Who'sWho in America®

Who'sWho in America®

Biographical Titles Currently Published by Marquis Who's Who

Who's Who in America
Who's Who in America Junior & Senior High School Version
Who Was Who in America
  Historical Volume (1607–1896)
  Volume I (1897–1942)
  Volume II (1943–1950)
  Volume III (1951–1960)
  Volume IV (1961–1968)
  Volume V (1969–1973)
  Volume VI (1974–1976)
  Volume VII (1977–1981)
  Volume VIII (1982–1985)
  Volume IX (1985–1989)
  Volume X (1989–1993)
  Index Volume (1607–1993)
Who's Who in the World
Who's Who in the East
Who's Who in the Midwest
Who's Who in the South and Southwest
Who's Who in the West
Who's Who in American Education
Who's Who in American Law
Who's Who in American Nursing
Who's Who of American Women
Who's Who of Emerging Leaders in America
Who's Who in Finance and Industry
Who's Who in Medicine and Healthcare
Who's Who in Science and Engineering
Index to Marquis Who's Who Publications
The *Official* ABMS Directory of Board Certified Medical Specialists

Who's Who in America®

1996

WHO'S WHO IN AMERICA
50th Edition
1899-1996

Volume 2
L–Z

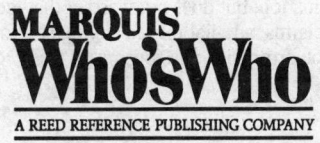

A REED REFERENCE PUBLISHING COMPANY

121 Chanlon Road
New Providence, NJ 07974 U.S.A.

Marquis Who's Who
Who's Who in America®

Vice President, Production—Directories	Dean Hollister
Editorial Director	Paul Canning
Research Director	Judy Redel
Senior Managing Editor	Fred M. Marks

Editorial

Senior Editor	Harriet Tiger
Associate Editor	Rose Marvin
Assistant Editors	Jennifer Cox
	Roger N. Generazzo
	Lisa A. Heft
	Andrea Lopez
	Matthew O'Connell
	Stephanie A. Palenque
	Josh Samber
	Rebecca Sultzbaugh

Editorial Services

Manager	Nadine Hovan
Supervisors	Debra Krom
	Mary Lyn Koval
Coordinator	Anne Marie C. Calcagno

Editorial Support

Manager	Sharon L. Gonzalez
Staff	J. Hector Gonzalez

Mail Processing

Supervisor	Kara A. Seitz
Staff	Shawn Johnston
	Cheryl A. Rodriguez
	Jill S. Terbell
	Scott Van Houten

Database Operations

Production Manager	Ren Reiner
Production Editors	Carl Edolo
	Lisa Martino

Research

Managing Research Editors	Anila Rao Banerjee
	William Cherf
Senior Research Editors	Patrick Gibbons
	Tanya Hurst
Associate Research Editors	Robert Docherty
	Hillary Eigen
	Connie Harbison
	Maura Roberts

Support Services

Assistant	Jeanne Danzig

Reed Reference Publishing

Chief Operating Officer Andrew W. Meyer **Executive Vice President, Business Development & Database Publishing** Peter E. Simon **Executive Vice President, Finance and Operations** Gwyn Williams **Senior Vice President, Marketing** Stanley Walker **Senior Vice President, Sales** Edward J. Roycroft **Vice President & Publisher** Sandra S. Barnes

Published by Marquis Who's Who, A Reed Reference Publishing Company.

Library of Congress Catalog Card Number 4-16934
International Standard Book Number   0-8379-0167-7 (set, Classic Edition)
                                      0-8379-0169-3 (volume 2, Classic Edition)
                                      0-8379-0171-5 (set, Deluxe Edition)
                                      0-8379-0173-1 (volume 2, Deluxe Edition)

Manufactured in the United States of America

Table of Contents

Preface

"WHO'S WHO IN AMERICA *shall endeavor to list those individuals who are of current national reference interest and inquiry either because of meritorious achievement or because of the positions they hold."*

Albert Nelson Marquis
Founder, 1899

When the first edition of **Who's Who in America** appeared in 1899, it presented itself as a new and untried experiment in the field of American reference book publishing. It was the first publication ever issued which claimed to be, in any comprehensive degree, a general biographical directory of notable American contemporaries.

Those interested in the production of the book looked forward to a favorable reception for it. But the event far outran the expectations. The enormous critical attention given to the work showed that **Who's Who in America** was regarded as one of the most important publications of the time. It was hailed everywhere as a valuable addition to indispensible reference sources.

A Standard Reference Work

A publisher of newspaper supplements in Chicago in the 1890s, A.N. Marquis noted the need for current information on city leaders, business people, and other professionals. He noted "[T]here are some excellent cyclopaedias...in which the notable lives of Americans, from Columbus to the man of a decade or so ago, are narrated...but the nature of such large compilations precludes any attempt to keep up with the times so far as presenting daily sought for information regarding living men and women. Yet the latter are precisely the persons whose careers are of the greatest interest to the largest number of people."

During the generations that have passed, **Who's Who in America** has garnered a worldwide reputation for presenting the most accurate, current biographical data available. Quickly establishing itself as a standard reference work, it has grown steadily in public favor, and today is recognized globally as the premier reference pertaining to notable living Americans.

The Golden 50th Edition

This edition continues to uphold the guiding principle set forth by A.N. Marquis in 1899: The editors of **Who's Who in America** continue to strive to identify and chronicle the achievements of men and women who have become the leaders in our society's political, cultural, and economic affairs.

As the course of history presents changing patterns in American leadership, Marquis records the impact of each emerging force: the rise of women to positions of influence; the role of the United States in a "global economy;" and the prominence of individuals in the growing fields of computer technology, health care, communications, athletics, and entertainment, to name but a few. While **Who's Who in America** focuses primarily on United States citizens, prominent individuals from other countries are profiled as well—an inevitable consequence of expanding mutual knowledge and recognition in an interdependent world.

Marquis Achievers: Then and Now

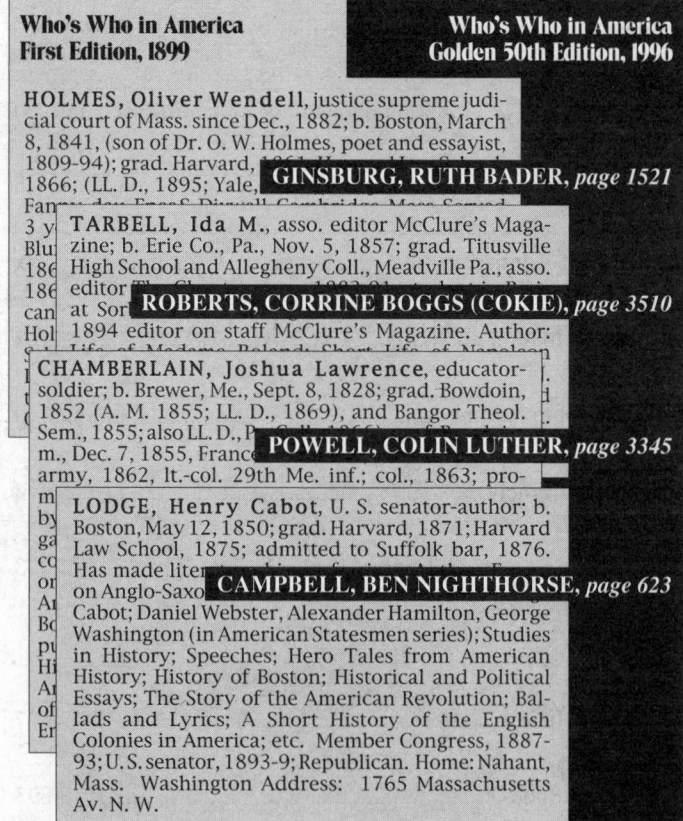

**Who's Who in America
First Edition, 1899**

**Who's Who in America
Golden 50th Edition, 1996**

HOLMES, Oliver Wendell, justice supreme judicial court of Mass. since Dec., 1882; b. Boston, March 8, 1841, (son of Dr. O. W. Holmes, poet and essayist, 1809-94); grad. Harvard, 1861; Harvard Law School, 1866; (LL. D., 1895; Yale, ...

GINSBURG, RUTH BADER, *page 1521*

TARBELL, Ida M., asso. editor McClure's Magazine; b. Erie Co., Pa., Nov. 5, 1857; grad. Titusville High School and Allegheny Coll., Meadville Pa., asso. editor ... at Sor ... 1894 editor on staff McClure's Magazine. Author: ...

ROBERTS, CORRINE BOGGS (COKIE), *page 3510*

CHAMBERLAIN, Joshua Lawrence, educator-soldier; b. Brewer, Me., Sept. 8, 1828; grad. Bowdoin, 1852 (A. M. 1855; LL. D., 1869), and Bangor Theol. Sem., 1855; also LL. D., ... m., Dec. 7, 1855, France ... army, 1862, lt.-col. 29th Me. inf.; col., 1863; pro-

POWELL, COLIN LUTHER, *page 3345*

LODGE, Henry Cabot, U. S. senator-author; b. Boston, May 12, 1850; grad. Harvard, 1871; Harvard Law School, 1875; admitted to Suffolk bar, 1876. Has made liter... on Anglo-Saxo...

CAMPBELL, BEN NIGHTHORSE, *page 623*

Cabot; Daniel Webster, Alexander Hamilton, George Washington (in American Statesmen series); Studies in History; Speeches; Hero Tales from American History; History of Boston; Historical and Political Essays; The Story of the American Revolution; Ballads and Lyrics; A Short History of the English Colonies in America; etc. Member Congress, 1887-93; U.S. senator, 1893-9; Republican. Home: Nahant, Mass. Washington Address: 1765 Massachusetts Av. N. W.

Marquis Notables																										
	Booker T. Washington	Alexander Graham Bell	Carrie Chapman Catt	Upton Sinclair	Thomas Alva Edison	John D. Rockefeller	Theodore Roosevelt	George M. Cohan	Carl Sandburg	D.W. Griffith	Henry Ford	Calvin Coolidge	Robert Goddard	Margaret Sanger	Charles Lindbergh	David Sarnoff	Jane Addams	Robert Frost	John L. Lewis	Eleanor Roosevelt	Orson Welles	Douglas MacArthur	Thomas E. Dewey	J. Robert Oppenheimer	Cole Porter	Ralph Bunche	Humphrey Bogart
Edition 1	2	3	4	5	6	7	8	9	10	11	12	13	14	15	16	17	18	19	20	21	22	23	24	25	26	27

One Principle Governs Selection

In 1899, Marquis Biographees numbered 8,602, or one person per 10,000 of U.S. population. In this Golden 50th Edition, Marquis Who's Who proudly presents the biographies of over 103,000 outstanding individuals. While our Biographees have grown in number, our selection standards remain stringent. Fewer than four in 10,000 people are included in **Who's Who in America**.

Biographees Selected for Who's Who in America

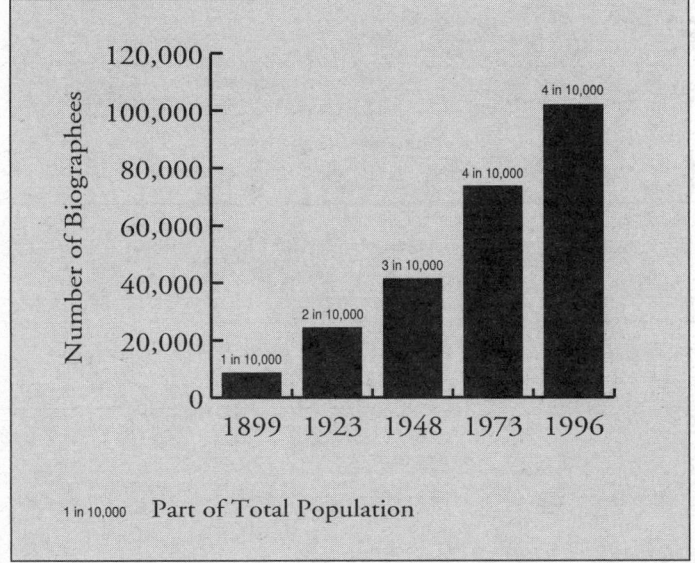

Selection is based solely on reference value. Individuals become eligible for listing by virtue of their positions and/or noteworthy achievements that have proven to be of significant value to society. An individual's desire to be listed is not sufficient reason for inclusion. Similarly, wealth or social position are not criteria. Of course, Marquis Who's Who has never charged a fee for publishing a biography, nor is purchase of the book ever a factor in the selection of Biographees.

Compiling the Most Accurate Biographical Data

Through fifty editions, the basic **Who's Who in America** compilation process has remained unchanged. As A.N. Marquis noted in his preface to the first edition: "The book is autobiographical, the data having been obtained from first hands...." Marquis's biographical information comes from the best sources available—the Biographees themselves.

Many steps are taken in the compilation of each edition of **Who's Who in America**. Potential Biographees are identified by Marquis researchers and editors. Candidates are sent data forms and are invited to submit complete biographical and career information. These data are reviewed to confirm that candidates meet the stringent selection criteria. Sketches are then prepared and sent to Biographees for prepublication checking.

In some cases, Marquis staff members compile and/or verify the biographical data through independent research. Sketches compiled in this manner are denoted by asterisks. For a small number of cases, where detailed information is not available at publication, the editors have written brief sketches with current career information; these are also indicated by asterisks.

To maintain its reputation for currency, and at the same time to adhere to space limitations, **Who's Who in America** undergoes meticulous review of selection criteria with each edition. Deletion of some names is inevitable; such deletion is not arbitrary. For example, if a Biographee has retired from active participation in a career or public life, the sketch may be excluded. In large part, it is career development that determines inclusion and continuation.

Annual publication enables **Who's Who in America** to bring users more new names and update more existing entries each edition. In all, over 22,400 new names appear in the Golden 50th Edition.

Responding to Your Reference Needs

An invitation for suggestions extended in the first edition brought forth the idea that a classified index would be an invaluable addition to **Who's Who in America.** The Marquis editors judged that it was "impossible to spare" the 100 estimated pages required to present the information thoroughly (no small consideration in a one-volume work) and the effort was "reluctantly abandoned."

As the publication grew to 73,500 Biographees in the two-volume forty-first edition, the necessity of a classified index eclipsed the limitations of space. Geographic and Professional Indexes were introduced in the forty-second edition, adding a third volume and making **Who's Who in America** an even more productive research tool. Through these indexes, users can identify and locate individuals in any of thirty-eight categories, as well as by country, state, or city.

Who's Who in America provides other useful reference features. This edition contains a cumulative Retiree Index of persons whose names were deleted from the forty-seventh through forty-ninth editions because they have retired from active work. This index enables the user to locate the last published biographical sketch of each listee.

There is also a Necrology of Biographees whose sketches appeared in the forty-ninth edition and whose deaths were reported prior to the closing of this edition. The sketches have been removed from the book. (For those Biographees whose deaths were reported prior to January 1993, complete biographical information, including date of death and place of interment, can be found in Volume X of Marquis **Who Was Who in America.**)

Finally, many of the women and men profiled in **Who's Who in America** have included in their biographies a listing of their avocations, thus providing additional insights into their personal lives and interests. Some of the sketches also end with an italicized feature, "Thoughts on My Life." The statement is written by the Biographees and reflects those principles, goals, ideals, and values that have been guidelines for success and achievement.

Our Challenge

Putting together a reference source as comprehensive as **Who's Who in America** is a monumental challenge. Over our long history, Marquis Who's Who researchers and editors have exercised diligent care in preparing each sketch for publication. Despite all precautions, however, errors do occasionally occur. Users of this directory are invited to notify the publisher to any such errors so that corrections can be made in a subsequent edition.

Board of Advisors

Marquis Who's Who gratefully acknowledges the following distinguished individuals who have made themselves available for review, evaluation, and general comment with regard to the publication of the Golden 50th Edition of *Who's Who in America*. The advisors have enhanced the reference value of this edition by the nomination of outstanding individuals for inclusion. However, the Board of Advisors, either collectively or individually, is in no way responsible for the selection of names appearing in this volume, nor does the Board of Advisors bear responsibility for the accuracy or comprehensiveness of the biographical information or other material contained herein.

Mindy Aloff
Free-lance Writer

James Arcara
President, Radio Division
Capital Cities/ABC, Inc.

Fred Basolo
Morrison Professor Emeritus
Department of Chemistry
Northwestern University

Willard L. Boyd
President
Field Museum of Natural History

Leighton E. Cluff
Veterans Administration Distinguished
  Physician and Professor of Medicine
University of Florida

Jean Dalrymple
Theater Producer and Director

Johann Deisenhofer
Professor of Biochemistry
Howard Hughes Medical Institute
  Research Laboratories
University of Texas Southwestern
  Medical Center

Richard L. Durbin
President, Chief Executive Officer
Durbin International

George E. Erikson
Professor of Medical Science
Brown University

Milton Friedman
Senior Research Fellow
Hoover Institution on War, Revolution
  and Peace

Phillip Grier
Executive Director
National Association of College and
  University Attorneys

Barbara Haskell
Curator
Whitney Museum of American Art

Elizabeth T. Kennan
President
Mount Holyoke College

Jill Krementz
Author and Photographer

Charles F. Larson
Executive Director
Industrial Research Institute, Inc.

John L. Lesher
President
Jack Lesher & Associates

James Levine
Artistic Director
Metropolitan Opera Association

John L. Marion
Chair
Sotheby's

Gerald F. Marshall
Consultant in Optics
Morgan Hill, California

Martin E. Marty
Professor
University of Chicago Divinity School

James A. Michener
Author

Ildaura Murillo-Rohde
Dean and Professor Emeritus
State University of New York, Brooklyn

Barbara G. Proctor
President, Chief Executive Officer
Proctor & Gardner Advertising

Mitchell T. Rabkin
President
Beth Israel Hospital

Linda Resnik
Executive Director
White House Conference on Library
  and Information Science

Louis Rukeyser
Economic Commentator
Host, *Wall Street Week with Louis
  Rukeyser*

John Fox Sullivan
President and Publisher
National Journal

James A. Van Allen
Carver Professor of Physics Emeritus
University of Iowa

Nicholas A. Veliotes
President
Association of American Publishers

Robert Wedgeworth
University Librarian
University of Illinois, Urbana

Elie Wiesel
Author
Professor of Philosophy
Boston University

Irwin Winkler
Film Producer
Chartoff-Winkler Productions

Standards of Admission

The foremost consideration in determining who will be admitted to the pages of *Who's Who in America* is the extent of an individual's reference interest. Reference value is based on either of two factors: 1) the position of responsibility held or 2) the level of significant achievement attained in a career of noteworthy activity. The majority of Biographees qualify for admission on the basis of the first factor, a specific position of responsibility. Incumbency in the position makes the person someone of high reference interest. The factor of position includes the following categories:

1. High-ranking members of the executive, legislative, and judicial branches of the United States government. This group includes, for example, the President of the United States, members of Congress, cabinet secretaries, chief administrators of selected federal agencies and commissions, and justices of the federal courts.

2. Military officers on active duty with the rank of Major General or higher in the Army, Air Force, and Marine Corps, and of Rear Admiral or higher in the U.S. Navy.

3. Specified state government officials. Among these are governors, lieutenant governors, secretaries of state, attorneys general, and treasurers. Also included under this standard are presidents of state senates, state university system administrators, chief state health officers, and officials of American territories.

4. Judges of state and territorial courts of the highest appellate jurisdiction.

5. High-level officials of principal cities, based on population. These officials include mayors, police chiefs, school superintendents, and other selected positions.

6. Leading government officials of Canada and Mexico. In Canada, this group includes the prime minister, premiers of the provinces, ministers of departments of the federal government, and justices of the highest courts. Examples in the Mexican government are the president of the country and cabinet secretaries of the national government.

7. Principal officers of major national and international businesses as defined by several quantitative criteria.

8. Ranking administrative officials of major universities and colleges. Some of the officers included in this category are president, provost, dean, and selected department heads.

9. Heads of leading philanthropic, cultural, educational, professional, and scientific institutions and associations. These institutions include, for example, selected foundations, museums, symphony orchestras, libraries, and research laboratories.

10. Selected members of certain honorary and professional organizations, such as the National Academy of Sciences, the National Academy of Design, the American College of Trial Lawyers, and the Royal Society of Canada.

11. Chief ecclesiastics of the principal religious denominations.

12. Recipients of major national and international awards, such as the Nobel and Pulitzer Prizes, the Academy Awards and the Antoinette Perry, or Tony Awards. Also included are winners of important professional awards, such as the American Institute of Architecture's Gold Medal for Architecture.

Admission by the second factor—significant achievement—is based on the application of objective criteria established for each field. An artist whose works are included in major museums qualifies for admission for noteworthy accomplishment. The professor who has made important research contributions in his field is of reference interest because of his outstanding achievements. Qualitative standards determine eligibility for every field.

In many instances there is considerable overlap between the two factors used for inclusion in *Who's Who in America*. For example, the head of a major library is in the book because of position, but reaching that responsibility also signifies important achievement. Similarly, a state governor not only holds a position that warrants inclusion; attaining that post also represents significant achievement in the political world. In both cases, the reference value of the biographical sketch is significant. Whether the person has been selected because of position or as a mark of achievement, the Biographee in *Who's Who in America* has noteworthy accomplishments beyond those of the vast majority of contemporaries.

Key to Information

[1] GIBSON, OSCAR JULIUS, [2] physician, medical educator; [3] b. Syracuse, N.Y., Aug. 31, 1937; [4] s. Paul Oliver and Elizabeth H. (Thrun) G.; [5] m. Judith S. Gonzalez, Apr. 28, 1968; [6] children: Richard Gary, Matthew Cary, Samuel Perry. [7] BA magna cum laude, U. Pa., 1960; MD, Harvard U., 1964. [8] Diplomate Am. Bd. Internal Medicine, Am. Bd. Preventive Medicine. [9] Intern Barnes Hosp., St. Louis, 1964-65, resident, 1965-66; clin. assoc. Nat. Heart Inst., NIH, Bethesda, Md., 1966-68; chief resident medicine U. Okla. Hosps., 1968-69; asst. prof. community health Okla. Med. Ctr., 1969-70, assoc. prof., 1970-74, prof., chmn. dept., 1974-80; dean U. Okla. Coll. Medicine, 1978-82; v.p. med. staff affairs Bapt. Med. Ctr., Oklahoma City, 1982-86, exec. v.p., 1986-88, chmn., 1988—; [10] mem. governing bd. Ambulatory Health Care Consortium, Inc., 1979-80; mem. Okla. Bd. Medicolegal Examiners, 1985—. [11] Contrb. articles to profl. jours. [12] Bd. dirs., v.p. Okla. Arthritis Found., 1982—; trustee North Central Mental Health Ctr., 1985—. [13] Served with U.S. Army, 1955-56. [14] Recipient R.T. Chadwick award NIH, 1968; Am. Heart Assn. grantee, 1985-86, 88. [15] Fellow Assn. Tchrs. Preventive Medicine; mem. Am. Fedn. Clin. Research, Assn. Med. Colls., AAAS, AMA, Masons, Shriners, Sigma Xi. [16] Republican. [17] Roman Catholic. [18] Avocations: swimming, weight lifting, travel. [19] Home: 6060 N Ridge Ave Oklahoma City OK 73126 [20] Office: Bapt Med Ctr 1986 Cuba Hwy Oklahoma City OK 73120

KEY

[1]	Name
[2]	Occupation
[3]	Vital statistics
[4]	Parents
[5]	Marriage
[6]	Children
[7]	Education
[8]	Professional certifications
[9]	Career
[10]	Career related
[11]	Writings and creative works
[12]	Civic and political activities
[13]	Military
[14]	Awards and fellowships
[15]	Professional and association memberships, clubs and lodges
[16]	Political affiliation
[17]	Religion
[18]	Avocations
[19]	Home address
[20]	Office address

Table of Abbreviations

The following abbreviations and symbols are frequently used in this book.

*An asterisk following a sketch indicates that it was researched by the Marquis Who's Who editorial staff and has not been verified by the Biographee.

A Associate (used with academic degrees only)
AA, A.A. Associate in Arts, Associate of Arts
AAAL American Academy of Arts and Letters
AAAS American Association for the Advancement of Science
AACD American Association for Counseling and Development
AACN American Association of Critical Care Nurses
AAHA American Academy of Health Administrators
AAHP American Association of Hospital Planners
AAHPERD American Alliance for Health, Physical Education, Recreation, and Dance
AAS Associate of Applied Science
AASL American Association of School Librarians
AASPA American Association of School Personnel Administrators
AAU Amateur Athletic Union
AAUP American Association of University Professors
AAUW American Association of University Women
AB, A.B. Arts, Bachelor of
AB Alberta
ABA American Bar Association
ABC American Broadcasting Company
AC Air Corps
acad. academy, academic
acct. accountant
acctg. accounting
ACDA Arms Control and Disarmament Agency
ACHA American College of Hospital Administrators
ACLS Advanced Cardiac Life Support
ACLU American Civil Liberties Union
ACOG American College of Ob-Gyn
ACP American College of Physicians
ACS American College of Surgeons
ADA American Dental Association
a.d.c. aide-de-camp
adj. adjunct, adjutant
adj. gen. adjutant general
adm. admiral
adminstr. administrator
adminstrn. administration
adminstrv. administrative
ADN Associate's Degree in Nursing
ADP Automatic Data Processing
adv. advocate, advisory
advt. advertising
AE, A.E. Agricultural Engineer
A.E. and P. Ambassador Extraordinary and Plenipotentiary

AEC Atomic Energy Commission
aero. aeronautical, aeronautic
aerodyn. aerodynamic
AFB Air Force Base
AFL-CIO American Federation of Labor and Congress of Industrial Organizations
AFTRA American Federation of TV and Radio Artists
AFSCME American Federation of State, County and Municipal Employees
agr. agriculture
agrl. agricultural
agt. agent
AGVA American Guild of Variety Artists
agy. agency
A&I Agricultural and Industrial
AIA American Institute of Architects
AIAA American Institute of Aeronautics and Astronautics
AIChE American Institute of Chemical Engineers
AICPA American Institute of Certified Public Accountants
AID Agency for International Development
AIDS Acquired Immune Deficiency Syndrome
AIEE American Institute of Electrical Engineers
AIM American Institute of Management
AIME American Institute of Mining, Metallurgy, and Petroleum Engineers
AK Alaska
AL Alabama
ALA American Library Association
Ala. Alabama
alt. alternate
Alta. Alberta
A&M Agricultural and Mechanical
AM, A.M. Arts, Master of
Am. American, America
AMA American Medical Association
amb. ambassador
A.M.E. African Methodist Episcopal
Amtrak National Railroad Passenger Corporation
AMVETS American Veterans of World War II, Korea, Vietnam
ANA American Nurses Association
anat. anatomical
ANCC American Nurses Credentialing Center
ann. annual
ANTA American National Theatre and Academy
anthrop. anthropological
AP Associated Press
APA American Psychological Association
APGA American Personnel Guidance Association
APHA American Public Health Association
APO Army Post Office
apptd. appointed
Apr. April
apt. apartment
AR Arkansas

ARC American Red Cross
arch. architect
archeol. archeological
archtl. architectural
Ariz. Arizona
Ark. Arkansas
ArtsD, ArtsD. Arts, Doctor of
arty. artillery
AS American Samoa
AS Associate in Science
ASCAP American Society of Composers, Authors and Publishers
ASCD Association for Supervision and Curriculum Development
ASCE American Society of Civil Engineers
ASHRAE American Society of Heating, Refrigeration, and Air Conditioning Engineers
ASME American Society of Mechanical Engineers
ASNSA American Society for Nursing Service Administrators
ASPA American Society for Public Administration
ASPCA American Society for the Prevention of Cruelty to Animals
assn. association
assoc. associate
asst. assistant
ASTD American Society for Training and Development
ASTM American Society for Testing and Materials
astron. astronomical
astrophys. astrophysical
ATLA Association of Trial Lawyers of America
ATSC Air Technical Service Command
AT&T American Telephone & Telegraph Company
atty. attorney
Aug. August
AUS Army of the United States
aux. auxiliary
Ave. Avenue
AVMA American Veterinary Medical Association
AZ Arizona
AWHONN Association of Women's Health Obstetric and Neonatal Nurses

B. Bachelor
b. born
BA, B.A. Bachelor of Arts
BAgr, B.Agr. Bachelor of Agriculture
Balt. Baltimore
Bapt. Baptist
BArch, B.Arch. Bachelor of Architecture
BAS, B.A.S. Bachelor of Agricultural Science
BBA, B.B.A. Bachelor of Business Administration
BBB Better Business Bureau
BBC British Broadcasting Corporation
BC, B.C. British Columbia

xi

BCE, B.C.E. Bachelor of Civil Engineering
BChir, B.Chir. Bachelor of Surgery
BCL, B.C.L. Bachelor of Civil Law
BCLS Basic Cardiac Life Support
BCS, B.C.S. Bachelor of Commercial Science
BD, B.D. Bachelor of Divinity
bd. board
BE, B.E. Bachelor of Education
BEE, B.E.E. Bachelor of Electrical Engineering
BFA, B.F.A. Bachelor of Fine Arts
bibl. biblical
bibliog. bibliographical
biog. biographical
biol. biological
BJ, B.J. Bachelor of Journalism
Bklyn. Brooklyn
BL, B.L. Bachelor of Letters
bldg. building
BLS, B.L.S. Bachelor of Library Science
BLS Basic Life Support
Blvd. Boulevard
BMI Broadcast Music, Inc.
BMW Bavarian Motor Works (Bayerische Motoren Werke)
bn. battalion
B.&O.R.R. Baltimore & Ohio Railroad
bot. botanical
BPE, B.P.E. Bachelor of Physical Education
BPhil, B.Phil. Bachelor of Philosophy
br. branch
BRE, B.R.E. Bachelor of Religious Education
brig. gen. brigadier general
Brit. British, Brittanica
Bros. Brothers
BS, B.S. Bachelor of Science
BSA, B.S.A. Bachelor of Agricultural Science
BSBA Bachelor of Science in Business Administration
BSChemE Bachelor of Science in Chemical Engineering
BSD, B.S.D. Bachelor of Didactic Science
BSEE Bachelor of Science in Electrical Engineering
BSN Bachelor of Science in Nursing
BST, B.S.T. Bachelor of Sacred Theology
BTh, B.Th. Bachelor of Theology
bull. bulletin
bur. bureau
bus. business
B.W.I. British West Indies

CA California
CAA Civil Aeronautics Administration
CAB Civil Aeronautics Board
CAD-CAM Computer Aided Design-Computer Aided Model
Calif. California
C.Am. Central America
Can. Canada, Canadian
CAP Civil Air Patrol
capt. captain
cardiol. cardiological
cardiovasc. cardiovascular
CARE Cooperative American Relief Everywhere
Cath. Catholic
cav. cavalry
CBC Canadian Broadcasting Company
CBI China, Burma, India Theatre of Operations
CBS Columbia Broadcasting Company
C.C. Community College
CCC Commodity Credit Corporation
CCNY City College of New York
CCRN Critical Care Registered Nurse

CCU Cardiac Care Unit
CD Civil Defense
CE, C.E. Corps of Engineers, Civil Engineer
CEN Certified Emergency Nurse
CENTO Central Treaty Organization
CEO chief executive officer
CERN European Organization of Nuclear Research
cert. certificate, certification, certified
CETA Comprehensive Employment Training Act
CFA Chartered Financial Analyst
CFL Canadian Football League
CFO chief financial officer
CFP Certified Financial Planner
ch. church
ChD, Ch.D. Doctor of Chemistry
chem. chemical
ChemE, Chem.E. Chemical Engineer
ChFC Chartered Financial Consultant
Chgo. Chicago
chirurg. chirurgical
chmn. chairman
chpt. chapter
CIA Central Intelligence Agency
Cin. Cincinnati
cir. circle, circuit
CLE Continuing Legal Education
Cleve. Cleveland
climatol. climatological
clin. clinical
clk. clerk
C.L.U. Chartered Life Underwriter
CM, C.M. Master in Surgery
CM Northern Mariana Islands
CMA Certified Medical Assistant
cmty. community
CNA Certified Nurse's Aide
CNOR Certified Nurse (Operating Room)
C.&N.W.Ry. Chicago & North Western Railway
CO Colorado
Co. Company
COF Catholic Order of Foresters
C. of C. Chamber of Commerce
col. colonel
coll. college
Colo. Colorado
com. committee
comd. commanded
comdg. commanding
comdr. commander
comdt. commandant
comm. communications
commd. commissioned
comml. commercial
commn. commission
commr. commissioner
compt. comptroller
condr. conductor
Conf. Conference
Congl. Congregational, Congressional
Conglist. Congregationalist
Conn. Connecticut
cons. consultant, consulting
consol. consolidated
constl. constitutional
constn. constitution
constrn. construction
contbd. contributed
contbg. contributing
contbn. contribution
contbr. contributor
contr. controller
Conv. Convention
COO chief operating officer
coop. cooperative

coord. coordinator
CORDS Civil Operations and Revolutionary Development Support
CORE Congress of Racial Equality
corp. corporation, corporate
corr. correspondent, corresponding, correspondence
C.&O.Ry. Chesapeake & Ohio Railway
coun. council
CPA Certified Public Accountant
CPCU Chartered Property and Casualty Underwriter
CPH, C.P.H. Certificate of Public Health
cpl. corporal
CPR Cardio-Pulmonary Resuscitation
C.P.Ry. Canadian Pacific Railway
CRT Cathode Ray Terminal
C.S. Christian Science
CSB, C.S.B. Bachelor of Christian Science
C.S.C. Civil Service Commission
CT Connecticut
ct. court
ctr. center
ctrl. central
CWS Chemical Warfare Service
C.Z. Canal Zone

D. Doctor
d. daughter
DAgr, D.Agr. Doctor of Agriculture
DAR Daughters of the American Revolution
dau. daughter
DAV Disabled American Veterans
DC, D.C. District of Columbia
DCL, D.C.L. Doctor of Civil Law
DCS, D.C.S. Doctor of Commercial Science
DD, D.D. Doctor of Divinity
DDS, D.D.S. Doctor of Dental Surgery
DE Delaware
Dec. December
dec. deceased
def. defense
Del. Delaware
del. delegate, delegation
Dem. Democrat, Democratic
DEng, D.Eng. Doctor of Engineering
denom. denomination, denominational
dep. deputy
dept. department
dermatol. dermatological
desc. descendant
devel. development, developmental
DFA, D.F.A. Doctor of Fine Arts
D.F.C. Distinguished Flying Cross
DHL, D.H.L. Doctor of Hebrew Literature
dir. director
dist. district
distbg. distributing
distbn. distribution
distbr. distributor
disting. distinguished
div. division, divinity, divorce
DLitt, D.Litt. Doctor of Literature
DMD, D.M.D. Doctor of Dental Medicine
DMS, D.M.S. Doctor of Medical Science
DO, D.O. Doctor of Osteopathy
docs. documents
DON Director of Nursing
DPH, D.P.H. Diploma in Public Health
DPhil, D.Phil. Doctor of Philosophy
D.R. Daughters of the Revolution
Dr. Drive, Doctor
DRE, D.R.E. Doctor of Religious Education
DrPH, Dr.P.H. Doctor of Public Health, Doctor of Public Hygiene
D.S.C. Distinguished Service Cross
DSc, D.Sc. Doctor of Science

DSChemE Doctor of Science in Chemical Engineering
D.S.M. Distinguished Service Medal
DST, D.S.T. Doctor of Sacred Theology
DTM, D.T.M. Doctor of Tropical Medicine
DVM, D.V.M. Doctor of Veterinary Medicine
DVS, D.V.S. Doctor of Veterinary Surgery

E, E. East
ea. eastern
E. and P. Extraordinary and Plenipotentiary
Eccles. Ecclesiastical
ecol. ecological
econ. economic
ECOSOC Economic and Social Council (of the UN)
ED, E.D. Doctor of Engineering
ed. educated
EdB, Ed.B. Bachelor of Education
EdD, Ed.D. Doctor of Education
edit. edition
editl. editorial
EdM, Ed.M. Master of Education
edn. education
ednl. educational
EDP Electronic Data Processing
EdS, Ed.S. Specialist in Education
EE, E.E. Electrical Engineer
E.E. and M.P. Envoy Extraordinary and Minister Plenipotentiary
EEC European Economic Community
EEG Electroencephalogram
EEO Equal Employment Opportunity
EEOC Equal Employment Opportunity Commission
E.Ger. German Democratic Republic
EKG Electrocardiogram
elec. electrical
electrochem. electrochemical
electrophys. electrophysical
elem. elementary
EM, E.M. Engineer of Mines
EMT Emergency Medical Technician
ency. encyclopedia
Eng. England
engr. engineer
engring. engineering
entomol. entomological
environ. environmental
EPA Environmental Protection Agency
epidemiol. epidemiological
Episc. Episcopalian
ERA Equal Rights Amendment
ERDA Energy Research and Development Administration
ESEA Elementary and Secondary Education Act
ESL English as Second Language
ESPN Entertainment and Sports Programming Network
ESSA Environmental Science Services Administration
ethnol. ethnological
ETO European Theatre of Operations
Evang. Evangelical
exam. examination, examining
Exch. Exchange
exec. executive
exhbn. exhibition
expdn. expedition
expn. exposition
expt. experiment
exptl. experimental
Expy. Expressway
Ext. Extension

F.A. Field Artillery
FAA Federal Aviation Administration
FAO Food and Agriculture Organization (of the UN)
FBA Federal Bar Association
FBI Federal Bureau of Investigation
FCA Farm Credit Administration
FCC Federal Communications Commission
FCDA Federal Civil Defense Administration
FDA Food and Drug Administration
FDIA Federal Deposit Insurance Administration
FDIC Federal Deposit Insurance Corporation
FE, F.E. Forest Engineer
FEA Federal Energy Administration
Feb. February
fed. federal
fedn. federation
FERC Federal Energy Regulatory Commission
fgn. foreign
FHA Federal Housing Administration
fin. financial, finance
FL Florida
Fl. Floor
Fla. Florida
FMC Federal Maritime Commission
FNP Family Nurse Practitioner
FOA Foreign Operations Administration
found. foundation
FPC Federal Power Commission
FPO Fleet Post Office
frat. fraternity
FRS Federal Reserve System
FSA Federal Security Agency
Ft. Fort
FTC Federal Trade Commission
Fwy. Freeway

G-1 (or other number) Division of General Staff
GA, Ga. Georgia
GAO General Accounting Office
gastroent. gastroenterological
GATE Gifted and Talented Educators
GATT General Agreement on Tariffs and Trade
GE General Electric Company
gen. general
geneal. genealogical
geod. geodetic
geog. geographic, geographical
geol. geological
geophys. geophysical
geriat. geriatrics
gerontol. gerontological
G.H.Q. General Headquarters
GM General Motors Corporation
GMAC General Motors Acceptance Corporation
G.N.Ry. Great Northern Railway
gov. governor
govt. government
govtl. governmental
GPO Government Printing Office
grad. graduate, graduated
GSA General Services Administration
Gt. Great
GTE General Telephone and Electric Company
GU Guam
gynecol. gynecological

HBO Home Box Office
hdqs. headquarters

HEW Department of Health, Education and Welfare
HHD, H.H.D. Doctor of Humanities
HHFA Housing and Home Finance Agency
HHS Department of Health and Human Services
HI Hawaii
hist. historical, historic
HM, H.M. Master of Humanities
HMO Health Maintenance Organization
homeo. homeopathic
hon. honorary, honorable
Ho. of Dels. House of Delegates
Ho. of Reps. House of Representatives
hort. horticultural
hosp. hospital
H.S. High School
HUD Department of Housing and Urban Development
Hwy. Highway
hydrog. hydrographic

IA Iowa
IAEA International Atomic Energy Agency
IATSE International Alliance of Theatrical and Stage Employees and Moving Picture Operators of the United States and Canada
IBM International Business Machines Corporation
IBRD International Bank for Reconstruction and Development
ICA International Cooperation Administration
ICC Interstate Commerce Commission
ICCE International Council for Computers in Education
ICU Intensive Care Unit
ID Idaho
IEEE Institute of Electrical and Electronics Engineers
IFC International Finance Corporation
IGY International Geophysical Year
IL Illinois
Ill. Illinois
illus. illustrated
ILO International Labor Organization
IMF International Monetary Fund
IN Indiana
Inc. Incorporated
Ind. Indiana
ind. independent
Indpls. Indianapolis
indsl. industrial
inf. infantry
info. information
ins. insurance
insp. inspector
insp. gen. inspector general
inst. institute
instl. institutional
instn. institution
instr. instructor
instrn. instruction
instrnl. instructional
internat. international
intro. introduction
IRE Institute of Radio Engineers
IRS Internal Revenue Service
ITT International Telephone & Telegraph Corporation

JAG Judge Advocate General
JAGC Judge Advocate General Corps
Jan. January
Jaycees Junior Chamber of Commerce
JB, J.B. Jurum Baccalaureus

JCB, J.C.B. Juris Canoni Baccalaureus
JCD, J.C.D. Juris Canonici Doctor, Juris
  Civilis Doctor
JCL, J.C.L. Juris Canonici Licentiatus
JD, J.D. Juris Doctor
jg. junior grade
jour. journal
jr. junior
JSD, J.S.D. Juris Scientiae Doctor
JUD, J.U.D. Juris Utriusque Doctor
jud. judicial

Kans. Kansas
K.C. Knights of Columbus
K.P. Knights of Pythias
KS Kansas
K.T. Knight Templar
KY, Ky. Kentucky

LA, La. Louisiana
L.A. Los Angeles
lab. laboratory
L.Am. Latin America
lang. language
laryngol. laryngological
LB Labrador
LDS Latter Day Saints
LDS Church Church of Jesus Christ of Latter
  Day Saints
lectr. lecturer
legis. legislation, legislative
LHD, L.H.D. Doctor of Humane Letters
L.I. Long Island
libr. librarian, library
lic. licensed, license
L.I.R.R. Long Island Railroad
lit. literature
litig. litigation
LittB, Litt.B. Bachelor of Letters
LittD, Litt.D. Doctor of Letters
LLB, LL.B. Bachelor of Laws
LLD, L.L.D. Doctor of Laws
LLM, L.L.M. Master of Laws
Ln. Lane
L.&N.R.R. Louisville & Nashville Railroad
LPGA Ladies Professional Golf Association
LPN Licensed Practical Nurse
LS, L.S. Library Science (in degree)
lt. lieutenant
Ltd. Limited
Luth. Lutheran
LWV League of Women Voters

M. Master
m. married
MA, M.A. Master of Arts
MA Massachusetts
MADD Mothers Against Drunk Driving
mag. magazine
MAgr, M.Agr. Master of Agriculture
maj. major
Man. Manitoba
Mar. March
MArch, M.Arch. Master in Architecture
Mass. Massachusetts
math. mathematics, mathematical
MATS Military Air Transport Service
MB, M.B. Bachelor of Medicine
MB Manitoba
MBA, M.B.A. Master of Business
  Administration
MBS Mutual Broadcasting System
M.C. Medical Corps
MCE, M.C.E. Master of Civil Engineering
mcht. merchant
mcpl. municipal
MCS, M.C.S. Master of Commercial Science

MD, M.D. Doctor of Medicine
MD, Md. Maryland
MDiv Master of Divinity
MDip, M.Dip. Master in Diplomacy
mdse. merchandise
MDV, M.D.V. Doctor of Veterinary
  Medicine
ME, M.E. Mechanical Engineer
ME Maine
M.E.Ch. Methodist Episcopal Church
mech. mechanical
MEd., M.Ed. Master of Education
med. medical
MEE, M.E.E. Master of Electrical
  Engineering
mem. member
meml. memorial
merc. mercantile
met. metropolitan
metall. metallurgical
MetE, Met.E. Metallurgical Engineer
meteorol. meteorological
Meth. Methodist
Mex. Mexico
MF, M.F. Master of Forestry
MFA, M.F.A. Master of Fine Arts
mfg. manufacturing
mfr. manufacturer
mgmt. management
mgr. manager
MHA, M.H.A. Master of Hospital
  Administration
M.I. Military Intelligence
MI Michigan
Mich. Michigan
micros. microscopic, microscopical
mid. middle
mil. military
Milw. Milwaukee
Min. Minister
mineral. mineralogical
Minn. Minnesota
MIS Management Information Systems
Miss. Mississippi
MIT Massachusetts Institute of Technology
mktg. marketing
ML, M.L. Master of Laws
MLA Modern Language Association
M.L.D. Magister Legnum Diplomatic
MLitt, M.Litt. Master of Literature, Master
  of Letters
MLS, M.L.S. Master of Library Science
MME, M.M.E. Master of Mechanical
  Engineering
MN Minnesota
mng. managing
MO, Mo. Missouri
moblzn. mobilization
Mont. Montana
MP Northern Mariana Islands
M.P. Member of Parliament
MPA Master of Public Administration
MPE, M.P.E. Master of Physical Education
MPH, M.P.H. Master of Public Health
MPhil, M.Phil. Master of Philosophy
MPL, M.P.L. Master of Patent Law
Mpls. Minneapolis
MRE, M.R.E. Master of Religious Education
MRI Magnetic Resonance Imaging
MS, M.S. Master of Science
MS, Ms. Mississippi
MSc, M.Sc. Master of Science
MSChemE Master of Science in Chemical
  Engineering
MSEE Master of Science in Electrical
  Engineering
MSF, M.S.F. Master of Science of Forestry

MSN Master of Science in Nursing
MST, M.S.T. Master of Sacred Theology
MSW, M.S.W. Master of Social Work
MT Montana
Mt. Mount
MTO Mediterranean Theatre of Operation
MTV Music Television
mus. museum, musical
MusB, Mus.B. Bachelor of Music
MusD, Mus.D. Doctor of Music
MusM, Mus.M. Master of Music
mut. mutual
MVP Most Valuable Player
mycol. mycological

N. North
NAACOG Nurses Association of the
  American College of Obstetricians and
  Gynecologists
NAACP National Association for the
  Advancement of Colored People
NACA National Advisory Committee for
  Aeronautics
NACDL National Association of Criminal
  Defense Lawyers
NACU National Association of Colleges
  and Universities
NAD National Academy of Design
NAE National Academy of Engineering,
  National Association of Educators
NAESP National Association of Elementary
  School Principals
NAFE National Association of Female
  Executives
N.Am. North America
NAM National Association of Manufacturers
NAMH National Association for Mental
  Health
NAPA National Association of Performing
  Artists
NARAS National Academy of Recording
  Arts and Sciences
NAREB National Association of Real Estate
  Boards
NARS National Archives and Record Service
NAS National Academy of Sciences
NASA National Aeronautics and Space
  Administration
NASP National Association of School
  Psychologists
NASW National Association of Social
  Workers
nat. national
NATAS National Academy of Television
  Arts and Sciences
NATO North Atlantic Treaty Organization
NATOUSA North African Theatre of
  Operations, United States Army
nav. navigation
NB, N.B. New Brunswick
NBA National Basketball Association
NBC National Broadcasting Company
NC, N.C. North Carolina
NCAA National College Athletic Association
NCCJ National Conference of Christians
  and Jews
ND, N.D. North Dakota
NDEA National Defense Education Act
NE Nebraska
NE, N.E. Northeast
NEA National Education Association
Nebr. Nebraska
NEH National Endowment for Humanities
neurol. neurological
Nev. Nevada
NF Newfoundland

NFL National Football League
Nfld. Newfoundland
NG National Guard
NH, N.H. New Hampshire
NHL National Hockey League
NIH National Institutes of Health
NIMH National Institute of Mental Health
NJ, N.J. New Jersey
NLRB National Labor Relations Board
NM New Mexico
N.Mex. New Mexico
No. Northern
NOAA National Oceanographic and Atmospheric Administration
NORAD North America Air Defense
Nov. November
NOW National Organization for Women
N.P.Ry. Northern Pacific Railway
nr. near
NRA National Rifle Association
NRC National Research Council
NS, N.S. Nova Scotia
NSC National Security Council
NSF National Science Foundation
NSTA National Science Teachers Association
NSW New South Wales
N.T. New Testament
NT Northwest Territories
nuc. nuclear
numis. numismatic
NV Nevada
NW, N.W. Northwest
N.W.T. Northwest Territories
NY, N.Y. New York
N.Y.C. New York City
NYU New York University
N.Z. New Zealand

OAS Organization of American States
ob-gyn obstetrics-gynecology
obs. observatory
obstet. obstetrical
occupl. occupational
oceanog. oceanographic
Oct. October
OD, O.D. Doctor of Optometry
OECD Organization for Economic Cooperation and Development
OEEC Organization of European Economic Cooperation
OEO Office of Economic Opportunity
ofcl. official
OH Ohio
OK Oklahoma
Okla. Oklahoma
ON Ontario
Ont. Ontario
oper. operating
ophthal. ophthalmological
ops. operations
OR Oregon
orch. orchestra
Oreg. Oregon
orgn. organization
orgnl. organizational
ornithol. ornithological
orthop. orthopedic
OSHA Occupational Safety and Health Administration
OSRD Office of Scientific Research and Development
OSS Office of Strategic Services
osteo. osteopathic
otol. otological
otolaryn. otolaryngological

PA, Pa. Pennsylvania

P.A. Professional Association
paleontol. paleontological
path. pathological
PBS Public Broadcasting System
P.C. Professional Corporation
PE Prince Edward Island
pediat. pediatrics
P.E.I. Prince Edward Island
PEN Poets, Playwrights, Editors, Essayists and Novelists (international association)
penol. penological
P.E.O. women's organization (full name not disclosed)
pers. personnel
pfc. private first class
PGA Professional Golfers' Association of America
PHA Public Housing Administration
pharm. pharmaceutical
PharmD, Pharm.D. Doctor of Pharmacy
PharmM, Pharm.M. Master of Pharmacy
PhB, Ph.B. Bachelor of Philosophy
PhD, Ph.D. Doctor of Philosophy
PhDChemE Doctor of Science in Chemical Engineering
PhM, Ph.M. Master of Philosophy
Phila. Philadelphia
philharm. philharmonic
philol. philological
philos. philosophical
photog. photographic
phys. physical
physiol. physiological
Pitts. Pittsburgh
Pk. Park
Pky. Parkway
Pl. Place
P.&L.E.R.R. Pittsburgh & Lake Erie Railroad
Plz. Plaza
PNP Pediatric Nurse Practitioner
P.O. Post Office
PO Box Post Office Box
polit. political
poly. polytechnic, polytechnical
PQ Province of Quebec
PR, P.R. Puerto Rico
prep. preparatory
pres. president
Presbyn. Presbyterian
presdl. presidential
prin. principal
procs. proceedings
prod. produced (play production)
prodn. production
prodr. producer
prof. professor
profl. professional
prog. progressive
propr. proprietor
pros. atty. prosecuting attorney
pro tem. pro tempore
PSRO Professional Services Review Organization
psychiat. psychiatric
psychol. psychological
PTA Parent-Teachers Association
ptnr. partner
PTO Pacific Theatre of Operations, Parent Teacher Organization
pub. publisher, publishing, published
pub. public
publ. publication
pvt. private

quar. quarterly
qm. quartermaster

Q.M.C. Quartermaster Corps
Que. Quebec

radiol. radiological
RAF Royal Air Force
RCA Radio Corporation of America
RCAF Royal Canadian Air Force
RD Rural Delivery
Rd. Road
R&D Research & Development
REA Rural Electrification Administration
rec. recording
ref. reformed
regt. regiment
regtl. regimental
rehab. rehabilitation
rels. relations
Rep. Republican
rep. representative
Res. Reserve
ret. retired
Rev. Reverend
rev. review, revised
RFC Reconstruction Finance Corporation
RFD Rural Free Delivery
rhinol. rhinological
RI, R.I. Rhode Island
RISD Rhode Island School of Design
Rlwy. Railway
Rm. Room
RN, R.N. Registered Nurse
roentgenol. roentgenological
ROTC Reserve Officers Training Corps
RR Rural Route
R.R. Railroad
rsch. research
rschr. researcher
Rt. Route

S. South
s. son
SAC Strategic Air Command
SAG Screen Actors Guild
SALT Strategic Arms Limitation Talks
S.Am. South America
san. sanitary
SAR Sons of the American Revolution
Sask. Saskatchewan
savs. savings
SB, S.B. Bachelor of Science
SBA Small Business Administration
SC, S.C. South Carolina
SCAP Supreme Command Allies Pacific
ScB, Sc.B. Bachelor of Science
SCD, S.C.D. Doctor of Commercial Science
ScD, Sc.D. Doctor of Science
sch. school
sci. science, scientific
SCLC Southern Christian Leadership Conference
SCV Sons of Confederate Veterans
SD, S.D. South Dakota
SE, S.E. Southeast
SEATO Southeast Asia Treaty Organization
SEC Securities and Exchange Commission
sec. secretary
sect. section
seismol. seismological
sem. seminary
Sept. September
s.g. senior grade
sgt. sergeant
SHAEF Supreme Headquarters Allied Expeditionary Forces
SHAPE Supreme Headquarters Allied Powers in Europe
S.I. Staten Island

S.J. Society of Jesus (Jesuit)
SJD Scientiae Juridicae Doctor
SK Saskatchewan
SM, S.M. Master of Science
SNP Society of Nursing Professionals
So. Southern
soc. society
sociol. sociological
S.P.Co. Southern Pacific Company
spkr. speaker
spl. special
splty. specialty
Sq. Square
S.R. Sons of the Revolution
sr. senior
SS Steamship
SSS Selective Service System
St. Saint, Street
sta. station
stats. statistics
statis. statistical
STB, S.T.B. Bachelor of Sacred Theology
stblzn. stabilization
STD, S.T.D. Doctor of Sacred Theology
std. standard
Ste. Suite
subs. subsidiary
SUNY State University of New York
supr. supervisor
supt. superintendent
surg. surgical
svc. service
SW, S.W. Southwest
sys. system

TAPPI Technical Association of the Pulp
   and Paper Industry
tb. tuberculosis
tchg. teaching
tchr. teacher
tech. technical, technology
technol. technological
tel. telephone
Tel. & Tel. Telephone & Telegraph
telecom. telecommunications
temp. temporary
Tenn. Tennessee
Ter. Territory
Ter. Terrace
TESOL Teachers of English to Speakers of
   Other Languages
Tex. Texas
ThD, Th.D. Doctor of Theology
theol. theological

ThM, Th.M. Master of Theology
TN Tennessee
tng. training
topog. topographical
trans. transaction, transferred
transl. translation, translated
transp. transportation
treas. treasurer
TT Trust Territory
TV television
TVA Tennessee Valley Authority
TWA Trans World Airlines
twp. township
TX Texas
typog. typographical

U. University
UAW United Auto Workers
UCLA University of California at Los
   Angeles
UDC United Daughters of the Confederacy
U.K. United Kingdom
UN United Nations
UNESCO United Nations Educational,
   Scientific and Cultural Organization
UNICEF United Nations International
   Children's Emergency Fund
univ. university
UNRRA United Nations Relief and
   Rehabilitation Administration
UPI United Press International
U.P.R.R. United Pacific Railroad
urol. urological
U.S. United States
U.S.A. United States of America
USAAF United States Army Air Force
USAF United States Air Force
USAFR United States Air Force Reserve
USAR United States Army Reserve
USCG United States Coast Guard
USCGR United States Coast Guard Reserve
USES United States Employment Service
USIA United States Information Agency
USMC United States Marine Corps
USMCR United States Marine Corps Reserve
USN United States Navy
USNG United States National Guard
USNR United States Naval Reserve
USO United Service Organizations
USPHS United States Public Health Service
USS United States Ship
USSR Union of the Soviet Socialist Republics
USTA United States Tennis Association

USV United States Volunteers
UT Utah

VA Veterans Administration
VA, Va. Virginia
vet. veteran, veterinary
VFW Veterans of Foreign Wars
VI, V.I. Virgin Islands
vice pres. vice president
vis. visiting
VISTA Volunteers in Service to America
VITA Volunteers in Technical Assistance
vocat. vocational
vol. volunteer, volume
v.p. vice president
vs. versus
VT, Vt. Vermont

W, W. West
WA Washington (state)
WAC Women's Army Corps
Wash. Washington (state)
WATS Wide Area Telecommunications
   Service
WAVES Women's Reserve, US Naval
   Reserve
WCTU Women's Christian Temperance
   Union
we. western
W. Ger. Germany, Federal Republic of
WHO World Health Organization
WI Wisconsin
W.I. West Indies
Wis. Wisconsin
WSB Wage Stabilization Board
WV West Virginia
W.Va. West Virginia
WWI World War I
WWII World War II
WY Wyoming
Wyo. Wyoming

YK Yukon Territory
YMCA Young Men's Christian Association
YMHA Young Men's Hebrew Association
YM & YWHA Young Men's and Young
Women's Hebrew Association
yr. year
YT, Y.T. Yukon Territory
YWCA Young Women's Christian
   Association

zool. zoological

Alphabetical Practices

Names are arranged alphabetically according to the surnames, and under identical surnames according to the first given name. If both surname and first given name are identical, names are arranged alphabetically according to the second given name.

Surnames beginning with De, Des, Du, however capitalized or spaced, are recorded with the prefix preceding the surname and arranged alphabetically under the letter D.

Surnames beginning with Mac and Mc are arranged alphabetically under M.

Surnames beginning with Saint or St. appear after names that begin Sains, and are arranged according to the second part of the name, e.g. St. Clair before Saint Dennis.

Surnames beginning with Van, Von, or von are arranged alphabetically under the letter V.

Compound surnames are arranged according to the first member of the compound.

Many hyphenated Arabic names begin Al-, El-, or al-. These names are alphabetized according to each Biographee's designation of last name. Thus Al-Bahar, Neta may be listed either under Al- or under Bahar, depending on the preference of the listee.

Also, Arabic names have a variety of possible spellings when transposed to English. Spelling of these names is always based on the practice of the Biographee. Some Biographees use a Western form of word order, while others prefer the Arabic word sequence.

Similarly, Asian names may have no comma between family and given names, but some Biographees have chosen to add the comma. In each case, punctuation follows the preference of the Biographee.

Parentheses used in connection with a name indicate which part of the full name is usually deleted in common usage. Hence Chambers, E(lizabeth) Anne indicates that the usual form of the given name is E. Anne. In such a case, the parentheses are ignored in alphabetizing and the name would be arranged as Chambers, Elizabeth Anne. However, if the name is recorded Chambers, (Elizabeth) Anne, signifying that the entire name Elizabeth is not commonly used, the alphabetizing would be arranged as though the name were Chambers, Anne. If an entire middle or last name is enclosed in parentheses, that portion of the name is used in the alphabetical arrangement. Hence Chambers, Elizabeth (Anne) would be arranged as Chambers, Elizabeth Anne.

Where more than one spelling, word order, or name of an individual is frequently encountered, the sketch has been entered under the form preferred by the Biographee, with cross-references under alternate forms.

Who's Who in America®
Biographies L–Z

LAABS, ALLISON C., hospital administrator; b. Milw., Nov. 30, 1944. BA, Catholic U. Am., 1967, MA, 1968; M Health Adminstrn., Cornell U., 1974. Various positions St. Anthony's Meml. Hosp., Effingham, Ill., 1968-71, asst. administr.; 1974-75; exec. v.p. St. Mary's Hosp. Med. Ctr., Grenn Bay, Wis., 1975-84; assoc. administr. St. John's Hosp., Springfield, Ill., 1984-85, administr., 1985-90, administr., CEO, 1990—. Mem. Wis. Hosp. Assn. Home: 10 Danbury Dr Springfield IL 62704 Office: St John's Hosp 800 E Carpenter St Springfield IL 62769-0002

LAALY, HESHMAT OLLAH, research chemist, roofing consultant, author; b. Kermanshah, Iran, June 23, 1927; came to Germany, 1951, Can., 1967, U.S., 1984; s. Jacob and Saltanat (Afshani) L.; m. Parvaneh Modarai, Oct. 7, 1963; (div. 1971); children: Ramesh, Edmond S.; m. Parivash M. Farahmand, Feb. 7, 1982. BS in Chemistry, U. Stuttgart, Germany, 1955; MS in Chemistry, U. Stuttgart, Republic of Germany, 1958, PhD in Chemistry, 1962. Chief chemist Kress Sohne, Krefeld, Germany, 1963-67; analytical chemist Gulf Oil Research Ctr., Montreal, Que., Can., 1967-70; material scientist Bell-Northern Research, Ottawa, Ont., Can., 1970-71; research officer NRC of Can., Ottawa, 1972-84; pres. Roofing Materials Sci. and Tech., L.A., 1984—; Patentee in field. Author: The Science and Technology of Traditional and Modern Roofing Systems, 1992 (World Lifetime Achievement award Am. Biog. Inst. 1992); patentee bi-functional photovoltaic single ply roofing membrane. Mem. AAAS (Can. chpt.), ASTM, Inst. Roofing and Waterproofing Cons., Single-Ply Roofing Inst., Assn. Profl. Engrs. Ontario, Am. Chem. Soc., Internat. Union of Testing and Rsch. Labs. for Material and Structures (tech. com. 75), Constrn. Specifications Inst., Nat. Roofing Contractors Assn., UN Indsl. Devels. Orgn., Internat. Conf. Bldg. Ofcls., Roofing Cons. Inst., Inst. for Roofing and Waterproofing Cons., Can. Standard Assn., Can. Gen. Standards Bd. Office: Roofing Materials Sci & Tech 9037 Monte Mar Dr Los Angeles CA 90035-4235

LAANE, JAAN, chemistry educator; b. Paide, Estonia, June 20, 1942; came to U.S., 1949; s. Robert Freidrich and Linda (Treufeldt) L.; m. Tiiu Virkhaus, Sept. 3, 1966; children: Christina J, Lisa A. BS in Chemistry, U. Ill., 1964; PhD in Chemistry, MIT, 1967. Asst. prof. of chemistry Tufts U., Medford, Mass., 1967-68; asst. prof. of chemistry Tex. A&M U., College Station, 1968-72, assoc. prof. of chemistry, 1972-76, prof. of chemistry, 1976—, chmn. div. of physical and nuclear chemistry, 1977-87, 93-94, dir. inst. for Pacific Asia, 1987-90; assoc. dean sci., 1994—; dep. exec. dir., sr. policy advisor Tex. A&M U./Koriyama, College Station, 1990-94; editor Jour. Molecular Structure, 1994—; reviewer numerous profl. jours. and grant agys., 1968—; cons. indsl. and govt. orgns., 1970—; vis. prof. U. Bayreuth, Fed. Republic Germany, 1979-80; speaker Tex. A&M Faculty Senate, College Station, 1985-86; dir. NATO Advanced Rsch. Workshop, Ulm, Germany, 1992. Contbr. numerous articles to profl. jours.; lectr. numerous sci. presentations. Pres., founder College Station Assn. for Gifted and Talented, 1982-83. Recipient 9 rsch. grants Robert A. Welch Found., 1970-95, 8 rsch. grants NSF, 1976-94, U.S. Sr. Scientist award Alex Von Humboldt Found., Fed. Republic Germany, 1979, Disting. Teaching award Tex. A&M Assn. Former Students. Fellow Am. Inst. Chemists; mem. Am. Chem. Soc. (sect. pres. 1977-78), Am. Phys. Soc. Soc. for Applied Spectroscopy, Coblentz Soc. (bd. dirs., treas. 1986-89), Tex. A&M Faculty Club (pres. 1987-88), Phi Beta Delta (pres. 1990-91). Achievements include research in molecular spectroscopy and vibrational potential energy functions of molecules, laser Raman spectroscopy, Raman difference spectroscopy, ft-infrared spectroscopy. Home: 1906 Comal Cir College Station TX 77840-4818 Office: Tex A&M U College Station TX 77843

LAANO, ARCHIE BIENVENIDO MAAÑO, cardiologist; b. Tayabas, Quezon, Philippines, Aug. 10, 1939; naturalized U.S. citizen; s. Francisco M. and Iluminada (Maaño) L.; m. Maria Esmeralda Eleazar, May 2, 1964; 1 child, Sylvia Marie. A.A., U. Philippines, 1958, B.S., 1959, M.D., 1963; postgrad. Command and Gen. Staff Sch., Ft. Totten, N.Y., Ft. Leavenworth, Kans., 1978-79, Oxford (Eng.) U., 1985-86, Cambridge (Eng.) U., 1986-87. Diplomate Am. Bd. Internal Medicine. Rotating intern Hosp. St. Raphael, New Haven, 1963-64; resident internal medicine, 1964-65; rotating resident pulmonary diseases Laurel Heights Hosp., Shelton, Conn., 1965; affiliated rotating resident Yale-New Haven Med. Ctr., 1965; resident internal medicine Westchester County Med. Ctr., Valhalla, N.Y., 1965-66, resident cardiology, 1966-67; resident fellow cardiology Maimonides Med. Ctr., Bklyn., 1967-68; rotating sr. resident cardiology Coney Island Hosp., Bklyn., 1967-68; fellow internal medicine Mercy Hosp., Rockville Centre, N.Y., 1968-70; med. dir. 54 Main St. Med. Ctr., Hempstead, N.Y., 1971-76, Bloomingdale's, Garden City, N.Y., 1972—, Esselte Pendaflex Corp., Garden City, 1976—; attending staff Nassau County (N.Y.) Med. Ctr., Hempstead Gen. Hosp.; practice medicine specializing in cardiology, internal medicine, Nassau County, 1971—; chief med. svcs., chief profl. svcs. U.S. Army 808th Sta. Hosp., Hempstead, N.Y., 1979—; brig. gen. 1st U.S. Army AMEDD Augmentation Detachment, Ft. Meade, Md., 1989—, M.C., chief of staff, chief profl. svcs. U.S. Army Meddac Hosp., Ft. Dix., N.J., 1990—; med. dir. Cities Svc. Oil Co. (CITGO), L.I. div., 1972—; mem. adv. bd. Guardian Bank, Hempstead, chmn. adv. coun., 1973-89; clin. prof. medicine SUNY at Stony Brook, 1979—; professorial lectr. medicine (cardiology) U.S. Mil. Acad.-Keller Army Med. Ctr., West Point, N.Y., 1979; affiliated teaching hosp. Harvard Med. Sch, 1979; vis. prof. Harvard U., 1979—; cons. physician ICC, Citgo, Liberty Mut. Ins. Co. Boston, 1972—, U.S. Dept. Transp.; post-doctoral in medicine-cardiovasc. diseases Brasenose Coll., Oxford U., U.K., 1985-65, post-doctoral in medicine-cardiology Corpus Christi Coll., Cambridge U., U.K., 1986-87; counsel White House Commn. on Mil. Medicine, 1988—. Perpetual benefactor Permanent Endowment Fund, U. Philippines Coll. of Medicine, Manila, 1987—, Dr. Archie B.M. Laano Scholarship Fund, U. Philippines, Diliman, Quezon City, 1987—. Decorated Silver Star, Bronze Star, Legion of Merit, Soldiers medal, Joint Svc. Command medal, Army Meritorious Svc. medal, Dept. Def. Joint Svc. Achievement award, Southwest Asia Svc. award-Desert Storm, others. Fellow Internat. Coll. Angiology, Am. Coll. Angiology, Am. Coll. Internat. Physicians, Internat. Coll. Applied Nutrition, Am. Soc. Contemporary Medicine and Surgery, Acad. Preventive Medicine, Internat. Acad. Med. Preventives, Philippine Coll. Physicians, Am. Coll. Acupuncture, N.Y. Acad. of Sci.; mem. AMA, Am. Coll. Cardiology, N.Y. Med. Soc., Nassau County Med. Soc., Am. Heart Assn., N.Y. Cardiol. Soc., World Med. Assn., Royal Soc. Medicine (overseas, London), Nassau Acad. Medicine, Am., N.Y. State, Nassau Soc. Internal Medicine, N.Y. Soc. Acupuncture for Physicians, Am. Geriatrics Soc., Nassau Physicians Guild, Res. Officers Assn. U.S., Assn. Mil. Surgeons, Assn. Philippine Physicians Am. (bd. govs. rep. N.Y. State 1984-86, v.p. 1988-89, chmn. com. nominations and election 1987-88. spl. counsel to pres. 1986-87), Philippine Med. Assn. Am. (spl. counsel 1988-89, bd. dirs. 1989-90, spl. counsel to pres, 1989-90, dir. continuing med. edn. 1990—, chmn. scholarship com. 1989—), Assn. Philippine Physicians of N.Y. (founding v.p., pres. 1985-87, pres. emeritus 1988—, chmn. com. on constitution and by-laws, nominations and election, med. coord. Internat. Games for Disabled Olympics 1984), Soc. Philippine Surgeons Am. (Medallion of Honor 1991), U.S. Knights of Rizal, U. Philippines Med. Alumni Soc. (pres. class of 1963, 1981—), U. Philippines Med. Alumni . bd. 1985—), Royal Soc. Medicine Club, The Oxford Club, Rolls Royce Club L.I., N.Y. Club (chmn. 1987—), West Point OfficersClub, Garden City Country Club, Phi Kappa Mu (overseas coord. U. Philippines 1985—), Beta Sigma (coun. adivsers Ea. U.S. 1990—, program chmn. 1975—, chmn. bd. 1978—, pres. 1978-79), Lions (Garden City program chmn. 1975—, chmn. bd. 1978—,

pres. 1978-79). Home: 80 Stratford Ave Garden City NY 11530-2531 Office: 230 Hilton Ave Ste 106 Hempstead NY 11550-8116

LABA, MARVIN, management consultant; b. Newark, Mar. 17, 1928; s. Joseph Abraham and Jean Cecil (Saunders) L.; m. Sandra Seltzer, Apr. 16, 1961 (div. May 1974); children: Stuart Michael, Jonathan Todd; m. Elizabeth Luger, June 11, 1974 (div. 1979). BBA, Ind. U., 1951. Buyer Bamberger's (Macy's N.J.), Newark, 1951-67; v.p., mdse. adminstr. Macy's N.Y., 1967-73; v.p., gen. mdse. mgr. Howland/Steinback, White Plains, N.Y., 1973-75, Pomeroy's, Levittown, Pa., 1975-76; v.p., gen. mdse. mgr., sr. v.p., exec. v.p. May Co. Calif., North Hollywood, 1976-79; pres., chief exec. officer G. Fox & Co. (div. of the May dept. stores), Hartford, Conn., 1979-82; pres. Richard Theobald & Asocs., L.A., 1983; pres., chief exec. officer Marvin Laba & Assocs., L.A., 1983—. With U.S. Army, 1946-48. Avocations: coins, tennis, theatre, travel. Office: Marvin Laba & Assoc 6255 W Sunset Blvd Ste 617 Los Angeles CA 90028-7407

LABADIE, GEORGE SHERMAN, retired art director; b. Dewey, Okla., Jan. 31, 1916; s. John and Minnie (Lunney) L.; m. Jeanne Elizabeth Woodson, June 24, 1939; children: John Woodson, Lynn Joyce Labadie Todd. Student, Sacramento Jr. Coll., 1934-37, Chouinard Art Inst., 1937-39, Art Ctr. Sch., 1938-39, UCLA, 1948. Art dir. Bishop-Conklin Co., L.A., 1940-42, 45-47, Mayers Co., L.A., 1947-49, Russel Harte & Assocs., L.A., 1949-52; sr. art dir. Erwin Wasey, Inc., L.A., 1952-58; exec. art dir. Donahue & Coe, Inc., L.A., 1958-62; advt. mgr. Equity Funding Corp. Am., Beverly Hills, Calif., 1964-65; pres., owner George S. Labadie Agy., Beverly Hills, 1966-72; exec. art dir. Mulle Breen & Rossi, Inc., Beverly Hills, 1972-90; retired, 1981; instr. Calif. Art Inst., Calabasas, 1987—; producer videos Art Video Prodns., Canoga Park, Calif., 1989-90; instr. workshops in field. Contbr. paintings to profl. mags. and contbr. paintings to authored art pubs. Recipient awards San Diego Watercolor Soc., 1982, Old Forge Arts Guild, 1982, 84, 86, Houston Watercolor Soc., 1987, 90, Allied Artists Am., 1987, La. Watercolor Soc., 1989. Mem. Allied Artists Am. (award 1987), Am. Watercolor Soc., Nat. Watercolor Soc. (bd. dirs., treas. 1987-88, nat v.p. 1995—), Midwest Watercolor Soc. (award 1986, 88, 90), Watercolor West (award 1986, 88), West Coast Watercolor Soc. Republican. Avocations: chess, photography, mineral prospecting, American Indian culture. Home: 22940 Calabash St Woodland Hills CA 91364-2714

LABALME, PATRICIA HOCHSCHILD, educational administrator; b. N.Y.C., Feb. 26, 1927; d. Walter and Kathrin (Samstag) Hochschild; m. George Labalme, Jr., June 6, 1958; children: Jennifer R., Henry G., Lisa G., Victoria A. B.A. magna cum laude, Bryn Mawr Coll., 1948; M.A., Harvard U., 1950, Ph.D., 1958. Instr. history Wellesley Coll., Mass., 1952-57; tchr. history Brearley Sch., N.Y.C., 1957-59; lectr. Barnard Coll., N.Y.C., 1961-77; adj. assoc. prof. history Hunter Coll., N.Y.C., 1979; lectr. NYU, N.Y.C., 1980-82; adj. prof. history NYU, 1986-87; assoc. dir. Inst. for Advanced Study, Princeton, N.J., 1982-88; sec. corp. Inst. for Advanced Study, Princeton, 1982-92, asst. to dir., 1992—; mem. adv. bd. G. K. Delmas Found., N.Y.C., 1976-79, trustee, 1979; trustee Am. Acad. in Rome, N.Y.C., 1979—; exec. dir. Renaissance Soc. Am., N.Y.C., 1982-85, trustee, 1982-89; bd. dirs. Quantum Chem. Corp., 1990-93. Author: Bernardo Giustiniani: A Venetian of the Quattrocento, 1969; contbg. editor: Beyond Their Sex: Learned Women of the European Past, 1980, A Century Recalled: Essays in Honor of Bryn Mawr College, 1987; contbr. articles to profl. jours. and publs. Trustee Brearley Sch., 1975-83, pres., 1978-82, hon. trustee, 1983—; trustee Lawrenceville Sch., 1986—. Recipient Caroline A. Wilby prize Radcliffe Coll., 1958. Mem. Am. Hist. Assn., Soc. for Renaissance Studies, Renaissance Soc. Am., Ateneo Veneto, Cosmopolitan Club, Harvard Club (N.Y.C.), Cream Hill Lake Assn. (West Cornwall, Conn.), Phi Beta Kappa. Office: Inst for Advanced Study Olden Ln Princeton NJ 08540-4920

LABAN, MYRON MILES, physician, administrator; b. Detroit, Mar. 9, 1936; s. Larry Max and Mary Marsha (Harris) LaB.; m. Rita Joyce Hochman, Aug. 17, 1958; children: Terry, Amy, Craig. B.A., U. Mich., Ann Arbor, 1957, M.D., 1967; M.Med. Sci., Ohio State U., Columbus, 1965. Diplomate Am. Bd. Phys. Medicine and Rehab. Intern Sinai Hosp., Detroit, 1961-62; resident Ohio State U. Hosp., 1962-65; assoc. dir. phys. medicine and rehab. Letterman Gen. Hosp., San Francisco, 1965-67; dir. phys. medicine and rehab. William Beaumont Hosp., Royal Oak, Mich., 1967—; Licht lecturer Ohio State U., 1986, clin. prof., 1993; clin. prof. Wayne State U., Detroit, 1990, clin. prof. Oakland U., Rochester, Mich., 1983; bd. dirs. Oakland County Med. Bd., Birmingham, Mich., 1982-87; rep. to Commn. on Phys. Medicine and Rehab., Mich. State Med. Soc. Contbr. chpts. in books, articles to profl. publs. Med. dir. Oakland County March of Dimes, Mich., 1969-83. Served to capt. U.S. Army, 1965-67. Fellow Am. Acad. Phys. Medicine and Rehab. (bd. dirs. 1980, pres. 1985-86, Bernard Baruch Research award 1961, R. Rosenthal Research award 1982, Zeiter lectureship, Disting. Clinician award 1991, "Top Doc" PM&R Det. Monthly 1993); mem. AMA, Am. Congress Rehab. Medicine, Am. Assn. Electromyography and Electrodiagnosis (program dir. 1972), Oakland County Med. Soc. (trustee 1983, pres.-elect 1987, pres. 1988-89), Mich. State Med. Soc., Mich. Acad. Phys. Med. and Rehab. (pres. 1982-84, judicial commr. 1991—, mem. editorial bd. Jour. Phys. Med. and Rehab.). Republican. Jewish. Avocations: gardening; ship modeling. Office: LMT Rehabilitation Assocs 3535 W Thirteen Mile Rd Ste 703 Royal Oak MI 48072

LABAREE, BENJAMIN WOODS, history educator; b. New Haven, Conn., July 21, 1927; s. Leonard Woods and Elizabeth Mary (Calkins) L.; m. Linda Carol Prichard, June 27, 1959; children: Benjamin Woods Jr., Jonathan Martin, Sarah Calkins. BA, Yale U., 1950; AM, Harvard U., 1953, PhD, 1957. Instr. history Conn. Coll., New London, 1957-58; from asst. prof. history to Allston Burr Sr. Tutor Harvard U., Cambridge, Mass., 1958-63; dean Williams Coll., Williamstown, Mass., 1963-67; assoc. to prof. history, 1963-77; Ephraim Williams Prof. Am. History, 1972-77; dir. Williams Coll.-Mystic Seaport Program/Mystic Seaport Mus., Mystic, Conn., 1977-89; dir. Ctr. for Environ. Studies Williams Coll., 1989-91; prof. history and environ. studies Williams Coll., Williamstown, 1989-92; prof. emeritus, 1992—; vis. prof. Trinity Coll., Conn., 1993, Williams Coll., 1994; dir. Munson Inst. Am. Maritime Studies, Mystic, 1974—; mng. editor Essex Inst. Hist. Collections, Salem, Mass., 1956-60. Author: Patriots and Partisans, 1962, The Boston Tea Party, 1964, America's Nation-Time, 1972, Colonial Massachusetts, 1979; co-author: New England and The Sea, 1972, Empire or Independence, 1976. Mem. Mt. Greylock Regional High Sch. Com., Williamstown, 1971-74. With USNR, 1945-46, ATO. Recipient Wilbur Cross award Conn. Humanities Coun., 1990, Samuel Eliot Morison award USS Constitution Mus., 1993. Mem. Am. Hist. Assn. (com. 1971-73), Am. Antiquarian Soc., Colonial Soc. Mass., Mass. Hist. Soc., Inst. for Early Am. History and Culture (coun. mem. 1983-86), others. Democrat. Congregationalist. Avocations: sailing, rowing, swimming. Home and Office: 2 Andrews Ln Amesbury MA 01913

LABARGE, MARGARET WADE, medieval history educator; b. N.Y.C., July 18, 1916; arrived in Can. 1940; d. Alfred Byers and Helena (Mein) Wade; m. Raymond C. Labarge, June 20, 1940 (dec. May 1972); children: Claire Labarge Morris, Suzanne, Charles, Paul. BA, Radcliffe Coll., 1937; LittB, Oxford (Eng.) U., 1939; LittD (hon.), Carleton U., Ottawa, Ont., Can., 1976; LLD (hon.), U. Waterloo, Ont., Can., 1993. Lectr. history U. Ottawa, Carleton U., 1950-62; adj. prof. history Carleton U., Ottawa, 1983—. Author: Simon de Montfort, 1962, A Baronial Household, 1965,

Gascony, 1980, A Small Sound of the Trumpet, 1987, others; contbr. articles to profl. jours. Chmn. bd. dirs. St. Vincent's Hosp., Ottawa, 1969-81; pub. rep. bd. dirs. Can. Nurses Assn., 1980-83; bd. dirs. Carleton U., 1984-93, Coun. on Aging, 1986-93 (pres., 1989-91). Recipient Alumnae Recognition award Radcliffe Coll., 1987. Fellow Royal Soc. Can.; mem. Medieval Acad., Order of Can., Phi Beta Kappa. Roman Catholic. Avocations: traveling, reading, walking. Home and Office: 402-555 Wilbrod St, Ottawa, ON Canada K1N 5R4

LABARGE, RICHARD ALLEN, financial analyst, educator; b. Salt Lake City, May 6, 1934; s. Oza Joseph and Mae (Erdman) LaB.; m. Catherine Eulalie Laurent, June 10, 1953 (div. 1979); children: R. Allen Jr., Catherine, Joseph Laurent, Nedra Anne, Eve Marie, Mary Evangeline, Louis E.R.; m. Karin Louise Peterson, June 28, 1980; 1 child, Robert E.J. AB, U. Mich., 1954; MA, Tulane U., 1955; PhD, Duke U., 1960. Chartered fin. analyst, 1982. Asst. prof. So. Methodist U., Dallas, 1957-60; treas., fin. analyst, spl. legis. analyst world hdqrs. Ford Motor Co., Dearborn, 1960-65; assoc. prof. Fla. State U., Tallahassee, 1965-67; prof. econs. and fin. U. New Orleans, 1967-89, chair dept., 1967-73; prof. Rutgers U., Camden, N.J., 1990-92; prin. Capital Choices, Inc., 1992—; fin. economist U.S. SEC, Washington, summer, 1977; cons. bd. regents State U. System Fla., Tallahassee, Miami, 1989; lectr. Fin. Analysts' Rev., Raleigh, N.C., 1989-92, Zurich, Switzerland, 1990, Bangkok, Thailand, 1993. Author: (monograph) Impact of United Front on Economic Development of Guatemala, 1960; contbr. articles to internat. profl. jours. Rsch. tng. fellow Social Sci. Rsch. Coun., Washington, 1956-57, Sr. Fulbright-Hays prof., Mexico, 1973-74. Mem. Assn. for Investment Mgmt. Rsch. N.Y. Soc. Security Analyst, Nat. Assn. Bus. Economists (New Orleans chpt., pres. 1972-73, 75-76), Mich. Alumni Assn. (New Orleans chpt., pres. 1985-89). Republican. Avocations: computer programming, travel. Home: 160 Ardmore Ave Haddonfield NJ 08033-1428 Office: Capital Choices Inc 160 Ardmore Ave Haddonfield NJ 08033-1428

LA BARGE, WILLIAM JOSEPH, tutor, researcher; b. Portis, Kans., June 27, 1943; s. Louis Joseph and Mary Genevieve (Colton) La B. AB, Ft. Hays State U., Hays, Kans., 1966, postgrad.d; 1980; postgrad.d, Cloud County C.C., Concordia, Kans., 1984. Cert. tchr., Kans. Depot agt. Mo. Pacific R.R., Lenora, Kans., 1971-77; correctional officer Kans. Dept. Corrections, Hutchinson, 1977; prodn. worker Becker Mfg. Co., Downs, Kans., 1978-79; ind. study Downs, 1983-88; pvt. tutor Templemere, Downs, 1988—. With USN, 1966-70. Mem. ASCD, Archaeol. Inst. Am., U.S. Naval Inst. Roman Catholic. Avocations: archaeology, history, toy soldiers, travel. Home and Office: 519 Blunt St Downs KS 67437-1713

LABARRE, CARL ANTHONY, retired government official; b. Sherwood, N.D., July 16, 1918; s. William Paul and Josephine K. LaB.; m. Persis Wester, Sept. 9, 1941; 1 son, William Paul, II. Student, U. Mont., 1936-40; postgrad., Naval Acad. Postgrad. Sch., 1945-46; grad., Naval War Coll., 1958-59, Advanced Mgmt. Program, Harvard U. Commd. ensign U.S. Navy, 1941, advanced through grades to capt., 1971; served in various fin., inventory control systems and purchasing assignments, to 1971; insp. gen. (Naval Supply Systems Command), to 1971; ret., 1971; dep. dir. materials mgmt. service GPO, Washington, 1971-75; dir. materials mgmt. service GPO, 1975, asst. public printer, supt. documents, 1975-82. Decorated Navy Commendation medal with V, Joint Service commendation medal, Legion of Merit with gold star; recipient Public Printers Disting. Service award, 1977, 81. Club: Harvard Bus. Sch. (Washington).

LABARRE, DENNIS W., lawyer; b. Binghamton, N.Y., Dec. 27, 1942. BA, Northwestern U., 1965; LLB, U. Va., 1968. Ptnr. Jones, Day, Reavis & Pogue, N.Y.C. Office: Jones Day Reavis & Pogue 599 Lexington Ave New York NY 10022-6030

LABATH, OCTAVE AARON, mechanical engineer; b. Milw., Sept. 22, 1941; s. Octave Adrain and Bertha Jane (Johnson) LaB.; m. Carole Marion Clay, Jan. 23, 1965; children—Melissa, Michelle, Mark. B.S. in Mech. Engring., U. Cin., 1964, M.S., 1969. Registered profl. engr., Ohio. v.p. engring. Cin. Gear Co., 1972—. Contbr. articles to profl. jours. Mem. Am. Gear Mfg. Assns., ASME. Methodist. Men's Club. Home: 5105 Kenridge Dr Cincinnati OH 45242-4831 Office: Cin Gear 5657 Wooster Pike Cincinnati OH 45227-4120

LABAY, EUGENE BENEDICT, lawyer; b. El Campo, Tex., July 20, 1938; s. Ben F. and Cecelia M. (Orsak) L.; m. Katharine Sue Ermis, Dec. 29, 1962; children—Michael, Joan, John, Paul, David, Patrick, Steven. B.B.A., St. Mary's U., San Antonio, 1960, J.D., 1965. Bar: Tex. 1965, U.S. Dist. Ct. (we. dist.) Tex. 1968, U.S. Dist. Ct. (no. dist.) Tex. 1973, U.S. Ct. Appeals (5th cir.) 1968, U.S. Ct. Appeals (11th cir.) 1981, U.S. Supreme Ct. 1980, U.S. Dist. Ct. (ea. dist.) Tex. 1986. Briefing atty. Supreme Ct. Tex., Austin, 1965-66; assoc. Cox & Smith Inc., San Antonio, 1966-71, ptnr., 1972-83, v.p., 1972-94; pvt. practice, 1994—. Served to 1st lt. U.S. Army, 1960-62. Mem. ABA, State Bar Tex. (chmn. sect. internat. law 1979-80), San Antonio Bar Assn., Fed. Bar Assn., Inter-Am. Bar Assn., Am. Judicature Soc., Catholic Lawyers Guild San Antonio, Phi Delta Phi, Roman Catholic. Clubs: Serra (San Antonio); KC (council grand knight 1982-83). Contbr. articles to legal jours. Home: 31720 Post Oak Trl Boerne TX 78006-4133 Office: 1140 Milam Bldg 115 E Travis St San Antonio TX 78205

LABBE, ARMAND JOSEPH, museum curator, anthropologist; b. Lawrence, Mass., June 13, 1944; s. Armand Henri and Gertrude Marie (Martineau) L.; m. Denise Marie Scott, Jan. 17, 1969 (div. 1972). BA in Anthropology, Univ. Mass., 1969; MA in Anthropology, Calif. State U., 1986; lifetime instr. credential in anthropology, State Calif. Curator collections Bowers Mus., Santa Ana, Calif., 1978-79, curator anthropology, 1979-86, chief curator, 1986-91, dir. rsch. and collections, 1991—; tchr. Santa Ana Coll., 1981-86, Calif. State U. Fullerton, 1982, 83, 88, U. Calif., Irvine, 1983, 87, 91, 93; trustee Balboa Arts Conservation Ctr., San Diego, 1989—, Ams. Found., Greenfield, Mass., 1985-94. Quintcentenary Festival Discovery, Orange County, Calif., 1990-91; mem. adv. bd. Elan Internat., Newport Beach, Calif., 1992—; trustee Mingei Internat. Mus., LaJolla, Calif., 1993—; inaugural guest lectr. Friends of Ethnic Art, San Francisco, 1988; hon. bd. dirs. Ethnic Arts Coun. of L.A. Author: Man and Cosmos, 1982, Ban Chiang, 1985, Colombia Before Columbus, 1986 (1st prize 1987), Leigh Wiener: Portraits, 1987, Colombia Antes de Colón, 1988 (honored at Gold Mus. Bogotá, Colombia, 1988), Images of Power: Master Works of the Bowers Museum of Cultural Art, 1992; co-author Tribute to The Gods: Treasures of the Museo del Oro, Bogotá, 1992, Guardians of the Life Stream: Shamans, Art and Power In Prehispanic Central Panama, 1995. Cons. Orange County Coun. on History and Art, Santa Ana, 1981-85; mem. Task Force on County Cultural Resources, Orange County, 1979; cons., interviewer TV prodn. The Human Journey, Fullerton, 1986-89; hon. mem. bd. dirs. L.A. Ethnic Arts Coun. With USAF, 1963-67. Recipient cert. of Recognition Orange County Bd. Suprs., 1982, award for outstanding scholarship Colombian Community, 1987; honored for authorship Friends of Libr., 1987, 88. Fellow Am. Anthrop. Assn.; mem. AAAS, Am. Assn. Mus., N.Y. Acad. Scis., S.W. Anthrop. Assn. Avocations: photography, travel. Home: 2854 Royal Palm Dr # C Costa Mesa CA 92626-3828

L'ABBÉ, GERRIT KAREL, chemist; b. Oostende, Belgium, Dec. 13, 1940; s. Bertram L'abbé and Marie-Rose Coenegrachts; m. Christianne Platteau, Aug. 17, 1967; children: Annick, Caroline. Lic. in Chemistry with highest honors, U. Leuven, Belgium, 1963; Dr. in Sci., U. Leuven, 1966. Postdoctoral fellow Erlangen, Fed. Republic Germany, 1967-68, Boulder, Colo., 1969-70; docent U. Leuven, 1972-75, prof. chemistry, 1975-77, prof. ordinarius, 1977—; rsch. dir. U. Leuven, 1972—. Contbr. 200 articles to profl. jours. Recipient Belgian-BP prize, 1959, P. Bruylants prize Chemici Lovanienses, 1966, bieninial prize Jour. Industrie Chimique Belge, 1968, award Japan Soc. for Promotion Sci., 1979, EuChem award European Cmtys. Chemistry Coun., 1993; Alexander von Humboldt fellow, 1967-68, Fulbright rsch. fellow, 1969-70, fellow Nat. Fund for Sci. Rsch., 1963-72. Fellow Brit. Royal Soc. Chemistry (chartered); mem. Am. Chem. Soc., Internat. Soc. Heterocyclic Chemistry, Belgian Royal Acad. Sci. (J.S. Stas medal 1966, Laureate 1972), Flemish Chem. Soc. (Breckpot prize 1983), Internat. Order of Merit. Home: Merellaan 33, 3210 Linden Belgium Office: U Leuven Dept Chemistry, Celestijnenlaan 200F, 3001 Heverlee Belgium

LABBÉ, PAUL, export corporation executive; b. Buckingham, Que., Can., Mar. 11, 1939; s. Arthur and Dorothy Frances (Gorman) L.; m. Kathryn Grace Cameron, July 10, 1965; Marie-Paule, Marc. Philippe, David, Robert. BA, U. Ottawa, 1961; BCL, McGill U., 1964; student, Ecole Nationale D'Administration, Paris, 1969, Harvard Grad. Sch. Bus., 1990. Bar: Que. 1965. Comml. sec. Can. Embassy, Paris, 1966-69; exec. asst. to minister Dept. Industry, Trade & Commerce, Ottawa, Ont., 1969-73; assoc. Interimco, Inc., 1973-75, pres., 1975-81; pres. CDN Indsl. Rev. Bd., 1981-85; commr. Fgn. Investment Rev. Agy., 1985; pres. Investment Can., Ottawa, 1985-91; commr. Fgn. Investment Rev. Agy., 1985; pres., CEO Export Devel. Corp., Ottawa, 1991—. Gov. Can. Comprehensive Auditing Found. Mem. Rideau Club, Hunt Club. Home: 216 Clemow Ave, Ottawa, ON Canada K1S 2B6 Office: Export Development Corp, 151 O'Connor St, Ottawa, ON Canada K1A 1K3

LABBETT, JOHN EDGAR, pet food products executive; b. Chesham, Bucks, Eng., June 19, 1950; came to U.S., 1987; s. Gordon F. and Sylvia (Dalton) L.; m. Mary McGagh, Jan. 30, 1976; children: Jennifer F., Alexander T. Audit clk. White Withers and Co., Bexhill, Eng., 1966-71; auditor Peat Marwick Mitchell, London, 1971-73; chief acct. Guild S&V Ltd., London, 1973-74; from fin. analyst to contr. Roneo Vickers Ltd., London, 1974-81; fin. contr. Cambridge (Eng.) Instruments Ltd., 1981-82; fin. dir. Linfood C&C Ltd. subsid. Dee Corp., Milton Keynes, U.K., 1982-85; fin. controller Dee Corp., Milton Keines, 1985-87; exec. v.p., chief fin. officer Hermans Sporting Goods, Inc., Carteret, N.J., 1987-93; v.p., CFO The Petfood Giant, Inc., 1994—. Fellow Inst. Chartered Accts. Eng. and Wales. Mem. Ch. Eng. Home: 597 Little Silver Point Rd Little Silver NJ 07739-1732

LABELLE, EUGENE JEAN-MARC, airport director general; b. Montreal, Que., Can., Nov. 26, 1941; s. Paul Eugene and Pauline (Brissette) L.; m. Louise Gingras; 1 child, Anne Marie. BA in Sci. and Math., U. Montreal, 1962, BS in Applied Scis. (civil engring.), 1967; postgrad. in transp. mgmt., various colls., 1975-85. Registered profl. engr., Que.; cert. expert of Internat. Aviation Orgn., expert of World Bank. With Transport Canada, 1967—; field engr. constrn. br. Que. region, 1967-68, design engr. constrn. br., 1968-71; mgr. engring. and maintenance svcs. Dorval, 1971-75; regional mgr. airport ops. Que. Region, 1975-80; acting airport gen. mgr. Dorval, 1980-81; mgr. airport mgr. & svcs. Mirabel, 1981-82; airport gen. mgr. Dorval, 1982-88; dir. gen. Montreal Airports, 1988-92; exec. v.p., COO Aeroports de Montreal, Canada, 1992-94, group v.p. planning and devel., 1994—; pres., gen. mgr. Aeroports de Montreal Svcs. Inc.; mem. planning missions, aerodrome engr. and/or mgmt. cons. for Internat. Civil Aviation Orgn. and World Bank, Congo, 1981, Cameroun, 1983, Chad, 1983, 84, 85, Senegal, 1984, Kenya, 1984, Jordan, 1985, Hdqrs., Montreal, 1986, Madagascar, 1985, Sierra Leone, Qatar, 1986, Turks and Caicos Islands, program evaluation officer, Kigali, Rwanda, 1986; aerodrome mgmt. cons. study of civil aviation reorgn., Conakry, (Guinea), World Bank Mission, 1986; ICAO Program Evaluation Officer, UN Tchad, 1987; aerodrome mgmt. cons., Warsaw, Poland, 1987; aerodrome engring cons., Kuwait, 1988, St. Vincent and the Grenadines, 1989, Uruguay, 1989; lectr. Civil Aviation Acad., Leningrad, USSR, 1990; aerodrome mgmt. advisor Santo Domingo, 1990; aerodrome mgmt. and engring. advisor Trinidad and Tobago, 1991, 92; UN program evaluation officer, Mózambique, 1990; aerodrome planning engr., Lebanon, 1993. Mem. ASCE, Chambre de Commerce de Montreal, Ordre des Ingenieurs du Quebec, Can. Inst.of Engrs., Fed. Inst. Mgmt., City of St. Laurent Chambre of Commerce, Am. Assn. Airport Execs., Airports Coun. Internat., Airports Conss. Coun., Can. Exporters Assn. Avocations: classical music, opera, reading, arts, golf. Home: 337 Perrault St, Rosemere, PQ Canada J7A 1C4 Office: Aeroports de Montreal, 1100 Rene-Levesque Blvd W 21st fl, Montreal, PQ Canada H3B 4X8

LABELLE, HUGUETTE, international agency executive; b. Rockland, Ont., Can.. PhD in Edn., U. Ottawa; hon. degree, Brock U., U. Sask., U. Ottawa, Carleton U., York U., U. Man., U. Windsor, Mt. St. Vincent U. Sr. mgmt. positions Indian and No. Affairs and Health and Welfare, Can., 1973-80; under-sec. of state Dept. Sec. of State, 1980-85; assoc. sec. to Cabinet, dep. clk. Privy Coun., 1985; chmn. Pub. Svc. Commn. Can., 1985-90; dep. min. Transport Can., 1990-93; pres. Can. Internat. Devel. Agy., Hull, Que., Can., 1993—; co-chair expert com. on health manpower mgmt. svs. WHO, 1987; cons. on health care planning and health scis. edn. to govts. of Haiti and Cuba, 1974-76; bd. dirs. Internat. Devel. Rsch. Ctr., Export Devel. Corp.. Internat. Ctr. for Human Rights and Dem. Devel.; mem. working group health and devel. policies Internat. Inst. for Sustainable Devel. and WHO; chancellor U. Ottawa. Pres./chmn. Can. Red Cross Soc.; bd. trustees Ottawa Gen. Hosp.; bd. dirs. Ottawa Health Scis. Ctr., Inc., Algonquin Coll., Ottawa-Carleton United Way, Internat. Ctr. for Human Rights and Dem. Devel. Named officer of Order of Can., 1990; recipient Vanier medal Inst. Pub. Administrn. of Can., 1993. Mem. Transp. Assn. Can., Can. Nurses Assn. (bd. dirs.). Office: Can Internat Devel Agy, 200 Promenade du Portage, Hull, PQ Canada K1A OG4

LABELLE, PATTI, singer; b. Phila., Oct. 4, 1944; d. Henry Holte; m. Armstead Edwards; children: Zuri, Stanley, Dodd. Singer Patti LaBelle and the Bluebelles, 1962-70; lead singer musical group LaBelle, 1970-76; solo performer, 1977—. Albums include Over the Rainbow, 1967, La Belle, 1971, Moon Shadows, 1972, Pressure Cookin', 1974, Chameleon, 1976, Patti LaBelle, 1977, Live at the Apollo, 1980, Gonna Take A Miracle-The Spirit's in It, 1982, I'm in Love Again, 1984, Winner in You, 1986, The Best of Patti LaBelle, Patti, Be Yourself, Burnin', 1991, Live (Apollo Theater), 1993, Gems, 1994; appeared in films A Soldier's Story, 1985, Beverly Hills Cop, 1985; appeared in TV movie Unnatural Causes, 1986, TV series A Different World, Out All Night, 1992. Recipient award of Merit, Phila. Art Alliance, 1987.Recipient Grammy award: best Rhythm & Blues vocal for "Burnin", 1991, Grammy nomination (Best Rhythym & Blues Female Vocal, 1994) for "All Right Now". Home: 8730 Sunset Blvd & PH-W Los Angeles CA 90069 Office: care MCA Records Inc 100 Universal City Plz Universal City CA 91608*

LABELLE, THOMAS JEFFREY, academic administrator; b. Owen, Wis., Sept. 21, 1941; s. Wendell Allen and Katherine (Dolan) LaB.; m. Nancy Reik, June 16, 1966 (dec. 1981); children: Katherine Anne, Jeanette Marie. AA, Pierce Coll., Woodland Hills, Calif., 1962; BA, Calif. State U., Northridge, 1964; MA, U. N.Mex., Albuquerque, 1967, PhD, 1969. Prof. UCLA, 1969-86, asst. dean edn., 1971-79, assoc. dean grad. div., 1980-86; prof. comparative and internat. edn. U. Pitts., 1986-90, dean Sch. Edn., 1986-90; v.p. acad. programs, provost Ga. State U., Atlanta, 1990-93; provost, v.p. acad. affairs and rsch. W.Va. U., Morgantown, 1993—; cons. InterAm. Found., U.S. AID, Ford Found., CBS, Acad. Ednl. Devel., Juarez and Assocs. Author: Education and Development in Latin America, 1972; Nonformal Education in Latin America, 1976; Nonformal Education in Latin America and the Caribbean; Stability, Reform or Revolution, 1986; Education and Intergroup Relations, 1985, Multiculturalism and Education, 1994. Vol. Peace Corps, Colombia, 1964-66. Grantee Fulbright Found., 1983, InterAm. Found., Latin America, 1984; recipient Andres Bello award 1st Class, Venezuela, 1987. Fellow Soc. Applied Anthropology; mem. Comparative and Internat. Edn. Soc. (pres. 1981), Coun. on Anthropology and Edn. (bd. dirs. 1977), Inter-Am. Found. (chmn. learning fellowship on social change), Golden Key, Omicron Delta Kappa, Phi Kappa Phi. Democrat. Office: W Va Univ Stewart Hall PO Box 6203 Morgantown WV 26506-6203

LABERNIK, MARY SUE, nurse; b. LaCrosse, Wis., Dec. 16, 1937; d. Raymond A. and Francis L. Fay; m. Theodore John Labernik, July 5, 1958; children: Debra Curry, Linda Himmelberger, Susan North, Laura Zeller, Daniel, Steven. Diploma, St. Mary's Sch. Nursing, Rochester, Minn., 1958; BA, Redlands U., 1974; BSN, Moorhead State U., 1982; MSN, U. N.D., Grand Forks, 1985. CCRN; cert. in nursing adminstrn.-advanced; cert. ACLS. Staff nurse Ely-Winton (Minn.) Hosp., 1959; office nurse D.E. Wagoner, MD., Oscoda, Mich., 1968-70; staff nurse Columbus Hosp., Great Falls, Mont., 1971-72; Victor Valley Hosp., Victorville, Calif., 1972-74, Meml. Hosp., Colorado Springs, 1974-75, Community Hosp., Colorado Springs, 1975-77; ICU staff nurse VA Med. Ctr., Fargo, N.D., 1977-82, head nurse, 1982-85, day supr., 1985-90; acting asst. chief nurse VA Med. Ctr., 1988-90, preceptorship tng. program, Mpls. Vets. Affairs Med. Ctr., 1990-91, asst. chief nurse, Ft. Wayne Vets. Affairs Med. Ctr., 1991—. Active ARC, 1965—. Mem. ANA, AACCN (pres. Fargo-Moorhead chpt. 1987-88, Critical Care Nurse of Yr. 1988-89), N.D. Nurses Assn., Midwest Nursing Rsch. Soc., Nurses Orgn. VA, NAFE, Sigma Theta Tau. Roman Catholic. Avocations: bridge, reading, skiing, hiking, bicycling. Home: 55016 Old Dover Blvd Fort Wayne IN 46835 Office: VA Med Ctr 2121 Lake Ave Fort Wayne IN 46805-5100

LA BLANC, CHARLES WESLEY, JR., financial consultant; b. Bayshore, L.I., N.Y., June 4, 1925; s. Charles Wesley and Anne (Dobson) LaB.; m. Marie Dolan, Oct. 26, 1963 (dec. Jan. 1985); children: Charles Wesley III, Gregory, Suzanne; m. Joan H. Trapp, Dec. 29, 1993. BS, Tufts Coll., 1949; MBA, NYU, 1952, PhD, 1956. Securities portfolio mgr. Manhattan Life Ins. Co., N.Y.C., 1952-57; asst. to pres. Magnavox Co., Ft. Wayne, Ind., 1957-60; security analyst C.W. LaBlanc & Assos., N.Y.C., 1960-62; treas. Macke Co., Cheverly, Md., 1962-72, dir., 1974-80; exec. v.p., sec.-treas., dir. After Six, Inc., Phila., 1972-84; pres. Bert Paley Ltd., Inc. subs., 1976-77; chmn. bd. Cymaticolor, 1983-84; chief fin. officer and dir. Standard Telecommunications Systems Inc., South Hackensack, N.J., 1983-87; pres. Standard Profit Sharing Fund, 1987—; bd. dirs. Acad. of Vocal Arts. Pres. Queens County Young Reps., 1955-57; bd. dirs. adv. council Temple U. With AC USNR, 1943-46. Fellow N.Y. Soc. Security Analysts; mem. Washington Soc. Investment Analysts, Fin. Analysts Phila., Fin. Execs. Inst., Am. Acctg. Assn., Am. Soc. Ins. Mgmt., Pub. Rels. Soc. Am., Nat. Assn. Bus. Economists, Nat. Investor Rels. Inst., Nat. Assn. Corp. Dirs., Phila. Securities Assn. (pres. 1991, bd. dirs.), Am. Stock Exch. Club, Union League, The Bond Club. Home: 370 Aubrey Rd Wynnewood PA 19096-1819 also: 111 N Pompano Beach Blvd Apt 1905 Pompano Beach FL 33062 also: 35487 Davis Wharf Rd Belle Haven VA 23306

LA BLANC, ROBERT EDMUND, consulting company executive; b. N.Y.C., Mar. 21, 1934; s. Charles Wesley and Anne R. (Dobson) La B.; m. Elizabeth Lammers, 1962; children: Elizabeth, Robert, Jeanne Marie, Paul, Michelle. B.E.E., Manhattan Coll., 1956; M.B.A., NYU, 1962. With Bell System, 1956-69; mem. tech. staff Bell Telephone Labs., 1961-62; seminar leader AT&T Long Lines, Cooperstown, N.Y., 1965-67; mktg. supr. AT&T Hdqrs., N.Y.C., 1967-68; planning engr. N.Y. Telephone, 1968-69; mgr. Salomon Bros., N.Y.C., 1969-73; v.p. Salomon Bros., 1973-75, gen. partner, 1975-79; vice chmn. Continental Telephone Corp., N.Y.C., 1979-81; pres. Robert E. LaBlanc Assocs., Inc., 1981—; bd. dirs. Storage Tech. Corp., M/A-COM, Inc., TIE/Comm. Inc., Tribune Co., Prudential Global Fund Inc., Contel Cellular Inc., Prudential Short-Term Global Income Fund, Inc., Prudential Pacific Growth Fund, Inc.; trustee Prudential U.S. Govt. Fund. Vice chmn. bd. trustees Manhattan Coll., 1987-93. Served to 1st lt. USAF, 1956-59. Named Wall St. Leading Analyst Instl. Investor Mag., 1973-78. Fellow Fin. Analysts Fedn.; mem. N.Y. Soc. Security Analysts (sr.), Assn. for Computing Machinery, Nat. Soc. Rate of Return Cons., Univ. Club, Marco Polo Club, Econ. Club. Republican. Roman Catholic.

LABODA, AMY SUE, writer; b. Phila., Sept. 10, 1962; d. Gerald and Sheila Lois (Plasky) L.; mem. Barry Lee Marz, Mar. 5, 1987; children: Rose Marie, Leah Ann. BA, Sarah Lawrence Coll., 1984. Vol. U.S. Peace Corps, Togo, 1985; flight instr., pilot Redwood Aviation, Santa Rosa, Calif., 1986, Qualiflight Tng., Ft. Worth, 1987-88; depts. editor Flying mag., N.Y.C., 1988-90; free-lance writer, mktg. cons. Ft. Myers, Fla., 1990—; mem. selection com. Am. Flyers Scholarship, Pal-Walkee, Ill., 1990—. Cons. editor textbook series: The Pilot's Manual, 2d edit., 1993; editor: Flying Ultralights, U.S. edit.; contbr. articles to various mags. Mem. NAFE, Exptl. Aircraft Assn., Aircraft Owners and Pilots Assn., Women in Aviation (internat. exec. bd. dirs.), Women's Scuba Assn., Diver's Alert Network. Avocations: scuba diving, soaring, skydiving.

LABODA, GERALD, oral and maxillofacial surgeon; b. Phila., Aug. 15, 1936; s. Lewis and Rose (Waldman) L.; m. Sheila Lois Plasky, Aug. 2, 1956; children: Amy, Michèle, Alane, Bruce. Student, Temple U., 1954-56, DDS, 1960; postgrad., U. Pa., 1960-61. Diplomate Am. Bd. Oral and Maxillofacial Surgery. Resident physician in oral and maxillofacial surgery Jefferson U., Phila., 1961-63; pvt. practice oral and maxillofacial surgery S.W. Fla. Oral Surgery Assocs., Ft. Myers, 1965—; postgrad. Sch. of Medicine; sr. dir. Barnett Bank of Lee County, Ft. Myers; chmn. bd. trustees S.W. Fla. Regional Med. Ctr., Ft. Myers, 1989-94, sec. bd. trustees, 1974—; med. dir. S.W. Fla. divsn. Columbia/HCA Hosp. Corp. Contbr. articles to profl. jours. Pres. YMCA of Lee County, 1976; pres. Found. for Lee County Pub. Schs., Ft. Myers, 1991; vice chmn. Downtown Redevel. Agy., Ft. Myers, 1985-93, chmn., 1993—; bd. dirs. United Way of Lee County, 1981. Fellow Am. Assn. Oral and Maxillofacial Surgeons (trustee Dist. III 1984-87, v.p. 1987-88, pres. 1989-90); mem. Fla. Soc. Oral and Maxillofacial Surgeons (pres. 1980-81), Fla. Dental Soc. of Anesthesiology (pres. 1978-79), S.W. Fla. Dental Soc. (pres. 1974). Republican. Jewish. Avocations: flying, skiing, scuba diving, white water rafting. Office: SW Fla Oral Surg Assocs Summerlin Med Park 5285 Summerlin Rd Fort Myers FL 33919-7602

LA BONTÉ, C(LARENCE) JOSEPH, weight management and lifestyle company executive; b. Salem, Mass., Sept. 23, 1939; s. Arthur and Alice Bella (Lecombe) LaB.; m. Donna Marie Chiaradonna, Aug. 2, 1959; children: Linda Jean, Joseph Michael. BS, Northeastern U., 1966, AME, 1968; MBA with distinction (Baker scholar), Harvard U., 1969. With H.P. Hood & Sons, Boston, 1958-63; project engr., mktg. coordinator Market Forge Co., Everett, Mass., 1963-67; with ARA Services, Inc., Phila., 1969-79, exec. asst. to pres., 1969-71, v.p., 1971-72, exec. v.p., 1976-79; pres. Western Co., Los Angeles, 1972-76; pres. chief operating officer, dir. Twentieth Century-Fox Film Corp., Beverly Hills, Calif., 1979-83; chmn., chief exec. officer The Vantage Group Inc., 1983-87, 90—; pres. chief operating officer Reebok Internat. Ltd., Stoughton, Mass., 1987-90; also bd. dirs. Reebok Internat., Stoughton, Mass.; chmn., CEO, Vantage Group, Inc., Palos Verdes, Calif., 1990-94; pres., CEO Jenny Craig, Internat., Del Mar, Calif., 1994—, also bd. dirs., mem. exec. com.; bd. dirs. several cos.; founder, pres. Am. Bus. Initiative for Free South Africa, 1990-95; bd. dirs. U.S.-SALEP, Washington. Founding dir. Souht African Fre Elections Fund, 1993-94; nat. bd. dirs. Big Bros. Am., 1970-74, pres., 1985-87; bd. dirs. L.A. Philharm. Assn., 1990-94, chmn. bd. dirs., 1994—; trustee Northeastern U., 1974-95; mem. Harvard U. Bus. Sch. Fund, 1991—; trustee orthopedic Hosp., L.A., 1980-86. Mem. Harvard U. Bus. Sch. Assn., Husky Assocs. Northeatern U., Huntington Soc., Human Rights Watch (Calif. exec. com.), Phila. Country Club Down Town Club, Vesper Club, Bankers Club San Francisco, 100 of L.A. Office: Jenny Craig Internat 445 Marine View Ave Ste 300 Del Mar CA 92014-3950

LABOON, ROBERT BRUCE, lawyer; b. St. Louis, June 14, 1941; s. Joseph Warren LaBoon and Ruth (Aab) LaBoon Freling; m. Ramona Ann Hudgins, Aug. 24, 1963; children: John Andrew, Robert Steven. BSC, Tex. Christian U., 1963; LLB cum laude, So. Meth. U., 1965. Bar: Tex. 1965. Ptnr. Liddell, Sapp, Zivley, Hill & LaBoon, Houston, 1965-86, 88—; vice chmn. and gen. counsel Tex. Commerce Bancshares, Inc., 1986-88; dir. Big Three Industries, Inc., Houston 1975—; dir. Tex. Commercep Bank, Gamma Biol. Inc., Tex. Med. Ctr. Bd. dir. The Houston Interat. Festival, Inst. Rehab. and Rsch. Internat. Ctr. Arbitration, The Greater Houston Partnership and Communities in Schs. Houston, Greater Houston Community Found.; adv. dir. Retina Rsch. Found.; trustee Tex. Christian U., The Kayser Found.; mem. Bd. of Visitors of the M.D. Anderson Cancer Ctr.-U. Cancer Found. Fellow Tex. Bar Found.; Am. Coll. of Trust and Estate Counsel; mem. ABA, Am. Law Inst., Tex. Assn. of Bank Counsel, Houston Bar Assn., State Bar Tex., Houston Club (pres.), River Oaks Country Club. Office: Liddell Sapp Zivley Hill & LaBoon LLP 3500 Tex Commerce Tower Houston TX 77002

LABORDE, ALDEN JAMES, oil company executive; b. Vinton, La., Dec. 18, 1915; s. Cliffe E. and Hilda (Moreau) L.; m. Margaret Bienuenu, Mar. 11, 1943; children: Susan, J. Monroe, John P., Stephanie, Jane. Student, La. State U., 1932-34; B.S., U.S. Naval Acad., 1938; DEng (hon.), Cath. U. Am., 1991. Engr., S.W. Richardson Oil Co., 1946-48; marine supt. Kerr McGee Oil Industries, 1948-52; pres. Ocean Drilling & Exploration Co., 1953-74, chmn. bd., c.e.o., 1974-77; offshore oil industry cons., 1977-85; chmn. bd., c.e.o. Gulf Island Fabrication Co., 1985—; chmn. All Aboard Devel. Corp. Trustee Catholic U. Am.; mem. bd. liquidation city debt, New Orleans; mem. New Orleans Sewage and Water Bd.; bd. adminstrs. Tulane U., 1975-85. Served from ensign to comdr. USNR, 1938-46. Decorated knight St. Gregory the Great, Vatican; recipient Order St. Louis medal, 1976; Disting. Achievement award Offshore Tech. Conf., 1977; St. Mary's Dominican Coll. medal, 1978; Loyola U. award; named to Fortune mag. Nat. Bus. Hall of Fame, 1985. Mem. Internat. Assn. Oilwell Drilling Contractors. (pres. 1973), Midcontinent Oil and Gas Assn. (pres. 1970-71), Nat. Petroleum Council, St. Vincent de Paul Soc. Home: 63 Oriole St New Orleans LA 70124-4517

LABORDE, JOHN PETER, retired international energy company executive; b. Marksville, La., Nov. 5, 1923; s. Cliffe E. and Hilda (Moreau) L.; m. Gene Zylks (div. 1974); children—John Tracy, Cliffe F., Gary L., John Peter, Mary Adrienne; m. Bethany Sanction Villere, 1983 (div. 1987); m. Sylvia R. McLellan, 1994. B.A., La. State U., 1947, J.D., 1949. Pvt. practice Marksville, La., 1949-50; div. land mgr. Richardson & Bass, New Orleans, 1950-56; pres., chief exec. officer Tidewater Inc. (formerly Tidewater Marine Service, Inc.), New Orleans, 1956-81, 87-94, chmn., chief exec. officer, 1968-94, cons., dir., 1995—; bd. dirs. United Gas Holding Corp. (dir. emeritus), Hibernia Nat. Bank New Orleans (dir. emeritus), Am. Bankers Ins. Group, Miami, Fla., Stolt Comex Seaway, S.A., Stone Energy Corp., Stewart Enterprises, Inc., Am. Bur. Shipping, N.Y.C.; mem. adv. council La. Sea Grant; mem. La. Oil and Gas Adv. Com. Past mem. editorial adv. bd. Offshore Mag.; mem. editorial adv. bd. Citybus. Mem. various coms., trustee Loyola U., New Orleans; mem. exec. com. So. Growth Policies Bd., 1976, 71; chmn. sustaining membership enrollment New Orleans Area council Boy Scouts Am., 1981; mem. U. New Orleans Met. Council for Continuing Higher Edn.; mem. Mayor New Orlean's Com. on Internat. Trade and Relations; mem. Mayor New Orleans' Bus. Devel. Council; mem. La. Gov.'s Energy Com. 100 Exec. Com.; mem. internat. policy forum, bd. govs. Council for Nat. Policy; bd. dirs., past v.p. and mem. exec. com. Council for Better La.; bd. dirs., past pres. Campanile Charities, Inc.; bd. dirs. Met. Crime Commn. New Orleans, La Fete, Ochsner Found.; trustee Pub. Affairs Research Council La., Inc.; mem. adv. com. La. Council Music and Performing Arts, Inc.; mem. New Orleans Charity Hosp. Found. Served to capt. U.S. Army, 1943-46. Mem. Mil. and Hospitalier Order St. Lazarus of Jerusalem; recipient one of ten Outstanding Persons' award Inst. Human Understanding, 1974, New Orleans Salesman of Yr. award Sales Mktg. Execs.' Assn., 1980, Humantarian award Nat. Jewish Hosp.-Nat. Asthm Ctr., 1983, Maritime Man of Yr. award Propeller Club, 1984, Significant Role Model award Young Leadership Coun., 1988, Disting. Citizen award Boy Scouts Am., 1995 ; named to Jr. Achievement Bus. Hall of Fame, 1985. Mem. ABA, La. Bar Assn., Chief Execs. Orgn., Nat. Ocean Industries Assn. (chmn. bd. 1980), C. of C. of New Orleans and River Region (chmn. nat. legis. com.), Bus. Coun. of New Orleans and River Region (past chmn.), Greater New Orleans Tourist and Conv. Commn., Inc., Nat. Coun. Fgn. Policy, World Bus. Coun. Bur. Govtl. Rsch., La. Region Regional Med. Program, Internat. House (pres. 1973), Petroleum Club New Orleans, Offshore Marine Svc. Assn. (past pres.), La. State U. Found., La. State U. Alumni Fedn. (pres. 1978-79, Disting. Alumnus award 1982, Outstanding Alumnus award 1983), La. State Law Ctr. Alumni Assn. (Disting. Alumnus award), 1993). Catholic. Clubs: Plimsoll of New Orleans, City Energy Club. Office: Tidewater Inc 1440 Canal St New Orleans LA 70112-2711

LABOVITZ, GEORGE HAROLD, business executive, educator; b. Boston, Apr. 19, 1940; s. Jacob and Janet (Bargad) L.; m. Susan Starr, Sept. 5, 1965; children: Elizabeth, Frank, Robert. BS, Boston U., 1961; MBA, Boston Coll., 1964; PhD, Ohio State U., 1968. Prof. Sch. Mgmt. Boston U., 1968—; pres. ODI, Burlington, Mass., 1977—. Contbr. articles to profl. jours. Trustee Children's Hosp. Meml. Ctr., Boston, 1985—. Capt. USAF, 1961-66. Recipient Disting. Alumni award Boston U., 198, Metcalf Cup and prize, 1979. Mem. APA, ASTD, Acad. Mgmt. Avocations: fishing, skiing, jogging, flying. Office: ODI 25 Mall Rd Burlington MA 01803-4176

LABREC, DAVID JOHN, lawyer; b. Mondovi, Wis., Aug. 25, 1948; s. Robert John and Ruth Marie (Miller) LaB.; m. Catherine Ann Gentry, Feb. 14, 1986; 1 child, Megan Elizabeth. BA, U. Tex.-El Paso, 1970; JD, St. Mary's U., 1973. Bar: Tex. 1973, U.S. Supreme Ct. 1977, U.S. Dist. Ct. (no., so., ea. and we. dists.) Tex. 1975, U.S. Ct. Appeals (5th cir.) 1976, U.S. Ct. Appeals (11th cir.) 1981. Sole practice, El Paso, 1973-74; chief trial atty. City of El Paso, 1975-80, 1st asst. city atty., 1978-80; gen. counsel Tex. Mcpl. League, Austin, 1980-85; gen. counsel TML Risk and Ins. Mgmt. Services, Austin 1982-85; Tex. City Atty.'s Assn., 1980-85; 1st asst. city atty. City of Dallas, 1985-87; ptnr. Strasberger & Price, Dallas, 1987—, also chief govtl. law practice group. Editor Tex. City Atty.'s Assn. Mcpl. Law Bull., 1980-85. Bd. dirs. El Paso County March of Dimes Assn., 1979-80; mem. legis. rev. task force City of El Paso, 1976-77. Mem. Nat. Inst. Mcpl. Law Officers (chmn. mcpl. ins. com. 1983, 85-86, chmn. litigation sect. 1986-93), Def. Research Inst. (vice chmn. govtl. liability com. 1983—), El Paso County Young Lawyers Assn. (bd. dirs. 1976-80), Tex. City Attys. Assn. (bd. dirs.), Phi Delta Phi. Home: 10122 Woodlake Dr Dallas TX 75243-5030 Office: Strasberger & Price 901 Main St Ste 4300 Dallas TX 75202-3794

LABRECQUE, RICHARD JOSEPH, manufacturing company executive; b. Lawrence, Mass., Dec. 19, 1938; s. Eugene N. and Ludivine M. (Roy) L.; m. Janet Marie Michaud, July 16, 1960; children: David R., Lisa M., Susan M. BSEE, Tufts U., 1962; MS in Indsl. Adminstrn., Union Coll., 1970. Mgr. mfg. engring. GE Aircraft Engine Group, Lynn, Mass., 1965-68; with Colt Industries, 1969-81; v.p., gen. mgr. Moloney div., St. Louis, 1969-72; pres. FM Pump div., Kansas City, Kans., 1973-78, Quincy (Ill.) Compressor div., 1979-81; with ITT Corp., Skokie, Ill., 1982—, pres. fluid handling div. 1982-84; corp. v.p., group gen. mgr. ITT Corp., N.Y.C., 1985—; pres. fluid transfer div. ITT Fluid Tech. Corp., Midland Pk., N.J., 1987—. Campaign chmn. United Way Wyandotte County, Kansas City, 1979. Mem. Hydraulic Inst. (v.p 1978, pres. 1979, chmn. 1980, bd. dirs. 1976—)

LABRECQUE, THEODORE JOSEPH, lawyer; b. Portland, Oreg., Mar. 8, 1903; s. Herman F. and Clara (Thibault) L.; m. Marjorie Uprichard, Jan. 31, 1931; children: Theodore J., Katherine Labrecque Skiba, Thomas G., Jeanne M. Labrecque Gagliano, Robert S., David F., Susan Labrecque Woolley, Barbara Anne Labrecque Danowitz. Ed., Manhattan Coll., 1920-21; LLB, Fordham U., 1924; LLD (hon.), Georgian Ct. Coll., 1986. Bar: N.J. 1925, ICC 1936, U.S. Tax Ct. 1943, U.S. Supreme Ct. 1957. Gen. practice law Red Bank, N.J., 1925-60; mem. Quinn, Parsons & Doremus, 1929-37, Parsons, Labrecque, Canzona & Blair, and predecessor firms, 1937-60; mem. N.J. Divsn. Tax Appeals, 1946-60, pres., 1956-60; judge N.J. Superior Ct., 1960-73; judge appellate div. Superior Ct., 1964-73; presiding judge part D appellate div. Superior Ct., 1972-73; of counsel Parsons & Cappiello and predecessor firms, Red Bank, N.J., 1973—. Chmn., Monmouth County Transp. Coordinating Com., 1973—; chmn. North Jersey Transit Adv. Com., 1980-87; mem. Monmouth County Hist. Commn., 1980-93. Recipient Salvation Army award, 1982, Boy Scoutings Joshua Huddy Disting. Citizen award, 1988, N.J. Gov.'s Charles A. Lindbergh Transp. award, 1992. Fellow Am. Coll. Trial Lawyers, Am. Bar Found.; mem. ABA, N.J. State Bar Assn. (pres. 1960), Essex County Bar Assn.. Monmouth Bar Assn., Am. Judicature Soc., Elks, Red Bank Lions Club (pres. 1939), Phi Delta Phi (hon.). Democrat. Roman Catholic. Home: 410 Rumson Rd Little Silver NJ 07739-1610 Office: 66 River Rd Fair Haven NJ 07704 also: Box 770 Red Bank NJ 07701

LABRECQUE, THOMAS G., banker; b. Long Branch, N.J., Sept. 17, 1938; s. Theodore Joseph and Marjorie (Uprichard) L.; m. Sheila English Cardone, June 16, 1962; children: Thomas, Douglas, Karen, Barbara. BA, Villanova U., 1960; postgrad., Amos Tuck Sch., 1969; NYU, 1965; D (hon.), Villanova U., U. Charleston, Drexel U., Marymount Coll. Mem. special devel. program The Chase Manhattan Corp., N.Y.C., 1964-65; with corp. portfolio adv.

group portfolio and investment banking dept. The Chase Manhattan Corp., 1965-66, asst. treas., 1966-67, second v.p., 1967-69, 1967-69, v.p. and mgr. correspondent bank portfolio advisory, 1969-70; assoc. sec. planning to corp. exec. office The Chase Manhattan Corp., N.Y.C., 1970-71, sr. v.p. bank portfolio group, 1971-74, exec. v.p. treasury dept. and treas., 1974-76, mem. mgmt. com., 1976-80; vice chmn., CEO The Chase Manhattan Corp. and The Chase Manhattan Bank, N.A., N.Y.C., 1980-81, responsible for comml. banking, retail banking, trust and fiduciary investment, ops. dept. and corp. systems functon, 1980-81, pres., 1981-90, chmn., CEO, 1990—, also bd. dirs., 1990—; bd. dirs. Pfizer, Inc., Alumax, Inc.; rep. on team that worked out the financial arrangements associated with the Am. hostages from Iran, Chase Manhattan Bank, 1980. Trustee Brookings Instn., Central Park Conservancy, N.Y. Pub. Libr.; bd. dirs. Fund for N.Y.C. Pub. Edn., United Way Tri-State, United Way N.Y.C.; bd. visitors Duke U. Fuqua Sch. Bus.; mem. Coun. Fgn. Rels., Trilateral Commn., Bus.-Higher Edn. Forum, Cystic Fibrosis Rsch. Devel. Coun.; mem. exec. com. Partnerships for Quality Edn. Mem. Bus. Coun., Bus. Roundtable, N.Y. Chamber of Commerce and Industry (bd. dirs.), N.Y.C. Partnership. Office: Chase Manhattan Bank NA 1 Chase Manhattan Plz New York NY 10081-1000*

LABRIE, FERNAND, physician; b. Quebec, Que., Can., June 28, 1937; s. François-Xavier and Rose-Alma (Dubois) L.; m. Nicole Cantin; children: Claude, Pierre, Danielle, Anne, Isabelle. BA magna cum laude, Laval U., 1957, MD magna cum laude, 1962, PhD in Endocrinology summa cum laude, 1966; postgrad., Univs. Cambridge and Sussex, 1966-69. Jr. intern l'Enfant-Jesus Hosp., Quebec, Que., Can., 1961-62; resident internal medicine L'Hôtel-Dieu de Québec, 1962-63; asst. prof. dept physiology Laval U., 1966-69; tutor dept. biochemistry Cambridge (Eng.) U., 1966-67, Sussex (Eng.) U., 1967-68; assoc. prof. dept. physiology Laval U., 1969—, dir. lab. molecular endocrinology, 1969—, prof. dept. physiology, 1974—; physician dept. medicine Le Centre Hospitalier of U. Laval, 1972—; dir. rsch. Laval U. Hosp. Rsch. Ctr., 1982—; head dept. physiology Laval U., 1990—; dir. med. rsch. group in molecular endocrinology, Med. Research Coun., 1973—; Keith Harrison meml. lectr. Endocrine Soc. Australia, 1984; mem. sci. com. Medicine-Scis., 1984-88; mem. med. adv. bd. Gairdner Found., Toronto, 1979-85; mem. adv. bd. Fondation de Recherche en Hormonologie, Paris, 1979-83; mem. selection panel Steacie Prize, 1982, 83; mem. mission of concertation minister for sci. and tech. Govt. of Que., 1982-84; mem. steering com. Task Force on Methods for Regulation of Male Fertility, WHO, Geneva, 1982; cons. study sect. Centre for Population Research, Nat. Inst. Childhood Diseases, NIH, Bethesda, Md., 1976, 77, 79, 80, 83, 84; mem. Sci. Coun. Can., 1984-87; mem. sci. com. 1st Internat. Congress on Neuroendocrinology, 1985-86; active Nat. Adv. Bd. Sci. and Tech., 1994—; invited speaker more than 600 symposia, confs., workshops, cong., U.S., Can., Europe, Asia. Assoc. editor Can. Jour. Biochemistry, 1973-78, Jour. Molecular and cellular Endocrinology, 1973-81; mem. editorial bd. Jour. Cyclic Nucleotide Research, 1974-80, Advances in Sex Hormone Research, Urban and Schwarzenberg, 1975-81, Endocrinology, 1977-81, Maturitas, 1979-83, Jour. Andrology, 1979-83, Hormones, 1982—, Contraceptive Delivery Systems, MTP Press Ltd., 1983—, Clin. and Investigative Medicine, 1985—, Clin. Endocrinology Monographs, 1977—, Jour. Clin. Investigation, 1977—, Jour. Endocrinological Investigation, 1983-87; mem. editorial com. Interface, 1984-87, sci. com., 1984-88; mem. editorial com. Hormones-reproduction-metabolisme, 1984—; mem. editorial bd. Jour. Steroid Biochemistry and Molecular Biology, 1987—; editor: Hypothalamus and Endocrine Functions, 1976, Clinical Neuroendocrinology, a pathophysiological approach, 1979, Prolactin and Prolactinomas, 1983, (with P. Mauvais-Jarvis and R. Sitruk-Ware) Medecine de la Réproduction, Gynécologie Endocrinienne, 1982, (with A. Belanger and A. Dupont) LHRH and Its Analogues, Basic and Clinical Aspects, 1984, (with L. Proulx) Endocrinology, 1984, (with V. K. Wenderoth) A New Approach to the Treatment of Prostate Cancer, 1985, (with others) Early Stage Prostate Cancer: Diagnosis and Choice of Therapy, 1989, (with others) Advances in Diagnosis and Treatment of Early Prostate Cancer, 1993. Pres. Le Fonds de la Recherche en Santé du Que., 1992—, mem. coun., 1981-87, Fondation du Centre Hospitalier de U. Laval, 1981—; trustee Fondation Skibec Alpin, 1981—; founding mem.; chmn. Skibec Alpin, 1980-85; v.p. Skibec, 1980-85; pres. Quebec Ski Show, 1980, 81, hon. pres., 1982, 84; coun. mem. Quebec Zone Water Ski Assn., 1979-80; founding pres. Quebec Water Ski Found., 1988; pres. organizing com., race chmn. Mont Ste.-Anne World Cup, 1983, 84; mem. coun. Can. Ski Assn., 1982-87; pres. Que. Water Ski Assn., 1987-89; coun. mem. Can. Water Ski Assn., 1987-89. Decorated chevalier Ordre de Malta, Order of Que., 1990, Order of Can., 1981; recipient medal city of Nice, 1977; award Fondation de Recherche en Hormologie, 1981, award MDS Health Group, 1981, award Fideides of C. of C. of Ste.-Foy, 1984, 85, medal Coll. de France, Paris, 1984, Excel award, 1985, Gloire de l'Escole award Laval U. Alumni, 1991; Rsch. Coun. Can. fellow, 1962-68, Centennial fellow, 1968-69, scholar, 1969-73; named Grand Quebecois, Met. Que. C. of C., 1991, Most Cited Can. Sci., Inst. Sci. Info., 1973-88; numerous other awards, honors. Fellow Royal Soc. Can. (program com. 1983-84, com. for McLaughlin medal 1983-84, pres. com. for McLaughlin medal 1983-84, mem. coun. 1983-84); mem. Coll. des Médecines et Chirurgiens de la Province de Que., Royal Coll. Physicians and Surgeons Can. (assoc.), AAAS, Assn. des Médecins de Langue Française du Can. (Fondamental rsch. award 1972), Assn. Canadienne-Française pour l'Avancement des Scis. (Vincent medal 1976), Soc. Study Reproduction (rsch. award 1980), Internat. Soc. Neuroendocrinology (sec.-treas. 1984-92, v.p. 1992—), Internat. Soc. Endocrinology (exec. com. 1984-88), Biochem. Soc. (Gt. Britain), Endocrine Soc., Can. Biochem. Soc., Can. Physiol. Soc. (Michel Sarrazin prize 1990), Club de Recherches Cliniques du Quebec (Michel Sarrazin prize 1990), Am. Soc. Cell Biology, Am. Fertility Soc., Tissue Culture Assn., Can. Soc. Clin. Investigation (pres. 1981-82, pres. program com. 1982), Cans. for Health Rsch. (bd. dirs. 1983-88), Can. Soc. Endocrinology and Metabolism (chmn. liaison com. 1975-84, pres. 1978-79), Am. Soc. Andrology (coun. 1982-85), N.Y. Acad. Scis., Royal Soc. Medicine (affiliate), Soc. Argentina de Urologia (miembro correspondiente), Société Française d'Endocrinologie (hon.), Am. Soc. Biol. Chemists, Can. Fertility and Andrology Soc., Soc. Obstetricians and Gynaecologists Can. (assoc.), Can. Investigators in Reproduction, Internat. Menopause Club, Internat. Soc. Andrology, Internat. Study Group Steroid Hormones, Am. Soc. Clin. Investigation, Société d'Andrologie de Langue Franaise (hon.). Home: 2989 Rue de la Promenade, Ste-Foy, Ste-Foy, PQ Canada G1W 2J5 Office: Laval U Hosp, 2705 Laurier Blvd, Quebec, PQ Canada G1V 4G2

LA BUDDE, KENNETH JAMES, librarian; b. Sheboygan Falls, Wis., Jan. 20, 1920; s. Arno Peter and Claire (Devoy) LaB. A.B., U. Wis., 1941, B.L.S., 1942; student, U. Chgo., 1943-44; M.A., U. Minn., 1948; Ph.D., 1954. Student asst. U. Wis. Library, 1939-42; sr. library asst. Milw. Pub. Library, 1942; librarian Sheboygan (Wis.) Press, 1944-46; instr. English Milton (Wis.) Coll., 1946-47; dir. libraries U. Mo. at Kansas City, 1950-85, asst. prof. history, 1958-61, assoc. prof., 1961, prof., 1962-85, prof. emeritus, 1985—. Contbr. articles profl. jours. Served with AUS, 1942-44. Recipient Thomas Jefferson award U. Mo., 1988. Mem. ALA, Am. Studies Assn., Bibliog. Soc. Am., Mo. Libr. Assn. (chmn. coll. and univ. div. 1954-55), Kansas City Posse of Westerners, Wis. Meml. Union, Mid-Continent Am. Studies Assn. (sec. 1963-64, arts editor jour. 1959-63), Orgn. Am. Historians, Soc. Archtl. Historians, Rockhill Tennis Club, Beta Phi Mu, Phi Kappa Phi, Phi Alpha Theta. Home: 309 Brush Creek Blvd Kansas City MO 64112-1788

LABUDDE, ROY CHRISTIAN, lawyer; b. Milw., July 21, 1921; s. Roy Lewis and Thea (Otteson) LaB.; m. Anne P. Held, June 7, 1952; children: Jack, Peter, Michael, Susan, Sarah. AB, Carleton Coll., 1943; JD, Harvard U., 1949. Bar: Wis. 1949, U.S. Dist. Ct. (ea. and we. dists.) Wis. 1950, U.S. Ct. Appeals (7th cir.) 1950, U.S. Supreme Ct. 1957. Assoc. Michael, Best & Friedrich, Milw., 1949-57, ptnr., 1958—; dir. DEC-Inter, Inc., Milw. Western Bank, Western Bancshares, Inc., Superior Die Set Corp., Aunt Nellie's Farm Kitchens, Inc. Bd. dirs. Wis. Hist. Soc. Found.; chmn., bd. dirs. Milw. div. Am. Cancer Soc. Served to lt. j.g. USNR, 1943-46. Mem. Milw. Estate Planning Coun. (past pres.), Wis. Bar Assn., Wis. State Bar Attys. (mem. tax sch., bd. dirs. taxation sect.), Univ. Club, Milw. Club, Milw. Country Club. Republican. Episcopalian. Home: 4201 W Stonefield Rd Mequon WI 53092-2771 Office: Michael Best & Friedrich 100 E Wisconsin Ave Ste 3300 Milwaukee WI 53202-4107

LABUDDE, SAMUEL FREEMAN, biologist, environmental activist; b. Madison, Wis., July 3, 1956; s. John Arthur and Bessie (Freeman) LaB. BA

in Biology, Ind. U., 1986. Fisheries biologist Nat. Marine Fisheries Svc., Seattle, 1987; staff biologist Marine Mammal Fund, San Francisco, 1987—, Earth Zóland Inst., San Francisco, 1987—; field biologist Earthtrust, Honolulu, 1989-90; field investigator Friends of Animals, Norwalk, Conn., 1990; EC marine policy cons. Humane Soc. of U.S., Washington, 1990-93. Contbg. author: (quar. jour.) Earth Zóland Jour., 1988-94. Coord. U.S. tuna boycott Earth Zóland Inst., San Francisco, 1988-90; lobbyist European comty. Humane Soc. of U.S., Brussels and Strasbourg, 1990-93; coord. U.S. Taiwan boycott Endangered Species Project, San Francisco and Washington, 1993-94. Recipient Goldman award for N.Am., Goldman Found., 1991, Founder's award for humane excellence ASPCA, 1989; named one of Am. Leaders under Age 40, Time Mag., 1994. Achievements include securing first documentary evidence of East Pacific dolphin slaughter by tuna industry in 1987, co-dir. U.S. campaign to end U.S. participation; organized and led high seas expedition in 1988 to obtain first documentary evidence of Asian driftnet fleets leading to 1989 UN resolution banning practice; organized and led U.S./internat. effort to implement U.S. trade sanctions against Taiwan for illegal wildlife trade, 1994. Office: Endangered Species Project E-205 Fort Mason Center San Francisco CA 94123

LABUNSKI, STEPHEN BRONISLAW, association executive; b. Jordanow, Poland, Sept. 24, 1924; came to U.S., 1928, naturalized, 1943; s. Wiktor and Wanda (Mlynarski) L.; m. Betty E. Marley, Oct. 2, 1947 (div. June 1963); children: Linda, Richard, Roger; m. Jeralyn LeBrun, Aug. 28, 1967. Student, U. Kansas City, Mo., 1946-49, George Washington U., 1950. Adminstrv. asst. to U.S. Congressman Richard W. Bolling, 1949-51; with Storz Broadcasting Co., 1954-57; v.p. ABC radio network, 1957; head broadcast div. Crowell Collier Pub. Co., 1958; v.p., gen. mgr. WMCA Radio/Straus Broadcasting Group, N.Y.C., 1958-65; pres. radio div. NBC, 1965-69; mng. dir. WMCA Radio, 1969-71; v.p., partner Chuck Blore Creative Services, 1971-75; exec. v.p. Merv Griffin Group Radio, 1975-77; exec. dir. Internat. Radio and TV Soc., N.Y.C., 1978—; Bd. dirs. Radio Advt. Bur., 1965-69, Nat. Assn. Broadcasters, 1965-67. Chmn. adv. com. Voice of Am., 1987-89; Democratic candidate for Mo. Legislature, 1948. With AUS and USAAF, 1943-46. Mem. Advt. Council. Home: 30 E 37th St New York NY 10016-3013 Office: 420 Lexington Ave New York NY 10170-0001

LACAGNINA, MICHAEL ANTHONY, judge; b. Rochester, N.Y., July 6, 1932; s. Frank and Josephine (LoMaglio) L.; m. Mary Laura Mantle, June 8, 1952; children: John Michael, Gina Laura, Frank Anthony. B.S. in Bus. Adminstrn, U. Ariz., 1955, LL.B., 1957. Bar: Ariz. 1957. Asst. U.S. atty. Tucson, 1958-60; partner firm Bilby, Shoenhair, Warnock & Dolph, Tucson, 1960-83; of counsel Bilby, Shoenhair, Warnock & Dolph, 1983-86; judge Div. II, Ariz. Ct. Appeals, 1984—, vice chief judge, 1985-87, chief judge, 1987-89. Served with USMCR, 1950-52. Fellow Am. Coll. Trial Attys., Ariz. Bar Found. (chmn. fellows 1986-87); mem. ABA, Ariz. Bar Assn., Pima County Bar Assn. (pres. 1981), Nat. Assn. R.R. Trial Attys., Am. Bd. Trial Advs. (nat. exec. com., nat. sec. 1981, nat. pres. 1983), Ariz. Judges Assn. (exec. com. 1985—), Tucson Def. Attys. (pres.), Phi Delta Phi, Alpha Kappa Psi. Democrat. Episcopalian. Home: 7100 E River Canyon Rd Tucson AZ 85715-2110 Office: Ariz Ct Appeals Div II 400 W Congress St Tucson AZ 85701-1352

LACAPRA, DOMINICK CHARLES, historian; b. N.Y.C., July 13, 1939; s. Joseph and Mildred (Sciascia) LaC.; m. Anne-Marie Hlasny, June 15, 1965 (div.); 1 dau., Veronique. B.A., Cornell U., 1961; Ph.D., Harvard U., 1970. Tutor Harvard U., Cambridge, Mass., 1967-69; asst. prof. history Cornell U. Ithaca, N.Y., 1969-74, assoc. prof., 1974-79, prof. history, 1979—; Goldwin Smith prof. European intellectual history Cornell U., Ithaca, 1985-92, Bryce and Edith M. Bowmar prof. humanistic studies, 1992—. Author: Emile Durkheim, 1972, A Preface to Sartre, 1978, "Madame Bovary" on Trial, 1982, Rethinking Intellectual History, 1983, History and Criticism, 1985, History, Politics and the Novel, 1987, Soundings in Critical Theory, 1989, Representing the Holocaust, 1994. Fulbright fellow France, 1961-62; Woodrow Wilson fellow Harvard U., 1962-63; sr. fellow Nat. Endowment for Humanities, 1979; recipient Disting. Teaching award Coll. Arts and Scis. Cornell U., 1979. Mem. MLA, Am. Hist. Assn., Internat. Assn. Philosophy and Lit., Soc. Phenomenological and Existential Philosophy, Soc. for the Humanities (dir.). Home: 119 Terrace Pl Ithaca NY 14850-4254 Office: Cornell U History Dept McGraw Hall Ithaca NY 14853

LA CELLE, PAUL LOUIS, biophysics educator; b. Syracuse, N.Y., July 4, 1929; s. George Clarke and Marguerite Ellen (Waggoner) La C. A.B., Houghton Coll., 1951; M.D., U. Rochester, 1959. Resident U. Rochester Med. Center-Strong Meml. Hosp., 1960-62; asst. prof. medicine U. Rochester, 1967-70, assoc. prof., 1970-74, prof., 1974—, chmn. dept. biophysics, 1977—; cons. to govt. Mem. Gates-Chili Sch. Bd., Rochester, 1964-72; trustee Houghton Coll., 1976—. Served to lt. USNR, 1952-55. NIH spl. fellow, 1965-66; recipient von Humboldt Sr. Scientist award, 1982-83. Mem. Biophys. Soc., Microcirculation Soc., European Microcirculation Soc., Alpha Omega Alpha. Achievements include research in biophysics of blood cells, physiology of microcirculation. Office: U Rochester Dept Biophysics 601 Elmwood Ave Rochester NY 14642-0001

LACEY, BEATRICE CATES, psychophysiologist; b. N.Y.C., July 22, 1919; d. Louis Henry and Mollie (Libowitz) Cates; m. John I. Lacey, Apr. 16, 1938; children: Robert Arnold, Carolyn Ellen. Student, Columbia U., 1935-38; A.B. with distinction, Cornell U., 1940; M.A., Antioch Coll., 1958. Mem. staff Fels Research Inst., Yellow Springs, Ohio, 1953-82; sr. investigator Fels Research Inst., 1966-72, sr. scientist, 1972-82; instr. Antioch Coll., Yellow Springs, 1956-63, asst. prof., 1963-68, assoc. prof., 1968-73, prof., 1973-82; Fels prof. psychiatry Wright State U. Sch. Medicine, 1977-82, clin. prof. psychiatry, 1982-89, Fels prof. emeritus, 1989—; acting sci. dir. Fels Research Inst., 1979-82. Assoc. editor Psychophysiology, 1975-78; reviewer Jour. Abnormal Psychology, Psychophysiology, Biol. Psychology, Cognitive Psychology, Sci.; contbr. articles to profl. jours.; researcher, author numerous publs. in psychophysiology of the autonomic nervous system. Recipient Disting. Sci. Contbn. award, Am. Psychol. Assn., 1976, Psychol. Sci. Gold Medal award, Am. Psychol. Found., 1985. Fellow Acad. Behavioral Medicine Research, Soc. Exptl. Psychologists, Am. Psychol. Soc. (William James fellow 1989); mem. Soc. Psychophysiol. Research (dir. 1972-75, pres. 1978-79), Soc. Neurosci., Phi Kappa Phi. Achievements include rsch. and publs. in psychophysiology of the autonomic nervous system. Home: 1425 Meadow Ln Yellow Springs OH 45387-1221

LACEY, CLOYD EUGENE, retired insurance company executive; b. New Lexington, Ohio, Mar. 12, 1918; s. Russell Anderson and Freda (Bahr) L.; m. Jane Linn Williams, Sept. 12, 1941; children: Thomas, Melinda Lacey Houfek, Janene Lacey Paulus. B.S. in Bus. Adminstrn., Ohio State U., 1941. Acct., asst. treas. Pioneer Mut. Casualty Co., Columbus, Ohio, 1945-51; various corp. positions Nationwide Ins. Cos., Columbus, 1951-73, v.p., asst. controller, 1973-75, v.p., corp. controller, 1975-78, v.p. Office of Treas., controller, 1978-81, sr. v.p. fin., 1981-82, ret., 1982. Served with U.S. Army, 1943-45. Republican. Methodist. *I believe in God and put my trust in him. I believe in treating other people fairly and in giving them credit for accomplishments. I believe in maintaining a high degree of integrity. I believe in diligence and determination in performing a task. I believe in striving for excellence.*

LACEY, FREDERICK BERNARD, lawyer, former federal judge; b. Newark, Sept. 9, 1920; s. Frederick Robert and Mary Agnes (Armstrong) L.; m. Mary C. Stoneham, May 20, 1944; children—Frederick Bernard, James, Virginia, Robert, Mary, Kathleen, John. A.B., Rutgers U., 1941; J.D., Cornell U., 1948; LL.D. (hon.), Montclair State Coll., 1971, Seton Hall U. 1973. Bar: N.Y. State bar 1948, N.J. bar 1952. Asso. firm Whitman & Ransom, N.Y.C., 1948-53; asst. U.S. atty. for N.J., 1953-55; U.S. atty., 1969-71; partner firm Shanley & Fisher, Newark, 1955-69; U.S. dist. judge for N.J., 1971-86; sr. litigation ptnr. LeBoeuf, Lamb, Greene & MacRae, N.Y.C. and Newark, 1986—. Served to lt. comdr. USNR, 1942-46. Mem. Order of Coif, Phi Beta Kappa. Office: LeBoeuf Lamb Greene & MacRae 125 W 55 th St New York NY 10022

LACEY, HUGH MATTHEW, philosophy educator; b. Sydney, Australia, Sept. 7, 1939; came to U.S., 1972; s. Owen Charles and Margaret Jane (Devine) L.; m. Maria Ines Rocha E. Silva, Aug. 14, 1966; children: Andrew David, Daniel Carlos. BA, U. Melbourne, Australia, 1962, MA, 1964; PhD,

Ind. U., 1966. Tutor in math. U. Melbourne, 1961-63; lectr. history and philosophy of sci. U. Sydney, 1966-68; prof. philosophy U. São Paulo, Brazil, 1969-72; prof. philosophy Swarthmore (Pa.) Coll., 1972, chmn. dept. philosophy, 1973-83, Eugene M. Lang Rsch. Prof. of Philosophy, 1993—; vis. prof. Temple U., Phila., spring 1983, Villanova U., fall 1984, Instituto de Teologia, São Paulo, spring 1988, fall 1992, Cen. Am. U., El Salvador, summer 1991. Author: A Linguagem Do Espaco E do Tempo, 1972; coauthor: Behaviorism, Science and Human Nature, 1982; co-editor: Towards a Society That Serves Its People: The Thought of El Salvador's Murdered Jesuits, 1991; cons. editor: Jour. for Theory of Social Behavior, 1977—, Behavior and Philosophy, 1987—, Jour. for Peace and Justice Studies, 1987—. Bd. dirs. Chester-Swarthmore Coll. Cmty. Coalition, 1993—. NSF fellow, 1975, 79, 83; Fulbright grantee, 1963; Research Found. of State of São Paulo grantee, 1969, 73. Mem. Philosophy of Sci. Assn., Am. Philos. Assn., Am. Psychol. Assn. (commn. on behavior modification 1974-77), Brazilian Soc. for the Advancement of Sci. Roman Catholic. Home: 4 Whittier Pl Swarthmore PA 19081-1142 Office: Swarthmore Coll Swarthmore PA 19081

LACEY, JOHN IRVING, psychologist, physiologist, educator; b. Chgo., Apr. 11, 1915; s. David and Cecelia (Burnstein) L.; m. Beatrice Lucile Cates, Apr. 16, 1938; children—Robert Arnold, Carolyn Ellen. A.B., Cornell U., 1937, Ph.D., 1941. Instr. Queen's Coll., Flushing, N.Y., 1941-42; mem. faculty Antioch Coll., 1946-77, prof. psychophysiology, 1956-77; mem. staff Fels Research Inst., Yellow Springs, Ohio, 1946-82, chief sect. behavioral physiology, 1946-82; Fels prof. psychiatry Wright State U. Med. Sch., 1977-82, prof. emeritus, 1982—; cons. USPHS, 1957-82, FDA, 1977-82; mem. bd. sci. counselors Nat. Inst. Aging, NIH, 1977-80;. Cons. editor Jour. Comparative and Physiol. Psychology, 1953-69, Jour. Psychosomatic Medicine, 1962-65, Jour. Psychophysiology, 1964-69, Jour. Physiol. Psychology; contbr. articles to profl. jours. Served to capt. USAAF, 1942-46. Centennial scholar Johns Hopkins U., 1976; recipient Psychol. Sci. Gold medal Am. Psychol. Found., 1985. Fellow Am. Psychol. Soc. (William James fellow 1989); mem. Soc. Psychophysiol. Research (award for disting. contbns. 1970, pres. 1961-62, dir. 1965-68), Am. Psychosomatic Soc. (bd. dirs. 1959-62), Soc. Exptl. Psychologists, Am. Psychol. Assn. (pres. div. physiol. and comparative psychology 1969-70, mem. council 1964-68, 70-73, 78-79, bd. dirs. 1974-77, Disting. Sci. Contbn. award 1976), AAAS (chmn. sect. 1985-86), Psychonomic Soc., Soc. for Neurosci., Acad. Behavioral Medicine Rsch., Internat. Brain Rsch. Orgn., Nat. Acad. Scis. (chair com. new techs. in cognitive psychophysiology with NRC 1988), Sigma Xi, Phi Kappa Phi. Home: 1425 Meadow Ln Yellow Springs OH 45387-1221

LACEY, JOHN WILLIAM CHARLES, management consultant; b. London, May 1, 1930; came to U.S., 1956; s. William J. and Florence (Farbus) L.; m. Edna Winifred Burns, July 28, 1951; children: Jonathan Charles, Erika Jane. B.A. with honors, Oxford U., 1952, M.A. with honors, 1956. Sr. sci. officer Govt. of U.K., 1952-60; U.S. liaison officer Brit. embassy, Washington, 1956-60; mgr. research and devel. spl. systems Control Data Corp., Bloomington, Minn., 1960-63, dir. ops., 1963; pres. Control Data subs. Control Corp., Bloomington, 1964-65, gen. mgr. Devel. and Standard Systems div., 1965, v.p. computer equipment group, 1966-67, v.p. corp. devel., 1967-71, v.p. sr. staff officer corp. plans and controls, 1971-73, sr. v.p. corp. plans and controls, chmn. mgmt. com., 1973-77; pres. Control Data Edn. Co., 1977-79, Control Data Info. and Edn. Systems Co., 1979-82; exec. v.p. Control Data Corp., 1982-86; cons. in field, 1986—; chmn. bd. Control Corp., Adcomp Corp., 1963-66; bd. dirs. Graco Corp., Instron Corp., LSC Inc. Bd. dirs. Jr. Achievement Greater Mpls., 1966-76, Mpls. Acquatennial, 1975-82, Guthrie Theater, 1983-88; bd. dirs. Computer Mus., 1982-86, trustee, 1986-93. With Brit. Royal Navy, 1948-49.

LACH, ALMA ELIZABETH, food and cooking writer, consultant; b. Petersburg, Ill.; d. John H. and Clara E. (Boeker) Satorius; diplome de Cordon Bleu, Paris, 1956; m. Donald F. Lach, Mar. 18, 1939; 1 dau., Sandra Judith. Feature writer Children's Activities mag., 1954-55; creator, performer TV show Let's Cook, children's cooking show, 1955; hostess weekly food program on CBS, 1962-66, performer TV show Over Easy, PBS, 1977-78; food editor Chgo. Daily Sun-Times, 1957-65; pres. Alma Lach Kitchens Inc., Chgo., 1966—; dir. Alma Lach Cooking Sch., Chgo.; lectr. U. Chgo. Downtown Coll., Gourmet Inst., U. Md., 1963, Modesto (Calif.) Coll., 1978, U. Chgo., 1981; resident master Shoreland Hall, U. Chgo., 1978-81; food cons. Food Bus. Mag., 1964-66, Chgo.'s New Pump Room, Lettuce Entertain You, Bitter End Resort, Brit. V.I., Midway Airlines, Flying Food Fare, Inc., Berghoff Restaurant, Hans' Bavarian Lodge, Unocal '76, Univ. Club Chgo.; columnist Modern Packaging, 1967-68, Travel & Camera, 1969, Venture, 1970, Chicago mag., 1978, Bon Appetit, 1980, Tribune Syndicate, 1982. Recipient Pillsbury award, 1958; Grocery Mfrs. Am. Trophy award, 1959, certificate of Honor, 1961; Chevalier du Tastevin, 1962; Commanderie de l'Ordre des Anysetiers du Roy, 1963; Confrerie de la Chaine des Rotisseurs, 1964; Les Dames D'Escoffier, 1982, Culinary Historians of Chgo., 1993. Mem. Am. Assn. Food Editors (chmn. 1959). Clubs: Tavern, Quadrangle (Chgo.). Author: A Child's First Cookbook, 1950; The Campbell Kids Have a Party, 1953; The Campbell Kids at Home, 1953; Let's Cook, 1956; Candlelight Cookbook, 1959; Cooking a la Cordon Bleu, 1970; Alma's Almanac, 1972; Hows and Whys of French Cooking, 1974; contbr. to World Book Yearbook, 1961-75, Grolier Soc. Yearbook, 1962. Home and Office: 5750 S Kenwood Ave Chicago IL 60637-1744 *The art of cooking rests upon one's ability to taste, to reproduce taste, and to create taste. To achieve distinction the cook must taste everything, study cookbooks of all kinds, and experiment constantly in the kitchen. I stress in my writing and teaching the logic of food preparation, for the cook who possesses logic, knows how to create dishes rather than being content merely to duplicate the recipes of others.*

LACH, JOSEPH THEODORE, physicist; b. Chgo., May 12, 1934; s. Joseph and Kate (Ziemba) L.; m. Barbara Ryan, June 26, 1965; children—Michael, Elizabeth. A.B., U. Chgo., 1953, M.S., 1956; Ph.D., U. Calif.-Berkeley, 1963. Rsch. assoc. in physics Yale U., Hew Haven, 1963-65, asst. prof. physics, 1966-69; physicist Fermi Nat. Accelerator Lab., Batavia, Ill, 1969—, chmn. dept. physics, 1974-75; chmn. Gordon Rsch. Conf. in Elem. Particle Physics, 1975; mem. joint rsch. program with USSR and People's Republic of China. Fellow Am. Phys. Soc., Physicians for Social Responsibility, Ill. Geol. Survey (rsch. affiliate). Home: 28W364 Indian Knoll Trail West Chicago IL 60185 Office: Fermilab PO Box 500 Batavia IL 60510-5000

LACHANCE, JANICE RACHEL, federal agency administrator, lawyer; b. Biddeford, Maine, June 17, 1953; d. Ralph L. and Rachel A. (Desnoyers) L. BA, Manhattanville Coll., 1974; JD, Tulane U., 1978. Bar: Maine 1978, D.C. 1982. Staff dir. subcom. on antitrust Ho. of Reps., Washington, 1982-83; adminstrv. asst. Congresswoman Katie Hall, 1983-84; asst. pres. sec. Mondale-Ferraro Campaign, Washington, 1984; press sec. Congressman Tom Daschle, 1985; ptnr. Lachance and Assocs., Washington, 1985-87; dir. communications and polit. action Am. Fedn. Govt. Employees (AFL-CIO), Washington, 1987-93; dir. policy and communications U.S. Office Pers. Mgmt., Washington, 1993—; vis. scholar Cornell U. 1972-73. Editor newsletter Govt. Standard, 1987-93. Mem. Delta Delta Delta, Phi Alpha Delta. Democrat. Roman Catholic. Office: US Office Pers Mgmt 1900 E St NW Ste 5F12 Washington DC 20415-0001

LACHANCE, PAUL ALBERT, food science educator, clergyman; b. St. Johnsbury, Vt., June 5, 1933; s. Raymond John and Lucienne (Landry) L.; m. Therese Cecile Cote; children: Michael P., Peter A., M.-Andre, Susan A. BS, St. Michael's Coll., 1955; postgrad., U. Vt., 1955-57; PhD, U. Ottawa, 1960; cert. in pastoral counseling, N.Y. Theol. Sem., 1981; DSc (hon.), St. Michael's Coll. 1982. Ordained deacon Roman Cath. Ch., 1977. Assigned to St. Paul's Ch. Princeton, N.J.; aerospace biologist Aeromed. Research Labs., Wright-Patterson AFB, Ohio, 1960-63; lectr. dept. biology U. Dayton, Ohio, 1963; flight food and nutrition coordinator NASA Manned Spacecraft Center, Houston, 1963-67; assoc. prof. dept. food sci. Rutgers U., New Brunswick, N.J., 1967-72, dir. Sch. Feeding effectiveness research project, 1969-72, prof., 1972—, faculty rep. to bd. trustees, 1988-90, dir. grad. program food sci., 1988-91, chmn. food sci. dept., 1991—, chmn. univ. senate, 1990-93; faculty rep. to bd. govs., 1990-94; cons. Nutritional Aspects of Food Processing; mem. sci. adv. bd. Roche chem. divsn. Hoffmann La Roche Co., 1976-88; mem. nutrition policy com. Beatrice

Foods Co., 1979-86; trustee religious ministries com. Princeton Med. Ctr.; bd. dirs. J.R. Short Milling Co., 1990—. Mem. editorial adv. bd., Sch. Food Service Research Rev., 1977-82, Jour. Am. Coll. Nutrition, 1986—, Jour. Med. Consultation, 1985—, Nutrition Reports Internat., 1963-83, Profl. Nutritionist, 1977-80; contbr. articles to profl. jours. Served to capt. USAF, 1960-63. Recipient Endel Karmas award for excellence in teaching food sci., 1988, WilliamCruess award for excellence in teaching Inst. Food Technologists, 1991. Fellow Inst. Food Technologists, Am. Coll. Nutrition; mem. Am. Assn. Cereal Chemists, AAAS, Am. Inst. Nutrition, N.Y. Inst. Food Technologists (chmn. 1977-78), Am. Soc. Clin. Nutrition, N.Y. Acad. Sci., Am. Dietetic Assn., Soc. Nutrition Edn., Am. Public Health Assn., Nat. Assn. Cath. Chaplains, Sociedad Latino Americano de Nutricion, Sigma Xi, Delta Epsilon Sigma. Home: 34 Taylor Rd Princeton NJ 08540-9521 Office: Rutgers U Food Sci New Brunswick NJ 08903-0231

LACHEMANN, MARCEL, professional baseball manager; b. L.A., June 13, 1941. BSBA, U. So. Calif., 1962. Former player Kansas City A's (moved to Oakland); pitching coach Calif. Angels, 1983-92, mgr., head coach, 1994—; pitching coach Fla. Marlins, 1992-94. Office: California Angels 2000 Gene Autry Way Anaheim CA 92806*

LACHEMANN, RENE GEORGE, professional sports manager; b. L.A., May 4, 1945. Attended, U. So. Calif. Minor league baseball player, 1964-72; with major league teams Kansas City, 1965-66, Oakland, 1968; minor league baseball team mgr., 1973-81; major league baseball team mgr. Seattle Mariners, 1981-83, Milw. Brewers, 1984; coach Boston Red Sox, 1984-86, Oakland Athletics, 1986-92; mgr. Fla. Marlins, 1993—. Named Southern League Mgr. of Yr., 1976. Office: Fla Marlins 2269 NE 199th St Miami FL 33180

LACHENBRUCH, ARTHUR HEROLD, geophysicist; b. New Rochelle, N.Y., Dec. 7, 1925; s. Milton Cleveland and Leah (Herold) L.; m. Edith Bennett, Sept. 7, 1950; children: Roger, Charles, Barbara. BA, Johns Hopkins U., 1950; MA, Harvard U., 1954, PhD, 1958. Registered geophysicist and geologist, Calif. Research geophysicist U.S. Geol. Survey, 1951—; vis. prof. Dartmouth Coll., 1963; mem. numerous adv. coms. and panels. Contbr. articles to sci. jours. Mem. Los Altos Hills (Calif.) Planning Commn., 1966-86. Served with USAAF, 1943-46. Recipient Spl. Act award U.S. Geol. Survey, 1970, Meritorious Service award, 1972, Disting. Service award U.S. Dept. Interior, 1978. Fellow AAAS, Am. Geophys. Union (Walter H. Bucher medal 1989), Royal Astron. Soc., Geol. Soc. Am. (Kirk Bryan award 1963), Arctic Inst. N.Am.; mem. Nat. Acad. Sci. Current work: solid-earth geophysics, terrestial heat flow, tectonophysics, permafrost; subspecialties: tectonics, geophysics. Office: US Geol Survey 345 Middlefield Rd Menlo Park CA 94025-3591

LACHENBRUCH, DAVID, editor, writer; b. New Rochelle, N.Y., Feb. 11, 1921; s. Milton Cleveland and Leah Judith (Herold) L.; m. Gladys Kidwell, Dec. 12, 1941; 1 child, Ann Leah Lachenbruch Zulawski. BA, U. Mich., 1942. Corr. Variety, also Detroit Times, 1940-42; reporter, asst. city editor, then wire editor Gazette & Daily, York, Pa., 1946-50; assoc. editor TV Digest with Consumer Electronics, Washington, 1950-58; mng. editor TV Digest with Consumer Electronics, 1959-68; editorial dir. TV Digest with Consumer Electronics, N.Y.C., 1968—; v.p. Warren Pub., Inc., Washington, 1962—. Columnist Electronics Now mag., Video mag.; co-author: The Complete Book of Adult Toys, 1983; contbr. articles to consumer mags., contbg. editor: N.Y. Times Ency. of TV; author: Videocassette Recorders—The Complete Home Guide, 1978, A Look Inside Television, 1985; cons. Acad. Am. Ency. Served with AUS, 1942-45. Inducted Video Hall of Fame, 1993. Mem. White House Corrs. Assn., Union Internat. de la Presse Electronique. Home: 77 7th Ave New York NY 10011-6645 also: 20 Cross Brook Rd Roxbury CT 06783-1211 Office: 276 5th Ave New York NY 10001-4509

LACHEY, JAMES MICHAEL, professional football player; b. St. Henry, Ohio, June 4, 1963. BA Mktg., Ohio State Univ., 1985. With San Diego Chargers, 1985-88, L.A. Raiders, 1988; offensive tackle Washington Redskins, 1988—. Named offensive tackle The Sporting News NFL All-Pro team, 1989-91. Played in Pro Bowl, 1987, 90-91. Office: Washington Redskins Dulles Intl Airport PO Box 17247 Washington DC 20041*

LACHMAN, EDWARD, cinematographer; b. Morristown, N.J., Mar. 31, 1946; s. Edward and Rosabel Lachman. BA, Harvard U., 1965; BFA summa cum laude, Ohio U., 1969. presenter seminars Harvard U., Columbia U., NYU, Ohio U. Co-dir. photography feature films Lords of Flatbush, 1973, Christo's Valley Curtain (Club Ribbon, Am. Film Festival 1974, Academy award nomination), Lightning over Water, Wim Winders, 1976, 79 (feature film prize German Film Festival), Stroszek LaSoufriere Werner Herzog, 1976 (awards Cannes, Berlin and N.Y. Film Festivals), Little Wars, Maroon Baghdadi (feature film award Cannes Film Festival, 1984), Mother Teresa (Acad. award nomination documentary, 1987); dir. photography Say Amen, Somebody, 1982 (awards Cannes and N.Y. Film Festival), Lightning Over Water, 1984 (Cannes, Berlin, N.Y. film festivals), Desperately Seeking Susan, 1985, Tokyo-Ga, 1985 (Cannes, Berlin, Venice and N.Y. Film Festivals), True Stories, 1986, Less Than Zero, 1987, Making Mr. Right, 1987, Mississipi Masala, 1991, London Kills Me, 1992, Light Sleeper, 1992, My New Gun, 1992. Recipient Best Cinematography award S. Am. Film Festival, 1988, Acad. award nomination for short subject, 1986. Mem. Internat. Photographers. Home: 43 E 19th St New York NY 10003-1304 also: Doug Apatow Agency 10559 Blythe Ave Los Angeles CA 90064

LACHMAN, LAWRENCE, business consultant, former department store executive; b. N.Y.C., Jan. 9, 1916; s. Charles and Dorothy (Rubin) L.; m. Judith Lehman, Apr. 8, 1945; children: Robert Ian, Charles Scott. BS summa cum laude, NYU, 1936. Controller James McCreery & Co., N.Y.C., 1938-46; treas., dir. Citizens Utilities Co., Stamford, Conn., 1946-47; treas. Bloomingdale's, N.Y.C., 1947-53; v.p. personnel and ops. Bloomingdale's, 1953-58, exec. v.p. adminstrn. and personnel, 1958-64, pres., chief exec. officer, 1964-69, chmn. bd., chief exec. officer, 1969-78; chmn. bd., chief exec. officer Bus. Mktg. Corp., 1978-80; bd. dirs. DFS Group Ltd., ADVO, Inc. Trustee NYU, 1974-90. Served to maj. USAAF, 1942-46. Decorated Bronze Star; French Legion of Honor; recipient Madden award N.Y. U., 1969. Home: 104 E 68th St Apt 5A New York NY 10021-5905

LACHMAN, MARGUERITE LEANNE, real estate investment advisor; b. Vancouver, B.C., Can., Mar. 16, 1943; came to U.S., 1955; d. Wilfred Harry and Claire Elisha (Silverthorn) L. BA, U. So. Calif., 1964; MA, Claremont Grad. Sch., 1966. With Real Estate Rsch. Corp., 1965-87; sr. v.p. Real Estate Research Corp., 1977-79, pres., CEO, 1979-87; mng. dir. Schroder Real Estate Assocs., 1987—, Schroder Mortgage Assocs., 1992—; bd. dirs. Chgo. Title and Trust, Lincoln Nat. Corp., Liberty Property Trust; frequent lectr. seminars and profl. groups. Author: (with Al Smith and Anthony Downs) Achieving Effective Desegregation, 1973, (with Susan Olson) Tax Delinquency in the Inner City, 1976, Emerging Trends in Real Estate, 1981, 82, 83, 84, 85, 86, 87, Decade to Decade, 1988, Demographics of Demand, 1992; contbr. articles to profl. jours. Trustee, v.p. Urban Land Inst., Urban Land Found. Mem. N.Y. Women's Forum, Inc., Comml. Club Chgo. Office: Schroder Real Estate Assocs 437 Madison Ave New York NY 10022-7001

LACHMAN, MORTON, writer, theatrical director and producer; b. Seattle, Mar. 20, 1918; s. Sol and Rose (Bloom) L.; m. Elaine Lachman, June 23, 1940; children: Joanne, Dianne, Robert. B.A., U. Wash., Seattle, 1939. Exec. producer TV series One Day at a Time, All in the Family, Archie Bunker's Place, Sanford, Gimme A Break, Kate & Allie; head writer, producer, dir. The Bob Hope Show; head writer Acad. Award shows; cowriter feature films Mixed Company, Yours, Mine & Ours. With AUS, 1942-45. Recipient Emmy award for directing The Girl Who Couldn't Lose, 1975. Clubs: El Caballero, Queens, Tamerisk, Rangoon Racquet. Address: 2780 Bottlebrush Dr Los Angeles CA 90077

LACHOWICZ, FRANCISZEK, foreign language educator; b. Poland, July 12, 1908; came to U.S., 1951; s. Ignacy and Anastazja (Szarejko) L.; m. Helena M. Pogonowska, Dec. 8, 1944; children: Barbara, Lech. MA, U. Warsaw, 1935; MS in Edn., U. Bridgeport, 1962, profl. diploma, 1966, MS in

Math., 1970. Asst. U. Warsaw, Poland, 1936-39; tchr. Polish Tchrs.' Coll., Univ. Edinburgh, Scotland, 1943-45; prin. Polish Bus. Coll., England, 1946-48; math. tchr. Masuk High Sch., Monroe, Conn., 1961-77, Housatonic Community Coll., Stratford, Conn., 1966-67; adj. assoc. prof. Sacred Heart U., Fairfield, Conn., 1978—. Contbr. articles to profl. jours. 2d lt. Polish Army, 1939-43. Mem. Polish Am. Hist. Soc., Polish Nat. Alliance, Kosciuszko Found., Polish Inst. Arts and Scis. Am., Polish Am. Edn. Soc. (first pres. 1973, pres. 1989), Jozet Pilsudski Inst., Polish Heritage Soc. (Man of the Yr. 1986), Polish Army Vet. Assn. Democrat. Roman Catholic. Avocations: chess. Home: 95 Houston Ave Bridgeport CT 06606-3041 Office: Sacred Heart Univ 5151 Park Ave Fairfield CT 06432-1023

LACHS, JOHN, philosopher, educator; b. Budapest, Hungary, July 17, 1934; s. Julius and Magda (Brod) L.; m. Shirley Marie Mellow, June 3, 1967; children: Sheila Marie, James Richard. B.A., McGill U., 1956, M.A., 1957; Ph.D., Yale, 1961. From asst. prof. to prof. philosophy Coll. William and Mary, 1959-67; prof. philosophy Vanderbilt U., 1967—, Centennial Prof., 1993—; chair Vanderbilt U. Faculty Senate, 1990-91. Author: Marxist Philosophy: A Bibliographical Guide, 1967, The Ties of Time, 1970, Intermediate Man, 1981, Mind and Philosophers, 1987, George Santayana, 1988, The Relevance of Philosophy to Life, 1995; editor: Animal Faith and Spiritual Life, 1967, Physical Order and Moral Liberty, 1969; co-editor: The Human Search, 1981; co-translator: Fichte, Science of Knowledge, 1970; contbr. numerous articles to profl. jours. Past chmn. Tenn. Com. for Humanities. Recipient Award for Advancement of Scholarship Phi Beta Kappa, 1962, Harris Harbison award for distinguished teaching Danforth Found., 1967, Chancellor's cup Vanderbilt U., 1970, Madison Sarratt prize excellence undergrad. teaching, 1972, Alumni Edn. award Vanderbilt U., 1991. Mem. Internat. Neoplatonic Soc., World Sociology Assn. (alienation rsch. com.), Am. Acad. Polit. and Social Sci., Am. Philos. Assn., Metaphys. Soc. Am. (pres.-elect), Royal Inst. Philosophy, Soc. Advancement Am. Philosophy (past pres.), Soc. Health and Human Values, C.S. Peirce Soc. (past pres.), Va. Philos. Assn., Tenn. Philos. Assn., So. Soc. Philosophy and Psychology, Hasting Ctr. Episcopalian. Home: 1968 Edenbridge Way Nashville TN 37215-5809 Office: Vanderbilt U 2305 W End Ave Nashville TN 37203-1700

LACITIS, ERIK, journalist; b. Buenos Aires, Argentina, Dec. 10, 1949; came to U.S., 1960, naturalized, 1965; s. Erik and Irene Z. L.; m. Malorie Nelson, Aug. 30, 1976. Student, Coll. Forest Resources, U. Wash., 1967-71. Editor U. Wash. Daily, 1970; pub. New Times Jour., 1970-71; reporter, popmusic cons. Seattle Post Intelligencer, 1972—; reporter, columnist Seattle Times, 1972; v.p.; treas. Malorie Nelson, Inc., 1980—. Recipient numerous awards from Wash. State chpt. Sigma Delta Chi; Nat. Headliners Club award, 1978; winner gen. interest competition Nat. Soc. Newspaper Columnists, 1987. Lutheran. Office: The Seattle Times PO Box 70 Fairview Ave N & John St Seattle WA 98111-0070

LACK, JAMES J., state senator, lawyer; b. N.Y.C., Oct. 18, 1944; s. Harry A. and Eve (Kaufman) L.; m. Therese M. Gutleber, Jan. 19, 1969; children: Katherine Shana, Jeremy David. B.A., U. Pa., 1966; J.D., Fordham U., 1969. Bar: N.Y. 1970. Counsel to N.Y. State Consumer Protection Bd., 1970-72; prin. asst. frauds bur. dist. attys. office County of Suffolk, 1972-73; commr. Suffolk County Dept. Consumer Affairs, Hauppauge, N.Y., 1974-77; pres. Better Bus. Bur. Met. N.Y., 1977-78; ptnr. Smyth & Lack, Huntington, N.Y., 1983—; mem. N.Y. Senate, 1979—; chmn. Senate Labor com., 1985-93, Majority Steering com., 1989-94, Senate com. on judiciary, 1994—, dep. majority whip, 1995—, Nat. Commn. Employment Policy; pres. Nat. Conf. State Legislatures, 1995—. Republican. Office: NY State Senate State Capitol Albany NY 12247

LACK, LEON, pharmacology and biochemistry educator; b. Bklyn, Jan. 7, 1922; s. Jacob and Yetta (Wolf) L.; m. Pauline Kaplan, Feb. 14, 1948; children: Elias David, Joshua Morris, Johanna Elaine, Adina Roberta, Evonne Clara. B.A., Bklyn. Coll., 1943; M.S., Mich. State Coll., 1948; Ph.D., Columbia U., 1953; postgrad. (Univ. postdoctoral fellow), Duke U., 1954-55. Instr. in pharmacology and exptl. therapeutics Johns Hopkins U. Sch. Medicine, 1955-59, asst. prof. pharmacology and exptl. therapeutics, 1959-63; asst. prof. physiology and pharmacology Duke U. Med. Center, 1964-66, prof. pharmacology, 1966-92, prof. emeritus pharmacology, 1992—, chief biochemist to clin. research, 1966-70; cons. E.I. DuPont de Nemours and Co., 1990-91, Monsanto, 1992-93. Contbr. numerous articles to profl. publs. Served with USAAF, 1943-46, PTO. Grantee NIH, 1960-90, OSHA, Ctr. for Disease Control, 1991-93. Mem. Am. Soc. Biol. Chemists, Am. Soc. Pharmacology and Exptl. Therapeutics. Jewish. Rsch. in pharmacology of cholesterol and lipids, pharmacology of intestinal bile salt transport, enzyme inhibitors relevant to prostatic cancer. Home: 2936 Welcome Dr Durham NC 27705-5556 Office: Duke U Med Ctr PO Box 3185 Durham NC 27715-3185

LACKENMIER, JAMES RICHARD, college president, priest; b. Lackawanna, N.Y., May 15, 1938; s. Harold and Margaret (Murphy) L. AB, Stonehill Coll., 1961; STL, Pontifical Gregorian U., Rome, 1965; AM, U.N.C., 1968; MA, U. Chgo., 1970. Ordained priest, Roman Catholic Ch. Tchr. English Notre Dame High Sch., Bridgeport, Conn., 1965-66, St. Peter's High Sch., Gloucester, Mass., 1966-68; chaplain St. Xavier Coll., Chgo., 1969-71; dir. collegiate formation Moreau Sem., Notre Dame, Ind., 1971-73; dir. campus ministry King's Coll., Wilkes-Barre, Pa., 1974-75, dir. devel., 1975-81, pres., 1981—. Bd. regents U. Portland, 1992—; bd. dirs. Stonehill Coll., 1986-92, Osterhout, 1987—, Mercy Hosp., 1989—, Com. on Econ. Growth, Earth Conservancy, 1992; adv. bd. Pa. Mountains coun. Boy Scouts Am., North Tier Advanced Tech. Ctr. Ben Franklin Partnership Program, 1983—, tuition acct. program Office of Gov., Commonwealth Pa., 1992; adv. group Coun. Higher Ed. Com., 1990; chmn. United Way Wyoming Valley, 1986; chmn. exec. com. Found. for Ind. Colls., adv. bd.; mem. hist. preservation com. City of Wilkes-Barre, 1995; bd. dirs. Greater Wilkes-Barre Partnership, Inc., instnl. affairs com. Commn. for Ind. Colls. and Univs., 1992. Mem. Wilkes-Barre C. of C., Westmoreland Club (bd. govs. local chpt. 1989-91), Mid. State Assn. Colls. and Schs. (commn. higher edn.), Pa. Assn. Colls. and Univs. (com. on acad. issues). Democrat. Lodges: Rotary Internat.; K.C. Office: King's Coll 133 N River St Wilkes Barre PA 18711-0802

LACKEY, LAWRENCE BAILIS, JR., retired architect, urban designer; b. Santa Fe, Nov. 7, 1914; s. Lawrence Bailis and Mary (McFie) L.; children: Merryl, Stephen Byrne. Student in liberal arts, U. N.Mex., 1936; BS in Architecture, U. Mich., 1938; postgrad. (Acad. fellow in town planning), Cranbrook Acad. Art, 1939-41; grad. seminar on computer aids in urban design, M.I.T., 1969. Registered architect, Calif., Alaska. Designer Eliel and Eero Saarinen, Bloomfield Hills, Mich., 1940-41, Wurster, Bernardi & Emmons, San Francisco, 1946-48; architect Skidmore, Owings & Merrill, San Francisco, 1948-54, John Lord King (Architect), San Francisco, 1954-56, John Carl Warnecke & Assocs., San Francisco, 1956-59; prin. Lawrence Lackey (Urban Design Cons.), San Francisco, 1959-63, Sasaki, Walker, Lackey & Assos., San Francisco, 1963-65, Lawrence Lackey & Assocs., San Francisco and San Rafael, Calif., 1965-75, Lawrence Lackey (Architect), San Rafael, Calif., 1978-91; cons. architect U. Alaska, 1959-71; mem. faculty U. Mont., 1964-71. Designer: preliminary concept Golden Gateway Redevel, San Francisco, 1956, U. N.Mex. Campus Devel. Plan, 1960, U. Mont. Campus Devel. Plan, 1964, Okla. Health Center Devel. Plan, Oklahoma City, 1968, U. Alaska Campus Devel. Plan, 1968, Sci. Teaching Complex Design Concept at, U. Kans. Med. Center, 1970, Creekside Center Complex, San Rafael, 1979. Mem. coordinating com. for redevel. San Francisco C. of C., 1955-58, chmn. com. urban design, 1971. Served as officer USN, 1942-45. Fellow AIA (dir. No. Calif. chpt. 1962); mem. San Francisco Planning and Urban Renewal Assn. (dir., mem. exec. com. 1959-63), San Francisco Planning and Housing Assn. (pres. 1956-59). Office: 623 Cherry Ave Sonoma CA 95476-4183

LACKEY, S. ALLEN, petroleum company executive, corporate lawyer. BBA, U. Miss., 1963, JD, 1968. Bar: Miss. 1968. Now v.p., gen. counsel Shell Oil Co., Houston. Office: Shell Oil Co 910 Louisiana St Houston TX 77002*

LACKLAND, JOHN, lawyer; b. Parma, Idaho, Aug. 29, 1939. A.B. Stanford U., 1962; J.D., U. Wash., 1964. Bar: Wash. 1965, U.S. Dist. Ct.

(we. dist.) Wash. 1965, (ea. dist.) Wash. 1973, U.S. Ct. Appeals (9th cir.) 1965, Conn. 1981, U.S. Dist. Ct. Conn. 1983, U.S. Supreme Ct. 1973, U.S. Dist. Ct. (so. dist.) N.Y. 1988. Assoc. firm Lane Powell Moss & Miller, Seattle, 1965-69; asst. atty. gen. State of Wash., Seattle, 1969-72; asst. chief State of Wash. (U. Wash. div.), 1969-72; v.p., sec., gen. counsel Western Farmers Assn., Seattle, 1972-76, Fotomat Corp., Stamford, Conn., 1976-80; ptnr. Leepson & Lackland, Westport, Conn., 1981-88, Lackland and Nalewaik, 1988-92; prin. Law Offices John Lackland, Lackland Assocs., Grand Junction, Colo., 1994—. Bd. dirs. Mercer Island (Wash.) United Ch., 1967-70, pres. bd. dirs., 1970; mem. land use plan steering com. City of Mercer Island, 1970-72; bd. dirs. Mercer Island Sch. Dist., 1970-73, v.p. bd., 1972, pres., 1973; trustee Mid-Fairfield Child Guidance Ctr., 1982-84, Norfield Congregational Ch., 1982-84.

LACKLAND, THEODORE HOWARD, lawyer; b. Chgo., Dec. 4, 1943; s. Richard and Cora Lee (Sanders) L.; m. Dorothy Ann Gerald, Jan. 2, 1970; 1 child, Jennifer Noel. BS, Loyola U., Chgo., 1965; MA, Howard U., 1967; JD, Columbia U., 1975; grad. U.S. Army Ranger Sch., 1968. Bar: N.J. 1975, U.S. Dist. Ct. N.J. 1975, Ga. 1982, U.S. Tax Ct. 1983, U.S. Supreme Ct. 1979, U.S. Dist. Ct. (no. dist.) Ga. 1982, U.S. Dist. Ct. (mid. dist.) Ga. 1985. Assoc. Dewey, Ballantine, Bushby, Palmer & Wood, N.Y.C., 1975-78; asst. U.S. atty. Dist. N.J., Newark, 1978-81; ptnr. Arnall Golden & Gregory, Atlanta, 1981-93, Lackland & Assocs., Atlanta, 1993—; adj. prof. law Ga. State U. Law Sch., 1989-94. Assoc. editor Columbia Human Rights Law Rev., 1974-75; contbr. articles to profl. jours. Adv. dir. Atlanta Bus. Devel. Ctr., Minority Bus. Devel. Council, Atlanta, 1983-91. Served with U.S. Army, 1967-71. Decorated Bronze Star with 1 oak leaf cluster, Purple Heart, Air Medal. Mem. ABA, N.J. Bar Assn., Ga. Bar Assn., Fed. Bar Assn., Gate City Bar Assn. Democrat. Roman Catholic. Home: 4400 Oak Ln Marietta GA 30062-6355 Office: Lackland Assocs 230 Peachtree St NW Ste 900 Atlanta GA 30303-1512

LACKNER, JAMES ROBERT, aerospace medicine educator; b. Virginia, Minn., Nov. 11, 1940; s. William and Lillian Mae (Galbraith) L.; m. Ann Martin Graybiel, Aug. 26, 1970. BSc, MIT, 1966, PhD, 1970. Asst. prof. psychology Brandeis U., Waltham, Mass., 1970-74, assoc. prof. psychology, 1974-79, Riklis prof. physiology dept. psychology, 1977—, chmn. dept. psychology, 1975-83, provost, dean faculty, 1986-89, dir. Ashton Graybiel Spatial Orientation Lab., 1982—; research assoc. dept. psychology and clin. research ctr. MIT, Cambridge, 1970-80; sci. adv. bd. Space Biomed. Research Inst., Houston, 1982—, Aphasia Research Ctr. Boston U. Sch. Med., 1977-82, Eunice Kennedy Shriver Ctr. Harvard U. Med. Sch., Cambridge, 1980—; sci. adv. panel astronaut longitudinal health program Johnson Space Ctr., NASA, 1983, exec. sec. space adaptation syndrome steering com., 1982-84, pre-adaption trainer working group, 1986—, artificial gravity working group, 1987—; fabricant com. life scis. experiments for a space sta., 1982; space scis. bd. sensory motor panel NAS, 1984-86; com. on hearing, bioacoustics and biomechanics NRC, 1985-89, com. on vision, 1987-92, com. on space, biology and medicine, 1991—, mem. com. virtual reality rsch. and devel., 1992—. Mem. editl. bd. Presence, 1992—, Jour. Vestib. Rsch.; contbr. more than 150 articles to sci. jours. Mem. Am. Soc. for Gravitational and Space Biology, Aerospace Med. Assn. (Arnold B. Tuttle award), Soc. for Neurosci., Psychonomics Soc., Internat. Brain Research Orgn., Barany Soc. (hon.), Internat. Acad. Astronautics (hon.). Achievements include research in human sensory-motor coordination and spatial orientation. Home: Boyce Farm Rd Lincoln MA 01773-4813 Office: Brandeis U Ashton Graybiel Lab PO Box 9110/415 South St Waltham MA 02154-9100*

LACKRITZ, MARC E., securities trade association executive; b. Columbus, Ohio, Sept. 29, 1946; m. Mary B. DeOreo, May 17, 1975; children: Anne, Katie, Sarah. AB in Pub. and Internat. Affairs, Princeton U., 1968; MPhil, Oxford U., 1971; JD cum laude, Harvard U., 1973. Asst. counsel U.S. Senate Watergate Com., Washington, 1973-74; dep. chief counsel U.S. Senate Budget Com., Washington, 1974-77; ptnr. Wald, Harkrader & Ross, Washington, 1977-84; staff dir., chief counsel U.S. Ho. Energy and Commerce subcom. telecommunications, consumer protection, fin., Washington, 1987-90; exec. v.p. Pub. Securities Assn., Washington, 1987-90; exec. v.p. Securities Ind. Assn., Washington, 1990-92, pres., 1992—; bd. dirs. Am. Coun. Capital Formation, Washington, Am. Univ. Adv. Bd. for MA in Fin. Econs. for Pub. Policy; bd. dirs., mem. adv. com. Fin. Acctg. Standards, Norwalk, Conn. Contbr. articles to profl. jours. Trustee Securities Industry Found. for Econ. Edn., Securities Industry Inst.; mem. fin. steering com. Clinton-for-Pres., Washington, 1991-92. Rhodes scholar 1968. Democrat. Jewish. Avocations: running, tennis, golf, writing. Office: Securities Industry Assn Ste 1000 1401 I St NW Washington DC 20005

LA CORTE, JOHN J., philosophy educator, historical society executive; b. Brooklyn, N.Y., July 25, 1944; s. John Napoleon and Marion Virginia (Loschiavo) L.; m. Mary Panettieri, July 9, 1967; children: Adriana Athena La Corte. BA, Loyola U., L.A., 1966; MA, U. So. Calif., L.A., 1970; PhD, U. So. Calif., 1971. Tchr. L.A. schs., 1965-67; chmn. philosophy dept. Calif. State U., Dominguez Hills, 1980-90, chmn. acad. senate, 1989-91, assoc. dean Sch. Fine Arts, 1988-91; mem. Assn. for Calif. State U. Profs., 1988—, Italian Hist. Soc. Am., N.J., 1991—; assoc. dir.Inst. for Study Cultural Diversity & Internationalization Calif. State U., Dominguez Hills, 1994—. Better World Soc. Am. (pres. 1991—), Brooklyn, N.Y. 1988 3837 Bluff St Torrance CA 90505 Office: Italian Hist Soc Am 111 Coumbia Hts Brooklyn NY 11201

LACOSTE, PAUL, lawyer, educator, university official; b. Montreal, Que., Can., Apr. 24, 1923; s. Emile and Juliette (Boucher) L.; m. Louise Marcil, Aug. 31, 1973 (div.); children: Helene, Paul-André, Anne-Marie. BA, U. Montreal, 1943, MA, 1944, Licenciate in Philosophy, 1946, Licenciate in Law, 1960; postgrad., U. Chgo., 1946-47; Docteur de l'Universite, U. Paris, 1948; LLD (hon.), McGill U., 1975, U. Toronto, 1978; D Univ. (hon.), Laval U., 1986. Bar: Que. 1960. Prof. philosophy U. Montreal, 1946-86, prof. law, 1960-68, 1985-87, vice rector, 1966-68, exec. vice rector, 1968-75, rector, 1975-85, prof. emeritus, 1987—; moderator, commentator CBC, 1956-63; mem. firm Lalande, Brière, Reeves, Lacoste et Paquette, Mont., 1964-66; mem. Royal Commn. on Bilingualism and Biculturism, 1963-71, Que. Superior Coun. Edn., 1964-68, Que. Coun. Univs., 1969-77; mem. Conf. Rectors and Prins. Que. Univs., 1967-85, pres., 1977-79; chmn. Fed. Commn. and coms. for the environ. assessment of Great-Whale hydraulic project, 1991—. Author: (with others) La crise de l'enseignement au Canada Francais, 1961, Justice et Paix scolaire, 1962, A Place of Liberty, 1964, Le Canada au seuil du siecle de l'abondance, 1969, Education permanente et potentiel universitaire, 1977; contbr. articles to profl. jours. Mem. Corp. de l'Ecole des Hautes Etudes Commerciales, 1975-85, Ecole Polytechnique, 1975-85, Corp. du Coll. Marie de France; bd. dirs. Clin. Rsch. Inst. of Montreal, 1975-85; pres. Assn. des universités partiellement ou entièrement de langue française, 1978-81. Mem. Assn. Univs. and Colls. of Can. (mem. com. of pres. 1975-85, v.p. 1977, pres. 1978-79), Assn. Commonwealth Univs. (dir. 1977-80). Home: 356 Woodlea, Ville Mont Royal, PQ Canada H3P 1R5 Office: Université de Montréal, CP 6128 Pavillon 2910 bur 6, Montreal, PQ Canada H3C 3J7

LACOUTURE, FELIPE ERNESTO, museum consultant; b. Mexico City, Feb. 25, 1928; s. Juan and Guadalupe (Fornelli) L.; m. Josefina Dahl Cortés, Nov. 21, 1959; children: Yvonne Josefina, Jacqueline, Geraldine, Verónica, Juan Felipe. Architect's degree, Universidad Nacional Autónoma de México, 1952; postgrad., Ecole du Louvre, Paris, 1952-53, Inst. de Cultura Hispánica, Universidad de Madrid, Spain, 1953-54; M in Visual Arts, U. Nacional Autonoma de Mexico, 1978; M in Museology, Inst. Nacional de Antropologia e Historia, 1981. Dir. Mus. Art and History in Ciudad Juárez, 1964-70; head dept. regional museums Nat. Inst. Anthropology and History, 1970-73; dir. San Carlos Mus., 1973-77; head dept. plastic arts Nat. Inst. Fine Arts, 1974-77; dir. Nat. Mus. History, Mexico City, 1977-82; permanent adv. museology Nat. Parks and Restoration of Monuments, 1983-85; prof. museology Churubusco Restoration Sch., 1971—; adviser in museology UNESCO, 1971-86; responsible for the program of integration new Mus. Documentation Ctr. (Coordinacion Nacional de Museos y Exposiciones) INAH-Mex.; expert appraiser Nat. Banking Commn. Mex., 1980-95. Decorated comendador Orden de Rio Branco, Brazil. Mem. Internat. Coun. Mus. (sec. Mexican nat. com.), Internat. Coun. Monuments and Sites, Colegio de Arquitectos de Mexico, Sociedad de Arquitectos Mexicanos.

Home and Office: Edificio 21 Depto 203, Villa Olimpica, Mexico City 14020, Mexico

LACOVARA, PHILIP ALLEN, lawyer; b. N.Y.C., July 11, 1943; s. P. Philip and Elvira Lacovara; m. Madeline E. Papio, Oct. 14, 1961; children: Philip, Michael, Christopher, Elizabeth, Karen, Daniel, Andrew. AB magna cum laude, Georgetown U., 1963; JD summa cum laude, Columbia U., 1966. Bar: N.Y. 1967, D.C. 1974, U.S. Supreme Ct. 1970. Law clk. to presiding justice U.S. Ct. Appeals D.C. Cir., 1966-67; asst. to solicitor gen. U.S. Washington, 1967-69; assoc. Hughes Hubbard & Reed, N.Y.C., 1969-71; ptnr. Hughes Hubbard & Reed, N.Y.C. and Washington, 1974-88; v.p., sr. counsel GE, Fairfield, Conn., 1988-90; mng. dir. gen. counsel Morgen Stanley & Co., N.Y.C., 1990-93; ptnr. Mayer, Brown & Platt, N.Y.C. and Washington, 1993—; spl. counsel to N.Y.C. Police Commr., 1971-72; dep. solicitor gen. U.S. Dept. Justice, Washington, 1972-73; counsel to spl. prosecutor Watergate Spl. Prosecution Force, 1973-74; lectr. law Columbia U.; adj. prof. Georgetown U. Law Ctr.; vis. lectr. various colls., univs.; mem. Jud. Conf. U.S. Ct. Circuit, 1973—; chmn. commn. on admissions and grievances U.S.T. Ct. Appeals for D.C. Circuit, 1980-86; spl. counsel U.S. Ho. of Reps. Com. on Standards Ofcl. Conduct, 1976-77; chmn. bd. trustees Public Defender Service for D.C., 1976-81; sec. exec. com. bd. visitors Columbia U. Sch. Law; pres. Columbia U. Sch. Law Alumni Assn., 1986-88; bd. govs. D.C. Bar, 1978-84, gen. counsel, 1985-87, pres., 1988-89, mem. legal ethics com., 1976-81, chmn. code subcom., 1977-81. Contbr. articles to profl. jours. Co-chair, Washington Lawyers Com. for Civil Rights Under Law, 1982-84; mem. D.C. Jud. Nomination Commn., 1981-85; bd. dirs. Legal Aid Soc. of N.Y.C., 1992—. Fellow Am. Coll. Trial Lawyers; mem. ABA (ho. of dels. 1978-89, vice-chmn. sect. individual rights and responsibilities 1985-87, 89-91, chmn. 1991-92), Am. Law Inst., Practicing Law Inst. (trustee), Cath. Interracial Coun. N.Y., Lawyers Com. for Human Rights (trustee 1991—), Legal Aid Soc. N.Y.C. (bd. dirs. 1992—), 1925 F St. Club, Lotos Club, Knights of Malta. Roman Catholic. Home: 39 Mill Rd New Canaan CT 06840-4305 Office: 1675 Broadway New York NY 10019

LACROIX, CHRISTIAN MARIE MARC, fashion designer; b. Arles, Bouche du Rhône, France, May 16, 1951; s. Maxime and Jeannette (Bergier) L. Grad., U. Valery, Montpelier, France, 1973. Asst. Hermes Co., Paris, 1978-79, Guy Paulin Co., Paris, 1980-81; chief designer Jean Patou Co., Paris, 1982-87; prin. Christian Lacroix Co., Paris, 1987—. Decorated chevalier des Arts et Lettres, 1992; recipient Golden Thimble award, 1986, 88, Coun. Fashion Designer Am. award, 1987, Prix Balzac, 1989, Das Goldene Spinnrad award Kreffeld, R.F.A., 1990. Roman Catholic. Office: Christian Lacroix, 73 Faubourg Saint-Honoré, 75008 Paris France

LACY, ALAN JASPER, retail executive; b. Cleveland, Tenn., Oct. 19, 1953; s. William J. and Mary (Leigh) L.; m. Caron Ann Cage, May 16, 1981; children: Daniel Alan, Brian Matthew. BSIM, Ga. Inst. Tech., 1975; MBA, Emory U., 1977. Chartered fin. analyst., 1982; fin. analyst Holiday Inns, Inc., Memphis, 1977-79; mgr. investor relations Tiger Internat., Los Angeles, 1979-80, Dart Industries, Los Angeles, 1980-81; dir. corp. fin. Dart & Kraft, Northbrook, Ill., 1981-82, asst. treas., 1982-83, treas., v.p., 1984-86, v.p. fin. and adminstrn. internat., 1987-88; v.p., treas., chief fin. officer Minnetonka Corp., Bloomington, Minn., 1988-89; sr. v.p. strategy and devel. Kraft Gen. Foods, Glenview, Ill., 1989-90, sr. v.p. fin., 1990-92, sr. v.p. fin., strategy, systems, 1992-93; v.p. fin. svcs. and systems Philip Morris Cos., 1993-95; sr. v.p. fin. Sears, Roebuck & Co., 1995—. Mem. Fin. Analysts Fedn., Economic Club (Chgo.), The Res. Bd.

LACY, ALEXANDER SHELTON, lawyer; b. South Boston, Va., Aug. 18, 1921; s. Cecil Baker and Lura Elizabeth (Byram) L.; m. Carol Jemison, Aug. 8, 1952; children: John Blakeway, Joan Elizabeth Chancey, Alexander Shelton. B.S. in Chemistry, U. Ala., 1943; LL.B., U. Va., 1949. Bar: Ala. 1949, U.S. Ct. Appeals (5th, 11th and D.C. cirs.) 1981, U.S. Supreme Ct. 1979. Assoc. Bradley, Arant, Rose & White, Birmingham, Ala., 1949-54; with Ala. Gas Corp., Birmingham, 1954-86; v.p., asst. sec., atty. Ala. Gas Corp., 1969-86, v.p., sec., atty., 1974-86; with Patrick and Lacy, Birmingham, 1986—. Pres., chmn. bd. Birmingham Symphony Assn., 1964-67; chmn. Birmingham-Jefferson Civic Center Authority, 1965-71. Served with USN, 1943-46. Mem. ABA, Ala. Bar Assn. (chmn. energy law com. 1984-86), Birmingham Bar Assn., Am. Gas Assn. (chmn. legal sect. 1983-85), Fed. Energy Bar Assn., Fed. Bar Assn., Am. Judicature Soc., The Club, Mountain Brook Club, Summit Club, Phi Gamma Delta, Phi Delta Phi. Episcopalian. Home: 3730 Montrose Rd Birmingham AL 35213-3824 Office: Patrick and Lacy 1201 Financial Ctr Birmingham AL 35203

LACY, BILL, college president; b. Madill, Okla., Apr. 16, 1933; s. Leon and Eunice L.; m. Susan Cavert Butler, Dec. 27, 1992; children: Jan, Kate, Shawn, Ross, Jessica. B.Arch., Okla. State U., 1955, M.Arch., 1958; D.F.A. (hon.), Miami U., Oxford, Ohio, 1985. Design architect Caudill, Rowlett, Scott, Houston, 1958-61; prof., assoc. chmn. dept. architecture Rice U., Houston, 1961-65; prof., dean sch. architecture U. Tenn., Knoxville, 1965-70; v.p. Omniplan, Dallas, 1970-71; dir. architecture and environ. arts Nat. Endowment Arts, Washington, 1971-77, dir. fed. design program, 1972-77; pres. Am. Acad. in Rome, N.Y.C., 1977-80, The Cooper Union, N.Y.C., 1980-88, SUNY, Purchase Coll., 1993—; archtl. cons. Fgn. Bldgs. Ops., Dept. State. Author: 100 Contemporary Architects, 1991, Angels and Franciscans, 1992; mem. editorial bd. Process: Architecture; contbr. articles, designs to profl. jours. Bd. dirs. Internat. Design Conf. Aspen, 1973-92; bd. dirs. Tiffany Found., Am. Archtl. Found.; cons. Rothschild Found., J. Paul Getty Trust; sec. Pritzker Prize Jury. With U.S. Army, 1955-57. Loeb fellow Harvard U., 1973. Fellow AIA; mem. Univ. Club. Office: 735 Anderson Hill Rd Purchase NY 10577-1400

LACY, CAROLYN JEAN, elementary education educator, secondary education educator; b. Marshall, Ark., Apr. 6, 1944; d. Charles Ira Bolch and Edna Evelyn Cherry; 1 child, Kelli Jean. AA with distinction, Riverside City Coll., 1980; BA, U. Calif., Riverside, 1982, postgrad., 1983; MEd, U.S. Internat. U., 1993. Cert. social sci. tchr., Calif. Educator Perris (Calif.) Elem. Sch. Dist., 1984-89, Rialto (Calif.) Unified Sch. Dist., 1989—; vol. Riverside Helpline, Calif., 1984-86; instr. Developing Capable People, Riverside, 1986-89; presenter, lectr. Jurupa Unified Sch. Dist., Riverside, 1990, Rialto Unified Sch. Dist., 1990; developer peer tutor program Perris Elem. Sch. Dist., 1989. Editor: (newsletter) Perris Lights, 1989. Active Students in Environ. Action, Riverside, 1978; mem. Riverside Helpline, 1984-86; mem. Riverside County Task Force for Self-Esteem; chess club dir., computer chmn. Dollahan Elem. Sch., Rialto Unified Sch. Dist., 1995—. Named Mentor Tchr. State of Calif., 1988. Mem. AAUW, NEA, Nat. Coun. for Self Esteem, Calif. Tchrs. Assn., U. Calif. Alumni Assn., Internat. Reading Assn., Phi Delta Kappa, Alpha Gamma Sigma. Democrat. Mem. LDS Ch. Avocations: painting, writing, gardening, reading, travel. Home: 4044 Wallace St Riverside CA 92509-6809

LACY, HERMAN EDGAR, management consultant; b. Chgo., June 21, 1935; s. Herman E. and Florence L.; m. Mary C. Lacy; children: Frederick H., Carlton E., Douglas H., Jennifer S., Victoria J., Rebecca M. BS in Indsl. Engring., Bradley U., 1957; MBA, U. Chgo., 1966. Cert. mgmt. cons. Plant mgr., indsl. engring. supr. Hammond Organ Co., Chgo., 1961-66; mgr. corp. indsl. engring. Consol. Packaging Corp., Chgo., 1966-68; mgr. mgmt. cons. Peat, Marwick, Mitchell & Co., Chgo., 1968-70; dir. ops. Wilton Enterprises, Inc., Chgo. 1970-77; v.p. gen. mgr. Intercraft Industries Corp., Chgo., 1978-79; pres. Helmco Cons. Assocs., Glenview, Ill., 1979—; instr. Roosevelt U., Oakton Coll., Harper Coll. Served to capt. USAF, 1957-61. Mem. Nat. Indsl. Engrs. (past pres., founder north suburban Ill. chpt.), Am. Mgmt. Assn., Nat. Coun. Phys. Distbn. Mgmt., Soc. Mfg. Engrs., Inst. Mgmt. Cons. Office: Helmco Cons Assocs 1920 Waukegan Rd Ste 202 Glenview IL 60025-1700

LACY, JAMES DANIEL, oil company executive; b. Cannel City, Ky., May 16, 1947; s. Steward and Mattie Lacy; m. Nancy Wehrle; children: Denise, Cathryn. BBA, Morehead State U., 1969. Prin., mgr. Lacy Photography, 1969-72; prin. Morgan Ambulance Service, 1970-71; dir. pub. rels. Lees Jr. Coll., 1972-75; asst. advt. and creative svcs. Ashland (Ky.) Oil Inc., 1975-77, mgr. creative svcs., 1977-78, mgr. media rels., 1978-80, dir. corp. media rels., 1980-81, dir. pub. rels., 1981-86, v.p. corp. communications, 1986—. Past pres. Ky. 1st Amendment Congress; mem. exec. bd. Morehead State U. Found. Inc., until 1991; mem. exec. com. Leadership Ky. Class 1986; past

bd. dirs. Jr. Achievement, Louisville Ballet; bd. dirs. St. Mary's Hosp. Named to Morehead State U. Alumni Hall of Fame. Mem. Pub. Rels. Soc. Am., Am. Petroleum Inst., Ky. Press Assn. (assoc. group), W.Va. Press Assn., Huntington C. of C. (bd. dirs.), Rotary. DEmocrat. Avocations: boating, tennis, fly fishing. Office: Ashland Oil Inc PO Box 391 Ashland KY 41105-0391

LACY, JAMES VINCENT, government official; b. Oakland, Calif., May 29, 1952; s. James C. and Roma (Stetsky) L.; m. Janice Payt, 1987. B.A. in Internat. Relations, U. So. Calif., 1974; JD., Pepperdine U., 1978; Cert. in Internat. Orgns., U. Geneva, 1973. Bar: Calif. 1978, D.C. 1983. Aide to Howard Jarvis, L.A., 1978-79; ptnr. Hoffenblum, Mollrich, Lacy, Inc., L.A., 1979-81; polit. cons. L.A., 1979-81; dep. dir. Office Bus. Liaison, U.S. Dept. Commerce, Washington, 1981-84, dir. Office Export Trading Co. Affairs, 1984-87, chief counsel for tech., 1989—; gen. counsel U.S. Consumer Product Safety Commn., 1987-89. Contbr. articles to legal jours. Chmn. bd. Young Ams. for Freedom, Inc., Sterling, Va., 1978-83; bd. dirs. Am. Conservative Union, 1979—; mem. exec. com. Young Republican Nat. Fedn., 1979-81; trustee Young Ams. Found., 1979—, U.S. Justice Found., 1979—; del. Rep. Nat. Conv., 1976; aide to del. Rep. Nat. Conv., 1980. Mem. Calif. Bar Assn., D.C. Bar Assn. Roman Catholic. Home: 24921 Seagate Dr Dana Point CA 92629-1920 Office: US Dept Commerce 14th & Constitution Ave NW Washington DC 20230-0002

LACY, JOHN FORD, lawyer; b. Dallas, Sept. 11, 1944; s. John Alexander and Glenda Arcenia (Ford) L.; m. Cece Smith, Apr. 22, 1978. BA, Baylor U., 1965; JD, Harvard U., 1968. Bar: Tex. 1968. Assoc. atty. Akin, Gump, Strauss, Hauer & Feld L.L.P., Dallas, 1968-72, ptnr., 1973-82; pres. Ford Lacy PC (affiliated with Akin, Gump et al.), Dallas, 1982—; chmn. Normandy Capital Co., Dallas, 1978—. Contbr. articles to profl. jours. Cofounder, co-chmn. pres.'s rsch. coun. U. Tex. Southwestern Med. Ctr., Dallas, 1985-91; dir., mem. fin. com. Vis. Nurse Assn. Tex., 1994-95. Served with U.S. Army, 1968-74. Rsch. fellow Southwestern Legal Found., Dallas. Mem. ABA, Dallas Bar Assn., State Bar Tex. (coun. bus. law sect. 1992-95). Home: 6412 Williams Pky Dallas TX 75205-1717 Office: Akin Gump Strauss et al Ste 4100 1700 Pacific Ave Dallas TX 75201-4618

LACY, JOSEPH NEWTON, architect; b. Kansas City, Mo., Oct. 6, 1905; s. John James and Theresa (Conboy) L.; m. Mary Duncan, Oct. 6, 1927 (dec. Aug. 1978); children: Mary-Louise, John Duncan, William Duncan; m. Martha E. Sadler, Apr. 19, 1980 (dec. Feb. 1987). B.Arch., U. Pa., 1927. Assoc. several archtl. firms in Phila., 1927-45; including Paul P. Cret, 1941-43, Louis I. Kahn, 1943-45; assoc. Eliel and Eero Saarinen, Bloomfield Hills, Mich., 1945-51; ptnr. Eero Saarinen & Assos., Bloomfield Hills, 1951-66; ret. Eero Saarinen & Assos., 1966. Mem. Coll. Fellows of AIA, Hon. Order Ky. Cols. Specialized in devel. of new bldg. materials. *Association with Eliel and Eero Saarinen, two of the great architects of modern times, gave me the opportunities to participate in the carrying out of my principles and goals of architecture. I became part of a team that designed such outstanding structures as the Jefferson Memorial Arch in St. Louis.*

LACY, LINWOOD A., JR., computer company executive; b. 1945. BS in Chem. Engring., U. Va., 1967, MBA, 1969. Sr. v.p., COO Micro D, Inc, 1982-83; sr. mgmt. position mktg. and merchandising Best Products, 1983-85; chmn., CEO Micro D, Inc., 1985-89, Ingram Micro, Inc., Santa Ana, Calif., 1989—. Office: Ingram Micro Inc 1600 E Saint Andrew Pl Santa Ana CA 92705-4926

LACY, MELVYN LEROY, plant pathology educator and researcher; b. Henry, Nebr., Oct. 24, 1931; married, 1954; 2 children. BS, U. Wyo., 1959, MS, 1961; PhD in Plant Pathology, Oreg. State U., 1964. From asst. prof. to assoc. prof., 1965-78; prof. plant pathology Mich. State U., 1978—. Mem. Am. Phytopath. Soc. (disting. svc. award), Can Phytopath Soc., Am. Potato Assn. Research in soil-borne fungus diseases, epidemiology, and control; pesticides for disease control; epidemiology, disease forecasting and disease management. Office: Mich State U Botany & Plant Pathology Dept East Lansing MI 48823*

LACY, NORRIS JOINER, French language and literature educator; b. Hopkinsville, Ky., Mar. 8, 1940; s. Edwin V. and Lillian Louise (Joiner) L. B.A., Murray State U., 1962; M.A., Ind. U., 1963; Ph.D., 1967. Lectr. Ind. U., 1965-66; asst. prof. to prof. U. Kans., Lawrence, 1966-88; prof. Washington U., St. Louis, 1988—; vis. assoc. prof. UCLA, 1975-76. Author: The Craft of Chretien de Troyes, 1980, The Arthurian Handbook, 1988, Reading Fabliaux, 1993; editor: Medieval French Miscellany, 1972, From Camelot to Joyous Guard, 1974, 26 Chansons d'amour de la Renaissance, 1975, The Comic Spirit in Medieval France, 1976, Essays in Early French Literature, 1982, L'Istoyre de Jehan Coquault, 1983, The Arthurian Encyclopedia, 1986, The Legacy of Chretien de Troyes, 1987, The Poetics of Love, 1989, Continuations: Essays in Honor of John L. Grigsby, 1989, The New Arthurian Encyclopedia, 1991, Conjunctures: Medieval Studies in Honor of Douglas Kelly, 1994, Medieval Arthurian Literature: A Guide to Recent Research, 1995; editor, translator: Tristan (Béroul), 1989, The Vows of the Heron, 1991, Lancelot-Grail: The Old French Arthurian Vulgate and Post-Vulgate in Translation, 1993—; editor in chief Summa Publs., Inc., 1981-86. Decorated knight Order of Acad. Palms (France); grantee Am. Philos. Soc., 1969, Am. Coun. Learned Socs., 1973, 85, NEH, 1975, 89-91. Mem. MLA, Medieval Acad. Am., Internat. Arthurian Soc. (hon. internat. pres.), Société Rencevals. Office: Dept Romance Lang Lit Washington U Saint Louis MO 63130

LACY, PAUL ESTON, pathologist; b. Trinway, Ohio, Feb. 7, 1924; s. Benjamin Lemmert and Amy Cass (Cox) L.; m. Emelyn Ellen Talbot, June 7, 1945; children: Paul E. Jr., Steven T. BA cum laude, Ohio State U., 1945, MD cum laude, MSc in Anatomy, 1948; PhD in Pathology, U. Minn.-Mayo Found., 1955; Doctor of Medicine (honoris causa), Uppsala (Sweden) U., 1977. Asst. instr. anatomy Ohio State U., Columbus, 1944-48; intern White Cross Hosp., Columbus, 1948-49; fellow in pathology Mayo Clinic, Rochester, Minn., 1951-55; postdoctoral fellow Washington U. Med. Sch., St. Louis, 1955-56, instr. pathology, 1956-57, asst. prof. pathology, 1957-61, asst. dean, 1959-61, assoc. prof. pathology, 1961, Mallinckrodt prof., chmn. dept. pathology, 1961-85, Robert L. Kroc prof. of pathology, 1985—; pathologist-in-chief Barnes & Allied Hosps., St. Louis, 1961-85, pathologist, 1985—. Served to capt. U.S. Army, 1949-51. Recipient Banting award Brit. Diabetes Assn., 1963, Am. Diabetes Assn., 1970, 3M Life Scis. award FASEB, 1981, Rous-Whipple award Am. Assn. Pathologists, 1984. Fellow AAAS, Am. Acad. Arts and Sci.; mem. NAS, Inst. Medicine. Avocations: horticulture, literature. Office: Washington Univ Med Sch Dept of Pathology 660 S Euclid Ave Saint Louis MO 63110-1010

LACY, ROBINSON BURRELL, lawyer; b. Boston, May 7, 1952; s. Benjamin Hammett and Jane (Burrell) L.; m. Elizabeth Coutrakon, Oct. 20, 1984. AB, U. Calif., Berkeley, 1974; JD, Harvard U., 1977. Bar: N.Y. 1978, U.S. Dist. Ct. (so. and ea. dists.) N.Y. 1979, U.S. Dist. Ct. (we. dist.) N.Y. 1992, U.S. Ct. Appeals (2d cir.) 1983, U.S. Ct. Appeals (10th cir.) 1990, U.S. Supreme Ct. 1990. Law clk. to judge U.S. Dist. Ct. (so. dist.) N.Y., N.Y.C. 1977-78; law clk. to chief justice Warren Burger U.S. Supreme Ct., Washington, 1978-79; assoc. Sullivan & Cromwell, N.Y.C., 1979-85, ptnr., 1985—. Mem. ABA, Assn. of Bar of City of N.Y., N.Y. State Bar Assn. Office: Sullivan & Cromwell 125 Broad St New York NY 10004-2400

LACY, STEVE, jazz musician; b. N.Y.C., 1934. Played soprano sax at Schillinger House, Boston; performed with Pee Wee Russell, Rex Stewart, Buck Clayton, Jimmy Rushing, Dicky Wells, Walter Page, N.Y.C., 1953-54; played with Cecil Taylor; then with Gil Evans' orch., 1957; formed quartet with Roswell Rudd, experimenting with chord-free improvisation and unusual song forms, early 1960s; formed sextet Paris, 1970; played regular duets with Mal Waldron, 1979—. Recordings include Soprano Sax (debut), 1957, Reflections: Steve Lacy Plays Thelonius Monk, 1958, Evidence (with Don Cherry), 1961, Paris Blues (with Gil Evans), Raps, 1977, Steve Lacy Three: New York Capers, 1979, The Way, 1979, Ballets, 1980, Herbe de L'Oubli & Snake Out (with Mal Waldron), 1981, Songs (with Brion Gysin), 1985, 86, Let's Call This (with Mal Waldron), Prospectus, 1986, Steve Lacy Two, Five & Six: Blinks, 1986, Steve Lacy Nine: Futurities, 1986, The Straight Horn of Steve Lacy, The Door (duos, trios, etc.), 1989, Anthem, 1990, Hot House (with Mal Waldron), 1991, Live at Sweet Basil, 1992, Steve

Lacy Solo, 1993; composed/played musical score Landing live for D. Dunn, 1992. Frequent winner Down Beat Mag. poll, best soprano saxist, 1992. Office: care BMG 1133 Ave Of The Americas New York NY 10036-6710*

LACZKO, BRIAN JOHN, theater director; b. Cleve., Aug. 7, 1952; s. Joseph John and Avonelle Dorothy (Toth) L.; m. Jill Maree Aude, Aug. 12, 1978; children: Brian John, Stefanie Dale. BA, Denison U., 1974; MA, W.Va. U., 1978. Prodn. mgr. Advent Theatre, Nashville, 1978-79; prodn. mgr. Tenn. Performing Arts Ctr., Nashville, 1980-81, dir. ops., 1981-82, asst. mng. dir., 1982-86; gen. mgr. Starwood Amphitheatre, Nashville, 1986-87; mng. dir. Tenn. Repertory Theatre, Nashville, 1987—; adjudicator Tenn. Arts Commn., Nashville, 1991—, chair adv. panel, 1992—; Met. Nashville Arts Commn., 1991—; mem. profl. cos. panel Opera-Musical Theatre Program NEA. Scenic and lighting dir. over 50 theater prodns. Mem. Am. Arts Alliance, Internat. Theatre Inst. of U.S., Theatre Communications Group, Nat. Alliance Musical Theatre Producers, Alliance Performing Arts Presenters, Tenn. Theatre Assn., Tennesseans for Arts, Nashville C. of C. Office: Tenn Repertory Theatre 427 Chestnut St Nashville TN 37203

LADANYI, BRANKA MARIA, chemist, educator; b. Zagreb, Croatia, Sept. 7, 1947; came to U.S., 1969; d. Branko and Nevenka (Zilic) L.; m. Marshall Fixman, Dec. 7, 1974. BSc, McGill U., Montreal, Can., 1969; M in Philosophy, Yale U., 1971, PhD, 1973. Vis. prof. of chemistry U. Ill., 1974; postdoctoral research assoc. Yale U., 1974-77, research assoc., 1977-79; asst. prof. chemistry Colo. State U., Ft. Collins, 1979-84, assoc. prof. chemistry, 1985-87, prof. chemistry, 1987—; vis. fellow Joint Inst. for Lab. Astrophysics, 1993-94. Assoc. editor Jour. Chem. Physics, 1994—; referee and contbr. articles to profl. jours. Fellow Sloan Found., 1982-84, Dreyfus Found., 1983-87; vis. fellow JILA, 1993-94; grantee NSF, NATO, 1983-89. Mem. AAAS, Am. Chem. Soc. (PRF grantee 1979-82, 1989-91), Am. Phys. Soc., NOW, Sigma Xi. Home: 1100 E Pitkin St Fort Collins CO 80524-3909 Office: Colo State U Dept Chemistry Fort Collins CO 80523

LADANYI, BRANKO, civil engineer; b. Zagreb, Croatia, Dec. 14, 1922; emigrated to Can., 1962, naturalized, 1967; s. Adalbert and Zora (Kniewald) L.; m. Nevenka Zilic, Dec. 14, 1946; children: Branka, Thomas, Marc. B.Civil Engring., U. Zagreb, 1947; Ph.D. in Soil Mechanics, U. Louvain, Belgium, 1959. Design engr. Dept. Transp., Zagreb, 1947-52; teaching asst. U. Zagreb, 1952-58; research engr. Belgian Geotech. Inst., Ghent, 1958-62; asso. prof., then prof. civil engring. Laval U., Quebec, Can., 1962-67; prof. civil engring. Ecole Poly., U. Montreal, 1967-94, prof. emeritus, 1994—, dir. North Engring. Centre, 1972—. Author papers in geotech. field, chpts. in books. Recipient Que. Sci. award Que. Ministry Edn., 1974, De Beer Geotech. award Belgian Geotech. Soc., 1986, Elbert F. Rice Meml. award ASCE and U. Ala. at Fairbanks, 1991. Fellow ASCE, Royal Soc. Can., Can. Acad. Engring., Engring. Inst. Can., Can. Soc. Civil Engring.; mem. ASTM, Order Engrs. Que., Can. Geotech. Soc. R.F. Legget Geotech. award 1981, Roger J.E. Brown Meml. award 1993), Can. Isnt. Mining and Metallurgy. Office: Dept Civil Engring, Ecole Poly CP 6079 Succ Centre-Ville, Montreal, PQ Canada *There is no end to learning.*

LADAR, JERROLD MORTON, lawyer; b. San Francisco, Aug. 2, 1933. AB, U. Wash., 1956; LLB, U. Calif., Berkeley, 1960. Bar: Calif. 1961, U.S. Supreme Ct. 1967. Law clk. to judge U.S. Dist. Ct. (no. dist.) Calif., 1960-61; asst. U.S. atty. San Francisco, 1961-70; chief criminal div., 1968-70; mem. firm MacInnis & Donner, San Francisco, 1970-72; prof. criminal law and procedure U. San Francisco Law Sch., 1962-83; pvt. practice San Francisco, 1970-94; ptnr. Ladar & Knapp, San Francisco, 1994—; lectr. Hastings Law Coll. Trial Advocacy, 1984—; chair pvt. defender panel U.S. Dist. Ct. (no. dist.) Calif., 1980-90; chair stats. and tech. subcom. Fed. Civicl Justice Reform Act Com. (no. dist.) Calif., 1990—; ct. appointed mem. Fed. Ct. Rules Revision Com. (no. dist.) Calif., 1994—; mem. continuing edn. of bar criminal law adv. com. U. Calif., Berkeley, 1978-83, 89—. Author: (with others) Selected Trial Motions, California Criminal Law Procedure and Practice, 1986, (supplements to) California Criminal Law and Procedure, 1987-92, (chpts.) Calif. Criminal Law and Procedure, 2d edit., 1993, Direct Examination-Tips and Techniques, 1982; co-author: Criminal Trial Tactics, 1985, 88, 89; co-author chpts. Grand Jury Practice, California Asset Forfeiture in California Criminal Law and Procedure 2d, U. Calif. Continuing Edn. of the Bar, 1994. Trustee Tamalpais Union High Sch. Dist., 1968-77, chmn. bd., 1973-74; mem. adv. com. Nat. PTA Assn., 1972-78; apptd. mem. criminal justice act com. U.S. Ct. Appeals (9th cir). Fellow Am. Bd. Criminal Lawyers; mem. ABA, San Francisco Bar Assn. (editor in Re 1974-76), State Bar Calif. (pro-tem disciplinary referee 1976-78, vice chmn. pub. interest and edn. com. criminal law sect., mem. exec. com. criminal law sect. 1980-87, editor Criminal Law Sect. News 1981-87, chmn. exec. com. 1983-84), Am. Inns of Ct. (exec. com. 1994—). Office: 507 Polk St Ste 310 San Francisco CA 94102-3339

LADAU, ROBERT FRANCIS, architect, planner; b. N.Y.C., Jan. 31, 1940; s. A. Ralph and Marguerite Louise (de Valois-Vignand) L.; m. Anne Horton, May 30, 1970. A.B., Columbia U., 1961, B.Arch., M.Arch., 1965. Chmn. bd. dirs., chief exec. officer Environers Inc., N.Y.C., 1964-66, dir., 1966-73; assoc. Rogers, Butler & Burgun, Architects, N.Y.C., 1966-69; prin. Robert F. Ladau, AIA Architect/Planner, N.Y.C., 1969-70, pres., 1973—; ptnr. Metcalf & Assocs. Architects & Engrs., Washington and N.Y.C. and founder and ptnr. Sir Robert Matthew, Metcalf & Ptnrs., London and Edinburgh, 1970-73; v.p. architecture A.M. Kinney Affiliation Architects & Engrs., Cin., N.Y.C., Chgo., Denver, L.A., San Juan and Basel, Switzerland, 1975-80; sr. v.p. Welton Becket Assocs., N.Y.C., 1980-84; pres., chief exec. officer The Miller Orgn., 1984-90; pres. Emery Roth & Sons Interior Design/Facilities Mgmt., 1990—; lectr. on planning, design health facilities; mem. nat. panel Am. Arbitration Assn. Bd. fellows Frick Collection; chmn. long range planning com. bd. govs. Columbia U. Club N.Y.; mem. Bedford (N.Y.) Conservation Bd., 1975-78. Contbr. articles to profl. jours. Co-author: Color in Interior Design and Architecture, 1988; designer numerous office and comml., health, ednl., urban, recreational, residential and indsl. facilities. Recipient Group Exhibit award Rockefeller Found., 1964; design awards Rockefeller Found., 1962, N.Y. Soc. Architects, 1966, Internat. Conf. Med. Primatology, 1974, Carnegie Heroism medal, 1989; William Kinne Fellows traveling fellow, 1965; registered architect, N.Y., N.J., Del., D.C., Conn. Mem. AIA, N.Y. Soc. Architects, N.Y. State Assn. Architects, Nat. Council Archtl. Registration Bds. (certified, Humane Soc. N.Y. (bd. advisors 1992-93, trustee 1993—). Clubs: Princeton, Mashomack, Quaker Hill. Home: Mooney Hill Rd Patterson NY 12563 Office: 560 Lexington Ave New York NY 10022-1906

LADD, ALAN WALBRIDGE, JR., motion picture company executive; b. L.A., Oct. 22, 1937; s. Alan Walbridge and Marjorie Jane (Harrold) L.; m. Patricia Ann Beazley, Aug. 30, 1959 (div. 1983); children: Kelliann, Tracy Elizabeth, Amanda Sue; m. Cindra Kay, July 13, 1985. Motion picture agt. Creative Mgmt., L.A., 1963-69; v.p. prodn. 20th Century-Fox Film Corp., L.A., 1973-74; sr. v.p. 20th Century-Fox Film Corp. (Worldwide Prodns. div.), Beverly Hills, Calif., 1974-76; pres. 20th Century-Fox Pictures, 1976-79, Ladd Co., Burbank, Calif., 1979-83; pres., chief oper. officer MGM/UA Entertainment Co. 1983-86; chief exec. officer MGM/UA Entertainment Co, from 1986, also chmn. bd. dirs.; chmn., chief exec. officer Metro-Goldwyn-Mayer Pictures, Inc., Culver City, Calif., 1993—until 1988; pres., chmn. Pathe Entertainment, L.A., 1989-90; co-chmn. MGM-Pathe, L.A., 1990-93, MGM, L.A., 1990-93; chmn., CEO MGM-Pathe Communications, L.A., 1991-93; pres. The Ladd Co., L.A., 1993—. Producer: (films) Walking Stick, 1969, A Severed Head, 1969, TamLin, 1970, Villian Zee and Co, 1971, Fear is the Key, 1973, Braveheart, 1995; exec. producer: (films) Nightcomers, 1971, Vice Versa, 1988, The Brady Bunch, 1995. Served with USAF, 1961-63. Office: The Ladd Co c/o Paramount 5555 Melrose Ave Los Angeles CA 90038

LADD, CHARLES CUSHING, III, civil engineering educator; b. Bklyn., Nov. 23, 1932; s. Charles Cushing and Elizabeth (Swan) L.; m. Carol Lee Ballou, June 11, 1954; children: Melissa, Charles IV, Ruth, Matthew. AB, Bowdoin Coll., 1955; SB, MIT, 1955, SM, 1957, ScD, 1961. Asst. prof. civil engring. MIT, 1961-64, assoc. prof., then-64, prof., 1970-94, dir. Ctr. Sci. Excellence in Offshore Engring., 1983-94, Edmund K. Turner prof., 1994—; gen. reporter 9th Internat. Conf. Soil Mechanics and Found. Engring., Tokyo, 1977; co-gen. reporter 11th Internat. Conf. Soil Mechanics and Found. Engring., San Francisco, 1985; mem. geotech. bd. NRC, 1992-94. Contbr. articles to profl. jours. Mem. Concord (Mass.) Republican Town

Com., 1968-82; commr. Concord Dept. Pub. Works, 1965-78, chmn., 1972-74. Mem. ASCE (hon., tech. prize 1969, Cores medal 1973, Norman medal 1976, Terzaghi lectr. 1986, exec. com. geotech. engring. divsn. 1989—, chmn. 1993-94), NAE, ASTM (Hogentogler award 1990), NSPE, Boston Soc. Civil Engrs. (bd. govs. 1972-81, pres. 1977-78), Transp. Rsch. Bd., Internat. Soc. Soil Mechanics and Found. Engring., Am. Soc. Engring. Edn., Assn. Engring. Firms Practicing in the Geoscis. Home: 7 Thornton Ln Concord MA 01742-4107 Office: MIT Dept Civil & Environ Engrng Cambridge MA 02139

LADD, CHERYL (CHERYL STOPPLEMOOR), actress; b. Huron, S.D., July 12, 1951; d. Dolores Katz; m. David Alan Ladd (div. 1980); m. Brian Russell, Jan. 3, 1981; children: Jordan, Elizabeth, Lindsay. Studies with Milton Kateselas. Mem. Music Shop musical group, 1968-70; Goodwill amb. to Childhelp U.S.A. (Woman of the World award 1987); spokesperson Retinitis Pigmentosa International. TV shows and movies include (animated) Josie and the Pussycats, 1970-72, The Ken Berry Wow Show, 1972, Satan's School for Girls, 1973, Charlie's Angels, 1977-81, Cheryl Ladd, 1979, Cheryl Ladd-Souvenirs, 1980, Cheryl Ladd: Scenes from a Special, 1982, Roots, Police Woman, Happy Days, Switch, When She Was Bad, 1979, Grace Kelly, 1983, Kentucky Woman, 1983, Romance on the Orient Express, 1985, A Death in California, 1985, Crossings, 1986, Blue Grass, 1988, Deadly Care, 1987, The Fulfillment of Mary Gray, 1989, Jekyll and Hyde, 1990, The Girl Who Came Between Them, 1990, Crash: The Mystery of Flight 1501, 1990, Daniel Steele's Changes, 1991, Locked Up: A Mother's Rage, 1991, Dead Before Dawn, 1992, Broken Promises, 1993, Dancing with Danger, 1994; stage appearances include Anything Goes, 1986, Hasty Heart; films include The Treasure of Jamaica Reef, 1975, Purple Hearts, 1984, Now and Forever, 1985, Millennium, 1989, Lisa, 1990, Poison Ivy, 1992, One West Waikiki, 1994; numerous TV commercials; albums include Cheryl Ladd, 1978, Dance Forever, 1979. Mem. AFTRA, SAG, AGVA.

LADD, DIANE, actress; b. Meridian, Miss., Nov. 29, 1943; m. Bruce Dern (div.); 1 child, Laura; m. William Shay, Jr. (div.). Grad., St. Aloysius Acad. Appearances include (films) The Wild Angels, 1966, The Reivers, 1969, Macho Callahan, 1970, Rebel Rousers, 1970, WUSA, 1970, White Lightning, 1973, Alice Doesn't Live Here Anymore, 1974, Chinatown, 1974, Embryo, 1976, The November Plan, 1976, All Night Long, 1981, Something Wicked This Way Comes, 1983, Black Widow, 1987, Plain Clothes, 1988, National Lampoon's Christmas Vacation, 1989, Wild at Heart, 1990, A Kiss Before Dying, 1991, Rambling Rose, 1991, Cemetery Club, 1992, Hold Me, Thrill Me, Kiss Me, 1992, Code Name: Chaos, 1992, Carnosaur, 1993, Father Hood, 1993, Spirit Realm, 1993, Obsession, 1994, Mrs. Milnck (also dir.), 1994, The Haunted Heart, 1995; (TV series) Alice, 1980-81; (TV movies) The Devil's Daughter, 1973, Thaddeus Rose and Eddie, 1978, Black Beauty, 1978, Willa, 1979, Guyana Tragedy: The Story of Jim Jones, 1980, Desperate Lives, 1982, Grace Kelly, 1983, I Married a Centerfold, 1984, Crime of Innocence, 1985, Celebration Family, 1987, Bluegrass, 1988, The Lookalike, 1990, Rock Hudson, 1990, Shadow of a Doubt, 1991, Hush Little Baby, 1994. Recipient award Brit. Acad., Spirit award, Golden Globe award, 3 Acad. award nominations, 4 Golden Globe nominations, Emmy nomination for Guest Actress in a Comedy Series (Grace Under Fire), 1994. Office: Diane Ladd Prodns Inc PO Box 17111 Beverly Hills CA 90209-3111*

LADD, EVERETT CARLL, political science educator, author; b. Saco, Maine, Sept. 24, 1937; s. Everett Carll and Agnes Mary (MacMillan) L.; m. Cynthia Louise Northway, June 13, 1959; children: Everett Carll, III, Corinna Ruth, Melissa Ann, Benjamin Elliot. A.B. magna cum laude, Bates Coll., 1959; Ph.D. (Woodrow Wilson fellow, Social Sci. Research Council fellow), Cornell U., 1964. Asst. dean students for pub. affairs Cornell U., Ithaca, N.Y., 1963-64; asst. prof. U. Conn., Storrs, 1964-67, assoc. prof., 1967-69, prof. polit. sci., 1969—; dir. for Social Inquiry, 1968—, co-exec. dir. Roper Ctr. for Pub. Opinion Research, 1977-79, exec. dir., pres. Roper Ctr. for Pub. Opinion Research, 1979—; research fellow Ctr. for Internat. Studies, Harvard U., Cambridge, Mass., 1969-75; adj. scholar Am. Enterprise Inst. Pub. Policy Research, 1978—; adv. editor in social scis. W.W. Norton & Co., 1977—; rsch. assoc. Ctr. for Study Social and Polit. Change, 1986—, Inst. for Study Econ. Culture, 1986—; trustee Nat. Coun. Pub. Polls, 1987-90. Author: Negro Political Leadership in the South, 1966, Ideology in America: Change and Response in a City, a Suburb and a Small Town, 1969, rev. edit., 1986, American Political Parties: Social Change and Political Response, 1970, (with M.I. Lipset) Professors, Unions and American Education, 1973, Academics, Politics and the 1972 Election, 1973, The Divided Academy: Professors and Politics, 1975, (with C.D. Hadley) Political Parties and Political Issues: Patterns in Differentiation Since the New Deal, 1973, Transformations of the American Party System: Political Coalitions from the New Deal to the 1970s, 2d edit., 1978, Where Have All the Voters Gone?, 1978, 2d edit., 1982, The American Polity, 1985, 5th edit., 1993, America at the Polls, 1994, 2nd edit., 1995; sr. editor Pub. Opinion mag., 1979-89, Am. Enterprise mag., 1990—; editor: Pub. Perspective mag., 1989—; columnist Christian Science Monitor, 1987—. Ford Found. fellow, 1969-70; Guggenheim fellow, 1971-72; Rockefeller Found. fellow, 1976-77; Hoover Instn. fellow, 1976-77, 79-80; Center Advanced Study in Behavioral Scis., 1979. Mem. Am. Polit. Sci. Assn., Am. Sociol. Assn., Am. Assn. Pub. Opinion Rsch., New Eng. Polit. Sci. Assn. (pres. 1982-83), Acad. Polit. Sci., Cosmos Club (Washington), Phi Beta Kappa, Delta Sigma Rho. Home: 86 Ball Hill Rd Storrs Mansfield CT 06268-2007 Office: Roper Center PO Box 440 Storrs Mansfield CT 06268-0440

LADD, JAMES ROGER, international business consultant; b. San Diego, Mar. 5, 1943; s. Robert Dwinell and Virginia Ruth (Dole) L.; m. Sharon Patricia Smith, Aug. 22, 1964; children—Brian Andrew, Jennifer Louise, Casey James. A.B., Duke U., 1964. C.P.A. With Deloitte Haskins & Sells, Seattle, 1964-79; mng. ptnr. Deloitte Haskins & Sells, Tokyo, 1979-84; nat. pers. ptnr. Deloitte Haskins & Sells, N.Y.C., 1984-86; area mng. ptnr. Deloitte Haskins & Sells, Seattle, 1986-89; mng. dir. Deloitte & Touche, Seattle, 1989-92; pres. Ladd Pacific Cons. Seattle, 1992—. Treas. United Way of King County, Seattle, 1977-79, 90-93, Japan-Am. Soc. Wash. State, 1994—; pres. Seattle Children's Home, 1979; bd. dirs. Corp. Coun. for Arts, 1986-92; bd. dirs., treas. Seattle Found., 1988—; bd. trustees Duke U., 1991-93; chair internat. bus. adv. coun. U. Wash., 1995—. Mem. AICPA, Wash. Soc. CPAs, Duke Alumni Assn. (nat. pres. 1991-92), Wash. Athletic Club, Rainier Club. Office: 1001 4th Ave Ste 3200 Seattle WA 98154-1075

LADD, JEFFREY RAYMOND, lawyer; b. Mpls., Apr. 10, 1941; s. Jasper Raymond and Florence Marguerite (DeMarce) L.; m. Kathleen Anne Crosby, Aug. 24, 1963; children: Jeffrey Raymond, John Henry, Mark Jasper, Matthew Crosby. Student, U. Vienna, Austria; BA, Loras Coll.; postgrad., U. Denver; JD, Ill. Inst. Tech. Bar: Ill. 1973, U.S. Dist. Ct. 1973. V.p. mktg. Ladd Enterprises, Des Plaines, Ill., 1966-70; v.p. mktg. and fin. Ladd Enterprises, Crystal Lake, Ill., 1966-70; ptnr. Ross & Hardies, Chgo., 1973-81, Boodell, Sears, et al., 1981-86, Bell, Boyd & Lloyd, Chgo., 1986—; spl. asst. atty. gen. for condemnation State of Ill., 1977-82. Former campaign chmn. Crystal Lake United Fund; bd. govs. Ill. State Colls. and Univs.; mem. Ill. Bd. Higher Edn.; bd. dirs. Regional Transp. Authority, Chgo., 1983-84; chmn. Met. Rail Bd., Chgo., 1984—; del. Ill. Constl. Conv., 1969-70, Nat. Rep. Conv., Kansas City, 1976, New Orleans, 1988, Houston, 1992. Mem. ABA, Chgo. Bar Assn., Nat. Assn. Bond Lawyers, Ill. Assn. Hosp. Attys., Am. Acad. Hosp. Attys., Crystal Lake Jaycees (Disting. Svc award), Crystal Lake C. of C. (past pres.), Econ. Club, Legal Club, The Attic Club, Bull Valley Golf Club, Woodstock Country Club. Roman Catholic. Avocations: golf, hunting, fishing, tennis, skiing. Office: Bell Boyd & Lloyd 3 First National Pla # 3300 Chicago IL 60602

LADD, JOSEPH CARROLL, retired insurance company executive; b. Chgo., Jan. 26, 1927; s. Stephen C. and Laura (McBride) L.; m. Barbara Virginia Carter, June 5, 1965; children: Carroll, Joseph Carroll, Barbara, Virginia, William. BA, Ohio Wesleyan U., 1950; CLU, Am. Coll., Bryn Mawr; D in Bus. Adminstrn. (hon.), Spring Garden Coll., 1985. Agt. Conn. Gen. Life Ins. Co., Chgo., 1950-53; staff asst. Conn. Gen. Life Ins. Co. 1953-54, mgr. Evanston (Ill.) br. office, 1954-60, dir. agys., 1960-62, mgr. Los Angeles br. office, 1963; v.p. sales Fidelity Mut. Life Ins. Co., Phila., 1964-67; sr. v.p. sales Fidelity Mut. Life Ins. Co., 1968, exec. v.p., 1969-71, pres., chief exec. officer, dir., 1971-84, chmn., chief exec. officer, dir., 1984-89, chmn., dir., 1989-91; ret.; bd. dirs. Corestates Fin., Phila. Suburban Corp., Phila. Electric Co. Trustee Bryn Mawr Hosp.; trustee United Way of S.E.

Pa.; trustee Phila. United Way, also gen. chmn. 1978 campaign; bd. dirs. Phila. YMCA. Served with USNR, 1945-46. Recipient Civic Achievement award Am. Jewish Com., 1978, Achiever's award WHEELS Med. and Specialized Transp., 1978, Ohio Wesleyan U. Life Achievement award Delta Tau Delta, 1982, William Penn award, Greater Phila. C. ofC. and PENJERDEL Coun., 1988, Robert Morris Citizenship award Valley Forge Coun. Boy Scouts Am., 1988; named YMCA Man of Yr., 1979, William Penn Found. Disting. Pennsylvanian, 1980. Mem. Greater Phila. C. of C. (dir., chmn. 1979, 83-84), Phila. Country Club, Union League Club (Phila.), Summer Beach (Fla.) Country Club.

LADDON, WARREN MILTON, lawyer; b. Washington, July 2, 1933; s. Misha and Hannah (Cooper) L.; m. Paula K. Cramer: children—Michael, Susan, Benjamin. B.S., Wilson Tchrs. Coll., 1955; J.D., U. Mich., 1962. Bar: Calif. 1963, D.C. 1966, Pa. 1967. Teaching assoc. Boalt Hall U. Calif.-Berkeley, 1962-63; trial and appellate atty. Dept. Labor, Washington, 1963-65; appellate atty. NLRB, Washington, 1965-67; assoc. Morgan Lewis & Bockius, Phila., 1967-71; ptnr. Morgan Lewis & Bockius, 1971-86; chief counsel CIGNA Corp., 1986—. Served to lt. (j.g.) USNR, 1956-59. Mem. ABA. Office: Cigna Corp One Liberty Pl 1650 Market St Philadelphia PA 19192-1520

LADEFOGED, PETER NIELSEN, phonetician; b. Sutton, Eng., Sept. 17, 1925; came to U.S., 1962; s. Niels Nielsen and Marie Frances (Foucard) L.; m. Jennifer Macdonald, Dec. 19, 1953; children: Lise, Thegn, Katie. M.A., U. Edinburgh, Scotland, 1951, Ph.D., 1959; DLitt (hon.), U. Edinburgh, 1993. Lectr. U. Edinburgh, 1953-61, U. Ibadan, Nigeria, 1959-60; rsch. fellow West African Langs. Survey, Nigeria, 1961-62; asst. prof. phonetics UCLA, 1962-63, assoc. prof., 1963-65, prof., 1965-91, prof. emeritus, 1991, rsch. linguist, 1991—; team leader East African Survey Lang. Use and Lang. Teaching, Uganda, 1968. Author: A Course in Phonetics; others. Served with Brit. Army, 1943-47. Fellow Acoustical Soc. Am. (Silver Speech Comm. medal 1994), Am. Speech and Hearing Assn., Am. Acad. Arts and Scis., Am. Speech Lang. and Hearing Assn.; mem. Linguistic Soc. Am. (pres. 1978), Internat. Phonetic Assn. (pres. 1986-91). Home: 2111 Kress St Los Angeles CA 90046-1525 Office: UCLA Dept Linguistics Los Angeles CA 90024

LADEHOFF, LEO WILLIAM, metal products manufacturing executive; b. Gladbrook, Iowa, May 4, 1932; s. Wendell Leo and Lillian A. L.; m. Beverly Joan Dreessen, Aug. 1, 1951; children: Debra K., Lance A. B.S., U. Iowa, 1957. Supt. ops. Square D Co., 1957-61; mfg. mgr. Fed. Pacific Electric Co., 1961; v.p. ops. Avis Indsl. Corp., 1961-67; pres. energy products Group Gulf & Western Industries, Inc., 1967-78; chmn. bd., pres., chief exec. officer, dir. Amcast Indsl. Corp., Ohio, 1978-95, also chmn. bd. dirs., 1995—; bd. dirs. Soc. Nat. Bank, Hobart Bros., Troy, Ohio. Mem. Dayton Area Progress Council. Served with USAF, 1951-54, Korea. Mem. Am. Foundrymen's Soc., Soc. Automotive Engrs., Dayton Area C. of C., Dayton One Hundred Club, Newcomen Soc., U. Iowa Alumni Assn., Moraine Country Club, Dayton Racquet Club, Ventana Canyon Country Club, Alpha Kappa Psi. Republican. Home: 1426 Finger Lakes Dayton OH 45459 Office: Amcast Indsl Corp PO Box 98 Dayton OH 45401-0098 also: Elkhart Products Corp 1255 Oak St Elkhart IN 46514-2277

LADEHOFF, ROBERT LOUIS, bishop; b. Feb. 19, 1932; m. Jean Arthur Burcham (dec. Feb. 1992); 1 child, Robert Louis Jr. Grad., Duke U., 1954, Gen. Theol. Sem., 1957, Va. Theol. Sem., 1980. Ordained deacon, priest The Episcopal Ch., 1957; Priest in charge N.C. parishes, 1957-60; rector St. Christopher's Ch., Charlotte, N.C., 1960-74, St. John's Ch., Fayetteville, 1974-85; bishop, co-adjutor of Oreg., 1985, bishop, 1986—. Office: Diocese of Oreg PO Box 467 Lake Oswego OR 97034-0467

LADEN, BEN ELLIS, economist; b. Savannah, Ga., Mar. 4, 1942; s. Bernard and Fannie Rachel (Cooper) L.; m. Susan Sherman, Aug. 16, 1964; children: Francine, Jonathan, Paul. A.B., Princeton U., 1963; Ph.D., Johns Hopkins U., 1969. Asst. prof. econs. Ohio State U., 1967-71; economist Fed. Res. Bd., 1971-74; v.p., chief economist T. Rowe Price Assocs., Balt., 1974-87; dir. fin. instns. regulation staff HUD, Washington, 1990-94; pres. Bel Assocs., Washington, 1994—. Author: Economic Trend, 1974-87; also articles. Fellow Nat. Assn. Bus. Economists (dir. 1981-87, pres. 1984-85); mem. Am. Econs. Assn. Jewish. Home: 3111 Rittenhouse St NW Washington DC 20015-1614 Each person has to find his own unique formula for success. My greatest achievements have come from the following elements. 1. A clear concept of priorities with persistent concentration on the highest priority. 2. Building structures which will continue to payoff in the future, rather than trying for immediate results. 3. Identifying those areas where my contribution could be the greatest and could be unique. 4. Always striving for the highest quality in my work. 5. Most important, learning from the experience of others and respecting the individual ways of other people.

LADEN, KARL, toiletries company executive; b. Bklyn., Aug. 10, 1932; s. Judah and Anna (Bernstein) L.; m. Judy Talisman, June 24, 1956; children—Ben, Ethan, Adam, Noam, Zev. B.S., U. Akron, Ohio, 1954; Ph.D., Northwestern U., 1957. Cons. Indsl. Bio-Test Labs., Northbrook, Ill., 1955-57; research chemist William Wrigley Jr. Co., Chgo., 1957-58; research mgr. Toni Co., Chgo., 1959-64; with Gillette Research Inst., Washington, 1964-76, v.p. biomed. scis., 1968-71, pres., 1971-76; v.p. research and devel. Carter Products Co., Cranbury, N.J., 1976-86; cons. tech. transfer, new product devel., 1986—. Contbg. editor, Nat. Beauty Sch. Jour., 1970-77; Contbr. articles to profl. jours. Recipient award Internat. Flavors and Fragrances, 1963, 67. Fellow Soc. Cosmetic Chemists (pres. 1977, then pub. 1978, editor jour. 1967-72, Mid-West chpt. award 1964, Lit. award 1969, Merit award 1972, Medal award 1979); mem. Am. Chem. Soc. Home: 31 Yafe Nof, Haifa Israel Office: PO Box 866 Freehold NJ 07728-0866

LADEN, SUSAN, publishing consultant; b. Washington, Aug. 3, 1942; d. Louis and Irene (Berenter) Sherman; m. Ben E. Laden, Aug. 16, 1964; children: Francine, Jonathan, Paul. AB, Vassar Coll., 1964. Caseworker Dept. Welfare, Balt., 1964-66; publ. Biblical Archaeology rev., Washington, 1976-94, Bible rev., Washington, 1984-94, Moment mag., Washington, 1987-94; pres. Laden & Assocs., 1994—; bd. dirs. Portfolio Travel, Washington. Treas. Lafayette Home and Sch. Assn., Washington, 1973-75; v.p. Jewish Ednl. Ventures, Boston, 1987-94; sec. Jewish Coun. for the Aging, Rockville, Md., 1992-94, treas. 1994. Mem. Bibl. Archl. Soc. (sec.-treas. 1977-94). Democrat. Home: 3111 Rittenhouse St NW Washington DC 20015 Office: Bibl Archl Soc 3000 Connecticut Ave NW Washington DC 20008

LADER, LAWRENCE, writer; b. N.Y.C., Aug. 6, 1919; s. Ludwig and Myrtle (Powell) L.; m. Jean MacInnis, Aug. 24, 1942 (div. Jan. 1946); m. Joan Summers, Sept. 27, 1961; 1 dau., Wendy Summers. A.B., Harvard U., 1941. With press dept. ABC, 1941-42; contbg. editor Coronet mag., 1946; feature editor Glamour mag., 1953; lectr. NYU, 1957-59, Philips Brooks Assns., Harvard, 1962—; regular contbr. Am. Heritage, Reader's Digest, N.Y. Times mags., others, 1941—; exec. dir. Hugh Moore Fund, 1966-67; fgn. corr. Arab-Israel War, 1948, other overseas assignments, 1951, 55, 57; adj. assoc. prof. journalism NYU, 1967-72. Author: Margaret Sanger, 1955, The Bold Brahmins, New England's War Against Slavery, 1961, Abortion, 1966; juvenile Margaret Sanger, 1969; Breeding Ourselves to Death, 1971, Foolproof Birth Control, 1972, Abortion II: Making the Revolution, 1973, Power on the Left: American Radical Movements since 1946, 1979, Politics, Power and the Church, 1987, Ru 486, 1991, A Private Matter, 1995. Chmn. exec. com. Nat. Abortion Rights Action League, 1969-72, chmn. bd., 1972-76; pres. Abortion Rights Mobilization, 1976—. Served to lt. AUS, 1942-46; officer-in-charge N.Y. Troop Information, Armed Forces Radio Service. Recipient Benjamin Franklin Mag. award, 1969, Cert. Distinction, NOW, 1989; named Feminist Majority Feminist of Yr., 1992. Mem. Authors Guild. Club: Harvard, Century Assn. (N.Y.C.). Home: 51 Fifth Ave New York NY 10003-4320

LADERMAN, EZRA, composer, educator, college dean; b. Bklyn., June 29, 1924. MA, Columbia U, 1952; studies with Otto Luening, D. Moore, P. Lang, Columbia U. Dir. music program Nat. Endowment for Arts, 1979-82; pres. Nat. Music Coun., 1985-89; dean Sch. Music Yale U., New Haven, 1989—; mem. Am. Composers Orch. Compositions include 7 symphonies, 8 string quartets, 6 operas, 150 compostions and 25 recordings; (dramatic operas) Jacob and the Indians, 1954, Goodbye to the Clowns, 1956, The

Hunting of the Snark, 1958, Sarah, 1959, Air Raid, 1965, Shadows Among Us, 1967, Galileo Galilei, 1978; (orchestral) Piano Concerto, 1939, Leipzig Symphony, 1945, Piano Concerto, 1957, 9 Symphonies, 1964-84, Flute Concerto, 1968, Viola Concerto, 1975, Violin Concerto, 1978, Piano Concerto No. 1, 1978, Concert for String Quartet and Orchestra, 1981, Cello Concerto, 1984; (vocal) oratorio The Eagle Stirred, 1961, oratorio The Trials of Galileo, 1967, cantata Columbus, 1975, oratorio A Mass for Cain, 1983; (chamber) Wind Octet, 1957, Clarinet Sonata, 1958, 8 String Quartets, 1959-85, Double Helix for Flute, Oboe, and String Quartet, 1968, Partita for Violin, 1982, Double String Quartet, 1983; (film scores) The Charter, 1958, The Invisible Aton, 1958, The Question Tree, 1962, Odyssey, 1964, The Eleanor Roosevelt Story, 1965, The Black Fox, 1965, Magic Prison, 1966, The Meaning of Modern Art, 1967, Confrontation, 1968, Image of Love, 1968, The Bible as Literature, 1972, Burden of Mystery, 1972; (television movie scores) Herschel, 1959, Invisible City, 1961, The Voice of the Desert, 1962, Eltanin, 1962, Grand Canyon, 1964, The Forgotten Peninsula, 1967, Our Endangered Wildlife, 1967, California the Most, 1968, Before Cortez, 1970, In the Fall of 1844, 1971, Cave People of the Philippines, 1972, Lamp Unto My Feet, 1978. Guggenheim fellow 1955, 58, 64; recipient Rome proze, 1963; Kennedy Center Friedheim Award, 2nd place, 1981. mem. Am. Acad. and Inst. of Arts and Letters, 1991. Office: Yale U Sch Music Office of Dean New Haven CT 06520*

LADERMAN, GABRIEL, artist; b. Bklyn., Dec. 26, 1929; s. Isidore and Leah (Stock) L.; m. Carol Ciavati, Feb. 12, 1953; children—Raphael, Michael. B.A., Bklyn. Coll., 1952; M.F.A., Cornell U., 1957. Faculty State U. N.Y., New Paltz, 1957-59, Pratt Inst., 1959-66; faculty Queens Coll., Flushing, N.Y., 1966—; chmn. Queens Coll., 1979-83; vis. prof. La. State U., Baton Rouge, 1966-67, Yale U., 1968, 81, 83, 89, 91, Viterbo Coll., 1969, 80, Art Students League, 1972-81, Boston U., 1973, N.Y. Studio Sch., Am. U., 1994—; dir. G.-T. Mus., 1980-84, Caumsett Summer Landscape Painting Program, 1980, 81; vis. critic, lectr. Yale U., Syracuse U., Bennington Coll., Vassar Coll., Rutgers U., Princeton, Cooper-Union, Phila. Coll. Art, Mus. Fine Arts, Boston, Md. Inst. Art, Swain Sch., Boston U., Boston Mus. Sch., Ind. U., Bard Coll., Kansas City Art Inst., Fla. State U., SUNY at New Paltz, Amherst Coll., Skowhegan Sch., Yale-Norfolk Sch., New York Studio Sch., Pratt Inst., N.Y. Inst. Tech., Boston Mus., Tyler Sch. of Temple U., U. R.I., U. N.H., Artists for Environment, Iowa State U., Hobart Coll., U. Wis., 1980, Md. Art Inst., 1980, Royal Sch. Art, Bangkok, Thailand, 1976, Nat. Art Sch., Jakarta, Indonesia, 1975, Art Sch., Surabaya, Indonesia, 1975, Victorian Coll. Art, Melbourne, Australia, 1975, Coll. Art, Ballarat, Australia, 1975, Prahran Coll., Melbourne, 1975, U. Minn., 1987, Yale U., 1987, State U. Calif. Arts seminars San Luis Obispo, 1986, Stanford U., 1987, 91, U. Calif., Santa Barbara, 1987, Calif. State U., Long Beach, 1987, Pa. Acad., 1988, Chautauqua Art Program, N.Y. Acad. Art, numerous others; USIS lectr., Japan, 1975; vis. lectr., critic Long Beach State Coll., 1987, Parsons Sch., 1991, Ox Bow Sch., 1991, N.Y. Acad., 1987, 91; vis. critic Chautauqua Art Sch., 1993; critic, lectr. Stanford U. Chautauqua Art Program, Bard Coll., Pa. Acad.; Disting. vis. prof. Am. Univ., Washington, 1994. Contbr. articles to profl. jours.; one man shows at Schoelkopf Gallery, 1964, 67, 70, 72, 74, 77, 86, 90, Hobart Coll., 1968, R.I. U., 1969, Temple U., 1971, La. State U., 1967, Bennington Coll., Ithaca Coll., R.I. U., So. U., Dart Gallery, Chgo., 1977, Savage Gallery, Boston, 1976, Meade Mus., Amherst Coll., 1983, Contemporary Realists Gallery, San Francisco, 1987, 90, Jessica Darraby Gallery, Los Angeles, 1987, Peter Tattistcheff Gallery, N.Y., 1994; exhibited in group shows at Whitney Mus., 1971, Mus. Modern Art, 1974, Corcoran Gallery, 1972, 76, Boston Mus., 1974, 75, Bklyn. Mus., 1952, 57, 59, 61, Library of Congress, 1957, 59, Gallery of Modern Art, 1972, N.Y. Cultural Center, 1972, Phila. Mus., 1970, Wadsworth Atheneum, 1976, Fogg Mus., 1976, Mpls. Inst. Arts, 1976, Milw. Art Center, 1977, Ft. Worth Art Mus., 1977, High Mus., 1977, San Francisco Mus. Modern Art, 1977, Pa. Acad., 1981, traveling shows sponsored by A.F.A., Smithsonian Instn., Library of Congress, Pa. Acad. Arts; represented in permanent collections Witherspoon Mus., Cleve. Mus., Mus. Fine Arts, Boston, Brandeis U. Art Mus., Chase-Manhattan Bank, A.D. White Mus. Cornell U., Nat. Gallery Art, Muzium Negara, Kuala Lumpur, Mead Mus. Amherst Coll., Glen S. Janss Collection Boise Art Mus., FMC Corp. Chgo., Archdiocese of Baton Rouge, Fidelity Bank Collection, Phila., Sierra Club. Recipient Research award CUNY, 1970-71, 75-76, 82, 86-87, 1988-89, Fed. Govt. Commn. through Interior Dept. for Bicentennial, 1974, award Rockefeller Found. at Bellagio, 1989, Altman Figure Painting prize Nat. Acad. Biennial, 1995; asst. Cornell U., 1955-57; L.C. Tiffany grantee, 1959; Fulbright fellow to Italy, 1962-63; Yaddo fellow, 1960, 62; Ingram Merrill fellow, 1975-76, 84, 90; J.S. Guggenheim fellow, 1989-90; NEA sr. grantee, 1983, 87-88; juror NEA, 1984, N.Y. State Council on Arts, 1985. Mem. Nat. Acad. (Proctor Portrait Prize Biennial Exhbn. 1993). Office: Queens Coll Flushing NY 11367

LADIN, EUGENE, communications company executive; b. N.Y.C., Oct. 26, 1927; s. Nat and Mae (Cohen) L.; m. Millicent Dolly Frankel, June 27, 1948; children: Leslie Hope, Stephanie Joy. B.B.A., Pace U., 1956; M.B.A., Air Force Inst. Tech., 1959; postgrad., George Washington U., 1966-69. Cost engr. Rand Corp., Santa Monica, Calif., 1960-62; mgr. cost and econ. analysis Northrop Corp., Hawthorne, Calif., 1962-66; dir. financial planning Communications Satellite Corp., Washington, 1966-70; treas., chief fin. and adminstrv. officer Landis & Gyr, Inc., Elmsford, N.Y., 1970-76; v.p., treas., comptroller P.R. Telephone Co., San Juan, 1976-77; v.p. fin. Comtech Telecommunications Corp., Smithtown, N.Y., 1977—; acting pres. Comtech Antenna Corp., St. Cloud, Fla., 1978-80; chmn., chief exec. officer Telephone Interconnect Enterprises/Sunshine Telephone Co., Balt., Md. and Orlando, Fla., 1980-82; pres. Ladin and Assocs., Cons. and Commodity Traders, Maitland, Fla., 1982-84; pres., chief fin. officer Braintech Inc., South Plainfield, N.J., 1984; sr. v.p. fin. officer Teltec Savs. Communications Co., Miami, Fla., 1984-88; chief fin. officer Hurwitz Group Inc., North Miami Beach, Fla., 1988-91; cons. pvt. practice, 1991—; assoc. prof. acctg. So. Ill. U., East St. Louis, 1960; assoc. prof. bus. U. Md., 1969-70; adj. prof. George Washington U., 1969-70; vis. prof. acctg. Pace U., 1970; cons. E. Ladin, Pembroke Pines, Fla., 1991—. Served to capt. USAF, 1951-60. Decorated Air Force Commendation medal; recipient Air Force Outstanding Unit award. Mem. Nat. Assn. Accts., Fin. Exec. Inst. Democrat. Jewish. Club: Flamingo Country Club. Avocations: golf, sailing. Home and Office: 13355 SE 16th Ct #401E Pembroke Pines FL 33027 An individual must have sufficient self esteem to sustain the courage of his convictions, a high degree of professional integrity, and his individual character. Society has adopted a philosophy of "walk the middle road".

LADINSKY, JUDITH LOUISE, preventive medicine educator; b. L.A., June 16, 1938; d. Irving and Eva (Freiden) Byers; m. Jack Ladinsky, July 16, 1961; children: Morissa, Mark. BS, U. Mich., 1960; MS, U. Wis., 1964, PhD, 1968. Project assoc. dept. genetics U. Wis., Madison, 1965-68, instr. preventive medicine, 1968-69, asst. prof. preventive medicine, 1969-75, assoc. prof. preventive medicine, 1975—; chmn. U.S. Com. for Sci. Coop. with Vietnam, 1985—; cons. Ministry of Health Vietnam, Laos; dir. Office Internat. Health Affairs Med. Schs., 1986—. Contbr. articles to profl. jours. Bd. dirs. Community Action Commn., Wis., 1975-80, Madison Community Health Ctr., Group Health Cooperative - HMO, 1980-85. Recipient rsch. grants, Rockefeller Found. and others., 1968—. Mem. Am. Pub. Health Assn. (chmn. sect., various offices), Am Soc. for Cell Biology, Assn. of Tchrs. of Preventive Medicine, Nat. Assn. Pub. Health Policy, Nat. Coun. Tchrs. of Preventive Medicine. Phi Kappa Phi (faculty award 1988), Sigma Xi. Office: Dept Preventive Medicine Univ Wis 1300 University Ave Madison WI 53706

LADJEVARDI, HABIB, historian; b. Tehran, Iran, May 28, 1938; came to U.S., 1950; s. Seyed Mahmoud and Tahereh (Kashani) L.; m. Mina Nassirzadeh, Aug. 3, 1962 (div. June 1979); children: Mahmoud, Mariam, Leila. BS, Yale U., 1961; MBA, Harvard U., 1963; DPhil, Oxford U., 1981. Personnel dir. Behshahr Ind. Group, Tehran, 1963-65, mktg. dir., 1966-69; pres. Paxan Corp., Tehran, 1969-70; chmn. bd. dirs. Container Corp. of Iran, 1969-79; founder, v.p. Iran Ctr. Mgmt. Studies, Tehran, 1970-79; sr. rsch. assoc. Harvard U. Bus. Sch., Cambridge, Mass., 1980-81; rsch. assoc. Harvard U. Ctr. for Middle Eastern Studies, 1981—, assoc. dir., 1987-90, dir. Iranian oral history project, 1981—; mem. acceptance coms. Tehran Stock Exch., 1973-76; lectr. Iran Ctr. for Mgmt. Studies, 1975-79; vis. fellow Oxford (Eng.) Ctr. Mgmt. Studies, 1976-79; v.p. exec. coun. Harvard U. Bus. Sch., 1978-79; exec. sec. Soc. for Iranian Studies, Cambridge, 1982-87; chmn. Iranian Studies Harvard U. Ctr. for Middle Eastern Studies, 1990—, chmn. pubs. com., 1990—. Author: Labor Unions & Autocracy in Iran, 1985,

Guide to the Iranian Oral History Collection, 1993; contbr. articles to profl. jours., chpts. to books. Mem. coun. of state Adminstrv. and Employment Affairs of Iran, 1972-76; dir. devel. and investment Bank of Iran, 1972-79; mem. ctrl. coun. Pres. of Univs. and Colls. of Iran, 1971-78; pres. Tahereh Found., Lincoln, Mass., 1982—. NEH grantee, 1984-87. Mem. Am. Hist. Assn., Young Presidents Orgn., Acad. Polit. Sci., N.Y. Acad. Scis., Iranian Assn. of Boston (founder, pres. 1988-91), Yale U. Class Coun., Yale Club of N.Y., Harvard Club of Boston. Democrat. Avocations: squash, skiing, grandchildren. Office: Harvard U Ctr Mid Eastern Studies 1737 Cambridge St Cambridge MA 02138-3016

LADJEVARDI, HAMID, fund manager; b. Tehran, Iran, June 11, 1948; came to U.S., 1948; s. Ahmad and Banoo (Barzin) L.; m. Manijeh Mirdamad, July 19, 1978; children: Adella, Lilly. BA in Econs., BA in Polit. Sci., U. Calif., Berkeley, 1971; MBA, Harvard U., 1973. Dep. mng. dir. Behshahr Indsl. Group, Tehran, 1974-79; vice chmn., fin. dir. Akam Group of Cos., Tehran, 1975-79; investment mgr., v.p. Morgan Stanley & Co., N.Y.C., 1980-92; gen. ptnr. Baltic Fund 1, N.Y.C., 1992—; instr. Fairleigh Dickinson U., Rutherford, N.J., 1984. Mem. Coun. Internat. Bus. Risk Mgmt., Fgn. Policy Assn., Carnegie Coun. on Ethics and Internat. Affairs, U.S. Senatorial Club, Harvard Club. Home: 66 Brite Ave Scarsdale NY 10583-1637 Office: Baltic Fund 745 5th Ave New York NY 10151-1698

LADLEY, KAREN J., nursing administrator, nurse; b. Pitts., Oct. 25, 1946; d. Wilbur D. and Florence M. (Fleishauer) Hostler; m. Stephen G. Ladley, Oct. 28, 1981; 1 child, Lauren. BSN, U. Cin., 1968; MSN, U. Calif., L.A., 1975. Dir. nursing Tri-City Med. Ctr., Oceanside, Calif., nursing quality assurance coord.; staff devel. coord. Huntington Meml. Hosp., Pasadena, Calif., clin. supr. Mem. Am. Orgn. Nurse Execs., NAFE. Home: 4002 Vista Way Oceanside CA 92056-4506

LADLY, FREDERICK BERNARD, health services and financial services company executive; b. Toronto, Ont., Can., July 14, 1930; s. John Bernard and Olivia Montgomery (Fenimore) L.; m. Sharon Mary Davidson; children: Patricia, Elizabeth, Katherine, Martha, Sarah, Meghan. B.A., U. Toronto. Gen. mgr. internat. ops. Can. Packers Inc., Toronto, 1973, v.p., 1974-78, dir., 1975-84, exec. v.p., 1978-84; pres., CEO Extendicare Health Svcs. Inc., Markham, 1984-94, Extendicare Inc. (formerly Crownx Inc.), Markham, 1992—; chmn., CEO United Health, Inc., Milw., 1984—; vice chmn. Crown Life Ins. Co., Regina, 1994—; chmn. Extendicare (Can.) Inc., Extendicare (U.K.) Ltd.; bd. dirs. Extendicare Inc., Crown Life Ins. Co., Cobi Foods, Inc.

LADMAN, A(ARON) J(ULIUS), anatomist, educator; b. Jamaica, N.Y., July 3, 1925; s. Thomas and Ida (Sobin) L.; m. Barbara Powers, 1948 (div. 1980); children: Susan Elizabeth, Thomas Frederick; m. Patricia A. Bergbauer, 1982; 1 child, Peter John. Student, Miami U., Oxford, Ohio, 1942-43; AB, NYU, 1947; postgrad., U. Cin., 1948-49; Ph.D., Ind. U., 1952. Teaching fellow anatomy U. Cin., 1948-49, Ind. U., 1949-52; instr. with Harvard Med. Sch., 1952-61, assoc., 1955-61; assoc. prof. U. Tenn. Med. Units, 1961-64; vis. assoc. prof. Yale, 1964; prof., chmn. dept. anatomy U. N.Mex. Sch. Medicine, Albuquerque, 1964-81; prof. anatomy Hahnemann U., Phila., 1981-94; prof. anatomy Med. Coll. Pa. and Hahnemann U. Sch. Medicine, Phila., 1995, adj. prof. anatomy and neurobiology, 1995—; dean Sch. Allied Health Professions Hahnemann U., 1981-84. Assoc. editor Anat. Record, 1967-68, editor-in-chief, 1968—; contbr. articles to profl. jours. Recipient Rsch. Career Devel. award USPHS, 1962-64; rsch. fellow Am. Cancer Soc., 1952-55, spl. rsch. fellow USPHS, 1955-57, 71-72. Fellow AAAS; mem. Am. Assn. Anatomists (exec. com. 1972-76, 2d v.p. 1980-81, 1st v.p. 1981-82), Am. Soc. for Cell Biology, Nat. Inst. Gen. Med. Scis. (rsch. cancer awards com. 1967-71), Electron Microscope Soc. Am. (exec. coun. 1974-76), Coun. Biol. Editors (sec. 1977-82), Histochem. Soc. Home: 103 Arbor Way Lansdale PA 19446-6433 Office: Med Coll Pa & Hahnemann U Broad And Vine Ms # 408 Philadelphia PA 19102

LADMAN, JERRY R., economist, educator; b. Sioux City, Iowa, Dec. 30, 1935; s. Harry L. and Amy I. (Swearingen) L.; m. Carmen Aida; children—Jeffrey, James, Michael, Stephanie. B.S., Iowa State U., 1958, Ph.D., 1968. Placement officer Coll. Agr., Iowa State U., Ames, 1963-65, research asst., 1965-67; asst. prof. Ariz. State U., 1967-72, assoc. prof., 1972-78, prof. econs., 1979—, dir. Ctr. for Latin Am. Studies, 1976-90; prof. agrl. econs. Ohio State U., Columbus, 1990—, chief of party Univ. Agribus. Partnership Project, Dominican Republic, 1990-95; program asst. Ford Found., Mexico City, 1971-72; vis. prof. Nat. Sch. Agr., Chapingo, Mex., 1965-67, 71-72, Ohio State U., 1979; vis. scholar Stanford U., 1975; hon. prof. Cath. U. Bolivia, 1986; participant U.S.-U.S.S.R. Cultural Exchange, 1986. Author: The Development of Mexicali Regional Economy, 1975, United States-Mexican Energy Relationships: Realities and Prospects, 1981, Modern Day Bolivia: The Legacy of the Revolution and Prospects for the Future, 1982, Mexico: A Country in Crisis, 1987, Redemocratization in Bolivia: A Political Economic Analysis of the Siles Suazo Government, 1982-1985, 1990; contbr. articles to profl. jours., chpts. to books. Chmn. troop com. Boy Scouts Am., Tempe, Ariz., 1976-84; bd. dirs. Friends of Mexican Art, 1977-86. Served to capt. USAR, 1958-65. Fulbright lectr., Ecuador, 1974. Mem. Am. Econ. Assn., Am. Agrl. Econ. Assn., Latin Am. Studies Assn., Pacific Coast Council Latin Am. Studies (treas. 1977-86, v.p. 1986, pres. 1987), Rocky Mountain Council Latin Am. Studies (bd. dirs. 1976-90), Phoenix Com. Fgn. Relations, Ariz.-Mex. Commn. (bd. dirs. 1982-90), Assn. Borderlands Scholars (pres. 1983-85), PROFMEX (bd. dirs. 1983-90). Office: Ohio State U Dept Agrl Econs 2120 Fyffe Rd Columbus OH 43210-1067

LADNER, JOYCE A., academic administrator; b. Hattiesburg, Miss.. BA in Sociology, Tougaloo Coll.; MA, PhD in Sociology, Washington U., St. Louis. Assoc. prof. dept. sociology Howard U., Washington, 1971-73, v.p. acad. affairs, 1990—, interim pres., 1994—; prof. Hunter Coll. CUNY, 1973-81. Author: Tomorrow's Tomorrow: The Black Woman, 1971, Mixed Families: Adoption Across Racial Boundaries; editor The Death of White Sociology, 1973, Adolescence and Poverty: Challenges for the 1990s, 1991; contbr. chpts. to over 20 books and articles to Washington Post, N.Y. Times, Ebony, others. Chair Mayor's Blue Ribbon Panel on Teenage Pregnancy Prevention for D.C, 1984-85; past chair Bd. Trans Africa Forum; past sec. Twenty-First Century Found.; bd. dirs. Recording for the Blind. Recipient DuBois-Johnson-Frazier Outstanding Scholarship award Am. Sociol. Assn., Joseph S. Himes Disting. Career award Assn. Black Sociologists, Acad. Excellence award Nat. Congress Black Faculty. Mem. Coalition of 100 Black Women (bd. dirs.). Office: Howard Univ Office of Pres 2400 Sixth St NW Ste 402 Washington DC 20059

LADNER, THOMAS E., lawyer; b. Vancouver, B.C., Can. Dec. 8, 1916. B.A., U. B.C., 1937; LLB, Osgoode Hall. Bar: B.C. bar 1940. Sr. partner firm Ladner Downs, Vancouver. Mem. Canadian, Vancouver bar assns., Law Soc. B.C. Office: PO Box 48600, 900-200 Burrard St, Vancouver, BC Canada V7X 1T2

LADOW, C. STUART, consultant financial services; b. Warren, Pa., Apr. 21, 1925; s. Clyde and Glendine (Bentley) LaD.; m. Donna Elizabeth Miller, Aug. 21, 1993; 1 child, Paul Stuart. B.A., Cornell U., 1947. With Gen. Electric Co., 1947-50; mgr. N.Y. region Gen. Electric Credit Corp., N.Y.C., 1950-80; v.p. gen. Electric Credit Corp., Stamford, Conn., 1971-80; pres. GECC Fin. Services, 1975-78, Color Tyme TV Rental div. Curtis Mathes Corp., Athens, Tex., 1980; sr. v.p. Yegen Assocs., Inc., Paramus, N.J. 1981-85; exec. v.p. Yegen Assocs., Inc., Paramus, 1985-87; pres. Yegen Equity Loan Corp., Paramus, N.J., 1987; fin. svcs. cons. Allison Park, Pa., 1988—; dir. Puritan Life Ins. Co.; Providence, Am. Bankers Ins. Group, Miami, Fla., 1980-81. Vice pres., bd. dirs. Jr. Achievement of Stamford, Inc., 1973-80; mem. exec. budget com., chmn. budget panel United Way of Stamford, 1973-80; chmn. Stamford chpt. Am. Cancer Soc., 1977; pres. Spring Meadow Condominium Assn., Wyckoff, N.J., 1983, trustee, 1983-88; moderator Emmanuel Bapt. Ch., Ridgewood, N.J., 1985-86; trustee North Hills Community Baptist Ch., 1988-91; dir. Hampton Twsp. Mcpl. Authority, Allison Park, Pa., 1991—, dir., treas. Baptist Homes of Western Pa., 1992—, pres. Arbors Homeowners Assn., Allison Park, 1992-93; trustee Cornell U. Class of 1947, 1992—. Served with USN, 1944-46, ETO. Recipient Community Service award Gen. Electric Credit Corp., 1976. Mem. Nat. Second Mortgage Assn. (pres. 1987-88, Outstanding Service award, Meritorious Svc. award 1989), Nat. Consumer Finance Assn. (certificate of appreciation),

Masons, Shriners, Cornell Club of Pitts. Republican. Baptist. Home and Office: 4211 Latour Ct Allison Park PA 15101-2968 *Ours is a great country that deserves the devotion and strong support of those who call it home. There can be few satisfactions in life greater than assisting in the moral, spiritual and career growth of those whom we have the opportunity to know and possibly influence.*

LA DU, BERT NICHOLS, JR., pharmacology educator, physician; b. Lansing, Mich., Nov. 13, 1920; s. Bert Nichols and Natalie (Kerr) La D.; m. Catherine Shilson, June 14, 1947; children: Elizabeth, Mary, Anne, Jane. B.S., Mich. State Coll., 1943; M.D., U. Mich., 1945; Ph.D. in Biochemistry, U. Calif., Berkeley, 1952. Intern Rochester (N.Y.) Gen. Hosp., 1945-46; research asso. N.Y.U. Research Service, Goldwater Meml. Hosp., N.Y.C., 1950-53; sr. asst. surgeon USPHS, Nat. Heart Inst., 1954-57; surgeon, later sr. surgeon, med. dir. Nat. Inst. Arthritis and Metabolic Disease, 1957-63; prof., chmn. dept. pharmacology N.Y.U. Med. Sch., 1963-74; prof. pharmacology U. Mich. Med. Sch., Ann Arbor, 1974-89, prof. emeritus, 1989—, chmn. dept., 1974-81. Contbr. articles to profl. jours. Served with AUS, 1943-45. Mem. AAAS, Am. Chem. Soc., N.Y. Acad. Sci. (pres.), Am. Soc. Biol. Chemistry, Am. Soc. Pharmacol. Therapeutics (pres.), Am. Soc. Human Genetics, Biochem. Soc. (Gt. Britain). Home: 817 Berkshire Rd Ann Arbor MI 48104-2630 Office: U Mich Med Sch 6322 Med Sci I Ann Arbor MI 48109-0572

LADUKE, NANCIE, lawyer, corporate executive; b. Mayfield, Ky.; m. Daniel E. LaDuke, 1978. BA, Wayne State U., 1962; JD, U. Detroit, 1976. Pvt. practice Detroit, 1976; atty. KMart, Troy, Mich., 1977-84, comml. law counsel, 1984-90, v.p., sec., 1991—. Office: KMart Corp 3100 W Big Beaver Troy MI 48084

LAESSIG, ROBERT H., artist; b. West N.Y., N.J., Nov. 15, 1913; s. Ernest and Martha (Weigert) L.; m. Isolde Helene Grosser, June 6, 1942; children: Thomas, Constance. B.F.A., Textile Sch., Pauen, Germany; postgrad., Art Students League, N.Y.C. Sr. art cons. Am. Greetings, Inc.; painting represented in collections Norfolk Mus. Art, Cleve. Mus. Art, Springfield Inst. Fine Art, Denver Mus. Art; designer personal Christmas cards Pres. Lyndon B. Johnson, 1964-66, Gov. Celeste, Ohio, 1983-90; works exhibited 100th anniversary Met. Mus., N.Y.C.; combat artist 13th Air Force; illustrator From the Fijis Through the Philippines; instr. condr. seminars; pub. of prints Art Beats, Salt Lake City; assoc. with Gallery One, Mentor, Ohio. Served with USAAF, 1942-46. Recipient award Am. Watercolor Soc., 1979, 81, 82, 83, award Ky. Watercolor Soc., 1984, Adirondack Nat. Show, Old Forge, N.Y., 1982, 83, Ohio Watercolor Soc., 1979-85, Pitts Watercolor Soc., 1981, award Mainstreams Marietta, Ohio, 1983. Mem. Nat. Acad., Am. Water Soc., Ohio Watercolor Soc. (Gold medal 1987, 88, other awards 1979-87), Dolphin Club. Lutheran. Home: 26376 John Rd Olmsted Falls OH 44138

LAESSIG, RONALD HAROLD, pathology educator, state official; b. Marshfield, Wis., Aug. 4, 1940; s. Harold John and Ella Louise (Gumz) L.; m. Joan Margaret Spreda, Jan. 29, 1966; 1 child, Elizabeth Susan. B.S., U. Wis.-Stevens Point, 1962; Ph.D., U. Wis.-Madison, 1965. Jr. faculty Princeton (N.J.) U., 1966; chief clin. chemistry Wis. State Lab. Hygiene, Madison, 1966-80, dir., 1980—; asst. prof. preventive medicine U. Wis.-Madison, 1966-72, assoc. prof., 1972-76, prof., 1976—, prof. pathology, 1980—; cons. Ctr. Disease Control, Atlanta; dir. Nat. Com. for Clin. Lab. Standards, Villanova, Pa., 1977-80; chmn. invitro diagnostic products adv. com. FDA, 1974-75; mem. rev. com. Nat. Bur. Standards, 1983-86. Mem. editorial bd. Med. Electronics, 1970—, Analytical Chemistry, 1970-76, Health Lab. Sci., 1970—; contbr. articles to profl. jours. Mem. State of Wis. Tech. Com. Alcohol and Traffic Safety, 1970-88. Sloan Found. grantee, 1966; recipient numerous grants. Mem. Am. Assn. Clin. Chemistry (chmn. safety com. 1984-86, bd. dirs. 1986-89, Natelson award 1989, Contbns. Svc. to Profession award 1990), Am. Pub. Health Assn. (Difco award 1974), Am. Soc. for Med. Tech., Nat. Com. Clin. Lab. Standards (pres. 1980-82, bd. dirs. 1984-87), Sigma Xi. Avocation: Woodworking. Office: State Lab Hygiene 465 Henry Mall Madison WI 53706-1578

LAESSIG, WALTER BRUCE, publishing executive; b. Englewood, N.J., Aug. 11, 1941; s. George Bruce Laessig and Eileen May (Codling) Roma; m. Susan Lamme, June 13, 1964; children: Katherine Anne, Sarah Eileen, Matthew Lamme. AB in History, Cornell U., 1963, MBA in Fin., 1966, LLB, 1966. Bar: N.Y. 1966, D.C. 1968. Atty. Nixon, Hargrave, Devans & Doyle, Rochester, N.Y., 1966-68, Martin, Whitfield & Thaler, Washington, 1968-70; minority economist, counsel Joint Econ. Com., U.S. Congress, Washington, 1971-75; minority tax counsel Com. on Ways and Means, U.S. Ho. Reps., Washington, 1975-77; gen. counsel Nat. Assn. REITs, Washington, 1977-79; atty. Laessig, Brown, Hearn & Clohan, Washington, 1979-84; v.p. Warren, Gorham & Lamont, N.Y.C., 1984-85, exec. v.p., 1986, pres., chief exec. officer, 1987-89; exec. v.p., chief oper. officer Thomson Profl. Pub., Stamford, Conn., 1989-90; pres., chief exec. officer The Argus Group, Washington, 1990—. Republican. Presbyterian. Office: The Argus Group 1101 Vermont Ave NW Ste 400 Washington DC 20005-3521

LAETTNER, CHRISTIAN DONALD, professional basketball player; b. Angola, N.Y., Aug. 17, 1969. Student, Duke U. Basketball player Minn. Timberwolves, 1992—. Named Most Outstanding Player in NCAA Divsn. 1A Tournament, 1991, Sporting News Coll. Player of Yr., 1992, Sporting News All-Am. First Team, 1992, Naismith award, 1992, Wooden award, 1992; mem. Gold medal Winning Olympic Team, Barcelona, Spain, 1992. Named to NBA All-Rookie first team, 1993; mem. NCAA Divsn. I Championship Teams, 1991-92. Office: Minn Timberwolves 600 1st Ave N Target Ctr Minneapolis MN 55403*

LA FALCE, JOHN JOSEPH, congressman, lawyer; b. Buffalo, N.Y., Oct. 6, 1939; s. Dominic E. and Catherine M. (Stasio) La F.; m. Patricia Fisher, 1979. BS, Canisius Coll., 1961; JD, Villanova U., 1964; LLD (hon.), Niagara U., 1979, St. Johns U., 1989; LHD (hon.), Canisius Coll., 1990; LLD (hon.), Villanova U., 1991. Bar: N.Y. 1964. Mem. N.Y. State Legislature, 1971-74, 94th-104th Congresses from 32nd (now 29th) N.Y. dist., Washington, D.C., 1975—. Capt. adj. gen. corps AUS. Democrat. Home: 35 Danbury Ln Buffalo NY 14217-2101 Office: US Ho of Reps Rm 2310 Rayburn House Office Bldg Washington DC 20515

LAFARGE, CATHERINE, dean; b. Paris, May 22, 1935. BA, Mt. Holyoke Coll., 1957; PhD in French, Yale U., 1966. Acting instr. French Yale U., 1964-66, instr. to asst. prof., 1966-74, assoc. prof., 1974-80; prof. French Bryn Mawr Coll., 1980—, chmn. dept. French, 1979-84; dean Grad. Sch. Arts and Scis., Bryn Mawr Coll. 1985—. Author: The Emergence of the Bourgeoisie, 1964, Reverie et Realite dans les Nuits de Paris de Restif de la Bretonne, 1975, Paris and Myth: One Vision of Horror, In: Studies in Eighteenth Century culture, vol. V, 1976, L'Anti-Fete dans le Nouveau Paris de L S Mercier, La Fete Revolutionnaire, 1977; author: (with J.P. Bouler) Les emprunts de mme Dupin L'Infortune litteraire des Dupin: Essai de bibliographie critique, Vol. CLXXXII, 1979, Studies on Voltaire & 18th Century: Catalogue topographique partiel des papiers Dupin-Rousseau disperse de 1951 à 58, Annales de la Societe Jean-Jacques Rousseau, Vol. XXXIX, 1980; editor: Dilemmes du Roman. Essays in Honor of Georges May, 1989. Bd. dirs. Grad. Record Examination, Test of English as a Fgn. Lang.; chmn. com. on langs. and lit. Yale U. Mem. Internat. Soc. 18th Century Studies, Am. Soc. 18th Century Studies, Soc. Francaise d'Etude 18th Siecle, Am. Assn. Tchrs. of French, Assn. Internat. Studies. Office: Bryn Mawr Coll Bryn Mawr PA 19010*

LA FARGE, TIMOTHY, plant geneticist; b. N.Y.C., Mar. 14, 1930; s. Louis Bancel and Hester Alida (Emmet) La F.; m. Anne Blackstone, Oct. 16, 1960 (div. Mar. 1964); m. Frances Madelyne Holst, Aug. 6, 1966 (dec. 1992); 1 child, Jason Emmet; m. Nkem R. Salako, Dec. 4, 1993. BA in Dance, Black Mountain Coll., 1952; BSc in Forestry, U. Maine, 1964; M Forestry, Yale U., 1965; PhD, Mich. State U., 1971. Forestry aid Forest Svc., Orono, Maine, 1962-64; lab. technician geology dept. Yale U., New Haven, 1965; rsch. forester USDA Forest Svc., Macon, Ga., 1965-69, plant geneticist Southeastern Sta., 1970-82; plant geneticist Nat. Forest System USDA Forest Svc., Atlanta, 1982—. Contbr. articles to profl. jours. Recipient Certs. of Merit, USDA Forest Svc., Atlanta, 1986, 88. Mem. AAAS, Soc. Am. Foresters. Democrat. Achievements include demonstration that back-

crossing and hybridization between shortleaf pine and loblolly pine can effectively produce fast-growing back-cross hybrids that are resistant to fusiform rust; application of Best Linear Prediction to analysis of unbalanced or messy progeny test data. Home: 2679 Tritt Springs Trace Marietta GA 30062-5266 Office: USDA Forest Svc 1720 Peachtree Rd NW Atlanta GA 30367

LAFAVE, ARTHUR J., JR., financial executive, lawyer; b. Cleve., Mar. 28, 1933; s. Arthur J. and Florence (Carr) L.; m. Carolyn Bone; children: Arthur III, Charles, Lisa, Anne, William, Evelyn. BA, Williams Coll., 1955; LLB, Yale U., 1958. Bar: Ohio. Assoc. Black & Apicella, Portland, Oreg., 1958-60, Arter & Hamen, Cleve., 1960-62; sr. group v.p., chief fin. officer Internat. Mgmt. Group, Cleve., 1982—. Home: 19900 Shaker Blvd Cleveland OH 44122-1871 Office: Internat Mgmt Group 1 Erieview Plz Ste 1300 Cleveland OH 44114-1715

LAFAVE, HUGH GORDON JOHN, medical association executive, psychiatrist, educator, consultant; b. Montmarte, Sask., Can., Apr. 28, 1929; s. Leslie Alexander and Mary (Flaman) L.; m. Joann Sanderson, June 1956; children: Bonnie Lynn, Leslie Hugh, Maria Delee. B.A. cum laude, U. Sask., 1951; M.D., McGill U., 1953. Diplomate: Am. Bd. Psychiatry and Neurology. Intern Detroit Receiving Hosp., 1953-54; gen. practice medicine Rockglen, Assiniboia, Sask., Can., 1954-56; resident Medfield State Hosp., 1956-57, 58-60, Inst. Living, Hartford, Conn., 1957-58; chief rehab. Medfield State Hosp., Harding, Mass., 1960-61; clin. dir. Sask. Hosp., Weyburn, Can., 1962-64, supt., 1964-66; assoc. commr. dept. mental hygiene State of N.Y., Albany, 1966-69; dir. Eleanor Roosevelt Devel. Services, Schenectady, 1969-76; exec. dir. psychiat. services br. Dept. Health-Sask., Can., 1976-79; exec. v.p. Can. Assn. Mentally Retarded (now Can. Assn. Community Living), Downsview, Ont., 1979-84; pvt. practice specializing in psychiatry Red Deer Regional Hosp, 1984-85; dir. rehab. programs Brockville Psychiatric Hosp, 1985-94; assoc. prof. Albany Med. Coll., N.Y., 1968-76, assoc. prof. pediatrics, 1971-76, prof.; assoc. dean, prof. N.Y. Sch. Psychiatry, Poughkeepsie, 1969-76; clin. assoc. prof. psychiatry. U. Sask. Med. Coll., 1976-83, U. Ottawa, 1985-94; pres. Wellness Can., Hugh Lafave Holdings Ltd., 1981—; med. dir. Smokers Treatment Ctr., Ottawa, 1993—; mem., chmn. exptl., spl. tng. rev. com. NIMH, Chevy Chase, Md., 1970-74; mem. editorial bd. Can.'s Mental Health, 1978-80; mem. rehab.-community psychiatry com. U. Ottawa, 1986-92; prin. investigator Health Innovation Grant Community Rehab. Program, 1990-93, Premier's Health Coun.'s Health Innovator Fund, 1991-93; pres. Cmty. Living Cons., 1994—. Author: (with others) State Hospitals—What Happens When They Close?, 1976, Is the Community Ready?; contbr. numerous articles to profl. jours. Mem. awards com. Kennedy Found., 1977-78; bd. dirs. Byrd Hoffman Found., Inc., N.Y.C., 1974-80, Family Focus, Brockville, Can., 1986-90. Recipient Outstanding Achievement Amethyst award, 1994. Mem. Can. Psychiat. Assn. (bd. dirs. 1976-79), Am. Psychiat. Assn., Can. Pub. Health Assn., Workshop, Inc. (profll. adv. com. 1970-75), Nat. Inst. Mental Retardation (assoc. 1984—), Can. Mental Health Assn. (Toronto) (consumer participation task force 1986-90), Royal Coll. Psychiatrists. Home: Box 424, Brockville, ON Canada K6V 5V6 Office: PO Box 13, Elgin, ON Canada *People, all kinds of people, their rights, their health, their wellbeing, have been the focus of my career and my life, without regret.*

LAFAVE, KENNETH JOHN, music critic, composer; b. Tucson, Dec. 4, 1951; s. Milton J. and Catherine Anne (Langdon) LaF.; m. Helena Claire Elling. MusB, U. Ariz., 1973, MusM, 1980. Arts writer The Ariz. Daily Star, Tucson, 1977-84; publicist The New York Philharmonic, N.Y.C., 1985-87; music editor The Kansas City (Mo.) Star, 1987—. Composer: (orch.) Clarinet Fantasy, 1981, Nightsongs, 1986 (commd. Tucson Symphony Orch.), (song cycle) Songs of G.M. Hopkins, 1986; contbr. articles and reviews to newspapers and periodicals, 1982—. Atlantic Ctr. for the Arts fellow, 1984. Mem. ASCAP, Music Critics Assn. Home: 6610 E First St Scottsdale AZ 85251 Office: The Ariz Republic 120 E Van Burren Phoenix AZ 85004

LAFAVE, LEANN LARSON, lawyer; b. Ramona, S.D., May 31, 1953; d. Floyd Burdette and Janice Anne (Quist) L.; m. Richard Curtis Finke, May 19, 1973 (div. Jan. 1978); 1 child, Timothy; m. Dwayne Jeffery LaFave, May 31, 1981 (div. 1992); children: Jeffrey, Allison. BS, U. S.D., 1974, JD with honors, 1977. Bar: S.D. 1977, U.S. Dist. Ct. S.D. 1977, U.S. Ct. Appeals (8th cir.) 1977, N.D. 1978, U.S. Dist. Ct. N.D. 1978. Asst. atty. gen. State of S.D., Pierre, 1977-78, 79-81; assoc. Bjella, Neff, Rathert & Wahl, Williston, N.D., 1978-79, Tobin Law Offices, P.C., Winner, S.D., 1981-83; assoc. dean, asst. prof. U. S.D. Sch. Law, Vermillion, 1983-86, dir. continuing legal edn., 1983-89, assoc. prof. law, 1986-89; ptnr. Aho & LaFave, Brookings, S.D., 1990-91; pvt. practice Brookings, 1991-92; asst. U.S. atty. U.S. Dist. S.D., 1992—; mem. S.D. Bd. Pardons and Paroles, 1987-90, chmn., 1989-90; comml. arbitrator Am. Arbitration Assn., 1985—; prof. Kilian C.C. Contbr. articles to profl. jours. Mem. planning coun. Nat. Identification Program for Advancement Women in Higher Edn. Adminstrn., Am. Coun. on Edn., S.D., 1984-90; bd. dirs. Mo. Shores Women's Resource Ctr., Pierre, 1980, W.H. Over Mus., Vermillion, 1986-87, S.D. Vol. Lawyers for Arts, 1987—, Brookings Interagy. Coun., 1990-91, Brookings Women's Ctr., 1990-94; sec. Mediation Ctr., Inc. Named S.D. Woman Atty. of Yr. Women in Law U. S.D., 1985. Mem. S.D. Bar Assn. (bd. govs. young lawyers sect. 1983-84), S.D. Mediation Assn., Epsilon Sigma Alpha (S.D. coun. sect. 1985-86). Republican. Episcopalian. Avocation: reading. Home: 1808 S Jefferson Ave Sioux Falls SD 57105-2415 Office: PO Box 1073 Sioux Falls SD 57101

LAFEBER, WALTER FREDERICK, history educator, author; b. Walkerton, Ind., Aug. 30, 1933; s. Ralph N. and Helen (Lidecker) LaF.; m. Sandra Gould, Sept. 11, 1955; children: Scot Nichols, Suzanne Margaret. B.A., Hanover Coll., 1955; M.A., Stanford, 1956; Ph.D., U. Wis., 1959. Asst. prof. history Cornell U., 1959-63, assoc. prof., 1963-67, prof., 1967-68, Noll prof. history, 1968—; Commonwealth lectr. U. London, Eng., 1973; Callander lectr. U. Aberdeen, 1987; Shaw lectr. Johns Hopkins U., 1989; Landmark prof. Am. U., 1992; Jefferson lectr. U. Calif., Berkeley, 1992; Mem. adv. com. hist. div. State Dept., 1971-75. Author: The New Empire...1860-1898, 1963, America, Russia and the Cold War, 7th edit, 1993, The Panama Canal, The Crisis in Historical Perspective, 1978, expanded edit., 1979, 2d edit., 1989, The Third Cold War, 1981, Inevitable Revolutions: The U.S. in Central America, 1983, 2d edit., 1992, The American Age...1750 to the Present, 1989, 2d edit. 1994, The American Search for Opportunity, 1865-1913, 1993; co-author: The American Century, 4th edit, 1991; America in Vietnam, 1985; editor: John Quincy Adams and American Continental Empire, 1965, America in the Cold War, 1969, American Issues Forum, Vol. 2, 1976, also others; co-editor: Behind the Throne, Essays in Honor of Fred Harvey Harrington, 1993; mem. editorial adv. bd., Polit. Sci. Quar. Recipient Gustavus Myers prize, 1985; Guggenheim fellow, 1990. Mem. Orgn. Am. Historians, Am. Hist. Assn. (exec. coun. 1994—), Albert Beveridge prize 1963), Am. Acad. Arts and Scis. Office: Cornell U Dept History McGraw Hall Ithaca NY 14853-4601

LAFER, FRED SEYMOUR, data processing company executive; b. Passaic, N.J., Mar. 17, 1929; s. Abraham David and Pauline (Braer) L.; m. Barbara Bernstein, Apr. 4, 1954; children: Deborah, Gordon, Diana. BIE, NYU, 1950, JD, 1961; LHD (hon.), William Paterson Coll., 1987. Bar: N.J. 1961. Sec. to Justice Hayden Proctor, N.J. Supreme Ct., 1961-62; partner firm Hoffman Humphreys Lafer, Wayne, N.J., 1962-67; sec., gen. counsel Automatic Data Processing, Inc., Clifton, N.J., 1967—; v.p. Automatic Data Processing, Inc., 1968-81, sr. v.p., 1981—; pres. N.J. Nets Profl. Basketball Team, 1984. Chmn. United Jewish Appeal Fedn. North Jersey, 1973-74; pres. Jewish Fedn. North Jersey, 1976-77; v.p. N.J. Bd. Edn., 1967-68; bd. dirs. Chilton Meml. Hosp., Pompton Plains, N.J., 1970-72; trustee William Paterson Coll. 1974—, vice-chmn. bd., 1977, chmn. bd., 1978-80; pres. Am. Friends of Hebrew U., 1985-89; exec. com. Washington Inst. Near East Policy, sec.-treas., 1993—. Served to lt. USAF, 1951-52. Mem. Computer Law Assn. (pres. 1972-74), Assn. Data Processing Service Orgns. (chmn. 1983), ABA. Office: ADP Inc 1 A D P Blvd Roseland NJ 07068-1728

LAFEVER, HOWARD NELSON, plant breeder, geneticist, educator; b. Wayne County, Ind., May 13, 1938; s. Samuel L. and Flossie B. (Ellis) L.; m. Kay M. Schutz, Aug. 30, 1958; children: Julie, Jeff. BS, Purdue U., 1959, MS, 1961, PhD, 1963. Instr. Wis. State U., LaCrosse, 1963; assoc. prof. Purdue U., West Lafayette, Ind., 1963; research geneticist USDA-Agrl.

Research Service, Starkville, Miss., 1963-65; plant breeder, prof. agronomy Ohio State U., Ohio Agr. Research and Devel. Ctr., Wooster, 1965-91; owner Sunbeam Extract Co., 1991—; cons. Ohio Found. Seeds, Croton, 1967—, Rohm & Haas Corp., Phila., 1975-78, Dow Chem. Co., 1987. Patentee Becker, Cardinal, Dynasty, Excel and Freedom wheats plus 14 other small grain varieties; contbr. numerous articles to profl. jours. Grantee John Deere, 1982-84, Eli Lilly, 1984, 85, Quaker Oats, 1984-91. Fellow Am. Soc. Agronomy (bd. dirs. 1982-84, assoc. editor 1982-85); mem. Assn. Ofcl. Seed Certifying Agys., Ohio Seed Improvement Assn. (dir. 1968-83, grantee 1975-91). Presbyterian. Club: Gnat Boxers (Wooster) (treas. 1983-84). Avocations: woodworking; golf. Home: 500 Danberry Dr Wooster OH 44691-7401

LAFF, SEYMOUR, health care executive. Chmn. bd. Rocky Mountain Health Care Group, Denver. Office: Rocky Mountain Health Care Corp 700 Broadway Denver CO 80203

LAFFERTY, BEVERLY LOU BROOKOVER, physician; b. Newark, Ohio, Aug. 15, 1938; d. Lawrence William and Rosie (Rey) Brookover; B.S., Ohio State U., 1959, M.D., 1963; diplomate Am. Bd. Family Practice; children—Marla Michele, William Brookover, Wesley Voris, Latour Rey. Intern Grant Hosp., Columbus, Ohio, 1963-64; practice medicine, West Union, Ohio, 1964-75, Sun City Center, Fla., 1975-79, Brandon, Fla., 1979-95; mem. staff Adams County Hosp., v.p., 1971-72, chief of staff, 1973-75; mem. staff Humana Hosp., Brandon, 1977-95, chmn. dept. family practice, 1984-86, hosp. trustee, 1984-92, chief of staff elect, 1986-88, chief of staff, 1988-90. Mem. AMA, Fla., Hillsborough County med. assns., Am. Acad. Family Physicians, Fla. Acad. Family Physicians, Alpha Lambda Delta, Alpha Epsilon Iota, Alpha Epsilon Delta (sec. 1958-59). Mem. Order Eastern Star. Home: 3913 John Moore Rd Brandon FL 33511-8020

LAFFERTY, CHARLES DOUGLAS JOSEPH, advertising agency executive; b. Rochester, Pa., Mar. 27, 1930; s. William Charles and Kathryn (Devine) L.; m. Inger Antionette Sorum, Nov. 17, 1967. BA, U. Pitts., 1956. Mgr. sales devel. Moloney Regan & Schmitt, N.Y.C., 1956-69; dir. mktg. exec. v.p. planning, corp. treas. Branham, Inc., N.Y.C., 1969-82, vice chmn. bd., 1982-83, chmn. bd., chief exec. officer, 1983—. Recipient The Sid Goldish award, Internat. Newspaper Promotion Assn. 1982. Mem. Marco Polo (audit com. mem.), Employee Stock Ownership Plan Assn. (bd. dirs. 1987—), Internat. Newspaper Advt. (com. mem.), Exec. Assn. Avocation: glider pilot. Home: 58 Red Coat Rd Westport CT 06880-1415 Office: Branham Newspaper Sales 60 E 42nd St Rm 2311 New York NY 10165-0001

LAFFERTY, JAMES MARTIN, physicist; b. Battle Creek, Mich., Apr. 27, 1916; s. James V. and Ida M. (Martin) L.; m. Eleanor J. Currie, June 27, 1942; children: Martin C., Ronald J., Douglas J., Lawrence E. Student, Western Mich. U., 1934-37; BS in Engring. Physics, U. Mich., 1939, MS in Physics, 1940, Ph.D. in Elec. Engring., 1946. Physicist Eastman Kodak Research Lab., Rochester, N.Y., 1939; physicist Gen. Electric Research Lab., Schenectady, 1940, 42-81; mgr. power electronics lab. Gen. Electric Research Lab., 1972-81; with Carnegie Instn., Washington, 1941-42; past pres. Internat. Union Vacuum Sci. Technique and Applications, 1980-83; People to People citizen ambassador program group leader for Vacuum Sci. and Tech. delegation to Europe, 1984, China, 1986, Australia, 1988, Soviet Union, 1990. Editor, contbg. author: Scientific Foundations of Vacuum Technique (Dushman), 1962; editor: Vacuum Arcs, Theory and Applications, 1980; asso. editor: Jour. Vacuum Sci. and Tech, 1966-69; Editorial bd.: Internat. Jour. Electronics, 1968-89; contbr. articles to profl. jours. Mem. greater consistory Ref. Ch.; trustee Schenectady Museum, 1967-73, sec., 1971-72, pres., 1972-73. Recipient Devel. award Bur. Naval Ordnance, 1946; Distinguished Alumnus citation U. Mich., 1953; IR-100 award, 1968. Fellow AAAS, IEEE (Lamme medal 1979), Am. Phys. Soc.; mem. Nat. Acad. Engring., Am. Vacuum Soc. (hon. life mem.; dir. 1962-70, sec. 1965-67, pres. 1968-69), U.S. Power Squadrons (comdr. Lake George squadron 1975-76, comdr. Dist. 2 1981-82, nat. rear comdr. 1987-91, treas. Ednl. Fund 1992—), Sigma Xi, Phi Kappa Phi, Iota Sigma, Tau Beta Pi. Patentee in field; inventor lanthanum boride cathode, 1950, hot cathode magnetron ionization gauge, 1961, triggered vacuum gap, 1966. Home: 1202 Hedgewood Ln Niskayuna NY 12309-4605

LAFFERTY, JOYCE G. ZVONAR, retired educator; b. Balt., July 9, 1931; d. George S. and Carolyn M. (Bothe) Greener; children: Barbara Z. Gunter, John G. Zvonar, David A. Zvonar. BS, Towson State, 1963; M. equivalent, Md. Inst. Coll. of Art, 1978. Cert. tchr., Md. Tchr., dept. chmn. Hampstead Hill. Jr. High Annex, Balt.; tchr. Forest Park Sr. High, Balt.; tchr., dept. chmn. Roland Park Mid. Sch., Balt. Mem. Nat. Art Edn. Assn., Internat. Soc. Artists, Balt. Tchrs. Union. Home: 1101 Gilcrest Ct Baltimore MD 21234-5924

LAFFERTY, RICHARD THOMAS, architect; b. Allentown, Pa., Dec. 12, 1932; s. Arthur M. and Emily (May) L.; m. Janece Fiore, Apr. 28, 1962; children: Alicia, Hope. BArch, Syracuse U., 1956. Registered architect, N.Y. Draftsman Sweeney-Burden, Architects, Syracuse, 1954-56, Gordon P. Schopfer, AIA, Syracuse, 1959-63; job capt. Sargent, Webster, Crenshaw & Folley, Syracuse, 1963-75, assoc., chief estimator, 1975-88; project architect V.I.P. Archtl. Assocs., Syracuse, 1988-90, assoc., 1989-90, project architect Schopfer Architects, 1990-93; architect, Richard T. Lafferty, 1993-94; architect, Fuligni-Fragola Architects, 1994—; instr. drafting Onondaga Community Coll., Syracuse, 1968-70, instr. codes, 1972-76, curriculum adviser archtl. tech., 1986—; curriculum adviser archtl. tech. SUNY, Delhi, 1984—; mem. N.Y. State Bd. Architecture, 1990—, chmn., 1995; sec. region II NCARB, 1995—. Adv. mem. Onondaga County Plumbing Bd., Syracuse, 1978—; curriculum adviser Nat. Tech. Inst. for Deaf, Rochester, N.Y., 1984—, mem. Uniform Code Syracuse/Watertown Bd. Rev., 1984—. Served to capt. USAF, 1956-59. Recipient, Matthew W. Del Gaudio award, 1983. Mem. AIA (energy com. 1981-85, profl. devel. com. 1981-85), Central N.Y. AIA (treas. 1978-79, pres. 1981, sec. 1989-94, editor newsletter 1978—, chmn. code com. 1983-84, 1989—), N.Y. State Assn. Architects (dir. 1980-84, mem. handicap com. 1983-84, pres. 1987, past pres. 1988, Pres. Medal 1991), N.Y. State Assns. of Professions (pres. 1991). Republican. Roman Catholic. Home and Office: Limeledge and Glover Rds Marcellus NY 13108

LAFFITTE, HECTOR MANUEL, federal judge; b. Ponce, P.R., Apr. 13, 1934; s. Miguel and Gilda (Colomer) L.; m. Nydia M. Rossy, June 13, 1958; children: Yasmin, Hector W., Bernice M., Walter M., Giselle M. BA, Interamerican U., 1955; LLB, U. P.R., 1958; LLM, Georgetown U., 1960. Bar: U.S. Dist. Ct. P.R. 1959, U.S. Ct. Appeals (1st cir.) 1959, Supreme Ct. P.R. 1959, U.S. Mil. Appeals 1960, U.S. Supreme Ct. 1976. Assoc. Hartzell, Fernandez & Novas, 1959-64; pvt. practice law, 1965-66; ptnr. Nachman, Feldstein, Laffitte & Smith, 1966-69, Laffitte & Dominguez, 1970-83; judge U.S. Dist. Ct. P.R., 1983—. Mem. ABA, Inst. Jud. Adminstrn. Office: US Dist Ct CH-142 Fed Bldg 150 Carlos Chardon Ave Hato Rey San Juan PR 00918

LAFFOON, CARTHRAE MERRETTE, management consultant; b. Wilkinsburg, Pa., Jan. 1, 1920; s. Carthrae Merrette and Kittie (Painter) L.; m. Helen Elizabeth Frisk, July 3, 1943; children: Judith Karin (Mrs. Wright), Catharine Elizabeth, Carthrae Merrette III (dec.), Barbara Louise. B.S., Mass. Inst. Tech., 1942. Jr. engr. rsch. lab. Westinghouse Electric Corp., Pitts., 1942-45; asst. project engr. aviation gas turbine div. Westinghouse Electric Corp., South Phila., 1945-47; asst. project engr. Ryan Aero. Co., San Diego, 1947-48; power plant group leader Ryan Aero. Co., 1948-49; jr. engr. San Diego Gas & Electric Co., 1950-53, asst. efficiency engr., 1953-58, asst. sta. chief, 1958-60, mech. engr., 1960-63, chief mech. engr., 1963, v.p. prodn., transmission, 1963-65, v.p. electric, 1965-70, sr. v.p., 1971-76; pres. C.M. Laffoon Cons., 1976—; pres., dir. Geothermal Generation, Inc., 1976-87, chmn., bd. dirs., 1987-89; ret. Elder Presbyn. Ch. Mem. ASME, Sigma Xi, Tau Beta Pi, Kiwanis. Republican. Home and Office: 1109 Merritt Ln El Cajon CA 92020-7851

LAFLEUR, GUY, public relations executive, professional hockey player; b. Thurso, Que., Can., Sept. 20, 1951; s. Rejean and Pierrette L.; m. Lise Barre, June 16, 1973; children: Martin, Mark. Student pub. schs. Mem. jr. hockey team Que. Remparts; player Montreal Canadiens Profl. Hockey Team., 1971-85, N.Y. Rangers, 1988-89; player Quebec Nordiques, 1989-91, dir. of corporate affairs, 1992-93; v.p. public relations Titrex, 1993—. Decorated

Order of Can.; recipient Art Ross trophy, 1976, 77; Conn Smythe trophy, 1977; Hart trophy, 1977. Office: Titrex, 4715 des Replats Room 150, Quebec, PQ Canada G2J 1B8*

LAFLEY, ALAN FREDERICK, retired banker; b. Stamford, Conn., Aug. 26, 1922; s. Alan George and Clara (Petersen) L.; m. Kathryn Margaret Irwin, Mar. 1, 1946; children: Alan George, Nora Kathryn, Jo Anne, Mary Patricia. B.B.A., Clarkson U. Polytech., N.Y., 1946; M.B.A., U. Mich., 1948. Asst. prof. Sch. of Bus.; placement dir. Clarkson U., 1948-50, Sch. Bus., Ind. U., Bloomington, 1950-51; with Gen. Electric Co., 1951-73; mgr. exec. personnel and compensation Gen. Electric Co., N.Y.C., 1968-73; v.p. personnel Chase Equipment Co., Buchanan, Mich., 1973-75; exec. v.p. human resources Chase Manhattan Bank, N.Y.C., 1975-84; mng. dir. Korn Ferry Internat., 1984-86; exec. in residence, vis. prof. U. Mich. Sch. Bus., Ann Arbor, 1984-85; cons., advisor, lectr. human resources mgr. Mem. adv. coun. Sch. Bus., Clarkson U. Served to 1st lt. U.S. Army and USAAF, 1942-46. Fellow Human Resources Policy Inst., Boston U.

LAFOLLETTE, CHARLES SANBORN, business consultant; b. Indpls., Sept. 3, 1929; s. Charles D. and Elizabeth (Sanborn) LaF.; m. Ellen Unwin McHugh, Apr. 24, 1954; children: Laetitia Amelia, Lizellen, Anne Unwin, Charles McHugh. A.B. cum laude, Harvard U., 1951, M.B.A., 1953. With Corning Glass Works, N.Y., 1955-70; asst. comptroller Corning Glass Works, 1961-64, asst. treas., financial v.p. internat., 1964-66; financial dir. Europe of Corning Glass Internat., Brussels, 1966-68; financial v.p. (Corning Glass subs. Sovirel), Paris, 1968-70; exec. v.p. finance, dir., mem. exec. com. Crown Zellerbach Corp., San Francisco, 1970-81; sr. v.p., chief fin. officer CBS Inc., N.Y.C., 1981-82; exec. v.p. US Leasing Internat., San Francisco, 1982-88, Chronicle Pub. Co., San Francisco, 1988-89, Calif. Energy Co., San Francisco, 1990-91; dir. Allendale Ins., U.S. Leasing; gov. Pacific Stock Exchange, San Francisco and Los Angeles; mem. fin. officers council Conf. Bd., 1976-91. Treas. European Rep. Nat. Com., 1970; bd. dirs. Arnot Art Gallery, Elmira, N.Y., 1963-67, Sta. KQED-TV, San Francisco Symphony, Nat. Urban Coalition; trustee Atlas Econ. Research Found., Archaeol. Inst. Am., Boston; chmn. audit adv. com. City and County San Francisco. Served with AUS, 1953-55. Clubs: University (N.Y.C.); Bankers, St. Francis Yacht, Pacific Union, Calif. Pacific Med. Ctr. Found.; Circle Gauloise (Brussels); Circle Interalliee (Paris). Home: 2620 Larkin St San Francisco CA 94109-1513

LA FOLLETTE, DOUGLAS J., secretary of state; b. Des Moines, June 6, 1940; s. Joseph Henry and Frances (Van der Wilt) LaF. B.S., Marietta Coll., 1963; M.S., Stanford U., 1964; Ph.D., Columbia U., 1967. Asst. prof. chemistry and ecology U. Wis.-Parkside, 1969-72; mem. Wis. Senate, 1973-75; sec. state State of Wis., Madison, 1975-79, 83—. Author: Wisconsin's Survival Handbook, 1971, The Survival Handbook, 1991. Mem. Council Econ. Priorities; mem. Lake Michigan Fed., Wis. Environ. Decade, 1971, S.E. Wis. Coalition for Clean Air, Dem. candidate for U.S. Congress, 1970, for Wis. lt. gov., 1978, for U.S. Senate, 1988. Recipient Environ. Quality EPA, 1976. Mem. Am. Fedn. Tchrs., Fedn. Am. Scientists, Phi Beta Kappa. Office: Office Sec State of Wis PO Box 7848 Madison WI 53707-7848

LAFONTAINE, PAT, professional hockey player; b. St. Louis, Feb. 22, 1965. With U.S. Olympic Hockey Team, 1984, N.Y. Islanders, 1983-91, Buffalo Sabres, 1991—; player All-Star game, 1988-91, 93. Recipient Dodge Performer Yr. award, 1989-90, Michel Briere award, 1982-83, Jean Beliveau trophy, 1982-83, Frank J. Selke trophy, 1982-83, Des Instructeurs trophy, 1982-83, Guy LaFleur trophy, 1982-83; named to Sporting News All-Star Team, 1989-90, Player of the Year Canadian Hockey League, 1982-83. Office: Buffalo Sabres Meml Auditorium 140 Main St Buffalo NY 14202*

LA FONTAINE, RAYMOND M., insurance company executive; b. 1926. Mem. Mass. Legislature, Boston, 1963-81; with Mass. Motor Vehicle Reinsurance Facility, Boston, 1974-84; pres. Commonwealth Auto Reinsurance, Boston, 1984—; chmn. house com. on ins. Mass. Legislature, Boston, 1963-81. Office: Commonwealth Auto Reinsurance 100 Summer St Boston MA 02110-2103

LAFONTANT-MANKARIOUS, JEWEL (MRS. NAGUIB S. MANKARIOUS), diplomat, lawyer; b. Chgo., Apr. 28, 1922; d. Cornelius Francis Stradford and Aida Arabella Carter; m. John Rogers, 1946 (dissolved 1961); 1 child, John W. Rogers Jr.; m. H. Ernest Lafontant, 1961 (dec. 1976); m. Naguib Soby Mankarious, Dec. 17, 1989. AB in Polit. Sci., Oberlin Coll., 1943; JD, U. Chgo., 1946; LLD (hon.), Cedar Crest Coll., 1973; D Humanitarian Svc. (hon.), Providence Coll., 1973; LLD (hon.), Ea. Mich. U., 1973; LHD (hon.), Howard U., 1974; LLD (hon.), Heidelberg Coll., 1975, Lake Forest Coll., 1977, Marymount Manhattan Coll., 1978, Oberlin Coll., 1979; LHD (hon.), Governor's State U., 1980, LLD (hon.), 1980; citation for pub. svc., U. Chgo., 1980; LLD (hon.), Chgo. Med. Sch., 1982, Loyola U. of Chgo., 1982, Roosevelt U., 1990. Bar: Ill. 1947. Asst. U.S. atty., 1955-58; sr. ptnr. Lafontant, et al., Chgo., 1961-83, Vedder, Price, Kaufman & Kammholz, Chgo., 1983-89; dep. solicitor gen. U.S. Dept. State, Washington, 1972-75, amb.-at-large, U.S. coord. for refugee affairs, 1989-93; ptnr. Holleb & Coff, Chgo., 1993—; bd. dirs. Mobil Corp., Continental Bank, Foote, Cone & Belding, Equitable Life Assurance Soc. U.S., Trans World Corp., Revlon, Inc., Ariel-Capital Mgmt., Harte-Hanks Communications, Inc., Pantry Pride, Inc., Revlon Group, Howard U.; past dir. Jewel Cos., Inc., TWA, Hanes Corp.; past mem. U.S. Adv. Commn. Internat. Edn. and Cultural Affairs, Nat. Coun. Minority Bus. Enterprises, Nat. Coun. on Ednl. Rsch.; past chmn. adv. bd. Civil Rights Commn.; mem. Pres.'s Pvt. Sector Survey Cost Control; pres. Exec. Exchange; past U.S. rep. to UN. Bd. editors: Am. Bar Assn. Jour. Former trustee Lake Forest (Ill.) Coll., Oberlin Coll., Howard U., Tuskegee Inst.; bd. govs. Ronald Reagan Presdl. Found.; mem. Martin Luther King, Jr., Fed. Holiday Commn.; dir. Project Hope; chmn. Ill. adv. com. U.S. Civil Rights Commn.; mem. bd. overseers Hoover Instn.; mem. nat. adv. bd. Salvation Army. Recipient Howard B. Shepard award Protestant Found., Little Flowers Sem. Soc., Svc. award U.S. Dept. Justice, Humanitarian award Opportunities Industrialization Ctrs. of Am., Inc., Candace award Nat. Coalition of Black Women, Adlai A. Stevenson II award for svc. and support UN, Par Excellence Svc. award People United to Save Humanity, Disting. Svc. award Interracial Coun. for Bus. Opportunity, 1988, Woman of Distinction award Nat. Conf. for Coll. Women Student Leaders and Women of Achievement, 1988, Abraham Lincoln Marovitz award B'nai Brith, 1989, Disting. Svc. to Law and Soc. award Ill. Bar Found., 1989, cert. of recognition Vietnamese Community Leaders in U.S., 1990, Wiley A. Branton Issues Symposium award 1991, United Charities Legal Aid Soc. award, 1991, Spl. Recognition award Assyrian Am. Nat. Found., 1992, Chgo. Chpt. of Links, Inc. award, 1992, CARE Humanitarian award, 1994, Luminary award Girl Scouts U.S., 1995, Raoul Wallenberg award Am. Com. for Shaare Zedek Med. Ctr., Jerusalem, 1995, others; named Hon. Citizen of Abilene, Tex., 1991; named one of One Hundred Most Influential Black Ams., Ebony Mag., 1973-74. Fellow Internat. Acad. Trial Lawyers; mem. NAACP (sec. Chgo. br.), ACLU (bd. dirs.), Chgo. Bar Assn. (bd. govs., Earl B. Dickerson award 1995), Comml. Club, Econs. Club (past bd. dirs.), Rotary Club. Home: 180 E Pearson St Apt 4004 Chicago IL 60611

LAFONTSEE, DANE, ballet company artistic director; b. Lansing, Mich., Nov. 9, 1946; s. Frank and Mary (Braily) LaF.; m. Dana Moore; 1 child, Liane Marie. Student, N.C. Sch. of the Arts, Winston-Salem, 1965-66. Dancer Nat. Ballet of Washington, 1966-67; dancer Pa. Ballet, Phila., 1967-86, ballet master, 1978-80, asst. to artistic dir., 1980-82, assoc. artistic dir., 1982-86; artistic dir. Nashville Ballet, 1986-90, Milw. Ballet, 1990—; bd. dirs. Tenn. Gov.'s Sch. for Arts; choreographer Pa. Ballet, Ballet Okla., Nashville Ballet, Milw. Ballet, Ballet Ariz., Lake Erie Ballet, 1978—; tchr. Nashville Inst. for Arts, 1986—; mem. vis. faculty Med. Coll. Wis. Toured with Rudolf Nureyev, 1973-74; choreographer numerous works for Pa. Ballet Repertory, champion ice dance team, 1986, (musical) Pirates of Penzance, 1988. Avocations: skiing, water skiing. Office: Milw Ballet 504 W National Ave Milwaukee WI 53204-1746

LA FORCE, JAMES CLAYBURN, JR., economist, educator; b. San Diego, Dec. 28, 1928; s. James Clayburn and Beatrice Maureen (Boyd) La F.; m. Barbara Lea Latham, Sept. 23, 1952; children: Jessica, Allison, Joseph. BA, San Diego State Coll., 1951; MA, UCLA, 1958, PhD, 1962. Asst. prof. econs. UCLA, 1962-66, assoc. prof., 1967-70, prof., 1971-93, prof. emeritus

1993—, chmn. dept. econs., 1969-78, dean Anderson Sch. Mgmt., 1978-93; acting dean Hong Kong U. Sci. & Tech., 1991-93; bd. dirs. Rockwell Internat., Eli Lilly & Co., Jacobs Engring. Group Inc., The Timken Co., The Black Rock Funds, Imperial Credit Industries, Inc., Payden & Rygel Investment Trust, Providence Investment Coun. Mut. Funds; chmn. adv. com. Calif. Workmen's Compensation. Author: The Development of the Spanish Textile Industry 1750-1800, 1965, (with Warren C. Scoville) The Economic Development of Western Europe, vols. 1-5, 1969-70. Bd. dirs. Nat. Bur. Econ. Rsch., 1975-88, Found. Francisco Marroquin, Lynde and Harry Bradley Found.; trustee Pacific Legal Found., 1981-86, Found. for Rsch. in Econs. and Edn., 1970—, chmn., 1977—; bd. overseers Hoover Inst. on War, Revolution and Peace, 1979-85, 86-93; mem. nat. coun. on humanities NEH, 1981-88; chmn. Pres.'s Task Force on Food Assistance, 1983-84. Social Sci. Research Council research tng. fellow, 1958-60; Fulbright sr. research grantee, 1965-66; Am. Philos. Soc. grantee, 1965-66. Mem. Econ. History Assn., Mont Pelerin Soc., Phi Beta Kappa. Office: UCLA Anderson Grad Sch Mgmt 405 Hilgard Ave Los Angeles CA 90095-1481

LAFORCE, WILLIAM LEONARD, JR., photojournalist; b. Albemarle County, Va., Aug. 24, 1940; s. William Leonard and Florence Alberta (Sandridge) LaF.; m. Dorothy Lee Kesler, June 8, 1963 (div. 1987); children: William Perry, Glenn Edward. Student, U. Va., 1958-60; B.S., Johns Hopkins U., 1967, M.Liberal Arts, 1972. Dir. photography Balt. Sun papers, 1962-74; chief photographer and graphics editor N.J. edit. N.Y. Daily News, N.Y.C., 1974-79, photojournalist N.Y. staff, 1979—; scholastic journalism faculty Columbia U., 1971-75; lectr. to various news and photography orgns. Judge Miss Delmarva Pageant, 1969-74; planning com. Balt. City Fair, 1971; pres. Rumsey Island Residents Assn., Joppa, Md., 1969-72, Rumsey House Restoration Found., 1968-70, Mountain Lakes (N.J.) Fire Dept., 1977-79; Democratic committeeman, Mountain Lakes, 1976-78; chmn. Wildwood Sch. Bd., 1976-77; mgr. Mountain Lakes Little League, 1981, 85-86; bd. dirs. Joppatowne Civic Assn., 1969-71, vice chmn. citizens nominating com., 1977-81; mem. Pedestrian Safety Com., 1976-80; bd. dirs. Mountain Lakes Hist. Soc., 1987—, Am. Police Hall of Fame, 1987—; Morris County disability commn., 1995—. Recipient Best Fire Photo in U.S. award Internat. Assn. Firefighters, 1967, Disting. Community Service award Jaycees, 1971, 1st Pl. Annapolis Fine Arts Festival, 1971, award for disting. community service Rumsey Island Residents Assn., 1972, Best Photo of Preakness Race award City of Balt., 1972, Page One award for best news photo in N.Y.C. Newspaper Guild, 1983, One Man Exhibition, Overseas Press Club, 1983; Best News Photo award N.Y. Press Club, 1984; 1st place Spot News award 2 N.J. Press Assn., 1985, 91, Best PIX Story award N.Y.C. Police, 1986, 1st place Gen. News award N.J. Press Assn., 1991, nominated for Pulitzer award, 1984, 91. Mem. Nat. Press Photographers Assn. (dir. Mid-Atlantic region 1977-81, Press's citation 1980, Bootstrap Leadership award 1981), Photographic Adminstrs. N.Y. (bd. dirs. 1986—, v.p. 1988—), N.Y. Press Photographers Club, N.J. Press Photographers, N.Y. Press Club. Home: PO Box 31 Mountain Lakes NJ 07046-0031 Office: NY Daily News 220 E 42d St New York NY 10017

LA FOREST, GÉRARD VINCENT, justice; b. Grand Falls, N.B., Can., 1926; s. Alfred and Philomène (Lajoie) La F.; m. Marie Warner, Dec. 27, 1952; children: Marie, Kathleen, Anne, Elizabeth, Sarah. Student, St. Francis Xavier U., 1944-46; BCL, U. N.B., 1949; BA in Jurisprudence (Rhodes scholar), Oxford (Eng.) U., 1951, MA, 1956; LLM (Univ. fellow), Yale U., 1965, JSD, 1966; LLD (hon.), Basel U., 1981; D Univ. (hon.), Ottawa U., 1985; DCL (hon.), U. N.B., 1985; LLD (hon.), St. Francis Xavier U., 1988, U. Alta., 1988, U. Moncton, 1988, St. Thomas U., 1988, Bates Coll., 1990. Bar: N.B. 1949; created Queen's Counsel 1968. Practiced law Grand Falls, 1951-52; adv. counsel legal br. Can. Dept. Justice, Ottawa, Ont., 1952-55; legal adv. Irving Oil and Assoc. Cos., St. John, N.B., 1955-56; assoc. prof. law U. N.B., 1956-63, prof., 1963-68; dean law U. Alta., Can., 1968-70; asst. dept. atty. gen. Can. Rsch. and Planning, Ottawa, 1970-74; mem. Law Reform Commn. of Can., Ottawa, 1974-79; on leave as exec. vice chmn. Can. Bar Assn. Com. on Constn., 1977-78; prof. law, dir. legis. drafting program U. Ottawa, 1979-81; judge Ct. Appeal N.B., 1981-85; justice Supreme Ct. of Can., Ottawa, 1985—; cons. to fed. and provincial govts., including appearances in constl. law cases before Supreme Ct. Can.; adv. to spl. counsel on const. to Minister of Justice and Prime Min. Can., 1967-70; mem. exec. com. Task Force on Computers and Privacy, 1971-72; chmn. Fed. Provincial Special Inquiry on Kouchibouguac Nat. Park, Expropriation, 1980-81; vis. prof. U. Montreal, 1962-63; professeur à la lecon U. Ottawa, 1971-78; lectr. in law McGill U., 1971, 79. Author: Disallowance and Reservation of Provincial Legislation, 1955, 2d edit., 1965, Extradition To and From Canada, 1961, 2d rev. edit., 1977, The Allocation of Taxing Power Under the Canadian Constitution, 1967, 2d rev. edit., 1981, Natural Resources and Public Property Under the Canadian Constitution, 1969, (with others) Le Territoire Québecois, 1970, (with assocs.) Water Law in Canada—The Atlantic Provinces, 1973; contbr. (with assocs.) numerous articles, revs. to profl. pubs. Recipient award of Merit, U. Montreal, 1993. Fellow Royal Soc. Can., World Acad. Art and Sci.; mem. Am. Coll. Trial Lawyers (hon.). Roman Catholic. Office: Supreme Ct Can, Wellington St, Ottawa, ON Canada K1A 0J1

LAFOREST, JAMES JOHN, retired electrical engineer; b. Tupper Lake, N.Y., Feb. 28, 1927; s. George Hector and Florence Alice (Trudel) L. B.S.E.E., Union Coll., 1957; M.E.E., Rensselaer Poly. Inst., 1964. Registered profl. engr., N.Y., Mass., Wyo., Colo. Engr. Gen. Electric Co., Pittsfield, Mass., 1951-58; research engr. Gen. Electric Co., 1959-69; application engr. Gen. Electric Co., Schenectady, 1970-77; sr. application engr. Gen. Electric Co., 1978-87, ret. Author: (with others) EHV Transmission Line Reference Book, 1968; editor-co-author: Transmission Line Reference Book, 1982. Bd. dirs., sec. Mohawk Opportunities in Mental Health, Schenectady, 1985. Fellow IEEE; mem. Sigma Xi. Democrat. Roman Catholic. Avocations: Alpine skiing, fishing, carpentry, travel, golf. Home: PO Box 3407 Schenectady NY 12303-0407

LA FOSSE, ROBERT, ballet dancer, choreographer; b. Beaumont, Tex.. Student, Marsha Woody Acad. of Dance; Studied with David Howard, Harkness House, N.Y.C., 1977. With Am. Ballet Theatre, N.Y.C., 1977-86, mem. corps de ballet, 1977-81, soloist, 1981-83, prin., 1983-86; prin. N.Y.C. Ballet, 1986—. Created roles at Am. Ballet Theatre in Cinderella, Lynne Taylor-Corbett's Great Galloping Gottschalk, John McFall's Follow the Feet, Kenneth MacMillan's The Wild Boy and Twyla Tharp's, Bach Partita; other Am. Ballet repertoire includes: La Bayadere, Billy the Kid, Clair de Lune, Don Quixote, Fancy Free, Giselle, Jardin Aux Lilas, Swan Lake Act II, The Leaves are Fading, Prodigal Son, Les Rendezvous, Symphonie Concertante, Rodeo, Other Dances, N.Y. Export: Op. Jazz, Romeo & Juliet, Dim Luster, Nutcracker, La Sonnambula & Coppelia; created roles at N.Y. City Ballet include Quiet City, Piccalo Balleto; repertoire at N.Y. City Ballet includes Slaughter on 10th Ave., Opus 19, The Dreamer, Raymonda Variations, Who Cares?, Davidsbundlertanze, Ballo del Regina, La Baiser de la Fee, Nutcracker, Prodigal Son, Dances at a Gathering, Scotch Symphony, Agon, Vienna Waltzes, Four Seasons, La Source, Union Jack, Dances Concertant, A Fool for You, Coppelia, Valse Triste, Western Symphony, Goldberg Variations in G Major, Donizetti Variations, Afternoon of a Faun; dancer: leading role in Dancin' (on Broadway), 1979, Dancing Hands, Live from Off Center, 1988; choreographer Giretry pas de deux Rappaccini's Daughter, 1985, (for Sch. Am. Ballet) Yesterdays, 1987, Woodland Sketches, N.Y.C. Ballet, 1988, Haydn Trumpet Concerto, 1989, Puss in Boots, 1990, Waltz Trilogy, 1991, I Have My Own Room, 1992, Four for 4, 1992, The Concert, 1993, The Nutcracker, 1993; starred in Jerome Robbins, Broadway, 1989; TV appearances: Ray Charles and N.Y.C. Ballet, PBS, 1989; also Am. Ballet Theatre at the Met (Triad), Am. Ballet Theatre in San Francisco (Jardin Aux Lilas, Great Galloping Gottschalk), Baryshnikov Dances Tharp (Push comes to Shore), Dance in America, Western Symphony, 1990, (movie) Nutcracker, 1993; author: Nothing to Hide: A Dancer's Life. Office: NYC Ballet NY State Theatre Lincoln Ctr Plz New York NY 10023

LAFRANKIE, JAMES V., water utility holding company executive; b. Elizabeth, Pa., Mar. 26, 1927; s. John Lewis and Susan Marie (Heidrick) L.; m. Nancy Louise Wiegel, June 12, 1954; children—Terence, James Jr., Jane, Donna, Kenneth, Mark, William. B.S. in Mgmt., Georgetown U., 1964. Office clk. Am. Water Works Co. Inc., Elizabeth, from 1948, now pres.; dir., exec. com. Am. Water Works Co. Inc., Voorhees, N.J. Mem. Am. Water

Works Assn. (Fuller award, hon. mem.), Nat. Assn. Water Cos. (past chmn. bd.). Republican. Roman Catholic. Home: 120 W Walnut Ave Moorestown NJ 08057-1808 Office: Am Water Works Co Inc 1025 Laurel Oak Rd PO Box 1770 Voorhees NJ 08043

LAFROSCIA, ERNEST JOHN, business executive; b. Bklyn., Sept. 19, 1930; s. Peter and Anna (Ferraiuolo) LaF.; m. Josephine Curella, Aug. 13, 1955; children: Donna Marie, Diane Elizabeth. BSEE, CCNY, 1957. Group leader AIL divsn. Eaton Corp., Deer Park, N.Y., 1957-69; dir. data sys. Gen. Instruments Corp., Hicksville, N.Y., 1969-73; v.p. devel. Nationwide Devel. Inc., Virginia Beach, Va., 1973-74; founder, CEO LFC Nationwide Inc., Central Islip, N.Y., 1974—. Sgt. USAF, 1948-52. Named Entrepreneur of the Yr., Ernst and Young, 1991. Mem. Mortgage Bankers Assn. Am., Nat. Assn. Mortgage Field Svcs. Inc. (bd. govs. 1988—), Am. Alliance Loan Mgmt. (bd. dirs. 1992—, v.p. 1994, pres. 1995). Avocations: golf, gardening, reading. Office: LFC Nationwide Inc Loudoun Gateway 45240 Business Park Dr Sterling VA 22170

LAFVING, BRIAN DOUGLAS, lawyer; b. Michigan City, Ind., Mar. 31, 1953; s. Allen Herschel and Barbara Joan (Rachow) L.; m. Diane Leigh Pierce, Aug. 16, 1975; children: Bridgette, Brandon, Brittany. BA, BFA, So. Meth. U., 1974, JD, 1977. Bar: Tex. 1977, U.S. Ct. Dist. (no. dist.) Tex., 1977. Assoc. Stalcup, Johnson, Meyers & Miller, Dallas, 1977-79, Baker, Glast, Riddle, Tuttle & Elliott, Dallas, 1979-80; ptnr. Glast & Miller, Dallas, 1980-83, Jones, Day, Reavis & Pogue, Dallas, 1983—. Mem. ABA, Tex. Bar Assn. Republican. Methodist. Office: Jones Day Reavis & Pogue 2300 Trammell Crow Ctr 2001 Ross Ave Dallas TX 75201-2911

LAGALLY, MAX GUNTER, physics educator; b. Darmstadt, Germany, May 23, 1942; came to U.S., 1953, naturalized, 1960; s. Paul and Herta (Rudow) L.; m. Shelley Meserow, Feb. 15, 1969; children—Eric, Douglas, Karsten. BS in Physics, Pa. State U., 1963; MS in Physics, U. Wis.-Madison, 1965, PhD in Physics, 1968. Registered profl. engr., Wis. Instr. physics U. Wis., Madison, 1970-71, asst. prof. materials sci., 1971-74, assoc. prof., 1974-77, prof. materials sci. and physics, 1977—, dir. thin-film deposition and applications ctr., 1982-93, John Bascom Prof. materials sci., 1986—, E.W. Mueller Prof. materials sci. and physics, 1993—; Gordon Godfrey vis. prof. physics, U. New South Wales, Sydney, Australia, 1987; cons. in thin films, 1977—; vis. scientist Sandia Nat. Lab., Albuquerque, 1975. Editor: (with others) Methods of Experimental Physics, 1985; editor: Kinetics of Ordering and Growth at Surfaces, 1990, (with others) Evolution of Surface and Thin-Film Microstructure, 1993; mem. editorial bd., also editor spl. issue Jour. Vacuum Sci. and Tech, 1978-81; prin. editor Jour. Materials Rsch., 1990-93; mem. editorial bd. Surface Sci., 1994; contbr. articles to profl. jours.; patentee in field. Max Planck Gesellschaft fellow, 1968, Alfred P. Sloan Found. fellow, 1972, H.I. Romnes fellow, 1976; Humboldt Sr. Rsch. fellow, 1992; grantee fed. agys. and industry. Fellow Am. Phys. Soc. (D. Adler award 1994, Davisson-Germer prize 1995), Australian Inst. Physics, Am. Vacuum Soc. (program and exec. coms. 1974-79, M.W. Welch prize 1991, trustee 1995—); mem. AAAS, Am. Soc. Metals Internat., Am. Chem. Soc. (colloid and surface chemistry divsn.), Materials Rsch. Soc. (medal 1994). Home: 5110 Juneau Rd Madison WI 53705-4744 Office: U Wis Materials Sci & Engring 1509 University Ave Madison WI 53706-1595

LAGAMMA, ROBERT RONALD, diplomat; b. N.Y.C., July 30, 1939; s. Frank and Rose (DiBennedetto) LaG.; m. Anita Vitacolonna, Sept. 16, 1963; children: Alisa, Matthew, Therese, Adrian, Florence. BA, Bklyn. Coll., 1961; MA, Boston U., 1971. With U.S. Info. Agy., various locations, 1963-72; dep. dir. U.S. Info. Agy., Milan, Italy, 1972-76; cultural rep. U.S. Info. Agy., Florence, Italy, 1976-78; dir. U.S. Info. Agy., Lome, Togo, 1978-81, Dakar, Senegal, 1984-88, Lagos, Nigeria, 1988-91; edini. coord. for Africa U.S. Info. Agy., Washington, 1982-84, dep. dir. Office African Affairs, 1991-93, dir. Office African Affairs, 1993—; dir. U.S. Edn. Abroad program U. Calif., Santa Barbara, 1981-82. Mem. Am. Fgn. Svc. Assn. Roman Catholic. Home: 1937 Barton Hill Rd Reston VA 22091 Office: US Info Agy Office African Affairs 301 4th St SW Washington DC 20540

LAGARIAS, JOHN SAMUEL, engineering executive; b. Rochester, N.Y., July 4, 1921; s. Soterios Nicholas and Aspacia (Basil) L.; m. Virginia Jane Clark, June 16, 1947; children: Jeffrey, Peter, Clark. BS in Physics, Rensselaer Poly. Inst., 1948; postgrad., Oak Ridge Sch. Reactor Tech., 1955-56. Registered profl. engr., Md. Rsch. engr. Westinghouse Electric Rsch. Labs., Pitts., 1948-51; mgr. metal products rsch. Koppers Co., Pitts., 1951-63; mgr. R&D Am. Instrument Co., Silver Spring, Md., 1963-64; pres. Resources Rsch., Inc., Reston, Va., 1964-71; dir. environ. quality Kaiser Engrs., Oakland, Calif., 1971-84; pres. Lagarias Assocs., Moraga, 1984—; lectr. civil engring. dept. U. Md., 1970-71; mem. tech. adv. com. Washington Coun. Govts., 1968-70, Commonwealth of Va., 1969-71; conf. chmn. 2d Internat. Clean Air Congress, Washington, 1970; bd. mem. Calif. Air Resources Bd., 1985—. Contbr. articles to profl. jours.; patentee electrostatic precipitators, analytical instruments and indsl. gas cleaning equipment. Planning commr. City of Moraga, Calif., 1975-82; mem. Calif. Air Resources Bd., 1986—. With AUS, 1943-46. Fellow Air Pollution Control Assn. (pres. 1968-69), Internat. Soc. for Electrostatic Precipitation (bd. dirs. 1984); mem. IEEE (sr. life), Am. Acad. Environ. Engrs. (diplomate). Home: 276 Donald Dr Moraga CA 94556-2310 Office: 2020 L St Sacramento CA 95814-4219

LAGER, HENRY S., transporation executive; b. 1942. BS in Bus. Adminstrn., U. Pa. Corp. dir. of compensation and benefits Eastern Airlines, 1967-77; v.p. personnel, group v.p. dental products co. Johnson & Johnson, 1977-88; v.p. personnel Pullman Co., Livingston, N.J., 1988-90, sr. v.p. human resources, 1990—. Office: The Pullman Co 3 Werner Way # 200 Lebanon NJ 08833-2223

LAGER, ROBERT JOHN, state agency administrator; b. Fairhope, Ala., Aug. 19, 1934; s. Edward Glen and Dorothy (Niemeyer) L. AB, Syracuse U., 1957; PhD, Georgetown U., 1970. Asst. prof. Russian Georgetown U., Washington, 1965-71; chmn. dept. Russian, 1971-78; exec. asst. Gov. Fob James, Montgomery, Ala., 1978-80; dir. Ctr. for Internat. Trade, Mobile, Ala., 1980—; exec. dir. Ala. Fgn. Trade Commn., Mobile, 1983—; dir. Coun. on Internat. Edn. Exchange, N.Y.C., 1969-78; Presdl. appointment to Ala. Export Coun.; cons. U.S. Dept. State, Voice of Am., Washington, 1969-78, Am. Coun. on Edn., Washington, 1975-78; adj. assoc. prof. Russian and Latin, U. South Ala., 1983—. Contbr. articles on Russian lang. and lit. to profl. jours. Trustee Ala. Inst. for Deaf and Blind, Talladega, 1979-86; mem. So. Growth Policies Bd.; bd. dirs. Mobile United. Served with USAF, 1956-60. Fellow Internat. Bus. Fellows; mem. Ala. World Trade Assn. (exec. dir. 1984-91), So. Ctr. for Internat. Studies (trustee 1986-95), Mobile Area C. of C. (cons. leadership program 1985, chmn. task force), Japan-U.S. Soc. Ala. (exec. com. 1989-93), Propeller Club, Phi Beta Kappa. Democrat. Roman Catholic. Avocations: sailing, tennis, reading, antique cars. Office: Ala Fgn Trade Commn 250 N Water St Rm 131 Mobile AL 36602-4091

LAGERFELD, KARL OTTO, fashion designer; b. Hamburg, Fed. Republic Germany, Sept. 10, 1938. Student, Lycee Montaigne, Paris. Owner Karl Lagerfeld Co., Biderman Industries, N.Y.C., 1984—; Karl Lagerfeld Co., Paris, 1984—; tchr. fashion U. Applied Art, Vienna, Austria. Fashion stylist (with Pierre Balmain), Paris, 1954-58, art mgr. (with Jean Patou), Paris, 1958-63, free-lance designer (with fashion houses including), Fendi, Rome, 1964-83, Chloe, Paris, 1964-83, Chanel, Paris, 1982—; designer Karl Lagerfeld Women's Wear, Inc., Karl Lagerfeld France, Inc., Paris, 1983—; producer perfume fragrances including, Chloe, Lagerfeld for Men, K.L. Decorated Bundesverdienst Kreuz (Fed. Republic Germany); recipient Golden Spinning Wheel Krefeld, 1980, Neiman-Marcus award, 1980, Munich Fashion Prize. Office: Karl Lagerfeld Co, 144 Champs Elysees, F-75008 Paris France

LAGIN, NEIL, property management executive; b. Bronx, N.Y., Jan. 10, 1942; s. Barney and Helen (Goldberg) L. Buyer Alexanders, N.Y.C., 1961-69; sales mgr. Halldon, Ltd., N.Y.C., 1969-79; mgr., ptnr. in concession Michele Craig, Westbury, N.Y., 1979-85; ptnr. ALW Trading, "9", N.Y.C., 1985-87; owner, operator Accent Foliage, Delray Beach, Fla., 1987-89; pres. Neil Lagin Property Mgmt., Neil's Landscape Svc., Boca Raton, Fla., 1988—. Author poetry; exhibitor photography shows, Ward Nasse Gallery-Salon, 1975-79, Timothy Blackburn Gallery, 1978, Washington Art Show and others. Notary pub., Fla., 1990; mem. nursery adv. bd. Habilitation Ctr.

for the Handicapped, Boca Raton, 1991—; mem. overall adv. com. Palm Beach County Ext., 1993—, sec., chair program rev. com.; bd. dirs. Greater Palm Beach Area Alzheimers Assn., 1993; mem. Environ. Resource Landscape Team; mem. Boca Raton Postal Customer Adv. Coun., 1994-96. Named Fla. Master Gardener, Inst. Food and Agrl. Scis., U. Fla., 1989, Best Landscaper in Boca Raton, South Fla. Newspaper Network, 1991, Best Local Vol. in Boca Raton, 1994. Mem. Internat. Palm Soc. (Palm Beach chpt.), Rare Fruit Coun. Internat. (Palm Beach chpt.), Boca Raton C. of C. (grad. leadership program 1991), Boca Raton Postal Customer Adv. Coun. Home and Office: 17730 Maplewood Dr Boca Raton FL 33487-2171

LAGO, MARY MCCLELLAND, English language educator, author; b. Pitts., Nov. 4, 1919; d. Clark Russell and Olive Arabella (Malone) McClelland; m. Gladwyn Vaile Lago, Mar. 4, 1944; children: Jane Hazel, Donald Russell. BA, Bucknell U., 1940; MA, U. Mo., 1965, PhD, 1969; DLitt (hon.), Bucknell U., 1981. Editorial asst. Friendship Press, N.Y.C., 1941-43, Congl. Ch. Nat. Hdqrs., N.Y.C., 1944-47; teaching asst. U. Mo., Columbia, 1964-70, lectr. English, 1971-77, assoc. prof., 1977-79, prof. English, 1979-88, Catherine Paine Middlebush prof. of English, 1988-89, prof. emeritus, 1990—; mem. dean's adv. com. Bucknell U., Lewisburg, Pa., 1979-81; hon. vis. prof. U. Manchester, 1985-86; vis. fellow St. Edmund's House, Cambridge U., 1982-83, vis. Bye-Fellow Selwyn Coll., 1991-92. Editor: Imperfect Encounter, 1972, (with K. Beckson) Max and Will, 1975, Rothenstein, Men and Memories, 1978, Burne-Jones Talking, 1980, Forster Number, Twentieth Century Literature, 1985 (with P.N. Furbank) Selected Letters of E.M. Forster, 2 vols., 1984, 85, (with Ronald Warwick) Perspectives in Time, 1989; author: Rabindranath Tagore, 1976, E.M. Forster: A Literary Life, 1994; mem. editorial bd.: Twentieth Century Lit., 1979—; translator (with Supriya Bari) The Broken Nest (Tagore), 1971; translator (with Krishna Dutta) Tagore Selected Stories, 1991; contbr. articles and revs. to mags. Convener community adv. bd. NPR/Sta. KBIA-FM, U. Mo., Columbia, 1979-88. Recipient Disting. Faculty award, Arts and Sci. Disting. Alumna award; rsch. grantee Am. Philos. Soc., 1966, 67, 72, NEH, 1980-83, Am. Coun. Learned Socs.; recipient summer rsch. stipend NEH, 1976. Mem. MLA, Soc. Authors (London), Univ. Women's Club (London), Phi Beta Kappa. Home: 13 Springer Dr Columbia MO 65201-5424 Office: U Mo Dept English 107 Tate Hall Columbia MO 65211

LAGORIA, GEORGIANNA MARIE, curator, writer, editor, visual art consultant; b. Oakland, Calif., Nov. 3, 1953; d. Charles Wilson and Margaret Claire (Vella) L.; m. David Joseph de la Torre, May 15, 1982; 1 child, Mateo Joseph. BA in Philosophy, Santa Clara U., 1975; MA in Museology, U. San Francisco, 1978. Exhbn. coordinator Allrich Gallery, San Francisco, 1977-78; asst. registrar Fine Arts Mus., San Francisco, 1978-79; gallery coordinator de Saisset Mus., Santa Clara, Calif., 1979-80, asst. dir., 1980-83, dir., 1983-86; dir. Palo Alto (Calif.) Cultural Ctr., 1986-91; ind. writer, editor and cons. mus. and visual arts orgns., Hawaii, 1991-95; dir. The Contemporary Mus., Honolulu, 1995—; V.p. Non-Profit Gallery Assn., San Francisco, 1980-82; bd. dirs. Fiberworks, Berkeley, Calif., 1981-85; field reviewer Inst. Mus. Services, Washington, 1985-87; adv. bd. Hearst Art Gallery, Moraga, Calif., 1986-89, Womens Caucus for Art, San Francisco, 1987—; mem. adv. bd. Weigand Art Gallery, Notre Dame Coll., Belmont, Calif. Curator exhbns. The Candy Store Gallery, 1980, Fiber '81, 1981; curator, author exhbn. catalogue Contemporary Hand Colored Photographs, 1981, Northern Calif. Art of the Sixties, 1982, The Artist and the Machine: 1910-1940, 1986; author catalogue, guide Persis Collection of Contemporary Art at Honolulu Advertiser, 1993; co-author: The Little Hawaiian Cookbook, 1994; coord. exhbn. selections Laila and Thurston Twigg-Smith Collection and Toshiko Takaezu ceramics for Hui No'eau Visual Arts Ctr., Maui, 1993; editor Nuhou (newsletter Hawaii State Mus. Assn.), 1991—; spl. exhbn. coord. Honolulu Acad. Arts, 1995. Mem. Arts Adv. Alliance, Santa Clara County, 1985-86; grant panelist Santa Clara County Arts Council, 1987. Exhbn. grantee Ahmanson Found., 1981, NEA, 1984, Calif. Arts Coun., 1985-89. Mem. Am. Assn. Mus., ArtTable, 1983—, Calif. Assn. Mus. (bd. dirs. 1987-89), Hawaiian Craftsmen (bd. dirs. 1994—), Honolulu Jr. League, Key Project (bd. dirs. 1993-94). Democrat. Roman Catholic. Avocations: dance, fiction writing. Home and Office: 47-665 Mapele Rd Kaneohe HI 96744

LAGOS, GEORGE PETER, lawyer; b. Concord, N.H., Oct. 23, 1954; s. Peter and Mary G. (Ahern) L.; m. Kathy Jean Bieniek, Nov. 21, 1981; children: Peter John, Andrew George, Stephen Charles. BA in History and Philosophy, Keene State Coll., 1976; JD, Franklin Pierce Law Sch., 1981. Bar: N.H. 1981, U.S. Dist. Ct. N.H. 1981, Mass. 1982. Counsel N.H. Ins. Group, Manchester, 1981-84, v.p., gen. counsel, sec., 1984-93; v.p., gen. counsel N.Am. Splty. Ins. Co., 1993, sr. v.p., gen. counsel, 1994—; pres., CEO Syndicated Svcs. Co., Inc., 1994—; adj. prof. U. N.H., 1986-87. Mem. ABA, N.H. Bar Assn., Manchester Bar Assn., Chartered Property Casualty Underwriters, N.H. Assn. Domestic Ins. Cos. (pres. 1985-87), N.H. Guaranty Assn., Fedn. Ins. and Corp. Counsel, N.H. Tennis Assn. (pres. 1985).

LAGOWSKI, BARBARA JEAN, writer, book editor; b. Adams, Mass., Nov. 9, 1955; d. Frances and Jeannette (Wanat) L.; m. Richard Dietrich Mumma III, Oct. 11, 1980; 1 child, Adam Dietrich. BA, U. South Fla., 1977; MA, Johns Hopkins U., 1978. Asst. editor Fred Jordan Books Grossett and Dunlap Pubs., N.Y.C., 1978-80; mng. editor Methuen Inc., N.Y.C., 1980-81; mng. assoc., sr. editor Bobb-Merrill Co. Inc., N.Y.C., 1981-84; editor New Am. Libr., N.Y.C., 1984-85; poet-in-the-schs. Hillsborough County Arts Council, Tampa, Fla., 1976-77; poet-in-residence Cloisters Children's Mus., Balt., 1977-78. Author: Silver Skates series, 1988-89; co-author: Good Spirits, 1986, Teen Terminators, 1989, How to Get the Best Public School Education for Your Child, 1991, The Sports Curmudgeon, 1993, How to Attract Anyone, Anytime, Anyplace, 1993. Mem. Authors Guild, Phi Kappa Phi. Home: 442 Dewey St Long Branch NJ 07740-5915

LAGOWSKI, J(OSEPH) J(OHN), chemist; b. Chgo., June 8, 1930; s. Joseph Thomas and Helen (Kasprzyczak) L.; m. Jeanne Wecker Mund, Feb. 13, 1954. B.S., U. Ill., 1952; M.S., U. Mich., 1954; Ph.D., Mich. State U., 1957; Ph.D. (Marshall scholar), Cambridge (Eng.) U., 1959. Asst. demonstrator and supr. in inorganic chemistry Cambridge U., 1958-59; asst. prof. chemistry U. Tex., Austin, 1959-63; assoc. prof. U. Tex., 1963-67, prof. chemistry and edn., 1967—, Piper prof., 1981. Author: (with G.W. Watt and L.F. Hatch) Chemistry, 1974, Chemistry in the Laboratory, 1964, The Structure of Atoms, 1964, The Chemical Bond, 1966, Modern Inorganic Chemistry, 1973; editor: Jour. Chem. Edn, 1979—. Recipient award Chem. Mfrs. Assn., 1981, Am. Chem. Soc. award in Chem. Edn., 1989. Fellow AAAS; mem. Am. Chem. Soc. (Union Carbide Corp. Chem. Edn. award 1989), Chem. Soc. (London), AAAS, Sigma Xi, Phi Lambda Upsilon. Office: U Tex Dept Chemistry Austin TX 78712

LAGRANGE, CLAIRE MAE, special education educator; b. Tarkio, Mo., Oct. 11, 1937; d. Floyd Gerald and Phyllis Geneva (Wilson) McElfish; m. Irving Joseph LaGrange, May 20, 1955; children: Raymond, Robert, Rhonda, Roger. BA, U. Southwestern La., 1983; MEd, Northwestern State U., 1990. Cert. English spl. edn., K-12 mild and moderate, assessment tchr., spl. edn., La. Tchr.'s aide St. Martin Parish Sch. Bd., Cecilia, La., 1979-82; tchr. English Florien (La.) High Sch., 1984-86; tchr. Zwolle (La.) High Sch., 1986-90, Cecilia Jr. High Sch., 1990-92, Cecilia High Sch., 1992—. Den mother Cub Scouts-Boy Scouts Am. Spokane, Wash., 1967-69; Sunday sch. tchr. First Friends Ch., Spokane, 1968-69. Fellow U. S.W. La Alumni Assn., Northwestern State U. Alumni Assn.; mem. ASCD, Coun. Exceptional Children, Nat. Educators Am., Nat. English Honor Soc., Internat. Reading Assn., La. Assn. Educators, La. Ednl. Assessment Tchrs. Assns., La. Reading Assn., St. Martin Assn. Educators. Avocations: sketching, reading, writing, crossword puzzles, camping. Home: 1052 Charles Marks Rd Arnaudville LA 70512-3820

LAGRONE, ALFRED HALL, electrical engineering educator; b. DeBerry, Tex., Sept. 25, 1912; s. William Taylor and Lena Enola (Westmoreland) LaG.; m. Dixie Louise Ballard, Sept. 8, 1955; children: Carrie Sue, Howard Tracy, Kimberly. B.S. in Elec. Engring, U. Tex., Austin, 1938, M.S., 1948, Ph.D., 1954. Distbn. engr. San Antonio Pub. Service Co., 1938-42; research engr. U. Tex., Austin, 1946-54; assoc. prof. U. Tex., 1954-60, prof., 1960-92, prof. emeritus, 1992—, dir. antennas and propagation lab., 1966—; Cons. ABC, Collins Radio Co., Honeywell, Inc., Tex. Nuclear Co.; chmn. U.S.

Commn. F of Union Radio-Scientifique Internationale, 1975—. Served to capt. USNR, 1942-46. Recipient Scott Helt Meml. award I.R.E., 1960. Fellow I.E.E.E. (nat. chmn. fellow com.); mem. Sigma Xi, Eta Kappa Nu, Tau Beta Pi. Home: 3925 Sierra Dr Austin TX 78731-3911

LAGUEUX, RONALD RENE, federal judge; b. Lewiston, Maine, June 30, 1931; s. Arthur Charles and Laurette Irene (Turcotte) L.; m. Denise Rosemarie Boudreau, June 30, 1956; children: Michelle Simone, Gregory Charles, Barrett James. AB, Bowdoin Coll., 1953; LLB, Harvard U., 1956. Assoc. then ptnr. Edwards and Angell Law Firm, Providence, R.I., 1956-68; assoc. justice Superior Ct. State of R.I., Providence, 1968-86; judge U.S. Dist. Ct., Providence, 1986—; exec. counsel to Gov. Chafee, R.I., 1963-65. Rep. candidate for U.S. Senate, 1964; corporator R.I. Hosp., Providence, 1965—; solicitor Southeastern New Eng. Province United Way, 1957-68. Mem. ABA, Bowdoin Coll. Alumni Council (past v.p., pres.), Am.-French Geneal. Soc. Home: 90 Greenwood Ave Rumford RI 02916-1934 Office: US Dist Ct Kennedy Plaza 214B US Courthouse Providence RI 02903

LAGUNOFF, DAVID, physician, educator; b. N.Y.C., Mar. 14, 1932; s. Robert and Cicele (Lipman) L.; m. Susan P. Powers, Mar. 8, 1958; children—Rachel, Liza, Michael. MD, U. Chgo., 1957. Rsch. asst. microbiology U. Miami, Coral Gables, Fla., 1951-53; intern U. Calif. San Francisco Hosp., 1957-58; postdoctoral fellow dept. pathology U. Wash., Seattle, 1958-59, trainee in pathology, 1959-60, instr. pathology, 1960-62, asst. prof., 1962-65, assoc. prof., 1965-69, prof., 1969-79; prof. dept. pathology St. Louis U., 1979—, chmn. dept. pathology, 1979-89, 91-95, asst. v.p., 1989-93; assoc. dean rsch. St. Louis U. Sch. Medicine, 1989-95. Nat. Heart Inst. fellow Carlsberg Laboratorium, Copenhagen, 1962-64, Nat. Cancer Inst. fellow Sir William Dunn Sch. Pathology, Oxford, Eng., 1970. Mem. AAAS, AAUP, Am. Soc. Cell Biology, Am. Assn. Pathologists, Assn. Pathology Chmn., Am. Assn. Immunologists. Office: St Louis Univ Sch Medicine Dept Pathology 1402 S Grand Blvd Saint Louis MO 63104

LAHAY, DAVID GEORGE MICHAEL, ballet company director; b. Barrie, Ont., Can., July 15, 1949; s. George Anthony and Edna Alice (Silverberg) LaH. B.A., Trent U., Peterborough, Ont., 1971; B.F.A. with honors, York U., Toronto, 1973. Prin. dancer Les Grands Ballets Canadiens, Montreal, 1978-87, asst. ballet master, 1987-91; prin. dancer Atlanta Ballet, 1978; ballet master Ottawa Ballet, 1991. Choreographer Canadian Heritage Festival, 1989, 90, 91. Can. Council grantee, 1973, 75, 78. Office: Alberta Ballet Nat Christie Ctr, 141 18th Ave, Calgary, AB Canada T2S 0B8

LAHEY, JOHN H., lawyer; b. Cleve., June 25, 1946. BS, Miami U., 1968; JD, Ohio State U., 1971. Bar: Ohio 1972. Ptnr. Jones, Day, Reavis & Pogue, Columbus, Ohio; adj. prof. law Capital Univ., 1980-83. Office: Jones Day Reavis & Pogue 1900 Huntington Ctr Columbus OH 43215

LAHEY, RICHARD THOMAS, JR., nuclear engineer, fluid mechanics engineer; b. St. Petersburg, Fla., Feb. 20, 1939; married, 1961; 3 children. BS, U.S. Merchant Marine Acad., 1960; MS, Rensselaer Polytechnic Inst., 1964; ME, Columbia U., 1966; PhD in Mechanical Engring., Stanford U., 1971. Engr. Knolls Atomic Power Lab., 1961-64; rsch. assoc. Columbia U., 1964-66; mgr. core & safety devel. nuclear energy divsn. Gen. Electric, 1966-75; chmn. dept. nuclear engring. Rensselaer Polytechnic Inst., Troy, N.Y., 1975-87, prof. nuclear engring. and engring. physics, 1987-89, prof. dept. chem. engring., 1987-89, Edward E. Hood, Jr. prof. engring., 1989—, dir. ctr. multiphase rsch., 1991—; mem. sci. adv. com. EG&G Idaho, Inc., 1976—; mem. Advanced Code Rev. Group & LOFT Rev. Group U.S. Nuclear Regulatory Commn., 1976—; commr. Engring. Manpower Commn., 1981—; pres. R.T. Lahey, Inc., 1981-83; adj. prof. U. Pisa, Italy and Claude Bernard U., France, 1987; Alexander von Humbolt, Sr. scientistfellow, 1994-95. Editor: Jour. Nuclear Engring. & Design, 1983—. Recipient Arthur Holly Compton award, 1989, Glenn T. Seaborg medal, 1992, E.O. Lawrence Meml. award U.S. Dept. Energy, 1988; Fulbright fellow Magdalen Coll., Oxford U., 1983-84. Fellow Am. Nuclear Soc. (Tech. Achievement award 1985), N.Y. Acad. Scis., Am. Soc. Engring. Edn. (Glen Murphy award 1985), Am. Soc. Mech. Engrs., Am. Inst. Chem. Engrs., Sigma Xi; mem. NAS. Research in two-phase flow and boiling heat transfer technology; nuclear reactor thermal-hydraulics and safety. Office: Rensselaer Poly Inst Dept Nuclear Engring & Physics 110 8th St Troy NY 12181-3522*

LAHOOD, RAY, congressman; b. Ill., Dec. 6, 1945; m. Kathleen (Kathy) Dunk LaHood; children: Darin, Amy, Sam, Sara. Student, Canton Jr. Coll., Ill.; BS in Edn. and Sociology, Bradley U., 1971. Tchr. Catholic and pub. jr. high schs., 1971-77; dist. administrv. asst. to congressman Tom Railsback, 1977; mem. Ill. Ho. of Reps., 1982; Chief of Staff Ho. of Reps.; mem. 104th Congress from 18th Ill. dist., 1995—; Mem. Agriculture Com., Transp. and Infrastructure Com. Bd. dirs. Economic Devel. Coun.; pres. sch. bd. Spalding and Notre Dame H.Schs., Bradley U. Nat. Alumni Bd.; svc. to Children's Hosp. Bd., Peoria Area Retarded Citizens Bd.; dir. Rock Island County Youth Svcs. Bur. Mem. ITOO Soc., Downtown Rotary Club, Holy Family Ch. (Peoria), Peoria Area C. of C. Roman Catholic. Office: US House Reps 2112 Rayburn House Office Bldg Washington DC 20515-1318 Office: US Rep Ray LaHood 100 NE Monroe Ste 100 Peoria IL 61602*

LAHOURCADE, JOHN BROSIUS, service company executive; b. San Antonio, Tex., Nov. 18, 1924; s. Frederic Eugene and Hildagarde (Brosius) L.; m. Mary Lou Williamson, Sept. 6, 1947; children: Lynne Breuer, Lee A., Lance. BBA, U. Tex., 1948. CPA, Tex. Staff acct. Stanolind Oil & Gas Co., Brownfield, Tex., 1948-51, Carneiro Chumney CPA's, San Antonio, 1951-55; ptnr. Bielstein, Lahourcade & Lewis CPA's, San Antonio, 1955-69; v.p. Luby's Cafeterias Inc., San Antonio, 1969-74, sr. v.p. fin., 1974-79, exec. v.p., 1979-82, pres., chief exec. officer, 1982-88, chmn., chief exec. officer, 1988-90, chmn. bd. dirs., 1990—; bd. dirs. First RepublicBank San Antonio, 1982-88. Trustee S.W. Tex. Meth. Hosp., San Antonio, 1974-83; adv. council U. Tex. Sch. Bus. Adminstrn. Found., Austin, 1986-89; bd. dirs. San Antonio Econ. Devel. Found., 1984-95. Mem. Tex. Soc. CPA's (bd. dirs. 1965-68), San Antonio CPA's (pres. 1964). Office: Luby's Cafeterias Inc PO Box 33069 San Antonio TX 78265-3069

LAHR, CHARLES DWIGHT, mathematics educator, college dean; b. Phila., Feb. 6, 1945; s. Charles and Helen L.; m. Dora (div.); children: Elena, Maria, Emilio; m. Beatriz Pastor, Conia, Katerina. A.B., Temple U., 1966; M.A., Syracuse U., 1968, Ph.D., 1971. Assoc. prof. math. Dartmouth Coll., Hanover, N.H., 1979-84, prof. math. and computer sci., 1984—, assoc. dean scis., dean grad. studies, 1981-84, dean of faculty, 1984-89; cons. Alfred P. Sloan Found., 1983-90; reviewer Math. Revs.; project dir. Fund for the Improvement of Post-Secondary Edn., Washington, 1982-85. Sloan Found. grantee, 1983, Fund for Improvement Postsecondary Edn. grantee, 1982. Mem. Am. Math. Soc., Math. Assn. Am., AAAS. Office: Dartmouth College 6188 Bradley Hanover NH 03755

LAHR, JACK LEROY, lawyer; b. Toledo, Aug. 5, 1934; s. Clarence L. and Josephine E. (Rosenbrook) L.; m. Greta Mars, Dec. 17, 1955 (div. 1987); children: Ellen, Julie; m. Joanna Rashon Hanes, Aug. 8, 1992. BS in Mech. Engring., U. Toledo, 1956; JD with honors, George Washington U., 1963. Bar: Va. 1963, DC 1963. Ptnr. Arent, Fox, Kintner, Plotkin & Kahn, 1971-80; ptnr. Foley & Lardner, Washington, 1980—; adj. prof. Georgetown U. Law Ctr., Washington, 1980-83. Author: (with E. Kintner) An Intellectual Property Law Primer, 2d edit., 1982. Served with USN, 1956-59. Mem. ABA (council adminstrv. law sect. 1971-74, chmn. administrv. law judges com. 1974-80), Order of Coif. Office: Foley & Lardner 3000 K St NW Washington DC 20007-5109

LAHR, JOHN, author; b. Los Angeles, July 12, 1941; s. Bert and Mildred (Schroeder) L.; m. Anthea Mander, Aug. 12, 1965; children: Christopher, David, James Anthony and Nicholas Dodds (twins) (dec.). B.A., Yale, 1963, Worcester Coll., Oxford, 1965; M.A., Worcester Coll., Oxford. Drama critic Manhattan East, 1966-68, New York Free Press, 1968-70, Evergreen Rev., 1968-71, Village Voice, 1969-72, The Nation, 1981-82, British Vogue, 1986-92, The New Yorker, 1992—; contbg. editor Harper's, 1979-83; lit. adviser Tyrone Guthrie Theatre, Mpls., 1968; lit. mgr. Repertory Theatre of Lincoln Center, 1969-71. Author: Notes on a Cowardly Lion: The Biography of Bert Lahr, 1969, Up Against the Fourth Wall, 1970, The Autograph Hound, 1973, Astonish Me, 1973, (with Jonathan Price) Life-

Show, 1973, Hot to Trot, 1974, Prick Up Your Ears: The Biography of Joe Orton, 1978 (Gay News lit. prize 1979), Coward: the Playwright, 1983, Automatic Vaudeville, 1984, (play) Diary of a Somebody, 1989, Dame Edna Everage and the Rise of Western Civilization: Backstage with Barry Humphries, 1991 (Roger Machell prize 1992); Editor: (with Anthea Lahr) Casebook on Harold Pinter's The Homecoming, 1969, The Complete Plays of Joe Orton, 1976, The Orton Diaries, 1987; co-producer: (film) Prick Up Your Ears, 1987. Mem. Rockefeller Theatre panel, 1969-73, Nat. Endowment for the Arts, 1969-73, Theatre Devel. Fund, 1970-73; Bd. dirs Choreoconcerts, 1966—. Recipient George Jean Nathan award for drama criticism, 1969; ASCAP-Deems Taylor award, 1980, 81. Mem. P.E.N. (dir.). Address: 11A Chalcot Gardens, London NW3 4YB, England

LAHTI, CHRISTINE, actress; b. Detroit, Apr. 5, 1950; d. Paul Theodore and Elizabeth Margaret (Tabar) L.; m. Thomas Schlamme, Sept. 4, 1983; 1 child, Wilson Lahti. BA in Speech, U. Mich., 1972; postgrad., Fla. State U., 1972-73; studies with William Esper, Uta Hagen, Herbert Berghof Studios. Actress: (stage prodns.) The Woods, 1978 (Theater World award 1979), Division Street, 1980, Loose Ends, 1981, Present Laughter, 1983, Landscape of the Body, 1984, The Country Girl, 1984, Cat on a Hot Tin Roof, 1985, Little Murders, 1987, The Heidi Chronicles, 1989, Three Hotels, 1993; regular mem. cast (TV series) Dr. Scorpion, 1978, The Harvey Korman Show, 1978, (TV films) The Last Tenant, 1978, The Henderson Monster, 1980, The Executioner's Song, 1982, Single Bars, Single Women, 1984, Love Lives On, 1985, Amerika, 1987, No Place Like Home, 1989, Crazy from the Heart, 1991, The Fear Inside, 1992, The Good Fight, 1985 (feature films) And Justice For All, 1979, Whose Life Is It, Anyway?, 1981, Swing Shift, 1984 (N.Y. Film Critics Circle award for best supporting actress 1985, Acad. award nomination 1985), Golden Globe award nomination 1985), Ladies and Gentlemen: The Fabulous Stains, 1985, Just Between Friends, 1986, Housekeeping, 1987, Season of Dreams, 1987, Stacking, 1988, Running on Empty, 1988, Gross Anatomy, 1989, Miss Firecracker, 1989, Funny About Love, 1990, The Doctor, 1991, Leaving Normal, 1992, Hideaway, 1995. Recipient Golden Globe award for Best Actress in a Miniseries or Motion picture Made for TV. Office: ICM 8942 Beverly Blvd Los Angeles CA 90048*

LAHTI, RICHARD, quality improvement administrator; b. East Chicago, Ind., May 16, 1943; s. Ivar John and Fannie (Panezich) L.; m. Margaret Alethe Dickson, Jan. 24, 1972; children: Sarah, Tom, David, Mari, Susan, John. Student, St. Joseph's Coll., 1969-70. Payroll analyst The Boeing Co., Seattle, 1964-69; mgr. Pare Inc., Madison, Wis., 1969-72; prodn. planner Revlon Co., Phoenix, 1973-78; mgr. The Boeing Co., Wichita, Kans., 1980—. With U.S. Army, 1961-64. Democrat. Congregationalist. Home: 6428 Rodeo St Wichita KS 67226-1414

LAHVIS, SYLVIA LEISTYNA, art historian, educator, curator; b. Ilion, N.Y., Dec. 6, 1936; d. Arthur Leistyna and Margareta Maresch; m. W. Frederick Lahvis, Nov. 12, 1960; children: Garet Paul, Matthew Arthur. BA, U. Rochester, 1958; MA, Oberlin Coll., 1972; PhD, U. Del., 1990. Curatorial asst. Yale U. Art Gallery, New Haven; curator New Milford (Conn.) Hist. Soc., 1975-78; co-curator Univ. Gallery U. Del., Newark, 1985; curatorial dir. The Sewell C. Biggs Mus. Am. Art, Dover, Del., 1993—; lectr. edn. dept. Albright-Knox Art Gallery, Buffalo; lectr. art history Wykeham Rise Sch., Washington, Conn.; instr. Canterbury Sch., New Milford; adj. prof. U. Del., 1986-87, Rutgers U., Camden, 1988, 91-92, dept. art history U. Del., 1989, Coll. Human Resources, 1988-89, adj. prof. dept. art history, 1989—, Master of Arts in Liberal Studies program, 1992—, U. Del; curator Index of Am. Sculpture, 1982-86, symposium com., 1985, student adv. com. art history dept., 1982-84; vis. asst. prof. Washington U., Chestertown, Md., 1989; presenter in field. Contbr. articles to art jours. Interpace and Clevepak Corp. fellow U. Del.; Henry Luce Found. grantee. Mem. Coll. Art Assn., Assn. Am. Mus., Soc. Archtl. Historians, Decorative Arts Soc., Nat. Trust for Hist. Preservation, Archives of Am. Art, Phi Kappa Phi, Phi Beta Kappa. Democrat. Mem. Unitarian Ch. Avocations: singing, designing. Home: 601 Wynyard Rd Wilmington DE 19803-2219 Office: Sewell C Briggs Mus Federal St Dover DE 19901

LAI, HIM MARK, writer; b. San Francisco, Nov. 1, 1925; s. Mark Bing and Hing Mui (Dong) L.; m. Laura Jung, June 12, 1953. AA, San Francisco Jr. Coll., 1945; BS in Engring., U. Calif., Berkeley, 1947. Mech. engr. Utilities Engring. Bur., San Francisco, 1948-51, Bechtel Corp., San Francisco, 1953-84; lectr. Chinese Am. history San Francisco State U., 1969, 72-75, U. Calif., Berkeley, 1978-79, 84; researcher, writer on Chinese Am. history San Francisco, 1967—; dir. Chinese of America 1785-1980 Exhbn. Chinese Cultural Found. San Francisco, 1979-80; mem. adv. bd. Chinese Am. Women's Project, 1981-83; coord. Chinese Am. In Search of Roots Program, 1991—; cons. proposed El Pueblo de L.A. State Hist. Park Chinese Am. Mus., 1987, 89, 93, Asian Am. Studies Program Chinese Materials Rsch. Collection, U. Calif., Berkeley, 1986-88; adj. prof. Asian Am. studies dept. San Francisco State U., 1990—; coord. Chinese Cmty. Hour, Cantonese radio program, 1971-84. Co-author: Chinese of America, 1785-1980: Exhibition Catalog, 1980, Island: Poetry and History of Chinese Immigrants on Angel Island, 1910-1940, 1980; author: A History Reclaimed: An Annotated Bibliography and Guide of Chinese Language Materials on the Chinese of America, 1986, From Overseas Chinese to Chinese American: History of Development of Chinese American Society During the Twentieth Century, 1992; assoc. editor: A History of the Chinese in California, A Syllabus, 1969; co-editor: Collected Works of Gilbert Woo, 1991; mem. editl. bd. Amerasia Journal, 1979—, Chinese America: History and Perspectives, 1986—; contbr. articles to profl. jours. Mem. Chinese Hist. Soc. Am. (pres. 1971, 76, 77, bd. dirs 1972-81, 84, 85-91, 93—), Chinese Culture Found. San Francisco (bd. dirs. 1975-85, 87-94, pres. 1982, bd. chairperson 1983, 84, 85, 93). Home: 357 Union St San Francisco CA 94133-3519

LAI, W(EI) MICHAEL, mechanical engineer, educator; b. Amoy, Fukien, China, Nov. 29, 1930; naturalized U.S. citizen, 1967; s. Chia-pan and Shue-Chin (Lo) L.; m. Linda Yu-ling Chu, Dec. 21, 1963; children: David, Michelle. BSCE, Nat. Taiwan U., 1953; MS in Engring. Mech., U. Mich., 1959, PhD, 1962. Asst. prof. mechanics Rensselaer Poly. Inst., Troy, N.Y. 1961-66, assoc. prof., 1967-77, prof., 1978-87, acting dept. chmn., 1986-87; prof. mech. engring. and orthopaedic bioengring. Columbia U., N.Y.C., 1987—. Author: Elements of Elasticity, 1965, Introduction to Continuum Mechanics, 1974, 3rd edit., 1993. Fellow ASME (Melville medal for Best Paper 1982, Best Paper award bioengring. divsn. 1991), Am. Inst. Med. and Biol. Engring.; mem. AAAS, Am. Soc. Biomechanics, Orthopaedic Rsch. Soc. Home: Apt 9H 215 W 95th St New York NY 10025-6340 Office: Columbia U Dept Mech Engring W 116th St New York NY 10027

LAIBINIS, PAUL EDWARD, chemical engineering educator; b. Wilkes-Barre, Pa., Dec. 8, 1963; s. Edward Bernard and Helen Jean (Draminski) L. BSChemE, BS in Chemistry, MIT, 1985; MA in Chemistry, Harvard U., 1987, PhD in Chemistry, 1991. Teaching/rsch. asst. Harvard U., Cambridge, Mass., 1985-91; postdoctoral fellow Calif. Inst. Tech., Cambridge, 1991-93; asst. prof. MIT, Cambridge, 1993-94, Texaco-Mangelsdorf asst. prof., 1994—; corr. Sci.-by-Mail, 1993—. Mem. AAAS, AIChE, Am. Chem. Soc. (Victor K. Lamer award divsn. colloid and surface sci. 1994). Republican. Roman Catholic. Achievements include contributions to more than 30 sci. publs.; 1 patent in area of thin films and nanotechnology. Avocations: hiking, swimming, racket sports, film, theater. Home: Apt 1 56 Winslow Somerville MA 02144 Office: MIT Dept Chemical Engring Cambridge MA 02139

LAIBLE, JON MORSE, retired mathematics educator, dean; b. Bloomington, Ill., July 25, 1937; s. Russell James and Margaret (Herold) L.; m. Jo Ann Ivens, June 14, 1959; children: Kathy Jo, Kenneth Russell, Jackie Ann Laible Muhs, Michael Howard. Student, Carleton Coll., 1955-57; BS, U. Ill., 1959; MA, U. Minn., 1961; PhD, U. Ill., 1967. Asst. prof. Western Ill. U., Macomb, 1962-64; asst. prof., assoc. prof. then prof. math. Ill. U., Charleston, 1964-80, dean Coll. Liberal Arts and Scis., 1980-93, dean Coll. Scis., 1993-94; ret. 1994. Chmn. citizens cons. council Unit #1 Pub. Schs., Charleston, 1975-78; adv. com. Sarah Bush Lincoln Health Ctr., Charleston, 1986-86. Recipient Outstanding Faculty Merit award Ea. Ill. Univ., 1978, Univ. Svc. award, 1991. Mem. Math. Assn. Am. (bd. govs. 1977-80, chmn. com. vis. lectrs. and cons. 1980-88, Disting. Svc. award Ill. sect. 1985), Ill.

Sect. Math. Assn. Am. (chmn. 1975, 94), Ill. Coun. Tchrs. Math., Sigma Xi. Democrat. Avocation: photography.

LAIDIG, WILLIAM RUPERT, retired paper company executive; b. Sterling, Ill., Feb. 3, 1927; s. George and Margaret Anne (Gnewuch) L.; m. Lorraine Mae Grom, Jan. 2, 1952; children: Ann Marie, Mary Katherine, Margaret Anne, William Andrew. B.S.M.E., Marquette U., 1949. Registered profl. engr., Ga., Ala., Wis., Ark. Engr. Inland Steel Products, 1949-50; engr. Nekoosa Papers Inc., Port Edwards, Wis., 1950-62, mgr., 1962-66; mgr. Nekoosa Papers Inc., Ashdown, Ark., 1966-72; mill mgr. Nekoosa Papers Inc., Port Edwards, Wis., 1972-75; v.p.; resident mgr. Gt. So. Paper Co., Cedar Springs., Ga., 1975-80, sr. v.p.; 1978-80, pres., 1980-84; exec. v.p Gt. No. Nekoosa Corp., Stamford, Conn., 1980-84, pres., chief exec. officer, chmn., dir., 1984-90; chmn. Jaakko Pöyry (USA), Inc., Raleigh, N.C., 1991-92; ret. Pres. Village of Port Edwards, Wis., 1966-67; trustee Marquette U., Milw.; bd. dirs Tasman Chile Ltd., 1993. Lt. USN, 1952-53. Roman Catholic. Club: Dothan Country (Ala.); Silver Spring Country (Conn.); Eagle Creek Country (Fla.). Lodges: K.C; Elks. Home (winter): PO Box 39 Manitowish Waters WI 54545-0039 Home (summer): PO Box 39 Manitowish Waters WI 54545-0039

LAIDLAW, ANDREW R., lawyer; b. Durham, N.C., Aug. 28, 1946. BA, Northwestern U., 1969; JD, U. N.C. 1972. Bar: Ill. 1972. Mem. Seyfarth, Shaw, Fairweather & Geraldson, Chgo. Contbr. articles to profl. jours. Mem. ABA (antitrust and securities law coms. 1982—), Barristers. Office: Seyfarth Shaw Fairweather & Geraldson Mid Continental Plz 55 E Monroe St Chicago IL 60603

LAIDLAW, HARRY HYDE, JR., entomology educator; b. Houston, Apr. 12, 1907; s. Harry Hyde and Elizabeth Louisa (Quinn) L.; BS, La. State U., 1933, MS, 1934; PhD (Univ. fellow, Genetics fellow, Wis. Dormitory fellow, Wis. Alumni Rsch. Found. fellow), U. Wis., 1939; m. Ruth Grant Collins, Oct. 26, 1946; 1 child, Barbara Scott Laidlaw Murphy. Teaching asst. La. State U., 1933-34, rsch. asst., 1934-35; prof. biol. sci. Oakland City (Ind.) Coll., 1939-41; state apiarist Ala. Dept. Agr. and Industries, Montgomery, 1941-42; entomologist First Army, N.Y.C., 1946-47; asst. prof. entomology, asst. apiculturist U. Calif.-Davis, 1947-53, assoc. prof. entomology, assoc. apiculturist, 1953-59, prof. entomology, apiculturist, 1959-74, assoc. dean Coll. Agr., 1960-64, chair apr. faculty, staff, 1965-66, prof. entomology emeritus, apiculturist emeritus, 1974—; coord. U. Calif.-Egypt Agrl. Devel. Program, AID, 1979-83. Rockefeller Found. grantee, Brazil, 1954-55, Sudan, 1967; honored guest Tamagawa U., Tokyo, 1980. Trustee, Yolo County (Calif.) Med. Soc. Scholarship Com., 1965-83. Served to capt. AUS, 1942-46. Recipient Cert. of Merit Am. Bee Jour., 1957, Spl. Merit award U Calif.-Davis, 1959, Merit award Calif. Central Valley Bee Club, 1974, Merit award Western Apicultural Soc., 1980, Gold Merit award Internat. Fedn. Beekeepers' Assns., 1986; recipient Disting. Svc. award Ariz. Beekeepers Assn., 1988. Cert. of Appreciation Calif. State Beekeepers' assn., 1987, award Alan Clemson Meml. Found., 1989; NIH grantee, 1963-66; NSF grantee, 1966-74. Fellow AAAS, Entomol. Soc. Am. (C.W. Woodworth award Pacific br. 1981, honoree spl. symposium 1990); mem. Am. Inst. Biol. Scis., Am. Soc. Naturalists, Am. Soc. Zoologists, Internat. Bee Rsch. Assn., Nat. Assn. Uniformed Svcs., Ret. Officers Assn. (2d v.p Sacramento chpt. 1984-86), Scabbard and Blade, Sigma Xi (treas. Davis chpt. 1959-60, v.p chpt. 1966-67), Alpha Gamma Rho (pres. La. chpt. 1933-34, counsellor Western Province 1960-66). Democrat. Presbyterian. Author books including Instrumental Insemination of Honey Bee Queens, 1977; Contemporary Queen Rearing, 1979; author slide set: Instrumental Insemination of Queen Honey Bees, 1976. Achievements include determination of cause of failure of attempts to artificially inseminate queen honey bees; invention of instruments and procedures to consistently accomplish same; elucidation of genetic relationships of individuals of polyandrous honey bee colonies; design of genetic procedures for behavioral study and breeding of honey bees for general and specific uses. Home: 761 Sycamore Ln Davis CA 95616-3432 Office: U Calif Dept Entomology Davis CA 95616

LAIDLAW, ROBERT RICHARD, publishing company executive; b. Berwyn, Ill., Mar. 25, 1923; s. John and Mabel Josephine (Howard) L.; m. Evangeline Rene Harrelson, Aug. 12, 1944; children—Andrew Robert, Kimberly, Lisa. Student, Dartmouth Coll., 1941-42; A.B., U. N.C., 1947, J.D., 1950. Sales rep. Laidlaw Bros. (textbook pubs.), River Forest, Ill., 1950-58; sales mgr. Laidlaw Bros. (textbook pubs.), 1958-60, exec. v.p., 1960-68, pres., 1968-85. Served with USNR, 1942-45. Congregationalist.

LAIDLER, DAVID ERNEST WILLIAM, economics educator; b. Tynemouth, Northumberland, Eng., Aug. 12, 1938; s. John Alphonse and Leonora (Gosman) L.; m. Antje Charlotte Breitwisch, Jan. 29, 1965; 1 dau., Nicole Joanna; m. Frances Joan Hutner, Aug. 1960 (div. 1964). B.Sc., London Sch. Econs., 1959; M.A., U. Syracuse, 1960; Ph.D., U. Chgo., 1964; M.A., U. Manchester, Eng., 1973. Temporary asst. lectr. London Sch. Econs., 1961-62; asst. prof. U. Calif.-Berkeley, 1963-66; lectr. econs. U. Essex, Colchester, Eng., 1966-69; prof. econs. U. Manchester, 1969-75; vis. prof. econs. Brown U., Providence, 1973; prof. econs. U. Western Ont., London, Can., 1975—; mem. econ. adv. panel to Marc Lalonde, minister fin., Ottawa, Ont., 1982-84; research coord. Macdonald Royal Commn., 1984-85; scholar in residence C.D. Howe Inst., 1990-91, adj. scholar, 1991—; mem. econs. com. Social Sci. Research Council, St. Britain, 1972-75; mem. program adv. com. Carnegie-Rochester Pub. Policy Conf. Series, Rochester, Pitts., 1978-79; Lister lecter. Brit. Assn. Advancement Sci., 1972. Author: The Demand for Money - Theories and Evidence, 1969, Introduction to Microeconomics, 1974, Essays on Money and Inflation, 1975, Monetarist Perspectives, 1982, Taking Money Seriously, 1990, The Golden Age of the Quantity Theory, 1991, (with W. Robson) The Great Canadian Disinflation, 1993; mem. editl. bd. Rev. Econ. Studies, 1970-75, Am. Econ. Rev., 1976-78, Can. Jour. Econs., 1977-79, Jour. Econ. Lit., 1978-91; assoc. editor: Jour. Money, Credit and Banking, 1979—. Rsch. grantee NSF, 1964-66, Social Sci. Rsch. Coun., 1971-76, Social Scis. and Humanities Rsch. Coun. Can., 1977-81, 94-99, 94—, Bradley Found., 1991—. Fellow Royal Soc. Can.; mem. Am. Econ. Assn., Can. Econ. Assn. (exec. com. 1980-83, pres. 1987-88). Home: 345 Grangeover Ave, London, ON Canada N69 4K8 Office: U Western Ont, Dept Econ, London, ON Canada N6A 5C2

LAIKIND, DONNA, psychotherapist, consultant; b. N.Y.C., Oct. 29, 1944; d. Charles and Eleanor (Boyarsky) Ressler; m. Jeffrey Laikind, June 29, 1969; children: Rachel Kate, Daniel Aaron. BA, Cornell U., 1965; MS in Counseling, Bank St. Coll. Edn., 1984; cert. in family therapy, Ackerman Inst. Family Therapy, 1990. Behavioral trainer McDermott & Assocs., N.Y.C., 1982-84; dir. orgnl. devel. Altro Health and Rehab., N.Y.C., 1985-86; family therapy cons. Family Dynamics, N.Y.C., 1987-90; psychosocial cons. Food Allergy Ctr., N.Y.C., 1990-91; family therapy cons. SCAN, N.Y.C., 1990—; pvt. practice N.Y.C. and Weston, Conn., 1987—; dir. Family Dynamics Inc., 1985—, chmn., bd. dirs., 1990-94; guest lectr. workshops in field. Contbr. articles to profl. jours. Bd. dirs U.S. Com. Sports for Israel, Maccabiah Games, N.Y.C., 1990—, mission dir., 1989, Ackerman Inst. Family Therapy, 1991—. Avocation: travel. Address: 37 Cedar Hills Rd Weston CT 06883

LAIMBEER, WILLIAM, manufacturing company executive; b. 1934; married. Mgr. Household Fin. Corp., Jacksonville, Fla., 1958-59; with Owens-Ill. Inc., 1959—, various mgmt. positions, 1959-75, v.p., 1975-76, corp. v.p., 1976-81, v.p., gen. mgr. forest products div., 1981-82, group v.p., 1982-84, exec. v.p., 1984—, also bd. dirs.; exec. v.p Stone Container Corp., Chgo., 1991—. Served with USMC, 1954-57. Office: Owens-Ill Inc & Forest Products Co 1 Seagate Toledo OH 43666-1000 also: Nekoosa Packaging Co 1660 Indianwood Cir Toledo OH 43694

LAINE, CLEO (CLEMENTINA DINAH DANKWORTH), singer; b. Southall, Middlesex, Eng. Oct. 28, 1927; d. Alexander and Minnie (Bullock) Campbell; m. George Langridge, 1947 (div.); m. John Philip William Dankworth, 1958; children: Stuart, Alec, Jackie. MA (hon.), Open U., 1975; MusD (hon.), Berklee Coll. Music, 1982. Vocalist Dankworth Orch., 1953-58; lead role in Seven Deadly Sins, Edinburgh, Scotland Festival and Sadlers Wells, 1961, in Showboat, 1972; acting roles Edinburgh Festival, 1966, 67, Colette, 1980; appeared in A Time to Laugh, Hedda Gabler, The Women of Troy, The Mystery of Edwin Drood, 1986 (Theatre World award, Tony award nomination, Drama Desk award nomination), Into the Woods, 1989

(L.A. Drama Critics award nomination); guest appearances symphony orchs. Eng. and abroad; numerous TV appearances and record albums; most recent albums That Old Feeling, 1985, Cleo Sings Sondheim, 1988, Woman to Woman, 1989, Jazz, 1991, Nothing Without You (with Mel Torme), 1992, Sailin' Through (with Dudley Moore), 1992, Cleo at Carnegie, 1993, Born on Friday, 1993, A Beautiful Thing, 1994, Blue and Sentimental, 1994; gold records: Feel The Warm, I'm a Song, Live at Melbourne; Platinum records: Best Friends, Sometimes When We Touch; author: Cleo, an autobiography, 1994. Decorated Order Brit. Empire, 1979; recipient Golden Feather award Los Angeles Times, 1973, Edison award, 1974, Grammy award for best female jazz vocal, 1985, Theatre World award, 1986; named Show Bus. Personality of Yr., Variety Club, 1977, Singer of Yr., TV Times, 1978; Tony nominee, 1986; recipient Theatre World award, 1986, Lifetime Achievement award N.A.R.M., 1990, Brit. Jazz award for best female vocalist, 1990. Office: care Sonoma-Hope Inc 179-9 Rte 46 W # 102 Rockaway NJ 07866*

LAINE, KATIE MYERS, communications consultant; b. Bluffton, Ohio, Oct. 2, 1947; d. George Emerson and Elanore (Keeney) Myers; m. Donald Edward Laine (div. Feb. 1990); 1 child, Brett Edward. BS in Edn., S.W. Tex. State U., 1970. Dir. vols. Austin (Tex.) Ctr. for Attitudinal Healing, 1983-86; talk show host Austin Cablevision, 1986-89; community rels. officer Laguna Gloria Art Mus., Austin, 1989-90; spl. events mgr. Ann Richards for Gov. Campaign, Austin, 1990—. Profl. TV talk show host Katie Laine and Friends. Mem. Mayor's Adv. Coun., Austin, 1989—, Austin Women's Polit. Caucus, 1989—, Emily's List, 1989—; vol. Mayor Lee Cooke Campaign, 1988, Ann Richards Campaign for Gov., 1989; tchr. Divorce Recovery Clinic. Mem. NOW, Women in Communications, Nat. Assn. for Corp. Speaker Activities, Paramount Producers. Avocations: speaking, TV prodn., reading, dancing. Home: 8703 United Nation Austin TX 78748 Office: Divorce Recovery & Family Resources Ctr Austin TX 78759

LAINE, RICHARD R., banking executive; b. 1940. Pres., CEO South Boston Savings Bank, Inc., 1968—, Boston Bancorp., Inc. Office: Boston Bancorp 460 W Broadway Boston MA 02127-2298

LAING, KAREL ANN, magazine publishing executive; b. Mpls., July 5, 1939; d. Edward Francis and Elizabeth Jane Karel (Templeton) Hannon; m. G. R. Cheesebrough, Dec. 19, 1959 (div. 1969); 1 child, Jennifer Read; m. Ronald Harris Laing, Jan. 6, 1973; 1 child, Christopher Harris. Grad., U. Minn., 1960. With Guthrie Symphony Opera Program, Mpls.., 1969-71; account supr. Colle & McVoy Advt. Agy., Richfield, Minn., 1971-74; owner The Cottage, Edina, Minn., 1974-75; salespromotion rep. Robert Meyers & Assocs., St. Louis Park, Minn., 1975-76; cons. Webb Co., St. Paul, 1976-77, custom pub. dir., 1977-89; pres. K.L. Publs., Inc., Bloomington, Minn., 1989—. Contbr. articles to profl. jours. Community vol. Am. Heart Assn. Am. Cancer Soc., Edina PTA; charter sponsor Walk Around Am., St. Paul, 1985. Mem. Bank Mktg. Assn., Fin. Instn. Mktg. Assn., Advt. Fedn. Am., Am. Bankers Assn., Direct Mail Mktg. Assn., St. Andrews Soc. Republican. Presbyterian. Avocations: painting; gardening; reading; traveling. Office: KL Publs 2001 Killebrew Dr Minneapolis MN 55425-1820

LAING, PENELOPE GAMBLE, art educator; b. Dallas, July 24, 1944; d. William Oscar and Beth (Robertson) G.; m. Richard Harlow Laing, June 29, 1970; children: Scott Emerson, Lindsey Elizabeth. BA in Art, N. Tex. State U., 1966; MFA, Edinboro State Coll., 1979. Cert. tchr., Tex. (life), N.C (Art all-level). Art cons. Lawrence (Kans.) Unified Sch. Dist., 1966-68; instr. art Ball State U., Muncie, Ind., 1969-71, Edinboro (Pa.) State U., 1976-77, Pitt C.C., Greenville, N.C., 1980-83; exec. dir. Pitt-Greenville Arts Coun., Greenville, 1983-84; free-lance designer, 1984-90; art tchr., head dept. art Pitt County Schs., 1990—; seminar participant N.C. Ctr. for Advancement of Tchg., 1993, tchr.-scholar, 1994. Bd. dirs., v.p. Pitt-Greenville Arts Coun., 1979-82; mem. adv. bd. Pitt County Schs., Greenville, 1985-87; pres. PTA S. Greenville Sch., 1986-87. Named Fellow, Tchr. Exec. Inst., Pitt County Edn. Found., Greenville, 1992; grantee Pitt County Edn. Found., 1991, 92, 93, N.C. Ctr. for Advancement Teaching, 1993, Tchr./scholar, 1994. Mem. Nat. Art Edn. Assn., N.C. Art Edn. Assn. (bd. dirs. 1992-94, chmn. elem. divsn. 1992-94), Surface Design Assocs. (N.C. rep.). Democrat. Avocations: travel, reading. Home: 204 Pineview Dr Greenville NC 27834 Office: 1325 Red Banks Rd Greenville NC 27858

LAING, ROBERT, production designer. Art dir.: (films) Travels with My Aunt, 1972 (Academy award nomination best art direction 1972), The Great Gatsby, 1974, True Lies, 1994; supervising art dir.: (films) Gandhi, 1982 (Academy award best art direction 1982); prodn. designer: (films) Frenzy, 1972, Night Games, 1980, High Road to China, 1983, The Doctor and the Devils, 1985, The Neverending Story II: The Next Chapter, 1990, (TV movies) Ellis Island, 1984, The Far Pavilions, 1984. Office: care Art Directors Guild 11365 Ventura Blvd #315 North Hollywood CA 91604*

LAINGEN, LOWELL BRUCE, diplomat; b. Odin Twp., Minn., Aug. 6, 1922; s. Palmer K. and Ida Mabel (Eng) L.; m. Penelope Babcock, June 1, 1957; children: William Bruce, Charles Winslow, James Palmer. B.A. cum laude, St. Olaf Coll., 1947; M.A. in Internat. Relations, U. Minn., 1949. Internat. rels. officer State Dept., 1949-50; joined U.S. Fgn. Svc., 1950; vice consul Hamburg, Germany, 1951-53; 3d sec. embassy Teheran, Iran, 1953-54; consul Meshed, Iran, 1954-55; asst., then officer chargé Greek affairs State Dept., 1956-60; 2d sec., then 1st sec. embassy Karachi, Pakistan, 1960-64; with Pakistan/Afghanistan affairs bur. State Dept., 1964-67; assigned Nat. War Coll., 1967-68; dep. chief mission to Afghanistan Kabul, 1968-71; country dir. Pakistan, Afghanistan and Bangladesh; country dir. State Dept., 1971-73, India, Nepal, Sri Lanka and the Maldives, 1973-74; acting dep. asst. sec. state for Near Eastern and South Asian affairs State Dept., 1974-75, dep. asst. sec. state for European affairs, 1975-76; ambassador to Malta, 1977-79; chargé d'affaires Am. Embassy, Teheran, Iran, 1979; held hostage by Iranian student militants, 1979-81; v.p. Nat. Def. U., Ft. McNair, Washington, 1981-86; exec. dir. Nat. Commn. Pub. Service, Washington, 1987-90; pres. Am. Acad. Diplomacy, 1991—. Home: 5627 Old Chester Rd Bethesda MD 20814-1035

LAIOU, ANGELIKI EVANGELOS, history educator; b. Athens, Greece, Apr. 6, 1941; came to U.S. 1959; d. Evangelos K. and Virginia I. (Apostolides) Laios; m. Stavros B. Thomadakis, July 14, 1973; 1 son, Vassili N. B.A., Brandeis U., 1961; M.A., Harvard U., 1962, Ph.D., 1966. Asst. prof. history Harvard U., Cambridge, Mass., 1969-72, Dumbarton Oaks prof. Byzantine history, 1981—; assoc. prof. Brandeis U., Waltham, 1972-75; prof. Rutgers U., New Brunswick, N.J., 1975-79, disting. prof., 1979-81; chmn. Gennadeion com. (Am. Sch. Classical Studies), Athens, Greece, 1981-84; dir. Dumbarton Oaks, 1989—. Author: Constantinople and the Latins, 1972, Peasant Society in the Late Byzantine Empire, 1977, Mariage, amour et parenté à Byznace, XIe-XIIIe siècles, 1992, Gender, Society and Economic Life in Byzantium, 1992, Consent and Coercion to Sex and Marriage in Ancient and Medieval Societies, 1993. Guggenheim Found. fellow, 1971-72, 79-80, Dumbarton Oaks sr. fellow, 1983-88, Am. Coun. Learned Socs. fellow, 1988-89. Mem. Am. Hist. Assn., Medieval Acad. Am., Societa Ligure di Storia Patria, Greek Com. Study of South Eastern Europe. Office: Dumbarton Oaks 1703 32nd St NW Washington DC 20007-2961

LAIR, ROBERT LOUIS, catering company executive; b. Albuquerque, Aug. 13, 1921; s. Louis E. and Inez B. (Mudd) L.; m. June Marie Moran, Aug. 9, 1941 (dec. Apr. 1983); children—Christopher Louis, Catherine Ann, Cynthia Susan; m. Therese C. Kronkowski, Sept. 15, 1984. With Boeing Airplane Co., 1940-53, dir. sub-contract adminstrn. USN, 1944-46, supr. materiel, 1947-53; with Cessna Aircraft Co., Wichita, Kans., 1953-83, sr. v.p., dir., 1969-83; chmn. bd. Precision Composites, Inc., 1984-87; co-owner Tee-C's Catering, 1987—. Bd. dirs. Jr. Achievement of Wichita, Midwest Cancer Inst. Mem. Falstaff Soc., Wichita Country Club, Rotary. Home: 105 N Woodlawn Ct Wichita KS 67218-1838

LAIRD, ALAN DOUGLAS KENNETH, mechanical engineering educator; b. Victoria, Can., Aug. 8, 1914; came to U.S. 1946, naturalized, 1955; s. George Alexander and Edna A (Foy) L.; m. Joyce Kathleen Morris, Nov. 3, 1941; children: William George, John Douglas, Linda Margaret. B.A.Sc. in Mech. Engring. U.B.C., 1940; M.S., U. Calif. at Berkeley, 1949, Ph.D., 1951. Engr. Def. Industries Ltd., Montreal, 1941-45, Leek and Co., Vancouver, Can., 1945-46; mem. faculty U. Calif. at Berkeley, 1948-80, prof. mech. engring., 1964-80, prof. emeritus, 1980—, dir. Sea Water Conversion

Lab., 1968-80, dir. emeritus Sea Water Conversion Lab., 1980—. Mem. ASME, Pi Tau Sigma. Home: 860 Sibert Ct Lafayette CA 94549-4925

LAIRD, CHARLES DAVID, zoology and genetics educator, researcher; b. Portland, Oreg., May 12, 1939; s. Charles Bruce and Mary (Gray) L.; m. Judith Helen Shepherd; children: Michael, John, Andrew, Jennifer. BA, U. Oreg., 1961; postgrad., U. Zürich, Switzerland, 1961-62; PhD, Stanford U., 1966. Postdoctoral fellow in microbiology and genetics U. Wash., Seattle, 1966-68, assoc. prof. zoology 1971-74, prof., 1975—, chmn. dept., 1985-89, adj. prof. genetics, 1975—, rsch. affiliate Child Devel. and Mental Retardation Ctr., 1988—; mem. Fred Hutchinson Cancer Rsch. Ctr., 1990—; asst. prof. zoology U. Tex., Austin, 1968-71. Contbr. articles to profl. jours. Recipient Career Devel. award NIH, 1969; fellow NSF, 1962, NIH, 1966. Fellow AAAS; mem. Am. Soc. Human Genetics, Genetic Soc. Am. Office: Fred Hutchinson Cancer Rsch Ctr 1124 Columbia St Seattle WA 98104-2092

LAIRD, DAVID, humanities educator emeritus; b. Marshfield, Wis., Oct. 17, 1927; s. Melvin Robert and Helen Melissa (Connor) L.; m. Helen Astrid Lauritzen, Sept. 10, 1955; 1 child, Vanessa Ann. PhB, U. Chgo., 1947; BA with highest honor, U. Wis., 1950, MA, 1951, PhD, 1955; postgrad., Courtauld Inst., 1953. Instr. to asst. prof. Oberlin Coll., 1955-58; mem. faculty Calif. State U., L.A., 1958—; chmn. dept. English Calif. State U., 1969-73, chmn. dept. Am. studies, 1977-79; Nat. Humanities Inst. fellow U. Chgo., 1978-79; sr. Fulbright lectr. U. Tunis, Tunisia, 1979-80; fellow Folger Shakespeare Libr., 1982; Fulbright lectr. Odense U. (Denmark), 1983-84; vis. prof. U. Ottawa, 1984-85; cons. to Choice. Mem. editorial bd. Jour. Forest History; contbr. articles on Shakespeare, Am. lit. and cultural history to profl. jours. Mem. Western Shakespeare Seminar, Friends of Huntington Libr. Recipient Outstanding Prof. award Calif. State U., 1987, Nat. Endowment for the Humanities Summer Seminar award Northwestern U., 1989; Uhrig Found. grantee, 1964-65; Fulbright fellow, 1953-54. Mem. MLA, Malone Soc., Am. Studies Assn., Phi Beta Kappa. Home: 565 N Milton Dr San Gabriel CA 91775-2203 Office: Calif State U Los Angeles CA 90032

LAIRD, EVALYN WALSH, lawyer; b. Chgo., Feb. 6, 1902; d. Edward Joseph and Mae E. (Tarr) Walsh; m. Charles Hamilton Laird, Aug. 8, 1925; children: Lois Hillmann, Betty Ann Hillmann (dec.), Charles Hamilton Laird, Jr. (dec.), Edward J. Laird, Jane Glynn. JD, DePaul U., Chgo., 1926; PhD cum honoris causa, Hamilton State U., 1973. Bar: Mich. 1982. Estate planner Prudential Ins. Co., Chgo., 1945-48; mgr. Edward J. Walsh Reporting Svcs., Chgo., 1948-60; owner Pvt. Law Practice, 1926; environ. chmn. Vilage of Grand Bch. Artist 10 oil paintings of family members, also paintings of dogs, cats, horses and scenery. Mem. personnel com. Girl Scouts of Chgo.; pres. 7th dist. Archdiocesan Coun. Cath. Women. Recipient 45th Yr. Citation for uninterrupted service Girl Scouts U.S., 1990. Mem. ABA, Ill. State Bar Assn., Chgo. Bar Assn. (honored for 50 yrs. membership 1991), Mich. State Bar, Ill. Women's Bar, Mich. Women's Bar, Berrien County Bar Assn., Skokie Valley Skating Club (hon.), Mich. City YMCA, Grand Beach Golf & Country Club. Democrat. Home and Office: 47104 Pine Ave Grand Beach New Buffalo MI 49117

LAIRD, JOHN B., newspaper publishing executive. V.p. sales and marketing Houston Chronicle, Tex. Office: Houston Chronicle Pub Co 801 Texas St Houston TX 77002-2906*

LAIRD, JOHN ROBERT, finance company executive; b. Erie, Pa., June 21, 1942; s. James Harris and Greta Doris (Campbell) L.; m. Ruth Jane Young, Jan. 30, 1965; children: James, Nancy, David. BS, Syracuse U., 1964, MBA, 1965; cert. Advanced Mgmt., Harvard U., 1983. With internat. info. mktg. Gould Inc., Chgo., 1968-77; sr. v.p., treas. Am. Express Co., N.Y.C., 1977-89; sr. exec. v.p. The Boston Co., 1989-90, chief exec. officer, 1990—, also chmn. bd. dirs. Active Internat. Multiple Sclerosis Socs., New Canaan, Conn. Lt. U.S. Army, 1966-68. Mem. Fin. Execs. Inst., Nat. Assn. Corp. Treasurers.

LAIRD, MARY See WOOD, LARRY

LAIRD, MELVIN ROBERT, former secretary of defense; b. Omaha, Sept. 1, 1922; s. Melvin R. and Helen (Connor) L.; m. Barbara Masters (dec. Jan. 1992); children: John, Alison, David; m. Carole Howard. B.A., Carleton Coll., 1942; LHD (hon.), Lincoln Coll., Ill., 1971; D Polit. Sci. (hon.), U. Pacific, 1968; HHD (hon.), St. Leo's Coll., 1969; LLD (hon.), U. Wis., 1982. Mem. Wis. Senate, 1946-52; chmn. Wis. Legis. Council; mem. 83d-91st Congresses; mem. Rep. Coordinating com. 83d-90th Congresses; sec. of def., 1969-73; dir. sr. counsellor nat. and internat. affairs Pres. Nixon, 1973-74; sr. counsellor nat. and internat. affairs Reader's Digest Assn., 1974—; bd. dirs. Met. Life Ins. Co., Northwest Airlines, IDS Mut. Fund Group, Sci. Applications Internat. Inc., Martin Marietta Corp.; bd. dirs. COMSAT Corp., chmn. bd., 1991—; bd. dirs. pub. oversight bd. SEC practice sect. AICPA. Author: A House Divided: America's Strategy Gap, 1962; Editor: The Conservative Papers, 1964, Republican Papers, 1968. Bd. dirs. World Rehab. Fund, Boys Clubs Am., George Washington U., Airlie Found., Laird Youth Leadership Found., Pres.'s Reagan Moscow Assessment Rev. Panel, 1987; trustee Kennedy Center; chmn. Nat. Election Commn., 1986; co-chmn. platform com. Rep. Nat. Conv., 1960, chmn., 1964. Decorated Order of Merit 1st class Fed. Republic Germany; commdr. Nat. Order Legion of Honor, France; recipient 15th Ann. Albert Lasker med. award; Man of Year award Am. Cancer Soc.-Nat. Assn. Mental Health; Humanitarian award John E. Fogarty Found. for Mentally Retarded, 1974; Presdl. Medal of Freedom, 1974, Harry S. Truman award, 1985. Mem. Mil. Order Purple Heart, 40 and 8, Am. Legion, VFW, DAV. Presbyterian (elder). Clubs: Burning Tree, Augusta Nat. Golf. Lodge: Masons. Office: 1730 Rhode Island Ave NW 212 Washington DC 20036

LAIRD, ROBERT WINSLOW, journalist; b. Chgo., Sept. 25, 1936; s. Robert Winslow and Evelyn (Emerson) L.; m. Marsa Radbill, Dec. 1, 1962; children—Michael Winslow, Joshua Radbill. B.A., Yale U., 1959. Reporter World Telegram and Sun, N.Y.C., 1963-66; dep. press sec. to Mayor John Lindsay N.Y.C., 1966-73; press sec. to Gov. Hugh Carey Albany, N.Y., 1974-76; opinions editor, weekly columnist Daily News, N.Y.C., 1977—. Vol. Peace Corps, Gebileh, Somalia, 1962-63; chmn. schs. com. Yale U Alumni, 1979-84. Recipient Editorial Writing award N.Y.C. Citizens Housing and Planning Coun., 1987; co-recipient Editorial Excellence award Nat. Assn. Edn. Writers, 1989. Mem. U.S. Paddle Tennis Assn. (bd. dirs. 1978-82, 87—). Avocation: paddle tennis. Home: 17 Stuyvesant Oval New York NY 10009-1920 Office: NY Daily News 220 E 42nd St Ste 817 New York NY 10017-5858

LAIRD, ROY DEAN, political science educator; b. Blue Hill, Nebr., July 15, 1925. B.A. in Biology, Hastings Coll., 1947; M.A. in Polit. Sci, U. Nebr., 1952; postgrad., U. Glasgow, Scotland, 1952-53; Ph.D., U. Wash., 1956. Research analyst CIA, Washington, 1956-57; asst. prof. U. Kans., Lawrence, 1957-62; assoc. prof. U. Kans., 1962-66, prof. polit. sci. and Soviet and Eastern European area studies, 1966-90, prof. emeritus, 1990—; cons. Spl. Ops. Research Office, Washington, 1960; guest researcher Inst. for Study of USSR, Munich, W. Ger., 1963-64; foreign internat. Conf. on Soviet and East European Agriculture, 1962. Author: Collective Farming in Russia, 1958, (with Betty A. Laird) Soviet Communism and Agrarian Revolution, 1958, The Soviet Paradigm: An Experiment in Creating a Monohierarchial Polity, 1970, To Live Long Enough: The Memoirs of Naum Jasny, Scientific Analysis, 1976; editor: (with Betty A. Laird) Soviet Agricultural and Peasant Affairs, 1963, The Future of Agriculture in the Soviet Union and Eastern Europe, 1977, (with Ronald A. Francisco and Betty A. Laird) The Political Economy of Collectivized Agriculture, 1979; author: (with Ronald A. Francisco and Betty A. Laird) The Politburo: Demographic Trend, Gorbachev and the Future, 1986, A Soviet Lexicon: Important Terms Concepts and Phrases, 1988, The Soviet Legacy, 1993; contbr. chpts. to books, articles to profl. jours. Rockefeller Found. fellow, 1963-64; NSF grantee, 1966, 67-68; NDEA-Fulbright Hays fellow, 1967; NASA grantee, 1971-72. Mem. AAUP, Am. Assn. Advancement of Slavic Studies, Cen. Slavic Assn., Conf. Soviet Agrl. and Peasant Studies (founder), Am. Polit. Sci. Assn., Western Slavic Studies Assn., Western Slavic Conf. (v.p. 1975-76), Kans. Polit. Sci. Assn., Midwest Conf. Slavic Studies.

Midwest Polit. Sci. Assn. Office: U Kans Dept Polit Sci Blake Hall Lawrence KS 66045

LAIRD, WILBUR DAVID, JR., librarian; b. Kansas City, Mo., Mar. 15, 1937; s. Wilbur David and Alma Blanche (Turner) L.; children: Wendy, Cynthia, Brian Andrew, David Alexander; m. Helen M. Ingram, July 12, 1984. Student, U. Wichita, 1959-60; BA, UCLA, 1965, MLS, 1966. Reference libr. U. Calif., Davis, 1966-67; acquisitions libr. U. Utah, 1967-70, asst. dir. for tech. svcs., 1970-71, assoc. dir., 1971-72; univ. libr. U. Ariz., Tucson, 1972-90; pres. Books West S.W., Tucson, 1990—. Author: Hopi Bibliography, 1977; editor: Books of the Southwest, 1977—. Bd. dirs. Westerners Internat., 1974-87, Tucson Civic Ballet, 1975-76, S.W. Pks. and Mon. Assn., 1993—. With USN, 1955-59. Mem. ALA, Ariz. State Libr. Assn. (pres. 1978-79), Western History Assn., Western Lit. Assn., Guild Ariz. Antiquarian Booksellers. Home: 3329 E 2d St Tucson AZ 85716 Office: Books West Southwest Inc 2452 N Campbell Ave Tucson AZ 85719-3368

LAIRD, WILLIAM EVERETTE, JR., economics educator, administrator; b. Hattiesburg, Miss., Feb. 4, 1934; s. William Everette and Mildred Alva (Howard) L.; m. Doris Anne Marley, Mar. 13, 1964; children: William Everette III, Andrew Marley, Glen Howard. B.S., Stetson U., 1956; M.A., George Washington U., 1958; Ph.D., U. Va., 1962. Asst. prof. Fla. State U., Tallahassee, 1960-66, assoc. prof., 1966-71, prof., 1971—; chmn. dept. econs. Fla State U., Tallahassee, 1974—. Contbr. articles to profl. jours. DuPont fellow, 1959-60; recipient awards Fla. State U. Grad. Research Council, 1965, 66, Faculty Devel. awards Fla. State U., 1971. Mem. Am. Econs. Assn., So. Econ. Assn. Democrat. Methodist. Clubs: Magna Charta Barons, Jamestowne Soc., St. Andrew Soc., Order of First Families of Va. Home: 1125 Mercer Dr Tallahassee FL 32312-2833 Office: Fla State U Dept Econs Tallahassee FL 32306

LAIRES, FERNANDO, concert piano educator; b. Lisbon, Portugal, Jan. 3, 1925; came to U.S., 1956; s. Joaquim Augusto and Clementina (Belfo) L.; m. Nelita True, Dec. 24, 1971. Artist diploma, Nat. Conservatory Music, Lisbon, 1945. Prof. piano Nat. Conservatory Music, Lisbon 1949-56; asst. prof. U. Tex., Austin, 1956-61; artist-in-residence, prof. piano Okla. Coll. Liberal Arts, Chickasha, 1961-68; artist-in-residence, chmn. piano dept. Interlochen (Mich.) Arts Acad., Interlochen, 1968-72; prof. piano Peabody Conservatory, Balt., 1972-87; adj. prof. piano Cath. U. Am., Washington, 1978—; artist faculty Eastman Sch. Music, Rochester, N.Y., 1992—; permanent guest prof. piano performance Shenyang (People's Republic of China) Conservatory of Music, 1989—; juror Tchaikowsky Internat. Piano Competition, Moscow, 1982, Van Cliburn Internat. Piano Competition, Ft. Worth, 1973, Gina Bachauer Internat. Piano Competition, Salt Lake City, 1978, 80, U. Md. Internat. Piano Competition, College Park, 1975, 77, 86, dir. U. Md. Internat. Piano Festival, 1979-81. Performed in cycle the 32 piano sonatas of Beethoven, 1944; dir.-founder 20-record Anthology Portuguese classical music, 1972-82; co-founder Pro-Arte Concert Soc., Portugal, 1949, The Am. Liszt Soc., 1964; contbr. articles to Clavier, The Piano Quar., Am. Music Tchr. Recipient Beethoven medal Harriet Cohen Internat. Music Awards, London, 1956, Franz Liszt medal Liszt Soc. Hungary, Budapest, 1984, Liszt medal for excellence Am. Liszt Soc., Inc., 1985, Liszt Commemorative medal Hungarian People's Rep., 1986; named Comdr. to Order of Prince Henry the Navigator, Portuguest Govt., 1984. Mem. European Piano Tchrs. Assn., Am. Liszt Soc., Inc. (pres. 1976-85, 89—), Music Tchrs. Nat. Assn., Am. Liszt Soc. (pres.). Avocations: travel, reading, writing. Home: 210 Devonshire Dr Rochester NY 14625-1905

LAITIN, DAVID DENNIS, political science educator; b. Bklyn., June 4, 1945; s. Daniel and Frances (Blumenkranz) L.; m. Delia Fortune; children: Marc Oliver, Anna Elizabeth. BA, Swarthmore (Pa.) Coll., 1967; PhD, U. Calif., Berkeley, 1974. Instr. Nat. Tchr. Edn. Ctr., Afgoy, Somalia, 1969; master Grenada Boys' Secondary Sch., West Indies, 1970-71; asst. prof. dept. polit. sci. U. Calif.-San Diego, La Jolla, 1977-80; prof., 1984-87, chmn., 1986-87; reader dept. polit. sci. U. Ife, Nigeria, 1979-80; prof. polit. sci., dir. Wilder House Ctr. for Study Politics, History and Culture U. Chgo., 1987—, William K. Kenan, Jr. prof., 1992—; expert witness fgn. affairs subcom. U.S. Ho. Reps., 1981. Author: Politics, Language and Thought: The Somali Expereience, 1966, Hegemony and Culture: Politics and Religious Change Among the Yoruba, 1986, Somalia: A Nation in Search of a State, 1987, Language Repertoires and State Construction in Africa, 1992. Fellow NEH, 1979-80, Howard Found., 1984-85, German Marshall Fund, 1984-85; coprin. investigator award NSF, 1993-95. Mem. Am. Polit. Sci. Assn. Office: U Chgo Dept Of Polit Sci Chicago IL 60637

LAITIN, JOSEPH, journalist, former government spokesman and public relations consultant; b. Bklyn., Oct. 2, 1914; s. Harry and Irene (Lubetkin) L.; m. Christine Henriette Houdayer (dec. Apr. 5, 1995), Apr. 26, 1961; children: Sigrid, Peter. Corr. United Press, Washington, 1941-45; fgn. corr. Reuters, Far East, Europe, Latin Am., 1945-50; chief corr. Research Inst. Am., Washington, 1950-52; freelance writer and broadcaster Hollywood, Calif., 1952-63; asst. to dir. Bur. of Budget, Washington, 1963-64; dep. press sec. to Pres. The White House, Washington, 1965-66; asst. to dir. for pub. affairs Office Mgmt. and Budget, Washington, 1966-74; asst. sec. pub. affairs Dept. Def., Washington, 1974-75; asst. administr. FAA, Washington, 1975-77; asst. sec. treasury U.S. Dept. Treasury, Washington, 1977-81; pvt. cons. govt. and pub. rels. Washington; advisor Hill & Knowlton, 1981-85; ombudsman Washington Post, 1986-88; sr. cons. Fleishman-Hillard, Inc., 1989-93; instr. Art Ctr. Sch. L.A., 1952-63, George Washington U., Washington, 1987; cons. Commn. on Selective Svc., 1966-67, Nat. Commn. on Causes and Prevention of Violence, 1968-70, Presdl. Commn. on Campus Unrest, 1970, Nat. Commn. on Exec., Legis. and Jud. Salaries, 1989, Paul Volcker Commn. on Pub. Svc., 1988-89; fellow media studies project Woodrow Wilson Ctr., 1990; mem. regional selection com. White House Fellows Program, 1994—. Recipient Calif. State Fair award for best radio documentary CBS The Changing Face of Hollywood, 1957; Disting. Public Service medal Dept. Def., 1975.

LAITNER, BILL, reporter. Health and fitness reporter Detroit Free Press. Office: Detroit Free Press Inc. 321 W Lafayette Blvd Detroit MI 48226

LAJEUNESSE, MARCEL, university administrator, educator; b. Mont-Laurier, Que., Can., June 28, 1942; s. Achille and Gertrude (Grenier) L.; m. Louise Beauregard, Dec. 20, 1975; 1 child, Anne. BA, U. Laval, Que., Can., 1964; B Bibliotheconomie, U. de Montreal, Que., Can., 1964, Licence ès Lettres, 1967, MA, 1968; PhD, U. Ottawa, Can., 1977. Prof. Coll. L'Outaouais, Hull, 1968-70, U. de Montreal, 1970—; prof. dir. Grad. Sch. Libr. and Info. Sci., 1987-94, assoc. dean for planning Faculty of Arts and Scis., 1994—; cons. Aupelf UREF, IDRC, Can. Internat. Devel. Agy. Agence de cooperation culturelle et technique, UNESCO. Author 9 books; contbr. numerous articles to profl. and scholarly jours. Mem. Conseil de la Langue Française, Que., 1987-91—. Mem. Assn. Libr. and Info. Sci. Edn., Assn. Internat. des Écoles de Scis. de l'Information, Assn. pour l'Avancement des Scis. et des Techniques de la Documentation, Corp. des Bibliothécaires professionnels de Québec, Inst. French Am. History, Bibliog. Soc. Can. Home: 126 Dobie, Mont-Royal, PQ Canada H3P 1S4 Office: FAS-Direction, U de Montreal, CP 6128 Succ A, Montreal, PQ Canada H3C 3J7

LAJOIE, ROLAND, army officer; b. Nashua, N.H., Aug. 11, 1936; s. Ernest Joseph and Alice (Bechard) L.; m. Joann Theresa Sinibaldi, Feb. 11, 1961; children: Michelle, Christopher, Renee. BA in Govt., U. N.H., 1958; MA in History, U. Colo., 1971; diploma, Army Command & Staff Coll., 1973, U.S. Army War Coll., 1981. Commd. 2d lt. U.S. Army, 1958, advanced through grades to maj. gen., 1991; served as asst. army attache Am. Embassy, Moscow, 1973-76; commandant U.S. Army Russian Inst., Garmisch, Fed. Republic Germany, 1976-79; bn. comdr. 1st Psychol. Ops. Bn., Ft. Bragg, N.C., 1979-80; rsch. fellow U.S. Army War Coll., Carlisle, Pa., 1980-81, Harvard U., Cambridge, Mass., 1980-81; army attache Am. Embassy, Moscow, 1981-83; chief of mission U.S. Mil. Liaison Mission, Berlin, Potsdam, German Dem. Republic, 1983-86; def. and army attache Am. Embassy, Paris, 1986-88; dir. U.S. On-Site Inspection Agy., 1988-91; dep. dir. internat. negotiations J5 The Joint Staff, Washington, 1991-92; assoc. dep. dir. for ops./mil. affairs CIA, Washington, 1992-94; dep. asst. to sec. of def., 1994—. Decorated Nat. Intel Disting. Svc. medal, Def. Disting. Svc. medal, Bronze Star, Legion of Merit, Def. Meritorious Svc., Def.

Superior Svc., Nat. Order Merit (France). Mem. VFW, Retired Officer Assn. Avocations: tennis, skiing. Home: 3727 Riverwood Rd Alexandria VA 22309

LA JONE, JAY ALLEN, lawyer; b. Oak Park, Ill., July 5, 1953; s. Joseph Frank and Lillian Margaret LaJ.; m. Teri Lynn Wuletich, Aug. 2, 1980; 1 child, Kathryn Jennifer. BA, Lawrence U., 1975; JD, Stanford U., 1978. Bar: Ill. 1978, U.S. Dist. Ct. (no. dist.) Ill. 1978, Tex. 1988. Assoc. Schiff, Hardin & Waite, Chgo., 1978-80; ptnr. Hopkins & Sutter, Chgo., 1980-87, Dallas, 1987—. Mem. ABA, State Bar Tex., Phi Beta Kappa. Office: Hopkins & Sutter 1717 Main St Ste 3700 Dallas TX 75201-4694

LAJTHA, ABEL, biochemist; b. Budapest, Hungary, Sept. 22, 1922; naturalized; married; 2 children. PhD in Chemistry, Eotvos Lorand U., Budapest, 1945; MD (hon.), U. Padua. Asst. prof. biochemistry Eotvos Lorand U., 1945-47; asst. prof. Inst. Muscle Rsch., Mass. 1949-50; sr. rsch. scientist N.Y. State Psychiat. Inst., 1950-57, assoc. rsch. scientist, 1957-62, prin. rsch. scientist, 1962-66; dir. N.Y. State Rsch. Inst. Neurochemistry, 1966—; prof. exptl. psychiatry Sch. Medicine NYU, 1971—; asst. prof. Coll. Physicians & Surgeons, Columbia U., 1956-69. Zoology Station fellow Italy, 1947-48, Rsch. fellow Royal Inst. Great Britain, 1948-49. Mem. Internat. Brain Rsch. Orgn., Am. Soc. Biol. Chemists, Am. Acad. Neurol., Am. Coll. Neuropsychopharmacol., Internat. Soc. Neurochem. (pres.), Am. Chem. Soc., Am. Soc. Neurochem. (pres.). Achievements include rsch. in neurochemistry, amino acid and protein metabolism of the brain and the brain barrier system. Office: Ctr Neurochem Nathan S Kline Inst Psy Rsc Orangeburg NY 10962

LAKAH, JACQUELINE RABBAT, political scientist, educator; b. Cairo, Apr. 14, 1933; came to U.S., 1969, naturalized, 1975; d. Victor Boutros and Alice (Mounayer) Rabbat; m. Antoine K. Lakah, Apr. 8, 1951; children: Micheline, Mireille, Caroline. BA, Am. U. Beirut, 1968; MPh, Columbia U., 1974, cert. Mid. East Inst., 1975, PhD, 1978. Assoc. prof. polit. sci. and world affairs Fashion Inst. Tech., N.Y.C., 1978—; asst. chairperson social scis. dept., 1989-95, chairperson social scis. dept., 1995—; asst. prof. grad. faculty polit. sci. Columbia U., N.Y.C., summer 1979, vis. scholar, 1982-83, also mem. seminar on Mid. East; guest faculty Sarah Lawrence Coll., 1981-82; cons. on Mid. East; faculty rsch. fellow SUNY, summer 1982. Fellow Columbia Faculty, 1970-73, NDEA Title IV, 1971-72; Mid. East Inst. scholar, 1976; Rockefeller Found. scholar, 1967-69. Mem. European Cmty. Studies Assn., Am. Polit. Sci. Assn., Fgn. Policy Assn., Internat. Studies Assn., Internat. Polit. Sci. Assn. Roman Catholic. Home: 41-15 94th St Queens NY 11373-1745 Office: 7th Ave At 27th St New York NY 10001-5992

LAKATTA, EDWARD GERARD, biomedical researcher; b. Scranton, Pa., May 10, 1944; s. Edward and Pauline Ann (Lucas) L.; m. Loretta Ellen Cantwell, July 28, 1968; children: Edward A., Christina, Lucas A. BS in Biology, U. Scranton, 1966; MD, Georgetown U., 1970. Intern Strong Meml. Hosp., Rochester, N.Y., 1970-71, asst. resident, 1971-72; clin. assoc. Gerontology Rsch. Ctr. cardiovascular sect. NIH, Nat. Inst. Child Health & Human Devel., Clin. Physiology Br., Balt., 1972-74; asst. in medicine Johns Hopkins Sch. Medicine, Balt., 1973-74; fellow in cardiology Georgetown U. Hosp., Washington, 1974-75; fellow in med. sci. Am. Coll. Physicians for 1975 dept. physiology Univ. Coll., London, 1975-76; fellow in med. sci. dept. cardiac medicine Cardiothoracic Inst., London, 1975-76; chief cardiovascular sect. clin. physiology Gerontology Rsch. Ctr., Nat. Inst. Aging NIH, Balt., 1976-85, chief Lab. Cardiovascular Sci., Gerontology Rsch. Ctr., Nat. Inst. Aging, 1985—, acting sci. dir. Nat. Inst. Aging, 1994—; prof. medicine Johns Hopkins Sch. Medicine, Balt., 1983—; prof. physiology Sch. Medicine U. Md., Balt., 1985—; vis. physician Bayview Med. Ctr., Balt., Md.; mem. ad hoc study sect. on animal model for study of pathogenesis of spl. heart muscle disease NIH, 1981; mem. ad hoc grant proposal reviews and site visit coms. VA and NSF; ad hoc reviewer Am. Jour. Physiology, Can. Jour. Physiology and Pharmacology, Circulation Rsch., Jour. Molecular and Cellular Cardiology, Sci.; mem. search com. for dir. Nat. Heart, Lung and Blood Inst., 1981, Gerontology Rsch. Ctr., 1988; chmn. intramural promotions and tenure review com. Nat. Inst. Aging, 1989-91; cons. in field. Editor for clin. scis. Exptl. Aging Rsch., 1982-89; assoc. editor Jour. Molecular and Cellular Cardiology, 1987—; mem. editorial bd. Jour. Gerontology, Jour. Molecular and Cellular Cardiology, Cardiosci., Current Problems in Geriatrics, Jour. Cardiovascular Electrophysiology; contbr. numerous articles to profl. jours., chpts. to books. Med. dir. USPHS, 1976. Recipient Paul Dudley White award Assn. Mil. Surgeons of U.S., 1992, Achievement in Aging award Allied Signal, 1993; Eli Lilly Med. Sci. fellow Am. Coll. Physicians, 1975. Fellow Am. Physiol. Soc. (cardiovascular sect.), Am. Heart Assn. (coun. basic sci., Cardiovascular B rsch. study com. 1987-89, application task force Mission to Elderly 1989-90, 90-91), Am. Soc. Clin. Investigation, Am. Assn. Physicians, Internat. Soc. for Heart Rsch. (coun.), Biophys. Soc.; mem. Physiol. Soc. (London). Avocation: fine wine and food. Home: 126 Briarcliff Ln Bel Air MD 21014 Office: Nat Inst Aging Lab Cardiovascular Sci Gerontology Rsch Ctr Rm 3D09 Baltimore MD 21224-2780

LAKE, ANN WINSLOW, lawyer; b. Lowell, Mass., May 14, 1919; d. Frank and Helen Jablonski; BS, Lowell State Coll., 1940; JD, U. Detroit, 1946; MA, Boston State Coll., 1964, Boston U., 1967; m. Thomas E. Lake, Sept. 5, 1942; children: Beverly Wilkes, Douglas, Warren. Tchr. schs. in Maine, Ga. and Detroit, 1940-43; admitted to Mass. bar, 1946; ind. practice, Dedham, Mass., 1946—; prof. law Salem (Mass.) State Coll., 1970-94, prof. emerita, 1990; mem. Mass. Commn. Study Labor Laws, 1974-79; mem. mktg. bd. ABA-GPS, 1993—; mem. ABA commn. coll. and univ. legal studies, 1994—. Mem. Mass. Adv. Commn. Acad. Talented Pupils, 1960-64, Mass. State Coll. Bldg. Authority, 1964-67, Mass. Com. to Recruit and Screen Candidates for Office Atty. Gen., 1974-78, U. Lowell Found., 1977-82; chmn. Dedham (Mass.) Coun. on Aging, 1993—. Recipient award Mass. State Coll. Alumni Assn., 1963, 64, 72, Mass. Assn. Mental Health, 1969, 72. Fellow Am. Bar Found. (life), Mass. Bar Found. (life); mem. Nat. Assn. Women Lawyers (pres. 1980-81), Polish Bus. and Profl. Women's Club Greater Boston (pres. 1977-79), Norfolk Mental Health Assn. (pres. 1972-73), Mass. Assn. Women Lawyers (pres. 1971-72), Assn. Mass. State Colls. Alumni (pres. 1961-64), Riverdale Improvement Assn. (pres. 1959). Republican. Address: 40 Sawyer Dr Dedham MA 02026-5701

LAKE, ANTHONY, federal official; married; 3 children. AB magna cum laude, Harvard U., 1961; PhD, Princeton U., 1974. Joined Fgn. Svc., Dept. State, Washington, 1962; U.S. vice consul Fgn. Svc., Dept. State, Saigon, Vietnam, 1963, Hue, Vietnam, 1964-65; spl. asst. to President U.S. for nat. security affairs Fgn. Svc., Dept. State, Washington, 1969-70; dep. policy planning for President U.S. Dept. State, Washington, 1977-81; Five Coll. Prof. Internat. Rels. Mount Holyoke Coll., 1981—; former sr. fgn. policy analyst Clinton-Gore Campaign; asst. to Pres. NSC, Washington, DC, 1993—. Author: The Tar Baby Option: America Toward Southern Rhodesia, 1976, Somoza Falling, 1989; co-author: Our Own Worst Enemy: The Unmaking of American Foreign Policy, 1984; editor: After the Wars, 1990; contbg. editor: Legacy of Vietnam: The War, American Society, and the Future of U.S. Foreign Policy, 1976. Office: Nat Security Coun 1600 Pennsylvania Ave NW Washington DC 20500-0001

LAKE, BRIAN JAMES, lawyer; b. Bloomfield, N.J., July 14, 1946; s. Walter H. and Bernice I. Lake; m. Virginia Ann Quirk, Nov. 27, 1971; children: Brian P., Timothy M. BA in Govt. cum laude U. Notre Dame, 1968; JD cum laude, U. Mich., 1971. Bar: Ind. 1972, Mich. 1971, Fla. 1972, U.S. Tax Ct. 1972. Assoc. Barnes & Thornburg, South Bend, Ind., 1972-77, ptnr., 1978—; seminar presenter, 1979-93. Bd. dirs. Family and Children's Ctr., Inc., Children's Campus, Inc.; bd. dirs., pres. Family and Children's Found., Inc.; bd. dirs., mem. exec. com. Michiana Pub. Broadcasting, 1978—, also past pres. 1st Lt. U.S. Army, 1972. Mem. ABA, Ind. Bar Assn., Mich. Bar Assn., Fla. Bar Assn., St. Joseph County Bar Assn., South Bend Country Club, Notre Dame Club St. Joseph Valley, Birchwood Farms Country Club. Roman Catholic. Avocations: sports, stock investing, photography. Office: Barnes & Thornburg 600 First Source Bk Ct 100 N Michigan St South Bend IN 46601-1630

LAKE, CAROL LEE, anesthesiologist, educator; b. Altoona, Pa., July 14, 1944; d. Samuel Lindsay and Edna Winifred (McMahan) L. BS, Juniata Coll., 1966; MD, Med. Coll. Pa., 1970. Intern Mercy Hosp., Pitts., 1970-71, resident in anesthesiology, 1971-73; staff anesthesiologist Pitts. Anesthesia Assocs., 1973-75; asst. prof. anesthesiology U. Va., Charlottesville, 1975-80, assoc. prof., 1980-89, prof. anesthesiology, 1989—; sr. assoc. examiner Am. Bd. Anesthesiology, Hartford, Conn., 1981—. Author: Cardiovascular Anesthesia, 1985; editor: Pediatric Cardiac Anesthesia, 1988, 2d edit., 1993; Clinical Monitoring, 1990, 2d edit., 1994. Fellow Am. Coll. Cardiology; mem. Assn. Cardiac Anesthesiologists (pres. 1987-88), Soc. Cardiovascular Anesthesiologists (bd. dirs. 1988-92), Assn. Univ. Anesthesiologists, Alpha Omega Alpha. Presbyterian. Avocations: music, entomology, gardening. Office: U Calif Davis Med Ctr 4150 V St Sacramento CA 95817

LAKE, DAVID S., publisher, lawyer; b. Youngstown, Ohio, July 17, 1938; s. Frank and Charlotte (Stahl) L.; m. Sandra J. Levin, Dec. 18, 1960 (div. Aug. 14, 1987); children: Joshua Seth, Jonathan Daniel. B.A. in Math, Youngstown State U., 1960; J.D. cum laude, Cleve. State U., 1965. Bar: Ohio 1965, D.C. 1970, U.S. Supreme Ct. 1969. Gen. counsel World Pub. Co., Cleve., 1965-68; dir. devel. Cath. U. Am., Washington, 1968-69; v.p., gen. counsel Microform Pub. Corp., Washington, 1969-70; dir. spl. projects Library Resources, Inc., Chgo., 1970-72; gen. mgr., partner Nat. Textbook Co., Skokie, Ill., 1972-76; pres. David S. Lake Pubs., Belmont, Calif., 1976-89, pres, owner, 1984-89; owner Lake Pub. Co., Belmont, 1989—. Contbr. to: Cleve. Marshall Law Rev, 1964. Served with USMC, 1960-62. Jewish. Office: Lake Pub Co 500 Harbor Blvd Belmont CA 94002-4021

LAKE, JOSEPH EDWARD, ambassador; b. Jacksonville, Tex., Oct. 18, 1941; s. Lloyd Euel and Marion Marie (Allen) L.; m. Sarah Ann Bryant (div.); children: Joseph Edward, Mary Elizabeth; m. Jo Ann Kessler, June 12, 1971; 1 child, Michael Allen. BA summa cum laude, Tex. Christian U., 1962, MA, 1967. Second sec. U.S. Embassy, Lagos, Nigeria, 1977-78; prin. officer and consul U.S. Consulate, Kaduna, Nigeria, 1978-81; with Fgn. Svc. Inst., Washington, 1981-82; first sec. U.S. Embassy, Sofia, Bulgaria, 1982-84, charge d'affaires, 1984, counselor, dep. chief mission, 1984-85; dep. dir. regional affairs , bur. East Asian and Pacific Affairs Dept. State, 1985-86; advisor U.S. delegation 41st UN Gen. Assembly, 1986; dir. ops. ctr. Dept. State, Washington, 1987-90; amb. to Rep. of Mongolia, Ulaanbaatar, 1990—. Contbr. articles to profl. jours. Mem. Am. Fgn. Svc. Assn. Office: US Embassy Ulaanbaatar Dept State Washington DC 20520

LAKE, KATHLEEN C., lawyer; b. San Antonio, Jan. 11, 1955; d. Herschel Taliaferro and Virginia Mae (Hylton) Cooper; m. Randall Brent Lake, Apr. 9, 1977; 1 child, Ethan Taliaferro. AB magna cum laude in Polit. Sci. with high honors, Middlebury Coll., 1977; JD with high honors, U. Tex., 1980. Bar: Tex. 1980, U.S. Ct. Appeals (5th cir.) 1981, U.S. Ct. Appeals (D.C. and 3d cirs.) 1984. Assoc. atty. Vinson & Elkins, Houston, 1980-88; ptnr. Vinson & Elkins, LLP, Houston, 1989—. Fellow Tex. Bar Found., Houston Bar Found.; mem. ABA, Fed. Energy Bar Assn., State Bar Tex., Tex. Law Rev. Assn. (life), Houston Bar Assn., Middlebury Coll. Alumni Assn. (com. mem. 1980—), Phi Beta Kappa, Phi Kappa Phi, Order of the Coif. Office: Vinson & Elkins LLP 2300 First City Twr 1001 Fannin Houston TX 77002-6760

LAKE, LARRY WAYNE, petroleum engineer; b. Del Norte, Colo., Jan. 31, 1946; s. Ralph Wayne and Ina Belle (Card) L.; m. Carole Sue Holmes, Mar. 22, 1975; children: Leslie Sue, Jeffrey Wayne. B.S., Ariz. State U., 1967, Ph.D., Rice U., 1973. Registered profl. engr., Tex. Prodn. engr. Motorola Co., Phoenix, 1968-70; sr. research engr. Shell Devel. Co., Houston, 1973-78; W.A. "Tex" Moncrief Centennial chair prof. U. Tex., Austin, 1978—; chmn. dept. petroleum engring.; cons. enhanced oil recovery. Recipient U. Tex. Engring. Found. award, 1979, Disting. Faculty Acad. award U. Tex., 1981, Grad. Engring. Council award, U. Tex., 1987. Mem. AICE, Soc. Mining Engrs., Soc. Petroleum Engrs. (mem. editorial rev. com., author video, Disting. Achievement award 1981), Soc. of Petroleum Engrs. (disting. lectr., bd. dirs., Reservoir Engr. award 1991). Baptist. Home: 4003 Edgefield Ct Austin TX 78731-2902 Office: U Tex Dept Petroleum Engring Austin TX 78712

LAKE, MAUREEN MAJOR, nurse; b. Birmingham, Ala., Aug. 23, 1948; d. Hubert William and Kathleen (Petty) Major; m. Douglas St. George Lake, Sept. 7, 1968; children: Matthew Major, Colleen Elizabeth. BSN, U. South Fla., 1978. RN. Staff nurse ICU St. Joseph's Hosp., Tampa, Fla., 1973-79; head nurse ICU Humana Biscayne Hosp., North Miami Beach, Fla., 1979-80; asst. dir. nursing Doctors Hosp., Hollywood, Calif., 1980-83; v.p nursing Mother Frances Hosp., Tyler, Tex., 1984—. Mem. Am. Nurses Assn., Nat. League for Nursing, Am. Assn. Critical-care Nurses (bd. dirs.). Republican. Avocations: travel, gardening. Home: 3802 Silverwood Dr Tyler TX 75701-9335

LAKE, SIMEON TIMOTHY, III, federal judge; b. Chgo., July 4, 1944; s. Simeon T. Jr. and Helen (Hupka) L.; m. Carol Illig, Dec. 30, 1970; children: Simeon Timothy IV, Justin Carl. BA, Tex. A&M, 1966; JD, U. Tex., 1969. Bar: Tex. 1969, U.S. Dist. Ct. (so. dist.) Tex. 1969, U.S. Ct. Appeals (5th cir.) 1969, U.S. Supreme Ct. 1976, U.S. Ct. Appeals (3d cir.) 1981, U.S. Dist. Ct. (no. dist.) Tex. 1983. From assoc. to ptnr. Fulbright & Jaworski, Houston, 1969-70, 72-88; judge U.S. Dist. Ct. (so. dist.) Tex., Houston, 1988—. Past editor Houston Lawyer. Served to capt. U.S. Army., 1970-71. Fellow Tex. Bar Assn., Houston Bar Assn., State Bar Tex., Am. Law Inst. Office: US Dist Ct 9535 US Courthouse 515 Rusk Ave Houston TX 77002-2603

LAKE, WILLIAM THOMAS, financial consultant; b. Ocean City, N.J., June 14, 1910; s. William Carson and Marie Cecelia (Kaiser) L.; m. V. Blair Torbert, Nov. 25, 1933 (div.); children: Donna Blair Lake Wright, Deborah Caren Lake Coates, Darelle Dee Lake Riabov, Carson Thomas; m. Dorothy Howell Caddelle, Mar. 1, 1968; 1 stepdau., Lynne E. Caddelle (Mrs. W. Dean Boecher). Grad., Rider Coll., Trenton, N.J., 1930. C.P.A., N.J., Pa., Mich., Calif., Colo., N.Y. Pub. acct. Lybrand Ross Bros. and Montgomery, Phila., 1932-39; controller Keystone Portland Cement Co., Phila., 1939-42; controller, treas. narrow fabric div. Burlington Mills, Allentown, Pa., 1946-48; controller Rouge plants Ford Motor Co., 1948-53; comptroller Curtiss Wright Corp., Wood Ridge, 1953-61, Gen. Dynamics Corp., 1961-68; v.p. finance aerospace and systems group Rockwell Internat., 1968-70; fin. cons., 1970—; pres. Talmud Internat. Mgmt. Co., Peripheral Engring. Inc.; treas. Talmud Internat. Ltd. Served to comdr. USNR, World War II; supply officer 4th Naval Dist., Naval Ordnance Plant York, Pa. Mem. Am. Inst. Profl. Cons. (charter), Fin. Execs. Inst. (life), AICPA (50 year hon. mem. award), N.J., Calif., Colo., Pa., Mich., N.Y. socs. CPAs, Am. Ordnance Assn., Navy League U.S. Presbyterian. Clubs: Masons (N.Y.C.) (32 deg.); Shriners; Economic (N.Y.C.), Engineers (N.Y.C.); Pinehurst Country. Home: 9 Oakwood Dr Queensbury NY 12804-1327

LAKEY, OTHAL H., bishop. Bishop Christian Meth. Episcopal Ch., Cin. Office: Christian Meth Episcopal Ch 6322 Elwynne Dr Cincinnati OH 45236-4014

LAKIER, NANCY S., health facility administrator; b. Ft. Madison, Iowa, Nov. 17, 1952; d. Bernard A. and Ruth Mary (Dyer) Mehmert; m. Richard Stephen Lakier, Nov. 12, 1983; 1 child, Andrea. BSN, Creighton U., 1975; MBA, U. Nebr., 1985. Staff and mdtt. mgmt. positions various orgns., 1975-83; v.p. nursing Children's Hosp., Omaha, 1983-86, Ft. Hamilton (Ohio)-Hughes, 1986-88, San Bernardino (Calif.) Community Hosp., 1989-90; assoc. administr. Scripps Meml. Hosp., La Jolla, Calif., 1990—; mem. nurse administrs. coun. of San Diego and Imperial Counties. Case Mgmt. and Critical Path Documentation System, 1991, CareTracs, 1991. Pres. alumni adv. bd. dirs. Creighton U., Omaha, 1984-88. Recipient Alumni Merit award Creighton U., Omaha, 1986, 87. Mem. Am. Orgn. Nurse Execs., Calif. Nurses Assn., VHA Nat. Nursing Adv. Bd. Avocations: walking, hiking, reading, gardening. Office: Scripps Meml Hosp 9888 Genesee Ave La Jolla CA 92037

LAKIER, THELMA, child development specialist, librarian; b. Pietersburg, Transvaal, S. Africa, May 28, 1941; came to U.S., 1978; d. Abraham and Berthe (MIchelsohn) Perlmann; m. Jeffrey Lakier, Dec. 20, 1964; children:

Beth, Louise. BA, U. Witaters, Johannesburg, S. Africa, 1962; Transvaal tchrs. higher diploma, Johannesburg Coll. Edn., S. Africa, 1963; postgrad., Erikson Inst., Chgo., 1988-91; MEd, Loyola U., Chgo., 1992. Cert. tchr., Mich. Tchr. Transvaal Edn. Dept., S. Africa, 1964, 66-72; libr. Libr. of Johannesburg, 1965; tchr. Hebrew Acad., San Francisco, 1972-74, Discovery Corner, Troy, Mich., 1982-88, Michael Reese Day Care, Chgo., 1988-89; child devel. specialist Luth. Gen. Children's Day Care Ctr., Des Plaines, Ill., 1989—; resource libr. for staff and parents, 1993—. Mem. Luth. Gen. Found Benefit Com., Chgo., 1989—. Mem. Nat. Assn. for Edn. of Young Children (workshop co-leader Chgo. chpt 1992), Assn. for Childhood Edn. Internat. Avocations: music, reading, needlework. Home: 2751 The Mews Northbrook IL 60062 Office: Luth Gen Children's Day Care 9375 Church St Des Plaines IL 60016

LAKIN, EDWIN A., retail executive; b. 1923. BA, Bklyn. Coll., 1946; student, NYU, 1946-48. CPA. Pvt. practice, 1948-50; with Julius Lefkowitz & Co., CPAs, N.Y.C., 1950-56; with Boscov's Department Store, Reading, Pa., 1956—, now pres. Office: Boscov's Department Store 4500 Perkiomen Ave Reading PA 19606-3202

LAKIN, JAMES DENNIS, allergist, immunologist; b. Harvey, Ill., Oct. 4, 1945; s. Ora Austin and Annie Pitranella (Johnson) L.; m. Sally A. Stuteville, July 22, 1972; children: Margaret K., Matthew A. PhD, Northwestern U., 1968, MD, 1969. Diplomate Am. Bd. Internal Medicine, Am. Bd. Allergy and Immunology. Dir. allergy rsch. Naval Med. Rsch. Inst., Bethesda, Md., 1974-76; clin. prof. U. Okla., Oklahoma City, 1976-89; dir. lab., chmn. allergy and immunology dept. Oxboro Clinics, Bloomington, Minn., 1989—; bd. dirs. Okla. Med. Rsch. Found., Oklahoma City, 1980-89; regional cons. Diver Alert Network, Duke U., Chapel Hill, N.C., 1987—; cert. diving med. officer NOAA, 1988. Co-author: Allergic Diseases, 1971, 3d edit., 1986; contbr. articles, revs. to profl. publs. Councilperson Our Lord's Luth. Ch., Oklahoma City, 1978-88, Faith Luth. Ch., Lakeville, Minn., 1990-91. Lt. comdr. USN, 1970-76. Fellow ACP, Am. Acad. Allergy and Immunology, Am. Coll. Chest Physicians; mem. Am. Assn. Immunologists. Achievements include research in characterization of the immunoglobulin system of the rhesus monkey, alterations in allergic reactivity during immunosuppression. Office: Oxboro Clinic 600 W 98th St Bloomington MN 55420-4773

LAKOFF, SANFORD, political scientist, educator; b. Bayonne, N.J., May 12, 1931; s. Herman and Gertrude (Robins) L.; m. Evelyn Schleifer, June 4, 1961. BA, Brandeis U., 1953; MA, Harvard U., 1955, PhD, 1959. Instr. to asst. prof. govt. Harvard U., Cambridge, Mass., 1958-65; assoc. prof. to prof. polit. sci. SUNY, Stony Brook, 1965-67; prof. polit. sci. U. Toronto, Ont., Can., 1967-74; prof. polit. sci. U. Calif., San Diego, 1974-92, rsch. prof., 1993—; acting dir. Inst. on Global Conflict and Cooperation U. Calif., 1988; cons. Commn. on MIT edn., Cambridge, 1970-71, NSF, Washington, 1979, Calif. Humanities Council, San Francisco, 1983-87. Author: Equality in Political Philosophy, 1964; co-author Science and the Nation, 1962, Energy and American Values, 1982, A Shield in Space?, 1989; editor Knowledge and Power, 1966; co-editor Strategic Defense and the Western Alliance, 1987. V.p. World Affairs Council of San Diego, 1985-86. Recipient Bowdoin Prize, Harvard U., 1955, Outstanding Community Service award U. Calif. San Diego, 1985, Outstanding Teacher award Warren Coll. U. Calif. San Diego, 1990; research grantee Carnegie Corp. N.Y, 1984; fellow Nat. Humanities Ctr., 1980-82; hon. fellow Brandeis U., 1989-94. Mem. Am. Polit. Sci. Assn. (council 1977-79), AAAS. Democrat. Jewish. Home: 3510 Dove Ct San Diego CA 92103-3904 Office: Univ Calif San Diego Dept Polit Sci 9500 Gilman Dr La Jolla CA 92093-0521

LAKRITZ, ISAAC, fundraising organization executive; b. Milw., June 11, 1952; s. Jeffrey and Deborah (Margolis) L.; m. Lea Winninger, May 22, 1982; children: Eli, Jacob, Atara. BA, U. Wis., Milw., 1973, MA, 1974. Cert. secondary sch. tchr. Coordinator Jewish Student Services Hillel, Milw., 1972-74; analyst Israel Ministry Social Welfare, Jerusalem, 1975-76; exec. dir. Jewish Nat. Fund Wis., Milw., 1977; devel. dir. Milw. Jewish Home, 1977-78; asst. dir. N.Y. Assn. for New Americans, N.Y.C., 1978-81; nat. youth dir. Zionist Orgn. Am., N.Y.C., 1981-84; asst. dir. Jacksonville (Fla.) Jewish Fedn., 1984-87, exec. v.p., 1987-90; exec. dir. east cen. region Am. Soc. for Technion, Detroit, 1990—. Chmn. Israel Com. Conf. Jewish Communal Service, 1982—. Recipient Top Pub. Rels. award in N.Am. Coun. Jewish Fedn. Mem. Assn. Jewish Community Orgn. Personnel, Phi Kappa Phi. Avocations: opera, stamps. Office: Am Technion Soc 29645 W 14 Mile Rd Farmington MI 48334-1666 *Our task is to build a more just and compassionate world. With mankind's considerable technical expertise, we have shown that we can accomplish just about anything we really desire. Let us create an environment where that which is right and kind is desirable.*

LAKSHMANAN, T.R., federal agency administrator, geography and environmental engineering educator, writer; m. Lata Chatterjee; children: Srobona, Indira. Corp. v.p. CONSAD Rsch. Corp., Pitts.; sr. analyst, assoc. Alan M. Voorhees Assocs.; prof. geography and environ. engring. Johns Hopkins U., 1973-78; founder, exec. dir. Ctr. for Energy and Environ. Studies Boston U.; first dir. Bur. Transp. Statistics U.S. Dept. Transp., Washington; vis. scholar Netherlands Inst. for Adv. Studies in the Humanities and Social Scis., Internat. Inst. for Applied Systems Analysis, Austria, Cambridge U., U.K., MIT; cons. UN, The World Bank, Japan's EPA, many govts. in Europe and Asia. Author 10 books; contbr. over 60 articles to profl. jours. Recipient James Anderson medal Assn. Am. Geographers. Mem. Clare Hall Coll. Cambridge U. (elected life). Office: Dept Transp Transp Statistics Bureau 400 7th St SW Washington DC 20590*

LAKSHMIKANTHAM, VANGIPURAM, mathematics educator; b. Hyderabad, India, Aug. 8, 1926; came to U.S., 1960, naturalized, 1966; s. Soroja Bukkapatnam, Feb. 22, 1942; children: Sreekantham, Neerada, Nirupama. MA, Osmania U., Hyderabad, 1955, PhD, 1958. Mem. faculty UCLA, 1960-61, Math. Rsch. Ctr., U. Wis., Madison, 1961-62; mem. Rsch. Inst. Advanced Studies, Balt., 1962-63; assoc. prof. U. Alta., Calgary, Can., 1963-64; prof., chmn. dept. math. Marathwada U., Aurangabad, India, 1964-66, U. R.I., Kingston, 1966-73, U. Tex., Arlington, 1973-88; prof., head dept. applied math. Fla. Inst. Tech., Melbourne, 1989—. Author 22 books; founder, editor: Jour. Nonlinear Analysis, Nonlinear World, Nonlinear Times and Digest, Stochastic Analysis and Applications, Mathematical Problems in Engineering; assoc. editor other jours.; contbr. over 250 rsch. articles to profl. publs. Mem. Am. Math. Soc., Indian Math. Soc., Soc. Indsl. and Aplied Math., Nat. Acad. Sci. India, Internat. Fedn. Nonlinear Analysts (founder). Office: Fla Inst Tech Dept Applied Math 150 W University Blvd Melbourne FL 32901-6967

LAKSHMINARAYANA, BUDUGUR, aerospace engineering educator; b. Shimoga, India, Feb. 15, 1935; came to U.S., 1963, naturalized, 1971; m. Saroja Lakshminarayana; children: Anita, Arvind. BME, Mysore U., India, 1958; PhD, U. Liverpool, Eng., 1963, DEng, 1981. Grad. trainee Steel Constrn. Co., Bangalore, India, 1957; asst. mech. engr. Kolar (India) Gold Mining Undertakings, 1958-60; rschr. in mech. engring. U. Liverpool, 1960-63, Leverhulme fellow, 1962-63; vis. asst. prof. aerospace engring. Pa. State U., University Park, 1963-65, asst. prof. aerospace engring., 1965-69, assoc. prof., 1969-74, prof., 1974-85, dir. computational fluid dynamics studies, 1980-87, disting. alumni prof., 1985-86, Evan Pugh prof., 1986—, dir. Ctr. for Gas Turbines and Power, 1994—; vis. fellow scientist Cambridge U., St. John's Coll., Eng., 1971-72; vis. assoc. prof. aeros. and astronautics MIT, 1972; vis. prof. dept. mech. engring. Indian Inst. Sci., 1979; aerospace engr. computational fluid mechanics group NASA Ames Rsch. Ctr., Moffett Field, Calif., 1979; CNRS vis. prof. Laboratoire de Mecanique des Fluides at d'Acoustique, Ecole Centrale de Lyon, France, 1987-88; vis. prof. Tech. U. of Aachen, Germany, 1988; adv. prof. Inst. Thermophysics Chinese Acad. Scis., 1993, Shanghai Jiao Tong U., China, 1993; cons. Pratt & Whitney Aircraft, GE Aircraft Engine Div., Garrett Turbines, Teledyne CAE, Inc.; UN, NATO/AGARD lectr.; Gen. Motors, Rolls Royce, 'European Space Agy.; mem. NASA adv. group on computational fluid dynamics, 1980; lectr. in field. Author book; editor 2 books; contbr. numerous articles on fluid dynamics, turbomachinery, computational fluid dynamics, turbulence modelling and acoustics to profl. publs. Recipient Henry R. Worthington N.Am. tech. award, 1977, sr. prof. Fulbright award, 1988, Arch. T. Colwell merit award Soc. Automotive Engrs., 1992; merit scholar Mysore U., 1953-57; grantee NSF, numerous others. Fellow AIAA (chmn. Cen. Pa. chpt. 1970, Pendrey Lit. award 1989, Airbreathing Propulsion award 1994),

ASME (Freeman Scholar award 1990). Office: Pa State U Coll Engring 153 Hammond Bldg University Park PA 16802

LAL, DEVENDRA, nuclear geophysics educator; b. Varanasi, India, Feb. 14, 1929; s. Radhe Krishna and Sita Devi (Gupta) L.; m. Aruna Damany, May 17, 1955 (dec. July 1993). BS, Banaras Hindu U., Varanasi, 1947, MS, 1949, DSc (hon. causa), 1984; PhD, Bombay U., 1960. Research student Tata Inst. of Fundamental Research, Bombay, 1949-60, research fellow, fellow, assoc. prof., 1960-63, prof., 1963-70, sr. prof., 1970-72; dir. Phys. Research Lab., Ahmedabad, India, 1972-83; sr. prof. Phys. Research Lab. Ahmedabad, 1983-89; vis. prof. UCLA, 1965-66, 83-84; prof. Scripps Instn. Oceanography, La Jolla, Calif., 1967—; fellow Phys. Rsch. Lab. Ahmedabad, 1989—. Editor: Early Solar System Processes and the Present Solar System, 1980, Biogeochemistry of the Arabian Sea, 1995. Recipient K.S. Krishnan Gold medal Indian Geophys. Union, 1965, S.S. Bhatnagar award for Physics, Govt. of India, 1971, award for Excellence in Sci. and Tech., Gedn. of Indian Chamber Com., 1974, Pandit Jawaharlal Nehru award for Scis., 1986, Group Achievement award NASA, 1986. Fellow Royal Soc London, Indian Nat. Sci. Acad., Indian Acad. Scis.; mem. NAS U.S.A. (fgn. assoc.), Third World Acad. Scis. (founding mem.), Indian Geophys. Union, NAS India, Royal Astron. Soc. (assoc.), Internat. Acad. Aeronautics, Internat. Union of Geodesy and Geophysics (pres. 1984-87), Am. Acad. Arts and Scis. (fgn. hon. mem.), Internat. Assn. Phys. Sch. of Ocean (hon. mem., pres. 1979-83), Geol. Soc. India (hon. fellow 1992). Hindu. Avocations: chess, photography, painting, math. puzzles. Office: U Calif Scripps Inst Oceanography GRD-0220 La Jolla CA 92093-0220

LAL, RATTAN, soil scientist, researcher; b. Karyal, Punjab, India, Sept. 5, 1944; came to U.S., 1987; s. Jagan Nath and Krishna Nath (Lakhanpal) Bhakri; m. Sukhvarsha Sharma, Dec. 12, 1971; children: Priya, Pratibha, Abhishek, Vivek. MS in Soils, I.A.R.I., New Delhi, India, 1965; PhD in Soil Physics, Ohio State U., 1968. Rsch. assoc. Rockefeller Found., New Delhi, India, 1963-65; rsch. assoc. Ohio Agrl. Rsch. and Devel. Ctr. Ohio State U., Wooster and Columbus, 1966-68; sr. rsch. fellow U. Sydney, N.S.W., Australia, 1968-69; soil physicist Internat. Inst. Tropical Agr., Ibadan, Nigeria, 1970-87, coord. UPS, 1985-87; assoc. prof. Ohio State U., Columbus, 1987-89, prof., 1989—; cons. World Bank, Washington, UN Devel. Program/Food and Agrl. Orgn., N.Y.C., Rome, Tropical R&D, Gainesville, Fla.; bd. dirs. Orgn. Tropical Studies, Durham, N.C. Author: Tropical Ecology and Physical Edaphology, 1987, Soil Erosion in the Tropics - Principles and Management, 1990; editor: Soil Erosion Research Methods, 1988, 94; co-editor: Tropical Agricultural Hydrology, 1981, Soil Management for Sustainability, 1991, 20 additional books. Recipient Merit award Indian Soc. Soil and Water Conservation, Dehradun, India, 1990, Disting. Scientist award ASIO, 1990. Fellow Am. Soc. Agronomy, Soil Sci. Soc. Am. (Internat. Soil Sci. award 1988, Soil Sci. Applied Rsch. award 1992), Third World Acad. Scis. (Disting. Scholar award 1994); mem. Internat. Soil Tillage Rsch. Orgn. (pres. 1988-91) World Assn. Soil and Water Conservation (pres. 1988-91), Sigma Xi (rsch. award 1995). Achievements include research on developing sustainable alternatives to shifting cultivation and bush fallow systems, soil erosion and its control, agricultural impact on soil and environmental degradation, soil process and greenhouse effect, soil compaction, anaerobiosis and other aspects of physical edaphology. Office: Ohio State U Dept Agronomy 2021 Coffey Rd Columbus OH 43210-1044

LALA, DOMINICK J., manufacturing company executive; b. N.Y.C., June 2, 1928; s. Joseph and Mary (Billera) L.; m. Nancy Bosco, Nov. 30, 1957; children: John, Steven, James, Thomas, Patrice. B.S., NYU, 1951. Mem. staff BDO/Seidman (CPAs), N.Y.C., 1951-62; v.p., contr. Universal Am. Corp., N.Y.C., 1962-68; sr. v.p. finance Paramount Pictures Corp., 1968-70; exec. v.p. Gould Paper Corp., 1970—. Served with AUS, 1946-47. Mem. AICPA, N.Y. State Soc. CPAs, Fin. Execs. Inst. Home: 10 Burnham Pl Manhasset NY 11030-2709 Office: Gould Paper Corp 315 Park Ave S New York NY 10010-3607

LALA, PEEYUSH KANTI, medical scientist, educator; b. Chittagong, Bengal, India, Nov. 1, 1934; came to U.S., 1963, to Can., 1967; s. Sudhangshu Bimal and Nani Bala (Chaudhuri) L.; m. Arati Roy-Burman, July 7, 1962 (dec.); children: Probal, Prasun; m. Shipra Bhattacareya, Nov. 6, 1992. MBBS, Calcutta (India) U., 1957, PhD in Med. Biophysics, 1962. Demonstrator pathology Calcutta Med. Coll., 1959-60, NRS Med. Coll., Calcutta, 1961-62; resident research assoc. Biol. and Med. Research div. Argonne (Ill.) Nat. Lab., 1963-64; research scientist lab radiobiology U. Calif. Med. Ctr., San Francisco, 1964-66; research scientist Biol. and Health Physics div. Chalk River (Ont., Can.) Nuclear Lab., 1967-68; from asst. prof. to assoc. prof. dept. anatomy McGill U., Montreal, Que., Can., 1968-77, prof. dept. anatomy, 1977-83; prof. dept. anatomy U. Western Ont., London, 1983—, chmn. dept. anatomy, 1983-93, prof. dept. oncology, 1990—; mem. grants panel MRC Can., Ottawa, Ont., 1983-87, 93—, NIH U.S.A., Bethesda, Md., 1977-86, Nat. Cancer Inst. Can., Toronto, 1987-90, Cancer Res. Soc., Montreal, 1987-90; mem. Cannaught com., Toronto, 1990-91; vis. prof. Walter and Eliza Hall Inst. Med. Res., U. Melbourne, Australia, 1977-78. Mem. editl. bd. Leukemia Rsch., 1977-86, Exptl. Hematology, 1974-77, Am. Jour. Reproductive Immunology, 1983-93, Early Pregnancy: Biology and Medicine, 1994—; assoc. editor Am. Jour. Anatomy, 1987-90; contbr. over 140 articles to profl. jours. Chmn. Bengali Cultural Ctr., Montreal, 1978-83. Grantee MRC Can., 1968—, NCI Can., 1968—, NIH U.S.A., 1976-79, Cancer Research Soc., 1978—; fellow Fulbright Found., 1962. Mem. Am. Assn. Cancer Research, Am. Assn. Anatomists, Can. Assn. Anatomists (chmn. awards com. 1987-89, v.p. and pres. elect 1989-90, pres. 1991-93, J.C.B. Grant award 1990), Internat. Soc. Exptl. Hematology, Soc. Leukocyte Biology, Am. Assn. Immunologists, Can. Soc. Immunologists, Internat. Soc. Reproductive Immunology (councillor 1986-89), Am. Soc. Reproductive Immunology (v.p. 1985-86). Achievements include discovery of new mode of cancer immunotherapy, resulting in a phase 2 human trial. Office: U Western Ont, Dept Anatomy, London, ON Canada N6A 5C1

LALANNE, JACK (FRANÇOIS HENRI LALANNE), physical fitness specialist, entrepreneur; b. San Francisco, Calif., Sept. 26, 1914; m. Elaine LaLane, 1959; children: Jon Allen, Yvonne, Janet (dec.). Opened first gym Jack LaLanne's Physical Culture Studio, Oakland, Calif., 1936; host The Jack LaLanne Show, 1956-70, Jack LaLanne and You, 1981-83. released Jack LaLanne's Glamour Stretcher Time (album), 1959, Jack LaLanne's Low Impact Plus Workout Featuring Kim Scott (video), 1988; books include: The Jack LaLanne Way to Vibrant Good Health, 1960, Foods for Glamour, 1961, For Men Only, with a Thirty-Day Guide to Looking Better and Feeling Younger, 1973, Revitalize Your Health: Improve Your Health, Your Sex Life & Your Look after Age Fifty, 1995. Address: PO Box 1023 Burbank CA 93406*

LALAS, ALEXI, professional soccer player; b. Birmingham, Mich.; s. Demetrius and Anne Lalas. BA in English, Rutgers U., 1991. Mem. U.S. Olympic Soccer Team, 1992, World Cup U.S. Soccer Team, 1993-94, Football Club Padova, Italian League, 1994—; mem. U.S. Olympic Festival Team, 1989, U.S. Pan-Am. Team, 1991. Mem. group Gypsies; rec. Woodland. Recipient Hermann trophy, 1991; named Coll. Soccer Player of Yr., 1991. Avocation: acoustic guitar. Office: FC Padova, 35100 Padova Italy*

LALIBERTE, GARLAND EVERETT, agricultural engineer; b. Walkerburn, Man., Can., Dec. 28, 1936; m. Audry Whitlock; 2 children: Tracy, Marnie. BS in Agrl. Engring., U. Sask., Can., 1956, MS, 1961; PhD, Colo. State U., 1966. Prof. U. Manitoba, Winnipeg, Can., 1967—. Fellow Agrl. Inst. Can. (mem. nat. coun. 1980-82), Can. Soc. Agrl. Engring. (charter, sr. mem. v.p. tech. 1971-73, pres. 1978-79, Maple Leaf award 1981); mem. Assn. of Faculties of Agr. in Can. (charter, bd. dirs. 1974-78, sec.-treas. 1974-75, pres. 1976-77, 77-78), Assn. Profl. Engrs. of Manitoba (coun. 1984-90, pres. 1988-89), Can. Agrl. Machinery Inst. (coun. 1983-85), Manitoba Econ. Innovation and Tech. Coun. Office: University of Manitoba, Prof of Agricultural Engineering, Winnipeg, MB Canada R3V 5V6

LALIBERTÉ-BOURQUE, ANDRÉE, museum director. Student, Queen's U., Ont., Can., 1960; U. Laval Sch. Liberal Arts, 1962-65, U. Laval Sch. Visual Arts, 1973-75; student Mus. Mgmt., Leicester U., Eng., 1987; student, Nat. Sch. Pub. Adminstrn., Québec, CAn., 1988. Tchr. visual arts Quebec,

Sillery, regional Scholar Commn. Tilly (Sainte Foy), Univ. Laval, 1973-77; tchr. Musée du Québec, 1977-78; dir., curator Galérie du Musée (Anse aux Barques), modern art Musée du Québec, 1979-86; chief curator Musée du Québec, 1986-88, gen. dir., 1988-93; curator Museé du Québec, Québec, Can., 1993—; mem. multidisciplinary cons. com. Region Tilly, 1974; dir. Studio Graphic Prodns., 1976-77; found. assoc. mem. Galerie sur la Côte, 1978-80; mem. Can. commn. examination cultural exports, 1988-91, study group profl. formation cultural sector Can., 1991, adminstrn. coun. Office tourism, Congress urban community Quebec, 1991-92; mem. various juries. Contbr. numerous articles, publications, interviews to profl. jours. Program com. Summer Festival Quebec, 1974-76; dir. regional com. Implantation Radio-Quebec, 1977; adminstrn. coun. Symphony Orch. Quebec, 1989-90; assembly govs. Univ. Quebec, 1990—, pres. com. arts teaching award Univ. Quebec, 1992. Recipient prize Prime Minister province Quebec, 1974, Prize Excellence Assn. Career Women Metropolis Quebec, 1988, cert. honor Fed. Bank Devel. Can. 1988. Mem. Internat. Com. Expositions Exchange (com. Internat. coun. mus. 1986-87, coun. adminstrn. 16th gen. conf., sec. exec com., pres. subcom. indemnification mus., organizer ann. reunion Dublin 1987), Assn. Can. Mus. (adhesion com. 1988-89, coun. adminstrn. 1988-90, pres. com. nominations 1989-90), Garrison Club (coun. adminstrn. 1990). Home: 4328 Turcotte, Cap-Rouge, PQ Canada G1Y 2P1 Office: Musée du Québec, 1 ave Wolfe-Montcalm, Quebec, PQ Canada G1R 5H3

LALINE, BRIAN J., newspaper editor; b. S.I., N.Y., Sept. 15, 1949; s. Joseph J. and Nancy (Duffy) L.; m. Carol P. Sadowski; children: Christopher, Peter, Kelly Anne. BA, LaSalle U., 1971; MS, Wagner Coll., 1972. From reporter to editor S.I. Advance, 1972—. Bd. dirs. Meals on Wheels, S.I., 1994-95, S.I. Bot. Garden, 1994-95; v.p. Staten Island Coun. Boy Scout of Am. Office: SI Advance 950 Fingerboard Rd Staten Island NY 10305

LALL, B. KENT, civil engineering educator; b. Feb. 4, 1939; m. Margaret Vivienne Boult, Nov. 30, 1970; 1 child, Niren Nicolaus. BS in Civil Engring., Panjab Engring. Coll., Chandigarh, India, 1961; ME in Hwy. Engring., U. Roorkee, India, 1964; PhD in Transp., U. Birmingham, Eng., 1969. Registered profl. engr. Commonwealth scholar U. Birmingham, 1966-69; lectr. Indian Inst. Tech., New Delhi, 1964-72, asst. prof., 1972-75; assoc. prof. U. Man., Winnipeg, Can., 1975-77; assoc. prof. civil engring. Portland (Oreg.) State U., 1977-84, prof., 1984—; vis. prof. U. Adelaide, South Australia, 1985; cons. Nat. Rds. Bd., Ministry of Works, Wellington, New Zealand, 1986. Contbr. articles to profl. jours. Vol. Meals on Wheels, Portland, 1991—. Fellow ASCE (chair transp. congress 1995, exec. com., chair urban transp. divsn. 1994-95, chair pub. transp. com. 1988-91, mem. high speed ground transport com.), S.W. Portland Rotary (bd. dirs. 1990-91, 95-96). Office: Portland State U Dept Civil Engring PO Box 751 Portland OR 97207-0751

LALLEY, FRANK EDWARD, federal government official; b. Woonsocket, R.I., Jan. 11, 1944; s. Frank Edward III and Lois Eva (Parkin) L.; m. Joyce Lynne Rynkiewicz, June 11, 1983; children: Jonathan, Robert, Adrienne, Andrea. B in Mgmt. Engring., Rensselaer Poly. Inst., 1965; MBA, So. Ill. U., 1971; postgrad., George Washington U., 1972-75. Ops. rsch. analyst U.S. Army, 1969-74; energy analyst FEA, Washington, 1974-77; dir. petroleum supply div. U.S. Dept. Energy, Washington, 1977-87; dir. Office Info., Mgmt. and Stats. U.S. Dept. Vets. Affairs, Washington, 1987-90; assoc. dep. asst. sec. Info. Resources Policies and Oversight U.S. Dept. Vets. Affairs, 1990-94, assoc. dep. asst. sec. Telecom., 1994—; co-chmn. publ. U.S. Refining Industry, Nat. Petroleum Coun., 1986, govt. liaison publ. U.S. Oil and Gas Outlook, 1987; mem. Nat. Performance Review, 1993; chmn. Interagency Com. Info. Resources Mgmt., 1994-95. Capt. USAF, 1965-69. Home: 13001 Shadwell Ct Woodbridge VA 22192 Office: Dept Vets Affairs 810 Vermont Ave NW Washington DC 20420-0002

LALLEY, RICHARD A., school system administrator. Supt. Brick Sch., Amherst, N.H., 1975—. Recipient N.H. Supt. of the Yr. awd., Am. Assn. of Sch. Adminstrs., 1993. Office: SAU # 39 Brick Sch PO Box 849 Amherst NH 03031

LALLI, CELE GOLDSMITH, editor; b. Scranton, Pa., Apr. 8, 1933; d. Arthur Langfeld and Viola Catherine (Wolfort) Goldsmith; m. Michael Anthony Lalli, Apr. 4, 1964; children—Francesca Ann, Erica Catherine. BA, Vassar Coll., 1955. From asst. editor to editor Amazing Sci. Fiction Stories, N.Y.C., 1955-65; mng. editor Modern Bride's Guide to Decorating Your First Home, N.Y.C., 1965-69; exec. editor Modern Bride, N.Y.C., 1969-81, editor-in-chief, v.p., 1982—. Co-author: Modern Bride Guide to Your Wedding and Marriage, 1984, Modern Bride Wedding Celebrations, 1992; author: Modern Bride Guide to Etiquette, 1993. Bd. dirs. Conn. Assn. for Children with Learning Disabilities, 1984-93. Recipient Invisible Little Man award West Coast Sci. Fiction Orgn., 1961; named to YWCA Acad. of Women Achievers, 1986. Mem. Am. Soc. Mag. Editors, Fashion Group. Republican. Roman Catholic. Office: Modern Bride Cahners Pub Co 249 W 17th St New York NY 10011-5300

LALLI, FRANK, magazine editor. Mng. editor Money mag., N.Y.C. Office: Money Magazine Time & Life Bldg Rockefeller Ctr 33rd fl New York NY 10020

L'ALLIER, JAMES JOSEPH, educational multimedia company executive, instructional designer; b. St. Paul, June 24, 1945; s. Charlemagne Joseph and Mildred Marie (LeVasseur) L'A.; m. Susan Kay Margulies, Apr. 28, 1973. BS magna cum laude, U. Wis., River Falls, 1969, MS, 1973; PhD, U. Minn., 1980. Instr. English River Falls Sr. High Sch., 1969-71, Stillwater (Minn.) Sr. High Sch., 1971-80; mgr. computer assisted instrn. Wilson Learning Corp., Mpls., 1980-83, dir. R&D, 1983-86; v.p. R&D Wilson Learning Interactive Tech. Group, Santa Fe, 1986-89; v.p. product devel. Nippon Wilson Learning, Tokyo, 1989-90; v.p. instructional systems Whole Systems International, Cambridge, Mass., 1990-93; v.p. product devel. Nat. Edn. Tng. Group, Naperville, Ill., 1993—; expert witness Universal Tng., Chgo., 1989-91. Author: (video prodns.) Who Shot the Terminal?, 1984, The Tenth Woman, 1987, Working Toward the Future, 1991, America's Workforce: A Vision for the Future, 1992; mem. editorial bd. Learning Age, Mpls., 1987-89; product reviewer Ednl. Tech., N.Y.C., 1981-83; assoc. editor Performance and Instrn., Washington, 1983-85. Curriculum chair Total Info. Ednl. Systems, St. Paul, 1971-76; fund raiser U. Minn. Alliance, Mpls., 1983-89; contbr. Am. Cancer Soc., Washington, 1987—; mem. pub. svc. com. Instructional Systems Assn., Sunset Beach, Calif., 1988—. U. Minn. Grad. Sch. Edn. sr. fellow, 1984; U.S. Dept. Labor grantee, 1991. Mem. U. Wis. Alumni Assn., Instructional Systems Assn. (conf. chair 1980, 84), U. Minn. Alumni Assn., Boston Computer Soc., Pres.'s Club U. Minn., Heritage Soc. U. Wis.; reviewer William H. Donner Found. Inc., N.Y.C., 1993—. Avocations: reading, photography, music, computer programming. Office: Nat Edn Tng Group 1751 W Diehl Rd Naperville IL 60563

L'ALLIER, JEAN-PAUL, mayor. BA, U. Montreal, 1959; LLM, U. Ottawa, 1962, diploma of superior studies, 1963. Mem. law firms Ville de Quebec, Ottawa and Hull, Ont., Can.; mem. law faculty U. Ottawa; rsch. officer Centre africain de formation et de recherches adminstratives pour le développment, Morocco, 1964-66; dir. coop. Ministry of Cultural Affairs Que., 1966-68; sec. gen. l'Office franco-que. pour la jeunesse, 1968, chmn. bd. dirs., 1970-76; mem. Deux-Montagnes Nat. Assembly Que., 1970-76; pres. Jean-Paul L'Allier & Assocs., 1976-89; mayor City of Que., 1989—; ministe youth recreation and sports Nat. Assembly Que., 1970, minister pub. svc., 1970-72, minister communications, 1970-75, minister cultural affairs, 1975-76, mem. treasury bd. and legislative com., 1970-76; pres. ministerial com. Quality of Life, 1970-76; gen. del. Que. in Belgium, 1981-84, hon. consul, 1985-88. Chmn. Orgn. World Heritage Cities, 1993. Decorated Légion d'honneur. Mem. Assn. internationale des maires francophones (v.p.). Office: Hôtel de Ville, 2 rue Desjardins CP 700, Quebec, PQ Canada G1R 4S9

LALLINGER, E. MICHAEL, savings and loan association executive; b. St. Louis, Aug. 17, 1915; s. Michael N. and Clara (Neiderhoff) L.; m. Johnetta Claire Ward, Jan, 14, 1948; children: Michael John, John Ward, Mary Jeanne. Student, Jefferson Coll., St. Louis, 1937. With RFC, 1941-51, asst. mgr. Dallas office, 1950-51; asst. regional commr. IRS, Dallas, 1952-56; exec. v.p. Gibraltar Savs. Assn., Houston, 1956-63; pres. Gibraltar Savs. Assn., 1963-80, chmn. bd., chief exec. officer, 1980-88, ret., 1988; also dir.; pres., chief exec. officer, dir. Imperial Corp. Am., from 1980; dir. First Internat. Bank,

Houston, Fed. Home Loan Mortgage Corp., Washington, First Tex. Savs. Assn.; tchr. individual and corp. tax acctg. Jefferson Coll., 1939-40. Capt., inf. AUS, 1942-46, ETO. Decorated Silver Star, Bronze Star, Purple Heart; Order Leopold Belgium; Croix de Guerre France). Mem. Nat. League Insured Savs. Assns., U.S. Savs. and Loan League, U.S. C. of C., Houston C. of C. Home: 2121 Kirby Dr Apt 52 Houston TX 77019-6065 Office: 1770 St James Pl Ste 605 Houston TX 77056-3405

LALLY, MICHAEL DAVID, writer, actor; b. Orange, N.J., May 25, 1942; s. James A. and Irene I. (Dempsey) L.; children: Caitlin Maeve, Miles Aaron. BA, U. Iowa, 1968, MFA, 1969. Instr. Trinity Coll., Washington, 1969-74; book reviewer Washington Post, 1974-77; editor Franklin Library div. Franklin Mint, 1976-79; editor, pub. various newspapers and presses including Iowa Defender, Some of Us Press, The Washington Review of the Arts, 1966-80, Venice mag., 1988-91, The Hollywood Rev., 1991; bd. dirs. The Print Center, Bklyn., 1972-75, Washington Film Classroom, 1970-72. Actor: (films) Last Rites, 1980, The Nesting, 1981, White Fang, 1991, Cool World, 1992, Basic Instinct, 1992; stage The Heroes, 1981, Balm in Gilead, 1983, The Rhythm of Torn Stars, 1988-89, Short Eyes, 1994; (TV) Cagney & Lacey, 1984, Berrengers, 1985, Hardcastle and McCormick, 1986, L.A. Law, 1989, Father Dowling's Mysteries, 1991, Caught in the Act, 1993, Diagnosis Murder, 1994, NYPD Blue, 1995; freelance writer, reviewer, actor, N.Y.C., 1975-82, screenwriter, actor, L.A., 1982—; author 20 books including Rocky Dies Yellow, 1974, German edit., 1982, Dues, 1974, Catch My Breath, 1976, 95, Just Let Me Do It, 1978, Attitude, 1982, Hollywood Magic, 1982; author, dir. (one-act play) Four Grown Men, N.Y.C., 1982, Hollywood Magic, L.A., 1983; co-author: (play) The Rhythm of Torn Stars, 1988-89; recorded poems on CD What You Find There, 1994; contbr. articles and poetry to profl. jours., newspapers, mags. Served with USAF, 1962-66. Recipient Discovery award N.Y. Poetry Center, 1972, award Poets Found., 1974; Nat. Endowment for Arts fellow, 1974, 81. Mem. Screen Actors Guild, Writers Guild Am., AFTRA, P.E.N.

LALLY, RICHARD FRANCIS, aviation security consultant, former association executive, former government official; b. Newark, Nov. 23, 1925; s. Francis J. and Helen (Fenney) L.; m. Doris P. Yasko, Sept. 10, 1949; children: Barbara J. Lally-Dittler, Joan E. Lally Stalder. B.S., Upsala Coll. 1950. Spl. agt. FBI, Atlanta, Cin. and Washington, 1951-60; area dir., chief gen. investigations Dept. Labor, Newark and Washington, 1960-63; dep. dir. compliance and security FAA, Washington, 1963-65; dir. compliance and security FAA, 1965-67; dir. investigations and security Dept. Transp., Washington, 1967-70; dir. equal opportunity Dept. Transp., 1967-70, dir. civil rights, 1970-72, dir. transp. security, 1972-74; dir. civil aviation security FAA, 1974-82; v.p. security Air Transport Assn. Am., 1982-91; aviation security consultant, 1991—. Served with AC U.S. Army, 1944-46. Recipient Exceptional Svc. citation Dept. Trans., 1969, Meritorious Achievement award, 1970, Sec.'s award, 1973, Superior Achievement award, 1970, Sec.'s award, 1973, Superior Achievement award, 1973, 76, Superior Achievement in Equal Opportunity award, 1977, Disting. Alumnus award Upsala Coll., 1979, Presdl. Rank Sr. Exec. award, 1980, Extraordinary Svc. award FAA, 1991, Internat. Security Mgmt. Assn. J. Paul Breslin Recognition award, 1993. Home and Office: Bay Colony 25 Indian River Dr Dagsboro DE 19939

LALLY, VINCENT EDWARD, atmospheric scientist; b. Brookline, Mass., Oct. 13, 1922; s. Michael James and Ellen Teresa (Dolan) L.; m. Marguerite Mary Tibert, June 5, 1949; children: Dennis V., Marianne Baugh, Stephen J. BS in Meteorology, U. Chgo., 1944; BSEE, MIT, 1948, MS in Engring. Adminstrn., 1949. Engr. Bendix-Friez, Balt., 1949-51; chief metall. equip. devel. Air Force Cambridge Rsch. Labs., Bedford, Mass., 1951-58; rsch. dir. Teledynamics, Phila., 1958-61; dir. Nat. Sci. Balloon Facility Nat. Ctr. for Atmospheric Rsch., Boulder, Colo., 1961-66, sr. scientist, 1966-91, sr. scientist emeritus, 1991—. Contbr. articles to sci. jours., chpt. to handbook in field. 1st lt. USAAC, 1942-46. Fellow Am. Meteorol. Soc. (Cleveland Abbe award 1990); mem. Inst. Navigation, Sigma Xi. Achievements include 7 patents for space inflatables, superpressure balloons, rocket instruments, communications techniques; made first balloon flight around the world, longest balloon flight; pioneered technology in measurements from radiosondes, aircraft and rockets. Avocations: running, golf, application of Monte Carlo techniques to gaming. Home: 4475 Laguna Pl # 305 Boulder CO 80303 Office: Nat Ctr Atmospheric Rsch PO Box 3000 Boulder CO 80307*

LALONDE, BERNARD JOSEPH, educator; b. Detroit, June 3, 1933; s. John Bernard and Fannie (Napier) LaL.; m. Barbara Elaine Eggenberger, Sept. 6, 1958; children—Lisa Renee, Michell Ann, Christopher John. A.B., U. Notre Dame, 1955; M.B.A., U. Detroit, 1957; Ph.D., Mich. State U. 1961. Asst. prof. mktg. U. Colo., Boulder, 1961-65; assoc. prof. Mich. State U., East Lansing, 1965-69; James R. Riley prof. mktg. and logistics Ohio State U., Columbus, 1969-85; Raymond E. Mason prof. transp. and logistics Ohio State U., 1985—. Author: Physical Distribution Management, 2d edit, 1968, Customer Service: A Management Perspective, 1988; Editor: Jour. Bus. Logistics; Jour. book and monographs editor, Am. Mktg. Assn.; Contbr. articles to profl. jours. Pres. Transp. Research Found. Recipient John Drury Sheehan award, 1976; Formerly Ford scholar; Gen. Electric fellow. Mem. Am. Marketing Assn., Regional Sci. Assn., Council Logistic Mgmt., Soc. Logistics Engrs., Beta Gamma Sigma, Alpha Kappa Psi. Roman Catholic. Home: 8538 Pitlochry Ct Dublin OH 43017-9709 Office: Ohio State U Coll Bus Logistics Rsch Group 421 Hagerty Hall Columbus OH 43210

LALONDE, MARC, lawyer, former Canadian government official; b. Ile Perrot, Que., Can., July 26, 1929; s. J. Albert and Nora (St-Aubin) L.; m. Claire Tetreau, Sept. 8, 1955; children: Marie, Luc, Paul, Catherine. BA, Coll. St. Laurent, Montreal, 1950; LLB, U. Montreal, 1964, LLM, 1955; M Econs. and Polit. Sci., Oxford (Eng.) U., 1957; LLD (hon.), U. Limburg, Maastrict; PhD (hon.), Limburg U., 1989; PhD honoris causa, Limburg U., The Netherlands. Bar: Que. 1955, Queen's Coun. 1971. Prof. bus. law and econs. U. Montreal, 1957-59; spl. asst. to Minister of Justice, Ottawa, Ont., Can., 1959-60; partner firm Gelinas, Bourque, Lalonde & Benoit, Montreal, 1960-68; policy adviser to Prime Minister Lester B. Pearson, Ottawa, 1967-68; prin. sec. to Prime Minister Pierre E. Trudeau, Ottawa, 1968-72; elected to House of Commons for Montreal-Outremont, 1972, minister of nat. health and welfare 1972-77, minister of state for fed.-provincial relations, 1977-78, minister responsible for status of women, 1975-78, minister of justice and atty. gen. Can., 1978-79, minister of energy, mines and resources 1980-82, minister of finance, 1982-84; ptnr. Stikeman, Elliott, Montreal; bd. dirs. Orléans Resources Inc., Cedar Group Inc., Citibank of Can., Camdev Corp.; chmn. bd. Hotel-Dieu de Montreal; advisor Internat. Coun. Presidium of Ukraine. Author: The Changing Role of the Prime Minister's Office, 1971. Decorated officer Order of Can.; recipient Dana award APHA, 1978. Mem. Internat. Coun. on Comml. Arbitration, Am. Arbitration Assn. (exec. bd. dirs.), Royal Coll. Physicians and Surgeons Can. Mem. Liberal Party. Home: 5440 Legare, Montreal, PQ Canada H3T 1Z4

LALONDE, ROBERT FREDERICK, state senator, retired; b. Bay City, Mich., Dec. 1, 1922; s. Joseph and Mildred Amanda (Brimmer) LaL.; m. Betty Ellen Schwartz, Aug. 2, 1941; 1 child, Rose Marie Tibbitts. BGE in Bus., U. Omaha, 1965. Airport mgr. Jackson Hole Airport, Jackson, Wyo., 1972-80; county commr. Teton County, Jackson, 1982-86, rental property owner, 1970-88; Wyo. state senator Jackson, 1989-95. Author: The Dangerous Trilogy, 1973. Chmn. Teton County Rep. Com., Jackson, 1975-77; del. Rep. Nat. Conv., Detroit, 1980; mem. Electoral Coll. Cheyenne, Wyo., 1980; sec. Wyo. Rep. party, 1980-82; chmn. Teton County Planning Commn., Jackson, 1973-78. Col. USAF, 1943-70. Mem. Am. Legion (comdr. 1989-94), Wyo. Airport Operators Assn. (founder, pres. 1973-75, Disting. Svc. award 1979), Jackson Hole C. of C. (pres. 1977-79, Citizen of Yr. 1975, Disting. Svc. award 1980), Rotary (pres. 1976-77). Christian Scientist. Avocations: hunting, fishing. Home: PO Box 1707 Jackson WY 83001-1707

LAM, DAVID C., lieutenant governor; b. Hong Kong; arrived in Can. 1967; Businessman, philanthropist; lt. gov. B.C., Province of B.C., Can. Office: Govt House, 1401 Rockland Ave, Victoria, BC Canada V8S 1V9

LAM, SIMON SHIN-SING, computer science educator; b. Macao, July 31, 1947; came to U.S., 1966; s. Chak Han and Kit Ying (Tang) L.; m. Amy Leung, Mar. 29, 1971; 1 child, Eric. B.S.E.E. with distinction, Wash. State U., 1969; M.S. in Engring., UCLA, 1970, Ph.D., 1974. Research engr. ARPA Network Measurement Ctr., UCLA, Los Angeles, 1971-74; research staff mem. IBM Watson Research Ctr, Yorktown Heights, N.Y., 1974-77; asst. prof. U. Tex.-Austin, Austin, 1977-79, assoc. prof., 1979-83, prof. computer sci., 1983—; David S. Bruton Centennial prof. U. Tex., Austin, 1985-88, anonymous prof., 1988—; chmn. dept. computer sci. U. Tex.-Austin, Austin, 1992-94. Editor-in-chief IEEE/ACM Transactions on Networking, 1995—; editor: Principles of Communication and Networking Protocols; contbr. articles to profl. jours. NSF grantee, 1978—; Chancellor's Teaching fellow UCLA, 1969-73. Fellow IEEE (Leonard G. Abraham prize 1975); mem. Assn. for Computing Machinery (program chmn. symposium 1983). Avocations: tennis, swimming, skiing, travel. Office: Univ Tex Dept of Computer Sci Austin TX 78712

LAMAGRA, ANTHONY JAMES, concert pianist, television host, music educator; b. Jersey City, Sept. 27, 1935; s. Anthony Carl and Irma Assunta L.; m. Susan Kate Ford, Sept. 1, 1968; children: Michael Anthony, Janet Lynn. B.Mus., Yale U., 1956, M.Mus., 1957; Ed.D., Columbia U., 1966. Dir. instrumental music Lincoln High Sch., Jersey City, 1960-62; dir. Keyboard Assocs. Ltd., Chappaqua, N.Y., 1962-65; instr. music Columbia U., 1962-65; with Manhattanville Coll. Purchase, N.Y., 1965—, prof., 1967—, dir. music, 1975—; dept. music chmn., 1971—; host Westchester Performs, UA Columbia Cablevision. Author: (with Marwick and Nagy) Creative Keyboard Piano Series, 1975. Served with U.S. Army, 1958. Recipient Hudson County Mus. Art Club, 1952. Mem. AAUP, Music Tchrs. Nat. Assn., Music Educators Nat. Conf. Office: Manhattanville Coll Purchase NY 10577

LAMAINA, LAWRENCE JOSEPH, JR., bank executive; b. Camden, N.J., Jan. 16, 1934; s. Lawrence Joseph Sr. and Josephine Catherine (Abretski) LaM.; m. Paula Rae Dwyer, July 26, 1958; children: Lawrence Joseph III, Jacquelyne Paula. BS, St. Joseph's U., 1956; postgrad., Am. U., 1959. Rutgers U., 1969. V.p. Girard Bank, Phila., 1960-73; exec. v.p., dir. Bank N.J., Moorestown, 1973-80, spres., dir., 1980-81; sr. v.p., regional adminstr. Hamilton Bank, Reading, Pa., 1981-84; chmn., chief exec. officer Farmers Bank and Trust Co., Hanover, Pa., 1984—. Mem. exec. council Boy Scouts Am., York Adams County, Pa., 1985-87, exec. com. Strand/Capitol Performing Arts Ctr., York, Pa., 1986-87, Penn Twp. Indls. Park Adv. Bd., York, 1987; co-chmn. United Way Campaign, Hanover, 1987. Served to comdr. USNR, 1957-87. Republican. Roman Catholic. Club: Arcadian (Hanover). Avocations: golf, tennis.

LAMALIE, ROBERT EUGENE, retired executive search company executive; b. Fremont, Ohio, June 3, 1931; s. Glennis and Mildred M. (Hetrick) L.; m. Dorothy M. Zilles, June 20, 1953; children: Deborah, Dawn, Elaine. BA, Capital U., Columbus, Ohio, 1954; postgrad., Case Western Res. U. Asst. dir. recruiting Xerox Corp., 1959-62; mgr. orgn. planning and profl. recruiting Glidden Co., 1962-65; search cons. Booz, Allen & Hamilton, Inc., Cleve., 1965-67; pres., chief exec. officer Lamalie Assocs., Inc., Tampa, Fla., 1967-84, chmn. bd. dirs., chief exec. officer, 1984-87, chmn. bd. dirs., 1987-88; pres. Robert Lamalie, Inc., Marco Island, Fla., 1988-90, ret., 1990. Served with U.S. Army, 1954-56, Korea.

LAMAN, JERRY THOMAS, mining company executive; b. Muskogee, Okla., Mar. 1, 1947; s. Thomas J. and Juanita J. (Pittman) L.; m. Lenora J. Laman, July 1, 1972; children: Troy T., Brian D. Silver Diploma, Colo. Sch. Mines, 1969. Refinery engr. ARCO, Torrance, Calif., 1969-71; chem. engr. Cleveland-Cliffs Iron Co., Mountain City, Nev., 1971-73, asst. mine supt., 1973-77; chief uranium metallurgist Cleveland-Cliffs Iron Co., Casper, Wyo., 1977-83; project mgr. In-Situ, Inc., Laramie, Wyo., 1983-85, v.p., 1985—; also bd. dirs. In-Situ, Inc.; pres. Solution Mining Corp., Laramie, Wyo., 1990—, also bd. dirs., 1990—. Mem. Soc. for Mining, Metallurgy and Exploration, Optimist (pres. Laramie club 1989). Avocations: golf, fishing. Home: 1085 Colina Dr Laramie WY 82070-5014

LAMANEC, TRACY, chemist, writer; b. Catskill, N.Y., Nov. 16, 1941; s. Julius Edward and Doris Irene (Gallon) L.; m. Eileen Mary Horan, June 22, 1963; children—Stephanie Jo., Michael Wright. A.A.S., Hudson Valley Community Coll., 1962; B.S., Union Coll., 1968. Chem. technician Gen. Electric Co., Schenectady, N.Y., 1962-68, analyst, 1968-79, sr. chemist, 1979-87; cons./microchem. materials characterization, Schenectady Materials and Processes Lab., Inc., 1987—; outdoor columnist, writer Schenectady Gazette, 1972-87. Author articles and weekly outdoor columns. Pres. Schenectady County Conservation Council, Inc., 1981, v.p. 1978-81, 82-87; sportsman's advocate, lobbyist, conservationist, environmentalist, youth instr. 4H; del. N.Y. State Conservation Council, Inc. Mem. Am. Soc. for Metals, Microbeam Analysis Soc., N.Y. State Outdoor Writers Assn. (dir., v.p. 1981-87), New Eng. Outdoor Writers Assn., Outdoor Writers Assn. Am. Clubs: Iroquois Rod and Gun (trustee 1978-87), Glenville Fish and Game (program dir.). Avocations: fishing; hunting; shooting sports; photography; flying.

LAMANTIA, CHARLES ROBERT, management consulting company executive; b. N.Y.C., June 12, 1939; s. Joseph Ferdinand and Catherine (Perniciaro) LaM.; m. Ann Christine Carmody, Sept. 16, 1961; children: Elise, Matthew. BA, Columbia U., 1960, BS, 1961, MS, 1962, ScD, 1965; grad. advanced mgmt. program, Harvard Bus. Sch., 1979. Cons. staff Arthur D. Little, Inc., Cambridge, Mass., 1967-77, v.p., 1977-81, pres., chief oper. officer, 1987-88, pres., chief exec. officer, 1988—; also bd. dirs.; pres., chief exec. officer Koch Process Systems, Westboro, Mass., 1981-86; mem. adv. coun. sch. engring. Columbia U., sch. mgmt. Boston Coll.; bd. dirs. State St. Boston Corp., 1993—; bd. govs. New Eng. Med. Ctr., 1989—; trustee Meml. Dr. Trust, 1988—. mem. bd. overseers Mus. Sci., Boston, 1988—, Sta. WGBH pub. broadcasting, 1991—, mem. Conf. Bd., 1989—; mem. Mass. Gov.'s Coun., Mass. Bus. Roundtable, 1992—. Lt. USN, 1965-67. NSF fellow, 1965; Sloan Found. fellow, 1962. Mem. Am. Inst. Chem. Engrs., Soc. Chem. Industries. Office: Arthur D Little Inc 25 Acorn Park Cambridge MA 02140-2390

LAMAR, HOWARD ROBERTS, educational administrator, historian; b. Tuskegee, Ala., Nov. 18, 1923; s. John Howard and Elma (Roberts) L.; m. Doris Shirley White, Sept. 3, 1959; children: Susan Kent, Sarah Howard. BA, Emory U., 1944; MA, Yale U., 1945, PhD, 1951. Instr. U. Mass., 1945-46, Wesleyan U., Middletown, Conn., 1944-49; mem. faculty Yale U., 1949—, prof. Am. History and history Am. West, 1964—, W.R. Coe prof. Am. history, 1970—, Sterling prof. history, 1987—, chmn. history dept., 1962-63, 67-70, dir. history grad. studies, 1964-67, fellow Ezra Stiles Coll., 1961—, dean, 1979-85, pres., 1992-93. Author: Dakota Territory, 1861-1889, 1956, The Far Southwest, 1846-1912, A Territorial History, 1966; also articles, reviews. Editor: (Joseph Downey) Cruise of the Portsmouth, 1958, Western Americana Series, 1961—, Reader's Encyclopedia of the American West, 1977, Gold Seeker: Adventures of A Belgian Argonaut in California, 1985; co-author, co-editor The Frontier in History: North America and Southern Africa Compared, 1981. Alderman, New Haven, 1951-53. Mem. Orgn. Am. Historians, Western History Assn. (pres. 1971-72), Am. Antquarian Soc., Elihu Soc., Phi Beta Kappa. Democrat. Home: 1747 Hartford Tpke North Haven CT 06473-1249 Office: Yale U Dept History New Haven CT 06520

LAMARRE, BERNARD, engineering, contracting and manufacturing advisor; b. Chicoutimi, Que., Can., Aug. 6, 1931; s. Emile J. and Blanche M. (Gagnon) L.; m. Louise Lalonde, Aug. 30, 1952; children: Jean, Christine, Lucie, Monique, Michèle, Philippe, Mireille. BSc, Ecole Poly., Montreal, Que., Can., 1952; MSc, Imperial Coll., U. London, 1955; LLD, St. Francis Xavier U., N.S., Can.; 1980; D in Engring. (hon.), U. Waterloo, Ont., 1984; LLD (hon.), U. Concordia, Montreal, 1985; D in Engring. (hon.), U. Montreal, 1985; D in Applied Sci. (hon.), U. Sherbrooke, Que., 1986; D in Bus. Adminstrn. (hon.), U. Chicoutimi, Que., 1987; D in Sci. (hon.), Queen's U., Kingston, Ont., 1987; D in Engring. (hon.), U. Ottawa, Ont., 1988, Tech. U. N.S., 1989, Royal Mil. Coll., Kingston, 1990. Structural and founds. engr. Lalonde-Valois, Montreal, 1955-60, chief engr., 1960-62, mgr., gen. mgr., pres. Valois, Lalonde, Valois, Lamarre, Montreal, 1962-72; chmn., chief exec. officer Lavalin Group, 1972-91; sr. advisor SNC-Lavalin Inc., 1991—; chmn. Ordre des Ingenieurs du Quebec, Montreal Design Inst., Société du Vieux

Port de Montreal. Bd. dirs. Telesystems Inc.; chmn. Bellechasse Santé Inc.; hon. chmn. Montreal Mus. Fine Arts, Coll. Stanislas, chmn. Soc. du Vieux Port de Montreal, 1991-94. Decorated officer Ordre nat. du Québec, Order of Can.; Athlone fellow, 1952. Fellow Engring. Inst. Can., Can. Soc. Civil Engring.; mem. ASCE, Order Engrs. of Que. (chmn.), Mont-Royal Club, Laval-sur-le Lac Club. Roman Catholic. Home: 4850 Cedar Crescent, Montreal, PQ Canada H3W 2H9

LAMARRE, DANIEL, public relations company executive; b. Trois Rivières, Que., Can., July 7, 1953; s. Gilles and Pauline (Perreault) L.; m. Josette Ferron, Oct. 21, 1979; children: Sébastien, Josianne. BA in Comm., Ottawa (Ont., Can.) U., 1976. Accredited in pub. rels. Journalist Le Nouvelliste, Stas. CKTM-TV and CKSM, Trois Rivières, 1969-79, Radio Can., Ottawa, 1973-74; dir. comm. Fedn. Caisses Populaires, Trois Rivières, 1974-77; dir. pub. rels. COGECO, Trois Rivières, 1977-78; supr. Cockfield Brown, Montreal, Que., 1978-81; v.p., gen. mgr. Burson-Marsteller, Montreal, 1981-84; sr. ptnr., exec. v.p. Nat. Pub. Rels., Montreal, 1984—. Co-author: Les relations publiques: une nouvelle force de l'enterprise moderne, 1986. Bd. govs. Sports Que., Montreal, 1994; v.p. XII World Congress, Toronto, 1991. Recipient Can. award in pub. rels. Can. Pub. Rels. Soc., 1987. Mem. Montreal C. of C. (pres. membership com. 1990-91). Avocations: hockey, golf, skiing, reading, theatre. Home: 2031 des Saules St, Saint Bruno, PQ Canada J3V 3Z9 Office: Nat Pub Rels, Ste 1600, 770 Sherbrooke St W, Montreal, PQ Canada H3A 1G1

LAMAS, LORENZO, actor, race car driver; b. Santa Monica, Calif., Jan. 20, 1958; s. Fernando Lamas and Arlene Dahl; m. Victoria Hilbert (div.); children: Alvaro Joshua, Shayne Dahl, Paton Lee; m. Kathleen Kinmont, Jan. 20, 1989 (div.). Grad., Farragut Acad., Pine Beach, N.J., 1975, Jim Russel Sch. Motor Racing, 1985. Ptnr. LeConte Driving Sch., Willow Springs, Calif., 1985—; driver Phil Conte Racing, Paramount, Calif., 1985—, driver competition in Internat. Motor Sports Assn. prototypes, 1988, 89. Appeared in films, Grease, 1978, Take Down, 1978, Tilt, 1979, Body Rock, 1984, Snake Eater, 1989, The Killing Streets, 1991, Night of the Warrior, 1991, also co-prodr. Snake Eater II: The Drug Buster, 1991, Final Impact, 1992, C.I.A., Code Name Alexa, 1992, Snake Eater III: His Law, 1992, Final Round, 1993, Bounty Tracker, 1993, The Swordsman, 1993, C.I.A. II: Target Alexa, 1994 (also dir.); (TV movies) Detour to Terror, 1980, Bad Blood, 1994; appeared in TV series, California Fever, 1979, Midland Heights, 1980, Falcon Crest, 1981-90, Dancin' to the Hits, 1986, Renegade Series, 1992. Winner Toyota Grand Prix of Long Beach, 1985. Democrat. Avocations: surfing; skiing; golf; motorcycles; karate. Office: care Lola Prodns 15250 Ventura Blvd Ste 710 Sherman Oaks CA 91403*

LAMATTINA, LAWRENCE E., advertising agency executive; b. Front Royal, Va., Sept. 5, 1943; s. Rosario John and Rosa Lee (Flick) L.; m. Elizabeth Ann Notaro, Oct. 29, 1967; children: Lisa, Laura. BA in Mktg., Pace U., 1967. Media planner/buyer Benton & Bowles, Inc., N.Y.C., 1968-70; media mgr. Scali, McCabe, Sloves, N.Y.C., 1970-71; exec. v.p., dir. media and programming Grey Advt. Inc., N.Y.C., 1971-81; dir. media and programming, exec. v.p. SSC&B/Lintas Worldwide, 1981—, chief operating officer, 1985—; speaker in field. Served with Air N.G., 1964-70. Mem. Am. Film Inst., Internat. Radio and TV Soc., Am. Assn. Advt. Agys.

LAMB, CHARLES F., minister; b. Maryville, Tenn., Dec. 18, 1934; s. C. Fred and Sadie Ellen (Tedder) L.; children: Elizabeth Susan, Linda Louise, Jennifer Janet; m. Betty Jane Zimmerman, Dec. 29, 1979. BA, Maryville Coll., 1956; MDiv, Grad. Sem. of Phillips U., 1961; D in Ministry, N.Y. Theol. Sem., 1990. Ordained to ministry Christian Ch., 1961. Pastor East Aurora Christian Ch., N.Y., 1961-71; assoc. regional min. Christian Ch., Disciples of Christ, Northeastern Region, Buffalo, N.Y., 1971-75; regional min. Christian Ch., Disciples of Christ, Northeastern Region, Buffalo, 1975—; mem. orgns. clergy and coun. of chs. Trustee Village of East Aurora, 1968-73; active environ. groups Conf. Mayors and Village Ofcls. N.Y., 1968-73. Mem. Conf. Regional Ministers and Moderators (pres. elect). Democrat. Office: 1272 Delaware Ave Buffalo NY 14209-2496

LAMB, FREDERIC DAVIS, lawyer; b. Oak Park, Ill., Nov. 23, 1931; s. Frederic Horace and Alice Emily (Davis) L.; m. Barbara Ann Bullard, Apr. 6, 1954; children: Deborah Ann Lamb Dunn, Jeffrey Davis. BA, Wabash Coll.; JD, U. Mich. Bar: Ohio 1957, Conn. 1989. Atty. Vick Chem. Co., N.Y.C. and Cin., 1956-63; v.p., counsel Merrell div. Richardson-Merrell Inc., Cin., 1964-80; asst. gen. counsel Richardson-Vicks Inc., Wilton, Conn., 1981-83, v.p., gen. counsel, sec., 1984-92; pvt. practice, 1993—. Mayor, councilman City of Forest Park, Ohio, 1971-75; mem. Forest Park Charter Commn., 1969-70; trustee Food Drug Law Inst., mem. scholarship com., 1985-92. Mem. ABA, Ohio Bar Assn., Westchester-Fairfield Corp. Counsel Assn., Am. Soc. Corp. Secs., Silver Spring Country Club (pres. 1989-91). Republican. Avocations: golf; tennis; boating. Home: 30 Keelers Ridge Rd Wilton CT 06897-1607 Office: PO Box 7414 180 Old Ridgefield Rd Wilton CT 06897

LAMB, GEORGE RICHARD, foundation executive; b. Cleve., Aug. 15, 1928; s. Harold George and Mildred (Oller) L.; m. Edith Mathews Read, June 18, 1955; children: Graham Read, George Kinsey, Gwynne Lamb Grimes. B.S., Ohio State U., 1953; M.S., Yale U., 1955. Mgr. Tinicum Wildlife Preserve, Phila., 1957-60; exec. sec. Pres. Task Force on Natural Beauty, Washington, 1964; fed. coord. White House Conf. Natural Beauty, Washington, 1965; program and policy staff Outdoor Recreation Resources Review Commn., Washington, 1960-61; budget examiner Bur. Budget, Exec. Office Pres., Washington, 1961-65; pres. Jackson Hole Preserve, N.Y.C., trustee, 1978—; trustee, v.p. Am. Conservation Assn., N.Y.C., 1978-94; assoc. philanthropy L.S. Rockefeller, N.Y.C., 1975—. Photographer (film) Birds of Tinicum, 1959. Mem. Palisades Interstate Park Commn., N.Y., N.J., 1973-75; pres. Rye Conservation Soc., N.Y., 1968; dir. Federated Conservationists Westchester County, 1965-82; pres. Audobon Soc. Cen. Atlantic States, Washington, 1964-65; trustee Coun. on Environment, N.Y.C., Greenacre Found., N.Y.C. With USAF, 1946-49. Fellow Internat. Council Bird Preservation, Cuba, P.R., 1956. Mem. Manursing Island Club, Campfire Club (Pleasantville, N.Y.), Tamarack Club. Office: 30 Rockefeller Plz Rm 5600 New York NY 10112-0001

LAMB, GORDON HOWARD, academic administrator; b. Eldora, Iowa, Nov. 6, 1934; s. Capp and Ethel (Hayden) L; m. Nancy Ann Painter; children: Kirk, Jon, Phillip. B in Music Edn., Simpson Coll., 1956; M of Music, U. Nebr., 1962; PhD, U. Iowa, 1973. Choral dir. Iowa pub. schs., Tama/Paullina, Sac City, 1957-68; asst. prof. music U. Wis., Stevens Point, 1969-70, U. Tex., Austin, 1970-74; prof., dir. divsn. music U. Tex., San Antonio, 1974-79, prof., v.p. acad. affairs, 1979-86; pres. Northeastern Ill. U., Chgo., 1986—. Author: Choral Techniques, 1974, 3d edit. 1988; editor: Guide for the Beginning Choral Director; contbr. articles to scholarly and profl. jours.; composer numerous pieces choral music. Served with U.S. Army, 1957-58. Recipient Most Supportive Pres. or Chancellor award Am. Assn. Colls. for Tchr. Edn., 1992. Mem. Am. Assn. Higher Edn., Am. Assn. State Colls. and Univs., Am. Choral Dirs. Assn. (life, chmn. nat. com. 1970-72). Office: Northeastern Ill U Office of Pres 5500 N Saint Louis Ave Chicago IL 60625-4625

LAMB, IRENE HENDRICKS, medical researcher; b. Ky., May 9, 1940; d. Daily P. and Bertha (Hendricks) Lamb; m. Edward B. Meadows. RN, Ky. Bapt. Hosp., Louisville; student, Berea (Ky.) Coll., Calif. State U., L.A. RN, Calif., Ky. Charge nurse, head nurse acute medicine, med. ICU, surgical ICU, emergency room various med. ctrs., 1963-67; staff nurse rsch. coronary care unit, 1968; asst. nurse coord., nurse coord. clin. rsch. ctr. U. So. Calif./L.A. County Med. Ctr., L.A. 1969-74; sr. rsch. nurse cardiology Stanford (Calif.) U. Sch. Medicine, 1974-85, rsch. coord. pvt. clin., 1988, dir. clin. rsch. pvt. cardiology group, 1989-92; clin. rsch. cons., cmty. health nurse Madison County Health Dept., Berea, Ky., 1993—. Co-author numerous articles to med. jours.; contbr. articles to nursing jours. and chpts. to med. books. Mem. Am. Heart Assn. (cardiovascular nursing sect.). Home: 208 Rockcastle St Berea KY 40403-1243

LAMB, JAMIE PARKER, JR., mechanical engineer, educator; b. Boligee, Ala., Sept. 21, 1933; s. Jamie Parker and Cletus (Hixson) L.; m. Nancy Catherine Flaherty, June 11, 1955; children: David Parker, Stephen Patrick. B.S., Auburn U., 1954; M.S., U. Ill., 1958, Ph.D., 1961. Asst. prof.

engring. mechanics N.C. State U., Raleigh, 1961-63; faculty mech. engring. U. Tex., Austin, 1963—; prof. U. Tex., 1970—, chmn. dept., 1970-76, assoc. dean engring., 1976-81, prof. faculty aerospace engring., 1981-88, chmn. dept., 1981-88, Ernest Cockrell Jr. Meml. prof., 1981—; dir. engring. program U. Tex.-Pan Am., 1993-94; cons. LTV Aerospace Corp., Dallas, Marshall Space Flight Center, Huntsville, Ala., Tracor, Inc., Austin, Rocketdyne, McGregor, Tex., ARO, Inc., Tullahoma, Tenn., Tex. Gas Transport Co., Austin; spl. cons. U. São Paulo, Brazil, 1974; cons. Mobil Oil Corp., Dallas, Gilbarco, Inc., Greensboro, N.C.; mem. bd. boiler rules Tex. Dept. Labor and Standards, 1977-81; mem. rev. panel postdoctoral assoc. NRC, 1981—, mem. U.S. nat. com. on theoretical and applied mechanics, 1985-89; chmn. 10th U.S. Nat. Congress Applied Mechanics, 1986. Assoc. tech. editor Jour. Fluids Engring., 1976-79; contbr. articles to profl. jours. Served to 1st lt. USAF, 1955-57. Recipient Joe J. King Profl. Engring. Achievement award U. Tex. at Austin, 1984, Disting. Alumnus award U. Ill. Dept. Mech. and Indsl. Engring., 1985, Centennial Alumnus award Auburn U. Dept. Mech. Engring., 1986. Fellow ASME (chmn. fluid mechanics tech. com. 1982-84, Founder's award Central Tex. sect. 1975, Leadership award 1976, 81, Centennial award 1980); assoc. fellow AIAA; mem. Am. Soc. Engring. Edn. (chmn. summer faculty programs com. 1978-80, chmn. mech. engring. div. 1979-80, bd. dirs. Profl. Interest Council I, 1981-82), Nat. Soc. Profl. Engrs., Sigma Xi, Pi Tau Sigma, Tau Beta Pi, Sigma Gamma Tau. Baptist. Home: 2605 Pinewood Ter Austin TX 78757-2136

LAMB, JERRY A., bishop; b. Denver, Sept. 4, 1940; m. Jane Onstad; 1 child, Katherine. BA in Philosophy, St. Thomas Coll.; MA in Theology, St. Thomas Sem. Ordained to Roman Catholic Archdiocese, 1965. Exec. asst. to Bishop of Oreg., elected 6th bishop of No. Calif., 1991—; rector Trinity Ch., Ashland, Oreg.; asst. to rector Emmanuel Ch., Coos Bay; coll. chaplain asst. All St.'s, Denver; dir. Camp St. Malo, Colo.; mem. standing com. Diocesan Coun., Commn. on Ministry; dep. 2 gen. convs. and provincial synods. Office: PO Box 131268 1322 27th St Sacramento CA 95816

LAMB, KATIE A., nursing educator; b. San Saba, Tex., Dec. 9, 1940; d. Wayne C. and Mable Ruth (Mackie) Towerton; m. Edward Lee Lamb, Aug. 27, 1961; children: John Edward, Janet Lea. BS, Union Coll., 1961; MSN, U. Cen. Ark., 1982; postgrad., U. Tenn. Staff nurse Porter Meml. Hosp., Denver, Washington Adventist Hosp., Takoma Park, Md.; dir. operating room Madison (Tenn.) Hosp.; dir. nursing div. So. Coll. of SDA, Collegedale, Tenn. Mem. Am. Nurses Assn., Tenn. Nurses Assn., NLN, Sigma Theta Tau.

LAMB, LESTER LEWIS, hospital administrator; b. Winchester, Va., Aug. 11, 1932; s. Lester Lewis and Nina Elizabeth (Higgs) L.; m. Mary Lou Watson, Aug. 11, 1956; children: Melissa, Amy, Elizabeth. BA, Richmond Coll., 1955, postgrad., 1955-56; MHA, Med. Coll. Va., 1958. Asst. dir. admissions, hosp. div. Med. Coll. Va., Richmond, 1956, adminstrv. resident, 1957; adminstrv. resident Shenandoah County Meml. Hosp., Woodstock, Va., 1957, Washington County Hosp., Hagerstown, Md., 1957-58; adminstr. Hampshire Meml. Hosp., Romney, W.Va., 1958-59, Marmet (W.Va.) Hosp., Inc., 1959-60; asst. dir. U. Va. Hosp., Charlottesville, 1961; adminstr. R.J. Reynolds-Patrick County Meml. Hosp., Stuart, Va., 1961-64, Shenandoah County Meml. Hosp., Woodstock, 1965-69, Mary Greely Meml. Hosp., Ames, Iowa, 1969-70; exec. dir. Radford (Va.) Cmty. Hosp., 1970-81, pres., 1981—; exec. v.p. Carilion Health System, 1989—; guest lectr., adj. asst. prof. Radford U., 1980-81; chmn. Va. Profl. Underwriters, Inc., 1984-87; chmn. Va. Hosp. Shared Svcs., Va. Healthcare Waste Mgmt. Coop., Vol. Hosp. Am. Mid-Atlantic. Mem. Va. Gov.'s Health Svcs. Cost Rev. Commn., 1978-82, Va. State Bd. Health, 1992—, chmn. 1993—. Fellow Am. Coll. Healthcare Execs., Royal Soc. Health; mem. Am. Hosp. Assn. (Va. del.), Va. Hosp. Assn. (pres. 1981-82), Med. Coll. Va. Hosp. Adminstrn. Alumni Assn. (sec., pres.), Roanoke Area Hosp. Council (pres. 1974), Psi Chi, Rotary (past pres.). Home: 116 Greenbrier Dr Radford VA 24141-3854 Office: Radford Community Hosp 700 Randolph St Radford VA 24141-2430

LAMB, PETER JAMES, meteorology educator, researcher, consultant; b. Nelson, New Zealand, June 21, 1947; came to U.S., 1971; s. George Swan and Dorothy Elizabeth (Smith) L.; m. Barbara Helen Harrison, Aug. 29, 1970; children: Karen Deborah, Brett Timothy. BA, U. Canterbury, Christchurch, New Zealand, 1969; MA with honours, U. Canterbury, Christ Ch., New Zealand, 1971; PhD, U. Wis., 1976. Asst. lectr. U. Canterbury, 1971; rsch. asst. U. Wis., Madison, 1971-76, rsch. assoc., 1976; lectr. U. Adelaide, Australia, 1976-79; sr. sci. Ill. State Water Survey, Champaign, 1979-91, section head, 1984-90; dir. Okla., Norman, 1991—; vis. rsch. assoc. U. Miami, Fla., 1978-79; adj. prof. U. Ill., Urbana, 1983-94; dir. Coop. Inst. Mesoscale Meteorol. Studies, Norman, 1991—; dir. Internat. Ctr. Disaster Rsch., 1994—; cons. Dept. State, Dept. Energy, Agy. Internat. Devel., Nat. Oceanic and Atmospheric Adminstrn., NSF, World Meteorol. Orgn., Kingdom of Morocco, U. Wis., U. Adelaide, Univs. Space Rsch. Assn., EPA, 1983—; site sci. atmospheric radiation measurement program Dept. Energy, 1992—. Co-author rsch. monographs, book chpt., numerous sci. papers. Coach Champaign Youth Soccer Orgn., 1983-91. Recipient more than 35 rsch. grants from U.S. Fed. Agys. including NSF, EPA, Dept. Energy, Nat. Atmospheric and Oceanic Adminstrn., Agy. Internat. Devel., MacArthur Found., Ins. Inst. for Property Loss Reduction. Fellow Am. Meteorological Soc. (chief editor Jour. Climate 1989—); mem. Royal Meteorological Soc. (Margary lectr. 1991), Am. Assn. State Climatologists, Sigma Xi. Achievements include research on heat transport by the Atlantic Ocean; investigations into the role of the ocean in causing droughts in Sahelian Africa, study of North American precipitation patterns. Home: 3616 Burlington Dr Norman OK 73072-3610 Office: Univ of Oklahoma CIMMS-Sarkeys Energy Ctr 100 E Boyd St Rm 1110 Norman OK 73069-5816

LAMB, ROBERT EDWARD, diplomat; b. Atlanta, Nov. 17, 1936; s. T.E. and Lois (Harris) L.; m. Lucille Trujillo, Jan. 13, 1962; children: Robert Edward, Anne Gretchen, Michael David. BA in Internat. Rels., U. Pa., 1962. Joined Fgn. Service, Dept. State, 1963; dir. fin. services Dept. State, Washington, 1975-77, dir. passport office, 1977-79; adminstrv. counsellor U.S. Embassy, Bonn, Fed. Republic Germany, 1979-83; asst. sec. of state for adminstrn. Dept. State, Washington, 1983-85; asst. sec. of state Diplomatic Security, 1985-89; U.S. Amb. to Cyprus Cyprus, 1990-93; spl. Cyprus coord., 1993-94; exec. dir. Am. Philatelic Soc., State Coll., Pa., 1994—. Served with USMC, 1958-61, 72—. Mem. Am. Philatelic Soc. (exec. dir. 1994). Home and Office: PO Box 8000 State College PA 16803

LAMB, ROBERT LEE, religious studies educator; b. Nevada, Mo., Aug. 18, 1930; s. Lifus E. and Miriam (McConnell) Lamb; m. Rhealene Bryant, Aug. 5, 1961; children: Robert Earl, Mary Rebecca, Miriam Elizabeth. BA, Stephen F. Austin State U., 1951; postgrad., Westminster Choir Coll., 1951-52; MA in Religious Edn., Southwestern Bapt. Sem., 1955, 83, PhD, 1964. Ordained to the gospel ministry, 1966. Min. of music and religious edn. First Bapt. Ch., Richardson, Tex., 1953-54; dir. Christian edn., civilian Vogelweh Army Chapel, Kaiserslautern, Germany, 1954-56; prof. religious edn. and religion Gardner-Webb U., Boiling Springs, N.C., 1962-76, 79-92, chair, dept. religious studies and philosophy, 1988-91; assoc. dir., nurse study sem. extension dept. So. Bapt. Sems., Nashville, Tenn., 1977-79; dean sch. divinity Gardner-Webb U., 1992—; chair, bd. dirs. Christian Svc. Corp., 1990-91; chair, pastoral ministries com. Kings Mountain Bapt. Assn., Shelby, N.C., 1990. Mem. Am. Acad. Religion, Soc. Bibl. Lit., Nat. Assn. Bapt. Profs. Religion, N.C. Bapt. Religious Edn. Assn. (past chair crisis support group, past pres., v.p.), Soc. for Scientific Study of Religion, So. Bapt. Religious Edn. Assn. (v.p. 1990-91), Bapt. State Conv. of N.C. (chair min. support adv. com. 1990-91), Lions Club (pres. Boiling Springs chpt. 1984). Home: 122 Clinton St Boiling Springs NC 28017 Office: Gardner-Webb U Boiling Springs NC 28017

LAMB, ROBERT LEWIS, electric utility executive; b. Goodland, Kans., Mar. 29, 1932; s. Perl and Josephine (Cullins) L.; m. Patricia Jean Kanuch, Sept. 6, 1953; children: Nancy Jo, David Lewis. BSEE, U. Kans., 1955. Engr. The Empire Dist. Electric Co., Joplin, Mo., 1955-67, distbn. engr., 1967-69; supt. engring. The Empire Electric Co., Joplin, 1969-74; v.p. customer services The Empire Dist. Electric Co., Joplin, 1974-78, exec. v.p., 1978-82, pres., chief exec. officer, 1982—, dir., 1978—; bd. dirs. Edison Electric Inst.; chmn. Mokan Power Pool, 1986-87, S.W. Power Pool, 1989-91. Pres. Joplin United Way, 1981, Joplin Indsl. Devel. Authority, 1992—; v.p., dir. Joplin So. Corp., 1974-90; bd. dirs. St. John's Regional Med. Ctr.,

Joplin, 1981-90, 91—, chmn., 1982-84, 92-94; trustee N.Am. Electric Reliability Coun., 1989-91; bd. dirs. Mo. So. State Coll., 1993—. Capt. USAF, 1955-58. Mem. Mo. Valley Elec. Assn. (pres. 1993-94), Joplin C. of C. (pres. 1979-80), Mo. C. of C. and Industry (bd. dirs. 1983—, treas. 1990-93, chmn. 1993—). Republican. Lutheran. Clubs: Twin Hills Country (Joplin); Kansas City (Mo.). Office: Empire Dist Electric Co 602 Joplin St PO Box 127 Joplin MO 64801

LAMB, SYDNEY MACDONALD, linguistics and cognitive science educator; b. Denver, May 4, 1929; s. Sydney Bishop and Jean Louisa (MacDonald) L.; m. Sharon Reese Rowell, June 17, 1956 (div. 1971); children: Christina, Sarah, Nancy; m. Susan Ellen Jones, May 15, 1977. BA, Yale U., 1951; PhD, U. Calif., Berkeley, 1958. From asst. to assoc. prof. linguistics U. Calif., Berkeley, 1958-64; from assoc. to prof. Yale U., New Haven, 1964-77; mng. ptnr. Semionics Assocs., Houston, 1977-93; prof. Rice U., Houston, 1980—; fellow Ctr. for Advanced Study in Behavioral Scis., Stanford, Calif., 1973-74. Author: Outline of Stratificational Grammar, 1966, (with others) Sprung from Some Common Source, 1991; inventor associative computer memory, 1977, 80, 4 patents; contbr. articles to profl. jours. NSF grantee, 1959-64, 66-70; Am. Council of Learned Soc. grantee, 1973-74. Mem. Linguistic Soc. Am. (exec. com. 1966-68), Linguistics Assn. of Can. and U.S. (pres. 1983-84), Houston Philos. Soc. (treas. 1985-86, v.p. 1991-92, pres. 1992-93). Avocations: singing, songwriting. Office: Rice U Dept of Linguistics Houston TX 77251

LAMB, URSULA SCHAEFER, history educator; b. Essen, Germany, Jan. 15, 1914; came to U.S., 1935, naturalized, 1949; d. Waldemar Joachim and Maria Katharina (Hoffman von Fallersleben) Schaefer; m. Willis Eugene Lamb, Jr., June 5, 1939. Student, U. Berlin, 1933-35, Smith Coll., 1935-36; M.A., U. Calif., Berkeley, 1937, Ph.D., 1949. Instr. and asso. Barnard Coll., Columbia U., N.Y.C., 1943-51; tutor Brasenose Coll. and Univ. Lectures, Oxford, Eng., 1958-61; lectr., sr. lectr., advisor to library Yale U., New Haven, 1961-74; prof. history U. Ariz., Tucson, 1974-85, prof. emeritus, 1985—; Eva G.R. Taylor lectr. Royal Inst. Navy, London, 1981, AAAS, Chgo., 1991, Brit. Soc. for History of Sci., Imperial Coll., London, 1993; hon. mem. Mortar Bd., 1984. Assoc. editor Hispanic Am. Hist. Rev, 1975-80; mem. editorial bd. Terrae Incognitae, 1978-84, 93, 94; author: Frey Nicolás de Ovando, 1956, 2d edit., 1977; translator, author: intro. A Navigator's Universe: The Libro de Cosmographia of 1538 (Pedro de Medina), 1972; contbr. articles to profl. jours. Recipient Disting. Svc. award Conf. Latin Am. Studies, 1990; Social Sci. Rsch. Coun. grantee, 1943, Am. Coun. Learned Socs. travel grantee, 1947, Guggenheim Meml. fellow, 1968; NEH sr. scholar, 1972-73, Am. Philos. Soc. travel grantee, 1975, NSF grantee, 1978-79; Jeannette Black fellow Brown U., spring, 1985. Mem. Conf. Latin-Am. History, Am. Hist. Assn. Conn. Acad. Arts and Scis., Soc. History of Discovery (pres. 1975-77, coun. mem. 1993, 94), Internat. Soc. History of Nautical Sci. and Hydrography (U.S. rep. 1976), Internat. Commn. maritime History (U.S. rep. 1977, 80), Soc. Spanish and Portuguese Hist. Studies, Instituto de Cultura Hispanica (Caracas), Soc. Hist. Sci. (com. for the quincentennial of discovery of Am.). Home: 848 N Norris Ave Tucson AZ 85719-5130 Office: Univ Ariz Dept History 215 Social Sci Tucson AZ 85721

LAMB, VINCENT P., industrial executive; b. 1932. With Parsons De Leuw Inc., Washington, 1955—, now exec. v.p. Office: Parsons De Leuw Inc 1133 15th St NW Washington DC 20005

LAMB, WILLIS EUGENE, JR., physicist, educator; b. L.A., July 12, 1913; s. Willis Eugene and Marie Helen (Metcalf) L.; m. Ursula Schaefer, June 5, 1939. BS, U. Calif., 1934, PhD, 1938; DSc (hon.), U. Pa., 1953, Gustavus Adolphus Coll., 1975, Columbia U., 1990; MA (hon.), Oxford (Eng.) U., 1956, Yale, 1961; LHD (hon.), Yeshiva U., 1965. Mem. faculty Columbia U., 1938-52, prof. physics, 1948-52; prof. physics Stanford U., 1951-56; Wykeham prof. physics and fellow New Coll., Oxford U., 1956-62; Henry Ford 2d prof. physics Yale U., 1962-72, J. Willard Gibbs prof. physics, 1972-74; prof. physics and optical scis. U. Ariz., Tucson, 1974—, Regents prof., 1990—; Morris Loeb lectr. Harvard U., 1953-54; Gordon Shrum lectr. Simon Fraser U., 1972; cons. Philips Labs., Bell Telephone Labs., Perkin-Elmer, NASA; vis. com. Brookhaven Nat. Lab. Recipient (with P. Kusch) Nobel prize in physics, 1955, Rumford premium Am. Acad. Arts and Scis., 1953; award Rsch. Corp., 1954, Yeshiva award, 1962; Guggenheim fellow, 1960-61, sr. Alexander von Humboldt fellow, 1992-94. Fellow Am. Phys. Soc., N.Y. Acad. Scis.; hon. fellow Inst. Physics and Phys. Soc. (Guthrie lectr. 1958), Royal Soc. Edinburgh (fgn. mem.); mem. Nat. Acad. Scis., Phi Beta Kappa, Sigma Xi. Office: U Ariz Optical Scis Ctr Tucson AZ 85721

LAMBERG, STANLEY LAWRENCE, medical technologist, educator; b. Bklyn., Oct. 2, 1933; s. Joseph and Ray C. (Miller) L.; m. Charlotte Frances Rothschild, June 15, 1963; children: Steven Kenneth, Eric Michael. BS, Bklyn. Coll., 1955; MA, Oberlin Coll.; MS, Tufts U., 1962; PhD, NYU, 1968. Chief lab. tech. dept. biochemistry Sch. Medicine Cornell U., N.Y.C., 1957-58; Charleton rsch. and USPHS fellow dept. physiology Tufts U., Boston, 1958-61; NIDR predoctoral trainee NYU, 1961-66; lectr. dept. biology CCNY, 1966-67; instr. to asst. prof. dept. biology Bklyn. Ctr., LIU, 1967-70; part-time asst. rsch. scientist Guggenheim Inst. for Dental Rsch., NYU, 1968-69; asst. prof. dept. biology SUNY, Farmingdale, 1970-71, asst. prof., 1971-73, assoc. prof., 1973-75, prof., 1975—. Co-author various lab. manuals. Adv. chmn. Boy Scouts Am., Hauppauge, N.Y., 1982—. Recipient Chancellor's award for Excellence in Teaching SUNY, 1976; NSF fellow, 1971, others. Mem. N.Y. State Histotech. Soc., Nat. Soc. Histotech., N.Y. State Soc. Med. Tech. (treas. 1980-93, bd. dirs. 1980-93, 94—), N.Y. Acad. Scis., Sigma Xi. Office: SUNY Dept Med Lab Tech Farmingdale NY 11787

LAMBERG-KARLOVSKY, CLIFFORD CHARLES, anthropologist, archaeologist; b. Prague, Czechoslovakia, Oct. 2, 1937; came to U.S., 1939; s. Carl Othmar von Lamberg and Bellina Karlovsky; m. Martha Louise Veale, Sept. 12, 1959; children: Karl Emil Othmar, Christopher William. A.B., Dartmouth Coll., 1959; M.A. (Wenner-Gren fellow), U. Pa., 1964, Ph.D., 1965; M.A. (hon.), Harvard U., 1970. Asst. prof. sociology and anthropology Franklin and Marshall Coll., 1964-65; asst. prof. anthropology Harvard U., 1965-69, prof., 1969-90, Stephen Phillips prof. archaeology, 1991—; curator Near Eastern archaeology Peabody Museum Archaeology and Ethnology, 1969—, mus. dir., 1977-90; assoc. Columbia U., 1969—; trustee Am. Inst. Iranian Studies, 1968—, Am. Inst. Yemeni Studies, 1976-77; dir. rsch. Am. Sch. Prehist. Rsch., 1974-79, 86—; trustee Am. Sch. Oriental Rsch., 1969-71, 86—, Centro di Richerche Ligabue, 1984; Rexhill archaeol. lectr. Brit. Acad., 1973; dir. archaeol. surveys in Syria, 1965, excavation projects at Tepe Yahya, Iran, 1967-75, Sarazm, Tadjikistan, USSR, 1985, archaeol. surveys in Saudia Arabia, 1977-80, USSR, 1990-91; corresponding fellow Inst. Medio and Extremo Orient, Italy; mem. UNESCO com. for sci. study of mankind, 1989—. Author: (with J. Sabloff) Ancient Civilizations: The Near East and Mesoamerica, 1979; editor: (with J. Sabloff) The Rise and Fall of Civilizations, 1973, Ancient Civilizations and Trade, 1975, Hunters, Farmers and Civilization, 1979, Archaeological Thought in America, 1988; author, gen. editor: Tepe Yahya: The Early Periods, 1986. Recipient medal Iran-Am. Soc., 1972; NSF grantee, 1966-75, 78-80, 93, Nat. Endowment for Arts grantee, 1977—, NEH grantee, 1977—. Fellow AAAS (chmn. USA/USSR archaeol. exch. program), Soc. Antiquaries Gt. Britain and Ireland (sec. N.Am. chpt. 1985-93), Am. Anthrop. Assn., N.Y. Acad. Sci., USSR Acad. Sci., Soc. Am. Archaeology, Archeol. Inst. Am., Instituto para Medio et Extrema Oriente; mem. German Archaeol. Inst., Danish Archaeol. Inst., Brit. Archaeol. Inst., Tavern Club (Boston). Office: Peabody Mus Archaeology & Ethnology 11 Divinity Ave Cambridge MA 02138-2019

LAMBERSON, JOHN ROGER, insurance company executive; b. Aurora, Mo., Aug. 16, 1933; s. John Oral Lamberson and Golda May (Caldwell) Tidwell; m. Virginia Lee, Aug. 10, 1957; 1 child. John Clinton. BA, U. Calif., Berkeley, 1954. Coach, tchr. Thousand Palms (Calif.) Sch., 1954-55; underwriter trainee Fireman's Fund Ins. Co., San Francisco, 1955; surety mgr. Safeco Ins. Co. (formerly Gen. Ins. Co.), San Francisco and Sacramento, Calif., 1957-61; pres., COO Willis Corroon Corp., N.Y.C., 1966-92, also bd. dirs., chmn. constrn. industry div., mem. exec. com., acquisition com.; pres., chmn. CEO Lamberson Koster & Co., San Francisco, 1992—; bd. dirs. Willis Corroon Group PLC, London, Consumers Benefit Life Ins. Co., Nova Group, U.S.; chmn., CEO Lamberson Koster and Co. Mem. Nat. Assn. Heavy Engring. Constructors (bd. dirs. 1985—, Golden Beavers award for outstanding svc. to industry), Constrn. Fin. Mgmt. Assn. (bd. dirs. 1987-91, exec. com.), Assoc. Gen. Contractors Am. (membership devel. com., past chmn. bd. dirs. nat. assoc. mems. coun.), Assoc. Gen. Contractors Calif. (bd. dirs. 1976), Nat. Assn. Surety Bond Producers (past nat. pres., regional v.p.), Am. Inst. Contractors, Soc. Am. Mil. Engrs., Young Pres. Orgn. (sem. leader), Bankers Club, Commonwealth Club, Sharon Heights Golf and Country Club, Bermuda Dunes Country Club, Rockaway Hunting Club. Home: 85 Greenoaks Dr Atherton CA 94027-2160 Office: Lamberson Koster & Co 580 California St San Francisco CA 94104

LAMBERT, BENJAMIN JOSEPH, III, optometrist, state legislator; b. Richmond, Va., Jan. 29, 1937; s. Benjamin Joseph and Mary Frances (Warden) L.; m. Carolyn Lee Morris, May 22, 1966; children: Benjamin J. IV, David Morris, Charles Justin, Ann Frances. BS, Va. Union U., 1959; OD, Mass. Coll. Optometry, 1962. Pvt. practice Richmond, 1963—; state senator Va. Gen. Assembly, Richmond, 1985—, state del., 1977-85; bd. dirs. Consol. Bank and Trust Co., Va. Power Co., Dominion Resources. Sec. bd. trustees Va. Union U.; bd. dirs. Va. Coll. Fund, Richmond Renaissance, Va. Randolph Found., Black History Mus., So. Regional Edn. Bd./Commn. of Edn. Quality; active NAACT, Richmond Crusade for Voters; former pres. North Richmond Jackson Ward Civic Assn., North Richmond YMCA; mem. Va. State Senate, 1986—, mem. com. on fin., com. on edn. and health, com. on privileges and elections, others; mem. Va. Ho. of Dels., 1978-85; mem. Gov's Commn. on Ednl. Opportunity for All Virginians, others. Mem. NAACP, Va. Optometric Assn., Am. Optometric Assn., Nat. Optometric Assn., Richmond Med. Soc., Thebans Beneficial Club, Omega Psi Phi, Alpha Beta Boule. Baptist. Office: 904 N 1st St Richmond VA 23219-1002

LAMBERT, DANIEL MICHAEL, academic administrator; b. Kansas City, Mo., Jan. 16, 1941; s. Paul McKinley and Della Mae (Rogers) L.; m. Carolyn Faye Bright, Dec. 27, 1969; children: Kristian Paige, Dennis McKinley. AB, William Jewell Coll., 1963; MA, Northwestern U., 1965; postgrad., Harvard U., 1965-66; PhD, U. Mo., Columbia, 1977. Dean student affairs William Jewell Coll., Liberty, Mo., 1970-77, exec. asst. to pres., 1977-80, v.p., 1980-85; pres. College Hill Investments Inc., Liberty, 1985-87, Baker U., Baldwin City, Kans., 1987—; bd. dirs. Ferrell Co., Liberty; dir. Kansas City Bd. of Trade, 1988-90; hon. trustee Dohto U., Japan. Bd. dirs. The Barstow Sch., Kans. Ind. Colls. Assn.; mem. Big Bros. and Big Sisters; trustee Midwest Rsch. Inst. Capt. U.S. Army, 1966-70, Vietnam. Recipient Civic Leadership award Mo. Mcpl. League, 1986. Mem. Nat. Assn. Intercollegiate Athletics (dir.). Club: KC (Alvamar). Home: 505 E 8th St Baldwin City KS 66006 Office: Baker U Office of Pres Baldwin City KS 66006

LAMBERT, DENNIS ALVIN, radio news director; b. Allegan, Mich., Sept. 14, 1947; s. Alvin Millard and Myrta Gertrude (Ellinger) L.; m. Pamela Sue Hoeksema, Dec. 20, 1969; children: Matthew Dennis, Nicole Leigh. BA, Mich. State U., 1971. Disc jockey Sta. WAOP, Osego, Mich., 1969; asst. news dir. Sta. WJIM, Lansing, Mich., 1969-75; news reporter Sta. WVIC, East Lansing, 1975-76; news and sports anchor Sta. WCAR, Detroit, 1976; news reporter, editor Sta. WXYZ, Detroit, 1976-84; mng. editor Sta. KTAR, Phoenix, 1984-85, news dir., 1985—. Recipient various news related awards Ariz. AP, 1984, 86, 87. Mem. Ariz. Press Club, Radio, TV and News Dirs. Assn. Avocations: golf, softball, little league. Office: Sta KTAR Radio 301 W Osborn Rd Phoenix AZ 85013-3921

LAMBERT, ELEANOR (MRS. SEYMOUR BERKSON), public relations executive, fashion authority, journalist; b. Crawfordsville, Ind.; d. Henry Clay and Helen Houghton (Craig) L.; m. Seymour Berkson, 1936 (dec.); 1 son, William Craig. Student, John Herron Art Inst., Chgo. Art Inst.; DFA (hon.), Parsons Sch. Design, 1993. Pioneer publicist for Am. art and artists and later for creative talents in Am. fashion; originator, coordinator Coty Am. Fashion Critics Award and Cotton Fashion Awards; originator, founder, coord. Nat. Fashion Press weeks and ann. Internat. Best Dressed polls, 1940—; original dir. ILGWU's consumer service program; producer large fashion shows; spl. cons. on uniforms WAC and U.S. Army Nurse Corps, 1943-45; mem. NRC advisory com. to Q.M. on Women's Mil Clothing; mem. advisory com. Costume Inst., Met. Mus. Art; apptd. by Pres. Johnson as mem. Nat. Council on Arts, 1965-66; founder, charter mem. Council Fashion Designers of Am., 1963; mem. N.Y. Mayor's Com. World Fashion Center; mem. Mayor's Hospitality Com., N.Y.; bd. dirs. N.Y. World's Fair, 1964; mem. Ednl. Found. for Fashion Industries. Author: syndicated column on women's interests She, World of Fashion, 1973. Recipient N.Y. Bd. of Trade gold medal award for outstanding contbns. to Am. fashion industries, 1960; Honor award Girls Clubs Am.; Matrix award in pub. rels. N.Y. Women in Communications, 1985; Lifetime Achievement awards Coun. Fashion Designers of Am., 1988, 94. Mem. N.Y. Fashion Group (v.p. 1961-63). Presbyterian. Home: 1060 5th Ave New York NY 10128-0104 Office: Eleanor Lambert Ltd 245 E 58th St New York NY 10022-1201

LAMBERT, ETHEL GIBSON CLARK, secondary school educator; b. Atlanta, Apr. 18, 1943; d. Robert Harold and Ethel (Gibson) Clark; m. Hugh Felder Lambert, June 27, 1964 (div. Nov. 3, 1988); children: Courtney, Elizabeth, Hugh Lambert Jr. BA, Oglethorpe U., Atlanta, 1965; MEd, Kennesaw State Coll., Marietta, Ga., 1992; postgrad., West Ga. Coll., Carrollton, 1995—. Lic. tchr. T-5, Ga. Tchr. Clayton County Bd. Edn., Jonesboro, Ga., 1965-66; Fulton County Bd. Edn., Atlanta, 1966-67; tchr. pre-sch. weekday program First Bapt. Ch., Gainesville, Ga., 1984-88; tchr. remedial edn. program Riverdale High Sch./Clayton County Bd. Edn., 1990—. Author: The Impact of Geography on the Campaigns of the Civil War Fought in Georgia, 1993, The Utilization of Georgia Historical Sites as a Teaching Methodology in Middle Grades Education, 1993, (juvenile) Obnoxious Bill, 1993, Research on Academic Motivation of Elementary, Middle and Secondary School Students in America, 1993. Den leader Cub Scouts Am., Gainesville, 1980-83; mem. Christian Businessmen's Prayer Breakfast, Atlanta, 1990-95. Mem. Profl. Assn. Ga. Educators, Order Ea. Star. Baptist. Avocations: swimming, water skiing, reading, walking, genealogy. Home: 1881 Myrtle Dr SW Apt 711 Atlanta GA 30311 Office: Riverdale High Sch 160 Roberts Dr Riverdale GA 30274

LAMBERT, EUGENE KENT, oncologist, hematologist; b. Hinsdale, Ill., Feb. 13, 1944; s. Eugene Nelson and Dorothy Louise (Diedrichson) L.; m. Maria Natalie Gonzalez,June 19, 1971; children: Carlotta Pilar, Danielle Suzanne, Jori Marie. BA, North Ctrl. Coll., Naperville, Ill., 1966; MD, U. Ill., Chgo., 1970. Diplomate Am. Bd. Internal Medicine, Am. Bd. Hematology, Am. Bd. Med. Oncology. Fellow in hematology Michael Reese Hosp., Chgo., 1976; fellow Northwestern U., Chgo., 1979; oncologist Wichita (Kans.) Clinic, 1979-81, Dreyer Med. Clinic, Aurora, Ill., 1981-86, Fond du Lac (Wis.) Clinic, 1986—; med. dir. at large Wis. divsn. Am. Cancer Soc., 1991—. Bd. dirs., Girl Scouts Am., Aurora, Ill., 1985-86, El Centro, Aurora, 1985-86. Lt. USNR, 1971-73. Mem. AMA, ACP, Am. Soc. Hematology, Am. Soc. Clin. Oncologists. Avocations: music, volley ball, reading, cross country skiing. Office: Fond du Lac Clinic 80 Sheboygan St Fond Du Lac WI 54935

LAMBERT, FREDERICK WILLIAM, lawyer, educator; b. Millburn, N.J., Feb. 12, 1943; m. Barbara E. Fogell, Aug. 13, 1965; children: Elisabeth, Mark. BA, U. Mich., 1965, JD, 1969. Bar: Ohio 1969, Fla. 1973, Calif. 1973, U.S. Supreme Ct. 1975. Law clk. to Stanley N. Barnes, U.S. Cir. Judge U.S. Cir. Ct., L.A., 1969-70; spl. asst. Office Legal Counsel U.S. Dept. Justice, Washington, 1970-71; law clk. to Justice William H. Rehnquist U.S. Supreme Ct., Washington, 1971-72; pvt. practice L.A., 1973-90; acting gen. counsel Itel Corp., San Francisco, 1981-82; prtnr. Adams, Duque & Hazeltine, L.A., 1985-90, chmn. bus. law dept., 1989-90; prof. Hastings Coll. Law, U. Calif., San Francisco, 1993—; vis. prof. law, 1990-92; vis. prof. Duke Law Sch., Durham, N.C., 1992-93. Mem. Calif. State Bar Assn. Home: 1531 Willard St San Francisco CA 94117

LAMBERT, GEORGE ROBERT, lawyer, insurance company executive; b. Muncie, Ind., Feb. 21, 1933; s. George Russell and Velma Lou (Jones) L.; m. Mary Virginia Ailing, June 16, 1956; children: Robert Allen, Ann Holt, James William. BS, Ind. U., Bloomington, 1955; JD, Ind. U. Chgo.-Kent Coll. Law, 1962. Bar: Ill. 1962, U.S. Dist. Ct. (no. dist.) Ill. 1962, Iowa 1984, Pa. 1988. V.p., gen. counsel, sec. Washington Nat. Ins. Co.,

Evanston, Ill., 1958-82; v.p., gen. counsel Washington Nat. Corp., Evanston, 1979-82; sr. v.p., sec., gen. counsel Life Investors Inc., Cedar Rapids, Iowa, 1982-88; v.p., gen. counsel Provident Mut. Life Ins. Co. Phila., 1988-95. Alderman, Evanston City Council, 1980-82. Served to lt. USAF, 1955-57. Mem. ABA (ho. of dels. 1987-89, chair life ins. law com. 1989-90, chair scope and correlation com. 1992-93, mem. tort and ins. practice sect.), Ill. State Bar Assn., Iowa State Bar Assn., Phila. Bar Assn., Pa. Bar Assn., Assn. of Life Ins. Counsel (past pres.), Am. Corporate Counsel Assn. (Del Valley chap., bd. dirs. 1992—). Home and Office: 2222 E Deerfield Dr Media PA 19063

LAMBERT, JEREMIAH DANIEL, lawyer; b. N.Y.C., Sept. 11, 1934; s. Noah D. and Clara (Ravage) L.; m. Vicki Anne Asher, July 25, 1959 (div.); children: Nicole Stirling, Alix Stewart, Leigh Asher; m. Sanda Kayden, Dec. 3, 1983; children: Clare Kayden, Hilary Kayden. A.B., Princeton U., 1955; LL.B., Yale U., 1959. Bar: N.Y. 1960, D.C. 1964, U.S. Ct. Appeals (5th cir.) 1964, U.S. Supreme Ct. 1964. Assoc. Cravath, Swaine & Moore, N.Y.C., 1959-63; pvt. practice law Washington, 1963-66; ptnr. Drew & Lambert, Washington, 1966-69; sr. ptnr. Peabody, Lambert & Meyers, Washington, 1969-84; ptnr. Lane & Mittendorf, Washington, 1991—; adj. prof. law Georgetown U., Washington, 1978-79; trustee Internat. Law Inst., Washington, 1983-88. Co-author: (with Lawrence White) Handbook of Modern Construction Law, 1982; editor: Economic and Political Incentives to Petroleum Development, 1990; contbr. articles to legal jours. 1st lt. USAR, 1966-67. Fulbright scholar U. Copenhagen, 1955-56. Mem. ABA, Am. Soc. Internat. Law, D.C Bar Assn., Bar Assn. of City of N.Y., Cosmos Club, Princeton Club, Yale Club, Chevy Chase Club. Office: Lane & Mittendorf 919 18th St NW Washington DC 20006-5503

LAMBERT, JOAN DORETY, elementary education educator; b. Trenton, N.J., Oct. 21, 1937; d. John William and Margaret (Fagan) Dorety; m. James E. Lambert Sr., June 25, 1960; children: Margi, Karen, James E., Kevin. BA, Georgian Ct. Coll., Lakewood, N.J., 1958. Cert. tchr., Pa., N.J Tchr. 2d and 3d grades combined Washington Elem. Sch., Trenton, 1958-61; tchr. kindergarten music St. Genevieve Sch., Flourtown, Pa., 1968-78, tchr. 3d grade, 1978—; producer, dir. musical shows for St. Genevieve Sch., 1970-78; demonstration classroom for writing process on computers Chestnut Hill Coll. Mem. Jr. League of Trenton, 1960-68, Jr. League of Phila., 1968-70. Teleflex Internat. grantee, 1989-92, Anna B. Stokes Meml. scholar, 1960, Met. Opera grantee, 1958-60. Mem. NEA. Republican. Roman Catholic. Avocations: walking, theater, reading, swimming, family activities. Home: 33 Coventry Ct Blue Bell PA 19422-2528 Office: St Genevieve Sch 1237 Bethlehem Pike Flourtown PA 19031-1902

LAMBERT, JOHN BOYD, chemical engineer, consultant; b. Billings, Mont., July 5, 1929; s. Jean Arthur and Gail (Boyd) L.; m. Jean Wilson Bullard, June 20, 1953 (dec. 1958); children: William, Thomas, Patricia, Cathy, Karen; m. Ilse Crager, Sept. 20, 1980. BS in Engring., Princeton U., 1951; PhD, U. Wis., 1956. Rsch. engr. E.I. DuPont de Nemours Co., Wilmington, Del., 1956-69; sr. rsch. engr. Fansteel, Inc., Balt., 1969, mktg. mgr./plant mgr., North Chicago, Ill., 1970-73, mgr. mfg. engring., Waukegan, Ill., 1974-80, corp. tech. dir., North Chicago 1980-86, gen. mgr. metals, 1987-90, v.p., corp. tech. dir., 1990-91; ind. cons. Lake Forest, Ill., 1991—; bd. dirs. Lake Forest Grad. Sch. Mgmt., 1984-91. Cont. to profl. publs. Sec. Del. Jr. C. of C., Wilmington, 1972-74. Recipient Charles Hatchett medal Inst. Metals, London, 1986. Mem. AICE, Am. Chem. Soc., Am. Soc. Metals, Sigma Xi. Episcopalian. Achievements include patents in field of dispersion-strengthened metals, refractory metals, chemical vapor deposition, both products and processes. Home and Office: 617 E Greenbriar Ln Lake Forest IL 60045-3214

LAMBERT, JOHN PHILLIP, financial executive, consultant; b. Davenport, Iowa, Aug. 17, 1944; s. Dale Edward Lambert and Phyllis Meeker; m. Carol Ann Moreira, Aug. 10, 1971; children: Dawn, Kimberly, Kim. BA, Augustana Coll., Rock Island, Ill., 1966. CPA, Ill. Sr. auditor Price Waterhouse, Chgo., 1966-71; sr. v.p. fin. Burger King Corp., Miami, Fla., 1971-82; exec. v.p., chief fin. officer W.R. Grace Restaurants, Irvine, Calif., 1983-84, Perkins Family Restaurants, L.P., Memphis, 1985-89; pvt. practice fin. cons. Sarasota, Fla., 1989—; fin. cons. to restaurant industry. Recipient All Am. Wrestler award NCAA, 1966; named one of Outstanding Young Men of Am., 1976. Mem. AICPA. Republican. Presbyterian. Avocations: reading, golf, boating, gardening. Home and Office: 3770 Prairie Dunes Dr Sarasota FL 34238-2853

LAMBERT, JOSEPH BUCKLEY, chemistry educator; b. Ft. Sheridan, Ill., July 4, 1940; s. Joseph Idus and Elizabeth Dorothy (Kirwan) L.; m. Mary Wakefield Pulliam, June 27, 1967; children: Laura Kirwan, Alice Pulliam, Joseph Cannon. BS, Yale U., 1962; Ph.D. (Woodrow Wilson fellow 1962-63, NSF fellow 1962-65), Calif. Inst. Tech., 1965. Asst. prof. chemistry Northwestern U., Evanston, Ill., 1965-69, assoc. prof., 1969-74, prof. chemistry, 1974-91, Clare Hamilton Hall prof. chemistry, 1991—; chmn. dept. Northwestern U., 1986-89, dir. integrated sci. program, 1982-85; vis. assoc. prof. Brit. Mus., 1973, Polish Acad. Scis., 1981, Chinese Acad. Scis., 1988. Author: Organic Structural Analysis, 1976, Physical Organic Chemistry through Solved Problems, 1978, The Multinuclear Approach to NMR Spectroscopy, 1983, Archaeological Chemistry III, 1984, Introduction to Organic Spectroscopy, 1987, Recent Advances in Organic NMR Spectroscopy, 1987, Acyclic Organonitrogen Stereodynamics, 1992, Cyclic Organonitrogen Stereodynamics, 1992, Prehistoric Human Bone, 1993; audio course Intermediate NMR Spectroscopy, 1973; editor in chief Journal of Physical Organic Chemistry; editorial bd. Magnetic Resonance Chemistry, Archaeometry; contbr. articles to sci. jours. Recipient Nat. Fresenius award, 1976, James Flack Norris award, 1987, Fryxell award, 1989, Nat. Catalyst award, 1993; Alfred P. Sloan fellow, 1968-70, Guggenheim fellow, 1973, Interacad. exch. fellow (U.S.-Poland), 1985, Air Force Office sci. rsch. fellow, 1990. Fellow AAAS, Japan Soc. for Promotion of Sci., Brit. Interplanetary Soc., Ill. Acad. Sci. (life); mem. Am. Chem. Soc. (chmn. divsn. hist. chemistry 1996), Royal Soc. Chemistry, Soc. Archaeol. Scis. (pres. 1986-87, assoc. editor Bull.), Phi Beta Kappa, Sigma Xi. Home: 1956 Linneman St Glenview IL 60025-4264 Office: Northwestern University Dept of Chemistry 2145 Sheridan Rd Evanston IL 60208-3113

LAMBERT, LLOYD TUPPER, writer, civic volunteer; b. Binghamton, N.Y., Apr. 3, 1901; s. Frank Lloyd and Lulu Maud (Tupper) L.; children: Richard Tupper, David William, Alec Lloyd. Student, Lowells Bus. Coll., Binghamton, N.Y. Sign-writer, display mgr. dept. store, Binghamton, 1916-17; vaudevillian N.Y., 1919-20; display mgr. dept. store, Binghamton, N.Y., 1921-27, Carl Co., Schenectady, N.Y., 1928-66; ski columnist Schenectady Gazette, Schenectady, 1944-71; ski radio broadcaster Sta. WPTR, Albany, N.Y., 1946-55; radio broadcaster Sta. WGY, Schdy, N.Y., 1955-72, Sta. WABY, Albany, 1972-81; founder The Hunter Mountain Mus., N.Y., 1976 (ski artifacts date back to 1750 from Norway Nat. Ski Hall of Fame, Mich.), N.Y. Capital Dist. Ski Coun., Albany, 1947. Author: Hunter Mountain News, Senior Mag., 1981—. With U.S. Army, 1917-19. Recipient Golden Quill, U.S. Ski Writers, 1988; Dedication to Skiing, Eastern Ski Writers, 1985; 70 years of Skiing, 1985; Golden Pass, U.S Olympic Team, 1989, Yugoslavia award in honor or 70 Plus Ski Club, 1991, Cortina, Italy award, 1993, Olympic Ski Team award. Mem. 70 Plus Ski Club (founder 1977, freelance writer), USCG Aux. (comdr.). Avocations: skiing and racing worldwide. Home and Office: 70 Plus Ski Club 104 Eastside Dr Ballston Lake NY 12019-2116

LAMBERT, MARTHA LOWERY, state legislator; b. Douglasville, Ga., Mar. 27, 1937; d. Edmond Davis and Mary (Daniel) Lowery; m. Paul Dean Lambert, June 13, 1959; children: Melanie Lynn, Kurt Phillip, Brett Cameron, Matthew Dean. Mem. N.Mex. Ho. of Reps., Santa Fe, 1981—; part-owner Premier Foods Inc., Albuquerque, 1989—. Pres. Albuquerque Dist. Dental Aux., 1971, Albuquerque Fed. Rep. Women, 1975; alt. del. Nat. Rep. Conv., Kansas City, Mo, 1976, Houston, 1992. Avocations: reading, bowling, skiing, snowmobiling, sports. Home: 616 Running Water Cir SE Albuquerque NM 87123-4162 Office: N Mex House of Reps State Capitol New Mexico State Capitol NM 87503

LAMBERT, MICHAEL MALET, hotel company executive; b. Liverpool, Eng., Sept. 30, 1930; came to Can., 1956, naturalized, 1968; s. Arthur Reginald and Kathleen (Backhouse) L.; m. Sally Ann Day, May 15, 1957;

children—Christopher Malet, Simon Day. Hotel gen. mgr. Western Internat. Hotels, Vancouver, B.C., Can., 1957-64; hotel gen. mgr. Calgary, Alta., 1964-68, Montreal, P.Q., Can., 1968-71, Washington, 1971-73; from v.p. to exec. v.p. Four Seasons Hotels Ltd., Toronto, Ont., Can., 1973-84; pres. Four Seasons Hotels Ltd., Singapore, 1984-85; regional v.p. Can. Pacific Hotels, 1985—; gen. mgr. Hotel Vancouver, 1985—. Served to lt. Army of Gt. Britain, 1949-50. Avocations: history; antiques; tennis; gardening; bridge. Office: Can Pacific Hotels Inc, 900 W Georgia St, Vancouver, BC Canada V6C 2W6

LAMBERT, NADINE MURPHY, psychologist, educator; b. Ephraim, Utah; m. Robert E. Lambert, 1956; children—Laura Allan, Jeffrey. Ph.D. in Psychology, U. So. Calif., 1965. Diplomate Am. Bd. Profl. Psychology, Am. Bd. Sch. Psychology. Sch. psychologist Los Nietos Sch. Dist., Whittier, Calif., 1952-53, Bellflower (Calif.) Unified Sch. Dist., 1953-58; research cons. Calif. Dept. Edn., Los Angeles, 1958-64; dir. sch. psychology tng. program U. Calif., Berkeley, 1964—; asst. prof. edn. U. Calif., 1964-70, asso. prof. 1970-76, prof., 1976—; assoc. dean for student svcs. U. Calif., Berkeley, 1988-94; mem. Joint Com. Mental Health of Children, 1967-68; cons. state depts. edn., Calif., Ga., Fla.; cons. Calif. Dept. Justice; mem. panel on testing handicapped people Nat. Acad. Scis., 1978-81. Author: School Version of the AAMD Adaptive Behavior Scale, 3d edit., 1993; co-author: (with Wilcox and Gleason) Educationally Retarded Child: Comprehensive Assessment and Planning for the EMR and Slow-Learning Child, 1974, (with Hartsough and Bower) Process for Assessment of Effective Functioning, 1981, (with Windmiller and Turiel) Moral Development and Socialization -- Three Perspectives, 1979; assoc. editor Am. Jour. Orthopsychiatry, 1975-81, Am. Jour. Mental Deficiency, 1977-80, others. With Hartsough and Sandoval Children's Attention and Adjustment Survey, 1990. Recipient Dorothy Hughes award for outstanding contbn. to ednl. and sch. psychology NYU, 1990, Tobacco Disease Related Rsch. award U. Calif., 1990-94, NIDA, 1994—, Dept. Transp., 1994-95; grantee NIMH, 1965-87, Calif. State Dept. Edn., 1971-72, 76-78. Fellow APA (coun. reps. div. sch. psychologists, bd. dirs. 1983-96, mem. bd. profl. affairs 1981-83, bd. ednl. affairs 1991-94, chmn. 1992-94, Disting. Svc. award 1980, award for disting. profl. contbns. 1986), Am. Orthopsychiat. Assn.; mem. NEA, Calif. Assn. Sch. Psychologists and Psychometrists (pres. 1962-63, Sandra Goff award 1985), Am. Ednl. Rsch. Assn. Office: U Calif Dept Edn Berkeley CA 94720-1670

LAMBERT, OLAF CECIL, hotel executive; b. Sherfield-on-London, Hampshire, Eng.; came to U.S., 1946; naturalized, 1958; s. Stanilas and Jeanne Claire (Helsen) Lubienski; m. Erla Saunders, Aug. 19, 1950. Grad. Ecole Hoteliere, Nice, France, 1937. Gen. mgr. Queensbury Hotel, Glens Falls, N.Y., 1956-57; resident mgr. Istanbul (Turkey) Hilton, 1957-58; resident mgr., asst. project mgr. Berlin Hilton, 1958-59; v.p., gen. mgr. Royal Orleans, New Orleans, 1959-65, Americana of N.Y., N.Y.C., 1965-66; gen. mgr. Chateau Louisiane, New Orleans, 1966—; treas. So. Motor Lodge, 1964—; pres. Dauphine Orleans Hotel Corp., Olaf Lambert and Assocs. Inc. New Orleans. served to flight lt. RAF, 1939-45; prisoner of war, 1942-45. Recipient Instns. Nat. Merit award Hotel Mgmt. Rev., 1958, Golden Host Merit award, 1964. Mem. Chaine des Rotisseurs, New Orleans Hotel Assn. (bd. dirs.). Hotel Sales Mgmt. Assn., Masons, Shriners. Office: 412 Dauphine St New Orleans LA 70112-3147

LAMBERT, PAUL CHRISTOPHER, lawyer, former ambassador; b. N.Y.C., Mar. 14, 1928; s. Prall Wilson and Lorena (Carroll) L.; m. Mary Lee, June 9, 1956; children: Jennifer, P. Christopher Jr. (dec.), John C., Mary W. AB, Yale U., 1950; JD, Harvard U., 1953. Bar: D.C. 1955, N.Y. 1956. Assoc. Milbank, Tweed, Hadley & McCloy, N.Y.C., 1955-66; ptnr. Whitman Breed Abbott & Morgan (formerly Breed, Abbott & Morgan), N.Y.C., 1966-90, 92—; U.S. amb. to Ecuador, 1990-92. Mem. N.Y. Rep. State Fin. Com., 1983-89; N.Y. del.-at-large Rep. Nat. Conv., 1984, 88, 92; mem. exec. com. N.Y. State Rep. Party, 1984-89, nat. fin. com. George Bush for Pres., 1988; chmn. The Empire Club, 1984-89; vice chmn. bd. govs. Assn. Yale Alumni, 1980-82, chmn. 1982-84; mem. Yale U. coun. 1980-84, hon. degree com., 1985-88, devel. bd., 1984-88; bd. dirs. Yale Alumni Fund, 1976-80, 82-84, Yale Alumni Publs. Inc., 1980-84; assoc. fellow Davenport Coll. Yale U., 1982—; bd. dirs. Nat. Soc. to Prevent Blindness, 1976-88, sec., 1976-84; trustee Brearley Sch., 1976-85, v.p. bd., 1978-85; trustee Hotchkiss Sch. 1973-81; sec., bd. dirs. Chamber Music Soc. of Lincoln Ctr., 1992—; Mayor's Commn. for Protocol, N.Y.C., 1994—. Cpl. U.S. Army, 1953-55. Recipient Yale medal, New Haven, 1988. Mem. ABA, N.Y. State Bar Assn., Assn. of Bar of City of N.Y., Century Assn., Down Town Assn. (N.Y.C.), Pilgrims of U.S., Coun. of Am. Ambassadors, River Club, Union Club, Rumson Country Club, Seabright Lawn Tennis Club (Rumson, N.J., sec. 1964-72, v.p. 1972-76, pres. 1976-82). Republican. Mem. Christian Ch. Avocations: politics, classical music, tennis, skiing. Office: Whitman Breed Abbott Morgan MetLife Bldg 200 Park Ave New York NY 10166

LAMBERT, RICHARD BOWLES, JR., science foundation program director, oceanographer; b. Clinton, Mass., Apr. 20, 1939; s. Richard Bowles and Dorothy Elisabeth (Peck) L.; m. Sherrill Faye Smith, July 4, 1964; 1 child, Lisa Beth Lauren. AB in Physics, Lehigh U., 1961; ScM in Physics, Brown U., 1964, PhD in Physics, 1966; postgrad., Goethe Institut, Germany, 1966, NATO Internat. Sch., Germany, 1966, Max Planck Inst. for Physics & Astrophysics, Germany, 1966. Fulbright Postdoctoral fellow Institut fur Stromungsmechanik Technische Hochschule, Munich, Germany, 1966-67; asst. prof. Grad. Sch. Oceanography U. R.I., 1968-74, assoc. prof. Grad. Sch. Oceanography, 1974; program dir. physical oceanography program NSF, Washington, 1975-77; rsch. oceanographer Sci. Applications Internat. Corp., 1977-79, mgr. ocean physics divsn., 1979-83, asst. v.p., 1980-83, sr. rsch. oceanographer, 1983-84; assoc. program dir. physical oceanography program NSF, Washington, 1984-91, program dir. physical oceanography program, 1991—; adv. com. NOAA; assoc. U.S. TOGA Project Office 1985-91; delegate Intergovernmental TOGA Bd.; delegation head Intergovernmental WOCE Panel; co-investigator R/V Trident Oceanographic Cruises, Feb. 1971 (21 days), Dec. 1971 (6 days), April 1974 (14 days), Nov. 1974 (19 days); chief scientist R/V Trident Oceanographic Cruises, Oct. 1971 (17 days), Nov. 1971 (8 days), April 1973 (15 days); co-investigator R/V Atlantis II Oceanographic Cruises, July 1973 (18 days). Contbr. articles to Jour. Fluid Mech. and other profl. jours. Bd. dirs. Christian Performing Artist's Fellowship, Fairfax, Va., 1993—. Mem. Am. Assn. Advancement Sci., Am. Geophysical Union, Am. Physical Soc., The Oceanography Soc. (life mem.). Phi Beta Kappa, Sigma Xi. Office: NSF Phys Oceanography Program 4201 Wilson Blvd Arlington VA 22203-1803

LAMBERT, ROBERT FRANK, electrical engineer, educator; b. Warroad, Minn., Mar. 14, 1924; s. Fred Joseph and Nutah (Gibson) L.; m. June Darlene Flatten, June 30, 1951; children—Cynthia Marie, Susan Ann, Katherine Cheryl. B.E.E., U. Minn., 1948, M.S. in Elec. Engring., 1949, Ph.D., 1953. Asst. prof. U. Minn. Inst. Tech., Mpls., 1953-54; assoc. prof. U. Minn. Inst. Tech., 1955-59, prof. elec. engring., 1959-94, prof. emeritus, 1964—; dir. propagation research lab. U. Minn., 1968-87; asso. dean U. Minn. (Inst. Tech.), 1967-68; asst. prof. Mass. Inst. Tech., 1954-55; cons. elec. engr., also in acoustics 1953—; guest scientist Third Phys. Inst., Göttingen, Fed. Republic Germany, 1964; vis. scientist NASA, Hampton, Va., 1979; dir. Inst. Noise Control Engring., Washington, 1972-95. Contbr. numerous articles to tech. jours. Served with USNR, 1943-46. Fellow IEEE, Acoustical Soc. Am. (assoc. editor jour. 1985-93); mem. Am. Soc. Engring. Edn., Am. Soc. Engring. Sci., AAAS, Inst. Noise Control Engring. (dir., John C. Johnson Meml. award), Sigma Xi, Tau Beta Pi, Eta Kappa Nu, Gamma Alpha. Lutheran. Rsch. in acoustics, communication tech. random vibrations. Home: 2503 Snelling Curve Saint Paul MN 55113-3111 Office: U Minn Inst Tech Dept Elec Engring Minneapolis MN 55455

LAMBERT, ROBERT LOWELL, scientific investigator; b. Mpls., Jan. 3, 1923; s. Luell E. and Amy (Schwerin) L.; m. Jean Louise Zavodney, Mar. 19, 1949; children: Thomas R., John N. Student, U. Utah, 1941-42, Tex. A&M Coll., 1943-44, Biarritz (France) Am. U., 1945; B.S., UCLA, 1947, M.B.A., 1948; grad. student, U. Minn., 1948-50; Ph.D., U. Beverly Hills, 1982. Instr. bus. adminstrn. U. Minn., 1948-50; with Budget Pack, Inc., Los Angeles, 1950-55; v.p. Budget Pack, Inc., 1954-55; with Riverside Cement Co. div. Amcord, Inc., Los Angeles, 1955-61; treas. Riverside Cement Co. div. Amcord, Inc., 1960-61; finance dir. Amcord, Inc., 1961-72, treas. 1972-75, 75-80, v.p., 1967-72, sec., 1972-74, sr. v.p., 1972-80; pres. dir. Inst. for Bus. Edn., Newport Beach, Calif., 1981-83; ind. investigator, author in field of chronobiological epidemiology, 1984—; former dir., officer various subsidiaries Amcord, Inc. Contbr. articles to profl. jours. Vice pres. Amcord Found., 1958-80. Served with inf. AUS, World War II, ETO. Decorated Combat Inf. badge, Bronze star with oak leaf cluster, Presdl. Unit citiation, Belgian Fourragere. Mem. AAAS, N.Y. Acad. Scis., Tau Kappa Epsilon, Beta Gamma Sigma, Alpha Kappa Psi. Lutheran. Clubs: Big Canyon Country (Newport Beach); Palm Desert Resort Country. Home: 13 Cool Brk Irvine CA 92715-3412

LAMBERT, SAMUEL WALDRON, III, lawyer, foundation executive; b. N.Y.C., Jan. 12, 1938; s. Samuel W. and Mary (Hamill) L.; m. Louisa Garnsey, Aug. 25, 1962; children—Louisa Kelly, Samuel William, Sarah Hamill. B.A., Yale U., 1960; LL.B., Harvard U., 1963. Bar: N.J. 1964, U.S. Tax Ct. 1975. Assoc Albridge C. Smith III, Princeton, N.J., 1964-67; ptnr. Smith, Cook, Lambert & Miller, and predecessors, Princeton, 1967-80; officer, dir. Smith, Lambert, Hicks & Miller, P.C., Princeton, 1981-87; ptnr. in charge of office Drinker, Biddle & Reath, 1988—; mng. ptnr., 1994—; dir., trustee Chem. Bank N.J, Peterson's Guides, Inc.; pres. The Bunbury Co., Princeton. Bd. dirs. Winslow Found., Windham Found., Curtis W. McGraw Found.; capt. Princeton Republican County Com., 1967-69. Served with USAR, 1963-69. Mem. Princeton Bar Assn. (pres. 1976-77), N.J. Bar Assn., ABA.

LAMBERT, STEVEN CHARLES, lawyer; b. Kingsport, Tenn., Aug. 22, 1947; s. M. Charles and Janet (Sultner) L.; m. Nancy B. Lambert, June 26, 1971; children: Shelley Elizabeth, Charles Burnette. BA, Duke U., 1969; JD, Georgetown U., 1974. Bar: D.C. 1975, U.S. Ct. Fed. Claims, U.S. Ct. Appeals (fed. cir.), U.S. Tax Ct. Law clk. to Chief Judge Wilson Cowen, U.S. Ct. Claims, Washington, 1974-75; assoc Wilkinson, Cragun & Barker, Washington, 1975-80; ptnr. Wilkinson, Cragun & Barker, 1980-82, Hamel & Park, Washington, 1982-88, Hopkins & Sutter, Washington, 1988—; mgr. litigation grp. Hopkins & Sutter, 1987-93; chmn. adv. coun. U.S. Ct. Claims, 1982-86, mem. adv. coun., 1986—, chmn. bicentennial commn., 1987-91. Co-author: Tax Ideas Desk Book, 1980; contbr. articles to profl. jours. Trustee Ferrum Coll.; mem. bd. pensions United Meth. Ch. With U.S. Army, 1970-72. Fellow Am. Bar Found.; mem. ABA (sec. litigation and natural resources), Am. Arbitration Assn., Claims Ct. Bar Assn. (pres. 1990-91), Fed. Cir. Bar Assn. (bd. dirs. 1986-88), Bar Assn. D.C. (bd. dirs. 1981-83). Methodist. Avocations: boating, fishing, tennis. Office: Hopkins & Sutter 888 16th St NW Washington DC 20006-4103

LAMBERT, WILLIAM G., journalist, consultant; b. Langford, S.D., Feb. 2, 1920; s. William G. and Blanche (Townsend) L.; m. Jean Kenway Mead, July 7, 1945; children: Kathryn, Heather Lambert Oxberry. Nieman fellow journalism, Harvard U., 1959-60. Reporter, news editor Enterprise-Courier, Oregon City, Oreg., 1945-50; reporter The Oregonian, Portland, 1950-59; anchor, news dir. KPTV, Oreg. Television, Inc., Portland, 1961-62; corr. Time mag., 1962-63; assoc. editor, staffwriter Life mag., N.Y.C., 1963-71; staff corr. Time-Life News Service, 1971-73; free-lance journalist, 1973; staff writer, cons. Phila. Inquirer, 1974-90; freelance journalist, libel litigation cons., 1990—; cons., U.S. commr. edn. Office of Edn., Washington, 1962. Served in U.S. Army, WWII, PTO, to maj. Res., ret. Decorated bronze star. Recipient Pulitzer prize for local reporting, 1957, Heywood Broun award, 1957, award for mag. reporting Sigma Delta Chi, 1967, Worth Bingham prize for distinguished reporting, 1967, Heywood Brown award, 1969, George Polk award for mag. reporting Abe Fortas articles, Sigma Delta Chi award, Nat. Headliners Club award, Page One award, 1970, Pa. Bar Assn. award, Phila. Bar Assn. award, Phila. Sigma Delta Chi award, AP Mng. Editors award (Pa.), 1981. Home: 529 Chandler Ln Villanova PA 19085-1026

LAMBERT, WILLIAM WILSON, psychology educator; b. Amherst, N.S., Can., May 10, 1919; s. Harry Brown and Alice Grace (Babcock) L.; m. Elisabeth Bird Carr, June 17, 1949; children: Hilary (Mrs. William M. Hopper), Holly Lee Alison (Mrs. Fred Nolting). A.B., Brown U., 1942; M.S., U. Nebr., 1943; Ph.D., Harvard U., 1951. Tech. aide NDRC, Washington, 1942-43; lectr. Harvard, Cambridge, Mass., 1949-50; asst. prof. Brown U., Providence, R.I., 1951-52; asst. prof. psychology, sociology and anthropology Cornell U., Ithaca, N.Y., 1952-55; assoc prof. Cornell U., 1955-60, prof., 1960—, dean Grad. Sch., 1974-81; cons. Fulbright Program, 1974-76; fellow Ctr. for Advanced Study, Palo Alto, Calif., 1954-55; Fulbright lectr. Oslo (Norway) U., 1957-58, U. Padua, Italy, 1973; Rockefeller exch. prof. U. Philippines, Quezon City, 1968-69; part-time longitudinal rsch. prof. U. Stockholm, 1965-66. Author: (with W.E. Lambert) Social Psychology, 1964, rev. edit., 1973, (with L. Minturn) Mothers of Six Cultures, 1963, (with G. Lindsey and others) Handbook of Social Psychology, 1969, (with R. Weisbrod) Comparative Perspectives in Social Psychology, 1971; Editor: (with E. Borgatta) Handbook Personality Theory and Research, 1968, (with H. Triandis) Handbook of Cross-Cultural Psychology, Vol. I, 1979. Served with USNR, 1943-46. NIH fellow, 1966-67; Guggenheim fellow, 1973. Fellow Am. Psychol. Assn. (mem. bd. sci. affairs 1970-73), AAAS; mem. Am. Sociol. Assn., Soc. for Cross-Cultural Research (pres. 1975-76), Phi Beta Kappa, Sigma Xi. Home: 1676 Hanshaw Rd Ithaca NY 14850-9102

LAMBERTH, ROYCE C., federal judge; b. 1943. BA, U. Tex., 1965, LLB, 1967. With civil dir. U.S. Atty's Office, Wasshington, 1974-77, asst. chief, 1977-78; chief U.S. Atty's. Office, 1978-87; judge U.S. Dist. Ct. (D.C. dist.), Washington, 1987—. Capt. (j.a.g.) U.S. Army, 1967-74. Mem. ABA (chmn. armed svcs. and vets. affairs com sect. adminstrv. law 1983-83), Fed. Bar Assn. (chmn. fed. litigation sect. 1986—), Jud. Conf. D.C. Cir. (arangements com. 1985, D.C. Bar., D.C. Bar Assn. (Cert. Appreciatio 1977), State Bar Tex. Office: US Dist Ct US Courthouse 3rd & Constitution Ave NW Washington DC 20001

LAMBERTI, MARJORIE, history educator; b. New Haven, Sept. 30, 1937; d. James and Anna (Vanacore) L. B.A., Smith Coll., 1959; M.A., Yale U., 1960, Ph.D., 1965. Prof. history Middlebury Coll., Vt., 1964—, Charles A Dana prof., 1984—. Author: Jewish Activism in Imperial Germany, 1978, State, Society and the Elementary School in Imperial Germany, 1989; mem. editorial bd. History of Edn. Quar., 1992—; contbr. articles to profl. jours. NEH fellow, 1968-69, 81-82; German Acad. Exch. Serv. rsch. grant, 1988. Fellow Inst. for Advanced Study (Princeton 1992-93); mem. Am. Hist. Assn., Conf. Group for Ctrl. European History, Leo Baeck Inst., Phi Beta Kappa. Home: 37 Gorham Ln Middlebury VT 05753-1016 Office: Middlebury Coll Dept History Middlebury VT 05753

LAMBERT LINCOLN, BLANCHE M., congresswoman; b. Helena, Ark., Sept. 30, 1960. BA, Randolph-Macon Woman's Coll., 1982. Sr. assoc The Pagonis & Donnelly Group, Inc., 1989-91; elected mem. 103rd Congress from 1st Dist., 1992. Office: US House of Representatives Office Of House Member Washington DC 20515

LAMBERTSEN, CHRISTIAN JAMES, environmental physiologist, physician, educator; b. Westfield, N.J., May 15, 1917; s. Christian and Ellen (Stevens) L.; m. Naomi Helen Hill, Feb. 5, 1944; children—Christian James, David Lee, Richard Hill, Bradley Stevens. B.S., Rutgers U., 1939; M.D., U. Pa., 1943. Prof. pharmacology and exptl. therapeutics, prof. medicine U. Pa. Sch. Medicine, 1946-87; founding dir. Inst. for Environ. Medicine, U. Pa. Med. Ctr., 1968—, disting prof. environ. medicine, 1985—; mem. adv. panel on med. scis. Office of Asst. Sec. Defense, 1954-61; sec. basic biol. sci. Bd. Med. Examiners, 1955-71; mem. Pres.'s Space Panel, 1967-70; mem. oceanographic adv. bd. Office of Asst. Sec. of Navy for R & D, 1968-77; mem. marine bd. Nat. Acad. Engring., 1973-77; adviser Office of Marine Resources, NOAA, 1972-76; med. adviser Ocean Systems Inc., Houston, 1960-83; med. dir. SubSea Intern, 1984—; chmn. com. Man in Space; Space Sci. Bd., NAS, 1960-62; chmn. life scis. adv. bd. McDonnell-Douglas Aircraft Corp., St. Louis, 1960-67; mem. research adv. bd. Mead-Johnson Corp., Evansville, Ind., 1960-67; sr. life scis. adviser Union Carbide Corp., Buffalo, N.Y., Westinghouse Elec. Corp., Annapolis, Md., 1972-74, Air Products and Chemicals Corp., Allentown, Pa., 1983-87; pres. Ecosystems Inc, Phila, 1972—. Editor: Underwater Physiology Symposium, II, III, IV, V, 1963-76; mem. editorial bd. Marine Tech. Soc. Jour., 1977-85. Contbr. articles to med., sci. jours. Served to maj. AUS, 1944-46. Decorated Legion of Merit; recipient Lindback award for Disting. Teaching, 1967; Aerospace Med. Assn. Tuttle award, 1970; Undersea Med. Behnke award, 1970; Dept. Def. Disting. Pub. Service medal, 1972; Marine Tech. Soc. award in Ocean Sci. and Engring., 1972; Dept. Navy Commendation Adv. Service, 1972; award in environ.

scis. N.Y. Acad. Scis., 1974; Disting. Pub. Service award USCG, 1976; NIH, USN, USAF, NASA, NOAA Research grantee. Fellow Aerospace Med. Assn. (v.p. 1968); mem. Am. Coll. Clin. Pharmacology and Chemotherapy, Am. Soc. Pharmacology and Exptl. Therapeutics, Am. Physiol. Soc., Am. Soc. Clin. Investigation, Assn. Am. Med. Colls., Internat. Acad. Astronautics, Internat. Astronautic Fedn., Internat. Union Physiol. Scis., Nat. Acad. Engring., John Morgan Med. Research Soc., Marine Tech. Soc., Peripatetic Med. Soc., Undersea Med. Soc. (founding pres.), Phila. County Med. Soc., Pa. Med. Soc., Phila. Maritime Mus., Phila. Physiol. Soc., Sigma Xi. Club: Cosmos (Washington). Home: 3500 Westchester Pike No 33 Newtown Square PA 19073 Office: Inst Environ Medicine 1 John Morgan Bldg U Pa Med Ctr Philadelphia PA 19104-6068

LAMBERTSEN, MARY ANN, human resources executive; b. Kane, Pa., Dec. 23, 1939; d. Arthur Nathaniel and Anna Marie (Peterson) Turnquist; m. John Franklin Lambertsen, Aug. 30, 1972. BS, Carnegie-Mellon U., 1961; MA, Columbia U., 1963; MS, Pace U., 1977. Tchr. math. Cleve. Pub. Schs., 1963-64; mgr. traffic Ohio Bell Telephone Co., Cleve., 1964-68, systems analyst, 1968-70, personnel analyst, 1970-71; specialist bus. systems Bell Telephone Labs., Piscataway, N.J., 1971-72; dist. mgr. personnel AT&T, N.Y.C., 1972-78; v.p. human resources Fisher-Price, East Aurora, N.Y., 1978-89, v.p. human resources and information systems, 1989-91; v.p. human resources Goulds Pumps, Seneca Falls, N.Y., 1991—; chmn. bd. N.Y. Fed. Res. Bank, Buffalo, 1986-91. Bd. dirs. Assn. for Retarded Children, Buffalo, 1985-92, trustee D'Youville Coll., 1990—. Recipient award SUNY-Buffalo, 1986; named Mgr. of Yr. Ctr. for Women in Mgmt./D'Youville Coll., 1986, YWCA Leader award, 1988. Mem. Profit Sharing Council Am. (bd. dirs. 1983—), Profit Sharing Research Found. (trustee 1982—). Club: The Women's Group (Buffalo). Office: Goulds Pumps 240 Fall St Seneca Falls NY 13148-1590

LAMBERTSON, DAVID FLOYD, ambassador; b. Sabetha, Kans., June 30, 1940; s. Alonzo Stagg and Anna Ruth (Shattuck) L.; m. Sacie Margaret Hooper, 1972; children: Jennifer Hall, David Hall, Dan Hall. BA, U. Redlands, 1962; postgrad., Occidental Coll., 1962, Georgetown U., 1963, Royal Coll. Def. Studies, London, 1981. Polit. officer U.S. Embassy, Saigon, Vietnam, 1965-68; dep. chief polit. sect. Am. Embassy, Tokyo, 1977-80; dep. chief mission Am. Embassy, Canberra, Australia, 1984-86, Seoul, Korea, 1986-87; consul U.S. Consulate, Medon, Indonesia, 1969-71; press spokesman U.S. delegation to Vietnam peace talks, Paris, 1971-73; dep. dir. office Japanese affairs U.S. Dept. State, Washington, 1975-77, dir. office Korean affairs, 1982-84, dep. asst. sec., from 1987; U.S. amb. to Thailand Bangkok, 1991—. Mem. Am. Fgn. Svc. Assn. Baptist. Office: Thailand Bangkok APO AP 96546

LAMBETH, THOMAS WILLIS, foundation executive; b. Clayton, N.C., Jan. 8, 1935; s. Mark Thomas and Ina Henrietta (Willis) L.; m. Donna Brooks Irving, July 18, 1964; children: Donna Catherine, Mark Hunter, Thomas Richard. AB in History, U. N.C., 1957; DHL (hon.), Pfeiffer Coll., Misenheimer, N.C., 1982. Reporter Winston-Salem Jour., 1959-60; adminstrv. asst. Gov. of N.C., 1961-65; staff mem. Smith Richardson Found., Greensboro, N.C., 1965-69; adminstrv. asst. Congressman Richardson Preyer, Washington, 1969-78; exec. dir. Z. Smith Reynolds Found., Winston-Salem, 1978—; acting dir. Kennedy Assasination Investigation, Washington, 1977; dir. Coun. on Founds., Washington, 1988-94, program chmn. ann. meeting, 1988-89; chmn. bd. Southeastern Coun. of Founds., Atlanta, 1985-87. Trustee, chmn. bd. U.N.C., Chapel Hill, 1969-83; chmn. Tchg. Fellow Commn., 1987-91, 93—. Recipient Disting. Alumnus award U.N.C., 1988. Mem. Alumni Assn. U.N.C. (pres. 1989-90). Democrat. Methodist. Home: 700 Yorkshire Rd Winston Salem NC 27106-5518 Office: Z Smith Reynolds Found 101 Reynolda Vlg Winston Salem NC 27106-5199

LAMBETH, VICTOR NEAL, horticulture, researcher; b. Sarcoxie, Mo., July 5, 1920; s. Odus Houston and Carrie (Woods) L.; m. Sarah Katherine Smarr, May 24, 1946; children: Victoria Kay, Debra Jean. B.S., U. Mo., 1942, M.A., 1948, Ph.D., 1950. Asst. prof. U. Mo., Columbia, 1950-51, assoc. prof., 1951-59, prof. dept. horticulture, 1959-91, prof. emeritus, 1991—; cons. horticulture to Thailand, Taiwan, Liberia; judge All-Am. Vegetable Trials, 1985-92. Inventor plant growth media, 1979; plant breeder tomato lines and cultivars; contbr. articles to profl. jours. Mem. Fin. Com. City of Columbia, Mo., 1970, mem. Bd. Zoning Adjustment, 1973-76, mem. Bd. Spl. Appeals, 1975-77. Served to lt. USN, 1943-46, PTO. Recipient Hort. award Mo. Hort. Soc., 1942; recipient Alumni Faculty award U. Mo. Alumni Assn., 1974; NSF grantee, 1982. Fellow Am. Soc. Hort. Sci. (grad. teaching award 1978); mem. Am. Soc. Plant Physiologists, Internat. Soc. Hort. Sci., Sigma Xi, Gamma Sigma Delta (pres. Mo. chpt. 1959-60). Methodist. Home: 1327 Lambeth Dr Columbia MO 65202-2466 Office: U Mo Dept Hort I-87 Agrl Bldg Columbia MO 65211

LAMBIRD, MONA SALYER, lawyer; b. Oklahoma City, July 19, 1938; d. B.M. Jr. and Pauline A. Salyer; m. Perry A. Lambird, July 30, 1960; children: Allison Lambird Watson, Jennifer Salyer, Elizabeth Gard, Susannah Johnson. BA, Wellesley Coll., 1960; LLB, U. Md., 1963. Bar: Okla. 1968, Md. Ct. Appeals 1963, U.S. Supreme Ct. 1967. Atty. civil div. Dept. Justice, Washington, 1963-65; sole practice law Balt. and Oklahoma City, 1965-71; mem. firm Andrews Davis Legg Bixler Milsten & Price, Inc. and predecessor firm, Oklahoma City, 1971—; minority mem. Okla. Election Bd., 1984—, vice-chmn., 1990—; mem. profl. responsibility tribunal Okla. Supreme Ct., 1984-90; Master of Bench, sec.-treas. Luther Bohanan Am. Inn of Ct., Oklahoma City, 1986—, pres., 1994—. Editor: Briefcase, Oklahoma County Bar Assn., 1976. Profl. liaison com. City Oklahoma City, 1974-80; mem. Hist. Preservation of Oklahoma City, Inc., 1970—; del. Oklahoma County and Okla. State Republican Party Conv., 1971—; Okla. City Orch. League Inc., legal advisor, 1973—, bd. dirs., 1973—; incorporator, bd. dirs. R.S.V.P. of Oklahoma County, pres., 1982-83; bd. dirs. Congregate Housing for Elderly, 1978—, Vis. Nurses Assn., 1983-86, Oklahoma County Friends of Library, 1980-91, The Support Ctrs., Inc., 1989—. Mem. ABA, Okla. Bar Assn. (pres. labor and employment law sect. bd. govs. 1992-94, pres.-elect 1995), Oklahoma County Bar Assn. (bd. dirs. 1986—, pres. 1990), Oklahoma County Bar Found. (pres. 1988), Jr. League Oklahoma City (bd. dirs. 1973-76, legal advisor), Oklahoma County and State Med. Assn. Aux. (dir.), Seven Sisters Colls. Club (pres. 1972-76), Women's Econ. Club (steering com. 1981-86). Methodist. Home: 419 NW 14th St Oklahoma City OK 73103-3510 Office: 500 W Main St Oklahoma City OK 73102-2220

LAMBORN, LEROY LESLIE, legal educator; b. Marion, Ohio, May 12, 1937; s. LeRoy Leslie and Lola Fern (Grant) L. A.B., Oberlin Coll., 1959; LL.B., Western Res. U., 1962; LL.M., Yale U., 1963; J.S.D., Columbia U., 1973. Bar: N.Y. 1965, Mich. 1974. Asst. prof. law U. Fla., 1965-69; prof. Wayne State U., 1970—; vis. prof. State U., Utrecht, 1981. Author: Legal Ethics and Professional Responsibility, 1963; contbr. articles on victimology to legal jours. Mem. Am. Law Inst., Nat. Orgn. Victim Assistance (bd. dirs. 1979-88, 90-91), World Soc. Victimology (exec. com. 1982-94). Office: Wayne State U Law Sch Detroit MI 48202

LAMBREMONT, EDWARD NELSON, JR., nuclear science educator; b. New Orleans, July 29, 1928; s. Edward Nelson and Caroline Josephine (Joachim) L.; m. Janice P. Savoy, Apr. 6, 1990; m. Mary Chris Bittle, May 30, 1981 (dec. Jan. 1987); m. Carol Jane Annis, June 16, 1951; children: Carol, Suzanne, John, Barbara. B.S., Tulane U., 1949, M.S., 1951; Ph.D., Ohio State U., 1958. Research entomologist U.S. Dept. Agr., Baton Rouge, 1958-66; assoc. prof. nuclear sci. La. State U., Baton Rouge, 1966-73, prof., 1973—, dir. Nuclear Sci. Ctr., 1974—; councilor Oak Ridge Assoc. Univs., 1971-79, bd. dirs., 1979-84, vis. scientist med. div., 1967-87; vis. scientist Internat. Atomic Energy Agy. Lab., Seibersdorf, Austria, 1988-90; cons. nuclear-related corps., 1978—. Contbr. articles to sci. jours. Served with U.S. Army, 1951-54, col. Res. (ret.). Grantee NIH, 1964-71; grantee NSF, 1971-77, U.S. Dept. Agr., 1979-83. Mem. Am. Nuclear Soc., Entomol. Soc. Am. (Deep South chpt.), Health Physic. Home: 2913 Calanne Ave Baton Rouge LA 70820-5408 Office: La State U Nuclear Sci Ctr Baton Rouge LA 70803

LAMBRIGHT, STEPHEN KIRK, brewing company executive; b. Kansas City, Mo., Dec. 3, 1942; s. Ray B. and Janet Lambright; m. Gail T. Tabler; children: Stephen K. Jr., James H., Sarah E., Catherine L. BS in Acctg., U.

Mo., 1965; JD cum laude, St. Louis U., 1968, MBA in Fin., 1977. Bar: Mo., 1968, Va. 1979, D.C. 1979; CPA, Mo. Tax acct. Arthur Andersen & Co., 1965-69; atty. Lashly, Caruthers, Thies, Rava & Hamel, 1970-77; asst. gen. counsel Anheuser-Busch Cos., St. Louis, 1977-78, exec. asst. chmn. bd., 1978-79; v.p., nat. affairs Anheuser-Busch Cos., Washington, 1979-81; v.p., industry and govt. affairs Anheuser-Busch Cos., St. Louis, 1981-83, mem. corp. policy com., 1981—, v.p. group exec., 1983—. Bd. dirs. St. Louis U.; chmn. legal and legis. com. C. of C of U.S.; mem. exec. com., treas. Shriner's Hosp. for Crippled Children; mem. Keep Am. Beautiful. Mem. Beer Inst., Northwestern U. Traffic Inst., Alcoholic Beverage Med. Rsch. Found. Presbyterian. Home: 415 Sheffield Estate Dr Saint Louis MO 63141-8523 Office: Anheuser-Busch Cos Inc 1 Busch Pl Saint Louis MO 63118-1849

LAMBRO, DONALD JOSEPH, columnist; b. Wellesley, Mass., July 24, 1940; s. Pascal and Mary (Lapery) L.; m. Jacquelyn Mae Killmon, Oct. 6, 1968; 1 son, Jason Phillip. B.S., Boston U., 1963. Reporter, Boston Traveler, 1963; freelance writer Washington, 1965-67; statehouse reporter UPI, Hartford, Conn., 1968-70; reporter UPI, Washington, 1970-80; columnist United Feature Syndicate, Washington, 1981—; commentator AP Radio Network, 1982-83, Nat. Pub. Radio, 1984-85; writer, host TV documentary Star Spangled Spenders, 1982; nat. editor Washington Times, 1987-88; chief polit. corr. Washington Times, 1988—. Author: The Federal Rathole, 1975; The Conscience of a Young Conservative, 1976; Fat City; How Washington Wastes Your Taxes, 1980; Washington-City of Scandals, 1984; Land of Opportunity, 1986. Albanian Orthodox.

LAMBRO, PHILLIP, composer, conductor, pianist; b. Wellesley, Mass., Sept. 2, 1935; s. Pascal and Mary (Lapery) L. Student, Music Acad. West, 1955. Piano debut Pianist's Fair, Symphony Hall, Boston, 1952; composer Miraflores for String Orchestra, Dance Barbaro for Percussion, Two Pictures for Solo Percussionist and Orchestra, Four Songs for Soprano and Orchestra, Toccata for Piano, Toccata for Guitar, Parallelograms for Flute Quartet and Jazz Ensemble, Music for Wind Brass and Percussion, Obelisk for Oboist and Percussionist, Structures for String Orchestra, Fanfare and Tower Music for Brass Quintet, Night Pieces for Piano, Biospheres for 6 Percussionists, Trumpet Voluntary, Eight Little Trigams for piano; composer, condr. for films including documentaries Energy on the Move, Mineral King; compositions performed by Leopold Stokowski, Philippe Entremont, Santiago Rodriguez, Phila. Orch., Rochester (N.Y.) Philharm., Balt. Symphony, Indpls. Symphony, Oklahoma Symphony, Denver Symphony, Europe, S.Am., Asia, Israel; condr. debut rec. of U.S. Internat. Orch. Active in population control, protection of animals, conservation; mem. NATO Tennis team, 1958-59. Served with inf. U.S. Army. Recipient award for best music for Mineral King, Nat. Bd. Rev., 1972. Mem. ASCAP, U.S. Tennis Assn., Raelian Movement, Tau Kappa Epsilon. Office: 1888 Century Park E Ste 1900 Los Angeles CA 90067-1723

LAMBROS, LAMBROS JOHN, lawyer, petroleum company executive; b. Sharon, Pa., 1935; s. John and Niki (George) L.; m. Cynthia Ryan, 1965; children: John F., Olivia W. A.B. magna cum laude in History and Lit, Harvard U., 1957, J.D., 1960. Bar: N.Y. 1961. Assoc. White & Case, N.Y.C., 1961-64; of counsel W.R. Grace & Co., N.Y.C., 1964-74, chief internat. counsel, 1970-74; v.p., gen. counsel Amerada Hess Corp., N.Y.C., 1974-76, sr. v.p., gen. counsel, 1976-80, sr. v.p., 1980-83, exec. v.p., dir., 1983-85; chmn., pres., chief exec. officer Norfolk Holdings Inc., Houston, 1986-93, also bd. dirs.; bd. dirs. 1st Empire State Corp. Home: 131 Goshen Rd Norfolk CT 06058-1301

LAMBROS, THOMAS DEMETRIOS, federal judge; b. Ashtabula, Ohio, Feb. 4, 1930; s. Demetrios P. and Panagoula (Bellios) L.; m. Shirley R. Kresin, June 20, 1953; children: Lesley P., Todd T. Student, Fairmount (W.Va.) State Coll., 1948-49; LLB, Cleve.-Marshall Law Sch., 1952. Bar: Ohio 1952. Ptnr. Lambros and Lambros, Ashtabula, 1952-60; judge Ct. Common Pleas, Jefferson, Ohio, 1960-67; judge U.S. Dist. Ct. (no. dist.) Ohio, Cleve., 1967—, chief judge, 1990—; mem. faculty Fed. Jud. Ctr.; innovator of summary jury trial. Contbr. articles legal publs. Mem. exec. bd. N.E. Ohio coun. Boy Scouts Am.; pres. Ashtabula county chpt. National Found. With U.S. Army, 1954-56. Recipient Disting. Svc. award Ashtabula Jr. C. of C., 1962; Outstanding Young Man of Ohio award Ohio Jaycees, 1963; Man of Yr. award Delta Theta Phi, 1969; Outstanding Alumnus award Cleve. Marshall Coll. of Law, 1974. Fellow Internat. Acad. Law and Sci.; mem. ABA, Ohio Bar Assn., Ashtabula County Bar Assn. (past pres.), Atty. Gen. Advocacy Inst. Office: US Dist Ct 106 US Courthouse 201 Superior Ave E Cleveland OH 44114-1203

LAMEL, LINDA HELEN, insurance company executive, former college president, lawyer; b. N.Y.C., Sept. 10, 1943; d. Maurice and Sylvia (Abrams) Treppel; 1 child, Diana Ruth Sands. BA magna cum laude, Queens Coll., 1964; MA, NYU, 1968; JD, Bklyn. Law Sch., 1976. Bar: N.Y. 1977, U.S. Dist. Ct. (3d dist.) N.Y. 1977. Mgmt. analyst U.S. Navy, Bayonne, N.J., 1964-65; secondary sch. tchr. Farmingdale Pub. Sch., N.Y., 1965-73; curriculum specialist Yonkers Bd. Edn., N.Y., 1973-75; program dir. Office of Lt. Gov., Albany, N.Y., 1975-77; dep. supt. N.Y. State Ins. Dept., N.Y.C., 1977-83; pres., chief exec. officer Coll. of Ins., N.Y.C., 1983-88; v.p. Tchr.'s Ins. and Annuity Assn., N.Y.C., 1988—; dir. Seneca (N.Y.) Ins. Co. Contbr. articles to profl. jours. Campaign mgr. lt. gov.'s primary race, N.Y. State, 1974. Mem. ABA (tort and ins. sect. chmn. 1985-86), N.Y. State Bar Assn. (exec. com. ins. sect. 1984-88), Assn. of Bar of City of N.Y. (chmn. med. malpractice com. 1989-91), Am. Mgmt. Assn. (ins. and risk mgmt. council), Fin. Women's Assn., Assn. Profl. Ins. Women (Woman of Yr. award 1988), Phi Beta Kappa (v.p. Phi Beta Kappa Assn. N.Y.C., 1992—), Kappa Delta Pi, Phi Alpha Theta. Office: 730 3rd Ave New York NY 10017-3206

One's life develops much like a patchwork quilt: there are opportunities to add color, texture, and design; and there are missed stitches and uneven seams. Each result is unique and adds value.

LAMENDOLA, WALTER FRANKLIN, huamn services, information technology consultant; b. Donora, Pa., Jan. 29, 1943. BA in English, St. Vincent Coll., 1964; MSWin Community Orgn., U. Pitts., 1966; diploma in Sociology and Social Welfare, U. Stockholm, 1970; PhD in Social Work, U. Minn., 1976. Community svcs. dir. Ariz. tng. programs State Dept. Mental Retardation, Tucson, 1970-73; assoc. prof. social welfare adminstrn. Fla. State U., 1976-77; pres., chief exec. officer Minn. Rsch. and Tech., Inc., 1977-81; assoc. prof., dir. Allied Health Computer Lab. E. Carolina U., 1981-84; prof., dir. info. tech. ctr. Grad. Sch. Social Work U. Denver, 1984-87; cons. info. tech., rsch. human svcs., 1987-90; v.p. rsch. The Colo. Trust, Denver, 1990-93, info. tech. and rsch. cons., 1993—; cons. European Network Info. Tech. & Human Svcs.; mem. adv. bd. ctr. human svcs. U. Southampton, Brit. Rsch. Coun. Univs., Human Svc. Info. Tech. Applications, CREON Found., Netherlands; lectr. conf., symposia, univs. U.S., Europe; mem. nat. adv. bd. Native Elder Health Resource Ctr., 1994—; cofounder Denver Free Net, 1993—; info. tech. cons. Healthy Nations Program Robert Wood Johnson Found., 1993—; evaluator Nat. Libr. Rsch. Program, Access Colo. grant, 1994, Nat. Info. Infrastruce grant Colo. State Libr.; cons. set up on the Internet for U.S. Cts.-Ct. Futures Network; rschr. telemedicine Ctr. for Mental Health Svcs., NIH, Frontier Mental Health Svcs. Network grant. Co-author: Choices for Colorado's Future, 1993, The Integrity of Intelligence: A Bill of Rights for the Information Age, 1992, Choices for Colorado's Future: Executive Summary, 1991, Choices for Colorado's Future: Regional Summaries, 1991; co-editor: A Casebook of Computer Applications in Health and Social Services, 1989; contbr. numerous articles to profl. jours. Capt. U.S. Army, 1966-69. Recipient Innovative Computer Application award Internat. Fedn. Info. Processing Socs., 1979; Nat. Lib. Rsch. Evaluator grantee, Colo., 1994—, Nat. Info. Infrastructure grantee Dept. Edn., State Libr. and Adult Literacy, 1994-95; Funds & Couns. Tng. scholar United Way Am., 1964-66, Donaldson Fund scholar, 1965-66, NIMH scholar, 1964-66, 73-76, St. Vincent Coll. Benedictine Soc. scholar, 1963-64; vis. fellow U. Southampton. Office: 4098 Field Dr Wheat Ridge CO 80033-4358

LAMER, ANTONIO, Canadian supreme court chief justice; b. Montreal, Can., July 8, 1933; s. Antonio and Florence (Storey) L.; m. Danièle Tremblay; children: Stephane, Melanie, Jean-Frederic. BA, Licentiate in Laws, U. Montreal, 1956; LLD (hon.), U. Moncton, 1981, U. Montreal, 1991, U. Toronto, 1992; D Univ. (hon.), U. Ottawa, 1987. Bar: Que. 1957. Justice Superior Ct. Que., 1969-78, Que. Ct. Appeal, 1978-80, Supreme Ct. Can.,

1980—; vice chmn. Nat. Law Reform Commn., 1971-75, chmn., 1975-78; prof. agrege U. Montreal, 1967—; read law with Cutler, Lamer, Bellemare & Assocs.; lectr. U. Montreal, Can. Jud. Conf.; former sr. ptnr. Cutler, Lamer, Bellemare & Assocs.; Que. Bar rep. govt. interdisciplinary com. on structures U. Que.; chmn. Can. Law Reform Commn., 1975. Served with Can. Army Res., 1952, hon. lt.-col. Decorated Knight, Order of St. John, 1993; recipient Order of Merit, U. Montreal, 1991. Mem. Privy Coun. Can., Can. Jud. Coun. (chmn.), Nat. Jud. Inst. (chmn.). Office: Supreme Ct Can, Wellington St, Ottawa, ON Canada K1A 0J1

LAMERE, ROBERT KENT, lawyer; b. Brockton, Mass., Feb. 24, 1926; s. Birney James and Margaret Monica (Kent) L.; m. Ruth Isabella Gardner, Feb. 15, 1985; children: Robert K. Jr., David R., Elizabeth J. AB, Harvard U., 1946; JD, Columbia U., 1949. Bar: Mass. 1949, U.S. Dist. Ct. Mass. 1950, U.S. Ct. Appeals (1st cir.) 1952, U.S. Supreme Ct. 1958. Assoc. Proctor & Devey, Boston, 1949-58; assoc. Sullivan & Worcester, Boston, 1958-61, ptnr., 1962-91, counsel, 1991—. Moderator Town of Milton, Mass., 1960-82. Ensign USNR, 1944-47, ETO. Mem. Boston Bar Assn., Mass. Bar Assn., ABA, Harvard Club, Duxbury Yacht Club. Democrat. Roman Catholic. Avocations: skiing, golf, reading, classical music. Home: 301 Berkeley St Boston MA 02116-2013 Office: Sullivan & Worcester 1 Post Office Sq Boston MA 02109-2103

LAMEY, WILLIAM LAWRENCE, JR., manufacturing company executive; b. Evanston, Ill., June 19, 1938; s. William Lawrence and Dorothy Matilda (Mann) L.; m. Barbara Mary Matulewicz, Oct. 7, 1961; children: William Lawrence III, Patricia, Elizabeth. B.S. in Bus. Adminstrn, Xavier U., 1960. C.P.A., Ill. Staff auditor Haskins & Sells, Chgo., 1960, 62-63, Celanese Corp., Charlotte, N.C., 1963-64; with DeSoto, Inc., Des Plaines, Ill., 1964—; treas. DeSoto, Inc., 1970-71, controller, 1971-73, asst. v.p. finance, 1973-74, v.p. fin., 1975—; assoc. bd. dirs.; bd. dirs. DeSoto Titanine Plc, DeSoto Far East, DeSoto Coatings Ltd., Japan Fine Coatings, Ltd. With AUS, 1961-62. Mem. AICPA, Ill. CPAs Soc., Fin. Execs. Inst., Chgo. Zool. Soc. Home: 1520 Chapel Ct Deerfield IL 60015-2213 Office: De Soto Inc 1700 S Mt Prospect Rd Box 5030 Des Plaines IL 60017

LAMIA, THOMAS ROGER, lawyer; b. Santa Monica, Calif., May 31, 1938; s. Vincent Robert, II and Maureen (Green) L.; m. Susan Elena Brown, Jan. 10, 1969; children: Nicholas, Katja, Jenna, Tatiana, Carlyn, Mignon. Student U. So. Calif., 1956, BS, 1961; student U. Miss., 1957-58; JD, Harvard U., 1964. Bar: Calif. 1965, U.S. Dist. Ct. (cen. dist.) Calif. 1965, D.C. 1980, U.S. Dist. Ct. D.C. 1980, U.S. Tax Ct. 1982, N.Y. 1990. Assoc. McCutchen, Black, Verleger & Shea, Los Angeles, 1964-66; lectr. in law U. Ife, Ile-Ife, Nigeria, 1966-67, U. Zambia, Lusaka, 1967-68; assoc. Paul Hastings, Janofsky & Walker, L.A., 1968-72, ptnr., 1972-80, Washington, 1980-87, N.Y., 1987—; bd. dirs. Acme Holdings, Inc. Mem. ABA (bus., banking, fed. regulation of securities com., SEC adminstrn., budget and legislation subcom., internat. law com.), Internat. Bar Assn. (product liability, false advt. and consumer protection com.), Harvard Law Sch. Assn., Nat. Aquarium Soc. (bd. dirs. 1982—). Office: Paul Hastings Janofsky Walker 399 Park Ave 31st flr New York NY 10022-4697

LAMIRANDE, ARTHUR GORDON, editor, organist; b. Holyoke, Mass., July 19, 1936; s. Joseph Armand Arthur and Marion Gordon (Beaton) L. AA, Holyoke Community Coll., 1956; student, Peabody Conservatory Music, 1956-57; BA, Am. Internat. Coll., 1959. Editorial asst. Merriam-Webster Dictionary, Springfield, Mass., 1959-61; instr. English dept. Chicopee (Mass.) High Sch., 1961-62; asst. editor Hawthorn Books, N.Y.C., 1962-63; editorial cons. N.Y.C., 1963-66, 73-81; assoc. editor N.Y. Acad. Scis., N.Y.C., 1966-67, Grune & Stratton Pub. Co., N.Y.C., 1967-68, H.S. Stuttman Co. N.Y.C., 1968-70; mng. editor United Pub. Co., Washington, 1970-71, Sci. and Medicine Pub. Co., N.Y.C., 1971-73; dir. editorial dept. Profl. Exam. Svc., N.Y.C., 1981-92, exec. editor, 1992-94; titular organist St. Catherine of Siena Ch., N.Y.C., 1994—. Contbr. articles to The Diapason, Lyrichord Discs, PES News; rec. artist (organ) Lyrichord Discs, N.Y.C., 1975; pianist. asst. organist Christ Ch. Cathedral, Springfield, Mass., 1960-61; organist, mus. dir. Ch. of Immaculate Conception, Astoria, N.Y., 1963-66; titular organist Ch. of Holy Name of Jesus, N.Y.C., 1973-82, St. Catherine of Siena Ch., N.Y.C., 1994—. Home and Office: 461 Fort Washington Ave New York NY 10033-4653 Office: Saint Catherine of Siena Ch 411 E 68th St New York NY 10021

LAMIRANDE, EMILIEN, historian, educator; b. St. Georges-de-Windsor, Que., Can., May 22, 1926; s. Armand and Valentine (Boucher) L.; m. Claire Guillemette, Apr. 3, 1971. B.A., U. Ottawa, 1949, Licentiate in Philosophy, 1950, M.A., 1951, Licentiate in Theology, 1955; Th.D., Innsbruck U., 1960; S.T.M., Union Theol. Sem., 1965. Lectr. U. Ottawa, Ont., Can., 1954-60, assoc. prof., 1960-64, prof., 1964-66; prof. St. Paul U., Ottawa, 1965-70, dean theology, 1967-69; prof. dept. religion U. Ottawa, 1971-88, chmn. dept. religious studies, 1972-74, prof. emeritus, 1988—. Author: Un siècle et demi d'études sur l'ecclésiologie de saint Augustin, 1962, L'Eglise céleste selon saint Augustin, 1963, Etudes sur l'ecclésiologie de saint Augustin, 1969, La situation ecclésiologique des Donatistes d'après saint Augustin, 1972, Church, State and Toleration: An Intriguing Change of Mind in Augustine, 1975, Le Père Georges Simard, O.M.I. (1878-1956). Un disciple de saint Augustin à l'Université d'Ottawa, 1981, Paulin de Milan et la 'Vita Ambrosii', 1983, Elisabeth Bruyère, fondatrice des soeurs de la Charité d'Ottawa (1818-1876), 1993; also numerous articles. Fellow Royal Soc. Can.; mem. Société canadienne de théologie (v.p. 1967-70), Can. Soc. Patristic Studies (v.p. 1977-83, hon. pres. 1985-87). Home: 6467 Tellier, Rock Forest, PQ Canada J1N 3B1

LAMIS, LEROY, artist, retired educator; b. Eddyville, Iowa, Sept. 27, 1925; s. Leo and Blanche (Bennett) L.; m. Esther Sackler, Aug. 13, 1954; children: Alexander, Jonas. B.A., N.Mex. Highlands U., 1953; M.A., Columbia U. 1956. mem. faculty dept. art Ind. State U., 1961—, prof., 1972-89, retired 1989; artist-in-residence Dartmouth Coll., 1970; founder PC ART, 1983. One-man sculpture exhbns. include, Staempfli Gallery, N.Y.C., 1966, 69, 73, Gillman Gallery, Chgo., 1967, Tacoma Mus., 1970, Fort Wayne Art Mus., 1968, Des Moines Art Center, 1970, La Jolla Mus., 1970, Ind. State U., 1976, Sheldon Swope Gallery, Terre Haute, Ind., 1979; Kinetic computer art exhbns. at Ben Shahn Gallery, William Patterson Coll. N.J., Ind. State U., 1985, Bronx Mus. Art, 1986, 55 Mercer Gallery, 1990, Indpls. Art Mus., 1992, Evansvill Mus. Sci. and Art, 1994; represented in permanent collections, Albright-Knox Mus., Des Moines Art Center, Whitney Mus. Am. Art, Joseph H. Hirshhorn Collection, Washington, Indpls. Mus., J.B. Speed Mus., Louisville. Author: (computer program) Eighty 5, 1985; creator, producer various computer software. Served with AUS, 1943. Recipient Award Commn. N.Y. State Coun. of the Arts, 1970. Mem. Am. Abstract Artists. Address: 332 White Oak Ln Terre Haute IN 47804

LAMKIN, BILL DAN, psychologist, educator, consultant; b. Cleburne, Tex., Feb. 26, 1929; s. Walter Lee and Evelyn Agnes (Watters) L.; m. Robbie Jane Stanley, Aug. 27, 1950; children: Louella Leigh, Rebecca Elizabeth, Melissa Jay. BA, Baylor U., 1950, MA, 1955; PhD, U. Tex., 1967. Tchr. English Bangs (Tex.) High Sch., 1950-53, Waco (Tex.) Schs., 1953-59; counselor Waco High Sch., 1959-60; dir. guidance Los Alamos (N.Mex.) Schs., 1960-65; research assoc. U. Tex., Austin, 1965-67; from asst. to assoc. to prof. Baylor U., Waco, 1967-81, prof. ednl. psychology, 1993—, dean Sch. Edn., 1981-93; cons. Region XII Edn. Svc. Ctr., Waco, 1967-79, New Horizons Residential Ctr., Goldthwaite, Tex., 1974—, Midway Home for Children, 1992—, Esperansa Home for Children, 1993—; teaching cons. Family Medicine Faculty Devel. Ctr., Waco, 1978-92. Contbr. articles to Jour. Med. Edn. Mem. APA, Assn. for Counseling and Devel., Am. Ednl. Rsch. Assn., Coll. of Preceptors. Democrat. Baptist. Home: 2608 Lake Oaks Rd Waco TX 76710-1616 Office: Baylor U Sch of Edn Waco TX 76798

LAMKIN, WILLIAM PIERCE, editor; b. Ansley, La., Oct. 17, 1919; s. John Mays and Carrie Ellen (Posey) L.; m. Irma Hazel Page, Dec. 30, 1948 (div.); children: John Page, Mary Jean, Carol Ellen; m. Jane Eagar Mills, Mar. 17, 1973. AB, U. N.C., 1948. Reporter Alexandria (La.) Daily Town Talk, 1941-43; copyreader Charlotte (N.C.) Observer, 1948-49, asst. city editor, night city editor, 1950-58, city editor, religion editor, 1958-61; news dir. Presbyn. Ch. U.S., 1961-78; editor Presbyn. Survey, Atlanta, 1978-80; editor and pub. Presbyn. Survey, 1980-83; editor Friendship mag., 1983—. With USAAF, 1943-45. Decorated D.F.C. (4), Air Medal (5). Democrat.

Home: 4201 Ridgehurst Dr Smyrna GA 30080-3114 Office: 57 Forsyth St NW Ste 900 Atlanta GA 30303-2213 *The most critical issue facing humankind as we approach the 21st century is how to assure world peace. I am convinced that the best approach is through friendship and understanding. We need organized efforts to "walk in other people's shoes". It goes without saying that a world of friends is a world of peace.*

LAMM, CAROLYN BETH, lawyer; b. Buffalo, Aug. 22, 1948; d. Daniel John and Helen Barbara (Tatakis) L.; m. Peter Edward Halle, Aug. 12, 1972; children: Alexander P., Daniel E. BS, SUNY Coll. at Buffalo, 1970; JD, U. Miami (Fla.), 1973. Bar: Fla., 1973, D.C., 1976, N.Y. 1983. Trial atty. frauds sect. civil div. U.S. Dept. Justice, Washington, 1973-78, asst. chief comml. litigation sect. civil div., 1978, asst. dir., 1978-80; assoc. White & Case, Washington, 1980-84, ptnr., 1984—; mem. Sec. State's Adv. Com. Pvt. Internat. law, 1988-91; arbitrator U.S. Panel of Arbitrators, Internat. Ctr. Settlement of Investment Disputes. Mem. bd. editors Can./U.S. Rev. Bus. Law, 1987-92; mem. editorial adv. bd. Inside Litigation; contbr. articles to legal publs. Fellow Am. Bar Found.; mem. ABA (chmn. young lawyers div., rules and calendar com., chmn. house membership com., chmn. assembly resolution com., sec. 1984-86, chmn. internat. litigation com. coun. 1991-94, sect. litigation, ho. dels. 1982—, nominating com. 1984-87, D.C. Cir. mem. standing com. fed. judiciary 1993—, com. scope and correlation of work), Am. Arbitration Assn. (arbitrator, com. on fed. arbitration act), Fed. Bar Assn. (chmn. sect. on antitrust and trade regulation), Bar Assn. D.C. (bd. dirs., sec.), D.C. Bar (bd. govs. 1987-93, steering com. litigation sect.), Am. Law Inst., Women's Bar Assn. D.C., Am. Soc. Internat. Law, Internat. Bar Assn. (bus. law sect., internat. litigation com.), Am. Turkish Friendship Coun. (bd. dirs., chair comml. com.), Am. Uzbekistan C. of C. (bd. dirs., sec., gen. counsel), Nat. Women's Forum, Columbia Country Club. Democrat. Home: 2801 Chesterfield Pl NW Washington DC 20008-1015 Office: White & Case 1747 Pennsylvania Ave NW Washington DC 20006-4604

LAMM, DONALD STEPHEN, publishing company executive; b. N.Y.C., May 31, 1931; s. Lawrence William and Aleen Antonia (Lassner) L.; m. Jean Stewart Nicol, Sept. 27, 1958; children: Douglas William, Robert Lawrence, Wendy Nicol. B.A. with high honors, Yale, 1953; postgrad., Oxford (Eng.) U., 1956. With W.W. Norton & Co. Inc., N.Y.C., 1956—; v.p. W.W. Norton & Co., Inc., 1968-76, pres., 1976-94, chmn., 1984—, also dir.; bd. dirs. W.W. Norton & Co., Ltd., London, Liveright Pub. Corp., Nat. Book Co., Scranton, Pa.; guest fellow Yale U., 1980, 85, Phi Beta Kappa lectr., 1994; Ida Beam disting. vis. prof. U. Iowa, 1987-88. Author: (with others) The Spread of Economic Ideas, 1989, Beyond Literacy, 1990; mem. editorial bd. Logos. Mem. coun. Woodrow Wilson Ctr., Inst. Early Am. History and Culture, Williamsburg, Va.; pres. Yale U. Press; past mem. coun., bd. dirs. Roper Ctr. Pub. Opinion Rsch.; bd. advs. The Yale Rev., bd. control U. Cal. Press. With AUS, 1953-55. Fellow Branford Coll., Yale U. Mem. Manuscript Soc., Coun. Fgn. Rels., Phi Beta Kappa (senator 1990—). Home: Woods End Rd New Canaan CT 06840 Office: W W Norton & Co Inc 550 Fifth Ave New York NY 10110-0001

LAMM, HARVEY H., foreign car and parts importer; b. Phila., Nov. 10, 1935; s. Edward S. and Rosalie Lamm; m. Sandra Budilov, May 3, 1964; children: Marla, Davin. Student, Pa. State U.; Drexel U. Exec. v.p. Subaru of Am. Inc., Pennsauken, N.J., 1967-70, chief operating officer, vice chmn. bd., 1970-75, chief exec. officer, dir., 1975—, pres., 1975-86, chmn., 1986—, also bd. dirs. Mem. Young Pres. Orgn. Office: Subaru Am Inc Subaru Pla 2235 Route 70 W Cherry Hill NJ 08002-3380

LAMM, MICHAEL EMANUEL, pathologist, immunologist, educator; b. Bklyn., May 19, 1934; s. Stanley S. and Rose (Lieberman) L.; m. Ruth Audrey Kumin, Dec. 16, 1961; children—Jocelyn, Margaret. Student, Amherst Coll., 1951-54; M.D., U. Rochester, 1959; M.S. in Chemistry, Western Res. U., 1962. Diplomate Am. Bd. Pathology. Intern, asst. resident in pathology Inst. Pathology Western Res. U. and Univ. Hosps. of Cleve., 1959-62; research assoc. NIMH, Bethesda, Md., 1962-64; asst. prof. pathology NYU Sch. Medicine, N.Y.C., 1964-68, assoc. prof., 1968-73, prof., 1973-81; prof. dept. pathology Case WEstern Res. U. Sch. Medicine, 1981—, chmn. dept., 1981—; vis. sci. dept. biochemistry, U. Oxford, 1968; vis. prof. dept. pathology, U. Geneva, 1976-77; mem. cancer spl. program adv. com. Nat. Cancer Inst., Bethesda, 1976-79, mem. bd. sci. counselors divsn. cancer biology, diagnosis and ctrs., 1993—; mem. sci. adv. com. Damon Runyon-Walter Winchell Cancer Fund, N.Y.C., 1978-82; mem. immunological scis. study sect. NIH, Bethesda, 1988-92; mem. immunotoxicology subcom. NRC, 1989-90; mem. toxin peer rev. panel Am. Inst. Biol. Sci., 1990—; bd. dirs. Univ. Associated for Rsch. and Edn. Pathology. Mem. editorial bds. Procs. Soc. Exptl. Biology and Medicine, 1973-82, Molecular Immunology, 1979-83, Jour. Immunol. Methods, 1980—, Jour. Immunology, 1981-85, Am. Jour. Pathology, 1982-92, Regional Immunology, 1988—, Modern Pathology, 1988—; contbr. articles to profl. jours. Recipient for excellence in teaching NYU Sch. Medicine, 1974; named Career Scientist Health Research Council, City of N.Y., 1966-75; NIH grantee, 1966-92. Fellow N.Y. Acad. Scis.; mem. Am. Assn. Pathologists (councilor 1986-88, sec. treas. 1988-90, v.p. 1990-91, pres. 1991-92), Am. Assn. Immunologists, Am. Soc. Biochemistry and Molecular Biology, Coll. Am. Pathologists, U.S. and Can. Acad. Pathology, Soc. for Exptl. Biol. Medicine, Clin. Immunology Soc., Soc. Mucosal Immunology, Am. Soc. Clin. Pathologists, Harvey Soc., Sigma Xi, Alpha Omega Alpha. Home: 2856 Glengary Rd Cleveland OH 44120-1731

LAMMERS, JOSEPH EDWIN, hospital executive; b. Archie, Mo., July 28, 1935; s. Melvin Edwin and Emma Victoria L.; m. Dorothy L. Howe, Sept. 14, 1957; children—Sean, Elizabeth, Kristen. B.S., Central Mo. State U., 1957. Office mgr. Firestone Tire and Rubber Co., Independence, Mo., 1957-60; area mktg. mgr. Phillips Petroleum Co., San Francisco, 1960-70; asst. adminstr. Independence (Mo.) Sanitarium and Hosp., 1970-79, exec. dir., 1979—; dir. Blue Cross, Profl. Standards Rev. Orgn. Bd. dirs. YMCA, 1982; pres. Am. Cancer Soc., 1979. Served with U.S. Army, 1958. Mem. Am. Hosp. Assn., Kansas City Hosp. Assn. (treas., chmn. bd. dirs. 1985—), Am. Coll. Hosp. Adminstrs., Mo. Hosp. Assn. (bd. dirs.). Am. Protestant Hosp. Assn., Independence C of C. (bd. dirs. 1979—, div. v.p. 1980-82; chmn.-elect 1985—). Mem. Reorganized Ch. of Jesus Christ of Latter-day Saints (ordained minister). Lodge: Kiwanis (pres. 1977) (Independence). Home: 4832 S Maybrook Ct Independence MO 64055-5372 Office: Independence Reg Health Ctr 1509 W Truman Rd Independence MO 64050-3436

LAMMERT, RICHARD ALAN, corporate lawyer; b. Pitts., Mar. 21, 1949; s. John Albert and Gladys Irene (Miller) L.; m. Susan Christine McLaren, Jan. 30, 1971; children: Ann, Adam. BA, Grove City Coll., 1971; JD, Duquesne U., 1975. Bar: Pa. 1975, U.S. Dist. Ct. (we. dist.) Pa. 1975, N.Y. 1985. Legal asst. Mellon Bank, N.A., Pitts., 1972-75, atty., 1975-76; assoc. counsel Equibank, Pitts., 1976-80, trust counsel, 1980-81, asst. gen. counsel, sr. v.p., 1981-84; gen. counsel, sr. v.p., sec. First Empire State Corp., Buffalo 1984—. Mem. N.Y. State Bar Assn., Allegheny County Bar Assn., Erie County Bar Assn. Republican. Lutheran. Club: Park Country. Home: 6405 Woodberry Ct East Amherst NY 14051-1547 Office: First Empire State Corp 1 Montana Ave Buffalo NY 14211-1638

LAMMERTSMA, KOOP, chemist, consultant; b. Makkum, Frysland, The Netherlands, Aug. 29, 1949. MS, U. Groningen, The Netherlands, 1975; PhD, U. Amsterdam, 1979. Postdoctoral fellow U. Coll. London, Eng., 1980, U. Erlangen, Nürnberg, Germany, 1980-81; rsch. fellow U. So. Calif., L.A., 1981-83; asst. prof. U. Ala., Birmingham, 1983-87, assoc. prof., 1987-92, prof., 1992—. Contbr. numerous articles to profl. jours. Mem. Am. Chem. Soc. Office: U Ala Uab # 221 Birmingham AL 35294-0001

LAMON, BEVERLY ANN, school system administrator; b. Howard Lake, Minn., Sept. 26, 1936; d. Erland Clifford and Vera Ella (Custer) Johnson; widowed, 1991; 1 child. Richard Lang. BS, Union Coll. 1959; MA, LaSierra U., 1993. Tchr. Firth Nebr.) Pub. Schs., 1962-64; tchr. libr. Brownton (Minn.) Pub. Schs., 1964-69, Maplewood Acad., Hutchinson, Minn., 1969-74, Ga.-Cumberland Acad., Calhoun, 1974-76; dean of women Dakota Adventist Acad., Bismark, N.D., 1977-79; assoc. supt. Minn. Adventist Schs., Maple Grove, 1980-87, supt., 1987—. Mem Assn. Supervision & Curriculum Devel., Assn. Seventh-Day Adventist Educators, Assn. Seventh-Day Adventist Sch. Adminstrs. Office: Minn Conf SDA 7384 Kirkwood Ct Maple Grove MN 55369-5270

LAMON, HARRY VINCENT, JR., lawyer; b. Macon, Ga., Sept. 29, 1932; s. Harry Vincent and Helen (Bewley) L.; m. Ada Healey Morris, June 17, 1954; children: Hollis Morris, Helen Kathryn Gurley. BS cum laude, Davidson Coll., 1954; JD with distinction, Emory U., 1958. Bar: Ga. 1958, D.C. 1965. Ptnr. Booth, Wade & Campbell, Atlanta, 1992—; adj. prof. law Emory U., 1960-79. Contbr. articles to profl. jours. Mem. adv. bd. Salvation Army, 1963—, chmn., 1975-79, nat. adv. bd., 1976-94, chmn., 1991-92; mem. Adv. Coun. on Employee Welfare and Pension Benefit Plans, U.S. Dept. Labor, 1975-79; mem. Pension and Benefits Reporter adv. bd. Bur. Nat. Affairs; bd. visitors Davidson Coll., 1979-89; trustee, pres. So. Fed. Tax Inst., Inc., 1965—; trustee Am. Tax Policy Inst., 1989—, Embry-Riddle Aero U., 1989—, Cathedral of St. Philip, Atlanta, 1989-95. 1st lt. AUS, 1954-56. Recipient Others award Salvation Army, 1979, Centennial Honoree, 1990. Fellow Am. Bar Found., Am. Coll. Trust and Estate Counsel, Am. Coll. Tax Counsel, Internat. Acad. Estate and Trust Law, Ga. Bar Found.; mem. ABA, Fed. Bar Assn., Atlanta Bar Assn., Am. Bar Retirement Assn. (bd. dirs. 1989—, pres. 1994-95), Am. Law Inst., Am. Pension Conf., So. Employee Benefits Conf. (pres. 1972), State Bar Ga. (chmn. sect. taxation 1969-70, vice chmn. commn. on continuing lawyer competency 1982-89), Am. Judicature Soc., Atlanta Tax Forum, Lawyers Club of Atlanta, Nat. Emory U. Law Sch. Alumni Assn. (pres. 1967), Practicing Law Inst., ALI-ABA Inst., CLUs Inst., Kiwanis Club of Atlanta (pres. 1973-74), Breakfast Club (pres. 1994), Peachtree Racket Club (pres. 1986-87), Capital City Club, Commerce Club (Atlanta), Cosmos Club, Univ. Club. (Washington), Phi Beta Kappa, Omicron Delta Kappa, Phi Delta Phi, Phi Delta Theta (chmn. community svc. day 1969-72, legal commr. 1973-76, prov. pres. 1976-79). Episcopalian. Home: 3375 Valley Rd NW Atlanta GA 30305-1150 Office: Booth Wade & Campbell Ste 1500 3100 Cumberland Dir NW Atlanta GA 30339-5939

LAMONE, RUDOLPH PHILIP, business educator; b. Wellsburg, W.Va., Dec. 20, 1931; s. Dominic and Maria (Branch) L.; m. Linda A. Hefler, Jan. 29, 1970. B.S., U. N.C., Chapel Hill, 1960, Ph.D, 1966. Instr. U. N.C., 1963-66; mem. faculty U. Md., College Park, 1966—, prof. mgmt. sci., 1971—, dean Coll. Bus. and Mgmt., 1973-92, prof., chair adv. bd. Michael Dingman Ctr. Entrepreneurship, 1993—; bd. dirs. Md. Ctr. Productivity and Quality of Working Life, EA Engring. Sci. and Tech. Inc.; chmn. govtl. rels. com. Am. Assembly Collegiate Schs. Bus., 1977-78; cons. Tatung Co., Taiwan; mem. adv. com. Md. Dept. Econ. and Cmty. Devel. Co-author: Linear Programming for Management Decisions, 1969, Marketing Management and the Decision Sciences, 1971, Production-Operations Management, 1972. Served with AUS, 1952-55. Mem. Acad. Mgmt., Inst. Mgmt. Scis., Am. Inst. Decision Scis., Md. C. of C. (dir.), Phi Beta Kappa, Beta Gamma Sigma. Democrat. Roman Catholic. Club: Annapolis Yacht (bd. dirs.). Office: U Md Dingman Ctr Entrepreneurship College Park MD 20742

LAMONICA, P(AUL) RAYMOND, lawyer, academic administrator, educator; b. Baton Rouge, June 10, 1944; s. Leonard and Olivia (Frank) L.; m. Dianne Davis, Aug. 23, 1971; children: Drew, Neal, Leigh. BA, La. State U., 1965, MA, 1966, JD, 1970. Bar, La. 1970. Law clk. to chief judge U.S. Dist. Ct. (we. dist.) La., 1970-71; assoc. Hebert, Moss & Graphia, Baton Rouge, 1971; judge pro tem 19th Jud. Dist. Ct., East Baton Rouge Parish, 1979; prof. La. State U. Law Sch., Baton Rouge, 1973-86; exec. counsel to La. Gov., 1983-84; U.S. atty. for mid. dist. La., 1986-94; vice chancellor, prof. law La. State U., Baton Rouge, 1994—; counsel La. Ho. of Reps., 1976-79, 80-83. Fellow Am. Bar Found.; mem. ABA, La. Bar Assn. (bd. govs. 1979). Republican. Roman Catholic. Office: La State U 210 LSU Law Ctr Baton Rouge LA 70803

LAMONT, BARBARA, television executive; b. Paget, Bermuda, Nov. 9, 1939; came to U.S., 1949; d. Theophilus and Muriel (Aird) Alcántara; m. Ludwig Gelobter, Dec. 20, 1959; children: Michel, David, Elisabeth. BA in Internat. Law, Sarah Lawrence Coll., 1960; MPA, Harvard U., 1985. Reporter Sta. WINS, N.Y.C., 1971-73; reporter, anchor Sta. WNEW-TV, N.Y.C., 1973-76; writer, reporter CBS News, N.Y.C., 1976-82; dir. ops. Nigerian TV Authority, Lagos, Nigeria, 1982-84; writer ABC News, N.Y.C., 1985-86; pres., CEO New Orleans Teleport, 1987—; adj. assoc. prof. journalism Columbia U., N.Y.C., 1980-82, 82-86. Author: City People, 1976; mem. editorial bd. Amsterdam News, N.Y.C., 1986—; contbr. articles to the N.Y. Times. Dist. leader N.Y. County Dem. Com., N.Y.C., 1969-72; mem. Coun. Elected Black Dems., N.Y.C., 1969-72; bd. dirs. Planned Parenthood N.Y.C., 1971; mem. Nat. Women's Polit. Caucus, Washington, 1972; mem. exec. coun. Kennedy Sch. Alumnae Assn., Cambridge, Mass., 1985—; mem. parents com. Williams Coll., Williamstown, Mass., 1986—; fiscal reform com. Urban League; mem. adv. bd. New Orleans Mus. of Art. Recipient AP award, 1973, Ret. Detectives award N.Y.C Detectives Assn., 1975. Mem. Nat. Assn. Broadcasters, New Orleans Ctr. for the Creative Arts, Greater New Orleans Exec. Assn. (bd. dirs.), Friends of New Orleans Ctr. for Creative Arts. Republican. Club: Harvard. Avocations: flying airplanes, tennis.

LAMONT, BARBARA GIBSON, librarian; b. Huntington, Ind., Nov. 8, 1925; d. Herbert Donald and Edith (VanAntwerp) LaM. A.B., Coll. William and Mary, 1947; M.A., Radcliffe Coll., 1952; M.S. in L.S, Simmons Coll., 1954. With Harvard Library, 1951-64; head librarian Douglass Coll., Rutgers U., 1964-67; head librarian Vassar Coll., 1967-83, head librarian emeritus, 1983—. Trustee Southeastern (N.Y.) Library Resources Council, 1967-73. Home: Andrews Rd Rural Route 2 Box 358 Lagrangeville NY 12540

LAMONT, CORLISS, philosopher, educator, author; b. Englewood, N.J., Mar. 28, 1902; s. Thomas William and Florence Haskell (Corliss) L.; m. Margaret H. Irish, June 8, 1928 (div.); children: Margaret Hayes (Mrs. J. David Heap), Florence Parmelee (Mrs. Ralph Antonides), Hayes Corliss, Anne Sterling (Mrs. George Jafferis); m. Helen Boyden Lamb, 1962 (dec. July 1975); m. Beth Keehner, July 24, 1986. Grad., St. Bernard's Sch., 1916, Phillips Exeter Acad., 1920; A.B. magna cum laude, Harvard U., 1924; postgrad., New Coll., Oxford (Eng.) U., 1924-25; Ph.D., Columbia U., 1932. Instr. philosophy Columbia, 1928-32, New Sch. Social Rsch., 1940-42; lectr. intensive study contemporary Russian civilization Cornell U., 1943, Social Studies Workshop on Soviet Russia, Harvard Grad. Sch. Edn., 1944; lectr. Columbia Sch. Gen. Studies, 1947-59, Columbia seminar assoc., 1971-91. Editor: Man Answers Death: An Anthology of Poetry, rev. edit., 1952, Dialogue on John Dewey, 1959, Dialogue on George Santayana, 1959, A Humanist Symposium on Metaphysics, 1960, Albert Rhys Williams: In Memoriam, 1962, The Trial of Elizabeth Gurley Flynn by the American Civil Liberties Union, 1968, The Thomas Lamonts in America, 1971, (with Lansing Lamont) Letters of John Masefield to Florence Lamont, 1979, (with Lansing Lamont) Collected Poems of John Reed, 1985, The John Reed Centenary, 1988, Dear Corliss: Letters From Eminent Persons, 1990; author: Issues of Immortality, 1932, The Illusion of Immortality, 5th edit, 1990, You Might Like Socialism: A Way of Life for Modern Man, 1939, The Peoples of the Soviet Union, 1946, A Humanist Funeral Service, 1947, Humanism as a Philosophy, 1949, The Independent Mind, 1951, Soviet Civilization, 1952, Freedom Is As Freedom Does: Civil Liberties in America, 1956, rev. edit., 1990, The Philosophy of Humanism, 7th edit., 1990, Freedom of Choice Affirmed, 1967, A Humanist Wedding Service, 1970, Remembering John Masefield, rev. edit. 1991, Lover's Credo, 1983, Voice in the Wilderness: Collected Essays of Fifty Years, 1974, Yes to Life: Memoirs of Corliss Lamont, 1981, rev. edit., 1991, A Lifetime of Dissent, 1988, Basic Pamphlet Series, 1952—; co-author: syllabus Introduction to Contemporary Problems in U.S. 1929, Russia Day by Day, (with Margaret I. Lamont), 1933; Frequent contbr. to periodicals; speaker radio, TV; vice chmn.: Jour. Philosophy. Bd. dirs. ACLU, 1932-54; pres. Bill of Rights Fund, 1954-69; chmn. Nat. Emergency Civil Liberties Com., 1965—, Nat. Coun.Am.-Soviet Friendship, 1943-46; Candidate for U.S. Senate Am. Labor Party, N.Y., 1952, Independent-Socialist Party, 1958; v.p., mem. exec. bd. Poetry Soc. Am., 1971-74. Recipient of N.Y. City Tchrs. Union Am. award, 1955, Gandhi Peace Award, 1981, Ethics in Action award, 1984, John Phillips award Phillips Exeter Acad., 1986-87. Mem. AAAS, Acad. Polit. Sci., NAACP, Am. Humanist Assn. (pres. emeritus 1992—, John Dewey Humanist award 1972, Humanist of Yr. award 1977), Acad. Am. Poets, PEN, Am. Philos. Assn., UN Assn., Phi Beta Kappa. Clubs: Columbia Faculty (N.Y.C.), Harvard (N.Y.C.). Indictment for contempt of the Congress effected by Sen. Joseph McCarthy dismissed by U.S. Appeals Ct., 1956. Address: 315 W 106th St New York NY 10025-3445

LAMONT, LANSING, journalist, public affairs executive, author; b. N.Y.C., Mar. 13, 1930; s. Thomas Stilwell and Elinor (Miner) L.; m. Ada Jung, Sept. 18, 1954; children: Douglas Ranlet, Elisabeth Jung Lamont Wolcott, Virginia Alden Lamont Cazedessus, Thomas Stilwell II. A.B., Harvard U., 1952; M.S. in Journalism with honors, Columbia U. 1958. Reporter, Washington Star, 1958-59; Washington corr. Worcester (Mass.) Gazette, also other New Eng. papers, 1959-60; sci. reporter Washington bur. Time mag., 1961-63, polit. reporter, 1964-68, corr., dep. chief London bur., 1969-71, chief Can. corr., chief Ottawa bur., 1971-73; chief UN bur. Time mag., N.Y.C., 1973-74; v.p., mng. dir. Can. Affairs The Americas Soc., 1981-91, sr. fellow, 1991-94. Author: Day of Trinity (alt. selection Lit. Guild Am.), 1965, Campus Shock, 1979; co-editor: Private Letters of John Masefield, 1979, Friends So Different: Essays on Canada and U.S. in the 1980's, 1989, Journey to the Last Empire: The Soviet Union in Transition, 1991, Breakup: The Coming End of Canada and the Stakes for America, 1994 (Notable Books of Yr., N.Y. Times). Mem. alumni bd. dirs. Harvard U., also chmn. nominating com. for overseers; trustee Milton Acad., Am. Mus. Natural History, N.Y.C., chmn. libr. com., fellow of libr. Nat. Inst. for Music Theatre; mem. Can.-Am. Com., 1984-94, Coun. Fgn. Rels. 1985—. Served to 1st lt., inf. U.S. Army, 1954-57. William Cullen Bryant fellow Met. Mus. Art, 1984—. Mem. Century Assn. (N.Y.C.), Harvard Club (N.Y.C.). Episcopalian. Home: 133 E 80th St New York NY 10021-0332 Office: 133 E 80th St New York NY 10021-0332

LAMONT, LEE, art management executive; b. Queens, N.Y.; m. August Tagliamonte, Apr. 30, 1951; 1 child, Leslie Lamont. With Nat. Concerts & Artists Group, N.Y.C., 1955-58; asst. Sol Hurok Concerts, N.Y.C., 1958-67; person rep. for concerts, rec. and TV Isaac Stern, N.Y.C., 1968-76; v.p. ICM Artists Ltd., N.Y.C., 1976-85; pres. ICM Artists Ltd. and ICM Artists (London) Ltd., N.Y.C., 1985-95, chmn. bd. dirs., 1995—; Mem. adv. com. Hannover (Germany) Internat. Violin Competition. Mem. US/USSR Trade and Econ. Coun., Am. Coun. on the Arts, Japan Soc., Asia Soc., Am. Symphony Orch. League (bd. dirs.), Bohemian Club. Avocations: painting, sculpture. Office: ICM Artists Ltd 40 W 57th St 16th Fl New York NY 10019

LAMONT, PETER, production designer, art director. Art dir.: (films) The Seven Percent Solution, 1976, The Spy Who Loved Me, 1977 (Academy award nomination best art direction 1977), The Boys from Brazil, 1978; prodn. designer: (films) For Your Eyes Only, 1981, Octopussy, 1983, Top Secret!, 1984, A View to a Kill, 1985, Aliens, 1986 (Academy award nomination best art direction 1986), The Living Daylights, 1987, Consuming Passions, 1988, Licence to Kill, 1989, Eve of Destruction, 1991, The Taking of Beverly Hills, 1992, True Lies, 1994. Office: The Lyons/Sheldon Agency 8344 Melrose Ste 20 Los Angeles CA 90069*

LAMONT, ROSETTE CLEMENTINE, Romance languages educator, theatre journalist, translator; b. Paris; came to U.S., 1941, naturalized, 1946; d. Alexandre and Loudmilla (Lamont) L.; m. Frederick Hyde Farmer, Aug. 9, 1969. B.A., Hunter Coll., 1947; M.A., Yale U., 1948, Ph.D., 1954. Tutor Romance langs. Columbia Coll., CUNY, 1950-54, instr., 1954-61, asst. prof., 1961-64, assoc. prof., 1965-67, prof., 1967—; mem. doctoral faculties, comparative lit., theatre, French and women's studies cert. program CUNY, 1968—; State Dept. envoy Scholar Exch. Program, USSR, 1974; rsch. fellow, 1976; lectr. Alliance Francaise, Maison Francaise of NYU; vis. prof. Sorbonne, Paris, 1985-86; vis. prof. theatre Sarah Lawrence Coll., 1994, 95. Author: The Life and Works of Boris Pasternak, 1964, De Vive Voix, 1971, Ionesco, 1973, The Two Faces of Ionesco, 1978, Ionesco's Imperatives: The Politics of Culture, 1993, Women on the Verge, 1993; translator: Days and Memory, 1990, Auschwitz and Alter, 1995; also contbr. to various books; mem. editl. bd. Western European Stages, also contbg. editor; European corr. Theatre Week; Columbia Dictionary of Modern European Literature; fgn. corr. Stages. Decorated chevalier, then officier des Palmes Academiques, officier des Arts et Lettres (France); named to Hunter Coll. Hall of Fame, 1991; Guggenheim fellow, 1973-74; Rockefeller Found. humanities fellow, 1983-84. Mem. PEN, MLA, Am. Soc. Theatre Research, Internat. Brecht Soc., Drama Desk (voting mem.), Internat. Assn. Theatre Critics, Phi Beta Kappa, Sigma Tau Delta, Pi Delta Phi. Club: Yale. Home: 260 W 72nd St New York NY 10023-2817 also: 51 W Chester St Nantucket MA 02554 Office: CUNY Queens Coll Dept Romance Langs Flushing NY 11367 *An educator does not merely impart knowledge: he or she communicates an attitude, a way of looking at the world. So does the writer. Through each creative mind the world is born anew.*

LAMONT, SANDERS HICKEY, journalist; b. Atlanta, Nov. 9, 1940; s. Louis Earnest and Dorothy Rebecca (Strickland) LaM.; m. Patricia Jean Taylor, Aug. 5, 1966; children—Patricia Ruth, Zachary Taylor. A.A., Marion Mil. Inst., Ala., 1960; B.A. in Journalism, U. Ala., 1962; postgrad. U. Mich., 1977-78. Reporter, bur. chief Gannett News Service, various locations, 1961-74; mng. editor Ft. Myers News Press, Fla., 1974-77; exec. editor Marietta Times, Ohio, 1978-80, Modesto Bee, Calif., 1980—; chmn. AP News Execs. Council, Calif., 1984-85. NEH journalism fellow, U. Mich., 1977-78; Pulitzer prize juror, 1984-85. Served to 1st lt. U.S. Army, 1963-65. Mem. Am. Soc. Newspaper Editors, AP Mng. Editors, Soc. Profl. Journalists. Methodist. Office: The Modesto Bee PO Box 5256 Modesto CA 95352-3928

LAMONT-HAVERS, RONALD WILLIAM, physician, research administrator; b. Wymondham, Norfolk, Eng., Mar. 6, 1920; came to U.S., 1955, naturalized, 1964; s. William Fredrick L.-H.; m. Gabrielson, Oct. 16, 1965; children—Wendy, Melinda, Ian. B.A., U. B.C., 1942; M.D. U. Toronto, 1946; diploma in internal medicine, McGill U., 1953. Intern Vancouver (B.C., Can.) Gen. Hosp., 1946-48; resident in internal medicine Queen Mary Vets. Hosp., Montreal, Que., Can., 1949-51; Canadian Arthritis and Rheumatism Soc. fellow Columbia Presbyterian Hosp., Coll. Physicians and Surgeons, Columbia U., N.Y.C., 1951-53; med. dir. Canadian Arthritis and Rheumatism Soc., B.C. div., Vancouver, 1953-55, Arthritis and Rheumatism Found., N.Y.C., 1955-64; instr. in medicine Coll. Physicians and Surgeons, Columbia U., 1955-64; assoc. dir. extramural programs NIAMD, Bethesda, Md., 1964-68, dep. dir., 1972-74; assoc. dir. extramural programs NIH, Bethesda, 1968-72; acting dir., dep. dir. NIH, Bethesda, Md., 1974-76, acting dir., 1975, dep. dir., 1974-76; dep. to gen. dir. for rsch. policy and admin. Mass. Gen. Hosp., Boston, 1976-87, v.p. rsch. and tech. affairs, 1987-90, sr. cons. for rsch., 1990—; dep. dir. Cutaneous Biology Rsch. Ctr. Mass. Gen. Hosp. and Harvard U., 1990—; del. USSR-Arthritis Exchange Program, 1964; U.S. coordinator U.S.-USSR Coop. Program in Arthritis, 1973-75.; Served with M.C. Royal Canadian Army, 1944-46. Recipient Golden Pen award Jour. Am. Phys. Therapy Assn., 1965; Superior Service award HEW, 1973; Spl. citation Soc. HEW, 1975. Fellow Royal Coll. Physicians (Can.); mem. Am. Coll. Rheumatology (dir. Met. Washington sect. 1964-66), N.Y. Rheumatism Assn. (pres. 1960), Arthritis Found. (dir. governing mem. 1966-80, pres. Mass. chpt. 1987-89), Am. Acad. Orthopaedic Surgeons (hon.), Am. Gastroent. Assn. (affiliate), Alpha Omega Alpha. Office: Mass Gen Hosp Bldg 149 13th St Charlestown MA 02129

LAMORE, GEORGE L., manufacturing company executive; b. Painesville, Ohio, Apr. 26, 1926; s. Albert and Augusta (Logan) L.; m. Jeannette Cowels, Apr. 26, 1947; 1 child, David G. Inside salesman Bearing, Inc., Cleve., 1942-43, outside salesman, 1946-50, dist. mgr. 1950-64, primary metals sales mgr., 1964-80, sr. v.p., 1980-82, pres., chief exec. officer, 1982-89, 1989—, also bd. dirs. Served with USN, 1943-46. Republican. Clubs: Avon Oak Country, Univ., Cleve. Athletic. Avocation: golf. Home: 1054 Creek Ln Cleveland OH 44116-2179 Office: Bearings Inc Box 6925 3600 Euclid Ave Cleveland OH 44115-2515

LAMOREAUX, PHILIP ELMER, geologist, hydrogeologist, consultant; b. Chardon, Ohio, May 12, 1920; s. Elmer I. and Gladys (Rhodes) L.; m. Ura Mae Munro, Nov. 11, 1943; children: Philip E Jr., James W., Karen L. BA, Denison U., 1943, PhD (hon.), 1972; MS, U. Ala., 1949. Registered profl. geologist, Ga., N.C., S.C., Tenn., Ind., Ariz., Ark., Fla. Wyo. Geologist U.S. Geol. Survey, Tuscaloosa, Ala., 1943-45, dist. geologist Groundwater Office, 1945-57, div. hydrologist Water Resources Programs, 1957-59; chief Ground Water Br. U.S. Geol. Survey, Washington, 1959-61; state geologist, oil and gas supr. Ala. Geol. Survey, Tuscaloosa, 1961-76; pres. P.E. LaMoreaux & Assocs Inc., Tuscaloosa, 1976-87, chmn. bd., 1987-90, sr. hydrologist, 1990—; mem. Karst Commn., 1961—; chmn. Hydrology Hazardous Waste Commn., 1983-91; lectr. Am. Geol. Inst. College Program,

1961-71, Am. Geophys. Union Coll. Program, 1961—, NSF, Ala. Acad. Sci. High Sch. Program, 1961—, No. Engring. and Testing, Salt Lake City, 1985, Ga. State U., Fla. State U., Vanderbilt U., Denison U., Auburn U., U. of Montpellier, France, U. Christ Church, New Zealand, University of Praetoria, Republic of South Africa; hydrogeology cons. to 30 fgn. countries. Editor in chief Jour. Environ. Geology and Water Scis., 1982—; editor in chief: Annotated Bibliography Carbonate Rocks, vols. 1-5; author numerous published articles in field. Mem. Nat. Drinking Water Adv. Coun. EPA, 1984-88, mem. Tech. Rev. Group Oak Ridge Nat. Lab., 1984-88; trustee Denison U. Recipient Comdrs. medal C.E., 1990. Mem. NAS (nat. rsch. coun. geotech. bd. 1990-92, water sci. and tech. bd. 1990-92, bd. on earth scis. and resources 1992—), AAAS, Ala. Acad. Sci., Ala. Geol. Soc., Am. Assn. Petroleum Geologists (acad. liaison com., del. to Ho. of Dels. 1970-72, com. for preservation samples and cores, chmn. divsn. geosci. hydrogeology com.), Am. Geol. Inst. (chmn. com. on publs. 1968-70, pres. 1971-72, Ian Campbell award 1990), Am. Geophys. Union, Am. Inst. Hydrology, AIME, Am. Inst. Profl. Geologists (chmn. com. on rels. with govtl. agencies 1967-70, bd. dirs. 1969-70), Am. Soc. Testing and Materials, Assn. Am. State Geologists (statistician 1966-69, chmn. liaison com. with fed. agencies 1968-70, pres.), Geol. Soc. Am. (1st chmn. hydrogeology group 1963, chmn. O.E. Meinzer award com. 1965, cons. on membership S.E. Sect. 1967-68, chmn. nominating com., bd. dirs., bd. trustees, publs. com.), Geol. Soc. London, Internat. Assn. Hydrogeologists (pres. 1977-80, v.p. 1973-77, mem. com. on water rsch., 1978-80), Internat. Water Resources Assn., Interstate Oil Compact Commn. (vice chmn. 1963, chmn. rsch. com.), Miss. Geol. Soc., NAE, Nat. Assn. Geology Tchrs., Nat. Rivers and Harbors Congress, Nat. Speleological Soc., Nat. Water Resources Assn., Nat. Water Well Assn., Soc. Econ. Geologists, Soc. Econ. Paleontologists and Mineralogists, Soil Conservation Soc. Am., Southeastern Geol. Soc., Ala. C. of C. (Pres.'s adv. com., Rep. of Energy, 1980), Geol. Soc. Am. (chmn.), numerous other orgns. and offices. Republican. Presbyterian. Avocations: golfing, photography, stamp collecting, coin collecting, gardening. Office: P E LaMoreaux & Assocs Inc 2610 University Blvd Tuscaloosa AL 35401-1566

LAMOREAUX, PHILIP ADDISON, investment management company executive; b. Vallejo, Calif., May 8, 1941; s. Page Halleck and Marjorie Ruth (Nelson) L.; m. Sonia Ann Zeltin, Aug. 13, 1965 (div. 1988); children: Anne Elizabeth, Brian Brook. BA, Stanford U., 1963; MBA, Harvard U., 1967. Analyst Dean Witter & Co., San Francisco, 1963-65; portfolio mgr. Am. Express Investment Mgmt. Co., San Francisco, 1967-74; gen. ptnr. Lamoreaux, Glynn & Assocs., San Francisco, 1974-83, Lamoreaux Ptnrs., San Francisco, 1983—; Lamoreaux Ventures, San Francisco, 1983-90, New West Capital Ptnrs., San Francisco, 1990-93. Pres. Interfaith Housing Found., Mill Valley, Calif. 1970-76; bd. dirs. Marin Theatre Co., Mill Valley, 1985-91; bd. dirs., treas. Hospice Marin, San Rafael, Calif. 1978-84. Mem. Western Venture Capital Assn., Security Analysts San Francisco, Olympic Club, Family (San Francisco), Mill Valley Tennis Club, Sausalito Yacht Club. Republican. Avocations: skiing, running, handball, tennis. Home: 1001 Bridgeway Ste 205 Sausalito CA 94965-3212 Office: 1505 Bridgeway Ste 125 Sausalito CA 94965-3212

LAMOREAUX, FREDERICK HOLMES, financial executive; b. Montreal, Que., Can., Dec. 10, 1941; s. Frederick Silas and Marie Paule (Dubuc) L.; children: David, John, Jenny. B.C., McGill U., 1964; M.B.A., Columbia, 1966. Fin. planning mgr. Cummins Engine Co., Columbus, Ind., 1966-67; mgr. acquisition analysis Am. Standard, N.Y.C., 1967-69; asst. to exec. v.p. Am. Standard, 1970-71; asst. treas. Fairchild Industries, Germantown, Md., 1971-72; v.p. fin. and adminstrn. Fairchild Space and Electronics div. Fairchild Industries, 1972-74; v.p. treas. Arvin Industries, Inc., Columbus, 1974-76; v.p., treas., chief fin. officer Arvin Industries, Inc., 1976-81, chmn. fin. com., dir., 1977-81; gen. partner Wolsey & Co., St. Louis, 1981—; chmn. bd., chief exec. officer Sabreliner Corp., St. Louis, 1983—. Trustee The Hill Sch. 1992—. Talcott fellow, 1965. Mem. Phi Gamma Delta, Beta Gamma Sigma. Clubs: University (N.Y.C.); St. Louis. Home: 54 Westmoreland Pl Saint Louis MO 63108-1244 Office: Sabreliner Corp 7733 Forsyth Blvd #1500 Saint Louis MO 63105

LAMORIELLO, LOUIS ANTHONY, professional hockey team executive; b. Providence, Oct. 21, 1942; s. Nicholas Schiano and Rose (Ventura) L.; m. Patricia A. Renaldo, Aug. 9, 1970; children: Christopher, Heidi, Timothy. BA in Math. and Econs., Providence Coll., 1963. Hockey coach Providence Coll., 1968-82, athletic dir., 1982-87; pres., gen. mgr. N.J. Devils, East Rutherford, 1987—; commr. Hockey East Assn., Providence, 1984-87; mem. hockey com. U.S. Olympics 1984, 88; pres. Am. Hockey Coaches Assn., 1982-83. Named to Hall of Fame Providence Coll. Athletic Dept., 1982, I.T.L.U.-Am. Hall of Fame, 1986, R.I. Hall of Fame, 1987. Mem. Nat. Collegiate Athletic Assn. (profl. devel. com. 1984-87). Office: NJ Devils PO Box 504 East Rutherford NJ 07073-0504*

LAMOS, MARK, artistic director, administrator, actor; b. Melrose Park, Ill., Mar. 10, 1946; s. Gustav and Ruth (Oechslin) L. BS, Northwestern U., 1969; hon. doctorate, Conn. Coll., 1990, U. Hartford, 1990, Trinity Coll., 1993. Artistic dir. Ariz. Theatre Co., Tucson, 1978, Calif. Shakespearean Festival, Visalia, 1980-81, Hartford (Conn.) State Co., 1980—. Stage appearances include (stage debut) Lovers, Lake Forest, Ill., (Broadway debut) Pvt. Bowers in Love Suicide at Schofield Barracks, ANTA Theatre, 1971, Another Part of the Forest, Chgo., 1971-72, as Abel in The Creation of the World and Other Business, N.Y.C., 1972, as Christian de Neuvillette in Cyrano, N.Y.C., 1973, title role in Hamlet, San Diego, 1977, as Rex in City Sugar, N.Y.C., 1978, as Feste in Twelfth Night, Stratford, Conn., 1978, as Octavius in Man and Superman, N.Y.C., 1978, A Month in the Country, Princeton, N.J., 1978-79, title role in Anatol, Hartford, Conn., 1984, as Dr. Rank in A Doll House, Hartford Stage Co., 1986, as Jack Worthing in The Importance of Being Earnest, Hartford Stage Co., 1989, others; toured as Solomon Rothschild in The Rothschilds, 1972; theater dir. Dear Liar, Guthrie Theatre, 1976; (Ariz. Theatre Co.) The Threepenny Opera, 1978, The Seagull, 1979, Twelfth Night, 1979; (Calif. Shakespearean Festival) Romeo and Juliet, 1979, The Taming of the Shrew, 1979, Hamlet, 1980, A Midsummer Night's Dream, 1980; (Hartford Stage Co.) Mackerel, 1977, The Beaux Stratagem, 1980, Cymbeline, 1981, Undiscovered Country, 1981, Antony and Cleopatra, 1981, Kean, 1982, The Greeks, 1982, The Great Magoo, 1982, The Portage to San Cristobal of A.H., 1983, The Misanthrope, 1983, The Three Sisters, 1984, The Tempest, 1985, Twelfth Night, 1985, Distant Fires, 1986, The Gilded Age, 1986, Pericles, 1987, Morocco, 1987, Hamlet, 1987, Hedda Gabler, 1988, The School for Wives, 1988, A Midsummer Night's Dream, 1988, Peer Gynt, 1989, The Importance of Being Earnest, 1989, The Illusion, 1990, The Miser, 1990, Our Country's Good, 1990, The Master Builder, 1991, Julius Caesar, 1991, All's Well That Ends Well, 1991, Hidden Laughter, 1992, Tartuffe, 1992, Martin Guerre, 1992, opera dir. Don Giovanni, St. Louis Opera, 1983, Arabella, Santa Fe Opera, 1983, The Aspern Papers, Dallas Opera, 1988, La Boheme, Glimmerglass Opera Theater, 1990, Il Re Pastore, Glimmerglass Opera Theater, 1991, The Turn of the Screw, Glimmerglass Opera Theater, 1992, Cosi fan Tutte, Portland Opera, 1993, Werther, Glimmerglass Opera Theater, 1993, Merchant of Venice, Hartford Stage, 1993, I Lombardi, Met. Opera, 1994, The Turn of The Screw, Seattle Opera, 1994, False Admissions, Hartford Stage, 1994, A Scourge of Hyacinths (world premiere), Munich Biennale, Germany; also dir. The Merchant of Venice, Stratford Festival, 1984, The Voyage of Edgar Allan Poe, Stora Teatern, Goteborg, Sweden, 1985, The School for Wives, La Jolla (Calif.) Playhouse, 1987, Desire Under the Elms, Pushkin Drama Theatre, Moscow, 1988, Measure for Measure, Lincoln Ctr., N.Y.C., 1989, Our Country's Good, Nederlander Theater, N.Y.C., 1991 (Tony nomination), The End of the Day, Playwrights Horizons, N.Y.C., 1992; TV appearance in School for Scandal, Great Performances, PBS, 1975; film appearance in Longtime Companion, Am. Playhouse Theatrical Films, 1989; author: (play) Some Other Time, 1970. Mem. Theater Comm. Group (trustee 1991—). Office: Hartford Stage Co 50 Church St Hartford CT 06103-1201

LAMOUREUX, CHARLES HARRINGTON, botanist, arboretum administrator; b. West Greenwich, R.I., Sept. 14, 1933; s. Emile and Cora May (Harrington) L.; m. Florence May Kettelle, Aug. 23, 1964; children: Mark Harrington, Anne Maile. BS in Botany, U. R.I., 1953; MS in Botany, U. Hawaii, 1955; PhD in Botany, U. Calif., Davis, 1961. From asst. to assoc. prof. botany U. Hawaii, Honolulu, 1959-71, prof., 1971—; chair dept. botany, 1962-65, 76-78, acting assoc. dean curriculum coll. arts and scis., 1976-77, 83, project coord. instrnl. assistance unit, 1977-79, assoc. dean acad.

affairs coll. arts and scis., 1985-91, dir. Lyon arboretum, 1992—; rsch. assoc. botany Bernice P. Bishop Mus., Honolulu, 1963—; vis. asst. prof. botany U. B.C., Can., summer 1963; vis. colleague dept. botany Canterbury U., Christchurch, New Zealand, 1965-66; mem. sci. adv. com. Pacific Tropical Bot. Garden (name changed to Nat. Tropical Bot. Garden), 1967-94; dir. summer inst. sci. amd math. tchrs. U.S. children Far East NSF, Chofu, Japan, 1968-71, reviewer, mem. various rev. panels; faculty mem. ctr. Pacific islands studies U. Hawaii, 1971—; guest sci. Nat. Biol. Inst. Indonesia, Bogor, 1972-73, 79-80; mem. adv. com. plants and animals quarantine br. Hawaii State Dept. Agr., 1973-79, 89—; study lectr./leader Smithsonian Assocs. Study Tours S.E. Asia, 1985, 86, 88-95, Melanesia, 1987; report reviewer U.S. Congl. Office Tech. Assessment; rschr. in field; bot. and ecol. cons. to various businesses and agys. including State Hawaii Dept. Bus. and Econ. Devel., UNESCO, UN Devel. Programme. Author: Trailside Plants of Hawaii's National Parks, 1976, (U.S. Nat. Pk. Svc. Dir.'s award 1977, Nat. Pks. Coop. Assn. Award of Excellence 1977-78), rev. edit., 1982; bd. editors Pacific Sci., 1965—, editor-in-chief, 1985-86; mem. editorial com. Allertonia, 1977-90; manuscript reviewer for various jours. and presses; contbr. articles to profl. jours. Active Hawaii Audubon Soc., 1959—, past pres., 1st v.p., Hawaiian Bot. Gardens Found., 1959-67, 1st v.p.; life mem. Conservation Coun. Hawaii, 1959—, state bd. dirs., mem. com. flora conservation, Hawaiian Bot. Soc., 1959—, trustee endowment fund, past pres., v.p., sec., treas., newsletter editor; mem. adv. com. Hawai'i Earth Day, 1990; bd. dirs. Friends Honolulu Bot. Garden, 1992—. Mem. Bot. Soc. Am., Am. Assn. Bot. Gardens and Arboreta, Hawaiian Acad. Sci. (councillor 1991-93, pres.-elect 1993, pres. 1994-95), Pacific Sci. Assn. (life, standing com. botany 1971—), Internat. Assn. Plant Taxonomists, Internat. Assn. Wood Anatomists. Avocations: photography, travel, opera. Home: 3426 Oahu Ave Honolulu HI 96822 Office: Harold L Lyon Arboretum 3860 Manoa Rd Honolulu HI 96822

LA MOY, WILLIAM THOMAS, library director, editor; b. Hartford, Conn., Jan. 27, 1953; s. Roy Henry and Margaret Mary (McKelligott) La M. BA in English Lang. and Lit. cum laude, Yale U., 1976; MS in Libr. and Info. Sci., Simmons Coll., 1988. Editor (with others) The Yale Edit. of Horace Walpole's Correspondence, New Haven, Conn., 1976-83; prodn. editor Garland Pub., Inc., Hamden, Conn., 1984-87; asst. libr. Essex Inst., Salem, Mass., 1989-90; dir. libr. Essex Inst., Salem, 1990-92; dir. James Duncan Phillips Libr. Peabody Essex Mus., Salem, 1992—. Editor: (quar. jour.) Essex Inst. Hist. Collections, Peabody Essex Mus. Collections. Recipient Publ. Design award Essex Inst. Hist. Collections, New Eng. Mus. Assn., 1991, Publ. Design award Peabody Essex Mus. Collections, New Eng. Mus. Assn., 1994, 95. Mem. ALA, Assn. Coll. and Rsch. Librs. (rare books and manuscripts sect.), Colonial Soc. Mass., Internat. Honor Soc. for Librarianship and Info. Svc. Office: James Duncan Phillips Libr Peabody Essex Mus East India Sq Salem MA 01970

LAMP, BENSON J., tractor company executive; b. Cardington, Ohio, Oct. 7, 1925; m. Martha Jane Motz, Aug. 21, 1948; children: Elaine, Marlene, Linda, David. BS in Agr. and B in Agrl. Engring., Ohio State U., 1949, MS in Agrl. Engring., 1952; PhD in Agrl. Engring., Mich. State U., 1960. Registered profl. engr., Ohio. Prof. agrl. engring. Ohio State U., Columbus, 1949-61, 87-91, prof. emeritus, 1991—; product mgr. Massey Ferguson Ltd., Toronto, Can., 1961-66; product planning mgr. Ford Tractor Ops. div. Ford Motor Co., Troy, Mich., 1966-71, mktg. mgr., 1971-76, bus. planning mgr., 1978-87; v.p. mktg. and devel. Ford Aerospace div. Ford Motor Co., Dearborn, Mich., 1976-78. Author: Corn Harvesting, 1962. Served to 2d lt. USAF, 1943-45. Fellow Am. Soc. Agrl. Engrs. (pres. 1985-86, Gold medal 1993), Country Club at Muirfield Village (Dublin, Ohio). Avocations: golf, tennis, bridge. Office: BJM Company Inc 6128 Inverurie Dr E Dublin OH 43017-9472

LAMP, FREDERICK JOHN, museum curator; b. Malvern, Pa., Nov. 20, 1944; s. Clyde Herman and Grace Ebersole (Landis) L.; m. Diane Frank, May 18, 1974 (div. 1984). BS, Kent State U., 1967; MA, Ohio U., 1971; PhD, Yale U., 1982. Adminstr., lectr. Mus. African Art, Washington, 1973-77; curator Balt. Mus. Art, 1981—. Author La Guinee, African Art of W Atlantic Coast. Contbr. articles to profl. jours. Nat. Mus. Act degree fellow, 1977-79; rsch. grantee Nat. Endowment Arts, 1976, 85, Social Sci. Rsch. Coun., 1979-81, 88, Smithsonian Instn., 1985, Fulbright, 1991-92, Nat. Gallery Art, 1995—. Mem. Coll. Art Assn., African Studies Assn. (Arts Council). Democrat. Avocation: collecting African Art. Office: Balt Mus Art Art Museum Dr Baltimore MD 21218-3898

LAMP, JOHN ERNEST, lawyer; b. Spokane, Wash., Jan. 17, 1943; s. Raymond Holmes and Marie (Cunningham) L.; m. Louise Edwards, June 26, 1976; children—Amanda Catherine Marie, Victoria Louise. B.A., Wash. State U., 1965; J.D., Willamette U., 1968. Bar: Wash. 1968. Asst. atty. gen. State of Wash., Olympia, 1968-69, 71-76; sr. asst. atty. gen. chief Spokane and Eastern Wash. br. Wash. State Atty. Gen.'s Office, 1976-81; U.S. Atty. Eastern Dist. Wash. State, 1981-91; spl. atty. to U.S. Atty. Gen., 1990-92. Mem. Atty. Gen.'s adv. com. U.S. Attys., 1983-86; apptd. to White House Conf. for Drug Free Am., 1987; apptd. to bd. dirs. Drug Watch Internat. Internat. Drug Strategy Inst., 1993. Capt. U.S. Army, 1969-71, Vietnam. Decorated Bronze Star; recipient Alumni Achievement award Wash. State U., 1986; recipient Medal Commitment Greater Spokane Substance Abuse Coun., 1989, Community Svc., Community Rels. Svc. award U.S. Dept. Justice, 1991. Mem. Wash. Bar Assn. Home: 3936 E 15th Ave Spokane WA 99223-5243 Office: Rock Pointe Corp Tower 316 W Boone Ave Ste 680 Spokane WA 99201-2346

LAMPARTER, WILLIAM C., printing and publishing consultant, digital printing and information systems specialist; b. Bklyn., July 13, 1929; s. William C. and Nadine (Lesch) L.; m. Ann E. Martyn; children: Ellen, Susan, David. B.S., Springfield (Mass.) Coll., 1951; M.S., Boston U., 1952. V.p. gen. mgr. Mead Digital Systems, 1975-78; pres. Nat. Assn. Printers and Lithographers, Teaneck, N.J., 1978-82, PrintCom Cons. Group, 1982—; staff cons. Rochester Inst. Tech.'s Lab. for Quality and Productivity in the Graphic Arts, mem. adv. com. to Sch. of Printing Mgmt. and Scis., adv. to Graphic Arts Tech. and Edn. Ctr.; internat. lectr. in field. Author: Forecast of Long-Term Business and Technological Trends in the Graphic Arts, 1968, transl. into Polish, Russian, 1973, The Electronic Superhighway Revolution - 1994-1997-2000-2010, 1994; prin. economist author Printing Industry Quar. Bus. Indicator Report, 1979-85, Ann. Tech. Impact Rev., 1985, Interpretive Tech. Analysis, 1986, Printing Industry Materials Mgmt. Newsletter, 1985-86; contbg. editor Printing News, 1978-90, Am. Printer, 1990—. Served with U.S. Army. Mem. Printing Industries Am. Inc., Nat. Assn. Printers and Lithographers, Tech. Assn. Graphic Arts, Rsch. and Engring. Coun. of Graphic Arts Industry Inc. (mem. exec. com.), Assn. for Graphic Arts Tng., World Future Soc., Am. Soc. Quality Control, Soderstrom Soc., Inst. of Printing (London), Nat. Printing Equip. Assn. (former bd. mem.), Sigma Delta Chi. Home and Office: 1020 Farm Creek Rd Waxhaw NC 28173-7793 *Commitment, developing people and combining their skills with the advantages of automation in a bottom-line oriented but innovative entrepreneurial atmosphere are the keys to success in today's changing business environment.*

LAMPE, FREDERICK WALTER, chemistry educator, consultant; b. Chgo., Jan. 5, 1927; s. Joseph Dell and Christine Wood (Phillips) L.; m. Eleanor Frances Coffin, Mar. 26, 1949; children: Joan Dell, Kathy Lee, Erik Steven, Beth Ann, Kristina Jean. BS, Mich. State Coll., 1950; AM, Columbia U., 1951, PhD, 1953. Research chemist Humble Oil and Refining Co., Baytown, Tex., 1953-56, sr. research chemist, 1956-59, specialist research, 1959-60; assoc. prof. Pa. State U., University Park, 1960-65, prof., 1965-92, prof. emeritus, 1992—; head dept. chemistry Pa. State U., University Park, 1983-88; Robert A. Welch Found. lectr., Tex., 1982, J.L. Franklin Meml. lectr., 1990; cons. Mobil Oil Corp, Pennington, N.J., 1961-69, Sci. Rsch. Instruments Corp., Balt., 1967-77, IBM Corp., Yorktown Heights, N.Y., 1980-85, Chemetron Corp., PPG Biomed., St. Louis, 1982-90, Polaroid Corp., Waltham, Mass., 1986-88, Marquett Electronics Corp., 1993—. bd. dirs. Vestec Corp., Houston. Author: (with H.R. Allcock) Contemporary Polymer Chemistry, 1981, 2d edit. 1990; patentee in field; contbr. 160 articles to profl. jours. Served with USN, 1944-46, ATO. NSF sr. postdoctoral fellow, 1966-67; recipient Sr. U.S. Scientist award Alexander von Humboldt Found., 1973-74, 84. Fellow Am. Physical Soc.; mem. Am. Chem. Soc., Am. Soc. for Mass Spectrometry (bd. dirs. 1981-83). Republican. Methodist.

Home: 542 Ridge Ave State College PA 16803-3441 Office: Pa State U Dept of Chemistry 152 Davey Lab University Park PA 16802-6300

LAMPEL, RONALD B., human resources executive; b. Bridgeport, Conn., Feb. 22, 1943; s. Ernest and Marion (Feldman) L.; m. Pamela Wininger, Apr. 23, 1973; children: Melissa, Benjamin, Amanda. BS in Econs., Rensselaer Poly. Inst., Troy, N.Y., 1964. Bank examiner Banking Dept., N.Y. State, N.Y.C., 1964-73; auditor Instl. Group Info. Corp., Great Neck, N.Y., 1973-78, v.p. human resources and adminstrn., 1978—. With U.S. Army, 1965-67. Mem. Am. Mgmt. Assn., Internat. Found. Employee Benefit Plans, Am. Soc. Personnel Adminstrn., Adminstrv. Mgmt. Soc., Am. Compensation Assn., Am. Payroll Assn. Avocations: reading, gardening, personal computers. Office: Instl Group Info Corp 1000 Northern Blvd Great Neck NY 11021-5305

LAMPEN, RICHARD JAY, lawyer, investment banker; b. New Brunswick, N.J., Nov. 12, 1953; s. J. Oliver and Miriam (Walsh) L.; m. Susan Matson, June 8, 1975; children: Katharine, Caroline. BA, John Hopkins U., 1975; JD, Columbia U., 1978. Bar: Fla. 1978, U.S. Dist. Ct. (so. dist.) Fla. 1978. From assoc. to ptnr. Steel Hector & Davis, Miami, Fla., 1978-86, co-chmn. corp. dept., 1992—; mng. dir. Salomon Bros. Inc., N.Y.C., 1986-92; bd. dirs. U.S. Can Corp., Roland Internat. Corp., All-Am. Bottling Corpl, INternat. Bank Miami, N.A. Miami. Fla. Bar Assn. (chmn. securities law com. 1985-86), mem. City Club (Miami, Fla.), Brickell Club (Miami), Exchange Club (N.Y.C.). Office: Steel Hector & Davis 200 S Biscayne Blvd Miami FL 33131

LAMPERT, JAMES B., lawyer; b. Montpelier, Vt., June 26, 1938; s. James Benjamin Lampert and Margery Frances (Mitchell) Lampert-Dudley; m. Mary Elizabeth Shugrue; children: Nicholas, Michael, Stephen. BSME, MIT, 1961; JD magna cum laude, Harvard U., 1964. Bar: Mass., U.S. Dist. Ct. Mass., U.S. Ct. Appeals (1st cir.) 1967, U.S. Patent and Trademark Office 1967, U.S. Ct. Appeals (fed. cir.) 1985. Sr. ptnr. Fish & Richardson, Boston, 1964-85; asst. prof. law Boston U., 1972-87; sr. ptnr. Hale and Dorr, Boston, 1985—. Capt. U.S. Army, 1964-66. Mem. Mass Bar Assn., Boston Patent Law Assn., Tau Beta Pi, Pi Tau Sigma, Sigma Xi. Avocations: sailing, skiing, swimming. Home: 148 Washington St Duxbury MA 02332-4523 Office: Hale and Dorr 60 State St Boston MA 02109-1803

LAMPERTI, JOHN WILLIAMS, mathematician, educator; b. Montclair, N.J., Dec. 20, 1932; s. Frank A. and Louise (Williams) L.; m. Claudia Jane McKay, Aug. 17, 1957; children—Matthew, Steven, Aaron, Noelle. B.S., Haverford Coll., 1953; Ph.D., Calif. Inst. Tech., 1957. Instr., then asst. prof. math. Stanford, 1957-62; research asso. Rockefeller Inst., 1962-63; faculty Dartmouth, 1963—, prof. math., 1968—; Sci. exch. visitor to USSR, 1970; vis. prof. U. Aarhus, Denmark, 1972-73; Nicaraguan Nat. U., 1990; cons. Am. Friends Svc. Com., 1980, 85, 91. Author: Probability: A Survey of the Mathematical Theory, 1966, Stochastic Processes: A Survey of the Mathematical Theory, 1977, What Are We Afraid Of? An Assessment of the "Communist Threat" in Central America, 1988. Fellow Inst. Math. Stats.; mem. ACLU, War Resisters League, Peace Action, Amnesty Internat., Fedn. Am. Scientists. Home: Upper Loveland Rd Norwich VT 05055 Office: Dartmouth Coll Dept Math Hanover NH 03755

LAMPI, JUANITA, principal. Prin. Loggers' Run Community Mid. Sch., Boca Raton, Fla. Recipient Blue Ribbon Sch. award U.S. Dept. Edn., 1990-91. Office: Loggers' Run Community Mid Sch 11584 W Palmetto Park Rd Boca Raton FL 33428

LAMPINEN, JOHN A., newspaper editor; b. Waukegan, Ill., Nov. 26, 1951; s. Walter Valentine and Patricia Mae Irene (Pruess) L.; m. Belinda Walter, Oct. 20, 1973; children: Amanda Michelle, Heidi Elizabeth. BS in Comm., U. Ill., 1973. Staff writer Paddock Cir. Newspapers, Libertyville, Ill., 1973-75; regional editor The Jour., New Ulm, Minn., 1975-76; various positions Daily Herald, Arlington Heights, Ill., 1976-90; asst. v.p.; mng. editor Daily Herald, Arlington Heights, 1990—. Avocations: baseball, long-distance running, coaching girls softball. Office: Daily Herald 217 W Campbell St Arlington Heights IL 60005-1459

LAMPKIN, M. MARTHA, architect, city planner; b. Decatur, Ill., Sept. 25, 1952; d. Louis William and Mary Estelle (Hayes) L. BArch, U. Notre Dame, 1975; MArch, M City Planning,, MIT, 1981. Registered arch., Ill., Mass.; cert. Nat. Coun. Archtl. Registration Bds. Arch. Metz, Train & Youngren, Inc., Chgo., 1975-77; asst. prof. architecture La. Tech U., Ruston, 1088-78; arch., planner Skidmore, Owings & Merrill, Boston, 1981-83, Chgo., 1985; urban designer Lane, Frenchman and Assocs., Inc., Boston, 1984-85; prin., v.p. Sasaki Assocs., Inc., Watertown, Mass., 1985—, also bd. dirs.; guest lectr., studio critic MIT, Harvard Grad. Sch. Design, Boston Archtl. Ctr., U. Notre Dame, Kent State U., Wentworth Inst. Tech., 1981—; bd. dirs. Nat. Archtl. Accrediting Bd., 1980-83, mem. accreditation team, 1979—. Co-author master plans for numerous univs., including Case Western Res. U., Ga. Inst. Tech., U. Ill., Iowa State U., Harvard U., U. Colo. Health Scis. Ctr., U. Lowell, Mass., U. Mass., Lowell, also Univ. Circle Master Plan, Cleve., Bank of Boston, Housatonic Corp. Ctr., Milford, Conn., Va. Ctr., Fairfax County, Campustown Revitalization Plan, Ames, Iowa, Ctrl. Area Circulator, Chgo., Ames Townscape Plan, Boston Common Garage Renovation, numerous others. Mem. design and engring. com. Artery Bus. Com., 1989—; mem. designer selection panel Mass. Turnpike Authority; trustee 1000 Friends of Mass., 1992; mem. Rotch Travelling Scholarship Com., 1990-95. Recipient 1st award in design Commonwealth of Mass., 1986; Loeb fellow Harvard UGrad. Sch. Design, 1991-92. Fellow AIA (chmn. regional and urban design com. 1992-94); mem. Boston Soc. Architects (bd. dirs. 1983—, co-chmn. ctrl. artery task force 1988—, mem. Hrleston Parker award jury 1993, chmn. nominating com. 1992, bd. dirs., commr. design 1988-90, chmn. urban design citation com. 1984, 87, design excellence in housing awards jury, 1990), New Eng. Women in Real Estate (steering com. 1991-94). Office: Sasaki Assocs Inc 64 Pleasant St Watertown MA 02172

LAMPL, PEGGY ANN, association administrator; b. N.Y.C., Dec. 12, 1930; d. Joseph and Alice L. B.A., Bennington Coll., 1952. Dir. program devel. dept. mental health AMA, Chgo., 1962-66; asst. dir. NIMH, HEW, Washington, 1967-69; public relations dir. League Women Voters of U.S., Washington, 1969-73; exec. dir. League Women Voters of U.S., 1973-78; dep. asst. Sec. of State for congressional relations Dept. State, Washington, 1978-80; dep. dir. Iris Schools Devel., 1982-83; exec. dir. Children's Def. Fund, Washington, 1984-89, LWV, Washington, 1989—. Club: Federal City. Home: 2500 Q St NW Washington DC 20007-4373

LAMPORT, FELICIA (MRS. BENJAMIN KAPLAN), writer; b. N.Y.C., Jan. 4, 1916; d. Samuel C. and Miriam (Dworsky) L.; m. Benjamin Kaplan, Apr. 16, 1942; children: James, Nancy Mansbach. B.A., Vassar Coll., 1937. Reporter N.Y. Jour., N.Y.C., 1935-36; dialogue sub-title writer MGM, N.Y.C., 1937-49; instr. expository writing Harvard U., 1980-88; instr. creative writing Harvard U. Extension, 1988—. Freelance writer for various mags., newspapers including N.Y. Times, 1949—; columnist for Boston Globe, 1981—; author: Mink on Weekdays, 1950, Scrap Irony, 1961, Cultural Slag, 1966; Light Metres, 1982; Political Plumlines, 1984. Bd. dirs. MacDowell Colony, 1970-80, Am. Chess Found., 1965-80. Mem. PEN, Author's Guild, Nat. Writers Union. Home: 2 Bond St Cambridge MA 02138-2308

LAMPORT, LESLIE B., computer scientist; b. N.Y.C., Feb. 7, 1941; s. Benjamin and Hannah (Lasser) L.; m. Carol Dahl Crum, Oct. 31, 1968 (div. Feb. 1978); 1 child, Jason Christopher. BS, MIT, 1960; MA, Brandeis U., 1963, PhD, 1972. Mem. faculty Marlboro (Vt.) Coll., 1965-69; systems analyst Mass. Computer Assocs., Wakefield, 1970-77; sr. computer scientist SRI Internat., Menlo Park, Calif., 1977-85; sr. cons. engr. Digital Equipment Corp., Palo Alto, Calif., 1985—. Patentee in field. Mem. NAE. Office: Digital Equipment Corp Systems Rsch Ctr 130 Lytton Ave Palo Alto CA 94301-1044

LAMPTON, LESLIE B., SR., oil industry executive; b. 1926; married. G-rad., U. Miss., 1947. With Joe T. Dehmer Distbr., Jackson, Miss., 1949-51, 53-54, Lampton Oil Co., Jackson, Miss., 1954-70; prin. Ergon Inc., Jackson,

Miss., 1970—, now chmn. With U.S. Navy, 1947-79, 1951-53. Office: Ergon Inc 2829 Lakeland Dr Jackson MS 39208-9798

LAMPTON, MASON HOUGHLAND, construction company executive; b. Louisville, Oct. 15, 1947; s. Dinwiddie Jr. and Nancy Amanda (Houghland) L.; m. Mary Lucile Hardaway, Jan. 22, 1972; children: Mason Hardaway, Lucile Houghland. BA, Vanderbilt U., 1969. Dir. of agys. Am. Life and Accident Ins. Co. of Ky., Louisville, 1972-77; v.p. The Hardaway Co., Columbus, Ga., 1977-80, pres., 1980—; bd. dirs. Total System Services, Inc. Bd. dirs. Synovus Fin. Corp., Columbus, 1993—; founder, race chmn. Columbus Steeplechase Callaway Gardens, Pine Mountain, Ga., 1985—. Mem. Associated Gen. Contractors, Bus. Council Ga., Columbus C. of C. (bd. dirs. named Bus. Leader of Yr. 1986). Democrat. Methodist. Club: Atlanta City, Capital City; Big Eddy, Green Island Country (Columbus); Little Harbor (Mich.); Pendennis (Louisville). Lodge: Moles. Office: Hardaway Co 945 Broadway PO Box 1360 Columbus GA 31993-5499

LAMSON, GEORGE HERBERT, economics educator; b. Hartford, Conn., Feb. 21, 1940; s. Arroll Liscomb and Marguerite (Brechbuhler) L.; m. Susan Kathryn Lippert, Sept. 7, 1968; children: Scott, Brandon. A.B., Princeton U., 1963; M.A., Northwestern U., 1966, Ph.D., 1971. Research asst. Northwestern U. Econ. Survery of Liberia, Monrovia, 1962-63; instr. dept. econs. Loyola U., Chgo., 1967-68, U. Conn., Storrs, 1968-69; asst. prof. then assoc. prof. dept. econs. Carleton Coll., Northfield, Minn., 1969-80, Williams prof., 1981—, chmn. dept., 1978-84; cons. Minn. Higher Edn. Coordinating Com., St. Paul, 1971-72; textbook reviewer John Wiley & Sons, N.Y.C., 1979-82; reviewer NSF grad. fellowship program, 1988-90; vis. prof. U. Internat. Bus. and Econs., Beijing, China, 1994. Intersocietal studies fellow Northwestern U., 1966-67; recipient Faculty Devel. awards 1979, 90-91. Mem. Am. Econ. Assn., Midwest Econ. Assn., Minn. Econ. Assn. (bd. dirs. 1981-83, pres. 1984). Republican. Home: 4485 Detelemark Rd Dundas MN 55019-4003 Office: Carleton Coll Dept Econs Northfield MN 55057

LAMSON, ROBERT WOODROW, retired school system administrator; b. L.A., Dec. 28, 1917; s. Ernest K. and Mabel (Mahoney) L.; m. Jeannette Juett, July 22, 1949; children: Robert Woodrow Jr., Nancy Virginia, Kathleen Patricia. BA, Occidental Coll., 1940; MA, U. So. Calif., 1955. Cert. tchr., prin., supt., Calif. Tchr. El Monte (Calif.) Sch. Dist., 1940-43; tchr. L.A. City Sch. Dist., 1945-49, prin., 1949-55, supr., 1955-57, adminstrv. asst., 1957-59, area supt., 1959-78; ret. 1978; agt. Keilholtz Realtors, La Canada, Calif., 1979—; instr. various colls. and univs. so. Calif., 1948—; a founder, v.p., bd. dirs. U.S. Acad. Decathlon, Cerritos, Calif., 1981-86. Bd. dirs. 10th Dist. PTA, L.A., 1965-78; chmn. Scout-O-Rama, Gt. Western coun. Boy Scouts Am., 1980. Lt. comdr. USNR, 1943-46, mem. Res. ret. Mem. Am. Assn. Sch. Adminstrs., Assn. Adminstrs. L.A., Alumni Occidental Coll. in Edn. (a founder, past pres., bd. dirs.), Town Hall, Nat. PTA (hon. life), Calif. PTA (hon. life, bd. dirs. 1978-80), 31st Dist. PTA (hon. life, bd. dirs. 1965-78, auditorium named in his honor 1978), Phi Beta Kappa, Alpha Tau Omega. Republican. Avocations: gardening, reading, coin and stamp collecting, investments. Home: 4911 Vineta Ave La Canada Flintridge CA 91011-2624 Office: Richard Keilholtz Realtors 727 Foothill Blvd La Canada Flintridge CA 91011-3405

LAMUNYON, CRAIG WILLIS, biology researcher; b. Fullerton, Calif., Feb. 2, 1960; s. Harold Lee and Bernardine Marie (Schutten) LaM.; m. Cynthia Ann Munson, Aug. 20, 1983; children: Diana Nicole, Kyle Clark. BA in Biology, Calif. State U., Fullerton, 1984; PhD in Chem. Ecology, Cornell U., 1992. Rsch. assoc. Cornell U., Ithaca, N.Y., 1992-93; rsch. assoc. dept. molecular and cellular biology U. Ariz., Tucson, 1993—; predoctoral trainee NIMH, Cornell U., 1990-92. Mem. AAAS, Entomol. Soc. Am., Animal Behavior Soc., Sigma Xi. Achievements include research in multiple mating and its implications in an arctiid moth, use and effect of an anal defensive substance in larval chrysopidae.

LAMY, MARTINE, dancer; b. Trois-Rivières, Que., Can.. Attended, Nat. Ballet Sch. Dancer Nat. Ballet Co., Can., 1983-90, prin. dancer, 1990—. Dance performances include Swan Lake, Giselle, The Sleeping Beauty, Don Quixote, La Fille Mal Gardée, The Taming of the Shrew, Coppelia, others. Recipient medals Jr. Women's Divsn. Moscow Internat. Ballet Competition, 1981. Office: Nat Ballet Co Can, 157 King St East, Toronto, ON Canada M5C 1G9*

LAN, DONALD PAUL, JR., lawyer; b. Orange, N.J., July 19, 1952; s. Donald Paul and Hannah Paula (Resnik) L.; m. Deborah Sue Rothenberg, Aug. 20, 1978; children: Jennifer Robyn, Adam Christopher, Eric Jacob. BS in Acctg., U. R.I., 1974; JD, Rutger U., 1977; LLM in Taxation, Georgetown U., 1982. Bar: N.J. 1977, D.C. 1978, Tex. 1983, U.S. Dist. Ct. N.J. 1977, U.S. Dist. Ct. (no. dist.) Tex. 1983, U.S. Ct. Claims 1978, U.S. Tax Ct. 1977, U.S. Ct. Appeals (fed. cir.) 1978, U.S. Ct. Appeals (5th cir.) 1984. Clk. to spl. trial judge U.S. Tax Ct., Washington, 1977-78; trial atty. tax div. U.S. Dept. Justice, Washington, 1978-82; assoc., ptnr. Shank, Irwin & Conant, Dallas, 1982-87; ptnr. Finley, Kumble Wagner et al, Dallas, 1987, Strasburger & Price, Dallas, 1988—; adj. prof. law So. Meth. U., 1990—; lectr. on tax controversy and litigation, 1983—. Named Outstanding Atty. tax div. U.S. Dept. Justice, 1980. Mem. ABA (ct. procedures com. tax sect. 1987, stds. in tax practice com. tax sect. 1992), State Bar Tex., Dallas Bar Assn., D.C. Bar Assn., Phi Kappa Phi, Beta Alpha Psi, Beta Gamma Sigma. Jewish. Avocation: all sports. Office: Strasburger & Price 901 Main St Ste 4300 Dallas TX 75202-3794

LANAHAN, JOHN STEVENSON, management consultant; b. Pitts., June 13, 1922; s. James S. and Katharine L. (Lauck) L.; m. Rosemary Lourdes Ford, Feb. 20, 1954; children—Margaret Kayne, Brian James, Ellen Ford. BA, Duke U., 1945; MBA, Harvard U., 1949. Sales mgr. Mid-Atlantic region Allen B. Dumont Labs., E. Paterson, N.J., 1950-53; sr. asso. Booz, Allen & Hamilton, Inc., N.Y.C., 1954-59; pres. Richmond Hotels, Inc., Va., 1959-69, Flagler System, Inc., Palm Beach, Fla., 1969-71, Carlton House Resort Inns, Inc., Richmond, 1971-73; exec. v.p. Braniff Internat. Hotels, Dallas, 1973-74; pres., chief exec. officer The Greenbrier, White Sulphur Springs, W.Va., 1975-80; sr. v.p.-comml. Chessie System, Inc. 1980-85; pres., mng. dir. Strategic Enterprises, Inc., 1986-89; dir. Figgie Internat. Inc., 1985—. Mem. adv. bd. W.Va. Found. for Ind. Colls.; chmn. bd. Richmond Forward, 1968; mem. bd. visitors Trinity Coll. Duke U., 1988-94. Served to lt. (j.g.) USNR, World War II. Named to Hotel Industry Hall of Fame, 1971; Hotel Mgr. of Yr. Am. Hotel and Motel Assn., 1979. Mem. Commonwealth Club of Richmond (bd. govs.), Rotary, Beta Theta Pi, Omicron Delta Kappa. Republican. Roman Catholic. Home: 36 Lower Tuckahoe East Richmond VA 23233

LANAM, LINDA LEE, lawyer; b. Ft. Lauderdale, Fla., Nov. 21, 1948; d. Carl Edward and Evelyn (Bolton) L. BS, Ind. U., 1970, JD, 1975. Bar: Ind. 1975, Pa. 1979, U.S. Dist. Ct. (no. and so. dists.) Ind. 1975, U.S. Supreme Ct. 1982, Va. 1990. Atty., asst. counsel Lincoln Nat. Life Ins. Co., Ft. Wayne, Ind., 1975-76, 76-78; atty., mng. atty. Ins. Co. of N.Am., Phila., 1978-79, 80-81; legis. liaison Pa. Ins. Dept., Harrisburg, 1981-82, dep. ins. commr., 1982-84; exec. dir., Washington rep. Blue Cross and Blue Shield Assn., Washington, 1984-86; v.p. and sr. counsel Union Fidelity Life Ins. Co., Am. Patriot Health Ins. Co., etc., Trevose, Pa., 1986-89; v.p., sr. counsel, corp. sec. Life Ins. Co. Va., Richmond, 1989—, also bd. dirs.; chmn. adv. com. health care legis. Nat. Assn. Ins. Commrs., 1985-87, chmn. long term care, 1986-87, mem. tech. resource com. on cost disclosure and genetic testing, 1993-95; mem. tech. adv. com. Health Ins. Assn. Am., 1986-89. Contbr. articles to profl. jours. Pres. Phila. Women's Network, 1980-81; chmn. city housing code bd. appeals Harrisburg, 1985-86. Mem. ABA, Richmond Bar Assn. Republican. Presbyterian. Office: Life Ins Co Va/ Aon Corp 6610 W Broad St Richmond VA 23230-1702

LANCASTER, ANTHONY, economics educator, consultant; b. Eccles, Eng., June 25, 1938; came to U.S., 1987; s. Stanley and Irene (Ashcroft) L.; m. Jane Lesley Heawood, June 1967; children: Clare, Thomas, Robert. BA, Liverpool U., 1959; PhD, Cambridge U., 1965; MA (hon.), Brown U., 1987. Prof. econometrics Hull (Eng.) U., 1973-88; prof. econs. Brown U., Providence, 1986—. Contbr. numerous articles to profl. jours. Mem. Econometric Soc., Inst. Math. Stats. Office: Brown U Dept Econs Box B Providence RI 02912

LANCASTER, BRUCE MORGAN, investment broker, adviser, lecturer, money manager; b. Meridian, Miss., Oct. 5, 1923; s. Reuben MacDowell and Margaret (Morgan) L.; m. Mary Elinor Bickham, Nov. 1, 1947; 1 son, Bruce Morgan II. B.S. with highest honors, Miss. State U., 1943; grad. student, Duke, 1946-47; Ph.D., Am. U., 1974. Instr. math. Miss. State U., 1943; joined U.S. Fgn. Service, 1947; 3d sec. embassy Nanking, Canton, Hong Kong, 1947-49; vice consul Hamburg, Germany, 1950-53; consul, 1954; Dutch and Swiss desk officer State Dept., 1955-57; pub. affairs officer State Dept. (European dir.), 1958; consul in charge Medellin, Colombia, 1959-61; Columbia and Argentine desk officer State Dept., 1961-63; dep. dir. State Dept., East Coast of Latin Am., 1963-65; dir. operations center, also dep. exec. sec. to sec. of state, 1965-67; consul gen. Stuttgart, Germany, 1967-69; fellow Imperial Defence Coll., London, 1970; country dir. Peru and Ecuador Dept. State, 1971-72; detailed S.E. Fed. Regional Council, Atlanta, 1973-74; sr. research assoc., lectr. Emory U., 1973-76; adj. faculty Johns Hopkins, 1977—; investment broker Paine Webber, Washington, 1979-87; investment banker Lancaster Investment Svcs., Washington, 1987—; polit. advisor, U.S. del. Law of Treaties, 1969; mem. Nat. Tax Adv. Bd., 1981-85, Paine Webber. Contbr. articles to profl. jours., also, chpts. to books. Campaign mgr. for Jimmy Carter in N.W. La., 1975-76; co-founder Futuros para Niños, 1960. Served to capt. USMCR, 1943-46, col. Res. ret. Recipient Crispus Attucks award for service to low income housing, 1978; Hoover fellow Yale, 1963. Mem. Marine CorpsCombat Corrs. Assn., Sigma Chi, Phi Kappa Phi. Episcopalian. Home and Office: 3611 Tupelo Pl Alexandria VA 22304-1844

LANCASTER, CARROLL TOWNES, JR., business executive; b. Waco, Tex., Mar. 14, 1929; s. Carroll T. and Beatrice (Hollaman) L.; student U. Tex., 1948-51, 52-53; m. Catherine Virginia Frommel, May 29, 1954; children—Loren Thomas, Barbara, Beverly, John Tracy. Sales coordinator Union Tank div. Butler Mfg. Co., Houston, 1954-56, sales rep., New Orleans, 1956-57, br. mgr., 1957-60; asst. to exec. v.p. Maloney-Crawford Mfg. Co., Tulsa, 1960-62; mktg. cons., sr. asso. Market/Product Facts, Tulsa, 1962-63; market devel. asst. Norriseal Controls div. Dover Corp., Houston, 1963-66; area dir. Arthritis Found., Houston, 1966-69, dir. S.W. div., 1969-70; exec. dir. United Cerebral Palsy Tex. Gulf Coast, 1971-74; exec. dir. Leukemia Soc. Am., Gulf Coast, 1974-76, Lancaster & Assos., 1976—. Christian edn. tchr., 1966-70, supr., 1971, asst. youth football coach, Bellaire, 1967-68, 70-71; mem. Houston-Galveston Area Health Commn. Study Group, 1972-76, co-chmn., 1976; dir., essayist Tex. Low Vision Council, 1976-79, sec.-treas., 1978-81, pres., 1981-85; pres. Bellaire Civic Action Club, 1987-88; del. Houston Interfaith Sponsoring Com., 1979-81; bd. dirs. Council Chs. Greater Houston, 1966-68, v.p., 1968. Served with USNR, 1946-48, 51-52. Recipient award for securing free blood for indigent Harris County Hosp. Dist., 1968. Mem. Am. Mktg. Assn., Huguenot Soc., San Marcos Acad. Ex-students Assn. (pres. 1982-84), SAR, Delta Sigma Phi. Episcopalian (vestryman 1975-78). Home: 4901 Holly St Bellaire TX 77401-5714 Office: PO Box 745 Bellaire TX 77402-0745

LANCASTER, CLAY, architecture/design educator, writer; b. Lexington, Ky., Mar. 30, 1917. Attended, Art Students League, N.Y., 1936; AB, U. Ky., 1938, MA, 1939; attended, Columbia U., 1944-50. Instr. in drawing Art Dept. U. Ky., 1938-39; staff theatre set design and constrn. Guignol Theatre, Lexington, Ky., 1939-43; asst. Avery Architecture Library Columbia U., 1944-45, warm librarian, 1944-49, lectr. dept. fine arts and archaeology, 1948-53; lectr. art dept. Vassar Coll., 1950-51; lectr. Cooper Union, 1951-53, Metropolitan Mus. Art/Columbia U., 1953; curator Prospect Park, Bklyn., 1966-67; lectr. Sch. Continuing Edn. NYU, 1968, 69; instr., lectr. Traphagen Sch., N.Y., 1956-58; adv. U.S. State Dept., 1951-53; vis. prof. Transylvania U., Lexington, 1979-81, U. Ky., 1979; Frederick Lindley Morgan prof. U. Louisville, Ky., 1983—; cons. Woodstock, Fayette COunty, Ky., Henry Clay Law Office, Sugar Hill, Woodford County, Big Spring Meeting House, Warwick, Mercer County, Liberty Hall, Franklin County, Ridgeway, Jefferson County, Peter Paul House, Fayette County, Mt. Hope, Robert Swain House, Nantucket, Mass., Eugene R. Black House, COlumbia Heights, N.Y., James W. Kennedy Residence, Mt. Eden, Cin., Ohio, Malverne, Va., Locust Grove, Stanardsville, Va. Author: (books) Back Streets and Pine Trees: The Work of John McMurtry, Nineteenth Century Architect-Builder of Kentucky, 1956, Architectural Follies in America, of Sheesn and Pine Trees: The Work of John McMurtry, Nineteenth Century Hammer, Sawtooth and Nail, 1960, The Periwinkle Steamboat, 1961, Old Brooklyn Heights: New York's First Suburb, 1961, Ante Bellum Houses of the Bluegrass, 1961, The Japanese Influence in America, 1963, Nantucket in the Nineteenth Century, 1979, The American Bungalow, 1985, Antebellum Architecture of Kentucky, 1991, Holiday Island: Nantucket Hostelries and Summer Life, 1992; contbr. articles to numerous jours. Guggenheim fellow, 1953, 64; recipient Cert. of Merit Mcpl. Art Soc. N.Y., 1962, Spl. citation Pres. Borough of Bklyn. Heights, Hall of Disting Alumni award U. Ky., 1975, Merit award Ala. Hist. Commn., 1975, Preservation award Lexington-Fayette County Historic Commn., 1979, Profl. award Ky. Heritage Coun. Preservation, 1979, John Wesley Hunt award for Historic Preservation Blue Grass Trust, 1986. Home: Rt 1 Box 2500 Oregon Rd Salvisa KY 40372

LANCASTER, EDWIN BEATTIE, insurance company executive; b. LeMars, Iowa, Aug. 1, 1916; s. Middleton John and Rosabelle (Beattie) L.; m. Marjorie Forshey, Sept. 1, 1951; children: Craig, Susan. B.A., U. Iowa, 1938, postgrad., 1938-39. With Met. Life Ins. Co., N.Y.C., 1939-81; actuary Met. Life Ins. Co., 1964-65, v.p., 1965-69, sr. v.p., 1969-71, sr. v.p., chief actuary, 1971-73, exec. v.p., 1973-81; pres., chief exec. officer Life Investors, Inc., Cedar Rapids, Iowa, 1982-83, vice chmn., 1983; v.p. Tillinghast, Nelson & Warren, N.Y.C., 1983-85; chief exec. officer Accident Fund of Mich., 1985-88; bd. dirs. Cedar Income Fund, Ltd. Mem. Mount Kisco Village Bd., N.Y. 1959-61; mem. Mount Kisco Planning Bd., 1957-59, 61-69, chmn., 1962-69; bd. dirs. U. Iowa Found., 1971—; trustee No. Westchester Hosp., 1976—. Served with AUS, 1941-46; to lt. col. USAAF. Fellow Soc. Actuaries (pres. 1970-71, bd. govs. 1963-73), Phi Beta Kappa. Methodist (trustee).

LANCASTER, H(AROLD) MARTIN, congressman; b. Patetown Community, N.C., Mar. 24, 1943; s. Harold Wright and Eva (Pate) L.; m. Alice Matheny; children: Ashley Elizabeth, Mary Martin. AB, U.N.C., 1965, JD, 1967. Asst. staff judge adv. 12th Naval Dist., San Francisco, 1968; staff judge adv. USN, USS Hancock, 1968-70; ptnr. Baddour, Lancaster, Parker, Hine & Keller P.A., Goldsboro, N.C., 1970-86; rep. N.C. Gen. Assembly, Raleigh, 1978-86; mem. 100th-103rd Congresses from 3d N.C. dist., Washington, D.C., 1987-94; mem. armed svcs. com., readiness subocm., mil. pers. subcom.; chmn. morale, welfare and recreation panel; small bus. com. Mcht. Marine and Fisheries com.; chmn. judiciary com. N.C. Ho. of Reps., 1983-86; chmn. hwy. safety com., 1981-83; chmn. congrl. study group on German, 1994, North Atlantic Assembly, 1989-94; mem. numerous other coms. Chmn. N.C. Arts Coun., 1977-81, Goldsboro Wayne Bicentennial Commn., 1975-76; pres. Community Arts Coun., 1973-74, Wayne Community Concert Assn., 1972-73; chmn. bd. trustees Wayne County Pub. Libr., 1979-80; chmn. Wayne chpt. ARC, 1978-79; mem. adv. bd. Z. Smith Reynolds Found.; deacon First Presbyn. Ch., 1972-75, elder, 1980-86. Recipient Disting. Svc. award Goldsboro Jaycees, 1977, N.C. Crime and Justice award Gov.'s Crime Commn., 1984, Spl. award Gov.'s Adv. Coun. for Persons with Disabilities, 1985, Valand award Mental Health Assn. N.C., 1985, Outstanding Legislators awards Neuse River Coun. Govts., N.C. Assn. Sch. Counselors, Nat. Security Leadership award, 1987, 89, 90, 91, 92, Sound Dollar award, 1988, 89, 90, Spirit of Enterprise award U.S. C. of C., 1989, 92, 93, Doer of Deeds award House Leadership, 1989, Pub. Health Svc. award N.C. Primary Care Assn., 1991, Charles Dick Medal of Merit, U.S. Nat. Guard Assn., 1992, Tad Davis Meml. award U.S. Mil. Sports Assn., 1992; named N.C. and U.S. Alumnus of Yr., 4-H, 1987. Mem. ABA, Assn. Trial Lawyers Am., N.C. Bar Assn. (bd. govs.), Eighth Jud. Dist. Bar Assn., N.C. Acad. Trial Lawyers (Outstanding Legislator award). Wayne County Hist. Soc. Lodges: Masons, Shriners, Elks. Office: US Ho of Reps 2436 Rayburn Ho Office Bldg Washington DC 20515

LANCASTER, JOHN HOWARD, civil engineer; b. Bklyn., July 3, 1917; s. George York and Alice Eliot (Littlejohn) L.; m. Phyllis Elaine Metcalf, June 1, 1938; children: Judith Ann, Barbara Jean, Marylin Sharon, Kathryn Joy, Debra Elizabeth. B.S., Worcester (Mass.) Poly. Inst., 1939. Registered profl. engr., N.Y., N.Mex.; lic. master mariner USCG. Engr. Austin Co., N.Y.C., 1939-40; engr. C.E., 1940-42; asst. to div. engr. C.E., N.Y.C., 1942-43; chief engring. and constrn. AEC, Upton, N.Y., 1946-54; chief project engr. Brookhaven Nat. Lab., Upton, 1954-72; asst. dir. Nat. Radio Astronomy Obs. and program mgr. very large array radiotelescope program,

Socorro, N.Mex., 1972-81; propr. John H. Lancaster & Assos. (cons. engrs.), 1950-72; cons. NRAO/Associated Univs. Inc., 1981—; cons. in field, 1970—; bd. dirs., sec. corp. Seven Seas Cruising Assn.; cons. NSF, 1970, Cornell U., 1971, Fermi Nat. Accelerator Lab., 1980. Bd. dirs. Good Samaritan Nursing Home; treas. Socorro Pub. Libr. With USNR, 1942-46. Recipient Meritorious Service award NSF, 1976. Mem. NSPE, N.Y. Soc. Profl. Engrs., N.Mex. Soc. Profl. Engrs., Rotary, Masons, Eastern Star (pres. N.Mex. tech. club), Sigma Xi, Alpha Tau Omega.

LANCASTER, JOHN LYNCH, III, lawyer; b. Dallas, Nov. 10, 1936; s. John Lynch Jr. and Loretta Charlotte (Delaney) L.; m. Jane Frances Riddle, Sept. 5, 1959; children: Delaney, John, Jim. Student, Washington and Lee U., 1954-56; BA, U. Tex., 1958, LLB, 1960. Bar: Tex. 1960; diplomate Am. Bd. Trial Advs. Ptnr. Jackson & Walker, L.L.P., Dallas, 1962—. Mayor Town of Highland Park, Tex., 1984-86. Fellow Am. Coll. Trial Lawyers; mem. Inn of Ct. (master). Office: Jackson & Walker LLP 901 Main St Ste 6000 Dallas TX 75202-3748

LANCASTER, KELVIN JOHN, economics educator; b. Sydney, Australia, Dec. 10, 1924; s. John Kelvin and Margaret Louise (Gray) L.; m. Deborah Grunfeld, June 10, 1963; children—Clifton John, Gilead. B.Sc., Sydney U., 1948, B.A., 1949, M.A., 1953; B.Sc. in Economics, London U., 1953, Ph.D., 1958. Asst. lectr.; lectr. London Sch. Economics, 1954-59; reader economics U. London, 1959-62; prof. polit. economy Johns Hopkins U., 1962-66; prof. econs., 1966-78, John Bates Clark prof. econs., 1978—; John Bates Clark prof. econs. Columbia U., N.Y.C.; Ford faculty fellow, 1968-69, chmn. dept. econs., 1970-73, 89-90, Wesley Clair Mitchell research prof., 1973-74; vis. prof. U. Birmingham, Brown U., 1961-62, CUNY, 1965-66, NYU, Australian Nat. U., 1969-77, Ottawa U., 1972; fellow Inst. Advanced Studies Hebrew U., Jerusalem, 1976-77; dir. Nat. Bur. Econ. Rsch., 1971-73; trustee BT Investment Funds, 1986—. Author: Mathematical Economics, 1968, Introduction to Modern Microeconomics, 1969, Consumer Demand: A New Approach, 1971, Modern Economics: Principles and Policy, 1973, Variety, Equity and Efficiency, 1979, Modern Consumer Theory, 1991; contbr. articles in economics to profl. jours. Served with Royal Australian Air Force, 1943-45. Fellow Econometric Soc., Am. Acad. Arts and Scis., Am. Econ. Assn. (disting.); mem. N.Y. State Econ. Assn. (pres. 1974-75). Home: 35 Claremont Ave New York NY 10027-6823 also: 8 Island View Dr Sherman CT 06784 Office: Columbia U Dept Econs New York NY 10027

LANCASTER, RALPH IVAN, JR., lawyer; b. Bangor, Maine, May 9, 1930; s. Ralph I. and Mary Brigid (Kelleher) L.; m. Mary Lou Pooler, Aug. 21, 1954; children: Mary Lancaster Miller, Anne, Elizabeth, Christopher, John, Martin. A.B., Coll. Holy Cross, 1952; LL.B., Harvard U., 1955; LLD (hon.), St. Joseph's Coll., 1991. Bar: Maine 1955, Mass. 1955. Law clk. U.S. Dist. Ct. Dist. Maine, 1957-59; ptnr. firm Pierce, Atwood, Scribner, Allen, Smith & Lancaster, Portland, Maine, 1961—; mng. ptnr. Pierce, ATwood, Scribner, Allen, Smith & Lancaster, 1993—; condr. trial advocacy seminar Harvard U.; lectr. U. Maine; chmn. merit selection panel U.S. Magistrate for Dist. of Maine, 1982, '88; bd. visitors U. Maine Sch. Law, 1991—, chair 1991-93; spl. master by appointment U.S. Supreme Ct. in State of N.J. vs. State of Nev. et al, 1987-88; mem. 1st Ctr. Adv. Com. on Rules, 1991—, legal adv. bd. Martindale Hubbell, 1990—. Mem. Diocese of Portland Bur. Edn. With U.S. Army, 1955-57. Mem. Maine Jud. Coun., Am Coll. Trial Lawyers (chmn. Maine 1974-79, bd. regents 1982-87, treas. 1985-87, pres. 1989-90), Maine Bar Assn. (pres. 1982), Cumberland County Bar Assn., Canadian Bar Assn. (hon.). Republican. Roman Catholic. Home: 162 Woodville Rd Falmouth ME 04105-1120 Office: 1 Monument Sq Portland ME 04101-4033

LANCASTER, ROBERT SAMUEL, lawyer, educator; b. Floyd, Va., July 9, 1909; s. Robert Tazwell and Rachel Elma (Barnard) L.; m. Ernestine Martha DeSporte, June 21, 1931; children: Ulysse (Mrs. Wallace Matthews), Evelyn Rachel (Mrs. David Tyrrell); m. Elizabeth Craig, Jan. 4, 1980 (dec.). B.A., Hampden-Sydney Coll., 1929, D.Litt. (hon.), 1980; M.A., U. South, 1934, D.C.L., 1979; student, Andrew Jackson Law U. Nashville, 1937; Ph.D., U. Mich., 1952. Bar: Va. 1937. Instr. Gulf Coast Mil. Acad., Gulfport, Miss., 1929-31; instr. Sewanee (Tenn.) Mil. Acad., 1931-38, 46-49, comdt. cadets, 1941-43; pvt. practice Pulaski, Va., 1938-41; mem. faculty U. of South, 1949—, acting dir. devel., 1965-66, prof. polit. sci., 1953—, dean men, 1951-56; dean U. of South (Coll. Arts and Scis.), 1957-69; Fulbright lectr. Coll. Arts and Scis., Baghdad, Iraq, 1955-56, Coll. Arts and Scis. and Coll. of Law, Seoul (Korea) Nat. U., 1964-65. Author: The Better Parts of a Life: An Authobiograhy, 1990; co-author: An Introduction to American Government, 1954; contbr. articles to legal jours. Trustee Duck River Electric Membership Corp.; mem. acad. adv. bd. U.S. Naval Acad., 1970-75. Served to lt. (s.g.) USNR, 1943-46. Fellow Internat. Inst. Arts and Letters; mem. Va. Bar Assn., Tenn. Bar Assn., So. Polit. Sci. Assn., Phi Beta Kappa, Chi Phi, Phi Kappa Phi, Sigma Upsilon, Tau Kappa Alpha, Pi Gamma Mu, Pi Sigma Alpha, Blue Key. Republican. Episcopalian.

LANCASTER, SALLY RHODUS, philanthropy consultant; b. Gladewater, Tex., June 28, 1938; d. George Lee and Milly Maria (Meadows) Rhodus; m. Olin C. Lancaster Jr., Dec. 23, 1960; children: Olin C. III, George Charles, Julie Meadows. BA magna cum laude, So. Meth. U., 1960, MA, 1979; PhD, East Tex. State U., 1983. Tchr. English, Tex. pub. schs., 1960-61, 78-79; sr. advisor Meadows Found., Inc., Dallas, 1979-94, also trustee and dir.; cons. to philanthropy sector, 1994—. Trustee So. Meth. U., 1980-88, East Tex. State U., regent 1987-93; Tex. del. White House Conf. on Tourism, 1995; adv. dir. Los Caminos del Rio Inc., dir. Inst. Nautical Archaeology; mem. adv. bd. Communities Found. Tex. Recipient Disting. Alumni award So. Meth. U., 1986, East Tex. State U., 1994, Citizenship Excellence award in philanthropy Dallas Hist. Soc., 1984. Mem. Am. Evaluation Assn., Conf. S.W. Founds., Council on Founds., Philos. Soc. of Tex., Phi Beta Kappa (assoc. pres. 1980-82, nat com. on assns. 1983-85), Am. Assn. Continuing Edn., World Future Soc. Presbyterian. Office: Meadows Foundation Inc Wilson Historic Block 3003 Swiss Ave Dallas TX 75204-6090

LANCASTER, TINA, real estate executive, small business owner, rancher; b. Austin, Tex., July 21, 1939; d. Ernest Thomas and Dorothy A. (Loya) Prado; children from a previous marriage: Christina M., Joseph P., M. Kathleen. Student, U. Notre Dame, St. Mary's Coll., South Bend, Ind., 1958-62, U. Pa., Austin Sch. of Bus./Real Estate, 1982-86. Cert. realtor, Tex. Owner, pres. Diversified Properties, Austin, 1972—; owner, publisher Austin Home & Gardens, 1978-84, San Antonio Homes & Gardens, 1978-84, The Catholic Journal, Austin, 1978-84; owner, pres. Diversified Prodns., Austin, 1978—; owner Escondido Internat. Bazaar, Austin, 1984—; Escondido Ranch, Austin, 1984—; owner, dir. Women's Health & Fitness Ctr., Austin, 1986-93, Diversified, USA, water purification and desalianation R & D; Diversified Cos., Diversified Worldwide; freelance hist. writer. Bd. dirs. Mayor's Alternative Sources of Income Com., Austin, 1982, Bowie High Sch., Austin, 1989-90. Named Most Successful Woman, Mexican-Am. Profl. Women's Assn., 1981. Mem. U.S. Bd. of Realtors, Tex. Bd. of Realtors, Austin Bd. of Realtors, Headliner's Club, Austin Club. Avocations: photography, writing, painting, traveling. Home: 2900 Frate Barker Rd Austin TX 78748-3522

LANCE, ALAN GEORGE, lawyer, legislator, attorney general; b. McComb, Ohio, Apr. 27, 1949; s. Cloyce Lowell and Clara Rose (Wilhelm) L.; m. Sheryl C. Holden, May 31, 1969; children: Lisa, Alan Jr., Luke. BA, S.D. State U., 1971; JD, U. Toledo, 1973. Bar: Ohio 1974, U.S. Dist. Ct. (no. dist.) Ohio 1974, U.S. Ct. Mil. Appeals 1974, Idaho 1978. Asst. pros. atty. Fulton County, Wauseon, Ohio, 1973-74; ptnr. Foley and Lance, Chartered, Meridian, Idaho, 1978-90; prin. Alan G. Lance, Meridian, Idaho, 1990-94; rep. Idaho Ho. of Reps., Boise, 1990-94, majority caucus chmn., 1992-94; atty. gen. State of Idaho, 1995—. Capt. AUS, 1974-78. Mem. Ohio Bar Assn., Idaho Bar Assn. (Idaho Trial Lawyers Assn., Meridian C. of C. (pres. 1983), Am. Legion (judge adv. 1981-90, state comdr. 1988-89, alt. nat. exec. com. 1992-94, nat. exec. com. 1994—), Elks. Republican. Avocations: hunting, fishing. Home: 1370 Eggers Pl Meridian ID 83642-6528 Office: PO Box 83720 Statehouse Rm 210 Boise ID 83720-0010

LANCE, GEORGE MILWARD, mechanical engineering educator; b. Youngstown, Ohio, Dec. 4, 1928; s. Ray Clifford and Louisa Brigetta (Emch) L.; m. Phyllis Joanne Sprague, Aug. 8, 1964; children: Kathryn, Deborah, John, Rebecca, George. B.S. in Mech. Engring, Case Inst. Tech., 1952, M.S.

in Instrumentation Engring, 1954. Registered profl. engr., Iowa. Instr. Case Inst. Tech., Cleve., 1952-54; research engr. TRW Inc., Cleve., 1954-56; lectr. Washington U., St. Louis, 1956-60; sr. systems engr. Moog, Inc., 1960-61; asst. prof., then prof. mech. engring. U. Iowa, Iowa City, 1961-91; prof. emeritus U. Iowa, 1991—; acting chair mech. engring. U. Iowa, Iowa City, 1972-74; asso. dean engring. U. Iowa, 1974-79; cons. McDonnell Aircraft, Boeing Airplane Co., Collins Radio Co., U.S. Army Weapons Command, CADSI. Served with USN, 1946-48. Mem. ASME, Am. Soc. Engring. Edn., Sigma Xi, Tau Beta Pi, Pi Tau Sigma. Patentee in valves. Home: 609 S Summit St Iowa City IA 52240-5657 Office: Univ Iowa Coll Engring Iowa City IA 52242

LANCE, LARRY KENT, insurance company executive; b. Laramie, Wyo., May 12, 1941; s. Dearl E. and Bessie L. (Hyde) L.; m. Anita Sue Rogler, Dec. 29, 1962; children: Steven, Stacey. BSBA, Pitts. State U., 1963. CLU. Group rep. Mut. Omaha, 1963-65; rep. group sales ITT Hartford Life Ins., Overland Park, Kans., 1965-68, zone mgr. group sales, 1968-71; asst. dir. sales ITT Hartford Life Ins., Hartford, Conn., 1971-75, v.p. group ops., 1975-80, sr. v.p. employee benefits divsn., 1980-86; exec. v.p. employee benefits divsn. ITT Hartford Life Ins., Simsbury, Conn., 1986—; pres. ITT-CEBSCO, Simsbury, Conn.; bd. dirs. Benefit Panel Svcs., Inc. Chmn. Gov.'s commn. pvt. and pub. responsibilities for financing long term care for elderly, 1987. Mem. Life Ins. Mgmt. Rsch. Assn. (bd. dirs. 1985-88), Am. Coun. Life Ins. (group ins. com. 1985-87), Health Ins. Assn. Am. (group com. 1985-88)., Assn. Pvt. Pension and Welfare Plans, Bus. Coalition on Health., Hartford C. of C. (com. aging Ams.). Avocations: golf, reading, photography. Office: Hartford Life Ins Co 200 Hopmeadow St Simsbury CT 06089-9793

LANCE, LEONARD, assemblyman; b. Easton, Pa., June 25, 1952; s. Wesley L. and Anne (Anderson) L. BA, Lehigh U., 1974; JD, Vanderbilt U., 1977; MPA, Princeton U., 1982. Law clk. to judges Warren County Ct., Belvidere, N.J., 1977-78; asst. counsel Office of N.J. Gov. Thomas H. Kean, Trenton, N.J., 1983-90; mem. N.J. Gen. Assembly, 1991—. Mem. Grandin Libr. Bd., Clinton, N.J., 1990—, N.J. Coun. for the Humanities, Trenton, 1994—; bd. trustees Newark Mus., 1995—. Mem. Princeton Club N.Y., Phi Beta Kappa. Republican. Home: PO Box 5240 Clinton NJ 08809-0240 Office: NJ Gen Assembly 119 Main St Flemington NJ 08822-1615

LANCHNER, BERTRAND MARTIN, lawyer, advertising executive; b. Boston, Oct. 3, 1929; s. Abraham Joseph and Mina (Grossman) L.; m. Nancy Nelson, Apr. 26, 1979; 1 son by previous marriage, David; 1 stepdau., Renate. B.A., Stanford U., 1951; postgrad., Columbia U. Grad. Sch. Bus., 1951-52, U. Vienna, Austria, summer 1955; J.D., Harvard U., 1955. Bar: N.Y. bar 1956. Asso. firm Sage, Gray, Todd & Sims, N.Y.C., 1955-57; atty. Warner Bros. Pictures, N.Y.C., 1957-59; asst. gen. counsel Dancer-Fitzgerald-Sample, N.Y.C., 1959-62; gen. counsel Lawrence C. Gumbinner Advt. Agy., N.Y.C., 1962-63; dir. bus. affairs and sports contract negotiations CBS-TV, N.Y.C., 1963-69; gen. counsel, exec. v.p. Videorecord Corp. Am., Westport, Conn., 1969-73; sr. v.p., sec., gen. counsel N.W. Ayer, Inc., N.Y.C., 1973—, also bd. dirs.; bd. dirs. 170 E. 79th St. Corp., Advt. Info. Services Inc., N.Y.C.; guest lectr. Yale U. Law Sch. Mem. adv. bd.: Communications and the Law. Mem. ABA, N.Y. State Bar Assn., Assn. of Bar of N.Y.C. (chmn. subcom. advt. agy. 1981-83), Copyright Soc. U.S., Am. Assn. Advt. Agys. (chmn. legal com. 1986-89), Am. Advt. Fedn. (mem. legal com.), Harvard Club of N.Y.C., Bridgehampton Tennis and Surf Club, East Hampton Tennis Club, Tennisport Club. Office: N W Ayer Inc Worldwide Plz 825 8th Ave New York NY 10019-7416

LAND, DAVID POTTS, lawyer; b. Lancaster, Pa., Mar. 29, 1944; s. William Ortlip and Jean (Potts) L.; m. Susan Delano, Aug. 20, 1966; children: Katherine, Stephen, Elizabeth. BA in Religion, Kenyon Coll., 1966; JD, Vanderbilt U., 1969. Bar: N.Y. 1970, U.S. Dist. Ct. (so. dist.) N.Y. 1972, U.S. Ct. Appeals (2d cir.) 1972. Assoc. Seward & Kissel, N.Y.C., 1969-71; asst. U.S. atty. State of N.Y., N.Y.C., 1971-75; assoc. Rosenman and Colin, N.Y.C., 1975-77; v.p., asst. gen. counsel Combustion Engring. Inc., Stamford, Conn., 1977-86; v.p., gen. counsel Brown Boveri Inc., White Plains, N.Y., 1986-87; v.p., sec., gen. counsel Asea Brown Boveri Inc., Purchase, N.Y., 1987-90; chief tax unit U.S. Attys. Office, N.Y.C., 1973-75. Pres. Saugatuck Shores Assn., Westport, Conn., 1982-85; mem. bd. deacons Saugatuck Congl. Ch., 1986—. Mem. ABA, Bklyn. Bar Assn. Home: 21 Marine Ave Westport CT 06880-6922 Office: Nixon Hargrave et al 437 Madison Ave New York NY 10022

LAND, GEOFFREY ALLISON, science administrator; b. Jeannette, Pa., July 9, 1942; s. Albert E. Jr. and Helene (Matthews) L.; m. Maxine McCluskey, Jan. 22, 1966; children: Kevin Jeffrey, Melissa Allison, Kyle Robert. MS in Biology (Biochemistry), Tex. Christian U., 1970; PhD in Microbiology/Immunology, Tulane U., 1973. Cert. clin. lab. dir. Am. Bd. Bioanalysis. Dir. mycology Wadley Institutes Molecular Medicine, Dallas, 1974-78; dir. mycology, assc. dir. microbiology U. Cin. Med. Ctr., 1978-81; dir. microbiology/immunology Meth. Med. Ctr., Dallas, 1981—, assoc. adminstrv. dir. pathology, 1990—; dir. histocompatibility Stewart Blood Ctr., Tyler, Tex., 1987—; sci. dir. pathology and labs. Meth. Med. Ctr., Dallas, 1991—; adj. full prof. biology Tex. Christian U., Ft. Worth, 1982—. Mem. rev. bd. Jour. Clin. Microbiology, 1980—; author: Pictorial Handbook of Medically Important Fungi, 1982, (with others) The Dermatophytes, 1992, Handbook of Applied Mycoses, 1991, Manual of Clinical Microbiology, 1992. Coach Denton (Tex.) Soccer Assn., 1981—; min. Tioga (Tex.) Ch. of Christ, 1985—; chmn.-elect Region 5 histocompatibility com. United Network for Organ Sharing, 1993. Recipient Svc. Above Self award Rotary Club. Mem. Mycol. Soc. Am. (pres. 1990-93, Billy H. Cooper-Meridian award 1992), Tex. Soc. Clin. Microbiology (pres. 1977-79, 81-83), N.Y. Acad. Sci., Am. Soc. Histocompatibility and Immunogenetics (commr 1995), Am. Soc. Microbiology. Mem. Ch. of Christ. Office: Meth Med Ctr 1441 N Beckley Ave Dallas TX 75203

LAND, GEORGE A., philosopher, writer, educator, consultant; b. Hot Springs, Ark., Feb. 27, 1933; s. George Thomas Lock and Mary Elizabeth Land; m. Jo A. Gunn, 1957 (dec. 1969); children—Robert E., Thomas G., Patrick A.; m. Beth Smith Jarman, 1987. Student, Millsaps Coll., 1952-54, U. Veracruz, Mexico, 1957-59; numerous hon. degrees U.S. and abroad. Program dir. Woodall TV Stas. of Ga., Columbus, 1951-52; ops. mgr. Lamar Broadcasting, Jackson, Miss., 1952-54; anthrop. research Cora, Huichole and Yaqui tribes, Latin Am. Mexico, 1955-60; dir. gen. Television del Norte (NBC), Mexico, 1960-62; v.p. Roman Corp., St. Louis, 1962-64; chmn. Transolve Inc., Cambridge, Mass., and St. Petersburg, Fla., 1964-68; chief exec., chmn. Innotek Corp., N.Y.C.; also pres. Hal Roach Studios, Los Angeles and N.Y.C., 1969-71; chmn. emeritus Turtle Bay Inst., N.Y.C., 1971-80; vice chmn. Wilson Learning Corp. Mpls., 1980-86; pres. Leadership 2000, Phoenix, 1986—; Inst. Transformational Research, Honolulu and Buffalo, 1980—; prof. Mankato State U., 1973-74; sr. fellow U. Minn., 1982—; cons.-in-residence Synplex Inc., N.Y.C.; AT&T, Forest Hosp., Des Plaines, Social Systems Inc., Chapel Hill, N.C., Children's Hosp., Nat. Med. Ctr., Washington, Herman Miller, Inc., Arthur Anderson & Co., Intermedics Orthopedics; Mem. Nat. Action Com. on Drug Edn., 1974-75; co-chmn. Syncon Conf., So. Ill. U., 1972-74; keynoter Emerging Trends in Edn. Conf., Minn., 1974, 75, Bicentennial Conf. on Limits to Growth, So. Ill. U., 1976, No. States Power Conf., 1975, U.S. Office of Edn., Nat. Conf. Improvements in Edn., 1979, World Conf. on Gifted, 1977, S.W. Conf. on Arts, 1977, World Symposium on Humanity, 1979, Four Corners Conf. on Arts, 1977, Chautauqua Inst., 1977, 78, Conf. Am. Art Tchrs. Assn., 1979, Internat. Conf. on Gifted, 1982, Japan Mgmt. Assn., Nat. Conf. of Art Curators, Chgo, 1985, others; keynoter, Nat. Conf. on Econ. Devel., Mex., 1988, Credit Union Roundtable, Tampa, Fla., 1988, Internat. Bihai Conf., Princeton, N.J., 1982, co-chmn. com. on society World Conf. Peace and Poverty, St. Joseph's U., Phila., 1968, Internat. Bahai Conf. Princeton U., 1987, Gov.'s Trade Corridor Conf., Phoenix, 1994, Cath. Hosp. Assn., Phila., 1994, Am. Assn. Adminstrs., Internat. Pub. Execs., 1994, Fed. Conf. Quality, Washington, 1994, MAC IS Nat. Conf., Orl., 1994, Innovative Thinking Conf., 1994, Ventaua Groupware Conf., 1994, Young Pres.' Orgn., Cannes, 1993, Austn. Conv. and Visitors Bureau, Pheonix, 1993, Profession Conv. Mgmt. Assn., Atlanta; mem. Nat. Security Seminar, U.S. Dept. Def., 1975; cons., keynoter corp. policy strategic seminars The Bell System, AT&T, 1978—; mem. faculty Edison Electric Grad. Mgmt. Inst., 1972-78; lectr., seminarian in transformation theory,

strategic planning and interdisciplinary research Menninger Found., U. Ga., Emory U., Waterloo (Can.) U., Office of Sec. HEW, Jamestown (N.Y.) Coll., Hofstra U., U.S. Office Edn., Calif. Dept. Edn., St. Louis U., Coll. William and Mary, Webster Coll., St. Louis, Wash. State Dept. Edn., U. Ky., So. Ill. U., St. John's U., Harvard U., U. South Fla., MIT, U. Veracruz, Children's Hosp. D.C., Gov.'s Sch. N.C., Scottsdale (Ariz.) Ctr. Arts, Humbolt U., East Berlin, AAAS, others; advanced faculty Creative Problem Solving Inst., SUNY, 1965—, S. Conn. Coll.; disting. lectr. Northwestern State U., La., State U. Coll. N.Y., Coll. of the Lakes, Ill.; cons. govt., industry and instns. in U.S. and abroad, including AT&T, IBM, Dow Chem., Dow Corning, DuPont, Hughes, TRW, 3M, Gen. Mills, Gen. Motors, Moore Corp., Branch Corp., Credit Union Nat. Assn., others. Author: Innovation Systems, 1967, Innovation Technology, 1968, Four Faces of Poverty, 1968, (as George T.L. Land) Grow or Die: The Unifying Principle of Transformation, 1973, Creative Alternatives and Decision Making, 1974, The Opportunity Book, 1980, (with Vaune E. Ainsworth), Breakpoint and Beyond, 1994, New Paradigm in Business, 1994,Forward to Basics; contbr. to profl. jours. and gen. mags. Fellow N.Y. Acad. Scis., World Bus. Acad.; mem. AAAS, Soc. Gen. Systems Rsch., Soc. Study Gen. Process (founding dir.), Am. Soc. Cybernetics (past v.p.), Creative Edn. Found. (trustee, Lifetime Achievement award 1993, New Paradigm in Bus. award 1994, colleague), Soc. Am. Value Engrs. (past dir.), World Future Soc., Com. for Future (colleague), Authors Guild, Authors League Am. Achievements include research on interdisciplinary unification, orginated transformation theory. Inventor computerassisted group creative thinking processes, "The Innovator," "CoNexus," "TeamWare" and others. Home: 7119 N Red Ledge Dr Paradise Vly AZ 85253-2847 Office: Leadership 2000 3333 N 44th St Phoenix AZ 85018-6461 *I was fortunate enough in my youth to experience and learn what has been the most important idea and principle in my life, the natural law of enrichment through diversity. This concept means that change and growth come about more by combining differentnesses than by adding likenesses. As in the biological world, where such behavior produces the vitality of hybrids, and as in chemistry, where the co-valent bonds of carbon make life possible, in human life we can also benefit immeasurably from using our differences as a creative way to grow anew. Thus, we can evolve beyond polarizations such as nationalism, racism, sexism, institutionalism and other obstacles that separate us and stunt our ability to realize the full community of Man.*

LAND, KENNETH CARL, sociology educator, demographer, statistician, consultant; b. Llano, Tex., Aug. 19, 1942; s. Otto Carl and Tillie (Lindemann) L.; m. Jacqueline Yvette Apere, Mar. 22, 1969; 1 child, Kristoffer Carl. B.A., Tex. Luth. Coll., 1964; M.A., U. Tex., 1966, Ph.D., 1969. Staff assoc. Russell Sage Found., N.Y.C, 1969-73; lectr. Columbia U., N.Y.C., 1970-73; assoc. prof. U. Ill.-Urbana, 1973-76, prof., 1976-81; prof. sociology U. Tex.-Austin, 1981-86; prof., chmn. dept. sociology Duke U., Durham, N.C., 1986—, John Franklin Crowell prof. sociology, 1990—. Editor: Social Indicator Models, 1975; Social Accounting Systems, 1981; Multidimensional Mathematical Demography, 1982; Forecasting in the Social and Natural Sciences, 1987; contbr. articles to profl. jours. Fellow Am. Statis. Assn., Am. Assn. for the Advancement of Sci.; mem. Sociol. Research Assn., Am. Sociol. Assn., Population Assn. Am., Am. Soc. Criminology. Lutheran. Office: Duke U Dept Sociology Durham NC 27706

LAND, REGINALD BRIAN, library administrator; b. Niagara Falls, Ont., Can., July 29, 1927; s. Allan Reginald and Beatrice Beryl (Boyle) L.; m. Edith Wyndham Eddis, Aug. 29, 1953; children—Mary Beatrice, John Robert Eddis. BA, U. Toronto, Ont., Can., 1949, BLS, 1953, MLS, 1956, MA, 1963. Catalogue copy editor T. Eaton Co. Ltd., Toronto, 1950-51; reference librarian Toronto Pub. Library, 1953-55; cataloguer U. Toronto Library, 1955-56, asst. librarian, 1959-63, assoc. librarian, 1963; head div. bus. and industry Windsor Pub. Library, Ont., Can., 1956-57; asst. editor Canadian Bus. Mag., Montreal, Que., Can., 1957-58, assoc. editor, 1958-59; exec. asst. to Minister Fin. of Can., Ottawa, Ont., 1963-64; prof. library sci. U. Toronto, 1964-78, part-time prof., 1978-93, prof. emeritus, 1993—, dean Faculty Library Sci., 1964-72; exec. dir. Ont. Legis. Library., Toronto, 1978-93. Author: Sources of Information for Canadian Business, 1962, 4th rev. edit., 1985, Eglinton: The Election Study of a Federal Constituency, 1965; founder, gen. editor: Directory of Associations in Canada, 1974, 16th rev. edit., 1995. Mem. Canadian Radio-TV and Telecommunications Commn., 1973-78. Decorated Knight Hospitaller Order of St. John of Jerusalem; recipient Kenneth R. Wilson Meml. award Bus. Newspapers Assn. Can., 1959, Disting. Achievement award Ont. Library Trustees Assn., 1968, Queen Elizabeth IIs Silver Jubilee medal, 1977, Spl. Librarianship award Can. Assn. for Spl. Librs. and Info. Svcs., 1991, 125th Anniversary Confederation Can. medal, 1992, Alumni Jubilee award U. Toronto Libr. & Info. Sci. Alumni Assn., 1994. Mem. Assn. Parliamentary Librarians in Can. (pres. 1982-84), ALA (chmn. com. on accreditation 1973-74), Canadian Library Assn. (pres. 1975-76), Ont. Library Assn. (1st v.p. 1962-63). Ont. Govt. Libraries' Council (chmn. 1984-85), Assn. for Library and Info. Sci. Edn. (pres. 1973-74), Bibliog. Soc. Can., Canadian Assn. for Grad. Edn. in Library Archival and Info. Studies (pres. 1966-67), Canadian Assn. Univ. Tchrs., Canadian Council Library Schs. (chmn. 1971-72), Inst. Profl. Librarians Ont. (pres. 1961-62), Ont. Council Library Schs. (chmn. 1968-72), Spl. Libraries Assn. (Member of Yr. award 1986 Toronto chpt.), Ont. Geneal. Soc., Ont. Coll. and Univ. Librs. Assn. (merit award 1992). Mem. Anglican Ch. Home: 18 Kirkton Rd, North York, ON Canada M3H 1K7

LAND, RICHARD DALE, minister, religious organization administrator; b. Houston, Nov. 6, 1946; s. Leggette Sloan and Marilee (Welch) L.; m. Rebekah Ruth Van Hooser, May 29, 1971; children: Jennifer, Richard Jr., Rachel. BA, Princeton U., 1969; ThM, New Orleans Bapt. Theol. Sem., 1972; D.Phil., U. Oxford, Eng., 1980. Ordained to ministry So. Bapt. Conv., 1969. Pastor S. Oxford Bapt. Ch., Oxford, Eng., 1972-75; prof. theology and ch. history Criswell Coll., Dallas, 1975-76, acad. dean, 1976-80, v.p. for acad. affairs, 1980-88; exec. dir. Christian Life Commn. So. Bapt. Conv., Nashville, 1988—; mem. exec. com. Nat. Coalition against Pornography, Cin., 1989—; bd. dirs. Bapt. Joint Com. Pub. Affairs, Washington, 1987-90, Nat. Pro-Life Religious Coun., Washington. Cons. editor Criswell Study Bible, 1979. Mem. Gov.'s Task Force on Welfare Reform, Austin, Tex., 1988, Pres.'s Campaign for a Drug-Free Soc., Washington, 1991—; bd. drs. Nat. Law Ctr., Arlington, Va., 1991—. Mem. Nat. Assn. Evangs. (Wheaton, Ill., bd. dirs. 1991—), Conf. on Faith and History, Evang. Theol. Soc., So. Bapt. Hist. Soc., Rotary. Office: Christian Life Commn 901 Commerce St Ste 550 Nashville TN 37203-3696

LANDA, HOWARD MARTIN, lawyer, business executive; b. Bklyn., Oct. 12, 1943; s. George and Lilli (Skolnik) L.; m. Nori Neinstein, Mar. 14, 1971; children—Alyson, David. B.A. (N.Y. State Regents scholar) Bklyn. Coll., 1964; J.D. (tuition scholar), U. Chgo., 1967. Bar: N.Y. 1968. Sole practice N.Y.C., 1968-69; assoc. Garfield, Solomon & Mainzer, N.Y.C., 1969-70, Szold, Brandwen, Meyers & Altman, N.Y.C., 1970-74; v.p., sec., gen. counsel IPCO Corp., White Plains, N.Y., 1974-90, also bd. dirs.; pres., mng. dir. Martin Hand Assocs., Inc., Greenwich, Conn., 1990-92, also bd. dirs.; owner Law Offices of Howard M. Landa, N.Y.C., 1990-94; counsel Rand Rosenzweig Smith Radley Gordon & Burstein L.L.P., N.Y.C., 1994—; lectr. Dental Lab. Conf., 1977. Mem. Mayor N.Y.C. Panel to Study Dept. Gen. Services' Div. Mcpl. Supplies, 1978-79; vice chmn. So. N.Y. chpt. Nat. Multiple Sclerosis Soc., 1988—. Mem. ABA, N.Y. County Lawyers Assn., Corp. Bar Assn. Office: 605 Third Ave New York NY 10158

LANDA, WILLIAM ROBERT, foundation executive; b. Jersey City, Dec. 4, 1919; s. G.B. and Henrietta (Elder) L.; m. Anne E. Longley, June 24, 1939; children: Susanne (Mrs. J.B. Moliere), Stephen R., Scott W., Richard W. Student, 1937-39. Salesman Sterling Drug, Inc., 1942-44; asst. export mgr. Taylor, Pinkham & Co., Inc., 1944-52; export mgr. Bates Fabrics, Inc., 1952-55; pres. Burlington Export Co. N.Y.C., 1955-62; v.p. Burlington Mills Corp., 1957-62, Burlington Industries, Inc., Greensboro, N.C., 1959-62, Warner Bros. Co., Bridgeport, Conn., 1962-66; pres. Warner Bros. Co. (Warner Bros. Internat.), 1962-66; exec. v.p. Turner Jones & Co., 1966-67, pres., 1967-68; group v.p. internat. Genesco, Inc. N.Y.C., 1968-70; v.p. Farah Mfg. Co., 1970-74; pres., dir. Holguin & Assos. Inc., El Paso, Tex., 1978-81; pres. Western Mktg. Corp., El Paso, 1981-85; spl. asst. to pres. Free/Congress Research and Edn. Found. Inc., Washington, 1986-89; dir. Affiliated Mfrs., Inc. North Branch, N.J., AMI-PRESCO; hon. consul of Belgium for West Tex. and State of N.Mex., 1981-86; Mem. Gen. Arbitration Council Textile Industry; mem. Nat. Export Council, 1965-66; cons. Internat. Mktg., 1988—. Decorated chevalier Order of Crown Belgium.

Mem. Commerce and Industry Assn. N.Y., Internat. Execs. Assn., U.S.C. of C. (spl. adv. com. on internat. trade), Am. Arbitration Assn., Beta Theta Pi. Presbyterian. Home: 2032 Birch Dr Culpeper VA 22701-4063

LANDAHL, HERBERT DANIEL, biophysicist, mathematical biologist, researcher, consultant; b. Fancheng, China, Apr. 23, 1913; (parents Am. citizens); s. Carl W. and Alice (Holmberg) L.; m. Evelyn Christine Blomberg, Aug. 23, 1940; children: Carl David, Carol Ann Landahl Kubai, Linda C. Landahl Shidner. Student, U. Minn., 1931-32; AB, St. Olaf Coll., Northfield, Minn., 1934; SM, U. Chgo., 1936, PhD, 1941. Rsch. asst. psychometric lab. U. Chgo., 1937-39, rsch. asst. math. biophysics, 1938-41, instr., 1942-45, asst. prof. com. on math. biology, 1945-48, assoc. prof., 1949-56, prof., 1956-68, acting. chmn., 1965-67; prof. biophysics and math. U. Calif., San Francisco, 1968-80, prof. emeritus, 1980—; cons. Respiratory Project, U. Chgo., 1944-46, toxicity lab. U. Chgo., 1947-51, USAF radiation lab., U. Chgo., 1951-67, dept. biomath. U. Tex., Houston, 1968-89; mem. NIH com. on epidemiology and biometry, Bethesda, Md., 1960-64. Coauthor: Mathematical Biophysics of Central Nervous System, 1945; contbr. approximately 190 sci. papers to various jours.; chief editor Bull. Math. Biophysics, 1973-80; mem. editorial bd. Computers in Biology and Medicine, 1971-90. Recipient Career Devel. award NIH, 1962-67, Career Achievement award Soc. Toxicology, 1987; grantee NIH, 1963-67. Fellow AAAS; mem. Biophys. Soc., Biometric Soc. (charter), Bioengring. Soc. (charter), Latin Am. Biomath. Soc. (charter), Soc. for Math. Biology (founding, pres. 1981-83). Home: 472 Lansdale Ave San Francisco CA 94127-1617 Office: U Calif-San Francisco PO Box 970 San Francisco CA 94143-0001

LANDAN, HENRY SINCLAIR, lawyer; b. Chgo., Aug. 4, 1943. BS, DePaul U., 1965, JD, 1969; LLM in Taxation, NYU, 1970. Bar: Ill. 1969, N.Y. 1971, U.S. Supreme Ct. 1976. Assoc. Altman, Kurlånder & Weiss, Chgo., 1969-70, Roberts & Holland, N.Y.C., 1970-72; sr. ptnr. Kamensky & Landan and predecessor, Chgo., 1972-84, Henry S. Landan, Chgo., 1984-88; of counsel Keck, Mahin & Cate, Chgo., 1988-90, ptnr., 1990—; counsel Caribbean Hotel Assn., Santurce, P.R., 1975-83. Contbg. author: Tax Planning for Professionals; contbr. articles to profl. jours. Mem. exec. com., dir. Young Men's Jewish Coun., Chgo., 1972-77; mem. Men's Coun., Mus. Contemporary Art, Chgo., 1977-84, pres., 1980-82; bd. dirs. Little City, Chgo., 1977-82; bd. dirs., mem. exec. com. Renaissance Soc. U. Chgo., 1984—; mem. Soc. Contemporary Art, Art Inst. Chgo., 1982—; mem. Contemporary Arts Coun., Chgo., 1994—; mem. bd. mgrs. Henry Horner Boys and Girls Club, 1992—. Named Life Dir., Young Men's Jewish Coun., 1980, Man of Yr., 1983. Mem. ABA, Ill. Bar Assn., N.Y. Bar Assn., Chgo. Bar Assn. Home: 120 W Kinzie St Chicago IL 60610-4508 Office: Keck Mahin & Cate 77 W Wacker Dr Ste 4900 Chicago IL 60601-1693

LANDAU, BERNARD ROBERT, biochemistry educator, physician; b. Newark, N.J., June 24, 1926; s. Morris Harry and Estelle (Kirsch) L.; m. Lucille Slosberg, Jan. 11, 1956; children: Steven Brian, Deborah Louise (dec.), Rodger Martin. S.B., MIT, 1947; Ph.D., Harvard U., 1950, M.D., 1954; MD (hon.), Karolinska Inst., 1993. Diplomate: Am. Bd. Internal Medicine. Intern Peter Bent Brigham Hosp., Boston, 1954-55; clin. assoc. Nat. Cancer Inst., Bethesda, Md., 1955-57; fellow in biochemistry Harvard U., 1957-58; sr. resident Peter Bent Brigham Hosp., 1958-59; asst. prof. medicine Case Western Res. U., 1959-62, assoc. prof., 1962-67, prof., 1969—, prof. biochemistry, 1979—; physician Univ. Hosps., 1969—; dir. dept. biochemistry Merck and Co., Rahway, N.J., 1967-69. Contbr. articles to profl. jours. Fellow Commonwealth fund, 1965-66, Fogarty Sr. Internat. fellow 1986-87, 93-94; grantee Am. Heart Assn., 1959-64; recipient William B. Peck Postgrad. Research award, 1961. Fellow AAAS; mem. Am. Fedn. Clin. Research, Am. Soc. Clin. Investigation, Assn. Am. Physicians, Am. soc. Biol. Chemists, Am. Physiol. Soc., Endocrine Soc., Central Soc. Clin. Research, Am. Diabetes Assn., Am. Thyroid Assn., Sigma Xi, Alpha Omega Alpha. Home: 19501 S Woodland Rd Cleveland OH 44122-2834 Office: University Hosps Cleveland 11100 Euclid Ave Cleveland OH 44106-5000

LANDAU, DAVID PAUL, physics educator; b. St. Louis, June 22, 1941; s. Bernard Israel and Selma (Goldstein) L.; m. Heidi Humpert, Aug. 28, 1966; children: Ladina Aviva, Anya Karina. BA, Princeton U., 1963; MS, Yale U., 1965, PhD, 1967. Chargé de recherche CNRS, Grenoble, France, 1967-68; lectr. Yale U., New Haven, 1968-69; asst. prof. physics U. Ga., Athens, 1969-73, assoc. prof., 1973-78, prof., 1978-84, rsch. prof., 1984—, dir. Ctr. for Simulational Physics, 1986—. Editor 7 books; author more than 200 sci. publs. Recipient Creative Rsch. medal U. Ga., 1981, sr. U.S. scientist prize Alexander von Humboldt Found., 1988. Fellow Am. Phys. Soc. (Jesse Beams award 1987). Jewish. Office: U Ga Ctr Simulational Physics Athens GA 30602

LANDAU, ELLIS, gaming company executive; b. Phila., Feb. 24, 1944; s. Manfred and Ruth (Fischer) L.; m. Kathy Suzanne Thomas, May 19, 1968 (div.); children: Rachel, David; m. Yvette Ehr Cohen, Nov. 1, 1992. BA in Econs., Brandeis U., 1965; MBA, Columbia U., 1967. Fin. analyst SEC, Washington, 1968-69; asst. treas. U-Haul Internat., Phoenix, 1969-71; v.p. treas. Ramada, Inc., Phoenix, 1971-90; CFO Boyd Gaming Corp., Las Vegas, Nev., 1990—. Home: 7895 Harbour Towne Ave Las Vegas NV 89113-1387 Office: Boyd Gaming Corp 2950 S Industrial Rd Las Vegas NV 89109-1100

LANDAU, HENRY GROH, geoenvironmental consulting engineer; b. N.Y.C., Mar. 1, 1943; s. Henry G. and Ann Marie (Skvarich) L.; m. Joyce Kathryn Van de Merlen, July 27, 1965; children: Greg, Amy, Michael. BS in Civil Engring., CCNY, 1965; MS in Geotech. Engring., Purdue U., 1966, PhD in Engring., 1973. Profl. engr., Wash. N.Y., Alaska. Civil engr. Geotechnica, Sao Paulo, Brazil, 1966-67; officer U.S. Army C.E., South Vietnam, 1967-70; sr. engr. Dames & Moore, Seattle, 1973-82; sr. prin. Landau Assocs., Inc., Edmonds, Wash., 1982—; vis. prof. Fed. U., Paraiba, Brazil, 1978-79; mem. Gov.'s Sci. Adv. Bd., Olympia, Wash., 1987-90, chmn., 1990—. Contbr. articles to profl. jours. Tutor math. & sci. Edmonds Sch. Dist.; scout leader Boy Scouts Am., Edmonds, 1986-90. 1st lt. U.S. Army, 1967-70, Vietnam. Mem. ASCE, Soc. Am. Mil. Engrs., Assn. Groundwater Scientists & Engrs. Avocations: bicycling, sailing, nature study, water sports. Office: Landau Assocs Inc 23107 100th Ave W Edmonds WA 98020-5017

LANDAU, IRWIN, magazine publishing company executive. BA, Bklyn. Coll., 1954; MS in Journalism, Columbia U., 1955. Reporter N.Y. Daily Mirror, 1951-55; asst. mng. editor Engring. News-Record, 1957-60; sr. editor Med. Econs., 1960-66; mng. editorr Consumer Reports, 1966-71, now editorial dir. Office: Consumer Reports 101 Truman Ave Yonkers NY 10703-1057

LANDAU, JACOB, artist; b. Phila. Dec. 17, 1917; s. Samuel and Deana (Kitaynick) L.; m. Frances Paul, May 5, 1949; children: Stephan Paul, Jonas Michael. Student, Phila. Coll. Art, 1936-39, New Sch., N.Y.C., 1948-49, 52-53, Acad. de la Grande Chaumiere, Paris, France, 1950-52. Prof. graphic art Pratt Inst., Bklyn., now prof. emeritus; founder, formerly learning coordinator integrative studies program; vis. scholar Memphis Acad. Arts, 1969, U. Notre Dame, Ind., 1969; graphic arts panelist N.J. Arts Council, 1969-73; vis. artist Skidmore Coll., Saratoga Springs, N.Y., 1971, Brookdale Coll., Lincroft, N.J., 1976, U. No. Mich., 1981, Ea. and Western Carolina Univs., Greenville and Cullowhee, N.C., 1982; panelist N.J. State Mus., Trenton, 1973, NYU, 1974, Rutgers U., New Brunswick, N.J., 1976; artist-in-residence U. No. Iowa, 1977; resident artist Pima Community College, Univ. Ariz., Tucson, 1984; tchr. Artist/Tchr. Inst., N.J. State Council on Arts, 1978-89; academician Nat. Acad. Design, N.Y.; cons. N.J. Dept. Higher Edn., 1974. One-man shows include Galerie LeBar, Paris, 1952, Art Alliance, Phila., 1954, 75, Art Ctr., New Brunswick, N.J., 1957, Samuel Fleisher Meml. Gallery, Phila., 1959, Assoc. Am. Artists Gallery, N.Y.C., 1960, 70, U. Maine, 1961, 71, Cober Gallery, N.Y.C., 1961, 63, Zora Gallery, L.A., 1964, Original Prints Gallery, San Francisco, 1965, Gallery 100, Princeton, N.J., 1966, Art Gallery, U. Notre Dame, 1969, A.A.A. Gallery N.Y., 1970, Print Club, Phila., 1970, Giraffe Gallery, L.A., 1970, Van Straaten Gallery, Chgo., 1970, Lunn Gallery, Washington, 1970, Jorgensen Auditorium, U. Conn. at Storrs, 1971, Bloomfield (N.J.) Coll., 1971, 72, Orpheus Ascending Gallery, Stockbridge, Mass., 1972, Galeria Pecanins, Mexico City, 1972, Imprint Gallery, San Francisco, 1973, Congregation Keneseth Israel, Elkins Park, Pa., 1974, ACA Galleries, N.Y.C., 1976,

Woodbridge (N.J.) Cultural Arts Commn., Schneider-Sato Gallery, Karlsruhe, Germany, 1977, N.J. Mus., 1981, U. Ga., 1982, Phila. Mus. Judaica, 1983, Phila. Coll. Art, 1985, Galerie Neuheisel, Saarbrucken, Fed. Republic Germany, Galerie Michael Hagen, Offenburg, Fed. Republic Germany, 1985, Martin Sumers Graphics, N.Y., 1988, Rider Coll., Lawrenceville, N.J., 1988, The Mariboe Gallery, Peddie Sch., Hightstown, N.J., 1992, Judah L. Magnes Mus., 1993, N.J. State Mus., 1994, Kenneth Israel, Elkins Park, Pa., 1995; numerous group shows, 1955—, latest include Four Painters, Art Alliance Phila., 1961, New Humanism, Nat. Sch. Plastics Arts, U. Mexico, 1963, regional exhbn., Pa. Acad. Fine Arts, 1964, N.J. and the Artist, N.J. State Mus., Trenton, 1965, Drawing Soc. Eastern Cen. Region, Phila. Mus. Art, 1965, N.J. Tercentenary Show, 1965, Contemporary N.J. Art, Newark Mus., 1965, Prize-Winning Am. Prints, circulating show, N.Y. State Council on Arts, 1967, Drawings U.S.A. St. Paul Art Ctr., 1968, Am. Prints Today, Mus. Art, Munson-Williams-Proctor Inst., Utica, N.Y., 1968, Selections from 50th Ann. Soc. Am. Graphic Artists, USIA Nr. East Traveling Show, 1970, Tamarind: A Renaissance of Lithography, circulating show, Internat. Exhbns. Found., 1971, SUNY Coll. at Brockport, 1972, Iowa State U., 1972, N.J. Arts Council, 1972, Art. Mus., Sao Paulo, Brazil, 1972, Am. Acad. Arts and Letters, 1973, 74, NAD, 1974, Washington Club, 1976, Soc. Am. Graphic Artists Show, 1976, 77, Am. Color Print Soc. 35th Exhbn., Phila., 1976, 1st Biennial N.J. Artists, 1977, State U., Potsdam, N.Y., 1978, Portsmouth Arts Ctr., Portsmouth, Va., 1979, Carnegie Mellon U., Pitts., 1980, Minn. Mus. Art, St. Paul, 1980, Worcester Art Mus., Worcester, Mass., 1981, Noyes Mus., Oceanville, N.J., 1983, 1991, Purdue U., W. Lafayette, Ind., 1986, Middlesex County Mus., Piscataway, N.J., 1987, FellowshipExhbn, The Monmouth Mus., 1988, Guild Hall Mus., East Hampton, N.Y., 1990, Rubelle and Norman Schafler Gallery, Pratt Inst. 1990-91, Mercer County (N.J.) Communtiy Coll., 1991, Printmaking Coun., Sommerville, N.J., 1991, Ellarslie Mus., renton, N.J., 1992; numerous nat. and internat. shows, 1953—, latest include woodcut annuals, Print Club Phila., 1955, 59, 92d, 95th, 97th Am. Watercolor Soc. anns., NAD, 1954, 62, 64, 12th-17th print biennials, Bklyn. Mus., 1960, 62, 64, 66, 68, 70, Xylon Internat., 1962, 65, Recent Paintings, U.S.A-The Figure, Mus. Modern Art, 1962, nominee exhbn., Nat. Inst. Arts and Letters, 1962, 65, 156th, 158th, 160th, 162d anns., Pa. Acad. Fine Arts, 1961, 63, 65, 67, graphics U.S.A., USIA traveling exhbn., 1963—, 19th, 20th print exhbns., Library of Congress, 1963, 66, 30th ann., Butler Art Inst., Youngstown, Ohio, 1965, Smithsonian invitational exhbn., White House, 1966, Nat. Drawing Exhbn., Rutgers U., 1975, Hawaii Nat. Print Exhbn, Honolulu Acad. Arts, 1975, Nat. Coll. Fine Arts, Miami Graphics, Biennial Met. Mus., Coral Gables, Fla., Boston Printmakers, De Cordova Mus., Lincoln, Mass., Hunterdon (N.J.) Art Center, 1977; also exhibited at Mus. Modern Art, N.Y.C., 1969, Whitney Mus., N.Y.C., 1969, Mus. Art, Phila., 1970, NAD 157th Ann. Ohio State U., 1982, Utopian Visions in Modern Art, Hirshhorn Mus. and Sculpture Garden, Washington, 1984, Third Internat. Biennial Print Exhbn., Hangzhou, People's Republic of China, 1989; represented in permanent collections Whitney Mus. Am. Art, Mus. Modern Art, Met. Mus., Pa. Acad. Fine Arts, art museums in Balt., Atlanta, New Orleans, Phila., Bklyn., Norfolk, Va., San Antonio, Tucson, Ariz., Malmo, Sweden, Nuremberg, Fed. Republic Germany, Slater Mus., Norwich, Conn., Library of Congress, Joseph J. Hirschhorn collection, also univs. Princeton, Rutgers, Maine, Minn., Syracuse, Yale, Ky., U. Calif. at Berkeley, U. Mass., U. South Fla., Columbia, Butler Inst., Youngstown, Ohio, M.H. DeYoung Mus., San Francisco, N.J. State Mus., Trenton, Bibliotheque Nationale, Paris, Lessing Rosenwald Collection, also pvt. collections, commns. include sketches of participants at Pacem In Terris II, 1967; print of Peace, Internat. Art Program, Nat. Collection Fine Arts, Smithsonian Instn., 1967; cycle of ten stained glass windows The Prophetic Quest, Keneseth Israel Congregation, Elkins Park, 1970; lithograph, Behold Jewish Ctr., Trenton, 1973, But if the Cause, Roten Galleries, Balt., 1976; etching, Einstein, Washington Print Club, 1982; lithograph, Thirty-Fourth Psalm, Jewish Family Svc. of Del. Valley, Trenton, N.J., 1988. Trustee N.J. Sch. Arts, 1981-85, Nat. Guild of Community Schs. of Arts; mem. nat. com. U. of Arts, Phila. Recipient Lessing Rosenwald Purchase award Print Club Phila., 1955, 59; recipient Woodcut prize Print Fair of Phila. Free library, 1960, Louis Comfort Tiffany award, 1962; recipinet hon. mention Am. Water Color Soc., 1962; recipient Paul F. Norton and Assn. Am. Artists awards Soc. Am. Graphic Artists, 1962, hon. mention Audubon Artists, 1965; named One of New Jersey's Five Finest Com. Curators and Critics, 1962; recipient Phila. Watercolor prize Pa. Acad. Fine Arts, 1963; First award N.J. Tercentenary Art Festival, 1963; fellow Tamarind Lithography Workshop, Los Angeles, 1965; Edna Pennypacker Stauffer prize Soc. Am. Graphic Artists, 1965; purchase awards Asso. Am. Artists, 1967; purchase awards Drawing U.S.A. '68, St. Paul Art Center; purchase awards Contemporary Graphic Art on Contemporary Law and Justice, Assn. Bar City N.Y.; Vera List purchase prize Soc. Am. Graphic Artists, 1972; Childe Hassam purchase award Am. Acad. Arts and Letters, 1973-74; purchase prize Nat. Drawing Exhbn., Rutgers U., 1975; Purchase prize Nat. Print Exhbn., Hunterdon; Purchase prize AAA Gallery, N.Y.C., 1977; Ann. award YM-YWHA, Union, N.J., 1984; Alumni Silver Star award Phila. Colls. Art, 1985; Grantee Nat. Arts Council, 1966; Grantee N.J. State Arts Council, 1974; Grantee Ford Found., 1975; Guggenheim Found. fellow, 1968-69; recipient N.J. State Arts Coun. fellowship, 1988, Gov.'s award for disting. svc. in arts and edn., 1989. Mem. Soc. Am. Graphic Artists. Home: 2 Pine Dr Roosevelt NJ 08555 Office & Studio: 30 Lake Dr PO Box 328 Roosevelt NJ 08555-0328 *For me, art is more than formal exploration or exploitation. Without it, we are an endangered and endangering species.*

LANDAU, KENNETH JEFFREY, lawyer; b. N.Y.C., Jan. 20, 1955; s. Seymour and Gilda (Schaeber) L.; m. Susan Beth Reich, Oct. 27, 1985. BA, CCNY, 1977; JD, SUNY, Buffalo, 1980. Assoc. Shayne, Dachs, Stanisci & Corker, Mineola, N.Y., 1980—; adj. asst. prof. Marymont Coll., N.Y.C.; instr. The Learning Annex, N.Y.C. Mem. ABA (vice chmn. econs. com. young lawyers div.), Nassau County Bar Assn. (v.p. young lawyer sect., com. profl. ethics). Office: 1501 Franklin Ave Mineola NY 11501-4802

LANDAU, LAURI BETH, accountant, tax consultant; b. Bklyn., July 21, 1952; d. Jack and Audrey Carolyn (Zuckernick) L. BA, Skidmore Coll., 1973; postgrad., Pace. U., 1977-79. CPA, N.Y., Oreg. Mem. staff Audrey Z. Landau, CPA, Suffern, N.Y., 1976-78; mem. staff Ernst & Whinney, N.Y.C., 1979-80, mem. sr. staff, 1980-82, supr., 1982-84; mgr. Arthur Young & Co., N.Y.C., 1984-87, prin., 1987-89; sr. mgr. Ernst & Young, N.Y.C. 1989-92; prnt. Landau & Landau, New City, N.Y., 1992—; speaker World Trade Inst., N.Y.C., 1987—, Nat. Tax Trade Coun., N.Y.C., 1989—. Composer songs. Career counselor Skidmore Coll., Saratoga Springs, N.Y., 1977—; mem. leadership com. Class of 1973, 83-85, pres., 1985-93, fund chmn., 1987-88, mem. planned gift com., 1989—. N.Y. State Regents scholar, 1970. Mem. Nat. Conf. CPA Practitioners, N.Y. State Soc. CPAs, Skidmore Coll. Alumni Assn. (mem. nominating com. 1989-92). Skidmore Alumni Club, German Shepherd Dog Am. Club. Democrat. Avocations: music, ballet, photography, sports. Office: 26 Firemens Meml Dr Ste 205A Pomona NY 10970

LANDAU, MARTIN, political science educator; b. N.Y.C., July 12, 1921; s. User Noah and Clara (Markowitz) L.; m. Bernice Feldman, July 11, 1943; children—Madeline, Claudia. A.B., Bklyn. Coll., 1947; M.A. in Pub. Adminstrn, N.Y., 1948; Ph.D., 1952; Docteur Honoris Causa, U. Paris, Dauphine, 1993. Vis. research prof. U. Calif. at Berkeley, 1969-71, prof. polit. sci., 1972—; Distinguished prof. City U. N.Y., Bklyn., 1970-72; lectr. orgn. and decision theory Fgn. Service Inst., U.S. Dept. State, Washington, 1969-72; cons. in field; chancellor Grad. Sch. Pub. Adminstrn., U.P.R., San Juan, 1970-71; Berkeley Exch. prof., Peking U., 1985; Phi Beta Kappa Nat. Lectr., 1984; dir. Berkeley-Hong Kong Project, 1984—. Author: Political Theory and Political Science; Studies in the Methodology of Political Inquiry, 1972; Chmn. editorial bd.: Polit. Sci, 1971—; mem. editorial bd.: Jour. Comparative Adminstrv. Studies, 1969—, Comparative Politics, 1970—, Jour. Theoretical Politics, 1988—, Jour. Behavioral Decision Making, 1988—. Served with Signal Corps AUS, 1941-45. Recipient Distinguished Teaching award Bklyn. Coll., 1963, E. Harris Harbison award gifted teaching Danforth Found., 1969-70, William E. Mosher award distinguished scholarship Soc. Pub. Adminstrn., 1970, 79; John Simon Guggenheim fellow, 1976-77; fellow Center Advanced Study in Behavioral Sci., 1976-77. Fellow Nat. Acad. Public Adminstrn.; mem. Am. Polit. Sci. Assn., Philosophy of Sci. Assn. Home: 1410 Summit Rd Berkeley CA 94708-2215 Office: U Calif Dept Polit Sci Berkeley CA 94720

LANDAU, MARTIN, actor; b. Bklyn., June 20, 1934; m. Barbara Bain (div.); children: Susie, Juliet. Student, Art Students League, Actors Studio. Staff artist, cartoonist N.Y. Daily News. Star TV series Mission: Impossible, 1966-69, Space 1999, 1974-77, others; TV appearances include Omnibus, Playhouse 90, G.E. Theatre, Gunsmoke, Twilight Zone; also TV movies Welcome Home, Johnny Bristol, 1972, Savage, 1973, The Death of Ocean View Park, 1979, The Harlem Globetrotters on Gilligan's Island, 1981, The Fall of the House of Usher, 1982, The Neon Empire, 1989, By Dawn's Early Light, 1990, Something to Live For: The Alison Gertz Story, 1992, Legacy of Lies, 1992 (Ace award), 1991, miniseries Joseph, 1995; films include Pork Chop Hill, North by Northwest, 1959, Stagecoach to Dancer's Rock, 1961, Cleopatra, 1962, Hallelujah Trail, 1964, The Greatest Story Ever Told, 1965, Nevada Smith, 1966, They Call Me Mr. Tibbs, 1970, Operation SNAFU, 1970, A Town Called Hell, 1971, Johnny Bristol, 1971, Black Gunn, 1972, Strange Shadows in an Empty Room, 1977, Meteor, 1979, The Last Word, 1979, Without Warning, 1980, Operation Moonbase Alpha, 1980, Earthright, 1980, Beauty and the Beast, 1981, Alone in the Dark, 1982, Trial by Terror, 1983, Tucker: The Man and His Dreams, 1988 (Acad. Award nominee 1988), Crimes and Misdemeanors, 1989, (Golden Globe award 1989, Acad. award nominee 1989) Paint It Black, 1990, Real Bullets, 1990, Firehead, 1991, Eye of the Widow, 1991, Mistress, 1992, Sliver, 1993, Intersection, 1994, Ed Wood, 1994 (Best Supporting Actor Acad. award 1994, Golden Globe award 1994, SAG award 1994, Am. Comedy award 1994, N.Y. Film Critics award 1994, L.A. Film Critics award 1994, Chgo. Film Critics award 1994, Nat. Soc. Film Critics award 1994, Boston Film Critics award 1994, Tex. Film Critics award 1994, Lifetime Achievement award Houston Film Festival 1994, Lifetime Achievement award Charleston Film Festival 1994), City Hall, 1995; stage appearances include Middle of the Night, Uncle Vanya, Stalag 17, Wedding Breakfast, First Love, The Goat Song, Dracula. Recipient Golden Globe award, 1967; Emmy nominee. Mem. Acad. Motion Picture Arts and Scis., Actors Studio (W. Coast dir.). Office: 7455 Palo Vista Dr Los Angeles CA 90046*

LANDAU, PETER EDWARD, editor; b. N.Y.C., July 16, 1933; s. Edward and Charlotte (Schmidt) L. A.B., Duke, 1955; M.S. in Econs, Columbia, 1959. Editorial asst. Newsweek mag., N.Y.C., 1955-57, asst. editor, 1958-61, assoc. editor, 1962-67; v.p. Tiderock Corp., 1967; sr. editor Instl. Investor, N.Y.C., 1968, mng. editor, 1968-70, editor, 1971-91, editor-at-large, 1991—. Home: 300 E 51st St New York NY 10022-7806 Office: Instl Investor 488 Madison Ave New York NY 10022-5702

LANDAU, RALPH, chemical engineer; b. Phila., May 19, 1916; s. Stanley and Deanna L.; m. Claire, July 14, 1940; 1 dau. B.S., U. Pa., 1937; Sc.D., MIT, 1941. Research asst. chem. engring. MIT, 1939-41; devel. engr. M.W. Kellogg Co., 1939, 41-43, 46; head chems. dept. Kellex Corp., 1943-45; exec. v.p., dir. Sci. Design Co., Inc., N.Y.C., 1946-63; pres. Halcon Internat., Inc., 1963-75, chmn., 1975-81; chmn. Halcon-SD Group, 1981-82, Listowel Inc., 1982—; cons. prof. econ. Stanford U.; fellow faculty Harvard Kennedy Sch.; bd. dirs. Alcoa Corp. Author papers, chpts.; patentee in field. Life mem. corp. MIT; life trustee U. Pa.; trustee Calif. Inst. Tech., Cold Spring Harbor Lab. Recipient Chem. Industry medal, Perkin medal, Nat. Medal Tech., John Fritz med. Mem. Nat. Acad. Engring. (v.p., Founders Award, 1994), Am. Acad. Arts and Scis., Sigma Xi, Tau Beta Pi. Clubs: Sky, Harvard, Princeton, Yale, Chemists (N.Y.C.), French (San Francisco). Office: Listowel Inc 2 Park Ave New York NY 10016-5603*

LANDAU, RICHARD L., physician, educator; b. St. Louis, Aug. 8, 1916; s. Milton S. and Amelia (Rich) L.; m. Claire Schmuckel, Dec. 4, 1943; children—James, Susan, Kay. B.S., M.D., Washington U., St. Louis, 1940. Intern U. Chgo. Clinics, 1940-41, resident, 1941-42; mem. faculty U. Chgo. Sch. Medicine, 1946—, prof. medicine, 1959-88, prof. medicine emeritus, 1988—; head sect. endocrinology, 1967-78. Editor: Perspectives in Biology and Medicine, 1973—; mem. editorial bd.: Jour. Lab. and Clin. Medicine, 1957-62, Ann. Rev. Medicine, 1959-68, Jour. AMA, 1981-89. Served to capt. M.C. AUS, 1943-46. Decorated Bronze Star. Mem. Endocrine Soc. (council 1962-65), Central Soc. Clin. Research, Am. Soc. Clin. Investigation, A.M.A., Chgo. Soc. Internal Medicine (pres. 1968). Spl. rsch. in endocrinologic aspects of reprodn., metabolic influence of progesterone. Home: 5732 S Kenwood Ave Chicago IL 60637-1719

LANDAU, SIDNEY I., publishing executive, lexicographer; b. N.Y.C., Apr. 11, 1933; s. Emanuel and Sadie Mildred (Halpern) L.; m. Sarah Gaston Bradford, June 19, 1959; children: Paul, Amy. BA in English, Queens Coll., 1954; MFA in Creative Writing, U. Iowa, 1959. Instr. English Miami U., Oxford, Ohio, 1959-61; editor, then editor in chief dictionaries Funk & Wagnalls, N.Y.C., 1961-70; editor in chief Doubleday Dictionary, Doubleday Roget's Thesaurus Doubleday & Co., N.Y.C., 1975-77; editor in chief Internat. Dictionary of Medicine and Biology, John Wiley & Sons, N.Y.C. 1977-88, mgr. med. jours., 1982-84, exec. editor medicine, 1985-87, pub. chemistry and life scis. sci.-tech. div., 1987-88; editorial dir. N.Am. br. Cambridge U. Press, N.Y.C., 1988—. Author: Dictionaries: The Art and Craft of Lexicography, 1984, paperback edit., 1989; contbr. numerous articles to profl. jours. With U.S. Army, 1954-56. Mem. MLA, Am. Dialect Soc., Dictionary Soc. N.Am. (pres. 1993—), Am. Coun. Learned Socs. (del. 1994—). Home: 50 W 96th St Apt 2A New York NY 10025-6527 Office: Cambridge U Press 40 W 20th St New York NY 10011-4211

LANDAU, WALTER LOEBER, lawyer; b. New Orleans, Sept. 9, 1931; s. Walter Loeber and Mae (Wilzin) L.; m. Barbara Jane Gordon, June 23, 1954; children: Donna Hardiman, Blair Trippe, Gordon Loeber. B.A., Princeton U., 1953; LL.B., Harvard U., 1956. Bar: N.Y. 1956, U.S. Dist. Ct. (so. dist.) N.Y. 1962, U.S. Supreme Ct. 1971. Assoc. firm Sullivan & Cromwell, N.Y.C., 1956-65; ptnr. Sullivan & Cromwell, 1966—; bd. dirs. Alumax, Inc., U.S. Life Ins. Co., N.Y.C.; mem. NYSE Legal Adv. Com. Trustee Reece Sch., N.Y.C.; mem. Met. Opera Assn.; bd. dirs. Opera Orch. of N.Y., N.Y.C. Opera, Manhattan Theater Club. Fellow Am. Bar Found.; mem. ABA, N.Y. State Bar Assn., Assn. Bar City N.Y., Am. Law Inst., N.Y. Law Inst. (pres.). Republican. Office: Sullivan & Cromwell 125 Broad St New York NY 10004

LANDAU, WILLIAM MILTON, neurologist; b. St. Louis, Oct. 10, 1924; s. Milton S. and Amelia (Rich) L.; m. Roberta Anne Hornbein, Apr. 3, 1947; children: David, John, Julia, George. Student, U. Chgo., 1941-43; M.D. cum laude, Washington U., St. Louis, 1947. Diplomate: Am. Bd. Psychiatry and Neurology (dir. 1967, pres. 1975). Intern U. Chgo. Clinics, 1947; resident St. Louis City Hosp., 1948; fellow Washington U., St. Louis, 1949-52, NIH, Bethesda, Md., 1952-54; instr. neurology Washington U., 1952-54, asst. prof., 1954-58, assoc. prof., 1958-63, prof., 1963—, dept. head, 1970-91, co-head dept. neurology and neur. surgery, 1975; chmn. Nat. Com. for Research in Neurol. and Communicative Disorders, 1980. Editorial bd.: Neurology, 1963, A.M.A. Archives Neurology, 1965, Annals Neurology, 1977. Mem. ACLU (trustee East Mo. 1966—), Am. Neurol. Assn. (pres. 1977), Am. Acad. Neurology, Assn. U. Profs. Neurology (pres. 1978), Soc. Neurosci., Am. Physiol. Soc., Am. Electro-encephalography Soc. Rsch. in neurophysiology. Office: Washington U Sch Med Dept Neurology 660 S Euclid Ave Saint Louis MO 63110-1010

LANDAUER, JERAMY LANIGAN, publishing company executive; b. Medford, Mass. Dec. 27, 1939; d. William Nicholas and Marion Elizabeth (Dorman) L. BA, Trinity Coll., Washington, 1961; cert., Harvard U., 1962; MBA, Columbia U., 1964. From mgr. direct mktg. to sr. v.p. direct mktg. Funk & Wagnalls, Inc., Ramsey, N.J., 1973-80; pres. Book Div. Times-Mirror Mags., N.Y.C., 1980-87; v.p., gen. mgr. Book Group Meredith Corp., Des Moines, 1987-88, pres. Book Group, 1988-91; pres. Landauer Corp., Des Moines, 1991—; bd. dirs. D.M.I.X., N.Y.C. Pres., bd. dirs. Girls' Club N.Y.C., 1986-87; bd. dirs. Trinity Coll., Washington, 1981-87, Des Moines Met. Opera, 1989—, Des Moines Symphony, 1989-91. Mem. Direct Mktg. Assn. (bd. dirs. 1984-91), Rotary.

LANDAUER, ROLF WILLIAM, physicist; b. Stuttgart, Germany, Feb. 4, 1927; came to U.S. 1938, naturalized, 1944; s. Karl and Anna (Dannhauser) L.; m. Muriel Jussim, Feb. 26, 1950; children—Karen, Carl, Thomas. SB, Harvard U., 1945, AM, 1947, PhD, 1950; DSc (hon.), Technion, 1991. Solid state physicist Lewis Lab., NACA (now NASA), Cleve., 1950-52; with IBM Research (and antecedent groups), 1952—; asst. dir. research IBM Research (T. J. Watson Research Center), Yorktown Heights, N.Y., 1966-69, IBM fellow, 1969—; Scott lectr. Cavendish Lab. 1991. Contbr. articles on solid state theory, computing devices, statis. mechanics of computational process to profl. jours. Served with USNR, 1945-46. Recipient Stewart Ballantine medal Franklin Inst., 1992, Centennial medal Harvard U., 1993. Fellow IEEE, AAAS, Am. Phys. Soc. (Buckley prize 1995); mem. NAE, NAS, European Acad. Scis. and Arts, Am. Acad. Arts and Scis. Achievements include initiating IBM programs leading to injection laser, large scale integration. Office: IBM Rsch Ct PO Box 218 Yorktown Heights NY 10598-0218

LANDAW, STEPHEN ARTHUR, physician, educator; b. Paterson, N.J., June 20, 1936; s. Louis and Ida (Machowsky) L.; children: Jared Lawrence, Nicole Renee. B.S., U. Wis., 1955; M.D., George Washington U., 1959; Ph.D., U. Calif., Berkeley, 1969. Cert. rsch. adminstr. Intern Mt. Sinai Hosp., N.Y.C., 1959-60; resident in internal medicine Mt. Sinai Hosp., 1960-61; fellow in hematology Med. Coll. Va., 1962-63; fellow in nuclear medicine Donner Lab., U. Calif., 1963-69, asst. physician, 1970-73; chief isotope lab. Highland-Alameda County Hosp., Oakland, Calif., 1970-73; asso. prof. SUNY, Syracuse, 1973-78; prof. SUNY, 1978—; asso. chief staff research and devel. VA Med. Center, Syracuse, 1973-94; vis. prof. Rockefeller U., N.Y.C., 1988; vis. physician Rockefeller U. Hosp., N.Y.C., 1988; pres. Ctrl. N.Y. Rsch. Corp., 1989-94. Contbr. in field. Served with U.S. Army, 1961-62. VA grantee, 1973-93; NASA grantee, 1976-82; recipient NASA Kosmos Achievement awards, 1975, 77. Fellow ACP; mem. Am. Soc. Hematology, Am. Fedn. Clin. Rsch., Am. Coll. Physician Execs., Soc. Pediat. Rsch., Soc. Rsch. Adminstrs., Soc. Exptl. Biology and Medicine, N.Y. Acad. Sci., Sigma Xi, Alpha Omega Alpha. Jewish. Home: 3159 Burrwood Dr Baldwinsville NY 13027-1708 Office: VA Med Ctr 800 Irving Ave Syracuse NY 13210

LANDE, JAMES AVRA, lawyer, engineering and construction company executive; b. Chgo., Oct. 2, 1930; s. S. Theodore and Helen C. (Hamburger) L.; m. Ann Mari Gustavsson, Feb. 21, 1959; children: Rebecca Susanne, Sylvia D. BA, Swarthmore Coll., 1952; JD, Columbia U., 1955; Bar: N.Y. 1958, Calif. 1967. Assoc. Rein, Mound & Cotton, N.Y.C., 1957-59; atty. VA, Seattle, 1959-61; Weyerhaeuser Co., Tacoma, 1961-63, Lande Assoc., San Francisco, 1963-67; atty. NASA, Ames Research Center, Moffett Field, Calif., 1967-70; house counsel Syntex Corp., Palo Alto, Calif., 1970-73; dir. contracts dept. Electric Power Research Inst., Palo Alto, Calif., 1973-81; corp. atty., dir contracts Lurgi Corp., Belmont, Calif., 1981-82; contracts mgr. Bechtel Corp., San Francisco, 1982-92, sr. contract mgr. Bay Area Rapid Transit Dist., Oakland, Calif., 1992—; adj. prof. U. San Francisco Sch. Law, 1972-73; lectr. law U. Santa Clara Sch. Law, 1984-82. Pres. Syntex Fed. Credit Union, 1971-72. Served with U.S. Army, 1955-57. Mem. Calif. Bar Assn., Fed. Bar Assn., Nat. Contract Mgmt. Assn. (past pres., dir Golden Gate chpt.), Lawyers Club of San Francisco.

LANDEGGER, CARL CLEMENT, machinery and pulp manufacturing executive; b. Vienna, Austria, Sept. 20, 1930; came to US., 1937, naturalized, 1947; s. Karl F. and Helena (Berger) L. BS in Social Sci., Georgetown U., 1951; children: Christine, Carl, Claudia, Cary, Celia, Gregory. Vice chmn., Parsons and Whittemore, Inc., N.Y.C., 1953—; with Black Clawson Co., N.Y.C., 1956—, exec. v.p., 1959-65, pres., 1965—, chmn., 1967—; chmn. St. Anne Nackawic Pulp & Paper Co.; vice chmn. Ala. River Pulp Co., Monroeville, Ala.; bd. dirs. Georgetown U., Gregorian U. Found. 1st lt. USAF, 1951-53. Mem. Explorers Club, Road Runners Club (bd. dirs.) Office: Black Clawson Co 405 Lexington Ave Fl 61 New York NY 10174-0001

LANDEL, ROBERT DAVIS, business administration educator, consultant; b. Birmingham, Ala., Feb. 23, 1940; s. Alden William and Helen (Davis) L.; m. Helen Brokhoff, June 13, 1964; children: Elizabeth Ann, Julie Lynn. BME, Ga. Inst. Tech., 1962, MS in Indsl. Mgmt., 1964, PhD in Indsl. Engring., 1970. Design engr. Chicago Bridge & Iron Co., Birmingham, 1962; buyer and indsl. engr. Westinghouse Electric Co., Staunton, Va., 1964-66; asst. prof. to prof. The Darden Sch. U. Va., Charlottesville, 1969-83, Henry E. McWane prof. bus. adminstrn., 1983—; cons. Southeastern Cons. Group, Charlottesville, 1970—. Author: Managing Productivity Through People, 1986; co-author: Production Operations Planning and Control, 1977, Aggregate Production Planning, 1984. Bd. mem. U.S. Senate Productivity Award Bd. in Va., Richmond, 1985-88. Recipient 1st Wachovia award The Darden Sch. U. Va., 1987. Mem. NAE (mfg. studies bd., com. on indsl. mobilization, 1988-89). Methodist. Avocation: tennis. Home: 1707 Old Forge Rd Charlottesville VA 22901-2111 Office: Univ Va The Darden Sch PO Box 6550 Charlottesville VA 22906-6550

LANDEL, ROBERT FRANKLIN, physical chemist, rheologist; b. Pendleton, N.Y., Oct. 10, 1925; s. Carlisle Oscar and Grace Elisabeth (McEachren) L.; m. Aurora Mamauag; children: Carlisle P., Grace P., Hans F., Robert F. Jr., Kevin L., Matthew N. BA, U. Buffalo, 1949, MA, 1950; PhD, U. Wis., 1954. Rsch. assoc. U. Wis., Madison, 1954-55; sr. rsch. engr. Jet Propulsion Lab. Calif. Inst. Tech., Pasadena, 1955-59, sect. mgr., 1959-85, sr. rsch. fellow CIT, 1966-69, sr. rsch. scientist Jet Propulsion Lab., 1980-92; cons., 1992—; rsch. affiliate Rancho Los Amigos Hosp., Downey, 1976—; vis. prof. Ecole Poly Fed., Lausanne, Switzerland, 1984, U. Philippines, Manila, 1993-94; cons. Sandia Nat. Labs., Albuquerque, 1983; mem. NASA Aircraft Fire Safety Tech. Panel, 1973-80; mem. U.S.-U.K. Working Group on Antimisting Aircraft Fuels, 1978-82, Joint Dept. Def./NASA Working Group on Mech. Properties of Solid Propellants, 1957-78, 85-92; cons. in field. Mem. editorial bd. various polymers jours.; contbr. over 90 articles to profl. jours.; patentee in field. Mem., officer YMCA Indian Guides, Altadena, Calif., 1960-74. With U.S. Army, 1943-45, ETO. French Govt. fellow Sadron Inst., Strasbourg, 1972, Sr. Fulbright fellow U. Naples, Italy, 1971-72; recipient Exceptional Sci. Achievement award, NASA, 1976, Exceptional Svc. medal, 1989, Humboldt Sr. Rsch. Scientist award, 1990. Fellow Am. Phys. Soc. (exec. com. high polymer physics div.); mem. Soc. Rheology (v.p. 1983-85, pres. 1985-87), Am. Chem. Soc., Sigma Xi (sec.-treas. Caltech chpt. 1974-75, v.p. 1975-76, pres. 1976-77). Avocations: skiing, backpacking, camping, photography, hiking.

LANDEN, ROBERT GERAN, historian, university administrator; b. Boston, July 13, 1930; s. Harry James and Evelyn Gertrude (Geran) L.; m. Patricia Kizzia, July 19, 1958; children—Michael Geran, Robert Kizzia, Jill Arnett, Amy Patricia. A.B., Coll. of William and Mary, 1952; M.A., U. Mich., 1953; A.M., Princeton U., 1958, Ph.D. (Ford Found. fellow), 1961. Asst. prof. social sci. Ball State U., Muncie, Ind., 1959-60; asst. prof. near eastern studies U. Mich., Ann Arbor, 1960-61; asst. prof. history Dartmouth, Hanover, N.H., 1961-66; asst. dean of freshmen Dartmouth, 1963-64, asso. prof. history, 1966-67; prof., head dept. history Va. Poly. Inst. and State U., Blacksburg, 1967-69; prof. history U. S.C., Columbia, 1969-75; asso. vice provost U. S.C., 1971-72, asso. provost, 1972-73; dean U. S.C. (Coll. of Social and Behavioral Scis.), 1972-75; prof. history U. Tex. at Arlington, 1975-77; dean U. Tex. at Arlington (Coll. Liberal Arts), 1975-77; prof. history U. Tenn., Knoxville, 1977-86; dean Coll. Liberal Arts, 1977-85; prof. history, v.p. acad. affairs, provost U. Montevallo, 1986-88; prof. history and humanities, dir. programs in the humanities Va. Poly Inst. and State U., Blacksburg, 1988—. Author: Oman Since 1856, 1967, The Emergence of the Modern Middle East, 1970, (with Abid Al-Marayati) The Middle East, Its Governments and Politics, 1972; contbr. articles to profl. jours. and book revs. to hist. publs. Served with AUS, 1953-55. Am. Coun. Learned Socs. fellow, 1965-66, Comparative Studies Ctr. Faculty fellow, 1965-66, Malone fellow, 1988. Fellow Middle East Studies Assn. of N. Am.; mem. Am. Hist. Assn., Middle East Inst., Theta Delta Chi, Phi Kappa Phi. Roman Catholic. Office: Va Poly Inst Office of Dir Programs Humanities Lane Hall Blacksburg VA 24061

LANDER, DAVID ALLAN, lawyer; b. St. Louis, Oct. 2, 1944; s. Louis and Edna (Schramm) L.; m. Carole Weissman Aug. 12, 1965; children—Brad, Rachel. B.A. cum laude, Bowdoin Coll., 1966; J.D., U. Chgo. 1969. Bar: Mo. 1969, U.S. Dist. Ct. (ea. dist.) Mo. 1969, U.S. Ct. Appeals (8th cir.) 1970. Atty., exec. dir. Legal Aid Soc St. Louis City-County, 1975-80; asst. prof. law, St. Louis 1973-75, instr., 1980—; ptnr. Thompson and Mitchell, St. Louis, 1981—; lectr. numerous programs on secured lending, bus. bankruptcy and workouts. Exec. com. Consumer Counseling Credit Service, St. Louis; dir. Legal Services Eastern Mo. Mem. ABA (chmn. com. on agrl. and agri-bus. fin.), Am. Coll. Bankruptcy, Am. Coll. Comml. Finance Attys., Am. Law Inst. (study com. on article 9 uniform comml. code), Mo.

Bar Assn., Bar Assn. Met. St. Louis. Contbr. articles to profl. jours. Office: Thompson & Mitchell 1 Mercantile Ctr Ste 3300 Saint Louis MO 63101-1622

LANDER, ERIC S., biologist, educator. Biology prof. MIT, Cambridge, Mass. Recipient MIT Convocation Program award, 1992. Office: MIT Dept Biology 77 Massachusetts Ave Cambridge MA 02139-4307

LANDER, JAMES ALBERT, retired military officer, state senator; b. Abbeville, S.C., Apr. 9, 1930; s. William Jones and Annie (Cheatham) L.; m. Jolene Patricia Smith, June 8, 1952; children: Theresa, Britt, Leslie, Victoria, Gail, Jean, David. BS, Lander Coll., 1986. Technician S.C. Nat. Guard, Abbeville, 1952-53; life ins. salesman Gulf Life Pilot, Met., Anderson, S.C., 1953-66; maj. U.S. Army, 1966-71; plans and ops. officer, chief of staff S.C. Army N.G., Columbia, 1971-85, maj. gen. mil., 1988-91; mem. S.C. Senate, Columbia, 1993—. Chmn. RSVP Adv. Com., 1991—, Newberry County Literacy Assn., 1991-93; deacon Newberry 1st Bapt. Ch., 1981; past chmn. Boy Scouts Am., Newberry. Decorated Bronze Star, Legion of Merit; recipient Order of Palmetto State of S.C., 1985, Palmetto Cross, 1991, Silver Beaver award Boy Scouts Am., 1990. Mem. Assn. U.S. Army, C. of C. Newberry, Exch. Club (pres.), Rotary, Maasons. Democrat. Baptist. Avocations: reading, gardening. Home: 2029 Main St Newberry SC 29108-3521 Office: SC Senate 601 Gressette Bldg Columbia SC 29202

LANDERS, ANN (MRS. ESTHER P. LEDERER), columnist; b. Sioux City, Iowa, July 4, 1918; d. Abraham B. and Rebecca (Rushall) Friedman; m. Jules W. Lederer, July 2, 1939 (div. 1975); 1 dau., Margo Lederer Howard. Student, Morningside Coll., 1936-39, LHD (hon.), 1964; hon. degree. Wilberforce (Ohio) Coll., 1972, Am. Coll. Greece, 1979, Meharry Med. Coll., 1981, Jacksonville U., 1983, St. Leo Coll., 1984, Fla. Internat. U., 1984, Med. Coll. Pa., 1985, New Eng. Coll., 1985, U. Wis., 1985, Lincoln Coll., 1986, Nat. Coll. Edn., 1986, Southwestern Adventist Coll., 1987, Duke U., 1987, Rosary Coll., 1989, U. Hartford, 1989, L.I. U., 1989, Med. Coll. Ohio, 1989, Roosevelt U., 1991, Ind. U., 1991, Howard U., 1991, Bellevue U., 1992, DePaul U., 1992, Ursinus Coll., 1992, Hillsdale Coll., 1993, St. Xavier U., 1993, Chgo. Theol. Sem., 1993, Barry U., 1993, Northwestern U., 1994. Syndicated columnist Chgo., 1955—; pres. Eppie Co., Inc., Chgo. Author: Since You Asked Me, 1962, Ann Landers Talks to Teen-agers about Sex, 1964, Truth is Stranger, 1968, Ann Landers Speaks Out, 1975, The Ann Landers Encyclopedia, 1978; also pub. svc. booklets and numerous mag. articles; syndicated columnist Los Angeles Times-Creators Syndicates. Chmn. Eau Claire (Wis.) Gray-Lady Corps, ARC, 1947-53; chmn. Minn.-Wis. council Anti-Defamation League, 1945-49; asst. Wis. chmn. Nat. Found. Infantile Paralysis, 1951-53; hon. nat. chmn. 1963 TB Christmas Seal Campaign; bd. sponsors Mayo Clinic, 1970; mem. sponsors com. Mayo Found.; nat. adv. bd. Dialogue for the Blind, 1972; adv. com. on better health services AMA; county chmn. Democratic Party Eau Claire; bd. dirs. Rehab. Inst. Chgo.; nat. bd. dirs. Am. Cancer Soc., Nat. Cancer Inst.; vis. com. bd. overseers Harvard Med. Sch.; mem. Pres.'s Commn. Drunk Driving; trustee Menninger Found., Nat. Dermatology Found., Am. Coll. Greece, Deree-Pierce Coll., Athens, Meharry Med. Sch., Hereditary Disease Found.; dirs. adv. bd. Yale Comprehensive Cancer Ctr. Recipient award Nat. Family Service Assn., 1965, Adolf Meyer award Assn. Mental Health N.Y., 1965, Pres.'s Citation and nat. award Nat. Council on Alcoholism, 1966, 2d nat. award, 1975, Golden Stethoscope award Ill. Med. Soc., 1967, Humanitarianism award Internat. Lions Club, 1967; plaque of honor Am. Friends of Hebrew U., 1968, Gold Plate award Acad. Achievement, 1969; Nat. Service award Am. Cancer Soc., 1971, Robert T. Morse award Am. Psychiat. Assn., 1972; plaque recognizing establishment of chair in chem. immunology Weizmann Inst., 1974, Jane Addams Public Service award Hull House, 1977, Health Achievement award Nat. Kidney Found., 1978, Nat. award Epilepsy Found. Am., 1978, James Ewing Layman's award Soc. Surg. Oncologists, 1979, citation for disting. service AMA, 1979, Thomas More medal Thomas More Assn., 1979, NEA award, 1979, Margaret Sanger award, 1979, Stanley G. Kay medal Am. Cancer Soc., 1983, 1st William C. Menninger medal for achievement in mental health, 1984, Albert Lasker pub. service award, 1985, Edwin C. Whitehead award, 1988, Community Svc. award Gateway Found.'s Citizen's Coun., 1989, Pub. Svc. award NIMH, 1989, award for outstanding pub. edn. Nat. Alliance for the Mentally Ill, 1990, Outstanding Pub. Svc. to Sci. award Nat. Assn. for Biomed. Rsch., 1990. Fellow Chgo. Gynecol. Soc. (citizen hon.); mem. LWV (pres. 1948), Brandeis U. Women (pres. 1960), Chgo. Econs. Club (dir. 1975), Harvard Club (Award 1994), Sigma Delta Chi. Clubs: Chgo. Econs. (dir. 1975), Harvard, Sigma Delta Chi. Office: Chgo Tribune 435 N Michigan Ave Chicago IL 60611 *I have learned that no matter how well-educated, well balanced or well bred a person may be, each of us is capable of doing something completely irrational—completely out of character at some time during our lives...and this doesn't mean we are crazy. It merely means we are human.*

LANDERS, JAMES MICHAEL (JIM LANDERS), international editor; b. San Francisco, Calif., Feb. 11, 1951; s. William Edward and Loretta Mae (Fouts) L.; m. Susan Ann Moran, Dec. 26, 1981; children: Amy Foster, Noelle Christine, Jessica Elizabeth. BA in English with honors, Va. Poly. Inst. and State U., 1974. Staff writer The Washington Post, 1971-74; freelance journalist Belfast, Northern Ireland, 1974; staff writer The Richmond (Va.) Mercury, 1975, The Trenton (N.J.) Times, 1975-77; features editor Arab News, Jeddah, Saudi Arabia, 1978-79; sr. editor Saudi Bus. & Arab Econ. Report, Jeddah, 1979-80; Washington corr. The Dallas Morning News, Washington, 1981-88; internat. editor The Dallas Morning News, Dallas, 1988-94, internat. affairs corr. Washington bur., 1994—. U.S. del. French-Am. Found., Taormina Young Leaders Conf., 1989. Named Outstanding Washington corr. Nat. Press Club, 1985, Finalist Pulitzer prize for Explanatory Journalism, N.Y.C., 1990; recipient World Hunger Media award World Hunger Yr., N.Y.C., 1990, Pulitzer prize for Internat. Reporting, 1994. Mem. Coun. Fgn. Rels., Am. Coun. on Germany, Dallas Com. Fgn. Rels. Roman Catholic. Avocations: running, camping, home renovation, model railroading. Home: 5208 Knoughton Way Centreville VA 22020-3336 Office: The Dallas Morning News Communications Ctr PO Box 655237 Dallas TX 75265-5237

LANDERS, RENÉE MARIE, law educator, government lawyer; b. Springfield, Ill., July 25, 1955; d. Robert Edward and Marvel Margaret (Neal) L.; m. Thomas L. Barrette, Jr., Aug. 2, 1980; 1 child, Nelson Landers Barrette. AB, Harvard U.-Radcliffe Coll., 1977; JD, Boston Coll., 1985. Bar: Mass. 1985, U.S. Dist. Ct. Mass. 1986, U.S. Ct. Appeals (1st cir.) 1986. Program devel. specialist Office Mass. Sec. State, Boston, 1978-79, chief adminstrv. asst. to sec., 1979-80, dep. state for pub. records, acting supr. pub. records, 1980, dep. sec. state Comml. Bur., 1980-82; law clk. to chief justice Mass. Supreme Jud. Ct., Boston, 1985-86; assoc. Ropes & Gray, Boston, 1986-88; asst. prof. law Boston Coll. Law Sch., Newton, Mass., 1988-93; dep. asst. atty. gen. Office of Policy Devel. U.S. Dept. Justice, 1993—; mem. subcom. co-chmn. gender bias study Mass. Supreme Jud. Ct., 1986-89, mem. racial and ethnic bias study, 1990-94. Mem. editl. bd. Mass. Law Rev., 1987-93, Am. Jour. Law and Medicine, 1989-93. Mem. bd. overseers Harvard U., 1991—; mem. Watertown (Mass.) Dem. Town Com., 1981-93, vice chmn., 1986-93; trustee Radcliffe Coll., 1987-89; bd. dirs., v.p Hist. Mass., Inc., 1989—, Big Sister Assn. Greater Boston, 1990-93; bd. dirs Mass. Eye and Ear Infirmary, 1993—. Mem. Boston Bar Assn. (com. 1988-91, chmn. com. on gender and justice 1989-93), Harvard U. Alumni Assn. (nominating com. for dirs. and overseers 1981-84, bd. dirs. 1990-92), Radcliffe Coll. Alumnae Assn. (pres. 1987-89, nominating com. 1983-84). Avocations: choral singing, jogging, tennis, reading. Office: Boston Coll Law Sch 885 Centre St Newton MA 02159-1156

LANDERS, STEVEN E., lawyer; b. N.Y.C., May 23, 1947. BA, Antioch Coll., 1969; JD, Harvard U., 1973. Gen. counsel N.Y. State Exec. adv. com. Sentencing, 1978-79; sec. N.Y. State adv. commn. Adminstrn. Justice, 1981-83; ptnr. Paul, Weiss, Rifkind, Wharton & Garrison, N.Y.C. and Paris. Mem. Internat. Bar Assn., Assoc. Bar City N.Y., D.C. Bar. Office: Paul Weiss Rifkind Wharton & Garrison, 199 Boulevard Saint Germain, 75007 Paris France

LANDERS, TERESA PRICE, librarian; b. N.Y.C., Dec. 28, 1954; d. Stanley and June Ethel (Novick) Price; m. Gary David Landers, Sept. 2, 1979; children: Joshua Price, Alisha Rose. BA in History cum laude, Williams Coll., 1976; MA in LS, U. Denver, 1978; postgrad., Ctrl. Wash. U.,

1980. Libr., asst. analyst Earl Combs, Inc., Mercer Island, Wash., 1979; reference libr. Yakima (Wash.) Valley Regional Libr., 1981-83, coord. youth svcs., 1983-84; libr. Tempe (Ariz.) Pub. Libr., 1984-85; supervisory libr. Mesa (Ariz.) Pub. Libr., 1985-90; head telephone reference Phoenix Pub. Libr., 1990-91, head bus. and scis., 1991—; cons. Fed. Dept. Corrections, Phoenix, 1991. Mem. Ariz. Right To Choose, Phoenix, 1992—. Mem. ALA, Ariz. Libr. Assn., Phoenix C. of C. (libr. rep. 1993—), Nat. Wildlife Fedn. (life), Beta Phi Mu. Democrat. Unitarian. Avocations: cooking, camping. Office: Phoenix Libr Bus & Scis Dept 12 E Mcdowell Rd Phoenix AZ 85004-1627

LANDERS, VERNETTE TROSPER, writer, educator, association executive; b. Lawton, Okla., May 3, 1912; d. Fred Gilbert and LaVerne Hamilton (Stevens) Trosper; m. Paul Albert Lum, Aug. 29, 1952 (dec. May 1955); 1 child, Rosemary, Marlin. AB with honors, UCLA, 1933, MA, 1935, EdD, 1953; Cultural doctorate (hon.) Lit. World U., Tucson, 1985. Tchr. secondary schs., Montebello, Calif., 1935-45, 48-50, 51-59; prof. Long Beach City Coll., 1946-47; asst. prof. Los Angeles State Coll., 1950; dean girls Twenty Nine Palms (Calif.) High Sch., 1960-65; dist. counselor Morongo (Calif.) Unified Sch. Dist., 1965-72, coordinator adult edn., 1965-67, guidance project dir., 1967; clk.-in-charge Landers (Calif.) Post Office, 1962-82; ret., 1982. V.p. sec. Landers Assn., 1965—; sec. Landers Vol. Fire Dept., 1972—; life mem. Hi-Desert Playhouse Guild, Hi-Desert Meml. Hosp. Guild; bd. friends Copper Mountain Coll., 1990-91; bd. dirs. sec. Desert Emergency Radio Service; mem. Rep. Senatorial Inner Circle, 1990-92, Regent Nat. Fedn. Rep. Women, 1990-92, Nat. Rep. Congl. Com., 1990-91, Presdl. Task Force, 1990-92; lifetime mem. Girl Scouts U.S., 1991. Recipient internat. diploma of honor for community service, 1973; Creativity award Internat. Personnel Research Assn., 1972, award Goat Mt. Grange No. 818, 1987; cert. of merit for disting. svc. to edn., 1973; Order of Rose, 1978, Order of Pearl, 1989, Alpha Xi Delta; poet laureate Center of Internat. Studies and Exchanges, 1981; diploma of merit in letters U. Arts, Parma, Italy, 1982; Golden Yr. Bruin UCLA, 1983; World Culture prize Nat. Ctr. for Studies and Research, Italian Acad.; 1984; Golden Palm Diploma of Honor in poetry Leonardo Da Vinci Acad., 1984; Diploma of Merit and titular mem. internat. com. Internat. Ctr. Studies and Exchanges, Rome, 1984; Recognition award San Gorgonio council Girl Scouts U.S., 1984—; Cert. of appreciation Morongo Unified Sch. Dist., 1984, 89; plaque for contribution to postal service and community U.S. Postal Service, 1984; Biographee of Yr. award for outstanding achievement in the field of edn. and service to community Hist. Preservations of Am.; named Princess of Poetry of Internat. Ctr. Cultural Studies and Exchange, Italy, 1985; community dinner held in her honor for achievement and service to Community, 1984; Star of Contemporary Poetry Masters of Contemporary Poetry, Internat. Ctr. Cultural Studies and Exchanges, Italy, 1984; named to honor list of leaders of contemporary art and lit. and apptd. titular mem. of Internat. High Com. for World Culture & Arts Leonardo Da Vinci Acad.; 1987; named to honor list Foremost Women 20th Century for Outstanding Contbn. to Rsch., IBC, 1987; Presdl. Order of Merit Pres. George Bush-Exec. Coun. of Nat. Rep. Senatorial Com., Congl. cert. of Appreciation U.S Ho. of Reps.; other awards and certs. Life fellow Internat. Acad. Poets, World Lit. Acad.; mem. Am. Personnel and Guidance Assn., Internat. Platform Assn., Nat. Ret. Tchrs. Assn., Calif. and Nat. Assn. for Counseling and Devel., Am. Assn. for Counseling and Devel. (25 yr. membership pin 1991), Nat. Assn. Women Deans and Adminstrs., Montebello Bus. and Profl. Women's Club (pres.), Nat. League Am. Pen Women (sec. 1985-86), Leonardo Da Vinci Acad. Internat. Winged Glory diploma of honor in letters 1982), Landers Area C. of C. (sec. 1985-86, Presdl. award for outstanding service, Internat. Honors Cup 1992-93), Desert Nature Mus., Phi Beta Kappa, Pi Lambda Theta (Mortar Bd., Prytanean UCLA, UCLA Golden Yr. Bruin 1983), Sigma Delta Pi, Pi Delta Phi. Clubs: Whittier Toastmistress (Calif.) (pres. 1957); Homestead Valley Women's (Landers). Lodge: Soroptimists (sec. 29 Palms chpt. 1962, life mem., Soroptimist of Yr. local chpt. 19, Woman of Distinction local chpt. 1987-88). Author: Impy, 1974, Talkie, 1975, Impy's Children, 1975; Nineteen O Four, 1976, Little Brown Bat, 1976; Slo-Go, 1977; Owls Who and Who Who, 1978; Sandy, The Coy, 1979; The Kit Fox and the Walking Stick, 1980; contbr. articles to profl. jours., poems to anthologies. Guest of honor ground breaking ceremony Landers Elem. Sch., 1989, dedication ceremony, 1991. Home: 632 N Landers Ln PO Box 3839 Landers CA 92285

LANDES, GEORGE MILLER, biblical studies educator; b. Kansas City, Mo., Aug. 2, 1928; s. George Y. and Margaret B. (Fizzell) L.; m. Carol Marie Dee, Aug. 30, 1953; children: George Miller Jr., Margaret Dee, John Christopher. A.B., U. Mo., 1949; M.Div., McCormick Theol. Sem., 1952; Ph.D., Johns Hopkins U., 1956. Minister to youth Second Presbyn. Ch., Balt., 1952-53, Govans Presbyn. Ch., Balt., 1953-56; instr. Old Testament Union Theol. Sem., N.Y.C., 1956-58, asst. prof. Old Testament, 1958-62, assoc. prof., 1962-70, prof., 1970—; ann. prof. Am. Sch. Oriental Research, Jersualem, Israel, 1967-68. Author: A Student's Vocabulary of Biblical Hebrew, 1961; editor, author: Report on Archaeological Work, 1975. Nettie F. McCormick fellow, 1952-54; Am. Council Learned Socs. fellow, 1967-68. Mem. Soc. Bibl. Lit., Amman Ctr. Archaeol. Rsch. (v.p. 1969-79), Am. Schs. Oriental Rsch. (sec. 1972-94), Phi Beta Kappa.

LANDES, ROBERT NATHAN, lawyer; b. N.Y.C., Dec. 24, 1930; s. Joseph William and Gertrude Ann (Sindeband) L.; m. Phyllis Markham, Apr. 16, 1964; children: Lucy Ann Harrop, Kathy Jill Braddock, Jeffrey Mark. A.B., Columbia U., 1952, LL.B. (Harlan Fiske Stone scholar), 1954. Bar: N.Y. 1954. Assoc Shearman & Sterling, N.Y.C., 1957-61; asst. gen. counsel, v.p. U.S. Industries, Inc., N.Y.C., 1961-73; exec. v.p., gen. counsel, sec. McGraw-Hill, N.Y.C., 1974—; bd. dirs. Greenwich House, Inc. Editor: Columbia Law Rev, 1953-54; contbr. corp. counsel column N.Y. Law Jour., 1986-87. Bd. dirs. McGraw-Hill Found.; bd. trustees Lawyers Com. for Civil Rights Under the Law, 1993—. Served as lt. (j.g.) USNR, 1954-57. Mem. ABA, N.Y. State, N.Y. County Bar Assns., Assn. Bar City N.Y. (com. corp. law 1978-81, sec., corp. law depts, 1985-88, internat. law com. 1981-84), Mag. Pubs. Assn. (chmn. legal affairs com. 1977-82, chmn. AAP lawyers com. 1983-85), Columbia Coll. Alumni Assn. (v.p., bd. dirs. 1974-76, 86-90), Soc. Columbia Grads., (pres., bd. dirs. 1985-88), Columbia Law Sch. Alumni Assn. (treas. 1994—), Vineyards Country Club (Naples, Fla.), Pelham Country Club, (N.Y.), The Club at Pelican Bay (Naples). Democrat. Home: 1192 Park Ave New York NY 10128-1314 Office: McGraw-Hill Inc 1221 Ave Of The Americas New York NY 10020-1001*

LANDES, ROBERT PAUL, architect; b. Houston, Jan. 29, 1926; s. Paul Washington and Walterene (Beasley) L.; m. Sarah Jeannine Early, May 22, 1954; children: Robert Paul Jr., Jennifer Lynn, Cindy Kay. BArch, U. Tex., 1950. Registered architect, Tex.; registered interior designer, Tex. Draftsman Ebasco Engrs., N.Y.C., 1948, Nunn & McGinty, Houston, 1949-50; designer, draftsman Bd. for Tex. State Hosps. and Spl. Schs., Austin, 1950-55; prin. Barnes, Landes, Goodman & Youngblood, Austin, 1955-88; prin., pres. BLGY, Inc., Austin, 1988—. Precinct chmn. Dem. Cen. Com., Austin, 1966-71; divsn. chmn. United Way, 1972; dir. Sunday sch. First Bapt. Ch., Austin, 1968-70, chmn. deacons, 1980. Cpl. U.S. Army, 1944-46. Mem. AIA (pres. Austin chpt. 1966-67), Austin Bass Club (Sportsmanship award 1981), Austin Woods and Waters Club (pres. 1965-66, Sportsman of Yr. 1976), N.E. Kiwanis (pres., bd. dirs. 1966-67, Top Fund Raiser award 1966-70), Delta Kappa Epsilon Alumni Club (v.p. 1957). Avocations: sports, fishing, music. Home: 7506 Greenhaven Dr Austin TX 78757-1706 Office: BLGY Inc 1600 W 38th St Ste 100 Austin TX 78731-6404

LANDES, WILLIAM M., law educator; b. 1939. AB, Columbia U., 1960, PhD in Econs, 1966. Asst. prof. econs. Stanford U., 1965-66; asst. prof. U. Chgo., 1966-69; asst. prof. Columbia U. 1969-72; assoc. prof. Grad. Ctr., CUNY, 1972-73; now prof. U. Chgo. Law Sch.; founder, chmn. Lexecon Inc.,1977—; mem. bd. examiners GRE in Econs., ETS, 1967-74. Mem. Am. Econ. Assn., Am. Law and Econ. Assn. (v.p. 1991-92, pres. 1992-93), Mont Pelerin Soc. Author: (with Richard Posner) The Economic Structure of Tort Law, 1987; editor: (with Gary Becker) Essays in the Economics of Crime and Punishment, 1974; editor Jour. Law and Econs., 1975-91, Jour. Legal Studies, 1991—. Office: U Chgo Sch Law 1111 E 60th St Chicago IL 60637-2702 also: Lexecon Inc 332 S Michigan Ave Chicago IL 60604-4301

LANDESMAN, FREDRIC ROCCO, theatre executive; b. St. Louis, July 20, 1947; s. Alfred and Paula (Berwald) L.; m. Heidi Prentice Ettinger, June 18, 1977; children: North, Nash, Dodge. BA, U. Wis., 1969; MFA, Yale U., 1972, DFA, 1976. Asst. prof. Sch. Drama, Yale U., New Haven, 1972-77; pres. Jujamcyn Theatres, N.Y.C., 1987—; bd. dirs. Municipal Arts Soc., 1989—; owner, mgr. The Cardinal Fund A Pvt. Hedge Fund, 1977-90; bd. dirs. Actor's Fund, N.Y.C., 1990—. Editor Yale/Theater mag., 1972-77; contbr. articles, revs. to profl. jours.; producer Broadway mus. Big River, Into the Woods, The Secret Garden. Bd. dirs. Ednl. Found. Am., Westport, Conn., 1980-87, Ettinger Found., N.Y.C., 1984—. Recipient Tony award Am. Theater Wing, 1985. Mem. League Am. Theaters and Producers (exec. bd. 1987—). Democrat. Jewish. Avocations: baseball, horse racing, country music, reading. *

LANDESMAN, HEIDI, set designer. Set designs include Big River, 1984 (Drama Desk award, Set Design, Tony award, Musical, 1985, Tony award, Scenic Designer); Secret Garden, 1990 (Drama Desk award, Set Design, Tony award, Scenic Designer, 1991), A Midsummer Night's Dream, 1982 (Obie award, Design), Painting Churches, 1982 (Obie award, Design). Office: Second Stage Ansonia Sta PO Box 1807 New York NY 10023-9453

LANDESS, FRED S., lawyer; b. Memphis, Jan. 27, 1933; s. Sterling Stone and Beulah Elizabeth (Melton) L.; m. Catherine Sue Lee, Dec. 27, 1953; children—Susan Elinor, Charles Barton, Catherine Elizabeth. Student, Wake Forest Coll., 1951-53; A.B., George Washington U., 1955; LL.B., U. Va., 1958. Bar: Va. 1958. Enforcement atty. NLRB, Washington, 1958-60; assoc., then ptnr. McGuire, Woods, Battle & Boothe, Charlottesville, VA., 1960—. Sec. Bd. Zoning Appeals, City of Charlottesville, Va., 1967-69; bd. dirs. YMCA, Charlottesville, 1975, Westminster Child Care Ctr., Charlottesville, 1978. Fellow Am. Coll. Real Estate Lawyers; mem. Charlottesville-Albemarle Bar Assn. (pres. 1983-84), Va. Bar Assn. (real estate com.), Va. State Bar (7th dist. disciplinary com. 1986-88, sec. 1987, chmn. 1987-88), Charlottesville-Albemarle Bd. Realtors (assoc.), Blue Ridge Homebuilders Assn. (assoc.). Democrat. Presbyterian. Clubs: Boar's Head Sports (Charlottesville). Avocations: tennis, sailing, gardening. Home: 806 Gilliams Mountain Rd Charlottesville VA 22903-9756

LANDFAIR, STANLEY W., lawyer; b. Elwood, Ind., July 9, 1954; s. Robert W. and Patricia (Wood) L.; m. Sherrie L. Sherman, Aug. 17, 1974 (div.); children: Jennifer, Monica, Stanley. BA, Butler U., 1975; JD, Georgetown U., 1978. Bar: Va. 1978. D.C. 1983, Calif. 1992. Commd. JAGC USN, 1975; sr. trial counsel U.S. Naval Legal Svcs. Office, Yokosuka, Japan, 1981; ptnr. McKenna & Cuneo, Washington D.C. and Calif., 1988—. Co-author Toxic Substances Control Act Handbook, 1989, Pesticide Regulation Handbook, 1991, Environmental Law Handbook, 1993; mem. editl. bd. Proposition 65 News. Home: 5981 Queenston St Springfield VA 22152 Office: McKenna & Cuneo 1575 I St Washington DC 20005 also: 444 S Flower St Los Angeles CA 90071

LANDGREBE, DAVID ALLEN, electrical engineer; b. Huntingburg, Ind., Apr. 12, 1934; s. Albert E. and Sarah A. L.; m. Margaret Ann Swank, June 7, 1959; children: James David, Carole Ann, Mary Jane. BSEE, Purdue U., 1956, MSEE, 1958, PhD, 1962. Mem. tech. staff Bell Telephone Labs., Murray Hill, N.J., 1956; electronics engr. Interstate Electronics Corp., Anaheim, Calif., 1958, 59, 62; mem. faculty Purdue U., West Lafayette, Ind., 1962—; dir. lab. for applications of remote sensing Purdue U., 1969-81, prof. elec. engring., 1970—, assoc. dean engring., 1981-84; rsch. scientist Douglas Aircraft Co., Newport Beach, Calif., 1964; dir. Univ. Space Rsch. Assn., 1975-78. Author: (with others) Remote Sensing: The Quantitative Approach, 1978. Recipient medal for exceptional sci. achievement NASA, 1973, William T. Pecora award NASA/U.S. Dept. Interior, 1990. Fellow IEEE (pres. Geosci. and Remote Sensing Soc. 1986-87, Sci. Achievement award 1992), Am. Soc. Photogrammetry and Remote Sensing; mem. AAAS, Am. Soc. for Engring. Edn., Sigma Xi, Tau Beta Pi, Eta Kappa Nu. Office: care Purdue U Dept Elec Engring West Lafayette IN 47907-1285

LANDGREBE, JOHN ALLAN, chemistry educator; b. San Francisco, May 6, 1937; s. Herbert Frederick and Janet Miller (Allan) L.; m. Carolyn Jean Thomson, Dec. 23, 1961; children—Carolyn Janet, John Frederick. B.S., U. Calif.-Berkeley, 1959; Ph.D., U. Ill., 1962. Asst. prof. U. Kans., Lawrence, 1962-67, assoc. prof., 1967-71, prof., 1971—, dept. chmn., 1970-80; vis. prof. U. Calif.-Berkeley, 1974. Author: Theory and Practice in the Organic Laboratory, 1973, 4th edit., 1993. NSF fellow, 1960-62; E. Watkins Faculty fellow U. Kans., 1963. Mem. Am. Chem. Soc., Royal Soc. of Chemistry, Phi Lambda Upsilon. Republican. Lutheran. Avocations: metal enameling; painting; camping; hiking. Home: 1125 Highland Dr Lawrence KS 66044-4523 Office: U Kansas Dept Chemistry Lawrence KS 66045

LANDGREN, CRAIG RANDALL, biology educator; b. St. Paul, Dec. 20, 1947; s. C. Robert and Alice Elizabeth (Ryder) L.; m. Susan Carina Gatwood, July 23, 1983. BA summa cum laude, Albion Coll., 1969; MA in Biology, Harvard U., 1970, PhD, 1974. Asst. prof. George Mason U., Fairfax, Va., 1974-77; vis. asst. prof. U. Oreg., Eugene, 1976-77; asst. prof. Middlebury Coll., Vt., 1977-82, assoc. prof., 1982-89, prof., 1989—, chmn. dept. biology, 1982-88, 92, 93—; dir. No. Studies program, 1984-87, chmn. natural scis. div., 1985-88; dir. SCIENS minority program, 1987-90, 92; dir. Reaccreditation Self-Study, 1989-90; dir. Freshman Seminar Program, 1990-91, dir. Writing Program, 1992-93; rsch. assoc. U. Oreg., 1978, 79, 80; exch. scientist U.S. Nat. Acad. Scis. program, Moscow and Kiev, 1980. Author: The Trees of the Middlebury College Campus, 1981; contbr. articles to profl. jours. Auditor Addison N.E. Union Supervisory Union, 1988-91, Lincoln Hist. Soc., 1989-92, Danforth Assocs. New Eng., 1989-93; devel. com., The Coll. Bd. ATP Biology Ach. Test, 1990-95, chair, 1992-95. Albion fellow, 1969. Mem. Sigma Xi, Phi Beta Kappa (pres. Beta of Vt. 1985-87), Omicron Delta Kappa, Phi Eta Sigma, Beta Beta Beta (founder George Mason U. chpt. 1976). Avocations: painting, cooking, stained glass, woodworking. Home: 16 Springside Rd Middlebury VT 05753 Office: Middlebury Coll Dept Biology Middlebury VT 05753-6151

LANDGREN, GEORGE LAWRENCE, electrical engineer, consultant; b. Duluth, Minn., July 22, 1919; s. Clarence Robert and Bertha Elizabeth (Borgeson) L.; m. Anna Jean Sinamark, July 26, 1943; children: Karen J., Nancy E., Larry A., David G. B.E.E., U. Minn., 1941; M.S.E.E., Northwestern U., 1955. Registered profl. engr., Ill. Elec. engr. Commonwealth Edison Co., Chgo., 1941-85. Served to capt. U.S. Army, 1942-46, PTO. Fellow IEEE (life, Best Paper 1973). Republican. Presbyterian.

LANDI, DALE MICHAEL, industrial engineer, academic administrator; b. Cleve., July 8, 1938; s. Lawrence Roy and Lillian (Caramell) L.; m. Mary Margaret Lipke, Mar. 23, 1974; children: Michael Kenneth, Kristin Marie. BS, Northwestern U., 1960, MS, 1963, PhD, 1965. Systems analyst Gen. Electric Corp., Chgo., 1960-61; research specialist Rand Corp., Santa Monica, Calif., 1965-68, assoc. dept. head, 1968-70, program dir., 1973-78, v.p., 1978-87; asst. budget dir. N.Y.C., 1970-71; asst. police commr. N.Y.C., 1971-73; v.p. SUNY, Buffalo, 1987—. Home: 238 Brantwood Rd Buffalo NY 14226-4306 Office: SUNY at Buffalo 516 Capen Hall Buffalo NY 14260

LANDIN, DAVID CRAIG, lawyer; b. Jamestown, N.Y., Aug. 1, 1946; s. David Carl and Rita Mae (Felthaus) L.; m. Susan Ann Gregory, July 11, 1970; children: Mary Stuart, Alexander Craig, David Reed. BA, U. Va., 1968, JD, 1972. Bar: Va. 1972, Pa. 1991, Tex. 1992, U.S. Supreme Ct. 1979. Ptnr. McGuire, Woods & Battle, Richmond, Va., 1972—, mgr. of product liability and litigation mgmt. group, 1987—; gen. counsel Va. Assn. Ind. Schs., 1989—, Coun. for Religion in Ind. Schs., 1990—. Trustee Va. Law Found., 1981—; v.p. 1986-87, pres. 1987-88; trustee St. Anne's Belfield Sch., Charlottesville, Va., 1984—; chmn. trusteeship com., 1985-87, exec. com. 1985—, sec. 1988—; mem. long-range planning com. Ch. Schs. of Episcopal Diocese Va., 1988-91. With USAR, 1968-74. Fellow Va. Law Found. (DRI Exceptional Performance citation 1988, product liability com. of internat. law sect.); mem. ABA (chmn. 1990), Va. Bar Assn. (chmn. young lawyers sect. 1979-80, chmn. com. on Issues of State and Nat. Importance 1982-90, chmn. judiciary com. 1990—), Va. Assn. Def. Attys. (regional v.p. 1982-84, pres. 1987-88, chmn. long range planning com. 1990—), Charlottesville-Albemarle Bar Assn. (sec., treas. 1975-77, chmn. young lawyers sect. 1975-78), Richmond Bar Assn., Def. Rsch. Inst., Country Club Va., Farmington Country Club, Commonwealth Club, N.Y. Athletic Club. Roman Catholic.

Avocations: squash, tennis. Home: 310 Oak Ln Richmond VA 23226-1639 Office: McGuire Woods Battle & Boothe 1 James River Plz Richmond VA 23219-3229

LANDINI, RICHARD GEORGE, university president, emeritus English educator; b. Pitts., June 4, 1929; s. George R. and Alice (Hoy) L.; m. Phyllis Lesnick, Nov. 26, 1952 (dec. Mar. 1992); children: Richard, Gregory, Matthew, Cynthia, Vincent. A.B., U. Miami, 1954, M.A., 1956; Ph.D., U. Fla., 1959; D.Civil Law, Quincy Coll., 1985; LLD, U. Miami, 1980, Baiko Jo Gakuin Coll., Japan, 1987. From asst. prof. to prof. English Ariz. State U., 1959-70, dean, 1968-70; prof. English, acad. v.p. U. Mont., 1970-75; pres. Ind. State U., 1975-92, prof. English, 1975—. Contbr. articles on lit. and higher edn. to profl. jours. Served with U.S. Army, 1948-51. Mem. Phi Beta Kappa, Phi Delta Kappa, Phi Kappa Phi, Phi Alpha Theta, Phi Kappa Phi, Sigma Tau Delta. Roman Catholic. Office: Ind State Univ Dept English Root Hall # A-288 Terre Haute IN 47809

LANDIS, DAVID MORRISON, state legislator; b. Lincoln, Nebr., June 10, 1948; BA, U. Nebr., Lincoln, 1970, JD, 1971; m. Melodee Ann McPherson, June 6, 1969; children: Matthew, Melissa. MPA U. Nebr., Omaha, 1984. Bar: Nebr. 1972; practice law, Lincoln, 1972-74; mem. Nebr. Legislature, 1978—, chmn. govt. mil. and vets. affairs com., 1983-87, chmn. banking, commerce and ins., 1988—; instr. Coll. Law U. Nebr., 1990—; adj. faculty mem. dept. pub. adminstrn. U. Nebr., Omaha, 1984, adj. mem. Coll. of Law, 1990—; adj. mem. bus. faculty Doane Coll., 1985—. Named Doane Coll. Tchr. of Yr., 1987, 88, 92. Bd. dirs. Lower Platte S. Natural Resources Dist., 1971-78; officer PTA, 1979-80; adminstrv. law judge Dept. Labor, 1977-78; mem. Nebr. Humanities Council. Mem. The Innocents Soc. (hon.), Golden Key Soc. (hon., U. Nebr.). Office: State Legislature State Capitol Lincoln NE 68509

LANDIS, EDGAR DAVID, services business company executive; b. Myerstown, Pa., Jan. 7, 1932; s. Edgar Michael and Anna Irene (Dubble) L.; m. Patrecia Ann Leininger, June 13, 1953; children—Susan Pauline, Jean Ann. B.S., Lebanon Valley Coll., 1953; M.B.A., U. Pa., 1957. C.P.A. Acct., audit supr. Peat, Marwick, Mitchell & Co., Phila., 1957-64; corp. controller, div. exec. v.p. Carlisle Corp., Pa., 1964-73; v.p., sr. v.p., now exec. v.p. CDI Corp., Phila., 1973—, also dir.; dir. affiliates in U.S. and Europe. Bd. dirs. Carlisle Sch. Dist., 1967-71, Carlisle City Airport, 1968-71, YMCA, Ardmore, Pa., 1981-87, chmn., 1984-88, YMCA, Phila., 1988—, vice chmn. 1991—. With U.S. Army, 1954-56, Japan. Mem. Lebanon Valley Coll. Alumni Assocs. (regional chmn. 1977-82). Republican. Methodist. Home: 222 Church Rd Ardmore PA 19003-3302 Office: CDI Corp 1717 Arch St Philadelphia PA 19103-2713

LANDIS, ELWOOD WINTON, retired newspaper editor; b. Wichita, Kans., June 14, 1928; s. Jacob Harrison and Christina (Fry) L.; m. Nancy Gauss, Nov. 22, 1961; children: Frederic, Laura. B.A., Friends U., Wichita, 1950; M.S. in Journalism, Northwestern U., 1953. Reporter Wichita Eagle, 1953; copy editor Omaha World-Herald, 1955-57; publicity dir. Bethany (Kans.) Coll., 1957-61; publs. dir. tchr. edn. project Central Mich. U., 1961-64; mng. editor Voice Newspaper, Mich. Edn. Assn., East Lansing, Mich., 1965-93. Mem. Williamston (Mich.) City Planning Commn., 1972-75; bd. dirs. Lansing Ballet Assn., 1980-81. Served with AUS, 1953-55. Recipient awards Edn. Press Assoc. Am. Mem. Sigma Delta Chi. Democrat. Home: 308 S Circle Dr Williamston MI 48895-1014

LANDIS, FRED, mechanical engineering educator; b. Munich, Mar. 21, 1923; came to U.S., 1947, naturalized, 1954; s. Julius and Elsie (Schulhof) L.; m. Billie H. Schiff, Aug. 26, 1951 (dec. Jan. 10, 1985); children—John David, Deborah Ellen, Mark Edward. B.Eng., McGill U., 1945; S.M., MIT, 1949, Sc.D., 1950. Design engr. Canadian Vickers, Ltd., Montreal, Can., 1945-47; asst. prof. mech. engring. Stanford U., 1950-52; research engr. Northrop Aircraft, Inc., Hawthorne, Calif., 1952-53; asst. prof. NYU, 1953-56, assoc. prof., 1956-61, prof., 1961-73, chmn. dept. mech. engring., 1963-73; dean, prof. mech. engring. Poly. U., Bklyn., 1973-74; dean Coll. Engring. and Applied Sci., U. Wis., Milw., 1974-83, prof. mech. engring., 1984-94; emeritus prof. U. Wis., Milw., 1994—; staff cons. Pratt & Whitney Aircraft Co., 1957-88. Cons. editor, Macmillan Co., 1960-68; cons. editorial bd.: Funk & Wagnalls Ency., 1969—, Compton's Ency., 1984—; contbr. numerous rsch. articles to profl. jours. and encys., including Ency. Britannica. Mem. Dobbs Ferry (N.Y.) Bd. Edn., 1965-71, v.p. 1966-67, 70-71, pres., 1967-68; bd. dirs. Westchester County Sch. Bds. Assn., 1969-70, v.p., 1970, pres., 1970-71; bd. dirs. Engring. Found. 1986-94. Fellow AIAA (assoc.), Am. Soc. Engring. Edn., ASME (hon. mem., div. exec. com. 1965-73, policy bd. 1973-89, v.p. 1985-89, 92—, bd. govs. 1989-91); mem. Sigma Tau, Tau Beta Pi, Pi Tau Sigma. Home: 2420 W Acacia Rd Milwaukee WI 53209-3306

LANDIS, GEOFFREY ALAN, physicist, writer; b. Detroit, May 28, 1955; s. John Lloyd and Patricia (Sheridan) L. BS and BEE, MIT, 1980; MS, MEE, PhD, Brown U., 1988. Staff scientist Spire Corp., Bedford, Mass., 1977-82; rsch. assoc. Solar Energy Rsch. Inst., Golden, Colo., 1986-87, NASA Lewis Rsch. Ctr., Cleve., 1988-90; physicist Sverdup Tech., Brook Park, Ohio, 1994-95; sr. engr. NYMA, Inc., Brook Park, 1994—; adj. prof. Ohio Aerospace Inst., Brook Park, 1990-92; sr. rsch. assoc. Ohio Aerospace Inst., 1995—; trustee Nat. Assn. Rocketry, Pa., 1977-81; mem. U.S. team Spacemodeling World Championships, Jambol, Bulgaria, 1978; tech. chmn. Vision 21 Conf., Cleve., 1990, 93. Editor: (procs.) Vision 21: Space Travel for the Next Millenium, 1991, Vision 21: Interdisciplinary Science and Engineering, 1993; author: (short story collection) Author's Choice Monthly, 1991 (Hugo award for best sci.-fiction short story 1992); author over 30 pub. sci.-fiction short stories; contbr. over 100 articles to profl. jours. Mem. AIAA, Am. Phys. Soc., Soc. Fiction Writers Am. (Nebula award 1990), Artemis Soc. Achievements include 4 patents; participation with MIT human-powered flight team for Chrysalis and Monarch aircraft; research in semiconductor physics, solar energy and astronautics. Office: NASA Lewis Rsch Ctr 302-1 2100 Brookpark Rd Cleveland OH 44135

LANDIS, GEORGE ARTHUR, career officer; b. Kane, Pa., Aug. 18, 1940; s. Norman Edward and Mazie Genetta (Shatto) L.; m. Sandra Kay Sanders, Dec. 28, 1963; children: Kirsten Kay Landis Lambert, Kelly Kay Landis Scott. BBA, Kent State U., 1963; MBA, Tex. Tech. U., 1970. Commd. 2d lt. U.S. Army, 1963, advanced through grades to brig. gen., 1990; student U.S. Army Transp. Sch., Ft. Eustis, Va., 1963, tng. officer, 1963-64; train comdr. transp. div. Hdqrs. Berlin Brigade, U.S. Army, Europe, 1964-66, rail transp. officer, 1966-67; comdr. 2d Transp. Co., 27th Transp. Bn., 8th Transp. Group, U.S. Army, Vietnam, 1967-68; hwy. ops. officer 8th Transp. Group, U.S. Army, Vietnam, 1968; student U.S. Army Transp. Sch., Ft. Eustis, 1968-69, Tex. Tech. U., Lubbock, 1969-70; ops. officer Hdqrs. U.S. Army terminal command Thailand, U.S. Pacific command, 1970-71; dep. comdr. U.S. Army terminal command, U.S. Pacific Command, 1971; instr. mgmt. tng. br. U.S. Army Transp. Sch., Ft. Eustis, 1971-72; student Cmmand and Gen. Staff Coll., Ft. Leavenworth, Kans., 1972-73; div. transp. officer Hdqrs. 82d Airborne div., Ft. Bragg, N.C., 1973-74, dep. G-4, 1974, chief plans and ops., 1974-75, security, plans and ops. officer div. support command, 1975-76; tng. with industry Nat. R.R. Passenger Corp., Washington, 1976-77; staff transp. officer Office of Dep. Chief of Staff for Logistics, Washington, 1977-78; comdr. 7th Transp. Bn., 1st Corps Support Command, Ft. Bragg, 1978-80; asst. chief of staff logistics 82d Airborne Div., Ft. Bragg, 1980-82; chief internat. logistics div. U.S. Pacific Command, Camp Smith, Hawaii, 1983-86; comdr. divsn. support command 25th Inf. Divsn., Schofield Barracks, Hawaii, 1986-88; asst. comdt. U.S. Army Transp. Sch., Ft. Eustis, 1988-90; commdg. gen. Mil. Traffic Mgmt. Command, Western Area, Oakland Army Base, Calif., 1990-91; dep. commdg. gen. for ops. and transp. 22d Theater Army Area Command, Dhahran, Saudi Arabia, 1991; spl. asst. Dep. Chief of Staff for Logistics, Dept. of the Army, Washington, 1992; commdg. gen. U.S. Army Pers. Info. Systems Command, Alexandria, Va., 1992—. Decorated Def. Supr. Svc. medal, Legion of Merit, Bronze Star, Def. Meritorious Svc. medal, Meritorious Svc. medal with three oak leaf clusters, Air medal, Army Commendation medal with three oak leaf clusters, Master Parachutist badge, Air Assault badge, Army Staff Identification badge. Mem. Nat. Def. Transp. Assn., Assn. of the U.S. Army, 82d Airborne Div. Assn., Armed Forces Comm. and Elecs. Assn. Avocations: family, handball, golf, jogging, photography. Office: US Army Pers Info Systems Command 200 Stovall St Alexandria VA 22332

LANDIS, JAMES DAVID, publishing company executive, retired, author; b. Springfield, Mass., June 30, 1942; s. Edward and Eve (Saltman) L.; m. Patricia Lawrence Straus, Aug. 15, 1964 (div.); children: Sara Cass; m. Denise Evelyn Tillar, July 20, 1983; children: Jacob Dean, Benjamin Nicholas. B.A. magna cum laude, Yale Coll., 1964. Asst. editor Abelard Schuman, N.Y.C., 1966-67; editor-sr. editor William Morrow & Co., N.Y.C., 1967-80, editorial dir., sr. v.p., pub. Quill trade paperbacks, 1980-85; sr. v.p. William Morrow & Co., 1985-91, pub., editor-in-chief, 1988-91; pub., editor-in-chief Beech Tree Books, 1985-87. Author: The Sisters Impossible, 1979, Daddy's Girl, 1984, Love's Detective, 1984, Joey and the Girls, 1987, The Band Never Dances, 1989, Looks Aren't Everything, 1990, Lying in Bed, 1995. Recipient Roger Klein award for editing, 1973; recipient Advocate Humanitarian, 1977. Mem. Phi Beta Kappa.

LANDIS, JOHN DAVID, film director, writer; b. Chgo., Aug. 3, 1950; s. Marshall David and Shirley (Magizner) L.; m. Deborah Nadoolman, July 27, 1980; 2 children. Mem. crew MGM film Kelly's Heroes; stuntman, writer-dir. Schlock, 1971, An American Werewolf in London, 1981; dir. Kentucky Fried Movie, 1977, National Lampoon's Animal House, 1978, Trading Places, 1983, Into the Night, 1985, Spies Like Us, 1985, Three Amigos, 1986, Coming to America, 1988, Oscar, 1991, Innocent Blood, 1992, Michael Jackson's Black or White, 1992, Beverly Hills Cop III, 1994, The Stupids, 1995; co-writer, dir. The Blues Brothers, 1980, Michael Jackson's Thriller; writer, dir., producer The Twilight Zone, 1983; frequent dir., exec. prodr. TV series Dream On, 1991— (ACE awards); exec. prodr. (TV series) Weird Science, 1994—, Sliders, 1995—, Campus Cops, 1995. Decorated chevalier dans L'Ordre des Arts et des Lettres (France), 1985; recipient numerous awards including NAACP Image awards, W.C. Handy award, People's Choice awards, internat. film festival awards. Mem. Writers Guild Am., Dirs. Guild Am., Screen Actors Guild, Acad. Motion Picture Arts and Scis. Office: care CAA 9830 Wilshire Blvd Beverly Hills CA 90212-1804

LANDIS, ROBERT M., lawyer; b. Fleetwood, Pa., 1920; s. Jacob B. and Bertha (Moyer) L.; m. Mary Elizabeth Hatton, Aug. 24, 1946; children: Christopher Hatton, Geoffrey Budd. AB, Franklin and Marshall Coll., 1941, LLD (hon.), 1991; JD, U. Pa., 1947. Bar: Pa. 1947. Assoc. firm Dechert, Price & Rhoads, Phila., 1947-54; ptnr. Dechert, Price & Rhoads, 1954—, chmn., 1981-84; chmn. Fed. Res. Bank, Phila., 1983-86; 1st dep. city solicitor Phila., 1952-53; mem. Pa. Supreme Ct. Advisory Judicial Qualifications Commn., 1968; mem. life U.S. Jud. Conf. Third Circuit; bd. dirs., chmn. comp. nominating com., mem. exec. com. Houghton Mifflin Co.; bd. dirs. Fed. Res. Bank Phila., chmn. 1983-86; chmn. Pa. Gov.'s Bd. Ethics, 1973-78; chmn. Bi-State Commn. Legislation Delaware River Port authority Pa.-N.J., 1976-77; chmn. adv. group Civil Justice Reform Act of 1990, U.S. Dist. Ct. (ea. dist.) Pa., 1991—; lectr. law sch. Temple U., 1987; adj. prof. law Villanova U., 1988. Co-chmn. Greater Phila. Partnership, 1977-79; bd. dirs. Greater Phila. Movement; pres. Children's Aid Soc. Pa., 1960-68; bd. dirs. Child Welfare League Am., 1964-66; pres. Fellowship Commn. Phila., 1972-74; past chmn. Pa. Council of Nat. Council on Crime and Delinquency; mem. advisory council Villanova Inst. Correctional Reform, 1972-79; steering com. NAACP Legal Def. Fund; assoc. trustee U. Pa., mem. bd. overseers Law Sch.; trustee Franklin and Marshall Coll.; bd. dirs. Nat. Jud. Coll., 1990—; chmn. bd. trustees Theodore F. Jenkins Law Library, 1970-71; elder, trustee First Presbyn. Ch., Lower Merion, Gladwyne, Pa. Fellow Am. Coll. Trial Lawyers (bd. regents 1981—), Am. Bar Found.; mem. Phila. Bar Assn. (numerous com. assignments, chmn. bd. govs. 1964, chancellor 1970—), Am. Bar Assn. (pres. Nat. Conf. Bar Presidents 1975-76, del. 1969-70, 77-78, bd. govs. 1982, state del. from Pa. 1992—, standing com. on fed. judiciary, chmn. standing com. on jud. improvements 1983-86), Pa. Bar Assn. (pres. 1981-82, ho. of dels. 1968—), Nat. Assn. R.R. Trial Counsel (pres. 1966-67), Am. Law Inst. (life), Am. Judicature Soc. (dir. 1974-77). Clubs: Franklin Inn (chmn.), Sunday Breakfast, Racquet, Phila. Country, Phila. Anglers, Broadacres Trouting Assn. Home: 1401 Monk Rd Gladwyne PA 19035-1314 Office: Dechert Price & Rhoads 4000 Bell Atlantic Tower 1717 Arch St Philadelphia PA 19103

LANDIS, WAYNE G., environmental toxicologist; b. Washington, Jan. 20, 1952; s. James G. and Harriet E. L.; m. Linda S.; children: Margaret Evelyn, Eva Armstrong. BA in Biology, Wake Forest U., 1974; MA in Biology, Ind. U., 1978, PhD in Zoology, 1979. Document mgr. Franklin Rsch. Ctr., Silver Spring, Md., 1979-81; rsch. biologist U.S. Army Chem. Rsch., Devel. & Engring. Ctr., Aberdeen Proving Ground, Md., 1982-89; dir., prof. Inst. Environ. Toxicology & Chemistry, Western Wash. U., Bellingham, 1989—. Contbr. numerous articles to profl. jours. Recipient Hankins scholarship Wake Forest U., 1972-74, U.S. Army Rsch. and Devel. Achievement award, 1984, Spl. Act award, 1985, Exceptional Performance award, 1986; named to Outstanding ILIR Rsch. Program, 1983, 84. Mem. AAAS, ASTM, Soc. Environ. Toxicology and Chemistry (Pacific NW chpt.), Genetics Soc. Am., Sigma Xi. Achievements include evaluation of aquatic toxicology of smoke, riot control materials and binary system compounds; devel. theory to predict response of biol. communities to chem. insults using resource competition models, of new methods for ecosystem anal. and applications of chaos theory to chem. impacts. Office: Western Wash U. Huxley Coll Environ Toxicology 516 High St Bellingham WA 98225-5946

LANDISMAN, MARK, geophysicist, educator; b. N.Y.C., Apr. 30, 1928; s. David and Rosa Landisman; m. Celia Turk, Aug. 3, 1960; children: Andrew Michael, Jessica, Carole Elizabeth. AB, Columbia U., 1949, PhD, 1959. Rsch. scientist Columbia U. at Lamont Geol. Obs., oceanographic cruises and geophys. field sites, 1949-64; prof. geophysics U. Tex. at Dallas, Richardson, 1964—; adj. prof. So. Meth. U., 1964—; vis. assoc. prof. U. Minn., 1962-63; vis. prof. U. Karlsruhe (Fed. Republic Germany), 1967; UNESCO expert in seismology Internat. Inst. Seismology and Earthquake Engring., Tokyo, 1972; invited contbr., keynote speaker internat. symposia on geophys. theory and computers. Contbr. articles to profl. jours. Bd. dirs., exec. sec., v.p., mem. exec. com. Heard Mus. and Wildlife Sanctuary, McKinney, Tex., 1978—. Mem. AAAS, Am. Geophys. Union, Am. Phys. Soc., Acoustical Soc. Am., European Assn. Exploration Geophysicists, Geol. Soc. Am., Seismol. Soc. Am., Seismol. Soc. Japan, Royal Astron. Soc. (U.K.), Dallas Geophys. Soc., U.S. Geodynamics Com., Sigma Xi. Achievements include development of first computer programs for gravity and magnetic signatures of two-dimensional models, seismic ray-mode duality, computation of global tremors from severe earthquakes, frequency-time analysis of multiply dispersed signals, generalized inversion models from inaccurate and incomplete data, seismic refraction-reflection and electrical properties of relatively wet earthquake-prone zone in the earth's crust; research in field of oceanographic precision depth recorder early seismic surface wave demarcation of global plate tectonic asthenosphere. Office: U Tex at Dallas PO Box 688 Richardson TX 75083

LANDMAN, BETTE EMELINE, academic administrator; b. Piqua, Ohio, July 18, 1937; d. Wilson Richard and Lois (Wilson) L. BS, Bowling Green State U., 1959; MA, Ohio State U., 1961, PhD, 1972. From instr. to asst. prof. anthropology Springfield (Mass.) Coll., 1963-67; asst. prof. Temple U., 1967-71; asst. prof. anthropology Beaver Coll., Glenside, Pa., 1971-76, dean, 1976-85, v.p. acad. affairs, 1980-85, acting pres., 1982-83, 85, pres., 1985—; bd. dirs. Abington (Va.) Meml. Hosp., 1986-93, Abington Meml. Hosp. Found., 1993—; mem. blood doner champaign ARC, chair Pa.-Jersey Region Higher Edn., 1990-91; mem. bd. advisors Coll. Physicians of Phila., 1994—. Recipient Disting. Teaching award Christian R. and Mary F. Lindback Found., 1973; NSF fellow, 1961-63, Wenner-Gren Found. for Anthrop. Rsch. fellow, 1965-66; named Disting. Dau. of Pa., 1992; Ann. Pa. Am. Coun. on Edn.-NIP award established in her honor, 1992. Mem. Am. Coun. Edn. (state coord. 1980-84, common on leadership devel. 1989-94, chmn. 1991-92, bd. dirs. 1993—), Assn. Am. Colls. (bd. dirs. 1986-91, vice chair 1989-90, chair 1990-91), Assn. Presbyn. Colls. and Univs. (exec. com. 1988-93, 95—, sec. 1989-90, v.p. 1990-91, pres. 1991-92), Pa. Assn. Colls. and Univs. (exec. com. 1992-93), Nat. Assn. Ind. Colls. and Univs. (common. on campus concerns 1991—, vice chmn. 1992, chmn. 1993), Sigma Xi, Phi Kappa Phi, Kappa Delta Pi. Office: Beaver Coll Office of Pres 450 S Easton Rd Glenside PA 19038-3295

LANDO, JEROME BURTON, macromolecular science educator; b. Bklyn., May 23, 1932; s. Irving and Ruth (Schwartz) L.; m. Geula Ahroni, Dec. 2, 1962; children: Jeffrey, Daniel, Avital. A.B., Cornell U., 1953; Ph.D., Poly.

Inst. Bklyn., 1963. Chemist Camille Dreyfus Lab., Research Triangle Inst., Durham, N.C., 1963-65; asst. prof. macromolecular sci. Case Western U., Cleve., 1965-68, assoc. prof., 1968-74, prof., 1974—; chmn. dept. Case Western, Cleve., 1978-85; dir. Macro-Epic (acad.-indsl. research program), 1985—; Erna and Jakob Michael vis. prof. Weizmann Inst. Sci., Rehovot, Israel, 1987; Lady Davis vis. prof. Technion, Haifa, Israel, 1992-93. Author: (with S. Maron) Fundamentals of Physical Chemistry, 1974; editorial adv. bd. Jour. Molecular Electronics, Polymers for Advanced Technologies, Jour. Materials Chemistry. Served to lt. U.S. Army, 1953-55. Named Alexander Von Humboldt Sr. Am. Scientist U. Mainz (Fed. Republic Germany), 1974, disting. alumnus Poly. U., 1990; recipient rsch. award Soc. Plastics Engrs., 1994. Fellow Am. Phys. Soc.; mem. Am. Chem. Soc., Am. Crustallographic Assn., Soc. Plastics Engrs., Sigma Xi. Jewish. Home: 21925 Byron Rd Cleveland OH 44122-2942 Office: Case Western Res U Dept Macromolecular Sci Kent Hale Smith Bldg 321 Cleveland OH 44106

LANDOLT, ARLO UDELL, astronomer, educator; b. Highland, Ill., Sept. 29, 1935; s. Arlo Melvin and Vesta (Kraus) L.; m. Eunice Jean Casper, June 8, 1966; 1 child, Jennifer; stepchildren: Lynda, Barbara, Vicky, Debra. B.A., Miami U., Oxford, Ohio, 1955; M.A., Ind. U., 1960, Ph.D., 1963. Mem. 1st wintering-over party Internat. Geophys. Year, Amundson-Scott South Pole Sta., Antarctica, 1957; asst. prof. physics and astronomy La. State U., 1962-65, asso. prof., 1965-68, prof., 1968—, dir. La. State U. Obs., 1970-88, acting chmn. dept. physics and astronomy, summers 1972-73, pres. faculty senate, 1979-80; program dir. astronomy sect. NSF, 1975-76; mem. governing bd. Am. Inst. of Physics, 1985-91, 95—; guest investigator Kitt Peak Nat. Obs., Tucson, Cerro Tololo Inter-Am. Obs.,Las Campanas Observatory, La Serena, Chile, Dyer Obs., Vanderbilt U., Goethe Link Obs., Ind. U. Rsch. grantee NSF, 1964, 66, 69, 71, 73, 75, 92-96, NASA, 1965, 92, Rsch. Corp., 1964, Air Force Office Sci., 1977-87, Space Telescope Sci. Inst., 1985-90, 92. Fellow AAAS (sec. Sect. D 1970-78); mem. Am. Astron. Soc. (sec 1980-89, 95—), Internat. Astron. Union (sec. U.S. nat. com. 1980-89), Royal Astron. Soc. (Eng.), Astron. Soc. Pacific, Am. Polar Soc., Am. Philatelic Soc., AAUP, Sigma Xi, Pi Mu Epsilon. Office: La State U Dept Physics And Astro Baton Rouge LA 70803

LANDOLT, ROBERT GEORGE, chemistry educator; b. Houston, Apr. 4, 1939; s. Robert Garland and Mary Ella (Campbell) L.; m. Margaret Ann Brown, June 8, 1962; children: Laura, Lisa, Robert. BA, Austin Coll., Sherman, Tex., 1961; PhD, U. Tex., 1965. Rsch. assoc. U. Ill., Urbana, 1965-67; asst. prof., assoc. prof. Muskingum Coll., New Concord, Ohio, 1967-80; sr. scientist Radian Corp., Austin, Tex., 1980-81; assoc. prof. chemistry Tex. Weslayan U., Ft. Worth, 1981-89, prof., 1989—; resident cons. Battelle Meml. Lab., Columbus, Ohio, 1974-75; cons. Naval Rsch. Lab., Washington, 1982-83; dir. rsch. div. Tex. Higher Edn. Coord. Bd., 1991. Contbr. articles on organic chemistry to profl. jours. Mem. AAAS, AAUP, Am. Chem. Soc. (Congl. fellow 1986-87), Sigma Xi. Office: Tex Weleyan U 1201 Wesleyan St Fort Worth TX 76105-1536

LANDON, FORREST M., newspaper editor; b. Pontiac, Mich., Sept. 24, 1933; s. DeWitt Dale Landon and Eleanor (Stevens) Landon Smith; m. Barbara Jean Patrick, Sept. 25, 1955; children—Jeffrey William, Tracy Alice. B. Journalism, U. Mo., 1955. Reporter Sta. WDBJ-AM-FM-TV, Roanoke, VA., 1955-59; news dir. Sta. WDBJ-AM-FM, Roanoke, VA., 1959-64; assoc. editorials editor Roanoke Times, VA., 1964-67, editorial page editor, 1967-71, assoc. editor, night mng. editor, mng. editor, 1971-82, exec. editor, v.p., 1982—; host weekly program pub. TV, Roanoke, 1968-79; tchr. journalism Hollins Coll., Va., 1970-74. Pres. Roanoke Valley Council Community Services, 1973-74, Roanoke Valley Indsl. Mgmt. Council, 1961. Mem. Soc. Profl. Journalists (pres. Blue Ridge chpt. 1977-78, award 1988), Va. Press Assn. (pres. 1993-94, award 1974), Va. A.P. Newspapers (pres. 1989-90), Va.A.P. Broadcasters (award 1958, 58, 60), Am. Soc. Newspaper Editors (FOI com. chmn. 1995), Torch Club (pres. Roanoke 1984-85). Unitarian. Home: 1603 Deyerle Rd SW Roanoke VA 24018-1313 Office: Roanoke Times & World-News PO Box 2491 201-209 W Campbell Ave Roanoke VA 24010-2491

LANDON, HARRY RAYMOND, utility company executive; b. Sherwood, Md., July 15, 1935; s. Harry Ellis and Goldey May (Harrison) L.; m. Jacquelyn Smith, Sept. 8, 1956; children: Roger Douglas, Richard Harrison. B.S., U. Md., 1957. Sales rep. Address-O-Graph & Multi-Graph Corp., Washington, 1958-59; personnel mgr. Chris-Craft Corp., Salisbury, Md., 1959-63; indsl. relations mgr. Eastern Shore Pub. Service Cos. of Md. and Va., Salisbury, 1973-76; v.p. Delmarva Power & Light Co., Wilmington, Del., 1976-78, sr. v.p., 1978—. Vice pres. Del. Chpt. ARC, Wilmington, 1980—; bd. dirs. Better Bus. Bur., 1982—; trustee Del. Council on Econ. Edn., Newark, Del., 1980—. Recipient Disting. Service award Salisbury Jr. C. of C., 1967; recipient Outstanding Service award United Fund of Wicomico County, (Md.), 1967. Mem. Southeastern Electric Exchange (chmn. indsl. relations sect. 1976), Eastern Shore Personnel Assn. (pres. 1970), Edison Electric Inst., Del. State C. of C. (dir. 1978—), Delta Sigma Pi. Republican. Methodist. Clubs: Rotary (Wilmington program chmn. 1981), Lions (Salisbury pres. 1976). Home: 116 Red Pine Cir Newark DE 19711-7000 Office: Delmarva Power & Light Co 800 N King St Wilmington DE 19801-3518

LANDON, JAMES HENRY, lawyer; b. Atlanta, Ga., Oct. 24, 1945; s. Ralph Henry and Gertrude Leola (Rew) L. BA, Vanderbilt U., Nashville, Tenn., 1967; JD, Harvard U., Cambridge, Mass., 1970. Bar: Ga. 1971, U.S. Dist. Ct. (no. dist.) Ga. 1971, U.S. Ct. Claims 1972, U.S. Supreme Ct. 1976, U.S. Tax Ct. 1980. Assoc. Hansell & Post, Atlanta, Ga., 1971-76, ptnr., 1976-89; ptnr. Jones, Day, Reavis & Pogue, Atlanta, Ga., 1989—; Adj. prof. Emory Law School, Atlanta, Ga., 1983-84; dir. TRC Temporary Serv., Inc., Atlanta, Ga., 1987—; mem. steering com. So. Pension Conf., Atlanta, Ga., 1985-88. Co-author: Transportation Politics in Atlanta, 1970; contbr. article to profl. jour. Gen. counsel Woodruff Arts Ctr., Inc., 1993—; trustee Atlanta Symphony Orchestra, 1981-87, 89—, The Hambidge Ctr. 1994—, Atlanta Med. Heritage, Inc., 1993—; trustee and sec. Atlanta Hist. Soc. 1985—; mem. community adv. bd. Jr. League of Atlanta, 1987-90. Mem. ABA, Ga. Bar Assoc., Atlanta Bar Assoc., Explorers Club of N.Y.C., Phi Beta Kappa. Presbyterian. Avocations: mountain climbing, hiking. Home: 1327 Peachtree St NE Apt 503 Atlanta GA 30309-3254 Office: Jones Day Reavis & Pogue 3500 One Peachtree Ctr 303 Peachtree St NE Atlanta GA 30308-3242

LANDON, JOHN CAMPBELL, medical research company executive; b. Hornell, N.Y., Jan. 3, 1937; s. Earl Shephard and Eleanor (Crane) L.; m. Nancy Ann Bachenheimer, Aug. 24, 1958; children: David Stephen, Martha Susan, Katherine Ellen, Peter Crane. BA in Biology, Alfred (N.Y.) U., 1959; MS in Biology, George Washington U., Washington, 1962, PhD in Biology, 1967. Biologist Nat. Cancer Inst., NIH, Bethesda, Md., 1960-65; virologist Litton Bionetics, Kensington, Md., 1965-68, dir. 1968-75; pres., dir. EG&G Mason Rsch. Inst., Worcester, Mass. 1975-82; pres., chief exec. officer, dir. Bioqual, Inc., Rockville, Md., 1982—; pres., chief exec. officer Sema, Inc., Rockville, 1986-91; pres., chief exec. officer, dir. chmn. bd. Diagnon Corp., Rockville, 1986—; chmn. bd. Diagnon Corp.; cons. EG&G, Worcester, Mass. 1982-85; reviewer ad-hoc com. NIH, Bethesda, Md., 1981—; mem. exec. com., bd. dirs., v.p. bd. Nat. Assn. Life Sci. Industries, 1975-78, 79-81. Contbr. articles to profl. jours. Bd. dirs Peirce Warwick Adoption Svc., Washington, 1970-79 (pres. 1972-75), Venture Expeditionary (pres. 1981-83), Washington, 1979-83; mem. credit com. Potomac Community Fed. Credit Union, 1982-85. Mem. AAAS, Am. Soc. Cell Biology, Am. Soc. Microbiology, N.Y. Acad. Scis., Sigma Xi. Office: Diagnon Corp 9600 Medical Center Dr Rockville MD 20850-3336

LANDON, JOHN WILLIAM, minister, social worker, educator; b. Marlette, Mich., Mar. 24, 1937; s. Norman A. and Merle Irene (Lawrason) L. BA, Taylor U., 1959; MDiv, Northwestern U., Christian Theol. Sem., 1962; MSW, Ind. U., 1966; PhD in Social Sci., Ball State U., 1972. Regional supr. Iowa Dept. Social Welfare, Des Moines, 1965-67; acting chmn. dept. sociology Marion (Ind.) Coll., 1967-69; asst. prof. sociology and social work Ball State U., Muncie, Ind., 1969-71; asst. prof. social work, coord. base courses Coll. Social Work U. Ky., Lexington, 1971-73, assoc. prof., coord. Undergrad. Program in Social Work Coll. of Social Work, 1974-85, prof., assoc. dean, 1985—; dir. social work edn. Taylor U., Upland, Ind., 1973-74. Author: From These Men, 1966; Jesse Crawford, Poet of the Organ, Wizard

of the Mighty Wurlitzer, 1974; Behold the Mighty Wurlitzer, The History of the Theatre Pipe Organ, 1983; The Development of Social Welfare, 1986. Mem. AAUP, Coun. on Social Work Edn., Nat. Assn. Social Workers, Am. Guild Organists. Home: 809 Celia Ln Lexington KY 40504-2305 Office: U Ky Coll Social Work Lexington KY 40506-0027

LANDON, MICHAEL DE LAVAL, historian, educator; b. St. John, N.B., Can., Oct. 8, 1935; came to U.S., 1960; s. Arthur Henry Whittington and Elizabeth Worthington (Fair) L.; m. Doris Lee Clay, Dec. 31, 1959 (div. May 1980); children: Clay de Laval, Letitia Elizabeth; m. Carole Marie Prather, Feb. 28, 1981. BA, Oxford (Eng.) U., 1958, MA, 1961; MA, U. Wis., 1962, PhD, 1966. Asst. master Manor House Sch., Horsham, Eng., 1957, Dalhousie Sch., Ladybank, Scotland, 1958, Lakefield (Ont.) Coll. Sch., 1958-60; asst. prof. history U. Miss., Oxford, 1964-67, assoc. prof., 1967-72, prof., 1972—. Author: The Triumph of the Lawyers, 1970, The Honor and Dignity of the Profession, 1979, Erin and Britannia, 1980. Commr. City Housing Authority, Oxford, 1983—, chmn., 1993—; lay Eucharistic minister Episcopal Ch. Am. Philos. Soc. Rsch grantee, 1967, 74. Fellow Royal Hist. Soc. (U.K.); mem. Am. Soc. for Legal History (sec.-treas. 1988—), Phi Kappa Phi, Eta Sigma Phi, Phi Alpha Theta. Episcopalian. Avocation: bird feeding. Home: 219 Bramlett Blvd Oxford MS 38655 Office: Univ of Miss Dept of History University MS 38677

LANDON, ROBERT GRAY, retired manufacturing company executive; b. Portsmouth, Ohio, Dec. 22, 1928; s. Herman Robert and Hazel Ruth (Tener) L.; m. Sarah A. Newpher, July 2, 1954; children: Geoffrey, Suzanne. Student, Cornell U., 1947-49; BA in Econs., U. Pa., 1955; grad. advanced mgmt. program, Harvard Bus., 1978. Loan officer Nat. City Bank, Cleve., 1955-60; SEC adminstr. Smith Kline Corp., 1960-64; controller, treas. Grumman Allied Industries, Inc., Garden City, N.Y., 1964-76; v.p. Grumman Allied Industries, Inc., 1977-82; v.p. investment mgmt. Grumman Corp., Bethpage, N.Y., 1978-79; pres. Grumman Ohio Corp., Worthington, Ohio, 1979-88. Served with AC USN, 1949-53. Clubs: The Oaks.

LANDON, ROBERT KIRKWOOD, insurance company executive; b. N.Y.C., Apr. 27, 1929; s. Kirk A. and Edith (Ungar) L.; m. Beulah Pair, Mar. 19, 1965; children: Chris, Kathleen Landon Staley, Kellyann Landon Spears. Student, U. Va., 1946-48; B.S., Ga. Inst. Tech., 1950. With Am. Bankers Life Assurance Co., Miami, Fla., 1952—; pres. Am. Bankers Life Assurance Co., 1960-74, chmn., chief exec. officer, 1974—; chmn. bd., chief exec. officer Am. Bankers Ins. Group Inc., Miami; pres. Landon Corp., Dover, Del., 1971—; charter mem. advisory bd. Fla. Internat. U., 1972-74. Trustee Kirk A. and Dorothy P. Landon Found., 1969—, Barry U. Served to lt. (j.g.) USNR, 1950-53. Mem. Coun. Internat. Visitors, World Bus. Coun., Scabbard and Blade, Grove Isle Club, Phi Gamma Delta. Republican. Congregationalist. Home: 2 Casuarina Concourse Coral Gables FL 33143-6502 Office: Am Bankers Ins Group Inc 11222 Quail Roost Dr Miami FL 33157-6543

LANDOVSKY, JOHN, artistic director; b. Riger, Latvia, Jan. 2, 1935; came to U.S., 1950; s. Jains and Olga (Kalnins) L. Dancer Weirtterberg Stadiis Opera House, Stuttgart, Fed. Republic Germany, 1965, Internat. Ballet Co., Chgo., 1960-70, Lyric Opera of Chgo., 1960-70; asst. prof. U. Ill., Urbana, 1976-80; director Duluth (Minn.) Ballet Co., 1980-82, Ballet Hawaii, Honolulu, 1982, Hawaii State Ballet, Honolulu, 1982—. Office: Hawaii State Ballet 1418 Kapiolani Blvd Honolulu HI 96814-3603

LANDOW, GEORGE PAUL, English literature and art educator, author; b. White Plains, N.Y., Aug. 25, 1940; s. Herman Irving and Lilian (Driver) L.; m. Ruth Beverly Macktez, May 22, 1966; children: Shoshana Macktez, Noah M., Serena. AB, Princeton U., 1961, MA, 1963, PhD, 1966; MA, Brandeis U., 1962; MA (hon.), Brown U., 1972. From instr. to prof. English Columbia U., N.Y.C., 1965-71; assoc. prof. Brown U., Providence, 1971-77, prof., 1978-83, prof. English and art, 1984—; vis. assoc. prof. English, U. Chgo., 1970-71; guest curator Mus. Art, R.I. Sch. Design, Providence, 1975-79; co-dir. NEH Summer Inst., Yale U., 1988; cons. Bank St. Coll. Edn., 1988-90; faculty fellow Inst. for Rsch. in Info. and Scholarship, Brown U., 1990-93; Brit. Acad. vis. prof. U. Lancaster, 1994; referee depts. English, history and art history at various univs. Author: The Aesthetic and Critical Theories of John Ruskin, 1971 (Gustave O. Arldt award 1972), William Holman Hunt and Typological Symbolism, 1979, Victorian Types, Victorian Shadows: Biblical Typology in Victorian Literature, Art and Thought, 1980, Images of Crisis: Literary Iconolgy, 1750 to the Present, 1982, Ruskin, 1985, Elegant Jeremiahs: The Sage from Carlyle to Mailer, 1986, Hypertext: The Convergence of Contemporary Critical Theory and Technology, 1992; editor: (with others) A Pre-Raphaelite Friendship: The Correspondence of William Holman Hunt and John Lucas Tupper, 1986, (with Paul Delaney) Hypermedia and Literary Studies, 1991, (with Paul Delaney) The Digital World: Text-Based Computing in the Humanities, 1993, Hyper Text Theory, 1994; assoc. editor Jour. of Computing in Higher Edn.; cons. editor: UMI Press, Ann Arbor, Mich., 1985-88; author electronic books: Dickens Web, 1990, 92, (with Jon Lauestedt) In Memoriam Web, 1992, Hypertext in Hypertext, 1994, Wriying at the Edge, 1995; contbr. chpts. and essays to profl. publs; evaluator manuscripts for various jours. Mem. supt.'s guidance council on gifted edn. Providence Sch., 1980-85, 87-90, v.p., 1982-84, pres., 1984-85; Nat. Fulbright selection com. for U.K., 1989-91, Grad. Record Exam., Lit. in English Com., 1990-95. Recipient Best Software award EDUCOM/NCRIPTAL, 1990; Woodrow Wilson fellow Brandeis U., 1961-62, Class of 1873 fellow Princeton U., N.J., 1962-64, Soc. for Humanities, Cornell U., 1968-69, Chamberlain Fellowship, Columbia U., summer 1969, Guggenheim Found., 1974, 78, vis. fellow Brasenose Coll., Oxford (Eng.) U., 1977, Vis. Rsch. fellow U. Southampton, 1995; Fulbright scholar Birkbeck Coll., U. London, 1964-65; grantee Council on Humanities, Columbia U., summer 1968, NEH, 1976, 77-79, summer 1984, Nat. Endowment Arts, 1984-85, R.I. Com. Humanities, 1985-86, Annenberg/Corp. for Pub. Broadcasting, 1985-87. Mem. Tennyson Soc., Ruskin Assn., Brown U. Faculty Club (bd. mgrs. 1985—, pres. 1988-89), Athenaeum Club (London), Rev. Club, Phi Beta Kappa. Jewish. Avocations: building miniatures and furniture, weightlifting. Office: Brown U Dept English Providence RI 02912

LANDOW-ESSER, JANINE MARISE, lawyer; b. Omaha, Sept. 23, 1951; d. Erwin Landow and Beatrice (Hart) Appel; m. Jeffrey L. Esser, June 2, 1974; children: Erica, Caroline. BA, U. Wis., 1973; JD with honors, George Washington U., 1976. Bar: Va. 1976, D.C. 1977, Ill. 1985. Lawyer U.S. Dept. Energy, Washington, 1976-83, Bell, Boyd & Lloyd, Chgo., 1985-86, Seyfarth, Shaw, Fairweather & Geraldson, Chgo., 1986-88, Holleb & Coff, Chgo., 1988—; co-chmn. Environ. Safety and Health Practice Group, 1993—, mem. exec. com., 1994—. Contbr. articles to profl. jours. Bd. dirs Bernard Zell Anshe Emet Day Sch. Parent-Tchr. Orgn. Mem. ABA, Chgo. Bar Assn. (vice chmn. environ. law com. 1990-91, chmn. 1991-92), Am. Jewish Congress Commn. on Women's Equality (bd. dirs. 1994—). Office: Holleb & Coff 55 E Monroe Ste 4100 Chicago IL 60603

LANDRIAULT, JACQUES EMILE, retired bishop; b. Alfred, Ont., Can., Sept. 23, 1921; s. Amedee and Marie-Louise (Brisebois) L. B.A., U. Ottawa; Licence in Theology, St. Paul U. Sem., Ottawa. Ordained priest Roman Cath. Ch., 1947; curate in Noranda Que.; chancellor Diocese Timmins, Ont., 1953; bishop of Cadi, titular bishop of Alexandria Ont., 1962-64, bishop of Hearst, 1964-71; bishop of Timmins 1971-90, bishop emeritus, 1990—; mem. Can. Conf. Cath. Bishops Commn.: Liturgy, Mission; mem. Ont. Episcopal Com. on Cath. Edn.; v.p. Ont. Cath. Episcopal Conf.; mem. Cath. Conf. Ont. Address: John Paul II Residence, 1243 Kilborn Pl Apt 206, Ottawa, ON Canada K1H 6K9

LANDRIGAN, PHILIP JOHN, epidemiologist; b. Boston, June 14, 1942; s. John Joseph and Frances Joan (Conlin) L.; m. Mary Florence Magee, Aug. 27, 1966; children: Mary Frances, Christopher Paul, Elizabeth Marie. A.B., Boston Coll., 1963; M.D., Harvard U., 1967; M.S., London Sch. Hygiene and Tropical Medicine, 1977, D.I.H., 1977. Diplomate Am. Bd. Pediatrics, Am. Bd. Preventive Medicine, Am. Bd. Occupational Medicine, Am. Coll. Epidemiology. Intern Cleve. Met. Gen. Hosp., 1967-68; resident in pediatrics Children's Hosp. Med. Ctr., Boston, 1968-70; fellow in pediatrics Harvard U. Med. Sch., Boston, 1969-70; clin. instr. pediatrics Emory U. Sch. Medicine, Atlanta, 1970-71; epidemic intelligence service officer Ctrs. for Disease Control, Atlanta, 1970-73; dir. research and devel. smallpox erradi-

cation program, 1973-74, chief environ. hazards activity, 1974-79; dir. div. Surveillance, Hazard Evaluations and Field Studies Nat. Inst. for Occupational Safety and Health, Cin., 1979-85; prof. community medicine and pediatrics Mt. Sinai Sch. Medicine, N.Y.C., 1985—; dir. div. environ. and occupational medicine Mt. Sinai Sch. Medicine, 1985-90; prof., chmn. dept. community medicine, 1990—; mem. bd. on toxicology and environ. health hazards Nat. Acad. Sci., Washington, vice chmn., 1981-86; clin. prof. environ. health Sch. Pub. Health U. Wash., Seattle, 1983—. Contbr. numerous articles on pediatrics, pub. health, epidemiology, occupational medicine and environ. medicine to med. jours.; cons. editor: Archives of Environ. Health, 1982—; Am. Jour. Indsl. Medicine, 1979—; editor-in-chief Environ. Research, 1987—. Recipient Vol. award Dept. HEW, 1973; recipient Pub. Health Service Career Devel. award, 1975, group citation as mem. of Ctr. for Disease Control beryllium rev. panel, 1978, Meritorious Service medal USPHS, 1985. Fellow Royal Soc. Medicine; mem. Inst. of MedicineInternat. Commn. on Occupational Health, Am. Pub. Health Assn., Am. Epidemiol. Soc., Soc. for Epidemiologic Research, AAAS. Home: 915 Stuart Ave Mamaroneck NY 10543-4124 Office: Mt Sinai Sch Medicine Dept Community Medicine 1 Gustave L Levy Pl New York NY 10029-6504

LANDRY, G. YVES, automotive company executive. Pres., CEO Chrysler Can. Ltd., Windsor, Ont., Can. Office: Chrysler Can Ltd, 2450 Chrysler Ctr PO Box 1621, Windsor, ON Canada N9A 4H6

LANDRY, JANE LORENZ, architect; b. San Antonio, Feb. 12, 1936; d. John Henry and Lulie Amanda (Sample) L.; m. Duane Eugene Landry, Sept. 8, 1956; children: Rachel, Claire, Ellyn, Jean. Student U. Tex., 1952-55, Yale U., 1955-56; BArch, U. Pa., 1957. Registered arch., Tex. Draftsman Wade, Gibson, & Martin, Corpus Christi, Tex., 1958-59; project arch. O'Neil Ford & Assoc., San Antonio, 1959-65; prin. Duane Landry, Arch., San Antonio, 1965-68, Dallas, 1968-76; ptnr. Landry & Landry, Archs. & Planners, Dallas, 1976—, Meyer, Landry & Landry, Archs. & Planners, Dallas, 1977-80; instr. San Antonio Coll., 1965. Dir. at large Interfaith Forum on Religion, Art and Architecture, 1991-94; mem. Liturgical Commn. Diocese of Dallas, 1978-90. Recipient design awards Interfaith Forum on Religion, Art and Architecture, 1985, 89, 90. Fellow AIA (mem. hist. resources com., design awards Dallas chpt. 1970, 75, 76, 77, 80); mem. Tex. Soc. Architects (design award 1969, 81). Roman Catholic. Office: Landry & Landry Archs & Planners 6319 Meadow Rd Dallas TX 75230-5140

LANDRY, JOHN BERNARD, III, data processing executive; b. Oak Park, Ill., Nov. 13, 1947; s. John Bernard Jr. and Madeline Marie (Ries) m. Ann C. Outchcunis, Mar. 19, 1978; children: Adam John, Jillian Kate. BSBA, Babson Coll., 1969. Acct. Shawmut Nat. Corp., Boston, 1970-72; exec. v.p rsch. and devel. McCormacy & Doge Corp., Naticu, Mass., 1972-85; chmn. Distbrn. Mgmt. Systems Inc., Lexington, Mass., 1985-87; exec. v.p. rsch. and devel. Cullinet Software Inc., Westwood, Mass., 1987—; bd. dirs. Cullinet Software Inc., Westwood, Language Technology Inc., Salem, Mass. Author: Software Development Technology, 1986. Served with U.S. Army, 1969-75. Mem. Mass. Computer Software Coun. (trustee 1987—), Assn. Data Processin Svc. Orgn. (dir. 1987—). Avocations: tennis, skiing. Office: Lotus Development Cor 55 Cambridge Pky Bedford MA 01730

LANDRY, PAUL LEONARD, lawyer; b. Mpls., Nov. 23, 1950; s. LeRoy Robert Landry and Alice Ruth (Swain) Stephens; m. Lisa Yvonne Yeo, Dec. 13, 1984; children: Marc, Lauren, Matthew. BA, Macalester Coll., 1974; postgrad., Georgetown U., 1976-77; JD, Boston U., 1977. Bar: Va. 1977, D.C. 1978, Minn. 1984, U.S. Dist. Ct. D.C., U.S. Dsit. Ct. Va., U.S. Dist. Ct. Minn., U.S. Ct. Appeals (D.C., 2d, 4th and 8th Cirs.). Dancer Dance Theater Harlem, N.Y.C., 1970-72; prin. dancer Dance Theatre Boston, 1972-75; atty. EPA, Washington, 1976-77; assoc. Reed, Smith, Shaw & McClay, Washington, 1977-83; officer, shareholder Fredrikson & Byron, P.A., Mpls., 1984—; adj. prof. law William Mitchell Coll. Law, St. Paul, 1985-89; mem. adv. bd. Minn. Minority Corp. Counsel Program, Mpls., Minn. Music Acad., Mpls., 1989—. Chmn., bd. dirs. Ind. Sch. Dist. 284 Bd. Edn., 1992-93; bd. dirs. Walker Art Ctr., Mpls., 1992—; advisor Kevin McCary Scholarship Fund, Flyte Tyme Found. Mem. ABA (coord. of minority ptnrs. adv. com., chmn. governance com.), Nat. Bar Assn., Minn. Bar Assn., D.C. Bar, Hennepin Conty Bar Assn., Corp. Coun. Assn. Minn. (bd. dirs.), Black Entertainment and Sports Lawyers Assn., Minn. Minority Lawyers Assn., Barristers. Avocations: golf, basketball. Office: Fredrikson & Byron PA 900 2d Ave S Ste 1100 Minneapolis MN 55402

LANDRY, ROBERT EDWARD, public policy consultant; b. Arvida, Que., Can., Apr. 9, 1929; children from previous marriage: Michael, Peter, Robert, Anthony, Liane, Joanne, Stephanie; m. Nicola E. Mandoli. Student, St. Francis Xavier U., Antigonish, N.S., 1945-48; BEE, McGill U., 1950. V.p external affairs Imperial Oil Ltd., Toronto, 1978-82, v.p., 1978-93; pres. Strategex Cons., Inc., Ottawa, 1993—. Mem. Fed. Cultural Policy Rev. Com., Ottawa, 1980-82; bd. dirs. Nat. Theatre Sch. Can., Montreal, 1981-92, chmn., 1986-88, U. Ottawa Heart Inst., 1993—, The Arts Network/Le Reseau des Arts, 1993-94; chmn. Nat. Arts Ctr., Ottawa, 1988-94, U. Ottawa, 1989—; coun. mem. World Arts Forum, Geneva. Mem. Rideau Club, Granite Club (Toronto). Avocations: cycling, squash, music, skiing, tennis. Office: Strategex Cons Inc, 541 Sussex Dr, Ottawa, ON Canada K1N 6Z6

LANDRY, ROGER D., publishing company executive; b. Montreal, Que., Jan. 26, 1934; s. Charle and Mabel (Desgroseillers) L.; m. Suzanne Shepherd; children—Johane, Charle, Genevieve. Student, Sir George Williams U., Montreal, 1953, Institut des Sci. Politiques, Paris, 1956. Mgr. mktg. services Bell Can., Montreal, 1957-63; insp. Que. Provincial Police, Montreal, 1963-65; dep. dir. 1967 World Exhbn., Montreal, 1965-68, Air Can., 1968-70; pres. Beauregard, Landry, Nantel & Assocs., Montreal, 1970-75; sr. v.p., chief adminstrv. officer ITT Can., Port Cartier, 1975-77; v.p. mktg. and pub. affairs Montreal Baseball Club Ltd., 1977-80; pres., pub. La Presse Ltd., Montreal, 1980—; chmn. Can. Press. Named Mktg. Man of Yr. Major League Baseball, 1980. Mem. Que. Dailies Inc. (bd. dirs.), Can. Daily Newspaper Assn. (bd. dirs.), Can. Pub. Relations Soc. (Médaille du Président 1980, Médaille Edouard-Montpetit 1984), Société de la Place des Arts (chmn. bd.), Order Can. (officer), Order Quebec (officer),Order Golden Lion, Sons of Italy, Grande Médaille de Vermeil de la Ville de Paris. Office: La Presse, 7 Rue St Jacques, Montreal, PQ Canada H2Y 1K9

LANDRY, SARA GRIFFIN, social worker; b. Thomaston, Ga., Sept. 17, 1920; d. John Carl and Mary Thelma (Abercrombie) Griffin; m. Thomas Leonard Perkins, Dec. 22, 1939 (dec. Jan. 27, 1945); 1 child, Thomas Leonard Perkins Jr.; m. George Kimball Landry, Dec. 19, 1949 (dec. Aug. 30, 1971). AB in Social Work magna cum laude, Wesleyan Coll., 1980; MS in Family Counseling, Mercer U., 1981. Receptionist Social Security Adminstrn., Macon, Ga., 1945-50, clerical, 1960-65, svc. rep., 1965-78; dir., organizer Bibb County Foster Grandparent Program, Macon, Ga., 1981-84; coord. rsch. project Med. Ctr. of Cen. Ga., Macon, Ga., 1986-87; social worker, bd. dirs. Bibb County Sr. Citizens Inc., Macon, Ga.; sec. bd. dirs. Bibb County Sr. Citizens, Inc., Macon, Ga., 1989-90, pres. bd. dirs., 1990-91; bd. dirs. grant chmn. Family Counseling Ctr., Macon, 1986-92, 94—. Contbr. articles, poems and various short stories to profl. jours. Bd. dirs., v.p., com. chmn. Am. Cancer Soc., Macon, 1956—, hon. life mem. 1993—; sec., com. chmn. John Women Bibb County, 1979—; mem. sec. Civic Woman's Club, Macon, 1955-61; mem. Coun. Cath. Women, St. Joseph's Parish, pres., 1956-58; mem., bd. dirs. Savannah Diocesan Coun. Cath. Women, 1957-59; bd. dirs. Macon Little Theatre, 1994—. Named Vol. of Yr., Bibb County Sr. Citizens, Inc., 1988, Am. Cancer Soc., 1987-88, Cherry Blossom Sr. Queen for Cmty. Svc., 1986, Fundraiser Honoree, Am. Cancer Soc., 1991; Sara Landry Day proclaimed in her honor Mayor of Macon, 1991. Mem. LWV, AAUW (pres. 1991-93), Wesleyan Coll. Alumnae Assn. (Sara Griffin Perkins Landry scholarship established for non-traditional age students 1994), Nat. Honor Soc., Macon Little Theatre. Democrat. Roman Catholic. Avocations: reading, swimming, travel, theater. Home: 3807 Drury Dr Macon GA 31204-1313

LANDRY, THOMAS HENRY, construction executive; b. Detroit, Nov. 2, 1946; s. Ernest E. and Charman A. (Iles) L.; m. Eileen K. Iannucci, June 22, 1968; children: Paul T., Christine M. BSBA, U. Dayton, 1968; MBA, Wayne State U., 1972. Project adminstr. A.J. Etkin Constrn. Co. Farmington Hills, Mich., 1971-79, exec. v.p., 1979-85, pres., chief oper. officer, 1985—; chmn. Fin., Design & Build, Inc., Birmingham, Mich., 1986—. Bd.

dirs. March of Dimes Metro Detroit, 1992—, United Cerebral Palsy Metro Detroit. With U.S. Army, 1968-70, Vietnam. Mem. Associated Gen. Contractors Am. (bd. dirs. Detroit chpt. 1987—), Engring. Soc. Detroit (vice-chmn. constrn. activities com. 1987—), Constrn. Specifications Inst. (bd. dirs. met. chpt. 1982—), Mich. Constrn. Users Coun., Detroit Soc. of Clubs, Lakeland Country Club. Roman Catholic. Office: AJ Etkin Constrn Co 30445 Northwestern Hwy Ste 250 Farmington Hills MI 48334

LANDRY, TOM (THOMAS WADE LANDRY), former professional football coach; b. Mission, Tex., Sept. 11, 1924; s. Ray and Ruth (Coffman) L.; m. Alicia Wiggs, Jan. 28, 1949; children—Thomas, Kitty, Lisa. BBA, U. Tex., 1949; BS in Indsl. Engring., U. Houston, 1952. Player N.Y. Yankees All-Am. Football Conf., 1949; player N.Y. Giants, 1950-53, player-coach, 1954-55, defensive coach, 1956-59; head coach Dallas Cowboys, 1960-89. Author: (with Gregg Lewis) Tom Landry: An Autobiography, 1990. Trustee Nat. Fellowship Christian Athletes, chmn. bd. Dallas chpt. Served with USAAF, World War II. Named to All-Pro team, 1954, to Pro Football Hall of Fame, 1990; coached winning Super Bowl teams, 1971, 77. Methodist (bd. govs.). Office: Landry Investment Group Inc 8411 Preston Rd Ste 720 Dallas TX 75225-5519

LANDSBERG, DENNIS ROBERT, engineering executive, consultant; b. Bklyn., Dec. 27, 1948; s. Nathan and Marilyn (Scherling) L.; m. Marjorie Ina Sahr, Aug. 18, 1974; children: Rebecca, Nancy, Jeniffer. BS in Aero. Engring., Poly. U., N.Y., 1969, MS, 1971; PhD, SUNY, Albany, 1975. Rsch. asst. Poly. Inst. N.Y., Bklyn., 1969-71; rsch. assoc. SUNY, Albany, 1971-75, Atmospheric Sci. Rsch. Ctr., Albany, 1976-79; pres. Assoc. Weather Svcs., Albany, 1979-85; v.p. W.S. Fleming & Assocs., Albany, 1977-85; pres. The Fleming Group, Syracuse, N.Y., 1986—. Author: (with R. Stewart) Improving Energy Efficiency in Buildings, 1980. Recipient Energy Conservation Design award Owens Corning Fiberglas, 1982; Soc. for Tech. Communications Mohawk Regional Mgmt. award, 1984. Mem. ASHRAE, AIAA, Am. Meteorol. Soc., Sigma Xi. Democrat. Jewish. Avocations: swimming, fishing, bowling, golf. Home: 6733 Harmony Dr Fayetteville NY 13066-1782 Office: The Fleming Group 6310 Fly Rd East Syracuse NY 13057-9325

LANDSBERG, LEWIS, endocrinologist, medical researcher; b. N.Y.C., Nov. 23, 1938. AB, Williams Coll., 1960; MD, Yale U., 1964. From instr. to asst. prof. medicine Sch. Medicine Yale U., 1969-72; from asst. prof. to prof. medicine Harvard Med. Sch., 1972-90; Irving S. Cutter prof., chmn. dept. medicine Med. Sch. Northwestern U., 1990—, dir. Ctr. Endocrinology, Metabolism & Nutrition, 1990—; assoc. physician Yale-New Haven Hosp., 1969-71, attending physician, 1971-72, Beth Israel Hosp., 1974-79, physician, 1979-88, sr. physician, 1988-90; attending physician West Haven VA Hosp., 1970-72; assisting physician Boston City Hosp., 1972-73, assoc. vis. physician, 1973-74; physician-in-chief dept. medicine Northwestern Meml. Hosp., 1990—. Fellow Am. Coll. Physicians; mem. AAAS, Am. Fedn. Clin. Rsch., Endocrine Soc., N.Y. Acad. Scis., AHA, Am. Soc. Pharmacology & Exptl. Therapeutics, Am. Physiology Soc., Am. Soc. Clin. Investigators, Assn. Am. Physicians. Achievements include rsch. in catecholamines and the sympathoadrenal system, nutrition and the sympathetic nervous system, obesity and hypertension. Office: Ctr Endocrinology Metabolism & Nutrition 10-555 Searle 303 E Chicago Ave Chicago IL 60611-3008

LANDSBERG, MICHELE, journalist; b. Toronto, July 12, 1939; d. Jack and Naomi Leah Landsberg; m. Stephen Lewis, May 30, 1963; children: Ilana Naomi, Avram David, Jenny Leah. BA, U. Toronto, 1962. Reporter Globe & Mail, Toronto, 1962-65, columnist, 1985-89; freelancer, 1965-71; editor, feature writer Chatelaine, 1971-78; columnist The Toronto Star, 1978-84, 89—, Globe and Mail, Toronto, 1985-88. Author: Women & Children First, 1982, Reading for the Love of It, 1986, This is New York, Honey! A Homage to Manhattan in Love & Rage, 1989. Recipient Nat. Newspaper award (columns), 1980, (feature writing) 81. Office: TorStar Newspapers Ltd, 1 Yonge St, Toronto, ON Canada M5E 1E6

LANDSEA, CHRISTOPHER W., meteorologist, educator. Prof. dept. atmospheric scis. Colo. State U. Recipient Banner I. Miller award Am. Meteorol. Assn., 1994. Office: Colorado St Univ Dept Atmospheric Science Colorado State University CO 80523*

LANDSMAN, EMANUEL ELBERT, manufacturing company executive; b. Bklyn., Jan. 10, 1937; s. Benjamin and Lillian F. (Neidich) L.; m. Sheila E. Tanzer, June 10, 1961; 1 child, Susan. B.S., MIT, 1958, M.S., 1959, E.E., 1960, Sc.D., 1966. Registered profl. engr., Mass. Vice pres. Am. Power Conversion, Burlington, Mass., 1981—, also bd. dirs. Served with USN, 1960-61. Mem. IEEE, Sigma Xi. Office: Am Power Conversion Corp 132 Fairgrounds Rd West Kingston RI 02892*

LANDSMAN, STEPHEN A., lawyer; b. Chgo., Aug. 28, 1942; s. Sam W. and Jeanne N. (Engerman) L.; m. Beth Landsman; children: Mark, Scott, Sari. B.S. in Econs., Wharton Sch. Fin., U. Pa., 1964; J.D. summa cum laude, U. Mich., 1967. Bar: Ill. 1967, U.S. Dist. Ct. (no. dist.) Ill. 1967, U.S. Ct. Appeals (7th cir.) 1967, U.S. Tax Ct. 1970. Assoc. Mayer, Brown & Platt, Chgo., 1967-69; assoc. Rudnick & Wolfe, Chgo., 1969-70, ptnr., 1970—. Contbr. articles to legal jours. Bd. dirs., treas. St. Joseph Hosp. Assocs., Chgo., 1978-82. Mem. Chgo. Bar Assn., Ill. Bar Assn., Am. Arbitration Assn., Order of Coif. Club: Standard, East Bank (Chgo.). Office: Rudnick & Wolfe 203 N La Salle St Ste 1800 Chicago IL 60601-1210

LANDSTROM, GAY LARAY, health facility administrator; b. Monterey, Calif., Sept. 15, 1960; d. John Dewey and Mary Jane (DuPont) Streeter; m. Brian Paul Landstrom, Apr. 26, 1986; 1 child, Noah Colin. BS in Nursing magna cum laude, Rush U., 1983; MS, U. Ill., Chgo., 1988. Asst. head nurse Rush-Presbyn. St. Luke's Med. Ctr., Chgo., 1985-86; nursing unit mgr. Mercy Ctr., Aurora, Ill., 1987-89; clin. nurse specialist Good Samaritan Hosp., Downers Grove, Ill., 1989-90; dir. nursing clin. ops. Good Samaritan Hosp., Downers Grove, Ill., 1990—. Mem. Oncology Nursing Soc., Sigma Theta Tau.

LANDUYT, BERNARD FRANCIS, economist, educator; b. Monmouth, Ill., Mar. 22, 1907; m. Meta Louise Bossong, June 2, 1928. BEd, Western Ill. Tchrs. Coll., 1929; AM, State U. Iowa, 1936, PhD, 1938; AM, Columbia U., 1943; LLD (hon.), U. Detroit, 1973; EdD (hon.), Cen. Mich. U., 1991. Tchr. pub. schs., 1926-31; tchr., prin., pub. high schs. P.I., 1931-35; instr. State U. Iowa, 1937-38; mem. faculty, dept. econ. and bus. adminstrn. U. Detroit, 1938-71, chmn., 1947-63, prof. econs., 1949-71, chmn. MBA Program, 1948-74, asst. dean Coll. Commerce and Fin., 1958-63, dean Coll. Commerce and Fin., 1963-71; dean emeritus Coll. Commerce and Fin. Coll. Bus. and Adminstrn. (formerly Coll. Commerce and Fin.), 1971—, disting. prof. adminstrn. Coll. Commerce and Fin., 1974—; lectr. OPM, 1958-63, Madonna U., 1960-93, Nat. Mgmt. Assn., 1960-78, divsn. mgmt. edn. U. Mich., 1969-90, Inst. for Career and Personal Devel., Ctrl. Mich. U., 1976-93, Chrysler Inst., 1976-78. Co-author: Administrative Strategy, 1961, Administrative Strategy and Decision Making, 1966. Mem. Detroit St. Ry. Commn., 1963-72, pres., 1970-72; mem. Detroit Rapid Transit Commn., S.E. Mich. Transp. Authority, 1967-72. Served as mil. govt. officer USNR, 1942-46; mem. jap. trade sub-commn. Allied Control Commn. for Italy econ., 1943, agrl. officer U.S. Mil. Govt. Saipan, 1944, chief salvage sect. U.S. Mil. Govt. Okinawa, 1945, ret. comdr. USNR. Decorated Bronze Star. Mem. Am. Econs. Assn., Assn. Social Econs., Naval Res. Assn., Navy League U.S., U.S. Naval Acad. Found., U.S. Naval Inst., Res. Officers Assn., Mil. Order World Wars, Order of Artus, Alpha Phi Omega, Beta Alpha Psi, Alpha Sigma Lambda, Beta Gamma Sigma, Delta Phi Epsilon, Kappa Delta Pi, Delta Mu Delta. Roman Catholic. Home: 31698 Southview St Beverly Hills MI 48025-4051

LANDWEHR, ARTHUR JOHN, minister; b. Northbrook, Ill., Mar. 8, 1934; s. Arthur John Sr. and Alice Eleanor (Borchardt) L.; m. Avonna Lee, Sept. 19, 1953; children: Arthur J. III, Andrea Lea Askow. BA, Drake U., 1956; BD, Garrett-Theol. Sem., 1959; DD (hon.), North Cen. Coll., 1980. Ordained minister in Meth. Ch. Pastor Lyndon (Ill.) United Meth. Ch., 1956-59, Marseilles (Ill.) United Meth. Ch., 1959-65, Faith United Meth. Ch., Lisle, Ill., 1965-69; sr. minister First United Meth. Ch., Elmhurst, Ill., 1969-75, Evanston, Ill., 1975-88; sr. minister Grace United Meth. Ch.,

Naperville, Ill., 1988—; trustee Garrett-Evang. Theol. Sem., Evanston, 1976—, 1st v.p. bd. trustees, 1977-86; del. to gen. conf. United Meth. Ch., 1976, 80, 84, 88, World Meth. Conf., Nairobi, Kenya, 1986; Wilson lectr., 1987; preacher Adams Sermon Bloomington, Ind., 1991, N.Mex. Ann. Conf., 1992, N.W. Tex. Conf., 1992. Author: In the Third Place, 1972; contbr. articles to profl. jours. Convenor Blue Ribbon Com. for Referendum on Expanded Gambling in Ill., 1994. Recipient citation for human rels. City of Lisle, 1969; study grantee World Coun. Chs., Sri Lanka, 1983, Ecumenical Inst. for Advanced Studies, Tantur, Israel, 1977. Mem. AAAS, Am. Acad. Religion, Am. Theol. Soc., Ill. Bar Assn. (interpfcl. cooperation com. 1991, Order St. Luke, Univ Club (pres. Evanston chpt. 1986-87). Home: 520 Highland Ave Naperville IL 60540-5423 Office: Grace United Meth Ch 300 E Gartner Rd Naperville IL 60540-7424 *It is evident to me that life is a gift surrounded in mystery. Like most mysteries, we wait for the moment of revelation in which there is a profound understanding. I've learned that without a radical lane life has no future.*

LANDWEHR, WILLIAM CHARLES, museum director; b. Milw., Sept. 19, 1941; s. Frank Albert and LaVerna Gertrude (Schumacher) L.; children—Leslie Lynne, Randall Scott, Eric Hampton, Christopher Whitney. B.S., U. Wis. Stevens Point, 1964; M.A., U. N.D., 1968. Curator Art Ctr. Gallery U. Wis.-Stout, Menomonie, 1968-69; dir. S.D. Art Mus., Brookings, S.D., 1969-71, Quincy (Ill.) Art Center, 1971-73; curator exhbns. Mint Mus. Art, Charlotte, N.C., 1973-76; dir. Springfield (Mo.) Art Mus., 1976-87, Lakeview Mus. of Arts and Scis., Peoria, Ill., 1987-89, Paine Art Ctr. and Arboretum, Oshkosh, Wis., 1989—; mem. adv. bd. Ringling Sch. Art and Design Fine Arts Dept., Sarasota, Fla., 1986-89. Author: Watercolor U.S.A. 1986, The Monumental Image, Ellen Murray: The Collection Series; (catalogue raisonnes) The Lithographs and Etchings of Philip Pearlstein, 1978, Robert Cottingham: A Print Retrospective, 1972-76; editor: Selections from the Permanent Collection of the Springfield Art Museum, 1980. Mem. Am. Assn. Mus., Am. Fedn. Arts (trustee 1978-80), Ill. Congress of Hist. Soc. and Mus. (trustee 1988-89), Midwest Mus. Conf., Wis. Fed. Mus. Lutheran. Home: 1931 Otter Ln Eagle River WI 54521-8817 Office: Paine Art Ctr and Arboretum 1410 Algoma Blvd Oshkosh WI 54901-7708

LANDY, BURTON AARON, lawyer; b. Chgo., Aug. 16, 1929; s. Louis J. and Clara (Ernstein) L.; m. Eleanor M. Simmel, Aug. 4, 1957; children: Michael Simmel, Alisa Anne. Student, Nat. U. Mex., 1948; B.S. Northwestern U., 1950; postgrad. scholar, U. Havana, 1951; J.D., U. Miami, 1952; postgrad. fellow, Inter-Am. Acad. Comparative Law, Havana, Cuba, 1955-56. Bar: Fla. 1952. Practice law in internat. field Miami, 1955—; ptnr. firm Ammerman & Landy, 1957-63, Paul, Landy, Beiley & Harper, P.A. and predecessor firm, 1964-94, Steel Hector & Davis, 1994—; lectr. Latin Am. bus. law U. Miami Sch. Law, 1972-75; also internat. law confs. in U.S. and abroad; mem. Nat. Conf. on Fgn. Aspects of U.S. Nat. Security, Washington, 1958; mem. organizing com. Miami regional conf. Com. for Internat. Econ. Growth, 1958; mem. U.S. Dept. Commerce Regional Export Expansion Council, 1969-74, mem. Dist. Export Council, 1978—; mem. U.S. Sec. State Adv. Com. on Pvt. Internat. Law; dir. Fla. Council Internat. Devel., 1977—, chmn. 1986-87; mem. U. Miami Citizens Bd., 1977—; chmn. Fla. del. S.E. U.S.-Japan Assn., 1980-82; mem. adv. com. 1st Miami Trade Fair of Ams., 1978; dir., v.p. Greater Miami Fgn. Trade Zone, Inc., 1978—; mem. organizing com., lectr. 4 Inter-Am. Aviation Law Confs.; bd. dirs. Inter-Am. Bar Legal Found.; participant Aquaculture Symposium Sci. and Man in the Ams., Mexico City, Fla. Gov's Econ. Mission to Japan and Hong Kong, 1978; mem. bd. exec. advisors Law and Econs. Ctr.; mem. vis. com. U. Miami Sch. Bus.; mem. internat. fin. council Office Comptroller of Fla.; founding chmn. Fla.-Korea Econ. Coop. Com., 1982—, Southeast U.S.-Korea Econ. Com., 1985—; chmn. Expo 500 Fla.-Columbus Soc., 1985-87; founding co-chmn. So. Fla. Roundtable-Georgetown U. Ctr. for Strategic and Internat. Studies, 1982-85; chmn. Fla. Gov's Conf. on World Trade, 1984—; gen. counsel Fla. Internat. Bankers Assn.; dir., former gen. counsel Fla. Internat. Ins. and Reins. Assn., chmn. Latin Am. Carribbean Bus. Promotion Adv. Counc. to U.S. Sec. of Commerce and Aid Adminstr; appointee Fla. Internat. Trade and Investment Coun.; mem. steering com. Summit of Ams., 1994—, co-chair point summit planning com. Contbg. editor Econs. Devel. Lawyers of the Ams., 1969-74; contbr. numerous articles to legal jours. in U.S. and fgn. countries. Chmn. City of Miami Internat. Trade and Devel. Com., 1984-86; chmn. internat. task force Beacon Coun. of Dade County, Fla., 1985, dir., chmn., 1991—; bd. dirs., exec. com. Internat. Comml. Dispute Resolution Ctr., Miami Internat. Arbitration and Mediation Inst.; appointed by Gov. of Fla. to Internat. Currency and Barter Commn., 1986; lectr. U. Miami Inter-Ban course for Latin Am. bankers; steering com. Summit of the Americas, Miami, 1994, co-chair post Summit Planning Com., 1994. With JAGC, USAF,. 1952-54, Korea; to maj. Res. Named Internat. Trader of Yr. Fla. Council Internat. Devel., 1980, Bus. Person of Yr., 1986; recipient Pan Am. Informatica Comunicaciones Expo award, 1983, Lawyer of Americas award U. Miami, 1984, Richard L. McLaughlin award Fla. Econ. Devel. Coun., 1993; named hon. consul gen. Republic of Korea, Miami, 1983-88, recipient Heung-in medal (Order of Diplomatic Service), 1986, Ministerial Citation, Min. of Fgn. Affairs, 1988; apptd. Hon. consul Ft. Lauderdale, Fla., 1991—. Fellow ABA Found. (chmn. com. arrangements internat. and comparative law sect. 1964-65, com. on Inter-Am. affairs of ABA 1985-87); mem. Inter-Am. Bar Assn. (asst. sec.-gen. 1957-59, treas. 11th conf. 1959, co-chmn. jr. bar sect. 1963-65, mem council 1969—, exec. com. 1975—, pres. 1982-84, Diploma de Honor 1987, William Roy Vallance award 1989), Spanish Am. Bar Assn., Fla. Bar Assn. (vice chmn. adminstrv. law com. 1965, vice chmn. internat. and comparative law com. 1967-68, chmn. aero. law com. 1968-69), Dade County Bar Assn. (chmn. fgn. laws and langs com. 1964-65), Internat. Ctr. Fla. (pres. 1981-82), World Peace Through Law Ctr., Miami Com. Fgn. Relations, Inst. Ibero Am. Derecho Aero., Am. Soc. Internat. Law, Council Internat. Visitors, Am. Fgn. Law Assn. (pres. Miami 1958), Bar of South Korea (hon. mem.), Greater Miami C. of C. (bd. govs. 1986—), Colombian-Am. C. of C. (bd. dirs. 1986—), Peruvian-Am. C. of C. (bd. dirs.), Phi Alpha Delta. Home: 605 Almeria Ave Coral Gables FL 33134 Office: Steel Hector & Davis 200 S Biscayne Blvd Miami FL 33131-2398

LANDY, JOANNE VEIT, foreign policy analyst; b. Chgo., Oct. 15, 1941; d. Fritz and Lucille (Stearns) Veit; m. Seymour Landy, Mar., 1959 (div. 1962); m. Nelson Lichtenstein, Mar., 1972 (div. 1976). BA in History, U. Calif., Berkeley, 1968; MA in History, U. Calif., Berkeley, 1970; MPH, Columbia U., 1982. Dir. N.Y. Met. Office, U. Chgo., N.Y.C., 1977-80; exec. dir. Campaign for Peace and Democracy, N.Y.C., 1982—; bd. dirs. Human Rights Watch, Helsinki. Editor: Peace & Democracy, 1984—. Recipient grant for rsch. and writing John D. and Catherine T. Mac Arthur Fedn. Program on Peace and Internat. Cooperation, Chgo., 1990-91. Mem. Coun. on Fgn. Rels., Phi Beta Kappa. Home: 2785 Broadway # 7A New York NY 10025 Office: Campaign for Peace and Democracy PO Box 1640 New York NY 10025

LANDY, RICHARD ALLEN, former geologist, consultant; b. Clearfield, Pa., Sept. 23, 1931; s. Gilbert Maxwell and Esther (Robinson) L.; m. Donna Jean Horst, Jan. 25, 1959; children: Richard A. Jr., Jennifer S. SB in Geology, MIT, 1953; MS in Mineralogy, Pa. State U., 1955, PhD in Mineralogy, 1961. Supervisory engr. Carborundum Co., Niagara Falls, N.Y., 1960-62; rsch. mineralogist Basic Inc., Bettsville, Ohio, 1962-63, mgr. quality assurance, 1963-65; cons., 1965-67; asst. prof. geology Allegheny Coll., Meadville, Pa., 1965-67; field officer Geol. Survey of Can., Ottawa, summer 1966, 67; rsch. mineralogist N.Am. Refractories Co., Curwensville, Pa., 1967-70; dir. rsch. N.Am. Refractories Co. State College, Pa., 1970-88; gen. mgr. N.Am. Refractories Co., Cleve., 1988-89, v.p. tech., 1989-91; dir. program devel. Ctr. for Advanced Materials, Pa. State U., 1992-93; cons. in field; mem. bd. examiners Pa. Quality Leadership Awards, 1994. Contbr. articles to profl. jours.; patentee in field. 1st lt. U.S. Army, 1953-55. Fellow Brit. Ceramics Soc.; mem. ASTM (Merit award 1989). Home: 1751 Princeton Dr State College PA 16803-3260

LANE, ALVIN HUEY, JR., management consultant; b. Dallas, May 2, 1942; s. Alvin Huey and Marianne (Halsell) L.; m. Melanie Kadane, June 21, 1963; children—Alvin Huey, III, Michael, Lance, Marianne. B.A. (Western Electric scholar, J. Venn Leeds scholar), Rice U., Houston, 1964, BA., 1965. Mgmt. positions with Procter & Gamble Mfg. Co., 1965-68; mgmt. cons. Ernst & Young, CPA's, Dallas, 1968-69; v.p. fin., sec. Balanced Investment Dynamics Co., Dallas, 1969-72, Dr Pepper Co., Dallas, 1972-80; sr. v.p. fin.,

sec. Dr Pepper Co., 1980-83; pres. Lane & Assocs., Dallas, 1983—; bd. dirs. Heartland Wireless Comms., Dallas, Love Bottling Co., Muskogee, Okla., Marketplace Christian Network, Dallas. Mem. Lakewood Country Club. Home: 3415 Colgate Ave Dallas TX 75225-4830 Office: Lane and Assocs 10440 N Central Expy Ste 610 Dallas TX 75231-2227

LANE, ALVIN S., lawyer; b. Englewood, N.J., June 17, 1918; s. Martin Lane and Nettie (Gans) Daniels; m. Terese P. Lyons, Apr. 24, 1949; children: Mary-Jo, Judith Lyons. Ph.B., U. Wis., 1940; LL.B., Harvard U., 1943. Bar: N.Y. 1947. Sr. ptnr. Wien, Lane & Malkin (now Wien, Malkin & Bettex), 1954-83; chmn. Rapidata, Inc., 1967-82; Mem. adv. bd. to N.Y. atty. gen. on art legis., 1966-71. Contbr. articles to art publs. and legal jours. Mem. bd. mgmt. Henry Ittleson Rsch. Ctr. Disturbed Children, Riverdale, N.Y., 1961-70; fellow Brandeis U., 1966—, nat. adv. coun. 20th Century Art Soc. High Mus. of Art, 1986—; sec., trustee Aldrich Mus. Contemporary Art, Inc., 1966-76; trustee Lexington Sch. Deaf, 1971; v.p., trustee Soho Ctr. Visual Artists, Inc., 1974-83; dir. Creative Artists Pub. Svc. Program, Inc., 1982-84; mem. drawing com. Whitney Mus. Am. Art, 1991-93; mem. The Elvehjem Mus. Art Coun., 1992—. Served as lt. USNR, 1942-46. Mem. Assn. of Bar of City of N.Y. (chmn. com. art 1963-65), N.Y. Artists Equity Assn. (dir. 1982-84). Clubs: Harvard (N.Y.C.), Riverdale Yacht. Home: 5251 Independence Ave Riverdale NY 10471-2825 Office: 35 E 38th St New York NY 10016-2523

LANE, ANN JUDITH, history and women's studies educator; b. N.Y.C., July 27, 1931; d. Harry A. and Elizabeth (Brown) Lane; children: Leslie Patricia, Joni Alexandra. BA, Bklyn. Coll., 1952; MA, NYU, 1958; PhD, Columbia U., 1968. Mng. editor Challenge Mag., NYU, 1953-56; asst. prof. Douglass Coll., Rutgers U., New Brunswick, N.J., 1968-71; prof. John Jay Coll., SUNY, 1971-83; vis. prof. Wheaton Coll., Norton, Mass., 1981-82; prof. history, dir. women's studies Colgate U., Hamilton, N.Y., 1983-90, U. Va., Charlottesville, 1990—. Author: To Herland and Beyond, 1990, Mary Ritter Beard: A Sourcebook, 1977, 2d edit., 1988, The Brownsville Affair, 1971; editor: Charlotte Perkins Gilman Reader, 1980, Herland: A Lost Utopian Novel, 1979. Chair Com. on Status of Women in the Profession, Orgn. of Am. Historians, 1992-95; dir. History Tchr. Inst., N.Y. Coun. for Humanities, summer 1985; mem. historians adv. com. Nat. Women's Hall of Fame, 1986—; bd. dirs. Louis M. Rabinowitz Found., 1972-76. Fellow, Berkshire Conf. Women Historians, 1988, Ford Found., 1981-82, Nat. Endowment for Humanities, 1980-81, Lilly Endowment, Inc., 1977-79, AAUW, 1959-60. Mem. AAUP (mem. com. on women 1987—), Orgn. Am. Historians (mem. Frederick Jackson Turner prize com. 1979), Women in Hist. Profession (exec. bd., coordinating com. 1971-74). Home: 2603 Jefferson Park Cir Charlottesville VA 22903-4133

LANE, ARTHUR ALAN, lawyer; b. N.Y.C., Dec. 2, 1945; s. George and Delys L.; m. Jane Ficocella, Dec. 30, 1972; 1 child, Eva B. BA, Yale U., 1967; JD, Columbia U., 1970, MBA, 1971. Bar: N.Y. 1971. Assoc. Webster, Sheffield, Fleischmann, Hitchcock & Brookfield, N.Y.C., 1971-72; asst. to div. counsel Liggett & Myers Inc., N.Y.C., 1973; assoc. Wickes, Riddell, Bloomer, Jacobi & McGuire, N.Y.C., 1974-78, Morgan, Lewis & Bockius, N.Y.C., 1979; ptnr. Eaton & Van Winkle, N.Y.C., 1980-94, DeForest & Duer, N.Y.C., 1994—. Mem. ABA, Assn. of Bar of City of N.Y., Soc. of Colonial Wars. Avocation: gardening. Home: 103 Brookside Dr Smithtown NY 11787-4456 Office: DeForest & Duer 90 Broad St New York NY 10004

LANE, BARBARA MILLER (BARBARA MILLER-LANE), humanities educator; b. N.Y.C., Nov. 1, 1934; d. George Ross Rede and Gertrude Miller; m. Jonathan Lane, Jan. 28, 1956; children: Steven Gregory, Eleanor. B.A., U. Chgo., 1953, Barnard Coll., 1956; M.A., Radcliffe Coll., 1957; Ph.D., Harvard U., 1962. Tutor history and lit. Harvard U., Cambridge, Mass., 1960-61; lectr. to prof. history Bryn Mawr Coll., Bryn Mawr, Pa., 1962-75, dir. Growth and Structure of Cities Program, 1971-89, Andrew W. Mellon prof. humanities, 1981—; vis. prof. Architecture, Columbia U., 1989; cons. NEH sr. fellowships, Washington, 1971-73, Time-Life Books, N.Y.C., 1975, Bauhaus, Dessau, 1991; advisor Macmillan Ency. of Architects, N.Y.C., 1979-82; vis. examiner U. Helsinki, 1991; vis. lectr. Technische Universität, Berlin, 1991. Author: Architecture and Politics in Germany, 1968, 85, Italian and German editions 1973, 86; co-author: Nazi Ideology Before 1933, 1978; contbg. author: Growth and Transformation of the Modern City, 1979, Macmillan Encyclopedia of Architects, 1982, Urbanisierung im 19. und 20. Jahrhundert, 1983, Perspectives in American History, 1984, The Evidence of Art: Images and Meaning in History, 1986, Art and Money, 1988, Nationalism in the Visual Arts, 1991, Moderne Architektur in Deutschland: Expressionismus und Neue Sachlichkeit, 1994; contbg. editor: Urbanism Past and Present, 1980-85; mem. bd. editors Archtl. History Found., 1988-94, Ctrl. European History 1992—; contbr. articles to profl. jours. Co-founder, dir., chmn. bd. dirs. New Gulph Child Care Ctr., Bryn Mawr, 1971-75; mem. Middle Atlantic Regional Com., Mellon Fellowships in the Humanities, 1985-87; mem. vis. com. Harvard U. Dept. History, 1986-92, Berlin Stadtforum (adv. coun. to Senator for Urban Devel. and Environment), 1991—. Fellow AAUW, 1959-60, Fels Found., 1961-62, Am. Council Learned Socs., 1967-68, John S. Guggenheim Found., 1977-78; sr. fellow Ctr. for Advanced Study in the Visual Arts, Nat. Gallery of Art, Washington, 1983; Am. Scandinavian Found. fellow, 1989; Wissenschaftskolleg zu Berlin fellow, 1990-91; NEH grantee, summer 1989; recipient Lindback award for excellence in tchg., 1988. Mem. Soc. Archtl. Historians (bd. dirs. 1977-80, Alice Davis Hitchcock award 1968, chmn. awards com. 1976, 82, chmn. jour. com. 1982-83), Conf. Group on Central European History (bd. dirs. 1977-79, chmn. awards com. 1987, structure and planning adv. com. 1993—), Am. Hist. Assn. (mem. council 1979-82, chmn. com. on Popular Mag. of History 1982), Coll. Art Assn., Phi Beta Kappa. Office: Bryn Mawr Coll Bryn Mawr PA 19010

LANE, BERNARD BELL, furniture company executive; b. Lynchburg, Va., Nov. 23, 1928; s. Edward Hudson and Myrtle Clyde (Bell) L.; m. Minnie Matthews Bassett, June 7, 1950; children: William R., Lucy H., Douglas B., Bernard Bell. B.S., U.S. Naval Acad., 1950. With Lane Co., Altavista, Va., 1954-87; v.p., then exec. v.p. Lane Co., 1960-76, pres., chmn. exec. com., 1976-81, chmn. bd., 1981-87. Commr. Va. Port Authority, 1986—; bd. dirs. Va. Poly. Inst. and State U. Ednl. Found., 1968-76, Food for the Hungry Inc., Scottsdale, Ariz., 1985— (chmn. bd. dirs. 1990); mem. Va. Gov.'s Adv. Bd. on Indsl. Devel., 1970-82, Va. Gov.'s Adv. Bd. on Revenue Estimates, from 1977-85; chmn. com. urol. rsch., endowment and devel. Duke U. Med. Ctr., 1974-82. Mem. Va. Mfrs. Assn. (bd. dirs. 1986-87). Methodist.

LANE, BRUCE STUART, lawyer; b. New London, Conn., May 15, 1932; s. Stanley S. and Frances M. (Antis) L.; m. Elizabeth Steinberg, Aug. 10, 1958; children: Sue Ellen, Charles M., Richard I. Student, Boston U., 1948-49; AB magna cum laude, Harvard U., 1952, JD, 1955. Bar: Ohio 1955, D.C. 1966, U.S. Ct. Claims 1960, U.S. Tax Ct. 1961, U.S. Supreme Ct. 1961. Assoc. Squire, Sanders & Dempsey, Cleve., 1955-59; sr. trial atty. tax div. Dept. Justice, Washington, 1959-61; tax atty. Dinsmore, Shohl, Barrett, Coates & Deupree, Cin., 1961-65; sec., asst. gen. counsel corp. and tax matters Communications Satellite Corp., Washington, 1965-69; v.p., gen. counsel Nat. Corp. Housing Partnerships, Washington, 1969-70; pres. Lane and Edson P.C., Washington, 1970-89; ptnr. Kelley Drye & Warren, Washington, 1989-93; mng. ptnr. Peabody & Brown, Washington, 1993—; bd. dirs. Nat. Found. for Affordable Housing Solutions. Co-editor-in-chief Housing and Devel. Reporter; author publs. and articles on tax, partnership and real estate. Incorporator, bd. dirs., past pres. D.C. Inst. Mental Health; past chmn. citizens Com. sect. 5 Chevy Chase, Md.; past mem. Montgomery County Hist. Preservation Commn., Md.; mem. historic coun. Crow Canyon Archeol. Ctr., Cortez, Colo. Maj. JAG, USAR, 1952-68. Mem. ABA, Am. Law Inst., Am. Coll. Real Estate Lawyers (pres. 1986-87), Anglo-Am. Real Property Inst., Phi Beta Kappa. Home: 3711 Thornapple St Chevy Chase MD 20815-4111 Office: Peabody & Brown 1255 23rd St NW Ste 800 Washington DC 20037-1434

LANE, BURTON (BURTON LEVY), composer; b. N.Y.C., Feb. 2, 1912; s. Lazarus and Frances Levy; m. Marion Seaman, June 28, 1935 (div. 1961); 1 dau.; m. Lynn Daroff Kaye, Mar. 5, 1961. Student, High Sch. of Commerce; studied piano with Simon Bucharoff. Former staff composer for Remick Music Pub. Wrote music for 2 songs in Three's a Crowd, 1930; 1 song in The Third Little Show, 1931; entire score for 9th edit. Earl Carroll's Vanities, 1931; 2 songs in Singin' the Blues, 1931; 1 song in Americana, 1932;

composed mus. scores for Hold on to Your Hats, 1940, Laffing Room Only (also lyricist), 1944, Finian's Rainbow, 1947, On a Clear Day You Can See Forever (Tony nomination, Grammy award with Alan Jay Lerner 1965 Carmelina, 1979 (Tony nomination); songs for motion pictures including Dancing Lady, 1933, Babes on Broadway, 1941, Royal Wedding, 1951, Give a Girl a Break, 1953, On a Clear Day You Can See Forever, 1966; animated film Heidi, 1979; composer music for Junior Miss, TV, 1958; composer songs in revue Mighty Fine Music!, off-Broadway, 1983; songs include Everything I Have is Yours, Tony's Wife, Moments Like This, There's A Great Day Coming Mañana, On a Clear Day, The Lady's In Love With You, I Hear Music, Too Late Now, When I'm Not Near The Girl I Love, I Love The Girl I'm Near, Come Back To Me, How Are Things In Glocca Morra?, Look To The Rainbow, How Could You Believe Me When I Said I Love You When You Know I've Been A Liar All My Life, Says My Heart, Stop!, You're Breaking My Heart, (I Like New York In June) How About You?, It's Time For A Love Song, In Our United State, Old Devil Moon, What Did I Have That I Don't Have, One More Walk Around The Garden. Recipient 2 Acad. Award nominations, award for Finian's Rainbow, Essex Symphony Soc. award, 1947, Mercer Lifetime Achievement award, Richard Rodgers Lifetime Achievement award ASCAP, 1992; inducted into Theatre Hall of Fame, 1993. Mem. ASCAP (bd. dirs.), Am. Guild Authors and Composers (pres. 1957-67, Sigmund Romberg award), Songwriters Hall of Fame (dir.). •

LANE, CAROL ANN, secondary school educator; b. Sayre, Pa., June 25, 1943; d. Harold J. and Evelyn (Ward) L. BS, East Stroudsburg State, 1965, MEd, 1972. Tchr. health, physical edn. Troy (Pa.) Area Sch. Dist., 1965—. Instr. sta. 1st aid ARC, Bradford, County. Recipient Outstanding Secondary Educators Am. award, 1973, Community Leaders & Noteworthy Ams. award, 1976, 300 Victory Club award, 1991. Mem. NEA, AAHPERD, Pa. Assn. Health, Phys. Edn., Recreation and Dance, Pa. Edn. Assn., Troy Area Edn. Assn., Women's Basketball Coaches Assn., Dist. IV Basketball Coaches Assn. (bd. dirs. 1990—). Republican. Methodist. Avocations: jogging, gardening. Home: RR 3 Box 4 Troy PA 16947-9401 Office: Troy High Sch 250 High St Troy PA 16947-1122

LANE, DAVID OLIVER, retired librarian; b. Flint, Mich., Oct. 17, 1931; s. Clinton Ellis and Mary Ailene (Sanders) L. B.A., U. Mich., 1958, A.M. in L.S, 1959; doctoral fellow, U. Chgo., 1968. Various library assignments, 1959-63; asst. dir. libraries Boston U., 1963-67; asst. univ. librarian U. Calif., San Diego, 1968-69; chief librarian, prof., dept. chmn. Hunter Coll., N.Y.C., 1969-90; Dir. NSF funded study of library acquisitions, 1967-68; chmn. Council Chief Librarians, City U. N.Y., 1972-75; trustee N.Y. Met. Reference Library Agy., 1978-87. Author: Study of the Decision Making Procedures for the Acquisition of Science Library Materials, 1968. Mem. A.L.A. (life), Assn. Coll. and Research Libraries, Beta Phi Mu. Home: 27D E Hill Dr Somers NY 10589

LANE, DIANE, actress; b. N.Y.C., 1963. Actress: (stage prodns.) Agamemnon, 1977, The Cherry Orchard, 1977, Runaways, 1978, Medea, Electra, The Trojan Woman, As You Like it, The Good Woman of Setzuan, (feature films) A Little Romance, 1979, Watcher in the Woods, 1980, Cattle Annie and Little Britches, 1981, National Lampoon Goes to the Movies, 1981, Six Pack, 1982, Ladies and Gentlemen, The Fabulous Stains, 1982, The Outsiders, 1983, Rumble Fish, 1983, The Cotton Club, 1984, Streets of Fire, 1984, Lady Beware, 1987, The Big Town, 1987, Vital Signs, 1990, Frankie & Johnny, 1991, Chaplin, 1992, Knight Moves, 1993, Indian Summer, 1993, Wild Bill, 1995, Judge Dredd, 1995; (TV movies) Child Bride of Short Creek, 1981, Miss All-America Beauty, 1982; appeared in TV miniseries, Lonesome Dove, 1989, The World's Oldest Living Confederate Widow Tells All, 1994. Mem. Actors' Equity Assn., AFTRA. Office: William Morris Agency 151 El Camino Beverly Hills CA 90212•

LANE, DOROTHY SPIEGEL, physician; b. Bklyn., Feb. 17, 1940; d. Milton Barton and Rosalie (Jacobson) Spiegel; m. Bernard Paul Lane, Aug. 5, 1962; children: Erika, Andrew, Matthew. BA, Vassar Coll., 1961; MD, Columbia U., 1965, MPH, 1968. Diplomate Am. Bd. Preventive Medicine, Am. Bd. Family Practice. Resident preventive medicine N.Y.C. Dept. Health Dist., 1966-68; project dir. children and youth project Title V, HHS N.Y.C. Dept. Health Dist., Rockaway, N.Y., 1968-69; med. cons. Maternal and Child Health Svc. HHS, Rockville, Md., 1970-71; asst. prof. preventive medicine Sch. Medicine SUNY, Stony Brook, 1971-76, assoc. prof., 1976-92; prof., 1992—; assoc. dean Sch. Medicine SUNY, Stony Brook, 1986—; chair dept. community medicine, dir. med. edn. Brookhaven Meml. Hosp. Med. Ctr., Patchogue, N.Y., 1972-86. Contbr. numerous articles to profl. jours. Mem. exec. com. Am. Cancer Soc., L.I. div., 1975—; corp. mem. Nassau Suffolk Health Systems Agy., L.I., 1977—; bd. dirs. Community Health Plan Suffolk, Hauppauge, 1986-91. Grantee HHS-USPHS, 1977-83, 83—, Nat. Cancer Inst., 1987—. Fellow APHA, Am. Coll. Preventive Medicine (regent 1988—), Am. Acad. Family Physicians, N.Y. Acad. Medicine, Am. Bd. Preventive Medicine (trustee). Office: SUNY Sch Medicine Health Scis Ctr L-4 Stony Brook NY 11794-8437

LANE, EDWARD WOOD, JR., retired banker; b. Jacksonville, Fla., Apr. 4, 1911; s. Edward Wood and Anna Virginia (Taliaferro) L.; m. Helen Spratt Murchison, Oct. 16, 1948; children: Edward Wood III, Helen Palmer, Anna Taliaferro, Charles Murchison. A.B., Princeton, 1933; LL.B., Harvard U., 1936. Bar: Fla. 1936. Partner firm McCarthy, Lane & Adams (and predecessors), Jacksonville, 1941-60; pres. Atlantic Nat. Bank, Jacksonville, 1961-74, chmn., 1974-85; chmn. First Union Nat. Bank of Fla. (formerly Atlantic Nat. Bank), Jacksonville, 1985-86, ret., 1986. Served to lt. comdr. USNR, World War II. Mem. Phi Beta Kappa. Clubs: Florida Yacht (Jacksonville), Timuquana Country (Jacksonville), River (Jacksonville), Univ. (Jacksonville); Ponte Vedra, Sawgrass. Home and Office: 3790 Ortega Blvd Jacksonville FL 32210-4333

LANE, FIELDING H., lawyer; b. Kansas City, Mo., May 6, 1926; s. Ralph Fielding and Nancy Lee (Greene) L.; m. Patricia Cecil Parkhurst, Jan. 25, 1980. B.S. in Bus. Adminstrn., U. Mo.-Columbia, 1948; LL.B. cum laude, Harvard U., 1951. Bar: Mo. 1951, Calif. 1956. Assoc. Watson Ess Marshall & Enggas, Kansas City, Mo., 1951-55; assoc. Thelen Marrin Johnson & Bridges, San Francisco, 1955-66, ptnr., 1967—. Served with USN, 1944-46; PTO; lt. comdr. Res. (ret.). Club: Olympic (San Francisco). Home: 165 Villa Terr San Francisco CA 94114 Office: Thelen Marrin Johnson & Bridges 2 Embarcadero Ctr Ste 2200 San Francisco CA 94111-3995

LANE, FREDERICK CARPENTER, investment banker; b. Boston, Aug. 28, 1949; s. Francis Robert and Edith (Lent) L.; m. Wendy Jane Evrard, June 9, 1973; children—Jesse Evrard, Eliza Evrard. A.B. cum laude, Harvard U., 1971, M.B.A. with distinction, 1975. C.P.A., Mass. Supr. Coopers & Lybrand CPAs, Boston, 1973-76; sr. v.p., prin. Donaldson, Lufkin & Jenrette, N.Y.C. and Boston, 1976-88; exec. v.p. Bessemer Securities Corp., N.Y.C., 1988-89; mng. dir. and dir. mergers and acquistions dept. Donaldson, Lufkin & Jenrette, N.Y.C., 1989—. Dir. Process Tech. Holdings, Gastonia, N.C. Racquet and Tennis Club (N.Y.C.), Harvard Club (Boston), Maugus Club (Wellesley, Mass.), Doubles Club (N.Y.C.). Republican. Episcopalian. Office: Donaldson Lufkin & Jenrette Securities Corp 140 Broadway New York NY 10005-1101

LANE, FREDERICK STANLEY, lawyer; b. Cumberland, Md., Jan. 16, 1915; s. Clifford Warren and Edith Persis (Mott) L.; m. Barbara Bentley, Mar. 6, 1943; children: Clifford Warren, Martha Cogswell, Susan Bonney, Jeffery Calvin. A.B. magna cum laude, Amherst Coll., 1936; LL.B., Harvard U., 1939. Bar: Mass. 1939. Assoc. Nutter, McClennen & Fish, Boston, 1939-50; ptnr. Nutter, McClennen & Fish, 1951-90; ret.; past trustee, clk. Hingham Instn. for Savs. Editor: Real Estate in Mid-Century, 1973; contbr. articles to profl. jours. Former trustee Virtual Law Library, Boston; former vice chmn. Council of Friends of Amherst Coll. Library. Served to lt. comdr. USNR, 1942-46. Recipient Richard B. Johnson Meml. award Mass. Conveyancers Assn., 1981. Fellow Am. Bar Found.; Mem. Boston Bar Assn., ABA (chmn. sect. real property, probate and trust law 1977-78), Anglo-Am. Real Property Inst. (chmn. 1982-83), Am. Coll. Real Estate Lawyers (pres. 1979-81), Mass. Conveyancers Assn. (pres. 1968-70), Abstract Club (pres. 1981-84), Phi Beta Kappa, Theta Delta Chi. Republican. Unitarian. Clubs: Union, Harvard, Fly Casters (pres. 1978-80). Home: 18 Ship St Hingham MA 02043-1816

LANE, GLORIA JULIAN, foundation administrator; b. Chgo., Oct. 6, 1932; d. Coy Berry and Katherine (McDowell) Julian; m. William Gordon Lane (div. Oct. 1958); 1 child, Julie Kay Rosewood. BS in Edn., Cen. Mo. State U., 1958; MA, Bowling Green State U., 1959; PhD, No. Ill. U., 1972. Cert. tchr. Assoc. prof. William Jewell Coll., Liberty, Mo., 1959-60; chair forensic div. Coral Gables (Fla.) High Sch., 1960-64; assoc. prof. No. Ill. U., DeKalb, 1964-70; prof. Elgin (Ill.) Community Coll., 1970-72; owner, pub. Lane and Assocs, Inc., San Diego, 1972-78; prof. Nat. U. San Diego, 1978-90; pres., chief exec. officer Women's Internat. Ctr., San Diego, 1982—; founder, dir. Living Legacy Awards, San Diego, 1984—. Author: Project Text for Effective Communications, 1972, Project Text for Executive Communication, 1980, Positive Concepts for Success, 1983; editor Who's Who Among San Diego Women, 1984, 85, 86, 90—, Systems and Structure, 1984. Named Woman of Accomplishment, Soroptimist Internat., 1985, Pres.'s Coun. San Diego, 1986, Center City Assn., 1986, Bus. and Profl. Women, San Diego, 1991, Woman of Yr., Girls' Clubs San Diego, 1986, Woman of Vision, Women's Internat. Ctr., 1990, Wonderwoman 2000 Women's Times Newspaper, 1991; recipient Independence award Ctr. for Disabled, 1986. Avocations: computers, painting, writing. Home and Office: 6202 Friars Rd Apt 311 San Diego CA 92108-1008

LANE, HANA UMLAUF, editor; b. Stockholm, Mar. 14, 1946; came to U.S., 1951, naturalized, 1957; d. Karel Hugo Antonin and Anatolia (Spitel) Umlauf; m. John Richard Lane, Feb. 16, 1980; 1 stepchild, Matthew John. A.B. magna cum laude, Vassar Coll., 1968; A.M. in Russian and East European Studies, Yale U., 1970. Asst. to exec. editor Newspaper Enterprise Assn., N.Y.C., 1970-72, sr. asst., asst. editor World Almanac div., 1972-75, assoc. editor World Almanac, 1975-80, spl. project editor, 1977-80; editor World Almanac and World Almanac Publs., N.Y.C., 1980-85; editor in chief Pharos Books, N.Y.C., 1984-91; editor Pharos Books, 1991-93; sr. editor John Wiley & Sons, 1993—. Editor: World Almanac Book of Who, 1980, World Almanac and Book of Facts, 1981-85; (with others) The Woman's Almanac, 1977. Democrat. Home: 140 Fairview Ave Stamford CT 06902-8040

LANE, HAROLD EDWIN, retired management educator, consultant; b. Malden, Mass., Aug. 19, 1913; s. Edwin George and Annabel (Fraser) L.; m. Constance Mason, June 1, 1940; children: Stephen Winslow, Harold Edwin, Nancy (Mrs. John H. Piper). BS, Boston U., 1936, MA, 1940. Asst. sec. Greater Boston Community Fund, 1940-42; sr. economist Nat. War Labor Bd., Boston, also Portland, Oreg., 1943-46; dir. personnel Sordoni Industries, Wilkes-Barre, Pa., 1946-47; dir. personnel and labor relations Sheraton Corp. Am., Boston, 1947-54; v.p. Sheraton Corp. Am., 1954-68; mgmt. cons., 1968-69; v.p. Fred Harvey, Inc., Chgo., 1969-70; assoc. prof. Bus. Coll., Mich. State U., East Lansing, 1970-78; prof. Bus. Coll. Mich. State U., East Lansing, 1978-81, prof. emeritus, 1981—; founding dir., prof. Sch. Hospitality Adminstrn. Boston U., 1981-93, prof. emeritus, 1993—; summer sch. instr. Cornell U., 1946-67; spl. lectr. Harvard.; Mem. Pres.'s Adv. Com. on Occupational Safety; mem. Council on Pres.'s Plans for Progress; nat. adv. com. Job Corps, Office Econ. Opportunity; chmn. Wage Deviation Bd. State Mich., 1974-78; participant seminar Harvard Bus. Sch., 1963; cons. Ford Found. N.J., 1963; seminar instr. Am. Mgmt. Assn., 1964. Author: (with Mark Van Hartesvelt) Essentials of Hospitality Management, 1983 ; mem. editorial bd. Jour. Managerial Issues, Pitts. State U., Southwest Bus. Rev., Southwest Tex. State U.; contbr. articles to profl. jours. Mem. Soc. Advancement Mgmt., Am. Mgmt. Assn., Am. Hotel and Motel Assn., Council on Hotel, Restaurant and Instnl. Edn., Internat. Assn. Hotel Mgmt. Schs., Internat. Hotel Assn., Nat. Restaurant Assn., AAUP, Friends East-West Center Honolulu, The Conf. Bd. Unitarian. Home: 9 Nutmeg Cir Laconia NH 03246 Office: Boston U Sch Hospitality Adminstrn 808 Commonwealth Ave Boston MA 02215-1206

LANE, JAMES GARLAND, JR., diversified industry executive; b. Roxobel, N.C., Jan. 15, 1934; s. James Garl and Josie (Wembrow) L.; m. Janet Benthall Miller, Oct. 8, 1954; children—Bernice, Frances, Garland, Amy. B.S. U. N.C. 1959. Mem. audit staff S.D. Leidesdorf & Co. Greenville, S.C., 1959-65; v.p. finance Computer Servicenters, Inc., Greenville, 1965-68; exec. v.p. dir. Synalloy Corp., Spartanburg, S.C., 1968-73; pres. dir. Synalloy Corp., 1968-70; v.p. divsn. exec. pension trust investment divsns., 1964-66, v.p. divsn. exec. pension trust investment divsns., 1966-68, chmn. investment policy com., 1968-78, sr. v.p., investment group exec., 1968-70, exec. v.p. fiduciary investment dept., 1978-90; pres., dir. Chase Investors Mgmt. Corp., N.Y.C., 1972-78; mng. dir. Cyrus J. Lawrence Inc., N.Y.C., 1978-82; sr. v.p., chief investment officer, head trust investment divsn. NBD Bank N.A., Detroit, 1982-94, mem. sr. mgmt., 1984-94; bd. dirs. Chateau Properties, Inc. Bd. dirs. Christian Camps Inc., 1978—, Baseball Chapel, 1994—, William Tyndale Coll., 1985—, chmn., 1995—; trustee Wheaton Coll., 1971—. Mem. Soc. Security Analysts., Fin. Analysts Soc. Detroit (pres. bd. dirs.), Econ. Club Detroit, Detroit Club, Grosse Pointe Yacht Club. Home: 24 Harbor Hill Rd Grosse Pointe MI 48236-3748 Office: NBD Bank NA 611 Woodward Ave Detroit MI 48226-3497

LANE, JAMES MCCONKEY, investment executive; b. Pitts., July 9, 1929; s. Mortimer Bliss and Mary (Knapp) L.; m. Arlyne Ruth Nelson, Dec. 16, 1950; children: James, Theodore, Thomas, Karen, David. BA, Wheaton Coll., 1952; MBA, U. Chgo., 1953; postgrad., NYU, 1956, U. Buffalo, 1960. Credit corr. John Plain & Co., Chgo., 1951; trainee Chase Manhattan Bank, N.Y.C., 1953-55, account mgr. investment adv. divsn., 1955-59, investment officer, 1959-62, 2nd v.p., 1962-64, v.p., mgr. corp. pension trust investments, 1964-66, v.p. divsn. exec. pension trust investment divsns., 1966-68, chmn. investment policy com., 1968-78, sr. v.p., investment group exec., 1968-70, exec. v.p. fiduciary investment dept., 1978-90; pres., dir. Chase Investors Mgmt. Corp., N.Y.C., 1972-78; mng. dir. Cyrus J. Lawrence Inc., N.Y.C., 1978-82; sr. v.p., chief investment officer, head trust investment divsn. NBD Bank N.A., Detroit, 1982-94, mem. sr. mgmt., 1984-94; bd. dirs. Chateau Properties, Inc. Bd. dirs. Christian Camps Inc., 1978—, Baseball Chapel, 1994—, William Tyndale Coll., 1985—, chmn., 1995—; trustee Wheaton Coll., 1971—. Mem. Soc. Security Analysts., Fin. Analysts Soc. Detroit (pres. bd. dirs.), Econ. Club Detroit, Detroit Club, Grosse Pointe Yacht Club. Home: 120 Pentland Ct Greer SC 29651

LANE, JEFFREY BRUCE, financial services company executive; b. Bklyn., June 25, 1942; s. Murray and Arlene (Avram) L.; m. Nancy Stern, June 24, 1982. BA, NYU, 1964; MBA, Columbia U., 1970. With Shearson Lehman Hutton, N.Y.C., CFO, vice chmn., 1983-84, COO, 1984-87, pres., 1987-90; pres. Primerica Holdings, N.Y., 1990-94; vice chmn. Smith Barney Harris Upham & Co. Inc., N.Y.C., 1991—; vice chmn. and dir. Smith Barney, Shearson Inc., N.Y.C.; vice chmn. bd. of govs. Am. Stock Exchange;. Bd. dirs. Woodmere Acad., N.Y., L.I. Jewish Hosp. Served to 1st lt. U.S. Army, 1966-68. Republican. Jewish. Office: Smith Barney Shearson Inc 1345 Ave of the Americas New York NY 10105

LANE, JOHN DENNIS, lawyer; b. Norwalk, Conn., Nov. 23, 1921; s. John J. and Theresa A. (Donnelly) L.; m. Elizabeth J. Galliher, Apr. 28, 1949; children: Elizabeth J., John Dennis, Margaret A., Robert E., Paul G. BS., Georgetown U., 1943, J.D., 1948. Bar: D.C. 1948, Conn. 1950. Atty. Office Chief Counsel, Bur. Internal Revenue, Washington, 1948-49; exec. sec. to U.S. Senator Brien McMahon, 1949-50; adminstrv. asst., 1950-52; pvt. practice Washington and Norwalk, 1953—; partner firm Hedrick & Lane, 1954—82, Wilkes, Artis, Hedrick & Lane, 1982—. Mem. council Adminstrv. Conf. U.S., 1961; bd. regents Georgetown U., 1979—. Served to capt. USMCR, 1943-45. Recipient Citation of Merit. Fellow Am. Bar Found.; mem. Am. Bar Assn. (chmn. standing com. unauthorized practice of law 1971-73, chmn. standing com. nat. conf. groups 1973-75, D.C. Cir. mem standing com. on fed. judiciary 1984-86, Fed. cir. mem. 1987-90), Fed. Communications Bar Assn. (pres.-elect 1990, pres. 1991-92), Am. Law Inst. Clubs: Met. (Washington), Army and Navy (Washington); Columbia Country (Chevy Chase, Md.). Home: 5045 Van Ness St NW Washington DC 20016-1960 Office: 1666 K St NW Washington DC 20006-2866 also: 4 Berkeley St Norwalk CT 06852

LANE, JOHN RODGER, art museum director; b. Evanston, Ill., Feb. 28, 1944; s. John Crandall Lane and Jeanne Marie (Rodger) L. Moritz; m. Inge-Lise Eckmann, 1992. B.A., Williams Coll., 1966; M.B.A. U. Chgo., 1971, A.M., Harvard U., 1973, Ph.D., 1976. Asst. dir. Fogg Art Mus., Cambridge, Mass., 1974; exec. asst. to dir., adminstr. curatorial affairs, asst. dir. curatorial affairs Bklyn. Mus., N.Y.C., 1975-80; dir. Carnegie Mus. Art, Pitts., 1980-86, San Francisco Mus. Modern Art, 1987—. Author: Stuart Davis: Art and Art Theory; 1978; co-editor: Abstract Painting and Sculpture in America, 1927-1944, 1983, Carnegie International, 1985; exec. editor: The Making of a Modern Museum/SFMOMA, 1995. Served to lt. USNR, 1966-69. Nat. Endowment Arts Mus. fellow, 1974-75. Mem. Assn. Art Mus. Dirs., Am. Assn. Museums, Internat. Council Museums, Coll. Art Assn. Office: San Francisco Mus Modern Art 151 3rd St San Francisco CA 94103-3107

LANE, JOSEPH M., orthopaedic surgeon, oncologist; b. N.Y.C., Oct. 27, 1939; s. Frederick and Madelaine Lane; m. Barbara Greenhouse, June 23, 1963; children: Debra, Jennifer. AB in Chemistry, Columbia U., 1957; MD, Harvard U., 1965. Surg. intern Hosp. U. Pa., Phila., 1965-66, resident in gen. surgery, 1966-67, resident, 1969-72, chief resident, 1972-73, chief MBD sect., 1973-76; rsch. assoc. NIH, NIDR, Bethesda, Md., 1967-69; rsch. fellow Phila. Gen. Hosp., 1969-70; chief MBD unit Hosp. Spl. Surgery, N.Y.C., 1976-93, dir. rsch. div., 1990-93; prof., chmn. orthopaedic surgery UCLA Med. Sch., L.A., 1993—, 1993—; assoc. dir. MultiPurpose Arthritis Ctr., N.Y.C., 1988-93; cons., collaborator Collagen Corp., Warsaw, Inc., Genetics Inst., Andover, Mass., EBI, Fairfield, N.J. Recipient N.Y. Mayoral Proclamation, 1988. Fellow Am. Acad. Orthopaedic Surgeons (Kappa Delta award 1973); mem. AMA, Am. Soc. Bone and Mineral Rsch., Med. Soc. State N.Y., Internat. Soc. Fracture Repair (bd. dirs.), Musculoskeletal Tumor Soc. (pres. 1982-83), Orthopaedic Rsch. Soc. (pres. 1984-85). Office: UCLA Med Sch Dept Orthopaedic Surgery 10833 Le Conte Ave Los Angeles CA 90095

LANE, KENNETH EDWIN, retired advertising agency executive; b. Orange, N.J., Sept. 30, 1928; s. Clarence Edwin and Erma Catherine (Kinser) L.; children by previous marriage—Kenneth, Laura, Linda, Katherine; m. Susan Spafford Zimmer, Sept. 13, 1980; stepchildren—Todd and Margaret Zimmer. B.A., U. Chgo., 1947, M.A., 1950. Mgr. media Toni div. Gillette Co., 1953-63; media dir. MacParland-Aveyard Co., 1963-64; asso. media dir. Leo Burnett Co., Chgo., 1964-71; mgr. media dept. Leo Burnett Co., 1971-75, sr. v.p. media services, 1975-84. Bd. dirs. Traffic Audit Bur. Maj. USAR ret. Mem. Am. Mktg. Assn. Advt. Agys., Media Dirs. Council., Phi Beta Kappa. Home: 834 N East Ave Oak Park IL 60302-1543 Office: Leo Burnett Agy Prudential Pla Chicago IL 60601

LANE, KENNETH JAY, jewelry designer; b. Detroit, Apr. 22, 1932; s. Mack and Beatrice (Holinstat) L. Student, U. Mich., 1951-52; B.F.A., R.I. Sch. Design, 1954. Mem. mdse. art staff Vogue, 1954-55; asst. designer Delman Shoes, N.Y.C., 1956-58; assoc. designer Christian Dior Shoes, N.Y.C., 1958-63; owner Kenneth Jay Lane, Inc., N.Y.C., 1963—. Recipient Coty award, 1967, Harpers Bazaar Internat. award, 1967, Maramodo di Capri Tiberio D'oro award, 1967, Tobe Coburn Award-Spl. Swarowski award, 1967, Neiman Marcus award, 1968. Office: Kenneth Jay Lane Inc 20 W 37th St New York NY 10018-7405

LANE, LARRY, performing company executive, theater educator; b. Cambridge, Mass., June 9, 1947; s. Robert Edwards and Helen Rita (Sobol) L.; m. Kathy Jeanne Lubar, June 10, 1981. BA, Harvard U., 1971; PhD, Stanford U., 1983.

LANE, LAURENCE WILLIAM, JR., retired U.S. ambassador, publisher; b. Des Moines, Nov. 7, 1919; s. Laurence William and Ruth (Bell) L.; m. Donna Jean Gimbel, Apr. 15, 1955; children: Sharon Louise, Robert Laurence, Brenda Ruth. Student, Pomona Coll., 1938-40, LLD (hon.), 1976; BJ, Stanford U., 1942; DHL (hon.), Hawaii Loa Coll., 1991. Chmn. bd. Lane Pub. Co.; pub. Sunset Mag., Sunset Books and Sunset Films; U.S. amb. to Australia and Nauru, 1985-89; ret., 1990; bd. dirs. Calif. Water Service Co., Crown Zellerbach Corp., Pacific Gas and Electric Co; bd. dirs., cons. Time Inc. Mag. Co.; bd. dirs. Oreg. Coast Aquarium, Internat. Bd. Advice, ANZ Bank; U.S. amb. and commr. Gen. Worlds Fair, Japan, 1975-76; hon. fellow Coll. Notre Dame, 1974. Former mem. adv. bd. Sec. Interior's Bd. Nat. Parks; mem. adv. council Grad. Sch. Bus., Stanford U., SRI; mem. Pres.'s Nat. Productivity Adv. Com.; mem. Pacific Basin Econ. Coun.; bd. dirs. Colonial Williamsburg Hotel Properties, Inc., Pacific Forum, CSI, Nat. Pks. Found.; vol. The Nat. Ctr.; bd. overseers Hoover Instn. War, Revolution and Peace; v.p. Am. Friends of the Australian Nat. Gallery; mem. exec. com. Ctr. for Australian Studies, U. Tex., Austin. Lt. USNR, World War II, PTO. Recipient Conservation Service award Sec. Interior; named hon. prof. journalism Stanford U. Mem. Newcomen Soc. N.Am., Pacific Asia Travel Assn. (life mem., chmn. 1980-81), Coun. of Am. Ambs., Los Rancheros Vistadores, Advt. Club San Francisco, No. Calif. Alumni Assn., Bohemian Club, Pacific Union, Men's Garden Club L.A., Alpha Delta Sigma. Republican. Presbyterian. Office: 3000 Sandhill Rd Ste 215 Menlo Park CA 94025-7116

LANE, LAWRENCE JUBIN, electrical engineer, consultant; b. Morganton, N.C., Feb. 19, 1927; s. Lawrence and Sarah Virginia (Jubin) L.; m. Gladys Verna Lee Hock, Dec. 25, 1947 (dec. 1975); children: Priscilla Gayle Lane Purks, Richard Jubin; m. 2d Helen Elizabeth Sollazzo, Dec. 19, 1975. B.E.E., N.C. State Coll., 1950; M.S.E.E., U. Va., 1972. Lic. profl. engr., Va. Engr. GE, Schenectady, N.Y., 1950-54; class supr. GE, Phila., 1954-55; devel. engr. GE, Waynesboro, Va., 1955-63, sr. devel. engr., 1963-78; sr. systems design engr. GE, Roanoke, Va., 1978-83, cons. engr., 1983—. Patentee in field. Pres. Stuarts Draft PTA, Va., 1960, 61. Served as petty officer USN, 1944-46, 50-51. Recipient Managerial award Gen. Electric Co., 1965. Fellow IEEE (chpt. chmn. 1982-83); mem. Eta Kappa Nu, Tau Beta Pi, Phi Eta Sigma, Phi Kappa Phi. Methodist. Home: 4868 Warrior Dr Salem VA 24153-5816 Office: GE 1501 Roanoke Blvd Salem VA 24153-6499 *Since my occupational accomplishments have been judged to be noteworthy, I am indeed fortunate. I thank God and Jesus Christ for my abilities and for the opportunities for such accomplishments.*

LANE, LEONARD CHARLES, manufacturing company executive; b. N.Y.C., Feb. 9, 1919; s. Harry and Hattie (Polatin) L.; m. Mildred Chasanow, Jan. 23, 1944; children: Arlene Lane Fisher, Stewart Franklin, Clifford Paul. BS, L.I. U., 1939; MA, Columbia U., 1942. Pres., dir. Pierce Sch. Radio and TV, N.Y.C., 1946-63; pres., trustee Nat. Sch. Home Study, N.Y.C., 1950-63; pres. Radio TV Tng. Am., N.Y.C., 1950-63; with Rapid Am. Corp., N.Y.C., 1955-82 exec. v.p., 1963-81, chmn. exec. com., 1963-81, vice chmn., 1981-84; chief exec. officer, chmn. bd. ILC Industries Inc., N.Y.C., from 1977, now chmn. bd.; bd. dirs. McCrory Corp., Rapid Am. Corp., J.J. Newberry Co.; vice chmn. Glen Alden Corp., Butler Bros. Author: Servicing Transistor Radios and Printed Circuits, 1961, New Shortcuts to TV Servicing, 1961, Industrial Electronics Made Easy, 1962, Simplified Radio Telephone License Course, 1971. Mem. nat. adv. com. Mexican Am. Edn., 1968-71; hon. trustee Temple Emanuel, Gt.Neck, N.Y. Served with inf. AUS, 1944-45. Mem. Nat. Tng. Labs. (trustee). Club: Glen Oaks Country. Office: ILC Industries Inc 888 7th Ave New York NY 10106-0001

LANE, LEONARD J., hydrologist; b. Tucson, Apr. 25, 1945; s. Edward M. and Audrey M. (Cutshaw) L.; m. Rose Mary Toon; children: Brian James, Leonard Brett. BS with distinction, U. Ariz., 1970, MS in Systems & Indsl. Engring., 1972; PhD in Hydrology & Water Resources, Colo. State U., 1975. Cert. erosion control specialist. Staff mem. Los Alamos Nat. Lab., 1981-82, 83-84; systems engr., coord. natural resource modeling activities ARS, 1989-91; hydrologist USDA-ARS, Tucson, 1970-72, 75-89, rsch. leader S.W. Watershed Rsch. Ctr., 1991—; cons. City of Tucson, Ariz. State U., San Diego State U., Los Alamos Nat. Lab., Washington State Dept. Ecology, Sabol Engring.; adj. assoc. prof. U. Ariz. Author or co-author over 140 publs. Recipient Outstanding Performance award, 1970, 77, 87, 88, 89, 92, Arthur S. Flemming award, 1982, Outstanding Performance award WEPP, 1989; named Mountain States Area Scientist of Yr., 1986. Mem. ASCE, AGU, ASAE (co-author outstanding paper award 1981, 90), AWRA, BGRG, SRM. Office: S W Watershed Rsch Ctr 2000 E Allen Rd Tucson AZ 85719-1520

LANE, LOIS N., artist; b. Phila., Jan. 6, 1948; d. Ervin C. and Celia (Genmankin) L.; m. Jared C. Bark, Jan. 24, 1979; 1 son, Theo Lane. Student, Yale Summer Sch. Music and Art, 1968; BFA, Phila. Coll. Art, 1969; MFA, Yale U., 1971. One-man shows, Arist Space, N.Y.C., 1974, Willard Gallery, N.Y.C., 1977, 79, 80, 83, 87, 89, Greenberg Gallery, St. Louis, 1980, Pa. Acad. Fine Arts, Phila., 1982, Nigel Greenwood Gallery, London, 1982, John Berggruen Gallery, San Francisco, 1987, Barbara Mathes Gallery, 1988, 89; group shows; represented permanent collections, Mus. Modern Art, N.Y.C., Whitney Mus. Am. Art, N.Y.C., Art Mus. S. Tex., Des Moines Art Ctr., Mus. Fine Arts, Houston. Grantee N.Y. State

Council on Arts, 1977; grantee Nat. Endowment for Arts, 1978. Office: Willard Gallery 12 E 12th St New York NY 10021

LANE, LOUIS, musician, conductor; b. Eagle Pass, Tex., Dec. 25, 1923; s. William Bartlett and Virginia (Gardner) L. B.Mus., U. Tex., 1943; Mus.M., Eastman Sch. Music, 1947; Mus.D. (hon.), Akron U., 1973, Cleve. State U., 1974, Kent State U., 1988. adj. prof. music Akron U., 1969-82; vis. prof. music U. Cin., 1973-75; artistic advisor, condr. Cleve. Inst. Music, 1982—; sr. lectr. music U. Tex., 1989-91. Mem., Cleve. Orch., 1947-73, assoc. condr., 1960-70, resident condr., 1970-73, condr., Akron (Ohio) Symphony Orch., 1959-83, co-condr., Atlanta Symphony Orch., 1977-83, prin. guest condr., Atlanta Symphony Orch., 1983-88, prin. condr., SABC Symphony Orch., Johannesburg South Africa, 1984-85, prin. guest condr., Dallas Symphony Orch., 1973-78, guest condr. in, Chgo., Seattle, St. Louis, Detroit, Houston, San Antonio, Vancouver, B.C., Can., Montevideo, Uruguay, Warsaw, Poland, Johannesburg, S.Africa, Helsinki, Finland, mus. dir., Lake Erie Opera Theatre, Cleve., 1964-72; co-dir., Blossom Festival Sch. of Cleve. Orch. and Kent State U., 1969-73; rec. artist for Columbia Records, Telarc Records. Served with F.A. AUS, 1943-46. Decorated chevalier l'Ordre des Arts et des Lettres de France; Recipient Mahler medal, 1971; Ditson award Columbia, 1972; Grammy award for best orch. rec., 1989. Home: 1808 Rockridge Pl NE Atlanta GA 30324-5264

LANE, MALCOLM DANIEL, biological chemistry educator; b. Chgo., Aug. 10, 1930; s. Malcolm Daniel Lane and Helga Sofia (Nielsen) Wilke; m. Patricia L. Sonquist, Mar. 17, 1951; children: Claudia J. Lane Fioranelli, M. Daniel Jr. BS, Iowa State U., 1951, MS, 1953; PhD, U. Ill., 1956. assoc. prof. Va. Poly. Inst., Blackburg, 1956-63, prof. biochemistry, 1963-64; assoc. prof. biochemistry Sch. Medicine N.Y.U., 1964-69, prof. biochemistry Sch. Medicine, 1969-70; prof. biochemistry Sch. Medicine Johns Hopkins U., Balt., 1970-78, DeLamar prof., dir. dept. biol. chemistry, 1978—. Mem. editorial bd.: Jour. Biol. Chemistry, 1969-74, 79-84, Biochem. et Biophysica Acta, 1968-70, 75-79, Archives Biochemistry and Biophysics, 1977-80, Ann. Revs. Biochemistry, 1980-84; exec. editor: Biochem./Biophys. Research Com., 1986—; contbr. numerous articles to profl. jours. Fellow Am. Acad. Arts and Sci.; mem. NAS, Am. Soc. Biochem. Molecular Biology (sec. 1987-89, program chmn. 1990-91, pres., William C. Rose award 1981), Am. Soc. Cell Biology, Am. Inst. Nutrition (Mead-Johnson award 1966), Am. Chem. Soc. Avocations: chamber music, boating, fishing, photography. Home: 5607 Roxbury Pl Baltimore MD 21209-4501 Office: Johns Hopkins U Sch Medicine 725 N Wolfe St Baltimore MD 21205-2105

LANE, MARGARET ANNA SMITH, property manager developer; b. Aspinwall, Pa., Nov. 26, 1918; d. Max Charles and Mary Ann (Jones) Smith; m. Frank A. Lane Jr., Feb. 7, 1954; 1 child, Alan Michael. AB, UCLA, 1940; MS, U. So. Calif., 1949. Cert. secondary tchr., Calif. Demonstration and tng. tchr. UCLA and U. Calif., Northridge, 1948-74; pvt. practice Cottonwood, Ariz., 1975—; tchr. dept. chmn. L.A. City Schs., 1948-74; sec.-treas. Silver Hoof, Inc., Sedona, Stone Pine Gallery, Ltd., Sedona. Mem. Pi Gamma Mu. Avocations: Native American cultures, art. Home: PO Box I-I West Sedona AZ 86340

LANE, MARILYN EDITH, treasurer, corporate executive; b. Calif., June 17, 1931; d. Frederick Ernest and Grace (Davage) Mockridge; m. Jack William Lane, Feb. 2, 1948 (dec. Jan. 1989); children: Adrienne G. Murphy, Jack William II, Jon F. Gen. officer worker Talney Mfg. Co., Los Angeles, 1951-52; with govt. products div. Rheem Mfg. Co., Downey, Calif., 1953-58; acct. Reed Necker, San Diego, 1960; v.p. treas. Anthony Industries, Inc., L.A., 1960—. Office: Anthony Industries Inc PO Box 22252 Los Angeles CA 90022-0252

LANE, MARK, lawyer, educator, author; b. N.Y.C., Feb. 24, 1927; s. Harry Arnold and Elizabeth (Brown) L.; m. Patricia Ruth Erdner, 1987; children: Anne-Marie, Christina. LLB, Bklyn. Law Sch., 1951. Bar: N.Y. 1951, D.C. 1995. Pvt. practice law N.Y.C. and Washington, 1952—; founder Mid-Harlem Community Parish Narcotics Clinic, 1953, East Harlem Reform Dem. Club, 1959; prof. law Cath. U., Washington, 1975-76; sr. ptnr. Lane & Assocs., 1986—; founder and dir. Citizens Commn. Inquiry; founder Wounded Knee Legal Def.-Offense Com., 1973, The Covered Wagon, Mountain Home, Idaho, 1971. Author: (books) Rush to Judgment, 1966, A Citizen's Dissent, 1968, Chicago Eye-Witness, 1969, Arcadia, 1970, Conversations with Americans, 1970, Executive Action, 1973, (with Dick Gregory) Code Name Zorro, 1977, The Strongest Poison, 1980, Plausible Denial, 1991, Murder in Memphis, 1993; prodr. films Rush to Judgment, 1967, Two men in Dallas, 1987, 92; prodr. plays Trial of James Earl Ray, 1978, Plausible Denial, 1992, Winds of Doctrine, 1994; prodr. screenplays, Arcadia, 1992, Slay the Dreamer, 1992, Plausible Denial, 1993; founder publs. Citizens Quar., 1975, Helping Hand, 1971. Mem. N.Y. State Assembly, 1960-62. With AUS, 1945-47. Home and Office: 105 2nd St NE Washington DC 20002-7303 *I do not believe that our fate is pre-ordained. I do believe that women and men, working together, can determine their own destiny and that the people write their own history. What moves me most directly into action is the fact that I hate bullies. What concerns me the most in contemporary America is the influence of the police and spy organizations with the national news media. Together these are bullies to contemplate and oppose.*

LANE, MARVIN MASKALL, JR., electronics company executive; b. Oak Park, Ill., Apr. 25, 1934; s. Marvin Maskall and Lucille Ernestine (Fischer) L.; m. Joan Agar Wheeler, June 28, 1958; children—Elizabeth Agar Anderson, Marlene Celia Christensen. B.S. in Elec. Engring, U. Wis., 1956, M.B.A. in Indsl. Mgmt, 1957. With Texas Instruments Inc., Dallas, 1958—; asst. v.p. Texas Instruments Inc., 1978-80, v.p., treas., 1980-82, v.p., controller, 1982—. Treasure, chmn. Tejas Girl Scouts Found., 1988-94; bd. dirs. Dallas Area Rapid Transit, 1986-93; mem. City of Dallas Jud. Nominating Commn. Mem. Fin. Execs. Inst. Presbyterian. Office: Tex Instruments Inc PO Box 655474 Dallas TX 75265-5474

LANE, MEREDITH ANNE, botany educator, museum director; b. Mesa, Ariz., Aug. 4, 1951; d. Robert Ernest and Elva Jewell (Shilling) L.; m. Donald W. Longstreth, Apr. 6, 1974 (div. Feb. 1985). BS, Ariz. State U., 1974, MS, 1976; PhD, U. Tex., 1980. assoc. prof. U. Colo., Boulder, 1980-88, assoc. prof., 1988-89; assoc. prof., dir. McGregor Herbarium U. Kans., Lawrence, 1989—; vis. asst. prof. U. Wyo., Laramie, 1985-86; vis. scholar U. Conn., Storrs, 1989; cons. editor McGraw-Hill Ency. of Sci. and Tech., N.Y.C., 1985-92. Contbr. 30 articles to profl. jours. Mem. Am. Soc. Plant Taxonomists (sec. 1986-88, program dir. 1986-90, councillor 1993-96, Cooley award 1982), Bot. Soc. Am. (editor 1990—, sect. chair 1984-86, sect. sec. 1986-90), Internat. Orgn. for Plant Biosystematics (councillor 1989-92), Internat. Assn. Plant Taxonomists, Calif. Bot. Soc. Democrat. Lutheran. Avocations: reading, conversation, country dance, hiking, furniture refinishing. Office: R. L. McGregor Herbarium 2045 Constant Ave Lawrence KS 66047-3729

LANE, MONTAGUE, physician, educator; b. N.Y.C., Aug. 28, 1929; s. George and Ada (Korn) L.; m. Chrsitine Laura; children: Laura Diane, Adam Reuben. B.A., N.Y. U., 1947; M.B., Chgo. Med. Sch., 1952, M.D., 1953; M.S., Georgetown U., 1957. Diplomate: Am. Bd. Internal Medicine (mem. subcom. on med. oncology 1981-83). Clin. assoc. Nat. Cancer Inst., NIH, 1954-56; sr. investigator Clin. Pharmacology and Exptl. Therapeutics Service; attending physician gen. med. br. Nat. Cancer Inst., 1957-60; assoc. in medicine George Washington U., Med. Sch., 1957-60; asst. prof., assoc. prof. depts. pharmacology and medicine Baylor Coll. Medicine, Houston, 1960-67; prof. depts. pharm. and medicine Baylor Coll. Medicine, 1967—, head div. clin. oncology dept. pharmacology, 1969-94, head sect. med. oncology dept. medicine, 1961-92; co-dir. cancer control sci. program Meth. Hosp. and Baylor Coll. Medicine, Houston, 1981-94; mem. study sect. Nat. Cancer Inst., 1966-69, mem. cancer clin. investigations review com., 1972-75; chmn. new agts. com. S.W. Cancer Chemotherapy study group; cons. drug evaluations AMA; cons. Merck Manual, U.S. Pharmacopeia, 1981-83; cons. interferon program Schering Corp., 1981-82; cons. com. on orphan drugs FDA, 1986—; cons. UNOMED, 1989-91; mem. adv. bd. Cancer Info. Dissemination and Analysis Ctr., Info Ventures, Inc., 1988-93; mem. sci. adv. bd. Health Infusion, Inc., 1991-94. Science editor: Cancer Research, 1970-80. External adv. bd. Howard U. Cancer Center, 1977-83. Named Disting. Alumnus Chgo. Med. Sch., 1971, Disting. Faculty Mem. Baylor Med. Alumni Assn., 1990. Fellow ACP; mem. Am. Inst.

Nutrition, Am. Soc. Clin. Oncology (program chmn. 1970), Am. Soc. Clin. Pharmacology and Exptl. Therapeutics (pres. 1971-72), Am. Soc. Pharmacology and Exptl. Therapeutics, Am. Soc. Hematology, Houston Soc. Internal Medicine (v.p. 1973-74, pres. 1984-85), Am. Assn. Cancer Rsch. (program com. 1990), Harris County Med. Soc. Home: 1514 Bissonnet St Houston TX 77005-1814 Office: Ste 1510 6560 Fannin St Houston TX 77030

LANE, NANCY, editor; b. N.Y.C., Dec. 20, 1938; d. Morton and Lillian (Gelb) L. A.B. in Am. Civilization, Barnard Coll., 1960. Mem. staff N.Y. Times, 1959-61; from asst. to assoc. editor Polit. Sci. Quar. and Procs. Acad. Polit. Sic., Columbia U., N.Y.C., 1962-70; from assoc. editor to mng. editor Am. Hist. Rev. Am. Hist. Assn., 1970-74; sr. editor Oxford U. Press, N.Y.C., 1974—. Mem. Am. Hist. Assn., Orgn. Am. Historians. Home: 45 W 10th St New York NY 10011 Office: Oxford U Press 200 Madison Ave New York NY 10016

LANE, NATHAN (JOSEPH LANE), actor; b. Jersey City, N.J., Feb. 3, 1956. Appeared in plays (off-Broadway) A Midsummer Night's Dream, (Broadway) Present Laughter, 1982-83, Merlin, N.Y.C., 1983, Love, N.Y.C., 1984, Raving, N.Y.C., 1984, She Stoops to Conquer, N.Y.C., 1984, The Common Pursuit, New Haven, 1984-85, A Backer's Audition, N.Y.C., 1985, Wind in the Willows, 1985, Measure for Measure, 1985, The Common Pursuit, 1986-87, Claptrap, N.Y.C., 1987, Broadway Bound, New Haven, L.A., 1991, On Borrowed Time, 1991, One of the Boys, 1982; (films) Ironweed, 1987, The Lemon Sisters, 1990, Joe Versus the Volcano, 1990, He Said, She Said, 1991, Frankie and Johnnie, 1991, Life With Mikey, 1993, Addams Family Values, 1993, (voice) The Lion King, 1994. Office: William Morris Agy 151 El Camino Beverly Hills CA 90212*

LANE, NEAL FRANCIS, university provost, physics researcher, federal administrator; b. Oklahoma City, Aug. 22, 1938; s. Walter Patrick and Harietta (Hattie) Charlotta (Hollander) L.; m. Joni Sue Williams, June 11, 1960; children: Christy Lynn Lane Saydjari, John Patrick. BS, U. Okla., 1960, MS, 1962, PhD, 1964, LHD (hon.), 1995; DSc (hon.), U. Ala., 1994, Mich. State U., 1995. NSF postdoctoral fellow, 1964-65; asst. prof. physics Rice U., Houston, 1966-69, assoc. prof., 1969-72, prof., 1972-84, 86-93, prof. space physics and astronomy, 1972-84, chmn. dept. physics, 1977-82, prof. space physics and astronomy, 1972-84, chmn. dept. of physics, 1977-82; dir. divsn. physics NSF, Washington, 1979-80; chancellor U. Colo., Colorado Springs, 1984-86; provost Rice U., 1986-93; dir. Nat. Science Foundation, Washington, D.C., 1993—; non-resident fellow Joint Inst. for Lab. Astrophysics U. Colo., Boulder, 1984-93, vis. fellow, 1965-66, 75-76; mem. commn. on phys. sci. math. and applications NRC, 1989-93; bd. overseers Superconducting Super Collider (SSC) Univs. Rsch. Assn., 1985-93; disting. Karcher lectr. U. Okla., Norman, 1983; disting. vis. scientist U. Ky., Lexington, 1980; mem. adv. com. math. and phys. sci. NSF, 1992-93. Co-author: Quantum States of Atoms, Molecules and Solids, Understanding more Quantum Physics; contbr. articles to profl. jours. Active Cath. Commn. Intellectual and Cultural Affairs, 1991. Sloan Found. fellow, 1967-71; recipient George Brown prize for superior teaching Rice U., 1973-74, 76-77. Fellow AAAS, Am. Phys. Soc. (councilor-at-large 1981-84, chmn. panel on pub. affairs 1983, exec. com. 1981-83, chmn. div. of electron and atomic physics 1977-78), Am. Acad. Arts and Scis.; mem. Am. Inst. Physics (gov. bd. 1984-87), Am. Assn. Physics Tchrs., Phi Beta Kappa, Sigma Xi (pres. elect 1992, pres. 1993). Roman Catholic. Avocations: tennis; squash. Office: NSF Office of Dir 4201 Wilson Blvd Arlington VA 22203-1803

LANE, NEWTON ALEXANDER, lawyer; b. Boston, June 16, 1915; s. Samuel B. and Eva (Robbins) L. AB, Harvard U., 1936, JD, 1939. Bar: Mass. 1939. Ptnr. emeritus Lane & Altman. Served with AUS, 1942-46. Mem. Phi Beta Kappa. Home: 704 Dedham St Newton MA 02159-2937 Office: Lane & Altman 101 Federal St Boston MA 02110-1842

LANE, PATRICK, poet; b. Nelson, B.C., Can., Mar. 26, 1939; s. A. S. Red and E. M. (Titsworth) L.; m. Carol Beala, 1972 (div.); children: Mark Hayden, Christopher Patrick, Kathryn Mary, Michael John, Richard Patrick. Grad. high sch., Vernon, B.C. Editor Very Stone House in Transit, Vancouver, B.C., Can., 1966-80; tchr. creative writing course Notre Dame Coll., 1966; writer-in-residence U. Man., Can., 1978, U. Ottawa, Ont., Can., 1980, U. Alta., Can., 1982, Libr. of Saskatoon, 1983, Globe Theatre Co. of Regina, 1985, Concordia U., Montreal, 1987, U. Toronto, 1989; lectr. U. Sask., 1988-89. Author: Letters From the Savage Mind, 1966, For Rita-In Asylum, 1967, Calgary City Jail, 1967, Sunflower Seeds, 1967, Separations, 1969, On The Street, 1970, Mountain Oysters, 1971, Hiway 401 Rhapsody, 1972, The Sun Has Begun to Eat The Mountain, 1972, Passing Into Storm, 1973, Beware The Months Of Fire, 1974, Certs, 1974, Unborn Things, 1975, For Riel in That Gawdam Prison, 1975, Albino Pheasants, 1977, If, 1977, Poems New and Selected, 1978 (Gov.-Gen. award for poetry 1978), (with Lorna Uher) No Longer Two People, 1979, There Are Still The Mountains, 1979, The Garden, 1980, The Measure, 1980, Old Mother, 1982, Woman in the Dust, 1983, A Linen Crow, A Caftan Magpie, 1985, Selected Poems, 1987, Winter, 1989, Miford and Me, 1989, Mortal Remains, 1991, How Do You Spell Beautiful, 1992; contbr. to anthologies. Sr. Can. Coun. Arts grantee, 1973, 76, 83, Ont. Arts Coun. grantee, 1974, 75, 78, Man. Sr. Arts grantee, 1979; recipient Poetry award York U., 1971. Mem. League Can. Poets. (v.p.), Writer's Union Can. Office: care Writer's Union of Canada, 24 Ryerson Ave, Toronto, ON Canada M5T 2P3

LANE, PETER, ornithologist; married. Author: Les Oiseaux du Québec, 1980, L'Alimentation des Oiseaux, 1985. Recipient Snowy Owl Conservation award Québec Zoological Gardens, 1992, Commemorative medal Confederation Can., 1993. Mem. Ornithologist's Club Québec, Cercle des Mycologues Québec. Office: 210 Chemin de l'Eperon CP 1654, Lac Beauport, PQ Canada G0A 2C0

LANE, REBECCA MASSIE, museum director. BA with distinction, U. Va., 1973, MA in History of Art, 1976. Curator, educator Va. Mus. Fine Arts, Richmond, 1975-80; research asst. mus. asst. Oak Ridge (Tenn.) Associated Univs., 1980-81; dir. Knoxville (Tenn.) Mus. Art, 1981-89; dir. coll. galleries and arts adminstrn. Sweet Briar (Va.) Coll., 1989—; field reviewer Inst. Mus. Svcs., Gen. Operating Support Competition, Washington, 1987, 89. Participant Leadership Knoxville, 1987; mem. crafts panel Tenn. Arts Commn., 1987-89, chmn., 1989. Recipient Artistic Merit award Knoxville Arts Council, 1985. Mem. Am. Assn. Museums, Museums of Knoxville (treas. 1982-86), Assn. Arts Adminstrn. Educators. Home: PO Box 15 Woodland Rd Sweet Briar VA 24595 Office: Sweet Briar Coll Pannell Ctr Sweet Briar VA 24595

LANE, ROBERT CASEY, lawyer; b. 1932. JD, Loyola U., 1960. Bar: Ill. 1960, Wash. 1969. Atty. U.S. Dept. Justice, Washington, 1960-61; assoc. Lewis, Overbeck & Furman, 1962-69; atty. Weyerhaeuser Co., Tacoma, 1969-77, asst. gen. counsel, 1977-80, v.p., gen. counsel, 1980—. Office: Weyerhaeuser Co Law Dept CH 2J28 Tacoma WA 98477

LANE, ROBERT G., lawyer; b. Chgo., Mar. 9, 1938. AB, Duke U., 1960; JD with distinction, U. Mich., 1963. Bar: Ill. 1963. Ptnr. Winston & Strawn, Chgo. Mem. ABA, Ill. State Bar Assn. Office: Winston & Strawn 35 W Wacker Dr Chicago IL 60601-1614

LANE, ROBERT GERHART, lawyer; b. Long Beach, Calif., Sept. 24, 1931; s. Herman G. and Adele (Steg) L.; m. Mary Ellaine Griffith, Aug. 29, 1953; children: John, Scott, David, Mary Katherine. A.B., U. So. Calif., 1953, MA in Polit. Sci., 1955, LLB, 1960. Bar: Calif. 1960, U.S. Dist. Ct. (cen. dist.) Calif. 1960, U.S. Ct. Appeals (9th cir.) 1964, U.S. Supreme Ct. 1971. Assoc. Paul, Hastings, Janofsky & Walker, Los Angeles, 1960-67, ptnr., 1967-93, mng. ptnr., 1986-91; gen. counsel U. So. Calif., L.A., 1993—. Mem. Town Hall, L.A., corp. bd. United Way, L.A.; chmn. Cmty. Issues Coun.; bd. councilors U. So. Calif., L.A.; mem. bd. alliance Natural History Mus. L.A. County; mem. Fellows of the Huntington Libr. Served to 1st lt. USAFR, 1954-57. Mem. ABA (Robinson Patman com. antitrust sect.), Calif. Bar

Assn., Los Angeles County Bar Assn., Order of Coif. Clubs: Jonathan (Los Angeles); Balboa Bay (Newport Beach, Calif.); Annandale Golf (Pasadena, Calif.). Office: U So Calif Office of Gen Counsel University Park ADM 352 Los Angeles CA 90089-5013

LANE, RONALD ALAN, lawyer; b. Ames, Iowa, July 15, 1950; s. Raymond Oscar and Beverly (Burdge) L.; m. Eileen Smietana, June 17, 1972; children: Andrew, Audrey. AB, Miami U., Oxford, Ohio, 1972; JD, Northwestern U., 1975; MBA, U. Chgo., 1987. Bar: U.S. Dist. Ct. (no. dist.) Ill. 1975, U.S. Ct. Appeals (7th cir.) 1975, U.S. Supreme Ct. 1975. Atty. Atchison, Topeka & Santa Fe Ry. Co., Chgo., 1975-78; from asst. gen. atty. to gen. atty. Santa Fe So. Pacific Corp., Chgo., 1979-86, gen. corp. atty., 1986-87; asst. v.p. pers. and labor rels. Atchison, Topeka & Santa Fe Ry. Co., 1987-90; v.p., gen. counsel Ill. Cen. R.R. Co., Chgo., 1990—. Office: Ill Central RR Co 455 N Cityfront Plz Chicago IL 60611

LANE, STEPHEN L., electronic equipment company executive; b. 1935; married. BA, U. Miami, 1957. With Kasselman and Co., N.Y.C., 1960-63, Emerson Radio Corp., No. Bergen, N.J., 1957-60; pres. Emerson Radio Corp., No. Bergen, 1963—, also bd. dirs. Office: Emerson Radio Corp PO Box 430 Parsippany NJ 07054-0430

LANE, SYLVIA, economist, educator; b. N.Y.C.; m. Benjamin Lane, Sept. 2, 1939; children: Leonard, Reese, Nancy. A.B., U. Calif., Berkeley, 1934, M.A., 1936; postgrad., Columbia U., 1937; Ph.D., U. So. Calif., 1957. Lectr., asst. prof. U. So. Calif., Los Angeles, 1947-60; asso. prof. econs. San Diego State U., 1961-65; assoc. prof. finance, assoc. dir. Ctr. for Econ. Edn. Calif. State U., Fullerton, 1965-69, chmn. dept. fin., 1967-69; prof. agrl. econs. U. Calif., Davis, 1969-82, prof. emerita, 1982—; prof. emerita and economist Giannini Found., U. Calif-Berkeley, 1982—; vis. scholar Stanford U., 1975-76; econ. cons. Pres.'s Com. Consumer Interests, 1966-72; cons. Calif. Adv. Commn. Tax Reform, 1963, Office Consumer Affairs, Exec. Office of Pres., 1972-77, FAO, UN, 1983. Author: (with E. Bryant Phillips) Personal Finance, 1963, rev. edit., 1979, The Insurance Tax, 1965, California's Income Tax Conformity and Withholding, 1968; also articles. Project economist Los Angeles County Welfare Planning Council, 1956-59; del. White House Conf. on Food and Nutrition, 1969, Pres.'s Summit Conf. on Inflation, 1974; mem. adv. com. Center for Bldg. Tech., Nat. Bur. Standards, 1975-79; Bd. dirs. Am. Council Consumer Interests, 1973, Consumers Union, 1974-76. Ford Found. fellow UCLA, 1963; Ford Found. fellow U. Chgo., 1965; fellow U. Chgo., 1968. Fellow Am. Agrl. Econ. Assn. (life, Sylvia Lane Fellowship Fund 1993); mem. Am. Econ. Assn., Am. Coun. Consumer Info., Omicron Delta Epsilon (pres. 1973-75, trustee 1975-83, chmn. bd. trustees 1982-84). Home: 1241 Grizzly Peak Blvd Berkeley CA 94708-2127 Office: U Calif Dept Agrl & Resource Econs Berkeley CA 94720 *Select goals carefully . . .*

LANE, WALTER RONALD, JR., advertising executive, educator; b. Wilmington, N.C., Sept. 2, 1940; s. Walter Ronald and Dorothy (Holmes) L.; m. Judy Carol Smith, Nov. 14, 1963 (dec. Oct. 1992); 1 child, Sheri Lynn Lane Bevil. AB, U. Ga., 1963, MA, 1964. Promotion mgr. Ga. Labs./Mentho-Mulsion Co., Wilmington, 1961-62; advt. copywriter LSP Advt., Wilmington, 1962; account exec. Am. Lithograph/Case-Hoyt, Atlanta, 1964-67; copywriter Rhodes Advt., Atlanta, 1967; creative dir. SLRS Comms., Athens, Ga., 1967-73, pres., 1973—; prof. U. Ga., Athens, 1973—; mktg. cons. Ga. Inst. Comty. and Area Devel., 1975-81; coord. Am. Assn. Advt. Agys. Inst. Advanced Advt. Studies, Atlanta, 1981-86; advt. mgr. Jour. Advt., 1987-90; mem. accrediting coun. Accrediting Bd. Journalism Colls., 1993—; judge Addy Awards, Peabody Screening Com. Co-author: Advertising Media Problem Solving, 1968, A Perspective for Advertising/Marketing in Emerging European Countries, 1990, Kleppner's Advertising Procedure, 10th edit., 1988, 11th edit., 1990, 12th edit., 1993; prodr. TV videos; contbr. articles to profl. jours. Grantee Newspaper Advt. Pubs. Assn., 1990, Warning Labels design grantee Am. Cancer Soc./Ga. Med. Coll., 1990. Mem. Am. Advt. Fedn. (bd. dirs., mem. coun. govs. 1992-93, chmn. acad. divsn. 1992-93, mem. acad. divsn. exec. com. 1993-96, Hileman Outstanding Educator award 1987, Outstanding Svc. award 1986), Am. Advt. Found. (bd. dirs. 1992-95), Am. Mktg. Assn., Am. Acad. Advt. Atlanta Advt. Club, Greater Augusta Advt. Club. Presbyterian. Avocations: photography, art, writing. Home: 193 Bent Tree Dr Athens GA 30606-1945 Office: SLRS Comms Inc PO Box 5488 Athens GA 30604-5488

LANE, WILLIAM C., JR., principal. Prin. Bonita Springs (Fla.) Mid. Sch. Recipient Blue Ribbon Sch. award U.S. Dept. Edn., 1990-91. Office: Bonita Springs Mid Sch 10141 W Terry St Bonita Springs FL 33923-4734

LANE, WILLIAM KENNETH, physician; b. Butte, Mont., Nov. 5, 1922; s. John Patrick and Elizabeth Marie (Murphy) L.; m. Gilda Antoinette Parision, Aug. 21, 1954; children: William S., Francine Deirdre. Student, U. Mont., 1940-41, M. St. Charles Coll., 1941-43; MD, Marquette U., 1946. Intern Queen of Angels Hosp., L.A., 1946-47, resident physician, 1954-56; pvt. practice internal medicine San Francisco, 1947-51; resident in urology VA Hosp., Long Beach, Calif., 1956-58; physician VA Hosp., Long Beach, Oakland and Palo Alto, Calif., 1958—; lectr. on psychology of the elderly Foothill Coll., Los Altos, 1972-74; rschr. in field. Bd. dirs., mem. No. Cheyenne Indian Sch.; mem. Josef Meier's Black Hills Theatrical Group, S.D., 1940. With U.S. Army, 1943-46, ETO, lt. USN, 1951-54, Korea. Mem. AMA, Am. Geriatrics Soc., Nat. Assn. VA Physicians, San Francisco County Med. Soc., Woodrow Wilson Ctr. (assoc.), St. Vincent de Paul Soc., Cupertino Landscape Artists (past pres.), Audubon Soc., Stanford Hist. Soc., San Jose Movie/Video Club, San Jose Camera Club. Roman Catholic. Avocations: oil and watercolor painting, hiking, mountain climbing, outdoor video camcorder photography. Home: 18926 Sara Park Cir Saratoga CA 95070-4164 Office: Stanford VA Med Ctr 3801 Miranda Ave # 171 Palo Alto CA 94304-1207

LANE, WILLIAM NOBLE, III, financial executive; b. Evanston, Ill., Aug. 2, 1943; s. William Noble and Marjorie Elizabeth (Hamilton) L.; children: Campbell, Heather, Carl. A.B., Princeton U., 1965. Salesman, Wallace Press, Inc., 1965-66; mgr. corp. planning Gen. Binding Corp., Northbrook, Ill., 1966-72; vice chmn. Gen. Binding Corp., 1978-82, chmn., 1983—; pres. Northwestco, Inc., Chgo., 1972-78; chmn. bd., pres., CEO Lane Industries, Inc., Northbrook, 1978—; chmn. bd. Lake View Trust & Savs. Bank, Chgo., N.W. Nat. Bank Chgo., Pioneer Bank & Trust Co., Northbrook Trust & Savs. Bank; dir. Hydraulic Component Services, Inc., Otis Assos. (architects), Schwaab, Inc. Trustee Rush Presbyn. St. Luke's Med. Center, Chgo., Lake Forest (Ill.) Acad., Chgo. Zool. Soc.; bd. govs. United Republican Fund Ill.; mem. Northwestern U. Assos.; econ. adv. council Princeton U.; bd. dirs. Irving Park YMCA, Chgo. Mem. Explorers Club. Episcopalian. Clubs: Winter (Lake Forest), Onwnetsia (Lake Forest); Princeton (N.Y.C.); Port Royal Beach (Naples, Fla.); Commonwealth (Chgo.), Univ. (Chgo.), Econ. (Chgo.); Adventurers. Office: Gen Binding Corp 1 GBC Plz Northbrook IL 60062-4195 also: Lane Fin Inc 1200 Shermer Rd Northbrook IL 60062 also: 4747 W Irving Park Rd Chicago IL 60641*

LANE, WILLIAM W., electronics executive; b. Roanoke, Va., Feb. 25, 1934; s. Melvin V. and Cecile (Lane); m. Ronnie G Lane, Sept. 14, 1978; children: Jonathan D., Drew H., Craig M. B.A., Bklyn. Coll., 1956; M.B.A., Cornell U., 1958. Vice pres. Major Electronics Corp., 1959-70, chmn., dir., 1970; v.p., dir. Internat. Transistor Corp., Burbank, Calif., 1971-73; vice chmn., dir. Internat. Chia Hsin, Taipai, Taiwan, 1973-76; chmn., dir. Emerson (H.K. Ltd.), Hong Kong, from 1976; chmn., CEO, dir. Emerson Radio Corp., North Bergen, N.J., 1974-91; pres. Majorette Enterprises, from 1961; chmn. MAJ EXCO Imports Inc., 1977-85, Emerson Computer Corp., 1989-91, H.H. Scott, Inc. Cardiac Resuscitator Corp., Portland, Oreg., Emerson Italy, Emerson Spain, Atlantic Shore 400 Cons. Corp., Emerson Investment Corp., Major Realty Corp., Emteck Tech. (U.K.) Ltd.; pres. W. Lane & Assocs. Inc., 1992—. Served with AUS, 1958-59. Mem. bus. adv. bd. U.S. Senate. Office: W Lane & Assocs 30 E 60th St Ste 903 New York NY 10021

LANER, RICHARD WARREN, lawyer; b. Chgo., July 12, 1933; s. Jack E. and Esther G. (Cohon) L.; m. Barbara Lee Shless, Aug. 15, 1954; children: Lynn, Kenneth. Student, U. Ill., 1951-54; BS, Northwestern U., 1955, LLB, 1956. Bar: Ill. 1956. Assoc. Laner, Muchin, Dombrow, Becker, Levin & Tominberg, Ltd., Chgo., 1956-62; ptnr. Muchin, Dombrow, Becker, Levin &

Tominberg, Ltd., Chgo., 1962—. Editor Northwestern Law Rev., 1954-56; contbr. articles to profl. jours. Mem. Chgo. Bar Assn. (chmn. com. labor law 1972-73), Chgo. Assn. Commerce and Industry, Order of Coif. Home: 1300 Edgewood Ln Northbrook IL 60062-4716 Office: Laner Muchin Dombrow Becker Levin & Tominberg Ltd 515 N State St Fl 28 Chicago IL 60610-4320

LANE-RETICKER, EDWARD, lawyer, educator; b. Chgo., Mar. 7, 1926; s. Edward and Jane Mary Reticker; m. Laura Ruth Lane, Aug. 9, 1947; children: Alison, Stoddard, Lydia. AB, Dartmouth Coll., 1947; LLB, Harvard U., 1952, grad. Advanced Mgmt. Program, 1979. Bar: N.C. 1954, Conn. 1960. Instr. Punahou Sch., Honolulu, 1947-49; mem. faculty U. N.C., Chapel Hill, 1952-56; assoc. prof. pub. law and govt. U. N.C., 1955-56; sr. researcher, then dir. research Conn. Pub. Expenditure Coun., Hartford, 1956-60; with Conn. Bank & Trust Co., Hartford, 1960-85; sec. Conn. Bank & Trust Co., 1966-85, gen. counsel, 1970-85; gen. counsel, sec. Bank of New Eng. Corp., 1985-91; of counsel Murtha, Cullina, Richter & Pinney, Hartford, 1992—; assoc. dir. Morin Ctr. Banking and Fin. Law Studies Boston U. Law Sch., 1992—. Lectr. Boston U. Law Sch., U. Conn. Law Sch.; pres. Mark Twain Meml., Hartford, 1975-78, Hartford Stage Co., 1980-82; dir. New Eng. Legal Found., 1988—. Ensign USNR, 1943-46; capt. Res. ret. Mem. Conf. State Bank Suprs. (chmn. adv. coun. 1977), N.C. Bar Assn., Conn. Bar Assn. (chmn. corp. counsel sect. 1979-82), Hartford Club, Univ. Club (Hartford). Home: 161 Four Mile Rd West Hartford CT 06107-3022 Office: Murtha Cullina Richter & Pinney City Pl # 1 Hartford CT 06103 also: Boston U Morin Ctr Banking and Fin Law Studies 765 Commonwealth Ave Boston MA 02215-1401

LANESE, HERBERT J., air and aerospace transportation manufacturing executive; b. 1945. V.p. Newport News Shipbuilding & Drydock Co., 1983-86, Tenneco Inc., 1986-89; sr. v.p. McDonnell Douglas Corp., 1989-92, exec. v.p., CFO, 1992—; also chmn. bd. McDonnell Douglas Fin. Corp., Long Beach, Calif., 1993—. Office: McDonnell Douglas Corp Lambert St. Louis Airport Saint Louis MO 63103 also: McDonnell Douglas Corp PO Box 516 Saint Louis MO 63166-0516*

LANEY, JAMES THOMAS, ambassador, educator; b. Wilson, Ark., Dec. 24, 1927; s. Thomas Mann and Mary (Hughey) L.; m. Berta Joan Radford, Dec. 20, 1949; children: Berta Joan Vaughan, James T., Arthur Radford, Mary Ruth Laney Reilly, Susan Elizabeth Castle. BA, Yale U., 1950, BD, 1954, PhD, 1966; DD (hon.), Fla. So. Coll., 1977; LHD (hon.), Rhodes Coll., 1979; HHD (hon.), Mercer U., 1980; LLD (hon.), DePauw U., 1985; DD (hon.), Wofford Coll., 1986; LHD (hon.), Millsaps Coll., 1988, Austin Coll., 1990, W.Va. Wesleyan Coll., 1990, Yale U., 1993; DD (hon.), Emory U., 1994; LLD (hon.), U. St. Andrews, Scotland, 1994, Alaska Pacific U., 1994. Chaplain Choate Sch., Wallingford, Conn., 1953-55; ordained to ministry Meth. Ch., 1955; asst. lectr. Yale Div. Sch., 1954-55; pastor St. Paul Meth. Ch., Cin., 1955-58; sec. student Christian movement, pres. Yonsei U., Seoul, Korea, 1959-64; asst. prof. Christian ethics Vanderbilt U. Div. Sch., 1966-69; dean Candler Sch. Theology, Emory U., 1969-77, pres. univ., 1977-93; U.S. amb. to Republic of Korea, 1993—; vis. prof. Harvard Div. Sch., 1974. Author: (with J.M. Gustafson) On Being Responsible, 1968; also essays. Pres. Nashville Community Rels. Coun., 1968-69; mem. Yale Coun. Com., 1972-77; bd. dirs. Fund Theol. Edn.; chmn. United Bd. Christian Higher Edn. in Asia, 1990-93; bd. dirs. Atlanta Symphony, 1979-91; chmn. bd. overseers com. to visit Harvard Div. Sch., 1980-85; mem. Yale U. Coun. Exec. Com., 1990-93; mem. Carnegie Endowment Nat. Commn. on Am. & the New World; mem. adv. com. Atlanta Project; chmn. so. dist. Rhodes Scholarship Com., 1980-90; bd. dirs. Atlantic Coun., 1987-93. With AUS, 1946-48. Selected for Leadership Atlanta, 1970-71; recipient Disting. Alumnus award Yale U. Div. Sch., 1979, 93; Kellogg award for leadership in higher edn., 1983; D.C. Macintosh fellow Yale U., 1965-66. Mem. Am. Soc. Christian Ethics, Soc. for Values Higher Edn. (pres. 1987-91), Coun. on Fgn. Rels., Atlanta C. of C., Commerce Club, Phi Beta Kappa, Omicron Delta Kappa.

LANEY, JOHN THOMAS, III, federal judge; b. Columbus, Ga., Mar. 27, 1942; s. John Thomas Jr. and Leila (Davis) L.; m. Louise Pierce, Nov. 23, 1974; children: Thomas Whitfield, Elizabeth Davis. AB, Mercer U., 1964, JD magna cum laude, 1966. Bar: Ga. 1965, U.S. Dist. Ct. (mid. dist.) Ga. 1966, U.S. Ct. Appeals (5th cir.) 1966, U.S. Ct. Mil. Appeals 1967, U.S. Ct. Appeals (11th cir.) 1981. Assoc. Swift, Pease, Davidson & Chapman, Columbus, 1970-73; ptnr. Page, Scrantom, Harris & Chapman, Columbus, 1973-86; judge mid. dist. Ga. U.S. Bankruptcy Ct., Columbus, 1986—. Co-editor-in-chief Mercer Law Rev., 1965-66; contbr. articles to profl. jours. Former pres., dir. Metro. Boys Club of Columbus. Capt. U.S. Army, 1966-70. Mem. ABA (judge adminstrv. divsn. Nat. Conf. Fed. Trial Judges), State Bar Ga. (chmn. gen. practice and trial sect. 1983-84, chmn. state disciplinary bd. 1984-85), Am. Judicature Soc., Nat. Conf. Bankruptcy Judges, Columbus Bar Assn., Inc. (pres. 1985-86), Rotary. Presbyterian. Office: US Bankruptcy Ct PO Box 1540 Columbus GA 31902

LANEY, LANDY B., supermarket chain executive; b. 1932; married. With Colonial Stores, Ashville, N.C., 1950-64; v.p. Ingles Markets Inc., Black Mountain, N.C., 1965-81; pres., COO Ingles Markets Inc., 1981—. Office: Ingles Markets Inc US Hwy 70 E Asheville NC 28711

LANEY, LEROY OLAN, economist, banker; b. Atlanta, Mar. 20, 1943; s. Lee Edwin and Paula Zel! (Bishop) L.; m. Sandra Elaine Prescott, Sept. 3, 1966; children: Prescott Edwin, Lee Olan III. B Indsl. Engring., Ga. Inst. Tech., 1965; MBA in Fin., Emory U., 1967; MA in Econs., U. Colo., 1974, PhD in Econs., 1976. Budget analyst Martin-Marietta Corp., Denver, 1971-72; economist Coun. Econ. Advisers, Washington, 1974-75; internat. economist U.S. Treasury Dept., Washington, 1975-78; sr. economist Fed. Res. Bank Dallas, 1978-88; prof. econs., chmn. dept. Butler U., Indpls., 1989-90; sr. v.p. 1st Hawaiian Bank, Honolulu, 1990—; chmn. Fed. Res. Com. on Internat. Rsch., Washington, 1981-83; vis. prof. U. Tex., Arlington and Dallas, 1978-85; adj. prof. So. Meth. U., Dallas, 1982-85. Editor bank periodicals, 1975-88; contbr. articles to profl. jours. Mem. Internat. Fin. Symposium, Dallas, 1982-85; Hawaii Coun. on Revenues. Lt. USN, 1967-71. Scholar Ga. Inst. Tech., 1961; rsch. fellow Emory U., 1965-67, teaching fellow U. Colo., 1972-73; rsch. grantee Butler U., 1989-90. Mem. Am. Econ. Assn., Western Econ. Assn., Indpls. Econ. Forum, Plaza Club, Honolulu Rotary, Omicron Delta Epsilon, Lambda Alpha, Kappa Sigma. Avocations: sailing, skiing, reading, tennis, jogging. Office: 1st Hawaiian Bank PO Box 3200 Honolulu HI 96847

LANEY, MICHAEL L., manufacturing executive; b. Los Angeles, Sept. 10, 1945; s. Roy and Wanda Laney; m. Marti Miller, Dec. 31, 1964; children: Tynna, Kristen. BS with honors, Calif. State U., Northridge, 1967; MBA, UCLA, 1969. CPA, Calif. Sr. tax acct. Haskins-Sells, Los Angeles, 1967-69; asst. prof. acctg. Calif. State U., Northridge, 1969-72; tax prin. M. Klaiman Acctg. Corp., Beverly Hills, Calif., 1972-75; pvt. practice acctg. Beverly Hills, 1975-80; v.p., controller Ducommun, Inc., Los Angeles, 1980-87; sr. v.p., fin. and adminstrn. Monarch Mirror Door Co. Inc., Chatsworth, Calif., 1987-92; v.p. ops. feature animation Walt Disney Pictures and TV (part of The Walt Disney Co.), Glendale, Calif., 1992-93; sr. v.p. ops. Warner Bros., Sherman Oaks, Calif., 1994—. Mem. Fin. Execs. Inst., Tax Execs. Inst., Am. Inst. CPA's, Calif. Soc. CPA's. Office: Warner Bros Feature Animation 15303 Ventura Blvd Ste 500 Sherman Oaks CA 91403-9999

LANFORD, LUKE DEAN, electronics company executive; b. Greer, S.C., Aug. 4, 1922; s. John D. and Ethel W. (Ballenger) L.; m. Donna Marie Cellar, Dec. 20, 1945 (dec. Apr. 29, 1984); 1 dau., Cynthia Lea Lanford Brown; m. Jacquelyn Sue Carr Bussell, Feb. 14, 1986. B.S.E.E., Va. Poly. Inst., 1943. With Western Electric Co. Inc., 1946-78; asst. mgr. tng. Western Electric Co., Inc., N.Y.C., 1957-60; mgr. engring. Western Electric Co., Inc., Kansas City, 1960-63; asst. works mgr. Western Electric Co., Inc., Allentown, Pa., 1963-65; plant mgr. Reading, Pa., 1965-69; gen. mgr. Indpls., 1969-78; dir. Met. Indpls. Television Assn., Inc., Sta. WFYI-TV, 1970—, pres., 1975-79. Served with U.S. Army, 1943-46. Mem. IEEE. Telephone Pioneers Am., Eta Kappa Nu, Tau Beta Pi, Phi Kappa Phi. Republican. Presbyterian. Home: 7810 Camelback Dr Indianapolis IN 46250-1840 Office: 2525 N Shadeland Ave Indianapolis IN 46219-1768

LANFORD, OSCAR ERASMUS, JR., retired university vice chancellor; b. Louisa County, Va., Dec. 19, 1914; s. Oscar E. and Ruth (Miller) L.; m. Caroline C. Sherman, Aug. 24, 1937 (dec. Jan. 1990); children—Oscar III, Caroline Aldrich (Mrs. William Eastman), Henry C. Sherman, William Armistead, Virginia Bowen (Mrs. Sedruddin Hemani); m. Esther Lund Arroe, Feb. 23, 1991. B.S., Va. Mil. Inst., 1934; A.M., Columbia, 1937, Ph.D., 1939. Research chemist Gold Dust Corp., 1934-36; instr. chemistry Columbia, 1937-40; prof. chemistry, chmn. dept. State U. N.Y. Coll., Albany, 1940-52; dean coll. State U. N.Y. Coll., 1952-61; first dir. Atmospheric Scis. Research Center, 1961; pres. Fredonia Coll., SUNY, 1961-70; dir. panel on univ. purposes and goals, gen. mgr. constrn. fund, vice chancellor SUNY, 1970-83, cons. univ. planning and mgmt., 1983—. Author textbooks, articles in sci. jours. Mem. Sigma Xi, Phi Lambda Upsilon. Club: University (Albany, N.Y.). Home and Office: 2567 Brookview Rd Castleton On Hudson NY 12033-9713

LANFORD, OSCAR ERASMUS, III, mathematics educator; b. N.Y.C., Jan. 6, 1940; s. Oscar E. and Caroline Clapp (Sherman) L.; m. Regina Victoria Krigman, Dec. 29, 1961; 1 child, Lizabeth Miller. BA, Wesleyan U., Middletown, Conn., 1960; MA, Princeton U., 1962, PhD, 1966; ScD (hon.), Wesleyan U., 1990. Asst., assoc. to prof. math. U. Calif., Berkeley, 1966-87; prof. math. Inst. des Hautes Etudes Scientiques, Bures-sur-Yvette, France, 1982-87. Recipient award in applied math and numerical analysis, U.S. Nat. Acad. Sci., 1986. Mem. Am. Math. Soc. Office: ETH-Zentrum, Dept Math, 8092 Zurich Switzerland

LANG, CAROL MAX, veterinarian, educator; b. Paris, Ill., Dec. 29, 1937; s. Acel G. and O. Nadine (Beaver) L.; m. Sylvia Smith, Jan. 10, 1965; children: Karen E., John A., Susan C. BS, U. Ill., 1959, DVM, 1961. Diplomate Am. Coll. Lab. Animal Medicine. Capt., vet. corp. Walter Reed Army Inst. Research, Washington, 1961-63; asst. prof. Pa. State U. Coll. Medicine, Hershey, 1966-69, assoc. prof., 1969-72, prof., 1972-84, George T. Harrell Jr. prof., 1984—, asst. dean continuing edn. 1984—. Contbr. over 130 articles to profl. pubs. Served to capt. U.S. Army, 1961-63. Recipient Research award Am. Assn. Lab. Animal Sci., 1980-81, Charles River award Am. Vet. Med. Assn., 1987; Bowman Gray Sch. Med. postdoctoral fellow, 1963-66. Mem. Am. Vet. Med. Assn., Am. Assn. Lab. Animal Sci., Am. Coll. Lab. Animal Medicine (past pres.). Home: 472 Hilltop Rd Hummelstown PA 17036-8512 Office: Pa State U Milton S Hershey Med Ctr PO Box 850 Hershey PA 17033

LANG, CECIL YELVERTON, English language educator; b. Walstonburg, N.C., Sept. 18, 1920; s. Wilton Earl and Lillie (Yelverton) L.; m. Violette Noelle Guérin-Lésé, Apr. 2, 1952; 1 child, François-Michel. AB, Duke U., 1941, AM, 1942; MA, Harvard U., 1947, PhD, 1949. Instr., then asst. prof. English Yale U., New Haven, 1949-57; assoc. prof. Claremont (Calif.) Grad. Sch., 1957-59; prof. Syracuse U., N.Y., 1959-65, U. Chgo., 1965-67; prof. Ctr. for Advanced Studies U. Va., Charlottesville, 1967-70, Commonwealth prof. English, 1970-84, John Stewart Bryan prof., 1984-91, prof. emeritus, 1991—. Editor: The Swinburne Letters. 6 vols., 1959-62, New Writings of Swinburne, 1964, The Pre-Raphaelites and Their Circle, 1968; co-editor: The Tennyson Letters, 3 vols., 1982-90. Served to 1st lt. USAAF, 1942-46. Guggenheim fellow, 1951-52; Fulbright fellow, 1951-52, Morse fellow, 1956-57. Fellow Brit. Acad. (corr.), Royal Soc. Lit., Arta Club (London). Home: 2401 Old Ivy Rd Apt 1507 Charlottesville VA 22903-4860 Office: Univ Va Dept Of English Charlottesville VA 22903

LANG, DANIEL S., artist; b. Tulsa, Mar. 17, 1935; s. Irving and Dorothy D. (Lauterer) L. B.F.A., Tulsa U., 1953; M.F.A., Iowa U., 1959. Asst. prof. art SUNY, Fredonia, 1959-60; Art Inst. Chgo., 1962-64, Washington U., St. Louis, 1964-65; vis. artist Ohio State U., 1968-69, U. South Fla., 1971, U. Utah, spring 1984; adj. prof. U. Utah, 1984—. One-man shows include Boston Mus. Fine Arts, 1961, Arthur Tooth & Sons, London, 1970, 74, Alexandra Monett Gallery, Brussels, Belgium, 1973, 78, Fairweather Hardin Gallery, Chgo., 1971, 77, 80, Il Gabbiano Gallery, Rome, 1975, DM Gallery, London, 1975, Gimpel & Weitzenhofer, N.Y.C., 1976, Fischbach Gallery, N.Y.C., 1977, 79, Graphik Internat. GMBH, Stuttgart, Germany, 1979, Richard Demarco Gallery, Edinburgh, Scotland, 1981, 83, Watson/ Willour Gallery, Houston, 1981, David Findlay Gallery, N.Y.C., 1981, 83, Sherry French Gallery, N.Y.C., 1984, Meredith Long Gallery, Houston, 1984, Washington Gallery, Glasgow, 1986, Phillips Gallery, Salt Lake City, 1988, Gilcrease Mus., Tulsa, 1989, Am. Stock Exch., N.Y.C., 1991, Galleria Civica, Seregno, Italy, 1991, The Hokin Gallery, Palm Beach, Fla., 1991, Taylor's Contemporary Gallery, Hot Springs, Alaska, 1992, Galleria Delle Art, Cittá di Castello, Italy, 1992, William Hardie Gallery, Glasgow, Scotland, 1992, Civic Gallery, Urbino, Italy, 1992, London Art Fair, 1994, Elliot Smith Gallery, St. Louis, 1994; group shows include Am. Fedn. of Arts travelling exhbn., 1968-69, U. Pa. Inst. Contemporary Art, 1970, Moore Coll. Art, 1971, Boston U., 1972, Joslyn Art Mus., Omaha and Sheldon Meml. Art Galleries, Lincoln, Nebr., 1973-74, Sherry French Gallery, 1983, 85, 86, Ruth Siegel Gallery, N.Y.C., 1989, Antarctica 2 man show sponsored by NSF, organized by Smithsonian Instn., 1976-79, America 1976 travelling exhbn., 1976-78, including stops at Fogg Art Mus. Harvard U., Wadsworth Atheneum, Hartford, Conn. and, Corcoran Gallery Art, Washington, Watson/de Nagy Gallery of Houston travelling exhbn., 1978-79, Hirschl & Adler Gallery, N.Y.C., 1980, Gerald Peters Gallery, 1993, Landfall Press, Chgo., 1993, Cline Fine Art Gallery, Sante Fe, 1994, U. Tulsa, 1994, numerous others; represented in permanent collections including Bklyn. Mus. High Mus. Art, Atlanta, Denver Art Mus., Mus. Modern Art, N.Y.C., Art Inst. Chgo., Library of Congress, Boston Public Library, Calif. Palace Legion of Honor, Nelson Rockefeller Collection, N.Y., Victoria and Albert Mus., London, Hunterian Art Gallery, U. Glasgow, Elliot Smith Gallery, St. Louis, 1994, The Cline Fine Art Gallery, Santa Fe, 1994, David Messum Gallery, London, 1995, other pub. and pvt. collections; designer sets for Orfeo, Kent Opera Co. Eng., later filmed by BBC, 1976. Served with U.S. Army, 1954-56. Home (winter): 38 W 56th St New York NY 10019 also: Montone (PG), 06014 Montone Italy

LANG, DOUGLAS STEWARD, lawyer; b. St. Louis, July 25, 1947; s. Ervin Jacob and Jacqueline Helen (Kratky) L.; m. Martha Kay Taylor, Aug. 25, 1973; children: Brian Chester and Christopher John (twins), Stewart Taylor. BS BA, Drake U., 1969; JD, U. Mo., 1972. Bar: Mo. 1972, Tex. 1973, U.S Dist. Ct. (ea. and we/ dists.) Tex. 1973, U.S. Dist. Ct. (no. dist.) Tex. 1973, U.S. Ct. Appeals (5th cir.) 1977. Law clk. to Hon. Fred L. Henley Mo. Supreme Ct., St. Louis, 1972-73; assoc. Weber, Baker & Allums, Dallas, 1973-78; ptnr. Gardere, Porter & DeHay, Dallas, 1978-79, Gardere & Wynne, Dallas, 1979—; speaker continuing legal edn. seminars. Bd. dirs. Univ. Park Elem. Sch Dads' Club, 1988-89, pres. 1990-91; chalice bearer and lay reader Ch. of Incarnation, Dallas, 1984—, mem. symposium on aging, 1990, co-chmn. annual ch. field day, 1988, 89, Sunday sch. tchr., 1982, 83, 90, vestry mem. 1990-95, Christian edn. com., 1992—, chair bldg. com., 1993—; baseball coach gradesch. teams YMCA, Dallas, 1988-89, football coach gradesch. teams, 1987-92, soccer coach gradesch. teams, 1983-86; campaign chmn., treas. Election Nathan L. Hecht, judge 95th dist. ct., Dallas, 1982; tribe chief Indian Guides, Dallas, 1985-87; mem. Dallas Mus. Art, 1986—; mem. Dallas County Rep. Men's Club, 1986—; bd. dirs. Girls' Adventure Trails, Inc., Dallas, 1986-92, chmn. facilities com., 1989-90, chmn. long range planning com., 1987-88; mem. troops com. Boy Scout Troop 72, Dallas, 1989—, asst. scoutmaster, 1992—, order of arrow; v.p. Park Cities Ctrl. Dads' Club, Dallas, 1990-91; pres. Univ. Park Grade Sch. Dad's Club 1990-91; bd. councillors U. Dallas, 1991—. Recipient Outstanding Svc. awd. Legal Svcs. North Tex., Dallas, 1991, Alumni Achievement award, Drake U., Des Moines, Iowa, 1992, Double D award Drake U., 1993. Fellow Tex. Bar Found. (sustaining life), Am. Bar Found., Dallas Bar Found. (trustee 1992—, exec. com. 1994-95); mem. ABA (litigation sect. 1974—, exec. com. Met. Bar Caucus 1991—, sec.-treas. 1992-93, pres.-elect 1993-94, pres. 1994-95), State Bar Tex. (coll. state bar Tex. 1992—, bd. dirs. 1992—, exec. com. 1994-95), Dallas Bar Assn. (bd. dirs. 1976-78, 80—, pres. 1991, chmn. exec. dir. search com. 1994, v.p. adminstrv. 1979, 88, v.p. activities 1989, chmn. strategic planning com. 1982-84, mem. numerous coms.), Dallas Assn. Young Lawyers (bd. dirs. 1975, v.p. 1976, treas. 1976, pres. 1977 Outstanding Young Lawyer in Dallas 1981), Tex. Young Lawyers Assn. (bd. dirs. 1976-78), Tex. Assn. Bank Coun. (co-chmn. litigation com. 1989, bd. dirs. 1990-94, v.p. 1994-95), Tex. Assn. Defense Counsel, Nat. Conf. Bar Press. (ex-officio, exec. coun. 1994-95), Am. Inn of Ct. (membership chmn. 1991, exec. com. 1991—), North Tex. Drake Alumni Assn. (pres. 1974-75),

Salesmanship Club of Dallas. Republican. Episcopal. Avocations: golf, hiking, rafting, camping. Office: Gardere & Wynne LLP 1601 Elm St Ste 3000 Dallas TX 75201-4761

LANG, ERICH KARL, physician, radiologist; b. Vienna, Austria, Dec. 7, 1929; came to U.S., 1950, naturalized, 1960; s. Johann Hans and Caecilia C. (Felkel) L.; m. Nicoli J. Miller, Apr. 21, 1956; children: Erich Christopher, Cortney Alexander Johann. Arbitur, Realgrymnasium, 1947; M.S., Columbia U., 1951; M.D., U. Vienna, 1953. Intern U. Iowa Hosps., Iowa City, 1954-55; resident in internal medicine U. Iowa Hosps., 1955-56; resident in radiology Johns Hopkins U. Hosp., Balt., 1956-59; radiologist Johns Hopkins U. Hosp., 1956-61; asst. prof. radiology Johns Hopkins U., 1956-61; radiologist, acting dir. radiology Methodist Hosp., Indpls., 1961-67; prof., chmn. dept. radiology La. State U. Med. Center, Shreveport, 1967-76, New Orleans, 1976-92; prof., chmn. dept. radiology La. State U., Tulane U. schs. medicine, 1976—; dir. radiology Charity Hosp., New Orleans, 1976-92; prof. radiology LSU, 1992—; adj. prof. urology La. State U. Med. Ctr., 1987—; guest prof. Uris Vienna, Austria, 1992-93, guest-vis. prof. UMD, N.J. Author numerous articles in field. Served as maj. M.C., U.S. Army, 1961-65. Fellow ACP, Soc. Vascular Surgeons, Am. Coll. Radiology, Billroth Med. Soc.; mem. Radiol. Soc. N. Am., Am. Roentgen Ray Soc., Soc. Nuclear Medicine, Soc. Acad.; Chmn. Radiology, Soc. U. Radiologists, La. New Orleans med. socs., Crescent City Radiol. Soc. Office: 1542 Tulane Ave New Orleans LA 70112-2825

LANG, EUGENE M., technology development company executive; b. N.Y.C., Mar. 16, 1919; s. Daniel and Ida L.; m. Theresa Volmar, Apr. 15, 1946; children—David A., Jane Lang, Stephen. BA, Swarthmore Coll., 1938; MS, Columbia U., 1940; postgrad., Bklyn. Poly. Inst., 1941-42; LLD (hon.), Swarthmore Coll., 1981, St. Paul's Coll., 1987, Columbia U., 1988, SUNY, 1987, St. Michaels Coll., 1988; LHD (hon.), Coll. New Rochelle, 1986, Bank St. Coll., 1986, New Sch. Social Research, 1987, Trinity Coll., Hartford, Conn., 1988; Dr. Pub. Svc. (hon.), R.I. Coll., 1988, CUNY, 1989, Springfield Coll., Mass., 1989, Yale U., 1989, Hunter Coll., 1990, Hobart Coll., 1990, Glassboro State Coll., 1990; LHD (hon.), Bard Coll., 1991; LLD, Lawrence U., 1991, U. Mo., 1993; LHD (hon.), Whitman Coll., 1993; LHD, Goucher Coll., 1994. Works mgr. Aircraft Screw Products, Inc., N.Y.C., 1941-46; founder, pres. Clark Chem. Co., Long Island City, N.Y., 1946-48; co-founder, exec. v.p. Heli-Coil Corp. (now divsn. of Black & Decker), Danbury, Conn., 1948-52; founder, chmn. REFAC Technology Devel. Corp., N.Y.C., 1952—; chmn. Electronic Rsch. Assn., Inc., Winsted, Conn., 1978-90; bd. dirs. other U S. and fgn. cos. Patentee. Contbr. articles on internat. bus., small bus. issues, technology transfer and venture capital projects to profl. pubs. Bus. chmn. Citizens for Humphrey-Muskie, N.Y., 1968; trustee, vice chmn. New Sch. Social Rsch., N.Y., 1978—; mng. dir. N.Y.C. Met. Opera Assn., 1978-93; bd. dirs. Columbia U. Grad. Sch. Bus., 1986—; adv. dir. Carnegie-Mellon Grad. Sch. Bus. Adminstrn., 1989—; dir. Mannes Coll. Music, 1989—; chmn. bd. dirs. Swarthmore Coll., Pa., 1981-88, emeritus, 1988—; chmn. Eugene M. Lang Found.; founding donor Eugene Lang Coll., New Sch. Social Rsch.; founder I Have A Dream program minority student edn. Recipient George Washington award Am.-Hungarian Fedn., 1982, Community Service award Booth Meml. Med. Ctr., N.Y., 1980, Disting. Service for Trusteeship Assn. Governing Bds., Washington, 1985, Brotherhood award NCCJ, 1985, John Jay award Conf. Ind. Colls. and Univs. of N.Y. State, 1986, Booth award Vols. of Am., 1986 presdl. citations, 1979, 85, Family of Man award nat. Council of Chs., 1986, Hubert H. Humphrey Humanitarian award Nat. Urban Coalition, 1986, Jefferson award Am. Inst. Pub. Service, 1986, Martin Luther King medal of Freedom, N.Y. State, 1987, Human Rights award N.J. Ednl. Assn., 1987, Front Page award N.Y. Daily News, 1987, Leadership award Nat. Urban League, 1987, Carter Humanitarian award NAACP, 1987, Salute award U.S. C. of C., 1987, Horatio Alger award Horatio Alger Found., 1987, Pub. Service award P.R. Family Inst., 1988, Friend of Edn. award NEA, N.Y., 1988, Fisher Disting. Service to Edn. award Council for Advancement and Support of Edn., 1988, Disting. Leadership award United Negro Coll. Fund, 1988, Val-Kill award Eleanor Roosevelt Found., 1988, Finley medal CCNY Alumni Assn., 1988, Evangeline Booth award Salvation Army, 1988, CESPA award Elem. Sch. Prins. Assn., 1989, Meridian award Children's Mus. Indpls., 1989, medal of distinction Barnard Coll., 1989, Leadership award Boston Partnership in Edn., Robie award Jackie Robinson Found., 1990, Point of Light citation President George Bush, Pub. Svc. award Boston Dept. Pub. Edn., 1991, Drum Major award So. Christian Leadership Conf., 1991, Trail Blazer award assn. Negro Bus. Women, 1991, Community Svc. award U.S Dept. Justice, 1991, Dodge award YMCA, 1992, S Henry Smith Pub. Svc. award Alfred U., 1992, Fgn. Trade Leadership award Charlotte World Trade Assn., 1992, Champion of Mentoring award Children's Crusade of R.I., Trustee's award Spelman Coll., 1993, Youth Svc. award Upward, Inc., Nat. Caring award, Recog. award Martin Luther King Com., Norman Vincent Peale award Norman Vincent Peale Fedn., 1994, Goodworks award Theaterworks USA. Mem. Licensing Exec. Soc. Club: University, Century (N.Y.C.), Yale (N.Y.C.). Home: 912 Fifth Ave New York NY 10021-4159 Office: REFAC Technology l Corp 122 E 42d St New York NY 10168

LANG, FRANCIS HAROVER, lawyer; b. Manchester, Ohio, June 4, 1907; s. James Walter and Mary (Harover) L.; m. Rachel Boyce, Oct. 20, 1934; children: Mary Sue, Charles Boyce, James Richard. A.B., Ohio Wesleyan U., 1929; J.D., Ohio State U., 1932. Bar: Ohio 1932. Practice in East Liverpool, Ohio, 1932-42, 45—; with War Dept., 1942-45; chmn. bd. First Fed. Savs. & Loan Assn., East Liverpool 1959-82; former pres., bd. dirs Walter Lang companies.; hon. bd. dirs. First Nat. Community Bank East Liverpool, Ohio. Past bd. dirs. YMCA, Mary Patterson Meml.; past pres. Columbiana council Boy Scouts Am. regional com., E. Central region; mem. at large Nat. council, 1968—; bd. dirs. Bd. Global Ministries of United Methodist Ch., 1968-76. Mem. Ohio State Bar Assn., Columbiana County Bar Assn. (past pres.), East Liverpool C. of C. (past pres.), Rotary (past dist. gov.), Masons (33d degree). Methodist. Home: Highland Colony East Liverpool OH 43920 Office: Potters Savs and Loan Bldg East Liverpool OH 43920

LANG, GEORGE, restaurateur; b. Székesfehérvár, Hungary, July 13, 1924; came to U.S., 1946, naturalized, 1950; s. Simon and Ilona (Lang) Deutsch; m. Jenifer Lang; children: Andrea, Brian, Simon John, Georgina Kathlyn. Student, U. Szeged, Hungary, 1945, Mozarteum, Salzburg, Austria, 1945-46, U. Stranieri, Perugia, Italy, 1950-51; LHD(hon.), Ind. Univ., 1994. Asst. banquet mgr. Waldorf-Astoria, 1953-58; v.p. sales and marketing Brass Rail Organ., 1958-60; v.p. Restaurant Assos. Industries, 1960-71; pres. George Lang Corp., N.Y.C., 1971—; owner (with Ronald Lauder) Gundel's Restaurant, Budapest, Hungary, 1990—; co-owner Tokaj and Eger Vineyard. Author: The Cuisine of Hungary, 1971, Lang's Compendium of Culinary Nonsense and Trivia, 1980, The Cafe des Artistes Cookbook, 1984; co-author: Gundel Album, 1993; cons. editor Time-Life Book div.'s Foods of the World series, 1966-70; columnist, assoc. editor Travel and Leisure mag.; contbr. to Ency. Brit., 1974, also columnist mags. Pub. mem. Am. Revolution Bicentennial Commn., 1969—, mem. exec. com., chmn. Festival U.S.A. coordinating art, internat. exchange and spl. events for Bicentennial celebrations. Address: 33 W 67th St New York NY 10023-6224 *Almost anyone can be creative given enough time, budget and space, but the ones who succeed today have the common denominator of being poets of the possible.*

LANG, H. JACK, advertising executive, author; b. Cleve., June, June 24, 1904; s. Hascal Charles and Rosetta (Stettiner) L.; m. Frances Wise, Aug. 10, 1935; children: Wendy, John. BA, Antioch Coll., 1928. Founder, pres. Lang, Fisher Stashower Inc. (name changed to Liggett-Stashower Inc. 1988), Cleve. Author: The Wit and Wisdom of Abraham Lincoln, 1941, Lincoln's Fireside Reading, 1965, Two Kinds of Christmases, 1965, The Rowfant Manuscripts (named one of best books of yr. Am. Inst. Graphic Arts 1979), newspaper syndicated feature and book Letters of the Presidents (George Washington medal Freedoms Found.), 1964; Lincoln's Log Cabin Library (George Washington medal Freedoms Found.), 1965, Letters in American History, 1982, Dear Wit: Letters From the World's Wits, 1990; editor: The Wolf Mag. of Letters, 1934—; collector autograph letters. Past trustee Planned Parenthood Cleve., Antioch U., Yellow Springs, Ohio; trustee Mt. Sinai Hosp., Cleve., 1947-60, hon. trustee, 1973—; past mem. exec. com. ARC, Cleve. Lt. col. USAAF, 1942-46. Named to Hall of Fame Cleve. Advt. Club, 1977. Mem. Manuscript Soc., Western Res. Hist. Soc., Rowfant

Club (fellow). Home: 1737 Andrews Rd Cleveland Heights OH 44118-1901 Office: 1228 Euclid Ave Cleveland OH 44115-1831

LANG, HANS JOACHIM, engineering company executive; b. Crailsheim, Germany, Nov. 17, 1912; came to U.S., 1920, naturalized, 1928; s. Karl Hermann and Marie (Muelberger) L.; m. Emily Ruth Crowl, Feb. 26, 1944; children—Helen Marie (Mrs. Fay Logan, Jr.), Jacqueline Ruth (Mrs. Kirk Weaver), Anne Michelle (Mrs. John Talbot), Robert Crowl. M.E., Stevens Inst. Tech., 1934; M.S., MIT, 1936. Registered profl engr., N.Y., N.J., Pa., Calif., Tex. Process engr. Standard Oil Co., N.J., 1936-41; chief process engr. Day & Zimmermann, Inc., Phila., 1942-50; project mgr. C.F. Braun & Co., Alhambra, Calif., 1950-59; mgr. European sales C.F. Braun & Co., 1959-62; v.p. N. Am. operations Lummus Co., Bloomfield, N.J., 1962-68; pres. J.F. Pritchard & Co., Kansas City, Mo., 1968-69; group pres. Internat. Systems and Controls Engring. Group of Cos., 1969-74; exec. v.p Procon Inc., Des Plaines, Ill., 1974-75; pres. Procon Inc., 1975-77, Lang Assos. Inc., Tenafly, N.J., 1978—; The Pritchard Corp., Kansas City, Mo., 1978-84. Author books and articles in field. Mem. Am. Bar Assn., State Bar Calif., Am. Inst. Chem. Engrs., ASME, Am. Assn. Cost Engrs. (award of merit 1983). Home and Office: 136 Westervelt Ave Tenafly NJ 07670

LANG, JOHN FRANCIS, lawyer; b. Bayonne, N.J., June 8, 1915; s. Lewis F. and Pauline M. (Norwich) L.; m. Eleanor Bradford Cook, Jan. 26, 1952; children: Elaine L. Cornett, Anita L. Knowlton. BA, Georgetown U., 1937; JD, Harvard U., 1940. Bar: N.Y. 1941, U.S. Dist. Ct. (so. dist.) N.Y., U.S. Ct. Appeals (2d cir.), U.S. Supreme Ct., 1947. Assoc. Buckley & Buckley, N.Y.C., 1940-41, Law Office of D. J. Mooney, N.Y.C., 1946-51, Nash, Ten Eyck, N.Y.C., 1951-53; ptnr. McNutt & Nash, N.Y.C., 1953-56; ptnr. Hill, Betts & Nash, N.Y.C., 1956-86, of counsel, 1986—; bd. dirs. numerous corps.; chmn. biennial seminar in Paris on ship and aircraft fin. Lt. comdr. USN, 1941-45. Decorated Knight Comdr. (Republic of Liberia). Mem. ABA, Internat. Bar Assn., Maritime Law Assn., Harvard Club of N.Y. Avocations: boating, skiing, travel, writing. Office: Hill Betts & Nash One World Trade Ctr New York NY 10048

LANG, K. D. (KATHERINE DAWN LANG), country music singer, composer; b. Consort, Alta., Can., 1961; d. Adam and Audrey L. Lang. Mem. Tex. swing fiddle band, 1982—; formed band The Reclines. Albums include A Truly Western Experience, 1984, Angel with a Lariat, 1986, Shadowland, 1988, Absolute Torch and Twang, 1990 (Can. Country Music Awards album of the yr.), Ingenue, 1992, Even Cowgirls Get the Blues (soundtrack), 1993; actress (film) Salmonberries, 1991. Recipient Can. Country Music awards, including Entertainer of Yr., 1989, Grammy award, 1990, 1993, Best Pop Female Vocal for Constant Craving, Grammy nomination Best Pop Female Vocal for Miss Chatelaine, 1994, William Harold Moon award Soc. of Composers, Authors and Music Publishers of Can., 1994. Office: Sire Records 75 Rockefeller Plz New York NY 10019-6989*

LANG, KURT, sociologist, educator, writer; b. Berlin, Jan. 25, 1924; came to U.S., 1936; s. Ernst and Ilse (Kass) L; m. Gladys Engel, June 9, 1950; children: Glenna Engel, Kevin Engel. BA, U. Chgo., 1949, MA, 1852, PhD, 1953. Rsch. analyst Office of U.S. Milit. Govt., Berlin, 1945-47; asst. prof. U. Miami, Fla., 1953-54; rsch. associate Can. Broadcasting Corp., Ottawa, Ont., 1954-56; from asst. to assoc. prof. Queens Coll. CUNY, Flushing, N.Y., 1956-62, assoc. prof., chair, 1963-64; prof. SUNY, Stony Brook, 1964-84, chair, 1965-68; prof. U. Wash., Seattle, 1984—, dir. Sch. Comm., 1984-87; vis. assoc. prof. U. Calif., Berkeley, 1962-63; cons. CBS, N.Y.C., 1964-65, Nat. Adv. Commn. Civil Disorder, Washington, 1967. Author: Collective Dynamic, 1961, Television and Politics, 1968, 84, Battle for Public Opinion, 1983, Etched in Memory, 1990. U.S. Army Rsch. Inst. grantee, 1975-78, NEH fellow, 1971, Woodrow Wilson Ctr. fellow, 1978-79, Nat. Humanities Ctr. fellow, 1983-84, Sr. Fullbright fellow, 1994. Mem. Am. Polit. Sci. Assn. (Disting. Career award in polit. comm. 1994), Am. Assn. Pub. Opinion Rsch. (coun. 1975-77, Disting. Contbn. award 1989), Am. Sociol. Assn. (Edward L. Bernays award 1952), Internat. Inst. Commn. Democrat. Avocations: art study, photography, jogging. Home: 1249 20th Ave E Seattle WA 98112-3530 Office: U Washington Dept Sociology Seattle WA 98195

LANG, MABEL LOUISE, classics educator; b. Utica, N.Y., Nov. 12, 1917; d. Louis Bernard and Katherine (Wedge) L. B.A., Cornell U., 1939; M.A., Bryn Mawr Coll., 1940, Ph.D., 1943; Litt.D., Coll. Holy Cross, 1975, Colgate U., 1978; L.H.D., Hamilton Coll. Mem. faculty Bryn Mawr Coll., 1943-91, successively instr., asst. prof., 1943-50, assoc. prof., 1950-59, prof. Greek, 1959—, chmn. dept., 1960-88, acting dean coll. 2d semester, 1958-59, 60-61; chmn. mng. com. Am. Sch. Classical Studies, Athens, 1975-80; chmn. admissions and fellowship com. Am. Sch. Classical Studies, 1966-72; Blegen disting. rsch. prof. semester I Vassar Coll., 1976-77; Martin classical lectr. Oberlin Coll., 1982. Co-author: Athenian Agora Measures and Tokens; author: Palace of Nestor Frescoes, 1969, Athenian Agora Graffiti and Dipinti, 1976; Herodotean Narrative and Discourse, 1984, Athenian Agor Ostraka, 1990; contbr. articles profl. jours. Guggenheim fellow, 1953-54; Fulbright fellow Greece, 1959-60. Mem. Am. Philos. Soc., Am. Acad. Arts and Scis., German Archaeol. Inst., Am. Philol. Assn., Soc. Promotion Hellenic Studies (Eng.), Classical Assn. (Eng.). Home: 905 New Gulph Rd Bryn Mawr PA 19010-2933

LANG, MARGO TERZIAN, artist; b. Fresno, Calif.; d. Nishan and Araxie (Kazarosian) Terzian; m. Nov. 29, 1942; children: Sandra J. (Mrs. Ronald L. Carr), Roger Mark, Timothy Scott. Student, Fresno State U., 1939-42, Stanford U., 1948-50, Prado Mus., Madrid, 1957-59, Ariz. State U., 1960-61; workshops with Dong Kingman, Ed Whitney, Rex Brandt, Millard Sheets, George Post. Maj. exhbns. include, Guadalajara, Mex., Brussels, N.Y.C., San Francisco, Chgo., Phoenix, Corcoran Gallery Art, Washington, internat. watercolor exhbn., Los Angeles, Bicentennial shows, Hammer Galleries, N.Y.C.; spl. exhbn. aboard, S.S. France, others, over 50 paintings in various Am. embassies throughout world; represented in permanent collections, Nat. Collection Fine Arts Mus., Smithsonian Instn.; lectr., juror art shows; condr. workshops.; interviews and broadcasts on Radio Liberty, Voice of Am. Bd. dirs. Phoenix Symphony Assn., 1965-69, Phoenix Musical Theater, 1965-69. Recipient award for spl. achievements Symphony Assn., 1966, 67, 68, 72, spl. awards State of Ariz., silver medal of excellence Internat. Platform Assn., 1971; honoree U.S. Dept. State celebration of 25 yrs. of exhbn. of paintings in embassies worldwide. 1989. Mem. Internat. Platform Assn., Ariz. Watercolor Assn., Nat. Soc. Arts and Letters (nat. dir. 1971-72, nat. art chmn. 1974-76), Nat. Soc. Lit. and Arts, Phoenix Art Mus., Friends of Mexican Art, Am. Artists Profl. League, English-Speaking Union, Musical Theater Guild, Ariz. Costume Inst., Phoenix Art Mus., Scottsdale Art Ctr., Ariz. Arts Commn. (fine arts panel 1990-91). Home: 6127 E Calle Del Paisano Scottsdale AZ 85251-4212 As a romantic impressionist I feel a tremendous exhilaration at being able to communicate my philosophy through my paintings. I look for God's beauty and mystery in all things, and as an artist, I feel very fortunate that I can eliminate the ugliness and the negatives and concentrate on the wonders of the universe around us.

LANG, MARVEL, urban affairs educator; b. Bay Springs, Miss., Apr. 2, 1949; s. Otha and Hattie (Denham) L.; m. Mozell Pentecost, Sept. 15, 1973; children: Martin E., Maya S. BA cum laude, Jackson State U., 1970; MA, U. Pitts., 1975; PhD in Urban/Social and Econ. Geography, Rural Settlement and Quantitative Methods/Computer Applications, Mich. State U., 1979; postgrad., St. John's Coll., Santa Fe, 1973, Miss. State U., 1979, Murray State U., 1980. Grad. teaching fellow dept. geography U. Pitts., 1970-72; instr. geography Jackson (Miss.) State U., 1972-74, asst. prof. geography, 1978-82, assoc. prof. geography, 1982-83; assoc. prof., dir. geography program Jackson (Miss.) State U. Ctr. Urban Affairs, 1983-84; grad. teaching & rsch. asst. dept. geography Mich. State U. Computer Inst. Social Sci. Rsch., East Lansing, 1974-76; grad. teaching fellow dept. geography Mich. State U., East Lansing, 1976-78; grad. asst. to dir. Mich. State U. Ctr. Urban Affairs, Coll. Urban Devel., East Lansing, 1977-78; dir. Ctr. Urban Affairs, assoc. prof. urban affairs programs Mich. State U., East Lansing, 1986-91, dir. Ctr. Urban Affairs, prof. urban affairs programs, 1991-93, prof. urban affairs programs, 1993—; profl. geographer Bureau of the Census, Washington, 1984-85, rsch. geographer, 1985-86; instr. geography Lansing C.C., 1976-78, vis. prof., 1990-91; vis. prof. grad. sch. edn. & allied professions Fairfield (Conn.) U., 1990, 91, Egeler correctional facility prison edn. program Spring Arbor Coll. Jackson, 1990, McNair summer rsch. opportunity program, Mich. State U. 1989, 90, Wilberforce U., 1991, 92; rsch.

cons. Mich. State U. Ctr. Urban Studies, 1978-79; prin. investigator NASA, 1979-81, Inst. Rsch., Devel. & Engring. in Nuclear Energy, 1980-81, U.S. Dept. Energy, 1980-82; co-prin. investigator & dir. U.S. Bureau of the Census, 1988—; mem. commn. geography & Afro-Am. fellowship U. Pitts, 1970-72; mem. numerous coms. Jackson State U., Mich. State U.; commentator on various radio and television programs; conductor seminars, workshops, and presentations; cons.; speaker in field. Author: (with others) The World at Your Fingertips: A Self Instructional Geography Handbook, 1991; editor: Contemporary Urban America: Problems, Issues and Alternatives, 1991, (with C. Ford) Black Student Retention in Higher Education, 1988, Strategies for Retaining Minorities in Higher Education, 1992; author (with others) Introduction to Remote Sensing of the Environment, 1982, Black Student Retention in Higher Education, 1988, Politics and Policy in the Age of Education, 1990, International Science, Technology, and Development: Philosophy, Theory and Policy, 1990, The Second Handbook of Minority Student Services, 1990, Contemporary Urban America: Problems, Issues, and Alternatives, 1991, The Guide to College Success: For Black Students Only, 1992, numerous tech. reports; mem. editorial bd. Jour. Urban Affairs, Urban Affairs Quarterly, 1992—; referee Urban Affairs Quarterly, Jour. Urban Affairs, Social Devel. Issues Jour., Econ. Devel. Quarterly, Urban Geography Jour.; contbr. articles and reviews to profl. jours. Mem. Gov.'s Coun. Selective Svc. in the State of Miss., 1969-80; bd. dirs. Boys and Girls Clubs of Lansing, 1986-89; chair bd. program com., bd. dirs. St. Vincent Children's Home/Catholic Social Svcs. of Lansing, 1986-89; mem. com. community rels. Tri-County Coun. Aging, 1987-89; mem. adv. com. Mich. Legis. Black Caucus Found., 1987—, hon. host Ann. Black History Month Celebration, 1989-91; mem. coordinating com. Friendship Baptist Ch. Acad. Enrichment Program, 1986-89; bd. dirs. Mich. Protection & Advocacy Svcs., 1991—; faculty advisor MSU Black Grad. Student's Assn., 1989-90; active CIC Acad. Leadership Devel. Program, 1989-90; cofounder, v.p. Black Men Inc. of Greater Lansing, 1992—. Acad. and Marching Band scholar Jackson State U., 1966-70; recipient Outstanding Leadership award Friendship Bapt. Ch. Laymen's League, 1988, Meritorious Svc. award Mich. Lelack Caucus Found., 1988; grantee Commn. on Geography and Afro-America and the Nat. Office of Edn., 1973, Jackson State U. Grad. Sch. Rsch. and Publ. Com., 1979, NASA, 1979-80, 80-81, U.S. Dept. Energy, 1980-81, 81-82, Inst. Rsch., Devel. & Engring. Nuclear Energy, 1980-81, NSF, 1980-82, Kellogg Found., 1981-84, Miss. Coun. Humanities, 1982-83, U.S. Bureau of the Census, 1988-90, C.S. Mott Found., 1990-93. Mem. Urban Affairs Assn. (nominating com. 1987-88, membership com. 1987—, site selection com. 1988-89, governing bd. 1989—, chair membership com. 1990-91, sec., treas. 1991-92, vice chair 1992—, chair 1993—), Assn. Am. Geographers (chair com. on the status of Afro-Am. geographers 1980-83, com. affirmative action 1983—, census adv. com. 1990—), Southeast Divsn. Assn. Am. Geographers (steering com. 1980-81, com. edn. 1981-86, program com. 1982), Nat. Coun. Geog. Edn. (remote sensing com. 1981-84), Assn. Advancement of Policy, Rsch. and Devel. in the Third World (conf. program planning com. 1988-89, chair health and population sect. 1988-89), Miss. Coun. Geog. Edn. (pres., chair program com. 1979-80), Population Assn. Am., Assn. Social and Behavioral Scientists, Mich. Acad. Scis., Sigma Rho Sigma Nat. Honor Soc., Gamma Theta Upsilon Nat. Honor Soc., Alpha Kappa Mu Nat. Honor Soc., Alpha Phi Alpha Frat., Inc. Home: 3700 Colchester Rd Lansing MI 48906-3418 Office: Mich State U Ctr Urban Affairs W-104 Owen Hall East Lansing MI 48824

LANG, NORTON DAVID, physicist; b. Chgo., July 5, 1940; s. Charles and Saddle (Bilow) L.; m. Enid Asher, June 8, 1969; children: Eugenie, Aaron. A.B. summa cum laude, Harvard U., 1962, A.M., 1965, Ph.D., 1968; postgrad. (Knox fellow), London Sch. Economics, 1962-63. Asst. research physicist, lectr. U. Calif., San Diego, 1967-69; mem. staff IBM Research Center, Yorktown Heights, N.Y., 1969—; Erwin W. Mueller meml. lectr., Pa. State U., 1992. Contbr. articles on theoretical physics to profl. jours.; asso. editor: Phys. Rev. Letters, 1980-83. Fellow N.Y. Acad. Scis., Am. Phys. Soc. (chmn. fellowship com. divsn. condensed matter physics 1985-87, Davisson-Germer prize 1977, chmn. Davisson-Germer Prize com. 1990); mem. Phi Beta Kappa. Office: IBM Rsch Ctr Yorktown Heights NY 10598

LANG, OTTO E., industry executive, former Canadian cabinet minister; b. Handel, Sask., Can., May 14, 1932; s. Otto T. and Maria (Wurm) L.; m. Adrian Ann Merchant, 1963-88; children: Maria (dec.), Timothy, Gregory, Andrew, Elisabeth, Amanda, Adrian; m. Deborah McCawley, 1989; stepchildren: Andrew, Rebecca. BA, U. Sask., 1951, LLB, 1953; BCL (Rhodes scholar), Oxford (Eng.) U., 1955; LLD (hon.), U. Man., 1987. Bar: Sask. 1956, Ont., Yukon and N.W.T 1972, Man. 1988; created Queen's counsel 1972. Mem. faculty Law U. Sask., 1956-68, asso. prof. law, 1958-61, prof., dean law, 1961-68; M.P. for Sask.-Humboldt, 1968-79; Canadian minister without portfolio, 1968-69, minister for energy and water, 1969, minister of manpower and immigration, 1970-72, minister of justice, 1972-75, 78-79, minister transport, 1975-79; minister-in-charge Canadian Wheat Bd., 1968-79; exec. v.p. Pioneer Grain Co. Ltd., James Richardson & Sons Ltd., Winnipeg, Man., Can., 1979-88; chmn. Transp. Inst., U. Man., Winnipeg, 1983-93; mng. dir. Winnipeg Airpots Authority, Inc., 1992-93; pres., CEO Centra Gas Manitoba, Inc., Winnipeg, 1993—; mem. Queen's Privy Coun. for Can.; hon. consul gen. for Japan, 1993—. Editor: Contemporary Problems in Public Law, 1967. Vice pres. Sask. Liberal Assn., 1956-62, fed. campaign chmn., Sask., 1963-64; campaign chmn. Winnipeg United Way, 1983. Roman Catholic. Clubs: Knights of Sovreign Order Malta; Bridge; Golf (St. Charles). Office: Centra Gas, 444 St Mary Ave, Winnipeg, MB Canada R3C 3T7

LANG, PEARL, dancer, choreographer; b. Chgo., May 1922; d. Jacob and Frieda (Feder) Lack; m. Joseph Wiseman, Nov. 22, 1963. Student, Wright Jr. Coll., U. Chgo.; D (hon.), Juilliard Sch. Music, 1995. Formed own co., 1953; faculty Yale, 1954-68; tchr., lectr. Juilliard, 1953-69; tchr., lectr. Jacobs Pillow, Conn. Coll., Neighborhood Playhouse, 1963-68, Israel, Sweden, Netherlands. Soloist, Martha Graham Dance Co., 1944-54; featured roles on Broadway include Carousel, 1945-47, Finian's Rainbow, 1947-48, Danced Marth Graham's roles in Appalachian Spring, 1974-76, Primitive Mysteries, 1978-79, Diversion of Angels, 1948-70, Herodiade, 1977-79; role of Solvieg opposite John Garfield Broadway include, ANTA Peer Gynt; choreographer: TV shows CBC Folio; co-dir. T.S. Eliot's Murder in the Cathedral, Stratford, Conn., Direction, 1964-66, 67, Lamp Unto Your Feet, 158, Look Up and Live TV, 1957; co-dir., choreographer: full length prodn. Dybbuk for CBC dir. numerous Israel Bond programs; assumed roles Emily Dickinson: Letter to the World, 1970; Clytemnestra, 1973; Jocasta in: Night Journey, 1974, for Martha Graham Dance Co.; choreographer: dance works Song of Deborah, 1952, Moonsung and Windsung, 1952, Legend, 1953, Rites, 1953, And Joy Is My Witness, 1954, Nightflight, 1954, Sky Chant, 1957, Persephone, 1958, Black Marigolds, 1959, Shirah, 1960, Apasionada, 1961, Broken Dialogues, 1962, Shore Bourne, 1964, Dismembered Fable, 1965, Pray for Dark Birds, 1966, Tongues of Fire, 1967, Piece for Brass, 1969, Moonways and Dark Tides, 1970, Sharjuhm, 1971, At That Point in Place and Time, 1973, The Possessed, 1974, Prairie Steps, 1975, Bach Rondelays, 1977, I Never Saw Another Butterfly, 1977, A Seder Night, 1977, Kaddish, 1977, Icarus, 1978, Cantigas Ladino, 1978, Notturno, 1980, Gypsy Ballad, 1981, Hanele The Orphan, 1981, The Tailor's Megilleh, 1981, Bridal Veil, 1982, Stravinsky's opera Oedipus Rex, 1982, Song of Songs, 1983, Shiru L'adonay, 1983, Tehilim, 1983, Sephardic Romance and Tfila, 1989, Koros, 1990, Eyn Keloheynu, 1991, Schubert Quartetsatz No. 12, 1993, Schubert Quartet 15 1st Mov., 1994. Founder Pearl Lang Dance Found.; mem. Boston Symphony, Tanglewood Fest. Recipient 2 Guggenheim fellowships; recipient Goldfadden award Congress for Jewish Culture, Achievement award Artists and Writers for Peace in the Middle East, Cultural award Workmen's Circle, Queens Coll. award, 1991, Jewish Cultural achievement award Nat. Found. for Jewish Culture, 1992. Mem. Am. Guild Mus. Artists. Home: 382 Central Park W New York NY 10025-6054

LANG, PHILIP DAVID, former state legislator, insurance company executive; b. Portland, Oreg., Dec. 16, 1929; s. Henry W. and Vera (Kern) L.; m. Marcia Jean Smith, May 29, 1952 (div. Oct. 1970); 1 son, Philip David, III; m. Virginia Ann Wolf, Feb. 16, 1980. Student, Lewis and Clark Coll., 1951-53, Northwestern Coll. Law, 1956. Police officer Oreg. State Police, Salem, 1953-55; claims adjuster Glenns Falls Ins. Co., Portland, 1955-57, Oreg. Automobile Ins. Co., Portland, 1959-61; adminstrv. asst. to mayor City of Portland, 1957-58; spl. agt., underwriter North Pacific Ins. Co.,

Portland, 1961-63; mgr. North Pacific Ins. Co., 1963-65, asst. v.p., 1965-80, v.p., 1980—; asst. v.p Oreg. Automobile Ins. Co., 1965-80, v.p., 1980—. Mem. Oreg. Ho. of Reps., 1960-79, speaker, 1975-79; Div. leader Multnomah County (Oreg.) Democratic Com., 1956-60, mem. precinct com., 1956—. Served with USAF, 1947-50. Mem. Oreg. Ins. Underwriters Assn., Theta Chi. Roman Catholic. Clubs: VFW, Masons, DeMolay (Legion Honor). Home: 5769 SW Huddleson St Portland OR 97219-6645 Office: PO Box 74 Portland OR 97207 *Success is achieved through commitment to, and perserverance in, all that is undertaken; balanced with tolerance and understanding of all persons.*

LANG, RICHARD A., lawyer; b. N.Y.C., Dec. 10, 1950. AB, Harvard U., 1972; JD, John Marshall Law Sch., 1975; LLM, Boston U., 1976. Bar: Ill. 1975, Mass. 1976. Ptnr. Kirkland & Ellis, Chgo. Mem. ABA, Ill. State Bar Assn. Office: Kirkland & Ellis 200 E Randolph Dr Chicago IL 60601-1809

LANG, RICHARD ARTHUR, mayor, educator; b. Modesto, Calif., June 22, 1937; s. Frank Herbert and Joyce C. (Crowell) L.; m. Judith Karen Haertling, June 29, 1957; children: Susan Diana, Richard Arthur Jr., Julie Diane. BA in Polit. Sci., Calif. State U., Fresno, 1959; MA in Mgmt. Sys., Chapman Coll., 1973. Cert. tchr., Calif., cert. adminstr., Calif. Vice prin. Roosevelt Jr. H.S., 1974-77, La Loma Jr. H.S., 1977-79; asst. prin. in charge of student pers. svcs. Downey H.S., 1980; prin. Modesto (Calif.) H.S., 1980-90; govt. tchr. Downey H.S., Modesto, 1990—; mayor City of Modesto, 1991—. Elected to City Coun., City of Modesto, 1977, 81, 85, 89, vice mayor, 1981, chmn. citizen housing and comty. devel. com., 1983-92, chmn. solid waste com., 1984-92, chmn. downtown renaissance com., 1986—, chmn. econ. devel., comty. & intergovtl. rels. com., transp. policy com., utility svcs. & franchise com., pub. projects, budget and Stanislaus County solid waste adv. coms.; mem. Presdl. Mayors Task Force on Urban Affairs, 1992—; chmn. Modesto Bi-Centennial Com.; bd. dirs. Stanislaus chpt. ARC, 1992—, Assn. Retarded Citizens, Hanot Found., United Way, Family Tree. Named Man of Yr., VFW, 1992, Friend of the Chamber, Hispanic C. of C., 1991. Mem. Nat. Assn. Secondary Sch. Prins., Assn. Calif. Sch. Adminstrs., Modesto Rotary Club, Moose (lodge # 675), Phi Delta Kappa. Methodist. Avocations: golf, fishing. Home: 2705 Stafford Way Modesto CA 95350 Office: 801 11th St Modesto CA 95354

LANG, RICHARD WARREN, economist; b. Mpls., Oct. 23, 1949; s. Norman George and Mildred Elizabeth (Sundheim) L.; m. Carol Jean Nelson, July 31, 1971; children—Scott, Erik. B.A., St. Olaf Coll., 1971; M.A., Ohio State U., 1973, Ph.D., 1977. From economist to sr. economist Fed. Res. Bank St. Louis, 1976-80; rsch. officer, v.p. Fed. Res. Bank Phila., 1980-84, sr. v.p., dir. rsch., 1984—; mem. faculty Ill. Bankers Sch., Carbondale, 1977-80, Pa. Bankers Sch., Lewisburg, 1981—. Contbr. articles to profl. jours. Mem. Am. Econ. Assn., Am. Fin. Assn., Nat. Assn. Bus. Economists, Phi Beta Kappa. Office: Fed Res Bank Phila 10 Independence Mall Philadelphia PA 19106

LANG, ROBERT TODD, lawyer; b. N.Y.C., July 2, 1924; s. Charles and Selma L.; m. Joann Lang, Aug. 4, 1949; children: William Gerald, James David, Nancy Adler, Carolyn Kay. BA, Yale U., 1945, LLB, 1947. Bar: N.Y., U.S. Dist. Ct. (so. dist.) N.Y. Assoc. Weil, Gotshal & Manges, N.Y.C., 1948-56; ptnr. Weil, Gotshal & Manges (P.C. since 1981), N.Y.C., 1956—. Bd. dirs. Lawyers' Com. for Human Rights. Recipient Golden Torch of Hope award City of Hope, 1971, Community Svc. award Brandeis U., 1982, Learned Hand award Am. Jewish Com., 1991. Mem. ABA (chmn. subcom. proxy solicitations/tender offers 1985-93, chmn. task force listing stds: self-regulatory orgn., ad hoc com. on instnl. investors, mem. task force on exec. compensation, task force on rev. of fed. securities laws, adv. com., chmn. task force hedge funds), N.Y. County Lawyers Assn. (chmn. corp. law com. 1971-76, spl. com. on legal opinion 1977-81), Am. Stock Exch. (spl. com. shareholder voting rights), Yale Club of N.Y.C., Harmonie Club, Sunningdale Country Club. Office: Weil Gotshal & Manges PC 767 Fifth Ave New York NY 10153-0002

LANG, RONALD ANTHONY, trade association executive; b. Bklyn., May 12, 1936; s. Andrew C. and Margaret (Peculis) L.; m. Diane A. Nemeth, June 6, 1961 (div. 1971); children: David, Christopher, Keri Ann; m. Sharon Y. Diehl, Feb. 12, 1982. BS in Math. Fordham U., 1958; postgrad. Harvard U., 1989. Writer, columnist Newsday, Garden City, N.Y., 1952-58; editor New Hyde Park (N.Y.) Courier, 1954-58; asst. to pres. Industry Svc. Burs., Inc., N.Y.C., 1958-64; pres. Synthetic Organic Chem. Mfrs. Assn., Washington, 1964—; mem. Indsl. Health Coun., Washington, 1977—; freelance writer, 1954—; chmn. Coun. Chem. Assns., Washington, 1976-82. Mem. editorial bd. Toxic Substances Jour., 1981-92, Environ. Econs. Jour., 1982-85. Mentor Gifted Students' Program Rachael Carson Intermediate Sch., Queens, N.Y., 1981-85; adv. com. Harvard Ctr. Risk Analysis. Recipient Award of Merit, Chem. Industry Assn., 1980. Mem. NAM (mem. assns. coun., bd. dirs. 1983-85, 89-92), Am. Soc. Assn. Execs., Societe de Chimie Industrielle, Mensa, Chemists' Club (trustee 1979-81), Fordham U. Club, Internat. Club of Washington, Harvard Club of Washington. Republican. Roman Catholic. Avocations: bridge, tennis, chess, bass fishing. Home: 4003 Whispering Ln Annandale VA 22003-2055 Office: Synthetic Organic Chem Mfrs Assn 1330 Connecticut Ave NW Ste 300 Washington DC 20036-1790

LANG, SERGE, mathematics educator; b. Paris, France, May 19, 1927; came to U.S. 1940; B.S., Calif. Inst. Tech., Pasadena, 1946; Ph.D., Princeton U., N.J., 1951. Instr. math. U. Chgo., 1953-55; prof. math. Columbia U., N.Y.C., 1955-70; vis. prof. math. Princeton U., N.J., 1970-71, Harvard U., Cambridge, Mass., 1971-72; prof. math. Yale U., New Haven, 1972—. Author numerous books in mathematics, contbr. chpts. to books, articles to profl. jours. Served as cpl. U.S. Army, 1946-47. Recipient Prix Carriere, Academie des Scis. Paris. Mem. Am. Math. Soc. (Cole prize). Avocations: piano, lute, politics. Office: Yale U Dept Math Yale Station Box 2155 New Haven CT 06520

LANG, STEPHEN R., lawyer; b. N.Y.C., Dec. 26, 1934; s. Charles Harry and Fannie (Lashow) L.; m. Audrey Joan Solomon, July 5, 1958; children: Donna, Michele, Patricia. BA, Bklyn. Coll., 1955, LLB, 1958. Bar: N.Y. 1958, U.S. Dist. Ct. (so. dist.) N.Y. 1962, U.S. Supreme Ct. 1968. Trial atty. antitrust div. U.S. Dept. Justice, Washington, 1958-62; assoc. Breed, Abbott & Morgan, N.Y.C., 1962-66, ptnr., 1966-86, presiding ptnr., 1986—. Mem. ABA, Fed. Bar Assn., Assn. Bar City of N.Y. Office: Breed Abbott & Morgan Citicorp Ctr 401 E 65th St Apt 16E New York NY 10021-6997

LANG, THERESA, investment banker; b. Hochhausen, Germany, Aug. 25, 1952; d. John and Theresa (Wendler) L.; m. Scott David St. Marie, Nov. 12, 1977; 1 child, Hanna. BA in Econs., Fordham U., 1974; MBA in Finance, UCLA, 1982. Assoc. investment banking A.G. Becker Paribas, N.Y.C., 1982-84; assoc. investment banking Merrill Lynch Capital Markets, N.Y.C., 1984-86, v.p. investment banking, 1986-89, dir. investment banking, 1989-92; sr. v.p., treas. Merrill Lynch & Co., Inc., 1992—. Office: Merrill Lynch and Co World Financial Ctr 250 Vesey St New York NY 10281-1012

LANG, THOMPSON HUGHES, publishing company executive; b. Albuquerque, Dec. 12, 1946; s. Cornelius Thompson and Margaret Miller (Hughes) L. Student, U. N.Mex., 1965-68. Americas, Mexico City, 1968-69. Advt. salesman Albuquerque Pub. Co., 1969-70, pres., treas., gen. mgr., dir., 1971—; pub., pres., treas., dir. Jour. Pub. Co., 1971—; pres., dir. Masthead, Internat., 1971—; pres. Magnum Systems, Inc., 1973—; pres., treas., dir. Jour. Ctr. Corp., 1979—; chmn. bd., dir. Starline Printing, Inc., 1985—; chmn. bd. dirs. Corp. Security and Investigation, Inc., 1986—; pres., bd. dirs. Eagle Systems, Inc., 1986—. Mem. HOW Orgn., Sigma Delta Chi. Home: 8643 Rio Grande Blvd NW Albuquerque NM 87114-1301 Office: Albuquerque Pub Co PO Drawer JT(87103) 7777 Jefferson St NE Albuquerque NM 87109-4343*

LANG, WILLIAM CHARLES, retail executive; b. Bronx, N.Y., Jan. 29, 1944; s. Harold C. and Katherine L. (Pratt) L.; m. Marilyn Warshow, June 27, 1965 (dec.); children: Kenneth William, Pamela Sue. B.S. magna cum laude, Lehigh U., 1965. C.P.A. Accounting supr. Peat, Marwick, Mitchell & Co., 1965-69; contr. Pueblo Internat., Inc., N.Y.C., 1970-72, v.p. fin., 1972-77; exec. v.p. adminstrn. and fin. Kenyon & Eckhardt, Inc., 1977-85;

exec. mng. dir. Finley, Kumble, Wagner, Heine, Underberg, Manley, Myerson & Casey, 1985-88; pres., chief fin. officer Furr's Inc., Lubbock, Tex., 1989-92; sr. v.p. fin. and adminstrn., chief fin. officer Duane Reade, N.Y.C., 1993—. Mem. Financial Execs. Inst., Am. Inst. C.P.A.'s, Nat. Accounting Soc., N.Y. State Soc. C.P.A.'s, Beta Gamma Sigma, Sigma Phi. Office: Duane Reade 49-29 30th Pl Long Island City NY 11101

LANG, WILLIAM WARNER, physicist; b. Boston, Aug. 9, 1926; s. William Warner and Lilla Gertrude (Wheeler) L.; m. Asta Ingard, Aug. 31, 1954; 1 son, Robert. B.S., Iowa State U., 1946, Ph.D., 1958; M.S., M.I.T., 1949. Acoustical engr. Bolt Beranek and Newman, Inc., Cambridge, Mass., 1949-51; instr. in physics U.S. Naval Postgrad. Sch., Monterey, Calif., 1951-55; cons. engr. E.I. du Pont de Nemours & Co., Wilmington, Del., 1955-57; mem. research staff M.I.T., 1958; physicist IBM, Poughkeepsie, N.Y., 1958-92; program mgr. acoustics tech. IBM, 1976-90, mem. sr. tech. staff, 1990-92; pres. Internat. Noise Control Engring., Poughkeepsie, 1991—. Editor: Designing for Noise Control, 1978. Pres. Noise Control Found., Poughkeepsie, 1975-92; adj. prof. physics Vassar Coll., 1979—; chmn. working group Internat. Orgn. Standardization, 1969—; chmn. tech. com. 29 Internat. Electrotech. Commn., 1975-84. Served with USN, 1944-47, 52. Decorated Meritorious Service medal; recipient Pro Silentio medal Hungarian Optical, Acoustical and Film Tech. Soc., 1989. Fellow AAAS, IEEE (Audio and Electroacoustics Achievement award 1970, dir. 1970-71, Centennial medal 1984), Audio Engring. Soc., Acoustical Soc. Am. (Silver medal 1984), Inst. Acoustics (U.K.); mem. Nat. Acad. Engring., Inst. Noise Control Engring./U.S.A. (pres. 1978), Rotary (pres. local club 1975-76). Episcopalian. Home: 29 Hornbeck Rdg Poughkeepsie NY 12603-4205 Office: Internat Inst Noise Control Engring PO Box 3067 Poughkeepsie NY 12603-3067

LANGACKER, PAUL GEORGE, physics educator; b. Evanston, Ill., July 14, 1946; s. George Rollo and Florence (Hinesley) L.; m. Irmgard Sieker, June 25, 1983. BS, MIT, 1968; PhD, U. Calif., Berkeley, 1972; MA, U. Pa., 1981. Postdoctoral assoc. Rockefeller U., N.Y.C., 1972-74; postdoctoral assoc. U. Pa., Phila., 1974-75, asst. prof. physics, 1975-81, assoc. prof. physics, 1981-85, prof. physics, 1985-93, William Smith Term prof. physics, 1993—; exec. com. Divsn. Particles & Fields of Am. Phys. Soc., Washington, 1989-91; mem. editorial bd. Phys. Rev., 1986-88, 91-93; sci. dir. Theoretical Advanced Study Inst., Boulder, Colo., 1990. Editor: Testing the Standard Model, 1991, Precision Tests of the Standard Electroweak Model, 1995. Recipient Humboldt award A.V. Humboldt Soc., 1987-88. Fellow Am. Phys. Soc., AAAS. Office: U of Pa Dept of Physics 2N10 David Rittenhouse Lab Philadelphia PA 19104

LANGACKER, RONALD WAYNE, linguistics educator; b. Fond du Lac, Wis., Dec. 27, 1942; s. George Rollo and Florence (Hinesley) L.; m. Margaret G. Fullick, June 5, 1966 (dec.). A.B. in French, U. Ill., 1963, A.M. in Linguistics, 1964, Ph.D., 1966. Asst. prof. U. Calif. at San Diego, La Jolla, 1966-70; asso. prof. U. Calif. at San Diego, 1970-75, prof. linguistics, 1975—. Author: Language and its Structure, 1968, Fundamentals of Linguistic Analysis, 1972, Non-Distinct Arguments in Uto-Aztecan, 1976, An Overview of Uto-Aztecan Grammar, 1977, Foundations of Cognitive Grammar I, 1987, Concept, Image and Symbol, 1990, Foundations of Cognitive Grammar II, 1991; assoc. editor: Lang, 1971-77, Cognitive Linguistics, 1989—; contbr. articles in field to profl. jours. Guggenheim fellow, 1978. Mem. Linguistic Soc. Am., Cognitive Sci. Soc., Soc. for Study Indigenous Langs. of Ams., Internat. Cognitive Linguistics Assn., AAUP, ACLU. Home: 7381 Rue Michael La Jolla CA 92037-3915 Office: U Calif at San Diego Dept Linguistics 0108 La Jolla CA 92093

LANGAN, JOHN PATRICK, philosophy educator; b. Hartford, Conn., Aug. 10, 1940; s. Eugene Edward and Sarah Cecilia (McCole) Langan. AB, Loyola U., Chgo., 1962; MA, Loyola U., 1966; BD, Woodstock Coll., N.Y.C., 1970; PhD, U. Mich., 1979. Ordained priest, Roman Cath. Ch. 1972. Instr. philosophy U. Mich., Ann Arbor, 1971-72; research fellow Woodstock Theol. Ctr., Washington, 1975-83; vis. asst. prof. social ethics Yale Div. Sch., New Haven, 1983; sr. fellow Woodstock Theol. Ctr., 1983—; acting dir., 1986-87; Rose F. Kennedy prof. Christian ethics Kennedy Inst. Ethics, Georgetown U., Washington, 1987—; bd. dirs. Georgetown U. Press, 1984—; vis. rsch. scholar Jesuit Inst. Boston Coll., 1993-94; mem. rsch. coun. Ctr. Strategic and Internat. Studies, 1993; cons. in field. Editor: The American Search for Peace, 1991, The Nuclear Dilemma and the Just War Tradition, 1986, Human Rights in the Americas: The Struggle for Consensus, 1982, Catholic Universities in Church and Society, 1993. Bd. dirs. Bon Secours Health System, 1990, Nat. Capital Presbytery, Health Care Ministries, Washington, 1989-92. Rackham Prize fellow, U. Mich., 1972-73. Mem. Am. Acad. Religion, Am. Philos. Assn., Cath. Theol. Soc. Am., Soc. Christian Ethics, Soc. Christian Philosophers, Soc. for Bus. Ethics, Internat. Studies Assn. Roman Catholic. Avocations: music, swimming. Office: Georgetown U 1437 37th St NW Washington DC 20007-2610

LANGBAUM, GARY ALAN, financial executive; b. N.Y.C., Dec. 16, 1948; s. Stanley and Anita (Grabel) L.; m. Risa Lynn Goldberg, Aug. 30, 1970; children: Lauren, Susanne. BS, U. Md., 1969, postgrad., 1969-70. CFA. Analyst Md. Nat. Bank, Balt., 1970-78, dir. rsch., 1978-82, head of investment, 1982-84; sr. rsch. analyst Northern Trust Co., Chgo., 1984-87, assoc. dir. rsch., 1987-88; dir. equity rsch., sr. v.p. Kemper Fin. Svcs., Chgo., 1988—. Recipient Best of Buyside award Institutional Investor Mag., 1989, 91. Mem. Assn. Investment Mgmt. and Rsch., Electrical Product Group N.Y., Consumer Analyst Group N.Y., Chgo. Analyst Soc. Avocations: travel, golf. Office: Kemper Fin Svcs 170 S La Salle St Chicago IL 60603-3408

LANGBAUM, ROBERT WOODROW, English language educator, author; b. N.Y.C., Feb. 23, 1924; s. Murray and Nettie (Moskowitz) L.; m. Francesca Levi Vidale, Nov. 5, 1950; 1 child, Donata Emily. A.B., Cornell U., 1947; M.A., Columbia U., 1949, Ph.D., 1954. Instr. English Cornell U., 1950-55, asst. prof., 1955-60; assoc. prof. U. Va., Charlottesville, 1960-63; prof. English U. Va., 1963-67, James Branch Cabell prof. English and Am. lit., 1967—; vis. prof. Columbia U., summer 1960, 65-66, Harvard U., summer 1965; mem. supervising com. English Inst., 1970-71, chmn., 1972; mem. Christian Gauss Book Award Com., 1984-86; U.S. Info. Svc. lectr. Japan, Taiwan, Hong Kong, 1988. Author: The Poetry of Experience: The Dramatic Monologue in Modern Literary Tradition, 1957, The Gayety of Vision: A Study of Isak Dinesen's Art, 1964, The Modern Spirit: Essays on the Continuity of Nineteenth and Twentieth Century Literature, 1970, The Mysteries of Identity: A Theme in Modern Literature, 1977, The Word from Below: Essays on Modern Literature and Culture, 1987, Thomas Hardy in Our Time, 1995; editor: The Tempest (Shakespeare), 1964; anthology The Victorian Age: Essays in History and in Social and Literary Criticism, 1967; mem. editorial bd. Victorian Poetry, 1963—, New Lit. History, 1969—, Bull. Rsch. in Humanities, 1977—, Studies in English Lit., 1978—, So. Humanities Rev., 1979—, Studies in Browning and His Circle, 1987—, Victorian Lit. and Culture, 1991—, Browning Studies, 1993. Served to 1st lt. M.I. AUS, 1942-46. Ford Found. fellow Center for Advanced Study, Stanford, Calif., 1961-62; Guggenheim fellow, 1969-70; sr. fellow Nat. Endowment for Humanities, 1972-73; Am. Council Learned Socs. grantee, 1961, 75-76; fellow Clare Hall, Cambridge U., Eng., 1978; U. Va. Ctr. Advanced Study fellow, 1982; resident scholar Bellagio Study and Conf. Ctr. Rockefeller Found., Italy, June 1987. Mem. MLA (del. assembly 1979-81), AAUP, PEN, Assn. Lit. Scholars and Critics, Phi Beta Kappa. Home: 223 Montvue Dr Charlottesville VA 22901-2022

LANGBEIN, JOHN HARRISS, lawyer, educator; b. Washington, Nov. 17, 1941; s. I. L. and M. V. (Harriss) L.; m. Kirsti M. Hiekka, June 24, 1973; children: Christopher, Julia, Anne. AB, Columbia U., 1964; LLB, Harvard U., 1968, Cambridge U., 1969; PhD, Cambridge U., 1971; MA (hon.), Yale U., 1991. Bar: D.C. 1969, Fla. 1970; barrister-at-law Inner Temple, Eng., 1970. Asst. prof. law U. Chgo., 1971-73, assoc. prof. law, 1973-74, prof. law, 1974-80, Max Pam prof. Am. and fgn. law, 1980-90; Chancellor Kent prof. law and legal history Yale U., New Haven, 1990—; commr. Nat. Conf. Commrs. on Uniform State Laws, 1984—; reporter Uniform Product Investor Act. Author: Prosecuting Crime in the Renaissance, 1974, Torture and the Law of Proof: Europe and England in the Ancient Regime, 1977, Comparative Criminal Procedure: German, 1977, (with L. Waggoner) Selected Statutes on Trusts and Estates, 1987, rev. edits., 1991, 92, 94, 95, (with B. Wolk) Pension and Employee Benefit Law, 1992, 2d edit., 1995;

contbr. numerous articles on law and legal history to profl. jours. Mem. ABA, Am. Coll. Trust and Estate Counsel, Am. Law Inst., Am. Soc. Legal History, Am. Hist. Assn., Selden Soc., Gesellschaft fuer Rechtsvergleichung, Am. Acad. of Arts and Scis., Internat. Acad. Estate and Trust Law, Internat. Acad. Comparative Law. Republican. Episcopalian. Office: Yale Univ Sch Law PO Box 208215 127 Wall St New Haven CT 06520-8215

LANGBO, ARNOLD GORDON, food company executive; b. Richmond, B.C., Can., Apr. 13, 1937; s. Osbjourn and Laura Marie (Hagen) L.; m. Martha Marie Miller, May 30, 1959; children: Sharon Anne, Maureen Bernice, Susan Colleen, Roderick Arnold, Robert Wayne, Gary Thomas, Craig Peter, Keith Edward. Student, U. B.C. Retail salesman Kellogg Co., Vancouver, 1956-57; dist. mgr. Kellogg Co., Prince George, B.C., 1957-60; supermarket salesman Kellogg Co., Vancouver, 1960; dist mgr. Kellogg Co., Winnipeg, Man., 1964-65; acct. mgr. Kellog Co. of Can., Ltd., Toronto, 1965-67; sales staff asst. Kellogg Co., Battle Creek, Mich., 1967-69, adminstrv. asst. to pres., 1969; exec. v.p. Kellogg Co. of Can. Ltd., London, Ont., 1970; v.p. sales and mktg. Kellogg Salada Can. Ltd., Toronto, 1971-74, sr. v.p. sales and mktg., 1974-76, pres., chief exec. officer, 1976-78; pres. food products div. Kellogg Co., Battle Creek, 1978-81; past exec. v.p. Kellogg Co., Battle Creek, group exec. v.p. 1983-86, exec. v.p., 1986—; pres. Kellogg Internat., Battle Creek, 1986—; pres. Mrs. Smith's Frozen Foods Co. (subs. Kellogg Co.), Battle Creek, 1983-85, chmn., chief exec. officer, 1985—; pres. Kellogg Internat., 1986—, pres., COO, internat. bd. dirs., 1990—; chmn., CEO Kellogg Co., Battle Creek, 1992—, also dir.; bd. dirs. Johnson & Johnson, Grocery Mfg. Am., Gilmore Int. Keyboard Festival. Vice-pres. Hockey Internat., Battle Creek; trustee Albion Coll.; mem. Canadian-Am. Com., B.C. Premier's Econ. Adv. Coun.; mem. adv. bd. J. L. Kellogg Grad. Sch. Mgmt., Northwestern U.; bd. dirs. Gilmore Internat. Keyboard Festival. Mem. Am. Frozen Food Inst. (bd. dirs., vice chmn. 1985), Grocery Products Mfrs. Can. (bd. dirs.), Tea Council of Can. (bd. dirs.). Office: Kellogg Co Box 3599 1 Kellogg Sq Battle Creek MI 49017-3534*

LANGDALE, GEORGE WILFRED, research soil scientist; b. Walterboro, S.C., Sept. 14, 1930; s. Benjamin Hayward and Hazel Ruth (Smith) L.; m. Eugenia Miles Boatwright, Aug. 28, 1955. B.S., Clemson Univ., 1957, MS, 1961; postgrad. N.C. State Univ., 1963-64; PhD, Univ. Ga., 1969. Rsch. soil scientist USDA, Agrl. Rsch. Svc., S.C., Ga., Tex., 1957—; cons. conservation tillage and soil erosion. Contbr. book chpts. and articles to profl. jours. Served with inf. U.S. Army, 1951-53, Korea. Kellogg fellow Agr. Policy Inst., 1963-64. Fellow Soil and Water Consoc. (H.H. Bennett award 1993), Am. Soc. Agronomy (pres. Ga. chpt. 1986-87), Soil Sci. Soc. Am.; mem. Soil Conservation Soc. Am. (chpt. pres. Tex. 1970-71, Ga. 1994-95), World Assn. Soil and Water Conservation, Internat. Soil Sci. Soc., Sigma Xi. Baptist. Avocations: conservation gardening, small game hunting, genealogy. Home: 125 Orchard Knob Ln Athens GA 30605-3427 Office: Southern Piedmont Conservation Research Center PO Box 555 Watkinsville GA 30677-0555

LANGDALE, JOHN WESLEY, timber executive; b. Valdosta, Ga., Feb. 8, 1917; s. Harley and Thalia (Lee) L.; m. Margaret Irene Jones, Dec. 19, 1946; children: Lee Mikuta, John Widr., Margaret Perryman. AB in Econs., U. Ga., 1939, JD, 1940. Mem. Ga. Ho. of Reps., Atlanta, 1949-52, Ga. State Senate, Atlanta, 1957-58; pres. The Langdale Co., Valdosta, 1976-82, vice chmn., 1983—; vice chmn. Langdale Industries Inc., 1986—; chmn. bd. dirs. Valdosta Fed. Savs. and Loan Assn., 1957—. Chmn. U. Ga. Bd. Regents, 1967-69. Served to lt. comdr. USNR, 1941-46, PTO. Decorated Bronze Star. Mem. Ga. Bar Assn. Republican. Baptist. Lodge: Rotary (pres. local chpt. 1948-49, dist. gov. 1967-68).

LANGDELL, ROBERT DANA, medical educator; b. Pomona, Cal., Mar. 14, 1924; s. Walter Irving and Florence Delsa (Reichenbach) L.; m. Alice E. Pritt, June 3, 1948; children—Robert Dana, Sara Ellen. Student, Pomona Coll., 1941-43; M.D., George Washington U., 1948. Intern Henry Ford Hosp., Detroit, 1948-49; mem. faculty Sch. Medicine, U. N.C., Chapel Hill, 1949—; assoc. prof. pathology Sch. Medicine, U. N.C., 1959-61, prof., 1961—; mem. hematology study sect. USPHS, 1968-71. Editor-in-chief Transfusion, 1972-82; assoc. editor Archives of Pathology and Laboratory Medicine, 1983—. Served to capt. M.C. AUS, 1955-56. USPHS sr. research fellow, 1957-61; Career Research fellow, 1962-66. Mem. Am. Assn. Blood Banks (pres. 1972-73), Am. Soc. Clin. Pathology, AMA, Coll. Am. Pathology (gov. 1977-83), N.C. Med. Assn. Episcopalian. Rsch. in blood coagulation and hemostasis. Home: 707 Williams Cir Chapel Hill NC 27516-1527

LANGDON, FRANK CORRISTON, political science educator, researcher; b. LaGrange, Ill., June 3, 1919; s. Ernest Warren and Julia Ida (Mondeng) L.; m. Virginia Irene Osborne, Nov. 11, 1922; children: Peter John, Marc Christopher. A.B., Harvard U., 1941, A.M., 1949; Ph.D., U. Calif.-Berkeley, 1953. Japanese Lang. Sch. intelligence officer U.S. Navy, Stillwater, Okla., 1945-46; econ. analyst Hdqrs. SCAP, Fgn. Trade div., Tokyo, 1946-47; instr. polit. sci. U. Calif. Far East Program, Korea, Japan, Guam, 1953-55; sr. lectr. Canberra U. Coll., Australia, 1955-58; prof. polit. sci. U. B.C., Vancouver, 1958-84, emeritus prof., 1984—, sr. research assoc., 1984—. Author: Politics in Japan, 1967, Japan's Foreign Policy, 1973, Politics of Canadian-Japanese Economic Relations, 1952-83, 83; co-editor, co-author: Japan in the Post Hegomonic World, 1993; co-editor, contbr.: Superpower Maritime Strategy in the Pacific, 1990. Served to lt. comdr. USNR, 1941-45. Mem. Assn. for Asian Studies, Can. Polit. Sci. Assn., Can. Asian Studies Assn., Japan Studies Assn. of Can., Internat. House Japan, Am. Polit. Sci. Assn. Democrat. Presbyterian. Club: Mokuyokai (Vancouver). Home: 4736 W 4th Ave, Vancouver, BC Canada V6T 1C2 Office: U BC Inst Internat Rels, C456 1866 Main Mall, Vancouver, BC Canada V6T 1Z1

LANGDON, GEORGE DORLAND, JR., association executive; b. Putnam, Conn., May 20, 1933; s. George Dorland and Anne Claggett (Zell) L.; m. Agnes Domandi; children—George Dorland, III, Campbell Brewster. A.B. cum laude (Coolidge scholar), Harvard Coll., 1954; M.A., Amherst Coll., 1957; Ph.D. (Coe fellow), Yale U., 1961; LHD (hon.), Colgate U. Instr. in history and Am. studies Yale U., 1959-62, asst. provost, lectr. in history, 1969-70, asso. provost, lectr. in history, 1970-72, dep. provost, lectr. in history, 1972-78; asst. prof. history Calif. Inst. Tech., 1962-64; asst. prof. Vassar Coll., 1964-67, asso. prof., 1967-68, spl. asst. to pres., 1968; pres., trustee Colgate U., 1978-88, pres. emeritus, 1988—; pres. Am. Mus. Natural History, N.Y.C., 1988-93; exec. chmn. Un Assn. of the U.S.A., N.Y.C., 1994—; bd. dirs. Quest for Value Dual Purpose Fund, Inc., Custodial Trust Co. Author: A History of New Plymouth 1620-1691, 1966 (State and Local Assn. of History award of Merit). Trustee The Kresge Found., St. Lukes/Roosevelt Hosp. Ctr., Wenner-Gren Found. for Anthrop. Rsch. Lt. U.S. Army, 1954-56. Fellow Pilgrim Soc.

LANGDON, GLEN GEORGE, JR., electrical engineer; b. Morristown, N.J., June 30, 1936; s. Glen George and Mildred (Miller) L.; m. Marian Elizabeth Jacobsen, Aug. 10, 1963; 1 child, Karen Joan. BSEE, Wash. State U., 1957, MSEE, U. Pitts., 1963; PhD, Syracuse U., 1968. Elec. engr. Wes-

tinghouse Electric Co., East Pittsburgh, Pa., 1960-62, applications programmer, Churchill Boro, Pa., 1962-63; engr. IBM Corp., Endicott, N.Y., 1963-73, research staff mem., San Jose, Calif., 1974-87; prof. computer engring. U. Calif., Santa Cruz, Calif., 1987—; vis. prof. U. São Paulo, Brazil, 1971-72; lectr. U. Santa Clara, 1975-78, Stanford U., 1984. Author: Logic Design: A Review of Theory and Practice, 1974; (with Edson Fregni) Projecto de Computadores Digitals, 1974; Computer Design, 1982. Patentee in field. Lt. Signal Corps., U.S. Army, 1958-59. Recipient Armed Svcs. Communications award Wash. State U., 1957, outstanding innovation award IBM, 1980, 91. Fellow IEEE, Computer Soc. of IEEE (standards com. 1969-70, 74-81, sec. 1982, edn. bd. 1983-86, pub. bd. 1984-85, 87-90, bd. govs. 1984-87, v.p. edn. 1986, Compcon gen. chair 1986, Hot Chips IV Symposium gen. chair 1992); mem. Assn. Computing Machinery (vice chmn. So. Tier chpt. 1973), SPIE, SMPTE, Sigma Xi. Home: 220 Horizon Way Aptos CA 95003-2739 Office: U Calif-Santa Cruz Dept Computer Engring Santa Cruz CA 95064

LANGDON, HERSCHEL GARRETT, lawyer; b. Lowry City, Mo., Oct. 6, 1905; s. Isaac Garrett and Della (Park) L.; m. Ethel Virginia Waterson, May 26, 1931 (dec. Apr. 1979); children: Richard G., Ann Virginia (Mrs. Charles Eugene Willoughby Ward); m. Miriam Pickett, May 17, 1982. B.A., U. Iowa, 1930, J.D., 1931. Bar: Iowa 1931. Since practiced in Des Moines; mem. firm Herrick, Langdon & Langdon (and predecessors), 1935—. Fellow Am. Coll. Trial Lawyers, Am. Bar Found.; mem. Am., Iowa, Polk County bar assns., Phi Beta Kappa, Delta Sigma Rho, Phi Delta Pi. Conglist. Club: Mason. Home: 3524 Grand Ave Apt 603 Des Moines IA 50312-4344 Office: 1800 Financial Ctr 7th and Walnut Des Moines IA 50309

LANGE, CARL JAMES, psychology educator; b. Seneca, Pa., June 1, 1925; s. Otto Carl and Rose Marie (Jetter) L.; m. Veronica Szelypecz, Jan. 14, 1950; children: David Carl, Veronica Jean. B.S., Duke U., 1945; M.S., U. Pitts., 1948, Ph.D., 1951. Lic. psychologist, Va. Project dir. Human Resources Research Office, George Washington U., 1953-60, dir. research, planning, 1960-69; asst. v.p. research George Washington U., 1969-75, v.p. adminstrn., research, prof. psychology, 1975-88, v.p. rsch., prof. psychology, 1988-89, prof. emeritus, 1989—; cons. NSF, Ford Found.; bd. dirs. Sch. for Contemporary Edn., Nat. Lab. Higher Edn., Eric Clearinghouse for Higher Edn., Southeastern Univs. Rsch. Assn. Contbr. articles in field to profl. jours.; bd. editors: Research in Higher Education. Served with USN, 1943-45. Fellow Am. Psychol. Assn.; mem. AAAS, Sigma Xi. Home: 7 Clarendon Ct Williamsburg VA 23188-1513

LANGE, CLIFFORD E., librarian; b. Fond du Lac, Wis., Dec. 29, 1935; s. Elmer H. and Dorothy Brick (Smithers) L.; m. Janet M. LeMieux, June 6, 1959; children: Paul, Laura, Ruth. Student, St. Norbert Coll., 1954-57; B.S., Wis. State U., 1959; M.S.L.S. (Library Services Act scholar), U. Wis., 1960, Ph.D. (Higher Edn. Act fellow), 1972. Head extension dept. Oshkosh (Wis.) Public Library, 1960-62, head reference dept., 1962-63; asst. dir. Jervis Library, Rome, N.Y., 1963-66; dir. Eau Claire (Wis.) Public Library, 1963-66; asst. dir. Lake County Public Library, Griffith, Ind., 1966-68; asst. prof. Sch. Library Sci., U. Iowa, 1971-73; dir. Wauwatosa (Wis.) Public Library, 1973-75; asst. prof. U. So. Calif., 1975-78; state librarian N.Mex. State Library, Santa Fe, 1978-82; dir. Carlsbad City Library, Calif., 1982—. Served with U.S. Army, 1958. Mem. ALA, Calif. Libr. Assn. Home: 3575 Ridge Rd Oceanside CA 92056-4952 Office: 1250 Carlsbad Village Dr Carlsbad CA 92008-1949

LANGE, CRYSTAL MARIE, nursing educator; b. Snover, Mich., Aug. 22, 1927; d. Bazil H. and Crystal S. (Hilborn) Morse; m. Elmer William Lange, June 10, 1961; children: Gregory, Frederick, Helen, Charles, G. Benson, Robert, Larry. BSN, U.Mich., 1949; MSN, Wayne State U., 1961; PhD, Mich. State U., 1972. Pvt. duty nurse, Richmond, Ind., 1949-50; asst. dir. nursing, nursing supr., instr. St. Mary's Hosp., Tucson, Ariz., 1950-58; night supr. Pima County Hosp., Tucson, 1958-59; asst. dir. Sch. Nursing, Saginaw Gen. Hosp., Mich., 1959-60; instr. to prof., chmn. div. Delta Coll., University Ctr., Mich., 1962-76; dean Sch. Nursing and Allied Health Scis., asst. to v.p. acad. affairs Saginaw Valley State Coll., University Center, 1976—, prof., dean, 1989—; mem. vis. com. Med. Ctr., U. Mich., 1978-81. Author: Leadership for Quality, 1966; Instructor's Guide - Nursing Skills and Techniques, 1969; The Use of the Auto-tutorial Laboratory and the Mobile Tutorial Unit in Teaching, 1969; Instructor's Guide - Nursing Skills and Techniques - Films 76-126, 1972; Instructor's Guide - Nursing Skills and Techniques - Films 127-151, 1971; Auto-Tutorial Techniques in Nursing Education, 1971; Future Education: Diagnosis Prescriptions Evaluation, 1971. Contbr. articles to profl. jours. Bd. dirs. Saginaw chpt. ARC, 1982—; Saginaw Vis. Nurse Assn., 1980—. Recipient award Mich. Acad. Sci., Arts and Letters, 1970, Monsour Found. Lectureship award Health Edn. Media Assn., 1977; NEH fellow, 1983. Fellow Am. Acad. Nursing; mem. Am. Acad. Arts and Scis., Am. Acad. Nursing (governing council, sec. 1978-80), AAUP (chpt. v.p. 1976, award citation 1970), Am. Ednl. Scis., Am. Nurses Assn., Mich. Nurses Assn., Saginaw Dist. Nurses Assn. (bd. dirs. 1976—), U. Mich. Alumnae Assn., Wayne State U. Alumnae Assn., Phi Kappa Phi, Sigma Theta Tau. Home: 4135 Kochville Rd Saginaw MI 48604-9750 Office: Saginaw Valley State U University Center MI 48710

LANGE, DAVID L., law educator; b. Charleston, Ill., Dec. 7, 1938; s. Charles W.S. and Mary Helen Lange; m. Teresa Tetrick, July 30, 1972; children—David, Adam, Daniel, Jennifer, William. BS, U. Ill., Urbana, 1960, LLB, 1964. Bar: Ill. 1964, N.C. 1989. Pvt. practice Chgo., 1964-71; gen. counsel media task force Nat. Commn. on Violence, Washington, 1968-69; gen. ptnr. Mediamix Prodns., 1970-71; assoc. prof. law Duke U., Durham, N.C., 1971-74; prof. law Duke U., 1974—; of counsel Parker, Poe, Adams & Bernstein, Charlotte, N.C., 1987—. Office: Duke U Sch Law Durham NC 27708

LANGE, JAMES BRAXTON, chemical company executive; b. Amory, Miss., Feb. 17, 1937; s. Oliver John and Sarah Nell (Gravlee) L.; m. Margaret Terry Terrell, Aug. 9, 1969. B.S. in Psychology, Millsaps Coll., 1960; B.S. in Bus, Miss. Coll., 1970, M.B.A., 1973; postgrad., Harvard U., 1979. Indsl. rep. Miss. CD, 1971-73; secs., treas. 1st Miss. Corp., Jackson, 1973-88; dir. investor rels. and corp. affaris Himont, Inc., Wilmington, Del., 1988-90; pres., chief exec. officer Columbia Gas Found., Wilmington, Del., 1990—; sec. Columbia Gas System Svc. Corp., Wilmington, 1990—; bd. dirs. Primex, Inc. Charter mem. Community Action Coun., 1972-74; group leader United Way campaign, 1970-73; mem. exec. com. YMCA; mem. com. on free enterprise Miss. Econ. Coun.; trustee Grand Opera House, 1990-93. With USN, 1960-63. Mem. Am. Soc. Corp. Secs., Am. Soc. Corp. Treas., Nat. Investor Rels. Inst., Am. Soc. Pers. Adminstrn., Miss. Mfrs. Assn., Jackson C. of C., Nat. Assn. Corp. Dirs., Naval Res. Assn. (pres.), Res. Officers Assn. (past v.p.), Navy League Jackson, Lions. Republican. Home: 4 Normandy Dr Chadds Ford PA 19317-9274 Office: Columbia Gas System PO Box 4020 Wilmington DE 19807-0020

LANGE, JESSICA, actress; b. Minn., Apr. 20, 1949; d. Al and Dorothy Lange; m. Paco Grande, 1970 (div. 1982); 1 child with Mikhail Baryshnikov, Alexandra; children with Sam Shepard: Hannah Jane, Samuel Walker. Student, U. Minn.; student mime, with Etienne DeCroux, Paris. Dancer Opera Comique, Paris; model Wilhelmina Agy., N.Y.C. Film appearances include King Kong, 1976, All That Jazz, 1979, How to Beat the High Cost of Living, 1980, The Postman Always Rings Twice, 1981, Frances, 1982 (Acad. award nominee 1982), Tootsie, 1982 (Acad. award 1983), Country, 1984, Sweet Dreams, 1985, Crimes of the Heart, 1986 (Acad. award nominee 1987), Everybody's All American, 1988, Far North, 1988, Music Box, 1989 (Acad. award nominee 1990), Men Don't Leave, 1990, Cape Fear, 1991, Night and the City, 1992, Blue Sky, 1994 (Golden Globe award Best Actress in a Drama 1995, Acad. award for Best Actress 1995), Losing Isaiah, 1995, Rob Roy, 1995; TV movies: Cat on a Hot Tin Roof, 1984, O' Pioneers!, 1992; in summer stock prodn. Angel on My Shoulder, N.C. 1980, Streetcar Named Desire, 1992. Office: Creative Artists Agy care Ron Meyer 9830 Wilshire Blvd Beverly Hills CA 90212*

LANGE, LESTER HENRY, mathematics educator; b. Concordia, Mo., Jan. 2, 1924; s. Harry William Christopher and Ella Martha (Alewel) L.; m. Anne Marie Pelikan, Aug. 17, 1947 (div. Oct. 1980); children: Christopher, Nicholas, Philip, Alexander; m. Beverly Jane Brown, Feb. 4, 1962; 1 son, Andrew. Student, U. Calif., Berkeley, 1943-44; B.A. in Math, Valparaiso U.,

1948; M.S. in Math, Stanford, 1950; Ph.D. in Math, U. Notre Dame, 1960. Instr., then asst. prof. math. Valparaiso U., 1950-56; instr. math. U. Notre Dame, 1956-57, 59-60; mem. faculty San Jose State U., Calif., 1960—, prof. math., head dept., 1961-70, dean Sch. Natural Scis. and Math., 1970—, dean Sch. Sci., 1972-88, emeritus prof. math., emeritus dean, 1988—; founder Soc. Archimedes at San Jose State U., 1982; now spl. asst. to dir. Moss Landing (Calif.) Marine Labs. Author text on linear algebra; sr. editor Calif. Math, 1981-84; contbr. to profl. jours. Served with inf. AUS, 1943-46, ETO. Danforth fellow, 1957-58; NSF faculty fellow, 1958-59. Fellow Calif. Acad. Scis.; mem. Math. Assn. Am. (bd. govs., L.R. Ford Sr. award 1972, George Polya award 1993), Calif. Math. Coun., London Math. Soc., Fibonacci Assn. (bd. dirs. 1987—), Nat. Coun. Tchrs. Home: 308 Escalona Dr Capitola CA 95010-3419 Office: Moss Landing Marine Labs Moss Landing CA 95039

LANGE, MARVIN ROBERT, lawyer; b. Bronx, Mar. 25, 1948; s. Arthur A. and Beatrice L. Lange; m. Ellen Metzger, Apr. 20, 1986; 1 child, Rebecca Hillary. BA, Queens Coll., 1968; JD, Harvard U., 1971. Bar: N.Y. 1972, U.S. Dist. Ct. (ea. and so. dists.) N.Y. 1975, U.S. Ct. Appeals (2d cir.) 1975, U.S. Supreme Ct. 1980, U.S. Ct. Appeals (6th cir.) 1986. Law clk. U.S. Dist. Ct., Phila., 1971-72; atty. FTC, Washington, 1972-75; assoc. Rosenman & Colin, N.Y.C., 1975-81, prtr., 1981-93; pvt. practice law, 1993—. Editor Harvard Law Rev., 1969-71. Mem. ABA. Jewish. Office: 777 Third Ave 19th Fl New York NY 10017

LANGE, PHIL C., retired education educator; b. North Freedom, Wis., Feb. 26, 1914; s. Richard Samuel and Martha (Grosinske) L.; m. Irene Oyen, June 8, 1940; children—Dena Rae, Richard (dec.). B.A., U. Wis., 1934, M.A., 1936, Ph.D., 1941. Tchr. Reeseville (Wis.) Pub. Sch., 1935-37; chmn. English dept. Wayland Jr. Coll. and Acad., Beaver Dam, Wis., 1937-39; instr. English, student teaching supr. Beloit (Wis.) High Sch., 1939-40; asst. instr. U. Wis., Madison, 1940-41, summers 1938, 39; chmn. psychology dept., dean men. Ariz. State Coll., Flagstaff, 1941-42; chmn. edn. dept. SUNY, Fredonia, 1942-50; prof. edn., coordinator student teaching Tchrs. Coll., Columbia U., 1950—; cons., expert for Dept. State, UNESCO, AID. Author, editor curriculum materials. Served with USNR, 1943-46. Recipient Filmstrip award Graphic Arts, 1966; Communication award Nat. Soc. Programmed Instrn., 1968; award Ednl. Press Assn. Am., 1969. Home: 727 Fox Hills Dr Sun City Center FL 33573-5127 Office: Tchrs Coll Columbia Univ New York NY 10027

LANGE, ROBERT DALE, internist, educator, medical researcher; b. Redwood Falls, Minn., Jan. 24, 1920; s. John Christian and Bertha Semelia (Eggen) L.; m. Mary Jane Adams, Sept. 16, 1944; children: Ruth Ann Lange Rehm, John Carl. B.A., Macalester Coll., 1941; M.D., Washington U., 1944. Diplomate: Am. Bd. Internal Medicine. Intern Barnes Hosp., St. Louis, 1944-45; asst. resident medicine U. Minn. Hosps., Mpls., 1945-46; fellow and instr. medicine U. Wash. Sch. Medicine, St. Louis, 1948-51; practice medicine specializing in internal medicine St. Louis, 1956-62, Knoxville, Tenn., 1964—; scientist Atomic Bomb Casualty Commn., Hiroshima and Nagasaki, Japan, 1951-53; rsch. assoc. VA Hosp., Mpls., 1953-54; mem. staff Eitel Hosp., Mpls., 1953-54; chief hematology Rsch. Lab. VA Hosp., St. Louis, 1956-62; asst. prof. medicine Washington U. Sch. Medicine, St. Louis, 1956-62; assoc. prof. medicine Med. Coll. Ga., Augusta, 1962-64; mem. staff Talmadge Hosp., Augusta, 1962-65, U. Hosp., Augusta, 1964-65, U. Tenn. Meml. Hosp., Knoxville, 1965; research prof. U. Tenn. Meml. Research Center, Knoxville, 1964-78; asst. dir. research U. Tenn. Meml. Research Center, Knoxville, 1966-76, dir. research, 1977-81; prof. medicine U. Tenn. Center for Health Services, Knoxville, 1970—; prof. U. Tenn. Meml. Research Center, 1978-85, prof. emeritus, 1985—; chmn. dept. med. biology, 1978-81; cons. to Oak Ridge Associated Univs., 1969-93, Abbott Labs Rev. Bd., 1974. Contbr. chpts. in hematology to med. books; contbr. numerous articles on research in hematology and exptl. medicine to profl. jours.; reviewer various med. jours., 1960—; editorial bd.: Exptl. Hematology, 1974-77. Served to maj., M.C. U.S. Army, 1954-56. Jackson Johnson scholar, 1941-44; recipient Cert. St. Paul Jr. Assn. of Commerce, 1941. Fellow A.C.P., Internat. Soc. Hematology; mem. Am. Soc. Hematology, Internat. Soc. Exptl. Hematology, Soc. of Research Administrs., Soc. Exptl. Biology and Medicine, Central Soc. Clin. Research, So. Soc. Clin. Investigation, Knoxville Soc. Internal Medicine, AMA (Cert. of Merit 1954), Tenn. Med. Assn., Knoxville Acad. Medicine, AAAS, AAUP, Sigma Xi, Alpha Omega Alpha, Pi Phi Epsilon. Methodist. Home: 8116 Bennington Dr Knoxville TN 37909-2301 Office: U Tenn Med Ctr 1924 Alcoa Hwy Knoxville TN 37920-1511

LANGE, VICTOR, language educator, author; b. Leipzig, Germany, July 13, 1908; came to U.S., 1932, naturalized, 1943; s. Walter and Theodora (Schellenberg) L.; m. Frances Mary Olrich, Feb. 23, 1945; children: Dora Elizabeth, Thomas Victor. Student, Thomasschule Leipzig, 1919-28, Oxford U., 1928, Sorbonne, 1929, U. Munich, 1929-30, U. Toronto; MA (Gertrude Davis exchange fellow 1930-31); Ph.D., U. Leipzig, 1934; H.L.D., Monterey Inst., 1978. Dir. Akademische Auslandsstelle, U. Leipzig, 1931-32; lectr. German, Univ. Coll., Toronto, 1932-38; asst. prof. German Cornell U., 1938-41, asso. prof., 1941-45, prof., 1945-57; prof. German lit. Princeton U., 1957—, John N. Woodhull prof. modern. langs., 1968-77, emeritus, 1977—; hon. prof. Free U., Berlin, 1962—; vis. prof. U. Calif.-Davis, Smith Coll., U. Chgo., Berkeley, U. Cologne, U. Heidelberg, Munich, Columbia U., U. Mich., NYU, CUNY, Yale U., La Jolla, etc.; examiner in chief for German Coll. Entrance Exam. Bd., 1942-50; external examiner U. Hong Kong, 1979; vis. prof. U. Auckland, New Zealand, 1974; Guggenheim fellow, 1950-51, 67, McCosh fellow, 1966-67, Fulbright lectr., Australia, 1969, Phi Beta Kappa vis. scholar, 1968-69, Nat. Endowment Humanities sr. fellow, 1973-74; fellow Humanities Research Centre, Canberra, Australia, 1977. Author: Die Lyrik und ihr Publikum im England des 18. Jahrhunderts, 1936, Kulturkritik und Literaturbetrachtung in Amerika, 1938, Modern German Literature, 1945, Goethe's Craft of Fiction, 1953, Contemporary German Poetry, 1964, The Reader in the Strategy of Fiction, 1973, Mann: Tradition and Experiment, 1976, (with W.R. Amacher) New Perspectives in German Literary Criticism, 1979, The Classical Age of German Literature, 1982, Goethe's Faust II, 1980, Illyrische Betrachtungen. Essays und Aufsätze aus dreissig Jahren, 1989, Goethe-Studien, 1990, Bilder, Ideen, Begriffe, 1991, Goethe, 1992; editor: Deutsche Briefe, 1940, The Sorrows of Young Werther, 1949, Goethe's Faust, 1950, Great German Short Stories, 1952, Lessings Hamburg Dramaturgy, 1962, Goethe's Wilhelm Meister, 1962, German Classical Drama, 1962, Goethe: Twentieth Century Views, 1968, Humanistic Scholarship in America, 1968, Goethes Werke, 1972; Munich edition Goethes Werke, vols. 6, 1 and 2, 1986; Goethe, 1992; trans.: Edith Wharton's Ethan Frome, 1948; editorial bd.: Rev. of Nat. Lits., Comparative Lit., 20th Century Lit.; contbr. to lit. jours. Decorated comdr.'s cross Order of Merit (German Fed. Republic); recipient Gold medal Goethe Inst., 1966, Friedrich-Gundolf prize German Acad. Lang. and Lit., 1966, Chancellor's citation U. Calif., 1985, Golden Goethe medal Weimar, 1993, Festschrift Aspekte der Goethezeit, editor T. Ziolkowski, 1977. Mem. Internat. Assn. Germanists (pres. 1965-70), Am. Soc. 18th Century Studies (pres. 1975-76), Goethe Soc. N.Am. (pres. 1980-89), Am. Tchrs. German, Modern Humanities Research Assn., German Acad. (Darmstadt), Am. Comparative Lit. Assn., Goethe Gesellschaft Weimar, Phi Beta Kappa. Home: 343 Jefferson Rd Princeton NJ 08540-3414

LANGEL, ROBERT ALLAN, III, geophysicist; b. Pitts., May 25, 1937; s. Robert Allan II and Fay Mildred (Harvey) L.; m. Carolyn May Wills, June 13, 1959; children: Kathleen Carol, Susan Lynn, Joy Christine. A.B., Wheaton Coll., 1959; M.S., U. Md., 1971, Ph.D., 1973. Physicist U.S. Naval Research Lab., 1959-62; physicist microwave antennas Goddard Space Flight Ctr., Greenbelt, Md., 1963-64, magnetospheric physicist, 1964-74, geophysicist magnetic fields satellite project, 1974—; vis. scholar Bullard Labs., Cambridge (Eng.) U., 1983-84, Purdue U., 1992-93, Copenhagen U., 1994. Spl. editor: (issue) Physics of the Earth and Planetary Interiors, 1976, Geophys. Rsch. Letters, 1982, Jour. Geophys. Rsch., 1985, J. Geomagn Geoelectr., 1992; assoc. editor Jour. Geophys. Rsch., 1991—; contbr. articles to sci. publs., chpts. books. Dir. youth Grace Brethren Ch., Temple Hills, Md., 1965-68; dir. coll.-career Berwyn Bapt. Ch., College Park, Md., 1975-89, dir. singles, 1989-91. Recipient Spl. Achievement award Goddard Space Flight Center, 1980, Group Achievement award, 1980, Exceptional Performance award, 1981, Medal for exceptional sci. achievement NASA, 1982. Fellow Am. Geophys. Union; mem. Internat. Assn. Geomagnetism and Aeronomy (vice chair Div. I 1983-87, chair working group on main field and secular variation 1987-91). Republican. Baptist. Home: 14910 Laurel Oaks Ln Laurel MD 20707-5518 Office: Goddard Space Flight Ctr Code 921 Greenbelt MD 20771 *My driving goal is to please God, which governs the things to which I commit myself and that I strive for integrity and faithfulness in what I do.*

LANGELLA, FRANK, actor; b. Bayonne, N.J., Jan. 1, 1940; m. Ruth Weil, Nov. 1977. Student, Syracuse U.; studies with Seymour Falk. Apprenticed Pocono Playhouse, Mountain Home, Pa., appeared Erie (Pa.) Playhouse, 1960, mem. original, Lincoln Center repertory tng. co., 1963; off-Broadway debut in The Immoralist, 1963; other stage appearances include: Benito Cereno, 1964, The Old Glory, 1964-65 (Obie award), Good Day, 1965-66 (Obie award), The White Devil, 1965-66 (Obie award), Long Day's Journey Into Night, The Skin of Our Teeth, The Cretan Woman, Yerma, all 1966, The Devils, Dracula, Iphigenia at Aulis, all 1967, A Cry of Players, 1968, Cyrano de Bergerac, 1971, A Midsummer Night's Dream, 1972, The Relapse, The Tooth of Crime, 1972, The Taming of the Shrew, 1973, The Seagull, 1974, Ring Round the Moon, 1975, Passion, 1983, Design for Living, 1984, After the Fall, 1984, Hurlyburly, 1985, Sherlock's Last Case, 1987, Booth, 1994, The Prince of Hamburg, Cleve. Playhouse Co., 1967-68, L.I. Festival repertory, 1968, Les Liaisons Dangereuses; Broadway debut in Seascape, 1974-75 (Drama Desk and Tony awards); stage directing debut in John and Abigail, 1969; performed in films Diary of a Mad Housewife, 1970 (Nat. Soc. Film Critics award), The Twelve Chairs, 1970, The Deadly Trap, 1972, The Wrath of God, 1972, Dracula, 1979, Those Lips Those Eyes, 1980, Sphinx, 1981, The Men's Club, 1986, Masters of the Universe, 1987, And God Created Woman, 1988, True Identity, 1991, 1492: Conquest of Paradise, 1992, Dave, 1993, Body of Evidence, 1993, Brainscan, 1994, Junior, 1994, Bad Company, 1995; TV appearances include: Benito Cereno, 1965, Good Day, 1967, The Mark of Zorro, 1974, The Ambassador, 1974, The Seagull, 1975, The American Woman: Portraits of Courage, 1976, Eccentricities of a Nightingale, 1976, Sherlock Holmes, Liberty, The Doomsday Gun, 1994. Bd. dirs. Berkshire Festival. Mem. Actors Equity, Screen Actors Guild. Office: Innovative Artists 1999 Ave of the Stars Ste 2850 Los Angeles CA 90067-6082*

LANGENBERG, DONALD NEWTON, academic administrator, physicist; b. Devils Lake, N.D., Mar. 17, 1932; s. Ernest George and Fern (Newton) L.; m. Patricia Ann Warrington, June 20, 1953; children: Karen Kaye, Julia Ann, John Newton, Amy Paris. B.S., Iowa State U., 1953; M.S., UCLA, 1955; Ph.D. (NSF fellow), U. Calif. at Berkeley, 1959; D.Sc. (hon.), U. Pa., 1985, MA (hon.), 1971. Electronics engr. Hughes Research Labs., Culver City, Calif., 1953-55; acting instr. U. Calif. at Berkeley, 1958-59; mem. faculty U. Pa., Phila., 1960-83; prof. U. Pa., 1967-83; dir. Lab. for Research on Structure of Matter, 1972-74; vice provost for grad. studies and research, 1974-79; chancellor U. Ill.-Chgo., 1983-90, U. Md. System, Adelphi, 1990—; maitre de conference associe Ecole Normale Superieure, Paris, France, 1966-67; vis. prof. Calif. Inst. Tech., Pasadena, 1971; guest researcher Zentralinstitut für Tieftemperaturforschung der Bayerische Akademie der Wissenschaften und Technische Universität München, 1974; dep. dir. Nat. Sci. Found., 1980-82. Rschr., contbr. to publs. on solid state and low temperature physics including electronic band structure in metals and semiconductors, quantum phase coherence and nonequilibrium effects in superconductors, sci. and edn. policy and rsch. adminstrn. Recipient John Price Wetherill medal Franklin Inst., 1975, Disting. Contribution to Research Adminstrn. award Soc. Research Adminstrs., 1983, Disting. Achievement Citation, Iowa State Alumni Assn., 1984, Significant Sig award Sigma Chi, 1985; fellow NSF, 1959-60, Alfred P. Sloan Found., 1962-64; Guggenheim Found., 1966-67. Fellow AAAS (pres. 1990), Am. Phys. Soc. (pres. 1993), Sigma Xi. Office: U Md System 3300 Metzerott Rd Adelphi MD 20783

LANGENBERG, FREDERICK CHARLES, business executive; b. N.Y.C., July 1, 1927; s. Frederick C. and Margaret (McLaughlin) L.; m. Jane Anderson Bartholomew, May 16, 1953; children: Frederick C., Susan Jane. BS, Lehigh U., 1950, MS, 1951; PhD, Pa. State U., 1955; postgrad. execs. program, Carnegie-Mellon U., 1962. With U.S. Steel Corp., 1951-53; vis. fellow MIT, 1955-56; with Crucible Steel Corp., Pitts., 1956-68, v.p. research and engring., 1966-68; pres. Trent Tube div. Colt Industries, Milw., 1968-70; exec. v.p. Jessop Steel Co., Washington, Pa., 1970, pres., 1970-75, also bd. dirs.; pres., bd. dirs. Am. Iron and Steel Inst., Washington, 1975-78; pres. Interlake Corp., Oak Brook, Ill., 1979-81, pres., chmn, chief exec. officer, 1981-91, also bd. dirs.; chmn. Langand Corp., Pitts., 1991—; bd. dirs. Carpenter Tech., Reading, Pa., The Interlake Corp., Chgo., Peoples Energy Corp., Chgo., Dietrich Industries, Inc., Pitts. Contbr. articles to tech. jours.; patentee in field. Trustee Piedmont Coll., Demorest, Ga. Served with USNR, 1944-45. Named Oak Brook Bus. Leader of the Yr., 1986, Disting. Bus. Leader, DuPage County, 1988; Alumni fellow Pa. State U., 1977; recipient Disting. Alumni award Pa. State U., 1989, Lehigh U., 1990. Fellow Am. Soc. Metals (disting. life mem. 1982, trustee, Pitts. Nite lectr. 1970, Andrew Carnegie lectr. 1976; David Ford McFarland award Penn State chpt. 1973); mem. AIME, Am. Soc. Metals, Metals Powder Industry Fedn., Phi Beta Kappa, Sigma Xi, Tau Beta Pi. Clubs: Duquesne, St. Clair Country (Pitts.), Congl., Burning Tree, Chgo. Golf, Chgo., Commercial (Chgo.), Laurel Valley, Rolling Rock (Ligonier, Pa.), Belleair County Club (Fla.), Desert Forrest (Ariz.), Carefree (Ariz.), Desert Mountain (Ariz.).

LANGENDERFER, HAROLD QUENTIN, accountant, educator; b. Swanton, Ohio, July 21, 1925; s. Omer Quintan and Minnie (Buckenmyer) L.; m. Joan Mary Etzrodt, June 17, 1950; children: Thomas, Amy, Jeffry, Chris. B.S. in Bus, Miami U., Oxford, Ohio, 1949; M.B.A., Northwestern U., 1950; D.B.A., Ind. U., 1954. C.P.A., Ind., N.C. Prof. intermediate acctg. Ind. U., Bloomington, 1952-53; KPMG Peat, Marwick prof. profl. acctg. U. N.C., Chapel Hill, 1953-93, prof. emeritus, 1993—; cons. mgmt. devel. to Ford Found., Cairo, 1961-63; tax cons. Co-author: C.P.A. Examination - A Comprehensive Review, 3d edit., 1979, Principles of Accounting, 1981, 4th edit., 1993, Income Tax Procedure, 1994; contbr. articles to acctg. jours. Served with U.S. Army, 1943-46. Named Acctg. Educator of Yr., Beta Alpha Psi, 1980. Mem. AICPA (Acctg. Educator of Yr. 1988), N.C. Assn. CPAs (pres. 1985-86, Acctg. Educator of Yr. 1986, Outstanding Svc. award 1989), Nat. Assn. Accts., Am. Acctg. Assn. (Outstanding Accounting Educator 1988), Am. Acctg. Assn. (pres. Chapel Hill lodge 1966). Roman Catholic. Home: 1074 Canterbury Ln Chapel Hill NC 27514-5612 Office: UNC CB 3490 Carroll Hall Chapel Hill NC 27599

LANGENDOEN, DONALD TERENCE, linguistics educator; b. Paterson, N.J., June 7, 1939; s. Garret and Wilhelmina (Van Dyk) L.; m. Sally Wicklund, Aug. 16, 1964, (div. Mar. 1982); 1 child, David; m. Nancy Susan Kelly, July 28, 1984. BS, MIT, 1961, PhD, 1964. Assoc. prof. Ohio State U., Columbus, 1964-68; vis. assoc. prof. Rockefeller U., N.Y.C., 1968-69; prof. Bklyn. C. and Grad. Ctr., CUNY, N.Y.C., 1969-88, U. Ariz., Tucson, 1988—; exec. officer grad. linguistics program, CUNY, N.Y.C., 1971-78; head dept. linguistics, U. Ariz., Tucson, 1988—; vis. scientist IBM T.J. Watson Research Ctr., Yorktown Heights, N.Y., 1986-87; sr. lectr. Fulbright, Utrecht, Holland, 1977. Co-author: The Vastness of Natural Languages, 1984; author: The London School of Linguistics, 1968. Fellow N.Y. Acad. of Scis., N.Y.C., 1977; named Ptnr. in Edn., Bd. of Edn., N.Y.C., 1982. Mem. AAAS, Linguistic Soc. of Am. (sec., treas. 1984-88), Assn. for Computational Linguistics, Assn. for Linguistic and Literary Computing. Office: U Ariz Dept Linguistics Tucson AZ 85721

LANGENFELD, DOUGLAS EUGENE, health care consultant, business advisor; b. Columbus, Ohio, Nov. 14, 1952; s. Eugene Clement Langenfeld and Phyllis Jane (McGath) Courtney; m. Carol Jean Jones, Sept. 7, 1974; 1 child, Eric Douglas. AB, Miami U., Oxford, Ohio, 1974, MBA, 1975. CPA, Ohio. With Ernst & Young, Columbus, 1975—, ptnr., 1986—; mem. task force to study Columbus conv. ctr., 1986-88; mem. task force to develop bus. plan Ameriflora 1992, Columbus, 1987-88. Bd. dirs. ARC, Columbus, 1982—, treas., 1991—; treas. Jazz Arts Group, Columbus, 1986-92. Named one of Ten Outstanding Young Citizens, Columbus Jaycees, 1987. Fellow Healthcare Fin. Mgmt. Assn. (dir. 1986-89, 94—); mem. AICPA, Ohio Soc. CPAs, Athletic Club Columbus, Columbus Country Club. Methodist.

LANGENHEIM, JEAN HARMON, biology educator; b. Homer, La., Sept. 5, 1925; d. Vergil Wilson and Jeanette (Smith) H.; m. Ralph Louis Langenheim, Dec. 1946 (div. Mar. 1961). BS, U. Tulsa, 1946; MS, U. Minn., 1949, PhD, 1953. Rsch. assoc. botany U. Calif., Berkeley, 1954-59, U. Ill., Urbana, 1959-61; rsch. fellow biology Harvard U., Cambridge, Mass.,

1962-66; asst. prof. biology U. Calif., Santa Cruz, 1966-68, assoc. prof. biology, 1968-73, prof. biology, 1973—; academic v.p. Orgn. Tropical Studies, San Jose, Costa Rica, 1975-78; mem. sci.adv. bd. EPA, Washington, 1977-81; chmn. com. on humid tropics U.S. Nat. Acad. Nat. Research Council, 1975-77; mem. com. floral inventory Amazon NSF, Washington, 1975-87. Author: Botany-Plant Biology in Relation to Human Affairs.; Contbr. articles to profl. jours. Grantee NSF, 1966-88; recipient Disting. Alumni award U. Tulsa, 1979. Fellow AAAS, AAUW, Calif. Acad. Scis., Bunting Inst.; mem. Bot. Soc. Am., Ecol. Soc. Am. (pres. 1986-87), Internat. Soc. Chem. Ecology (pres. 1986-87), Assn. for Tropical Biology (pres. 1985-86), Soc. for Econ. Botany (pres. 1993-94). Home: 191 Palo Verde Ter Santa Cruz CA 95060-3214 Office: U Calif Dept Biology Sinsheimer Labs Santa Cruz CA 95064

LANGENHEIM, RALPH LOUIS, JR., geology educator; b. Cin., May 26, 1922; s. Ralph Louis and Myrtle (Helmers) L.; m. Jean C. Harmon, Dec. 23, 1946; m. Virginia A.M. Knobloch, June 5, 1963; children: Victoria Elizabeth, Ralph Louis III; m. Shirley B. Ate, May 1, 1970; stepchildren: Judy Grigg, Lynn Ate, Kathleen Majack; m. Casey Diana, Mar. 6, 1993; stepchildren: Eric Steckler, Matthew Diana. B.S., U. Tulsa, 1943; M.S., U. Colo., 1947; Ph.D., U. Minn., 1951. Registered profl. geologist, Wyo. Teaching asst. U. Tulsa, 1941-43, U. Colo., 1947; fellow U. Minn., 1947-48, teaching asst., 1948-50; asst. prof. Coe Coll., 1950-52; asst. prof. paleontology U. Calif., Berkeley, 1952-59, curator Paleozoic and early Mesozoic fossil invertebrates, 1952-59; asst. prof. geology U. Ill., Urbana, 1959-62; asso. prof. U. Ill., 1962-67, prof., 1967-92, prof. emeritus, 1993—; also curator fossil invertebrates Mus. Nat. History, 1988-92, curator emeritus, 1993—; with Instituto Geologico Nacional de Colombia, summer 1953; Geol. Survey Can., summer 1958, Geol. Survey Iran, fall 1973, Geol. Survey Republic of China, fall 1981; ptnr. Lanman Assocs., Cons. Geologists, 1974—; cons., mem. faculty geology and mining depts. Poly. U., Albania, fall 1992; vis. disting. prof. U. Nev., Las Vegas, 1994; book rev. editor Jour. Geol. Edn., 1990—. Assoc. editor Jour. Paleontology, 1995—. Served with USNR, 1943-46; lt. comdr. Res., ret. Mem. AAAS, Paleontol. Soc. (sec. 1962-70), Geol. Soc. Am., Soc. Econ. Paleontologists and Mineralogists, Am. Assn. Petroleum Geologists, Soc. Geologique Suisse, Ill. Geol. Soc. (sec. 1978, v.p. 1979, pres. 1980), Internat. Assn. Cindaria Specialists (treas. 1977-79), Nat. Assn. Geology Tchrs., Ill. Acad. Sci., Rocky Mountain Biol. Lab., Petroleum Soc., Explorers Club, Sigma Xi. Rsch. and publs. in stratigraphy and paleontology. Home: 401 W Vermont Ave Urbana IL 61801-4928

LANGER, ANDREW J., advertising agency executive. Formerly pres. The Marschalk Co. (now Lowe & Ptnrs.), N.Y.C.; pres., U.S. creative dir. Lowe Marschalk Inc., N.Y.C., creative dir., 1989—; CEO Lowe & Ptnrs./SMS, N.Y.C.; bd. dirs. Am. Assn. Advt. Agys. Office: 1114 Ave of the Americas New York NY 10036

LANGER, ARTHUR MARK, mineralogist; b. N.Y.C., Feb. 18, 1936; s. Morton Livingston and Ruth Regina (Lewitz) L.; m. Catherine Chilcott Josi, apr. 11, 1977; children: Erica Margaret, Andrew Michael, Elliott Mark, Christopher Morton. BA, Hunter Coll., 1956; MA, Columbia U., 1962, PhD, 1965. Exploration geologist Rosario Exploration Chibougamau Mining and Smelting, 1956; field asst. in geology Beartooth Mountains, Mont. Columbia U., N.Y.C., 1957-58, teaching asst. dept. geology, 1958-59, cons. mineralogist, 1960-65, rsch. asst. dept. geology 1961-64; lectr. CUNY, 1964-65, mem. grad. faculty, 1982—; rsch. assoc. environ. medicine, dept. medicine Mt. Sinai Hosp., N.Y.C., 1965-67, asst. prof. dept. community medicine, 1967-68; assoc. prof. mineralogy, dept. community medicine Mt. Sinai Sch. Medicine, N.Y.C., 1968-86, 87-88, head phys. scis. sect., assoc. dir. Environ. Scis. Lab., 1969-86, sci. adminstr. Environ. Scis. Lab., 1983-84, assoc. prof. Ctr. for Polypeptide and Membrane Rsch., 1986-88; rsch. assoc. dept. mineral scis. Am. Mus. Natural History, N.Y.C., 1979—; dir. Environ. Scis. Lab. Inst. of Applied Scis. CUNY, 1988—, dep. dir. Ctr. Applied Studies of the Environment, 1992—; adj. assoc. prof. mineralogy grad. div. CUNY, 1968-69; expert cons. NIH, 1974—, WHO, 1975—, Nat. Heart, Lung and Blood Inst., 1975—, EPA, 1975—, Nat. Inst. for Environ. Health Scis., 1975—, Nat. Inst. for Occupational Safety and Health, 1975—; EPA Superfund cases, 1985—; other regional consultations; cons. Inst. Pub. Health, Norway, 1977, Ministry of Mines, South Africa, 1977, Internat. Agy. Rsch. Cancer, 1976, 86, Internat. Program Chem. Safety (WHO), 1985, Internat. Fedn. Bldg. Wood Workers, 1989; mem. internat. coms. on pollution and health. Assoc. editor Environ. Rsch., 1978-85, adv. editor, 1985-87; asst. editor Am Jour. Indsl. Medicine, 1980-85, assoc. editor, 1985-86; mem. editorial rev. bd. Journ. Environ. Pathology and Toxicology, 1978-82, Jour. Environmental Pathology, Toxicology and Oncology, 1983—; mem. editorial adv. bd. Advances in Modern Eenviron. Toxicology, 1981-82; manuscript reviewer many jours.; reviewer, author fed. and industry documents, 1978—; contbr. chpts. to books, articles and abstracts to profl. jours. and symposia proc. Recipient award Dept. Geology, Hunter Coll., 1956, Dust Rsch. award Polachek Found., 1965-67, Career Scientist award Nat. Inst. Environ. Health Scis., 1969-74; named to Hall of Fame, Hunter College-CUNY, 1978; grantee Health Rsch. Coun., 1966-67, 75-77, Polacheck Found., 1966-68, NIH, 1967-78, Johns-Manville Corp., 1968-73, Am. Cancer Soc., 1971-74, 80-81, EPA, 1973, Ford Motor Co., 1973-75, Nat. Inst. Occupational Safety and Health, 1976-79, 82-84, Nat. Inst. Environ. Health Scis, 1978-86, Nat. Cancer Inst., 1979-81, Mobil Found., 1979—, Vanderbilt Talc Co., 1988, Battelle, Columbus, 1988—, Consumer Products Safety Commn., 1987-90, Ga. Pacific, 1989-91, others. Fellow Collegium Ramazzini, Geol. Soc. Am., Mineral. Soc. Am., N.Y. Acad. Scis.; mem. Phi Beta Kappa, Sigma Xi. Home: 6 Rochambeau Dr Hartsdale NY 10530-3008 Office: CUNY Brooklyn Coll Brooklyn NY 11210

LANGER, ELLEN JANE, psychologist, educator, writer; b. N.Y.C., Mar. 25, 1947; d. Norman and Sylvia (Tobias) L. BA, NYU, 1970; PhD, Yale U., 1974. Cert. clin. psychologist. Asst. prof. psychology The Grad. Ctr. CUNY, 1974-77; assoc. prof. psychology Harvard U., Cambridge, Mass., 1977-81; prof. Harvard U., 1981—; cons. NAS, 1979-81, NASA; mem. div. on aging Harvard U. Med. Sch., 1979—. mem. psychiat. epidemiology steering com., 1982-90; chair social psychology program Harvard U., 1982—, chair Faculty Arts and Scis. Com. of Women, 1984-88. Author: Personal Politics, 1973, Psychology of Control, 1983, Mindfulness, 1989; editor: (with Charles Alexander) Higher Stages of Human Development, 1990, (with Roger Schank) Beliefs, Attitudes, Reasoning & Decision, 1994; contbr. articles to profl. and scholarly jours. Guggenheim Fellow, grantee NIMH, NSF, Soc. for Psychol. Study of Social Issues, Milton Fund, Sloan Found., 1982. Fellow Computers and Soc. Inst., Am. Psychol. Assn. (Disting. Contributions to Psychology in the Public Interest award 1988); mem. Soc. Expl. Social Psychology, Phi Beta Kappa, Sigma Xi. Democrat. Jewish. Avocations: theater, horseback riding, tennis. Office: Harvard U Dept Psychology 33 Kirkland St Cambridge MA 02138-2044

LANGER, GLENN ARTHUR, cellular physiologist, educator; b. Nyack, N.Y., May 5, 1928; s. Adolph Arthur and Marie Catherine (Doscher) L.; m. Beverly Joyce Brawley, June 5, 1954 (dec. Nov. 1976); 1 child, Andrew; m. Marianne Phister, Oct. 12, 1977. BA, Colgate U., 1950; MD, Columbia U., N.Y.C., 1954. Diplomate Am. Bd. Internal Medicine. Asst. prof. medicine Columbia U. Coll. Physicians and Surgeons, N.Y.C., 1963-66; assoc. prof. medicine and physiology UCLA Sch. Medicine, 1966-69, 1969—, Castera prof. of cardiology, 1978—, assoc. dean rsch., 1986-91, dir. cardiovascular rsch. lab., 1987—; Griffith vis. prof. Am. Heart Assn., L.A., 1979; cons. Acad. Press, N.Y.C., 1989—. Editor: The Mammalian Myocardium, 1974, Calcium and the Heart, 1990; mem. editorial bd. Circulation Rsch., 1971-76, Am. Jour. Physiology, 1971-76, Jour. Molecular Cell Cardiology, 1974—; contbr. over 170 articles to profl. jours. Capt. U.S. Army, 1955-57. Recipient Disting. Achievement award Am. Heart Assn. Sci. Coun., 1982, Heart of Gold award, 1984, Cybulski medal Polish Physiol. Soc., Krakow, 1990, Pasarow Found. award for Cardiovascular Sci., 1993; Macy scholar Josiah Macy Found., 1979-80. Fellow AAAS, Am. Coll. Cardiology; mem. Am. Soc. Clin. Investigation, Am. Assn. Physicians. Achievements include research on control of cardiac contraction. Office: UCLA Sch Medicine Los Angeles CA 90024

LANGER, HORST, financial corporate executive. Chmn. Siemens Corp. subs. Siemens A.G., Munich, N.Y.C. Office: Siemens Corp 1301 Avenue Of The Americas New York NY 10019-6022

LANGER, JAMES STEPHEN, physicist, educator; b. Pitts., Sept. 21, 1934; s. Bernard F. and Liviette (Roth) L.; m. Elinor Goldmark Aaron, Dec. 21, 1958; children: Ruth, Stephen, David. B.S., Carnegie Inst. Tech., 1955; Ph.D., U. Birmingham, Eng., 1958. Prof. physics Carnegie-Mellon U., Pitts., 1958-82, assoc. dean, 1971-74; prof. physics U. Calif., Santa Barbara, 1982—, dir. Inst. for Theoretical Physics 1989—. Contbr. articles to profl. jours. Vice pres. physics Com. Concerned Scientists, 1979—. Guggenheim fellow, 1974-75; Marshall scholar, 1955-57. Fellow AAAS, Am. Acad. Arts and Scis., Am. Phys. Soc. (chair elect divsn. condensed matter physics, chair nominating com.); mem. NAS, N.Y. Acad. Scis. Democrat. Jewish. Home: 1130 Las Canoas Ln Santa Barbara CA 93105-2331 Office: U Calif Inst Theoretical Physics Santa Barbara CA 93106

LANGER, LAWRENCE LEE, English educator, writer; b. N.Y.C., June 20, 1929; s. Irving and Esther (Strauss) L.; m. Sondra Weinstein, Feb. 21, 1951; children: Andrew, Ellen. BA, CCNY, 1951; AM, Harvard U., 1952, PhD, 1961. Teaching fellow Harvard U., Cambridge, Mass., 1954-57; instr. English U. Conn., Storrs, 1957-58; instr. English Simmons Coll., Boston, 1958-61, asst. prof., 1961-66, assoc. prof., 1966-72, prof., 1972-76, Alumnae prof., 1976-92, Alumnae prof. emeritus, 1992—; Fulbright prof. Am. lit. U. Graz, Austria, 1963-64; cons. U.S. Holocaust Meml. Mus., Washington, 1991—. Author: The Holocaust and The Literary Imagination, 1975, The Age of Atrocity, 1978, Versions of Survival, 1982, Holocaust Testimonies, 1991 (Nat. Book Critics Cr. award for Criticism 1991), Art From the Ashes: A Holocaust Anthology, 1994, Admitting the Holocaust: Collected Essays, 1994. Sr. rsch. fellow NEH, 1978-79, 89-90. Mem. MLA, PEN. Office: Simmons Coll Dept English 300 The Fenway Boston MA 02115 also: care Yale Univ Press Authors Mail 92A Yale Sta New Haven CT 06520

LANGER, LEONARD O., JR., radiologist, educator; b. Mpls., Oct. 16, 1928; s. Leonard Otto and Louise (Buro) L.; m. Rollie Helen Segal, Sept. 13, 1952; children: Maren, Sara, Elizabeth, Kristen. BA summa cum laude, U. Minn., 1950, BS, 1951, MD, 1953. Diplomate Am. Bd. Radiology. Intern Salt Lake County Hosp., Salt Lake City, 1953-54; resident in radiology U. Mich. Hosp., 1956-59; instr. radiology U. Pitts. Med. Sch., 1959-60; from instr. to assoc. prof. radiology U. Minn. Med. Sch., Mpls., 1961-66; radiologist Suburban Radiologie Cons., Mpls., 1966-78, 84-89; prof. U. Wis. Med. Sch., Madison, 1978-84; clin. assoc. prof. radiology U. Minn. Med. Sch., Mpls., 1966-78; clin. prof. U. Minn., 1984—; cons. clin. genetics divsn. U. Wis. Med. Sch., 1984—; skeletal dysplasia program, U. Minn. Med. Sch., 1984—; mem. com. Internat. Nomenclature of Constl. Diseases of Bone, Paris, 1969—. Author: Bone Dysplasias, 1974; contbr. over 100 articles to profl. med. jours. Served to capt. USAF, 1953-56. Fellow Am. Coll. Radiology; mem. Internat. Skeletal Soc. (cons. editor Skeletal Radiology 1976-89), Soc. Pediatric Radiology, Radiological Soc. N.Am., Bone Dysplasia Soc., Little People Am. (hon. life, med. adv. bd., 1966—). Democrat. Avocations: swimming, skiing, tennis. Home: 1235 Yale Pl Apt 710 Minneapolis MN 55403-1945

LANGER, RALPH ERNEST, journalist; b. Benton Harbor, Mich., July 30, 1937; s. Ralph L. and Mary (Skuda) L.; m. Katherine B. McGuire, June 25, 1960; children: Terri B., Tammi L. Student, Central Mich. U., 1955-57; B.A. in Journalism, U. Mich., 1957-59. Telegraph editor, reporter Grand Haven (Mich.) Daily Tribune, 1959-60; mng. editor Port Angeles (Wash.) Evening News, 1962-66; copy desk Detroit Free Press, 1966-68; asst. mng. editor Dayton Jour. Herald, 1968, mng. editor, 1968-75; editor Everett (Wash.) Herald, 1975-81; mng. editor Dallas Morning News, 1981-83, exec. editor, 1983-86, v.p., 1986-91, sr. v.p., exec. editor, 1991—. Pres. Freedom of Info. Found. Tex., 1985-89, Nat. Freedom of Info. Coalition, 1992-93, Coun. of Presidents, 1991-92.. 1st lt. U.S. Army, 1960-62. Mem. Am. Soc. Newspaper Editors, Press Club Dallas (pres. 1985-86), A.P. Mng. Editors Assn. (bd. dirs. 1980—, sec. 1989, v.p. 1990, pres. 1990-91), Coun. of Pres.'s (founding pres. 1992-93), AP Mng. Editors Assn. Found. (pres. 1991-92), Scabbard and Blade, Alpha Phi Gamma, Sigma Phi Epsilon. Office: Dallas Morning News Comm Ctr PO Box 655237 Dallas TX 75261

LANGER, RAY FRITZ, retired insurance executive; b. Manchester, N.H., Apr. 29, 1921; s. Fritz Bruno and Clara (Lindh) L.; m. Myrtle Elaine Sargent, May 23, 1942; 1 child, Barry Frederick. Cert., U. N.H., 1940. Chief statistician N.H. Ins. Co., Manchester, 1942-71; chief statistician, asst. sec. N.H. & Am. Internat. Group, Manchester, 1972-84, asst. sec., 1984-91; cons. N.H. Group, Manchester. Selectman Town of Hooksett, N.H, 1970-78, councilor, 1988-91, state rep., 1993—; pres. Hooksett-ites Sr. Citizens, 1993—. Capt. USAF, 1943-46, PTO, 1955-57, Korea, ret. 1981. Mem. Soc. Ins. Accts. (past pres.), Am. Legion. Republican. Methodist. Avocations: hunting, fly fishing, painting.

LANGER, RICHARD J., lawyer; b. Rockford, Ill., June 10, 1944; s. John W. and Dorothy E. (Brunn) Langrehr; m. Audrey A. Russo, Jan. 28, 1967; children: Kathleen M., Michael R. BS, U. Ill., 1967; JD, U. Wis., 1974. Bar: Wis. 1974, U.S. Dist. Ct. (we. dist.) Wis. 1974. Assoc. Ela, Esch, Hart & Clark, Madison, Wis., 1974-76; ptnr. Stolper, Koritzinsky, Brewster & Neider, Madison, 1976-91, Michael, Best & Friedrich, Madison, 1991—. Author: Guide to Property Classification, 1986, Workbook For Wisconsin Estate Planners, 1991, also articles. Sec. Combat Blindness Found., Madison, 1988—. Fellow Am. Coll. Trust and Estate Coun.; mem. ABA, State Bar Wis., Madison Estate Coun. Avocations: scuba diving, traveling, bicycling. Home: 1502 Windfield Way Madison WI 53562-3808 Office: Michael Best & Friedrich 1 S Pinckney St Madison WI 53703-2808

LANGER, ROBERT MARTIN, retired chemical engineering company executive, consultant; b. Boston, May 29, 1925; s. Samuel Morton and Ethel (Shlivek) L. B.Engring., Yale U., 1945, D.Engring., 1952; S.M., MIT, 1948. Sales mgr. The Badger Co., Inc., Cambridge, Mass., 1968-70; dep. mng. dir. Badger B.V., The Hague, The Netherlands, 1970-74, mng. dir., 1974-78; v.p., project adminstrn. The Badger Co., Inc., Cambridge, 1978-80; sr. v.p. Badger Am., Inc., Cambridge, 1981-83; v.p., treas. The Badger Co., Inc., Cambridge, 1983-87. Served to lt. j.g. USNR, 1945-46. Mem. Am. Inst. Chem. Engrs. (Charles M.A. Stine award 1991). Home: 280 Commonwealth Ave Boston MA 02116-2422

LANGER, ROBERT SAMUEL, chemical, biomedical engineering educator; b. Albany, N.Y., Aug. 29, 1948; s. Robert Samuel Sr. and Mary (Swartz) L.; m. Laura Feigenbaum, July 31, 1988; children: Michael David, Susan Katherine, Samuel Alexander. BS, Cornell U., 1970; ScD, MIT, 1974. Rsch. assoc. Children's Hosp. Med. Ctr., Boston, 1974—; asst. prof. MIT, Cambridge, Mass., 1978-81, assoc. prof., 1981-85, prof., 1985-89, Germeshausen prof., 1989—; bd. dirs. Alkermes, Cambridge, Omniquest, N.H., Acusphere, Cambridge; tchr. Group Sch., Cambridge, 1971-73; endowed lectr. U. P.R., 1983, Case Western Res. U., 1986, U. Mich., 1987, U. Wash., 1988, U. Kans., 1989, U. Calif. San Francisco, 1991, U. Wis. 1991, Ga. Inst. Tech., 1991, Ohio State U. 1991, U. Pitts., 1992, Purdue U., 1992, U. Del., 1993, Pa. State U., 1993, Beth Israel Hosp., 1994, Cornell U., 1994; cons. to numerous cos. including Genentech, San Francisco, 1981—, Merck Sharpe and Dohme, 1981-85; sci. advisor Cygnus, Redwood City, Calif., 1987—, Perspetive Biosystems, Cambridge, 1991—. Author: (with D. Cincotta and K. Cole) Group School Chemistry Curriculum, 1972, (with W. Thilly) Laboratory in Applied Biology, 1978, Analytical Practices in Biochemistry, 1979, (with W. Hrusheysky and F. Theeuwes) Temporal Control of Drug Delivery, 1990, (with D. Wise), Medical Applications on Controlled Release, Vols. I and II, 1984; editor: (with R. Steiner, P. Weisz) Angiogenesis, 1992; contbr. more than 500 articles to profl. pubs.; patentee in field. Union Oil fellow 1970-71, Chevron fellow 1971-72; cited for Outstanding Patent in Mass., Intellectual Property Owners Inc., 1989. Fellow Soc. Biomaterials (Clemson award 1990) ; mem. NAS, Nat. Acad. Engring., Inst. Medicine of NAS, Am. Inst. Med. and Biol. Engrs. (founding fellow), AIChE (Food, Pharm. & Bioengring. award, 1986, Profl. Progress award 1990, Charles M. Shine Materials Sci. and Engring. award 1991), Am. Acad. Arts and Scis., Soc. for Biomaterials (Clemson award 1990), Am. Chem. Soc. (recipient Creative Polymer award, 1989, Phillips Applied Polymer Sci. award 1992, Pearlman Meml. lectr. award 1992), Am. Assn. Pharm. Scis. (Disting. Pharm. Sci. award 1993), Internat. Soc. Artificial Internal Organs (Organon-Teknika award 1991), Biomed. Engring. Soc. (bd. dirs. 1991-94, Whitaker lectr. 1994), Controlled Release Soc. (bd. govs. 1981-85, chmn. regulatory affairs com. '1985-89, pres. 1991-92, Founders award 1989, Outstanding

---

Pharm. Paper award 1990, 92), Am. Soc. Artificial Internal Organs (mem. program com. 1984-87), Internat. Soc. Artificial Internal Organs. Avocations: magic, jogging. Office: MIT Dept Chem Engring 77 Massachusetts Ave Cambridge MA 02139

LANGER, STEVEN, consultant human resources management and industrial psychology; b. N.Y.C., June 4, 1926; s. Israel and Anna (Glaisner) L.; BA in Psychology, Calif. State U., Sacramento, 1950; MS in Pers. Svc., U. Colo., 1958; PhD, Walden U., 1970; Lic. psychologist, Ill.; m. M. Jacquline White, Oct. 11, 1965 (dec. 1969); children: Bruce, Diana, Geoffrey; m. Elaine Catherine Brewer, Dec. 29, 1979 (dec. Feb. 1992). Asst. to pers. dir. City and County of Denver, 1956-59; pers. dir. City of Pueblo (Colo.) 1959-60; pers. cons. J.L. Jacobs & Co., Chgo., 1961-64, adminstrv. mgr., 1966-67; sales selection mgr. Reuben H. Donnelly Corp., Chgo., 1964-66; pres. Abbott, Langer & Assocs., Crete, Ill., 1967—; vis. prof. mgmt. Loyola U., Chgo., 1969-71; community prof. behavioral scis. Purdue U., Calumet campus, Hammond, Ind., 1973-75. Mem. Ill. Psychol. Assn. (chmn. sect. indsl. psychologists 1971-72), Chgo. Psychol. Assn. (pres. 1974-75, 94-95), Greater Chgo. Assn. Indsl./Orgnl. Psychology, Soc. Human Resources Mgmt. (accredited, chmn. research award com. 1966-69), Am. Compensation Assn., Chgo. Compensation Assn. (sec. 1976-77), Mensa (pres. Chgo. chpt. 1972-74). Unitarian. Contbr. numerous reports and articles on indsl. psychology and personnel mgmt. to profl. publs. Home: 309 Herndon St Park Forest IL 60466-1132 Office: Abbott Langer & Assoc 548 1st St Crete IL 60417-2199

LANGERAK, ESLEY OREN, retired research chemist; b. Pella, Iowa, Oct. 28, 1920; s. William Henry and Grace Dena (Vander Linden) L.; m. Elizabeth Jane Rhodes, Nov. 18, 1944; children—Kristin, Lisbeth, Peter. B.S. in Chemistry, Central Coll., Iowa, 1941; M.S., U. Del., 1947, Ph.D. in Organic Chemistry, 1949. High sch. tchr. Garden Grove Consol. Sch., Iowa, 1941-42; research chemist, supr., lab mgr. DuPont Co., Wilmington, Del., 1949-81; compensation mgr. chems. and pigments dept. DuPont Co., 1981-85; ret., 1985. Contbr. articles to profl. jours. Served with Ordnance, U.S. Army, 1942-46, PTO. Republican. Presbyterian. Club: DuPont Country. Patentee in field (3).

LANGERMANN, JOHN W. R., institutional equity salesperson; b. N.Y.C., Aug. 14, 1943; m. Karen Elizabeth Stives, Jan. 14, 1995. BA with highest honors, Lehigh U., 1965. Ptnr., sales mgr. L.F. Rothschild, Unterberg, Towbin, Boston, 1977-87; sr. v.p. County Nat. West Securities, Boston, 1987-90; v.p. Piper, Jaffray & Hopwood, Boston, 1990-92; sr. v.p. Needham & Co., Inc., Boston, 1993-94; mng. dir. instl. sales Ladenburg, Thalmann & Co., Inc., Boston, 1994—. Mem. Internat. Soc. Security Analysts, Kansas City Soc. Fin. Analysts. Avocations: vintage sports car racing, curling, sculling. Home: Stonehenge Farm Dover MA 02030 Office: Ladenburg Thalmann & Co Inc 10 Post Office Sq Boston MA 02109

LANGEVIN, LOUIS-DE-GONZAQUE, bishop; b. Oka, Can, Oct. 31, 1921. BA, Seminaire de Philosophie de Montreal, 1944; postgrad. in theology, Scolasticat des Peres Blancs, Ottawa, 1946-50; Lic. in Theology, Gregorian U., Rome, 1957; Lic. in Holy Scripture, Sainte a l'Institut Biblique, Rome, 1957. Ordained priest Roman Catholic Ch. Provincial priest Blancs d'Afrique, Montreal, Que., Can; aux. bishop Diocese de St Hyacinthe, 1974-79, titular bishop, 1979—; pres. Episcopal Commn. on Social Communications Conf. Cath. Bishops Can.; mem. Comm. for the Lay Apostate Conf. Bishops of Que. Decorated chevalier de l'Ordre du Saint-Sepulcre de Jerusalem lieutenance du Can., a Montreal, 1975, chevalier de Colomb du 4e Degre Assemblee Antoine Girouard de Saint-Hyacinthe Province de Que., Can. Home and Office: Eveche de Saint Hyacinthe, 1900 rue Girouard ouest CO 190, Saint Hyacinthe, PQ Canada J2S 7B4

LANGEVIN, THOMAS HARVEY, higher education consultant; b. St. Paul, Mar. 20, 1922; s. Thomas E. and Myrtle (Damsgard) L.; m. Pearl E. Mattfeld, Aug. 29, 1942; children: Dennis, Timothy. B.S., Concordia Tchrs. Coll., Seward, Neb., 1947; M.A., U. Neb., 1949, Ph.D., 1951. Quarantine insp. USPHS, 1943-45; grad. asst., asst. instr. U. Neb., 1947-51; prof. Concordia Tchrs. Coll., 1951-63, dean coll., 1961-63, acting pres., 1961-63; dir. long-range planning project Luth. Ch.-Mo. Synod, 1964-65; also cons. Bd. Higher Edn.; acad. v.p. Pacific Luth. U., 1965-69; pres. Capital U., Columbus, Ohio, 1969-79; pres. emeritus Capital U., 1979—; pres. Thomas H. Langevin Assoc., LadyLake, Fla., 1979—; prin. Registry for Interim Coll. and Univ. Pres., 1992—; chmn. Luth. Edn. Conf. N.Am., 1980-87; cons. Battelle Inst., 1979-87; cons., vis. fellow Battelle Seattle Rsch. Ctr., 1976. Co-chmn. Tacoma Area Urban Coalition Edn. Task Force, 1967-69; mem., past chmn. Ohio Com. Pub. Programs in Humanities; former exec. com. Fedn. Pub. Programs in Humanities; former mem. Ohio Higher Edn. Facilities Commn.; former mem. Commn. on Future Lutheran Edn., Luth Edn. Conf. N.Am., pres., 1977-78; bd. dirs. Nat. Urban League, 1979-80; Mem Columbus Urban League; Former mem. Met. Columbus Sch. Com.; bd. dirs. Tacoma Citizens Com. Pub. TV, 1967-69, Design for Progress Tacoma, 1969, Tacoma Area Urban Coalition, 1967-69; bd. rev. Air U.; former adv. com. Center Sci. and Industry, Columbus; asso. in urban affairs Nat. Inst. Pub. Affairs; bd. control Concordia Coll., Portland, Oreg., 1965-69; bd. overseers Acad. Contemporary Problems, Columbus, 1972-75; trustee Columbus Symphony Orch., pres., 1979-81; past trustee Columbus Sch. Girls, Columbus Met. Area Community Action; hon. trustee Internat. Council of Mid-Ohio; past bd. govs. Goodwill Industries Central Ohio, Salesian Inner City Boys' Club; past bd. dirs., pres. Blue Cross Central Ohio; bd. dirs. Options, Learning Connections, Franklin County Heart Br.; Columbus Area Mental Health Center; bd. dirs. Battelle Meml. Inst. Found., chmn. 1977-78; mem. bd. dirs. Nationwide Corp. Served with USCGR, 1943-45. Recipient Carnegie grant, postdoctoral fellow Center for Study Higher Edn., U. Mich., 1963-64. Mem. Assn. Ind. Colls. and Univs. Ohio (chmn. 1971-74), Orgn. Am. Historians, Nebr., Ohio hist. socs., Am. Assn. Higher Edn., Newcomen Soc. N.Am., Navy League U.S. (past dir. Columbus council), Columbus Area C. of C. (dir. 1971-74). Lutheran. Club: Columbus Rotary (dir.). Home: 441 San Pedro Drive Lady Lake FL 32159

LANGEVOORT, DONALD CARL, law educator; b. Paterson, N.J., Feb. 20, 1951; s. Garrett William and Kathleen Marjorie (Schneider) L.; m. Joni Jackson, Aug. 10, 1985. BA, U. Va., 1973; JD, Harvard U., 1976. Bar: D.C. 1976, U.S. Supreme Ct. 1980. Assoc. Wilmer, Cutler & Pickering, Washington, 1976-78; spl. counsel SEC, Washington, 1978-81; Lee S. and Charles A. Speir prof. law Vanderbilt U., Nashville, 1981—. Author: Insider Trading Regulation; co-author (with Cox and Hillman); Securities Regulation: Cases and Materials. Home: 9433 Chenoweth Pl Brentwood TN 37027-8701 Office: Vanderbilt U Sch Law 21st Ave S Nashville TN 37240

LANGFORD, CHARLES DOUGLAS, state legislator, lawyer; b. Montgomery, Ala., Dec. 9, 1922; s. Nathan G. and Lucy B. (Brown) L. BS, Tenn. State U., Nashville, 1948; LLB, Cath. U. of Am., 1952, JD, 1967. Bar: Ala. 1953, U.S. Dist. Ct. (mid. dist.) Ala. 1954, U.S. Ct. Appeals (5th cir.) 1969, U.S. Supreme Ct. 1976, U.S. Ct. Appeals (11th cir.) 1982. Ptnr. Gray, Langford, Sapp, McGowan, Gray & Nathanson, Montgomery, Ala., 1968—; mem. Ala. State Senate, Montgomery, 1983—. Officer St. John A.M.E. Ch. With U.S Army, 1943-46. Mem. Elks (past exalter ruler So. Pride lodge), Alpha Phi Alpha. Democrat. Home: 918 Grove St Montgomery AL 36104-4738 Office: 400 S Union St Ste 205 Montgomery AL 36104-4316

LANGFORD, DEAN TED, lighting and precision materials company executive; b. Princeton, Ill., June 19, 1939; s. Claude Robert and Dorothy Aeileen (Tuckerman) L.; m. Nancy Hirsch; children: Douglas T., John P. B.S. in Math. and Aero. Engring., U. Ill., 1962, LHD, Salem State Coll. 1990. Regional sales mgr. IBM-N.E. Region, Westport, Conn., 1980-81, corp. dir. mgmt. devel., Armonk, N.Y., 1981-82, group dir., communications, Ryebrook, N.Y., 1982-83; v.p. mktg. GTE Communications Systems, Stamford, Conn., 1983-84; pres. GTE Elec. Products, Danvers, Mass., 1984-93, Osram Sylvania Inc., Danvers, Mass., 1993—. Mem. bd. advisers Sch. Engring., U. Ill.-Chgo., 1984-92; mem. actuele Northeastern U., 1984; trustee Civic Edn. Found. Lincoln-Filene Ctr., Tufts U.; mem. corp. bd. Mass. Gen. Hosp. Mem. U. Ill. Alumni Assn. (bd. dirs.), Alliance to Save Energy (bd. dirs.), Nat. Assn. of Mfg. (bd. dirs.), Nat. Elec. Mfg. Assn. (bd. dirs.), Phys. Sci. Inc. (bd. dirs.), Salem Country Club. Avocations: biking, golf, skiing. Home: 345 Beacon St Boston MA 02116-1102 Office: Osram Sylvania Inc 100 Endicott St Danvers MA 01923

LANGFORD, JAMES JERRY, lawyer; b. Birmingham, Ala., May 19, 1933; s. N.B. and Margaret Elizabeth (Fuller) L.; m. Mary Elizabeth Fryant, Mar. 21, 1958; children: Jan Carol Langford Hammett, Joel Fryant. BS, U. So. Miss., 1955; JD, U. Miss., 1970. Bar: Miss. 1970, U.S. Dist. Ct. (no. and so. dists.) Miss. 1970, U.S.C. Appeals (5th cir.) 1971, U.S. Ct. Appeals (11th cir.). Agt. Met. Life Ins. Co., Jackson, Miss., 1957-58; sales rep. Employers Mut. of Wausau, Jackson, 1958-64; v.p. Reid-McGee Ins. Co., Jackson, 1964-67; assoc. Wells Marble & Hurst, Jackson, 1970-73, ptnr., 1973-90, sr. ptnr., mng. ptnr. 1990—. Editor-in-chief Miss. Law Jour., 1969-70. Mem. U.S. Naval Inst., Annapolis, Md. 1st lt. U.S. Army, 1955-57. Mem. ABA, Fed. Bar Assn. (pres. Miss. chpt. 1981-82), Fedn. Ins. and Corp. Counsel, Nat. Assn. RR Trial Counsel, Miss. Bar Found., Miss. Bar Assn., Miss. Def. Lawyers Assn. (pres. 1992-93), Def. Rsch. Inst. Country Club Jackson, Phi Delta Phi, Omicron Delta Kappa, Pi Kappa Alpha. Presbyterian. Avocations: military history, baseball. Home: 12 Plum Tree Ln Madison MS 39110-9620 Office: Wells Marble & Hurst PO Box 131 Jackson MS 39205-0131

LANGFORD, JAMES ROULEAU, university press administrator; b. South Bend, Ind., June 12, 1937; s. Walter McCarty and Alice M. (Joubert) L.; m. Margaret Marie Hammerot, Aug. 30, 1968 (div. 1980); 1 child, Joshua; m. Jill Ann Justice, July 16, 1981; children: Trevor J., Emily A. Ph.B., Aquinas Inst., 1960, M.A. in Philosophy, 1961, M.A. in Theology, 1964, S.T.L., 1965. Instr. theology St. Thomas Coll., St. Paul, 1965-67; editor Doubleday & Co., N.Y.C., 1967-69; exec. editor U. Mich. Press, Ann Arbor, 1969-74; dir. U. Notre Dame Press, Ind., 1974—; bd. dirs. Assn. Am. Univ. Presses, 1981-83. Author: Galileo, Science and the Church, 1966, rev., 1971, 3d edit., 1992, The Game Is Never Over, 1980, rev., 1982, The Cub Fan's Guide to Life, 1984, Runs, Hits and Errors, 1987, Rookie: The Story of a Seaon, 1990. Democrat. Roman Catholic. Home: 21550 New Rd Lakeville IN 46536-9342 Office: U Notre Dame Press Notre Dame IN 46556 My life as a scholar, publisher and writer has brought me into contact with many of the most intelligent, creative and important people of our time. Those I admire most are the ones of whom it can be said "They never lost their sense of humor."

LANGFORD, ROLAND EVERETT, military officer, environmental scientist, author; b. Owensboro, Ky., Apr. 11, 1945; s. John Roland and Mary Helen (Cockriel) L.; m. Son-Hee Shin, Dec. 18, 1971; children: John Everett, Lee Shin. AA, Armstrong State Coll., 1965; BS, Ga. So. Coll., 1967; MS, U. Ga., 1971, PhD, 1974; grad., U.S. Army Command and Gen. Staff Coll., 1985; postgrad. in health physics, U. N.C., 1988-91. Cert. indsl. hygienist; registered hazardous substances profl., sanitarian, Ariz.; diplomate Am. Acad. Sanitarians. Instr. Savannah (Ga.) Sci. Mus., 1971-72; Bainbridge (Ga.) Jr. Coll., 1973-74; asst. prof. chemistry Ga. Mil. Coll., Milledgeville, 1975-77; asst. prof. Ga. So. Coll., Statesboro, 1977-78; commd. capt. U.S. Army, 1978, advanced through grades to lt. col., 1992; chief chemistry sect. U.S. Army Acad. Health Scis., Ft. Sam Houston, Tex., 1978-79; sanitary engr. U.S. Army Environ. Hygiene Agy., Aberdeen Proving Ground, Md., 1979-81; comdr. environ. sanitation detachment Taegu, Republic of Korea, 1981-83; environ. sci. officer Ft. Huachuca, Ariz., 1984-88; chief occupational health rsch. U.S. Army Biomed. R&D Lab., Ft. Detrick, Md., 1991-92; comdr. med. rsch. detachment Walter Reed Army Inst. Rsch., Wright-Patterson AFB, Ohio, 1992—; panel mem. Comprehensive Assistance to Undergrad. Sci. Edn., NSF, 1975-77; judge Internat. Sci. Fair, San Antonio, 1979; mem. sci. rev. panel NIH, 1986—; adj. faculty St. Leo's Coll., San Antonio, 1978-79, U. Md., Taegu and Pusan, Korea, 1981-83. Co-author: Hazardous Materials Training Program for International Union of Operating Engineers, 1988, Fundamentals of Hazardous Materials Incidents, 1990, Drug Abuse in the Workplace, 1994; contbr. articles to profl. jours. Active Boy Scouts Am., Ft. Sam Houston, 1978-79; mem. parish coun., lay minister Holy Family Parish, Ft. Huachuca, 1985-88; advisor Med. Explorer Post, Ft. Huachuca, 1986-88; lay minister St. Thomas More Ch., 1988-91. Fellow Am. Inst. Chemists; mem. Am. Acad. Indsl. Hygiene (cert.), Am. Chem. Soc., Nat. Environ. Health Assn. (cert. hazardous materials profl.), Korean Chem. Soc., Royal Asiatic Soc. (bd. dirs. 1982-83), Assn. Mil. Surgeons U.S., Am. Acad. Sanitarians (cert.), Health Physics Soc., Am. Water Works Assn., Am. Indsl. Hygiene Assn., Am. Acad. Health Physics (assoc.). Republican. Roman Catholic. Avocations: ham radio, oriental studies, photography. Home: 509 Phelps Cir Dayton OH 45433-1324 Office: US Army Med Rsch Detachment Wright Patterson AFB Dayton OH 45433

LANGFORD, WALTER MARTIN, retired greeting card and gift wrap manufacturing executive; b. Steubenville, Ohio, Jan. 2, 1931; s. Martin and Ola Belle (Stiff) L.; m. Winifred Claire Major, Mar. 14, 1953; children: Martin B., Janet R., Steven M. BS in Acctg., U. Kans., 1952; JD, Ill. Inst. Tech., 1971. With Am. Can Co., 1956-66; internal audit mgr. All-Steel, Inc., Aurora, Ill., 1966-68, div. controller, 1968-71, dir. corp. services, 1971-77; v.p. adminstrn. Gibson Greetings, Inc., Cin., 1977-79; v.p. ops. Cleo Wrap Corp. div. Gibson Greetings, Inc., Memphis, 1979-87, exec. v.p., gen. mgr., 1987-90; bd. dirs., corp. sec. Gibson Greetings, Inc., Cin., 1978-90. Mem. adv. bd. State Tech. Inst., Memphis, 1986-91; bd. dirs. Jr. Achievement of Memphis, 1985-91, Theatre Memphis, 1994—; bd. trustees LeMoyne-Owen Coll., 1991—, chmn., 1994—. Lt. (j.g.) USNR, 1952-56, Korea. Mem. Ill. Bar Assn. Lodge: Rotary. Avocation: book collecting. Office: Gibson Greetings Inc 4025 Viscount Ave Memphis TN 38118-6106

LANGHAM, MICHAEL, theatrical director; b. Somerset, Eng., Aug. 22, 1919; s. Seymour and Muriel (Andrews Speed) L.; m. Helen Burns, July 8, 1948 (div. 1972); 1 son, Christopher; m. Ellin Gorky, 1972. Student, Radley Coll., Abingdon, Eng., 1933-37, London U., 1937-39; D.Lit. (hon.), McMaster U., 1962, St. Scholastica Coll., 1973; LL.D., U. Toronto, 1966. Engaged in theatrical profession, 1946—; dir. prodns. Arts Council Midland Theatre Co., 1946-48, Sir Barry Jackson's Birmingham Repertory Theatre, 1948-50, Glasgow Citizens' Theatre, 1953-54; artistic dir. Guthrie Theater, Mpls., 1971-79, including direction of Relapse, 1972, Oedipus the King, 1972, 73, The Government Inspector, 1973, The Merchant of Venice, 1973, King Lear, 1974, Love's Labor's Lost, 1974, The School for Scandal, 1974, Private Lives, Measure For Measure, 1975, The Matchmaker, 1976, Winter's Tale, 1977; dir. Theatre Center, The Juilliard Sch., N.Y.C., 1980—, Julius Caesar, Stratford-upon-Avon, 1950, Stratford, Ont., 1955, The Gay Invalid, London, 1950, Pygmalion, London, 1951, The Other Heart, London, 1951, Old Vic Co., prodn., Othello at Berlin Festival, also London, 1951; Brit. Council lectr., Australia, 1952; dir. Richard III, Belgian Nat. Theatre, 1952, The Merry Wives of Windsor, The Hague, 1953, artistic dir. Stratford (Ont.) Shakespearean Festival, 1955-67, including direction of Hamlet, 1957, Henry IV, Part I, 1958, Much Ado About Nothing, 1958, Romeo and Juliet, 1960, Coriolanus, 1961, Love's Labour's Lost, 1961, Taming of the Shrew, 1962, Cyrano de Bergerac, 1962, Troilus and Cressida, 1963, Timon of Athens, 1963, King Lear, 1964, The Country Wife, 1964; also prodns. Love's Labour's Lost and Timon of Athens at Festival Theatre, Chichester, Eng., 1964; dir. prodns. Hamlet, Stratford-upon-Avon, 1956, Merchant of Venice, 1960, Much Ado About Nothing, 1961, Henry V, Edinburgh Festival, 1956, Two Gentlemen of Verona, London, 1957, A Midsummer Night's Dream, London, 1960, Andorra, N.Y.C., 1963, Twelfth Night, Am. Place Theatre, 1982; compiler, dir. univ. tour prodns., Can. and U.S. on Shakespearean comedy, 1962; author, dir. prodns. The Affliction of Love for TV, 1963; Artistic cons. prodns., LaJolla (Cal.) Theater Project, 1965. Served with Brit. Army, 1939-45. Office: The Juilliard Sch Drama Div 144 W 66th St New York NY 10023-6547

LANGHAM, NORMA, playwright, educator, poet, composer, inventor; b. California, Pa.; d. Alfred Scrivener and Mary Edith (Carter) L. BS, Ohio State U., 1942; B in Theatre Arts, Pasadena Playhouse Coll. Theatre Arts, 1944; MA, Stanford U., 1956; postgrad., Summer Radio-TV Inst., 1960, Pasadena Inst. Radio, 1944-45. Tchr. sci. California High Sch., 1942-43; asst. office pub. info. Denison U., Granville, Ohio, 1955; instr. speech dept. Westminster Coll., New Wilmington, Pa., 1957-58; instr. theatre. California U., Pa., 1959, asst. prof., 1960-62, assoc. prof., 1962-79, prof. emeritus, 1979—, co-founder, sponsor, dir. Children's Theatre, 1962-79; founder, producer, dir. Food Bank Players, 1985, Patriot Players, 1986, Noel Prodns., 1993. Writer: (plays) Magic in the Sky, 1963, Founding Daughters (Pa., Nat. DAR awards 1991), Women Whisky Rebels (Pa., Nat. DAR awards 1992), John Dough (Freedoms Found. award 1968), Who Am I?, Hippocrates Oath, Gandhi, Clementine of '49, Soul Force, Dutch Painting, Purim, Music in Freedom, The Day the Moon Fell, Job Johnson; composer, lyricist (plays) Why Me, Lord?, (text) Public Speaking; co-inventor computer driving game. Recipient Exceptional Acad. Svc. award Pa. Dept. Edn., 1975, Appreciation award Bicentennial Commn. Pa., 1976, Gregg award Calif. U. of Pa. Alumni Assn., 1992; Henry C. Frick Ednl. Commn. grantee. Mem. AAUW (co-founder Calif. br., 1st v.p. 1971-72, pres. 1972-73, Outstanding Woman of Yr. 1986), DAR, Theatre Assn. Pa., Internat. Platform Assn. (Poetry award 1993, 94), Calif. U. Pa. Assn. Women Faculty (founder, pres. 1972-73), Calif. Cmty. Choir, Calif. Hist. Soc., Washington County Hist. Soc., Dramatists Guild, Whisky Rebellion Task Force, Mensa, Alpha Psi Omega, (Omicron Nu. Presbyterian (elder). Home: PO Box 459 California PA 15419-0459

LANGHANS, EDWARD ALLEN, drama and theater educator; b. Warren, Pa., Mar. 11, 1923; s. Allen Milton and Frances Allen L. BA, U. Rochester, 1948, MA in English, 1949; M.A. in Theatre, U. Hawaii, 1951; Ph.D. in Theatre, Yale U., 1955. Asst. prof. drama U. Tex., Austin, 1955-57; asst. prof. drama and theatre U. Hawaii, Honolulu, 1957-64; assoc. U. Hawaii, 1964-71, prof., chmn. dept., 1971-85, assoc. dean arts and humanities, 1987, prof. emeritus, 1988—; vis. prof. Tufts U., 1967-68; rsch. prof. George Washington U., 1975-76. Author: (with Philip Highfill and Kalman Burnim) A Biographical Dictionary of Actors, Actresses, Musicians, Dancers, Managers and Other Stage Personnel in London 1660-1800, 16 vols., 1973-93, Five Restoration Theatrical Adaptations, 1980, Restoration Promptbooks, 1981, Eighteenth-Century British and Irish Promptbooks, 1987; co-author: An International Dictionary of Theater Language, 1985; contbr. articles to The New Grove Dictionary of Opera, 4 vols., 1992; dir., designer numerous plays. Bd. dirs. Honolulu Theatre for Youth, 1958-63, Hawaii Theatre Council, 1965-70, Hawaii Theatre Festival, 1978-82. Served with USAAF, 1942-47. Decorated Air medal, D.F.C.; Nat. Endowment for Humanities grantee, 1975-76, 85-86; Folger Shakespeare Library fellow, 1970-73. Mem. Am. Assn for Theatre in Higher Edn., Soc. Theatre Research, Am. Soc. Theatre Research. Home: 1212 Punahou St Apt 3402 Honolulu HI 96826-1026

LANGHENRY, JOHN GODFRED, JR., lawyer; b. Chgo., Feb. 10, 1933; s. John Godfred and Julia Margaret (Hoffman) L.; m. Eleanor L., Dec. 1, 1956; children: Barbara, John, Mark, Mary Patricia, Paul, Thomas, Matthew. BS, Loyola U., Chgo., 1954, JD, 1956. Bar: Ill. 1956, U.S. Dist. Ct. (no. dist.) Ill. 1959, U.S. Supreme Ct. 1971. Assoc. Hinshaw & Culbertson, Chgo., 1959-64, ptnr., 1965—; lectr. med. malpractice, hosp. law, civil practice and procedure Ill. Inst. Continuing Legal Edn.; lectr. med. loss prevention Ill. State Med. Soc.; faculty mem. trial advocacy workshop for practicing attys. Loyola U. Chgo. Sch. Law. Contbr. articles to profl. jours. Bus. chmn. Crusade of Mercy, Arlington Heights, Ill., 1966-67; chmn. safety commn. Village of Arlington Heights, 1967-69, mem. planning commn., 1969-72; trustee lay adv. bd. Sacred Heart of Mary High Sch., Rolling Meadows, Ill., 1972-76, 1st pres., 1972-73; mem. fin. com. Our Lady of the Wayside Ch., Arlington Heights, 1981-82; chmn., 1981-82; Loyola U. Sch. Law Alumni Assn., pres. 1973-74, Ill. Right to Life Com., chmn. 1975-76; chmn. fund raising St. Viator High Sch., Arlington Heights, mem. lay adv. bd., 1983-84, v.p. 1985-86. Served to 1st lt. USAF, 1956-59. Fellow Am. Coll. Trial Lawyers; mem. ABA, Ill. Bar Assn., Chgo. Bar Assn., Am. Soc. Hosp. Attys., Am. Bd. Trial Advs. (charter Ill. br., treas. 1988), Def. Rsch. Inst., Fedn. Ins. Counsel (chmn. med. malpractice com. 1979-80), Soc. Trial Lawyers Ill. (treas. 1986, sec. 1987, v.p. 1988, pres. 1989), Ill. Def. Counsel (pres. 1973-74), Trial Lawyers Club Chgo. (pres. 1970-71), Big Foot Country Club (Fontana, Wis.). Roman Catholic. Office: Hinshaw Culbertson 222 N La Salle St Ste 300 Chicago IL 60601-1081

LANGHOLZ, ROBERT WAYNE, lawyer, investor; b. Sioux City, Iowa, Jan. 17, 1930; s. Harry H. and Alvina (Bockhop) L.; m. Patricia Wilson Wheeler, Mar. 6, 1994; children: Robert Wayne, Laurence Henry, Kristofer Page. B.S. with distinction, U. Iowa, 1951, J.D., 1956. Bar: Iowa 1956, Okla. 1957. Research asst. to prof. Frank R. Kennedy, U. Iowa Coll. Law, 1955-56; trainee Gulf Oil Corp., 1956; mem. firm Carlson, Lupardus, Matthews, Holliman & Huffman, Tulsa, 1956-67; ptnr. Holliman, Langholz, Runnels, Holden, Forsman & Sellers, Tulsa, 1967—; chmn. bd., chief exec. officer Skinner Bros. Co. Inc., Geophys. Research Corp., Indel-Davis Inc.; bd. dirs. F&M Bank & Trust Co. Trustee Herbert Hoover Presdl. Libr. Assn., West Branch, Iowa; nat. trustee Nat. Jewish Ctr. for Immunology and Respiratory Medicine, Denver. Served with USAF, 1951-53. Mem. ABA, Iowa Bar Assn., Okla. Bar Assn., Young Pres. Orgn., World Pres. Orgn., Summit Club, So. Hills Country Club (Tulsa), Eldorado Country Club (Indian Wells, Calif.). Methodist. Home: 4033 S Yorktown Pl Tulsa OK 74105-3412 Office: Holarud Bldg 10 E 3rd St Ste 400 Tulsa OK 74103-3620

LANGILL, GEORGE FRANCIS, hospital administrator, educator; b. Ottawa, Ont., Can., Dec. 31, 1946; s. Roy Joseph and Margaret (O'Hara) L.; m. Lorraine Diane Bavazeau, Aug. 10, 1947; children: Norman, Barbara Ann, Kendra, Leonard. BSc with honors, Ottawa U., 1971, MHA, 1973. Adminstrv. coordinator N.S. Dept. Health, 1973-74; asst. exec. dir. Royal Ottawa Hosp., 1974-79; assoc. exec. dir. Rehab. Ctr., Ottawa, 1979-83; chief exec. officer Royal Ottawa Health Care Group, 1983—; adj. prof., part-time lectr. Faculty Adminstrn., Ottawa U., 1979—; mem. faculty health care adminstrn. WHO, Montreal, 1983—; bd. dirs., mem. exec. com. Can. council Rehab. of Disabled, Toronto, 1985—. Contbr. articles to profl. jours. Mem. Ottawa Bd. Trade, 1986. Mem. Can. Coll. Health Service Execs., Am. Coll. Health Execs., Am. Assn. Mental Health Adminstrs. Clubs: L'Cercle (Ottawa) Cedarhill Golf and Country (Nedean, Ont. Can.). Avocations: skiing, hockey, golf. Office: Royal Ottawa Health Care, Group, 1145 Carling Ave, Ottawa, ON Canada K1Z 7K4

LANGLAND, JOSEPH THOMAS, author, emeritus educator; b. Spring Grove, Minn., Feb. 16, 1917; s. Charles M. and Clara Elizabeth (Hille) L.; m. Judith Gail Wood, June 26, 1943; children—Joseph Thomas, Elizabeth Langland, Paul. B.A., U. Iowa, 1940; M.A., 1941; D.Litt. (hon.), Luther Coll., 1974. Instr. in English Dana Coll., Blair, Nebr., 1941-42; part-time instr. U. Iowa, 1946-48; asst. prof., then asso. prof. U. Wyo., 1948-59; mem. faculty U. Mass., Amherst, 1959-79; prof. English U. Mass., 1964-79, prof. emeritus, 1979—; dir. program for M.F.A. in writing, 1964-70, 78-79; vis. lectr. U. B.C., U. Wash., Seattle, San Francisco State U.; poetry reader, lectr., U.S. and Europe. Author: poems For Harold, 1945, The Green Town, 1956, The Wheel of Summer, 1963, 2d edit., 1966, An Interview and Fourteen Poems, 1973, The Sacrifice Poems, 1975, Any Body's Song (Nat. Poetry Series), 1980, (poem with etchings) A Dream of Love, 1986, Twelve: Preludes & Postludes, 1988, Selected Poems, 1991, 2d edit., 1992; co-editor: poems Poet's Choice, 1962, 83, The Short Story, 1956; co-translator: poems Poetry From the Russian Underground, 1973. Served to capt., inf. AUS, 1942-46, ETO. Ford fellow in humanities Harvard-Columbia U. 1953-54; Amy Lowell Poetry fellow, 1955-56; Arts and Humanities fellow in poetry, 1966-67; recipient Melville Cane prize poetry Poetry Soc. Am., 1964; named Living Art Treasure in Lit., New Eng. Arts Biennial, 1985. Democrat. Home: 16 Morgan Cir Amherst MA 01002-1131

LANGLANDS, ROBERT PHELAN, mathematician; b. New Westminster, Can., Oct. 6, 1936; came to U.S., 1960; s. Robert and Kathleen (Phelan) L.; m. Charlotte Lorraine Cheverie, Aug. 13, 1956; children: William, Sarah, Robert, Thomasin. BA, U. B.C., 1957, MA, 1958, DS honoris causa, 1985; PhD, Yale U., 1960; DSc (hon.), McMaster U., 1985, CUNY, 1985; D in Math. (hon.), U. Waterloo, 1988; DSc (hon.), U. Paris, 1989, McGill U., 1991, Toronto U., 1993. From instr. to asso. prof. Princeton (N.J.) U., 1960-67; prof. math. Yale U., New Haven, 1968-72. Inst. Advanced Study, Princeton, 1972—. Author: Euler Products, 1971, (with H. Jacquet) Automorphic Forms on GL (2), 1970, On the Functional Equations Satisfied by Eisenstein Series, 1976, Base Change for GL (2), 1980, Les Débuts d'une Formule des Traces Stable, 1983. Recipient Wilbur Lucius Cross medal Yale U., 1975, Common Wealth award Sigma Xi, 1984, Mathematics award Nat. Acad. Sci., 1988. Fellow Royal Soc. London, Royal Soc. Can.; mem. NAS, Am. Math Soc. (Cole prize 1982), Can. Math. Soc. Office: Inst Advanced Study Sch Math Olden Ln Princeton NJ 08540

LANGLEBEN, MANUEL PHILLIP, physics educator; b. Poland, Apr. 9, 1924; emigrated to Can., 1929, naturalized, 1935; s. David and Charna Molly (Shabason) L.; m. Rose Cohen, May 25, 1948; children—Adrian, David, Louise. B.Sc., McGill U., Can., 1949, M.Sc., 1950, Ph.D., 1953. Postdoctoral fellow Meteorol. Office, Dunstable, Eng., 1953-54; research asso. McGill U., Montreal, Que., 1954—; asst. prof. physics McGill U., 1960-62,

assoc. prof., 1962-68, prof., 1968-90, prof. emeritus, 1990—, dir. Centre for No. Studies and Rsch., 1977-80; mem. sub-com. snow and ice, asso. com. geotech. research Nat. Research Council Can., 1968-74; mem. working group on ice reconnaissance and glaciology Canadian Adv. Com. on Remote Sensing, 1971-75; mem. panel on ice, subcom. Arctic oceanography Canadian Com. on Oceanography, 1973-84; mem. adv. bd. Ea. Arctic Marine Environ. Studies, 1977-83; mem. Working Group on Arctic Regions and Atmospheric Interactions, Can. Global Change Program, Internat. Geosphere-Biosphere Programme, 1988—. Contbr. articles sci. jours. Served with Royal Can. Navy, 1941-45. Fellow Royal Soc. Can.; mem. Canadian Assn. Physicists, Royal Meteorol. Soc., Glaciological Soc., Am. Geophy. Union, Sigma Xi. Home: 4753 Grosvenor, Montreal, PQ Canada H3W 2L9

LANGLEY, BEVERLY, critical care nurse; b. Monticello, N.Y., July 26, 1948; d. Herbert and Joyce (Rennolds) Sklarew; m. Victor Langley, Oct. 1972; children: Clark, Aaron, Michelle. AS, Broward Community Coll., Davie, Fla., 1972; BS, Nova U., Davie, Fla., 1985. Head nurse CCU North Broward Hosp. Dist., Ft. Lauderdale, Fla.; nursing coord. North Broward Hosp. Dist., asst. dir. nursing, dir. nursing. Mem. Human Rights Advocacy Com., Dist. X, Broward County, Fla., Com. for Licensure, South Fla. Hosp. Assn., Transitional Planning Com., Broward County Health Planning Coun.; mem. Broward County Mental Health Coalition; adv. bd. Nursing Spectrum mag. Mem. Am. Assn. Critical Care Nurses, Am. Orgn. Nurse Execs., S. Fla. Orgn. of Nurse Execs.

LANGLEY, CHIARA MARIA BINI, society executive, research scientist; b. Castelfranco Emilia, Mo, Italy, June 26, 1934; came to the U.S., 1954; d. Giovanni and Maria (Cavallini) Bini; m. Robert B. Sexton, Aug. 20, 1958 (div. June 1969); children: John Andrew, Marta A., Michael R.; m. Rolland A. Langley, Apr. 12, 1978. Student. U. Bologna, Italy, 1954-55; BS in Biology, Kans. State U., 1959; postgrad., Sonoma State Coll., 1974-75, San Francisco State U., 1976-80. Histology lab. tech., rsch. assoc. Nat. Cancer Found. Kans. State U., Manhattan, Kans., 1955-60; radiochem. technician Aerojet-Gen. Nucleonics, San Ramon, Calif., 1960-65; med. lab. tech. various orgns., Calif., 1969-71; sr. med. tech., microbiology supr. Ukiah (Calif.) Gen. Hosp., 1971-75; bacteriologist Pediatric Clinic, Ukiah, 1972-75; sr. med. tech. Clin. Labs., VA Med. Ctr., San Francisco, 1976; adminstrv. asst. to the chief, lab. supr., sr. technician Immunology Rsch., VA. Med. Ctr., San Francisco, 1976-82; rsch. adminstr., rsch. scientist Kuzell Inst Arthritis Rsch. Inst. Med. Scis., Pacific Med. Ctr., San Francisco, 1981-82; pres. GCBL Enterprises, Inc., 1984-86; dir. internat. rels. IDEA of San Francisco, Calif., 1986-90; vis. scholar Dr. Peter Witschi's Lab., Oak Ridge (Tenn.) Nat. Lab./Biology Divsn., 1982; fundraiser Loudon Healthcare Found., Leesburg, Va., 1993; mem., advisor World Meml. Fund for Disaster Relief, London, 1993; advisor internat. exchanges Notre Dame Acad., Middleburg, Va., 1994; bd. dirs. Fund Internat. Youth Coop., Ctr. Profl. Tng. and Internat. Exchanges, Moscow. chairperson fin. com. Oak Ridge Art Ctr., 1982-83, v.p., 1983-84; active Italian Regional Events, 1984-87, San Francisco/Moscow Med. Exchange Program, 1987-89; bd. dirs. Juvenile Diabetes Found. Internat. of San Francisco, 1988-90; establisher The Clara Lux Found., 1988-90; amb. Internat. Fedn. Keystone Youth Orgns., 1991—; mem. bd., internat. coor., amb. Internat. Fedn. Multiple Sclerosis Socs., 1991—; v.p., amb. World Meml. Fund for Disaster Relief USA, 1994—. Recipient U.S. Govt. Fulbright scholarship, Pi Beta Phi scholarship, Kans. State Fedn. Women scholarship, 1955-56, AAUW scholarship, 1955-57, Pvt. commendation Chief of Surgery, Ukiah Gen. Hosp., 1972, Am. Soc. Med. Techs./Mgmt. Tng. grant, 1973. Republican. Roman Catholic. Avocations: art, music, antiques, old buildings restoration, sports. Home and Office: 1341 28th St NW Washington DC 20007-3101

LANGLEY, GEORGE ROSS, medical educator; b. Sydney, N.S., Can., Oct. 6, 1931; s. John Goerge Elmer and Freda Catherine (Ross) L.; m. Jean Marie Ballantyne, June 22, 1957; children: Joanne Marie, Mark Ross, Richard Graham. B.A., Mt. Allison U., 1952; M.D., Dalhousie U., 1957. Intern Victoria Gen. Hosp., Halifax, N.S., 71957; resident Victoria Gen. Hosp., 1958, Toronto (Ont.) Gen. Hosp., 1960, U. Melbourne, Australia, 1961, U. Rochester, N.Y., 1962; John and Mary Markle scholar in acad. medicine Dalhousie U., Halifax, 1963-68; from lectr. to prof. medicine Dalhousie U., 1963-69, prof., chmn. dept. medicine, 1974-82; chief of service medicine Camp Hill Hosp., Halifax, 1969-74; head dept. medicine Victoria Gen. Hosp., 1974-82; chmn. clin. investigation grants com. Med. Research Council, 1976-78; chmn. clin. and epidemiol. research adv. com., bd. dirs. Nat. Cancer Inst., 1978-86. Contbr. articles to sci. jours. Decorated Queen's Jubilee medal, 1977; recipient Inst. medal Nat. Cancer Inst. Can., 1985. Fellow Internat. Soc. Hematology, Royal Coll. Physicians and Surgeons (v.p., coun., Wightman vis. prof. 1990), ACP (bd. govs. 1973-78), Royal Coll. Physicians (Edinburgh); mem. Can. Hematology Soc. (pres. 1976-78), Can. Soc. Clin. Investigation, Am. Soc. Hematology, Can. Soc. Oncology, Alpha Omega Alpha. Mem. United Ch. Can. Home: 6025 Oakland Rd Halifax, NS Canada B3H 1N9 Office: Victoria Gen Hosp, Ste 8-024, Halifax, NS Canada B3H 2Y9

LANGLEY, LYNNE SPENCER, newspaper editor, columnist; b. West Palm Beach, Fla., June 4, 1947; d. George Hosmer and Elwa June (Harries) Spencer; m. William A. Langley, Oct. 10, 1970. student, Glasgow U., Scotland, 1967-68; BA with honors, Coll. of Wooster, 1969. Feature writer, asst. women's editor Palm Beach Times, West Palm Beach, 1969-70; asst. editor Brunswick (Maine) Times Record, 1971; investigative reporter Maine Times, Topsham, 1971-75; asst. mng. editor York County Coast Star, Kennebunk, Maine, 1976-78; environ. and med. editor, nature columnist Charleston (S.C.) Post and Courier Newspapers, 1979—; editor Maine Audubon Soc. News, 1975-76; stringer Newsweek mag., 1971-75; speaker in field; freelance writer. Author: Nature Watch, 1987. Recipient Media award S.C. Assn. Mentally Retarded, 1985. Mem. Charleston Mus., S.C. chpt. Nature Conservancy. Recipient Media awards Charleston County Parks and Recreation Commn., 1985, Am. Diabetes Assn. S.C. chpt., 1989, Communicator of Yr. award S.C. Wildlife Fedn., 1983, Writing awards S.C. Press Assn., 1987. Mem. Am. Hort. Soc., Nat. Audubon Soc., Charleston Natural History Soc. (Media award 1985), Garden Writers Assn. Am., PEO (sec. chpt. D Maine 1975-76, corr. sec. chpt. J S.C. 1986-88), Sigma Delta Chi. Home: PO Box 97 Adams Run SC 29426-0097 Office: 134 Columbus St Charleston SC 29403-4800

LANGLINAIS, JOSEPH WILLIS, academic administrator; b. San Antonio, Aug. 12, 1922; s. Joseph Willis and Marie Nellie (St. Julien) L. B.S. in Edn, U. Dayton, 1943; S.T.D., U. Fribourg, Switzerland, 1954. Joined Soc. Mary, 1940; ordained priest Roman Cath. Ch., 1952; tchr. high schs. in Mo., Ill. and Man., Can., 1943-48; dir. admissions Chaminade Coll. Prep. Sch., St. Louis, 1957-59; dir. Archdiocesan High Sch. Sodality Union St. Louis, 1958-59, Marianist Novitiate, LaFayette, Wis., 1959-63; mem. faculty St. Mary's U., San Antonio, 1963—, dean Sch. Arts and Scis., 1964-75, acad. v.p., 1975-81, dir. instnl. self-study, 1970-72, 82-84, chmn. theology dept., 1981-83, dean Sch. Humanities and Soc. Scis., 1986, chaplain Sch. of Bus., 1988—, Univ. Prof., 1993—; pres. Cen. Cath. Marianist High Sch., San Antonio, 1987-91; dir. semester in Puebla, Mex. St. Mary's U., 1994. Contbr.: Cath. Ency. Am., Encyclopedic Dictionary of Religion. Mem. AAUP, Cath. Theol. Soc. Am., Mariological Soc. Am., Archaeol. Soc. Am., Torch Internat., Rotary. Home: 1 Camino Santa Maria San Antonio TX 78228

LANGLITZ, HAROLD N., pension fund administrator. Exec. dir. N.Y. State Teachers Retirement Fund, Albany, N.Y., 1967—. Office: Tchr's Retirement System 10 Corporate Woods Dr Albany NY 12211-2395

LANGMEAD, JEFFREY P., insurance company executive; b. 1935. With data processing Honeywell Corp., Boston, L.A., 1957-62; with Carte Blanche, L.A., 1962-68; with data processing Southern Calif. Blue Cross, L.A., 1968-69, Mass. Blue Cross, Boston, 1970-75; v.p. N.H./Vt. Blue Cross, Concord, N.H., 1975-80; v.p. benefits adminstrn. Blue Cross of N.Y., N.Y.C., 1980-82; sr. v.p. Blue Cross Blue Shield of Tex., Richardson, Tex., 1982—. Office: Blue Cross Blue Shield of Tex 901 S Central Expy Richardson TX 75080-7399

LANG-MIERS, ELIZABETH ANN, lawyer; b. Mpls., Nov. 26, 1950; d. Ervin J. Jr. and Jacqueline H. (Kratky) Lang; m. Jeb. S. Miers, July 29, 1978; children: Ellen Lang Miers, James L. Miers. BA, U. Mo., 1972, JD,

1975. Bar: Mo. 1975, Tex. 1977, U.S. Ct. Appeals (5th cir.), U.S. Supreme Ct. Law clk. to presiding justice Mo. Supreme Ct., Jefferson City, 1975-76; ptnr. Locke, Purnell, Rain, Harrell, Dallas, 1976—. Mem. editorial bd. Mo. Law Review. Mem. Dallas County Med. Soc. Aux., bd. dirs. Met. YWCA; bd. dors., chairperson adv. bd. Women's Resource Ctr. Leadership Dallas, Leadership Tex., Leadership Am. Recipient Am. Jurisprudence awards 1973, 74. Mem. ABA, Tex. Bar Assn., Dallas Bar Assn. (chmn. media rels com. 1985, chair lawyer referral svc., v.p., sec.-treas., bd. dirs., exec. com 1987—, chmn. bd. dirs., vice-chair), Tex. Young lawyers Assn. (com. chair) Dallas Assn. Young Lawyers (com. chair), State Bar (com. chair). Episcopalian. Office: Locke Purnell Rain Harrell 2200 Ross Ave Ste 2200 Dallas TX 75201-6776

LANGMORE, JOHN PRESTON, biophysicist, educator; b. Santa Monica, Calif., Jan. 2, 1947; s. Herbert C. and Elizabeth (Harmon) L.; children: Ian, Katherine. BS in Physics, Stanford U., 1968; PhD in Biophysics, U. Chgo., 1975. Asst. prof. biology U. Mich., Ann Arbor, 1979-85, assoc. prof. biology, 1985-91, chmn. dept. biophysics, 1989—, prof. biology, 1991—.

LANGMUIR, CHARLES HERBERT, geology educator; b. Chalk River, Ont., Can., Nov. 24, 1950; came to U.S., 1954; s. David Bulkeley and Marianna (Lawrence) L.; m. Diane Marie Langmuir, Sept. 22, 1973; 1 child, Molly Kathryn. BA, Harvard U., 1973; MS, SUNY, Stony Brook, 1978, PhD, 1980. From asst. to assoc. prof. Lamont-Doherty Geol. Observatory Columbia U., Palisades, N.Y., 1981-88, prof., 1988—; Arthur D. Storke Meml. prof., 1989—; vis. scientist Inst. de Physique du Globe, Paris, 1989-90; mem. adv. com. on ocean scis. NSF, 1990-93; mem. lithosphere panel Joint Oceanographic Instns. for Deep Earth Sampling, 1984-87; chmn. Conf. on Sci. Ocean Drilling II, Work Group on Mantle-Crust Interactions, 1986-87; mem. steering com. Ridge Interdisciplinary Global Experiments, 1990-93; chmn. coord. com. Project French-Am.-Ridge Atlantic, 1989—; mem. steering com. Inter Ridge, 1992—. Editor: Earth and Planetary Sci. Letters, 1989—; mem. editorial bd. Chem. Geology, 1985—; contbr. over 40 articles to profl. jours. Alfred Sloan Rsch. fellow, 1983-85, Henry Shaw fellow Harvard U., 1974. Fellow Am. Geophys. Union (fellows com. 1995—); mem. Geol. Soc. Am. Office: 37 Iroquois Ave RFD 1 Box 86 Palisades NY 10964

LANGRAN, ROBERT WILLIAMS, political science educator; b. N.Y.C., Feb. 15, 1935; s. Robert Joseph and Leona Gertrude (Williams) L.; m. Eleanor Victoria Groh, Dec. 26, 1959; children—Irene, Elizabeth, Thomas. B.S. with honors, Loyola U., Chgo., 1956; M.A., Fordham U., 1959; Ph.D., Bryn Mawr Coll., 1965. V.p. prof. polit. sci. Villanova U., Pa., 1959—. Contbr. articles to profl. publs. Served to 1st lt. U.S. Army, 1956-58. Mem. Am. Polit. Sci. Assn., Supreme Ct. Hist. Soc. Office: Villanova U Villanova PA 19085

LANGROCK, KARL FREDERICK, former academic administrator; b. Toeterville, Iowa, Jan. 26, 1927; s. Lee Henry and Alice Dora (Grube) L.; m. Rose Marie Meyer, June 4, 1950; children: Laura Sue, Charles Alan. BA, U. No. Iowa, 1949; MA, U. Iowa, 1951; MDiv, Luth. Sch. Theology, Chgo., 1955; LittD (hon.), Grand View Coll., 1989. Pastor Lake Park Luth. Ch., Milw., 1955-57; Resurrection Luth. Ch., Franklin Park, Ill., 1957-62, Luth. Ch. of the Holy Spirit, Deerfield, Ill., 1962-69; asst. to pres. Berea (Ky.) Coll., 1969-72; pres. Grand View Coll., Des Moines, 1972-88; free-lance writer, 1988—. Mem. Iowa Coll. Aid Commn., Des Moines, 1980-84, Luth. Social Services of Ill., Chgo., 1962-70, pres., 1968-70. Served in USN, 1945-46. Mem. Iowa Assn. Independent Colls. and Univs. (bd. dirs. 1972-87, chmn. 1986-87), Council of Luth. in Am. Colls. (pres. 1978), Phi Eta Sigma. Address: 2234 NE Douglas St Newport OR 97365-1837

LANGROCK, PETER FORBES, lawyer; b. N.Y.C., Feb. 2, 1938; s. Frank Langrock; m. Joann Murphy, July 4, 1960; children: Frank, Catherine, Eric. BA, U. Chgo., 1958, JD, 1960. Bar: Vt. 1964, U.S. Supreme Ct. 1966. State's atty. Addison County, Vt., 1960-65; sr. ptnr. Landrock Sperry Life & Wool, Middlebury, Vt., 1965—; commr. Nat. Conf. Commrs. on Uniform State Laws. Chmn. Vt. Breeders Stake Bd., 1984-90. Mem. ABA (chmn. individual rights and responsibilities sect. 1980-81, del. 1982-83, ho. of dels. 1984-93), Am. Law Inst. Avocations: horse breeding and raising, fishing, hunting. Home: Rd Lower Plains Rd Salisbury VT 05769 Office: 15 S Pleasant St PO Box 351 Middlebury VT 05753-0351

LANGSDORF, ALEXANDER, JR., physicist; b. St. Louis, May 30, 1912; s. Alexander S. and Elsie (Hirsch) L.; m. Martyl S. Schweig, Dec. 31, 1941; children: Suzanne M., Alexandra. B.A., Washington U., St. Louis, 1932; Ph.D., M.I.T., 1937. NRC fellow U. Calif.-Berkeley, 1938; instr. Washington U., 1939-43; physicist Argonne (Ill.) Nat. Lab., 1943-77, sr. physicist, 1947-77; Mem. Dist. 211 High Sch. Bd., 1970-73. Assoc. editor Applied Physics Letters, 1978-91. Recipient Alumni award Washington U., 1958. Fellow Am. Phys. Soc. Home: 645 S Meacham Rd Schaumburg IL 60193-4366

LANGSLEY, DONALD GENE, psychiatrist, medical board executive; b. Topeka, Oct. 5, 1925; s. Morris J. and Ruth (Pressman) L.; m. Pauline R. Langsley, Sept. 9, 1955; children: Karen Jean, Dorothy Ruth, Susan Louise. B.A., SUNY, Albany, 1949; M.D., U. Rochester, 1953. Diplomate: Am. Bd. Psychiatry and Neurology (dir. 1976-80), Nat. Bd. Med. Examiners. Intern USPHS Hosp., San Francisco, 1953-54; resident psychiatry U. Calif., San Francisco, 1954-59; NIMH career tchr. in psychiatry U. Calif., 1959-61; candidate San Francisco and Chgo. insts. for psychoanalysis, 1958-67; asst. prof., assoc. prof. psychiatry U. Colo. Sch. Medicine, 1961-68; prof., chmn. dept. psychiatry U. Calif., Davis, 1968-77. U. Cin., 1977-81; prof. dept. psychiatry Northwestern U. Sch. Medicine, Chgo., 1981—; mem. psychiatry edn. com. NIMH, 1969-75; exec. v.p. Am. Bd. Med. Spltys., 1981-91; trustee Ednl. Commn. for Fgn. Med. Graduates, 1983-91; mem. adv. com. on Grad. Med. Edn. Dept. Def., 1986-87; bd. govs. EcuMed, 1983-85; bd. dirs. Nat. Resident Matching Program, 1982, sec. 1984-87, 89-91, pres. 1987-89. Author: The Treatment of Families in Crisis, 1968, Mental Health Education in the New Medical Schools, 1973, Peer Review Manual for Psychiatry, 1976, Handbook of Community Mental Health, 1981, Evaluating the Skills of Medical Specialists, 1983, Legal Aspects of Certification & Accreditation, 1983, Trends in Specialization, 1985, Hospital Privileges & Specialty Medicine, 1986, 2d edit., 1991, How To Evaluate Residents, 1986, How to Select Residents, 1988, Health Policy Issues in Graduate Medicine Education, 1992; contbr. articles to med. jours. Served with AUS, 1943-46; med. officer USPHS, 1953-54. Recipient Spl. awards Colo. Assn. for Mental Health, 1968, Spl. awards Sacramento Area Mental Health Assn. 1973. Fellow Am. Psychiat. Assn. (Hofheimer award 1971, pres. 1980-81, chmn. peer rev. com. 1975-77, Kiewit lectr. 1990, Adminstrv. Psychiatry award 1993), Am. Coll. Psychiatrists; mem. Ctrl. Calif. Psychiat. Soc. (pres. 1973-74), Colo. Psychiat. Soc. (pres.-elect 1967-68), Soc. Med. Adminstrs. Home: 9445 Monticello Evanston IL 60203-1117 Office: 980 N Michigan Ave #1500 Chicago IL 60611

LANGSTAFF, DAVID HAMILTON, commercial industry executive; b. Paris, June 12, 1954; s. E. Kennedy and Percy (Lee) L.; m. Cynthia Shauer, Aug. 26, 1978; children: Meredith Avery, Christopher Maxim. BA cum laude, Harvard U., 1977, MBA, 1981. Assoc. First Boston Internat., Athens, Greece, 1977-78, Blyth Eastman Dillon & Co., Athens, 1978-79; prin. Langstaff Design & Mgmt., Cambridge, Mass., 1980-81; assoc. Inverness Group, Houston, 1981-82, v.p. corp. fin., mgr. mergers and acquisitions, 1983-84; sr. v.p., chief exec. officer, sec., treas. Space Industries Inc., Houston, 1984—. Founder, mem. bd. advisors Harvard U. Ensemble, Boston; bd. dirs. Boston Premiere Ensemble, 1981—, Houston Symphony Orch., 1987—; mem. exec. com. Houston Grand Opera, 1986-87. Democrat. Avocations: music, athletics, squash, skiing, counseling. Home: 6628 Rutgers St Houston TX 77005-3853 Office: Space Industries Inc 101 Courageous Dr League City TX 77573

LANGSTAFF, GARY LEE, food service marketing executive; b. Cherry Point, N.C., Aug. 21, 1948; s. Harold A. and Ruth (Means) L.; m. Claudia Gramps, Jan. 8, 1977; children: Danielle, Brett Allyn. BA in History, Polit. Sci., U. Calif., Santa Barbara, 1970; BS in Internat. mgmt., Thunderbird Grad. Sch. Bus., 1971, M in Internat. Mgmt., 1972. Account exec. Benton & Bowles, N.Y.C., 1972-77 v.p. account supr., 1977-79; sr. v.p., mgmt. supr. Benton & Bowles, N.Y.C. and Chgo., 1979-81; pres. Envision Systems, Inc.,

Westport, Conn., 1981-85; exec. v.p. Triparte Corp., Fresno, Calif. 1983-85; also bd. dirs. Triparte Corp., Fresno; gen. mgr. Wieden & Kennedy, Inc., Los Angeles, 1985; sr. v.p. mktg. Hardee's Food Systems, Rocky Mount, N.C., 1985-86, exec. v.p. mktg., 1986-89; exec. v.p. mktg. Burger King Corp., Miami, Fla., 1989-91; prin. Retail Resolve, Inc., Steamboat Springs, Colo. 1991—; pres. TPR Resources, Inc., Steamboat Springs, Colo., 1992—. Bd. Dirs. Rocky Mount Acad., 1987-88. Republican. Office: Retail Resolve Inc 29950 Emerald Meadows Ln Steamboat Springs CO 80487

LANGSTAFF, GEORGE QUIGLEY, JR., retired footwear company executive; b. Paducah, Ky., July 28, 1925; s. George Quigley and Katherine Elizabeth (Irion) L.; m. Maureen Black, Dec. 27, 1946; children: Patricia (Mrs. Charles Poole), Lynne (Mrs. Steve Frederick), Katherine (Mrs. George Stockman). B.A., U. of South, 1948; grad., Advanced Mgmt. Program, Harvard U., 1978. Mfg. mgr. Genesco, Inc., Nashville, 1948-59; mktg. mgr. Genesco, Inc., 1959-70, group pres., 1970-73, v.p., chief operating offr., 1974-78, exec. v.p., 1978-80; pres., chief exec. officer Footwear Industries Am., Inc., Phila., 1981-85. Pres. Nashville Mental Health Assn., 1970, Episcopal Churchmen of Tenn., 1966; trustee, alumni v.p. U. of the South; mem. Rep. State Exec. Com., 1952-53; bd. dirs. United Fund, Jr. Achievement; vestry St. George's Episcopal Ch., sr. warden, 1966, 89, 90. With USNR, 1943-46. Home: 6001 Andover Dr Nashville TN 37215-5731

LANGSTAFF, JOHN MEREDITH, musician; b. Bklyn., Dec. 24, 1920; s. Bridgewater Meredith and Esther Knox (Boardman) L.; m. Diane Guggenheim; 1 child, Carol; m. Nancy Graydon Woodbridge, Apr. 3, 1948; children—John Elliot, Peter Gerry, Deborah Graydon. Student, Curtis Inst. Music, Juilliard Sch. Music, Columbia U. Author (books) Frog Went a-Courtin', 1955 (Caldecott prize 1955), Over in the Meadow, 1957, On Christmas Day in the Morning, 1959, The Swapping Boy, 1960, Ol' Dan Tucker, 1963, Hi! Ho! The Rattlin' Bog, 1969, Jim Along, Josie, 1970, Gather My Gold Together, 1971, The Golden Vanity, 1971, Soldier, Soldier, Won't You Marry Me?, 1972, The Two Magicians, 1973, Shimmy, Shimmy Coke-a-pop!, 1973, St. George and the Dragon, 1973, A-Hunting We will Go, 1974, A Season for Singing, 1974, Sweetly Sings the Donkey, 1976, Hot Cross Buns, 1978, The Christmas Revels Songbook, 1985, Sally Go Round The Moon, 1986, What A Morning!, 1987, Climbing Jacob's Ladder, 1991, I Have A Song To Sing-O, 1994; recitals, U.S., Can., Eng., Iceland, Europe, rec. for, Odeon-Capital, Jupiter, RCA-Victor, Nixa, Renaissance, Tradition, HMV, Desto, Weston Woods, Revels Records, Minstrel Records; soloist with, Cantata Singers, N.Y. Philharmonic, Nat. Symphony, Montreal Symphony Orch., Little Orch. Soc., N.Y. Oratorio Soc., Collegium Musicum, Stratford Shakespeare Festival, Eng.; dir. music dept., Potomac Sch., Washington, 1953-68, Shady Hill Sch., Cambridge, Mass., 1969-72; faculty, Simmons Coll., Boston, 1970-86, Wheelock Coll., Boston, 1974-79, Mass. Coll. Art, 1977, Boston Coll., 1979, U. Conn., 1977-79, Lesley Coll., 1978—; artistic dir., Young Audiences Mass., 1972-81, adv. bd., 1981—; artist-lectr., Assn. Am. Colls. Served as 1st lt., inf. AUS, World War II. Recipient Hope S. Dean Meml. award Found. for Children's Books, 1991. Mem. Actors Equity, Country Dance and Song Soc. Am., Internat. Folk Music Council, English Folk Song Soc. (founder and dir. Christmas Revels 1956, 57, 66, 70—, Spring Revels 1972—, Sea Revels 1983—). Office: Revels Inc One Kendall Sq Bldg 600 Cambridge MA 02139*

LANGSTON, MARK EDWARD, professional baseball player; b. San Diego, Aug. 20, 1960; m. Michelle Langston; 1 child, Katie. Student, San Jose State U. Baseball player Seattle Mariners, 1981-89, Montreal Expos, 1989—, California Angels, 1989—. Named AL Rookie Pitcher of Yr. 1984 by the Sporting News, Am. League All-Star Team, 1987, 91-93; recipient AL Gold Glove, 1987-88, 1991-94. Office: care Calif Angels Anaheim Stadium 200 State College Blvd Anaheim CA 92806*

LANGSTON, PAUL T., music educator, university dean, composer; b. Marianna, Fla., Sept. 15, 1928; s. Howard McGhee and Rosa (Jeffries) L.; m. Esther Howard, Aug. 12, 1950; children: Claire Beth, Erin, Howard. Pvt. study with, Nadia Boulanger, 1962, 63; diploma, Conservatoire Americaine, France; BA, U. Fla., 1950; MS in Music, So. Bapt. Theol. Sem., 1953; SMD, Union Theol. Sem., 1963; DMus (hon.), Stetson U., 1985. Organistchoirmaster St. John's Bapt. Ch., Charlotte, N.C., 1953-60; instr. music theory Davidson Coll., 1959-60; mem. faculty Stetson U., De Land, Fla., 1960—; dean Sch. Music, Stetson U., 1963-85, William Kenan Jr. prof. music, 1986—, prof. and dean music emeritus, 1993—; asso. condr. Charlotte Oratorio Singers, 1986-93; dir. Fla. Internat. Music Festival, Fla. Internat. Music Festival Inst.; research fellow Inst. Sacred Music, Yale U., 1985. Composer organ, choral works.; oratorio Petros (premier Nov. 1983). Recipient Hand award for outstanding rsch., 1993. Mem. Am. Guild Organists, Hymn Soc., Coll. Music Soc., Music Tchrs. Nat. Assn., Nat. Assn. Schs. of Music (undergrad. commn., McEniry award teaching excellence), Assn. Anglican Musicians, Omicron Delta Kappa, Pi Kappa Lambda, Delta Tau Delta. Home: 313 N Salisbury Ave Deland FL 32720-4054

LANGSTON, ROY A., insurance company consultant; b. Dallas, Feb. 13, 1912; s. Lamar Q. and Gertrude (McDaniel) L.; m. Edna Earle Scott, 1936; 1 dau., Peggy Langston Schieffer. Student, Dallas Sch. Law, Mountain View Coll., Dallas. With Trinity Universal Ins. Co., 1929-33; with Traders & Gen. Ins. Co., 1933-73, dir., Franklin Life Ins. Co., 1953-56, pres., chief exec. officer, 1956-73; founder Traders Indemnity Co., 1962; past pres. Tex. Assn. Fire & Casualty Cos. Mem. Mason (32 degree, Shriner), Pioneer Club, High Noon (Dallas) Club, Oak Cliff Shrine Club (pres.). Methodist. Home: 2032 W Five Mile Pky Dallas TX 75224-3608

LANGTON, BRYAN D., hotel executive. Chmn., CEO Holiday Inns, Inc., Memphis, Tenn. Office: Holiday Inn Inc 3796 Lamar Ave Memphis TN 38118 Office: Holiday Inn Worldwide 3 Ravinia Dr Ste 2000 Atlanta GA 30346-2149 Office: Holiday Inn Worldwide, Woluwe Off Pk 1 101 Rue Neerveld, 1200 Brussels Belgium

LANGTON, CLEVE SWANSON, advertising executive; b. N.Y.C., Sept. 1, 1950; s. Raymond Benedict and Viola (Swanson) L.; m. Patricia Scott, July 16, 1976; children: Elizabeth Renwick, Cleve, Jr. B.A., NYU, 1972; M.B.A. Columbia U., 1974. Product mgr. Gen. Foods Corp., White Plains, N.Y., 1974-76; sr. account exec. Dancer Fitzgerald Sample, N.Y.C., 1976-79; v.p., account supr. D'Arcy MacManus Masius, N.Y.C., 1979-83, corp. v.p. bus. devel. worldwide, DMB&B, N.Y.C., 1983-89; corp. sr. v.p. DDB Needham Worldwide, 1990-92; corp. exec. v.p. multinat. nat. client devel., 1993—. Bd. dirs. Columbia U. Grad. Sch. Bus., St. Bartholomew Sch. Club: Metropolitan (N.Y.C.). Office: DDB Needham Worldwide Inc 437 Madison Ave New York NY 10022-7001

LANGTON, RAYMOND BENEDICT, III, manufacturing company executive; b. N.Y.C., Oct. 26, 1944; s. Raymond B. II and Viola M. (Swanson) L.; m. Regina M. Rose, July 20, 1968; children: Raymond B. IV, Tyler J. BA in History, U. Va., 1966; MBA, U. Pa., 1971. Dir. sales and mktg. Continental Forest Industries (Continental Group), Greenwich, Conn., 1974-78, dir. planning and devel., 1978-79; v.p. mktg. bus. devel. Fram (Allied Signal), Providence, 1979-81, v.p. gen. mgr. div. indsl. filtration, 1981-83, v.p. ops., 1983-86; pres. SKF Automotive Products, King of Prussia, Pa., 1986-87, SKF Bearing Industries Co., King of Prussia, 1987-91; pres., chief exec. officer SKF USA Inc., King of Prussia, 1991—, also bd. dirs.; mem. regional adv. bd. First Fidelity Bank. Mem. Antifriction Bearing Mfrs. Assn. (treas. 1990, vice chmn., chmn. 1993). Office: SKF USA Inc 1100 1st Ave King Of Prussia PA 19406

LANGWAY, CHESTER CHARLES, JR., geological sciences educator; b. Worcester, Mass., Aug. 15, 1929; s. Chester Charles and Agnes Hedwig (McLush) L.; children: Nancy, Mary, JoAnn, Thomas. A.B., Boston U., 1955, MA., 1956; Ph.D., U. Mich., 1965; PhD (hon.), U. Bern, Switzerland, 1991. Research geologist, glaciologist U.S. Army Snow, Ice, and Permafrost Research Establishment, Wilmette, Ill., 1956-59; research geologist, glaciologist U.S. Army Cold Regions Research and Engring. Lab., Hanover, N.H., 1961-65, chief snow and ice br. research div., 1966-77; prof. geol. scis. SUNY-Buffalo, Amherst, 1975—, chmn. dept. geol. scis., 1975-90; cons. Ecology and Environ., Inc., Buffalo, 1981. Served with U.S. Army, 1946-48; with USAF, 1948-52. Recipient cert. of achievement Cold Regions Research and Engring. Lab., 1978; Mount Langway, Antarctica designated in his

honor by NSF, 1971. Fellow Am. Geophys. Union, Geol. Soc. Am., Artic Inst. N.Am.; mem. Royal Danish Acad. Arts & Scis., Internat. Glaciol. Soc., AAAS, N.Y. Acad. Scis., Collegium Disting. Alumni Boston U., Phi Kappa Phi. Office: SUNY Buffalo Dept Geology 4240 Ridge Lea Rd Buffalo NY 14226-1016

LANGWIG, JOHN EDWARD, retired wood science educator; b. Albany, N.Y., Mar. 5, 1924; s. Frank Irving and Arlene Stone (Dugan) L.; m. Margaret Jacquelyn Kirk, Aug. 31, 1946; 1 dau., Nancy Ann Langwig Davis. B.S., U. Mich., 1948; M.S., Coll. of Forestry, SUNY, Syracuse, 1968, Ph.D., 1971. Asst. to supt. Widdicomb Furniture Co., Grand Rapids, Mich., 1948-50; salesman John B. Hauf Furniture, Inc., Albany, N.Y., 1950-51; asst. mgr. furniture dept. Montgomery Ward Co., Menands, N.Y., 1951-52; office mgr. U.S. Plywood Corp., Syracuse, 1952-65; instr. wood products engring. SUNY Coll. Forestry, Syracuse, 1969-70; asst. prof. wood sci. Okla. State U. Stillwater, 1971-74; prof., head dept. forestry Okla. State U., 1974-81, prof. wood sci., wood products extension specialist, 1982-86, mem. faculty council, 1983-86; mem. Gov.'s Com. on Forest Practices, 1975-77. Contbr. articles to profl. jours. Served with AUS, 1943-45. NSF fellow, 1966-68. Mem. Soc. Am. Foresters, TAPPI, Forest Products Research Soc. (regional bd. dirs. 1983-89, regional rep. to nat. exec. bd. 1983-86), Soc. Wood Sci. and Tech., Okla. Acad. Sci., Okla. Forestry Assn. (bd. dirs. 1982-83), Council Forestry Sch. Execs., Sigma Xi, Xi Sigma Pi., Gamma Sigma Delta, Alpha Zeta, Phi Kappa Phi. Episcopalian. Home: 33 Liberty Cir Stillwater OK 74075-2015 Office: Okla State U Dept Forestry Stillwater OK 74078 *My graduate education began after a seventeen year career in the forest products industry. This additional education broadened my life, and opened up a rich new world of experience beyond my greatest expectations. I commend to all young people the pursuit of a maximum education, as one of life's most worthy efforts.*

LANGWORTHY, AUDREY HANSEN, state legislator; b. Grand Forks, N.D., Apr. 1, 1938; d. Edward H. and Arla (Kuhlman) Hansen; m. Asher C. Langworthy Jr., Sept. 8, 1962; children: Kristin H., Julia H. BS, U. Kans., 1960, MS, 1962; postgrad., Harvard U., 1989. Tchr. jr. high sch. Shawnee Mission Sch. Dist., Johnson County, Kans., 1963-65; councilperson City of Prairie Village, Kans., 1981-85; mem. Kans. State Senate, 1985—; del. Midwestern Conf. State Legislatures, 1989; alt. del. Nat. Conf. State Legislatures, 1985-87, del., 1987—, nominating com., 1990-92. City co-chmn. Kassebaum for U.S. Senate, Prairie Village, 1978; pres. Jr. League Kansas City, Mo., 1977, Kansas City Eye Bank, 1982-85; mem. bd. Greater Kansas City ARC, 1975—, pres., 1984, chmn. midwestern adv. coun., 1985-86, nat. bd. govs., 1987-93; mem. Johnson County Community Coll. Found., 1989—; mem. Leadership Kans., Gateway Today Program, 1991; bd. dirs. Kans. Wildlife & Parks Fund; trustee Found. on Aging, 1992—; mem. nat. adv. panel Child Care Action Campaign, 1988—. Recipient Outstanding Vol. award Cmty. Svcs. Award Found., 1983, Confidence in Edn. award Friends of Edn., 1984, Pub. Svc. award as Kans. Legislator of Yr., Hallmark Polit. Action Com., 1991, Clara Barton honor award Greater Kansas City ARC, Intergovtl. Leadership award League Kans. Municipalities, 1994. Mem. LWV, Women's Pub. Svc. Network, U. Kans. Alumni Assn. Episcopalian. Avocations: hunting, running, family. Home: 6324 Ash St Shawnee Mission KS 66208-1369

LANGWORTHY, EVERETT WALTER, association executive, natural gas exploration company executive; b. West Springfield, Mass., Aug. 17, 1918; s. Walter Carr and Lucy Anne (Laurent) L.; m. Mary Jane Mateer, Nov. 30, 1946 (dec. Oct. 1966); children—John Alan, Jo Ann Langworthy Sears, Robert Carr; m. Joan E. Scott, Feb. 27, 1982; stepchildren—Russell, Michael, Gregory. B.A., U. Mass., 1940; M.A., George Washington U., 1964; grad., Nat. War Coll., 1964. Commd. 2d lt. U.S. Army, 1943; commd. capt. U.S. Air Force, 1947; advanced through grades to col., 1963, ret., 1972; v.p. ops. Meteor Aero Inc., Gaithersburg, Md., 1972-76; sec. contest and record bd. Nat. Aero. Assn., Washington, 1976-80; exec. v.p. Nat. Aero. Assn., 1980—; v.p. LABCO Inc., Martinsburg, W.Va., 1974—; gen. ptnr. M&E Assocs., Gaithersburg, 1976—; dir. Acad. Model Aeronautics, Reston, Va. Contbr. articles and columns on aerospace activities to profl. publs. U.S. rep. Fedn. Aeronautique Internat., Paris, 1980—. Decorated DFC, Air medal African Campaign award, Berlin Air Life medal; recipient Paul Tissandier diploma Fedn. Aeronautique Internationale, 1987. Mem. Nat. Aviation Club (elder statesman aviation 1990), Aero Club Washington, Air Force Assn., Ret. Officers Assn., Soaring Soc. Am. (bd. dirs. 1980—), U.S. Hang Gliding Assn. (bd. dirs. 1980—), VFW. Republican. Club: Lakewood Country (Rockville, Md.). Avocations: golf; writing. Home: 13701 Charity Ct Germantown MD 20874-2965 Office: Nat Aeronautic Assn 1815 Ft Myer Dr Arlington VA 22209-1805

LANGWORTHY, ROBERT BURTON, lawyer; b. Kansas City, Mo., Dec. 24, 1918; s. Herman Moore and Minnie (Leach) L.; m. Elizabeth Ann Miles, Jan. 2, 1942; children: David Robert, Joan Elizabeth Langworthy Tomek, Mark Burton. A.B., Princeton U., 1940; J.D., Harvard U., 1943. Bar: Mo. 1943, U.S. Supreme Ct 1960. Practiced in Kansas City, 1943—; assoc., then mem. and v.p. Linde, Thomson, Langworthy, Kohn & Van Dyke, P.C., 1943-91; pres., mng. shareholder Blackwood Langworthy & Schmelzer, P.C., Kansas City, Mo., 1991—; lectr. on probate, law sch. CLE courses U. Mo. Kansas City. Mem. bd. editors Harvard Law Rev., 1941-43; contbr. chpts. to Guardian Desk Book of Mo. Bar. Mem. edn. appeal bd. U.S. Dept. Edn., 1982-86; commr. Housing Authority Kansas City, 1963-71, chmn., 1969-71; chmn. Bd. Election Commrs. Kansas City, 1973-77; chmn. bd. West Ctrl. area YMCA, 1966; mem. bd. Mid-Am. region YMCA, 1970-83, vice chmn., 1970-73, chmn., 1973-78; pres. Met. Bd. Kansas City (Mo.) YMCA (now YMCA of Greater Kansas City), 1965, bd. dirs., 1965—, mem. nat. bd. 1971-78, 79-83; bd. dirs. YMCA of the Rockies, 1974—, bd. sec., 1994—; chmn. bd. trustees Sioux Indian YMCAs, 1983—; bd. dirs. Armed Svcs. YMCA, 1984-85; pres. Met. Area Citizens Edn., 1969-72; chmn. Citizens Assn. Kansas City, 1967; bd. dirs. Project Equality Kans.-Mo., 1967-80, pres., 1970-72, treas., 1972-73, sec., 1973-76; 1st v.p. Human Resources Corp. Kansas City, 1969-71, 72-73, bd. dirs., 1965-73; hon. v.p. Am. Sunday Sch. Union (now Am. Missionary Fellowship), 1965—; vice chmn. bd. trustees Kemper Mil. Sch., 1966-73; U.S. del. YMCA World Coun., Buenos Aires, 1977, Estes Park, Colo., 1981, Nyborg, Denmark, 1985; bd. dirs. Mo. Rep. Club, 1960—; del., mem. platform com. Nat. Rep. Conv., 1960; Rep. nominee for U.S. Congress, 1964; mem. gen. assembly Com. on Representation Presbyn., 1991—, moderator, 1993-94; commr. to gen. assembly Presbyn. Ch., 1984; moderator Heartland Presbyn., 1984. Lt. (j.g.) USNR, 1943-46; now capt. Res. ret. Mem. ABA, Kansas City Bar Assn. (chmn. probate law com. 1988-90, living will com. 1989-91), Mo. State Bar (chmn. probate and trust com. 1983-85, chmn. sr. lawyers com. 1991-93), Lawyers Assn. Kansas City, Harvard Law Sch. Assn. Mo. (v.p. 1973-74, pres. 1974-75, 85-87), Univ. Club (Kansas City), Leawood (Kans.) Country Club. Presbyterian (elder). Home: 616 W 69th St Kansas City MO 64113-1937 Office: 1220 Washington St Ste 300 Kansas City MO 64105-2245

LANGWORTHY, THOMAS ALLAN, microbiologist, educator; b. Oak Park, Ill., Aug. 7, 1943; s. Thomas Earl and Jean Carolyn (Hruby) L.; m. Pamela Joyce Tanis, May 15, 1965 (div. 1985); children; Jocelyn Ann, Jennifer Elise; m. Jane Rae Heckenlively, Sept. 15, 1988. AB, Grinnell Coll., 1965; PhD, U. Kans., 1971. Asst. prof. U. S.D., Vermillion, 1973-78, assoc. prof., 1978-82, prof., 1982-91, prof., chair, 1991—; Alexander von Humboldt preistrager and guest prof. U. Regensburg, Germany, 1984-85; cons. EG&G Idaho, Idaho Falls, 1984—. Contbr. articles to profl. jours. and chpts. to books; mem. editorial bd. Applied and Environ. Microbiology, 1987—. Fellow Am. Acad. Microbiology; mem. Am. Soc. for Microbiology, AAAS, Internat. Orgn. for Mycoplasmology, Sigma Xi. Office: U SD Sch Medicine 414 E Clark St Vermillion SD 57069-2307

LANGWORTHY, WILLIAM CLAYTON, college official; b. Watertown, N.Y., Sept. 3, 1936; s. Harold Greene and Carolyn (Peach) L.; m. Margaret Joan Amos, Sept. 6, 1958; children: Kenneth, Geneva. B.S. magna cum laude, Tufts U., 1958; Ph.D., U. Calif.-Berkeley, 1962. Asst. prof. Alaska Meth. U., Anchorage, 1962-65; assoc. prof., 1967-72, prof., 1972-73, assoc. dean Sch. Letters Arts and Scis., 1970-73; prof. chemistry Calif. Poly. State U., San Luis Obispo, 1973-76, head dept. chemistry, 1973-76; dean Sch. sci. and Math Calif. Poly. State U., San Luis Obispo, 1976-83; v.p. acad. affairs Ft. Lewis Coll., Durango, Colo., 1983—. Author: monograph Environmental Educa-

tion, 1971; contbr. articles to profl. jours. Treas. Coun. Concerned Citizens, Inc., Arroyo Grande, Calif., 1976-83; mem. Clean Air Coalition, San Luis Obispo, 1978-83; active Mozart Festival, 1981-82; bd. dirs. Durango Choral Soc., 1984-93, bd. dirs. Durango Stage Co., 1990—, pres., 1992-94. Mem. AAAS, AAHE, Am. Chem. Soc., Coun. Colls. Arts and Scis. (bd. dirs. 1982), Sierra Club, Phi Beta Kappa, Sigma Xi, Kappa Mu Epsilon, Phi Kappa Phi.

LANHAM, BETTY BAILEY, anthropologist, educator; b. Statesville, N.C., Aug. 12, 1922; d. Clyde B. and Naomi (Bailey) L. B.S., U. Va., 1944, M.A., 1947; Ph.D., Syracuse U., 1962. Mem. faculty River Falls State Tchrs. Coll., 1948-49, U. Md., 1949-50, Wakayama U., Japan, 1951-52, Randolph Macon Women's Coll., 1954-55, Oswego State Tchrs. Coll., 1956-58, Hamilton Coll., 1961-62, Ind. U., 1962-65, Western Mich. U., 1965-67, Albany Med. Coll., 1967-70, Guyana U., 1969-70; prof. anthropology Indiana U. of Pa., 1970-88, prof. emeritus, 1988—. Contbr. articles to jours. Wenner-Gren Found. for Anthrop. Research predoctoral fellow, 1951-52; AAUW predoctoral research fellow, 1959-60. Mem. Am. Anthrop. Assn., Assn. Asian Studies, Soc. Psychol. Anthropology, Caribbean Studies Assn. Democrat. Home: 2529 Willard Dr Charlottesville VA 22903-4225

LANHAM, URLESS NORTON, curator; b. Grainfield, Kans., Oct. 17, 1918; s. Urless R. and Frankie V. (Norton) L.; m. Caroline Jane Combs, Sept. 1, 1945; children: Robert, Margaret, Carl. B.A. cum laude, U. Colo., 1940; Ph.D., U. Calif., Berkeley, 1948; postgrad., UCLA, La Jolla, 1940-42, U. Chgo., 1945-46. Asst. prof., research asso. U. Mich., Ann Arbor, 1948-62; asso. prof. Monteith Coll., Wayne State U., 1959-62; vis. curator, asso. curator entomology U. Colo. Mus., Boulder, 1962-73, curator, 1973-89, prof. natural history, 1973-89, prof. emeritus, 89—; mem. Tunisian expdn., 1976; asst. prof. biophysics U. Colo. Med. Center, Denver, 1968-71; vis. lectr. Arctic-Alpine Inst., Dept. Devel. Biology, 1966-67; vis. investigator Carnegie Mus. Pitts., 1982; editor biol. sci. curriculum studies Am. Inst. Biol. Scis., 1963-66; cons. Smithsonian Instn., Washington, 1967. Author: The Fishes, 1962, The Insects, 1964, Origins of Modern Biology, 1968, German transl., 1972; The Bone Hunters, 1973, 91, The Enchanted Mesa, 1974, The Sapphire Planet, 1978, transl. into Arabic and Spanish; also tech. papers; adv. editor, Columbia U. Press, 1964-72. Served to capt. USAAF, 1942-46, PTO. Mem. Kans. Entomol. Soc., Phi Beta Kappa, Sigma Xi. Home: 2670 Stephens Rd Boulder CO 80303-5762 Office: U Colo Museum Campus Box 218 Boulder CO 80309

LANIAK, DAVID KONSTANTYN, utility company executive; b. Rochester, N.Y., Sept. 10, 1935; s. Konstantyn and Anastasia (Andrieve) L.; m. Carol Hammond, Sept. 19, 1959; children: Mark, Todd. BEE, Rochester Inst. Tech., 1958; MBA, U. Rochester, 1985. Elec. engr. Rochester Gas and Electric Corp., 1959-75, supt. meter dept., 1975-78, div. supt., 1978-80, v.p. electric system planning, operation, 1980-82, v.p. corp. planning, 1982-87, sr. v.p. gas, electric distbn., corp. planning, 1988-90, sr. v.p. gas, electric distbn., customer svcs., 1990-94; exec. v.p., COO, 1994—; bd. dirs. Rochester Gas & Electric Corp., Empire State Energy Rsch. Corp., Telog Instruments, Inc. ACC Corp. Mem. IEEE, Rochester Engring. Soc. Republican. Avocations: tennis, golf, fishing. Home: 10 Harvest Ln Rush NY 14543-9764 Office: Rochester Gas & Electric Corp 89 East Ave Rochester NY 14649-0001

LANIER, BOB, professional sports team executive, former basketball player; b. Buffalo, Sept. 10, 1948. Student, St. Bonaventure U., 1966-70. Basketball player Detroit Pistons, 1970-79, Milw. Bucks, 1980-84; actor various commls., 1984—; asst. basketball coach Golden State Warriors, 1994—. Mem. NBA All-Star Team, 1972-79, 82; named Most Valuable Player NBA All-Star Team, 1974. Office: Golden State Warriors Oakland Coliseum Oakland CA 94621-1918*

LANIER, JAMES ALFRED, III, aquarium administrator; b. Norfolk, Va., Sept. 28, 1941; s. James Alfred and Mary Elizabeth (Baughan) L.; m. Hope Baldwin, AUg. 1, 1964; children: Hope Baldwin Holly, David Ludwell, Andrew Lee. BA, U. Va., Charlottsville, 1963; MA, William and Mary Coll., Williamsburg, Va., 1972, PhD, 1981. Lt. Y.S. Naval Res., N.Y., 1963-67; edn. program dir. Va. Inst. Marine Sci., Gloucenter Pt., Va., 1971-80; dir. ednl. programs N.J. Marine Sci. Consortium, Princeton, N.J., 1980-82; dir. N.C. Aquarium Ft. Fisher, Kure Beach, N.C., 1982—; pres. elect Friends Pub. Radio, Wilmington, N.C., 1990-91; immed. past pres. Greater Wilmington C. of C, WIlmington, N.C., 1990. Contbr. articles to profl. jours. Recipient Gov's. award, Governor N.C., Raleigh, 1990, Pres. award Nat. Marine Educators Assn., 1989. Mem. Wilmington Rotary Club. Democrat. Episcopalian. Avocations: aquariums, bonsai, gardening. Home: 4212 Appleton Way Wilmington NC 28412-7312 Office: North Carolina Aquarium PO Box 130 Kure Beach NC 28449-0130

LANIER, JOHN HICKS, apparel company executive; b. Nashville, Apr. 12, 1940; s. Sartain and Claudia Gwynn (Whitson) L.; m. Jane M. Darden, Oct. 15, 1966; children: Jay, Liza, Stephen. B.A., Vanderbilt U., 1962; M.B.A., Harvard U., 1964. Pres., chmn., chief exec. officer Oxford Industries, Inc., Atlanta, 1981—; bd. dirs. Shaw Industries, Inc., Dalton, Ga., Crawford & Co., Trust Co. of Ga. Assocs. Trustee, Henrietta Egleston Hosp. for Children, The Westminster Schs., Atlanta; bd. dirs. Piedmont Hosp., Atlanta. Served with USAFR, 1964-65. Mem. Am. Apparel Mfrs. Assn. (past bd. dirs.). Republican. Office: Oxford Industries Inc 222 Piedmont Ave NE Atlanta GA 30308-3306

LANIER, ROBERT C. (BOB LANIER), mayor; b. Baytown, Tex., 1931. Student, Lee Coll., Univ. N.Mex.; grad. in law with hons., U. Tex. Former reporter The Baytown Sun and The Austin Am.-Statesman.; law assoc. Baker & Botts; then pvt. practice; mayor Houston, 1992—. Chmn. Tex. Highway and Pub. Transp. Commn., Houston Met. Transit Authority; founder Houston Community Coll.; founder, chmn. Bd. Hope Ctr. Wilderness Camp. Office: Office of the Mayor PO Box 1562 Houston TX 77251-1562

LANIER, THOMAS, chemical and export company executive; b. Cienfuegos, Cuba, Sept. 18, 1923; came to U.S., 1938; s. Joseph and Irene (Medina) L.; divorced; children: Margie, Robert, George, Thomas Emil; m. Julie Gonzalez, May 1, 1980. Student, Bowens Bus. Coll., 1939-40, Latin Am. Inst., 1940-41; BBA, Havana U., 1948; postgrad., St. Mary's U., San Antonio, 1955. Mgr. sales Joskes of Tex., San Antonio, 1949-51; mgr. office investment corp. San Antonio, 1951-55; v.p. internat. sales Sun-X Internat. Export Corp. San Antonio, 1955-59; pres. Sun-X Internat. Ltd., Houston, 1963-66; pres., mgr. Tri-X Internat. Co., North Bergen, 1963—; pres., chief exec. officer Lanier Shipping Co., Inc., North Bergen, N.J., 1966-87; internat. trade cons. Falor Assocs. Inc., North Bergen, 1987—; Factory Assocs. & Exporters, East Hanover, N.J., 1987—. Served with USAF, 1943-45. Recipient E award U.S. Govt. 1963. Mem. Am. Soc. Internat. Execs., C. of C. of Shipping (pres. North Bergen 1982-88), Bogota (N.J.) Tenants Assn., Am. Radio Relay League. Democrat. Roman Catholic. Avocations: amateur radion, stamp collecting, lecturing. Office: Tri-X Internat Co 7500 Bergenline Ave North Bergen NJ 07047-5401

LANIGAN, DENIS GEORGE, retired advertising agency executive; b. Eng., Jan. 25, 1926; widowed; 2 children. Ed., Cambridge (Eng.) U. With J. Walter Thompson Co., 1952-87; mgr. J. Walter Thompson Co., Frankfurt, Germany, 1959-64; mng. dir. J. Walter Thompson Co., London, 1964-74; pres. European div. J. Walter Thompson Co., 1974-80; vice chmn. adminstrn. J. Walter Thompson Co., N.Y.C., 1980-82; dir., chief operating officer J. Walter Thompson Co. and JWT Group, N.Y.C., 1982-86; bd. dirs. Marks & Spencer, U.K., 1987—, TSB Bank plc, 1987-90; chmn. MM&K Ltd., U.K., 1988-91; chmn. N.Am. Adv. Group; mem. Brit. Overseas Trade Bd. Office: Michael House, 47 Baker St, London W1A 1DN, England

LANIGAN, ROBERT J., packaging company executive; b. Bklyn., Apr. 26, 1928; s. John F. and Katherine (Sheehy) L.; m. Mary Elizabeth McCormick, Dec. 30, 1950; children—J. Kenneth, Betty Jane Lanigan Snavely, Kathryn Ann Lanigan Pilewskie, Jeanne Marie Lanigan Schafer, Suzanne Marie Lanigan Georgetti. A.B. in Econs., St. Francis Coll., N.Y.C., 1950; B.A. (hon.), Nathaniel Hawthorne Coll., Antrim, N.H., 1979. Pres. domestic ops. Owens-Ill., Inc., Toledo, 1976-79, pres. internat. ops., 1979-82, pres., 1982-86, chief oper. officer, 1982-84, chief exec. officer, 1984-90, chmn. bd., 1984-

91, chmn. emeritus, 1991—; bd. dirs. Chrysler Corp., Detroit, Sonat, Inc., Birmingham, Ala., Dun & Bradstreet Corp., N.Y.C., Sonat Offshore Drilling, Inc., Houston. Pres. Toledo Symphony Orch.; hon. trustee Toledo Mus. Art. Recipient achievement award St. Francis Coll. Alumni Assn., 1980. Mem. Burning Tree (Bethesda, Md.) Club, Quail Creek Country Club (Naples, Fla.), Belmont Country Club (Perrysburg, Ohio). Roman Catholic. Avocations: fishing; hunting; golf; tennis. Home: 13145 Valewood Dr Naples FL 33999 Office: Owens-Ill Inc 1 Seagate Toledo OH 43666-0001

LANING, J. HALCOMBE, retired computer scientist; b. Kansas City, Mo., Feb. 14, 1920; s. J. Halcombe and Mary Alice (Knox) L.; m. Betty Arleen Kolb, June 27, 1943; children: Christine, James, Susan, Linda. Student, Kansas City Jr. Coll., 1936-38; SBChemE, MIT, 1940, postgrad., 1941, PhD in Applied Math., 1947; postgrad., Brown U., 1941-42. Engr. Watertown (Mass.) Arsenal Govt. U.S., 1942-45; group leader instrumentation lab. MIT, Cambridge, 1945-73; head dept. C.S. Draper Lab., Cambridge, 1973-88, sr. tech. advisor, 1988-89. Author: Random Processes in Automatic Control, 1956; creator computer programs; patentee in field. C.S. Draper fellow, 1982-85. Mem. NAE, Assn. Computing Machinery, Am. Math. Soc., Soc. for Indsl. and Applied Math., AIAA, IEEE, Inst. Mgmt. Scis.

LANING, RICHARD BOYER, naval officer, writer, retired; b. Washington, Jan. 1, 1918; s. Richard Henry and Marguerite (Boyer) L., m. Ruth Richmond, Sept. 5, 1942; children: Christine, Lucille. BSEE, U.S. Naval Acad., 1940; MS in Biophysics & Nuclear Physics, U. Calif., Berkeley, 1950; postgrad., U.S. Nat. War Coll., 1960. Officer USS Yorktown, 1940-41; officer USS Hornet Boolittle Raid, Battle of Midway, Tokyo, 1941-42; exec. officer USS Salmon Pacific Fleet, 1942-44; nuclear weapons planner OPNAV, Washington, 1953-54; commdg. officer 5 subs. including commng. 2d nuclear sub. USS Seawolf, 1956; first Polaris tender USS Proteus USN, Scotland, 1960-62; asst. chief of staff Submarines Pacific USN, Pearl Harbor, Hawaii, 1962-63; ret. USN, 1963; corp. planner, mgr. biotech. programs United Aircraft Corp., Hartford, Conn., 1963-73; life ins. underwriter Equitable of Iowa, Orlando, Fla., 1973-77; writer Orlando, Fla., 1977—; cons. in field. Contbr. articles to profl. jours. Mem. U.S. Naval Inst., Naval Acad. Alumni, Fleet Res. Assn., Navy League, Adm. Nimitz Fedn., U. Calif. Alumni, Futurist Soc., Greater Orlando C. of C., Nat. Space Soc., Navy Submarine League, Univ. Club Winter Park, Mil. Order of World Wars, Retired Officers Assn. Avocations: swimming, racquetball, computer art. Home and Office: 5955 Turnbull Dr Orlando FL 32822-1740

LANING, ROBERT COMEGYS, retired physician, former naval officer; b. Haiti, Sept. 20, 1922; s. Richard Henry and Marguerite C. (Boyer) L.; m. Alice Teresa Lech, Sept. 9, 1961; 1 dau., Maria Laning LeBerre. BA, U. Va.; MA, Ohio State U.; MD, Jefferson Med. Coll., 1948. Diplomate: Nat. Bd. Med. Examiners, Am. Bd. Surgery. Intern Jefferson Hosp., Phila., 1948-50; enlisted USN, 1950, advanced through grades to rear adm., 1973, mem. astronaut recovery teams, 1960-66; chief of surgery Naval Hosp., San Diego, 1967-71; med. dir. Naval Hosp., Yokosuka, Japan, 1972-73; med. officer Pacific Fleet, 1973-75; asst. chief Bur. Medicine and Surgery for Operational Med. Support, Washington, 1975-77; dep. dir. surg. service Cen. Office, VA, Washington, 1977-79, dir. surg. service, 1979-87. Fellow ACS (gov. 1984-87); mem. Am. Assn. Mil. Surgeons, Soc. Med. Cons. to Armed Forces (pres. 1988-89, bd. dirs.), Ret. Officers Assn. Roman Catholic. Home: 6532 Sunny Hill Ct Mc Lean VA 22101-1639

LANITIS, TONY ANDREW, market researcher; b. Port Said, Egypt, May 29, 1926; came to U.S., 1929; s. Christopher and Helen (Joanides) L.; m. Anne Mortimer, Feb. 4, 1947 (div. 1951); 1 son, Philip; m. Gertrude Letesse, June 14, 1959; 1 dau., Melissa. BS in Econs., NYU, 1950, MA, 1951. Assoc. research dir. Morey, Humm & Warwick, N.Y.C., 1954-55; sr. group supr. Colgate-Palmolive Co., N.Y.C., 1955-60; sr. v.p. SSC & B: Lintas Worldwide, Inc., N.Y.C., 1960-89, dir. rsch., 1960-87, dir. market planning and rsch., 1987-89; market planning and rsch. cons. N.Y.C., 1989—; instr. Ulster County C.C., 1993—; guest lectr. NYU, 1970-72, Pace Coll., 1970-73, L.I. U., 1968-70; lectr. in field. Cons. editor Psychology and Mktg. Jour., 1983—; contbr. articles to profl. jours. Bd. dirs. Port Chester (N.Y.) Coun. Arts, 1981-89, Unison Art and Learning Ctr., New Paltz, N.Y., 1990-92. Served with U.S. Army, 1944-46. Named Marketer of Month Kansas City, Am. Mktg. Assn, 1972. Mem. Am. Mktg. Assn., Advt. Research Found., Advt. Agy. Research Dirs. Council, Am. Psychol. Assn., Inst. Mgmt. Sci., Market Research Council, Communications Research Council. Club: Commerce. Home: 59 Lake Hill Rd Kingston NY 12401-8440

LANKFORD, DUANE GAIL, investment banker, mountaineer; b. Ft. Collins, Colo., July 18, 1932; s. William Oliver and Mary Martha (Lago) L.; m. Eleanor Polly, June 18, 1955 (div. 1983); children: Scott, Kurt Edwin, Rebecca Ann; m. Margaret Ekkanasing, Nov. 8, 1991. Student, Colo. State Coll. of Edn., 1950-51, Denver U., 1952-55. Lic. stockbroker over 40 states security commns. Mgr. Dial Fin., Denver, 1953-59; mgr. investment banking Peters Writer & Christianson, Denver, 1959-60, E.I. DuPont De Nemours, Denver, 1960; mgr. mcpl. investment banking Bache & Co., Denver, L.A., N.Y.C., 1961-68; v.p. sales Fin. Programs, Inc., San Francisco, 1968-69; fin. advisor Lankford & Co., Denver, 1969; mgr. muni bonds W.E. Hutton & Co., Denver, 1969-71; owner/operator Lankford & Co., Denver, 1972—, The Wilderness Inst./Lankford Mountain Guides, Denver, 1978—; chmn. Denver Lenders Exch., 1957-58; cons. advisor numerous cities, towns, states and corps.; expert witness in investment banking and mountaineering; cons. numerous legal firms; cons./advisor numerous fed. agys. Contbr. articles to profl. jours. Worldwide mountaineer numerous maj. peaks. Mem. Am. Alpine Club, Pioneers. Republican. Avocations: internat. mountaineering, internat. travel, philosophy, opera, classical music.

LANKFORD, FRANCIS GREENFIELD, JR., education educator emeritus; b. Morattico, Va., Feb. 14, 1906; s. Francis Greenfield and Alma (Coulbourne) L.; m. Florence Fleet, June 4, 1935; children: William Fleet, Francis Greenfield III. B.S., Randolph-Macon Coll., 1928, LL.D., 1959; M.A., U. Va., 1932, Ph.D., 1938. High sch. prin., 1928-31; from instr. to prof. edn. U. Va., Charlottesville, 1932-55; dir. research Richmond Pub. Schs., 1943-44; pres. Longwood Coll., Farmville, Va., 1955-65; prof. edn., dir. office instl. analysis U. Va., 1965-72, sesquicentennial scholar, 1971-72, Commonwealth prof., 1972, prof. edn. emeritus, 1972; edn. adviser Ford Found.-U. Chgo. Pakistan Edn. Project, 1962-63; Dir. study high sch. edn. Va. C. of C., 1942-43; dir. div. ednl. research internat. U. Va., 1951-55; mem. Charlottesville (Va.) Sch. Bd., 1952-55. Co-author: Mathematics for the Consumer, 1947, 2d edit., 1953, Basic Ideas of Mathematics, 1953, Algebra One and Algebra Two, 1955, Essential Mathematics, 1961, 2d edit., 1967, 3d edit., 1975, Contemporary Algebra I, 1962, Contemporary Algebra II, 1963, Algebra One, 1969, 72, Algebra Two, 1969, 72, 77, Numbers and Operations, 1970, Consumer Mathematics, 1971, 2d edit., 1974, author, 1981, also articles.; Departmental editor: Math. Tchr, 1953-57. Campaign chmn. Prince Edward Community Chest, 1958. Recipient Disting. Alumnus award U. Va. Sch. Edn., 1977; Gen. Edn. Bd. fellow U. Mich., 1939-40. Mem. Nat. Council Tchrs. Math. (v.p. 1955-57), Raven Soc., Phi Beta Kappa, Omicron Delta Kappa, Phi Delta Kappa (distinguished service award U. Va. chpt. 1944). Democrat. Home: 2600 Barracks Rd Apt 396 Charlottesville VA 22901-2196

LANKHOF, FREDERIK JAN, publishing executive; b. Mar. 4, 1949; came to U.S., 1983; s. Adriaan Pieter and Janny (Baas) L; m. Joyce Ganimian, May 31, 1983; children: Lauren, Nora. Attended, U. Amsterdam. Editorial asst. Meulenhoff Pub. Co., Amsterdam, The Netherlands, 1968-72; free-lance copy editor, proofreader, translator The Netherlands, 1972-83; bookseller, libr. asst. N.Y.C., 1983-86; pres., owner i.b.d., Ltd., Kinderhook, N.Y., 1989—; pres. E.J. Brill (USA), Inc., Kinderhook, 1986—; Nedbook New York, Inc., Kinderhook, 1990—; Internat. Bur. Fin. Documentation, Kinderhook, 1993—. Trustee Kinderhook Meml. Libr., 1994—. Avocations: reading, writing, translations, publishing. Home: 24 Hudson St Kinderhook NY 12106 Office: E J Brill USA Inc 24 Hudson St Box 467 Kinderhook NY 12106

LANKTON, STEPHEN RYAN, family therapist, management consultant; b. Lansing, Mich., May 29, 1947; s. Stanley R. and Mary Lou (Cook) L.; children: Stephen, Shawn Michael, Alicia Michelle. Student, Lansing Community Coll., 1966-68; BA, Mich. State U., 1972; MSW (scholar), U. Mich., 1974. Diplomate Am. Bd. Examiners in Clin. Social Work, NASW,

Am. Hypnosis Bd. for Clin. Social Work; lic. marriage and family therapist, Fla. Youth outreach YMCA, Lansing, 1969-70; residential youth treatment Camp Highfields, Inc., Onondaga, Mich., 1970-73; instr. psychology Jackson (Mich.) Community Coll., 1974-78; clin. social worker Family Services of Jackson, 1974-78; mem. tng. staff. Huron Valley Inst., Dexter, Mich., 1978-79; pvt. practice psychology Gulf Breeze, Fla., 1980—; adj. instr. psychology U. West Fla., 1980—. Author: Practical Magic: The Clinical Application of Neuro Linguistic Programming, 1980; editor Ericksonian Monographs, 1984—; author: The Answer Within: A Clinical Framework of Ericksonian Hypnotherapy, 1983, Enchantment and Intervention in Family Therapy: Training in Ericksonian Approaches, 1986, Tales of Enchantment: A Collection of Goal Directed Metaphors for Adults and Children in Therapy, 1989, The Blammo-Surprise!: A Story to Help Children Overcome Fear, 1988. Fellow Am. Acad. Pain Mgmt., Am. Assn. Marriage and Family Therapy (approved supr., clin. mem.); mem. Internat. Transactional Analysis Assn., Acad. Cert. Social Workers, Soc. Clin. and Exptl. Hypnosis, Am. Acad. Phychotherapists, Internat. Soc. Hypnosis, Fla. Soc. Clin. Phynosis, Am. Soc. Clin. Hypnosis (approved cons.), Am. Family Therapy Assn. (clin. teaching mem.). Avocation: scuba diving. Office: PO Box 958 Gulf Breeze FL 32562-0958

LANMON, DWIGHT PIERSON, museum director; b. Pueblo, Colo., July 28, 1938; s. Ira Dwight and Elaine Glea Pierson (Curtis) L.; m. Ann Lorraine Welling, Jan. 10, 1970. Student, Knox Coll., 1956-58; B.A., U. Colo., 1960; postgrad., UCLA, 1961-66; M.A., U. Del., 1968. Asst. curator, assoc. curator, and in charge of conservation Winterthur Mus., Del., 1968-73; dep. dir. Corning Mus. Glass, N.Y., 1973-81, dir., 1981-92; CEO, dir., trustee Winterthur (Del.) Mus., 1992—; trustee Rockwell Mus., Corning, 1983-92, pres., 1988-92, chmn. exec. com., 1988-92, acting dir., 1986-88; trustee Corning Mus. Glass, 1981-95. Author: (with Arlene Palmer) John Frederick Amelung, 1976, 2d edit. 1981, (with Paul Hollister) Paperweights, 1978, (with David B. Whitehouse) Glass in the Robert Lehman Collection, 1993. Winterthur fellow, 1966-68. Fellow Soc. Antiquaries of London; mem. Internat. Assn. History of Glass (sec.-gen. 1981-85), Internat. Coun. Mus., Assn. Art Mus. Dirs., Am. Assn. Mus., Census of Stained Glass (dir. 1980-92), Paperweight Collectors Assn. (bd. dirs. 1991-92), Walpole Soc., Blair House Fine Arts Com., Chevaliers de Tastevin. Office: Henry Francis Du Pont Winterthur Mus RR 52 Winterthur DE 19735

LANNAMANN, RICHARD STUART, executive recruiting consultant; b. Cin., Sept. 4, 1947; s. Frank E. and Grace I. (Tomlinson) L. AB in Econs., Yale U., 1969; MBA, Harvard U., 1973; divorced; children: Thomas Cleveland, Edward Payne, John Stewart. Investment analyst U.S. Trust Co. N.Y., N.Y.C., 1969-71; rsch. analyst Smith, Barney & Co., N.Y.C., 1973-75, 2d v.p., 1975-77, v.p. successor firm rsch. dir. Smith Barney Harris Upham & Co., 1977-78; v.p. Russell Reynolds Assocs., Inc., N.Y.C., 1978-83, mng. dir. 1983-86, 87—; sr. v.p. Mgmt. Asset Corp., Westport, Conn., 1986-87. Dir. Boy's Choir Harlem. Mem. N.Y. Soc. Security Analysts, Internat. Soc. of Fin. Analysts, Assn. for Investment Mgmt. and Rsch., Inst. Chartered Fin. Analysts, Riverside Yacht Club, Yale Club of N.Y., Links Club. Home: 51 Forest Ave Old Greenwich CT 06870-1526 Office: 200 Park Ave New York NY 10166-0001

LANNER, MICHAEL, research administrator, consultant; b. Montreal, Que., Can., Sept. 14, 1943; came to U.S., 1969; s. Hyman Alter and Anne P. (Rasnikopf) L.; m. Bluma Pauline Weiskopf, Dec. 27, 1946; children: Brian, Jennifer, Lisa. BS, Loyola U., Montreal, Que., Can., 1968. Cert. rsch. adminstr. Sr. rsch. technician McGill U., Montreal, 1964-69; sr. rsch. assoc. Beth Israel Hosp., Boston, 1969-80, rsch. mgr., 1980-84, deputy dir. rsch., 1984-88, dir. rsch., 1988—; pvt. practice Boston, 1987—; instr. in medicine Harvard Medical Sch., 1992—. Contbr. articles to Biochemistry, Diabetes, Nature. Active Stoughton (Mass.) Town Meeting, 1985—, Stoughton Youth Commn., 1988—; mem. Stoughton Sch. Com., 1989—. Grantee NIH, 1980—, 1990. mem. Soc. Rsch. Adminstrs. (bd. dirs., sec 1990-91), Mass. Soc. Med. Rsch. (mem. policy bd. 1989—). Achievements include patents for Convertible Animal Cage, Insert for Animal Cage. Office: Beth Israel Hosp 330 Brookline Ave Boston MA 02215-5491

LANNERT, ROBERT CORNELIUS, manufacturing company executive; b. Chgo., Mar. 24, 1940; s. Robert Carl and Anna Martha (Cornelius) L.; m. Kathleen A. O'Toole, July 10, 1965; children: Jacqueline, Krista, Kevin, Meredith. B.S. in Indsl. Mgmt., Purdue U., 1963; M.B.A., Northwestern U., 1967; grad. Advanced Mgmt. Program, Harvard U., 1978. With Navistar Internat. Transp. Corp. (formerly Internat. Harvester), Chgo., 1963—; staff asst. overseas fin., 1967-70; asst. mgr., treas. and contr. IH Finanz AG, Zurich, Switzerland, 1970-72; mgr. overseas fin. corp. hdqrs. Navistar Internat. Transp. Corp., Chgo., 1972-76, asst. treas., 1976-79; v.p., treas. Navistar Internat. Corp., Chgo., 1979-90, exec. v.p., chief fin. officer, 1990—, also bd. dirs.; bd. dirs. NITC, Harbour Assurance Co., Bermuda, Navistar Fin. Corp., Chgo. Mem. adv. bd. to dean Krannert Sch. Purdue U. Mem. Fin. Execs. Inst. Home: 130 N Grant St Hinsdale IL 60521-3334 Office: Navistar Internat Corp 455 N Cityfront Plaza Dr Chicago IL 60611-5503

LANNES, WILLIAM JOSEPH, III, electrical engineer; b. New Orleans, Oct. 12, 1937; s. William Joseph Jr., and Rhea Helen (Simon) L.; m. Patricia Anne Didier, Jan. 17, 1961: children: David Mark, Kenneth John, Jennifer Anne. BEE, Tulane U., 1959; MEE, U.S. Naval Postgrad. Sch., 1966; registered profl. engr. Commd. 2d lt. U.S. Marine Corps, 1959, advanced through grades to maj., 1967, served as electronics officer, ops. officer, until 1970; substation engr. La. Power & Light, New Orleans, 1970-71, utility engr., 1971-76, system relay engr., 1976-77, system substation engr., 1977-79, engring. supr. for substations, 1979-83, substation engring. mgr., 1983-86, dir. systems engring., 1986—, v.p. systems engring., 1986-88, with cen. engring., 1988-89; sr. v.p. Energy Supply Fossil, 1989-91; v.p. svc. and support Entergy Corp., 1991-92; assoc. dean rsch. & grad. studies Coll. Engring., U. New Orleans, 1992—; dir. U. New Orleans EPRI Community Initiative Ctr., 1993—; assoc. dir. Ctr. Energy Resources Mgmt., 1993—; dir. Engring. Mgmt. Program, 1995—; instr. Delgado Jr. Coll., 1973-74; instr. elec. engring. U. New Orleans, 1979-80; dir. 5th Dist. Savs. and Loan, 1982—; speaker profl. confs. Contbr. articles to profl. jours. Committeeman New Orleans Area Coun., Boy Scouts Am., 1972-76; vol., United Way 1975, 76, 81; treas., PTA 1971; vol. tchr. Confraternity of Christian Doctrine, 1972; mem. bus. adv. coun. Our Lady of Holy Cross Coll., 1981-86; chmn. engring. adv. coun. U. New Orleans; bd. dirs. New Life in La.; vol. coach New Orleans Recreation Dept., 1973; mem. La. Employees Com. on Polit. Action, Tulane Univ. Engring. Coun., New Orleans Archiocesan Pastoral Coun., 1988-91; mem. adv. bd. Bridge House, 1992—. Decorated Bronze Star; Cross of Gallantry Republic S. Vietnam; recipient cert. of merit, Mayor New Orleans, 1964; registered profl. engr.; La. Mem. Electric Power Rsch. Inst. (industry advisor), Edison Electric Inst. (systems and equipment com.), Soc. Power Rsch. and Implementation (chmn. 1987—), Southeastern Electric Exchange (substation com. 1977-85), IEEE (sr., profl. mem., Outstanding Svc. award, 1976, chmn. New Orleans sect. 1981-82, Edward Freitag award 1988, Region 3 Outstandin Engr. award 1991), Power Engring. Soc. (Prize Paper award 1988), Sigma Xi, Eta Kappa Nu. Republican. Roman Catholic. Office: Coll Engring U New Orleans New Orleans LA 70148

LANNIE, PAUL ANTHONY, lawyer; b. Hayti, Mo., Feb. 21, 1954; m. Donna Dean; children: Heather, Anthony. BA magna cum laude, Vanderbilt U., 1974, JD, 1978. Bar: Tex. Assoc. Johnson & Swanson, Dallas, 1978-83; exec. v.p. BusLease, Inc., Dallas, 1983-87, Greyhound Lines, Inc., Dallas, 1987-91; v.p. and gen. counsel Baroid Corp., Houston, 1991—. Bd. dirs. Dallas Indstrl. Devel. Corp., 1985-87; exec. mem. Trust Dallas Assn., 1990. Mem. Order Coif, Phi Beta Kappa. Office: Baroid Corp 3000 N Sam Houston Pky E Houston TX 77032

LANNON, JOHN JOSEPH, energy holding company executive; b. Springfield, Ill., Apr. 8, 1937; s. Richard James and Anne (Malone) L.; m. Arlene Joan Mularski, Sept. 2, 1976; children—John Joseph, Susan Kay, Laura Colleen; stepchildren—Kurt Henry, Karen Joan, Lynne Eileen. B.S., U. Ill., 1961; M.B.A., U. Chgo., 1970. C.P.A., Ill. Tax and audit sr. Arthur Andersen & Co., Chgo., 1961-66; with No. Ill. Gas Co., 1966-84, treas., 1973-75, v.p., controller, 1975-77, v.p. central div., 1977-78, v.p., controller, 1978-83, v.p., 1983-84; v.p. controller NICOR Inc., Naperville, Ill., 1978-83, v.p., 1983-84, v.p. fin., 1984-87, sr. v.p., chief fin. officer, 1988—; dir. Chgo. Community Ventures, Inc., 1975-85, sec., 1976-85; dir. State Bank Saunemin,

Ill., NICOR Oil and Gas Exploration. Bd. dirs. Taxpayers Fedn. Ill., 1979—, chmn., 1988-89. Served with U.S. Army, 1956-58. Mem. Acctg. Rsch. Assn., Am. Gas Assn. (chmn. application acctg. prins. com. 1974-75, mem. acctg. adv. council 1982—, chmn. 1982-83), Fin. Execs. Inst., Midwest Gas Assn. (chmn. acctg. and fin. sect. 1974-75), Ill. Soc. C.P.A.'s, U. Ill. Coll. Commerce Alumni Assn. (pres. 1977-78), Chgo. Assn. Commerce and Industry, Econ. Club Chgo. Roman Catholic. Office: NICOR Inc 1844 W Ferry Rd Naperville IL 60563-9662*

LANNON, LINNEA, newspaper editor. Book review editor Detroit Free Press. Office: Detroit Free Press 321 W Lafayette Blvd Detroit MI 48226*

LANNUTTI, JOSEPH EDWARD, physics educator; b. Malvern, Pa., May 4, 1926; s. Sabatino and Elizabeth (Alleva) L.; m. Margaret Elizabeth Judge, Apr. 24, 1954; children: Dominique, John, Kathryn. BS, Pa. State U., 1950; MS, U. Pa., 1953; PhD, U. Calif., Berkeley, 1957. Adminstrv. asst. Pa. Railroad Co., Phila., 1943-47; theoretical physicist N. Am. Aviation, Inc., Downey, Calif., 1952-53; rsch. asst. U. Calif., Berkeley, 1953-57; prof. physics Fla. State U., Tallahassee, 1959—, dir. High Energy Physics Lab., 1959—, dean, co-dir. Coll. Engring., 1981-84; dir. Supercomputer Computations Rsch. Inst. Supercomputer Computations Rsch. Inst., Tallahassee, 1984-93, assoc. v.p. rsch., 1992—; bd. dirs. U. Rsch. Assn., Washington; mem. High Energy Physics Adv. Panel, Dept. Energy, Washington, 1983-90. Contbr. articles to profl. jours. Bd. dirs. Oak Ridge (Tenn.) Associated U., 1972-88, Southeastern U. Rsch. Assn., Washington, 1983-84. Sgt. U.S. Army, 1944-46, ETO. Recipient rsch. grant NSF, 1958-60, rsch. contracts U.S. Dept. Energy, 1960—, 1983—. Fellow Am. Phys. Soc., Tallahassee C. of C. Democrat. Roman Catholic. Office: Fla State U Superconductor Computations Rsch Inst 400 SCL Tallahassee FL 32306*

LANO, CHARLES JACK, management auditor; b. Port Clinton, Ohio, Apr. 17, 1922; s. Charles Herbin and Antoinette (Schmitt) L.; m. Beatrice Irene Spees, June 16, 1946; children—Douglas Cloyd, Charles Lewis. B.S. in Bus. Adminstrn. summa cum laude, Ohio State U., 1949. C.P.A., Okla. With U.S. Gypsum Co., 1941-46, Ottawa Paper Stock Co., 1946-47; accountant Arthur Young & Co. (C.P.A.'s), Tulsa, 1949-51; controller Lima div. Ex-Cell-O Corp., 1951-59, electronics div. AVCO Corp., 1959-61, Servomation Corp., 1961; asst. comptroller Scovill Mfg. Co., Waterbury, Conn., 1961-62, comptroller, 1962-67; controller CF&I Steel Corp., Denver, 1967-69; v.p., controller CF&I Steel Corp., 1969-70; controller Pacific Lighting Corp., 1970-76; exec. v.p. Arts-Way Mfg. Co., Armstrong, Iowa, 1976-85; mgmt. auditor City of Anaheim, Calif., 1985—. Served with USMCR, 1942-45. Mem. Am. Inst. C.P.A.'s, Calif. Soc. C.P.A.'s, Inst. Internal Auditors. Home: 6274 E Calle Jaime Anaheim CA 92807-4005 Office: Civic Ctr 200 S Anaheim Blvd Anaheim CA 92805-3820

LANOIS, DANIEL, record producer, musician, popular; b. Hull, Que., Can., 1951; s. Guy and Jill Lanois. Founder, prodr. Grant Ave. Studio, Ont., Can., 1980-85; indep. prodr., 1981—. Solo albums include Arcadie, 1989, For the Beauty of Wynona, 1993; prodr. albums by Martha and the Muffins, Brian Eno, U2 (Grammy award The Joshua Tree 1987), Peter Gabriel, Robbie Robertson, Bob Dylan, The Neville Brothers. Grammy award, Best Producer (with Brian Eno for U2's Achtung Baby),1993. Office: Opal/ Warner Bros 3300 Warner Blvd Burbank CA 91510*

LANOU, ROBERT EUGENE, JR., physicist, educator; b. Colchester, Vt., Feb. 13, 1928; s. Robert E. and Flora G. (Goyette) L.; m. Cornelia Rockwell Wheeler, May 14, 1960; children: Katharine, Gregory, Elizabeth, Steven. BS, Worcester Poly. Inst., 1952; PhD, Yale U., 1957. Physicist Lawrence Berkeley (Calif.) Lab., 1956-59; asst. prof. physics Brown U., Providence, 1960-63, assoc. prof., 1963-67, prof., 1967—, chair dept. physics, 1986-92; cons. Brookhaven Nat. Lab., Upton, N.Y., Los Alamos (N.Mex.) Nat. Lab.; sci. advisor Gov. State of R.I., Providence, 1986-88. Contbr. articles to profl. jours. With USN, 1946-48, ETO. Grantee Dept. Energy, 1960—, NSF, 1995—. Fellow AAAS, Am. Phys. Soc.; mem. Sigma Xi, Tau Beta Pi. Achievements include research in experimental particle physics and astrophysics. Home: 90 Keene St Providence RI 02906-1508 Office: Brown U Dept Physics Providence RI 02906

LANOUE, ALCIDE MOODIE, medical corps officer, health care administrator; b. Tonawanda, N.Y., Nov. 2, 1934; s. Alcide and Isabelle LaNoue; children: Claire L., Alcide J., George E., Michelle; m. Beth Gortner, Dec. 20, 1986. B.A., Harvard U., 1956; M.D., Yale U., 1962. Diplomate Am. Bd. Orthopedic Surgery. Commd. lt. U.S. Army Med. Corps, 1966, advanced through grades to maj. gen., 1988; intern Brooke Army Med. Ctr., Ft. Sam Houston, Tex., 1960-61, resident in orthopedic surgery 1963-66; mem. staff 2d Surg. Hosp., Republic of Vietnam, 1966-67, 24th Evacuation Hosp., Republic of Vietnam, 1967, Valley Forge Gen. Hosp., Phoenixville, Pa., 1967-70, 71-73, Command & Gen. Staff Coll., Ft. Leavenworth, Kans., 1970-71, Walter Reed Army Med. Ctr., Washington, 1973-77, Hanau Clinic, Fed. Republic Germany, 1977-80; comdr. U.S. Army MEDDAC, Ft. Stewart, Ga., 1980-82; mem. staff U.S. Army MEDDAC, Ft. Benning, Ga., 1982-84; comdg. gen. Dwight David Eisenhower Army Med. Ctr., Ft. Gordon, Ga., 1984-86; comdt. Acad. Health Scis., U.S. Army, Ft. Sam Houston, Tex., 1986—; now dep. surgeon gen. Surgeon Gen.'s Office, Falls Church, Va.; also commander Army Medical Command, Fort Sam Houston, San Antonio, Tex., 1994—; now surgeon general Dept. Army, General's Office. Contbr. chpts. to books, articles to profl. jours. Decorated Bronze Star, Legion of Merit, Meritorious Service medal with 3 oak leaf clusters. Fellow ACS; mem. Am. Acad. Orthopedic Surgery. Office: Surgeon Gen's Office 5109 Leesburg Pike # 6 Falls Church VA 22041-3201

LA NOUE, TERENCE DAVID, artist, educator; b. Hammond, Ind., Dec. 4, 1941; s. George David and Lois (Lilly) L.; m. Ann Marcus, Oct. 15, 1977; children: Daniel, Alexandra. BFA, Ohio Wesleyan U., 1964; Fulbright meister student, Hochschule fur Bildenden Kunste, West Berlin, 1964-65; MFA, Cornell U., 1967. Prof. Trinity Coll., Hartford, Conn., 1967-72, CUNY, N.Y.C., 1972-85, NYU, 1987. Works represented in various museums, including Whitney Mus., Guggenheim Mus., Bklyn. Mus., Albright-Knox Mus., Corcoran Gallery Art, Carnegie Inst., Power Inst. Fine Arts, Sydney, Australia, Musé D'art et Archeologie, Toulon, France, Musée de Strasbourg, France, Mus. Contemporary Art, Teheran, Iran, Mus. Modern Art, N.Y.C.; monograph, Terence La Noue, Ashton Dore, 1992. Grantee Fulbright Found., Berlin, 1964-65, NEA, 1972-73, 83-84, Guggenheim Found., 1982-83. Office: 714 Broadway New York NY 10003-9506

LANOUETTE, WILLIAM JOHN, writer, public policy analyst; b. New Haven, Sept. 14, 1940; s. Joseph Francis and Gertrude Veronica (Thiede) L.; m. JoAnne Marie Sheldon, Apr. 12, 1969; children: Nicole Marie, Kathryn Ann. Student, USCG Acad., 1958-59; A.B., Fordham Coll., 1963; M.Sc., London Sch. Econs. and Polit. Sci., U. London, 1966, Ph.D., 1973. Researcher, reporter Newsweek, N.Y.C., 1961-64; news editor Radio Sta. WVOX AM-FM, New Rochelle, N.Y., 1964; Am. lectr. Hansard Soc. for Parliamentary Govt., London, 1967-68, 70-71; profl. staff mem., rsch. and tech. programs subcom. Govt. Ops. Com. Ho. of Reps., Washington, 1967; legis. asst. to U.S. Rep. John S. Monagan, Washington, 1967-68; staff writer Nat. Observer, Washington, 1969-70, 72-77; staff corr. Nat. Jour., Washington, 1977-82, contbg. editor, 1982-83; communications dir. World Resources Inst., Washington, 1983-85, sr. assoc., 1985; Washington corr. Bull. Atomic Scientists, 1989-90; sr. evaluator energy and science issues U.S. Gen. Acctg. Office, Washington, 1991—; founder Internat. Soc. Panetics. Author: Genius in the Shadows, a Biography of Leo Szilard, 1993. Recipient Forum award, 1974; fellow John F. Kennedy Sch. Govt., Harvard U., 1988-89; guest scholar Wilson Ctr., Smithsonian Instn., 1989. Democrat. Club: Potomac Boat (Washington). Home: 326 5th St SE Washington DC 20003-2048

LANPHER, E. GIBSON, ambassador to Zimbabwe. U.S. amb. to Zimbabwe Dept. of State, Harare. Office: Zimbabwe Dept of State Washington DC 20521-2180

LANPHIER, DAVID J., judge; b. Omaha, Feb. 7, 1945; s. Lawrence Anthony and virginia (Kelly) L.; m. Patricia Quinn, Oct. 16, 1963; children: David Lanphier, Jr., Dominic, Krista, Elizabeth. AB, Creighton U., Omaha, 1967; JD, Fordham Law Sch., N.Y.C., 1971. Law clk. to hon. John W.

Delehant Omaha, 1971-72; assoc. atty. Morsman, Fike, Sawtell & Davis, Omaha, 1972-75; dir. McGill, Koley, Parsonage & Lanphier, Omaha, 1975-90, Croke, Huck, Kasher, Lanphier, DeWitt & Anderson, Omaha, 1990-92; supreme ct. judge Nebr. Supreme Ct., Lincoln, 1993—. Mem. City Omaha Personnel Bd., 1984-89, Charter review Conv., Omaha, 1988, State Crime Commn., Lincoln, Nebr., 1992. Mem. ABA, Nebr. Bar Assn., Omaha Bar Assn. Office: Nebraska Supreme Ct 2413 State Capitol Lincoln NE 68509

LANS, ASHER BOB, lawyer; b. N.Y.C., Dec. 4, 1918; s. Arthur Louis and Sophie (Bob) L.; m. Barbara Eisner, Dec. 5, 1946 (div.); children: Deborah, Stephen, Alan; m. Mary Themo, Nov. 1, 1966 (div.); 1 child, Tracy; m. Shirley Johnson, June 26, 1967 (div.); 1 child, Andrea Elisabeth; m. Margaret Catherine Clancy, June 12, 1993. AB, Dartmouth Coll., 1938; MA, Columbia U., 1939; LLB, Yale U., 1944. Bar: N.Y. 1945, U.S. Supreme Ct., U.S. Ct. Appeals (2d dir.), U.S. Tax Ct., U.S. Dist. Ct. (so. and ea. dists.) N.Y. Law clk. Trustees of Assoc. G&E Corp., 1942-44; rsch. asst. Yale U., New Haven, 1944; assoc. Coudert Bros., 1945-47; ptnr. Lans, Goldstein, Golenbock & Abrams, N.Y.C., 1948-50; pvt. practice N.Y.C., 1951-57, 69; ptnr. Kramer & Lans, N.Y.C., 1958-65, Lans & Fink, N.Y.C., 1966-68, Lans, Feinberg & Cohen, N.Y.C., 1970-84, Summit, Rovins & Feldesman, N.Y.C., 1984-91; of counsel Jackson & Nash, N.Y.C., 1991—; dir., sec. Charbert, Inc. and related cos., N.Y.C., 1964—, J.K. Gallery, Inc., 1994—. Co-author: Studies in World Public Order, 1960; contbr. articles to profl. jours. Mem. Alumni Coun., Dartmouth Coll., Hanover, N.H., 1988-92; elector Spanish Portuguese Synagogue, N.Y.C., 1971—; bd. dirs. Gramercy Neighborhood Assn., 1993—. Mem. ABA, Yale Club. Democrat. Jewish. Home: 24 Gramercy Park S New York NY 10003-1700 Office: Jackson & Nash 330 Madison Ave New York NY 10017-5001

LANSAW, CHARLES RAY, rendering industry consultant; b. Middletown, Ohio, Mar. 5, 1927; s. Edward Curtis and Lura (Tyra) L.; m. Joan Betty Kalbaugh, July 4, 1949; children: Charles E., Gail D., Leslie J., Kristi L. Student, Miami U., Oxford, Ohio, 1947-48; student engring., U. Cin., 1949-51. Chief engr., sales mgr. Dupps Co., Germantown, Ohio, 1950-85; pres. C.R. Lansaw, Inc., Germantown, 1985—. Mem. Germantown Planning Commn.; bd. mem. Germantown Pub. Libr., 1991—. With USNR, 1944-46. Mem. U.S. Power Squadron (past officer Dayton), Rotary (pres. Germantown 1987-88). Avocations: sailing, woodworking, tennis. Home: 73 Sue Dr Germantown OH 45327-1628 Office: 41 N Main St Germantown OH 45327-1319

LANSBURY, ANGELA BRIGID, actress; b. London, Oct. 16, 1925; came to U.S., 1940; d. Edgar and Moyna (Macgill) L.; m. Peter Shaw, Aug. 12, 1949; children: Anthony, Deirdre. Student, Webber-Douglas Sch. Drama, London, 1939-40, Feagin Sch. Drama, N.Y.C., 1940-42; LHD (hon.), Boston U., 1990. Host 41st, 42d and 43d Ann. Tony Awards, 45th Ann. Emmy Awards. Actress with Metro-Goldwyn-Mayer, 1943-50; films include: Gaslight, 1944 (Acad. award nomination), National Velvet, 1944, The Picture of Dorian Gray, 1944 (Golden Globe award, Acad. award nomination), The Harvey Girls, 1946, The Hoodlum Saint, 1946, Till the Clouds Roll By, 1946, The Private Affairs of Bel Ami, 1947, If Winter Comes, 1948, Tenth Avenue Angel, 1948, State of the Union, 1948, The Three Musketeers, 1948, The Red Danube, 1949, Samson and Delilah, 1949, Kind Lady, 1951, Mutiny, 1952, Remains to be Seen, 1953, A Life at Stake, 1955, The Purple Mask, 1956, A Lawless Street, 1956, Please Murder Me, 1956, The Court Jester, 1956, The Long Hot Summer, 1958, Reluctant Debutante, 1958, Summer of the 17th Doll, 1959, A Breath of Scandal, 1960, Dark at the Top of the Stairs, 1960, Season of Passion, 1961, Blue Hawaii, 1961, All Fall Down, 1962, Manchurian Candidate, 1962 (Golden Globe award, Acad. award nomination), In the Cool of the Day, 1963, Dear Heart, 1964, The World of Henry Orient, 1964, Out of Towners, 1964, The Greatest Story Ever Told, 1965, Harlow, 1965, The Amorous Adventures of Moll Flanders, 1965, Mister Buddwing, 1966, Something for Everyone, 1970, Bedknobs and Broomsticks, 1971, Death on the Nile, 1978, The Lady Vanishes, 1980, The Mirror Crack'd, 1980, The Pirates of Penzance, 1982, The Company of Wolves, 1983, Beauty and the Beast, 1991; star TV series Murder She Wrote, 1984— (Golden Globe awards 1984, 86, 91, 92, 10 Emmy nominations, Lead Actress - Drama); appeared in TV mini-series Little Gloria, Happy at Last, 1982, Lace, 1984, Rage of Angels, part II, 1986; other TV movies include: The First Olympics-Athens 1896, A Talent for Murder, Gift of Love, 1982, Shootdown, 1988, The Shell Seekers, 1989, The Love She Sought, 1990, Mrs. 'Arris Goes to Paris, 1992; appeared in plays Hotel Paradiso, 1957, A Taste of Honey, 1960, Anyone Can Whistle, 1964, Mame (on Broadway), 1966, 83 (Tony award for Best Mus. Actress 1966), Dear World, 1968 (Tony award for Best Mus. Actress 1969), All Over (London Royal Shakespeare Co.), 1971, Gypsy, 1974 (Tony award for Best Mus. Actress 1975, Sarah Siddons award), The King and I, 1978, Sweeney Todd, 1979 (Tony award for Best Mus. Actress 1979, Sarah Siddons award), Hamlet, Nat. Theatre, London, 1976. Named Woman of Yr., Harvard Hasty Pudding Theatricals, 1968, Comdr. of British Empire by Queen Elizabeth II, 1994; inducted Theatre Hall of Fame, 1982; recipient British Acad. award, 1991. Office: Bldg 426 100 Universal City Plz Universal City CA 91608

LANSBURY, EDGAR GEORGE, theatrical producer; b. London, Jan. 12, 1930; came to U.S., 1941, naturalized, 1953; s. Edgar Isaac and Charlotte Lillian (McIldowie) L.; m. Rose Anthony Kean, Aug. 12, 1955; children: James, Michael, David, George, Brian, Kate. Ed., UCLA. Designer stock and off-Broadway prodns., 1953-55; art dir. ABC-TV, 1955, CBS-TV, 1955-62, Channel 13, N.Y.C., 1962-63; motion picture art dir., 1963-64; formed Edgar Lansbury Prodns. Inc., 1; prod. in theatre and films, 1964—; chmn. The Acting Co.; bd. dirs. Story Line Press. Producer Broadway plays: First One Asleep Whistle, 1966, The Subject Was Roses, 1964, That Summer-That Fall, 1967, The Only Game in Town, 1968, Promenade, 1970, Look to the Lilies, 1970, Engagement Baby, 1971, Godspell, 1971, Elizabeth I, 1972, The Night That Made America Famous, 1974, The Magic Show, 1974, Gypsy, 1975, American Buffalo, 1977, Broadway Follies, 1981, O, Pioneer!, 1989, Club XII, 1990, Amphigorey, 1992, Any Given Day, 1993; films The Subject was Roses, 1968, Godspell, 1973, The Wild Party, 1974, Squirm, 1976, Blue Sunshine, 1978, He Knows You're Alone, 1980, The Clairvoyant, 1982, Summer Girl, 1983, A Stranger Waits, 1986; dir. Without Apologies, 1989, All the Queen's Men, 1989, Advice from a Caterpillar, 1990, The Country Club, 1992. Pres. Agni Yoga Soc.; pres. Nicholas Roerich Museum, N.Y.C.; bd. govs. League N.Y. Theatres and Producers. Served with U.S. Army, 1951-53. Recipient N.Y. Art Dirs. award for best comml. film, 1963, N.Y. Outer Critics Circle award, 1965; N.Y. Critics Circle award, 1965; Antoinette Perry award for best produced play, 1965; nomination for Antoinette Perry award for best mus. play, 1977; N.Y. Critics Circle award for best drama, 1977. Office: Edgar Lansbury Prodns 450 W 42nd St Ste 2C New York NY 10036-6814

LANSDALE, DARYL L., retail executive; b. 1940. Student, Okla. State U. Pres., CEO Handy Dan, Handy City & Housewroks, San Antonio, 1976-87, Lone Star Hardware, Inc., 1987-88; pres., COO Scotty's Inc., Winter Haven, Fla., 1988—. Office: Scotty's Inc 5300 Recker Hwy Winter Haven FL 33880-1256

LANSER, HERBERT RAYMOND, financial planner; b. Hollywood, Calif., Dec. 10, 1932; s. Hugo and Anna (Strandlund) L.; divorced; children: Lynn (dec.), Deborah, Cynthia, Karen, Rick; m. Judy Kay Skousen; children: Zachary, Joshua, Ezekiel. Cert. fin. planner. With Herb Lanser Fin. Svc's., San Mateo, Calif., 1956-62, financial planner, 1962-83, cons., 1971-83; fin. planner Herb Lanser Fin. Svc's., Morro Bay, Calif., 1986-92; cons., fin. planner Lanser Vermiculture Svc's., Herb Lanser Fin. Svc's., Nurnberg, Fed. Republic Germany, 1983-85; cons. various orgns., 1975-92. Author: Profit From Earthworms, 1976; contbr. articles to profl. jours. Sgt. U.S. Army, 1953-55. Named Nat. Sales Leader Prudential Ins. Co. Europe, 1985, 1987. Mem. Assn. Life Underwriters (v.p. San Luis Obispo, Calif. chpt.), Morro Bay C. of C. (chmn. econ. devel. com., v.p. 1991, pres. 1992). Republican. Avocation: photography. Studio: PO Box 834 Morro Bay CA 93443

LANSING, ALLAN MEREDITH, cardiovascular surgeon, educator; b. St. Catherines, Ont., Can., Sept. 12, 1929; s. George Clayton and Annie Irene (Scott) L.; m. Donna Joanne Alford, Aug. 25, 1951; children—Ann, Peter, Michele. Student, U. Western Ont., London, 1949, MD magna cum laude, 1953, PhD in Physiology, 1957; LHD (hon.), Bellarmine Coll., 1985; DSc (hon.), Transylvania U., 1985. Intern Victoria Hosp., London, Ont., Can.,

1953-54; resident in surgery U. Western Ont. and associated hosps., London, 1954-55, 57-58, U. Ill. Research and Ednl. Hosp., Chgo., 1958-59; asst. prof. surgery U. Western Ont., London, Ont., Can., 1961-63; assoc. prof. surgery U. Louisville, 1963-69, prof. surgery, 1969-84; dir. The Heart Inst. Audubon Regional Med. Ctr., Louisville, 1983—; bd. dirs. Nat. Kidney Found., Louisville and Western Ky., 1985. Contbr. articles to profl. jours. Bd. dirs. Bellarmine Coll., Louisville, Transylvania U., Lexington, Ky. Decorated comdr. Order of Balboa; recipient Med. Alumni Gold medal U. Western Ont. Faculty of Medicine, 1953, Gold medal Alpha Kappa Kappa, 1953, Honorable G. Ferguson trophy, 1953, Nat. Humanitarian award Nat. Jewish Hosp. Ctr., Silver Beaver award Boy Scouts Am., Pres.'s medal Dominican Republic, Presdl. Point of Light, 1991, Bell award Louisville, 1994; named Outstanding Kentuckian, Derby Festival Com., 1980; John and Mary Markle scholar, 1961-66, Paul Harrris fellow. Fellow ACS, Royal Coll. Surgeons Can., Am. Coll. Cardiology; mem. Warren H. Cole Soc., Romanian Acad. Sci., Romanian Coll. Cardiology, Pan Am. Cardiovascular Soc. Rotary. Mem. United Ch. of Can. Avocations: tennis; reading. Office: 2266 Medical Arts Bldg 1169 Eastern Pky Louisville KY 40217-1401

LANSING, SHERRY LEE, motion picture production executive; b. Chgo., July 31, 1944; d. Norton and Margo L.; m. William Friedkin. BS summa cum laude in Theatre, Northwestern U., 1966. Tchr. math. public high schs. Los Angeles, 1966-69; model TV commls. Max Factor Co., 1969-70, Alberto-Culver Co., 1969-70; story editor Wagner Internat. Prodn. Co., 1972-74, dir. west coast devel., 1974-75; story editor MGM, 1975-77, v.p. creative affairs, 1977; v.p. prodn. Columbia Pictures, 1977-80; pres. 20th Century Fox Prodns., 1980-82; founder Jaffee-Lansing Prodns., 1982—; chmn. Paramount Pictures' Motion Picture Group, 1992—. Appeared in movies Loving, 1970, Rio Lobo, 1970; exec. story editor movies, Wagner Internat., 1970-73; v.p. prodn., Heyday Prodns., Universal City, Calif., 1973-75; exec. story editor, then v.p. creative affairs, MGM Studios, Culver City, Calif., 1975-77; sr. v.p. prodn., Columbia Pictures, Burbank, Calif., 1977-80, pres., 20th Century-Fox Prodns., Beverly Hills, Calif., 1980-83; ind. producer., Jaffe-Lansing Prodns., Los Angeles, 1983-91; producer Racing With the Moon, 1984,Firstborn, 1984, Fatal Attraction, 1987, The Accused, 1988, Black Rain, 1989, School Ties, 1992, Indecent Proposal, 1993; TV exec. producer When the Time Comes,1987, Mistress, 1992. Office: Paramount Pictures Corp 5555 Melrose Ave Los Angeles CA 90038-3197*

LANSKY, ZENA, surgeon; b. Phila., Apr. 18, 1942; d. Jacob and Thelma Lansky. BA summa cum laude, U. Pa., 1963; MD, Med. Coll. Pa., 1967. Diplomate Am. Bd. Surgery, 1975. Intern Montefiore Hosp., 1968-69; resident in surgery Bellevue Hosp., 1968-72, chief resident in surgery, 1971-72, instr. surgery, 1971-72; teaching asst. NIH, 1970, 71; mem. med. staff Morton F. Plant Hosp., Largo Med. Ctr., Clearwater Community Hosp.; med. dir. Gulf Coast Home Health Care, 1990; pres. Metabolic Cons. Inc. Infusion Co., pharmacy; mem. nat. med. adv. bd. New Eng. Critical Care, 1985; mem. adv. bd. Ind. Home Health Care, 1984-91. Mem. editorial bd. Nutritional Support mag., 1987; contbr. articles to profl. jours.; inventor gastrostomy tube, long term venous catheter repair kit, gastrostomy tube and percutaneous endoscopic kit. Bd. dirs. Pinellas County chpt. Am. Cancer Soc., 1980-85. Fellow ACS, Southeastern Surg. Congress; mem. Am. Soc. Parenteral and Enteral Nutrition (bd. dirs. 1989), Fla. Med. Assn., Fla. Assn. Nutritional Support (pres. 1986-87), Pinellas County Med. Soc. Office: Metabolic Cons Inc 412 S Missouri Ave Clearwater FL 34616

LANSNER, KERMIT IRVIN, editor, consultant; b. N.Y.C., May 9, 1922; s. David and Anna (Gordon) L.; m. Fay Gross, Sept. 10, 1948; children: Gabrielle, Erica. B.A., Columbia U., 1942; postgrad., Harvard U., 1947, Columbia U., 1948; Fulbright scholar, Sorbonne, Paris, 1950. Asst. prof. philosophy Kenyon Coll., 1948-50; asso. editor Art News mag., 1953-54; mem. staff Newsweek mag., 1954-73, sr. editor, 1959-61, exec. editor, 1961-65, mng. editor, 1965-69, editor, 1969-72, contbg. editor, columnist, 1972-77; editor-in-chief Newsweek Books, 1972-73; cons. Louis Harris & Assocs., 1973-76, sr. v.p., 1976-82; editor-in-chief Fin. World mag., 1983-89, editorial dir., 1989—. Columnist; contbr. New Republic, Kenyon Rev., Art News. Served to lt. USNR, 1942-46. Mem. Council Fgn. Relations, Century Assn., Phi Beta Kappa. Home and Office: 317 W 80th St New York NY 10024-5701

LANTAY, GEORGE CHARLES (WAGNER), school psychologist, psychotherapist, consultant; b. N.Y.C., Aug. 1, 1942; s. George Sylvester and Geraldine LeMae (Ogline) L.; BA, Hope (Mich.) Coll., 1965; MA, U. Ill., 1968; postgrad. in phys. therapy NYU, 1971-72; postgrad. in phys. and recreation therapy L.I. U., 1978-79; student physician asst. program Touro Coll., 1982-83; postgrad. in U.S. customs and law World Trade Inst., 1989—; postgrad. in E. Asian and African Studies St. John's U., 1993—; postgrad in electronics engring. tech. Tech. Career Inst., N.Y.C., 1993, cert. EPA Bergen County Tech. Schs., 1995; children by previous marriage: Scott Christopher, Christina, Susan Kimberly, Erica; m. Susannah Hewson, Dec. 31, 1992; 1 child, George Mason. Asst. prof. psychology Westminster Coll., Princeton, N.J., 1969-70; behavioral scientist, dir. Wagner Assocs., Princeton, 1969—; mgmt. tng. assoc. Western Elec. Co., N.Y.C., 1970; phys. therapist asst. Jewish Meml. Hosp., N.Y.C., 1970-72; sch. psychologist St. Agnes Cathedral High Sch., Rockville Centre, 1976—; ednl. cons. Test Preparation Centers, Riverdale, N.Y., 1975-79; intern psychologist N.Y. State Dept. Mental Hygiene, 1973-75; psychologist Odyssey House Parents Program, Wards Island, N.Y., 1973; adj. prof. behavioral scis. N.Y. Inst. Tech., Old Westbury, L.I., 1974-75; bd. dirs. div. field services N.Y. Testing and Guidance Center, Flushing, 1976—; with Adult Edn. Program Bergen County Tech. Schs., 1994-95. bd. dir. Shangri-La Day Camps, N.Y.C., 1976—; seminar instr. Nat. Traffic Safety Inst., N.Y.C., 1988—; asst. dir. aftersch. program Pub. Sch. 234, N.Y.C., 1988; founder Separation Encounter; contbr. Pres.'s Commn. Mental Health, 1977-78; cons. Eastern Regional Inst. Edn., N.Y.U. Med. Sch. Dept. Psychiatry, Newark Council Social Agys., N.Y.C. Bd. Edn., Astor Program Intellectually Gifted Children, N.Y.C. Bd. Edn., Evaluation and Placement Unit, 1977-78, N.Y.C. Bd. Edn. Spl. Edn. Div., Queens Region, 1983, Office Contracted Services, 1983-86, Camp Northwood for Learning Disabilities, summer 1977, Esperanza Day Treatment Center, N.Y.C., 1981-82; psychologist United Cerebral Palsy of N.Y. State, 1986; field ops. supr. N.Y. regional office U.S. Census Bur., 1990; presch. sch. psychologist and outreach coord. St. Mark's Inst. for Community Mental Health, N.Y.C., 1990—; preschool psychologist Karen Horney Clinic Therapeutic Nursery Program, N.Y.C., 1992—; contbr. Commrs. Adv. Council on Vocat. Rehab., N.Y. State Edn. Dept., 1978-79; asst. dir. after school program P.S. 234, N.Y.C., 1988; registrar Ind. Order of Forresters USA, 1991; sales coord. NSA wings program, Northeast Region, USA. Named an Outstanding Young Man of Am., 1975; cert. sch. psychologist, cert. emergency med. technician, N.Y. State; qualified mental retardation profl., N.Y. State. Mem. Am. Psychol. Assn., AAUP, Am. Ednl. Research Assn., Am. Assn. Sex Educators, Counselors and Therapists, Am. Phys. Therapy Assn. Am. Acad. Physicians Assts., Air Pollution Control Assn. Clubs: St. Bartholomew's Community, Downtown Glee (N.Y.C.). Author: Activities for Learning Disabled Children, 1980, Radon in Homes & What You Can Do to Protect Your Family's Health, 1987; contbr. articles to Ch. Herald mag.; research on underachievement and masculine identification. Home and Office: 28 Greenwich Ave New York NY 10011-8346

LANTHIER, CLAUDE, Canadian government official; b. Montreal, PQ, Can., Jan. 24, 1933; s. Ulric and Berthe (Sauvé) L.; m. Violet d Rafaëlo Pietroniro, Sept. 8, 1956; children: Marc, Anne-Marie. Arbitrator engr. examiner Order Architects of Quebec, 1961-; sr. ptnr. Claude Lanthier, Jean Saia & Assocs., 1959-84; 1st elected M.P. House of Commons, 1984; parliament sec. to min. finance, 1984-85, parliament sec. to min. for sci. & tech., 1986, parliament sec. to min. pub. works, 1987; pres. perm. com. on employment, work and immigration House of Commons, 1987; various pos. as cons. engr. and expert arbitrator; chmn. Canadian sect. Internat. Joint Commn. Mem. Ordre des Ingén. du Québec, Engring. Inst. Can., Arbitrators Inst. Can., Am. Arbitration Inst., Environmental Assessment Assn. Singapore Internat. Arbitration Ctr., Vancouver Arbitration Ctr. Office: Internat Joint Commn, 100 Metcalfe St 18th Fl, Ottawa, ON Canada K1P 5M1*

LANTHIER, JOHN SPENCER, accounting company executive; b. Montreal, Can., 1940; m. Diane Safford, Sept. 16, 1961; children: Sherrill, Suzanne, John, Sara. Student, McGill U., Montreal. Fin. chartered acct.

Ontario Inst., 1982. With Peat, Marwick Mitchell & Co., Montreal, 1960-72, ptnr., 1972-77; mng. ptnr. Peat Marwick's London (merger Thorne Ernst & Whinney 1989), Ontario, Can., 1977-82; mng. ptnr. Peat Marwick's London, Can., 1982-84, Toronto, Can., 1984-89; vice-chmn. KPMG Peat Marwick Thorne, Toronto, Can., 1989-93; chmn., chief exec. KPMG Can. Toronto, Can., 1993—; past chmn. bd. Goodwill Industries Toronto. Trustee United Way Greater Toronto, 1985-90, vice chmn., treas., mem. exec. com., 1986-89; mem. gov. coun. U. Toronto, 1989—; dir. United Way Centraide Can., 1990-92; chair area wide United Way, Toronto, 1994—. Office: KPMG Canada, 40 King St W Scotia Pla Box 122, Toronto, ON Canada M5H 3Z2

LANTHIER, RONALD ROSS, retired manufacturing company executive; b. Montreal, Que., Can., May 2, 1926; s. Emile Edgar and Edith (Martin) L.; m. Jacqueline Barbara Dyment; children: April Carolyn, Bonnie Alice, Ronald Dyment, Andrea Elizabeth, John Elliott. Chartered Accountant, McGill U., 1952. Pub. accountant, 1944-51; chief accountant St. Lawrence Flour Co., 1951-52; controller Canadian Underwriters Assn., 1952-54; div. controller Canadian Aviation Electronics Co., 1954-56; treas. Webb & Knapp, Can., 1956-62; dir. adminstrn., mem. exec. com. Greenshields, Inc. (investment dealers), 1962-67; v.p. finance, treas., mem. exec. com. Canadian Marconi Co., 1967-72; v.p. finance, dir., mem. exec. com. Macdonald Tobacco, Inc., 1972-75; pres. Lanco Mgmt. Ltd., 1975—; v.p. finance MacDonald Stewart Textiles, 1976-77; v.p. fin., mem. exec. com. Electrolux Can., 1978-79; pres. Robert R. Bramhall & Assos. (Can.) Ltd., 1980-81; sr. v.p. Camflo Mines Ltd., 1981-84; v.p. fin. Starnav Corp., 1984-86; v.p. fin. svcs., 1987—. Mem. Inst. Chartered Accts. Que. and Ont., Phi Kappa Pi. Anglican. Home: 100 Westview Dr Rural Rt 1, Gormley, ON Canada L0H 1G0 Office: V R Fin Svcs, 2 Lansing Sq Ste 101, North York, ON Canada M2J 4P8

LANTIERI, MICHAEL, special effects expert. Films include Heartbeeps, 1981, The Last Starfighter, 1984, Fright Night, 1985, My Science Project, 1985, Back to School, 1986, Poltergeist, 1986, Star Trek IV: The Voyage Home, 1986, The Witches of Eastwick, 1987, Moving, 1988, Who Framed Roger Rabbit?, 1988, Back to the Future II, 1989 (Acad. award nominee for best visual effects 1989), Caddyshack II, 1989, Indiana Jones and the Last Crusade, 1989, Nothing But Trouble, 1991, Hook, 1991 (Acad. award nominee 1991), Death Becomes Her, 1992, Jurassic Park, 1993 (Acad. award 1993). Office: IATSE Local 44 11500 Burbank Blvd North Hollywood CA 91601*

LANTOS, PETER R(ICHARD), industrial consultant, chemical engineer; b. Budapest, Hungary, July 18, 1924; came to U.S. 1939; naturalized citizen; s. Ernest and Bertha (Wigner) L.; m. Janice Kirchner, Dec. 20, 1947 (div. 1982); children: Geoffrey P., Greggory P., Gabrielle, Giselle. BChemE, Cornell U., 1945, PhD in Chem. Engring., 1950. Devel. chemist GE, Pittsfield, Mass., 1946-47; rsch. engr. E. I. Du Pont Nemours & Co., Wilmington, Del., 1950-55, supr. rsch., 1955-60; mgr. application and product devel. Celanese Plastics Co., Clark, N.J., 1961-63, mgr. R & D, 1964-69; dir. devel. Sun Chem. Corp., Carlstadt, N.J., 1969-70, v.p. R & D, 1970-75; gen. mgr. div. plastics Rhodia Inc., N.Y.C., 1975-76; dir. R & D Arco Polymers, Inc., Phila., 1976-77, v.p. R & D, 1978-79; pres. Target Group, Inc., Phila., 1980—. Contbr. over 30 articles to profl. jours. Pres. Bal. Health, Kennett Square, Pa., 1955-59. Mem. Am. Chem. Soc. (chmn. div. chem. mktg. and econs. 1988-89), Am. Inst. Chem. Engrs., Assn. Cons. Chemists and Chem. Engrs., Soc. Plastics Engrs., Soc. Plastics Industry. Home: PO Box 27247 Philadelphia PA 19118-0247 Office: Target Group Inc 1000 Harston Ln Erdenheim PA 19038

LANTOS, THOMAS PETER, congressman; b. Budapest, Hungary, Feb. 1, 1928; m. Annette Tillemann; children: Annette, Katrina. B.A., U. Washington, 1949, M.A., 1950; Ph.D., U. Calif.-Berkeley, 1953. Mem. faculty U. Wash., San Francisco State U., 1950-83; TV news analyst, commentator, sr. econ. and fgn. policy adviser to several U.S. senators; mem. Presdl. Task Force on Def. and Fgn. Policy, 97th-104th Congresses from 11th (now 12th) Calif dist., 1981—; ranking minority mem., mem. internat. rels. subcom. on internat. ops. and human rels., chmn. internat. rels. subcom. on western hemisphere human rights, mem. gov. reform and oversight com.; founder study abroad program Calif. State U. and Coll. System. Mem. Millbrae Bd. Edn., 1950-66. Democrat. Office: US Ho of Reps 2217 Rayburn HOB Washington DC 20515-0512*

LANTZ, CHARLES ALAN, chiropractor, researcher; b. Haywood County, N.C., Dec. 15, 1947; s. Harry Adrian and Betty Elizabeth (Stewart) L.; m. Susan Ruppalt (div. June 1971); children: Heather Leigh; m. Judith Daye Wagner (div. May 1990); children: Sky Micah, Spring Laurel, Miriah Lee. Cert. in French, U. Lyon, France, 1969; BS in Zoology, U. N.C., 1971, PhD in Pharmacology, 1978; D Chiropractic magna cum laude, Life Chiropractic Coll., Marietta, Ga., 1987. Postdoctoral fellow Johns Hopkins U., Balt., 1977-81; assoc. prof. biochemistry Life Chiropractic Coll., 1982-87, assoc. rsch. prof., 1987-90; chief rsch. Life Chiropractic Coll.-West, San Lorenzo, Calif., 1990—; mem. adv. bd. Chiropractic Rsch. Jour., 1988—; mem. rsch. adv. com. Found. for Chiropractic Edn. and Rsch., Arlington, Va., 1990—; mem. exec. com. Consortium for Chiropractic Rsch., Sunnyvale, Calif., 1990—; mem. commn. Consensus Conf. To Establish Guidelines for Chiropractic Quality Assurance and Practice Parameters. Mem. Am. Chiropractic Assn. (cons. on technique 1992—), Calif. Chiropractic Assn., Mich. Chiropractic Coun. (hon.), Internat. Chiropractors Assn. Achievements include development of mathematical theory for thin-film dialysis, developing a theoretical basis for chiropractic-the vertebral subluxation complex. Home: 492 Scenic Rd Fairfax CA 94930 Office: Life Chiropractic Coll West 2005 Via Barrett San Lorenzo CA 94580

LANTZ, DAVID CARSON, mathematics educator; b. Topton, Pa., Nov. 15, 1946; s. Carson Oliver and Harriet Mary (Smith) L. BS in Secondary Edn., Kutztown U., 1968; MA, U. Kans., 1972, PhD, 1975. Tchr. Palmyra (Pa.) Area High Sch., 1968; vis. asst. prof. U. Nebr., Omaha, 1975-76; vis. instr. U. Ga., Athens, 1976-77; prof. Colgate U., Hamilton, N.Y., 1977—; vis. prof. Purdue U., West Lafayette, Ind., 1984-75, 90-91. Mem. Am. Math. Soc., Math. Assn. Am. Home: RR 2 Box 324 Hamilton NY 13346-9802 Office: Colgate U Math Dept Hamilton NY 13346

LANTZ, GEORGE BENJAMIN, JR., business executive, college executive, consultant; b. Buckhannon, W.Va., Feb. 6, 1936; s. George Benjamin and Georgia Myrtle (Bodkin) L.; m. Mary Sue Powell, Feb. 25, 1957; children—Mary Lynne, Marsha, Kimberly, Rebecca, Todd. AB with honors, W.Va. Wesleyan Coll., 1960; LLD, W.Va. Wesleyan Coll., 1993; STB with honors, Boston U., 1964, PhD, 1971. Minister United Meth. Pastorates, W.Va. and Mass., 1956-75; mem. faculty W.Va. Wesleyan Coll., Buckhannon, 1967-73, chmn. div. humanities, prof. humanities and religion, 1974-75; asst. to pres., ACE fellow Ohio Wesleyan U., Delaware, 1973-74; dean coll. Mount Union Coll., Alliance, Ohio, 1975-80, pres., 1980-85; v.p. adminstrn. and devel. Nesco, Inc., Hudson, Ohio, 1985-88; pres. U. Indpls., 1988—; cons. Coun. Ind. Colls., Washington, 1982—; chmn. The Nat. Bank Indpls. Trustee W.Va. Wesleyan Coll., 1986-88; bd. dirs. Dollars for Scholars Program, Ind.; bd. dirs. Ind. Coll. of Ind., Salvation Army Adv. Bd. Mem., Ind. Law Enforcement Tng. Bd., Ind. State chpt. Nat. Multiple Sclerosis Soc., Ind. Higher Edn. Telecom. System, Bus. Encouraging Success for Tomorrow, Meridian Mut. Ins.; chmn. bd. dirs. Greater Indpls. Progress Com.; bd. dirs. Internat. Fedn. for Bus. Edn.; mem. United Way Cen. Ind. Indpls. Downtown Inc., Japan-Am. Soc. of Ind., Inc., Benjamin Harrison Meml. Commn., English Speaking Union, Ind. Soc. of Chgo.; bd. adv. Greater Johnson County Cmty. Found.; mem. adv. group Midwest Partnership Ind. Colls., Blue Ribbon panel Indpls. Bus. Jour., Mayor's Global Initiative Task Force, Mayor's Operation Respect Network Com., Ind., Ind. Bus./Higher Edn. Forum; bd. dirs. Indpls. Conv. and Visitors Assn.; trustee Cypress Am. Archeol. Rsch. Inst.; elder South Ind. Conf. United Meth. Ch. With U.S. Army, 1954-56. Recipient Cokesbury Grad. award Meth. Bd. Higher Edn. Fellow Am. Coun. Edn.; mem. AAUP, Nat. Assn. Ind. Colls. and Univs. (commn. on financing higher edn.), Am. Assn. Higher Edn. (bd. dirs.), Nat. Assn. Schs. and Colls. of United Meth. Ch. (pres. 1993—), mem. com. on internat. edn.), Internat. Assn. Univ. Pres, Soc. Bibl. Lit., North Ctrl. Assn. Colls. and Schs. (commr. 1978-85, cons., evaluator); Indpls. C. of C., Economic Club, Columbia Club, Skyline Club, Kiwanis. Home: 4051 Otterbein Ave Indianapolis IN 46227-3618 Office: U Indpls Office Pres 1400 E Hanna Ave Indianapolis IN 46227-3630

LANTZ, JOANNE BALDWIN, university chancellor emerita; b. Defiance, Ohio, Jan. 26, 1932; d. Hiram J. and Ethel A. (Smith) Baldwin; m. Wayne E. Lantz. BS in Physics and Math., U. Indpls., 1953; MS in Counseling and Guidance, Ind. U., 1957; PhD in Counseling and Psychology, Mich. State U., 1969; LittD (hon.), U. Indpls., 1985; LHD (hon.), Purdue U., 1994; LLD (hon.), Manchester Coll., 1994. Tchr. physics and math. Arcola (Ind.) High Sch., 1953-57; guidance dir. New Haven (Ind.) Sr. High Sch., 1957-65; with Ind. U.-Purdue U., Fort Wayne, 1965—, interim chancellor, 1988-89, chancellor, 1989-94, chancellor emerita, 1994—. Contbr. articles to profl. jours. Mem. Ft. Wayne Econ. Devel. Adv. Bd. and Task Force, 1988-91, Corp. Coun., 1988-94; bd. advisors Leadership Ft. Wayne, 1988-94; mem. adv. bd. Ind. Small. Bus. Devel. Ctr., 1988-90; trustee Ancilla System, Inc., 1984-89, chmn. human resources com., 1985-89, exec. com., 1985-89; trustee St. Joseph's Med. Ctr., 1983-84, pers. adv. com. to bd. dirs., 1978-84, chmn., 1980-84; bd. dirs. United Way Allen County, sec., 1979-80; bd. dirs. Anthony Wayne Vocat. Rehab. Ctr., 1969-75. Mem. Fort Wayne Ind.-Purdue Alumni Soc. (hon. mem. 1987), Am. Psychol. Assn., AAUW (internat. fellowship com. 1986-88, prog. com. 1981-83, Am. women fellowship com. 1978-83, chmn. 1981-83, trust rsch. grantee 1980), Southeastern Psychol. Assn. (referee conv. papers 1987, 88), Ind. Sch. Women's Club (v.p. prog. chair 1979-81), Pi Lambda Theta, Sigma Xi, Delta Kappa Gamma (editorial bd. 1986-88, gen. chair conv. 1985-86, dir. N.E. region 1982-84, adminstrv. bd., exec. bd. 1982-84, leadership devel. com.). Avocations: swimming, reading, knitting, boating.

LANTZ, KENNETH EUGENE, consulting firm executive; b. Altoona, Pa., Mar. 9, 1934; s. William Martin and Alice Lucretia (Glass) L.; m. D. Arlene Yocum, Nov. 28, 1959; children—Antonia Marie, Theresa Antoinette. B.S. cum laude, Fordham U., 1956. Cons. Sutherland Co., 1960-62; spl. rep. IBM, Los Angeles, 1962-67; dir. info. services Loyola-Marymount U., Los Angeles, 1967-70; pres. CBIS, Los Angeles, 1970-72, Kennett Lantz Assocs., Los Angeles, 1977-82; mgr. fin. systems Occidental Life Ins. Los Angeles, 1973-77; dir. systems Sayre & Toso, Los Angeles, 1982-83; prin. Atwater, Lantz, Hunter & Co., Los Angeles, 1983—; lectr. computing topics Technology Transfer Inst., 1987-88. Author: The Prototyping Methodology, 1984. Contbr. articles to profl. jours. Served to 1st lt. USAF, 1957-60. Mem. Future of Automation Roundtable (dir. 1983—), Ins. Acctg. and Systems Assn. (Nat. Merit award 1984), First Friday Friars Club. Republican. Roman Catholic.

LANTZ, NORMAN FOSTER, electrical engineer; b. Pekin, Ill., June 8, 1937; s. Norman Gough and Lenore (Elsbury) L.; m. Donnis Maureen Ballinger, Sept. 7, 1958 (div. Aug. 1991); children: Katherine, Deborah, Norman Daniel; m. Judith Eliane Peach, Dec. 7, 1991. BSEE, Purdue U., 1959, MSEE, 1961. System engr. GE Co., Phila., 1961-72; mem. tech. staff The Aerospace Corp., El Segundo, Calif., 1972-75, mgr., 1975-79, dir., 1979-83, prin. dir., 1983-90, sr. project engr., 1991—; dir. Internat. Found. for Telemetering, Woodland Hills, Calif., 1985—. 2d lt. U.S. Army, 1960-61. Mem. AIAA (sr.), IEEE, Internat. Test and Evaluation Assn., Am. Mgmt. Assn. Office: The Aerospace Corp El Segundo CA 90245-4691

LANTZ, PHILLIP EDWARD, corporate executive, consultant; b. Laramie, Wyo., Sept. 21, 1938; s. Everett Delmer and Elizabeth Mary (Stratton) L.; m. Paula Bogel, June 16, 1962; children: Kirk Edward, Eric William. BA in Math., U. Colo., 1960; MA in Math., U. Wyo., 1966; MS in Ops. Rsch., Johns Hopkins U., 1972. Grad. teaching asst. U. Wyo., Laramie, 1964-65; sr. engr. Applied Physics Lab. Johns Hopkins U., Silver Spring, Md., 1965-70; v.p. Ops. Rsch. Inc., Silver Spring, Md., 1970-72; dir. Tetra Tech. Inc. Arlington, Va., 1972-74; pres., chief exec. officer Systems Planning and Analysis, Inc., Falls Church, Va., 1974—, also bd. dirs. Lt. USN, 1960-64. Home: 2911 Eddington Ter Alexandria VA 22302-3503 Office: Systems Planning and Analysis Inc 200 N Beauregard St Alexandria VA 22311-1811

LANTZ, WILLIAM CHARLES, lawyer; b. Rochester, Minn., July 3, 1946; s. Charles E. and Doris (Greenwood) L.; m. Vickie L. Erickson, May 17, 1972; children: Charles Eric, Andrew William. BA, Hamline U., 1968; JD, U. Minn., 1971. Bar: Minn. 1971. From assoc. to ptnr. Dorsey & Whitney, Rochester, 1975—. Served to lt. JAGC, USNR, 1971-75. Mem. Minn. Bar Assn., Olmsted Bar Assn. Methodist. Lodge: Kiwanis. Home: 807 Sierra Ln NE Rochester MN 55906-4230 Office: Dorsey & Whitney 201 1st Ave SW Ste 340 Rochester MN 55902

LANYI, ALEXANDER SANDOR, rail transportation executive; b. Budapest, Hungary, Jan. 30, 1937; arrived in Can., 1957; s. Imre and Ilona (Balla) L.; m. Aniko Friedman, Aug. 16, 1964 (dec. 1989); children: Thomas, Peter, Susan. BS, Sir George Williams U., Montreal, Que., Can., 1963. Rsch. analyst CP Ltd., Montreal, 1967-69, asst. statistician, 1969-72, sr. statistician, 1972-73, mgr. costs and oper. stats., 1973-74; mgr. profit analysis CP Rail, Montreal, 1974-78, asst. dir. acctg., 1978-79, dir. profit analysis and devel., 1979-80, asst. contr. devel., 1980-81, contr., 1981—, v.p., 1985-89, exec. v.p., CFO, 1989—; bd. dirs. Toronto (Ont., Can.) Terminals Ry. Co., Shawinigan (Ont.) Ry. Co., Soo Line Corp., Canpac Car Inc., Incan Superior. Mem. Assn. Am. R.R.s (chmn. acctg. div. 1987). Office: CP Rail, PO Box 6042, Sta A, Montreal, PQ Canada H3C 3E4

LANYI, JANOS KAROLY, biochemist, educator; b. Budapest, Hungary, June 5, 1937; came to U.S., 1957, naturalized, 1962; s. Istvan and Klara (Rosthy) L.; m. Carol Ann Giblin, Sept. 15, 1962 (div. Dec. , 1984); children: Clara Aileen, Sean Renton, Gabriella; m. Brigitte Schobert, Mar. 27, 1988. Student, Eotvos Lorand U. Scis., Budapest, 1955-56; B.S., Stanford U., 1959; M.A., Harvard U., 1961, Ph.D., 1963. Postdoctoral fellow Stanford U. Sch. Medicine, 1963-65; Nat. Acad. Scis. resident assoc. NASA-Ames Research Ctr., 1965-66; sr. scientist NASA-Ames Research Ctr., Moffett Field, Calif., 1966-80; prof. physiology and biophysics U. Calif.-Irvine, 1980—; vis. fellow Cornell U., 1976. Recipient NASA medal for exceptional sci. achievement, 1977; recipient H. Julian Allen award for best sci. paper Ames Research Ctr., 1978, Alexander von Humboldt award for Sr. U.S. Scientists W.Ger., 1979-80. Mem. Am. Soc. Biol. Chemists, Biophys. Soc., Am. Soc. Microbiology, Hungarian Acad. Scis. (fgn.), Phi Beta Kappa, Sigma Xi. Office: U Calif Dept Physiology Biophy Irvine CA 92717

LANYON, ELLEN (MRS. ROLAND GINZEL), artist, educator; b. Chgo., Dec. 21, 1926; d. Howard Wesley and Ellen (Aspinwall) L.; m. Roland Ginzel, Sept. 4, 1948; children: Andrew, Lisa. BFA, Art Inst. Chgo., 1948; MFA, U. Iowa, 1950; Fulbright fellow, Courtauld Inst., U. London, 1950-51. Tchr. jr. sch. Art Inst. Chgo., 1952-54; past tchr. day sch., tchr. Rockford Coll., summer 1953, Oxbow Summer Sch. Painting, Saugatuck, Mich., 1961-62, 67-70, 71-72, 78, 88, 94, U. Ill., Chgo., 1970, U. Wis. Extension, 1971-72, Pa. State U., 1974, U. Calif., 1974, Sacramento State U., 1974, Stanford U., 1974, Boston U., 1975, Kans. State U., 1976, U. Mo., 1976, U. Houston, 1977; assoc. prof. Cooper Union, N.Y.C., 1980-93; ret., 1993; founder, sec.-treas. Chgo. Graphic Workshop, 1952-55; participant Yaddo, 1973, 75, 76, Ossabow Island Project, 1976; adj. vis. prof. So. Ill. U., 1978, No. Ill. U., 1978, SUNY, Purchase, 1978, Cooper Union, N.Y.C., 1978-79, Parsons Sch. Design, N.Y.C., 1979; disting. vis. prof. So. Ill. U., 1980, U. Calid. Davis, 1980, Sch. Visual Arts, N.Y.C., 1980-83; vis. artist U. N.Mex., 1980, So. Ill. U., 1984, Sch. Art Inst., Chgo., 1984, U. Tenn., Md. Inst., Northwestern Grad. Sch., 1988, U. Pa., U. Iowa, 1991, 92, Anderson Ranch Workshop, 1994, Aspen Design Conf., 1994; vis. prof. U. Iowa, 1991-92; bd. dirs. Oxbow Summer Sch. Painting, 1972-82, emeritus, 1982—. One woman shows, Superior St. Gallery, Chgo., 1960, Stewart Richart Gallery, San Antonio, 1962, 65, Fairweather Hardin Gallery, Chgo., 1962, Zabriskie Gallery, N.Y.C., 1962, 64, 69, 72, B.C. Holland Gallery, Chgo., 1965, 68, Ft. Wayne Art Mus., 1967, Richard Gray Gallery, Chgo., 1970, 73, 76, 79, 82, 85, Madison Art Center, 1972, Nat. Collection at Smithsonian Instn., 1972, Odyssia Gallery, Rome, 1975, Krannert Performing Arts Center, 1976, Oshkosh Pub. Mus., 1976, U. Mo., 1976, Harcus Krakow, Boston, 1977—, Fendrick Gallery, Washington, 1978, Ky. State U., 1979, Ill. Wesleyan U., 1979, U. Calif. Davis, 1980, Odyssia Gallery, N.Y., 1980, Landfall Press, 1980, Alverno Coll., Milw., 1981, Susan Caldwell, Inc., N.Y.C., 1983, N.A.M.E. Gallery, Chgo., 1983, Printworks, Ltd., Chgo., 1989, 93 Pretto Berland Hall, N.Y.C., 1989, Struve Gallery, Chgo., 1990, 93, Berland Hall Gallery, N.Y.C., 1992, Sioux City Art Mus., Iowa, 1992, U. Iowa Mus. Art, 1994, Andre Zarre Gallery, N.Y.C., 1994; retrospective exhibitions, Krannert Art Mus., McNay Art Mus., Chgo. Cultural Ctr., Stamford Mus., U. Tenn.; exhibited group shows, 1946—, including traveling exhbns., Am. Fedn. Arts,

1946-48, 50, 53, 57, 65, 66, 69; Art Inst. Chgo., 1946-47, 51-53, 55, 57-58, 60-62, 64, 66, 67, 68, 69, 71, 73, Corcoran Gallery Art, 1961, 76, Denver Art Mus., 1950, 52, Exhbn. Momentum, Chgo., 1948, 50, 52, 54, 56, Library of Congress, 1950, 52, Met. Mus. Art, 1952, Mus. Modern Art, 1953, 62, Phila. Mus. Art, 1946, 47, 50, 54, San Francisco Mus. Art, 1946, 50, U. Ill., 1953, 54, 57, Drawing Soc., Nat. Traveling Exhbn., 1965-66, The Painter and The Photograph traveling exhbn., 1964-65; Nostalgia traveling show, 1968-69, Violence,, Mus. Contemporary Art, Chgo., 1969, Birds and Beasts,, Graham Gallery, N.Y.C., 1969-71; Ill. Painters, Ill. Arts Council, 1968-71; Ill. painters: Beyond Illustration, HMH Publs. Europe, 1971, Chgo. Imagists, 1972, Chgo. Sch, 1972, Am. Women, 1972, Artists Books, 1973; Bicentennial America 76 traveling exhibit, 1976; Chgo. Connection, 1976-77, Downtown Whitney, N.Y.C., 1978—, Queens Mus., 1978, Dayton Art Inst., 1978, Odyssia Gallery, N.Y.C., 1979, Chgo. Cultural Center, 1979, Aldrich Mus. Contemporary Art, 1980, Bklyn. Mus., 1980, Walker Art Center, 1981, also Lisbon, Venice biennales, Voorhees Mus. Rutgers U., Mus. Contemporary Art, Chgo., Milw. Art. Mus., Art of the Quilt traveling exhibition, 1985—, Made In America Berkeley Art Mus., 1987, Art of the Screen traveling exhibition, 1986—, Lines of Vision: Drawings by Contemporary Women, 1989, Symbolism: Cooper Union, 1989, Randall Gallery, St. Louis, 1991, Printworks Ltd., Chgo., 1991, 92, Berland/Hall, N.Y.C., 1991, The Cultural Ctr., Chgo., 1992, Matnan Locks Gallery, Phila., 1992, Art Inst. Chgo., 1992, Andre Zarre Gallery, N.Y.C., 1993-94, 95, Nat. Mus. Women in Arts, Washington, 1994, 95; represented in permanent collections Art Inst. Chgo.; Denver Art Mus., Library of Congress, Inst. Internat. Edn., London, Finch Coll., N.Y., Krannert Mus., U. Ill., U. Mass., N.J. State Mus., Ill. State Mus., Bklyn. Mus., Mus. Contemporary Art, Chgo., Nat. Coll. Fine Arts, Walker Art Ctr., Mpls., Boston Pub. Library, Des Moines Art Center, Albion Coll., Met. Mus., McNay Art Inst., Albion Coll., Kans. State U., U. Dallas, U. Houston, Cornell U., also numerous pvt. collections; mural paintings: Working Men's Coop. Bank Boston, 1979, State of Ill. Bldg., Chgo., 1985, State Capitol, Springfield, Ill., 1989, City of Miami Beach, Art in Public Places project, Police and Court Facility, 1993; published: Wonder Production Vol. I, 1971, Jataka Tales, 1975, Transformations, 1976, Transformations II (Endangered), 1983 ; editorial bd.: Coll. Art Jour., 1982-92; illustrator: The Wandering Tattler, 1975, Perishible Press, 1976—, Red Ozier Press, 1980—. Recipient Armstrong prize Art Inst. Chgo., 1946, 55, 77, Town and Country purchase prize, 1947, Blair prize, 1958, Palmer prize, 1962, 64, Chan prize, 1961, Vielehr prize, 1967, Logan prize, 1981; purchase prize Denver Art Mus., 1950; purchase prize Library of Congress, 1950; Cassandra Found. award, 1970; Nat. Endowment for Arts grantee, 1974, 87; Herewood Lester Cook Found. grantee, 1981. Mem. Coll. Art Assn. (dir., exec. com. 1977-80), Delta Phi Delta. Address: 138 Prince St New York NY 10012-3135

LANYON, WESLEY EDWIN, retired museum curator, ornithologist; b. Norwalk, Conn., June 10, 1926; s. William J. and Frances A. (Merrill) L.; m. Vernia E. Hall, Jan. 29, 1951; children: Cynthia Hall, Scott Merrill. A.B. in Zoology, Cornell U., 1950; Ph.D., U. Wis., 1955. Interpretive specialist Nat. Park Service, summers 1947-51; instr. zoology U. Ariz., 1953-56; asst. prof. Miami U., Oxford, Ohio, 1956-57; asst. curator birds Am. Mus. Natural History, N.Y.C., 1957-63, assoc. curator, 1963-67, curator, 1967-88; resident dir. Kalbfleisch Field Research Sta., 1958-74; adj. prof. biology City U. N.Y., 1968-87; expdns. for mus. to C.Am. and Mexico, 1959, 60, 63, West Indies, 1960, 65, 66, S. Am., 1967-80. Contbr. articles to profl. jours. Fellow Am. Ornithologists Union (Brewster award 1968, pres. 1976-78); mem. Cooper, Wilson ornithol. socs., Eastern Bird Banding Assn., Ecol. Soc. Am., Soc. Study Evolution, Soc. Systematic Zoology, Linnaean Soc. N.Y., Sigma Xi. Home: RR 2 Box 219 Louisa VA 23093-9802

LANZ, ROBERT FRANCIS, corporate financial officer; b. Greenwich, Conn., Oct. 30, 1942; s. John Edwin and Katheryn Loretto (Jernan) L.; m. Elizabeth Kienlen, Nov. 11, 1967; children—Christopher, Jennifer. B.A., LaSalle Coll., Phila., 1964; postgrad., Law Sch., Fordham U., 1966-67; M.B.A., U. Conn., 1975. Corp. trust officer Chase Manhattan Bank, N.Y.C., 1966-71; cons. Stone & Webster, N.Y.C., 1971; sr. cons. EBASCO Services, N.Y.C., 1971-73; v.p., treas. Pacific/Corp., Inc., Portland, Oreg., 1973—; treas. Pacific/Corp., Inc., 1985—; sr. v.p. Pacific/Corp. Credit, Inc., Portland, Oreg., 1986—; pres. Willamette Devel. Corp. Mem. legal budget com. City of Lake Oswego, Oreg., 1975-80. Served with U.S. Army, 1964-66. Mem. Edison electric Inst. (fin. com. 1980-85), Northwest Electric Light and Power Assn. Democrat. Roman Catholic. Avocations: travel; languages; golf. Home: 17351 Canyon Dr Lake Oswego OR 97034-6711 Office: PacifiCorp 851 SW 6th Ave Portland OR 97204-1337

LANZA, FRANK C., electronics executive; b. 1931. BS, Heralds Engring. Coll., 1956. Project engr. Philco Western Devel. Labs., 1957-59; v.p. Textron Corp., Providence, 1960-72; with Loral Corp., N.Y.C., 1972—, v.p.—, 1973-79, exec. v.p., 1979-81, corp. pres., chief operating officer, 1981—, also bd. dirs. Served with USCG, 1953-55. Office: Loral Corp 600 Third Ave 36th Fl New York NY 10016

LANZAFAME, SAMUEL JAMES, manufacturing company executive; b. Canastota, N.Y., Oct. 9, 1950; s. James Charles and Sarah Ann (Aiello) L.; m. Janet Mangan, Nov. 23, 1974; children: Bethany, Erin, John. BA, Holy Cross U., 1972; MBA magna cum laude, Notre Dame U., 1974. Project coordinator Oneida (N.Y.) Ltd., 1975-76, mgr. mktg. research and bus. devel., 1977-78, corp. mgr. spl. projects, 1979-80, br. mgr. No. Ireland subsidiary, 1980-82, sr. v.p. Camden Wire subsidiary, 1983-84, pres. Camden Wire subsidiary, 1985-86, corp. pres., 1986—. Avocations: running, gardening. Office: Ctrl Locating Svc Ltd 6489 Ridings Rd Syracuse NY 13206-1112

LANZANO, RALPH EUGENE, civil engineer; b. N.Y.C., Dec. 26, 1926; s. Ralph and Frances (Giuliano) L.; B.C.E., NYU, 1959. Engring. aide Seelye, Stevenson, Value, Knecht, N.Y.C., 1957-58; jr. civil engr. N.Y.C. Dept. Public Works (name changed to N.Y.C. Dept. Water Resources), 1960-63, asst. civil engr., 1963-68; civil engr., 1968-71; sr. san. engr. Parsons, Brinckerhoff, Quade & Douglas, N.Y.C., 1971-72; civil engr. N.Y.C. Dept. Water Resources, 1972-77, N.Y.C. Dept. Environ. Protection, 1978-90; ret., 1990. Registered profl. engr., N.Y. Mem. NRA (life), ASCE (life), ASTM, Nat. N.Y. socs. profl. engrs., Water Environ. Fedn., Am. Water Works Assn., Am. Public Health Assn., Am. Fedn. Arts (contbg.), U.S. Inst. Theatre Tech., NYU Alumni Assn., Am. Nat. Theatre and Acad., Lincoln Center Performing Arts, Film Soc. Lincoln Ctr., N.Y.C. Ballet Guild, Asia Soc., Nat. Fire Protection Assn., N.Y. Pub. Libr. (friend), Sta. WNET-TV (Thirteen), U.S. Lawn Tennis Assn. (life), Nat., Internat. wildlife fedns., Bible-A-Month-Club, Nat. Parks and Conservation Assn., Nat. Geog. Soc., Nat. Audubon Soc., Am. Automobile Assn., Bklyn. Bot. Garden, Am. Mus. Natural History, Metro. Mus. Art, Chi Epsilon. Home: 17 Cottage Ct Huntington Station NY 11746-1104

LANZEROTTI, LOUIS JOHN, physicist; b. Carlinville, Ill., Apr. 16, 1938; s. Emanuel Louis and Mary Pauline (Orienti) L.; m. Mary Yvonne DeWolf, June 19, 1965; children: Mary Yvonne, Louis DeWolf. BS, U. Ill., 1960; MA, Harvard U., 1963, PhD, 1965. Postdoctoral fellow AT&T Bell Labs., Murray Hill, N.J., 1965-67, mem. tech. staff, 1967-82, Disting. mem. tech. staff, 1982—; adj. prof. U. Fla., Gainesville, 1978—; mem. Polar rsch. bd. NRC, Washington, 1982-91, space sci. bd., 1980-94; chmn. Space Studies Bd., 1988-94; phys. sci. Com. NASA, Washington, 1975-79; chmn. space and earth sci. adv. comm., 1984-88, adv. coun., 1984-94; mem. adv. com. on future U.S. space program, 1990. V.P.'s space policy adv. bd., 1992-93, v.p. blue ribbon advisory com. on re-design of space station, 1993-94. Co-author: Particle Diffusion in Rad. Belts, 1974; co-editor 2 books related to space physics, 1977, 79; contbr. over 400 tech. papers to profl. jours. V.p. Harding Twp. (N.J.) Sch. Bd., 1982-90, com., 1993—. Recipient Antarctic Svc. medal U.S., 1979, Disting. Pub. Svc. award NASA, 1982, 1988, 94, Achievement award Blackburn Coll. Alumni Assn., 1993; mountain named in his honor in Antarctica; minor planet 5504 named in his honor. Fellow Am. Phys. Soc., Am. Geophys. Union, AAAS; mem. NAE, Internat. Acad. Astronautics. Office: AT&T Bell Labs 600 Mountain Ave New Providence NJ 07974-2008

LANZILLOTTI, ROBERT FRANKLIN, economist, educator; b. Washington, June 19, 1921; s. Vincent and Gilda S. (Incutti) L.; m. Patricia Joy Jackson, Oct. 27, 1945; children—Robert J. (dec.), Donna J. Student, Dartmouth Coll., 1943; B.A., Am. U., 1946, M.A., 1947; Ph.D., U. Calif.,

Berkeley, 1953; D.D.L. (hon.), Tampa U., 1979; D.D.S. (hon.), Fla. Inst. Tech., 1979. Teaching fellow U. Calif. at Berkeley, 1947-49; mem. faculty Wash. State U., 1949-61, prof. econs., 1959-61; research assoc. Brookings Instn., 1956-57, 1974-75; prof. econs., chmn. dept. Mich. State U., 1961-69; prof. econs., dean Coll. Bus. Adminstrn., U. Fla., Gainesville, 1969-86, Eminent Scholar chair in Am. econ. instns., 1986; mem. U.S. Price Commn., 1971-72; bd. dirs. Jim Walter Corp., Citizens and So. Bank Corp., Fla. Power Corp., Bank of Ormond Beach, Fla., Talquin Corp., Bottom-Line Assoc., Fla. Progress Corp.; chmn. Econ. Adv. Bd. to Gov. of Fla., 1973—; cons. Mich. Bankers Assn., attys. gen., Calif., Wis., Minn., Ill., Mich., Oreg., Washington; attys. gen. also Fed. Trade Commn., U.S. Dept. Justice, U.S. Govt. Accounting Office, U.S. Comptroller of the Currency, U.S. Census Bur. Author: Hard-Surface Floor Covering Industry, 1955, Pricing, Production & Marketing Policies of Small Manufacturers, 1964, Banking Structure in Michigan, 1945-63, 1966; co-author: Pricing in Big Business, 1959, Phase II in Review: The Price Commission Experience, 1975, Economic Effects of Government Mandated Costs, 1979; editor: The Conglomerate Corporation, 1981; contbr. profl. jours. Served to lt. (j.g.) USNR, 1943-45; lt. comdr. Res. Decorated Bronze Star (2); NATO fellow, 1964. Mem. Am. Econ. Assn., So. Econ. Assn. (1st v.p. 1972-73), Fla. Coun. of 100, Phi Beta Kappa (hon.), Beta Gamma Sigma, Omicron Delta Kappa.

LANZINGER, KLAUS, language educator; b. Woergl, Tyrol, Austria, Feb. 16, 1928; came to U.S., 1971, naturalized, 1979; m. Aida Schuessl, June, 1954; children—Franz, Christine. B.A., Bowdoin Coll., 1951; Ph.D., U. Innsbruck (Austria), 1952. Research asst. U. Innsbruck, 1957-67; assoc. prof. modern langs. U. Notre Dame (Ind.), 1967-77, prof., 1977—, resident dir. fgn. study program, Innsbruck, 1969-71, 76-78, 82-85; acting chmn. dept. Modern and Classical Languages, U. Notre Dame, fall 1987, chmn. dept. German and Russian, 1989—. Author: Epik im amerikanischen Roman, 1965, Jason's Voyage: The Search for the Old world in American Literature, 1989. Editor: Americana-Austriaca, 5 vols., 1966-83. Contbr. numerous articles to profl. jours. Bowdoin Coll. fgn. student scholar, 1950-51; Fulbright research grantee U. Pa., 1961; U. Notre Dame summer research grantee Houghton Library, Harvard U., 1975, 81. Mem. MLA, Deutsche Gesellschaft für Amerikastudien, Thomas Wolfe Soc. Home: 52703 Helvie Dr South Bend IN 46635-1215 Office: Dept German Russian Langs & Lits U Notre Dame Notre Dame IN 46556

LANZL, LAWRENCE HERMAN, medical physicist; b. Chgo., Apr. 8, 1921; s. Hans and Elsa (Seitz) L.; m. Elisabeth Farber, Sept. 18, 1947; children: Eric Lawrence, Barbara Jane. B.S., Northwestern U., 1943; M.S., U. Ill., 1947, Ph.D., 1951. Diplomate: Am. Bd. Health Physics (dir. 1969-73), Am. Bd. Radiology (mem. physics exam. com. 1977-83). Asst. dept. astronomy Dearborn Obs.; interim instr. dept. physics Northwestern U., Evanston, Ill., 1941-43; jr. physicist Metall. Lab., Manhattan Project, U. Chgo., 1944, Los Alamos (N.Mex.) Sci. Lab. Manhattan Project, U. Calif., 1944-45; research asst. dept. physics U. Ill., Urbana, 1946-50; asso. physicist naval reactor div. Argonne (Ill.) Nat. Lab., 1951; sr. physicist U. Chgo., Argonne Cancer Research Hosp., 1951-55, research physicist, 1955-56; asst. prof. U. Chgo., 1956-59, asso. prof., 1959-68, prof. dept. radiology and Franklin McLean Meml. Research Inst., 1968-80, prof. emeritus, 1980—; prof. Rush Med. Coll., Chgo., 1980—; prof., chmn. dept. med. physics Coll. Health Scis. and Grad. Coll., Rush U., Chgo., 1982—; 1st officer divsn. life scis. IAEA, Vienna, Austria, 1967-68; cons. Pan Am. Health Orgn., 1993, Internat. Atomic Energy Agy., 1994; radiation hazard control expert Ill. Bd. Radiation Physics, 1960; mem. Radiation Protection Adv. Coun. State Ill., 1966—, chmn., 1971—; mem. Med. Use Adv. Bd. State Ill., 1974—. Author: (with others) Moving Field Radiation Therapy, 1962, Radiation Accidents and Emergencies in Medicine, Research and Industry, 1965, Atlas of Radiation Dose Distributions, 1972; editor: Recent Developments in Digital Imaging, 1985; contbr. (with others) articles to profl. jours. Mem. DBM Adv. Panel for Californium Program AEC, 1969-73; cons. Nat. Cancer Inst., 1968-88; cons. therapeutic radiology service, sect. radiation physics Hines (Ill.) VA Hosp., 1969-87, chmn. adv. panel on radiation safety and protection, 1973-80; mem. coun. Marie Sklodowska-Curie Meml. Found., Warsaw, Poland, 1989—. Recipient Commendation VA, Washington, 1975, Alumni Honor award for disting. svc. U. Ill., 1984, Landauer award Midwest chpt. Am. Assn. Physicists in Medicine/Health Physics Soc., 1989; Evans scholar Northwestern U., 1940-43; Lawrence H. Lanzl Inst. of Med. Physics named in his honor. Fellow Am. Coll. Radiology (mem. commn. human resources 1976-88), Health Physics Soc. (editor assn. jour. 1979-83), Am. Assn. Physicists in Medicine (pres. 1966-67, chmn. Commn. on Accreditation 1981-89, Spl. Recognition award Midwest chpt. 1977, chmn. local arrangements 1969-86, mem. com. on tng. med. physicists 1976-90, William D. Coolidge award 1978, Farrington Daniels award 1984, Landauer Meml. award 1989); mem. Am. Phys. Soc., Internat. Orgn. Med. Physics (U.S. del. 1973-85, v.p. 1982-85, pres. 1985-89, editor Med. Physics World 1982-85), Radiol. Soc. N. Am. (mem. asso. sci. coms. 1972-82), Nat. Council Radiation Protection and Measurements (mem. sci. coms. 1967-92), AAAS, Radiation Research Soc., Am. Nuclear Soc. (Midwest), Hosp. Physicists' Assn. (U.K.), Internat. Radiation Protection Assn., Assn. Med. Physicists India, Chinese Soc. Med. Physics (hon.), Internat. Union Phys. and Engring. Scis. in Medicine (coun. 1985-94, pres. 1988-91, past pres. 1991-94), Sigma Xi (Disting. Scientist Mem. award 1989, J.M. Paul Meml. award 1992). Unitarian. Club: Quadrangle. Office: Rush-Presbyn-St Luke's Med Ctr Dept Med Physics 1653 W Chicago IL 60612

LANZONI, VINCENT, medical school dean; b. Kingston, Mass., Feb. 23, 1928; s. Vincent and Caroline (Melloni) L.; m. Phoebe Krey, June 12, 1960; children: Karen, Susan, Margaret. BS, Tufts U., 1949, PhD, 1953; MD, Boston U., 1960. USPHS fellow Tufts U., 1953-54; intern in medicine Boston City Hosp., 1960-61, resident and fellow in medicine, 1961-65; asst. prof. pharmacology Boston U., 1964-67, assoc. prof. medicine and pharmacology, 1967-73, prof., 1973-75; assoc. dean Sch. Medicine, 1969-75; prof. U. Medicine and Dentistry N.J., Newark, 1975—, dean N.J. Med. Sch., 1975-87, interim dean Grad. Sch. Biomed. Scis., 1987—; bd. dirs., sec.-treas. Postgrad. Med. Inst., 1972-75; bd. dirs. Mass. Health Research Inst., Mass. Registration in Nursing, Roxbury Neighborhood Clinic. Served to lt. Navy, USAF, 1954-56. Researcher cardiovascular pharmacology, hypertension. Office: NJ Med Sch 100 Bergen St Newark NJ 07103-2407

LAO, LANG LI, nuclear fusion research physicist; b. Hai Duong, Vietnam, Jan. 28, 1954; came to U.S., 1972; s. Thich Cuong and Boi Phan (Loi) L.; m. Ngan Hua, Dec. 22, 1979; children: Bert J., Brian J. BS, MS, Calif. Inst. Tech., 1976; MS, U. Wis., 1977, PhD, 1979. Staff scientist Oak Ridge (Tenn.) Nat. Lab., 1979-81, TRW, Redondo Beach, Calif., 1981-82; prin. scientist Gen. Atomics, San Diego, 1982—. Contbr. articles to sci. jours. Fellow Am. Phys. Soc. (co-recipient excellence in plasma physics rsch. award 1994). Achievements include being world leader in equilibrium analysis of magnetic fusion plasma physics experiments; developed a widely used computer code essential for successful operation and interpretation of tokamak fusion experiments. Office: General Atomics 3550 General Atomics Ct San Diego CA 92121

LAO, MARDONIO MAGADAN, history educator, researcher, farmer; b. Bukidnon, The Philippines, Dec. 24, 1950; s. Cecilio and Sotera Lao; m. Agnes Grace Cruzado, Jan. 4, 1975; children: Diane Love Grace, Marza Lee Gem, Debrah Lily. BA cum laude, Silliman U., The Philippines, 1974; MA, U. The Philippines, 1978, PhD in History, 1984. Instr. Silliman U., Dumaguete City, 1973-74; instr. Ctrl. Mindanao U., Musuan, The Philippines, 1974-78, asst. prof., 1978-84, chmn. dept. Social Scis., Coll. Arts and Scis., 1978-80, asst. dean Coll. Arts and Scis., 1984, assoc. prof., 1984-86, acting dean Coll. Arts and Scis., 1985-86, prof., 1986—, secy. grad. sch., 1987-88, officer-in-chg. grad. sch., 1989-90, univ. and bd. regents secy., 1993—; coord. instn. bldg. program Nat. Sci. and Tech. Authority, 1986, Mindanao Univs. Sci. Consortium, 1986; speaker numerous confs. and orgns. in field. Author: History of Cagayan de Oro, 1622-1901, 1980, Bukidnon in Historical Perspective, vol. 1, 1985, Bukidnon in Historical Perspective, vol. 2, 1992; contbr. articles to profl. jours. Recipient Silliman U. Honor Scholarship award, 1970-73, Ctrl. Mindanao U. Faculty Scholarship award, 1976-78, 80-84, Ctrl. Mindanao U. Rsch. grant 1975-76, Philippine Social Sci. Rsch. award 1977, 83, Pride of Heritage award Internat. Press. Rsch. Devel. Progress Inc., 1989, Toyota Found. Internat. Rsch. award 1989-92. Mem. Nat. Rsch. Coun. The Philippines, Philippine Hist. Assn., Ctrl. Mindanao Media Practitioners, Phi Kappa Phi. Home and Office: Ctrl Mindanao Univ Musuan Bukidnon 8710, The Philippines

LAOS, JEFFERY BAFFERT, health services specialist; b. Tucson, Oct. 11, 1954; s. Roy Elias and Annie (Baffert) L.; m. Carren Lee Wood, Jan. 7, 1984; children: Jeffrey Wood Jr., Jarred Wood. BS in Health Svcs., U. Ariz., 1983, postgrad., 1985—; cert. mgmt., Western Internat. U., Phoenix, 1985. Emergency med. technician II A&A Ambulance, Tucson, 1973-77; dialysis technician Dialysis Found. So. Ariz., Tucson, 1977-81, projects mgr., 1981-83; dept. mgr. renal service St. Joseph's Med. Ctr., Phoenix, 1983-85; adminstr., chief executive officer Desert Dialysis Ctr., Tucson, 1985-86; cons. Dialysis Cons., Inc., Littleton, Colo., 1987—; pres., cons. Jeffrey B. Laos & Assocs., Tucson, 1987—; instr. U. Ariz., Tucson, 1975-77, Pima Community Coll., Tucson, 1976-79. Contbr. articles to profl. jours. Bd. mem. Nat. Kidney Found. Ariz., Tucson, 1985, Catholic Community Svcs. Ariz., Tucson, 1985; mem. Republican Com., Pima County, Tucson, 1977. Recipient Outstanding Citizen of Tucson award, Mayor of Tucson, 1972, 88; speakers award, Lions Internat. Tucson, 1987. Mem. Nat. Renal Adminstrs. Assn., U. Ariz. Alumni Assn., We. Internat. U. Mgmt. Soc. Republican. Roman Catholic. Avocations: golf, organized league basketball, painting. Office: Laos & Assocs 9300 N Eagle Dancer Dr Las Tablas NM 87541-9999

LAPALOMBARA, JOSEPH, political science educator; b. Chgo., May 18, 1925; s. Louis and Helen (Teutonico) LaP.; m. Lyda Mae Ecke, June 22, 1947 (div.); children—Richard, David, Susan; m. Constance Ada Bezer, June, 1971. A.B., U. Ill., 1947, A.M., 1950; A.M. (Charlotte Elizabeth Proctor fellow, Class of 1883 fellow), Princeton U., 1952, Ph.D., 1954; student, U. Rome (Italy), 1952-53; M.A. (hon.), Yale U., 1964. Instr., then asst. prof. polit. sci. Oreg. State Coll., 1947-50; instr. politics Princeton U., 1952; mem. faculty Mich. State U., 1953-64, prof. polit. sci., 1958-64, head dept., 1958-63; prof. polit. sci. Yale U., 1964—; Arnold Wolfers prof., 1969—, chmn. dept. polit. sci., 1974-78, 82-85; prof. Sch. of Orgn. and Mgmt., 1979-84; dir. Instn. for Social and Policy Studies, 1987-92; chmn. Council Comparative and European Studies, 1966-71; cultural attache, first sec. U.S. embassy, Rome, 1980-81; vis. prof. U. Florence, Italy, 1957-58, U. Calif.-Berkeley, 1962, Columbia U., 1966-67, U. Turin, 1974, U. Catania, 1974; cons. FCDA, 1956, Carnegie Corp., 1959, Brookings Instn., 1962, Ford Found., 1963-76, Twentieth Century Fund, 1965-69, AID, 1967-68, Fgn. Svc. Inst., 1968-72, 74-76, Ednl. Testing Svc., 1970-75, Alcoa, 1978-80, Rohm & Haas, 1975-76, GE, 1978-80, Union Carbide, 1981-92, Montedison, 1984-85, Ente Nazionale Idrocarburi, 1983-93, Guardian Industries, 1990-93, Praxair, 1992—, Swiss Bank Corp., 1994—, Athena, 1994-95; sr. rsch. assoc. Conf. Bd. N.Y., 1976-81; pres. Italian-Am. Multimedia Corp. N.Y., 1988—. Author: The Initiative and Referendum in Oregon, 1950, The Italian Labor Movement: Problems and Prospects, 1957, Guide to Michigan Politics, rev. edit, 1960, (with Alberto Spreafico) Elezioni e Comportamento Politico in Italia, 1963, Bureaucracy and Political Development, 1963, Interest Groups in Italian Politics, 1964, Italy: The Politics of Planning, 1966, (with Myron Weiner) Political Parties and Political Development, 1966, Clientela e Parentela, 1967, Burocracia y desarrolo politico, 1970, Crises and Sequences of Political Development, (with others), 1972, Politics Within Nations, 1974, (with Stephen Blank) Multinational Corporations and National Elites: A Study in Tensions, 1975, Multinational Corporations in Comparative Perspective, 1976, Multinational Corporations and Developing Countries, 1979, A Politica nos Interior das Nações, 1982, Democracy, Italian Style, 1987, Democrazia all'italiana, 1988, Die Italiener: oder Demokratie als Lebenskunst, 1988, Democratie à l'italienne, 1990; bd. editors Midwest Jour. Polit. Sci, 1956-57, Yale U. Press, 1965-72, 73-76, ABC-CL10, 1976—, Global Perspectives, 1983—; mem. editorial bd. Comparative Politics, 1968—, Jour. Comparative and European Studies, 1969—, Am. Jour. Polit. Sci, 1976-80; Italian Jour., 1988; editor series comparative politics Prentice-Hall Co., 1971-85; mem. editorial adv. bd. Jour. Comparative Adminstrn, 1970-74, Adminstrn. and Soc, 1974—; adv. bd. ABC Polit. Sci; N.Am. editor: Mediterranean Observer, 1981-86; editor in chief Italy, Italy, 1988—; contbr. articles to profl. jours. Exec. com. Inter U. Consortium Polit. Research, 1968-70; staff mem. Social Sci. Research Council, 1966-73; chmn. West European fgn. area fellowship program Social Sci. Research Council-Am. Council Learned Socs., 1972-74, mem., 1974-75; dir. Mich. Citizenship Clearing House, 1955. Decorated knight comdr. Order of Merit, Republic of Italy, Fulbright scholar, 1952-53, 57-58, Penfield scholar U. Pa., 1953; fellow Social Sci. Rsch. Coun., 1952-53, Ctr. Advanced Study Behavioral Scis., 1961-62, Rockefeller Found., 1963-64, Ford Found., 1969, Guggenheim Found., 1971-72; recipient Guido Dorso prize, Italy, 1984, Medal of Honor, Italian Constitutional Ct., 1993, Presidency of Italian Republic, 1993. Mem. Am. Acad. Arts and Scis., Conn. Acad. Arts and Scis., Am. Acad. in Rome (trustee 1984-94), Social Sci. Research Council (com. comparative politics 1958-72), Am. Polit. Sci. Assn. (exec. coun. 1963-65, exec. com. 1967-68, v.p. 1979-80, mem. conf. group on Italian politics and soc. 1978, conf. pres. 1984-85), So. Polit. Sci. Assn., Midwest Polit. Sci. Assn., Am. Soc. Pub. Adminstrn., Am. Acad. Polit. and Social Sci., Soc. for Italian Hist. Studies, Societá Italiana di Studi Elettorali, Consiglio Italiano di Scienze Sociali, Phi Beta Kappa, Phi Kappa Phi, Phi Eta Sigma. Clubs: Yale of N.Y., Elizabethan, Morys Assn., East India. Home: 50 Huntington St New Haven CT 06511-1333

LAPATIN, PHILIP STUART, lawyer; b. Balt., Feb. 18, 1949; s. Joseph Abraham and Sara (Union) L.; m. Donna Linda Greenglass, June 11, 1972; children: Sheri Meredith, Adam Blake. BA, Cornell U., 1971; JD, Boston U., 1973. Bar: Mass. 1973, U.S. Ct. Appeals (1st cir.) 1983. With Gaston & Snow, Boston, 1973—, ptnr., 1981—; lectr. Nat. Assn. Realtors, 1979, N.W. Ctr. Profl. Edn., 1985—; clk. Greater Boston Real Estate Bd., 1976—, bd. dirs. Author: Residential Landlord-Tenant Law, 1977, Consumer Protection in Massachusetts, 1978, Real Estate Standard Forms Guide, 1986 (pamphlets) Brokerage Law Series, 1982-87. Bd. dirs. New Eng. Non-Profit Housing Corp., Concord, N.H., 1978. Recipient cert. of appreciation Providence Bd. Realtors, 1980, Mass. Assn. Realtors, 1983. Mem. ABA, Boston Bar Assn., Phi Beta Kappa. Office: Gaston & Snow 1 Federal St Boston MA 02110-2003

LAPAYOWKER, MARC SPENCER, radiologist; b. Phila., Sept. 19, 1927; s. Adolph H. and Anna E. (Hoberman) L.; m. Isabel Rose Gordy, May 2, 1930; children: Andrew, Janet. BA, Temple U., 1950, MD, 1954. Diplomate Am. Bd. Radiology. Assoc. radiologist Temple U., Phila., 1960-70; prof. radiology Temple U., 1969-83; dir. diagnostic radiology Temple U. Hosp., Phila., 1975-83; pres. Montgomery County Med. Imaging, Willow Grove, Pa., 1985-92; chmn. dept. radiology Abington Meml. Hosp., Abington, Pa., 1983-92; sr. radiologist Abington (Pa.) Meml. Hosp., 1992—; bd. dirs. Schuylkill River Devel. Corp. Contbr. articles to profl. jours. Pres. Phila. Roentgen Ray Soc., 1975-76; bd. dirs. Walnut St. Theatre, 1993—, Phila. Chamber Ensemble, 1994—. Lt. comdr. USNR, 1955-57. Named Radiologist of Yr. Pa. Radiologic Soc., 1988. Fellow Am. Coll. Radiology (bd. chancellors 1987-82, chmn. com. on coding and nomenclature 1983-90), Am. Inst. Ultrasound; mem. AMA. Jewish. Avocations: photography, sailing. Home: 2301 Cherry St Apt 16E Philadelphia PA 19103-1043 Office: Radiology Group of Abington 1200 York Rd Abington PA 19001-3788

LA PENTA, ROBERT VINCENT, electronics company executive; b. Yonkers, N.Y., Aug. 20, 1945; s. John Peter and Nancy Ann (DeIanni) La P.; 1 child, Robert Vincent Jr. BBA, Iona Coll., 1967. CPA, Tex. Sr. acct. Deloitte Haskins & Sells, N.Y.C., 1967-72; corp. v.p., controller Loral Corp., N.Y.C., 1972—; bd. dirs. Travel Video Systems, Inc., N.Y.C., 1984—. Mem. Am. Inst. CPA's, Fin. Execs. Inst., Assn. Govt. Fin. Execs. Office: Loral Corp 600 3rd Ave New York NY 10016-1901

LAPHAM, LEWIS HENRY, editor, author, television host; b. San Francisco, Jan. 8, 1935; s. Lewis Abbot and Jane (Foster) L.; m. Joan Brooke Reeves, Aug. 10, 1972; children: Lewis Andrew, Elizabeth Delphina, Winston Peale. Grad., Hotchkiss Sch., 1952; BA, Yale U., 1956; postgrad., Cambridge U., 1956-57; LLD, Hampden-Sydney Coll., Va. Reporter San Francisco Examiner, 1957-60, N.Y. Herald Tribune, 1960-62; author, editor USA-1, N.Y.C., 1962, Saturday Evening Post, N.Y.C., 1963-67; writer Life mag., Harper's, N.Y.C., 1968-70; mng. editor Harper's, N.Y.C., 1971-75; editor Harper's, 1975-81, 83—; TV host weekly series Bookmark, PBS, also host, author documentary series America's Century. Author: (essays) Fortune's Child, 1980, Money and Class in America, 1988, Imperial Masquerade, 1989, The Wish for Kings, 1993. Mem. Council on Fgn. Relations. Club: Century Assn. (N.Y.C.). Office: Harper's Mag 666 Broadway New York NY 10012-2317

LAPIDES, JACK, urologist, medical educator; b. Rochester, N.Y., Nov. 27, 1914; s. Harry and Emma (Seldow) L.; m. Alice Jean Hatt, June 1948 (dec. Oct. 1971); m. Roberta de Vries Stadt, Sept. 1975 (dec. June 1993). B.A., U. Mich., 1936, M.A., 1938, M.D., 1941. Diplomate: Am. Bd. Urology. Rockefeller Research asso. fellow physiology U. Mich. Grad. Sch., 1936-38; intern U. Mich. Hosp., 1941-42, asst. resident surgery, 1946-47, resident sect. urology, dept. surgery, 1947-50; research fellow urology U. Chgo., 1947; USPHS postdoctorate fellow Nat. Cancer Inst., 1948-50; instr. urology U. Mich. Med. Sch., 1950-52, asst. prof. surgery, 1952-55, asso. prof., 1955-64, prof. surgery sect. urology, 1964-84, prof. emeritus surgery, 1984—, head sect. urology, 1968-83; chief sect. urology Wayne County Gen. Hosp., 1950-83, VA Hosp., 1952-83. Author: Fundamentals of Urology, 1976; Contbg. author chpts. in numerous med. texts, also articles. Served with USAAF, 1942-46. Recipient award for disting. achievement U. Mich. Med. Ctr. Alumni Soc., 1994. Mem. Soc. Pediatric Urology, Washtenaw County Med. Soc., Fla. Urol. Soc., AMA, ACS, Am. Urol. Assn., Am. Assn. Genitourinary Surgeons, Pan-Am. Med. Assn., Phi Beta Kappa, Sigma Xi, Phi Eta Sigma, Phi Sigma, Phi Kappa Phi, Alpha Omega Alpha (Paul Zimskind award 1987, Ramon Guiteras award 1987, Pediatric Urology medal 1989, Premier F. Brantley Scott award 1993). Home: 2805 N Wagner Rd Ann Arbor MI 48103-1765

LAPIDES, JEFFREY ROLF, corporate executive; b. Balt., June 16, 1954; s. Morton M. and Joan Elisabeth (Sherbow) Winston; m. Kathy Lee Bortner, June 19, 1977; children: Jessica, David, Benjamin. BA, Clark U., Mass., 1976; MS in Physics, U. Md., 1979; Ph.D., U. Md., College Park, 1981. Research asst. NASA-Goddard, Greenbelt, Md., 1976-81; staff fellow NIH, Bethesda, Md., 1981-82; dir. intra-corp. devel. Allegheny Beverage Corp., Cheverly, Md., 1982-83; v.p. info. systems, 1983-85, sr. v.p. strategic planning, 1985-86; exec. v.p. Alleco, Cheverly, Md., 1986-88, pres., 1988; pres. Service Am. subs. Alleco, 1986-87, Jeffrey R. Lapides and Assocs., Inc., Columbia, Md., 1989-90; v.p. comml. products Essex Corp., Columbia, Md., 1990—. Mem. Am. Phys. Soc., Phi Beta Kappa. Office: Essex Corp 9150 Guilford Rd Columbia MD 21046-1891

LAPIDES, JULIAN LEE, state senator, lawyer; b. Balt., Sept. 17, 1931; s. Solomon M. and Doris (Racusin) L.; m. Linda Zeva Fishman, 1964. BS, Towson State U., 1955; LLB, U. Md., 1961. Tchr. sci. pub. schs., 1956-60; admitted to Md. bar, 1965; practice law, Balt., 1965—; mem. Md. Ho. of Dels., 1963-67, Md. State Senate, 1967—; mem. senate budget and taxation com., 1967—, co-chmn. joint com. legis. ethics, joint budget and audit com. Mem. Md. State Arts Council, 1967—, Md. Hall Records Commn., Md. State Planning Commn., Md. State Housing Policy Commn.; pres. Mt. Royal Democratic Club. Served with AUS, 1954-56. Recipient Md. Pub. Health Assn. Ann. Achievement award, 1971, Nat. Kidney Found. Disting. Service award, 1971, Young Democrat of Md. Outstanding State Ofcl. award, 1973, Cert. of Merit Common Cause Md., 1982. Mem. Am. Antiquarian Soc. (council 1983—). Address: 1528 Bolton St Baltimore MD 21217-4203 Office: Md State Senate Office Bldg Annapolis MD 21401

LAPIDUS, ALLAN E., lawyer; b. Chgo., 1943; s. Bernard Lapidus; m. Ghita Lapidus, 1980; children: David, Laura. BS, U. Wis., 1964; JD, U. Mich., 1967. Bar: Ill. 1967, U.S. Dist. Ct. (no. dist.) Ill. 1970, U.S. Dist. Ct. (so. dist.) Ill. 1972, U.S. Dist. Ct. (ctrl. dist.) Ill. 1974, U.S. Ct. Appeals (7th cir.) 1971, U.S. Supreme Ct. 1972. Trial atty. FCC, Chgo., 1967-69; asst. U.S. atty. No. Dist. Ct. Ill., Chgo., 1969-73; ptnr. Vedder, Price, Kaufman & Kammholz, Chgo., 1973—; panel atty. Fed. Defender Program, Chgo. Cooperating atty. ACLU, Chgo. Mem. Chgo. Bar Assn. Office: Vedder Price Kaufman & Kammholz 222 N La Salle St Chicago IL 60601-1003

LAPIDUS, ARNOLD, mathematician; b. Bklyn., Nov. 6, 1933; s. Morris and Mollie L.; m. Nancy Beatrice Latner, Aug. 9, 1952. BS, Bklyn. Coll., 1956; MS, PhD, N.Y. U., 1967. Research scientist Courant Inst., N.Y.C., 1956-68; computer application math. analyst Goddard Inst. for Space Studies, N.Y.C., 1968-70, math. analyst programming methods, 1970-71, sr. mem. tech. staff computer scis., 1971-73; assoc. prof. quantitative analysis Fairleigh Dickinson U., Teaneck, N.J., 1973-83, prof., chair dept. computer and decision systems, 1983-85; sr. engr. Singer Electronic Systems Corp., Little Falls, N.J., 1986-87; owner Advanced Math. Co., Englewood, N.J., 1987—; pvt. practice Englewood, 1987—. Contbr. articles to profl. publs. Mem. AAAS, AAUP, Math. Assn. Am., Am. Math. Soc., Soc. Indsl. and Applied Math. Home and Office: 160 Rockwood Pl Englewood NJ 07631-5028

LAPIDUS, JULES BENJAMIN, association executive; b. Chgo., May 1, 1931; s. Leo R. and Lillian D. (Davidson) LaP.; m. Anne Marie Liedman, June 8, 1970; children: Steven, Amy, Mark, Marilyn. B.S., U. Ill., 1954; M.S., U. Wis., 1957, Ph.D., 1958. Prof. medicinal and pharm. chemistry Ohio State U., 1958-84; assoc. dean Grad. Sch., 1972-74, dean Grad. Sch., 1974-84, vice provost for research, 1974-82; pres. Council Grad. Schs., 1984—; Mem. pharmacology and toxicology tng. com. NIH, 1965-67, pharmacology program com., 1971-74; mem. Grad. Record Examination Bd., 1982—. Mem. AAAS, Am. Chem. Soc. Office: Coun Grad Schs 1 Dupont Cir NW Ste 430 Washington DC 20036-1110

LAPIDUS, MORRIS, retired architect, interior designer; b. Odessa, Russia, Nov. 25, 1902; came to U.S., 1903, naturalized, 1914; s. Leon and Eva (Sherman) L.; m. Beatrice Perlman, Feb. 22, 1929 (dec. 1992); children: Richard L., Alan H. Student, NYU, 1921-23; B. Arch., Columbia, 1927. With Warren & Wetmore, N.Y.C., 1926-28, Arthur Weisner, N.Y.C., 1928-30; asso. architect Ross-Frankel, Inc., N.Y.C., 1930-42; prin. Morris Lapidus Assos., 1942-86; keynote speaker Conv. Preserving the Recent Past, U.S. Dept. Interiors, 1995. Author: Architecture-A Profession and a Business, 1967, Architecture of Joy, 1979, Man's Three Million Odyssey, 1988, A Pyramid in Brooklyn, 1989, Morris Lapidus: The Architect of the American Dream, 1992 (English and German edits. by Martina Duttmann); architect-designer: Fontainebleau Hotel, Miami Beach, Fla., 1954, Eden Roc Hotel, 1955, Americana Hotel, Bal Harbor, Fla., 1956, Sheraton Motor Inn, N.Y.C., 1962, Internat. Inn, Washington, 1964, Fairfield Towers, Bklyn., 1966, Summit Hotel, N.Y.C., 1966, Paradise Island Hotel, Nassau, 1967, Paradise Island Casino, Nassau, 1968, Out-Patient and Rehab. Center, continuing care wing Mt. Sinai Hosp, Miami Beach, Fla., 1967, Research Bldg, 1981, congregation Beth Tfiloh, Pikesville, Md., 1967, Internat. Hdqrs. of Jr. Chamber Internat., Coral Gables, Fla., 1968, Americana Hotel, N.Y.C., 1968, Cadman Plaza Urban Redevel., Bklyn., 1969, Miami Internat. Airport, 1969-74, Penn-Wortman Housing Project, Bklyn., 1971, Bedford-Stuyvesant Swimming Pool and Park, Bklyn., 1970, El Conquistador Hotel, P.R., 1969, Trelawney Beach Hotel, Jamaica, W.I., 1973, Greater Miami Jewish Fedn. Hdgrs, 1970, Hertz Skycenter Hotel, Jacksonville, Fla., 1971, Aventura, Miami, 1971, U. Miami (Fla.) Concert Hall, 1972, Griffin Sq. Office Bldg, Dallas, 1972, U. Miami Law Library, 1975, Citizens Fed. Bank Bldg, Miami, 1975, Miami Beach Theater of Performing Arts, 1976, Ogun State Hotel, Nigeria, 1977, Exhbn. Designers, Forum Design, Linz, Austria, 1980; others; assoc. architect: Keys Community Coll, Key West, Fla., 1977, Churchill Hotel London, Grandview Apt. Complex, 1980, La Union Ins. Bldg., Guayaquil, Ecuador, 1983, Daniel Tower Hotel, Herzlea, Israel, 1983, Colony Performing Arts Ctr., 1983, Jabita Hotel, Nigeria, 1984; lectr. store, hotel design; one-man exhibit 40 Yrs. Art and Architecture, Lowe Gallery, Miami U., 1967, Fedn. Arts and Archtl. League N.Y., 1970, Weiner Galleries, 1972, Exhibit 55 Yrs. Architecture, Rotterdam, The Netherlands, 1992; exhibited at Bass Mus. of Art, 1994, Columbia U., 1995; monograph pub. in Basil's Switzerland, 1992. Mem. Miami Beach Devel. Commn., 1966-67. Winner nat. competition S.W. Urban Renewal Program in Wash., internat. competition for trade ctr. on The Portal Site in Washington; recipient Justin P. Allman award Wallcovering Wholesaler's Assn., 1963; Outstanding Specifications award Gypsum Drywall Contractors Internat., 1968; cert. merit N.Y. Soc. Architects, 1971; NYU Alumni Achievement award, 1955. Mem. Miami Beach C. of C. (gov.), Kiwanis. Achievements include initial use of modern in merchandising field; areas of work include housing, hosps., hotels, shopping ctrs., office bldgs., religious instns. Home: 3 Island Ave Miami FL 33139-1363

LAPIDUS, NORMAN ISRAEL, food broker; b. N.Y.C., July 20, 1930; s. Rueben and Laurette (Goldsmith) L.; m. Myrna Sue Cohen, Nov. 20, 1960; children: Robin Anne, Jody Beth. BBA, CCNY, 1952; postgrad. internat. Relations, CCNY, NYU, 1957-60. Salesman Rueben Lapidus Co., N.Y.C.,

1954-56, pres., 1960—; sales trainee Cohn-Hall-Marx, N.Y.C., 1955; salesman to v.p. Julius Levy Co., Millburn, N.J., 1964-66, pres., 1966—; salesman Harry W. Freedman Co., Millburn, N.J., 1975-76, v.p., treas., 1976-84, pres., 1984—; pres. Julius Levy/Rueben Lapidus and Harry W. Freedman Cos. div. Pezrow Corp., Millburn, N.J., 1985-86, L&H Food Brokers, Millburn, N.J., 1986-87. Mem. Maplewood (N.J.) Bd. Adjustment, 1975-82; gen. chmn. Maplewood Citizens Budget Adv. Com., 1977-79, chmn. Maplewood United Jewish Appeal Drive, 1975-76, 83-84; vice-chmn. Maplewood First Aid Squad Bldg. Fund Dr., 1978-79; co-founder Citizens for Charter Change in Essex County (N.J.), 1974, mem. exec. bd., 1974—, treas., 1983-84; founder, chmn. Music Theatre of Maplewood; pres. Maplewood Civic Assn., 1983-85; bd. mgrs. Essex County unit Am. Cancer Soc., v.p., 1984-87, chmn. 1991—; mem. adv. bd. Essex County Coll., West Essex, N.J., chairperson bd., 1991—; mem., sec., bd. dirs. KnollCrest Neighborhood Assn., 1994—; active local theatricals. Served with U.S. Army, 1952-54, Korea. Recipient Leadership Medallion United Jewish Appeal, 1970, 84. Mem. Nat. Food Brokers Assn. (regional dir., Cert. Exceptionally Meritorious Svc.), Nat. Food Svc. Sales Com., Met. Food Brokers Assn. (chmn. 1982-90), Assn. Food Industries (bd. dirs.), Nat. Food Processors Assn., Young Guard Soc., Old Guard Soc., CCNY Alumni Assn., U.S. Navy Inst., Acad. Polit. Sci., Archaeol. Inst. Am., Nat. Trust for Historic Preservation, Assn. Food Distbrs., Knollcrest Homeowners Assn. (bd. trustees), LWV, Am. Legion, Lions (bd. dirs.), B'nai Brith. Republican. Jewish. Club: Maplewood Glee. Home: 9 Lockhaven Ct Bedminster NJ 07921-1728 Office: 2204 Morris Ave Ste 310 Union NJ 07083-5914

LAPIER, THEODORE, lawyer; b. Kansas City, Sept. 2, 1953; s. Rae Theodore and Alice (Daley) LaP.; m. Kathy Feldman, May 17, 1986; children: Danielle, Andrew Theodore. BA, U. Pa., 1972-76; JD, Fordham U., 1976-79. Bar: N.Y. 1980. Assoc. Willkie Farr & Gallagher, N.Y.C., 1979-88, ptnr., 1989-93; ptnr. Berlack, Israels & Liberman, N.Y.C., 1993—. Avocations: sailing, golf. Office: Berlack Israels & Liberman 120 W 45th St New York NY 10036-4041

LAPIERRE, DOMINIQUE, writer, historian, philanthropist; b. Chatelaillon, France, July 30, 1931; s. Jean and Luce (Andreota) L.; m. Dominique Conchon, Apr. 5, 1980. Student (Fulbright Exchange scholar), U. Polit. Sci., Paris, 1950-51; B.A., Lafayette Coll., Easton, Pa., 1952, LittD (hon.), 1982. Editor Paris Match News mag., 1955-67. Author: The City of Joy, 1985 (Christopher award 1986), Beyond Love, 1991; co-author: Is Paris Burning?, 1964, ...Or I'll Dress You in Mourning, 1967, O Jerusalem, 1971, Freedom at Midnight, 1975, The Fifth Horseman, 1980. Founder, pres. Action Aid for Lepers' Children of Calcutta. Decorated comdr. Order of Tastevin; recipient Gold medal of the City of Calcutta for humanitarian action, 1987. Home: 26 Ave Kleber, 75116 Paris France Office: care Morton Janklow Lit Agy 598 Madison Ave New York NY 10022

LAPIN, HARVEY I., lawyer; b. St. Louis, Nov. 23, 1937; s. Lazarus L. and Lillie L.; m. Cheryl A. Lapin; children: Jeffrey, Gregg. BS, Northwestern U., 1960, JD, 1963; LLB in Taxation, Georgetown U., 1967. Bar: Ill. 1963, Fla. 1980, Wis. 1985. Cert. tax lawyer, Fla. Bar. Atty., Office Chief Counsel, IRS, Washington, 1963-65; trial atty. Office Regional Csl., IRS, Washington, 1965-68; assoc., then ptnr. Fiffer & D'Angelo, Chgo., 1968-75; pres. Harvey I. Lapin, P.C., Chgo., 1975-83; mng. ptnr. Lapin, Hoff, Spangler & Greenberg, 1983-88, Lapin, Hoff, Slaw & Laffey, 1989-91, ptnr. Gottlieb and Schwartz, Chgo., 1992-93; prin. Harvey I. Lapin & Assocs., P.C., Northbrook, Ill., 1993—; instr. John Marshall Law Sch., 1969—; facility adv. lawyers asst. program Roosevelt U., Chgo.; mem. cemetery adv. bd. Ill. Comptroller, 1974—. C.P.A., Ill. Mem. Chgo. Bar Assn. (chmn. tax exempt orgns. subcom., sect. taxation, 1988-90), Ill. Bar Assn., ABA, Fla. Bar Assn. (Fla. cert. tax specialist), Wis. Bar Assn. Jewish. Asst. editor Fed. Bar Jour., 1965-67; contbg. editor Cemetery Business and Legal Guide and Funeral Service Business and Legal Guide; contbr. articles to trade assn. jours. Office: Harvey I Lapin & Assocs PC PO Box 1327 Northbrook IL 60065

LAPINE, JAMES ELLIOT, playwright, director; b. Mansfield, Ohio, Jan. 10, 1949; s. David Sanford and Lillian (Feld) L.; m. Sarah Marshall Kernochan, Feb. 24, 1985; 1 child, Phoebe. BA, Franklin and Marshall Coll., Lancaster, Pa.; hon. degree, Franklin and Marshall Coll., 1994; MFA, Calif. Inst. of Arts, Valencia. Author: dir.: (plays) Photograph, 1977 (Obie award 1977), Table Settings, 1980 (George Oppenheimer/Newsday award), Twelve Dreams, 1983, Sunday in the Park with George, 1984 (N.Y. Drama Critics' Circle award 1984, Pulitzer prize for drama 1984), Into the Woods, 1987 (Tony award 1988, N.Y. Drama Critics' Circle award 1988, Drama Desk award 1988), Falsettoland, 1990 (2 Tony awards 1992), Luck, Pluck and Virtue (La Jolla Playhouse), 1993, Passion, 1994 (Tony award 1994); dir.: March of the Falsettos, 1982, Merrily We Roll Along (La Jolla Playhouse), A Midsummer Night's Dream, A Winter's Tale, 1988, (films) Impromptu Passion, 1990, Life with Mikey, 1993. Recipient 4 Drama Desk awards, Outer Critics Circle award, Evening Standard award, Olivier award; Guggenheim fellow. Mem. Dramatists Guild. Office: care Sam Cohn Internat Creative Mgmt 40 W 57th St New York NY 10019-4001*

LAPINSKI, DONALD, elementary school principal. Prin. Dick Scobee Elem. Sch., Auburn, Wash. Recipient Elem. Sch. Recognition award U.S. Dept. Edn., 1989-90. Office: Dick Scobee Elem Sch 1031 14th St NE Auburn WA 98002

LAPINSKI, TADEUSZ ANDREW, artist, educator; b. Rawamazowiecka, Poland, June 20, 1928; s. Tadeusz Alexander and Valentina (Kwiatkowska) L. MFA, Acad. Fine Arts, Warsaw, Poland, 1945. Prof. U. Md., College Park, 1973—. One-man shows include Mus. Modern Art, N.Y.C., also mus. in Washington, São Paulo and Rio de Janeiro, Brazil, Turin, Italy, Belgrade, Yugoslavia and Vienna, Austria, Regional Mus. of Torun, Poland, 1992, Plock Mus. and Libr., Poland, 1993, Regional Mus. of Zyrardow, Poland, 1994, Sci. Soc. Plock, 1993, Dist. Mus. City of Zyrardow, Poland, 1994, Zyrardow Mus. of Art, Poland, 1994; group shows include Nat. Royal Acad., London, biennial exhbns. in Venice, Italy, Paris, Buenos Aires, Argentina, John Guggenheim Gallery Exhibition, Coral Gables, Fla., 1988, numerous others; retrospective exhibition Nat. Mus. Torun, Poland, 1956-92; represented in permanent collections Mus. Modern Art, N.Y.C., Libr. of Congress, Washington, Nat. Mus. Am. Art, Washington, mus. in São Paulo, Warsaw and Cracow, Poland, others. Recipient Gold medal Print Festival, Vienna, 1979, Silver medal World Print '80, Paris, medal City of Zamosc, Poland, 1980, UNESCO prize Paris, Statue of Victory 85 World prize, Italy, Achievement award Prince George's County, 1989, Cultural Achievement award Am. Polish Art award U. Md., 1991, Am. Polish Arts Assn. award, 1991; T. Lapinski day proclaimed by mayor of Washington, 1981; named Man of Yr. Md. Perspectives Mag., 1984, Internat. Man of Yr. Intern., Art award City Plock, Poland, 1994. Mem. Soc. Graphic Art, Painters and Sculptors Soc. N.J. Office: U Md Dept Art College Park MD 20742

LAPLANTE, JOHN BAPTISTE, naval officer; b. St. Joseph, Mo., June 6, 1940; s. John Jessup and Naomi Katherine (Klaus) LaP.; m. Phyllis Elaine De Bartolo, Dec. 12, 1964; children: John Baptiste, Elizabeth Gamelin. BS in Gen. Engring., U.S. Naval Acad., Annapolis, Md., 1962; MS in Internat. Affairs, George Washington U., 1973. Commd. ensign USN, 1962, advanced through grades to vice adm., 1988; exec. officer USS San Bernardino, San Diego, 1974-76; flag lt. Surface Force Pacific, San Diego, 1976-78; comdg. officer USS Thomaston, San Diego, 1978-80; exec. officer USS Belleau Wood, San Diego, 1980-83; br. head Naval Ops., Washington, 1983-85; fellow Strategic Studies Group, Newport, R.I., 1985-86; comdg. officer USS Coronado, Pearl Harbor, Hawaii, 1986-88; comdr. Logistic Force Pacific, Pearl Harbor, 1988-90, Amphibious Group 2, Norfolk, Va., 1990-91; comdr. amphibious forces Gulf War USN, 1991; dir. logistics The Joint Staff, 1992—. Contbr. articles to profl. jours. Roman Catholic. Avocation: golf. Home: Quarters O Navy Yard Washington DC 20374 Office: Joint Chiefs of Staff 4000 Joint Chiefs of Staff Washington DC 20318

LA PLATA, GEORGE, federal judge; b. 1924; m. Frances Hoyt; children: Anita J. La Plata Rard, Marshall. AB, Wayne State U., 1951; LLB, Detroit Coll. Law, 1956. Pvt. practice law, 1956-79; judge Oakland County (Mich.) Cir. Ct., Pontiac, 1979-85, U.S. Dist. Ct. (ea. dist.) Mich., Ann Arbor, 1985—; prof. Detroit Coll. Law, 1985-86. Trustee William Beaumont Hosp., 1979—, United Found. 1983—. Served to col. USMC 1943-46. 52-54. Mem. ABA, Oakland County Bar Assn., Hispanic Bar Assn. Lodge: Optimists. Office: US Dist Ct 200 E Liberty St Ste 400 Ann Arbor MI 48104-2121 Office: US District Court US Courthouse PO Box 7760 Ann Arbor MI 48107-7760

LAPOE, WAYNE GILPIN, retired business executive; b. Waynesburg, Pa., July 13, 1924; s. James Lindsay and Mary (Gilpin) LaP.; m. Margaret Louise Clark, Feb. 21, 1953; children: Deborah Jean, Marqui Lynne. B.A., Pa. State U., 1947. With personnel and sales depts. Armstrong Cork Co. Lancaster, Pa., 1947-53, Chgo., 1947-53 San Francisco 1947-53; personnel dir. Safeco Ins. Group., 1953-63, v.p., 1963-86; v.p. Safeco Corp., Seattle, 1976-80, sr. v.p., 1980-86; v.p. Gen. Ins. Co. Am., 1963-86, Safeco Ins. Co. Am., 1963-86, Safeco Life Ins. Co., 1963-86, First Nat. Ins. Co. Am., Seattle, 1963-86, Safeco Nat. Ins. Co., St. Louis, 1972-86. Mem. White House Conf. Children and Youth, 1960, Mus. Flight, Seattle, Ocean Liner Mus., N.Y.C.; bd. dirs. Ind. Colls. Washington. Served to capt. USAAF, 1943-46, USAF, 1951-52. Decorated D.F.C.; decorated Air medal with three oak leaf clusters. Mem. Am. Polit. Items Collectors (past pres.), Am. Aviation Hist. Soc., SS Hist. Soc. Am., Assn. Des Amis Des Paquebots, Nat. Trust Hist. Preservation, Phi Kappa Tau. Republican. Home: 11986 Lakeside Pl NE Seattle WA 98125-5955

LAPOINTE-PETERSON, KITTIE VADIS, choreographer, ballet school director, educator; b. Chgo., June 4, 1915; d. Samuel Joseph and Katie (Parbst) Andrew; m. Arthur Joseph LaPointe, Dec. 17, 1938 (dec. Apr. 1985); children: Janice Deane, Suzanne Meta; m. Ray Burt Peterson, Feb. 2, 1992. Studies with, Marie Zvolanek, Chgo., 1921-28, Laurent Novikoff, Chgo., 1928-35, Edward Caton, Chgo., 1928-35; student, Royal Danish Ballet, Copenhagen, 1926. Dancer Chgo. Civic Opera, 1929-32, Century of Progress, Chgo., 1933-34, Stone-Camryn Ballet, Chgo., 1934-35, Mary Vandas Dancers, Chgo., 1935-38, Balaban-Katz Theaters, Chgo., 1935-36; tchr., choreographer Studio of Dance Arts, Chgo., 1952-68, Herrstrom Sch., Chgo., 1968-72; dir. Le Ballet Petit Sch., Chgo., 1972-92. Soloist in Michael Fokine's Co., 1935. Mem. Danish Brotherhood and Sisterhood (pres. 1962-65, 72-75, Midwest dist. pres. 1972-74), Chgo. Outdoor Art League (sec. 1975-79, Manor Garden Club. Avocations: cooking, writing, gardening. Home: 5843 W Peterson Ave Chicago IL 60646-3907

LAPONCE, JEAN ANTOINE, political scientist; b. Decize, France, Nov. 1925; s. Fernand and Fernande (Ramond) L.; m. Joyce Price, July, 1950; children: Jean-Antoine, Marc, Patrice; m. Iza Fiszhaut, Apr. 10, 1972; 1 child, Danielle. Diploma, Institut d'études politiques, Paris, 1947; Ph.D., UCLA, 1955. Instr. U. Santa Clara, 1956; asst. prof. polit. sci. U. B.C, Can., Vancouver, 1956-61; assoc. prof. U. B.C., 1961-66, prof., 1966—; dir. Inst. Interethnic Rels. U. Ottawa, 1993—. Author: The Protection of Minorities, 1961, The government of France under the Fifth Republic, 1962, People vs Politics, 1970, Left and Right, 1981, Langue et territoire, 1984, Languages and Their Territories, 1987. Fellow Royal Soc. Can. (pres. Acad. Humanities and Social Scis. 1988-91); mem. Can. Polit. Sci. Assn. (pres. 1972-73), Am. Polit. Sci. Assn., French Polit. Sci. Assn., Internat. Polit. Sci. Assn. (pres. 1973-76). Office: U BC Dept Polit Sci, Vancouver, BC Canada V6T 1Z1

LAPORTE, CLOYD, JR., retired manufacturing executive, lawyer; b. N.Y.C., June 8, 1925; s. Cloyd and Marguerite (Raeder) L.; m. Caroline E. Berry, Jan. 22, 1949; children—Elizabeth, Marguerite, Cloyd III. AB, Harvard U., 1946, JD, 1949. Bar: N.Y. 1949. Assoc. mem. firm Cravath, Swaine & Moore, N.Y.C., 1949-56; dir. adminstrn. Metals div. Olin Corp., N.Y.C., 1957-66; legal counsel Dover Corp., N.Y.C., 1966-93, sec., 1971-93. 2d lt. A.C. AUS, WWII. Mem. Harvard Club (N.Y.C.). Home: Gipsy Trail Club Carmel NY 10512

LAPORTE, GERALD JOSEPH SYLVESTRE, lawyer; b. Windsor, Ont., Can., Oct. 16, 1946; came to U.S., 1948, naturalized, 1954; s. Rosaire Joseph and Catherine Rose (Sylvestre) L. Ba, Sacred Heart Sem. Coll., 1968; STB, St. Paul U., Ottawa, Ont., 1971; BTh, U. Ottawa, 1971; MA, Georgetown U., 1974; JD, George Washington U., 1976. Bar: Mich. 1976, D.C. 1977. Legis. asst. to U.S. Congressman William J. Randall, Washington, 1971-75; law clk. to U.S. Dist. Judge, Washington, 1976-77; assoc. Wilmer, Cutler & Pickering, Washington, 1977-82, Nutter, McClennen & Fish, Washington, 1987; sr. spl. counsel, Office Gen. Counsel, SEC, Washington, 1982-85; counsel to SEC Commr., 1985-87; ptnr. Patton Boggs, L.L.P., Washington, 1988—. Mng. editor George Washington Law Rev., 1975-76. Mem. ABA (sect. on bus. law, devels. in investment svcs. com., fed. regulation of securities com., subcom. SEC adminstrn., budget and legis.), Nat. Assn. Bond Lawyers (vice chmn. securities law and disclosure com.), Nat. Assn. Stock Plan Profls. Democrat. Roman Catholic. Home: 3154 Key Blvd Arlington VA 22201-5037 Office: Patton Boggs LLP 2550 M St NW Washington DC 20037

LAPORTE, LEO FREDERIC, earth sciences educator; b. Englewood, N.J., July 30, 1933; s. Leo Frederic and Edea (Giacobbe) L.; m. Mary G. Dunlap, 1956 (div. 1983); children: Leo G., Eva R.; m. Margaret Liniecki, 1985; 1 child, Noel A. Student, Fordham Coll., 1951-53; A.B., Columbia U., 1956, Ph.D., 1960. From instr. to prof. dept. geol. scis. Brown U., Providence, 1959-71; prof. bd. earth scis. U. Calif.-Santa Cruz, 1971-94, prof. emeritus, 1994, chmn., 1972-75, dean div. natural scis., 1975-76, provost Crown Coll., 1993—, assoc. acad. vice chancellor for undergrad. edn., 1994—; vis. prof. Yale U., 1964; geologist N.Y. State Geol. Survey, 1962-64; petroleum research cons.; mem. com. geol. scis. Nat. Acad. Sci.-NRC, 1970-72; sec. U.S. Nat. Com. Hist. Geology, 1991-93, chair, 1994—. Author: Ancient Environments, 1968, 79, 89, Encounter with the Earth, 1975; prin. author: The Earth and Human Affairs, 1972; editor: Reefs in Time and Space, 1974, Evolution and the Fossil Record, 1978, Simple Curiosity: Family Letters of George G. Simpson, 1987; contbr. articles profl. jours. Recipient President's award Am. Assn. Petroleum Geologists, 1969; U. Calif. Santa Cruz Alumni Disting. Teaching award, 1980. Fellow AAAS, Geol. Soc. Am., Calif. Acad. Sci.; mem. History of Sci. Soc., History of Earth Scis. Soc. (pres. 1994), Soc. Vertebrate Paleontology, Soc. Econ. Mineralogists and Paleontologists (chmn. research com., paleontology councilor, editor PALAIOS 1984-89, pres. 1995—). Office: U Calif Crown Coll Santa Cruz CA 95064

LAPOSATA, JOSEPH SAMUEL, army officer; b. Johnstown, Pa., Oct. 3, 1938; s. Joseph Thomas and Mary Marie (Coco) L.; m. Anita Marie Sabo, Aug. 12, 1961; children: Joseph S. Jr., David G., Matthew M. BS, Indiana U. Pa., 1960; MS, Cornell U., 1968; grad., Command and Gen. Staff Coll., Leavenworth, Kans., 1971, Indsl. Coll. Armed Forces, Washington, 1980. Commd. 2d lt. U.S. Army, 1960, advanced through grades to lt. gen., 1991; asst. chief of staff for logistics 5th Inf. Div., Ft. Polk, La., 1978-79; chief war res. div. Office Dep. Chief of Staff for Logistics, Hdqrs. Dept. Army, Washington, 1980-81; comdr. 8th Support Group, U.S. Army So. European Task Force, Livorno, Italy, 1981-84; dep. comdr., chief of staff U.S. Army So. European Task Force, Vicenza, Italy, 1984; exec. to dep. chief of staff for logistics Hdqrs. Dept. Army, Washington, 1984-86, dir. plans and ops., 1986-88; comdg. gen. U.S. Army Material Command-Europe, Heidelberg, Fed. Republic Germany, 1988-89; dep. chief of staff for logistics U.S. Army Europe and 7th Army, Heidelberg, 1989-91; chief of staff Allied Forces So. Europe, Naples, Italy, 1991-93; Presdl. appointee as sec. Am. Battle Monuments Commn., Washington, 1994-95; ret. Decorated Def. DSM, DSM (I), Legion of Merit (3), Bronze Star (2); knight comdr. Republic of Italy; recipient Man of Yr. award Interclub Coun., Johnstown, Pa., 1990, Disting. Alumnus award Ind. U. of Pa., 1992; inducted into Quartermaster Hall of Fame, 1994. Mem. Assn. U.S. Army (pres. European dept. 1989-91), Quartermaster Assn., Rotary. Roman Catholic. Avocation: golf. Home: 2420 Stirrup Ln Alexandria VA 22308

LAPP, JAMES MERRILL, clergyman, marriage and family therapist; b. Lansdale, Pa., July 20, 1937; s. John E. and Edith (Nice) L.; m. Nancy Swartzentruber, Mar. 1, 1936; children: Cynthia Ann, J. Michael. B.A., Eastern Mennonite Coll., 1960; B.D., Goshen Bibl. Sem., 1963; D.Min. Drew U., 1981. Ordained to ministry Mennonite Ch., 1963. Pastor Belmont Mennonite Ch., Elkhart, Ind., 1961-63; paster Perkasie Mennonite Ch., Pa., 1963-72, Albany Mennonite Ch., Oreg., 1972-81; dir. campus ministries Goshen Coll., Ind. 1981-87; tchr. Christopher Dock Mennonite High Sch., Lansdale, Pa., 1963-70; moderator Pacific Coast Conf. on Mennonite Ch., Oreg., 1977-79, Mennonite Gen. Assembly, Lombard, Ill., 1985-87; gen. sec., gen. bd., 1988—. Contbr. articles to Mennonite Ch. publs. Democrat.

Avocations: gardening, baking, walking. Home: 210 Oak Ln Goshen IN 46526-5026 Office: Mennonite Church Gen Bd 421 S 2nd St Rm 600 Elkhart IN 46516-3243

LAPP, JOHN ALLEN, religious organization administrator; b. Lansdale, Pa., Mar. 15, 1933; s. John E. and Edith Ruth (Nyce) L.; m. Alice Weber, Aug. 20, 1955; children: John Franklin, Jennifer Lapp Lerch, Jessica. BA, Ea. Mennonite Coll., 1954; MA, Case Western Res. U., 1958; PhD, U. Pa., 1968. From instr. to prof. history Ea. Mennonite Coll., Harrisonburg, Va., 1958-69; exec. sec. peace sect. Mennonite Cen. Com., Akron, Pa., 1969-72, exec. sec., 1985—; prof. history, dean Goshen (Ind.) Coll., 1972-79, prof. history, provost, 1979-84; rep. Ch. World Svc. and Witness, N.Y.C., 1985—; observer World Coun. Chs., Canberra, Australia, 1991. Author: Mennonite Church in India 1897-1962, 1972, The View from East Jerusalem, 1980; editor: Peacemaking in a Broken World, 1970; columnist Christian Living mag., 1963-80; mem. editorial bd. Mennonite Quar. Rev., 1972—; contbr. articles to profl. jours. Visitor N. Cen. Assn. Schs. and Colls., Chgo., 1976-84; pres. Rockingham Coun. on Human Rels, Harrisonburg, 1962-65; v.p. Va. Coun. on Human Rights, Richmond, 1965-69. Mem. Conf. on Faith and History, Mennonite Hist. Soc. (pres. 1972-84). Home: 13 Knollwood Dr Akron PA 17501-1113 Office: Mennonite Cen Com PO Box 500 21 S 12th St Akron PA 17501-0500

LAPPE, FRANCES MOORE, author, lecturer; b. Pendleton, Oreg., Feb. 10, 1944; d. John and Ina (Skrivvars) Moore; m. Marc Lappe, Nov. 11, 1967 (div. 1977); children: Anthony, Anna; m. J. Baird Callicott, Dec. 1, 1985 (div. 1991); m. Paul Martin DuBois, Aug. 19, 1991. BA in History, Earlham Coll., 1966; PhD (hon.), St. Mary's Coll., 1983, Lewis and Clark Coll., 1983, Macalester Coll., 1986, Hamline U., 1987, Earlham Coll., 1988, Kenyon Coll., 1989, U. Mich., 1990, Nazareth Coll., 1990, Niagara Coll., 1993. Co-founder, mem. staff Inst. for Food and Devel. Policy, Oakland, 1975-90; co-founder, co-dir. Ctr. for Living Democracy, Brattleboro, Vt., 1990—. Author: Diet for A Small Planet, 1971, 75, 82, 91, Mozambique and Tanzania: Asking the Big Questions, 1979, What To Do After You Turn Off the T.V., 1985, Rediscovering America's Values, 1989; (with Joseph Collins) Food First: Beyond the Myth of Scarcity, 1977, Aid as Obstacle, 1980, Now We Can Speak, 1984, Nicaragua: What Difference Could a Revolution Make?, 1984, World Hunger: Twelve Myths, 1986; (with Rachel Schurman and Kevin Danaher) Betraying the National Interest, 1987, (with Schurman) Taking Population Seriously, 1990, (with Paul Martin Du Bois) The Quickening of America: Rebuilding Our Nation, Remaking Our Lives, 1994. Named to Nutrition Hall of Fame Ctr. for Sci. and Pub. Interest, 1981; recipient Mademoiselle Mag. award, 1977; World Hunger Media award, 1982, Right Livelihood award, 1987. Office: Ctr Living Democracy RR 1 Black Fox Rd Brattleboro VT 05301-9801

LAPPEN, CHESTER I., lawyer; b. Des Moines, May 4, 1919; s. Robert C. and Anna (Sideman) L.; m. Jon Tyroler Irmas, June 29, 1941; children—Jonathan Bailey, Timothy, Andrea L., Sally Morris. A.B. with highest honors in Econs, U. Calif., 1940; LL.B. magna cum laude (Faye diploma), Harvard, 1943. Bar: Calif. bar 1943. Practice in Los Angeles, 1946—; sr. partner firm Mitchell, Silberberg & Knupp, 1949—; advisory bd. Bank Am., 1962-65; chmn. bd., dir. Zenith Nat. Ins. Corp., 1975-77; bd. dirs. Arden Group, Inc. (chmn. exec. com. 1978), Data Products Corp. (chmn. fin. com.), City Nat. Bank Corp.; trustee, pres. Citinat. Devel. Trust; bd. dirs., chmn. bd. Pacific Rim Holding Corp. Editor-in-chief: Harvard Law Rev, 1942-43. Chmn. bd. trustees Immaculate Heart Coll., 1981-88; trustee UCLA Found.; v.p., dir. Ctr. for Childhood. Served as spl. agt. CIA AUS, 1943-46. Mem. ABA, Los Angeles Bar Assn. (dir. 1953), Los Angeles Jr. Bar Assn. (pres. 1953), Beverly Hills (Calif.) Bar Assn., Harvard Law Sch. Alumni Assn. So. Calif. (pres. 1973-82), Artus (hon.). Republican. Office: Mitchell Silberberg & Knupp 11377 W Olympic Blvd Los Angeles CA 90064-1625

LAPPIN, JOAN E., financial executive; b. Cleve., Nov. 16, 1943; d. Jack W. Berger and Eleanore E. (Bloomfield) Shallant; m. John W. Lappin, Nov. 11, 1972 (div. May 1989); children: Jessica S., Joshua H. BA, U. Wis., 1964; MBA, NYU, 1972. CFA. Sr. analyst Equity Rsch. Assocs., N.Y.C., 1966-69; asst. to pres. FAS Internat., Westport, Conn., 1970-71; sr. rsch. analyst Seidlitz & Co., N.Y.C., 1971-72, Dreyfus Corp., N.Y.C., 1973-80; v.p. Mfrs. Hanover Trust, N.Y.C., 1980-83, Arnhold & S. Bleichroeder, N.Y.C., 1983-86; pres. Gramercy Capital Mgmt. Corp., N.Y.C., 1986—. Active Women's Campaign Fund. Mem. N.Y. Soc. Security Analysts, Media & Entertainment Analysts of N.Y., Am. Women Entrepreneurs, Fin. Women's Assn., N.Y. Yacht Club, Ida Lewis Yacht Club, Nat. Arts Club. Avocations: sailing, photography. Office: Gramercy Capital Mgmt Corp 515 Madison Ave New York NY 10022-5403

LAPPIN, RICHARD C., corporate executive; b. Detroit, Dec. 16, 1944; s. Thomas Gerald and Helen Marie (Manor) L.; m. Mary Ann Hopkinson; children: Sean, Reid; children from previous marriage: Jill, Richard, Nicole. BA in Mgmt., Econs. and Psychology, U. Detroit, 1968. Corp. mgr. indsl. engring. AMC Corp., Southfield, Mich., 1972-75, corp. mgr. fin., 1975-77; internat. ops. exec. Chrysler Corp., Highland Park, Mich., 1977-79; v.p. ops. Distbn. and Controls divsn. Gould Inc., Rolling Meadows, Ill., 1979-80; gen. mgr. ball and roller divsn. Hoover Uniroyal, Ann Arbor, Mich., 1980-82; asst. to pres. Northop Def. Systems, Rolling Meadows, 1982-86; group v.p. electronics, corp. v.p bus. devel. RTE Corp., Brookfield, Wis., 1986-88; pres. N.Am. Automotive Products Champion Spark Plug, Toledo, Ohio, 1988—; pres., chief exec. officer Doehler-Jarvis/Farley Inc., Toledo, 1988—; chief exec. officer So. Fastner/Farley Inc., Statesville, N.C. 1989—; pres., chief oper. officer Farley Industries, Chgo., 1991—; vice-chmn. Fruit of the Loom, Inc., Chgo. Office: Fruit of the Loom Inc 233 S Wacker Dr Chicago IL 60606*

LAPSLEY, JAMES NORVELL, JR., minister, pastoral theology educator; b. Clarksville, Tenn., Mar. 16, 1930; s. James Norvell and Evangeline (Winn) L.; m. Brenda Ann Weakley, June 4, 1953 (dec. May 1989); children: Joseph William, Jacqueline Evangeline; m. Helen Joan Winter, Feb. 24, 1990. BA, Rhodes Coll., 1952; BD, Union Theol. Sem., 1955; PhD (Div. Sch. fellow, Rockefeller fellow), U. Chgo., 1961. Ordained to ministry Presbyn. Ch., 1955; asst. min. Gentilly Presbyn. Ch., New Orleans, 1955-57; instr. Princeton (N.J.) Theol. Sem., 1961-63, asst. prof., 1963-67, assoc. prof., 1967-76, prof. pastoral theology, 1976-80, Carl and Helen Egner prof. pastoral theology, 1980-92, acad. dean, 1984-89, prof. emeritus, 1992—; mem. editl. bd. Jour. Pastoral Care, 1966-69, 1971—; bd. dirs. N.W. Maricopa UN Assn., 1994—, v.p., 1995. Editor: The Concept of Willing, 1967, Salvation and Health, 1972, Renewal in Late Life Through Pastoral Counseling, 1992; editor: (with B.H. Childs, D.W. Waanders), Festschrift: The Treasure of Earthen Vessels, 1994; chmn. editl. bd. Pastoral Psychology Jour., 1975-84. Bd. dirs. Westminster Found., Princeton U., 1970-76. Danforth fellow Menninger Found., 1960-61. Mem. Am. Acad. Religion, Phi Beta Kappa. Presbyterian. Home: 16610 N Meadow Park Dr Sun City AZ 85351-1758

LAQUEUR, MARIA, association executive; b. San Francisco, Sept. 25, 1942; d. Gert Ludwig and Mary Alice (Murphy) L.; m. William Gerald Hamm, Feb. 12, 1983. BA German, Am. Univ., 1965, MA German/Linguistics, 1968; MPA, U. of No. Colo., 1978. German lang. cataloger Libr. of Congress, Washington, 1965-70, assoc. catalog editor, 1970-76, asst. dir. NUC proj., 1976-81; assoc. pub. Bemrose UK, Ltd., London, 1981-85; exec. dir. Assoc. of Part-time Profls., Falls Church, Va., 1988—. Author: Flexible Work Options: A Selected Bibliography, 1990; co-author: Breaking Out of 9 to 5, 1994. Fellow U.S. Office Edn., 1967. Home: 508 Council Ct NE Vienna VA 22180 Office: Assn of Part Time Profls Crescent Plaza 7700 Leesburg Pike Ste 216 Falls Church VA 22043-2615

LAQUEUR, WALTER, history educator; b. Breslau, Germany, May 26, 1921; s. Fritz and Else (Berliner) L.; m. Barbara Koch, May 29, 1941; children: Sylvia, Shlomit. Grad. Johannesgymnasium, Breslau, 1938; student, Hebrew (Jerusalem) U.. 1938-39; HHD (hon.), Hebrew Union Coll., 1988, Adelphi U., 1993, Brandeis U., 1994. Agrl. worker Palestine, 1940-44; newspaper corr., free-lance author, 1944-55; founder, editor Survey, London, Eng., 1955-67; vis. prof. Johns Hopkins, 1957, U. Chgo., 1958, Harvard, 1977; dir. Inst. Contemporary History, Wiener Library, London, 1964-92; prof. history ideas and politics Brandeis U., Waltham, Mass., 1967-72; prof. history U. Tel Aviv, 1970-80; chmn. internat. research council Ctr. Strategic

and Internat. Studies, Washington, 1973—; univ. prof. govt. Ctr. Strategic and Internat. Studies Georgetown U., Washington, 1977-91. Author: Communism and Nationalism in the Middle East, 1956, The Soviet Union and the Middle East, 1959, Young Germany, 1962, Russia and Germany, 1966, The Fate of the Revolution, 1967, The Road to War, 1967, The Struggle for the Middle East, 1969, Europe Since Hitler, 1970, Out of the Ruins of Europe, 1971, Confrontation: The Middle East and World Politics, 1974; A History of Zionism, 1972, Weimar, 1975, Guerrilla, 1976, Terrorism, 1977, Guerrilla Reader, 1977, Terrorism Reader, 1978, A Continent Astray, 1979, The Missing Years, 1980, Political Psychology of Appeasement, 1980, Farewell to Europe, 1981, The Terrible Secret, 1981, America, Europe, and the Soviet Union, 1983, Germany Today, 1985, A World of Secrets, 1985, The Age of Terrorism, 1987, The Long Road to Freedom: Russia and Glasnost, 1989, Stalin, 1991, Thursday's Child Has Far to Go, 1992, Black Hundred, 1993, The Dream That Failed, 1994; co-editor, founder: Jour. Contemporary History, 1966—; founder, editor: Washington Papers, 1972—. Recipient 1st Distinguished Writer's award Center Strategic and Internat. Studies, 1969, Inter Nationes award, 1985, Grand Cross of Merit German Fed. Republic, 1987. Office: Ctr Strategic and Internat Studies 1800 K St NW Washington DC 20006-2200

LARA, ADAIR, columnist, writer; b. San Francisco, Jan. 3, 1952; d. Eugene Thomas and Lee Louise (Hanley) Daly; m. James Lee Heig, June 18, 1976 (div. 1989); children: Morgan, Patrick; m. William Murdock LeBlond, Nov. 2, 1991. BA in English, San Francisco State U., 1976. Reader Coll. of Marin, Kentfield, Calif., 1976-83; freelance editor, 1983-86; mng. editor San Francisco Focus mag., 1986-89; exec. editor San Francisco mag., 1988-89; columnist San Francisco Chronicle, 1989—. Author: History of Petaluma: A California River Town, 1982, Welcome to Earth, Mom, 1992, Slowing Down in a Speeded-up World, 1994, At Adair's House, More Columns by America's Funniest Formerly Single Man, 1995; contbr. articles to profl. publs. Recipient Best Calif. Columnist award AP, 1990. Democrat. Avocations: reading, photography, travel, softball, biking. Office: San Francisco Chronicle 901 Mission St San Francisco CA 94103-2905

LARAGH, JOHN HENRY, physician, scientist, educator; b. Yonkers, N.Y., Nov. 18, 1924; s. Harry Joseph and Grace Catherine (Coyne) L.; m. Adonia Kennedy, Apr. 28, 1949; children: John Henry, Peter Christian, Robert Sealey; m. Jean E. Sealey, Sept. 22, 1974. MD, Cornell U., 1948. Diplomate Am. Bd. Internal Medicine. Intern medicine Presbyn. Hosp., N.Y.C., 1948-49; asst. resident Presbyn. Hosp., 1949-50; cardiology trainee Nat. Heart Inst., 1950-51; rsch. fellow N.Y. Heart Assn., 1951-52; asst. physician Presbyn. Hosp., 1950-55, asst. attending, 1954-61, assoc. attending, 1961-69, attending physician, 1969-75, pres. elect med. bd., 1972-74; mem. faculty Coll. Physicians and Surgeons Columbia U., 1950-75, prof. clin. medicine, 1967-75, spokesman exec. com. faculty coun., 1971-73; vice chmn. bd. trustees for profl. and sci. affairs Presbyn. Hosp., 1974-75; dir. Hypertension Ctr., chief nephrology div. Columbia-Presbyn. Med. Ctr., 1971-75; Hilda Altschul Master prof. medicine, dir. Hypertension and Cardiovascular Ctr., N.Y. Hosp.-Cornell Med. Ctr., 1975-; chief cardiology div., 1975-95; cons. USPHS, 1964—. Editor-in-chief Am. Jour. Hypertension, Cardiovascular Reviews and Reports; Editor: Hypertension Manual, 1974, Topics in Hypertension, 1980, Frontiers in Hypertension Rsch., 1981; editor Hypertension: Pathophysiology, Diagnosis, and Management, 1990, 1995; editorial bd.: Am. Jour. Medicine, Am. Jour. Cardiology, Kidney Internat., Jour. Clin. Endocrinology and Metabolism, Hypertension, Jour. Hypertension, Circulation, Am. Heart Jour., Procs. of Soc. Exptl. Biology and Medicine, Heart and Vessels. Mem. policy adv. bd. hypertension detection and follow-up program Nat. Heart and Lung Inst., 1971, bd. sci. counselor, 1974-79; chmn. U.S.A.-USSR Joint Program in Hypertension, 1977-93. With U.S. Army, 1943-46. Recipient Stouffer prize Med. Rsch., 1969, J.K. Lattimer award Am. Urol. Assn., 1989, Robert Tigerstedt award Am. Soc. Hypertension, 1990, John P. Peters award Am. Soc. Nephrology, 1990. Lifetime Achievement in Medicine award N.Y. Acad. Medicine, 1993, Disting. Alumnus award Cornell U. Med. Coll.. 1993; subject of Time Mag. cover story, 1975; Most Frequently Cited Scientist: Top Ten Advances in Cardiopulmonary Medicine, 1946-75. Fellow Am. Coll. Cardiology; mem. ACP (Master), Am. Heart Assn. (chmn. med. adv. bd. coun. high blood pressure rsch. 1968-72), Am. Soc. Clin. Investigation, Assn. Am. Physicians, Assn. Univ. Cardiologists, Endocrine Soc., Am. Soc. Nephrology, Am. Soc. Hypertension (founder, 1st pres. 1986-88), Internat. Soc. Hypertension (pres. 1986-88), Harvey Soc., Kappa Sigma, Nu Sigma Nu, Alpha Omega Alpha, Winged Foot Golf Club (Mamaroneck, N.Y.), Shinnecock Hills Golf Club (Southampton, N.Y.). Achievements include research on hormones and electrolyte metabolism and renal physiology, mechanisms of edema formation and on causes and treatments of high blood pressure. Home: 27 Overlook Dr Southampton NY 11968 Office: NY Hosp-Cornell Med Ctr 525 E 68th St (Starr 4) New York NY 10021 *In my research, a key resource has been the ability to look at everyday clinical phenomena differently, to recognize and develop new ideas and principles about human physiology. These perceptions enable hypotheses and experiments for creation and synthesis of new knowledge that redirects medical thinking.*

LARAYA-CUASAY, LOURDES REDUBLO, pediatric pulmonologist, educator; b. Baguio, Philippines, Dec. 8, 1941; came to U.S., 1966; d. Jose Marquez and Lolita (Redublo) Laraya; m. Ramon Serrano Cuasay, Aug. 7, 1965; children: Raymond Peter, Catherine Anne, Margaret Rose, Joseph Paul. AA, U. Santo Tomas, Manila, Philippines, 1958, MD cum laude, 1963. Diplomate Am. Bd. Pediatrics. Resident in pediatrics U. Santo Tomas Hosp., 1963-65, Children's Hosp. Louisville, 1966-67, Charity Hosp. New Orleans-Tulane U., 1967-68; fellow child growth and devel. Children's Hosp. Phila., 1968-69; fellow pediatric pulmonary and cystic fibrosis programs St. Christopher's Hosp. for Children, Phila. 1969-71; rsch. assoc., 1971-72; clin. instr. Tulane U., New Orleans, 1967-68; asst. prof. pediatrics Temple Health Scis. Ctr., Phila., 1972-77; assoc. prof. pediatrics Thomas Jefferson Med. Sch., Phila., 1977-79; assoc. prof. pediatrics U. Medicine & Dentistry N. J., Robert Wood Johnson Med. Sch., New Brunswick, 1980-85, prof. clin. pediatrics, 1985—; dir. pediatric pulmonary and cystic fibrosis program U. Medicine and Dentistry, Robert Wood Johnson Med. Sch., New Brunswick, 1981—. Co-editor: Interstitial Lung Diseases in Children, 1988. Recipient Pediatric Rsch. award Mead Johnson Pharm. Co., Manila, 1965. Fellow Am. Coll. Chest Physicians (steering com., chmn. cardiopulmonary diseases in children 1976—), Am. Acad. Pediatrics (tobacco free generation rep. 1986-92); mem. Am. Ambulatory Pediatric Soc., Am. Thoracic Soc., Am. Sleep Disorder Assn., N.J. Thoracic Soc. (chmn. pediatric pulmonary com. 1986-91, governing coun. mem. 1981—), Am. Coll. Physician Execs., Lung Club. Avocation: pianist. Home: 100 Mercer Ave Spring Lake NJ 07762 Office: UMDMJ Robert Wood Johnson Med Sch CN19 New Brunswick NJ 08903

LARCH, BILLIE BENTLEY, nursing administrator; b. Texarkana, Tex., Aug. 26, 1919; d. William Calvin and Lula Marie (Cowley) Bentley; m. Monroe P. Larch, Mar. 26, 1936; children: James Monroe, Michael B. BSN, U. Ark., Little Rock, 1962; MSN, U. Cen. Ark., Conway, 1971; MA in Gerontology, U. Little Rock, 1987. Cert. gerontol. nurse and psychiat. clin. specialist nurse. Nurse cons. Ark. Dept. Mental Health, Little Rock, 1978; assoc. chief nursing svc. for edn. John L. McClellan VA Hosp., Little Rock, 1972-85; exec. dir. Ark. State Nurses Assn., Little Rock, 1989-92; nurse cons. Larch Cons. Svcs., 1992—; health care specialist Children and Family Divsn. Ark. Dept. Human Svcs., 1993—; mem. nursing faculty Allied Health, U. Ark., 1973-76; med. rschr. for pros. and def. trial lawyers, 1992—. Developer small group work program Chronically and Mentally Ill, Ark., 1966—; organizer Ark. affiliate chpt. Am. Diabetes Assn., 1973, bd. dirs. 1973-79; healthcare specialist Ark. Dept. Human Svcs., Children and Family Divsn., 1993—. Recipient Gold Star award Atty. Gen.'s Office, 1989; named to Hall of Fame in Nursing, Ark. State Nurses Assn., 1988. Mem. Nat. League for Nursing (Linda Richards award 1969), Ark. Gerontol. Soc. (bd. dirs. 1982-92, 93—). Home: 8422 Kling Rd Mabelvale AR 72103-3614

LARCHE, JAMES CLIFFORD, II, state agency administrator; b. Mobile, Ala., Nov. 27, 1946; s. James Clifford and Alma (Dunn) L.; m. Mary Cecilia Whelchel, June 6, 1969 (div. 1972); m. Jan Pirkle, May 7, 1994. A.B., Ga. State U., 1974. Claims examiner Employees' Retirement System, Atlanta, 1969-73, div. dir., 1973-84, dep. dir., 1985—; with Nat. Conf. State Social Security Adminstrs., Atlanta, 1973—, regional v.p., 1978-80, sec., 1980-82, first v.p., 1982-83, pres., 1983-84, chmn. fed.-state procedures com., 1984-85.

Served with N.G., 1968-74. Roman Catholic. Home: PO Box 38056 Atlanta GA 30334-0056 Office: State Social Security Adminstrs 2 Northside Ste 300 Atlanta GA 30318-7778

LARDIERI, ANTHONY J., school system administrator. Supt. Fontana (Calif.) Unified Sch. Dist. State finalist Nat. Supt. Yr., 1993. Office: Fontana Unified Sch Dist 9680 Citrus Ave Fontana CA 92335-5571

LARDNER, GEORGE, JR., journalist; b. N.Y.C., Aug. 10, 1934; s. George Edmund and Rosetta (Russo) L.; m. Rosemary Schalk, July 6, 1957; children: Helen, Edmund, Richard, Charles, Kristin (dec.). AB summa cum laude in Journalism, Marquette U., 1956, MA, 1962. Reporter The Worcester (Mass.) Telegram, 1957-59, The Miami (Fla.) Herald, 1959-63; reporter The Washington Post, 1963-64, 66—, columnist, 1964-66; bd. dirs. Fund for Investigative Journalism, Washington. Recipient Byline award Marquette U., 1967, Front-page Nat. News award Washington-Balt. Newspaper Guild, 1984, 86, Pulitzer Prize for feature writing, 1993. Mem. Congl. Press Gallery. Roman Catholic. Home: 5604 32nd St NW Washington DC 20015 Office: Washington Post 1150 15th St NW Washington DC 20071

LARDNER, HENRY PETERSEN (PETER LARDNER), insurance company executive; b. Davenport, Iowa, Apr. 5, 1932; s. James Francis and Mary Catharine (Decker) L.; m. Marion Cleaveland White, Dec. 28, 1954; children: Elisabeth, Emily Decker, David, Peter, Sarah (dec.). B.S.E. (Indsl. Engring.), U. Mich., 1954; M.A., Augustana Coll., 1982. C.P.C.U. Indsl. engr. Cutler-Hammer, Milw., 1954; Agt. H.H. Cleaveland Agcy., Rock Island, Ill., 1956-60; with Bituminous Ins. Cos., Rock Island, 1960—; exec. v.p. Bituminous Ins. Cos., 1968-72, pres., 1972—; also bd. dir.; pres., bd. dir. Bitco Corp., 1973—; bd. dirs. Old Republic Internat., 1985—. Bd. govs. State Colls. and Univs., 1971-80; trustee Black Hawk Coll., 1964-72; mem. Ill. Bd. Higher Edn., 1976-77; chmn. Ill. State Scholarship, 1982-85. Served with AUS, 1954-56. Home: 3227 29th Ave Rock Island IL 61201-5568 Office: Bitco Corp 320 18th St Rock Island IL 61201-8716

LARDNER, RING WILMER, JR., author; b. Chgo., Aug. 19, 1915; s. Ring Wilmer and Ellis (Abbott) L.; m. Silvia Schulman, Feb. 19, 1937 (div. 1945); children: Peter, Ann; m. Frances Chaney, Sept. 28, 1946; 1 child, James; stepchildren: Katharine, Joseph. Student, Princeton, 1932-34. Reporter N.Y. Daily Mirror, 1935; press agt. Selznick Internat. Pictures, Culver City, Calif., 1935-37; screenwriter various cos., 1937-82; freelance writer, 1982—. Screenwriter: (with Michael Kanin) Woman of the Year, 1942 (Acad. award 1942), (with Leopold Atlas) Tomorrow the World, 1944, (with Albert Maltz) Cloak and Dagger, 1946, (with Philip Dunne) Forever Amber, 1947, (with Terry Southern) The Cincinnati Kid, 1965, M*A*S*H, 1970 (Acad. award 1970), The Greatest, 1977; author: (novels) The Ecstasy of Owen Muir, 1955, All for Love, 1985, The Lardners: My Family Remembered, 1976; also TV and movie pieces; collaborator Broadway mus. Foxy, 1964. Mem. Writers Guild Am. (Screen Laurel award 1989, Ian McLellan Hunter Meml. award for lifetime achievement 1992).

LARDY, HENRY ARNOLD, biochemist, biological sciences educator; b. Roslyn, S.D., Aug. 19, 1917; s. Nick and Elizabeth (Gebetsreiter) L.; m. Annrita Dresselhuys, Jan. 21, 1943; children: Nick, Diana, Jeffrey, Michael. B.S., S.D. State U., 1939, D.Sc. (hon.), 1979; M.S., U. Wis., 1941, Ph.D., 1943. Mem. faculty U. Wis.-Madison, 1945—, assoc. prof. biochemistry, 1947-50, prof., 1950-88, Vilas prof. biol. scis., 1966-88; prof. emeritus, 1988—. Co-editor: The Enzymes. Pres. Citizens vs. McCarthy, 1952. Recipient Paul-Lewis award enzyme chemistry Am. Chem. Soc., 1949, Neuberg medal Am. Soc. European Chemists, 1956, award in agr. Wolf Found., 1981, Nat. award for agrl. excellence, 1982, Amory prize Am. Acad. Arts and Scis., 1984, Carl Hartman award Soc. Study of Reproduction, 1984, W.C. Rose award Am. Soc. Biochemistry and Molecular Biology, 1988, Hilldale award U. Wis., 1988. Fellow Wis. Acad. Arts, Scis. and Letters; mem. Nat. Acad. Sci., Am. Chem. soc. (chmn. biol. divsn. 1958), Am. Soc. Biol. Chemists (pres. 1964), Am. Philos. Soc., Golden Retriever Club Am. (pres. 1962), Am. Acad. Arts and Scis. (Amory Prize 1984), Endocrine Soc., Japanese Biochem. Soc. (hon.), Am. Soc. Biochem. Molecular Biol. (pres. 1964). Home: 1829 Thorstrand Rd Madison WI 53705-1052

LARDY, NICHOLAS RICHARD, economics educator; b. Madison, Wis., Apr. 8, 1946; s. Henry Arnold and Annrita (Dresselhuys) L.; m. Barbara Jean Dawe, Aug. 29, 1970; children: Elizabeth Brooke, Lillian Henry. BA, U. Wis., 1968; MA, U. Mich., 1972, PhD, 1975. Asst. prof. Yale U., New Haven, 1975-79, assoc. prof., 1979-83, asst. dir. econ. growth ctr., 1979-82; assoc. prof. U. Wash., Seattle, 1983-85, chair China program, 1984-89, prof., 1985—, dir. The Henry M. Jackson Sch. Internat. Studies, 1991—; bd. dirs. Nat. Com. on U.S.-China Rels., N.Y.C., 1987—; chmn. Com. on Advanced Study in China; vice chmn. com. on scholarly comm. with China, NAS, Washington, 1991—; bd. dirs. Com. on Internat. Rels. Studies with People's Republic China, 1989-92, Program for Internat. Studies in Asia, 1993—; mem. bd. mgrs. The Blakemore Found., 1993—. Author: Economic Growth and Distribution in China, 1978, Agriculture in China's Modern Economic Development, 1983, China's Entry into the World Economy, 1987, Foreign Trade and Economic Reform in China, 1978-90, 92, China in the World Economy, 1994, (policy study) Economic Policy Toward China in the Post-Reagan Era, 1989; mem. editl. bd. The China Quar. (London), China Econ. Rev., Jour. Asian Bus. Rsch. fellow Am. Coun. Learned Socs., 1976, 78-79, 89-90, Henry Luce Found., Inc., 1980-82; faculty rsch. grantee Yale U., 1976, 78. Mem. Am. Econ. Assn., Assn. for Asian Studies (nominating com. 1986-87), Assn. for Comparative Econ. Studies (exec. com. 1986-88). Avocations: skiing, squash, tennis, sailing. Home: 3802 110th Pl NE Bellevue WA 98004-7760 Office: U Wash Sch of Internat Studies Seattle WA 98195

LARDY, SISTER SUSAN MARIE, prioress; b. Sentinel Butte, N.D., Nov. 9, 1937; d. Peter Aloysius and Elizabeth Julia (Dietz) L. BS in Edn., U. Mary, Bismarck, N.D., 1965; MEd, U. N.D., 1972. Entered Order of St. Benedict, Bismarck, 1957. Elem. tchr. Cathedral Grade Sch., Bismarck, 1958-67, Christ the King Sch., Mandan, N.D., 1967-68, 70-72, St. Joseph's Sch., Mandan, 1968-70; asst. prof. edn. U. Mary, Bismarck, 1972-80; adminstr., asst. prioress Annunciation Priory, Bismarck, 1980-84, prioress, major superior, 1984—; pres., bd. dirs. St. Alexius Med. Ctr., Bismarck, 1984—, Garrison (N.D.) Meml. Hosp., 1984—. U. Mary, Bismarck, 1984—. Chair Health Commn. of Diocese of Bismarck, 1991. Mem. Delta Kappa Gamma. Home: 7520 University Dr Bismarck ND 58504-9653

LAREAU, MARYBETH BASS, marketing professional; b. N.Y.C., July 12, 1941; d. James Gordon and Marjorie (Mestell) B.; m. Gerard Arthur Lareau, June 6, 1970 (div. Nov. 1984). AB in Biology, Bucknell U., 1963. V.p., creative group head Dancer Fitzgerald Sample, Inc., N.Y.C., 1966-78; sr. v.p., creative dir. Norman Craig & Kummel, N.Y.C., 1978-79; creative dir., pres. Lareau & Assocs., N.Y.C., 1980—; guest lectr. St. John's U., N.Y.C., 1980-83; adj. instr. Fashion Inst. Tech. SUNY, N.Y.C., 1982-87. Contbr. articles to mags., jours.; prin. works include L'eggs Pantyhose, 1974-78, corp. advt. campaign Gen. Electric Corp., 1981. Recipient ANDY award Advtg. Club N.Y., 1975, EFFIE award Am. Mktg. Assn., 1976. Mem. Internat. Wine and Food Soc., Advt. Women N.Y. (chair pub. svc. com. 1986-88), Women's Direct Response Group, Direct Mktg. Club N.Y. Unitarian. Avocations: horseback riding, photography, writing. Home and Office: 140 W End Ave New York NY 10023-6131

LAREAU, RICHARD GEORGE, lawyer; b. Woonsocket, R.I., June 11, 1928; s. Hector R. and Agnes P. (Valley) L.; m. Thelma Johnson, Aug. 11, 1970; 1 son, Alan Hartland; 1 son by previous marriage, William Wheeler Mohn. BA, St. Michael's Coll., Winooski Park, Vt., 1949; JD, U. Minn., 1952. Bar: Minn. 1952. Ptnr. Oppenheimer, Wolff & Donnelly, St. Paul, Mpls., 1956—; bd. dirs. Ceridan, Bloomington, Minn., Nash Finch Co., Mpls., Merrill Corp., St.Paul, No Techs. Internat. Corp., Lino Lakes; trustee Mesabi Trust, N.Y.C.; sec AVECOR Cardiovascular Inc., Plymouth, Minn. Sec., bd. dir. Minn. Cooperation Office for Small Bus. and Job Creation, Mpls.; bd. dirs. Minn. Project on Corp. Responsibility, Mpls. 1st lt. USAF, 1952-56. Mem. ABA, Minn. Bar Assn., Hennepin County Bar Assn., Mpls. Club. Avocation: fishing. Home: 20750 Linwood Rd Excelsior MN 55331-9386 Office: Oppenheimer Wolff & Donnelly 3400 Plz VII 45 S 7th St Minneapolis MN 55402-1607

LAREN, KUNO, investment banker; b. Tallinn, Estonia, Sept. 29, 1924; came to U.S., 1946, naturalized, 1953; s. Alexander and Jenny (Ozolit) L.; m. Mary Boondas, Nov. 18, 1950; children: Inga, Guy, Philip, Anders. Student, U. Stockholm, 1944-46; B.A., Park Coll., 1948; M.A., NYU, 1950. Securities analyst Shearson, Hammill & Co., N.Y.C., 1953-59; mgr. investment research Jesup & Lamont, N.Y.C., 1959-62; v.p. investment banking and research McDonnell & Co., N.Y.C., 1962-70; treas. Kumala Inc., N.Y.C., 1970—; pres. U.S. Securities Corp., N.Y.C., 1971—; bd. dirs., mem. exec. com. Servicemaster Industries, Inc., Downers Grove, 1968-83; pres. Pennate Corp., N.Y.C., 1983—; chmn. Quality Industries, Inc., Thibodaux, La., 1989—, Grand Enterprise Ltd., N.Y.C., 1986—; bd. dirs. Ages Health Svcs. Inc., Rockland, Mass., Plastic Tech. Enterprise Corp., N.Y.C. Mem. Princeton Club of N.Y. State. Office: 320 Lexington Ave New York NY 10016-2645

LARESE, EDWARD JOHN, management company executive; b. Kimball, W.Va., Mar. 7, 1935; s. Innocente and Velia (Pais) L.; m. Julianne Falotico, Aug. 15, 1964. Student, U. Ky., 1953-54; AB in Acctg., Duke, 1957. CPA, N.C., N.Y. Acct. Price Waterhouse & Co., N.Y.C., 1957-65; mgr.-fin. acctg. Ea. Air Lines, Inc., N.Y.C., 1965-67, asst. to sr. v.p. fin. and adminstrn., 1968-70, asst. contr. fin. planning and analysis, 1970-72; v.p., contr. Eastern Air Lines, Inc., 1972-76; v.p. planning and control IU Internat., Inc., Phila., 1976-79; CEO, pres. Altair Airlines, Inc., 1979-81; mgmt. cons. Berwyn, Pa., 1981-84; exec. v.p., CFO Finalco Group, Inc., McLean, Va., 1984-89; mgmt. cons. Warrenton, Va., 1989-91; v.p. fin. and adminstrn., CFO Star Techs., Inc., Sterling, Va., 1992-94; pres., CEO Scala, Inc., Herndon, Va., 1994—. Loaned exec. Dade County (Fla.) United Fund, 1965, corp. chmn., 1975-76. With USAFR, 1958-64. Mem. AICPA, Air Transp. Assn. (vice chmn. corp. acctg. com.), N.Y. Soc. CPAs, N.C. Assn. CPAs, Fin. Execs. Inst., Duke U. Alumni Assn., Bath Club (Miami Beach, Fla.), Radnor Hunt Club (Berwyn, Pa.), Warrenton Hunt Club, Ashland Bassetts Club, Springs Club, Fauquier Club, Sigma Nu. Republican. Episcopalian. Home: 8372 Elway Ln Warrenton VA 22186 Office: Scala Inc Ste 202 2323 Horse Pen Rd Herndon VA 22071

LARGE, G. GORDON M., data processing company executive; b. Phila., Apr. 4, 1940; s. James M. and Sarah Morris (Ellison) L.; m. Janet G. Leith, 1964 (div. 1978); children: Christopher M., Allison G.; m. Theresa A. M. Misiorek, Nov. 30, 1978. BA, Princeton U., 1962; MBA, U. Pa., 1963. V.p. Smith, Barney & Co., Inc., N.Y.C., 1963-73; adminstr. N.J. State Energy Office, Trenton, 1974-75; exec. dir. N.J. Cabinet Energy Com., Trenton, 1974-75; v.p. Mathematica, Inc., Princeton, N.J., 1975-81, Mathematica Products Group, Inc., Princeton, 1981-84, Martin Marietta Data Systems, Greenbelt, Md., 1986-88; sr. v.p., chief fin. officer Palladian Software, Inc., Cambridge, Mass., 1986-88, Pansophic Systems, Inc., Lisle, Ill., 1988-91; sr. v.p., fin. and adminstrn. CFO Systems Ctr. Inc., Reston, Va., 1992-93; exec. v.p., CFO Card Establishment Svcs., Inc., Melville, N.Y., 1993—. Mem. Fin. Execs. Inst. Avocations: running, tennis, photography, music. Office: Card Establishment Svcs Inc 265 Broadhollow Rd Melville NY 11747-4802

LARGE, JAMES MIFFLIN, JR., banker; b. Phila., Mar. 15, 1932; s. James Mifflin and Sarah Morris (Ellison) L.; m. Carol E. Large, Sept. 30, 1978; children: James Mifflin III, Richard C., Ginny, Dudly, Jon. Postgrad., Stonier Grad. Sch. Banking; BSE, Princeton U. Exec. v.p., chmn. credit policy Centran Corp., Pa., 1975-82; chmn. bd., pres. First Nat. Bank, Allentown, Pa., 1982-85; vice chmn. Meridian Bancorp, Reading, Pa., 1984-85; exec. v.p., asst. to pres. 1st Interstate Bancorp, L.A., 1986, 89; chmn. chief exec. officer Anchor Savs. Bank FSB, Hewlett, N.Y., 1989—; also chmn., CEO Anchor Bancorp, Inc., Hewlett, N.Y.; also bd. dirs. Author: Planning Secondary Defenses Against Loan Losses; contbr. articles to trade jours. Served with USN, 1955-59. Mem. Corinthian Yacht Club (Phila.), Piping Rock Club (N.Y.). Episcopalian. Home: 14 Underhill Rd Locust Valley NY 11560-2216 Office: Anchor Savings Bank 1420 Broadway Hewlett NY 11557-1352

LARGE, JOHN ANDREW, library and information service educator; b. Mexborough, Yorkshire, Eng., Mar. 27, 1947; arrived in Can., 1989; s. Gordon and Winifred Mary (Tompkins) L.; m. Valerie Merle Wilson, Aug. 30, 1972; children: Amanda Fiona, Kirsty Jane. BSc in Econs., London U., 1968, diploma in libr., 1973; PhD, Glasgow U., Scotland, 1973. Asst. libr. Glasgow U. Libr., 1973-74; libr. Inst. Soviet and East European Studies, Glasgow U., 1974-78; prin. lectr. Coll. Librarianship Wales, Aberystwyth, 1978-89; prof., dir. Grad. Sch. Libr. and Info. Studies McGill U., Montreal, Que., Can., 1989—; vice chmn. U.K. Online User Group, London, 1987-89; chmn. Can. Coun. Libr. Schs., 1991-93; external examiner U. W.I., 1991—, U. Ibadan, Nigeria, 1992—. Author: The Foreign-Language Barrier, 1983, The Artificial Language Movement, 1985, A Modular Curriculum for Information Studies, 1987; co-author: Online Searching: Principles and Practice, 1990; editor: Manual of Online Search Strategies, 1988, 2d edit., 1992, CD-ROM Information Products: An Evaluative Guide vol. 1, 1990, vol. 2, 1991, vol. 3, 1992; mem. editl. adv. bd. Jour. Librarianship and Info. Sci., 1992—; editor jour. Edn. for Info., 1983—, CD-ROM Info. Products, 1993. Rsch. grantee Brit. Libr. R&D Dept., 1981-82, 85-86, European Space Agy., 1983-85; IBM Acad. Info. Exch. fellow, 1991-92, Social Sci. and Humanities Rsch. Coun. fellow, 1991-94; recipient Commemorative medal for 125th Anniversary of the Confedn. of Can., 1992. Mem. ALA, Am. Soc. for Info. Sci., Can. Libr. Assn., Spl. Librs. Assn., Assn. Libr. and Info. Sci. Edn., Que. Libr. Assn. Avocation: music listening and playing. Office: McGill U Grad Sch Libr and Info. Studies 3459 McTavish, Montreal, PQ Canada H3A 1Y1

LARGEN, JOSEPH, retailer, furniture manufacturer, book wholesaler; b. Union, N.J., June 13, 1940; s. Fred and Wilma Largen; children: Lori, Lisa. B.S. in Econs., U. Mo., 1963. Mgmt. trainee R.R. Donnelly Corp., Chgo., 1964-67; distbn. mgr., material control and distbn. Warwick Electronic Co., Niles, Ill., 1967-69; with Brodart, Inc., 1969—; v.p. prodn. Brodart, Inc., Williamsport, Pa., 1973-75; exec. v.p. Brodart, Inc., 1975-78, pres., 1978—. Served with USCG, 1963-64. Home: 3213 W Wheeler St Apt 306 Seattle WA 98199-3200 Office: Brodart Co 500 Arch St Williamsport PA 17701-7809

LARGEY, KATHLEEN KIERNAN, lawyer, marketing director; b. Montclair, N.J., Sept. 13, 1958; d. Robert Edward and Patricia Ann (Brunetto) K.; m. Thomas L. Largey. BA, Wellesley (Mass.) Coll., 1980; JD, U. Notre Dame, 1985. Bar: Ill. 1985, N.J. 1987, Mass. 1988. Assoc. Wildman, Harrold, Allen & Dixon, Chgo., 1985-87; dir. client svcs. Campbell & Assocs., Boston, 1987-93, Fish & Richardson, Boston, 1993—. Mem. Nat. Law Firm Mktg. Assn. (treas. 1991-92, pres.-elect 1992-93, pres. 1993), Phi Beta Kappa. Office: Fish & Richardson 225 Franklin St Boston MA 02110-2809

LARIBÉE, JACQUES, conservationist. Recipient Snowy Owl Conservation award Québec Zoological Gardens, 1993. Home: 194 Ouellet, Rimanski, PQ Canada G5L 4R5*

LARIMER, DAVID GEORGE, federal judge; b. Rochester, N.Y., Mar. 3, 1944; s. John and Mary (Sullivan) L.; m. Karen Moore, July 29, 1967; children: Amy, Beth, John. BA, St. John Fisher Coll., 1966; JD, Notre Dame U., 1969. Bar: N.Y. 1970, D.C. 1971. Law clk. to Hon. Joseph C McGarraghy U.S. Dist. Ct. (D.C. dist.), 1969-70; asst. U.S. atty. U.S. Dept. Justice, Washington, 1970-73, Rochester, 1973-75; with Beckerman, Davidson, Cook & Fink, Rochester, 1975-78, Lapine & Larimer, 1978-79; chief appellate law asst. Supreme Ct. (4th Dept.), Rochester, 1979-81; mem. firm Greisberger, Zicari, McConville, Cooman & Morin, Rochester, 1982-84;

U.S. magistrate U.S. Dist. Ct., Rochester, 1983-87; judge U.S. Dist. Ct. (west dist.) N.Y., Rochester, 1987—; law instr. St. John Fisher Coll., Rochester, 1979-81. Office: US Dist Ct 100 State St 250 US Courthouse Rochester NY 14614

LARIVIERE, RICHARD WILFRED, Asian studies educator, consultant; b. Chgo., Jan. 27, 1950; s. Wilfred Francis and Esther Irene (Kallestad) L.; m. Janis Anne Worcester, June 5, 1971; 1 child, Anne Elizabeth. BA, U. Iowa, 1972; PhD, U. Pa., 1978. Lectr. U. Pa., Phila., 1978-79; asst. prof. U. Iowa, Iowa City, 1980-82; prof. U. Tex., Austin, 1982—, Ralph B Thomas Regents prof. Asian studies, 1993—; ptnr. Sinha & Lariviere Internat. Comms. Cons.; dir. Ctr. for Asian Studies, dir. Nat. Resource Ctr. for South Asia, founder bus. seminar in India Seminar; cons. Perot Systems Corp., Dallas, 1993—. Author: Ordeals in Hindu Law, 1981, Narada Smrti, 1989. Fellow NEH, 1979-83. Fellow Royal Asiatic Soc.; mem. Am. Oriental Soc., Am. Inst. Indian Studies (sr.fellow 1989, 95, v.p. 1990), Assn. Asian Studies. Lutheran. Office: U Tex Asian Studies Mail Code G9300 Austin TX 78727

LARIZADEH, M(OHAMMED) R(EZA), business educator; b. Tehran, Iran, Apr. 14, 1947; came to U.S., 1966; s. Hassan and Nosrat (Saremi) L.; m. Dianne Ellen Pincus, Mar. 25, 1973; children: Dariush, Darya Anna. BA in Econs., Bus., UCLA, 1972, cert. in acctg., 1974. Cert. colls. teaching credential, Calif. (life); lic. real estate agent, Calif. Auditor Peat, Marwick & Mitchell, Los Angeles, 1972-74; controller Petromain Constrn. Co., Tehran, 1975-77; v.p. fin. Pilary Marine Shipping Co., Tehran, 1977-79; prof. Iranian Inst. Banking, Tehran, 1975-78; pres. Audicount Acctg. and Auditing Group, L.A., 1984—; prof. bus. and acctg. East L.A. Coll., 1980-87, vice-chmn. dept. bus. and acctg., 1987—, chmn. dept. bus. adminstrn., 1988—; prof. acctg. Santa Monica (Calif.) Coll., 1987—; mgmt. cons. L.P. Assocs. Mfg. Co., Los Angeles, 1981—; mng. dir. Barrington Enterprises, Los Angeles; prof. Santa Monica (Calif.) Coll., 1987. Author/translator: Accounting/Auditing, 1975. Mem. NEA, Internat. Fedn. Bus. Edn., Am. Mgmt. Assn., Am. Acctg. Assn., Faculty Assn. Calif. C.C.s, Am. Fedn. Tchrs., Calif. Tchrs. Assn., Am. Entrepreneur Assn., Nat. Assn. Realtors, Am. Assn. Pub. Accts., Calif. Assn. Bus. Educators, Calif. Assn. Realtors, Nat. Soc. Pub. Accts., Calif. Bus. Edn. Assn., Internat. Fedn. Bus. Inst. Mgmt. Accts., UCLA Alumni Assn. (life), Alpha Kappa Psi.

LARK, RAYMOND, artist, art scholar; b. Phila., June 16, 1939; s. Thomas and Bertha (Lark) Crawford. Student, Phila. Mus. Sch. Art, 1948-51, Los Angeles Trade Tech. Coll., 1961-62; B.S., Temple U., 1961; L.H.D., U. Colo., 1985. Ednl. dir. Victor Bus. Sch., Los Angeles, 1969-71; public relations exec. Western States Service Co., Los Angeles, 1968-70; owner, mgr. Raymond Lark's House of Fine Foods, Los Angeles, 1962-67; exec. sec. to v.p Physicians Drug and Supply Co., Phila., 1957-61; lectr. L.A. Trade Tech. Coll., 1973, Compton (Calif.) Coll. 1972, Nat. Secs. Assn., Hollywood, Calif., UCLA, U. Utah, Salt Lake City, 1993, numerous others. One-man shows include, Dalzell Hatfield Galleries, Los Angeles, 1970-80, Arthur's Gallery Masterpieces and Jewels, Beverly Hills, Calif., 1971, Dorothy Chandler Pavillion Music Center, L.A., 1974, Honolulu Acad. Arts, 1975, UCLA, 1983, U. Colo. Mus., 1984, Albany State Coll. Art Gallery, Albany, Ga., 1988, Utah Mus. Fine Arts, Salt Lake City, 1989, Mind's Art Gallery, Dickinson U., Dickinson, N.D., 1989, Trinton Mus. Art, Santa Clara, Calif., Greenville (N.C.) Mus. of Art, 1993, others; group exhbns. include, Smithsonian Instn., 1971, N.J. State Mus., Trenton, 1971, Guggenheim Mus., N.Y.C., 1975, Met. Mus. Art, 1976, La Galerie Mauffe, Paris, 1977, Portsmouth (Va.) Mus., 1979, Ava Dorog Galleries, Munich, W. Ger., 1979, Accademia Italia, Parma, 1980, Ames Art Galleries and Auctioneers, Beverly Hills, 1980, Le Salon des Nations at Centre International d'Art Contemporain, Paris, 1983; represented in permanent collections, Library of Congress, Ont. Coll. Art, Toronto, Mus. African and African Am. Art and Antiquities, Buffalo, Carnegie Inst., numerous others; art commns. for TV and film studios include, All in the Family, Carol Burnett Show, Maude, The Young and the Restless, Universal City Studios, Palace of the Living Arts, Movie Land Wax Mus.; author works in field; author and contbr. more than 50 scholarly treatises on art, edn. and the hist. devel. of Black Ams., chpts. to encyclopedias and textbooks, articles to jours., introductions to mus. exhbn. catalogues. Recipient gold medal Acad. Italia, 1980, also numerous gold medals and best of show awards, 3 presdl. proclamations; award Internat. Platform Assn.; Dr. Raymond Lark Day proclaimed by State of Md., 1994; grantee Nat. Endowment Arts, ARCO Found., Colo. Humanities Program, Adolph Coors Beer Found. Mem. Art West Assn. (pres. 1968-70). Address: PO Box 76169 Los Angeles CA 90076-0169 I was telling people that I was Black, proud, and beautiful long before it became fashionable to be very dark. I never felt, "I am the greatest." However, I never had an inferiority complex. I always knew that I had God-given talent, character, and good common sense. In addition, I have always had great confidence in God and in myself. While I am not a soothsayer and never will be a braggart, I knew my art would be recognized. For whatever recognition I have received, I have worked extremely hard and have paid my dues.

LARKIN, ALFRED SINNOTT, JR., newspaper editor; b. Boston, May 13, 1947; s. Alfred Sinnott and Lillian Louise (Brunswick) L.; children: Kristin, Jessica, Hannah, Matthew. Reporter Boston Herald, 1968-72; reporter Boston Globe, 1972-74, asst. met. editor, 1974-76, reporter, 1977-81, Sunday mag. editor, 1981-82, asst. mng. editor local news, 1982-86, dep. mng. editor, 1986-88, mng. editor Sunday edition, 1988-90, mng. editor adminstrn., 1990—. Nieman fellow Harvard U., 1977. Office: Boston Globe 135 Morrissey Blvd Dorchester MA 02125-3338

LARKIN, BARRY LOUIS, professional baseball player; b. Cin., Apr. 28, 1964; m. Lisa Davis. Student, U. Mich., 1982-85. Baseball player Cincinnati Reds, 1985—. First baseball player twice named MVP of Big Ten Athletic Conf.; two-time All-Am. honors; named MVP, Rookie of Yr. and to All-Star team, 1988-94, to Topps' Triple-A All-Star team, 1986, All-Star teams by Sporting News, 1988-92, AP, 1990, UPI, 1990, Maj. League Baseball, 1988-91, 93, to N.L. Silver Slugger team, 1988-92; recipient Gold Glove award, 1994. Achievements include mem. U.S. Olympic Baseball Team, 1984, World Series Team, 1990. Office: Cin Reds 100 Riverfront Stadium Cincinnati OH 45202-3590*

LARKIN, EUGENE DAVID, artist, educator; b. Mpls., June 27, 1921; s. John Peter and Martha Lavinia (Vandevere) L.; m. Audrey Jean Krueger, Jan. 29, 1947; children: Andrew, Alan. BA, U. Minn., 1946, MA, 1949. Mem. faculty dept. art Kans. State Coll., Pittsburg, 1949-54; head printmaking dept., chmn. divsn. fine arts Mpls. Sch. Art, 1954-69; prof. design dept. U. Minn., St. Paul, 1969—, prof. emeritus design, housing and apparel, 1991—. One man exhbns. include, Mpls. Inst. Arts, 1957, 60, 68, Syracuse U., 1962, Walker Art Center, Mpls., 1967, New Forms Gallery, Athens, Greece, 1967, U. Kans., 1972, Macalester Coll., 1974, U. Minn., St. Paul, 1973, 78, 87, 91; group exhbns. include, Phila. Printmakers Club, 1966, 20 American Artists, Geneva, Switzerland, 1964, Big Prints, N.Y. U., 1968, Midwestern Printmakers, Walker Art Center, 1973, Cabo Frio Internat. Print Biennial, Brazil, 1983, Nat. Works on Paper, Minot State Coll., 1986, 17th Annual Works on Paper SW State U., San Marcos, Tex., 4th Annual North Coast Coll. Soc. Exhbn., Hiram Coll., Hudson, Ohio, 1988, 20th Annual Works on Paper Dulin Nat. Knoxville, Knoxville Mus. Art, 1988, Paepcke Meml. Bldg. Gallery, 1993, Aspen Inst. and Music Assoc. of Aspen, 1993; represented in permanent collections, Mus. Modern Art, N.Y.C., Nat. Mus. S.Africa, Capetown, Library Congress, Chgo. Art Inst., Mpls. Inst. Arts, U. Minn. Gallery, Des Moines Art Center, U. Tenn., Kans. State Tchrs. Coll., Minn. Mus. Art, Nat. Collection Fine Arts, Smithsonian Instn; author: Design: The Search for Unity, 1988. Recipient juror's award Rockford Internat. Print and Drawing Biennale, 1983. Mem. Coll. Art Assn. Am. Home: 64 Groveland Ter Minneapolis MN 55403-1103

LARKIN, JOAN, poet, English educator; b. Boston, Apr. 16, 1939; d. George Joseph and Celia Gertrude (Rosenberg) Moffitt; m. James A. Larkin, Dec. 23, 1966 (div. 1969); 1 child, Kate. BA, Swarthmore Coll., 1960; MA, U. Ariz., 1969. Asst. prof. English CUNY-Bklyn. Coll., 1969-94, ret., 1994; assoc. faculty MFA program Goddard Coll.; mem. guest faculty poetry writing Sarah Lawrence Coll., Bronxville, N.Y., 1984-86, fall 1988; vis. instr. Hartwick Coll., Manhattan Theatre Club, Gainesville, Tenants Harbor and Cummington workshops; poet-in-residence Writers Community, Manhattan, West Side YMCA. Author: (poems) Housework, 1975, A Long Sound, 1986, (rec. poetry reading) A Sign I Was Not Alone, 1980; co-editor: Gay and Lesbian Poetry in Our Time: An Anthology, 1988 (Lambda Lit. award 1988), Amazon Poetry, 1975, Lesbian Poetry, 1981; editor: The Women Writers Calendar, 1982, 83, 84; contbr. poems to periodicals including Am. Poetry Rev., Conditions, Ms., Paris Rev., Sinister Wisdom, The Village Voice, Aphra, Endymion, The Lamp in the Spine, Global City Rev., Am. Rev., Genesis West, Sojourner. Nat. Endowment for Arts fellow in poetry, 1987-88, N.Y. Found. for Arts fellow in poetry, 1987-88; Creative Artists Pub. Svc. Program grantee N.Y. State Coun. Arts, 1976, 80.

LARKIN, JOHN MONTAGUE, microbiology educator, researcher; b. Phila., Apr. 7, 1936; s. Jesse Walter and Mary Schofield (Montague) L.; children: Laura, Jennifer. BS, Ariz. State U., 1961, MS, 1963; PhD, Wash. State U., 1967. Teaching asst. Ariz. State U., Tempe, 1961-63; rsch. asst. Wash. State U., Pullman, 1963-67; asst. prof. microbiology La. State U., Baton Rouge, 1967-73, assoc. prof., 1973-81, prof., 1981—, assoc. dean grad. sch., 1994—. Author: Laboratory Manual for Microbiology, 3d edit. 1991; contbr. over 50 articles to profl. jours., chpts. to books; author 2 computer programs. With USMC, 1957-59. NSF grantee 1983, NIH grantee, 1979, Nat. Hatch Act grantee, 1988, Nat. Sea grantee, 1990. Mem. Am. Soc. for Microbiology (chmn. gen. microbiology divsn. 1980-81, 95-96). Republican. Episcopalian. Avocations: golf, tennis, computers, archaeology. Office: La State U Grad Sch Baton Rouge LA 70803

LARKIN, JOHN PAUL, II, state legislator; b. Rutland, Vt., Dec. 2, 1969; s. John Paul and Ann Marie (Canfield) L. BA, U. Vt., 1992. Lic. securities broker, life and health ins. agt.; V.t. Mem. Vt. Ho. of Reps., Montpelier, 1992—; state vice-chmn. Am. Legis. Exch. Coun., Washington, 1993—; chair Fair Haven Green-Up Day. Vice-chmn. Fair Haven Rep. Com., Freshman GOP, 1992-94; co-chair Vt. Rep. Youth Outreach com., 1993—; trustee pub. funds Town of Fair Haven, 1994—. Mem. Nat. Rep. Legislator's Assn., Vt. Vets. Action Group, Alzheimer's Assn. (Green Mountain chpt. 1994—), Sons of the Am. Legion, Fair Haven C. of C. Roman Catholic. Avocations: basketball, snowboarding, golf. Home: PO Box 92 Fair Haven VT 05743

LARKIN, LEE ROY, lawyer; b. Oklahoma City, Aug. 11, 1928; s. William Patrick and Agnes (Matthis) L.; m. Mary Jane Langston, Apr. 17, 1965; children—James William, John Patrick (dec.). B.S., Oklahoma A&M U., Stillwater, 1950; M.A., Vanderbilt U., 1952; LL.B., William Mitchell U., St. Paul, 1959. Bar: Minn. 1959, Tex. 1963, D.C. 1963. Economist U.S. Dept. Agr., Washington, 1953; economist, lawyer Pillsbury, Mpls., 1953-62; pfnr. Harris & Larkin, Houston, 1963-65; sr. pfnr. Andrews & Kurth, Houston, 1966—; speaker Continental Legal Edn. Officer, Sharpstown Civic Assn., Houston, 1966—; elder St. Philip Presbyn. Ch., Houston; moderator Presbytery of New Covenant, Houston, 1980. Served to capt. USAR, 1951-58. Fellow Tex. Bar Found., Houston Bar Found.; mem. ABA, State Bar Tex., Houston Bar Assn.. Am. Intellectual Property Assn., Houston Intellectual Property Assn., Riverbend Country Club, Houston Club, Rotary (pres. 1978-79), Delta Theta Phi. Avocations: golf; tennis; ranching. Home: 3725 Wickersham Houston TX 77027 Office: Andrews & Kurth 4200 Tex Commerce Towers Houston TX 77002

LARKIN, LEO PAUL, JR., lawyer; b. Ithaca, N.Y., June 19, 1925; s. Leo Paul and Juanita (Wade) L. AB, Cornell U., 1948, LLB, 1950. Bar: N.Y. 1950, U.S. Dist. Ct. (so. dist.) N.Y. 1951, U.S. Supreme Ct. 1967. Assoc., pfnr., sr. counsel Rogers & Wells and predecessor firms, N.Y.C., 1950—. Served with U.S. Army, 1943-45. Mem. ABA, Fed. Bar Coun., Univ. Club, Sky Club, Phi Beta Kappa, Phi Kappa Phi, Theta Delta Phi. Home: 200 E 66th St Apt 1804B New York NY 10021-6728 Office: Rogers & Wells 200 Park Ave Ste 5200 New York NY 10166-0005

LARKIN, MICHAEL JOHN, newspaper editor, journalist; b. Boston, Sept. 27, 1950; s. Alfred Sinnott and Lillian Louise (Brunswick) L.; m. Sarah Jane Wood, July 6, 1970 (div. 1985); children—Jonathan Michael, Joshua Stuart; m. Alison Rose Biggs, June 1, 1986. B.A. in English, U. Mass., 1973. News copy editor Boston Globe, 1974-76, sports copy editor, 1976-80, asst. bus. editor, 1980-82, Sunday editor, 1982, mag. editor, 1982-85, living/arts editor, 1985-89, sr. asst. met. editor zoned editions, 1989-92, Sunday editor, 1992-95; asst. mng. editor, 1995—. Office: Boston Globe PO Box 2378 Boston MA 02107-2378

LARKIN, MICHAEL JOSEPH, retail food executive; b. N.Y.C., June 6, 1941; s. John Thomas and Mary (Finnerty) L.; m. Sandra L. Pagano, July 15, 1978; 1 child, Lisa. BBA, Iona Coll., 1963; postgrad., Cornell U., 1970. Supermarket mgr. Grand Union Co., N.Y.C., 1963-69; dist. mgr. Grand Union Co., Syracuse, N.Y., 1969-71; dir. ops., 1971-75; div. v.p. Grand Union Co., Mt. Kisco, N.Y., 1975-78; regional v.p. Grand Union Co., Elmwood Park, N.J., 1978-84; ops. v.p. The Atlantic and Pacific Tea Co., Montvale, N.J., 1984-85, group v.p., 1985-87, sr. v.p. ops., 1987-89, exec. v.p. ops., 1989—, chief oper. officer, 1991—; pres. Daitch Shopwell Co., N.Y.C., 1986—. With USMC, 1960-65. Named Man of Yr. Cath. Inst. of Food Industry, N.Y.C., 1986, Boys Town of Italy, 1993; recipient award of merit Deborah Hosp., Browns Mill, N.J., 1988. Republican. Roman Catholic. Home: 15 Windmill Dr Morristown NJ 07960-5971 Office: Great Atlantic & Pacific Tea Co Inc 2 Paragon Dr Montvale NJ 07645

LARKIN, MOSCELYNE, retired artistic director, dancer; b. Miami, Okla., Jan. 14, 1925; d. Reuben Frances and Eva (Matlogova) L.; m. Roman Jasinski, Dec. 24, 1943 (dec. 1991); 1 child, Roman. Studied with Serge Grigorieff, Lubov Tchernicheva, Mikhail Mordkin, Anatole Vilzak, Vincenzo Celli; hon. doctorate of Fine Arts, U. of Tulsa, 1991. With Ballet Russe, 1941-47, Ballet Russe de Monte Carlo, 1948-52; prima ballerina Radio City Music Hall, N.Y.C., 1951-52; with Alexandra's Danilova's Great Moments of Ballet touring co., 1952-54; established Tulsa Sch. Ballet, from 1956; artistic dir. Tulsa Civic Ballet, 1956-76, Tulsa Ballet Theater, 1976-91; artistic dir. emerita Tulsa Civic Ballet, 1991—. Dance performances include Mikhail Forkine's Paganini and Les Sylphides; Leonid Massine's Le Beau Danube, Symphonie Fantastique, Les Presages; George Balanchine's Concerto Barocco, Night Shadow, Cotillion; Agnes De Mille's Rodeo; David Lichine's Graduation Ball; Michael Maule's The Carib Peddler. Recipient Dance Mag. award, 1988, Gov. Arts award, 1988, Rogers State Coll. Lynn Riggs award, 1989, award of Am.,1992; named to Tulsa Press Clubb Headliner award, Okla. Hall of Fame, 1979, Tulsa Hall of Fame, 1988, Okla. Womens Hall of Fame, 1993, and numerous others. Mem. Southwestern Regional Ballet Assn. (exec. v.p. 1963-76), Nat. Assn. Regional Ballet. Home: 5414 S Gillette Ave Tulsa OK 74105-6434 Office: Tulsa Ballet Theatre 4512 S Peoria Ave Tulsa OK 74105-4563

LARKIN, PETER ANTHONY, zoology educator, university dean and official; b. Auckland, New Zealand, Jan. 11, 1924; arrived in Can., 1929; s. Frank Wilfrid and Caroline Jane (Knapp) L.; m. Lois Boughton Rayner, Aug. 21, 1948; children: Barbara, Kathleen, Patricia, Margaret, Gillian. BA, MA, U. Sask., Can., 1946, LLD (hon.), 1989; DPhil (Rhodes scholar), Oxford U., 1948; DSc (hon.), U. B.C., 1992. Bubonic plague survey Govt. of Sask., 1942-43; fisheries investigator Fisheries Rsch. Bd. Can., 1944-46; chief fisheries biologist B.C. Game Commn., 1948-55; asst. prof. U. B.C., 1948-55, prof. dept. zoology, 1959-63, 66-69; prof. Inst. Animal Resource Ecology, 1969—, also dir. fisheries, 1955-63, 66-69, head dept. zoology, 1972-75, dean grad. studies, 1975-84, assoc. v.p. rsch., 1980-86, v.p. rsch., 1986-88, univ. prof., 1988—; hon. life gov. Vancouver Pub. Aquarium; mem. Can. nat. com. Sci. Com. on Problems of Environment, WHO, 1971-72; mem Killam selection com. Can. Can., 1974-77; mem. Sci. Coun. Can., 1971-76, Nat. Rsch. Coun. Can. 1981-84, Can. Com. on Seals and Sealing, 1981-86, Can. Inst. Advanced Rsch., 1982-85, Nat. Scis. and Engring. Rsch. Coun. Can., various govtl. rsch. coms.; mem. Internat. Ctr. for Living Aquatic Resources Mgmt., 1977, chmn. bd. dirs., 1991-93; bd. dirs. B.C. Packers, 1980—; mem. bd. govs. Internat. Devel. Rsch. Coun., Can., 1987-93; mem. Nat. Sci. Eng. Rsch. Coun. Can., 1987-93; pres. Rawson Acad., 1988-91; commr. B.C.U-tilities Commn., 1993—; mem. interim gov. coun. U. No. B.C., 1991-93. Contbr. articles to profl. jours. Pres. B.C. Conservation Found., 1987-90; temporary commr. B.C. Utilities Commn., 1993—; trustee Vancouver Hosp., 1994—. Recipient Centennial medal (govt. of Can.), 1967, Silver Jubilee medal, 1977, Can. Sport Fishing Inst. award, 1979; Nuffield Found. fellow, 1961-62. Fellow Royal Soc. Can.; mem. Internat. Limnological Assn., Am. Fisheries Soc. (award of excellence 1983, Carl R. Sullivan Conservation award 1993), B.C. Natural Resources Conf. (pres. 1954), B.C. Wildlife Fedn.. Can. Soc. Zoologists (pres. 1972, Fry medal 1978), Can. Assn. Univ. Rsch.

Adminstrn. (pres. 1979), Am. Inst. Fisheries Biologists (Outstanding Achievement award 1986). Home: 4166 Crown Crescent, Vancouver, BC Canada V6R 2A9 Office: U BC Fisheries Ctr, 2204 Main Mall, Vancouver, BC Canada V6T 1Z4

LARKIN, WILLIAM VINCENT, JR., oil field service company executive; b. N.Y.C., July 19, 1953; s. William Vincent and Gloria Ann (Stone) L.; m. Margaret Catherine Gunn, Nov. 12, 1988; children: William Vincent III, Jeremy Stone. AB cum laude, Harvard U., 1976; M Pub. and Pvt. Mgmt., Yale U., 1980. Intern White House, 1975; staff acct. Price Waterhouse & Co., N.Y.C., 1976-78; mktg. asst. AMF Ben Hogan Co., Ft. Worth, 1980-81; asst. to pres. AMF Biol. & Diagnostic Co., Seguin, Tex., 1981-82; mktg. mgr. AMF Tuboscope, Houston, 1982-83, mgr. mill div., 1983-84; v.p. Tuboscope Inc., Houston, 1984-91; pres., COO Tuboscope Vetco Internat., Houston, 1991-93, pres., CEO, 1993—. Mem. Young Pres.'s Orgn., Petroleum Equipment Suppliers Assn., Nomads, Yale Sch. Mgmt. Alumni Assn. (chmn. nominating com. 1980-82), A.D. Club (Cambridge, Mass.), Harvard Club (N.Y.C.), Yale Club (Houston). Republican. Episcopalian. Avocations: woodworking, golf, tennis. Home: 360 Westminster Dr Houston TX 77024-5608 Office: Tuboscope Inc 2919 Holmes Rd Houston TX 77051

LARMORE, JENNIFER, mezzo-soprano; b. Atlanta, 1960. Debuted in La Clemenza di Tito, France; repertoire includes Rossini's Rosina, L'Enfant et les Sortileges, Giulio Cesare, Donna Elvira, Rossini's Isabella and Adele, Monteverdi's Ottavia, Bellini's Romeo, Cenerentola, Dorabella. Office: Columbia Artists Mgt Inc Foster Div 165 West 57th St New York NY 10019*

LARNED, WILLIAM EDMUND, JR., international development and venture capital company executive; b. Albany, N.Y., July 3, 1919; s. William Edmund and Augusta Danforth (Geer) L.; m. Margaret Auguste Klipstein, Jan. 22, 1943; children: Gay, William August, Cynthia Troy. B.S., U.S. Mil. Acad., 1943. Commdt. 2d lt. U.S. Army, 1943, advanced through grades to maj., 1953; small unit comdr. (3d and 4th Mech. Cav. groups), ETO, 1943-46; with CIC, Europe, U.S., 1946-52; gen. staff officer Dept. Army, Washington, 1953-55; ret. Dept. Army, 1955; mgr. market planning Servomechanisms, Inc., N.Y.C., Los Angeles, 1956-59; chief requirements br. Ramo-Wooldridge div. TRW, Canoga Park, Calif., 1959-60; pres., bd. dirs. DMS, Inc. div. McGraw-Hill Pubs., Greenwich, Conn., Beverly Hills, Calif., 1960-70; pres., bd. dirs. Internat. Bus. Services Corp., Greenwich, Conn., 1970-72; v.p., bd. dirs. GMS Assos. Internat., Arlington, Va., 1971-73; exec. v.p. Halaby Internat. Corp., Greenwich, 1973-85, also bd. dirs.; pres., bd. dirs. William Larned, Inc., Greenwich, 1985—. Author: The Aerospace Marketing Handbook, 1960, Aerospace Market Intelligence Report, 1961. Home: 37 Burying Hill Rd Greenwich CT 06831-3045

LA ROCCA, ISABELLA, artist; b. El Paso, Apr. 14, 1960; d. Remo and Alicia Estela (Gonzalez) La R. BA, U. Pa., 1984; MFA, Ind. U., 1993. Freelance photographer N.Y.C., 1986-90; assoc. instr. Ind. U., Bloomington, 1991-93; instr. Herron Sch. Art, Indpls., 1992; vis. asst. prof. Ind. U., 1994—; asst. prof. DePauw U., 1994—. One-woman shows include Notre Dame U., Ctr. Photography Woodstock, N.Y., Moore Coll., Pa., 1994; exhibited in group shows at Bellevue Gallery, 1992, 494 Gallery, N.Y.C., 1993. Ind. U. CIC Minority fellow, 1990-91; Jewish Found. Edn. Woman scholar, 1990; recipient Friends Photography Ferguson award, 1993.

LAROCCA, JAMES LAWRENCE, lawyer; b. N.Y.C., Aug. 29, 1943; s. Elias D. and Claire (Walsh) L.; m. Dale Maizels, May 9, 1971; children: Joshua, amy, Michael. BA, Hofstra U., 1964; JD, Cath. U. Am., 1974; LHD (hon.) Hofstra U., 1993. Bar: D.C. 1974, Fla. 1974. Mem. staff US Ho. of Reps., 1969-73; counsel to vice-chmn. Nat. Commn. Water Quality, Washington, 1974-75; dep. sec. to gov., dir. N.Y. State Office Fed. Affairs, Washington, 1975-77; commr. energy N.Y. State and chmn. N.Y. State Energy R & DAuthority, 1977-83; trustee Power Authority State of N.Y., Albany, 1982-89; commr. transp. N.Y. State, 1983-85; pres., CEO L.I. Assn., Inc., 1985-93; sr. pfnr. Cullen and Dykman, Garden City, 1993—; bd. dirs. European Am. Bank. Host: (TV program) Long Island Talks Business, 1986-93. Mem. adv. council Sch. Bus. Hofstra U., 1984—; chair Touro Coll. Law Ctr., Suffolk County Comml. and Indsl. Incentive Bd.; bd. visitors Marine Scis. Rsch. Ctr., SUNY-Stony Brook; bd. dirs. Nature Conservancy Long Island; mem. Gov.'s Task Force on Coastal Resources, 1990-92; co-chmn. Suffolk Vietnam Vets. Meml. Commn.; mem. State Commn. on Constl. Revision, 1993—, Gov. Coun. Fiscal and Econ. Priorities. Mem. Temp. State Commn. on Constitutional Revision; vice chmn. L.I. Housing Ptnrship; mem. coun. of SUNY at Stony Brook, Gov.'s Sch.-Bus. Alliance Task Force . Lt. USN, 1965-68, Vietnam. Recipient George M. Estabrook award Hofstra U., 1988, Charles Evans Hughes award Am. Soc. for Pub. Adminstrn., 1985. Mem. ABA, Fed. Bar Assn., D.C. Bar, State Bar Fla. Democrat. Home: 8 Beardsley Ln Lloyd Harbor Long Island NY 11743 Office: Cullen & Dykman 100 Quentin Roosevelt Blvd Garden City NY 11530-4850

LAROCHE, GLORIA ROSEMARIE, pilot; b. Pitts., June 17, 1946; d. William Edward and Lillian Marie (Brovchuk) LaR.; 1 child, Kathryn Alexandra. Student, George Peabody Coll., Nashville, 1966-70, Mountain View Coll., Dallas, 1974-76, Dallas Bapt. Coll., 1977. Lic. flight instr., ground instr., airline transport pilot, flight engr. Chief flight instr., FAA pilot examiner, safety counselor Piper S.W., Inc., Dallas, 1973-77; simulation instr. Mountain View Coll., Dallas, 1977; DC-3 1st officer Airgo Airlines, Dallas, 1977-78; 1st officer Evergreen Airlines, Marana, Ariz., 1978-79, Transam. Airlines, Oakland, Calif., 1979-80, Zantop Airlines, Ypsilanti, Mich., 1980-81; Convair capt. Interstate Airlines, Little Rock, 1981-82, Boeing 727 capt., 1983-85; Boeing 727 capt. Connie Kalitta Svcs., Ypsilanti, 1985-89; instr. B-727 flight engr. Flight Internat., Atlanta, 1982-83; Boeing 727 pilot instr. United Airlines, Denver, 1989—. Mem. Internat. Soc. Women Airline Pilots (Capt.'s Club), Archaeological Inst. Am., Mensa, Ukrainian Nat. Women's League Am. Democrat. Ukrainian Orthodox. Avocations: genealogy, sewing, knitting, snow skiing, cooking. Home: 2451 York St Denver CO 80205-5708 Office: United Airlines Flight Tng Ctr Stapleton Airport Denver CO 80207

LA ROCHELLE, PIERRE-LOUIS, civil engineering educator; b. Quebec, Que., Can., Aug. 20, 1928; s. Emile Joseph and Juliette Marie (Coulombe) LaR.; m. Rachel Gratia Bedard, July 11, 1958 (dec. Aug. 1991); children—Judith, Sophie, Anne. B.A., Seminaire De Quebec, Can., 1950; B.Sc. in Civil Engring., U. Laval, Quebec, 1954, M.Sc., 1956; Ph.D., U. London, 1960. Registered profl. engineer, Que. Asst. prof. engring. U. Laval, Quebec, 1960-63, head dept. civil engring., 1963-67, prof. engring., 1968—, dir. grad. studies civil engring., 1992-94; cons. in geotech. engring., dam design and constrn. Hydro-Quebec, SNC, Golder, others, Can. Contbr. articles to profl. jours. Recipient Can. Geotech. Soc. Prize, 1975, R.F. Leggett award, 1977, Queen Elizabeth Jubilee's medal Can. Govt., 1978. Fellow Engring. Inst. Can.; mem. ASCE, ASTM (Hogentogler award 1985), Royal Soc. Can. Internat. Com. on Landslides (pres, 1981-89), Yacht Club (Sillery, Que.; commdr. 1982). Avocations: sailing, skiing, golfing, music. Home: 2328 Des Hospitalieres, Sillery, PQ Canada G1T 1V7 Office: U Laval Dept Civil Engring, Cite Universitaire, Quebec, PQ Canada G1K 7P4

LAROCHELLE, RICHARD CLEMENT, tanning company executive; b. Lewiston, Maine, July 21, 1945; s. Paul H. and Jeannette D. (Jean) L.; m. Constance T. Normand, June 10, 1966; children—Anne Marie, Paul, Christie, Marc, Peter. B.A., U. Maine, 1971; M.B.A., Northeastern U., 1976. Cert. mgmt. acct. Prodn. scheduling mgr. A.C. Lawrence Co., South Paris, Maine, 1971-73; adminstrv. supt. A.C. Lawrence Leather Co., Peabody, Mass., 1973-76; v.p., treas. Nat. Tanning and Trading Corp., Peabody, 1976-79; exec. v.p. Hermann Loewenstein Inc., Johnstown, N.Y., 1980-82; pres. Irving Tanning Co., Hartland, Maine, 1982—, CEO, 1992—; bd. dirs. Vista Resources Inc. Com. chmn. Boy Scouts Am., Johnstown, N.Y., 1981-82; trustee YMCA, Johnstown, 1982; trustee Boys/Girls Club, Waterville, Maine, 1985. Served with USN, 1965-69. Mem. Nat. Leather Industries Am. (treas. 1982-84, 92—, chmn 1984-86, chmn. targeted export assistance com. 1986-90, exec. com. 1982—). Avocations: personal investing, personal computing. Home: 21 Eustis Pkwy Waterville ME 04901-4901 Office: Irving Tanning Co Main St Hartland ME 04943

LAROCK, BRUCE EDWARD, civil engineering educator; b. Berkeley, Calif., Dec. 24, 1940; s. Ralph W. and Hazel M. (Lambert) L.; m. Susan E. Gardner, June 17, 1968; children: Lynne M., Jean E. BS in Civil Engring., Stanford U., 1962, MS in Civil Engring., 1963, PhD, 1966. Registered profl. engr., Calif. Asst. prof. U. Calif., Davis, 1966-72, assoc. prof., 1972-79, prof., 1979—; sr. vis. fellow U. Wales, Swansea, 1972-73; U.S. sr. scientist Tech. U., Aachen, Germany, 1986-87. Author: (with D. Newnan) Engineer-in-Training Examination Review, 3d edit., 1991; contbr. over 70 tech. articles to profl. jours. Mem. ASCE, Sigma Xi, Tau Beta Pi. Lutheran. Avocation: duplicate bridge. Office: U Calif Davis Dept Civil & Eviron Engring Davis CA 95616-5294

LA ROCQUE, EUGENE PHILIPPE, bishop; b. Windsor, Ont., Can., Mar. 27, 1927; s. Eugene Joseph and Angeline Marie (Monforton) LaR. B.A., U. Western Ont., 1948; M.A., Laval U., 1956. Ordained priest Roman Catholic Ch., 1952, consecrated bishop, 1974; asst. parish priest Ste. Therese Ch., Windsor, 1952-54; registrar, then dean men, lectr. Christ The King Coll., U. Western Ont., 1956-64; asst. spiritual dir. St. Peter's Sem., 1964-65; prin., dean King's Coll., 1965-68; pastor St. Joseph's Ch., Rivière-aux-Canards, Ont., 1968-70, Ste. Anne's Ch., Tecumseh, 1970-74; bishop of Alexandria-Cornwall, Ont., 1974—; dean Essex County, 1970-73; trustee Essex County Roman Cath. Separate Sch. Bd., 1972-74; 1st chmn. liaison com. Can. Jewish Congress Can. Coun. Chs. and Can. Cath. Conf. Bishops, 1977-84; mem. pro-life com., 1992-94; pres. Ont. Conf. Cath. Bishops, 1992—; pres. Fedn. Couns. Priests of Can., 1973-74. Mem. KC (3d degree, chaplain Ont. 1977-87). Address: 200 Montreal Rd, Box 1388, Cornwall, ON Canada K6H 5V4
Belief in God, who creates my unique human life and has a loving plan and concern for each of his children, sustains me amidst the strains, challenges and turmoils of life.

LAROCQUE, JUDITH ANNE, federal official; b. Hawkesbury, Ont., Can., Sept. 27, 1956; d. Jean Olier Edouard and Elizabeth Robina (Murray) LaR.; m. Andre Roland Lavoie, Mar. 15, 1991. BA with honours, Carleton U., Ottawa, Ont., 1979, MA, 1992. Notary Pub., Ont. Adminstrv. asst. Internal Audit Directorate, Pub. Svc. Commn., Ottawa, 1979; writer, researcher Prime Min.'s Office, Ottawa, 1979; spl. asst. Office Leader of Opposition, Ottawa, 1980-82; com. clk. coms. and pvt. legis. br. Can. Ho. of Commons, Ottawa, 1982-84, legis. asst. to Govt. House leader, 1984-85, head of House Bus. Office of Govt. House Leader, 1985-86; pres. Queen's Privy Coun. for Can. and min. responsible for regulatory affairs, Ottawa, 1985-86; exec. asst. to min. justice and atty. gen. Can., Ottawa, 1986-89; chief staff Office Leader Govt. in Senate and min. responsible for fed.-provincial rels., Ottawa, 1989-90; sec. to gov. gen. and herald chancellor Govt. House, Ottawa, 1990—; sec. Gen. Order Can., Order Mil. Merit. Fellow Heraldry Soc. Can. (hon.). Office: Govt House, 1 Sussex Dr, Ottawa, ON Canada K1A 0A1

LAROCQUE, MARILYN ROSS ONDERDONK, public relations executive; b. Weehawken, N.J., Oct. 14, 1934; d. Chester Douglas and Marion (Ross) Onderdonk; B.A. cum laude, Mt. Holyoke Coll., 1956; postgrad. N.Y. U., 1956-57; M. Journalism, U. Calif. at Berkeley, 1965; m. Bernard Dean Benz, Oct. 5, 1957 (div. Sept. 1971); children: Mark Douglas, Dean Griffith; m. 2d, Rodney C. LaRocque, Feb. 10, 1973. Jr. exec. Bonwit Teller, N.Y.C., 1956; personnel asst. Warner-Lambert Pharm. Co., Morris Plains, N.J., 1957; editorial asst. Silver Burdett Co., Morristown, 1958; self-employed as pub. rels. cons., Moraga, Calif., 1963-71, 73-77; pub. relations mgr. Shaklee Corp., Hayward, 1971-73; pub. rels. dir. Fidelity Savs., 1977-78; exec. dir. No. Calif. chpt. Nat. Multiple Sclerosis Soc., 1978-80; v.p. pub. rels. Cambridge Plan Internat., Monterey, Calif., 1980-81; sr. account exec. Hoefer-Amidei Assocs., San Francisco, 1981-82; dir. corp. communications, dir. spl. projects, asst. to chmn. Cambridge Plan Internat., Monterey, Calif., 1982-84; dir. communications Buena Vista Winery, Sonoma, Calif., 1984-86, asst. v.p. communications and market support, 1986-87; dir. communications Rutherford Hill Winery, St. Helena, Calif., 1987-88; pres. LaRocque Pub. Rels. and Pub. Affairs, Napa, Calif., 1989; pres. LaRocque Profl. Svcs., Inc., 1991—; instr. pub. rels. U. Calif. Extension, San Francisco, 1977-79. Mem. exec. bd., rep-at-large Oakland (Calif.) Symphony Guild, 1968-69, Napa County Landmarks, Inc.; co-chmn. pub. rels. com. Oakland Mus. Assn., 1974-75; cabinet mem. Lincoln Child Ctr., Oakland, 1967-71, pres. membership cabinet, 1970-71, 2d v.p. bd. dirs., 1970-71; bd. dirs. Calif. Spring Garden and Home Show, 1971-77, 1st agrl. Dist., 1971-77, Dunsmuir House and Gardens, 1976-77; mem. Calif. State Rep. Cen. Com., 1964-66; v.p. Piedmont coun. Boy Scouts Am., 1977. Mem. U. Calif. Alumni Assn., Pub. Rels. Soc. Am. (chpt. dir. 1980-82; accredited), Sonoma Valley Vintners Assn. (dir. 1984-87), Internat. Wine and Food Soc. (Marin chpt.), San Francisco Mus. Soc., Smithsonian Assocs., Sonoma Valley C. of C. (bd. dirs. 1984-87), Napa County Landmarks Inc. (bd. dirs., 1993-94), Am. Assn. Univ. Women (Napa Valley chpt.), Napa Valley Republican Women, Knights of the Vine (master lady 1985-90), Mount Holyoke Coll. Alumnae Club, Silverado Country Club, DAR (vineyard trails chpt.). Office: LaRocque Profl Svcs Inc 1800-A Soscol Ave Napa CA 94559-1345

LAROSA, ROBERT A., trade association executive; b. Boston, May 29, 1938; s. Alphonso LaRosa and Lillian D. (Cacciotta) Pierce; m. Naida L. Janes, July 30, 1961; children: Robert A. Jr., Terry Ann Champion, Jon A., Deana Marie Stevens. Student, Bentley Coll., 1963. Pres. Associated Industries of Mass. Svc. Corp., Boston, 1959—; chmn., pres. Mass. Employers Ins. Exch., Boston, 1989—; governing bd. Workers Compensation Rating Bur., Boston, 1990—. With U.S. Army, 1955-58. Mem. Am. Soc. Assn. Execs. (bd. dirs. 1988-89, mgmt. edn. award 1983, 84). Home: 2 Harwood Dr PO Box 533 Monument Beach MA 02553 Office: Associated Industries Mass 222 Berkeley St Boston MA 02116

LAROSE, ROGER, former pharmaceutical company executive, former university administrator; b. Montreal, Que., Can., July 28, 1910; s. Alfred and Anna (Contant) L.; m. Rita Dagenais, Aug. 10, 1936 (dec. Oct. 1960); 1 child, Louise Larose Cuddihy; m. Julienne Begin, Aug. 4, 1961. B.A., U. Montreal, 1929, B.Sc. in Pharmacy, 1932; Licentiate in Social, Polit., and Econ. Scis, 1934. Asst. prof. pharmacy U. Montreal, 1934; dean Faculty Pharmacy, 1960-65, vice rector, 1969-79; with Ciba Co. Ltd., Montreal, 1936-71; v.p. Ciba Co. Ltd., 1958-68, pres., 1968-71, dir., 1958-71; pres. Ciba-Geigy Can. Ltd., 1971-73, dep. chmn. bd., 1973-78, chmn. bd., 1978-82; vice chmn. bd., mem. exec. com. Bank Canadian Nat., 1969-80; mem. Sci. Council Can., 1966-71; pres. com. Sci. Council on Health Scis., 1969-73. Bd. dirs. Institut recherches cliniques de Montreal, 1968—, Hotel-Dieu de Montreal, 1969-79; pres. Hopital St-Luc de Montreal, 1978-88; bd. govs. Can. Bankers Inst., 1973-80; pres. Montreal Symphony Orch., 1978-79, pres. and mng. dir., 1979-81; pres. Chamber Orch. I Musici de Montreal, 1984-88; bd. dirs. Que. Hosp. Assn. Decorated officer Order Can. Mem. Acad. Pharmacy (France) (hon.), Pharm. Soc. Gt. Britain (hon.), Can. Hosp. Assn. (bd. dirs. 1985-89, George Findlay Stephen award 1990), St.-Denis Club (Montreal). Home: 404-205 Côte Ste. Catherine Rd, Outremont, PQ Canada H2V 2A9

LA ROSSA, JAMES M(ICHAEL), lawyer; b. Bklyn., Dec. 4, 1931; s. James Vincent and Marie Antoinette (Tronolone) La R.; m. Gayle Marino, Sept. 20, 1958; children—James M., Thomas, Nancy, Susan. B.S., Fordham U., 1953, J.D., 1958. Bar: N.Y. 1958, U.S. Dist. Ct. N.Y. 1961, U.S. Supreme Ct. 1969. Pvt. practice law N.Y.C., 1958-62, 67-74, 76—; asst. U.S. atty. Eastern Dist. N.Y., Bklyn., 1962-65; pfnr. firm Lefkowitz & Brownstien, N.Y.C., 1965-67, La Rossa, Shargel & Fishetti, N.Y.C., 1974-76, La Rossa, Brownstein & Mitchell, N.Y.C., 1980-82, La Rossa, Axenfeld & Mitchell, N.Y.C., 1982-84, La Rossa, Cooper, Axenfeld, Mitchell & Bergman, N.Y.C., 1984-85; now pfnr. La Rossa, Mitchell & Ross, N.Y.C.; participant Debate on Legal Ethics Criminal Cts. Bar Assn. Queens County, N.Y., 1978, Criminal Trial Advocacy Workshop, Harvard U. Law Sch., 1978. Author: White Collar Crimes: Defense Strategies, 1977, Federal Rules of Evidence in Criminal Matters, 1977, White Collar Crimes, 1978. Served to 1st lt. USMC, 1953-55. Recipient Guardian of Freedom award B'nai B'rith, 1978. Mem. ABA, N.Y. State Bar Assn. (Criminal Law Practitioner of Yr. 1990, 91), Fed. Bar Counsel, Assn. Bar City N.Y. Office: LaRossa Mitchell & Ross 41 Madison Ave New York NY 10010-2202

LAROUCHE, LYNDON H., JR., economist; b. Rochester, N.H., Sept. 8, 1922; s. Lyndon H. Sr. and Jesse (Weir) L.; m. Helga Zepp, 1977; 1 child, Daniel. Student, Northeastern U. 1940-47. Mgmt. cons. L.H. LaRouche

Rsch., 1942-66; founder, contbg. editor Exec. Intelligence Rev., 1975—; chmn. adv. com. Nat. Dem. Policy Com., 1980-83; mem. Internat. Ecology Acad., 1993—. Contbr. books and articles on politics, econs. and energy related issues. Presdl. candidate, 1976, 80, 84, 88, 92; candidate 10th Congl. Dist. Va., 1990; mem. internat. adv. bd. Schiller Inst.; bd. dirs. Fusion Energy Found., 1981-87. Mem. Club of Life. Office: care Exec Intelligence Rev PO Box 17390 Washington DC 20041

LARPENTEUR, JAMES ALBERT, JR., lawyer; b. Seattle, Aug. 6, 1935; s. James Albert and Mary Louise (Coffey) L.; m. Hazel Marie Arntson, Apr. 23, 1965 (div. 1983); children: Eric James, Jason Clifford; m. Katherine Annette Bingham, Nov. 8, 1986; 1 adopted child, Brenda Mon Fong. BS in Bus., U. Oreg., 1957, LLB, 1961. Bar: Oreg. 1961, U.S. Dist. Ct. Oreg. 1961, U.S. Tax Ct. 1962, U.S. Ct. Appeals (9th cir.) 1962, U.S. Supreme Ct. 1965. Assoc Schwabe Williamson & Wyatt, Portland, Oreg., 1961-69, ptnr., 1969-82, sr. ptnr., 1982—, mem. exec. com., 1989-92. Dir. exec. com. Portland Rose Festival Assn., 1975—, pres., 1987; ex-officio dir. Portland Visitors Assn., 1981—; bd. dirs., mem. exec. com. Providence Child Ctr. Found., 1983-94, chmn. exec. com. 1986-87; pres., bd. dirs. Willamette Light Brigade, 1987—, Cath. Charities Portland, 1989-92. Capt. U.S. Army, 1959-67. Mem. Oreg. Bar Assn. (editor, writer, speaker numerous continuing legal edn. programs, chmn. bus. law sect. 1986-87, real estate, estate planning, securities regulation sects.), Multnomah Athletic Club (pres. 1984), Univ. Club Portland, Waverley Country Club, Arlington Club, City Club of Portland. Avocations: golf, tennis, skiing, squash. Home: 324 NW Lomita Ter Portland OR 97210-3321 Office: Schwabe Williamson & Wyatt 1211 SW 5th Ave Portland OR 97204-3713

LARR, PETER, banker; b. Indpls., Jan. 17, 1939; s. David and Marjorie Kathleen (Hearne) L.; m. Rosamond Holmes Woodfield, July 7, 1962; children—Alexia Aisha, Diana Kirsten, David Hearne. B.A., Princeton U., 1960. Asst. mgr. London and Beirut brs. Chase Manhattan Bank, 1961-67, v.p., div. exec. land transp., 1976-78, v.p., group exec. credit tng. and devel., 1978-80, v.p., div. exec. commodity fin., 1983-85; sr. v.p., bus. exec. nat. corr. banking Chase Manhattan Bank, N.Y.C., 1983-85; sr. v.p., exec. domestic instl. banking Chase Manhattan Bank, 1985-90, v.p., risk asset rev. exec., 1990-95; sr. v.p. sr. credit and porfolio mgmt. exec. Asia Chase Manhattan Bank, Hong Kong, 1995—. Assoc. vestry Christ Ch., Rye, N.Y., 1983-85; planning commr., City of Rye, 1992-95. Mem. Assn. Res. City Bankers (assoc., bank pay systems com. 1984-90), Am. Bankers Assn. (chmn. corp. banking divsn. 1988-94), Robert Morris Assn. N.Y. (pres.), Princeton Club, Am. Yacht Club, Apawamis Club. Avocations: tennis, golf, genealogical rsch. Office: Chase Manhattan Bank, World Trade Ctr, 280 Gloucester Rd, Hong Kong Hong Kong

LARRABEE, DONALD RICHARD, publishing company executive; b. Portland, Maine, Aug. 8, 1923; s. Henry Carpenter and Marion (Clapp) L.; m. Mary Elizabeth Rolfs, Oct. 9, 1948; children—Donna Louise, Robert Rolfs. Student, Syracuse U., 1941-43. Reporter Portland Press Herald, 1941-43, Syracuse Post Standard, 1943; reporter Griffin-Larrabee News Bur., Washington, 1946-54; mng. editor Griffin-Larrabee News Bur., 1954-67, bur. chief, 1967-69, owner, 1969-78; dir. Washington office. Assn. State of Maine, 1978-89; dir. Nat. Press Bldg. Corp., 1973-85. Bd. dirs. Nat. Press Found., 1978—. Served with USAAF, 1943-45. Mem. Me. Soc. Washington (pres. 1950-53), Corrs. for Congl. Press Galleries (standing com. 1959-60), White House Corrs. Assn. Conglist. (moderator 1962). Clubs: Gridiron (Washington), National Press (Washington) (sec. 1953-54, treas. 1966-67, mem. bd. 1969, pres. 1973). Home and Office: 4704 Jamestown Rd Bethesda MD 20816-2923

LARRABEE, MARTIN GLOVER, biophysics educator; b. Boston, Jan. 25, 1910; s. Ralph Clinton and Ada Perkins Miller L.; m. Sylvia Kimball, Sept. 10, 1932 (div. 1944); 1 son, Benjamin Larrabee Scherer; m. Barbara Belcher, Mar. 25, 1944; 1 son, David Belcher Larrabee. B.A., Harvard, 1932; Ph.D., U. Pa., 1937; M.D. (hon.), U. Lausanne, Switzerland, 1974. Research asst. fellow U. Pa., Phila., 1934-40; assoc to assoc. prof. U. Pa., 1941-49; asst. prof. physiology Cornell U. Med. Coll., N.Y.C., 1940-41; assoc. prof. Johns Hopkins U., Balt., 1949-63, prof. biophysics, 1963—. Contbr. articles to scientific jours. Mem. Am. Physiol. Soc., Biophys. Soc., Am. Soc. Neurochemistry, Internat. Neurochem. Soc., Nat. Acad. Scis., Soc. for Neurosci. (treas. 1970-75), Physiol. Soc. (asso., Eng.), Phi Beta Kappa. Clubs: Appalachian Mountain, Sierra, Mountain of Md. Rsch. on circulatory, respiratory and nervous systems of animals, especially on synaptic and metabolic mechanisms in sympathetic ganglia, 1934—; wartime research on oxygen lack, decompression sickness, nerve injury, infrared viewing devices, 1941-45. Home: Glen Meadows 11630 Glen Arm Rd Glen Arm MD 21057 Office: Johns Hopkins U Biophysics Dept Baltimore MD 21218

LARRIMORE, RANDALL WALTER, manufacturing company executive; b. Lewes, Del., Apr. 27, 1947; s. Randall A. and Irene (Faucett) L.; m. Judith Cutright, Aug. 29, 1970; children: Jacob, Alex. BS, Swarthmore (Pa.) Coll., 1969; MBA, Harvard U., 1971. Product mgr. Richardson-Vick, Wilton, Conn., 1971-75; sr. engagement mgr. McKinsey & Co., N.Y.C., 1975-80; pres. Pepsi-Cola Italia, Rome, 1980-83, Beatrice Home Specialties, Inc. (name changed to Twentieth Century Cos., Inc.), Skokie, Ill., 1983-87; pres., chief exec. officer MasterBrand Industries, Inc., 1988—; v.p. Am. Brands, Inc., 1988—; chmn. Moen Inc., 1990—, chief exec. officer, 1990-94; adv. bd. Nat. Home Ctr. Show, 1990-93. Bd. dirs. Winnetka Congl. Ch., 1989-90; mem. hardware/home improvement coun. City of Hope, 1991—, pres. 1991-93; mem. adv. bd. Nat. Home Ctr. Show, 1990-93; commr. Landmark Preservation Coun., Winnetka, 1992—. Mem. Plumbing Mfg. Inst. (bd. dirs 1991-93). Home: 830 Sheridan Rd Winnetka IL 60093-1929 Office: MasterBrand Industries Inc 510 Lake Cook Rd Deerfield IL 60015-5610 also: Am Brands Inc 1700 E Putnam Ave Box 819 Old Greenwich CT 06870

LARROCA, RAYMOND G., lawyer; b. San Juan, P.R., Jan. 5, 1930; s. Raymond Gil and Elsa Maria (Morales) L.; m. Barbara Jean Strand, June 21, 1952 (div. 1974); children—Denise Anne Sheehan, Gail Ellen, Raymond Gil, Mark Talbot, Jeffrey William. B.S.S. Georgetown U., 1952, J.D., 1957. Bar: D.C. 1957, U.S. Supreme Ct. 1960. Assoc., Kirkland, Fleming, Green, Martin & Ellis, Washington, 1957-64; ptnr. Kirkland, Ellis, Hodson, Chaffetz & Masters, Washington, 1964-67, Miller, Cassidy, Larroca & Lewin, Washington, 1967—. Served with arty. U.S. Army, 1948-49, to 1st lt., inf., 1952-54. Mem. ABA, D.C. Bar, Bar Assn. D.C., The Barristers. Republican. Roman Catholic. Clubs: Congl. Country (Potomac, Md.); University (Washington). Office: 2555 M St NW Ste 500 Washington DC 20037-1353

LARROQUETTE, JOHN BERNARD, actor; b. New Orleans, Nov. 25, 1947; s. John Edgar Larroquette and Berthalla (Oramous) Helmstetter; m. Elizabeth Ann Cookson, July 4, 1975; children: Lisa Katherina, Jonathan Preston, Benjamin Lawrence. Grad. high sch., New Orleans. Plays include: The Crucible, Enter Laughing, Endgame; numerous appearances in TV shows including Baa Baa Black Sheep; Dan Fielding in Night Court, NBC, 1983-92 (Best Actor Emmy award, 1985, 86, 87, 88), The John Larroquette Show, 1993— (Best Actor Emmy award nominee 1994); feature films include: Altered States, 1980, Stripes, 1981, Cat People, 1982, Twilight Zone: The Movie, 1983, Choose Me, 1983, Star Trek III: The Search for Spock, 1984, Hysterical, 1984, Meatballs, Part II, 1984, Summer Rentals, 1985, Blind Date, 1987, Second Sight, 1989, Madhouse, 1990, Tune in Tomorrow, 1990, Richie Rich, 1994; TV film appearance Hot Paint, 1988; narrator Texas Chainsaw Massacre, 1974, One Special Victory, NBC, 1991. Avocation: collecting first edition books. Office: 1033 Gayley Ave Ste 208 Los Angeles CA 90024

LARROUILH, MICHEL, banker; b. Pessac, Gironde, France, July 27, 1935; came to U.S., 1984; s. Robert L.; m. Martine Cullmann; children: Frederic, Caroline, Stephane, Alexandre. Gen. sec. Banque Nat. de Paris, St. Quentin, France, 1960-61, Saigon, Vietnam, 1961-64; dep. gen. mgr. BICI subs. Banque Nat. de Paris, Dukar, Senegal, 1965-71; gen. mgr., chief exec. officer Banque Nat. de Paris, Bombay, 1972-75; mgr. dir. United Bank for Africa subs. Banque Nat. de Paris, Lagos, Nigeria, 1975-80; dir. dept. R & D internat. div. Banque Nat. de Paris, Paris, 1981-82; gen. mgr. BNP Group, Sydney, Australia, 1982-83; pres., chief exec officer Bank of West subs. BNP Group, San Francisco, 1984—. Office: Bank of the West 180 Montgomery St San Francisco CA 94104-4204

LARROWE, CHARLES PATRICK, economist, educator; b. Portland, Oreg., May 1, 1916; s. Albertus and Helen (Maginnis) L.; 1 child, Peter (dec.). B.A., U. Wash., Seattle, 1946, M.A., 1948; Ph.D., Yale U., 1952. Asst. instr. econs. U. Wash., 1946-49, Yale U., 1949-52; assoc. prof. U. Utah, 1952-56; mem. faculty Mich. State U., East Lansing, 1956-89; prof. econs. Mich. State U., 1961-89, faculty grievance ofcl., 1976-80, 88-89; cons. to govt. Author: Shape-Up and Hiring Hall, 1955, Harry Bridges, 2d edit., 1977, Lashing Out, 1982. Served in Am. Field Service, 1942-43; Served with AUS, 1943-45. Decorated Silver Star, Purple Heart with oak leaf cluster, Combat Infantryman's badge; grantee Rabinowitz Found., 1962. Mem. ACLU, NAACP, Amnesty Internat., Rolls-Royce Owners' Club. Democrat. Home: 537 Gunson St East Lansing MI 48823-3525 Office: Mich State Univ Dept Econs East Lansing MI 48824

LARRY, DAVID HEATH, lawyer; b. Pitts., Dec. 24, 1941; s. Ralph Heath and Eleanor Elizabeth (Ketler) L.; m. Elizabeth Lowe Satler, Dec. 7, 1968; children: Demian Heath, Christa Elizabeth. BA in Philosophy, Williams Coll., 1963; JD, U. Oreg., 1976. Bar: Oreg. 1976, D.C. 1979. Counsel to chmn., mem. NLRB, Washington, 1976-78; asst. county counsel Lane County, Eugene, Oreg., 1979; assoc. McGuiness & Williams, Washington, 1979-81; from assoc. to ptnr. Epstein Becker & Green, Washington, 1981-90; Manatt Phelps & Phillips, Washington, 1990—. Office: Manatt Phelps & Phillips 1200 New Hampshire Ave NW Washington DC 20036-6801

LARRY, R. HEATH, lawyer; b. Huntingdon, Pa., Feb. 24, 1914; s. Ralph E. and Mabel (Heath) L.; m. Eleanor Ketler, Sept. 10, 1938; children: David Heath, Dennis Ketler, Thomas Richard. A.B., Grove City Coll., 1934, LL.D., 1964; J.D., U. Pitts., 1937. Bar: Pa. 1937, D.C. 1937. Pvt. practice, 1937-38; atty. Nat. Tube Co., 1938-44, sec., dir., 1944-48; gen. atty. U.S. Steel Corp., Pitts., 1948-52; asst. gen. solicitor U.S. Steel Corp., 1952-58, adminstrv. v.p. labor relations, 1958-66, exec. v.p.-adminstrn., 1966-69, vice chmn. bd., 1969-77; pres. N.A.M., 1977-80; of counsel Reed Smith Shaw & McClay, Washington, 1980—; dir. emeritus Textron, Inc. Bd. visitors U. Pitts. Sch. Law; trustee Grove City Coll.; former trustee Conf. Bd. Mem. Am. Iron and Steel Inst. Presbyn. Clubs: Met. (Washington); Economic (N.Y.C.); Gulf Stream Golf, Delray Beach Yacht, Gulf Stream Bath and Tennis, Little; Bermuda Run Country Club. Home: 4333 N Ocean Blvd Apt 3A Delray Beach FL 33483-7559 also (summer): Bermuda Village 3107 Advance NC 27006

LARSEN, ANNE, editor; b. Blue Island, Ill., Apr. 13, 1941; d. Robert Edward and Ruth Elizabeth (Hunke) Schnare; m. Eric Everett Larsen, June 5, 1965; children: Flynn, Gavin. BA, Carleton Coll., 1963; MA, U. Wis., 1965. Support svcs., researcher Sta. WNET-TV, N.Y.C., 1972-74; freelance book reviewer, writer Village Voice, Chgo. Tribune, Parents mag., N.Y.C., 1974-76; assoc. editor fiction Redbook mag., N.Y.C., 1976-83; free-lance editor and cons. Redbook, Mademoiselle, Seventeen, Cosmopolitan, Esquire, N.Y.C., 1983-85; editor, fiction Kirkus Rev., N.Y.C., 1985-87, editor, 1987-94, fiction editor, 1995—. Mem. Nat. Book Critics Circle, Am. Soc. Mag. Editors, Women's Media Group, Friends of Poets and Writers, Friends of PEN. Office: Kirkus Svc Inc Kirkus Reviews 200 Park Ave S New York NY 10003-1503

LARSEN, EDWIN MERRITT, retired chemist, educator; b. Milw., July 12, 1915; s. Howard Reynolds and Ella (Tees) L.; m. Kathryn Marie Behm, Aug. 17, 1946; children—Robert, Lynn, Richard. B.S., U. Wis., 1937; Ph.D., Ohio State U., 1942. Chemist Rohm & Haas, Phila., 1937-38; teaching asst. Ohio State U., 1938-42; group leader Manhattan Dist. polonium project Monsanto Chem. Co., 1943-46; mem. faculty dept. chemistry U. Wis.-Madison, 1942-43, 46-86, prof., 1958-86, assoc. chmn. dept., 1977-86; mem. Wis. Fusion Tech. Inst.; vis. prof. U. Fla., 1958; Fulbright lectr. Technische Hochschule, Vienna, Anorganische Institut, 1966-67. Author: Transitional Elements, 1965; contbr. articles to profl. jours. on synthesis in liquid aluminum trihalides and on role of chemistry in development of fusion energy. Fellow AAAS; mem. Am. Chem. Soc. (chmn. Wis. sect.), Am. Nuclear Soc., Wis. Acad. Scis., Arts and Letters, Sigma Xi (chmn. Wis. chpt.), Phi Lambda Upsilon. Home: 109 Standish Ct Madison WI 53705-5131

LARSEN, ERIK, art history educator; b. Vienna, Austria, Oct. 10, 1911; came to U.S., 1947, naturalized, 1953; s. Richard and Adrienne (Schapringer de Csepreg) L.; m. Lucy Roman, Oct. 4, 1932 (dec. 1981); children: Sigurd-Yves, Annik-Eve., Erik-Claude (dec.); m. Anna Gallup Moses, May 8, 1982 (div. Sept. 1986); m. Katharina Ehling, Oct. 21, 1989. Candidate, Institut Superieur d'Histoire de l'Art et d'Archéologie, Brussels, 1931; Licentiate, Louvain (Belgium) U., 1941; Docteur en Archéologie et Histoire de l'Art, 1959; D. honoris causa, Janus Pannonius U., Pécs, Hungary, 1992. Dir., editor-in-chief on semi-ofcl. cultural mission for Belgian Govt. Pictura, art mag., Brussels, Rio de Janeiro, Brazil, 1946-47; research prof. art Manhattanville Coll. of Sacred Heart, 1947-55; instr. CCNY, 1948-55; lectr, then vis. prof. Georgetown U., 1955-58, assoc. prof. fine arts, 1958-63, prof., 1963-67, head dept. fine arts, 1960-67; prof. history of art U. Kans., 1967-80, prof. emeritus, 1980—; dir. Center for Flemish Art and Culture, 1970-80; cons. old masters' paintings, guest-prof. U. Salzburg, Austria, 1988. Author: books, the most recent being La Vie, Les Ouvrages et Les Eleves de Van Dyck, 1975, Calvinistic Economy and 17th Century Dutch Art, 1979, Anton van Dyck, 1980, Rembrandt, Peintre de Paysages: Une Vision Nouvelle, 1983, Japanese edit., 1992; Seventeenth Century Flemish Painting, 1985, The Paintings of Anthony van Dyck, 2 vols., 1988; contbr. numerous articles, revs. to profl. publs., newspapers. Mem. Kans. Cultural Arts Commn., 1971-73; mem. Kans. Cultural Arts Adv. Council, 1973-79. Served with Belgian Underground, 1942-45. Decorated knight's cross Order Leopold, knight's cross Order of Crown, officer Order Leopold (Belgium); officer Order of Rio Branco (Brazil); recipient prix Thorlet, laureate Inst. France, Académie des sciences morales et politiques, 1962; Internat. Hon. Citizen, New Orleans, 1989; named hon. Ky. col., 1977. Fellow Soc. Antiquaries of Scotland; mem. Appraisers Assn. Am., Association des Diplomés en Histoire de l'Art et Archéologie de L'Université Catholique de Louvain, Académie d'Aix-en Provence (France) (corr.), Académie de Mâcon (France) (asso.), Académie d'Alsace (France) (titular), Comité Cultural Argentino (hon.), Schweizerisches Institut fuer Kunstwissenschaft (Zurich, Switzerland), Academia di Belle Arti Pietro Vanucci (Perugia, Italy) (hon.), Royal Soc. Arts (London) (Benjamin Franklin fellow); correspondent-academician Real Academia de Bellas Artes de San Telmo (Malága, Spain), Real Academia de Bellas Artes de San Jorge (Barcelona, Spain), Accademia Tiberina (Rome), Académie Royale D'Archéologie de Belgique (fgn. assoc.). Home: 511 S Washington St Beverly Hills FL 34465

LARSEN, GARY LOY, physician, researcher; b. Wahoo, Nebr., Jan. 10, 1945; s. Allan Edward and Dorothy Mae (Hengen) L.; m. Letitia Leah Hoyt, Dec. 22, 1967; children: Kari Lyn, Amy Marie. BS, U. Nebr., 1967; MD, Columbia U., 1971. Diplomate Am. Bd. Pediatrics, Am. Bd. Pediatric Pulmonology (chmn. 1990-92)/. Pediatric pulmonologist Nat. Jewish Ctr. for Immunology & Respiratory Medicine, Denver, 1978—; mem. faculty U. Colo. Sch. Medicine, Denver, 1978—, dir. sect. of pediatric pulmonary medicine, 1987—, prof. pediatrics, 1990—. Contbr. articles to profl. jours. Major M.C., U.S. Army, 1974-76. NIH med. rsch. grantee NIH, 1981—. Mem. Am. Thoracic Soc. (chmn. pediatric assembly 1987-88), Soc. Pediatric Rsch., Phi Beta Kappa, Alpha Omega Alpha. Lutheran. Office: Nat Jewish Ctr Immunology & Respiratory Medicine 1400 Jackson St Denver CO 80206-2761

LARSEN, GLEN L., school system administrator. Supt. Deshler (Nebr.) Schs., 1968-71, Fullerton (Nebr.) Pub. Schs., 1971-81, Adams Ctrl. Jr./Sr. High Sch., Hastings, Nebr., 1981—. Recipient Nebr. Superintendent of the Yr. award Am. Assn. of Sch. Adminstrs., 1991. Mem. Nebr. Sch. Athletics Assn. (dmn. region IV). Office: Adams Ctrl Jr Sr High Sch PO Box 1088 Hastings NE 68902

LARSEN, JONATHAN ZERBE, journalist; b. N.Y.C., Jan. 6, 1940; s. Roy Edward and Margaret (Zerbe) L.; m. Katharine Wilder, May 28, 1966; m. Jane Amsterdam, Aug. 31, 1985; 1 child, Edward Roy. B.A., Harvard U., 1961, M.A.T., 1963. Chicago bur. chief Time mag., N.Y.C., 1965-66; corr. Time mag., Chgo., 1966-68, Los Angeles, 1968-70; bur. chief Time mag., Saigon, Vietnam, 1970-71; asso. editor Time mag., 1972-73; editor New Times mag., N.Y.C., 1974-79; Nieman fellow Harvard U., 1979-80; news editor Life mag.,

1980-81, sr. editor, 1981-82; free-lance writer, 1982-88; editor-in-chief The Village Voice, N.Y.C., 1989-94. Trustee Natural Resources Def. Council., Cambridge Coll.; bd. dirs. Larsen Fund. Recipient Clarion award, 1986. Home: Finch Farm Vail Ln North Salem NY 10560

LARSEN, PAUL EMANUEL, religious organization administrator; b. Mpls., Oct. 5, 1933; s. David Paul and Myrtle (Grunnet) L.; m. Elizabeth Helen Taylor, Mar. 19, 1966; children: Kristin, Kathleen. BA, Stanford U., 1955; MDiv, Fuller Theol. Sem., 1958; STD, San Francisco Theol. Sem., 1978. Ordained to ministry Evang. Ch., 1963. Asst. pastor Evang. Ch., Eagle Rock, Calif., 1958-59; pastor Pasadena, Calif., 1963-70, Peninsula Covenant Ch., Redwood City, Calif., 1971-86; pres. Evang. Covenant Chs., Chgo., 1986—; chmn. meeting U.S. ch. leaders, 1992—. Author: Wise Up and Live, Mission of a Covenant. Home: 24 The Landmark Northfield IL 60093 Office: Evang Covenant Ch 5101 N Francisco Ave Chicago IL 60625-3611

LARSEN, RALPH IRVING, environmental research engineer; b. Corvallis, Oreg., Nov. 26, 1928; s. Walter Winfred and Nellie Lyle (Gellatly) L.; B.S. in Civil Engring., Oreg. State U., 1950; M.S., Harvard U., 1955; Ph.D. in Air Pollution and Indsl. Hygiene, 1957; m. Betty Lois Garner, Oct. 14, 1950 (dec. Feb. 1989); children: Karen Larsen Cleeton, Eric, Kristine Larsen Burns, Jan Alan; m. Anne Harmon King, Aug. 3, 1991; children: Vikki King Ball, Terri King Reading, Cindi King King. San. engr. div. water pollution control USPHS, Washington, 1950-54; chief tech. service state and community service sect. Nat. Air Pollution Control Adminstrn., Cin., 1957-61; with EPA and Nat. Air Pollution Control Adminstrn., 1961—, environ. rsch. engr. Atmospheric Rsch. and Exposure Assessment Lab., Rsch. Triangle Park, N.C., 1971—; air pollution cons. to Poland, 1973, 75, Brazil, 1978; condr. seminars for air pollution researchers, Paris, Vienna and Milan, 1975; adj. lectr. Inst. Air Pollution Tng., 1969—; Falls of Neuse community rep. City of Raleigh (N.C.), 1974—. Recipient Commendation medal USPHS, 1979. Mem. Air and Waste Mgmt. Assn. (mem. editorial bd. jour. 1971-88), Conf. Fed. Environ. Engrs., USPHS Commd. Officers Assn. (past br. pres.), Sigma Xi. Republican. Mem. Christian and Missionary Alliance Ch. (elder). Contbr. over 55 articles to profl. jours. Home: 4012 Colby Dr Raleigh NC 27609-6045 Office: Md # 76 Epa Research Triangle Park NC 27711 *God issued me a 1928-model body. It works best, for others and me, as I read a chapter of the Owner's Manual (The Holy Bible) first thing each morning.*

LARSEN, RALPH S(TANLEY), health care company executive; b. Bklyn., Nov. 19, 1938; s. Andrew and Gurine (Henningsen) L.; m. Dorothy M. Zeitfuss, Aug. 19, 1961; children: Karen, Kristen, Garret. BBA, Hofstra U., 1962. Mfg. trainee, then supr. prodn. and dir. mfg. Johnson & Johnson, New Brunswick, N.J., 1962-71? v.p. ops., v.p. mktg. McNeil Consumer Products Co. div. Johnson & Johnson, Ft. Washington, Pa., 1977-81; pres. Becton Dickenson Consumer Products, Paramus, N.J., 1981-83; pres. Chicopee div. Johnson & Johnson, New Brunswick, 1983-85; co. group chmn. Johnson & Johnson, New Brunswick, N.J., 1985-86, vice chmn., exec. com., bd. dirs., 1986-89, chmn. bd., pres., CEO, 1989—, also bd. dirs., mem. exec. com.; bd. dirs. N.Y. Stock Exch., Xerox Corp. Bd. dirs. United Ways of Tri-State, Unicef. Mem. Bus. Coun. (vice chmn.), Bus. Roundtable (policy com.). Republican. Avocations: skiing, boating, art. Office: Johnson & Johnson 1 Johnson Johnson Plz New Brunswick NJ 08933

LARSEN, RICHARD GARY, accounting firm executive; b. Tampa, Fla., Nov. 28, 1948; s. Dagfinn T. Larsen and Elizabeth M. (Koch) Thompson; m. Harriet Taylor Jones, Dec. 19, 1970; children—Jonathan Daniel, Alice Taylor. BBA in Acctg., George Washington U., 1971, JD, 1974; postgrad., Columbia U., 1985. Bar: Va. 1974; CPA, D.C., Va. Mem. staff U.S. Senate, Washington, 1967-73; ptnr. Ernst & Young, Washington, 1973—; adj. prof. U. Md., College Park, 1976-78, Am. U., Washington, 1977-78. Mem. ABA, Va. Bar Assn. (AICPA, Md. Soc. CPAs, Univ. Club (Washington), Coral Beach and Tennis Club (Bermuda), Chatham Beach and Tennis Club, Eastward Ho Country Club (Chatham), Columbia Country Club (Chevy Chase), Belle Haven Country Club, Capitol Hill Club. Home: 319 S St Asaph St Alexandria VA 22314 Office: Ernst & Young 1225 Connecticut Ave NW Washington DC 20036-2604

LARSEN, RICHARD LEE, former city manager, business, municipal and labor relations consultant, arbitrator; b. Jackson, Miss., Apr. 16, 1934; s. Homer Thorsten and Mae Cordelia (Amidon) L.; m. Virginia Fay Alley, June 25, 1955; children: Karla, Daniel, Thomas (dec.), Krista, Lisa. B.S. in Econs. and Bus. Adminstrn, Westminster Coll., Fulton, Mo., 1959; postgrad., U. Kans., 1959-61. Fin. dir. Village of Northbrook, Ill., 1961-63; city mgr. Munising, Mich., 1963-66, Sault Ste. Marie, Mich., 1966-72, Ogden, Utah, 1972-77, Billings, Mont., 1977-79; mcpl. cons., 1979—, pub./pvt. sector labor relations cons., arbitrator, 1979—; elected mayor City of Billings, 1989—; dep. adm. chmn. Greater Mich. Found., 1968. Bd. dirs. Central Weber Sewer Dist., 1972-77; chmn. labor com. Utah League Cities and Towns, 1973-77, Mont. League Cities and Towns, 1977-79; bd. dirs., coach Ogden Hockey Assn., 1972-77, Weber Sheltered Workshop, 1974-77, Billings YMCA, 1980-86, Rimrock Found., 1980-86; chmn. community relations council Weber Basin Job Corps Center, 1973-77. Served with USCG, 1953-57. Recipient Cmty. Devel. Disting. Achievement awards Munising, 1964, Cmty. Devel. Disting. Achievement awards Sault Ste. Marie, 1966-70, Citizen award Dept. of Interior, 1977, Alumni Achievement award Westminster Coll., 1990, Dist. award of merit Boy Scouts Am., 1993, Silver Beaver award Boy Scouts Am., 1994; named Utah Adminstr. of Yr., 1976. Mem. Internat. City Mgmt. ASsn. (L.P. Cookingham career devel. award 1974, Clarence Ridley in-service tng. award 1979), Utah City Mgrs. Assn. (pres. 1972-74), Greater Ogden C. of C. (dir.), Phi Gamma Delta. Mem. LDS Ch. Club: Rotary. Home and Office: 1733 Parkhill Dr Billings MT 59102-2358

LARSEN, ROBERT DHU, lawyer; b. Stoughton, Wis., Oct. 20, 1922; s. Hans Christian and Helen Charlotte (Sobye) L.; m. Mary Lee Matheson, May 5, 1959 (div. 1973); children: Brooke, Christopher Dhu. AB, U. Wis., 1947; JD with honors, U. N.C., 1950. Bar: N.C. 1950, D.C. 1952, U.S. Supreme Ct. 1957, N.Y. 1959. Law clk. to presiding judge U.S. Ct. Appeals (4th cir.), Charlotte, N.C., 1950-51; from assoc. to ptnr. Rogers & Wells (and predecessors), N.Y.C., 1951-90; retired, 1990. Editor-in-chief U. N.C. Law Rev., 1950. Chmn. bd. trustees Pine Manor Coll., Chestnut Hill, Mass., 1981-84. Served to capt. inf. U.S. Army, 1943-46. Mem. Order of Coif. Democrat. Episcopalian. Home: 40 E 88th St New York NY 10128-1176

LARSEN, ROBERT LEROY, artistic director; b. Walnut, Iowa, Nov. 28, 1934; s. George Dewey and Maine M. (Mickel) L. MusB, Simpson Coll., Indianola, Iowa, 1956; MusM, U. Mich., 1958; MusD, Ind. U., 1972. Music prof. Simpson Coll., 1957—, chmn. music dept., 1965—; founder, artistic dir. Des Moines Met. Opera, 1973—. Mus. coach Tanglewood, Lenox, Mass., 1963, Oglebay Pk. (W.Va.) Opera, 1965, Chgo., N.Y. studios; condr.; stage dir. Simpson Coll., Des Moines Met. Opera, Miss. Opera, U. Ariz.; solo pianist, accompanist numerous recitals; adjudicator Met. auditions and competitions, Mpls., Chgo., Kansas City, Mo., Tulsa, San Antonio; stage dir., condr. operas, Simpson Coll., Des Moines Met. Opera, 1973—; editor Opera Anthologies by G. Schirmer; piano rec. artist for G. Schirmer Libr. Recipient Gov's. award State of Iowa, 1974. Mem. Am. Choral Dir. Assn., Nat. Opera Assn., Music Tchrs. Nat. Assn., Pi Kappa Lambda, Phi Kappa Phi, Phi Mu Alpha Sinfonia (faculty advisor). Presbyterian. Avocations: reading, theatre, coaching students. Office: Des Moines Metro Opera 106 W Boston Ave Indianola IA 50125-1836

LARSEN, STEVEN, orchestra conductor; b. Oak Park, Ill., Feb. 10, 1951; s. Edwin Earnest and Sylvia Viola Larson; divorced; children: Vanessa, Krista; m. Martha Jane Bein, Mar. 21, 1993. MusB, Am. Conservatory Music, Chgo., 1975; MusM, Northwestern U., 1976. Cert. Nederlandse Dirigenten Kursus. Orch. dir.; instr. music theory, chair instrumental dept Am. Conservatory Music, Chgo., 1976-82; music dir. Opera Theatre of San Antonio, 1987-90; orch. dir. Rockford (Ill.) Symphony Orch., 1991—; music dir., acting artistic dir. Chgo. Opera Theater, 1981-92; lectr. opera performance Chgo. Musical Coll., 1984—. Mem. Rockford South Rotary. Office: Rockford Symphony Orch 711 N Main Rockford IL 61103

LARSEN, TERRANCE A., bank holding company executive. BA, U. Dallas, 1968; PhD, Tex. A&M U., 1971. With Phila. Nat. Bank, from 1977, sr. v.p., 1980-83, exec. v.p., from 1983; exec. v.p Corestates Fin. Corp.

(parent), Phila., 1983-86, pres., 1986—, COO, 1986-87, chmn. CEO, 1988—; also bd. dirs. Office: Core States Fin Corp NE Corner Broad & Chestnut Sts PO Box 7618 Philadelphia PA 19101-7618•

LARSEN, WILLIAM LAWRENCE, materials science and engineering educator; b. Crookston, Minn., July 16, 1926; s. Clarence M. and Luverne (Carlisle) L.; m. Gracie Lee Richey, June 19, 1954; children—Eric W., Thomas R. B.M.E., Marquette U., 1948; M.S., Ohio State U., 1950, Ph.D. 1956; postgrad., U. Chgo., 1950-51. Registered profl. engr., Iowa. Research assoc. Ohio State U., Columbus, 1951-56; research metallurgist E. I. duPont de Nemours & Co., Wilmington, Del., 1956-58; metallurgist Ames Lab., AEC, Iowa, 1958-73; assoc. prof. Iowa State U., Ames, 1958-73, prof. materials sci. and engring., 1973-93; cons. metallurgical engring., 1960—. Contbr. articles to profl. jours. Served with USN, 1944-46. Mem. ASM Internat., ASTM, Am. Soc. Engring. Edn., Nat. Assn. Corrosion Engrs. (cert.), The Minerals, Metals and Materials Soc., Nat. Collegiate Honors Coun. Home: 335 N Franklin Ave Ames IA 50014-3424 Office: Iowa State U Ames IA 50011

LARSEN-BASSE, JORN, mechanical/materials engineering educator, researcher, consultant; b. Maribo, Denmark, Oct. 14, 1934; came to U.S. 1962; s. Asger Bernhard Bjerregaard and Ragnhild Sofie (Jorgensen) Larsen Badse; m. Margarita Simpson, Mar. 31, 1959; 1 child, Kai Erik. MSME, Royal Danish Tech. U., Copenhagen, 1958, PhD in Metallurgy, 1961. Registered mech. engr., Denmark; cert. corrosion specialist, U.S. Rsch. metallurgist Soderfors Bruk, Soderfors, Sweden, 1961-62; rsch. assoc. Stanford (Calif.) U., 1963-64; prof. mech. engring. U. Hawaii, Honolulu, 1964-86; chmn. dept. U. Hawaii, 1976-81, 82-85; prof. mech. engring. Ga. Inst. Tech., Atlanta, 1986-91; program dir. NSF, Washington, 1988—; cons. Honolulu, 1964-86; vis. prof. U. NSW, Sydney, Australia, 1978, Tsinghua U., Beijing, 1983; vis. researcher in tribophysics Commonwealth Sci. and Indsl. Rsch. Orgn., Melbourne, Australia, 1979. Assoc. editor Jour. Tribology, 1989-91; contbr. numerous articles to profl. jours. Mem. ASME, Metall. Soc. of AIME, Am. Soc. for Metals, Am. Soc. for Engring. Edn., Nat. Assn. Corrosion Engrs., Sigma Xi. Home: 6200 Perthshire Ct Bethesda MD 20817-3348 Office: NSF 4201 Wilson Blvd Arlington VA 22230-0001

LARSON, ALAN PHILIP, federal official; b. Osage, Iowa, July 19, 1949; s. Philip Harold and Marilyn (Lack) L.; m. Nancy Ruth Naden, June 3, 1972; children: NAthan Christopher, Lara Marie, Philip Gardner. BA, U. Iowa, 1971, MA, 1978, PhD, 1982. Econ. officer U.S. Embassy Dept. of State, Kinshasa, Zaire, 1975-77; dep. dir. Dept. of State, Washington, 1978-82; counselor for econ. and comml. affairs U.S. Embassy Dept. of State, Kingston, Jamaica, 1982-84; exec. asst. to undersec. Dept. of State, Washington, 1984-86, dep. asst. sec. for internat. energy, 1986-87, prin. dep. asst. sec. for econs. and bus., 1987-90; U.S. amb. to OECD Paris, 1990—. Office: 19, rue de Franqueville, 75016 Paris France

LARSON, ALLAN LOUIS, political scientist, educator, lay church worker; b. Chetek, Wis., Mar. 31, 1932; s. Leonard Andrew and Mabel (Marek) L. BA magna cum laude, U. Wis., Eau Claire, 1954; PhD, Northwestern U., 1964. Instr. Evanston Twp. (Ill.) High Sch., 1958-61; asst. prof. polit. sci. U. Wis., 1963-64; asst. prof. Loyola U., Chgo., 1964-68, assoc. prof., 1968-74, prof., 1974—. Author: Comparative Political Analysis, 1980, (essay) The Human Triad: An Introductory Essay on Politics, Society, and Culture, 1988; (with others) Progress and the Crisis of Man, 1976; contbr. articles to profl. jours. Assoc. mem. Paul Galvin Chapel, Evanston, Ill. Norman Wait Harris fellow in polit. sci. Northwestern U., 1954-56. Mem. AAAS, ASPCA, AAUP, Humane Soc. U.S., Northwestern U. Alumni Assn., Am. Polit. Sci. Assn., Am. Acad. Polit. and Social Sci., Acad. Polit. Sci., Midwest Polit. Sci. Assn., Spiritual Life Inst., Anti-Cruelty Soc., Nat. Wildlife Fedn., Noetic Scis. Inst., Humane Soc. U.S., Kappa Delta Pi, Pi Sigma Epsilon. Roman Catholic. Home: 2015 Orrington Ave Evanston IL 60201-2911 Office: Loyola U 6525 N Sheridan Rd Damen Hall Rm 915 Chicago IL 60626 *We are each of us mysteries to ourselves. We are on a life-long search for meaning: questions about where we have come from, what we are doing and where we are going. The deepest desires of a person embody the spiritual quest. The Kingdom of God tells us where to place our priorities. Life is short. No one is untouched by tragedy. We are reminded every day of our finiteness. We care because it is our nature to care. Christianity teaches a reverence for life that urges us to transcend narcissism and selfishness.*

LARSON, APRIL U., bishop. Pastor; bishop Southeastern Minn. Synod, Evang. Luth. Ch. in Am., 1992—. Office: Evang Luth Ch in Am SE Minn Synod Assissi Heights, Box 4900 Rochester MN 55903

LARSON, BENNETT CHARLES, solid state physicist, researcher; b. Buffalo, N.D., Oct. 9, 1941; s. Floyd Everet and Gladys May (Hogen) L.; m. Piola Anne Taliaferro, June 6, 1969; children—Christopher Charles, Andrea Kay. B.A. in Physics, Concordia Coll., Moorhead, Minn., 1963; M.S. in Physics, U. N.D., 1965; Ph.D. in Physics, U. Mo., 1970. Rsch. physicist, group leader x-ray diffraction, sect. head thin films and microstructures solid state div. Oak Ridge Nat. Lab., Tenn., 1969—. Contbr. numerous articles to profl. jours. Recipient Sidhu award Pitts. Diffraction Soc., 1974. Fellow Am. Phys. Soc.; mem. Am. Crystallographic Assn. (Bertram E. Warren Diffraction Physics award 1985), Materials Research Soc. Office: Oak Ridge Nat Lab Solid State Dv Oak Ridge TN 37831

LARSON, BRENT T., broadcasting executive; b. Ogden, Utah, Sept. 23, 1942; s. George Theodore and Doris (Peterson) L.; m. Tracy Ann Taylor; children: Michelle, Brent Todd. Student, pub. schs., Los Angeles; diploma in radio operational engring., Burbank, Calif., 1962. Owner, mgr. Sta. KAIN, Boise, Idaho, 1969-77; owner, operator Sta. KXA Radio, Seattle, 1975-83, Sta. KYYX Radio, Seattle, 1980-83, Sta. KGA Radio, Spokane, Wash., 1978-84, Sta. KUUZ Radio, Boise, 1976-82, Sta. KOOS Radio, North Bend, Oreg., 1980-81, Sta. KODL Radio, The Dalles, Oreg., 1974-80, Sta. KKWZ Radio, Richfield, Utah, 1980—, Sta. KSVC Radio, Richfield, 1980—, Sta. KSOS-FM & AM, Salt Lake City, 1984—; v.p. Casey Larson Fast Food Co., Oreg. and Idaho, 1976-94, Imperial Broadcasting Corp., Idaho, 1970—, Sta. KSOS FM & AM, 1983—; pres. First Nat. Broadcasting Corp., 1970—; v.p. Larson-Wynn Corp., 1974—, Brentwood Properties, Ogden, 1977—; pres. Sta. KSIT Broadcasting, Rock Springs, Wyo., 1980—, Gold Coast Communications Corp., Oreg., 1980-81, Sevier Valley Broadcasting Co., Inc., Utah, 1980—, Brent Larson Group Stas., Western U.S., 1969—; v.p. mktg. Internat. Tourist Foods Corp., Boise, 1983—; ptnr. Larson Tours and Travel, Burley, Idaho, 1977-87; founder 1st Nat. TV Div., 1990; bd. dirs. Casey-Larson Foods Co., La Grande, Oreg. Bd. dirs. Met. Sch., 1981—. Served with U.S. Army, 1961-63. Mem. Am. Advt. Fedn., Nat. Assn. Broadcasters, Nat. Radio Broadcasters Assn., Wash. Broadcasters Assn., Oreg. Broadcasters Assn., Idaho Broadcasters Assn., Utah Broadcasters Assn., Citizens for Responsible Broadcasting (bd. dirs.). Republican. Mormon. Home: 4014 Beus Dr Ogden UT 84403-3208 Office: First Nat Broadcasting Corp 385 24th St Ste 820 Ogden UT 84401-1446

LARSON, BRIAN FOIX, architect; b. Eau Claire, Wis., July 6, 1935; s. Albert Foix and Dorothy Jean (Thompson) L.; m. Mildred Anne Nightswander, Feb. 13, 1961; children: Urban Alexander, Soren Federick. BArch, U. Ill., 1959. Registered architect, Wis., Minn., Colo., Mass., N.H. Architect-in-tng. Geometrics, Inc., Cambridge, Mass., 1959-60, Bastille Halsey Assoc., Boston, 1960-62; ptnr. Larson, Playter, Smith, Eau Claire, 1962-72; v.p. Larson, Hestekins, Smith, Ltd., Eau Claire, 1962-80, Ayres Assocs., Eau Claire, 1980—; sec. Wis. Bd. Archtl. Examiners, 1985-88, chmn., 1988-89; master juror Nat. Coun. Archtl. Rev. Bd. Bldg. Design Exam, 1987—. Prin. works include One Mill Plaza, Laconia, N.H. (Honor award New Eng. Regional Council AIA 1974), Eau Claire County Courthouse, Wis. (Honor award Wis. Soc. Architects 1978), St. Croix County Courthouse, Wis. Mem. Hist. Bldg. Code Adv. Com., Wis., 1985. Mem. AIA, Wis. Soc. Architects (pres. 1983), Wis. Architects Found. (bd. dirs.), Soc. Archtl. Historians. Home: 215 Roosevelt Ave Eau Claire WI 54701-4065 Office: Ayres Assocs PO Box 1590 Eau Claire WI 54702-1590

LARSON, CHARLES FRED, association executive; b. Gary, Ind., Nov. 27, 1936; s. Charles F. and Margaret J. (Taylor) L.; m. Joan Ruth Grupe, Aug. 22, 1959; children: Gregory Paul, Laura Ann. BSME, Purdue U., 1958; MBA summa cum laude, Fairleigh Dickinson U., 1973. Registered profl.

engr., N.J. Project engr. Combustion Engring., Inc., East Chicago, Ind., 1958-60; sec. Welding Rsch. Council, N.Y.C., 1960-70, asst. dir., 1970-75; exec. dir. Indsl. Rsch. Inst., Inc., N.Y.C., 1975—. Assoc. editor Jour. Pressure Vessel Tech., 1973-75; mem. bd. advisors Who's Who in Am. Mem. Wyckoff (N.J.) Bd. Edn., 1973-78, pres., 1976-77; reader In Touch Networks, Inc., N.Y.C., 1979-89; chmn. 43d Nat. Conf. on Advancement Rsch. Fellow AAAS; mem. ASME, NSPE, Am. Soc. Assn. Execs., Coun. Engring. and Sci. Soc. Execs., Soc. Rsch. Adminstrs., Univ. Club, Kenwood Club. Republican. Methodist. Office: Indsl Rsch Inst Inc 1550 M St NW Washington DC 20005-1708

LARSON, CHARLES LESTER, television writer, producer, author; b. Portland, Oreg., Oct. 23, 1922; s. Charles Oscar and Ina May (Couture) L.; m. Alice Mae Dovey, Aug. 25, 1966; 1 stepson, Wyn Donavan Malotte. Student, U. Oreg., 1940. Contract writer MGM Studios, Culver City, Calif., 1943-46; freelance mag. writer, 1941-51. Assoc. producer: TV program Twelve O'Clock High, 1964; producer: TV program The FBI, 1965-68, The Interns, 1970-71, Cades County, 1971-72; exec. producer: TV program Nakia, 1974; producer: TV movie Crime Club, 1973; co-creator: TV series Hagen, 1979-80; author: The Chinese Game, 1969, Someone's Death, 1973, Matthew's Hand, 1974, Muir's Blood, 1976, The Portland Murders, 1983. Mem. Writers Guild Am. West, Producers Guild, Mystery Writers Am. (spl. award 1974), Authors League Am. Democrat. Home: 14205 SE 38th St Vancouver WA 98684-3912

LARSON, CHARLES ROBERT, naval officer; b. Sioux Falls, S.D., Nov. 20, 1936; s. Eldred Charles and Gertrude Edythe (Jensen) L.; m. Sarah Elizabeth Craig, Aug. 19, 1961; children: Sigrid Anne, Erica Lynn, Kirsten Elizabeth. B.S. in Marine Engring, U.S. Naval Acad., 1958. Commd. ensign USN, 1958, advanced through grades to adm., 1990; naval aviator, attack pilot, 1958-63, nuclear power, submarine tng., 1963-64, assigned nuclear subs., 1964-76, naval aide to the Pres., 1969-71, comdg. officer USS Halibut, 1973-76, comdr. submarine devel. group, head operational deep submergence program, 1976-78, chief naval ops. staff Strategic Submarine Programs, 1978-79; dir. long range planning group Washington, 1978-82; comdr. submarines Mediterranean, 1982-83; supt. U.S. Naval Acad. Annapolis, Md., 1983-86; comdr. 2d Fleet, 1986-88; dir. plans, policies and ops. DCNO, 1988-90; comdr. U.S. Pacific Fleet, 1990-91, U.S. Pacific Command, Hawaii, 1991-94; supt. U.S. Naval Acad. 1994—; v.p. U.S. Naval Inst., 1994—. Mem. USO Coun., Honolulu, 1990-92; mem. Honolulu area coun. Boy Scouts Am., 1990-94. Decorated Def. D.S.M. (6), Legion of Merit (3), Bronze Star medal, others; named Disting. Eagle Scout, Balt. area coun. Boy Scouts Am., 1985; White House fellow, 1968-69. Mem. Coun. on Fgn. Rels. Home: 1 Buchanan Rd Annapolis MD 21402 Office: 121 Blake Rd Annapolis MD 21402

LARSON, CLARENCE EDWARD, association executive; b. Cloquet, Minn., Sept. 20, 1909; s. Louis Ludwig and Caroline Hilda (Ullman) L.; m. Gertrude Ellen Ruben, May 17, 1934 (dec. June 1952); 1 child, Robert Edward; m. Jane Ritchie Warren, Apr. 20, 1957; children—Lawrence Ernest, Lance Stafford (dec.). B.S., U. Minn., 1932; Ph.D., U. Calif.-Berkeley, 1937. Chmn. chemistry dept. Coll. of Pacific, Stockton, Calif., 1937-42; project dir., mgr. Union Carbide Corp., Oak Ridge, 1942-50; mgr. corp. research Union Carbide Corp., N.Y.C., 1955-61; pres. nuclear div. Union Carbide Corp., Oak Ridge, 1961-69; dir. Oak Ridge Nat. Lab., 1950-55; commr. AEC, Washington, 1969-74; pres. Pioneers Sci. and Tech. Hist. Assn., Washington, 1982—; chmn. Nat. Battery Adv. Commn., Washington, 1975-81. Patentee separation process for uranium. Recipient Disting. Achievement award Am. Soc. for Advancement Mgmt., 1963. Fellow Am. Nuclear Soc., Am. Inst. Chemists; mem. NAE, Am. Chem. Soc., Cosmos Club (Disting. Svc. award 1991), Knights of Malta, Rotary, Sigma Xi, Tau Beta Pi. Republican. Avocations: amateur radio; computers; scuba diving; photography; golf. Home: 6514 Bradley Blvd Bethesda MD 20817-3248

LARSON, DALE IRVING, lawyer; b. Mpls., Aug. 12, 1937; s. Irving Sigurd and Clara (Markeson) L.; m. Janet Marie Watson, June 22, 1960; children: Mark Dale, Scott Matthew. Student, Moorhead State U., 1958-61; BA, U. Minn., 1962, LLB, 1965. Bar: Minn. 1965, U.S. Dist. Ct. Minn. 1965, U.S. Ct. Appeals (8th cir.) 1968, U.S. Ct. Appeals (4th cir.) 1971, U.S. Supreme Ct. 1972, U.S. Dist. Ct. (so. dist.) N.Y. 1984, U.S. Dist. Ct. (no. dist.) Calif. 1987, U.S. Ct. Appeals (9th cir.) 1987, U.S. Ct. Appeals (7th cir.) 1992. News editor, reporter Sta.-KYJB TV., Fargo, N.D., 1960-61, Sta.-WCCO TV., Mpls., 1961-62; with Robins, Davis & Lyons, Mpls., 1963-64, assoc., 1965-70, ptnr., 1970-80; exec. ptnr. Robins, Zelle, Larson & Kaplan, Mpls., 1980-88; ptnr., mng. ptnr. Zelle & Larson, Mpls., 1988—; lectr. U. Minn. Contbr. articles to profl. jours. Precinct chmn. Rep. Party, Mpls., 1968; bd. dirs. Fund for Legal Aid Soc., Mpls., 1983—, chmn., 1986-88, Fed. Appointment Com., Mpls., 1988; chief exec. officer Minn. Bus. Partnership, Mpls., 1986-88. With U.S. Army, 1955-58. Fellow Internat. Soc. Barristers; mem. ABA, Internat. Bar Assn., Minn. State Bar Assn., Hennepin County Bar Assn. (bar nomination com. 1988), Fedn. Ins. Counsel, Mpls. Club, Mpls. Athletic Club. Avocations: skiing, sailing, tennis, lecturing on trial practice. Office: Zelle & Larson 33 S 6th St Ste 4400 Minneapolis MN 55402-3710

LARSON, DAYL ANDREW, architect; b. Denver, Aug. 13, 1930; s. Andrew and Esther (Freiberg) L.; m. Kay W. Larson; children: Linda, Lesli, Lucy. BS in Architecture, BSBA, U. Colo., 1953. Pres. Haller & Larson Architects, Denver, 1962-92. Served to capt. C.E., U.S. Army, 1953-55. Fellow AIA (pres. Denver chpt. 1978, pres.-elect 1986-87); mem. Colo. AIA (pres.). Home: 2153 S Beeler Way Denver CO 80231-3409 Office: Haller & Larson 1621 18th St Denver CO 80202-1266

LARSON, DONALD CLAYTON, physics educator, consultant; b. Wadena, Minn., Jan. 29, 1934; s. Clyde Melvin and Selma (Wilson) L.; m. Susan Dunnet, July 17, 1960; children: Tor Frederick, Jun Dunnet (dec.), Erika Rose. BS, U. Wash., 1956; SM, Harvard U., 1957, PhD, 1962. Asst. prof. U. Va., Charlottesville, 1962-67; assoc. prof. Drexel U., Phila., 1967-83, full prof., 1983—; vis. prof. Univ. Chile, Santiago, 1969, 73, Tel-Aviv (Israel) U., 1984, 92; vis. scientist Naval Air Devel., Warminster, Pa., summers 1981-91; cons. NIST, Gaithersburg, Md., 1984-95. Author: Physics of Thin Films, vol. VI, 1971, Experimental Methods in Preparation and Measurement of Thin Films, vol. II, 1974. Mem. Optical Soc. Am., Phi Beta Kappa, Tau Beta Pi, Sigma Xi. Home: 409 Drew Ave Swarthmore PA 19081-2407 Office: Drexel U Physics Atmospheric Sci Dept Philadelphia PA 19104

LARSON, DOYLE EUGENE, electronics company executive, retired air force officer; b. Madelia, Minn., Oct. 2, 1930; s. Edgar Louis and Gyneth Mae (Weldy) L.; m. Lois James, May 29, 1953; children: James, Nancy, Mary, Mark. Student, Macalester Coll., 1948-51; BA, Hardin-Simmons U., 1962; postgrad., Armed Forces Staff Coll., 1965, Air War Coll., 1971; MS in Polit. Sci., Auburn U., 1971. Enlisted USAF, 1951, commd. 2d lt., 1953, advanced through grades to maj. gen., 1977; sr. mil. rep. Nat. Security Agy., Pentagon, 1971-72; asst. for joint matters, asst. chief staff for intelligence Hdqrs. USAF, 1972-73, dir. policy and resource mgmt., dep. chief staff for intelligence, 1973-74; dir. intelligence Pacific Command, Camp H.M. Smith, Hawaii, 1974-77; dep. chief staff for intelligence Hdqrs. SAC, Offutt AFB, Omaha, 1977-79; comdg. gen. Security Svc., 1979-83; comdr. Electronic Security Command, San Antonio, 1979-83; dir. Joint Electronic Warfare Ctr., San Antonio, 1980-83; ret., 1983; chief exec. officer Centurion Enterprises, 1983—. trustee Macalester Coll. Decorated DSM, Legion of Merit with 2 oak leaf clusters, Air medal with 3 oak leaf clusters; named to Order of the Sword. Mem. Minn. Air Force Assn. (nat. v.p.). Lutheran. Home: 13509 York Ave S Burnsville MN 55337-1844 Office: PO Box 29385 San Antonio TX 78229-0385

LARSON, EARL RICHARD, federal judge; b. Mpls., Dec. 18, 1911; s. Axel R. and Hannah (Johnson) L.; m. Cecill Frances Carlgren, Dec. 30, 1939; children: Jane, Earl R. BA, U. Minn., 1933, LLB, 1935. Bar: Minn. 1935. Judge U.S. Dist. Ct. Minn., Mpls., 1961-77, sr. judge, 1977—. Lt. USNR, 1943-46. Recipient Outstanding Achievement award U. Minn., 1978. Office: US Dist Ct 661 US Courthouse 110 S 4th St Minneapolis MN 55401-2216

LARSON, GARY, cartoonist; b. Tacoma, Wash., Aug. 14, 1950; s. Vern and Doris Larson; married. BA in Communications, Wash. State U., 1972. Jazz

musician, 1973-76; with music store, Seattle, 1976-77, Humane Soc., Seattle, 1978-80; cartoonist Seattle Times, 1978-79; syndicated cartoonist The Far Side Chronicle Features Syndicate, San Francisco, 1979-84, Universal Press Syndicate, Kansas City, Mo., 1984-94; prodr. books and calendars. Exhbns. include The Far Side of Sci. (exhibited at Calif. Acad. Scis., 1987, Smithsonian Instn., 1987, Denver Mus. Natural History, L.A. County Mus., Shedd Aquarium, Chgo., other mus.), The Far Side of the Zoo, Wash. Pk. Zoo, Portland, Oreg., 1987; author: (cartoon collections) The Far Side, 1982, Beyonf the Farside, 1983, In Search of The Far Side, 1984, Bride of the Far Side, 1985, Valley of the Far Side, 1985, It Came from the Far Side, 1986, The Far Side Observer, 1987, Hound of the Far Side, 1987, Night of the Crash-Test Dummies, 1988, Wildlife Preserves, 1989, The Prehistory of the Far Side: A 10th Anniversary Exhibit, 1989, Weiner Dog Art, 1990, Unnatural Selections, 1991, Cows of Our Planet, 1992, The Chickens are Restless, 1993, The Cuse of Madame "C", 1994, (cartoon anthologies) The Far Side Gallery, 1984, The Far Side Gallery II, 1986, The Far Side Gallery III, 1988, The Far Side Gallery IV, 1993; television animation Gary Larson's Tales from the Far Side, 1994. Recipient award for Best Humor Panel, Nat. Cartoonists Soc., 1986, Reuben award for Outstanding Cartoonist of Yr. Nat. Cartoonists Soc., 1991, Max and Moritz prize for best internat. comic strip panel Internat. Comics Salon, 1993, other awards. Avocation: jazz music. Office: Universal Press Syndicate 4900 Main St 9th Fl Kansas City MO 64112

LARSON, GEORGE CHARLES, magazine editor, writer; b. Mar. 31, 1942; s. George Lester and Mildred Caroline (Frehner) L.; m. Valarie Ann Thompson, Aug. 20, 1946; children: Evan Richard; Alice Lynn and Keely Mae (twins). BA, Harvard U., 1964. Staff writer Scholastic Mag., N.Y.C., 1971; regional editor, mng. editor Flying Mag., N.Y.C., 1972-78; tech. editor Bus. & Comml. Aviation Mag., White Plains, N.Y., 1980-85; editor Air & Space/Smithsonian Mag., Washington, 1985—. Author: Fly on Instruments, The Blimp Book. Served with U.S. Army, 1966-70, Vietnam.

LARSON, GERALD LEE, auditor; b. Billings, Mont., Apr. 18, 1937; s. Phillip Antone and Eunice (LaPoint) L. Student, U. Nev., 1955-59; AS, Western Nev. U., 1975. Mil. pers. mgr. Nev. Air NG, Reno, 1973-81; mgr. employee rels. Nev. Mil. Dept., Carson City, 1981-82, mil. pers. mgr., 1982-88; auditor Nev. State Indsl. Ins., Reno, 1989-92; sr. auditor Nev. State Indsl. Ins., Carson City, 1992—. State pres. Nev. Enlisted NG Assn., Carson City, 1988-87; nat. conf. chmn. Enlisted Assn. NG U.S., Reno, 1989; project chmn. 40th ann. book Nev. Air NG, 1988. CM Sgt. Nev. Air NG, USAF, 1955-88. Named Outstanding Sr. Non-Commissioned Officer of Yr., Nev. Air NG, 1979. Avocations: travel, gardening. Office: State Indsl Ins System 515 E Musser St Carson City NV 89714

LARSON, HARRY ROBERT, investment banking executive; b. Chgo., Oct. 13, 1945; s. Harry John and Alice Marie Larson; m. Charlene Marie Grenier; children: Christopher, Elizabeth, Erik, Brandon. BSBA, Roosevelt U., 1968. Contr. Halsey Stuart & Co. Inc., Chgo., 1967-73; with dept. sales Bache Halsey Stuart Inc., N.Y.C., 1973-79; sr. v.p. 1st Interstate Bank Calif. N.Y.C., 1979-85; pres. Chem. Securities Inc., N.Y.C., 1985-89, 1st Chgo. Capital Markets, Inc., 1989—; vice chmn. Mcpl. Securities Rulemaking Bd., Washington, 1989. Mem. Pub. Securities Assn. Home: 180A Old Sutton Rd Barrington Hi IL 60010-9383 Office: First Chicago Capital Markets Inc 1 First National Plz Chicago IL 60670

LARSON, HARRY THOMAS, electronics engineer; b. Berkeley, Calif., Oct. 16, 1921; s. Harry Homer and Edna Clara (Petersen) Larson; m. Merry Evelyn Otteson, Dec. 26, 1956 (div. Dec. 1975); children: Kristin Eve Beltz, Margit Merry Mills, Megan Marie Hoyt. BSEE summa cum laude, U. Calif., Berkeley, 1947; MSEE, UCLA, 1954. Computer engr. Inst. for Numerical Analysis Nat. Bur. Standards, L.A., 1949-51; mem. tech. staff Advanced Electronics Lab. Hughes Aircraft Co., Culver City, Calif., 1951-54; dept. mgr. bus. applications of computers Ramo-Wooldridge Co., Inglewood, Calif., 1954-56; asst. div. dir. command and control Systems, aero. div. Philco-Ford Co., Newport Beach, Calif., 1956-68; asst. div. dir. software and computing ctr. TRW Systems, Redondo Beach, Calif., 1968-69; dir. planning Calif. Computer Products, Anaheim, 1969-74; sr. scientist Hughes Aircraft, Fullerton, Calif., 1978-87; pres. Larbridge Enterprises Cons., Laguna Hills, Calif., 1970—; mem. Army Sci. Bd., Washington, 1988-92; contbd. to NASA's Mission Control Ctr. in Houston for Gemini, Apollo, Skylab and shuttle missions, Field Army tactical command and control system, first random access computer memory, early airborne digital computer, first keyboard and cathode ray tube data entry device (terminal), first-of-a-kind applications of computers in banks, factories, pension trust funds, payroll, acctg., truck scheduling, R.R. car routing, car body design and manufacture, automobile assembly plant inventory control, electrical power distbn. network, steel hot roll mill, computer programming methodologies (modularization, report generator, table-driven software), founds. for display tech. and large screen displays; lectr. workshops, conf. sessions, 1954-74. Editor Proc. Inst. Radio Engrs. 1961; editor and pub. The Larbridge Letter, 1973-76; co-editor Handbook of Automation, Computation and Control, 1972; contbr. articles to profl. jours., computer publs.; patentee in field. 1st lt. USAF, 1942-45. Fellow IEEE (life; Centennial medal); mem. IEEE Computer Soc. (co-founder, nat. chmn. 1954-55), Soc. for Info. Display, Am. Fedn. Info. Processing Socs. (bd. govs. 1956-60), Los Escribientes (San Clemente, Calif.), Sigma Xi, Tau Beta Pi, Eta Kappa Nu. Avocations: writing, photography. Home and Office: Larbridge Enterprises 236 Calle Aragon Apt A Laguna Hills CA 92653-3492

LARSON, INGEGERD ELIN, immunology/arthritis nurse; b. Alfta, Sweden, Oct. 5, 1930; came to U.S. 1936; d. Jonas and Elin (Johansson) Larsson. Grad., Hartford Hosp. Sch. Nursing, 1953; BA in Biblical Edn., Columbia (S.C.) Bible Coll., 1958; BS in Nursing, U. Pa., 1969; MS in Health Edn., St. Joseph's U., 1986. RN, Conn., Pa. Staff nurse Hartford (Conn.) Hosp., 1953-58; staff nurse, instr. Tulloch Meml. Hosp., Tangier, Morocco, 1960-65; staff nurse Thomas Jefferson U. Hosp., Phila., 1965-69; instr. in nursing Thomas Jefferson Hosp. Sch. Nursing, 1969-75; staff nurse rehab. unit Bollnäs, Sweden, 1975-76; staff nurse med.-surgical clinics to rheumatology clinics Phila. VA Med. Ctr., 1977—. Mem. Assn. Rheumatology Health Profls. Avocations: reading, traveling. Office: Phila VA Med Ctr Univ & Woodland Aves Philadelphia PA 19104

LARSON, JERRY L., state supreme court justice; b. Harlan, Iowa, May 17, 1936; s. Gerald L. and Mary Eleanor (Patterson) L.; m. Debra L. Christensen, July 17, 1993; children: Rebecca, Jeffrey, Susan, David. BA, State U. Iowa, 1958, JD, 1960. Bar: Iowa. Partner firm Larson & Larson, 1961-75; dist. judge 4th Jud. Dist. Ct. of Iowa, 1975-78; justice Iowa Supreme Ct., 1978—. Office: Supreme Ct Iowa State Capital Bldg Des Moines IA 50319

LARSON, JOHN DAVID, life insurance company executive, lawyer; b. Madison, Wis., July 6, 1941; s. Lawrence John and Anna Mathilda (Furseth) L.; M. Evelyn Vie Smith, Jan. 22, 1966 (div. Apr. 1980); children: Eric John, Karen Annette; m. Nancy Jay With, Nov. 29, 1980; stepchildren: Anne Elizabeth, Christopher Allen. BBa, U. Wis., 1963, JD, 1965, MBA, 1966. Bar: Wis. 1965, U.S. Ct. Mil. Appeals 1966; CPA, Wis.; CLU, chartered fin. cons. With Nat. Guardian Life Ins. Co., Madison, 1969—; exec. v.p., treas. Nat. Guardian Life Ins. Co., 1973, pres., dir., 1974—, pres., chief exec. officer, 1989—; dir. Firstar Bank Madison, N.A., TV Wis., Inc., Madison, KELAB, Inc., Madison. Chmn. Madison chpt. ARC, 1974-75; pres. United Way Dane County, 1975; pres. Wis. Nat. Guard Assn., 1992—. With U.S. Army, 1966-69, brig. gen. Wis. Army N.G. Recipient Know Your Madisonian award Wis. State Jour., 1973. Mem. ABA, State Bar Wis., Wis. Inst. CPAs, Am. Soc. CLUs, Am. Soc. Chartered Fin. Cons., Madison C. of C. (dir. 1976-80), U. Wis. Bus. Alumni (bd. dirs. 1986-90). Lutheran. Clubs: Maple Bluff (dir. 1974-80), Rotary. Home: 401 New Castle Way Madison WI 53704-6070 Office: PO Box 1191 Madison WI 53701-1191

LARSON, JOHN HYDE, retired utilities executive; b. Phila., Sept. 15, 1930; s. Roy Frank and Olive (Alden) L.; m. Priscilla Hibbs Beane; children: Michael Alden, Christopher Hibbs, Cynthia Ann. BA, Trinity Coll., 1953; M City Planning, MIT, 1955. Vice-pres. The Potomac Edison Co., Hagerstown, Md., 1969-72; treas. Allegheny Power System, Inc., N.Y.C., 1973-79; v.p. fin. Conn. Energy Corp., Bridgeport, Conn., 1980-85, pres., chief exec. officer, 1985-89; exec. v.p., chief operating officer So. Conn. Gas. Co., Bridgeport, Conn., 1981-85; pres., chief exec. officer So. Conn. Gas. Co.,

Bridgeport, 1985-89; acting dir. fin. City of Bridgeport, 1989-90; chmn. mgmt. adv. com. City of Bridgeport, Conn., 1990-93; chmn. selectman's com. on ops. improvement Westport, Conn., 1991; bd. dirs. Bay State Gas Co. Westborough, mass., Bolt Tech., Inc.; Norwalk, Conn., So. Conn. Health Care Systems, Inc. Vice chmn. Bridgeport Hosp., 1991-93; chmn. Nova Med. Corp., 1991-95; hon. chmn. capital funds drive Family Svcs. Woodfield. Recipient Corp. Leadership award MIT, 1987, Century Svc. award Bridgeport Boys and Girls Club, 1991, Richard P. Bodine Community Leadership award, 1993. Mem. New Eng. Gas Assn. (chmn. 1988-89). Home: Mount Hunger Rd Barnard VT 05031

LARSON, JOHN WILLIAM, lawyer; b. Detroit, June 24, 1935; s. William and Sara Eleanor (Yeatman) L.; m. Pamela Jane Wren, Sept. 16, 1959; 1 dau., Jennifer Wren. BA with distinction, honors in Economics, Stanford, 1957; LLB, Stanford U., 1962. Bar: Calif. 1962. Assoc. Brobeck, Phleger & Harrison, San Francisco, 1962-68, ptnr., 1968-71, 73—, chmn. exec. com., mng. ptnr., 1988-92, chmn. of firm, CEO, 1993—; asst. sec. Dept. Interior, Washington, 1971-73; exec. dir. Natural Resources Com., Washington, 1973; counsellor to chmn. Cost of Living Coun., Washington, 1973; faculty Practising Law Inst.; bd. dirs. Measurex Corp. Mem. 1st U.S.-USSR Joint Com. on Environ.; mem. bd. visitors Standord U. Law Sch., 1974-77, 85-87, 95—; pres. bd. trustees The Katherine Branson Sch., 1980-83; bd. dirs. Bay Area Coun (chmn. bd.), San Francisco C. of C. With AUS, 1957-59. Mem. ABA, Calif. Bar Assn., Order of Coif, Pacific Union Club, Burlingame Country Club, Bohemian Club. Home: PO Box 349 Ross CA 94957-0349 Office: Brobeck Phleger & Harrison Spear St Tower 1 Market Plz San Francisco CA 94105-1019

LARSON, JOSEPH STANLEY, environmentalist, educator, researcher; b. Stoneham, Mass., June 23, 1933; s. Gustave Adolph and Marian (Kelly) L.; m. Wendy Nichols, Nov. 23, 1958; children: Marion Elizabeth, Sandra Frances. BS, U. Mass., 1956, MS, 1958; PhD, Va. Poly. Inst., 1966. Registered profl. forester, Maine. Exec. sec. Wildlife Conservation, Inc., Boston, 1958-59; state ornithologist Mass. Div. Fisheries and Wildlife, Boston, 1959-60; head conservation edn. div. Natural Resources Inst., U. Md., Annapolis, 1960-62, rsch. asst. prof., LaVale, 1965-67; wildlife rsch. biologist U.S. Fish and Wildlife Svc., Amherst, Mass., 1967-69; prof., dir. The Environ. Inst., U. Mass., Amherst, 1969—; cons. in field. Contbr. articles to profl. jours. Recipient Chevron Conservation award, 1990; grantee in field. Mem. AAUP (pres. Mass. chpt. 1976-77), AAAS, Wildlife Soc. (cert. wildlife biologist), Ecol. Soc. Am. (cert. sr. ecologist), Am. Assn. Mammalogists, Nat. Wetlands Tech. Coun. (exec. chmn.), Mass. Audubon Soc. (bd. dirs.), U.S. Nat. Ramsar Com. (chmn.), Internat. Union for Conservation of Nature and Natural Resources (ecology commn.) (Switzerland), Faculty Univ. Club, Cosmos Club, Sigma Xi, Xi Sigma Pi, Phi Sigma. Congregationalist. Home: 27 Arnold Rd Pelham MA 01002-9757 Office: U Mass Environ Inst Blaisdell House Box 30820 Amherst MA 01003-0820

LARSON, KERMIT DEAN, accounting educator; b. Algona, Iowa, Apr. 7, 1939; s. Loren L. and Hansena Laurena (Andersen) L.; m. Nancy Lynne Weber, June 17, 1961; children: Julie Renee, Timothy Dean, Cynthia Lynne. A.A., Ft. Dodge Jr. Coll., 1960; B.B.A., U. Iowa, 1962, M.B.A., 1963; D.B.A., U. Colo., 1966. C.P.A., Tex. Mem. faculty U. Tex., Austin, 1966—; Arthur Andersen & Co. Alumni prof. emeritus U. Tex., 1975—, chmn. dept. accounting, 1971-75; vis. asso. prof. Tulane U., New Orleans, 1970-71; cons. sales tax audit litigation, pvt. anti-trust litigation, expropriation ins. arbitration. Author: (with Paul Miller) Fundamental Accounting Principles, 1978, 13th edit., 1993, Financial Accounting, 6th edit., 1995, (with Charlene Spoede and Miller) Fundamentals of Financial and Managerial Accounting, 1994; contbr. articles to profl. jours. Mem. AICPA, Am. Acctg. Assn. (v.p. 1978-79), Tex. Soc. CPAs, Beta Gamma Sigma, Beta Alpha Psi. Baptist. Home: 1310 Falcon Ledge Dr Austin TX 78746-5120 Office: 823 Congress Ave Ste 1500 Austin TX 78701-2457

LARSON, LARRY, librarian; b. El Dorado, Ark., July 18, 1940; s. Willie Lee and Myrtle Elizabeth (McMaster) L.; m. Dorothy Ann Bing, Apr 23, 1966; 1 child, Larisa Ann. BS, Ouachita Baptist U., 1962; MLS, George Peabody Coll., 1967. Asst. librarian, media specialist Hall High Sch., Little Rock, 1962-65; asst. librarian, circulation Ark. Tech. U., Russellville, 1965-67; asst librarian reference Hendrix Coll., Conway, Ark., 1967-73; head librarian U. Ark., Monticello, 1973-75; librarian, dir. N. Ark. Regional Library, Harrison, 1975-85, Ft. Smith (Ark.) Pub. Library, 1985—. Bd. dirs. Ft. Smith Hist. Soc., 1986-90; treas. bd. dirs. Pub. Awareness Com., Ft. Smith, Ark., 1986—. Mem. ALA (chair pub. libr. div. 1980), Ark. Libr. Assn. (vice chair membership com. 1968, Disting. Svc. award 1985, chair pub. libr. divsn., 1993), Ark. Libr. Devel. Dist. (chair 1985-87), Ark. Adminstrs. Pub. Librs. (chair 1988-89, del. Ark. govs.' conf. on librs. 1990), Noon Exchange Club. Democrat. Baptist. Avocations: gardening, woodworking. Home: 3114 S Enid St Fort Smith AR 72903-4445 Office: Ft Smith Pub Libr 61 S 8th St Fort Smith AR 72901-2415

LARSON, MARK ALLAN, financial executive; b. Milw., June 24, 1948; s. Owen Earl and Alice May (Ulmen) L.; m. Linda Rosalie Wohlschlaeger, Jan. 3, 1970; children: Craig Allan, Emily Lin. BA, Ripon Coll., 1970; postgrad., Washington U., St. Louis, 1971-74; postgrad. in bus., St. Louis U., 1974-76. Personnel supr. Barnes Hosp., St. Louis, 1970-71; various fin. and mgmt. positions Bank Bldg. Corp., St. Louis, 1971-76, G.D. Searle & Co., Skokie, Ill., Geneva, Switzerland, 1976-85; sr. v.p., chief fin. and admistrv. officer Leaf Inc., Bannockburn, Ill., 1985-89; v.p. internat. devel. and adminstrn. Carlson Cos., Inc., Mpls., 1990-91; exec. v.p. fin. and adminstrn., travel and mktg. groups, 1992-93, exec. v.p. ops. and internat., mktg. groups, 1993-95; sr. v.p. fin. and treasury, CFO, Internat. Distillers & Vintners N.Am., Hartford, Conn., 1995—. Home: 3485 Christine Dr Maple Plain MN 55359-9100

LARSON, MAURICE ALLEN, chemical engineer, educator; b. Missouri Valley, Iowa, July 19, 1927; s. Albert Juluis and Grace Elizabeth (Chambers) L.; m. Ruth Elizabeth Gugeler, Dec. 5, 1953; children: Richard Alan (dec.), Janet Ann, John Albert. BS, Iowa State U., 1951, PhD, 1958. Chem. engr. Dow Corning Corp., Midland, Mich., 1951-54; teaching asst. Iowa State U., 1954-55, instr. dept. chem. engring., 1955-58, asst. prof., 1958-61, assoc. prof., 1961-64, prof., 1964—, Anson Marston Disting. prof., 1977—, chmn. dept. chem. engring., 1978-83; cons. AID, Kharagpur, India, 1968, USIA, Amman, Jordan, 1983, 84, 85; Shell vis. prof. Univ. Coll., London, 1971-72; sci. exchange visitor, Czechoslovakia and Poland, 1974; vis. prof. U Queensland, Australia, summer 1981, U. Manchester Inst. Sci. and Tech., Eng., 1984-85; guest prof. Tianjin U., Peoples Republic of China, 1982; hon. lectr. Mid. Am. State U. Assn., 1986-87; Dow Corning Australia Bicentennial lectr., Sydney, 1988. Author: (with A.D. Randolph) Theory of Particulate Processes, 1971, 2d edit., 1988; contbr. (with others) articles to profl. jours. With U.S. Army, 1946-47. Recipient H.A. Webber Teaching award Iowa State U., 1967, Western Electric Fund award Am. Soc. Engring. Edn., 1970, Faculty citation Iowa State U. Alumni, 1972, Gov.'s Sci. medal State of Iowa, 1990, D.R. Boylan Eminent Faculty award Iowa State U., 1990; NSF fellow, 1965-66. Fellow Am. Inst. Chem. Engrs. (pres. Iowa 1970-71); mem. Am. Chem. Soc. (chmn. div. fertilizer and soil chemistry 1975), Am. Soc. Engring. Edn., Lions (pres. Ames club 1979-80), Sigma Xi, Tau Beta Pi, Phi Lambda Upsilon, Phi Kappa Phi. Democrat. Methodist. Home: 2710 Thompson Dr Ames IA 50010-4759

LARSON, MEL, retired hotel facility executive, corporate executive, helicopter pilot; b. Detroit, Oct. 1, 1929; s. Algot E. and Oleta M. (Murphy) L.; m. Marilyn Gowens, Jan. 14, 1979. Grad. high sch., Plymouth, Mich., 1946. Track owner, auto racing driver, promoter, publicist, 1953-73; v.p. pub. rels., advt. C.W. Pine, Phoenix, 1964-68; various promotional positions Mint Hotel/Casino, 1968-73; mktg. dir. Circus Circus Hotel/Casino, Las Vegas, Nev., 1974-75, v.p. mktg., 1976-85; corp. v.p. mktg. Circus Circus Enterprises, Inc., Las Vegas, 1985-87, exec. v.p., 1987-92; ret., 1992; also bd. dirs. Circus Circus Enterprises, Inc., Las Vegas. Sgt. USAF, 1948-52. Mem. Nat. Assn. Stock Car Auto Racing, Helicopter Assn. Internat., Helicopter Club Am.

LARSON, MICHAEL LEN, newspaper editor; b. St. James, Minn., Feb. 3, 1944; s. Leonard O. and Lois O. (Holte) L.; m. Kay M. Monahan, June 18, 1966; children: Christopher, David, Molly. BA, U. Minn., 1966; MBA, Mankato State U., 1986. Mng. editor Paddock Circle Inc., Libertyville, Ill.,

1972-74, New Ulm (Minn.) Journal, 1974-76, Republican-Eagle, Red Wing, Minn., 1976-79; editor Mankato (Minn.) Free Press, 1979—. Bd. dirs. Valley Indsl. Devel. Corp., Mankato, 1985—, also treas.; mem. adv. bd. Minn. State U. Bus. Sch. Served with U.S. Army, 1966-68, Vietnam. Recipient five First Place awards for investigative reporting Minn. Newspaper Assn., 1969, 71, 72, 76, 78, First Place award for feature writing, Suburban Newspapers Am., 1974. Mem. Minn. AP (pres. 1988—), Kiwanis. Roman Catholic. Avocation: bicycling. Home: 35 University Ct Mankato MN 56001-4182 Office: Mankato Free Press 418 S 2nd St Mankato MN 56001-3727

LARSON, REED EUGENE, association executive; b. Smith County, Kans., Sept. 27, 1922; s. George Christian and Edith Hazel (Whitney) L.; m. Marjorie Jeanne Hess, Aug. 31, 1947; children: Patricia Kay Larson Sween, Barbara Ann Larson Finnegan, Marcia Lynn Larson Craig. Student, Kans. Wesleyan U., 1940-41, Ohio State U., 1943-44; B.S. in E.E, Kans. State U., 1947. Design engr. Stein Labs., Atchison, Kans., 1947-48; processing engr. Coleman Co., Wichita, Kans., 1948-54; exec. v.p. Kansans for the Right to Work, Wichita, 1954-58; exec. v.p. Nat. Right-to-Work Com., Washington, 1959-76, pres., 1976—; exec. v.p. Nat. Right-to-Work Legal Def. Found., Washington, 1968-73, pres., 1973—; chmn. Hallmark Bank & Trust, 1984-94, F&M Bank-Hallmark, 1994—. Served with AUS, 1943-46. Recipient Seldon Waldo award U.S. Jaycees, 1956; Silver Anvil award Public Relations Soc. Am., 1966; James J. Kilpatrick award Internat. Platform Assn., 1980; Awarded Doctor of Laws Campbell U., 1988. Mem. Mont Pelerin Soc., Phila. Soc., Eta Kappa Nu, Tau Beta Pi. Baptist. Clubs: Kansas Jaycees (pres. 1953-54), Rotary, Am. Legion. Home: 7803 Antiopi St Annandale VA 22003-1405 Office: 8001 Braddock Rd Springfield VA 22151-2110

LARSON, ROBERTA M., children's theater director; b. Heidelberg, Fed. Republic of Germany, Mar. 22, 1960; came to U.S., 1960; d. Edmund A. and Maureen (Cort) Wilhelm; m. James Larson, May 1, 1984; children: Tess, Max. BA, U. Kans., 1982, MA, 1984. Mng. dir. Emmy Gifford Children's Theater, Omaha, 1984—. Office: Emmy Gifford Childrens Theater 3504 Center St Omaha NE 68105-2424

LARSON, ROLAND ELMER, health care executive; b. Chgo., Jan. 21, 1939; s. Elmer Gustav and Anna (Alphida) L.; m. Noel Kathleen Brennan, June 28, 1969; children: Eric R., Jennifer L., Melissa K. BA, Augustana Coll., 1961; MHA, U. Iowa, 1963; postgrad., Harvard U., 1978. Adminstrv. asst. U. Vt. Med. Ctr., Burlington, 1962-64; assoc. adminstr. Roger Williams Hosp., Providence, 1964-73; v.p. adminstrn. Norwalk (Conn.) Hosp., 1973-81; pres., chief exec. officer Nashoba Community Hosp., Ayer, Mass., 1981-88; v.p. Charles River Assn., Boston, 1988-90; cons. Charles River Assocs., Boston, 1990—; ind. healthcare cons. Harvard, Mass., 1990—. Chmn. Harvard (Mass.) Coalition Against Drugs and Alcohol, Opportunities, Inc., Providence, 1966-68, Greater Norwalk Community Coun., 1980; bd. dirs. Nat. Arthritis Found., N.Y.C., 1967-71, Am. Cancer Soc., Stamford, Conn., 1978-81. Fellow Am. Coll. Healthcare Execs.; mem. Cen. Mass. Hosp. Coun. (chmn. 1987-88), Rotary. Avocations: sailing, bicycling, golf, squash, woodworking. Home: 28 Candleberry Ln Harvard MA 01451-1641 Office: Larson & Assocs 28 Candleberry Ln Harvard MA 01451

LARSON, ROY, journalist, publisher; b. Moline, Ill., July 27, 1929; s. Roy W. and Jane (Beall) L.; m. Dorothy Jennisch, June 7, 1950; children: Mark, Bruce, Jodie, Bradley. A.B., Augustana Coll., Rock Island, Ill., 1951; M.Div., Garrett Theol. Sem., 1955. Ordained to ministry Methodist Ch. 1956; min. Covenant United Meth. Ch., Evanston, Ill., 1963-68, First United Meth. Ch., Elmhurst, Ill., 1968-69; religion editor Chgo. Sun-Times, 1969-85; pub. The Chgo. Reporter, 1985-94; exec. dir. Garrett-Medill Ctr. for Religion and News Media, Evanston, Ill., 1995—. Home: 1508 Hinman Evanston IL 60201-9999 Office: Garrett-Medill Ctr 2121 Sheridan Rd Evanston IL 60201

LARSON, RUSSELL EDWARD, university provost emeritus, consultant agriculture research and development; b. Mpls., Jan. 2, 1917; s. Karl Sam and Belle (Wing) L.; m. Margaret Agnes Johnson, Aug. 19, 1939; children: Gayle Margaret, Beverly Jean, Russell Troy. BS, U. Minn., 1939, MS, 1940, PhD, 1942; DSc (hon.), Delaware Valley Coll. Sci. and Agr., 1966. Asst. prof. U. R.I., Kingston, 1941-44; asst. prof. Pa. State U., University Park, 1944-45, assoc. prof., 1945-47, prof., 1947—, head dept. horticulture, 1952-62, dean Coll. Agriculture, 1963-72, provost, 1972-77; sci. advisor Am. Cocoa Rsch. Inst., McLean, Va., 1975-87; cons. Agriculture R & D, State Coll. Pa., 1977—. Contbr. 46 tech. articles on plant sci. to profl. jours. Recipient Outstanding Alumnus award U. Minn., 1961. Fellow AAAS, Am. Soc. Hort. Sci. (pres. 1963-64, L.H. Vaughan award 1948); mem. Am. Genetic Assn., Am. Inst. Biol. Sci., Sigma Xi. Republican. Lutheran. Avocations: gardening, golf, fishing. Home: 608 Elmwood St State College PA 16801-7053 Office: Pa State U 6 Tyson Bldg University Park PA 16802

LARSON, RUSSELL GEORGE, magazine and book publisher; b. Waukesha, Wis., May 4, 1942; s. George Arthur and Dorothy Edna (Hanneman) L.; m. Barbara Kay Krsek, Aug. 1, 1964; children—Eric, Craig, Denise. A.A.S., Milw. Sch. Engring., 1962. Tech. writer various publs., 1962-69; assoc. editor Model Railroader Mag., Milw., 1969-75, mng. editor, 1975-77, editor, 1977-93, v.p. editorial, 1989-93, sr. v.p. editorial, 1993—; pub. Model Railroader Mag., Trains Mag., Classic Toy Trains Mag., Collecting Toys Mag., Astronomy Mag., Earth Mag. Kalmbach Books, Greenberg Books, Milw., 1991—. Author: N Scale Primer, 1973, Beginner's Guide to N Scale Model Railroading, 1990, Beginner's Guide to Large Scale Model Railroading, 1994. Mem. Soc. Tech. Communication. Lutheran. Avocations: golf, model railroading, reading, travel. Office: Kalmbach Pub Co PO box 1612 21027 Crossroads Cir Waukesha WI 53186-4055

LARSON, SANDRA MAE, nursing educator; b. Chgo., Apr. 21, 1944; d. Richard Milward and Eldred Gertrude (Piehl) Blackburn; m. Eric Richard Larson, Nov. 25, 1967; children—Sarah, Keith. B.S., No. Ill. U., 1966, M.S., 1978. R.N., Ill. Nursing educator Lutheran Hosp., Moline, Ill., 1968-70; charge nurse ICU, Peninsula Hosp., Burlingame, Calif., 1970-72; staff nurse Illini Hosp., Silvis, Ill., 1972-76; nursing educator Black Hawk Coll., Moline, 1976—; mem. audit com. Rock Island County Health Dept., Ill., 1983—; presenter radio program on stress Sta. KIIK, Moline, 1980; interviewer Am. Cancer Soc., Moline, 1982, 84, 86. Co-author Anatomy and Physiology Testbank, 1994. Mem. Am. Nurses Assn., Ill. Nurses Assn. (bd. dirs. 5th dist. 1979-82, treas., 1982-84, pres. 1984-86, 1st v.p. 1986-87, pres. 1988-92, 2nd v.p., 1993-95), Sigma Theta Tau. Democrat. Roman Catholic. Avocations: camping; reading. Home: 3009 29th St Moline IL 61265-6950 Office: Black Hawk Coll 6600 34th Ave Moline IL 61265

LARSON, SIDNEY, art educator, artist, writer, painting conservator; b. Sterling, Colo., June 16, 1923; s. Harry and Ann Levin; m. George Ann Madden, Aug. 30, 1947; children: Sara Catherine, Nancy Louise. BA, U Mo., 1949, MA in Art, 1950. Prof. art Columbia Coll., Mo., 1951—; art curator State Hist. Soc. Mo., 1962—; painting conservator, Columbia, 1960—. Exhibited paintings and drawings in group shows in Midwest, Washington, N.Y. and Japan; executed murals Daily News, Rolla, Mo., Shelter Ins., Columbia, Mo., Guitar Bldg., Columbia, Mcpl. Bldg., Jefferson City, Mo., Centerre Bank, Columbia, chs. in Okla. and Ark. Adv. Mo. State Council on Arts, 1960, Boone County Courthouse, Columbia. Served with USN, 1943-46, PTO. Fellow Huntington Hartford Found., 1962; rRecipient Commendation award Senate of State of Mo., 1977, 87, Nat. Prof. of Yr. award, Bronze medalist, Mo. State Prof. of Yr. award Coun. for Advancement and Support Edn., 1987, Disting. Svc. award State Hist. Soc. Mo., Mo. State Arts Coun. award, 1991. Mem. Am. Inst. Conservation of Hist. and Artistic Works (assoc. mem.), Nat. Assn. Mural Painters. Avocations: world travel, reading. Home: 2025 Crestridge Dr Columbia MO 65203-1803 Office: Columbia Coll Dept Art Columbia MO 65216

LARSON, WARD JEROME, lawyer, retired banker; b. Mpls., Mar. 3, 1924; s. Philip Jerome and Inez (Sandstrom) L.; m. Phyllis Jean Lindahl, June 18, 1949; children—Eric, Peter, David, Barbara. BA, North Central Coll., Naperville, Ill., 1948; LLB, Harvard U., 1951. Bar: Ill. 1951. Atty. First Nat. Bank Chgo., 1951-56; asst. trust officer, v.p. DuPage Trust Co., Glen Ellyn, Ill., 1956-62; with Fed. Res. Bank Chgo., 1962-80, v.p., gen. counsel, sec., 1968, sr. v.p., gen. counsel, sec., 1970-80; sole practice law Glen Ellyn, 1980—; Chmn. ins. com. Fed. Res. Banks, 1968-80; mem. adminstrv.

bd. Fed. Res. Employee Benefits System, 1970-74, vice chmn., 1973-74. Mem. bd. edn. Sch. Dist. 41, Glen Ellyn, Ill., 1961-67, pres., 1964-67; chmn. estate planning com. North Cen. Coll., 1962-68, trustee, 1980-81, planned giving officer, 1987-90; chmn. trustees 1st United Meth. Ch., Glen Ellyn, 1968-69, chmn. coun. ministries, 1969-71, chmn. membership commn., 1973-75, chmn. social concerns com., 1977, membership sec., 1985-90, lay leader, 1979, 90-93; lay mem. ann. conf. United Meth. Ch. No. Ill., 1992—, mem. conf. coun. fin. and adminstrv.; bd. dirs., v.p. B.R. Ryall YMCA, Glen Ellyn, 1968-70; bd. dirs. United Meth. Found.-North Ill. Conf., 1973-76; mem. exec. com. Chgo. chpt. March of Dimes, 1978-80; mem. Council Laity Garrett-Evang. Theol. Sem., 1984—; planned giving cons. Ctl. DuPage Hosp., 1992—. Served to 1st lt., inf. AUS, 1943-46. Mem. ABA, Alumni Assn. North Central Coll. (dir. 1976—, sec. 1977-78, pres. 1980-81, nat. chmn. ann. fund 1983-92, Outstanding Alumnus award 1986). Home and Office: 822 Saddlewood Dr Glen Ellyn IL 60137-3202

LARSON, WILFRED JOSEPH, chemical company executive; b. N.Y.C., July 12, 1927; s. Fred Wilfred and Mabel Louise (Messier) L.; m. Joan Jesslyn Tilford, Sept. 4, 1949; children: Linda Sue, Robert Wilfred. B.S. in Econs., U. Pa., 1951; postgrad., U. Chgo., 1958-59, Seton Hall U., 1960-61, U. Cin., 1964-65. With Ward Foods, N.Y.C., 1953-63; contr., chief fin. officer Ward Foods, 1961-63; with Drackett Co., Cin., 1963-79; fin. v.p. Drackett Co., 1966-67, adminstrv. v.p., 1967-68, exec. v.p., 1969-79; pres. Bristol-Myers Products Can., 1977-79; v.p. Bristol-Myers Squibb Co., 1981-92; pres. Westwood Squibb Pharms., Inc., 1979-92; past chmn. Western N.Y. Tech. Devel. Ctr.; bd. dirs First Empire State Corp., M&T Bank, Pratt & Lambert, Bryant & Stratton. Pres., trustee Cin. Adolescent Clinic, Inc., 1968-80; trustee, past chmn. Women's & Children's Rsch. Found., Children's Hosp.; past chmn., bd. dirs. Greater Buffalo YMCA; trustee, past treas. Studio Arena Theatre; chmn. SUNY-Buffalo Sch. Pharmacy centennial, 1986; past trustee Calspan/UB Rsch. Ctr.; past vice chmn., bd. dirs. Buffalo Children's Hosp.; chmn. bd. dirs. Buffalo Philharm. Orch. Soc., Inc., 1986-91; vice chmn. bd. dirs. Greater Buffalo Devel. Found., 1987-92; bd. dirs. Buffalo Fine Arts Acad., 1988-91, Am. Symphony Orch. League, 1989-91, U. at Buffalo Found., 1990—; mem. community coun. Roswell Park Meml. Inst., 1988—. With USNR, 1945-47, AUS, 1951-53. Named Buffalo/Niagara Sales and Mktg. Exec. of Yr., 1985, Disting. Citizen of Yr. Boy Scouts Am., 1987, Ann. Alumni award Niagara Frontier Exec. of Yr., U. Buffalo Sch. Mgmt., 1987; recipient Disting. Pub. Svc. award SUNY Buffalo Alumni Assn., 1986, Outstanding Citizens award Buffalo News, 1987, Man of Yr. award West Side Bus. and Taxpayers Assn., 1989, Bus. Exec. of Yr. award Nat. Assn. Accts. Buffalo chpt., 1989. Mem. Fin. Execs. Inst. (treas., sec. 1965-68), Greater Buffalo C. of C. (bd. dirs. 1989-92, Western New Yorker of Yr. award 1992, Patron of the Arts award 1993), Leland (Mich.) Country Club, Queen City Club, Moorings Country Club, Naples, Fla., Commonwealth Club of Cin., Buffalo Club. Republican. Episcopalian (vestryman, treas. 1966-69). Home: 88 Oakland Pl Buffalo NY 14222-2030 Office: 100 Forest Ave Buffalo NY 14213-1091

LARSSON, HANS LENNART, match company executive; b. Varberg, Sweden, Feb. 21, 1942; s. John S. and Margit (Silven) L.; m. Ann-Christine; children—Johan, Charlotta. M.B.A., U. Lund. With Skandinaviska Banken, Stockholm, 1968-69, SCA, Sundsvall, 1970-71; exec. v.p. Gotaverken, Gothenburg, 1972-77; exec. v.p. Swedish Match Co., Stockholm, 1977-85, pres., chief exec. officer, 1985—. Office: Esselte Bus Systems Inc 71 Clinton Rd Garden City NY 11530-4711

LA RUE, CARL FORMAN, lawyer; b. Ann Arbor, Mich., Aug. 4, 1929; s. Carl D. and Evelina F. La R.; children: Steven, Edward; m. Ann Williams Lindbloom, June 28, 1971; stepchildren: Eric, Sarah Relyea. A.B., Harvard U., 1952; LL.B., U. Mich., 1957. Bar: Ohio 1957, Ill. 1964, Calif. 1969. Assoc. firm Fuller & Henry, Toledo, 1957-59; asst. U.S. atty. for Northwestern Ohio, Dept. Justice, 1959-61; staff atty. Trinova Corp. (then Libbey-Owens-Ford Co.), Toledo, 1961-64; v.p., gen. counsel, sec. Trinova Corp., Toledo, 1978-87; ptnr. Marshall & Melhorn, Toledo, 1988-89, counsel, 1989—; sr. atty. Armour and Co., Chgo., 1964-68; asst. gen. counsel Rockwell Internat., Los Angeles, 1968-78. With U.S. Army, 1952-54. Mem. ABA, Ohio Bar Assn., Toledo Bar Assn., Toledo Club, Toledo Tennis Club, Westowne Tennis Club. Home: 3553 Brookside Rd Toledo OH 43606-2610 Office: Marshall & Melhorn 4 Seagate Toledo OH 43604-1520

LA RUE, HENRY ALDRED, consultant, former oil company executive; b. Denver, Aug. 13, 1927; s. Robert Hughes and Leona Spencer (Wood) La R.; m. Marion Hardin Klein, Aug. 22, 1954. B.S. in Bus. Adminstrn., U. Kans., 1951. Pres. Pacific Gulf Oil Co., Tokyo, 1973-74; exec. v.p. Gulf Oil Middle East Co., Pitts., 1974-75, Gulf Sci. and Tech. Co., Pitts., 1975-82; pres. Gulf Research and Devel. Co., Pitts., 1975-82, Pitts. Applied Rsch. Corp., U. Pitts. Applied Rsch. Ctr., 1986-88; vice chmn. Pitts. Applied Rsch. Ctr., 1988-92; chief exec. officer Alle-Kiski Revitalization Corp., 1989-90; cons. in field. Bd. dirs. Gulf Oil Corp. Found., Pitts., 1976-82, Franklin Rsch. Ctr., Phila., 1981-86, Colo. Sch. Mines Rsch. Inst., Golden, 1981-87; v.p., dir. Bio Rsch. Ctr. Co., Tokyo, 1973-84; mem. adv. bd. Mellon Inst., Pitts., 1977-83; sec. Salvation Army Greater Pitts., 1980—; mem. Bell Acres Borough Coun., 1992, vice chmn., 1994. Recipient achievement award indsl. research Slippery Rock U. Mem. Am. Petroleum Inst., Am. C. of C. (pres. Seoul, Korea 1970-71, 1st v.p. Taipei, Taiwan 1972-73), Duquesne Club, Edgeworth Club, Sewickley Heights Golf Club, Beta Theta Pi, Delta Sigma Pi. Republican. Episcopalian. Home: 129 Woodcock Drive Rd Sewickley PA 15143-8356 Office: Pitts Applied Research Corp 100 William Pitt Way Pittsburgh PA 15238-1327

LA RUE, (ADRIAN) JAN (PIETERS), musicologist, educator, author; b. Kisaran, Sumatra, Indonesia, July 31, 1918; s. Carl Downey and Evelina Brown (Forman) LaR.; m. Helen Claire Robison, Aug. 21, 1940; children: Charlotte (Mrs. Jonathan L. Isaacs), Christine (Mrs. Dan Honig). SB, Harvard, 1940, PhD, 1952; M.F.A., Princeton, 1942. Instr. music Wellesley Coll., 1942-43, 46-48, asst. prof., 1948-50, asso. prof., 1950-57, chmn. dept. music, 1950-57; prof. NYU, 1957-88; prof. emeritus N.Y.U., 1988—, exec. dean arts and sci., 1962-63, chmn. dept. music, 1970-73, dir. grad. studies in music, 1973-80; vis. prof. UCLA, 1947, U. Mich., 1962, Bar Ilan U., Israel, 1980; first musicologist-in-residence Mozart Festival, The Kennedy Ctr., Washington, 1975. Author: Guidelines for Style Analysis, 1970, 2d edit. 1992, A Catalogue of 18th-Century Symphonies, 1988, Vol.1, Thematic Identifier; co-author: (with M. Ohmiya) Methods and Models for Comprehensive Style Analysis, 1988; contbg. author: Die Musik in Geschichte und Gegenwart, 1968, Grove's Dictionary of Music and Musicians, 1980; editor: Congress Report of the Internat. Musicological Soc., 2 vols., 1961, Festschrift Otto Erich Deutsch, 1963, Festschrift Gustave Reese: Aspects of Medieval and Renaissance Music, 1966; contbr. numerous articles on 18th century symphony and concerto, musical analysis, watermarks, music manuscripts and computer applications to profl. jours. Mem. coun. Smithsonian Instn., 1967-73; mem. Zentralinstitut für Mozartforschung, Salzburg (Austria) Mozarteum, 1969—. 1st lt. Transp. Corps, AUS, 1943-46. Fellow Ford Found., 1954, Fulbright Found., 1954-56, Am. Coun. Learned Socs., 1964, Guggenheim Found., 1965; grantee NEH, 1978, 80-84; honored with publ. of Studies in Musical Sources and Style: Essays in Honor of Jan LaRue, 1990. Mem. Music Library Assn., Soc. Ethnomusicology, Am. Musicological Soc. (pres. 1966-68), Am. Soc. Eighteenth-Century Studies (exec. bd. 1978-80), Phi Beta Kappa. Home: Woods End Rd New Canaan CT 06840 Office: NYU Dept Music Dept Music New York NY 10003-6757

LARUE, PAUL HUBERT, lawyer; b. Somerville, Mass., Nov. 16, 1922; s. Lucien H. and Germaine (Choquet) LaR.; m. Helen Finnegan, July 20, 1946; children: Paul Hubert, Patricia Seward, Mary Hogan. PhB, U. Wis., 1947, JD, 1949. Bar: Ill. 1955, Wis. 1949, U.S Supreme Ct. 1972. Instr. polit. sci. dept. U. Wis., 1947-48; mem. staff Wis. Atty. Gen., 1949-50; trial atty., legal adviser to commr. FTC, 1950-55; pvt. practice, Chgo.; mem. Chadwell & Kayser, Ltd., 1955-90; ptnr. Vedder, Price, Kaufman & Kammholz, 1990-93, of counsel, 1993—; speaker profl. meetings. Mem. Com. Modern Cts. in Ill., 1964; mem. Ill. Com. Constl. Conv., 1968, Better Govt. Assn., 1966-70, Lawyers com. Met. Crusade of Mercy, 1967-68, lawyers' com. United Settlement Appeal, 1966-68; apptd. pub. mem. Ill. Conflict of Interest Laws Commn., 1965-67. Served with AUS, 1943-45, ETO; as capt JAGC, USAFR, 1950-55. Fellow Ill. Bar Found. (life); mem. ABA (mem. council sect. antitrust law 1980-83, chmn. Robinson-Patman Act com. 1975-78), 7th Cir. Bar Assn., Chgo. Bar Assn. (chmn. antitrust com. 1970-71), Wis. State

Bar, Met. Club. Roman Catholic. Contbr. articles to profl. jours. Home: 250 Cuttriss Pl Park Ridge IL 60068 Office: Vedder Price Kaufman & Kammholz 222 N La Salle St Ste 2600 Chicago IL 60601-1194

LARUE, PAUL HUBERT, JR., lawyer; b. Madison, Wis., July 17, 1950; s. Paul Hubert and Helen (Finnegan) L.; m. Nancy Karen Whiting, Dec. 17, 1983; children: Madeleine, Michelle, Michael. BA cum laude, Yale U., 1972; JD, Cornell U., 1975. Bar: Ill. 1975, U.S. Dist. Ct. (no. dist.) Ill. 1975; U.S. Tax Ct. 1993. Assoc. Lord, Bissell & Brook, Chgo., 1975-83, ptnr., 1984—. Mem. Chgo. Coun. on Foreign Rels., 1993. Mem. ABA, Chgo. Bar Assn., Yale Club of Chgo., Rotary (Chgo. chpt.). Home: 124 Robsart Rd Kenilworth IL 60043-1213 Office: Lord Bissell & Brook 115 S La Salle St Chicago IL 60603-3801

LARUSSA, JOSEPH ANTHONY, optical company executive; b. N.Y.C., May 10, 1925; s. Ignacio and Jennie (Bellone) LaR.; m. Stella M.A. Braconnier, July 2, 1946; children—Joseph, Raymond Paul, Debra Marie. BME, CCNY, 1949; M.S., Columbia U., 1955, postgrad. math., mechanics, 1955-59; postgrad. math., physics, NYU, 1959-62; diploma in Infrared Tech., U. Mich. Registered profl. engr., N.Y. V.p. charge advanced engring. Farrand Optical Co., Inc., Valhalla, N.Y., 1952, sr. v.p., tech. dir., 1952-88; pres., chief oper. officer Tech. Innovation Group Inc, Pleasantville, N.Y., 1988-90, Electro Visual Engring. Inc., Yorktown Heights, N.Y., 1991—. Designed Mercury, Gemini, Apollo LM visual spaceflight simulators for NASA; designed space shuttle Aft and Ohd visual simulators for NASA, others for USAF. Patentee in field; contbr. articles profl. publs. Served with inf. AUS, World War II, ETO. Mem. AIAA (DeFlorez award 1968), Tau Beta Pi, Pi Tau Sigma. Home: 451 Rutledge Dr Yorktown Heights NY 10598-5011

LA RUSSA, TONY, JR. (ANTHONY LA RUSSA, JR.), professional baseball manager; b. Tampa, Fla., Oct. 4, 1944; m. Elaine Coker, Dec. 31, 1973; 2 daus.: Bianca, Devon. Student, U. Tampa; BA, U. So. Fla., 1969; LLB, Fla. State U., 1978. Bar: Fla. 1979. Player numerous major league and minor league baseball teams, 1962-77; coach St. Louis Cardinals orgn., 1977; mgr. minor league team Knoxville, 1978, Iowa, 1979; coach Chgo. White Sox, 1978, mgr., 1979-86; mgr. Oakland A's, 1986—; mgr. All-Star team, 1988, coach, 1984, 87. Named Maj. League Mgr. of Yr. Baseball Writers' Assn. Am., 1983, 88, AP, 1983, Sporting News, 1983, Am. League Mgr. of Yr., 1988. Office: Oakland Coliseum 7000 Coliseum Way Oakland CA 94621-1918*

LARWOOD, LAURIE, psychologist; b. N.Y., 1941; PhD, Tulane U., 1974. Pres., Davis Instruments Corp., San Leandro, Calif., 1966-71, cons., 1969—; asst. prof. orgnl. behavior SUNY, Binghamton, 1974-76; assoc. prof. psychology, chairperson dept., assoc. prof. bus. adminstrn. Claremont (Calif.) McKenna Coll., 1976-83, Claremont Grad. Sch., 1976-85; prof., head dept. mgmt. U. Ill.-Chgo., 1983-87; dean sch. bus. SUNY, Albany, 1987-90; dean Coll. Bus. Adminstrn., U. Nev., Reno, 1990-92; dir. Inst. Strategic Bus. Issues, 1992—; mem. western regional advisory coun. SBA, 1976-81; dir. The Mgmt. Team; pres. Mystic Games, Inc. Mem. Acad. Mgmt. (editl. rev. bd. Rev. 1977-82, past chmn. women in mgmt. div., managerial consultation divsn., tech. and innovation mgmt. divsn.), Am. Psychol. Assn., Assn. Women in Psychology. Author: (with M.M. Wood) Women in Management, 1977; Organizational Behavior and Management, 1984, Women's Career Development, 1987, Strategies-Successes-Senior Executives Speak Out, 1988, Women's Careers, 1988, Managing Technological Development, 1988; mem. editl. bd. Sex Roles, 1979—, Consultation, 1986-91, Jour. Orgnl. Behavior, 1987—, Group and Orgn. Mgmt., 1982-84, editor, 1986—; founding editor Women and Work, 1983, Jour. Mgmt. Case Studies, 1985-87. Contbr. numerous articles, papers to profl. jours. Home: 2855 Sagittarius Dr Reno NV 89509-3885 Office: U Nev Coll Bus Adminstrn Reno NV 89557

LASAGA, ANTONIO C., geochemistry educator, researcher; b. Havana, Cuba, Dec. 17, 1949; came to U.S., 1961; s. Antonio and Margarita (Casañas) L.; m. Evelyn F. Fumagali; children: Peter M., Daniel A. BA, Princeton U., 1971; MS in Physics, Harvard U., 1974, PhD in Chem. Physics, 1976; MS (hon.), Yale U., 1984. Lectr. Harvard U., Cambridge, Mass., 1976-77; from asst. prof., assoc. prof. to prof. Pa. State U., State College, 1977-84; prof. geochemistry Yale U., New Haven, Conn., 1984—; mem. adv. bd. NSF, 1977-81; pvt. cons. geochemistry, New Haven, 1982—. Editor: Kinetics of Geochemical Processes, 1981; editor-in-chief Chem. Geology, Amsterdam, The Netherlands, 1987—; assoc. editor Am. Jour. Sci., 1986—. Vol. Centro San Jose, New Haven, 1988—. Named Fairchild Disting. fellow Calif. Inst. Tech., Pasadena, 1989; Guggenheim Found. fellow, 1988; Clare Hall Coll. life fellow, Cambridge U., Eng. Fellow Mineral. Soc. Am. (life, Ann. award 1986); mem. Geochem. Soc. (councillor 1987—, F.W. Clarke medal 1979, v.p. 1991-93, pres. 1993—), Internat. Geochem. Soc. (v.p. 1992-94). Roman Catholic. Avocations: guitar, singing, tennis, squash, swimming. Office: Yale U PO Box 6666 210 Whitney Ave New Haven CT 06511-3748

LASAGE, JOHN DAVID, public relations firm executive; b. Gary, Ind., May 6, 1937; s. Harold and Natalie (Marich) LaS.; m. Carol Lee Monson, June 17, 1962; children: Laura, Catherine. B.A. in Journalism, U. Mich., 1959. Publicity writer U.S. Gypsum Co., Chgo., 1960-64; account exec. Burson-Marsteller, Chgo., 1964-70; supr. Burson-Marsteller, 1970-78, gen. mgr. Chgo., 1978-83, exec. v.p. central region, 1980-91, pres., CEO Chgo., 1992—. Bd. dirs. Urban Gateways, Chgo., 1978-80; bd. dirs. Community Renewal Soc., 1975-78, Eastern Seal Soc., 1980—; Boy Scouts Am., 1982—. Recipient Golden Trumpet Publicity Club Chgo., 1968. Mem. Pub. Relations Soc. Am. (accredited Silver Anvil 1972, accredited Silver Anvil 1980). Congregationalist. Clubs: Publicity (Chgo.); Chicago. Office: Burson-Marsteller 1 E Wacker Dr Chicago IL 60601-1801*

LASAGNA, LOUIS CESARE, medical educator; b. N.Y.C., Feb. 22, 1923; s. Joseph and Carmen (Boccignone) L.; m. Helen Chester Gersten; children: Nina, David, Maria, Kristin, Lisa, Peter, Christopher. BS, Rutgers U., 1943; MD, Columbia U., 1947; DSc (hon.), Hahnemann U., 1980, Rutgers U., 1983. Asst. prof. medicine Johns Hopkins U., Balt., 1954-57, asst. prof. pharmacology, 1954-59, assoc. prof. medicine, 1957-70, assoc. prof. pharmacology, 1959-70; prof. pharmacology and toxicology U. Rochester, 1970-86, prof. medicine, 1970-86; dean Sackler Sch. Tufts U., 1984—, prof. pharmacology and psychiatry, 1984—. Author: The Doctors' Dilemmas, 1962, Life, Death and the Doctor, 1968, Phenylpropanolamine, A Review, 1988; editor: Controversies in Therapeutics, 1980, Sr. asst. surgeon USPHS, 1952-54. Recipient Oscar B. Hunter award Am. Soc. Clin. Pharmacology, 1975, ASPET award Am. Soc. Pharmacology and Exptl. Therapeutics, 1976, Lilly prize Brit. Pharmacological Soc., 1985, Rutgers U. award, 1993, J. Allyn Taylor Internat. prize in Medicine, 1993; named Disting. prof. Tufts U., 1994. Mem. Inst. Medicine of NAS, Am. Coll. Neuropsychopharmacology (pres. 1979-80). Republican. Roman Catholic. Home: 256 Woodland Rd Auburndale MA 02166-2707 Office: Tufts U Sackler Sch Grad Biomed Sci 136 Harrison Ave Boston MA 02111-1800

LA SALLE, ARTHUR EDWARD, historic foundation executive; b. New Orleans, Aug. 9, 1930; s. Rene Charles and Jeanne Matilda (Senac) La S.; divorced; children—Carl Alan, Adam David, Jeanne Ambre Victoria. Student Holy Name of Jesus Coll. Founder, pres. Am. R.R. Equipment Assn., Asheville, N.C., 1960—; founder Trains of Yesterday Mus., Hilliard, Fla., 1964-73; owner, restorer Brush Hill mansion, Irwin, Pa., 1973-77; lessee, restorer Springfield mansion, Fayette, Miss., 1977—; founder, pres. Hist. Springfield Found., Fayette, 1977—; cons. Smithsonian Instn., 1959, 75, Japanese Nat. Rys., Tokyo, 1968, Henry Ford Mus., 1975 City of Natchez, Miss., 1985, Old South Soc., Church Hill, Miss., 1985—; cons. in field; lectr. in field. Author: The Marriage of Andrew Jackson at Springfield Plantation; contbr. articles to profl. jours. Mem. Ry. and Locomotive Hist. Soc., Nat. Trust for Historic Preservation, Natchez Hist. Soc., U.S. Naval Inst. Avocations: historical preservation and study; writing; painting. Home and Office: Springfield Plantation RR 1 Box 201 Fayette MS 39069-9527

LASAROW, WILLIAM JULIUS, federal judge retired; b. Jacksonville, Fla., June 30, 1922; s. David Herman and Mary (Hollins) L.; m. Marilyn Doris Powell, Feb. 4, 1951; children: Richard M., Elisabeth H. BA, U. Fla., 1943; JD, Stanford U., 1950. Bar: Calif. 1951. Counsel judiciary com. Calif. Assembly, Sacramento, 1951-52; dep. dist. atty. Stanislaus County, Modesto, Calif., 1952-53; pvt. practice law L.A., 1953-73; bankruptcy judge U.S. Cts.,

---

L.A., 1973-94; chief judge U.S. Bankruptcy Ct., Central dist., Calif., 1973-92; judge Bankruptcy Appellate Panel 9th Fed. Cir., 1980-82; fed. judge U.S. Bankruptcy Ct., L.A., 1973; faculty Fed. Jud. Ctr. Bankruptcy Seminars, Washington, 1977-82. Contbg. author, editor legal publs.; staff: Stanford U. Law Review, 1949. Mem. ABA, Am. Coll. Bankruptcy, Am. Bankruptcy Inst., L.A. County Bar Assn., Wilshire Bar Assn., Blue Key, Phi Beta Kappa, Phi Kappa Phi. Home: 11623 Canton Pl Studio City CA 91604-4164 Office: US Bankruptcy Ct 1534 Roybal Federal Bldg 255 E Temple St Los Angeles CA 90012-3334

LASCALA, ANTHONY CHARLES, financial company executive; b. Pittston, Pa., June 30, 1924; s. Anthony Dominic and Margaret (Mazzitelli) LaS.; m. Deborah Sherwood, Apr. 25, 1980; 1 child, Linda Andrews. Major appliance buyer Montgomery Ward, 1946-54; hard goods merchandiser Federated Dept. Stores, Los Angeles, 1954-56; v.p. mktg. Tappan O'Keefe & Merritt Co., Mansfield, Ohio, 1956-72; sr. v.p. Citizens Savs. & Loan, San Francisco, 1973-75; exec. v.p. Great Western Fin. Corp., Beverly Hills, Calif., 1975—, pres. retail banking and customer services div., 1981—; with Great Western Savs. & Loan, Beverly Hills, Calif., 1975-81; chmn., pres., chief exec. officer Great Western Bank, White Plains, N.Y., 1987—; bd. dirs. Great Western Brokerage, Beverly Hills, Calif.; chmn., dir. GW Fin. Direct Mktg. Co., Beverly Hills. Exec. v.p. Big Bros. Greater Los Angeles, 1979-80, pres., 1981-82, bd. dirs., 1976—; chmn. bd. Young Musicians Found., Los Angeles, 1984-85. Recipient Belding awards Advt. Club Los Angeles, 1977, 78. Club: Bel Air Country (Los Angeles). Avocations: music; photography; travel. Office: Gt Western Fin Corp 8484 Wilshire Blvd Beverly Hills CA 90211-3227

LASCH, ROBERT, former journalist; b. Lincoln, Neb., Mar. 26, 1907; s. Theodore Walter and Myrtle (Nelson) L.; m. Zora Schaupp, Aug. 22, 1931 (dec. 1982); children: Christopher (dec. 1994), Catherine; m. Iris C. Anderson, Sept. 14, 1986. A.B., U. Nebr., 1928; postgrad. (Rhodes scholar), Oxford, 1928-31; Nieman fellow, Harvard, 1941-42. Reporter, state editor, editorial writer Omaha World-Herald, 1931-41; editorial writer, then chief editorial writer Chgo. Sun and Sun-Times, 1942-50; editorial writer St. Louis Post-Dispatch, 1950-57, editor editorial page, 1957-71, ret. Contbr. to: Newsmen's Holiday, 1942; Author: For a Free Press, 1944 (Atlantic Monthly prize), Breaking The Building Blockade, 1946. Recipient; St. Louis Civil Liberties award, 1966; Pulitzer prize for distinguished editorial writing, 1966. Home: 685 La Posada Cir #703 Green Valley AZ 85614-2246

LASCHER, ALAN ALFRED, lawyer; b. N.Y.C., Dec. 8, 1941; s. Morris Julius and Sadie Lillian (Chassen) L.; m. C. Amy Weingarten, July 12, 1969; children: David, Lauren, Alexandra, Carlyn. BS, Union Coll., 1963; LLB, Bklyn. Law Sch., 1967. Bar: N.Y. 1967. Assoc. Kramer, Leven et al, N.Y.C., 1969-75; ptnr. real estate dept. Weil, Gotshal & Manges, N.Y.C., 1975—; mem. law com. N.Y. Real Estate Bd., N.Y.C., 1981—. Served to sgt. USAF, 1968-69. Named Real Estate Lawyer of Yr. Am. Lawyer, 1982. Mem. Am. Coll. Real Estate Lawyers (mem. Resolution Trust Corp. and Bankruptcy coms.). Office: Weil Gotshal & Manges 767 5th Ave New York NY 10153-0001

LASCHUK, ROY BOGDAN, lawyer; b. Saskatoon, Sask., Can., Aug. 13, 1932; s. Nicholas and Agatha (Schyhol) L.; m. Tairroyn Riley, Aug. 21, 1964; children: Tonia Jane, Stephen Clare, Graham Christopher. BA, U. Sask., 1953, LLB, 1955. Bar: Sask.; created Queen's counsel 1978. Assoc. firm Balfour, Moss, Milliken, Laschuk & Kyle (and predecessors), Regina, Sask., 1956-61; ptnr. Balfour Moss and predecessor firms, Regina, Sask., 1961-94, of counsel, 1994—; mem. Crown Investment Rev. Commn., vice chmn. 1983-84. Bd. dirs. Regina Housing Authority, 1973—; chmn. 1987-94. Mem. Law Soc. Sask., Can. Bar Assn. (council) Regina Bar Assn. (life, dir. 1975—, v.p. 1977-78, pres. 1978, chmn. health law sect. 1990-93), Canadian Petroleum Assn. (chmn. legal com. Sask. 1972-78), Can. Assn. Occupational Therapists (hon. exec. mem. 1970-75), Royal United Svcs. Inst., Sask. Track and Field Assn. (dir. 1983-85), Assiniboia Club, Rotary (pres. 1967-68). Baptist. Home: 629 Senanus Dr, Saanichton BC Canada V8M 1S6 Office: 700-2103 11th Ave, Regina, SK Canada S4P 4G1

LASH, JONATHAN, environmental law executive; b. N.Y.C., Aug. 12, 1945; s. Joseph P. and Trude W. (Wenzel) L.; m. Eleanor Scattergood, Apr. 27, 1968; children: Elissa, Matthew, Emily. BA, Harvard Coll., 1967; MA in Edn., Cath. U., 1971, JD, 1974. Atty. Natural Resources Def. Coun., Washington, 1978-85; commr. Vt. Dept. Environ. Conservation, Waterbury, 1985-87; sec. Vt. Agy. Natural Resources, Waterbury, 1987-90; dir. Environ. Law Ctr. Vt. Law Sch., South Royalton, 1990-93; pres. World Resources Inst., Washington, 1993—; cons. sci. adv. bd. U.S. EPA, Washington, 1989-90, Inst. for Sustainable Communities, South Royalton, 1991-92, World Bank, Washington, 1992, Pew Charitable Trusts, Phila., 1992-93; co-chair Pres.'s Coun. on Sustainable Devel., Washington, 1993—; chair Nat. Commn. Superfund; mem. adv. bd. TATA Energy Rsch. Inst.; internat. adv. Keidanren Com. on Nature Conservation; bd. dirs. Keystone Ctr. Co-author: The Synfuels Manual, 1980, A Season of Spoils, 1984. Vol. Peace Corps, Dominican Republic, 1967-70; bd. dirs. Vt. Law Sch., The Putney Sch., Alliance to Save Energy; mem. Earth Coun. Democrat. Mem. Soc. of Friends. Office: World Resources Inst 1709 New York Ave NW Washington DC 20006-5206

LASH, MYLES PERRY, hospital administrator; b. Detroit, May 31, 1946; s. Irving and Rose (Simkovitz) L.; m. Linda Pauline Borger, June 19, 1968; children: Alissa Beth, David Howard. B.S., Wayne State U., 1968; M.Hosp. Adminstrn., U. Mich., 1970. Asst. to exec. dir. Peoples Community Hosp. Authority, Wayne, Mich., 1970-72; asst. prof. Grad. Program Hosp. Adminstrn., Ohio State U., Columbus, 1970-72; adminstr. Ohio State U. Hosps., Columbus, 1973-79; exec. dir. Med. Coll. Va., Richmond, 1979-85; nat. dir. health care Arthur Young Co., Washington, 1985-86; pres. The Lash Group-Health Care Cons., Washington, 1986—. Contbr. articles to profl. jours. Bd. dirs. Univ. Hosp. Consortium, 1980-85, pres., 1985. Mem. U. Mich. Hosp. Adminstrn. Alumni Assn. (pres.), Am. Hosp. Assn., Am. Coll. Hosp. Adminstrs. (Robert S. Hudgens Meml. award 1982). Home: 6708 Bonaventure Ct Bethesda MD 20817-4026 Office: 555 13th St NW Washington DC 20004-1109

LASH, STEPHEN SYCLE, auction company executive; b. Boston, Feb. 10, 1940; s. Samuel George and Carolyn Virginia (Sycle) L.; m. Wendy Lehman, Oct. 29, 1967; children: Abigail Sycle, William Lehman. BA, Yale U., 1962; MBA, Columbia U., 1966. V.p. Bali Footwear, Inc., Marlborough, Mass., 1962-64, 66-68, S.G. Warburg and Co., London, N.Y.C., 1968-76; v.p. Christies, N.Y.C., 1976-80, sr. v.p., 1980-84, exec. v.p., 1984-93, vice chmn., 1993—; also bd. dirs. Christies Internat. PLC. Founder, pres. Ocean Liner Mus., N.Y.C., 1983-88, co-chmn., 1988—; commr. N.Y.C. Landmarks Preservation Commn., 1973-76; bd. dirs. N.Y. Landmarks Conservancy, N.Y.C., 1975—, chmn., 1992-95; bd. dirs. Preservation League N.Y., Albany, 1986—. With USCGR, 1962-67. Pan Am. Union fellow, 1965. Mem. Yale Alumni Assn. Metro N.Y. (pres. 1987-90). Clubs: River, Mill Reef, Century Assn. Home: 151 E 79th St New York NY 10021-0434 Office: Christie Manson & Woods Internat Inc 502 Park Ave New York NY 10022-1108

LASH, STEVEN M., hospital administrator. Fin. analyst Interracial Coun. Bus. Opportunity, L.A., 1975-76, Pacific Health Resources, L.A., 1976-77; contr. Sharp Meml. Hosp., San Diego, 1977-81; CFO San Diego Hosp. Assn., San Diego, 1981-85; sr. v.p. fin. and bus. devel. Sharp HealthCare, San Diego, 1985—.

LASHBROOKE, ELVIN CARROLL, JR., legal educator, consultant; b. Dec. 14, 1939; s. Elvin Carroll Sr. and Lois Lenora (Weger) L.; m. Margaret Ann Jones, Dec. 19, 1964; children: Michelle Ann, David C. BA, U. Tex., 1967, MA, 1968, JD, 1972, LLM, 1977; PhD, Mich. State U., 1993. Bar: Tex. 1972, Fla. 1973. Legis. counsel Tex. Legis. Coun., Austin, 1972-75; pvt. practice law Austin, 1975-77; asst. prof. coll. of law DePaul U. Chgo., 1977-79, Stetson U., St. Petersburg, Fla., 1979-80; assoc. prof. sch. law Notre Dame, Ind., 1981-85; prof., chmn. bus. law dept. Mich. State U., East Lansing, 1985—, assoc. dean adminstrn. Eli Broad Coll. Bus., 1993—; pvt. practice cons. East Lansing, 1986—; instr. St. Edward's U., Austin, 1975-76. Author: Tax Exempt Organizations, 1985, The Legal Handbook of Business Transactions, 1987; contbr. articles to profl. jours. Mem. ABA, Tex. Bar

---

Assn., Fla. Bar Assn., Am. Arbitration Assn., Fin. Mgmt. Assn. Avocation: computers. Home: 6435 Island Lake Dr East Lansing MI 48823-9735 Office: Mich State U Office of Dean Eli Broad Coll Bus East Lansing MI 48824-1122

LASHELLE, CHARLES STANTON, lawyer, insurance company executive; b. Colorado Springs, Colo., June 25, 1947; s. Stanton Duane and Glenna (Bloom) LaS.; m. Pamela Montross, Aug. 24, 1968; children: Rebecca, Karen. BA, U. No. Colo., 1969; JD, Creighton U., 1972. Bar: Nebr. 1972, U.S. Dist. Ct. Nebr. 1972, U.S. Tax Ct. 1980, U.S Ct. Appeals (8th cir.) 1980, U.S. Supreme Ct. 1980; CLU. Mktg. rep. Teton Nat. Life Ins. Co., Greeley, Colo., 1968-69; v.p., assn. gen. counsel Mut. Protective & Medico Life, Omaha, 1973-83; sr. v.p. adminstrn. Am. Founders Life Ins. Co., Austin, Tex., 1983-87; exec. v.p. adminstrn. Nat. Western Life Ins. Co., Austin, 1987-92; pres., CEO Tex. Life and Health Ins. Guaranty Assn., Austin, 1992—; pres. Comml. Adjusters Inc., Austin, 1988-92. Bd. dirs. Variety Club, Omaha, 1983, Nat. Orgn. Life & Health Guaranty Assns., 1993—, chair confederation life task force, 1994—; vice chmn. Mayor's Task Force on Drugs and Drug Abuse, 1990-91. Capt. USAR, 1972-76. Mem. ABA, Nebr. Bar Assn., Am. Soc. CLUs, Am. Coun. Life Ins., Greater Austin C. of C. (legis. com.), Sertoma Club (Round Rock, Tex.). Republican. Methodist. Avocations: golf, reading. Home: 1821 Possum Trot St Round Rock TX 78681-1710

LASHOF, JOYCE C., public health educator; b. Phila.; d. Harry and Rose (Brodsky) Cohen; m. Richard K. Lashof, June 11, 1950; children: Judith, Carol, Dan. AB, Duke U., 1946; MD, Women's Med. Coll., 1950; DSc (hon.), Med. Coll. Pa., 1983. Dir. Ill. State Dept. Pub. Health, 1973-77; dep. asst. sec. for health programs and population affairs Dept. Health, Edn., and Welfare, Washington, 1977-78; sr. scholar in residence IOM, Washington, 1978; asst. dir. office of tech. assessment U.S. Congress, Washington, 1978-81; dean sch. pub. health U. Calif., Berkeley, 1981-91, prof. pub. health Sch. Pub. Health, 1981-94, prof. emerita, 1994—; co-chair Commn. on Am. after Roe vs. Wade, 1991-92; mem. Sec.'s Coun. Health Promotion and Disease Prevention, 1988-91. Recipient Alumni Achievement award Med. Coll. Pa., 1975. Mem. editl. bd. Wellness Letter, 1983—, editl. com. Ann. Rev. of Pub. Health, 1987-90. Avocation: hiking. Home: 601 Euclid Ave Berkeley CA 94708-1331 Office: U Calif-Berkeley Sch Pub Health 19 Earl Warren Hall Berkeley CA 94720

LASHUTKA, GREGORY S., mayor, lawyer; b. N.Y.C., 1944; m. Catherine Adams; children: Stephanie, Michael, Nicholas, Lara. BS, Ohio State U., 1967; JD, Capital U., 1974. Bar: Ohio, 1974, Fla., D.C., 1975. Former ptnr. Squire, Sanders & Dempsey, Columbus, Ohio; elected mayor City of Columbus, 1991—; former Columbus City Atty. Past chmn. Columbus-Area Sports Devel. Corp.; 1st v.p. Nat. League of Cities; comentator of the Ohio State U. Football Color, 1983-90; active civic and charitable orgns. including Charity Newsies Assocs., Nat. Football Found., Ohio State U. Varsity "O". Served to lt., USN. Named Mcpl. Leader of the Yr., Am. City and County mag., 1993. Office: Office of the Mayor City Hall Room 247 90 W Broad St Columbus OH 43215-9014

LASICH, VIVIAN ESTHER LAYNE, secondary education educator; b. Hopewell Twp., Pa., Dec. 17, 1935; d. Charles McClung and Harriette Law (George) Layne; m. William G. Lasich, Apr. 10, 1958; children: C. Laurence, Celeste M., Michelle R. AB, Geneva Coll., 1956; MA in Edn., No. Mich. U., 1970, postgrad. Secondary tchr. Freedom (Pa.) High Sch., 1956-57; elem. educator Gilbert Elem. Sch., Gwinn, Mich., 1967-69; lang. arts educator Gwinn Mid. Sch., 1970—; adv. bd. community arts panel Coun. for Arts, Mich., 1979-81; at-large rep U. Peninsula adv. panel Mich Dept. Edn./ Arts, 1976-79; mem. sch. improvement team 1988-91, 93-94, middle sch. concept team, 1992—; dist. curriculum strategy action team, 1993-94; dist. profl. devel. strategy team, 1993-94; mem. sounding bd. Middle Sch., 1994—, dist. sch. improvement team, 1994—. Author: Prophets Without Honor: Teachers, Students & Trust, 1991. V.p. Marquette (Mich.) Community Theatre, 1962-63 bd. dirs. 1963-74, mem. 1961-92; pres. Marquette Arts Coun. 1973-74, v.p 1972-73, bd. dirs. 1970-78, mem. 1970-84; pres. Upper Peninsula Arts Coordinating Bd. 1976-78, v.p. 1974-76, bd. dirs. 1978-84; bd. dirs. Mich. Community Theatre Assn. 1972-73; bd. dirs. Mich Community Arts Agys., 1976-79. Recipient Committment to Excellence award Marquette Community Theatre, 1965. Devotion to Arts Development award Upper Peninsula (Mich.) Arts Coord. Bd. 1979. Mem. ASCD, NEA, AAUW, Mich. Edn. Assn., Phi Delta Kappa. Presbyterian. Avocations: rsch. writing, theatrical direction and performance, vocal music. Home: 508 Pine St Marquette MI 49855 Office: Gwinn Area Community Schs Gwinn MI 49841

LASIECKA, IRENA M., mathematics educator; b. Warsaw, Poland, Feb. 4, 1948; came to U.S., 1978; d. Antoni and Janina (Krzeminska) Lech; m. Stanislaw Lasiecki, June 22, 1971 (div. 1979); 1 child, Paul; m. Roberto Triggieni. BA, U. Warsaw, 1971, MS, 1972, PhD, 1975; postgrad., UCLA, 1978-79. Researcher Polish Acad. Scis., Warsaw, 1975-78; vis. asst. prof. UCLA, 1979-81; assoc. prof. math. U. Fla., Gainesville, 1981-84, prof., 1984-87; prof. U. Va., Charlottesville, 1987—. Editor Jour. on Control, Soc. Indsl. and Applied Math., 1982, Applied Math., 1984—; Internat. Jour. Math., 1985, Computational Optimization and Applications, 1991. Recipient award Polish Acad. Scis., 1976, Creative Extension award NSF, 1986. Mem. Internat. Fedn. Imfo. Processing. Roman Catholic. Avocations: sports, music, theater. Office: U Va Dept Applied Math Charlottesville VA 22901

LASKAWY, PHILIP A., accounting and management consulting firm executive; b. 1941. With S. D. Leidesdorf & Co., 1961-78, ptnr., 1971-78; ptnr. Ernst & Whinney (acquired S. D. Leidesdorf 1978), 1978-85, vice chmn., mng. ptnr. N.Y. region, 1983-93; chmn., CEO Ernst & Young (merger of Ernst & Whinney and Arthur Young 1993), 1993—, also bd. dirs. Office: Ernst & Young 277 Park Ave New York NY 10172*

LASKER, DAVID RAYMOND, newspaper editor, musician; b. N.Y.C., Apr. 21, 1950; arrived in Can., 1974; s. Joseph Leon and Mildred (Jaspen) L. BA in History of Art cum laude, Yale U., 1972, MMus, 1974. Double-bassist Winnipeg (Man., Can.) Symphony Orch., 1974-84; freelance archtl. journalist, Toronto, Ont., Can., 1984-89; editor Contract mag., Toronto, 1989-91; editor fashion and design The Globe and Mail, Toronto, 1991—; prin. dobule-bassist North York Symphony Orch. Author: (children's book) The Boy Who Loved Music, 1979 (ALA Notable Book award). Avocations: collecting classical vinyl records, high-end audio, bodybuilding. Home: 533 Logan Ave, Toronto, ON Canada M4K 3B3 Office: The Globe and Mail, 444 Front St W, Toronto, ON Canada M5V 2S9

LASKER, GABRIEL WARD, anthropologist, educator; b. York, Eng., Apr. 29, 1912; s. Bruno and Margaret Naomi (Ward) L.; m. Bernice Kaplan, July 31, 1949; children: Robert Alexander, Edward Meyer, Ann Titania. Student, U. Wis., 1928-30; A.B., U. Mich., 1934; A.M., Harvard U., 1940, Ph.D., 1945. Instr. English Chiao T'ung U., Peking, China, 1936-37; teaching fellow in anatomy Harvard Med. Sch., 1941-42; mem. faculty dept. anatomy Wayne State U. Sch. Medicine, Detroit, 1946—, asst. prof., 1947-55; assoc. prof., 1955-64; prof. Wayne U. Sch. Medicine, 1964-82, prof. emeritus, 1982—; visiting commoner Churchill Coll. Cambridge U., 1983-84; conducted Wayne U.-Viking Fund field trip to Mexico to study effects of migration on phys. characteristics of Mexicans, 1948. Author: Physical Anthropology, The Evolution of Man, Surnames and Genetic Structure; editor: Yearbook of Phys. Anthropology, 1945-51, Human Biology, 1953-87, Research Strategies in Human Biology: Field and Survey Studies, 1993; contbr. articles to profl. jours. Fellow Am. Anthrop. Assn., AAAS (v.p. 1968); mem. Am. Assn. Phys. Anthropologists (sec.-treas. 1947-51, v.p 1960-62, pres. 1963-65, Charles Darwin award 1993), Am. Assn. Anatomists, Human Biology Council (pres. 1982-84), Soc. Study Human Biology (U.K.), Asociación Mexicana de Antropología Biológica, Sigma Xi. Office: 540 E Canfield St Detroit MI 48201-1928

LASKER, JONATHAN LEWIS, artist; b. Jersey City, July 30, 1948; s. Lester and Henrietta Selma (Gross) L. Student, Sch. Visual Arts, N.Y.C., 1975-77, Calif. Inst. Arts, 1977. One-man exhbns. include Landmark Gallery, N.Y., Gunnar Kaldewey, Dusseldorf, Fed. Republic Germany, 1981, Annette Gmeiner, Kirchzarten, Fed. Republic Germany, 1984, Tibor de Nagy, N.Y.C., 1984, 86, Michael Werner, Cologne, Fed. Republic Germany,

1986, 87, 90, Massimo Audiello, N.Y.C., 1986, 88, 89, Anders Tornberg, Lund, Sweden, 1987, 90, Gian Enzo Sperone, Rome, 1988, 91, Sperone Westwater Gallery, N.Y.C., 1991, 93, Lars Bohman, Stockholm, 1991, 94, Inst. Contemporary ArtU. Pa., Phila., 1992, Thaddaeus Ropac Gallery, Paris, 1992, Witte de With Ctr. Contemporary Art, Rotterdam, 1993, Rhona Hoffman Gallery, Chgo., 1993, numerous others; selected group exhbns. include Mus. Ludwig, Cologne, Wacoal Art Ctr., Tokyo, 1985, Rose Art Mus. Brandeis U., Waltham, Mass., 1986, Corcoran Gallery Art, Washington, 1987, Aldrich Mus. Contemporary Art, Ridgefield, Conn., 1987, Roos Mus., Malmo, Sweden, U. N. Tex., Denton, J.B. Speed Mus., Louisville, Alta. Coll. Art., Edmonton, Can., Contemporary Arts Ctr., Cin., Santa Fe Community Coll., Gainesville, Fla., Met. Mus. Art, N.Y.C., 1988, Stedelijk Mus., Amsterdam, The Netherlands, 1989, Marc Richards Gallery, L.A., Scott Hansen Gallery, N.Y.C., 1990, Pace Gallery, N.Y.C., 1990, Sperone Westwater Gallery, N.Y.C., 1991, 94, Gallery Modern Art, Bologna, Italy, 1991, Hirshhorn Mus. and Sculpture Garden, Washington, 1991, Mus. Contemporary Art of Dayton Art Inst., 1992, Documenta IX, Kassell, Germany, Gallerie Nächst Sankt Stefan, Vienna, 1992, Thaddaeus Ropac, Paris, 1992, Ruth Bloom Gallery, L.A., 1993, Hayward Gallery, London, 1994, Ctr. for the Fine Arts, Miami, 1994, numerous others; in pub. collections Corcoran Gallery, Hirshhorn Mus. and Sculpture Garden, Washington, Mus. Ludwig, Cologne, Wacoal Art Ctr., Tokyo, Whitney Mus. Am. Art, N.Y.C., Moderna Museet, Stockholm, Fond Nat. d'Art Contempor Ain, Paris; critiqued numerous art books, catalogs, mags. including Beyond Boundaries: New York's New Art (Jerry Saltz), N.Y. Art Now, The Saatchi Collection (Dan Cameron), The Silent Baroque (Christian Leigh editor), Interpreting Contemporary Art (Rainer Crone and David Moos), Art at the End of the Social (Collins and Milazzo), Art Since Mid-Century: 1945 to the Present (Daniel Wheeler), Art News (Feb. 1990, Apr. 1992), Le Monde (June 1992). NEA fellow, 1987, 89. Office: care Sperone Westwater Gallery 142 Greene St New York NY 10012-3236

LASKER, JOSEPH L., artist, illustrator; b. N.Y.C., June 26, 1919; s. Isidore and Rachel (Strollowitz) L.; m. Mildred Jaspen, Nov. 28, 1948; children: David Raymond, Laura, Evan. Student, Cooper Union Art Sch., evenings 1936-39, Escuela Universitaria de Bellas Artes, Mexico, 1948. Tchr. Coll. City N.Y., 1947; vis. assoc. prof. art U. Ill., 1953-54. Exhibited oneman shows Kraushaar Galleries, N.Y.C., most recently 1990; works represented in permanent collections Whitney Mus., Cal. Palace Legion of Honor, Phila., Springfield Mus., Mass., Joseph Hirschorn Collection, Balt. Mus., Munson-Williams Proctor Inst., Phila. Mus. Art; murals in Calumet (Mich.) P.O., Millbury, Mass., Henry Street Settlement Play House, N.Y.C.; author, illustrator juvenile books: Mothers Can Do Anything, 1972, He's My Brother, 1974, Tales of a Seadog Family, 1974, Merry Ever After (best illustrated children's book, N.Y. Times, 1976, Notable Bk. of Yr. Am. Library Assn. 1977), 1976, The Strange Voyage of Neptune's Car, 1977, Lentil Soup, 1977, Nick Joins In, 1980, The Do-Something Day, 1982, The Great Alexander the Great, 1983, Tournament of Knights, 1986; illustrator numerous other children's Books. Served with U.S. Army, 1941-45. Abbey Meml. scholar, 1946, 47; Prix de Rome fellow, 1950, 51; Guggenheim fellow, 1954; Benjamin Altman prize (figure) Nat. Acad. Design, 1958, 80; grantee Nat. Inst. Arts and Letters, 1968. Mem. Nat. Acad. Design. Office: care Kraushaar Galleries 724 5th Ave New York NY 10019-4106

LASKER, MORRIS E., federal judge; Judge, U.S. Dist. Ct. (so. dist.) N.Y. Office: US Dist Ct 90 Devonshire St Boston MA 02109

LASKEY, RICHARD ANTHONY, biomedical device executive; b. N.Y.C., Oct. 24, 1936; s. Charles Lewis and Gertrude Ann (Stolzenthaler) L.; m. Frances M. Pollack, June 29, 1975; children: Victoria Ann, Deborah Lea. Student CCNY; BS in Chemistry, Ohio, MS in Organic Chemistry; PhD in Organic Chemistry, Sussex (Eng.) U., 1970; LLB, U. Chgo., 1972; MD (hon.), Med. Coll. S.A., 1975, fellow, Psychiatry 1976; postgrad. in ob-gyn, U. Pa., 1989-94. Diplomate Am. Bd. Examiners in Psychotherapy. Head sect. med. products, lab. mgr. Hydron Labs., North Brunswick, N.J., 1967-73; v.p. biomed. rsch. Datascope Corp., Paramus, N.J., 1973-82; pres. rsch. Millbrook Labs., Inc., Rochelle Park, N.J., 1982—; cons. in field. Mem. N.Y.C. Aux. Police, 1963-65. Recipient Doctor's award Chgo. Med. Coll., 1975; fellow Am. Acad. Behavioral Sci., 1976. Fellow Am. Inst. Chemist; mem. NRA, AAAS, Md. Med. Soc., Idaho Med. Soc., Nat. Med. Soc., Internat. Coll. Physicians and Surgeons, Am. Inst. Chemist, Am. Psychotherapy Assn., Nat. Psychol. Assn., Assn. Advancement Med. Instrumentation, Soc. Rsch. Adminstrs. Biomed. inventor, patentee. Home: PO Box 133 Washington NJ 07882-0133 Office: PO Box 125 Rochelle Park NJ 07662-0125

LASKIN, BARBARA VIRGINIA, legal association administrator; b. Chgo., July 2, 1939; d. Cyril Krieps and Gertrude Katherine (Kujawa) Szymanski; children: Dawn Katherine Doherty, Amy Lynn Anderson. BA, U. Ill., Chgo., 1967; MA, Am. U. Beirut, 1978, Georgetown U., 1985. Asst. buyer Carson, Pirie, Scott & Co., Chgo., 1967-69; fgn. svc. officer Dept. State, Washington, 1969-79; mgr. gift shops Marriott Hotels, Washington, 1979-81; office mgr. Robt Schwinn & Assoc., Bethesda, Md., 1983-85; exec. dir. Internat. Acad. Trial Lawyers, San Jose, Calif., 1985—. Fellow Rotary Club San Jose; mem. AAUW (v.p. 1987), Am. Soc. Assn. Execs., Meeting Planners Internat., Internat. Spl. Events Soc. (v.p. edn. 1995), Profl. Conservation Mgrs. Assn. Roman Catholic. Office: Internat Acad Trial Lawyers 4 N 2nd St Ste 175 San Jose CA 95113-1306

LASKIN, DANIEL M., oral and maxillofacial surgeon, educator; b. Ellenville, N.Y., Sept. 3, 1924; s. Nathan and Flora (Kaplan) L.; m. Eve Pauline Mohel, Aug. 25, 1945; children: Jeffrey, Gary, Marla. Student, NYU, 1941-42; BS, Ind. U., 1947; MS, U. Ill., 1951. Diplomate: Am. Bd. Oral and Maxillofacial Surgery, Am. Soc. Osseointegration (hon.). Mem. faculty U. Ill., Chgo., 1949-84; prof. dept. oral and maxillofacial surgery U. Ill., 1960-84, head dept., 1973-84, clin. prof. surgery, 1961-84, dir. temporomandibular joint and facial pain research center, 1963-84; prof., chmn. dept. oral and maxillofacial surgery Med. Coll. Va., 1984—; dir. temporomandibular joint and facial pain rsch. ctr. MCV, 1984—; head dept. dentistry MCV Hosp., Richmond, 1986—; former attending oral surgeon Edgewater, Swedish Covenant, Ill. Masonic, Skokie Valley Community hosps., all Chgo.; former chmn. dept. oral surgery Cook County Hosp., Chgo.; cons. oral surgery to Surgeon Gen. Navy, 1977—; mem. dental products panel fDA, 1988-92, cons., 1993—; Francis J. Reichmann lectr., 1971, Cordwainer lectr., London, 1980. Author: Oral and Maxillofacial Surgery, Vol. I, 1980, Vol. II, 1985; contbr. articles to profl. jours.; editor-in-chief: Jour. Oral and Maxillofacial Surgery, 1972—; mem. editorial bd. Internat. Jour. Oral and Maxillofacial Surgery, 1978-88, Topics in Pain Mgmt., Densat, Internat. Jour. Oral and Maxillofacial Implants, Quintessence Internat., Revista Latino America Cirugia Traumatologia Maxilofacial, Virginia Dental Jour., Jour. Dental Rsch.; mem. internat. editorial bd. Headache Quar. Nat. hon. chmn. peer campaign A.A.O.M.S. Edn. and Rsch. Found., 1990. Recipient Disting. Alumni Service award Ind. U., 1975; William J. Gies editorial award hon. mention, 1975-77, 80, 88, 90, 91, 93; 1st prize, 1978-79, 84, 87, 89, 92; Simon P. Hullihen Meml. award, 1976; Arnold K. Maislen Meml. award, 1977; Thomas P. Hinman medallion, 1980; W. Harry Archer Achievement award for research, 1981; recipient Heidbrink award, 1983; Disting. Alumnus award Ind. U. Sch. Dentistry, 1984; Rene Lefort medal, 1985; Semmelweis medallion Semmelweis Med. U., 1985; Golden Scroll award Internat. Coll. Dentists, 1986; Internat. award Friends Sch. Dental Medicine, U. Conn. Health Ctr., Donald B. Osbon award, 1991, Achievement medal Alpha Omega, 1992, Norton M. Ross Excellence in Clin. Rsch. award, 1993, Va. Commonwealth U. Faculty award of Excellence, 1994; Zendium Lecture, 1989; fellow in gen. anesthesia Am. Dental Soc. Anesthesiology; fellow in dental surgery Royal Coll. Surgeons Eng.; Edward C. Hinds lectureship, 1990; named Disting. Practitioner Nat. Acads. Practice, 1992, Hon. Diplomate, Am. Soc. Osseointegration, 1992. Fellow AAAS, Am. Coll. Dentists, Internat. Coll. Dentists, Am. Acad. Implant Prosthodontists (academia), Acad. Internat. Dental Studies (hon.), Glascow Royal Coll. of Physicians (hon.), Internat. Assn. Oral and Maxillofacial Surgeons (hon., exec. com. 1980—, pres. 1983-86, sec. gen. 1989—); mem. Ill. Splty. Bd. Oral Surgery, ADA (adv. com. advanced edn. in oral surgery 1968-75, cons. Council on Dental Edn. 1968-82, mem. Commn. on Accreditation 1975-76), Am. Assn. Oral and Maxillofacial Surgeons (editor Forum 1965—, disting. service award 1972, pres. 1976-77, research recognition award 1978, William J. Gies award 1979, dedication 73d ann. meeting and sci. sessions 1991), Internat. Assn. Dental Research, , Am. Dental Soc.

Anesthesiology (pres. 1976-78), Am. Soc. Exptl. Pathology, Am. Assn. Dental Editors, Royal Soc. Medicine, Brazilian Coll. Oral and Maxillofacial Surgery and Traumatology (hon.), Chilean Soc. Oral and Maxillofacial Surgery (hon.), Hellenic Assn. Oral Surgery (hon.), Sadi Fontaine Acad. (hon.), Internat. Congress Oral Implantologists (hon.), Soc. Maxillofacial and Oral Surgeons South Africa (hon., assoc. life), Am. Dental Bd. Anesthesiology (pres. 1983-92), Nat. Chronic Pain Outreach Assn. (adv. bd.), Japanese Soc. for Temporomandibular Joint (hon.), AmLaser in Dentistry (hon. life), Internat. Study Group for the Advancement of TMJ Arthroscopy (hon.), William F. Harrigan Soc., Odontographic Soc., Can. Assn. Oral and Maxillofacial Surgeons (hon.), Sigma Xi, Omicron Kappa Upsilon. Rsch. and publs. on connective tissue physiology and pathology, particularly cartilage and bone metabolism, craniofacial growth, oral maxillofacial surgery, and pathology of temporomandibular joint. Office: Med Coll Va Dept Oral and Maxillofacial Surgery PO Box 566 Richmond VA 23204-0566

LASKIN, LEE B., lawyer, state senator; b. Atlantic City, June 30, 1936; student Am. U., Temple U.; Rutgers U., 1960; m. Andrea Solomon; 1 dau., Shari. Bar: N.J.; asst. atty. City of Camden (N.J.), from 1962; asst. U.S. atty. N.J., 1964-68; mem. N.J. Gen. Assembly, 1968-70; mem. Camden County Bd. Chosen Freeholders, 1970-73; mem. N.J. Senate, 1977-92; judge N.J. Superior Ct., 1994—; mcpl. atty. Audubon, Berlin Borough, Berlin Twp., Clementon, Laurel Springs, Mt. Ephraim and Waterford, N.J., and Winslow Twp.; counsel Bellmawr Bd. Edn., Berlin Zoning Bd., Camden County Welfare Bd., Non-Resident Taxpayers Assn., Animal Welfare Assn., Brith Sholom Fed. Credit Union, Camden Hebrew Fed. Credit Union, United Fed. Savs. and Loan Assn., Div. 880 Amalgamated Transit Union, Local 18 of Am. Fed. Tech. Engrs., Camden Fire Officers Assn., Am. Postal Workers Union, Fuel Mchts. Assn., Glendale Nat. Bank; field counsel Fed. Nat. Mortgage Assn.; founder, 1st chmn. Glendale Nat. Bank; del. Rep. Nat. Conv., 1984. Served with USMCR. Office: NJ State Senate 1878 Route 70 E Cherry Hill NJ 08003-2090

LASKO, WARREN ANTHONY, mortgage banker, economist; b. Bklyn., June 29, 1940; s. Albert Anthony and Mildred (Hoyer) L.; m. Lorraine Gevertz; children: Karen, Erika. AB in Econs., Columbia U., 1962, MA in Econs., 1969. V.p. mortgage backed securities Govt. Nat. Mortgage Assn., Washington, 1977-81, 81-82, exec. v.p., 1982-85; v.p. strategic planning Fed. Nat. Mortgage Assn., Washington, 1981; exec. v.p. Mortgage Bankers Assn. Am., Washington, 1985—. Bd. dirs. Boys & Girls Homes Montgomery County, Chevy Chase, Md.; mem. Greater Washington Research Ctr., Washington, Chesapeake Bay Found., The Nature Conservancy, Chevy Chase. Recipient Cert. of Merit, U.S. Dept. Housing and Urban Devel., 1979, Disting. Svc. award U.S. Govt., 1982. Mem. Columbia Club. Home: 3211 Leland St Bethesda MD 20815 Office: Mortgage Bankers Assn of Am 1125 15th St NW Washington DC 20005-2707

LASKOWSKI, LEONARD FRANCIS, JR., microbiologist; b. Milw., Nov. 16, 1919; s. Leonard Francis and Frances (Cyborowski) L.; m. Frances Bielinski, June 1, 1946; children—Leonard Francis III, James, Thomas. B.S., Marquette U., 1941, M.S., 1948; Ph.D., St. Louis U., 1951. Diplomate: Am. Bd. Microbiology. Instr. bacteriology Marquette U., 1946-48; mem. faculty St. Louis U., 1951—, prof. pathology and internal medicine, Div. Infectious Diseases, 1969-90, prof. emeritus, 1990—, assoc. prof. internal medicine, 1977-90—; dir. clin. microbiology sect. St. Louis U. Hosps. Labs., 1965—; cons. clin microbiology Firmin Desloge Hosp., St. Louis U. Group Hosps., St. Marys Group Hosps.; cons. bacteriology VA Hosp.; asst. dept. chief Pub. Health Lab., St. Louis Civil Def., 1958—; cons. St. Elizabeths Hosp., St. Louis County Hosp., St. Francis Hosp. Contbr. articles to profl. jours. Health and tech. coordinator for Latin Am. projects Peace Corps, 1962-66. Served with M.C. AUS, 1942-46. Fellow Am. Acad. Microbiology; mem. Soc. Am. Bacteriologists, N.Y. Acad. Scis., Am., Mo. pub. health assns., AAUP, Med. Mycol. Soc. Am., Alpha Omega Alpha. Home: 6229 Robertsville Rd Villa Ridge MO 63089-2617 Office: 1402 S Grand Blvd Saint Louis MO 63104-1004

LASKOWSKI, MICHAEL, JR., chemist, educator; b. Warsaw, Poland, Mar. 13, 1930; came to U.S., 1947, naturalized, 1955; s. Michael and Maria (Dabrowska) L.; m. Joan Claire Heyer, Nov. 29, 1957; children: Michael Christopher, Marta Joan. B.S. magna cum laude, Lawrence Coll., 1950; Ph.D. (NIH fellow), Cornell U., 1954, postgrad., 1954-55; postgrad., Yale U., 1955-56. Research asst. Marquette U., 1949-50; instr. Cornell U., 1956-57; asst. prof. chemistry Purdue U., 1957-61, asso. prof., 1961-65, prof., 1965—; chmn. Gordon Rsch. Conf. Physics and Phys. Chemistry Biopolymers, 1966, Proteolytic Enzymes and Their Inhibitors, 1982; mem. study sect. NIH, 1967-71, NSF, 1989, sci. adv. bd. Receptor, Inc., 1993—, Khepri Pharms., Inc., 1993—. Mem. editorial bd. Archives Biochemistry and Biophysics, 1972-90, Biochemistry, 1973-78, Jour. Protein Chemistry, 1981—, Jour. Biol. Chemistry, 1983-88; contbr. articles to profl. jours. Recipient McCoy award Purdue U., 1975; co-recipient award in biol. scis. Alfred Jurzykowski Found., 1977. Mem. Am. Chem. Soc. (chmn. sect. 1968-69, treas. div. biol. chemistry 1981-84, councillor 1985-88), Am. Soc. Biol. Chemists, Biophys. Soc., Protein Soc., AAAS, AAUP, Polish Acad. Arts, Sci. Am., ACLU, Sigma Xi. Home: 222 E Navajo St West Lafayette IN 47906-2155 Office: Purdue U Dept Chemistry West Lafayette IN 47907 A scientist who claims a small subfield of science as his personal fief should strive to leave it simpler and more coherent than he originally found it.

LASKOWSKI, RICHARD E., retail hardware company executive; b. 1941. With Ace Hardware Corp., Oak Brook, Ill., 1962—, now chmn. bd. dirs., also pres. subs. Office: Ace Hardware Corp 2200 Kensington Ct Oak Brook Mall IL 60521*

LASKY, DAVID, lawyer, corporate executive; b. N.Y.C., Nov. 12, 1932; s. Benjamin and Rebecca (Malumed) L.; m. Phyllis Beryl Sumper, Apr. 14, 1957; children—Jennifer Lee, Robert Barry. BA, Bklyn. Coll., 1954; LLB, Columbia U., 1957. Bar: N.Y. 1957. Atty. N.Y.C. R.R. Co., 1957-62; with Curtiss-Wright Corp., N.Y.C., 1962—; corp. counsel Curtiss-Wright Corp., 1966-67, gen. counsel, 1967-93, v.p., 1972-80, sr. v.p., 1980-93, sec. 1989-93, pres., 1993—; Chmn. zoning bd. appeals, Ramapo, N.Y., 1968-72. Dir. v.p. Oak Trail Homeowners Assn., 1987-90. Served with AUS, 1957-58. Mem. ABA (chmn. com. corp. law depts. 1992-93), N.Y. Bar Assn., Phi Beta Kappa. Office: 1200 Wall St W Ste 501 Lyndhurst NJ 07071-3616

LASKY, LAURENCE D., lawyer; b. Chgo., June 26, 1940. BA, DePaul U., 1962; JD magna cum laude, Northwestern U., 1965. Bar: Ill. 1965. Ptnr. Sidley & Austin, Chgo. Office: Sidley & Austin 1 First Nat Plz Chicago IL 60603

LASKY, MOSES, lawyer; b. Denver, Nov. 2, 1907; s. Juda Eisen and Ida (Grossman) L.; m. Ruth Helen Abraham, July 6, 1933; children: Morelle, Marshall. A.B. magna cum laude, U. Colo., 1926, J.D., 1928; LL.M., Harvard U., 1929. Bar: Calif. 1930, U.S. Supreme Ct 1947. Asst. dept. econs. U. Colo., 1925-26; salesman, local sales mgr. R.C. Barnum Co., Cleve., 1927-28; asso. Brobeck, Phleger & Harrison, San Francisco, 1929-41; partner Brobeck, Phleger & Harrison, 1941-79, Lasky, Haas, Cohler & Munter, San Francisco, 1979-94; Lasky, Haas & Cohler, San Francisco, 1994—; instr. Golden Gate Law Sch., 1934-35; sr. adv. bd. U.S. Ct. Appeals (9th cir.) 1984-90, chmn., 1989-90. Contbr. articles in legal field and on Jewish life to jours. and mags. Pres. bd. dirs. San Francisco Mus. Modern Art, 1963, 64, now life trustee; pres. Regional Arts Coun. San Francisco 1963-64; v.p. bd. dirs. San Francisco Art Inst., 1964; trustee War Meml. San Francisco, 1969-75; co-chmn. San Francisco Crime com., 1968-71; bd. dirs. The Exploratorium, San Francisco, 1979—; bd. overseers L.A. br. Hebrew Union Coll.; nat. Jewish com. Am. Jewish Com., 1947-55. Recipient Disting. Alumnus award U. Colo. Law Sch., 1977, U. Colo. medal, 1983, 50 Yr. award Am. Bar Found., 1989. Fellow Am. Coll. Trial Lawyers; mem. ABA, Phi Beta Kappa, Delta Sigma Rho. Home: 10 Mountain Spring Ave San Francisco CA 94114-2118 Office: 505 Sansome St Fl 12 San Francisco CA 94111-3106

LASNICK, JULIUS, fabric company executive; b. 1929; married. Student, N.C. State Univ. With Milliken & Co., 1951-78; pres. M Lowenstein Corp., N.Y.C., 1978—; exec. v.p. Spring Industries Inc., 1986—. With U.S. Army, 1953-55. Home: 39 Cayman Pl West Palm Beach FL 33418 also: M Lowenstein Corp 1430 Broadway New York NY 10018

LASORDA, THOMAS CHARLES (TOMMY LASORDA), professional baseball team manager; b. Norristown, Pa., Sept. 22, 1927; s. Sam and Carmella (Covatto) L.; m. Joan Miller, Apr. 14, 1950; children: Laura, Tom Charles. Student pub. schs., Norristown. Pitcher Bklyn. Dodgers, 1954-55, Kansas City A's, 1956; with L.A. Dodgers, 1956—; mgr. minor league clubs L.A. Dodgers, Pocatello, Idaho, Ogden, Utah, Spokane, Albuquerque, 1965-73; coach L.A. Dodgers, 1973-76, mgr., 1976—. Author: (with David Fisher) autobiography The Artful Dodger, 1985. Served with U.S. Army, 1945-47. L.A. Dodgers winner Nat. League pennant, 1977, 78, 81, 88, winner World Championship, 1981, 88; 2d Nat. League mgr. to win pennant first two yrs. as mgr.; named Nat. League Mgr. Yr. UPI, 1977, AP, 1977, 81, Baseball Writers' Assn. Am., 1988, Sporting News, 1988; recipient Milton Richman Meml. award Assn. Profl. Baseball Players Am. Mem. Profl. Baseball Players Am. Roman Catholic. Club: Variety of Calif. (v.p.). Office: care Los Angeles Dodgers 1000 Elysian Park Ave Los Angeles CA 90012-1112*

LASRY, JEAN-MICHEL, mathematics educator; b. Paris, Oct. 29, 1947; m. Elisabeth du Boucher; children: Laura, Romain, Julien. M. in Econs., U. Paris-Assas, 1970; these d'etat in math., U. Paris IX, 1975. Rsch. fellow Ctr. Nat. Recherche Scientifique, Paris, 1971-78; prof. Paris-Dauphine U., 1978—, chmn. math. dept., 1980-83; cons. Compagnie Bancaire, Paris, 1988-91; mem. exec. bd. Caisse des Depots, 1991-94; CEO Caisse Autonome de Refinancement, Paris. Contbr. articles in math., econ. and fin. to profl. jours. Mem. Am. Math. Soc., Soc. Mathematiques apliquies et industrielles (bd. dirs.), Soc. Mathematique de France, Assn. Francaise de Finance, Ecole de la Cause Freudienne.

LASS, E(RNEST) DONALD, communications company executive; b. Neptune N.J., Jan. 15, 1938; s. Ernest W. and Frances F. (Felger) L.; m. Elsa Green, Aug. 6, 1960 (div. 1968); children: Deborah, Mark Donald; m. 2d Jean L. Taylor, Dec. 17, 1978. B.A., Lafayette Coll., 1960; M.S. in journalism, Columbia U., 1961. Asst. mng. editor Asbury Park Press, N.J., 1968-74, exec. editor, 1974-80, editor, 1980—, pub., 1990—; pres. Asbury Park Press Inc., 1980—, Press Broadcasting Co., Asbury Park, 1980—. Bd. dirs. Shore Area YMCA, Asbury Park, 1978—, pres., 1981-83; bd. dirs. Monmouth Boys Club, 1977—, Monmouth coun. Boy Scouts Am., 1985-89, Journalism Resource Inst., Rutgers U., 1983—, Am. Cancer Soc., Monmouth, 1985—; chmn Monmouth Coll. Assocs., 1985-86; bd. visitors Columbia U. Grad. Sch. Journalism; bd. overseers Rutgers U.; mem. Monmouth Coll. Coun. Pub. Affairs. Recipient Editorial Comment award N.J. Press Assn., 1980, Disting. Service award Greater Asbury Park Jaycees, 1968, Meritorious Service award Monmouth-Ocean Chiropractic Assn., 1976; Disting. Pub. Service award Monmouth council Boy Scouts Am., 1985. Mem. Am. Soc. Newspaper Editors, Newspaper Assn. Am., Nat. Conf. Editorial Writers (pres. 1987, chmn. 1988), N.J. Press Assn., Nat. Assn. Broadcasters, Nat. Assn. TV Programming Dirs., Greater Asbury Park C. of C. (pres. 1972-74), Sigma Delta Chi, Delta Upsilon. Presbyterian. Office: Asbury Pk Press Inc PO Box 1550 3601 Hwy 66 Neptune NJ 07754-1550 also: Sta WTKS-FM 600 Courtland St Ste 100 Orlando FL 32804-1313

LASSAR, SCOTT R., lawyer; b. Evanston, Ill., Apr. 5, 1950; s. Richard Ernest and Jo (Ladenson) L.; m. Elizabeth Levine, May 22, 1977; children: Margaret, Kate. B.A., Oberlin Coll., 1972; J.D., Northwestern U., 1975. Bar: Ill. 1975. Former dep. chief spl. prosecutions divsn. no. dist. Office U.S. Atty., Chgo.; former ptnr. Keck, Mahin & Cate, Chgo.; now 1st asst. U.S. atty. no. dist. Office U.S. Atty., Chgo. Home: 1544 Sheridan Rd Highland Park IL 60035-3447 Office: US Attys Office 219 S Dearborn St Chicago IL 60604-1702

LASSAW, IBRAM, sculptor, painter; b. Alexandria, Egypt, May 4, 1913; s. Philip and Bertha (Zaleski) L.; m. Ernestine Blumberg, Dec. 15, 1944; 1 dau., Denise. Student, Clay Club, 1927-32, Beaux Arts Inst. Design, N.Y.C., 1930-31, CCNY, 1931-32; student art, Amédée Ozenfant, ArtsD (hon.), L.I. U., 1990, DFA (hon.), 1990. Benjamin N. Duke prof. Duke U., 1962-63; tchr. U. Calif. at Berkeley, 1965-66, Am. U., 1950, Colo. Coll., Colorado Springs, 1965; adj. faculty Southampton (L.I.) Coll., 1966—; vis. prof. Brandeis U., 1975, Mt. Holyoke Coll., 1978. One-man shows Kootz Gallery, N.Y.C., 1951, 52, 54, 58, 60, 63, 64, MIT, 1958, Duke U., 1963, Benson Gallery, 1966, Gertrude Kasle Gallery, Detroit, 1968, Zabriskie Gallery, N.Y.C., 1977, Mus. Art, Carnegie Inst., Pitts., 1983, Whitney Mus., N.Y., 1984, Sid Deutsch Gallery, N.Y.C., 1986, The Third Dimension, Whitney Mus. Am. Art, 1984, Sid Deutsch Gallery, N.Y.C., Sculpture Am., Internat. Biennial of Contemporary Sculpture, Matera, Italy, 1990, Harmon-Meek Gallery, Naples, Fla., 1991, others; exhibited at museums, univs., art insts. in U.S., Japan, France, Italy, Holland, Denmark, Switzerland, Eng., S. Am., USSR; also Internat. Exhbn. Sculpture, Musée Rodin, Paris, 1956, retrospective, Heckscher Mus., Huntington, N.Y., 1973, Smithsonian Instn., 1975, Whitney Mus. Am. Art, 1976, 78, U. N.Mex., Albuquerque, 1977, Guild Hall Mus., East Hampton, N.Y., 1978, 88, Nat. Mus. Am. Art, Washington, 1989, Baruch Coll., N.Y.C., 1994; group shows Hirschhorn Mus., Washington, 1982, Ten Sculptors of N.Y. Sch., 1992, M. Silverman Gallery, L.A., 1992; represented in permanent collections Nat. Gallery, Washington, Mus. Modern Art, N.Y.C., Whitney Mus. Am. Art, N.Y.C., Museu de Arte Moderna, Rio de Janeiro, Brazil, Gallery Contemporary Art, Carnegie-Mellon U., Pitts., Balt. Mus. Art, Kalamazoo U., St. Louis, Albright Knox Art Gallery, Buffalo, Wadsworth Atheneum, Hartford, Conn., Fogg Mus. of Harvard U., Newark Mus., Worcester (Mass.) Art Mus., U. Calif. Mus., Berkeley, U. N.C., Greensboro, Birla Mus., Calcutta, India, Israel Mus., Jerusalem, Wichita (Kans.) Art Mus., Bklyn. Mus., Corcoran Gallery, Washington, Guggenheim Mus., N.Y.C., Nat. Galllery, Washington, McNay Art Mus., San Antonio, Rhode Island Sch. Design, Met. Mus., Sheldon Art Gallery, Nat. Gallery, Washington, Anital Saposky Gallery, N.Y., Chgo. Internat. Art Expo., McNay Art Mus., San Antonio, RISD; works in pvt. collections including, Nelson Rockefeller, William A. M. Burden, Nat. Gallery, Washington; one of five U.S. reps. to, Venice Biennale, 1954; prin. commns. include: large sculpture Pillar of Fire, Temple Beth-El, Springfield, Mass., 1953; sculptures, Temple Beth-El, Providence, 1954, Sculpture Pantheon, Celanese Bldg., N.Y.C., also residential archtl. sculpture, Work reproduced in numerous books. Served as pvt. AUS, World War II. Mem. Am. Abstract Artists (pres. 1946-48), Am. Acad. Arts and Letters, Century Assn. Pioneer welding techniques in sculpting. Home and Studio: PO Box 487 East Hampton NY 11937-0487

LASSELL, MICHAEL JOHN, writer, editor; b. N.Y.C., July 15, 1947; s. Michael Joseph and Catherine Elizabeth (Harnett) L. BA, Colgate U., 1969; MFA, Calif. Inst. Arts, 1973, Yale U., 1976. Assoc. editor L.A. Weekly, Los Angeles, 1983-85; theater critic Los Angeles Herald-Examiner, Los Angeles, 1985-87; mng. editor L.A. Style Mag., Los Angeles, 1985—. Author: Poems For Lost and Unlost Boys, 1986 (Amelia award 1986); contbr. poems and articles to various jours. Democrat. Office: L A Style 6834 Hollywood Blvd Los Angeles CA 90028-6175

LASSEN, ROBERT MAURIE, graphic artist, photographer, editor; b. N.Y.C., June 7, 1935; s. Ben and Beatrice (Barmak) L.; m. Olivia Veronia Cheatham, 1957 (dec. Mar. 1985). BA, CCNY, 1959, postgrad., 1965-68; cert., Germain Sch. Photography, N.Y.C., 1978. Graphic artist Ben Lassen Studio, N.Y.C., 1950-68; prin. Lassen Advt., N.Y.C., 1968-80; owner, CEO Graphic Art Resource Assocs., N.Y.C., 1980—. Community activist Hudson Towers Tenant Assn., N.Y.C., 1970-89. Avocations: chess, theoretical cosmology, Civil War history, crossword puzzles, photographic excursions. Home and Office: 257 W 10th St # 5E New York NY 10014-2508

LASSER, HOWARD GILBERT, chemical engineer, consultant; b. N.Y.C., Nov. 24, 1926; s. Milton and Tessie (Rosenthal) L.; m. Barbara Ann Katz, Aug. 24, 1950; children: Kathy, Ellen Lasser-LeVee, Alan. BSChemE, Lehigh U., 1950; postgrad., Columbia U., 1951; Dr.Ing., Darmstadt Tech. Inst., Germany, 1956. Registered profl. engr., D.C., Va., Calif. Chem. engr. Belvoir Rsch. Engring. & Devel. Ctr., Ft. Belvoir, Va., 1950-55, 58-72; materials engr. Naval Sea Systems Command, Washington, 1956-57, chem. engr., 1955-56; materials engr. Naval Facilities Engring. Command, Alexandria, Va., 1972-82; chem. engr. Materials Rsch. Cons., Alexandria & Springfield, Va., 1982—. Author: Design of Electroplating Facilities, 1990; contbr. articles to profl. jours. Fellow AAAS, Oil and Colour and Surface Finishers Chemists Assn., Am. Inst. Chemists; mem. Am. Electroplaters Soc., AIChE, NACE Internat. (cert.), ASM INternat., Steel Structures

Painting Coun., Tau Beta Pi, Sigma Xi, Alpha Chi Sigma, Pi Delta Epsilon. Achievements include 6 patents in electroplating and metal finishing; description of thermodynamic properties of carbon dioxide; development of thermotropic dyes for aluminum oxides; over 500 publs. in materials and chemical engineering. Home: 5912 Camberly Ave Springfield VA 22150-2438 Office: Materials Rsch Cons 1121 King St Alexandria VA 22314-2924

LASSER, JOSEPH ROBERT, investment company president; b. N.Y.C., Sept. 25, 1923; s. Milton and Tessie (Rosenthal) L.; m. Ruth Jean Pollak, May 4, 1925; children: James, Carol Lasser Kornblith, Jean. BS, Lehigh U., 1946; MBA, NYU, 1951. Sr. analyst Lewisohn and Co., N.Y.C., 1946-51; dir. research Walston and Co., N.Y.C., 1951-55, Wertheim and Co., N.Y.C., 1956-67; ptnr. Shufro, Rose, Ehrman and Stanley Marks, Lasser & Co., N.Y.C., 1967-75; sr. portfolio mgr. C.J. Lawrence, N.Y.C., 1975-76; ptnr., sr. portfolio mgr. Neuberger & Berman, N.Y.C., 1977—. Treas. Bronx House, N.Y., 1978—; past trustee United Jewish Appeal/Fedn. Jewish Philanthropies, mem. bd. overseers. 1st lt. USAF, 1943-45. Decorated Air medal with three bronze oak leaf clusters, one silver oak leaf cluster; recipient 1st Lit. award Soc. Paper Money, 1976. Mem. Am. Numismatic Soc. (councillor 1990-93), N.Y. Soc. Security Analysts, Chartered Fin. Analysts Assn., N.Y. Stock Exchange (allied), Phi Beta Kappa, Princeton Club (N.Y.C.), Quaker Ridge (Scarsdale N.Y.). Home: 119 Cushman Rd Scarsdale NY 10583-3405 Office: Neuberger & Berman 605 3rd Ave New York NY 10158-3698

LASSERRE, JEAN PAUL, reinsurance company president; b. Mirande, France, Feb. 2, 1942; s. Henry and Renée (Bertin) L. Degree in engring., Ecole Centrale, Paris, 1965; MBA, Insead, Fontainebleau, France, 1977. Design engr. S.O.M., Chgo., 1965; project engr. Eurochemic, Mol, Belgium, 1966; area mgr. mid. east OTH Internat., Paris, 1972; internat. contracts mgr. CMP-EI, Paris, 1977; with SCOR Group, Paris, 1981; pres. SCOR Reins. Co. of Can., Toronto, Ont., 1987. Mem. Reins. Rsch. Coun. (bd. dirs., v.p.), Cercle Can. (bd. dirs.), French Can. C. of C. (bd. dirs.). Office: Scor Reinsurance of Canada, 123 Front St W, Toronto, ON Canada M5J 2M2

LASSERS, WILLARD J., judge; b. Kankakee, Ill., Aug. 24, 1919; s. Henry and Sylvia (Oppenheim) L.; m. Elisabeth Stern, June 30, 1946; 1 dau., Deborah. A.B., U. Chgo., 1940, J.D., 1942. Bar: D.C. 1941, Ill. 1942, U.S. Supreme Ct. 1965. Practiced in Chgo., 1946-78; practice with Alex Elson, Chgo., 1946-48, Elson and Cotton, 1948-49; atty. RFC, Chgo., 1950-51, Office Price Stablzn., Chgo., 1951-53; individual practice law Chgo., 1953-60; partner Elson, Lassers and Wolff, Chgo., 1960-78; judge Circuit Ct. Cook County, Chgo., 1978—; lectr. taxation U. Chgo., 1954-55. Author: (with Alex Elson and Aaron S. Wolff) Civil Practice Forms Annotated, Illinois and Federal, 1952, 65, Scapegoat Justice: Lloyd Miller and the Failure of the Legal System, 1973; reviser: Fletcher Corporation Forms, 5 vols, 1957-60. Mem. Gov.'s Com. to Study Consumer Credit Laws, 1962-63; chmn. Com. Ill. Govt., 1962-63; Bd. dirs. Ill. div. ACLU, to 1978. Served with AUS, 1943-46. Mem. Ill., Chgo. bar assns. Am. Arbitration Assn. (mem. panel labor arbitrators 1965-78). Home: 1509 E 56th St Chicago IL 60637-1910 Office: Richard J Daley Center Chicago IL 60602

LASSETER, CHARLES ERWIN, energy company executive; b. Freeport, Tex., Sept. 11, 1932; s. Charles Roy and Mary (Erwin) L.; m. Dorothy Jean Fausullo, Nov. 24, 1957; 1 child, Michael C. B.B.A. in Acctg., U. Tex., 1954. C.P.A. Acct., Harrell Drilling Co., Houston, 1958-62; dir. acctg. Union Tex. Petroleum, Houston, 1962-70; v.p., sec., controller ADA Resources, Houston, 1970-74; v.p., controller Anadarko Prodn. Co., Houston, 1974-79; v.p., controller Panhandle Eastern Pipe Line Co., Kansas City, Mo., 1979-83; sr. v.p., controller Panhandle Eastern Corp., Houston, 1983-88, group v.p., chief fin. officer, 1989—; group v.p., controller Panhandle Eastern Pipe Line & Trunkline Gas Co., 1988. Treas. St. Michael's Episcopal Ch., Houston, 1969. Served with U.S. Army, 1954-56; Korea. Mem. Fin. Execs. Inst., Petroleum Acctg. Soc. (pres. Houston 1970-71), Am. Inst. C.P.A.s, Tex. Soc. C.P.A.s. Republican. Episcopal. Clubs: Warwick, Houston City, Yorkwood Civic (pres. 1970). Home: 10815 Creektree Dr Houston TX 77070-3931 Office: Panhandle Ea Corp 5400 Westheimer St PO Box 1642 Houston TX 77251-1642

LASSETER, EARLE FORREST, lawyer; b. Gadsden, Ala., Dec. 26, 1933; s. Thomas Hobart and Mildred (Williamson) L.; m. Sally Elizabeth Bork, Sept. 2, 1961; children: Sally Fernald, David Forrest. BS, Auburn U., 1957; LLB, U. Ala., 1966. Bar: Ala. 1966, Ala. Supreme Ct. 1966, U.S. Ct. Military Appeals 1970, U.S. Dist. Ct. D.C. 1971, U.S. Ct. Internat. Trade 1971, D.C. 1972, U.S. Supreme Ct. 1972, Ga. 1987, Ga. Supreme Ct. 1988, U.S. Ct. Appeals Ga. 1988, U.S. Dist. Ct. (no. and mid. dists.) Ga. 1988, U.S. Ct. Vet. Appeals 1992. Commd. U.S. Army, 1958, advanced through grades to col., 1987; dep. staff judge adv. Hdqs. 1st Cav. Div., Republic of Vietnam, 1968-69; exec. officer Hdqs. U.S. Army Europe, Heidelberg, Germany, 1969-70; dep. staff judge adv. U.S. Army, Berlin, 1970-72; student Command and Gen. Staff Coll., Ft. Leavenworth, Kans., 1972; staff judge adv. 82d Airborne Div., Ft. Bragg, N.C., 1972-75; legal advisor Mil. Assistance Command and Am. Embassy, Taipei, Taiwan, 1975-77; staff judge adv. U.S. Army Mil. Police Sch., Ft. McClellan, Ala., 1977-79, U.S. Army Inf. Ctr., Ft. Benning, Ga., 1979-83; student U.S. Army War Coll., Carlisle Barracks, Pa., 1983; staff judge adv. U.S. Army Forces Command, Ft. McPherson, Ga., 1983-87; ret., 1987; ptnr. Pope, McGlamry, Kilpatrick & Morrison, Atlanta, Columbus, Ga., 1988—. Contbr. articles to profl. jours. Pres. Ft. Benning Sch. Bd., 1980-82. Served to 2d lt. U.S. Army. Decorated Purple Heart, Bronze Star with Oak Leaf Cluster, Legion of Merit, Meritorious Svc. medal with two Oak Leaf Clusters; recipient Joint Svcs. Commendation medal, Air medal, Army commendation medal, Master Parachutists Wings, Taiwan. Mem. ABA (mem. 1991-92), Ga. State Bar, Ala. State Bar, Ala. Trial Lawyers Assn. (bd. govs. 1989—), Ga. Trial Lawyers Assn., Army-Navy Country Club (Arlington, Va.), Army-Navy Club (Washington), Green Island Country Club, Harmony Club. Avocations: golf, tennis, running. Home: 6855 Ranch Forest Dr Columbus GA 31904-2428 Office: Pope McGlamry Kilpatrick & Morrison 720 Broadway Columbus GA 31901-2921

LASSETER, KENNETH CARLYLE, pharmacologist; b. Jacksonville Fla., Aug. 12, 1942; s. James and Retta (Shad) L.; BS, Stetson U., 1963; MD, U. Fla., 1967; m. Kathy G. Marks, Aug. 6, 1977; children—Kenneth C. III, Susan, Frank L. Diplomate Am. Bd. Clin. Pharmacology. Intern, resident in medicine U. Ky. Med. Center, 1967-71; asst. prof., assoc. prof. pharmacology and medicine U. Miami Med. Sch., 1971-81, clin. assoc. prof., 1981—; adj. assoc. prof. pharmacology, Barry U., 1986—; v.p., dir. Clin. Pharmacology Assos., Inc., Miami, 1981—. Served with USAR, 1971-76. Recipient William B. Peck Sci. Research award Interstate Postgrad. Med. Assn., 1976, research award Alpha Omega Alpha, 1967. Fellow Am. Coll. Clin. Pharmacology; mem. ACP, Am. Soc. Pharmacology and Exptl. Therapeutics, Am. Soc. Clin. Pharmacology and Therapeutics, Sigma Xi. Republican. Contbr. articles to profl. jours. Home: 552 Ocean Dr Key Largo FL 33037 Office: Clin Pharmacol Assocs 2060 NW 22d Ave Miami FL 33142

LASSITER, KENNETH T., photography educator, consultant; b. Richmond, Va., Jan. 2, 1935; s. B. Taylor and Euzelia (Duke) L.; m. Carol Lester, Apr. 9, 1960; children: Karen, Keith. BS, Va. Poly. Inst. and State U., 1957; MS (hon.), Brooks Inst. Photography, 1992. Engr. Eastman Kodak Co., Rochester, N.Y., 1957-60, tech. editor, 1960-69, dir. publs., 1970-84, dir. photo trade rels., 1984-93, mgr. photo edn., 1989-93; retired, 1993; mng. dir. Palm Beach (Fla.) Photo Workshops, 1993-94; mem. pres.'s coun. Internat. Ctr. Photography, N.Y.C., 1985-93; dir. Photographic Art & Sci. Found., Oklahoma City, 1984-95. Author: Executive Producer: Techniques of the Masters Videoconference Series; author or editor numerous Kodak publs. Mem. Soc. for Imaging Sci. and Tech. (sr., bd. dirs. 1965—), Friends of Photography, Nat. Press Photographers Assn., Soc. for Photographic Edn. Republican. Presbyterian. Avocations: boating, photography, music.

LASSITER, PHILLIP B., insurance company executive. Chmn., CEO, pres. Ambac Inc., N.Y.C. Office: Ambac Inc One State Street Plaza New York NY 10004

LASSITER, RONALD CORBETT, oil company executive; b. Houston, Aug. 2, 1932; s. Mance and Pauline Marie (Lloyd) L.; m. Ella Lee Moechel,

Dec. 26, 1951; children: Rona Lee, James Mance, Jennifer Lynn, Lynda Fay. B.A., Rice U., 1955; M.B.A., Harvard U., 1964. Sr. v.p. corp. devel. Zapata Corp., Houston, 1970-71, exec. v.p. natural resources, 1971-74, chief oper. officer natural resources products, 1974-77, dir., sr. exec. v.p. natural resource products, 1977-78, pres., chief operating officer, 1978-83, chief exec. officer, 1983, chief exec. officer, chmn. bd., 1986—, also dir.; bd. dirs. Zapata Off-Shore Co., Zapata Haynie Corp., Pesquera Zapata, Tidewater, Inc., Zapata Exploration Co., Daniel Industries, Inc. Mem. editorial bd. Offshore mag. Mem. dean's adv. bd. Coll. Bus. Adminstrn., U. Houston. Mem. AIME, Soc. Mining Engrs., Petroleum Club, Forum Club. Office: Zapata Corp Zapata Tower PO Box 4240 Houston TX 77210-4240

LASSLO, ANDREW, medicinal chemist, educator; b. Mukacevo, Czechoslovakia, Aug. 24, 1922; came to U.S., 1946, naturalized, 1951; s. Vojtech Laszlo and Terezie (Herskovicova) L.; m. Wilma Ellen Reynolds, July 9, 1955; 1 child, Millicent Andrea. MS, U. Ill., 1948, PhD, 1952, MLS, 1961. Rsch. chemist organic chems. div. Monsanto Chem. Co., St. Louis, 1952-54; asst. prof. pharmacology, divsn. basic health scis. Emory U., 1954-60; prof. and chmn. dept. med. chemistry Coll. Pharmacy, U. Tenn. Health Sci. Ctr., 1960-90, Alumni Disting. Svc. prof. and chmn., dept. medicinal chemistry, 1989-90, professor emeritus, 1990—; cons. Geschickter Fund for Med. Research Inc., 1961-62; rsch. contractor U.S. Army Med. R & D Command, 1964-67; dir. postgrad. tng. program sci. librarians USPHS, 1966-72; chmn. edn. com. Drug Info. Assn., 1966-68, bd. dirs., 1968-69; dir. postgrad. tng. program organic medicinal chemistry for chemists FDA, 1971; exec. com. adv. council S.E. Regional Med. Library Program, Nat. Library of Medicine, 1969-71; chmn. regional med. library programs com. Med. Library Assn., 1971-72; mem. pres.'s faculty adv. council U. Tenn. System, 1970-72; chmn. energy authority U. Tenn. Center for Health Scis., 1975-77, chmn. council departmental chmn., 1977, 81; chmn. Internat. Symposium on Contemporary Trends in Tng. Pharmacologists, Helsinki, 1975. Producer, moderator (TV and radio series) Health Care Perspective, 1976-78; editor: Surface Chemistry and Dental Inteuments, 1973, Blood Platelet Function and Medicinal Chemistry, 1984; contbr. numerous articles in sci. and profl. jours.; mem. editorial bd. Jour. Medicinal and Pharm. Chemistry, 1961, U. Tenn. Press, 1974-77; composer (work for piano) Synthesis in C Minor, 1968; patentee in field. Trustee First Bohemian Meth. Ch., Chgo., 1950-52, mem. bd. stewards, 1950-52; mem. ofcl. bd. Grace Meth. Ch., Atlanta, 1955-60; mem. adminstrv. bd. Christ United Meth. Ch., Memphis, 1964-72, 73-75, 77-79, 81-83, 88-90, chmn. commn. on edn., 1965-67, chmn. bd. Day Sch., 1967-68. Served to capt. M.S.C., USAR, 1953-62. Recipient Research prize U. Ill. Med. Ctr. chpt. Sigma Xi, 1949, Honor Scroll Tenn. Inst. Chemists, 1976, Americanism medal DAR, 1976; U. Ill. fellow, 1950-51; Geschickter Fund Med. Research grantee, 1959-65, USPHS Research and Tng. grantee, 1958-64, 66-72, 82-89, NSF research grantee, 1964-66, Pfeiffer Research Found. grantee, 1981-87. Fellow AAAS, Am. Assn. Pharm. Scientists, Am. Inst. Chemists (nat. councilor for Tenn. 1969-70), Acad. Pharm. Rsch. and Sci.; mem. ALA (life), Am. Chem. Soc. (sr.), Am. Pharm. Assn., Am. Soc. Pharmacology and Exptl. Therapeutics (chmn. subcom. pre and postdoctoral tng. 1974-76, mem. edn. com. ednl. and profl. affairs 1974-78), Sigma Xi (pres. elect U. Tenn. Ctr. for Health Sci. chpt. 1975-76, pres. 1976-77, Excellence in Rsch. award 1989), Beta Phi Mu, Phi Lambda Sigma, Rho Chi. Methodist. Achievements include 7 U.S. and 11 foreign patents in field; identification of platelet aggregation-inhibitory specific functions in synthetic organic molecules; design and synthesis of novel human blood platelet aggregation inhibitors, novel compound for mild stimulation of central nervous system activity; research on relationships between structural features of synthetic organic entities, their physicochemical properties and their effects on biologic activity. Home and Office: 5479 Timmons Ave Memphis TN 38119-6932 Of all the pleasures a human being can savor, none exceeds the satisfaction of a genuine sense of accomplishment. It undergirds all elements of creative living and surmounts vicissitudes exceeding conventional human endurance.

LASSMAN, MALCOLM, lawyer; b. Bklyn., June 9, 1938; M. Barbara Turley (div.); children: Scott, Robin, Amy; m. Vivienne McIntosh; 1 child, Justine. BA, Washington & Lee U., 1960, LLB cum laude, 1963. Bar: Va. 1963, D.C. 1965. Ptnr. Akin, Gump, Strauss, Hauer & Feld, Washington. Jewish. Lodge: Masons. Home: 2883 Audubon Ter NW Washington DC 20008-2309 Office: Akin Gump Strauss Hauer & Feld Ste 400 1333 New Hampshire Ave NW Washington DC 20036-1564

LASSNER, FRANZ GEORGE, historian, educator; b. Leipzig, Germany, May 6, 1926; s. Oscar and Marga (Treskow) L.; m. Marguerite Sansone, Aug. 18, 1961; children: Alexander Nicholas, John Paul. A.B. in History, Rutgers U., 1947; M.A. in History, Georgetown U., 1951, Ph.D. in Govt., 1960. With various research projects Georgetown U., Washington, 1951-62; research supt. Russian Studies Project, Washington, 1956-57; research assoc., curator spl. collections Hoover Inst., Stanford, Calif., 1962-63; dir. Herbert Hoover Presdl. Libr., West Branch, Iowa, 1963-67; dir. archives Hoover Inst., Stanford, 1969-74, spl. rep., 1974—; dir. devel. Phila. Coll. Textiles and Sci., 1974-76; sr. v.p. programs Freedoms Found., Valley Forge, 1977-91; adj. prof. history Temple U., Phila., 1992-93; adj. prof. history Atlantic C.C., N.J., 1992—. Mem. adv. bd. Internat. Telecommunications Inst., Houston, 1984-89; bd. dirs. St. Lawrence Inst., Montreal, 1985-89. Mem. World Affairs Coun. Greater Valley Forge (bd. dirs. 1991-93), Lambda Chi Alpha, Delta Phi Alpha. Roman Catholic. Home: 1069 Michigan Ave Cape May NJ 08204

LASSWELL, MARCIA LEE, psychologist, educator; b. Oklahoma City, July 13, 1927; d. Lee and Stella (Blackard) Eck; m. Thomas Lasswell, May 29, 1950; children: Marcia Jane, Thomas Ely, Julia Lee. B.A., U. Calif., Berkeley, 1949; M.A., U. So. Calif., 1952; postgrad., U. Calif., Riverside, U So. Calif., U. N.C. Individual practice psychotherapy, marriage/family therapy Claremont, Calif.; asst. prof. Pepperdine Coll., Los Angeles, 1959-60; asst. prof. psychology behavioral sci. dept. Calif. State U., Pomona, 1960-64; asso. prof. Calif. State U., 1965-69 prof., 1970—, chmn. dept., 1964-69; asso. clin. dir. Human Relations Center, U. So. Calif., 1975—; vis. assoc. prof. Scripps Coll., 1968-69, U. So. Calif., 1969-70, Occidental Coll., 1971-72; lectr. various Calif. univs.; mem. staff spl. project alcoholics and narcotics offenders Calif. Prison System, 1970-73; mem. CAJI. Accreditation Com. Secondary Schs. and Colls., 1965—; mem. commn. accreditation for marriage and family tng. U.S. Dept. Edn., 1981-87. Author: College Teaching of General Psychology, 1967, Love, Marriage and Family, 1973, No-Fault Marriage, 1976, Styles of Loving, 1980, Marriage and Family, 1982, rev. edit., 1987, 91, Equal Time, 1983. Recipient Outstanding Tchrs. award Calif. State U., 1971, Outstanding Contbn. to Marriage and Family Therapy, 1991, Disting. Clin. Mem. award Calif. Assn. Marriage and Family Therapists, 1995. Fellow Am. Assn. Marital and Family Therapy (bd. dirs. 1970-72, 87-91, pres. elect 1993-95, pres. 1995-97); mem. AAAS, Nat. Coun. Family Rels. (exec. com. 1978-80), Am. Acad. Family Therapy, So. Calif. Assn. Marital and Family Therapy (pres. 1972-73), Alpha Kappa Delta, Phi Delta Gamma, Pi Gamma Mu. Home: 800 W 1st St #2908 Los Angeles CA 90012

LAST, MICHAEL P., lawyer; b. Chgo., July 31, 1946; s. Jules Hilbert and Muriel Esther (Ruekberg) L.; m. Yong-Hee Chyun, Dec. 1970 (div.); m. Jane Antoinette Nooy Bunnell, May 29, 1993. BA magna cum laude, Lawrence U., 1968; JD cum laude, Harvard U., 1971. Bar: Mass. 1971. Ptnr., head Real Estate, Environ. Law Dept. Warner & Stackpole, Boston, 1972-84; ptnr., head Environ. Law Dept. Gaston & Snow, Boston, 1984-91; ptnr., cochair Environ. Law sect. Mintz, Levin, Cohn, Ferris, Glovsky and Popeo P.C., Boston, 1991—; mng. dir. ML Strategies, Inc., Boston, 1991—; bd. dirs. Newell Enterprises Inc., 1983-87; co-chair Am. Law Inst./ABA Ann. Course Study Minimizing Liability for Hazardous Waste Mgmt.; lectr. in field. Contbr. articles to profl. jours. Chair wetlands regulation review bd. Mass. Dept. Environ. Quality Engring., 1983-85, Town Wellesley Wetlands Protection Com., 1980-82; mem. Town Wellesley Planning Bd., 1983-88; rep. Town Meeting, Wellesley; mem. review bd. Mass. Dep. Environ. Protection, 1991-92; mem. bd. environ. mgmt. Mass. Dept. Environ. Mgmt., 1991—, chmn., 1994—; founder, pres. Santa Fe Coun. Environ. Excellence, 1991—; mem. contp. gifts com. Boston Museum Fine Arts Capital Fund Drive, 1979; vice chair open space plan implementation com. Town Wellesley, Mass., 1978-79; trustee Mass. Eye and Ear Infirmary, 1990—, New Eng. Aquarium, 1995—; trustee, bd. govs. exec. com. Newton-Wellesley Hosp., 1987-94, chmn. joint trustee staff com., 1992-93. 1st Lt. USAF, 1971-72. Warren Hurst Stevens scholar Lawrence U., 1964. Mem. ABA (standing com. environ. law 1989-91, natural resources sect., corp., banking, bus. law sect.,

real property, probate, trust law sect.), Boston Bar Assn. (bd. dirs. 1984-87, chair environment com. 1979-81, chair urban affairs sect. 1983-87, co-chair mcpl. planning process com. 1983-87), Greater Boston C. of C. (real estate devel. com. 1979-80, co-chair Boston 2000 project review com. 1982-90, Boston 2000 steering com. 1983-90, co-chair adv. com. Devel. Design Guideline Study Downtown Boston 1983-92), Phi Beta Kappa. Avocations: canoeing, cross country skiing, camping. Office: Mintz Levin Cohn Ferris Glovsky & Popeo PC One Financial Center Boston MA 02111

LASTER, DANNY BRUCE, animal scientist; b. Scotts Hill, Tenn., Nov. 29, 1942; married 1960; 2 children. BS, U. Tenn., 1963; MS, U. Ky., 1964; PhD in Animal Breeding, Okla. State U., 1970. Rsch. specialist U. Ky., Lexington, 1965-68; asst. prof. endocrinology Iowa State U., 1970-71; rsch. leader reproduction rsch. unit, Clay ctr., agr. rsch. svc. USDA, Nebr., 1971-78; nat. program leader, assoc. dep. adminstr. beef and sheep USDA, 1981-88; dir. Roman L. Hruska Meat Animal Rsch. Ctr. Clay Ctr., Nebr., 1988—. Mem. Am. Soc. Animal Sci. Office: USDA Roman L Hruska Meat Animal Rsch Ctr MARC PO Box 166 Clay Center NE 68933-0166

LASTER, LEONARD, physician, consultant, author; b. N.Y.C., Aug. 24, 1928; s. Isaac and Mary (Ehrenreich) L.; m. Ruth Ann Leventhal, Dec. 16, 1956; children: Judith Eve, Susan Beth, Stephen Jay. AB, Harvard U., 1949, MD, 1950. Diplomate Nat. Bd. Med. Examiners, Am. Bd. Internal Medicine (gastroenterology). From intern to resident in medicine Mass. Gen. Hosp., Boston, 1950-53; fellow gastroenterology Mass. Meml. Hosp., 1958-59; vis. investigator Pub. Health Rsch. Inst., N.Y.C., 1953-54; lt. commd. USPHS, 1954, advanced through grades to asst. surgeon gen. (rear adm.), 1971; mem. staff Nat. Inst. Arthritis, Metabolic and Digestive Diseases, NIH, Bethesda, Md., 1954-73, chief digestive and hereditary diseases, 1969-73; spl. asst., then asst. dir. human resources President's Office Sci. and Tech., 1969-73; exec. dir. Assembly Life Scis., also dir. med. scis. NAS-NRC, 1973-74; ret. USPHS, 1973; v.p. acad. affairs and clin. affairs Med. Ctr., also dean Coll. Medicine, prof. medicine Downstate Med. Ctr., SUNY, Bklyn., 1974-78; pres. Oreg. Health Scis. U., Portland, 1978-87, prof. medicine, 1978-87; chancellor U. Mass. Med. Ctr., Worcester, 1987-90, disting. univ. prof. medicine and health policy, 1990—, chancellor emeritus, 1990—; bd. dirs. Thermo Cardiosystems, Inc., Protein Engring. Corp., Inc., Cambridge, Mass.; cons. mgmt. and productivity of R & D programs for numerous pharm. corps.; R & D strategic planning, corp. corp. health care programs for multinat. paper corp. and private rsch. found.; lab investigator Marine Biol. Lab., Woods Hole, Mass., summers 1962-69, organizer symposia on nat. policy and biomed. scis., summers 1971-72, libr. reader, summers 1973-76. Author articles on gastrointestinal disease, inborn errors of metabolism, devel. biology; contbr. OP-ED column and other pieces to Washington Post, essays to Hosp. Practice and MD Mag. Bd. dirs. Found. Advanced Edn. Scis., Bethesda, 1965-69, Bedford Stuyvesant Family Health Ctr., Bklyn., 1975-78, Med. Rsch. Found., Oreg., 1979-87, Oreg. Symphony, 1979-85, Oreg. Contemporary Theatre, 1981-83; pres. Burning Tree Elem. Sch. PTA, Bethesda, 1972-73; bd. dirs. Internat. Artists Series, Worcester, 1988-91, Mass. Biotech. Ctrs. for Excellence, Boston, 1988—, Mass. Biotech. Rsch. Inst., Worcester, 1988-90, Worcester Bus. Devel. Corp., 1988-91; cochmn. United Way Cen. Mass., COMEC Campaign, 1989; exec. com. Worcester Econ. Club, 1988-91; mem. citizen gov. bd. Worcester Fights Back, 1990—; chmn. corp. liaison com. Marine Biol. Lab., 1991—; mem. Worcester Com. Fgn. Rels. (affiliated with Coun. Fgn. Rels.), 1992—. With USPHS, 1952-73. Fellow ACP; mem. Am. Fedn. Clin. Rsch., Am. Gastroenterol. Assn., Am. Soc. Biol. Chemists, Am. Soc. Clin. Investigation (emeritus), Marine Biol. Lab. Corp., Harvey Soc. N.Y., Portland C. of C. (dir. 1980-84), Mass. Med. Soc. (pub. rels. com.), Worcester Dist. Med. Soc., Worcester Club, Cosmos Club (Washington), Harvard Club (N.Y.C.), Univ. Club (Portland, Oreg.), Phi Beta Kappa, Sigma Xi. Home: 47 Pine Arden Dr West Boylston MA 01583-1024 Office: U Mass Med Ctr 55 Lake Ave N Worcester MA 01655-0002 Education is nurturing excellence in others and facilitating its spread as an infectious disease.

LASTER, RALPH WILLIAM, JR., insurance company executive, accountant; b. Hutchinson, Kans., Oct. 4, 1951; s. Ralph William Sr. and Peggy Edith (O'Connell) L.; m. Jerri Laster, May 26, 1971; children: Tarissa Marie, Damian Michael. BSBA, Emporia (Kans.) State U., 1974. Staff acct. Deloitte, Haskin & Sells, Kansas City, Mo., 1974-76, Mize, Houser, Mehlinger & Kimes, Topeka, 1976-78; ptnr. Gregg, Prichard & Laster CPA's, Winfield, Kans., 1978-81; v.p. chief fin. officer, sec. Am. Investors Life Ins. Co., Inc., Topeka, 1981-84, exec. v.p., chief fin. officer, sec., 1985-88, also bd. dirs.; exec. v.p. chief fin. officer, sec., treas. AmVestors Fin. Corp., Topeka, 1986-88, vice-chmn., chief exec. officer, 1988, chmn., chief exec. officer, 1988—; bd. dirs. AmVestors Fin. Corp., Topeka, AmVestors Investment Group, Topeka, Am. Investors Sales Group, Topeka. Methodist. Home: 5646 SW 33rd St Topeka KS 66614-4517 Office: Am Investors Life Ins Co Inc 415 SW 8th Ave Topeka KS 66603-3913

LASTER, RICHARD, biotechnology executive, consultant; b. Vienna, Austria, Nov. 10, 1923; came to U.S., 1940; naturalized, 1944; s. Alan and Caroline (Harband) L.; m. Liselotte Schneider, Oct. 17, 1948; children: Susan Laster Rubenstein, Thomas. Student U. Wash., 1941-42; BChE cum laude, Poly. Inst. Bklyn., 1943; postgrad. Stevens Inst. Tech., 1945-47. With Gen. Foods Corp., 1944-82, corp. rsch. and devel., Hoboken, N.J., 1944-58, ops. mgr. Franklin Baker div., Hoboken, N.J., Atlantic Gelatin div., Woburn, Mass., 1958-64, mgr. rsch. devel. Jell-O div., White Plains, N.Y., 1958-64, corp. mgr. quality assurance, White Plains, 1964-67, ops. mgr. Maxwell House div., White Plains, 1967-68, exec. v.p. Maxwell House div., 1968-69, pres. Maxwell House div., 1969-71, corp. group v.p., White Plains, 1971-73, exec. v.p. Gen. Foods Corp., 1974-82, also dir., rsch., devel. and food-away-from-home, 1975-82; bd. dirs. DNA Plant Tech. Corp., 1982-94, chmn., 1988-94, CEO, 1982-92, pres. 1982-91; mgmt. cons., 1994—; bd. dirs. RiceTec, Bowater Inc., Peptor Ltd.; mem. sch. bd. Chappaqua, N.Y., 1971-74, pres., 1973-74; chmn., mem. bd., 1st v.p. United Way of Westchester, 1978; chmn. adv. com. Poly. Inst. Westchester, 1977; trustee Poly. Inst. N.Y., 1978—; mem. ncall. coun. SUNY, Purchase; chmn. Purchase Coll. Found., 1986—; mem. corp. N.Y. Botanical Garden; mem. adv. panel to chancellor SUNY, Albany; mem. subcom. Export Adminstrn. Pres.'s Export Coun., 1995; chmn. Westchester Edn. Coalition, 1992—; dir. SciencePort, 1993—, Westchester Holocaust Commmn., 1994. Recipient Disting. Alumnus award. Fellow Poly. Inst. N.Y. Mem. AAAS, N.Y. Acad. Scis., Am. Inst. Chem. Engrs. (Food and Bioengring. award 1972), Am. Chem. Soc., Am. Inst. Chemists, Tau Beta Pi, Phi Lambda Upsilon. Contbr. articles on food sci. to profl. publs. Patentee in field. Home: 23 Round Hill Rd Chappaqua NY 10514-1622 Office: Richard Laster 103 S Bedford Rd Mount Kisco NY 10549-3440

LASTINGER, ALLEN LANE, JR., banker; b. Atmore, Ala., Aug. 16, 1942; s. Allen Lane and Sue Belle (Bevis) L.; m. Shirley Delores Taylor, May 1, 1965; children—Randall Lane, Lindsey Kathleen, Amy Delores. B.B.A., U. Fla., 1965, 1971; postgrad. Stonier Grad. Sch. Banking, Rutgers U., 1979-81; A.M.P., Harvard U., 1982. Fin. analyst Barnett Banks Fla., Inc., Jacksonville, 1971-75, asst. v.p., 1975, pres., chief exec. officer Barnett Bank, Gainesville, Fla., 1976-80; exec. v.p. community banking Barnett Banks Fla., 1980-82, sr. exec. v.p. community banking, 1982-84, vice-chmn., 1984-88, vice chmn., chief banking officer, 1988-91, pres., chief oper. officer, 1991—; dir. Barnett Banks, Inc.; vice-chmn. Enterprise Florida, Inc. Served with USN, 1966-70. Mem. Bankers Roundtable. Republican. Episcopalian. Office: Barnett Banks Inc PO Box 40789 Jacksonville FL 32203-0789

LASTMAN, MELVIN D., mayor; b. Toronto, Ont., Can., Mar. 9, 1933; s. Louis and Rose L.; m. Marilyn Lastman, Nov. 15, 1953; children—Dale, Blayne. Pres. Bad Boy Furniture & Appliances, Toronto, 1955-76; mayor North York, Ont., 1972—; bd. govs. North York Gen. Hosp.; commr. York-Finch Gen. Hosp. Found. Active Pride of Israel Synagogue, North York br. Can. Red Cross, Sunnybrook Med. Ctr., Ont. Men's ORT, Can. ORT Orgn., Parents Against Drugs, North York YMCA, Vol. Ctr. Met. Toronto, North York Mental Health Council, North York Srs. Ctr., North York Hydro Commn., North York chpt. Heart and Stroke Found. Ont., Can. Found. for Ileitis and Colitis, Ont. Audio Libr. Svc., March of Dimes, Shalom Food Project, Good Cheer Russian Language Radio Program, Can. Assn. Riding for Disabled, St. John Ambulance Canine Theory Program, Metro Toronto; patron Kidney Found. Can.; hon. chmn. Children's Wish Found. Ont., Alcohol and Drug Svc. Network North York, Hugh MacMillan Med. Ctr.,

Leukemia Rsch. Fund, St. John's Rehab. Hosp.; active Chi-Ping Dance Group, Kolinka Contemporary Dance Co., North York Singers. Recipient Ursaki award Can. Sales and Mktg. Execs. Mem. North York C. of C., Older Adult Ctrs. Assn., B'Nai Brith Can., Juvenile Diabetes Found. Can. Can. Cancer Soc. (Willowdale Unit), March of Dimes, Caritas Project, Can. Soc. Yad Vashem (bd. dirs.), Assn. Children with Learning Disabilities, North York Symphony, Kiwanis Club of North York. Clubs: Kinsmen, North York Civitan. Lodges: B'nai Brith, Rotary, Kiwanis. Home: 19 Widefird Pl, North York, ON Canada M2N 5S5 Office: City of North York, 5100 Yonge St, North York, ON Canada M2N 5V7

LASTOWKA, JAMES ANTHONY, former federal agency executive, lawyer; b. Chester, Pa., Oct. 1, 1951; s. Joseph Edward and Mary A. (O'Malley) L.; m. Sandra L. Pugh, Apr. 28, 1979; children: Conor David, Carey Anna, Austin Tucker. BA in Econs. cum laude, Syracuse U., 1973; JD, Georgetown U., 1976. Bar: Pa. 1976, D.C. 1990, U.S. Ct. Appeals (a4th, 5th, 9th, 10th, 11th, D.C. cirs.) 1981. Staff atty. U.S. Occupational Safety and Health Rev. Commn., Washington, 1976-78, asst. gen. counsel, 1979-80; supervisory atty. Fed. Mine Safety and Health Rev. Commn., Washington, 1978-79, dep. gen. counsel, 1980-81, gen. counsel, 1981-84, commr., 1984-90; with Jones, Day, Reavis & Pogue, Washington, 1992—. Contbr. editor Occupational Hazards Mag. Mem. ABA (mem. labor law sect., com. occupational safety and health law, com. natural resources, energy and environ. law). Office: McDermott Will & Emery 1850 K St NW Washington DC 20006-8087

LATAIF, LAWRENCE P., lawyer; b. Fall River, Mass., Nov. 1, 1943; s. Louis and Linda Adele (Salwan) L.; m. Noha Nader, Dec. 29, 1979; children: Nicole, Lawrence Jr., Diana. BA, Brown U., 1965; JD, Georgetown U., 1968, LLM, 1970. Bar: D.C. 1969, U.S. Ct. Appeals (D.C. cir.) 1969, U.S. Ct. Mil. Appeals 1969, U.S. Supreme Ct. 1973, Va. 1974, U.S. Tax Ct. 1979. Asst. U.S. atty. U.S. Dept. Justice, Washington, 1970-73; pvt. practice Arlington, Va., 1974-75; ptnr. Lataif & Bernsen, Arlington, 1976-77; pvt. practice Fairfax, Va., 1978-85; of counsel Jones, Day, Reavis & Pogue, Washington, 1986-88, ptnr., 1989-91; ptnr. McDermott, Will & Emery, Miami, Fla., 1991-95; prin. Lawrence P. Lataif, P.A., Ft. Lauderdale, Fla., 1995—. Bd. advisors: Corp. Counsel's Guide to Business-Related Immigration, 1989—; contbr. articles to Wall St. Jour. and profl. jours. Mem. bd. overseers Children's Hosp., Boston, 1993—. Prettyman fellow Georgetown U. Law Sch., 1968. Mem. Am. Immigration Lawyers Assn. Office: 1500 N Federal Hwy Ste 202 Fort Lauderdale FL 33308

LATANÉ, BIBB, social psychologist; b. N.Y.C., July 19, 1937; s. Henry Allen and Felicite Gillman (Bibb) L.; m. Deborah Ruth Richardson; children by previous marriage: Julia Gillman, Claire Augusta, Henry Arbiter. B.A., Yale U., 1958; Ph.D., U. Minn., 1963. Mem. faculty dept. social psychology Columbia U., N.Y.C., 1962-68; prof. psychology, dir. behavioral scis. lab. Ohio State U., Columbus, 1968-82; prof. psychology, dir. Inst. Research Social Sci. U.N.C.-Chapel Hill, 1982-90; prof. psychology Fla. Atlantic U., Boca Raton, 1990—. Contbr. articles to profl. jours. Guggenheim fellow, 1974-75; James McKeen Cattell fellow, 1981-82; NSF, Office of Naval Research grantee. Mem. Am. Psychol. Assn. (council rep. 1971-75), Soc. Personality and Social Psychology (pres. 1976-79, Campbell award 1986), Midwestern Psychol. Assn. (pres. 1981-84), Acad. Mgmt., AAAS (Socio-Psychol. prize 1968, 80), Am. Sociol. Assn., Animal Behavior Soc., Internat. Assn. Applied Psychology. Home: 4521 S Ocean Blvd Boca Raton FL 33487-4235 *We know so much, yet have so much to learn about each other that the science of behavior will continue to vitalize and be vital.*

LATANISION, RONALD MICHAEL, materials science and engineering educator, consultant; b. Richmondale, Pa., July 2, 1942; s. Stephen and Mary (Kopach) L.; m. Carolyn Marie Domenig, June 27, 1964; children—Ivan, Sara. BS, Pa. State U., 1964; PhD in Metall. Engring., Ohio State U., 1968. Postdoctoral fellow Nat. Bur. Standards, Washington, 1968-69; research scientist Martin Marietta, Balt., 1969-73, acting head materials sci., 1973-74; dir. H.H. Uhlig Corrosion Lab. MIT, Cambridge, 1975—, Shell Disting. prof. materials sci. and engring., 1983-88, dir. Materials Processing Ctr., 1984-91; co-founder ALTRAN Materials Engring. Corp., Boston, 1992—; mem. tech. adv. bd. Modell Devel. Corp., Framingham, Mass., 1987—; sci. advisor com. on sci. and tech. U.S. Ho. of Reps., 1982-83; chmn. ad hoc com. Mass. Advanced Materials Ctr., Boston, 1985—; mem. adv. bd. Mass. Office Sci. and Tech.; co-PI, NSF/SSI project PALMS. Editor: Surface Effects in Crystal Plasticity, 1977, Atomistics of Fracture, 1983, Chemistry and Physics of Fracture, 1987, Advances in Mechanics and Physics of Fracture, 1981, 83, 86; contbr. articles to profl. jours. Recipient sr. scientist award Humboldt Found., 1974-75, David Ford McFarland award Pa. State U., 1986; named Henry Krumb lectr. AIME, 1984, Disting. Alumnus, Ohio State U. Coll. Engring., 1991; hon. alumnus MIT, 1992. Fellow Am. Soc. Metals Internat., Nat. Assn. Corrosion Engrs. (A.B. Campbell award 1971, Willis R. Whitney award 1994); mem. NAE, Am. Soc. Metals (govt. and pub. affairs com. 1984), New Eng. Sci. Tchrs. (founder, co-chmn.), Nat. Materials Adv. Bd. Roman Catholic. Office: MIT Materials Sci & Engring 77 Massachusetts Ave Rm 8202 Cambridge MA 02139-4307

LATCHUM, JAMES LEVIN, federal judge; b. Milford, Del., Dec. 23, 1918; s. James H. and Ida Mae (Robbins) L.; m. Elizabeth Murray McArthur, June 16, 1943; children: Su-Allan, Elizabeth M. A.B. cum laude, Princeton U., 1940; J.D., U. Va., 1946. Bar: Va. 1942, Del. 1947. Assoc. Berl, Potter & Anderson, Wilmington, 1946-53; partner Berl, Potter & Anderson, 1953-68; judge U.S. Dist. Ct. Del., Wilmington, 1968-73; chief judge U.S. Dist. Ct. Del., 1973-83, sr. judge, 1983—; New Castle County atty. Del. Hwy. Dept., 1944-50; asst. U.S. atty., 1950-53; atty. Del. Interstate Hwy. Div., 1955-62, Delaware River and Bay Authority, 1962-68. Chmn. New Castle County Democratic Com., 1953-56, Wilmington City Com., 1959-63. Served to maj. Insp. Gen. Corps AUS, 1942-46, PTO. Mem. ABA, Del. Bar Assn., Va. Bar Assn., Order of Coif, Sigma Nu Phi. Presbyn. Clubs: Wilmington, Univ. Office: US Dist Ct 844 N King St # 34 Wilmington DE 19801-3519

LATEEF, YUSEF (BILL EVANS), composer, educator; b. Chattanooga, 1920. BA, Manhattan Sch. Music, MA in Music Edn., 1975; EdD, U. Mass., 1975. Tchr. saxophone Stan Kenton Summer Jazz Clinics, 1963; past. assoc. prof. music Manhattan C.C.; lectr. colls.; vis. prof. music Mass. and Hampshire Coll., Amherst. Leader quartet, N.Y.C. 1960; featured with Charles Mingus, 1960-61, Babatundi Olatunji, 1961-62, with Cannonball Adderley Combo, European Tour, 2 years; now combo leader; musician various instruments including tenor saxophone, flute, oboe, Middle Eastern and Asian instruments; recs. on Impulse, Prestige, Landmark labels, others; records include Part of the Search; albums include The Boeue Yusef Lateef, The Diverse Yusef Lateef, The Gentle Giant, Hush 'n Thunder, Blues for Orient, Cry-Tender, Eastern Sounds, Expression!, Gentle Giant with W.K. Barron, Imagination with Doug Watkins, Into Something with Elvin Jones, Live Session, The Many Faces of Yusef Lateef, Plays for Lovers, Sounds of Yusef, Live at Pep's, Club Date, Little Symphony, Yusef Lateef's Flute Book of the Blues, Lateef in Nigeria, 1985, Gong, 1957, Jazz for the Thinker, 1985, Morning with Curtis Fuller, Nocturnes with Schick, C. Salvo, P. Tucker, 1989, Other Sounds with W. Harding, H. Lawson, E. Farrow, D. Jackson, 1957, 89; composer symphany Do I (Tahira) recorded with the Hamburg Germany Radio Orch. Recipient Grammy award for best new-age performance, 1987.

LATELLA, ROBERT NATALE, brewing company executive, lawyer; b. N.Y.C., Oct. 4, 1942; s. Donato and Santa (Codraro) L.; m. Christine Smith, June 4, 1966; children: Daivid Christopher, Patrick Smith. BA, Fordham Coll., 1964; LLB, Vanderbilt U., 1967; LLM in Corp. Law, NYU, 1968. Bar: N.Y. 1967. Assoc. Harter, Secrest & Emery, Rochester, N.Y., 1968-75, ptnr., 1976-82; mng. ptnr.; 1980-82; exec. v.p., chief fin. officer, gen. counsel Case Hoyt Corp., Rochester, 1982-86; exec. v.p., chief ops. officer Genesee Corp., Rochester, 1986—; also bd. dirs.; regional bd. dirs. Marine Midland Bank, Rochester. Trustee Monroe C.C., Rochester, 1984—, vice chmn., 1991—; trustee Highland Hosp., Rochester, 1986—, vice chmn., 1991-94, chmn., 1994—; trustee Buffalo Bills Found., Inc., 1990—. Mem. ABA, N.Y. State Bar Assn., Monroe County Bar Assn. Democrat. Roman Catholic. Club: Oak Hill Country (Rochester). Office: Genesee Brewing Co Inc 445 St Paul St Rochester NY 14605-1726

LATHAM, ALLEN, JR., manufacturing company consultant; b. Norwich, Conn., May 23, 1908; s. Allen and Caroline (Walker) L.; m. Ruth Nichols, Nov. 11, 1933 (dec. 1992); children: W. Nichols, Harriet Latham Robinson, David W., Thomas W.; m. Charlotte T. Goldsmith, July 4, 1992. B.S. in Mech. Engring, MIT, 1930, Sloan fellow, 1936. Devel. engr. E.I. duPont, Belle, W.Va., 1930-35; engr.; treas. Polaroid Corp., Cambridge, Mass., 1936-41; engr., v.p. Arthur D. Little, Cambridge, 1941-66; pres. Cryogenic Tech., Waltham, Mass., 1966-71; founder Haemonetics, Braintree, Mass., 1971—. Recipient New Eng. Inventor award, 1987, Morton Grove-Rasmussen award Am. Assn. Blood Banks, 1989; named Engr. of Yr. Socs. New Eng. Engring., 1970. Mem. AAAS, ASME (hon.), AIChE, Instrument Soc. Am., Nat. Acad. Engring. Club: Country (Brookline, Mass.). Patentee in blood processing equipment and processes. Home: 143 Whitcomb Ave Jamaica Plain MA 02130-3436 Office: Haemonetics 400 Wood Rd Braintree MA 02184-2486

LATHAM, DUDLEY EUGENE, III (DEL LATHAM), printing and paper converting executive; b. New Rochelle, N.Y., Sept. 28, 1943; s. Dudley E. Latham Jr. and Virginia Lois (Jarman) Latham Brodhagen; m. Kathleen Boylson, Apr. 2, 1965; children: Elizabeth, Clifford, Gregory, Thomas, Mark, John, Andrew. BA, U., 1967; postgrad., De Paul U., 1969. Sales rep. Hoffman LA Roche, Nutley, N.J., 1967-69, Permacel div. Johnson & Johnson, New Brunswick, N.J., 1969-71, Addison Wesley Pub. Co., Redding, Mass., 1971-72; gen. mgr. Midwest Tape Corp., Madison, Wis., 1972-76; pres. Roll Products, St. Mary's, Kans., 1976—; dir. St. Therese Acad., Madison, Wis., 1974-86. Chmn. Arts in Park, 1993—; city planning commr., 1994—; mem. St. Mary's C. of C. (bd. dirs. 1993—, sec. 1993-94, pres. 1994-95). Mem. Topeka Country Club, Phi Sigma Kappa. Republican. Roman Catholic. Avocation: band director. Home: 101 E Mission St Saint Marys KS 66536-1526 Office: Roll Products Inc 511 W Palmer St Saint Marys KS 66536-1627

LATHAM, JAMES DAVID, lawyer; b. Lowell, Mass., Apr. 18, 1942; s. Ernest Hargreaves and Anne Crowdis (MacIvor) L.; m. Pauline Page, Apr. 14, 1972; children: James Benjamin, Timothy David. AB, Dartmouth Coll., 1964; LLB, Boston U., 1967. Bar: Mass. 1967, U.S. Dist. Ct. Mass. 1968. Assoc. Goldman & Curtis, Lowell, 1967-72; ptnr. Goldman, Curtis, Leahey & Latham, Lowell and Boston, 1972-74; assoc. counsel ITT Sheraton Corp., Boston, 1974-78, sr. counsel, 1978-80, asst. gen. counsel, 1982-84, v.p., 1984-92, sr. v.p., sec., gen. counsel, 1992—; gen. counsel Sheraton Mgmt. Corp., London, 1980-84. Chmn. Lowell Rep. City Com., 1972. Mem. Vesper Country Club, The Internat. Club. Episcopalian. Office: ITT Sheraton Corp 60 State St Boston MA 02109-1815

LATHAM, JEAN LEE, writer; b. Buckhannon, W.Va., Apr. 19, 1902; d. George Robert II and Winifred Ethelda (Brown) L. A.B., W.Va. Wesleyan Coll., 1925, Litt.D., 1956; B.D.E., Ithaca Coll., 1928; M.A., Cornell U. 1930; student, W.Va. Inst. Tech., 1942. Head English dept. Upshur County High Sch., 1926-27; substitute tchr. speech W.Va. Wesleyan Coll., 1927; tchr. dramatic and acad. depts. Ithaca Coll., 1928-29; editor in chief Dramatic Pub. Co., Chgo., 1930-36; free lance writer, 1936-41, 45—; Trainer insps. Signal Corps U.S. War Dept., 1943-45; substitute librarian Warm Springs Found., summer 1951. Playwright: The Blue Teapot, 1932, Old Doc, 1941, Gray Bread, 1941, Senor Freedom, 1941, The Nightmare, 1953; Author: Do's and Don'ts of Drama, 1935, The Story of Eli Whitney, 1953, Medals for Morse, 1954, Carry On, Mr. Bowditch, 1955 (Jr. Literary Guild selection, Newbery Medal, hon. mention Internat. Bd. Books for Young People), Trail Blazer of the Seas, 1956, This Dear Bought Land, 1957 (Jr. Lit. Guild selection 1957), On Stage, Mr. Jefferson, 1958, Young Man in a Hurry; The Story of Cyrus W. Field, 1958, Nutcracker, Puss in Boots, Jack the Giant Killer, Hop O' My Thumb, When Homer Honked, The Dog that Lost His Family, The Cuckoo Who Couldn't Count, The Man Who Never Snoozed, Drake: The Man They Called a Pirate, 1960, Man of the Monitor: The Story of John Ericsson, 1962, The Chagres: Power of the Panama Canal, 1964, Sam Houston: Hero of Texas, 1965, Retreat to Glory, The Story of Sam Houston, 1965, George W. Goethals: Panama Canal Engineer, 1965, The Frightened Hero, 1965, David Glasgow Farragut: Our First Admiral, 1967, The Columbia: Powerhouse of North America, 1967, Anchor's Aweigh: The Story of David Glasgow Farragut, 1968, Far Voyager: The Story of James Cook, 1970, Rachel Carson: Who Loved the Sea, 1973, Who Lives Here?, 1974, What Tabbit the Rabbit Found, 1974, Elizabeth Blackwell: Pioneer Woman Doctor, 1975; Recorded: Carry On Mr. Bowditch (for Talking Books), 1956. Publicity dir. South Pinellas chpt. A.R.C., St. Petersburg, Fla., 1949; Bd. dirs. Friends of U. Miami (Fla.) Library. Mem. Nat. League Am. Pen Women, Women's Aux. U.S. Power Squadron, Phi Kappa Phi, Zeta Phi Eta. Democrat. Methodist. Club: Zonta. Home: 12 Phoenetia Ave Apt 1 Coral Gables FL 33134-3414 *I grew up in a home where BELIEF was the net under the tightrope walker. It was not tangled around his ankles. A home where I dared to believe was the secret of success.*

LATHAM, JOSEPH AL, JR., lawyer; b. Kinston, N.C., Sept. 16, 1951; s. Joseph Al and Margaret Lee (Tyson) L.; m. Elaine Frances Kramer, Dec. 19, 1981; 1 child, Aaron Joshua. BA, Yale U., 1973; JD, Vanderbilt U., 1976. Bar: Calif. 1976, U.S. Dist. Ct. (cen. dist.) Calif. 1977, U.S. Ct. Appeals (9th cir.) 1977, U.S. Dist. Ct. (no. and so. dists.) Calif. 1978, Ga. 1980, U.S. Dist. Ct. (no. dist.) Ga. 1981, U.S. Ct. Appeals (5th and 11th cirs.) 1981, U.S. Dist. Ct. (mid. dist.) Ga. 1982, D.C. 1984. Assoc. Paul, Hastings, Janofsky & Walker, Orange County and L.A., 1976-80, Atlanta, 1980-83; ptnr. Paul, Hastings, Janofsky & Walker, Orange County and L.A., 1987—; chief counsel to bd. mem. NLRB, Washington, 1983-85; staff atty. U.S. Commn. on Civil Rights, Washington, 1985-86; instr. advanced profl. program U. So. Calif. Law Ctr., 1988, lectr. law, 1989—. Articles editor Vanderbilt Law Rev., 1975-76; editorial asst. Employment Discrimination Law, 2d edit., 1983; contbr. articles to Barron's, ABA Jour., Litigation, Employee Rels. Law Jour. Mem. ABA (labor and employment law sect.), Calif. Bar Assn., Ga. Bar Assn., D.C. Bar Assn., Order of Coif. Republican. Episcopalian. Office: Paul Hastings Janofsky & Walker 555 S Flower St 23d Fl Los Angeles CA 90071-2371

LATHAM, LARRY LEE, state administrator, psychologist; b. Dallas, June 27, 1945; s. James L. Latham and Sara B. (MacClaine) Dulaney; m. Helen Marie Bumpass, Dec. 19, 1966; children: Wade Lee, Ryan Justin. BS in Psychology, U. North Tex., 1966, MS in Psychology, 1967; PhD in Psychology, U. Ala., 1977. Lic. psychologist, Ala. Psychologist Outwood State Sch., Dawson Springs, Ky., 1967-69; psychologist, unit coord. Denton (Tex.) State Sch., 1969-72; dir. habilitation W.D. Partlow Devel. Ctr., Tuscaloosa, Ala., 1972-77; dir. applied rsch. Ala. Dept. Mental Health and Mental Retardation, Tuscaloosa, 1977-81; dir. L.B. Wallace Devel. Ctr. Ala. Dept. Mental Health and Mental Retardation, Decatur, 1981-84; assoc. commr. for mental retardation Ala. Dept. Mental Health and Mental Retardation, Montgomery, 1984-91; dir. Bur. Orgnl. Devel., Montgomery, 1991—; dir. Greil Psychiat. Hosp./ Ala. Dept. Mental Health and Mental Retardation, 1987; pres. Human Svcs. Pers. Specialist, Inc. Bd. dirs. Foster Grandparents Ky., 1967-69, Ala. Spl. Olympics, 1984-91, Ala. Devel. Disabilities Coun., 1984-91. Fellow Am. Assn. Mental Retardation (pres. Ala. chpt. 1988-89). Avocations: woodworking, golf. Office: Greil Meml. Psychiat Hosp 2140 Upper Wetumpka Rd Montgomery AL 36107 *In this age it is best to remember that just because your values are not valued does not mean that you are wrong.*

LATHAM, LAVONNE MARLYS, physical education educator; b. Garrison, Iowa, Mar. 17, 1942; d. Harry August and Vona Irene (Loveless) Hilmer; m. Robert Allen Latham Jr., July 21, 1979. BA, U. Iowa, 1964; postgrad., No. Ill. U., 1985, Western Ill. U., 1970-88, Bemidji State U., 1979. Cert. tchr.; Ill. Tchr. phys. edn., elem. computer coord. Erie (Ill.) Community Unit 1, 1964—; head counselor Camp Lenore Owaissa, Hinsdale, Mass., 1964-78. Mem. NEA, AAHPER, Ill. Assn. Health, Phys. Edn. and Recreation, U. Iowa Alumni Assn., Ill. Edn. Assn., Erie Tchrs. Assn. (pres. 1982-83), Nat. Audubon Soc., Nature Conservancy, Delta Kappa Gamma. Baptist. Avocations: violin, computers, photography, travel, outdoor activities. Home: 1002 6th St Erie IL 61250 Office: Erie Community Unit 1 600 6th Ave Erie IL 61250-9452

LATHAM, TOM, congressman; b. Hampton, Iowa, July 14, 1978; s. Willard and Evelyn L.; m. Kathy Swinson, 1975; children: Justin, Jennifer,

Jill. Student, Watrburg Coll., Iowa State U. Bank teller, bookkeeper Brush, Colo., 1970-72; ind. ins. agent Fort Lupton, Colo., 1972-74; mktg. rep. Hartford Ins. Co., Des Moines, 1974-76; with Latham Seed Co., Alexander, Iowa, 1976—; now v.p., co-owner Latham Seed Co.; mem. 104th Congress from 6th Iowa dist., 1995—; Mem. congressman Fred Grandy's agriculture com.; sec. Republican Party of Iowa; rep. 5th dist. Republican State Ctrl. com.; co-chair Francklin County Republican Ctrl. com.; whip Iowa del. Republican Nat. Conv., 1992. Past chair Francklin County Extension Coun.; mem. Nazareth Lutheran Ch., past pres.; citizens adv. coun. Iowa State U. Mem. Am. Soybean Assn., Am. Seed Trade Assn., Iowa Farm Bur. Fedn., Iowa Soybean Assn., Iowa Corn Growers Assn., Iowa Seed Assn., Agribusiness Assn. of Iowa. Lutheran. Office: US House Reps 516 Cannon House Office Bldg Washington DC 20515-1505*

LATHAM, WELDON HURD, lawyer; b. Bklyn., Jan. 2, 1947; s. Aubrey Geddes and Avril (Hurd) L.; m. Constantia Beecher, Aug. 8, 1948; children—Nicole Marie, Brett Weldon. BA, Howard U., 1968; JD, Georgetown U., 1971; postgrad. George Washington U., 1975-76. Bar: D.C. 1972, U.S. Ct. Appeals (D.C. cir.) 1972, U.S. Ct. Mil. Appeals 1974, U.S. Ct. Claims 1975, U.S. Supreme Ct. 1975, Va. 1981, U.S. Ct. Appeals (fed. cir.) 1988. Mgmt. cons. Checchi & Co., Washington, 1968-71; atty. Covington & Burling, Washington, 1971-73; sr. atty. Fed. Energy Adminstrn., Washington, 1974; asst. gen. counsel Exec. Office Pres., Office Mgmt. and Budget The White House, 1974-76; atty. Hogan & Hartson, Washington, 1976-79; gen. dep. asst. sec. HUD, 1979-81; v.p., gen. counsel Sterling Systems, Inc. (subs. PRC), exec. asst., counsel to chmn., CEO, and assoc. gen. counsel Planning Rsch. Corp., McLean, Va., 1981-86; mng. ptnr. Reed Smith Shaw & McClay, McLean, Va., 1986-91; sr. ptnr. Shaw, Pittman, Potts & Trowbridge, Washington, 1992—; adj. prof. Howard U. Law Sch., Washington, 1972-82; guest prof. U.Va., Charlottesville, 1976-90; mem. Va. Gov.'s Bus. and Industry Adv. Com. on Crime Prevention, 1983-85, Va. Gov.'s Regulatory Reform Adv. Bd., 1982-84; chmn. task force SBA, 1982; legal counsel Md. Mondale for Pres. Campaign, 1984. Columnist Minority Bus. Entrepreneur Mag., 1991—. Mem. Washington steering com. NAACP Legal Def. Fund, 1975—, Fairfax County Airports Adv. com., 1987-88; bd. dirs., gen. counsel Northern Va. Minority Bus. and Profl. Assn., 1985-92; trustee Va. Commonwealth U., Richmond, 1986-90; bd. dirs. Washington Urban League, 1986-90, U. D.C. Found., 1982-87, Washington Coun. Lawyers, 1973, bd. dirs. Profl. Svcs. Coun., 1983-88; bd. dirs. Minority Bus. Legal Def. and Edn. Fund, 1989-91; appointee Greater Washington Bd. Trade, Blue Ribbon Task Force on Home Rule, 1985-86, bd. dirs., exec. com., chmn. regional affairs com., corp. sec., 1990-93; trustee George Mason U., Fairfax, Va., 1990-94; prin. coun. for Excellence in Govt., 1989—; mayor D.C. Internat. Ins. Adv. Commn., 1994—; chair bus. adv. com., 1994—; co-chair UNCF Sportsfest Fundraiser, 1994—; gen. counsel's Honors Program Office of Sec. Capt. USAF, 1973-94. Recipient SES Effective Mgr. award HUD, 1980, Nat. Assn. for Equal Achievement Opportunity in Higher Edn. 1987. Mem. ABA (vice-chmn. subcom. pub. contract law sect. 1988-93), Fed. Bar Assn., Nat. Bar Assn., D.C.C. of C. (gen. counsel 1979), State Va. Bar Assn., Washington Bar Assn., Bar Assn. D.C., Nat. Lawyers Club Washington, Nat. Contract Mgmt. Assn. Mem. editorial adv. bd. Washington Bus. Jour., 1985-87. Home: 7004 Natelli Woods Ln Bethesda MD 20817-3924 Office: Shaw Pittman Potts & Trowbridge 2300 N St NW Washington DC 20037-1122

LATHAM, WILLIAM PETERS, composer, former educator; b. Shreveport, La., Jan. 4, 1917; s. Lawrence L. and Eugenia (Peters) L.; m. Joan Seyler, Apr. 18, 1946; children: Leslie Virginia, William Peters, Carol Jean. Student, Asbury Coll., Wilmore, Ky., 1933-35, Cin. Conservatory Music, 1936-38; B.Sc. in Music Edn, U. Cin., 1938; B.Mus., Coll. Music Cin., 1940, M.Mus., 1941; Ph.D., Eastman Sch. Music, 1951; pupil composition with, Eugene Goossens, Howard Hanson, Herbert Elwell. Mem. faculty N. Tex. State Tchrs. Coll., 1938-39, Eastern Ill. State Tchrs. Coll., 1946; mem. faculty State Coll., Iowa, 1946-65, prof. music, 1959-65; prof. composition Sch. Music, U. N. Tex., Denton, 1965-84; dir. grad. studies Sch. Music, U. N. Tex., 1969-84, disting. prof., 1978-84, prof. emeritus, 1984—. Composer numerous works, 1938—, including works for orch., band, chorus, chamber groups, soloists, one opera, and one ballet; compositions since 1980 include (chorus) Gaudeamus Academe, 1981, Bitter Land, 1985, My Heart Sings, 1988, Missa Novella, 1989; (chamber music) Ion, The Rhapsode for clarinet and piano, 1985, Metaphors, three songs for soprano, 1988, A Green Voice, cantata for soprano and tenor, 1989, The Sacred Flame, cantata for baritone and Orch., 1990, Vital Signs for chorus of unchanged voices, Tex., 1991, Excelsior K-2, for Orch. 1994, Requiem for My Love, three songs for high voice, 1994. Served to 2d lt. AUS, 1942-46. Scholar in composition Cin. Coll. Music, 1939-41; recipient numerous awards and commns. Mem. ASCAP (ann. awards 1962—), Coll. Mus. Soc., Phi Mu Alpha, Pi Kappa Lambda. Home: PO Box 50373 Denton TX 76206-0373

LATHE, ROBERT EDWARD, management and financial consultant; b. Balt., Apr. 8, 1945; s. Warren Calvin Sr. and Margaret Mary (Cavey) L.; m. Hermina Yeghnazarian, Apr. 13, 1967; children: Michelle Gayaneh, Mellina Margaret. MSc in Mgmt., U. Dublin, 1985. Metrology/field engr. Bendix Field Engring. Corp., Balt., 1967-68; quality assurance supr. space seismology lab. Bendix Aerospace Systems Divsn., Ann Arbor, Mich., 1968-72; programs mgr. Iran Aircraft Industries, Tehran, 1972-76; mgmt. cons. Alexander Proudfoot Co., Chgo., 1977-78; program mgr., field engr. Harris-PRD Electronics Divsn., Syosset, N.Y. & Isfahan, Iran, 1978-80; ops. dir. Airmotive Ireland Ltd., Dublin, 1980-84; project mgr. Handley-Walker Co., Inc., Valencia, Calif., 1986-87; owner, pres. Hyrel Bus. Svcs., Glendale, Calif., 1987-90; fin. planner, investment advisor IDS Fin. Svcs. Inc., Glendale, 1990—. Sgt. USAF, 1963-67, Vietnam. Mem. Am. Legion, La Crescenta C. of C. Avocations: microcomputers, golf, swimming, ten-pin bowling. Home: 543 Milford St # 4 Glendale CA 91203-1697

LATHEM, EDWARD CONNERY, librarian, editor, educator; b. Littleton, N.H., Dec. 15, 1926; s. Belton Gilreath and Myrtie Etta (Connery) L.; m. E. Elizabeth French, Nov. 27, 1957. A.B., Dartmouth Coll. 1951; M.S., Columbia U., 1952; D.Phil., Oxford U., 1961. With library Dartmouth Coll., 1952-78, librarian, 1968-78, dean of libraries, 1973-78, Bezaleel Woodward fellow, 1978—, couns. to pres., 1982—; officer, dir. Stinehour Press Inc., 1958-77, Plymouth Cheese Corp., 1959—, N. Country Pub. Co., 1970-78, Vt. Provisioners Inc., 1972-82, Meriden-Stinehour Inc., 1977-95; copub. Coös County Democrat, 1970-78; fence viewer Hanover, N.H., 1962—; adv. editor Dodd, Mead & Co., 1974-84; corp. mem. Hanover Improvement Soc., 1971—; trustee N.H. Hist. Soc., 1956-76, Howe Libr., Hanover, 1967-87, Dr. Seuss Found., 1985—, William L. Bryant Found., 1986—; pres. Assn. Rsch. Librs., 1976-77. Organizer microfilm edit. Papers of Daniel Webster, 1971; initiator Univ. Press of New Eng; editor and compiler: numerous books including (with Hyde Cox) Selected Prose of Robert Frost, 1966, Interviews with Robert Frost, 1966, (with Lawrance Thompson) Robert Frost and the Lawrence, Mass. High Sch. Bulletin, 1966, Your Son, Calvin Coolidge, 1968, The Poetry of Robert Frost, 1969, A Concordance to the Poetry of Robert Frost, 1971, (with Lawrance Thompson) Robert Frost: Poetry and Prose, 1972, Calvin Coolidge Says, 1972, Chronological Tables of American Newspapers 1690-1820, 1972, Robert Frost 100, 1974, 76 United Statesiana, 1976, North of Boston Poems (R. Frost), 1977, Thirteen Colonial Americana, 1977, The Dartmouth Experience (John Sloan Dickey), 1977, American Libraries as Centers of Scholarship, 1978, Robert Frost: A Biography (Lawrance Thompson and R.H. Winnick), 1981, (with Hyde Cox) Prose Jottings of Robert Frost, 1982, Stories of Life: North and South (Erskine Caldwell), 1983, Rudolph Ruzicka: Speaking Reminiscently, 1986, On the Teaching of Creative Writing (Wallace Stegner), 1989, A Vermont 14, 1992, Robert Frost: Seasons, 1992, On the Teaching and Writing of History (Bernard Bailyn), 1994. Mem. Phi Beta Kappa. Clubs: Century, Dartmouth (N.Y.C.); St. Botolph (Boston). Office: Dartmouth Coll 213 Baker Library Hanover NH 03755

LATHLAEN, ROBERT FRANK, retired construction company executive; b. Phila., May 25, 1925; s. Clarence Delcamp and Anna Marie (Schwab) L.; m. Nancy Nichols, May 1949 (div. July 1983); children: Margaret, Gail, Carol Sue; m. Margot von Harten, May 4, 1985. BSCE, Drexel U., 1945; SMCE, MIT, 1946. Registered profl. engr., N.Y. With W.J. Barney Corp., N.Y.C., 1946-94, pres., 1972-91, chmn. bd., 1991-94; vis. prof. Ea. Carolina U., 1993; adj. assoc. prof. NYU, 1984-91. Trustee St. Vincent's Hosp. and Med. Ctr., N.Y.C., 1986-90. Mem. ASCE (life), Assoc. Gen. Contractors (bd. dirs., chmn. various coms. 1976—, chmn. bldg. divsn. 1991), Gen. Bldg.

Contractors N.Y. State (pres. 1975-76), N.Y. Bldg. Congress (bd. dirs. 1975-80), Am. Arbitration Assn. (dir. 1986-94, exec. com. 1987-93, chmn. nat. constrn. industry arbitration com. 1989-90). Mem. Ch. of Christ. Avocations: writing fiction; bicycle riding; swimming; bird watching.

LATHROP, ANN, librarian, educator; b. L.A., Nov. 30, 1935; d. Paul Ray and Margaret (Redfield) W.; divorced; children: Richard Harold, John Randolph, Rodney Grant. BA in History summa cum laude, Ea. N.Mex. U., 1957; MLS, Rutgers U., 1964; PhD, U. Oreg., 1988. Cert. elem. tchr., Calif.; cert. libr., Calif. adminstrv. credential, Calif. Elem. sch. tchr. Chalfont (Pa.) Boro Sch., 1960-61, Livingston Elem. Sch., New Brunswick, N.J., 1961-63, Rosedale Elem. Sch., Chico, Calif., 1964-65; libr. Chico (Calif.) H.S., 1965-72, Princeton (Calif.) H.S., 1972-73, Santa Maria (Calif.) H.S., 1973-77; libr. coord. San Mateo County Office Edn., Redwood City, Calif., 1977-89; assoc. prof. Calif. State U., Long Beach, 1989-92, prof., 1993—; dir. Calif. Software Clearinghouse, Calif. State U. Long Beach. Author: Online Information Retrieval as a Research Tool in Secondary School Libraries, 1988; co-author: Courseware in the Classroom, 1983; editor: Online and CD-ROM Databases in School Libraries, 1989, the 1988-89 Educational Software Preview Guide, 1988, Technology in the Curriculum Recource Guides, 1988; editor, founder: (jours.) The Digest of Software Reviews: Education, 1983-86, Software Reviews on File, 1985-86; editor: (database) California Online Resources in Education, 1989; contbr. chpts. to books, articles to prof. jours. Mem. ALA, NEA, Am. Assn. Sch. Librs., Assn. State Tech. Using Tchr. Educators, Calif. Faculty Assn., Calif. Media and Libr. Educators Assn., Calif. Reading Assn., Computer Using Educators, Internat. Soc. for Tech. in Edn., Phi Delta Kappa. Avocations: traveling, camping. Office: Calif State U 1250 Bellflower Blvd Long Beach CA 90840-1402

LATHROP, GERTRUDE ADAMS, chemist, consultant; b. Norwich, Conn., Apr. 28, 1921; d. Williams Barrows and Lena (Adams) L. B.S., U. Conn., 1944; M.A., Tex. Woman's U., 1953, Ph.D., 1955. Devel. chemist on textiles/Alexander Smith & Sons Carpet Co. Yonkers, N.Y., 1944-52; research assoc. textiles Tex. Woman's U., 1952-56; chief chemist Glasgo Finishing Plant div. United Mchts. & Mfrs., Inc., Conn., 1956-57; chief chemist Old Fort Finishing Plant div. United Mchts. & Mfrs., Inc., N.C., 1957-63; research chemist United Mchts. Research Ctr., Langley, S.C., 1963-64; lab. mgr. automotive div. Collins & Aikman Corp., Albemarle, N.C., 1964-78; chief chemist, lab. mgr. Old Fort Finishing Plant div. United Mchts., 1979-83. Treas. 1st Congl. Ch., Asheville, N.C., 1985-87, bd. deacons, 1990-93; tax-aide counselor to elderly IRS, 1984—, Am. Assn. Ret. Person, Widowed Person Svcs., Asheville-Buncombe County, Inc., 1990-91, pres. Widowed Persons Svcs., 1992—; active RSVP Land of Sky, 1989-92; pub. Rels. com. Swannanoa Valley, N.C., Am. Assn. Ret. Persons, 1984-92, v.p., 1992, treas., 1993-94. Recipient Disting. Alumni award U. Conn. Sch. Family Studies, 1980-81. Mem. ASTM (chmn. transp. fabrics on flammability com. 1973-75), Am. Chem. Soc. (emeritus), Am. Assn. Textile Chemists and Colorists (emeritus, sec., rsch. chmn., treas., vice chmn. 1962-64, chmn. edn. com. Piedmont sect. 1977-78), Bus. and Profl. Women's Club (chpt. pres. 1974-76, Woman of Yr. award 1979, 80), Iota Sigma Pi (chmn. mem.-at-large). Home and Office: PO Box 1166 Black Mountain NC 28711-1166

LATHROP, IRVIN TUNIS, retired academic dean, educator; b. Platteville, Wis., Sept. 23, 1927; s. Irvin J. and Marian (Johnson) L.; m. Eleanor M. Kolar, Aug. 18, 1951; 1 son, James I. B.S., Stout State Coll., 1950; M.S., Iowa State U., 1954, Ph.D., 1958. Tchr. Ottumwa (Iowa) High Sch., 1950-55; mem. faculty Iowa State U., 1957-58, Western Mich. U., 1958-59; mem. faculty Calif. State Coll., 1959-88, prof. indsl. arts, 1966-88, chmn. dept. indsl. edn., 1969-88, assoc. dean extended edn., 1978-88, prof. emeritus, 1988—; cons. Naval Ordnance Lab., Corona, Calif., 1961-63. Author: (with Marshall La Cour) Photo Technology, 1966, rev. edit., 1977, Photography, 1979, rev. edit., 1992, The Basic Book of Photography, 1979, Laboratory Manual for Photo Technology, 1973, (with John Lindbeck) General Industry, 1969, rev. edit., 1977, 86, (with Robert Kunst) Photo-Offset, 1979; Editorial cons.: (with Robert Kunst) Am. Tech. Soc; Contbr. (with Robert Kunst) articles to profl. jours. Mem. adv. com. El Camino and Orange Coast Coll.; mem. Orange County Grand Jury, 1989-90, Orange County Juvenile Justice Commn., 1991—. Mem. Nat. Soc. for Study Edn., Am. Council Indsl. Arts Tchr. Edn., Am. Vocat. Assn., Nat. Assn. Indsl. and Tech. Tchrs., Internat. Tech. Assn., Am. Ednl. Research Assn., Epsilon Pi Tau, Psi Chi, Phi Delta Kappa, Phi Kappa Phi. Home: PO Box 3430 Laguna Hills CA 92654-3430 Office: 1250 N Bellflower Blvd Long Beach CA 90840-0004

LATHROP, MITCHELL LEE, lawyer; b. L.A., Dec. 15, 1937; s. Alfred Lee and Barbara (Mitchell) L.; m. Denice Annette Davis; children: Christin Lorraine Newlon, Alexander Mitchell, Timothy Trewin Mitchell. B.Sc., U.S. Naval Acad., 1959; J.D., U. So. Calif., 1966. Bar: D.C. 1966, Calif. 1966, U.S. Supreme Ct. 1969, N.Y. 1981; registered environ. assessor, Calif. Dep. counsel Los Angeles County, Calif., 1966-68; with firm Brill, Hunt, DeBuys and Burby, L.A., 1968-71; ptnr. Macdonald, Halsted & Laybourne, L.A. and San Diego, 1971-80; sr. ptnr. Rogers & Wells, N.Y.C., San Diego, 1980-86; sr. ptnr. Adams, Duque & Hazeltine, L.A., San Francisco, N.Y.C., San Diego, 1986-94, exec. com. 1986-94, firm chmn., 1992-94; sr. ptnr. Luce, Forward, Hamilton & Scripps, San Diego, N.Y.C., San Francisco, L.A., 1994—; presiding referee Calif. Bar Ct., 1984-86, mem. exec. com., 1981-88; lectr. law Calif. Judges Assn., Practicing Law Inst. N.Y., Continuing Edn. of Bar, State Bar Calif., ABA. Author: State Hazardous Waste Regulation, 1991, Environmental Insurance Coverage, 1991, Insurance Coverage for Environmental Claims, 1992. Western Regional chmn. Met. Opera Nat. Coun., 1971-81, v.p., mem. exec. com., 1971—, now chmn.; trustee Honnold Libr. at Claremont Colls., 1972-80; bd. dirs. Music Ctr. Opera Assn., L.A., sec., 1974-80; bd. dirs. San Diego Opera Assn., 1980—, v.p., 1985-89, pres.-elect, 1993, pres., 1994—; bd. dirs. Met. Opera Assn., N.Y.C.; mem. nat. steering coun. Nat. Actors Theatre, N.Y. Capt. JAGC, USNR, ret. Mem. ABA, N.Y. Bar Assn., Fed. Bar Assn., Fed. Bar Council, Calif. Bar Assn., D.C. Bar Assn., San Diego County Bar Assn. (chmn. ethics com. 1980-82, bd. dirs. 1982-85, v.p. 1985), Assn. Bus. Trial Lawyers, Assn. So. Calif. Def. Counsel, Los Angeles County Bar Assn. (pres. 1970-72), Soc. Colonial Wars in Calif. (gov. 1970-72), Order St. Lazarus of Jerusalem, Friends of Claremont Coll. (dir. 1975-81, pres. 1978-79), Am. Bd. Trial Advocates, Judge Advocates Assn. (dir. Los Angeles chpt. 1974-80, pres. So. Calif. chpt. 1977-78), Internat. Assn. Def. Counsel, Brit. United Services Club (dir. Los Angeles 1973-75), Mensa Internat., Calif. Soc., S.R. (pres. 1977-79), Calif. Club (Los Angeles), Valley Hunt Club (Pasadena, Calif.), Met. Club (N.Y.C.), The Naval Club (London), Phi Delta Phi. Republican. Home: 455 Silver Gate Ave San Diego CA 92106-3327 Office: Luce Forward Hamilton and Scripps 600 W Broadway 26th Fl San Diego CA 92101 also: Citicorp Ctr 153 E 53d St 26th Flr New York NY 10022

LATHROPE, DANIEL JOHN, legal educator, administrator. BSBA, U. Denver, 1973; JD, Northwestern U., 1977; LLM, NYU, 1979. Bar: Ariz. 1977, Calif. 1978. Assoc. Evans, Kitchel & Jenckes, Phoenix, 1977-78; instr. law NYU, 1979-80; assoc. prof. Calif. U., Hastings, 1980-86; prof. Calif. U., 1986—, assoc. acad. dean, 1986-87, acting dean, 1987-88, acad. dean, 1988-90. Author: (with Lind, Schwarz and Rosenberg) Fundamentals of Corporate Taxation, 3d edit., 1991, Fundamentals of Partnership Taxation, 4th edit., 1994, The Alternative Minimum Tax-Compliance and Planning with Analysis, 1994, (with Schwarz) Black Letter on Federal Taxation of Corporations and Partnerships, 1991, 2d edit., 1994. Mem. Order of Coif, Beta Alpha Sigma. Office: U Calif Hastings Coll Law 200 Mcallister St San Francisco CA 94102-4976

LATIES, VICTOR GREGORY, psychology educator; b. Racine, Wis., Feb. 2, 1926; s. Simon Gregory and Rima (Kapnik) L.; m. Martha Ann Fisher, July 29, 1956; children: Nancy, Andrew, Claire. A.B., Tufts U., 1949; Ph.D., U. Rochester, N.Y., 1954. Ford Found. teaching intern Brown U., 1954-55; instr., asst. prof. dept. pharmacology Johns Hopkins U. Sch. Medicine, 1955-65; assoc. prof. U. Rochester Sch. Medicine and Dentistry, 1965-71, prof. dept. biophysics, psychology, pharmacology, 1971-93, dir. toxicology tng. program, 1978-91, 95-96, dir. environ. studies program, prof. dept. environ. medicine, 1992—; mem. preclinical psychopharmacology research rev. com. NIMH, 1967-71; mem. bd. on toxicology and environ. health hazards Nat. Acad. Sci.-NRC, 1977-80, mem. toxicology info.

program com., 1981-85; mem. sci. rev. com. for health research EPA, 1981-89. Editor: Jour. Exptl. Analysis of Behavior, 1972-76, exec. editor, 1966-72, 76—; editor: (with B. Weiss) Behavioral Toxicology, 1975, Behavioral Pharmacology, 1976; mem. editorial bd.: Jour. Pharmacology and Exptl. Therapeutics, 1965-71, Psychopharmacology, 1968-78, 81-89, The Behavior Analyst, 1980-82, Experimental and Clinical Psychopharmacology, 1993—; contbr. articles to profl. jours. Served with USN, 1944-46. Fellow Am. Psychol. Assn. (pres. div. psychopharmacology 1968-69, div. exptl. analysis of behavior 1979-82, bd. sci. affairs 1983-85), Behavioral Pharmacology Soc. (pres. 1966-68), Am. Soc. Pharmacology and Exptl. Therapeutics, Assn. for Behavior Analysis, Soc. Toxicology, Am. Psychol. Soc., Soc. for Exptl. Analysis of Behavior (sec.-treas. 1966—). Home: 55 Dale Rd E Rochester NY 14625-2137 Office: U Rochester Medical Ctr Dept Environ Medicine Box EHSC Rochester NY 14642

LATIMER, ALLIE B., lawyer, government official; b. Coraopolis, Pa.; d. Lawnye S. and Bennie Latimer. BS, Hampton Inst., 1947; JD, Howard U., 1953, MDiv, 1986, DMin, 1988; LLM, Cath. U., 1958; postgrad., Am. U. 1960-61. Bar: N.C. bar 1955, D.C. bar 1960. Vol. in projects Am. Friends Service Com., N.J. and, Europe, 1948-49; correctional officer Fed. Reformatory for Women, Alderson, W.Va., 1949-51; personnel clk. NIH, Bethesda, 1953-55; realty officer Mitchell AFB, N.Y., 1955-56; with Office Gen. Counsel, GSA, Washington, 1957-76; chief counsel Office Gen. Counsel, GSA, after 1966, asst. gen. counsel, 1971-76, gen. counsel, 1977-87; asst. gen. counsel NASA, 1976-77; spl. counsel Gen. Svcs. Adminstrn., Washington, 1987—; past chmn. central office com. Fed. Women's Program, GSA; mem. membership and budget com. Health and Welfare Council, 1967-72. Bd. dirs. D.C. Mental Health Assn., pres., 1977-79; bd. dirs. Friendship House, Washington; elder Presbyn. Ch.; pres. Interacial Council, 1964-75; chmn. Presbyn. Econ. Devel. Corp., 1975-81; mem. governing bd. Nat. Council Chs. of Christ in U.S.A. Recipient GSA Sustained Superior Service award, 1959, Meritorious Service award, 1964, Commendable Service award, 1964, Pub. Service award, 1971, Outstanding Performance award, 1971, Presdl. Rank award, 1983, Disting. Service award, 1984. Mem. ABA, Nat. Bar Assn. (sec. 1966-74), Fed. Bar Assn., Washington Bar Assn., N.C. Bar Assn., Nat. Bar Found. (dir. 1970-71, pres. 1974-75), Hampton Alumni Assn. (pres. Washington chpt. 1970-71), Howard Law Alumni Assn. (v.p. 1962-63) alumni assns), Links (pres. Washington chpt. 1971-74, nat. v.p. 1976-80), Federally Employed Women (founder, 1st pres.). Home: 1721 S St NW Washington DC 20009-6117

LATIMER, KENNETH ALAN, lawyer; b. Chgo., Oct. 26, 1943; s. Edward and Mary (Schiller) L.; m. Carole Ross, June 23, 1968; children: Cary, Darren, Wendy. BS, U. Wis., 1966; JD with honors, George Washington U., 1969. Bar: D.C. 1969, Ill. 1970. Atty. U.S. Office of Comptroller, Washington, 1969-70; assoc. Berger, Newmark & Fenchel, Chgo., 1970-74, ptnr., 1975-86; ptnr. Holleb & Coff, Chgo., 1986—; guest speaker Ill. Inst. for Continuing Legal Edn., Chgo., 1975-87. Pres. North Suburban Jewish Community Ctr., Highland Park, Ill., 1985; bd. dirs. Jewish Community Ctrs. of Chgo., 1985—. Mem. Ill. Bar Assn. (chmn. secct. coun. on comml. banking and bankruptcy 1990-91), Standard Club. Avocations: jogging, travel, tennis. Office: Holleb & Coff 55 E Monroe St Ste 4100 Chicago IL 60603-5803

LATIMER, LINDA GAY, small business owner; b. Washington, Oct. 3, 1943; d. Harry Allen and Beverly Elizabeth (Gosman) Latimer; m. 1963 (div. 1980); children: Debra Ann, Troy Christopher. Pers. mgr. Bozell & Jacobs, Palo Alto, Calif., Coakley Heagerty Advt., Santa Clara, Calif., 1982-85; owner The People Advertisers, Milpitas, Calif., 1985—; lectr. in field; resume evaluator job fairs/career fairs; seminar presenter Women in Bus., 1990. Contbr. articles to profl. jours. Mem. Women in Bus., Milpitas C. of C. Republican. Avocations: racquetball, cycling, tennis, public speaking. Office: The People Advertisers 259 W Calaveras Blvd Milpitas CA 95035

LATIMER, PAUL JERRY, non-destructive testing engineer; b. Springfield, Tenn., July 21, 1943; s. Paul Daniel and Juanita Inez (Richey) L.; m. Sylvia Susan Cole, June 6, 1966; children: Zachary Nathaniel, Matthew Jason. BS in Physics with honors, U. Tenn., 1966, MS in Physics, 1979, PhD in Physics, 1983. Devel. engr. Oak Ridge (Tenn.) Nat. Lab., 1980-81; faculty rsch. assoc. Ohio State U., Columbus, 1981; rsch. asst. U. Tenn., Knoxville, 1981-83; sr. rsch. engr. Babcock and Wilcox, Lynchburg, Va., 1983—. Patentee in field. Co-leader cub pack Lynchburg Area coun. Boy Scouts Am., 1983-84; vol. United Way, 1994. Mem. Am. Soc. Non-destructive Testing, Sigma Pi Sigma. Avocations: martial arts, hiking, lapidary, mineral collecting. Home: 303 Juniper Dr Lynchburg VA 24502-5661 Office: Babcock and Wilcox Lynchburg Rsch Ctr Lynchburg VA 24506

LATIMER, ROY TRUETT, museum executive; b. Albany, Tex., Aug. 23, 1928; s. Charles Lee and Zora Neil (Brock) L.; m. Judith Gail Johnson, Nov. 26, 1955 (div. 1975); children: Jeff, Laura, Tiffany; m. Harriet Calvin, Nov. 20, 1976. BA, Hardin-Simmons U., 1951. Owner Gen. Ins. Agy., Abilene, Tex., 1951-55; alumni dir. Hardin-Simmons U., Abilene, 1955-62; dir. pub. relations Tex. Assn. of Realtors, Austin, 1962-65; exec. dir. Tex. Hist. Commn., Austin, 1965-81, Tex. Hist. Found., Austin, 1972-81; v.p. pub. relations and mktg. Spaw Glass, Inc., Houston, 1981-85; pres. Houston Mus. Natural Sci., Houston, 1986—; pres. Nat. Conf. State Hist. Preservation Officers, 1974-75; bd. advisors Nat. Trust for Hist. Preservation, Washington, 1981-88. Mem. Tex. Ho. Reps., Austin, 1952-62; bd. devel. Hardin-Simmons U., 1974—; bd. dirs. Downtown Houston Assn., 1983—, past pres.; bd. dirs. Rice Design Alliance, Houston, 1983-87; chmn. S. Main Ctr. Assn., 1991-93. Mem. Houston C. of C., South Main Ctr. Assn. (bd. dirs. 1988—). Presbyterian. Avocations: running, canoeing, backpacking, travel. Home: 2807A Midlane St Houston TX 77027-4909 Office: Houston Mus Natural Sci 1 Hermann Circle Dr Houston TX 77030-1749

LATINI, ANTHONY A., insurance company financial executive; b. Chester, Pa., June 8, 1942; s. Angelo and Mildred (Gardner) L.; m. M. Katherine Kraft; children: Anthony A., Diane Marie. B.S., St. Joseph U., 1964. Tax mgr. Price Waterhouse & Co., Phila., 1971; dir. taxes Colonial Penn Group, Phila., 1971-76, treas., 1976-79, sr. v.p., treas., 1979-86, exec. v.p. fin. ops., 1987; chief fin. officer Pa. Conv. Authority, 1988; v.p., asst. comptr. Prudential Ins. Co. Am., South Plainfield, N.J., 1988-91, v.p. investment ops., systems and reporting, 1991—. Bd. mgrs. Children's Hosp. of Phila., 1985—, mem. common. long range planning com. Mem. Fin. Execs. Inst., Tax Execs. Inst., Soc. Ins. Accts., Nat. Assn. Corp. Treas., Internat. Assn. Fin. Planners, Am. Inst. C.P.A.s, Pa. Inst. C.P.A.s. Avocations: skiing; boating; tennis. Office: Three Gateway Ctr 12th Fl Prudential Ins Co Am 100 Mulberry St Newark NJ 07102-4004

LATINI, NANCY JANE, special education administrator; b. Buhl, Minn., Mar. 20, 1943; d. Nazzareno Thomas and Josephine (Pervenanze) L. BS, U. Minn., 1965; MS, St. Cloud State U., 1975; PhD, U. Minn., 1985. Cert. adminstr., Minn., Oreg. Spl. edn. tchr., trainer, adminstr. Mpls. Pub. Schs., 1965-90; spl. edn. adminstr. North Clackamas Sch. Dist., Milwaukie, Oreg., 1990—; cons. to univs.; mem. adv. bd. Spl. Edn. Adv. State Edn. Agy., Minn., 1985-88, Assn. for Retarded Citizens, Clackamas, 1990. Editor: Special Education Learning Disabilities Research, 1985. Mem. Coun. for Exceptional Children, Coun. of Adminstrs. in Spl. Edn., Delta Kappa Gamma, Phi Delta Kappa. Office: North Clackamas Sch Dist 1903 SE Oak Grove Blvd Portland OR 97267-2621

LATIOLAIS, RENÉ LOUIS, natural resources company executive, chemical engineer; b. New Orleans, July 21, 1942; s. Lewis W. and Elise (Kernion) L.; m. Joan Filizola, Mar. 31, 1962; children: Renelle Latiolais Brame, Craig A., Christopher A. BChemE, La. State U., 1965; grad. mgmt. devel. program, Harvard U., 1978. Registered profl. engr. Chem. and prodn. engr. Freeport Sulphur Co., Port Sulphur, La., 1965-68, prodn. supt., 1968-74, ops. mgr., 1974-78; asst. to pres. Freeport Sulphur Co., New Orleans, 1978-79; asst. mgr. corp. devel. Freeport Minerals Co., N.Y.C., 1979, exec. v.p., 1984; pres. Nat. Potash Co. (sub. Freeport Minerals Co.), N.Y.C., 1979-84; v.p. dir. ops. rev. and investor relations Freeport Minerals Internat., N.Y.C., 1982; sr. v.p. Freeport-McMoRan Inc., New Orleans, 1986—; pres., chief exec. officer Freeport-McMoRan Resource Ptnrs., New Orleans, 1988—. Patentee sulphur well sealing method, apparatus and method mining of subterranean sulphur. Mem. Am. Soc. Petroleum Engrs. Republican. Roman Catholic. Avocations: golf, tennis, sailing, skeet shoot-

ing. Office: Freeport-McMoRan Inc 1615 Poydras St New Orleans LA 70112-1217

LATNO, ARTHUR CLEMENT, JR., telephone company executive; b. Ross, Calif., May 14, 1929; s. Arthur Clement and Marie (Carlin) L.; m. Dorothy Sheldon Guess, June 27, 1953; children—Jeannine Marie, Michele Claire, Arthur Clement III, Mary Suzanne, Patrice Anne. B.S., Santa Clara U., 1951. With Pacific Tel. & Tel. Co., San Francisco, 1952-92; v.p. Pacific Tel. & Tel. Co., 1972-78, exec. v.p., 1978-92; former amb. accorded by Ronald Reagan, 1988; chmn. U.S. Delegation to World Telecom. Conf. Australia; bd. dirs. WestAm. Bank, WestAm. Bancorp. Bd. dirs. Marin Gen. Hosp.; bd. dirs., former chmn. Calif. Inst. Fed. Policy Rsch.; chmn. adv. bd. Berkeley program in bus. and social policy U. Calif; trustee St. Mary's Coll. Calif. Mem. Meadow Club, Knights of Malta, Alpha Sigma Nu. Home: 67 Convent Ct San Rafael CA 94901-1333

LATORRE, L. DONALD, chemical company executive; b. Amsterdam, N.Y., Sept. 19, 1937; s. Matthew Albert and Nancy (Donato) LaT.; m. Gloria Jean Lojpersberger, Nov. 5, 1940; children: L. Donald Jr., David S., Craig M., Amy E. BS, Lowell Tech. Inst., 1960; MS, Union Coll., 1967. Tech. sales rep. Ritter Chem. Corp., Amsterdam, 1960-66; market research, planning mgr. Diamond Shamrock, Cleve., 1967-69; market mgr. Diamond Shamrock Splty. Chems. Div., Cleve., 1969-73; comml. devel. mgr. BASF Wyandotte (Mich.) Corp., 1973-74; mktg. mgr. BASF Wyandotte Corp. Urethanes Div., 1974-79; div. mgr. BASF Wyandotte Corp. Styropor Div., Parsippany, N.J., 1980-82; exec. v.p., bd. dirs. Velcro, U.S.A., Manchester, N.H., 1982-84; sr. v.p., gen. mgr. splty. chems. div. Engelhard Corp., Menlo Park, N.J., 1984-88, v.p., pres. pigments and additives div., 1988-90, sr. v.p., COO, 1990-95, pres., COO, 1995—, also bd. dirs.; bd. dirs. N.E. Chemcat Corp. Officer Jr. C. of C., Amsterdam, 1962; bd. dirs. Manchester C. of C., 1982-84; bd. dirs. Syracuse Pulp and Paper Found., 1984—, engring. adv. bd. Mercer U., Macon, Ga., 1987—; trustee Ind. Coll. Fund. N.J., 1991—. Mem. Nat. Assn. Corp. Dirs., Mfrs.' Alliance for Productivity and Innovation. Office: Engelhard Corp 101 Wood Ave S Iselin NJ 08830

LATORRE, ROBERT GEORGE, naval architecture and engineering educator; b. Toledo, Jan. 9, 1949; s. Robert James and Madge Violette (Roy) L. BS in Naval Architecture and Marine Engring. with honors, U. Mich., 1971, MS in Engring., 1972; MSE in Naval Architecture, U. Tokyo, 1975, PhD in Naval Architecture, 1978. Asst. prof. U. Mich., Ann Arbor, 1979-83; assoc. prof. U. New Orleans, 1984-87, prof. naval architecture, marine engring., 1987, prof., chair naval architecture, marine engring., 1989—; assoc. prof. mech. engring., U. Tokyo, 1986-87; rsch. scientist, David Taylor Naval R & D Lab., Bethesda, Md., 1980, 81, Bassin d'Essais des Carenes, Paris, 1983; cons. in field. Contbr. to profl. publs. Mem. Soc. Naval Architects, Royal Inst. Naval Archtects Gt. Britain, ASME, Soc. NAval Architects Japan, Am. Soc. engring. Edn. (program chmn. ocean engring. divsn. 1989-93O, Japan Club New Orleans. Roman Catholic. Home: 300 Lake Marina Dr New Orleans LA 70124-1676 Office: U New Orleans 911 Engineering Bldg New Orleans LA 70148

LA TOURETTE, JOHN ERNEST, academic administrator; b. Perth Amboy, N.J., Nov. 5, 1932; s. John Crater and Charlotte Ruth (Jones) LaT.; m. Lillie M. Drum, Aug. 10, 1957; children—Marc Andrew, Yanique Renee. B.A., Rutgers U., 1954, M.A., 1955, Ph.D., 1962. Instr. Rutgers U., New Brunswick, N.J., 1960-61; asst. and assoc. prof. SUNY, Binghamton, 1961-76; chair dept. econs. SUNY, 1967-75, provost grad. studies, 1975-76; dean grad. sch., vice provost grad. studies Bowling Green (Ohio) State U., 1976-79; v.p., provost No. Ill. U., DeKalb, 1979-86; acting pres. No. Ill. U., 1984-85, pres., 1986—; vis. prof. Karlsruhe (W. Ger.) U., 1974; research prof. Brookings Inst., 1966-67; vis. scholar Ariz. State U., 1969, 70; lectr. Econs. Inst., U.S. Colo., 1966; dir. NSF Departmental Sci. Devel. Grant, 1970-75, First Am. Bank, DeKalb, 1985—, Higher Edn. Stategic Planning Inst., Washington, 1984-88; cons. North Cen. Assn., 1983—. Contbr. articles to profl. jours. Served to capt. USAF, 1955-58. Ford Found. grantee, 1963; SUNY Found. grantee, 1963, 65, 70. Mem. Am. Econ. Assn., Can. Econ. Assn. (fin. acctg. adv. standards coun. 1991—). Home: 3734 N Pine Grove Ave Apt 304 Chicago IL 60613-4161 Office: No Ill U Office of Pres De Kalb IL 60115

LATOURETTE, STEVEN C., congressman; b. Cleve., July 22, 1954; m. Susan LaTourette; 4 children. BA in Hist., U. Mich., 1976; JD, Cleve. State U., 1979. Asst. pub. defender Lake County Pub. Defender's Office, 1980-83; assoc. Cannon, Stern, Aveni & Krivok, Painesville, 1983-86; with Baker, Hackenberg & Collins, Painesville, 1986-88; prosecutingatty. Lake County Prosecutor Office, 1988-93; mem. U.S. Ho. of Reps., Washington, 1994—; mem. Com. on Transp. & Infrastructure, subcom. pub. bldgs. & econ. devel., surface transp., & water resources and environ. U.S. Ho. of Reps., also vice-chmn. investigations and oversight subcom., mem. com. Reform and Oversight, D.C. subcom., mem. com. Small Bus., subcoms. Tax & Fin. and Govt. Programs, mem. U.S. Holocaust Meml. Coun., 1995—. Office: US House Reps 431 Cannon House Office Bldg Washington DC 20515-3519*

LATOURRETTE, JAMES THOMAS, retired electrical engineering and computer science educator; b. Miami, Ariz., Dec. 26, 1931; s. Emery Everest and Carrie B. (Hoffman) LaT.; m. Muriel Ashe, Aug. 28, 1955; children: Mary Beth, John Emery, James Thomas, Joanne. B.S., Calif. Inst. Tech., 1953; M.A. (Gen. Communication Co. fellow), Harvard U., 1954, Ph.D. (NSF fellow), 1958. Research assoc., lectr. physics Harvard U., 1957-59; physicist Gen. Electric Research Lab., Schenectady, 1960-62; sr. supervisory scientist TRG, Inc., Melville, N.Y., 1962-66; sect. head TRG div. Control Data Corp., Melville, 1966-67; prof. elec. engring. and computer sci. Poly. U. (formerly Poly. Inst. Bklyn. and Poly. Inst. N.Y.), Farmingdale, N.Y., 1967-93, prof. emeritus, 1993; assoc. dir. Weber Rsch. Inst., Poly. U., 1987-90. Contbr. articles to profl. jours. NSF postdoctoral fellow Physikalisches Institut der U. Bonn, Germany, 1959-60. Mem. AAAS, IEEE, IEEE Computer Soc., N.Y. Acad. Sci., Assn. for Computer Machinery, Sigma Xi, Tau Beta Pi. Home: 2 Candlewood Ct Huntington NY 11743-1827 Office: Poly Univ Rt 110 Farmingdale NY 11735

LATSHAW, JOHN, entrepreneur; b. Kansas City, Dec. 10, 1921; s. Ross W. and Edna (Parker) L.; m. Barbara Haynes, Nov. 13, 1954 (div. Dec. 1975); children: Constance Haynes, Elizabeth Albright Latshaw Reid-Scott. Student, Kansas City Jr. Coll., 1938-40; BS, Mo. U., 1942. Mgr. trading dept. Harris, Upham & Co., 1943-49; ptnr. Uhlmann & Latshaw, 1949-53; ptnr. E.F. Hutton & Co. (merger with Uhlmann & Latshaw), 1954-87, exec. v.p., mgn. dir., 1987—; chmn. bd. dirs., chief exec. officer B.C. Christopher & Co., 1987-89, chmn. emeritus, 1989-90; chmn., chief exec. officer Conchemco Inc.; chmn., chief exec. officer, mng. dir. Latshaw Enterprises, 1990—; chmn. bd. dirs. Bus. Communications, Inc., Install, Maintain and Repair, Inc., Interior Designs, Inc.; mem. Kansas City Bd. Trade; gov. Midwest Stock Exchange, 1966-68; moderator, opening speaker Plenary Panel on Needs and Opportunities in Key Bus. Sectors, Miami Conf. on the Caribbean, 1980; pres. World Cable Ltd. Past Chmn. Key Men's Council; past pres. Friends of Zoo, 1970; mem. exec. com. Religious Heritage Am., Starlight Theatre, Performing Arts Kansas City; v.p., mem. exec. bd. Am. Cancer Soc., 1970, 71; mem. Jackson County and Crusade Adv. Com., Gov.'s Com. on Higher Edn.; bd. dirs. Kansas City Theatre Guild Council, The Curry Found., Am. Urban Devel. Found., Kansas City Crime Commn.; trustee City Employees Pension Plan, St. Andrew's Episcopal Ch. Meml. and Res. Trust Fund, U. Mo., Kansas City; bd. govs. Am. Royal, Agrl. Hall of Fame, 1976-77; exec. bd. Kansas City Area council Boy Scouts Am. 1970-72, adv. bd., 1973, chmn. patriotism program, 1970; hon. bd. dirs. Rockhurst Coll.; past pres. Kansas City Soccer Club, Inc.; mem. exec. com. N.Am. Soccer League, 1968, 69; bd. govs. Invest-In-Am. Nat. Council; mem. Central Region exec. com.; regional chmn. Invest-in-Am. Week Liaison, 1958—; mem. fin. com. Mayor's Profl. Theater; mem. Univ. Assos. of U. Mo. of Kansas City; chmn. hon. trustees YWCA, 1968-69; trustee Midwest Research Inst.; mem. chancellor's adv. council Met. Community Colls., 1976-77; mem. pres.'s council bd. hon. trustees Kansas City Art Inst.; mem. Pres.' Scholarship Club Avila Coll.; bd. dirs., mem. fin. com. Mayor's Christmas Tree Assn.; chmn. bd. trustee Conservatory of Music; community adv. com. U. Mo. Kansas City Sch. Nursing; mem. Civic Council Greater Kansas City; chmn. Brotherhood Citation Dinner for NCCJ, 1980; trustee Westminster Coll., 1981; hon. bd. govs. Hyman Brand Hebrew Acad.; adv. com. Metro Energy Ctr., 1982; mem. NASA adv. bd. to Pres. U.S., 1983-86.

Recipient citation of merit U. Mo., 1957, Golden Eagle award Nat. Invest in Am. Coun., 1970, Chaturathabhorn of Most Exalted Order of White Elephant award, Thailand, 1983; named hon. consul Thailand, Royal Consulate Gen., 1986, The Knight Comdr. of the Most Noble Order of the Crown of Thailand, 1993; decorated Knight Hospitaller of Malta Sovereign Order St. John Jerusalem. Mem. Internat. Trade Assn. (chmn. bd.), Kansas City C. of C. (dir., past pres.), Bus. and Profl. Assn. Western Mo. (mem. adv. bd.), Kansas City Security Traders Assn. (past pres.), Nat. Security Traders Assn. (past exec. v.p.), Wine Soc. of World, Order Jim Daisy, Sigma Nu. Episcopalian (trustee). Clubs: Carriage, Mission Hills Country. Home and Office: 3 Dunford Cir Kansas City MO 64112-2362

LATTANZIO, STEPHEN PAUL, astronomy educator; b. Yonkers, N.Y., June 29, 1949; s. Anthony Raymond and Anella Lattanzio; m. Barbara Regina Knisely, Aug. 14, 1976; children: Gregory Paul, Timothy Paul. BA in Astronomy, U. Calif., Berkeley, 1971; MA in Astronomy, UCLA, 1973, postgrad., 1973-75. Planetarium lectr. Griffith Obs., Los Angeles, 1973-75; instr. astronomy El Camino Coll., Torrance, Calif., 1974-75; planetarium lectr. Valley Coll., Los Angeles, 1975; prof. astronomy Orange Coast Coll., Costa Mesa, Calif., 1975—; planetarium dir., 1975—; mem. adv. commn. Natural History Found. Orange County, Calif., 1988-91; scientific advisor instructional TV series Universe: The Infinite Frontier, 1992—. Co-author: Study Guide for Project: Universe, 1978, 2d rev. edition 1981; textbook reviewer, 1978—; co-screenwriter Project: Universe instructional TV series episode, 1979; contbr. articles to profl. jours. Mem. Astron. Soc. Pacific, Nat. Space Soc., The Planetary Soc., Space Studies Inst. Sigma Xi (assoc.), Phi Beta Kappa. Avocation: astronautics. Office: Orange Coast Coll 2701 Fairview Rd Costa Mesa CA 92626-5561

LATTES, RAFFAELE, physician, educator; b. Torino, Italy, May 22, 1910; came to U.S., 1940, naturalized, 1947; s. Attilio Marco and Dolce (Noemi) L.; m. Eva H. Hahn, 1936; children—Conrad George (dec.), Robert George. M.D. U. Torino 1933; D.M.S., Columbia, 1946. Diplomate: Am. Bd. Pathology. Tng. surgery, surg. pathology U. Torino Med. Sch., 1934-38; instr. pathology Woman's Med. Coll. Pa., Phila., 1941-43; asst. prof. pathology N.Y. Postgrad. Hosp. and Med. Sch., 1944-48; instr. surg. pathology Coll. Phys. and Surg., Columbia, 1943-46, asst. prof., 1948-49, asso. prof. surgery, surg. pathology, 1949-51, prof. surgery, surg. pathology, 1950-78, prof. emeritus, 1978—, spl. lectr. in surgery, 1978, dir. lab. surg. pathology, 1951-78. Fellow A.M.A., Coll. Am. Pathologists, N.Y. Acad. Medicine, Internat. Acad. apathology; mem. N.Y. Path. Soc., Am. Assn. Pathologists and bacteriologists, A.A.A.S., Am. Assn. Cancer Rsch., Am. Soc. Clin. Pathologists, Arthur Purdy Stout Soc. Surgical Pathologists. Home: 597 Rutland Ave Teaneck NJ 07666-2947 Office: Coll Physicians and Surgeons 630 W 168th St New York NY 10032-3702

LATTIMER, GARY LEE, physician; b. Nanticoke, Pa., Dec. 4, 1939; s. Paul Floyd and Gene Elizabeth L.; m. Patricia Sara Weise, June 14, 1958; children: Toni Jo, Gregory Weise. M.D., Temple U., 1966; postgrad., Jefferson Med. Coll., 1970-72. Intern Allentown (Pa.) Hosp.; resident Presbyn.-Univ. Hosp., Phila., 1969-70; resident Jefferson Med. Coll. Hosp., Phila., 1970-71, chief med. resident, 1971-72; chief infectious diseases Allentown-Sacred Heart Hosp. Center, 1972-80; assoc. prof. medicine U. N.D., 1980-81, chief infectious diseases, 1980-81; chief infectious diseases New Britain (Conn.) Gen. Hosp., 1981—; assoc. prof. medicine U. Conn., 1981-83; dir. infectious diseases Williamsport Hosp., Divine Providence Hosp., 1983—. Author: Legionnaires' Disease, 1981; contbr. articles to profl. jours. Served with M.C. U.S. Army, 1967-69. Decorated Bronze Star; recipient Disting. Service award Pa. chpt. Am. Legion. Fellow ACP; mem. Am. Soc. Microbiology, AAAS, Nat. Found. Infectious Diseases, Am. Legion. Office: 904 Campbell St Williamsport PA 17701-3166

LATTIMER, JOHN KINGSLEY, physician, educator; b. Mt. Clemens, Mich., Oct. 14, 1914; s. Eugene and Gladys Soulier (Lenfestey) L.; m. Jamie Elizabeth Hill, Jan. 1948; children: Evan, Jon, Gary. AB, Columbia U., 1935, MD, 1938, ScD, 1943; student, Balliol Coll., Oxford (Eng.) U., 1944, Med. Field Svc. Sch., Paris, 1945. Diplomate Am. Bd. Urology. Surg. intern Meth.-Episcopal Hosp., N.Y.C., 1938-40; urol. resident Squier Urol. Clinic Presbyn. Hosp., N.Y.C., 1940-43, dir. Squier Urol. Clinic, 1955-80, dir. urol. svc., 1955-80, also dir. urology Sch. Nursing; staff asst., instr. urology Columbia Coll. Physicians and Surgeons, 1940-53, asst. prof. clin. urology, 1953-55, prof. urology, chmn. dept. urology, 1955-80; vis. prof. Med. Coll. S.C., Med. Coll. Va., Mayo Clinic Med. Sch., Rochester, Minn., 1977, Boston U. Tufts U., U. Oreg., Ind. U., UCLA, Leeds Med. Sch. U. Witwatersrand, South Africa; guest lectr. Akron City Hosp., 1977, Reno Surg. Soc., 1977; chief urology Babies Hosp., Vanderbilt Clinic, Frances Delafield Hosp., N.Y.C., 1955; cons. urology VA, N.Y.C., 1947-80, USPHS Hosp., S.I., N.Y.C., Meth. Hosp., Bklyn., Englewood (N.J.), Yonkers (N.Y.) gen. hosps., Harlem, Roosevelt, St. Lukes hosps. (all N.Y.C.); mem. com. surgery in Tb, genito-urinary Tb VA; med. cons. Time mag.; cons. to com. on therapy Nat. Tb Assn.; mem. expert adv. panel biology human reprodn. WHO; mem. N.Y. Supreme Ct. Med. Arbitration Panel, 1975; Am. Urol. Assn. rep. to NRC-Nat. Acad. Scis.; mem. tng. grants com. NIH, 1968-72. Contbr. over 350 articles on urology and history to various publs., also chpts. in books; guest author New Eng. Jour. Medicine; rschr., writer, speaker on assassinations of Pres. Lincoln and Kennedy, and Nuremberg Trials. Trustee Presbyn. Hosp., 1974-78; mem. vis. com. Ft. Ticonderoga Mus.; mem. vis. com. sect. arms and armour Met. Mus. Art, 1978; chmn. book com. Englewood Hist. Soc., 1984—; mem. Dallas Coun. World Affairs, Phila. Coun. World Affairs; official historian City of Englewood, N.J. Maj. M.C., AUS, 1943-46; med. officer at Nuremberg Trials, 1945-46. Decorated Croix de Guerre (France and Belgium); recipient Joseph Mather Smith prize for rsch. kidney disease Columbia U., 1943, honor award for meritorious work in field of Tb Am. Acad. Tb Physicians, also prizes for sci. exhibits, gold medal alumni assn. Coll. Physicians and Surgeons 1971, Disting. Svc. award 1993, Hugh Young medal for outstanding work in infectious diseases 1973, Belfield medal Chgo. Urol. Soc., Burpeau medal N.J. Acad. Medicine, Edward Henderson Gold medal Am. Geriatrics Soc., 1978, Gt. medal City of Paris, 1979, Normandy Liberation medal Soc. French War Vets., Nat. Kidney Fedn. medal, 1987, Am. Acad. Pediatrics Urology medal, 1987; Richard Chute lectr., 1973, Stoneburner lectr. Med. Coll. Va., 1973. Fellow ACS (chmn. adv. com. urology 1962-64, gov. 1966-79, com. on undergrad. tng. 1967-80, chmn. nominating com. 1976-77, com. to study size and composition of bd. govs.), AMA (prize rsch. kidney Tb 1953), Am. Acad. Pediatrics (chmn. com. on pediatric urology, pres. sect. urology 1973-79); mem. AAAS, Am. Assn. Clin. Urologists, Assn. Am. Med. Colls., Clin. Soc. Genito-Urinary Surgeons (pres. 1984), N.Y. Acad. Sci. (trustee), N.Y. Acad. Medicine (chmn. genito-urinary sect. 1956-57, trustee 1978-84, v.p. 1986-87, chmn. bldg. com. 1982-87), Am. Assn. Genito-Urinary Surgeons (pres. 1982), Am. Urol. Assn. (pres. 1975-76, chmn. com. on pediatric urology, pres. N.Y. sect. 1966, exec. com. 1967-80, com. on surgery, rev. and long range planning com., editorial bd. Jour. Urology 1965-68, chmn. com. to gather info. about urology, chmn. coordinating coun. for urology, chmn. nominating com. 1976-77, 1st prize for clin. rsch. 1950, 60, Ramon Guiterez medal 1980), Am. Thoracic Soc., AAUP, Soc. U. Urologists (pres. 1969), Nat. Inst. Social Scis., St. Nicholas Soc., Assn. Mil. Surgeons Harvey Soc., Nat. Tb Assn., N.Y. State Pediatrics Soc., N.Y. Med. Socs., New York County Med. Soc., So. Pediatric Urology (pres. 1961-62), Brit. Assn. Urol. Surgeons (corr.), N.Y. Soc. Surgeons, N.Y. Soc. Professions, Internationale Société d'Urology (v.p. 1967-73, pres.1973-79), Assn. Pediatric Urology (pres. 1961), Spanish Urol. Assn. (hon.), Paleopathology Assn., Charles A. Lindbergh Soc. (ofcl. historian City of Englewood 1990), Dallas Surgical Soc., Japanese Urol. Assn. (hon.), Italian Urol. Assn. (hon.), SAR, Assn. Mil. Historians, Soc. War 1812, Mil. Order Fgn. Wars U.S., Order of Founders and Patriots, Arms and Armour Soc. N.Y., Arms and Armour Soc. Eng., Arms and Armour Soc. Gueurnsey, Soc. Colonial Wars, Englewood Hist. Soc., Manuscript Soc., Revolutionary War Round Table of N.Y., Abraham Lincoln Soc., Lincoln Soc. N.Y., Wis., Ill., Fla., Washington, Civil War Surgeons (hon.), Am. Legion, 82d Airborne Div. Assn., 101st Airborne Div. Assn., Res. Officers Assn., Metropolitan Club, Sigma Xi. Office: Columbia U Med Sch New York NY 10032

LATTIN, ALBERT FLOYD, banker; b. Everett, Wash., May 23, 1950; s. Albert S. and Erma Victoria (Hunt) L. Student, U. Nairobi, Kenya, 1970-71, Am. U. Cairo, Egypt, 1972; BA, Antioch U., 1973; MA, NYU, 1979; MBA, Columbia U. 1984. Asst. curator The Bklyn. Mus., 1973-76, assoc. 1976-79; sec. of the mus. Solomon R. Guggenheim Mus., N.Y.C., 1979-80,

cons. in arts, 1980-83; banker Bankers Trust Co., N.Y.C., 1984-93; v.p. CS 1st Boston, N.Y.C., 1993-95, CS First Boston Corp., N.Y.C., 1995—; dir. trustee Mus. Holography, N.Y.C., 1980-87; bd. adv. Gallery Assn. N.Y. State, 1988—; treas. The Theban Found., 1991—. Editor, researcher book and catalogue Africa in Antiquity: The Arts of Ancient Nubia and the Sudan, 1978; organizer exhibition/movie The Heritage of Islam, 1982. Mem. Bklyn. Hist. Soc., Bklyn. Heights Assn., 1986—. Mem. Am. Banking Assn., Urban Land Inst., Internat. Council of Mus., Am. Assn. Mus., Internat. Assn. Egyptologists, Roundout Valley Country Club, Columbia Club. Home: 242 Henry St Brooklyn NY 11201-4662 Office: CS First Boston Corp 55 E 52d St New York NY 10055

LATTIS, RICHARD LYNN, zoo director; b. Louisville, May 31, 1945; s. Albert Francis and Jean Elizabeth (Baker) L.; m. Sharon Louise Elkins, June 22, 1968; children Michael David, Robert Brian, Theodore James. BS in Biol., U. Louisville, 1967, MS in Ecol., 1970. Asst. curator edn. Bronx (N.Y.) Zoo, 1974-75, curator edn., 1975-78; chmn. edn. The Wildlife Conservation Soc., 1978-80; dir. city zoos N.Y. Zoological Soc., 1980-93, v.p. conservation parks and aquariums, 1993—; lectr., cons. zoos, aquariums, nature ctrs.; past cons. Time-Life Wild Wild World Animals film series; appeared Who's Who in the Zoo WNBC-TV, N.Y.C. Sgt. USAR, 1970-76. Mem. AAAS, Am. Assn. Zool. Parks and Aquariums (bd. dirs., bd. regents, govt. affairs. com.), Nat. Hist. Soc., Soc. Conservation Biol., Zoo Biol., Sigma Xi. Avocations: fishing, photography, golf, gardening, bird watching. Home: 1650 Maxwell Dr Yorktown Heights NY 10598 Office: Wildlife Conservation Soc The Bronx Zoo Bronx NY 10460

LATTMAN, LAURENCE HAROLD, retired academic administrator; b. N.Y.C., Nov. 30, 1923; s. Jacob and Yetta (Schwartz) L.; m. Hanna Renate Cohn, Apr. 12, 1946; children—Martin Jacob, Barbara Diane. BSChemE, Coll. City N.Y., 1948; MS in Geology, U. Cin., 1951, PhD, 1953. Instr. U. Mich., 1952-53; asst. head photogeology sect. Gulf Oil Corp., Pitts., 1953-57; asst. prof. to prof. geomorphology Pa. State U., 1957-70; prof., head dept. geology U. Cin., 1970-75; dean Coll. of Mines U. Utah, 1975-83, dean Coll. Engring., 1978-83; pres. N.Mex. Tech., Socorro, 1983-93, pres. emeritus, 1993—; bd. dirs. Pub. Svc. Co. of N.Mex.; cons. U.S. Army Engrs., Vicksburg, Miss., 1965-69, also major oil cos. Author: (with R.G. Ray) Aerial Photographs in Field Geology, 1965, (with D. Zillman) Energy Law; Contbr. articles to profl. jours. Served with AUS, 1943-46. Fenneman fellow U. Cin., 1953. Fellow Geol. Soc. Am.; mem. Am. Assn. Petroleum Geologists, Am. Soc. Photogrammetry (Ford Bartlett award 1968), Soc. Econ. Paleontologists and Mineralogists, AIME (Disting. mem. 1981, Mineral Industries Edn., award 1986—), Assn. Western Univs. (chmn. bd. dirs. 1986-87), Sigma Xi. Home: 6433 Glen Oak NE Albuquerque NM 87111-6506

LATTO, LEWIS M., JR., broadcasting company executive; b. Duluth, Minn., Jan. 21, 1940; s. Lewis M. and Ethel S. L.; divorced; children: Aaron, Caroline. B.A., U. Minn., 1963. Owner, mgr. Sta. KXTP, Duluth, 1965-94, Sta. WAKX-FM, 1974-94; owner Sta. WEVE AM-FM, Eveleth, Minn., 1978—, Sta. KGPZ-FM, Grand Rapids, Minn., 1995—. Mem. Duluth City Council, 1969-75, pres., 1974. Mem. Nat. Radio Broadcasters Assn. (dir.), Minn. Broadcasters Assn. (pres. 1992-93). Republican. Methodist. Office: Northland Radio Stas 5732 Eagle View Dr Duluth MN 55803-9498

LATZ, G. IRVING, II, manufacturing company executive; b. Ft. Wayne, Ind., Feb. 12, 1920; s. G. Irving and Carrie (Stiefel) L.; m. Janet Horwitz Simon, Oct. 16, 1949; children: Sara Rose, G. Irving III. BS in Econs., U. Pa., 1941; MBA, U. Chgo., 1971. Trainee F.R. Lazarus Co., Columbus, Ohio, 1941; with Wolf & Dessauer Co., Ft. Wayne, 1946-66, treas., 1947-66, pres., 1957-66; dir. Model Cities, Columbus, 1967-68; cons. urban affairs Michael Reese Hosp. and Med. Ctr., Chgo., 1973-74; cons. econ. urban affairs, 1974-80; prin. Latz Assocs., Ft. Wayne, 1974-80; pres. Sci-Agra, Inc., Ft. Wayne, 1980—; exec. dir. Ft. Wayne Future, Inc., 1984-80; hon. bd. dirs. Ft. Wayne Nat. Bank. Gen. chmn. Ft. Wayne Fine Arts Found., 1958-67, pres., 1967-69; gen. chmn. Ft. Wayne United Fund; pres. Ind. Retail Coun., 1965-66; bd. dirs. Ft. Wayne Jewish Fedn., United Community Svcs. With AUS, 1941-46. Mem. Ft. Wayne C. of C. (v.p.), Ft. Wayne Country Club. Home: 1919 S Hadley Rd Fort Wayne IN 46804-1461

LATZER, RICHARD NEAL, investment company executive; b. N.Y.C., Jan. 6, 1937; s. Paul John and Alyce A. Latzer; B.A., U. Pa., 1959, M.A., 1961; m. Ellen Weston, Sept. 5, 1965; children—Steven, David. Security analyst Mut. Benefit Life Ins. Co., Newark, 1963-66; portfolio mgr. Equitable Life Ins., Washington, 1966-68; securities analyst Investors Diversified Services, Mpls., 1968-69, dir. cert. and ins. investments, 1969-77, v.p. cert. and ins. investments, 1977-84; v.p. cert. and ins. investments IDS Fin. Services, Inc., 1984-86, IDS Fin. Corp., 1987-88; v.p. investments, IDS Reins. Co., 1986-88; asst. treas. Investors Syndicate Life Ins. & Annuity Co., Mpls., 1969-72; v.p. IDS Life Ins. Co., Mpls., 1973-80, v.p. investments, 1980-88; v.p. Investors Syndicate of Am., 1973-77, v.p. investments, 1977-84; v.p. Investors Syndicate Title & Guaranty Co., 1977-83, investment officer IDS Life Ins. Co. of N.Y., 1977-88; v.p. investments IDS Life Capital Resource Fund I, Inc., 1981-88 ; IDS Spl. Income Fund, Inc., 1981-88, Am Enterprise Life Ins. Co., 1986-88, Reinsurance Co. 1986-88; IDS Life Series Fund, 1986-88; IDS Life Managed Fund, Inc., 1986-88, IDS Property Casualty, 1987-88; v.p. IDS Realty Corp. 1987-88; pres., chmn. bd., bd. dirs. Real Estate Svcs. Co., 1986-88; IDS Life Moneyshare Fund, Inc., 1981-88 ; IDS Cert. Co., 1984-88 ; chmn. bd., dir. IDS Real Estate Services Co., 1983-86; v.p. Fireman's Fund Am. Life Ins. Co., 1985-86; dir. Investors Syndicate Devel. Corp., Mpls., 1970-88 , Nuveen Realty Corp., Mpls., 1976-80; sr. v.p., chief investment officer Transamerica Corp., San Francisco, 1988—, pres., CEO Transamerica Investment Svcs., Inc., San Francisco 1988—; dir., chief investment officer, chmn. investment com. Transamerica Occidental Life Ins. Co., L.A., 1989—, Transamerica Life Ins. and Annuity Co., L.A., 1989—; dir., chief investment officer, mem. investment com. Transamerica Ins. Group, Woodland Hills, 1988-93; bd. dirs., mem. exec. com. Transamerica Realty Svcs., Inc., San Francisco, 1988—, dir. Transamerica Realty Investment Corp., San Francisco 1988—; chmn. pension investment com. Transamerica Corp., San Francisco, 1988—, dir. Transamerica Cash Res. Inc., L.A., 1989-90, Transamerica Income Shares, 1989—; dir., mem. investment com. Transamerica Life Ins. Co. Can., Toronto, 1991—; chief investment officer, mem. operating com. ARC Reinsurance Corp., Honolulu, 1993—. Served to lt., USN, 1960-63. Chartered fin. analyst. Mem. Security Analysts San Francisco, Chartered Fin. Analysts. Office: 600 Montgomery St San Francisco CA 94111-2702

LAU, CHARLES KWOK-CHIU, architect, architectural firm executive; b. Hong Kong, Oct. 19, 1954; came to U.S., 1973; s. Oi-Ting and Wai-Han L. BFA in Environ. Design, U. Hawaii Manoa, Honolulu, 1977. Registered architect, Hawaii. Designer CJS Group Architects, Honolulu, 1977-78, Fox Hawaii, Honolulu, 1978-80, Wimberly Allison Tong & Goo, Honolulu, 1980-82, Architects Hawaii, Honolulu, 1982-84; assoc., designer Stringer & Assocs., Honolulu, 1984-85; pres. AM Ptrns., Inc., Honolulu, 1985—; instr. U. Hawaii, Honolulu, 1987. Principal works include Crystal Fantasy, Hyatt Regency Hotel, Honolulu, 1988 (Merit award Hawaii chpt. AIA 1988), Dole Cannery Sq., Honolulu, 1989 (Merit award Hawaii Renaissance 1989), Danelle Christie's, Ala Moana Hotel, Honolulu, 1989 (Hawaii Region award Illuminating Engring. Soc. N.Am. 1989, Grand and Nat. Grand awards Hawaii Renaissance 1989, Tiger Restaurant, Lahaina, Hawaii, 1990 (Gold Key Excellence in Interior Design award Am. Hotel and Motel Assn. 1990, Nat. and Merit awards Hawaii Renaissance 1990), La Pierre du Roi, ANA Kalakaua Ctr., Honolulu, 1990 (Grand and Nat. Grand awards 1990), Crazy Shirts, Honolulu, 1991 (Grand and Overall awards Hawaii Hawaii Renaissance 1991), Grand Hyatt Wailea, Maui, Hawaii, 1992 (Merit award Hawaii chpt. AIA 1992), Carrera y Carrera, Ala Moana Ctr., Honolulu, 1992 (Merit award Hawaii chpt. AIA 1992), Danelle Christie's, Outrigger Waikiki Hotel, Honolulu, 1992 (Merit award Hawaii Renaissance 1992), Exec. Ctr. Hotel, Honolulu, 1992 (Merit award Hawaii Renaissance 1992), Centre Ct. Restaurant, Honolulu, 1993 (Merit award Hawaii Renaissance 1993), Lann Huli, Kailua, 1993 (Spl. Recognition award Parade of Homes 1993), 218 Plantation Club Dr., Kapalua, Maui, 1993 (Interior Design award Am. Soc. Interior Design 1993), Royal Garden Restaurant, Alamoana Hotel, Honolulu, 1994 (Brand and Overall award Hawaii Renaissance, 1994, Lani Huli, Kailua Hawaii 1994 (Project of Yr., City and County of Honolulu 1994). Mem. AIA (mem. design award jury selection com. Honolulu chpt. 1990), C.

of C. Hawaii, Chinese C. of C. Hawaii, Pacific Club. Office: AM Partners Inc 1164 Bishop St Ste 1000 Honolulu HI 96813

LAU, CHERYL A., former state official. BM, Ind. U.; JD, U. San Francisco. Bar: 1986. Formerly dep. atty. gen. Nev. Motor Vehicles and Pub. Safety Dept., Carson City, Nev.; sec. of state, State of Nev. State of Nev., Carson City, 1991-94; gen. coun. U.S. Ho. of Reps., Washington, 1995—. Office: House of Reps 219 Cannon House Office Bldg Washington DC 20515

LAU, H. LORRIN, physician, inventor; b. Honolulu, Hawaii, Apr. 21, 1932; s. Henry S. and Helen (Lee) L.; m. Maureen Lau; children: David, Marianne, Mike, Mark, Linda. AB cum laude, Harvard U., 1950-54; MD, Johns Hopkins U., 1954-58, MPH, 1970-71. Asst. prof. Sch. Med. Johns Hopkins U. (Balt.), 1964-82; assoc. prof. U. Hawaii, 1982-84; chief ob-gyn. St. Francis West Hosp., Honolulu, 1980-92, Kuakini Hosp., Honolulu, 1994-95. Fellow AMA; mem. ACOG, Internat. Soc. Biology and Medicine. Inventor pregnancy tests, introduced alphafetoprotein tests into obstetrics in USA, 1971. Home: 925 14 Ave Honolulu HI 96816 Office: 1010 S King St Honolulu HI 96814

LAU, IAN VAN, safety research engineer, biomechanics expert; b. Macao, Apr. 4, 1950; came to U.S., 1969; s. Wai-Hung L.; m. Helen Ting, Jan. 5, 1973; 1 child, Lisa Alison. BS, U. Mass. at Lowell, 1973; PhD, Johns Hopkins U., 1977. Rsch. engr. GM Rsch. Labs., Warren, Mich., 1978-86, sr. staff engr., 1986—; head dept. automotive safety and health GM, 1993—; mgr. USCAR safety consortium for Gen. Motors, Ford and Chrysler. Contbr. articles on injury prevention in car crashes (Caldwell award 1988, 89, 91); discoverer viscous injury index (Hwy. Safety award 1988); inventor safety steering wheel (McCuen award 1989) side impact dummy. Mem. Soc. Automotive Engrs. (Isbrandt Safety Engring. award 1986, 87, 91), Biomed. Engring. Soc. Republican. Roman Catholic. Avocation: racquetball. Office: GM Rsch Labs Automotive Safety & Health Warren MI 48090

LAU, LAWRENCE JUEN-YEE, economics educator, consultant; b. Guizhou, China, Dec. 12, 1944; came to U.S., 1961, naturalized, 1974; s. Shai-Tat and Chi-Hing (Yu) Liu; m. Tamara K. Jablonski, June 23, 1984. BA with great distinction, Stanford U., 1964; MA, U. Calif.-Berkeley, 1966, PhD, 1969. Acting asst. prof. econs. Stanford U. Palo Alto, Calif. 1966-67, asst. prof., 1967-73, assoc. prof., 1973-76, prof., 1976—, Kwoh-Ting Li prof. econ. devel., 1992—; co-dir. Asia/Pacific Rsch. Ctr., 1992—; cons. The World Bank, Washington, 1976—; vice chmn. Bank of Canton of Calif. Bldg. Corp., San Francisco, 1981-85; dir. Bank of Canton of Calif., San Francisco, 1979-85; dir. Property Resources Equity Trust, Los Gatos, 1987-88; vice-chmn. Complete Computer Co. Far Eat Ltd., Hong Kong, 1981-89. Co-author: (with D.T. Jamison) Farmer Education and Farm Efficiency, 1982, Models of Devlopment: A Comparative Study of Economic Growth in South Korea and Taiwan, 1986, rev. edit., 1990; contbr. articles to profl. jours. Adv. bd. Self-Help for Elderly, San Francisco, 1982—; bd. dirs. Chiang Ching-Kuo Found. for Internat. Scholarly Exch., 1989—; govs. coun. econ. policy advisors State of Calif., 1993—. John Simon Guggenheim Meml. fellow, 1973; fellow Ctr. for Advanced Study in Behavioral Scis., 1982; Overseas fellow Churchill Coll., Cambridge U., Eng., 1984. Fellow Econometric Soc.; mem. Academia Sinica, Conf. Research in Income and Wealth. Republican. Episcopalian. Office: Stanford U Dept Econs Stanford CA 94305

LAU, MICHELE DENISE, advertising consultant, sales trainer, television personality; b. St. Paul, Dec. 6, 1960; d. Dwyane Udell and Patricia Ann (Yri) L. Student, U. Minn., 1979-82. Pub. rels. coord. Stillwater (Minn.) C. of C., 1977-79; asst. mgr. Salkin & Linoff, Mpls., 1982, store merchandiser, sales trainer, 1982-83; rental agt. Sentinel Mgmt. Co., St. Paul, 1983-84; account exec. Community Svc. Publs., Mpls., 1984-85, frwy. news supr., 1985, asst. sales mgr., 1985-86; asst. sales mgr. St. Paul Pioneer Press Dispatch, 1986-91; pres. Promotional Ptnrs., Eden Prairie, Minn., 1991—; on-air personality Sta. WCCO II Cable TV Mpls., 1988-89, co-host Afternoon Midwest, 1989—; co-host Home Shopping Show, host Minn. Voices, Fox 29; cons. U. Minn. Alumni mag., 1986-89. Author merchandising and sales tng. manuals. Fund-raiser sustaining program YMCA, Mpls., 1986, Jr. Achievement, St. Paul, 1988; cons. Muscular Dystrophy Assn., St. Paul, 1988-89; bd. dirs. St. Paul Jaycees. Mem. NAFE, Nat. Assn. Home Builders, Mpls. Builder Assn. (amb.), Metro-East Profl. Builders Assn. (spl. events com.), Advt. Fedn., The Newspaper Guild, Internat. Platform Assn., Speakeasy Club. Lutheran. Avocations: tennis, golf, aerobics. Home and Office: Promotional Ptnrs 8033 Belair Ln Eden Prairie MN 55347

LAUB, ALAN JOHN, engineering educator; b. Edmonton, Alta., Can. Aug. 6, 1948; came to U.S., 1970; naturalized, 1984; BSc with honors, U. B.C., 1969; MS, U. Minn., 1972, PhD, 1974. Asst. prof. Case Western Res. U., Cleve., 1974-75; vis. asst. prof. U. Toronto, Can., 1975-77; rsch. scientist MIT, Cambridge, Mass., 1977-79; assoc. prof. U. So. Calif., L.A., 1979-83; prof. U. Calif., Santa Barbara, 1983—, chmn. dept. elec. and computer engring., 1989-92. Contbr. articles to profl. jours. Fellow IEEE; mem. IEEE Control Systems Soc. (pres. 1991, Disting. Mem. award 1991, control systems tech. award 1993), Soc. Indsl. Applied Math., Assn. Computing Machinery. Avocations: bridge, tennis. Office: U Calif Dept Elec & Computer Engring Santa Barbara CA 93106-9560

LAUB, WILLIAM MURRAY, retired utility executive; b. Ft. Mills, Corregidor, Philippines, July 20, 1924; s. Harold Goodspeed and Marjorie M. (Murray) L.; m. Mary McDonald, July 26, 1947; children: William, Andrew, Mary, David, John. BSBA, U. Calif., Berkeley, 1947, LLB, 1950. Bar: Calif. 1951. Practice law Los Angeles, 1951-55; with Southwest Gas Corp., Las Vegas, Nev., 1948-88; v.p., gen. counsel Southwest Gas Corp., 1958-60, exec. v.p., 1960-64, pres., chief exec. officer, 1964-82, chmn., chief exec. officer, 1982-88. Pres. Boulder Dam Area council Boy Scouts Am., 1967-69, So. Nev. Indsl. Found., 1967-68, So. Nev. Meth. Found., 1967-74; chmn. Nev. Equal Rights Commn., 1966-68; Clinton Clark County Republican Central Com., 1964-66; nat. committeeman Nev. Rep. Com., 1968-80; trustee Sch. Theology at Claremont, Calif., 1977—; trustee Inst. Gas Tech., 1983-89; nat. bd. advisors, coll. bus. and pub. adminstrn. The U. Ariz., 1985-89; bd. dirs. Alliance for Acid Rain Control, 1985-89. Served to lt. (j.g.) USNR, 1941-45. Mem. ABA, Am. Gas Assn. (bd. dirs., chmn. 1986-87), Pacific Coast Gas Assn. (chmn. 1983), Calif. Bar Assn., Nat. Coal Coun., Jonathan Club, Pauma Valley Country Club, Spanish Trail Golf and Country Club, Las Vegas Country Club. Office: 2810 W Charleston Blvd Ste 53 Las Vegas NV 89102-1906

LAUBACH, ROGER ALVIN, accountant; b. Riegelsville, N.J., July 3, 1922; s. Harry and Daisy (Cyphers) L.; diploma in bus. adminstrn. Churchman Bus. Coll., Easton, Pa., 1941; B.S. cum laude in Acctg., Rider U., 1949. CPA, N.Y., N.J. Acct., Coopers & Lybrand, C.P.A.s, N.Y.C., 1949-60; asst. to treas. Coca-Cola Bottling Co. N.Y., N.Y.C., 1960-63; mgr. audits and systems Atlantic Research Corp., Alexandria, Va., 1964-65; controller Ely-Cruikshank Co., Inc., realtors, N.Y.C., 1965-71, asst. treas, 1966-67, treas., dir., 1967-71; dir. Phila. Acctg. Center, Ogden Food Service Corp., 1971-72, treas., 1972-77; dir. corp. auditing Ogden Corp., N.Y.C., 1977-79; contr. Burlington County Community Action Program, Burlington, N.J., 1981-84. Served with U.S. Army, 1942-46; ETO. Decorated Bronze Star. Mem. AICPA, Inst. Internal Auditors, N.Y. State, N.J. socs. CPAs, Real Estate Bd. N.Y., SAR, VFW, Am. Legion, 100th Inf. Div. Assn., Soc. Colonial Wars, Delta Sigma Pi (pres. 1948). Lutheran (treas., council). Home: 39 Southgate Rd Mount Laurel NJ 08054-2932

LAUBENSTEIN, VERNON ALFRED, state agency administrator; b. Fredonia, Wisc., Mar. 17, 1933; s. Edwin R. and MArtha (Parlow) L.; m. Barbara Jean Swanson, Oct. 15, 1960; children: Jeffrey, Elizabeth, Katherine, Scott, Suzanne. BA, Ripon (Wisc.) Coll., 1954; MBA, Ind. U., 1955. Contracts and compliance mgr. Kemper Group, Long Grove, Ill., 1957-88; mgmt. ops. analyst State Of Ill., Chgo., 1988—; township supr. Schaumburg Twp., Hoffman Estates, Ill., 1969—. Pres. Twinbrook YMCA, Schaumburg, 1970-71, Twp. Suprs. of Ill., Astoria, 1988-89, Rep. Orgn. of Schaumburg, 1967-68; bd. dirs. Suburban Cook-DuPage Health Sys. Agy., Oak Park, Ill. 1976-81, Twp. Ofcls. of Ill., Astoria, 1981-85. 1st MSC U.S. Army, 1955-57. Recipient Twinbrook award Twinbrook YMCA, 1975, Friend of Elk Grove-Schaumburg Twp. Mental Health Ctr. award, 1983. Republican.

Lutheran. Avocations: fishing, camping, politics. Home: 125 Westover Ln Schaumburg IL 60193-1154 Office: Schaumburg Twp 25 Illinois Blvd Hoffman Estates IL 60194

LAUBER, JOHN K., research psychologist; b. Archbold, Ohio, Dec. 13, 1942; s. Kenneth Floyd and Fern Elizabeth (Rupp) L.; m. Susan Elizabeth Myers, Sept. 16, 1967; 1 stepchild, Sarah H. BS, Ohio State U., 1965, MS, 1967, PhD, 1969. Rsch. psychologist U.S. Naval Tng. Equipment Ctr., Orlando, Fla., 1969-73; chief aero. human factors office NASA Ames Rsch. Ctr., Moffett Field, Calif., 1973-85; mem. Nat. Transp. Safety Bd., Washington, 1985-95; v.p. corporate safety and compliance Delta Air Lines, Atlanta, 1995—; mem. aeros. adv. com. NASA, 1987—, U.S. Air Force Studies Bd., NAS, Washington, 1987-89; mem. RE&D adv. com. FAA, 1995—; bd. govs. Flight Safety Found., 1995—. Contbr. articles to profl. jours. Recipient Industry Svc. award Air Transport World, N.Y.C., Disting. Svc. award Flight Safety Found., Tokyo, 1987, Joseph T. Nall Meml. award Nat. Air Traffic Contrs. Assn., 1992, Paul T. Hansen Lectureship award, 1993, Forrest & Dominique Bird award Civil Aviation Med. Assn., 1994. Fellow Aerospace Med. Assn. (chmn. aviation safety com. 1978-82, R. F. Longacre award 1990).; mem. Human Factors Soc. Democrat. Avocations: sailing, flying, amateur radio, cooking. Office: Delta Air Lines Dept 025 Hartsfield Internat Airport Atlanta GA 94035

LAUCHENGCO, JOSE YUJUICO, JR., lawyer; b. Manila, Philippines, Dec. 6, 1936; came to U.S., 1962; s. José Celis Sr. Lauchengco and Angeles (Yujuico) Sapota; m. Elisabeth Schindler, Feb. 22, 1968; children: Birthe, Martina, Duane, Lance. AB, U. Philippines, Quezon City, 1959; MBA, U. So. Calif., 1964; JD, Loyola U., L.A., 1971. Bar: Calif. 1972, U.S. Dist. Ct. (cen. dist.) Calif. 1972, U.S. Ct. Appeals (9th cir.) 1972, U.S. Supreme Ct. 1975. Banker First Western Bank/United Calif. Bank, L.A., 1964-71; assoc. Demler, Perona, Langer & Bergkvist, Long Beach, Calif., 1972-73; ptnr. Demler, Perona, Langer, Bergkvist, Lauchengco & Manzella, Long Beach, 1973-77; sole practice Long Beach and L.A., 1977-83; ptnr. Lauchengco & Mendoza, L.A., 1983-92; pvt. practice L.A., 1993—; mem. commn. on jud. procedures County of L.A., 1979; tchr. Confraternity of Christian Doctrine, 1972-79; counsel Philippine Presdl. Commn. on Good Govt., L.A., 1986. Chmn. Filipino-Am. Bi-Partisan Polit. Action Group, L.A., 1978. Recipient Degree of Distinction, Nat. Forensic League, 1955. Mem. Criminal Cts. Bar Assn., Calif. Attys. Criminal Justice, Calif. Pub. Defenders Assn., L.A. County Bar Assn., Assn. Trial Lawyers Am., Calif. Trial Lawyers Assn., L.A. Trial Lawyers Assn., Philippine-Am. Bar Assn. (bd. dirs.), U. Philippines Vanguard Assn. (life), Beta Sigma. Roman Catholic. Lodge: K.C. Avocations: classical music, opera, romantic paintings and sculpture, camping, shooting. Office: 3545 Wilshire Blvd Ste 247 Los Angeles CA 90010-9999

LAUCK, ANTHONY JOSEPH, artist, retired art educator, priest; b. Indpls., Dec. 30, 1908; s. Anthony Peter and Marie Elizabeth (Habig) L. Diploma in fine arts, John Herron Art Sch., 1936; AB, U. Notre Dame, 1942, DFA (hon.), 1980; cert. in carving, painting, Corcoran Sch. Art, 1948. Entered Congregation of Holy Cross, 1937; ordained priest Roman Catholic Ch., 1946; priest aux. St. Martin's Ch., Washington, 1946-48, Holy Cross Ch., N.Y.C., 1948-49; priest aux. univ. ch. U. Notre Dame, Ind., 1950, mem. faculty dept. art univ. ch., 1950-82, assoc. prof. sculpture univ. ch., 1958-70, prof. sculpture, 1970-72, emeritus prof., 1973—, head dept., 1960-67, dir. Univ. Art Gallery, 1962-74, dir. emeritus, 1974—; Chmn. art jury Nat. Sacred Heart Drawing Competition, Xavier U., 1956. Exhibited, John Herron Art Inst., Ind. State Fair, Indpls., Corcoran Gallery Art, Nat. Mus. Art, Washington, N.A.D., Audubon Artists, N.Y.C., Pa. Acad. Fine Arts, Phila., Conn. Acad. Fine Art, Hartford, Provincetown (Mass.) Art Assn., Newport (R.I.) Art Assn., sculpture retrospective, U. Notre Dame, 1980-81, Snite Mus.Art, 1993; represented permanent collections, Phila. Mus. Art, Corcoran Gallery Art, Pa. Acad. Fine Arts, Norfolk Mus. Art, South Bend Art Ctr., Indpls. Mus. Art, Snite Mus. Art, Notre Dame U., Ind. State Museum, Indpls., Grand Rapids Art Mus., Evansville Mus. Arts and Sci., Ball State U. Art Mus., Gary Art Center, Hartwick Coll., Krasl Art Ctr., Midwest Mus. of Am. Art, Ind., St. Joseph, Mich., Midwest Mus. of American Art, Elkhart, Ind. ,also pvt. collections; contbr. articles on sacred art to jours. and mags. Recipient Fairmount Park purchase prize Third Sculpture Internat., 1949, George D. Widener Gold medal for sculpture Am. art exhbn. Pa. Acad. Art, 1953, John Herron Art Inst. citation, 1957, 1st prize for sculpture Newport Art Assn., Peterson Sculpture Purchase award, 1991, Sculpture Purchase prize Midwest Mus. Am. Art, 1992; inducted medalist Ind. Acad., 1973. Mem. Audubon Artists, St. Joseph Valley Watercolor Soc., No. Ind. Artist, Ind. Artists Club, Nat. Sculpture Soc. N.Y. Home: Moreau Seminary Notre Dame IN 46556 Office: U Notre Dame Snite Mus Art Notre Dame IN 46556 *My work does not enter vitally into the main currents of American life, this busy, mechanized, space-oriented, scientific world of the late 20th century. What interest can such a world have in these silent little sacred images? It's up to them, nevertheless, to exercise some aesthetic attraction upon those who can see what I've tried to reveal. I do hope, of course, that these images may implant a warm, deep reminder into a few hearts and minds.*

LAUDA, DONALD PAUL, university dean; b. Leigh, Nebr., Aug. 7, 1937; s. Joe and Libbie L.; m. Sheila H. Henderson, Dec. 28, 1966; children: Daren M., Tanya R. B.S., Wayne State Coll., 1963, M.S., 1964; Ph.D., Iowa State U., 1966. Assoc. dir. Communications Center U. Hawaii, 1966-67; assoc. prof. indsl. arts St. Cloud (Minn.) State Coll., 1967-69; asst. dean Ind. State U., 1970-73; chmn. tech. edn. W.Va. U., 1973-75; dean Sch. Tech., Eastern Ill. U., Charleston, 1975-83, Calif. State U., Long Beach, 1983—; cons. in field. Author: Advancing Technology: Its Impact on Society, 1971, Technology, Change and Society, 1978, 2d edit., 1985; contbr. articles to profl. jours. Pres. Council on Tech. Tchr. Edn.; dir. Charleston 2000 Futures Project, 1978-81. Served with USAR, 1957-59. EPDA research fellow, 1969-70; Eastern Ill. U. faculty research grantee, 1971. Mem. Future Soc. Internat. Tech. Edn. Assn., Coun. Tech. Tchr. Educators (Tchr. of Yr. award 1978, pres.), World Future Soc., Internat. Tech. Edn. Assn. (pres. 1990), World Coun. Assn. Tech. Edn., Am. Vocat. Assn., Phi Kappa Phi (pres. 1993), Epsilon Pi Tau (Laureate citation 1982). Office: Calif State U Coll Health & Human Svcs Long Beach CA 90840 *Jobs and careers come through a great deal of effort, education, but, most importantly, through the help of others. It is this input that helps one clarify goals, gain new insights, and synthesize information. The process is reciprocal in that one helps others grow. Reflecting on the past always brings to mind people rather than degrees, positions, salaries, etc. When one loses sight of this, he/she is missing the greatest achievement of life.*

LAUDEMAN, LESLIE, nursing administrator, oncological nurse; b. Santa Monica, Calif., Nov. 6, 1960; d. Hal Cella and Janet (Graham) L. BSN, U. Ariz., 1982; MSN, UCLA, 1988. RN, Calif.; ANA advanced adminstrv. cert. Staff nurse St. Joseph Med. Ctr., Burbank, Calif., Kenneth Norris-U. So. Calif. Cancer Ctr., L.A.; nurse mgr. bone marrow transplant, oncology unit UCLA Med. Ctr. Mem. Am. Orgn. Nurse Execs. (coun. nurse mgr. affiliates), Oncology Nurses Soc. (cert.).

LAUDER, ESTÉE, cosmetics company executive; b. N.Y.C.; m. Joseph Lauder (dec.); children: Leonard, Ronald. LLD (hon.), U. Pa., 1986. Chmn. bd. Estée Lauder Inc., 1946—. Author: Estée: A Success Story, 1985. Named One of 100 Women of Achievement Harpers Bazaar, 1967, Top Ten Outstanding Women in Business, 1970; recipient Neiman-Marcus Fashion award, 1962; Spirit of Achievement award Albert Einstein Coll. Medicine, 1968; Kaufmann's Fashion Fortnight award, 1969; Bamberger's Designer's award, 1969; Gimbel's Fashion Forum award, 1969; Internat. Achievement award Frost Bros., 1971; Pogue's Am. Fashion award, 1975, Golda Meir 90th Anniversary Tribute award, 1988; decorated chevalier Legion of Honor France, 1978; medaille de Vermeil de la Ville de Paris, 9, 1979; 4th Ann. award for Humanitarian Service Girls' Club N.Y., 1979; 25th Anniversary award Greater N.Y. council Boy Scouts Am., 1979; L.S. Ayres award, 1981; Achievement award Girl Scouts U.S.A., 1983; Outstanding Mother award, 1984; Athena award, 1985; Pres. award Cosmetic Exec. Women, 1989, Neiman-Marcus Fashion award, 1992; honored Lincoln Ctr., World of Style, 1986; 1988 Laureate Nat. Bus. Hall of Fame. Office: Estée Lauder Cos 767 Fifth Ave New York NY 10153-0002*

LAUDER, EVELYN, cosmetics executive; b. Vienna; m. Leonard Lauder, 1959; children: William, Gary. Attended, Hunter Coll. Sr. corp. v.p. Estée Lauder Cos., N.Y.C. Photographer: (book) The Seasons Observed, 1994. Founder Breast Cancer Rsch. Found., 1993. Office: Estée Lauder Cos 767 Fifth Ave New York NY 10153*

LAUDER, LEONARD ALAN, cosmetic and fragrance company executive; b. N.Y.C., Mar. 19, 1933; s. Joseph H. and Estée (Mentzer) L.; m. Evelyn Hausner, July 5, 1959; children: William Phillip, Gary Mark. BS, Wharton Sch., U. Pa., 1954. With Estée Lauder, Inc., N.Y.C., 1958—, exec. v.p., 1962-72, pres., 1972-82, pres., chief exec. officer, 1982—; vice chmn. bd. CFTA, 1977-79, 1976-79. Trustee Aspen Inst. for Humanistic Studies, 1978—, U. Pa., Phila., 1977—; pres. Whitney Mus. Am. Art, 1977—; bd. dirs. Adv. Commn. on Trade Negotiations, Washington, 1983-87; bd. govs. Joseph H. Lauder Inst. Mgmt. and Internat. Studies, 1983—. Lt. USNR, 1955-58. Mem. Chief Execs. Orgn., French-Am. C. of C. in U.S. (coun. frn. relations). Office: Estée Lauder Cos 767 5th Ave New York NY 10153-0001*

LAUDER, VALARIE ANNE, editor, educator; b. Detroit, Mar. 1; d. William J. and Murza Valerie (Mann) L. AA, Stephens Coll., Columbia, Mo., 1944; postgrad. Northwestern U. With Chgo. Daily News, 1944-52, columnist, 1946-52; lectr. Sch. Assembly Service, also Redpath lectr., 1952-55; freelance writer for mags. and newspapers including N.Y. Times, Yankee, Ford Times, Travel & Leisure, Am. Heritage, 1955—; editor-in-chief Scholastic Roto, 1962; editor U. N.C., 1975-80, lectr. Sch. Journalism, 1980—; gen. sec. World Assn. for Pub. Opinion Rsch., 1988-95; nat. chmn. student writing project Ford Times, 1981-86; pub. rels. dir. Am. Dance Festival, Duke U., 1982-83, lectr., instr. continuing edn. program, 1984; contbg. editor So. Accents mag., 1982-86. Mem. nat. fund raising bd. Kennedy Ctr., 1962-63. Recipient 1st place award Nat. Fedn. Press Women, 1981; 1st place awards Ill. Women's Press Assn., 1950, 1951. Mem. Pub. Rels. Soc. Am. (treas. N.C. chpt. 1982, sec. 1983, v.p. 1984, pres.-elect 1985, pres. 1986, chmn. council of past pres., chmn. 25th Ann. event 1987, del. Nat. Assembly 1988-94, S.E. dist. officer, nat. nominating com. 1991), Women in Communications (v.p. matrix N.C. Triangle chpt. 1984-85), N.C. Pub. Rels. Hall of Fame Com., DAR, Soc. Mayflower Desc. (bd. dir. Ill. Soc. 1946-52), Chapel Hill Hist. Soc. (bd. dir. 1981-85, 94—, chmn. publs. com. 1980-85), Chapel Hill Preservation Soc. (bd. trustees 1993—, nominating com. 1994), N.C. Press Club (3d v.p. 1981-83, 2d v.p. 1983-85, pres. 1985, 1st pl. awards 1981, 82, 83, 84), Univ. Woman's Club (2d v.p. 1988), The Carolina Club, The Nat. Press Club. Office: U NC Sch Journalism and Mass Comm CB 3365 Chapel Hill NC 27599-3365

LAUDISE, ROBERT ALFRED, research chemist; b. Amsterdam, N.Y., Sept. 2, 1930; s. Anthony Thomas and Harriette Elizabeth (O'Neil) L.; m. Joyce Elizabeth DeSilvia, Aug. 24, 1957; children: Thomas Michael, Margaret Joyce, John David, Mary Elizabeth, Edward Robert. B.S. in Chemistry, Union Coll., Schenectady, N.Y., 1952; Ph.D. in Chemistry (A.D. Little fellow), MIT., 1956. Mem. Tech. staff Bell Telephone Labs., Murray Hill, N.J., 1956-60; head crystal chemistry rsch. dept. Bell Telephone Labs., 1960-72, asst. dir. materials research lab., 1972-74, dir. materials research lab., 1974-77, dir. phys. and inorganic chemistry research lab., 1977-87, dir. materials chemistry rsch. lab., 1988-90, dir. materials and processing rsch. lab., 1990-92, adj. dir. chem. rsch., 1994—; vis. prof. U. Aix, Marseilles, France, 1971, Hebrew U., Jerusalem, 1972, Shandong U., China, 1980; cons. Pres.'s Sci. Com., 1960-64; adv. com. Nat. Bur. Standards, 1970-78; solid state scis. com. NRC, 1977-81; adv. com. NASA, 1977-82; adj. prof. MIT, 1988—, Rutgers U., 1991—. Author: The Growth of Single Crystals, 1970; editor: Jour. Crystal Growth, 1978-94, Jour. Materials Rsch., 1994—; contbr. articles to sci. jours. Recipient Sawyer award, 1974. Fellow AAAS, Am. Mineral Soc., Am. Ceramic Soc. (Orton award lectr. 1994); mem. NAS, NAE, Internat. Orgn. Crystal Growth (pres. award 1981), Am. Assn. Crystal Growth (pres. 1971-77), Am. Chmn. Soc. (Materials Chemistry prize 1990), Electrochem. Soc., Am. Crystal Soc., Fedn. Math. Soc. (pres. 1995—). Roman Catholic. Patentee in field. Home: 65 Lenape Ln Berkeley Heights NJ 07922-2333 Office: Bell Telephone Labs 600 Mountain Ave New Providence NJ 07974-2010

LAUDONE, ANITA HELENE, lawyer; b. Boston, Sept. 14, 1948; d. Vincent A. and Wanda L.; m. Colin E. Harley, May 20, 1978; children: Clayton Thomas, Victoria Spencer. A.B., Conn. Coll., 1970; J.D., Columbia U., 1973. Bar: N.Y. 1974. Law clk. to judge Fed. Dist. Ct., N.Y.C., 1973-74; asso. Davis Polk & Wardwell, N.Y.C., 1974-78; assoc. Shearman & Sterling, N.Y.C., 1978-79; with Phelps Dodge Corp., N.Y.C., 1979-85; corp. sec. Phelps Dodge Corp., 1980-85, v.p., corp. sec., 1984-85. Editor: Columbia Law Rev., 1973. Home: 510 North St Greenwich CT 06830-3439

LAUENSTEIN, MILTON CHARLES, management consultant; b. Webster Groves, Mo., Feb. 16, 1926; s. Milton Charles and Helen (Scholz) L.; m. Helen Smith, Feb. 5, 1949; children: Paul C., Kurt, Maria, Fritz. BS, Purdue U., 1945; MBA, U. Chgo., 1960. Tech. svc. engr. Norton Co., Worcester, Mass., 1948-51; with silicone products dept. GE Co., Waterford, N.Y., Cleve. and Chgo., 1951-57; cons. mktg. and corp. planning A.T. Kearney & Co., Chgo., 1957-60; dir. long range planning Bell & Howell Co., Chgo., 1960-62; pres. Ventron Corp., Beverly, Mass., 1962-76, Lauenstein & Assoc., Inc. (mgmt. cons.), Wenham, Mass., 1977-91; pres. Telequip Corp., Littleton, Mass., 1979-80, chmn., 1989—; bd. dirs. Helix Tech. Corp., Waltham, Mass., Tech/Ops. Sevcon Corp., Boston; chmn. bd. dirs. Telequip Corp., Hollis, N.H.; sr. lectr. bus. U. Chgo., 1961-62, 79-80; adj. prof. mgmt., 1983-85; exec.-in-residence Coll. Bus. Adminstrn. Northeastern U., Boston, 1980-83. Author: What's Your Game Plan?, 1986; contbns. editor Jour. Bus. Strategy. Trustee, treas. Vt. Studio Ctr., Johnson; chm., Wenham Dem. Town Com., 1967-72. With USNR, 1943-46. Fellow emeritus Am. Inst. Chemists. Avocations: painting, sailing, tennis. Home and Office: 90 Hesperus Ave Gloucester MA 01930-5273

LAUER, ELIOT, lawyer; b. N.Y.C., Aug. 17, 1949; s. George and Doris (Trenk) L.; m. Marilyn Steinberg, June 5, 1977; children: Tamar Rachel, Ilana Jennifer, Michael Jonathan, Samuel Geoffrey. BA, Yeshiva U., 1971; JD cum laude, Fordham U., 1974. Bar: D.C. 1975, N.Y. 1975, U.S. Dist. Ct. (so. and ea. dists.) N.Y. 1975, U.S. Ct. Appeals (2d cir.) 1975, U.S. Supreme Ct. 1984. Assoc. Curtis, Mallet-Prevost, Colt & Mosle, N.Y.C., 1974-82, ptnr., 1982—. Counsel Keren-Or Inc., N.Y.C., 1985—; bd. dirs. Hebrew Acad. Long Beach, N.Y., 1985—, Young Israel Lawrence, Cedarhurst, N.Y., 1984—. Mem. ABA, N.Y. State Bar Assn., Assn. of Bar of City of N.Y., Fed. Bar Council, Am. Arbitration Assn. (arbitrator 1979—), Nat. Futures Assn. (arbitrator 1983—). Republican. Office: Curtis Mallet-Prevost Colt & Mosle 101 Park Ave New York NY 10178-0061

LAUER, JAMES LOTHAR, physicist, educator; b. Vienna, Austria, Aug. 2, 1920; came to U.S., 1938, naturalized, 1943; s. Max and Friederike (Rappaport) L.; m. Stefanie Dorothea Blank, Sept. 5, 1955; children: Michael, Ruth. A.B., Temple U., 1942, M.A., 1944; Ph.D., U. Pa., 1948; postgrad., U. Calif., San Diego, 1964-65. Scientist Sun Oil Co., Marcus Hook, Pa., 1944-52; spectroscopist Sun Oil Co., 1952-64, sr. scientist, 1965-77; asst. prof. U. Pa., 1952-55; lectr. U. Del., 1952-58; research fellow mech. engring. U. Calif., San Diego, 1964-65; research prof. mech. engring. Rensselaer Poly. Inst., Troy, N.Y., 1978-85; prof. mech. engring. Rensselaer Poly. Inst., 1985-93, prof. mech. engring. emeritus 1993—; rsch. sci. Ctr. Magnetic Recording Rsch. U. Calif., San Diego, 1993—; sr. faculty, summer rsch. fellow NASA-Lewis Rsch. Ctr., 1986, 87; vis. prof. Ctr. for Magnetic Rec. Rsch., U. Calif., San Diego, 1991; cons. Digital Equipment Corp., 1992—; NASA-Lewis Rsch. Ctr., 1993—. Author: Infrared Fourier Spectroscopy—Chemical Applications, 1978; author numerous tech. papers. Active Penn Wynne Civic Assn., 1959-77, Country Knolls Civic Assn., 1978-93. Sun Oil Co. fellow, 1964-65, Air Force Office Sci. Rsch. grantee, 1974-86, NASA Lewis Rsch. Ctr. grantee, 1974-86, Office Naval Rsch. grantee, 1979-82, Army Rsch. Office grantee, 1985-89, NSF grantee, 1987—. Mem. Am. Chem. Soc. (emeritus), Am. Phys. Soc., Soc. Applied Spectroscopy, Materials Rsch. Soc., Optical Soc. Am. (emeritus), Sigma Xi. Jewish. Patentee in field. Home: 7622 Palmilla Dr Apt 78 San Diego CA 92122-5049 Office: U Calif San Diego Ctr Magnetic Recording La Jolla CA 92093 *My advice to those contemplating a career in experimental research is to give much thought to these points: (1) interest, enthusiasm, willingness to work are only basics, (2) a loving and understanding wife is essential, and (3) the*

knowledge that one can create one's own success at any time is the driving force.

LAUER, JEANETTE CAROL, history educator, author; b. St. Louis, July 14, 1935; d. Clinton Jones and Blanche Aldine (Gideon) Pentecost; m. Robert Harold Lauer, July 2, 1954; children: Jon, Julie, Jeffrey. BS, U. Mo., St. Louis, 1970; MA, Washington U., St. Louis, 1973, PhD, 1975. Assoc. prof. history St. Louis Community Coll., 1974-82; assoc. prof. history U.S. Internat. U., San Diego, 1982-90, prof., 1990-94; dean Coll. of Arts and Scis., San Diego. Author: Fashion Power, 1981, The Spirit and the Flesh, 1983, Til Death Do Us Part, 1986, Watersheds, 1988, The Quest for Intimacy, 1991, 2nd edit., 1993, No Secrets, 1993, The Joy Ride, 1993, For Better or Better, 1995. Woodrow Wilson fellow, 1970, Washington U. fellow, 1971-75. Mem. Am. Hist. Assn., Orgn. Am. Historians. Democrat. Presbyterian. Home: 18147 Sun Maiden Ct San Diego CA 92127-3102

LAUER, ROBERT LEE, consumer products executive; b. Crook, Colo., Oct. 25, 1933; s. Martin F. and Mary A. (Hofsetz) L.; m. Mary Redman, Aug. 25, 1956; children: Anne, Lisa, John. B.S. in Journalism and Pub. Relations, Bowling Green State U., 1956. Mgr. Procter & Gamble, Cin., 1962-69; account supr. Harshe-Rotman & Druck, Los Angeles, 1969-70; mgr. corp. relations Clorox Co., Oakland, Calif., 1970-77; dir. pub. affairs S.C. Johnson & Son, Racine, Wis., 1977-81; v.p. corp. affairs Sara Lee Corp., Chgo., 1981-93, sr. v.p., 1993—; pres. Sara Lee Found. Bd. dirs. Pub. Affairs Coun., Washington, Advt. Coun., Inc., Internat. Theatre Festival Chgo., Arthur Page Soc., Second Harvest Nat. Food Bank Network. Mem. Pub. Rels. Soc. Am., Econ. Club Chgo., Chgo. Club, Univ. Club, Execs. Club, Commonwealth Club. Office: Sara Lee Corp 3 First National Pla Chicago IL 60602

LAUERSEN, NIELS HELTH, physician, educator; b. Denmark, Sept. 10, 1939; came to U.S., 1967, naturalized, 1977; s. Bernhard and Maria L. M.D. cum laude, U. Copenhagen, 1967, Cornell U., 1968. Diplomate: Am. Bd. Ob-Gyn. Intern, then resident in ob-gyn N.Y. Hosp.-Cornell U. Med. Center, 1968-72, assoc. prof., 1972-79; assoc. prof. ob-gyn Mt. Sinai Sch. Medicine, N.Y.C., 1979-83; prof. ob-gyn N.Y. Med. Coll., 1983—. Author: It's Your Body, A Woman's Guide to Gynecology, 1978, new version, 1993, Clinical Perinatal Biochemical Monitoring, 1981, Principles of Microsurgical Techniques in Infertility, 1982, Listen to your Body, 1982, Childbirth With Love, 1983, Modern Management of High-Risk Pregnancy, 1983, PMS: Premenstrual Syndrome and You, 1984, It's Your Pregnancy, 1987, The Endometriosis Answer Book, 1988, A Woman's Body, 1989, Getting Pregnant, 1990, You're in Charge, 1993; also numerous articles. Served with Danish Air Force, 1958-60. Recipient Profl. Service award AMA, 1979, 80, 82, 84, 86, 88, 92. Fellow Am. Coll. Obstetricians and Gynecologists (award 1977), Soc. Gynecol. Investigation, Am. Fertility Soc., N.Y. Obstet. Soc., N.Y. Gynecol. Soc., Soc. of Perinatal Medicine; mem. AFTRA, N.Y. Gynecol. Soc., N.Y. Soc. Reproductive Medicine, Author's Guild Am. Home: 750 Park Ave New York NY 10021-4252 Office: 784 Park Ave New York NY 10021-3553 *Through helping others, you will help yourself.*

LAUFER, BEATRICE, composer; b. N.Y.C.; d. Samuel and Fanny (Silverman) L.; m. Theodore Lassoff, Oct. 2, 1940 (dec. 1955); 1 child, Samuel; m. Seymour H. Rinzler, Oct. 19, 1969 (dec. 1970). Student Juilliard Sch. Music, 1944. Composer: Symphony No. 1 (performed by Eastman-Rochester Symphony Orch., 1945-46, performance Germany and Japan under auspices of State Dept., 1948, performed by Nat. Gallery Orch., Washington, 1982), Dance Festival (performed by Eastman-Rochester Symphony, 1946-47); choral compositions include: Under the Pines, Spring Thunder performed Tanglewood, 1949, Song of the Fountain, inter-racial chorus, UN Freedom celebration, 1952; Small Concerto for Chamber Orch. performed McMillan Theatre, Columbia, 1949-50; Ile, opera, world premiere Royal Opera Co., Stockholm, Sweden, 1958, recorded by Yale U. Orch. 1978, Broadcast Nat. Pub. Radio, 1980, 87, performed in Chinese at Nanjing U. World Conf. on O'Neill, Shanghai Opera House, June 1988; Second Symphony performed by Oklahoma City Orch., 1961; premiere concerto at Donnell Library Ctr., 1962; premiere performance Prelude and Fugue for Orch., Brevard Music Ctr., N.C., 1964, Cry! orchestral prelude, Orch. of Am., Town Hall, 1966, Lyric string trio, Bowdoin Coll. Contemporary Music Festival, 1966, performed with Eastman-Rochester Symphony, 1968, Shreveport Symphony Orch., 1978, Berkshire Symphony Orch., 1981; In the Throes performed Shreveport Symphony, 1980, New Orleans Symphony Orch., 1982, Berkshire Symphony Orch., 1985; Conn. Found. of Arts grantee for performance And Thomas Jefferson Said (symphonic version performed by S.W. Floridan Symphony Orch., 1987), Norwalk Symphony Orch., 1976, 3 excerpts performed by USAF Chamber Players, Washington, 1985, premiere version for concert band baritone solo performed by The Goldman Meml. Band, 1986, also at the Aspen (Colo.) Music Festival, 1987, orchestral performance We Hold These Truths, S.W. Fla. Symphony, Nov. 1987; master ceremonies Young Am. Artists, radio sta. WNYC; hostess The Conductor Speaks series sta. WNYC. Mem. ASCAP, Am. Symphony Orch. League, Am. Music Ctr. Address: PO Box 3 Lenox Hill Sta New York NY 10021

LAUFER, DONALD L., lawyer; b. Neptune, N.J., May 31, 1933. AB, Columbia U., 1955, LLB, 1957. Bar: N.Y. 1958, U.S. Dist. Ct. (so. dist.) N.Y. 1961. Law clk. to Hon. Harold R. Medina U.S. Ct. Appeals (2nd cir.), 1957-58; ptnr. Winston & Strawn, N.Y.C. Mem. ABA, N.Y. County Lawyers Assn., Assn. Bar City N.Y. Office: Winston & Strawn 175 Water St New York NY 10038-4918

LAUFER, HANS, developmental biologist, educator; b. Germany, Oct. 18, 1929; s. Sol and Margarete (Freundlich) L.; m. Evelyn Green, Oct. 31, 1953; children: Jessica, Marc, Leonard. B.S., CCNY, 1952; M.A., Bklyn. Coll., 1953; Ph.D. (James fellow), Cornell U., Ithaca, N.Y., 1957. Research and teaching asst. Cornell U., 1953-57; NRC fellow Carnegie Instn. of Washington, 1957-59; asst. prof. biology Johns Hopkins U., 1959-65; assoc. prof. U. Conn., Storrs, 1965-72; prof. U. Conn., 1972—; vis. prof. Karolinska Inst., Stockholm, 1972, Charles U., Prague, 1974, Yale U., 1980, Harvard U., 1987-89; participant Nat. Acad. Scis.-Czechoslovak Acad. exchange program, 1974, 77; ad hoc mem. study sect. tropical medicine NIH, 1981, mem., 1982-85; Conklin Meml. fellow Marine Biology Lab., Woods Hole, Mass., 1956, Lalor fellow, 1962, 63, mem. staff, embryology course, 1968-72, mem. corp., 1962—, corp. trustee, 1978-82, mem. exec. com., 1979-80; vis. scholar Case Western Res. U., 1962; mem. NSF-NATO Fellowship Rev. Panel, 1974, 76. Contbg. author numerous books; assoc. editor Jour. Exptl. Zoology, 1969-73, 90-93, Archives Insect Physiology and Biochemistry, 1983—, Invertebrate Reprodn. and Devel., 1984-86, mng. editor, 1991—; contbr. numerous articles to profl. jours. Recipient Rsch. Svc. award NIH, 1989, Marcus Singer medal for rsch., 1986; NATO Sr. fellow, 1972; NIH Spl. fellow, 1973; sr. fellow Lady Davis Trust, Hebrew U., 1988; Japan Soc. Promotion of Sci. fellow, 1980; Rosenstiel scholar Brandeis U., 1973. Fellow AAAS (chmn. sect. biology 1975), Royal Entomology Soc. London (fgn. fellow, elected); mem. Internat. Soc. Devel. Biology, Assn. Rsch. Couns. (nat. bd. on grad. edn. of conf. bd. 1971-75), Am. Soc. Zoology (chmn. divsn. developmental biology 1981-82), Soc. Devel. Biology, Am. Soc. Cell Biology, European Soc. Comparative Endocrinology, Am. Assn. Advancement Aging Rsch., Internat. Soc. Differentiation, Tissue Culture Assn. (coun. 1979-82), World Agrl. Soc. Home: Apt 1112 345 Buckland Hills Dr Manchester CT 06040-3333 Office: U Conn Dept Molecular & Cell Biology U-125 Storrs Mansfield CT 06268

LAUFF, GEORGE HOWARD, biologist; b. Milan, Mich., Mar. 23, 1927; s. George John and Mary Anna (Klein) L. B.S., Mich. State U., 1949, M.S., 1951; postgrad., U. Mont., 1951, U. Wash., 1952; Ph.D., Cornell U., 1953. Fisheries research technician Mich. Dept. Conservation, 1950; teaching asst. Cornell U., 1952-53; instr. U. Mich., 1953-57, asst. prof., 1957-61, asso. prof., 1961-62; research asso. Gt. Lakes Research Inst., U. Mich., 1954-59; dir. U. Ga. Marine Inst., 1960-62; asso. prof. U. Ga., 1960-62; research coord. Sapelo Island Research Found., 1962-64; dir. Kellogg Biol. Sta., 1964-90; prof. dept. fisheries and wildlife and zoology Mich. State U., East Lansing, 1964-91, prof. emeritus, 1991—; mem. cons. and rev. panels for Smithsonian Inst., Nat. Water Commn., NSF, Nat. Acad. Sci., Am. Inst. Biol. Sci., U.S. AEC, Inst. Ecology, others. Editor: Estuaries, 1967, Experimental Ecological Reserves, 1977. Served with inf. U.S. Army, 1944-46. Office of

Naval Research grantee; U.S. Dept. Interior grantee; NSF grantee; others. Fellow AAAS; mem. Am. Inst. Biol. Sci., Am. Soc. Limnology and Oceanography (pres. 1972-73), Ecol. Soc. Am., Freshwater Biology Assn., INTECOL, Societas Internationalis Limnologiae, Orgn. Biol. Field Stas., Sigma Xi, Phi Kappa Phi. Home: 3818 Heights Dr Hickory Corners MI 49060-9504 Office: 3700 E Gull Lake Dr Hickory Corners MI 49060-9516

LAUFMAN, HAROLD, surgeon; b. Milw., Jan. 6, 1912; s. Jacob and Sophia (Peters) L.; m. Marilyn Joselit, 1940 (dec. 1963); children: Dionne Laufman Weigert, Laurien Laufman Kogut; m. June Friend Moses, 1980. BS, U. Chgo., 1932; MD, Rush Med. Coll., 1937; MS in Surgery, Northwestern U., Chgo., 1946, PhD, 1948. Diplomate: Am. Bd. Surgery. Intern Michael Reese Hosp., Chgo., 1936-39; resident in gen. surgery St. Marks Hosp., London, Northwestern U. Med. Sch., Cook County Hosp., Hines VA Hosp., 1939-46; mem. faculty Northwestern U., 1941-65; from clin. asst. to prof., attending surgeon Passavant Meml. Hosp., Chgo., 1953-65; prof. surgery, history of medicine Albert Einstein Coll. Medicine, N.Y.C., 1965-82, prof. emeritus, 1982—; dir. Inst. Surg. Studies, Montefiore Hosp. and Med. Center, Bronx, N.Y., 1965-81; pvt. practice gen. and vascular surgery Chgo., 1941-65, N.Y.C., 1965-81; ret. professorial lectr. surgery Mt. Sinai Sch. Medicine, N.Y.C., 1979—; attending surgeon Mt. Sinai Hosp., N.Y.C., 1979-83; cons., lectr. in field; chmn. FDA Classification Panel Gen. and Plastic Surgery Devices, 1975-78; pres. Harold Laufman Assocs., Inc. 1977—, sr. ptnr., 1988—; pres. HLA Systems. Author: (with S.W. Banks) Surgical Exposures of the Extremities, 1953, 2d edit., 1986, (with R.B. Erichson) Hematologic Problems in Surgery, 1970, Hospital Special Care Facilities, 1981, The Veins, 1986; chmn. editorial bd.: Diagnostica, 1974-79; mem. editorial bd.: Surgery, Gynecology and Obstetrics, 1974-92, Infection Control, 1980-88, Med. Instrumentation, 1972-83, Med. Rsch. Engring., 1972-79; contbr. articles to sci. publs. Chmn. bd. dirs. N.Y. Chamber Soloists, 1974-80, Chamber Music Conf. and Composers Forum of the East, 1975-91. Maj. AUS, 1942-46. Named Disting. Alumnus Rush Med. Coll., 1993. Fellow ACS; mem. Assn. Advancement Med. Instrumentation (pres. 1974-75, chmn. bd. 1976-77), Am. Assn. Hosp. Cons., Am. Med. Writers Assn. (pres. 1968-69), Am. Surg. Assn., Société Internationale de Chirurgie, Western Surg. Assn., Cen. Surg. Assn., N.Y. Surg. Soc., Soc. Vascular Surgery, Internat. Cardiovascular Soc., Soc. Surgery Alimentary Tract, Surg. Infection Soc. (councillor 1980-84), Sigma Xi, Alpha Omega Alpha, Phi Sigma Delta, Zeta Beta Tau. Jewish. Clubs: Standard (Chgo.); Harmonie (N.Y.C.); Willow Ridge Country (Harrison, N.Y.). Home and Office: 31 E 72nd St New York NY 10021-4146

LAUFMAN, LESLIE RODGERS, hematologist, oncologist; b. Pitts., Dec. 13, 1946; d. Marshall Charles and Ruth Rodgers; m. Harry B. Laufman, Apr. 25, 1970 (div. Apr. 1984); children: Hal, Holly; m. Rodger Mitchell, Oct. 9, 1987. BA in Chemistry, Ohio Wesleyan U., 1968; MD, U. Pitts., 1972. Diplomate: Am. Bd. Internal Medicine and Hematology. Intern Montefiore Hosp., Pitts., 1972-73, resident in internal medicine, 1973-74; fellow in hemotology and oncology Ohio State Hosp., Columbus, 1974-76; dir. med. oncology Grant Med. Ctr., Columbus, 1977-92; practice medicine specializing in hematology and oncology Columbus, 1977—; bd. dirs. Columbus Cancer Clinic; prin. investigator Columbus Cmty. Clin. Oncology Program, 1989—. Contbr. articles to profl. jours. Mem. AMA, Am. Women Med. Assn. (sec./treas. 1985-86, pres. 1986-87), Am. Soc. Clin. Oncology, Southwest Oncology Group, Nat. Surg. Adjuvant Project for Breast and Bowel Cancers. Avocations: tennis, piano, sailing, hiking, travel. Office: 393 E Town St # 109 Columbus OH 43215-4741 also: 8100 Ravine'S Edge Ct Worthington OH 43235

LAUGHERY, JACK ARNOLD, restaurant chain executive; b. Guthrie Center, Iowa, Feb. 25, 1935; s. Gerald Reve and Mildred Eva (Ansberry) L.; m. Helen Herboth, Sept. 14, 1968; children: Brenda, Kelly, Christine, Sarah. B.C.S., U. Iowa, 1957; grad. exec. program, U. N.C., Chapel Hill, 1976. Salesman Conn. Gen. Ins. Co., 1957-62; with Sandy's Systems, 1962-72, pres., 1969-72, chief operating officer, 1970-72, chief exec. officer, 1971-72; exec. v.p. Hardee's Food Systems, Inc., Rocky Mount, N.C., 1972-73, pres., 1973—, chief operating officer, 1973-75, chief exec. officer, 1975-89, chmn. bd., 1983—; chmn. bd., pres., chief exec. officer Imasco, USA, Rocky Mount, 1983—; dir. First Union Nat. Bank, Charlotte, N.C. Bd. dirs. Wesleyan Coll., Rocky Mount, Mary Frances Ctr., Tarboro, N.C., N.C. Zool. Soc. Served with AUS, 1957-60. Mem. Nat. Restaurant Assn., N.C. Restaurant Assn., Rocky Mount C. of C. (dir. 1976—, pres. 1985), Am. Mgmt. Assn. Republican. Episcopalian. Home: 1730 Hunter Hill Rd Rocky Mount NC 27804-1734 Office: Hardee's Food Systems Inc 1233 Hardees Blvd Rocky Mount NC 27804-2815*

LAUGHERY, KENNETH RONALD, psychology educator; b. Rowes Run, Pa., Oct. 3, 1935. BS, Carnegie-Mellon U., 1957, MS, 1959, PhD, 1961. With SUNY, Buffalo, 1963-72, U. Houston, 1972-84; Herbert S. Autrey prof. psychology Rice U., Houston, 1984—. Office: Rice U Dept Psychology 6100 Main St Houston TX 77005-1827

LAUGHLIN, CHARLES WILLIAM, agriculture educator, research administrator; b. Iowa City, Iowa, Dec. 9, 1939; s. Ralph Minard and Geraldine (O'Neill) L.; m. Barbara Waln, Dec. 17, 1966; children: Shannon Morris, Charles Tudor. BS, Iowa State U., 1963; MS, U. Md., 1966; PhD, Va. Tech., 1969. Asst. extension nematologist U. Fla., Gainesville, 1968-69; asst. prof., extension nematologist Mich. State U., East Lansing, 1969-73, assoc. prof., asst. dir. acad. and student affairs, 1973-78, prof., asst. dean, dir. acad. and student affairs, 1978-80; prof., dept. head plant pathology and weed sci. Miss. State U., Starkville, 1980-83; prof., assoc. dir. Ga. Agrl. Expt. Sta. U. Ga., Athens, 1983-92; dir. co., Agrl. Expt. Sta. Colo. State U., Ft. Collins, 1992—; cons. Brazilian Ministry of Edn. and Culture, Brasilin, Brazil, 1975-77, Brazilian Nat. Agrl. Rsch. Agy., 1978, W.K. Kellogg Found., Battle Creek, Mich., 1983—. Latin Am. Inst. of Creativity, São Paulo, Brazil, 1991. Recipient Colleague award Creative Edn. Found., 1988. Mem. Soc. Nematologists, Am. Phytopathological Soc., Brazilian Soc. Nematologists. Avocations: creative problem solving, outdoors recreation. Address: 16 Administration CSU Fort Collins CO 80523-0001

LAUGHLIN, DAVID EUGENE, materials science educator, metallurgical consultant; b. Phila., July 15, 1947; s. Eugene L. and Myrtle M. (Kramer) L.; m. Diane Rae Seamans, June 13, 1970; children—Jonathan, Elizabeth, Andrew, Daniel. B.Sc., Drexel U., 1969; Ph.D., MIT, 1973. Asst. prof. materials sci. Carnegie-Mellon U., Pitts., 1974-78, assoc. prof., 1978-82, prof., 1982—; rsch. scientist Oxford (Eng.) U., 1985. Editor: Solid-Solid Phase Transformations, 1982; category editor of copper: Am. Soc. Metals-Nat. Bur. Stds. Phase Diagram Program, 1981-94; assoc. editor: Metall. Trans., 1982-87, editor, 1987—; contbr. more than 170 articles to profl. jours. Mem. sch. bd. Trinity Christian Sch., Pitts., 1976-85, 87—, pres., 1978-83, sec., 1988-91, pres., 1991-94; ruling elder Covenant Presbyn. Ch., Pitts., 1982—; foster parent Children's Home of Pitts., 1984-90; bd. dirs. Christian Schs. Internat. 1991—. Recipient Ladd Teaching award Carnegie-Mellon U., 1975; postdoctoral fellow Nat. Acad. Scis., 1974. Fellow Am. Soc. Metals; mem. Metallurgical Soc. of AIME, Am. Sci. Affiliation, Materials Rsch. Soc. Orthodox Presbyterian. Avocations: sports; books. Home: 2357 Mcnary Blvd Pittsburgh PA 15235-2779 Office: Carnegie-Mellon U Dept Materials Sci Eng Pittsburgh PA 15213

LAUGHLIN, FELIX B., lawyer; b. New Orleans, Dec. 4, 1942; m. Betty Gayle Laughlin. BS with honors, U. Tenn., 1967, JD with honors, 1967; LLM, Georgetown U., 1971. Bar: Tenn. 1967, D.C. 1972, U.S. Ct. Claims 1969, U.S. Tax Ct. 1968, U.S. Dist. Ct. D.C. 1972, U.S. Ct. Appeals (D.C. cir.) 1988, U.S. Ct. Appeals (fed. cir.) 1992, U.S. Supreme Ct. 1970. With interpretation divsn. Office Chief Counsel IRS, 1967-71; assoc. Dewey Ballantine, Washington, 1972—, mem., 1975—. Dir. Friends of U.S. Nat. Arboretum, Nat. Bonsai Found. Mem. ABA (tax sect.), Fed. Bar Assn. (chmn. tax sect. 1989), Met. Club (Washington), George ˊ own Club (Washington), Order of Coif, Sigma Alpha Epsilon, Phi Eta Sigma, Phi Kappa Phi, Phi Delta Phi. Office: Dewey Ballantine 1775 Pennsylvania Ave NW Washington DC 20006-4605

LAUGHLIN, GREGORY H. (GREG LAUGHLIN), congressman; b. Bay City, Tex., Jan. 21, 1942. BA, Tex. A&M U.; LLB, U. Tex. Asst. dist. atty. Harris County, Tex., 1970-74; pvt. practice Tex.; mem. 101st-103rd Congresses from 14th Tex. dist., Washington, D.C., 1989—. With AUS; col. USAR. Office: US Ho of Reps 442 Cannon Washington DC 20515

LAUGHLIN, HENRY PRATHER, physician, psychiatrist, educator, author, editor; b. Hagerstown, Md., June 25, 1916; s. John Royer and Myrtle Frances (Binkley) L.; m. Marion Page Durkee, June 2, 1941; children: Constance Ann Kuhn, John Royer II, Robert Scott, Barbara Hilton Galant, Deborah Page Mayer. Student, Johns Hopkins U. 1936,1938; BS, Ursinus Coll., 1937, ScD, 1976; MD, Temple U., 1941; D Social Sci., U. Louisville 1978; LittD, Albright Coll., 1994; PSD, Washington Coll., 1995. Diplomate Am. Bd. Psychiatry and Neurology, Nat. Bd. Med. Examiners. Pvt. practice Md., 1947-92; faculty psychiatry George Washington U, 1947-83; clin. prof. psychiatry George Washington U., 1948-83; disting. vis. prof. U. Louisville, 1974-89, adj. prof. emeritus, 1989; vis. prof. 60 med. ctrs. around the world, 1950-93; pres. Nat. Psychiat. Endowment Fund, Washington, Frederick, Md.,1957-91; pres. Med. Coun. of the Washington Met. area, 1959-1961; exec. dir. Nat. Inst. of Emerging Tech., Frederick, 1989-92, mem.; bd. dirs. Ursinus Coll., Collegeville, Pa., 1967-77, life mem. 1985; cons. 14 U.S. agys., Washington, 1974-79; asst. or assoc. examiner Am. Bd. Psychiatry and Neurology, 1948-82; cons. editor in psychoanalysis Psychosomatics, N.Y., 1977-87; cons. Walter Reed Army Med. Ctr., 1949-57, Nat. Naval Med. Ctr., 1972-79; co-founder, bd. dirs. Robert R. Luce Inc. Pubs., Washington, 1957-62; owner Montgomery House, Bethesda, Md. 1959-84, owner Kings Park Plz., Hyattsville, Md., 1965—; co-developer So. Manor Country Club, Boca Raton, Fla., 1970-73; dir., sec., 1982-84, dir., 1987-94, Galaxy Cos., Frederick, Md.; bd. dirs. Frederick Trading Co., 1991—, Capital Investment Co., Washington, 1959-62; co-founder, v.p., treas. Alaska-N.Am. Investment Co., Washington, 1958-62; chief psychiatry and neurology, 1954-64, attending staff, cons. to 1977, emeritus staff 1977—, Suburban Hosp., Bethesda, Md.; cons., emeritus staff Frederick Meml. Hosp., 1976-94, mem. hon. staff, 1994—. Author: The Neuroses in Clinical Practice, 1956, Mental Mechanisms, 1963, The Neuroses, 1967, 70, The Ego and Its Defenses, 1970, 79, 17 other books; assoc. editor Md. Med. Jour., 1988—; assoc. editor Physician's Practice Digest, 1989-92, editor, 1992-94, editor emeritus, 1994—; contbr. more than 148 articles and revs. to profl. jours., reports, chpts. to books. Pres. CAMPER, U.S. Park Svc. Catoctin Mountain Park, 1987-90, bd. dirs., 1980—, Md. Sheriffs Youth Ranch, Frederick County, 1989-90, bd. dirs., 1994—; grand marshal Nat. Independence Day parade, Washington, 1988, 89, Grand Marshal emeritus 1989—; capt. USN Admiral's Team, Lander, Wyo., One Shot Unit, 1997; bd. assocs. Hood Coll., 1988—; trustee, Francis Scott Key Meml. Found., 1988—; pres. Dr. Henry P. and M. Page Durkee Laughlin Found., 1991—. With M.C., USN, 1941-47. Decorated six medals with four battle stars; recipient Disting. Alumni award Ursinus Coll., 1966, the Laughlin prize established in his hon., Royal Coll. Physicitrists of Great Britain, 1979—, Laughlin Profl./Ursinus Coll. faculty achievement award established in his honor, 1988, three Salute to Excellence awards, 1990-92, 6 gov.'s citations State of Md., from 1969, hon. citizenship/comms. various states, 1st Internat. Patriot's award OAS, 1993, Pres. Spl. Achievement award Md. Sheriffs Youth Ranch, 1993, others. Fellow Am. Psychiat. Assn. (life), Am. Soc. of Physician Analysts (founder, hon. lifetime pres. 1982), Royal Coll. Psychiatrists (hon.), Am. Coll. of Psychiatrists (pres. 1963-65), hon. mem. National Accreditation Assn. in pyschoanalysis, 1978—, Am. Coll. of Psychoanalysts (founder, 1st and 8th pres., hon. life pres. 1979, established Laughlin Fellowship program, 1994—, Laughlin fellow, 1977, Gold medals 1965, 76, plaque for significant contbns. as hon. life pres. 1994), USN Psychiatrists (commodore 1978-80, hon. life commodore 1980), USN Admirals Team (capt. 1991), Med. and Chirurg. Faculty of Medicine Md. (mem. coun. 1962-73, 88-92), emeriSoc. Psychoanalytic pysicians, 1987—, Montgomery County Med. Soc. (pres. 1959-60, emeritus mem. 1985), hon. mem Titus Harris Psychiatric Soc. of Tex., Frederick County Med. Soc. emeritus (pres. 1991, 92, 93), SAR (MD soc. pres. 1987-88, Md. surgeon 1994-95, v.p. gen. nat. soc. 1988, surgeon gen. 1990-91, various nat. coms. 1986—, numerous awards), Nat. Congress of Patriotic Orgns. (inaugural pres. emeritus 1991) Am. Legion, U.S. Soc. SAR (trustee 1989-91, inaugural pres. coun. of pres. Md. Soc. 1992-94, inaugural pres. emeritus, 1994—), Gov. Md. Sons and Dau. of the Pilgrims (hon. gov. 1995), Gen. Soc. War of 1812, Pan Am. Bldg. Orgn. Am. States (1st Internat. Patriots award 1993), Rotary. Avocations: philately, geneology, philanthropy, big game hunting, marksmanship. Home: Freehold Park 7977 Timmons Rd Union Bridge MD 21791-7699

LAUGHLIN, JAMES, publishing company executive, writer, lecturer; b. Pitts., Oct. 30, 1914; s. Henry Hughart and Marjory (Rea) L.; m. Margaret Keyser, Mar. 13, 1942 (div. 1952); children: Paul, Leila; m. Ann Clark Resor, May 19, 1956 (dec. Nov. 1987); children: Robert (dec.), Henry; m. Gertrude Huston, Dec. 5, 1991. A.B., Harvard U., 1939; Litt.D. (hon.), Hamilton Coll., 1969, Colgate U., 1978; H.H.D. (hon.), Duquesne U., 1980; L.H.D., Yale U., 1982, Brown U., 1984, Bellarmine Coll., 1987, St. Joseph's Coll., Hartford, 1993. Founder New Directions (now New Directions Pub. Corp.), N.Y.C., 1936; pres. New Directions (now New Directions Pub. Corp.), 1964—; Intercultural Publs., Inc; pub. Perspectives, USA and Perspectives supplements The Atlantic Monthly Jour.; cons. Indian So. Langs. Book Trust, Madras, 1955; vis. Regents prof. U. Calif., San Diego, 1974; Ida Bean vis. prof. U. Iowa, 1981; chmn. creative writing panel Inst. Internat. Edn. Conf. on Arts Exchange, 1956—; adj. prof. English, Brown U., 1983, 85. Author: Some Natural Things, 1945, A Small Book of Poems, 1948, The Wild Anemone and Other Poems, 1957, Selected Poems, 1960, The Pig, 1970, In Another Country, 1978, Stolen and Contaminated Poems, 1984, The House of Light, 1986, Selected Poems, 1986, The Owl of Minerva, 1987, Pound as Wuz, 1987, William Carlos Williams and James Laughlin: Selected Letters, 1989, The Bird of Endless Time, 1990, Kenneth Rexnroth and James Laughlin: Selected Letters, 1991, Random Essays, Random Stories, 1991, The Man in the Wall, 1993, Delmore Schwartz and James Laughlin: Selected Letters, 1993, Collected Poems, 1994, Ezra Pound and James Laughlin: Selected Letters, 1994, (novella) Angelica, 1992; profiled in New Yorker; contbr. mags. and books.; collector lit. mags. (little mag. type); active prodn. documentary films on modern poets, 1983—. Bd. dirs. Goethe Bi-Centennial Found., 1949, Aspen (Colo.) Inst. Humanities, 1950; mem. Nat. Citizens Commn. for Internat. Cooperation, U.S. Nat. Commn. for UNESCO, 1960-63, Nat. Commn. for Internat. Coop. year, 1966; past trustee Allen-Chase Found.; mem. vis. com. German Princeton U.; mem. vis. com. dept. Romance langs. Harvard U.; co-trustee Merton Legacy Trust, 1969—; trustee Rosenbach Found., Phila., to 1981. Decorated chevalier Legion of Honor; hon. fellow Coll. Five, U. Calif., Santa Cruz, 1972—; recipient Disting. Svc. award Am. Acad. Arts and Letters, 1977, award for pub. PEN, 1979, Carey-Thomas citation Pubs. Weekly, 1978, Conn. Arts Comn. award, 1986, Nat. Book Found. medal for Disting. Contbn. to Am. Letters, 1992. Mem. Am. Acad. Arts and Scis., Am. Acad. Arts and Letters, Alta Ski Lifts Co. (formerly Salt Lake City Winter Sports Assn.; dir. 1939—, v.p. 1958), Alta Lodge Co. (v.p. 1948-58, pres. 1958-59), PEN, Asia Soc. (chmn. publs. com. 1959-67), Grolier Assn. (N.Y.C.), Harvard Club of N.Y.C. Office: New Directions Pub Corp 80 8th Ave New York NY 10011-5126

LAUGHLIN, JAMES RODNEY, health care company executive; b. Birmingham, Ala., Dec. 4, 1946; s. James Earl and Gwen (Campbell) L.; m. Gail Bruton, Aug. 6, 1971; children: Micah Garrick, James Matthew, Mary Elizabeth. BBA, Ga. State U., 1969, MBA, 1972. Mgr. acctg. So. Bell Telephone Co., Atlanta, 1969-74; assoc. cons. acct. Touche Ross and Co., Atlanta, 1974-75; exec. v.p. devel. and adminstrv. svcs. Charter Med. Corp., Macon, Ga., 1975—, also bd. dirs.; bd. dirs. 1st Macon Bank. Served with USAR, 1969-75. Mem. Fedn. Am. Hosps. (bd. govs. 1979—), Nat. Assn. Pvt. Psychiatric Hosps. (trustee 1988), Am. Lung Assn. (bd. dirs. 1986-87). Republican. Presbyterian. Club: Idle Hour Country (Macon, Ga.). Avocations: collecting wine, running, deep sea fishing. Home: 1591 Buckline Way Dunwoody GA 30338-5656 Office: Charter Med Corp 577 Mulberry St Macon GA 31201-2728

LAUGHLIN, JOHN SETH, physicist, educator; b. Canton, Mo., Jan. 26, 1918; s. Sceva Bright and Catherine (Goodall) L.; m. Barbara Kester, Jan 14, 1943; children—Catherine Ann, Frances Elizabeth, Janet Judd; m. Eunice Chapin Beyersdorf, June 23, 1979. A.B., Willamette U., 1940, D.Sc., 1968; M.S., Haverford Coll., 1942; Ph.D., U. Ill., 1947. Diplomate: Am. Bd. Radiology. Research physicist OSRD, 1944-45; asst. prof. dept. physics U. Ill., 1946-48, assoc. prof. radiology, 1951-52; attending physicist Meml. Hosp., chmn. dept. med. physics, 1952-89; chief div. biophysics Sloan-Kettering Inst., N.Y.C., 1952-89; vis. prof. Sloan-Kettering Inst., 1966-72; prof. biophysics Sloan Kettering div. Cornell U. Grad. Sch., 1955—; prof. radiology Cornell U. Med. Coll., 1970—; dir. N.E. Center for Radiol. Physics, 1974-85; chmn. med. radiation adv. com. Bur. Radiol. Health, 1976-79; John Wiley Jones lectr. Rochester Inst. Tech., 1977. Author: Physical Aspects of Betatron Therapy, 1954; editor: Medical Physics, 1988—. Recipient Distinguished Service Alumni award U. Ill. Coll. Engring., 1972; Alumni citation Willamette U., 1964; Disting. Service award Health Physics Soc., 1982. Fellow Am. Phys. Soc., Am. Coll. Radiology (Gold medalist), N.Y. Acad. Scis., Am. Inst. Med. and Biol. Engring, Sigma Xi; mem. AAAS, Am. Soc. Therapeutic Radiology and Oncology (Gold medal 1993), Health Physics Soc. (pres. 1960-61), Assn. Tchrs. Physics, Radiol. Soc. N.Am., Soc. Nuclear Medicine (dir., Aebersold award 1984), Am. Radium Soc. (Gold medal 1986), Internat. Orgn. Med. Physics (v.p. 1965-69, pres. 1969-72), Radiation Research Soc. (pres. 1970-71), Am. Assn. Physicists in Medicine (pres. 1964-65, chmn. sci. com. 1968-75, Coolidge award 1974), Am. Coll. Med. Physicists (Williams award 1992). Mem. Soc. of Friends. Home: 48 Graham Rd Scarsdale NY 10583-7256 Office: 1275 York Ave New York NY 10021-6007

LAUGHLIN, NANCY, newspaper editor. Nation/world editor Detroit Free Press. Office: Detroit Free Press Inc 321 W Lafayette Blvd Detroit MI 48226*

LAUGHREN, TERRY, marketing executive; b. Trenton, N.J., July 6, 1940; s. Donald Dunn and Hazel Melinda (Rogers) L.; children: Laurie Margot, B. Kenneth, Brandon Keith. BSBA with honors, Boston U., 1961. Brand mgr. Procter & Gamble Co., Cin., 1963-70; dir. mktg. Internat. Playtex Corp., N.Y.C., 1970-71; dir. corp. mktg. Mattel Inc., Hawthorne, Calif., 1971-72; pres., CEO Metaframe Corp. (subs. of Mattel), Elmwood Park, N.J., 1972-75; exec. v.p. J. Walter Thompson, Detroit and N.Y.C., 1976-80; pres. FTTL Media Co., 1981—; pres., mng. ptnr. Screenvision Cinema Network, N.Y.C., 1981-89, chmn., 1990. 1st lt. U.S. Army, 1961-63. Mem. Young Pres.'s Orgn., Nat. Alumni Coun. Boston U. (chmn.), Econ. Club Detroit, Adcraft Club, Friar's Club, Beta Gamma Sigma. Republican. Office: FTTL Media Co Inc 311 W 43rd St Ste 903 New York NY 10036-6413

LAUGHTON, KATHARINE L, career officer; b. L.A., Dec. 9, 1942; d. Herman and Mary-Alice (McCunniff) H.; m. Robert James Laughton, Oct. 16, 1972. Attended, Vassar Coll., 1960-61; BA, U. Calif., Riverside, 1964; dist. grad., Navy War Coll., 1986. Dep. dir. mgmt. info. svcs. Military Sealift Command, 1977-79; commdg. officer Military Sealift Command, Pt. Canaveral, 1979-82; program mgr. Naval Data Automation Command, 1982-84; spl. asst. inspector gen. U.S. Navy, 1984-86; head ADP svcs. commdr. n chief U.S. Atlantic, Norfolk, Va., 1986-87. Recipient medal of merit for excellence in tech. Armed Forces Communications & Elecs. Assn., 1991, Parsons award for scientific and Tech. progress Navy League, 1990. Mem. AFCEA (internat. v.p.), Vassar Club. Episcopalian. Avocation, crafts. Office: Navy Department Washington DC 20350-2000

LAULICHT, MURRAY JACK, lawyer; b. Bklyn., May 12, 1940; s. Philip and Ernestine (Greenfield) L.; m. Linda Kushner, Apr. 4, 1965; children: Laurie Hasten, Pamela Hirt, Shellie Davis, Abigail. Ba, Yeshiva U., 1961; LLB summa cum laude, Columbia U., 1964. Bar: N.Y. 1965, N.J. 1968, U.S. Supreme Ct. 1976. Mem. legal staff Warren Commn., Washington, 1964; assoc. Kaye, Scholer, Fierman, Hays & Handler, N.Y.C., 1965-68; ptnr. Lowenstein, Sandler, Brochin, Kohl & Fisher, Newark, N.J., 1968-79, Pitney, Hardin, Kipp & Szuch, Florham Park, N.J., 1979—. Mem. N.J. Consumer Affairs Adv. Com., 1991-93; chmn. N.J. Commn. on Holocaust Edn., 1992—; pres. Jewish Edn. Assn., 1981-84; chmn. Community Rels. Com., 1988-91. Recipient Julius Cohn Young Leadership award Jewish Fedn. Metrowest, 1976. Mem. ABA, N.J. State Bar Assn. (dist. X ethics com. 1986-89, bd. editors N.J. Law Jour. 1986-93), N.J. Lawyer Mag. (chmn. 1993—). Democrat. Avocations: computers, communal activities. Home: 18 Crestwood Dr West Orange NJ 07052-2004 Office: Pitney Hardin Kipp & Szuch PO Box 1945 200 Campus Dr Florham Park NJ 07932-1012

LAUMANN, EDWARD OTTO, sociology educator; b. Youngstown, Ohio, Aug. 31, 1938; m. Anne Elizabeth Solomon, June 21, 1980; children: Christopher, Timothy; children by previous marriage: Eric, Lisa. AB summa cum laude, Oberlin Coll., 1960; MA, Harvard U., 1962, PhD, 1964. Asst. prof. sociology U. Mich., Ann Arbor, 1964-69, assoc. prof., 1969-72; prof. sociology U. Chgo., 1973—; George Herbert Mead Disting. Service prof., 1985—, chmn. dept., 1981-84, dean div. of social scis., 1984-92, provost, 1992-93; bd. govs. Argonne Nat. Lab., 1992-93. Author: Prestige and Associations in an Urban Community, 1966, Bonds of Pluralism, 1973, (with Franz U. Pappi) Networks of Collective Action, 1976, (with John P. Heinz) Chicago Lawyers, 1982, (with David Knoke) The Organizational State, 1987, (with John P. Heinz, Robert Nelson and Robert Salisbury) The Hollow Core, 1993, (with John Gagnon, Robert Michael, Stuart Michaels) The Social Organization of Sexuality, 1994, (with Robert Michael, John Gagno, Gina Kolata) Sex in America, 1994; editor Am. Jour. Sociology, 1978-84, 95—. Mem. sociology panel NSF, Washington, 1972-74; commr. CBASSE, NRC, 1986-91; v.p., trustee NORC; trustee U. Chgo. Hosps., 1992-93. Fellow AAAS; mem. Sociol. Rsch. Assn., Am. Sociol. Assn., Population Assn. Am. Office: U Chgo 5848 S University Ave Chicago IL 60637

LAUN, LOUIS FREDERICK, government official; b. Battle Creek, Mich., May 19, 1920; s. Louis Frederick and Roena (Graves) L.; m. Margaret West, Jan. 25, 1947; children: Nancy, Kathryn Webb, Margaret. B.A., Yale U., 1942. Asst. advt. mgr. Bates Fabrics, Inc., N.Y.C., 1946-48; asst. to pres., indsl. and public relations Bates Mfg. Co., Lewiston, Maine, 1948-55; advt. dir., out-of-town sales mgr. Burlington Industries, N.Y.C., 1955-57; gen. merchandising mgr. Celanese Fibers Co., N.Y.C., 1957-60; v.p., dir. mktg. Celanese Fibers Co., 1960-63, exec. v.p. mktg., 1963-64; pres. Celanese Fibers Mktg. Co. div. Celanese Corp., 1964-71, also v.p. corp., 1964-71; assoc. adminstr. ops. SBA, Washington, 1973; dep. adminstr. SBA, 1973-77; pres. Am. Paper Inst., N.Y.C., 1977-86; asst. Sec. Commerce for Internat. Econ. Policy Dept. of Commerce, Washington, 1986-89; exec. br. commr., Commn. on Security and Cooperation in Europe, 1988-89; cons. Nat. Exec Svc. Corp, 1989—; U.S. pulp and paper rep. food and agrl. orgns. UN; bd. dirs. Overseas Pvt. Investment Corp., Noranda Aluminum, Inc.; exec. br. mem. Commn. on Security and Cooperation in Europe (Helsinki Commn.). Bd. dirs. N.Y. Bd. Trade, Better Bus. Bur. N.Y., Alliance to Save Energy, Bus. Adv. Com. on Fed. Reports, Citizens Against Govt. Waste; indsl. asst. to chmn. Opportunities Industrialization Centers Am.; nat. adv. council SBA; chmn. Republican Industry Workshop program; field dir. Com. for Re-election of Pres., 1972; trustee Taft Sch.; mem. exec. com. President's Pvt. Sector Survey on Cost Control. Served with USMCR, 1942-46. Decorated Bronze Star; recipient Human Rights award Anti-Defamation League, 1968; Achievement award Textile Vets. Assn., 1970; named Young Man of Yr. Lewiston-Auburn C. of C., 1953, Man of Yr. Textile Salesman Assn., 1970, Man of Yr. Fabric Salesmen's Guild, 1971; Gold medal for disting. service SBA, Citation Merit Taft Sch., 1988. Mem. Color Assn. U.S. (sec.), Man-Made Fiber Producers Assn. (chmn. 1967-69), Yale Club (N.Y.C.), Sleepy Hollow Country Club (Scarborough, N.Y.), Met. Club (Washington), Mid-Ocean Club (Bermuda). Home: 25 Spring Ln Chappaqua NY 10514-2607

LAUNER, DALE MARK, screenwriter; b. Cleve., May 19, 1952; s. Sol John and Estelle Launer. Student, Calif. State U., Northridge. Ind. screenwriter Calif., 1986—. Screenwriter: (films) Ruthless People, 1986, Blind Date, 1987; screenwriter, exec. prodr.: (films) Dirty Rotten Scoundrels, 1988; screenwriter, dir., prodr.: (films) Love Potion #9, 1991; screenwriter, prodr.: (films) My Cousin Vinny, 1992. Democrat. Jewish. Home: 118 1/2 Pacific St Santa Monica CA 90405 Office: 20th Century Fox 10201 W Pico Blvd Bldg 1 Ste 148 Los Angeles CA 90035

LAUPER, CYNDI, musician; b. Queens, N.Y., June 20, 1953. Studied with Katie Agresta, N.Y., 1974. Toured with Doc West's Disco Band Flyer; mem. musical group Blue Angel, N.Y.C. 1980. Featured in German TV music program; rec. artist: (album) She's So Unusual, 1983, A Night To Remember, 1989, Hat Full of Stars, 1993; co-writer: (songs) Girls Just Want to Have Fun, She Bop, Money Changes Everything, Time After Time, Goonies R Good Enough, 1985, True Colors, 1986, A Night to Remember, 1989; contbr. A Very Special Christmas, 1992, vol. 2, 1993; star: (videos) Girls Just Want to Have Fun, Time After Time, others; film debut: Vibes, 1988, (other films) Life with Mikey, 1993; TV appearances include The Tonight Show, The David Letterman Show, Mad About You (Emmy nomination, Guest Actress - Comedy Series, 1994); concert tours in Japan, Australia, Hawaii and Eng. Named one of Women of Yr., 1984, Best Female Video Performer, MTV Video Music Awards, 1984, Best Female Performer, Am. Video Awards, 1985; recipient 6 Grammy awards, 1985, 2 Am. Video awards, 1985. *

LAUPUS, WILLIAM EDWARD, physician, educator; b. Seymour, Ind., May 25, 1921; s. John George and Laura Kathryne (Hancock) L.; m. Evelyn Estelle Fike, Mar. 6, 1948; children: Patricia, John Richard, Laura (dec.), William Edward. B.S., Yale, 1943, M.D., 1945. Diplomate Am. Bd. Pediatrics (ofcl. examiner 1966-90, mem. exec. bd. 1972-77, pres. 1976-77). Intern N.Y. Hosp.-Cornell Med. Center, 1945-46; resident, 1948-51; instr. pediatrics Cornell U. Sch. Medicine, 1950-52; asst. prof., then asso. prof., prof. pediatrics Med. Coll. Ga., 1959-63; prof. pediatrics, chmn. dept. Med. Coll. Va., Va. Commonwealth U., Richmond, 1963-75; pediatrician-in-chief Med. Coll. Va. Hosps.; prof. pediatrics Sch. of Medicine East Carolina U., 1975-89; dean Sch. of Medicine East Carolina U., 1975-82; dean Sch. of Medicine and vice chancellor div. Health Scis. East Carolina U., 1982-89, dean emeritus, 1989—; prof. preventive medicine and pediatrics East Carolina U. Sch. Medicine, 1989-91; pres. Am. Bd. Med. Specialists, 1984-86. Contbr. to: Nelson's Textbook of Pediatrics, 1964, 69, 75, Kendig's Respiratory Diseases in Children, 1969, 72, 77, Gellis and Kagen's Current Therapy, 1969-77. Pres. Richmond Area Community Council, 1973-75. Served with AUS, 1946-48. Mem. Am. Acad. Pediatrics (past pres. Va. chpt.), Am. Pediatric Soc., AMA, N.C. Med. Soc., Pitt County Med. Soc., Alpha Omega Alpha, Phi Kappa Phi. Office: Welco Consulting PO Box 20007 Greenville NC 27858-0007

LAUR, BERNARD PAUL, radio executive; b. Milw., Feb. 5, 1964; s. Joseph Edwin and Ruth Bernadine (Beiswenger) L. BA, U. Minn., 1987. Program asst. WLOL Radio, Mpls., 1984-87; program producer WISN WLTQ Radio, Milw., 1987; promotion dir. WMIL WOKY Radio, Milw., 1988-89, WMYX WEMP Radio, Milw., 1989—; gen. ptnr. L.T. Entertainment, Milw., 1991—. Bd. dirs. Great Lakes Hemophilia Found., Milw. Roman Catholic. Avocations: football, softball, golf, hunting. Office: WMYX WEMP Radio 11800 W Grange Ave Hales Corners WI 53130-1035

LAUR, WILLIAM EDWARD, retired dermatologist; b. Saginaw, Mich., Nov. 17, 1919; s. Vertner Linton and Ruth Gae (Eyre) L.; m. Mary Elizabeth Kirby, Dec. 31, 1943; children: Eric, Edward, John, J. Michael. BS, Mercer U., Macon, Ga., 1941; MD, U. Mich., 1943; MS in Medicine, Wayne State U., Detroit, 1949. Diplomate Am. Bd. Dermatology. Intern John Sealy Hosp., Galveston, Tex., 1943; resident Wayne State U., Detroit, 1946-49; pvt. practice Amarillo, Tex., 1949-75; pres. High Plains Dermatology Ctr., P.A., Amarillo, 1975-90; ret.; cons. VA, USAF, 1952-90; assoc. prof. Tex. Tech. Health Sci. Ctr., Amarillo, 1965-90. Contbr. articles to profl. jours. including Archives of Dermatology, Internat. Jour. Dermatology, Cutis, So. Med. Jour., Jour. Am. Acad. Dermatology, Panhandle Med. Soc. Bull., Urologic and Cutaneous Rev. Dir. Moon Watch, NASA, Amarillo, 1956. Capt. U.S. Army, 1944-46; ETO(. Fellow Am. Acad. Dermatology; mem. AMA, Noah Worcester Dermatological Soc., Potter Randall County Med. Soc. (pres. 1964). Avocations: cooking, duplicate bridge, computer activities. Home: 1607 Fannin St Amarillo TX 79102

LAURANCE, DALE R., oil company executive; b. Ontario, Oreg., July 6, 1945; s. Rolland D. and Frances S. (Hopkins) L.; m. Lynda E. Dolmyer, Sept. 11, 1966; children—Catherine Mange, Brandy Nichole, Holly Elizabeth. B.S. in Chem. Engring., Oreg. State U., 1967; M.S. in Chem. Engring., U. Kans., 1971, Ph.D. in Chem. Engring., 1973. Mem. mgmt., research staff E.I. DuPont de NeMours, Lawrence, Kans., 1967-77; mgr. process technology Olin Corp., Lake Charles, La., 1977-80; bus. mgr. urethanes Olin Corp., Stamford, Conn., 1980-82, gen. mgr. urethane and organics, 1982-83; sr. v.p. Occidental Chem. Corp., Darien, Conn., 1983-84; exec. v.p. Occidental Petroleum Corp., Los Angeles, 1984-91, exec. v.p., sr. oper. officer, 1991—, also bd. dirs.; chmn. adv. bd., mem. dept. chem. and petroleum engring., U. Kans., Lawrence, 1985—. Contbr. articles to profl. jours. Patentee in field. Recipient Disting. Engring. Svc. award Sch. Engring., U. Kans., 1991. Mem. Am. Petroleum Inst., Chem. Mfrs. Assn., Soc. Chem. Industry, L.A. Area C. of C. (bd. dirs.). Republican. Club: Riveria Country (Los Angeles). Office: Occidental Petroleum Corp 10889 Wilshire Blvd Los Angeles CA 90024-4201

LAURANCE, LEONARD CLARK, marketing researcher, educator and consultant; b. Perth, Australia, Aug. 20, 1932; came to U.S., 1963; s. Thomas Clark and Lorna Ruby (Spencer) L.; m. Lorraine Joan Harwood, June 10, 1954 (div. 1960); 1 child, Beverley Lorraine; m. Judith Ellen Krickan, Sept. 8, 1962; children: Cynthia Ellen, Amanda Lee. Gen. mgr. Ketchikan & No. Terminal Co. Inc., Ketchikan, Alaska, 1963-65; regional mgr. Alaska Steamship Co., Ketchikan, 1965-68; pres. Alaska World Travel Inc., Ketchikan, 1968-72, Leisure Corp., Ketchikan, 1972-85, AlaskaBound, Inc., Ketchikan, 1985-88, Mariner Inc., Ketchikan, 1988—; faculty mem. U. Alaska SE, Ketchikan, 1987—, Juneau, 1995; dir. mktg. Taquan Air, Ketchikan, 1991—; bd. dirs. Hist. Ketchikan, Inc. Mem. Alaska Mktg. Coun., Juneau, 1979-84, chair, 1982-84; mem. SE Alaska Tourism Coun., Juneau, 1982-86, chair, 1982-83; mem. mgmt. com. Sheffield Hotels, Anchorage, 1980-85; chair Alaska Marine Hwy. Task Force, Juneau, 1983-84, UAS Coll. Coun., 1982-83; mem. Ketchikan Gen. Hosp. Adv. Bd., 1973-84, chair, 1979; assemblyperson Ketchikan Gateway Borough, 1976-82. Recipient North Star award Alaska Visitors Assn., 1977, Gov.'s award State of Alaska, 1984, Presdl. award Ketchikan C. of C., 1970. Mem. Alaska Visitors Assn. (bd. dirs. 1969-93, advisor to bd. 1994—, pres. 1972-73, hon. life 1994), Alaska Tourism Mktg. Coun., Ketchikan Visitors Bur. (bd. dirs. 1980—, chair 1983-84), UAS Visitor Ind. Program (adv. bd. 1986—). Republican. Episcopalian. Avocations: sportfishing, swimming, community service, tourism research. Office: Mariner Inc 5716 S Tongass PO Box 8800 Ketchikan AK 99901-3800

LAUREN, RALPH, fashion designer; b. Bronx, N.Y., Oct. 14, 1939; s. Frank and Frieda Lifshitz; m. Ricky Low Beer, Dec. 30, 1964; children: Andrew, David, Dylan. Student, CCNY; DFA (hon.), Pratt U., 1988. Salesperson Brooks Bros., N.Y.C.; asst. buyer Allied Stores, N.Y.C.; rep. Rivetz Necktie Mfrs., N.Y.C.; neckwear designer Polo divsn. Beau Brummel, N.Y.C., 1967-69; founder Polo Fashions, Inc., N.Y.C., 1968—; established Polo Men's Wear Co., N.Y.C., 1968—, Ralph Lauren Womenswear, N.Y.C., 1971—, Polo Leathergoods, 1978—, Polo/Ralph Lauren for Boys, 1978—, Polo/Ralph Lauren Luggage, 1982—, Ralph Lauren Home Collection, 1983—; launched fragrances Polo for Men, Lauren for Women, 1979—; chmn. Polo Ralph Lauren Corp. (flagship store N.Y.C., 65 other stores in U.S. and 140 stores worldwide); launched Safari fragrance for women, 1990, Safari for men, 1992, Polo Sport, 1994. Served in U.S. Army. Recipient Coty Am. Fashion awards, 1970, 73, 74, 76, 77, 81, 84, also Coty Hall of Fame award for Menswear and Womenswear, Tommy award Am. Printed Fabrics Coun., 1971, Neiman Marcus Disting. Svc. award, 1973, Am. Fashion award, 1975, award Coun. Fashion Designers Am., 1981, CFDA Lifetime Achievement award, 1992. Office: Polo Ralph Lauren Corp 650 Madison Ave New York NY 10022-1004

LAURENCE, DAN H., author, literary and dramatic specialist; b. N.Y.C., Mar. 28, 1920. B.A., Columbia U., 1946; M.A., N.Y. U., 1950. Performed in profl. theatre, 1932-41; writer, performer Armed Forces Radio, 1942-45; writer for radio, TV U.S. and Australia, 1946-48; grad. asst. NYU, 1950-52, assoc. prof. English, 1962-67, prof., 1967-70; instr. Hofstra U., 1953-58; editor Readex Microprint Corp., 1959-60; lit. and dramatic adv. Estate of George Bernard Shaw, London, 1973-90; vis. prof. Hofstra U., 1969, U. Tex., 1974-75; vis. fellow Inst. Arts and Humanistic Studies, Pa. State U., 1976; spl. cons. Humanities Research Center, U. Tex., Austin, 1975-77; Andrew W. Mellon prof. humanities Tulane U., New Orleans, 1981; Montgomery fellow Dartmouth Coll., 1982; disting. vis. prof. humanities Guelph U. (Ont., Can.), 1983, U. B.C. (Can.), 1984; adj. prof. drama Guelph U., 1986-91; literary advisor, mem. acting ensemble of Shaw Festival, Ont., 1982-90, assoc. dir., 1987—. Author: (with Leon Edel) Henry James: a bibliography, 3d edit, 1981, Robert Nathan: A Bibliography, 1960, Bernard Shaw: A Bibliography, 1983; playwright: The Black Girl in Search of God, 1977; editor: Uncollected Writings of Bernard Shaw: How to Become A Musical Critic, 1961, Platform and Pulpit, 1961, (with David H. Greene) The Matter with Ireland, 1962, Selected Non-Dramatic Writings of Shaw, 1965, Col-

lected Letters of Bernard Shaw, 4 vols., 1965-88, Bernard Shaw's Collected Plays with Their Prefaces, 7 vols., 1970-74, (with Daniel J. Leary) Flyleaves, 1977, Shaw's Music, 1981, (with James Rambeau) Agitations, 1985, (with Martin Quinn) Shaw on Dickens, 1985, (with Nicholas Grene) Bernard Shaw, Lady Gregory, and the Abbey, 1993, (with Daniel J. Leary) Shaw: Complete Prefaces, vol. 1, 1993, vol. 2, 1995, Theatrics, 1995. Served with USAAF, 1942-45, PTO. John Simon Guggenheim Meml. fellow, 1960, 61, 72, Pres.'s medal Hofstra U., 1990. Mem. Royal Acad. Dramatic Art (assoc.), Phi Beta Kappa, Phi Alpha Theta, Alpha Psi Omega, Phi Gamma Delta. Home: # P-213 102 W Rampart Dr San Antonio TX 78216-6757

LAURENCE, JEFFREY CONRAD, immunologist; b. N.Y.C., Oct. 21, 1952; s. Harry and Stephanie (Maderic) L.; m. Linda Dusenbury, July 4, 1987; 1 child, Auden. BA summa cum laude, Columbia U., 1972; MD, U. Chgo., 1976. Diplomate Am. Bd. Internal Medicine. Rsch. assoc. Inst. for Cancer Rsch., Osaka, Japan, 1974-75; intern, resident, then hematology fellow N.Y.C. Hosp.-Cornell, 1976-79; assoc. physician The Rockefeller U., N.Y.C., 1980-84; asst. prof. Cornell U. Med. Coll., N.Y.C., 1982-87, assoc. prof., 1988-91, assoc. prof. with tenure, 1991—; dir. Lab. AIDS Rsch. Cornell Med. Coll., N.Y.C., 1986—; sr. dir. Immune Tech., Inc., N.Y.C., 1986—; sr. scientist Am. Found. AIDS Rsch., N.Y.C. and Beverly Hills, Calif., 1986—. Author (play) Many Happy Returns, 1982; editor-in-chief The AIDS Reader, 1991—; editor AIDS Targeted Info. Newsletter, 1987-92; assoc. editor AIDS Rsch. and Human Retroviruses, AIDS, 1987—; cons. editor Infections in Medicine, 1987—; patentee in field. Recipient Clinician-Scientist award Am. Heart Assn., 1980-85; William S. Paley Found. fellow, 1982-84; Henry Luce Found. scholar, 1974, Rhodes scholar-elect, 1973. Mem. NIH (mem. study sect.), AMA, Am. Fedn. Clin. Rsch., Am. Soc. Microbiology, Phi Beta Kappa. Episcopalian. Avocations: collecting ancient med. books and sci. instruments, contemporary art. Home: 86 Brookside Dr Greenwich CT 06831-5345 Office: The NY Hosp-Cornell Med Ctr Dept Medicine Lab AIDS Rsch 411 E 69th St New York NY 10021-4873

LAURENCE, MICHAEL MARSHALL, magazine publisher, writer; b. N.Y.C., May 22, 1940; s. Frank Marshall and Edna Ann (Roeder) L.; m. Patricia Ann McDonald, Mar. 1, 1969; children—Elizabeth Sarah, John Marshall. A.B. cum laude, Harvard U., 1963. Sr. editor Playboy mag., Chgo., 1967-69, contbg. editor, 1969-72, asst. pub., 1977-82; mng. editor Oui mag., Chgo., 1973-77; editor/pub. Linn's Stamp News, Sidney, Ohio, 1982—, also columnist Editor's Choice; co-founder, dir. U.S. 1869 Pictorial Research Assocs., 1975-82. Author: (Playboy's Investment Guide, 1971; also articles. Editor: U.S. Mail and Post Office Assistant, 1975. Recipient G.M. Loeb award for disting. mag. writing U. Conn., 1968. Mem. Internat. Soc. Philatelic Journalists, U.S. Philatelic Classics Soc. (Elliott Perry award 1975; bd. dirs. 1975-81), Harvard Club (N.Y.C.), Collectors Club Chgo. (bd. dirs. 1978-82), Collectors Club N.Y.C. Avocations: stamp collecting; gardening. Office: Linn's Stamp News 911 S Vandemark Rd Sidney OH 45365-8983

LAURENCE, ROBERT LIONEL, chemical engineering educator; b. West Warwick, R.I., July 13, 1936; s. Lionel Gerard and Gertrude Sara (Lefebvre) L.; m. Carol Leah Jolicoeur, Sept. 7, 1959; children: Jonathan, Lisa, Andrew. BSChemE, MIT, 1957; MSChemE, U. R.I., 1960; PhDChemE, Northwestern U., 1966; DSc (honoris causa), Inst. Nat. Poly., 1989. Rsch. engr. Gen. Dynamics, Groton, Conn., 1957-59, E. I. du Pont de Nemours, Wilmington, Del., 1960-61; field svc. engr. E. I. du Pont de Nemours, Beaumont, Tex., 1961-63; asst. prof. chem. engring. Johns Hopkins U., Balt., 1965-68; rsch. engr. Monsanto Co., Springfield, Mass., 1968; assoc. prof. U. Mass., Amherst, 1968-73, head dept. chem. engring., 1982-89, prof., 1973—; vis. prof. Imperial Coll., London, 1974-75, Coll. de France, Paris, 1982-83; invited prof. ENSIGC, Toulouse, France, 1990; vis. rsch. fellow GE, Schenectady, 1989; cons. UN Devel. Program, Argentina, 1978, 80, Beijing, 1982; mem. Conseil Technologique Groupe Rhone-Poulenc, Paris, 1988—. Fellow Am. Inst. Chem. Engrs., Am. Inst. Chemists; mem. Am. Chem. Soc., Soc. Plastics Engrs., Am. Soc. Engring. Edn., Sigma Xi, Tau Beta Pi. Roman Catholic. Avocation: rugby. Office: U Mass Dept Chem Engring Amherst MA 01003

LAURENSON, ROBERT MARK, mechanical engineer; b. Pitts., Oct. 25, 1938; s. Robert Mark and Mildred Othelia (Frandsen) L.; m. Alice Ann Scroggins, Aug. 26, 1961; children: Susan Elizabeth Laurenson Matchael, Shari Lynn. Student, Drury Coll., 1956-58; BS in Mech. Engring., Mo. Sch. Mines, 1961; MS in Mech. Engring., U. Mich., 1962; PhD in Mech. Engring. (NASA tng. grantee), Ga. Inst. Tech., 1968. Registered profl. engr., Mo. Dynamics engr. McDonnell Douglas Corp., St. Louis, 1962-64, sr. dynamics engr., 1968-71, group engr., 1971-74, staff engr., 1974-75, tech. specialist, 1975-78, sr. tech. specialist, 1978-81, sect. chief, 1981-85, prin. tech. specialist, 1985-87, br. chief, 1987-89, prin. mgr. engring., 1989-92; prin. tech. specialist, systems engring. mgr. McDonnell Douglas Aerospace, Seabrook, Md., 1992-93, sr. mgr., 1993-95; asst. dir. engring., 1995—; participant 14th Midwestern Mechanics Conf., 1975; lectr. engring. mechanics St. Louis U., part-time 1969-71; adj. assoc. prof. U. Mo.-Rolla Grad. Engring. Ctr., St. Louis, 1980-88; participant Symposium on Dynamics and Control of Large Flexible Spacecraft, Blackburg, Va., 1977, In-Space Tech. Experiments Workshop NASA, 1988, Damping '89 Conf., 1989; mem. panel Am. Astronautica Soc. Symposium on Dynamics and Control of Nonrigid Spacecraft, UCLA, 1974. Contbr. articles to profl. jours.; reviewer profl. jours. Vestryman Episcopal Ch., 1972-76, sr. warden, 1976, usher chmn., 1978-80, Sunday sch. tchr., 1980-84, chmn. every mem. canvas, 1983, mem. steering com., 1983-88, chmn. steering com., 1987-88, mem. search com., 1984-85, mem. exec. com., 1991-92, warden, 1991-92; mem. Commn. on Ministry, Diocese of Mo., 1985-91, chmn., 1989-91; mem. standing com. Diocese of Mo., 1990-92; trustee Corp. of Episcopal Diocese of Mo., 1990-92, mem. seminarian com., 1993-95, chair seminarian com., 1994-95; engring. mentor Holy Trinity Episcopal Day Sch. Fellow ASME (structures materials com. aerospace divsn. 1975-84, com. chmn. 1979-81, session organizer, chmn. ann. meeting, 1975, participatant ann. meeting, 1986, 89, mem. exec. com. aerospace divsn. 1980-85, sec.-treas. 1981-82, vice-chmn. 1982-83, chmn. 1983-84, Flag award aerospace divsn. 1990, mem. Guggenheim medal bd. 1989-92, mem. conf. organizing com., session chmn. Structure, Structural Dynamics and Materials Conf. 1977, chmn. tech. program 1978, gen. co-chmn. 1979, gen. chmn. 1981, mem. SDM planning com. 1978-82, chmn. 1981-82, session chmn. 1985, 88, adv. com. 1978-82, participant 1979, 83, 86, 90, mech. engring. evaluator Accreditation Bd. Engring. and Tech. 1985-91, organizer symposium on microgravity fluid mechanics 1986, mem. planning com. edn. conf. 1986, editor Advances in Aerospace Structures 1982, Proc. of 1986 Edn. Conf. The Decade Ahead, bd. engring. edn. K. thru 12 task force 1992-93, bd. pre-coll. edn. 1992—, 1st alt. nat. nominating com. 1993-94, engring. accreditation com. 1993—, exec. com. 1993-95, rep. on Am. Assn. Engring. Soc. precoll. edn. coun. 1994—); mem. AIAA (sr., gen. chmn. dynamics specialist conf. 1981, session chmn. 1987), Edison Electric Inst. (adv. com. power engring. edn. forgivable loan program 1993-94), Sigma Xi, Pi Tau Sigma, Tau Beta Pi, Phi Kappa Phi, Sigma Phi Epsilon. Home: 1104 Jasper Ct Crofton MD 21114 Office: McDonnell Douglas Aerospace 7404 Executive Pl Seabrook MD 20706

LAURENT, LAWRENCE BELL, communications executive, former journalist; b. Monroe, La., Mar. 9, 1925; s. Lewis Emeal and John Ethel (Dawkins) L.; m. Margaret F. Goodwillie, Nov. 1, 1949; children—Richard Sandford, Arthur Halliday, Margaret Funsten, Elizabeth MacLean. Student, U. Va., 1946-49; pvt. study with Dr. W.Y. Elliott, 1954-56, Dr. Franklin Dunham, 1957-58. With Bluefield (W.Va.) Daily Telegraph, 1949-50, Charlottesville (Va.) Daily Progress, 1950-51; with Washington Post, 1951-82, radio-TV editor, 1953-82, radio-TV editor emeritus, 1982—; cons. Assn. Ind. TV Stas., 1982-85, dir. communication, 1985-86, v.p. communication, 1986-91; congl. cons., 1991—; editor-in-residence Broadcast Pioneers Library, 1985—; adj. prof. communications Am. U., Washington, 1963-85; chmn. editorial bd. TV Quar., 1973-74, bd. dirs., 1974—; guest prof. Syracuse U., 1965; vis. prof. U. Detroit, 1967, George Washington U., 1982—; formerly judge Alfred I. duPont awards, Saturday Rev. Lit. TV awards, Sigma Delta Chi pub. service TV awards, Humanitas awards. Editor, author: (with Newton N. Minow) Equal Time, 1964; Contbr. to books, mags. Trsutee Human Family Edn. and Cutlrual Inst.; bd. dirs. Pioneers Edn. Fund., Inc., 1984-94, trustee, 1995—. With USNR, 1943-46. Recipient Front Page award Am. Newspaper Guild, 1964, Disting. Tchr. award Am. U., 1978, TV Acad.'s Silver Circle award 1988; named to Broadcast Pioneers' Hall of Fame, 1984; du Pont Journalism scholar U. Va. Mem. AAUP, NATAS (life), VFW (life), DAV (life), Nat. Press Club, White

House Corrs. Assn., Washington Post E-Streeters, Am. Legion (life), Sigma Delta Chi, Pi Delta Epsilon, Theta Chi. Episcopalian. Home: 215 Jefferson St Alexandria VA 22314-4323

LAURENT, PIERRE-HENRI, history educator; b. Fall River, Mass., May 15, 1933; s. Henri and Harriet (Moriarty) L.; m. Virginia Blanco, 1958; children: Paul-Henri, Bradford Webb, Nicole, Alexa. A.B., Colgate U., 1956; A.M., Boston U., 1960, Ph.D., 1964. Instr. hist. economy Boston U., 1961-64; asst. prof. history Sweet Briar Coll., 1964-66; vis. asst. prof. history U. Wis., Madison, 1966-67; asst. prof. history Tulane U., New Orleans, 1967-68, assoc. prof., 1968-70; assoc. prof. history Tufts U., Medford, Mass., 1970-75, prof., 1975—, chmn. dept., 1987-89, adj. prof. diplomatic history/Fletcher Sch. Law and Diplomacy, 1977, 84, chmn. Exptl. Coll., 1973-75, acting dir. internat. relations program, 1979, dir. internat. relations program, 1984-88; co-dir. Internat. Relations Inst. Tufts U., France, 1979-80; acad. dir. Tufts European Ctr., France, 1994—; mem. history devel. bd. Ednl. Testing Svc. of Princeton, 1979-82; instr. JFK Inst. Polit., Harvard U., Cambridge, 1989; mem. nat. screening com. Fulbright-Hays program Inst. Internat. Edn., 1988-91; rsch. assoc. Ctr. for Internat. Affairs, Harvard U. Mem. editorial bd. Jour. Social History, 1966-74; sect. editor Am. Hist. Rev., 1967-77; contbr. chpts. to books, articles to profl. jours., mags., encys. Served with USAF, 1956-58. NATO fellow, 1967, NEH fellow, 1969, Paul-Henri Spaak Found. fellow, 1976-77; Sweet Briar Faculty rsch. grantee, 1965, Tufts Faculty rsch. grantee, 1972, Inst. European Studies-Exxon Ednl. Fund grantee, 1983; Fulbright Rsch. scholar, 1992-93. Fellow Inst. des Rels. Internationales, Acad. Assoc. Atlantic Coun.; mem. AAUP (exec. com. Mass. State Conf. 1974-76, pres. Tufts U. chpt. 1982-84), European Cmty. Studies Assn. (exec. com. 1988-92, 95—, chmn. 1991-92), Belgian-Am. Edn. Found. (bd. govs. 1986-90). Office: Tufts Univ Dept Of History Medford MA 02155

LAURENTS, ARTHUR, playwright; b. N.Y.C., July 14, 1917; s. Irving and Ada (Robbins) L. BA, Cornell U., Ithaca, N.Y., 1937. Radio script writer, 1939-40. Author: (novels) The Way We Were, 1972, The Turning Point, 1977 (screen plays) The Snake Pit, 1948, Rope, 1948, Caught, 1948, Anna Lucasta, 1949, Anastasia, 1956, Bonjour Tristesse, 1958, The Way We Were, 1973, The Turning Point, 1977 (Writer Guild Am. award), (plays) Home of the Brave, 1946, The Bird Cage, 1950, The Time of the Cuckoo, 1952, A Clearing in the Woods, 1956, Invitation to a March, 1960, The Enclave, 1973, Scream, Houston, 1978, Johnson Sings Again, 1995, The Radical Mystique, 1995, (mus. plays) West Side Story, 1957, Gypsy, 1959, Do I Hear A Waltz?, 1964, Hallelujah, Baby, 1967 (Tony award), Nick and Nora, 1991; screenwirter, co-producer (film) The Turning Point, 1977 (Golden Glove award, Nat. Bd. Rev. award); co-author; dir.: (dramatic prodns.) My Mother was a Fortune Teller, 1978 (Drama Desk award), The Madwoman of Central Park West, (radio plays in anthologies) Radio Drama in Action, 1945, Best One Act Plays of 1944-45, 1945-46, dir.: (Broadway prodns.) Invitation to a March, 1960, I Can Get It For You Wholesale, 1962, La Cage aux Folles (Tony award for Best Dir. 1984); writer, dir.: (Broadway prodns.) Invitation to a March, 1960, Anyone Can Whistle, 1964, The Enclave, 1973, (one-act play) A Loss of Memory (Best Short Plays of 1983); dir. (London prodn.) Gypsy, 1973, N.Y. revival, 1974 (Drama Desk award), La Cage aux Folles, 1983, Australian prodn. (Best Dir's. award 1985, London prodn. 1986), Birds of Paradise, 1987, Gypsy, revival, 1989, Nick and Nora, 1991. Served with AUS, 1941-45. Recipient Variety Radio award, 1945, Am. Acad. Arts and Letters award; co-recipient Sidney Howard award, 1946. Mem. Dramatists Guild Council, P.E.N., Authors League, Screenwriters Guild, Acad. Motion Picture Arts and Scis., Theatre Hall of Fame. Home: PO Box 582 Quogue NY 11959-0582

LAURENZO, VINCENT DENNIS, industrial management company executive; b. Des Moines, May 31, 1939; s. Vincent C. and B.J. (Garver) L.; m. Sherrill S. Mullen, Sept. 10, 1960; children: Lisa, David, Susan, Nancy, James. B.B.A., U. Notre Dame, 1961; M.B.A., U. Mich., 1964. With Ford Motor Co., Dearborn, Mich., 1961-66; plant controller Massey Ferguson Inc., 1967-70; with parent co. Massey Ferguson Ltd., Toronto, Ont., Can., 1971—, dir. fin. Am. div. 1977-78, v.p., comptr. Massey Ferguson Ltd., 1978-80, sr. v.p. planning and adminstrn., 1980—; pres. Varity Corp. (formerly Massey Ferguson Ltd.), Toronto, 1981-88; vice chmn. bd. Varity Corp. (formerly Massey Ferguson Ltd.), Buffalo, 1988—, vice chmn., pres., 1988-94; ret., 1994, vice chair bd. dirs. Roman Catholic. Office: Varity Corp 672 Delaware Ave Buffalo NY 14209-2202

LAURET, CURTIS BERNARD, JR., international marketing professional; b. Vicksburg, Miss., Mar. 17, 1945; s. Curtis Bernard and Ora Belle (Scott) L.; m. Mary Lorraine Fontenot, Sept. 12, 1964; children: Curtis B. III, Charles E., Christopher S., Craig T. Student, La. State U., 1963—. CLU. Dist. mgr. Nat. Life & Accident Co., Baton Rouge, 1967-74; cons. Life Ins. Mktg. Rsch. Assn., Hartford, Conn., 1974-77; asst. dir., then dir. ednl. svcs. Life Ins. Mktg. Rsch. Assn., 1977-81, dir. co. rels., 1981-83; v.p. co. rels. Life Underwriter Tng. Coun., Washington, 1983-85, v.p. mktg., 1985-87, sr. v.p. mktg., 1987-94, sr. v.p. internat., 1994—; mem. faculty Life Underwriter Tng. Coun., Washington, 1970-74. Contbr. articles to profl. publs. Mem. parish coun. St. Catherine Ch., Simsbury, Conn., 1975-81; counselor Boy Scouts Am., Conn. and Md., 1975-86; mem. Intercounty Connector Task Force, Rockville, Md., 1985-87. Fellow Life Underwriter Tng. Coun., Limra Leadership Inst.; mem. Nat. Assn. Life Underwriters, Gen. Agts. and Mgrs. Assn., Internat. Ins. Soc., K.C., La. Soc. Washington, Choral Ministry of St. Patrick's, Worldwide Marriage Encounter. Democrat. Avocations: reading, computers, tennis, bicycling. Office: Life Underwriter Tng Coun 7625 Wisconsin Ave Bethesda MD 20814-3560

LAURETA, ALFRED, federal judge; b. Ewa, Oahu, Hawaii, May 21, 1924; s. Laureano and Victoriana (Pascua) L.; m. E. Evelyn Reantillo, Feb. 21, 1953; children: Michael, Gregory, Pamela Ann, Lisa Lani. B.Ed., U. Hawaii, 1947, teaching cert., 1948; LL.B., Fordham U., 1953. Bar: Hawaii. Partner firm Kobayashi, Kono, Laureta & Ariyoshi, Honolulu, 1954-59; adminstr. to U.S. Congressman Inouye, 1959-63; dir. Hawaii Dept. Labor and Indsl. Relations, 1963-67; judge 1st Circuit Ct., Honolulu, 1967-69, 5th Circuit Ct., Kauai, 1969-78; U.S. Dist. Ct. No. Mariana Islands, Saipan, 1978—. Mem. Nat. Council Juvenile Ct. Judges, Am. Judicature Soc., Hawaii Bar Assn., Kauai Bar Assn. Democrat. Office: US Dist Ct PO Box 687 Saipan MP 96950-0687

LAURI, JOHN PETER, hospital administrator; b. Marquette, Mich., Apr. 25, 1946; s. T.J. and Elsie Elizabeth (Storstrang) L.; m. Cynthia Judith Barr, June 22, 1968; children—Brian Barr, Christian Matthew. B.A., Morehead State U., 1968; M.A. in Health Care Adminstrn., George Washington U., 1972. Cert. secondary tchr., Mich. High sch. tchr. Roseville Pub. Schs., Roseville, Mich., 1968-70; adminstrv. resident Baptist Med. Ctrs., Birmingham, Ala., 1971-72; asst. adminstr. Foote Meml. Hosp., Jackson, Mich., 1972-73; assoc. adminstr. Foote Meml. Hosp., Jackson, 1973-78; adminstr. Miami Heart Inst., Fla., 1978—; mem. S. Fla. Hosp. Assn., Miami, 1979-84, chmn., 1982-83; adj. prof. U. Miami Grad. Program, 1982—. Mem. Miami Beach Health Adv. Bd., 1984—; mem. Miami Beach Task Force, 1984—, Becon Council, Miami, 1984—. Mem. Greater Miami C. of C., Miami Beach C. of C., Am. Coll. of Hosps. Adminstrs. Am. Hosp. Assn., Fla. Hosp. Assn. (dir.). Republican. Presbyterian. Club: LaGorce County (Miami Beach). Avocations: golf; tennis; boating. Home: 2005 Linden Lake Rd Fort Collins CO 80524

LAURIE, JAMES ANDREW, journalist, broadcaster; b. Eustis, Fla., June 16, 1947; s. Andrew Louis and Geneva Lavina (Pryor) L. B.A. in History, Am. U., Washington, 1970; postgrad. George Washington U. Free-lance writer and reporter Metromedia-TV, Washington, 1969, 73-74, Phnom Penh, Cambodia and Saigon, Vietnam, 1970-71; reporter NBC News, Saigon, 1971-73, 75, Tokyo, 1976-78; with ABC News, 1978—, corr., bur. chief, Hong Kong, 1978-81, opened 1st Am. radio-TV bur. in Peking, 1981, bur. chief, Peking, 1981-82, chief Asia corr., Tokyo, 1983-88, corr., bur. chief Moscow, 1989-91; sr. corr., bur. chief Moscow ABC News, London, 1991—. Writer, narrator: (ABC Closeup documentaries) Japan: Myths behind the Miracle, 1981, The Unruly Dragon: China's Yellow River, 1988, Soviet segment ABC Spl. "Beyond the Cold War", 1989; covered Mikhail Gorbechev in Cuba, East Germany, Rome, Malta, 1989, Tien An Men Crushing of Democrats Movement, 1989, Gorbachev summit in U.S., 1990, Bush-Gorbachev summit, Moscow, 1991, coup d'etat Moscow, 1991, Somalia Famine, 1992,

Iraq Crisis, 1993, Bosnia Crises, 1993, Israeli-Palestinian Negotiations, 1993, Russian Crisis October, 1993, South African elections, 1994, U.S. operation in Haiti, 1994. Recipient George Foster Peabody Broadcasting award for reporting fall of Saigon, 1976; Columbia-Dupont award for ABC Closeup documentary Cambodia: This Shattered Land, 1981; award for radio news coverage of assassination of Philippine leader Benigno Aquino, Overseas Press Club, 1983; Emmy award, 1987. Office: ABC News London Bur, 8 Carburton St, London W1P 7DT, England

LAURIE, JOHN VELDON, business financial executive, accountant; b. Granby, Que., Can., July 2, 1952; s. Veldon Earl and Lillian Ruby (Wickens) L.; m. Linda Enrica Dominick, Dec. 6, 1952; children: Krista, Courtney. BS, Bishop's U., Lennoxville, Que., 1974; degree in acctg., McGill U., 1977. Chartered acct. Acct. Peat, Marwick Mitchell & Co., Montreal, Que., 1974-78; tax specialist Peat, Marwick Mitchell & Co., Toronto, 1978-82; tax mgr. George Weston Ltd., Toronto, 1982-84, asst. treas., 1984-86, treas., 1986-93, v.p., treas., 1993—. Mem. Inst. Chartered Accts. Avocations: golf, skiing, squash, hockey. Home: 14 Squirewood Rd, Willowdale, ON Canada M2J 4T3 Office: George Weston Ltd, 22 St Clair Ave E, Toronto, ON Canada M4T 2S7

LAURIE, MARILYN, communications and computer company executive; b. N.Y.C.; d. Abraham and Irene Gold; m. Robert Laurie; children: Amy, Lisa. BA in English, Barnard Coll., 1959; MBA, Pace U., 1975. Responsible for environ. programs AT&T, N.Y.C., 1971-75, established electronic media program, 1975-78, exec. speeches, policy statements, 1978-79, advt. mgr., 1979-80; exec. dir. AT&T Bell Labs., 1980-83; v.p. AT&T Bell Labs., N.J., 1983-84, AT&T, N.J., 1984-85; group v.p. AT&T, 1986-87; sr. v.p. AT&T, Basking Ridge, N.J., 1987—; chmn. AT&T Found., N.Y.C. Author articles on environ. issues. Co-founder Environ. Action Coalition, 1970; co-originator Earth Day, 1970; bd. dirs. N.Y.C. Ballet, N.Y.C Pub. Edn. Fund. Recipient Gold Key award Pub. Rels. News, WEAL award Women's Equity Action League, 1985, Women in Comm. Matrix award, 1988, Human Rels. award Am. Jewish Com., 1995; named to YWCA Acad. Women Achievers, 1984; named Pub. Rels. All Star, Inside Pub. Rels. Mag., 1993. Mem. Pub. Rels. Seminar (officer), Arthur Page Soc. (bd. officer), N.Y.C. Partnership (mem. exec. com.), Women's Forum. Avocations: reading, tennis. Office: AT&T 295 N Maple Ave RM 434213 Basking Ridge NJ 07920 also: AT&T Foundation 1301 Ave of the Americas New York NY 10019

LAURIE, PIPER (ROSETTA JACOBS), actress; b. Detroit, Jan. 22, 1932; 1 child. Motion picture debut in Louisa; other motion pictures include The Prince Who Was A Thief, Until They Sail, The Hustler (Acad. award nominee 1962), Carrie, 1976 (Acad. award nominee 1976), Tim, 1978, Return to Oz, 1985, Children of a Lesser God, 1986 (Acad. award nominee 1986), Appointment with Death, 1988, Other People's Money, 1990, Rich in Love, 1992, Trauma, 1993, Wrestling Ernest Hemingway, 1993, The Grass Harp, 1995; TV appearances include Days of Wine and Roses, Playhouse 90, The Deaf Heart, The Ninth Day, G.E. Theatre, Play of the Week, Hallmark Hall of Fame, Nova: Margaret Sanger, The Woman Rebel, In the Matter of Karen Ann Quinlan, Rainbow, Skag, The Thorn Birds, 1983; TV films include The Bunker, 1981, Love, Mary, 1985, Mae West, 1985, Promise, 1986, Toughlove, 1985, Lies and Lullabies, 1993, Shadows of Desire, 1994, Fighting for My Daughter, 1995; TV series: Twin Peaks, 1990-91 (Golden Globe award 1990), Traps, 1994; appeared Broadway play Glass Menagerie, 1965, off-Broadway plays Rosemary and the Alligators, 1961, The Innocents, 1971, Biography, 1980, Zelda, 1986, The Destiny of Me, 1992, The Cherry Orchard, 1993. Recipient Emmy award Acad. TV Arts and Scis., 1987; named Woman of Yr., Harvard U. Hasty Pudding, 1962. Mem. Acad. Motion Picture Arts and Scis. Address: William Morris Agy care Jonathan Howard 151 S El Camino Dr Beverly Hills CA 90212-2704

LAURIE, RONALD SHELDON, lawyer; b. San Francisco, June 30, 1942; s. Charles M. and Mimosa (Ezaoui) L.; m. Mina Heshmati, June 1, 1986. BS in Indsl. Engring., U. Calif., 1964; JD, U. San Francisco, 1968. Bar: Calif. 1969, U.S. Ct. Appeals (9th cir.) 1969, U.S. Patent Office 1969, U.S. Supreme Ct. 1971, U.S. Ct. Appeals (fed. cir.) 1972. Programmer, sys. engr. Lockheed Missiles & Space Co., Sunnyvale, Calif., 1960-64; patent atty. Kaiser Aluminum & Chem. Co., Oakland, Calif., 1968-70; ptnr. Townsend and Townsend, San Francisco, 1970-88, Irell & Manella, Menlo Park, Calif., 1988-91, Weil, Gotshal & Manges, Menlo Park, 1991-94, McCutchen, Doyle, Brown & Emersen, San Francisco, 1994—; lectr. in computer law Stanford Law Sch., 1993—; adv. NAS, U.S. Copyright Office and U.S. Patent and Trademark Office, Washington, Office Tech. Assessment U.S. Congress, World Intellectual Property Orgn., Geneva. Co-editor: International Intellectual Property, 1992; contbr. articles to profl. jours. Mem. Internat. Intellectual Property Assn. (mem. exec. com.), State Bar Calif. (mem. exec. com. intellectual property sect.), Computer Law Assn. (bd. dirs.). Avocation: vintage auto racing. Home: 107 Acacia Ave Belvedere CA 94920-2309 Office: McCutchen Doyle Brown & Emersen Three Embarcadero Ctr San Francisco CA 94111

LAURIN, PIERRE, finance company executive; b. Charlemagne, Que., Can., Aug. 11, 1939. MBA, U. Montreal, 1963; D in Bus. Adminstrn., Harvard U., 1969; PhD (hon.), Concordia U., Montreal, 1983. Dean bus. sch. U. Montreal, 1975-82; v.p. planning and adminstrn. Alcan Co. of Can., 1982-87; vice chmn., dir. gen. Merrill Lynch Can. Inc., Montreal, 1987—. Author mgmt. textbook. Named officer Order Can. Office: Merrill Lynch Can Inc, 1800 McGill College Ave Ste 2500, Montreal, PQ Canada H3A 3J6

LAURITZEN, JOHN RONNOW, banker; b. Mpls., Mar. 28, 1917; s. Max R. and Margaret (Flannery) L.; m. Elizabeth Ann Davis, Nov. 4, 1939; children: Bruce Ronnow, Ann Davis (Mrs. Ray Page). Student, Princeton, 1937-38, U. Minn., 1939, U. Wis. Sch. Banking 1947-49; LLD (hon. causa), Dana Coll. With First Nat. Bank, Omaha, 1943-, v.p., 1949-61, grad., 1967-70, chmn. bd. dirs., chmn. exec. com., 1971—, also bd. dirs., chmn. emeritus bd. dirs. Emerson State Bank, Iowa, First State Bank, Loomis, Nebr., Washington County Bank, Blair, Nebr., Farmers & Mchts. State Bank, Bloomfield, Nebr., Burt County State Bank, Tekamah, Nebr., Harlan County Bank, Alama, Nebr., Farmers Savs. Bank, Shelby, Iowa, 1st Nat. of Nebr., Inc., Lauritzen Corp., Omaha, Emerson Ins. Agy., Inc., Blair Ins. Agy., Inc., Burt County Ins. Agy., Inc., Farmers & Mchts. Co. of Bloomfield, Farmers & Ranchers Svc. Co., Fin. Svc. Co., First Nat. Credit Corp., Valley State Bank in S.D., First Nat. Bank, North Platte, Nebr., First Nat. Bank, Columbus, Nebr., Beatrice State Co., First Security Savs., First Nat. Bank Kansas City, Kans., First Nat. Bank Fort Collins, Colo., Shelby County State Bank, Harlan, Iowa. Mem. Omaha Club, Omaha Country Club, Univ. Cottage Club (Princeton, N.J.), Alexandria Golf Club, Minnesouri Club, Island Country (Club (Marco Island, Fla.) (founder). Home: 6621 Underwood Ave Omaha NE 68132-2617 Office: 1st Nat Bank 1st National Ctr Omaha NE 68102 also: 1963 Caxambas Dr Marco Island FL 33937 also: Home Owners Assn 12892 Minnesouri Club Rd NE Alexandria MN 56308

LAURITZEN, PETER OWEN, electrical engineering educator; b. Valparaiso, Ind., Feb. 14, 1935; s. Carl W. and Edna B. (Seebach) L.; m. Helen M. Janzen, Apr. 6, 1963; children: Beth K., Margo S. B.S., Calif. Inst. Tech., 1956; M.S., Stanford U., 1958, Ph.D., 1961. Asso. evaluation engr. Honeywell Aero. Div., Mpls., 1956-57; mem. tech staff Fairchild Semiconductor Div., Palo Alto, Calif., 1961-65; asst. prof. elec. engring. U. Wash., Seattle, 1965-68; prof. U. Wash., 1968-73, prof., 1973—, adj. prof. social mgmt. of tech., 1977-83; engring. mgr. Avtech Corp., Seattle, 1979-80; cons. x-ray div. Chgo. Bridge & Iron Works, 1967-71, 78, Eldec Corp., 1982-91, Energy Internat., 1986-88; conf. chair IEEE Power Electronics Specialist Conf., 1993. Pres. Coalition for Safe Energy, Wash. Citizens Group, 1975-76. Danforth asso., 1966-78; NASA-Am. Soc. Engring. Edn. summer faculty fellow, 1974. Mem. IEEE, Am. Soc. Engring. Edn., AAAS. Home: 7328 58th Ave NE Seattle WA 98115-6257 Office: U Wash Elec Engring Dept PO Box 352500 Seattle WA 98195-2500

LAURSEN, PAUL HERBERT, retired university educator; b. Ord, Nebr., Mar. 28, 1929; s. Ejvind L. and Jacobine E. (Jorgensen) L.; m. Marcia Gail Thompson, Aug. 23, 1959; children: Brett Paul, Scott Warren. B.A. cum laude, Dana Coll., Blair, Nebr., 1954; Ph.D. (duPont teaching fellow 1958-59), Oreg. State U., 1961; NSF vis. fellow, UCLA, 1967-68. Mem. faculty Nebr. Wesleyan U., Lincoln, 1959-93; prof. chemistry Nebr. Wesleyan U.,

1964-93, head dept., 1961-76, chmn. div. natural scis. and math., 1966-67, 68-71, chmn. faculty, 1973-76, acad. dean, 1976-78, provost, 1978-87, trustee, bd. govs., 1973-76; dir. student sci. tng. projects NSF, 1971-75; dir. Nebr. State Sci. Talent Search, 1974-80; lectr. U. Md Munich campus, 1987-88. Active local Boy Scouts Am., 1970-75, Habitat for Humanity, 1993—; treas. Citizens Environ. Improvement, 1971-73; co-chair Transition Team, Nebr. Synod of the New Luth. Ch., 1986-87; mem. com. appeals Evang. Luth. Ch. Am., 1987-93, mem. discipline com., 1993—; mem. Bd. Regents Dana Coll. 1990—. With AUS, 1951-53. Recipient Honor Faculty award Nebr. Wesleyan U. Trustees, 1969, Disting. Alumnus award Dana Coll., 1975. Mem. Am. Chem. Soc. (sec. Nebr. sect. 1989), AAAS, Nebr. Acad. Scis. (pres. 1970-71), Sigma Xi, Phi Lambda Upsilon, Sigma Pi Sigma, Phi Kappa Phi. Club: Polemic. Address: 3148 N 75th Street Ct Lincoln NE 68507-2139

LAURUS (LAURUS SKURLA), archbishop; b. Ladomirova, Czechoslovakia, Jan. 1, 1928; s. Michael Ivan and Helen Michael (Martinik) Skurla. BTh, Holy Trinity Sem., 1954. joined Holy Trinity Monastery, 1946; ordained deacon Russian Orthodox Ch. Abroad, 1950, ordained priest, 1957, consecrated bishop, 1967, elevated to archbishop, 1981. Instr. Old Testament Holy Trinity Sem., Jordanville, N.Y., 1960-65, instr. patristics, 1959-93, instr. moral theology, 1973-76, insp., 1958-67, dean, 1973-76, abbot, 1976—, rector, chmn. bd., 1976—; bishop Diocese of Manhattan, 1967-76; bishop, then archbishop Diocese of Syracuse, 1976—; sec. Synod of Bishops, 1967-77, 1986—; pres. St. John of Kronstadt Meml. Fund, 1976—. Editor Calendar, 1976—, Orthodox Life, 1991—, Orthodox Russia, 1991—; contbr. articles to ch. publs. and periodicals. Mem. Orthodox Palestine Soc. 1986—. Home: Holy Trinity Monastery Jordanville NY 13361 Office: Synod of Bishops 75 E 93d St New York NY 10128

LAUSE, MICHAEL FRANCIS, lawyer; b. Washington, Mo., Aug. 3, 1948; s. Walter Francis and Junilla Rose (Marquart) L.; m. Ann G. Hellman, Aug. 29, 1981; children: Andrew Edward, Scott Michael. BA, St. Benedict's Coll., 1970; JD, U. Ill., 1973. Bar: Mo. 1973. Ptnr. Thompson & Mitchell, St. Louis, 1973—; mem. mgmt. com. Thompson & Mitchell, St. Louis, 1988-90, co-chmn. corp. dept., 1990—. Gen. counsel Mo. Health and Ednl. Facilities Authority, 1986—. Mem. ABA, Mo. Bar Assn., St. Louis Bar Assn., Nat. Assn. Bond Lawyers, Bellerive Country Club, Racquet Club, Noonday Club. Roman Catholic. Home: 11106 Hermitage Hill Rd Saint Louis MO 63131-3323 Office: Thompson & Mitchell One Mercantile Ctr Ste 3400 Saint Louis MO 63101

LAUTENBACH, TERRY ROBERT, information systems and communications executive; b. Cin., Aug. 10, 1938; s. Robert C. and Frances M. (Herbert) L.; m. Carole Wuest; children: Jennifer, Susan, Julie, Martha, Mary, Anne. B in Physics, Xavier U., 1959, LLD (hon.), 1977. Pres. data processing div. IBM Corp., White Plains, N.Y., 1976-78; pres. World Trade Ams., Far East Corp. Mt. Pleasant, N.Y., 1978-83; v.p. mktg. Purchase, N.Y., 1984-85; pres. communication products div. White Plains, 1985-86, group exec., info. systems and communications group, 1986-88; sr. v.p. gen. mgr. IBM U.S., 1988—; bd. dirs. Arkwright Mut. Ins. Co., Xavier U. V.p Darien Library, Conn., 1988. Clubs: Tokeneke, Wee Burn. Home: Shennamere Rd Darien CT 06820-6225 Office: IBM Corp 2000 Purchase St Purchase NY 10577-2597

LAUTENBACHER, CONRAD CHARLES, JR., naval officer; b. Phila., June 26, 1942; s. Conrad Charles and Dorthea Henrietta (Jensen) L.; m. Susan Elizabeth Scheihing, June 20, 1964; children: Elizabeth Lautenbacher Katz, Conrad John. BS, U.S. Naval Acad., 1964; MS, Harvard U., 1965, PhD, 1968. Commd. ensign USN, 1964, advanced through grades to vice adm., 1994; aide to Vice Chief Naval Ops., Chief Naval Ops. USN, Washington, 1974-75; exec. officer USS Benjamin Stoddert USN, Pearl Harbor, Hawaii, 1975-77; program analyst Chief Naval Ops. USN, Washington, 1977-80; comdg. officer USS Hewitt USN, San Diego, 1980-82; dir. program planning Chief Naval Ops. USN, Washington, 1982-86; comdg. officer Naval Sta., Norfolk USN, Va., 1986-88; insp. gen. U.S. Pacific Fleet Hdqrs. USN, Pearl Harbor, 1988-90; comdr. Cruiser-Destroyer Group 5 San Diego, 1990-91; dir. force structure, resources and assessment J-8, Joint Staff, Washington, 1991-94; spl. asst. to asst. sec. navy USN, 1994; commdr. U.S. Third Fleet, 1994—. Decorated D.S.M., Legion of Merit with 3 gold stars, Meritorious Svc. medal with 2 gold stars, Navy Commendation medal, Navy Achievement medal. Mem. U.S. Naval Inst.. Lutheran. *Life is about people and relationships. True happiness begins with sensitivity and responsiveness to the needs of others.*

LAUTENBERG, FRANK R., senator; b. Paterson, N.J., Jan. 23, 1924; s. Samuel and Mollie L.; children: Ellen, Nan, Lisa, Joshua. BS, Columbia U., 1949; DHL, Hebrew Union Coll., Cin. and N.Y.C., 1977; PhD (hon.), Hebrew U., Jerusalem, 1978. Founder Automatic Data Processing, Inc., Clifton, N.J., 1952-55; exec. v.p adminstrn. Automatic Data Processing, Inc., 1955-69, pres., 1969-75, chief exec. officer, 1975-82, chmn. bd.; mem. U.S. Senate from N.J., 1982—. Commr. Port Authority N.Y. and N.J., 1978-82, N.J. econ. devel. coun.; trustee Sch. Bus., Columbia U.; nat. pres. Am. Friends Hebrew U., 1973-74; former gen. chmn., pres. Nat. United Jewish Appeal, 1975-77; mem. bd. overseers N.J. Symphony Orch.; mem. Pres.'s Coun. on the Holocaust; founder Lautenberg Center for Gen. and Tumor Immunology, Med. Sch., Hebrew U., Jerusalem, 1971; mem. fin. council Nat. Democratic Com. Served with Armed Forces, 1943-46, ETO; bd. mem. Montclair Art Mus., mem. adv. bd. Interfaith Hunger Appeal; trustees Tri-County Scholarship fund. Recipient Torch of Learning award Am. Friends Hebrew U., 1971, Scopus award, 1975. Mem. Nat. Assn. Data Processing Service Orgns. (pres. 1968-69, dir. from 1974), Patrons Soc. Met. Opera. Office: US Senate Hart Senate Ofc Bldg Washington DC 20510-0004

LAUTENSCHLAGER, PEGGY ANN, prosecutor; b. Fond du Lac, Wis., Nov. 22, 1955; d. Milton A. and Patsy R. (Oleson) L.; m. Rajiv M. Kaul, Dec. 29, 1979 (div. Dec. 1986); children: Joshua Lautenschlager Kaul, Ryan Lautenschlager Kaul; m. William P. Rippl, May 26, 1989; 1 child, Rebecca Lautenschlager Rippl. BA, Lake Forest Coll., 1977; JD, U. Wis., 1980. Bar: Wis., U.S. Dist. Ct. (we. dist.). Pvt. practice atty. Oshkosh, Wis., 1981-85; dist. atty. Winnebago County Wis., Oshkosh, 1985-88; rep. Wis. Assembly, Fond du Lac, 1988-92; U.S. attorney U.S. Dept. of Justice, Madison, Wisc., 1992-93; apptd. mem. Govs. Coun. on Domestic Violence, Madison, State Elections Bd., Madison. Active Wis. and Fond du Lac County Dem. Parties, 1976—, Dem. Nat. Com., Washington, 1992-93; mem. com. U. Wis. 1989—. Named Legislator of Yr., Wis. Sch. Counselors, 1992, Legislator of Yr., Wis. Corrections Coalition, 1992. Mem. Wis. Bar Assn., Fond du Lac County Bar Assn., Fond du Lac Assn. for Retarded Citizens, Fond du Lac Women in Mgmt., Fond du Lac Morning Optimists, Fond du Lac LWV, Phi Beta Kappa. Avocations: gardening, house renovation, sports, cooking, needlecrafts. Home: 1 Langdon St # 211 Madison WI 53702

LAUTER, JAMES DONALD, stockbroker; b. L.A., Sept. 3, 1931; s. Richard Leo and Helen M. (Stern) L.; BS, UCLA, 1956; m. Neima Zwieli, Feb. 24, 1973; children: Walter James (dec.), Gary. Market rsch. mgr. Germain's Inc., L.A., 61; sr. v.p investments, former branch mgr. Dean Witter Reynolds, Inc., Pasadena, Calif., 1961—. With Armed Forces, 1954-56. Recipient Sammy award L.A. Sales Execs. Club, 1961. Mem. AARP, UCLA Alumni Assn.), Pasadena Bond Club, Bruin Athletic Club. Home: 17237 Sunburst St Northridge CA 91325-2922 Office: Dean Witter Reynolds Inc 55 Lake Ave Ste 800 Pasadena CA 91101

LAUTERBACH, HANS, pharmaceutical company executive; b. 1934; married. With Bayer AG, Leverkusen, Germany, 1951-91; pres. diagnostic divsn. Miles Inc., Tarrytown, N.Y., 1992—. Office: Miles Inc 1 Mell Bk Ctr Ste 5300 Pittsburgh PA 15219

LAUTERBACH, ROBERT EMIL, steel company executive; b. Erie, Pa., May 31, 1918; s. Emil and Inez (Ricci) L.; m. Jane Stonerod; children: Jeffrey R., Marsha J., Mark S. BBA, Westminster Coll., 1939; postgrad., U. Pitts., 1939-41; LLD (hon.), Wheeling Coll., 1975. With Wheeling-Pitts. Steel Corp. and subs., 1939-78; treas. Johnson Steel & Wire Co., 1947-50, asst. sec. parent firm, 1950-52, sec., 1952-58, v.p., 1958-68; treas. v.p Wheeling Pitts. Steel Corp., 1968-70, pres., 1970—, chmn., 1973-78, also bd. dirs.; bd. dirs. H.H. Robertson Co., Covenant Luth Ins. Co. Bd. dirs. United Way of All County, Boy Scouts Am.; treas. local br. Am. Cancer Soc., 1953-62; pres. Mt. Lebanon Libr. Bd., 1962-73; pres. bd. trustees Westminster

Coll., 1970-85. With AUS, 1943-46. Recipient George Washington Honor medal Freedoms Found. at Valley Forge. Mem. Am. Petroleum Inst., Am. Iron and Steel Inst., Duquesne Club, Laurel Valley Golf Club, Rolling Rock Club, Fox Chapel Golf Club. Home: 115 Forest Dr Pittsburgh PA 15238-2103

LAUTERBORN, ROBERT F., advertising educator; b. Albany, N.Y., Apr. 3, 1936; s. Ferdinand Raymond and Julia Marie (O'Brien) L.; m. Sylvia Ann Stebbings, Sept. 28, 1963; children: Michael Alan, David Ian. BA in English, Columbia U., 1956; postgrad., Syracuse U., 1957. Advt. sales rep. Syracuse (N.Y.) Herald Jour., 1957-60; mgr. creative programs Gen. Electric, Schenectady, N.Y., 1960-76; dir. mktg. communications, corp. advt. Internat. Paper, N.Y.C., 1976-86; James L. Knight prof. advertising U. N.C., Chapel Hill, 1986—; bd. dirs. Sawyer Riley Compton, Atlanta; prin. Morgan, Anderson & Co., N.Y.C., 1990—. Co-author: Integrated Marketing Communications, 1992; columnist (mag.) Advt. Age; radio commentator Sta. WUNC; contbr. articles to profl. jours. Mem. Bus. Mktg. Assn. (chmn. 1994—), Advt. Rsch. Found., Am. Advt. Fedn., Assn. Nat. Advertisers (vice-chmn. 1985-86), Am. Acad. Advt., Mktg. Sci. Inst., Nat. Advt. Rev. Bd., Sigma Alpha Epsilon. Republican. Roman Catholic. Home: 1403 Gray Bluff Trail Chapel Hill NC 27514-9126

LAUTERBUR, PAUL C(HRISTIAN), chemistry educator; b. Sidney, Ohio, May 6, 1929. BS, Case Inst. Tech., 1951; PhD, U. Pitts., 1962; PhD (hon.), U. Liege, Belgium, 1984; DSc (hon.), Carnegie Mellon U., 1987; DSc (med. hon.), Corpernicus Med. Acad., Cracow, Poland, 1988; DSc (hon.), Wesleyan U., 1989, SUNY, Stony Brook, 1990; DEng (hon.), Rennselaer Poly. Inst., 1991. Rsch. asst. and assoc. Mellon Inst., Pitts., 1951-53, fellow, 1955-63; assoc. prof. chemistry SUNY, Stony Brook, 1963-69, prof. chemistry, 1969-84, with, 1963-85, rsch. prof. radiology, 1978-85, univ. prof., 1984-85; prof. (4) depts. U. Ill., Urbana, 1985—; Disting. Univ. prof. Coll. Medicine U. Ill., Chgo. 1990—. Contbr. articles to profl. jours.; mem. editorial bds.; mem. sci. couns. Cpl. U.S. Army, 1953-55. Recipient Clin. Rsch. award Lasker Found., 1984, Nat. Medal of Sci., U.S.A., 1987, Fiuggi Internat. prize Fondazione Fiuggi, 1987, Roentgen medal, 1987, Gold medal Radiol. Soc. N.Am., 1987, Nat. Medal of Tech., 1988, Gold medal Soc. Computed Body Tomography, 1989, The Amsterdam (Alfred Heineken) prize in medicine, 1989, Laufman-Greatbatch award Assn. for Advancement Med. Intrumentation, 1989, Leadership Tech. award Nat. Elec. Mfr. Assn., 1990, Bower award and prize for achievement in sci. Benjamin Franklin Nat. Meml. Commn. of the Franklin Inst., 1990, Internat. Soc. Magnetic Resonance award, 1992, Kyoto prize, Inamori Foundation, 1994. Fellow AAAS, Am. Phys. Soc. (Biol. Physics prize 1983); mem. NAS, Am. Chem. Soc., Soc. Magnetic Resonance in Medicine (Gold medal 1982). Office: U Ill-Urbana-Champaign 1307 W Park St Urbana IL 61801-2332

LAUTERSTEIN, JOSEPH, cardiologist; b. Vienna, Austria, Dec. 1, 1934; came to U.S., 1940; s. Bernard and Hajnalka (Stern) L.; m. Erika Stein, Jan. 24, 1964 (dec. Aug. 1990); children: Deborah Ann, Brenda Rose; m. Elisabeth Spiegl Lazaroff, Nov. 27, 1994. BA, Syracuse U., 1955; MD, U. Vienna, 1964. Lic. physician, N.Y. Intern, then resident in internal medicine The Bklyn. Cumberland Med. Ctr., 1964-66, 68-69, fellow in cardiology, 1969-70; attending physician, cons. internal medicine and cardiology Hamilton Ave. Hosp., Monticello, N.Y., 1970-78; attending physician, cons. internal medicine and cardiology Community Gen. Hosp. Sullivan County, Harris, N.Y., 1970—, chief cardiology, 1971—, chief of staff, 1981-82; mem. courtesy staff dept. internal medicine and cardiology The Bklyn. Hosp. Ctr., 1971—; clin. asst. dept. internal medicine and cardiology St. Vincent's Hosp. and Med. Ctr. N.Y., 1974-80, asst. attending physician, 1981-86, assoc. attending physician, 1987-94, attending physician, 1995—; with Sullivan Internal Medicine Group, P.C., Monticello, 1970—; dir. ICU Community Gen. Hosp. Sullivan County, 1971-79, dir. CCU, 1978—, dir. spl. diagnostics, 1984—, pres. med. bd., 1981-82; mem. pacemaker task force Empire State Med. Sci. and Ednl. Found., 1985-89; med. dir. Sullivan County EMT-D Program, 1989—; police surgeon Village of Monticello, 1974—, Sullivan County, 1972—; med. advisor Monticello Vol. Ambulance Corps, 1970-80, 89—; mem. Sullivan County Emergency Svcs. Coun., 1990, 91. Co-contbr. articles to Jour. Cardiovascular Surgery, Annals of Thoracic Surgery, Angiology, Chest. Trustee Cmty. Gen. Hosp. Sullivan County, 1981-82, Cmty. Gen. Hosp. Found., 1990—; mem. Nat. Ski Patrol, 1979—, med. advisor So. N.Y. region, 1989-94, med. advisor So. Catskill sect., 1994—; patroller Holiday Mountain Ski Patrol, 1979—. Capt. M.C., USAF, 1966-68. Fellow Am. Coll. Cardiology (N.Y. State chpt., del. to N.Y. Med. Soc. Ho. Dels. 1991—, councilor 1991—, com. mem. 1990—), Am. Coll. Chest Physicians (assoc.), Am. Coll. Angiology, Internat. Coll. Angiology, N.Y. Cardiological Soc. (exec. bd. dirs. 1982—, mem. various coms.), N.Y. Acad. Medicine; mem. AMA, Am. Geriatrics Soc., Am. Soc. Internal Medicine, Soc. for Critical Care Medicine, N.Y. Acad. Scis., N.Am. Soc. for Pacing and Electrophysiology, Med. Soc. State of N.Y., others. Office: Sullivan Internal Medicine Group PC 370 Broadway Monticello NY 12701-1155

LAUTIER, YVES LAURENT, physician; b. Tlemcen, Algeria, May 1, 1941; came to U.S., 1970; s. Etienne Georges and Georgette Adelaide (Herrmann) L.; m. Eloise Walne Dabney, July 19, 1969; children: Claire Dabney, Erik Laurent. MD, U. Montpellier, France, 1969. Diplomate Am. Bd. Psychiatry and Neurology. Intern Medical Coll. Va., Richmond, 1970-71, jr. asst. resident, 1971-72, asst. resident, 1972-73, sr. asst. resident, 1973-74; pvt. practice psychiatry McLean, Va., 1974-83, Pensacola, Fla., 1983—; medical dir. Baptt. Hosp., Pensacola, Fla., 1983—; chief psychiatry svc., 1987—. Mem. AMA, Am. Psychiat. Assn. Episcopalian. Avocations: triathlon competitions, sailing. Home: 2942 Coral Strip Pkwy Gulf Breeze FL 32561 Office: 4400 Bayou Blvd Ste 51 Pensacola FL 32503

LAUTZ, LINDSAY ALLAN, retained executive search consultant; b. San Bernardino, Calif., Dec. 24, 1947; s. Carl Ernest and Carole Mae (Lindsay) L.; m. Laurie Ann Morgan, June 20, 1970; children—Christopher, Kathryn, Amy. BS, U. So. Calif., 1971, postgrad., 1971. Adminstrv. mgr. Associated Freight Lines, Los Angeles, 1969-73; with Fromm & Sichel, Inc., San Francisco, 1973-81; treas. and fin. officer Fromm & Sichel, Inc., 1977-81; co-founder, pres., chief exec. officer Positive Video, Ltd. subs. Groupe Andre Perry, Inc., Montreal, Que., Can., 1981-88; founder, chmn. Morgan Board Works, Inc., San Francisco, 1989-90; prin. Korn/Ferry Internat., San Francisco, 1990-92; ptnr. Wilkinson and Ives, San Francisco, 1992—. Exec. producer Makaha Skate Classic, spl. interest home video; inventor skate bd. product Instant Ollie. Founder Havens Dads Club, Piedmont, Calif. With USAR, 1971-77. Mem. Assn. Exec. Search Cons., Calif. Exec. Recruiters Assn., Internat. Assn. Corp. Pers. Recruiters, Commerce Assocs. (pres.), U. So. Calif. Bay Area Alumni Assn., Pi Kappa Alpha. Republican. Home: 321 Bedford Pl Moraga CA 94556-2106 Office: Wilkinson and Ives Ste 550 One Bush St San Francisco CA 94104

LAUTZENHEISER, BARBARA JEAN, insurance executive; b. LaFeria, Tex., Nov. 15, 1938; d. Fred E. and Verna V. L. B.A. with high distinction, Nebr. Wesleyan U., 1960. Actuarial trainee Bankers Life Ins. Co. Nebr. Lincoln, 1960-64; programmer and systems analyst, 1964-65, asst. actuary, 1965-69, assoc. actuary 1969-70, 2d v.p., actuary, 1970-72, v.p., actuary, 1972-80; sr. v.p. Phoenix Mut. Life Ins. Co., Hartford, Conn., 1980-84; pres. Montgomery Ward Life Ins. Co., Montgomery Ward Ins. Co., Forum Ins. Co., Schaumberg, Ill., 1984-85; prin. Lautzenheiser & Assocs., Hartford, 1986—; spokesperson for ins. industry, testifier U.S. Senate and Ho. of Reps. coms., commns. and state legislatures; featured on TV, nat. mags. and newspaper articles; mem. Interim Actuarial Standard Bd., 1985-88, Actuarial Standard Bd., 1988-89; chmn. Com. for Fair Ins. Rates, 1983—. Contbr. articles to profl. jours. Mem. Lincoln Electric System Adminstrv. Bd., 1977-79; bd. dirs. Nebr. Wesleyan U., 1977-82, 89—, Am. Coll., 1987—. Recipient Corp. Woman award Women Bus. Owners of N.Y., 1983, C.H. Poindexter award for disting. achievement and exceptional svc. to the assn. and ins. industry Nat. Assn. Life Cos., 1989. Fellow Soc. Actuaries (pres. 1982-83, dir. 1975-80, 81-85, exec. com. 1981-84, chmn. adminstrn. and fin. com. 1981-82), Conf. Cons. Actuaries; mem. Am. Acad. Actuaries (dir. 1974-77, chmn. com. on publs. 1980-81), Nebr. Actuaries Club (dir. 1969-70, 71-74, chmn. 1973-74, pres. 1972-73, sec., treas. 1971-72), Life Office Mgmt. Assn. (corp. fin. planning com. 1974-81, chmn. 1976-78), Am. Council Life Ins. (risk classification com. 1973-81), Greater Hartford C. of C. (nat. policies panel 1980-84). Home: 17 Huntingridge Dr South Glastonbury CT 06073-3614 Office: City Place II Fl 11 Hartford CT 06103

LAUTZENHEISER, MARVIN WENDELL, computer software engineer; b. Maximo, Ohio, Feb. 19, 1929; s. Milton Leander and Mary Lucetta (Keim) L.; m. Jean Bethene Baker, Oct. 26, 1946 (div. Nov. 1986); children: Constance Kay, Thomas Edward, Jan Stephen; m. Paula Ann Keane, Mar. 10, 1990. BS in Math., Mt. Union Coll., 1953. Spl. agt. FBI, Washington, 1953-59; computer analyst Tech. Ops., Washington, 1959-64; pres. Anagram Corp., Springfield, Va., 1964-83; computer analyst Onyx Corp., McLean, Va., 1983, Inmark, Springfield, 1983-84, Memory Scis., McLean, 1984-85; software scientist Zitel Corp., San Jose, Calif., 1985—. Inventor, designer in field. Mem. Mensa, Am. Iris Soc. Avocations: theatre pipe organ, hybrid iris gardening. Home: 7216 Neuman St Springfield VA 22150 Office: Zitel Corp 47211 Bayside Pky Fremont CA 94538-6517

LAUVEN, PETER MICHAEL, anesthesiologist; b. Leverkusen, Fed. Republic of Germany, May 13, 1948; s. Peter Aloysius and Katharina (Oedekoven) L.; m. Anne-Kareen Wetje, Nov. 7, 1970; children: Anne-Laureen, Lars-Peter. Diploma in Chem., U. Bonn, Fed. Republic of Germany, 1970, Dr. rer. nat., 1974, Dr. med., 1979, priv.-dozent, 1985. Teaching asst. Inst. Organic Chem. U. Bonn, Fed. Republic of Germany, 1970-76, scientist Inst. Anaesthesiology, 1976-79, physician, 1979—, anaesthesiologist, 1983—, asst. dir., 1983-85, vice-chmn., 1985-92, prof. of anaesthesia, 1986—, chmn. dept. Anaesthesiology & Surg. ICU, 1993—; mem. German Fed. Drug Admission Com., 1987—. Author, co-editor: Das Zentralanticholinergische Syndrom, 1985, Klinische Pharmakologie und rationale Arzneimitteltherapie, 1992; author, editor: Anasthesie und der Geriatrische Patient, 1989, Postoperative Schmerztherapie, 1991. Recipient scholarship Stipendien Fonds der Chemischen Inst., Frankfurt, 1970, Paul Martini award, Paul Martini Found., Bonn, 1988. Mem. Gesellschaft Deutscher Chemiker, Deutsche Gesellschaft für Anaesthesiologie und Intensiv Medizin, Am. Soc. Anaesthesiology (affiliate), Am. Soc. Regional Anaesthesia, European Acad. Anaesthesiology, European Soc. Regional Anaesthesia, European Soc. Intensive Care Medicine, European Soc. Anaesthesiology, N.Y. Acad. of Scis. Home: Haendelstr 22, D-33604 Bielefeld Germany Office: Clinic Anaesthesiology and Intensive Care, Teutoburger Str 50, D-33604 Bielefeld Germany

LAUX, JAMES MICHAEL, historian, educator; b. La Crosse, Wis., Nov. 4, 1927; s. William M. and Clara (Smelser) L.; m. Barbara I. Robertson, 1952; children: Robert James, Stephen Andrew, Frederick Lawrence. Student, Wis. State U., 1946-48; BS, U. Wis., 1950; MA, U. Conn., 1952; PhD, Northwestern U., 1957. Instr. history Wis. State U., La Crosse, 1955-57; asst. prof. U. Cin., 1957-65, assoc. prof., 1965-69, prof., 1969-89, prof. emeritus, 1989—; vis. prof. Northwestern U., Evanston, Ill. 1966-67. Author: In First Gear, 1976, The European Automobile Industry, 1992; co-author: Revolution Automobile, 1977; co-editor: French Revolution, 1968; translator Right Wing in France, 1966; co-editor French Hist. Studies, 1985-92, Napoleon, 1989. With USN, 1945-46. Fulbright scholar, France, 1954-55; recipient Rieveschl award, U. Cin., 1981. Mem. Am. Hist. Assn., Soc. French Hist. Studies, Soc. Automotive Historians, Amis Fondation l'Automobile Marius Berliet. Home: 5179 Shore View Run Cincinnati OH 45248-6837

LAVAIL, JENNIFER HART, neurobiologist, educator, researcher; b. Evansville, Ind., Apr. 2, 1943; d. L. Paul and Ruth (Lensing) Hart; children: Matthew H., Katherine H. BA, Trinity Coll., Washington, 1961-65; PhD, U. Wis., 1970. Postdoctoral fellow dept. neuropathology Harvard Med. Sch., Cambridge, Mass., 1970-73, instr., 1973-74, asst. prof., 1974-76; assoc. prof. anatomy U. Calif., San Francisco, 1976-83, prof., 1983—; bd. sci. counselors Nat. Inst. Neurol. and Communicative Disorders and Stroke, NIH, 1988-92. Woodrow Wilson fellow Ford Found., 1965-66; Alfred P. Sloan fellow Sloan Found., 1976-79. Mem. Am. Assn. Anatomists (v.p. 1988-90, Charles Judson Herrick award 1975). Office: U Calif Dept Anatomy PO Box 452 San Francisco CA 94143

LAVALLE, GERALD J., state senator; b. Pa., Jan. 25, 1932; s. Peter J. and Marie L. (Pagley) LaV.; m. Darla J. Winkle; children: Mark, Peter. BSBA, Geneva Coll., 1956; MEd, Westminster Coll., 1971. With Pitts. Bridge & Iron, 1959, Laborers Local 833, New Brighton, Pa.; with car shop, scrap dock Pa. R.R.; tchr., staff mem. football and baseball teams Midland H.S., Midland and Rochester, Pa., 1959-64; tchr. acctg., bus. math. and econs., football coach Rochester H.S., 1964-83; mem. Pa. Senate, 1990—. Pres. Rochester Borough Coun., 1974-76; mayor Borough of Rochester, 1976-89; chmn. bd. Beaver County Commn., 1984-90; mem. steering com. Southwestern Pa. Growth Alliance, 1989-90; mem. Beaver County Corp. for Econ. Devel., 1989-90. Served to lt. col. USMC and Res. Office: 239 Brighton Ave Rochester PA 15074

LAVALLE, IRVING HOWARD, decision analysis educator; b. Hancock, N.Y., Apr. 24, 1939; s. Irving Howard and Louise Hartshorne (Wood) LaV. A.B., Trinity Coll., Conn., 1960; M.B.A., Harvard U., 1963, D.B.A. 1966. Asst. prof. A.B. Freeman Sch. Bus., Tulane U., New Orleans, 1965-68; assoc. prof. A.B. Freeman Sch. Bus., Tulane U., 1968-71; prof. A.B. Freeman Sch. Bus., Tulane U., New Orleans, 1971-93; Francis Martin prof., 1993—; chmn. Decision Analysis SIG, Balt., 1980-82, So. Cons. Group, Inc., New Orleans, 1981—. Author: Introduction to Probability, Decision and Inference, 1970; Fundamentals of Decision Analysis, 1978; also articles; editor various profl. jours. Ford Found. fellow, 1964. Mem. Royal Statis. Soc., Inst. Mgmt. Scis., Ops. Research Soc. Am., Inst. Math. Stats., Econometric Soc. Episcopalian. Avocations: music; photography; woodworking. Home: 726 Foucher St New Orleans LA 70115-1311 Office: Tulane U Freeman Sch Bus St Charles Ave New Orleans LA 70118-5669

LAVALLEE, H.-CLAUDE, chemical engineer, researcher; b. Cap-Santé, Que., Can., July 28, 1938; s. Henri Lavallée and Yvonne Lavallée-Légaré; m. Ginette Morissette, June 25, 1966. BScA, Univ. Laval, Que., 1964, MScA, 1965, DSc, 1970. Rschr. Def. Rsch. Establishment of Valcartier Govt. of Can., Que., 1965-67; prof. chem. engring. U. Que. at Trois-Rivières, 1970-74; sr. engr. pulp & paper industry Ministry of Environment-Govt. of Que., Quebec City, 1974-87, head pulp & paper industry, 1980-87; dir. Pulp & Paper Rsch. Ctr. U. Que. at Trois-Rivières, 1987—; pres. H.C. Lavallée Inc., Donnacona, Que., 1989—; cons. Roche Ltée, Québec City, 1988—; administr. John Meunier Inc., Montréal, 1991—, Centre des technologies du gaz naturel, Montréal, 1992—. Contbr. articles to profl. jours., chpts. to books. Recipient Prize Raimbeault de Montigny Conf. Technologique, Point-au-Pic, 1990, Prize of excellence SNC-Lavalin Assn. Qué. Technique de l'eau, 1993. Mem. TAPPI, Can. Pulp and Paper Assn., Ordre des Ingénieurs du Qué. Roman Catholic. Office: Ctr Rsch Pulp & Paper, 3351 Blvd des Forges, Trois Rivieres, PQ Canada G9A 5H7

LAVALLEY, FREDERICK J. M., lawyer; b. May 23, 1947; m. Christine Dengler. AB, Stanford U., 1969; JD, U. Pa., 1972. Bar: Pa. 1972. Ptnr. Morgan, Lewis & Bockius, Phila. Chmn. Francis W. Sullivan Found. Mem. Phila. Club. Office: Morgan Lewis & Bockius 2000 One Logan Sq Philadelphia PA 19103

LAVATELLI, LEO SILVIO, retired physicist, educator; b. Mackinac Island, Mich., Aug. 15, 1917; s. Silvio E. and Zella (Cunningham) L.; m. Anna Craig Henderson, June 14, 1941 (dec. Sept. 1966); children: Nancy Jack, Mark Leo; m. Celia Burns, Jan. 23, 1967 (dec. May 1976); 1 stepchild, Faith Stendler (dec.); m. Barbara Gow, Nov. 22, 1976 (div. Jan. 1979); stepchildren: Ann Deemer, Lindsay Deemer; m. Olwen Thomas, Mar. 4, 1982; stepchildren: Alice Ann Williamson (Mrs. Michael W. Cone), Caroline Hill Williamson, Thomas Holman Williamson, Hugh Stuart Williamson. BS, Calif. Inst. Tech., 1939; MA, Princeton U., 1943, Harvard U., 1949; PhD, Harvard U., 1951. Instr. physics, chemistry, algebra, calculus, symbolic logic Deep Springs (Calif.) Jr. Coll., 1939-41; instr. Princeton (N.J.) U., 1941; rsch. asst. Manhattan Dist. Office Sci. R&D, Nat. Def. Rsch. Coun., Princeton, 1942-43; jr. staff mem. Los Alamos (N.Mex.) Nat. Lab. (formerly Manhattan Dist. Site Y), 1943-46; rsch. asst. Harvard U. Cambridge, Mass., 1946-50; asst. prof. physics, staff mem. Control Systems Lab. U. Ill., Urbana, 1950-55, assoc. prof., 1955-58; prof., 1958-79, prof. emeritus, 1979—; mem. one of measuring groups and design team for "Trinity", the Alamogordo atomic bomb test, 1945; mem. design team orbit plotting/control cir. logic FM new cyclotron project Harvard U., 1946; observer air/ground exercises U.S. Dept. Def., Waco, Tex., 1952; observer joint air exercises NATO, Fed. Republic Germany, 1955; mem. project quick-fix Control Sys. Lab., 1953; cons. Ill.

group Phys. Sci. Study Com., 1956-57, Sci. Teaching Ctr., MIT, 1966, Tehran (Iran) Rsch. Unit, U. Ill., 1970; participant info. theory in biology conf. U. Ill., 1952. Producer silent film cassettes on orbit graphing U. Ill., 1964; co-interviewee video tape Logical Thinking in Children and Science Education, Nat. Japanese TV, Tokyo, 1970; phys. sci. cons. The Macmillan Science Series, 1970 edit.; The Macmillan Co., N.Y.C., 1967-70; contbr. articles and revs. to profl. publs. Co-moderator discussion Fedn. Atomic Scientists, 1945, 1947. Recipient Univ. of Ill. Undergrad. Teaching award U. St. Andrews, Scotland, 1965; John Simon Guggenheim Meml. fellow U. Bologna, Italy, 1957. Fellow Am. Phys. Soc.; mem. Harvard Faculty Club (non-resident). Avocations: music, painting, art history, books, movies. Home: RFD 2 Box 510 Spring Hope NC 27882-9543

LAVE, CHARLES ARTHUR, economics educator; b. Phila., May 18, 1938; s. Israel and Esther (Axlerod) L.; 1 child, Rebecca. BA, Reed Coll., 1960; PhD, Stanford U., 1968. Mem. faculty U. Calif., Irvine, 1966—, prof. econs., chmn. dept. econs., 1978-85, 89-92; vis. prof., vis. scholar Hampshire Coll., 1972, Stanford U., 1974, MIT, 1982, Harvard U., 1982, U. Calif., Berkeley, 1988, 94. Author: (with James March) An Introduction to Models in the Social Sciences, 1975, Energy and Auto Type Choice, 1981, Urban Transit, 1985, others. Trustee Reed Coll., Portland, Oreg., 1978-82; bd. dirs. Nat. Bur. Econ. Rsch., Cambridge, 1991—; chmn. bd. Irvine Campus Housing Authority, Inc., 1982—. Served with USAF, 1957. Recipient Pyke Johnson award Transp. Rsch. Bd., 1987, Extraordinarius award U. Calif., 1993. Fellow Soc. Applied Anthropology; mem. Am. Econ. Assn., AAAS, Transp. Research Bd. Office: U Calif Dept Econs Irvine CA 92717

LAVE, JUDITH RICE, economics educator; came to U.S., 1961; d. J.H. Melville and G.A. Pauline (Lister) Rice; m. Lester Bernard Lave, June 21, 1965; children: Tamara Rice, Jonathan Melville. BA in Econs., Queen's U., Kingston, Ont., Can., 1957-61; MA in Econs., Harvard U., 1964, PhD, 1967; LLD, Queen's U., 1994. Lectr., asst. prof. econs. Carnegie Mellon U., Pitts., 1966-73, assoc. prof., 1973-78; dir. econ. analysis Office of Sec., Dep. of Asst. Sec. Planning and Evaluation, Washington, 1978-79; dir. office of rsch. Health Care Fin. Administrn., Washington, 1980-82; prof. health econs. U. Pitts., 1982—; cons. Nat. Study Internal Medicine Manpower, Chgo., 1976, Wash. State Hosp. Assn., 1984, Horty, Springer & Mattern, Pitts., 1984, Hogan and Hartson, Washington, 1989, Ont. Hosp. Assn., Conn. Hosp. Assn., 1991; cons. various agys. U.S. HHS (formerly U.S. HEW), 1971-89; mem. adv. panel Robert Wood Johnson Found., Princeton, N.J., 1983-84, Leonard Davis Inst., Phila., 1984, U.S. Congress, 1977, 82, 83—; com. mem. Inst. Medicine Coms., Washington, 1975-91, Project 2000 Commn. on Future of Podiatry, Washington, 1985-86. Editl. bd. Wiley Series in Health Svcs., 1989-90, Health Svcs. Rsch., 1970-74, Inquiry, 1979-82, AUPHA Press, 1986, Jour. of Health Policy Politics and Law; co-author: Hospital Construction Act - An Evaluation of the Hill Burton Program, 1948-73, 74, Health Status, Medical Care Utilization and Outcome: A Bibliography of Empirical Studies (4 vols.) 1989, Providing Hospital Services, 1989; contbr. numerous articles to profl. jours. Mem. Prospective Payment Assessment Commn., 1993—, planning com. ARC, Pitts., 1986—; mem. rev. com. United Way, Pitts., 1988-90; bd. dirs. Craig Ho., Pitts., 1976-77. Woodrow Wilson fellow, 1961-62. Mem. Assn. Health Svcs. Rsch. (pres. 1977-88, bd. dirs. 1983-93), Found. for Health Svcs. Rsch. (pres. 1988-89, bd. dirs 1983—), Am. Pub. Health Soc., Am. Econ. Soc. (com. mem.), Inst. Medicine, Nat. Acad. Social Ins. Democrat. Home: 1008 Devonshire Rd Pittsburgh PA 15213-2914 Office: U Pitts A649 Pub Health Pittsburgh PA 15213

LAVECK, GERALD DELOSS, physician, educator; b. Seattle, Apr. 19, 1927; s. DeLoss Francis and Helen Marie (Keller) LaV.; m. Beverly Beers Vander Veer, July 22, 1976; children: Gerald DeLoss, Roxanne M., Julie B., Amy B., Jill M. B.S., U. Wash., 1948, M.D., 1951. Clin. clk. Rainier Sch., Buckley, Wash., 1958-62; head crippled children's service Wash. Health Dept., 1962-63; clin. prof. pediatrics Georgetown U., Washington, 1966-73; clin. prof. U. Wash., Seattle, 1973—; dir. research Bur. Community Health Services, USPHS, Rockville, Md., 1976-77; med. cons. Region X, USPHS, Seattle, 1977-85. With USPHS, 1953-55, 72-85, ret., 1985. Recipient Superior Service award HEW, 1966. Fellow Am. Acad. Pediatrics, Am. Pub. Health Assn., Assn. Mental Deficiency. Home: 6633 NE Windermere Rd Seattle WA 98115-7942

LAVELLE, ARTHUR, anatomy educator; b. Fargo, N.D., Nov. 29, 1921; s. Frank and Lillie (Hanson) LaV.; m. Faith Evelyn Wilson, 1947; 1 dau., Audrey Anne. B.S., U. Wash., 1946; M.A., Johns Hopkins, 1948; Ph.D., U. Pa., 1951. USPHS postdoctoral fellow U. Pa., Phila., 1951-52; mem. faculty dept. anatomy U. Ill. Coll. Medicine, Chgo., 1952—; assoc. prof. U. Ill. Coll. Medicine, 1958-65, prof., 1965-87, prof. emeritus, 1987—; vis. prof. UCLA, 1968-69; cons. Galesburg (Ill.) State Rsch. Hosp., 1965-68; mem. Biol. Stain Commn., 1953-93, trustee, 1978-93, pres., 1981-86, v.p., 1991-92. Mem. editorial bd. Biotechnic and Histochemistry, 1989-93; contbr. articles to profl. jours. USPHS research grantee, 1953-70; Cerebral Palsy Found. grantee, 1964-68; Guggenheim fellow, 1968-69. Mem. Am. Assn. Anatomists, Am. Soc. Cell Biology, Soc. Developmental Biology, AAAS, Soc. Neurosci., Sigma Xi. Office: 1853 W Polk St Chicago IL 60612-4316

LAVELLE, AVIS, federal administration official; b. Chgo., Mar. 5, 1954; d. Adolph Eugene and Mai Evelyn (Hicks) Sampson. BS in Comms. cum laude, U. Ill., 1975. Announcer, pub. affairs dir. Sta. WTAX Radio, Springfield, Ill., 1977-78; news dir., anchor Sta. WLTH Radio, Gary, Ind., 1978-79; reporter, anchor Stas. WJJD/WJEZ, Chgo., 1979-84; chief polit. reporter Sta. WGN-Radio/TV, Chgo., 1984-88; campaign press sec. Richard M. Daley for Mayor, Chgo., 1988-89; mayoral press sec. Officer of the Mayor, Chgo., 1989-92; nat. press sec. Clinton/Gore for Pres., Little Rock, Ark., 1992; spl. asst. to chmn. Vernon Jordan Presdl. Transition, Washington, 1992-93; asst. sec. pub. affairs U.S. Dept. Health and Human Svcs., Washington, 1993—. Bd. dirs. Project Image, Inc., Chgo., 1988-89, Human Resources Devel. Inst., Chgo., 1988; mem. steering com. Black Adoption Taskforce of Ill., Chgo., 1987; mem. Delta Sigma Theta Pub. Svc., Chgo., 1973—. Recipient African Am. Bus. and Profl. Women award Dollars and Sense Mag., 1989, Women at Work award Nat. Commn. Working Women, 1980, First Place Team award AP, 1984. Democrat. Office: Dept of Health & Human Services Public Affairs 200 Independence Ave SW Washington DC 20201

LAVELLE, MICHAEL JOSEPH, economist, academic administrator; b. Cleve., Dec. 28, 1934; s. Michael Joseph and Helen Victoria (Wiejek) L. Student, Xavier U., 1953-57; AB, Loyola U., Chgo., 1958, Licentiate in Philosophy, 1960; PhD in Econs., Boston Coll., 1966; postgrad., Harvard U. Russian Rsch. Ctr., 1965-83; Lic. Theol., Hochschule für Philosophie und Theologie, Frankfurt, Fed. Republic Germany, 1969. Book rev. editor Rev. Social Economy, 1963-65; dir. social ministry S.J., Detroit, 1970-75, provincial superior, 1977-83; dir. summer urban program John Carroll U., Cleve., 1970, dean Bus. Sch., 1975-77, acad. v.p. 1984-88, pres. 1988—. Trustee Cleve. Ctr. for Econ. Edn., 1975-88, St. Joseph's U., Phila., 1984-90, Loyola Coll., Balt., 1986-92, Boston Coll., Chestnut Hill, Mass., 1989—, Xavier U., Cin., 1986—, Le Moyne Coll., Syracuse, N.Y., 1993—; mem. Leadership Cleve., 1988-89, Assn. Jesuit Coll. and Univ., 1988—, The Nat. Conf., 1989—, The SO Club, Cleve., 1988—, A Bus./Clergy Dialogue, Cleve., 1988—; Fgn. Area Fellowship Program fellow, 1963-65. Mem. Am. Assn. for Advancement Slavic Studies, Assn. for Comparative Econ. Studies, Assn. for Social Econs., Union Club. Democrat. Roman Catholic. Avocation: cooking. Home and Office: John Carroll U 20700 N Park Blvd Cleveland OH 44118-4520

LAVELLE, PAUL MICHAEL, lawyer; b. Scranton, Pa., July 19, 1956; s. James Gregory and Helen Delores (Borys) L.; m. Sue Swan, May 24, 1980. BS, U. Scranton, 1978; JD, Loyola U., New Orleans, 1981. Bar: La. 1981, U.S. Dist. Ct. (ea., mid. dists.) La., U.S. Dist. Ct. (we. dist.) La. 1985, U.S. Ct. Appeals (5th cir.) 1981. Assoc. Montgomery, Barnett, Brown & Read, New Orleans, 1981-86, ptnr., 1986-90; ptnr. Guste, Barnett & Shushan, New Orleans, 1991—; chair Nat. High Sch. Mock Trial Championship, Inc., 1991-92. Mem. ABA (assembly del. young lawyers divsn. 1987-88), La. Bar Assn. (chmn. h.s. mock trial 1988, rep. exec. coun. young lawyers sect. 1988), Def. Rsch. Inst., Internat. Assn. Def. Counsel, Assn. Transp. Practitioners, Order Ky. Cols. (hon.), La. Assn. Def. Counsel.

Democrat. Roman Catholic. Avocations: camping, hiking, racquetball. Office: Guste Barnett & Shushan 639 Loyola Ave Ste 2500 New Orleans LA 70113-7103

LAVENANT, RENE PAUL, JR., lawyer; b. Highland Park, Ill., Feb. 6, 1925; s. Rene Paul and Marie C. (Nack) L.; m. Marjorie Ann Witter; children: Hilary, Mark, Amelie. B.S., Northwestern U., 1945; LL.B., Stanford U., 1949. Bar: Calif. 1949, N.Y. 1962, Tex. 1978. Successively atty., sr. atty., regional gen. counsel Mobil Oil Corp. and affiliates, Los Angeles, 1949-73, Casper, Wyo., 1949-73, Billings, Mont., 1949-73, N.Y.C., 1949-73, Paris and London, 1949-73; ptnr. in charge London office Fulbright & Jaworski LLP, Houston, 1973-78; sr. ptnr. Fulbright & Jaworski, Houston, 1978—. Mem. ABA, Houston Bar Assn. Home: Lafayette Pl Houston TX 77036 Office: Fulbright & Jaworski 1301 Mckinney St Houston TX 77010-3049

LAVENAS, SUZANNE, writer, editor, consultant; b. Buenos Aires, Dec. 17, 1942; came to U.S., 1955; d. Carlos Fernando and Mary (Sharp) Lavenas; m. Wesley First, Jan. 9, 1982. Student, Antioch Coll., 1960-64, 65-66. Computer programmer N.Y. Telephone, N.Y.C., 1966-68; prodn. editor, then copy editor Travel Weekly, N.Y.C., 1968-76, chief copy editor, 1976-79; mng. editor Indsl. Chem. News, N.Y.C., 1981-82; editor, writer, cons. N.Y.C., 1986—. Author numerous articles. Mem. Overseas Press Club, Soc. Silurians. Republican. Episcopalian. Avocations: reading, cooking, computer hacking, walking, cinema. Home: 236 Edgemere St Montauk NY 11954-5249

LAVENDER, ROBERT EUGENE, state supreme court justice; b. Muskogee, Okla., July 19, 1926; s. Harold James and Vergene Irene (Martin) L.; m. Maxine Knight, Dec. 22, 1945; children—Linda (Mrs. Dean Courter), Robert K., Debra (Mrs. Thomas Merrill), William J. LL.B, U. Tulsa, 1953; grad., Appellate Judges Seminar, 1967, Nat. Coll. State Trial Judges, 1970. Bar: Okla. bar 1953. With Mass. Bonding & Ins. Co., Tulsa, 1951-53, U.S. Fidelity & Guaranty Co., Tulsa, 1953-54; asst. city atty. Tulsa, 1954-55, practice, 1955-60; practice Claremore, Okla., 1960-65; justice Okla. Supreme Ct., 1965—, chief justice, 1979-80; guest lectr. Okla. U., Oklahoma City U., Tulsa U. law schs. Republican committeeman, Rogers County, 1961-62. Served with USNR, 1944-46. Recipient Disting. Alumnus award U. Tulsa, 1993. Mem. ABA, Okla. Bar Assn., Rogers County Bar Assn., Am. Judicature Soc., Okla. Jud. Conf., Phi Alpha Delta (hon.). Methodist (adminstrv. bd.). Club: Mason (32 deg.). Home: 2910 Kerry Ln Oklahoma City OK 73120-2507 Office: US Supreme Ct Okla Rm 1 State Capitol Oklahoma City OK 73105

LAVENGOOD, LAWRENCE GENE, management educator, historian; b. Tulsa, June 30, 1924; s. Lawrence Wilbur and Elizabeth (Gardner) L.; m. Gloria M. deLeon, Aug. 27, 1947; children: Jessica, Abigail, Timothy, Rachel. M.A., U. Chgo., 1947, Ph.D., 1953. Asst. prof. bus. history Northwestern U., Evanston, Ill., 1953-59, assoc. prof., 1959-69, chmn. dept. policy and environ., 1980-82, prof. bus. history and policy and environ., 1970-94, prof. emeritus, 1994—; mem. Com. on Ethics in Bus. Edn., 1977-79; cons. on mgmt. devel. edn. U.S. and European corps.; U.S. faculty coord. Sasin Grad. Inst. Bus. Administrn., Chulalongkorn U., Bangkok, 1983-95. Editor, contbr.: Moral Man and Economic Enterprise, 1967. Mem. Bd. Edn. Ill. elem. dist. 65, Evanston, 1967-72, 75, 78. Recipient Ann. Kellogg Alumni Choice award, 1992. Mem. Bus. History Conf. Democrat. Presbyterian. Office: Kellog Grad Sch Mgmt Northwestern U Evanston IL 60201

LAVENSON, JAMES H., hotel industry executive; b. Phila., 1919. Grad., Williams Coll., 1941. Chmn. CEO SYR Corp., 1976-88; pres. Lavenson Mgmt. Enterprises, Inc., N.Y.C., 1976—, Plaza Hotel, N.Y.C. 1972-75, Sunwear, Inc.; chmn. Doxsee Food Co.; pres. Lavenson Bur. Advt., Inc., 1950-64; dir. Sonesta Hotels, TLC Corp.; chmn. Pine Tree Computers, Camden, Maine; bd. dirs. Am. Field Svc., Chief Exec. Forum. Author: Selling Made Simple, Sensuous Animal, Think Strawberries, How to Earn a MBWA Degree. Trustee Thomas Coll. Office: 12 Norumbega Dr Camden ME 04843-1746

LAVENSON, SUSAN BARKER, hotel corporate executive, consultant; b. L.A., July 26, 1936; d. Percy Morton and Rosalie Laura (Donner) Barker; m. James H. Lavenson, Apr. 22, 1973; 1 child, Ellen Ruth Stancliff. BA, Stanford U., 1958, MA, 1959; PhD (hon.), Thomas Coll., 1994. Cert. gen. secondary credential tchr., Calif. Tchr. Benjamin Franklin Jr. High Sch., San Francisco, 1960; tchr. French dept. Lowell High Sch., San Francisco, 1960-61; v.p. Monogram Co., San Francisco, 1961-62; creative dir. Monogram Co., N.Y.C., 1973-76; pres. SYR Corp., Santa Barbara, Calif., 1976-89; ptnr. Lavenson Ptnrs., Camden, Maine, 1989—; mem. commn. on co-edn. Wheaton Coll., Norton, Mass., 1985-87; mem. Relais et Chateaus, Paris, 1978-79; cons. World Bank Recruitment Divsn., 1993; bd. dirs. Pinetree Computer Systems, Rockport, Maine. Author: Greening of San Ysidro 1977 (Conf. award 1977). Trustee Camden Pub. Libr., 1989—, v.p., 1991-93; vice chair bd. trustees Thomas Coll., Waterville, Maine; trustee Atlantic Ave Trust; founding pres. Maine chpt. Internat. Women's Forum, 1991—. Mem. Camden Yacht Club, Stanford Alumni Assn., Com. of 200 (treas. 1985-86), Phi Delta Kappa. Home and Office: 12 Norumbega Dr Camden ME 04843-1746

LAVENTHOL, DAVID ABRAM, newspaper editor; b. Phila., July 15, 1933; s. Jesse and Clare (Horwald) L.; m. Esther Coons, Mar. 8, 1958; children: Peter, Sarah. BA, Yale U., 1957; MA, U. Minn., 1960; LittD (hon.), Dowling Coll., 1979; LLD (hon.), Hofstra U., 1986. Reporter, news editor St. Petersburg (Fla.) Times, 1957-62; asst. editor, city editor N.Y. Herald-Tribune, 1963-66; assoc. mng. editor Washington Post, 1966-69; assoc. editor Newsday, L.I., N.Y., 1969, exec. editor, 1969, editor, 1970-78, pub., chief exec. officer, 1978-86; group v.p. newspapers Times Mirror Co., L.A., 1981-86, sr. v.p., 1987-93, pres., 1987-93; pub., chief exec. officer L.A. Times, 1989-93; editor-at-large Times Mirror Co., L.A., 1994—; mem. Pulitzer Prize Bd., 1982-91, chmn., 1988-89; chmn. Internat. Press Inst., 1992—, vice chmn., 1985-93; dir. Am. Press Inst., 1988—. Bd. dirs. United Negro Coll. Fund, 1988, Times Mirror Found., 1987, Mus. Contemporary Art, L.A., 1989—, chmn., 1993—; bd. dirs. Associated Press, 1992—, Columbia Journalism Sch., 1993—. With Signal Corps AUS, 1953-55. Recipient Columbia Journalism award for Disting. Svc., 1994. Mem. Am. Soc. Newspaper Editors (chmn. writing awards bd. 1980-83), Council Fgn. Relations. Clubs: Century (N.Y.C.), Regency (L.A.). Office: LA Times Times Mirror Sq Los Angeles CA 90053-3816

LAVENTHOL, HENRY L(EE) (HANK LAVENTHOL), artist, etcher; b. Phila., Dec. 22, 1927; s. Lewis Jacob and Sadye Aileen (Horwitz) L.; m. Josephine P. Weitjens, Mar. 26, 1965. B.A., Yale U., 1947; postgrad., Columbia U., 1948-51, New Sch. Social Research, 1952-53, Academia di Bell Arte, Florence, Italy, 1961-62. Sr. acct. Laventhol Horwath & Co. N.Y.C., 1948-51; v.p. Wings Shirt Co., Inc., N.Y.C., 1951-61; guest lectr. N.Y. U., 1955, Pratt Graphic Center, N.Y.C., 1974. One-man shows include John Whibley Gallery, London, 1963-69, Galerie Goldoni, Florence, 1962, Galerie de la Madeleine, Brussels, 1962, Die Brucke, Dusseldorf, Fed. Republic Germany, 1964, Galerie Ganzoni, Geneva, 1964, Galerie de Sfinx, Amsterdam, The Netherlands, 1967, Bodley Gallery, N.Y.C., 1968-71, Mickelson Gallery, Washington, 1973, Frank Fedele Fine Arts, N.Y.C., 1980, 81, 82, Werner Gallery, N.Y.C., 1989; exhibited in group shows at Phila. Mus. Art, 1969, Print Club Phila, 1969-86, Bibliotheque Nationale Paris, 1979, Associated Am. Artists, 1968-86, Shippee Gallery, N.Y.C., 1987; represented in permanent collections, Nat. Gallery Art, Washington, IBM Corp., Armonk, N.Y., N.Y. Public Library, N.Y.C., Yale U. Art Gallery, Cigna Corp., Hartford, Conn., Forbes Coll., Pepsico, Purchase, N.Y., Lowe Mus. Art, Miami, Fla., Duke U. Mus. Art, Reuben A. Donnelley, White Plains, N.Y., Free Library Phila., Citicorp Collection, N.Y.C., Erbamont N.A., White Plains, Bibliotheque Nationale, Paris, Evansville Mus., Ind., Warnaco, Bridgeport, Conn., E.M. Warburg Pincus & Co., N.Y.C., NYNEX Corp., White Plains, N.Y.; contbr. etchings to books Le Miroir Aux Alouettes, 1973, Eyedeas, 1980, Crises, 1980. Mem. Artists Equity Assn. Home: 805 Hanover St Yorktown Heights NY 10598

LAVERGE, JAN, tobacco company executive; b. Amsterdam, Netherlands, Nov. 17, 1909; came to U.S., 1934, naturalized, 1942; s. Hendrik Johannes and Margaretha (Van Gelder) L.; m. Henriette Amelia Boelen, May 21, 1935; children—Bart Jan, Eva S., Charlotte M. M.E., Higher Tech. Sch., Amsterdam, 1930. With Am. Tobacco Co., Amsterdam, 1930-34; with Universal Leaf Tobacco Co., Inc., Richmond, Va., 1934—; asst. v.p. Universal Leaf Tobacco Co., Inc., 1946-51, v.p., 1951-66, sr. v.p., 1966-78, dir., 1953—, chmn. exec. com., 1974-78, cons., 1978-81, dir. emeritus, 1981—. Served to maj. AUS, 1943-46. Decorated U.S. Legion of Merit, Croix de Guerre France; Netherlands Order Orange Nassau. Home: 6120 St Andrews Ln Richmond VA 23226-3213 Office: Universal Bldg Broad and Hamilton Richmond VA 23230

LAVERNE, MICHEL MARIE-JACQUES, international relations consultant; b. Paris, June 1, 1928; s. Charles Henri Andre and Anne Marie Henriette (Bour) L.; m. Genevieve Laverne Pierès, June 29, 1963; children: Beatrice, Thierry, Loic Heaulme, Christophe, Matthieu. MBA, Ecole des Hautes Etudes Commerciales, 1953; postgrad., Centre de Perfectionnement dans l'Adminstrn. des Affaires, 1960. Various mktg., adminstrn. and fin. positions Shell Group Cos., internat. locations, 1954-73; account exec. Union d'Etudes et Investissements (subs. Credit Agricole), Paris, 1973-76; v.p. fin. Salmon et Cie, Paris, 1976-81; chief exec. officer Cartonneries de St. Germain, 1977-79, Papeteries Maunoury, 1979-80; exec. Generale Biscuit, Athis-Mons, France, 1981-83; former chmn. bd. Generale Biscuit, Italy; pres., CEO Mother's Cookies, Oakland, Calif., 1983-91, Mother's Cookies/ Gen. Biscuit Am., 1990-91; assoc. MLG Plus Cons., Oakland, 1991—, Eurosite, Oakland, 1992—. Commr. Internat. Trade and Fgn. Investment Commn., City of Oakland. Mem. Conseiller du Commerce Exterieur de la France (pres. U.S.A. N.W. sect.). Roman Catholic. Avocations: sailing, skiing, photography, hunting. Home and Office: MLG Plus Cons 8 Marr Ave Oakland CA 94611-3131 Address: Grand Pas, 41230 Vernou-en-Sologne France

LAVERS, RICHARD MARSHALL, lawyer; b. Oak Ridge, Tenn., Apr. 15, 1947; s. Willard Douglas and Athena Vashti (Compton) L.; m. Christine Anne Jandl, June 2, 1973; children: Christian Douglas, Ansley McKay, Ti-Patrice, Rickey Elizabeth. BA, U. Mich., 1968; postgrad., Columbia U., 1968-69; JD cum laude, U. Mich., 1972; postdoctoral, U. Wis., 1977-81. Bar: Colo. 1972, U.S. Dist. Ct. (Colo.) 1972, U.S. Ct. Appeals (10th cir.) 1975, Wis. 1978, La. 1983, U.S. Dist. Ct. (mid. dist.) La. 1983, U.S. Ct. Appeals (5th cir.) 1983, N.Y. 1986. Dep. dist. atty. 9th Jud. Dist., Glenwood Springs, Colo., 1972-73; assoc. Martin Dumont, Glenwood Springs, 1972-74, Rovira, Demuth & Eiberger, Denver, 1974-76; assoc. resident counsel Nat. Presto Industries, Eau Claire, Wis., 1976-82; asst. counsel Ethyl Corp., Baton Rouge, 1982-87; ptnr. Mulcahy & Wherry, S.C., Milw., 1987-90, Michael, Best & Friedrich, Milw., 1990-94; gen. counsel RMT, Inc., Madison, Wis., 1994—; gen. counsel Wis. World Trace Ctr., 1987-91; bd. dirs. Nexus Internat., Ltd.; adj. prof. bus. law Cardinal Stritch Coll. Mem. editorial bd. U.S. Trademark Assn., Guide to the Internat. Sale of Goods Conv., Bus. Laws Inc. Bd. dirs. Milw. Kickers, Soccer Club, Inc., pres., 1992—; counsel U.S., Rep. Steve Gunderson campaign, Eau Claire, Wis., 1980. With USAR, 1969-73. Mem. ABA, N.Y. Bar Assn., Wis. Bar Assn. (bd. dirs. internat. practice sect. 1992—), La. Bar Assn., Eau Claire Jaycees (bd. dirs. 1976-80), Meridian Club (pres. 1981). Republican. Congregationalist. Office: Michael Best & Friedrich 100 E Wisconsin Ave Milwaukee WI 53202-4107

LAVERTY, BRUCE, curator; b. Phila., Nov. 20, 1958; s. John Patterson and Barbara Shirley (McKee) L.; m. Wendy S. Emrich, Sept. 14, 1985; children: Allison B., Susan L. BA, La Salle Coll., 1979. Asst. dir. N.W. Phila. Hist. Site Survey, 1979-80; manuscripts libr. Hist. Soc. Pa., Phila., 1980-83; archivist Athenaeum of Phila., 1983-88, curator of architecture, 1988—; juror Charles E. Peterson Prize Hist. Am. Bldgs. Survey, Washington, 1998—; cons. Phila. Archdiocese Hist. Resource Ctr., Phila., 1994—. Bd. dirs. Old York Rd. Christian Endeavor, Phila., 1975-93, Whosoever Gospel Mission & Rescue Home, Phila., 1992—. Grantee NEA, 1993. Mem. Soc. Am. Archivists, Mid-Atlantic Regional Archivists Conf. Democrat. Avocations: reading, travel, racquetball. Office: Athenaeum Phila 219 S 6th St Philadelphia PA 19106

LAVERTY, ROGER MONTGOMERY, III, food products executive, lawyer; b. Los Angeles, June 12, 1947; s. Roger M. and Joan Ruth (Wright) L.; m. Melinda Hodell, July 10, 1970 (div. July, 1980); m. Jill B. Rosenbaum, Oct. 12, 1982; children: Rory, Geoffrey, Molly. BA, Stanford U., 1969, JD, 1972. Bar: Calif. 1972. Atty. Bodkin, McCarthy & Sargent, Los Angeles, 1975-79; gen. counsel Thriftimart, Inc., Los Angeles, 1979-82, v.p., 1982-84; sr. v.p. Smart & Final Iris Corp., Los Angeles, 1984-87, pres., 1988—. Served to lt. USN, 1972-75. Mem. Calif. Bar Assn. Republican. Clubs: Los Angeles Country, Los Angeles Athletic. Avocations: tennis, cycling, golf, fishing. Home: 320 16th St Manhattan Beach CA 90266-4621 Office: Smart & Final Stores 524 Chapala St Santa Barbara CA 93101

LAVERY, DANIEL P., management consultant; b. N.Y.C., June 28, 1932; B.S. with honors, Manhattan Coll., 1954; M.B.A., Rutgers U., 1963; m. Doris E. Guenther, Oct. 23, 1954; children—Daniel, Brian, Kevin, Michael. Mem. prodn. mgmt. staff, photo products dept. E.I. DuPont de Nemours & Co., Inc., 1954-65; div. mgr. Anken Industries, Williamstown, Mass., 1965-71; gen. mgr. Dymo Industries, N.Y.C., 1971-73; dir. cons. studies Quantum Sci. Corp., N.Y.C., 1973-79; mgr. strategic mktg. ITT, N.Y.C., 1979-80; sr. dir. market research Western Union, 1980-82; v.p. Pactel, Inc., mgmt. cons., N.Y.C., 1982-83; ptnr. Palo Alto Mgmt. Group, Wyckoff, N.J., 1983—. Served as capt. USAF, 1955-57. Mem. Inst. Mgmt. Cons. (cert. mgmt. cons.), Am. Arbitration Assn. (panel mem. 1985—). Office: Palo Alto Management Group Inc 458 Sicomac Ave Wyckoff NJ 07481-1120

LAVEY, KENNETH HENRY, advertising agency executive, designer; b. Palermo, Calif., Aug. 25, 1923; s. Rudolph Charles and Margaret S. (Williams) L.; m. Joann Lucile Miller, July 11, 1948; children: Brian Benton, Neil Bruce. B.A., Calif. Coll. Arts and Crafts, 1948; grad., Pratt Inst., 1949. With L. W. Frolich (pharm. advt. co.), N.Y.C., 1949-72; creative dir. L. W. Frolich (pharm. advt. co.), 1962-66, sr. v.p., dir. creative planning, 1966-72; co-founder Lavey Wolff Swift, Inc. (health care communications agy.), N.Y.C., 1972; exec. v.p., dir. creative services Lavey Wolff Swift, Inc. (health care communications agy.), from 1972, now vice chmn., creative dir.; lectr. Pratt Inst., 1976-77; participant Ten Alumni exhibit, 1962, Fifty Alumni exhibit, 1966; panel mem. Pharm. Advt. Club Seminar. Designer (with Harvard Med. Sch. dept. physiology), anatomical graphics. Served with USAAF, 1943-46. Recipient Student medal for advt. design Pratt Inst., 1949. Mem. Art Dirs. Club N.Y., Am. Ethical Union, Riverdale-Yonkers Ethical Soc. (v.p. 1969-71, 76-77), Riverdale-Yonkers Soc. Ethical Culture (pres. 1990-93). Office: Lavey Wolff Swift Inc 488 Madison Ave New York NY 10022-5702

LAVEY, STEWART EVAN, lawyer; b. Newark, July 24, 1945; m. Suzanne Laurence, July 9, 1972. AB, Syracuse U., 1967; JD, Fordham U., 1970. Bar: N.Y. 1971, N.J. 1987, Pa. 1988, D.C. 1988. Assoc. Kelley Drye & Warren, N.Y.C., 1970-71, Emil, Kobrin, Klein & Garbus, N.Y.C., 1971-72, Zimet Haines Moss & Goodkind, N.Y.C., 1972-75; asst. sec., asst. gen. counsel Norlin Corp., N.Y.C., 1975-78; sec., asst. gen. counsel Norlin Corp., 1978-85; of counsel Shanley & Fisher, P.C., Morristown, N.J., 1985-87, ptnr., 1987—; adj. assoc. prof. law Fordham U., N.Y.C., 1976-79, adj. prof., 1980—; lectr. Fordham U. Continuing Legal Edn., 1991—. Mem.: Fordham Law Rev, 1968-70. Mem. Am. Bar Assn., N.Y. State Bar Assn.; mem. of Bar of City of N.Y., N.J. Bar Assn. (securities law com.), Pa. Bar Assn., D.C. Bar Assn. Office: Shanley & Fisher PC 131 Madison Ave Morristown NJ 07960-6086

LAVEZZI, JOHN CHARLES, art history educator, archaeologist; b. Chgo., July 7, 1940; s. Francis M. and Dorothy M. (Kopal) L. AB magna cum laude, Cath. U. Am., 1962; MA, U. Cin., 1965; postgrad., Am. Sch. Classical Studies, Athens, Greece, 1967-70; PhD, U. Chgo., 1973. Sec. Am. Sch. Classical Studies at Athens, 1968-70; asst. prof. Sch. Art Bowling Green (Ohio) State U., 1973-80, assoc. prof., 1980—; sr. assoc. mem. Am. Sch. Classical Studies at Athens, 1972—, rsch. assoc. Corinth Excavations, 1972—. Contbr. articles to profl. jours. Mem. Toledo Mus. Art. Recipient CUA Stratemeier award, 1962, Medici Circle teaching awards, 1986, 94; grantee Am. Philos. Soc., 1973. Mem. Archeol. Inst. Am., Midwest Art History Soc., Soc. for Preservation of Greek Heritage, Nat. Geographic Soc.,

Phi Beta Kappa (pres. chpt. 1992), Phi Alpha Theta, Blue Key, Delta Epsilon Sigma, Phi Eta Sigma. Roman Catholic. Office: Bowling Green State U Sch Art Bowling Green OH 43403

LA VIA, MARIANO FRANCIS, physician, pathology and laboratory medicine educator; b. Rome, Jan. 29, 1926; came to U.S., 1952; s. Vincenzo and Carmela (Carbone) La V.; m. Martha Ann Tillson, Dec. 26, 1959 (div. 1972); children: William, Maria, Charles, Jacqueline, Susan, Christopher, Thomas; m. June F.S. Bailey, Oct. 19, 1991. MD, U. Messina, Italy, 1949. Internship, residency A.M. Billings Meml. Hosp., U. Chgo., 1952-57; pathology fellow U. Rome, Italy, 1949-52; rsch. asst. pathology U. Chgo., 1952-57; resident in pathology A.M. Billings Hosp., U. Chgo., 1952-57; instr. anatomy U. Chgo., 1957-60; asst. prof. pathology U. Colo. Med. Ctr., Denver, 1960-67, assoc. prof. pathology, 1967-68; prof. pathology and lab. medicine Bowman Gray Sch. Medicine, Wake Forest U., Winston-Salem, N.C., 1968-71, Sch. Medicine, Emory U., Atlanta, 1971-79, Med. U.S.C., Charleston, 1979—. Contbr. numerous articles to profl. jours. Pres. Advocacy Coun. for Persons with Disabilities, 1994. Recipient NIH Rsch. Career Devel. award, 1962-68. Fellow AAAS; mem. Am. Soc. Investigative Pathology, Clin. Cytometry Soc. (pres.), Am. Assn. Immunologists, Clin. Immunology Soc., others. Avocations: photography, pipe collecting. Office: Med U SC 171 Ashley Ave Charleston SC 29425-0001

LAVIDGE, ROBERT JAMES, marketing research executive; b. Chgo., Dec. 27, 1921; s. Arthur Wills and Mary Beatrice (James) L.; m. Margaret Mary Zwigard, June 8, 1946; children: Margaret, Kathleen, William, Lynn Elizabeth. AB, DePauw U., 1943; MBA, U. Chgo., 1947. Analyst Pepsodent div. Lever Bros., Chgo., 1947-48, new products mktg. rsch. mgr. Pepsodent div., 1948-49; asst. dir. mktg. Am. Meat Inst., Chgo., 1950-51; ptnr. Elrick, Lavidge and Co., Chgo., 1951-56; pres. Elrick and Lavidge, Inc., Chgo., 1956-86; pres. emeritus Elrick and Lavidge, Inc., Scottsdale, Ariz., 1987—; lectr. mktg. research, sales adminstrn. Northwestern U., 1950-80; mem. Nat. Mktg. Adv. Com., 1967-71, also exec. com. Trustee Village Western Springs, Ill., 1957-61, pres., 1973-77; trustee McCormick Theol. Sem., 1981-90, 92—; mem. adv. council U. Chgo. Grad. Sch. Bus. With USNR, 1943-46. Mem. Am. Mktg. Assn. (v.p. 1963-64, pres. 1966-67, trustee found. 1992—, chmn.), Internat. Rels. Soc. (chmn. 1961-65), Econ. Club Phoenix, De Pauw U. Alumni Assn. (pres. 1967-68), Klinger Lake Club (Mich.), Paradise Valley Country Club, Phi Beta Kappa, Beta Gamma Sigma, Sigma Delta Chi, Pi Sigma Alpha, Delta Upsilon. Presbyterian.

LAVIN, BERNICE E., cosmetics executive; b. 1925; m. Leonard H. Lavin, Oct. 30, 1947; children: Scott Jay, Carol Marie, Karen Sue. Student, Northwestern U. Vice chairperson of bd., sec.- treas. Alberto-Culver Co.; dir., v.p., sec.- treas. Alberto-Culver U.S.A., Inc.; sec.- treas., dir. Alberto-Culver Internat., Inc., Draper Daniels Media Svcs., Inc.; v.p., sec.-treas. Sally Beauty Co., others. Office: Alberto-Culver Co 2525 Armitage Ave Melrose Park IL 60160-1163

LAVIN, CHARLES BLAISE, JR., realtor, association executive; b. Balt., Aug. 13, 1940; s. Charles Blaise and Dorothy (Sturla) L.; m. Eileen Donohue, Sept. 3, 1966; children—Charles, Michael, Kristine, Philip. Student, U. Balt., 1958-62, U.S. Army Sch. Mil. Intelligence, 1962. Exec. dir. New Eng. chpt. Associated Builders and Contractors, Waltham, Mass., 1968-78; exec. v.p. Am. Subcontractors Assn., Washington, 1978-81; exec. asst. to dep. sec. for housing HUD, Washington, 1981-82; exec. v.p. Nat. Assn. Plumbing, Heating and Cooling Contractors, Washington, 1982-87; exec. dir. and lobbyist Nat. Burglar and Fire Alarm Assn., Washington, and Cen. Sta. Alarm Assn., Bethesda, Md., 1987-90; realtor Prudential Preferred Properties, Laurel, Md., 1990-95; exec. dir. Nat. Duckpin Bowling Congress, Balt., 1995—; trustee Assoc. Splty. Contractors, Constrn. Jurisdictional Dispute Bd., 1983-85; chmn. P6 County Real Estate Bd., 1993—. Vice chmn. bd. dirs., chmn. fin. com. Laurel-Beltsville Gen. Hosp. (Md.), 1982-84; mem. Budget Com. Hopkinton, Mass., 1975-77, Planning Commn., 1977-78; bd. dirs. Young Republicans Balt., 1966. Served with CIC U.S. Army, 1962-65. Mem. New Eng. Soc. Assn. Execs., (Greater Washington Soc. Assn. Execs. (dir.), Am. Soc. Assn. Execs., Am. Legion, U.S.C. of C., D.C. Basketball Ofcls. Assn., Internat. Assn. Basketball Ofcls., Washington Dist. Football Ofcls. Assn., Sons of Italy, KC, Am. Legion Post 60 (comdr. 1994—), Loyal Order of Moose, West Laurel Recreational Coun. (pres. 1993—, chmn. legis. com. real estate bd.). Republican. Roman Catholic. Home: 7006 Redmiles Rd Laurel MD 20707-3244 Office: Nat Duckpin Bowling Cong 4991 Fairview Ave Baltimore MD 21090

LAVIN, JOHN HALLEY, editor, author; b. Queens County, N.Y., Oct. 27, 1932; s. John Joseph and Dorothy Monica (Halley) L.; m. Bernadette Manning, Mar. 2, 1957; children—John Stephen, Michael James, Eileen Mary, Monica Anne. B.A., Queens Coll., 1958; health adminstrv. devel. program, Cornell U., 1969. Editor L.I. Graphic (weekly), 1958; copy editor New Haven Register, 1958-59; newsman, state news editor A.P., Newark, 1959-65; gen. news supr. A.P., N.Y.C., 1965-66; editor-winter Med. Econs. Co., mag. pubs., Oradell, N.J., 1966-82; Atlantic bur. chief Soccer Am. Mag., 1977-78; sr. editor, news div. chief. mem. editorial bd. Med. Econs., 1968-73; editor RN, 1973-75, Nursing Opportunities, 1973-75, RN Recruiter, 1974-75, Geriatric Cons., 1982-94, Pharmacy World News, 1985-86, Contemporary Sr. Health, 1989-93; with Cardiology World News, 1982—. Author: Stroke: From Crisis to Victory, 1985; contbr. articles to profl. and gen. interest publs. Publicity chmn. Glen Rock (N.J.) Cub Scouts and Boy Scouts Am., 1968-73; founder, mem., trustee Glen Rock Jr. Soccer Club. Served with USN, 1951-55, Korea. Recipient Jesse H. Neal award 1970-74. Served with USN, 1951-55, Korea. Recipient Jesse H. Neal award Am. Bus. Press, 1976, cert., 1976; Journalism award Am. Acad. Family Physicians, 1981. Mem. Soc. Prfol. Journalists. Roman Catholic. Home: 106 Delbrook Way Marco Island FL 33937-4605 *An editor's primary responsibility is to his reader. If he has performed his corporate duties well, endeared himself to his publisher, pleased his writers and advertisers, fed his ego among his fellow editors, but has allowed the editorial excellence of his publication to be compromised, he has not met his primary responsibility. If he loses touch with the copy or the reader, he is no longer an editor; he is a manager. And he might as well be in some other business.*

LAVIN, LEONARD H., personal care products company executive; b. Chgo., 1919; married. BA, U. Wash., 1940. With Lucien Lelong, 1940-46; with Leonard H. Lavin Co., 1951-55, Alberto-Culver Co., Melrose Park, Ill., 1955—, chmn., pres., CEO, now chmn., bd. dirs. Served to lt. commdr. USNR, 1941-45. Office: Alberto-Culver Co 2525 Armitage Ave Melrose Park IL 60160-1163

LAVIN, LINDA, actress; b. Portland, Maine, Oct. 15, 1937; d. David J. and Lucille (Potter) L. BA, Coll. William and Mary, Williamsburg, Va., 1959. Debut: (Off-Broadway) Oh, Kay!, 1960, (Broadway) A Family Affairs, 1962; appearances in revues Wet Paint, 1965, The Game Is Up, 1965, The Mad Show, 1966; with nat. touring company On a Clear Day You Can See Forever, 1966-67; mem. acting company Eugene O'Neil Playwrights' Unit, 1968; other stage appearances include It's a Bird... It's a Plane... It's Superman, 1966, Something Different, 1967, Little Murders, 1969, Cop-Out, 1969, The Last of the Red Hot Lovers, 1969 (Tony nominee), Story Theatre, 1970, The Enemy is Dead, 1973, Love Two, 1974, The Comedy of Errors, 1975, Dynamite Tonite!, 1975, Six Characters in Search of an Author, Am. Repertory Theatre, Cambridge, Mass., 1983-84 season, Broadway Bound, 1986 (Tony award 1987), Gypsy, 1990, The Sisters Rosensweig, 1993, Death Defying Acts, 1995; film appearances: See You In The Morning, 1989, I Want to Go Back Home, 1989; star: (TV series) Alice, 1976-85 (Golden Globe award 1979); star and prodr.: (TV series) Room for Two, 1992—; prodr.: (PBS TV miniseries) The Sunset Gang, 1991; other TV appearances on Phyllis, Family, Rhoda, Harry O; TV movies include: The Morning After, 1974, Like Mom, Like Me, 1978, A Matter of Life and Death, 1981, Another Woman's Child, 1983, A Place To Call Home, Lena: My One Hundred Children. Recipient Sat. Rev., Outer Critics Circle awards for Little Murders, Theater World award for Wet Paint. Office: Metropolitan Talent Agy 4526 Wilshire Blvd Los Angeles CA 90010*

LAVIN, MATTHEW T., horticultural educator. Prof. biology dept. Mont. State U., Bozeman. Recipient N.Y. Botanical Garden award Botanical Soc. Am., 1993. Office: care Dept Biology Montana State U Bozeman MT 59717-0002*

LAVIN, THOMAS J. A., investment banker; b. N.Y.C., Nov. 2, 1949; s. Thomas and Kathleen (Monahan) L.; m. Elizabeth Hickey, Aug. 26, 1977; children: Thomas L., Katherine Elizabeth, Margaret Ann, John Patrick. BA, Wesleyan Coll., 1971; MBA, Harvard U., 1978. Assoc. to mng. dir. First Boston Corp., N.Y.C., 1985—. Office: First Boston Corp Pk Ave Pla 55 E 52nd St New York NY 10055-0002

LAVINE, ALAN, columnist, writer; b. Sharon, Pa., Feb. 17, 1948; s. Milton and Doris (Helfman) L.; m. Gail Jeanne Liberman, Dec. 20, 1991. BA, Kent State U., 1970; MA, U. Akron, 1973; MBA, Clark U., 1981. Dir. of rsch. Donoghue Orgn., Holliston, Mass., 1981-83; syndicated columnist Boston & West Palm Beach, Fla., 1984—; presenter papers in field ann. meeting AAAS, 1972, ann. meeting Mass. Psychol. Assn., Wellesley, 1978, ann. meeting APA, 1979, Nat. Symposium on Rsch. in Art, U. Ill., 1980; guest lectr. Cornell U., 1990, 91, 92, 93. Author: Diversify: Investor's Guide to Asset Allocation Strategies, 1990 (alt. selection Fortune Book Club), Your Life Insurance Options, 1993 (endorsed Inst. CFPs), Improving Your Credit and Reducing Your Debt, 1994 (endorsed Inst. CFPs), Getting Started in Mutual Funds, 1994, Diversify Your Way to Wealth, 1994 (alt. selection Fortune Book Club), 50 Ways to Mutual Fund Profits, 1995; contbr. articles to Am. Jour. Zoology, Psychol. Reports, New Eng. Econ. Energy Project Reports, Fin. Planning. Mem. Nat. Writers Union. Home: H2 3606 Alder Dr West Palm Beach FL 33417 Office: Alan Lavine Inc 3951 N Haverhill Rd # 210 West Palm Beach FL 33417

LAVINE, GARY J., utility executive. BS, Syracuse U., 1971, JD, 1973. Bar: N.Y. 1979. Asst. gen. counsel Niagara Mohawk Power Corp, Syracuse, N.Y., 1986-87, v.p., gen. counsel, sec., 1987-90, sr. v.p., gen. counsel, 1990—. Office: Niagara Mohawk Power Corp 300 Erie Blvd W Syracuse NY 13202-4250*

LAVINE, HENRY WOLFE, lawyer; b. Phila., Apr. 21, 1936; s. Samuel Phillips and Sarah Pamela (Leese) L.; m. Meta Landreth Doak, Feb. 20, 1960 (div. Feb. 1980); children: Lisa, Lindsay; m. Martha Putnam Cathcart; children: Samuel Putnam, Gwenn Cathcart. BA, U. Pa., 1957, JD, 1961. Assoc. Squire, Sanders & Dempsey, Cleve., 1961-70; ptnr. Squire, Sanders & Dempsey, Washington, 1970-85, mng. ptnr. Washington office, 1985-91; sr. mng. ptnr., 1991—; dir. Greater Washington Bd. of Trade. Trustee Fed. City Coun., Washington; bd. assocs. Gallaudet U.; mem. The Bretton Woods Com. Mem. Siasconset Casino Club, Met. Club. Office: Squire Sanders & Dempsey 1201 Pennsylvania Ave NW PO Box 407 Washington DC 20044

LAVINE, JOHN M., journalism educator, newspaper publisher; b. Duluth, Minn., Mar. 20, 1941; s. Max H. and Frances (Hoffman) L.; m. Meryl Esta Lipton, June 1, 1980; children: Miriam, Marc, Max. B.A., Carleton Coll., Minn., 1963; postgrad., U. Minn., 1963; LL.D. (hon.), Emerson Coll., Boston, 1975. Pub., editor Lavine Newspaper Group, Chippewa Falls, Wis., 1964-89; pub. Ind. Media Group, Profl. Publs., Inc., 1984-94; Cowles prof. media mgmt. and econs. U. Minn., Mpls., 1984-89; prof., dir. Newspaper Mgmt. Ctr. a joint program Northwestern U. Kellogg Grad. Sch. Mgmt./ Medill Sch. Journalism, Evanston, Ill., 1989—; pres. Newspaper Cons. Inc., Evanston, 1993—; cons., lectr. in field, vis. prof. numerous profl. and ednl. instns.; participant numerous profl. confs. Author: China, 1980; The Constant Dollar Newspaper, 1980; Managing Media Organizations, 1988; contbr. chpts. to books, articles to profl. jours. Recipient numerous awards for excellence in mgmt. and journalism. Mem. Newspaper Assn. Am., Am. Soc. Newspapers Editors, Inter Am. Press Assn., Inland Daily Press Assn. (chmn., pres. 1984-85), Wis. Newspaper Assn. (life). Home: 727 Sheridan Rd Evanston IL 60202-2501 Office: Newspaper Mgmt Ctr 1845 Sheridan Rd Evanston IL 60208-0815

LAVINE, LAWRENCE NEAL, investment banker; b. Providence, Sept. 20, 1951; s. Avery B. and Pearl (Burbil) L.; m. Pamela Ferne Selby, Jan. 3, 1981; 1 child, Jason. BS summa cum laude, Northwestern U., 1974; MBA with highest distinction, Harvard U., 1976. V.p. Kidder, Peabody & Co. Inc., N.Y.C., 1976-87; mng. dir. Donaldson, Lufkin & Jenrette, N.Y.C., 1987—. Dir. Nat. Downe Syndrome, N.Y.C.; trustee Providence YMCA Camp Fuller. Mem. Harvard Club of N.Y., Harvard Bus. Sch. Club of N.Y., Sunningdale Country Club. Avocations: running, tennis, golf. Office: Donaldson Lufkin & Jenrette Securities Corp 140 Broadway New York NY 10005-1101

LAVINE, STEVEN DAVID, college president; b. Sparta, Wis., June 7, 1947; s. Israel Harry and Harriet Hauda (Rosen) L.; m. Janet M. Sternburg, May 29, 1988. BA, Stanford U., 1969; MA, Harvard U., 1970; PhD, 1976. Asst. prof. U. Mich., Ann Arbor, 1974-81; asst. dir. arts and humanities Rockefeller Found., N.Y.C., 1983-86, assoc. dir. arts and humanities, 1986-88; pres. Calif. Inst. Arts, Valencia, 1988—; adj. assoc. prof. NYU Grad. Sch. Bus., 1984-85; cons. Wexner Found., Columbus, Ohio, 1986-87; selection panelist Input TV Screening Conf., Montreal, Can., and Granda, Spain, 1985-86; cons., panelist Nat. Endowment for Humanities, Washington, 1981-85; faculty chair Salzburg Seminar on Mus., 1989; co-dir. Arts and Govt. Program, The Am. Assembly, 1991. Editor: The Hopwood Anthology, 1981, Exhibiting Cultures, 1991, Museums and Communities, 1992; editor spl. issue Prooftexts jour., 1984. Bd. dirs. Sta. KCRW-FM (NPR), 1989—, J. Paul Getty Mus., 1990—, Inst. for African Humanities, Northwestern U., 1990—, Am. Coun. on the Arts, 1991—, L.A. Philharm. Assn., 1994—, Endowments, Inc., Bond Portfolio for Endowments, Inc., 1994—. Recipient Class of 1923 award, 1979, Faculty Recognition award, 1980 U. Mich.; Charles Dexter traveling fellow Harvard U., 1972, Ford fellow, 1969-74, vis. rsch. fellow Rockefeller Found., N.Y.C., 1981-83. Jewish. Office: Calif Inst Arts Office Pres 24700 Mcbean Pky Santa Clarita CA 91355-2397

LAVINGTON, MICHAEL RICHARD, venture capital company executive; b. Purley, Surrey, Eng., Feb. 21, 1943; came to U.S., 1972; s. Richard H. and Patricia (Young) L.; m. June Watford, Aug. 13, 1966; children: Susan, Victoria. B.A., Cambridge U., 1964; M.A., Columbia U., 1965; Ph.D., Lancaster U., (Eng.), 1968. Dir. Ralli Australia, 1969-71, Bowater America, N.Y.C., 1971-74; pres. Kay Jewelers Inc., Alexandria, Va., 1974-90, Watford Investment Corp., Fredericksburg, Va., 1990—. Gov. St. Stephen's and St. Agnes Sch., Alexandria, 1981—; trustee Ch. Schs. in Diocese of Va., 1989—.

LAVINSKY, LARRY MONROE, lawyer, consultant; b. N.Y.C., Oct. 23, 1929; s. Isaac A. and Rose (Zuroff) L.; m. Dena Mazell, Mar. 20, 1960; children: Joshua, Avram, Ezra. Bar: N.Y. 1953, U.S. Ct. Appeals 2d cir. 1958, U.S. Ct. Appeals 3d cir. 1978, U.S. Supreme Ct. 1961. Assoc. Baer, Marks, Frieman, Berliner & Klein, N.Y.C., 1953-57; law clk. U.S. Dist. Ct. (so. dist.) N.Y., 1957-59; assoc. Proskauer, Rose, Goetz & Mendelsohn, N.Y.C., 1959-67, ptnr., 1967—; spl. cons. on desegregation N.Y.C. Bd. Edn., 1973-74. Contbr. articles to profl. jours.; pub. TV appearances, 1978, 79. Chmn. nat. law com. Anti-Defamation League, B'nai B'rith, 1972-76, chmn. nat. civil rights com., 1976-80, vice chmn. nat. com., 1980-86, sec. nat. com., 1986-88; founding mem. Comm. on Equal Edn. Opportunity, 1978. Mem. ABA (Post-Bakke task force 1978-80, affirmative action com. 1981-86), New York County Lawyers Assn. (chmn. civil rights com. 1988-90), Assn. Bar City N.Y. Office: Proskauer Rose et al 1585 Broadway New York NY 10036-8200

LAVITT, MEL S., investment banking professional; b. Denver, Sept. 9, 1937; s. Al R. and Ruth Lucille (Friedman) L.; m. Wendy Susan Adler, Sept. 10, 1959; children—Kathy, John, Meredith. A.B. in Am. Civilization, Brown U., Providence, 1959. Assoc. Bear Sterns & Co., N.Y.C., 1959-62; ptnr. C.E. Unterberg Towbin, N.Y.C., 1962-77; adminstrv. mng. dir. L.F. Rothschild, Unterberg, Towbin, N.Y.C., 1977-87; pres. Lavitt Mgmt., Park City, Utah, 1987-92; mng. dir. Unterberg Harris, 1992—; bd. dirs. Emerald Systems Corp., Jabil Circuit Co.; fin. advisor Netframe Systems Inc. Mem. Harmonie Club, N.Y. Road Runners Club. Avocations: running, skiing, collecting American Indian art, biking. Home: 15 E 91st St New York NY 10128-0648 also: PO Box 74 Park City UT 84060-0074

LA VO, CARL PALMER, JR., newspaper editor, author; b. Oakland, Calif., Sept. 3, 1944; s. Carl Palmer and Irene Hilda (Braaten) L.; m. Mary Anne Ferber, May 31, 1975; 1 child, Genevieve Lamielle. BS in Journalism, U. Fla., 1973. Sports writer Fresno (Calif.) Bee newspaper, 1959-61; news editor, reporter Gainesville (Fla.) Sun newspaper, 1972-73; reporter Bucks

County Courier Times, Levittown, Pa., 1973-75, polit. writer, 1975-77, assoc. editor, 1978—; free-lance writer Levittown, Pa., 1972—. Author: Back from the Deep, 1994; editor: Nat. Speleological Soc. Mag. U. Fla. branch, 1968-71; contbr. articles to nat. and regional mags. Pres. Hope Lutheran Parent-Tchr. League, Levittown, 1985-87; trustee Hope Lutheran Ch., 1987-91, Friends of Pennwood Libr., 1995—. Recipient 1st place Features Writing award, 1975 and 2nd place Page 1 Design award Pa. Newspaper Publishers Assn., 1987. Mem. Author's Guild, Sigma Delta Chi. Avocations: tennis, horticulture. Home: 20 Oaktree Dr Levittown PA 19055-1526 Office: Bucks County Courier Times 8400 Rt 13 Levittown PA 19057

LAVOIE, LIONEL A., physician, medical executive; b. St. Brieux, Sask., Can., Aug. 24, 1937; s. Athanase T. and Ella Marie (Mevel) L.; m. Mary Tina Luchewski, Oct. 12, 1964; children: Robert, Michelle, Nicole, Andrea. BA, Ottawa U., Ont., Can., 1958, MD, 1964. Intern, then resident Univ. Hosp., Sask.; assoc. clin. prof. family medicine U. Sask., 1978—; chief of staff Melfort (Sask.) Union Hosp., 1985-90; commr. Med. Care Ins. Commn., 1984-88. Chmn. Melfort Dist. Minor Sports, 1978-80, Melfort Pks. and Recreation, 1983-86, Sask. Summer Games 1988, 1986-88. Recipient Ramstead award Jaycees of Province Sask., 1975, Dedication award Sask. Parks, Recreation and Culture, 1988, Community Recreation award Melford C. of C., 1989, Commemorative medal 125th Anniversary Can. Confed., 1993. Mem. Can. Med. Assn. (bd. dirs. 1978-83, pres. elect 1989-90, pres. 1990-91), Sask. Med. Assn. (bd. dirs. 1971-76, v.p. 1974, pres. 1975), Can. Acad. Sports Medicine, Am. Geriatric Soc., Coll. Family Physicians Can. (sec. Sask. province 1967-70), Sask. Acad. Sports Medicine (pres. 1986-88), Coun. Med. Assn. (chmn. 1985-89), Sask. Paraplegic Assn. (bd. dirs. 1978—), Can. Cancer Soc. (adv. com. Sask. div. 1986—), Nat. Aerospace Med. Assn., KC (grand knight 1980-81), Rotary (pres. Melfort club 1987-88). Avocations: golf, curling, horticulture. Home: 402 Stovel E, Melfort, SK Canada S0E 1A0 Office: Can Med Assn, 1867 Alta Vista Dr, Ottawa, ON Canada K1G 0G8

LAVOIE, SERGE, principal dancer; b. Lachine, Que., Can., Jan. 30, 1963; s. Jean Claude and Therese (Larr) L. Student, Nat. Ballet Sch., Toronto, 1979-82. Prin. dancer Northern Ballet Theatre, Manchester, Eng., 1981, 82; dancer Nat. Ballet Can., Toronto, Ont., 1982-84, 2d soloist, 1986-87, 1st soloist, 1987-88, prin. dancer, 1988—. Appeared in Raymonda Act III, Don Quixote, La Sylphide, Onegin, Napoli, The Nutcracker, Symphony in C, Romeo and Juliet, Elite Syncopations; featured in Here We Come, Endangered Species, Reminiscence, Components; created roles in L'Ile inconnue, Blue Snake, Pastorale, The Miraculous Mandarin, The Actress; appeared in Quartet, Khachaturian Pas de Deux, 1983; appeared with stars and soloists of Can. Ballet in Etc!, On Occasion, Pastel, Swan Lake,(Italy, 1985); debuted as Prince in Swan Lake, 1985-86; danced lead in Transfigured Night and Elite Syncopations; debuted as Solor in La Bayadere Act III, as James in La Sylphide, as guest artist with London Festival Ballet; appeared with Basel Ballet in Switzerland, 1986-87 in Coppelia and The Sleeping Beauty; performed with Berlin Opera Ballel in Theme and Variations, 1987, at La Scala in Milan in The Nutcracker, in France, Italy and the U.S. with Nureyev, at Spoleta Festival in Australia; appeared with Can. Ballet Company in Concerto Barocco, Second Movement of Barocco, Forgotten Land, Death of a Lady's Man, Song of the Earth, Symphony in C, Alice, Steptext, Diana and Acteon Pas de Deux, 1987; appeared with Boston Ballet in La Sylphide, The Nutcracker, Monotones I, Sacre du Printemps, Don Quixote, Esmeralda Pas De Deux, Coppelia, Swan Lake, 1988, 89. Recipient 1st prize Internat. Ballet Competition, Moscow, 1980, Silver medal 1st N.Y.C. Internat. Ballet, 1984. Office: National Ballet of Canada, 157 King St East, Toronto, ON Canada M5C 1G9*

LAVOND, DAVID G., psychology educator. Assoc. prof. depts. psychology & biological scis. U. So. Calif., L.A. Recipient Troland Rsch. award NAS, 1994. Office: Depts Psychology Biol Scis U Southern Calif Los Angeles CA 90024*

LAW, BERNARD FRANCIS CARDINAL, archbishop; b. Torreon, Mex., Nov. 4, 1931; s. Bernard A. and Helen A. (Stubblefield) L. B.A., Harvard U., 1953; postgrad., St. Joseph Sem., St. Benedict, La., 1953, Pontifical Coll. Josephinum, Worthington, Ohio, 1955. Ordained priest Roman Catholic Ch., 1961, consecrated bishop, 1973; editor Natchez-Jackson diocesan paper, Jackson, 1963-68; exec. dir. U.S. Bishops Com. for Ecumenical and Interreligious Affairs, 1968-71, chmn., from 1975; vicar gen. Diocese of Natchez-Jackson, 1971-73; bishop Diocese of Springfield-Cape Girardeau, Mo., 1973-84; archbishop Archdiocese of Boston Brighton, Mass., 1984—; created cardinal, 1985; mem. adminstrv. com. Nat. Conf. Cath. Bishops, from 1975; mem. communication com. U.S. Cath. Conf., 1974, mem. adminstrv. bd., from 1975; mem. Vatican Secretariat for Promoting Christian Unity, from 1976; consultor Vatican Commn. Religious Relations with the Jews, from 1976; chmn. bd. Pope John XXIII Med.-Moral Research and Edn. Ctr., St. Louis, 1980-82; ecclesiastical del. of Pope John Paul II for matters pertaining to former Episcopal priests, 1981. Trustee Pontifical Coll. Josephinum, 1974-85, Nat. Shrine of Immaculate Conception, from 1975; bd. regents Conception (Mo.) Sem. Coll., from 1975. Office: Cardinal's Residence 2121 Commonwealth Ave Brighton MA 02135-3193*

LAW, CHUNG KING, aerospace engineering educator, researcher; b. Shanghai, People's Republic of China, Sept. 21, 1947; came to U.S., 1969; s. Chun and Chin (To) Lo; m. Helen Kwan-Mei Chen, Aug. 11, 1973; children: Jonathan, Jennifer, Jeffrey. BS, U. Alberta, Edmonton, Can., 1968; MS, U. Toronto, Can., 1970; PhD, U. Calif., San Diego, 1973. Assoc. sr. rsch. engr. GM Rsch. Lab., Warren, Mich., 1973-75; from assoc. prof. to prof. Northwestern U., Evanston, Ill., 1976-84; prof. U. Calif. Davis, 1984-88; rsch. staff Princeton (N.J.) U., 1975-76, prof., 1988—. Recipient Curtis W. McGraw award Am. Soc. Engring. Edn., 1984. Fellow AIAA (Propellants and Combustion award 1994), ASME; mem. Combustion Inst. (Silver medal 1990). Office: Princeton U Engineering Quad Dept Mech/Aerospace Engring Princeton NJ 08544-1019*

LAW, CLARENE ALTA, innkeeper, state legislator; b. Thornton, Idaho, July 22, 1933; d. Clarence Riley and Alta (Simmons) Webb; m. Franklin Kelso Meadows, Dec. 2, 1953 (div. July 1973); children: Teresa Meadows Jillson, Charisse Meadows Haws, Steven Riley; m. Creed Law, Aug. 18, 1973. Student, Idaho State Coll., 1953. Sec., sub. tchr. Grand County Schs., Cedar City, Utah, 1954-57; UPI rep. newspaper agy. Moab, Utah Regional Papers, Salt Lake City and Denver; auditor Wort Hotel, Jackson, Wyo., 1960-62; innkeeper, CEO Elk Country Motels, Inc., Jackson, Wyo., 1962—; rep. Wyo. Ho. of Reps., Cheyenne, 1991—, chmn. house travel com., 1993—, mem. bank bd. State of Wyo., 1991—; bd. dirs. Jackson State Bank, Snow King Resort. Chmn. sch. bd. dirs. Teton County Schs., Jackson, 1983-86. Named Citizen of Yr. Jackson C. of C., 1976, Bus. Person of Yr. Jackson Hole Realtors, 1987, Wyo. Small Bus. Person SBA, 1977. Mem. Wyo. Lodging and Restaurant Assn. (pres., chmn. bd. dirs. 1988-89, Big Wyo. award 1987), Internat. Leisure Hosts (bd. dirs. Phoenix chpt. 1991-94), Soroptimists (charter), BPW (Woman of Yr. 1975). Republican. Mem. LDS Ch. Avocations: travel, study. Home: Box 575 43 W Pearl Jackson WY 83001 Office: Elk County Motels Inc 43 W Pearl Jackson WY 83001

LAW, DAVID HILLIS, physician; b. Milw., July 24, 1927; s. David Hillis Law III and Hazel Janice (May) Young; m. Patricia Bicking Thornton, Sept. 14, 1949; children: Linda Clark, Wendy, David, Kimberly Rankin, Cassandra. BS, Cornell U., 1950, MD, 1954. Resident in internal medicine Cornell U. Med. Coll., N.Y.C., 1954-57, fellow in gastroenterology, 1957-59; dir. personnel health services N.Y. Hosp., Cornell Med. Ctr., N.Y.C., 1959-60; asst. adminstrn. assoc., prof. medicine, chief gastroenterology Vanderbilt U. Med. Coll., Nashville, 1960-69; prof., vice chmn. dept. medicine U. New Mex. Sch. Med., Albuquerque, 1969-85; chief med. services Vets. Adminstrn. Med. Ctr., Albuquerque, 1969-85; dir. med. services Vets. Adminstrn. Cen. Office, Washington, 1985-86, dep. asst. chief med. dir. for clin. services, 1986-89, asst. chief med. dir. clin. affairs, 1989-91, acting dep. assoc. chief med. dir. for hosp.-based svcs., 1991—, assoc. dep. chief med. dir. for clin. program, 1993—; mem. human rsch. com. Los Alamos (N.Mex.) Sci. Lab., 1972-80; sabbatical dept. clin. physiology Karolinska Inst., Stockholm, 1980; bd. dirs. officer N.Mex. Nutrition Improvement Program, 1970-75; sub-com. chmn. U.S Pharmacopeia Commn. on Revision, 1975-80; lectr. in field. Editor, Parenteral Nutrition; mem. editorial bd., Am. Jour. Digestive Diseases, 1968-74; rev. numerous med. jours.; contbr. articles to numerous

profl. jours. Bd. dirs., officer Albuquerque Friends of Music, 1975-85; mem. Nat. Digestive Disease Adv. Bd., 1989—; mem. Interdepartmental Digestive Disease Coordinating Com. Cpl. U.S. Army, 1945-46. Named Tchr. and Attending Physician of Yr. Dept. Medicine House Staff, 1985. Fellow ACP (gov. 1989—); mem. AMA (lectr.), Western Assn. Physicians, Western Soc. Clin. Rsch., Am. Gastroenterol. Assn., Am. Inst. Nutrition, Alpha Omega Alpha. Republican.. Presbyterian. Avocation: travel. Office: Vets Adminstrn Cen Office 810 Vermont Ave NW Washington DC 20420-0002

LAW, DAVID HOLBROOK, safety engineer; b. Camp Lejeune, N.C., Aug. 10, 1946; s. Edwin Augustus and Adria (Kellogg) L.; m. Katharine Jones, Aug. 19, 1989; children: Christine Renee, Jessie Marie, Matthew McCarron. BSCE, George Washington U., 1973. Registered profl. engr.; Calif; cert. safety profl. Supt. Aetna Casualty & Surety Co., Fairfax, Va., 1969-85; v.p. Alton Ins. Agy., Arlington, Va., 1985—; cons. in constrn. safety and risk mgmt. Mem. Am. Soc. Safety Engrs. (2d v.p. 1988-89, 1st v.p. 1989-90, pres. elect 1990-91, pres. 1991-92). Democrat. Mem. Unitarian Universalist Ch. Avocations: woodworking, music, Scrabble. Home: 5400 Panola Ct Springfield VA 22151-1718 Office: Alton Ins Agy Inc 1735 Jeff David Hwy Ste 900 Arlington VA 22202

LAW, FLORA ELIZABETH (LIBBY LAW), retired community health and pediatrics nurse; b. Biddeford, Maine, Sept. 11, 1935; d. Arthur Parker and Flora Alma (Knutti) Butt; m. Robert F. Law, 1961; children : Susan E., Sarah F., Christian A., Martha F.; m. John F. Brown, Jr., 1982. BA, Davis and Elkins (W.Va.) Coll., 1957; postgrad., Cornell U.-N.Y. Hosp., N.Y.C., 1960; BSN, U. Nev., Las Vegas, 1976, MS in Counseling Edn., 1981. RN, Nev.; cert. sch. nurse. Staff nurse So. Nev. Community Hosp. (now Univ. Med. Ctr.), Las Vegas, 1975-76; relief charge nurse Valley Psychiat. Inst. Las Vegas, 1976; pub. health nurse Clark County Dist. Health Dept., Las Vegas, 1977-78; sch. nurse Clark County Sch. Dist., Las Vegas, 1978-94; ret., 1994. Chair task force on sch. nursing Nev.'s Commn. for Profl. Standards in Edn.; mem. nurse practice act revision com. Nev. State Bd. Nursing. Mem. Nat. Assn. Sch. Nurses (past state dir., sch. nurse liaison Clark County Tchrs. Assn.), NEA, Clark County Assn. Sch. Nurses (past pres.), Sigma Theta Tau. Home: 3420 Clandara Ave Las Vegas NV 89121

LAW, FREDERICK MASOM, engineering educator, structural engineering firm executive; b. Newark, Mar. 8, 1934; s. Frederick T. and Evelyn (Masom) L.; m. Margaret Mary Maus, Oct. 27, 1956; children: Carolyn Jean, Frederick Masom. B.S. Engring., Princeton U., 1956; M.S., N.J. Inst. Tech., 1962; Ph.D., Rutgers U., 1965. Registered profl. engr., Mass., R.I., N.Y., N.J., Pa., Fla., S.C. Structural engr. H.N.T.& B. Engrs., N.Y.C., 1956-57, 60-61, Austin Co., Roselle, N.J., 1961-63; asst. prof. engring. Newark Coll. Engring., 1963-68; assoc. prof. Pa. State U., Middletown, 1968-70; prof., chmn. dept. civil engring. U. Mass., North Dartmouth, 1970—; prin. Frederick M. Law, P.E., South Dartmouth, 1970—; pres. Timberspan Bridges Inc., South Dartmouth, 1983—; vice chmn. Mass. Bd. Registration Profl. Engrs. and Land Surveyors, 1977-82; mem. jury Am. Inst. Steel Constrn. Prize Bridge Competition, 1982. Served to 1st lt. AUS, 1957-60, ETO. Recipient Grand Conceptor Cons. Engrs. Council Am., 1978. Fellow ASCE; mem. Nat. Soc. Profl. Engrs., Mass. Soc. Profl. Engrs. (Outstanding Engring. Achievement 1978), Am. Soc. Engring. Edn., Soaring Soc. Am. Home: 10 Swift Rd South Dartmouth MA 02748-3717 Office: U Mass Dept Civil Engring Old Westport Rd North Dartmouth MA 02747

LAW, GORDON THEODORE, JR., library director; b. Norwood, Mass., Oct. 27, 1945; s. Gordon Theodore and Laura (Andersen) L.; m. Pam Marilyn Baxter, Sept. 29, 1990;. BA in History, SUNY, Albany, 1967, MA in Social Scis., 1968, MLS, 1972. Tchr. Mynderse Acad., Seneca Falls, N.Y., 1968-71; dir. Krannert Libr., Purdue U., West Lafayette, Ind., 1983-93; head reference and info. svcs. Cornell U., Ithaca, N.Y., 1972-83, dir. Catherwood Libr., 1993—. Author: A Guide to Information on Closely Held Corporations, 1986; editor recent publ. feature Indsl. and Labor Rels. Rev., 1974-83. Mem. ALA, Com. Indsl. Rels. Librs., Spl. Librs. Assn., Indsl. Rels. Rsch. Assn. Office: Cornell U Martin P Catherwood Libr 237 Ives Hall Ithaca NY 14853-3901

LAW, JANET MARY, music educator; b. East Orange, N.J., Mar. 8, 1931; d. Charles and Mary Ellen (Keavy) Maitland; m. William Howard Law, Dec. 13, 1952; children: Robert Alan, Gail Ellen. Lic. Practical Nurse, St. Barnabas Sch., 1971; BA magna cum laude, Fairleigh Dickinson U., Rutherford, N.J., 1981; tchr. tng. course, Westminster Choir Coll., 1990—; Queens U., Canada, 1993. Registered Suzuki tchr., Suzuki piano tchr., traditional piano tchr. Staff nurse psychiat. unit St. Barnabas Med. Ctr., Livingston, N.J., 1972-78; office nurse, asst. to pvt. physician North Arlington, N.J., 1978-79; dir., owner B Sharp Acad., Rutherford, N.J., 1979-83; founder, tchr. piano music preparatory div. Fairleigh Dickinson U., Rutherford, 1983-89; founder, coord. piano divsn. Garden State Acad. Music, Rutherford, N.J., 1989-94; tchr. piano divsn. Garden State Acad. Music, Rutherford, 1989—; Suzuki piano coord., tchr. Suzuki piano program, coord. Suzuki piano divsn. Montclair (N.J.) State U., 1994—. Author: Keyboard Kapers, 1983; inventor music games, 1983. Mem. Music and Performing Arts Club, Profl. Music Tchrs. Guild N.J. Inc., Suzuki Assn. of the Ams. Avocation: concerts. Home: 169 Hillcrest Dr Wayne NJ 07470-5629 Office: Garden State Acad Music 88 Park Ave Rutherford NJ 07070-1957 Office: Montclair State University Music Prep Divsn Upper Montclair NJ 07043

LAW, JOHN HAROLD, biochemistry educator; b. Cleve., Feb. 27, 1931; s. John and Katherine (Frampton) L.; m. Nancy Jean Floyd, June 8, 1956. BS, Case Inst. Tech., Cleve., 1953; PhD, U. Ill., 1957; D hon. causa, U. Sofia, 1995. Postdoctoral fellow Harvard U., Cambridge, Mass., 1958-59, from instr. to asst. prof. biochemistry, 1960-65; instr. Northwestern U., Evanston, Ill., 1959-60; prof. U. Chgo., 1965-81; prof. U. Ariz., Tucson, 1981-91, Regents prof., 1991—, chmn. dept. biochemistry, 1981-86, dir. biotech. program, 1986-92; dir. Ctr. Insect Sci., 1993; assoc. dean coll. agr. U. Ariz., Tucson, 1988-90; mem. gov. bd. Internat. Ctr. Insects, Nairobi, Kenya, 1980-87; mem. bd. trust Gordon Rsch. Conf., 1992—; mem. coun. Am. Soc. Biochem. Molecular Biology, 1993—. Recipient Gregor Mendel medal Czech Acad. Sci., 1992, J.E. Purkinje medal Czech Acad. Sci., 1994. Fellow AAAS; mem. NAS, Am. Soc. Biochem. Molecular Biology, Am. Chem. Soc., Entomol. Soc. Am. Home: 2540 E 7th St Tucson AZ 85716-4702 Office: U Ariz Dept Biochemistry BioScis W 345 Tucson AZ 85721

LAW, JOHN MANNING, retired lawyer; b. Chgo., Dec. 5, 1927; s. Fred Edward and Elisabeth (Emmons) L.; m. Carol Lufkin Ritter, May 14, 1955; children: John E., Lucy L., Frederick R., Beth K. Student, U. Chgo., 1944-45, St. Ambrose Coll., 1945; BA, Colo. Coll., 1948; JD, U. Colo., 1951. Bar: Colo. 1951, Ill. 1952, U.S. Dist. Ct. Colo. 1952, U.S. Ct. Appeals (10th cir.) 1954. Atty. trust dept. Harris Bank, Chgo., 1951-52; ptnr. Law, Nagel & Clark, Denver, 1958-84, also bd. dirs.; ptnr. Law & Knous, Denver, 1984-93; retired Law, Knovs, Denver, 1993; mem. law com. Colo. Bd. Law Examiners, 1971-81, Colo. Ofcls. Compensation Commn., 1985-89. Mem. Moffatt Tunnel Commn., Denver, 1966-90. Capt. USNR, 1945-77, ret. Fellow Colo. Bar Found. (charter); mem. ABA (legal assistance to mil. person 1972-77, past chair), Colo. Bar Assn. (mem. bd. govs. 1968-71), Denver Bar Assn. (trustee 1971-74), Internat. Soc. Barristers, Law Club, Univ. Club Denver, Denver Country Club. Republican. Presbyterian. Home: 3333 E Florida Ave Apt 35 Denver CO 80210-2541

LAW, LLOYD WILLIAM, geneticist; b. Ford City, Pa., Oct. 28, 1910; s. Craig Smith and Cora Jane (Whiteley) L.; m. Bernette Bohen, May 4, 1942; children: Lloyd William, David Bradford. B.S., U. Ill., 1931; A.M., Harvard U., 1935, Ph.D. (Austin fellow), 1937; Harvard Sheldon fellow, Stanford U., 1937-38. Tchr. high sch. Charleston, Ill., 1931-34; Finney-Howell Med. research fellow Jackson Meml. Lab., Bar Harbor, Maine, 1938-41; Commonwealth Fund fellow Jackson Meml. Lab., 1941-42, research assoc. 1946, sci. dir., 1947; now trustee; geneticist Nat. Cancer Inst., Bethesda, Md., 1947-52; head leukemia studies sect. Nat. Cancer Inst., 1952—, chief lab. cell biology, 1970—; mem. sci. directorate, 1970-90; Panel mem. com. on growth NRC, 1952-56; mem. pharmacology and exptl. therapeutics study sect. NIH, 1955—; mem. screening panel cancer chemotherapy Nat. Service Center, 1955—; mem. adv. bd. Nat. Blood Research Found., 1954—; adv. bd. cancer research Am. Cancer Soc., 1965—, mem. panel on etiology of cancer, 1960—; sci. bd. Children's Cancer Fund Am., 1956—; bd. sci. advisers

Roswell Park (N.Y.) Cancer Inst., 1957—; expert adv. com. cancer WHO, 1960-80; mem. U.S.A. nat. com. Internat. Union Against Cancer, 1969-78; mem. bd. sci. advs. Chemotherapy Found. N.Y., 1974—; mem. bd. sci. advisers Ludwik Cancer Found., 1980—, chmn., 1985. Author: Advances in Cancer Research Vol. II, 1954, Vol. XXXII, 1980, Leukemia Research, 1955, Origins of Resistance to Toxic Agents, 1955; other books in field; editor: Tumour Antigens; contbr. articles to profl. jours., books and pamphlets. Served as capt. 2d Air Force USAAF, 1942-46. Recipient Anne Frankel Rosenthal award AAAS, 1955; USPHS Meritorious Service award, 1965; G.H.A. Clowes Meml. award in cancer research, 1965; Allesandro Pascoli prize, 1969; Disting. Service medal USPHS, 1969; G.B. Mider lecture award NIH, 1970. Mem. Soc. Exptl. Biology and Medicine, N.Y. Acad. Sci., Am. Soc. Exptl. Pathology, Am. Assn. Cancer Rsch. (dir. 1956-59, 65—, pres. 1967-68), Italian Cancer Soc., Royal Soc. Medicine, Am. Immunology Assn., Am. Assn. Cancer Rsch. (hon. 1987), Europe Assn. Cancer Rsch. (hon. 1987). Home: 9810 Fernwood Rd Bethesda MD 20817-1512 Office: Nat Cancer Inst Pub Health Service Rockville Pike Bethesda MD 20892

LAW, MARK EDWARD, electrical engineer, educator; b. St. Paul, July 19, 1959; s. Paul Rock and Bernice Edna (Brookshaw) L.; m. Alison Leigh Retz, May 30, 1981; children: Christopher, Heather. BS CprE, Iowa State U., 1981; MSEE, Stanford U., 1982, PhD in Elec. Engring., 1988. Engr. Hewlett Packard, 1982-84; rsch. asst. Stanford (Calif.) U., 1984-87, rsch. assoc., 1988; asst. prof. elec. engring. U. Fla., Gainesville, 1988-93, assoc. prof. elec. engring., 1993—; presenter, spkr. in field; vice chmn. tech. adv. bd. tech. computer aided design program Los Alamos (N.Mex.) Nat. Lab.; session chmn. various tech. meetings in field. Author: Floods/Floops User's Manual, 1993; contbr. articles to profl. jours., chpts. to books. Nat. Merit scholar, 1977-81; grantee NSF, 1992—, SRC, 1989-94, 93-94, IBM, 1991-93; NSF presdl. fellow, 1992; recipient Young Faculty Devel. award IBM, 1988, Tech. Excellence award Semiconductor Rsch. Corp., 1993, Outstanding Young Alumnus award Iowa State U., 1994, Profl. Progress award Coll. Engring. Iowa State U., 1994. Mem. IEEE (sr., guest editor publ. 1991), Am. Soc. Engring. Edn., Am. Phys. Soc., Electrochem. Soc., Sigma Xi, Phi Beta Pi, Phi Kappa Phi. Avocations: soccer, beer brewing. Office: U Fla 339 Larsen Hall Gainesville FL 32611-6200

LAW, MICHAEL R., lawyer; b. Rochester, N.Y., Nov. 30, 1947; s. George Robert and Elizabeth (Stoddart) L.; m. Cheryl Heller. BS, St. John Fisher Coll., 1969; JD, U. Louisville, 1975. Bar: N.Y. 1976, U.S. Dist. Ct. (we. dist.) N.Y. 1976, U.S. Supreme Ct. 1982. Assoc., Wood, P.C., Rochester, 1976-77; pvt. practice, Rochester, 1977-78; assoc. Sullivan, Peters, et al, Rochester, 1978-80, ptnr., 1980-81; ptnr. Phillips, Lytle, Hitchcock, Blaine & Huber, Rochester, 1982—. Editor (newsletter) 1986 Trial Techniques. Counselor, exec. com. Camp Good Days and Spl. Times, Rochester, 1984—. Served with USAR, 1968-74. Mem. Monroe County Bar Assn. (judiciary com. 1981-88, ethics and personal injury com. 1988—), N.Y. State Bar Assn. (trial sect., ins. negligence com.), ABA (trial law sect., trial techniques com.), N.Y. State Trial Lawyers (bd. dirs.), Genesee Valley Trial Lawyers Assn. (treas., 1992-93, pres.-elect 1993-95, pres. 1995—), Nat. Spinal Cord Injury Assn. (bd. dirs. Rochester chpt. 1990-92). Republican. Roman Catholic. Home: 3373 Elmwood Ave Rochester NY 14610-3425 Office: Phillips Lytle Hitchcock Blaine & Huber 1400 First Federal Plz Rochester NY 14614-1909

LAW, SYLVIA A., law educator; b. 1942. BA, Antioch Coll., 1964; JD, NYU, 1968. Bar: N.Y. 1968, Pa. 1970. Lawyer Reginald Heber Smith Community Columbia Ctr. Social Welfare Policy and Law, 1968-69; lectr. London Sch. Econ. & Polit. Sci., 1969-70; staff dir. Pa. Health Law Project, 1970-73; asst. prof. NYU, N.Y.C., 1973-76, assoc. prof., 1976-79, prof. law, dir. Arthur Garfield Hays civil liberties meml. program, 1979—; vis. prof. Harvard U., 1984, CUNY at Queens, 1989. Author: (with others) Political and Civil Rights, vol. 2, 1978, (with W.S. Polan) Pain and Profit: The Politics of Malpractice, 1978; contbr. articles to profl. jours. Sec. Alan Guttmacher Inst., 1978; chmn. Non-Traditional Employment for Women, 1985—. Mem. ACLU, SALT (treas. 1974-75), Nat. Lawyer's Guild. Office: NYU Dept Law New York NY 10016

LAWAND, THOMAS A., research engineer. BChemE, McGill U., 1957, diploma engring. aspects arid land dev., 1963, MS in Agrl. Engring., 1968. Rsch. engr. Brace Rsch. Inst., Faculty of Engring. McGill U.-Macdonald campus, Ste. Anne de Bellevue, Que., Can., 1959-70; dir. field ops. Brace Rsch. Inst., Faculty of Engring. McGill U.-Macdonald campus, Ste. Anne de Bellevue, Que., 1970-71, dir. Brace Rsch. Inst., Faculty of Engring., 1971-87, dir. internat. ops. Brace Rsch. Inst., Faculty of Engring., 1987—; project coord. energy program devel. studies UN Univ., Tokyo; cons. in field. Contbr. numerous articles to profl. jours. Mem. ASHRAE, Corp. Profl. Engrs. Que., Internat. Solar Energy Soc., Solar Energy Soc. Can. Inc. Office: McGill U Brace Rsch Inst, PO Box 900 2111 Lakeshore Rd, Sainte Anne de Belle, PQ Canada H9X 3V9

LAWARE, JOHN PATRICK, retired banker, federal official; b. Columbus, Wis., Feb. 20, 1928; s. John Henry and Ruth (Powles) L.; m. Margery Ann Ninabuck, Dec. 22, 1952; children: John Kevin, Margaret Ann. BA in Biology, Harvard, 1950; grad., Advanced Mgmt. Program, 1975; MA in Polit. Sci., U. Pa., 1951; LHD (hon.), Suffolk U., D in Polit. Sci. (hon), Northeastern U. Trainee Chem. Bank & Trust Co., N.Y.C., 1953-54, with credit dept., 1954-56, asst. sec., 1957-60, asst. v.p., 1960-62, v.p., 1962-65, v.p. in charge mktg. div., 1965-68, sr. v.p., 1968-72; sr. v.p. in charge holding co. ops. Chem. N.Y. Corp., from 1972; pres., dir. Shawmut Corp., 1978-88, Shawmut Bank of Boston N.A., 1978-80, chmn., dir., 1980-88; pres., dir. Shawmut Assn., Inc., 1978-80; chmn., CEO Shawmut Corp., 1980-88; mem. bd. govs. FRS, Washington, 1988-95, ret., 1995; pres., dir. Devonshire Fin. Svc. Corp., 1978-88; chmn., treas. Boston Clearing House Assn., Inc.; Shawmut Corp. subs.; mem. Internat. Fin. Conf.; chmn. Mass. Bankers Assn., 1982-83, Assn. Bank Holding Cos., 1986-87. Trustee, vice chmn., chmn. fin. com. Northeastern U., 1981-88; trustee, mem. fin. com. Mt. Holyoke Coll., 1984-88; chmn. Children's Hosp. Med. Ctr., 1989-91; past chmn., bd. dirs. Mass. Bus. Roundtable; chmn. coordinating com. Boston Bus. Leaders Orgn.; trustee Holyoke Coll., 1983-88, Northeastern U., 1982-83, vice chmn. 1985-88, chmn. fin. com., 1985-88. 2d lt. USAF, 1951-53. Recipient Disting. Citizen award Minuteman Coun. Boy Scouts Am., Chief Exec. Officer of Yr. award Northeastern U. Coll. Bus., Outstanding Citizen award B'nai B'rith-Antidefamation League. Mem. Assn. Bank Holding Cos. (past chmn. and dir.). Office: PO Box 30083 Sea Island GA 31561

LAWATSCH, FRANK EMIL, JR., lawyer; b. Avenel, N.J., May 11, 1944; s. Frank Emil and Jessie Margaret L.; m. Deanna Conover, May 25, 1969; children: Amanda, Abigail, Frank. BA, Colgate U., 1966; JD, Cornell U., 1969. Bar: N.Y. 1969, Pa. 1992, N.J. 1993. Assoc. Shearman & Sterling, N.Y.C., 1969-78; sr. v.p., gen. counsel, sec. Midlantic Corp., Edison, N.J., 1978-91; sr. v.p., gen. counsel PNC Bank Corp., Pitts., 1991-92; ptnr. Crummy, Del Deo, Dolan, Griffinger & Vecchione, Newark, 1993—. Mem. ABA, N.J. Bar Assn., Pa. Bar Assn., Assn. of Bar of City of N.Y., Am. Soc. Corp. Secs. Episcopalian. Home: 11 The Fairway Upper Montclair NJ 07043 Office: Crummy Del Deo Dolan Griffinger & Vecchione One Riverfront Plz Newark NJ 07102

LAWES, PATRICIA JEAN, art educator; b. Mathis, Tex., June 28, 1940; d. Thomas Ethan and Alma Dena (Pape) Allen; m. Elmer Thomas Lawes, Apr. 9, 1960; children: Linda Lee, Tracy Dena. BA in Art Edn., U. Wyo., 1976; MA in Curriculum and Instruction, Leslie Coll., 1988. Cert. tchr., Wyo. Elem. art tchr. Laramie County Sch. Dist. # 1, Cheyenne, Wyo., 1977—, facilitator elem. art. and gifted edn., 1979-87; ret. Laramie County Sch. Dist. #1, 1994; owner, sec. Dundele Limited Liability Co., Mesa, Ariz., 1994—; artist in the sch. Mesa, Ariz., 1994-95; judge F.E. Warren AFB Artist Craftsman Show, Cheyenne, 1988-92, adjudicator for music festival for Assn. of Christian Sch Internat., Tempe, Ariz. Author, mem. visual arts task force various curricula; Author; dir: The Apron Caper, 1989 (recognition 1990), Oh Where Oh Were Have Those Little Dawgs Gone, 1989 (recognition 1990); exhibitions include Wyoming Artists Assn., Wyo., 1977, Washington Congressional Exhibit, 1977-78. Recipient Cert. of Appreciation Mayor Erickson, Cheyenne, 1986, MWR Vol. Recognition F.E. Warren Moral, Welfare, Recreation Dept., Cheyenne, 1988-93; grantee Coun. on Arts, Cheyenne, 1987-91. Mem. NEA, Am. Fedn. Tchrs., Nat. Art Edn. Assn., Wyo. Assn. Gifted Edn. (bd. dirs., southeast rep. 1986—, presenter, chmn. state assn. awards 1992—), Wyo. Arts Alliance for Edn. (presenter, bd. dirs.

1987—, sec. 1988-91, visual arts task force, chmn. state arts awards 1990-92), Wyo. Coun. Arts (slide bank 1986—), Wyo. Odessey of Mind (bd. dirs. 1991-92), Wyo. Women's Fedn. Club (chmn. state safety 1972-75), Order of Eastern Star (presiding officer, worthy matron 1984-85, grand officer 1990-91,), Daughters of Nile. Avocation: art, hiking, traveling, photography, storytelling. Office: Laramie County Sch Dist # 1 2810 House Ave Cheyenne WY 82001-2860

LAWHON, JOHN E., III, lawyer, former county official; b. Denton, Tex., Dec. 14, 1934; s. John E. and Gladys (Barns) L.; m. Tommie Collins, Aug. 27, 1967; 1 son, David Collins. Student, U. N.Tex., 1951-53; BBA, U. Houston, 1958, JD, 1958. Bar: Tex. 1958; cert. specialist in criminal law, family law. Asst. dist. and county atty. Denton County, Tex., 1958-61; dist. and county atty., 1961-77; dir. Southridge, Inc., Denton, 1962-72, Lawyers Title Agy. Denton, 1965-74; Legal adviser Denton City-County Day Nursery, 1972-80; tchr. bus. law U. North Tex. (formerly North Tex. State U.), Denton, 1969-71; mem. acad. bd. Tex. Criminal Justice Council, 1973-79; univ. atty. Tex. Woman's U., 1977-83, gen. counsel, 1983—; sec. bd. regents, 1987—. Bd. dirs. Denton County Welfare Coun., 1970-78, Denton Community Coun., 1978-79, 80-82; mem. Denton Forum; chmn. Denton County ARC, 1985-87, Denton County Probation Adv. Bd., 1985-92; mem. City of Denton Land Use Com., 1986-88. Mem. Tex. Bar Assn., Denton Bar Assn. (pres. 1968-69, bd. dirs. 1978-81), Tex. Dist. and County Attys. Assn. (bd. dirs. 1964-66), Denton Jaycees (sec. 1961), Denton C. of C., Tex. Assn. State Univ. Attys. (pres. 1983-84, Denton County crim. justice task force 1992-93). Baptist (deacon 1968—). Lodges: KP, Kiwanis (bd. dirs. 1981-86, pres. 1984-85). Home: 2810 Carmel St Denton TX 76205-8310 Office: Tex Woman's U Adminstrn Tower Bldg PO Box 23025 Denton TX 76204-1025

LAWHON, TOMMIE COLLINS MONTGOMERY, child development/family living educator; b. Shelby County, Tex., Mar. 15; d. Marland Walker and Lillian (Tinsley) Collins; m. David Baldwin Montgomery, Mar. 31, 1962 (dec. Aug. 1964); m. John Lawhon, Aug. 27, 1967; 1 child, David Collins. B.S., Baylor U., 1954; M in Home Econs. Edn. in Home Econs., Tex. Woman's U., 1964, Ph.D., 1966. Cert. tchr., Tex., home economist, family life educator. Tchr., Victoria Pub. Schs. (Tex.), 1954-55; stewardess, supr. Am. Airlines, Dallas/Fort Worth, 1955-62; prof. home econs. Ea. Ky. U., Richmond, 1966-67, U. North Tex., Denton, 1968—; profl. presenter Profl. Devel. Inst., U. North Tex., 1981—, mem. faculty senate 1984-90, chmn. com. on coms., 1987-88, com. status of women, 1984-87, mem. faculty salary study com., 1989-95, chmn., 1989-91, mem. tradition com., 1989-95, recorder, 1989-91; bd. dirs. Univ. union, 1985-88, mem. Status of Women Com., 1984-87, mem. Com. on Coms., 1986-89, chmn. 1987-88, vice chmn., 1988-89, mem. mentor com., 1990—, mem. benefits com., 1994—, vice chair, 1994-95. Co-author: Children are Artists, 1971; Hidden Hazards for Children and Families, 1982; editor: What to do with Children, 1974; Field Trips for Children, 1984; contbr. articles to profl. jours. Chmn., United Way North Tex. State U., 1980-81; chmn. crusade Am. Cancer Soc., Denton County, 1982-83; chmn. nominating com. First Bapt. Ch., Denton, 1983-84, 84-85; advisor North Tex. Student Coun. on Family Rels., 1994—. Recipient Presdl. award Tex. Council on Family Rels., 1979, Fessor Graham award North Tex. State U., 1980, Svc. award Am. Cancer Soc., 1983, Outstanding Home Economists Alumni award Baylor U., 1985, Moore-Bowman award, 1994; named Honor Prof. North Tex. State U., 1975. Mem. Tex. Council on Family Rels. (pres. 1977-79, chmn. policy advisor com. 1986-88, nominating com. 1986-88, 94—, chair 1994—, mem. family life edn. com. 1994—), Denton Assn. for Edn. of Young Children (pres. 1970-72, 84-85, 85-86, v.p. 1986-87), Tex. Assn. Coll. Tchrs. (nominating com. 1988-89, 89-90, v.p. 1990-92, v.p. U. North Tex. chpt. 1987-88, pres. 1988-89, 89-90), Tex. Home Econs. Assn. (chmn. FLCD nominating com. 1983-84, chmn. child devel. and family rels. sect. 1988-90, sect. rep. THEA bd. 1989-90, Nat. Council on Family Rels. (com. 1982-83), North Tex. Home Econs. Inter-orgnl. Council (advisor 1983-85), Phi Delta Kappa (pres. local chpt. 1991-92), Alpha Iota/Phi Upsilon Omicron (advisor 1970-82, chmn. nat. com. 1984-87, nat. bd. dirs. edn. found. 1990-94, com. pubs. 1991-92, vice chair ednl. found. 1992-94). Democrat. Clubs: Tri D (v.p. Baylor U. 1953-54); Univ. Grad. (pres. Tex. Woman's U. 1965-66). Office: U North Tex Coll Edn Denton TX 76203

LAWHON, WILLIAM GRIFFITH, lawyer; b. Evanston, Ill., Apr. 9, 1942; s. James Griffith and Virginia (Vinson) L.; m. Elaine Seewald, Sept. 4, 1965; children: Leslie, Christine, Laura. BA, U. Tex., 1964, JD, 1967. Bar: Texas 1967, U.S. Dist. Ct. (so. dist.) Tex. 1976, cert. comml., residential, farm and ranch real estate law, Tex. Bd. Legal Specialization, 1985. Assoc. Butler & Binion, Houston, 1967-76, ptnr., 1976—; Mem. ABA, 1967-87. Mem. Tex. Bar Assn., Houston Bar Assn., Order of Barristers. Office: Butler & Binion 1000 Louisiana St Ste 1400 Houston TX 77002-5009

LAWI, DAVID STEVEN, energy, agriservice and thermoplastic resins industries executive; b. Baghdad, Iraq, Aug. 3, 1935; came to U.S., 1946, naturalized, 1952; s. Steven David and Marcelle (Masry) L.; m. Anne Shamash, June 9, 1968; children—Nicole, Neil. A.A. in Sci, N.Y. State Coll., 1955. Registered rep. Bear, Stearns & Co., N.Y.C., 1956-62; dir. Adobe Brick & Supply, West Palm Beach, Fla., 1962-64; v.p. Molly Corp., Reading, Pa., 1962-64; gen. mgr. United Shoe Machinery Corp., Reading, 1964-65; a founder, sec., treas., mem. exec. com. dir. Unimax Group Inc. (formerly Riker-Maxson Corp.), N.Y.C., 1966-80; also dir. all subs., v.p., treas. Telepictures Corp., N.Y.C., 1980-81, chmn. fin. com., sec., 1980-86; exec. v.p., sec. Helm Resources, Inc., Greenwich, Conn., 1980—, also bd. dirs.; bd. dirs. sec. Teletrak Advanced Tech. Systems, Inc., 1983—, Continuing Care Assocs., 1982—; sec., bd. dirs., chmn. exec. com. Seitel Inc. (formerly Seismic Enterprises, Inc.), 1982-84, now bd. dirs.; advisor Lorimar-Telepictures (acquired by Warner Comm., Inc. 1989), 1986—, now Time-Warner, 1990—; bd. dirs., chmn. exec. com. Intersystems, Inc. (formerly Bamberger Polymers, Inc.), Unipix Entertainment, Inc. (formerly Majestic Entertainment, Inc.); bd. dirs. Cliff Engle Ltd. Served with AUS, 1968. Home: Ramapo Trail Harrison NY 10528 Office: Helm Resources Inc 93 Mason St Greenwich CT 06830-5502

LAWING, JACK L., lawyer, corporate executive; b. 1938. A.B., U. N.C., 1960; J.D., Harvard U., 1964. Assoc., Berry & Blesoe, 1964-67; atty. Reynolds Metal Co., 1967-69; div. counsel Litton Industries, Inc., 1969-71; atty. Tenn. Eastman Co. div. Eastman Kodak Co., 1971-76; gen counsel, v.p., sec. Gold Kist Inc., Atlanta, 1976—. Office: Gold Kist Inc 244 Perimeter Center Pky NE Atlanta GA 30346-2302

LAWLER, JAMES EDWARD, physics educator; b. St. Louis, June 29, 1951; s. James Austin and Dolores Catherine Lawler; m. Katherine Ann Moffatt, July 21, 1973; children: Emily Christine, Katie Marie. BS in Physics summa cum laude, U. Mo., Rolla, 1973; MS in Physics, U. Wis., 1974, PhD in Physics, 1978. Rsch. assoc. Stanford (Calif.) U., 1978-80; asst. prof. U. Wis., Madison, 1980-85, assoc. prof., 1985-89, prof., 1989—; product devel. cons. Nat. Rsch. Group, Inc., Madison, 1977-78; cons. GE, Schenectady, N.Y., 1985—, Teltech, Inc., 1990—; mem. exec. com. Gaseous Electronics Conf., 1987-89, treas., 1992-94, DAMOP program com., 1993—. Editor: (with R.S. Stewart) Optogalvanic Spectroscopy, 1991; contbr. articles to profl. jours. Schumberger scholar U. Mo., 1971-72; Grad. fellow Wis. Alumni Rsch. Found., 1973-74, NSF, 1974-76, H.I. Romnes Faculty fellow U. Wis., 1987. Fellow Am. Phys. Soc. (Will Allis prize 1992), Optical Soc. Am.; mem. Sigma Xi. Achievements include patent for Echelle Sine Bar for dye laser cavity; development of laser diagnostics for glow discharge plasmas, of methods for measuring accurate atomic transition probabilities and radiative lifetimes. Office: U Wis Dept of Physics 1150 University Ave Madison WI 53706-1390

LAWLER, JAMES RONALD, French language educator; b. Melbourne, Australia, Aug. 15, 1929; married, 1954; 2 children. BA, U. Melbourne, 1950, MA, 1952; DUniv., U. Paris, 1954. Lectr. French U. Queensland, Australia, 1955-56; sr. lectr. U. Melbourne, 1957-62; prof., head dept. U. Western Australia, 1963-71; prof., chmn. dept. UCLA, 1971-74; McCulloch prof. Dalhousie U., Halifax, N.S., Can., 1974-79; prof. French U. Chgo., 1979—, Edward Carson Waller Disting. Svc. prof., 1983—; vis. prof. Coll. de France, 1985; chmn. vis. com. Romance Langs. and Lits. Harvard U., 1991-94. Author: Form and Meaning in Valery's Le Cimetiere Marin, 1959, Lecture de Valery: Une Etude de Charmes, 1963, The Language of French Symbolism, 1969, The Poet as Analyst, 1974, Rene Char: The Myth and the

Poem, 1978, Edgar Poe et les Poetes Francais, 1989, Rimbaud's Theatre of the Self, 1992, Baudelaire and the Moral Dialectic, 1996; co-author: Paul Valery; Poems, 1971, Paul Valery: Leonardo, Poe, Mallarme, 1972; editor: An Anthology of French Poetry, 1960, Paul Valery: An Anthology, 1977, Paul Valery, 1991; founding editor Essays in French Literature, 1966, Dalhousie French Studies. Decorated officier Palmes Academiques; Brit. Coun. interchange scholar, 1967; Australian Acad. Humanities fellow, 1970, Guggenheim Found. fellow, 1974, NEH fellow, 1985. Mem. MLA, Am. Assn. Tchrs. French, Internat. Assn. French Studies (v.p. 1974—). Rsch. in modern French poetry, poetics, 20th century novel. Office: U Chgo Dept Romance Langs & Lit 1050 E 59th St Chicago IL 60637

LAWLER, RICHARD FRANCIS, lawyer; b. Providence, Mar. 24, 1945; s. Richard F. and Priscilla (Lenihan) L.; m. Jacqueline Marie Depuy, Oct. 2, 1976; children: James, Christopher. BA, Yale U., 1967; JD, Columbia U., 1973. Bar: Conn. 1974, N.Y. 1980. Assoc. atty. Wiggin & Dana, New Haven, 1973-76; asst. U.S. atty. U.S. Atty's. Office So. Dist. N.Y., N.Y.C., 1976-80; ptnr. Whitman Breed Abbott & Morgan, N.Y.C., Greenwich, Conn., 1980—. Lt. (j.g.) USN, 1969-70. Fulbright scholar Colombia, S.Am., 1967-68. Mem. Field Club Greenwich (bd. govs. 1993—). Office: Whitman Breed Abbott Morgan 2 Greenwich Plz Greenwich CT 06830-6353 Also: 200 Park Ave New York NY 10166

LAWLER, SUSAN GEORGE, elementary education educator; b. Evergreen Park, Ill., June 23, 1940; d. Louis Lawrence and Elsie Marie (Velk) George; m. Jerome Charles Lawler, Feb. 23, 1963; children: Susan Elizabeth, Kathleen Marie. BS in Edn., Mt. Mary Coll., 1961; MEd, Nat. Louis U., Evanston, Ill., 1991. Tchr. Oak Lawn (Ill.) Sch. Dist. 123, 1961-65, Palos Community Sch. Dist. 118, Palos Park, Ill., 1975—; pres. Parent-Faculty Orgn. Sch. Dist. 230, Orland Park, Ill., 1982-85. Sec. Ishnala Homeowners Assn., Palos Heights, Ill., 1972-75; active Neighborhood Watch, City of Palos Heights, 1988—. Mem. AAUW (chair Ishnala chpt. 1975-77), internat. Reading Assn., Nat. Coun. Tchrs. English, Ill. Reading Assn., Palas Edn. Assn. (pres. 1992—), Mt. Mary Coll. Alumni Assn. (co-chair Chgo. chpt. 1992—), Phi Delta Kappa. Avocations: reading, bridge, taking classes, golf, walking. Home: 12932 S Comanche Dr Palos Heights IL 60463-2618 Office: Palos Community Sch Dist 118 8800 W 119th St Palos Park IL 60464-1004

LAWLESS, JAMES L., editor, columnist; b. Des Moines, Mar. 26, 1932; s. James L. and Mary O. (Gray) L.; m. Mary Belle McPherson; children: Kathleen, Maureen, Michael, Martha, Kerry, Dan. BA, Drake U., 1954. Editor, columist Des Moines Register, Des Moines, 1956—; columnist Gannett News Svc. Alexandria, Va., 1986—. Chmn. Clive (Iowa) Planning & Zoning, 1970-80; mem. bd. adjustment, Clive, 1980-90. Lt. (j.g.) USNR, 1954-56. Nat. Press Found. fellow, 1986. Republican. Roman Catholic. Avocations: tennis, travel, swimming. Home: 6137 Pleasant Dr Des Moines IA 50312-1217 Office: The Des Moines Register 715 Locust St Des Moines IA 50309-3724

LAWLESS, ROBERT WILLIAM, academic administrator; b. Baytown, Tex., Feb. 13, 1937; s. James Milton and Belva Ambaline (Mode) L.; m. Marcella Jane Emmert; children: Christopher, Cheryl, Diana. B.S., U. Houston, 1964; Ph.D., Tex. A&M U., 1968. Instr., asst. prof. Tex. A&M U., College Station, 1967-69; prof., sr. vice chancellor U. Houston, 1969-82; v.p., chief fin. officer S.W. Airlines, Dallas, 1982-85, exec. v.p., chief oper. officer, 1985-89; cons. Tex. Hosp. Assn., Austin, 1966-82, banks, savs. and loans, 1970-72, NASA, 1970; pres. Tex. Tech U. and Tex. Tech. U. Health Scis. Ctr., Lubbock, 1989—; ind. dir. Salomon Bros. Asset Mgmt. Co., 1991—, Cen. and S.W. Corp., 1981—; chmn.Coun. of Pub. Univ. Pres. and Chancellors, Tex. higher edn. system, 1993—. Contbr. articles to profl. jours. Mem. formula adv. com. Tex. State Coordinating Bd., Austin, 1977-89; chmn. bd. dirs. Coll. Football Assn., 1990-92; mem. Citizens Commn. on the Tex. Jud. System, 1991-93. Recipient Teaching Excellence award U. Houston, 1972, Disting. Faculty award Coll. Bus. Alumni, 1971, Disting. Alumni award Lee Coll., 1984, U. Houston, 1990. Office: Tex Tech U Office of President Lubbock TX 79409-2013

LAWLESS, RONALD EDWARD, transportation executive; b. Toronto, Ont., Can., Apr. 28, 1924. Student, McGill U., Montreal, U. Toronto, Concordia U. Mem. express dept. CN Rail, Toronto, 1941-43, numerous positions, 1946-61, officer employee relations, 1961-62, gen. supt.-express Great Lakes region, 1962-69; system mgr. container devel. CN Rail, Montreal, Que., 1969-70; gen. mgr. express and intermodal systems CN Rail, Montreal, Que., 1970-72, v.p. freight sales, 1972-74, v.p. mktg., 1974-79, pres., 1979-85, pres., chief operating officer, 1987; pres., chief oper. officer Can. Nat. Railways, Montreal, Que., 1985-87, pres., chief exec. officer, 1987—, also bd. dirs.; pres., chief exec. officer VIA Rail Can. Inc., Montreal, Que., 1989—, also bd. dirs.; chmn., pres., chief exec. officer Grand Trunk Corp., Grand Trunk Western R.R. Co., Cen. Vt. Ry. Inc., Duluth, Winnipeg & Pacific R.R. Co.; Concordia Bd. Govs. (1973-90), Dome Consortium Investments Inc., Ry. Assn. of Can. (chmn.), Can. Transp. Edn. Found. Bursary Bd., U. Manitoba Adv. Com., Old Brewery Mission, Montreal Bd. Trade Heritage Found., Bishop's U.; bd. dirs. Assn. Am. Rys. Campaign chmn. Lakeshore Gen. Hosp. Bldg. Fund., Centraide, 1992—; co-chmn., hon. v.p Scouts Can. With RCAF, 1943-46. Decorated Knight Order of St. John; named Can.'s Transp. Man of Yr., 1986; recipient Achievement award Nat. Transp. Week Can. (Quebec chapt.), 1990. Fellow Chartered Inst. Transport; mem. Can. Inst. Traffic and Transp. (hon.), Nat. Freight Transp. Assn., N.Y. Traffic Club, Toronto Ry. Club, Transp. Club Toronto, Montreal Bd. Trade, Can. Ry. Club, Traffic Club Montreal, Can. Club N.Y., Can. Club of Montreal, McGill Assocs., Beaconsfield Golf Club, Mount Royal Club, St. James Club, The Vancouver Club, Corp. Adv. Com. Wanuskewin Heritage Pk. Avocations: golf, reading. Office: Via Rail Canada Inc, 2 Pl Ville-Marie CP 8116 Succ A, Montreal, PQ Canada H3C 3N3 also: 935 Lagauchetiere St W, Montreal, PQ Canada H3B 2M9

LAWLESS, SARAH MADISON, theatrical executive; b. Milw., Feb. 1, 1934; d. Frederick William and Geraldine (Conover) Madison; m. Donald Buzard (div.); m. James J. Lawless, May 7, 1971; children: Julia, Mary, David Buzard. BS, Northwestern U., 1953. Assoc. mng. dir. Guthrie Theatre, Mpls., 1969-71; dir. communications Dayton Hudson Corp., Mpls., 1971-79; v.p. Padilla & Speer, Mpls., 1979-81; exec. dir. The Children's Theatre, Mpls., 1981-84, Denver Ctr. Theatre Co., 1984—. Bd. dirs. Children's Chorale, Denver, 1987—, TCG, N.Y.C., 1988—, League of Resident Theatres, N.Y.C., 1986-88, Am. Arts Alliance. Mem. Internat. Assn. Theatre for Children and Young People. Office: Denver Ctr Theatre Co 1245 Champa St Denver CO 80204-2104

LAWLEY, ALAN, materials engineering educator; b. Birmingham, Eng., Aug. 29, 1933; s. Archibald and Millicent A. (Olorenshaw) L.; m. Nancy A. Kressler, Mar. 26, 1960; children—Carolyn Ann, Elizabeth Ann, Jennifer Ann. B.Sc., U. Birmingham, 1955, Ph.D., 1958. Research asso. U. Pa., 1958-61; mgr. research labs. Franklin Inst. Labs., 1961-66; A.W. Grosvenor prof. materials engring. Drexel U., Phila., 1969—; head dept. Drexel U., 1969-79; cons. to govt., industry. Editor in chief Internat. Jour. Powder Metallurgy; contbr. chpts. to books, articles to profl. jours. Recipient Disting. Svc. award Metal Powder Industries Fedn., 1991. Fellow Am. Soc. Metals; mem. AIME (pres. 1987), Minerals, Metals and Materials Soc. (pres. 1982), Am. Soc. Engring. Edn., Inst. Materials, Microscopy Soc. Am., APMI Internat., Sigma Xi, Phi Kappa Phi, Tau Beta Pi, Alpha Sigma Mu. Home: 336 Hathaway Ln Wynnewood PA 19096-1925 Office: Drexel Univ Dept Materials Engring Philadelphia PA 19104

LAWLOR, HELEN ANNE, database publisher; b. Phila., July 20, 1944; d. Walter John and Nellie (Branka) Quinn; m. John Francis Lawlor, Nov. 10, 1967 (div. June 1985). BS, Chestnut Hill Coll., 1966; MS, St. Joseph's U., 1976; MBA, U. Pa., 1989. Comm. indexer Inst. for Sci. Info., Phila., 1967-74, mgr. comm. indexing, 1974-76, asst. dir., 1976-77, dir., 1977-82, v.p., 1982-85, sr. v.p., 1985-89, exec. v.p., 1989—; bd. trustees, fin. com. PALINET, 1989-92. Mem. Am. Chem. Soc. (chmn. div. chem. info. 1989, founder and recording sec. local chpt.'s chem. info. group 1980-82, editor Chem. Info. Bull. 1977-82), Pa. Inst. Chemists (sec. 1981-82), Chem. Notation Assn. (sec. 1976-79, v.p. 1979, pres. 1980), Nat. Fedn. Abstracting and Info. Svcs. (pres. 1989-90), Union League Phila. Republican. Roman Catholic. Avocations: music (trumpet, piano), reading, walking. Office: ISI 3501 Market St Philadelphia PA 19104-3389

LAWN, JOHN C., professional baseball team executive, former federal government official; b. Bklyn., June 2, 1935. BA, St. Francis Coll., 1957; MA, St. John's U., 1964. Spl. agt. FBI, 1967; supr. hdqrs. FBI, Washington, 1973-77, sect. chief hdqrs., 1979-80; asst. agt. asst. in charge FBI, Kansas City, Mo., 1977-79; spl. agt. in charge FBI, San Antonio, 1980-82; dep. adminstr. Drug Enforcement Adminstrn., Washington, 1982-84, adminstr., 1985-90; v.p., chief of ops. New York Yankees, 1990-95; chmn., CEO The Century Coun., L.A., 1995—. Capt. USMC, 1957-61. Office: New York Yankees Yankee Stadium Bronx NY 10451

LAWNICZAK, JAMES MICHAEL, lawyer; b. Toledo, Sept. 11, 1951; m. Christine Nielsen, Dec. 31, 1979; children: Mara Katharine, Rachel Anne, Amy Elizabeth. BA, U. Mich., 1974, JD, 1977. Bar: Mich. 1977, Ill. 1979, Ohio 1989. Law clk. to the Honorable Robert E. DeMascio U.S. Dist. Ct. (ea. dist.) Mich., Detroit, 1977-79; assoc. Levy and Erens, Chgo., 1979-83; assoc. then ptnr. Mayer, Brown & Platt, Chgo., 1983-88; ptnr. Calfee, Halter & Griswold, Cleve., 1988—. Mem. Chgo. Bar Assn. (subcom. on bankruptcy 1983-88), Cleve. Bar Assn. (bankruptcy com.). Home: 14039 Fox Hollow Dr Novelty OH 44072-9719 Office: Calfee Halter & Griswold Ste 1800 800 Superior Ave Cleveland OH 44114

LAWRANCE, CHARLES HOLWAY, civil and sanitary engineer; b. Augusta, Maine, Dec. 25, 1920; s. Charles William and Lois Lyford (Holway) L.; m. Mary Jane Hungerford, Nov. 22, 1947; children: Kenneth A., Lois R., Robert J. BS in Pub. Health Engring., MIT, 1942; MPH, Yale U., 1952. Registered profl. engr., Calif. Sr. san. engr. Conn. State Dept. Health, Hartford, 1946-53; assoc. san. engr. Calif. Dept. Pub. Health, L.A., 1953-55; chief san. engr. Koebig & Koebig, Inc., Cons. Engrs., L.A., 1955-75; engr., mgr. Santa Barbara County Water Agy., Santa Barbara, Calif. 1975-79; prin. engr. James M. Montgomery Cons. Engrs., Pasadena, Calif., 1979-83; v.p. Lawrance, Fisk & McFarland, Inc., Santa Barbara, 1983—. Author: The Death of the Dam, 1972; co-author: Ocean Outfall Design, 1958; contbr. articles to profl. jours. Bd. dirs. Pacific Unitarian Ch., Palos Verdes Peninsula, Calif., 1956-60, chmn. bd. 1st lt. USMCR, 1942-46, PTO. Fellow ASCE (life, Norman medal 1966); mem. Am. Water Works Assn. (life), Am. Acad. Environ. Engrs. (life diplomate), Water Environment Fedn. (life). Republican. Unitarian. Home: 1340 Kenwood Rd Santa Barbara CA 93109

LAWRENCE, ALBERT JAMES, association executive; b. Chgo., Feb. 5, 1947; s. Leo M. and Ruth (Rymph) L.; m. Mary Ellen Grimes. AB in Creative Writing, U. Mo., 1971, MEd in Lang. Art., 1975, MA in English Lit., 1977. Tchr. English Lincoln, Nebr., 1977-80; mng. editor Chess Life mag., 1981-82; asst. dir. U.S. Chess Fedn., New Windsor, N.Y., 1982-83; assoc. dir. U.S. Chess Fedn., New Windsor, 1983-88, exec. dir., 1988—. Author short stories; contbr. numerous articles on chess to profl. publs. Co-chmn. Coun. of Nat. Resource Orgns., VA; bd. dirs. Lincoln Chess Found.; capt. Lincoln Logs, nat. chess league team. With U.S. Army, Vietnam. Decorated Bronze Star; recipient Adminstr.'s award VA, 1977. Home: 52 Youngblood Rd Montgomery NY 12549-1915 Office: US Chess Fedn 186 Route 9W New Windsor NY 12553-7624

LAWRENCE, ALBERT WEAVER, insurance company executive; b. Newburgh, N.Y., Aug. 4, 1928; s. Claude D. and Janet (Weaver) L.; m. Barbara Corell, June 28, 1950; children: David, Janet, Elizabeth. BSAE in Engring., Cornell U., 1950; grad. advanced mgmt. program, Rensselaer Poly. Inst., 1975. Ins. agt., exec., 1953—; founder, chmn. A.W. Lawrence and Co. Inc., Schenectady and Albany, N.Y., 1954-82; chmn. bd. dirs. Lawrence Agy. Corp., Albany, 1982—, Lawrence Ins. Group Inc., Albany, 1986—, Lawrence Group Inc., Schenectady, 1986—; mem. Cornell Engring. Adv. Coun.; bd. dirs. Ctr. for Econ. Growth, Inc., Capital Dist. Ctr. for Econ. Devel., Schenectady Indsl. Devel. Corp., Mech. Tech., Inc., Latham, N.Y. Trustee Russell Sage Coll., Troy, N.Y., Rensselaer Poly. Inst., Sunnyview Hosp. and Rehab. Ctr.; past pres. Schenectady Girls Club, Family and Child Svc. Schenectady; bd. dirs. Ind. Living for Physically Disabled, St. Clare's Hosp., Proctor's Theatre, N.Y. State Olympic Regional Devel. Authority, 1989; co-founder Lawrence Inst. for Physically Disabled Rsch.; past chmn. Schenectady United Fund Drive, Jr. Achievement Capital Dist. With U.S. Army, 1946-47. Recipient Sca-Nec-Ta-De Civic award, 1967. Mem. Schenectady C. of C. (past pres.), Schenectady Hist. Soc. (past bd. dirs.), Mohawk Golf Club, Cornell Club (N.Y.C.), N.Y. Athletic Club, N.Y. Yacht Club, No. Lake George Yacht Club (past commodore), U. Club Albany, Ft. Orange Club Albany, Rotary Club (past pres.). Republican. Mem. First Dutch Reformed Ch. Home: 708 Riverview Rd Rexford NY 12148-1433 Office: Lawrence Group Inc 108 Union St Schenectady NY 12305

LAWRENCE, BARBARA, information manager; b. N.Y.C., Dec. 16, 1944; d. Seth and Aline (Greenberg) L.; m. Allen I. Laskin. BA in Chemistry, U. Vt., 1965; student, Yale U., New Haven, 1965-66. Jr. organic chemist Burroughs Wellcome & Co., Tuckahoe, N.Y., 1966-67; asst. documentation scientist Schering Corp., Bloomfield, N.J., 1967-69; info. chemist, group head, database mgmt. Exxon Research & Engring., Linden, N.J., 1979-82; head, info. service unit Exxon Corp. Research & Environ. Health Division, East Millstone, N.J.; div. dir. tech. info. AIAA, N.Y.C., 1982-94; v.p. Rsch. Peterson's Guides, Inc., Princeton, N.J., 1994—; U.S. del. NATO Adv. Group for Aerospace R & D, Paris 1984-91; pres., dir. Nat. Fed. Abstract and Info. Svcs., Phila. 1985-90. Contbr. articles to pubs. Mem. Nat. Orgn. for Women, Princeton N.J. Mem. AIAA, Nat. Info. Standards Orgn. (standards devel. com. 1993—), Am. Chem. Soc., Am. Soc. for Info. Sci., Spl. Librs. Assn. Avocations: gardening, swimming. Home: 383 S Middlebush Rd Somerset NJ 08873-9531 Office: Peterson's Guides PO Box 202 Princeton NJ 08540

LAWRENCE, BARRY HOWARD, lawyer; b. N.Y.C., June 3, 1942; m. Eleanor Luskin, June 27, 1965. BS, UCLA, 1963, J.D., 1966. Bar: Calif. 1966. Dep. atty. gen. State of Calif., 1967-68; prof. law California Coll. Law, 1967-69, asst. dean, 1969; with Mazirow, Forer, Lawrence, Cunningham & Giden, Inc., Los Angeles, 1968-82; ptnr. Mazirow, Forer, Lawrence, Cunningham & Giden, Inc., 1972-82, Manatt, Phelps, Rothenberg & Tunney, 1982-84; former ptnr. Finley, Kumble, Wagner, Heine, Underberg, Manley & Casey; now ptnr. Kaye, Scholer, Fierman, Hays & Handler, L.A.; instr. real estate law Los Angeles City Sch. Dist.; instr. bus. law Los Angeles Valley Coll.; instr. real estate and constrn. UCLA; mem. faculty Calif. Assn. Realtors Grad. Program; mem. Calif. Commn. Profl. Devel. Real Estate Industry in Calif., 1978, Calif. Corporations Commn. Escrow Law, 1981-83; TV host Fin. Network, 1982; legal counsel Calif. Escrow Assn., 1978-83; legis. counsel Homebuilders Coun., 1982; panelist Continuing Edn. Bar Real Estate Programs, 1985—. Served with USAR, 1966-72. Mem. Calif. Bar Assn., L.A. County Bar Assn. (mem. exec. com. real estate sect. 1987). Office: Kaye Scholer Fierman Hays & Handler 1999 Ave Of The Stars Ste 1600 Los Angeles CA 90067

LAWRENCE, BRYAN HUNT, investment banking executive; b. N.Y.C., July 26, 1942; s. Bryan and Suzanne (Walbridge) L.; m. Elizabeth D. Lawrence, Sept. 25, 1965; children: Bryan R., E. Corey. BA, Hamilton Coll., 1964; MBA, Columbia U., 1966. Assoc. Dillon, Read & Co. Inc., N.Y.C., 1966-70, v.p., 1971-74, sr. v.p., 1975-81, mng. dir., 1982—; bd. dirs. Meenan Oil, Inc., Tulsa, D & K Wholesale Drug, St. Louis, Transmontaigne Oil Co., Denver, Fintube, L.P., Tulsa, Willbros Group Inc., Panama, Interenergy Corp., Denver, Benson Petroleum, Calgary, Alta., Cavell Energy, Calgary, PetroSantander Inc., Houston. Trustee Hamilton Coll., Clinton, N.Y., 1991-94. Republican. Home: 116 E 63rd St New York NY 10021-7343 Office: Dillon Read & Co Inc 535 Madison Ave New York NY 10022-4212

LAWRENCE, CALEB JAMES, bishop; b. Lattie's Brook, N.S., Can., May 26, 1941; s. James Otis and Mildred Viola (Burton) L.; m. Maureen Patricia Cuddy, July 18, 1966; children: Fiona, Karen, Sean. B.A., Dalhousie U., Halifax, N.S., 1962; B.S.T., U. of King's Coll., Halifax, 1964, D.Div. (hon.) 1980. Ordained priest Anglican Ch. of Canada, 1965. Missionary priest St. Edmund's Anglican Parish, Gt. Whale River, Que., Can., 1965-74, rector, 1974-79; canon St. Jude's Cathedral, Frobisher Bay, N.W.T., Can., 1974-75; archdeacon of Arctic Que. Diocese of the Arctic, Toronto, Ont., Can., 1975-79; bishop Diocese of Moosonee, Schumacher, Ont., 1980—; mem. coun. of north Anglican Ch. Can., 1979—, mem. gen. synod, 1980—; mem. Anglican Coun. N.Am. and Caribbean, 1983-86. Translator liturgical services, hymns into Cree, 1970-80. Canon W.H. Morris travelling scholar U. of King's Coll., 1964. Home: PO Box 830, Schumacher, ON Canada P0N 1G0 Office: Anglican Ch of Can, Diocese of Moosonee, PO Box 841, Schumacher, ON Canada P0N 1GO

LAWRENCE, CHARLES EDMUND, architect; b. Victoria, Tex., Jan. 24, 1927; s. Robert Lee and Josephine Amelia (Jecker) L.; m. Nancy Mell, June 23, 1951; children: Lise, Charles Mell, Mia Michele, Joshua Jon. Student, Tex. A&M U., 1944-45; B.Arch., U. Tex., 1951. Designer Caudill Rowlett Scott, Inc., Bryan, Tex., 1951-58; dir. design Caudill Rowlett Scott, Inc., 1958-72, ptnr., 1958-67; sr. v.p. CRS, Inc. (CRSS, Inc.), Houston, 1967-82, ret., design cons., 1982-85; vis. prof. Rice U. Sch. Architecture, 1960, U. Houston Sch. Architecture, 1991; mem. adv. bd. Ednl. Facilities Lab., Sch. Constrn. System Devel. Project Calif., 1961-63; mem. adv. council U. Tex. Sch. Architecture, 1975—. Prin. works include Jesse Jones Hall for Performing Arts, Edwin Thomas Hall for Performing Arts, Ky. Ctr. for Performing Arts, Energy Control Ctr. H.L.& P., U. of Petroleum and Minerals, King Abdul Aziz Acad., U.S. Embassy, Saudi Arabia, Orange County Performing Arts Ctr. Served with USN, 1945-46. Fellow AIA; mem. Tex. Soc. Architects. Roman Catholic. Home: 11715 Timberknoll St Houston TX 77024-6305 Office: 1111 W Loop S Houston TX 77027

LAWRENCE, CHARLES R., law educator; b. 1943. BA, Haverford Coll., 1965; JD, Yale U., 1969. Bar: Mass. 1970, Calif. 1973. Asst. prof. San Francisco U., 1974-77, assoc. prof., 1977-80, prof. law Stanford (Calif.) U., 1986—. Author: (with Dreyfuss) The Bakke Case: The Politics of Inequality, 1979. Mem. ABA, SALT. Office: Stanford Law Sch Nathan Abbott Way Stanford CA 94305

LAWRENCE, DAVID, JR., newspaper editor, publisher; b. N.Y.C., Mar. 5, 1942; s. David Sr. and Nancy Wemple (Bissell) L.; m. Roberta Phyllis Fleischman, Dec. 21, 1963; children: David III, Jennifer Beth, Amanda Katherine, John Benjamin, Dana Victoria. BS, U. Fla., 1963; postgrad. advanced mgmt. program, Harvard U., 1983; LHD (hon.), Siena Heights Coll., Adrian, Mich., 1985; HHD (hon.), Lawrence Inst. Tech., Detroit, 1986; LHD (hon.), No. Mich. U., 1987; LD (hon.), Barry U., 1991, Fla. Meml. U., 1992, Northwood U., 1993; U. Fla., 1993. Reporter, news editor St. Petersburg (Fla.) Times, 1963-67; news editor Style/Washington Post, 1967-69; mng. editor Palm Beach (Fla.) Post, 1969-71, Phila. Daily News, 1971-75; exec. editor Charlotte (N.C.) Observer, 1975-76, editor, 1976-78; exec. editor Detroit Free Press, 1978-85, pub., chmn., 1985-89; pub., chmn. The Miami Herald, 1989—. Bd. dirs., vice-chair Dade Community Found.; bd. dirs. U. Fla. Found., Fla. Coun. of 100, United Way of Dade County; trustee Ctr. for Fine Arts. Named Disting. Alumnus, U. Fla., 1982; recipient Nat. Human Rights award Am. Jewish Com., 1986, First Amendment Freedoms award Anti-Defamation League, 1988, Ida Wells Nat. award for advancement of minorities Nat. Assn. Black Journalists and Nat. Conf. of Edit. Writers, 1988, John S. Knight Gold medal Knight-Ridder, 1988, Silver Medallion award NCCJ, 1992, Disting. Svc. award Nat. Assn. Schs. Journalism and Mass Comm., 1992, Scripps Howard First Amendment award, 1993, Nat. Assn. of Minority Media Execs. lifetime achievement award. Mem. Am. Soc. Newspaper Editors (pres. 1991-92), Inter Am. Press Assn. (officer), Miami Club. Office: The Miami Herald 1 Herald Plz Miami FL 33132-1609

LAWRENCE, DAVID M., health facility administrator; b. 1940. MD, U. Ky., 1966; MPH, U. Wash., 1973. Intern in internal medicine, pediat.; with Kaiser Found. Health Plan and Hosps., Oakland, Calif., 1981—, now chmn., CEO; various professorships, directorships and fellowships with U. Wash., Johns Hopkins U., U. Ky.; dir. Pacific Gas and Electric Co., 1994—, Hewlett Packard, Healthcare Forum, Bay Area Coun., Urban Strategies Coun., CCAC. Mem. APHA, Am. Hosp. Assn., Am. Coll. Preventive Medicine, Calif. Assn. Hosps. and Health Sys., Group Health Assn. of Am., Western Consortium for Pub. Health, Calif. Bus. Roundtable Collective Bargaining Forum. Office: Kaiser Found Health Plan & Hosp 1 Kaiser Plz Oakland CA 94612

LAWRENCE, DAVID MICHAEL, lawyer, educator; b. Portland, Oreg., Dec. 26, 1943; s. Robert A. and Maude (Davis) L.; m. Alice Oviatt, June 18, 1966. A.B., Princeton U., 1965; J.D., Harvard U., 1968. Asst. prof. Inst. Govt., U. N.C., Chapel Hill, 1968-71, assoc. prof., 1971-76, prof. pub. law and govt., 1976-94; Kenan prof. pub. law and govt. U. N.C., Chapel Hill, 1994—; counsel N.C. Local Govt. Study Commn., 1972-73, N.C. Open Meetings Study Commn., 1978-79. Author: Local Government Finance in North Carolina, 2d edit., 1991 (award for excellence Rsch. and Publs. Govt. Fin. Officers Assn. U.S. and Can. 1991); contbr. law articles to profl. jours. Chmn. Durham (N.C.) Hist. Dist. Commn., 1985-89. Recipient Herald prize Princeton U., 1965. Mem. N.C. State Bar, Campus Princeton U. Club. Democrat. Office: University of NC Knapp Bldg Clb # 3330 Chapel Hill NC 27599

LAWRENCE, DEAN GRAYSON, retired lawyer; b. Oakland, Calif.; d. Henry C. and Myrtle (Grayson) Schmidt; A.B., U. Calif.-Berkeley, 1934, J.D., 1939. Admitted to Calif. bar, 1943, U.S. Dist. Ct., 1944, U.S. Ct. Appeals, 1944, Tax Ct. U.S., 1945, U.S. Treasury Dept. 1945, U.S. Supreme Ct., 1967; asso. Pillsbury, Madison & Sutro, San Francisco, 1944, 45; gen. practice Oakland, 1946-50, San Jose, 1952-60, Grass Valley, 1960-63, 66—; county counsel Nevada County, 1964-65. Nevada County Bd. Suprs., 1969-73, chmn., 1971. Vol. animal welfare movement; sec. Nev. County Humane Animal Shelter Bd., 1966-86; state humane officer, 1966-82; pres. Nev. County Humane Soc., 1974-86; mem. Humane Soc. U.S., Fund for Animals; pres. Humane Information Svc., 1992—; bd. dirs. Nevada County Health Planning Council, Golden Empire Areawide Health Planning Council, 1974, 75; trustee Grass Valley Pub. Libr., 1962-64. Mem. People for Ethical Treatment of Animals, Doris Day Animal League, Farm Animal Reform Movement, Performing Animal Welfare Soc., Pet Adoption League, Bus. and Profl. Women's Club, AAUW, Animal Protection Inst. Am. (Humanitarian of Yr. 1986), Animal Legal Defense Fund, Golden Empire Human Soc. (Lifetime Achievement award 1990), League Unbiased Women, Phi Beta Kappa, Sigma Xi, Kappa Beta Pi, Pi Mu Epsilon, Pi Lambda Theta. Episcopalian. Office: PO Box 66 Grass Valley CA 95945-0066

LAWRENCE, GEORGE HUBBARD CLAPP, investment company executive; b. Bronxville, N.Y., Aug. 9, 1937; s. Christopher and George-Anne (Collin) L.; student Columbia Coll., N.Y.C., 1956-58; B in Profl. Studies, Pace U., 1975; m. Suzanne Spear, June 4, 1966; children—Christopher C., Arthur W. Assoc. W.E. Hutton & Co., N.Y.C., 1960-64, R.W. Pressprich & Co., N.Y.C., 1964-67, G.H. Walker & Co., N.Y.C., 1967-70; v.p. Lawrence Investing Co., Inc., Bronxville, 1971-78, pres., chief exec. officer, 1978-88, chief exec. officer, chmn. bd., 1988—; dir. Pearce, Urstadt, Mayer & Greer, Scarsdale Nat. Bank. Pres., Charles Edison Meml. Youth Fund, 1971-75; exec. bd. Westchester Putnam council Boy Scouts Am.; chmn. Westchester Heart Fund, 1977-78; bd. govs. Lawrence Hosp.; chmn. Westchester County Tricentennial Commn., 1981-82; chmn. Westchester County Hist. Soc.; mem. nat. adv. council SBA, 1971-77; bd. dirs. Kensico Cemetery, Legal Aid Soc. Westchester; mem. Republican State Com.; mem. staff Richard M. Nixon, 1968-69; dir., officer Westchester County Assn., 1973—; trustee Shubert Theatre, New Haven, Conn.; Sarah Lawrence Coll. Mem. Nat. Assn. Realtors, N.Y. State Assn. Realtors, Westchester County Real Estate Bd. Episcopalian. Clubs: Mill Reef Ltd., Adirondack League, Bedford Golf and Tennis, Links, Capitol Hill, St. Nicholas Soc. Home: Guard Hill Rd Bedford NY 10506 Office: Lawrence Investing Co Inc 244 Westchester Ave White Plains NY 10604-2900

LAWRENCE, GERALD GRAHAM, management consultant; b. U.K., June 21, 1947; came to U.S., 1962, naturalized, 1967; s. Raymond Joseph and Barbara Virginia L.; 1 child, Ian Andrew. BA in Math., Northeastern U., 1970, MA in Econs., 1973; MBA, U. Pa., 1975. Optics rsch. technologist Polaroid Corp., Cambridge, Mass., 1968-70; intern Corning Glass Works, Inc., N.Y.C., 1974; asst. brand mgr. Procter and Gamble, Cin., 1975-76; assoc. Theodore Barry & Assocs., N.Y.C., 1976-79; dir. performance improvement systems Stone & Webster Mgmt. Cons., N.Y.C., 1979-84; mgr. utility MAS Deloitte Haskins & Sells, N.Y.C., 1984-86; pres. PMC Mgmt. Cons., Inc., Three Bridges, N.J., 1986—; advisor Commerce & Econ. Devel. Dept. State of N.J.; speaker in field. Designer: auditor system nuclear power plant constrn; innovator; quality assurance for profl. cons. svcs; contbr.

articles to profl. jours. Econs. fellow Northeastern U., 1973, adminstrv. fellow Wharton Sch. U. Pa., 1975. Home: 11 Thistle Ln Flemington NJ 08822-9706 Office: PMC Mgmt Cons PO Box 332 Three Bridges NJ 08887-0332

LAWRENCE, GLENN ROBERT, federal administrative law judge; b. N.Y.C., Nov. 8, 1930; m. Nina M. Scaturro; children: David P., Eric A. JD, Bklyn. Law Sch., 1954; BA, U. Louisville, 1968; MA, Cath. U., 1977. Bar: N.Y. 1955, D.C. 1973, U.S. Supreme Ct. 1976. Atty. N.Y.C. Legal Aid, 1955-57; ptnr. Lawrence & Lawrence, N.Y.C., 1957-64; agt. N.Y. State, Babylon, N.Y., 1964-66; atty. U.S. Army Engrs., Washington, 1966-69; assoc. chief trial atty. U.S. Dept. Navy, Washington, 1969-78; judge adminstrv. law HEW, Camden, N.J., 1978-79, U.S. Dept. Labor, Washington, 1979-93, SEC, Washington, 1993—; mem. bd. contract appeals U.S. Dept. Labor, Washington, 1981-93; adj. prof. law George Mason U., Fairfax, Va., 1980-83, Cen. Mich. U., Washington, 1981—, Nat. Jud. Coll. U. Nev., Reno, 1984-88; lectr. Banares Hindu U., Varanasi, India, 1988, Law Coll., Ernakulum, Cohin, India, 1989, Washington Lee U., Lexington, Va., 1990; mem. adv. com. Georgetown U. State Cts. and Toxic Torts, 1991; advisor judiciary Leadership Devel. Coun. Inc., 1990—, Fed. Bar Found., 1993—; chmn. rsch. divsn., 1993—. Author: Condemnation Law, 1969. Bd. dirs. Democracy Devel. Initiative. Mem. ABA (chmn. nat. conf. adminstrv. law judges edn. com. 1985-90, chmn. internat. conf. jud. edn. London 1985, pres. fed. adminstrv. law judge conf. 1984-85, chmn. edn. jud. adminstrn. div. 1987-91, chmn. conf. new demands for effective judging, Honolulu 1989, chmn. conf. jud. ethics, Chgo., 1990, chmn. jud. edn. standards program 1991—, vice chmn. govt. lawyers com. sr. lawyers div. 1991—), Fed. Bar Assn. (chmn. adminstrv. judiciary com. 1984-88, continuing edn. bd. 1988-91, chmn. judiciary sect. 1989-91, sect. coordinator FBA exec. com. 1992-94, editor Fed. Jurist 1991—, chair pub. rels. com. 1993—), Trial Lawyers Assn. (pres. adminstrv. 1970-79). Office: SEC 450 5th St NW Washington DC 20549

LAWRENCE, HENRY SHERWOOD, physician, educator; b. N.Y.C., Sept. 22, 1916; s. Victor John and Agnes (Whalen) L.; m. Dorothea Wetherbee, Nov. 13, 1943; children: Dorothea, Victor, Geoffrey. AB, NYU, 1938, MD, 1943. Diplomate Am. Bd. Internal Medicine. Mem. faculty NYU, N.Y.C., 1947—; John Wyckoff fellow in medicine NYU, 1948-49, dir. student health, 1950-57, head infectious disease and immunology div., 1959—, prof. medicine, 1961-79, Jeffrey Bergstein prof. medicine, 1979—, co-dir. med. svcs., 1964—, dir. Cancer Ctr., 1974-79; dir. Ctr. for AIDS Rsch., 1989-94; vis. physician Tisch Hosp., Bellevue Hosp., 1964—; cons. medicine Manhattan VA Hosp., 1964—; infectious disease program com. VA Rsch. Svc., 1960-63; cons. allergy and immunology study sect. USPHS, 1960-63, chmn., 1963-65; assoc. mem. commn. on streptococcal and staphylococcal diseases Armed Forces Epidemiol. Bd., Dept. Def., 1956-74; mem. coms. Nat. Acad. Scis.-NRC, 1957-65, chmn. com. transplantation, 1963-65; mem. NRC, 1970-72; mem. allergy and infectious disease panel Health Rsch. Coun., N.Y.C., 1962-75, co-chmn., 1968-75; mem. sci. adv. council Am. Cancer Soc., 1973-75. Editor: Medical Clinics of North America, 1957, Cellular and Humoral Aspects of Hypersensitive States, 1959, (with M. Landy) Mediators of Cellular Immunity, 1969, (with Kirkpatrick and Burger) Immunobiology of Transfer Factor, 1983; mem. editorial bd. Transplantation, Ann. of Internal Medicine; founder, editor in chief: Cellular Immunology. Served to lt. M.C. USNR, World War II. Commonwealth Fund fellow Univ. Coll., London, 1959; recipient Research Career Devel. award USPHS, 1960-65, prize Alpha Omega Alpha, 1943; Meritorious Sci. Achievement award NYU Alumni Assn., 1970, von Pirquet Gold medal Ann. Forum on Allergy, 1972, Award for Disting. Achievement in Sci. of Medicine ACP, 1973, Sci. Achievement award Am. Coll. Allergists, 1974, Sci. medal N.Y. Acad. Medicine, 1974, Bristol Sci. award Infectious Diseases Soc. Am., 1974, Charles V. Chapin medal, 1975, Lila Gruber honor award Am. Acad. Dermatology, 1975, Alumni Achievement award NYU Washington Sq. Coll., 1979. Fellow ACP (Bronze medal 1973), Am. Acad. Allergy (hon.), Royal Coll. Physicians and Surgeons Glasgow (hon.); mem. Nat. Acad. Scis., Assn. Am. Physicians, Am. Soc. for Clin. Investigation, Am. Assn. Immunologists, Soc. for Exptl. Biology and Medicine (editorial bd. procs.), Interurban Clin. Club, Harvey Soc. (sec. 1957-60, lectr. 1973—, councillor 1974-77), Peripatetic Clin. Soc., Infectious Diseases Soc. (charter, councillor 1970-72, Bristol Sci. award 1974), Royal Soc. Medicine (affiliate) (Eng.), Internat. Transplantation Soc. (chmn. constn. com., councillor), Société Française d'Allergie (corr.), Alpha Omega Alpha. Achievements include discovery of Transfer Factor - a product of lymphocytes (T-cells) which confers and/or augments immunity to mycobacterial, viral and fungal infections when administered to non-immune individuals; research on mechanisms tissue damage and homograft rejection in man. Home: 343 E 30th St New York NY 10016-6417

LAWRENCE, JACOB, artist, educator; b. Atlantic City, Sept. 7, 1917; s. Jacob and Rosealee (Armstead) L.; m. Gwendolyn Knight, July 24, 1941. Student, Harlem Art Workshop, N.Y.C., 1932-39; scholar, Am. Artists Sch., N.Y.C., 1938-39; AFD, Denison U. 1970; DFA (hon.), Pratt Inst., 1970, Colby Coll., 1976, Md. Inst. Coll. Art, 1979, Carnegie-Mellon U., 1981, Yale U., 1986, Spelman Coll. 1987, Rutgers U., 1988, Parsons Sch. Design, N.Y.C., 1988; LHD (hon.), Howard U., 1988, Tulane U., 1989. Artist Yaddo Found., Saratoga, 1954-55; instr. Pratt Inst. Art Sch., N.Y.C., 1958-65, Art Students League, N.Y.C., 1967-69, New Sch. Social Rsch., N.Y.C., 1966-71; artist in residence Brandeis U., 1965—; coord. of the arts Pratt Inst., 1970—, prof. art, 1970; prof. art U. Wash., Seattle, 1970-83, prof. emeritus, 1983—; Disting. Faculty lectr. U. Wash., 1978. Exhibits include John Brown Series, under auspices Am. Fedn. Art, 1947, 30 paintings on history U.S., Alan Gallery, 1957, mural GSA, Jamaica, N.Y.; one-man shows include Migration Series, Mus. Modern Art, 1944, Downtown Gallery, N.Y.C., 1941, 43, 45, 47, 50, 53, M'Bari Artists and Writers Club, Nigeria, 1962, Terry Dintenfass Gallery, N.Y.C., 1963, Francine Seders Gallery, Seattle, 1985; works included Johnson Wax Co. World tour group exhbn., 1963, U.S. State Dept. group exhbn. in, Pakistan, 1963, retrospective exhbn., Whitney Mus. Am. Art, 1974, traveling retrospective Exhbn., Seattle Art Mus., 1986-87; commd. for graphic impressions 1977 Inauguration, Washington, mural commd., Kingdome Stadium, Seattle, 1979, Mural Howard U., 1980, 85, U. Wash., 1985, others; represented in, Met. Mus. Art, Mus. Modern Art, Whitney Mus., Phillips Meml. Gallery, Wash., Portland (Oreg.) Mus., Worcester (Mass.) Mus., Balt. Mus. Art, Wichita Art Mus., Albright Art Gallery, Buffalo, AAAL, N.Y.C., Mus. Modern Art, Sao Paulo, Brazil, R.I. Sch. Design, Va. Mus. Fine Arts, Bklyn. Mus., IBM Corp., Container Corp. Am., various univs.; Author: Harriet and the Promised Land, 1968; illustrator: Aesop's Fables, 1970; (book catalogue for retrospective exhbn.: Jacob Lawrence-American Painter, 1986; executed mural Theatre, 1985; executed, instatted mural Orlando Fla. Internat. Airport, 1988. Mem. bd. govs. Skowhegan Sch. Painting and Sculpture; mem. Fulbright Art Com., 1966-67, Wash. State Arts Commn., 1976—; elector Hall of Fame for Gt. Americans, 1976—. Rosenwald fellow, 1940, 41, 42, Guggenheim fellow, 1945; recipient purchase prize Artists for Victory, 1942, purchase prize Atlanta U., 1948, Opportunity mag. award, 1948; Norman Wait Harris medal Art Inst. Chgo., 1948; Acad. Arts and Letters grantee, 1953; Chapelbrook Found. grantee, 1955; recipient 1st prize in mural competition for UN Bldg. Nat. Council U.S. Art, Inc., 1955, Retrospective Exhbn. with Definitive Catalogue Ford Found., 1960, Retrospective Exhbn. with Definitive Catalogue Whitney Mus. Modern Art, 1974; works selected as part of exchange exhibit with Soviet Union, 1959; Spingarn medal NAACP, 1970; ann. citation Nat. Assn. Schs. Art, 1973; recipient U.S. Gen. Svcs. Adminstrn. Design award, 1990, Nat. Medal of Arts award Pres. of U.S., 1990, Gold medal Nat. Arts Coll N.Y., 1993. Mem. Artist Equity Assn. (past. sec., pres. N.Y. chpt. 1957), Nat. Endowment for Arts, Nat. Arts and Letters, Nat. Coun. Arts. Address: 4316 37th Ave NE Seattle WA 98105-5629 *As an artist, I hope to contribute something of value to life in general and to my fellowman in particular. I hope that when my life ends... I would have added a little beauty, perception and quality for those who follow. During my lifetime also...I hope to learn and add further motivation, insight and dimension as to my own thinking.*

LAWRENCE, JAMES BLAND, advertising executive; b. Houston, July 22, 1947; s. Harding Luther and Jimmie Georgia (Bland) L.; m. Marie Therese Heckethorn, Feb. 7, 1976 (div. 1981); m. Pamela Douglas Moffat, Sept. 7, 1985. BA in Psychology, U. So. Calif., 1970, MA in Comm./Cinema, 1975. Account exec. KTVV TV, Austin, Tex., 1974, KXAS TV, Dallas, 1975-77; v.p. pub. affairs Braniff Internat., Dallas, 1977-78; v.p. Pacific & Asia Braniff

Internat., Hong Kong, 1978-80; v.p. govt. and internat. affairs Braniff Internat., Dallas, 1980-81; v.p. Wells, Rich, Greene, Inc., N.Y.C., 1981-82; sr. v.p., mng. dir. Wells, Rich, Greene, Inc., Detroit, 1983-88, exec. v.p., mng. dir., 1988-90; exec. v.p. Wells, Rich, Greene, Inc., N.Y.C., 1990—. Dir. producer documentary film: Honky Tonk Heros, 1975. Active Foster Parents Plan, Warwick, R.I., 1988—; mem. Met. Affairs Corp., Detroit, 1989. Mem. Detroit Inst. Arts, Am. Assn. Advt. Agencies, Wilderness Soc., Nat. Wildlife Fedn., Greenfield Village/Henry Ford Mus., Adcraft Club, Fairlane Country Club, Waccabuc Country Club (N.Y.). Avocations: tennis, sailing. Office: Wells Rich Greene Inc 9 W 57th St New York NY 10019-2600

LAWRENCE, JAMES KAUFMAN LEBENSBURGER, lawyer; b. New Rochelle, N.Y., Oct. 8, 1940; s. Michael Monet and Edna (Billings) L.; m. George-Ann Adams, Apr. 5, 1969; children: David Michael, Catherine Robin. AB, Ohio State U., 1962, JD, 1965. Bar: Ohio. 1965, U.S. Dist. Ct. (so. dist.) Ohio 1971, U.S. Ct. Appeals (6th cir.) 1971, U.S. Ct. Appeals (4th cir.) 1978. Field atty. NLRB, Cin., 1965-70; ptnr. Frost & Jacobs, Cin., 1970—; adj. prof. econs. dept. and Coll. of Law, U. Cin., 1975—; adj. prof. negotiations Antioch U., 1993—; master Potter Stewart Inn of Ct., Cin., 1987—, treas., 1988-90; tchg. fellow Harvard Negotiation Project, 1991; chmn. adv. panel on reappointment of magistrate judges U.S. Dist. Ct. for So. Dist. of Ohio, 1993—. Contbr. articles to profl. jours. Mem. nat. coun. Coll. Law Ohio State U., 1974—; mem. steering com. Leadership Cin., 1985-89; pres. Alumni Assn. Coll. Law Ohio State U., 1984-85; mem. Cincinnatus Assn., 1975—, pres., 1985-86; mem. Seven Hills Neighborhood Houses, Cin., 1973—, pres., 1992-94; bd. dirs. Beechwood Home, Cin., 1973-85, St. Ursula Villa Sch., Cin., 1983-86; adv. bd. Emerson Behavioral Health Svcs., 1990—, chmn., 1995—; chmn. Labor Dept., 1979-89; trustee Ctr. for Resolution of Disputes, Inc., 1988-91, treas., 1990-91; mem. Gov.'s Ops. Improvement Task Force, 1991. Mem. ABA, Fed. Bar Assn., Cin. Bar Assn. (chmn. labor law com. 1979-82, chmn. comm. adv. com. 1994—), Ohio State Bar Assn. (vice chmn. labor and employment law sect. 1987-90, chmn. 1990-92), Indsl. Rels. Rsch. Assn. (bd. govs. 1977-80), Univ. Club, Cin. Athletic Club. Avocations: collecting movie posters, biking. Home: 3592 Raymar Dr Cincinnati OH 45208-1560 Office: Frost & Jacobs 2500 PNC Ctr 201 E Fifth St Cincinnati OH 45202-4124

LAWRENCE, JEROME, playwright, director, educator; b. Cleve., July 14, 1915; s. Samuel and Sarah (Rogen) L. BA, Ohio State U., 1937, LHD (hon.), 1963; DLitt, Fairleigh Dickinson U., 1968; DFA (hon.), Villanova U., 1969; LittD, Coll. Wooster, 1983. Dir. various summer theaters Pa. and Mass., 1934-37; reporter, telegraph editor Wilmington (Ohio) News Jour., 1937; editor Lexington Daily News, Ohio, 1937; continuity editor radio Sta. KMPC, Beverly Hills, Calif., 1938-39; sr. staff writer CBS, Hollywood, Calif. and N.Y.C., 1939-42; pres., writer, dir. Lawrence & Lee, Hollywood, N.Y.C. and London, 1945—; vis. prof. Ohio State Univ., 1969, Salzburg Seminar in Am. Studies, 1972, Baylor Univ., 1978; prof. playwriting Univ. So. Calif. Grad. Sch., 1984—; co-founder, judge Margo Jones award, N.Y.C., 1955—; co-founder, pres. Am. Playwrights Theatre, Columbus, Ohio, 1970-85; bd. dirs. Am. Conservatory Theatre, San Francisco, 1970-80, Stella Adler Theatre, L.A., 1987—, Plumstead Playhouse, 1986—; keynote speaker Bicentennial of Bill of Rights, Congress Hall, Phila., 1991; hon. mem. Nat. Theatre Conf., 1993; adv. bd. Am. Theatre in Lit. Contemporary Arts Ednl. Project, 1993—. Scenario writer Paramount Studios, 1941; master playwright NYU Inst. Performing Arts, 1967-69; author-dir. for: radio and television UN Broadcasts; Army-Navy programs D-Day, VE-Day, VJ-Day; author: Railroad Hour, Hallmark Playhouse, Columbia Workshop; author: Off Mike, 1944, (biography, later made into PBS-TV spl.) Actor: Life and Times of Paul Muni, 1978 (libretto and lyrics by Lawrence and Lee, music by Billy Goldenberg); co-author, dir.: (album) One God; playwright: Live Spelled Backwards, 1969, Off Mike, (mus. with Robert E. Lee) Look, Ma, I'm Dancin', 1948 (music by Hugh Martin), Shangri-La, 1956 (music by Harry Warren, lyrics by James Hilton, Lawrence and Lee), Mame, 1966 (score by Jerry Herman), Dear World, 1969 (score by Jerry Herman), (nonmus.) Inherit the Wind (translated and performed in 34 langs., named best fgn. play of year London Critics Poll 1960), Auntie Mame, 1956, The Gang's All Here, 1959, Only in America, 1959, A Call on Kuprin, 1961, Diamond Orchid (revised as Sparks Fly Upward, 1966), 1965, The Incomparable Max, 1969, The Crocodile Smile, 1970, The Night Thoreau Spent in Jail, 1970, (play and screenplay) First Monday in October, 1978, (written for opening of Thurber Theatre, Columbus) Jabberwock: Improbablilities Lived and Imagined by James Thurber in the Fictional City of Columbus, Ohio, 1974, (with Robert E. Lee) Whisper in the Mind, 1994, The Angels Weep, 1992, (novel) A Golden Circle: A Tale of the Stage and the Screen and Music of Yesterday and Now and Tomorrow and Maybe the Day After Tomorrow, 1993; Decca Dramatic Albums, Musi-Plays; contbg. editor Dramatics mag., mem. adv. bd., contbr. Writer's Digest; Lawrence and Lee collections at Libr. and Mus. of the Performing Arts, Lincoln Ctr., N.Y., Harvard's Widener Libr., Cambridge, Mass., Jerome Lawrence & Robert E. Lee Theatre Rsch. Inst. at Ohio State U., Columbus, est. 1986. A founder, overseas corr. Armed Forces Radio Service; mem. Am. Theatre Planning Bd.; bd. dirs. Nat. Repertory Theatre, Plumstead Playhouse; mem. adv. bd. USDAN Center for Creative and Performing Arts, East-West Players, Performing Arts Theatre of Handicapped., Inst. Outdoor Drama; mem. State Dept. Cultural Exchange Drama Panel, 1961-69; del. Chinese-Am. Writers Conf., 1982, 86, Soviet-Am. Writers Conf., 1984, 85; Am. Writers rep. to Hiroshima 40th Anniversary Commemorative, Japan, 1985; mem. U.S. Cultural Exchange visit to theatre communities of Beijing and Shanghai, 1985; adv. coun. Calif. Ednl. Theatre Assn., Calif. State U., Calif. Repertory Co., Long Beach, 1984—. Recipient N.Y. Press Club award, 1942, CCNY award, 1948, Radio-TV Life award, 1948, Mirror awards, 1952, 53, Peabody award, 1949, 52, Variety Showmanship award 1954, Variety Critics poll 1955, Outer-Circle Critics award 1955, Donaldson award, 1955, Ohioana award,Ohio Press Club award, 1959, Brit. Drama Critics award, 1960, Moss Hart Meml. award, 1967, State Dept. medal, 1968, Pegasus award, 1970, Lifetime Achievement award Am. Theatre Assn., 1979, Nat. Thespian Soc. award, 1980, Pioneer Broadcasters award, 1981, 95, Diamond Circle award, 1995, Ohioana Library career medal, Master of Arts award Rocky Mountain Writers Guild, 1982, Centennial Award medal Ohio State U., 1970, William Inge award and lectureship Independence Community Coll., 1983, 86—, Disting. Contbr. award Psychologists for Social Responsibility, 1985, ann. awards San Francisco State U., Pepperdine U., Career award Southeastern Theatre Conf., 1990; named Playwright of Yr. Baldwin-Wallace Coll. 1960; named to Honorable Order of Ky. Colonels, 1965, Tenn. Colonels, 1988; named to Theater Hall of Fame, 1990. Fellow Coll. Am. Theatre, Kennedy Ctr.; mem. Nat. Theatre Conf. (hon.), Acad. Motion Picture Arts and Scis., Acad. TV Arts and Scis. (2 Emmy award 1988), Authors League (coun.), ANTA (dir., v.p.), Ohio State U. Assn. (dir.), Radio Writers' Guild (founder, pres.), Writers Guild Am. (dir., founding mem. Valentine Davies award), Dramatists Guild (coun.), ASCAP, Calif. Ednl. Theatre Assn. (Profl. Artist award 1992), Century Club N.Y., Phi Beta Kappa, Sigma Delta Chi. Avocations: traveling, photography, swimming. *I want people to leave the theatre after seeing a play I have written feeling as if they were taller human beings, as if their souls had been sandpapered. A work must have meanings many layers deep so that it illumines our lives and our times.*

LAWRENCE, JOHN ALAN, legislative staff director; b. Paterson, N.J., July 5, 1949; s. Elias David and Sylvia (Gilbert) L.; m. Deborah Ann Phillips, July 4, 1989; 1 child, Samuel Phillips. AB, Oberlin Coll., 1970; PhD in U.S. History, U. Calif., Berkeley, 1979. Legis. asst. U.S. Rep. George Miller, Washington, 1975-76, adminstrv. asst., 1976-93; staff dir. Subcom. on Labor Standards, Washington, 1979-83; assoc. staff Com. on Budget, Washington, 1983-89; dep. polit. dir. for no. Calif. Dukakis for Pres., San Francisco, 1988; staff dir. Com. on Natural Resources, U.S. Ho. of Reps., Washington, 1991—. Office: Natural Resources 1324 Longworth Ofc Bldg Washington DC 20515

LAWRENCE, JOHN KIDDER, lawyer; b. Detroit, Nov. 18, 1949; s. Luther Ernest and Mary Anna (Kidder) L.; m. Jeanine Ann DeLay, June 20, 1981. AB, U. Mich., 1971; JD, Harvard U., 1974. Bar: Mich. 1974, U.S. Supreme, 1977, D.C. 1978. Assoc. Dickinson, Wright, McKean & Cudlip, Detroit, 1973-74; staff atty. Office of Judge Adv. Gen., Washington, 1975-78; assoc. Dickinson, Wright, McKean, Cudlip & Moon, Detroit, 1978-81; ptnr. Dickinson, Wright, Moon, VanDusen & Freeman, Detroit, 1981—. Exec. sec. Coun. on Fgn. Rels. Com., 1988—; trustee Ann Arbor (Mich.) Summer Festival, Inc., 1990—; patron Founders Soc. Detroit Inst. Arts,

1979—. With USN, 1975-78. Mem. AAAS, ABA, Am. Law Inst., Fed. Bar Assn., State Bar Mich., D.C. Bar Assn., Am. Judicature Soc., Internat. Bar Assn., Am. Hist. Assn., Detroit Club, Econ. Club Detroit, Phi Eta Sigma, Phi Beta Kappa. Democrat. Episcopalian. Office: Dickinson Wright Moon VanDusen & Freeman 500 Woodward Ave Ste 4000 Detroit MI 48226-3425

LAWRENCE, JOYCE WAGNER, health facility administrator, educator; b. N.Y.C., Apr. 3, 1942; d. Edward William and Bertha Beatrice (Merz) Wagner; m. William Robert Lawrence, Feb. 9, 1969; 1 child, Rebecca Suzanne. Diploma, Washington Hosp. Ctr., 1963; BS, St. Joseph's Coll., Windham, Maine, 1990. Cert. health care mgr., Va. Supr. Profl. Support Svcs., Virginia Beach, Va.; supr., asst. dir. nursing Med. Staff Svcs., Virginia Beach; supr. Health Care Resources, Inc., Norfolk, Va.; corp. dir. instr., coord. med./cna programs Tidewater Tech, Virginia Beach, Va.; instr. nurse aide program LTH, Norfolk. Lt. (j.g.) USNR, 1968-70. Recipient South Hampton Rds. Women-In-Transition award YWCA, 1991. Mem. Oncology Nurses Assn. (chmn., sec. local chpt.), Hampton Roads Home Health Assn. (chmn. com.), Southeastern Va. Am. Soc. Tng. and Devel., ABWA. Home: 1617 Ashton Dr Virginia Beach VA 23464-7717

LAWRENCE, KEN, columnist; b. Chgo., Nov. 11, 1942; s. Lawrence Edward and Mary Ewing (Glickauf) Burg; m. Patricia Rose Bridges, Feb. 6, 1964 (div. Sept. 1980); children: Vernon H. Davis, Max E.; m. Elizabeth Ann Sharpe, 1984 (div. Feb. 1993); m. Kathleen Wunderly, Feb. 24, 1995. Student, Shimer Coll., 1959-61, Roosevelt U., 1962-63, 68. Freelance film technician Chgo. and Gary, Ind., 1959-71; corr. Southern Conf. Ednl. Fund, Jackson, Miss., 1971-75; editor Greenwood Press & Univ. Press of Miss., Jackson, 1976; columnist Covert Action Info. Bull., Washington, 1979—, Stamp Collector, Albany, Oreg., 1982-86, Linn's Stamp News, Sidney, Ohio, 1987—; Am. Philatelist, State College, Pa., 1991—; dir. Am. Friends Svc. Com., Jackson, 1977-79, Anti-Repression Resource Team, Jackson, 1979-93. Author: Linn's Plate Number Coil Handbook, 1990, (booklet) The New State Repression, 1980; editor: Mississippi Slave Narratives, 5 vols., 1976, The Philatelic Communicator, 1989-94; contbr. (book) Dirty Work 2-The CIA in Africa, 1979. Trainer United Meth. Voluntary Svc., N.Y.C., 1980-83; organizer Nat. Anti-Klan Network, Atlanta, 1980-85; bd. dirs. South African Mil. Refugee Aid Fund, N.Y.C., 1977-85. Recipient Rosebud, MORE Journalism Rev., 1975, Cert. of Merit, Miss. Hist. Soc., 1976. Mem. Am. Philatelic Soc. (dir.-at-large 1991-93, sec. 1993—, Rsch. medal 1988), Am. Philatelic Congress, Jackson Philatelic Soc. (v.p. 1990-91, pres. 1992-93), Bur. Issues Assn. (gov. 1989—). The Manuscript Soc. Avocations: stamp collector, traveling. Office: PO Box 8040 State College PA 16803-8040

LAWRENCE, LINDA HIETT, retired school system administrator, writer; b. Phoenix, July 26, 1939; d. Lydle and Hazeldell (Sutton) Hiett; children: Pamela Lee Reardon, Annabel Virginia Urrea. BA, U. Ariz., 1961; MA, Ariz. State U., 1985, EdD, 1986. Cert. sch. supt., prin., tchr., Ariz. Prin. Washington Elem. Sch. Dist. 6, Phoenix, 1980-83; prin. Dysart Unified Sch. Dist. 89, Peoria, Ariz., 1985-87, asst. supt., 1987-88; supt. Cottonwood Ariz. Oak Creek Sch. Dist. 6, 1988-91; cons., writer, 1991—; adj. prof. No. Ariz. U., 1990-91. Author: Adventures in Arizona, 1991; co-author: History of Jerome and Verde Valley, 1991. Trustee Marcus J. Lawrence Home. NSF grantee for Math; recipient USC's 100 Outstanding Supts. award. Mem. Sacred Heart Alumni Assn., Ariz. State U. Alumni Assn. (chpt. pres.), Ariz. Humanities Coun. Assn., Phoenix Zoo, Friends of Our Brothers and Sisters, Scared Heart Alumni Assn., Ariz. State U. Alumni Assn., Phi Delta Kappa.

LAWRENCE, LOUIS JAMES, JR., automotive company executive; b. Nashville, Apr. 7, 1935; s. Louis J. and Mary H. (Bethel) L.; m. Kay L. Smitherman; children—Cathy, Louis III, Larry, Linda, Lisa, Lori, Lana. BS in Indsl. Engring., U. Tenn., 1959; MBA, Ea. Mich. U., 1970. Engr. Trane Co., La Crosse, Wis., 1959-63; with Ford Motor Co., Dearborn, Mich., 1963-77; vice pres., gen. mgr. Philco Ford Co., Toronto, Ont., Can., 1977-79; corp. v.p. prodn. ops. Bendix Corp., Southfield, Mich., 1979-82; pres., chief exec. officer Goetze Corp. of Am., Muskegon, Mich., 1982-86; sr. v.p. AMCA Internat. Ltd., Hanover, N.H., 1986—. Bd. cons. Ea. Mich. U., Ypsilanti, 1980—. Sr. research fellow U. Chgo., 1957. Mem. Soc. Automotive Engrs., Detroit Engring. Soc., Am. Mgmt. Assn. (v.p. mfg. council 1981—, trustee 1981—). Roman Catholic. Clubs: Plum Hollow Country (Southfield); Century (Muskegon); Spring Lake Country, Farmington Hunt (Mich.). Home: 8 The Courtyard Hanover NH 03755 Office: AMCA Internat Ltd Dartmouth Nat Bank Bui Hanover NH 03755

LAWRENCE, M. LARRY, ambassador; b. Chgo., Aug. 16, 1926; s. Sidney A. and Tillie (Astor) L.; m. Shelia; 4 children. B in Sociology, U. Ariz., 1948. Lic. gen. contractor; lic. real estate and insurance broker. Chmn., pres., chief exec. officer Del Properties, Inc., 1963-86; chmn., chief exec. officer Hotel del Coronado Corp., Coronado, Calif., 1986-93; U.S. amb. to Switzerland, Bern, 1993—; bd. dirs. Federal Home Loan Bank San Francisco; chmn. bd., chief exec. officer, or ptnr. numerous cos. including China Basin Ltd., Coronado Properties, Ltd., Danilo Gardens, Del Properties Inc., Garden Villas Ltd., HDC Properties, Hotel Del Coronado Corp., JKL Ltd., Lawrence-Woodglen Ptnrship. Ltd., Magnolia Gardens Ltd., Poolside Assocs., Resort Supply Internat., Ridan Gardens, So. Calif. Fin. Ltd., West Coast Fin. Ltd., others. Mem. San Diego county Commn. on Bicentennial U.S. Constitution, Exec. Com. Joan Kroc Hospice Ctr., Calif. State Commn. on Tourism and Visitor Services, adv. bd. U. San Diego Sch. Bus. Adminstrn., Urban Coalition task force com. on housing, Vietnam Vets. Leadership Program of San Diego, archtl. selection com. Convention Ctr. City and County San Diego, San Diego Civic Light Opera Assn., select com. Am.'s Cup Task Force, 1987; commr. Calif. Senate Adv. Commn. Cost Control in State Govt., chmn. fin. instns. subcom.; chmn. United Crusade, United Jewish Appeal, Israel Bonds Campaign, Tri-Hosp. Dr. San Diego County Charter Rev. Com.; bd. dirs. Neighborhood House, World Affairs Council; charter life mem. San Diego State U. History Research Ctr.; vice chmn. 1985 Nobel Peace Prize Nominating Commn.; chmn., trustee Citizens United; pres. San Diego Community Service Orgn.; active Dem. coms., Ind. and Calif.; mem. nat. fin. council Dem. Nat. Com., 1978-82, steering com. Re-election Com. Pres. Carter, 1979-80, site selection com. 1984 Dem. Nat. Conv., 1982, Dem. Bus. Council, 1982—, del. selection com. Calif. Dem. Party, 1983, nat. adv. bd. Ctr. Nat. Policy, 1984; founder Dem. Found. San Diego County, 1986-87; trustee Dem. Party Victory Fund, 1987-88, others. Recipient Alumni Achievement award U. Ariz., 1987; named Man of the Yr., City of Coronado, 1984, San Diego Citizen Yr., 1984; named to Hon. Order Ky. Cols. Mem. Navy League, Rest and Aspiration Soc., U. San Diego Pres.'s Club (life), Am. Merchant Marine Vet. Assn., Rotary. Office: Am Embassy, Jubilaeumstrasse 93, 3005 Bern Switzerland

LAWRENCE, MERLE, medical educator; b. Remsen, N.Y., Dec. 26, 1915; s. George William and Alice Rutherford (Bowne) L.; m. Roberta Ashby Taylor Harper, Aug. 8, 1942; children—Linda Alice, Roberta Harper Lawrence Henderson, James Bowne. A.B., Princeton, 1938, M.A., 1940, Ph.D., 1941. NRC fellow Johns Hopkins Hosp., 1941; asst. prof. psychology Princeton, 1946-50; assoc. prof., 1950-52; assoc. research Lempert Inst. Otology, N.Y.C., 1946-52; assoc. prof. dept. otolaryngology U. Mich. Med. Sch., 1952-57, prof. otolaryngology, 1957-85, prof. emeritus, 1985—; research assoc. Inst. Indsl. Health, 1952—; prof. psychology U. Mich. Coll. Lit. Sci. and Arts, 1957—; dir. Kresge Hearing Research Inst., 1961-83; mem. sci. rev. bd. Deafness Research Found., 1960-66, 82-84; Nat. Adv. Neurol. and Communicative Disorders and Stroke Council, 1976-79; mem. communicative disorders research tng. com. Nat. Inst. Neurol. Diseases and Blindness, 1961-65; mem. communicative scis. study sect. div. research grants NIH, 1965-69, chmn., 1967-69, mem. communicative disorders rev. com., 1972-76; cons. Surgeon Gen. U.S. Army office Aviation Medicine, 1963-70. Served as naval aviator USNR, 1941-46, 50-51, PTO; Served as naval aviator USNR, Korean conflict, PTO. Decorated Purple Heart, Air medal with nine gold stars; recipient Sec. Navy Commendation, award merit Am. Acad. Ophthalmology and Otolaryngology, 1965, award merit Assn. Research in Otolaryngology, 1979; award merit Am. Otol. Soc., 1967, guest of honor, 1986; Distinguished Service award Princeton Class of 1938, Rsch. Achievement award Am. Acad. Audiology, 1992. Fellow AAAS, Am. Acad. Otolaryngology-Head and Neck Surgery, Otosclerosis Study Group, Am. Laryngol., Rhinolog. and Otolaryngol. Soc.; mem. Acoustical Soc., Am. Mich. Acoustical Soc. (pres. 1956), Am. Acad. Ophthalmology and Otolaryngology, Am. Otological Soc. (cons. bd. trustees

research fund), Collegium Oto-Rhino-Laryngologicum Amicitiae Sacrum, Soc. U. Otolaryngologists, Assn. Research Otolaryngology, Am. Auditory Soc. (council 1978-82), Walter P. Work Soc., Am. Tinnitus Assn., Quarter Century Wireless Assn. Clubs: Rotary (pres. 1978-79), Centurion, Mich. Masters Swim. Home (winter): 1535 Shorelands Dr E Vero Beach FL 32963-2648 Home (summer): 2029 Vinewood Blvd Ann Arbor MI 48104-3613

LAWRENCE, MERLOYD LUDINGTON, editor; b. Pasadena, Calif., Aug. 1, 1932; d. Nicholas Saltus and Mary Lloyd (Macy) Ludington; m. Seymour Lawrence, June 21, 1952 (div. 1984); children: Macy, Nicholas; m. John M. Myers, 1985. A.B., Radcliffe Coll., 1954, M.A., 1957. With Houghton Mifflin Co., 1955-57; free lance translator, 1957-65; editor, treas., v.p. Seymour Lawrence Inc., Boston, 1965-83; pres. Merloyd Lawrence, Inc., Boston, 1983—. Translator works of Flaubert and Balzac, modern French fiction, German and Swedish children's books.; contbr. articles to nat. mags. Treas., v.p. Milford House Properties, Ltd., N.S., Can., 1975-80; trustee Milton (Mass.) Acad., 1974-82; mem. com. clin. investigations Beth Israel Hosp. Mem. Am. Translators Assn., New Eng. Forestry Found. (exec. bd. 1989—), Mass. Audubon Soc. (dir. 1974—, exec. com. 1992-95), Phi Beta Kappa. Home: 102 Chestnut St Boston MA 02108-1120 Office: 102A Chestnut St Boston MA 02108-1120

LAWRENCE, PATRICIA ANN, obstetrician-gynecologist; b. Rocky Mount, N.C., Mar. 31, 1926; d. Graham Vance and Vera Lynn (Burnette) L. Student, Queens Coll., 1942-43, U. N.C., Chapel Hill, 1943-46; MD, U. Va., 1950. Diplomate, Am. Bd. Ob-Gyn. Resident in ob.-gyn. Ind. U. Med. Ctr., Indpls., 1950-54; pvt. practice Charlotte, N.C., 1955—; mem. staff Carolinas Med. Ctr., exec. com. dept. ob.-gyn., 1983-87, chmn. search com., 1988. Contbr. articles to med. jours. Pres. Mecklenburg unit Am. Cancer Soc., Charlotte. Named Outstanding Career Woman, Cen. Charlotte Assocs., 1968. Fellow Am. Coll. Obstetricians and Gynecologists, South Atlantic Assn. Obstetricians and Gynecologists; mem. AMA, N.C. Med. Assn., Mecklenburg County Med. Soc., So. Med. Assn., N.C. Ob-Gyn Soc., Raintree Country Club, Tower Club, Jefferson Club, Farmington Country Club. Democrat. Baptist. Avocation: raising Thoroughbred horses. Home: 1908 Sterling Rd Charlotte NC 28209-1610 Office: 1001 Blythe Blvd Ste 402 Charlotte NC 28203-5866

LAWRENCE, PAUL ROGER, retired organizational behavior educator; b. Rochelle, Ill., Apr. 26, 1922; s. Howard Cyrus and Clara (Luther) L.; m. Martha G. Stiles, Dec. 14, 1948; children: Anne Talcott, William Stiles. Student, Grand Rapids Jr. Coll., 1939-41; AB, Albion Coll., 1943; MBA, Harvard U., 1947, DCS, 1950. Mem. faculty Harvard U. Bus. Sch., Boston, 1947-91, asst. prof., 1951-56, assoc. prof., 1956-61, prof. organizational behavior, 1961-68, Donham prof. organizational behavior, 1968; retired, 1991; dir. Hollingsworth and Vose Co. Author: (with others) Renewing American Industry, 1983, HRM, Trends and Challenges, 1985, Behind the Factory Walls, 1990. Served to lt. USNR, 1943-46. Fellow Acad. Mgmt.; mem. Am. Sociol. Assn. Home: 17 Willard St Cambridge MA 02138-4836 Office: Cumnock Hall Soldiers Fld Boston MA 02163

LAWRENCE, RAY VANCE, chemist; b. Vance, Ala., July 6, 1910; s. William Monroe and Frances (Ray) L.; m. Barbara New, June 22, 1935; children: Robert Craig, Richard Vance. BS, U. Ala., Tuscaloosa, 1931; MS, U. Tenn., Knoxville, 1933. Instr. chemistry Marion (Ala.) Mil. Inst., 1932-33; chemist TVA, Muscle Shoals, Ala., 1933-38, Naval Stores Sta., Olustee, Fla., 1938-41, Naval Stores Rsch. Div., Washington, 1941-43; head rosin rsch. So. Regional Rsch. Lab., New Orleans, 1943-50; head rosin rsch. Naval Stores Rsch. Lab., Olustee, 1950-58, dir., 1958-73; cons. Naval Stores, Lake City, Fla., 1973—; lectr. terpene chemistry U. Fla., Gainesville, 1953-57; lectr. Nanjing (China) Forestry U., 1979. Columnist, assoc. editor Naval Stores Rev., 1977-90; contbr. articles to profl. jours.; patentee in field. Mem Am. Chem. Soc. (chmn. Fla. sect. 1965, Fla. award 1971), Am. Oil Chemists Soc. Presbyterian. Home and Office: Apt 453 5900 Wilson Blvd Arlington VA 22205-1550

LAWRENCE, RICHARD WESLEY, JR., foundation administrator; b. N.Y.C., Jan. 16, 1909; s. Richard Wesley and Ruth (Earle) L.; m. Marjorie Fitch, June 23, 1933 (dec. Feb. 1945); children: Ruth Earle Lawrence Wilson (dec.), Alida L. Currey; m. Elizabeth Hand Wadhams, Apr. 13, 1946 (dec. Nov. 1987); 1 child, Elizabeth Lawrence. B.S., Princeton U., 1931; LL.B., Columbia U., 1934. Bar: N.Y. 1935. Former chmn. bd. Printers Ink Pub. Co., Bankers Comml. Corp.; v.p., dir. Umont Mining, Inc. Chmn. Adirondack Park Agy., 1971-75; chmn. Commr. Edn.'s com. on Reference and Rsch. Libr. Resources; mem. Gov.'s Commn. on Future of Adirondacks, Gov.'s Commn. on Adirondacks in the 21st Century; past chmn. coun. State U. Coll., Plattsburgh; past chmn. bd. trustees North Country C.C.; pres. Crary Edn. Found. Capt. USAAF, 1942-44; lt. col. ret. Recipient North Country citation St. Lawrence U., 1969, Conservation award Garden Club of Am., 1982, Disting. Service award Potsdam Coll., 1987, Founders award Adirondack Hist. Assn., 1991. Mem. N.Y. State Hist. Assn. (Velma Moore award), N.Y. State Hist. Assn. (trustee), Essex County Hist. Soc.; mem. Explorers Club, Union League, Princeton Club (N.Y.C.), Ausable Club. Home: Elizabethtown NY 12932 Office: PO Box 427 Elizabethtown NY 12932-0427

LAWRENCE, ROBERT ALLEN, lawyer; b. Scranton, Pa., Dec. 25, 1935; s. Karl Manning and Edith Mary (Richards) L.; div.; children: Allan, Richard, Brian, Robert. BS, Columbia U., 1962; JD, George Washington U., 1966. Bar: Va. 1966. Asst. commonwealth atty. Commonwealth of Va., Fairfax, 1967-68; asst. county atty. County of Fairfax, Fairfax, 1969; ptnr. Fried, Fried, Klewans and Lawrence, Fairfax, 1970-73, Hazel and Thomas, P.C., Falls Church, Va., 1974—; counsel No. Va. Bldg. Assn., Fairfax, 1976-79; lectr. on zoning law. Chmn. planning and land use com. Fairfax County C. of C., 1985-86; bd. dirs. Southeast Fairfax Devel. Corp., 1987-88. With USAF, 1954-58. Mem. ABA (coun.), Va. State Bar, Fairfax Bar Assn., Homeowners Warranty Corp. (life dir.). Avocations: music, golf. Office: Hazel and Thomas PO Box 12001 3110 Fairview Pk Dr Ste 1400 Falls Church VA 22042

LAWRENCE, ROBERT SWAN, physician, educator, academic administrator; b. Phila., Feb. 6, 1938; s. Thomas George and Catherine (Swan) L.; m. Cynthia Starr Cole, July 1, 1960; children: Job Scott, Matthew Swan, Hannah Starr, Jin Sook, Sang Bo. AB magna cum laude, Harvard U., 1960, MD, 1964. Intern, then resident in internal medicine Mass. Gen. Hosp., 1964-66, 69-70; surgeon USPHS, 1966-69; asst. prof., then assoc. prof. medicine, chief div. community medicine Med. Sch. U. N.C., 1970-74; div. primary care Med. Sch. Harvard U., 1974-91, assoc. prof. medicine Med. Sch., 1980-81, Charles S. Davidson assoc. prof. medicine Med. Sch., 1981-91; chmn. dept. medicine Cambridge (Mass.) Hosp., 1980-91; adj. prof. NYU Sch. of Medicine, 1992-95; prof. health policy & mgmt. Johns Hopkins Sch. Hygiene & Pub. Health, 1995—; mem. com. human rights NAS; chmn. bd. health promotion and disease prevention IOM, 1981-86, chmn. com. health and human rights, 1990—; chmn. U.S. Preventive Svc. Task Force, HHS, 1984-89, active mem., 1990—; fellow Ctr. for Advanced Study in Behavioral Scis., 1988-89; dir. health scis. Rockefeller Found., 1991-95; assoc. dean for profl. edn. Johns Hopkins Sch. Hygiene & Pub. Health, 1995—. Editor Am. Jour. Preventive Medicine, 1990-92; contbr. articles and chpts. in books. Bd. dirs. Physicians for Human Rights, Teachers Coll., Columbia U., Am.'s Watch. Recipient Maimonides prize, 1964. Fellow ACP, Am. Coll. Preventive Medicine (Spl. Recognition award 1988); mem. Inst. Medicine, Am. Pub. Health Assn., Soc. Gen. Internal Medicine (pres. 1978-79), Soc. Tchrs. Preventive Medicine (Spl. Recognition award 1993), Phi Beta Kappa. Home: Highfield House 112 4000 N Charles St Baltimore MD 21218 Office: Johns Hopkins Sch Hygiene & Pub Health 615 N Wolfe St Baltimore MD 21205-2179

LAWRENCE, RUDDICK CARPENTER, public relations executive; b. Marquette, Mich., Jan. 5, 1912; s. Willard Carpenter and Verna (Ruddick) L.; m. Barbara Dole, June 5, 1937 (div. 1971); children: Dana Ann Lawrence Wetstone, Sara Hilary Lawrence Engelharth, Megan Elizabeth Lawrence Cumming, Jean Hathaway Lawrence Petri, Ruddick C. Daniel Dole; m. Cherry McDonnell Swasey, Oct. 27, 1973; stepchildren: Leslie Denison Black, Caroline McDonnell Black Blydenburgh. B.A. in Journalism cum laude, U. Wash., 1934. Dir. publicity Detroit Inst. Arts, 1934-36; assoc. dir.

World Adventure Series, Detroit, 1934-36; mgr. Western div. Am. Boy mag., Chgo., 1936-39; Phila. and So. mgr. Fortune mag., Time, Inc., 1939-44, N.Y. mgr., assoc. advt. mgr., 1946-50; dir. sales devel. TV network, dir. promotion, planning, devel. radio and TV networks NBC, N.Y.C., 1950-53; v.p. N.Y. Stock Exchange, 1953-68, Conoco Inc. (now DuPont Co.), 1968-77; pres. Lawrence Assocs., 1977—. Trustee Sarah Lawrence Coll., 1954-69, chmn. bd. trustees, 1964-69; bd. mgrs. N.Y. Bot. Garden, 1968-92; hon. chmn., bd. dirs. N.Y. Bd. Trade, 1968-92, pres., chmn., 1978-80; bd. dirs. Internat. Film Found., 1956—, World Adventure Series, 1952-80, N.Y. State Festival, 1981-93; gov. Invest-in-Am. Nat. Coun. Inc., 1954-91; hon. pres. U.S.-Arab C. of C., pres. 1976-79, 82-83. Served from lt. (j.g.) to lt. USNR, 1944-46; staff requirements rev. bd. Office Sec. Navy, Chief Naval Ops. Decorated Star of Jordan, Cedars of Lebanon. Mem. Pub. Rels. Soc. N.Y., Pilgrims Soc., Explorers Club, Circumnavigators Club, Bronxville Field Club, Rockefeller Luncheon Club, Univ. Club, Econ. Club, Shelter Island Yacht Club, Phi Kappa Psi (chmn., trustee Endowment Fund Corp. 1960-88, Disting. Alumnus award 1988), Sigma Delta Chi. Episcopalian. Home: 3 Wellington Cir Bronxville NY 10708-3011 also: Menantic Rd PO Box 1052 Shelter Island NY 11964-1052 Office: 122 E 42nd St Ste 1700 New York NY 10168-0001

LAWRENCE, SALLY CLARK, academic administrator; b. San Francisco, Dec. 29, 1930; d. George Dickson and Martha Marie Alice (Smith) Clark; m. Henry Clay Judd, July 1, 1950 (div. Dec. 1972); children: Rebecca, David, Nancy; m. John I. Lawrence, Aug. 12, 1976; stepchildren: Maia, Dylan. Docent Portland Art Mus., Oreg., 1958-68; gallery owner, dir., Sally Judd Gallery, Portland, 1968-75; art ins. appraiser, cons. Portland, 1975-81; interim dir. Mus. Art. Sch., Pacific Northwest Coll. Art, Portland, 1981, asst. dir., 1981-82, acting dir., 1982-84, dir., 1984-94, pres., 1994—; bd. dirs. Art Coll. Exch. Nat. Consortium, 1982-91, pres., 1983-84. Bd. dirs. Portland Arts Alliance, 1987—; Assn. Ind. Colls. of Art and Design, 1991—. Mem. Nat. Assn. Schs. Art and Design (bd. dirs. 1984-91, treas. bd. dirs. 1994—), Oreg. Ind. Coll. Assn. (bd. dirs. 1981—, exec. com. 1989—, pres. 1992—). Office: Pacific NW Coll of Art 1219 SW Park Ave Portland OR 97205-2430

LAWRENCE, SANFORD HULL, physician, immunochemist; b. Kokomo, Ind., July 10, 1919; s. Walter Scott and Florence Elizabeth (Hull) L. AB, Ind. U., 1941, MD, 1944. Intern Rochester (N.Y.) Gen. Hosp., 1944-45; resident Halloran Hosp., Staten Island, N.Y., 1946-49; chief med. svce. Ft. Ord Regl. Hosp., 1945-46; dir. biochemistry rsch. lab. San Fernando (Calif.) VA Hosp.; asst. prof. UCLA, 1950—; cons. internal medicine and cardiology U.S. Govt., Los Angeles County; lectr. Faculte de Medicine, Paris, various colls. Eng., France, Belgium, Sweden, USSR, India, Japan; chief med. svc. Ft. Ord Regional Hosp.; chmn. Titus, Inc., 1982—. Author: Zymogram in Clinical Medicine, 1965; contbr. articles to sci. jours.; author: Threshold of Valhalla, Another Way to Fly, My Last Satyr, and other short stories; traveling editor: Relax Mag. Mem. Whitley Heights Civic Assn., 1992—; pres. Halloran Hosp. Employees Assn., 1947-48. Served to maj. U.S. Army, 1945-46. Recipient Rsch. award TB and Health Assn., 1955-58, Los Angeles County Heart Assn., 1957-59, Pres. award, Queen's Blue Book award, Am. Men of Sci. award; named one of 2000 Men of Achievement, Leaders of Am. Sci., Ky. Col., named Hon. Mayor of West Point, Ky. Mem. AAAS, AMA, N.Y. Acad. Scis., Am. Fedn. Clin. Research, Am. Assn. Clin. Investigation, Am. Assn. Clin. Pathology, Am. Assn. Clin. Chemistry, Los Angeles County Med. Assn. Republican. Methodist. Avocations: bridge, comml. pilot, pianist, organist. Home: 2014 Whitley Ave Los Angeles CA 90068-3235 also: 160 rue St Martin, 75003 Paris France

LAWRENCE, STEVE, entertainer; b. Bklyn., July 8, 1935; s. Max Leibowitz; m. Eydie Gorme, Dec. 29, 1957; children: David, Michael. Former mem. cast The Tonight Show; host Steve Lawrence Show, CBS-TV, 1965; has starred (with Eydie Gorme) in TV spls. honoring Gershwin, Porter and Berlin (7 Emmy awards); TV appearances include: Police Story, Murder She Wrote; also numerous TV guest appearances; performer night clubs; made stage debut in What Makes Sammy Run, 1964; co-starred: (with Eydie Gorme) in Golden Rainbow, N.Y.C., 1967; co-host: (TV series) Foul-Ups, Bleeps and Blunders, 1984; TV miniseries: Alice in Wonderland, 1985; albums include Through the Years, At the Movies, Together Forever, The Best of Steve and Eydie, 1990. Hon. chmn. entertainment com. Cerebral Palsy; bd. govs. Brookdale Hosp., N.Y.C. Served with AUS, 1958-60. Recipient N.Y. Drama Critics award for best male performance in mus. comedy, 1964, TV Critics Circle award for achievement in music 1976-77, Grammy for album We've Got Us (with Eydie Gorme). Club: Friars (N.Y.C.) (gov.). Office: care William Morris Agy Inc 151 S El Camino Dr Beverly Hills CA 90212-2704*

LAWRENCE, THOMAS PATTERSON, public relations executive; b. Phila., Nov. 20, 1946; s. Granville Allen and Rebecca (Patterson) L.; m. Peggy Wilson, Nov. 1, 1986. BA in Journalism, Fla. So. Coll., 1968. Reporter Nashville Banner, 1968-70; account exec. Holder, Kennedy & Co., Nashville, 1971-78, exec. v.p., 1978-79; ptnr. Dye, Van Mol & Lawrence, Nashville, 1980—. Mem. Nat. Investor Rels. Inst., Nashville Soc. Fin. Analysts Inc., Nashville City Club, Hillwood Country Club. Republican. Presbyterian. Office: Dye Van Mol Lawrence 209 7th Ave N Nashville TN 37219 office: Dye, Van Mol & Lawrence 126 2nd Ave Nashville TN 37201

LAWRENCE, VICKI SCHULTZ, singer, dancer, comedienne; b. Los Angeles, Mar. 26, 1949; d. Howard Axelrad and Ann Alene (Loyd) L.; m. Alvin Adolph Schultz, Jr., Nov. 16, 1974; children: Courtney Allison, Garrett Lawrence. Student, UCLA, 1967-70. Toured as entertainer with Johnny Grant, Vietnam, 1968. Appearances include (TV series) The Carol Burnett Show, CBS, 1967-78, Mama's Family, 1983-90, 87; hostess: (game shows) Win, Lose or Draw, 1987-89; recs. include The Night the Lights Went Out in Georgia (Gold record 1973); host Group W syndicated daytime talk show Vicki, 1992—. Recipient Emmy award for Burnett show, 1976. Republican. Lutheran. Avocations: needlepoint, sailing. Office: VICKI! Group W Productions 3000 W Alameda Avenue Burbank CA 91523*

LAWRENCE, WALTER, JR., surgeon; b. Chgo., May 31, 1925; s. Walter and Violette May (Matthews) L.; m. Susan Grayson Shryock, June 20, 1947; children: Walter Thomas, Elizabeth, William Amos, Edward Gene. Student, Dartmouth Coll., 1943-44; PhB, U. Chgo., 1944, SB, 1945, MD with honors, 1948. Diplomate Am. Bd. Surgery (examiner 1974-78, sr. mem. 1978-). Intern Johns Hopkins, 1948-49, asst. resident, 1949-51; fellow Meml. Sloan-Kettering Cancer Center, 1951-52, 54-56, research fellow, 1956, asst. mem., asst. attending surgeon, 1957-60, assoc. mem., assoc attending surgeon, 1960-66; practice medicine specializing in surgery N.Y.C., 1956-66, Richmond, Va., 1966—; instr. surgery Cornell U., 1957-58, asst. prof. clin. surgery, 1958-63, clin. assoc. prof., 1963-66; vis. investigator Queen Victoria Hosp., East Grinstead, Eng., 1964-65; prof. surgery Med. Coll. Va., Richmond, 1966—, chmn. div. surg. oncology, 1966-90, exec. vice chmn. dept. surgery, 1966-73, acting chmn., 1973-74, Am. Cancer Soc. prof. clin. oncology, 1972-77; dir. Cancer Ctr., 1974-88, dir. emeritus, 1988—; mem. surgery test com. Nat. Bd. Med. Examiners, 1973-77; med. dir.-at-large Va. div. Am. Cancer Soc., 1967—, med. v.p. Am. Cancer Soc., 1975-77, pres., 1977-79, mem. nat. coun. for rsch. and clin. investigation, 1974-78, nat. del., mem. profl. edn. com., 1982—, bd. dirs., 1985—, vice chmn., chmn. M&S com. 1986-88, chmn. M&S exec. com., 1989-90, pres. elect, 1990-91, pres., 1991-92; bd. sci. counsellors Nat. Cancer Inst., 1978-82, chmn. surg. oncology rsch. devel. com.; mem. N.C.A.B., 1988-94; governing coun. U.I.C.C., 1994—. Author: (with J.J. Terz) Cancer Management, 1977, (with J.J. Terz, J.P. Neifeld) Manual of Soft Tissue Surgery, 1983; mem. editorial bd. Va. Med., 1977—; Jour. Surg. Oncology, 1978—, assoc. editor, 1991—; editor Jour. Cancer Edn., 1986—; asst. editor Cancer, 1962-65, assoc. editor, 1991—; contbr. articles to med. jours. Served with USNR, 1942-46; Served with U.S. Army, 1952-54. Recipient Cancer Rsch. award Alfred P. Sloan Found., 1964; J. Shelton Horsley award Am. Cancer Soc., 1973; Disting. Svc. award U. Chgo., 1976; Va. Commonwealth U. Univ. Award for Excellence, 1988, Disting. Faculty award Med. Coll. Va. Alumni Assn., 1988, Va. Cultural Laureate award, 1992, OBICI award, 1992, Dean's award for Disting. Svc., 1992; named to Humera Soc. (hon.), 1992. Fellow ACS (commn. on cancer 1973-85, chmn. 1979-81), N.Y. Acad. Scis., Royal Soc. Medicine; mem. AAAS, Am. Assn. Cancer Edn., Am. Assn. Cancer Rsch., Am. Gastroenterol. Assn. (coun. on cancer 1972-76), Am. Surg. Assn., AMA, Halsted Soc. (past pres.), James Ewing Soc., Soc. Head and Neck Surgeons, Am. Soc. Clin. Oncology Am. Radium Soc. (exec. coun. 1985-876), Soc. Surgery

Alimentary tract (founder), Soc. Surg. Oncology (exec. com. 1976-77, v.p. 1977-78, pres. 1979-80, chmn. exec. coun. 1980-81), Soc. Univ. Surgeons, Surg. Biol. Club III (founding mem.), Transplantation Soc., Collegium Internat. Chirurgiae Digestive, Southeastern Surg. Congress, Pan Am. Med. Assn., Société Internationale de Chirurgie, Va. Surg. Soc. (v.p. 1973-74), Richmond Surg. Soc. (pres. 1986-87), Richmond Acad. Medicine (trustee 1986-87, 1st v.p. 1988), So. Surg. Assn., Argentine Surg. Assn. (hon.), Sigma Xi, Alpha Omega Alpha. Home: 6501 Three Chopt Rd Richmond VA 23226-3118 Office: Med Coll Va Hosps 1200 E Broad St PO Box 11 Richmond VA 23298

LAWRENCE, WAYNE ALLEN, publisher; b. Cin., Dec. 11, 1938; s. Clarence E. and Edna M. (Newman) L.; m. Carol SueAnn Wisecup, July 28, 1959; children: Jeffrey Thomas, Jon Christopher, Jeremy Wayne. Student public schs., Seaman, Ohio. Advt. salesman Amos Press, Inc., Sidney, Ohio, 1957-61; v.p. Amos Press, Inc., 1973-83, sr. v.p., 1983-92, ret., 1992, also bd. dirs.; pub. Stamp World, Linns Stamp News, 1977-82; v.p. advt. Coin World, Sidney, 1973-78; advt. mgr. World Coins, Sidney, 1964-68, advt. dir., 1968-73, v.p. 1973-77; adv. mgr. Numis. Scrapbook, Sidney, 1967-68, advt. dir., 1968-73, v.p. advt., 1973-78; pub. Cars & Parts, Sidney, 1978-85; propr., dir. Sidney Camera, 1981-87; pres. Scott Pub. Co., 1984-92. Contbr. articles and editorials on coins, stamps and cars to Amos publs. Bd. dirs. Shelby County (Ohio) United Way, 1970-76, 1st United Meth. Ch., Sidney, 1982—; bd. dirs. Sidney-Shelby County United Way, 1982-85, sec., 1985; mem. U.S. Assay Commn., 1975. Mem. Am. Mgmt. Assn., Am. Numis. Assn., Am. Philatelic Assn., Numis. Lit. Guild, Am. Stamp Dealers Assn., Mag. Pubs. Assn., Am. Motorcycle Assn., Soc. Automotive Historians. Lodge: Moose. Home: 10 Southmoor Shore Dr Saint Marys OH 45885-9501 Office: 911 S Vandemark Rd Sidney OH 45367-0001

LAWRENCE, WILLARD EARL, mathematics, statistics and computer science educator emeritus; b. Chassell, Mich., Apr. 8, 1917; s. William and Ruth Marie (Messner) L.; m. Lorayne Adalayde Williams, June 12, 1943; children—Victoria (Mrs. Joseph C. Barton), Barbara (Mrs. Timothy F. Columbia), Joan (Mrs. James A. Wilger), Willard, Mark. Student, Ripon Coll., 1947-49; B.S., Marquette U., 1951, M.S., 1953; postgrad., U. Wyo., summer 1959, Iowa State U., summer 1961; M.S., U. Wis., 1962, Ph.D., 1964. Prof. math. and statistics Marquette U., Milw., 1953-87; prof. emeritus math., statistics and computer sci. Marquette U., 1987—, chmn. dept., 1973-79; statis. cons. Author: Introduction to the Theory of Probability, 1967; Probability: An Introductory Course, 1970. Served with USAAF, 1941-45. Decorated Bronze Star medal; NSF faculty fellow, 1961-62. Mem. Math. Assn. Am., Wis. Geol. Soc. Roman Catholic. Home: 13865 Adelaide Ln Brookfield WI 53005-4967 Office: Marquette U Katharine Reed Cudahy Hall Milwaukee WI 53233

LAWRENCE, WILLIAM DORAN, physician; b. Tampa, Fla., Sept. 3, 1926; s. Joseph Daniel and Gladys Irene (Lamb) Lawrence; m. Mardelle Laura Wright, June 18, 1950; children: Jodi Werhanowicz, Patricia Lawrence, Susan Hunter. BA, State U. Iowa, 1948, MD, 1951. Diplomate Am. Bd. Ob-Gyn. Intern Parkland Hosp., Dallas, 1951-52; family doctor Hereford, Tex., 1952, 53, 56; resident, preceptorship Northwestern Hosp., Mpls., 1954-55, 57-61; pvt. practice Phoenix, 1957—. Contbr. articles to profl. jours. Physician World Brotherhood Exch. and So. Bapt. Mission, India, Africa, 1963-83. With USNR, 1944-46. Recipient Drithomas Dooley medal Maricopa County Med. Soc., 1979. Mem. Ariz. Med. Assn. Republican. Avocations: flying, fishing, hunting. Home: 32 E Marshall Ave Phoenix AZ 85012-1318

LAWRENCE, WILLIAM JOSEPH, JR., retired corporate executive; b. Kalamazoo, Feb. 1, 1918; s. William J. and Borgia M. (Wheeler) L.; m. Doris Luella Fitzgerald, Aug. 19, 1955; children: Aaron Frances, Cleve Moren, Julie Anne, William III. A.B., Kalamazoo Coll., 1941. Engaged in personal investments; dir. emeritus, treas. Superior Pine Products Co.; chmn. bd. dir. Channel 41, Inc.; dir. LPI. Trustee Kalamazoo Found., Borgess Hosp.; trustee emeritus Kalamazoo Coll. Served with AUS, 1942-46. Mem. Kalamazoo C. of C. Roman Catholic. Clubs: Kiwanian, Gull Lake Country, Park. Home: PO Box 37 Richland MI 49083-0037 Office: 1000 Old Kent Bank Bldg Kalamazoo MI 49007

LAWRENCE, WILLIAM PORTER, former naval officer, academic administrator; b. Nashville, Jan. 13, 1930; s. Robert Landy and Tennie (Brewer) L.; m. Diane Wilcox, 1974; children: William Porter, Laurie, Fritz, Wendy. BSEE, U.S. Naval Acad., 1951; MS in Internat. Affairs, George Washington U., 1974; LHD (hon.), Fisk U., 1980. Commd. ensign U.S. Navy, 1951, advanced through grades to vice adm., 1980, designated naval aviator, 1952; test pilot, service in Korea and Vietnam; prisoner-of-war Vietnam, 1967-73; dir. aviation programs div. Navy Dept., Washington, 1975-78; supt. U.S. Naval Acad., 1978-81; comdr. U.S. 3d Fleet, 1981-83; chief naval pers. Dept. Navy, Washington, 1983-86; ret., 1986; chair leadership U.S. Naval Acad., 1986—. Author poem Oh Tennessee My Tennessee (composed as prisoner-of-war, designated state poem of Tenn.), 1970. Decorated D.S.M. with 3 oak cleaf clusters, Silver Star with 2 oak leaf clusters, D.F.C., Air medal, Bronze Star with oak leaf cluster, Purple Heart with oak leaf cluster; recipient Gold medal Nat. Football Hall of Fame, 1979, Theodore Roosevelt award Nat. Collegiate Athletic Assn., Liberty Bowl's Disting. Svc. award, 1984, Tenn. Outstanding Achievement award, 1986, Citizen of Yr. award Mil. Chaplains Assn., 1986; first Naval Aviator to fly twice the speed of sound, Mercury Astronaut candidate. Mem. VFW, Assn. Naval Aviation (pres.), Naval Inst., Am. Legion, Rotary. Methodist. Home: 303 Kyle Rd Crownsville MD 21032-1842

LAWRENCE, ZAN, computer consultant; b. Cedar Rapids, Iowa, Jan. 19, 1945; s. Stanley Alexander and Doris (Cornelius) L. Student, Calif. State-Fullerton, 1973-75. Sales cons. Computerland, Newport Beach, Calif., 1979-80, 85-86; regional sales mgr. Microbyte Electronic, Newport Beach, 1981-85; sr. sales rep. Pac Tel Infosystems, Irvine, Calif., 1986-87, MIS Triple Crown Industries, Santa Ana, Calif., 1987-88; owner Western Computer Systems, Laguna Beach, Calif., 1988—. Author: (tng. manual) Effective Sales of AT&T, 1985. Sponsor Children's Hosp., Orange, Calif., 1988; quartermaster Orange County Marine Inst., Dana Pt., Calif., 1988. Served with USMC, 1963-66. Republican. Avocations: music, flying, sports car racing, sailing.

LAWRIE, DUNCAN H., computer science educator, consultant; b. Chgo., Apr. 26, 1943; s. John Lawrie and Annabel (Harwood) McKenna; m. Linda K. Zapf, June 1, 1974. BA, De Pauw U., 1966; BSEE, Purdue U., 1966; MS, U. Ill., 1969, PhD, 1973. Asst. prof. U. Ill., Urbana, 1973-79, assoc. prof., 1979-84, prof., 1984—, head dept. computer sci., 1990—. Contbr. numerous articles to profl. jours.; patentee computer memory. Fellow IEEE (editor-in-chief transp. parallel and distributed systems); mem. IEEE Computer Soc. (pres. 1991), Assn. Computing Machinery. Office: U Ill Dept Computer Sci 1304 W Springfield Urbana IL 61801

LAWRIE, HENRY DEVOS, JR., lawyer; b. Evanston, Ill., Oct. 21, 1942; s. Henry DeVos and Mary Jane (Carothers) L.; m. Audrey Masessa, Sept. 10, 1968 (div. 1982); children: Henry, Clayton; m. Debra L. Wray, May 10, 1986; children: Cameron, Travis. BA, Bowdoin Coll., 1964; JD, Northwestern U., 1967. Assoc. Hopkins & Sutter, Chgo., 1967-74, ptnr., 1974-94, chmn. employee benefits sect.; ptnr. Gardner, Carton & Douglas, Chgo., 1994—; speaker in field. Contbr. articles to profl. jours. Trustee Back of the Yards Coun., Chgo., 1978-92, Beverly Farms Sch., Alton, Ill., 1975-90, Roycemore Sch., Evanston, 1985-90. Hardy scholar Northwestern Law Sch., 1966. Mem. ABA, Univ. Club, Law Club. Avocations: flying, diving, skiing, sailing. Home: 2275 Drury Ln Northfield IL 60093

LAWRIE, ROBERT GEORGE, lawyer; b. Toronto, Ont., Can., Mar. 22, 1945; s. James Chester and Hazel Jean (O'Dell) L.; m. Barbara Lynne Johnston, Feb. 26, 1972 (div. Nov. 1987); children: Katherine Anne, Robyn Samantha. BA in Econs., U. Toronto, 1968, LLB, 1971. Assoc. Zimmerman & Winters, Toronto, 1971-72; ptnr. Lawrie, Coleman & McTavish, Mississauga, Ont., Can., 1978-81; sr. counsel Mobil Oil Co. N.Y.C., 1979-81; gen. counsel BP Can. Inc., Toronto, 1981; v.p. law dept. Husky Oil Ops. Inc., Calgary, Alta., Can., 1982—; chmn. Dash Air Corp., Newport Beach, Calif., 1983; assoc. gen. counsel Tenneco Oil Co., Houston, 1984—; co-chmn. industry creditors com. Texaco Bankruptcy, N.Y.C., 1987; bd. dirs. Net Corp., Toronto, Lorry Corp., Toronto, Dash Air Corp., Newport Beach. Hellyer nat. chmn. Progressive Conservative Party, Ottawa, Can., 1976. Mem. Can. Am. Bar Assn. (sec., treas. 1987-88), ABA, Am. Corp. Counsel Assn., Can. Bar Assn. Clubs: Mississaugua, Jonathan (Los Angeles). Avocations: jogging, photography, piano. Office: Tenneco 1100 Milam St Ste 805 Houston TX 77002-5502

LAWROSKI, HARRY, nuclear engineer; b. Dalton, Pa., Oct. 10, 1928; s. Alexander and Nancy (Lutchka) L.; m. Mary Ann DeWoody, Oct. 6, 1962. B.S. in Chem. Engring, Pa. State U., 1950, M.S., 1956, Ph.D., 1959. Research and devel. work in petroleum refining Pa. State U., 1950-58; instr., thesis advisor Argonne (Ill.) Nat. Lab., 1958-63; supt., asso. project dir. exptl. breeder reactor II power plant Idaho Nat. Engring. Lab., 1968-73; gen. mgr. quality assurance and environmental services Nuclear Services Corp., Campbell, Calif., 1973-76; asst. gen. mgr. nuclear fuel processing and waste mgmt. tech. Idaho chem. programs Allied Chem. Corp., Idaho Falls, 1976-79; cons., 1979—; lectr. Idaho Acad. Scis.; cons. in field; chmn. sci. and tech. project 1990 Idaho Centennial Celebration. Author. Named Outstanding Engring. Alumnus Pa. State U., 1981. Fellow Am. Nuclear Soc. (treas. 1973-77, dir. 1969-77, pres.-elect 1979-80, pres. 1980-81), Am. Inst. Chem. Engrs. (chmn. nuclear engring. div. 1974), Skull and Bones, Sigma Xi, Tau Beta Pi, Sigma Tau, Phi Lambda Upsilon. Clubs: Rotary, Elks. Patentee in field. Home: PO Box 717 Wilson WY 83014-0717

LAWRY, SYLVIA (MRS. STANLEY ENGLANDER), association executive; b. N.Y.C.; d. Jack and Sonia (Tager) Friedman; m. Michael Lawry, Mar. 1944 (div. 1946); m. Stanley Englander, Apr. 1957 (dec. 1968); children: Franklin Miles, Steven Jon. A.B., Hunter Coll., 1936. Law practice and hearing reporter for State Arbitrator, 1937-40; sponsored by N.Y.C., 1942-43; Law practice and hearing reporter for U.S. Atty.'s office, N.Y., 1943-44; asst. dir. radio prodn. Civilian Def. Reporting; founded Nat. Multiple Sclerosis Soc., N.Y.C., 1946; exec. dir. Nat. Multiple Sclerosis Soc., until 1982, now founder-dir., 1982—; sec. Internat. Fedn. Multiple Sclerosis Soc., 1967—. Mem. President's Com. on Employment of Handicapped. Recipient Disting. Svc. award Nat. Health Coun., Pres. Reagan's Volunteer Action award, 1987. Mem. APHA, Acad. Polit. Sci., Am. Judicature Soc., Rehab. Internat. Office: Nat Multiple Sclerosis Soc 733 3d Ave New York NY 10017

LAWS, ELLIOTT PEARSON, federal agency administrator; b. N.Y.C., May 4, 1956; s. James Garfield and Elvira Johanna (Freeman) L.;m. Karen Marie Jackson, June 22, 1991. BA, St. John's U., Jamaica, N.Y., 1977; JD, Georgetown U., 1980. Bar: N.Y., D.C. Law clk. Office of Chief Counsel, Army C.E., Washington, 1978-80; asst. dist. atty. N.Y. County Water Enforcement Divsn. Office Enforcement & Compliance Monitoring, U.S. EPA, Washington, 1980-84, atty., 1984-85; trial atty. environ. def. sect. Dept. of Justice, Washington, 1985-87; assoc. Patton, Boggs & Blow, Washington, 1987-91, ptnr., 1991-93; asst. administr. Office Solid Waste & Emergency Response, U.S. EPA, Washington, 1993—. Co-author: Clean Water Handbook, Govt. Inst., 1990, Environ. Law Handbook, 1991, Clean Air Law and Regulation, 1992; Contributing author in field. Office: EPA Solid Waste & Emergency Response 401 M St SW Washington DC 20460 Office: US EPA 5101 401 M St NW Washington DC 22046

LAWS, PRISCILLA WATSON, physics educator; b. N.Y.C., Jan. 18, 1940; d. Morris Clemens and Frances (Fetterinan) Watson; m. Kenneth Lee Laws, June 3, 1965; children: Kevin Allen, Virginia. BA, Reed Coll., 1961; MA, Bryn Mawr Coll., 1963, PhD, 1966. Asst. prof. physics Dickinson Coll., Carlisle, Pa., 1965-70; assoc. prof. Dickinson Coll., Carlisle, 1970-79, prof. physics, 1979—, chmn. dept. physics and astronomy, 1982-83; cons. in field. Author: X Rays: More Harm than Good?, 1977, The X-Ray Information Book, 1983; contbr. numerous articles to profl. jours.; assoc. editor Am. Jour. Physics, 1989—. Vice-pres. Cumberland Conservancy, 1972-73, pres. 1973; bd. dirs. Pa. Alliance for Returnables, 1974-77; asst. sec., treas. Carlisle Hosp. Authority, 1973-76; pres. bd. Carlisle Day Care Ctr., 1973-74. Fellow NSF, 1963-64, grantee, 1989-95, Commonwealth of Pa., 1985-86, U.S. Dept. Edn. Fund for Improvement of Post-Secondary Edn., 1986-89, 89-93, AEC; recipient Innovation award Merck Found., 1989, Educom Incriptal award for curriculum innovation in sci. labs., 1989, award Sears Roebuck and Co., 1990, award Outstanding Software Devel. Computers in Physics Jour., 1991, Pioneering Achievement in Edn. award Dana Found., 1993. Mem. Am. Assn. Physics Tchrs. (Disting Svc. citation 1992), Fedn. Am. Scientist, Sigma Xi, Sigma Pi Sigma, Omicron Delta Kappa. Democrat. Home: 10 Douglas Ct Carlisle PA 17013-1714 Office: Dickinson Coll Dept of Physics & Astronomy Carlisle PA 17013

LAWS, ROBERT E., diversified company executive; b. 1927; married. BA, Ind. U., 1949, MA, 1955. With Indpls. Morris Planning Corp., 1949-59, Economy Fin. Corp., 1959-69; with ITT Consumer Services Corp., N.Y.C., 1969—, v.p., 1973—, now chmn., pres., chief exec. officer, also bd. dirs.; also sr. v.p. parent co. ITT Corp. Office: ITT Consumer Svcs Corp 1330 6th Ave New York NY 10019-5422

LAWSON, A(BRAM) VENABLE, retired librarian; b. South Boston, Va., Jan. 9, 1922; s. Abram Venable and Vivien Strudwick (Moseley) L.; children—Janet Lee, Abram Venable, Mary Vivian. B.A., U. Ala., 1946; M.Ln., Emory U., 1950; D.L.S., Columbia U., 1969. Auditor Socony Mobil Oil Co., 1947-48; teller 1st Nat. Bank, Altavista, Va., 1948-49; library asst. Harvard Coll. Library, 1951-54; head reference dept. Atlanta Pub. Libr., 1954-56, coord. pub. svcs., 1956-60; asst. prof. Fla. State U., 1960-65; dir. div. librarianship Emory U., Atlanta, 1965-89; vis. prof. Clark Atlanta U., 1989-90. Active Friends of Atlanta Fulton Pub. Libr., 1987—; advisor Friends of Librs. USA, 1990-93; bd. dirs. Episcopal Charities Found. With USAF, 1942-46. Recipient George Virgil Fuller award Columbia U., 1964, Nick Davies award Friends of Atlanta Fulton Pub. Libr., 1993. Mem. ALA, AAUP, Assn. Libr. and Info. Sci. Edn., Southeastern Libr. Assn., Ga. Libr. Assn. (Nix-Jones award for disting. svc. to Ga. librarianship 1989). Home: 1065 Briarcliff Rd NE Atlanta GA 30306-2619

LAWSON, ANDREW LOWELL, JR., defense industry company executive; b. Macon, Ga., Jan. 16, 1938; s. Andrew Lowell and Valerie Ula (Brazzeal) L.; m. Carol Belle Few, Dec. 31, 1961; children: Andrew L. III, Steven Brian. Student, Mercer U., 1955; cert., Middle Ga. Coll., 1956-58; BS in Math, U. Ga., 1960. Contract price analyst WRAMA, Robins AFB, Ga., 1960-64; with E-Systems, Inc., Greenville, Tex., various fin. positions, 1964-70; v.p. fin., div. controller Huntington, Ind., 1970-73; corp. v.p., controller Dallas, 1973; corp. v.p., div. v.p. fin. & adminstrn. Greenville, 1973-78, corp. v.p., gen. mgr. Greenville div., 1978-83; sr. v.p., group exec. aircraft systems group Dallas, 1983-87, exec. v.p., 1987—; also bd. dirs. Deacon Ridgecrest Bapt. Ch., Greenville. Served with USNR, 1955-63. Mem. Aerospace Industries Assn., Am. Def. Preparedness Assn., Armed Force Communications and Electronic Assn., Assn. U.S. Army, Air Force Assn., Navy League, Old Crows. Office: E-Systems Inc PO Box 660248 Dallas TX 75266-0248

LAWSON, BEN F., lawyer, international legal consultant; b. Marietta, Okla., Feb. 7, 1939; s. Woodrow W. and Lennie L. (McKay) L.; children: Nicole, Benjamin C. BBA, U. Houston, 1965, JD, 1967. Bar: Tex. 1967. Atty. Monsanto/Burmah Oil, Houston, 1967-72; mgr. internat. acquisitions Oxy (formerly Cities Svc. Co.), Houston, 1972-78; gen. atty. Damson Oil Corp., Houston, 1978-81; gen. counsel, v.p. Newmont Oil Co., Houston, 1981-86; pvt. practice internat. law Houston, 1986—; cons. internat., 1987—. Contbr. numerous articles to profl. jours. Staff sgt. USAF, 1959-65. Fellow Houston Bar Found.; mem. ABA, Am. Corp. Counsel Assn. (chmn. oil and gas com. 1986-87). Republican. Avocations: fishing, antiques. Address: 3027 Bernadette Ln Houston TX 77043-1302

LAWSON, BILLIE KATHERINE, elementary school educator; b. Cleveland, Tenn., Jan. 15, 1943; d. William Taylor and Katherine Beatrice (Kelley) L. BS in Elem. Edn., Lee Coll., 1970; postgrad., Exeter (Eng.) U., 1975; MEd, U. Tenn., 1975; postgrad., Trevecca Nazarene Coll., Nashville, 1989. Cert. elem. tchr., Tenn. Tchr. Prospect Sch., Cleveland, 1970-76, Trewhitt Elem. Sch., Cleveland, 1976—; mem. Gov.'s Coun. Gore del. 3rd Congl. Dist. Conv., Tenn. 1988. Recipient 4-H Leader award, 1985. Mem. NEA (local rep. to nat. conv.), Nat. Coun. Tchrs. of Math., Tenn. Edn. Assn. (local rep. to state conv.), Bradley County Edn. Assn. (treas., schs. rep., mem. coms.), U. Tenn. Alumni Assn., Lee Coll. Alumni Assn. Democrat. Baptist. Avocations: reading, travel. Home: 198 Charles Cir SE Cleveland TN 37323-8814 Office: Trewhitt Elem Sch 610 Kile Lake Rd SE Cleveland TN 37323-8446

LAWSON, BILLY JOE, educational administrator; b. Longview, Tex., Sept. 15, 1941; s. Roy Lawson, Sr.; m. Velma Pryor, Jan. 20, 1963 (div. 1988); children: Keely N., Billy J., Jr. BS, Wiley Coll., 1965; M Natural Sci., Okla. U., 1968; M of Sci. Teaching, Tex. So. U., 1974. Tchr. chemistry and biology, coach Luling (Tex.) Ind. Sch. Dist., 1963-65, Palestine (Tex.) Ind. Sch. Dist., 1965-78; tchr. chemistry and biology, coach to asst. prin. Tyler (Tex.) Ind. Sch. Dist., 1978-92; pres. Tyler Area Alliance of Black Sch. Educators, 1989-92. Steering com. Leadership Tyler, 1992-93; mentor Martin Luther King Scholars, U. Tex., Tyler, 1992-93. Recipient award of Recognition, Tex. High Sch. Coaches Assn., 1986, Tex. Assn. Basketball Coaches, 1985; named Coach of Decade, Tyler Courier Times, 1975-85. Mem. Nat. Assn. Secondary Sch. Prins., Tex. Assn. Secondary Sch. Prins., ASCD, NAACP, Phi Delta Kappa, Kappa Alpha Psi (life mem.), others. Avocations: golf, basketball, travel. Office: Tyler ISD 1120 NNW Loop 323 Tyler TX 75702

LAWSON, D. DALE, public relations executive. Sr. labor policy analyst Govt. Rsch. Corp; v.p. Hill and Knowlton Pub. Affairs Worldwide; sr. prin./dir. labor policy Capitoline Internat. Group, 1991—. Office: Capitoline Internat Group Ltd 1615 L St NW # 1150 Washington DC 20036-5610

LAWSON, DAVID E., architect; b. Eau Claire, Wis., Apr. 12, 1937; s. Ralph E. and Guida (Mahon) L.; m. Mary A. Gease, Dec. 29, 1984; children from previous marriage: Eric, Kent, Keith. BArch, U. Ill., 1960. Lic. architect Wis., Va., Iowa, Mich. Pa. Archtl. intern Tannenbaum & Koehnen, Milw., 1961-63; project mgr. Cashin & Goodwin, Madison, Wis., 1963-64; project architect Law Law Potter & Nystrom, Madison, 1964-66; exec. v.p. Potter Lawson Architects, Madison, 1966—; bd. dirs. Associated Randall Bank, Madison, Downtown Madison Ptnrs. Inc. Architect: McPhee Physical Edn. Bldg., Eau Claire, Wis., 1970 (Honor award Wis. Soc. Arch.), Wis. Power and Light Control Ctr., 1977 (Honor award Wis. Soc. Arch.). Mem. City of Madison Urban Design Task Force, 1973; chmn. Archtl. Engring. Div. Dame County (Wis.) United Way, 1981; bd. dirs. Friends U. Wis. Arboretum, Madison, 1977-80. Named Dane County's Top Architectural Exec., Madison Mags. Survey of 1000 Bus. Leaders, 1994. Fellow AIA (bd. dirs. 1983-85, v.p. 1986, chmn. govt. affairs adv. bd., nat. registration law adv. task force, 1979-88, chmn. AIA design build task force 1989-91); mem. Wis. Soc. Archs. (chmn. legis. com 1974-81, v.p., pres. elect 1977, pres. 1978, recipient first Golden award for disting. svc. to profession 1985), Nat. Archtl. Accrediting Bd. (exec. com. 1987-88), Madison Club (bd. dirs. 1988-92, v.p. 1989-90, pres. 1990-91), Nakoma Country Club. Lutheran. Home: 2145 Middleton Beach Rd Middleton WI 53562-2904 Office: Potter Lawson Inc PO Box 44964 Madison WI 53744-4964

LAWSON, DAVID JERALD, bishop; b. Princeton, Ind., Mar. 26, 1930; s. David Jonathon and Bonnetta A. (White) L.; m. Martha Ellen Pegram, July 16, 1950; children: John Mark, Karen Sue Lawson Eynon. A.B., U. Evansville, 1955; M.Div., Garrett Theol. Sem., 1959; D.D., U. Evansville, 1977. Ordained to ministry United Methodist Ch. Bishop United Meth. Ch., Wis., 1984-92, Ill., 1992—; trustee Ill. Wesleyan Coll., McKendree Coll. MacMurray Coll., Meth. Health Svcs., Peoria, No. Ctrl. Coll., Naperville, Ill., 1984-92; pres. United Meth. Bd. Disciplineship; also chairperson; mem. com. theol. edn. World Meth. Coun., also mem. exec. com.; mem. originating steering com. New Africa U.; mem. Ill. Conf. of Churches, Coun. of Bishop's to Study the Ministry. Author monograph: Administrative Spirituality; contbr. articles to profl. jours.

LAWSON, EVE KENNEDY, ballet mistress; b. Washington, Mar. 28, 1964; d. John and Elizabeth Lawson. Student, Sch. Am. Ballet, N.Y.C., 1972-83. Prin. dancer State Ballet Mo., Kansas City, 1983-87; dancer Miami City Ballet, Miami Beach, Fla., 1988-94, coord. edn., 1993—, ballet mistress, 1994—. Created prin. roles in ballet Voyager (Bolender), 1984, Miniatures (Gamonet), 1990, Tango Tonto (Gamonet), 1991. Office: Miami City Ballet 905 Lincoln Rd Miami Beach FL 33139

LAWSON, F. D., bishop. Bishop Ch. of God in Christ, Stillwater, Okla. Office: Ch of God in Christ PO Box 581 Stillwater OK 74076-0581

LAWSON, FRANCIS COLIN, chemical company executive; b. Apr. 7, 1917; s. James and Alice (Gamble) L.; m. Mary Aileen Behan, Oct. 21, 1942; children: Paul, Judy, Tony, Moya, Clare, Margaret, James. From various clerical positions to asst. sales mgr. of subs. Australian Consol. Industries Ltd., Melbourne, 1932-50; sec. Gibson Chem. Industries Ltd., Melbourne, 1950-62, dep. mng. dir. 1970-75, mng. dir., 1975-83, chmn. bd., 1983—. Fellow Cert. Practising Accts., Australian Inst. Mgmt. Roman Catholic. Avocations: golf, public speaking. Home: 7 Limeburners Way, Portsea Victoria 3944, Australia Office: Gibson Chem Industries Ltd, 350 Reserve Rd/Cheltenham, Melbourne Victoria, Australia

LAWSON, H(ERBERT) BLAINE, JR., mathematician, educator; b. Norristown, Pa., Jan. 4, 1942; s. Herbert Blaine and Mary Louise (Corson) L.; m. Carolyn Elaine Pieroni, June 6, 1964 (div. Sept. 1977); children: Christina Corson, Heather Brooke. AB, ScB in Applied Mat. and Russian Lit., Brown U., 1964; MS in Math., Stanford U., 1966, PhD in Math., 1968. Lectr. math. U. Calif., Berkeley, 1968-70, assoc. prof., 1971-74, prof., 1974-80, asst. dean, 1975-77; Disting. prof., chmn. SUNY, Stony Brook, 1978—; vis. asst. prof. IMPA, Rio de Janeiro, 1970-71; vis. prof. Inst. des Hautes Etudes Scientifiques, Bures-sur-Yvette, France, 1977-78, Ecole Poly., Palaiseau, France, 1983-84; bd. dirs. U.S.-Brazilian Math. Exch., Stony Brook and Rio de Janeiro; trustee Math. Scis. Rsch. Inst., Berkeley; chmn. Nat. Com. Math. NAS, Washington, 1989-91; mem. Inst. Advanced Study, Princeton U., 1973-74; lectr. in minimal submanifolds, 1971. Author: The Theory of Gauge Fields in 4 Dimensions, 1985, Spin Geometry, 1989; editor Jour. Differential Geometry, Topology, The Princeton Mat. Series; contbr. articles to profl. jours. Sloan Found. fellow, 1971, Guggenheim Found. fellow, 1983, Japan Soc. Promotion Sci. fellow, 1985. Mem. Am. Math. Soc. (coun. 1988—, editor jour., Steele prize 1975), Math. Assn. Am. Achievements include construction of minimal surfaces in the 3-dimensional sphere, construction of foliations on higher dimensional spheres; characterization of boundaries of analytic varieties; co-creation of Calibrated Geometries; research on basic results on manifolds on non-positive curvature, on spaces of positive scalar curvature, on stability results for Yang-Mills fields, and on structure of Chow Varieties. Home: 29 North Rd Stony Brook NY 11790-1009

LAWSON, JANE ELIZABETH, bank executive; b. Cornwall, Ont., Can.; d. Leonard J. and Margaret L. BA, LLB, U. N.B., Can., 1971. With law dept. Royal Bank Can., Montreal, Que., Can., 1974-78, sr. counsel, 1978-84; v.p., corp. sec. Royal Bank Can., Montreal, Que., 1988-92, sr. v.p., sec., 1992—. Mem. Can. Bar Assn., N.B. Bar Assn., Que. Bar Assn., Inst. Chartered Secs. and Adminstrs., Inst. Corp. Dirs., Inst. Donations and Pub. Affairs Rsch. (fin. com.), Am. Soc. Corp. Secs., Mt. Royal Tennis Club. Office: Royal Bank Can PO Box 6001, 1 Place Ville Marie, Montreal, PQ Canada H3C 3A9

LAWSON, JENNIFER, broadcast executive; b. Birmingham, Ala., June 8, 1946; d. Willie DeLeon and Velma Theresa (Foster) L.; m. Elbert Sampson, June 1, 1979 (div. Sept. 1980); m. Anthony Gittens, May 29, 1982; children: Kai, Zachary. Student, Tuskegee U., 1963-65; MFA, Columbia U., 1974; LHD (hon.), Teikyo Post U., Hartford, Conn., 1991. Assoc. producer William Greaves Prodns., N.Y.C., 1974-75; asst. prof. film studies Bklyn. Coll., 1975-77; exec. dir. The Film Fund, N.Y.C., 1977-80; TV coord. Program Fund Corp. for Pub. Broadcasting, Washington, 1980-83, assoc. dir. TV Program Fund, 1983-89, dir. TV Program Fund, 1989; exec. v.p. programming PBS, Alexandria, Va., 1090-95; v.p. internat. Pub. TV, Washington, 1984-88; panelist Fulbright Fellowships, Washington, 1988-90. Author, illustrator: Children of Africa, 1970; illustrator: Our Folktales, 1968, African Folktales: A Calabash of Wisdom, 1973. Coord. Nat. Coun. Negro Women, Washington, 1969. Avocations: painting, reading. Office: PBS 1838 Ontario Pl Washington DC 20009

LAWSON, JOHN H., university official; b. Gloucester, Mass.; s. Howard Vincent and Alice Louise (Carpenter) L.; m. Helen Louise De Lotto, July 3, 1948 (dec. 1981); children—John, Paula, Jay; m. Sally W. Ward, Mar. 7, 1983. B.S., U. N.H., 1949, Ed.M., 1952; Ed.D., Boston U., 1958; postgrad., Guilford Coll., 1970; Aspen Humanities Inst., 1968, Columbia U. Supt.'s Workshop, 1963, Harvard Advanced Adminstry. Inst., 1962-72, Northeastern U. (hon.), 1982. Tchr. sch. sci. and social studies, coach Antrim, N.H. 1949-51; supervising prin. Salisbury (Mass.) Meml. Sch., 1951-55; supt. schs. Salisbury and Newbury, Mass., 1955-57, Hamilton-Wenham, Mass., 1957-61, Hingham, Mass., 1961-65, Shaker Heights, Ohio, 1965-76, Lexington, Mass, 1976-81; commr. edn. Commonwealth Mass., Quincy, 1982-86; prof. ednl. adminstrn. U. N.H., Durham, 1986-91, officer dept. labor rels., 1991-93, dir. alumni affairs, 1993—; vis. lectr.; adj. prof. Boston U., Northeastern U., Case Western Reserve U., Harvard U., Ind., U., Cleve. State U., U. Akron, U. Tex., U. Nebr., John Carroll U. Contbr. articles to profl. jours. Bd. dirs. Sci. Mus., Mus. Fine Arts, Bay State Skills Corp; trustee Econ. Edn. Council; mem. Boston U. Nat. Alumni Council, Cleve. Commn. on Higher Edn., N.C.A.T.E. Accreditation Com. on Sch. Adminstrn., M.I.T. Bd. Overseers, Mass. Telecommunications Commn., Bd. Library Commrs., Mass. State Consortium Com. for Gifted/Talented, Gov.'s Task Force on Edn. Job-Training Partnership Act; pres. U. N.H. Alumni Assn.; mem. state adv. com. Globe Scholastic Art Awards; founding dir. Teacher and Learning Ctr. Bd. Mem. Nat. Suburban Sch. Supts. (pres.), AASA (higher edn. com.), ASCD, Edn. Commn. of the States, Council of Chief State Sch. Officers (vice chmn. policies and priorities com.), Phi Delta Kappa. Home: 7 Bucks Hill Rd Durham NH 03824-3202 Office: U NH Elliott Alumni Ctr Durham NH 03824

LAWSON, JOHN QUINN, architect; b. Tucumcari, N.Mex., Apr. 11, 1940; s. Tom L. and Mable Marie (Hagglund) L.; m. Elizabeth Jo Waddel, June 4, 1961 (div. 1980); children: Bevan Eugene, Cary Augusta; m. Lorna Miriam Katz, Feb. 20, 1981. BA, Rice U., 1961, BSArch, 1962; MFA in Architecture, Princeton U., 1964. Registered architect, Pa., N.J. Staff architect Doxiadis Assocs., Phila., 1961, Collins, Uhl, Hoisington, Princeton, N.J., 1963, Frank Schlesinger, Doylestown, Pa., 1964, Kneedler Mirick & Zantzinger, Phila., 1964; staff architect Mitchell/Giurgola Architects, Phila., 1965-71, assoc., 1972-73, ptnr., 1974-85; ptnr. John Lawson Architects, Phila., 1986—; mem. adj. faculty Grad. Sch. Fine Arts U. Pa., 1972-87; chmn. archtl. adv. bd. Spring Garden Coll., Phila., 1986-92. Prin. works include United Way hdqrs. bldg., Phila., 1971, Lang Music Bldg. Swarthmore (Pa.) Coll., 1973, Nat. Hist. Park maintenance bldg., Phila., 1981, Columbia Ave. Sta. improvements, Phila., 1983, all recipients Pa. Soc. Architects awards. V.p. Logan Sq. Neighborhood Assn., Phila., 1971-72; mem. Community Leadership Seminar Alumni, Phila., 1982-85; cons. Friends of Starr Garden, Inc., Phila., 1989. Lowell M. Palmer fellow Princeton U., 1964, NEA Mid-Career fellow Am. Acad. in Rome, 1980. Fellow AIA (mem. architecture for edn. com. 1976-85, chmn. urban design com. Phila. chpt. 1986—); mem. Pa. Soc. Architects, Soc. Hill Civic Assn., City Pks. Assn. (bd. dirs. 1988—), Awbury Arboretum Assn. (bd. dirs. 1989—), Soc. Hill Towers (coun. 1994—). Democrat. Office: John Lawson Architects 812 Chestnut St Fl 2 Philadelphia PA 19107-5104

LAWSON, JONATHAN NEVIN, academic administrator; b. Latrobe, Pa., Mar. 27, 1941; s. Lawrence Winters and Mary Eleanor (Rhea) L.; m. Leigh Farley (div.); children: Paul, Joshua, Jacob; m. Paula Cross. AA, York Coll. Pa., 1962; BFA, Tex. Christian U., 1964, MA, 1966, PhD, 1970. Dir. composition St. Cloud (Minn.) State U., 1971-77, assoc. dean, 1977-81; asst. vice chancellor Minn. State U. System, St. Paul, 1980-81; dean liberal arts Winona (Minn.) State U., 1981-84; dean arts and scis. U. Hartford, West Hartford, Conn., 1984-86; sr. v.p., dean of faculty U. Hartford, 1986—; pres. Bus. Sch. U. Hartford, Paris, 1990-94. Author: Robert Bloomfield, 1980; editor: Collected Works: Robert Bloomfield, 1971; contbr. articles and papers to scholarly pubs; assoc. editor Rhetoric Soc. Quar., St. Cloud, 1974-79. Mem. regional adv. bd. Greater Hartford C.C., 1992-94; mem. bd. trustees Hartford Coll. for Women, 1992-94. Mem. Am. Coun. Edn., Coun. Fellows Alumni, Coun. Liberal Learning, Assn. Gen. and Liberal Studies, Assn. Am. Colls., N.E. Assn. Schs. and Colls. (chmn. commn. on instns. higher edn. 1992—), Asian Studies Consortium (chmn. bd.), Lambda Iota Tau (hon.), Alpha Chi (hon.). Democrat. Episcopalian. Avocations: fishing, camping, writing. Home: 207 Bloomfield Ave West Hartford CT 06117-1503

LAWSON, RANDALL CLAYTON, II, financial executive; b. Wabash, Ind., June 20, 1948; s. Randall Clayton and Evelyn Beatrice (Wright) L.; m. Julie Ann Severin, June 30, 1973; children: Randall Clayton III, Erin Elizabeth. BS, Butler U., 1970. CPA, Ind., Ohio. Jr. acct. Price Waterhouse, Indpls., 1970-73; sr. acct. Price Waterhouse, Indpls. and Cin., 1973-76; audit mgr. Price Waterhouse, Cin., 1976-79; unit devel. contr. Ponderosa, Inc., Dayton, Ohio, 1979-81, asst. corp. contr., 1981-82, corp. contr., 1982-84, v.p., corp. contr., 1984-85, sr. v.p., chief acctg. officer, 1985-87, sr. v.p., CFO, 1987; v.p., CFO Tad Tech. Services Corp., Cambridge, Mass., 1988-89; v.p. fin. HydroLogic, Inc., Asheville, N.C., 1993; dir. mgmt. acctg. Rust Indsl. Cleaning Inc., Ashland, Ky., 1994—; adj. prof. Wilmington Coll., 1991; bus. cons., 1987—. Mem. agy. audit com. United Way Greater Cin., 1975; mem. fin. and resource allocation com. United Way Greater Dayton, 1985, mem. com. on agy. fin., 1986-87. Mem. AICPA, Ohio Soc. CPAs, Fin. Execs. Inst., Phi Kappa Psi. Republican. Presbyterian. Clubs: Queen City Assn. (bd. dirs. 1978) (Cin.), Dayton Racquet. Lodge: Elks. Avocations: golf; tennis; reading; antiques; crafts. Home: 3229 Hanna Ave Cincinnati OH 45211-6848

LAWSON, RICHARD LAVERNE, trade association executive, retired military officer; b. Fairfield, Iowa, Dec. 19, 1929; s. Vernon C. and Wilma Aletha (Rabel) L.; m. Joan Lee Graber, Aug. 28, 1949; children: Leslie D., Wendy L., Richard H., Randolph S. BSChemE, Parsons Coll., 1951, MSChemE, 1951; grad., Nat. War Coll.; MPA, George Washington U., 1964; PhD (hon.), Centenary Coll., 1980; PhD in Polit. Sci. (hon.), Boston U., 1985. Enlisted US Army USA, 1946, advanced through grades to sgt. maj.; transferred to USAF and advanced through grades to gen., 1951; mil. asst. to Pres. The White House, Washington, 1973-75; dir. plans HQ USAF, Washington, 1975-77; comdr. 8th Air Force, Barksdale AFB, La., 1977-78; dir. Joint Chiefs of Staff, Washington, 1978-80; U.S. rep. to milit. com. NATA, Brussels, Belgium, 1980-81; chief of staff Supreme HQ Allied Powers Europe, Mons, Belgium, 1981-83; deputy comdr. in chief HQ U.S. European Command, Stuttgart, Germany, 1983-86; retired USAF, 1986; pres. Nat. Coal Assn., Washington, 1987-95, also bd. dirs.; pres., CEO Nat. Mining Assn., 1995—; Chmn. Internat. Com. Coal Rsch., Washington, 1987—, Trade Assn. Liaison Coun., Washington, 1992-93, Bus. Com. Atlantic Coun., Washington, 1987—; chmn. global climate com. U.S. Energy Assn., 1994—. Decorated Def. DSM with 1 oak leaf cluster, DSM with 1 oak leaf cluster, Legion of Merit with 1 oak leaf cluster, Soldiers medal, Bronze Star, Air medal with 1 oak leaf cluster, USAF Commendation medal with 3 oak leaf clusters, Republic of Vietnam Gallantry Cross with Palm, Joint Chiefs of Staff Identification Badge, Presdl. Svc. Badge, Armed Forces Expeditionary medal, Vietnam Svc. medal with 4 oak leaf clusters, USAF Overseas Long Tour ribbon with 1 oak leaf cluster, USAF Longevity Svc. award ribbon with 7 oak leaf clusters. Mem. U.S. Energy Assn. (bd. dirs.), Washington Inst. Fgn. Affairs, World Energy Coun., Nat. Energy Found. Home: 6910 Clifton Rd Clifton VA 22024-1524 Office: Nat Mining Assn 1130 17th St NW Washington DC 20036-4604

LAWSON, ROBERT BERNARD, psychology educator; b. N.Y.C., June 20, 1940; s. Robert Bernard Sr. and Isabella Theresa (McPeake) L.; children: Christina Megan, Steven Robert, Jennifer Erin. BA in Psychology, Monmouth Coll., 1961; M.A. in Psychology, U. Del., 1963, Ph.D. in Psychology, 1965. Mem. faculty U. Vt., Burlington, 1966—; asst. prof. psychology U. Vt., 1966-69, assoc. prof., 1969-74, prof., 1974—, assoc. v.p. acad. affairs, 1978, assoc. v.p. research, dean Grad. Coll., 1978-86, dir. gen. exptl. psychology, 1989-90; chair dept. pub. adminstrn., 1990—; cons. Mgmt. Systems, 1986—; vis. scholar Stanford U., 1986-87; pres. Alliance Mgmt. Cons. Group, Burlington, 1987—, N.E. Assn. Grad. Schs., Princeton, N.J., 1983-86; bd. dirs. Grad. Record Exams-ETS, Princeton, 1984-88. Author: (with S.G. Goldstein and R.E. Musty) Principles and Methods of Psychology, 1975, (with W.L. Gulick) Human Stereopsis: A Psychophysical Approach, 1976. Bd. govs. Vermont Public Radio, Inc., 1978-86, dir.; 1979-80. Recipient numerous grants NIH, NSF, USDA; numerous awards from Nat. Eye Inst. Mem. AAAS, Psychonomic Soc., Council Grad. Schs., N.Y. Acad.

Scis., Am. Psychol. Assn., Am. Eastern psychol. assns. Avocations: running, reading, playing tennis. Office: U Vt Dept Psychology John Dewey Hall Burlington VT 05405-0134

LAWSON, ROBERT WILLIAM, JR., retired lawyer; b. South Boston, Va., Sept. 20, 1908; s. Robert William and Mary Easley (Craddock) L.; m. Virginia Peyton Broun, Nov. 19, 1938; children: Robert William III, Fontaine Broun, Lewis Peyton. BA, Hampden-Sydney Coll., 1930, LLD, 1992; LLB, U. Va., 1935. Bar: Va. 1934, W.Va. 1935, U.S. Ct. Appeals (4th cir.) 1950. Assoc. Steptoe & Johnson, Charleston, W.Va., 1935-41; ptnr. Steptoe & Johnson, Charleston, 1941-62, sr. ptnr., 1962-84, of counsel, 1984-89; dir. Fed. Res. Bank Richmond, 1967-75, dep. chmn., 1968-71, chmn., 1972-75. Trustee Episcopal High Sch., 1961-67, Hampden-Sydney Coll., 1950-77; chancellor Protestant Episcopal Diocese W.va., 1956-77. Lt. comdr. USNR, 1944-46. Fellow Am. Bar Found.; mem. ABA (state del. 1975-84, bd. govs. 1984-86), Am. Law Inst., Am. Judicature Soc. (bd. dirs. 1985-89), 4th Cir. Jud. Conf. (life), Rotary. Democrat. Avocations: golf; reading. Home: 10 Grosscup Rd Charleston WV 25314-1210

LAWSON, WILLIAM DAVID, III, cotton company executive; b. Jackson, Miss., Oct. 30, 1924; s. William David Jr. and Elizabeth Vaiden (Barksdale) L.; m. Elizabeth Coppridge Smith, June 9, 1948; children: Margaret Lawson Headrick, William David IV, Susan Barksdale, Thomas Nelson. BS, Davidson Coll., 1948; MBA, U. Pa., 1949. Trainee T.J. White and Co., Memphis, 1949-52; v.p. W.D. Lawson and Co., Gastonia, N.C., 1952-70, pres., 1971-81; pres. Lawson, Lewis & Peat, Gastonia, 1981-85, Lawson Cotton Co., Gastonia, 1985—; v.p. Hohenberg Bros. Co. div. Cargill Inc., Memphis, 1988—; hon. dir. 1st Union Nat. Bank, Gastonia. Bd. dirs. Sister Cities Com., Gastonia; elder Presbyn. ch. Named Cotton Man of Year Cotton Digest, 1969, 76. Mem. Nat. Cotton Coun. (pres. 1975-76), Am. Cotton Shippers Assn. (pres. 1968-69), Atlantic Cotton Assn. (pres. 1957-58), Cotton Coun. Internat. (pres. 1972-73), Am. Cotton Exporters Assn. (pres. 1979-80), Newcomen Soc., Gaston County C. of C. (pres. 1972-73), Am. Legion, Gaston Country Club, Gastonia City Club, Rotary (pres. 1964-65, dist. gov. 1995-96), Kappa Sigma. Clubs: Gaston Country, Gastonia City. Avocations: scuba diving, tennis, jogging. Home: 1341 Covenant Dr Gastonia NC 28054 Office: Lawson Cotton Co 509 E Main Ave Gastonia NC 28054-7124 also: Hohenberg Bros Co 266 S Front St Memphis TN 38103-3803

LAWSON, WILLIAM HOGAN, III, electrical motor manufacturing executive; b. Lexington, Ky., Feb. 3, 1937; s. Otto Kirsky and Gladys (McWhorter) L.; divorced; children—Elizabeth, Cynthia. B.S. in Mech. Engring. Purdue U., 1959; M.B.A., Harvard U., 1961. Gen. mgr. service div. Toledo Scale Corp., 1964-68; exec. v.p., chief ops. officer Skyline Corp., Elkhart, Ind., 1968-85; chmn. bd. dirs., chief exec. officer Franklin Elec. Co., Inc., Bluffton, Ind., 1985—, also bd. dirs.; bd. dirs. JSJ Corp., Skyline Corp., Am. Electronics Co., Plc., Sentry Ins. (a Mut. Ins. Co.); chmn. bd. Oil Dynamics, Inc.; instr. U. Toledo, 1966-67. Trustee Ind. Inst. Tech., Am. Ground Water Trust. With U.S. Army, 1961-63. Mem. Harvard U. Bus. Sch. Assn., Ft. Wayne Country Club, Summit Club Ft. Wayne, St. James Club (London). Republican. Presbyterian. Home: 7126 Blue Creek Dr Fort Wayne IN 46804-9421 Office: Franklin Electric Co Inc 400 E Spring St Bluffton IN 46714-3737

LAWSON DONADIO, CAROLINA ANNA, foreign language educator, translator; b. Naples, Italy, Mar. 11, 1920; d. Joseph and Concetta (Bartolomeo) Donadio; m. Allan Leroy Lawson, Sept. 15, 1945; 1 child, John. Laurea in European langs., lit., instns., Western Group Instituto Universitario Orientale, Naples, Italy, 1946; PhD in French and Italian, Tulane U., 1971. Lectr. overseas div. U. Md., Leghorn, Italy, 1952; tchr. Warren Easton High Sch., New Orleans, 1958-61; teaching asst. Tulane U., New Orleans, 1961-64; instr. Tex. Christian U., Ft. Worth, 1964-65; lectr. Downtown ctr., U.Chgo., 1967-73, U. Akron, Ohio, 1975-76; pvt. practice lectr., translator, ind. scholar, freelance writer Moncks Corner, S.C., 1985—; vis. prof. Kent (Ohio) State U., 1977-84. Author: (textbook) Nuove Letture di Cultura Italiana, 1975; fgn. lang. editl. reviewer Ency. Brit. Chgo., 1971; rev. editor: Italian Culture, 1984-61; contbr. many articles and revs. in lit. criticism, art history, textbooks of fables, fairy tales and biographies to profl. and fgn. lang. publs. Recipient cert. of proficiency in Japanese lang. and culture Tokyo Coll., 1958. Mem. MLA, Am. Assn. Tchrs. of Italian, Am. Assn. Italian Studies, Am. Assn. Tchrs of French, Nat. Italian-Am. Found. Republican. Roman Catholic. Avocations: classical music, painting, sports, world travel.

LAWSON-JOHNSTON, PETER ORMAN, foundation executive; b. N.Y.C., Feb. 8, 1927; s. John R. and Barbara (Guggenheim) L.; m. Dorothy Stevenson Hammond, Sept. 30, 1950; children: Wendy, Tania, Peter, Mary. Reporter, yachting editor Balt. Sun Papers, 1951-53; exec. dir. Md. Classified Employees Assn., Balt., 1953-54; pub. info. dir. Md. Civil Def. Agy., Pikesville, 1954-56; sales mgr. Feldspar Corp. subs. Zemex Corp. (formerly Pacific Tin Consol.), N.Y.C., 1956-60, v.p. sales, 1961-66, v.p. 1966-72, chmn., 1972-81, bd. dirs., 1959—; v.p. Zemex Corp., N.Y.C., 1964-72, vice chmn. 1972-75, pres., 1975-76, chmn., 1975—, also bd. dirs.; chmn. Anglo Energy, Inc., 1973-86; trustee Solomon R. Guggenheim Found. (operating Guggenheim Mus., N.Y.C. and Peggy Guggenheim Collection, Venice, Italy), 1964—, v.p. bus. adminstrn., 1965-69, pres., 1969-95, chmn., 1995—; dir. Harry Frank Guggenheim Found., 1968—, chmn., 1971—; ptnr. Guggenheim Bros., 1962-70, sr. ptnr., 1971—; ltd. ptnr. emeritus Alex. Brown & Sons, Inc.; pres., bd. dirs. Elgerbar Corp.; bd. dirs. McGraw Hill Inc., Nat. Rev. Inc. Trustee The Lawrenceville Sch., pres. 1990—; bd. dirs. Coun. for U.S. and Italy. Served with AUS, 1945-47. Recipient Gertrude Vanderbilt Whitney award Skowhegan Sch. Painting and Sculpture, 1986, Ellis Island Medal of Honor, Nat. Ethnic Coalition Orgns., 1993. Mem. Pilgrims of U.S., Carolina Plantation Soc., U.S. Srs. Golf Assn., Edgartown Yacht Club, Edgartown Reading Room Club, Green Spring Valley Hunt Club, River Club, Century Assn., Links, Nassau Gun Club, Bedens Brook Club, Pretty Brook Tennis Club, Md. Club, Seminole Golf Club, Island Club, Brook Club (N.Y.C.), Yeamans Hall Club. Republican. Episcopalian. Home: 215 Carter Rd Princeton NJ 08540-2104 Office: Solomon R Guggenheim Found 527 Madison Ave New York NY 10022-4304

LAWTON, CHARLES See HECKELMANN, CHARLES NEWMAN

LAWTON, EUGENE ALFRED, banking executive; b. Yonkers, N.Y., Mar. 30, 1936; s. Charles Phineas and Jean (Pagnotta) L.; m. Elizabeth Anne Nicoletti, Oct. 20, 1956; children: Glenn Michael, Gary Paul, Melissa Anne. Student, Westchester Community Coll., 1954-56, Am. Inst. Banking, 1958-63, Sch. Bank Adminstrn. U. Wis., 1971. Cert. info. systems auditor. With Nat. Bank Westchester, White Plains, N.Y., 1956-61; sr. auditor County Trust Co., White Plains, 1961-68; v.p., auditor City Trust, Bridgeport, Conn., 1968-77; sr. v.p. Bay Banks Inc., Boston, 1978-85; pres., chief exec. officer, dir. Innovative Internal Controls, Inc., 1986—. Active Boy Scouts Am. Mem. Nat. Assn. Cert. Fraud Auditors (cert.), Bank Adminstrn. Inst. (guest lectr.), Am. Mgmt. Assn., Am. Inst. Banking, EDP Auditors Assn., Inst. Internal Auditors, Mass. Bankers Assn. Republican. Roman Catholic. Club: Masons. Home and Office: 55 Paul Revere Rd Lexington MA 02173-6636

LAWTON, FLORIAN KENNETH, artist, educator; b. Cleve., June 20, 1921; s. Maximillian and Mary L.; m. Lois Mari Ondrey, June 19, 1948; children: Kenneth R., David F., Dawn M., Patricia A. Student, Cleve. Sch. Art, 1941-43, Cleve. Inst. Art, 1948-51, John Huntington Polytech. Inst., 1946-50. Instr. Cooper Sch. Art, Cleve., 1976-80, Cleve. Sch. Art, 1980-82; cons., instr. Orange Art Ctr., Pepper Pike, Ohio, 1978—; cons. in field, juror, 1968—. Exhbns. include Am. Watercolor Soc., N.Y., Cleve. Mus. Art, Butler Mus. Youngstown, Ohio, Canton (Ohio) Mus., Massillon (Ohio) Mus., Nat. Arts Club, N.Y.C., Pitts. Watercolor Soc., Audubon Artists, N.Y.C., Salmagundi Club, N.Y.C., Parkersburg (W.Va.) Art Ctr., Boston Mills Arts Festival, Peninsula, Ohio, Marietta (Ohio) Coll., many others; 25 yrs. retrospective exhbn. Amish paintings, Butler Inst. Am. Art, 1989; represented in collections including Am. Soc. Metals, Ctrl. Nat. Bank, Diamond-Shamrock, Diocese Cleve., Kaiser Found., Ohio Conservation Found., Nat. City Bank Ohio, TRW, Standard Oil Co., Huntington Bank, Nat. Mennonite Mus., Lancaster, Pa., Ohio Bell Telephone Co., Day-Glo Corp., Soc. Bank Corp., numerous others U.S. and internat., also pvt. col-

lections; featured mags., calendars; Mill Pond Press; cons., artist (documentary) Amish Romance, 1979; official Coast Guard artist. Cons. Aurora (Ohio) Community Libr., 1990—. Cpl. USAF, 1943-46, PTO. Recipient Disting. Alumni award Garfield Hgts. (Ohio) High Sch., 1990. Mem. Ohio Watercolor Soc. (signature award 1983), Am. Watercolor Soc. (signature, charter, Grand Buckeye award 1983), Am. Watercolor Soc. (signature, Strathmore award 1977), Nat. Watercolor Soc. (signature), Akron Soc. Artists, Assoc. Audubon Artists, Artists Fellowships Inc. (N.Y.), Ky. Watercolor Soc., Midwest Watercolor Soc., Pa. Watercolor Soc., Ga. Watercolor Soc., NOVA, Whiskey Painters Am., Rotary Club Chagrin Valley (Paul Harris fellow 1989). Office: 410-29 Willow Cirle Aurora OH 44202

LAWTON, JONATHAN FREDERICK, screenwriter; b. Riverside, Calif., Aug. 11, 1960; s. Harry Wilson and Georgeann Leona (Honegger) L.; m. Teresa Ann Neely, Mar. 17, 1988. Student, Calif. State U., Long Beach, 1978-83. Freelance editor L.A., 1978-88, freelance screenwriter, 1988—. Screenwriter: (short films) The Artist, Renesance; (feature films) Pretty Woman, 1989 (Writers' Guild award nomination 1990, British Academy award nomination 1990), (with Barry Primus) Mistress, 1992, Under Siege, 1992, (with Damon Wayans) Blankman, 1994; screenwriter, dir.: (as J.D. Athens) Cannibal Women in the Avocado Jungle of Death, 1989, (as J.D. Athens) Pizza Man, 1991, The Hunted, 1995; editor: (films) Talking Walls, 1986. Mem. Writers' Guild Am., Acad. Motion Picture Arts & Scis., British Acad. Film & Television. •

LAWTON, JOSEPH J., JR., lawyer; b. Syracuse, N.Y., Aug. 8, 1926; m. Mary Clarke; children: Joe, Jeff, Eileen, Dan, Sara. BS, Niagara U., 1950; JD, St. John's U., 1953. Bar: N.Y. 1953, U.S. Dist. Ct (no. dist.) N.Y. 1954, U.S. Ct. Appeals (2d cir.) 1966, U.S. Supreme Ct. 1970. Atty. Schoeneck & King, Syracuse, N.Y., 1953; Arbitrator Am. Coll. Construction Arbitrators, 1982-90; adv. com. Legal Adv. Counsel Am. Subcontractors Assn., Washington, 1974-90, chmn. 1983-85; lectr. in field. Mem. ABA (forum Constrn. Industry), Am. Arbitration Assn. (constrn. adv. counsel 1982-90, panel arbitrators), Am. Subcontractors Assn. (chpt. atty. ctrl. N.Y. chpt. 1971-93), N.Y. State Bar Assn. (ins. sect. constrn. and surety com. 1961-90, chmn. 1967-71, continuing legal edn. com. 1973-74, chmn. 1975-77, legal edn. and admission to Bar 1980-81, chmn. 1982-84), Constrn. Specification Inst. (ctrl. N.Y. chpt.). Avocations: education, golf, travel, archtl. design, photography. Home: 3371 E Lake Rd Skaneateles NY 13152-9001 Office: Bond Schoeneck & King 1 Lincoln Ctr Fl 18 Syracuse NY 13202-1324

LAWTON, LOIS, health facility administrator; b. Lucedale, Miss., Sept. 2, 1934; d. Floyd Jefferson and Ernestine (Cooley) Eubanks; m. Frank Willingham Lawton, Aug. 17, 1952; children: Deaver Lamar, Wesley Maxwell, Alice Sandra Lawton Hogue, Sarah Diane. Student, Clark Coll., 1952-53, Miss. Coll., 1953-54, Desoto C.C., 1969. Cert. health unit coord. Nat. Assn. Health Unit Coords. Kindergarden supt., tchr. Union Ave. Bapt. Ch., Memphis, 1967-73; health unit coord. Meth. South Hosp., Memphis, 1973-76, Richmond (Va.) Meml. Hosp., 1976-77; coord., trainer health unit coords. Henrico Drs. Hosp., Richmond, 1978-88, health unit coord., 1990—; presenter, coord. seminars in field. Editor newsletter Regional 8 Communicates, 1985-90, Chapter Chatter, 1990-93; author: The History of NAHUC, 1988. Mem. Nat. Assn. Health Unit Coords., Inc. (lead regional rep. 1985-90, regional rep. 1985-90, bd. dirs. 1985-95, treas. capital area chapt. 1989-95, chair various coms. 1990-93, mem. ad hoc task force 1990-93, mem. fiscal affairs com. 1990-95, pres.-elect 1990-93, pres., CEO 1993-95, Disting. Svc. award 1990). Baptist. Avocations: flower and vegetable gardening. Home: 11602 Lothbury Ln Richmond VA 23233-4025 Office: NAHUC Ste S-104 1821 University Ave Saint Paul MN 55104-2869

LAWTON, NANCY, artist; b. Gilroy, Calif., Feb. 28, 1950; d. Edward Henry and Marilyn Kelly (Boyd) L.; m. Richard Enemark, Aug. 4, 1984; children: Faith Lawton, Forrest Lawton. BA in Fine Art, Calif. State U., San Jose, 1971; MFA, Mass. Coll. Art, 1980. artist-in-residence Villa Montalvo Ctr. Arts, Los Gatos, Calif., 1971, Noble & Greenough Sch., Dedham, Mass., 1990. One-woman shows include The Bklyn. Mus., 1983, Victoria Munroe Gallery, N.Y.C., 1993; group shows include San Francisco Mus. Modern Art, 1973, The Bklyn. Mus., 1980, 83, Staempfli Gallery, N.Y.C., 1984, The Ark. Art Ctr. Mus., Little Rock, 1984, 88, 92, 93, Victoria Munroe Gallery, 1985, 87, 88, 92, Butler Inst. Am. Art, Ohio, 1988, Smith Coll. Mus. Art, Mass., 1988, NAD, N.Y.C., 1988, Reynolds Gallery, Richmond, 1994; public collections include The Ark. Art Ctr. Mus., Art Inst. Chgo., Bklyn. Mus., Nat. Mus. Am. Art, Smithsonian Inst., Washington. Scholar Mellon Found., 1982; N.Y. State Creative Artists grantee, 1983, N.Y. State Arts Devel. Fund grantee, 1989. Home and Office: 49 Monument Rd New Orleans MA 02653

LAWTON, THOMAS, art gallery director; b. Somerset, Mass., Feb. 5, 1931; s. John Henry and Beatrice Alice (Miller) L. B.S., Durfee Tech. Inst., 1953; M.F.A., U. Iowa, 1959; Ph.D., Harvard U., 1970. Asst. curator Freer Gallery Art, Washington, 1967-70, curator Chinese Art, 1970-71, asst. dir., 1971-77, dir., 1977-87; concomitant dir. Arthur M. Sackler Gallery, Washington, 1982-87, sr. rsch. scholar, 1987—. Author: Chinese Figure Painting, 1973, Chinese Art of the Warring States Period, 1983, New Perspectives on Chu Culture During the Eastern Zhou Period, 1991; co-author: Freer: A Legacy of Art, 1993. Grantee Ford Found., 1959-61; grantee JDR 3d Fund (China), 1966-67; Fulbright fellow, 1963-66; scholar Harvard U., 1961-63. Club: Cosmos (Washington). Home: 420 4th St SE Washington DC 20003-2005 Office: Arthur M Sackler Gallery 1050 Independence Ave SE Washington DC 20003-3920

LAWTON, WILLIAM BURTON, bank executive; b. 1927; widowed. Student, U. Tex. Farmer, rancher Tex., 1971-74; with Calcasieu-Marine Nat. Bank, Lake Charles, La., 1974—, now chmn. With USN, WWII. Office: Calcasieu-Marine Nat Bank PO Box 3402 One Lakeshore Dr Lake Charles LA 70602

LAWYER, WILLIAM GROVE, foundation administrator; b. York, Pa., Apr. 5, 1943; s. Clarence Martin and Katherine E. (Frei) L.; m. Sharon L. Wilderson, June 13, 1965; children: Katherine E., William G. III. BA, Duke U., 1965; MA, Yale U., 1969. Tchr. U.S. Peace Corps, Philippines, 1965-67; tchr., administr. Rye (N.Y.) Country Day Sch., 1969-78; exec. dir. Greenburgh Nature Ctr., Scarsdale, N.Y., 1978—; mem. steering com. Coalition Living Mus., 1980—; Sound Hudson Nature Ctrs., 1981—; cons. Council Park Friends, Jamesville, N.Y., 1985. contbr. articles to N.Y. Times 1987-89. Elder Presbyn. Ch., Rye, 1987—; publicity chmn. Westchester Youth Symphony Orch., 1985. Democrat. Avocations: running, tennis, swimming, guitar, concerts. Office: Greenburgh Nature Ctr Dromore Rd Scarsdale NY 10583

LAX, KATHLEEN THOMPSON, federal judge. BA, U. Kans., 1967; JD, U. Calif., L.A., 1980. Law clk. U.S. Bankruptcy Ct., L.A., 1980-82; assoc. Gibson, Dunn & Crutcher, L.A., 1982-88; judge U.S. Bankruptcy Ct., L.A., 1988—; bd. dirs. L.A. Bankruptcy Forum, 1988—; bd. govs. Fin. Lawyers Conf., L.A., 1991-92, 94—. Bd. editors: Calif. Bankruptcy Jour., 1988—. Office: US Bankruptcy Court Rm 1334 255 E Temple St Los Angeles CA 90012

LAX, MELVIN, theoretical physicist; b. Bklyn., Mar. 8, 1922; s. Morris and Rose H. L.; m. Judith Heckelman, June 26, 1949; children: R. Laurie, David A., Jonathan R., Naomi A. B.A. in Physics (Charles Hayden scholar 1938-42), NYU, 1942; M.S. in Physics; M.S. (fellow in applied math. 1942-43), MIT, 1943, Ph.D. (fellow in physics 1943-46, research asso. 1946-47), 1947. Mem. faculty Syracuse (N.Y.) U., 1947-55, Princeton U., 1961, Oxford (Eng.) U., 1961-62; mem. tech. staff AT&T Bell Labs., Murray Hill, N.J., 1955-72; head theoretical physics research dept. Bell Labs., 1962-64, cons., 1972—; Disting. prof. physics CCNY, 1971—; cons. to govt. and industry. Author books and numerous papers in field; bd. editors Phys. Rev., 1958-60, 84-86; editor: Advanced Series in Applied Physics, 1988—; mem. adv. bd. Modern Physics Letters, Internat. Jour. Modern Physics; editorial bd. Quantum Optics, 1992-94. Fellow Am. Phys. Soc. (publs. com. 1980-83); mem. NAS (sec. applied scis., math. and engring. class 1989-92), Am. Phys. Soc.-Chinese Phys. Soc. (telecomm. com. 1995—), Optical Soc. Am. (publs. tech. com. 1991-94, optics letters rev. com. 1995—). Jewish. Home: 12 High St Summit NJ 07901-2413 Office: CCNY 138th St and Convent Ave New York NY 10031

LAX, PETER DAVID, mathematics educator; b. Budapest, Hungary, May 1, 1926; came to U.S., 1941, naturalized, 1944; s. Henry and Klara (Kornfeld) L.; m. Anneli Cahn, 1948; children: John, James D. BA, N.Y. U., 1947, PhD, 1949; DSc (hon.), Kent State U., 1976; DSC (hon.), Brown U., 1993; Dr. honoris causa, U. Paris, 1979; D. Natural Scis. (hon.), Technische Hochschule Aachen, Germany, 1988; DSc (hon.), Herriot Walt U., 1990; D. (hon.), Leningrad State U., 1991, U. Md. Baltimore County, 1993; PhD (hon.), Tel Aviv U., 1992, Beijing U., 1993. Asst. prof. NYU, 1949-57, prof., 1957—; dir. Courant Inst. Math. Scis., 1972-80. Author: (with Ralph Phillips) Scattering Theory, 1967, Scattering Theory for Automorphic Functions, 1976, (with A. Lax and S.Z. Burstein) Calculus with applications and computing, 1976, Hyperbolic Systems of Conservation Laws and the Mathematical Theory of Shock Waves, 1973. Mem. Pres.'s Com. on Nat. Medal of Sci., 1976, Nat. Sci. Bd., 1980-86. Served with AUS, 1944-46. Recipient Semmelweis medal Semmelweis Med. Soc., 1975, Nat. Medal Sci., 1986, Wolf Prize, 1987. Mem. AAAS, NAS (applied math. and numerical analysis award 1983), Am. Math. Soc. (pres. 1979-80, Norbert Wiener prize 1973, Leroy P. Steele prize 1993), Math. Assn. Am. (bd. govs., Chauvenet prize 1974), Soc. Indsl. and Applied Math., Acad. des Scis. (fgn. assoc.), Russian Acad. Sci. (fgn. assoc.), Acad. Sinica (hon.), Hungarian Acad. Sci. (hon.). Office: Courant Inst Math Scis 251 Mercer St Rm 912 New York NY 10012-1185

LAY, DONALD POMEROY, federal judge; b. Princeton, Ill., Aug. 24, 1926; s. Hardy W. and Ruth (Cushing) L.; m. Miriam Elaine Gustafson, Aug. 6, 1949; children: Stephen Pomeroy (dec.), Catherine Sue, Cynthia Lynn, Elizabeth Ann, Deborah Jean, Susan Elaine. Student, U.S. Naval Acad., 1945-46; BA, U. Iowa, 1948, JD, 1951; LLD (hon.), Mitchell Coll. Law, 1985. Bar: Nebr. 1951, Iowa 1951, Wis. 1953. Assoc. Kennedy, Holland, DeLacy & Svoboda, Omaha, 1951-53, Quarles, Spence & Quarles, Milw., 1953-54, Eisenstatt, Lay, Higgins & Miller, 1954-66; judge U.S. Ct. Appeals (8th cir.), 1966—, chief judge, 1980-92, senior judge, 1992—; faculty mem. on evidence Nat. Coll. Trial Judges, 1964-65, U. Minn. Law Sch., William Mitchell Law Sch.; mem. U.S. Jud. Conf., 1980-92. Mem. editorial bd.: Iowa Law Rev., 1950-51; contbr. articles to legal jours. With USNR, 1944-46. Recipient Hancher-Finkbine medal U. Iowa, 1980. Fellow Internat. Acad. Trial Lawyers; mem. ABA, Nebr. Bar Assn., Iowa Bar Assn., Wis. Bar Assn., Am. Judicature Soc., Assn. Trial Lawyers Am. (bd. govs. 1963-65, Jud. Achievement award), Order of Coif, Delta Sigma Rho (Significant Sig award 1986, Herbert Harley award 1988), Phi Delta Phi, Sigma Chi. Presbyterian. Office: US Ct Appeals 8th Cir 316 N Robert St Rm 560 Saint Paul MN 55101

LAY, KENNETH LEE, diversified energy company executive; b. Tyrone, Mo., Apr. 15, 1942; s. Omer and Ruth E. (Reese) L.; m. Linda Ann Phillips, July 10, 1982; children: Robyn Anne, Mark Kenneth, Todd David, Elizabeth Ayers, Robert Ray. BA, U. Mo., 1964, MA, 1965; PhD, U. Houston, 1970. Corp. economist Exxon Corp., Houston, 1965-68; asst. prof. and lectr. in econs. George Washington U., 1969-73; tech. asst. to commr. FERC, 1971-72; dep. undersec. for energy Dept. Interior, 1972-74; v.p. Fla. Gas Co. (now Continental Resources Co.), Winter Park, Fla., 1974-76, pres., 1976-79; exec. v.p. The Continental Group, 1979-81; pres., chief operating officer, dir. Transco Energy Co., Houston, 1981-84; chmn., chief exec officer Houston Natural Gas Corp., 1984-85; pres., chief exec. officer, chief operating officer, dir. HNG/InterNorth (now Enron Corp.), Omaha, 1985—, also chmn. bd. dirs., Houston; asst. prof. George Washington U.; bd. dirs. Eli Lilly & Co., Trust Co. West, Compaq Computer Corp.; past chmn. Greater Houston Partnership; mem. President's Coun. on Sustainable Devel. Sec. Energy Adv. Bd.; former chmn. bd. regents U. Houston, Bus. Coun. for Sustainable Energy Future; Houston Host Com. for 1992 Rep. Nat. Conv.; co-chmn. 1990 Houston Econ. Summit Host Com. Decorated Navy Commendation award; N.A.M. fellow; State Farm fellow; Guggenheim fellow. Mem. Nat. Petroleum Coun. (bd. dirs.), River Oaks Country Club, Phi Beta Kappa. Republican. Methodist. Office: Enron Corp PO Box 1188 Houston TX 77251-1188

LAY, NORVIE LEE, legal educator; b. Cardwell, Ky., Apr. 17, 1940; s. Arlie H. and Opha (Barnes) L.; 1 dau., Lea Anne. B.S., U. Ky., 1960; J.D., U. Louisville, 1963; LL.M. (Cook fellow), U. Mich., 1964, S.J.D., 1967. Bar: Ky. 1963. Asst. prof. law U. Louisville, 1964-67, assoc. prof., 1967-70, 1970—; asst. dean U. Louisville (Sch. Law), 1971-73, assoc. dean, 1973-84, acting dean, 1981-82; vis. prof. Southwestern U. Sch. Law, summer 1983, N.Y. Law Sch., 1983-84, Coll. of Law U. Iowa, summer 1989. Author: Tax and Estate Planning for Community Property and the Migrant Client, 1970; contbr. articles to profl. jours. Trustee St. Joseph's Infirmary, 1974-78, S.W. Jefferson Community Hosp., 1979-80, Suburban Hosp., 1981-84, Humana-Audubon Hosp., 1985-88, U. Louisville Law Sch. Alumni Found., from 1982-85; bd. dirs. Louisville Ballet, from 1982-88, Louisville Theatrical Assn., 1985-88, Louisville Art Gallery, 1984-87, Watertower Art Assn., 1986-89, Chamber Mus. Soc. of Louisville, 1985-88, Louisville Chorus, 1985-88, Ky. Contemporary Theatre, 1984, Ky. Country Day Sch., 1985-88, Ky. Arts Coun., 1991—; mem. Nat. Conf. Commrs. Uniform State Laws. Recipient Scholarship Key Delta Theta Phi, 1963, Outstanding Graduating Sr. award Omicron Delta Kappa, 1963. Fellow Am. Coll. of Trust and Estate Counsel (mem.), Am. Coll. Tax Counsel; mem. ABA, Ky. Bar Assn., Louiville Bar Assn., Am. Judicature Soc. Republican. Baptist. Office: U Louisville Sch Law Belknap Campus Louisville KY 40292

LAY, THORNE, geosciences educator; b. Casper, Wyo., Apr. 20, 1956; s. Johnny Gordon and Virginia Florence (Lee) L. BS, U. Rochester, 1978; MS, Calif. Inst. Tech., 1980, PhD, 1983. Rsch. assoc. Calif. Inst. Tech., Pasadena, 1983; asst. prof. geosciences U. Mich., Ann Arbor, 1984-88, assoc. prof., 1988-89; prof. U. Calif., Santa Cruz, 1989—. cons. Woodward Clyde Cons., Pasadena, 1982-84; dir. Inst. Tectonics, 1990-94, chmn. earth sci. dept., 1994—. Contbr. more than 120 peer-reviewed articles to sci. jours. NSF fellow, 1978-81, Guttenberg fellow Calif. Inst. Tech., 1978, Lilly fellow Eli Lilly Found., 1984, Sloan fellow, 1985-87, Presidential Young Investigator, 1985-90. Fellow Royal Astron. Soc., Am. Geophys. Union (Macelwane medal 1991), Soc. Exploration Geophysicist, Seismol. Soc. Am., AAAS. Home: 32 Eastridge Dr Santa Cruz CA 95060-9999 Office: U Calif Santa Cruz Earth Sci Bd Santa Cruz CA 95064

LAYBOURNE, EVERETT BROADSTONE, lawyer; b. Springfield, Ohio, Oct. 26, 1911; s. Lawrence Everett and Jean (Broadstone) L.; m. Dorrise Barclay, Sept. 19, 1936 (dec. Nov. 1973); m. Ottilie Kruger, July 31, 1974. B.A., Ohio State U., 1932; J.D., Harvard, 1935. Bar: Calif. bar 1936. Mem. firms Macdonald, Schultheis & Pettit, 1936-40; mem. firms Schultheis & Laybourne, 1940-54, Schultheis, Laybourne & Dowds, 1954-68, Laybourne, Keeley & MacMahon, 1968-69; sr. partner Macdonald, Halsted & Laybourne, Los Angeles, 1969-88; of counsel Baker & McKenzie, Los Angeles, 1988-93; dir. Viking Industries, Pacific Energy Corp., McBain Instruments, Coldwater Investment Co., Brouse-Whited Packaging Co., Calif. Energy Co. Trustee Brite-Lite Corp. Calif.; Calif. UN Day, 1960; regional vice chmn. U.S. Com. for UN, 1961-64; mem. adv. council Stamp Out Smog, 1963-75; mem. spl. rev. com. Los Angeles Air Pollution Control Dist., 1964-65; bd. dirs. Fedn. Hillside, Canyon Assos., Los Angeles, 1952-59, chmn. bd., 1957-59; bd. dirs. WAIF, Inc., 1977—, chmn. bd., 1978—; bd. dirs. UN Assn. U.S.A., 1964-65; bd. dirs. Ralph M. Parsons Found., 1977—, v.p., 1978—; trustee, sec. Beta Theta Pi Scholastic Found. So. Calif. 1947-58. Served as lt. USNR, 1944-46. Recipient Commendation Los Angeles City Council, 1957, Ohio State U. Alumni Centennial award, 1970, Alumni Citizenship award, 1988. Mem. Big Ten Univs. Club So. Calif. (pres. 1941-42), L.A. Bar Assn. (exec. com. internat. law sect. 1968-74), World Affairs Coun., Selden Soc., Roscomare Valley Assn. (pres. 1952-54), Calif. Club, Bel-Air Country Club, Phi Beta Kappa. Republican. Episcopalian (sr. warden 1966-67). Office: 555 W 5th St 35th Fl Los Angeles CA 90013-1024

LAYBOURNE, GERALDINE, broadcasting executive; b. Plainfield, N.J., 1947; married; 2 children. BA, Vassar Coll., 1969; MS, U. Pa., 1971. Former high sch. tchr.; dir. with Nickelodeon, 1980—, creator Nick at Nite, 1985—, pres.; also vice chmn. MTV Networks. Office: MTV Networks 1515 Broadway New York NY 10036-5702

LAYCOCK, ANITA SIMON, psychotherapist; b. Cheyenne, Wyo., Dec. 17, 1940; d. James Robert and Dorothy (Dearmin) Simon; m. Maurice Percy Laycock, June 18, 1965(dec. 1976); 1 child, (dec.). BA, U. Wyo., 1962,

MA, 1971. Lic. counselor, Wyo., nationally cert. addiction specialist. Grad. student counselor, psychometrist Wyo. State Prison, Rawlins, 1971-73; counselor, trainer Dept. of Insts. State of Colo., Denver, 1973-75; counselor, tchr. supr. Jefferson County Evaluation-Diagnostic Ctr., Rawlins, 1975-78; psychometrist Wyo. State Penitentiary, Rawlins, 1978-79; counselor, therapist Rocky Mountain Arts and Scis., Cheyenne, 1979-81; counselor, therapist supr., dir. SWARA, Rock Springs, Wyo., 1981-85; therapy dir. St. Joseph Residential Treatment, Torrington, Wyo., 1985-88; dir. psychiatric unit Nat. Med. Enterprises Hill-Haven-Pk. Manor, Rawlins, 1988-89; chief exec. officer Simon-Laycock & Assocs., Rawlins, 1989—; cons. Kids in Distressed Situations, Rawlins, 1990-91, Child Devel. Ctr., Rawlins, 1991—; dir. Pub. Offender and Forensic Mental Health Program, Rawlins, 1988-91. Author: (programs) related to sex offenders. Pres. Cheyenne City Panhellenic, 1965-68. Named Miss Wyo.-Miss Universe, 1960; named Miss Wool of Wyo., 1965. Mem. ACA, Nat. Sex Offenders Counselors, Nat. Assn. Drug and Alcohol Counselors, Pub. Offenders Counselors Assn., Western Corrections Assn., Wyo. Assn. Addiction Specialists (pres. 1988—). Avocations: profl. animal trainer, artist. Home: PO Box 3027 Cheyenne WY 82009 Office: Simon Laycock & Assocs 1716 Yellowstone hwy Cheyenne WY 82009

LAYCOCK, ERIC PAUL, hospital administrator; b. Toronto, Ont., Can., Mar. 12, 1949; s. Earl Russel and Iva Marie (Posthill) L.; m. Brigitte Sieck Laycock, Feb. 7, 1968; children: Kimberly, Christopher. BA in Econs., U. Western Ont., London, 1972; diploma in hosp. adminstrn., U. Toronto, 1974. Adminstrv. resident Scarborough (Ont.) Centenary Hosp., 1973-74, adminstrv. asst., 1974-76, asst. exec. dir. med. svcs., 1976-80; dir. hosp. svcs. North York Gen. Hosp., Toronto, 1980-82; sr. v.p. Royal Victoria Hosp., Barrie, Ont., 1982—; owner Healthcare Assocs., Ont., 1980. Author: How We Care: A Quality Assurance Program for Canadian Hospitals, 1984, Emergency Services Action Plan, 1990; contbr. articles to profl. publs. Pres. Simcoe County area Can. Red Cross Soc., Barrie, Ont., 1989-94, developer emergency svcs. response plan; dir. Ont. Red Cross, Toronto, 1991-94; sec. Simcoe County Hosp. Coun.; mem. Dist. Health Coun. Fellow Am. Coll. Hosp. Adminstrs. (mem. regents adv. coun.); mem. Barrie Golf and Country Club (pres.). Avocations: golf, woodworking.

LAYCOCK, HAROLD DOUGLAS, law educator, writer; b. Alton, Ill., Apr. 15, 1948; s. Harold Francis and Claudia Anita (Garrette) L.; m. Teresa A. Sullivan, June 14, 1971; children: Joseph Peter, John Patrick. BA, Mich. State U., 1970; JD, U. Chgo., 1973. Bar: Ill. 1973, Tex. 1974, U.S. Dist. (no. dist.) Ill. 1973, Tex. 1974, U.S. Dist. Ct. (we. dist.) Tex. 1975, U.S. Ct. Appeals (5th and 11th cirs.) 1975, U.S. Supreme Ct. 1976, U.S. Ct. Appeals (6th cir.) 1987, U.S. Ct. Appeals (8th cir.) 1994. Law clk. to judge U.S. Ct. Appeals (7th cir.), Chgo., 1973-74; pvt. practice Austin, Tex., 1974-76; asst. prof. U. Chgo., 1976-80, prof., 1980-81; prof. U. Tex., Austin, 1980—, endowed professorships, 1983-88, assoc. dean for acad. affairs, 1985-86, endowed chair, 1988—, assoc. dean for rsch., 1991—; vis. prof. U. Mich., 1990; reporter com. on motion practice III. Jud. Conf., 1977-78. Author: Modern American Remedies, 1985, 2d edit., 1994, The Death of the Irreparable Injury Rule, 1991; mem. bd. advisors Religious Freedom Reporter, 1990—; contbr. articles to law revs. Mem. adv. bd. Consumer Svcs. Orgn., Chgo., 1979-80; mem. exec. bd. Ctr. for Ch./State Studies, DePaul U., Chgo., 1982-87; mem. adv. com. on religious liberty Presby. Ch. U.S.A., 1983-88, advisor restatement of restitution, 1984-85; v.p. St. Francis Sch., 1990-92, pres. 1992—; mem. bd. advisors J.M. Dawson Inst. Ch./State Studies, Baylor U., 1990—. Fellow Internat. Acad. for Freedom of Religion and Belief; mem. AAUP (mem. com. on status of women in acad. profession 1982-85), Am. Law Inst., Chgo. Coun. Lawyers (v.p. 1977-78), Assn. Am. Law Schs. (chmn., sec. on remedies 1983, 94). Home: 4203 Woodway Dr Austin TX 78731-2034 Office: U Tex Law Sch 727 E 26th St Austin TX 78705-3224

LAYCRAFT, JAMES HERBERT, judge; b. Veteran, Alta., Can., Jan. 5, 1924; s. George Edward and Hattie (Cogswell) L.; m. Helen Elizabeth Bradley, May 1, 1948; children: James B., Anne L. BA, U. Alta., Edmonton, 1950; LLB, U. Alta., 1951; LLD (hon.), U. Calgary, Alta., 1986. Bar: Alta. Barrister Nolan Chambers & Co., Calgary, 1952-75; justice trial div. Supreme Ct. of Alta., Calgary, 1975-79; justice Ct. of Appeal of Alta., Calgary, 1979-85, chief justice of Alta., 1985-91, ret., 1991. Contbr. articles to law jours. Served to lt. Royal Can. Arty., 1941-46, PTO. Mem. United Ch. of Can. Avocations: amateur radio, fishing.

LAYDEN, FRANCIS PATRICK (FRANK LAYDEN), professional basketball team executive, former coach; b. Bklyn., Jan. 5, 1932; m. Barbara Layden; children: Scott, Michael, Katie. Student, Niagara U. High sch. basketball coach L.I., N.Y.; head coach, athletic dir. Adelphi-Suffolk Coll. (now Dowling Coll.); head basketball coach, athletic dir. Niagara U., Niagara Falls, N.Y., 1968-76; asst. coach Atlanta Hawks, 1976-79; gen. mgr. Utah Jazz, Salt Lake City, 1979-88, head coach, 1981-88, v.p. basketball ops., until 1988, pres., 1989—. Bd. dirs. Utah Soc. Prevention Blindness; bd. dirs. Utah chpt. Multiple Sclerosis Soc., Utah Spl. Olympics. Served to 1st lt. Signal Corps, AUS. Office: Utah Jazz Delta Ctr 301 West South Temple Salt Lake City UT 84101*

LAYMAN, EMMA MCCLOY (MRS. JAMES W. LAYMAN), psychologist, educator; b. Danville, Va., Feb. 25, 1910; d. Charles Harold and Anna (Fisher) McCloy; m. James Walter Layman, Dec. 12, 1936 (dec. May 5, 1978). A.B., Oberlin Coll., 1930; M.A., NYU, 1931; Ph.D., U. Iowa, 1937; L.H.D. (hon.), Iowa Wesleyan Coll., 1981. Diplomate: Am. Bd. Examiners Profl. Psychology. Psychol. examiner Iowa Psychopathic Hosp., Iowa City, 1934-35, 37; clin. psychologist Mich. Children's Inst., Ann Arbor, 1935-36; supr. psychol. services Iowa Bd. Social Welfare, Des Moines, 1937-41; assoc. prof. psychology Woman's Coll., U. N.C., 1947-52; supervisory clin. psychologist Brooke Army Hosp., Ft. Sam Houston, 1952-54; chief psychologist Children's Hosp., Washington, 1954-60; head dept. psychology Iowa Wesleyan Coll., Mt. Pleasant, 1960-75, assoc. prof., 1960-61, prof., 1961-75, emeritus, 1975—, asst. acad. dean, 1964-65, chmn. social sci. div., 1969-75, dir. East Asian studies, 1963-75, dir. internat. studies, 1970-75; pvt. practice clin. psychology, 1941—; lectr. U. Chattanooga, 1946-47; vis. prof. edn. Duke, summers 1948-50; adj. prof. U. Md., 1954-60; lectr. Howard U., 1956-60; cons. Walter Reed Army Hosp., 1956-60. Author: Mental Health Through Physical Education and Recreation, 1955, Airesboro Castle, 1974, Buddhism in America, 1976, also articles. Pres. Oberlin-Wellington bd. Ch. Women United; bd. dirs. Intergenerational House; pres. class of 1930 Oberlin Coll., also mem. alumni coun.; mem. Spectrum Community Club. Lt. USNR, 1943-46. Fellow APA, Acad. Clin. Psychology; mem. Inter-Am. Psychol. Soc., Am. Assn. Chinese Studies, AAUW (br. treas.), Phi Beta Kappa, Sigma Xi. Episcopalian. Home: 154 Kendal Dr Oberlin OH 44074-1907

LAYMAN, LAWRENCE, naval officer; b. Laclede County, Mo., Oct. 28, 1930; s. Archibald A. and Zoe Ellen (Hoke) L.; m. Carmen Elizabeth Meyer, Oct. 5, 1953; children: Linda Carmen, Lawrence, Harry Arthur, John Robert. B.S., U.S. Naval Acad., 1952; M.S. in Internat. Affairs, George Washington U., 1972. Commd. ensign U.S. Navy, 1952, advanced through grades to rear adm., 1979; service to Korea and Vietnam; dep. comdr. Naval Telecommunications Command, 1978-79; dir. command, control and communications systems U.S. European Command, 1979-81; vice dir. Def. Communications Agy., Washington, 1981-83; dir. Naval Communications, Washington, 1983-86; dir. space command and control Office Chief Naval Ops., Washington, 1986-89, ret., 1989. Decorated D.S.M., Def. Superior Svc. medal with oak leaf cluster, Legion of Merit with Gold Star, Bronze Star with combat V, Meritorious Svc. medal. Home: 3429 Silver Maple Pl Falls Church VA 22042-3545

LAYMAN, MARK LESLIE, journalist; b. Waynesboro, Va., Sept. 25, 1958; s. G. Edward and Virginia (Ramsey) L. BA in Polit. Sci. magna cum laude, Roanoke Coll., 1980; grad. Poynter Inst. Media Studies, 1994. Reporter The Roanoke (Va.) Times and World-News, 1982-93; night metro editor Roanoke (Va.) Times & World-News, 1993—. Contbg. writer: Collier's Year Book, P.F. Collier Inc., N.Y.C., 1985-93. Home: 2610 Derwent Dr SW Roanoke VA 24015-2618 Office: Roanoke Times & World News PO Box 2491 Roanoke VA 24010-2491

LAYMAN, WILLIAM ARTHUR, psychiatrist, educator; b. West New York, N.J., Feb. 8, 1929; s. Frank Kyle and Lucy Geraldine (Rooney) L.; 1 child, William Kraft. Student, NYU, 1946, 48; B.S. cum laude, St. Peter's Coll., 1951; M.D., Georgetown U., 1955. Diplomate: Am. Bd. Psychiatry and Neurology. Intern Hackensack (N.J.) Hosp., 1955-56; resident in psychiatry Lyons (N.J.) VA Hosp., 1956-57, Fairfield Hills Hosp., Newtown, Conn., 1957-58; fellow in psychiatry Yale U., 1958-59; instr. psychiatry Seton Hall Coll. Medicine, 1959-61, asst. prof., 1961-65; assoc. prof. psychiatry N.J. Med. Sch., Newark, 1965-74; clin. prof. N.J. Med. Sch., 1974-77, prof., 1977—; practice medicine specializing in psychiatry Hackensack, NJ, 1959—; dep. chmn. ednl. services, dept. psychiatry and mental health sci. N.J. Med. Sch., 1976-83, acting chmn. dept. psychiatry and mental health sci., 1983-86; cons. Hackensack Hosp.; mem. staff Coll. Hosp. Contbr. articles to profl. jours. Served with U.S. Army, 1946-48. Fellow Am. Psychiat. Assn. (life); mem. AAUP, N.J. Med. Soc., Bergen County Med. Soc. Office: UMDNJ-ADMC 15 (1510) 30 Bergen St Newark NJ 07107-3000

LAYNE, JAMES NATHANIEL, vertebrate biologist; b. Chgo., May 16, 1926; s. Leslie Joy and Harriet (Hausmann) L.; m. Lois Virginia Linderoth, Aug. 26, 1950; children: Susan Kimberly, Jamie Linderoth, Susan Nell, Rachel Pratt. BA, Cornell U., 1950, PhD, 1954. Grad. teaching asst. Cornell U., Ithaca, N.Y., 1950-54; assoc. prof. zoology Cornell U., 1963-67; asst. prof. zoology So. Ill. U., Carbondale, 1954-55; asst. prof., then asso. prof. biology U. Fla., 1955-63; asst. curator, then asso. curator mammals Fla. State Mus., Gainesville, 1955-63; research asso. Fla. State Mus., 1963-65; dir. research, then exec. dir. Archbold Biol. Sta.; Archbold curator mammals Am. Mus. Natural History, 1967-85; sr. rsch. biologist Archbold Biol. Sta., 1985-94, sr. rsch. biologist emeritus, 1994—; rsch. assoc. Fla. State Collection of Arthropods, Am. Mus. Natural History; vis. scientist primate ecology sect. Nat. Inst. Neurol. Diseases and Blindness, summers 1961-62. Contbr. articles and chpt. to profl. jours. and books. Hon. Trustee Fla. Defenders of Environment; bd. dirs. Fla. Audubon Soc.; mem. Fla. Nongame Wildlife Adv. Council, Peace River Basin Bd., Fla. Panther Tech. Adv. Council. Served with USAAF, 1944-46. Fellow AAAS; mem. Am. Soc. Zoologists, Am. Soc. Mammalogists (pres. 1970-72, hon. mem. 1993, C. Hart Merriam award 1976), Ecol. Soc. Am., Soc. for Study of Evolution, Am. Soc. Naturalists, Wildlife Soc., Wildlife Disease Assn., Nature Conservancy (trustee Fla. chpt.), Fla. Acad. Scis. (pres. 1984-85, medalist 1995), Orgn. Biol. Field Stas. (pres. 1986-87), Phi Beta Kappa, Sigma Xi, Phi Kappa Phi, Phi Sigma. Office: Archbold Biol Sta PO Box 2057 Lake Placid FL 33852-2057

LAYSON, WILLIAM MCINTYRE, research consulting company executive; b. Lexington, Ky., Sept. 24, 1934; s. Zed Clark and Louise (McIntyre) L.; m. Robin Dale Fort, July 28, 1982. B.S., MIT, 1956, Ph.D., 1961; postgrad., U. Sydney, Australia, 1957-58. Research scientist European Ctr. Nuclear Research, Geneva, 1960-62; research scientist U. Calif.-Berkeley, 1962-64; mem. tech. staff Pan Am World Airways, Patrick AFB, Fla., 1964-67; research scientist Gen. Research Corp., Rosslyn, Va., 1967-70; dir. Sci. Applications Internat. Corp., McLean, Va., 1970—, sr. v.p., chmn. incentives com., 1975-93; coord. def. nuclear programs, 1975—, chmn. ethics com., 1994—; pres. Langley Sch., 1995—; dir. Langley Sch., 1992—; pres. Layson's Buffalo Trace Farms, 1976—. Fulbright scholar U. Sydney, Australia, 1957-58. Mem. Am. Def. Preparedness Assn. Democrat. Presbyterian (elder). Avocations: church activities, jogging, swimming, skiing. Home: 8301 Summerwood Dr Mc Lean VA 22102-2213 Office: Sci Applications Internat Corp 1710 Goodridge Dr Mc Lean VA 22102-3701

LAYTON, BILLY JIM, composer; b. Corsicana, Tex., Nov. 14, 1924; s. Roy William and Jimmie Vera (Franks) L.; m. Evro Zeniou, Feb. 2, 1949; children: Alexis Roy, Daphne Niobe. Mus.B., New Eng. Conservatory Music, 1948; Mus.M., Yale U., 1950; postgrad. (Alfred M. Hertz Travelling fellow), U. Calif. at Berkeley, 1964, Ph.D., Harvard U., 1960. Faculty New Eng. Conservatory Music, 1959-60, Harvard U., 1960-66; prof. State U. N.Y. at Stony Brook, 1966-92, chmn. dept. music, 1966-72, 82-85. Composer: Five Studies for Violin and Piano, 1952, An American Portrait; symphonic overture, 1953, Three Dylan Thomas Poems; mixed chorus, brass sextet, 1954-56, String Quartet in Two Movements, 1956, Three Studies for Piano, 1957, Divertimento, 1958-60, Dance Fantasy for Orchestra, 1964. Rome Prize fellow, 1954-57; grantee Nat. Inst. Arts and Letters, 1958; Guggenheim fellow, 1963; grantee Thorne Music Fund, 1968-70; Recipient Creative Arts award Brandeis U., 1961. Mem. Am. Music Center (dir. 1972-74), Am. Soc. Univ. Composers (founding), A.S.C.A.P., Am. Musicological Soc., Coll. Music Soc. (mem. council 1970-72), Internat. Soc. Contemporary Music (U.S.A. sect. 1968-70), Soc. for Music Theory (founding). Home: 4 Johns Rd East Setauket NY 11733-3020

LAYTON, DONALD HARVEY, banker; b. Bklyn., May 9, 1950; s. Irving and Charlotte (Bell) L.; m. Sandra Lynn Lazo, June 1, 1974; children: Todd Samuel, Ross Charles. SB in Econs., MIT, 1972, SM in Econs., 1972; MBA, Harvard U., 1974. Rsch. asst. Harvard Bus. Sch., Boston, 1974-75; trainee Mfrs. Hanover Trust Co., N.Y.C., 1975-76, asst. sec., 1976-78, asst. v.p., 1976-78, v.p., 1978-83, sr. v.p., 1983-86, sr. mng. dir., 1986-90, group exec., 1990-91; sr. exec. v.p. Chemical Bank, 1992—; chmn. Chem. Futures & Options, Chgo., 1983—. Treas. 305 E 24th St Owners Corp., N.Y.C., 1984-92. Baker scholar Harvard U., 1974. Home: 885 Park Ave New York NY 10021 Office: Chem Bank 270 Park Ave New York NY 10017

LAYTON, EDWIN THOMAS, JR., science and technology history educator, writer; b. Los Angeles, Sept. 13, 1928; s. Edwin Thomas Layton and Virginia Louise (Yarnell) Meyer; m. Barbara Jean Wyman, May 2, 1952 (dec. Apr. 1978); 1 child, George Mowry; m. Margaret Ruth Brubacher Kirby, Nov. 24, 1982; 1 step-son, David Kirby. BA in History, UCLA, 1950, MA in History, 1953, PhD in History, 1956. Instr. U. Wis., Madison, 1955-56, Ohio State U., Columbus, 1956-60; asst. prof. Purdue U., Lafayette, Ind., 1960-65; assoc. prof. Case Western Res. U., Cleve., 1965-75; prof. history of sci. and tech. dept. mech. engring. U. Minn., Mpls., 1975-94, Inst. Tech. prof., 1994—; cons. Iron Bridge Trust, U.K., summer 1986. Author: The Revolt of the Engineers, Social Responsibility and the American Engineering Profession, 1971, rev. edit. 1985, Dexter prize 1971, A Regional Union Catalog of Manuscripts Relating to the History of Science and Technology, 1971; author, co-editor: The Dynamics of Science and Technology, 1978, History of Heat Transfer, 1988; editor: Technology and Social Change in America, 1973; adv. editor Technology and Culture, Bus. and Profl. Ethics Jour., 1981—; contbr. chpts. to books, articles to profl. jours. Mem. Nuclear Manpower Studies Commn., NRC, Washington, 1981. AEC fellow Summer Inst. Oak Ridge, Tenn., 1963, NSF grantee 1965-70, 67-69, 71, 74-75, 77-78, 79-80, 81, 85. Fellow AAAS (chmn. sect. L 1989-90); mem. ASME (affiliate, history and heritage com. 1981), Soc. for History of Tech. (numerous coms. 1971-78, pres. 1985-86, Leonardo da Vinci medal 1990), History of Sci. Soc. (adv. editor ISIS 1979-81), Midwest Junto for History Sci. (pres. 1985-86, pres.-elect 1995-96), Soc. for Social Studies Sci. (exec. bd. 1978-79), Soc. Philosophy and Tech., Faculty Club (U. Minn.). Democrat. Episcopalian. Home: 2816 Webster Ave S Minneapolis MN 55416-1846 Office: Univ of Minn Dept of Mech Engring 111 Church St SE Minneapolis MN 55455-0150

LAYTON, JOHN C., federal agency administrator; b. East Stroudsburg, Pa., Oct. 9, 1944; s. Charles O. and Jeanne (Carlton) L.; m. Laura Bick, June 8, 1991; children: Gwen Ann, Susan Carlton. BS in Commerce, Rider Coll., 1966. Auditor Litton Industries, East Orange, N.J., 1969-72; spl. agt. FBI, Washington, 1972-80; dep. inspector gen. NASA, Washington, 1983-84; inspector gen. U.S. Dept. Treasury, Washington, 1984-86, U.S. Dept. Energy, Washington, 1986—. Served to 1st lt. U.S. Army, 1966-69. Mem. Assn. Govt. Accts. (chmn. ethics bd. 1985), Fed. Investigators Assn. (treas. 1982, bd. dirs. 1983-85), Soc. of Former Agts. of the FBI. Methodist. Office: Dept of Energy Inspector Gen 1000 Independence Ave SW Washington DC 20585-0002

LAYTON, ROBERT, lawyer; b. N.Y.C., Jan. 19, 1931; s. Benjamin and Ruth (Beck) L.; m. Joan Levy, May 17, 1967 (div. Jan. 1976); children: Elisabeth, Julie. BA, U. Mich., 1951; LLB, Yale U., 1954. Teaching fellow Stanford Law Sch., Palo Alto, Calif., 1957-58; atty. U.S. Dept. Justice, Washington, 1958-62; assoc., ptnr. Gilbert, Sewell & Young, N.Y.C., 1962-73; ptnr. Layton and Sherman, N.Y.C., 1973-84; Surrey & Morse, N.Y.C., 1984-85, Jones, Day, Reavis & Pogue, N.Y.C., 1986—. Served to sgt. U.S.

Army, 1954-56. Club: Yale (N.Y.C.). Office: Jones Day Reavis & Pogue 745 5th Ave # 29 New York NY 10151-0002

LAYTON, RODNEY EUGENE, controller, newspaper executive; b. Lusk, Wyo., Feb. 27, 1954; s. Raymond Dwight Layton and Mary Elizabeth (Miller) Spencer; m. Susan Carol Jouhnson, Jan. 8, 1977; children: Joshua, Elise, Caleb. Ba in Polit. Sci./Econs., Kearney State, 1977; student, U. Nebr. 1978-80. CPA, Nebr. Auditor State of Nebr., Lincoln, 1979-80; staff auditor Arthur Andersen, Houston, 1980-81; audit sr. McDermott & Miller, Grand Island, Nebr., 1981-82; internal audit mgr. Berkshire Hathaway, Inc., Omaha, 1982-86; internal auditor Norwest Bank Corp., Omaha, 1986-89; treas., controller Buffalo News, 1989—. Treas. Citizens Advocacy, Grand Island, 1981; treas., pres. Crippled Children's Camps, Inc., Buffalo, 1989-93; treas., bd. dirs. Cradle Beach Camp, Buffalo, 1989-94. Mem. AICPAs, Nebr. Soc. CPAs, Internat. Newspaper Fin. Execs. Avocations: tennis, golf, piano. Home: 3076 Green View Ter Hamburg NY 14075-3404 Office: Buffalo News 1 News Plz Buffalo NY 14203-2994

LAYTON, WILLIAM GEORGE, computer company executive, management consultant, human resources executive; b. Missouri Valley, Iowa, Sept. 11, 1931; s. George Holbert and Margaret (Wilson) L.; m. Caroline R. Tiffany, June 27, 1953; children: Kathleen Layton Medl, Sara Layton Howe, Thomas William. B.A., Coe Coll., 1953; M.A., U. Ill., 1955. Indsl. rels. trainee Procter & Gamble Co., Cin., 1955-57, pers. specialist, 1957-62; indsl. rels. mgr. Procter & Gamble Co., France, 1962-66; pers. mgr. European Tech. Ctr. Procter & Gamble Co., 1966-69, pers. mgr. internat., 1969-72; v.p. human resources Food Svc. div. Heublein, Inc., Louisville, 1972-77; sr. v.p. human resources Holiday Inns, Inc., Memphis, 1977-83; sr. ptnr. Johnson-Layton Co. Mgmt. Cons., L.A. and St. Petersburg, 1985-95; pres. CompCom, Inc., 1994—. Bd. dirs., pres. Jr. Achievement of Memphis, 1981-83; mem. Tenn. Jobs Tng. Coordinating Coun., 1982-88; mem. Pvt. Industry Coun. of Memphis and Shelby County, 1982-88; mem. Pres.'s Coun., Rhodes Coll., Memphis, 1983-90; mem. Tenn. Coun. Vocat. and Tech. Edn., 1984-88. Served with USAF, 1953-55. Mem. Soc. for Human Resources Mgmt., Am. Mgmt. Assn. (human resources coun. 1981-83), Inst. Mgmt. Cons. (cert. mgmt. cons.), Coun. Mgmt. Cons. (1987—, Sr. Examiner Sterling Quality award Fla. 1994), Phi Beta Kappa. Republican. Presbyterian. Lodge: Rotary. Office: 1135 Pasadena Ave S #307 Saint Petersburg FL 33707

LAYTON, WILLIAM ISAAC, mathematics educator; b. Cameron, Mo., Sept. 26, 1913; s. Joseph Evening and Mary Rebecca (Leighton) L.; m. Eva James Wade Layton, Mar. 28, 1941; children: Mary Layton Wells, Gay Layton Aycock. BS, U. S.C., 1934, MS, 1935; PhD, Vanderbilt U., 1948. Cert. tchr., S.C., Fla. Math. tchr. Greer High Sch., Greer, S.C., 1935-36, Rome High Sch., Rome, Ga., 1937-39; math. dept. head Albany Sr. High Sch., Albany, Ga., 1939-40; math. tchr. Peabody Demonstration, Nashville, Tenn., 1940-41; math. and engring. drawing tchr. Amarillo Coll., Amarillo, Tex., 1941-46; math. dept. head Austin Peay State Univ., Clarksville, Tenn., 1946-48; assoc. prof. math. Auburn Univ., Auburn, Ala., 1948-49; dean of instrn. Frostburg State Coll., Frostburg, Md., 1949-50; prof. math. and statistics Stephen F. Austin State Univ., Nacogdoches, Tex., 1950-79; math prof. Newberry (S.C.) Coll., Newberry, S.C., 1979-92; prof. emeirus Newberry (S.C.) Coll., 1992—, chmn. math., computer sci. and physics, 1982-92, acting chair dept. maths., computer sci. and physics, 1992-93. Author: An Analysis of Certification Requirements for Teachers of Mathematics, 1949, (with others) College Algebra, 1956, Mathematics of Finance, 1958, College Arithmetic, 1959, 2d edit., 1971, Essential Business Mathematics, 1977; contbg. author to The Mathematics Teacher. Pres., founder East Tex. Council of Tchrs. of Math. Recipient Alumni Disting. Prof. award Stephen F. Austin State Univ., 1976, Meritorious Svc. award Nat. Coun. Tchrs. Math., 1984, Fifty Yrs. Teaching award, 1987; named Prof. of Yr., Newberry Coll., 1988, 92. Mem. Am. Math. Soc. (pres. Tex. sect.), Math. Assn. Am., S.C. Coun. Tchrs. Math., S.C. Acad. Sci., Rotary (pres. S.C. 1987), Phi Beta Kappa, Sigma Xi, Phi Delta Kappa, Pi Mu Epsilon. Presbyterian. Home: 2421 Fulmer Ave Newberry SC 29108-2009 Office: Newberry Coll Newberry SC 29108

LAYVA, DAVID, lawyer; b. Cleve., Feb. 2, 1950; s. Paul M. and Celia L. (Pepe) L.; m. Suzan Layva, Jan. 8, 1982; (div. 1990); children: Vanessa, Laura. Ba cum laude, Cleve. State U., 1973; JD, Cleve. Marshall Coll. 1976; MLT, Georgetown U., 1983. Bar: Ohio 1976, Fla. 1977, D.C. 1980, W.Va. 1982, U.S. Dist. Ct. (no. dist.) Ohio 1977, U.S. Tax Ct. 1984, Ohio Supreme Ct. 1976, Fla. Supreme Ct. 1977, W.Va. Supreme Ct. 1982. Counsel Bar Assn. Greater Cleve., 1977-79; assoc. Silverstein & Mullins, Washington, 1980-87; ptnr. Avey & Steptoe, Charles Town, W.Va., 1982-90, Steptoe & Johnson, Charles Town, 1990-92, Jackson & Kelly, Charles Town, 1992—. Mem. W.Va. Bar Assn., Fla. Bar, D.C. Bar. Home: 34 Heritage Sq Harpers Ferry WV 25425 Office: Jackson & Kelly 700 E Washington St Charles Town WV 25414

LAYZELL, THOMAS D., academic administrator. Chancellor Bd. Govs. U., Springfield, IL. Office: Bd Govs Univs 700 E Adams St Ste 200 Springfield IL 62701-1601

LAYZER, DAVID, astrophysicist, educator; b. Ohio, Dec. 31, 1925; married; 6 children. A.B., Harvard U., 1947, Ph.D. in Theoretical Astrophysics, 1950. NRC fellow, 1950-51; lectr. astronomy U. Calif., Berkeley, 1951-52; research assoc. physics Princeton (N.J.) U., 1952-53; research assoc. Harvard U., Cambridge, Mass., 1953-55, research fellow, lectr., 1955-60, prof. astronomy, 1960-80, Donald H. Menzel prof. astrophysics, 1980—. Recipient Bok prize, 1960. Mem. Am. Acad. Arts and Sci., Am. Astron. Soc., Internat. Astron. Union, Royal Astrin. Soc. Office: Harvard U Ctr for Astrophysics 60 Garden St Stop 31 Cambridge MA 02138-1596*

LAZAGA, JOSE IGNACIO, airline executive; b. Havana, Cuba, Oct. 18, 1937; came to U.S., 1957; s. Jose Ignacio and Ada Olimpia (Diaz) L.; m. Esther Mae Arencibia; children: Edward Joseph, Deborah Diana Lazaga Nodar, Lisa Marie Harvey. BA, H.H. Maristas Coll., Havana, 1957; postgrad., U. Miami, 1957-59. Reservations supr. Tan Airlines, Miami, Fla., 1959-61; sta. mgr. Lanica Airlines, Miami, 1961-65, regional sales mgr., 1965-67; gen. traffic and sales mgr. Lanica Airlines, Managua, Nicaragua and Miami, 1967-71; sales mgr. Lan Chile Airlines, Miami, 1971-72; sales mgr. N.Am. Aerocondor Airlines, Miami, 1972-74, dir. sales systems, 1974-75, v.p. sales for N.Am. and Europe, 1975-79; v.p. mktg. and sales Tan-Sahsa Airlines, Miami, 1979-82; v.p. mktg. and sales Faucett-Peru Airlines, Miami, 1982-84, v.p. interline system, 1984—, also bd. dirs.; chief exec. officer CAF Airline Corp., Miami, 1984—, also bd. dirs.; bd. dirs. Caribbean Airlines Ltd., TFC Mgmt. Corp., sr. v.p. Faucett-Peru Airlines, North Am., The Caribbean, 1991—; comml. dir. APA Internat. Airlines, Caribbean Airlines Ltd., chmn. bd. dirs. Interworld Rep. Served with U.S. Army, 1959. Mem. Am. Soc. Travel Agts., S.Am. Travel Assn. (officer), Interline Mgrs. Assn., Airline Mktg. and Sales Execs., Airline Mgmt. Council, Airline Vets. Assn. Republican. Roman Catholic. Club: Airlines Exec. (Miami). Avocations: travel, tennis, water skiing. Office: CAF Airline Corp 7220 NW 36th St Ste 245 Miami FL 33166

LAZAR, ANNA, chemist; b. Budapest, Hungary, Jan. 10, 1931; came to U.S. 1956; d. Lajos and Maria (Grits) Varga; m. Josseph Lazar, Apr. 11, 1955 (div. 1969); 1 child, Julie Anna. Diploma, Eötvös Lorand Sci. U., Budapest, 1955. Chemist Harvard U., Boston, 1957-59, Arthur D. Little, CAmbridge, Mass., 1959-61, Wilkens Instrument and Rsch., Lafayette, Calif., 1961-62, Stanford (Calif.) U., 1962-63, Hercules Inc., Wilmington, Del., 1964-69, Cancer Rsch. Inst., Fox Chase Phila., Pa., 1969-70, Food and Drug Administrn., Phila., 1970—. Roman Catholic. Home: 428 W Montgomery Ave Haverford PA 19041

LAZAR, LUDMILA, concert pianist, educator; b. Celje, Slovenia; married; two children. MusB, Roosevelt U., 1963, MusM, 1964; D of Musical Arts, Northwestern U., 1987. Faculty Roosevelt U., Chgo., 1967—; prof. piano Chgo. Musical Coll. Roosevelt U., 1988—; chmn. keyboard dept. Roosevelt U., Chgo., 1983—. Roosevelt U. rsch. grantee, 1988; recipient Goethe Inst. award, 1987; named to All Star Profs. Team Chgo. Tribune, 1993. Mem. AAUP, Music Tchrs. Nat. Assn. (master tchr. cert. 1991), European Piano Tchrs. Assn., Ill. State Music Tchrs. Assn., Soc. Am. Musicians (pres., v.p.),

Coll. Music Soc., Mu Phi Epsilon (pres., v.p.). Office: Roosevelt U 430 S Michigan Ave Chicago IL 60605-1301

LAZAR, RAYMOND MICHAEL, lawyer, educator; b. Mpls., July 16, 1939; s. Simon and Hessie (Teplin) L; m. Susan Leah Krantz, Dec. 27, 1966; children: Mark, Deborah. BBA, U. Minn., 1961, JD, 1964. Bar: Minn. 1964, U.S. Dist. Ct. Minn. 1964. Spl. asst. atty. gen. State of Minn., St. Paul, 1964-66; sole practice Mpls., 1966-72; ptnr. Lapp, Lazar, Laurie & Smith, Mpls., 1972-86; ptnr., officer Fredrikson & Byron P.A., Mpls., 1986—; lectr. various continuing edn. programs, 1972—; adj. prof. law U. Minn., Mpls., 1983—. Fellow Am. Acad. Matrimonial Lawyers; mem. ABA, Minn. Bar Assn., Hennepin County Bar Assn. (chair family law sect. 1978-79, chair divsn. laws and procedures com. family law sect. 1993-94. Home: 1611 W 22nd St Minneapolis MN 55405-2402 Office: Fredrikson & Byron PA 1100 Internat Centre 900 2nd Ave S Minneapolis MN 55402-3314

LAZAR, THEODORE AARON, retired manufacturing company executive, lawyer; b. Chgo., July 16, 1920; s. Philip and Rena (Goodman) L.; m. Betty Jean Papermaster, July 6, 1952; children: Mark D., Paul A., Nancy Paula. JD, John Marshall Law Sch., Chgo., 1951. Bar: Ill. 1951, Wis. 1962, Ohio 1966. Sole practice, Chgo., 1951-62; asst. corp. counsel City of Chgo., 1956-59; atty. NLRB, Chgo. and Los Angeles, 1962-65; corp. counsel Lancaster Colony Corp., Columbus, Ohio, 1965-83, v.p. law, 1983-88, ret., 1988. Served as sgt. U.S. Army, 1942-46. Mem. Columbus Bar Assn., Indsl. Rels. Rsch. Assn. Home: 270 Bryant Ave Columbus OH 43085-3009

LAZAROVIC, KAREN, money manager, investment consultant; b. Bklyn., June 30, 1947; d. Alex and Lillian (Kurlanchik) Schwartzberg; children: Laura, Michael. BA cum laude, Bklyn. Coll., 1968. Proofreader Consumers Handbook, Great Neck, N.Y., 1975-77; sports dept. asst. N.Y. Post, N.Y.C., 1977-78, fin. dept. asst., 1978-79, reporter fin., 1979-84, columnist and editor fin., 1984-89; editor, pub. Wall St. Monitor newsletter, 1983-88; pres. KLP Capital Mgmt. Inc., 1989—; adv. to various companies on corp. fin. issues. Poetry pub. various jours. Avocations: tennis, photography.

LAZARUS, ALLAN MATTHEW, retired newspaper editor; b. New Orleans, Nov. 21, 1927; s. Harry Adolph and Edna Mary (Wodiker) L.; m. Martha Elizabeth Ellis, July 26, 1946; children—Kenneth Wayne, Virginia Lynn. B.A. in History, Centenary Coll., 1951. Copy boy The Times, Shreveport, La., 1944-45, reporter, 1945-46, telegraph editor, 1947-58, news editor, 1958-69, mng. editor, 1969-90; Pulitzer Prize Juror, 1978. Served as cpl. USAF, 1946-47. Mem. AP Mng. Editors Assn. (bd. dirs. 1975-80), La.-Miss. AP Assn. (pres. 1977-78), Sigma Delta Chi (pres. chpt. 1971-72). Roman Catholic. Home: 7713 Tampa Way Shreveport LA 71105-5701

LAZARUS, ARLIE GARY, retail corporate executive; b. N.Y.C., Jan. 29, 1938; s. Leon and Celia L.; m. Gloria Hindman, Mar. 29, 1959; children—Mark, Lee, Lisa. B.S., Hunter Coll., 1959. Acct. Eisner & Lubin (C.P.A.'s), N.Y.C., 1959-64; controller Miracle Mart, Inc., N.Y.C., 1964-68; fin. v.p. Jamesway Corp., Secaucus, N.J., 1968-73; exec. v.p. Jamesway Corp., 1973-76, pres., 1977-90; bd. dirs., mem. adv. bd. Discount Store News. Mem. Internat. Mass Retailing Assn. (bd. dirs.). Jewish. Office: Jamesway Corp 40 Hartz Way Secaucus NJ 07094-2479

LAZARUS, ARNOLD ALLAN, psychologist, educator; b. Johannesburg, Republic of South Africa, Jan. 27, 1932; came to U.S. 1963; s. Benjamin and Rachel Leah (Mosselson) L.; m. Daphne Ann Kessel, June 10, 1956; children: Linda Sue, Clifford Neil. BA with honors, U. Witwatersrand, 1956; MA, U. Witwatersrand, Johannesburg, 1957, PhD, 1960. Diplomate: Am. Bd. Profl. Psychology, Am. Bd. Med. Psychotherapists (fellow), internat. Acad. Behavioral Medicine, Counseling and Psychotherapy. Pvt. practice clin. psychology Johannesburg, 1959-63, 64-66; vis. asst. prof. dept. psychology Stanford (Calif.) U., 1963-64; prof. psychology Temple U. Med. Sch., Phila., 1967-70; dir. clin. tng. Yale U., New Haven, 1970-72; disting. prof. Rutgers U., New Brunswick, N.J., 1972—; mem. adv. bd. Psychologists for Social Responsibility, 1984—; cons. in field. Author: 15 books including Behavior Therapy and Beyond, 1971, Multimodal Behavior Therapy, 1976, The Practice of Multimodal Therapy, 1981, rev. edit., 1989, In the Mind's Eye, 1984, Martial Myths, 1985, Mind Power: Getting What You Want Through Mental Training, 1987, The Essential Arnold Lazarus, 1991, A Dialogue eiht Arnold Lazarus, 1991, Don't Believe It For a Minute!, 1993, Abnormal Psychology; edtl. bd. sci. jours.; contbr. articles to profl. jours. Recipient Disting. Svc. award Am. Bd. Profl. Psychology, Disting. Career Achievement award Am. Bd. Med. Psychotherapists, Outstanding Contbns. to Mental Health award Psychiat. Outpatient Ctrs. of the Americas, 1991. Fellow APA (Disting. Psychologist award divsn. of psychotherapy 1992), Am. Bd. Profl. Psychology (diplomate), Internat. Acad. Eclectic Psychotherapists, Acad. Clin. Psychology; mem. Am. Acad. Psychotherapy, Assn. for Advancement Psychotherapy, Nat. Acads. Practice in Psychology (disting.), Soc. for Exploration of Psychotherapy Integration. Home: 56 Herrontown Cir Princeton NJ 08540-2924 Office: Rutgers U PO Box 819 Piscataway NJ 08855 *Whatever modicum of success I may have achieved is probably due, in large part, to my view of parity as a way of life. I am committed to the notion that there are no superior human beings—we are all different, indeed unique, but equal. While some people possess superior skills and abilities, this does not make them superior human beings. To respect others for their exceptional capacities, but never to deify them, enables one to learn from others instead of envying them and denigrating oneself. This egalitarian view transforms acquisitiveness, power, and aggression into love, intimacy, and productive activity.*

LAZARUS, ARTHUR, JR., lawyer; b. Bklyn., Aug. 30, 1926; s. Arthur and Frieda (Langer) L.; m. Gertrude Chiger, Jan. 8, 1956; children: Andrew Joseph, Edward Peter, Diana Ruth. BA with honors, Columbia U., 1946; JD, Yale U., 1949. Bar: N.Y. 1951, D.C. 1952, U.S. Supreme Ct. 1954. Assoc. Fried, Frank, Harris, Shriver & Jacobson, Washington, 1950-57, ptnr., 1957-91, mng. ptnr. Washington office, 1974-86; of counsel Sonosky, Chambers, Sachse & Endreson, Washington, 1994—. Trustee Arena Stage, 1987—. Home: 3201 Fessenden St NW Washington DC 20008-2032

LAZARUS, CHARLES, retail toy company executive; b. 1923; married. With Lash Distributors Inc., 1958-67; with Interstate Stores Inc. (acquired by Toys "R" Us Inc., 1978), from 1967, sr. v.p., 1971-76, pres., chief exec. officer, from 1976; with Toys "R" Us Inc., Rochelle Park, N.J., 1970—; now chmn. Toys "R" Us Inc., Paramus, N.J.; also bd. dirs. Toys "R" Us Inc., Rochelle Park, N.J. Office: Toys R Us Inc 461 From Rd Paramus NJ 07652-3524*

LAZARUS, DAVID, physicist, educator; b. Buffalo, Sept. 8, 1921; s. Barney B. and Lillian (Markel) L.; m. Betty Jane Ross, Aug. 15, 1943; children: Barbara, William, Mary Ann, Richard. B.S., U. Chgo., 1942, M.S., 1947, Ph.D., 1949. Instr. electronics U. Chgo., 1942-43, electronics engr., 1946-49, instr. physics, 1949; research assoc. radio research lab. Harvard, 1943-45; mem. physics faculty U. Ill., Urbana, 1949—, prof., 1959—; vis. prof. U. Paris, 1968-69, M.I.T., 1978-79, Harvard U., 1978-79; vis. scientist Am. Inst. Physics, N.Y.C., 1962-69; cons. Phys. Sci. Study Com., 1957-59, Hallicrafters Co., Chgo., 1957-69, Gen. Electric Co., Cin., 1960-68, Gen. Atomic, La Jolla, Calif., 1962-63, Lawrence Radiation Lab., 1967-68, Sandia Lab., 1970-72, Addison-Wesley Pub. Co., Reading, Mass., 1964-80; dir. Council on Materials Sci., U.S. Dept. Energy, 1981-85. Author: (with H. de Waard) Modern Electronics, 1966, (with R.I. Hulsizer) The World of Physics, 1972, (with M. Raether) Practical Physics: How Things Work, 1979; also articles. Guggenheim fellow, 1968-69. Fellow AAAS, Am. Phys. Soc. (coun. 1974-78, 80-91, exec. com. 1980-91, editor-in-chief 1980-91, publs. com. 1980-91, exec. com. div. contensed matter physics 1968-70, 74-78, chmn. New Materials prize com. 1976, chmn. Buckley prize com. 1979); mem. Am. Inst. Physics (governing bd. 1981-92, exec. com. 1981-89, publs. policy com. 1981-92). Home: 502 W Vermont Ave Urbana IL 61801-4931

LAZARUS, FRED, IV, college president; b. N.Y.C., Jan. 1, 1942; s. Fred and Irma (Mendelson) L.; m. Jonna Gaee, Nov. 27, 1970; children: Anna Mendelson, Fred Lazarus V. B.A., Claremont McKenna Coll., 1964; M.B.A., Harvard U., 1966. Staff assoc. Nat. Council for Equal Bus. Opportunity, Washington, 1969-71; pres. Washington Council for Equal Bus. Opportunity, 1971-74; exec. asst. to chmn. Nat. Endowment for Arts, Wash-

ington, 1975-78; pres. Md. Inst. Coll. Art, Balt., 1978—; vice chmn. Md. Ind. Colls. and Univs. Assn.; vice chmn. Assn. Ind. Colls. Art and Design; trustee Alliance for Ind. Colls. Art, 1978-91, chmn., 1984-86, 89-91; founding chmn. Nat. Coalition for Edn. in Arts, 1988-90. Trustee St. Paul's Sch.; trustee, sec. Am. Coun. for Arts, Md. Art Place; trustee emeritus Ptnrs. for Livable Places; bd. dirs. Afro-Am. Newspapers; chmn. Balt. Coun. for Equal Bus. Opportunity Md. Art Place. Recipient mayor's art award, City of Balt., 1988. Mem. Harvard Club (N.Y.C.). Office: Md Inst Coll Art 1300 W Mount Royal Ave Baltimore MD 21217-4134

LAZARUS, GEORGE MILTON, newspaper columnist; b. Worcester, Mass., June 16, 1932; s. Milton George and Urania (Costa) L.; m. Karen Jayne Sippel, Mar. 1, 1969; children: Lana Elizabeth, Tara Lisanne. BBA, Clark U., 1954; MS in Journalism, Northwestern U., 1957. Staff writer AP, Chgo., 1957-59; asst. editor Printers' Ink mag., Chgo., 1959-61; fin. news reporter Chgo. Daily News, 1961-69, mktg. news columnist, 1961-69; mktg. columnist Chgo. Today, 1969-72, Chgo. Tribune, 1972—, Adweek's Mktg. Week, 1982-90, N.Y. Daily News, 1984-90; speaker, cons. in field; commentator radio Sta. WGN, 1991—; former commentator stas. WMAQ, WLAK, all Chgo.; instr. advt. North Park Coll., 1957-58. Author: Marketing Immunity, 1988; contbr. articles to mags. Recipient Marshall Field award for editorial contbns., 1966-67, Nat. Headliners award, 1971, Compton Advt. award for best newspaper article on advt., 1983. Mem. Merchandising Execs. Club Chgo. (pres. 1979-80, dir.), Lambda Chi Alpha, Alpha Delta Sigma, Sigma Delta Chi. Club: Flossmoor Country. Home: 1214 Western Ave Flossmoor IL 60422-1636 Office: The Chicago Tribune 435 N Michigan Ave Chicago IL 60611-4001

LAZARUS, GERALD SYLVAN, physician; b. N.Y.C., Feb. 16, 1939; s. Joseph W. and Marion (Goldstein) L.; m. Sandra Jacob, Sept. 3, 1961 (dec. 1985); children: Mark, Elyse, Lynne, Laura; m. Audrey Fedyszyn Jakubowski, Apr. 7, 1990. B.A., Colby Coll., 1959; M.D., George Washington U., 1963. Intern, then resident U. Mich., Ann Arbor, 1963-64; resident in medicine U. Mich., 1964-65; NIH research asso. NIH, Bethesda, Md., 1965-68; resident in dermatology Harvard U., Cambridge, Mass., 1968-70; research fellow Strangeways Labs., Cambridge, Eng., 1970-72; assoc. prof. medicine, co-dir. dermatology tng. program Albert Einstein Med. Coll., N.Y.C., 1972-75; J. Lamar Callaway prof. Duke U., Durham, N.C., 1977-82; chief dermatology Duke U., 1975-82; Milton B. Hartzell prof. U. Pa. Sch. Medicine, Phila., 1982—, chmn. dept. dermatology, 1982-93; dean Sch. Medicine U. Calif., Davis, 1993—; mem. study sect. NIH, 1976-80. Author: (with L. Goldsmith) Diagnosis of Skin Disease, 1980, (with Herman Beerman) Tradition of Excellance: History of Dermatology at Univ. Pa. Sch. of Medicine; asso. editor: Jour. Investigative Dermatology, 1977-82; contbr. numerous articles to profl. jours. Served with USPHS, 1965-68. Carl Herzog fellow Am. Dermatology Assn., 1970-72; Johon Simon Guggenheim fellow U. Geneva, 1986; sr. investigator Arthritis Found., 1972-77; grantee NIH. Fellow ACP, Assn. Am. Physicians, Am. Soc. Clin. Investigation; mem.Am. Dermatol. Assn., Soc. Investigative Dermatology (dir.), Biochem. Soc., Am. Acad. Dermatology (Sultzberger award 1986). Republican. Jewish. Office: U Calif Sch Medicine Office Of The Dean Davis CA 95616

LAZARUS, KENNETH ANTHONY, lawyer; b. Passaic, N.J., Mar. 10, 1942; s. John Joseph and Margaret (Di Cenzo) L.; m. Marylyn Jane Flemming, Aug. 13, 1966; children: Maggi Ann, John, Joseph. Ba, U. Dayton, 1964; JD, U. Notre Dame, 1967; LLM in Taxation, George Washington U., 1971. Bar: N.J. 1967, U.S. Tax Ct. 1970, U.S. Ct. Claims 1970, U.S. Supreme Ct. 1971, D.C. 1976. Trial atty. U.S. Dept. Justice, 1967-71; assoc. counsel and chief counsel to Minority Com. on Judiciary, U.S. Senate, 1971-74; assoc. counsel to Pres. U.S., 1974-77; ptnr. Ward, Lazarus & Grow, Washington, 1977-91; of counsel Dixon & Dixon, Washington, 1991—; mem. adv. bd. Sch. Law Dayton U., 1975-85; adj. prof. Sch. Law Georgetown U., 1979—; mem. U.S. Adv. Com. on Trade Negotiations, 1983-87; chmn. Sailors and Mchts. Bank and Trust Co., Vienna, Va., 1987-89. Mem. adv. bd. Houston Jour. Internat. Law, 1983-90; contbr. numerous articles to profl. publs. U.S. reporter to UN, 1975-77; mem. adv. coun. Rep. Nat. Com., 1977-80; mem. Presdl. transition team Office of Pres.-Elect, 1980-81; caucus mgr. George Bush Rep. Conv., 1988; bd. trustees Internat. Law Inst., pres., 1990—. Mem. ABA, D.C. Bar Assn., Fed. Bar Assn., N.J. Bar Assn., Am. Judicature Soc., Am. Law Inst. Home: Ste 716 4501 Connecticut Ave NW Washington DC 20008 Office: 1850 M St NW Ste 450 Washington DC 20036

LAZARUS, MARGARET LOUISE, film producer and director; b. N.Y.C., Jan. 22, 1949; d. Leon A. and Paula (Plesser) L.; children: Michael Lazarus Renner, Matthew Lazarus Renner. BA cum laude, Vassar Coll., 1969; MS in Broadcast, Film, Boston U., 1972. Researcher Westinghouse Broadcasting/Parallel Prodns., Boston, 1970-71; producer, writer Sta. WNAC-TV, Boston, 1971-72; producer, dir. Cambridge (Mass.) Documentary, 1973—, also pres., 1980-90; cons., bd. dirs. Cambridge Community TV, 1987-94. Producer, dir. (films) Taking Our Bodies Back, 1974, Rape Culture, 1976, 83, Eugene Debs and the American Movement, 1977, Killing Us Softly, 1979, Calling the Shots, 1982, Pink Triangles, 1984, The Last Empire, 1986, Still Killing Us Softly, 1987, Hazardous Inheritance, 1989, Not Just a Job, 1990, Advertising Alcohol, 1991, Life's Work, 1993, Defending Our Lives, 1993 (Academy Award, Best Documentary Short Subject); co-author: The New Our Bodies, Ourselves, 1984. Counselor, mem. Alliance Against Sexual Coercion, Cambridge, 1977-81; peace commr. City of Cambridge, 1988-91. Recipient London Film Festival award, 1982, Mannheim (Fed. Republic Germany) Film Festival award, 1982, Berlin Film Festival award, 1982, Red Ribbon Am. Film Festival award, 1983, Melbourne (Australia) Film Festival award, 1983, 1st place Am. Jour. Nursing, 1984, 1st place Nat. Council on Family Relations, 1984, 93, Blue Ribbon award Am. Film Festival, 1987, 91, U.S.A. Film Festival award 1987, World Peace Film Festival award, 1987, Global Village Film Festival award, 1985, Filmosav award India, 1988, Golden Babe award Chicago Ednl. Film Festival, 1988, Silver Apple award Nat. Ednl. Film Festival, 1991, 94, Seattle Film Festival Silver Placque award, 1993, Chgo. Internat. Film Festival award 1993, Exceptional Merit in Media award, 1993, PASS award Nat. Coun. on Crime and Delinquency, Chris award Columbus Internat. Film Festival, 1993, Outstanding Film of the Year award New England Film and Video Festival, 1994.

LAZARUS, MELL, cartoonist; b. N.Y.C., May 3, 1927; s. Sidney and Frances (Mushkin) L.; m. Eileen Hortense Israel, June 19, 1949; children: Marjorie, Suesan, Catherine. Cartoonist-writer Miss Peach, 1957—; author anthologies Miss Peach, Miss Peach, Are These Your Children?, Momma, We're Grownups Now!; novels The Boss is Crazy, Too, 1964, The Neighborhood Watch, 1986; plays Everybody into the Lake, Elliman's Fly, Lifetime Eggcreams, 1969-70; juvenile Francine, Your Face Would Stop a Clock, 1975; co-author Miss Peach TV spl. programs Turkey Day Pageant and Annual Heart Throb Ball. Trustee Internat. Mus. Cartoon Art. With USNR, 1945, USAFR, 1951-54. Mem. Nat. Cartoonists Soc. (pres. 1989-93, chmn. membership com. 1965, nat. rep., Humor Strip Cartoonist of Yr. 1973, 79, Reuben award 1981), Writers Guild Am. West, Nat. Press Club, The Century Assn., Newspaper Features Coun. (bd. dirs.), Sigma Delta Chi. Office: Creators Syndicate Inc 5777 W Century Blvd Los Angeles CA 90045

LAZARUS, RICHARD STANLEY, psychology educator; b. N.Y.C., Mar. 3, 1922; s. Abe and Matilda (Marks) L.; m. Bernice H. Newman, Sept. 2, 1945; children—David Alan, Nancy Eve. A.B., City Coll. N.Y., 1942; M.S., U. Pitts., 1947, Ph.D., 1948; Dr. honoris causa, Johannes Gutenberg U., Mainz, Fed. Republic Germany, 1988. Diplomate in clin. psychology Am. Bd. Examiners in Profl. Psychology. Asst. prof. Johns Hopkins, 1948-53; psychol. cons. VA, 1952—; assoc. prof. psychology, dir. clin. tng. program Clark U., Worcester, Mass., 1953-57; assoc. prof. psychology U. Calif. at Berkeley, 1957-59, prof. psychology, 1959-91, prof. emeritus U.—; prin. investigator Air Force contracts dealing with psychol. stress, 1951-53, USPHS grant on personality psychol. stress, 1953-70; NIA, NIDA, and NCI grantee on stress, coping and health, 1977-81, MacArthur Found. research grantee, 1981-84; USPHS spl. fellow Waseda U., Japan, 1963-64. Author 18 books, numerous publs. in profl. jours. Served to 1st lt. AUS, 1943-46. Recipient Disting. Sci. Achievement award Calif. State Psychol. Assn., 1984, Div. 38 Health Psychology, 1989; Guggenheim fellow, 1969-70; Army Rsch. Inst. rsch. grantee, 1973-75. Fellow AAAS, APA (Disting. Sci. Contbn. award 1989); mem. Western Psychol. Assn., Argentina Med. Assn. (hon.).

Home: 1824 Stanley Dollar Dr Apt 3B Walnut Creek CA 94595-2833 Office: Univ Calif Dept Psychology Berkeley CA 94720

LAZARUS, ROCHELLE BRAFF, advertising executive; b. N.Y.C., Sept. 1, 1947; d. Lewis L. and Sylvia Ruth (Eisenberg) Braff; m. George M. Lazarus, Mar. 22, 1970; children: Theodore, Samantha, Benjamin. AB, Smith Coll., 1968; MBA, Columbia U., 1970. Product mgr. Clairol, N.Y.C., 1970-71; account exec. Ogilvy & Mather, N.Y.C., 1971-73, account supr., 1973-77, mgmt. supr., 1977-84, sr. v.p., 1981—; account group dir., 1984-87; gen. mgr. Ogilvy & Mather Direct, N.Y.C., 1987-88, mng. dir., 1988-89, pres., 1989-91; pres. Ogilvy & Mather, N.Y.C., 1991-94, pres. N. Am., 1994—. Bd. dirs. Ann Taylor, Advt. Edn. Found., YMCA, Nat. Women's Law Ctr.; mem. Com. of 200; mem. bus. com. Solomon R. Guggenheim Mus.; mem. bd. overseers Columbus Bus. Sch.; trustee Smith Coll., Columbia Presbyn. Hosp. Recipient YWCA Women Achievers award, 1985, Matrix award, 1995. Mem. Am. Assn. Advt. Agys. (bd. dirs.), Advt. Women N.Y. (Woman of Yr. 1994). Home: 106 E 78th St New York NY 10021 Office: Ogilvy & Mather Direct Worldwide Plz 309 W 49th St New York NY 10019-7316

LAZARUS, STEVEN S., management consultant, marketing consultant; b. Rochester, N.Y., June 16, 1943; s. Alfred and Ceal H. Lazarus; m. Elissa C. Lazarus, June 19, 1966; children: Michael, Stuart, Jean. BS, Cornell U., 1966; MS, Poly. U. N.Y., 1967; PhD, U. Rochester, 1974. Pres. Mgmt. Systems Analysis Corp., Denver, 1977—; dir. Sci. Application Intern Corp., Englewood, Colo., 1979-84; assoc. prof. Metro State Coll., Denver, 1983-84; sr. v.p. Pal Assocs. Inc., Denver, 1984-85; with strategic planning and mktg. McDonnell Douglas, Denver, 1985-86; mktg. cons. Clin. Reference Systems, Denver, 1986—; assoc. exec. dir. Ctr. Rsch. Ambulatory Health Care Adminstrn., Englewood; sp. cons. State of Colo., Denver, 1976-81; mktg. cons. IMX, Louisville, Ky., 1986-87; speaker Am. Hosp. Assn., Chgo., 1983—; speaker Med. Group Mgmt. Assn., 1975—. Author chpts. to books; patentee med. quality assurance. NDEA fellow U. Rochester, 1968-71. Mem. Inst. Indsl. Engring. (sr.), Med. Group Mgmt. Assn., Operations Research Soc. Am. Lodge: Optimists (program chmn. Denver club 1976-78). Home: 7023 E Eastman Ave Denver CO 80224-2845 Office: MSA Corp 4949 S Syracuse St Ste 300 Denver CO 80237

LAZAY, PAUL DUANE, telecommunications manufacturing company executive; b. Phila., June 2, 1939; s. Louis and Thea (Lindberg) L.; m. Joan Elizabeth Robinson, Sept. 2, 1961; 1 child, Thomas. BS, Trinity Coll., 1961; PhD, MIT, 1968. Supr. optic measurement Bell Labs., Murray Hill, N.J., 1969-83; v.p. engring. ITT-EOPD, Roanoke, Va., 1983-86; v.p. engring. Telco Systems Fiber Optics Div., Norwood, Mass., 1986-87, v.p. mktg., 1987-88, pres., gen. mgr., 1987-88; pres., chief exec. officer Telco System, Inc., Norwood, 1988-94, bd. dir.; bd. dirs. SpecTran Corp., Sturbridge, Mass., United Techs. Photonics, Bloomfield Conn. Contbr. articles on fiber optics to profl. jours.; patentee in field. Mem. IEEE, Am. Physics Soc., Optical Soc. Am., Sigma Xi.

LAZEAR, EDWARD PAUL, economics and industrial relations educator, researcher; b. N.Y.C., Aug. 17, 1948; s. Abe and Rose (Karp) L.; m. Victoria Ann Allen, July 2, 1977; 1 child, Julia Ann. A.B., UCLA, 1971, A.M., 1971; Ph.D., Harvard U., 1974. Asst. prof. econs. U. Chgo., 1974-78, assoc. prof. indsl. relations, 1978-81, prof. indsl. relations, 1981-85, Isidore and Gladys Brown prof. urban and labor econs., 1985-92; sr. fellow Hoover Instn. Stanford (Calif.) U., 1985—, coord. domestic studies Hoover Instn. 1987-90, prof. econs. and human resource mgmt. Grad. Sch. Bus., 1992—; econ. advisor to Romania, Czechoslovakia, Russia, Ukraine, Georgia; rsch. assoc. Nat. Bur. Econ. Rsch., Econs. Rsch. Ctr. of Nat. Opinion Rsch. Ctr.; fellow Inst. Advanced Study, Hebrew U., Jerusalem, 1977-8; lectr. Inst. Advanced Study, Vienna, 1983-84, Nat. Productivity Bd., Singapore, 1982, 85; vis. prof. Inst. des Etudes Politiques, Paris, 1987; Wicksell lectr., Stockholm, 1993. Author: (with J.P. Gould) Microeconomic Theory, 1989, Personell Economics, 1995, Economic Transition in Russia and Eastern Europe, 1995; (with R. Michael) Allocation of Income Within the Household, 1988; founding editor Jour. Labor Econs., 1982—; assoc. editor Jour. Econ. Perspectives, 1986-89; contbr. numerous articles to scholarly jours. NSF grad. fellow, 1971-74. Fellow Econometric Soc.; mem. Am. Econs. Assn. Home: 277 Old Spanish Trl Portola Valley CA 94028-8129 Office: Stanford U Grad Sch Bus Stanford CA 94305-5015 also: Hoover Inst Stanford CA 94305-6010

LAZECHKO, D. M. (MOLLY LAZECHKO), former state legislator; b. Innisfail, Alta., June 3, 1926; came to U.S., 1960; d. Archibald Donald and Violet Georgina (Adams) Manuel; m. Walter Vladmir Lazechko, Apr. 16, 1960; children: William Donald, Robert James. BA, Boise State U., 1976. Cert. elem. tchr. Tchr. Olds Sch. Dist., Stewart Sch., Alta., 1945-46, Innisfail (Alta.) Sch. Dist., 1946-50; tchr., vice prin. Calgary (Alta.) Sch. Dist., 1950-59; exchange tchr. Edinburgh, Scotland, 1954-55; math tutor mgr. Title I, Boise, Idaho, 1974-76; elem. tchr. Boise (Idaho) Sch. Dist., 1976-87; jr. high tchr. Chpt. I, Boise, 1987-88; ret., 1988-90; mem. Idaho Ho. of Reps., Boise, 1991, 92; pres. div. I Alta. Tchrs. Assn., Calgary, 1958-59, Whittier PTA, Boise, 1969-70, 73-74; pres., 3d v.p. Dist. 8 Idaho State PTA, 1973-75; sec., elem. dir. Boise (Idaho) Edn. Assn., 1978-81. Treas. LWV, Boise, 1988-90, House Dems. Campaign. Com., Boise, 1991-92; precinct capt. Ada County Dems. Dist. 16, Boise, 1988-90; sec. Boise Ret. Tchrs., 1989-90, pres., 1993-94; bd. mem. Boise Neighborhood Housing Svcs., 1990-92, Cmty. Contbn. Ctr., 1991-92, Idaho Housing Coalition, 1991-92; gov. appt. to bd. of Idaho Coun. on Domestic Violence, 1994—; bd. dirs. Epilepsy League of Idaho, 1993-94; candidate Idaho Legis. Ho. Reps., 1994. Mem. NEA, Idaho Edn. Assn., Idaho Conservation League, Idaho Women's Network, Grassroots Women's Lobby, Idaho Citzen's Network. Episcopalian. Avocations: politics, reading, swimming.

LAZENBY, FRED WIEHL, insurance company executive; b. Chattanooga, Jan. 13, 1932; s. John Wesley and Adela (Valenzuela) L.; m. Virginia Banks; children: Kathryn Wesley, Grace Woodard. BA cum laude, Vanderbilt U., 1954. CLU. With Nat. Life & Accident Ins. Co., Nashville, 1956— from agt. to pres., 1956-83; chmn. bd., chief exec. officer Southlife Holding Co., Nashville, 1983-94; chmn. CEO SouthCap Corp., 1994—; Premier Life Ins. Co., 1995—; past chmn. Life Insurers Conf.; bd. dirs. Nashville Bank of Commerce. Trustee Life Underwriting Tng. Coun., 1978-82; mem. bd. advisors Massey Sch.; chmn. Nashville Community Found. 1st lt. U.S. Army, 1954-56. Mem. Life Ins. Mgmt. Rsch. Assn. (bd. dirs 1985-88, past chmn. communication cos. exec. com.), Belle Meade Country Club, Cumberland Club, Carolina Yatch Club, Rotary. Republican. Methodist. Avocations: tennis, golf, skiing. Office: SouthCap Corp 211 7th Ave N Nashville TN 37219-1822

LAZENBY, GAIL R., library director; b. Charlotte, N.C., May 6, 1947; d. James Yates and Marian Elizabeth (Church) Rogers. BA, Salem Coll., 1969; MLS, U. N.C., 1971. Cert. libr., Ga. Br. libr. Atlanta Pub. Libr., 1970-77; br. coord. Dekalb Libr. System, Decatur, Ga., 1977-82; asst. dir. West Ga. Regional Libr., Carrollton, 1982-83; asst. dir. Cobb County Pub. Libr., Marietta, Ga., 1983-90, dir., 1991—. Mem. Leadership Cobb, Cobb County, 1985-86. Mem. ALA, Ga. Libr. Assn. (2d v.p. 1987-83), Southeastern Libr. Assn. (v.p.-pres. elect 1990-92, pres. 1992-94), Kiwanis Club Marietta (bd. dirs. 1991-92, sec. 1992-93, sec.-treas. 1993-94, pres. 1995-96). Office: Cobb County Public Lib 266 Roswell St SE Marietta GA 30060-2005

LAZERSON, EARL EDWIN, university president emeritus; b. Detroit, Dec. 10, 1930; s. Nathan and Ceil (Stashefsky) L.; m. Ann May Harper, June 11, 1966; children from previous marriage: Joshua, Paul. BS, Wayne State U., Detroit 1953; postgrad., U. Leiden, Netherlands, 1957-58; MA, U. Mich., 1954; PhD, 1982. Mathematician Inst. Def. Analyses, Princeton, N.J., 1960-62; assoc. prof. math. Washington U., St. Louis, 1962-65, 66-69; vis. assoc. prof. Brandeis U., 1965-66; mem. faculty So. Ill. U., Edwardsville, 1969—, prof. math., 1973—, chmn. dept. math. studies, 1972-73, dean Sch. Sci. and Tech., 1973-76, univ. v.p, provost 1975-77, pres., 1980-93; pres. emeritus, 1994—. Chmn. Southwestern Ill. Devel. Authority, City of East St. Louis Fin. Adv. Authority; active Leadership Coun. Southwestern Ill., Gateway Ctr. Met. St. Louis, Inc., St. Louis Symphony Soc.; trustee Jefferson Nat. Expansion Meml. Assn., Ill. Econ. Devel. Bd. Recipient Sr. Teaching Excellence award Standard Oil Found., 1970-71. Mem. Am. Math. Soc., Math. Assn. Am., European Math. Soc., London Math. Soc., Soc.

Mathematique France, Fulbright Alumni Assn., Sigma Xi. Home: 5 Hidden Valley Ln Edwardsville IL 62025-3706

LAZERSON, JACK, pediatrician, educator; b. Bronx, Jan. 9, 1936; s. Mayer and Jennie (Gerson) L.; (div.); children: David, Deborah, Darlene, Donna; (div.); 1 child, Samuel. AB, NYU, 1957; MD, U. Chgo., 1961. Diplomate Am. Bd. Pediatrics. Rotating internship L.A. County Gen. Hosp., 1961-62; resident in pediatrics Stanford-Palo Alto (Calif.) Hosp., 1962-64; chief resident in pediatrics, instr. U. Wash. Hosp., Seattle, 1966-67; asst. prof. dept. pediatrics Sch. of Medicine Stanford U., 1969-72; from asst. to assoc. prof. dept. pediatrics U. So. Calif., L.A., 1972-76; assoc. prof. dept. pediatrics U. Wis., Milw., 1976-79; prof. dept. pediatrics Sch. of Medicine U. Calif., Davis, 1979-86, prof. dept. pathology, 1980-86; prof., chmn. dept. pediatrics Sch. of Medicine U. Nev., 1986-94; prof. dept. pediatrics Sch. Medicine, 1986—; chief hemophilia svc. Children's Hosp. Stanford U. Sch. of Medicine, 1969-72; assoc. hematologist div. hematology and oncology Children's Hosp. L.A., 1972-76. Contbr. numerous articles to profl. jours. Bd. dirs. hemostasis program Milw. Children's Hosp., 1976-79; med. dir. Great Lakes Hemophilia Found., 1976-79. Armour and Hyland Labs. grantee, 1969-72, 72-76, Med. Coll. of Wis. grantee, 1976-79, HEW grantee, 1976-79, Cutter Labs. grantee, 1981-82, 82-83; recipient Rsch. Funds award U. Calif.-Davis, 1981-82, Outstanding Alumnus award U. Chgo., 1981. Fellow Am. Acad. Pediatrics; mem. Am. Fedn. for Clin. Rsch., N.Y. Acad. Scis., Nat. Hemophilia Found., Am. Chem. Soc. (biochemistry sect., med. chemistry sect.), Hemostasis Assn. of Calif., Internat. Soc. Thrombosis and Hemostasis, Am. Heart Assn. Coun. on Thrombosis Basic Sci. Coun., Am. Soc. Hematology, Am. Soc. for Exptl. Pathology, World Fedn. Hemophilia, Am. Assn. Blood Banks, Am. Soc. Pediatric (hematology and oncology credentials and by-laws com., membership com.), Alpha Omega Alpha. Office: U Nev Sch Medicine 2040 W Charleston Blvd Ste 200 Las Vegas NV 89102-2206

LAZIO, RICK A., congressman, lawyer; b. Amityville, N.Y., Mar. 13, 1958; s. Anthony and Olive E. (Christensen) L. AB in Polit. Sci., Vassar Coll., 1980; JD, Am. U., 1983. Bar: N.Y. 1984, U.S. Dist. Ct. (ea. and so. dists.) N.Y., 1985. Asst. dist. atty. Suffolk County Rackets Bureau, Hauppauge, N.Y., 1983-88; exec. asst. dist. atty. Suffolk County, N.Y., 1987-88; village atty. Village of Lindenhurst, N.Y., 1988-93; mng. ptnr. Glass, Lazio and Glass, Esqs., Babylon, N.Y., 1988-93; mem. Suffolk County Legislature from 11th Dist., N.Y., 1989-93; mem. 103d-104th Congresses from 2nd N.Y. dist., Washington, 1993—; dep. majority whip; budget com. banking subcom.; chmn. subcom. on housing and cmty. opportunity; mem. capital markets, securities and govt. sponsored enterprises. Mem. admissions com. Vassar Coll., N.Y.; past pres. West Islip Rep. Club. Mem. Suffolk County Bar Assn. Roman Catholic. Avocations: numismatics, guitar. Office: US Ho of Reps 314 CHOB Washington DC 20515

LAZOR, THEODOSIUS (HIS BEATITUDE METROPOLITAN THEODOSIUS), archbishop; b. Canonsburg, Pa., Oct. 27, 1933; s. John and Mary (Kirr) L. AB, Washington and Jefferson Coll., 1957, DD (hon.), 1973; BD, St. Vladimir's Orthodox Theol. Sem., 1960; postgrad., Ecumenical Inst., Bossey, Switzerland, 1961; DD (hon.), St. Vladimir's Orthodox Theol. Sem., 1986; DHL (hon.), Georgetown U., 1988. Tonsured monk Orthodox Ch. in Am., 1961, ordained priest, 1961; priest Nativity of Holy Virgin Mary Ch., Madison, Ill., 1961-66; elected bishop of Washington, 1967, Sitka and Alaska, 1967, Pitts. and, W.Va., 1972; elected primate of Orthodox Ch. in Am., Met. All Am. and Can.; archbishop of N.Y., 1977, archbishop of Washington and Met. of All Am. and Can., 1981—. Address: Orthodox Ch Am PO Box 675 RR 25 Box 675 # A Syosset NY 11791

LAZORKO, ANTHONY, JR., art director; b. Phila., June 5, 1935; s. Anthony and Rose (Rudnick) L.; m. Marguerite Francis Biddle, Aug. 1, 1959; children: Jonathan, Paul, Catherine. Student, Pa. Acad. Fine Arts, U. Pa. Staff artist Phila. Bull., 1950-60, asst. art dir., 1960-74, art dir., 1974-80, asst. news art dir., 1980-82; staff artst St. Louis Post-Dispatch, 1982, asst. news art dir., 1982-85, news art dir., 1985—; art dir. Blavat Advt., Erdenheim, Pa., 1968-82. Treas. Powelton Civic Club, Phila., 1966; pres. Powelton '76, Phila., 1971. Mem. Soc. Newspaper Design, Hist. Soc. Pa. Avocations: travel, music, history. Home: 816 Ann Ave Saint Louis MO 63104-4135

LAZZARA, BERNADETTE See PETERS, BERNADETTE

LAZZARO, ANTHONY DEREK, university administrator; b. Utica, N.Y., Jan. 31, 1921; s. Angelo Michael and Philomena (Vanilla) L.; m. Shirley Margaret Jones, Dec. 20, 1941; 1 child, Nancy. B.S. in Indsl. Engring., U. So. Calif., 1948; LL.D. with honors, Pepperdine U., 1974. Registered prof. engr., Calif. Asst. bus. mgr. U. So. Calif., L.A., 1948-60, asst. bus. mgr., dir. campus devel., 1960-65, asso. bus. mgr., dir. campus devel., 1965-71, asso. v.p. bus. affairs, 1971-72, v.p. bus. affairs, 1972-86, sr. v.p. bus. affairs, 1986-88, univ. v.p., 1988-91, v.p. emeritus, 1991—; cons. HEW. Editorial cons. College and University Business, 1955-58. Mem. nat. adv. coun. United Student Aid Funds, N.Y.C., 1974-77, chmn., 1976-77; dir. Rep. Fed. Savs. & Loan Assn. and subs. corps., L.A., 1961-88; spl. studies cons. div. higher edn. Office Edn. HEW, 1956-59; mem. citizens com. Palos Verdes Bd. Edn., 1955-57; mem. Hoover urban renewal adv. com. Community Redevl. Agy. City of L.A., 1960-88. Lt. USNR, 1941-46. Mem. Nat. Assn. Coll. and Univ. Bus. Officers (pres. 1978-79, dir. 1972-80, chmn. goals and programs com. 1978, chmn. large inst. com. 1986-87, Disting. Bus. Officer award 1986), Western Assn. Coll. and Univ. Bus. Officers (pres. 1971-72), Soc. Coll. and Univ. Planning, Blue Key, Golden Key, Phi Kappa Phi, Tau Beta Pi. Club: Jonathan (Los Angeles). Home: 4012 Via Largavista Palos Verdes Estates CA 90274 Office: Los Angeles CA 90089-1454

LE, TON DA, horticulturist, researcher; b. Hanoi, Vietnam, Apr. 10, 1935; U.S. citizen; s. Liem Da and Sam Thi; m. Norma Olivia Benitez, Apr. 9, 1981; children: Patricia D., Natalie D., Minh Dang. BSA, U. Fla., 1963, MSA in Fruit Crops, 1965, PhD in Hort. Sci., 1975. Dir.-mgr. Dalat Hort. Expt. Sta., Vietnam, 1965-68; specialist Ministry of Agr., Saigon, Vietnam, 1969-71, Ministry of Edn., Saigon, 1971-72; horticulturist Div. Tropical Rsch., United Brands, La Lima, Honduras, 1976-82; dir. rsch. Frutos Tropicales, S.A., Dominican Republic, 1982-84; horticulturist Chiquita Brands Internat., 1984-86; dir. applied rsch. Chiquita Brands Internat., Fla., 1986-92; dir. agrl. extension and quality assurance Latin Am. ops. Del Monte Fresh Produce Co., San Jose, Costa Rica, 1993-94; dir. tech. svcs. Del Monte Fresh Produce Co., Nogales, Ariz., 1994—. Contbr. articles to profl. jours. Ford Found. fellow, 1975, U.S. AID scholar, 1960-65, 72-75. Mem. Am. Soc. for Hort. Sci., Fla. State Hort. Soc., Sigma Xi, Gamma Sigma Delta, Alpha Zeta. Republican. Avocations: classical music, astrology, tennis. Office: Del Monte Fresh Produce NA Inc 19 Kipper St Rio Rico AZ 85648

LEA, GEORGE A., JR., retail food executive; b. Pine Bluff, Ark., Apr. 8, 1950; s. George A. and Lois (Hogg) L.; m. Martha Elizabeth Quinn Stuckey, Sept. 16, 1972 (div. 1987); children: George A. III, Robert Quinn, Lois Anne Elizabeth. BA in Econs. and Bus., Hendrix Coll., 1972. CPA, Ark. Acct. Glenn Railsback & Co., Pine Bluff, Ark., 1972-77; pres. CEO The Mad Butcher, Inc., Pine Bluff, 1977—. Elder Presbyn. Ch. Mem. AICPA, Ark. Soc. CPA, Ark. Grocers and Retail Mchts. (vice chmn. 1994). Home: 501 Carter Dr Pine Bluff AR 71602 Office: The Mad Butcher Inc PO Box 1020 Pine Bluff AR 71613

LEA, LOLA STENDIG, lawyer; b. N.Y.C., Sept. 20, 1934; d. Hershel and Sophie (Golub) Stendig; m. Robert M. Lea, Sept. 12, 1953 (div. Apr. 1976); 1 child, Jennie. B.A. cum laude, NYU, 1954; LL.B., Yale U., 1957. Bar: N.Y. 1958, Maine 1989. Law clk. to U.S. dist. judge So. Dist. N.Y., 1957-59, asst. U.S. atty., 1959-61; assoc. C.C. Davis, N.Y.C., 1961-67; mem. firm Davis & Cox, N.Y.C., 1967-71, Lea, Goldberg & Spellun (P.C.), N.Y.C., 1971-77, Trubin, Sillcocks, Edelman & Knapp, N.Y.C., 1977-80; counsel Parker & Duryee, 1983-86, mem., 1987-88; spl. counsel to N.Y. 1st dept. joint interprofl. com. Drs. and Lawyers, 1972-78; lectr. Practising Law Inst., N.Y.C., 1969-70, 74, 79; spl. mediator Med. Malpractice Mediation part Supreme Ct. N.Y., 1971-80; chmn. N.Y. State Commn. Investigation, 1981-83. Fellow Am. Bar Found.; N.Y. Bar Found.; mem. N.Y. Bar Assn. (del. 1972-77, 87-88, mem. exec. com. 1976-77), Assn. Bar City N.Y. (chmn. grievance com. 1978-80, chmn. medicine and law com. 1969-71, chmn. spl.

com. on drug laws 1986-88, mem. other coms.), N.Y. County Lawyers Assn. (dir. 1978-81). Home: PO Box 356 South Freeport ME 04078-0356 Office: 22 Arnold Rd Freeport ME 04032-6025 also: 529 Fifth Ave New York NY 10017-4608

LEA, LORENZO BATES, lawyer; b. St. Louis, Apr. 12, 1925; s. Lorenzo Bates and Ursula Agnes (Gibson) L.; m. Marcia Gwendolyn Wood, Mar. 21, 1953; children—Victoria, Jennifer, Christopher. BS, MIT, 1946; JD, U. Mich., 1949; grad. Advanced Mgmt. Program, Harvard U., 1964. Bar: Ill. 1950. With Amoco Corp. (formerly Standard Oil Co. Ind.), Chgo., 1949—, asst. gen. counsel, 1963-71, assoc. gen. counsel, 1971-72, gen. counsel, 1972-78, v.p., gen. counsel, 1978-89. Trustee Village of Glenview (Ill.) Zoning Bd., 1961-63; bd. dirs. Chgo. Crime Commn., 1978—; Midwest Council for Internat. Econ. Policy, 1973—; Chgo. Bar Found., 1981—; Chgo. Area Found. for Legal Services, 1981—; bd. dirs. United Charities of Chgo., 1973—, chmn., 1985—. Served with USNR, 1943-46. Mem. ABA, Am. Petroleum Inst., Am. Arbitration Assn. (dir. 1980—), Ill. Bar Assn., Chgo. Bar Assn., Assn. Gen. Counsel, Order of Coif, Law Club, Econs. Club, Legal, Mid-Am. (Chgo.), Glen View, Wyndemere, Hole-In-The-Wall, Sigma Xi. Republican. Mem. United Ch. of Christ.

LEA, SCOTT CARTER, retired packaging company executive; b. New Orleans, Nov. 14, 1931; s. Leonard G. and Helen (Stoughton) L.; m. Marilyn Ruth Blair, Oct. 25, 1957; children: Scott, Nancy B., Mark S. BA, Amherst Coll., 1954; MBA, U. Pa., 1959. Sales and mktg. positions Riegel Paper, 1959-66, sales mgr. folding carton dept. southeastern div., 1966-67, gen. sales mgr., 1967-69, v.p. folding carton dept., 1969-71; v.p. bd. conversion div. Rexham Corp., Charlotte, N.C., 1971-73; v.p. packaging group Rexham Corp., 1973-74, pres., 1974-90; chmn. bd. Rexham Industries, Inc., 1990-92; bd. dirs. Lance, Inc., Speizman Industries, Inc. Trustee Johnson C. Smith U., Charlotte, N.C. With U.S. Army, 1954-57. Mem. Charlotte C. of C. (bd. dirs. 1977-78), Carmel Country Club, Quail Hollow Country Club, Wild Dunes Club (Isle of Palms, S.C.). Home: 3704 Stone Ct Charlotte NC 28226-7343 Office: 5821 Fairview Rd Ste 200 Charlotte NC 28209-3649

LEA, STANLEY E., artist, educator; b. Joplin, Mo., Apr. 5, 1930; s. Everett G. and Edna F. L.; m. Ruth Lowe, Aug. 19, 1951; children: Kristy Ruth, Kraig, Kelly B. B.F.A., Pitts. State U., 1953; M.F.A., U. Ark., 1961. Prof. art Sam Houston State U., Huntsville, 1961-90, 93—, Mexican Field Sch., Puebla, Mexico, 1963-65; vis. artist prof. Mus. Fine Arts, Houston, 1968, 69, 70; prof. art study abroad program London, 1977-78. Juror various art exhibits, 1970-81; workshop demonstrator, E. Tex. State U., Commerce, 1977, 10th ann. color print symposium, Tex. Tech. U., Lubbock, 1983; one-man shows paintings and/or prints, Valley House Gallery, Dallas, 1963, Moody Gallery, Houston, 1976, Sol Del Rio, San Antonio, 1978, 89, Adelle M. Fine Arts, Dallas, 1978, Dubose Gallery, Houston, 1980, Cultural Activities Ctr., Temple, Tex., 1982, Tex. A&M U., College Station, 1986, Mus. at E. Tex., Lufkin, 1989; numerous group shows, latest being Moody Gallery, Houston, 1975, 77, Pecan Square Gallery, Austin, Tex., 1977, Waco Art Center, Waco, Tex., 1977, East Tex. State U., Commerce, 1977, Galveston (Tex.) Art Center, 1978, Twenty Five Nat. Printmaker, Lubbock, Tex., 1978, Beaumont (Tex.) Art Mus., 1978, Art League of Houston, 1978, Gates Gallery, Port Arthur, Tex., 1979, Ars Longa, Houston, 1974, Laguna Gloria Mus., Austin, 1979; represented in permanent collections, Library of Congress, Washington, Brit. Mus., London, Mus. Fine Arts, Houston, USIA, N.Y.C., N.Y. Public Library, N.Y.C., Mpls. Inst. Art, Kalamazoo Inst. Art, Boise (Idaho) Gallery of Art, Madison (Wis.) Art Center, Spiva Art Center, Joplin, Mo., Ft. Worth Art Mus., Cleve. Mus., Inst. Mexicano Norteamericana de Relationes, Mexico City, Smithsonian Inst., Washington, also corp. and pvt. collections. (Recipient numerous awards, latest being, Southwest Graphics Invitational award 1971, Dimensions IX Exhbn. award 1974, 68th Nat. Tex. Fine Arts Exhbn. 1979.) Sam Houston State U. grantee, 1970, 74. Mem. Coll. Art Assn., So. Graphics Council. Home: 3324 Winter Way Huntsville TX 77340-8919 Office: Sam Houston State Univ Huntsville TX 77341

LEAB, DANIEL JOSEF, history educator; b. Berlin, Aug. 29, 1936; s. Leo and Herta (Marcus) L.; B.A., Columbia U., 1957, M.A., 1961, Ph.D., 1969; m. Katharine Kyes, Aug. 16, 1964; children—Abigail Elizabeth, Constance Martha, Marcus Rogers. With Columbia U., 1966-73, Seton Hall, 1974—; pub., co-editor Am. Book Prices Current; mng. editor Labor History; dir. Bancroft-Parkman. Fellow Met. Mus. Art.; mem. Historians of Am. Communism (gen. sec.). Clubs: Century, Grolier. Home: PO Box 1216 Washington Depot CT 06793-0216

LEACH, ANTHONY RAYMOND, financial executive; b. Gerrards Cross, Eng., Nov. 11, 1939; came to U.S., 1969; s. John Raymond Geoffrey and Edith Eileen (Blackburn) L.; m. Shirley Ann Kidd, Apr. 17, 1965; children: Mark Irwin, Amanda Jane, Christopher John. Supr. Ernst & Whinney, London, 1957-63, San Francisco, 1967—; mgr. Ernst & Whinney, Paris, 1963-69; mgr. fin. acctg. Occidental Petroleum Corp., Los Angeles, 1965-74, asst. controller, 1974-81, v.p. acctg., 1981-91, v.p. contr., exec. v.p., CFO, 1991—. Fellow Inst. Chartered Accts.; mem. Fin. Execs. Inst. Club: Palos Verdes Breakfast. Office: Occidental Petroleum Corp 10889 Wilshire Blvd Los Angeles CA 90024-4200

LEACH, FRANKLIN ROLLIN, biochemistry educator; b. Gorman, Tex., Apr. 2, 1933; s. Frank Rollin and Jewel Laurie (Casey) L.; m. Mary Kathleen Kincaid, Jan. 26, 1956 (dec. 1969); children: Carolyn Ann, Janet Lynne, Barbara Naomi; m. Anna Belle Coke, Feb. 27, 1970; stepchildren: Alan Charles Coke, Barry Neil Coke, Carol Ann Coke. BA, Hardin-Simmons U., 1953; PhD, U. Tex., Austin, 1957. Rsch. asst. U. Tex., Austin, 1953-56, Hite rsch. fellow, 1956-57; Nat. Rsch. Coun. fellow med. sci. U. Calif., Berkeley, 1957-59; rsch. assoc., then assoc. prof. Okla. State U., Stillwater, 1959-65, prof. biochemistry and molecular biology, 1966—, assoc. dept. head, 1990—; rsch. fellow Calif. Inst. Tech., Pasadena, 1965-66; cons. Kerr-McGee Co., Edmond, Okla., 1970-72, 3M Co., St. Paul, 1981-85, Idexx, 1994—, Teltex, 1994; interim dept. head biochemistry Okla. State U., 1990. Author: Biochemical Indicators of Subsurface Pollution, 1980; editor Okla. Acad. Sci., 1990—; contbr. over 90 articles to sci. jours. Pres.'s fellow, Soc. Am. Bacteriologists, 1960; recipient rsch. career devel. award, Nat. Cancer Inst., 1962-72. Mem. Am. Soc. Biochemistry and Molecular Biology, Am. Soc. Microbiology, AAAS, Am. Soc. Photobiology, Am. Chem. Soc., Coun. Biology Editors, Protein Soc., Stillwater Flying Club (pres. 1968-86). Avocations: hunting, reading, photography. Home: 1101 N Lincoln St Stillwater OK 74075-4033 Office: Okla State U Dept Biochemistry Stillwater OK 74078

LEACH, JAMES ALBERT SMITH, congressman; b. Davenport, Iowa, Oct. 15, 1942; s. James Albert and Lois (Hill) L.; m. Elisabeth Foxley, Dec. 6, 1975; 1 child, Gallagher. BA, Princeton U., 1964; MA, Johns Hopkins U., 1966; postgrad., London Sch. Econs., 1966-68. Mem. staff Congressman Donald Rumsfeld, 1965-66; U.S. Fgn. Service officer, 1968-69, 70-73; spl. asst. to dir. OEO, 1969-70; mem. U.S. del. Geneva Disarmament Conf., 1971-72, UN Gen. Assembly, 1972, UN Natural Resources Conf., 1975; pres. Flamegas Companies Inc., Bettendorf, Iowa, 1973-76; chmn. bd. Adel Wholesalers, Inc., Bettendorf, 1973-76; mem. 95th-104th Congresses from 1st Iowa dist., 1977—; chmn. banking and fin. svcs. com., merint. rels. com.; mem. U.S. Adv. Commn. Internat. Ednl. and Cultural Affairs, 1975-76. Chmn. Iowa Rep. Directions '76 Com. Episcopalian. Office: 2186 Rayburn Washington DC 20515-1501*

LEACH, JOHN F., newspaper editor, journalism educator; b. Montrose, Colo., Aug. 6, 1952; s. Darrell Willis and Marian Ruth (Hester) L.; m. Deborah C. Ross, Jan. 2, 1982; children: Allison, Jason. BS in Journalism, U. Colo., 1974, MA in Journalism, 1979; MA in Am. Studies, U. Sussex, Falmer, Brighton, Eng., 1983. News reporter Boulder (Colo.) Daily Camera, 1974-79; news reporter Ariz. Republic, Phoenix, 1979-85, asst. city editor, 1985-93; news editor Phoenix Gazette, 1993-94, asst. mng. editor, 1994—; faculty assoc. Ariz. State U., Tempe, 1990—; pres., dir. First Amendment Funding Inc., Phoenix. Bd. Regents scholar U. Colo., 1970, Rotary Found. scholar, 1982. Mem. Ariz. Press Club (treas. 1984-86, pres. 1986-87), Investigative Reporters and Editors, Soc. Profl. Journalists, Reporter's Com. for Freedom of Press. Home: 4313 E Calle Redonda Phoenix AZ 85018-3733 Office: Phoenix Gazette 300 E Van Buren St Phoenix AZ 85004-2227

LEACH, JOHN FRANK, transportation executive; b. New Ross, Ireland, Mar. 11, 1921; came to U.S., 1921; s. John Reginald and Evelyn Muriel (Ard) L.; m. Lee Marie Serre, Dec. 1, 1945; children: John Michael, Suzanne Lee Leach, Earnest. B.A. in Indsl. Mgmt., Wayne State U. Tool and diemaker apprentice Ford Motor Co., Dearborn, Mich., 1934-38; various mfg. positions to mgr. Ford Engine Plant, Cleve., 1938-54; dir. mfg. positions from v.p. mfg. Studebaker-Packard Corp., Detroit, 1954-56; various positions from v.p. mfg. and pres. Amphenol Electronics Corp.; exec. v.p., chief oper. officer Bunker Ramo Corp., Chgo., 1956-72; pres., chief exec. officer Arcata Corp., Menlo Park, Calif., 1972-82, chmn. bd., 1982-85; pres., chief oper. officer Consol. Freightways Inc., Menlo Park, 1990-91; ptnr. Sequoia Assocs., Menlo Park, 1982—; chmn. bd. Acme Fixture Co., Oakland, Calif.; bd. dirs. Consol. Freightways, Palo Alto, (vice chmn. 1991—), Nat. Safe Depository, San Jose, Calif., Basic Am. Foods Inc., San Francisco, Newell Industries, Lowell, Mich., Champion Rd. Machinery Co., Ltd., Goderich, Ont., Can., Pacific Fruit Growers & Packers, Inc., Wenatchee, Wash., Snow Mountain Pine Lumber Co., Hines, Oreg. Chmn. steering com. Friends of Radiology, Stanford U. Med. Ctr.; bd. dirs. Bus. Sch., U. Calif., Berkeley. 2d lt. USAAF. Recipient Medal of Honor Electronic Industries Assn., 1972. Mem. Elec. Industries Assn. (chmn., chief exec. officer Washington chpt. 1971-72, EIA medal of honor 1973), Desert Horizons Country Club, Menlo Country Club, Palo Alto Club, Lincoln Club of No. Calif. (past chmn.). Office: Consol Freightways Inc 3000 Sand Hill Rd Ste 1 Menlo Park CA 94025-7116

LEACH, JOSEPH LEE, English language educator, author; b. Weatherford, Tex., May 2, 1921; s. Austin Felix and Eula Lee (Gose) L.; m. Dorothy Ann Stuart, June 5, 1958; children—Joseph Lee, Jonathan Stuart, Anne Stuart, Christopher Bryan, Timothy Peter, Hilary, Melinda. B.A., So. Methodist U., 1942; Ph.D., Yale U., 1948. Prof. English U. Tex., El Paso, 1947-86, prof. emeritus, 1986—; prof. U. Ark., Fayetteville, 1957, European div. U. Md., 1957-58. Author: The Typical Texan, 1972, Bright Particular Star, 1970, Sun Country Banker, 1989; editor: A Treasury of American Folklore (Botkin), 1981; co-editor: World Literature Written in English, 1969; contbr. articles on history and English to scholarly publs., articles to popular mags. Pres. Festival Theatre, El Paso, 1969, El Paso County Hist. Soc., 1961. Served with inf. AUS, 1946-47. U. Tex. Research grantee, 1969-70. Mem. MLA, Nat. Coun. Tchrs. English, Sierra Club (pres. El Paso group 1970-71), Yale Club, Rotary, Pi Kappa Alpha. Republican. Episcopalian. Home: 735 De Leon Dr El Paso TX 79912-4945

LEACH, MAURICE DERBY, JR., librarian; b. Lexington, Ky., June 23, 1923; s. Maurice Derby and Sallie Eleanor (Woods) L.; m. Virginia Stuart Baskett, Mar. 16, 1953; 1 dau., Sarah Stuart. A.B., U. Ky., 1945; B.L.S., U. Chgo., 1946. Bibliographer Dept. State, 1947-50; fgn. service officer Dept. State (USIS); vice consul, attache Dept. State (USIS), Cairo and Alexandria, U.A.R., Beirut, 1950-59; chmn. dept. library sci. U. Ky., 1959-66; regional program officer Ford Found., Beirut, 1967-68; univ. librarian, prof. Washington and Lee U., Lexington, Va., 1968-85, prof., asst. to pres., 1985-88; library adviser Nat. Library, Egypt, Lebanon and acad. libraries in Middle East. Contbr. articles to profl. jours. Served with AUS, 1948-49. Mem. English Speaking Union (pres. Lexington br. 1970-75), Va. Libr. Assn. (pres. 1976), Assn. Preservation of Va. Activities (dir. Lexington br. 1989-91), Rockbridge Hist. Soc., SAR (v.p. 1990-93). Episcopalian. Home: 1 Courtland Ctr Lexington VA 24450-1813

LEACH, MICHAEL GLEN, publisher; b. Chgo., Aug. 19, 1940; s. Glen E. and Sara Faith (Giarrizzo) L.; M.A., St. Mary of the Lake Coll., 1966; m. Vickie Louise Jacobi, Oct. 3, 1969; children—Christopher, Jeffrey. Adminstr., Cath. Charities of Chgo., Maryville Acad., 1966-68; v.p., sr. editor Seabury Press, N.Y.C., 1969-80; sr. v.p., asso. pub. The Crossroad Pub. Co., N.Y.C., 1981-83; pres. The Continuum Pub. Corp., N.Y.C., 1980-83; exec. v.p., assoc. pub. The Crossroad/Continuum Pub. Cos., N.Y.C. 1983-90; pres., pub. The Crossroad/Continuum Pub. Group, 1990-92; COO and pub. The Crossroad Pub. Co., N.Y.C., 1993—. Mem. Assn. Am. Pubs., Protestant Ch.-Owned Pubs. Assn., Religious Pubs. Group (pres. 1991-92), Nat. Book Critics Circle, Cath. Book Pubs. Assn. (pres. 1989-90), Riverside Acres Community Assn. (pres. 1988). Roman Catholic. Author: I Know It When I See It: Pornography, Violence and Public Sensitivity, 1975; The Boy Who Had Everything, 1977; Don't Call Me Orphan, 1979; contbr. articles to profl. jours. Home: 49 Long Meadow Rd Riverside CT 06878-1125 Office: 370 Lexington Ave New York NY 10017-6503

LEACH, RALPH F., banker; b. Elgin, Ill., June 24, 1917; s. Harry A. and Edith (Sanders) L.; m. Harriet C. Scheuerman, Nov. 18, 1944; children: C. David, H. Randall, Barbara E. A.B., U. Chgo., 1938. Investment analyst Harris Trust & Savs. Bank, Chgo., 1940-48, Valley Nat. Bank, Phoenix, 1948-50; chief govt. finance sect. Fed. Res. Bd., Washington, 1950-53; treas. Guaranty Trust Co., N.Y.C., 1953-59; v.p. Guaranty Trust Co., 1958-59; v.p., treas. Morgan Guaranty Trust Co., N.Y.C., 1959-62; sr. v.p., treas. Morgan Guaranty Trust Co., 1962-64, exec. v.p., treas. 1964-68, vice chmn. bd. dirs., 1968-71, chmn. exec. com., 1971-77; chmn. bd. dirs. Energy Conversion Devices, Inc., Troy, Mich. Served to capt. USMCR, 1940-45. Mem. Coral Ridge Country Club, Phi Kappa Psi. Home: 4211 NE 25th Ave Fort Lauderdale FL 33308-5706 Office: Energy Conversion Devices Inc 1675 W Maple Rd Troy MI 48084-7197

LEACH, RICHARD HEALD, political scientist, educator; b. Denver, May 30, 1922; s. Richard Edwards and Helen Caroline (Heald) L.; m. Betty Carroll, Sept. 5, 1947; 1 son, Christopher Alan. A.B., Colo. Coll., 1944; M.A., Princeton U., 1949, Ph.D., 1951. Asst. prof. Ga. Inst. Tech., Atlanta, 1949-53; staff assoc. So. Regional Edn. Bd., Atlanta, 1953-55; asst. prof. to prof. emeritus Duke U., Durham, N.C., 1955—; vis. disting. prof. Citadel, Charleston, S.C., 1976; vis. scholar Australian Nat. U., 1975,83; cons. U.S. Adv. Commn. on Intergovt'l. Relations, Am. Coll. Testing Program. Co-author: In Quest of Freedom, 1959, reissued, 1981, State and Local Government: The Third Century of Federalism, 1988; author: Governing the American Nation, 1967, American Federalism, 1970, Intergovernmental Relations in the 1980's, 1983. Mem. Durham City County Merger Study Commn., 1971-73; mem. Ill. Commn. of Scholars, 1975-77. Fulbright scholar U. Amsterdam, 1967-68. Mem. Am. Soc. Pub. Adminstrn. Clubs: Cosmos (Washington); Princeton (N.Y.C.). Lodge: Rotary. Home: 1313 Woodburn Rd Durham NC 27705-5740

LEACH, ROBERT ELLIS, physician, educator; b. Sanford, Maine, Nov. 25, 1931; s. Ellis and Estella (Tucker) L.; m. Laurine Seber, Aug. 20, 1955; children: Cathy, Brian, Michael, Craig, Karen, Diane. A.B., Princeton U., 1953; M.D., Columbia U., 1957. Resident orthopedic surgery U. Minn., 1957-62; orthopedic surgeon Lahey Clinic, Boston, 1964-68; chmn. dept. Lahey Clinic, 1968-70; prof., chmn. dept. Boston U. Med. Sch., 1970—; lectr. Tufts U. Med. Sch., Medford, Mass., 1971—; head physician U.S. Olympic Team, 1984; chmn. sports medicine coun. U.S. Olympic Com., 1984-93. Editor-in-chief Am. J. Sports Med.; contbr. articles to profl. jours. Served to lt. comdr. USNR, 1962-64. Am., Brit., Canadian Orthopedic Travelling fellow, 1971; Sports Medicine Man of the Yr., 1988. Mem. Am. Acad. Orthopedic Surgeons, Continental Orthopedic Soc. (sec. 1966), Am. Orthopedic Assn. (pres. 1994), Am. Orthopedic Soc. Sports Medicine (pres. 1983), Longwood Cricket Club. Home: 40 Rockport Rd Weston MA 02193-1428 Office: 230 Calvary St Waltham MA 02154

LEACH, ROBIN, producer, writer, television host; b. London, Aug. 29, 1941; came to U.S., 1963; s. Douglas Thomas and Violet (Phillips) L. Diploma, Nat. Union Journalists, 1961. Reporter Harrow (Eng.) Observer, 1958-63, Daily Mail, London, 1961-63; mag. ed. NY mag., N.Y.C., 1964-67; show bus. editor The Star, N.Y.C., 1964-79; reporter Cable News Network, N.Y.C., 1979-80; entertainment reporter Entertainment Tonight, N.Y.C., 1980-83; exec. producer Leach Entertainment Enterprises, N.Y.C., 1983—. Author: The Go Book & Roll Manual, 1966, 2d rev. edit., 1967, Lifestyles of the Rich and Famous, 1986; producer: (TV shows) Lifestyles of the Rich and Famous, 1984 (Emmy nomination), Runaway with the Rich and Famous, The Rich and Famous Worlds Best, 1985, 86, 87, 88, 89, 90, 91, Fame, Fortune & Romance; host: KNBC-TV Year in Review, 1986, (Emmy award), Supermodel of the World, 1986, Home Videos of the Stars, 1991. Mem. AFTRA, Screen Actors Guild. Avocations: tennis, gourmet cooking. Office: Leach Entertainment Features 885 2nd Ave New York NY 10017

LEACH, RONALD GEORGE, university dean, librarian; b. Monroe, Mich., Feb. 22, 1938; s. Garnet William and Erma (Erbadine) L.; m. Joy Adeline Moore, Dec. 21, 1956; children—Ronald George, Debra Mabel, Catherine Louise, Shane John. B.S in Secondary Edn, Central Mich. U., 1966; M.A. in L.S. (U.S. Office Edn. fellow 1968-69), U. Mich., 1969; Ph.D. in Higher Edn. Adminstrn, Mich. State U., 1980. Head libr. Ohio State U., Mansfield, 1969-70; asst. dir., then acting dir. libr. Lake Superior State Coll., Sault Ste. Marie, Mich., 1970-76; assoc. dir. librs. Central Mich. U., 1976-80; dean libr. svcs. Ind. State U., Terre Haute, 1980-93, assoc. v.p. info. svcs., dean of librs., 1994—; tchr. libr. sci. and edn., mem. accreditation teams N. Central Assn. Author articles in field. Served with N.G., 1955-61. Mem. ALA, INFORMA (steering com. 1990—), Assn. Coll. and Rsch. Librs., Libr. Info. and Tech. Assn., Ind. Libr. Assn., Am. Soc. Info. Sci., Libr. Adminstrn. and Mgmt. Assn. (pres. 1985-86), Online Computer Libr. Ctr. User Council (exec. com. 1986, 88). Home: 4815 E Wolf Tree Ave Terre Haute IN 47805-9414 Office: Ind State U Terre Haute IN 47809

LEACH, RUSSELL, judge; b. Columbus, Ohio, Aug. 1, 1922; s. Charles Albert and Hazel Ark (Thatcher) L.; m. Helen M. Sharpe, Feb. 17, 1945; children: Susan Sharpe Snyder, Terry Donnell, Ann Dunham Samuelson. B.A., Ohio State U., 1946, J.D., 1949. Bar: Ohio 1949. Clk. U.S. Geol. Survey, Columbus, 1948-49; reference and teaching asst. Coll. Law, Ohio State U., 1949-51; asst. city atty. City of Columbus, 1951, 53-57, city atty., 1957-63, presiding judge mcpl. ct., 1964-66; ptnr. Bricker & Eckler, 1966-88, chmn. exec. com., 1982-87; judge Ohio Ct. Claims, 1988—. Commr., Columbus Met. Housing Authority, 1968-74; chmn. Franklin County Republican Com., 1974-78. Served with AUS 1942-46, 51-53. Named One of 10 Outstanding Young Men of Columbus, Columbus Jaycees, 1956, 57. Mem. ABA, Ohio Bar Assn. (council of dels. 1970-75), Columbus Bar Assn. (pres. 1973-74, Svc. medal 1993), Am. Judicature Soc., Pres.' Club Ohio State U., Am. Legion, Delta Theta Phi, Chi Phi. Presbyterian. Home: 1232 Kenbrook Hills Dr Columbus OH 43220-4968 Office: Ohio Ct Claims 65 E State St Ste 1100 Columbus OH 43215-4265

LEACH, SHERYL, television show character creator; b. Athens, Tex.; d. B.J. Stamps; m. Jim Leach; 1 child. Sch. tchr. Tex.; writer DLM Inc., Allen, Tex.; devel. Barney & the Backyard Gang video series (now Barney & Friends) PBS-TV, 1987. Creator of Barney the Dinosaur TM, 1987; devel. Barney and the Backyard Gang video series and numerous others. Office: Lyons Group Ste 1600 2435 N Central Expy Richardson TX 75080-2722

LEACH, WILLIAM RILEY, writer, historian; b. New Brunswick, N.J., Feb. 12, 1944; s. Thomas Edward and Esther Matilda (Lee) L. BA, Rutgers U., 1965; MA, Cornell U., 1968; PhD, U. Rochester, 1976. Asst. prof. U. South, Sewannee, Tenn., 1979-80; asst. prof. NYU, N.Y.C., 1980-81, fellow N.Y. Inst. for Humanities, 1981-91; adj. prof. history Columbia U., N.Y.C., 1993; ind. writer, 1993—; Mellon fellow Wesleyan U., Middletown, Conn., 1978-79, U. Rochester, 1977-78. Author: True Love and Perfect Union: The Feminist Reform of Sex and Society, 1980, Land of Desire: Merchants Power, and the Rise of a New American Culture, 1993 (finalist nat. book award, Herbert Hoover book prize 1993). NEH fellow, Washington, 1983, Woodrow Wilson Found. internat. fellow, Washington, 1984, Guggenheim Found. fellow, N.Y.C., 1993. Avocations: amateur lepidoptery, gardening, improvisational piano playing. Home and Office: 225 W Shore Dr Carmel NY 10512

LEACHMAN, CLORIS, actress; b. Des Moines, June 30, 1930; m. George England, 1953 (div. 1979); 5 children. Ed., Northwestern U. Actress: (films) including Kiss Me Deadly, 1955, Butch Cassidy and the Sundance Kid, 1969, W.U.S.A., 1970, The People Next Door, 1970, Lovers and Other Strangers, 1970, The Steagle, 1971, The Last Picture Show, 1971 (Acad. award for best supporting actress 1971), Charles and the Angel, 1972, Happy Mother's Day...Love, George, 1973, Dillinger, 1973, Daisy Miller, 1974, Young Frankenstein, 1974, Crazy Mama, 1975, High Anxiety, 1977, The Mouse and His Child, 1977 (voice), Foolin' Around, 1979, The North Avenue Irregulars, 1979, The Muppet Movie, 1979, Scavenger Hunt, 1979, Yesterday, 1979, Herbie Goes Bananas, 1980, History of the World, Part 1, 1982, Shadow Play, 1986, My Little Pony, 1986 (voice), Walk Like a Man, 1987, Hansel and Gretel, 1987, Prancer, 1989, Love Hurts, 1990, Texasville, 1990, Walter and Emily, 1991, My Boyfriend's Back, 1993, The Beverly Hillbillies, 1993, A Troll in Central Park, 1994 (voice), Storytime, 1994, Nobody's Girls, 1994; TV series including Lassie, 1957, Route 66, Laramie, Trials of O'Brien, Mary Tyler Moore Show, Phyllis, 1975-77, Facts of Life, The Nutt House, 1989; (TV movies) including Silent Night, Lonely Night, 1969, Suddenly Single, 1971, Haunts of the Very Rich, 1972, Brand New Life, 1973, Dying Room Only, 1973, Crime Club, 1973, Death Sentence, 1974, Thursday's Game, 1974, Hitchhike!, 1974, The Migrants, 1974, A Girl Named Sooner, 1975, Ladies of the Corridor, The New Original Wonder Woman, 1975, Death Scream, 1975, Someone I Touched, 1975, It Happened One Christmas, 1977, Long Journey Back, 1978, Mrs. R.'s Daughter, 1979, Willa, 1979, S.O.S. Titanic, 1979, The Acorn People, 1981, Advice to the Lovelorn, 1981, Miss All-American Beauty, 1982, Dixie: Changing Habits, 1983, The Demon Murder Case, 1983, Ernie Kovacs, Between the Laughter, 1984, Deadly Intentions, 1985, Love is Never Silent, Danielle Steele's Fine Things, 1990, In Broad Daylight, 1991, A Little Piece of Heaven, 1991, Fade to Black, 1993, Without a Kiss Goodbye, 1993, Spies, 1993, Miracle Child, 1993, Double, Double, Toil and Trouble, 1993, Between Love and Honor, 1995; (TV miniseries) Backstairs at the White House, 1979; theater appearance in Grandma Moses: An American Primitive, Washington, 1990; guest appearance: The Love Boat, 1976. Recipient 6 Emmy awards. Address: Met Talent Agy 4526 Wilshire Blvd 3d Fl Beverly Hills CA 90212*

LEACHMAN, ROGER MACK, librarian; b. Stillwater, Okla., June 3, 1942; s. Oakley Thaddeus and Mildred Violet (McNeff) L.; m. Nancy Jo Lordeman, Aug. 25, 1973; children—Emily Anne, James Oakley. A.B., U. Pa., 1967; M.S., U. N.C., 1973. Planner Pa. State Planning Bd., Harrisburg, 1967-68; rsch. libr. U. Va., Charlottesville, 1973-74, info. svcs. libr., 1974-76, dir. reference svcs., 1976-84, rare book bibliographer, 1984-88; coord. Southeast Libr. System, Rochester, Minn., 1988—. Contbr. articles to profl. jours. Served with U.S. Army, 1965-67. Gov's. fellow U. Va., Charlottesville, 1968-69. Mem. ALA, MEMO, MLA. Episcopalian. Avocations: bibliography; backpacking. Home: 822 4th St SW Rochester MN 55902-2914 Office: Southeast Libr System 107 W Frontage Rd N # 52 Rochester MN 55901-0343

LEADABRAND, RAY L., engineering executive, defense industry consultant; b. Pasadena, Calif., Oct. 12, 1927; s. Russell Lewis and Monica Laurel (Irwin) L.; m. Mildren Helen Armbruster, Apr. 2, 1955; 1 child, Paul Lewis. AA, Visalia Jr. Coll., 1948; BS, San Jose State U., 1950; MSEE, Stanford U., 1955. Project leader SRI Internat., Menlo Park, Calif., 1955-62, dir., 1962-69, exec. dir., 1969-77, v.p., 1977-79, sr. v.p. Sci. Applications Internat. Corp., Los Altos, Calif., 1986-89; past mem. Naval Studies Bd. Nat. Rsch. Coun., Washington, adv. com. Def. Intelligence Agy., Washington, 1983-92. Contbr. articles to profl. jours. Served with USN, 1945-46. Fellow IEEE; mem. AIAA (sr.), Am. Geophys. Union, Armed Forces Comm. and Electronics Assn., Assn. Unmanned Vehicle Systems, Am. Bonanza Soc. (bd. dirs.), Assn. Old Crows. Club: Cosmos (Washington). Avocation: private pilot. Home: 80 Joaquin Rd Menlo Park CA 94028-8115

LEADBETTER, MARK RENTON, JR., orthopaedic surgeon; b. Phila., Nov. 7, 1944; s. Mark Renton and Ruth (Protzeller) L.; m. Letitia Ashby, July 28, 1973 (div. June 1990); m. Jan Saker, 1991. BA, Gettysburg Coll., 1967; MSc in Hygiene, U. Pitts., 1970; MD, Temple U., 1974. Surg. intern Univ. Hosps., Boston, 1974-75, resident in surgery, 1975-76; emergency room physician Sturdy Meml. Hosp., Attleboro, Mass., 1976-78; resident in orthopaedics U. Pitts., 1978-81; orthopaedic physician Rockingham Meml. Hosp., Harrisonburg, Va., 1981-82, courtesy staff, 1982—; pvt. practice, Staunton, Va., 1982—; mem. active staff King's Daus. Hosp., Staunton, 1982—; active staff Samaritan Hosp., Moses Lake, Wash.; courtesy staff Columbia Basin Hosp., Ephrata, Wash. Contbr. articles to med. jours.; patentee safety syringes, safety cannulas. Mem. Am. Coll. Sports Medicine, So. Med. Assn., So. Orthopaedic Assn., County Med. Soc., Nat. Futures Assn. (assoc.). Republican. Avocations: flying, skiing, raising bird dogs. Home: 660 Coolidge St Moses Lake WA 98837-1877

LEAF, ALEXANDER, physician, educator; b. Yokohama, Japan, Apr. 10, 1920; came to U.S., 1922, naturalized, 1936; s. Aaron L. and Dora (Hural) L.; m. Barbara Louise Kincaid, Oct. 1943; children—Caroline Joan, Rebecca Louise, Tamara Jean. B.S., U. Wash., 1940; M.D., U. Mich., 1943; M.A., Harvard, 1961. Intern Mass. Gen. Hosp., Boston, 1943-44; mem. staff Mass. Gen. Hosp., 1949—, physician-in-chief, 1966-81; resident Mayo Found., Rochester, Minn., 1944-45; research fellow U. Mich., 1947-49; practice internal medicine Boston, 1949-90; faculty Med. Sch., Harvard, 1949—, Jackson prof. clin. medicine, 1966-81, Ridley Watts prof. preventive medicine, 1980-90, chmn. dept. preventive medicine and clin. epidemiology, 1980-90, Jackson prof. clin. medicine emeritus, 1990—; Disting. physician VA Medical Ctr. Brockton/W. Roxbury Hosps., Boston, 1990—. Served to capt. M.C. AUS, 1945-46. Recipient Outstanding Achievement award U. Minn., 1964; vis. fellow Balliol Coll., Oxford, 1971-72; Guggenheim fellow, 1971-72; named Disting. Physician, VA, 1991—. Fellow Am. Acad. Arts and Scis.; mem. NAS, ACP (master), Inst. Medicine, Am. Soc. Clin. Investigation (past pres.), Am. Physiol. Soc., Biophys. Soc., Assn. Am. Physicians (Kober medal 1995). Home: 1 Curtis Cir Winchester MA 01890-1703 Office: Mass Gen Hosp Boston MA 02114

LEAF, HOWARD WESTLEY, retired air force officer, military official; b. Menominee, Mich., Sept. 22, 1923; s. Joseph Conrad and Hilda Eugene (Lavoy) L.; m. Madonna Anne Ronan, May 21, 1955; children: Mary Beth, Barbara Anne, Timothy, Anne Marie, Thomas, James. B.S., Colo. Sch. Mines, 1950; M.S., St. Louis U., 1955; grad., Command and Staff Coll., 1961, Indsl. Coll. Armed Forces, 1969. Commd. 2d lt. U.S. Air Force, 1951, advanced through grades to lt. gen., 1980, ret., 1985; aviation cadet, 1950-51; jet pilot Korea, 1952-53; test pilot, 1955-60, geophysicist, 1961-64; ops. officer (49th Tactical Fighter Wing), Europe, 1965; squadron comdr. S.E. Asia, 1966; staff officer (Hdqrs. USAF), 1966-68, 69-71; wing comdr. 1st and 366th Tactical Fighter Wings, 1971-74; dep. chief staff for requirements Tactical Air Command, 1974-76; comdr. Air Force Test and Evaluation Ctr., Kirtland AFB, N.Mex., 1976-80; insp. gen. U.S. Air Force, Washington, 1980-83, asst. vice chief of staff, 1983-85; sr. v.p. BDM Internat. Corp., McLean, Va., 1984-91; dir. test and evaluation Hdqrs. USAF The Pentagon, Washington, 1992—; mem. Air Force Sci. Adv. Bd. Decorated D.S.M., Silver Star, Legion of Merit, D.F.C.; recipient Eugene M. Zuckert Mgmt. Award, 1978, Disting. Achievement award Colo. Sch. Mines, 1982. Mem. Internat. Test and Evaluation Assn. (sr. adv. bd.). Presbyterian. Home: 8504 Brook Rd Mc Lean VA 22102-1505 Office: Hdqs USAF TE 4E-995 The Pentagon Washington DC 20330

LEAF, PAUL, producer, director, writer; b. N.Y.C., May 2, 1929; s. Manuel and Anna (Dardick) L.; m. Nydia Ellis, Oct. 22, 1955; children: Jonathan, Alexandra, Ellen. BA in Drama with honors, CCNY, 1952. pres. Sea Gate Co. Dir., prodr.: 17 Broadway prodns., including The Subject Was Roses, 1964, films include: Judge Horton and the Scottsboro Boys, 1976 (Peabody award), Desperate Characters, 1972, Hail to the Chief, 1973, Sister Aimee, 1977, Every Man a King, 1977, Top Secret, 1979, God, Sex and Apple Pie, 1995, TV prodns. include Sgt. Matlovich vs. the U.S. Air Force, 1978; author: Comrades, 1985, Red, Right, Returning, 1987. Founder, chmn. Santa Monica Arts Commn., Santa Monica Arts Found.; founder, cons., bd. dirs. Santa Monica Coll. Art, Design and Architecture, 1990—. Served with U.S. Army, 1952-54. Decorated Meritorious Service medal; recipient 20 internat. festival and profl. awards, including Venice, 1967, London, 1967, 68, 69, N.Y., 1967, 68, 69, Berlin, 1972. Mem. Dirs. Guild Am., Writers Guild Am. Home: 2800 Neilson Way Santa Monica CA 90405-4025

LEAF, ROBERT JAY, dental insurance consultant; b. Mt. Vernon, N.Y., July 27, 1944; s. Jules William and Evelyn (Schneider) L.; m. Jeanette Ann Benjamin, June 17, 1973; children: Jeremy Robert, David Evan. DMD, Harvard U., 1969. Pres. Universal Profl. Ctrs., N.Y.C., 1971-74; dentist in pvt. practice N.Y.C., 1973-80; pres. Am. Dental Examiners, Inc., N.Y.C., 1978—, Better Benefits, Inc., N.Y.C., 1990—; pres., founder LeafRe Reins. Co., Ariz., 1993—; founder Dental Health Alliance, 1994; cons. Guardian Life Ins. Co., N.Y.C., 1979, Prin. Life Ins. Co., Iowa, 1981, 93, Mass. Mut. Life Ins. Co., 1983, 94, Equitable, N.Y., 1985, Empire Blue Cross, 1986, Prudential, N.J., 1987, Gen. Mills, Minn., 1988, Aetna, Conn., 1989, Am. Airlines, Tex., 1990, Protective Life Ins. Co., Alabama, 1991, Gen. Am. Life Ins. Co., 1992, 94, Blue Cross/Blue Shield, R.I., 1993, Fortis Benefits Ins. Co., Mo., 1988, 93, Chubb Life Ins. Co. Am., N.H., 1993, Jefferson Pilot Life, 1994, Trustmark Life, 1994, Delta Dental Minn., 1994; lectr. at nat. confs. on dental ins., vol. dental ins., and managed dental care, group officers round table, 1985. Author: The Dental Logic System, 1984, The Dental Learning System, 1987; also articles; devel. vol. dental ins. plan. Bd. dirs. Jewish Community Ctr., Harrison, N.Y., 1992. Mem. ADA, Dental Soc. State of N.Y., First Dist. Dental Soc., Acad. Gen. Dentistry, Am. Assn. Dental Cons., Am. Soc. for Preventive Dentistry. Avocations: sailing, skiing, reading. Office: Am Dental Examiners Inc 370 7th Ave Ste 1206 New York NY 10001-3900

LEAF, ROBERT STEPHEN, public relations executive; b. N.Y.C., Aug. 9, 1931; s. Nathan and Anne (Feinman) L.; m. Adele Ornstein, June 8, 1958; 1 child, Stuart Nathan. B.J., U. Mo-Columbia, 1952, M.A., 1954. Account exec. Herbert Kaufman, N.Y.C., 1956-57; various positions Marsteller Orgn., N.Y.C., 1957-65; v.p., gen. mgr. Marsteller Internat., Brussels, 1965-68; v.p. Marsteller Internat., Europe, 1968-70; pres. Burson-Marsteller Internat. and Marsteller Internat., London, 1970-81; chmn. Burson-Marsteller Internat., London, 1985—; dir. Burson-Marsteller Ltd., (Eng.), Burson-Marsteller Inc. (U.S.), Burson-Marsteller, (Japan), Burson-Marsteller Intermarkets, Bahrain, Burson-Marsteller S.E.A., (Singapore), Burson-Marsteller Ltd., (Hong Kong), Burson-Marsteller Gmbh, Germany; dir. Burson-Marsteller S.A. (Belgium), (France); dir. Burson-Marsteller S.P.A., (Italy), Burson-Marsteller S.A., (Switzerland), Burson-Marsteller Pty., (Australia), Burson-Marsteller, China. Contbr. articles to profl. pubs. Mem. Public Relations Soc. Am., Inst. Pub. Relations Eng., Pub. Relations Consultancy Assn. (London), Fgn. Press Assn., Pub. Relations Soc. Am., Alpha Pi Zeta, Kappa Tau Alpha. Club: Hurlingham (London). Home: 3 Fursecroft George St, London W1, England Office: Burson Marsteller Internat, 24-28 Bloomsbury Way, London WC1A 2PX, England

LEAF, ROGER WARREN, business consultant; b. New Rochelle, N.Y., Aug. 3, 1946; s. Harold Edwin and Mabel (Erickson) L.; m. Judith Blaine Edds, Sept. 23, 1978; children: Spencer W., Andrew B. BA in Econs., Heidelberg Coll., 1968; MBA, NYU, 1978. V.p. pub. fin. Dean Witter Reynolds Inc., N.Y.C., 1974-81; prin. corp. fin. Morgan Stanley & Co., Inc., N.Y.C., 1981-84; v.p. pub. fin., The First Boston Corp, N.Y.C., 1984-87, dir. mcpl. securities, 1988-91, chief oper. officer fixed income divsn., 1991-93; pres. R.W. Leaf & Co., 1993—. Trustee All Souls Sch., N.Y.C., 1984-90, treas. 1984-88. 1st lt. USAR, 1969-72. Mem. Waccabuc Country Club (N.Y.). Office: RW Leaf & Co 100 Park Ave New York NY 10017

LEAHEY, LYNN, editor-in-chief. Editor-in-chief Soap Opera Digest, N.Y.C. Office: Soap Opera Digest 888 7th Ave New York NY 10106*

LEAHIGH, ALAN KENT, public relations executive; b. Chgo., Dec. 25, 1944; s. Leland Jean and Rena Matilda (Rodda) L.; m. Lorrie Lynn Johnson, Aug. 19, 1967; children: Matthew Alan, Nathan Andrew. BA, Ill. Wesleyan U., 1967; MA, U. Mo., 1971. Reporter, editor Daily Pantagraph, Bloomington, Ill., 1965-71; tchr. Joliet (Ill.) Pub. Sch. Dist., 1969-71; assoc. dir. pub. info. Am. Dental Assn., Chgo., 1971-75, dir. pub. info., 1976-77, editor ADA News, 1978-80; v.p. Pub. Communications Inc., Chgo., 1981-83, sr. v.p., ptnr., 1983-90, exec. v.p., 1990—; v.p. Living Learning Devel. Corp., Wheaton, Ill., 1980-89, Marian Park Inc., Wheaton, 1980-89; lectr. workshops in field. Contbr. articles to profl. jours. Mem. Wheaton Hist. Preservation Soc., 1978—; chmn. Wheaton Community TV Cmmn., 1986—. Mem. Pub. Rels. Soc. Am. (Silver Anvil award 1982, 85, 86, 93), Soc. Profl. Journalists, Chgo. Publicity Club, Am. Hosp. Assn., Chgo. Headline Club, Masons. Presbyterian. Office: Pub Communications Inc 35 E Wacker Dr Chicago IL 60601-2102

LEAHY, GERALD PHILIP, hospital administrator; b. Vancouver, B.C., Canada, Feb. 16, 1936; married. B. U. Portland, 1959; MHA, St. Louis U., 1961. Adminstrv. asst. Sacred Heart Med. Ctr., Spokane, Wash., 1961-63, asst. adminstr., 1963-68, assoc. adminstr., 1968-81, exec. v.p., 1981-88, pres., chief exec. officer, 1988—. Mem. Am. Coll. Healthcare Execs., Am. Hosp.

Assn. (del. 1979-81, reg. adv. bd. 1977-83) Wash. Hosp. Assn. (chmn. 1977-78, bd. dirs. 1970-82). Home: 4925 S Perry St Spokane WA 99223-6337 Office: Sacred Heart Med Ctr PO Box 2555 Spokane WA 99220-2555

LEAHY, MICHAEL JOSEPH, newspaper editor; b. Chgo., Feb. 24, 1939; s. Joseph Michael and Elizabeth Catherine (Keefe) L.; m. Harriet Smith Friday, Sept. 18, 1971; children—Christine Elizabeth, Thomas Joseph, Christopher Michael. A.B., Georgetown U., 1961; M.S. in Journalism, Columbia U., 1966. Copy boy, news clk., copy editor N.Y. Times, N.Y.C., 1961-71, asst. to met. editor, 1971-73, editor L.I. Weekly, 1973-77, editor Conn. Weekly, 1977-81, travel editor, 1982-86, editor arts & leisure sect., 1986-90, dep. editor The Week in Review, 1990-92, real estate editor, 1992—Editor: (with A.M. Rosenthal, A. Gelb and N. Kerr) The Sophisticated Traveler series. Bd. advisors Georgetown Coll., 1990—; mem. edn. com. St. David's Sch., 1991-93. 1st lt. U.S. Army, 1961-64. Pulitzer Traveling fellow Columbia U., 1967. Mem. Georgetown Libr. Assocs. (trustee 1981-94), Columbia Journalism Alumni (pres. 1981-83), Century Assn. Roman Catholic. Office: NY Times Co 229 W 43rd St New York NY 10036-3913

LEAHY, PATRICK JOSEPH, senator; b. Montpelier, Vt., Mar. 31, 1940; s. Howard and Alba (Zambon) L.; m. Marcelle Pomerleau, Aug. 25, 1962; children: Kevin, Alicia, Mark. B.A., St. Michael's Coll., Vt., 1961; J.D., Georgetown U., 1964. Bar: Vt. 1964, D.C. 1979, U.S. Ct. Appeals (2d cir.) 1966, Vt. Fed. Dist. Ct. 1965, U.S. Supreme Ct. 1968. State's atty. Chittenden County, Vt., 1966-75; U.S. senator from Vt., 1975—, ranking minority mem. com. on agrl. nutrition and forestry, subcom. on fgn. ops., jud. subcom. antitrust, bus. routes & competition, mem. judiciary com., mem. appropriations com. mem. appropriations com., vice chmn. senate intelligence com., 1985-86; mem. World Hunger bd.; bd. visitors U.S. Mil. Acad. West Point, Gallaudet Coll., Nat. Coll. Deaf, Washington; mem. Senate Dem. Steering & Coordination Com. Recipient 1st amendment award Soc. Profl. Journalists. Mem. Nat. Dist. Attys. Assn. (v.p. 1971-74). Office: US Senate 433 Russell Senate Office Washington DC 20510*

LEAHY, T. LIAM, management consultant; b. Camp Legeunne, N.C., Apr. 15, 1952; s. Thomas James and Margaret May (Munnelly) L.; m. Shannon Kelly Brooks, Apr. 21, 1990. BS, St. Louis U., 1974, MA, 1975; postgrad., Hubbard Coll. of Adminstrn., L.A., 1989. V.p. sales Cablecom Inc., Chgo., 1978-81, Kaye Advt., N.Y.C., 1981-83; group pubr. Jour. Graphics Pub., N.Y.C., 1983-85; gen. mgr. Generation Dynamics, N.Y.C., 1985-86; pres. Leahy & Assocs., N.Y.C., 1982-86, Tarzana, Calif., 1982—; assoc. Am Coun. of Execs. Assoc., Glendale, 1991—; bd. dirs. Cons. Assn., Laser Impact, Austin, Tex., comprotek Svcs. Inc., DBA Laser Impact, Austin, Art Boom Internat., Inc., Santa Clarita, Calif. Contbr. articles to profl. jours. Fellow Effective Mgmt. Ctrs. (sr.); mem. Am. Coun. Execs. (bd. dirs. 1993-95), Turnaround Mgmt. Assn., L.A. C. of C. Avocations: musician, computer systems design, producer TV/film. Office: Leahy & Assocs 19131 E Nadia Way Reseda CA 91335-3827

LEAHY, WILLIAM F., insurance company executive, lawyer; b. N.Y.C., July 28, 1913; s. William F. and Anna (Murphy) L.; m. Catherine Patricia Carlin, Oct. 19, 1940; children: William C., Michael J. Pre-law certificate, Coll. City N.Y., 1936; LL.B. cum laude, Bklyn. Law Sch., 1939, LL.M. 1940. Bar: N.Y. 1940. With Met. Life Ins. Co., N.Y.C., 1932-78; assoc. gen. counsel Met. Life Ins. Co., 1962-65, v.p. real estate financing, 1965 and after, sr. v.p. 1976-78; sr. real estate cons. Goldman Sachs Realty Co., 1979-85; adv. bd. N.Y. State Tchrs. Retirement System. Served to lt. col. USAAF, 1941-46. Mem. ABA. Home: 6152 N Verde Trail Apt D122 Boca Raton FL 33433-2419 also: 24 Cliff Dr Sag Harbor NY 11963-1805

LEAK, MARGARET ELIZABETH, insurance company executive; b. Atlanta, Sept. 9, 1946; d. William Whitehurst and Margaret Elizabeth (Whitsitt) L. BS in Psychology, Okla. State U., 1968; postgrad., U. Okla., 1968-69, Cornell U., 1976-78; grad. advanced mgmt. program, Harvard U., 1983-84. Editor communications Eastern State Bankcard Assn., N.Y.C., 1969-71; sr. edn. specialist Citibank, N.Y.C., 1971-73; adminstrv. devel. NBC, N.Y.C., 1973-74; mgr. tng. and devel. Atlantic Mut. Cos., Property/Casualty Ins., N.Y.C., 1974-76, sec. human resources, 1976-78, v.p. human resources, 1978-84, v.p. human resources and corp. communications, 1984-86, sr. v.p. adminstrv. services, 1987—. Office: Atlantic Mut Cos 3 Giralda Farms Madison NJ 07940-1004

LEAK, ROBERT E., management consultant; b. Charlotte, N.C., Sept. 15, 1934; s. James Pickett and Cornelia (Edwards) L.; m. Martha Councill, Aug. 25, 1956; children: Robert E., James Councill. B.S., Duke U., 1956; M.S., U. Tenn., 1957. With Pan Am. Petroleum Co., Lafayette, La., 1957-59, Allied Securities Corp., Raleigh, N.C., 1961-62, Cameron Brown Mortgage Co., Raleigh and Charlotte, 1962-64; with N.C. Dept. Natural and Econ. Resources, Raleigh, 1959-61, 64-76; dir. econ. devel. N.C. Dept. Natural and Econ. Resources, until 1976; dir. S.C. State Devel. Bd., Columbia, 1976-84; pres. Research Triangle Park Found., N.C., 1984-88; prin. Leak-Goforth Co., LLC, Raleigh, N.C., 1988—; mem. U.S. Dept. Commerce Small Bus. Adv. Council; also vice-chmn. Dist. Export Council; leader industry organized govt. approved trade and indsl. devel. missions to, Can., Europe, S.Am., Australia, Far East. Bd. dirs. Raleigh YMCA, S.C. Tech. and Comprehensive Edn., N.C. Symphony Fedn.; bd. dirs., mem. adv. bd. Duke Hosp.; bd. Duke Alumni Assn. Mem Am. Indsl. Devel. Council (past pres.), Nat. Assn. State Devel. Agys. (past pres.). Episcopalian. Home: 3301 Landor Rd Raleigh NC 27609-7012 Office: Ste 2700 150 Fayetteville St Mall Raleigh NC 27601

LEAKE, DONALD LEWIS, oral and maxillofacial surgeon, oboist; b. Cleveland, Okla., Nov. 6, 1931; s. Walter Wilson and Martha Lee (Crowe) L.; m. Rosemary Dobson, Aug. 20, 1964; children: John Andrew Dobson, Elizabeth, Catherine. AB, U. So. Calif., 1953, MA, 1957; DMD, Harvard U., 1962; MD, Stanford U., 1969. Diplomate Am. Bd. Oral and Maxillofacial Surgery. Intern Mass. Gen. Hosp., Boston, 1962-63; resident Mass. Gen. Hosp., 1963-64; postdoctoral fellow Harvard U., 1964-66; practice medicine specializing in oral and maxillofacial surgery; assoc. prof. oral and maxillofacial surgery Harbor-UCLA Med. Ctr., Torrance, 1970-74, dental dir., chief oral and maxillofacial surgery, 1970—, prof., 1974—; assoc. dir. UCLA Dental Rsch. Inst., 1979-82, dir., 1982-86; prof. extranjero Escuela de Graduados, Asociacion Medica Argentina, 1990—; cons. to hosps.; dental dir. coastal health services region, Los Angeles County, 1974-81; oboist Robert Shaw Chorale, 1954-55; solo oboist San Diego Symphony, 1954-59. Contbr. articles to med. jours.; rec. artist: (albums on Columbia label) The Music of Heinrich Schütz, Stockhausen, Zeitmasse for 5 Winds, Schönberg, Orchestra Variations-Opus 31; freelance musician various film studio orchs. Carmel Bach Festival, 1949, 52-53, 67-81, numerous concerts with Coleman Chamber Music, The Cantata Singers, Boston, Garden St. Chamber Players, Cambridge, Baroque Consortium, L.A., Corona Del Mar Baroque Festival, others; world premieres (oboe works) by Darius Milhaud, William Kraft, Alice Parker, Mark Volkert, Eugene Zádor, Robert Linn. Mem. Commn. on the Future of Rose-Hulman Inst. Tech., Terre Haute, Ind., 1992-93. Recipient 1st prize with greatest distinction for oboe and chamber music Brussels Royal Conservatory Music Belgium, 1956. Fellow ACS; mem. AAAS, ASTM, Internat. Assn. Dental Rsch., Internat. Assn. Oral Surgeons. Soc. Biomaterials, Biomed. Engring. Soc. (sr. mem.), L.A. County Med. Assn., N.Y. Acad. Sci., L.A. Acad. Medicine, European Assn. Maxillofacial Surgeons, Brit. Assn. Oral and Maxillofacial Surgeons, Internat. Gesellschaft fur Kiefer-Gesichts-Chirurgie, Internat. Soc. Plastic, Aesthetic and Reconstructive Surgery, Phi Beta Kappa, Phi Kappa Phi. Clubs: Harvard (Boston and N.Y.C.). Achievements include patents for work related to bone reconstruction, 1974, 82, 90. Home: 2 Crest Rd W Rolling Hills CA 90274 Office: Harbor-UCLA Med Ctr 1000 W Carson St Torrance CA 90502-2004 also: Harbor UCLA Profl Bldg 21840 S Normandie Ave Ste 700 Torrance CA 90502

LEAKE, PRESTON HILDEBRAND, tobacco research executive; b. Proffit, Va., Aug. 8, 1929; s. Perry Hansford and Lydia Viola (Cox) L.; m. Elizabeth Ann Kelly, Dec. 5, 1954; children: Luther Hildebrand, Lawrence Albert. BS, U. Va., 1950; MA, Duke U., 1953, PhD, 1954. Rsch. supr. Allied Chem. Corp., Hopewell, Va., 1954-60; asst. rsch. dir. Albemarle Paper Mfg. Co., Richmond, Va., 1960-65; asst. to mng. dir. The Am. Tobacco Co., Hopewell, 1965-68, asst. mng. dir., 1968-70, asst. R & D dir., 1970-87, dir. R & D, 1987-88, v.p. rsch., 1988-91, ret., 1991; adj. prof. organic chemistry Va.

Commonwealth U., 1963-64; tobacco industry rep. to Coun. for Tobacco Rsch., 1977-88; chmn. bd. dirs. Tobacco Inst. Testing Lab., 1977-88; adv. bd. chem. abstracts Va. Jr. Acad. Sci., 1986-88, mem. planning com., 1991-95; mem. Congl. Study Com., 1984-88. Patentee amino acid synthesis and tobacco cigarette filter; contbr. articles to profl. jours. Chmn. Providence Jr. High Sch. PTA, Midlothian, Va., 1968-70, Clover Hill High Sch. PTA, 1971-72; chmn. bd. trustees Chesterfield County (Va.) Pub. Librs., 1974-77; mem. County Sch. Adv. Com., Chesterfield, 1969-70; judge chemistry sect. Jr. Acad. Sci., 1991-92; mem. Hopewell Community and Indsl. Panel for Environ. Improvement, 1992—. Recipient Army Chem. Corp fellowship, 1950-52, Allied Chem. fellowship, 1952-54. Mem. Am. Chem. Soc. (treas. 1966, sec. 1967, mng. vice-chmn. 1968, chmn. 1970, mem. People to People Goodwill Tour to England, Norway, USSR, Czechoslovakia, East and West Germany 1971, Disting. Svc. award 1976), Am. Inst. Chemists (chmn. 1962), Va. Acad. Sci., Computer Users Group (pres. Richmond chpt. 1984-86), James River Catfish Club (keeper of keys 1978-80), Rotary (sec. Hopewell 1992), Sigma Xi, Phi Lambda Upsilon. Home: 401 Delton Ave Hopewell VA 23860-1815

LEAL, GEORGE D., engineering company executive; b. 1934. B in Civil Engring., MA, Santa Clara U., 1959. With Dames & Moore, Inc., L.A., 1959—, CEO, 1981—, now CEO, pres.; bd. dirs. BW/IP Internat. Inc. Office: Dames & Moore Inc 911 Wilshire Blvd Ste 700 Los Angeles CA 90017-3436*

LEAL, HERBERT ALLAN BORDEN, former university chancellor, former government official; b. Beloeil, Que., Can., June 15, 1917; s. Frederick William and Marie Ange (Ranger) L.; m. Muriel Isobel, Mar. 21, 1942; children: Kathleen Mary Leal Clark, Allan Ross, James Frederick. B.A. with honors in History, McMaster U., 1940; LL.M., Harvard U., 1957. Bar: Called to Ont. bar 1948. Read law with Frank Erichsen-Brown, Toronto, 1945-48; mem. firm Erichsen-Brown & Leal, Toronto, 1948-50; lectr. Osgoode Hall Law Sch., 1950-56, vice dean, prof., 1956-58, dean, prof., 1958-66; dep. atty. gen. Ont., 1977-81; chancellor McMaster U., Hamilton, Ont., 1977-86; chmn. Ont. Law Reform Commn., 1966-77, vice chmn., 1981-89; spl. lectr. Law Soc. Upper Can., 1951, 57, 60, 66, 77, Faculty of Law, U. Toronto, 1972-77; mem. council Medico-Legal Soc. Toronto, 1960, 1st v.p., 1968, pres., 1969. Contbr. articles to legal and profl. jours. Mem. exec. com. Toronto br. Can. Red Cross Soc., 1959-64; convion. spl. com. Assn. Am. Law Schs., Assn. Can. Law Tchrs. Can.-Am. Coop., 1962-66; commmr. Ont. Uniform Law Conf. Can., 1963-86, pres., 1977-78; mem. adv. com. Can. Civil Liberties Assn. Ont., 1965-66; mem. faculty Can. Jud. Conf., 1969-73, dir., 1969-70; mem. Can. del. Hague Conf. on Pvt. Internat. Law, 1968, 72, 76, chief of del., 1980; chief Can. del. Internat. Diplomatic Conf. on Wills, Washington, 1973; chmn. spl. com. uniform law Conf. Internat. Conventions Pvt. Internat. Law, 1971-81. With Royan Can. Arty., 1943-45; reeve Village of Tweed, 1991-94. Decorated officer Order of Can.; recipient Gov. Gen. medal McMaster U., 1939; A. G. Alexander scholar, 1939; Rhodes scholar, 1940. Mem. Law Soc. Upper Can. (medal 1987), Toronto Arty. Officers Assn., Assn. Can. Law Tchrs. (pres. 1959-60), African Students Found. (bd. dirs.). Club: Masons.

LEAL, LESLIE GARY, chemical engineering educator; b. Bellingham, Wash., Mar. 18, 1943; s. Leslie Arthur and Esther Vivian (Jones) L.; m. Mary Ann Seelye, June 11, 1965; children: Heather Noel, Kameron Brie, Farrah Aimee. BS, U. Wash., 1965; MS, Stanford U., 1967, PhD, 1969. Asst. prof. chem. engring. Calif. Inst. Tech., Pasadena, 1970-75, assoc. prof., 1975-78, prof., 1978-89, Chevron Disting. prof., 1986-89; prof., chmn. dept. chem. and nuclear engring. U. Calif., Santa Barbara, 1989—; cons. Firestone Rsch., Akron, Ohio, 1981-88, Dynamics Tech., Torrance, Calif., 1982-90, Richards of Rockford, Ill., 1975-79, Dowell-Schlumbargar, Tulsa, Okla., 1985-88, U. Okla. Fracturing Fluid Characterization Facility Project, 1991—; active U.S. Nat. Com. on Theoretical and Applied Mechanics, 1991—, chmn. 1994—; lectr. in field. Assoc. editor Internat. Jour. Multiphase Flow, 1985—; mem. editl. bd. Experiments in Fluids, 1994—, Ann. Revs. Fluid Mechanics, 1985-90, Jour. Colloid and Interface Sci., AIChE Jour. Tchr.-scholar grantee Camille and Henry Dreyfus Found., 1975; fellow John Simon Guggenheim Found., 1976. Fellow Am. Phys. Soc.; mem. NAE (mem. membership policy com. 1994—), AIChE (William H. Walker award 1993, Allan P. Colburn award 1978, tech. achievement award So. Calif. sect. 1978, chmn. nat. program com. in fluid mechanics 1984-89), Nat. Rsch. Coun. (mem. space studies bd. com. on microgravity rsch. 1993—), Soc. Rheology, Am. Soc. for Engring. Edn., Phi Beta Kappa, Tau Beta Pi, Phi Sigma Upsilon. Methodist. Home: 1560 Hillcrest Rd Santa Barbara CA 93103-1841 Office: U Calif Dept Chem and Nuclear Engring Santa Barbara CA 93106

LEAMAN, DAVID MARTIN, cardiologist; b. Lancaster, Pa., Apr. 24, 1935; s. Benjamin Denlinger and Elise Mae (Martin) L.; m. Doris Jean Heisey; children: Gretchen Jane, Heidi Jean, Erika Ingrid. Student, Franklin & Marshall Coll., 1956-58; BA, Eastern Mennonite Coll., 1960; MD, Temple U., 1964. Intern Mary Hitchcock Hosp., Hanover, N.H., 1964-66; resident U. Vt., Burlington, 1968-71; asst. prof. medicine Pa. State U., Hershey, 1971-77, assoc. prof., 1977-84, prof., 1984—; chief div. of cardiology, 1984—; asst. dean for student affairs, 1987-91, asst. dean for admissions, 1991-94. Contbr. articles to med. jours. Sch. dir. Lower Dauphin Sch. Dist., Hummelstown, Pa., 1977-83. Served with USPHS, 1966-68. Named Alumnus of Yr. Eastern Mennonite Coll., 1985. Fellow Am. Coll. Cardiology, Am. Coll. Chest Physicians, ACP, Soc. Cardiac Angiology, Am. Heart Assn. (mem. council on clin. cardiology, Service Recognition award 1981, Disting. Service award 1985, bd. dirs. Pa. affiliate 1975—), Alpha Omega Alpha. Republican. Mennonite. Avocations: reading, photography. Office: Pa State Univ Hershey Med Ctr PO Box 850 Hershey PA 17033-0850

LEAMAN, J. RICHARD, JR., paper company executive; b. Lancaster, Pa., Sept. 22, 1934; s. J. Richard and Margaret B. (Leaman); m. Helen Brown, June 15, 1957; children: Lynda B., J. Richard, III. BA, Dartmouth Coll., 1956, MBA, 1957; PhD (hon.), Widener U., 1988. With Scott Paper Co., Phila., 1960—, v.p. comml. products, 1975-78; exec. v.p. mktg. and sales Scott Paper Co., 1978—, pres. Packaged Products div., 1983—, dir., 1986; pres. Scott Worldwide, 1986; vice chmn. Scott Paper Co., 1991-94; pres. S.D. Warren Co. div. Scott Paper, 1991-95; bd. dirs. Church & Dwight Co., Inc., Pep Boys, S.D. Warren Holdings. Vice chmn. exec. com., trustee Widener U., 1987; mem. conf. bd.'s coun. Global Bus. Mgmt.; trustee Tyler Arboretum. Capt. USAF, 1957-61. Recipient Disting. Performance in Mgmt. award Widener U. Mem. Conf. Bd.'s Coun. on Global Bus. Mgmt. Republican. Episcopalian. Clubs: Dartmouth (Phila.). Home: 317 Boot Rd Malvern PA 19355-3317 Office: Scott Paper Co Scott Plz Philadelphia PA 19113

LEAMAN, JACK ERVIN, landscape architect, community/regional planner; b. Mason City, Iowa, Jan. 24, 1932; s. Theodore R. and Dorothy M. (Schrum) L.; m. Darlene A. McNary, June 15, 1952; children: Jeffrey A., Danna J., Jay M., Duree K. B.S. in Landscape Architecture and Urban Planning, Iowa State U., 1954, M. Community and Regional Planning, 1982. Registered landscape architect, Calif., Iowa, Minn., N.Mex. Landscape architect Sam L. Huddleston Office, Denver, 1954-55, Phillips Petroleum Co., Bartlesville, Okla., 1955-58; landscape architect for Price Tower and residence with architect Frank Lloyd Wright Bartlesville, Okla., 1957-58; planning technician Santa Barbara County, Calif., 1958-60; planning cons. Engring. Planners, Santa Barbara, 1960-63; planning dir. City of Santa Barbara, 1963-66, City of Mason City, 1971-72; landscape architect, planning cons. Midwest Research Inst., Kansas City, Mo., 1972-74, Hansen, Lind, Meyer, Iowa City, Iowa, 1974-76, Sheffler, Leaman, Rova, Mason City, 1976-78, RCM Assocs., Inc., Hopkins, Minn. and Ames, Iowa, 1978-82; planning dir. City-County Planning, Albuquerque, 1982-86, City of Colorado Springs, Colo., 1986-90; landscape architect, pvt. practice planning cons. Mason City, Iowa, 1990-92; assoc. ptnr., landscape architect, community/regional planner Yaggy Colby Assocs., Mason City, 1992—. Recipient Residential Landscape Design award Calif. Landscape Contractors Assn., 1962, Design Achievement award Coll. of Design Iowa State U., 1988. Fellow Am. Soc. Landscape Architects (chpt. pres. 1967-68, 90-91, trustee Iowa 1980-82, N.Mex. 1982-86, Award of Excellence 1954); mem. Am. Inst. Cert. Planners, Am. Planning Assn. (chpt. pres. Iowa 1969-70), Urban Land Inst., Tau Sigma Delta.

LEAMON, TOM B., industrial engineer, educator; b. Ossett, Yorkshire, U.K., Apr. 16, 1940; came to U.S., 1980; s. Harold and Dorothy (Wilde) L.; m. Geraldine Bland, July 1, 1967; children: Amanda Charlotte, Jonathan Barton, Genevieve Emma. BS in Chemistry, U. Manchester, U.K., 1961; MS in Indsl. Engring., Inst. Tech., Cranfield, U.K., 1964; MS in Applied Psychology, U. Aston, Birmingham, U.K., 1970; PhD in Indsl. Engring. Production Mgmt., Inst. Tech., Cranfield, 1982. Chartered engr.; chartered profl. ergonomist. Indsl. engr. Ilford (Eng.) Ltd., 1961-62; mgr. ergonomics Pilkington Ltd., St. Helens, Eng., 1964-71; dir. masters course Inst. Tech., Cranfield, 1970-75; head ergonomics br. Nat. Coal Bd., Burton-upon-Trent, U.K., 1975-80; dir. grad. program in occupational safety U. Ill., Chgo., 1981-82; prof., chmn. No. Ill. U., DeKalb, 1982-87, acting dean, 1985-86; prof., chmn. Tex. Tech. U., Lubbock, 1987-91; v.p., dir. rsch. ctr. Liberty Mut. Ins. Group, Hopkinton, Mass., 1991—. Trustee Am. Soc. Safety Engrs. Found. Named 1985 Disting. Lectr., Coll. Lake County. Fellow Inst. Prodn. Engrs. (Sir Ben Williams Silver medal 1969), Human Factors Soc. (chmn. indsl. ergonomics 1983-85), Ergonomics Soc.; mem. Inst. Indsl. Engrs. (chmn. ergonomics div. 1990-91, Spl. citation for outstanding contbns. to the enhancement of ergonomics); Am. Soc. Safety Engrs., Sigma Xi. Office: Liberty Mutual Rsch Ctr 71 Frankland Rd Hopkinton MA 01748-1231

LEAP, DARRELL IVAN, hydrogeologist; b. Huntington, W.Va., Oct. 19, 1937; s. Willis Ivan and Bertie Estal (Messinger) L.; m. Wilma Ann Elkins, Feb. 24, 1962 (div. 1977); m. Myra Kay McCammon, May 14, 1983. BS, Marshall U., 1960; MA, Ind. U., 1966; PhD, Pa. State U., 1974. Registered profl. hydrogeologist; cert. profl. geologist. Geologist, hydrologist S.D. Geol. Survey, Vermillion, S.D., 1966-71; hydrologist U.S. Geol. Survey, Denver, 1974-80; assoc. prof. Purdue U., West Lafayette, Ind., 1980-93, prof., 1993—; pvt. cons. West Lafayette, 1985—; cons. U.S. EPA, Washington, 1990—, U.S. Nuclear Regulatory Com., Washington, 1992—; disting. guest spkr. 1st Nat. Ground-Water Conf., Seoul, Korea, 1994; apptd. Ind. Hazardous Waste Facility Siting Authority, 1993; co-prin.investigator IBM-Purdue environmental rsch. project. Contbr. articles to profl. jours.; composer vocal and choral music. Singer Bach Chorale Singers, Lafayette, 1981-92, bd. dirs., 1992, pres., 1993—; bd. dirs. Water Conservancy Dist., Battleground, Ind., 1992. Lt. USNR, 1960-65. Mem. Am. Geophys. Union, Geol. Soc. Am. (com. chair 1991-92), Nat. Assn. Ground Water Scientists and Engrs., Ind. Water Resources Assn. (pres. 1982-83). Republican. Presbyterian. Achievements include research development of two new ground water tracing methods, three new ground water modeling methods, method to test relative retardation of substances in the ground; first to report influence of pore pressure on dispersivity; application of boundary-fitted coordinate system method to modeling of ground-water flow; modeling effects of climate change on ground water flow and transport. Office: Purdue U Dept Earth and Atmospheric Scis West Lafayette IN 47907-1397

LEAR, ERWIN, anesthesiologist, educator; b. Bridgeport, Conn., Jan. 1, 1924; s. Samuel Joseph and Ida (Ruth) L.; m. Arlene Joyce Alexander, Feb. 15, 1953; children—Stephanie, Samuel. MD, SUNY, 1952. Diplomate Am. Bd. Anesthesiology, Nat. Bd. Med. Examiners. Intern L.I. Coll. Hosp. Bklyn., 1952-53; asst. resident anesthesiologist Jewish Hosp., Bklyn., 1953-54; sr. resident Jewish Hosp., 1955, asst., 1955-56, adj., 1956-58, assoc. anesthesiologist, 1958-64; attending anesthesiologist Bklyn. VA Hosp., 1958-64, cons., 1977—; assoc. vis. anesthesiologist Kings County Hosp. Ctr., Bklyn., 1957-80; staff anesthesiologist Kings County Hosp. Ctr., 1980-81; vis. anesthesiologist Queens Gen. Hosp. Ctr., 1955-67; dir. anesthesiology Queens Hosp. Ctr. Jamaica, 1964-67, cons., 1968—; chmn. dept. anesthesiology Catholic Med. Ctr., Queens and Bklyn., 1968-80; dir. anesthesiology Beth Israel Med. Ctr., Bklyn., 1955-58; clin. instr. SUNY Coll. Medicine, Bklyn., 1955-58; clin. asst. prof. SUNY Coll. Medicine, 1958-64, clin. assoc. prof. 1964-71, clin. prof., 1971-80, prof., vice-chmn. clin. anesthesiology, 1980-81; prof. anesthesiology Mt. Sinai Sch. Medicine, 1981-94, Albert Einstein Coll. of Medicine, 1994—. Author: Chemistry Applied Pharmacology of Tranquilizers; contbr. articles to profl. jours. Served with USNR, 1942-45. Fellow Am. Coll. Anesthesiologists, N.Y. Acad. Medicine (sec. sect. anesthesiology 1985-86, chmn. sect. anesthesiology 1986-87); mem. AMA, Am. Soc. Anesthesiologists (chmn. com. on by-laws 1982-83, dir. 1981—, ho. of dels. 1973—, editor newsletter 1984—, chmn. adminstrv. affairs com., 1987—), N.Y. State Bd. Profl. Med. Conduct, N.Y. State Soc. Anesthesiologists (chmn. pub. relations 1963-73, chmn. com. local arrangements 1968-73, dist. dir. 1972-73, v.p. 1974-75, pres. 1976, bd. dirs. 1972, past com. 1977-81, assoc. editor Bulletin 1963-77, editor Sphere 1978-84), N.Y. State Med. Soc. (chmn. sect. anesthesiology 1966-67, sec. sect. 1977-81), N.Y. County Med. Soc., SUNY Coll. Medicine Alumni Assn. (pres. 1983, trustee alumni fund 1980), Alpha Omega Alpha. Address: Harriman Dr Sands Point NY 11050

LEAR, EVELYN, soprano; b. Bklyn., Jan. 8, 1930; m. Thomas Stewart; children: Jan, Bonni. Vocal student in, N.Y.C.; student, N.Y. U., Hunter Coll. Song recitals, Phillips Gallery, Washington; mem. Juilliard Sch. Music Workshop; recital, Town Hall, N.Y.C., 1955; lead in Marc Blitzstein's Reuben, Reuben; performed Strauss's Four Last Songs with London Symphony Orch., 1959; mem. Deutsche Oper, 1959, appeared in Lulu at Vienna Festival, 1962, The Marriage of Figaro at Salzburg Festival, 1962, debut, Vienna State Opera, 1964, Frankfurt Opera, 1965, Covent Garden, 1965, Kansas City (Mo.) Performing Arts Found., 1965, Chgo. Lyric Opera, 1966, La Scala Opera, 1971, also in Brussels, San Francisco, Los Angeles, Buenos Aires, debut at Met. Opera as Lavinia in Mourning Becomes Electra, 1967, mem. co., 1967—; roles include Tosca, Manon, Marshallin, Desdemona, Mimi, Dido, Donna Elvira, Marina, Tatiana; TV appearance in La Boheme, 1965; numerous solo appearances, 1960—; appeared in film Buffalo Bill, 1976; rec. artist Angel Records, Deutsche Grammophon. Recipient Concert Artists Guild award 1955, Liederabend, Salzburg Festival 1964, Grammy award for best operatic recording (Marie in Wozzeck) 1965; Fulbright scholar, 1957. Address: care Zemsky/Green Divsn Columbia Artists Mgmt Inc 165 W 57th St New York NY 10019

LEAR, JOHN, writer, editor; b. nr. Allen, Pa., Aug. 10, 1909; s. Charles D. and Esther M. (Sourbeer) L.; m. Dorothy Leeds, Sept. 26, 1931 (dec. May 1965); m. Marie Nesta, Aug. 28, 1966. D.Sc. (hon.), Dickinson Coll., 1968. Editor Daily Local News, Mechanicsburg, Pa., 1927-28; reporter Patriot, Harrisburg, 1928-34; writer-editor A.P., Phila., Chgo., N.Y.C., Washington, Buenos Aires; roving assignments A.P., Eastern U.S., Can., S.Am., 1934-42; coordinator info. staff gov. P.R., 1942-43; radio news writer Press Assn., N.Y.C., 1943; free lance mag. corr., 1944-48; mng. editor Steelways mag., 1948-49; chief articles editor Collier's mag., 1949-50, assoc. editor, 1950-53; cons. publs. IBM Corp., 1953-54; dir. spl. atomics and automation studies Research Inst. Am., 1954-55; sci. editor Sat. Rev., 1956-71, sr. editor, 1971-72; v.p. Bauer Engring., Inc., 1972; v.p.-chief editor Bauer, Sheaffer & Lear, Inc., Chgo., 1972-75; chief editor Keifer & Assos., Inc., 1975-76; Am. corr. New Scientist, London, 1956-62; editorial cons. Russell Sage Found., 1967-68, Inst. for Social Research, U. Mich., 1972-73; columnist King Features Syndicate, 1973; editorial cons. Rockefeller Found., 1978-82; cons. Office of Tech. Assessment, U.S. Congress, 1975; publs. cons. Acad. Forum, Nat. Acad. Scis., 1976. Author: Forgotten Front, 1942, Kepler's Dream, 1965, Recombinant DNA—The Untold Story, 1978; contbg. editor: World Press Rev, 1976-84; sci. editor Pa. mag., 1982-83; editor Pa. Press Bur., Pa. Newspaper Pubs. Assn., 1986; columnist The Gettysburg Times, 1986-87. Recipient Disting. Svc. to Journalism medal Sigma Delta Chi, 1950, 60, Westinghouse prize AAAS, 1951, Albert Lasker Med. Journalism award, 1952. Mem. AARP. Home: 4570 Larch Dr Apt 181 Harrisburg PA 17109-5105

LEAR, NORMAN MILTON, producer, writer, director; b. New Haven, July 27, 1922; s. Herman and Jeanette (Seicol) L.; children: Ellen, Kate B. Lear LaPook, Maggie B.; m. Lyn Davis; 1 child, Benjamin Davis. Student, Emerson Coll., 1940-42, HHD, 1968. Engaged in pub. relations, 1945-49; founder Act III Comms., 1987—. Comedy writer for TV, 1950-54; writer, dir. for TV and films, 1954-59; producer: films Come Blow Your Horn, 1963, Never Too Late, 1965; prodr., screenwriter: Divorce American Style, 1967, The Night They Raided Minsky's, 1968; writer, producer, dir.: Cold Turkey, 1971; exec. prodr. film Start the Revolution Without Me, The Princess Bride, Breaking In, Fried Green Tomatoes; creator, dir.: TV shows TV Guide Awards Show, 1962, Henry Fonda and the Family, 1963, Andy Williams Spl., also, Andy Williams Series, 1965, Robert Young and the Family, 1970; exec. prodr., creator-developer: TV shows All in the Family, 1971 (4 Emmy awards 1970-73, Peabody award 1977), Maude, 1972; Sanford and Son, 1972, Good Times, 1974, The Jeffersons, 1975, Hot L Baltimore, 1975, Mary Hartman, Mary Hartman, 1976, One Day At a Time, 1975, All's Fair, 1976, A Year at the Top, 1977, All That Glitters, 1977, Fernwood 2 Night, 1977, The Baxters, 1979, Palmerstown, 1980, I Love Liberty, 1982, Sunday Dinner, 1991, The Powers That Be, 1992, 704 Hauser, 1994; creator a.k.a. Pablo, 1984; exec. producer Heartsounds, 1984. Pres. Am. Civil Liberties Found. So. Calif., 1973—; trustee Mus. Broadcasting; bd. dirs. People for the American Way; founder Bus. Enterprise Trust. Served with USAAF, 1942-45. Decorated Air medal with 4 oak leaf clusters; named One of Top Ten Motion Picture Producers, Motion Picture Exhibitors, 1963, 67, 68, Showman of Yr., Publicists Guild, 1971-77, Assn. Bus. Mgrs., 1972, Broadcaster of Yr., Internat. Radio and TV Soc., 1973; Man of Yr. Hollywood chpt. Nat. Acad. Television Arts and Scis., 1973; recipient Humanitarian award NCCJ, 1976, Mark Twain award Internat. Platform Assn., 1977, William O. Douglas award Pub. Counsel, 1981, 1st Amendment Lectr. Ford Hall Forum, 1981, Gold medal Internat. Radio and TV Soc., 1981. Disting. Am. award, 1984, Mass Media award Am. Jewish Com. Inst. of Human Relations, 1986, Internat. award of Yr., Nat. Assn. TV Program Execs., 1987; inducted into TV Acad. Hall of Fame, 1984. Mem. Writers Guild Am. (Valentine Davies award 1977), Dirs. Guild Am., AFTRA, Caucus Producers, Writers, and Dirs. Office: Act III Communications 1999 Ave of the Stars #500 Los Angeles CA 90067

LEAR, ROBERT WILLIAM, holding company executive; b. Canon City, Colo., May 10, 1917; s. Louis and Bertha (May) L.; m. Dorothy Schureman, Sept. 16, 1941; children—William S., Andrew R. B.A. U. Colo., 1938; M.B.A. with distinction, Harvard, 1940. Market research analyst U.S. Steel Corp., 1940-43; sales promotion mgr. Duff-Norton Co., 1946-47; corp. dir. marketing services Am. Standard Co., 1947-61; v.p. marketing Carborundum Co., 1961-64, group v.p., 1964-67; pres., dir. Indian Head Inc., 1967-72; pres., chief exec. officer, chmn., dir. F. & M. Schaefer Corp., N.Y.C., 1972-77; exec.-in-residence Columbia Grad. Bus. Sch., 1977—; Woodrow Wilson vis. fellow, 1987; bd. dirs. Welsh, Carson, Anderson Assocs. Venture Funds, Cambrex Corp., Korea Fund, Scudder, Stevens & Clark Instnl. Funds, others; ind. gen. prtnr. Equitable Capital Prtrs. Author: How to Turn Your MBA into a CEO, 1987, Pressure Points, 1992. Bd. dirs. Waveny Care Center. Served as lt. USNR, 1943-46. Clubs: Harvard (N.Y.C.); New Canaan Country, Blind Brook, Mill Reef. Home: 429 Silvermine Rd New Canaan CT 06840-4320 Office: Columbia U 206 Uris Hall # F New York NY 10027

LEARN, ELMER WARNER, agricultural economics educator, retired; b. Sayre, Pa., Jan. 19, 1929; s. John Walter and Naomi Ruth (Warner) L.; m. Theresa Arlene Green, Sept. 22, 1956; children—Diane Marie, Linda Jean. B.S., Pa. State U., 1950, M.S., 1951, Ph.D., 1957; student, U. Minn., 1954-55. Grad. research asst., instr. Pa. State U., 1950-51, 53-54, 55-56; successively asst. prof., assoc. prof., prof. U. Minn., 1956-69, head dept. agrl. econs., 1963-64, asst. to pres. then exec. asst. to pres., also dir. planning, 1964-69; prof., exec. vice chancellor U. Calif.-Davis, 1969-84, prof., 1984-92; cons. 9th Dist. Fed. Res. Bank, 1962. Mem. Natl. Agrl., 1962-65. Contbr. articles on agrl. policy, prices, fgn. trade policy to profl. jours. Served with AUS, 1951-53. Recipient Grad. Student award Am. Farm Econs. Assn., 1956. Mem. AAUP, Am. Agrl. Econs. Assn., Phi Kappa Phi, Gamma Sigma Delta. Home: 1702 Sycamore Ln Davis CA 95616-0809

LEARY, CAROL ANN, academic administrator; b. Niagara Falls, N.Y., Mar. 29, 1947; d. Angelo Andrew and Mary Josephine (Pullano) Gigliotti; m. Noel Robert Leary, Dec. 30, 1972. B.A, Boston U., 1969; MS, SUNY, Albany, 1970; PhD, Am. Univ., 1988. Asst. to v.p. for student affairs, dir. women's programs Siena Coll., Loudonville, N.Y., 1970-72; asst. dir. housing Boston U., 1972-78; dir. residence Simmons Coll., Boston, 1978-84, assoc. dean, 1984-85; assoc. dir. The Washington Campus, Washington, 1985-86; adminstrv. v.p., asst. to pres. Simmons Coll., Boston, 1988-94; pres. Bay Path Coll., Longmeadow, Mass., 1995—. Chair, coll. and univ. devel. com. St. Francis Homeless Shelter, Boston, 1990—. Fellow SUNY, Albany, 1969-70, Am. U., 1986-88; Ednl. Policy Fellowship Program fellow, 1990-91. Mem. Coun. for the Advancement and Support of Edn., Am. Assn. Higher Edn., Am. Coun. Edn. (rep. Mass. div. 1991—), Phi Beta Kappa. Avocations: classic movies, traveling overseas, hiking. Office: Bay Path Coll Office of the President 588 Longmeadow St Longmeadow MA 01106

LEARY, DAVID EDWARD, university dean; b. L.A., May 5, 1945; married; 3 children. BA in Philosophy, San Luis Rey Coll., 1968; MA in Psychology, San Jose State Coll., 1971; PhD in History of Sci., U. Chgo., 1977. Instr. psychology Holy Names Coll., Oakland, Calif., 1972-74, U. Calif. Extension Svcs., Berkeley, 1972-74; counseling psychologist Howard Inst., Oakland, 1972-74; instr. psychology San Jose (Calif.) State U. Extension Svcs., 1973-74, San Francisco State U. Extension Svcs., 1973-74, U. Calif. at Santa Cruz Extension Svcs., Monterey, 1973-74, U. Chgo., 1975; asst. prof. history and philosophy of psychology U. N.H., Durham, 1977-81, co-dir. grad. program in history and theory psychology, 1977-89, assoc. prof. psychology and humanities, 1981-87, chmn. dept. psychology, 1986-89, prof. psychology, history and humanities, 1987-89; prof. psychology, dean arts and scis. U. Richmond, Va., 1989—; vis. asst. prof. psychology Grad. Theol. Union, Berkeley, 1971-72; fellow Ctr. Advanced Study in Behavioral Scis., Stanford, Calif., 1982-83; co-dir. summer inst. on history of social sci. inquiry, 1986; assoc. prof. humanities Summer Program Cambridge U., Eng., 1984; presenter in field. Author: A Century of Psychology as Science, 2d rev. edit., 1992 (Assn. Am. Pub. award 1986), An Introduction to the Psychology of Guilt, 1975; editor: Metaphors in the History of Psychology, 1990; author: (with others) The Encyclopedia of Higher Education, 1992, Writing the Social Text: Poetics and Politics in Social Science Discourses, 1992, Annual Review of Psychology, 1991, Metaphors in the History of Psychology, 1990, Reflections on The Principles of Psychology: William James After a Century, 1990, Psychology in Twentieth-Century Thought and Society, 1987, Psychology in its Historical Context, 1985, Thinkers of the 20th Century, 1984, Studies in Eighteenth-Century Culture, 1984, The Problematic Science: Psychology in Nineteenth Century Thought, 1982; contbr. articles to profl. jours. Grantee NEH, 1982-83, 91-94, Social Sci. Rsch. Ctr. Faculty Support, U. N.H., 1988, Coll. Liberal Arts Faculty Rsch. Support, U. N.H., 1987-88, Ctrl. U. Rsch. Found. U. N.H., 1979, 87, Mellon Found., 1986, NSF, 1980-82, 82-83; rsch. fellow History Psychology Found., 1980, summer fellow NEH, 1979, U. N.H., 1978, grad. fellow U. Chgo., 1975-77. Fellow Am. Psychol. Soc.; mem. AAAS, APA (centennial lectr. on history of psychology 1979-80, 91-92, fellow divsn. 24 1988—, fellow divsn. 1 1983—, pres. divsn. 26 1983-84, fellow divsn. 26 1982—, pres. divsn. 24 1994-95), Am. Assn. Higher Edn., Am. Conf. Acad. Deans (bd. dirs. 1994—), Am. Hist. Assn., Assn. Am. Colls. (grantee 1990-91), Soc. History of Sci. in Am., Cheiron: Internat. Soc. History of Behavioral and Social Scis., Forum History of Human Sci., History of Sci. Soc., Phi Beta Kappa (hon.). Office: Univ Richmond Office Dean Arts & Scis Richmond VA 23173

LEARY, DENIS, comedian; b. 1958; m. Ann Lembeck; children: Jack, Devin. BA in English, Emerson Coll., 1979. Films: National Lampoon's Loaded Weapon I, 1993, The Sandlot, 1993, Who's the Man?, 1993, Judgment Night, 1993, Demolition Man, 1993, Gunmen, 1994, The Ref, 1994, Operation Dumbo Drop, 1995; off Broadway appearances No Cure for Cancer, 1991-92, Birth, School, Work, Death, 1993; TV spls. No Cure for Cancer, 1993, MTV Unplugged, 1993, A-hole, 1993; alkbum No Cure for Cancer, 1993. Office: c/o William Morris Agency 151 S El Camino Dr Beverly Hills CA 90212-2704 Office: Full Circle Mgmt 929 N Larabee St Ste 16 West Hollywood CA 90069*

LEARY, MICHAEL WARREN, journalist; b. Rice Lake, Wis., Apr. 15, 1949; s. Warren Denis and Patricia (Berigan) L.; m. Janice Marie Kalmar, Sept. 5, 1970; children: Meghan, Evan, Kieran. Student, U. Innsbruck, Austria, 1968-69; AB cum laude, U. Notre Dame, 1971; MS, Columbia U., 1972. Reporter Phila. Inquirer, 1972—; nat. corr. Houston Bur., 1983-86, asstc. city editor, Phila., 1986-87, European corr., London, 1987-90, editor Book Rev. sect., 1990-93, assoc. editor, mem. editorial bd., 1993—. Dir. Chestnut Hill Fathers Club. Recipient Silver Gavel award ABA, 1981. Home: 7153 Crittenden St Philadelphia PA 19119-1217 Office: Philadelphia Inquirer PO Box 8263 400 N Broad St Philadelphia PA 19101

LEARY, THOMAS BARRETT, lawyer; b. Orange, N.J., July 15, 1931; s. Daniel and Margaret (Barrett) L.; m. Stephanie Lynn Abbott, Dec. 18, 1954,

June 3, 1991; children: Thomas A., David A., Alison Leary Estep. AB, Princeton U., 1952; JD, Harvard U., 1958. Bar: N.Y. 1959, Mich. 1972, D.C. 1983. Assoc. White & Case, N.Y.C., 1958-68, ptnr., 1968-71; atty.-incharge antitrust Gen. Motors Corp., Detroit, 1971-77, asst. gen. counsel, 1977-82; ptnr. Hogan & Hartson, Washington, 1983—. Served to lt. USNR, 1952-55. Mem. ABA. Office: Hogan & Hartson Columbia Sq 555 13th St NW Washington DC 20004-1109

LEARY, TIMOTHY, psychologist, author; b. Springfield, Mass., Oct. 22, 1920; s. Timothy and Abigal (Ferris) L.; m. Rosemary Woodruff, Dec. 12, 1967; m. Barbara Chase, Dec. 18, 1978; children: Susan, John Busch, Zachary; remarried Rosemary Woodruff, Mar. 21, 1995. Student, Holy Cross Coll., 1938-39, U.S. Mil. Acad., 1940-41; AB, U. Ala., 1943; MS, Wash. State U., 1946; PhD in Psychology, U. Calif. at Berkeley, 1950. Asst. prof. U. Calif. at Berkeley, 1950-55; dir. psychol. research Kaiser Found., Oakland, Calif., 1955-58; lectr. Harvard, 1959-63; first guide League Spiritual Discovery, 1964—; pres. producer Futique Inc. (electronic books), 1985—; psychol. cons. to mgmt., 1983-63; cons. Mass. Dept. Corrections, 1961-63, Afghanistan Export Assn., 1966-69; Interactive Software Cons., Xor, 1981, Electronic Arts, 1981, Activision, 1986, Epyx, 1988, Autodesk, 1989; keynote speaker Ars Futura, Barcelona, Spain, 1989, Siggraph, Dallas, 1990, Ars Electronica, Linz, Austria, 1990, Cyberthon, San Francisco, 1990, Cyberarts, Pasadena, Libertian Party Nat. Conv., Chgo., Design Forum Symposium, Matsue, Japan, 1991, Am. Humanist Psychology Conv., 1993, Lalapaloosa Festival, 1993; founder Conscious-Net Electron Bulletin Bd., 1994. Producer: Psychedelic Celebrations, 1965-66; writer, actor: (film) Turn On, Tune In, Drop Out, 1967, Volcano of Love, 1991; author: Social Dimensions of Personality, 1950, Interpersonal Diagnosis of Personality, 1950, Multilevel Assessment of Personality, 1951, Psychedelic Experience, 1964, Psychedelic Reader, 1965, Psychedelic Prayers, 1964, High Priest, 1968, Politics of Ecstasy, 1968, The Psychology of Pleasure, 1969, Jail Notes, 1970, Confessions of a Hope Fiend, 1973, Neurologic, 1973, Terra II, 1973, The Intelligence Agents, 1978, Exo-Psychology, 1979, What Does Women Want?, 1979, Changing My Mind, 1982, Flashbacks: An Autobiography, 1983, 1983, Infopsychology, 1987, The Cybernetic Societies of the 21st Century, 1987, Greatest Hits, 1990, Virtual Reality and Telepresence, 1991, Chaos & Cyber Culture, 1994, The Adventures of Huck Getty, 1994, High Priest, 1995; actor: (film) Cheech & Chong's Nice Dreams, 1981, Return Engagement with G. Gordon Liddy, 1984, Hard Knocks, Showscan, 1987, Moonlighting, 1988, Medium Rare, 1988, Imagine with John Lennon, 1989, Fatal Skies, 1989, Shocker, 1989, Chamelion Blue, 1990, Chill Me, Thrill Me, 1991, Roadside Prophets, 1991, Super Force, 1991, Ted and Venus, 1991, Banana Chip Love, 1991, Volcano of Love, 1992, Roadside Prophet, 1992, Ted and Venus, 1992, Sex Police, 1993, Cyberpunk with Billy Idol, 1993, Brisco County Jr., 1994, (with Retinalogic) Chaos Engineering, 1994; (recordings) Give Peace a Chance, 1969, (with J. Lennon) Seven Up, 1973, (with Jimi Hendrix) You Can Be Anything This Time Around, 1970, TranceFormation (with Psychic TV), 1992, Brain Exchange (with Hyperdelic Video), 1992, How to Operate Your Brain, 1993, With Retinalogic, 1993, (with Richard Chase) Five Generations that Changed American Culture in the 20th Century, 1994, Gilocepter (with Ministry), 1994, (with Aileen Getty) Dying is a Team Sport, 1994; designer interactive computer programs Mind Mirror, Life Adventure, 1985, Head Coach Master Mind; designer reactive videoware program for Mental Fitness, software program Neuromancer, 1986, Intercom Ednl. Software, 1989; designer CD Rom program Wonderland Park. Candidate for gov., Calif., 1969-70; mem. Alcor Cryonics Life Extension Found., 1991. Served with U.S. Army, 1942-45. Mem. AFTRA, Screen Actors Guild, Am. Courseware Assn. (pres. 1989), Hemlock Soc. Address: PO Box 69886 Los Angeles CA 90069-0886

LEARY, WILLIAM JAMES, educational administrator; b. Boston, Oct. 1, 1931; s. John Gilbert and Josephine Marie (Kelley) L.; m. Joann Linda Parodi, June 25, 1960; children: Lorraine, Lisa, Linda. S.B., Boston Coll. 1953; M.Ed., Boston State Coll., 1954; postgrad. (Fulbright fellow), Sophia U., Tokyo, 1967; cert. advanced study, Harvard U., 1972, Ed.D., 1973; Ed.D., Boston U., 1971. Tchr. pub. schs. Boston, 1957-67; chmn. dept. social studies Dorchester High Sch., Boston, 1967-68; dir. curriculum Boston Dist. Pub. Schs., 1969-72, supt. schs., 1972-75; exec. dir. Met. Planning Project, Newton, Mass., 1975-77; supt. schs. Rockville Centre, N.Y., 1977-82, North Babylon, N.Y., 1982-84, Broward County, Ft. Lauderdale, Fla., 1984-88; supt. Gloucester (Mass.) Pub. Schs., 1989-93; assoc. prof. dept. ednl. leadership U. Miss., University, 1993—; assoc. in edn. Harvard U. Grad. Sch. Edn., 1972-75; adj. prof. edn. Boston U., 1973-75, C.W. Post Ctr., L.I. U., 1979-84, Fla. Internat. U., 1984-88, Salem (Mass.) State Coll., 1990-93; prof. Suffolk U., 1975-77; mem. meml. scholarship fund com. Harvard U., 1977-82; TV commentator Channel 5, Boston, 1975-76; producer edn. programs New Eng. Cablevision, 1989-93; keynote speaker Harvard U. Grad. Sch. Edn., 1976, NYU, 1980. Edn. columnist Boston Herald, 1975-78, L.I. News, 1982-84, Gloucester Times; edn. commentator New Eng. Cablevision, 1989-93; contbr. articles to profl. jours. Edn. coord. Boston chpt. United Way, 1974, Rockville Centre United Fund, 1979-80, Broward County chpt., 1985-87; trustee Mus. Fin. Arts, Boston, 1972-77; bd. dirs. Boston Youth Symphony, 1972-77, Edn. Devel. Ctr., 1972-77, Broward Com. of 100, Boys Club Broward County, 1985-88; mem. nat. alumni bd. Boston U., 1975—; mem. vis. com Suffolk U., 1978-80; adv. bd. Harvard N.Y. Alumni Forums, 1980-84; mem. L.I. Regional Planning Bd., 1983-84, Gov.'s Task Force on Alt. Edn., Fla., 1986-88; mem. Atty. Gen.'s edn. adv. com., Mass., 1991-93. Recipient Friend of Youth award Hayden Goodwill Boys' Home, 1973, Ida M. Johnston Outstanding Alumni award Boston U. Sch. Edn., 1976, Man of Yr. award Pope's Hill Assn., 1976, Jenkins Meml. award for ednl. leadership N.Y. State Council, PTA, 1980, Ednl. Leadership award L.I. chpt. NCCJ, 1980, Broward County Med. Aux., 1984, Lifetime Achievement award Matignon H.S. Alumni, 1995; selected as mem. Exec. Educator 100, Nat. Sch. Bd. Assn., 1987. Mem. ASCD (nat. commn. on supervision 1984-85), Am. Assn. Sch. Adminstrs. (del. assembly 1991, 92, 93, resolutions com. 1988-89, 93-94, 94-95, 95—), Am. Hist. Assn., Assn. for Asian Studies, Nat. Coun. Social Studies (nat. urban affairs com. 1977-80), Mass. Assn. Sch. Supts., Mass. Atty. Gen.'s Adv. Group, Harvard Club Boston, Harvard Club N.Y.C., Boston Coll., Varsity Club, KC, Rotary, Am. Legion, Phi Delta Kappa. Roman Catholic. Office: Grad Sch of Edn Univ of Mississippi PO Box 563 University MS 38677-0563 *A person's ability for creative and imaginative thinking is limited only by his/her fear to dream.*

LEASE, GARY LLOYD, religion educator, dean; b. Hollywood, Calif., Sept. 27, 1940; s. Rex Lloyd Lease and Isabelle (Riehle) Reynolds; m. Patricia Ann Metkovich, Sept. 10, 1966 (div. 1986); 1 child, Dylan; m. Dorothea Ann Ditchfield, Aug. 26, 1988. BA, Loyola U. L.A., 1962; ThD, U. Munich, 1968. Prof. history of consciousness U. Calif., Santa Cruz 1973—, assoc. chancellor, 1989-90, dean of humanities, 1990—; investigator various archaeol. excavations, 1974, 76, 80, 81. Author: Witness to The Faith, 1971; contbr. articles to profl. jours. Instr. hunter safety Calif. Dept. Fish and Game, 1971—. Fellow Nat. Def. Found., 1962, Danforth Found., 1967, NEH, 1971-72, Fulbright Commn., 1984. Mem. Am. Acad. Religion, Am. Hist. Assn., Am. Schs. Oriental Rsch., Am. Rsch. Ctr. in Egypt, Am. Soc. for Study Religion. Democrat. Office: U Calif History of Consciousness Santa Cruz CA 95064

LEASE, MARTIN HARRY, JR., retired political science educator; b. Plainfield, Ind., Aug. 15, 1927; s. Martin Harry and Beatrice Irene (Krebs) L.; m. Jeanne Marie Lachance, Sept. 6, 1969; children—Deborah Eileen, Joshua Martin. B.A., Ind. U., 1953, M.A., 1955, Ph.D., 1961. Instr. polit. sci. U. Miami, Coral Gables, Fla., 1955-56; instr. U. Minn., Duluth, 1957-61, asst. prof., 1961-65, assoc. prof., 1965-70, prof., 1970-94, asst. dean grad. sch., 1968-77, acting acad. vice-provost, 1977-79, polit. sci. dept. head, 1979-83, dir. overseas program, Eng., 1983-84; ret.; vis. lectr. Lakehead U., Thunder Bay, Ont., Can., 1975. Del. Democratic Nat. Conv., 1968; active local party offices including head of Duluth mayor's office; election cons. local radio and TV, Duluth; mem. fed. dist. ct. com. on Celebration Bicentennial U.S. Constn. Nat. Ctr. for edn. in Politics fellow, 1962-63. Mem. Western Polit. Sci. Assn. (research group), Minn. Polit. Sci. Assn. (bd. dirs. 1966-68), Ctr. for Study of Presidency. Mem. Democratic Farm Labor Party. Avocations: fishing; gardening. Office: U Minn-Duluth Polit Sci Dept 302 B Cina Hall Duluth MN 55812

LEASE, RICHARD JAY, police science educator, former police officer; b. Cherokee, Ohio, Dec. 10, 1914; s. Harold and Mabelle (Fullerton) L.; m.

Marjorie Faye Stoughton, Sept. 2, 1939 (div. Apr. 1957); children: Richard Jay II, William Harley; m. Jane Etta Omer, Jan. 16, 1960; stepchildren: Janet Radifera, Joyce Carson, Julia Marvin, Catherine Warren; adopted children: Alan Fudge, Stephen V. Graham. Student, Wittenberg U., 1932-33; BA, U. Ariz., 1937, MA, 1961; postgrad., Ind. U., 1950, 60, Ariz. State U., 1956, 63-65, 67—; grad., U. Louisville So. Police Inst., 1955. Grad. asst . U. Ariz., Tucson, 1937-38; with Tucson Police Dept., from 1938; advanced from patrolman to sgt., also served as safety officer Pima County Sheriff's Dept., Tucson, 1953, patrol supr., 1953-55, investigator, 1955-56; tchr. sci. pub. schs. Tucson, 1957-59; lectr. dept. adminstrn. Ind. U., Bloomington, 1960-65; asst. prof. dept. police sci. N.Mex. State U., Las Cruces, 1965—; cons. law enforcement problems HEW, 1960, Indpls. Police Dept., 1962, Harrisburg Community Coll. Police Sci. Dept., 1967, Phoenix Police Dept., 1968—; advisor police tng. programs several small city police depts., Ind., 1960-63, Indpls., 1962; mem. oral bd. for selection of chief in Bateville, Ind., 1962, oral bd. for selection sgts. and lts., Las Cruces Police Dept., 1966—. Author: (with Robert F. Borkenstein) Alcohol and Road Traffic: Problems of Enforcement and Prosecution, 1963, The Dreams, Hopes, Recollections and Thoughts of a Professional Good Samaritan; cons. editor Police, various rsch. publs. on chem. intoxification tests, psychol. errors of witnesses, reading disabilities, delinquency. Participant numerous FBI seminars; active youth work, philanthropy, among Am. Indians in Southwest; founder awards outstanding ROTC cadets N.Mex. State U., 1967—; founder Wiltberger ann. awards Nat. Police Combat Pistol Matches; scoutmaster Yucca council Boy Scouts Am., 1966—. Served to 1st lt. USMCR, 1942-45, PTO. Fellow Am. Acad. Forensic Scis. (sec. gen. sect.); mem. Internat. Assn. Chiefs of Police, Internat. Assn. Police Profs., Brit. Acad. Forensic Scis., Can. Soc. Forensic Sci., Am. Soc. Criminology, Ret. Officers Assn., Assn. U.S. Army (2d v.p. 1969—), NEA, N.Mex. Edn. Assn., N.Mex. Police and Sheriffs Assn., Internat. Crossroads, NRA (benefactor mem.), Marine Corps League (life), Sigma Chi. Lodges: Masons, Elks. Home and Office: 2145 Boise Dr Las Cruces NM 88001-5149

LEASE, ROBERT K., lawyer; b. Cleve., 1948. AB magna cum laude, Dartmouth Coll., 1970; JD cum laude, U. Conn., 1976. Bar: Ohio. Ptnr. Baker & Hostetler, Cleve. Mem. Phi Beta Kappa. Office: Baker & Hostetler 3200 Nat City Ctr 1900 E 9th St Cleveland OH 44114-3485

LEASE, RONALD CHARLES, financial economics educator; b. Davenport, Iowa, Feb. 3, 1940; s. Mace Duane and Mary Virginia (Marsh) L.; m. Judy Ellen Gifford, Aug. 24, 1962; 1 child, Tracy Rene. BS in Engring., Colo. Sch. Mines, 1963; MS, Purdue U., 1966, PhD, 1973. Metall. engr. Aluminum Co. Am., 1963-69; prof. U. Utah, Salt Lake City, 1973-86; prof., chmn. Tulane U., New Orleans, 1986-90, endowed prof., assoc. dean, 1988-90; endowed prof. U. Utah, Salt Lake City, 1990—; vis. assoc. prof. U. Chgo., 1978-79; vis. prof. U. Mich., Ann Arbor, 1985-86. Mem. editorial bd. Jour. Fin. Rsch., Phoenix, 1987-93, Fin. Mgmt., Tampa, 1986—, Jour. Corp. Fin., Pitts., 1993—; contbr. articles to profl. jours. Mem. Am. Fin. Assn., Western Fin. Assn., Fin. Mgmt. Assn. (editor Survey and Synthesis in Fin. 1984-90, pres. 1992-93), Phi Kappa Phi, Beta Gamma Sigma. Home: 1409 Spring Ln Salt Lake City UT 84117-6710 Office: U Utah Eccles Sch Bus Salt Lake City UT 84112

LEASON, JODY JACOBS, newspaper columnist; b. Margarita, Venezuela, June 8, 1926; came to U.S., 1928; d. Jose Cruz Caceres and Graciela Rodriguez; m. Russell L. Jacobs (div.); 1 child, Jessica Jacobs Vitti; m. Barney Leason, Dec. 29, 1976. BA, Hunter Coll., 1940's. Assoc. fashion editor Women's Wear Daily, N.Y.C., 1969-70; West Coast fashion editor Women's Wear Daily, Los Angeles, 1957-69; London fashion editor Women's Wear Daily, N.Y.C., 1970-72; soc. editor L.A. Times, 1972-86. Author: (novel) The Right Circles, 1988. Avocations: needlework, gardening.

LEATH, KENNETH THOMAS, research plant pathologist, educator; b. Providence, Apr. 29, 1931; s. Thomas and Elizabeth (Wootten) L.; m. Marie Andreozzi, Aug. 1955; children: Kenneth, Steven, Kevin, Maria Beth. BS, U. R.I., 1959; MS, PhD, U. Minn., 1966. Rsch. plant pathologist U.S. Regional Pasture Rsch. Lab. USDA-ARS, 1966-94; prof. Pa. State U., 1966-94; pvt. agrl. cons. Boalsburg, Pa., 1994—; advisor numerous state and nat. orgns. Contbr. numerous articles to profl. jours. With USN, 1951-55. Mem. Elks. Achievements include research on root diseases and systemic wilts of forage species.

LEATHAM, JOHN TONKIN, business executive; b. Chgo., July 4, 1936; s. Chester and Betty (Collins) L.; m. Sheila K. Andersen, Sept. 13, 1958; children: Lisa M., John A., Bronwen Gay, Douglas Q. B.A., Lawrence U., Appleton, Wis., 1958. Asst. cashier, lending officer Continental Ill. Nat. Bank & Trust Co., Chgo., 1962-68; with Reliance Group, Inc., N.Y.C., 1968-79; sr. v.p., chief financial officer Reliance Group, Inc., 1971-72, exec. v.p., chief operating and chief financial officer, 1972-79, dir., mem. exec. com., 1974-79; investment and merchant banker, 1979—; chmn., dir. Security Health Ptnrs., 1994—; vice chmn., dir. CliniCorp, Inc., West Palm Beach, Fla., 1992-94; pres., CEO Clinicorp Midwest, Inc., 1992-93; bd. dirs., mng. dir. Scuul Ltd.; trustee Endowment Realty Investors Inc., 1987—; nat. dir. Reading is FUN-damental, Inc., 1975-91. Trustee Lawrence U., 1981—; chmn., 1990-92; trustee The Common Fund, 1987—, Endowment Advisers, Inc., Fairfield Ptnrs., Inc., 1990—, chmn., 1992—. 1st lt. USAF, 1958-62. Decorated Air Force Commendation medal. Mem. Lawrence U. Alumni Assn. (v.p. 1963-70, dir. 1963-71). Home: 1925 Calvin Ct Riverwoods IL 60015

LEATHER, RICHARD BRENK, mineral company executive; b. N.Y.C., Feb. 2, 1932; s. Basil Henry and Elizabeth Marie (Brenk) L.; m. Penelope Jessie Pope, May 28, 1960; children: Edward, Ann, Charles. B.A., Yale U., 1953; cert., U. Paris, 1952; LL.B., Harvard U., 1958. Bar: N.Y. 1959. Assoc. Chadbourne Parke Whiteside & Wolff, 1958-66, ptnr., 1966-70; atty. Newmont Mining Corp., N.Y.C., 1970-71, gen. counsel and sec., 1971-74, v.p., gen. counsel, 1975-78, sr. v.p., 1978-79, exec. v.p., 1979-88; vice-chmn. Newmont Mining Corp., Denver, 1988-92, Newmont Gold Co., Denver, 1988-92; chmn. bd. Foote Mineral Co., Exton, Pa., 1980-88; bd. dirs. Newmont Gold Co., So. Peru Copper Corp., Tri Med Supply Corp. Trustee L.W. Frohlich Found., N.Y.C., Denver Art Mus.; mem. vis. com. Met. Mus. Art. With AUS, 1954-56. Mem. ABA, Copper Devel. Assn. (sec. 1972-83), Smelter Environ. Rsch. Assn. (trustee 1974-80), Am. Bur. Metal Stats. (trustee 1974-88). Clubs: Racquet and Tennis (N.Y.C.), N.Y. Yacht; Manhasset Bay Yacht (Port Washington, N.Y.); Metropolitan (Washington); University (Denver), N.Y.C. Yacht Club. Office: Newmont Mining Corp 1700 Lincoln St Denver CO 80203-4501

LEATHER, VICTORIA POTTS, college librarian; b. Chattanooga, June 12, 1947; d. James Elmer Potts and Ruby Lea (Bettis) Potts Wilmoth; m. Jack Edward Leather; children: Stephen, Sean. BA cum laude, U. Chattanooga, 1968; MSLS, U. Tenn., 1978. Libr. asst. East New Orleans Regional Libr., 1969-71; libr. Erlanger Nursing Sch., Chattanooga, 1971-75; chief libr. Erlanger Hosp., Chattanooga, 1975-77; dir. Eastgate Br. Libr., Chattanooga, 1977-81; dir. libr. svcs. Chattanooga State Tech. Community Coll., 1981—. Mem. Allied Arts, Hunter Mus., High Mus. Art. Mem. ALA, Southeastern Libr. Assn., Tenn. Libr. Assn. (chair legislation com.), Chattanooga Area Libr. Assn. (pres. 1978-79), Tenn. Bd. Regents Media Consortium (chair 1994-95), Phi Delta Kappa. Episcopalian. Avocations: reading, needlework, traveling.

LEATHERBEE, WILLIAM BELL, architect; b. Hanover, N.H., Apr. 13, 1938; s. John Howland and Helen Luscombe (Ullmann) L.; m. Tabitha Susan Allen, July 2, 1960 (div. 1987); children: Lydia Leah, Rachel Lyn. BA, Harvard Coll., 1959; MArch, U. Pa., 1963. Registered architect, Pa., N.J., Md.; lic. planner, N.J. Designer H2L2 Architects/Planners, Phila., 1963-64, Vincent G. Kling Assocs., Phila., 1964-65; architect Bower & Fradley Architects, Phila., 1965-68; project mgr. Richard Martin & Assocs., Phila., 1968-69; pvt. practice Phila. 1969—; pres. Benezet Ct., Inc., Phila., 1973-80; archtl. critic. instr. Drexel U., Phila., 1972-83. Prin. works include rehabilitation of low income single family houses Allegheny West Found., 1993, Group Home for Boys, Phila., 1991, S.W. Sr. Ctr. for Phila. Corp. for Aging, 1989; cons. architect for shopping ctrs., N.C., S.C., Kans. Dir., chmn. properties and bldgs. coms. Boys and Girls Clubs Phila., 1984—. Lt. comdr. USCGR Reserve, 1959-70. Recipient award for excellence in masonry design Delaware Valley Masonry Inst., 1978, Legion of Honor award Chapel of the Four Chaplains, 1985. Mem. AIA (dir. Phila. chpt. 1983-84, Disting. Bldg. award 1972), Am. Arbitration Assn., Nat. Trust for Historic Preservation, Nat. Assn. Housing and Redevel. Ofcls. (dir., treas. 1974-90), Pa. Soc. Architects AIA (Dist. Bldg. award). Avocations: sailing, skiing, gardening. Office: Leatherbee & Assocs Architects & Planners 1504 South St Philadelphia PA 19146

LEATHERDALE, DOUGLAS WEST, insurance company executive; b. Morden, Man., Can., Dec. 6, 1936; came to U.S., 1968; s. Walter West and Lena Elizabeth (Gilligan) L.; children—Mary Jo, Christopher. B.A., United Coll., Winnipeg, Man., 1957. Investment analyst, officer Gt. West Life Assurance Co., Winnipeg, 1957-68; assoc. exec. sec. Bd. Pensions, Luth. Ch., Mpls., 1968-72; exec. v.p. then v.p. St. Paul Investment Mgmt. Co., subs. St. Paul Cos., Inc., 1972-77; v.p.-fin. St. Paul Cos., Inc., 1974-81, sr. v.p.-fin., 1981-82, exec. v.p., 1982-89, also dir., pres., chief oper. officer, 1989-90, chmn., pres., chief exec. officer, 1990—; bd. dirs. St. Paul Fire and Marine Ins. Co., St. Paul Land Resources, Inc., St. Paul Real Estate of Ill., Inc., John Nuveen & Co. Inc., St. Paul Properties, Inc., St. Paul Oil and Gas Corp., St. Paul Fire & Marine Ins. Co. (U.K.) Ltd., St. Paul Mercury Ins. Co., St. Paul Guardian Ins. Co., St. Paul Surplus Lines Ins. Co., Nat. Ins. Wholesalers, Atwater McMillian, 77 Water St., Inc., Ramsey Ins. Co., St. Paul Risk Services, Inc., St. Paul Plymouth Ctr., Inc. Athena Assurance Co., St. Paul Fin. Group, Inc., Graham Resources, Inc., Carlyle Capital, L.P., United HealthCare Corp. Mem. Twin Cities Soc. Security Analysts, Fin. Execs. Inst. Club: Minnesota (St. Paul). Avocation: horses. Office: St Paul Cos Inc 385 Washington St Saint Paul MN 55102-1309*

LEATHERMAN, HUGH KENNETH, SR., state senator, business executive; b. Lincoln County, N.C., Apr. 14, 1931; s. John Bingham and Ada Annis (Gantt) L.; m. Jean Helms, Nov. 11, 1978; children: Sheila Dianne, Hugh Kenneth, Karen Ann, Joyce Lynn, Amy Jean, Sarah Ada. BS in Civil Engring., N.C. State U., 1953; HHD (hon.), Francis Marion Coll., 1987. Engr., then sec. Florence (S.C.) Concrete Products Inc., 1955-72, pres., 1972-93; sec. Hugh-Stan Inc., Myrtle Beach, 1974—; mem. S.C. Senate, 1980—; commr. S.C. Dept. Consumer Affairs. Deacon 1st Bapt. Ch. Named Legislator of Yr., 1982. Home: 1817 Highland Ave Florence SC 29501-5419 Office: 205 Gressette Bldg Columbia SC 29202

LEAVELL, WILLIAM A., publisher, editor; b. Montgomery, Ala., Apr. 12, 1923; William A. and Myrtle I. (Watson) L.; m. Patty J. Shobe, June 24, 1927; William A. III, Melissa I. BA, U. Ala., 1945; MA, George Washington U., 1947, PhD, 1949. Owner Leavell & Assocs., Belleair, Fla., 1950-62; columnist "Keep Off The Grass" syndicated column, 1963-73; editor, pub. Washington Report, Editor Release Svcs. (Washington Report), St. Petersburg, Fla., 1974—; regular guest on several radio and TV stas. Author: (novel) As Honest As Times Permit, 1974. Adminstrv. asst. Congressman Arthur Winstead Washington 1947-49. With USAF 1944-45. Home: 3610-38th Ave S # 88 Saint Petersburg FL 33711 Office: Editors Release Svcs PO Box 10309 Saint Petersburg FL 33733-0309

LEAVEN, GLORIOUS SHARPLESS, special education educator, reading specialist; b. Hampstead, N.C., Sept. 27, 1941; d. James Edward Sr. and Lecola (Shepard) Sharpless; div.; children: Grady Funderburk, Bryan Funderburk. BS, Winston-Salem State U., 1964. Cert. tchr., N.C. Tchr. Annandale Elem. Sch., Hampstead, 1964-68; tchr. spl. edn. Topsail High Sch., Hampstead, 1968-72; reading specialist Topsail High Sch., Topsail Mid. Sch., Hampstead, 1972—. Mem. NEA, N.C. Assn. Educators, Internat. Reading Assn. (pres. Cafe Fear coun. 1992—), N.C. Reading Assn., South Pender Alumni Assn. (sec. tng. 1991-92), Winston-Salem State U. Alumni (fin. sec. 1989-92), Olivet Social Women Club (treas. 1990-92). Democrat. Baptist. Avocations: piano, drawing, writing, storytelling, singing. Home: 336 Shepards Rd Hampstead NC 28443-2928 Office: Topsail Mid Sch 17447 Us Highway 17 N Hampstead NC 28443-7320

LEAVENGOOD, VICTOR PRICE, telephone company executive; b. Ocala, Fla., June 2, 1924; s. Hansel Devane and Mildred (Price) L.; m. Elizabeth Lee Bird, Sept. 12, 1950; children: Sally (dec.), Ann, Hansel. BSBA, U. Fla., 1947; MBA, Harvard U., 1949. Bus. mgr. Ocala (Fla.) Star Banner (daily newspaper), 1952-59; circulation dir. Tampa (Fla.) Tribune, 1959-60, dir. community affairs, 1960-64; asst. v.p. Gen. Telephone Co. Fla., Tampa, 1964-70; sec., treas. Gen. Telephone Co. Fla., 1970-87. Pres. Hills County Community Coordination Council, 1964-65, Tampa Econ. Opportunity Council, 1965-66, Fla. Clergy Econ. Edn. Found., 1964-68; bd. dirs. Blue Cross Blue Shield of Fla., Lowry Park Zoo, Fla. Aquarium, West Cen. Fla. Area Agy. on Aging, Japan-Am. Soc. Cen. Fla., Suncoast council Girl Scouts U.S.A.; bd. advisors U. South Fla. Contemporary Art Mus.; trustee Fla. Mental Health Inst.; chmn. Tampa Bay Internat. Super Task Force, Fla. Mchts. Assn., Tampa Commn. on Pub. Art; pres. United Fund Greater Tampa Inc., 1964-68, treas., 1970-75; pres. Fla. chpt. United Way, 1969-79; mem. Fla. Council Mental Health Tng. and Research, 1967-74, Pres.'s Round Table, Eckerd Coll., St. Petersburg, Fla., 1969—, pres.'s council U. South Fla., 1974—, Hillsborough County Hosp. Authority; treas. U. South Fla. Found., 1975-80, pres., 1982-83. Comdr. USNR, 1942-47. Mem. Greater Tampa C. of C. (bd. dirs.), Fla. C. of C. (edn. com. 1968-71), U.S. C. of C. (edn. com.), Phi Eta Sigma, Phi Delta Theta.; mem. Ye Mystic Krewe of Gasparilla. Democrat. Methodist (ofcl. bd.). Clubs: University (Tampa), Tampa, Tampa Yacht and Country (Tampa). Home: 4516 W Sylvan Ramble St Tampa FL 33609-4214

LEAVITT, AUDREY FAYE COX, television programming executive; b. Old Hickory, Tenn., June 1, 1932; d. James Aubrey and Bernice (Hudnall) Cox; student David Lipscomb Secondary Sch. and Coll., 1947, Tenn. Sch. Broadcasting, 1949-50, Vanderbilt U., 1948-50; children: Jack, Teresa. Woman commentator, continuity chief radio sta. WGNS, Murfreesboro, Tenn., 1949-50; announcer, continuity chief, traffic dir. Sta. KDWT, Stamford, Tex., 1950-51; sales account exec. Sta. KMAC, San Antonio, 1952; continuity chief, announcer Sta. KEYL-TV, San Antonio, 1952-54, also firm dir.; film buyer, mgr. Sta. WOAI-TV, San Antonio, 1954-68, ops. mgr. film, video-tape traffic, continuity, 1968-71; film and videotape operations mgr., film buyer Sta. KENS-TV, San Antonio, 1972-79; exec. v.p. Jim Thomas & Assocs., San Antonio, 1979-80; owner Communique Internationalé, TV programming syndication, 1981—; Faye Leavitt Advt., 1990—; Strategic Planning Services; exec. producer TV series The Lone Star Sportsman Show; writer, exec. producer and dir. TV series Weather or Not; writer, producer gourmet cooking show For Men Only, The Great Age, 1988; hostess radio series Our Turn, 1994—. Pub. rels dir., advt. dir. The Madison Retirement Community, San Antonio, 1991—. Mem. NAFE, Nat. Pub. Rels. Soc., Internat. Platform Assn., Alamo Heights C. of C. (bd. dirs.), San Antonio Conservation Soc., San Antonio Livestock and Rodeo Exposition, San Antonio Apt. Assn. (publicity chmn.), Yellow Rose Tex., World Affairs Council. Office: PO Box 6493 San Antonio TX 78209-0493

LEAVITT, CHARLES LOYAL, English language educator, administrator; b. Randolph, Maine, Apr. 30, 1921; s. Charles Warren Franklin and Alice Mabel (Sparrow) L.; m. Emily Raymond Stewart, June 12, 1951 (dec. 1966); m. Virginia Louise Kracke, Sept. 6, 1969. Diploma in Edn., U. Maine, Farmington, 1941; BS in Edn., U. So. Maine, 1946; MA in English, Boston U., 1947; PhD in English, U. Wis., 1961; MLS, Columbia U., 1969. Cert. tchr. English and history, elem., secondary, coll. Tchr. pub. schs., Vanceboro, Maine, 1941-42; tchr., prin. pub. schs., York Village, Maine, 1945-47; instr. English and history Endicott Jr. Coll., Beverly, Mass., 1947-48; assoc. prof. English Lyndon State Coll., Lyndon Center, Vt., 1948-53, 54-55; teaching asst. in English U. Wis., Madison, 1953-54, 55-59; instr. Wayne State U., Detroit, 1959-61; assoc. prof. Montclair (N.J.) State Coll. 1961-68; v.p. sec., dir. edn. Universal Learning Corp., N.Y.C., 1968-69; assoc. dir. admissions Sarah Lawrence Coll., Bronxville, N.Y., 1970-71; dir. continuing edn., asst. dean, prof. Bloomfield (N.J.) Coll., 1971-74; chmn. liberal arts, prof. Coll. of Ins., N.Y.C., 1975-86, prof. emeritus, 1987—. Author: Ten Lit. Study Guides, 1964-66; cons. editor Monarch Lit. Guides, N.Y.C., 1963-68; author chpt. in book. Treas. Youth Community Funds, York Village, Maine, 1946-47; asst. scoutmaster Boy Scouts Am., York Village, 1946-47; v.p. Overseas Neighbors, Montclair, 1974-75; tchr. Adult Sch. of Montclair, 1963-68. With USAAF, 1942-45. Named Most Popular Prof., Montclair State Coll., 1967, Prof. of Yr., Coll. of Ins., 1978; yearbook dedications Lyndon State Coll., 1950, Bloomfield Coll., 1974, Coll. of Ins.,

1987; Nat. Audubon scholar, Garden Clubs York Village, 1947. Mem. AAUP, MLA, Coll. English Assn., Internat. Platform Assn., Princeton Club (N.Y.C.), Faculty Columbia U. Club, New Eng. Soc. N.Y.C. Club, Kiwanis (trustee Manhattan found. 1989—). Republican. Baptist. Home: 93 Stonebridge Rd Montclair NJ 07042-1632 Office: One Insurance Pla 101 Murray St New York NY 10007-2165

LEAVITT, DANA GIBSON, management consultant; b. Framingham, Mass., Dec. 4, 1925; s. Luther C. and Margaret (Gibson) L.; m. Frances Smith, Apr. 12, 1952; children: Margaret Gibson, Jonathan. BA, Brown U., 1948; postgrad., Harvard U. Bus. Sch., 1954-55. Home office rep. Aetna Life Ins. Co., Boston, also Long Beach, Calif., 1949-54; v.p., sec.-treas., exec. v.p. N. Am. Title Ins. Co., Oakland, Calif., 1955-64; pres. Transam. Title Ins. Co., Oakland, 1964-72; v.p. Transam. Corp., 1969-71, group v.p., 1971-77, exec. v.p., 1977-81; bd. dirs. Chgo. Title and Trust Co., Chgo. Title Ins. Co., World Minerals, Inc., Am. Ctr. for Wine, Food, and the Arts, Napa Valley, Calif. Bd. dirs. Children's Hosp. Med. Ctr. and Found., 1969-72; trustee Lewis and Clark Coll., Portland, Oreg., 1972-75, Queen of Valley Hosp., Napa, Calif., 1988-90, Nat. Wildflower Rsch. Ctr., Austin, Tex., 1988-90, pres., 1991-94, Brown U., Providence, 1973-78, trustee emeritus, 1978—. With USMCR, WWII. Mem. World Presidents Orgn. (bd. dirs. 1986), Delta Kappa Epsilon. Republican. Clubs: Brown U. of No. Calif, Harvard Bus. Sch. of No. Calif, Napa Valley Country; Bohemian (San Francisco). Office: 2201 Third Ave Napa CA 94558

LEAVITT, DAVID ADAM, writer; b. Pitts., June 23, 1961; s. Harold Jack and Gloria (Rosenthal) L. BA, Yale U., 1983. Reader, editorial asst. Viking-Penguin Inc., N.Y.C., 1983-84. Author: Family Dancing, 1984 (Nat. Book Critics Circle award nomination 1984, PEN-Faulkner award nomination 1985), The Lost Language of Cranes, 1986, Equal Affections, 1988, A Place I've Never Been, 1990, While England Sleeps, 1993; editor: The Penguin Book of Gay Short Fiction, 1994; contbr. to periodicals including Esquire, Harper's, New Yorker, N.Y. Times Book Rev., Village Voice, others. Recipient Willets prize for fiction Yale U., 1982, O. Henry Award, 1984; Nat. Endowment for Arts grantee, 1985; vis. fgn. writer Inst. Catalan Letters, Barcelona Spain, 1989; Guggenheim fellow, 1990. Mem. PEN. Office: c/o Andrew Wylie Wylie, Aitken and Stone, Inc 250 W 57th St Ste 2114 New York NY 10107*

LEAVITT, HAROLD JACK, management educator; b. Lynn, Mass., Jan. 14, 1922; s. Joseph and May (Lopata) L.; m. Gloria Rosenthal, Jan. 31, 1943 (dec.); children—John, Emily, David; m. Jean Lipman-Blumen. B.A. Harvard Coll., 1943; M.S., Brown U., 1944; Ph.D., Mass. Inst. Tech., 1949. Asst. prof. psychology Rensselaer Poly. Inst., 1949-50; assoc. prof. Sch. Bus., U. Chgo., 1954-58; prof. indsl. adminstrn. and psychology GSIA, Carnegie Inst. Tech., 1958-66; Walter Kenneth Kilpatrick prof. orgn. behavior and psychology Grad. Sch. Bus., Stanford U., 1966-90, prof. emeritus, 1990; vis. prof. London Grad. Sch. Bus. Studies, 1972; v.p. Nejelski & Co., 1951-53; cons. European Prod. Agy., Paris, 1956; faculty prin. Mgmt. Analysis Ctr., Inc., 1971—. Author: (with H. Bahrami) Managerial Psychology, 5th edit., 1988, (with W. Dill and H. Eyring) The Organizational World, 1973, Corporate Pathfinders, 1986; co-editor: Organizations of the Future, 1974. Served to lt. (j.g.) USNR, 1944-46. Fellow Am. Psychol. Assn. Home: 1520 E California Blvd Pasadena CA 91106 Office: Stanford U Grad Sch Bus Stanford CA 94305

LEAVITT, HORACE MADISON, JR., communications company executive, former naval officer; b. Long Beach, Calif., Apr. 26, 1929; s. Horace Madison and Gertrude (Webb) L.; m. Nancy Dohring, July 16, 1955; children—Horace Madison III, Lisa Grace. B.S. in Naval Sci., U.S. Naval Acad., 1953; B.S.E.E. in Ordnance Engring., U.S. Naval Postgrad. Sch., Monterey, Calif., 1961. Commd. ensign U.S. Navy, 1953, advanced through grades to capt., 1973; comdg. officer USS Carbonero, 1965-67; mgr. Rewson Program, 1978-82, ret., 1982; sr. v.p. Western Union Corp., Upper Saddle River, N.J., 1983—; pres. Advanced Transmission Systems Div., Upper Saddle River, N.J., 1988—. Mem. IEEE, Old Crows (gold award 1981). Republican. Avocation: fishing. Home: 3 Yeoman Dr Saddle River NJ 07458-1123 Office: Western Union Corp 1 Lake St Saddle River NJ 07458-1813

LEAVITT, JEFFREY STUART, lawyer; b. Cleve., July 13, 1946; s. Sol and Esther (Dolinsky) L.; m. Ellen Fern Sugerman, Dec. 21, 1968; children: Matthew Adam, Joshua Aaron. AB, Cornell U., 1968; JD, Case Western Res. U., 1973. Bar: Ohio 1973. Assoc. Jones, Day, Reavis & Pogue, Cleve., 1973-80, ptnr., 1981—. Contbr. articles to profl. jours. Trustee Bur. Jewish Edn., Cleve., 1981-93, v.p. 1985-87; trustee Fairmount Temple, Cleve., 1982—, v.p. 1985-90, pres., 1990-93; trustee Citizens League Greater Cleve., 1982-89, 92-94, pres., 1987-89; trustee Citizens League Rsch. Inst., Cleve., 1989—, Great Lakes Region of Union Am. Hebrew Congregations, 1990-93; mem. bd. gov. Case Western Res. Law Sch. Alumni Assn., 1989-92; sec. Kulas Found., 1986-88, 93—, asst. treas., 1989-92. Mem. ABA (employee benefits coms. 1976—), Midwest Pension Conf. Jewish. Home: 25961 Annesley Rd Cleveland OH 44122-2437 Office: Jones Day Reavis & Pogue N Point 901 Lakeside Ave E Cleveland OH 44114-1116

LEAVITT, JEROME EDWARD, childhood educator; b. Verona, N.J., Aug. 1, 1916; s. Thomas Edward and Clara Marie (Sonn) L.; m. Florence Elizabeth Wilkins, Aug. 23, 1963. B.S., Newark State Coll., 1938; M.A., N.Y. U., 1942; Ed.D., Northwestern U., 1952. Tchr. pub. schs. Roslyn Heights, N.Y., 1938-42; instr. Sperry Gyroscope, Bklyn., 1942-45; prin., supr. pub. schs. Los Alamos, N.Mex., 1945-49; prof. elem., exec. asst. to dean Portland (Oreg.) State U., 1952-66; prof. edn. U. Ariz., Tucson, 1966-69; prof. elem. edn.; coordinator Child Abuse Project, Calif. State U., Fresno, 1969-81; pres. Jerome Leavitt, Inc., 1981—. Author: Nursery-Kindergarten Edn., 1958, Carpentry for Children, 1959, By Land, By Sea, By Air, 1969, The Beginning Kindergarten Teacher, 1971, America and Its Indians, 1971, The Battered Child, 1974, Herbert Sonn: Yosemite's Birdman, 1975, Child Abuse and Neglect: Research and Innovation, 1983, others; contbr. articles to profl. jours. Mem. ASCD (life), NEA (life), Assn. Childhood Edn. Internat. (life), Soc.Profs. Edn., Calif. Tchrs. Assn., Profs. Curriculum, Phi Delta Kappa, Kappa Delta Pi, Epsilon Pi Tau. Home and Office: Villa Campana 6653 E Carondelet Dr Apt 124 Tucson AZ 85710-2138

LEAVITT, JOAN KAZANJIAN, state health official, physician; b. Boston, Jan. 14, 1926; d. Varaztad Hovannes and Marion V. (Hanford) Kazanjian; m. Don K. Leavitt; children—Mark S., Lynda Donn. A.B., Radcliffe Coll., 1947; M.A., Smith Coll., 1949; M.D., Boston U., 1953. Intern in pediatrics Boston City Hosp., 1953-54, resident in pediatrics, 1954-55; resident in pediatrics Mass. Gen. Hosp., Boston, 1955-56, 57-58; pediatrician Comanche County (Okla.) Guidance Center, 1959; practice medicine specializing in pediatrics Altus, Okla., 1959-64; med. dir. Jackson County (Okla.) Health Dept., 1960-67, Kay County (Okla.) Health Dept., 1967-76; chief maternal and child health service Okla. Health Dept., Oklahoma City, 1976; dep. commr. for personal health services Okla. Health Dept., 1976-77, commr. of health, 1977-93. Mem. AMA, Okla. State Med. Assn., Okla. Public Health Assn., Oklahoma County Med. Soc., Assn. State and Territorial Health Ofcls. (pres. 1985-86), Sigma Xi. Office: 1000 NE Tenth St PO Box 53551 Oklahoma City OK 73152

LEAVITT, JOEL, consumer products company executive. Exec. v.p. Springfield Sugar and Pdts. Co., Suffield, Conn., 1953—. Office: Springfield Sugar & Pdts Co 1120 Harvey Ln Suffield CT 06078

LEAVITT, JULIAN J., wholesale food company executive; b. 1928. Student, Harvard U., 1950. With Springfield Sugar & Products Co., Suffield, Conn., 1953—; now pres. Office: Springfield Sugar & Products Co 1120 Harvey Ln Suffield CT 06078-2447

LEAVITT, LEWIS A., pediatrician, medical educator; b. N.Y.C., Nov. 7, 1941; s. Isidore and Sarah (Fishkowitz) L.; m. Judith E. Walzer, July 2, 1966; children—Sarah Abigail, David Isaac. B.S., U. Chgo., 1961, M.D., 1965. Diplomate Am. Bd. Pediatrics. Intern, resident Albert Einstein Coll. Medicine, Jacobi Hosp., Bronx, N.Y., 1965-68; prof. pediatrics U. Wis., Madison, 1984—; head infant devel. lab. Waisman Ctr. Mental Retardation and Human Devel., 1973—. Contbr. articles to profl. jours. Served to lt.

comdr. USN, 1968-70. Mem. Soc. Research in Child Devel., Am. Acad. Pediatrics. Office: U Wis 1500 Highland Ave Madison WI 53705-2280

LEAVITT, MICHAEL OKERLUND, governor, insurance executive; b. Cedar City, Utah, Feb. 11, 1951; s. Dixie and Anne (Okerlund) L.; m. Jacalyn Smith; children: Michael Smith, Taylor Smith, Anne Marie Smith, Chase Smith, Weston Smith. BA, So. Utah U., 1978. CPCU. Sales rep. Leavitt Group, Cedar City, 1972-74, account exec., 1974-76; mgr. underwriting Salt Lake City, 1976-82; chief operating officer, 1982-84, pres., chief exec. officer, 1984—, gov., state of Utah, 1993—; bd. dirs. Pacificorp, Portland, Oreg., Utah Power and Light Co., Salt Lake City, Great Western Thrift and Loan, Salt Lake City. Utah Bd. Regents, chmn. instl. coun. So. Utah State U., Cedar City, 1985-89; campaign chmn. U.S. Sen. Orrin Hatch, 1982, 88, U.S. Sen. Jake Garn, 1980, 86; cons. campaign Gov. Norman Angerter, 1984; mem. staff Reagan-Bush '84. 2d lt. USNG, 1969-77. Named Disting. Alumni So. Utah State Coll. Sch. Bus., 1986. Mem. Chartered Property Casualty Underwriters. Republican. Mormon. Avocation: golf. Office: Office of the Governor 210 State Capitol Building Salt Lake City UT 84114-1202*

LEAVITT, MICHAEL P(AUL), performing arts manager and concert producer; b. N.Y.C., Dec. 9, 1944; s. Harry and Bertha (Mandell) L.; m. Nancy J. Redden, April 2, 1964; children: Amy, Sarah. BA, Kans. Weslayan U., 1965; MA, Queens Coll., 1967; M in Philosophy, CUNY, 1975. Adminstrv. dir. Gregg Smith Singers, N.Y.C., 1978-79; exec. dir. Horizon Concerts, N.Y.C., 1978-79; mng. dir. Allied Artists Bur., N.Y.C., 1979—, Beethoven Soc., 1979-85; mng. dir. MPL Advt. for Arts, N.Y.C., 1981—; pres. MPL Prodns. Mem. Music Library Assn., Nat. Assn. Performing Arts Mgrs. and Agts. Home: 195 Steamboat Rd Great Neck NY 11024-1739 Office: MPL Advt for the Arts 170 W 74th St New York NY 10023-2350

LEAVITT, THOMAS WHITTLESEY, museum director, educator; b. Boston, Jan. 8, 1930; s. Richard C. and Helen M. (Pratt) L.; m. Jane O. Ayer, June 23, 1951 (div. 1969); children: Katherine, Nancy, Hugh; m. Lloyd B. Carter, Sept. 14, 1978 (div. 1985); mem. Michele C. McDonald, Apr. 20, 1991; children: Zachary Leavitt, Collin McDonald. A.B., Middlebury (Vt.) Coll., 1951; M.A., Boston U., 1952; Ph.D., Harvard, 1958. Asst. to dir. Fogg Mus., Harvard, 1954-56; exec. dir. fine arts com. People to People Program, 1957; dir. Pasadena (Calif.) Art Mus., 1957-63, dir. Santa Barbara (Calif.) Mus. Art, 1963-68; dir. Andrew Dickson White Mus. Art, Cornell U., Ithaca, N.Y., 1968-73; Herbert F. Johnson Mus. Art, 1973-91; univ. prof. history art Cornell U., 1968-91, prof. emeritus, 1991—; interim dir. R.I. Sch. Design Mus. of Art, 1993-94, Newport Art Mus., 1994-95; Dir. mus. program Nat. Endowment for Arts, 1971-72, mem. museum panel, 1972-75; vice chmn. Council on Museums and Edn. in Visual Arts, 1972-76; trustee Gallery Assn. N.Y. State, 1972-78; mem. mus. panel N.Y. State Council Arts, 1975-78, 1980-82; chmn. art adv. com. Nat. Air and Space Mus., 1988—. Author exhbn. catalogs, articles. Trustee Am. Fedn. Arts, 1972-91; bd. dirs. Am. Arts Alliance, 1976-82, Ind. Sector, 1980-84; bd. govs. N.E. Mus. Conf., 1973-76; bd. trustees Williamstown Regional Art Conservation Lab., 1979-91, pres., 1984-87. Mem. Assn. Art Mus. Dirs. (pres. 1977-78, trustee 1978-80), Am. Assn. Museums (council 1976-79, v.p. 1980-82, pres. 1982-85). Home: 25 Waterway Rd Saunderstown RI 02874-3906

LEAVY, EDWARD, judge; m. Eileen Leavy; children: Thomas, Patrick, Mary Kay, Paul. AB, U. Portland, 1950, LLB, U. Notre Dame, 1953. Dist. judge Lane County, Eugene, Oreg., 1957-61, cir. judge, 1976; magistrate U.S. Dist. Ct. Oreg., Portland, 1976-84, judge, 1984-87, cir. judge U.S. Ct. Appeals (9th cir.), 1987—. Office: US Ct Appeals Pioneer Courthouse 555 SW Yamhill St Ste 216 Portland OR 97204

LEAVY, HERBERT THEODORE, publisher; b. Detroit, July 10, 1927; s. Morris and Thelma (Davidson) L.; m. Patricia J. Moran, June 20, 1953; children: Karen, Kathryn, Jill, Jacqueline. B.S. in Journalism, Ohio U., 1951. Supervisory editor Fawcett Books, N.Y.C., 1951-60; v.p.; editorial dir. Davis Publs., N.Y.C., 1960-69; founder, pres. Internat. Evaluations, Hauppage, N.Y., 1969-70; pub. dir. Countrywide Publs. Inc., N.Y.C., 1970-75; pres. Communications Devel. Co., N.Y.C., 1975-79; editorial dir. Watson-Guptil Publs., N.Y.C., 1979-80; pres. Books from Mags., Inc., Smithtown, N.Y., 1980—; Resumes Unltd., Smithtown, 1984—. Author: 101 Fast Track Resumes, The Pleasure, Executive Handbook, Vegetarian Times Cookbook, McCall's Houseplant and Indoor Landscaping Guide, Working Mother Cookbook, Carpentry, Shoe and Leather Repair at Home, The Complete Book of Beards and Moustaches, Air Conditioning-Repair and Maintenance, Designing and Building Beds, Lofts and Sleeping Areas, Wallcovering, Floor Stripping and Refinishing, Packing and Moving, Recreational Vehicles, Appliance Repair, Plumbing Handbook, Successful Small Farms; numerous others. 1st sgt. USAF, 1945-47. Mem. Sales Exec. Club, Am. Soc. Mag. Editors, Nat. Sporting Goods Assn., Am. Mgmt. Assn., Mag. Advts. Sales Club, Electronics Press Club, U.S. Tennis Ct. and Track Builders Assn., Am. Motorcycle Assn., Am. Horse Council, Author's Guild, Motorcycle Industry Council, Nat. Indoor Tennis Assn., Bus./Profl. Advt. Assn., Sigma Delta Chi. Office: Resumes Unlimited 222 E Main St Ste 107A Smithtown NY 11787

LEAVY, PAUL MATTHEW, management consultant; b. Jackson, Mich., Apr. 15, 1923; s. Paul Matthew and Myrtle Victoria (Robertson) L.; m. Jeanne Marie Le Mieux, Jun. 7, 1944; children: Paula Jeanne, William Thomas. BS, U.S. Naval Acad., 1944. Commd. ensign USN, 1944, advanced through grades to lt., resigned, 1954; advanced projects mgr. Laboratory for Electronics, Boston, 1954-59; pres. Trident Corp., Cambridge, 1959-62; mgr. radiation divsn Sanders Assocs., Nashua, N.H., 1962-72; v.p. EOPD ITT, Roanoke, Va., 1972-78; mktg. mgr. west GTE Mountain View, Calif., 1978-84; dir. devel. programs Teledyne CME, Santa Clara, 1984-91; pres. Paul Leavy Assocs., San Jose, 1991—; bd. dirs. Optical Shields, Inc., Menlo Park, Calif. Contbr. articles to profl. jours. Mem. Soc. Photo-Optical Instrumentation Engs., AIAA, Soc. Old Crows, Unmanned Vehicle Assn. Republican. Achievements include invention and development of active OCM and IRCM systems; development of first successful C.W. Sensing Laser Radar, of CHEM/BIO Mass Spectrometer, of high speed laser wavelength agility, of novel communications systems. Home: 8388 Riesling Way San Jose CA 95135-1480

LEB, ARTHUR STERN, lawyer; b. Cleve., June 26, 1930; s. Ernest A. and Bertha (Stern) L.; m. Lois Shafron, Oct. 21, 1932; children: Gerald P., Judith A., Robert B. AB, Columbia Coll., 1952; JD, Case Western Res. U., 1955. Bar: Ohio 1955, U.S. Supreme Ct., 1965. Ptnr. Leb & Halm, Canton, Ohio, 1961-84, Amerman, Burt & Jones, L.P.A., Canton, 1985-90, Buckingham, Doolittle & Burroughs, 1991—; founding mem., exec. com. Ohio Coun. Sch. Bd. Attys., 1976-84, pres. 1983. Served to 1st lt. JAGC, USAF, 1955-57. Recipient Merit award Ohio Legal Ctr. Inst., 1964. Fellow Ohio Bar Found.; mem. ABA, Stark County Bar Assn. (pres. 1985-86), Ohio Bar Assn.

LEBANO, EDOARDO ANTONIO, foreign language educator; b. Palmanova, Italy, Jan. 17, 1934; s. Nicola and Flora (Puccioni) L.; came to U.S. 1957, naturalized, 1961; m. Mary Vangeli, 1957; children: Tito Nicola, Mario Antonio. Student Biennio, U. Florence, 1955; M.A., Catholic U. Am., 1961, Ph.D., 1966. Tchr. high sch., Florence, Italy, 1955-57; Italian lang. specialist Bur. Programs and Standards, CSC Washington, 1958; lang. instr. Sch. Langs., Fgn. Services Inst., Dept. State, Washington, 1959-61; lectr. Italian, U. Va., Charlottesville, 1961-66; asst. prof. Italian, U. Wis.-Milw., 1966-69; assoc. prof., assoc. chmn. dept. French and Italian, 1969-71; assoc. prof. dept. French and Italian, Ind. U., Bloomington, 1971-83, prof. 1983—, dir. Scuola Italiana, Middlebury Coll., Vt., 1987. Author: A Look at Italy, 1976; Buon giorno a tutti, 1983; L'insegnamento dell'italiano nei colleges e nelle universita del nordamerica, 1983. Contbr. articles to profl. jours. Recipient Uhrig award Faculty U. Wis., 1968. Decorated Cavaliere nell'ordine al Merito della Repubblica Italiana. Mem. MLA, AAUP, Am. Assn. Tchrs. Italian (sec. treas. 1980-84, pres. 1984-87, Disting. Svc. award 1994), Dante Soc. Am., Renaissance Soc. Am., Boccaccio Soc. Am., Nat. Italian Am. Found., Am. Italian Hist. Assn., Am. Assn. Italian Studies, Midwest MLA. Home: 715 N Plymouth Rd Bloomington IN 47408-3066 Office: Ind U Ctr for Italian Studies Bloomington IN 47405

LEBARON, EDOARDO WAYNE, JR., lawyer; b. San Rafael, Calif., Jan. 7, 1930; s. Edward Wayne and Mabel Butler (Sims) LeB.; m. Doralee M.

LeBaron, June 4, 1954; children: Edward Wayne, William Bruce, Richard Wilson. BA, Coll. Pacific, 1950; LLB, George Washington U., 1959. Bar: Calif. bar 1960, Tex. bar 1960, Nev. bar 1967. Football quarterback Washington Redskins, 1952-59; with Dallas Cowboys, 1960-63; exec. v.p. Nevada Cement Co., 1964-65; mem. firm Wynne & Wynne, Dallas, 1960-63, Bible, McDonald & Carano, Reno, 1966-68, Laxalt & Berry, Carson City, Nev., 1969-70; partner firm Jones, Jones, Bell, LeBaron and Brown, Las Vegas, Nev., 1970-76; gen. mgr. Atlanta Falcons Football team, 1977-85; ptnr. Powell, Goldstein, Murphy & Frazer, 1986-89, Pillsbury, Madison & Sutro, 1989-94; ret., 1994; bd. dirs. Tom Brown, Inc.; ptnr LeBaron Ranches. Served with USMC, 1950-52. Decorated Purple Heart, Bronze Star; named Sportsman of Year in Ga., 1978-79; named to Coll. Football Hall of Fame, 1980. Mem. ABA, Sutter Club, Northridge Country Club. Republican. Office: Pillsbury Madison & Sutro 400 Capital Mall Ste 1700 Sacramento CA 95814

LE BARON, JOSEPH EVAN, diplomat; b. Nampa, Idaho, Sept. 3, 1947; s. Carlos Stannard and Truellen Ruth (Davis) McCracken; m. Elinor Rae Drake, Mar. 3, 1973; 1 child, Petra Drake. BS, Portland State U., Oreg., 1969; MA, Princeton U., 1978, PhD, 1980. Consular officer U.S. Embassy, Doha, Qatar, 1980-82; polit. officer U.S. Embassy, Amman, Jordan, 1982-83, econ./commercial officer, 1983-84; staff aide to amb. U.S. Embassy, Ankara, Turkey, 1984-85; polit. officer U.S. Consulate Gen., Istanbul, Turkey, 1985-87; desk officer for Lebanon U.S. State Dept., Washington, 1987-89; fgn. affairs advisor to majority leader U.S. Senate, Washington, 1989-90; consul gen. U.S. Consulate Gen., Dubai, United Arab Emirates, 1991-94; dep. amb. U.S. Embassy, Manama, Bahrain, 1994—. With USAF, 1970-74. Recipient Sinclaire award Disting. Lang. Study Am. Fgn. Svc. Assn., Washington, 1992; rsch. fellow for Sudan Social Sci. Rsch. Coun., N.Y.C., 1978-79; Nat. Defense Fgn. Lang. fellow Princeton U., 1976-78; Princeton U. fellow, 1976. Office: US Embassy Bahrain Dept Of State Washington DC 20520

LEBARRON, SUZANNE JANE, librarian; b. Tyndall, S.D., May 29, 1945; d. Ford and Eunice (Venne) LeB. BA, Coll. of Great Falls, 1967; MA, U. Minn., 1972. Prin. libr. asst. Stanford (Calif.) U., 1967-68; reference asst. Great Falls (Mont.) Pub. Libr., 1968-70; pre-profl. Mpls. Pub. Libr., 1970-72, community librarian Sumner Community Libr., 1972-74, librarian, 1974-78; NEH project dir. Minn. Office Libr. Devel. and Svc., Mpls., 1978-79; assoc. librarian. N.Y. State Libr., Albany, 1979-81; div. dir. Ky. Dept. for Librs. and Archives, Frankfort, 1981-86; dep. state librarian. Conn. State Libr., Hartford, 1986-89; state librarian. Wyo. State Libr., Cheyenne, 1990—; Author: Humanities in Minnesota, 1979; co-author: Serials for Libraries, 1979, Networking in Kentucky, 1981; editor: Directory of Humanities Research People in New York, 1980. Mem. ALA (councilor 1978-80, 84-88, 89—, chair com. on orgn. 1990-92), Wyo. Libr. Assn. Avocations: reading, swimming. Office: Wyo State Libr 2301 Capitol Ave Cheyenne WY 82001

LEBEAU, CHARLES PAUL, lawyer; b. Detroit, Dec. 11, 1944; s. Charles Henry Jr. and Mary Barbara (Moran) L.; m. Victoria Joy (Huchin), May 15, 1970; children: Jeffrey Kevin, Timothy Paul. AA, Macomb County Community Coll., Warren, Mich., 1967; BA, Wayne State U., 1969; JD, U. Detroit, 1972; grad. tax program, NYU Sch. Law, 1972-73. Bar: Mich. 1973, U.S. Tax Ct. 1973, Calif. 1987, U.S. Ct. Internat. Trade. 1988, U.S. Supreme Ct. 1988, U.S. Dist. Ct. (so. dist.) Calif. 1988. Tax atty. Ford Motor Co., Dearborn, Mich., 1973-75; assoc. Hoops & Huff, Detroit, 1975-76, Miller, Canfield, Paddock & Stone, Detroit, 1976-78; tax mgr. Oceaneering Internat., Santa Barbara, Calif., 1978-79; tax counsel Signal Cos. Inc., Beverly Hills and La Jolla, Calif., 1979-83; assoc. Gray, Cary, Ames & Frye, San Diego, 1983-84; of counsel James Watts Esq., La Jolla, 1985, Murfey, Griggs & Frederick, La Jolla, 1986; pvt. practice La Jolla and San Diego, 1987—; lectr. grad. tax program Golden Gate U., San Diego, 1979-87; adj. prof. law U. San Diego, 1982-85, 88-89; mem. Law Rev., U. Detroit, 1971-72; lectr. in taxation. Contbr. articles on internat. tax to profl. jours.; monthly tax case commentator Taxes Internat., London, 1981-85. Campaign coord. United Way, Santa Barbara, 1979. Mem. ABA, Mich. Bar Assn., Calif. Bar Assn., San Diego County Bar Assn., Pi Sigma Alpha. Republican. Roman Catholic. Avocations: sailing, tennis, walking. Home: 1999 Via Segovia La Jolla CA 92037-6441 Office: Law Offices Charles LeBeau Ste 1070 4660 La Jolla Village Dr San Diego CA 92122-4601

LEBEAU, HECTOR ALTON, JR., management consultant, former confectionary company executive; b. Hartford, Conn., July 2, 1931; s. Hector Alton and Gladys (Chester) LeB.; m. Joan Michaelson, May 31, 1955; children: Linda, Jane, Michael, Leslie. B.S., U. Tex., 1960; Program for Mgmt. Devel., Harvard U., 1965. With mktg. dept. Gen. Foods, White Plains, N.Y., 1960-73; v.p., gen. mgr. Consol. Brands div. Gulf & Western, N.Y.C., 1973-78; with sales and mktg. dept. Timex, Middlebury, Conn., 1978-80; v.p. fields ops. Schweppes U.S.A., Stamford, Conn., 1980-82, pres., 1982-84; pres. Rose Holland House, 1984-85, Cadbury U.S.A., 1985-88; sr. v.p. Cadbury Schweppes Inc., Stamford, Conn., 1985-88; pres. The Marcon Group, 1988—; pres., CEO Am. Candy Co., Selma, 1995—. Mem. Stanford Bd. Reps., 1966-69; mem. nat. com. Explorers, Boy Scouts Am., 1970-71; trustee St. Augustine Arts Assn., 1994—; pres. Marsh Creek Homeowners Assn., 1994—. Capt. USAF, 1954-58. Elected dean Nat. Candy Wholesalers Assn., 1988. Mem. Beta Gamma Sigma. Republican. Clubs: Union League (N.Y.C.); Cedar Point Yacht (Westport, Conn.); Marsh Creek Country Club (St. Augustine, Fla.). Office: One 10th St Ste 101 Saint Augustine FL 32084

LEBEC, ALAIN, investment banker; b. Dunkerque, Nord, France, Apr. 25, 1950; came to U.S., 1971; m. Leah M. Koncelik, June 27, 1981; children: Gabriel, Christina, Xavier. Diplome d'Ingenieur, Ecole Poly., Paris, 1971; MBA, Northwestern U., 1973. Mng. dir. A.G. Becker & Co., N.Y.C., 1973-84; mng. dir. investment banking group Merrill Lynch & Co., N.Y.C., 1984—. 2d lt. French Army, 1971. Office: Merrill Lynch & Co World Fin Ctr North Tower New York NY 10281-1330

LEBECK, WARREN WELLS, commodities consultant; b. Chgo., Mar. 13, 1921; s. Emil and Hazel (Wells) L.; m. Dorothy Lester, Feb. 1, 1943; children: Sara Beth, Kenneth, Clayton A., Frederick E. BA, North Central Coll., Naperville, Ill., 1942. With Montgomery Ward & Co., Chgo., 1941-42, 46-54; with Chgo. Bd. Trade, 1954-79, sec., then exec. v.p., 1957-73, pres., 1973-77, sr. exec. v.p., 1977-79; pvt. practice cons. Chgo., 1979—; past dir. Bank of Hinsdale, Ill.; past chmn. bd., pres. South Loop Improvement Project; mem. U.S. Agrl. Policy Adv. Com., 1976-87; trustee Nat. Agrl. Forum, 1983-86; bd. dirs., exec. com. U.S. Feed Grains Council, 1978-90, Agrl. Council Am., 1980-90; bd. dirs., exec. com. Nat. Grain Trade Council, 1968-90, chmn., 1988-89; bd. dirs., exec. com. Nat. Futures Assn., 1982—. Former mem. bd. edn. Downers Grove (Ill.) Twp. High Sch. Served with USNR, 1942-45. Home and Office: 1060 Burning Tree Rd Pinehurst NC 28374-9271

LEBED, HARTZEL ZANGWILL, insurance company executive; b. Columbia, Pa., Mar. 1, 1928; m. Ann Kronick, June 12, 1956; children: Holly, Jay, Alex (dec.). BS in Commerce, U. N.C., 1950. With Conn. Gen. Life Ins. Co., Hartford, 1950—; v.p. group sales, 1971-73, sr. v.p. group pension ops., 1973-76, exec. v.p. group pension ops. and reinsurance ops., 1976-78, exec. v.p. chief investment officer, 1978-82; pres. Conn. Gen. Corp. subs. CIGNA Corp., 1982-85; exec. v.p. CIGNA Corp., Hartford, 1982-85, pres., 1985-88; interim pres. U. Hartford, 1988-89; bd. dirs. Kaman Corp. Campaign mem. U.S. Holocaust Mus., Washington; regent U. Hartford. With USN, 1945-47. Mem. Phi Beta Kappa. Home: 3278 Degas E Palm Bch Gdns FL 33410-1276

LEBEDOFF, DAVID M., lawyer, author; b. Mpls., Apr. 29, 1938; s. Martin David and Mary Louise (Galanter) L.; m. Randy Louise Miller, Feb. 7, 1981; children: Caroline, Jonathan, Nicholas. BA magna cum laude, U. Minn., 1960; JD, Harvard U., 1963. Bar: Minn. 1963. Spl. asst. atty. gen. Atty. Gen. of Minn. St. Paul, 1963-65; spl. counsel U.S. Senator Walter F. Mondale, Washington, 1966; pvt. practice law Mpls., 1967-81; ptnr. Lindquist & Vennum, Mpls., 1981-91, Briggs & Morgan, Mpls., 1991—; spl. master U.S. Dist. Ct., Mpls., 1974-75. Author: The 21st Ballot, 1969, Ward Number Six, 1972, The New Elite, 1981; contbr. articles to profl. jours. Bd. regents U. Minn., Mpls and St. Paul, 1977-89, chmn. bd. 1987-89; chmn. Mpls. Inst. Arts, 1989-91 bd. dirs. 1991—; bd. dirs. Blake Sch., U. Minn. Found. Recipient Outstanding Achievement award U. Minn., 1991. Mem. Mpls. Club (bd. dirs.), Minikahda Club, Phi Beta Kappa. Home: 1738

Oliver Ave S Minneapolis MN 55405-2222 Office: Briggs & Morgan 2400 IDS Ctr 80 S 8th St Minneapolis MN 55402-2113

LEBEDOFF, JONATHAN GALANTER, federal judge; b. Mpls., Apr. 29, 1938; s. Martin David and Mary (Galanter) L.; m. Sarah Sargent Mitchell, June 10, 1979; children: David Shevlin, Ann McNair. BA, U. Minn., 1960, LLB, 1963. Bar: Minn. 1963, U.S. Dist. Ct. Minn. 1964, U.S. Ct. Appeals (8th cir.) 1968. Pvt. practice Mpls., 1963-71; judge Hennepin County Mcpl. Ct., State Minn., Mpls., 1971-74; dist. ct. judge State of Minn., Mpls., 1974-91; U.S. magistrate judge U.S. Dist. Ct., St. Paul, 1991—; mem. Gov.'s Commn. on Crime Prevention, 1971-75; mem. State Bd. Continuing Legal Edn.; mem. Minn. Supreme Ct. Task Force for Gender Fairness in Cts., mem. implementation com. of gender fairness in cts. Jewish. Avocations: reading (biographies, history), family, bridge. Office: 570 US Courthouse 110 South 4th St Minneapolis MN 55401

LEBEDOFF, RANDY MILLER, lawyer; b. Washington, Oct. 16, 1949; m. David Lebedoff; children: Caroline, Jonathan, Nicholas. BA, Smith Coll., 1971; JD magna cum laude, Ind. U., 1975. Assoc. Faegre & Benson, Mpls., 1975-82, ptnr., 1983-86; v.p., gen. counsel Star Tribune, Mpls., 1989—; asst. sec. Star Tribune Cowles Media Co., Mpls., 1990—. Bd. dirs. Minn. Opera, 1986-90, YWCA, 1984-90, Planned Parenthood Minn. 1985-90, Fund for Legal Aid Soc., 1988—, Abbott-Northwestern Hosp., 1990-94. Mem. Newspaper Assn. (legal affairs com. 1991—, mem. history com. 1990-94, Minn. U. Dist. Ct.), Order of Coif. Home: 1738 Oliver Ave S Minneapolis MN 55405 Office: Star Tribune 425 Portland Ave Minneapolis MN 55488

LEBEDOW, AARON LOUIS, consulting company executive; b. Chgo., Aug. 19, 1935; s. Isidor and Fannie (Perchikoff) L.; m. Madeleine Hellman; children: Ellen, Francine, Sheri, Sherri Michaels, Tracey Michaels. B.S. in Indsl. Engring, Ill. Inst. Tech., 1957; M.B.A., U. Mich., 1958. Cert. mgmt. cons. Asst. marketing mgr. Imperial-Eastman, Chgo., 1960-61; mgr. Corplan Assos., Chgo., 1961-66; chmn. bd. Technomic, Inc., Chgo., 1966-87, Technomic Consultants Internat., Deerfield, Ill., 1987-93, Global Marketactics, L.L.C., Chgo., 1993—; Global Devel. Network, L.L.C., 1993—. Bd. dirs. Coun. for Jewish Elderly. Served to 1st lt. USAF, 1958-60. Mem. Am. Mgmt. Assn., Am. Mktg. Assn., Tau Epsilon Phi. Mem. B'nai B'rith. Office: Global Marketactics LLC 150 S Wacker Dr Ste 450 Chicago IL 60606-4101

LEBEL, ROBERT, bishop; b. Trois Pistoles, Que., Can., Aug. 11, 1924; s. Wilfrid and Alexina (Belanger) L. L.Theol., St. Paul U., Ottawa, 1950; D.Theol., Athenee Angelicum, Rome, 1951. Ordained priest Roman Cath. Ch., 1950, consecrated bishop, 1974; tchr. theology Major Sem., Rimouski, Que., 1951-65; rector Major Sem., 1963-65, Minor Sem., 1965-68; tchr. dogmatic theology U. Rimouski, 1970-74; aux. bishop St. Jean, Que., 1974-76; bishop Valleyfield, Que., 1976—. Contbr. ch. publs. Mem. Roman Synod on the Christian Family, 1980. Mem. Assemblee des Eveques Que., Conf. Can. Cath. Bishops, Soc. Canadienne de Theologie (theology commn.), KC. Address: 11 de l'Eglise, Valleyfield, PQ Canada J6T1J5

LEBENSFELD, HARRY, manufacturing company executive; b. N.Y.C., Aug. 25, 1904; s. Samuel and Bertha (Wolfshaut) L.; m. Edith Goldman, Sept. 15, 1937; 1 dau., Lynne Pasculano. With UIS, Inc. (formerly United Indsl. Syndicate, Inc.) N.Y.C.; mem.—now chief exec. officer, chmn. bd. Mem. Harmony Club. Home: 980 5th Ave New York NY 10021-0126 Office: UIS Inc 600 5th Ave New York NY 10020-2302*

LEBENZON, CHRIS, film editor. Editor: (documentary) (with Robert K. Lambert and Ian Masters) The Secret Life of Plants, 1978, (films) Demon, 1977, The Private Files of J. Edgar Hoover, 1978, (with Marshall M. Borden, Martin Bram, and Dennis Dolan) Wolfen, 1981, A Breed Apart, 1984, (with Scott Wallace and Mark Warner) Weird Science, 1985, Death of an Angel, 1985, (with Billy Weber) Top Gun, 1986 (Academy award nomination best film editing 1986), (with David Handman and Jon Poll) Weeds, 1987, (with Michael Tronick and Weber) Beverly Hills Cop II, 1987, (with Tronick and Weber) Midnight Run, 1988, Revenge, 1990, (with Weber) Days of Thunder, 1990, Batman Returns, 1992, Josh and S.A.M., 1993, Ed Wood, 1994. Office: care Lawrence Mirisch The Mirisch Agency 10100 Santa Monica Blvd Ste 700 Los Angeles CA 90067*

LEBER, LESTER, advertising agency executive; b. Newark, June 11, 1913; s. David and Hattie Leber; m. Ruth Schwarz, Mar. 29, 1940 (div. 1968); m. Magdalena Maurer, July 15, 1968; children: Frederick, Laura Wood, Daniel. BA, Columbia U., 1934. Various positions Grey Advt., N.Y.C., 1935-52; founder, hon. chmn. Leber Katz Ptnrs., N.Y.C., 1952-72. Columnist: Saturday Evening Post, 1950, Tide, 1952, Advertising Age, 1960. Served with USN, 1943-45; Pearl Harbor. Home: 95706 Overseas Hwy Key Largo FL 33037-2046 Office: FCB/Leber Katz Ptnrs 767 5th Ave New York NY 10153-0001

LEBER, STEVEN EDWARD, film producer, corporate executive; b. Bklyn., Dec. 12, 1941; s. David and Selma (Teitelbaum) L.; m. Marion Susan Greiffenhagen, Feb. 6, 1966; children: Michelle, Jill, Jordan. BA in Mgmt. and Acctg., Northeastern U., 1964. Agt. William Morris Agy., N.Y.C., 1964-72; pres. Contemporary Communications Corp., N.Y.C., 1972—; producer Leber and Krebs, Inc., N.Y.C., 1972—; pres. Global Sports & Arts, Ltd., N.Y.C., 1989—; pres. Tyumen Cons. Group, Inc., cons. Tyumen region, Russia; founder Hollywood Stores; voting mem. Tony Selection Com., N.Y.C., 1977—. Producer: Jesus Christ Superstar-Touring Co., N.Y.C., 1972-78, Beatlemania-Broadway, 1977-84, 1st Pro-Skating Championships-ABC Wide World of Sports, 1981-83, Tennis Championships, 1981-83, Moscow Circus-Circus Prodn., Inc., N.Y.C., 1988—(Family Show of Yr. award Performance mag. 1989), Moscow Circus (Family Show of Yr. award Performance mag. 1990), Teenage Mutant Ninja Turtles* "Coming Out of Their Shells", 1990; producer Animated Films, Russia. Mem. H.E.L.P. (found. to aid homeless), N.Y.C., 1988—; bd. dirs. Children's Med. Ctr., Great Neck, N.Y., 1985—, Five Towns United Way; fund raiser Armenian Earthquake Fund, Washington/N.Y.C., 1988; exec. producer Concert for Bangledesh, 1971. Mem. NARAS (voting), N.Y. League Theatrical Producers, N.Y. Internat. Festival arts (bd. mem. 1989), Friars Club, Innercircle Club (Washington). Office: Circus Prodns Inc 155 E 55th St Apt 6H New York NY 10022-4040

LEBLANC, HUGH LINUS, political science educator, consultant; b. Alexandria, La., Oct. 30, 1927; s. Moreland Paul and Carmen Marie (Haydel) LeB.; m. Shirley Jean Smith, Feb. 28, 1953; children: Leslie Ann, Alexander Hugh. BA, La. State U., 1948; MA, U. Tenn., 1950; PhD, U. Chgo., 1958. Asst. prof. George Washington U., Washington, 1955-58, assoc. prof., 1959-63, prof., 1964-90, prof. emeritus dept. polit. sci., 1991—, chmn. dept., 1963-65, 70-76, 82-88; v.p. Area Inc., Arlington, VA, 1961-63. Author: American Political Parties, 1982, (with D. Trudeau Allensworth) The Politics of States and Urban Communities, 1971; contbr. articles to polit. sci. jours. Served to lt. (j.g.) USNR, 1944-45, 52-55. Named Outstanding Prof. Interfraternity Council, George Washington U., 1968. Mem. Country Club of Fairfax (Va.). Home: 3403 Barger Dr Falls Church VA 22044-1202

LEBLANC, HUGUES, philosophy educator; b. Ste-Marie de Beauce, Que., Can., Mar. 19, 1924; came to U.S., 1946, naturalized, 1952; s. Edmond and Alice (Caron) L.; m. Virginia Southall Graham, June 10, 1950 (div. Apr. 1983); children—Gabrielle, Suzanne, Stephen. MA, U. Montreal, Que., 1946, hon. doctorate, 1980; PhD, Harvard U., 1948; hon. doctorate, Dalhousie U., 1982, U. Que., Montreal, 1985. Prof. philosophy Bryn Mawr (Pa.) Coll., 1948-67, Temple U., Phila., 1967-92, U. Que., Montréal, 1992—. Author: An Introduction to Deductive Logic, 1955, Statistical and Inductive Probabilities, 1962, Techniques of Deductive Inference, 1966, Deductive Logic, 1972, Truth, Syntax and Modality, 1973, Truth-Value Semantics, 1976, Existence, Truth and Probability, 1982, Essays on Epistemology and Semantics, 1983; also numerous papers on logic, philosophy of logic and probability theory. Fulbright fellow, 1953-54; Guggenheim fellow, 1965-66. Mem. Royal Soc. Can., Assn. for Sympolic Logic (exec. com. 1958-61, treas. 1979-91, 82-85), Soc. for Exact Philosophy (v.p. 1978-80, pres. 1980-82). Home: 460 Champ de Mars Apt 502, Montreal, PQ Canada H2Y 1B4

LEBLANC, JAMES E., financial services company executive; b. 1942. BA, Providence Coll., 1964. With GE Credit Corp., Stamford, Conn., 1964-82; chief oper. officer Northwest Acceptance Corp., Portland, Oreg., 1982-85; pres. Pacificorp Credit, 1985-88; chmn., pres., chief exec. officer Whirlpool Fin. Corp., Benton Harbor, Mich., 1988—; also v.p. Whirlpool Corp., Benton Harbor; bd. dirs. Shoreline Fin. Corp., Shoreline Bank, Cornerstone Alliance. Office: Whirlpool Fin Corp 553 Benson Rd Benton Harbor MI 49022-2664

LEBLANC, L(OUIS) CHRISTIAN, architect; b. Heidelberg, Bavaria, Fed. Republic Germany, July 5, 1957; s. Louis Carroll LeBlanc and Gladys Jane Everett; m. Janet Beverly Frances Mulholland; children: Jacob Bodalski (stepchild), L. Christian Jr., Francesca Helen. BS in Design, Clemson U., 1980, MArch, 1982. Architect FJ Clark Inc., Anderson, S.C., 1982-86, Freeman & Major Architects Inc., Greenville, S.C., 1987-88, Narramore & Assocs., Inc., Greenville, 1988-89, Greene & Assocs., Inc., Greenville, 1989—. Mem. AIA. Republican. Roman Catholic. Avocations: languages, sailing. Home: 213 Oregon St Greenville SC 29605-1050 Office: Greene & Assocs Architects Inc 704 E Washington St Greenville SC 29601-3035

LEBLANC, ROGER MAURICE, chemistry educator; b. Trois Rivières, Que., Can., Jan. 5, 1942; s. Henri and Rita (Moreau) L.; m. Micheline D. Veillette, June 26, 1965; children: Daniel, Hughes, Marie-Jose, Nancy. BSc, U. Laval, 1964, PhD, 1968. NRC postdoctoral fellow Davy Faraday Rsch. Lab. Royal Inst. Great Britain, London, 1968-70; prof. phys. chemistry U. Que., Trois-Rivières, 1970-93, chmn. dept., 1971-75, dir. Biophysics Rsch. Group, 1978-81, chmn. Photobiophysics Rsch. Ctr., 1981-91; prof., chmn. dept. chemistry U. Miami, Coral Gables, Fla., 1994—; hon. prof. Jilin U., Chang Chun, China, 1992. Recipient Barringer award Spectroscopy Soc. Can., 1983, Medaille du Merite Universitaire du Que. a Trois-Rivieres, 1987, Commemorative medal for 125th Anniversary of Confedn. Can., 1993. Fellow Chem. Inst. Can. (Noranda award 1982, John Labatt Ltd. award 1992); mem. Am. Chem. Soc., Assn. Canadienne Francaise pour l'Avancement des Sciences (Prix Vincent 1978), Am. Soc. Photobiology, Biophys. Soc., European Photochem. Assn. Roman Catholic. Home: 9335 SW 77th Ave Apt 251 Miami FL 33156 Office: Univ Miami Dept Chemistry Cox Sci Bldg Rm 315 1301 Memorial Dr Coral Gables FL 33124-0431

LEBLANC, ROMÉO, Canadian government official; b. Memramcook, N.B., Can., Dec. 18, 1927; s. Philias and Lucie LeB.; m. Diana Fowler; 4 children. BA, St. Joseph U., 1948, BEd, 1951; postgrad., Paris U., 1953-55; DCL (hon.), Mount Allison U., New Brunswick, 1977; D Pub. Adminstrn. (hon.), U. de Moncton, New Brunswick, 1979. Tchr. Drummond High Sch., New Brunswick, Can., 1951-53; Prof., New Brunswick Tchrs. Coll., Fredericton, Can., 1955-59; journalist, correspondent Radio Can., Ottawa, 1960-62, United Kingdom, 1962-65, U.S.A., 1965-67; founding pres. CBC/Radio-Can. Correspondent's Assn., 1965; press sec. to Right Hon. Lester B. Pearson, 1967-68, Right Hon. Pierre Elliott Trudeau, 1968-71; asst. to pres. and dir. pub. rels. l'Universite de Moncton, Can., 1971-72; M.P. from Westmorland-Kent, New Brunswick dist. Ho. of Commons, Can., 1972-74; min. Ministry of State Fisheries, 1974-76, Ministry of Fisheries and the Environ., 1976-79, Ministry of Fisheries and Oceans, 1980-82, Ministry of Pub. Works, 1982-84, Canada Mortgage and Housing Corp., 1982-84, Nat. Capital Commn., 1982-84; mem. Can. Senate, 1984-95, speaker, 1993-95; governor general Govt. Can., 1995—; official rep. Govt. Can. USSR, Poland, Cuba., United Kingdom, France, 1974-84; mem. del. U.N. Law of the Sea Conf., 1974-79; cabinet com. mem. External Affairs and Econ. Affairs Govt. Can., 1974-82, Comm. Cabinet, 1974-84; comm. Comm. Cabinet, 1976-81, Priorities and Planning Cabinet, 1975-84; Social Affairs Cabinet, 1984; mem. senate com. Internal Econ., Budgets and Administration., 1984-93, chmn., 1989-93; mem. senate com. Fgn. Affairs, 1986-94, Sub. Com. on Security and Nat. Defense, 1992-94; vis. scholar Inst. Can. Studies, Carleton U.; part time faculty mem. Can. studies Concordia U., Montreal. Mem. Canada France Parliamentary Assn., Internat. Assn. French Speaking Parliamentarians. Office: Office of the Governor General, Rideau Hall 1 Sussex Dr, Ottawa, ON Canada K1A 0A1

LEBLANC, RUFUS JOSEPH, SR., geology educator, consultant, researcher; b. Erath, La., Oct. 12, 1917; s. Aladain and Orore (Nunez) LeB.; m. Alva Mae Broussard, Mar. 10, 1940; children: Rufus Jr., Paul, Lucille. BS in Geology, La. State U., 1939, MS in Geology, 1941. Chief geologist Mississippi River Commn., Baton Rouge, 1941-48; rsch. geologist, then mgr. geol. rsch. Shell Oil Co., Shell Devel. Co., Houston, 1948-86; prin. Rufe LeBlanc Sch. Sediments, Houston, 1986—. Contbr. numerous articles to profl. jours. Fellow Geol. Soc. Am. (sr.); hon. life mem. Am. Assn. Petroleum Geologists (Best Paper award 1974, assoc. editor jour. 1975-81, Sidney Powers Meml. award 1988), Soc. for Sedimentary Geology, Gulf Coast Assn. Geol. Socs., Houston Geol. Soc. Republican. Roman Catholic. Avocation: music collector. Home and Office: 3751 Underwood St Houston TX 77025-1805

LEBLANC, TINA, dancer; b. Erie, Pa.; m. Marco Jerkunica, May 1988. Trained, Carlisle, Pa. Dancer Joffrey II Dancers, N.Y.C., 1982-83, The Joffrey Ballet, N.Y.C., 1984-92; prin. dancer San Francisco Ballet, 1992—; guest tchr. Ctrl. Pa. Youth Ballet, 1992, 94. Work includes roles in (with San Francisco Ballet) Con Brio, Bizet Pas de Deux, Swan Lake, Nanna's Lied, Handel -- A Celebration, La fille mal gardée, Rubies, Tchaikovsky Pas de Deux, Seeing Stars, The Nutcracker, La Pavane Rouge, Company B; (with other companies) The Green Table, Les Presages, Le sacre du printemps, Les Noces, Light Rain, Romeo and Juliet, Runaway Train, Empyrean Dances, La Vivandière. Recipient Princess Grace Found. award, 1988. Office: San Francisco Ballet 455 Franklin St San Francisco CA 94102

LEBLANG, STEVEN CRAIG, television executive; b. N.Y.C., Aug. 13, 1959; s. Allan and Barbara Joan (Chapin) L. BA, SUNY, Oswego, 1981. Media buyer Grey Advt., N.Y.C., 1981-83; program analyst MMT Sales, Inc., N.Y.C., 1983-85; dir. domestic research Metromedia Producers Corp., Hollywood, Calif., 1985-86; dir. research 20th Century Fox TV, Beverly Hills, Calif., 1986, v.p. TV research, 1987-88; v.p. programming Fox TV Stas., Inc., Beverly Hills, Calif., 1988-90; exec. v.p. programming LBS Communications, L.A., 1990—. Home: 12703 Tiara St North Hollywood CA 91607-1024 Office: LBS Communications 9220 W Sunset Blvd West Hollywood CA 90069-3501

LEBLOIS, AXEL, computer company executive; b. 1949. Student in Econs., Ecole Nationale des Sciences Politiques; student in Philosophy, U. Paris; MBA, INSEAD. With Compagnie Europeenne de Publication; pres. French ops. Internat. Data Corp., France, 1983-86; pres., CEO IDG Comm. 1986-91; vice chmn. Internat. Data Group, 1986-91; chmn., CEO Internat. Data Corp, 1986-91; pres., CEO H N Bull Info. Systems, Billerica, Mass., 1991—. Office: H N Bull Information Systems Technology Park Billerica MA 01821

LEBLOND, CHARLES PHILIPPE, anatomy educator, researcher; b. Lille, France, Feb. 5, 1910; s. Oscar and Jeanne (Desmarchelier) L.; m. Gertrude Sternschuss, Oct. 22, 1936; children—Philippe L., Paul N., Pierre F., Marie Pascale. L.Sc., U. Lille, 1932; M.D., U. Paris, France, 1934, D. Sc., 1945; Ph.D., U. Montreal, 1942; DSc Acadia (hon.), McGill U., 1982, York U., 1985. Asst. histology U. Lille and U. Paris, France, 1934-35; Rockefeller fellow anatomy Yale, 1935-37; charge biology div. Lab. Synthese Atom, Paris, 1937-40; research fellow U. Rochester, N.Y., 1940-41; mem. faculty McGill U., Montreal, Que., Can., 1941-92; prof. anatomy McGill U., 1948—, chmn. dept., 1957-75. Author: L'Acide Ascorbique dans les Tissues et sa Detection, 1936, Radioautography as a Tool in the Study of Protein Synthesis, 1965, also over 300 articles mainly on cell and tissue dynamics. Fogarty scholar NIH, 1975. Fellow Royal Soc. London, Royal Soc. Can. Am. Assn. Anatomy, Canadian Assn. Anatomists. Home: 68 Chesterfield St, Montreal, PQ Canada H3Y 2M5

LEBLOND, PAUL HENRI, oceanographer, educator; b. Que., Can., Dec. 30, 1938; s. Sylvio and Jeanne (Lacerte) LeB.; m. Josee Michaud (div. 1985); children: Michel, Philippe, Anne. BA, Laval U., Quebec, 1957; BS, McGill U., Montreal, Que., 1961; PhD, U. B.C., Vancouver, Can., 1964; DSc (hon.). Meml. U., Newfoundland, 1992. Prof. depts. oceanography and physics U. B.C., Vancouver, 1965, assoc. dean faculty of sci., 1982-85, head dept. oceanography, 1987-92, dir. program earth and ocean scis. 1992—; chmn. Can.

nat. com. World Ocean Circulation Expt., 1987-92; program leader Ocean Prodn. Enhancement Network, Can., 1991-93. Co-author: Waves in the Oceans, 1978; contbr. articles to profl. jours. Bd. dirs. Can. Ctr. for Fisheries Innovations, 1993—; mem. Fisheries Resource Conservation Coun., 1993—. Fellow Royal Soc. Can.; mem. Can. Meteorol. and Oceanographic Soc. (Pres.'s prize 1981, Tully medal 1991), Am. Geophys. Union. Avocations: hiking, history. Office: U BC, Dept Oceanography, Vancouver, BC Canada V6T 1Z4

LEBLOND, RICHARD FOARD, internist, educator; b. Seattle, July 17, 1947; s. Donald E. and Ruth Elizabeth (Foard) LeB.; m. Anita Caraig Carcia, Dec. 28, 1994; children: Sueno Emmeline, Edgardo Alan. AB, Princeton U., 1969; MD, U. Wash., 1972. Diplomate Am. Bd. Internal Medicine (bd. dirs. 1993—). Intern Harlem Hosp., N.Y.C., 1972-73; resident in medicine, clin. fellow in oncology U. Wash., Seattle, 1975-78; pvt. practice, Livingston, Mont., 1978—; dir. Livingston Meml. Hosp., 1979-91, 94—, chmn. bd. dirs., 1984-91; clin. asst. prof. medicine Mont. State U., Bozeman, 1979—, U. Wash., 1991—, U. Calif., San Francisco, 1991-92; acting instr. Makerere U. Kampala, 1991-92; bd. dirs. Deaconess Rsch. Found., Billings, Mont., 1993. Dir. Park County Friends of the Arts, Livingston, 1981-87, Livingston Cmty. Trust, 1986-91. Recipient Regional Trustee of Yr. Am. Heart Assn., 1989. Fellow ACP; mem. AMA, Mont. Med. Assn., Am. Soc. for Internal Medicine, Nat. Rural Health Assn. Avocations: fishing, hunting, hiking, reading, gardening. Home: Rt 62 Box 3196 Livingston MT 59047 Office: Park Clinic PC 1001 River Dr Livingston MT 59047

LEBLOND, RICHARD KNIGHT, II, banker; b. Cin., Nov. 16, 1920; s. Harold R. and Elizabeth (Conroy) LeB.; m. Sara Cordial Chapman, Dec. 11, 1948; children—Mary, Richard, E. Chapman, Elizabeth, David, Virginia, William, Thomas, Sara, Joseph. B.A., Princeton U.; D.C.S. (hon.), St. John's U., Jamaica, N.Y., 1978. Exec. v.p. Chem. Bank, N.Y.C., 1968-73; vice-chmn. bd. Chem. Bank, 1973-85, sr. advisor, 1985—; chmn. bd. Chem. Bank & Trust of Fla., 1988—; bd. dirs. Ingersoll Internat., Inc., Rockford, Ill., Bedford Stuyvesant D&S Corp., Bklyn. Served to 1st It. U.S. Army, 1943-46, PTO. Mem. N.Y. State Bankers Assn. (pres. 1979-80), Harvard Bus. Sch. Assn. (pres. 1975-76). Republican. Roman Catholic. Office: Chem Bank 11 W 51st St 2d Fl New York NY 10019

LEBO, WILLIAM C., JR., hotel corporation executive, lawyer. BA, Vanderbilt U., 1965, JD, 1968. Bar: N.Y. 1968, Tenn. 1975. Assoc. Shearman & Sterling, 1968-72; atty. Am. Can Co., 1972-74; counsel Agrl. Chemicals Group W.R. Grace & Co., 1974-82; v.p., gen. counsel, sec. Summa Corp., 1982-85; sr. v.p., gen. counsel Hilton Hotels Corp., Beverly Hills, Calif., 1985—. Office: Hilton Hotels Corp 9336 Civic Center Dr Beverly Hills CA 90210-3964

LEBOEUF, RAYMOND WALTER, manufacturing company executive; b. Chgo., Dec. 30, 1946; s. Raymond O'Dillon and Opal Rosalind (Powell) LeB.; m. Loralee Ann Sawyer, Jan. 24, 1968; children—Mandy, Whitney. BA, Northwestern U., 1967; MBA, U. Ill., 1970. Analyst Ford Motor Co., Detroit, 1970-73; asst. comptroller Union Bank, Los Angeles, 1973-74; mgr. banking Ford Motor Co., Detroit, 1974-80; treas. PPG Industries, Inc., Pitts., 1980-84, controller, 1984-86, v.p. purchasing, 1986-88, v.p. finance, 1988-94, exec. v.p., 1994—. Mem. Fin. Execs. Inst. (dir. 1983-84). Office: PPG Industries Inc 1 PPG Pl Pittsburgh PA 15272-0001

LEBOR, JOHN FRANCIS, retired department store executive; b. Portland, Oreg., Mar. 22, 1906; s. John G. and Jettie P. (Cook) L.; m. Violette Steinmetz, Oct. 7, 1931 (dec. Feb. 11, 1983); children: Andrew Scott, John Cook (dec. Jan. 1990), m. Dorothy Patrick Burns, Sept. 22, 1984. B.B.A., U. Oreg., 1928; M.B.A., Harvard U., 1930. Investment analyst Scudder, Stevens & Clark, N.Y.C., 1930-33; financial staff Radio-Keith-Orpheum Corp., 1933-40; sec.-treas. York (Pa.) Corp., 1940-46; treas. Federated Dept. Stores, Inc., Cin., 1946-51; v.p., treas., dir. Federated Dept. Stores, Inc., 1951-57, v.p., dir., 1958-60, exec. v.p., dir., 1960-65; trustee The Gateway Trust, Cin. Mem. Phi Beta Kappa, Beta Gamma Sigma, Beta Alpha Psi, Alpha Kappa Psi. Episcopalian. Clubs: Queen City (Cin.), The Beach; Old Guard Soc. Palm Beach Golfers (Palm Beach, Fla.); Turtle Creek (Tequestra, Fla.), Westchester Country (Rye, N.Y.). *An important guiding principle for evaluating myself and others has been dependability and a record of "mission accomplished," as opposed to offering alibis.*

LEBOUITZ, MARTIN FREDERICK, financial services industry executive, consultant; b. Phila., May 16, 1946; s. William and Sylvia (Magen) L.; m. Helene A. Pepe, Oct. 15, 1977; 1 child, Clarke S. BS, U.S. Air Force Acad., Colorado Springs, Colo., 1971; MA, The Fletcher Sch. of Law and Diplomacy, 1972. Asst. v.p. Bankers Trust Co., N.Y.C., 1976-82; v.p. mgr. of planning Barclays Bank of N. Am., N.Y.C., 1982-85; v.p. corp. devel. Chase Manhattan Bank, N.Y.C., 1985-88; v.p. planning and devel. Paine Webber Group Inc., N.Y.C., 1988-90; prin. DRI/McGraw-Hill, N.Y.C., 1990-91; mng. dir. Fin. Svcs. Cons., N.Y.C., 1991-95; v.p. dir. strategy wholesale oper. products The Chase Manhattan Bank, N.A., Bklyn., 1995—. Bd. dirs., chmn. sch. rels. com. N.Y. chpt. Fletcher Sch. Capt. USAAF, 1971-76. Mem. Planning Forum (chmn. program com. N.Y. chpt.), Assn. for Corp. Growth, Am. Mgmt. Assn., USAF Acad. Alumnae (treas. N.Y. metro area chpt.), Harvard Club, Fletcher Sch. Club N.Y. (chmn. sch. rels. com.). Office: The Chase Manhattan Bank NA 21st Fl 4 Chase Metrotech Ctr Brooklyn NY 11245

LEBOVITZ, HAROLD PAUL (HAL LEBOVITZ), journalist; b. Cleve., Sept. 11, 1916; s. Isaiah and Celia (Levy) L.; m. Margie Glassman, Feb. 20, 1938; children: Neil Ross, Lynn Gail. BA, Case Western Res. U., 1938; MA, Western Res. U., 1942. Sci. tchr., coach Euclid (Ohio) High Sch., 1938-46; reporter, baseball writer, columnist Cleve. News, 1946-60; columnist Cleve. Plain Dealer, 1960-84, sports editor, 1964-84; columnist The Sporting News, 1970-92, Gannett Syndicate, 1979-82; dir. Cleve. Jewish News, 1971-89; baseball umpire, 1937-50, football ofcl., 1940-71, basketball ofcl., 1940-60; Cleve. corr. Sporting News, 1950-64. Author: Pitchin' Man, 1948; (with Phil R. Gilman) Springboards to Science, 1967; contbg. editor: Webster's New World Dictionary, 1983—; syndicated columnist several Ohio newspapers, 1984—; contbr. articles to various periodicals; inventor outdoor playground game Four Sq. Tennis. Mem. recreation com. University Heights, Ohio, 1965-75; bd. dirs. Jewish Community Ctr., Cleve., 1962-63, Alumni Assn. Adelbert Coll. Case-Western Res. U., 1969-83. Named Citizen of Yr. City of University Heights, 1964, Sportsman of Yr. B'rith Emeth Men's Club, 1964, Top Sportswriter Cotron Twelve of Atlantic Fleet, 1961, Sporting News Top Feature Writer, 1963-64; recipient ten best writing awards Cleve. Newspaper Guild, 1948-60, Greater Cleve. Football Coaches Golden Deeds award, 1987; inducted into Glenville High Sch. Hall of Fame, 1980, Ohio Baseball Hall of Fame, 1984, Greater Cleve. Softball Hall of Fame, 1989, Sport Media Assn. of Cleve. Hall of Fame, 1990, Cleve. Journalism Hall of Fame, 1991. Mem. Baseball Writers Assn. (pres. 1965-66, bd. dirs. 1966-67), Ohio Sports Editors Assn. (pres. 1965-66), Cleve. Football Ofcls. Assn., Ohio Football Ofcls. Assn., Cleve. Umpires Assn., Sigma Delta Chi (Disting. Svc. award 1981, Mel Harder Disting. Svc. award 1992). Home: 2380 Edgerton Rd Cleveland OH 44118-3726

LEBOW, BENNETT S., communications executive; b. Phila., 1938; 1 child, Geri. BEE, Drexel U.; postgrad., Princeton U. Prin. DSI Systems Inc., Rockville, Md., from 1961, B.S. LeBow Inc.; chmn. Western Union Corp., Upper Saddle River, N.J., New Valley Corp. (formerly Western Union Corp.), Upper Saddle River, 1993—. Office: Brook Management 65 E 55th St New York NY 10022-3219 Office: Mai Basic Four Inc 14101 Myford Rd Tustin CA 92680-7020 also: New Valley Corp 1 Mack Centre Dr Paramus NJ 07452*

LEBOW, IRWIN LEON, electronics engineering consultant; b. Boston, Apr. 27, 1926; s. Samuel and Ruth (Tobey) L.; m. Grace H. Hackel, July 8, 1951; children: Judith, William, David. Sb, MIT, 1948, Ph.D., 1951. Staff mem. MIT Lincoln Lab., 1951-60, assoc. leader satellite communications surface techniques group, 1960-65, leader, 1965-70, assoc. head communications div., 1970-72, assoc. head data systems div., 1972-75, mem. steering com., 1970-75; chief scientist, assoc. dir. tech. Def. Communications Agy., Washington, Dept. Def., Washington, 1975-81; v.p. engring. Am. Satellite Co., Rockville, Md., 1981-84; v.p. Systems Research and Applications Corp., Arlington, Va., 1984-87; ind. cons. Washington, 1987—. Author: (with

others) Theory and Design of Digital Machines, 1962, The Digital Connection, 1990, Information Highways and Byways, 1995. Served with USNR, 1944-46. Awarded rank of Meritorious Sr. Exec., 1980; recipient Meritorious Civilian Service medal Dept. Def., 1981. Fellow Am. Phys. Soc., IEEE; mem. AAAS, Armed Forces Communications and Electronics Assn., Sigma Xi. Home and Office: 2800 Bellevue Ter NW Washington DC 20007-1366

LEBOW, MARK DENIS, lawyer; b. Harrisburg, Pa., Apr. 2, 1940; s. Sylvan and Ruth M. (Lebowitz) L.; m. Catherine Maugee, Nov. 12, 1972 (div. 1982); m. Patricia Edith Harris, Jan. 30, 1988; children: Michael, Jeffrey, Alexandra. AB, Yale U., 1961; JD, Harvard U., 1964. Bar: N.Y. 1965, U.S. Ct. Appeals (2d cir.) 1965, U.S. Dist. Ct. (so. and ea. dists.) N.Y. 1966. Assoc. Coudert Bros., N.Y.C., 1965-71, ptnr., 1972—; chmn. N.Y.C. CSC, 1979-92. Chmn. St. Francis Friends of the Poor, Inc., 1991—. Lt. USNR, 1964-71. Home: 1067 Fifth Ave New York NY 10128 Office: Coudert Bros 1114 Ave of the Americas New York NY 10036

LEBOWITZ, ALBERT, lawyer, author; b. St. Louis, June 18, 1922; s. Jacob and Lena (Zemmel) L.; m. Naomi Gordon, Nov. 26, 1953; children—Joel Aaron, Judith Leah. A.B., Washington U., St. Louis, 1945; LL.B., Harvard U., 1948. Bar: Mo. bar 1948. Assoc. Frank E. Morris, St. Louis, 1948-55; partner firm Morris, Schneider & Lebowitz, St. Louis, 1955-58, Crowe, Schneider, Shanahan & Lebowitz, St. Louis, 1958-66; counsel firm Murphy & Roche, St. Louis, 1966-67, Murphy & Schlapprizzi, St. Louis, 1967-81; partner firm Murphy, Schlapprizzi & Lebowitz, 1981-86; editor lit. quar. Perspective, 1961-80; of counsel Donald L. Schlapprizzi, P.C., 1986—, John T. Murphy, Jr., 1986-88. Author: novel Laban's Will, 1966, The Man Who Wouldn't Say No, 1969, A Matter of Days, 1989; also short stories. Served as combat navigator USAAF, 1943-45, ETO. Decorated Air medal with 3 oak leaf clusters. Mem. ABA, Mo., St. Louis bar assns., Phi Beta Kappa. Home: 743 Yale Ave Saint Louis MO 63130-3120 Office: Gateway One On The Mall 701 Market St Ste 1550 Saint Louis MO 63101

LEBOWITZ, CATHARINE KOCH, state legislator; b. Winchester, Mass., June 30, 1915; d. William John and Carolyn Sophia (Kistinger) Koch; m. Murray Lebowitz, Sept. 21, 1971 (dec. Oct. 1978). Student Northeastern U., 1948-49, Boston Coll., 1949-52. Sec. ERA, Bangor, Augusta, Maine, 1935-38, WPA, Portland, Maine, 1938-42; personnel officer, exec. sec. USN, Portland, 1942-47; exec. sec. Clark Babbitt, Boston, 1947-48; adminstrv. asst. Moore Bus. Forms, Boston, 1948-52; apt. mgr., wholesale appliance div. Coffin-Wimple Inc., 1952-62, clerk U.S. Dist. Ct. Bangor (No. dist), 1962-79; sec. Portland Credit Bur., 1980-86; mem. Bangor City Council, 1985-87; mem. Maine State Legislature, 1982-92; bd. dirs. Eastern Transportation, 1989-94; mem. Bus. Adv. Coun., 1991—; active Program Rev. Subcom., 1991—; mem. adv. com. RSVP, 1987—, bd. dir., bus. adv. coun., and chmn. sub com. project with industry RSVP, 1992—; mem. adv. coun. Eastern Maine Tech. Coll., 1992—; bd. dirs. Rural Health Ctrs. Maine, Inc., 1992—; adv. bd. Maine Ctr. for the Arts, U. Maine, 1992—. Sec. Symphony Women, Bangor, 1964-84; bd. dirs. Opera House Com., Bangor, 1978-94; del. Rep. Nat. Conv., 1984, 88; mem. Spl. Task Force to Study Child Abuse, 1985-92; legis. com. United Way of Penobscot Valley, 1988-93, bd. mem., 1993—; adv. com. Maine Devel. Found., 1984-92; adv. bd. Aftercare, 1990, planning bd. St. Joseph Hosp., 1987-92, dir., v.p. St. Joseph Hosp. Aux., 1994—, Bangor City Hosp. Aux., 1988—; bd. dirs. Penobscot Theater, 1990; accredited Beauty Pageant judge, 1986—. Recipient Civilian Meritorious Service award USN, Portland Maine, 1946; named Hon. Alumnus Secretarial Sci., Husson Coll., 1980. Mem. Credit Women Internat. (tress. 1975-77, Credit Woman of Yr. 1969), Credit Profls., 1988-92, Bangor Community Theater (tress. 1973—, award 1973), U. Maine Maine Masque Theater (judge 1983-90), Maine N.G. Assn. (hon.), Maine Air N.G. (hon.), Nat. Assn. Retired Fed. Employers (v.p. bd. dirs. 1994—, sec. 1994), Credit Women Bangor (sec. 1965-67), Bangor Dist. Nursing Assn. (corp. mem. at large), Bangor C. of C. (mem. consumer rels. coun. 1981-90, coord. 150th anniversary prodn. Music Man 1984) Bangor Hist. Soc. (bd. dirs. 1993—, exec. bd. sec. 1994—), Penobscot County Extension Svc. (bd. dir. 1995), Penobscot County Republicans, Penobscot County Rep. Women's Club (sec. 1979), Bangor City Rep. Club (bd. dirs., tress. 1993—), Newcomb Soc., Ret. Fed. Employees (v.p. 1994), Zonta Club (pres. Bangor 1962-64, 80-82, v.p. 1994, Outstanding Leader 1991), Mgmt. Club.

LEBOWITZ, HARVEY M., lawyer; b. Balt., Dec. 13, 1929; s. Samuel and Lillian (Caplan) L.; m. Eunice Levin, Aug. 4, 1955; children: Harrison, Bonnie, Fran. LLB, U. Md., Balt., 1954, JD, 1969. Assoc. Hoffberger & Hollander, Balt., 1955-61; ptnr. Gordon, Feinblatt, Rothman, Hoffberger & Hollander, Balt., 1961-79; judge U.S. bankruptcy ct. Dist. Md., Balt., 1979-82; ptnr. Frank, Bernstein, Conaway & Goldman, Balt., 1982-91, Whiteford, Taylor & Preston, Balt., 1991—; tchr. U. Balt., 1975-79; mem. faculty seminars on bankruptcy, various cities, 1979—. Author: Bankruptcy Deskbook, 1st Edit., 1986, Bankruptcy Deskbook, 2d Edit., 1990; author course material for various seminars. Mem. 4th Cir. Judicial Conf. With U.S. Army, 1954-55. Fellow Am. Coll. Bankruptcy, Md. Bar Found.; mem. ABA, Bankruptcy Bar Assn. Md. (dir. 1989—, pres. 1994—), Balt. City Bankruptcy Bar Assn., Assn. Former Bankruptcy Judges, Barristers Club (treas. 1991), E-Streeters Club. Democrat. Jewish. Avocations: tennis, travel, music. Office: Whiteford Tayler & Preston 7 Saint Paul St Ste 1400 Baltimore MD 21202

LEBOWITZ, JOEL LOUIS, mathematical physicist, educator; b. May 10, 1930; came to U.S., 1946, naturalized, 1951; m. Estelle Mandelbaum, June 21, 1953. BS, Bklyn. Coll., 1952; MS, Syracuse U., 1955, PhD, 1956; hon. doctorate, Ecole Poly. Federale, Lausanne, Switzerland, 1977. NSF postdoctoral fellow Yale U., New Haven, 1956-57; mem. faculty Stevens Inst. Tech., Hoboken, N.J., 1957-59; mem. faculty Yeshiva U., N.Y.C., 1959-77, prof. physics, 1965-77, acting chmn. Belfer Grad. Sch. Sci., 1964-67, chmn. dept., 1967-76; prof. math. and physics, dir. Ctr. for Math. Scis. Rutgers U., New Brunswick, N.J., 1977—. Co-editor: Phase Transitions and Critical Phenomena, 1980, editor Jour. Statis. Physics, 1975—, Studies in Statis. Mechanics, 1973—, Com. Math. Physics, 1973—; contbr. articles to profl. jours. Recipient Boltzmann medal Internat. Union Pure and Applied Physics, 1992, Max Planck Rsch. award, 1993, Delmar S. Fahrney medal Franklin Inst., 1994; Guggenheim fellow, 1976-77. Fellow AAAS, Am. Phys. Soc., N.Y. Acad. Scis. (pres. 1979, A. Cressy Morrison award in natural scis. 1986); mem. NAS, AAUP, Am. Math. Soc., Phi Beta Kappa, Sigma Xi. Office: Rutgers U Ctr Math Sci Rsch Busch Campus-Hill Ctr New Brunswick NJ 08903

LEBOWITZ, MARSHALL, publishing company executive; b. Boston, Mar. 4, 1923; s. Max Nathan and Rissah (Zangwill) L.; m. Charlotte Lily Meyersohn, Aug. 7, 1949; children: Wendy Ann, Marian Kay, Mark Louis. AB, Harvard U., 1942. Statis. analyst U.S. WPB, Washington, 1942-43; periodicals mgr. J.S. Canner & Co. Inc., Needham Heights, Mass., 1946-68, gen. mgr., 1968-86, v.p., 1987—; v.p. Plenum Pub. Corp., 1977—. Mem. Natick (Mass.) Planning Bd., 1964-69, chmn., 1968-69; mem. Natick Town Meeting, 1954—, chmn. town by-laws revision com., 1965-67; pres. Greater Framingham Mental Health Assn., 1963-64, dir. 1954-63; mem. Greater Framingham Mental Health Area Bd., 1972-78, v.p., 1974-75, pres., 1975-77; mem. Regional Drug Rev. Bd., 1973; chmn. Natick Regional Vocat. Sch. Planning Com., 1974-77; mem. Natick Sch. Com., 1978-81, clk., 1979-81; chmn. legis. impact study commn. Town of Natick, 1980; chmn. town commn. to rev. by-laws and mcpl. charter, 1980-90; mem. trustees adv. coun. Leonard Morse Hosp., 1973-91, vice chmn., 1974-77, mem. mental health adv. com., 1972-91; chmn. Natick Land-Use Com., 1983—; mem. Mcpl. Charter Rev. Com., 1985-88, Framingham-Natick Golden Triangle Planning Com., 1988-93; trustee Morse Inst. Libr., 1989—; bd. dir. Framington-Natick Cemetery Assn., 1991—; mem. Mcpl. Facilities Planning Com., 1994—. With AUS, 1943-46. Jewish (fin. sec. temple 1954-56, treas. 1952-54, vice-chmn. bd. 1958-59). Home: 2 Abbott Rd Natick MA 01760-1913 Office: 10 Charles St Needham MA 02194-2900

LEBOWITZ, MICHAEL DAVID, epidemiologist; b. Bklyn., Dec. 21, 1939; s. Harry and Rachel (Dick) L.; m. Joyce Marian Schmidt, Sept. 9, 1960; children: Jon A., Kira L., Debra M. AB, U. Calif., 1961, MA, 1965; PhC, U. Wash., 1969, PhD, 1971. Rsch. assoc. preventive medicine U. Wash., Seattle, 1967-70, rsch. assoc. environ. health, 1970-71; asst. prof. internal medicine U. Ariz., Tucson, 1971-75, assoc. prof. internal medicine, 1975-80, prof. internal medicine, 1980—, asst. dir. div. respiratory sci., 1974-84, assoc.

dir. Respiratory Sci. Ctr., 1985—, dir. epidemiol. grad. program, 1994—; vis. fellow Postgrad. Cardiothoracic Inst. U. London, 1978-79; vis. prof. Groningen U., The Netherlands, 1993, U. Pisa, Italy, 1993cons. US NIH, Bethesda, Md., 1975—, US EPA, Washington, 1969—, WHO, 1979—, Italian Nat. Rsch. Coun., 1979—, Polish Nat. Inst. Hygiene and Acad. Scis., 1981—, Hungarian Nat. Inst. Hygiene, 1989—, Pan Am. Health Orgn., 1985—, numerous others; co-chmn. indoor air pollutants commn. NAS/NRC, Washington, 1979-81, WHO Guidelines for Indoor Air in Environ. Epidemiol., 1983, WHO/EURO Monographs on Indoor Air Quality, 1982—. Mem. editl. bd. Jour. Behavioral Medicine, 1977-93, Jour. Air Pollution Control Assn., 1984-88, Pediatric Pulmonology, 1990—, Archives Environ. Health, 1990—, Am. Rev. Respiratory Diseases, 1993—; co-editor WHO/Euro Biol. Contaminants, 1990, WHO Euro Priorities in Environ. Epidemiol.; assoc. editor Jour. Toxicology Indsl. Health, 1984—, Jour. Expos. Analysis Environ. Epidemiology, 1992—; contbr. over 400 articles to profl. jours., chpts. to books and monographs. Chmn. Pima County Air Quality Adv. Coun., Tucson, 1975-78; cons. Ariz. State Dept. Health Svcs., 1972—, Ariz. Lung Assn., 1971—, State Dept. Environ. Quality, 1987—, Gov. of Ariz., 1987—; senator U. Ariz. Faculty Senate, Tucson, 1976-78. Recipient Ariz. Clean Air award Ariz. Lung Assn., 1987; numerous epidemiology/disease grants and contracts, NIH, EPA, FDA, EPRI and others, 1964—. Fellow Am. Coll. Epidemiology, Am. Coll. Chest Physicians; mem. Am. Epidemiol. Soc., Am. Thoracic Soc., Internat. Epidemiol. Assn., European Respiratory Soc., Soc. Epidemiol. Rsch., Internat. Soc. Environ. Epidemiology, Internat. Soc. Expn. Assessment, Hungar Soc. Health (hon.). Office: U Ariz Coll Medicine Respiratory Scis Ctr 1501 N Campbell Ave Tucson AZ 85724-0001

LEBRECHT, THELMA JANE MOSSMAN, reporter; b. Indpls., Feb. 21, 1946; d. Elmore Somerville and Lois Thelma (Johnson) Mossman; m. Roger Dublon LeBrecht, May 4, 1968. BS in Journalism, U. Fla., 1968. Pub. affairs reporter WBT and WBTV, Charlotte, N.C., 1967-72; freelance reporter Toronto and N.Y.C., 1972-76; reporter KYW Newsradio, Phila., 1976-80; editor ABC Radio Network, N.Y.C., 1980-81; reporter AP Broadcast, Washington, 1981—. Mem. Radio and TV Corrs. Assn. in U.S. Capitol (chmn. 1991). Office: AP Broadcast 1825 K St NW Washington DC 20006-1202

LE BUHN, ROBERT, investment executive; b. Davenport, Iowa, May 2, 1932; s. Dick and Mable (Blom) LeB.; m. Jo-Ann Fitzsimmons, June 19, 1954 (dec. Aug. 1991); children: Anne, Ellen, Robert, Richard. B.S. Northwestern U., 1954; M.B.A., U. Pa., 1957. Security analyst Cyrus J. Lawrence & Sons, N.Y.C., 1957-62; v.p. Eppler & Co., Inc., Morristown, N.J., 1962-72; independent fin. cons., 1972-80; mng. dir. Rothschild, N.Y.C., 1980-84; chmn. Investor Internat. (U.S.), Inc., N.Y.C., 1984-94; bd. dirs. Cambrex, Inc., USAIR Group, Inc., Acceptance Ins. Cos., Inc., Lomas Fin. Corp., Enzon Corp.; pres. Geraldine R. Dodge Found. Served to lt. (j.g.) USNR, 1954-56. Home: Fawn Hill Dr New Vernon NJ 07976

LE CAM, LUCIEN MARIE, mathematics educator; b. Croze Creuse, France, Nov. 18, 1924; came to U.S., 1950; s. François Marie and Marie Renée (Jouanno) Le C.; m. Louise E. Romig, Apr. 19, 1952; children—Denis A., Steven D., Linda M. Licence es Scis., U. Paris, 1947; grad. student, Sorbonne, Paris, 1947-48; Ph.D., U. Calif. at Berkeley, 1952. Mem. faculty U. Calif. at Berkeley, 1952—, from asst. to assoc. prof. stats., 1953-57, prof. stats., 1961-91, Miller prof., 1971-72, prof. math., 1973-91, chmn. dept., 1961-65, prof. emeritus, 1991—. Author: Asymptotic Methods in Statistical Decision Theory, 1986, (with Grace Lo Yang) Asymptotics in Statistics, 1990. Dir. Centre de Recherches Mathématiques, U. Montreal, 1972-73. Fellow AAAS, N.Y. Acad. Scis., Am. Acad. Arts and Scis., Inst. Math. Statistics (pres. 1972-73); mem. Internat. Statis. Inst., Internat. Chinese Statis. Assn., Am. Math. Soc., Bernoulli Soc. (council 1973), Am. Statis. Assn., Sigma Xi. Home: 101 Kensington Rd Kensington CA 94707-1011 Office: Univ Calif Berkeley CA 94720-3860

LE CARRÉ, JOHN (DAVID JOHN MOORE CORNWELL), author; b. Poole, Dorset, Eng., Oct. 19, 1931; s. Ronald Thomas Archibald and Olive (Glassy) Cornwell; m. Alison Ann Sharp, Nov. 27, 1954 (div. dissolved 1972); children: Simon, Stephen, Timothy; m. Valerie Jane Eustace, 1972; 1 son, Nicholas. Student, Bern (Switzerland) U., 1948-49; B.A. in Modern Langs., Lincoln Coll., Oxford (Eng.) U., 1956; hon. doctorate, U. Exeter, 1990. Tutor Eton Coll., Berkshire, Eng., 1956-58; mem. Brit. Fgn. Service, 1959-64; 2d sec. embassy Brit. Fgn. Service, Bonn, Germany, 1961-63; consul Brit. Fgn. Service, Hamburg, Germany, 1963-64. Author: Call for the Dead, 1960, A Murder of Quality, 1962, The Spy Who Came in From the Cold, 1963 (Mystery Writers of Am. Novel of Yr., 1963, Brit. Crime Novel of Yr. award 1963), The Looking-Glass War, 1965, A Small Town in Germany, 1968, The Naive and Sentimental Lover, 1971, Tinker Tailor Soldier Spy, 1973, The Honourable Schoolboy, 1977 (James Tait Black Meml. prize, Crime Writers Assn. gold dagger), Smiley's People, 1980 (televised 1982), The Little Drummer Girl, 1983, A Perfect Spy, 1986, The Russia House, 1989 (Nikos Kasanzakis prize 1991), The Secret Pilgrim, 1991, The Night Manager, 1993, Our Game, 1995, Our Game, 1995. Recipient Somerset Maugham award 1964, Edgar Allen Poe award Mystery Writers Am., 1965, Gold dagger Crime Writers Assn., 1978, Black Meml. award, 1978, Grand Master award Mystery Writers Am., 1986, Malaparte prize, 1987, Diamond Dagger award Crime Writers Assn., 1988; Lincoln Coll., Oxford hon. fellow, 1984. Office: David Higham Assocs Ltd, 5-8 Lower John St Golden Sq, London W1R 4HA, England

LECERF, OLIVIER MAURICE MARIE, construction company executive; b. Merville-Franceville, France, Aug. 2, 1929; s. Maurice and Colette (Lainé) L.; m. Annie Bazin de Jessey, Jan. 11, 1958; children: Christophe, Véronique, Nicolas, Patricia. Baccalauréat A in Philosophy, 1946; diploma Inst. Polit. Studies Paris, 1950; M. Law, U. Paris, 1950; diploma Indsl. Studies Ctr., U. Geneva, 1960. Asst. mgr. Omnium pour l'importation et l'exportation, Paris, 1951-56; asst. mgr. Ciments Lafarge, Can., 1956-57, and Brazil, 1958-59, asst. mgr. fgn. dept., 1961, adj. comml. dir., Paris, 1962-64, pres., chief exec. officer Lafarge Cement N.Am., Vancouver, B.C., Can., 1965, pres. Lafarge Can. Que., Montreal, 1968, pres. Lafarge Can. Ltd., 1969, gen. mgr. Can. Cement Lafarge, Montreal, 1970, exec. gen. mgr., Paris, 1971-73, chmn., chief exec. officer (now Lafarge Coppée), 1974—, hon. chmn., 1989—, also dir.; dir. Compagnie de St Gobain, L'Oréal, SEB SA, others; mem. adv. com. Morgan Stanley, dir., chmn. financière Lafarge Coppée. With inf. French Army, 1950-51; lt. Res. Decorated officer de la Legion d'Honneur, commandeur Ordre National du Merite. Contbr. articles to profl. jours. Home: 8 rue Guy de Maupassant, 75116 Paris France Office: Lafarge, 61 rue des Belles Feuilles, 75116 Paris France

LECHASE, RAYMOND WAYNE, construction company executive; b. Rochester, N.Y., Mar. 24, 1944; s. Raymond F. and Rachel (Palumbo) LeC.; m. Beverly A. Carroll, Oct. 24, 1962; children: Raymond F., Jacqueline M. LeChase Frate. BSBA, John Carroll U., 1965; JD, SUNY, Buffalo, 1968. Bar: N.Y. 1968. Atty. Johnson, Reif and Mullan, Rochester, N.Y., 1968-71; ptnr. LaDuca, Offen and LeChase, Rochester, 1971-79; sec., contract mgr. Raymond LeChase, Inc., Rochester, 1979-81, pres. CEO, 1981—; ptnr. Raymond LeChase Co., Rochester, 1981—; chair edn. com. Gen. Bldg. Contractors; mem. bd. advisors Nazareth Coll.; mem. adv. coun. Rochester Inst. Tech. Bd. Cooperative Ednl. Svcs. # 1, Monroe County Coll. Vice-chmn. bd. trustees Rochester Mus. and Sci. Ctr.; bd. trustees St. John Fisher Coll., Ctr. for Govt. Rsch., Inc., Bricklayers and Allied Craftsmen Funds; mem. exec. bd. Otetiana coun. Boy Scouts Am. Mem. ABA, Constrn. Specification Inst., Assn. Gen. Contractors, Rochester Housing Partnership (steering com.), Rochester Area C. of C. (bd. trustees), Rochester Yacht Club, Oak Hill Country Club. Office: Raymond LeChase Inc 300 Trolley Blvd Rochester NY 14606

LECHAY, JAMES, artist, emeritus art educator; b. N.Y.C., July 5, 1907; s. Charles and Augusta (Wolfson) L.; m. Rose David, Mar. 26, 1934; children: Jo, Daniel. A.B., U. Ill., 1928; D.F.A. (hon.), Coe Coll., 1961. Asst. prof. art U. Iowa, 1945-49; assoc. prof. 1949-56, prof. 1956-75, prof. emeritus, 1975—; tchr. Stanford U., 1949, N.Y. U., 1953, Skowhegan (Maine) Sch. Painting and Sculpture, 1961; artist in residence Tamarind Inst., 1973; vis. artist New Asia Coll., Chinese U. of Hong Kong, 1976, Parsons Sch. Design, Provincetown, Mass., 1981—; Studio Art Sch. of Aegean, Samos, Greece, 1986, 87, 88. Exhibited in numerous one-man shows including N.Y.C., others in, Trieste, Italy, Chgo., Cedar Rapids, Iowa City, Des Moines Art Center, Louisville, Springfield, Ill., Ft. Dodge, Cedar Falls and Davenport, Iowa Wesleyan U., Sioux City, Iowa, Wellfleet, Mass., Palardy Gallery, Montreal, Que., Can., Dartmouth Coll., Hanover, N.H., SUNY, Binghamton; exhibited group shows Met. Mus. Art, N.Y.C., Pa. Acad. Fine Arts, Provincetown Art Assn., Mass., Va. Mus. Fine Arts, Bklyn. Mus., Chgo. Art Inst., Phillips Meml. Gallery, Whitney Mus. Am. Art, Corcoran Gallery Art, Carnegie Instn., Copenhagen City Gallery, Denmark, others; represented permanent collections, Nat. Collection Fine Arts Smithsonian Instn., Pa. Acad. Fine Arts, U. Ariz., U. Iowa, Bklyn. Mus., New Britain Inst., U. Nebr., Memphis Mus. Ill. Wesleyan U., Chgo Art Inst., Wichita Art Center, Philbrook Mus., Tulsa, Des Moines Art Center, Coe Coll., Joslyn Art Mus., U. No. Iowa, Springfield (Mo.) Art Mus., Rochester Meml. Gallery, others, also pvt. collections. Recipient Norman Wait Harris bronze medal, 52 ann. exhbn. Am. Painting, Art Inst. Chgo., 1941, Lambert purchase prize Pa. Acad., 1942; represented hon. mention for water color Art Inst. Chgo., 1943, prize for oil 2d Ann. Portrait of Am. Exbhn., 1945, hon. mention Denver Mus., 1946, 1st prize for oil Iowa State Fair Exhbn., 1946, 51, 53, 55, 1st prize First Biennial Walker Art Ctr., Mpls., 1947, Minn. Centennial award, 1949, Edmundson trustee prize Des Moines Art Ctr., 1950, 1st prize, 1952, 53, 1st prize Davenport Mcpl. Art Gallery, 1950, Rosenfield Collection purchase prize Des Moines Art Ctr., 1959, Childe Hassam purchase prize, 1974, Benjamin Altman prize NAD, 1977, 91, Henry Ward Ranger Fund purchase prize, 1979, 86, Edwin Palmer Meml. award, 1981, Adolph and Clara Obrig prize NAD, 1993, 95. Mem. NAD. Office: Kraushaar Galleries 724 5th Ave New York NY 10019-4106

LECHELT, EUGENE CARL, psychology educator; b. Edmonton, Alta., Can., Dec. 26, 1942; s. Adolph Carl and Natalie (Klapstein) L.; m. Sandra Dona Morris, Dec. 18, 1965; 1 child, David Patrick. B.Sc., U. Alta., 1964, M.Sc., 1966, Ph.D., 1969. Research assoc., lectr. Princeton U., N.J., 1969-72; asst. prof. dept. psychology U. Alta., Edmonton, 1972-76, assoc. prof., 1976-82, prof., 1982—, chmn., 1986—. Recipient Rutherford Teaching award, 1985, Vol. award Fed. Govt. of Can., 1994; U. Alta. fellow, 1968-69; Social Scis. Research Council Can. fellow, 1978-79. Mem. Psychonomic Soc., Can. Psychol. Assn., AAAS, N.Y. Acad. Scis., Sigma Xi. Home: 11723-91 Ave, Edmonton, AB Canada T6G 1B1 Office: U Alta, Dept Psychology, Edmonton, AB Canada T6G 2E9

LECHEVALIER, HUBERT ARTHUR, microbiology educator; b. Tours, Indre et Loire, France, May 12, 1926; came to U.S., 1948; s. Jean Gaston and Marie (Delorme) L.; m. Mary Pfeil, Apr. 10, 1950; children: Marc, Paul. L és Sci., Laval U., 1947, MS, 1948, DSc (hon.), 1983; PhD, Rutgers U., 1951. Asst. prof. Rutgers U., New Brunswick, N.J., 1951-56, assoc. prof., 1956-66, prof. microbiology, 1966-91, assoc. dir. Waksman Inst., 1980-88; prof. emeritus, 1991—; vis. scientist Acad. of Scis. USSR, Moscow, 1958-59, Pasteur Inst., Paris, 1961-62;. Author: (with others) A Guide to the Actinomycetes and Their Antibiotics, 1953, Neomycin--Its Nature and Practical Application, 1958, Antibiotics of Actinomycetes, 1962, Three Centuries of Microbiology, 1965, Hungarian transl., 1971, The Microbes, 1971, Macrophages and Cellular Immunity, 1972, Microbial Ecology, 1974, The Development of Applied Microbiology at Rutgers, 1982; contbr. numerous articles to profl. jours.; 4 patents. Trustee Am. Type Culture Collection, Rockville, Md., 1973-79. Recipient Lindback award 1976, Bergey award 1989; inducted into N.J. Inventors Hall of Fame, 1990. Mem. Soc. Française de Microbiology (hon.), Soc. for Indsl. Microbiology (Charles Thom award 1982).

LECHNER, ALFRED JAMES, JR., federal judge; b. Elizabeth, N.J., Jan. 7, 1948; s. Alfred J. and Marie G. (McCormack) L.; m. Gayle K. Peterson, Apr. 3, 1976; children—Brendan Patrick, Coleman Thomas, Mary Kathleen. B.S., Xavier U., Cin., 1969; J.D., U. Notre Dame, 1972. Bar: N.J. 1972, N.Y. 1973; U.S. Dist. Ct. N.J. 1972, U.S. Dist. Ct. (so. and ea. dists.) N.Y. 1974, U.S. Ct. Appeals (2d cir.) 1974, U.S. Ct. Appeals (3d cir.) 1980, U.S. Supreme Ct. 1975. Assoc. Cadwalader, Wickersham & Taft, N.Y.C., 1972-75, MacKenzie, Welt & Duane, Elizabeth, N.J., 1975-76; ptnr. MacKenzie, Welt, Duane & Lechner, Elizabeth, 1976-84; judge Superior Ct. State N.J., 1984-86; judge U.S. Dist. Ct. N.J., 1986—. Mem. Union County (N.J.) adv. bd. Catholic Community Services, 1981-83, chmn., 1982. Maj. USMCR. Fellow Am. Bar Found.; mem. Assn. Fed. Bar of State N.J. Roman Catholic. Clubs: Friendly Sons of St. Patrick (pres. 1982), Union County. Note and comment editor Notre Dame Law Rev., 1972; contbr. articles to legal jours. Office: US Dist Ct Martin Luther King Jr Fed Bldg & PO Box 999 Newark NJ 07102

LECHNER, BERNARD JOSEPH, consulting electrical engineer; b. N.Y.C., Jan. 25, 1932; s. Barnard Joseph and Lillian Veronica (Stevens) L.; m. Joan Camp Mathewson, Nov. 21, 1953. BSEE, Columbia U., 1957; postgrad., Princeton U., 1957-60. Mem. tech. staff RCA Labs., Princeton, N.J., 1957-62, project leader, 1962-67, group head, 1967-77, lab. dir., 1977-83, staff v.p., 1983-87; cons. Princeton, 1987—; cons. expert on TV matters including high definition TV and flat-panel displays; bd. dirs. Palisades Inst., N.Y.C.; chmn. advr. commn. Mercer County Coll., Trenton, N.J., 1968-85. Contbr. articles to profl. jours.; holder 10 patents. Reader Recording for the Blind, Princeton, 1967-72. Served to cpl. U.S. Army, 1953-55. Recipient David Sarnoff Gold medal RCA Corp., 1962. Fellow Soc. for Info. Display (pres. 1978-80, other offices, Frances Rice Darne award 1971, Beatrice Winner award 1983), IEEE (chpt. chmn. 1964-66, Best Paper award Solid State Circs. Conf. 1966); mem. Soc. Motion Picture & TV Engrs., Am. Relay Radio League, Sigma Xi, Tau Beta Pi, Eta Kappa Nu. Episcopalian. Club: Princeton Sqs. (pres. 1981-87). Avocations: amateur radio, sq. dancing, philately, sailing, swimming. Address: 98 Carson Rd Princeton NJ 08540

LECHOLOP, STEPHEN K., medical center administrator; b. Dillon, S.C., Sept. 11, 1953; s. Michael Stephen Lecholop and Miriam Edna Kinon Sanders; m. Carol Roberts, Nov. 26, 1976; children: Stephen K. II, Timothy R. BSBA, The Citadel, Charleston, S.C., 1975; MBA, Golden Gate U., San Francisco, 1977; MS in Health Svcs. Adminstrn., Ctrl. Mich. U., 1987. Dir. patient adminstrn. Hill Hosp., Ogden, Utah, 1978-79, dir. med. resource mgmt., 1979-80; dir. patient affairs Eglin Regional Hosp., Ft. Walton Beach, Fla., 1980-82; adminstr. Fairford (U.K.) Clinic, 1982-84; assoc. to chief Med. Svc. Corps Surgeon Gen. Office, Washington, 1984-87; chief human resources Regional Office S.W., San Antonio, 1987-91; adminstr. Bergstrom Hosp., Austin, Tex., 1991-93; regional dir. managed care Wilford Hall Med. Ctr., San Antonio, 1993—. Bd. dirs. McAllister Park, San Antonio, 1994—, Blue Gray Ednl. Soc., Washington, 1994—, Donald Wagner Scholarship, San Antonio, 1994—. Col. USAF, 1975—. Named Fed. Young Healthcare Adminstr., AMSUS, 1987. Fellow Am. Coll. Healthcare Execs. (regent 1993—); mem. Am. Coll. Managed Care Adminstrs. (adv. coun. 1995), Healthcare Execs. Group of Wilford Hall. Avocations: golf, music. Home: 17206 Fawn Cloud Ln San Antonio TX 78248 Office: Managed Care Wilford Hall Med Ctr/MC 2200 Bergquist Dr Ste #1 Wilford Hall U S A F Hosp TX 78236

LECKER, ABRAHAM, former banker; b. Rumania, Mar. 29, 1916; came to U.S., 1957; s. Schaje and Lisa (Schimmel) L.; m. Minnie Kamenetzky, Aug. 29, 1954; 1 dau., Lisa Joy. MBA, Cert. Assn. Brit. Inst. Bankers, London, 1947; LLB, Sch. Law, Tel Aviv, 1957; postgrad., Harvard Bus. Sch. With banks in Palestine, 1934-36, Barclays Bank DCO, Palestine, 1936-49; dep. treas., comptroller City of Haifa, Israel, 1949-57; with Exchange Nat. Bank, Chgo., 1957-81; v.p., cashier Exchange Nat. Bank, 1966-73, exec. v.p., 1973-81, dir., 1971-75. Served with Brit. Army, World War II; Served with Israeli Army, 1948-49. Former mem. Am. Jewish Com., Brit. Inst. Bankers, Am. Inst. Bankers, Ill. Mfrs. Assn., Bankers Assn. Fgn. Trade, Internat. Bus. Coun. Chgo., Ill. C. of C., Svc. Corps Ret. Execs. (vol.), Exec. Svc. Corps., Internat. Exec. Svc. Corps. B'nai B'rith. Home: 3750 N Lake Shore Dr Chicago IL 60613-4238

LECKERLING, JON PETER, lawyer; b. Bklyn., Aug. 17, 1948; s. Edward W. and A. Jeanne (Rohrbach) L.; m. Nancy Reihl, July 11, 1970; children: Peter B., Christian E. BS, U.S. Mil. Acad., 1970; JD, Washington & Lee U., 1978. Bar: Conn. 1978. Ptnr. Thompson, Weirs & Barclay, New Haven, 1978-86; v.p., gen. counsel Armtek Corp., New Haven, 1986-88, Echlin, Inc., Branford, Conn., 1990—; mng. dir. Long Wharf Capital Ptnrs., Inc., New Haven, 1988-90; bd. dirs. Brad Eaves, Inc., Madison, Conn. Editor: Washington & Lee U. Law Rev., 1976-78. Capt. U.S. Army, 1970-75. Mem.

ABA, Conn. Bar Assn., New Haven County Bar Assn., Am. Soc. Corp. Secs. Congregational. Home: 19 Grove Ave Madison CT 06443-3257 Office: Echlin Inc 100 Double Beach Rd Branford CT 06405-4906

LECKEY, ANDREW A., financial columnist; b. Chgo., Sept. 22, 1949; s. Alexander and Ellen (Martin) L. B.A., Trinity Coll., Deerfield, Ill., 1971; M.A. in Journalism, U. Mo., 1975; postgrad., Columbia U., 1978-79, Rutgers U., 1981. Fin. editor Oreg. Statesman, Salem, 1975-76; statehouse reporter Phoenix Gazette, 1976-78; fin. columnist Chgo. Sun-Times, 1979-85, Chgo. Tribune and N.Y. Daily News 1985—; fin. commentator Sta. WBEZ, Chgo., 1981-83, Sta. WLS-TV, Chgo., 1983—; syndicated fin. columnist Los Angeles Times Syndicate, 1983-85, Tribune Media Services, 1985—; fin. commentator WLS-TV. Author: Make Money with the New Tax Laws, 1987. Office: WLS-TV 190 N State St Chicago IL 60601-3302 also: Chgo Tribune Co 435 N Michigan Ave Chicago IL 60611

LECKIE, FREDERICK ALEXANDER, mechanical engineer, educator; b. Dundee, Scotland, Mar. 26, 1929; came to U.S., 1978; s. Frederick and Mary Baxter (Barclay) L.; m. Alison Elizabeth Wheelwright, Mar. 30, 1957; children—Gavin Frederick, Gregor Wheelwright, Sean Charles. B.Sc., St. Andrews U., 1949; M.S., Stanford U., 1955, Ph.D., 1957; M.A., Cambridge U., 1958. Cons. civil engr. Mott, Hay & Anderson, London, 1949-51; research asst. Hannover (Ger.) U., 1957-58; lectr. in mech. scis. Cambridge (Eng.) U., 1958-68; fellow, tutor, dir. studies Pembroke Coll., 1959-68; prof. engring. U. Leicester, Eng., 1968-78; prof. theoretical and applied mechanics U. Ill., Urbana, 1978-88; head dept. U. Ill., 1984-88; prof., chmn. dept. mech. engring. U. Calif., Santa Barbara, 1988—. Mem. editorial bd. various tech. jours., including Engring. scis.; author: Matrix Methods in Elastomechanics, 1963, Mechanical Vibrations, 1963, Engineering Plasticity, 1968. Trustee Stoneygate Sch., Leicester, 1974-78, Bedales Sch., Hampshire, 1974-78. Fellow Am. Acad. Mechanics; mem. ASME. Home: 1177 N Ontare Rd Santa Barbara CA 93105-1937 Office: Univ Calif Dept Mech Engring Santa Barbara CA 93106

LECKIE, JAMES OLIVER, engineering educator; b. Denver, May 9, 1939; s. Edward and Maria Anna (Valdez) L.; m. Malinda Ann Mahrt, Feb. 11, 1962; children: Carmela, Raúl, Rafael. BS, San Jose State U., 1964; SM, Harvard U., 1965, PhD, 1970. Asst. prof. engring. San Jose Calif.) State U., 1969-70; asst. prof. engring. Stanford (Calif.) U., 1970-74, assoc. prof., 1974-81, prof., 1981—. Author: Other Homes and Garbage, 1975, More Other Homes and Garbage, 1981, Water chemistry Laboratory Manual, 1980; editor Particulates in Water, 1980. Recipient Engring. award of Distinction San Jose State U., 1983; Fulbright-Hays fellow Internat. Communications Agy., 1979; Mellon Found. fellow, 1974; Stanford U. fellow, 1982. Mem. Geochem. Soc., Am. Chem. Soc., ASCE (Rudolf Hering medal 1981), Am. Soc. Limnology and Oceanography. Office: Stanford U Dept Civil Engring Stanford CA 94305

LE CLAIR, CHARLES GEORGE, artist, retired dean; b. Columbia, Mo., May 23, 1914; s. Carl Amie and Marie (Fess) LeC.; m. Margaret Foster, May 30, 1945 (dec. Nov. 1992). BS, MS, U. Wis., 1935; posgrad., Academie Ranson, Paris, 1937; grad. study, Columbia U., 1940-41. Instr. art U. Ala., 1935-36, asst. prof., head dept., 1937-42; asst. prof. art, head dept. Albion Coll., 1942-43; tchr. painting and design Albright Art Sch., Buffalo, 1943-46; assoc. prof., head dept. Chatham Coll., 1946-52, prof., 1952-60; dean Tyler Sch. Art, Temple U., Phila., 1960-74; dean emeritus Tyler Sch. Art, Temple U., 1981—, prof. painting, 1974-81, chmn. painting and sculpture dept., 1979-81; established Tyler Sch. Art, Rome, Italy, 1966. Author: The Art of Watercolor, 1985, rev. edit. full color, 1994, Color in Contemporary Painting, 1991; contbg. author: Everything You Ever Wanted to Know About Oil Painting, 1994; works exhibited Pa. Acad., Met. Mus. Art, Carnegie Inst., Whitney Mus., Corcoran Mus., Chgo. Art Inst., Richmond Mus., Butler Mus. Art, Am. Watercolor Soc., Bklyn. Mus.; one-man shows include Carnegie Inst., 1954, Salpeter Gallery, N.Y.C., 1956, 59, 65, Rochester Inst. Tech., 1958, Phila. Art Alliance, 1962, 73, Franklin and Marshall Coll., 1969, Galleria 88, Rome, 1970, Left Bank Gallery, Wellfleet, 1983, 87, 40-yr. Retrospective, Temple U., 1978, Visual Images, Wellfleet, 1978, 79, 80, Am. Acad. and Inst. Arts and Letters, 1978, Gross-McCleaf Gallery, Phila., 1979, 81, 96, More Gallery Phila., 1983, 87, 89. Fellow Fund for Advancement Edn. Ford Found., 1952-53; named Pitts. Artist of Year, 1957. Subject of Elizabeth Leonard's book Painting Flowers, 1986. Home: 1810 Rittenhouse Sq Philadelphia PA 19103-5837

LECLERC, DENISE, college dean; 3 children. BSc Pharm., U. Montreal, Que., MSc Pharm. in Bacteriology, diploma in hosp. pharmacy, 1962, PhD, 1966. Prof. health adminstrn. and hosp. pharmacy U. Montreal, 1966-70, dean faculty of pharmacy, 1990—; prof., rschr. Institut Nat. Rsch. Sci., U. Que., 1970-71; pres., dir. gen. coun. of pharmacology Dept. Social Affairs, Que., 1971-75; dir. bur. drug quality Drugs Directorate, Health Protection Br. Health and Welfare, Can., 1975-82; exec. dir. Can. blood com. Conf. Ministers of Health and Health and Welfare Can., 1982-88; dir. gen. Health Ins. Directorate Health and Welfare Can., 1988-90; gov. Coll. Pharmacists of Que., 1969-73; cons. in field; lectr. U. Paris XI, 1991 mem. Can. delegation to World Health Assembly, Geneva, 1978, to Pan-Am. Conf., Granada Island, 1978, to Coun. of Europe, Strasbourg, 1984; rep. Health and Welfare Can. to GATT, 1981; mem. Can. Delegation to China, 1982; coord. study on plasma fractionation Interprovincial Conf. Ministers of Health of Can., 1987-88; mem. Bur. Coord. of teaching hosps. affiliated with U. Montreal, 1990—. Mem. blood svcs. adv. com. Can. Red Cross Soc., 1982-89; mem. Nat. Adv. Com. on AIDS, 1984-85; U. Montreal rep. to bd. dirs. St.-Luc Hosp., 1991—. Recipient award of achievement Can. Pharm. Assn., 1990; named Woman of Yr., 1991. Mem. World Assn. Francophone Faculties of Pharmacy (v.p. 1990—), Assn. Deans of Faculties of Pharmacy of Can. (pres. 1993—). Office: U Montreal, Faculty of Pharmacy, Montreal, PQ Canada H3C 3J7

LECLERC, PAUL, library director; b. Lebanon, N.H., May 28, 1941; s. Louis and M. Juliette (Trottier) LeC; m. Judith Ginsberg, Oct. 26, 1980; 1 child, Adam Louis. BS, Coll. Holy Cross, 1963; student, U. Paris, 1963-64; MA, Columbia U., 1966, PhD with distinction, 1969; LHD (hon.), L.I. U., 1994, Coll. of the Holy Cross, 1994. Assoc. prof. French Union Coll., Schenectady, 1969-79, chmn. dept. modern langs. and lit., 1972-77, chmn. humanities div., 1975-77; univ. dean for acad. affairs CUNY, 1979-84; provost and acad. v.p. Baruch Coll., CUNY, 1984-88; pres. Hunter Coll. CUNY, 1988-93; pres., CEO New York Public Library, 1994—; bd. dirs. N.Y. Alliance for Pub. Schs., N.Y.C., 1981-84, El Museo del Barrio, The Feminist Press; pres. N.Y. Tchr. Edn. Conf. Bd., Albany, N.Y., 1983-84. Author: Voltaire and Crebillon Pere, 1972, Voltaire's Rome Sauvée, 1992; co-editor: Lettres d'André Morelet, vol. I, 1991, vol. II, 1994; contbr. articles to profl. jours. Decorated officier Palmes Académiques (France); grantee NEH, 1971, 79, Am. Coun. Learned Socs., 1973, Ford Found., 1979. Mem. MLA, Am. Soc. for 18th Century Studies. Office: NY Pub Libr Fifth Ave & 42nd St New York NY 10018

LECLERCQ, JACQUES JEAN, retail grocery execrutive; b. Brussels, Aug. 15, 1929; came to U.S., 1981; s. Jean Louis and Marguerite (Francois) LeC.; m. Therese Blaton, Sept. 12, 1954 (div. 1983); 1 child, Sophie; m. Winnie Mae Chandler, Mar. 16, 1983; 1 child, Sophie. BSBA, U. Antwerp, 1951. With La Couverture, Alost, Belgium, 1954-57, Dehaize The Lion Am., Inc., Atlanta, 1957—; dir. Food Lion, Inc., Salisbury, N.C., 1974—, Johnson Wax/Belgium, Brussels, Le Lion/Belgium; pres. Delhaize/Am., Atlanta, 1981—; site cons. Wakefern Food Corp., Edison, N.J., 1987—. Res. It. Belgian Army, 1952-54. Decorated Order of Merit French Govt., Order of Merit Belgian Govt., Order of Merit Italian Govt. Mem. Food Mktg. Inst., Internat. Assn. Chain Stores, World Trade Club, Tastevin Club, Cherokee Club. Republican. Roman Catholic. Avocations: swimming, travel. Home: 3224 W Andrews Ct NW Atlanta GA 30305-2015 Office: Delhaize The Lion Am Inc 950 E Paces Ferry Rd NE Atlanta GA 30326-1119

LECOMPTE, ELIZABETH, theater director; b. Summit, N.J., Apr. 28, 1944. BS, Skidmore COll., 1967. Dir. Wooster Group, N.Y.C., 1980—. Director: Frank Dell's The Temptation of Saint Antony, 1987, Brace Up!, 1991, Fish Story, 1993, The Emperor Jones, 1994, The Hairy Ape, 1995. MacArthur fellow, 1995; recipient Obie award for Point Judith. Office: The Wooster Group PO Box 654 Canal St New York NY 10013*

LECOMPTE, ROGER BURTON, management consultant; b. Cin., May 22, 1942; s. Joseph Edward and Lefa May (Ayars) LeC.; m. Margaret Morgan, 1969 (div. 1971); m. Helen Lida Smits, Aug. 28, 1976; 1 child, Theodore Edward. BA, U. Cin., 1965; MBA, U. Pa., 1975. Cons. alt. delivery systems Blue Cross Assn., Chgo., 1971-73; asst. to pres. Albert Einstein Med. Ctr., Phila., 1975-77; cons. Lewin & Assocs., Washington, 1977-81; v.p. planning Middlesex Hosp., Middletown, Conn., 1981-93; ind. cons., 1993—; prin. The Futures Group, Glastonbury, Conn., 1993—; pres. LeCompte & Co., 1993—; bd. dirs. Aetna Health Plan of So. New Eng.; vol. US Peace Corps, Kumba, Cameroon, 1965-67; vice-chmn. Vis. Nurses of Lower Valley, Essex, Conn., 1983-86. Author/editor: Prepaid Group Practice Manual, 1973. Mem. bd. edn. Essex Elem. Sch., 1985-91, chmn. sch. bldg. com., 1987-93; vestryman St. John's Episcopal Ch., Essex, 1988-92. Democrat. Home: 81 Main St Ivoryton CT 06442

LE COMTE, EDWARD SEMPLE, author, educator; b. N.Y.C., May 28, 1916; s. John Radway and Mary (Semple) Le C.; m. Marie Munzer, Jan. 19, 1945; 1 son, Douglas Munzer. A.B., Columbia, 1939, A.M., 1940, Ph.D. 1943. Instr. English Columbia, 1943-45; asst. prof. English U. Calif.-Berkeley, 1945-48; asst. prof. English Columbia U., 1948-56, assoc. prof., 1956-64; prof. English SUNY-Albany, 1964-81, prof. emeritus, 1981—. Author: Endymion in England: The Literary History of a Greek Myth, 1944, Yet Once More: Verbal and Psychological Pattern in Milton, 1953, A Dictionary of Last Words, 1955, The Long Road Back, 1957, He and She, 1960, A Milton Dictionary, 1961, Grace to a Witty Sinner: A Life of Donne, 1965, The Notorious Lady Essex, 1969, The Man Who Was Afraid, 1969, Milton's Unchanging Mind, 1973, Poets' Riddles: Essays in Seventeenth-Century Explication, 1975, Sly Milton: The Meaning Lurking in the Contexts of His Quotations, 1976, Milton and Sex, 1978, The Professor and the Coed, 1979, A Dictionary of Puns in Milton's English Poetry, 1981, I, Eve, 1988, Milton Re-viewed: Ten Essays, 1991, Carnal Sin, 1994; also various articles in scholarly jours. on 17th Century lit.; editor: Paradise Lost and Other Poems, 1961, Justa Edovardo King, 1978. Mem. Milton Soc. (hon. scholar), P.E.N., MLA, Phi Beta Kappa. Home: PO Box 143 North Egremont MA 01252-0143

LECOURS, MICHEL, electrical engineering educator; b. Montreal, Que., Can., Aug. 1, 1940; s. Henri and Germaine (L'Archeveque) L.; m. Almut Lange, July 14, 1966; children: Christiane, Mireille, Jean-Yves. BScA, Ecole Poly., Montreal, 1963; PhD, Imperial Coll., London, 1966. Registered profl. engr., Que. Mem. sci. staff Bell-No. Rsch., Ottawa, Ont., Can., 1971-72; prof. elec. engring. U. Laval, Quebec City, Que., 1967—, head dept., 1975-77, vice dean, 1977-85; cons. Lab-Volt (Que.) Ltd., Quebec City, 1981—; vis. researcher Nippon Tel. & Tel., Yokosuka, Japan, 1986. Contbr. numerous articles on electronics and communications to sci. jours.; patentee for short range high resolution radar. Recipient ann. merit award Ecole Poly., 1986. Fellow Can. Soc. for Elec. and Computer Engring., Engring. Inst. Can.; mem. IEEE (sr.), Order Engrs. Que. (sr.). Office: Laval Univ, Dept Elec Engring, Quebec, PQ Canada G1K 7 P4

LE DAIN, GERALD ERIC, retired Canadian Supreme Court justice; b. Montreal, Que., Can., Nov. 27, 1924; s. Eric George and Antoinette Louise (Whithard) Le D.; m. Cynthia Roy, Sept. 13, 1947; children—Jacqueline, Catherine, Barbara, Caroline, Eric, Jennifer. B.C.L., McGill U., Montreal, 1949; LLD (hon.), McGill U., 1985; Docteur del'Universite, U. Lyon, France, 1950; LL.D. (hon.), York U., Toronto, 1976, Concordia U., Montreal, 1976; D.C.L. (hon.), Acadia U., N.S., 1978. Bar: Que. 1949, Ont. 1968; created Queen's counsel 1961. Asso. prof. law McGill U., 1953-59, prof., 1966-67; dean, prof. Osgoode Hall Law Sch., York U., 1967-72, prof., 1972-75; practiced law with Walker, Martineau & Co., Montreal, 1950-53; with legal dept. CDN Internat Pap Co., Montreal, 1959-61; ptnr. Riel, LeDain & Co., Montreal, 1961-66; judge Fed. Ct. of Appeal of Can., Ottawa, Ont., 1975-84; judge Supreme Ct. Can., Ottawa, 1984-88, ret., 1988. Contbr. articles to legal jours. Chmn. Commn. of Inquiry Into Non-Med. Use of Drugs (Le Dain Commn.), 1969-73. Served with arty. Can. Army, 1943-46, France, Germany. Recipient Elizabeth Torrance Gold medal McGill U., 1949, Companion of the Order of Can., 1989, Justice Gerald LeDain award, Drug Policy Found., ,1990; MacDonald Travelling scholar, 1949-50. Club: Rideau (Ottawa).

LEDBETTER, CALVIN REVILLE, JR. (CAL LEDBETTER), political science educator, university dean, former legislator; b. Little Rock; s. Calvin Reville Sr. and Virginia Mae (Campbell) L.; m. Mary Brown Williams, July 26, 1953; children: Grainger, Jeffrey (dec.), Snow. BA, Princeton U., 1951; LLB, U. Ark., 1954; PhD, Northwestern U., 1960. Bar: Ark., 1954. Pvt. practice Little Rock, 1954; mem. faculty dept. polit. sci. U. Ark., Little Rock, 1960—, now prof., head dept., 1968-78, dean, 1978-88; cons. law enforcement program, advisor pre-law program; mem. Ark. Ho. of Reps., 1967-76; chmn. spl. legis. com. on legis. orgn.; vice chmn. legis. com. state agys. and govt. affairs; cons. pub. schs.; mem. Nat. Adv. Com. on Criminal Justice Goals and Standards; mem. adv. com. Nat. Inst. Law Enforcement and Criminal Justice; election night analyst for Ark. congl. and Presdl. elections ABC, 1964-84. Co-author: Politics in Arkansas: The Constitutional Experience, 1972, The Arkansas Plan: A Case Study in Public Policy, 1979, Arkansas Becomes a State, 1985, Carpenter from Conway: George W. Donaghey as Governor of Arkansas 1909-1913, 1993; contbr. articles, book reviews to profl. jours. Mem. Ark. Adv. Coun. on Pub., Elem. and Secondary Edn.; Gov.'s rep. So. Regional Growth Policies Bd.; mem. Ark. Legis. Coun.; del. Ark. Constl. Conv., 1979, v.p., 1979-80; chmn. law enforcement and criminal justice task force Nat. Legis. Conf. Former chmn. coll. and univ. sect. United Fund; del. Dem. Nat. Conv., 1968, 84; mem. exec. com. Ark. Young Dems.; bd. dirs. Health and Welfare Coun. Pulaski County; trustee Philander Smith Coll., chmn. council community advisers; sec. bd. dirs. St. Vincent's Infirmary; bd. dirs. Ark. Humanities Coun., 1989-93, v.p., 1991-93, pres. 1993-94; bd. trustees Ark. Mus. Sci. and History. Served with JAGC AUS, 1955-57. Recipient award for outstanding contbn. to humanities Little Rock Arts and Humanities Commn., 1993; named Educator of Yr., Greater Little Rock Fedn. Women's Clubs, 1968. Mem. ABA, Ark. Bar Assn. (Writing Excellence award 1985-86), Pulaski County Bar Assn., Nat. Conf. State Legislators (exec. com.), Nat. Conf. Acad. Deans (pres. 1987-88), Am. Polit. Sci. Assn., So. Polit. Sci. Assn., Ark. Polit. Sci. Assn. (pres. 1980-81), Ark. Acad. Sci., Am. Acad. Polit. and Social Sci., Ark. Hist. Assn., Ark. Edn. Assn., Pulaski County Hist. Soc. (bd. dirs. 1988-90), Ark. Hist. Commn. (v.p. 1989—, pres. 1990—), Rotary (pres. West Little Rock chpt. 1987-88). Presbyterian. Home: 4322 I St Little Rock AR 72205-2054 Office: Univ Ark Little Rock Polit Sci Dept Little Rock AR 72204

LEDBETTER, DAVID OSCAR, lawyer; b. Santa Rosa, Calif., Mar. 16, 1950; s. Oscar Smith Ledbetter and Nova Nell (Huckaby) Kramer; m. Judith Louise Fischer, Dec. 14, 1976; children: Hannah J., Jordan B. BA, U. Redlands, 1972; JD, Hastings Coll. Law, 1977. Bar: Calif. 1977, D.C. 1986, Va. 1987. Assoc. Moran, Urich & Evans, San Francisco, 1977-79; trial atty. land and natural resource divsn. U.S. Dept. Justice, Washington, 1979-85; assoc., counsel, ptnr. Hunton & Williams, Richmond, Va., 1985—; bd. adv. Chem. Waste Litigation Reporter, Washington, 1983—. Co-author: Environmental Law Practice Guide, 1992; co-author, editor: Outline RCRA, Cercla Enforcement Issues and Holdings, 1994; contbr. articles to profl. jours. Bd. dirs. John Tyler C.C. Found., Chester, Va., 1992—; ednl. adv. coun. Charles City (Va.) County Vocat., 1987—. Mem. ABA (vice chair spl. com. toxic and environ. torts), Va. State Bar Assn., Calif. Bar Assn., Bar Assn. D.C., Environ. Law Inst., Charles City Ruritan Club. Democrat. Methodist. Avocations: gardening, fishing. Home: 16530 The Glebe Ln Charles City VA 23030 Office: Hunton & Williams 951 East Byrd St Richmond VA 23219-4074

LEDBETTER, JEFFREY A., immunologist. Rsch. fellow dept. immunnother Oncogen, 1981—. Office: Bristol-Myers Squibb Pharm Rsch Inst Dept Cell Immunology 3005 First Ave Seattle WA 98121-1069*

LEDBETTER, RANDI RAE, obstetrican/gynecologist; b. Portland, Oreg., June 24, 1952; d. James Edward Wagenblast and Shiela Faye (Mathis) Rhyne; m. Gordon Kirk Ledbetter, Feb. 14, 1971. BA in Biology, Linfield Coll., 1974; MD, Oreg. Health Scis. U., 1978. Diplomate Am. Bd. Ob-Gyn., Am. Bd. Family Practice. Intern, resident Family Practice Residency of Idaho, Boise, 1978-81; pvt. practice Boise Family Practice, 1981-88; resident in ob-gyn. Kaiser Found. Hosp., San Francisco, 1988-91; pvt. practice Women's Healthcare Assocs., Portland, Oreg., 1991—; chmn. laparoscopy com. ob-gyn. dept. St. Vincent's Hosp., Portland, 1993—. Mem. women's task force Women's Life, Boise, 1985-88. Fellow Am. Coll. Ob-Gyn.; mem. Oreg. Med. Assn., Washington County Med. Soc. (bd. dirs.), Porsche Club Am., Sports Car Club Am., Team Continental (dir. med.). Republican. Avocations: autoracing, gardening, computers. Home: 12929 NW Laidlaw Rd Portland OR 97229 Office: Women's Healthcare Assocs 9155 SW Barnes Rd Ste 340 Portland OR 97225

LEDDICOTTE, GEORGE COMER, business executive, consultant; b. Oak Ridge, Tenn., May 28, 1947; s. George W. Leddicotte and Virginia (Comer) Leddicotte Stratton; m. Connie Laverne Sterrett, Jan. 25, 1969; 1 child, Matthew Sterrett. BA in Polit. Sci., U. Mo., 1970. Cert. relocation profl. Customer service supr. Crown Zellerbach, San Francisco, 1973-74; exec. recruiter Christopher & Long, St. Louis, 1974; regional ops. mgr. Curtin Matheson Scientific, Inc., Houston, 1974-80; regional mgr./mng. cons. Merrill Lynch Relocation Mgmt., White Plains, N.Y., 1980-82, regional v.p. nat. accounts, 1982-83, regional v.p. govt. svcs., 1983-84; dir. govt. svcs. Coldwell Banker Relocation Mgmt., Washington, 1984-85; dir. sales., account mgmt. Homequity, Wilton, Conn., 1985-87; v.p. nat. sales Premier Relocation Svcs., Inc., Irvine, Calif., 1987-88; v.p., sr. mng. cons. Premier Decision Mgmt., Irvine, 1988—; pres., CEO Feasibility Inc., Raleigh, N.C., 1988—; pres., COO Carolina Relocation Group, Rocky Mount, N.C., 1994. Pub. Relocation Update, 1993—. First lt. U.S. Army, 1970-72, Korea. Mem. Am. Mktg. Assn., Am. Mgmt. Assn., Soc. for Human Resource Mgmt., Employee Relocation Coun. Avocations: sailig, golf, skiing. Home and Office: Feasibility Inc 8000 Glenbrittle Way Raleigh NC 27615-4737

LEDDY, SUSAN, nursing school educator; b. N.J., Feb. 23, 1939; d. Bert B. and Helen (Neumann) Kun; children: Deborah, Erin. BS, Skidmore Coll., 1960; MS, Boston U., 1965; PhD, NYU, 1973; cert., Harvard U., 1985. Chair dept. nursing Mercy Coll., Debbs Ferry, N.Y.; dean sch. nursing U. Wyo., Laramie, dean coll. health scis.; dean Sch. Nursing Widener U., Chester, Pa., 1988-93; postdoctoral fellow U. Pa., 1994—. Author: (with M. Pepper) Conceptual Bases of Professional Nursing, 1985, 3d edit., 1993. Bd. dirs. Springfield Hosp., 1992-94. Mem. NLN (bd. dirs. and 1st v.p. 1985-87).

LEDEBUR, LINAS VOCKROTH, JR., lawyer; b. New Brighton, Pa., June 18, 1925; s. Linas Vockroth and Mae (McCabe) L.; m. Conne Ryan, July 3, 1969; children: Gary W., Sally, Nancy, Sandra. Student, Geneva Coll., Beaver Falls, Pa., 1943, 45-46, Muhlenberg Coll., Allentown, Pa., 1943-44; J.D., U. Pitts., 1949. Bar: Pa. 1950. Assoc., then ptnr. Ledebur, McClain & Ledebur, New Brighton, 1950-63; trust mktg. mgr. Valley Nat. Bank Ariz., Phoenix, 1963-72; ptnr. Ledebur & Ledebur, New Brighton, 1972-76; sr. v.p., mgr. state trust div. Fla. Nat. Banks Fla., Inc., Jacksonville, 1976-81; sr. v.p. Fla. Nat. Bank, Jacksonville, 1977-81; pres. Northeastern Trust Co. Fla., N.A., Vero Beach, 1982-86; exec. v.p. PNC Trust Co. Fla., N.A., 1986-87; sole practice Beaver, Pa., 1987—; instr. bus. law Geneva Coll., 1951-52, 88—; past pres. Central Ariz. Estate Planning Council. Chmn. Beaver County chpt. Nat. Found.-March of Dimes, Pa., 1950-63; chmn. com. corrections Pa. Citizens Assn., 1958-63; bd. dirs., counsel Beaver County Mental Health Assn., 1962-63; bd. dirs. Maricopa County chpt. ARC, Ariz. 1968-72. Served with USMC, 1943-45, 51-53. Mem. ABA, Pa. Bar Assn. Home: 652 Bank St Beaver PA 15009-2728

LEDEEN, ROBERT WAGNER, neurochemist, educator; b. Denver, Aug. 19, 1928; s. Hyman and Olga (Wagner) L.; m. Lydia Rosen Hailparn, July 2, 1982. B.S., U. Calif., Berkeley, 1949; Ph.D., Oreg. State U., 1953. Postdoctoral fellow in chemistry U. Chgo., 1953-54; rsch. assoc. in chemistry Mt. Sinai Hosp., N.Y.C., 1956-59; rsch. fellow Albert Einstein Coll. Medicine, Bronx, N.Y., 1959; asst. prof. Albert Einstein Coll. Medicine, 1963-69, assoc. prof., 1969-75, prof., 1975-91; prof., dir. div. neurochemistry U. Medicine and Dentistry N.J., Newark, 1991—. Contbr. articles to profl. jours.; dep. chief editor Jour. Neurochemistry. Mem. neurol. scis. study sect. NIH; mem. study sect. Nat. Multiple Sclerosis Soc. NIH grantee, 1963—; Nat. Multiple Sclerosis Soc. grantee, 1967-74; recipient Humboldt prize, Javits Neurosci. Investigator award. Mem. Internat. Soc. Neurochemistry, Am. Soc. Neurochemistry, Am. Chem. Soc., Am. Soc. Biol. Chemists, N.Y. Acad. Sci. Jewish. Achievements include discoveries in the biochemistry of brain glycolipids and myelin. Home: 8 Donald Ct Wayne NJ 07470-4608 Office: U Medicine and Dentistry NJ Dept Neuroscis 185 S Orange Ave Newark NJ 07103-2714

LEDER, PHILIP, geneticist, educator; b. Washington, Nov. 19, 1934; married; 3 children. A.B., Harvard U., 1956, M.D., 1960. Research assoc. Nat. Heart Inst., Nat. Cancer Inst.; lab chief molecular genetics Nat. Inst. Child Health and Human Devel., NIH, 1972-80; prof. genetics Harvard U. Med. Sch., Boston, Mass., 1980—, now John Emory Andrus prof. genetics; sr. investigator Howard Hughes Med. Inst. Co-author: Molecular Basis of Blood Diseases, 1987; co-editor: Molecular Medicine, 1994. Recipient Albert Lasker Med. Rsch. award, 1987, Nat. Medal of Sci., 1989. Mem. NAS, Inst. Medicine. *

LEDER, SANDRA JUANITA, elementary school educator; b. Stuttgart, Ark., Apr. 17, 1942; d. Everett Samuel and Lorene (Payer) L. BS, U. Cen. Ark., 1963; MEd, McNeese State U., 1976, EdS, 1979; PhD, Fla. State U., 1984. Cert. tchr. grades 1-8, supr., prin., aerospace edn., supr. student tchrs., La.; cert. pvt. pilot. Elem. tchr. DeWitt (Ark.) Pub. Schs., 1963-66, Gillett (Ark.) Pub. Schs., 1966-69; math. tchr. Tulsa County, Tulsa, Okla., 1970; tchr. Calcasieu Parish, Lake Charles, La., 1971-94, Episcopal Day Sch., Lake Charles, La., 1994—; condr., dir. numerous aerospace camps, 1980—; chmn., judge sci. fairs; com. mem. and chmn. self-study com. So. Assn. Colls. and Schs., 1985-86; arranger numerous tours and workshops in field. Manuscript rev. panel Sci. Scope, 1988-91, writer, 1992; TV interviews, 1991—; radio and ednl. TV appearances, Tchr. in Space applicant, 1985; contbr. Metric Curriculum Guide for La., 1978; presenter in field; contbr. articles to profl. jours. Vol. reader NEA, 1990; active outreach com. Episcopal Ch. of Good Shepherd, 1994; pres. Lake Charles Regional Airport Authority, 1991, 95, sec., 1993, v.p. 1994, pres., 1995; mem. gen. adv. coun. Sowela Tech. Inst. 1990; active Mayor's Commn. for Women, 1986-91, fall conf. chmn. resource fair, 1988; founder Lake Charles Ninety-Nines Challenger Ctr.; pres. La. Nat. Airshow Bd., 1993-95, sec. 1993—; bd. dirs. Chenault Airpark Aviation Mus., 1994—; tour organizer. Recipient S.W. Region Frank Brewer Aerospace Edn. award CAP, 1990, Excellence in Aviation Edn. Championship award S.W. region FAA, 1989, Acad. Edn. award Women's History Month, Lake Charles, Great Expectations Tchr. award Sta. KPLC-TV, 1993, Pinnacle award, 1993, NEWMAST award NASA, 1986, STEP award, 1993, Outstanding Young Astronaut Chpt. Leader award 1993; grantee Space Acad., 1988, South Ctrl. Bell, 1991, 93, Olin Corp., 1994. Mem. Nat. Sci. Tchrs. Assn., Nat. Space Soc., La. Assn. Educators (del. to convs. 1977-79, 84, 86), Aircraft Owners and Pilots Assn., Delta Kappa Gamma (pres. 1992-94, legis. com. 1985-86, chair social com. 1987-89, comms. com. chair 1990, 94-95), Kappa Kappa Iota, Phi Delta Kappa. Republican. Episcopalian. Office: Episcopal Day Sch Ch of Good Shepherd 715 Kirkman St Lake Charles LA 70601

LEDERBERG, JOSHUA, geneticist, educator; b. Montclair, N.J., May 23, 1925; s. Zwi Hirsch and Esther (Goldenbaum) L.; m. Marguerite S. Kirsch, Apr. 5, 1968; children: David Kirsch, Anne. BA, Columbia U., 1944; PhD, Yale U., 1947. With U. Wis., 1947-58; prof. genetics Sch. Medicine, Stanford (Calif.) U., 1959-78; pres. Rockefeller U., N.Y.C., 1978-90, Univ. prof., 1990—; bd. dirs. Ann. Revs., Inc., Palo Alto, Calif.; adj. prof. Columbia U., 1990—; mem. adv. com. med. scis. WHO, 1971; mem. bd. sci. advisors Affymax N.V., Palo Alto, Hewlett Packard Inc., Palo Alto, Bellcore, Livingston, N.J., Aviron, Belmont, Calif.; cons. U.S. Def. Sci. Bd., U.S. Dept. Energy, NSF, NIH, NASA, ACDA. Trustee Camille and Henry Dreyfus Found.; bd. dirs. Chem. Industry Inst. Toxicology, N.C. With USN, 1943-45. Recipient Nobel prize in physiology and medicine for rsch. in genetics of bacteria, 1958, U.S. Nat. Medal of Sci., 1989; Sackler Found. scholar. Fellow AAAS, Am. Philos. Soc., Am. Acad. Arts and Scis., N.Y. Acad. Medicine (hon.), Acad. Universelle Cultures (Paris); mem. Inst. Medicine of NAS, Coun. Fgn. Rels., Royal Soc. London (fgn.), N.Y. Acad. Scis. (chmn.), Ordre des Lettres et des Arts (fgn.). Office: Rockefeller U 1230 York Ave Ste 400 New York NY 10021-6341

LEDERER, EDITH MADELON, journalist; b. N.Y.C., Mar. 27, 1943; d. Samuel B. Weiner and Frieda (Rich) Weiner Lederer; adopted d. Irving A. Lederer. B.S. with distinction, Cornell U., 1963; M.A., Stanford, 1964. With Sci. Service, Washington, 1964-65; free-lance writer, 1965-66; mem. staff AP, 1966—, South Vietnam, 1972-73; chief bur. AP, Lima, Peru, 1975; chief Caribbean services, San Juan, P.R., 1975-78; corr. Hong Kong, 1978-81, London, 1982-90, 91—; corr. Gulf War, Saudi Arabia, 1990-91. Recipient resolution Calif. Assembly, 1974, Nat. Press Club award, 1993, Nat. Headliner award, 1994. Mem. Mortar Bd., Phi Kappa Phi, Omicron Nu, Sigma Delta Chi. Address: care Asso Press 50 Rockefeller Plz New York NY 10020-1605 *Women should take more risks to live their dreams, which otherwise turn to nightmares of frustration as empty years pass. It is better to fail and touch the essence of life than to stand forever on the threshold as a gutless spectator.*

LEDERER, MRS. ESTHER P. See LANDERS, ANN

LEDERER, JACK LAWRENCE, personnel director, human resources specialist; b. Oak Park, Ill., July 19, 1940; s. Ludwig George and Netta O. (Olsen) L.; m. Diane D. Lederer, Sept. 1, 1962; children: Chris, Kevin, Kathy. BA in Psychology, Ohio Wesleyan U.; MBA, George Washington U. Career devel. specialist, pers. rsch. specialist, mgmt. intern Nat. Security Agy., 1962-65; regional pers. mgr., corp. mgr. equal employment opportunity, corp. mgr., mgmt. devel. Eastern Airlines Inc., 1965-69; mgr. corp. pers. Celanese Corp., 1969-72; dir. employee rels. multigraphics div. Addressograph-Multigraph Corp., d1972-73; dir. corp. pers. Allis Chalmers Corp., 1974; corp. dir. compensation and manpower resources Fiat-Allis Inc., 1974-75; ptnr., exec. v.p. Meredith Assocs. Inc., 1975-79; pres. Meredith Assocs. Inc. (merged with Alexander & Alexander), 1979-83, Meredith, Lederer & Assocs. Inc., 1983-86; co-founder, pres. Pers. Corp. Am., Norwalk, Conn., 1986-93; Compo Consulting Group, Westport, Conn., 1994—. Founder Conn. POP Warner Football, Weston; chmn. Weston Pks. and Recreation Commn. Def. Dep. fellow National Security Agency. Mem. Nat. Urban League (trustee 1979—). Republican. Office: Compo Consulting Group 495 Post Rd E Westport CT 06880

LEDERER, JEROME, aerospace safety consultant, engineer; b. N.Y.C., Sept. 26, 1902; m. Sarah Bojarsky, Nov. 1, 1935; children: Nancy, Susan. BSc in Mech. Engring., NYU, 1924, M.Engring., 1925. Registered profl. engr., N.Y. Chief engr. Aero Ins. Underwriters, N.Y.C., 1929-40; dir. safety bur. CAB, Washington, 1940-42; mgr. Airlines War Tng. Inst., 1942-44, U.S. Strategic Bombing Survey, 1945; pres., Flight Safety found., 1947-67, pres. emeritus, 1967—; dir. Cornell-Guggenheim Aviation Safety Rsch. Ctr., N.Y.C., 1950-67; dir. Office Manned Space Flight Safety, NASA, Washington, 1967-70, dir. safety, 1970-72; ret., 1972; adj. prof. Inst. Safety and System Mgmt., U. So. Calif. ret.; past mem. adv. council Inst. Nuclear Power Ops., Atlanta, 1980-85; cons., Laguna Hills, Calif., 1974—. Author books and articles on aviation and space safety. Recipient NASA Exceptional Service medal, Daniel Guggenheim medal, Wright Bros. trophy, Amelia Earhart medal, Ziolkowski and Yuri Gagarin medals, Soviet Fedn. Cosmonauts, Von Baumhauer medal Royal Dutch Aero. Soc., Laura Taber Barbour award, many others; named to Safety and Health Hall of Fame Internat., Space Hall of Fame Internat. Fellow AIAA (hon.), Am. Astronautics Assn., Soc. Automotive Engrs., Royal Aero. Soc., Human Factors Soc.; mem. NAE, Airline Pilots Assn. (hon.), Mil. Order Daedalions (hon.), Wings Club (N.Y.). Home: 468D Calle Cadiz-D Laguna Hills CA 92653

LEDERER, MARIE A., state legislator; b. Phila., Oct. 24, 1927; d. Donato and Edith (Vitacolonna) Panosetti; ed. Phila. Public Relations Inst., 1966-67, Temple U., 1973-76; m. William J. Lederer, June 17, 1950; children—Doneda M. Lederer Guyon, William M., Regina M. Instr. polit. sci. Temple U., Phila., 1976-77; exec. dir. Jackson for Pres. Com., 1976; del. Dem. nat. conv., 1976, 84; voter registration chmn. Dem. exec. com., 1978-79; administrv. asst. to Congressman Joseph F. Smith, Pa., 1981-82; asst. to Dep. Auditor Gen. of Pa., 1985; now mem. Pa. Ho. Reps., Harrisburg, Pa. Dir. Southeastern Pa. Heart Assn., 1968-71; mem. bd. dirs. Balch Inst., ARC, U.S.S. Cruiser Olympia Ship; mem. Phila. Art Alliance. Recipient Pa. Ho. of Reps., 1974, certs. of merit U.S. Ho. of Reps., 1982. Roman Catholic. Clubs: Am. Legion Ladies Aux., Hist. Ships Assn., Mexican Soc. Home: 1237 Shackamaxon St Philadelphia PA 19125-3913 Office: Pa Ho of Reps State Capitol Harrisburg PA 17120

LEDERER, MARION IRVINE, cultural administrator; b. Brampton, Ont., Can., Feb. 10, 1920; d. Oliver Bateman and Eva Jane (MacMurdo) L.; m. Francis Lederer, July 10, 1941. Student, U. Toronto, 1938, UCLA, 1942-45. Owner Canoga Mission Gallery, Canoga Park, Calif., 1967—; cultural heritage monument Canoga Mission Gallery, 1974—; Vice pres. Screen Smart Set women's aux. Motion Picture and TV Fund, 1973—; founder sister city program Canoga Park-Taxco, Mexico, 1963; Mem. mayor's cultural task force San Fernando Valley, 1973—; mem. Los Angeles Cultural Affairs Commn., 1980-85. Mem. Los Angeles Cultural Affairs Commn., 1980-85. Recipient numerous pub. service awards from mayor, city council, C. of C. Mem. Canoga Park C. of C. (cultural chmn. 1973-75, dir. 1973-75). Presbyn. Home: PO Box 32 Canoga Park CA 91305-0032 Office: Canoga Mission Gallery 23130 Sherman Way Canoga Park CA 91307-1402

LEDERER, PETER DAVID, lawyer; b. Frankfurt, Fed. Republic Germany, May 2, 1930; came to U.S., 1938; s. Leo and Alice (Freistadt) L.; m. Norma Jean Taylor, June, 1955 (div. 1966); 1 child, Patricia Ann; m. Midori Shimanouchi, Dec. 16, 1966. BA, U. Chgo., 1949, JD, 1957, M Comparative Law, 1958. Bar: Ill. 1959, U.S. Supreme Ct. 1966, N.Y. 1967. Law and behavioral sci. research fellow U. Chgo. Law Sch., 1958-59; ptnr. Baker & McKenzie, Zurich, Switzerland, 1960-66; ptnr. Baker & McKenzie, N.Y.C., 1966-94, of counsel, 1994—; dir. Nuc. Electric Ins. Ltd., Nuc. Mutual Ltd. Mem. vis. com. U. Miami Law Sch., Coral Gables, Fla., 1974—, U. Chgo. Law Sch., 1988-91; adv. bd. Wildlife Preservation Trust Internat., Phila.; dir. Asian-Am. Legal Def. & Edn. Fund, N.Y.C., The Midori Found.; pres. bd. trustees The Calhoun Sch., N.Y.C., 1980-83. With ASS, 1951-53. Mem. ABA, Assn. Bar City of N.Y. (chmn. com. on nuclear law 1987-88, del. to the Union Internat. des Avocats 1989—), Internat. Nuclear Law Assn. Office: Baker & McKenzie 805 Third Ave 29th fl New York NY 10022-7513

LEDERER, RICHARD HENRY, writer, educator, columnist; b. Phila., May 26, 1938; s. Howard Jules and Leah (Perry) L.; m. Rhoda Anne Spangenberg, Aug. 25, 1962 (div. 1986); m. Simone Johanna van Egeren, Nov. 29, 1991; children: Howard Henry, Anne Labarr, Katherine Lee. BA, Haverford Coll., 1959; student, Harvard U., 1959-60, M of Arts and Teaching, 1962; PhD, U. N.H., 1980. Tchr., coach St. Paul's Sch., Concord, N.H., 1962-89; lectr. in field. Author: Anguished English, 1987, Get Thee To a Punnery, 1988, Crazy English, 1989, The Play of Words, 1990, The Miracle of Language, 1991, More Anguished English, 1993, Building Bridge, Literary Trivia, 1994, Nothing Risqué, Nothing Gained, 1995, Adventures of a Verbivore, 1995, The Write Way, 1995; weekly columnist Looking at Language; contbr. over 1000 articles to jours.; broadcaster various radio stas.; numerous TV appearances. Recipient Lifetime Achievement award Columbia Scholastic Press Assn., N.Y.C., 1989; named Internat. Punster of Yr. Internat. Save the Pun Found., Toronto, Can., 1990. Mem. Phi Beta Kappa, Phi Delta Kappa. Avocations: tennis, cards, film. Home: 5 Merrimack St Concord NH 03301 *Whatever you hear about the closing of the American mind and cultural illiteracy, there has never been a more passionate moment in the history of the American love affair with language than right now. I'm exceedingly fortunate to have written books that embrace that passion.*

LEDERER, WILLIAM JULIUS, author; b. N.Y.C., Mar. 31, 1912; s. William J. and Paula (Franken) L.; m. Ethel Hackett, Apr. 21, 1940 (div. Jan. 1965); children: Brian, Jonathan, Bruce; m. Corinne Edwards Lewis, July 1965 (div. May 1970). B.S., U.S. Naval Acad. 1936; assoc. Nieman fellow, Harvard U., 1950-51. Enlisted USN, 1930, commd. ensign, 1936, advanced through grades to capt., 1952, ret., 1958; Far East corr. Reader's Digest, 1958-63; lectr. colls. and univs., 1949—. Author in residence, Harvard U., 1996-97; Author: All the Ship's at Sea, 1950, The Last Cruise, 1950, Spare Time Article Writing for Money, 1953, Ensign O'Toole and Me, 1957, A Nation of Sheep, 1961, Timothy's Song, 1965, Pink Jade, 1966, (with Eugene Burdick) The Ugly American, 1958, Sarkhan, 1965, Our Own Worst Enemy, 1967, (with Don D. Jackson) The Mirages of Marriage, 1968,

---

(with Joe Pete Wilson) Complete Cross-Country Skiing and Ski Touring, 1970, (with others) Marriage for and Against, Marital Choices, A Happy Book of Happy Stories, I, Giorghos, 1984, Creating a Good Relationship, 1984. Mem. Signet Soc., Authors Guild, Acad. Orthomolecular Psychiatry, European Acad. Preventive Medicine, Internat. Acad. Preventive Medicine, Internat. Coll. Applied Nutrition, Sigma Delta Chi. Clubs: Lotos, Trap Door Spiders, National Press, Harvard Faculty. Address: P O Box 248 Peacham VT 05862-0248 *If one works at being joyful and physically functional, almost everything else seems to come along on its own. Put energy into the "here and now" and do not distract from it by worrying about either the past or the future.*

LEDERIS, KAROLIS PAUL (KARL LEDERIS), pharmacologist, educator, researcher; b. Noreikoniai, Lithuania, Aug. 1, 1920; arrived in Can., 1969; s. Paul Augustus and Franciska (Danisevicius) L.; m. Hildegard Gallistl, Feb. 28, 1952; children: Aldona Franciska, Edmund Paul. Diploma, Tchrs. Coll., Siauliai, Lithuania, 1939; BSc, U. Bristol, U.K., 1958, PhD, 1961, DSc, 1968. Jr. lectr., then lectr. and reader U. Bristol, 1961-69; prof. pharmacology U. Calgary, Alta., Can., 1969-89, prof. emeritus, 1989—; vis. prof. univs. in Fed. Republic Germany, Austria, Chile, Argentina, Sri Lanka, Switzerland, Lithuania, France, , USA, USSR, 1963-79, U. Bristol, 1979, U. Kyoto, Japan, 1980; career investigator, mem., chair grants com. Med. Rsch. Coun., Ottawa, Ont., Can., 1970-89, coun. mem., exec., 1983-90; mem. internat. com. Centres Excellence Networks, Ottawa, 1988-89. Author, editor: 5 books on hypothalamic hormones; editor in chief Jour. Exptl. and Clin. Pharmacology, 1977-89; contbr. approximately 350 book chpts. and articles to profl. jours.; patentee hormonal peptides. Recipient Upjohn award in pharmacology, 1990, various fellowships and scholarships in U.K., Fed. Republic of Germany, U.S. Fellow NAS, Royal Soc. Can.; mem. Western Pharmacological Soc. (pres. 1982-83), pharm., physiol., endocrinological, biochem. socs. U.K., Can., U.S., Lithuanian Club (London), Men's Can. Club, Cabot Yacht and Cruise Club (Bristol). Avocations: music, sailing, fishing, hunting, golf. Home: 147 Carthew St, Comox, BC Canada V9M 1T4 Office: U Calgary, Health Scis Centre, Calgary, AB Canada T2N 4N1

LEDERMAN, BRUCE RANDOLPH, lawyer; b. N.Y.C., Oct. 12, 1942; s. Morris David and Frances Lederman; m. Ellen Kline, Aug. 4, 1979; children: Eric, Jeffrey, Joshua. Cert., U. London, 1963; BS Econs. cum laude, U. Pa., 1964; LLB cum laude, Harvard U., 1967. Bar: U.S. Dist. Ct. (cen. dist.) Calif. 1967. Law clk. to Hon. Irving Hill U.S. Dist. Ct. Cen. Dist., L.A., 1967-68; sr. ptnr. Latham & Watkins, L.A., 1968—. Avocations: bicycle riding, real estate investments. Office: Latham & Watkins 633 W 5th St Los Angeles CA 90071-2005

LEDERMAN, FRANK L., scientist, research center administrator; b. Buffalo, Aug. 19, 1949; s. Sol J. and Carol S. (Dankman) L.; m. Daphna Kaplansky, Aug. 8, 1993. BS in Math., Carnegie-Mellon U., 1971, MS in Physics, 1971; MS in Physics, U. Ill., 1972, PhD, 1975. Fellow U. Pa., Phila., 1975; physicist R & D ctr. GE Corp., Schenectady, N.Y., 1976-78, mgr. ultrasound program, 1978-80, mgr. energy systems mgmt. br., 1981-82, acting mgr. liaison ops., 1983-84, mgr. power electronics systems br., 1984-87, mgr. programs and resources, 1988; v.p., dir. rsch. Noranda Inc., Pointe Claire, Que., Can., 1988-91, sr. v.p. tech., 1992-95; v.p. rsch., devel. and engring. Aluminum Co. Am., Alcoa Center, Pa., 1995—. Contbr. articles to profl. jours.; patentee in field. Mem. IEEE, IRI, Am. Phys. Soc. Home: 4011 Pin Oak Ln Murrysville PA 15668 Office: Alcoa Tech Ctr 100 Technical Dr New Kensington PA 15069

LEDERMAN, IRA SETH, insurance executive, lawyer; b. N.Y.C., Apr. 25, 1953; m. Carol Susan Jupiter; children: Rachael, Aaron. Bar: N.Y. 1980. Assoc. Rein Mound and Cotton, N.Y.C., 1979-83; assoc. counsel W.R. Berkley Corp., Greenwich, Conn., 1983-86, v.p., ins. counsel, 1986-89, v.p., asst. gen. counsel, 1989—. Mem. ABA, N.Y. County Lawyers Assn., The Corp. Bar Assn., Am. Soc. Corp. Secs. Office: W R Berkley Corp 165 Mason St Greenwich CT 06830-6608

LEDERMAN, LAWRENCE, lawyer, writer, educator; b. N.Y.C., Sept. 8, 1935; s. Herman Jack and Lillian (Rosenfeld) L.; children: Leandra, Evin. B.A., Bklyn. Coll., 1957; LL.B., N.Y.U., 1966. Bar: N.Y. 1968; Law clk. chief justice Calif. Sup. Ct., 1966-67; assoc. Cravath, Swaine & Moore, N.Y.C., 1968-74; ptnr. Wachtell, Lipton, Rosen & Katz, N.Y.C., 1975-91; ptnr., chmn. corp. practice Milbank, Tweed, Hadley & McCloy, 1991—; adj. prof. law N.Y.U. Law Sch. Law, 1974—; Chmn. bd. Phoenix House Devel. Corp., mem. Phoenix House Found. Author: Tombstones: A Lawyer's Tales from the Takeover Decades, 1992. Bd. dirs. One to One Partnership Inc. Served with U.S. Army, 1957-59. Mem. ABA, N.Y. State Bar Assn., Order of the Coif . Contbr. articles to profl. jours. Office: Milbank Tweed Hadley & McCloy 1 Chase Manhattan Plz New York NY 10005-1401

LEDERMAN, LEON MAX, physicist, educator; b. N.Y.C., July 15, 1922; s. Morris and Minna (Rosenberg) L.; m. Florence Gordon, Sept. 19, 1945; children: Rena S., Jesse A., Heidi R.; m. Ellen Carr, Sept. 17, 1981. B.S., CCNY, 1943, DSc (hon.), 1980; A.M., Columbia U., 1948, Ph.D., 1951; DSc (hon.), No. Ill. U., 1984, U. Chgo., 1985, Ill. Inst. Tech., 1987. Assoc. in physics Columbia, N.Y.C., 1951; asst. prof. Columbia, 1952-54, assoc. prof., 1954-58; prof. Columbia U., 1958-89, Eugene Higgins prof. physics, 1972-79; Frank L. Sulzberger prof. physics U. Chgo., 1989-92; dir. Fermi Nat. Accelerator Lab., Batavia, Ill., 1979-89, dir. emeritus, 1989—; Pritzker prof. physics Ill. Inst. Tech., Chgo., 1992—; dir. Nevis Labs., Irvington, N.Y., 1962-79; guest scientist Brookhaven Nat. Labs., 1955; cons. Nat. Accelerator Lab., European Orgn. for Nuclear Rsch. (CERN), 1970—; mem. high energy physics adv. panel AEC, 1966-70; mem. adv. com. to div. math. and phys. scis. NSF, 1970-72; sci. advisor to gov. State of Ill., 1989-93. Author: Quarks to the Cosmos, 1989, The God Particle, 1993; also over 200 articles. 1st lt. Signal Corps, AUS, 1943-46. Recipient Nat. Medal of Sci., 1965, Townsend Harris medal CUNY, 1973, Elliot Cresson medal Franklin Inst., 1976, Wolf prize, 1982, Nobel prize in physics, 1988, Enrico Fermi prize, 1992; Guggenheim fellow, 1958-59, Ford Found. fellow European Ctr. for Nuclear Rsch., Geneva, 1958-59, fellow NSF, 1967. Fellow AAAS (pres. 1990-91, chmn. 1992-93), Am. Phys. Soc.; mem. NAS, Italian Phys. Soc., Aspen Inst. Physics (pres. 1990-92), Ill. Math. Sci. Acad. (vice chmn. 1985—), Tchrs. Acad. for Math. and Sci. in Chgo. (co-chmn. 1990—). Office: Ill Inst Tech Dept Physics 3300 S Federal St Chicago IL 60616-3732

LEDERMAN, LEONARD LAWRENCE, government research executive; b. N.Y.C., Nov. 23, 1931; s. Hyman G. and Yetta (Dreyfus) L.; m. Florence Krinsky, May 19, 1956; children: Hugh Daniel, Steven Mark, Michael Jay. BA in Econs., CCNY, 1953; MA in Econs., NYU, 1957; postgrad., Columbia U., 1955-56, Princeton U., 1957-58. Statistician Barnard Rsch. Inc., N.Y.C., 1953-54; rsch. analyst Maidenform Inc., Bayonne, N.J., 1954-58; asst. mgr. mfg. dept., exec. sec. comm. on sci. and tech., also comml. use atomic energy U.S. C. of C., Washington, 1958-62; fellow, sr. rsch. advisor Battelle Meml. Inst., Washington, 1963-70; dep. head Office Econ. and Manpower Studies; dir. Office Exploratory Rsch. and Problem Assessment, Rsch. Applied to Nat. Needs Directorate, NSF, Washington, 1970-72; detailed to Exec. Office of Pres. as program mgr. Productivity in New Tech. Opportunities Program, 1971-72; dir. Office Nat. R & D Assessment, 1972-76; acting dep. asst. dir. planning and programs Directorate for Sci., Technol. and Internat. Affairs, 1976-77, dep. asst. dir. and dir. strategic planning and assessment, 1977-82, 90—, dir. strategic planning and assessment, sr. staff assoc., 1983-86; head spl. analytical studies NSF, Washington, 1987-90, sr. staff assoc. for strategic planning and assessment, 1990-92; sr. staff assoc., dir. rsch. on sci. and tech. Directorate for Social, Behavioral and Econ. Scis. NSF, 1992—; with White House Office of Sci. and Tech. Policy, 1983; cons. Pres.'s Task Force on Hwy. Safety. Author: An Analysis of the Allocation of Federal Budget Resources as an Indicator of National Goals and Priorities, 2 vols, 1969, Federal Funding and National Priorities, 1971; Analysis of Programs, Expenditures, and Research and Development, 1971; contbg. author: A Review of the Relationship Between Research and Development and Economic Growth/Productivity, 1971; contbr. articles to profl. jours. Recipient certificates of accomplishment for staff work NSF, 1972, 74, Spl. Achievement award NSF, 1972, Outstanding Performance rating for Nat. Research and Devel. Assessment Program NSF, 1974, Superior Accomplishment award NSF, 1979. Mem. AAAS, Am. Econ. Assn., Am. Mgmt. Assn., World Future Soc. Home: 5602 Ridgefield Rd

Bethesda MD 20816-1253 Office: NSF 4201 Wilson Blvd Ste 995 Arlington VA 22230-0001

LEDERMAN, MARIE JEAN, English language educator; b. Bklyn., Dec. 28, 1935; d. Samuel and Gladys (Leeshutz) Candel; m. Theodore Lederman, June 28, 1957 (div. 1963); 1 child, Mark; m. Martin Benis, 1977. B.S. magna cum laude, NYU, 1957, Ph.D. 1966; M.A. Bklyn. Coll. 1963. Tchr. English, N.Y.C. Bd. Edn., 1957-59, cons., 1975-76, 78-79; instr. NYU, 1965-66; asst. prof. N.Y.C. Community Coll., 1966-68; asst. prof. SEEK program CUNY, 1968-69, successively asst. prof., assoc. prof., prof. Baruch Coll., 1969-79, 88-91, prof. emerita, 1991—, cons. chancellor's SEEK task force 1975, univ. dean acad. affairs, 1979-85; dean for freshman skills La Guardia Community Coll. Long Island City, 1985-87; cons. Mohawk Valley Community Coll., Utica, N.Y., 1980, Tex. A&I U., 1984, U. Toronto, 1984, Framingham State Coll., 1987, Woodrow Wilson Fellowship Found., 1985, Dept. Higher Edn. State of N.J., 1989-91; cons. U. Minn., 1989-90. Chgo. State U., 1991-92. Exhibited works at Pen and Brush Club, Salamagundi Club; mem. editl. bd. Jour. Basic Writing, 1987—; contbr. articles to profl. jours. Bd. dirs. Jean Cocteau Repertory Theatre, v.p., 1988—. Recipient CUNY faculty research award, 1976-78; Fund for Improvement of Postsecondary Edn. grantee, 1981-87. Mem. Internat. Sculpture Ctr., Nat. Sculpture Soc., Art Students League, Burr Artists, Visual Individualists United. Democrat. Jewish.

LEDERMAN, MICHAEL G., consumer products company executive; b. 1953. With Goldman Sachs & Co., 1980-86; partner Japonica Partners, 1987—; pres. Sunbeam Oster Co. Inc., Providence, R.I. Office: Sunbeam Oster Co Inc 200 E Las Olas Blvd # 2100 Fort Lauderdale FL 33301-2248

LEDERMAN, PETER (BERND), environmental services executive, consultant; b. Weimar, Germany, Nov. 16, 1931; came to U.S., 1939, naturalized, 1945; s. Ernst M. and Irmgard R. (Heilbrunn) L.; m. Susan Storr, Aug. 25, 1957; children: Stuart M., Ellen L. BSE, U. Mich., 1953, MSE, 1957, PhD, 1961. Instr., U. Mich., 1959-61; research engr. Esso Research Labs., Baton Rouge, La., 1961-63; sr. engr. Esso Research & Engring. Co., Florham Park, N.J., 1963-66; asso. prof. chem. engring. Poly. Inst. Bklyn., 1966-72, adj. prof., 1972-75; dir. Ind. Waste Treatment Research Lab., EPA, Edison, N.J., 1972-75, dir. indsl. and extractive processes research, Washington, 1975-76; v.p. Cotrell Environ. Scis. Div., Research Cottrell, Bound Brook, N.J., 1976-80; v.p. hazard/toxic materials mgmt. Roy F. Weston, Inc., Edison, N.J., 1980-92; dir. Ctr. for Environ. Engring. and Sci. NJIT, Newark, 1993—, rsch. prof. chem. engring., 1992—; mem. NRC-Nat. Acad. Sci. Rev. Panel, Office Recycled Tech., U.S. Bur. Standards, 1980-83; mem. com. decontamination and decomissioning nuclear gaseous diffusion plants; mem. expert panel PCBs Agy. for Toxic Substances and Disease Registry. Mem. editorial bd. Environ. Progress, Chem. Engring. Progress, Hazardous Waste Mgmt. Jour. Mem. exec. bd. Watchung Area council Boy Scouts Am. 1970-86; assoc. editor AWMA Jour., mem. affirmative action adv. com. New Providence (N.J.) Bd. Edn., 1979-83. Served with AUS, 1953-55. Recipient Silver medal EPA, 1976. Fellow Am. Inst. Chem. Engrs. (chmn. profl. devel. com., chmn. N.J. sect., chair environ. div., Larry K. Cecil award 1987, dir. AICHE Found.); mem. ASME, AAAS, NAM, Am. Chem. Soc., Am. Soc. Engring. Edn., Nat. Soc. Profl. Engrs., Am. Acad. Environ. Engrs. (diplomate, trustee, Stanley Kappe award 1993), Am. Arbitration Assn., Am. Assn. of Eng. Soc. (chain environ. comm.), U. Mich. Engring. Alumni Soc. (chair, bd. dirs.), Sigma Xi, Phi Kappa Phi, Phi Lambda Upsilon. Contbr. numerous articles on environ. regulations, solid waste mgmt., hazardous waste mgmt., computer tech. to profl. jours. Home: 17 Pittsford Way New Providence NJ 07974-2428 Office: NJIT Newark NJ 07102

LEDERMAN, STEPHANIE BRODY, artist; b. N.Y.C.; d. Maxwell and Ann (Rockett) Brody. Student, U. Mich.; BS in Design, Finch Coll.; MA in Painting, L.I. U., 1975. One-person exhbns. Franklin Furnace, N.Y.C., 1979, Kathryn Markel Fine Arts, N.Y.C., 1979, 81, 83, Kaciare/Brown Gallery, N.Y.C., 1988, 89, Real Artways, Hartford, Conn., 1984, Alfred U., 1990, Hal Katzen Gallery, N.Y.C., 1992, Hillwood Art Mus., Brookville, N.Y., 1992, Casements Mus., Ormond Beach, Fla., 1994, Broward Cmty. Coll., Ft. Lauderdale, Fla., 1994, Hebrew Home for the Aged, N.Y.C., 1994-95, Galerie Caroline Corre, Paris, 1995; exhibited in numerous group shows including Newark Mus., 1983, Met. Mus. Art, N.Y.C., 1986, Queens Mus., 1989, Basel Art Fair, 1989, Caroline Corre, Paris, 1991, R.I. Mus. Art, 1991, Am. Acad. Arts & Letters, N.Y.C., 1992, Guild Hall Mus., East Hampton, N.Y., 1993, Ind. Mus. Art, Terre Haute, 1993, Jewish Mus., N.Y.C., 1993; represented in permanent collections Newark Mus., Mus. Modern Art, Prudential Ins., Bertelsmann Music Group, Guild Hall Mus., East Hampton, L.I., Chase Manhattan Bank, N.Y. Health and Hosp. Corp., Victoria & Albert Mus., London, Doubleday Books. Recipient Hassam and Speicher purchase award Am. Acad. and Inst. Arts and Letters, 1988; grantee Creative Artists Pub. Svc., 1977, Ariana Found. for Arts, 1985, Artists Space, 1987, E.D. Found., 1991, Lancaster Group, U.S.A. Comm. award, 1991, Spl. Opportunity stipend N.Y. State Coun. Arts, 1992, 94, Heuss Ho. project Lower Manhattan Cultural Coun., 1992. Studio: 85 N 3d St 5th Fl Brooklyn NY 11211

LEDFORD, FRANK FINLEY, JR., surgeon, army officer; b. Jacksonville, Fla., Apr. 22, 1934; s. Frank F. and Hazel H. (Barrette) L.; m. Marilyn Sue Kain, Aug. 23, 1957; 1 child, Cheryl Lynn. B.S., U. Dayton, 1955; M.D., U. Cin., 1959; postgrad., Indsl. Coll. Armed Forces, 1976—. Diplomate: Am. Bd. Orthopedic Surgery. Commd. 2d lt. U.S. Army, 1958, advanced through grades to lt. gen., 1988; surgeon, 1958-69; intern Brooke Army Hosp., San Antonio, 1959-60; resident in surgery Womack Army Hosp., 1960-61; resident in orthop. surgery Letterman Gen. Hosp., San Francisco, 1961-64; resident in pediat. orthop. surgery Phoenix Crippled Childrens Hosp., 1964-65; chief orthopedic surgery (Army Hosp.), Landstuhl, W.Ger., 1969-71; dep. commr. (Army Hosp.), Heidelberg, W.Ger., 1971-72; asst. chief surg. cons. Office of Surgeon Gen., Washington, 1972-73; chief grad. med. edn. Office of Surgeon Gen., 1973-76; comdr. U.S. Army Hosp., Fort Riley, Kans., 1977-80, Ft. Benning, Ga., 1980; dir. profl. services Office of Surgeon Gen., U.S. Army, Washington, 1980-82; comdr. Letterman Army Med. Ctr. San Francisco, 1982-85; chief surgeon U.S. Army Europe, 1985-88; The Surgeon Gen. Dept. of the Army, Heidelberg, Germany, 1988-92; pres. S.W. Found. for Biomedical Rsch., San Antonio, 1992—; clin. prof. Health Sci. Ctr. U. Tex., San Antonio, 1993—; clin prof. surgery Uniformed Services U. Health Scis. Contbr. articles to med. jours. Fellow ACS, Am. Acad. Orthopedic Surgeons, Am. Coll. Physician Execs.; mem. AMA, Assn. Mil. Surgeons, Soc. Mil. Orthopedic Surgeons. Methodist. Clubs: Bohemian. Address: SW Found For Biomedical Research PO Box 28147 San Antonio TX 78228-0146*

LEDFORD, HANNA MAY, state official; b. Athens, Ga., Sept. 11, 1946. AB in Journalism, U. Ga., 1964. Reporter Marietta (Ga.) Daily Jour., 1968-69; info. specialist Ga. Dept. Industry Trade and Tourism, Atlanta, 1969-76, asst. dir. tourist divsn., 1976-83, dir. tourist divsn., 1983—, dep. commr., 1986—; pres. Welcome South Ctr., Atlanta, 1993—; bd. dirs. Cecil B. Day Sch. Hospitality Adminstrn. Recipient Unity Appreciation award Travel Industry Ga. Assn., 1989, Disting. Achievement in Journalism John E. Drewry award Henry W. Grady Coll. Journalism U. Ga., 1994; named Resolution Outstanding Leader, Ga. Ho. of Reps., 1987, Top Ten Atlanta Businesswomen, Atlanta Bus. Chronicle, 1990. Mem. Ga. Hospitality and Travel Assn. (bd. dirs., Travel Industry Leader of Yr. 1985), Southeast Tourism Soc. (bd. dirs., Travel Dir. of Yr. 1986, Pres. award 1993), Travel South USA (bd. dirs., chmn. 1991-93). Office: State of Ga Industry Trade & Tourism Dept PO Box 1776 Atlanta GA 30301

LEDFORD, JACK CLARENCE, retired aircraft company executive, former air force officer; b. Blairsville, Ga., Sept. 1, 1920; s. Jack Raymond and Clara Mae (Duckworth) L.; m. Pauline F. Knight, Dec. 9, 1973; children: Barbara Jan (Mrs. Russell J. Thomas), Jack Michael, Joseph Dan. B.S., Ohio State U.; M.B.A. George Washington U. Commd. 2d lt. Air Corps U.S. Army, 1941; advanced through grades to brig. gen. USAF, 1965; dep. chief staff Def. Atomic Support Agy., Washington, 1958-61; dir. spl. projects USAF, 1961-63; asst. dir. CIA, 1963-66; dir. inspection USAF, 1966-61; comdr. 12th Strategic Air Div., Tucson, 1968-70; ret., 1970; v.p. area devel. So. Ariz. Bank & Trust Co., Tucson, 1970-71; v.p. Hughes Aircraft Internat. Service Corp., 1971-85. Pres. Old Pueblo Boys Club.; bd. dirs. Tucson United Community Campaign, Catalina council Boy Scouts Am., Pima County Air

Mus. Decorated D.S.C., D.S.M. (2), Legion of Merit, Air Medal, Purple Heart; Order of Flying Cloud and Banner China). Mem. Air Force Assn. Skyline Country Club (Tucson), Calif. Yacht Club (L.A.), Delta Upsilon.

LEDFORD, RICHARD ALLISON, food science educator, food microbiologist; b. Charlotte, N.C., June 30, 1931; s. Travis Allison and Sarah (Moon) L.; m. Martha Ann Worley Jan. 26, 1957; children: Richard Jr. (dec.), Roeby, Ann, Jeanne, Robert. BS, N.C. State U., 1954, MS, 1958; PhD, Cornell U., 1961. Dir. food lab. N.Y. State Agr. & Markets, Albany, 1961-64; asst. prof. food sci. Cornell U., Ithaca, N.Y., 1964-70, assoc. prof., 1970-80, prof., 1980—, chmn. dept., 1972-77, 85—; dir. Inst. Food Sci. 1988—. Served to 1st lt. U.S. Army, 1954-56. Mem. Am. Soc. Microbiology, Inst. Food Technologists, Am. Dairy Sci. Assn. Lodge: Rotary. Office: Cornell U Dept Food Sci 114 Stocking Hall Ithaca NY 14853-7201

LEDFORD, SANDRA, principal. Prin. Harding Mid. Sch., Cedar Rapids, Iowa. Recipient Blue Ribbon Sch. award, 1990-91. Office: Harding Mid Sch 4801 Golf St NE Cedar Rapids IA 52402-5738

LEDGER, WILLIAM JOE, physician, educator; b. Turtle Creek, Pa., 1932. B.A., Princeton U., 1954; M.D., U. Pa., 1958; M.S., Temple U., 1964. Diplomate Am. Bd. Ob-Gyn. Intern Hamot Hosp. Assn., Erie, N.Y., 1958-59; resident Temple U. Hosp., Phila., 1961-64; attending physician Women's Hosp.-Mich. Med. Ctr., 1964-72; assoc. prof. U. Mich., Ann Arbor; prof. U. So. Calif., L.A.; Given Found. prof., chmn. ob-gyn. Cornell U. Med. Coll., N.Y.C. Served to capt. USMC, 1959-61. Fellow ACS, Am. Coll. Ob-Gyn. Office: Cornell U Med Coll 411 E 69th St New York NY 10021-5697*

LEDLEY, ROBERT STEVEN, biophysicist; b. N.Y.C., June 28, 1928. DDS, NYU, 1948; MA, Columbia U., 1949. Rsch. physicist Columbia U. Radiation Labs., Columbia, 1948-50; instr. physics Columbia U., 1949-50; vis. scientist Nat. Bur. Standards, 1951-52; physicist, 1953-54; ops. rsch. analyst Johns Hopkins U., 1954-56; assoc. prof. elec. engring George Washington U., 1957-60; instr. pediatric. Johns Hopkins U., Sch. Medicine, 1960-63; prof. elec. engring. George Washington U., 1968-70; prof. physiology, biophysics & radiology Georgetown U., from 1970; pres., rsch. dir. Nat. Biomed. Rsch. Found., from 1960; pres. Digital Info. Sci. Corp., 1970-75. named to Nat. Inventor Hall of Fame, 1990. Mem. Soc. Math Biophys., Inst. Elec. & Electronics Engrs., Biphys. Soc., N.Y. Acad. Sci., Pattern Recognition Soc. Office: Georgetown U Nat Biomed Rsch Found 3900 Reservoir Rd NW Washington DC 20007-2187*

LEDOGAR, STEPHEN J., diplomat; b. N.Y.C., Sept. 14, 1929; m. Marcia Hubert, Sept. 16, 1967; children: Lucy, Charles. BS, Fordham U., 1954, LLB, 1958. Bar: N.Y. 1959. Surety claims atty. Chubb & Son, N.Y.C., 1954-59; with Fgn. Svc., 1959—; press spokesman, U.S. del. Vietnam Peace Talks, Paris, 1967-72; with U.S. Mission to NATO, 1973-76; spl. asst. to undersec. of state, 1976-77; dir. Office of NATO Affairs, 1977-80; mem. State Dept. Senior Seminar, 1980-81; dep. chief of mission U.S. Mission to NATO, Brussels, 1981-87; amb., U.S. rep. European Conventional Stability Negotiations and Mutual and Balanced Force Reductions Talks, 1987-89, amb. and head U.S. Del. to Negotiations on Conventional Armed Forces in Europe, 1989, amb. and U.S. rep. Conference on Disarmament, 1989—. Lt. USN, 1949-52, USNR, 1954-60 (Naval Aviator). Office: US Del to Conf Disarmament, 11 Rte de Pregny, 1292 Geneva Switzerland

LEDOUX, CHRIS LEE, country musician; b. Biloxi, Miss., Oct. 2, 1948; s. Alfred Hector and Bonnie Jeanette (Gingrich) LeDoux; m. Peggy Jo Rhoades, Jan. 4, 1972; children: Clayton, Ned, Will, Cindi, Beau. AA, Sheridan (Wyo.) Coll., 1969. With rodeo, 1971-81, musician, 1972—; rancher Wyo., 1976—. Songwriter, singer 22 albums of songs with Western themes, 1972—, recent recordings include Western Underground, 1991, (with Garth Brooks) Watcha Gonna Do With a Cowboy, 1992, Under This Old Hat, 1993, (with Garth Brooks) Best of Chris LeDoux, 1994. Sculptor (Best Bronze of Show, State of Wyo. 1985, Best Art of Show, State of Nev., 1986). State spokesman, Wyo. State Centennial, 1990. Mem. Profl. Rodeo Cowboy Assn. (World Champion Bareback Broncs, 1976). Avocations: Wyo. rancher, give music concerts with Western Underground. Office: ACS Inc 3015 Leeville Rd Mount Juliet TN 37122-3911

LEDOUX, HAROLD ANTHONY, cartoonist, painter; b. Port Arthur, Tex., Nov. 7, 1926; s. Antoine Ovide and Pauline Zulma (Bernard) LeD.; m. Jeanne Labbe, 1964 (div. 1979); children—Lorraine Marthe, Noelle Pauline. Grad., Thomas Jefferson High Sch., Port Arthur, Tex., 1944; student, Chgo. Acad. Fine Arts, 1948-49. Cartoonist, illustrator N.Am. Syndicate, 1965—. Cartoonist, Famous Funnies, N.Y.C., 1950-53; asst. cartoonist: syndicated comic strip Judge Parker, 1953-65; represented in permanent collection Mus. of Gulf Coast, Port Arthur, Tex. Advisor Council for Devel. of French in La. Served with U.S. Mcht. Marine, 1944-47. Recipient Atlantic War Zone Bar War Shipping Adminstrn. Mem. Nat. Cartoonists Soc., Comics Council, Southwestern Watercolor Soc. Club: Alliance Française. Address: N Am Syndicate 235 E 45th St New York NY 10017

LEDSINGER, CHARLES ALBERT, JR., hotel, gaming executive; b. Memphis, Jan. 1, 1950; s. Charles Albert Ledsinger Sr. and Betty L. (Clark) Heller; m. Anita Clarendon, May 11, 1974; children: Leila Grace, Katherine Elise. BA in English, U. Va., 1972; MBA in Fin., Memphis State U., 1977. Restaurant mgr. Boudreaux and Shoup Enterprises, Atlanta, 1972-74; comml. property mgr. Hoover Morris, Enterprises, Atlanta, 1974-75; fin. analyst Holiday Inns, Inc., Memphis, 1978-79, mgr. investor rels., 1980, exec. asst. to pres., 1980-83; v.p. fin. and adminstrn. Embassy Stes., Irving, Tex., 1983-87; v.p. project fin. Holiday Corp., Memphis, 1987-90; v.p., treas. The Promus Cos., Memphis, 1990, sr. v.p., chief fin. officer, 1990—; bd. dirs. Tenn. Restaurant Co., Perkins Mgmt. Co., Inc., Friendly Ice Cream Corp. Mem. exec. bd. Chickasaw coun. Boy Scouts Am., 1993—; trustee St. Mary's Episcopal Sch., 1994—; bd. dirs. Memphis Devel. Found., 1992—. Office: The Promus Cos 1023 Cherry Rd Memphis TN 38117-5423

LE DUC, ALBERT LOUIS, JR., computer services director; b. Montgomery, Ala., Feb. 1, 1937; s. Albert Louis and Rachel Nancy (Wineinger) LeD. Student Duke U., 1954-55; B.A., Fla. State U., 1958, M.S., 1960; m. Ellen Heath, June 18, 1960; children: Albert Louis III, Candy Andrew. Civilian mathematician Army Rocket Guided Missile Agy., Huntsville, Ala., 1958, 59; mathematician analyst RCA Svc. Co., Patrick AFB, Fla., 1960-63, programming leader, 1963-67, project mgr., Eglin AFB, Fla., 1967-69, mktg. adminstr., Cherry Hill, N.J., 1969-71; tech. dir. Ind. U., Bloomington, 1971-77; dir. analysis programming Miami-Dade Community Coll., Miami, Fla., 1977-89, dir. computer svcs., 1989—; part-time instr. Fla. State U., 1958-60, Brevard Engring. Coll., 1961-62, Ind. U., 1972-77. Bd. dirs. Coll. and Univ. Machine Records Conf., 1979-87. Recipient Frank Martin award Coll. and Univ. Machine Records Conf., 1985. Mem. Assn. Computing Machinery (Best Paper award 1973), Profl. Assn. for Computing and Info. Tech. in Higher Edn. (best paper award 1986), CAUSE (bd. dirs. 1993—, Elite award 1993). Author: The Computer for Managers, 1972. Home: 10321 SW 107th St Miami FL 33176-3473 Office: 11011 SW 104th St Miami FL 33176-3330

LE DUC, DON RAYMOND, lawyer, educator; b. South Milwaukee, Wis., Apr. 7, 1933; s. Raymond Joseph and Roberta (Jones) Le D.; m. Alice Marie Pranica, Oct. 24, 1959; children—Paul, Marie. B.A., U. Wis., 1959, Ph.D, 1970; J.D., Marquette U., 1962. Bar: Wis. 1962. Assoc. firm Arnold, Murray & O'Neill, Milw., 1962-63; Ford fellow in comparative law U. Wis.-Madison, 1963-64; pvt. practice Green Bay, Wis., 1964-67; assoc. prof. U. Wis.-Madison, 1973-76, prof., 1976-84; chmn. Western European studies program U. Wis., 1979-80; Reagan prof. telecommunications U. Ala., University, 1984-86, chmn. doctoral program, 1984-86; chief counsel Wis. Dept. Ins., Madison, 1967-69; asst. prof. communications law U. Md., 1970-71; assoc. prof. Ohio State U. 1971-73; prof. U. Wis., Milw., 1986—, chmn. dept. mass comm., 1991—; dir. Comparative Telecommunications Research Center, Madison, 1974-84. Author: Cable Television and the FCC, 1973, Issues in Broadcast Regulation, 1974, Beyond Broadcasting: Patterns in Policy and Law, 1986, (with Dwight Teeter) Law of Mass Communications, 1995; editor Client mag., 1973-77; assoc. editor Jour. Broadcasting, 1974—; comm. 1978—; contbr. articles to profl. pubs. Chief counsel Wis. Gov.'s Task Force on Telecommunications, 1971-72; cable TV advisory com. mem. FCC, 1972-76. Served as spl. agt. CIC U.S. Army, 1954-57. Recipient

award Ohio State U., 1971, Wis. Alumni Research Found., 1974, 75, 77; grantee Am. Philos. Soc., 1975, 77; research fellow NATO, 1979; research fellow Council European Studies, 1979. Mem. FCC, Wis. bar assns., Broadcast Edn. Assn., Internat. Inst. Communication. Republican. Roman Catholic. Home: 1800 Fairhaven Dr Cedarburg WI 53012-9100 Office: U Wis-Milw Dept Mass Communicatio Milwaukee WI 53201

LEDUC, JOHN ANDRE, lawyer; b. Oberlin, Ohio, Apr. 13, 1954. AB summa cum laude, Princeton U., 1975; JD cum laude, Harvard U., 1978. Bar: Ohio 1978, Ill. 1984. Ptnr. Winston & Strawn, Chgo.; adj. prof. law U. Chgo., 1985-91; active Fed. Income Tax Project Tax Adv. Group. Contbr. articles to profl. jours. Mem. ABA (mem. corp. tax com. tax sect. 1985—), Ill. Bar Assn., Chgo. Bar Assn., Am. Law Inst. Office: Winston & Strawn 35 W Wacker Dr Chicago IL 60601-1614

LEDWIDGE, PATRICK JOSEPH, lawyer; b. Detroit, Mar. 17, 1928; s. Patrick Liam and Mary Josephine (Hooley) L.; m. Rosemary Lahey Mervenne, Aug. 3, 1974; stepchildren—Anne Marie, Mary Clare, John, David, Sara Mervenne. A.B., Coll. Holy Cross, 1949; J.D., U. Mich., 1952. Bar: Mich. 1952. Assoc. firm Dickinson, Wright, Moon, Van Dusen & Freeman, Detroit, 1956-63; ptnr. Dickinson, Wright, Moon, Van Dusen & Freeman, 1964—. Served to lt. j.g. U.S. Navy, 1952-55. Mem. Mich. Bar Assn., Detroit Bar Assn., Am. Law Inst. Roman Catholic. Clubs: Detroit, Detroit Athletic, Detroit Golf. Home: 777 N Williamsbury Rd Bloomfield Village MI 48301-2521 Office: Dickinson Wright et al 1 Detroit Ctr 500 Woodward Ave Ste 4000 Detroit MI 48226-3423

LEDWIG, DONALD EUGENE, association executive, former public broadcasting executive, former naval officer; b. Lubbock, Tex., Mar. 2, 1937; s. Paul Lawrence and Rose L.; m. Gail Wilcox, Jan. 30, 1965; children: Donald Eugene Jr., David W. BS, Tex. Tech. U., 1959; MBA, George Washington U., 1973; Disting. Grad. Naval War Coll., 1977. Commd. ensign, U.S. Navy, 1959, advanced through grades to capt., 1980, ship's officer U.S. Pacific Fleet, 1959-65, 77-79, staff Adm. H.G. Rickover, Nuclear Propulsion Program, 1966-72; dir. contract policy Naval Material Command, Washington, 1979-81, dep. comdr. Naval Electronic Systems Command, Washington, 1981-84, ret. 1984; v.p., treas. Corp. for Pub. Broadcasting, Washington, 1984-86, pres., chief exec. officer, 1987-92; exec. dir. Am. Prodn. and Inventory Control Soc., Falls Church, Va., 1992—. Decorated Legion of Merit; recipient Barrow Meml. award Hastings Coll. Law, 1989, Nat. Captioning Inst. Award, 1990, Disting. Alumnus award Tex. Tech U., 1992. Mem. Am. Soc. Assn. Execs., Nat. Press. Club, Nat. Assn. Mfrs., Army and Navy Club, Army/Navy Country Club. Office: APICS 500 W Annandale Rd Falls Church VA 22046-4205

LEDWITH, JAMES ROBB, lawyer; b. Bryn Mawr, Pa., Feb. 14, 1936; s. Richard W. (dec.) and Elizabeth T. Ledwith; children: Cheryl D., James Robb Jr., Scott W.; m. Katherine Hoffman, Dec. 2, 1978. AB, Princeton U., 1958; LLB, U. Pa., 1963. Bar: Pa. 1964. Assoc. Pepper, Hamilton & Scheetz, Phila., 1963-71, ptnr., 1971—. Bd. dirs., trustee Coll. Settlement Phila.; bd. dirs., trustee, asst. sec., treas., past pres. bd. trustees Kuhn Day Camp; sec., trustee Curtis Inst. Music, Mary Louise Curtis Bok Found. Lt. USNR, 1958-60. Fellow Am. Coll. Trust and Estate Counsel (past bd. regents past Pa. chmn.); mem. ABA (past chmn. com. on adminstrn. estates sect. real property, probate and trust law sect.), Pa. Bar Assn. (past chmn. sect. real property, probate and trust law), Pa. Bar Inst. (bd. dirs., past pres.), Phila. Bar Assn. (past chmn., exec. com. probate and trust law com.), Nat. Assn. Estate Planning Couns. (past bd. dirs., past pres.). Republican. Presbyterian. Avocations: tennis, squash, music (piano). Office: Pepper Hamilton & Scheetz 3000 Two Logan Sq 18th Arch St Philadelphia PA 19103

LEDWITH, JOHN FRANCIS, lawyer; b. Phila., Oct. 3, 1938; s. Francis Joseph and Jane Agnes (White) L.; m. Mary Evans, Aug. 28, 1965; children—Deirdre A., John E. A.B., U. Pa., 1960, J.D., 1963. Bar: Pa. 1965, U.S. Dist. Ct. (ea. dist.) Pa. 1965, U.S. Ct. Appeals (3rd cir.) 1965, U.S. Supreme Ct. 1970, N.Y. State, 1984. Assoc. Joseph R. Thompson, Phila., 1965-71; mem. Schubert, Mallon, Wallheim & deCindis, Phila., 1971-81, LaBrum & Doak, Phila., 1981—. Author: (with others) Philadelphia CP Trial Manual, 1982. Bd. dirs. Chestnut Hill Community Assn., Phila., 1975, 76. Served to E-6 USCG, 1963-71. Mem. ABA, Phila. Bar Assn., Pa. Bar Assn., Def. Research Inst., Fedn. of Ins. Corp. Coun. Republican. Roman Catholic. Clubs: Racquet (Phila.), Phila. Cricket; Avalon Yacht (N.J.) (commodore 1982). Office: LaBrum and Doak 1818 Market St Fl 2900 Philadelphia PA 19103-3629

LEDYARD, JOHN ODELL, economics educator, consultant; b. Detroit, Apr. 4, 1940; s. William Hendrie and Florence (Odell) L.; m. Bonnie Higginbottom, May 23, 1970; children: Stephen, J. Henry, Meg. BA, Wabash Coll., 1963; PhD, Purdue U., 1967. Asst. prof. Carnegie-Mellon U., Pitts., 1967-70; prof. Northwestern U., Evanston, Ill., 1970-85; prof. Calif. Inst. Tech., Pasadena, 1985—, exec. officer for social sci., 1989-92, chmn. div. humanities and social scis., 1992—. Contbr. articles to profl. jours. Fellow Econometric Soc.; mem. Pub. Choice Soc. (pres. 1980-82), Econ. Sci. Assn. (exec. com. 1986—). Office: Calif Inst of Tech Dept Econs Pasadena CA 91125

LEDYARD, ROBINS HEARD, lawyer; b. Nashville, Oct. 14, 1939; s. Quitman Robins and Alma Elizabeth (Stevenson) L.; m. Julia Bordeaux Gambill, Dec. 19, 1962; children: Stevenson Gambill, Quitman Robins II, Margaret Dabney. BA, Vanderbilt U., 1965, JD, 1966. Bar: Tenn. 1966, U.S. Supreme Ct. 1975. Atty. Nat. Life & Accident Ins. Co., Nashville, 1966-68; asst. counsel Nat. Life & Accident Ins. Co., 1968-69, asso. counsel, 1969-70, counsel, 1970-72, asso. gen. counsel, 1972-75, gen. counsel, 1975-80; partner Bass, Berry & Sims, 1980—; tchr. C.L.U.s, 1967-75. Asst. editor: Vanderbilt Law Rev., 1965-66; contbr. articles to profl. jours. Active United Way, Nashville, 1967—, Heart Fund, 1970-73; vice chmn. United Diocesan Givers, 1975; bd. dirs. St. Thomas Hosp., 1990—. With USMC, 1958-61. Recipient Bennett Douglas Bell Meml. prize, 1966; Marr scholar, 1965-66. Mem. ABA, Am. Coun. Life Ins. (chmn. tax com. 1978-80), Assn. Life Ins. Counsel (chmn. tax com. 1979-80), Tenn. Bar Assn., Nashville Bar Assn., Internat. Assn. Ins. Counsel, Global Leaders for the South, Order of Coif, Phi Delta Phi, Alpha Tau Omega. Democrat. Roman Catholic. Clubs: Belle Meade Country, Capitol of Nashville, KC. Home: 1215 Chickering Rd Nashville TN 37215-4519 Office: 2700 First American Ctr Nashville TN 37238

LEE, ADRIAN ISELIN, JR., journalist; b. Miami, Fla., Nov. 6, 1920; s. Adrian Iselin and Adriana Lanier (Owen) L.; m. Marie Lainé Santa Maria, Oct. 14, 1950; children: Adrian Iselin III, Catherine Taney, Thomas Sim, William Owen, Anne Marie, Louisa Carrell. BA, Spring Hill Coll., Mobile, Ala., 1943. With The Bulletin, Phila., 1948—; gen. assignment reporter The Bulletin, 1960—, editorial writer, 1967-72, columnist op-ed page, 1972-82; with Phila. Daily News, 1982-88; speech and op-ed writer U.S. Atty. Gen. Edwin Meese III, 1988-89; writer CBS Radio News, 1989—; tchr. editorial writing, dept. journalism Temple U. Active Chestnut Hill Community Assn. Lt. (j.g.) USNR, 1943-46, PTO. Decorated Navy Unit Commendation medal. Mem. Nat. Press Club, Pen and Pencil Club, Phila. Press Assn. (prize for coverage Pres. F. Kennedy assassination 1963), Sigma Delta Chi (prize for column writing 1978). Republican. Roman Catholic. Home and Office: Penns Wood Apt F-20 20 E Haws Ln Flourtown PA 19031-2048

LEE, ALLAN WREN, clergyman; b. Yakima, Wash., June 3, 1924; s. Percy Anson and Agnes May (Wren) L.; m. Mildred Elaine Ferguson, June 16, 1946; 1 dau., Cynthia Ann. B.A., Phillips U., Enid, Okla., 1949; M.A., Peabody Coll. Tchrs., 1953; B.D., Tex. Christian U., 1955, D.D. (hon.), 1968. Ordained minister Christian Ch. (Disciples of Christ), 1949; pastor chs. in Tex. and Wash., 1955-60; gen. sec. World Conv. Chs. of Christ, Dallas, 1971-92; mem. gen. bd. Christian Ch., 1971-73; pres. Seattle Christian Ch. Missionary Union, 1964-66, Wash.-No. Idaho Conv. Christian Chs., 1966; TV panel mem. Am. Religious Town Hall, 1988—. Author: Bridges of Benevolence, 1962, Wit and Wisdom, 1963, The Burro and the Bibles, 1968, Under the Shadow of the Nine Dragons, 1969, Reflections Along the Reef, 1970, Disciple Down Under, 1971, Meet My Mexican Amigos, 1972, One Great Fellowship, 1974, Fifty Years of Faith and Fellowship, 1980, Recollections of a Dandy Little Up-to-Date Town, 1985, also articles. TV panel mem. Am. Religious Town Hall, 1988—; bd. dirs. Melissa/Pub. Libr., 1992-94. Recipient Disting. Service citation Children's Home Soc. Wash., 1967, Disting. Service award Bremerton Jaycees, 1959; Jamaica Tourist Bd. citation, 1984. Mem. Disciples of Christ Hist. Soc. (founder, life mem.), Religious Conv. Mgrs. Assn. (v.p. 1972-92), Am. Bible Soc. (nat. adv. coun. 1985-94), Seattle Civitan (pres. 1962-64, lt. gov. Orewa dist. 1965). Club: Seattle Civitan (pres. 1962-64, lt. gov. Orewa dist. 1965). Home and Office: 2112 Stone Creek Dr Plano TX 75075 *I make every effort to live a life patterned after the life and teachings of the Man of Nazareth, Jesus Christ—that is, to be compassionate, understanding, peaceful and loving.*

LEE, ALVIN A., literary educator, scholar, author; b. Woodville, Ont., Can., Sept. 30, 1930; s. Norman Osborne and Susanna Elizabeth (Found) L.; m. Hope Arnott, Dec. 21, 1957; children: Joanna, Monika, Fiona, Alison, Margaret. B.A., U. Toronto, Ont., Can., 1953, M.A. in English, 1958, Ph.D., 1961; M.Div., Victoria U., Toronto, 1957. Teaching fellow in English U. Toronto, 1957-59; asst. prof. English McMaster U., Hamilton, Ont., 1960-65; assoc. prof. McMaster U., 1966-70, prof., 1970-92, prof. emeritus, 1990-92, asst. dean Sch. Grad. Studies, 1968-71, dean Sch. Grad. Studies, 1971-73, acad. v.p., 1974-79, pres., vice-chancellor, 1980-90, pres. emeritus, 1994—; Northrop Frye prof. literary theory U. Toronto, 1992; mem. Western Ont. coun. Conf. Bd. Can., 1983-90; mem. adv. bd. Medieval Renaissance History, 1991—. Author: James Reaney, Twayne's World Authors Series, 49, 1968, The Guest-Hall of Eden: Four Essays on the Design of Old English Poetry, 1972; editor: (with Hope Arnott Lee) Wish and Nightmare, 1972, Circle of Stories: One, 1972, Two, 1972, The Garden and the Wilderness, 1973, The Temple and the Ruin, 1973, The Peaceable Kingdom, 1974, (with Robert D. Denham) The Legacy of Northrop Frye, 1994; gen. editor: McMaster Old English Studies and Texts; editorial bd. English Studies in Canada, 1982-88; mem. editorial com. Collected Works of Northrop Frye, 1993—; contbr. articles to profl. jours. Trustee, mem. exec. com. Chedoke-McMaster Hosps., 1980-90; mem. Community Edn. Coordinating Com., 1981-90; mem. Council Ont. Univs., 1980-90, vice chmn., 1981-83, chmn., 1983-85, mem. exec. com., 1981-87; mem. Health Scis. Liaison Com., 1980-90; dir. Council Ont. Univ. Holdings Ltd., 1981-90; mem. chancellors coun. Victoria U., U. Toronto, 1983—; hon. bd. dirs. Operation Lifeline, Hamilton, 1980-90; hon. Patron Opera Hamilton, 1982-90; vice chmn. bd., mem. exec. com. Royal Bot. Gardens, Hamilton, 1980-90, chmn. provincial and fed. relations com., 1981-90, vice chmn. sci. and ednl. com., 1981-90, mem. nominating com., 1981-90; vice chmn. bus. adv. conf. Regional Municipality of Hamilton-Wentworth, 1983-90; chmn. fund-raising liaison com. McMaster Hosps. Found/McMaster U., 1983-90; hon. patron Edn. Found. of Fedn. Chinese Can. Profls., Ont., 1984-90; mem., vice chair Can. Merit Scholarship Found., 1990-93; bd. dirs. Art Gallery Hamilton, 1991-94; mem. adminstrn. bd. McMaster Mus. Art; active Hamilton Region Conservation Authority Found., 1992-94. Mem. MLA, Mediaeval Acad. Am., Assn. Univs. and Colls. Can. (coun. univ. pres. 1980—), Hamilton Assn. Advancement Lit., Sci. and Art (hon. pres. 1980-88), Can. Inst. Advanced Rsch., Internat. Assn. Anglo-Saxonists, Corporate-Higher Edn. Forum, McMaster U. Alumni Coun. (hon. pres. 1980-90), McMaster U. Letterman's Assn. (hon.), Hamilton and Dist. C. of C. (dir., mem. program com. 1982-90). Office: McMaster U, 1280 Main St W, Hamilton, ON Canada L8S 4L9

LEE, AMY SHIU, biochemist, educator; b. Canton, Peoples Republic of China, Aug. 5, 1947; d. Chi To and Siu Yu (Wong) Shiu; m. Paul L. Lee, Jan. 15, 1972; children: May, Andrew. B.A, U. Calif., Berkeley, 1970; PhD, Calif. Tech. Inst., Pasadena, 1975. Asst. prof. biochemistry sch. medicine U. So. Calif., L.A., 1980-83, assoc. prof., 1984-87, prof., 1988—; group leader gene regulation program comprehensive cancer ctr. U. So. Calif., 1987—; mem. study sects. NIH, Washington, 1981—. Mem. AAAS, Am. Soc. Biol. Chemist, Am. Soc. Microbiologists, Am. Cancer Soc. Office: U So Calif Sch Medicine 1441 Eastlake Ave Los Angeles CA 90033-1048

LEE, ANDRÉ LAFAYETTE, hospital administrator; b. Detroit, Aug. 14, 1943; s. Clyde and Laura D. (Davis) L.; m. Katrina (Siu.); children—Andre, Bryan, Tracey, Robyn. B.S., Mich. State U., 1966; M.P.A., Cornell U., 1972; D.P.A., Nova U., Fort Lauderdale, 1978. Cert. med. technologist Am. Soc. Clin. Pathologists. Adminstr., Highland Park Hosp., Mich., 1972-76; adminstr. Sumby Hosp., River Rouge, Mich., 1976-78; asst. adminstr. St. Joseph Hosp., Fort Wayne, Ind., 1978-81; adminstr. Hubbard Hosp., Nashville, 1981-87; pres. Urban Health Assocs., Nashville, 1987—; asst. prof. Shaw Coll., Detroit, 1976-77; assoc. prof. Ind. U. Grad. Sch., Fort Wayne, 1978-80; adj. prof. Eastern U., Ann Arbor, Mich., 1976-78; asst. prof. Meharry Med. Coll., Nashville, 1981—; asst. prof. Tenn. State U., 1994—. CEO United Cmty. Hosp., Detroit; owner, Friendship Hospice, Nashville, New Orleans, Natchez, Detroit. Author: Teach Your Child Healthy Habits, 1978; newspaper/cartoonist: Frost Illustrated, 1978-79. Contr. articles to profl. jours. Served to capt. U.S. Army, 1968-70. Fellow Am. Coll. Hosp. Adminstrn. (numerous coms.), Am. Acad. Med. Adminstrn. (state bd. dirs. 1981—); mem. Nat. Assn. Health Sci. Execs. (pres. 1985), NAACP. Methodist. Club: Optimist (River Rouge). Avocation: cartooning. Home: 100 Riverfront Apts #108 Detroit MI 48216 Office: United Cmty Hosp 2401 20th St Detroit MI 48216

LEE, ARTHUR VIRGIL, III, biotechnology company executive; b. Detroit, Nov. 24, 1920; s. Arthur Virgil and Emily S. (Burry) L.; m. Elizabeth Hoppin Chafee, Dec. 8, 1945 (div.); children: Arthur C., Sherrill Ann Rosoff, William J., Henry C.; m. Jean Austin LaMothe, Dec. 30, 1967. BA, Williams Coll., 1942; Indsl. Adminstr. (World War II MBA), Harvard Bus. Sch., 1943. With McKesson & Robbins, Inc., Memphis, 1946-47; ops. mgr. Providence div. McKesson & Robbins, Inc., 1947-63, v.p., mgr. Providence div., 1954-59, with Boston div., 1959-63, with Pitts. div., 1963; asst. dean Harvard U. Bus. Sch., Cambridge, Mass., 1964-65, dir. corp. rels., 1965-72, dir. resources, 1972-73; v.p. Lesley Coll., Cambridge, 1973-77; dir. corp. rels. Tufts U., Medford, Mass., 1977-79; pres. Biotec Internat., Ltd., Williamstown, Mass., 1979—; bd. dirs. Atec Internat. Ltd., Beratec, Ltd., Content Agrl. Products, Ltd., Jamaica. Bd. dirs. New Eng. Drug Exchange, 1956-63; trustee Am. Coll. Switzerland, 1978-82, Williamstown Theatre Festival, 1984-94, trustee emeritus, 1994—; mem. Weston Town Fin. Com., 1961-66; mem. adv. bd. Coll. Pharmacy, U. R.I., 1957-58. Lt. USNR, 1942-46. Mem. Taconic Golf Club, Alpha Delta Phi. Congregationalist. Home and Office: 1549 Green River Rd Williamstown MA 01267-0354

LEE, BARBARA A., federal magistrate judge. AB, Boston U., 1959; LLB, Harvard Law Sch., 1962. Bar: Conn. 1962, N.Y. 1966. Atty. Poletti Freidin Prashker Feldman & Gartner, 1968-74, ptnr., 1974-82; pvt. practice N.Y.C., 1983-87; U.S. magistrate judge U.S. Dist. Ct. (so. dist.), N.Y., 1988—; adj. prof. law Seton Hall U., So. Orange, N.J., 1984-87. Mem. com. on ecumenical and inter-religious affairs of Roman Cath. Archdiocese of N.Y., 1983—. Mem. Fed. Magistrate Judges Assn., Assn. Bar City of N.Y. (mem. adminstrv. law com. 1973-74, mem. fed. cts. com. 1981-84, mem. com. on state cts. of superior jurisdiction 1984-87, mem. libr. com. 1989-92), Nat. Assn. Women Judges, N.Y. Assn. Women Judges, N.Y. County Lawyers Assn. Office: US Courthouse 500 Pearl St New York NY 10007-1312

LEE, BARBARA ANNE, educator, lawyer; b. Newton, N.J., Apr. 9, 1949; d. Robert Hanna and Keren (Dalrymple) L.; m. James Paul Begin, Aug. 14, 1982; 1 child, Robert James. B.A., U. Vt., 1971; M.A., Ohio State U., 1972; J.D., Georgetown U., 1982; Ph.D., Ohio State U., 1977. Bar: N.J. 1983, U.S. Dist. Ct. N. J. 1983. Instr., Franklin U. Columbus, Ohio, 1974-75; rsch. asst. Ohio State U., Columbus, 1975-77; policy analyst Dept. Edn., Washington, 1978-80; dir. data trends Carnegie Found., Princeton, N.J., 1980-82; asst. prof. Grad. Sch. Edn., Rutgers U., 1982-84; asst. prof. Inst. Mgmt. and Labor Rels., Rutgers U., New Brunswick, N.J., 1984-88, assoc. prof. 1988-94, prof. 1994—, acting assoc. provost 1995—; mem. Study Group on Excellence in Higher Edn., Nat. Inst. Edn., 1983-84; project dir. Carnegie Corp., N.Y.C., 1982-84. Corse fellow U. Vt., 1971; recipient John F. Kennedy Labor Law award Georgetown U., 1982; grantee Bur. Labor-Mgmt. Rels. and Coop. Programs, 1985-86. Mem. ABA, N.J. Bar Assn. (exec. com. labor and employment law sect. 1987—, women's rights sect.), Mercer County Bar Assn., Princeton Bar Assn., Am. Ednl. Rsch. Assn., Indsl. Rels. Rsch. Assn., Acad. Mgmt., Assn. Study Higher Edn. (legal counsel 1982-88), Nat. Assn. Coll. and Univ. Attys. (vice chair editorial bd. 1986-89, chair 1995—, chair publs. com. 1988-91, bd. dirs. 1990—) Author: Academics in Court, 1987; co-author: The Law of Higher Education, 3d edit., 1995;

---

contbr. numerous articles to profl. jours. Office: Rutgers U IRHR Dept Inst Mgmt & Labor Rels PO Box 5062 New Brunswick NJ 08903-5062

LEE, BERNARD SHING-SHU, research company executive; b. Nanking, People's Republic of China, Dec. 14, 1934; came to U.S., 1949; s. Wei-Kuo and Pei-fen (Tang) L.; m. Pauline Pan; children: Karen, Lesley, Tania. BSc, Poly. Inst. Bklyn., 1956, DSc in Chem. Engring., 1960. Registered profl. engr., N.Y., Ill. With Arthur D. Little, Inc., Cambridge, Mass., 1960-65; with Inst. Gas Tech., Chgo., 1965-78, pres., 1978—; chmn. M-C Power Corp., Burr Ridge, Ill.; bd. dirs. NUI corp., Bedminster, N.J., Nat. Fuel Gas Co., Buffalo, Peerless Mfg. Co., Dallas, Energy BioSystems Corp., The Woodlands, Tex., New Eng. Gas Assn.; chmn. SGT, Shanghai, People's Republic of China. Contbr. more than 60 articles to profl. jours. Recipient Outstanding Personal Achievement in Chem. Engring. award Chem. Engring. mag., 1978. Fellow AAAS, Am. Inst. Chem. Engrs. (33d inst. lectr. 1981); mem. AIME, Am. Chem. Soc., Am. Gas Assn. (Gas Industry Rsch. award 1984), Econ. Club Chgo. Office: Inst Gas Tech 1700 S Mt Prospect Rd Des Plaines IL 60018

LEE, BETTY REDDING, architect; b. Shreveport, La., Dec. 6, 1919; d. Joseph Alsop and Mary (Byrd) Redding; m. Frank Cayce Lee, Nov. 22, 1940 (dec. Aug. 1978); children: Cayce Redding, Clifton Monroe, Mary Byrd (Mrs. Kent Ray). Student La. State U., 1936-37, 37-38, U. Calif. War Extension Coll., San Diego, 1942-43; student Centenary Coll., 1937; attended Roofing Industry Ednl. Inst., 1980-82, 84, 86-88, 89-90, 93, Better Understanding Roofing Systems Inst., 1989. Sheetmetal worker Consol.-Vultee, San Diego, 1942; engring. draftsman, 1943-45; jr. to sr. archtl. draftsman Bodman & Murrell, Baton Rouge, 1945-55; sr. archtl. draftsman to architect Post & Harelson, Baton Rouge, 1955-58; assoc. arch. G. Ross Murrell, Jr., Baton Rouge, 1966-70; staff arch. Charles E. Schwing & Assos., Baton Rouge, 1966-71, Kenneth C. Landry, Baton Rouge, 1971, 73-74; design draftsman Rayner & McKenzie, Baton Rouge, 1972-73; cons. arch. and planner Office Engring. and Cons. Svcs., La. Dept. Health and Human Resources, Baton Rouge, 1974-82; arch. roofing and weatherproofing sect. La. Dept. Facility Planning and Control, 1982—. Author Instructions to Designers for Roofing Systems for Louisiana Public Buildings; co-author: Building Owners Guide for Protecting and Maintaining Built-Up Roofing Systems, 1981; designed typical La. country store for La. Arts and Sci. Ctr. Mus. Recipient Honor award Schuller BURSI Group, 1989, 90, 91, 92, 93. Mem. La. Assn. Children with Learning Disabilities, 1967-69, Multiple Sclerosis Soc., 1963—, CPA Aux., 1969-69, PTA, 1953-66; troop leader Brownies and Girl Scouts U.S.A., 1959-60; asst. den mother Cub Scouts, 1955-57. Licensed architect. Mem. ASTM, Nat. AIA, AIA La., AIA Baton Rouge (first woman mem.), DAR, Constrn. Specifications Inst. (charter mem. Baton Rouge chpt.) So. Bldg. Code Congress Internat., Miss. Roofing Contractors Assn. (first woman hon.), Nat. Roofing Contractors Assn., La. Inst. Bldg. Scis. (founding mem. 1980), Roof Cons. Inst. (govt. liaison mem.), Jr. League Baton Rouge., Le Salon du Livre Club, Kappa Delta. Republican. Episcopalian. Home: 1994 Longwood Dr Baton Rouge LA 70808-1247 Office: Capitol Sta PO Box 94095 Baton Rouge LA 70804-9095

LEE, BEVERLY ING, educational administrator; b. Honolulu, Oct. 10, 1932; d. Tim Sheu and Helen (Heu) Ing; m. Daniel David Lee, June 21, 1962; children: Helen Ann Esq, Terence Daniel, Scott David. BA, Coll. of the Pacific, Stockton, Calif., 1954; MA, Columbia U., 1957. Policewoman Honolulu Police Dept., 1957-61; counselor Ewa Elem., Highlands Intermediate and Waipahu High Schs., 1961-69; adminstr. Dept. Edn. State of Hawaii, Honolulu, 1969-89; contr., v.p., pres. Classic Travel, Honolulu, 1988—; bd. dirs. Hawaii State Employee's Credit Union, Honolulu, 1986-91, 93—, vice chairperson, 1994, chairperson, 1995, John Howard Assn., Honolulu, 1985-92. Mem., chairperson Gov.'s Commn. on Honolulu, 1985-93. Mem. AAUW (life), Hawaiian Airlines Travel Agy. (adv. bd. 1991-93), Mahalo Airlines Travel Agy. (adv. bd. 1994—), Travel U. Internat. (adv. bd. 1994—), Casey Family (adv. bd. 1986—), Prevent Child Abuse Hawaii (bd. dir. 1975—), Child & Family Svcs. (bd. dir. 1975-85), Delta Kappa Gamma, Tri Delta. Avocations: travel, plants, photography. Office: Classic Travel 1413 S King St Ste 201 Honolulu HI 96814-2505

LEE, BRANT THOMAS, lawyer, federal official; b. San Francisco, Feb. 17, 1962; s. Ford and Patricia (Leong) L.; m. Marie Bernadette Curry, Sept. 20, 1991. BA in Philosophy, U. Calif., Berkeley, 1985; JD, Harvard U., 1990, M in Pub. Policy, 1994. Bar: Calif. 1992. Counsel subcom. on Constitution, U.S. Senate Judiciary Com., Washington, 1990-92; assoc. Breon, O'Donnell, Miller, Brown & Dannis, San Francisco, 1992—; dep. staff sec., spl. asst. to Pres. (acting) Washington, 1993. Trustee Chinese for Affirmative Action, San Francisco, 1992—; bd. dirs. Conf. Asian Pacific Am. Leadership, Washington, 1990-92; staff mem. Dukakis for Pres., Boston, 1988. Mem. Bar Assn. San Francisco, Nat. Asian Pacific Am. Bar Assn. Office: Breon O'Donnell Miller et al 71 Stevenson St San Francisco CA 94105-2934

LEE, BRENDA (BRENDA MAE TARPLEY), singer, entertainer; b. Lithonia, Ga., Dec. 11, 1944; m. Ronnie Shacklett; children: Julie, Jolie. First appeared on Red Foley Ozark Jubilee Show, 1956; appeared in Opryland USA Show, Nashville, Music! Music! Music! Starring Brenda Lee, 1988; appeared in film Smokey and the Bandit II, 1980, in cable TV spl. Legendary Ladies, 1986, in PBS spl. Shake Rattle and Roll, 1988; recs. include Brenda Lee, 1960, Sincerely, 1961, All Alone Am I, 1962, By Request, 1964, Bye Bye Blues, 1966, 10 Golden Years, 1966, Memphis Portrait, 1970, Now, 1975, and many others; recent albums include Brenda Lee, 1991, Anthology Vols. 1 & 2, 1991, Greatest Hits Live, 1992. Recipient Gov.'s award Nat. Acad. Rec. Arts and Scis., 1984. Address: Brenda Lee Entertainments care Ronnie Shacklett PO Box 101188 Nashville TN 37210-1188*

LEE, BRIAN EDWARD, lawyer; b. Oceanside, N.Y., Feb. 29, 1952; s. Lewis H. Jr. and Jean Elinor (Andrews) L.; m. Eleanor L. Barker, June 5, 1982; children: Christopher Martin, Alison Ruth, Danielle Andrea. AB, Colgate U., 1974; JD, Valparaiso U., 1976. Bar: N.Y. 1977, U.S. Dist. Ct. (so. and ea. dists.) N.Y. 1978, U.S.C. Ct. Appeals (2nd cir. 1992). Assoc. Marshall, Bellofatto & Callahan, Lynbrook, N.Y., 1977-80, Morris, Duffy, Ivone & Jensen, N.Y.C., 1980-84; sr. assoc. Ivone, Devine & Jensen, Lake Success, N.Y., 1984-85, ptnr., 1985—. Pres., trustee Trinity Christian Sch. of Montville Inc., N.J., 1985—. Mem. ABA, N.Y. State Bar Assn., N.Y. County Lawyers Assn., Christian Legal Soc. Republican. Baptist. Home: 292 Jacksonville Rd Pompton Plains NJ 07444-1511 Office: Ivone Devine & Jensen 2001 Marcus Ave Lake Success NY 11042-1024

LEE, BURNS WELLS, public relations executive; b. St. Louis, July 21, 1913; s. Channing B. and Rae (Wells) L.; m. Pauline Slocum, Apr. 10, 1939 (div.); m. Kathleen Booth Strutt, July 1, 1960. A.B., Occidental Coll., 1935. Publicity dir. Benton & Bowles, Inc., N.Y.C., Hollywood, 1939-42; sr. specialist war savs. staff Treasury Dept., Washington, 1942-43; pub. relations mgr. Rexall Drug Co., Los Angeles, 1946-49; pres. Bergen & Lee, Inc., Los Angeles, 1949—. Served as pub. relations officer USMCR, 1943-46. Mem. Pub. Rels. Soc. Am. (chmn. com. standards of profl. practice 1951, regional v.p. 1952-53, chmn. pub. rels. reference round table 1954-55, chmn. eligibility com. 1962, chmn. grievance bd. 1965-66, chmn. spl. task force on pub. rels. 1975-77, 1st ann. professionalism award L.A. chpt. 1964), Regional Plan Assn. So. Calif. (dir. 1970-84), L.A. C. of C. (chmn. pub. rels., bus. outlook conf. 1974, mem. exec. com., internat. commerce coun. 1979-83, 85-89), GrandPeople (L.A., mem. bd. dirs. 1988-92),Exec. Svc. Corps (cons. L.A. chpt. 1991—), Publicity Club L.A., Rotary L.A. (editor weekly publ. 1993—). Home: 870 Rome Dr Los Angeles CA 90065-3215 Office: 123 S Figueroa St Ste 200B Los Angeles CA 90012-2469

LEE, CARLA ANN BOUSKA, nursing educator; b. Ellsworth, Kans., Nov. 26, 1943; d. Frank J. and Christine Rose (Vopat) Bouska; m. Gordon Larry Lee, July 8, 1967. RN, Marymount Coll., Salina, Kans., 1964; BSN, U. Kans., 1967; MA, Wichita State U., 1972, EdS, 1975, M in Nursing, 1984; PhD, Kans. State U., 1988. RN; cert. family and adult nurse practitioner, advanced nurse adminstr., med.-surg. nurse clin. specialist. Staff, charge nurse Ellsworth (Kans.) County Vet. Meml. Hosp., 1964-65; critical, coronary, and surg. nurse Med. Ctr. U. Kans., Kansas City, 1966-67; asst. dir., chief instr. sch. nursing Wesley Sch. Nursing, Wichita, Kans., 1967-74; asst. prof. Wichita State U., 1974-92; asst. prof., dir. nurse practitioner

---

program Ft. Hays State U., Hays, Kans., 1992—; lectr. Wichita State U., 1972-74; cons. Hays Med. Ctr./Family Healthcare Ctr., 1993—, Baker U., Northeastern U., Boston; mem. adv. coun. Kans. Newman Coll.; adv. bd. Kans. Originals, Kans. Dept. Econ. Devel. Project, Wilson; mem. grad. faculty U. Kans., 1993—, Wichita State U., 1993—; rschr. in field. Author: (with Barrett) Fluids & Electrolytes: A Basic Approach, 3d edit., 1984 (poetry) Seasons: Marks of Life, 1991 (Golden Poet award 1991), (booklet) Czechoslavakian History, 1988; author, editor History of Kansas Nursing, 1987; contbr. articles to profl. jours. Co-founder Kans. Nurses Found., pres., trustee; vol. ARC, 1967-90, bd. dirs., 1977-90; mem. researcher Gov.'s Commn. Health Care, Topeka, 1990; city coord. campaign Sec. State, 1986; vol., lectr. Am. Heart Assn., Am. Cancer Soc., 1967—; election judge Sedgwick County, Kans., 1989—. Nurse Practitioner Tng. grantee U.S. Health and Human Svcs.; named Outstanding Community Leader, Jaycees, Alumnus of Yr., Kansas U., Marymount Coll.; recipient Tchr. award Mortar Bd. Fellow Am. Acad. Nursing; mem. ANA (credentialing ctr.), Kans. State Nurses Assn. (bd. dirs., treas.), Kans. Alliance of Advanced Nurse Practitioner's (founder, pres.), Great Plains Nurse Practitioner's Soc. (founder, pres.), Alpha Eta (Wichita State U. chpt. pres.). Republican. Roman Catholic. Avocations: poetry, music, gardening, writing, sewing. Home: 1367 N Westlink St Wichita KS 67212-4238 Office: Ft Hays State U 600 Park St Hays KS 67601-4059

LEE, CATHERINE, sculptor, painter; b. Pampa, Tex., Apr. 11, 1950. BA, San Jose State U., 1975. artist-in-residence Mpls. Coll. Art & Design, Minn. Inst. Art, 1982; vis. asst. prof. painting U. Tex., San Antonio, 1983; adj. asst. prof. Columbia U., N.Y.C., 1986-87. Group exhbns. include Albright-Knox Mus., Buffalo, 1987, Biennale de Sculpture, Monte Carlo, Monaco, 1991, Mus. Folkwang, Essen, Germany, 1992, Stadtiche Galerie im Lenbachhaus, Munich, 1992, Neue Galerie Der Stadt Linz, Austria, 1992, Cleve. Mus. of Art, 1993, The Tate Gallery, 1994, many others. Creative Artists Pub. Svc. fellow, 1978; NEA grantee, 1989. Office: 106 Spring St New York NY 10012 also: Galerie Karsten Greve, Wallrafplatz 3, 5000 Koln Germany also: Galerie Lelong 20 W 57th New York NY 10019

LEE, CHARLES, retired English language and literature educator, arts critic; b. Phila., Jan. 2, 1913; s. Benjamin and Lillian (Potash) Levy; divorced; children: Myles E., Gail M. A.B., U. Pa., 1933, M.A., 1936, Ph.D., 1955. Lit. editor Boston Herald-Traveler, 1936-40; contbg. reviewer N.Y. Times Book Review, 1942-58; Lit. editor Phila. Record, 1940-47; contbg. reviewer Phila. Evening Bulletin, 1947-49; faculty U. Pa., 1949-65, prof. communications, 1959-65, prof. English, 1959-83, emeritus prof. English, 1983—; vice dean Annenberg Sch. Communications, 1959-65; roving critic WCAU radio, 1960-65, WCAU-TV, 1965-73; entertainments editor WCAU radio, 1974-79; roving critic WFLN-AM & FM, 1979—; creative cons. Four-Star Internat., Hollywood. Exhibited: one-man art show Janet Fleisher Gallery, Phila., 1972, Faculty Club, U. Pa., 1985, 89, Designer's Corner Gallery, 1990, Burrison Gallery, U. Pa., 1991, 93; author Exile: A Book of Verse, 1936, How to Enjoy Reading, 1939, An Almanac of Reading, 1940, Weekend at the Waldorf, 1945, North East, South, West, 1945, The Twin Bedside Anthology, 1946, Snow, Ice and Penguins, 1950, I'll Be Waiting, 1958, The Hidden Public, 1958; Editor (author preface): The State of the Nation, 1963, Sevens Come Eleven, 1972, Ten Sevens, 1982, Love, Life and Laughter, 1990. Recipient 1st award for meritorious achievement in journalism U. Pa., 1944, achievement award Logan Square East, 1991, citation City of Phila., 1993. Mem. Soc. Am. Historians, A.A.U.P., Phi Beta Kappa. Home: Presdl Apts Philadelphia PA 19131 *Savor the sun. Study the dust. Enjoy what you can. Endure what you must.*

LEE, CHARLES ROBERT, telecommunications company executive; b. 1939; married. BS in Metall. Engring., Cornell U., 1962; MBA, Harvard U., 1964. Mgr. bus. research U.S. Steel Co., 1964-70; v.p., dir. Victor Palmiere Co., 1970-79; sr. v.p. fin. Columbia Pictures Industries., 1979-83; sr. v.p. fin. and planning GTE Corp., Stamford, CT, 1983-88, pres., chief oper. officer, 1989-92, chmn., chief exec. officer, 1992—; also bd. dirs.; also pres. Contel Corp., Stamford, Conn.; bd. dirs. Travelers Corp., USX Corp., Contel Cellular Corp. Mem. Fin. Execs. Inst., Nat. Planning Assn. (com. on new Am. realities), Stanwich Club. Office: GTE Corp 1 Stamford Forum Stamford CT 06904 also: Anglo-Can Tel Co, 8750 Cote de Liesse Rd, Montreal, PQ Canada H41 1H3*

LEE, CHARLES TOMERLIN, lawyer; b. N.Y.C., Feb. 20, 1950; s. Thomas Bailey and Sarah (Tomerlin) L.; m. Leslie Simmons, May 19, 1979; children: Thomas, Leslie. BA, Harvard U., 1972; JD, Columbia U., 1976. Assoc. Webster & Sheffield, N.Y.C., 1976-84; assoc., now ptnr. Paul, Hastings, Janofsky & Walker, Stamford, Conn., 1984—. Founder, pub. Noonmark mag., 1967; founder Harvard Ind., 1969. Chmn. Urban Redevel. Commn., Stamford, 1984-91; dir. Hartman Found., 1984—. Mem. Harvard Club N.Y.C. (sec. 1990—). Avocations: history, hiking, skiing. Office: Paul Hastings Janofsky & Walker 1055 Washington Blvd Fl 9 Stamford CT 06901-2222

LEE, CHESTER MAURICE, government official; b. New Derry, Pa., Apr. 6, 1919; s. Joseph and Mary L.; m. Rose McGinnis, Apr. 18, 1942; children: Suzanne D., David J., Virginia A., Nancy M. B.S., U.S. Naval Acad., 1941; postgrad., George Washington U., 1962-63. Nat. War Coll., 1962-63. Commd. ensign U.S. Navy, 1941, advanced through grades to capt., 1961; comdg. officer U.S.S. Rodman, Charleston, S.C., 1952-53; instr. Gen. Line Sch., Monterey, Calif., 1953-56; with Spl. Projects Office, Bur. Naval Weapons, Washington, 1956-58, 60-62; comdg. officer U.S.S. Gyatt, Norfolk, 1958-60; comdr. Destroyer Div. 132, Long Beach, 1963-64; with Office Sec. Def., Washington, 1964-65; ret., 1965; with NASA, Washington, 1965-87; dir. Apollo Mission NASA, 1969-72, program dir. Apollo/Soyuz Test Project, 1973-75, dir. space transp. systems utilization, 1975-81, dir. customer services, 1981-87, asst. assoc. adminstr. Office of Space Flight, from 1987; now v.p. Spacehab Inc., Washington. Decorated Navy Commendation medal; recipient 2 Exceptional Service medals, 1969, 3 Distinguished Service medals, 1973, 75, 87, Distinguished Service medals NASA., Outstanding Leadership medal; Pres.' Rank of Meritorious Exec. with Sr. Exec. Service. Fellow AIAA (assoc.), Am. Astronautic Soc. Office: Spacehab Inc 600 Maryland Ave SW Ste 530 Washington DC 20024-2520

LEE, CHIN O., physiologist, educator; b. Tanyang, Choongbuk, Korea, June 8, 1939; came to U.S., 1968; s. Yoon Hee and Kyung Duk (Song) L.; m. Kwang-Hee Kim, Sept. 20, 1969; children: Albert, Daniel. BS, Seoul Nat. U., 1965; PhD, Ind. U., 1972. Postdoctoral fellow U. Chgo., 1972-76; asst. prof. Cornell U. Med. Coll., Ithaca, N.Y., 1976-81, assoc. prof., 1981-86, full prof., 1986-92, adj. prof., 1993—; prof., dept. life scis. Pohang U. Sci. and Tech., Korea, 1992—. Author 40 jour. articles and review papers. Recipient Louis N. Katz Basic Sci. prize Am. Heart Assn., 1974, Established Investigator, 1976; Pfizer award Outstanding Rsch., Internat. Soc. Heart Rsch., 1986; Overseas Vis. fellow British Heart Found., London, 1990. Mem. Am. Physiol. Soc. (editorial bd. 1981-90), Biophys. Soc., Soc. General Physiol., Am. Heart Assn., Korean Scientist Engrs. Assn. (pres. 1989-90 councillor). Home: 1161 York Ave New York NY 10021-7940 Office: Cornell U Med Coll 1300 York Ave New York NY 10021-4805

LEE, CHIN-TIAN, academic administrator, agricultural studies educator; b. Chiayi, Taiwan, June 22, 1940; came to U.S., 1967; s. Pau-Tong and Wu-May (Yang) L.; m. Shu-Teh Kuo, June 22, 1969; Corinna T., Frances T. BS, Nat. Taiwan U., Taipei, 1964, MS, 1967; MS, U. Wis., 1969, PhD, 1971. Rsch. asst. Nat. Taiwan U., Taipei, 1965-67; rsch. asst. U. Wis., Madison, 1967-71, biologist, 1971-74; asst. prof. U. Guam, Mangilao, 1974-80; assoc. prof. U. Guam, Manigilao, 1980-87, prof., 1987—; dean coll. agriculture, 1989—; dir. Guam Coop. Extension Svc., Mangilao, 1989—, Guam Agrl. Expt. Sta., Mangilao 1989—; cons. South Pacific Commn., Suva, Fiji, 1978. Contbr. articles to profl. jours. Vice-chmn. bd. dirs. Chinese Sch. Guam, Harmon, 1984-88, advisor, 1989-91, chmn., 1992—. 2d lt. Taiwanese Air Force, 1965. Recipient Outstanding Prof. award 19th Guam Legislature; grantee USDA, 1981-89. Mem. Chinese Assn. Agrl. Sci., Asian Assn. Colls. and Univs. (bd. dirs. 1989—), We. Assn. Agrl. Exptl. Sta. Dirs., Am. Soc. Agronomy, Am. Soc. Horticultural Sci., Epsilon Sigma Phi. Avocations: reading, gardening, traveling, swimming, fishing. Home: Y-Papao Estates 156 Bengbing St Dededo GU 96912 Office: U Guam Coll Agriculture Coll Agriculture UDG Sta Mangilao GU 96923

LEE, CHONG-SIK, political scientist, educator; b. Anju, Korea, July 30, 1931; came to U.S., 1954, naturalized, 1969; s. Bong-Joo and Bong-kye (Moon) L.; m. Myung-Sook Woo, Mar. 19, 1962; children—Sharon, Gina, Roger. B.A., UCLA, 1956, M.A., 1957; Ph.D., U. Calif., Berkeley, 1961. Instr. polit. sci. U. Colo., Boulder, 1960-61, Dartmouth Coll., Hanover, N.H., 1961-63; asst. prof. U. Pa., Phila., 1963-65; assoc. prof. U. Pa., 1965-73, prof., 1973—; dir. Anspach Inst. Diplomacy and Fgn. Affairs, 1980-85, chmn. grad. program internat. relations, 1980-85; chmn. joint com. on Korean Studies Social Sci. Research Council and Am. Council Learned Socs., 1970-77. Author: The Politics of Korean Nationalism, 1963, Counterinsurgency in Manchuria: The Japanese Experience, 1931-40, 1967, (with Robert A. Scalapino) Communism in Korea, 1973, The Life of Kim Kyu-sik, 1974, Materials on Korean Communism, 1945-47, 1977, The Korean Workers' Party: A Short History, 1978, Revolutionary Struggle in Manchuria: Chinese Communism and Soviet Interest, 1922-1945, 1983, Japan and Korea: The Political Dimension, 1985; (with Mike Langford) Korea: Land of Morning Calm, 1988, Recollections of Anti-Japanese Revolutionaries, 1988, Korea Briefing, 1990, 91, North Korea in Transition, 1991, In Search of a New Order in East Asia, 1991; mem. editorial bd.: Asian Survey, 1973—, Jour. N.E. Asian Studies, 1982—, Orbis, 1980-86. Mem. Task Force on Equal Ednl. Opportunity and Quality Edn., Pa. Higher Edn. Planning Commn., 1977. Social Sci. Rsch. Coun. grantee, 1963, 66-67, 72, 73-74, Rockefeller Found. grantee, 1965-66, Hoover Inst. grantee, 1980, Yonkang Found. grantee, 1990-93; Ford Found. faculty fellow, 1969-70. Mem. Am. Polit. Sci. Assn. (Woodrow Wilson Found. award for best book in polit. sci. 1974), Assn. Asian Studies. Home: 8 Cypress Ln Berwyn PA 19312-1005 Office: Univ Pa Dept Polit Sci Philadelphia PA 19104-6215

LEE, CHOOCHON, physics educator, researcher; b. Seoul, Korea, June 8, 1930; came to U.S., 1962; s. Yoon Young and Soon Ye (Rhee) L.; m. Chung Sun Yun, Apr. 9, 1960; children: John Taihee, Jane Eun Kyoung, Carol Eunmee. BS in Physics, Seoul Nat. U., 1953, MS in Physics, 1957; PhD in Physics, U. Ill., 1968. From instr. to asst. prof. Seoul Nat. U., 1957-62; rsch. assoc. U. Ill., Urbana, 1968; rsch. physicist U. Montreal, Que., Can., 1968-75; assoc. prof. Korea Advanced Inst. Sci. and Tech., Seoul, Taejon, 1975-78, prof., 1978-92, Korea Telecom. Found. prof. physics, 1992—; pres. Korea Advanced Inst. Sci. and Tech., Seoul, 1980-92; vis. scholar Harvard U., Cambridge, Mass., 1982-83, 87-88. Author: Physics of Semiconductor Materials and Applications, 1986; contbr. over 130 articles to profl. jours. Recipient Presdl. Sci. prize Pres. Korean Govt., 1985, Incheon prize in Acad. Achievement, 1993, Order of Rose of Sharon, 1995. Mem. IEEE, Am. Phys. Soc., Korean Phys. Soc. (pres. 1991-93), Soc. Info. Display (bd. dirs. 1991—). Methodist. Achievements include discovery of negative staerblewronski experiment; first to confirm mechanism of Controversial State III annealing in gold, to explain persistent photocontercivity in a-Si:H and a-Si:H/a-SiN multilayers; 1st observation of persistent photo conductivity in porous silicon. Home: 237 Kajong-dong KIT Apt 15-201, Yusongku Taejon 305-350, Republic of Korea Office: Korea Advanced Inst Sci and Tech, 373-1 Kusong-dong Yusong-ku, Taejon 305-701, Republic of Korea

LEE, CHRISTOPHER FRANK CARANDINI, actor, author; b. London, May 27, 1922; s. Geoffrey Trollope and Estelle Marie (Carandini) L.; m. Birgit Kroencke, Mar. 17, 1961; 1 child, Christina Erika. Student Brit. schs. With theatrical and film industry, 1947—; films include Corridor of Mirrors, 1947, The Curse of Frankenstein, 1956, Dracula, 1958, The Three Musketeers, 1974, The Four Musketeers, 1975, The Man with the Golden Gun, 1974, Airport 77, 1977, Caravans, 1978, Return from Witch Mountain, 1978, Circle of Iron, 1979, The Passage, 1979, The Wicker Man, 1974, Jaguar Lives, 1979, 1941, 1980, Bear Island, 1980, The Salamander, 1981, An Eye for an Eye, 1981, Safari 3000, 1982, The Last Unicorn, 1982, The Return of Captain Invincible, 1983, House of the Long Shadows, 1984, Murder Story, 1989, The Return of the Musketeers, 1989, Gremlins 2, 1990, Honeymoon Academy, 1990, Gremlins II: The New Batch, 1990, Police Academy: Mission to Moscow, 1994; appeared in TV miniseries: The Pirate, 1978, Captain America II, 1979, Goliath Awaits, 1981, The Far Pavilions, 1984, Roadtrip, Mio My Mio, The Girl; TV movies include: Poor Devil, 1973, Once Upon a Spy, 1980, Charles and Diana: A Royal Love Story, 1982, The Disputation, Metier du Seigneur, Shaka Zulu, Around the World in Eighty Days, Treasure Island; author: autobiography Tall Dark and Fearsome, 1977, The Great Villains, 1979, Archives of Evil. Served with RAF, 1941-45. Decorated Polonia Restituta, Czechoslovak Medal for Valor, officer Arts, Lettres et Scis., France. Mem. Screen Actors Guild, Brit. Actors Equity, Variety, Clubs Internat. Conservative. Mem. Ch. of Eng. Clubs: Hon. Company Edinburgh Golfers; Bucks's (London); Travellers (Paris); Bel-Air Country (Los Angeles). Office: Don Buchwald & Assoc 9229 Sunset Blvd Ste 710 Los Angeles CA 90069*

LEE, CHRISTOPHER HEINZ, destination management consultant; b. San Diego, Mar. 13, 1965; s. Phillip Craig and Ilse (Blömer) L. Mgr. mktg. Westin Bonaventure Hotel, L.A., 1985-86, Calif. Leisure Cons., L.A., 1986-87; owner, v.p. Mktg. Inspired Mgmt., San Diego, 1987-89; div. v.p. Bill Communications, N.Y.C., 1988-89; owner, pres. Calif. Leisure Cons., San Diego, 1989—; cons. in field. Mem. sales com. San Diego Conv. and Visitors Bur., 1990. Named Abrams Attrdige Outstanding Leader, 1983. Mem. Execs. Assn., San Diego C. of C. (mem. com. 1990). Republican. Roman Catholic. Avocations: skiing, scuba, soccer, golf, tennis. Office: Calif Leisure Consultants 1775 Hancock St Ste 280 San Diego CA 92110-2036

LEE, CLEMENT WILLIAM KHAN, association administrator; b. N.Y.C., Feb. 7, 1938; s. William P. and Helen M. BTh, Concordia Coll., 1958; MDiv, Concordia Theol. Sem., 1962; MA, New Sch. for Social Research, 1976. Asst. exec. dir. Greater Detroit Luth. Ctr., 1962; editor Detroit and Suburban Luth. Newspaper, 1963; assoc. communications dir. Met. Detroit Council of Chs., 1964; dir. media ops. Am. Bible Soc., N.Y.C., 1967; dir. media relations Luth. Council U.S.A., N.Y.C., 1971-82, asst. exec. dir. communications and interpretation, 1977-82; dir. dept. telecommunications Luth. Ch. in Am., N.Y.C., 1983-87; dir. electronic media Episcopal Ch., N.Y.C., 1987-93, program dep. for communication, 1989-93, Episcopal telecomm. dir., 1993—; media cons. Luth. Ch.-Mo. Synod, Spaulding for Children, Metro News of Metro N.Y., Synod of Luth. Ch. Am., archtl. newsletter Window, Luth. Deaconess Assn., Concordia Coll., Bronxville, Physicians for Social Responsibility, Wheatridge Found., Luth. Sch. Theology, Chgo.; chmn. broadcast ops. com. Nat. Council Chs. of Christ U.S.A., 1976-80; vice chmn. bd. mgrs. Communications Commn., 1977-80; chmn. inter-faith Media Data System, 1981; mem. TV awards com. N.Y. Council Chs.; mgr. Lutherans-in-Media Conf. I and II, 1980, Luth. Audio-Visual Conf., 1981; project dir. Lambeth Conf. Inter-Anglican Telecommunication Network, 1988; internat. computer network resource leader Religious Communications Congress 90, 1990; bd. dirs. FACTA TV News, Inc.; pres. N.Y. chpt. Religious Pub. Rels. Coun.; telecommunication cons. World Coun. of Chs., Canberra Assembly, 1990-91, Episc. Bd. Theol. Edn., 1993—. Editor: Media Alert newsletter, 1980-86, Luth. Communication newsletter, 1983-87, Episcopal Media Adv. newsletter, 1989—; creator children's TV series Storyline; producer multi-image sequences, Augustana Jubilee, 1980, multi-image program Proclaim, 1984, multi-image effects, Milw. Conv., 1986, (films) Mission on Six Continents, 1975, Room for a Stranger, 1978, Winter Wheat, 1982; exec. producer, One in Mission, 1985, Gathering of the Family, 1988, Doers of the Word, 1988, The Tully-Freeman Report, 1988, Outpourings of Love, 1989, Faith on a Tightrope, 1989, Fresh Winds Blowing, 1989, Prophecy Fulfilled in Me, 1990, President Carter Center Health Video, 1990, To Walk in Beauty, 1990, Pathways for Peace, 1990, Word in the World, 1991, Executive Council Presents, 1991, Cantenbury in North Carolina, 1992. Mem. Metro N.Y. Synod Evangelical Luth. Ch. in Am. Communication Commn., Religious Pub. Rels. Coun.; mem. communication dept. nat. adv. com. Evang. Luth. Ch. in Am.; chair Telecomm. Task Force Lambeth Anglican Bishops Confs., 1988, Bldg. Restoration com. St. John's Episc. Ch., N.Y.C., 1993-95; gov. Inter-Anglican Info. Network Quest Internat. Mgmt. team, 1992—. Recipient award Detroit Press Club Found., 1963, silver medal Internat. Film and TV Festival, 1975, 79, Creative Excellence award U.S. Indsl. Film Festival, 1986, Brit. Telecommunications award, 1988, Polly Bond award, 1989, 90, 91, 92, N.Y. TV Festival finalist, 1990. Mem. Assn. Edn. Communication Tech., Internat. Assn. Bus. Communicators, Internat. TV Assn., World Assn. Christian Communication (chmn. N.Am. broadcast sect. 1975), Nat. Interfaith Cable Coalition VISN (members' com.), Satellite TV Network (bd. dirs.), Episcopal Cathedral Teleconferencing Network

---

(steering com.). Office: Episcopal Ch Nat Office 815 2nd Ave New York NY 10017-4503

LEE, DAI-KEONG, composer; b. Honolulu, Sept. 2, 1915; s. Hoo and Young Kun (Lee) L.; m. Dorothy Isabelle Moncur. Student in pre-medicine, U. Hawaii, 1933-36; scholarship student with Roger Sessions, N.Y.C., 1937-38; fellowship student under Frederick Jacobi, Juilliard Grad. Sch., 1938-41; fellowship student under Aaron Copland, Berkshire Music Ctr., summer 1941; M.A. under Otto Luening, Columbia U., 1951. bd. dirs. Am. Music Ctr., N.Y.C., 1960-69. Recorded Prelude, Hula, Symphony No. 1, Polynesian Suite; wrote mus. score for motion picture Letter from Australia, 1945; guest condr., ABC Symphony, Sydney, Australia, 1944-45; composer: orchestral works including Prelude and Hula, 1939, Hawaiian Festival Overture, 1940, Introduction and Allegro for Strings, 1941, Golden Gate Overture for Chamber Orch., 1941, Polynesian Suite, Symphony No. 1, 1941, revised 1947, Symphony No. 2, 1952; chamber works including String Quartet No. 1, 1947, Sonatina for Piano, 1947, Incantation and Dance for Piano and Violin, 1948, Introduction and Allegro for Cello and Piano, 1947; opera Open the Gates, produced by Blackfriars, N.Y.C., 1951; ballet Waltzing Matilda, 1951; mus. score Teahouse of the August Moon, produced by Maurice Evans-George Shaeffer, 1953; Polynesian Suite for Orch., 1958, Violin Concerto, 1947, revised 1955, Mele Olili for Chorus, Solo and Orch., 1960, Canticle of the Pacific, 1968; mus. play Noa-Noa, 1972; Mortal Thoughts of a Buddhist Monk for baritone, chorus and orch., 1976; one-act opera Ballad of Kitty the Barkeep, 1979; mus. plays Jenny Lind, 1981, Gauguin, Maker of Sea and Sky, 1994; Concerto Grosso for string orch., 1952, rev., 1985; contbr. articles to music mags., newspapers. Served with AUS, 1942-45, PTO. Received Albert Metz commn. for violin concerto, 1946; received CBS commn. for Introduction and Allegro for Strings, 1941, Inst. Mus. Art commn. for one-act opera, Poet's Dilemma, 1940; recipient hon. mention Prix de Rome competition Am. Acad. in Rome, 1942; Guggenheim fellow, 1945, 51. Mem. ASCAP, League Composers, Allied MacDowell Club, Dramatists Guild. Composer orchestral, symphonic, chamber music; 1st orchestral work Valse Pensieroso, performed Honolulu Symphony Orch., 1936; works performed by N.Y. Philharm., Eastman Rochester Philharm., Mpls., San Francisco, Cin., CBS, Nat., Montreal, Manila, N.Y.C. Phila., symphony orchs.; under direction of Kurtz, Monteux, Mitropoulos, Goosens, Barlow, Caston, Dixon, Stokowski, Stoessel, Pelletier, Wallenstein, others. Home: 245 W 104th St New York NY 10025-4249

LEE, DAN M., state supreme court justice; b. Petal, Miss., Apr. 19, 1926; s. Buford Aaron and Pherbia Ann (Camp) L.; m. Peggy Jo Daniel, Nov. 27, 1947 (dec. 1952); 1 child, Sheron Diane Lee Anderson; m. Mary Alice Gray, Sept. 30, 1956; 1 child, Dan Jr. Attended, U. So. Miss., 1946; LLB, Jackson Sch. Law, 1949; JD, Miss. Coll., 1970. Bar: Miss. 1948. Ptnr. Franklin & Lee, Jackson, Miss, 1948-54, Lee, Moore and Countiss, Jackson, Miss., 1954-71; county judge Hinds County, Jackson, 1971-77; circuit judge Hinds-Yazoo Counties, Jackson, 1977-82; assoc. justice Miss. Supreme Ct., Jackson, 1982-87, presiding justice, 1987—. Served with U.S. Naval Aviation, 1944-46. Mem. ABA, Hinds County Bar Assn., Miss. State Bar Assn., Aircraft Owners and Pilots Assn., Am. Legion, VFW. Democrat. Baptist. Lodges: Masons, Odd Fellows.

LEE, DAVID JAMES, lawyer; b. Oak Park, Ill., Oct. 7, 1947; s. Bruce David and Jane (Roberts) L.; m. Julia Nelson, May 5, 1990; 1 child, Carson. BS in Chem. Engring. cum laude, Wash. U., 1969; JD, U. Chgo., 1972. Bar: N.Y. 1975, U.S. Dist. Ct. (so. and ea. dist.) N.Y. 1975, U.S. Dist. Ct. (we. dist.) N.Y. 1981, U.S. Ct. Appeals (2d crct.) 1975, U.S. Ct. Appeals (10th crct.) 1979, U.S. Ct. Appeals (4th crct.) 1980, U.S. Ct. Appeals (fed. crct.) 1984, U.S. Supreme Ct. 1990. Summer assoc. Wolfe, Hubbard, Leydig, Voit & Osann, Chgo., 1970, Kirkland & Ellis, Chgo., 1971; law clk. to Hon. Luther M. Swygert U.S. Ct. of Appeals (7th crct.) Ill., Chgo., 1972-73; assoc. Cravath, Swaine & Moore, N.Y.C., 1973-77; ptnr. Fish & Neave, N.Y.C., 1977—; speaker in field. Contbr. articles to law revs. and jours. Mem. ABA, Am. Intellectual Property Law Assn., Assn. of the Bar of City of N.Y. (trademarks and copyrights com. 1988—, chmn. fed. legislation subcom.), N.Y. Patent, Trademark and Copyright Law Assn. (publs. com. 1987-91, patent legislation com. 1989-91). Office: Fish & Neave 1251 Avenue Of The Americas New York NY 10020-1104

LEE, DAVID MORRIS, physics educator; b. Rye, N.Y., Jan. 20, 1931; s. Marvin and Annette (Franks) L.; m. Dana Thorangkul, Sept. 7, 1960; children: Eric Bertel, James Marvin. AB, Harvard U., 1952; MS, U. Conn., 1955; PhD, Yale U., 1959. Instr. of physics Cornell U., Ithaca, N.Y., 1959-60, asst. prof. physics, 1960-63, assoc. prof. physics, 1963-68, prof. physics, 1968—; vis. scientist Brookhaven Nat. Lab., Upton, N.Y., 1966-67; vis. prof. U. Fla., Gainesville, 1974-75, 94, U. Calif., San Diego, La Jolla, 1988; vis. lectr. Peking U., Beijing, China, 1981; chair municipal Joseph Fourier U., Grenoble, France, 1994. Contbr. articles to Phys. Rev. Letters, Phys. Rev., Physica and Nature. With U.S. Army, 1952-54. John Simon Guggenheim fellow Guggenheim Found., 1966-67, 74-75, Japan Soc. Promotion of Scis. fellow, 1977; recipient Sir Francis Simon Meml. prize British Inst. of Physics, 1976. Fellow AAAS, Am. Phys. Soc. (Oliver Buckley prize 1981); mem. Am. Acad. Arts and Scis., Nat. Acad. Scis. Achievements include co-discovery of superfluid 3He, of the tricritical point of 3He-4He mixtures; co-observation of spin waves in spin polarized hydrogen gas. Office: Cornell U Physics Dept Clark Hall Ithaca NY 14853

LEE, DAVID STODDART, investment counselor; b. Boston, Jan. 12, 1934; s. George Cabot and Kathleen Bowring (Stoddart) L.; m. Lucinda Hopkins, Apr. 29, 1972; children: Alexander Putnam, Madeline Jackson, Alice Ingalls. A.B., Harvard U., 1956, M.B.A., 1960. V.p., dir. Lee Higginson Corp., N.Y.C., 1960-65; mng. dir., Scudder, Stevens and Clark, Boston, 1965—; dir., pres., asst. treas. Scudder Investor Svcs., Inc. (formerly Scudder Fund Distbrs.); pres., trustee Scudder Calif. Tax Free Trust, Scudder Cash Investment Trust, Scudder U.S. Treasury Money Fund, Scudder Mcpl. Trust, Scudder State Tax Free Trust, Scudder Tax Free Money Fund, Scudder Tax Free Trust; v.p., trustee Scudder Equity Trust, Scudder GNMA Fund, Scudder Portfolio Trust; v.p. Scudder Devel. Fund, Scudder Funds Trust, Scudder Mut. Funds, Inc., Scudder Investment Trust, Scudder Variable Life Investment Fund, The Argentina Fund, Inc., The Brazil Fund, Inc., The Korea Fund, Inc., The Latin America Dollar Income Fund, Inc., Scudder New Asia Fund, Inc., Scudder New Europe Fund, Inc., Scudder World Income Opportunties Fund, Inc.; v.p., asst. treas. Scudder Global Fund, Inc., Scudder Internat. Fund, Inc.(chmn., dir.), AARP Cash Investment Funds, AARP Growth Trust, AARP Income Trust, AARP Tax Free Income Trust; v.p., dir. Scudder Svc. Corp. Trustee Cotting Sch. for Handicapped Children, Boston, 1974—, New Eng. Med. Ctr., 1974—, The Winsor Sch., 1991—; bd. dirs. Rogerson House, 1978—; corporator Mass. Gen. Hosp., 1975—. Lt. (j.g.) USN, 1956-58. Mem. Soc. Chartered Fin. Analysts (chartered investment counsellor). Republican. Episcopalian. Clubs: Country, Somerset (Boston). Office: 2 International Pl Boston MA 02110

LEE, DON YOON, publisher, academic researcher and writer; b. Seoul, Korea, Apr. 7, 1936; came to U.S., 1957; s. Yoo-ehn and Ch'i-ho (Kim) L. BA, U. Wash., 1963; MA, St. John's U., Jamaica, N.Y., 1967; MS, Georgetown U., 1971; MA, Ind. U., 1975, 90. Founder, pub. Eastern Press, Inc., Bloomington, Ind., 1981—. Author: History of Early Relation Between China and Tibet, 1981, An Introduction to East Asian and Tibetan Linguistics and Culture, 1981, Learning Standard Arabic, 1988, An Annotated Bibliography of Selected Works on China, 1981, Light Literature and Philosophy of East Asia, 1982, An Annotated Bibliography on Inner Asia, 1983, An Annotated Archaeological Bibliography of Selected Works on Norther and Central Asia, 1983, Traditional Chinese Thoughts: The Four Schools, 1990, others. Office: Eastern Press Inc PO Box 881 Bloomington IN 47402-0881

LEE, DONALD JOHN, federal judge; b. 1927. AB, U. Pitts. 1950; LLB, Duquesne U., 1954. Bar: Pa. Supreme Ct. 1955; U.S. Supreme Ct. 1984. Assoc. George Y. Meyer and Assocs., 1954-57; law clk. to Hon. Rabe F. Marsh Jr. U.S. Dist. Ct., Pa., 1957-58; assoc. Willner, Wilner and Kuhn, 1958-61; ptnr. Dougherty, Larrimer & Lee, Pitts., 1961-84, 86-88; judge Ct. Commnon Pleas of Allegheny County, Pa., 1984-86, 88-90, U.S. Dist. Ct. (we. dist.) Pa., Pitts., 1990—; councilman Borough of Green Tree, 1963-65, solicitor, 1963-84, 86-88; spl. asst. atty. gen. Office of Atty. Gen. Commonwealth of Pa., 1963-74; spl. legal counsel Home Rule Study Commn.,

---

Municipality of Bethel Park and Borough of Green Tree, 1973-74, City of Pitts., 1978-80, various municipalities, 1970-86; chmn. Home Rule Charter Transition Com. Bethel Park, 1978. Mem. ad hoc com. Salvation Army. With USN, 1945-47. Mem. ABA, Allegheny County Bar Assn., St. Thomas More Legal Soc., Western Pa. Consevancy, Am. Youth Hostel, Ancient Order of Hibernians, Knights of Equity, Woodland Hills Swim Club, Gaelic League. Office: US Dist Ct 7th Grant St Rm 916 Pittsburgh PA 15219

LEE, DONALD YOUNG (DON LEE), publishing executive, editor, writer; b. Tokyo, Dec. 11, 1959; s. Victor Young and Jean Ann (Kim) L. BA in English, UCLA, 1982; MFA in Creative Writing, Emerson Coll., 1986. Writing instr. Emerson Coll., Boston, 1985-89; mng. editor Ploughshares, Boston, 1988-92, dir., 1992—; panelist NEA Lit. Program, Washington, 1991-92; cons. AGNI, Boston, 1993, Asian Pacific Am. Jour., 1994. Contbr. short stories, articles to jours. St. Botolph Club Found. fellow, 1990, 91. Mem. PEN Am. New Eng. (bd. dirs.). Democrat. Office: Ploughshares Emerson Coll 100 Beacon St Boston MA 02116-1511

LEE, DOUGLAS A., music educator; b. Carmel, Ind., Nov. 3, 1932; s. Ralph Henley and Flossie Ellen (Chandler) Lee; m. Beverly Ruth Haskell, Sept. 2, 1961. MusB with High Distinction, DePauw U., 1954; MusM, U. Mich., 1958, PhD, 1968; postgrad., U. Md., 1985. Instr. Nat. Mus. Camp, Interlochen, Mich., 1959-62; instr. Mt. Union Coll., Alliance, Ohio, 1959-61, chmn. keyboard instrn., 1959-61; asst. prof. Music Wichita (Kans.) State U., 1964-68, assoc. prof., 1968-74, coord. Music History and Lit., 1968-71, coord. grad. studies in Music, 1969-70, chmn. dept. Musicology, 1971-74, prof. Music, 1974-86, administrv. intern, v.p. bus. affairs, 1983; pvt. practice event coord., 1974-85; prof. Musicology Vanderbilt U., Nashville, 1986—, coord. Music History and Lit., advisor, 1987—; radio commentator Sta. KMUW-FM, 1969-76; judge various competitions, Mu Phi Epsilon, 1980, Kans. Music Tchrs. Assn., 1975-83, Baldwin Found. awards, 1979, 80; program annotator Nashville Symphony Orch., 1988—; cons. U.S. Dept. Edn. Jacob Javits fellowship program, 1988, 89, United Meth. Publishing Ho., 1988, Mayfield Pub. Co., 1990. Author: The Instrumental Works of Christoph Nichelmann: The Thematic Index, 1971, Franz Benda: A Thematic Catalogue of His Works, 1984: editor: Christoph Nichelmann: Clavier Concertos in E Major and A Minor, 1977, Six Sonatas for Violin and Bass by Franz Benda, with Embellishments, 1981; contbr. articles to The New Grove Dictionary of Music and Musicians, 1980, The New Grove Dictionary of Music in the United States, 1986; contbr. articles to profl. jours., chpts. to books. With U.S. Army, 1955-57, Japan. Rector Scholar Found., 1950-54; Rackham fellow U. Mich., 1961-65, fellow NEH, 1980, 85, Am. Philos. Soc., 1980, Kans. Arts Coun., 1985, Tenn. Arts Coun., 1988, 89. Mem. Am. Musicological Soc. (program chmn. Midwest chpt. 1984, South-Ctrl. chpt. 1989, nat. coun. 1986, pres. South-Ctrl. chpt. 1990-91), Music Tchrs. Nat. Assn. (editor 1971-90), Am. Soc. Eighteenth Century Studies, Coll. Music Soc., Sonneck Soc. Am. Music (program coord. 1987-88, editor The Sonneck Soc. Bull. 1988-900. Episcopalian. Avocation: photography. Office: Vanderbilt U 2400 Blakemore Ave Nashville TN 37212-3406

LEE, E. BRUCE, electrical engineering educator; b. Brainerd, Minn., Feb. 1, 1932; s. Ernest R. and Hazel B. Lee; m. Judith P. Paine, Apr., 1954; children: Brian, Kevin, Timothy, Joel, Cara, Elizabeth. AA, Brainerd State Coll., 1952; BSME, U. N.D., 1955, MSME, 1956; PhD, U. Minn., 1960. Rsch. engr. Honeywell, Inc., Mpls., 1955-63; assoc. prof. U. Minn., Mpls., 1963-65, prof., 1966—; head dept. elec. engring., 1976-82, acting head elec. engring. dept., 1983-84, assoc. dir. Ctr. for Control Sci., 1984—; cons. Nat. Sci. Found., Washington, 1978-80, Fulbright (CIES), Washington, 1980-82. Author: Foundations of the Optimal Control Theory, 1986. Fellow: IEEE. Home: 1705 Innsbruck Pky Minneapolis MN 55421-2003 Office: U Minn Elec Engring Dept 200 Union St SE Minneapolis MN 55455-0154

LEE, E. DENISE, council woman; d. Lenora Lee; 1 child, Tammy Hudson. Student, Fla. A&M U., Edward Waters Coll. Council woman City of Jacksonville, Fla., 1982—. Bd. Fla. League of Cities, 1987-88, vice chmn. intergovernmental affairs com.; del. Fla. Dem. Conf. Home: 1140 W 10th St Jacksonville FL 32209-5605 Office: Jacksonville City Coun 220 E Bay St Jacksonville FL 32202-3429

LEE, EDWARD BROOKE, JR., real estate executive, fund raiser; b. Silver Spring, Md., Oct. 25, 1917; s. E. Brooke Lee and Elizabeth (Wilson) Aspinwall; m. Camilla Edge, Apr. 15, 1944 (div. Feb. 1983); children: Camilla Lee Alexander, E. Brooke III, Kaiulani Lee Kimbrell, Katherine Blair Lee St. John, Richard Henry, Elizabeth Ashe Somerville; m. Deborah Roche, Apr. 30, 1983; children: Samuel Phillips II, Regina Blair. AB, Princeton U., 1940; student, The Infantry Sch., 1942; postgrad. bus. sch., Harvard U., 1957. Cert. real estate broker Md., D.C., Va. Various indsl. positions to nat. account mgr. Scott Paper Co., Phila., 1940-62; comml. broker Shannon and Luchs, Washington, 1962-83, Merrill Lynch Comml. Realty, Washington, 1983-89, Prudential Preferred Properties, Bethesda, Md., 1989—; pres. E. Brooke Lee Properties, Inc., Montgomery County, Md., 1979—; fund raiser key gifts Nat. Found. for Cancer Research, Bethesda, Md., 1985—; v.p. Ga. Ave. Properties, Montgomery County, Ga.-Conn., Inc., Montgomery County, Conn. Aspen, Inc., Montgomery County, 1962—; sec.-treas. Brooke Lee Family, Inc., Montgomery County, 1962—. Author numerous sales articles for purchasing mags. Chmn. Drug Action Coalition, Inc., fin. v.p., bd. dirs., 1966-70; rep. candidate for Mayor of Washington, 1982, rep. primary candidate for U.S. Senate, State of Md., 1986. Served to capt. inf. U.S. Army, 1943-45, ETO. Named Realtor Assoc. of Yr., Washington Bd. of Realtors, 1984. Mem. Harvard Bus. Sch. Club (pres. 1962, exec. v.p. 1975), Princeton Club of Washington (sec., bd. dirs. 1970-75), Princeton Club of N.Y., Nat. Account Mktg. Assn. (pres. 1959-62). Republican. Episcopalian. Clubs: Met., Chevy Chase Country (Washington). Lodge: Kiwanis. Avocations: tennis, hunting, swimming, sailing, skating. Home: 208 Primrose St Chevy Chase MD 20815-3323 Office: Nat Found Cancer Rsch 7315 Wisconsin Ave Bethesda MD 20814-3202 also: Prudential Preferred 4733 Bethesda Ave Ste 100 Bethesda MD 20814

LEE, EDWARD L., bishop; b. Fort Washington, Pa., 1934; m. Kathryn Fligg, 1961; 1 child, Kathryn E. Grad. cum laude, Brown U., 1956; MDiv, Gen. Theol. Seminary, 1959. Ordained diaconate, priesthood Episc. Ch., 1959. Curate St. Holy Trinity, Phila., 1959-64; Episc. advisor Univ. Christian Movement Temple Univ., Phila., 1964-73; rector St. James Ch., Florence, Italy, 1973-82, St. John's Ch., Washington, 1982-89; bishop Diocese We. Mich., Kalamazoo, 1989—; Sunday, pastoral asst. Ch. Annunciation, Phila.; parish cons. St. Peters Ch., Germantown; lectr. homiletics Phila. Divinity Sch.; nat. chair Episc. Peace Fellowship, 1970-73; with Convocation of Am. Chs. Europe, pres. coun. advice; dep. Gen. Conv., 1976, 79; chair Coun. Coll. Preachers; active Washington Diocesan Coun., chmn. exec. com.; com. inquiry on the nuclear issues Diocesan Peace Commn. former chair bd. advisors Am. Internat. Sch. Florence. Office: Episcopal Church Ctn 2600 Vincent Ave Kalamazoo MI 49008-3438

LEE, ELIZABETH BOBBITT, architect; b. Lumberton, N.C., July 9, 1928; d. William Osborne and Catharine Wilder (Bobbitt) Lee. Student Salem Coll., 1945-47; B.Arch. with honors, N.C. State Coll., 1952. Registered architect, N.C., 1955, S.C., 1964. Assoc. William Coleman, Architect, Kinston, N.C., 1952-55; Skidmore, Owens & Merrill, N.Y.C., 1955-56; prin. Elizabeth B. Lee, FAIA, Architect, Lumberton, N.C., 1956-73, 82—; sr. ptnr. Lee & Thompson, Architects, Lumberton, 1973-82. Bd. dirs. Robeson Little Theatre, Lumberton, 1977-80, N.C. Dance Theatre, Winston-Salem, N.C., 1980-85, Robeson County Community Concerts, Lumberton, 1980-87; trustee N.C. State U., Raleigh, 1983-92; mem. bd. endowment N.C. State U., 1993—. Recipient cert. recognition Randolph E. Dumont Design Program, 1970, Disting. Alumna award, Salem Coll., 1989. Fellow AIA (nat. dir. 1983-85; officeholder N.C. chpt., 1959, v.p. 1978, pres. 1979, bd. dirs. 1980, pres. eastern sect. N.C. chpt., 1975, bd. dirs. S. Atlantic Regional Council, 1977-79); mem. Jr. League (pres. Lumberton chpt., 1968), Robeson County Heart Assn. (pres. 1970), N.C. Design Found., N.C. Archtl. Found. (pres. 1982-83), Lumberton Jr. Service League (pres. 1968), N.C. State Alumni Assn. (bd. dirs. 1982-85, chmn. Robeson county chpt.), Phi Kappa Phi. Democrat. Presbyterian. Home: 906 N Chestnut St Lumberton NC 28358-4801 Office: 407 Elm St PO Box 1067 Lumberton NC 28359

LEE, ELOISE R., nursing educator and administrator; b. Bklyn., Nov. 12, 1930; d. Louis John and Edna Mae (Loeffler) Herberger; m. Winsor A. Lee,

Sept. 6, 1953; children: Christopher, Bryant, Preston. BSN cum laude, Adelphi U., 1952; MEd, Lehigh U., 1969, EdD, 1985; MS in Nursing, Gwynedd-Mercy Coll., 1989. Cert. gerontol. nurse specialist. Clin. instr. Albert Einstein Sch. Nursing, Phila.; asst. dir. nursing Allentown (Pa.) Hosp., 1963-65; assoc. prof. Northampton Community Coll., Bethlehem, Pa., 1970-75; prof. nursing, dir. gerontology inst. Cedar Crest Coll., Allentown, 1975-90, chairperson dept. nursing, 1990—. Contbr. articles to profl. jours. Mem. Pa. League for Nursing (chmn. Area 2), Pa. Nurses Assn. (commn. on nursing practice, commn. on nursing edn., bd. dirs. Dist. 2), Sigma Theta Tau (Theta Rho chpt.).

LEE, EUGENE, theatrical set designer; b. Beloit, Wis., Mar. 9, 1939; m. Franne Newman. Student, Carnegie-Mellon U., Yale U. Designer sets for Broadway shows Dude, 1972, The Skin of Our Teeth, 1975, Some of My Best Friends, 1977, Sweeney Todd, 1979 (Tony award), Gilda Radner Live From New York, 1979; designer Trinity Square Co., R.I., 1968—; TV work includes Saturday Night Live, (film) Hammett, 1983; other prodns. include End Game, 1965, 66, Slave Ship, 1969, Son of Man and the Family, 1970, Candide (revival), 1974 (Tony award), Agnes of God, 1983, The Ballad of Soapy Smith, 1983. Office: N York Performing Arts Centre, 5040 Young St, North York, ON Canada M2N 6R8

LEE, E(UGENE) STANLEY, industrial engineer, mathematician, educator; b. Hopeh, China, Sept. 7, 1930; came to U.S., 1955, naturalized, 1961; s. Ing Yah and Lindy (Hsieng) L.; m. Mayanne Lee, Dec. 21, 1957 (dec. June 1980); children: Linda J., Margaret H.; m. Yuan Lee, Mar. 8, 1983; children—Lynn Hua Lee, Jin Hua Lee, Ming Hua Lee. BS, Chung Cheng Inst. Tech., Republic of China, 1953; MS, N.C. State U., 1957; PhD, Princeton U., 1962. Research engr. Phillips Petroleum Co., Bartlesville, Okla., 1960-66; asst. prof. Kans. State U., Manhattan, 1966-67; assoc. prof. Kans. State U., 1967-69, prof. indsl. engring., 1969—; prof. U. So. Calif., 1972-76; cons. govt. and industry. Author: Quasilinearization and Invariant Imbedding, 1968, Coal Conversion Technology, 1979, Operations Research, 1981, Fuzzy and Evidence Reasoning, 1995; editor: Energy Sci. and Tech., 1975—; assoc. editor Jour. Math. Analysis and Applications, 1974—, Computers and Mathematics with Applications, 1974—; editorial bd. Jour. Engring. Chemistry and Metallurgy, 1989—, Jour. of Nonlinear Differential Equations, 1992—, Jour. Chinese Fuzzy Systems Assn., 1995—. Grantee Dept. Def., 1967-72, Office Water Resources, 1968-75, EPA, 1969-71, NSF, 1971—, USDA, 1978-90, Dept. Energy, 1979-84, USAF, 1984-88. Mem. Soc. Indsl. and Applied Math., Ops. Rsch. Soc. Am., N. Am. Fuzzy Info. Processing Soc., Internat. Neural Network Soc., Sigma Xi, Tau Beta Pi, Phi Kappa Phi. Office: Kans State U Dept Indsl Engring Manhattan KS 66506 *Nothing can replace hard work and persistence.*

LEE, GEORGE C., civil engineer, university administrator; b. Peking, China, July 17, 1933; s. Shun C. and J. T. (Chang) L.; m. Grace S. Su, July 29, 1961; children—David S., Kelvin H. B.S., Taiwan U., 1955; M.S. in Civil Engring., Lehigh U., 1958, Ph.D., 1960. Research assoc. Lehigh U., 1960-61; mem. faculty dept. civil engring. SUNY, Buffalo, 1961—; prof. SUNY, 1967—, chmn. dept., 1974-77, dean sch. of engring. and applied scis., 1978—; head engring. mechanics sect. NSF, Washington, 1977-78; assoc. dir. Calspan-U. Buffalo Rsch. Ctr., 1985-89; acting dir. Nat. Ctr. for Earthquake Engring. Rsch., 1989-90, dir., 1992—; sci. cons. Nat. Heart Lung and Blood Inst., NSF. Author: Structural Analysis and Design, 1979, Design of Single Story Rigid Frames, 1981, Cold Region Structural Engineering, 1986, Stability and Ductility of Steel Structures Under Cyclic Loading, 1991; contbr. articles to profl. jours. in areas of structural design, nonlinear structural mechanics, biomed. engring. and cold region structural engring. Recipient Adams Meml. award Am. Welding Soc., 1974; Superior Accomplishment award NSF, 1977. Mem. ASCE, Am. Welding Soc., Welding Research Council, Structural Stability Research, Council, Am. Soc. Engring. Edn., AAAS, Sigma Xi, Chi Epsilon, Tau Beta Pi. Office: SUNY Buffalo 412 Bonner Hall Buffalo NY 14260-0001*

LEE, GEORGE TERRY, JR., lawyer; b. Dallas, Oct. 28, 1935; s. George Terry and Isabel (Breckenridge) T.; m. Natalie Blythe Henderson, Aug. 17, 1957; children: George Terry III, Blythe, Rebecca, Hamilton. BA, Yale U., 1957; LLB, Stanford U., 1960. Assoc. Goldberg, Fonville, et al, Dallas, 1960-65; gen. counsel George A. Fuller Co. and OKC Corp., Dallas, 1965-73; ptnr. Akin, Gump, Strauss, Hauer & Feld, L.L.P., Dallas, 1973—. Trustee Found. for Arts, Dallas, 1963—; St. Mark's Sch. of Tex., Dallas, 1966-72; bd. dirs. Dallas Mus. Fine Arts; pres. Brit-Am. Commerce Assn., Dallas, 1986. Fellow (life) Tex. Bar Found.; mem. ABA, University Club (N.Y.C.), Brook Hollow Golf Club (Dallas), Koon Kreek Klub (Athens, Tex.), Crescent Club (Dallas). Home: 3101 Greenbrier Dr Dallas TX 75225-4603 Office: Akin Gump Strauss Hauer & Feld LLP 1700 Pacific Ave Ste 4100 Dallas TX 75201-4618

LEE, GLENN RICHARD, medical administrator, educator; b. Ogden, Utah, May 18, 1932; s. Glenn Edwin and Thelma (Jensen) L.; m. Pamela Marjorie Ridd, July 18, 1969; children—Jennifer, Cynthia. B.S., U. Utah, 1953, M.D., 1956. Intern Boston City Hosp.-Harvard U., 1956-57, resident, 1957-58; clin. assoc. Nat. Cancer Inst., NIH, 1958-60; postdoctoral fellow U. Utah, 1960-63; instr. U. Utah Coll. Medicine, 1963-64, asst. prof. internal medicine, 1964-68, assoc. prof., 1968-73, prof., 1973—; assoc. dean for acad. affairs, 1973-76, dean, 1978-83; chief of staff Salt Lake VA Med. Ctr., 1985-95. Author: (with others) Clinical Hematology, 9th edit, 1993; Contbr. (with others) numerous articles to profl. jours.; editorial bd.: (with others) Am. Jour. Hematology, 1976-79. Served with USPHS, 1958-60. Markle Found. scholar, 1965-70; Nat. Inst. Arthritis, Metabolic and Digestive Disease grantee, 1977-82. Mem. A.C.P., Am. Soc. Hematology, Am. Soc. Clin. Investigation, Western Assn. Physicians, Am. Inst. Nutrition. Mem. LDS Ch. Home and Office: 3781 Ruth Dr Salt Lake City UT 84124-2331

LEE, GRIFF CALICUTT, civil engineer; b. Jackson, Miss., Aug. 17, 1926; s. Griff and Lida (Higgs) L.; m. Eugenia Humphreys, July 29, 1950; children: Griff Calicutt III, Robert H., Carol E. B.E., Tulane U., 1948; M.S., Rice U., 1951. Civil engr. Humble Oil & Refining Co., New Orleans, Houston, 1948-54; design engr. J. Ray McDermott & Co., Inc., New Orleans, 1954-66; chief engr. J. Ray McDermott & Co., Inc., 1966-75, group v.p., 1975-80, v.p., group exec., 1980-83; cons. engr. Griff C. Lee Inc., 1983—; mem. vis. com. dept. civil engring. U. Tex.; mem. adv. bd. Tulane U., Rice U., MIT; mem. marine bd. NRC. Contbr. articles to profl. jours. Served with USN, 1944-46. Named Outstanding Engring. Alumnus Rice U., 1991. Mem. NAE, ASCE (hon.), Am. Bur. Shipping, Am. Concrete Inst., Am. Welding Soc., Soc. Petroleum Engrs., Am. Petroleum Inst., Internat. House Club, City Club, Bienville Club, New Orleans Country Club, Rotary. Presbyterian. Home: 6353 Carlson Dr New Orleans LA 70122-2803 Office: 1010 Common St New Orleans LA 70112-2401

LEE, HOWARD DOUGLAS, university president; b. Louisville, Ky., Mar. 15, 1943; s. Howard W. and Margaret (Davidson) L.; m. Margaret Easley, Nov. 20, 1965; children: Gregory Davidson, Elizabeth Anna. BA in English, U. Richmond, 1964; ThM, Southeastern Seminary, Wake Forest, N.C., 1968; PhD in Religion, U. Iowa, Iowa City, 1971. Prof. religion, devel. dir. Va. Intermont Coll., Bristol, 1971-73; dir. univ. relations Wake Forest (N.C.) U., 1973-78; v.p. devel. Stetson U., DeLand, Fla., 1978-80, v.p. planning and devel., 1980-83, exec. v.p., 1984-86, pres.-elect, 1986-87, pres., 1987—. Contbr. articles to profl. jours. Founding dir. Atlantic Ctr. for Arts, New Smyrna Beach, Fla., 1978—; chmn. DeLand C. of C., 1944, Volusia County Vision Com., 1994-95. Named Cen. Fla. Fundraiser of Yr. Nat. Assn. Fundraising Execs. 1985. Mem. So. Assn. Colls. and Schs. (exec. coun. 1993-94), Rotary, Deland Country Club, Omicron Delta Kappa. Avocations: running, golf, woodworking/antiques, reading. Office: Stetson U Campus Box 8258 421 N Boulevard Deland FL 32720

LEE, HWA-WEI, librarian, educator; b. Canton, China, Dec. 7, 1933; came to U.S., 1957, naturalized, 1962; s. Luther Kan-Chun and Mary Hsiao-Wei (Wang) L.; m. Mary F. Kratochvil, Mar. 14, 1959; children: Shirley, James, Pamela, Edward, Charles, Robert. BEd, Taiwan Normal U., 1954; MEd, U. Pitts., 1959, PhD, 1964; MLS, Carnegie Mellon U., 1961. Asst. libr. U. Pitts. Librs., 1959-62; head tech. svcs. Duquesne U. Libr., Pitts., 1962-65; head libr. U. Pa., Edinboro, 1965-68; dir. libr. and info. ctr. Asian Inst. Tech., Bangkok, Thailand, 1968-75; assoc. dir. librs., prof. libr. adminstrn. Colo. State U., Fort Collins, 1975-78; dean librs., prof. Ohio U.,

Athens, 1978—; cons. FAO, UNESCO, U.S. AID, World Bank, Internat. Devel. Rsch. Ctr., Asia Found.; del.-at-large White House Conf. Libr. and Info. Svcs., 1991. Author: Librarianship in World Perspectives, 1991, Fundraising for the 1990s: The Challenge Ahead, 1992; exec. editor Jour. Ednl. Media and Libr. Sci., 1982—; mem. editorial bd. Internat. Communications in Libr. Automation, 1974-76; mem. editor bd. Jour. Libr. and Info. Sci, 1975-78, Libr. Acquisition: Practice and Theory, 1976-83; contbr. articles to profl. jours. Recipient Disting. Svc. award Libr. Assn. of China (Taiwan), 1989. Mem. ALA (councilor 1988-92, 93—), John Ames Humphry/Forest Press award 1991), Acad. Libr. Assn. Ohio, Am. Soc. Info. Sci., Asian-Pacific Am. Librs. Assn. (Disting. Svc. award 1991), Internat. Fedn. Libr. Assns. and Instns. (standing com. univ. librs. and other gen. rsch. librs. 1989-93), Assn. Coll. and Rsch. Librs. Chinese-Am. Librs. Assn. (Disting. Svc. award 1983), Internat. Assn. Orientalist Librs., Ohio Libr. Assn. (bd. dirs. 1991-92, Libr. of the Yr. 1987), Online Computer Libr. Ctr. (users coun. 1987-91), Ohio Chinese Acad. and Profl. Assn. (founding pres. 1988-90). Home: 19 Mulligan Rd Athens OH 45701-3734 Office: Ohio U Alden Libr Athens OH 45701

LEE, ISAIAH CHONG-PIE, social worker, educator; b. Ma-kung, Taiwan, Jan. 31, 1934; s. Ju-Nie Chen and Chioh L.; m. Ho-Mei Chen, Feb. 8, 1960; children—Jense, Jenfei. Dr.P.H., UCLA, 1972. Lic. clin. social worker, family, marriage and child counselor. Dist. dir. public health social work Los Angeles County Health Dept., 1970-72; assoc. prof. social work Calif. State U., Long Beach, 1972-78, prof. social work, 1978—, chmn. dept., 1980-86, dir. Internat. Inst. Social Work, 1982—; vis. prof. family medicine Kaoshiung Med. Coll., 1989, med. sociology, 1993-94. Author: Medical Care in a Mexican American Community, 1972, Health Care Need of the Elderly Chinese in Los Angeles, 1979, Youth Leadership in Immigrant Communities, 1986, Yin-Yang Theory in Chinese Medicine, 1987, Selective Readings in Social Work, 1988, Community Organizing—Chinese-American Perspectives, 1992. Sec. bd. dirs. Oriental Healing Arts Inst., Calif.; founder Formosan Presbyterian Ch. of Orange County, 1978; pres. bd. dirs. Formosan Presbyn. Ch. Orange County, 1978-79; chmn. Asian Presbyn. Council So. Calif., 1980-81; chmn. Internat. Task Force Nat. Comm. on Self-Devel. of People United Presbyn. Ch., 1980-84; advisor social econ. group World Coun. on Chs., Geneva, 1980-84; adv. bd. Asian Am. Community Mental Health Tng. Center, Los Angeles, 1972-77; v.p. Pacific Asian-Am. Center, Santa Ana, Calif., 1981-82, pres., 1982-84; founder Calif. Inst. of Human Care, 1988. 2d lt. Chinese Army, 1954-55. Fellow Soc. Clin. Social Work; mem. Oriental Social Health Soc. (founder, pres. 1970-72), AAUP, Council Social Work Edn., Chinese-Am. Social Workers Assn. USA, (founder, pres. 1985-88), Nat. Assn. Social Workers, Acad. Cert. Social Workers, American-Am. Profl. Assn. USA (pres. 1993—). Democrat. Office: Calif State U Dept Social Work Long Beach CA 90840

LEE, J. DANIEL, JR., insurance company executive; b. Pitts., Mar. 11, 1938; s. John Daniel and Frances Emma (Schimid) L.; m. Betty Williams, Oct. 22, 1961; children—John, Michael, Julie. A.B., Duke U., 1960; M.B.A., U. N.C. 1963; postgrad., Dartmouth Coll., 1984. Investment analyst, gen. investment mgr. Prudential Ins. Co Am., Jacksonville, Fla., 1963-70; gen. investment mgr. Prudential Ins. Co Am., Newark, 1974-77; asst. v.p. Tchrs. Ins. and Annuity Assn. of Am., N.Y.C., 1978, 2d v.p., 1978-80, v.p., 1980-83, mgr. securities div., 1983, sr. v.p., 1983, investment area mgr., 1984, exec. v.p., 1984—. Mem. Mortgage Bankers Assn., Urban Land Inst., Internat. Council Shopping Ctrs. Avocations: golf; salt-water fishing. Office: Tchrs Ins & Annuity Assn Am 730 3rd Ave New York NY 10017-3206

LEE, J. E., bishop. Bishop Ch. of God in Christ, Dallas. Office: Ch of God in Christ 1701 Turtle Point Dr De Soto TX 75115-2747

LEE, JACK (JIM SANDERS BEASLEY), broadcast executive; b. Buffalo Valley, Tenn., Apr. 14, 1936; s. Jesse McDonald and Nelle Viola (Sanders) Beasley; m. Barbara Sue Looper, Sept. 1, 1961; children: Laura Ann, Elizabeth Jane, Sarah Kathleen. Student, Wayne State U., 1955-57; BA, Albion Coll., 1959. Cert. radio mktg. cons. Announcer Sta. WHUB-AM, Cookeville, Tenn., 1956; news dir., program dir. Sta. WALM-AM, Albion, Mich., 1957-59; radio-TV personality WKZO-Radio-TV, Kalamazoo, 1960-62; prodn. dir. Stas. WKMH-WKNR, Detroit, 1962-63; gen. mgr. Sta. WAUK-AM-FM, Waukesha, Wis., 1963-65; asst. program mgr. Sta. WOKY, Milw., 1965-70; program mgr. Sta. WTMJ-WKTI, Milw., 1970-76; gen. mgr. Sta. WEMP-WMYX, Milw., 1976-88; pres. Jack Lee Enterprises Ltd., Milw., 1977—; pres., CEO, Milw. Area Radio Stas., 1989—; instr. dept. mass communication U. Wis.-Milw., 1972-81; adviser Nat. Baha'i Info. Office. With U.S. Army, 1959, 61-62; maj. CAP, 1964—. Decorated Army Commendation medal. Mem. AFTRA, Milw. Advt. Club, Omicron Delta Kappa, Alpha Epsilon Rho. Home and Office: 277 W N Chicory Ln # 2793 Pewaukee WI 53072 *It is a constant struggle to balance my greatest gift—the ability to express myself—with my biggest failing—the inability to keep my mouth shut.*

LEE, JAMES A., health facility finance executive; b. Red Level, Ala., Dec. 19, 1939; s. H. Alton Lee; m. Charlotte Phillips, Dec. 19, 1963 (div. July 1971); children: Phillip, Michele, Jenifer; m. Melanie Cooper, Dec. 14, 1973; children: Christopher, Amanda. BBA in Acctg., Jacksonville State U., 1964; MS in Hosp. and Health Adminstrn., U. Ala., 1980. CPA, Ala. Sr. acct. Macke, Eldredge, McIntosh, Birmingham, Ala., 1964-67, Touche, Ross, Bailey & Smart, Birmingham, 1967-68; bus. functions mgr. Druid City Hosp., Tuscaloosa, Ala., 1968-71; sr. assoc. adminstr., fin. Univ. Ala. Hosp., Birmingham, 1971—; asst. prof. Dept. Pub. Health, Univ. Ala. Birmingham, 1980—; asst. prof. Dept. Pub. Health, Univ. Ala. Birmingham, 1984—. Mem. Health Care Fin. Mgmt. Assn., Ala. Soc. CPA's, Am. Inst. CPA's, Am. Hosp. Assn., Am. Coll. Hosp. Adminstrs. Republican. Baptist. Home: 109 Pemberton Pl Pelham AL 35124-2817 Office: U Ala 1675 University Blvd # 540 Birmingham AL 35233

LEE, JAMES EDWARD, JR., educational administrator; b. Pitts., Mar. 9, 1939; s. Willard and Gladys Hilda (Jenkins) L.; m. Daisy Mae Tibbs, June 29, 1977; children: Stephen Michael, Monica Michelle, Brian Patrick, Priscilla Demone. BS, Wayne State U., 1962, EdS, 1969; MA, U. Mich., 1964; postgrad., Mich. State U., Wayne State U., U. Minn., U. Colo. 1964-92. Ctrl. Mich. U. Cert. tchr., adminstr., Mich. Tchr. Miller, Durfee and Michael Jr. High Schs., Detroit, 1962-67; team leader Nat. Tchr. Corps, Detroit, 1967-69; dept. head Noble Jr. High Sch., Detroit, 1969-74; asst. prin. MacKenzie High Sch., Detroit, 1974-80; asst. prin. Drew Mid. Sch., Detroit, 1980, prin., 1980—; instr. Wayne State U., Detroit, 1967-69, edn. cons., 1970-71; instr. Wayne C.C., 1967-81; prin. adult evening sch., 1974-80, summer gifted program, Detroit, 1986-92; mem. profl. stds. commn. for sch. adminstrs. Mich. Dept. Edn., 1992—, mem. adminstrv. waiver com., 1992-94. Contbg. author: The Development of Micro Teaching as an Evaluative Instrument in Teacher Training, 1969, (manual) The Principalship, 1990. Co-chair ednl. audit com. Oak Park (Mich.) Sch., 1988-90; bd. dirs. Scott Community Ctr., Detroit, 1988—; adv. bd. Adrian/Scott program to inspire readiness for ednl. success, Detroit, 1990—; adv. coun. Christ Child House, Detroit, 1990-92. With USMC, 1956-58. Recipient Prins. and Educators award Booker T. Washington Bus. Assn., Detroit, 1986, 90, Citation for Outstanding Leadership Detroit Bd. Edn., 1986; named finalist Boss of Yr., Detroit chpt. Am. Bus. Women's Assn., 1987. Mem. Nat. Assn. Secondary Sch. Prins., Nat. Mid. Sch. Assn., Mich. Assn. Supervision and Curriculum Devel., Mich. Assn. Secondary Sch. Prins. (exec. bd. 1986-88, Outstanding Mid. Level Prin. of Yr. 1991), Mich. Assn. Mid. Sch. Educators (bd. dirs. 1988-91). Avocation: tennis. Home: 22580 Saratoga St Apt 2102M Southfield MI 48075-5947 Office: Charles R Drew Mid Sch 9600 Wyoming St Detroit MI 48204-4669

LEE, JAMES JIEH, environmental educator, computer specialist; b. I-Lan, Taiwan, Aug. 27, 1939; came to U.S.A. 1968; s. Yun Ping and Lien Hwa (Kuo) L.; m. Margie J. Feng, March 31, 1965; 1 child: Jean H. BA, Taiwan Normal U., Taipei, 1962; MA, U. Minn., 1970, postgrad., 1971. Cert. high sch., univ. tchr. Taiwan. Tchr. I-Lan High Sch., 1962-64; instr. Ta-Tung & Taiwan Normal U., 1964-68; rsch. asst. U. Minn., Mpls., 1968-71, rsch. assoc., 1971-77; computer specialist U.S. Dept. Commerce, Silver Spring, Md., 1977-83; sr. computer system analyst U.S. Pub. Health Svc., Rockville, Md., 1983-92; planning dir. Ctr. for Taiwan Internat. Rels., Washington,

1990—; with Internat. Environ. Protection Assn., Washington, 1988-90, also bd. dirs. 1986—; bd. dirs. Asia Resource Ctr., Washington, 1993—; exec. dir. Constitution Movement for Taiwan, Washington, 1993—; chmn. Formosan Human Rights Assn. Washington chpt., 1976—. Co-author: (with others) Introduction to Human Geography, 1966, Yun-Wu Social Sci., 1971; author: Minnesota Taxing Jurisdictions, 1976, Return to Nature, 1991. Bd. dirs. Formosan Assn. Pub. Affairs, Washington, 1982-92. Recipient automation data processing/extramural rsch. USPHS, 1991. Mem. World Watch, Nat. Resource Def. Coun., Am. Solar Energy Soc., Union of Concerned Scientists, Sierra Club. Avocations: traveling, hiking. Home: 14306 Parkvale Rd Rockville MD 20853-2530

LEE, JAMES MATTHEW, Canadian politician; b. Charlottetown, PEI, Can., Mar. 26, 1937; s. James Matthew and Catherine (Blanchard) L.; m. Patricia Laurie, July 2, 1960; children: Jason, Laurie Ann, Patti Sue. P.C., St. Dustans U., 1956. Mem. provincial parliament from, 5th Queens Riding, 1975-82; minister Health and Social Service-Province of P.E.I., Charlottetown, from 1979, Tourism, Parks and Conservation, 1980; premier, pres. Exec. Council-Province P.E.I., Charlottetown, 1981-86. Mem. Can. Pension Commn., 1986—, Privy Council Can., 1982. Mem. Can. Jaycees (internat. senate 1983), United Comml. Travellers Am. (past sr. councillor), Coun. for Can. Unity (provincial pres. 1988). Roman Catholic.

LEE, JAMES MICHAEL, religious education educator, publisher; b. Bklyn., Sept. 29, 1931; s. James and Emma (Brenner) L.; m. Marlene Mayr, Oct. 16, 1976; children: James V, Michael F.X., Patrick John. A.B., St. John's U., 1955; A.M., Columbia U., 1956, Ed.D, 1958. Tchr. gen. sci. N.Y.C. secondary sch., 1955-56, chmn. sci. dept. and coordinator audiovisual aids, 1956-59, substitute tchr. adult edn., 1955-60; lectr. Hunter Coll. Grad. Sch., N.Y.C., 1959-60, Sch. Edn. Seton Hall U., South Orange, N.J., 1959; asst. prof. grad. dept. edn. St. Joseph Coll., West Hartford, Conn., 1959-62, U. Notre Dame, South Bend, Ind., 1962-65; assoc. prof. U. Notre Dame, 1965-68, prof., 1968-77, chmn. dept. grad. studies in edn., 1966-71, dir. religious edn. program, 1967-77; prof. U. Ala. at Birmingham, 1977—, chmn. dept. secondary instrn. and ednl. founds., 1977-79; lectr. Chaplain's Sch., Air U., 1985-88; subject matter expert, lectr. GS-16 Chaplain Corps, USN, 1990-91, hon. chaplain, 1991; mem. Birmingham Diocesan Bd. Edn., 1981-89; founder, pub. Religious Edn. Press; cons. in field. Author: Principles and Methods of Secondary Education, 1963, Guidance and Counseling in Schools, Foundations and Processes, 1966, Purpose of Catholic Schooling, 1968, Shape of Religious Instruction, 1971, The Flow of Religious Instruction, 1973, Forward Together, 1973, The Content of Religious Instruction, 1985; sr. author: The Delivery of Religious Education in the Sea Services, 1991; editor, contbr.: Seminary Education in a Time of Change, 1965, Readings in Guidance and Counseling, 1966, Catholic Education in the Western World, 1967, Toward a Future for Religious Education, 1970, The Religious Education We Need, 1977, The Spirituality of the Religious Educator, 1985, Handbook of Faith, 1990; corr. editor Panorama: An Internat. Jour. Religious Edn. and Values. Fulbright sr. research scholar U. Munich, 1974-75; Religious Edn. Assn. Lilly research tng. fellow, 1974-75, 85. Fellow Soc. for Sci. Study Religion; mem. NEA, N.Am. Profs. of Christian Edn., Assn. Profs. and Rschrs. in Religious Edn. (exec. com. 1972-73, 78-80), Am. Ednl. Rsch. Assn., Nat. Soc. Study Edn., Religious Edn. Assn. (rsch. com. 1970-76, bd. dirs. 1979-89), Religious Rsch. Assn., Fulbright Alumni Assn. Home: 5316 Meadow Brook Rd Birmingham AL 35242-3315

LEE, JANIE C., art gallery owner; b. Shreveport, La., Apr. 22, 1937; d. Birch Lee and Joanna (Glassell) Wood; m. David B. Warren, Jan. 2, 1980. Student, Nat. Cathedral Sch., 1951-55; BA, Sarah Lawrence Coll., 1959. Asst. to Cheryl Crawford, Actors Studi o, N.Y.C., 1962-63; co-prodr. Off Broadway Theatre Co., N.Y.C., 1963-65; owner, pres. Janie C. Lee Gallery, Dallas, 1967-74, Houston, 1973—; owner, pres. Janie C. Lee Master Drawings, N.Y.C., 1983—; mem. art appraisal panel IRS, Washington, 1987-94. Prodr. ann. catalogue on 20th Century drawings, 1979—; prodr., editor: Mark di Suvero Catalogue, Houston Graphic Soc. Mem. Alumnae Bd. Sarah Lawrence Coll. (1972-74). Mem. Art Dealers Assn. Am. (bd. dirs. 1980-88, 1992—, v.p 1984-88). Avocation: study of Italian life and culture. Office: Janie C Lee Gallery 1209 Berthea St Houston TX 77006-6411

LEE, JEN-SHIH, biomedical engineering educator; b. Kwangtong, China, Aug. 22, 1940; parents Y. and Yao-Ze (Lai) L.; m. Lian-Pin Ma Lee, June 11, 1966; children: Lionel, Grace, Albert. BS, Nat. Taiwan U., 1961; MS, Calif. Inst. Tech., 1963, PhD, 1966. Advance rsch. fellow San Diego Heart Assn., U. Calif., San Diego, 1966-69; asst. prof. dept. Biomedical Engring. U. Va., Charlottesville, 1969-74, assoc. prof., 1974-83, prof., 1983—, chmn. dept. Biomedical Engring., 1988—. Editor: Microvascular Mechanics, 1988; assoc. editor Jour. Biomech. Engring., 1987-93; contbr. articles to Jour. Applied Physiology, Jour. Biomech. Engring., others. Recipient Rsch. Career Devel. award NIH, 1974-80. Fellow ASME, Am. Inst. Med. and Biol. Engring.; mem. IEEE, Am. Physiol. Soc., Microcirculatory Soc., Biomed. Engring. Soc. (bd. dirs. 1991-93, pres. 1994—). Office: U Va Dept Biomed Engring Box 337 Charlottesville VA 22908

LEE, JEROME G., lawyer; b. Chgo., Feb. 23, 1924; m. Margo B. Lee, Dec. 23, 1947; children—James A., Kenneth M. B.S. Ch.E., U. Wis., 1947; J.D., NYU, 1950. Bar: N.Y. 1950, U.S. Supreme Ct. 1964. Assoc. firm Jeffery, Kimball, Eggleston, N.Y.C., 1950-52; assoc. firm Morgan, Finnegan, Durham & Pine, N.Y.C., 1952-59; ptnr. Morgan, Finnegan, Pine, Foley & Lee, N.Y.C., 1959-86; sr. ptnr. Morgan & Finnegan, N.Y.C., 1986—; lectr. in field. Author: (with J. Gould) Intellectual Property Counseling and Litigation, 1988, USPTO Proposals to Change Rule 56 and the Related Rules Regarding a Patent Applicant's Duty of Candour, Patent World, 1992; contbr. articles to legal jours. in patent and trademark litigation splty. Served to sgt. U.S. Army, 1944-46. Fellow Am. Bar Found.; mem. ABA (chmn. com. fed. practice and procedure, chmn. com. Ct. of Appeals Fed. Cir., chmn. com. on ethics and profl. responsibility, standards com., mem. fed. cir. adv. com. 1992—), Am. Intellectual Property Law Assn. (bd. dirs. 1984-90, pres. 1991), Assn. Trial Lawyers Am., Am. Judicature Soc., Internat. Fedn. Indsl. Property Attys., Found. for Creative Am. (bd. dirs.), N.Y. Bar Assn., assn. of Bar of City of N.Y., N.Y. County Bar Assn., N.Y. Patent, Trademark and Copyright Law Assn. (bd. dirs. pres. 1981), more. Home: Apt 558 2110 Harbourside Dr Longboat Key FL 34228-4278 Office: Morgan & Finnegan 345 Park Ave New York NY 10154-0001

LEE, JERRY CARLTON, university administrator; b. Roanoke, Va., Nov. 21, 1941; m. Joan Marie Leo; 1 child, Zan. BA, W.Va. Wesleyan Coll., 1963; postgrad., W.Va. U. Grad. Sch. Indsl. Relations, 1963-64, U. Balt. Sch. Law, 1967-69; MA, Va. Poly. Inst., 1975, EdD, 1977; LLD (hon.), Gallaudet U., 1986. Mgmt. trainee Gen. Motors Corp., 1964-65; v.p. adminstrn. Comml. Credit Indsl. Corp., Washington, 1965-71; dir. gen. services Gallaudet Coll., Washington, 1971-77, asst. v.p. bus. affairs, 1978-82, v.p. adminstrn. and bus., 1982-84; pres. Gallaudet U. (formerly Gallaudet Coll.), Washington, 1984-88, Nat. U., San Diego, 1989—. Hon. bd. dirs D.C. Spl. Olympics; commn. in adminstrn. org. Rehab. Internat.; bd. dirs People to People, Deafness Research Found.; hon. advocacy bd. Nat. Capital Assn. Coop. Edn.; mem. Personnel Policies Forum Bur. Nat. Affairs. Served with USAR, 1966-72. Recipient Nat. Service award, Hon. Pres. award Council for Better Hearing and Speech, 1986, One-of-a-Kind award People-to-People, 1987, Advancement Human Rights & Fundamental Freedoms award UN, 1984, Alumni award Va. Poly. Inst., 1985, Pres.' award Gallaudet Coll. Alumni Assn., Gallaudet Community Relations award, U.S. Steel Found. Cost Reduction Incentive award Nat. Assn. Coll. and Univ. Bus. Officers, award Am. Athletic Assn. Deaf, 1987. Mem. Am. Assn. Univ. Adminstrs. (Eileen Tosney award 1987), Consortium of Univs. Washington Met. Area (exec. com.), Nat. Collegiate Athletic Assn. (pres.' commn.), Nat. Assn. Coll. Aux. Services (jour. adv. bd.; journalism award), Alpha Sigma Pi (Man of Yr. award 1983-84). Lodge: Sertoma (life, found. nat. adv. com.). Avocations: tennis, long distance running, weightlifting. Office: Nat Univ 4025 Camino Del Rio S San Diego CA 92108-4107

LEE, JOE, federal judge. BJ, U. Ky., 1952, JD, 1955. Bar: Ky., U.S. Dist. Ct. (ea. dist.) Ky., U.S. Ct. Mil. Appeals, U.S. Supreme Ct. Law clk. to chief justice Ky. Supreme Ct.; law clk. to dist. judge U.S. Dist. Ct. (ea. dist) Ky.; counsel to congl. subcom. U.S. Ho. of Reps.; bankruptcy judge U.S. Bankruptcy Ct., Lexington, Ky., 1961—; adj. prof. U. Ky. Coll. Law, 1972-

92. Editor-in-chief Am. Bankruptcy Jour., 1982-90; author: Bankruptcy Practice Manual, 1981, 84-87; contbr. of more than 40 articles to profl. jours. Treas., bd. dirs. Emerson Ctr., Inc. With USAF, 1943-49. Recipient Henry T. Duncan Meml. award for disting. jud. svc. Fayette County Bar Assn. 1986. Fellow Am. Bar Found.; mem. ABA (chmn. com. on consumer bankruptcy 1977-82), Ky. Bar Assn. (Outstanding Judge award 1991), Fed. Bar Assn. Nat. Bankruptcy Conf. (chmn. com. on individual debtor 1982—), Nat. Conf. Bankruptcy Judges (pres. 1973-74, sec. 1979-90, com. on legis. 1973-77, Herbert M. Bierce Disting. Jud. Svc. award 1983). Office: US Bankruptcy Ct PO Box 1111 Lexington KY 40588-1111

LEE, JOE R., food products company executive; b. 1940; married. Store mgr. Red Lobster Inns, Lakeland, Fla., 1967-69, supr., dir. ops., 1969-72, v.p. ops., 1972-75, pres., CEO, 1976-79; pres. Gen. Mills Restaurant, Inc. 1979-91; with Gen. Mills, Inc., Mpls., 1970—, v.p., 1976-80, exec. v.p., 1980-91, exec. v.p. fin., 1991-92, CFO, 1992, vice-chmn., 1992—, also bd. dirs., 1985—. Office: Gen Mills Inc 1 General Mills Blvd Minneapolis MN 55426-1347

LEE, JOHN CHONGHOON, SR., financial executive, international laywer; b. Seoul, Korea, July 4, 1928; came to U.S., 1948; s. Sung Han and Song Soh (Chae) L.; m. Mary Aniela Cyrulik, May 6, 1967; children: Suzanne, Daniel, Judy, Jeannette, John Jr. BSFS, Georgetown U., 1954; univ. doctorate in laws, faculty of laws, U. Paris, 1957. Spl. asst. to Korean ambassador UN, Geneva, Switzerland, 1955; v.p. Stanford Corp., Washington, 1958-60; chmn., pres. Overseas Investment Corp., Washington, N.Y.C., 1961-70, 76—; chmn. Amfico Corp./Allnations Devel. Bank, 1971-76; co-chmn. Brit. Indsl. Bank, London, 1965-68; chmn., pres. Agronomica Internat. (USA) Ltd.; spkr. internat. law soc. Am. U., 1987-88; founder Global Econ. Action Inst., N.Y.C., Washington; participant World Conf. Econ. and Social Order, Beneva, 1983; bd. dirs., chmn. logistic com. Fulbright Assn. Fulbright scholar, 1950-54. Office: Agronomica Internat Ltd PO Box 70 Gaithersburg MD 20884-0070

LEE, JOHN EDWARD, JR., government official; b. Pickens County, Ala., May 29, 1933; s. John Edward and Lois Juanita (Stallings) L.; BS, Auburn U., 1957, MS, 1958; PhD, Harvard U., 1969; m. Mary Alice Herren, Feb. 8, 1958 (div. 1987); children: Mary Elizabeth, John Edward III, James Whitfield; m. Marie Elizabeth Dougan, May 28, 1988; 1 child, Anne M. Dougan Clark. Instr., rsch. asst. Auburn U., 1958-59; teaching fellow Harvard U., 1961-62; agrl. economist Econ. Rsch. Svc., U.S. Dept. Agr., Washington, 1962-67, chief agrl. fin. br., 1967-71, dir. farm prodn. econs. div., 1971-73, commodity econs. div., 1973-76, nat. econs. div., 1976-81, administr., 1981-93; head dept. agrl. econs. Miss. State U., 1993—; mem. Pres.'s Commn. Productivity in the Food Industry, 1971-72; mem. Joint Coun. on Food and Agrl. Scis., 1981-93; mem. exec. com. Gt. Plains Agrl. Council, 1984-89; bd. dirs. Grad. Sch. USDA, 1985-89; pres. Am. Agrl. Econs. Assn. Found., 1991-93. Served with Signal Corps, U.S. Army, 1953-55. Fellow Am. Agrl. Econs. Assn. (gov. bd. found.); mem. Agrl. History Soc., Internat. Assn. of Agrl. Economists, Internat. Agribusiness Mgmt. Assn. (bd. dirs.), Methodist. Contbr. articles to profl. jours. Home: 4 Lakes Blvd Starkville MS 39759-3157 Office: Miss State Univ Mississippi State MS 39762-9755

LEE, JOHN FRANCIS, international management consulting company executive, author; b. Boston, Sept. 19, 1918; s. Michael Francis and Catherine Mary (Arrigal) L.; m. Helene Zinka Comes, May 13, 1946 (div.); children: Anne-Marie Lee Buckband, Robert Paul, Virginia Louise Lee Linden, Jacqueline, Lee Arthur. S.B., The Citadel, 1947; S.M., Harvard U., 1948; Sc.D., U. London, 1968; Litt.D. (hon.), U. Malaga, 1972. Registered profl. engr., Maine, D.C. Asst. prof. to assoc. prof., U. Maine, Orono, 1948-52; Broughton disting. prof. engring. N.C. State U., Raleigh, 1952-61; pres. SUNY-Stony Brook, 1961-62; special advisor, cons. NSF, 1962; pres., chief exec. officer Internat. Devel. Services, Inc., Washington, 1962-71; pres., chief exec. officer Promotorco, S.A. (Europe), Luxembourg, 1971-79; pres., chief exec. officer, Intercontinental Mgmt. Cons., Inc., Torrance, Calif., 1979-84; pres., chief exec. officer Calif. Tech. Cons., 1984-89, ret., 1989; dir. internat. firms; vis. prof. Calif. State Univ. system. Participant White House Conf. Internat. Cooperation, 1965; ambassador ICEM-Argentina Negotiations; participant State Dept. Foreign Policy Conf., 1970-71. Served to maj. U.S. Army, 1941-45. Decorated Bronze Star, Purple Heart; order Southern Cross (Brazil), Order Bernardo O'Higgins (Chile) chevalier Legion D'Honeur (France); named Ambassador of Good Will, State of N.C., 1961. Mem. Am. Foreign Service Assn., IEEE, AIAA, Optical Soc. Am., Soc. Photo-optical Instrumentation and Engring., Internat. Soc. Hybrid Microelectronics, Sigma Xi, Tau Beta Pi, Pi Tau Sigma. Unitarian. Clubs: Cosmos, International (Washington); Jockey (Paris). Author: Theory and Design of Steam and Gas Turbines, 1954, 2nd edit., 1961; co-author: Thermodynamics, 1955, 2nd edit., 1962; Statistical Thermodynamics, 1963, 2nd edit., 1973; others; contbr. articles to profl. jours. Home: 250 Knoll Rd Apt 143 San Marcos CA 92069-1592

LEE, JOHN FRANKLIN, retired lawyer, retired association executive; b. Idaho Falls, Idaho, Dec. 7, 1927; s. Wilford D. and Lorine (Hutchinson) L.; m. Patricia Anne Mason, Sept. 15, 1950; children: Randall Mason, Laurelei, John F. B.A., Brigham Young U., 1950; J.D., George Washington U., 1956; diploma, Stonier Grad. Sch. Banking, Rutgers U., 1966. Bar: Utah, D.C. 1956. Atty. SEC, 1956-59; practice in Salt Lake City, 1959-64; asst. to chmn. Fed. Deposit Ins. Corp., Washington, 1964-66; gen. counsel Fed. Deposit Ins. Corp., 1966-68; pres. N.Y. Clearing House Assn., N.Y.C., 1968-93; retired, 1993. Served to lt. comdr. USNR, 1945-46, 51-54. Mem. Order of Coif.

LEE, JOHN J., petroleum, fertilizer company executive; b. 1933. With Barber Oil Co., N.Y.C., 1970-80, Fibre Sullivan Resources Co., 1980-83; pres. Lee Devel. Corp., 1983—; chmn. d., CEO Seminole Fertilizer Corp., 1989—; pres Tosco Corp. Office: SFC Holding Corp 72 Cummings Point Rd Stamford CT 06902-7912

LEE, JOHN JIN, lawyer; b. Chgo., Oct. 20, 1948; s. Jim Soon and Fay Yown (Young) L.; m. Jamie Pearl Eng, Apr. 30, 1983. BA magna cum laude, Rice U., 1971; JD, Stanford U., 1975; MBA, 1975. Bar: Calif. 1976. Assoc. atty. Manatt Phelps & Rothenberg, L.A., 1976-77; asst. counsel Wells Fargo Bank N.A., San Francisco, 1977-79, counsel, 1979-80, v.p., sr. counsel, 1980, v.p., mng. sr. counsel, 1981—; mem. governing com. Conf. on Consumer Fin. Law, 1989-93. Bd. dirs. Asian Bus. League of San Francisco, 1981—; gen. counsel, 1981. Fellow Am. Coll. Consumer Fin. Svcs. Attys., Inc., (bd. regents 1995—), mem. ABA (chmn. subcom. on housing fin., com. on consumer fin. svcs., bus. law sect. 1983-90, vice chmn. subcom. securities products, com. consumer fin. svcs. bus. law sect. 1991—), Consumer Bankers Assn. (lawyers com.), Soc. Physics Students, Stanford Asian-Pacific Am. Alumni/ae Club (bd. dirs. 1989-93, v.p. 1989-91). Democrat. Baptist. Office: Wells Fargo Bank NA Legal Dept 111 Sutter St San Francisco CA 94104-4504

LEE, JOHN MARSHALL, mathematics educator; b. Phila., Sept. 2, 1950; s. Warren W. and Virginia (Hull) L.; m. Pm Weizenbaum, May 26, 1984; children: Nathan Lee Weizenbaum, Jeremy Lee Weizenbaum. AB, Princeton U., 1972; student, Tufts U., 1977-78; PhD, MIT, 1982. Systems programmer Tex. Instruments, Princeton, N.J., 1972-74; Geophys. Fluid Dynamics Lab., NOAA GFDL/NOAA, Princeton, 1974-75; tchr. math. and physics Wooster Sch., Danbury, Conn., 1975-77; programmer and cons. info. processing svcs. MIT, Cambridge, Mass., 1978-82; asst. prof. math. Harvard U., Cambridge, 1982-87; asst. prof. math. U. Wash., Seattle, 1987-89, assoc. prof. math., 1989—; sr. tutor Harvard U., Cambridge, 1984-87. Contbr. articles to profl. jours. Rsch. fellow NSF, 1982. Mem. Am. Math. Soc. (Centennial fellow 1989). Avocations: hiking, wine tasting. Home: 5637 12th Ave NE Seattle WA 98105-2603 Office: Univ Wash Math Dept Box 354350 Seattle WA 98195-4350

LEE, JOHN PATRICK, hospital administrator; b. Portland, Oreg., Apr. 29, 1942; s. Patrick and Margaret Ann (Molahan) L.; m. Feb. 27, 1965; children—Kevin, Kelly, Jason. B.B.A. U. Portland, 1964, M.B.A., 1973; M.P.A. in Hosp. Administrn., UCLA, 1970. Asst. administr. fin. and gen. adminstrn. Good Samaritan Hosp. and Med. Center, Portland, 1970-75; dep. adminstr., St. Vincent's Hosp. and Med. Center, Portland, 1975-79;

adminstr. Providence Med. Center, Portland, 1979-89; regional v.p. Sisters of Providence Health System, 1989—. Served to capt. Med. Service Corps, USAF, 1964-68. Fellow Am. Coll. Hosp. Adminstrs., Hosp. Adminstrv. Mgmt. Assn. Office: Sisters of Providence 1235 NE 47th Ave Ste 299 Portland OR 97213-2966

LEE, JONATHAN OWEN, financial services company executive, lawyer; b. Boston, Mar. 12, 1951; s. Herbert C. and Mildred (Schiff) L.; m. Barbara Ruth Cole, Mar. 24, 1984; children: Suzanna Cole, Alexander Philip. AB in Architecture, U. Calif., Berkeley, 1973; JD, Boston Coll., 1976. Bar: Mass. 1976. Staff atty. SEC, N.Y.C., 1976-79; gen. ptnr. Lee Capital Holdings, Boston, 1979—; chmn. bd. dirs. Dartmouth Finishing Corp., New Bedford, Mass., 1984—; Globe Metall., Inc., Cleve., 1986—; So. Energy Homes, Inc., Adison, Ala., 1989—; bd. dirs. 1st Security Svcs., Inc., Boston, Hyde Athletic Industries, Inc., Peabody, Mass. Micromedia New Eng., Norwood, P.A.R. Assocs., Inc., Boston. Bd. dirs. Combined Jewish Philanthropies, Boston, 1987—; mem. bd. overseers Mus. Fine Arts, Boston. Mem. Young Presidents Orgn., Explorers Club. Office: Lee Capital Holdings 1 International Pl Boston MA 02110-2600

LEE, JONG HYUK, accountant; b. Seoul, Korea, May 6, 1941; came to U.S., 1969, naturalized, 1975; s. Jung Bo and Wol Sun L. B.A., Sonoma State U., Rohnert Park, Calif., 1971; M.B.A. in Taxation, Golden Gate U., San Francisco 1976. CPA, Calif.; m. Esther Kim, Jan. 24, 1970. Cost acct., internal auditor Foremost-McKesson Co., San Francisco, 1971-74; sr. acct. Clark, Wong, Foulkes & Barbieri, CPAs, Oakland, Calif., 1974-77; pres. J.H. Lee Accountancy Corp., Oakland, 1977-89, Bay Cities Restaurants, Inc. Wendy's Franchise, 1989—; instr. Armstrong Coll., Berkeley, Calif., 1977-78; lectr. acctg., dir. sch. of bus. The U.S.-Korea Bus. Inst., San Francisco State U.; adv. bd. mem. Ctr. for Korean Studies, Inst. of East Asian Studies U. Calif, Berkeley. Bd. dirs. Korean Residents Assn., 1974, Multi-svc. Ctr. for Koreans, 1979, Better Bus. Bur., 1984-87; chmn. caucus Calif.-Nev. ann. conf. United Meth. Ch., 1977; commr. Calif. State Office Econ. Opportunity, 1982-86; pres. Korean-Am. Dem. Network; mem. Dem. Nat. Fin. Coun.; regional chmn. Adv. Coun. on Peaceful Unification Policy, Republic of Korea; commr. Asian Art Mus. San Francisco, 1988-91. With Korean Marine Corps, 1961-64; 1st lt. Calif. State Mil. Res. Mem. Am. Inst. CPAs, Nat. Assn. Asian Am. CPAs (bd. dir.), Am. Acctg. Assn., Nat. Assn. Accts., Internat. Found. Employee Benefit Plans, Calif. Soc. CPAs, Oakland C. of C., Korean Am. C. of C. (pres. Pacific North Coast, Rotary. Democrat. Author tax and bus. column Korea Times, 1980. Home: 180 Firestone Dr Walnut Creek CA 94598-3645 Office: 369 13th St Oakland CA 94612-2636

LEE, JOSEPH WILLIAM, sales executive; b. Florence, S.C., Sept. 19, 1943; s. Warner Lou and Rosalee (Hyman) L.; m. Rita Martin, Sept. 8, 1962; children: Mark Stephen, Allison Lynette. Grad. high sch., Florence. Clk. Atlantic Coast Line R.R., Florence, 1962-69; sales rep. Durham (N.C.) & So. Rwy., 1969-74; dist. sales mgr. Westmoreland Coal Sales Co., Charlotte, N.C., 1974-82; v.p. purchasing Westmoreland Coal Sales Co., Phila., 1982-85, v.p. purchasing distbn., 1985-88, v.p. purchasing and northern sales, 1988-91; sr. v.p. Westmoreland Coal Sales Co., Phila., Pa., 1991, 1991—; also bd. dirs. Westmoreland Coal Sales Co.; bd. dirs. Ea. Coal & Coke Corp., ECC Leasing Co., Westmoreland Energy, Inc. Mem. N.C. Coal Inst., So. Coals Conf., Inc. (trustee 1989-92). Republican. Office: Westmoreland Coal Sales Co 200 S Broad St Philadelphia PA 19102-3803

LEE, JUNE WARREN, dentist; b. Boston, Feb. 24, 1952; d. Earl Arnold and Rosemary Regina (Leary) Warren; m. William Lee, July 25, 1976; children: Jaime Michelle, Daniel William. BA, Brandeis U., 1973; DDS, Georgetown U., 1977; student, U.S. Dental Inst., 1985-87. Pvt. practice, Boston, 1977—; chair gen. arrangements YDC 21, Yankee Dental Congress. Mem. Altrusa Club of Quincy, Mass., 1979—, Cunningham Sch. PTO, Milton, Mass. 1987—, Parent-Adv. Coun., Collicot Elem. Sch., Milton, 1986-87; dental instr. Cunningham Sch., 1987—; dental screening, Healthworks, Neponset Health Ctr., Boston, 1981-84. Master Acad. Gen. Denistry (coun. ann. meetings and internat. confs., past pres. New Eng. Mastertrack program, pres.-elect Mass chpt., past chmn. editl. rev. bd. Audiodent); fellow Am. Coll. Dentists, Internat. Coll. Dentists, Acad. Dentistry Internat.; mem. ADA, Mass. Dental Soc., South Shore Dist. Dental Soc. (chmn.-elect 1991, chmn. 1992), Am. Orthodontic Soc., Am. Acad. Gnathologic Orthopedics, Am. Assn. for Functional Orthodontics, Am. Assn. Women Dentists (sec. 1987, v.p. 1988, pres.-elect 1989, pres. 1990, A.T. Cross Co. Women of Achievement award 1985), Women's Dental Soc. Mass. (sec. 1978, v.p. 1979-81, pres. 1981-83), Mass. Dentists Interested in Legislation, Chestnut Hill Rsch. Study Club. Roman Catholic. Avocations: travel, geneology, reading, writing, celtic music. Office: 383 Neponset Ave Dorchester MA 02122-3197

LEE, KATHARINE CAECILIA, art museum administrator; b. Detroit, Dec. 12, 1941; d. Sherman E. and Ruth (Ward) L.; m. Bryan S. Reid Jr. BA magna cum laude, Vassar Coll., 1963; MA, Harvard U., 1966. Curatorial asst. Toledo Mus. Art, 1968-69, asst. curator, 1969-70; dir. exhbns. Renaissance Soc., U. Chgo., 1971-73; curator of collections David & Alfred Smart Gallery, U. Chgo., 1973-79; lectr. dept. art U. Chgo., 1978-79; curator The Ackland Art Mus., U. N.C., Chapel Hill, 1979-82; asst. dir. Art Inst. Chgo., 1982-86, dep. dir., 1986-91; dir. Va. Mus. of Fine Arts, Richmond, 1991—. Chmn. vis. com. Vassar Coll., The Frances Lehman Loeb Art Ctr.; bd. dirs. Richmond Children's Mus., 1992, Agecroft Hall, Richmond, Va., 1992—; The Trust for Mus. Exhbns., 1993—; adv. bd. Getty Trust, Mus. Mgmt. Inst., 1993—, James Madison U. Honors Program, 1992—, Commonwealth coun. Girl Scouts U.S., 1992—. Recipient Ford Found. mus. curatorial tng. internship, Toledo Mus. Art, 1966-68; Fulbright fellow, The Sorbonne and Inst. d'Art et Archaeologic, Paris, 1963-64. Mem. Assn. of Art Mus. Dirs., Am. Assn. Mus. (bd. dirs. 1992—, chmn. nat. program com. 1994 ann. meeting 1993-94), Coll. Art Assn. (com. on conservation of archival materials 1987). Office: Va Mus of Fine Arts Office of the Director 2800 Grove Ave Richmond VA 23221-2466

LEE, KATHRYN ELLEN, corporate lawyer; b. Highland Park, Mich., Sept. 2, 1958; d. Brendan Joseph and Elise Alexandra (Worobetz) L.; m. Albert E. Bender, May 1, 1993. BA in Econs., U. Mich., 1980; JD, U. Ga., 1985. Law assoc. Shumacker & Thompson, Chattanooga, 1985-88, Altman, Kritzer & Levick, Atlanta, 1989-92; corp. counsel real estate The Home Depot, Inc., Atlanta, 1992—. Avocations: fly fishing, rowing, baseball. Office: Home Depot 2727 Paces Ferry Rd NW Atlanta GA 30339

LEE, KENNETH, physicist; b. San Francisco, July 3, 1937; s. Kai Ming and Ah See Lee; A.B. with honors in Physics, U. Calif., Berkeley, 1959. Ph.D., 1963; m. Cynthia Ann Chu, June 28, 1959; children—Marcus Scott, Stephanie Denise. Research physicist Varian Assocs., Palo Alto, Calif., 1963-68; mem. research staff, mgr. IBM, San Jose, Calif., 1968-83; dir. memory techs. Southwall Techs., Palo Alto, Calif., 1983-84; sr. v.p. product devel. Domain Tech., Milpitas, Calif., 1984-89; chief tech. officer, exec. v.p. engring. Quantum Corp., Milpitas, Calif., 1989—. 1 child Anne H. Physics Soc.; sr. mem. IEEE; mem. Phi Beta Kappa, Sigma Xi. Contbr. articles to profl. jours.; patentee in field. Home: 20587 Debbie Ln Saratoga CA 95070-4827 Office: Quantum Corp 500 Mccarthy Blvd Milpitas CA 95035-7909

LEE, KENNETH STUART, neurosurgeon; b. Raleigh, N.C., July 23, 1955; s. Kenneth Lloyd and Myrtle Lee (Turner) L.; m. Cynthia Jane Anderson, May 23, 1981; children: Robert Alexander, Evan Anderson. BA, Wake Forest U., 1977; MD, East Carolina U., 1981. Diplomate Nat. Bd. Med. Examiners, Am. Bd. Neurol. Surgeons; med. lic. N.C., Ariz. Intern then resident in neurosurgery Wake Forest U. Med. Ctr., Winston-Salem, N.C., 1981-88; fellow Barrow Neurol. Inst., Phoenix, 1988-89; clin. assoc. prof. neurosurgery East Carolina U., Greenville, N.C., 1989-93; clin. assoc. prof. neurosurgery, 1994—. Assoc. editor Current Surgery, 1990—; contbr. 30 articles to profl. jours. and 5 chpts. to books. Mem. Ethicon Neurosurgical Adv. Panel, 1989—. Bucy fellow, 1988. Fellow Am. Heart Assn. (stroke coun.); mem. AMA, N.C. Med. Soc., Am. Assn. Neurol. Surgeons, Am. Soc. Stereotactic and Functional Neurosurgery, So. Med. Assn., Congress Neurol. Surgeons, N.C. Nuerosurgical Soc. (sec.-treas. 1991=93, pres. 1994—), Alpha Omega Alpha. Democrat. Baptist. Achievements include research on the efficacy of certain surgical procedures, particularly carotid endarterectomy, in the prevention of strokes. Home: 3600 Baywood Ln Greenville

NC 27834-7630 Office: Ea Carolina Neurosurg 2325 Stantonsburg Rd Greenville NC 27834-7546

LEE, KUO-CHUAN, horticulture educator; b. Yungchia, CheKiang, China, Sept. 23, 1933; s. Yu-lone and Shu-wai Chang Lee; m. Margaret S.C. Ou, Dec. 20, 1969; 1 child, Elsa P.J. BS, Nat. Chung-Hsing U. TaiChung, Republic of China, 1958; MS, Kans. State U., 1967, PhD, 1971. Rsch. assoc. Kans. State U., Manhattan, 1972-75; assoc. prof. Nat. Chung-Hsing U., 1975-79, chmn. dept. horticulture, 1979-82, dir. Grad. Inst. of Horticulture, 1979-82, prof. Grad. Inst. of Horticulture, 1979—, editor Jour. Agr. and Forestry, Coll. Agr., 1992-94. Contbr. articles to profl. jours. Recipient Teaching award Ministry of Edn., Republic of China, 1990. Mem. Chinese Soc. Horticulture Sci. (mem. editorial bd. jour. 1991—, Acad. award 1989), Phi Dau Phi, Sigma Xi, Gamma Sigma Delta. Avocations: music appreciation, friends. Address: 4223 East Dr Butler PA 16001 Office: Dept Horticulture, Nat Chung Hsing U, Taichung 40227, Taiwan

LEE, KUO-HSIUNG, medicinal chemistry educator; b. Kaohsiung, Taiwan, Jan. 4, 1940; came to U.S., 1965; s. Ching-Tsung Lee and Chin-Yeh Yang; m. Lan-Huei Chen; children: Thomas Tung-Ying, Catherine Tung-Ling. BS, Kaohsiung Med. Coll., Taiwan, 1961; MS, Kyoto U., Japan, 1965; PhD, U. Minn., 1968. Postdoctoral scholar dept. chemistry UCLA, 1968-70; asst. prof. Sch. Pharmacy, U. N.C., Chapel Hill, 1970-74, assoc. prof., 1974-77, prof. medicinal chemistry, 1977-91, dir. natural products lab., 1983—, Kenan prof. medicinal chemistry, 1991—; adj. prof. Koahsiung Med. Coll., 1977—; mem. devel. therapeutics contract rev. com. Nat. Cancer Inst., NIH, 1984-88, bio-organic and natural products chemistry study sect., 1990-94; cons. natural products program div. life scis. NSC, Taiwan, 1986-87, Food and Drug Bur., Dept. Health, Exec. Yuan of Republic of China, Taiwan, 1986-92, Genelabs, Inc., Redwood City, Calif., 1988—, Nat. Rsch. Inst. Chinese Medicine, Taiwan, 1989—, Sphinx Pharms. Corp., Durham, N.C., 1990—; sci. advisor Nat. Lab. Foods and Drugs, Dept. Health, Exec. Yuan of Republic of China, Taiwan, 1990—; mem. sci. adv. bd. Pharmagenesis, 1992—; mem. acad. adv. com. plannint sect. Nat. Health Rsch. Inst., Dept. Health, 1992—. Mem. editl. adv. bd. Abstracts of Chinese Medicines, 1986—, Oriental Healing Arts Internat. Bull., 1987—, Bot. Bull. Academia Sinica, 1988—, The Chinese Pharm. Jour., 1988—, Jour. Pharm. Scis., 1990-92, Jour. Chinese Medicine, 1990—, Internat. Jour. Oriental Medicine, 1989—, Kaohsiung Jour. Med. Sci., 1992—, Internat. Jour. Pharmacognosy, 1991—, Jour. Nat. Prod., 1994—; contbr. numerous rsch. articles to profl. jours. Grantee NIH, Am. Cancer Soc., U.S. Army, 1971—; recipient Soine Meml. award U. Minn., 1990, Achievement award Genelabs, 1993, Lifu Acad. award Chinese Medicine, 1994, T.M. Tu Sci. award, 1995. Fellow AAAS, Chem. Soc., Am. Soc. Pharm. Scientists, Acad. Pharm. Sci.; mem. Am. Chem. Soc., Am. Soc. Pharmacognosy, Am. Pharm. Sci., Am. Assn. Coll. Pharm., Phytochemistry Soc. N.Am., Soc. Syn. Organic Chemistry. Achievements include patents on synthesis of anti-cancer drugs, antifungal agts., anti-AIDS compounds; discovery of over 800 novel plant antitumor agts. and synthetic analogs; elucidation of structure-activity relationships, mechanisms of action of bioactive products. Office: U NC Sch Pharmacy Chapel Hill NC 27599-7360

LEE, LANSING BURROWS, JR., lawyer, corporate executive; b. Augusta, Ga., Dec. 27, 1919; s. Lansing Burrows and Bertha (Barrett) L.; m. Natalie Krug, July 4, 1943; children: Melinda Lee Clark, Lansing Burrows III, Bothwell Graves, Richard Hancock. BS, U. Va., 1939; postgrad U. Ga. Sch. Law, 1939-40; JD, Harvard U., 1947. Bar: Ga. 1947. Former corp. officer Ga.-Carolina Warehouse & Compress Co., Augusta, 1957-89, pres., chief exec. officer, 1989—, co-owner Ga.-Carolina Warehouse Co. Chmn. bd. trustees James Brice White Found., 1962—; sr. warden Episc. Ch., also chancellor, lay min; sr. councillor The Atlantic Coun. of the U.S.; bd. dirs. Med. Coll. Ga. Found., Kanuga Endowment, Inc. Capt. USAAF, 1942-46. Fellow Am. Coll. Trust & Estate Counsel, Ga. Bar Found.; mem. Harvard U. Law Sch. Assn. Ga. (pres. 1966-67), Augusta Bar Assn. (pres. 1966-67), Soc. Colonial Wars Ga., Ga. Bar Assn. (former chmn. fiduciary law sect.), U.S. Supreme Ct. Hist. Soc., U. Va. Thomas Jefferson Soc. of Alumni, Internat. Order St. Luke, Augusta Country Club, Harvard Club of Atlanta, The Pres.'s Club of Med. Coll. Ga. Home: 2918 Bransford Rd Augusta GA 30909-3004 Office: Law Offices Lansing B Lee Jr 699 Broad St Ste 904 Augusta GA 30901-1456

LEE, LEO OU-FAN, Far Eastern languages educator; b. Honan, China, Apr. 9, 1939; came to U.S., 1962; s. Lucas Yung-kang and Yuan (Chou) L. BA, Taiwan U., Taipei, 1961; MA, Harvard U., 1964, PhD, 1970. Instr. Dartmouth Coll., Hanover, N.H., 1968-70; lectr. Chinese U., Hong Kong, 1970-71; asst. prof. Princeton (N.J.) U., 1972-76; assoc. prof. Ind. U., Bloomington, 1976-82; prof. U. Chgo., 1982-90, UCLA, 1990-94, Harvard, Cambridge, Mass., 1994—. Author: The Romantic Generation of Modern Chinese Writers, 1973, Voices from the Iron House, 1987; editor: Lu Xun and His Legacy, 1985; co-editor: Modern Chinese Stories and Novellas, 1981, (jour.) Chinese Lit. in Translation, 1976—; contbr. essays, articles and revs. to profl. jours. Fellow NEH, 1979-80, Wang Inst. Chinese Studies, 1985-86, Guggenheim Meml. Found., 1986-87. Mem. Assn. for Asian Studies (bd. dirs. 1977-79). Avocation: classical music. Home: 16 Leonard Ave Cambridge MA 02139 Office: 2 Divinity Ave Cambridge MA 02138

LEE, LOW KEE, electronics engineer, consultant; b. Oakland, Calif., Feb. 12, 1916; s. Hing Wing and Yan Hai (Louie) L.; m. Alice Jing, Nov. 29, 1953; children: Elliott James, Elizabeth Joanne. BS, U. Calif., Berkeley, 1937, MS, 1939; PhD, Calif. Western U., 1977. Group leader Aerophysics Lab., Los Angeles, 1944-50; lab. mgr. Stanford Research Inst., Menlo Park, Calif. 1950-55; asst. to dir. Gen. Mills, Mpls., 1955-57; dept. mgr. product engring. TRW, Redondo Beach, Calif., 1957-62, asst. dir. product assurance, 1962-78, ret., 1978; cons. Omni Corp., Rancho Santa Fe, Calif., 1983—, Control Data Inc., City of Industry, Calif. Co-author: Design and Construction of Electronic Equipment, 1961; contbr. to books, encys. Fellow IEEE, Chinese Am. Inst. Engrs. and Scientists (pres. San Francisco 1945-46, trustee 1979-81, 89-91, Meritorious award 1985), Masons. Home: 4479 Deerberry Ct Concord CA 94521-4513

LEE, MARGARET BURKE, college administrator; b. San Diego, Dec. 28, 1943; d. Peter John and Margaret Mary (Brown) Burke; m. Donald Harry Lee, June 30, 1973; children: Katherine Louise, Kristopher Donald. BA summa cum laude, Regis Coll., 1966; MA with honors, U. Chgo., 1970, PhD, 1978. Asst. to humanities MIT, Cambridge, 1969; instr. Dover-Sherborn High Sch., Dover, 1973-75; instr. Alpena Community Coll., Mich., 1975-80, dean liberal arts, 1980-82; dean instrn. Kalamazoo Valley Community Coll., 1982-85; v.p. Oakton Community Coll., Des Plaines, Ill., 1985—; cons. evaluator North Cen. Assn., Chgo., 1982—, commr.-at-large, 1988—; cons., field faculty Vt. Coll., Montpelier, 1982—; mem. admissions com. Ill. Math and SCi. Acad., 1988—; bd. gov.'s North Cook Ednl. Svc. Ctr., 1988—; bd. dirs. North Cook Ednl. Svc. Ctr., 1989—, vice-chair, 1990-91; mem. Bd. Edn. Dist. 39, Wilmette, Ill., 1990-92, chair, 1992—. Mem. Career Edn. Planning Dist., Kalamazoo, 1982, Kalamazoo Forum/ Kalamazoo Network, 1982, Needs Assessment Task Force, 1984. Ford Found. fellow, 1969-73; Woodrow Wilson Found. fellow, 1975; fed. grantee, 1978-84. Mem. Am. Assn. Community and Jr. Colls., Mich. Assn. Community Coll. Instrnl. Adminstrs. (pres. 1983-85), Mich. Occupational Deans Adminstrs. Coun. (exec. bd. 1983-85), Mich. Women's Studies Assn. (honors selection com. 1984), North Cen. Assn. Acad. Deans (pres. 1988—), Kalamazoo Consortium Higher Edn. (pres.'s coun. coordinating com. 1982-85), Kalamazoo C of C. (vocat. edn. subcom. indsl. coun. 1982), North Cen. Assn. Acad. Deans (v.p., pres. 1985-87). Democrat. Lutheran. Avocations: quilt collecting, reading, listening to classical music, sports spectating, theatre-going. Home: 2247 Lake Ave Wilmette IL 60091-1410 Office: Oakton CC 1600 E Golf Rd Des Plaines IL 60016

LEE, MARGARET NORMA, artist; b. Kansas City, Mo., July 7, 1928; d. James W. and Margaret W. (Farin) Lee; PhB, U. Chgo., 1948; MA, Art Inst. Chgo., 1952. Lectr. U. Kansas City, 1957-61; cons. Kansas City Bd. Edn., Kansas City, Mo., 1968-86; guest lectr. U.Mo.-Columbia, 1983, 85, 87, 89, 91, 93; one-woman shows Univ. Women's Club, Kansas City, 1966, Friends of Art, Kansas City, 1969, Fine Arts Gallery U. Mo. at Columbia, 1972, All Souls Unitarian Ch. Kansas City, Mo., 1978; two-Woman show Rockhurst Coll., Kansas City, Mo., 1981 exhibited in group shows U. Kans., Lawrence, 1958, Chgo. Art Inst., 1963, Nelson Art Gallery, Kansas City, Mo., 1968,

74, Mo. Art Show, 1976, Fine Arts Gallery, Davenport, Iowa, 1977; represented in permanent collections Amarillo (Tex.) Art Center, Kansas City (Mo.) Pub. Library, Park Coll., Parksville, Mo. Mem. Coll. Art Assn. Roman Catholic. Contbr. art to profl. jours.; author booklet. Home and Studio: 4109 Holmes St Kansas City MO 64110-1127

LEE, MARIANNA, editor; b. N.Y.C., Aug. 23, 1930; d. Isaac and Charlotte (Steiner) Lubow; m. Edward Lee, June 17, 1968 (div. 1978); 1 child, Susanna. BA, Smith Coll., 1952; postgrad, Columbia U., 1952-53; postgrad., Oxford (Eng.) U., 1957-58. Asst. editor Watson-Guptill Publs., N.Y.C. 1958-59; chief copy editor Grolier, Inc., N.Y.C., 1960-61; mng. editor Portfolio & Art News Ann., N.Y.C., 1961-62; assoc. editor Parade Publs., N.Y.C., 1962-66; mng. editor The Johns Hopkins Press, Balt., 1966-68, U. Tex. Press, Austin, 1968-69; sr. publs. mgr. Scripps Inst. of Oceanography, La Jolla, Calif., 1979-82; mng. editor Harcourt Brace and Co., San Diego, 1982—. Contbr. articles to profl. jours. Democrat. Jewish. Avocations: piano, painting, fell walking, speaking. Office: Harcourt Brace and Co 525 B St San Diego CA 92101

LEE, MARILYN (IRMA) MODARELLI, law librarian; b. Jersey City, Dec. 8, 1934; d. Alfred E. and Florence Olga (Koment) Modarelli; m. Alfred McClung Lee III, June 8, 1957 (div. July 1985); children: Leslie Lee Ekstrand, Alfred McClung IV, Andrew Modarelli. BA, Swarthmore (Pa.) Coll., 1956; JD, Western New Eng. Sch. of Law, 1985. Bar: Mass. 1986. Claims rep., supr. region 1I Social Security Adminstrn., Jersey City, 1956-59; law libr. County of Franklin, Greenfield, Mass., 1972-78; libr. I Franklin Law Libr. Mass. Trial Ct., Greenfield, 1978—; mem. Franklin County Futures Lab Task Force (Mass. Cts.), 1994—. Chmn. Franklin County (Mass.) Regional Tech., Turners Falls, 1974-76, Sch. Bldg. Com., 1974-76; mem. Franklin County Planning Bd., 1988-93, mem. exec. bd., 1993—; clk. Franklin County Tech. Sch., 1976-81; vice chmn. Greenfield Planning Bd., 1987—; mem. Greenfield Sch. Bldg. Com., 1995—. Mem. Mass. Bar Assn., Franklin County Bar Assn. (chmn. lawyer referral com. 1992-94, vice chmn. 1994—, chmn. libr. com. 1992—), Law Librs. of New Eng. (treas. 1993—), Am. Assn. Law Librs., Greenfield Charter (com. clk. 1979-83), Swarthmore Alumni Coun. Avocations: swimming, gardening. Office: Mass Trial Ct Franklin Law Libr 425 Main St Greenfield MA 01301-3313

LEE, MARTIN YONGHO (KYUNG-JOO LEE), mechanical engineer; b. Apr. 13, 1937; s. Yee Whan and Myo Ryun (Choi) L.; m. Su Ja Bang, Nov. 29, 1969; children: Mu Young, Tae Young. BSME, Han Yang U., Seoul, Republic of Korea, 1964. Lic. stationary engr., N.Y.; lic. energy mgmt. engrs. 1st class, indsl. power boiler-turbine oper. engrs. 1st class, Korea. Start-up engr. Sam-Chuch Power Plant, 1963-66; jr. engr. U.S. Army, Camrhan Bay, Vietnam, 1966-69; startup engr. power plant Korea Electric Power Co., Seoul, 1969-75; stationary engr. CUNY, N.Y.C., 1981-92, Queens, 1981-92; stationary engr. N.Y. Police Dept., N.Y.C., 1992—. Mem. Assn. Energy Engr., Co-Generation Assn. Home: 14628 34th Ave Flushing NY 11354-3134 Office: Police Hdqs NYC 1 Police Plz New York NY 10038-1403

LEE, MELVIN JOSEPH, minister; b. New Orleans, Dec. 25, 1929; s. John and Isabelle (Green) L.; m. Dorothy Peterson, June 5, 1971; children: Betty, Barbara, Joseph, Edward. BS in Chemistry, So. U., New Orleans, 1970; MDiv, Union Bapt. Theol. Sem., New Orleans, 1988, ThM, 1989. Ordained to ministry Bapt. Ch., 1984. Assoc. min. 3d Missionary Bapt. Ch., St. Bernard, La., 1984-87, pastor, 1987—, chair deacon bd., 1974-84; coroner's investigator Orleans Parish, New Orleans, 1982—; bd. dirs. So. Gen. Missionary Bapt. Assn., New Orleans, 1987—, chmn. bldg. com., 1988-92. Author: What Baptists Should Know, 1991; contbr. articles to profl. jours. Chmn. St. Bernard Cmty. Devel. Corp., 1988-93. Sgt. USAF, 1947-52. Democrat. Home: 7514 Dwyer Rd New Orleans LA 70126-4220 Office: 3d Missionary Bapt Ch 206 Armstrong Rd PO Box 1012 Saint Bernard LA 70085 *Man's action are controlled by his beliefs. Therefore, to change a man's actions—change his beliefs.*

LEE, MICHELE, actress; b. L.A., June 24, 1942; d. Jack and Sylvia Helen (Silverstein) Dusick; m. James Farentino, Feb. 20, 1966 (div. 1983); 1 son, David Michael; m. Fred Rappoport, Sept. 27, 1987. Actress roles include (Broadway play) How to Succeed in Business Without Trying, 1962-64, Seesaw, 1973, (movies) How to Succeed in Business With Really Trying, 1967, The Love Bug, 1969, Dark Victory, 1975, Bud and Low, 1976, A Letter to Three Wives, 1985, Single Women, Married Men, 1989, The Fatal Image, 1990, My Son Johnny, 1991, (TV movie) Broadway Bound, 1992, When No One Would Listen, 1993, Big Dreams Broken Hearts: The Dottie West Story, 1995, (TV series) Knots Landing, 1979-93 (Outstanding Lead Actress award Soap Opera awards 1992). Recipient Top Star of Tomorrow award Motion Picture Exhibitors of U.S. and Can., 1967, Drama Desk award Broadway Critics, 1973, Outer Critics Circle award, 1973; nominated for Antoinette Perry award, 1973-74, Emmy for Knots Landing, 1981-82.

LEE, MING CHO, set designer; b. Shanghai, China, Oct. 3, 1930; came to U.S., 1949, naturalized, 1961; s. Tsufa F. and Ing (Tang) L.; m. Elizabeth Rapport; 3 children. B.A., Occidental Coll., 1953, LHD (hon.), 1975; postgrad. in theatre arts, UCLA; student art, Chang Kuo-Nyen, Shanghai; DFA (hon.), Parsons Sch. Design, 1986. Apprentice, asst. designer Jo Mielzinger, 5 yrs.; art dir., designer in residence San Francisco Opera, fall 1961; prin. designer Juilliard Opera Theatre and Am. Opera Ctr. of Juilliard Sch. Music, from 1964; tchr. set design Yale U. Drama Sch., 1968—, co-chair, 1979—; tchr. theatre program NYU, 1967-69; set designer Yale Repertory Theatre, 1981-82; adj. prof., scene design adviser Yale U., New Haven; cons. in field; former mem. theatre projects com. N.Y.C. Planning Bd.; mem. adv. council U.S.-China Arts Exchange; trustee Nat. Design Archive. First sets designed for theatre, The Internal Machine, Phoenix, N.Y.C., 1958; designer sets: off-Broadway prodns. The Crucible, 1958, Triad, 1958, Walk in Darkness, 1963, Othello, 1964, Gandhi, 1970, Manhattan Project Seagull, 1974, Cuban Swimmer/Dog Lady, 1984; Broadway prodns. The Moon Besieged, 1962, Mother Courage, 1963, 78, Conversation in the Dark, 1963, Slapstick Tragedy, 1966, A Time for Singing, 1966, Little Murders, 1967, Here's Where I Belong, 1968, King Lear, 1968, Billy, 1969, La Strada, 1969, Lolita, 1971, Two Gentlemen of Verona, 1971, Much Ado About Nothing, 1972, All God's Children Got Wings, 1975, The Glass Menagerie, 1975, 83, For Colored Girls, 1976, Romeo and Juliet, 1977, Caeser and Cleopatra, 1977, The Shadow Box, 1977, Angel, 1979, The Grand Tour, 1978, K2, 1983, most recent work Execution of Justice, 1986; prin. designer, N.Y. Shakespeare Festival, 1962-73, designer N.Y. Shakespeare Festival various theatres and touring group shows, including The Merchant of Venice, 1962, The Tempest, 1962, King Lear, 1962, Macbeth, 1962, Anthony and Cleopatra, 1963, As You Like It, 1963, A Winter's Tale, 1963, Twelfth Night, 1963, Hamlet, 1964, 72, Othello, 1964, Electra, 1964, A Midsummer Night's Dream, 1964, Love's Labour's Lost, 1965, Coriolanus, 1965, Troilus and Cressida, 1965, The Taming of the Shrew, 1965, Henry V, 1965, All's Well That Ends Well, 1966, Measure for Measure, 1966, Richard III, 1966, The Comedy of Errors, 1967, Titus Andronicus, 1967, Hair, 1967, Henry IV, Parts I and II, 1968, Romeo and Juliet, 1968, Ergo, 1968, Peer Gynt, 1969, Electra, 1969, Cities in Bezique, 1969, Invitation to a Beheading, 1969, The Wars of the Roses (Henry VI, Parts I, II, and III, and Richard III), 1970, Sambo, 1969, 70, Jack MacGowran in the Works of Samuel Beckett, 1970, Timon of Athens, 1971, Two Gentleman of Verona, 1971, The Tale of Cymbeline, 1971, Older People, 1972, Much Ado About Nothing, 1972, Wedding Band, 1972; designer sets: plays King Lear, N.Y.C., 1968, Lolita, 1971, My Love in Philadelphia, 1971, Remote Asylum, Los Angeles, 1971, Henry IV, Part I, Los Angeles, 1972, Volpone, Los Angeles, 1972, Two Gentlemen of Verona, London, 1973, Lear, New Haven, 1973, The Crucible, Arena Stage, Washington, 1967, The Tenth Man, 1968, Room Service, 1968, The Iceman Cometh, 1968, The Night Thoreau Spent in Jail, 1970, Our Town, 1972, Inherit the Wind, 1973, Julius Caeser, 1975, The Ascent of Mount Fuji, 1975, Waiting for Godot, 1976, For Colored Girls, Los Angeles, 1977, Shadow Box, New Haven, 1977, Twelfth Night, Stratford, Conn., 1978, Hamlet, Washington, 1978, Don Juan, Washington, 1978, The Glass Menagerie, Mpls., 1979, Plenty, Washington, 1980, K2, Washington, 1982, Execution of Justice, Washington, 1985, numerous others; ballets for troupes of Jose Limon, Martha Graham, Gerald Arpino, Alvin Ailey including Missa Brevis, 1958, Three Short Dances, 1959, A Look at Lightning, 1962, Sea Shadow, 1963, Adriadne, 1965, The Witch of Endor, 1965, Olympics, 1966, Night Wings, 1966, Elegy, 1967, The Lady of the House of Sleep, 1968,

Secret Places, 1968, A Light Fantastic, 1968, Anim, 1969, The Poppet, 1969, Myth of a Voyage, 1973, Don Juan, 1973, Whisper of Darkness, 1974, In-Quest of the Sun, 1975, The Leaves Are Fading, 1975, The Tiller in the Fields, 1978, The Owl and the Pussycat, 1978, Dream of the Red Chamber, 1983, Les Noces, 1985, Tangled Night, 1986, Sephardic Songs, Intermezzo; set designer: opera cos., including Peabody Arts Theatre of Peabody Inst., Balt., 1959-63; designer: Peabody Arts Theatre prodns. The Turk in Italy, The Old Maid and the Thief, The Fall of the City, La Boheme, Amahl and the Night Visitors, The Pearl Fishers, Werther, Hamlet; Empire State Music Festival prodns. Katya Kabanova, 1960, Peter Ibbetson, 1960, The Pearl Fishers, 1961; Balt. Civic Opera prodns. Tristan and Isolde, 1962; Opera Co. of Boston prodn. Madama Butterfly, 1961, Turandot, 1983; Met. Opera Nat. Co. prodns. Madama Butterfly, 1965, Marriage of Figaro, 1966; Opera Soc. Washington prodn. Bombarzo, 1967; N.Y.C. Opera prodns. Don Rodrigo, 1966, Julius Caeser, 1966, Le Coq d'Or, 1967, Bombarzo, 1968, Faust, 1968, Roberto Devereaux, 1972, Susannah, 1971, Maria Stuarda, 1972, Contes D'Hoffman, 1972, Anna Bolena, 1973, Idomeneo, 1975, Attila, 1981, Alceste, 1982; Hamburgische Staatsoper prodns. Julius Caeser, Hamburg, Fed. Republic Germany, 1969, Lucia di Lammermoor, Hamburg, 1971; Juilliard Opera Theatre and Am. Opera Ctr. of Juilliard Sch. Music prodns. Katya Kabanova, 1964, Il Tabarro, 1964, Gianni Schicchi, 1964, Fidelio, 1965, The Magic Flute, 1965, The Trial of Lucullus, 1965, The Rape of Lucrezia, 1967, L'Ormindo, 1968, The Rake's Progress, 1970, Il Giuramento, 1970, also prodns. at Lyric Opera Chgo., Covent Garden, London, Houston Grand Opera, Teatro Colon, Buenos Aires, San Francisco Opera, Dallas Civic Opera, Kennedy Ctr., Washington, Chilean Opera Soc., Santiago, associated Opera Co. Am.; one-man shows of water colors and design, Los Angeles, N.Y.C., Calif. Water Color Soc., Los Angeles County Art Show, Ohio U., Athens, Capricorn Gallery, N.Y.C., Compass Gallery, N.Y.C.; Library and Mus. Performing Arts, N.Y.C., Mus. City of N.Y., Design '70; designer: Mobile Unit, N.Y. Shakespeare Festival, Florence Sutro Anspacher Theatre, N.Y. Shakespeare Festival, Estelle R. Newman Theatre, N.Y. Shakespeare Festival, Garage Theatre, Harlem Sch. Arts. Bd. dirs. Pan Asian Repertory Theatre, Chen and Dancers; mem. citizens cultural adv. com.; mem. nat. adv. bd. Drama League N.Y.; mem. adv. bd. Theatre at Storm King. Recipient 1st Joseph Maharam award for Electra, 1965, Maharam award for Ergo, 1968, Off-Broadway award Show Bus., 1969, Tony award nomination, 1970, Spl. award Nat. Opera Inst., 1980, Tony award for set design for Broadway play K-2, 1983, Outer Critics Circle award, 1983, Drama Desk award, 1983, Maharam award, 1983, Mayor's award of Honor for Arts and Culture, 1984, 12 Qinyun award for Art and Culture China Inst., 1984, Los Angeles Drama Critics Circle award for Traveller in the Dark, 1985, Hollywood Drama-Logue Critics award for Traveller in the Dark, 1985; named Man of Yr., Chinatown Planning Commn., 1986; Guggenheim fellow, 1988—. Mem. United Scenic Artists Local Union 829 (v.p. 1969-71), Mcpl. Arts Soc. (bd. dirs.). Office: care Drama Sch Yale U 205 Park St West Haven CT 06516-6044 also: 12 E 87th St New York NY 10128-0524

LEE, MORDECAI, religious agency adminstrator, political scientist; b. Milw., Aug. 27, 1948; s. Jack Harold and Bernice (Kamesar) L.; 1 child, Ethan. BA, U. Wis., 1970, MPA, Syracuse U., 1972, PhD, 1975. Guest scholar Brookings Instn., Washington, 1972-74; legis. asst. to Congressman Henry Reuss, Washington, 1975; asst. prof. polit. sci. U. Wis.-Whitewater and Parkside, 1976; mem. Wis. Ho. Reps., 1977-82; mem. Wis. Senate, 1982-89; exec. dir. Milw. Jewish Coun. Cmty. Rels., 1990—; adj. prof. govt. U. Wis.-Milw. Jewish.

LEE, NELDA S., art appraiser and dealer, film producer; b. Gorman, Tex., July 3, 1941; d. Olan C. and Onis L.; A.S. (Franklin Lindsay Found. grantee), Tarleton State U., Tex., 1961; B.A. in Fine Arts, N. Tex. State U., 1963; postgrad. Tex. Tech. U., 1964. San Miguel de Allende Art Inst., Mexico, 1965; 1 dau., Jeanna Lee Pool. Head dept. art Ector High Sch., Odessa, Tex., 1963-68. Bd. dirs. Odessa YMCA, 1970, bd. dirs. Am. Heart Assn., Odessa, 1975; fund raiser Easter Seal Telethon, Odessa, 1978-79; bd. dirs. Ector County (Tex.) Cultural Center, 1979—, Tex. Bus. Hall of Fame, 1980-85; bd. dirs., mem. acquisition com. Permian Basin Presdl. Mus., Odessa, 1978; bd. dirs., chairperson acquisition com. Odessa Art Mus., 1979—; pres. Mega-Tex. Prodns., TV and movie producers; pres. Ector County Democratic Women's Club, 1975, Nelda Lee, Inc., Odessa; appointee Tex. Commn. Arts, 1993—. Group exhbns. include El Paso, Tex., New Orleans. Recipient Designer-Craftsman award El Paso Mus. Fine Arts, 1964. Mem. Am. Soc. Appraisers (sr.), Nat. Tex. Assn. Art Dealers (pres. 1978—), Odessa C. of C. Contbr. articles to profl. jours. Office: Nelda Lee Inc PO Box 4268 Odessa TX 79760-4268

LEE, PATRICIA HURESTON, lawyer; b. Chgo., Apr. 27, 1957; d. Louis Calvin and Emma (Arthur) Hureston; m. Darryl Michael Lee, Aug. 10, 1981; 1 child, Brandon Louis. BA, Northwestern U., 1979, JD, 1982. Bar: Ill. 1982, U.S. Dist. Ct. (no. dist.) Ill. 1982. Lawyer Legal Assistance Found., Chgo., 1982-84; corp. atty. McDonald's Corp., Oak Brook, Ill., 1984—; bd. dirs. Minority Legal Edn. Resources, Chgo., 1987—. Adv. dir. Children's Rights Project, 1986—. Recipient Black and Hispanic Achievement award, YMCA, 1988. Mem. ABA, Nat. Bar Assn., Chgo. Bar Assn., Oak Brook Bar Assn. Roman Catholic. Avocations: travel, movies, softball. Office: McDonald's Corp 1 McDonalds Plz Hinsdale IL 60521

LEE, PATRICK A., physics educator; b. Hong Kong, Sept. 8, 1946; m. Jeanne M. Tran, June 7, 1970; children: Eric, Brian. BS, MIT, 1966, PhD, 1970. Gibbs instr. Yale U., New Haven, 1970-72; asst. prof. U. Wash., Seattle, 1973-74; mem. tech. staff Bell Labs., Murray Hill, N.J., 1974-82; prof. physics MIT, Cambridge, 1982—. Fellow Am. Phys. Soc. (Oliver Buckley prize 1991); mem. NAS, Am. Acad. Arts and Scis. Office: MIT Dept of Physics Rm 12-117 Cambridge MA 02139

LEE, PAUL CHING-LAI, banker, real estate developer; b. Tainan, Taiwan, Republic of China, Dec. 10, 1943; came to the U.S., 1978; s. Lau Teh and Koy (Lin) L.; m. Mary S. Lin, June 8, 1966; children: Patty S., Kathy S. B in Commerce, Nat. Cheng-Kung U., Tainan, 1966. Pres. Oriental Trade Internat. Corp., N.Y.C., 1978-81; Taiwan Christian Svcs., Inc., N.Y.C., 1982—; Teco Industry (USA) Corp., N.Y.C., 1978—; vice chmn. Great Ea. Bank, N.Y.C., 1990—; bd. dirs. Five Giants, Inc., San Francisco, Seven Giants, Inc., N.Y.C., 1984—, 136-09 Realty, Inc., N.Y.C. Lt. U.S. Army, 1966-67, Taiwan. Mem. Am. Reformed Ch. Avocations: golf, travel, tai-chi, swimming, ping-pong. Home: 106 Jarvis Ave Staten Island NY 10312-5772 Office: Great Ea Bank 41-48 Main St Flushing NY 10355

LEE, PAUL KUO-LUNG, electronics engineer, researcher; b. Taipei, Republic of China, Aug. 7, 1942; came to U.S.; 1966; s. Ching-Yuan and Chong (Chang) L.; m. Ying-Ming Yang, Aug. 8, 1970; children: Karen, Sharon. BSEE, Nat. Taiwan U., 1965; MSEE, Ill. Inst. Tech., 1968, PhD in Elec. Engring., 1972. Elec. engr. Magnavox Co., Ft. Wayne, Ind., 1968-69; instr. Ill. Inst. Tech., Chgo., 1971; mem. tech. staff MITRE Corp., Bedford, Mass., 1972-80, lead engr., 1980-86, group leader, 1986-94; chmn. internat. conf. sessions, sr. prin. systems engr. Lockheed Sanders, Nashua, N.H., 1995—. Contbr. articles to profl. jours. and conf. proc. Charter mem. Reg. Presdl. Task Force, 1990—. Inland Steel Co. fellow, 1969-70, N.Y. Acad. Scis. fellow, 1984. Mem. IEEE (sr.), AIAA (sr.), Pioneer Investment Club (pres. 1977-80). Republican. Avocations: music, photography, hiking. Home: 257 E Emerson Rd Lexington MA 02173-2110 Office: Lockheed Sanders Nashua NH 03061

LEE, PAUL L., lawyer; b. N.Y.C., 1946. AB, Georgetown U., 1969; JD, U. Mich., 1972. Bar: N.Y. 1974. Law clk. to Hon. Walter R. Mansfield U.S. Ct. Appeals (2d cir.), 1973-74; spl. asst. to gen. counsel U.S. Treas. Dept. 1977-78, exec. asst. to dep. sec., 1978-79; dep. supt. and counsel N.Y. State Banking Dept., 1980-81; ptnr. Shearman & Sterling, N.Y.C., 1982-94; exec. v.p., gen. counsel Republic N.Y. Corp., N.Y.C., 1994—. Editor-in-chief Mich. Law Rev., 1971-72. Office: Republic NY Corp 452 Fifth Ave New York NY 10018

LEE, PEGGY (NORMA DELORES EGSTROM), singer, actress; b. Jamestown, N.D., May 26, 1920; d. Marvin Engstrom; m. Dave Barbour, 1943 (div. 1951); 1 dau., Nicki; m. Brad Dexter, Jan. 4, 1955 (div. 1955); m. Dewey Martin, Apr. 25, 1956; Jack del Rio, Mar., 1964 (div. 1964). Grad. high sch. Singer Sta. WDAY, Fargo, N.D.; various singing engagements

Mpls.; vocalist Will Osborne's band, Doll House, Palm Springs, Ambassador Hotel West, Chgo., Americana Hotel, Basin St. East, Benny Goodman's Band, 1941-43; singer concerts with Benny Goodman at Melodyland Theatre, Anaheim, Calif., Circle-Star Theatre, San Carlos, Calif. Author: (verse) Softly, With Feeling, 1953; screen appearances include Mr. Music, 1950, The Jazz Singer, 1953, Pete Kelly's Blues, 1955; performer Revlon Revues CBS-TV, 1960; actor Gen. Electric Theater, 1960; composer for films including Johnny Guitar, About Mrs. Leslie; composer musical score (cartoon) Tom Thumb; lyricist, voice talent Lady and the Tramp; rschr., program writer, performer The Jazz Tree Philharm. Ctr. for Performing Arts, N.Y.C., 1963; recordings include Golden Earrings, You Was Right Baby, It's A Good Day, Manana, and I Don't Know Enough About You, Is That All There Is (Grammy award 1969), I'm A Woman, Mirrors, There'll Be Another Spring, 1948, 1985, You Can Depend On Me, Seductive, Peggy Lee Sings With Benny Goodman, 1988, Peggy Lee Sings the Blues, 1988, Vol. 1-The Early Years, 1990, Classics, 1993, Love Held Lightly, 1993, Moments Like This, 1993. Named Best Female Vocalist by Metronome, Downbeat mags., 1946; recipient Most Popular Vocalist citation Billboard, 1950; Nat. Acad. of Recording Arts & Sciences Lifetime Achievement Award, 1994. Office: care Irvin Arthur & Assoc 9363 Wilshire Blvd Ste 212 Beverly Hills CA 90210-5418*

LEE, PETER JAMES, bishop; b. Greenville, Miss., May 11, 1938; s. Erling Norman and Marion (O'Brien) L.; m. Kristina Knapp, Aug. 28, 1965; children: Stewart, Peter James Jr. AB, Washington and Lee U., 1960; MDiv, Va. Theol. Sem., 1967; postgrad. Duke U. Law Sch., 1963-64; DD (hon.), Va. Theol. Sem., 1984, St. Paul's Coll., Lawrenceville, Va., 1985, U. of the South, 1993. Ordained priest Episc. Ch., 1968, bishop, 1984. Newspaper reporter, editor Pensacola, Fla., Richmond, Memphis, 1960-63; deacon St. John's Cathedral, Jacksonville, Fla., 1967-68; asst. min. St. John's Ch. LaFayette Sq., Washington, 1968-71; rector Chapel of the Cross, Chapel Hill, N.C., 1971-84; bishop coadjutor Episcopal Diocese of Va., Richmond, 1984-85, bishop, 1985—; pres. trustees of the funds Diocese of Va., 1985—; dir. Presiding Bishop's Fund for World Relief, 1986-93. Rector bd. trustees Episcopal H.S., Alexandria, Va., 1985—; chmn. Meml. Trustees, Richmond, Am. Friends the Episcopal Diocese Jerusalem; bd. advisors Christian Children's Fund, Wash. Nat. Cathedral. Mem. Phi Beta Kappa, Omicron Delta Kappa. Office: Diocese Va 110 W Franklin St Richmond VA 23220-5010

LEE, PHILIP RANDOLPH, medical educator; b. San Francisco, Apr. 17, 1924; married, 1953; 4 children. AB, Stanford U., 1945, MD, 1948; MS, U. Minn., 1956; DSc (hon.), MacMurray Coll., 1967. Diplomate Am. Bd. Internal Medicine. Asst. prof. clin. phys. medicine & rehab. NYU, 1955-56; clin. instr. medicine Stanford (Calif.) U., 1956-59, asst. clin. prof., 1959-67; asst. sec. health & sci. affairs U. Calif., San Francisco, 1967-69, chancellor, 1969-72, prof. social medicine, 1969—, dir. inst. health policy studies, 1972-93; asst. sec. U.S. Dept. of Health & Human Services, Washington, D.C., 1993—; mem. dept. internal medicine Palo Alto Med. Clinic, Calif., 1956-65; cons. bur. pub. health sec. USPHS, 1958-63, adv. com., 1978, nat. commn. smoking & pub. policy, 1977-78; dir. health svc. office tech. cooperation & rsch. AID, 1963-65; dep. assst. sec. health & sci. affairs HEW, 1965, asst. sec., 65-69, mem. nat. coun. health planning & devel., 1978-80; co-dir. inst. health & aging, sch. nursing U. Calif., San Francisco, 1980—; pres. bd. dirs. World Inst. Disability, 1984—; mem. population com. Nat. Rsch. Coun.- Nat. Acad. Sci., 1983-86; mem. adv. bd. Scripps Clinic & Rsch. Found., 1980—. Author over 10 books; contbr. articles to profl. jours. Recipient Hugo Schaefer medal Am. Pharm. Assn., 1976. Mem. AAAS, AMA, ACP, Am. Pub. Health Assn., Am. Fedn. Clin. Rsch., Am. Geriatric Soc., Assn. Am. Med. Colls., Inst. Medicine-Nat. Acad. Sci. Achievements include research in arthritis and rheumatism, especially Rubella arthritis, cardiovascular rehabilitation, academic medical administration, health policy. Office: Dept. of Health & Human Servs Public Health Service 200 Independence Ave SW Washington DC 20201-0004*

LEE, R. MARILYN, employee relations executive. BA in Polit. Sci., U. Calif., Santa Barbara, 1969; JD, U. Pacific, 1977. Dep. city atty. City of L.A., 1977-82; corp. dir. human resources The Times Mirror Co., L.A., 1982-90; v.p. employee rels. L.A. Times, 1990—; regent U. Calif. Bd. Regents, 1986-88; bd. dirs. L.A. Times Fund, L.A. Times Credit Union; mem. adv. bd. Women in Bus. Legis. aide congl. offices, Washington, 1970-74; bd. trustees U. Calif. Santa Barbara Found., Calif. Summer Sch. of Arts. Mem. Newspaper Pers. Rels. Assn., Calif. State Bar Assn., L.A. County Bar Assn. (labor and employment law com.), Soc. Human Resource Planning, McGeorge Sch. Law (alumni rep.), Alumni Assn. U. Calif. (pres. 1987-88, bd. dirs. 1983-89). Office: LA Times Times Mirror Sq Los Angeles CA 90012

LEE, RAPHAEL CARL, plastic surgeon; b. Sumter, S.C., Oct. 29, 1949; s. Leonard Powell and Jean Maurice (Langston) L.; m. Kathleen Kelley; children: Rachel, Catherine. BS, U. S.C., 1971; MS, Drexel U., 1975; MD, Temple U., 1975; ScD, MIT, 1979. Diplomate Am. Bd. Plastic Surgeons, Am. Bd. Surgery, Nat. Bd. Med. Examiners. Asst. resident in surgery U. Chgo. Hosps., resident in surgery, 1979-80, chief resident gen. surgery, 1980-81, attending plastic surgery, 1989—; sr. asst. resident plastic surgery Mass. Gen. Hosp., Boston, 1983, chief resident, 1983; attending plastic surgeon Cambridge Hosp., 1983-89; assoc. in surgery Brigham and Women's Hosp., 1984-89; cons. in plastic surgery West Roxbury VA Hosp., 1984-86, chief plastic surgery sect., surgery dept., 1986-89; assoc. surgeon The Children's Hosp., 1985-89; active staff New England Deaconess Hosp., 1985-89; acting chief, sect. of plastic and reconstructive surgery U. Chgo., 1992-93; dir. Electrical Trauma Program, 1991—; med. dir. U. Chgo. Burn Unit, 1991—; asst. prof. of surgery Harvard Med. Sch., 1984-89; Karl R. VanTassel asst. prof. of electrical and bioengring. MIT, 1983-89, assoc. prof. of bioengring. and surgery Harvard MIT, Divsn. of Health Scis. and Tech., 1983-89; assoc. prof. surgery U. Chgo. 1989-92; assoc. prof. of anatomy and organismal biology, U. Chgo. 1989-92, prof. surgery anatomy and organismal biology, 1992—; ad hoc mem. radiologic study sect. NIH, 1994—; mem. pres. adv. com. on patents, software and licensing U. Chgo., 1994—, mem. com. on appointments and promotions, biol. scis. divsn., 1994—, mem. critical care com., 1993—, chmn. rsch. com. dept. surgery, 1992—, mem. clin. laser com., 1990—; co-dir., organizer symposium, 1994—. Author: Electrical Injury, Multidisciplinary Approach, 1994; editor: Electrial Trauma; editl. bd. Bioelectromagnetics, 1993—; contbr. numerous articles to profl. jours. Recipient Sr. Clin. Paper award Midwest Assn. of Plastic Surgeons, 1994, Searle Scholar award The Searle Found., 1985-88; named Am. 100 Brightest Young Scientists Sci. Digest, 1984; MacArthur Prize fellow John D. and Catherine T. MacArthur Found., 1981-86. Fellow ACS (Schering Scholar in Surgery 1978); mem. IEEE, AAAS, Am. Burn Assn., Am. Phys. Soc., Am. Soc. for Cell Biology, Am. Soc. of Plastic and Reconstructive Surgeons (James Barrett Brown award 1988), Assn. for Acad. Surgery (sr. mem.), Bioelectric Repair and Growth Soc. (membership chmn. 1986-88, scientific coun. mem. 1991-93), Bioelectrochem. soc., Bioelectromagnetics Soc. (scientific coun. 1994), Biophys. Soc., Chgo. Soc. of Plastic Surgery, Chgo. Surg. Soc., Electrochem. Soc. Nat. Med. Assn. (plastic surgery sect chmn. 1989-91), N.Y. Acad. of Sci., Plastic Surgery Rsch. Coun. (program com. 1993-95), Soc. for Phys. Regulation in Biology and Medicine (scientific program com. 1993, pres.-elect 1994), Soc. of Univ. Surgeons, Tau bet Pi, Alpha Omega Alpha, Sigma Xi. Achievements include patent for oriented tissue-equivalent materials, treatment of hypertrophic would healing disorders with clcium channel blockers, control of dermal scarring, feedback limitation of electric shock injury by telemetry, methods and compositions of polymers and cell membrane repair, method for the improvement of scar size and appearance, control of wound scar productions, methods and composition of a polymer for repair of electrical injury, use of calcium antagonists for treating scars. Office: U Chgo Hosps Pritzker Sch Medicine-Surgery MC6035 5841 S Maryland Ave Chicago IL 60637

LEE, R(AYMOND) WILLIAM, JR., apparel company executive; b. Richmond, Va., Apr. 24, 1930; s. Raymond William and Sally (Beal) L.; m. Marianne Hollingsworth, June 21, 1952; children: Lelia, Carol, Raymond William, III, Sally. A.B., Duke U., 1951. With Oxford Industries, Inc., Atlanta, 1955—; in men's wear Oxford Industries, Inc., 1970-77, v.p. fin. and adminstrn. 1977-86; adv. bd. Allendale Ins. Co., 1982; mem. adv. com. U.S. Dept. of Commerce, 1982—; exec. v.p. fin. and adminstrn. Oxford Industries, Inc., 1986—; bd. dirs. Major Leasing. Vice-chmn. Ga. Rep. party, 1981-83; bd. dirs. Ga. Coop. Svcs. for Blind, 1974—, pres., 1979-80. With USMCR, 1951-53. Mem. Am. Apparel Mfrs. Assn. (dir. 1964-70),

Men's Fashion Assn. (dir. 1974-86), Father's Day Council (dir. 1975-85); dir. Ga. Regents Global Ctr., 1993—. Republican. Episcopalian. Clubs: Cherokee Town and Country (treas. 1977-78, dir. 1979-83, pres. 1982-83); Fripp Island; Dataw; Capitol Hill; Kiwanis. Home: 6265 Riverside Dr NW Atlanta GA 30328-3623 Office: Oxford Industries Inc 222 Piedmont Ave NE Atlanta GA 30308-3306

LEE, REX E., university president, lawyer; b. Los Angeles, Feb. 27, 1935; s. Rex E. and Mabel (Whiting) L.; m. Janet Griffin, July 7, 1959; children: Diana, Thomas Rex, Wendy, Michael, Stephanie, Melissa, Christie. B.A. Brigham Young U., 1960; J.D., U. Chgo., 1963. Bar: Ariz., D.C., Utah. Law clk. Justice Byron R. White, U.S. Supreme Ct., 1963-64; atty. Jennings, Strouss & Salmon, 1964-72, ptnr., 1967-72; founding dean J. Reuben Clark Law Sch., Brigham Young U., Provo, Utah, 1972-81; solicitor gen. U.S.A., Washington, 1981-85; ptnr. Sidley & Austin, Washington, 1985-89; pres. Brigham Young U., Provo, Utah, 1989—; asst. U.S. atty-gen. in charge civil div. Justice Dept., Washington.; lectr. Am. Inst. Trade, 1966-68, U. Ariz. Sch. Law, 1968-72; George Sutherland prof. law Brigham Young U., 1985—. Mem. gen. bd. Young Men's Mut. Improvement Assn., Ch. of Jesus Christ of Latter-day Saints, 1958-60; bd. dirs. Theodore Roosevelt council Boy Scouts Am., 1967-72. Mem. Am. Law Inst. Home: 2840 Iroquois Dr Provo UT 84604-4318 Office: Brigham Young U D346 ASB Provo UT 84602

LEE, RICHARD, martial arts educational executive; b. Hartford, Conn., Feb. 5, 1942; children: Christopher Lee Cuvelier, Stacy Ann Cuvelier. Attended, Foothill Coll. Exec. v.p. U.S. Chinese Kuoshu Fedn.; founder, pres. East West Martial Arts Schs., Alamo, Calif., 1967—; pres., head instr., sys. master Internat. Chinese Bok Fu Kenpo Assn.; coach U.S. Team at 1st World Kung Fu Championships, Taiwan, 1975, U.S. Kung Fu Kuoshu Team 7th World Championships, Republic of China, 1992; founder, grand master Bok-Fu Chinese Kenpo. Achieved 10th degree Black Belt in Chinese Kenpo. Shotokan, Tai kwon do; avocations: travel, spl. interest cars, antiques. Office: East-West Karate Sch 140 C Alamo Plaza Alamo CA 94507

LEE, RICHARD DIEBOLD, law educator, consultant; b. Fargo, N.D., July 31, 1935; s. Sidney Jay and Charlotte Hannah (Thompson) L.; m. Patricia Ann Taylor, June 17, 1957; children—Elizabeth Carol, Deborah Susan, David Stuart. B.A., Stanford U., 1957; J.D., Yale U., 1960. Bar: Calif. 1961. U.S. Dist. Ct. (no. dist.) Calif. 1961, U.S. Ct. Appeals (9th cir.) 1961. Dep. atty. gen. Office of Atty. Gen., Sacramento, 1960-62; assoc. McDonough, Holland, Schwartz, Allen & Wahrhaftig, Sacramento, 1962-66, ptnr., 1966-69; asst. dean U. Calif. Sch. Law, Davis, 1969-73, assoc. dean, 1973-76; assoc. prof. law Temple U. Sch. Law, Phila., 1976-77, vis. prof., 1975-76, prof., 1977—; dir. profl. devel. Baker & McKenzie, Chgo., N.Y.C., 1981-83; dir. Am. Inst. for Law Tng., Phila., 1985—; trustee Law Sch. Admission Council, Washington, 1976-78; mem. internat. adv. com. Internat. Juridical Org., Rome, 1977—; mem. bd. advisors Lawyer Hiring and Tng. Report, Chgo., 1983—; mem. Grad. and Profl. Fin. Aid Council, Princeton, N.J., 1974-80. Author: (coursebook) Materials on Internat. Efforts to Control the Environment, 1977, 78, 79, 80, 84, 85, 87. Co-editor: Materials for the 12th, 13th, 14th Orientation in the U.S. Legal System coursebook, 1982, 83, 84, 85, 86. Contbr. articles to profl. jours. Bd. dirs. Lung Assn. of Sacramento-Emigrant Trails, 1962-69, pres., 1966-68; bd. dirs. Sacramento County Legal Aid Soc., 1968-74, pres., 1971-72; chmn. bd. overseers Phila. Theol. Inst., 1984—, bd. dirs., 1979-80, 84—; mem. bd. of council Episcopal Community Services, Phila., 1984—. Mem. ABA (chmn. various coms.), Pa. Bar Assn., Am. Law Inst. Democrat. Episcopalian. Club: Yale (N.Y.C.). Home: 2001 Sacramento St # 4 San Francisco CA 94109-3342 Office: Morrison & Foerster 345 California St San Francisco CA 94104

LEE, RICHARD KENNETH, building products company executive; b. Birmingham, Eng., Dec. 10, 1942; came to U.S., 1964; s. Kenneth Jesse Lee and Eleanor Margaret (Bellsham) Dean; m. Melinda Elena Noback, Aug. 20, 1966; children: Sonja Eleanor, Alyssa Claire. BSc with upper 2d class honours, No. Poly. U. London, 1964; MS in Inorganic Chemistry, Northwestern U., 1965; PhD in Inorganic Chemistry, U. London, 1968. Various corp. rsch. positions UOP Inc., Des Plaines, Ill., 1965-74, mgr. catalyst R & D automotive products divsn., 1974-77; v.p., gen. mgr. portable battery div. Gould Inc., St. Paul, 1977-82; v.p., gen. mgr. Elgar Corp., an Onan/McGraw Edison Co., San Diego, 1982-85; v.p. R & D, Pharmaseal div. Baxter Healthcare Corp., Valencia, Calif., 1985-88; v.p. strategic bus. ops. Manville Sales Corp., Denver, 1988-92; pres., chief exec. officer Rocklite Inc., Denver, 1992—; adj. prof. masters tech. program U. Coll., U. Denver, 1993-95. Author: (videotape) U.S. Competitiveness—A Crisis?, 1992; patentee for vehicle emission control system. Chmn. Summit 91, Denver, 1991, mem. organizing com. Summit 92, Pacoima, Calif., 1992; bd. dirs. Indsl. Rsch. Inst., Inc., Washington, 1991-92. Recipient IR-100 award Indsl. R & D, 1978; Fulbright travel scholar, 1964-65. Mem. Rocky Mountain World Trade Ctr. (vice chmn. 1992-94, co-chmn. 1992-94, bd. dirs. 1990-95), Denver C of C. Office: Rocklite Inc PO Box 44423 Denver CO 80201-4423 *The quality of life for U.S. citizens in the early 21st Century will be primarily determined by the results of U.S. industry and government efforts to improve our ability to commercialize technology successfully.*

LEE, RICHARD VAILLE, physician, educator; b. Islip, N.Y., May 26, 1937; s. Louis Emerson and Erma Natalie (Little) L.; m. Susan Bradley, June 25, 1961; children: Matthew, Benjamin. B.S., Yale U., 1960, M.D. cum laude, 1964. Diplomate: Am. Bd. Internal Medicine, Am. Bd. Family Practice. Intern Grace-New Haven Hosp., 1964-65, asst. resident in internal medicine, 1965-66, 69-70; fellow in inflammatory disease Yale U., New Haven, 1970-71; practice medicine specializing in internal medicine New Haven, 1969-76, Buffalo, 1976—; family practice Poplar, Mont., 1966-68, Chester, Mont., 1968-69; asst. prof. medicine Yale U., 1971-74, assoc. prof. clin. medicine, 1974-76; prof. medicine SUNY, Buffalo, 1976—, prof. pediatrics, 1985—; adj. prof. anthropology, 1989—; prof. obstetrics, 1992—, chief div. gen. internal medicine, 1979-82, chief div. maternal and adolescent medicine, 1982—, chief div. geog. medicine, 1991—; dir. primary care ctr. Yale-New Haven Hosp., 1975-76, dir. med. clinics, 1971-75; chief med. svc. Buffalo VA Hosp., 1976-79; head dept. medicine Children's Hosp. Buffalo, 1979—; chief med. officer WHO Collaborating Ctr. for Health in Housing, 1995—, Wito Collaboration Ctr. for Health and Housing, 1995—; cons. internal medicine N.Y. Zool. Soc., 1973—; cons. physician Buffalo Zool. Soc., 1980—; aviation med. examiner, 1980—. Sr. editor Current Obstetric Medicine, 1989—; corr. editor Jour. Obstetrics and Gynecology, London, 1989—; mem. editorial bd. Internat. Jour. Environ. Health, 1994—; cons. editor Am. Jour. Medicine, 1976-86; contbr. articles on gen. medicine and infectious diseases to med. jour., also articles on med. problems during pregnancy; contbr. chpts. to books on obstetrics. Served with USPHS, 1966-68. Fellow ACP, Am. Acad. Family Practice, Royal Geog. Soc., Royal Soc. Medicine; mem. AMA, N.Y. Acad. Sci., Am. Fedn. Clin. Rsch., Soc. Gen. Internal Medicine, Am. Soc. Tropical Medicine and Hygiene, Infectious Diseases Soc. Am., Soc. Obstetric Medicine (pres. 1991-93), Great Lakes Interurban Clin. Club, Alpha Omega Alpha. Home: 7664 E Quaker St Orchard Park NY 14127-2015 Office: 219 Bryant St Buffalo NY 14222-2006

LEE, ROBERT, association executive, former theological educator, consultant, author; b. San Francisco, Apr. 28, 1929; s. Frank and Shee (Fong) L.; m. May Gong, Feb. 4, 1951; children: Mellanie Lynn, Marcus Arthur, Matthew John, Wendy Gale, Michele Miko. A.B., U. Calif.-Berkeley, 1951; M.A., Pacific Sch. Religion, 1953; B.D. magna cum laude, Union Theol. Sem., 1954; Ph.D., Columbia U., 1958. Ordained to ministry United Ch. Christ, 1954; transferred to U.P. Ch., 1961; Western regional exec. sec. Chinese Student Christian Assn., 1949-50; assoc. sec. Stiles Hall, Univ. YMCA, Berkeley, Calif., 1950-52; dir. rsch. Protestant Council N.Y., 1954; from instr. to asst. prof. ch. and community Union Theol. Sem., 1955-61; lectr. philosophy Mills Coll. Edn., 1956-57; Margaret Dollar prof. social ethics, dir. Inst. Ethics and Soc., San Francisco Theol. Sem., 1961-83; v.p. acad. affairs Alaska Pacific U., 1983-85; pres., dir. Enfield Resources, 1985-87; dean Internat. Student Studies Heald Coll. Inst. of Tech., San Francisco, 1987-88; rsch. cons. Ctr. for Pacific Rim, U. San Francisco, 1989—; asst. v.p., dir. Asian Am. Philanthropy, United Way of Bay Area, 1990—; coord. community rels. Peace Corps., 1991—; prof., area chmn. Grad. Theol. Union, 1962-70; vis. prof. Union Theol. Sem., summer 1964, Internat. Christian U., Tokyo, Japan, 1964-65, Assn. S.E. Asian Sems., Hong Kong, 1966; vis. scholar Stanford Grad. Sch. Bus., 1971-72; co-optd staff World Council Chs. Conf. Ch. and Soc., Geneva, 1966; lectr., TV appearances, 1956—;

cons. ISI Corp., 1971-72, World Coll. West, 1977-83, Coun. on Founds., 1989—; theologian-in-residence Windward Coalition, Kilua, Hawaii, 1980; moderator Inst. Religion and Social Studies, Jewish Theol. Sem., 1960; assoc. Columbia Seminar, 1961; sr. fellow East-West Center, Honolulu, 1972-73; bd. advisors Waldn U.; nursing home care specialist Found. Health Corp., 1987; mem. exec. com. Calif. State Bar Ct., 1989—. Author: Social Sources of Church Unity (selected for Kennedy White House Library), 1960, Religion and Leisure in America, 1964, Directory of Centers for the Study of Society, 1965, Stranger in the Land, 1967, The Schizophrenic Church, 1969, The Promise of John C. Bennett, 1969, (with Marjorie Casebier) The Spouse Gap, 1971, Marriage Enrichment Sharing Sessions, 1979, China Journal, 1980, Faith and the Prospects of Economic Collapse, 1981, Guide to Chinese American Philanthropy and Charitable Giving Patterns, 1990; editor: Cities and Churches, 1962, (with Martin E. Marty) Religion and Social Conflict, 1964, The Church and The Exploding Metropolis, 1965, Action/Reaction; Pacific Theol. Rev., (book revs. edit.) East/West; contbr. to profl. jours., books. Mem. adv. com. problems met. soc. U.P. Ch., 1961—, Center Study Democratic Instns., Coll. Marin, 1965—; bd. sponsors Christianity and Crisis; bd. dirs. Chinese for Affirmative Action, Am. Soc. Christian Ethics, Ctr. for Family in Transition, Family Svc. Agy. of Marin, Festival Theatre Found., Pacific S.W. Student YMCA, ISI Trust Fund, ISI Growth Fund, ISI Income Fund, Found. for Theol. Edn. S.E. Asia; asst. v.p., bd. dirs. Asian Am. and Internat. Philanthropy, United Way Bay Area: bd. dirs. Marin Chinese Culture Ctr.; commn. Marin County Human Rights Comm., 1995—; hon. chairperson U.N 50 Marin Com., 1995—. Recipient Martin Luther King, Jr. Humanitarian award Marin County, 1994. Mem. Religious Rsch. Assn. (book rev. editor jour. 1959-65), Am. Sociol. Assn., Soc. Religion Higher Edn., Soc. for Sci. Study Religion, Center for Ethics and Social Policy, United Presbyn. Found. (trustee), Asians and Pacific Islanders in Philanthropy, Nan Hai Art Ctr. (trustee). Home: 717 Montecillo Rd San Rafael CA 94903-3135

LEE, ROBERT, telecommunications executive; b. Los Angeles, Sept. 19, 1948; s. Ben Yow and Ngun Hung (Chin) L.; m. Carolyn Louise Coffman, Sept. 11, 1971; children: Robyn Jennifer, Tracy Christine. BS, U. So. Calif., Los Angeles, 1970; MBA, U. Calif., Berkeley, 1972. With Pacific Telephone, 1972—; asst. mgr. Los Angeles, 1972-74; mgr. Los Angeles, Huntington Pk., El Segundo, Calif., 1975-78; dist. mgr. Inglewood, Buena Pk., El Segundo, Torrance, Calif., 1978-80; div. mgr. Torrance, San Francisco, Calif., 1983-84; gen. mgr. San Francisco, San Ramon, Calif., 1984-85; v.p.-ops. San Francisco, 1986; v.p.-consumer market San Ramon, 1986-87, exec. v.p.-mktg., 1987—. Recipient Asian Am. Achievement award Orgn. Chinese Ams., Los Angeles, 1985, Corp. Leadership award Asian Bus. League, San Francisco. Democrat. Avocations: tennis, jogging, travel, theater. Office: Pacific Bell 2600 Camino Ramon Rm 3100cn San Ramon CA 94583-5041

LEE, ROBERT DORWIN, public affairs educator; b. Detroit, Jan. 14, 1939; s. Robert Dorwin Sr. and Virginia (Stanow) L.; m. Barbara Marvin, June 4, 1968; children: Robert, Craig, Cameron. BA, Wayne State U., 1960; MA, Syracuse (N.Y.) U., 1963, PhD, 1967. From asst. to prof. Pa. State U., University Park, 1966—; head pub. adminstrn. dept., 1988-94; prof. hotel, restaurant, and recreation mgmt., 1994—. Author: Public Personnel Systems, 3d edit., 1993; lead author: Public Budgeting Systems, 5th edit., 1994. Avocations: backpacking, swimming, bicycling. Home: 672 Devonshire Dr State College PA 16803-3231 Office: Pa State U Sch Hotel Restaurant & Rec 201 Mateer Bldg University Park PA 16802

LEE, ROBERT EARL, physician; b. North Sydney, N.S., Can., Sept. 26, 1928; came to U.S. 1928, naturalized, 1942; s. Matthew and Amy Roberts (Moulton) L.; m. Sally Gosling, June 23, 1953 (annuled 1967); children: Diane, Cynthia, Susan, Robert; m. Elaine Katherine Chapleau, Dec. 15, 1967. AB, Colgate U., 1948; MD, Cornell U., 1952. Diplomate Am. Bd. Internal Medicine. Intern N.Y. Hosp., Cornell Med. Ctr., N.Y.C., 1952-53, resident, 1955-56, asst. clin. prof. internal medicine Med. Coll.; fellow Manhattan VA Hosp., N.Y.C., 1956-57; cons. internal medicine N.Y. Hosp., Cornell Westchester Div., 1958, dir. med. services, 1967-80, attending physician Burke Rehab., White Plains, 1957-71, cons., 1971—; attending physician White Plains Hosp., N.Y., 1957—, St. Agnes Hosp., White Plains, 1971—; cons. in medicine Dobbs Ferry Hosp., N.Y., 1968-90; pres. White Plains Hosp. Med. Staff, 1975-76; mem. Westchester County Bd. Mgrs., Div. Lab. and Research, 1970, chmn. 1984—. Bd. dirs. Westchester Council Social Agencies, 1972-77; sr. warden Ch. of St. James the Less, Scarsdale, N.Y., 1988; vol. vol. advisor Scarsdale Ambulance Corps., 1977—; v.p. Greenburgh Nature Ctr., Scarsdale, 1982-84. Served to 1st lt. U.S. Army, 1953-55. Named to Am. Soc. Most Venerable Order of St. John of Jerusalem, 1984 (comdr.). Mem. Westchester County Med. Soc., N.Y. State Med. Soc., ACP, Westchester County Med. Soc. (bd. dirs. 1970-72). Republican. Episcopalian. Clubs: Fox Meadow Tennis (Scarsdale) (pres. 1986-87); Union League, Church (N.Y.C.). Home: 9 Old Windy Bush Rd New Hope PA 18938 Office: Heathcote Med Assocs PC 50 Popham Rd Scarsdale NY 10583-4253

LEE, ROBERT LLOYD, pastor, religious association executive; b. Escanaba, Mich., Jan. 3, 1943; s. Lloyd Benjamin and Eleanor Mae (Lence) L.; m. Gloria Jeanne James, June 3, 1967; children: Adam Robert, Amy Vicary Lee Skogerboe. BA, Augsburg Coll., 1965; MDiv, Free Luth. Sem., 1968; ThM, Bethel Theol. Sem., 1988. Ordained min. Luth. Ch., 1968. Pastor Tioga (N.D.) Luth. Parish, 1966-72, Grace & Zion Luth. Chs., Valley City, N.D., 1972-79, Helmar Luth. Ch., Newark, Ill., 1990-92; prof. hist. theology Free Luth. Schs., Mpls., 1979-89; pres. Assn. Free Luth. Congregations, Mpls., 1992—. Author: Fever Saga, 1987, Do the Work of An Evangelist, 1990; editor The Luth. Ambassador, 1990-93. Co-chmn. Luth. Estonian Am. Friends, 1992—. Mem. Valdres Samband, Norwegian-Am. Hist. Assn., N.Am. Manx Assn. Office: Assn Free Luth Congregations 3110 E Medicine Lake Blvd Minneapolis MN 55441-3008

LEE, ROBERT SANFORD, psychologist; b. Bklyn., Nov. 16, 1924; s. Mark and Celia (Edelstein) L.; m. Barbara Kaplan, June 9, 1963 (div. 1980); children: David, Daniel. Student, U. Chgo., 1943-46; B.A., NYU, 1947, Ph.D., 1956. Psychologist, N.Y. Program dir. U.S. Bur. Census, N.Y.C., 1947-50; research assoc. NYU, 1952-58; asst. dir. The Psychol. Corp., N.Y.C., 1959-61; research advisor for communications IBM, Armonk, N.Y., 1961-81; sr. v.p. McCann-Erickson, Inc., N.Y.C., 1981-84; assoc. prof. mktg. Lubin Grad. Sch. Bus. Pace U., N.Y.C., 1984—. Author: (with Chein, Gerard and Rosenfeld) The Road to H, 1964. Served with U.S. Army, 1943-45. Recipient Kurt Levin award N.Y. State Psychol. Assn., 1994. Mem. AAAS, Am. Psychol. Assn. for Pub. Opinion research (exec. council 1967-68, 71-72), Am. Psychol. Assn., N.Y. Assn. for Pub. Opinion Research, Am. Mktg. Assn. Home: 277 W 10th St ph-b New York NY 10014-2583 Office: Pace U LGSB 1 Pace Plz New York NY 10038-1598

LEE, ROBIN S., surgeon, researcher; b. Pitts., Nov. 28, 1957; d. Lamont and Patricia Anne (Flaherty) S.; 1 child, Zoe Bryson Mayfield. BA, Swarthmore Coll., 1980; MD, Harvard U., 1990. Intern U. Calif. San Francisco, 1990-91, resident gen. surgery, 1991-93; rsch. fellow Mass. Gen. Hosp., Boston, 1993—. Resident scholar Am. Coll. Surgeons, 1994. Office: Mass Gen Hosp TBRC 149 13th St Boston MA 02129

LEE, RONALD BARRY, marketing company executive, retired military officer; b. N.Y.C., May 26, 1932; s. Kermit James and Lillian Bryant (Jackson) L.; m. Nancy Jean Kowalk, Oct. 10, 1985; children: Brett Michael, Brooke Alexandria; 1 child by previous marriage: Dean Eric. B.S. in Engring, U.S. Mil. Acad., 1954; M.B.A., Syracuse U., 1964; PhD (ABD), Am. Univ., 1975; LL.D., Western New Eng. Coll., 1969; M.A., Am. U., 1977, postgrad., 1977-79. Commd. 2d lt. U.S. Army, 1954, advanced through grades to maj., 1965; communications officer 3d Armored Corps, 1965; radio and wire communications constrn. engring. Okinawa, 1956-59; part-time radio announcer Sta. KSBK, Okinawa, 1957-59; instr. orgn. and staff procedures U.S. Army Signal Sch., 1960-61, instr. plans and operations Vietnamese 9th Div., 1962-63; chief electronic system sect., evaluation br. systems analysis Army Material Command, 1964-65; White House fellow, 1965-66, resigned commn., 1966; mem. staff Lawrence F. O'Brien, The White House, 1965; asst. to postmaster gen., 1965-66, dir. office planning and systems analysis, 1966-68; asst. provost, dir. Center for Urban Affairs; prof. Mich. State U., 1968-69; asst. postmaster gen. for planning and marketing,

1969-72; with Xerox Corp., Stamford, Conn., 1972-73, White Plains, N.Y., 1973-75; regional mgr. Xerox Corp., Des Plaines, Ill., 1975-78; mgr. govt., edn. and med. mktg. Xerox Corp., Rochester, N.Y., 1978-79; mgr. bus. and community affairs Xerox Corp., Washington, 1979-82; pres. Phoenix Group Internat. Ltd., Washington, 1982-89; exec. v.p. Devl. Mgmt. Group, Inc., Chgo., 1989-90; pres. Vantage Mktg. Internat. Inc., 1991—, Phoenix Group Internat., Ltd., 1991—; exec. v.p. G/DEC Internat., Ltd., 1992—; lectr. in field. Contbr. articles to profl. jours., chpts. to books; poet. Mem. Weston (Conn.) Police Commn., 1973-75; trustee Western New Eng. Coll., 1969-75; bd. advisers, trustee Woodrow Wilson Sch. (Princeton), 1969-75; bd. dirs. Zion Investment Assn., 1970-76, Jr. Achievement Greater Washington, 1979-89, NCCJ, 1980-89, Comty. Found. Greater Washington, 1980-89, Duke Ellington Sch. Arts, 1980-89, Workshops for Careers in the Arts, 1980-89; adv. bd. Nat. Assn. Sickle Cell Diseases, 1972—; chmn. bd. trustees Capital Children's Mus., 1979-89; mem. D.C. Mayor's Pvt. Industry Coun., 1979-89. Decorated Army Commendation medal with oak leaf cluster; named Neighbor of Month Springfield, Mass., June 1950; jr. singles champion New Eng. Tennis Assn., 1950; recipient Arthur S. Flemming award, 1968. Mem. NAACP, Nat. Urban League, Am. West Point Grads., Assn. Syracuse Army Comptrs., Am. Soc. Pub. Adminstrn., White House Fellows Assn. (1st pres. 1966), Am. Acad. Polit. and Social Sci., Beta Gamma Sigma, Alpha Phi Alpha. Office: Vantage Marketing Internat Inc 4200 Wisconsin Ave NW Washington DC 20016

LEE, RONALD DEMOS, demographer, economist, educator; b. Poughkeepsie N.Y., Sept. 5, 1941; s. Otis Hamilton and Dorothy (Demetracopoulou) L.; m. Melissa Lee Nelken, July 6, 1968; children: Sophia, Isabel, Rebecca. BA, Reed Coll., 1963; MA, U. Calif.-Berkeley, 1967; PhD, Harvard U., 1971. Postdoctoral fellow Nat. Demographic Inst., Paris, 1970-71; asst. prof. to prof. U. Mich., Ann Arbor, 1971-79; prof. demography and econs. U. Calif.-Berkeley, 1979—; chair NAS Com. on Pop., 1993—; cons. in field; dir. Ctr. Demography and Econs. of Aging. Peace Corps. vol., Ethiopia, 1963-65. NIH fellow, 1965-67; NSF fellow, 1968-69; Social Sci. Research Council fellow, 1970-71; NIH grantee, 1973—; Guggenheim fellow, 1984-85. Mem. Population Assn. Am. (pres. 1987), Am. Econ. Assn., Internat. Union Sci. Study of Population. Democrat. Author: Econometric Studies of Topics in Demographic History, 1978; Population Patterns in the Past, 1977, others; contbr. articles to profl. jours. Mem. NAS. Home: 2933 Russell St Berkeley CA 94705-2333 Office: Dept of Demography 2232 Piedmont Ave Berkeley CA 94704

LEE, RUTH DAVIDSON, tax collector; b. Jackson County, Ind., July 15, 1935; d. Miles and Elsie M. (George) Davidson; m. Robert Alexander Lee, Sept. 8, 1956; children: Joan Reneé Weeks, Robyn Ann Lorenz, Robert Anthony. Student, Fla. Jr. Coll., 1979, 80, 82, Jacksonville U., 1989-90. Cert. tax collector. Clk. Prudential Ins. Co., Jacksonville, Fla., 1955-56; office staff Green Cove Hosiery Co., Green Cove Springs, Fla., 1956-59; asst. tax collector Clay County Tax Collector's Office, Green Cove Springs, 1959-84; tax collector Clay County, 1985—. Bd. dirs. Area Coun. Aging, Clay County, 1991—, Am. Cancer Soc., Orange Park, Fla., 1992—, Clay County Cmty. Svcs., 1992—, Penney Retirement Cmty., Penney Farms, Fla., 1992—; past bd. dirs. Green Cove Bus. Coun., current mem.; chair precinct Clay County Dem. Exec. Com.; mem. 4-H "500" Club Clay County 4-H Club Found., Green Cove Springs; patron life mem. Clay County Fair Bd. Recipient Super Server award Leukemia Soc. Am., 1991, Celebrity Waiters award Am. Cancer Soc., 1988, Presdl. award Green Cove Bus. Coun., 1985. Mem. Orange Park C. of C. (past dir., Govt. Affairs award 1985-88, past v.p.). Baptist. Avocations: cooking, gardening, painting, crafts. Home: 734 Myrtle Ave Green Cove Springs FL 32043

LEE, SALLY A., editor-in-chief; m. Rob Niosi. Grad., Durham U., Eng.; Clark U., Mass. Lectr. Clark U., Mass.; reporter Worcester (Mass.) Telegram; mng. editor Worcester (Mass.) Monthly; spl. features editor Woman's World mag., N.Y.C.; articles editor Woman's Day mag., N.Y.C.; sr. editor Redbook mag. N.Y.C.; editor-in-chief YM/Young & Modern mag., N.Y.C., 1994—; corr. E! Entertainment Network. Office: YM/Young & Modern 685 Third Ave New York NY 10017

LEE, SARAH TOMERLIN, design executive; b. Union City, Tenn.; d. Charles Granville and Dorothy (Robinson) Tomerlin. B.A., Randolph Macon Women's Coll., 1932. Copyeditor Vogue mag. JBK, N.Y.C., 1939-45; v.p. Lord and Taylor, N.Y.C., 1959-65; pres. Fashion Group, N.Y.C., 1960-63; editor-in-chief House Beautiful mag., N.Y.C., 1965-71; pres. Tom Lee Ltd., N.Y.C., 1971-93, Beyer Tom Lee Interiors, N.Y.C., 1993—; cons. to pres. Fashion Inst. Tech., 1971-74. Editor: American Fashion. Vice pres. N.Y. Landmarks Conservancy. Recipient Penny-Mo. Magazine award, 1967, Fashion Inst. award, 1981, Women Bus. Owners N.Y. Entrepreneurial award, 1981, Am. Inst. Interior Decorators Project award, 1982, Decorators Club medal of honor, 1982, Interior Design Project award Am. Soc. Interior Designers, 1987, award of Spl. Distinction, Restaurant & Instns., 1987, 1st Pl. Resort Splty. award Restaurant Hospitality, 1988, Platinum Circle award, 1988, Interior Design award Restaurant Hospitality, 1989, Interior Design Project award Am. Soc. Interior Designers, 1990; named to Interior Design Mag. Hall of Fame, 1986; named Woman of Yr. by Exec. Women in Hospitality, 1988, Designer of Distinction, Am. Soc. Interior Designers, 1990. Mem. Decorators Club (v.p.), Craft Council N.Y. bd. dirs. 1965-75, emeritus 1983). Clubs: Cosmopolitan (N.Y.C.), Nat. Arts (N.Y.C.). Office: Beyer Blinder Belle Tom Lee Interiors 41 E 11th St New York NY 10003

LEE, SHERMAN EMERY, art historian, curator; b. Seattle, Apr. 19, 1918; s. Emery H. and Adelia (Baker) L.; m. Ruth A. Ward, Sept. 3, 1938; children: Katharine C. (Mrs. Bryan Reid), Margaret A. (Mrs. Stephen Bachenheimer), Elizabeth K. (Mrs. William Chiego), Thomas W. B.A., M.A., Am. U.; Ph.D., Western Res. U. Curator, Far Eastern art Detroit Inst. Art, 1941-46; with dept. arts and monuments, div. civil info. and edn. sect. Gen. Hdqrs. SCAP, Tokyo, 1946-48; asst. dir., then asso. dir. Seattle Mus. Art, 1948-52; curator Oriental art Cleve. Mus. Art, 1952-57, dir., 1958-83; prof. art Western Res. U. 1962-83; adj. prof. U. N.C., Chapel Hill, 1983—. Author: Chinese Landscape Painting, rev. edit., 1962, (with Wen Fong) Streams and Mountains Without End, 1955, Japanese Decorative Style, 1961, History of Far Eastern Art, 5th edit., 1994, (with W.K. Ho) Chinese Art under the Mongols, 1968, Reflections of Reality in Japanese Art, 1983, Past, Present, East and West, 1983; editor: On Understanding Art Museums, 1977. Trustee Amon Carter Mus. Western Art, Isamu Noguchi Found. Served from ensign to lt. (j.g.) USNR, 1944-46. Decorated Legion of Honor; Order North Star; Order of Sacred Treasure 3d class. Mem. Am. Acad. Arts and Scis., Asia Soc. (hon. trustee), Japan Soc., Century Assn. (N.Y.C.). Home: 102 Dixie Dr Chapel Hill NC 27514-6615 Office: Univ NC Dept Art Chapel Hill NC 27514

LEE, SHIH-YING, mechanical engineering educator; b. Peking, China, Apr. 30, 1918; came to U.S., 1942, naturalized, 1952; s. Tse-Kung and Pei-Jour (Tao) L.; m. Lena Yin, Aug. 18, 1973; children: Carol Sana, David, Linda Grace, Eileen M. Sc.D., MIT, 1945. Bridge design engr. Chinese Govt., 1940-41, hydraulic power research engr., 1941-42; design engr. Cram & Ferguson Co., Boston, 1945-47; research engr. MIT, Cambridge, 1947-52, mem. faculty, 1952-74, prof. mech. engring., 1966—; chmn., chief exec. officer Setra Systems Inc., Acton, Mass. Mem. Nat. Acad. Engrs. Inventor field instrumentation, fluid power control. Home: Huckleberry Hl Lincoln MA 01773 Office: Setra Systems 45 Nagog Park Acton MA 01720-3413

LEE, SHUISHIH SAGE, pathologist; b. Soo-chow, Kiang Su, China, Jan. 5, 1948; came to U.S., 1972, naturalized, 1979; d. Wei-ping Wilson and Min-chen (Sun) Chang; m. Chung Seng Lee; children: Yvonne Claire, Michael Chung. M.D. Nat. Taiwan U., 1972; Ph.D., U. Rochester, 1976. Resident in pathology Strong Meml. Hosp., Rochester, N.Y., 1976-78; Northwestern Meml. Hosp., Chgo., 1978-79; dir. cytology and electron microscopy Parkview Meml. Hosp., Ft. Wayne, Ind., 1979—; clin. asst. prof. Ind. U. Med. Sch. Contbr. articles to profl. jours. Fellow Coll. Am. Pathologists, Am. Soc. Clin. Pathologists; mem. AMA, Ind. Med. Assn., N.E. Ind. Pathologists Assn. (sec. 1984), Ind. Assn. Pathologists, N.Y. Acad. Scis., Am. Assn. Pathologists, Am. Soc. Cytology, Internat. Acad. Pathology, Internat. Acad. Cytology, Buckeye Soc. Cytology, Electron Microscopy Soc. Am. Home: 5728 Prophets Pass Fort Wayne IN 46845 Office: Parkview Meml Hosp 2200 Randallia Dr Fort Wayne IN 46805-4699

LEE, SIDNEY PHILLIP, chemical engineer, state senator; b. Pa., Apr. 20, 1926; s. Samuel L. and Mollie (Heller) L. B.Sc., U. Pa., 1939; McMullin fellow, Cornell U., 1939-40, then M.Ch.E. Chem. engr. Atlantic Richfield Co., 1938-42; sr. chem. engr., 1942-45; pres. Dallas Labs., 1945—, Assoc. Labs., Dallas, 1945—, West Indies Investment Co., 1957—; chmn. exec. com. West Indies Bank & Trust Co.; dir. mem. exec. com. Am. Ship Bldg. Co.; prin. West Indies Investment Co., St. Croix, 1956—. writer of Lee Lets Loose column for local Carribean newspapers. Mem. V.I. Senate, 1976—, now v.p.; chmn. com. govt., com. on fin. ops. V.I. Govt. Democratic nat. committeeman for V.I., 1969—; mem. V.I. Bd. Edn., 1969—. Fellow Am. Inst. Chemists; sr. mem. Am. Inst. Chem. Engring., Am. Inst. Mining and Petroleum Engring.; mem. Am. Assn. Ret. Persons (chmn. legis. com. 1984—), Tau Beta Pi, Sigma Tau. Clubs: Rotary (pres. 1971-73), Lions (pres. 1960). Home and Office: 135 E 54th St Apt 11C New York NY 10022-4511 Office: PO Box 15705 Dallas TX 75215 *In retrospect, elation from supposed triumphs or defeats is blurred in memory; and of greater importance is the quality of one's life or how one played the game.*

LEE, SPIKE (SHELTON JACKSON LEE), filmmaker; b. Atlanta, Mar. 20, 1957; s. William and Jacqueline (Shelton) L.; m. Tonya Lewis; 1 child: Satchel Lewis Lee. BA, Morehouse Coll., 1979; MA in filmmaking, NYU, 1983. Dir., writer films Joe's Bed-Stuy Barber Shop: We Cut Heads, 1982 (student dir. award Acad. Motion Pictures Arts and Scis.), She's Gotta Have It, 1986 (New Generation award L.A. Film Critics, Prix de Jeunesse, Cannes Film Festival 1986), School Daze, 1988, Do the Right Thing, 1989, Mo' Better Blues, 1990, Jungle Fever, 1991, Malcolm X, 1992, Crooklyn, 1994; other film appearances include: Drop Squad, 1994; author: Spike Lee's Gotta Have It: Inside Guerilla Filmmaking, 1987, Uplift the Race: The Construction of School Daze, 1988, Do the Right Thing: A Spike Lee Joint, 1989, Mo' Better Blues, 1990, By Any Means Necessary: The Trials and Tribulations of the Making of "Malcolm X", 1992. Trustee Morehouse Coll., 1992—. Office: 40 Acres & a Mule 124 Dekalb Ave Ste 2 Brooklyn NY 11217-1201

LEE, STAN (STANLEY MARTIN LIEBER), cartoon publisher, writer; b. N.Y.C., Dec. 28, 1922; s. Jack and Celia (Solomon) Lieber; m. Joan Clayton Boocock, Dec. 5, 1947; 2 dau., Joan C., Jan (dec.). Student pub. schs., N.Y.C.; hon. degree, Bowling Green State U. Copy writer, then asst. editor, editor Timely Comics (became Atlas Comics), N.Y.C., 1939-42; editor, creative dir. Atlas (became Marvel Comics) Comics, until 1961; creative dir., editor-in-chief Marvel Comics, 1961-70, pub., 1970—; creative dir. Marvel Prodns., 1980—; adj. prof. popular culture Bowling Green (Ky.) State U.; coll. lectr., TV script editor. Creator, former writer and editor Fantastic Four, Incredible Hulk, Amazing Spiderman, numerous others; author: Origins of Marvel Comics, 1974, Son of Origins, 1975, Bring On The Bad Guys, 1976, Mighty Marvel Strength & Fitness Book, 1976, Mighty Marvel Superheroes Fun Book, 1976, The Marvel Comics Illustrated Version of Star Wars, 1977, The Amazing Spiderman Vol. No. 3, 1977, The Superhero Women, 1977, The Mighty World of Marvel Pin-up Book, 1978, The Mighty Marvel Superhero Fun Book Vol. No. 3, 1978, The Silver Surfer, How to Draw Comics the Marvel Way, 1978, Marvel's Greatest Superhero Battles, 1978, Incredible Hulk, 1978, Marvelous Mazes to Drive You Mad, 1978, Fantastic Four, 1979, Doctor Strange, 1979, Complete Adventures of Spider-Man, 1979, Captain America, 1979, The Best of the Worst, 1979, Marvel Word Games, 1979, Omnibus Fun Book, 1979, Dunn's Conundrum, 1985, The Best of Spider-Man, 1986, Marvel Team-Up Masterworks, 1987, The Amazing Spiderman, No. 2, 1980, Hulk Cartoons, 1980, Marvel Masterworks Vol. 2: Fantastics Four, 1987, X-Men, 1987, Marvel Masterworks, Vol. 1: Amazing Spider-Man, 1987, Masterworks, Vol. 6: Fantastic Four, 1988, Silver Surfer: Judgement Day, 1988, Silver Surfer: Parable, 1988, Spider-Man, 1988, Avengers, 1988, The God Project, 1990, Silver Surfer: The Enslavers, 1990, Marvel Masterworks, Vol. 13: Fantastic Four, 1990, Best of Marvel Comics, 1991, Night Cat, 1991, Marvel Masterworks, Vol. 17: Daredevil, 1991, Marvel Masterworks, Vol. 18: Thor, 1991, Spider-Man Wedding, 1991, Spider-Man Masterworks, 1992, Uncanny X-Men Masterworks, 1993, Marvels Greatest Super Battles, 1994, The Ultimate Spiderman, 1994, The Very Best of Spiderman, 1994, The Incredible Hulk: A Man-Brute Berserk, 1995, others. Served with AUS, 1942-45. Recipient Alley Award, 1963-68; Comic Art Award, Soc. for Comic Art Rsch. & Preservation, 1968; Eureka Award, Il Targa 1970; Publisher of the Year, Periodical & Book Assn. of America, 1978; ann. award Popular Culture Assn., 1974. Mem. (founder), Acad. Comic Book Arts (award 1973), Nat. Acad. TV Arts and Scis., Nat. Cartoonists Soc., AFTRA. Club: Friars (N.Y.C.). Office: Marvel Comics Group 387 Park Ave S New York NY 10016-8810 also: Cowles Syndicate Inc 235 E 45th St New York NY 10017

LEE, STANLEY, physician, educator; b. Newburgh, N.Y., Aug. 27, 1919; s. Philip H. and Bessie (Stember) L.; m. Ann Rosenthal, Dec. 23, 1947; children: Nancy E., Edward J. and Kenneth R. BA, Columbia U., 1939; M.D., Harvard U., 1943. Diplomate: Am. Bd. Internal Medicine. Intern, resident, fellow in medicine and pathology Mt. Sinai Hosp., N.Y.C., 1943-44, 46-49; research asst., asst. attending physician Mt. Sinai Hosp., 1949-59; practice medicine, specializing in internal medicine N.Y.C.; dir. hematology Maimonides Med. Center, Bklyn., 1959-71; dir. medicine Jewish Hosp. and Med. Center, 1971-77; asso. prof. SUNY Downstate, Bklyn., 1959-69; prof. SUNY Downstate, 1969-91; Dean faculty, 1978-81, acting pres., 1979-81; dean Coll. Medicine; v.p. med. affairs Coll. Medicine, 1981-82, prof. emeritus, 1991—. Served with AUS, 1944-46. Decorated Combat Med. badge. Fellow A.C.P.; mem. Am. Soc. Hematology, Am. Soc. Human Genetics, Am. Soc. Clin. Oncology, Am. Rheumatism Assn., Soc. Exptl. Biology and Medicine, Harvey Soc., N.Y. Acad. Medicine, AAAS, Am. Fedn. Clin. Research. Jewish. Club: Harvard (N.Y.C.). Office: Brookdale Hosp Med Ctr Brooklyn NY 11212

LEE, STEPHEN E., lawyer, educator; b. Hutchinson, Minn., July 24, 1938; s. E.S. and Vivian D. (Hed) L.; m. Donna M. Smutka, Aug. 15, 1959 (div. 1978); children: Katherine, Christopher, Elizabeth; m. Todd Stansbury, May 15, 1981; children: David, Anne. BA, U. Minn., 1960, LLB, 1963. Bar: Calif. 1964, Minn. 1964, Ariz. 1972. Assoc. Faegre & Benson, Mpls., 1964-68; prof. Ariz. State U., Tempe, 1969-82; ptnr. Brown & Bain, Phoenix, Tuscon, Calif., and Palo Alto, Calif.; adj. prof. Ariz. State U., Tempe, 1983—; vis. prof. Cornell U. Law Sch., Ithaca, N.Y., 1972, Southampton (Eng.) U., 1981; bd. dirs. Babbitt Bros. Trading Co., Flagstaff, Ariz., 1987-91. Bd. dirs., gen. counsel Ariz. Civil Liberties Union, Phoenix, 1972—, ACLU, N.Y.C., 1990—. Mem. ABA, Ariz. Bar Assn., Am. Law Inst. Democrat. Congregational. Home: 4402 N 56th St Phoenix AZ 85018-3109 Office: Brown & Bain 2901 N Central Ave Ste 2000 Phoenix AZ 85012-2740

LEE, STEPHEN W., lawyer; b. New Castle, Ind., Oct. 25, 1949; s. Delmer W. Lee and Loma F. (Thurston) McCall; m. Pamela A. Summers, Aug. 2, 1969; children: Erin E., Stephanie M. BS, Ball State U., 1971; JD summa cum laude, Ind. U., 1977. Bar: Ind. 1977, U.S. Dist. Ct. (so. dist.) Ind. 1977, U.S. Ct. Appeals (7th cir.) 1977, U.S. Supreme Ct. 1982. Officer, lt.(j.g.) USNR, Phila., 1971-74; law clk. U.S. Dist. Ct. (no. dist.) Ind., Ft. Wayne, 1977-78; assoc. Barnes, Hickam, Pantzer & Boyd, Indpls., 1978-82; assoc. Barnes & Thornburg, Indpls., 1982-83, ptnr., 1984—. Editor-in-chief: Indiana Law Jour., 1976-77. Dir. Ind. Repertory Theatre, Indpls., 1986-91; exec. coun. Ind. U. Alumni Assn., Bloomington, 1989; dir. Ind. U. Sch. of Law Alumni Assn., Bloomington, 1984-90, pres., 1991-92. Mem. ABA, Ind. State Bar Assn., Indpls. Bar Assn. (chmn. bus. sect. 1985), 7th Cir. Bar Assn., Highland Golf & Country Club. Republican. Avocations: golf. Office: Barnes & Thornburg 11 S Meridian St Indianapolis IN 46204

LEE, SUL HI, library administrator; b. Taegu, Korea, July 13, 1936; s. Sang Moo and Won Nim L.; m. Seol Bong Ryu, Sept. 6, 1962; 1 child, Melissa Jemee. B.A., Bowling Green State U., 1961; M.A., U. Toledo, 1964, U. Mich., 1966. Reference libr. Toledo Pub. Libr., 1961-67; supr. info. analysts Owens-Ill., Inc., 1967-68; dir. Ctr. for Libr. and Info. Sys., U. Toledo, 1968-70; assoc. dir. libr. Eastern Mich. U., Ypsilanti, 1970-73; assoc. dir. libr. U. Rochester, N.Y., 1973-75; dean libr. svcs. Ind. State U., Terre Haute, 1975-78; dean univ. libr. U. Okla., Norman, 1978—; prof. Sch. Libr. and Info. Studies, 1988—. Author: Library Orientation, 1972, A Challenge for Academic Libraries, 1973, Planning-Programing-Budgeting System, 1973, Library Budgeting, 1977, Emerging Trends in Library Organization, 1978, Serials Collection Development: Choices and Strategies, 1981, Reference Service: a Perspective, 1983, Library Fundraising, 1984, Issues in Acquisitions, 1984, Access to Scholarly Information, 1985, Pricing and Cost of

Monographs and Serials, 1987, Acquisitions, Budgets and Materials Costs, 1988, The Impact of Rising Costs of Serials and Monographs on Library Services and Programs, 1989, Library Material Costs and Access to Information, 1990, Budgets for Acquisitions, 1991, Vendor Evaluation and Acquisitions Budgets, 1992, Collection Assessment and Acquisitions Budgets, 1993, The Role and Future of Special Collections in Research Libraries, 1993, Declining Acquisitions Budgets, 1994; editor Jour. Library Adminstrn., 1987—. Mem. ALA (com. on accreditation 1981-83, mem. coun. 1986-90, coun. com. on coms. 1988-89), Assn. Rsch. Librs. (chair com. mgmt. rsch. librs. 1987-89, bd. dirs. 1991—), Greater Midwestern Rsch. Librs. Consortium (chair 1994—), U. Mich. Sch. Libr. Sci. Alumni Soc. (pres. 1983-84). Office: U Okla 401 W Brooks St Norman OK 73069-8824

LEE, SUNG W., electronics executive. Pres., cfo Samsung Semiconductor Inc., San Jose, Calif., 1991—; with Samsung Group, Korea, 1970-91. Office: Samsung Semiconductor Inc 3655 N 1st St San Jose CA 95134

LEE, T. GIRARD, architect; b. Washington, Nov. 3, 1938; m. T. Girard and Dorothy (Thomas) L.; m. Paula Stephan, June 17, 1961; children: Kenneth Robert, Jennifer Margaret Dowd, Rebecca Susan Clark, Nancy Elizabeth. BArch, Miami U., 1961. Registered architect M.D., D.C., Va., W.Va. Architect intern various architects offices, Silver Spring, Md., 1965-68; assoc., architect Bagley & Soule Architects, Chevy Chase, Md., 1968-69; sole propriator Lee & Assoc., Bethesda, Md., 1969-71; ptnr. Bagley, Soule, Lee Architects, Chevy Chase, 1971-84, Lee Warner & Assocs., Annapolis, Md., 1984-90; v.p., treas., prin. Lee-Warner Architects, Inc., Annapolis, Md., 1990—. Chmn. bd. mgmt. Bethesda Chevy Chase YMCA, 1976-77; bd. trustees United Way and Nat. Capitol Area, Washington, 1977-80; bd. dirs. Anne Arundel County YMCA, Annapolis, Md., 1986-91. Mem. AIA (pres. Potomac Valley chpt. 1974-75, treas. Chesapeake Bay chpt. 1985-91, pres. Md. Soc. of Architects 1978-79), Rotary Club of Annapolis, Annapolis Yacht Club. Republican. United Methodist. Avocations: golf, tennis, sailing, jogging. Home: 754 Robin Hood Hl Sherwood Frst MD 21405 Office: Lee Warner Architects Inc 126 Cathedral St Annapolis MD 21401-2704

LEE, THOMAS ALEXANDER, accountant, educator; b. Edinburgh, Scotland, May 18, 1941; s. Thomas Henderson and Dorothy Jane (Norman) L.; m. Ann Margaret Brown, Sept. 14, 1963; children: Sarah Ann, Richard Thomas. Chartered acct., Inst. Chartered Accts.Scotland, Edinburgh, 1964; tax acct., Inst. Tax, Glasgow, Scotland, 1965; MS, U. Strathclyde, Glasgow, Scotland, 1969, DLitt, 1984. Audit asst. Edinburgh, 1959-64, Glasgow, 1964-66; lectr. U. Strathclyde, 1966-69, U. Edinburgh, 1969-73; prof. U. Liverpool, Eng., 1973-76, U. Edinburgh, 1976-90; dir. rsch. Inst. Chartered Accts. Scotland, 1983-84; prof. U. Ala., 1990—; dir. PhD program, 1991—; vis. prof. U. Md., 1986, U. Utah, 1987-88, U. Edinburgh, Scotland, 1991-94, Deakin U., 1994—. Assoc. editor Brit. Acctg. Rev., Auditing Rsch. Jour.; mem. editorial bd. various jours., 1971—. Trustee Acad. Acctg. Historians. Mem. Fellow Royal Soc. Arts; mem. Inst. Chartered Accts. Scotland (coun. 1989-90), Inst. Taxation. Presbyterian. Avocations: church, road running, cricket history. Office: U Ala PO Box 870220 Tuscaloosa AL 35487-0220

LEE, THOMAS HENRY, electrical engineer, educator; b. Shanghai, China, May 11, 1923; came to U.S., 1948, naturalized, 1953; s. Y. C. and Nan Tien (Ho) L.; m. Kin Ping, June 12, 1948; children—William F., Thomas H. Jr., Richard T. B.S.M.E., Nat. Chiao Tung U., Shanghai, 1946; M.S.E.E., Union Coll., Schenectady, 1950; Ph.D., Rensselaer Poly. Inst., 1954. Registered profl. engr., Pa. Mgr. research and devel. Gen. Electric Co., Phila., 1959-74; mgr. strategic planning Fairfield, Conn., 1974-78, staff exec., 1978-80; prof. elec. engring. MIT, Cambridge, 1980-84, 87—; dir. Internat. Inst. for Applied Systems Analysis, Laxenburg, Austria, 1984-87; pres. Tech. Assessment Group, Schenectady, 1980-84, Ctr. for Quality Mgmt., Cambridge, Mass., 1990—. Author: Physics and Engineering of High Power Switching Devices, 1973, Energy Aftermath, 1989; patentee in field. Recipient Davis medal for outstanding engring. accomplishment Rensselaer Poly. Inst., 1987. Fellow IEEE (Power Life award 1980, Haraden Pratt award 1983), AAAS; mem. NAE, Swiss Acad. Engring. Sci., Power Engring. Soc. (pres. 1974-76). Office: 150 Cambridge Park Dr Cambridge MA 02140

LEE, THOMAS J., aerospace scientist; b. Wedowee, Ala., 1935; m. Jean Gullatt; children: Kevin, Patrick. BS in Aero. Engring., U. Ala., 1958; grad. advanced mgmt. program, Harvard U., 1985; PhD (hon.), U. Ala., Huntsville, 1993. Registered profl. engr., Ala. Aero. rsch. engr. U.S. Army Ballistic Missle Agy., Redstone Arsenal, Ala., 1958-60; systems engr. Marshall Space Flight Ctr., Huntsville, Ala., 1960-69, tech. asst. to tech. dep. dir., 1969-73, mgr. Sortie lab task team, 1973-74, mgr., 1974-80, dep. dir., 1980-89, dir., 1989-94, spl. asst. to NASA adminstrn. for access to space, 1994—. Recipient Medal for Exceptional Svc, Outstanding Leadership medal, Equal Opportunity award NASA, Meritorious Exec. award, 1988, Disting. Exec. award, 1991, Executive Excellence Disting. Svc. award Sr. Execs. Assn. Profl. Devel. League, 1992, Werner Von Braun Space Flight trophy Hunstville chpt. Nat. Space Club, 1993; named to Ala. Engring. Hall of Fame, 1993; Disting. Engring. fellow U. Ala. Fellow AIAA (Von Braun award for Excellence in Space Program Mgmt. 1992). Home and Office: 230 Walden Ln New Market AL 35761-9599

LEE, TIEN SHUEY, chemical firm executive; b. Yunnan, China, Nov. 11, 1925; came to U.S., 1954; s. Chien and In-Ho (Wang) L.; m. Laura Teng, Aug. 31, 1963; children: Everett, Lawrence. BS, Chung-Cheng Inst. Tech., China, 1948; MA, U. Oregon, 1956; PhD, Purdue U., 1963. Instr., asst. prof. Chung-Cheng Inst. Tech., Republic of China, 1948-54; research assoc. Harshaw Chem. Co., Cleve., 1963-66; sr. staff chemist Union Carbide Corp., Cleve., 1966-74; proj. mgr. corrosion and deposit control Drew Chem. Corp., Boonton, N.J., 1974-76; mgr. research and devel. Gould, Inc., Rolling Meadows, Ill., 1976-79; task mgr. Argonne (Ill.) Nat. Lab., 1979-85; pres. Sci. Resources, Inc., Palatine, Ill., 1985—; chmn. bd. SA Techs., Inc., Nanjing, China, 1988-90. Contbr. articles to profl. jours.; patentee in field. Mem. Electrochem. Soc. (chmn. Cleve. sect. 1972, George Heise medal 1973),Nat. Assn. Corrosion Engrs., Am. Chem. Soc., Sigma Xi, Phi Lambda Epsilon. Avocations: reading, music, travel. Office: Sci Resources Inc 1058A Whytecliff St Palatine IL 60067-5846

LEE, TOM STEWART, judge; b. 1941; m. Norma Ruth Robbins; children: Elizabeth Robbins, Tom Stewart Jr. BA, Miss. Coll., 1963, JD cum laude, U. Miss., 1965. Ptnr. Lee & Lee, Forest, Miss., 1965-84; pros. atty. Scott County, Miss., 1968-71; judge Scott County Youth Ct., Forest, 1979-82; mcpl. judge City of Forest, 1982; judge U.S. Dist. Ct. (so. dist.) Miss., Jackson, 1984—. Asst. editor: Miss. Law Jour. Deacon, Sunday sch. tchr. Forest Bapt. ch.; pres. Forest Pub. Sch. Bd., Scott County Heart Assn.; bd. visitors Miss. Coll. Law Sch.; lectr. Miss. Coll., 1993. Served to capt. USAR. Named one of Outstanding Young Men Am. Mem. Miss. Bar Assn., Scott County Bar Assn., Forest C. of C. (bd. dirs.), Forest Jaycees (past pres., Disting. Service award), Ole Miss. Alumni Assn. (pres.), Miss. Coll. Alumni Assn. (bd. dirs.), Am. Legion. Office: US Dist Ct 245 E Capitol St Ste 110 Jackson MS 39201-2411

LEE, TONG HUN, economics educator; b. Seoul, Korea, Nov. 20, 1931; came to U.S., 1955, naturalized, 1968; s. Chong Su and Yun (Lee) L.; m. Yul Jah Ahn, June 11, 1960; children: Bruce Keebeck, James Keewon. B.S., Yon-Sei U., 1955; Ph.D., U. Wis., 1961. Asst. prof. econs. U. Tenn., Knoxville, 1962-64; assoc. prof. U. Tenn., 1964-67; prof. econs. U. Wis., Milw., 1967—; chmn. dept. econs., 1978-82. Author: Interregional Intersectoral Flow Analysis, 1973; Contbr. articles to profl. jours. NSF grantee, 1965-67, 73-75. Mem. Am. Econ. Assn., Am. Fin. Assn., Am. Statis. Assn., Econometric Soc. Home: 3743 W Fairway Heights Dr Thiensville WI 53092-2271 *Success comes from determination, persistence and hard work, but the ultimate measure of success is derived from the inner life of a person.*

LEE, TSUNG-DAO, physicist, educator; b. Shanghai, China, Nov. 25, 1926; s. Tsing-Kong L. and Ming-Chang (Chang); m. Jeannette Chin, June 3, 1950; children: James, Stephen. Student, Nat. Chekiang U., Kweichow, China, 1943-44, Nat. S.W. Assoc. U., Kunming, China, 1945-46; PhD, U. Chgo., 1950; DSc (hon.), Princeton U., 1958; LLD (hon.), Chinese U., Hong Kong, 1969; DSc (hon.), CCNY, 1978. Research assoc. in astronomy U. Chgo., 1950; research assoc., lectr. physics U. Calif., Berkeley, 1950-51; mem. Inst. for Advanced Study, Princeton (N.J.) U., 1951-53, prof. physics, 1960-63;

asst. prof. Columbia U., N.Y.C., 1953-55, assoc. prof., 1955-56, prof., 1956-60, 63—; adj. prof., 1960-62, Enrico Fermi prof. physics, 1963—, Univ. prof., 1984—; Loeb lectr. Harvard U., Cambridge, Mass., 1957, 64. Editor: Weak Interactions and High Energy Nutrino Physics, 1966, Particle Physics and Introduction to Field Theory, 1981. Decorated grande ufficiale Order of Merit (Italy); recipient Albert Einstein Sci. award Yeshiva U., 1957, (with Chen Ning Yang) Nobel prize in physics, 1957, Ettore Majorana-Erice-Sci. for Peace prize, 1990. Mem. NAS, Acad. Sinica, Am. Acad. Arts and Scis., Am. Philos. Soc., Acad. Nazionale dei Lincei, Acad. Sci. China. Office: Columbia U Dept Physics Morningside Heights New York NY 10027*

LEE, TUNG-KWANG, pathologist, cancer researcher; b. Wuchang, China, Oct. 6, 1934; came to U.S., 1980; s. Jie-Tsai Lee and Chong-Wen Ding; m. You-An Sun, Jan. 30, 1974; 1 child, Hao. MD, Shanghai First Med. Coll., 1955. Resident in surgery and pathology Yubei Med. Sch., Henan, China, 1957-60, tchr. pathology, 1960-78, assoc. prof., 1979-80; Brandshaw fellow Bowman Gray Sch. of Medicine, Winston-Salem, N.C., 1980-81, rsch. assoc., 1981-85; rsch. instr. East Carolina U. Sch. Medicine, Greenville, N.C., 1985-87, rsch. asst. prof., 1988—; researcher and speaker in field. Author: (with others) Rheumatology, 1985, Ovarian Tumors, 1984, Clinical Cytology, 1981; contbr. 47 articles to profl. jours. Bd. dirs., chmn. membership com. Eastern Carolina Multicultural Ctr., Greenville, 1992—. Brown F. Finch Found. grantee 1993. Mem. Am. Assn. Cancer Rsch., Internat. Acad. Cytology, Sigma Xi. Avocation: classical music. Home: 1403 Evergreen Dr Greenville NC 27858 Office: East Carolina U Sch of Medicine Moye Blvd Greenville NC 27834

LEE, TUNNEY FEE, urban planning educator; b. Taishan, Guangdong, China, Oct. 22, 1931; came to U.S., 1938; s. Kwang Lien and Kam Kwai (Chan) L.; m. Irene Friedman, Apr. 18, 1957; children: Thea, Kaela, Dara. BArch, U. Mich., 1954. Registered architect, Mass. Designer Geodesics, Inc, Raleigh, N.C., 1954-55, Marcel Breuer, Architect, N.Y.C., 1955, Ulrich Franzen, Architect, N.Y.C., 1956, I.M. Pei Assocs., Architects, N.Y.C., 1958-59; chief of planning design Boston Redevel. Authority, 1960-66; chief designer Marcou O'Leary, Planners, Washington, 1966-68; prin. Tunney Lee, Architect, Washington, 1968-70; prof. dept. urban studies and planning MIT, Cambridge, Mass., 1970-93, head dept., 1986-90; prof. dept. architecture, head dept. Chinese U., Hong Kong, 1990—; coord. Citizens Adv. Com. Copley Pl., Boston, 1977-80; city rep. for Cambridge, Boston Transp. Planning Rev., 1970-72. Co-author: Development Politics, 1980; contbr. articles to profl. jours. Bd. dirs. Asian Community Devel. Corp., Boston, 1988-90, South Cove Community Health Ctr., Boston, 1981-87, Oxfam Am., Boston, 1986-88; chmn. Decennial Census Commn., Boston, 1987; dep. commr. Mass. Div. Capital Planning and Ops., Boston, 1983-86. Fulbright fellow U. Rome, 1956-57. Democrat. Office: Chinese Univ of Hong Kong, Dept of Architecture, Shatin Hong Kong

LEE, VERNON ROY, minister; b. Jackson, Miss., Feb. 1, 1952; s. Samuel Rayford and Evie Mae (Abel) L.; m. Rhonda Sue Parker, Nov. 6, 1970; 1 child, Shannon Grant. Pastor Mt. Moriah Bapt. Ch., Junction City, Ark., 1971-72, Pleasant Grove Bapt. Ch., El Dorado, Ark., 1972-74, Pilgrims Rest Bapt. Ch. Spearsville, La., 1974-76, Bethany Bapt. Ch., Bastrop, La., 1976-78, 1st Bapt. Ch., Taylor, Ark., 1978-83, Farmington Bapt. Ch., Corinth, Miss., 1983-86, Wyatt Bapt. Ch. El Dorado, 1986—. Trustee Southeastern Bapt. Coll., Laurel, Miss., 1983-86, Ctrl. Bapt. Coll., Conway, Ark., 1992—; vol. Boy's Clubs, El Dorado, 1986-91, YMCA, Corinth, 1983-86. Mem. Bapt. Missionary Assn. Am. (v.p. 1986-88, pres. 1990-92, clk. missionary com. 1989-91, asst. ch. adv. com. 1992—), Miss. Bapt. Assn. (pres. 1984-86). Avocations: golf, fishing, basketball, softball. Home and Office: Wyatt Bapt Ch 4621 W Hillsboro St El Dorado AR 71730

LEE, WALLACE WILLIAMS, JR., retired hotel executive; b. Nacogdoches, Tex., June 28, 1915; s. Wallace Williams and Caryl (Ames) L.; m. Doris Card, Sept. 19, 1942; children: Doris Lee Bessette, Frederic Williams. B.S. in Hotel Adminstrn, Cornell U., 1936; postgrad. in Advanced Bus. Mgmt, Columbia, 1954. Cert. hotel adminstr. Asst. mgr. Broadmoor Hotel, Colorado Springs, Colo., 1938-42; resident mgr. Hotel Thayer, West Point, N.Y., 1945-47; mgr. Hotel Anderson (Ind.), 1947-48; resident mgr. Hotel Roosevelt, N.Y.C., 1951-53; v.p., gen. mgr. Hotel Roosevelt, 1954; asst. mgr. Waldorf-Astoria, N.Y.C., 1948-51; mgr. Waldorf-Astoria, 1954-59, v.p., resident mgr., 1959-61; v.p., gen. mgr. The Barclay and Park Lane Hotels, N.Y.C., 1961-63; group v.p. accommodations Howard Johnson Co., 1963-80; dir. Smiley Bros., Inc., 1981—, mem. exec. com., 1982-87. Vice chmn. AH/MA adv. com. to Statler Found., 1966-72; mem. exec. bd. Greater N.Y. coun. Boy Scouts Am., 1960-71, mem. exec. bd. Boston Coun., 1971-79, chmn. camping Northeast region, 1972-73; bd. dirs., 1960-71, v.p. bd. dirs. YMCA of Greater N.Y., 1965-71; bd. dirs. Travelers Aid Soc., N.Y.C., 1959-66; trustee Am. Hotel Found., 1973-78; pres. Hospitality, Lodging and Travel Rsch. Found., 1975-80; trustee Christ Ch. Meth. N.Y.C., 1959-64, chmn. ocfl. bd., 1963-64; trustee Congl. Ch., Sherman, Conn., 1965-68, deacon, 1981-83; assoc. 1st Presbyn. Ch., Orlando, Fla., 1990—. Served to capt. AUS, 1942-45. Recipient Silver Beaver award Boy Scouts Am., 1964, Disting. Achievement in Edn. and Advancing Profession of Innkeeping award Hotel and Restaurant Mgmt. Soc. NYU, 1964, award of merit Am. Hotel and Motel Assn., Hosp. Travel Rsch. Found., 1980; named Man of Yr. YMCA Neighbor Youth Br. Greater N.Y., 1961; named to Hall of Fame Hospitality Mag., 1965. Mem. Cornell Soc. Hotelmen (pres. 1953-54, trustee Found. 1991—), Am. Security Coun., Conn. Soc. Mayflower Desc., Ednl. Inst., Timber Trails Club (pres. 1966-67). Congregationalist. Home (summer): 172 Rt 37 S Sherman CT 06784 Home (winter): 1055 Kensington Park Dr Altamonte Springs FL 32714-1940

LEE, WALTER WILLIAM, JR., film writer, consultant, publishing executive; b. Eugene, Oreg., Aug. 16, 1931; s. Walter William and Okria LaVelle (Mooney) L.; m. Frances Eve Olveda, May 9, 1959; children: Cindy Lee Kimmick, Steven Marco. BS with honors, Calif. Inst. Tech., 1954; postgrad., U. Calif., Berkeley, 1954-55. Cert. Motion Picture Assn. Am. Film writer Howard Hughes, Culver City, Calif., 1955-59; v.p., dir. Tech. Communications, Inc., L.A., 1959-62; sr. project engr., film writer, coord. Hughes Aircraft Co., El Segundo, Calif., 1962-89; pres. Chelsea-Lee Books, L.A., 1972—; v.p. dir. Sci. Fiction Cons. of Hollywood, Inc., L.A., 1980-94; cons. L.A. Film Expn., 1975, Lucasfilm/20th Century Fox, L.A., 1979, 86, CBS spl. E.T. & Friends/Warner Bros., L.A. and Burbank, Calif., 1982. Editor: Pendulum mag., 1952-54, It mag., 1955-58; editor, compiler Reference Guide to Fantastic Films, 1972, vol. 2, 1973, vol. 3, 1974 (Spl. award World Sci. Fiction Conv. 1975); author: (with Richard Delap) Shapes, 1987; mem. bd. advisors Who's Who in Entertainment, 1991-93; contbr. articles to profl. jours., The New Ency. of Sci. Fiction, 1988. Mem. Community Adv. Coun., L.A., 1975-79. Recipient Film award Internat. Film Producers Assn., 1967. Mem. Am. Film Inst. Democrat. Avocation: collecting sci. fiction, fantasy and horror film reference material. Office: PO Box 66273 Los Angeles CA 90066-0273

LEE, WILLIAM CHARLES, federal judge; b. Fort Wayne, Ind., Feb. 2, 1938; s. Russell and Catherine (Zwick) L.; m. Judith Anne Bash, Sept. 19, 1959; children—Catherine L., Mark R., Richard R. A.B., Yale U., 1959; J.D., U. Chgo., 1962. Bar: Ind. 1962. Ptnr., Parry, Krueckeberg & Lee, Fort Wayne, 1964-70; dep. pros. atty. Allen County, Fort Wayne, 1963-69, chief dep., 1966-69; U.S. atty. No. Dist. Ind., Fort Wayne, 1970-73; ptnr. Hunt, Suedhoff, Borror, Eilbacher & Lee, Fort Wayne, 1973-81; U.S. Dist. judge No. Dist. Ind., Fort Wayne, 1981—; instr. Nat. Inst. Trial Advocacy. Contbd. numerous publications and lectrs. in the field. Co-chmn. Fort Wayne Fine Arts Operating Fund Drive, 1978; past bd. dirs., v.p., chmn. Fort Wayne Philharm. Orch.; past bd. dirs., v.p. Hospice of Fort Wayne, Inc.; past bd. dirs. Fort Wayne Fine Arts Found., Fort Wayne Civic Theatre, Neighbors, Inc., Embassy Theatre Found.; past bd. dirs., pres. Legal Aid of Fort Wayne, Inc.; past mem. ch. coun., v.p. Trinity English Lutheran Ch. Council; past trustee Fort Wayne Community Schs., 1978-81, pres., 1980-81; trustee Fort Wayne Mus. Art, 1984-90; past bd. dirs., pres. Fort Wayne-Allen County Hist. Soc. Griffin scholar, 1955-59; chmn. Fort Wayne Cmty. Schs Scholarship Com.; bd. dirs. Arts United of Greater Fort Wayne, Fort Wayne Ballet. Weymouth Kirkland scholar, 1959-62; named Ind. Trial Judge of the Yr, 1988. Fellow Am. Coll. Trial Lawyers, Ind. Bar Found.; mem. ABA, Allen County Bar Assn., Ind. State Bar Assn., Fed. Bar Assn., Seventh Cir. Bar Assn., Phi Delta Phi, Benjamin Harrison Am. Inn of Ct., North Side High Alumni Assn. (bd. dirs. pres.), Fort Wayne Rotary Club (bd. dir.). Republican. Lutheran. Office: US Dist Ct 2145 Fed Bldg 1300 S Harrison St Fort Wayne IN 46802-3426

LEE, WILLIAM CHIEN-YEH, communications executive, educator; b. London, July 20, 1932; came to U.S., 1958; s. Chou Ying and Fang-Teh (Chang) L.; m. Margaret Mei-Pai, Oct. 6, 1964; children: Betty, Lily. B.Sc., Chinese Naval Acad., Tyoching, Taiwan, 1954; M.S., Ohio State U., Columbus, 1960; Ph.D., Ohio State U., 1963. Mem. tech. staff Bell Labs., Holmdel, N.J., 1964-73; engring. specialist Bell Labs., Whippany, N.J., 1974-78; sr. scientist ITT Def. Communications Div., Nutley, N.J., 1979-81, sr. scientist, mgr., 1982-85; v.p. Pactel Cellular, Inc., 1985-92; chief scientist, v.p. Pactel Corp., 1992-94; v.p., chief sci. AirTouch Comm., Inc., Danville, Calif., 1994—. Author: Mobile Communications Engineering, 1982, Mobile Communications Fundamental Design, 1986, 2d edit., 1993, Mobile Cellular Telecommunication Systems, 1989, 2nd edit., 1995; patentee in field. Named Disting. Alumnus Ohio State U., 1990. Fellow IEEE, Radio Club Am.; mem. Cellular Telecommunications Indsl. Assn. (co-chmn. sub-com. advanced radio tech. 1987-88), IEEE Vehicular Tech. Soc. (Svc. Appreciation cert. 1991, pub. chmn., Avant Garde award 1990, mem. internat. radio consultative com.). *Use mathematics to solve problems; use physics to interpret results; use counter examples to check outcomes; use pictures to memorize the importance.*

LEE, WILLIAM FRANKLIN, III, association administrator; b. Galveston, Tex., Feb. 20, 1929; s. William Franklin Jr. and Anna Lena (Keis) L.; m. Jacqueline Tyler; children: William Franklin IV, Robert Terry, Patricia Lynn, Peggy Ann. MusB, N. Tex. State U., 1949, MS, 1950; MusM, U. Tex., 1956, PhD, 1956. Prof. music St. Mary's U., San Antonio, 1952-55; asst. to dean fine arts U. Tex., 1955-56; chmn. dept. music Sam Houston State Coll., 1956-64; dean Sch. Music U. Miami (Fla.), 1964-82; provost, exec. v.p., 1982-86, disting. prof.; composer in residence, 1986-88; dir. arts Fla. Internat. U., Miami, 1988-90; dean coll. fine arts and humanities U. Tex., San Antonio, 1990-95; exec. dir. Internat. Assn. Jazz Educators, 1995—. Performances with Houston, Dallas symphony orchs., performances with Gene Krupa and Artie Shaw, guest clinician, condr., composer, 1952—; composer, author, arranger more than 100 published works.; author: Music Theory Dictionary, 1962; also articles, music publs.; biographer, discographer of Stan Kenton, 1981; editor, co-founder: Southwestern Brass Jour., 1958, Belwin New Dictionary of Music and Musicians, 1988. Mem. AAUP, ASCAP (recipient 26 awards 1968— including Deems Taylor awards 1981, 85), Nat. Assn. Am. Composers and Condrs., Music Educators Nat. Conf., Am. Fedn. Musicians, Music Tchrs. Nat. Assn., Pi Kappa Lambda, Kappa Kappa Psi, Phi Mu Alpha. Office: Internat Assn Jazz Educator PO Box 724 Manhattan KS 66502

LEE, WILLIAM GENTRY, lawyer; b. St. Louis, Apr. 2, 1944; s. Gentry and Wilma (Elliott) L.; m. Carter Kerr, Aug. 9, 1969; children: William Gentry Jr., Kathryn Carter. BA cum laude, Harvard U., 1966; JD, U. Okla., 1969. Bar: Okla. 1969, Tex. 1972. Assoc. Vinson & Elkins, Houston, 1973-81, ptnr., 1981—; mem. com. on revision of corp. laws bus. law sect. State Bar of Tex., 1975—. Editor: Okla. Law Rev., 1967-69; contbr. articles to profl. jours. Adminstrv. bd. mem. Cho-Yeh Camp and Conf. Ctr., Livingston, Tex., 1990-94, deacon 1st Presbyn. Ch. of Houston, 1979-83, elder, 1984—. Capt U.S. Army JAGC, 1969-73. Named to Order of Coif U. Okla., 1969. Mem. Allegro, Houston Club, Houston Ctr. Club, River Oaks Country Club. Republican. Avocations: tennis, golf. Home: 3665 Overbrook Ln Houston TX 77027-4127 Office: Vinson & Elkins Ste 3635 1001 Fannin St Houston TX 77002-6710

LEE, WILLIAM JOHN, petroleum engineering educator, consultant; b. Lubbock, Tex., Jan. 16, 1936; s. William Preston and Bonnie Lee (Cook) L.; m. Phyllis Ann Bass, June 10, 1961; children: Anne Preston, Mary Denise. B in Chem. Engring., Ga. Inst Tech., 1959, MSChemE, 1961, PhD in Chem. Engring., 1963, NAE, 1993, Ga. Tech. Acad. Disting. Engring. Alumni, 1994. Registered profl. engr., Tex., Miss. Sr. rsch. specialist Exxon Prodn. Rsch. Co., Houston, 1962-68; assoc. prof. petroleum engring. Miss. State U., Starkville, 1968-71; tech. advisor Exxon Co., Houston, 1971-77; prof. petroleum engring. Tex. A&M U., College Station, 1977—, holder Noble chair in petroleum engring., 1985-93, Peterson chair in petroleum engring., 1993—; dir. Crisman Inst. for Petroleum Reservoir Mgmt. at Tex. A&M U., 1987-93; exec. v.p. S.A. Holditch & Assocs., Inc., College Station, 1979—. Author: Well Testing, 1982. Recipient award of excellence Halliburton Edn. Found., 1982, Meritorious Engring. Teaching award Tenneco, Inc., 1982, Disting. Teaching award Assn. Former Students, Tex. A&M U., College Station, 1983; Tex. Engring. Experiment Sta. fellow, 1987-88, sr. fellow 1990. Mem. Soc. Petroleum Engrs. (disting., chmn. edn. and accreditation com. 1985-86, disting. lectr. 1980, disting. faculty achievement award 1982, Reservoir Engring. award 1986, Regional service award 1987, disting. svc. award 1992). Presbyterian. Avocation: travel. Home: 3100 Rolling Gln Bryan TX 77807 Office: Tex A&M U Petroleum Engring Dept College Station TX 77843

LEE, WILLIAM MARSHALL, lawyer; b. N.Y.C., Feb. 23, 1922; s. Marshall McLean and Marguerite (Letts) L.; m. Lois Kathryn Plain, Oct. 10, 1942; children: Marsha (Mrs. Stephen Derynck), William Marshall Jr., Victoria C. (Mrs. Larry Nelson). Student, U. Wis., 1939-40; BS, Aero. U., Chgo., 1942; postgrad., UCLA, 1946-48, Loyola U. Law Sch., L.A., 1948-49; JD, Loyola U., Chgo., 1952. Bar: Ill. 1952. Thermodynamicist Northrop Aircraft Co., Hawthorne, Calif., 1947-49; patent agt. Hill, Sherman, Meroni, Gross & Simpson, Chgo., 1949-51, Borg-Warner Corp., Chgo., 1951-53; ptnr. Hume, Clement, Hume & Lee, Chgo., 1953-72; pvt. practice Chgo., 1973-74; ptnr. Lee and Smith (and predecessors), Chgo., 1974-89, Lee, Mann, Smith, McWilliams, Sweeney & Ohlson, Chgo., 1989—; v.p. Power Packaging, Inc. Speaker and contbr. articles on legal topics. Pres. Glenview (Ill.) Citizens Sch. Com., 1953-57; v.p. Glenbrook High Sch. Bd., 1957-63. Lt. USNR, 1942-46, CBI. Recipient Pub. Svc. award Glenbrook High Sch. Bd., 1963. Mem. ABA (chmn. sect. patent, trademark and copyright law 1986-87, sect. fin. officer 1976-77, sect. sec. 1977-80, sect. governing coun. 1980-84, 87-88), Ill. Bar Assn., Chgo. Bar Assn., 7th Fed. Cir. Bar Assn., Internat. Patent Law Assn., Am. Intellectual Property Law Assn., Intellectual Property Law Assn. Chgo., Licensing Execs. Soc. (pres. 1981-82, treas. 1977-80, trustee 1974-77, 80-81, 82-83, internat. del. 1980—), Phi Delta Theta, Phi Alpha Delta. Republican. Home: 84 Otis Rd Barrington IL 60010 Office: 209 S La Salle St Chicago IL 60604-1202

LEE, WILLIAM SAUL (BILL LEE), artist, writer; b. Bklyn., Nov. 15, 1938; s. Arthur Martin and Clara (Levine) Levy; m. Dona Ruth Johnson-Lee; 1 child, Jennifer Catherine. Grad. high sch., N.Y.C. Humor editor Penthouse Publs., N.Y.C., 1976—; tchr. satiric art Sch. Visual Art; lectr. slide shows of satiric art. Author: 7 books including Insecurity is Better Than No Security at All, (comic strip and lit. format) Investigative Cartooning; featured cartoonist San Francisco Chronicle, Leescapes, The New Yorker, Playboy, Penthouse, Omni, Esquire, Cosmopolitan, Nat. Lampoon, and others; nationally syndicated cartoonist: Lee Scapes, Tribune Media Svcs.; one-man art show at Visual Arts Ctr., N.Y.C., 1974; works exhibited in group shows at Castelli Gallery, N.Y.C., 1972, Motreal Fair, 1974, Hansen Galleries, N.Y.C., 1975, Van Gogh Mus., Holland, 1975, Kew Gardens, London, 1975, Greene St. Gallery, N.Y.C., 1986, Broome St. Gallery, 1987, Atrium Gallery, 1989. Recipient Internat. Humor award Montreal Expo, 1971, L.A. Metro Arts Festival, 1986, 87. Mem. Nat. TV Acad., Writers Guild, Motion Picture Acad., Mus. of Broadcasting, Nat. Cartoonist Soc., Soc. Illustrators, Am. Inst. Graphic Arts, Soc. Publ. Designers, Tarreytown Group. Avocations: drawing, writing, painting, sculpting.

LEE, WILLIAM STATES, retired utility executive; b. Charlotte, N.C., June 23, 1929; s. William States and Sarah (Everett) L.; m. Janet Fleming Rumberger, Nov. 24, 1951; children—Lisa, States, Helen. BS in Engring. magna cum laude, Princeton U., 1951. Registered profl. engr., N.C., S.C. With Duke Power Co., Charlotte, 1955-94, engring. mgr., 1962-65; v.p. engring. Duke Power Co., 1965-71, sr. v.p., 1971-75, exec. v.p. 1976-77, pres., chief operating officer, 1978-82, chmn., CEO, 1982-94, also dir., mem. mgmt. and fin. com.; retired, 1994; mem. U.S. Com. on Large Dams, 1963—; bd. dirs. Liberty Corp., J.P. Morgan Co., Morgan Guaranty Trust Co., Knight-Ridder, Nat. Instruments. Bd. dirs. United Cmty. Svcs., Found. of the Carolinas; trustee Queen's Coll., U. N.C., Charlotte Found., Presbyn. Hosp. Found. With C.E. USNR, 1951-54. Named Outstanding Engr. N.C.

Soc. Engrs., 1969. Fellow ASME (George Westinghouse gold medal 1972, James N. Landis medal 1991), ASCE; mem. Nat. Acad. Engring., Nat. Soc. Profl. Engrs. (Outstanding Engr. award 1980), Edison Electric Inst. (dir. econs. and fin. policy com., dir.), Charlotte C. of C. (chmn. 1979), Am. Nuclear Soc., Phi Beta Kappa, Tau Beta Pi. Presbyn. (ruling elder). Office: Duke Power Co 526 S Church St EC12P Charlotte NC 28201-1006

LEE, WONYONG, physicist, educator; b. Ham Hung, Korea, Dec. 29, 1930; came to the U.S., 1953; s. Zae Taek and Ho Soon (Kim) L.; m. Soo Fong, July 29, 1961; 1 child, Adrian. BS, Calif. Tech. U., 1957; PhD, U. Calif., Berkeley, 1961. Rsch. assoc. LBL, Berkeley, Calif., 1961-62; rsch. assoc. Columbia U., N.Y.C., 1962-64, asst. prof., 1964-67, assoc. prof., 1967-72, prof., 1972—. Alfred Sloan fellow, 1965-67, Guggenheim fellow, 1979. Fellow Am. Phys. Soc. Home: 29 Sheldon St Ardsley NY 10502-2504 Office: Columbia U Dept Physics New York NY 10027

LEE, YOUNG JACK, federal agency administrator; b. Seoul, Republic of Korea, Feb. 25, 1942; came to U.S., 1969; s. Kyung Ho and Taekyo (Chung) L.; m. Kiran Jung, Mar. 31, 1967; children: Hyung Joo, Taejoo J., Minjoo L. BEE, Seoul Nat. U., 1964; MS in Stats., Ohio State U., 1972, PhD in Stats., 1974. Asst. prof. U. Md., College Park, 1974-79; math. statistician NIH, Bethesda, Md., 1979-89, br. chief, 1989—. Mem. Am. Statis. Soc., Clin. Trial Soc., Biometrics Soc. Office: NIH Bldg 6100 Rm 7B13 Bethesda MD 20892

LEE, YOUNG WOO, financial executive; b. Seoul, Republic of Korea, July 13, 1941; came to U.S., 1971; s. Jong J. and Boo S. (Kim) L.; m. Julie D. Cho, Sept. 23, 1973; children: Sammuel S., Grace. BS in Acctg., Calif. State U., Hayward, 1974. CPA, Colo. Sr. immigration officer Kimpo Internat. Airport, Korea, 1966-71; internal auditor, asst. treas., controller Am. Home Shield Corp., Santa Rosa, Calif., 1978-86, treas., v.p. fin., 1986—; treas. Am. Mortgage Service Inc., Compu Fund Inc., Dublin, Calif., 1982-85. Recipient Acad. award Korean and Am. Women's Club, 1974, Pres.'s award for Disting. Service, Am. Home Shield Corp., 1981. Mem. AICPA. Mem. Adventist Ch. Home: 4676 Los Gatos Ct Santa Rosa CA 95403-1499 Office: Am Home Shield Corp 90 S E St Santa Rosa CA 95404-6500

LEE, YUAN T(SEH), chemistry educator; b. Hsinchu, Taiwan, China, Nov. 29, 1936; came to U.S., 1962, naturalized, 1974; s. Tsefan and Pei (Tasi) L.; m. Bernice Wu, June 28, 1963; children: Ted, Sidney, Charlotte. BS, Nat. Taiwan U., 1959; MS, Nat. Tsinghua U., Taiwan, 1961; PhD, U. Calif., Berkeley, 1965. From asst. prof. to prof. chemistry U. Chgo., 1968-74; prof. U. Calif., Berkeley, 1974—, also former prin. investigator Lawrence Berkeley Lab. Contbr. numerous articles on chem. physics to profl. jours. Recipient Nobel Prize in Chemistry, 1986, Ernest O. Lawrence award Dept. Energy, 1981, Nat. Medal of Sci., 1986, 90, Peter Debye award for Phys. Chemistry, 1986; fellow Alfred P. Sloan, 1969-71, John Simon Guggenheim, 1976-77; Camille and Henry Dreyfus Found. Tchr. scholar, 1971-74, Harrison Howe award, 1983. Fellow Am. Phys. Soc.; mem. NAS, AAAS, Am. Acad. Arts and Scis., Am. Chem. Soc. Office: U Calif Dept Chemistry Berkeley CA 94720*

LEE, YUNG-KEUN, physicist, educator; b. Seoul, Korea, Sept. 26, 1929; came to U.S., 1953, naturalized, 1968; s. Kwang-Soo and Young-Sook (Hur) L.; m. Ock-Kyung Pai, Oct. 25, 1958; children—Ann, Arnold, Sara, Sylvia, Clara. B.A., Johns Hopkins, 1956; M.S., U. Chgo., 1957; Ph.D., Columbia, 1961. Research scientist Columbia U., N.Y.C., 1961-64; prof. physics Johns Hopkins U., Balt., 1964—; vis. mem. staff Los Alamos Sci. Lab., 1971; vis. researcher Institut Scis. Nucléaires, Grenoble, France, 1975; cons. Idaho Nat. Engring. Lab., 1988—. Contbr. articles to profl. jours. Mem. Am. Phys. Soc. Democrat. Methodist. Club: Johns Hopkins. Home: 1318 Denby Rd Baltimore MD 21286 Office: Johns Hopkins U 34th and Charles Sts Baltimore MD 21218

LEEBERN, DONALD M., distilled beverage executive; b. 1938. Pres. Georgia Crown Distributing, Columbus, Ga., 1960—. Office: Georgia Crown Distributing PO Box 7908 Columbus GA 31908-7908

LEEBRON, DAVID WAYNE, law educator; b. Phila., Feb. 12, 1955. BA, Harvard U., 1976, JD, 1979. Bar: N.Y. 1982, Pa. 1981, Hawaii 1980. Law clk. Judge Shirley Hufstedler, L.A., 1979-80; assoc. Cleary, Gottleib, Steen & Hamilton, N.Y.C., 1981-83; prof. Sch. Law NYU, 1983-89, Columbia U., N.Y.C., 1989—. Office: Columbia U Sch Law 435 W 116th St New York NY 10027-7201

LEECH, CHARLES RUSSELL, JR., lawyer; b. Coshocton, Ohio, July 29, 1930; s. Charles Russell and Edna (Henry) L.; m. Patricia Ann Tubaugh, June 20, 1953; children—Charles Russell III, Timothy David (dec.), Wendy Ann. A.B. cum laude, Kenyon Coll., 1952; J.D., Ohio State U., 1955; M.A., U. Toledo, 1969. Bar: Ohio 1955. Assoc. Fuller & Henry and predecessor firms, Toledo, 1957-64, ptnr., 1964—. Mng. editor: Ohio State Law Jour., 1955. Mem. exec. com. alumni council Kenyon Coll., 1967-72, trustee coll., 1974-80. Served with USNR, 1955-57. Fellow Ohio State Bar Found.; mem. Am., Ohio, Toledo bar assns., Kenyon Coll. Alumni Assn. Maumee Valley (past pres.), Beta Theta Pi, Phi Delta Phi. Republican. Home: 10953 Springbrook St Whitehouse OH 43571-9674 Office: 1 SeaGate 17th Fl Toledo OH 43603-2088

LEECH, JAMES WILLIAM, manufacturing and technology company executive; b. St. Boniface, Man., Can., June 12, 1947; s. George Clarence and Mary Elizabeth (Gibson) L.; m. Jacqueline Roberts Hilton; children: Jennifer Hilton, Joanna Marjorie, James Andrew Douglas. BS in Math. and Physics with hons., Royal Mil. Coll. Can., 1964; MBA, Queen's U., Can., 1973. Exec. asst. to pres. Commerce Capital Corp., Ltd., Montreal, Que., Can., 1973-74, v.p., 1974-75; exec. v.p. Commerce Capital Trust Co., Calgary, Alta., Can., 1976-78; sr. v.p. Eaton/Bay Fin. Services Ltd., Toronto, Ont., Can., 1979; pres., bd. dirs. Unicorp Canada Corp., Toronto, 1979-88; pres., CEO, bd. dirs. Union Energy, Inc., Toronto, 1985-93, Disys Corp., Toronto, 1993—; bd. dirs. Harris Steel Group, Inc., 20/20 Fin. Corp. Vice chmn. adv. coun. sch. bus. Queens U., 1979-83, mem. gen. coun., 1978—, mem. investment com. bd. trustees, 1980—, trustee, 1984—, mem. fund coun., 1988—; bd. dirs., chmn., pres., mem. exec. com. Can. Stage Co., 1989-94; bd. dirs. Toronto Arts Coun., 1994—. D.I. McLeod scholar, 1971-73; Seagram rsch. fellow, 1983, Samuel Bronfman Found. fellow, 1973, Transp. Devel. Agy. fellow, 1972. Mem. Young Pres. Orgn. (upper Can. chpt.), The Nat. Club, Ranchmen's Club, Granite Club, Glencoe Club. United Ch. Can. Home: 70 Garfield Ave, Toronto, ON Canada M4T 1E9 Office: Disys Corp-No 10 Airport Sq, 2600 Skymark Ave, Mississauga, ON Canada L4N 5B2

LEECH, JOHN DALE, lawyer; b. Cleve., Apr. 3, 1939; s. George Alfred and Mary Virginia (Merrell) L.; m. Patricia Jeanne Higgins, July 15, 1961; children: Kathryn, Carolyn, Krista, Karlyn. BA with honors, Williams Coll., 1961; LLB, Duke U., 1964. Bar: Ohio 1964, U.S. Dist. Ct. (no. and ea. dists.) Ohio 1965, U.S. Ct. Appeals (6th cir.) 1968, U.S. Ct. Appeals (4th cir.) 1974, U.S. Supreme Ct. 1988. Assoc. Arter & Hadden, Cleve., 1964-72; ptnr. Calfee, Halter & Griswold, Cleve., 1972—, mem. exec. com., 1989-92; chmn. health care law sect., antitrust. Councilman, pres. coun. Mayfield Village, Ohio, 1970-74, mayor, 1974-75; trustee Regional Income Tax Agy., Cuyahoga County, Ohio, 1974-75; pres. Hillcrest Hosp., Cleve., 1980-84, chmn. bd., 1986-88; bd. dirs. Cleve. Dialysis Ctr., 1984-89; del. Congress Hosp. Trustees, Chgo., 1986—; chmn., trustee Health Trustee Inst., Cleve., 1986-90; trustee Am. Hosp. Assn., 1993—, mem. exec. com., trustee various coms., Chgo., 1987—, bd. mentor, 1984—; testimony House Ways & Means Subcom., 1987, 93; trustee sec. Health Hill Hosp., 1988—. Mem. ABA (various coms., antitrust and healthcare sects.), Soc. Ohio Hosp. Attys., Ohio Bar Assn., Greater Cleve. Bar Assn., Cleve. Country Club, Union Club. Republican. Avocations: golf, tennis, photography, reading, hiking. Home: 10149 Cedar Rd Chesterland OH 44026-3301 Office: Calfee Halter & Griswold 800 Superior Ave E Ste 1800 Cleveland OH 44114

LEECH, NOYES ELWOOD, lawyer, educator; b. Ambler, Pa., Aug. 1, 1921; s. Charles S. and Margaret Owens (Reid) L.; m. Louise Ann Gallagher, Apr. 19, 1954; children: Katharine, Gwyneth. AB, U. Pa., 1943, JD, 1948. Bar: Pa. 1949. Assoc. Dechert, Price & Rhoads (and predecessors), Phila., 1948-49, 51-53; mem. faculty law U. Pa., Phila., 1949-57; prof.

U. Pa., 1957-78, Ferdinand Wakeman Hubbell prof. law, 1978-85, William A. Schnader prof. law, 1985-86, prof. emeritus, 1986—. Co-author: The International Legal System, 3d edit., 1988; gen. editor: Jour. Comparative Bus. and Capital Market Law, 1978-86. Mem. Order of Coif, Phi Beta Kappa. Office: U Pa Law Sch 3400 Chestnut St Philadelphia PA 19104-6204

LEEDER, ELLEN LISMORE, language and literature educator, literary critic; b. Vedado, Havana, Cuba, July 8, 1931; came to U.S., 1959; d. Thomas and Josefina (Jorge) Lismore; m. Robert Henry Leeder, Dec. 20, 1957; 1 child, Thomas Henry. Doctora en Pedagogía, U. Havana, Cuba, 1955; MA, U. Miami, 1966, PhD, 1973. Lang. tchr. St. George's Sch., Havana, 1952-59; from part-time instr. to full prof. Spanish Barry U., Miami Shores, Fla., 1960-75, prof. Spanish, 1975—, chmn. dept. for lang., 1975-76, coord. of Fgn. Lang., 1976-89; dir. Spanish immersion program, 1986-88; part-time prof. Miami-Dade C.C., 1974-75; vis. prof. U. of Madrid, 1982; prof. Forspor Program Studies Abroad, 1989, 90; cons. HEH, 1981-83; judge Assiacion Criticas y Comentariastas del Arte, Miami, 1985—; judge Silver Knight Awards, 1979-83; oral examiner juror Dade County Pub. Schs., Miami, 1986-87. Author: El Desarraigo en Las Novelas de Angel Maria de Lera, 1978, Justo Sierra y el Mar, 1979, Dimension Existencial en la Narrativa de Lera, 1992. Bd. dirs. Vis. Nurse Assn., 1978-80. Mem. MLA, South Atlantic MLA, Am. Coun. Teaching Fgn. Langs., Am. Assn. Tchrs. Spanish and Portuguese (pres. 1978-84, v.p. 1984-87), Fla. Fgn. Assn., Circulo de Cultura Panamericano, Assn. Internat. Hispanistas, Assn. Cubana de Plojeres Universitarias (orricer), Cuban Women Assn., Phi Alpha Theta, Kappa Delta Pi, Sigma DXelta Pi, Alpha Mu Gamma, Coral Gables Country Club. Avocations: tennis, piano, singing, numismatics. Home: 830 SW 101st Ave Miami FL 33174-2836 Office: Barry Univ 11300 NE 2nd Ave Miami FL 33161-6628

LEEDER, STUART L. SANDY, real estate financial executive; b. N.Y.C., Jan. 24, 1943; s. Arthur and Sophie (Ollander) L.; m. Diane Caplin, Oct. 19, 1975; children: Asher, Shira, Akiva, Shoshana. BA, SUNY, Binghamton, 1964; MBA, Columbia U., 1967. Vol. Peace Corps, Niger, 1967-69; controller Celenese Corp., N.Y.C., 1969-70, Peter Max Enterprises, N.Y.C., 1970-72, Property Svcs. Co., San Jose, Calif., 1973; ptnr. Lincoln Property Co., Foster City, Calif., 1979—; v.p., controller Lincoln Property Co., San Mateo, Calif., 1974—; mem. adv. coun. Nat. Inst. Real Estate Taxation, New London, Conn., 1993. Author: My Personal Operation Moses, 1984. Bd. dirs. Am. Assn. Ethiopian Jews, San Francisco Bur. Jewish Edn. Mem. Real Estate Tax Inst. (bd. dirs.). Jewish. Office: Lincoln Property Co Inc 101 Lincoln Centre Dr San Mateo CA 94404-1130

LEEDOM, ERIN, dancer. Attended, Am. Ballet Sch., Joffrey Ballet Sch. Dancer Oakland (Calif.) Ballet, until 1988; dancer Ballet West, Salt Lake City, 1988-90, prin. artist, 1990—. Dance performances include Giselle, Coppelia, Death and the Maiden, Green Table Cake Walk, Daphnis and Cloe, Romeo & Juliet, Anna Karenina, The Dream, The Nutcracker, The Gilded Bat, Sleeping Beauty, Rosalinda, Cinderella. Office: Ballet West 50 West 200 South Salt Lake City UT 84101*

LEEDOM, JOHN NESBETT, distribution company executive, state senator; b. Dallas, July 27, 1921; s. Floyd H. and Gladys Lorraine (Nesbett) L.; m. Betty Lee Harvey, Mar. 17, 1956; children: Joann, Judy, Eddie Kennedy, Danny Kennedy, Linda, John Nesbett. B.S.E.E., Rice U., 1943. Engr., Naval Research Lab., Washington, 1943-45; asst. sales mgr. Sprague Products Co., North Adams, Mass., 1945-50; founder, chief exec. officer Wholesale Electronic Supply, Inc., Dallas, 1950—; pres. Levco, Inc., 1973—; mem. Tex. Senate, 1980—. Chmn. Dallas County Republican Com., 1962-66, mem. state exec. com., 1966-68; mem. Dallas City Council, 1975-80. Author The Group and You. Served to lt. (j.g.), USNR, 1943-45. Mem. Nat. Electronic Distbrs. Assn. (pres. 1971-72), Nat. assn. Wholesale Distbrs. (pres. 1972-73), IEEE, Mil. Order World Wars, Navy League, Tau Beta Pi. Office: 2809 Ross Ave Dallas TX 75201-2595

LEEDS, CHARLES ALAN, publishing executive; b. Mpls., Aug. 20, 1951; s. Charles Phillips and Irene (Pollard) L.; m. Karen Sue Biggs-Leeds, Aug. 2, 1986; children: Charles Austin, Tyler Dixon. BA, Drake U., 1973, MPA, 1978. Mktg. coord. Register and Tribune Syndicate Inc., Des Moines, Iowa, 1973-79; sales mgr. Washington Post Writers Group, Washington, 1979-89; pres. and editorial dir. L.A. Times Washington Post News Svc., Washington, 1989—; asst. professorial lectr. George Washington U., Washington, 1986, 88. Mem. Internat. Press Inst. (assoc.), Soc. Profl. Journalists, Sigma Delta Chi, Kappa Tau Alpha. Presbyterian. Avocations: jogging, tennis. Home: 4714 17th St N Arlington VA 22207-2031 Office: LA Times-WA Post News Svc 1150 15th St NW Washington DC 20071-0001

LEEDS, DEBRA ANN, primary school educator; b. Lewistown, Mont., Dec. 28, 1951; d. Marvin Arnold and Velda Irene (Todd) Duty; 1 child, Franklin Todd. BS, Mont. State U., 1974; MS, No. Mont. Coll., 1977. Tchr. 1st grade Havre (Mont.) Pub. Schs., 1974-82, tchr. kindergarten, 1982-86, lang. tchr., 1986—, mem. curriculum com., 1990-91; prin. Highland Park Elem., 1992—; presentor chpt. I, Helena, Mont., No. Mont. Coll., Havre, 1989-91, tchr., 1991. Chmn., St. Jude's Sch. Bd., Havre, 1985-90; pres. St. Jude Parish Bd., Havre, 1986-88. Mem. NEA, Mont. Reading Coun., Mont. Edn. Assn., Sch. Administrs. Mont. Assn. Elem. Sch. Prins. (scholar 1992), Havre Edn. Assn. (sec. 1976, Tchr. of Yr. 1991), Havre Jaycees (Hill County's Outstanding Young Montanan 1991, Tchr. of Yr. 1991), No. Mont. Coll. Alumni Assn. (exec. bd. dirs. 1986—, v.p. 1988-89, pres. 1990-91, keynote speaker state chpt. I 1992), Kappa Delta Pi. Republican. Roman Catholic. Avocations: music, drama, reading, golfing. Office: Havre Pub Schs 801 4th St Havre MT 59501-3747

LEEDS, DOUGLAS BRECKER, advertising agency executive, theatre producer; b. N.Y.C., Mar. 15, 1947; s. Richard Henry and Nancy Ann (Brecker) L.; m. Christine Castler, Jan. 14, 1980; 1 child, Victoria Brecker. BS, Babson Coll., 1970. V.p., dir. Auto Data Systems, Inc., Natick, Mass., 1970-72; dir. leasing Beacon Cos., Inc., Boston, 1972-77; account exec. Thomson-Leeds Co., Inc. div. The WPP Group, N.Y., 1977-84, exec. v.p., 1985-88, pres., 1988—, chief exec. officer, 1989—; chmn. ednl. rels. com. Point of Purchase Advt. Inst., 1986—, elected bd. dirs., 1989, vice chmn., 1994—; bd. dirs. Checker Board Found. Co-producer: (Broadway musical) Streetheat, 1985; assoc. producer: (Broadway play) Sleight of Hand, 1986; patentee in field. Chmn., founder Lobby Gallery Assocs. Whitney Mus. Am. Art, N.Y.C., 1983-90; trustee Guild Hall of East Hampton (Mus. and Theatre), 1990-92, John Drew Theatre; chmn. men's com. Boys Club N.Y., 1989; bd. dirs. chmn. Friends Henry Street Settlement House, N.Y.C., 1977-80; trustee Whitney Mus. Am. Art, 1992—; co-chmn. membership com., 1993—, Worcester Acad., 1982-85, Babson Coll., 1979-86, also co-chmn. devel. and pub. affairs com.; spl. projects com., The Soc. of Meml. Sloan-Kettering Cancer Ctr.; bd. dirs. Am. Theatre Wing, 1991—, mem. adminstrn. com. Tony Awards. Mem. Babson Coll. Alumni Assn. (bd. dirs., v.p. 1975-79), Union Club, Doubles Club, Royal Tennis Court Club (Middlesex, Eng.). Office: Thomson-Leeds Co Inc 450 Park Ave S New York NY 10016-7320

LEEDS, ROBERT LEWIS, JR., marketing and management educator; b. N.Y.C., Feb. 9, 1930; s. Robert Lewis and Elisabeth (Bandler) L.; m. Irene Osterweil, July 9, 1958 (div.); children: Leslie Anne, Robert Lewis III; m. Joan Wrigley, Sept. 27, 1984. B.A., Amherst Coll., 1951; M.B.A., U. Pa., 1953. With Manhattan Industries, Inc. (formerly Manhattan Shirt Co.), N.Y.C., 1955-76; v.p. marketing Manhattan Industries, Inc., 1958-65, exec. v.p., 1965-66, chmn. bd., chief exec. officer, 1966-74; also dir.; v.p. corporate devel. Benrus Corp., 1976-78; adv. bd. Mfrs. Hanover Trust Co., 1973-74; part-time faculty Bklyn. Coll., 1979, Pace U., 1979-81, Marymount Manhattan Coll., 1982—; Disting. lectr. mktg. and mgmt.; dir. Exec. MBA Program, U. South Fla., 1982—. Bd. dirs. Hillside Hosp., Glen Oaks, N.Y.; mem. mktg. com. Morton Plant Hosp., 1984—Served with USAF, 1953-55. Recipient award for Civic Endeavour Textile Vets, Assn., 1968; award Young Men's Assn., 1971. Mem. Men's Fashion Assn. (chmn. bd. 1972-74, dir.). Home: 215 Midway Is Clearwater FL 34630-2316

LEEDY, DANIEL LONEY, ecologist; b. Butler, Ohio, Feb. 17, 1912; s. Charles Monroe and Bernice Camilla (Loney) L.; m. Barbara E. Sturges, Nov. 25, 1945 (dec. Mar. 12, 1988); children: Robert Raymond, Kathleen Eleanor; m. Virginia Lee Bittenbender, Sept. 22, 1989. A.B. with honors,

Miami U., Oxford, Ohio, 1934, B.Sc., 1935; M.Sc., Ohio State U., 1938, Ph.D., 1940. Asst. geology and zoology depts. Miami U., 1933-35; instr. wildlife mgmt. Ohio State U., 1940-42; leader Ohio Coop. Wildlife Research Unit, 1945-48; biologist charge coop. wildlife research units U.S. Fish and Wildlife Service, Washington, 1949-57; mem. biol. sci. com. Dept. Agr. Grad. Sch., 1950-75; pres. Wildlife Soc., 1952, exec. sec., 1953-57; chief br. wildlife research U.S. Fish and Wildlife Service, 1957-63; chief div. research Bur. Outdoor Recreation, Dept. Interior, 1963-65; water resources research scientist Office Water Resources Research, 1965-74; ret., 1974; sr. scientist Nat. Inst. Urban Wildlife, Columbia, Md., 1975—. Contbr. over 100 articles to profl. publs. Served to capt. USAAF, 1942-45. Decorated Bronze medal; Recipient cert. of merit Nash Conservation Awards program, 1953; Am. Motors Conservation award, 1958; U.S. Dept. Interior Disting. Service award, 1972; Disting. Alumni award Ohio State U., 1975; Daniel L. Leedy Urban Wildlife Conservation award established in his honor Nat. Inst. Urban Wildlife, 1985. Fellow AAAS; mem. Wildlife Soc. (hon., Aldo Leopold award for disting. service to wildlife conservation 1983), Am. Ornithologists Union (elective mem.), Wilson Ornithol. Soc., Am. Fisheries Soc., Sigma Xi. Clubs: Field Biologists, Cosmos (Washington). Home: 12401 Ellen Ct Silver Spring MD 20904-2905

LEEDY, ROBERT ALLAN, SR., retired lawyer; b. Portland, Oreg., Aug. 5, 1909; s. Harry E. and Loretta (Viles) L.; m. Annapauline Rea, Sept. 14, 1935; children: Douglas Harry, Robert Allan, Jr. J.D., U. Oreg., 1933. Bar: Oreg. 1933. Practiced in Portland, 1934-86; former mem. firm Bullivant, Houser, Bailey, Pendergrass, and Hoffman, ret.; U.S. commr., 1943-56; Mem. Oreg. Bar Examiners, 1947-48, chmn., 1949. Chancellor Episcopal Diocese Oreg., 1970-83. Mem. ABA, Oreg. Bar Assn. (pres. 1953), Multnomah County Bar Assn., Western Bar Conf. (pres. 1952), Alpha Tau Omega, Phi Delta Phi. Home: 2839 NW Fairfax Terr Portland OR 97210 Office: Pioneer Towers Portland OR 97204

LEEFE, JAMES MORRISON, architect; b. N.Y.C., Aug. 28, 1921; s. Charles Clement and Suzanne (Bernhardt) L.; m. Miriam Danziger, Oct. 31, 1949; 1 dau., Molly Elizabeth. Cert., U.S. Mcht. Marine Acad., 1943; B.Arch., Columbia U., 1950. Practice architecture San Francisco, 1955-60; chief architect power and indsl. div. Bechtel Inc., San Francisco, 1960-64; prin. urban designer Bechtel Inc., 1974-80; chief architect San Francisco Power div. Bechtel Power Corp., 1980-89; v.p., asst. sec. Bechtel Assos. (P.C.), N.Y., 1978-89; v.p. Bechtel Assos. (P.C.), D.C. and Va., 1978-89; pvt. cons. architect Sausalito, Calif., 1989—; ptnr. Leefe & Ehrankrantz Architects, San Francisco, 1964-68; v.p. Bldg. Systems Devel. Inc., San Francisco and Washington, 1965-70; also dir.: dir. architecture Giffels Assos. Inc., Detroit, 1971-74; lectr. in architecture Columbia U., 1951-52, U. Calif., Berkeley, 1954-60; mem. faculty U. for Pres's. Young Pres's. Orgn., 1967; adj. prof. U. Detroit, 1971-72; mem. adv. bd. Nat. Clearing House for Criminal Justice Planning and Architecture, 1974-76. Works include Mus. West of Am. Craftsmen's Council, San Francisco, 1964 (Archtl. Record award for interior design 1971), Wells Hydrocombine Dam and Power Generating Facility, Columbia River, Wash., 1965, Boundary Dam, Pend Orielle River, Wash., 1965 (Am. Public Power Assn. honor award 1975), Detroit Automobile Inter-Ins. Exchange Corp. Hdqrs, Dearborn, Mich., 1972 (Detroit chpt. AIA honor award 1975), PPG Industries Research Center, Allison Park, Pa., 1973 (Detroit chpt. AIA honor award 1975, Am. Inst. Steel Constrn. Archtl. award of excellence 1975, Mich. Soc. Architects honor award 1976), Gen. Electric Research Center, Twinsburg, Ohio, 1973 (Detroit chpt. AIA honor award 1977), Appliance Buyers Credit Corp. Hdqrs. Office, Benton Harbor, Mich., 1974 (Engring. Soc. Detroit Design award 1976), Standard Tng. Bldg. Commonwealth Edison, 1989-90, Strybing Arboretum, San Francisco, 1990; contbr. articles to profl. jours.; originator various techniques for analysis of human factors in the working environment. Chmn. bd. Mus. West of Am. Crafts Coun., San Francisco, 1966-68; vice chmn. Franklin (Mich.) Hist. Dist. Commn., 1973-74; trustee So. Marin Land Trust. With U.S. Mcht. Marine, 1942-46. Recipient Hirsh Meml. prize Columbia U., 1950, 1st prize (with Miriam Leefe) Dow Chem. Co. Competition for Interior Design, 1960. Fellow AIA; hon. mem. Internat. Union Architects Working Group Habitat, trustee, So. Marin Land Trust. Home and Office: James Leefe FAIA Architect 131 Spencer Ave Sausalito CA 94965-2022 *I think of architecture as a celebration of life, of the buildings we make for ourselves as stepping stones on the path of history. This forces me to be an optimist, always searching to find a manifestation of the joy of being in my work.*

LEEGE, DAVID CALHOUN, political scientist, educator; b. Elkhart, Ind., May 18, 1937; s. Harold Martin and Nellie Josephine (Bliss) L.; m. Patricia Ann Schad, June 8, 1963; children—David McChesney, Lissa Maria, Kurt Johannes. B.A., Valparaiso U., 1959; postgrad., U. Chgo., 1959-60; Ph.D., Ind. U., 1965. Instr. social sci. Concordia Coll., River Forest, Ill., 1962-64; asst. prof. polit. sci., dir. pub. opinion survey unit U. Mo., Columbia, 1964-68; assoc. prof., dir. survey research center SUNY, Buffalo, 1968-70; assoc. prof. U. Ill., Chgo., 1970-72; prof. U. Ill., 1972-76, head dept., 1972-73; prof. govt. and internat. studies U. Notre Dame, Ind., 1976—; dir. center for study of contemporary society U. Notre Dame, 1976-85, dir. London program, 1982, dir. program for research on religion, church and society, 1984—; dir. Hesburgh Program in Pub. Service, 1987-92; program dir. for polit. sci. NSF, 1974-76; vis. prof. York U., Toronto, Ont., Can., 1970, U. Mich., 1971, 73, U. Leuven, Belgium, 1980, Cath. U. Am., 1985-86. Author: (with Wayne Francis) Political Research, 1974, (with Lyman Kellstedt) Rediscovering the Religious Factor in American Politics, 1993; editor: The Missouri Poll, 1965-68, (with Joesph Gremillion) The Notre Dame Study of Catholic Parish Life Report Series, 1984-89; contbr. articles to profl. jours. Mem. bd. overseers Am. Nat. Election Studies, 1990—, chair, 1994; del. ICORE, 1993—; mem. coun. ICPSR, 1966-69. Mem. Am. Polit. Sci. Assn. (sect. officer, program com., chmn. task force com.), Midwest Polit. Sci. Assn. (chair nominating com., mem. coun., program co-chair). Lutheran. Home: 51971 S Shoreham Ct South Bend IN 46637-1358 Office: U Notre Dame Dept Govt Notre Dame IN 46556

LEEHEY, PATRICK, mechanical and ocean engineering educator; b. Waterloo, Iowa, Oct. 27, 1921; s. Florance Patrick and Monica (White) L.; m. Dorothy Feltus, Feb. 3, 1944; children—Patrick M., David J., Christopher M., Jonathan R., Susan E., Jennifer A. B.S., U.S. Naval Acad., 1942; postgrad., U.S. Naval Postgrad. Sch., 1946-47; Ph.D., Brown U., 1950. Commd. ensign USN, 1942, advanced through grades to capt., 1962; hydrofoil project officer, 1951-53; design supt. Puget Sound Naval Shipyard, 1956-58; head ship silencing br. USN Bur. Ships, 1958-63; head acoustics lab. David Taylor Model Basin, 1963-64; ret., 1964; assoc. prof. naval architecture MIT, 1964-66, prof., 1966-71, prof. mech. and ocean engring., 1971—; liaison scientist ONR, London, 1984-85; cons. Bath Iron Works, Rand Corp., Litton Industries, Office Naval Research. Mem. Am. Math. Soc., Acoustical Soc. Am., Am. Soc. Naval Engrs. Patentee in field. Home: 48 Bellevue Rd Swampscott MA 01907-1517 Office: MIT Rm 3-262 Cambridge MA 02139

LEEKLEY, JOHN ROBERT, lawyer; b. Phila., Aug. 27, 1943; s. Thomas Briggs and Dorothy (O'Hora) L.; m. Karen Kristin Myers, Aug. 28, 1965; children: John Thomas, Michael Dennis. BA, Boston Coll., 1965; LLB, Columbia U., 1968. Bar: N.Y. 1968, Mich. 1976. Assoc. Curtis, Mallet-Prevost, Colt & Mosle, N.Y.C., 1968-69, Davis Polk & Wardwell, N.Y.C., 1969-76; asst. corp. counsel Masco Corp., Taylor, Mich., 1976-77, corp. counsel, 1977-79, v.p., corp. counsel, 1979-88, v.p., gen. counsel, 1988—. Bd. visitors Columbia U. Law Sch., N.Y.C., 1994—; active Freedom Twp. Bd. Tax Appeals, 1984-85. Mem. ABA (com. long range issues affecting bus. practice 1976—), Mich. State Bar Assn. Democrat. Roman Catholic. Avocations: hunting, fishing, outdoor activities. Office: Masco Corp 21001 Van Born Rd Taylor MI 48180-1340

LEEKLEY, MARIE VALPOON, secondary education educator; b. Honolulu, Mar. 28, 1941; d. Amil Richard and Florence Haruko (Soken) V.; m. John Darwin Leekley, Jr., June 26, 1965; children: Katherine Joan, Tracy Ann Kehaunani. BS, Carroll Coll., Waukesha, Wis., 1963; MEd, Nat. Coll. Edn., Evanston, Ill., 1990. Dir. Christian edn. Kamehameha Sch. Girls, Honolulu, 1963-64; elem. tchr. Milw. Pub. Schs., 1965-67; vol. Marianas Edn. Dept. Peace Corps, Saipan, Mariana Islands, 1967-69, dist. coord. tchr. edn., 1969-71; tchr. Ethan Allen Sch. for Boys, Wales, Wis., 1977—; tchr. adult basic edn. Waukesha County Tech. Coll., Pewaukee, Wis., 1977—.

Mem. Menomonee Falls (Wis.) Pub. Schs. Bd. Edn., 1990—; bd. dirs. Comprehensive Ednl. Svcs. Agys., West Allis, Wis., 1991—. Recipient vol. appreciation award Greater Menomonee Falls Com., 1991, Boardmanship award Wis. Assn. Sch. Bds., 1991, 92, 93. Mem. ASCD, Correctional Edn. Asn., Nat. Sch. Bd. Assn., Wis. Assn. School and Continuing Edn., Wis. Vocat. Assn., Wis. Edn. Assn. Methodist. Home: W148n7590 Woodland Dr Menomonee Falls WI 53051-4522 Office: Ethan Allen Sch for Boys PO Box 900 Wales WI 53183-0900

LEEMAN, CAVIN PHILIP, psychiatrist, educator; b. N.Y.C., Jan. 16, 1932; s. Stephen and May (Cavin) L.; m. Susan Epstein, Aug. 11, 1957 (div. 1983); children: Eve, Jennifer, Raphael; m. Diane Leenheer Zimmerman, Feb. 18, 1984. AB, Harvard U., 1952, MD, 1959. Diplomate Am. Bd. Psychiatry and Neurology. Intern in medicine Mass. Gen. Hosp., Boston, 1959-60; resident in psychiatry Mass. Mental Health Ctr., Boston, 1960-62; resident in psychiatry Beth Israel Hosp., Boston, 1962-64, asst. in psychiatry, 1964-83; instr. in psychiatry Harvard Med. Sch., Boston, 1966-75; chief of psychiatry Framingham (Mass.) Union Hosp., 1973-83; lectr. Harvard Med. Sch., 1975-83; chief of psychiatry VA Med. Ctr., Bklyn., 1983-85; clin. dir. psychiatry Univ. Hosp., Bklyn., 1985—; assoc. clin. prof. Boston U. Sch. Medicine, 1974-83; clin. prof. psychiatry SUNY Health Sci. Ctr., Bklyn., 1984—. Contbr. articles to profl. publs. Fellow Am. Psychiat. Assn.; mem. Assn. for Acad. Psychiatry, Am. Assn. Gen. Hosp. Psychiatrists, Acad. Psychosomatic Medicine, N.Y. Acad. Medicine, Physicians for Social Responsibility, Physicians for Human Rights, Soc. Bioethics Cons. Office: SUNY Health Sci Ctr Box 1203 450 Clarkson Ave Brooklyn NY 11203-2012

LEEMAN, SUSAN EPSTEIN, neuroscientist, educator; b. Chgo., May 9, 1930; d. Samuel and Dora (Gubernikoff) Epstein; m. Cavin Leeman (div.); children: Eve, Raphael, Jennifer. BA, Goucher Coll., 1951; MA, Radcliffe Coll., 1954, PhD, 1958; DS (hon.), SUNY, Utica, 1992; hon. degree, Goucher Coll., 1993. Instr. Harvard Med. Sch., Boston, 1958-59; postdoctoral fellow Brandieis U., Waltham, Mass., 1959-62, 62-66, rsch. assoc., adj. asst. prof., asst. rsch. prof., 1966-68, 68-71; asst. prof. Harvard Med. Sch., 1972-73, assoc. prof., 1973-80; prof. U. Mass. Med. Ctr., Worcester, 1980-92, dir. interdept. neurosci. program, 1984-92; prof. Boston U. Sch. Medicine, 1992—. Recipient Burroughs Wellcome Vis. Professorship award U. Ky., 1992, Women's Excellence in Sci. award Fedn. Am. Socs. for Exptl. Biology, 1993, Fred Conrad Koch award 1994. Mem. NAS (197th Lilly lectr. 1994, Fred Conrad Koch award 1994). Office: Boston U Sch Medicine Dept Pharmacology 80 E Concord St Boston MA 02118

LEEMANS, WIM PIETER, physicist; b. Gent, Belgium, June 7, 1963. BS in Elec. Engring., Free U. Brussels, 1985; MS in Elec. Engring., UCLA, 1987, Ph.D. in Elec. Engring., 1991. Teaching asst. UCLA, 1986-87, rsch. asst., 1987-91; staff scientist Lawrence Berkeley Lab., Berkeley, Calif., 1991—; group leader exptl. beam physics group, 1994—; presenter numerous seminars. Contbr. articles to profl. jours. Recipient Simon Ramo award., Am. Physical Soc., 1992; grad. scholar IEEE Nuclear and Plasma Soc., 1987. Fellow Belgian Am. Ednl. Found., Francqui Found.; mem. IEEE (Nuclear and Plasma scis. soc. grad scholar 1987), SPIE, Am. Phys. Soc. (Simon Ramo award 1992), Royal Flemish Engrs. Soc. Achievements include research in high intensity laser-plasma interaction, interaction of relativistic electrons with lasers and plasmas, novel radiation sources, advanced accelerator concepts, non-linear dynamics of tree electron lasers. Office: Lawrence Berkeley Lab Divsn Accelerator Fusion Rsch 1 Cyclotron Road MS 71-259 Berkeley CA 94720

LEEMING, FRANK, JR., newspaper editor, publisher; b. Oklahoma City, Aug. 10, 1938; s. Frank and Louise (Linder) L.; m. Sally Schuske, 1960 (div. 1968); children: Patricia, Frank III; m. Joyce Barnett, Oct. 28, 1973; children: Dusty, Scott, Lewis. B in Bus. and Pub. Adminstrn., U. Mo., 1960. Reporter St. Louis Dispatch, 1960-69; corr. Life Mag., St. Louis, 1967-69; editorial editor Lindsay-Schaub Newspapers, Decatur, Ill., 1969-70; bus. editor The Phila. Inquirer, 1970-71, city editor, 1972, asst. to exec. editor, 1973-75, circulation sales and mktg. mgr., 1976-78; circulation sales and mktg. mgr. Daily News, Phila., 1976-78; pub. Kinsport (Tenn.) Times-News, 1978-83; editor, pub. Jour. of San Juan Islands, Friday Harbor, Wash., 1983—. Contbr. editorials, news series and columns. Bd. dirs. Econ. Devel. Coun. San Juan County, Wash., 1986-89. Mem. Lions. Presbyterian. Avocations: boating, reading, computers. Home: RR 1 Box 179 Courtland MS 38620-9725 Office: Leeming Communications Co PO Box 519 301 Tucker Ave Friday Harbor WA 98250-8021

LEENER, JACK JOSEPH, advertising executive; b. Sierra Madre, Calif., Apr. 18, 1926; s. Edward I. and Gertrude (Krushen) L.; m. Anne Gertrude Frank, Sept. 12, 1948; children: Kathy Ellen, Craig Ellis, Douglas Scott. B.A., UCLA. Publicity dir. Los Angeles Jaycees, 1947-49; account exec. West Marquis, Inc., Los Angeles, 1949-54; account supr. Stromberger, LaVene, McKenzie, Los Angeles, 1954-59; adv. dir. Tidewater (Getty) Oil Co., Los Angeles, 1959-64; exec. v.p. Eisaman, Johns & Laws, Los Angeles, 1964—. Bd. dirs. UCLA Bruin Bench, Los Angeles, 1950—, pres., 1962; bd. dirs. Sherman Oaks Little League, Los Angeles, 1964-77, pres., 1968; bd. dirs. Hollywood YMCA, Los Angeles, 1980-81, Hollywood Human Services Project, 1983. Served with U.S. Army, 1944-45. Clubs: Western Advt. Golfers (pres. 1958); Milline Club of So. Calif. (Los Angeles) (bd. dirs. 1962-70), So. Calif. Advt. Tennis Soc. (pres. 1988-89). Office: Eisaman Johns & Laws Inc 5700 Wilshire Blvd # 600 Los Angeles CA 90036-3659

LEENEY, ROBERT JOSEPH, newspaper editor; b. New Haven, May 10, 1916; s. Patrick Joseph and Mary Alice (Ross) L.; m. Anne King Coyne, June 28, 1941; children: Robert Joseph, David Coyne, Anne Patricia. Student pub. and pvt. schs.; L.H.D. (hon.), U. New Haven, 1983, Albertus Magnus Coll., 1989. Reporter, book page editor, drama critic New Haven Register, 1940-47, editorial writer, 1947-55; editor editorial page New Haven Jour.-Courier, New Haven Register, 1956-61, exec. editor, 1961-72, editor, 1972-81, editor emeritus, 1981, v.p./dir., 1970—; v.p., sec. Register Pub. Co.; dir. Conn. Savs. Bank.; examiner adminstrv. reports, editor Ofcl. Digest State Reports, Conn., 1951-52. Columnist. Conn. pub. info. chmn. Am. Cancer Soc.; v.p. Arts Council Greater New Haven; mem. Conn. Edn. Council, Edn. Commn. of States, Conn. Commn. on Freedom of Info., 1981—; bd. dirs. St. Raphael's Hosp. Found., Long Wharf Theatre, New Haven, 1990; trustee Albertus Magnus Coll., 1984, Conn. Found. Open Govt. Served with USAAF, World War II. Named to New Eng. Journalism Hall of Fame, 1977; recipient Seal of the City award for disting. cmty. svc., 1994. Mem. Nat. Conf. Editl. Writers, Am. Soc. Newspaper Editors, New Eng. Soc. Newspaper Editors (pres. 1961), New Eng. AP News Execs. Assn. (pres. 1977), Conn. Editl. Assn., Conn. Cir. AP (pres.), New Haven C. of C. (v.p., dir., Disting. Svc. award), Outer Circle, N.H. Colony Hist. Soc., Kiwanis, Woodbridge Club, Mory's Club, Quinnipiak Club, Sigma Delta Chi (pres. Conn. chpt. 1963-69). Home: R 69 424 Carrington Hill Rd Bethany CT 06525 Office: New Haven Register 40 Sargent Dr New Haven CT 06511-5939*

LEEPA, ALLEN, artist, educator; b. N.Y.C., Jan. 9, 1919; s. Harvey and Esther (Gentle) L. Student (scholar), The New Bauhaus Sch., 1937-38; scholar, Hans Hofmann Sch., 1938-39; B.S., Columbia U., 1942, M.A. (scholar), 1948, Ed.D. 1960. Art instr. Hull Sch., Chgo., 1937-38, Bklyn. Art Center, 1939-40, Met. Mus., N.Y.C., 1940-41, St. Marks Center, N.Y.C., 1941-42; draftsman Acrotorque Co., Conn., 1942, Glen Martin Aircraft, N.Y.C., 1942-44; prof. art Mich. State U., 1945-84, ret. prof. emeritus; mem. Leepa Gallery of Fine Art, Tarpon Springs, Fla., 1987-90. Author: The Challenge of Modern Art, 1949, 95, Abraham Rattner, 1974; contbr.: (anthologies) The New Art, 1966, 68, The Humanitites in Contemporary Life, 1960, Minimal Art; art editor: The Centennial Rev. Arts and Scis. Jour., 1959-62; one man shows Artists Gallery, N.Y.C., 1953, La Cours D'Ingres, Paris, 1961, Artists Mart, Detroit, 1969, Duke U., 1981; group shows include Mus. Modern Art, N.Y.C., 1953, VII Bienal, São Paulo, Brazil, 1963, Prado Mus., Madrid, Spain, 1963, Detroit Inst. Arts, 1948, 50, 56, 80, Pa. Acad. Fine Arts, 1951, 63; represented in permanent collections Mich. State U., Grand Rapids (Mich.) Mus., South Bend (Ind.) Mus.; lifetime work Tampa Mus. Fine Art. Fulbright award to Paris, 1950-51; Ford Found. grantee Brazil, 1970; recipient numerous prizes for paintings including: 1st prize statewide mural competition, Mich. 1983; 1st prize abstract painting Guld Hall Mus., East Hampton, N.Y., 1985. Mem. Mich. Acad. Arts, Scis., Letters. Office: Mich State U Art Dept East Lansing MI 48823

LEEPER, MICHAEL EDWARD, retired army officer, retired corporation executive; b. Republic, Pa., Jan. 28, 1917; s. Samuel and Elizabeth (Augustine) L.; m. Betty Jane Marshall, June 5, 1943 (dec.); children: Michael E., Richard A., James R.; m. Mary Hoke Austin, July 20, 1974. B.S., U. Pitts., 1940; M.B.A., Stanford U., 1949; grad., Indsl. Coll. Armed Forces, 1961. Credit mgr. finance div. Ford Motor Co., Uniontown, Pa., 1940-41; commd. 2d lt. U.S. Army, 1942, advanced through grades to brig. gen., 1969; ret., 1971, staff positions as comptroller, procurement and mil. logistics, 1942-71; G-4 8th U.S. Army, Korea, 1970-71; chmn. bd. Aloha Corp., Honolulu, 1973—; pres. DRC of Hawaii, Inc., Honolulu, 1974-78; asst. to pres. Lucky Devel. Co. Ltd., 1978-84; ret., 1984. Decorated D.S.M., Legion of Merit, Army Commendation medal (U.S.); Order of Merit (Korea). Mem. Beta Gamma Sigma, Lambda Chi Alpha. Clubs: Lion, Rotarian. Home: 7400 Crestway Dr Apt 620 San Antonio TX 78239-3091

LEER, STEVEN F., mining executive. Pres., ceo Arch Mineral Corp., St. Louis. Office: Arch Mineral Corp City Place One Saint Louis MO 63141

LEES, BENJAMIN, composer; b. Harbin, China, Jan. 8, 1924; came to U.S., 1925; Studied piano, with K.I. Rodetsky, 1931, Marguerite Bitter, 1945-48; composition, with Halsey Stevens at U. So. Calif. 1945-48, with George Antheil, 1949-54. Prof. composition Peabody Conservatory, Queen's Coll., Manhattan Sch. Music. Composer: Profile, 1952, Declamations for piano and strings, 1953, Symphony Number 1, 1953, Number 2, 1958, Piano Concerto Number 1, 1955, Divertimento Burlesca, 1957, Songs of the Night for Soprano and Orch., 1952, Violin Concerto, 1958, Prologue, Capriccio and Epilogue, 1958, Concerto for Orch., 1959, Concertante Breve, 1959, Interlude for Strings, 1957, Visions of Poets for Soprano and Tenor Solo; Chorus and Orch., 1961; The Gilded Cage; chamber music String Quartet Number 1, 1952; Evocation for Solo Flute, 1953, Violin Sonata Number 1, 1953, Movement da Camera for Flute, Clarinet, Cello and Piano, 1954, String Quartet Number 2, 1955, Three Variables for Winds and Piano, 1956; piano Sonata for Two Pianos, 1951; Toccata, 1953, Fantasia, 1954, Kaleidoscopes, 1959, Sonata Breve, 1956, Six Ornamental Etudes, 1957; songs Cyprian Songs for baritone, 1961; Concerto for Oboe and Orch, 1964, Piano Sonata 4, 1965, Piano Concerto 2, 1966, Symphony No. 3, 1968; opera Medea in Corinth, 1970; Study for Solo Cello, 1972, Sonata No. 2 for Violin and Piano, 1973, Etudes for Piano and Orch., 1974, Labyrinths for Symphonic Band, 1975, Variations for Piano and Orch., 1975, Passacaglia for Orch., 1976, Concerto for Woodwind Quintet and Orch., 1976, Staves soprano and piano, 1977; Scarlatti Portfolio; transcriptions for orch., 1978; Dialogue for Cello and Piano, 1977, Paumanok for mezzo-soprano with piano, 1980; Omen for soprano with piano, 1980; Sonata for cello and piano, 1981, String Quartet No. 3, 1982, Double Concerto for piano, cello and orch., 1982, Concerto for brass choir and orch., 1983, Portrait of Rodin (orch.), 1984, Symphony No. 4 (Memorial Candles), 1985, Odyssey II for solo piano, 1986, Symphony # 5, 1988, String Quartet No. 4, 1989, Sonata for Violin and Piano # 3, 1989, Concerto for Horn and Orch., 1991, Mirrors for solo piano, 1992, Borealis for orch., 1993, Echoes of Normandy, 1994. Recipient Fromm Found. award, 1953; William and Noma Copley Found. award, 1955; UNESCO award, 1958; Sir Arnold Bax medal, 1958; Composers award Lancaster Symphony Orch., 1985; Guggenheim fellow, 1954, 66; Fulbright fellow, 1956. Address: 28 Cambridge Rd Great Neck NY 11023

LEES, BRIAN PAUL, state senator; b. Amesbury, Mass., July 25, 1953; Phillip and Patricia (Wenzel) L.; m. Nancy Ward, Aug. 2, 1980. BSBA, Salem State Coll., 1975. Staff asst. U.S. Senator Edward Brooke, Washington, 1976-79; product devel. mgr. Westvaco Corp., Springfield, Mass., 1980-89; state senator Mass. Senate, Boston, 1989—, asst. minority leader, 1991-92; minority leader, 1993—. Corporator Springfield YMCA, Springfield Libr. and Mus., Brightside Children's Ctr.; bd. trustees Willie Ross Sch. for Deaf; mem. Internat. Trade Adv. Bd. Recipient Leadership award Greater Springfield chpt. NOW, 1989, Pub. Svc. award Springfield Pomona Grange, 1992, Legislator of Yr. award Western Mass. Orgn. Nursing Execs., 1994; named Headliner of Yr., Valley Press Club, 1988, Hampden County Am. Legion Legislator of Yr., 1992. Office: 527 Main St Springfield MA 01151-2208

LEES, MARJORIE BERMAN, biochemist, neuroscientist; b. N.Y.C., Mar. 17, 1923; d. Isadore I. and Ruth (Rogalsky) Berman; m. Sidney Lees, Sept. 17, 1946; children: David E., Andrew, Eliot. BA, Hunter Coll., 1943; MS, U. Chgo., 1945; PhD, Harvard U., Radcliffe Coll., 1951. Assoc. biochemist, asst. biochemist McLean Hosp., Belmont, Mass., 1953-62; rsch. assoc. Darmouth Med. Sch., Hanover, N.H., 1962-66; assoc. biochemist McLean Hosp., Belmont, 1966-76; prin. assoc. sr. rsch. assoc. Harvard Med. Sch., Boston, 1966-85; biochemist E.K. Shriver Ctr., Waltham, Mass., 1976—; prof. biochemistry (neurology) Harvard Med. Sch., Boston, 1985—; biochemist Mass. Gen. Hosp., Boston, 1976—; assoc. dir. biochemistry E.K. Shriver Ctr., Waltham, 1982-90, dir. biochemistry, 1990-93, assoc. dir. mental retardation rsch. ctr., 1994—; mem. adv. com. biomed. and behavioral rsch. NASA/NIH, 1990—; mem. sci. adv. com. Nat. Multiple Sclerosis Soc., 1988-93. Chief editor Jour. of Neurochemistry, 1986-90; author (with others) books; contbr. articles to profl. jours. Mem. adv. coun. Nat. Inst. Neurological Disorders, Bethesda, Md., 1979-82; chmn. Radcliffe Grad. Soc., Cambridge, Mass., 1978-80. Predoctoral fellow USPHS, 1947-50, postdoctoral fellow Am. Cancer Soc., 1951-53; Javits Neurosci. grantee NIH, 1983-90, 91-97, prin. grantee NIH, 1962—; named to Hunter Coll. Hall of Fame, 1982. Mem. Am. Soc. Biochemistry and Molecular Biology, Internat. Soc. Neurochemistry (treas. 1975-81, pres. 1983-85), Soc. for Neurosci., Am. Assn. Neuropathology (assoc.), Internat. Soc. Neuroimmunology, N.Y. Acad. Scis., Am. Women in Sci., Phi Beta Kappa. Office: E K Shriver Ctr 200 Trapelo Rd Waltham MA 02154-6332

LEES, MARTIN HENRY, pediatrician, educator; b. London, May 11, 1929; came to U.S., 1958; s. David William and Lilian Thomson (White) L.; m. Elizabeth McMahon, Sept. 5, 1959; children: Deborah Ann, Jacqueline Mary, Christina Beth. MBBS, London U., 1955, MD, 1962. Diplomate: Am. Bd. Pediatrics, Am. Bd. Pediatric Cardiology, Am. Bd. Fetal/Neonatal Medicine. Intern South Devon Hosp., Plymouth, Eng., 1955-57; resident in pediatrics Hosp. Sick Children, 1957; sr. resident, fellow in pediatric cardiology Boston Children's Hosp., 1958-61; asst. prof. McGill U., Montreal, Que., Can., 1961-62; prof. pediatrics U. Oreg. Health Ctr., Portland, 1963—. Fellow Royal Coll. Physicians (London); mem. Am. Heart Assn., Am. Pediatric Soc., Soc. Pediatric Rsch. Home: 17 Abelard St Lake Oswego OR 97035-2340 Office: Pediatric Cardiology 2801 N Gantenbein Ave Portland OR 97227-1623

LEES, SIDNEY, research facility administrator, bioengineering educator; b. Phila., Apr. 17, 1917; s. Charles K. and Bess Rose (Segal) L.; m. Marjorie Berman, Sept. 17, 1947; children—David E.B., P. Andrew, Eliot Jay. A.B., Coll. City N.Y., 1938; S.M., Mass. Inst. Tech., 1948, Sc.D., 1950. Observer U.S. Weather Bur., 1938-40; meteorol. instrument engr. U.S. Signal Corps, 1940-43; research assoc. Mass. Inst. Tech., 1947-50, asst. prof. aero. dept., 1950-57; cons. engr., 1957-62; prof. engring. Thayer Sch., Dartmouth, 1962-66; head bioengring. dept., sr. mem. staff Forsyth Inst. Research and Advanced Study, Boston, 1966—; hon. rsch. assoc. dept. med. biophysics U. Manchester, England, 1990—; adj. prof. Northeastern U., 1980; vis. scientist U. Amsterdam, 1975; chmn., 1965; Joint Automatic Control Conf., Research Conf. on Instrumentation Sci., 1971; Conf. on Ultrasonics in Bioengring. and Biophysics, 1978. Co-author: Instrument Engineering 3 vols, 1952-55; Editor: Air, Space and Instruments, Draper Anniversary vol, 1963. Contbr. articles to profl. jours. Served with AUS, 1943-46. Mem. Am. Phys. Soc., ASME, IEEE, Engring. in Medicine and Biology Soc. IEEE (chmn. region I 1980—), Sigma Xi (pres. Dartmouth chpt. 1964-65). Home: 50 Eliot Memorial Rd Newton MA 02158-2704 Office: Forsyth Dental Center 140 The Fenway Boston MA 02115

LEESER, DAVID O., materials engineer, metallurgist; b. El Paso, Tex., Aug. 3, 1917; s. Oscar D. and Rose R. (Goodman) L.; m. Marilyn Bachman Kalina, Mar. 18, 1945; children: Barbara H., Joyce N. BSc in Mining, U. Tex., El Paso, 1943; MSc in Materials Sci., Ohio State U., 1950; postgrad., U. Fla., 1962, U. Mich., 1985. Registered profl. engr. Ohio, Calif., Ariz. Mining engr. Bradley Mining Co., Stibnite, Idaho, 1943-44; rsch. engr. Battelle Meml. Inst., Columbus, Ohio, 1944-50; assoc. metallurgist Argonne Nat. Lab., Lemont, Ill., 1950-54; mgr. staff metallurgist Atomic Power Devel. Assn., Detroit, 1954-61; chief scientist, materials Chrysler Corp./

Missiles, Cape Canaveral, Fla., 1961-68; chief metallurgist Chrysler Corp., Amplex div., Detroit, 1968-75; sr. staff engr. Burroughs Corp. (Unisys), Plymouth, Mich., 1975-86; prin. materials cons., forensic engr. D.O. Leeser, Profl. Egnr., Scottsdale, Ariz., 1987—; materials cons. fgn. tech. divsn. Wright-Patterson AFB, Dayton, Ohio, 1958-80; charter mem. Missile, Space and Range Pioneers, Cape Canaveral, 1967—; organizer Fla. Indsl. Exhbn., Orlando, 1968; U.S. del. 2d World Metall. Congress, Chgo., 1957, Internat. Conf. on Peaceful Uses of Atom, Geneva, 1958, Internat. Atomic Energy Agy. Conf., Vienna, Austria, 1961. Contbr. articles on nuclear radiation effects on structural materials, flame deflector materials for rockets, forensic investigations to profl. publs. Vice-pres. Manzanita Villas Home Owners Assn., Scottsdale, 1990—. Recipient citation War Manpower Commn., 1945, U.S. Sci. R&D Office, 1946, Appreciation award State of Fla., 1968; Engr. of Yr. Fla. Engring. Soc.-Canaveral Coun. Tech. Socs., 1967, Outstanding Alumnus of Yr., U. Tex. at El Paso, 1969; recipient Apollo Achievement award NASA, 1969, Exemplary Action award Burroughs Corp., 1986. Mem. Am. Soc. materials Internat., Sigma Xi. Achievements include collaboration on development of atomic bomb, Apollo space program, first nuclear-powered naval vessel; pioneering studies on effects of nuclear radiation on materials. Home: 11515 N 91st St Unit 151 Scottsdale AZ 85260-6899 Office: DO Leeser Profl Engr 11515 N 91st St Unit 151 Scottsdale AZ 85260-6899

LEE-SMITH, HUGHIE, artist, educator; b. Eustis, Fla., Sept. 20, 1915; s. Luther and Alice (Williams) Smith; m. Mabel Louise Everett, 1940 (div. 1953); 1 child, Christina; m. Helen Nebraska, 1965 (div. 1974); m. Patricia Thomas-Ferry, 1978. Student, Art Sch. of Detroit Soc. Arts and Crafts, 1934-35; grad., Cleve. Inst. Art, 1938; B.S., Wayne State U., 1953. Instr. painting Grosse Pointe War Meml., Mich., 1956-66, Studio-on-the-Canal, Princeton, N.J., 1959-64; art tchr. Princeton Country Day Sch., 1964-65; artist-in-residence Howard U., 1969-71; instr. painting Art Students League, N.Y.C., 1972-87, ret., 1987; adj. prof. Trenton State Coll., 1972-73. Oneman shows include Detroit Artists Market, Howard U. Gallery, Washington, Grand Central Art Galleries, N.Y.C., Janet Nessler Gallery, N.Y.C., Chgo., June Kelly Gallery, N.Y.C., Butler Inst. Am. Art, Youngstown, Ohio, Chgo. Cultural Ctr., Greenville (S.C.) Mus. Art, others; exhibited group shows Cleve. Mus. Art, Detroit Inst. Arts, Butler Inst. Am. Art, Youngstown, Bklyn. Mus., Wadsworth Atheneum, Boston Mus., San Francisco Mus., Mus. Modern Art, Whitney Mus., Am. Acad, and Inst. Arts and Letters, N.Y.; represented in permanent collections Met. Mus., Phila. Mus., Detroit Inst. Arts, Parrish Mus., Southampton, L.I., N.J. State Mus., Standard Oil of Ohio, AT&T, Wadsworth Atheneum, U. Mich., Wayne State U., Schomburg Coll., N.Y.C., Howard U., Nat. Mus. Am Art, U.S. Navy Art Ctr., Chase Manhattan Bank, N.Y.C., Forbes Mag. Collection, N.Y.C., Kidder & Peabody Co., N.Y.C., Mus. Internat. Art, Sofia, Bulgaria, Century Assn., N.Y.C., Lagos (Nigeria) Mus. With USN, 1944-45. Recipient Thomas B. Clark prize NAD, 1959, Ranger Fund purchase award NAD, 1963, 77, prize Allied Artists Am., 1958, Emily Lowe award, 1957, Founders prize Detroit Inst. Arts, 1953, Audubon Artist prizes, 1982, 83, 85, 86, cert. of commendation USN, 1974, Art Achievement award Wayne State U., Key to the City of Hartford award, Conn.; others; named Mich. Painter of Yr. Detroit News, 1953. Mem. Artists Equity Assn. (bd. dirs.), Allied Artists Am., Princeton Art Assn., Mich. Acad. Sci., Arts and Letters, NAD (mem. coun., awards juries), Audubon Artists (pres. 1980-82, exhbn. coord.), Artists Fellowship (trustee, v.p. 1985-88), Century Assn., Lotos Club (N.Y.C.). Home: 152A Chatham Dr Cranbury NJ 08512-3824

LEESON, DAVID BRENT, electronics company executive; b. Cleve., Apr. 12, 1937; s. Herman Lee and Sylva (Metzenbaum) L.; m. Rosa Riordan, June 7, 1958 (div. 1972); children: High Lawrence, Melinda Anita; m. Barbara Splane, Apr. 14, 1980. B.S., Calif. Inst. Tech., 1958; S.M. in Electronics Engring., MIT, 1959; Ph.D., Stanford U., 1962. Mem. tech. staff Hughes Aircraft, Culver City, Calif., 1954-64; dir. microwave lab. Applied Tech., Palo Alto, Calif., 1964-68; chmn., chief exec. officer, founder Calif. Microwave, Inc., Sunnyvale, Calif., 1968-93; chmn. emeritus, dir. Calif. Microwave, Sunnyvale, Calif., 1993—, No. Calif. D.X. Found., Stanford; chmn. Wireless Info. Networks Forum (WINForum industry assoc.), 1993; consulting prof. dept. elec. engring. Stanford (Calif.) U., 1994—. Author: Physical Design of Yagi Antennas, 1992; contbr. articles to profl. jours. Named Entrepreneur of Yr., Stanford Grad. Sch. Bus., 1979; recipient MIT Corp. Leadership award, 1987. Fellow IEEE; mem. Am. Electronics Assn. (bd. dirs. 1980-82), Electronics Industries Assn. (bd. govs. 1983-84). Avocations: sports car racing (nat. champion), amateur radio. Office: Calif Microwave Inc 985 Almanor Ave Sunnyvale CA 94086

LEESTMA, ROBERT, federal agency administrator, educator; b. Detroit, Oct. 15, 1927; s. Richard and Jeanne (Nivarre) L.; m. Margaret Elizabeth Bell, Aug. 13, 1955. AB, U. Mich., 1949, AM, 1951, PhD, 1956. Rsch. teaching asst., cmty. adult edn. program U. Mich., Ann Arbor, 1949-50; tchr. English and social studies Ann Arbor pub. schs., 1950-51; asst. dir. Audio-Visual Edn. Ctr., lectr. sch. edn. U. Mich., 1951-55, assoc. prof., dir. Peace Corps tng. program, 1961-64; ICA edn. and mass. comm. advisor Govt. of Vietnam, Vietnam, 1955-58; edn. adviser Govt. of Thailand, 1958-61; dep. chief edn. div. Bur. Africa, AID, 1964-65; dir. Office Multilateral Policy and Programs, Multilateral Policy Planning Staff, Bur. Ednl. and Cultural Affairs, Dept. State, 1965-67; asst. to asst. sec. edn. for internat. edn. HEW, 1967-68; dir. Inst. Internat. Studies, assoc. commr. internat. edn. U.S. Office Edn., 1968-74, assoc. commr. instl. devel. and internat. edn., 1974-79; dep. dir. planning and implementation Office Edn. for Overseas Dependents, U.S. Dept. Edn., 1980-82; assoc. dir. dissemination and improvement of practice Nat. Inst. Edn., 1982-83, assoc. dir. field initiated and internal studies, 1984-85; dir. U.S. study edn. in Japan, Office Ednl. Rsch. and Improvement Dept. Edn., 1986-89; v.p. internat. programs Am. Assn. State Colls. and Univs., Washington, 1989-91; dir. spl. studies staff, Office Ednl. Rsch. and Improvement Dept. Edn., 1991-94; also policy advisor Edn. Rsch. and Devel. Bur., AID, 1992-94; interim dir. Nat. Libr. Edn., 1994; mem., chmn. and/or adviser U.S. dels. internat. confs.; U.S. rep., chmn. edn. com. OECD; U.S. rep. governing coun. Internat. Bur. Edn.; UNESCO; mem. Indo-U.S. Subcomm. on Edn. and Culture, U.S.-Egyptian Joint Working Group on Edn. and Culture, U.S.-Japan Culcon Edn. Com., U.S. Nat. Commn. for UNESCO; alt. mem. U.S.-Japan Friendship Commn., also Am. panel Joint Culcon Com.; mem. adv. com. Hanna Collection, Hoover Instn., Com. on Edn. and Successor Generation of Atlantic Coun. U.S. Author, coauthor and or editor books, chpts. and articles in profl. jours., including Japanese Education Today, 1987, Japanese Educational Productivity, 1992. With AUS, 1946-47. Payne scholar U. Mich., 1951-52, Hinsdale scholar, 1953-54. Mem. Am. Ednl. Rsch. Assn., Comparative and Internat. Edn. Soc., Assn. Asian Studies, Phi Delta Kappa. Home: 2712 George Mason Pl Alexandria VA 22305-1620 Office: Nat Libr Edn Dept Edn 555 New Jersey Ave NW Washington DC 20208

LEET, MILDRED ROBBINS, corporate executive, consultant; b. N.Y.C., Aug. 9, 1922; d. Samuel Milton and Isabella (Zeitz) Elowsky; m. Louis J. Robbins, Feb. 23, 1941 (dec. 1970); children: Jane, Aileen; m. Glen Leet, Aug. 9, 1974. BA, NYU, 1942; LHD (hon.), Coll. Human Svcs., 1988; LLD honoris causa, Marymount Coll., Tarrytown, N.Y., 1991; HHD, Lynn U., 1993; D Humanitarian Svc. (hon.), Norwich U., 1994. Pres. women's div. United Cerebral Palsy, N.Y.C., 1951-52; bd. dirs. United Cerebral Palsy, 1953-55; rep. Nat. Coun. Women U.S. at UN, 1957-64, 1st v.p. chmn. 1964-68, hon. pres., 1968-70; sec., v.p. conf. group U.S. Nat. Orgns. at UN, 1961-64, 76-78, vice chmn., sec., 1962-64, mem. exec., 1961-65, 75—, chmn. hospitality info. svc., 1960-66; vice chmn. exec. com. NGO's UN Office Public Info., 1976-78, chmn. ann. conf., 1977; chmn. com. on water, desertification, habitat and environment Conf. NGO's with consultative status with UN/ECOSOC, 1976—; mem. exec. com. Internat. Coun. Women, 1960-73, 1977-93; chmn. program planning com., women's com. OEO, 1967-72; chmn. com. on natural disasters N.Am. Com. on Environment, 1973-77; N.Y. State chmn. UN Day, 1975; ptnr. Leet & Leet (cons. women in devel.), 1978—; co-founder Trickle Up Program, 1979—, co-pres., 1991—. Contbr. articles to profl. jours.; editor UN Calendar & Digest, 1959-64, Measure of Mankind, 1963; editorial bd.: Peace & Change. Co-chmn. Vols. for Stevenson, N.Y.C., 1956; vice chmn. task force Nat. Dem. Com., 1969-72; commr. N.Y. State Commn. on Powers Local Govt., 1970-73; chmn. Coll. for Human Svcs., 1985—; former mem. bd. dirs. Am. Arbitration Assn., New Directions, Inst. for Mediation and Conflict Resolution, Spirit of Stockholm; bd. dirs. Hotline Internat.; v.p. Save the Children Fedn., 1986-93; rep. Internat. Peace Acad. at UN, 1974-77, Internat. Soc. Community Devel., 1977—; del. at large 1st Nat. Women's Conf., Houston, 1977; chmn. task force on internat. interdependence N.Y. State Women's Meeting, 1977; mem. Task Force on Poverty, 1977—; chmn. Task Force on Women, Sci. and Tech. for Devel., 1978; U.S. del. UN Status of Women Commn., 1978, UN Conf. Sci. and Tech. for Devel., 1979, co-dir. Trickle Up Program, Inc, 1979—; Brazzaville Centennial Celebration, 1980; mem. global adv. bd. Internat. Expn. Rural Devel., 1981—; mem. Coun. Internat. Fellows U. Bridgeport, 1982-88; trustee overseas edn. fund LWV, 1983-91; v.p. U.S. Com. UN Devel. Fund for Women, 1983—; mem. Nat. Consultative Com. Planning for Nairobi, 1984-85; co-chmn. women in devel. com. Interaction, 1985-91; mem. com. of cooperation Interam. Commn. of Women, 1986; bd. dirs. Nat. Women's Conf. Com., 1986-87; adv. com. Am. Assn. Internat. Aging, 1986-90; mem. Overseas Devel. Bd., 1988—; bd. dirs Internat. Devel. Conf., 1991— Recipient Crystal award Coll. Human Svcs., 1983, Ann. award Inst. Mediation and Conflict Resolution, 1985, Woman of Conscience award Nat. Coun. Women, 1986, Temple award Inst. Noetic Scis., 1987, Presdl. Edn Hunger award, 1987, Giraffe award Giraffe Project, 1987, Woman of the World award Eng.'s Women Aid, 1989; co-recipient Rose award World Media Inst., 1987, Human Rights award UN Devel. Fund for Women, 1987, (with Glen Leet) Pres.'s medal Marymount Manhattan Coll., 1988, Leadership award U.S. Peace Corps, Woman of Vision award N.Y.C. NOW, 1990, Matrix award Women in Comm., Inc., Spirit of Enterprise award Rolex Industries, 1990, Ann. award Interaction, 1990, Citation, Pres. Bush's Ann. Points of Light Award, 1992, Internat. Humanity award ARC Overseas Assn., 1992, Excellence award U.S. Com. for UNIFEM, 1994, Champion of Enterprise award Avon, 1994, Achievement award NYU-Washington Square Coll. Alumni Assn., 1995. Mem. AAAS, Women's Nat. Dem. Club, Women's Forum Inc., Cosmopolitan Club, Princeton Club. Home and Office: 54 Riverside Dr New York NY 10024

LEET, RICHARD HALE, oil company executive; b. Maryville, Mo., Oct. 11, 1926; s. Theron Hale and Helen Eloise (Rutledge) L.; m. Phyllis Jean Combs, June 14, 1949; children: Richard Hale II, Alan Combs, Dana Ellen. B.S. in Chemistry, N.W. Mo. State Coll., 1948; Ph.D. in Phys. Chemistry, Ohio State U., 1952. Rsch. chemist Standard Oil Co., Whiting, Ind., 1953-64; dir. long-range and capital planning, mktg. dept. Am. Oil Co., Chgo., 1964-68; mgr. ops. planning, mfg. dept. Am. Oil Co., 1968-70; regional v.p. Am. Oil Co., Atlanta, 1970-71; v.p. supply Am. Oil Co., Chgo., 1971-74; v.p. planning and adminstrn. Amoco Chems. Corp., Chgo., 1974-75; v.p. mktg. Amoco Chems. Corp., 1975-77, exec. v.p., 1977-78, pres., 1978-83; dir. Amoco Corp., Chgo., 1983-91, vice chmn., 1991-92; retired, 1992; bd. dirs. Gt. Lakes Chem., Vulcan Materials Corp., ITW, Landauer, Inc. Former chmn. bd. mgrs. Met. YMCA, Chgo.; former pres. Boy Scouts Am.; former chmn. bd. Am. Indsl. Health Coun.; former bd. visitors Emory U., 1970-71; vice chmn. found. bd. Ohio State U; trustee Brenau U. With USNR, 1944-46. Mem. Am. Chem. Soc., Am. Chem. Industry (exec. com.), Am. Petroleum Inst. (bd. dirs.), Société Industrielle de Chemie, Chem. Mfrs. Assn. (dir.), Phi Sigma Epsilon, Gamma Alpha. Office: Lighthouse Acres PO Box 1686 Gainesville GA 30503-1686

LEETCH, BRIAN JOSEPH, hockey player; b. Corpus Christi, Tex., Mar. 3, 1968. Student, Boston Coll. With N.Y. Rangers, 1986—; mem. U.S. Olympic hockey team, 1988, Team USA for 1991 Can. Cup Tournament, Stanley Cup championship team, 1994. Named mem. U.S. Coll. first-team All-Am. team, 1987, Sporting News NHL Rookie of Yr., 1989, Player of the Year, Hockey East, 1986-87, Rookie of the Year, 1986-87, Sporting News All-Star team, 1991-92; recipient Calder Meml. trophy for NHL Rookie of Yr., 88, 1989, James Norris Meml. trophy for best defenseman, 1991, 92, Conn Smythe trophy, 1993-94. Office: NY Rangers Madison Sq Garden 4 Pennsylvania Plz New York NY 10001*

LEETE, WILLIAM WHITE, artist; b. Portsmouth, Ohio, June 12, 1929; s. Bernard Emerson and Lois Trowbridge (Denison) L.; m. Doris Louise Knight, Sept. 19, 1952; children: Amy MacDonald, Robin Schodt. B.A., Yale U., 1951, B.F.A., 1955, M.F.A., 1957. Mem. faculty dept. art U. R.I., Kingston, 1957—; now prof., acting chmn. dept. U. R.I., 1968, 69-70, 76. Represented in permanent collections, De Cordova Mus., Lincoln, Mass., Cleve. Mus., Worcester Mus., R.I. Hosp., Trust Bank, also various pvt. collections. Served with USMC, 1951-53. Mem. AAUP, Coll. Art Assn., Siggraph, Boston Computer Soc. Home: 202 Silver Lake Ave Wakefield RI 02879-4231 Office: U RI Dept Art Kingston RI 02881

LEETSAR, JAAN, government official; b. Jõgeva, Estonia, Apr. 3, 1946; s. Inno and Sselma (Sömer) L.; m. Ene Unt, Sept. 26, 1975; children: Erkki, Martti, Selma Sömer. Hydromelioration Engr., Estonian Acad. Agr., Tartu, 1971; postgrad., Acad. Scis. Estonia, Tallinn, 1986; M Economy, Acad. Agr. Latvia, 1987. Chief engr. Com. EstonianState Meliorisation and Hydroeconomy, Tallinn, 1971-78; head dept. tech. works Nat. Inst. Rojection and Rsch., 1978-82; head dept. Estonian Land Improvement Project, Tallinn, 1982-90; dir. gen. Estonian Farmers Ctr. Union, Tallinn, 1990-92; min. Min. Agr., Tallinn, 1992—; chief Estonian Farmers Centre Union, Tallinn, 1988-94. Author 2 books. Mem. NLKP (The Communist Party of the Soviet Union), Estonia, 1971-89; mem. mgmt. bd. Estonian Ctrl. Land Fraction, 1989—. Mem. All Union Assn. Sojuzvodprojekt (mem. bd. 1974-78), Soc. Acad. Coop. Avocations: music, research works, fishing, boating, trip. Office: Embassy of Estonia 1030 15th St NW Ste 1000 Washington DC 20005-1503

LEEVER, HAROLD, chemical company executive; b. Detroit, May 21, 1914; s. Guy Harold and Mary (MacGregor) L.; m. Ruth Ann Salter, Oct. 5, 1935; children: Suzanne Hart, Thomas, John, Daniel, Andrew. BSChemE, Mich. State U., 1936; PhD (hon.), Post Coll., 1947. From chief chemist to v.p. McDermid Inc., Waterbury, Conn., 1938-54, pres., 1954-77, chmn. bd., 1977—. Patentee in field. Chmn. bd. Post Coll., Waterbury, 1965—; chmn. United Way, Waterbury, 1959, 81. Recipient Hiram Hayden award Boy Scouts Am., Silver Beaver award Boy Scouts Am.; named Industrialist of Yr., Conn. chpt. United Ch. of Christ, Man of the Yr. Waterbury United Way, 1989, Outstanding Fund Raiser of Conn. Nat. Soc. Fund Raising Execs., 1988. Lodge: Rotary. Home: 366 Guilds Hollow Rd Bethlehem CT 06751-1607 Office: MacDermid Inc 245 Freight St Waterbury CT 06702-1802

LEEVY, CARROLL MOTON, medical educator, hepatology researcher; b. Columbia, S.C., Oct. 13, 1920; s. Isaac S. and Mary (Kirkl) L.; m. Ruth S. Barboza, Feb. 4, 1956; children: Carroll Barboza, Maria Secora. AB, Fisk U., 1941; MD, U. Mich., 1944; ScD (hon.), N.J. Inst. Tech., 1973, U. Nebr., 1989; HHD (hon.), Fisk U., 1981; M, Am. Coll. Physicians, 1991. Intern Jersey City Med. Ctr., 1944-45, resident, 1945-48, dir. clin. investigation, 1947-57; fellow Banting-Best Inst., U. Toronto, Ont., Can., 1953; research assoc. Harvard U. Med. Sch., Cambridge, Mass., 1959; assoc. prof. U. Medicine and Dentistry of N.J., 1960-64, prof., 1964, Disting. prof., 1990—; physician in chief Univ. Hosp., 1975-91; dir. Liver Ctr. U. Medicine and Dentistry N.J., 1983-85; dir. div. hepatology and nutrition N.J. Med. Sch., 1959-75, acting chmn. dept. medicine, 1966-68, chief of medicine, 1968-71, chmn. dept. medicine, 1975-91; disting. prof. medicine Univ. Hosp., physician in chief, 1975-91; acting chmn. Sammy Davis Jr. Nat. Liver Inst., 1984-86, pres., sci. dir., 1989—; dir. N.J. Med. Sch. Liver Ctr., 1991—; chief of medicine VA Hosp., East Orange, N.J., 1966-71; coms. NIH, 1965—, FDA, 1970-80, VA, 1971—, Alcohol and Nutrition Found., 1970-80, Am. Liver Found., 1979-84, Health Care Fin. Adminstrn., 1990—; mem. nat. commn. on digestive disease, 1978, expert com. on chronic liver disease WHO, 1978; mem. adv. com. Health and Human Svcs., 1989-93; mem. nat. adv. com. liver transplantation Health Care Fin. Adminstrn., 1991—. Author: Practical Diagnosis and Treatment of Liver Disease, 1957, Evaluation of Liver Function in Clinical Practice, 1965, 2d edit., 1974, Liver Regeneration in Man, 1973, The Liver and Its Diseases, 1973, Diseases of the Liver and Biliary Tract, 1977, Guidelines for Detection of Drug and Chemical-Induced Hepatotoxicity, 1979, Alcohol and the Digestive Tract, 1981, Standardization of Nomenclature, Diagnostic Criteria and Prognosis for Diseases of the Liver and Biliary Tract, 1994; contbr. numerous articles to med., sci. jours.; patentee in field. Bd. dirs. U. Cape Town, South Africa, 1984—; mem. Cmty. Congl. Ch. Recipient Modern Med. award, 1972, Edward Ill award, 1973, United Negro Coll. Fund award, 1980, Key to City of Newark, 1981, Key to City of Columbia, S.C., 1987, Nat. Med. Assn. award, 1987. Mem. NAACP, Am. Assn. for Study of Liver Diseases (pres.

1967-68, chmn. steering com. 1968-74, disting. svc. award 1991), Internat. Assn. for Study of Liver (pres. 1970-74, chmn. criteria com. 1972—), Am. Gastroenterol. Assn. (mem. edn. and tng. com. 1967-71), Assn. Profs. Medicine (Robert Williams disting. chmn. award 1991), ACP (mem. publs. com. 1969-74, master), AMA (vice-chmn., chmn. program com. sect. on gastroenterology 1971-74), Assn. Am. Physicians, Soc. Exptl. Biology and Medicine, Am. Soc. Clin. Nutrition, Am. Inst. Nutrition, AAAS, Nat. Med. Assn., Am. Fedn. Clin. Rsch., Assn. Acad. Minority Physicians (pres. 1986-88, chmn. bd. trustees 1988—), Internat. Com. on Informatics in Hepatology (chmn. 1986—), Internal Hepatology Informatics Group (chair 1984-93), Phi Beta Kappa, Alpha Omega Alpha, Sigma Pi Phi. Home: 35 Robert Dr Short Hills NJ 07078-1525 Office: U Medicine and Dentistry NJ Med Sch 100 Bergen St Newark NJ 07103-2407

LEFCOE, VANN H., lawyer; b. Portsmouth, Va., Dec. 3, 1943; s. Robert R. and Dorothy (S.) L.; m. Sandra E., Aug. 22, 1965; 1 child, Marnie L. BS in Commerce, U. Va., 1964, LLB, 1967. Bar: Va. 1967, D.C. 1973; U.S. Supreme Ct. 1973. Lawyer Portsmouth, Va., 1967-70; asst. atty. gen. Commonwealth of Va., Richmond, 1970-73; ptnr. Livesay & Lefcoe, Portsmouth, 1973-88, McGuire, Woods, Battle & Boothe, Norfolk, Va., 1988—. Author: Virginia Corporations, 1981. Chmn. Portsmouth Planning Commn., 1988—. Mem. Va. State Bar (exec. com. 1987—). Home: 5000 Oakhill Ave Portsmouth VA 23703-5215 Office: McGuire Woods Battle Boothe PO Box 3767 Norfolk VA 23514-3767

LEFEBER, EDWARD JAMES, SR., physician; b. Wauwatosa, Wis., June 1, 1911; s. Cornelius George and May (McCord) L.; m. Ellie Hancock Weisiger, June 4, 1938; children: Edward James, Jr., Robert Randolph, John Courtney, Ann Elizabeth, Donald Louis, Nancy Ellen. B.S., U. Wis., 1934, M.D., 1936. Intern, resident in medicine Med. Coll. Va. Hosps., Richmond, 1936-40; mem. faculty Med. Br., U. Tex., Galveston, 1940-88, clin. assoc. prof. medicine, 1951-83, clin. prof. medicine and family practice, 1983-88, dir. Student Health Service, 1943-46; practice medicine, specializing in internal medicine Internal Medicine Assocs., Galveston, 1948-88; chief outpatient service Galveston office Houston Regional Office, VA, 1946-48; cons. gastroenterology USPHS Hosp., Galveston, 1952-53; pres. staff St. Mary's Infirmary, Galveston, 1961; mem. adv. com. on nursing home affairs Tex. Dept. Health, 1976-82. Bd. dirs. Galveston chpt. ARC, 1958-78; mem. Galveston Civic Orch., 1957-60; mem. Tex. Bd. Licensure for Nursing Home Adminstrs., 1979-88; bd. dirs. Moody House, 1964-65, 67-71, med. dir. Diplomate Am. Bd. Internal Medicine. Fellow ACP; mem. Galveston County Med. Soc. (pres. 1954, sec.-treas. 1948-53), AMA, Tex., So. med. assns., Am., Tex. (pres. 1977) socs. internal medicine, Am. Soc. Gastro-Intestinal Endoscopy, Tex. Club Internists, Phi Chi. Episcopalian (past vestryman). Club: Masons. Died Jan. 3, 1988. Home: 2927 Bernardo De Galvez Ave Galveston TX 77550-7753 Office: 200 University Blvd Galveston TX 77550-2711

LEFEBVRE, GABRIEL FELICIEN, retired chemical company executive; b. N.Y.C., Feb. 29, 1932; s. Gabriel F. and Harriett Blanche (Terrill) L.; m. Doris Jeanette Germain, Oct. 26, 1952; children: David Marshall, Richard Terrill, Kathryn Louise. B.S., Webb Inst. Naval Arch., 1952. Registered profl. engr., Ky., Ohio. Ptnr. Leco, Inc., Paducah, Ky., 1962-63; engring. supr. B.F. Goodrich Chem. Group, Calvert City, Ky., 1963-76; plant mgr. B.F. Goodrich Chem. Group, Louisville, 1977-78; gen. mgr. Chlor-Alkali B.F. Goodrich Chem. Group, Cleve., 1978-82, v.p PVC intermediates, 1982-83, gen. mgr. PVC intermediates, 1982-83, v.p. facilities mgmt., 1983-85, pres. Convent Chem. Corp., 1978-83, dir., 1978-83; v.p. LaPorte Chem. Corp. B.F. Goodrich Chem. Group, 1982-83; v.p. ops. Geon Vinyl div., 1985-87, v.p. regulatory affairs, 1987-91; tech. mgr. Abadan Petrochem Co., Tehran, Iran, 1976-77. Served to lt. USNR, 1952-56. Mem. ASME, Nat. Soc. Profl. Engrs. Episcopalian. Home: 5195 Hilltop Ln Cleveland OH 44131-1136

LEFEBVRE, GREN GORDON, school superintendent; b. Buffalo, May 2, 1943; s. Gordon and Anne B. (Finch-Noyes) L.; m. Mary Margaret Hill, Aug. 20, 1966; children: Lisa Jackman, Christopher. BS, Purdue U., 1966 MS, 1967, EdS, 1982. Lic. sch. supt., Ind. Tchr./coach Darlington (Ind.) High Sch., 1967-70, Coal Creek Cen. High Sch., New Richmond, Ind., 1970-71, North Montgomery High Sch., Crawfordsville, Ind., 1971-76; prin. Waynetown (Ind.) Elem.-Jr. High Sch., 1976-87, Northridge Mid. Sch., Crawfordsville, 1987-91; supt. North Montgomery Community Sch. Corp., Linden, Ind., 1991—; cons. on stress mgmt. Mem. Town of Darlington Town Bd., pres., 1977-85; bd. dirs. Montgomery County United Fund, 1984—, Youth Svcs. Bur., Crawfordsville, 1986-92, Montgomery County Boys Club, 1978-84, Montgomery County coun. Boy Scouts Am., 1980-82. Mem. Am. Soc. Notaries, Ind. Assn. Pub. Sch. Supts., Darlington Community Assn., Ind. High Sch. Athletic Assn., Am. Legion, Darlington Conservation Club, Lions, Elks, Phi Beta Kappa. Republican. Episcopalian. Avocations: antiques, travel, raising cats, reading. Home: PO Box 176 Darlington IN 47940-0176 Office: North Montgomery Cmty Sch Corp PO Box 70 Linden IN 47955-0070

LEFER, ALLAN MARK, physiologist; b. N.Y.C., Feb. 1, 1936; s. I. Judah and Lillian G. (Gastwirth) L.; m. Mary E. Indoe, Aug. 23, 1959; children—Debra Lynn, David Joseph, Barry Lee and Leslie Ann (twins). BA, Adelphi Coll., 1957, Western Res. U., 1959; PhD (NSF fellow), U. Ill., Urbana, 1962. Instr. physiology, USPHS-NIH fellow Western Res. U., 1962-64; asst. prof. physiology U. Va., 1964-69, assoc. prof., 1969-71, prof., 1972-74; vis. prof. Hadassah Med. Sch., Jerusalem, 1971-72; prof., chmn. dept. physiology Jefferson Med. Coll., Thomas Jefferson U., Phila., 1974—; dir. Ischemia-Shock Research Inst., 1980—; cons. Merck & Co., Upjohn Co., Genetech Inc., Syntex Inc., Ciba-Geigy, NIH, Protein Design Labs, Bristol-Myers Squibb, Cytel Corp.; Wellcome Found. vis. prof., 1985-86, Pfizer vis. prof. cardiovascular medicine, 1995; Nat. Bd. Med. Examiners, Step 1, 1993-95. Author: Pathophysiology and Therapeutics of Myocardial Ischemia, 1977, Prostaglandins in Cardiovascular and Renal Function, 1979, Cellular and Molecular Aspects of Shock and Trauma, 1983, Leukotrienes in Cardiovascular and Pulmonary Function, 1985; mng. editor: Eicosanoids, 1988-93; cons. editor Circulatory Shock, 1973-80; field editor Jour. Pharmacology and Exptl. Therapeutics, 1994—; mem. editl. bd. Critical Care Medicine, Shock, Am. Jour. Physiology, Endothelium, Drug News and Perspectives; contbr. to World Book Ency. Sci. Yearbook, 1979; contbr. over 550 sci. articles to profl. jours. Active Acad. Com. on Soviet Jewry, 1970—; chmn. United Jewish Appeal, 1973-74; coach basketball and baseball Huntingdon Valley Athletic Assn., 1975-78. Recipient Pres. and Visitor's prize in research U. Va., 1970. Fellow Am. Coll. Cardiology; mem. AAAS, Am. Physiol. Soc., Am. Soc. Pharmacology and Exptl. Therapeutics, Internat. Heart Rsch. Soc., Am. Heart Assn. (established investigator 1968-73, fellow circulation coun., nat. grant rev. com. 1993-95), Pa. Heart Assn. (rsch. com.), Shock Soc. (chmn. membership com., pres. 1983-84, chmn. devel. com. 1985-89, chmn. internat. rels. com. 1993), Internat. Fed. Shock Socs. (coun. 1994—), Soc. Exptl. Biology and Medicine, Israel Soc. Physiology and Pharmacology, Phila. Physiol. Soc. (pres. 1978-79), Sierra Club, B'nai B'rith (Charlottesville chpt., v.p. 1967-68, chmn. Va. Hillel 1970-71), Sigma Xi. Democrat. Home: 3590 Walsh Ln Huntingdon Valley PA 19006-3226 Office: Thomas Jefferson Univ 1020 Locust St Philadelphia PA 19107-6731

LEFERMAN, NORMAN BRUCE, marketing professional; b. Stamford, Conn., Nov. 17, 1945; s. Irving Herman and Eleanor (Weil) L.; m. Nancy Louise Weintraub, June 18, 1967; children: Lori, Randi, Marc. BS, Rensselaer Polytechnic Inst., 1967; MBA, U. Conn., 1970. Research supr. BBDO, Inc., N.Y.C., 1968-70; consumer research, mgr. Supermarkets Gen., N.Y.C., 1971; assoc. research dir. BBDO, Inc., N.Y.C., 1972-73, mgr., mktg. info. services; exec. v.p. Consumer Response Corp., N.Y.C., 1975-76; pres. Leferman Assocs., Inc., 1977—. Arthur: Handbook of Package Design Research, 1980; contbr. articles to profl. jours. Bd. trustees Bi-cultural Day Sch., Stamford, 1980—; bd. dirs. Roxbury Little League, Stamford. Mem. Am. Mktg. Assn. Jewish. Avocation: tennis. Office: Leferman Assocs Inc 22 Knapp St Stamford CT 06907-1700

LEFEVER, ERNEST W., political philosopher, author, former institute president; b. York, Pa., Nov. 12, 1919; m. Margaret Louise Briggs, 1951; children: David, Bryce. AB, Elizabethtown Coll. 1942; BD in Christian ethics, Yale U., 1945, PhD, 1956. Field sec. World Alliance of YMCA's, U.K. and W. Ger., 1945-48; internat. affairs specialist Nat. Council Chs., N.Y.C., 1952-54; mem. faculty govt. U. Md., 1956-57; mem. research staff, acting head fgn. affairs div. Library of Congress, Washington, 1957-59; fgn. affairs staff Sen. Hubert Humphrey of Minn., 1959-60; research assoc. Washington Center Fgn. Policy Research, Johns Hopkins U., 1960-61; sr. staff Inst. Def. Analyses, Washington, 1961-64; sr. fellow fgn. policy studies Brookings Instn., 1964-76; founder, pres. Ethics and Public Policy Center, Washington, 1976-89; sr. fellow, 1989—; asst. sec. state for human rights and humanitarian affairs designate, 1981; professorial lectr. dept. govt. Georgetown U.; lectr. Nat. War Coll., Army, Navy and Air Force War colls., Japan Def. Coll., numerous univs.; cons. sec. Dept. State, 1981-83; mem. Internat. Inst. Strategic Studies, London, 1960-89; participant numerous internat. confs. Author: Ethics and U.S. Foreign Policy, 1957, (with others) Profile of American Politics, 1960, Crisis in the Congo, 1965, Uncertain Mandate: Politics of the U.N. Congo Operation, 1967, Spear and Scepter: Army, Police, and Politics in Tropical Africa, 1970, (with others) Ethics and World Politics, 1972, TV and National Defense, 1974, Amsterdam to Nairobi: The World Council of Churches and the Third World, 1979, Nuclear Arms in the Third World: U.S. Policy Dilemma, 1979, (with others) The CIA and the American Ethic, 1980; Editor: Arms and Arms Control, 1962, Will Capitalism Survive?, 1979; co-editor: The Apocalyptic Premise: Nuclear Arms Debated, 1982, Nairobi to Vancouver: The World Council of Churches and the World, 1975-87, 1987, Perestroika: How New Is Gorbachev's New Thinking?, 1989; mem. editorial bd. Policy Rev.; editorial adv. bd. The Washington Times; contbr. articles to profl. jours. and newspapers. Mem. Md. State Commn. Values in Edn., 1979-83. Mem. Washington Inst. Fgn. Affairs, Coun. Fgn. Rels., Johns Hopkins U. Soc. Scholars, Soc. Values in Higher Edn., Phila. Soc. (1st v.p. 1986-87), Cosmos Club (Washington, Yale Club (Washington and N.Y.C.). Home: 7106 Beechwood Dr Chevy Chase MD 20815 Office: 1015 15th St NW Washington DC 20005-2605 *My pious Protestant parents taught me that serving humanity was the highest earthly good, that fame and wealth were unworthy goals. During my youth I sought to pursue this high purpose mainly through social service, including three years of volunteer relief work in postwar Europe, where I saw the tragic suffering caused by Nazism and communism. Convinced that the fundamental battle was in the realm of ideas because they had profound consequences for good or evil, I thereafter sought to advance freedom, justice, and peace primarily by the written and spoken word.*

LEFEVER, MICHAEL GRANT, state agency administrator; b. Lancaster, Pa., Sept. 12, 1947; s. Norwood Grant and Frances (Gillespie) LeF.; m. M. Malissa Burnette, 1989; 1 child, Grant Burnette. BA in English, Presbyn. Coll., 1969; MPA, U. S.C., 1976. Claims rep. Underwriters Adjusting Co., Columbia, S.C., 1972-73; project administr. CATAYTIC, Inc., Charlotte, N.C., 1973-75; dep. dir. S.C. Dept. Juvenile Placement and Aftercare, Columbia 1977-81, dir., 1981; asst. commr. for adminstrn. S.C. Dept. Youth Svcs., Columbia, 1981-82, dep. commr., 1982-86; exec. dir. S.C. Worker's Compensation Commn., 1986—; interim commr. S.C. Dept. of Juvenile Justice, 1993; chmn. Serious and Violent Offender Study Com., Columbia, 1981-86; bd. dirs. State Agy. Dirs. Orgn., 1991—, v.p. 1992, pres. 1993—; bd. dirs. Ctr. for Cancer Treatment and Rsch. Richland Meml. Hosp., 1992, exec. com. 1994—, vice chmn., 1995—; S.C. State Quality Network, 1992—; cons. Gov.'s Children Coordinating Cabinet, Columbia, 1981-86. Pres. Palmetto State Alumni chpt. Theta Chi, Columbia, 1973-83, Columbia Area Alumni Assn., Presbyn. Coll. 1988-89, Columbia, 1979; pres. Windcrest Villas Homeowners Assn., North Myrtle Beach, S.C., 1983-90; trres. Planned Parenthood Cen. S.C., 1988-91, Bd. Assocs., 1991—; mem. adv. com. on pub. adminstrn., exec. com. U. S.C., 1988— Served with U.S. Army, 1970-71. Named Outstanding Pub. Adminstr., 1986. Mem. Nat. Youth Work Alliance (chmn. 1982-83), Am. Soc. for Pub. Adminstrn. (trees. S.C. chpt. 1987—), Mental Health Assn. Midlands, So. Assn. of Worker's Compensation Administrs. (exec. com. 1986—), Internat. Assn. Indsl. Accident Bds. and Commns. (chmn. adminstrn. and proc. com. 1989-93, exec. com. 1993—), S.C. Youth Workers Assn. (bd. dirs. 1979-83), Presbyn. Coll. Alumni Assn. (bd. dirs. until 1990, pres. 1988-89, Outstanding Young Alumnus award 1981). Home: 2721 Wheat St Columbia SC 29205

LEFEVRE, DAVID E., lawyer, professional sports team executive; b. Cleve., Oct. 25, 1944; s. Fay A. and Mary (Eaton) LeF. B.A., Yale U., 1966; J.D., U. Mich., 1971. Bar: N.Y., U.S. Dist. Ct. (so. and ea. dists.) N.Y. Assoc. Reid & Priest, N.Y.C., 1971-78, ptnr., 1979—; owner Houston Astros Baseball Club, 1979-84, Cleve. Indians Baseball Club, 1984-86; dir. Tampa Bay Lightning, NHL; bd. dirs. Lightning Arena, Inc.; chmn. bd. dirs. Chertsey Corp.; bd. dirs. TDC (USA) Inc.; bd. govs. NHL, 1992—. Bd. dirs. Tampa Downtown Partnership; vol. Peace Corps, Uruguay, 1966-68. Named Hon. Alumnus, Cleve. State U., 1985. Mem. ABA, Canyon Club (pres. Armonk, N.Y. 1986—), Nippon Club, Japan Soc., Alexis de Tocqueville Soc. Office: Tampa Bay Lightning 501 E Kennedy Blvd Tampa FL 33602 also: Reid & Priest 40 W 57th St New York NY 10019-4001

LEFEVRE, ELBERT WALTER, JR., civil engineering educator; b. Eden, Tex., July 29, 1932; s. Elbert Walter Sr. and Hazie (Davis) LeF.; m. Joyce Ann Terry, Nov. 28, 1957; children: Terry Ann, Charmaine Rene, George Walter, John Philip. BS in Civil Engring, Tex. A&M U., 1957, MS in Civil Engring, 1961; PhD, Okla. State U., 1966. Registered profl. engr., Ark., Tex. Faculty Tex. A&M U., Bryan, 1958, Tex. Technol. Coll., Lubbock, 1959-63, Okla. State U., Stillwater, 1963-66, U. Ark., Fayetteville, 1966—; head dept. civil engring. U. Ark., 1971-82, dean engring., 1982-83; sr. v.p. Engring. Svcs., Inc., Springdale, Ark., 1973—; dir. Nat. Rural Transp. Study Ctr., 1992—; mem. Ark. State Bd. Registration for Profl. Engrs. and Land Surveyors, 1984—, pres., 1989, 94; mem. Nat. Coun. Examiners for Engring. and Surveying, 1984—, v.p. So. zone, 1991-93, mem. accreditation bd. engring. and tech., 1985-91. Served to 1st lt. AUS, 1953-56. Fellow ASCE (pres. Mid-South sect. 1972, chmn. dist. 14 1977-80, dist. 14 1983-86), Inst. Engrs. of Ireland; mem. NSPE (v.p. profl. engrs. in edn. 1982, v.p. S.W. region 1984-86, pres. 1989-90), Transp. Rsch. Bd., Am. Soc. Engring. Edn. (pres. midwest sect. 1976-77), Ark. Soc. Profl. Engrs. (pres. 1979-80, Outstanding Ark. Engr. 1980) Masons, Rotary (pres. 1973), Sigma Xi, Chi Epsilon, Tau Beta Pi, Phi Beta Delta. Home: 300 Paradise Ln Springdale AR 72762-3832 Office: Univ Ark Dept Civil Engring Fayetteville AR 72701 *I owe a great debt to those whose efforts have provided me the opportunity to accomplish these things. Personal relationships dwarf the honors I have received.*

LEFEVRE, PERRY DEYO, minister, theology educator; b. Kingston, N.Y., July 12, 1921; s. Johannes and Faye (McFerran) LeF.; m. Carol Baumann, Sept. 14, 1946; children: Susan Faye, Judith Ann, Peter Gerret. AB, Harvard U., 1943; BD, Chgo. Theol. Sem., 1946, DD, 1992; PhD, U. Chgo., 1951. Ordained to ministry Congl. Ch., 1946. Instr. religion Franklin and Marshall Coll., 1948-49; asst., then assoc. prof. religion Knox Coll., 1949-53, Fed. Theol. Sem., U. Chgo., 1953-61; prof. constructive theology Chgo. Theol. Sem., 1961-92, dean of faculty, 1961-81, acting dean, 1990-91. Author: The Prayers of Kierkegaard, 1956, The Christian Teacher, 1958, Introduction to Religious Existentialism, 1963, Understandings of Man, 1966, Philosophical Resources for Christian Thought, 1968, Conflict in a Voluntary Association, 1975, Understandings of Prayer, 1981, Aging and the Human Spirit, 1981, Radical Prayer, 1982; editor: Paul Tillich: The Meaning of Health, 1984, Spiritual Nurture and Congregational Development, 1984, Daniel Day Williams Essays in Process Theology, 1985, Pastoral Care and Liberation Praxis, 1986, Bernard Meland Essays in Constructive Theology, 1988, Creative Ministries in Contemporary Christianity, 1991, Modern Theologies of Prayer, 1995. Mem. Phi Beta Kappa. Address: 5757 S University Ave Chicago IL 60637-1507

LEFEVRE, THOMAS VERNON, retired utility company executive, lawyer; b. Dallas, Dec. 5, 1918; s. Eugene H. and Callie E. (Powell) L.; m. Lillian Herndon Bourne, Oct. 12, 1946; children: Eugene B., Nicholas R., Sharon A., Margot P. BA, U. Fla., 1939, LLB, 1942; LLM, Harvard U., 1946. Bar: Fla. 1945, N.Y. 1947, D.C. 1951, Pa. 1955, U.S. Supreme Ct. 1953. Atty. IRS and various firms, N.Y.C., Washington, and Phila., 1946-55; ptnr. Morgan, Lewis & Bockius, Phila., 1956-79; pres., chief exec. officer UGI Corp., Valley Forge, Pa., 1979-85, chmn., 1983-89; chmn. G.P. Hospitality, Inc., 1981—; mem. Commr.'s Adv. Group IRS, 1976-77. Bd. dirs. Zool. Soc. Phila., 1982-91, WHYY Inc., 1982—; chmn. U. Arts, 1986-89; trustee Franklin Inst., 1980-89, Fox Chase Cancer Ctr., 1979-88. With USMC, 1942-46. Fellow ABA (vice chmn. govn. rels. sect. of taxation 1976-79), Am. Bar Found.; mem. Pa. Bar Assn., Phila. Club, Merion Cricket Club, Merion Golf Club, Sankaty Head Golf Club, Nantucket Yacht Club. Episcopalian.

Office: Fidelity Ct Bldg Ste 145 259 Radnor Chester Rd Wayne PA 19087-5240

LE FEVRE, WILLIAM MATHIAS, JR., brokerage company executive; b. Muskegon, Mich., Dec. 22, 1927; s. William Mathias and Crystal (Atkinson) LeF.; m. Ada Marie Cannon, 1949 (div. 1973); children—Marie L. Keidel, Jeanne L. Van Vlandren, William Mathias III, Suzanne C.; m. Mathilda Bock Maguire, 1976. Grad., Phillips Exeter Acad., 1946; student, U. Mich., 1946-48. Floor ptnr. Arthur Wiesenberger & Co., N.Y.C., 1956-60; assoc. oddlot broker DeCoppet & Doremus, N.Y.C., 1961-64; v.p. Carter, Walker & Co. Inc., N.Y.C., 1964-68, Bruns, Nordeman & Co., N.Y.C., 1969-71; dir. research Sade & Co., Washington, 1972-73, Mack Bushnell & Edelman, N.Y.C., 1973-74; v.p. investment strategy Granger & Co., N.Y.C., 1974-80, Purcell, Graham & Co., N.Y.C., 1980-86; sr. v.p. market strategy Advest Inc., N.Y.C., 1986-91, Tucker Anthony Inc., N.Y.C., 1991-93, Sutro & Co., San Francisco, 1991-93; sr. market analyst Ehrenkrantz King Nussbaum Inc., N.Y.C., 1993—; mem. N.Y. Stock Exchange, 1958-64; assoc. mem. Am. Stock Exchange, 1960-62; speaker various colls., univs. and indsl. assns., 1977—. Editor: Monday Morning Market Memo, 1973—; contbr. market commentary radio and TV, 1980—. Mem. Assn. for Investment Mgmt. and Rsch. (profl. conduct com. 1977—), N.Y. Soc. Security Analysts, Fin. Analysts Phila. Home: 132 E 35th St New York NY 10016-3892 also: 78 Grassy Hill Rd Old Lyme CT 06371 Office: Ehrenkrantz King Nussbaum Inc 635 Madison Ave New York NY 10022-1009

LEFF, ALAN RICHARD, medical educator, researcher; b. Pitts., May 23, 1945; s. Maurice D. and Grace Ruth (Schwartz) L.; m. Donna Rae Rosene, Feb. 14, 1975; children: Marni, Karen, Alison. AB cum laude, Oberlin Coll., 1967; MD, U. Rochester, 1971. Diplomate Am. Bd. Internal Medicine, Am. Bd. Pulmonary Disease. Intern U. Mich. Hosp., Ann Arbor, 1971-72, resident, 1974-76; fellow U. Calif.-San Francisco, 1976-77, postdoctoral fellow, 1977-79; asst. prof. medicine U. Chgo., 1979-85, assoc. prof.medicine and clin. pharm., 1985-89, prof. medicine, anesthesia and critical care and clin. pharm., 1989—, prof. cell physiology, 1992—, prof. pediatrics, 1993—, prof. pharm. and physical scis., 1993—, dir. pulmonary medicine service, 1984-87, dir. Pulmonary Function Lab., 1979-87, chief sect. pulmonary and critical care medicine, 1987—; dir. NIAID Asthma and Allergic Dis. Coop. Rsch. Ctr., Chgo., 1993—; advisor San Francisco Dept. Pub. Health, 1977-79, Chgo. Dept. Health, 1979—; bd. dirs. Chgo. Lung Assn., 1984-93. Cons. editor Jour. Clin. Invest., editorial bd. Am. Jour. Physiology, Jour. Applied Physiology; editor Am. Jour. Respir. Critical Care Medicine, 1994—; assoc. editor Am. Rev. Respiratory Disease, 1989-94, Pulmonary Pharm., 1987; contbr. articles to profl. jours. Served with USPHS, 1972-74. Recipient Citation of merit Chgo. Lung Assn., 1974; Leopold Schepp Found. fellow, 1967-69. Fellow Am. Coll. Chest Physicians; mem. Am. Fedn. Clin. Research (councilor 1983-86), Am. Soc. Clin. Investigation, Am. Physiological Soc., Cent. Soc. for Clin. Investigation, Assn. Am. Physicians, Sigma Xi. Avocation: music. Home: 5730 S Kimbark Ave Chicago IL 60637-1615 Office: U Chgo Pritzker Sch Medicine Div Biological Scis MC 6076 5841 S Maryland Ave Chicago IL 60637-1463

LEFF, ILENE J(OAN), management consultant, corporate and government executive; b. N.Y.C., Mar. 29, 1942; d. Abraham and Rose (Levy) L.; BA cum laude, U. Pa., 1964; MA with honors, Columbia U., 1969. Statis./ computer analyst McKinsey & Co., N.Y.C., 1969-70, rsch. cons., 1971-74, mgmt. cons., N.Y.C. and Europe, 1974-78; dir. exec. resources Revlon, Inc., N.Y.C., 1978-81, dir. human resources, 1981-83, dir. personnel. 1983-86; cons. APM Inc., 1986-88, ind. mgmt. cons., 1988-93, 95—; dep. asst. sec. for mgmt. HUD, Washington, 1993-94; rsch. asst. U. Pa., Phila., 1964-65; employment counselor State of N.J., Newark, 1965-66; tchr., Newark, 1966-69; lectr. Grad. Program in Pub. Policy, New Sch. for Social Rsch., Wharton Sch., Duke U.; chmn. com. on employment and unemployment, mem. exec. com. Bus. Rsch. Adv. Coun., U.S. Bur. Labor Stats., 1980; sr. del. econ. rels. and trade Sino-U.S. Conf., 1986. Ops. coun. Jr. Achievement Greater N.Y., 1975-78; cons. com. for Econ. Devel., N.Y. Hosp., Regional Plan Assn., Am. Cancer Soc.; vol. for dep. mayor for ops N.Y.C., 1977-78 Mem. N.Y. Human Resource Planners (trustee 1984), Fin. Women's Assn. N.Y. (exec. bd., 1977-78, 83-84), The Fashion Group (treas. 1989). Contbr. issue papers and program recommendations to candidates for U.S. Pres., U.S. Senate and Congress, N.Y. State Gov., mayor N.Y.C.

LEFF, JOSEPH NORMAN, yarn manufacturing company executive; b. N.Y.C., Dec. 17, 1923; s. Phillip and Lillian (Wiesen) L.; m. Joyce Hochberg, June 12, 1954 (div. 1958); 1 child, Julie; m. Juanita Hughey, Dec. 17, 1967; 1 child, Valerie. BS, Columbia U., 1944, AB, 1946. Treas. Nat. Spinning Co. Inc., N.Y.C., 1949-63, pres., chief exec. officer, 1963-83, chmn., chief exec. officer, 1983—. Mem. bd. visitors Columbia Coll., N.Y.C., 1987-92; trustee Park Ave. Synagogue, N.Y.C., 1987-95; bd. dirs., pres. 92nd St. YM/ YWHA, N.Y.C., 1994—; bd. dirs. Inst. Textile Tech., Va., 1982—. With U.S. Army, 1944-45. Mem. Woolknit Assocs. (bd. dirs.), Acrylic Coun. (pres. 1988—). Jewish. Clubs: Harmonie (pres. 1974-75) (N.Y.C.); Quaker Ridge Golf (Scarsdale, N.Y.).

LEFF, ROBERT S., computer company executive; b. 1947. BA, MS, SUNY at Albany. With RCA Labs., 1971, Neisner Bros., Inc., 1971-72, BASF Wyandotte Corp., 1972-78, Transaction Tech., 1978-80; pres. Merisel Internat. (formerly Softsel Computer Products), from 1980, co-chmn. bd., 1985—. Office: Merisel Internat 200 Continental Blvd El Segundo CA 90245-4510

LEFF, SANDRA H., gallery director, consultant; b. N.Y.C., Dec. 24, 1939; d. I. Bernard and Rose (Kupfer) L. BA, Cornell U., 1960; MA, Inst. Fine Arts, N.Y.C., 1969. Editorial asst. Indsl. Design Mag., N.Y.C., 1960-61; instr., asst. Mus. of City of N.Y., 1962-65; assoc. print dept. Sotheby Parke Bernet, N.Y.C., 1969-73; rsch. asst. Daniel Chester French Exhibit, Washington, 1975-77; dir. Am. painting Graham Gallery, N.Y.C., 1977-93. Author: (exhbn. catalogs) Thomas Anshutz: Paintings, Watercolors and Pastels, 1979, Guy Pène du Bois: Painter, Draftsman and Critic, 1979, Helen Torr, 1980, John White Alexander: Fin-de-Siècle American, 1980, Jan Matulka & Vaclav Vytlacil, 1992. Ford Found. fellow, 1967. Mem. Phi Beta Kappa. Avocations: reading, traveling, jogging, film, photography.

LEFFEK, KENNETH THOMAS, chemist, educator; b. Nottingham, Eng., Oct. 15, 1934; emigrated to Can., 1959, naturalized, 1966; s. Thomas and Ivy Louise (Pye) L.; m. Janet Marilyn Wallace, Sept. 26, 1958; children: Katharine, Geoffrey. B.S., Univ. Coll., London, 1956, Ph.D., 1959. Asst. prof. chemistry Dalhousie U., Halifax, N.S., 1961-67; assoc. prof. Dalhousie U., 1967-72, prof., 1972-94, dean grad. studies, 1972-90; Chmn. Atlantic Provinces Interuniv. Com. on Scis., 1975-77. Contbr. articles on phys.-organic chemistry to profl. jours. Leverhulme fellow U. Kent (Eng.), 1967-68. Fellow Chem. Inst. Can., Royal Soc. Arts (London); chmn. Atlantic Can. chpt. 1987-91); mem. Chem. Inst. Can., London, Chem. Inst. Can. (nat. dir. tech. and sci. affairs 1980-83, nat. v.p. 1985-86, pres. 1986-87). Club: Waegwoltic (Halifax). Office: Dalhousie U Chemistry Dept, Coburg Rd, Halifax, NS Canada B3H 4J3

LEFFELL, DAVID JOEL, surgeon, dermatologist, educator, researcher; b. Montreal, Feb. 28, 1956; came to U.S., 1973; s. Allen Bernard and Freda (Deckelbaum) L. BS, Yale U., 1977; MD, McGill U., Montreal, 1981. Diplomate Am. Bd. Dermatology, Am. Bd. Internal Medicine. Resident in internal medicine Meml. Sloan-Kettering Cancer Ctr., N.Y.C., 1981-84; instr. medicine Cornell U. Sch. Medicine, N.Y.C., 1983-84; lectr., fellow dermatologic surgery U. Mich., Ann Arbor, 1987-88; resident in dermatology Yale U. Sch. Medicine, New Haven, 1984-86, assoc. prof. dermatology, plastic surgery and otolaryngology, 1988—, chief Mohs micrographic surgery and laser surgery, 1988—, dir. Yale skin cancer detection program, 1988—; sci. advisor Nat. Hereditary Hemorrhagic Telangiectasia Found., New Haven, 1991—. Mem. editl. bd. Archives of Dermatology; contbg. editor Jour. Dermatologic Surgery and Oncology; assoc. editor Med. and Surg. Dermatology; inventor laser fluorescence device to measure photoaging. Recipient Frederic Mohs award Skin Cancer Found., 1988, 91. Home: 69 Mumford Rd New Haven CT 06515-2431 Office: Yale Sch Medicine 333 Cedar St New Haven CT 06510-3289

LEFFERTS, GEORGE, writer, producer, director; b. Paterson, N.J.. B.A. in Engring. (Nat. Merit scholar, William Rose scholar), Drew U., 1940; B.A.

in English, U. Mich., 1942. Exec. producer, writer, dir. NBC, 1947-57; pres. George Lefferts Assocs., 1968—; exec. prodr. ABC, 1966-67, Time-Life Films, 1980-81; tchr. John Hopkins U., Balt., 1989-90, Rutgers U., 1992—; prodr., writer, dir. Network for Continuing Med. Edn., 1990—; program cons. ABC, 1981. Exhibited sculpture, Sculpture Gallery, N.Y.C., 1980; producer: series Report from America, U.S. Dept. State, Tactic, Am. Cancer Soc., others; (Recipient Nat. Media award 1961, Fame award 1962, Fgn. Press award 1963, Golden Globe award 1967, Plaudit award Producers Guild 1968, 69, Cine Golden Eagle award 1974, Peabody award 1970, 75, 1st prize San Francisco Film Festival 1970; nominee Humanitas Prize 1988); author: plays Nantucket Legend, 1960, The Boat, 1968, Hey Everybody, 1969; columnist N.Y. Observer, Litchfield County Times, 1984-87 (1st prize New England Journalism award, 1984, 85); also author mag. articles, works on piano method, syndicated columns, others; prodns. include Biographies in Sound (Peabody award 1956), NBC Theatre, (Ohio State award 1955), Kraft Theatre, Armstrong Circle Theatre, Studio One, Lights Out, Frank Sinatra Show; spl. program Pain, 1971, Bravo Picasso!, 1972, What Price Health; program NBC Investigative Reports, 1972 (Albert Lasker award), CBS, Ben Franklin Series (Peabody award 1975, Emmy award 1975), Ryan's Hope, 1977 (Emmy award 1977), Purex Specials, 1966 (Emmy award 1966), The People vs. Jean Harris, 1981; exec. producer, writer, dir., NBC, Spls. for Women (2 Emmy awards 1965); series (Emmy award 1962), 1961 (Golden Globe award 1961); exec. producer: series Breaking Point, 1962-64 (Producers Guild Plaudit award 1963), CBS, Smithsonian Spls., 1974-75, ABC, Wide World of Entertainment, 1973-74, Bing Crosby Prodns., 1962-64; exec. producer: Wolper Prodns., 1974-75, Time/Life Films, 1978-79; original films produced include: series The Living End, 1959, The Stake, 1960, The Teenager, 1965, The Harness, 1972, The Night They Took Miss Beautiful, 1977, Bud & Lou, 1978, Mean Dog Blues, 1979, The Search for Alexander the Great, 1981, Dressed to Kill, 1980; producer: series Hallmark Hall of Fame, 1969-70, Never Say Goodbye, 1987 (Emmy award 1988, Humanitas Award nomination 1988), TV play Teacher, Teacher, 1974 (Emmy award 1974). Served with AUS, 1942-45. Mem. Nat. Acad. TV Arts and Scis., Am. Acad. Motion Picture Arts and Scis., Christopher Morley Knothole Assn. Club: South Bay Cruising (Babylon, (N.Y.).

LEFFERTS, GILLET, JR., architect; b. N.Y.C., May 6, 1923; s. Gillet and Helen Willets (Lambert) L.; m. Lucia Beverly Hollerith, Apr. 21, 1951; children: Helena Gillet (dec.), Robert Beverly, John Willets, Sarah Fox, David Hollerith. A.B., Williams Coll., 1947; M.F.A., Princeton, 1950. Apprentice Moore & Hutchins, N.Y.C., 1947-48, 50-55; assoc. Moore & Hutchins, 1955-66, ptnr., 1967-72; partner Hutchins, Evans & Lefferts, N.Y.C., 1972-89; mem. William A. Hall Partnership, Architecture and Planning, N.Y.C., 1990—; instr. Mechanics Inst., N.Y.C., 1955-58. Architect: master plan and ednl. facilities SUNY-Binghampton, 1956—, Buffalo, 1981-85; master plan Coll. Agr., Malaya, 1970, St. Johnland Nursing Home, L.I., N.Y., 1976, Clark Gymnasium, Cooperstown, N.Y., 1986, Nat. Baseball Hall of Fame and Mus. Expansion, Cooperstown, 1988-89, 93-94, Scholes Libr. Coll. Ceramics, Alfred U., 1992. Mem. zoning bd. appeals Town of Darien, Conn., 1961-69, mem. planning and zoning commn., 1969-77, chmn., 1973-77, mem. bd. selectmen, 1983-89; pres. Darien Hist. Soc., 1982-83; mem. bd. trustees Darien Pub. Libr., 1991—. With USAAF, 1943-46. Decorated Air medal with oak leaf cluster. Fellow AIA; mem. Fairfield County Alumni Assn. Williams Coll. (v.p. 1965-67), Nat. Inst. Archtl. Edn. (chmn. bd. trustees 1963-65, treas. 1970-73), Delta Psi. Episcopalian. Clubs: Century Assn. (N.Y.C.), Williams (N.Y.C.); Norwalk (Conn.); Yacht. Office: 42 E 21st St New York NY 10010-7201

LEFFERTS, WILLIAM GEOFFREY, physician, educator; b. Towanda, Pa., Mar. 24, 1943; s. William LeRoy and Beatrice (Smith) L.; m. Susan Lynn Hiles, Oct. 31, 1970. B.A., Hamilton Coll., 1965; M.D., Hahnemann Med. Coll., 1969. Intern Hahnemann Hosp., 1969-70; resident in internal medicine Cleve. Clinic Hosp., 1970-73, chief med. resident, 1972-73; asst. prof. internal medicine Hahnemann Med. Coll., 1973-77; assoc. prof. Med. Coll. Pa., 1977-82, dir. primary care unit, 1978-82, dir. div. gen. internal medicine, 1979-82; staff physician Cleve. Clinic Found., 1982—. Fellow ACP. Office: 9500 Euclid Ave Cleveland OH 44195-0001

LEFFLER, CAROLE ELIZABETH, mental health nurse, women's health nurse; b. Sidney, Ohio, Feb. 18, 1942; d. August B. and Delores K. Aselage; children: Veronica, Christopher. ADN, Sinclair Community Coll., Dayton, Ohio, 1975. Cert. psychiat. nurse coord. Nurse Grandview Hosp, Dayton, 1961-76; substitute sch. nurse Fairborn (Ohio) City Schs., 1981-82; dir. nursing Fairborn Nursing Home, 1983; psychiat. nurse coord. Dayton Mental Health Ctr., 1984—; head bd. 1199. Vol., instr., disaster health nurse ARC; officer, leader, camp nurse for Girl Scouts, Boy Scouts; Ch. Parish Coun. Recipient Fleur de Lis award Girl and Boy Scouts, Svc. award ARC, Fairborn Mayor's Cert. of Merit for Civic Pride, State of Ohio Govs. award Innovation Ohio. Mem. ANA, Ohio Nurses Assn. Home: 29 W Bonomo Dr Fairborn OH 45324-3407

LEFFLER, MELVYN P., history educator; b. N.Y.C., May 31, 1945; s. Louis and Mollie (Fuchs) L.; m. Phyllis Konan, Sept. 1, 1968; children: Sarah Ann, Elliot. BS, Cornell U., 1966; PhD, Ohio State U., 1972. Asst. prof. Vanderbilt U., Nashville, 1972-77, assoc. prof., 1977-86; internat. affairs fellow Coun. Fgn. Rels. Dept. Def., Washington, 1979-80; prof. U. Va., Charlottesville, 1986-94, Edward R. Stettinius prof. history, 1994—, chmn. hist. dept., 1990—. Author: The Elusive Quest, 1979, A Preponderance of Power, 1992 (Bancroft, Ferrell & Hoover prizes 1993), The Specter of Communism, 1994; contbr. articles to profl. jours. Fellow Woodrow Wilson Internat. Ctr., 1979, Am. Coun. Learned Socs., 1984, Nobel Peace Inst., 1994. Mem. Am. Hist. Assn., Orgn. Am. Hists., Soc. Hists. Am. Fgn. Rels. (v.p. 1993, future pres., Bernath Article prize 1984). Jewish. Home: 1612 Concord Dr Charlottesville VA 22901 Office: U Va History Dept Randall Hall Charlottesville VA 22903

LEFKOVITS, ALBERT MEYER, dermatologist; b. N.Y.C., June 30, 1937; s. Aaron Melchior and Muriel (Mark) L.; A.B., Cornell U., 1958; M.D. (Lederle research fellow), N.Y. Med. Coll., 1962; m. Cheryl Beth Kornberg, Apr. 25, 1971; children—Ari Nathan, Lauren Blair. Intern, Newark Beth Israel Hosp., 1962-63; resident in dermatology Kings County Hosp. Center, SUNY, Downstate Med. Center, Bklyn., 1963-65; chief resident dermatology Mt. Sinai Hosp., N.Y.C., 1965-66, research fellow in dermatology, 1966-67, asst. attending physician, 1966—; practice medicine specializing in dermatology, N.Y.C., 1966—; asst. attending physician Beekman-Downtown Hosp., N.Y.C., 1968-75; instr. dermatology Mt. Sinai Sch. Medicine, 1966-68, clin. asso. dermatology, 1968-73, asst. prof., 1974, acad. council, 1973-78 1886—; instr. dermatology N.Y. Med. Coll., 1966-69. Alumni fund-raising chmn. Horace Mann Sch., 1976-78; treas. Mt. Sinai Alumni, 1988-90, sec., 1991-93, v.p., 1993-95, pres. 1995—. Served to maj. M.C., AUS, 1969-71. Recipient Fredrick Wise Dermatology award N.Y. Acad. Medicine, 1965, Torch of Liberty award Anti-Defamation League, 1987, Maimonides award Keren Or Found. for Handicapped Blind Children, 1994. Mem. Harvey Soc., Soc. Investigative Dermatology, Dermatology Found., Soc. Tropical Dermatology, Am. Acad. Dermatology, AMA, Internat. Soc. Human and Animal Mycology, Mycology Soc. of Ams., N.Y. Acad. Scis., Am. Physicians Fedn. (trustee, exec. com.), Jewish Chautauqua Soc. (life), Dermatology Soc. Greater N.Y. (pres.), N.Y. State Med. Soc., Cornell Alumni Assn. N.Y. (bd. govs. 1974-76) Med. Adv. Bd. Skin Cancer Found. 1986—. Jewish (dir. congregation Emanu-El men's club). Clubs: Town, Cornell (N.Y.C.); Lawrence Yacht (fleet surgeon 1982-83, sec. 1984, treas. 1985, commodore 1987). Address: 1040 Park Ave New York NY 10028-1032

LEFKOW, JOAN HUMPHREY, judge; b. Kans., Jan. 9, 1944; d. Otis L. and Donna Grace (Glenn) Humphrey; m. Michael F. Lefkow, June 21, 1975; children: Maria Aithne, Helena Claiborne, Laura Bethany, Margaret Frances. AB, Wheaton Coll., 1965; JD, Northwestern U., 1971. Bar: Ill. 1971, U.S. Dist. Ct. (no. dist.) Ill. 1972, U.S. Ct. Appeals (7th cir.) 1972, U.S. Ct. Appeals (5th cir.) 1980. Law clerk to Hon. Thomas E. Fairchild U.S. Ct. Appeals (7th cir.), 1971-72; atty. Lega Assistance Found. Chgo. 1972-75; adminstrv. law judge Ill. Fair Employment Practices Commn., 1975-77 chief adminstrv. law judge, 1977-79; instr. sch. law U. Miami, Fla., 1980-81; exec. dir. Cook County Legal Assistence Found., 1981-82; now magustrate judge U.S. Dist. Ct. (no. dist.) Ill. Editor Northwestern U. Law Rev. Active PTA. Mem. Chgo. Bar Assn. (legal aid com. 1982), Chgo. Coun. Lawyers (gov. bd. 1975-77), 7th Cir. Bar Assn. Episcopalian. Office:

Everett McKinley Dirksen Bldg 219 S Dearborn St Rm 2402 Chicago IL 60604

LEFKOWITZ, HOWARD N., lawyer; b. Utica, N.Y., Oct. 28, 1936; s. Samuel I. and Sarah Lefkowitz; m. Martha Yelon, June 16, 1958; children: Sarah, David. BA, Cornell U., 1958; LLB, Columbia U., 1963. Bar: N.Y. 1963, Fla. 1979, D.C. 1981. Ptnr. Proskauer Rose Goetz & Mendelsohn, N.Y.C., 1963—; chmn. joint com. to study, Office of Sec. of State, mem. tri-bar opinion com., remedies subcom. Editor Columbia Law Rev., 1963. Served to lt. (j.g.) USN, 1958-61. Kent scholar Columbia U. Law Sch. Mem. ABA (mem. ltd. liability partnership subcom. of bus. sect. 1993—), Assn. of Bar of City of N.Y. (chmn. com. on corp. law 1990-93), N.Y. County Lawyers Assn. (chmn. com. on comm. entertainment and arts-related law 1983-86). Office: Proskauer Rose Goetz & Mendelsohn 1585 Broadway New York NY 10036-8200

LEFKOWITZ, LAWRENCE, lawyer; b. Bklyn., Feb. 5, 1938; s. Mortimer and Sylvia Lefkowitz; m. Janet Goldblatt, Sept. 3, 1961; children: James, Karen, Diane. AB, Franklin and Marshall Coll., 1959; JD, Columbia U., N.Y.C., 1962. Bar: N.Y. 1962. Atty., examiner SEC, Washington, 1962-64; assoc., ptnr. Guzik and Boukstein, N.Y.C., 1964-73; ptnr. Reavis and McGrath, N.Y.C., 1973-77; v.p. legal, sec. Ampal-Am. Israel Corp., N.Y.C., 1977-90, pres., 1990—; counsel Bank Hapoalim, B.M., 1990—. Commr. Hartsdale (N.Y.) Pub. Parking Dist., 1973-92. Mem. ABA. Democrat. Jewish. Avocations: fishing, tennis. Office: Ampal-American Israel Corp 10 Rockefeller Plz New York NY 10020-1903

LEFKOWITZ, MARY ROSENTHAL, Greek literature educator; b. N.Y.C., Apr. 30, 1935; d. Harold L. and Mena (Weil) Rosenthal; m. Alan L. Lefkowitz, July 1, 1956 (div.); children: Rachel, Hannah; m. Hugh Lloyd-Jones, Mar. 26, 1982. BA, Wellesley Coll., 1957; AM, Radcliffe Coll., 1959, PhD, 1961. Instr. Greek Wellesley (Mass.) Coll., 1960-63, asst. prof. Greek and Latin, 1964-69, assoc. prof. Greek and Latin, 1969-75, prof. Greek and Latin, 1975-79; Andrew W. Mellon prof. in the humanities Wellesley (Mass.) Coll., 1979—; vis. prof. U. Calif., Berkeley, 1978; vis. fellow St. Hilda's Coll., 1979-80, Corpus Christi Coll., 1991. Author: Heroines and Hysterics, 1981, Lives of the Greek Poets, 1981, Women in Greek Myth, 1986, First Person Fictions, 1991; co-editor: Women's Life in Greece and Rome, 1982, 2d edit., 1992. Fellow NEH, 1979-80, 91, ACLS, 1972-73, Hon. fellow St. Hilda's Coll., Oxford, 1994—. Mem. Am. Philol. Assn. (bd. dirs. 1974-77), Class Assn. New Eng. (pres. 1972-73). Home: 15 W Riding St Wellesley MA 02181-6914 Office: Wellesley Coll 106 Central St Wellesley MA 02181-8252

LEFKOWITZ, ROBERT JOSEPH, physician, educator; b. N.Y.C., Apr. 15, 1943; s. Max and Rose (Levine) L.; children: David, Larry, Cheryl, Mara, Joshua; m. Lynn Tilley, May 26, 1991. B.A., Columbia U., 1962, M.D., 1966. Diplomate: Am. Bd. Internal Medicine. Assoc. prof medicine Duke U., Durham, N.C., 1973-77, prof. medicine, 1977—; James B. Duke prof. medicine, 1982—; prof. biochemistry, 1985—; investigator Howard Hughes Med. Inst., Durham, 1976—. Author: Receptor Binding Studies in Adrenergic Pharmacology, 1978, Receptor Regulation, 1981, Principles of Biochemistry, 1983. Am. Heart Assn. established investigator, 1973-76, Basic Rsch. prize, 1990; recipient Young Scientist award Passano Found., 1978, George Thorn award Howard Hughes Med. Inst., 1979, Oppenheimer award, 1982, Gordon Wilson medal Am. Clin. and Climatol. Assn., 1982, Lita Annenberg Hazen award, 1983, outstanding rsch. award Internat. Soc. for Heart Rsch., 1985, H.B. van Dyke award Coll. Physicians and Surgeons Columbia U., 1986, Steven C. Beering award Ind. U. Sch. Medicine, 1986, N.C. award in Sci., 1987, Internat. award Gairdner Found., 1988, Novo Nordsk Biotech. award, 1990, Biomed. Rsch.award Assn. Am. Med. Colls., 1990, City of Medecin award, N.C., 1991, Columbia U. Coll. of Physicians and Surgeons Alumnus award for Disting. achievements in medicine, 1992, Bristol-Meyers Squibb award for Disting. achievement in Cardiovascular rsch., 1992, The Giovani Lorenzini Prize for Basic Biomedical Rsch., 1992, Columbia U. coll. of Physicians and Surgeons Joshep Mather Smith Prize, 1993. Mem. Am. Soc. Biol. Chemists, Am. Soc. Clin. Investigation (counselor, 1982-85, pres.-elect 1986-87, pres. 1987-88), Assn. Am. Physicians (treas. 1989—), Am. Soc. Pharmacology and Exptl. Therapeutics (John J. Abel award 1978, Goodman and Gilman award 1986), Endocrine Soc., Am. Fedn. Clin. Research (sec.-treas. 1980-83, mem. nat. council 1978-83), NAS, Am. Acad. Arts and Scis., Japanese Biochem.soc. (hon.), Am. Heart Assn. Basic Rsch. Soc. Office: Duke Univ Med Ctr PO Box 3821 Durham NC 27710-0001

LEFRAK, FRANCINE, theatre and film producer; b. N.Y.C., Oct. 18, 1950; d. Samuel J. and Ethel (Stone) LeF. Student L'Ecole Superieure de Neufchatel, Switzerland, 1966, Sarah Lawrence Coll., Florence and Greece, 1970; BA, Finch Coll., 1972. Art appraiser Sotheby Parke Bernet, N.Y.C., 1976; mem. chmn's. coun. Metro. Mus. of Art; bd. dirs. Women's Project and Prodns., BMI Found.; associated with production Broadway play Ain't Misbehavin', 1978, Children of Lesser God, 1979; co-producer March of The Falsettos, N.Y.C., Los Angeles, (Best Musical Outer Critics Circle 1981), 1981, Crimes of The Heart (Best Play Tony nomination 1982) N.Y.C., Nat. Tour, 1981-82, They're Playing Our Song, London, 1980, Nine (Best Musical Outer Critics Circle 1982, Best Musical Drama Desk award 1982, Best Musical Tony award 1982), N.Y.C., 1982-84, My One and Only (Best Musical Tony Nomination 1983), N.Y.C., Leader of the Pack (Best Musical Tony Nomination 1985), N.Y.C., 1985; associated with Noises Off (Best Play Tony Nomination 1984), N.Y.C., Nat. Tour, 1984-85, Cafe Crown (Best Set Design award 1989); developer films for 20th Century Fox, Warner Bros., Walt Disney Prodns., Tri-Star/Columbia Pictures, 1985—; exec. prodr.: Prison Stories: Women on the Inside, 1990 (Ciné Golden Eagle award, 4 ACE noms.), Blood Brothers: The Joey Dipaolo Story, 1992 (Cable ACE award, Ciné Golden Eagle award, Silver award Houston Film Festival, Blue Ribbon Am. Film & Video Assn., Beacon award for Community Svcs., Pixie award Found. for Film & TV); co-prodr.: Miss Rose White, 1992 (recipient 4 Emmy awards, 10 Emmy noms., The Humanitas prize); exec. prodr. HBO film A Body to Die For: The Aaron Henry Story, 1994; co-exec. prodr.: Mi Vida Loca, 1994, ABC/Hallmark Hall of Fame film Redwood Curtain, 1995; exec. prodr. HBO film In Hitler's Shadow, 1995. Mem. League Am. Theatres Producers. Avocations: hiking, aerobic exercising; art collecting; shipwrecks. Office: LeFrak Prodns The Whole Picture Co 40 W 57th St Ste 409 New York NY 10019-4001

LEFRAK, RICHARD STONE, real estate developer; b. N.Y.C., Aug. 29, 1945; s. Samuel J. and Ethel (Stone) LeF.; m. Karen Tucker, Sept 7, 1969; children: Harrison, James. BA, Amherst Coll., 1967; JD, Columbia U., 1970. Bar: N.Y. Pres. The Lefrak Orgn. Inc., N.Y.C., 1975—; gov. Real Estate Bd., N.Y.C.; bd. dirs. Sequa Corp. Bd. dirs. Samuel J. and Ethel LeFrak Found., N.Y. State Banking Bd., 1985-90. Mem. Young President's Orgn., Lotos Club, Met. Club, Explorers Club. Office: The Lefrak Orgn Inc 97-77 Queens Blvd Forest Hills NY 11374

LEFRAK, SAMUEL J., housing and building corporation executive; b. N.Y.C., Feb. 12, 1918; s. Harry and Sarah (Schwarz) LeF.; m. Ethel Stone, May 14, 1941; children: Denise, Richard, Francine, Jacqueline. Grad., U. Md., 1940; postgrad., Columbia U., Harvard U.; LLD (hon.), U. of Studies, Rome, 1971, N.Y. Law Sch., 1974, Colgate U., 1979; HHD (hon.), Pratt Inst., 1988, U. Md., 1990, Queens Coll., 1994, Mich. State U., 1995. Pres. Lefrak Orgn., 1948—, chmn. bd., 1975—; creator, sponsor, builder Lefrak City, Battery Park City, Gateway Pla., Newport Complex; mem. adv. bd. Sta. WHLI, 1955; commr. Landmarks Preservation Commn., N.Y.C., 1966; commr. pub. works Borough Manhattan, 1956-58; commr. Interstate Sanitation Commn., 1958; Saratoga Springs Commn., 1962—; mem. adv. bd. Chem Bank.; guest lectr. Harvard Grad. Sch. Bus. Adminstrn., 1971, Yale, 1975, NYU, 1977; guest speaker Fin. Women's Assn., N.Y., 1975; guest lectr. Princeton U., U. Haifa, 1983, Oxford U., 1984, Pratt Inst., 1987, Harvard U., 1987, Columbia Sch. Bus., 1988, Wharton Sch. Bus., 1989, Sch. Bus. NYU, 1989; speaker UN, 1988; featured speaker Instl. Investment Real Estate Conf., 1975, Fed. Home Loan Bank Conf., 1990; guest lectr. Japanese Govt., Finnish Govt., Switzerland, 1987; U.S. del. Internat. Conf. Housing and Urban Devel., Switzerland, 1967; dir. N.Y. World's Fair Corp., 1964-65; N.Y. Indsl. Devel. Corp., 1975—, chmn. bd. L.I. Post; pres. N.Y.C. Comml. Devel. Corp., 1967-71, chmn., 1971—; founding mem. World Business Coun., Inc., 1970; mem. Pres.'s Com. Employment Handicapped; spl. cons. urban affairs State Dept., 1969; mem. adv. coun. Real Estate Inst., N.Y. U.,

1970—; mem. gov. fin. Pres.'s Club U. Md., 1971, com. N.Y. State Traffic Safety Council, 1966; bd. visitors Sch. Law, Columbia U., 1983; commr. Saratoga-Capital dist. N.Y. State Park and Recreation Commn., 1973; mem. real estate coun. exec. com. Met. Mus. Art, 1982; mem. N.Y.C Pub. Devel. Corp., Nat. Energy Coun., U.S. Dept. Commerce, Mayor's Com. on Housing Devel., N.Y.C., 1974—; mem. exec. com. Citizen's Budget Com. for N.Y.C, Inc., 1975—; mem. Gov. Cuomo's Adv. Coun., 1983, N.Y. State Gov.'s Task Force on Housing, 1974; establish Lefrak Lecture Series, U. Md., 1982; creator, developer residential and business property. Vice chmn.-at-large ARC, N.Y.; mem. U.S. com. UN Orgn., 1957; chmn. nat. bd. Histadrut, 1967—; mem. Israel Bonds Prime Minister Com., 1980; dir. Ronald McDonald House, 1986; chmn. bldg. com. Saratoga Performing Arts Ctr.; mem. Fifth Ave. Assn.; dir., chmn. real estate div. Greater N.Y. Fund; hon. com. AAU; Queens chmn. United Greek Orthodox Charities, 1973; chmn. Celebrity Sports Night-Human Resources Ctr., 1973-74, Sports Assn. Hebrew U. of Jerusalem, 1979; patron Met. Mus. Art; sponsor Israel Philharm. Orch., Jan Groth Exhibit, Guggenheim Mus.; trustee, dir. Beth-El Hosp.; bd. dirs. USO, Citizens Housing and Planning Council, N.Y., 1957—; Interfaith Movement, Diabetics Found., Queens Cultural Assn., Consumer Credit Counseling Svc. Greater N.Y., Astoria Motion Picture and TV Ctr. Found.; trustee N.Y. Law Sch., Queens Art and Cultural Ctr., Jewish Hosp. at Denver, N.Y Civic Budget Com.; trustee, med. adv. bd. Brookdale Hosp. Med. Ctr., Pace U.; mem. exec. bd. Greater N.Y. couns. Boy Scouts Am.; founder Albert Einstein Sch. Medicine; mem. Bretton Woods Com.; bd. govs. Invest-in-Am. Nat. Coun.; mem. task force on energy conservation Div. Community Housing, 1981—; mem. com. N.Y. State Traffic Safety Coun., 1966; chmn. Scandinavia Today, 1981—; bd. visitors Sch. Law Columbia U., 1983; mem. adv. bd. The Explorer's Club, 1984; mem. Nat. Com. on U.S.-China Rels. Inc.; bd. dirs. Inst. Nautical Archaeology; trustee Queens Coll., 1989; adv. dir. Met. Opera, 1990; conf. bd. Keynote Address-Annual Fin. Seminar, 1987; mem. Lambda Alpha Internat. bd. trustees Guggenheim Mus., 1993; mem. bd. trustees Dana Farker Cancer Inst. Harvard Med. Sch., 1992. Decorated officer Order of Lion of Finland, 1980, Medment, 1980; officer Order St. John of Jerusalem Knights of Malta, 1982; Order of the North Star of Sweden, 1982; comdr. Royal Norwegian Order of Merit, 1987; recipient Mayor N.Y.C award outstanding citizenship, 1960; Nat. Boys Club award, 1960; Citizen of Year award B'nai Brith, 1963; Am. Achievement award, 1984; Disting. Achievement award, 1967; Man of Year award VFW, 1963; Brotherhood award NCCJ, 1964; Chief Rabbi Herzog gold medal; Torah Fellowship citation Religious Zionist Am. 1966; John F. Kennedy Peace award, 1966; Man of Year award Bklyn. Community Hosp., 1967; Builder of Excellence award Brandeis U., 1968; Master Builder award N.Y. Cardiac Ctr., 1968; Disting. Citizen award M Club Found. U. Md., 1970; Disting. Alumnus award U. Md. Alumni Assn., 1970; Disting. Citizen and Outstanding Community Svc. award United Way, 1986; Am. Achievement award Ency. Britannica, 1984; Am. Eagle award nat. coun. Investn-in Am., 1972; Exec. Sportsman award Human Resources Ctr., 1973; Archtl. award Fifth Av. Assn., 1974; Excellence in Design award Queens C. of C., 1974; Flame Truth award Fund Higher Edn., 1986; elected hon. citizen Md. 1970; Citizen of Yr. award Bklyn. Philharm. Orch., 1983; dedication of Samuel J. LeFrak Hall U. Md., 1982, LeFrak Gymnasium, Amherst Coll., 1986, LeFrak Moot Ct., N.Y. Law Sch., 1990, LeFrak Meadow, N.Y.C., 1991; LeFrak Lecture Series at U. Md. established, 1982; Comdr. of the Royal Norwegian Order of Merit, presented by King Olav V, 1987; Rough Riders award Boy Scouts Am., 1987; Torch of Progress Assoc. Builders and Owners Greater N.Y.; award Soc. Fgn. Consuls, 1988, Gold medal and Man of Yr. award Israel Bonds Found., 1990, Developer of the Yr. Associated Builders and Owners of Greater N.Y., 1990; award Assn. Graphics Arts, 1990, Disting. Citizen of World award UN, 1994, Alumni Hall of Fame award U. Md., 1995; named to Nat. Sales Club Hall of Fame, 1990. Mem. Sales Execs. Club N.Y. (dir.), United Hunts Racing Assn., Philharm. Symphony Soc. N.Y., Explorers Club (dir.), Newcomen Soc. U.S., Phi Kappa Phi, Tau Epsilon Phi (established Samuel J. LeFrak scholarship award 1975). Clubs: U. Md. Pres.'s (mem. Gov. N.Y. Inc.), Lotos (bd. dirs. 1975—, Merit award 1973), Grand Street Boys, Friars (dir. Found.), Advertising, Economic, Downtown Athletic (N.Y.C.); Town, Turf and Field; Cat Cay (Nassau, Bahamas); Xanadu Yacht (Freeport, Grand Bahamas); Palm Bay (Miami Beach, Fla.); Seawane; Ocean Reef (Key Largo); Sag Harbor Yacht (L.I.). Lodges: Masons (32d degree), Shriners. Office: LeFrak Orgn Inc 97-77 Queens Blvd Rego Park NY 11374*

LEFSTEIN, NORMAN, lawyer, educator; b. Rock Island, Ill., July 16, 1937; s. George M. and Rose Lefstein; m. Leah M. Lefstein, Apr. 15, 1962 (div.); children: Lisa, Adam, Susan. Student, Augustana Coll., 1955-58; LL.B., U. Ill., 1961; LL.M., Georgetown U., 1964. Bar: Ill. 1961, D.C. 1963. Asst. U.S. atty. Washington, 1964-65; project dir. Nat. Council Juvenile Ct. Judges, Chgo., 1965-68; staff mem. Dept. Justice, Washington, 1968-69; dep. dir. Pub. Defender Service for D.C., 1969-72, dir., 1972-75; assoc. prof. law U. N.C., Chapel Hill, 1975-79, prof., 1979-87; dean, prof. Ind. U. Sch. Law, Indpls., 1988—; vis. prof. Duke U., 1976-77, fall 1978; chmn. Ind. Pub. Defender Commn., 1990—. Bd. editors U. Ill. Law Forum, 1959-61. Mem. ABA (council criminal justice sect. 1979-88, chmn. 1986-87, reporter Project to Update ABA Criminal Justice Standards 1977-85), Nat. Legal Aid and Defender Assn. (bd. dirs., mem. exec. com. 1975-80), Order of Coif. Home: 3405 Bay Point Dr Indianapolis IN 46240-2451 Office: Ind U Sch Law 735 W New York St Indianapolis IN 46202-5194

LEFT, JOAN MARILYN, principal; b. Bayonne, N.J., Aug. 21, 1940; d. William A. and Amelia P. (Jakowicz) Lapinski; m. Anthony Patrick Left, Aug. 4, 1962; children: Susan, Carol, Barbara, Patricia. BA in Sci. Edn., Jersey City State Coll., 1962; MA, U. Ala., Birmingham, 1981, EdS, 1992, EdD in Ednl. Leadership, 1994. Cert. elem. tchr., Ala. Sci. tchr. Pont Pleasant (N.J.) Elem. Sch., 1962-63; biology tchr. Lakewood (N.J.) High Sch., 1964-67; lab. instr. Georgia Ct. Coll., Lakewood, 1968-67; tchr. St. Francis Xavier Sch., Birmingham, Ala., 1974-85, Phileo Sch., Birmingham, 1985-86, Pinson (Ala.) Elem. Sch., 1986-90; asst. prin. Cahaba Heights Elem. Sch., Birmingham, 1991-93, Leeds (Ala.) Elem., 1993-94; prin. Greystone Elem. Sch., Birmingham, 1994—; cons., presenter in field; mentor tchr. First-Yr. Tchr. Scholar Program. Author papers in field. Grantee Nat. Sci. Tchrs Assn., Gen. Aviation Mfrs. Assn., Ala. Dept. Econ. & Conservation Affairs, Am. South Bank. Mem. NAESP, NEA, ASCD, Ala. Edn. Assn., Ala. Sci. Tchrs. Assn., Nat. Coun. Tchrs. Math., Women Educator's Network (v.p. 1991-93, pres. 1993—), Jefferson County Edn. Assn., Phi Delta Kappa (v.p.), Kappa Delta Pi. Home: 5291 Amber Hills Rd Birmingham AL 35210 Office: Greystone Elem Sch Hoover AL 35242

LEFTON, AL PAUL, JR., advertising executive; b. Wilmington, Del., July 11, 1928; s. Al Paul and Clara Belle (Ginns) L.; m. Amarilice Miller, Dec. 28, 1951; children: Alice, Marie, Al Paul III. BA, Yale U., 1950. With Al Paul Lefton Co., Inc., Phila., 1950—; v.p., sec. Al Paul Lefton Co., Inc., Phila. and N.Y.C., 1961-64, pres., chief exec. officer, 1964—. Bd. dirs. Eaglesville Sanitarium, 1965-79, Mann Music Ctr., Phila. 1975—, Univ. Arts, 1980—, Med. Coll. Pa., 1978-89, No. Home for Children, 1965-86; mem. Mayor's Com. on Culture and Arts, 1992—. With AUS, 1951-53. Clubs: Yale (N.Y.C., Phila.); Union League (Phila.). Office: Al Paul Lefton Co Inc Rohm & Haas Bldg Independence Mall W Philadelphia PA 19106

LEFTON, HARVEY BENNETT, gastroenterologist, educator, author; b. Cleve., May 17, 1944; s. Nat L. and Edith (Waintrup) L.; m. Paulette Lipkowitz, Aug. 24, 1968; children: Allison Rachel, Daniel Adam. BS, U. Pitts., 1966; MD, Jefferson Med. Coll., Phila., 1970. Cert. Nat. Bd. Med. Examiners, Am. Bd. Internal Medicine, Am. Bd. Gastroenterology. Intern medicine Cleve. Clinic, 1970-71, resident internal medicine, 1971-72, fellow gastroenterology, 1972-74; chief gastroenterology Scott AFB, Belleville, Ill., 1974-76; asst. clin. prof. medicine Med. Coll. Pa., Phila., 1976-78, assoc. clin. prof. medicine, 1978-81, clin. prof. medicine, 1981—; cons. gastroenterology Friends Hosp., Belmont Psychiat. Hosp., Pa., 1980—. Contbr. articles to profl. jours. Maj. USAF, 1974-76. Fellow ACP, Am. Coll. Gastroenterology, Coll. Physicians Phila.; mem. Am. Soc. Gastroenterology Endoscopy, Pa. Soc. Gastroenterology. Home: 559 Long Ln Huntingdon Valley PA 19006 Office: 2 Bala Plz Ste IL 22 Bala Cynwyd PA 19004

LEFTWICH, HAL WEST, health facility administrator; b. Richmond, Va., Oct. 21, 1955; Louis J. Jr. and R. Arvella (Donahoe) L. AA, Fla. Tech. U., 1977; BBA, La. Ky. U., 1978; MHA, Xavier U., Cin., 1980. Asst. administr. Greenville (S.C.) Hosp. System, 1980-82; v.p. med. svcs. Kissimmee (Fla.) Meml. Hosp., 1982-84; v.p. adminstrn. Parrish Med. Ctr., Titusville, Fla.,

1984-91; chmn. planning, zoning commn. City of Titusville, Fla., 1990; adminstr. Quorum Health Resources Brooksville (Fla.) Regional Hosp., 1991—; cons. Sunbelt Emergency Med. Services, Orlando, Fla., 1985-86; pres. Brevard County CPR, Inc., Melbourne, Fla., 1986-90. Bd. dirs., chmn. multisvc. agencies budget task group United Way, 1989-91. Recipient achievement award United Way of Osceola County, 1985. Fellow Am. Coll. Health Care Execs.; mem. Am. Hosp. Assn., Fla. Hosp. Assn., U. Ctrl. Fla. Alumni Assn. (bd. dirs. 1988-91), Aircraft Owners and Pilots Assn., Mensa, Rotary. Republican. Methodist. Home: 24050 Martin Dr Brooksville FL 34601-5237 Office: Brooksville Regional Hosp Quorum Health Resources 55 Ponce De Leon Blvd Brooksville FL 34605-0037

LEFTWICH, RICHARD HENRY, economist, educator; b. Burden, Kans., Feb. 1, 1920; s. Rush F. and Nellie (Bailiff) L.; m. Maxine Ellen Dieterich, Mar. 11, 1945; children: Judith E. (dec.), Gregory V., Bradley R. BA, Southwestern Coll., 1941; MA, U. Chgo., 1948, PhD, 1950. From asst. prof. to assoc. prof. econs. Okla. State U. Stillwater, 1948-55, prof. econs., 1955-75, head dept. econs., 1966-75, regent prof. econs., 1975-85, dir. Market Economy Edn. Ctr., 1980-85, Ford Found. faculty research fellow, 1959-60; vis. prof. U. Chgo., 1962-63; Disting. vis. prof. Am. U. Cairo, 1977, Tunghai U. (Taiwan), 1981, Trinity U., 1989-90, Southwestern Coll., 1990-91, Austin Peay State U., 1991-92; vis. scholar Paul Quinn Coll., 1985-86; mem. GRE advanced econs. com. Ednl. Testing Svcs., 1969-75, chmn. GRE advanced econs. com., 1972-75; Mid-Am. State Univs. Assn. hon. lectr., 1980. Author: The Price System and Resource Allocation, 1955, (with R.D. eckert) 10th edit., 1988, An Introduction to Economic Thinking, 1969, A Basic Framework for Economic, 1980, (with D.E.R. Gay) 3d edit., 1987, Productivity in Ency. Americana, 1992; co-author: (with Ansel M. Sharp) The Economics of Social Issues, 1974, 11th edit., 1994. Served with USAAF, 1942-45. Decorated Bronze Star; recipient Amoco Found. outstanding tchr. award, 1980, Merrick Found. teaching award on Am. free enterprise system, 1981, Freedoms Found. Leavy award for excellence in teaching pvt. enterprise, 1982. Mem. Am. Econs. Assn., Midwest Econ. Assn. (pres. 1977), So. Econ. Assn. (pres. 1965), Southwestern Econs. Assn. (pres. 1984-85), Southwestern Social Sci. Assn., Western Social Sci. Assn. (pres. 1973), Beta Gamma Sigma (disting. scholar 1977-78). Home and Office: 316 E Rusgan Dr Bloomington IN 47408

LÉGARÉ, HENRI FRANCIS, archbishop; b. Willow-Bunch, Sask., Can., Feb. 20, 1918; s. Phillippe and Amanda (Douville) L. B.A., U. Ottawa, 1940; theol. student, Lebret, Sask., 1940-44; M.A., Laval U., 1946; Dr. Social Sci., Cath. U. Lille, France, 1950; LL.D. (hon.), Carleton U., Ottawa, 1959, Windsor (Ont.) U., 1960, Queens U., Kingston, Ont., 1961, U. Sask., 1963, Waterloo (Ont.) Luth. U., 1965, U. Ottawa, Can., 1984; Doctor of Univ., U. of Ottawa. Ordained priest Roman Cath. Ch., 1943; prof. sociology Laval U., 1947, U. Ottawa, 1951; exec. dir. Cath. Hosp. Assn. Can., 1952-57; dean faculty social scis. U. Ottawa, 1954-58, pres., 1958-64; provincial Oblate Fathers, Winnipeg, Man., 1966-67; bishop of Labrador, 1967-72; archbishop Grouard-McLennan, Alta., 1972—. Contbr. articles to profl. jours. Chmn. Canadian Univs. Found., 1960- 62. Decorated grand cross merit Order Malta, 1964; order merit French Lang. Assn. Ont., 1965. Mem. Assn. Canadian Univs. (pres. 1960-62), Can. Conf. Cath. Bishops (pres. 1981-83), Internat. Assn. Polit. Sci. Address: Archbishop's House, CP 388, McLennan, AB Canada T0H 2L0

LEGATE, STEPHEN, ballet dancer; b. Portland, Oreg.. Student, Marylynn's Ballet Arts, Riverside, Calif.. Nat. Ballet Sch. With Nat. Ballet Can.; soloist San Francisco Ballet, 1991-92, prin. dancer, 1992—. Appeared in ballets Nanna's Lied, Rubies, The Concert, La Pavane Rouge, Seeing Stars, Handel- a Celebration, Beads of Memory, The Four Seasons, Nutcracker, La Fille mal gardee, Connotations, The End, Don Quixote, Nutcracker, La Ronde, Voluntaries, Daphnis and Chloe, Sphinx, Tagore, Swan Lake, Pastorale, Forgotten Land, Transfigured Night, Blue Snake, The Second Detail, Le Corsaire, Onegin; appeared in TV prodns. The Merry Widow, Alice. Named Best Male Dancer, Internat. Competition for Erik Bruhn Award, 1989. Office: San Francisco Ballet 455 Franklin St San Francisco CA 94102*

LEGATES, JOHN CREWS BOULTON, information scientist; b. Boston, Nov. 19, 1940; s. Eber Thomson and Sybil Rowe (Crews) LeG.; m. Nancy Elizabeth Boulton, Apr. 28, 1993. BA in Math., Harvard U. 1962. Edn. svcs. mgr. Telcomp Dept. Bolt Beranek & Newman, Cambridge, Mass., 1966-67; v.p. Washington Engring. Svcs., Cambridge, 1967-69; v.p., co-founder Cambridge Info. Systems, 1968-69; v.p., founder Computer Adv. Svc. to Edn., Wayland, Mass., 1966-72; exec. dir. Educom Interuniversity Communications Coun., Boston, 1969-72; founder, mng. dir. Program on Info. Resources Policy Harvard U., 1973—, founder, pres. Ctr. Info. Policy Rsch., 1978—; cons. in field. Contbr. articles to profl. jours. Bd. dirs. Nat. Telecommunications Conf., Washington, 1979. Kent fellow, 1964. Mem. NAS/NRC (telecommunications privacy, reliability and integrity panel), IEEE, Nat. Sci. Found., Soc. for Values in Higher Edn. Episcopalian. Club: Nashuba Valley Hunt (Pepperell, Mass.) (pres. 1974-80). Avocations: sailing, fox-hunting, mountaineering, classical music. Home: PO Box 6331 Lincoln MA 01773

LEGENDRE, LOUIS, biological oceanography educator, researcher; b. Montreal, Que., Can., Feb. 16, 1945; s. Vianney and Marguerite (Venne) L. BA, U. Montreal, 1964, BSc, 1967; PhD, Dalhousie U., Halifax, 1971. Postdoctoral fellow U. Paris VI, Villefranche-sur-Mer, 1971-73; rsch. assoc. U. Laval, Quebec City, Que., 1973, asst. prof., 1974-77; assoc. prof. U. Laval, Quebec City, 1977-81, prof., 1981—; v.p. Groupe interuniversitaire de recherches océanographi3u du Que., 1989—; group chmn. Natural Scis. and Engring. Rsch. Coun. Can., Ottawa, 1989-92. Co-author: (with P. Legendre) Numerical Ecology, 1983; contbr. articles to profl. jours. Decorated Knight of Malta; recipient Léo-Pariseau award Assn. canadienne-française pour l'avancement des sciences, 1985, Michel-Jurdant award, 1986. Fellow Royal Soc. of Can., mem. Am. Soc. Limnology and Oceanography, Environment & Policy Soc. (bd. dirs. 1990-92). Office: U Laval, Dept Biology, Sainte-Foy, PQ Canada G1K 7P4

LEGER, WALTER JOHN, JR., lawyer; b. New Orleans, Nov. 11, 1951; s. Walter John Sr. and Mildred Veronica (Brown) L.; m. Catherine Ann Buras, Aug. 4, 1973; children: Walter John III, Rhett Michael, Elizabeth Catherine. BA, La. State U., 1973; JD, Tulane U., 1976. Bar: La. 1976, U.S. Dist. Ct. (ea. dist.) La. 1976, U.S. Dist. Ct. (ea. dist.) La. 1976, U.S. Dist. Ct. (we. dist.) La. 1978, U.S. Ct. Appeals (5th and 11th cirs.) 1981, U.S. Supreme Ct. 1981, U.S. Dist. Ct. (mid. dist.) La. 1989. Assoc. Phelps, Dunbar, Marks, Claverie & Smith, New Orleans, 1976-78; ptnr. George & George, New Orleans, 1978-79; sr. ptnr. Leger & Mestayer, New Orleans, 1979—; pres. CBL Barge Co., 1979—; lectr. law Tulane U. 1983-85, U. New Orleans, Para-Legal Inst., 1987-88; adv. bd. dirs. First Nat. Bank of St. Bernard, Chalmette, La.; bd. dirs Bergeron Marine Svc., Inc., New Orleans, Ryan Marine, Inc., Pearlington, Miss. Chmn. March of Dimes, Met. New Orleans and Southeastern La., 1980-84; adv. com. bd. commrs. Port of New Orleans, 1986-88; bd. dirs. St. Bernard Community Coll. Found., Chalmette, La., 1986-92; bd. dirs. vice chmn. Nunez Community Coll., Chalmette, 1992—; adv. counsel St. Bernard Parish Home Rule Charter Commn., 1988, econ. devel. commn., 1989—, pers. bd., 1990—, chmn. Appointments Rev. Bd.; Disting. fellow Govt. Leadership Inst., U. New Orleans. Named one of People to Watch in 1982 New Orleans Mag., 1982. Mem. ABA, Fed. Bar Assn., Assn. Trial Lawyers Am., La. Trial Lawyers Assn. (pres.'s adv. council 1982-88, bd. govs. 1984—, exec. com. 1991—), Miss. Trial Lawyers Assn., Maritime Law Assn., Southeastern Admiralty Law Inst., La. State U. Fedn. (pres.-elect St. Bernard chpt. 1986-87), St. Bernard Council St. C. of C. (chmn. 1986, 92—), New Orleans/River Region C. of C. (bd. dirs. 1986—, vice-chmn. bd. dirs. 1987-88), Omicron Delta Kappa. Democrat. Roman Catholic. Avocations: jogging, sailing, tennis. Home: 20 Carolyn Ct Arabi LA 70032 Office: Leger & Mestayer 600 Carondelet St New Orleans LA 70130-3511

LEGERE, LAURENCE JOSEPH, government official; b. Fitchburg, Mass., Jan. 2, 1919; s. Laurence Joseph and Aurore Hermine (Bean) L.; m. Mary Yesley Keville, Oct. 25, 1973. B.S., U.S. Mil. Acad., 1940; M.P.A., Harvard, 1948, A.M. (Littauer fellow), 1949, Ph.D., 1951. Commd. 2d lt. U.S. Army, 1940, advanced through grades to col., 1959; asst. prof. internat. relations U.S. Mil. Acad., 1945-47; student Nat. War Coll., 1960-61; asst. to mil. rep. of Pres. U.S., Washington, 1961-62; sr. staff mem. NSC, Washington, 1962-63; ret., 1966; sr. staff mem. Center for Internat. Studies, M.I.T., Cambridge, 1966-67; dir. office nat. security studies Bendix Corp., Ann Arbor, 1967-68; dir. internat. and social studies div. Inst. Def. Analyses, Arlington, Va., 1968-74; def. advisor U.S. Mission to NATO, Brussels, 1974-89, ret., 1989; mem. policy panel on Europe UN Assn., 1967-69. Contbg. author, editor: The President and the Management of National Security, 1969; Contbr. numerous articles on foreign and def. policies to profl. jours. Decorated Silver Star, Legion of Merit, Bronze Star, Purple Heart, Disting. Civilian Service medal; recipient Presdl. Service Badge, 1956-57, 61-63, medal Outstanding Pub. Service, 1976, medal Disting. Pub. Service, 1978, 81, 87, Presdl. award for Disting. Fed. Civilian Svc., 1989. Mem. Internat. Inst. Strategic Studies. Clubs: Army-Navy (Washington). Office: 1073 Riverbend Dr Advance NC 27006

LEGERTON, CLARENCE WILLIAM, JR., gastroenterologist, educator; b. Charleston, S.C., July 8, 1922; s. Clarence William and Winnie Davis (McMaster) L.; m. Mitzi Foster Herrin, May 31, 1958; children: Clarence William, Mary Pringle, Gregg McMaster. Student, Davidson Coll., 1939-43, BS, 1942; MD, Med. Coll. S.C., 1946. Intern Univ. Hosp., Balt., 1946-47, med. resident, 1947-48; med. resident Duke U. Sch. Medicine, 1951-52, fellow in gastroenterology, 1952-53, instr. medicine, 1950-53; practice medicine specializing in gastroenterology Conway, S.C., 1953-56, Charleston, 1956-66; prof. medicine, dir. div. gastroenterology Med. U. S.C., Charleston, 1966-92; asst. to pres. Med. U. S.C., 1975-80, prof. Emeritus, 1992; vis. prof. Royal United Hosp., Bath, Eng., 1987; cons. Cambridge U. Sch. Medicine (Eng.), 1978; trustee Nat. Found. for Ileitis and Colitis, 1976—; bd. dirs. Coalition Digestive Disease Orgns., 1982—; mem. nat. digestive diseases adv. bd. NIH, Washington; chmn. com. on digestive diseases rsch. ctrs. Nat. Inst. Digestive Diseases, Diabetes, and Kidney Diseases, Washington. Med. dir. Nat. Miss U.S.A. Pageant, 1977-79; dir. Citizens and So. Nat. Bank, Charleston; chmn. Charleston Bd., 1974—; bd. dirs. Nations Bank, Charleston, 1992—; vice chmn. Charleston Commn. Public Works, 1959-76; chmn. water supply City of Charleston; pres. Charleston Symphony Orch. Assn., 1967-68; chmn. bd. dirs. Legerton & Co., Inc.; Mem. City Council Charleston, 1959-76, mayor pro-tem, 1960; pres. Charleston County Democratic Conv., 1960; trustee Montreat-Anderson Coll., vice chmn., 1962-74, chmn., 1974-78; trustee Queens Coll., 1965—; bd. visitors Davidson (N.C.) Coll., 1979—, trustee, 1982-84; bd. visitors Warren Wilson Coll., Swannanoa, N.C., 1993—; chmn. bd. Charleston Mcpl. Auditorium; chmn. adv. bd. Comprehensive Health Planning Council, Charleston, Berkeley and Dorchester Counties. Served to capt. AUS, 1948-50. Named Disting. Alumnus, Med. U. of S.C., 1986; recipient Alumni Svc. award Davidson Coll., 1988. Master ACP (gov. S.C. 1978-82); fellow Am. Coll. Gastroenterology (gov. for S.C. 1978-82), Am. Gastroenterology Assn. (chmn. com. on pub. policy and govt. rels. 1982—; governing bd. 1985); mem. S.C. Soc., New Eng. Soc. (pres. 1992—), Coun. Med. socs. (rep. 1980-84), Nat. Alumni Assn. Davidson Coll. (pres. 1983-84), Alpha Omega Alpha, Sigma Phi Epsilon, Alpha Kappa Alpha. Presbyterian (ruling elder 1956—, pres. corp. 1965—, moderator 1963). Clubs: Carolina Yacht (Charleston); Biltmore Forest Country (Asheville, N.C.); The Club at Seabrook Island. Home: 2 1/2 Atlantic St Charleston SC 29401-2746 *I believe life confers upon each individual a responsibility to his Creator, his community, his family, and his own person. This responsibility is discharged by the demonstration of religious faith through both precept and example, by involvement in various forms of community service for the betterment of society, by faithfulness to the family unit, and by a concern for the avoidance of those things which impair personal health, whether mental or physical.*

LEGG, BENSON EVERETT, federal judge; b. Balt., June 8, 1947; s. William Mercer Legg and Beverly Bladen (Mann) Mason; m. Kyle Prechtl Legg; children: Jennifer, Charles, Matthew. AB, Princeton U., 1970; JD, U. Va., 1973. Bar: Md. 1973. Law clk. to Hon. Frank A. Kaufman, Balt., 1973-74; assoc. Venable, Baetjer & Howard, Balt., 1975-81, ptnr., 1982-91; judge U.S. Dist. Ct., Dist. Md., Balt., 1991—; spl. reporter appeals com. and standing com. on rules of practice and procedure Ct. Appeals Md., 1983-85; faculty mem. nine day intensive trial advocacy program Md. Inst. Continuing Profl. Edn. for Lawyers, Inc., 1987—; program on appellate advocacy, 1988; lectr. and panelist in field. Contbr. articles to profl. jours., chpts. to books. Bd. dirs. ctrl. Md. chpt. ARC, 1979-88, past chpt. gen. counsel.; mem. secondary schs. com. Princeton U., 1986-88, adv. bd. Nat. Aquarium in Balt., 1987—. Mem. ABA (bus. torts litigation com. 1987), Md. State Bar Assn., Inc. (chmn. econs. of litigation com. 1981-82), Bar Assn. Balt. City (vice-chmn. continuing legal edn. com. 196-87, chmn. 1987-88, exec. coun. 1987-88, judiciary com. 1989-90), The Serjeant's Inn Law Club. Office: US Dist Ct 101 W Lombard St Rm 340 Baltimore MD 21201

LEGG, WILLIAM JEFFERSON, lawyer; b. Enid, Okla., Aug. 20, 1925; s. Garl Paul and Mabel (Gensman) L.; m. Eva Imogene Hill, Dec. 16, 1950; children: Melissa Lou, Eva Diane, Janet Sue. Grad., Enid Bus. Coll., 1943; student, Pittsburg State U., 1944; BBA, U. Tex., Austin, 1946; JD, U. Tulsa, 1954. Bar: Okla. 1954, U.S. Supreme Ct., U.S. Ct. Appeals (10th cir.), U.S. Dist. Ct. (we. dist.) Okla. With aviation sales Phillips Petroleum Co., 1946-48; atty. Marathon Oil Co., 1954-61; pvt. practice Oklahoma City, 1962—; ptnr. Andrews Davis Legg Bixler Milsten & Price, Inc. and predecessor firms, Oklahoma City, 1962—, pres., 83-86, also dir., 1973-77, 80-81, 83-86, 90, sec., 1975-80, 82-83, 90, now sr. counsel and adv. dir., 1991—; adj. profl. law Oklahoma City U., 1975-80; lectr. Okla. U. Law Sch., 1986; dir., v.p. internat. oil cos., Turkey, Australia, Brunei; dir., gen. counsel N.J. Nat. Resources Co., 1986-91; dir. Skillpath Inc., Kansas City, Mo., 1995—; lectr. energy seminars. Contbr. articles to profl. jours. Ordained Reorganized Ch. of Jesus Christ of Latter Day Saints, 1964, dist. pres., 1975-80, br. pres., 1986-91, evangelist, 1993—; mem. com. Okla. Gov.'s Energy Adv. Council, 1973, Okla. Blue Ribbon Com. on natural gas well allowables, 1983; trustee Am. Inst. Discussion, 1962-88, chmn., 1969-72, now mem. exec. com.; counsel; trustee Jenkins Found. Research, sec., 1975-81; trustee Restoration Trails Found., 1975; trustee Graceland Coll., Lamoni, Iowa, 1986—, mem. exec. com., chmn. bus. affairs com., 1988—; trustee Met. Library Endowment Trust, 1986—, treas. 1988—; chmn. investment com.; rsch. fellow Southwestern Legal Found., Dallas, 1989—. With USN, 1943-46, lt. (j.g.) USNR, 1946-66. Mem. ABA, Internat. Bar Assn., Okla. Bar Assn. (past com. chmn.), Oklahoma County Bar Assn. (past com. chmn.), Internat. Assn. Energy Econs., Econ. Club Okla., Men's Dinner Club, Petroleum Club. Home: 3017 Brush Creek Rd Oklahoma City OK 73120-1855 Office: Andrews Davis Legg Bixler Milsten & Price Inc 500 W Main St Oklahoma City OK 73102-2220

LEGGE, CHARLES ALEXANDER, federal judge; b. San Francisco, Aug. 24, 1930; s. Roy Alexander and Wilda (Rampton) L.; m. Janice Meredith Sleeper, June 27, 1952; children: Jeffrey, Nancy, Laura. AB with distinction, Stanford U., 1952, JD, 1954. Bar: Calif. 1955. Assoc. Bronson, Bronson & McKinnin, San Francisco, 1956-64, ptnr., 1964-84, chmn., 1978-84; judge U.S. Dist. Ct. (no. dist.) Calif., San Francisco, 1984—. Served with U.S. Army, 1954-56. Fellow Am. Coll. Trial Lawyers; mem. Calif. Bar Assn. (past chmn. adminstrv. justice com.). Republican. Clubs: Bohemian, World Trade (San Francisco) Orinda (Calif.) Country. Office: US Dist Ct PO Box 36060 16700 Valley View Ave Ste 300 La Mirada CA 90638-5841

LEGGE KEMP, DIANE, architect, landscape architect; b. Englewood, N.J., Dec. 4, 1949; d. Richard Claude and Patricia (Roney) L.; m. Kevin A. Kemp; children: Alloy Hudson, McClelland Beebe, Logan Roney. BA, Stanford U., 1972; M in Architecture, Princeton U., 1975. Architect Northrop, Kaelber & Kopf, Rochester, N.Y., 1971, Michael Graves, Architect, Princeton, 1972-75, The Ehrenkrantz Group, N.Y.C., 1975-77; ptnr. Skidmore Owings & Merrill, Chgo., 1977-89; prin. Diane Legge Kemp Architecture and Landscape Consulting, Riverside, Ill., 1989-93, pres., 1993—; pres. DLK Architecture, 1993—; chair Princeton U. adv. bd. Sch. Architecture, 1991—; dir. Newhouse Archtl. Found., Chgo., 1991—. Designer, architect: Boston Globe Satellite Printing Plant, 1984, Mfrs. Hanover Plaza, Wilmington, 1987, Herman Miller Showroom, Chgo., 1988, Arlington Internat. Racecourse, 1989, Phila. Newspapers Expansion and Retrofit, 1989, Navy Pier Reconstrn., 1990, McCormick Place Retrofit and Expansion, 1991, L.A. Times Master Plan, 1992, CRSS capital project mgmt. Chgo. Park Dist., 1993, Chgo. Hist. Blvds. Restoration, 1993, St. Ignatius Prep. Master Plan, 1993, Roosevelt Rd. Reconstruction, Chgo., 1993, Field, Shedd, Adler Mus. Campus, Goodman Theater, Chgo., 1995, Job Corps Tng. Campus, 1995, Chgo. Area Circulator Urban Design, 1995.

Mem. bd. govs. Sch. of Art Inst., Chgo., 1991—; dir., past pres. Soc. for Contemporary Art, Chgo., 1991—. Recipient 40 under 40 award N.Y. Archtl. League, 1986. Fellow AIA; mem. Nat. Coun. Archtl. Registration Bds., Am. Soc. Landscape Architects, Urban Land Inst. Avocations: piano, flute, skiing, sailing, gardens. Office: DLK Architecture 410 S Michigan Ave Chicago IL 60605-1302

LEGGETT, DONALD YATES, academic administrator; b. Windsor, N.C., Oct. 31, 1935; s. Turner Carter Leggett and Ruby (Harden) Lanier; m. Nancy Lou Porter, Aug. 17, 1980; 1 stepson, Clayton Porter Johnston. BS in Phys. Edn., Social Studies, East Carolina U., 1958, MA in Edn., 1962; postgrad., N.C. State U., 1966-67. Tchr., coach Benhaven (N.C.) High Sch., 1958-59, Buies Creek (N.C.) High Sch., 1959-64; coach, tchr., Needham B. Broughton High Sch., Raleigh, 1964-66; asst. prin. Needham B. Broughton High Sch., Raleigh, 1966-70; dir. alumni affairs East Carolina U., Greenville, N.C., 1970-73; dir. alumni affairs and founds. East Carolina U., Greenville, 1973-79, dir. alumni rels., 1979-85, asst. to vice chancellor for instl. advancement, 1985-92, assoc. vice chancellor for alumni rels., 1992—; acting dir. Regional Devel. Inst., 1993; driver tng. coord. Raleigh City Sch. System, 1964-66; mem. numerous coms. at East Carolina U., 1970—. Editor East Carolina U. Alumni pubs. 1979-85; contbr. articles to alumni pubs. Past mem. bd. dirs. Pitt County Boys Club, Pitt-Greenville Arts Coun. (past mem. steering com.); former bd. dirs. Ea. N.C. Village of Yesteryear; former vice chmn. Pitt-Greenville Conv. and Visitors Authority, bd. dirs., 1995—. Named Boss of Yr. Greenville Jaycees, 1976. Mem. Coun. for Advancement and Support of Edn., East Carolina U. Pirate Club, Pitt-Greenville C. of C., Kiwanis Club (past bd. dirs. Univ. City), Greenville Golf and Country Club, Phi Kappa Phi, Phi Delta Kappa. Baptist. Avocations: wood working, gardening. Home: 110 Kimberley Dr Greenville NC 27858-6721

LEGGETT, GLENN, former English language educator, academic administrator; b. Ashtabula, Ohio, Mar. 29, 1918; s. Glenn H. and Celinda (Sheldon) L.; m. Doris Ruth James, June 14, 1941 (dec.); children: Leslie Ann (Mrs. David K. Leonard), Susan Cady (Mrs. Michael Baxter Jones), Celinda Sheldon, Joanna Ruth (Mrs. Alan Sinnwell); m. Russelle Seeberger Jones, Mar. 11, 1973; children: Brian Edward Jones, Sarah Lorene Jones (Mrs. Timothy Krumm). A.B. Middlebury (Vt.) Coll., 1940, LL.D., 1971; M.A., Ohio State U., 1941, Ph.D., 1949; L.H.D., Rockford Coll., 1967, Ripon Coll., 1968, Coll. Idaho, 1974, Grinnell Coll., 1975; LL.D., Morningside Coll., 1975; Litt.D., Lawrence U., 1968. Instr. in English Mass. Inst. Tech., 1942-44; instr., then asst. prof. English Ohio State U., 1946-52; asso. prof. English U. Wash., 1952-58, asst. to pres., 1958-61, vice provost, 1961-63, provost, 1963-65; prof. English, pres. Grinnell Coll., 1965-75, pres. emeritus, 1979—; v.p. corporate communications Deere & Co., 1975-79; Mem. commn. English Coll. Entrance Exam. Bd., 1957-65, trustee, 1965-76, vice chmn., 1970-72, chmn., 1972-74; pres. Mayflower Retirement Homes, Inc., 1986-88. Author: (with Mead and Kramer) Handbook for Writers, 12th edit., 1995, A Conservative View, The New Professors, 1960; editor: Twelve Poets, 1959, (with Daniel and Beardsley) Theme and Form: An Introduction to Literature, 4th edit., 1975, (with Daniel) The Written Word, 1960, (with Steiner) Twelve Poets, alt. edit., 1967, Years of Turmoil: Years of Change, 1978, Teacher to Teacher: Selected Papers on Teaching, Writing, and Higher Education, 1979. Chmn. Ill.-Iowa Assn. Children with Learning Disabilities, 1976-79; bd. dirs. Quad-Cities Grad. Study Center, 1975-79, chmn., 1977-79; chmn. Conf. Coll. Composition, 1959, Iowa Coll. Found., pres., 1974-75; trustee Marycrest Coll., 1975-80; curator Stephens Coll., 1976-83; mem. exec. com. Iowa Natural Heritage Found., 1979-93; mem. Iowa Natural Resources Commn., 1982-83; bd. dirs. Stewart Library, pres., 1987-88. Served with USNR, 1944-46. Danforth grantee, 1971; recipient Edward S. Noyes award Coll. Bd., 1979. Mem. MLA, Nat. Council Tchrs. English (chmn. coll. sect. 1963-65, chmn. survey undergrad. curriculum in English 1964-67, task force career edn. 1978-79), Iowa Assn. Pvt. Colls. (pres. 1969-71), Assoc. Colls. Midwest (chmn. 1971-73), Chi Psi. Conglist. Home: 6 College Park Rd Grinnell IA 50112-1207

LEGGETT, JAMES DANIEL, church administrator; b. Williamston, N.C., Oct. 21, 1939; s. James S. and Hazel Louise (Wynn) L.; m. Clara Faye Watts, June 25, 1961; children: James Jr., Joseph Talmadge, Cynthia Faye, John David. BA, Pembroke State U.; ThB, Holmes Coll. of the Bible, hon. doctorate, 1988. Ordained to ministry Pentecostal Holiness Ch., 1960. Pastor Swan Quarter Pentecostal Holiness Ch., 1962-64, Pinetown Pentecostal Holiness Ch., 1962-64, Mt. Olive Pentecostal Holiness Ch., Pembroke, 1964-70, Culbreth Meml. Pentecostal Holiness Ch., Falcon, 1970-86; assn. gen. supt. Internat. Pentecostal Holiness Ch., Bethany, Okla., 1989-93, vice chmn., 1993—; exec. dir. Evangelism USA; pres. Extension Loan Fund; supr. N.C. Conf., 1986-89; mem. Evangelical Curriculum Commn., writer Sunday Sch. lit.; instr. extension classes Holmes Coll. of the Bible, Emmanuel Coll. Sec. bd. trustees Holmes Coll. of the Bible, past bd. dirs. Office: Pentecostal Holiness Ch 7300 NW 39th Expy Bethany OK 73008-2340

LEGGETT, JOHN CARL, sociology educator; b. Detroit, Sept. 18, 1930; s. Norval John and Eileen Elizabeth (McVeigh) L.; m. Iris Leja Leggett (div. Feb. 1989); children: Britt Erika, Shannon Kelley. BA, U. Mich., 1954, MA in Polit. Sci., 1956, MA in Sociology, 1958, PhD in Sociology, 1962. Various positions U. Mich., Ann Arbor, 1954-62, lectr. dept. sociology, rsch. assoc. Sch. Social Work, 1961-62; instr. sociology U. Calif., Berkeley, 1962-63, asst. prof., 1963-64, rsch. assoc., 1964-65; asst. prof. Simon Fraser U., Berkeley, 1966-67; assoc. prof. Simon Fraser U., 1967-70; lectr. sociology U. Calif., Davis, 1968, lectr. black studies, 1971; assoc. prof. sociology Rutgers U., New Brunswick, N.J., 1971—; vis. assoc. prof. Sacramento State Coll., 1967-68; prof. U. Conn., 1968-69; vis. lectr. U. B.C. (Can.), Vancouver, 1970; cons. to labor union, including United Farm Union, AFL-CIO. Author: Class, Race and Labor: Working Class Consciousness in Detroit, 1968, paperback edit., 1971, Race, Class and Political Consciousness, 1973, Taking State Power, 1973, (with others) Allende, His Exit and Our Times, 1978, Whither Black Studies, 1971, The American Working Class, 1979, Mining the Field, A Photo History of American Farm Worker Struggles, 1991, Newspaper Analysis: The Natural History of a Counter-Revolutionary News Story, 1993, The 18 Stages of Romantic Love, 1995; co-author (with Suzanne Malm) The Eighteen Stages of Love, 1995; contbr. numerous articles and book revs. prof. publ. Active Free Speech Movement, Berkeley, 1964, Farm Labor Support Com., Berkeley and Delano, Calif., 1965, Vietnam Day Com., Berkeley, 1965-66, Rainbow Coalition Cen. N.J., 1984—; officer, organizer Socialist Youth League, 1951-54; mem. Socialist Party, 1958-64, New Democratic Party, 1967-70, United Farm Workers; candidate for local polit. offices; union ofcl.; chmn. Raritan Inst. With USN, 1949-50. Recipient Disting. Faculty Person award Livingston Coll. Assn. Grads., 1987, Alfred McClyng Lee award Sociological Abstracts Inc., 1994; Ford Found. fellow, 1954-55; Social Sci. Rsch. Coun. grantee, 1960-61, 64, Can. Coun. grantee, 1968-70, Trans-Action Mag. grantee, 1984-85. Mem. AAUP (officer, grievance counselor Rutgers U.), Am. Sociol. Soc., So. Sociol. Soc., Midwestern Sociol. Soc., North Cen. Sociol. Soc., Assn. for Humanist Sociology, Soc. for Study Social Problems, Students for Dem. Soc. (charter Ann Arbor chpt. 1960). Avocations: white water canoeing, mountain climbing, softball. Home: 320 Lawrence Ave Highland Park NJ 08904-1840 Office: Rutgers U Dept Sociology New Brunswick NJ 08904

LEGGETT, ROBERTA JEAN (BOBBI LEGGETT), association executive; b. Kankakee, Ill., Nov. 30, 1926; d. Clyde H. and Sybil D. (Billings) Karns; m. George T. Leggett, Aug. 25, 1956. Sec. Cardov div. Chemetron Corp., Chgo., 1951-60; sec., asst. mgr. Ravisloe Country Club, Homewood, Ill., 1961-65; sec. Nationwide Paper Co., Chgo., 1966-68; exec. dir. Am. Bd. Oral and Maxillofacial Surgery, Chgo., 1969-87. Mem. Chgo. Soc. Assn. Execs., Conf. Med. Soc. Execs. of Greater Chgo., Profl. Secs. Internat. Methodist.

LEGGETT, WILLIAM C., biology educator, educational administrator; b. Orangeville, Ont., Can., June 25, 1939; s. Frank William and Edna Irene (Wheeler) L.; m. Claire Holman, May 9, 1964; children: David, John. AB, Waterloo U. Coll., 1962; MSc, U. Waterloo, 1965; PhD, McGill U., 1969; DSc, U. Waterloo, 1992; LLD, Wilfred Laurier U., 1994. Research scientist Essex (Conn.) Marine Lab., 1965-70, rsch. assoc., 1970-73; asst. prof. McGill U., Montreal, Que., Can., 1970-72, assoc. prof., 1972-79, prof., 1979—, chmn. dept. biology, 1981-85, dean of sci., 1986-91, acad. v.p., 1991-94; prin. Queen's U., Kingston, Ont., Can., 1994—; chmn. bd. Huntsman Marine Lab., 1980-89; pres. Groupe Interuniversitaire de Recherche Oceanographique du

Que., 1986-91; chmn. grant selection com. for population biology Natural Scis. and Engring. Research Council Can., 1980-81, chmn. grant selection com. for oceans, 1986-87. Mem. editorial bd.: Can. Jour. Fisheries and Aquatic Sciences, 1980-85, Le Naturaliste Canadien, 1980-91, Can. Jour. Zoology, 1982-86; contbr. in field. Recipient Dwight D. Webster award Am. Fisheries Soc., 1989, Award for Excellence for Fisheries Edn., 1990, Fry medal Can. Soc. Zoologists, 1990, Outstanding Biologist award Can. Coun. Biol. Chmn., 1993; grantee in field. Fellow Rawson Acad., Royal Soc. Can.; mem. Am. Fisheries Soc. (pres. North-East div. 1977-78), Can. Com. for Fishery Research, Can. Soc. Zoologists; Am. Soc. Limnology and Oceanography, Am. Soc. Naturalists. Office: Queens University, Kingston, ON Canada K7L 3N6

LEGLER, DONALD WAYNE, university dean, dentist; b. Mpls., Oct. 2, 1931; s. Ernest W. and Almira (Elness) L.; m. Janice Carol Cleworth, June 21, 1938; children: Lori, Lee, Catherine, Christian. BS, U. Minn., 1954, DDS, 1956; PhD, U. Ala., 1966. Lic. dentist Ala., Colo., Minn. Chmn. dept. oral biology U. Ala., Birmingham, 1968-71, 76-80, assoc. prof. dentistry, 1968-74, assoc. prof. microbiology Med. Ctr., 1969-80, asst. dean Sch. Dentistry, 1971-74, assoc. dean for adminstrv. affairs Sch. Dentistry, 1974-75, prof. dentistry, 1974-77, asst. dean for adminstrn., 1977-80; prof. dentistry, assoc. dean for rsch. and advanced edn. Sch. Dentistry U. Minn., Mpls., 1980-83, dir. Ctr. for Aging, 1981-83; prof. dentistry, dean Coll. Dentistry U. Fla., Gainesville, 1983—; curriculum cons. So. Assn. Colls. and Schs., Atlanta, 1973-75. Swedish Med. Rsch. Coun. fellow, 1966-67. Mem. ADA (curriculum cons. coun. on dental edn. 1974-88, commn. on nat. dental exams. 1993—), Fla. Dental Assn. (Dentist of Yr. award 1988), Internat. Assn. Dental Rsch., Am. Assn. Dental Schs. (chmn. coun. deans 1989-90). Office: U Fla Coll Dentistry PO Box 100405 Gainesville FL 32610-0405

LEGLER, MITCHELL WOOTEN, lawyer; b. Alexandria, Va., June 3, 1942; s. John Clarke and Doris (Wooten) L.; m. Harriette Dodson; children: John Clarke, Dorothy Trumbull, Harriette Holland. BA in Polit. Sci. with honors, U. N.C., 1964; JD, U. Va., 1967. Bar: Va. 1967, Fla. 1967. Pres. Commander, Legler, Werber, Dawes, Sadler & Howell, Jacksonville, Fla., 1976-91; mng. ptnr. Foley & Lardner, Jacksonville, 1991—; chmn. Fla. Bar Consumer Protection Law Com. Editorial bd. Va. Law Rev., 1966-67. Mem. Va. Bar Assn., Fla. Bar Assn. (lectr. continuing legal edn.); Order of Coif, Phi Beta Kappa, Phi Eta Sigma, Delta Upsilon, Delta Theta Phi. Office: Foley & Lardner 200 N Laura St Jacksonville FL 32202-3527

LEGO, PAUL EDWARD, retired corporation executive; b. Centre County, Pa., May 16, 1930; s. Paul Irwin and Sarah Elizabeth (Montgomery) L.; m. Ann Sepety, July 7, 1956; children: Paul Gregory, Debra Ann, Douglas Edward, Michael John. BS in Elec. Engring. U. Pitts., 1956, M.S., 1958. With Westinghouse Electric Corp., 1956—; gen. mgr. Westinghouse semiconductor div. Westinghouse Electric Corp., Pitts., 1970-74; gen. mgr. electronic tube div. Westinghouse Electric Corp., Elmira, N.Y., 1974-75; bus. unit gen. mgr. electronic components divs. Westinghouse Electric Corp., Pitts., 1975-77; v.p., gen. mgr. lamp divs. Westinghouse Electric Corp., Bloomfield, N.J., 1977-80; exec. v.p. electronics and control group Westinghouse Electric Corp., Pitts., 1980-83, exec. v.p. control equipment, 1983-85, sr. exec. v.p. corp. resources, 1985-87, pres., COO, 1988-90, chmn., CEO, 1990-93, also bd. dirs.; ret., 1993; pres. Intelligent Enterprises, Pitts., 1993—; chmn. bd. Commonwealth Aluminum Corp., Louisville, 1995—; bd. dirs. PNC Bank Realty Holding Co., USX Corp., Consol. Natural Gas Co., Lincoln Electric Co. Trustee U. Pitts.; chmn. bd. visitors U. Pitts. Sch. Engring.; bd. overseers N.J. Inst. Tech., Newark, 1979—. With AUS, 1948-52. Recipient Westinghouse Order of Merit 1975, Disting. Alumni award U. Pitts. Sch. Engring., 1986, Bicentennial Medallion of Distinction award U. Pitts., 1987. Mem. Am. Soc. Corp. Execs., Valley Brook Country Club, Duquesne Club, The Club Pelican Bay (Naples, Fla.), Laurel Valley Golf Club, Rolling Rock Club (Ligonier, Pa.). Republican. Roman Catholic. Office: Exec Assocs One PPG Place Ste 2210 Pittsburgh PA 15222-1318 *I believe that every individual in an organization should take ownership of his or her job and have the authority and responsibility to make continuous improvements in the processes by which the objectives of that job are accomplished. This approach will produce the lowest possible cost for that job and, collectively, for the company, with the highest level of quality and customer service.*

LEGOFFIC, FRANCOIS, biotechnology educator; b. Pluzunet, France, Nov. 10, 1936; s. Laurent and Marie LeGoffic; m. Marie-Thérèse Castel, Nov. 28, 1957; 1 child, Marc. Dr 3e Cycle, U. Paris, 1962, Dr Sci., 1963. Various positions Nat. Ctr. Sci. Rsch., France, 1962-74; prof. Ecole Nationale Supérieure de Chimie de Paris, 1975—; bd. dirs. UA 1389 du Centre Nat. de la Recherche Scientifique; vis. prof. Rolla U., 1975. Contbr. over 350 articles to Organic Chemistry, Biochemistry, Biotechnology and Microbiology; holder 20 patents. Recipient award Chem. Soc. France, 1968, Acad. Pharmacy, 1971, Acad. Scis., 1993; named Officier palmes academiques, 1994. Achievements include rsch. on total synthesis of natural compounds of therapeutic value, mechanism of resistance of bacteria to antibiotics, mechanism of action of antibiotics, enzyme inhibitors as drugs in antibacterial, antifungal and anticancer area, biotechnology, such as new membranes, immobilized enzymes and cells, enzymes in organic synthesis, valorization of molecules from marine origin and the use of antibodies in environmental analytical chemistry and biosensors design as well as the devel. of new bioprocesses. Home: 42 rue Jean Georget, 92140 Clamart France Office: ENSCP, 11 rue Pierre Marie Curie, 75231 Paris France

LE GRAND, CLAY, former state justice; b. St. Louis, Feb. 26, 1911; s. Nicholas and Mary Margaret (Leifield) Le G.; m. Suzanne Wilcox, Dec. 30, 1935, (wid.); children: Mary Suzanne Le Grand Murray, Julie A. Le Grand Ekstrand, Nicholas W.; m. Margaret Morris Burrows, Dec. 11, 1993. Student, St. Ambrose Coll., Davenport, Iowa, 1928-31; LL.B. Catholic U. Am., 1934. Bar: Iowa 1934. Practice law Davenport, 1934-57; judge Dist. Ct., 1957-67; justice Supreme Ct. Iowa, Davenport, 1967-83; of counsel Stanley, Rehling, Lande & Van Der Kamp, Davenport, 1983-92, Noyes, O'Brien, Gosma and Brooke, Davenport, 1992-95; Noyes & Gosma, Davenport, 1995—; lectr. St. Ambrose Coll. 1957-67. Recipient award for outstanding achievement in field of law and the cts. Cath. U. Am., 1969; award of merit for profl. achievement St. Ambrose Coll., 1976. Mem. Am., Iowa, Scott County bar assns., Am. Judicature Soc., Inst. Jud. Adminstrn. Home: 4130 Northwest Blvd Apt 32 Davenport IA 52806-4234 Office: Noyes & Gosma Ste 106 400 Main St Davenport IA 52801

LEGRAND, MICHEL JEAN, composer; b. Paris, Feb. 24, 1932; came to U.S., 1955; s. Raymond and Marcelle Legrand; children: Hervé, Benjamin, Eugénie. Diploma, Conservatoire Nationale Superieur de Musique, Paris, 1951. Composer, conductor, 1965—. Composer (score, song adaptation) I Will Wait for You, 1965 (3 Acad. award nominations), Windmills of Your Mind, 1968 (Acad. award 1968), film scores include Summer of 42, 1970 (Acad. award 1970), Brian's Song, 1971, Lady Sings the Blues, 1972, The Three Muscateers, 1973, Ode to Billy Joe, 1975, The Other Side of Midnight, 1977, Atlantic City, 1980, The Mountain Men, 1980, Melvin and Howard, 1980, Never Say Never Again, 1983, Yentl, 1984 (Acad. award 1984), The Pickle, 1993, Ready to Wear, 1994, also over 100 albums; arranger (album) I Love Paris, 1954; contbr. jazz pianist with numerous orchs. including Pitts. Symphony, Minn. Orch., Buffalo Philharm.; collaborated with various artists including Barbara Streisand, Sarah Vaughan, Jack Jones, Lena Horne, Dame Kiri Te Kanawa, Ray Charles, Miles Davis; dir. (film) 5 Days in June, 1989. Mem. Dramatists Guild, Songwriters Guild of Am., Am. Fedn. Musicians, AFTRA, ASCAP, Acad. Motion Picture Arts and Scis. (Oscar award 1967, 70, 83). Avocations: boating, airplane pilot, tennis, horseback riding. Office: c/o Jim DiGiovanni 157 W 57th St PH-B New York NY 10019*

LEGRANDE, WILLIAM HUNT, biology educator; b. Shreveport, La.; s. Clay Charles and Annie Elizabeth (Beard) LeG. BS, La. State U., 1971, MS, 1974; PhD, Ohio State U., 1978. Prof. biology U. Wis., Stevens Point, 1977—, dir. Mus. Natural History, 1984—. Mem. Am. Soc. Ichthyologists and Herpetologists, Am. Fisheries Soc., Ichthyological Soc. Japan, Assn. Southeastern Biologists, Soc. Study Evolution, Soc. Systematic Zoology, Sigma Xi. Democrat. Baptist. Office: U Wis Mus Natural History Dept Biology Stevens Point WI 54481

LEGRICE, STEPHEN, magazine editor. Exec. editor Star Mag., Tarrytown, N.Y. Office: Star Mag 660 White Plains Rd Tarrytown NY 10591*

LEGTERS, LYMAN HOWARD, historian; b. Jamestown, N.Y., Feb. 15, 1928; s. Lyman H. and Nettie (Saunders) L.; m. Marie Bird; children: Lyman, Matthew, Nettie, Douglas. AB, U. Mich., 1949; MA, Boston U., 1956; PhD, Free U. Berlin, 1958. Assoc. dir. U. Pitts., 1958-59; assoc. prof. Am. U., Washington, 1959-62; specialist, chief U.S. Office Edn., Washington, 1962-65; prof. George Washington U., Washington, 1965-66; prof. emeritus history of Russia and Ea. Europe U. Wash., Seattle, 1966—; project dir. States and Socs. in E.-Cen. Europe, 1988—; vis. prof. Columbia U., N.Y.C., 1973, U. Warsaw, Poland, 1982; bd. dirs. Hist. Abstracts, Santa Barbara, Calif., 1970-78. Author: Eastern Europe: Transformation and Revolution, 1945-91, 1992; co-author, editor: German Democratic Republic, 1978, Marxism and Good Society, 1981, Western Society After the Holocaust, 1983, Native Americans and Public Policy, 1992, American Indian Policy, 1994, Critical Perspectives on Democracy, 1994. Served as sgt. U.S. Army, 1951-53. Sr. fellow William O. Douglas Inst., 1977—, Kennan Inst., 1978; recipient Arts and Humanities award U. Wash. Grad. Sch., 1986. Democrat. Avocations: gardening, woodcraft. Office: William O Douglas Inst 5410 Maple Glen Rd Langley WA 98260-8253

LE GUIN, URSULA KROEBER, author; b. Berkeley, Calif., Oct. 21, 1929; d. Alfred Louis and Theodora (Kracaw) Kroeber; m. Charles A. Le Guin, Dec. 22, 1953; children: Elisabeth, Caroline, Theodore. B.A., Radcliffe Coll., 1951; M.A., Columbia, 1952. Vis. lectr. or writer in residence numerous workshops and univs., U.S. and abroad. Author: Rocannon's World, 1966, Planet of Exile, 1966, City of Illusion, 1967, The World For World is Forest, 1967, A Wizard of Earthsea, 1968, The Left Hand of Darkness, 1969, The Tombs of Atuan, 1971, The Lathe of Heaven, 1971, The Farthest Shore, 1972, The Dispossessed, 1974, The Wind's Twelve Quarters, 1975, A Very Long Way from Anywhere Else, 1976, Orsinian Tales, 1976, The Language of the Night, 1979, Leese Webster, 1979, Malafrena, 1979, The Beginning Place, 1980, Hard Words, 1981, The Eye of the Heron, 1982, The Compass Rose, 1982, King Dog, 1985, Always Coming Home, 1985, Buffalo Gals, 1987, Wild Oats and Fireweed, 1988, A Visit from Dr. Katz, 1988, Catwings, 1988, Solomon Leviathan, 1988, Fire and Stone, 1989, Catwings Return, 1989, Dancing at the Edge of the World, 1989, Tehanu, 1990, Searoad, 1991, Blue Moon Over Thurman Street, 1993, Wonderful Alexander and the Catwings, 1994, Going Out With Peacocks, 1994, A Fisherman of the Inland Sea, 1994; also numerous short stories, poems, criticism, screenplays. Recipient Howard D. Vursell award Am. Acad. Arts and Letters, 1991, Pushcart prize, 1991, Boston Globe-Hornbook award for excellence in juvenile fiction, 1968, Nebula award (novel) 1969, (novel and story) 1975, (story) 1975, (novel) 1990, Hugo award (novel) 1969, (story) 1973, (novella) 1973, (novelette) 1988, Gandalf award, 1979, Kafka award, 1986, Newbery honor medal, 1972, Nat. Book award, 1972, H.L. Davis award Oreg. Inst. Literary Arts, 1992, Hubbub annual poetry award, 1995, Asimov's Reader's award, 1995. Mem. Sci. Fiction Research Assn., Sci. Fiction Writers Assn., Authors League, PEN, Writers Guild West, NOW, NARAL, Phi Beta Kappa. Office: c/o Virginia Kidd PO Box 278 Milford PA 18337-0278 also: c/o Matthew Bialer William Morris Agy 1350 Ave of the Americas New York NY 10019

LEGUM, JEFFREY ALFRED, automobile company executive; b. Balt., Dec. 16, 1941; s. Leslie and Naomi (Hendler) L.; m. Harriet Cohn, Nov. 10, 1968; children: Laurie Hope, Michael Neil. BS in Econs. Wharton Sch., U. Pa., 1963; grad. Chevrolet Sch. Merchandising and Mgmt., 1966. With Park Circle Motor Co., Balt., 1963—, exec. v.p., 1966-77, pres. Legum Chevrolet-Nissan, 1977-89, also dir.; ptnr. Pkwy. Indsl. Ctr., Dorsey, Md., 1969-91; ltd. ptnr. Circle Ltd. Partnership, Glen Burnie, Md., 1991; v.p., dir. P.C. Parts Co., 1967—; v.p. Westminster Motor Co. (Md.), 1967-72, pres., dir., 1972—; pres. One Forty Corp., Westminster, 1972—; dir., exec. com. United Consol. Industries, 1970-73; dist. chmn. Chevrolet Dealers Council, 1975-77, chmn. Washington zone, 1982-83. Chmn. transp. div. Associated Jewish Charities, Balt., 1966-69; mem. Md. Nat. Svc. Acad. Review Bd., 1975-77, Bus. Adv. Bd. to Atty. Gen., 1985-87; trustee The Legum Found., Balt., 1967—; trustee Balt. Mus. Art, 1992—, mem. fine arts accessions com., 1992—, mem. investment com., 1992—, mem. exec. com., 1993, contr., 1994—; trustee The Park Sch. Balt., 1979-94, chmn. investment com., 1980—, mem. exec. com., chmn. fin. com., treas., 1981-91; pres.'s com. U. Toronto, 1983—; bd. dirs. Assoc. Placement Bur. (Jewish Vocat. Svc.), Balt., 1964-76, v.p., 1972-76; adv. bd. The Competitive Edge, Albuquerque, 1977-81; mem. investment com. Balt. Hebrew Congregation, 1980—, bd. electors, 1990-93; bd. dirs. Preakness Celebration, Inc., 1988-89, Associated Jewish Community Fedn. Balt., 1992—; mem. adv. coun., exec. com. Wilmer Eye Inst., The Johns Hopkins Hosp., 1991; mem. instl. rev. bd. for human subjects rsch. Johns Hopkins Bayview Med. Ctr., 1992—. Recipient award of honor Assoc. Jewish Charities of Balt., 1967, 68; Cadillac Master Dealer award, 1980-88, 91; Cadillac Pinnacle of Excellence award, 1986; Young Pres.'s Orgn. Cert. Appreciation, 1984; Nissan Nat. Merit Master award, 1982-88; Chevrolet Nat. Svc. Supremacy award, annually 1979-89, Sales Giant award Automotive News, 1987, Minute of Gratitude The Park Sch. Bd. Trustees, 1994. Mem. Md. New Car and Truck Assn., Young Pres. Orgn. (pres.'s forum 1977-92), World Pres.' Orgn., Benjamin Franklin Assocs., Johns Hopkins Assocs., Carroll County C. of C., Md. Hist. Soc. (exec. com. Library of Md. History 1981-90), Chesapeake Pres.' Orgn., Suburban Club (Baltimore County), U. of Pa., Center Club, U. Toronto Faculty Club (hon.). Home: 10 Stone Hollow Ct Baltimore MD 21208-1860 Office: 1829 Reisterstown Rd Baltimore MD 21208-6301

LEHAN, RICHARD D'AUBIN, English language educator, writer; b. Brockton, Mass., Dec. 23, 1930; s. Ralph A. and Mildred L.; m. Ann Evans, June 11, 1960; 1 son, Edward Scott. B.A., Stonehill Coll., 1952; M.A., Boston Coll., 1953; Ph.D., U. Wis., 1958. Mem. faculty U. Wis.-Madison, 1953-57, U. Tex.-Austin, 1958-62; mem. faculty dept. English UCLA, 1962—, prof. English, 1969—, chmn. dept. English 1971-73; Fulbright exchange prof. Moscow State U., USSR, 1974-75. Author: F. Scott Fitzgerald, 1966, Theodore Dreiser, 1969, Literary Existentialism, 1973, The Great Gatsby: The Limits of Wonder, 1990. Recipient Disting. Teaching award U. Tex., 1961, UCLA, 1970; Fulbright award, 1975; Guggenheim fellow, 1978-79, Pres.'s Rsch. fellow U. Calif., 1988-89. Home: 333 S Oakhurst Dr Beverly Hills CA 90212-3505 Office: UCLA Dept English Los Angeles CA 90024-1530

LEHISTE, ILSE, language educator; b. Tallinn, Estonia, Jan. 31, 1922; came to U.S., 1949, naturalized, 1956; d. Aleksander and Julie M. (Sikka) L. Dr.Phil., U. Hamburg (Ger.) 1948; Ph.D., U. Mich., 1959; D.Univ. (hon.), U. Essex (Eng.), 1977; Dr. Phil. (hon.), U. Lund (Sweden), 1982, U. Tartu, Estonia, 1989. Lectr. U. Hamburg, 1948-49; assoc. prof. modern langs. Kans. Wesleyan U., 1950-51, Detroit Inst. Tech., 1951-56; rsch. assoc. U. Mich., 1957-63; faculty Ohio State U., Columbus, 1963-87, prof. linguistics, 1965-87, prof. emeritus, 1987—, chmn. dept., 1965-71, 85-87; dir. Linguistic Inst. Ohio State U., 1970; vis. prof. U. Cologne, Germany, 1965, UCLA, 1966, U. Vienna, 1974, U. Tokyo, 1980. Author 11 books; latest being Lectures on Language Contact, 1988; contbr. articles to profl. jours., book revs. Guggenheim fellow, 1969, 75; grantee Am. Council Learned Socs., 1971; fellow Center for Advanced Study in Behavioral Scis., 1975-76. Fellow AAAS, Am. Acad. Arts and Scis., Acoustical Soc. Am.; mem. MLA, Linguistic Soc. Am. (exec. com. 1971-73, pres. 1980), Internat. Soc. Phonetic Scis., Societas Linguistica Europaea. Home: 985 Kennington Ave Columbus OH 43220-4018

LEHMAN, ARNOLD LESTER, museum official, art historian; b. N.Y.C., July 18, 1944; s. Sidney and Henrietta F. L.; m. Pamela Gimbel, June 21, 1969; children—Nicholas Richard, Zachary Gimbel. B.A., Johns Hopkins, 1965, M.A., 1966; M.A., Yale U., 1968, Ph.D., 1973. Chester Dale fellow Met. Mus. Art, N.Y.C., 1969-70; lectr. art history Cooper Union and Hunter Coll., 1969-72; dir. Urban Improvements Program, N.Y.C., 1970-72, Parks Council of N.Y.C., 1972-74, Met. Mus. and Art Centers, Miami, Fla., 1974-79, Balt. Mus. Art, 1979—; adj. prof. dept. art history Johns Hopkins U., 1986-93; dir. or trustee several corps. and non-profit orgns. Author: The Architecture of Worlds Fairs 1900-1939, 1972, The New York Skyscraper: A History of its Development 1870-1939, 1974; editor: Oskar Schlemmer, 1986; also various mus. catalogs. Trustee several non-profit orgns. Mem. Assn.

Art Mus. Dirs. (trustee 1987-93, pres. 1990-91), Harmonie Club (N.Y.C.). Office: Baltimore Mus Art Art Museum Dr Baltimore MD 21218-3898

LEHMAN, CHRISTOPHER M., international business consultant; b. Phila., Dec. 15, 1948; s. John F. and Constance (Cruice) L.; m. Maureen Daly, Oct. 1971; children: Brian Thomas, Robert Francis, Christopher M. BA, St. Joseph's Coll., 1971; MA in Law and Diplomacy, Fletcher Sch., 1974, MA in Internat. Rels., 1974, PhD in Internat. Rels., 1993. Research assoc. Fgn. Policy Research Inst., Phila., 1974-76; legis. asst. Senator Harry Byrd, Washington, 1976-78, Senator John Warner, Washington, 1979-81; office dir. Dept. State, Washington, 1981-83; spl. asst. to Pres. The White House, Washington, 1983-85; sr. v.p. Black, Manafort, Stone & Kelly, Alexandria, Va., 1985-87; pres. Commonwealth Cons. Corp., Washington, 1987—; bd. dirs. Handheld Computer Systems, Inc. Bd. advisors KIDS Found.; chmn. bd. Northern Va. Scholarship Trust. Served with USNR, 1969-71. H.B. Earhart fellow, 1971, 72, 73; vis. fellow Ctr. for Internat. Devel. and Conflict Mgmt., U. Md.

LEHMAN, DONALD RAY, chemical company executive; b. Chickasha, Okla., Apr. 19, 1947; s. Theodore and Elva (Walker) L.; m. Laura Elizabeth Decker, Aug. 30, 1968; children: Shelby Lynn, Shana Beth, John David. B-SchemE, Okla. State U., 1969. Prodn. supt. Celanese Chem. Co., Pampa, Tex., 1976-79; process engr. supt. Celanese Chem. Co., Houston, 1979-81; mgr. internat. planning Celanese Chem. Co., Dallas, 1981-82, mgr. new bus. devel., 1982-83; tech. mgr. Celanese Chem. Co., Bishop, Tex., 1983-85; plant mgr. Celanese Chem. Co., Pampa, 1985-87; dir. bus. svcs. and ops. Hoechst-Celanese Corp., Portsmouth, Va., 1987-88; dir. methyl chems. Hoechst-Celanese Corp., Dallas, 1988-89, v.p., gen. mgr. methyl and oxo chemicals, 1989-90, v.p., gen. mgr. monomers and acetyl chems., 1990—; bd. dirs. Nat. Methanol Co., Al-Jabail, Saudi Arabia. Pres. Richardson (Tex.) Girls Soccer Assn., 1988, Pampa Indsl. Found., 1986; bd. dirs. Coronado Community Hosp., Pampa, 1986, Horas Alegras Presch. Mem. Rotary, Lions (v.p.). Republican. Methodist. Office: Hoechst Celanese Ste 100 1601 Lyndon B Johnson Fwy Dallas TX 75234-6034

LEHMAN, DOYLE, superintendent. Supt. South Adams Schs., South Berne, Ind. Recipient State Finalist for Nat. Supt. of Yr. award, 1992. Office: South Adams Schs 1027 US 27 South Berne IN 46711

LEHMAN, EDWARD WILLIAM, sociology educator, researcher; b. Regensburg, Germany, Feb. 7, 1936; came to U.S., 1939; s. William and Kate (Hoffman) L.; m. Ethna V. O'Flannery, May 26, 1962; 1 child, Robert. B.S., Fordham U., 1956, M.A., 1959; Ph.D., Columbia U., 1966. Lectr. Fordham U., 1958-59; vis. research sociologist dept. psychiatry Montefiore Hosp., Bronx, N.Y., 1959-61; lectr. Sch. Nursing, Columbia U., N.Y.C., 1964-67; research sociologist Cornell U. Med. Coll., N.Y.C., 1961-67; asst. prof., then assoc. prof. sociology NYU, 1967-78; prof., 1978—; chmn. dept., 1978-84, 93—; assoc. dir. Ctr. Policy Research, N.Y.C., 1976-85, sr. research assoc., 1969-89; mem. minority adv. com. N.Y. State Dept. Mental Hygiene, 1981-90. Author: Political Society: A Macrosociology of Politics, 1977, Coordinating Health Care: Explorations in Interorganizational Relations, 1975, The Viable Polity, 1992; editor: (with others) A Sociological Reader in Complex Organizations, 1980. Served as capt. U.S. Army, 1957. Mem. Am. Sociol. Assn., Am. Polit. Sci. Assn. Democrat. Roman Catholic. Home: 1 Washington Square Vlg New York NY 10012-1606

LEHMAN, EDWIN, minister, head of religious organization. Pres. Luth. Ch. Can., Winnipeg, Man.

LEHMAN, GEORGE MORGAN, food sales executive; b. Chgo., Apr. 28, 1938; s. George Daniel and Margaret Marie (Cunningham) L.; m. Kathleen Marie Loftus, June 30, 1962; children: Robert Patrick, Daniel Joseph, Kathleen Marie, Michael Francis, William Terrance, Marilyn Elizabeth. BS, Marquette U., 1960; postgrad., Marquette Law Sch., 1962. Salesman, area mgr., city mgr. Am. Dist. Telegram Co., Chgo., 1964-79; security cons. A.I.C. Security Systesm, Chgo., 1981-83; exec. acct. mgr. Murphy Butter & Egg Co., Chgo., 1984-90; acct. exec. Badger/Murphy Food Svc., Chgo., 1990—; assoc. mem. Chef's De Cuisine, Chgo., 1985—. V.p. Sch. Dist. 126, Oak Lawn, Ill.; coach, umpire, v.p. Oak Lawn Little League; coach YMCA Basketball, Oak Lawn Pk. Dist. Basketball. Recipient Those Who Excell in Edn. award Ill. Assn. Sch. Bds., 1991, Cert. of Achievement, 1992. Mem. Beverly Stamp Club, Delta Sigma Pi. Roman Catholic. Avocations: stamps, basketball, darts. Home: 10733 Lawler Ave Oak Lawn IL 60453-5113 Office: Badger/Murphy Food Svc 700 N Western Ave Chicago IL 60612-1218

LEHMAN, HARRY JAC, lawyer; b. Dayton, Ohio, Aug. 29, 1935; s. H. Jacques and Mildred (Benas) L.; m. Linda L. Rocker, June 7, 1964 (div. Mar. 1977); children: Sara Beth, Adam Henry, Matthew Daniel; m. Patricia L. Steele, Aug. 30, 1980; 1 child, Alexandra Steele. BA, Amherst Coll., 1957; JD, Harvard U., 1960. Bar: Ohio 1960. Assoc. Burke, Haber & Berick, Cleve., 1960-61; assoc. Falsgraf, Kundtz, Reidy & Shoup, Cleve., 1961-66, ptnr., 1967; of counsel Benesch, Friedlander, Coplan & Aronoff, Cleve., 1971-80; ptnr. Jones, Day, Reavis & Pogue, Columbus, 1980—; adj. prof. law Ohio State U., Columbus, 1980-84, 86-87; mem. Bd. Bar Examiners, State of Ohio, Columbus, 1983-85. Contbr. articles to profl. jours. Mem. Ohio Ho. of Reps., Columbus, 1971-80; chmn. House Judiciary Com., 1975-80; mem. Ohio Elections Com., Columbus, 1983-88, State Underground Parking Com., Columbus, 1983-87, chmn., 1984-86. Served with USAR, 1960-66. Named one of Ten Outstanding Young Men, Cleve. Jaycees, 1968-69; recipient Disting. Service award NAACP, 1968, Outstanding Freshman Legislator award Ohio Legis. Correspondents Assn., 1971-72, Disting. Service award Ohio Edn. Assn., 1972, Most Effective Legislator award Ohio Legis. Correspondents Assn., 1973-74, Pub. Service award Ohio Pub. Defender Assn., 1974, Outstanding Pub. Service award Ohio Pub. Transit Assn., 1978, Disting. Service award ACLU Ohio Found., 1978, Most Effective Legislator 112th Gen. Assembly Ohio award Columbus Monthly Mag., 1980, Most Effective Legislator 113th Gen. Assembly Ohio award Columbus Monthly Mag. Mem. ABA, Ohio Bar Assn., Columbus Bar Assn., Cleve. Bar Assn., Columbus Athletic Club, Ohio State U. Golf Club, New Albany Country Club. Democrat. Jewish. Avocations: reading, golf, family. Home: 2642 Charing Rd Columbus OH 43221-3628 Office: Jones Day Reavis & Pogue 41 S High St Ste 1900 Columbus OH 43215-6196

LEHMAN, JAMES ALDEN, economist, educator; b. St. Charles, Ill., Oct. 20, 1947; s. Harold Richard and Elsie (Landis) L.; m. Kay Laura Behrens, Sept. 25, 1973; children: Max Behrens, Sophie Behrens. BA, Davidson Coll., 1973; MA, Duke U., 1976, PhD, 1981. Lectr. Kobe (Japan) U., 1977-80; asst. prof. Pitzer Coll., Claremont, Calif., 1981-87, assoc. prof., 1987-93, prof., 1993—; exec. dir. Thomas J. Watson Found., 1993—; vis. asst. prof. UCLA. 1982. Contbr. articles to profl. jours. Recipient fellowship Thomas J. Watson Found., 1973, Durfee Found., 1987. Mem. Am. Econ. Assn., Western Econ. Assn. (assoc. editor Econ. Inquiry 1985—). Democrat. Presbyterian. Avocations: tennis, hiking, cycling, singing. Office: 217 Angell St Providence RI 02906-2120

LEHMAN, JAMES ORTEN, library director; b. Apple Creek, Ohio, Dec. 22, 1932; s. Willis Albert and Sarean Aldula (Amstutz) L.; m. Dorothy Anna Amstutz, Sept. 5, 1953; children: Lynn, Orval, Gerald, Beverly, Alan. BA, Ea. Mennonite Coll., Harrisonburg, Va., 1959; MLS, Kent State U., 1965, cert. advanced studies in libr. sci., 1969. Prin., tchr. Cen. Christian High Sch., Kidron, Ohio, 1955-57, 59-60; libr., tchr. Cen. Christian High Sch., Kidron, 1961-68; asst. libr. Ea. Mennonite Coll. and Sem., 1969-73, prof. libr. sci., 1973—; mem. exec. com. Mennonite Ch., Goshen, Ind., 1973-77, 87-93; chmn. hist. com. Va. Mennonite Conf., Harrisonburg, Va., 1975—; chmn. Ea. Mennonite Assoc. Librs. and Archives, Lancaster, Pa., 1977-89; various positions Sonnenberg Mennonite Ch., Lindale Mennonite Ch., 1955—. Author congl. and community histories in Ohio, 1964, 74, 75, 78, 80, 86, 90; contbr. numerous articles to religious jours. Served alt. mil. duty Univ. Hosp., Cleve., 1953-55. Mem. ALA, Va. Libr. Assn., Am. Assn. for State and Local History, Ohio Hist. Soc., Mennonite Ch. Hist. Assn., Lancaster Mennonite Hist. Soc., Mennonite Historians Ea. Pa., Kidron Community Hist. Soc., Shenandoah Valley Mennonite Historians. Office: Ea Mennonite Univ Libr 1200 Park Rd Harrisonburg VA 22801-2462

LEHMAN, JOHN F., JR., industrialist; b. Phila., Sept. 14, 1942; s. John F. and Constance (Cruice) L.; m. Barbara Wieland, 1975; children: John F., Alexandra, Grace. B.S. in Internat. Relations, St. Joseph's Coll., 1964; B.A. in Law with honors, MA in Internat. Law and Diplomacy, Cambridge U., 1967; Ph.D. in Internat. Relations, U. Pa., 1974. Sr. staff mem. Nat. Security Council, 1969-74; dep. dir. U.S. Arms Control and Disarmament Agy., 1975-77; pres. Abington Corp., 1977-81; sec. of Navy Washington, 1981-87; mng. dir. Paine Webber, 1988-91; chmn. J.F. Lehman & Co. N.Y.C., 1991—, Sperry Marine Inc., N.Y.C., 1993—; bd. dirs. Ball Corp., Sedgwick Group, plc, ISO, Inc. Author: Command of the Seas, 1989, Making War, 1992. Capt. USNR, 1968—.

LEHMAN, KARL FRANKLYN, accountant; b. Lowville, N.Y., Aug. 15, 1942; s. Addison E. and Mary L. (Zehr) L.; m. Elaine K. Hartsough, Aug. 2, 1964; children: Karleia Janel, Regan Scott, Anjanette Joy. BA, Goshen Coll., 1963; MBA, Columbia U., 1965. CPA, Ind.; N.Y.; cert. real estate broker, Ind. Staff acct., CPA Arthur Andersen & Co., CPA's, N.Y.C., 1965-68; mgr., CPA McGladrey & Co., CPA's, Davenport, Iowa, 1968-71; v.p., sec.-treas. ADM Industries, Inc., Elkhart, Ind., 1971-74; treas., contr. Globestar Industries, Inc., Elkhart, 1974-80; assoc. prof. acctg. Goshen (Ind.) Coll., 1980-83; pres. Karl F. Lehman & Assocs., PC CPA's, Goshen, 1980—, also bd. dirs.; mem. Creation Design and Mfg., Inc., Elkhart, Pioneer Homes, Inc., Goshen. Mem. AICPA, N.Y. State Soc. CPA's. Home: 3500 Calumet Ave Elkhart IN 46514-4408 Office: Karl F Lehman & Assocs PC 316 S 3rd St Goshen IN 46526-3710 also: Karl F Lehman and Assocs PC 615 W Bristol St Elkhart IN 46514-2900 also: Karl F Lehman & Assocs PC 445 S Van Buren St Shipshewana IN 46565-9176 also: Karl F Lehman & Assocs PC 1001 N Main St Nappanee IN 46550-1016

LEHMAN, LAWRENCE HERBERT, consulting engineering executive; b. N.Y.C., Apr. 30, 1929; s. Samuel and Shirley (Freiberg) L.; m. Susan E. Green, June 29, 1957; children: Scott Jeffrey, Christopher Adam. BCE, NYU, 1949; MBA, Iona Coll., 1978. Registered profl. engr., N.Y., N.J., Ky., Ill., Mass., Conn., Ind., Pa. Project engr. Andrews & Clark (Cons. Engrs.), N.Y.C., 1951-57; project mgr. Barstow, Mulligan & Vollmer (Cons. Engrs.), N.Y.C., 1957-59; chief engr., ptnr. Vollmer Assos. (Cons. Engrs.), N.Y.C., 1959-67; chief exec. officer, dir. Berger, Lehman Assos. (P.C.), Rye, N.Y., 1967—. Recipient Third award U.S. Steel Corp., 1966, Bridge award Pre-stressed Concrete Inst., 1975, Honor award Nat. ACEC, 1995, others. Fellow ASCE (life); mem. NSPE, Am. Cons. Engrs. Coun., Soc. Am. Mil. Engrs., Transp. Rsch. Bd., Am. Ry. Engring. Assn., Internat. Assn. Bridge and Structural Engrs., Am. Rd. and Transp. Builders Assn., Am. Arbitration Assn. (nat. panel arbitrators), N.Y. Assn. Cons. Engrs. (Engring. Excellence awards 1975, 79, 90, 95), Conn. Engrs. in Pvt. Practice, West County Profl. Engrs. Soc. (Engr. of Yr. award 1991), The Moles, High Speed Rail Assn. Home: 10 Chester Dr Rye NY 10580-2204 Office: 411 Theodore Fremd Ave Rye NY 10580-1410

LEHMAN, LOIS JOAN, medical librarian; b. Danville, Pa., Apr. 25, 1932; d. Harold M. and Leona (Shuey) L. B.A., Pa. State U., University Park, 1954; M.S., Columbia U., 1959. Librarian Lankenau Hosp., Phila., 1959-66; reference librarian Sch. Medicine, U. Pa., Phila., 1966-68; asst. librarian head pub. services Coll. Medicine, Pa. State U., Hershey, 1968-71, acting librarian, 1971-72, librarian, 1972—. Mem. Med. Libr. Assn., Am. Acad. Health Scis. Libr. Dirs., Health Scis. Librs. Consortium (bd. dirs.), Interlibr. Delivery Svc. of Pa. (bd. dirs.), Quentin Riding Club. Avocation: owner of thoroughbred race horse. Office: Pa State U Coll Medicine George T Harrell Libr The Hershey Med Ctr Hershey PA 17033

LEHMAN, MARK E., lawyer; b. Bklyn., Mar. 14, 1951; s. Edward Berton and Aileen Sally (Tarrow) L.; m. Diane Carol Goller, Aug. 15, 1976; children: David, Abigail. BA, Columbia Coll., 1973; JD, NYU, 1976. Bar: N.Y. 1977, U.S. Dist. Ct. (so. dist.) N.Y. 1977. Litigation atty. Merrill Lynch, Pierce, Fenner & Smith, Inc., N.Y.C., 1976-79; gen. coun. Bear Stearns & Co. Inc., N.Y.C., 1979—; arbitrator Am. Stock Exchange, Nat. Assn. Securities Dealers. Mem. Securities Industry Assn., Future Industry Assn. Office: Bear Stearns Co Inc 245 Park Ave New York NY 10167-0001

LEHMAN, ORIN, retired state official; b. N.Y.C., Jan. 14, 1922; s. Allan S. and Evelyn (Schiffer) L.; children: Susan, Brooke, Sage. BA, Princeton U., 1942; MA, NYU, 1956, PhD, 1961; LHD (hon.), Hartwick Coll., 1962, Marist Coll., 1993; LLD (hon.), Manhattan Coll., 1985. Economist Lehman Bros., N.Y.C., 1947-52; pub. and chmn. Colgreene Pub., Inc., Hudson, N.Y., 1951-59; chmn. Colgreene Broadcasting Co., Catskill, N.Y., 1958-75, Picket Prodn., Inc., N.Y.C., 1968-75; commr. N.Y. State Office of Parks, Recreation and Hist. Preservation, Albany, 1975-94; State Commn. for Restoration of the Capitol, 1979; adv. U.S. del. UN Conf. Trade and Devel., 1964-68; chmn. N.Y. State Gov.'s Com. on Employment of Handicapped, 1956-65; mem. public adv. bd. Econ. Cooperation Adminstrn., 1950-52; mem. U.S. Nat. Commn. for UNESCO, 1968-71; chmn. N.Y.C. Bd. Corrections, 1974-75; mem. exec. com. N.Y.C. Criminal Justice Coordinating Com., 1974-75. Trustee, past chmn. New Sch. Social Research, N.Y.C., Parsons Sch. Design; trustee, chmn. Just-One-Break, Inc.; trustee, past exec. dir. Eleanor Roosevelt Meml. Found.; bd. dirs. Ednl. Broadcasting Corp., 1965-74; pres. N.Y. Citizens Com. Public Higher Edn., 1964-68. Served to capt. U.S. Army, 1942-47. Decorated D.F.C., Bronze Star, Purple Heart; recipient Disting. Svc. award Nat. Govs. Assn, 1992, citations Anti-Defamation League, citations N.Y. Jaycees, citations N.Y. State Jaycees, citations Pres.'s Com. on Employment of Handicapped, citations CSC U.S., citations CCNY, citations Marist Coll., citations Taft Sch., Pres.'s Pub. Svc. award Nature Conservancy, Pugsley medal Nat. Park Found., 1989. Office: 20 E 69th St 4C New York NY 10021

LEHMAN, PAUL V., minister. Dir. Haitian Ministy Dist. of the Christian and Missionary Alliance. Office: 211 College Ave Nyack NY 10960

LEHMAN, RICHARD LEROY, lawyer; b. Johnstown, Pa., Feb. 4, 1930; s. John S. and Deliah E. (Chase) L.; m. Lucia M. Ragnone; children: Ann Laurie, Leslie Ann, Lucia Marie. AB in Social Work, U. Ky., 1957; LLB, U. Detroit, 1960. Bar: Mich. 1961, U.S. Dist. Ct. (ea. dist.) Mich. 1961, U.S. Ct. Appeals (6th cir.) 1961. Pvt. practice Detroit; ptnr. Garan, Lucow, Miller, Lehman, Seward & Cooper, 1961-79; pres. Home Bldg. Plan Svc., Inc., Portland, Oreg., 1979-82; pres., gen. counsel Matvest Inc., Farmington Hills, Mich., 1980-86; pres. Xi Industries, Flint, Mich., 1982-86; ptnr. Lehman & Valentino, P.C., Bloomfield Hills, Mich., 1986-95; pres. Premiere Packaging, Inc., Flint, 1987-91, chmn., CEO, 1990—; vis. lectr. U. Detroit Law Sch., 1970-74, also Inst. Continuing Legal Edn. Mem. exec. com. pres.'s cabinet U. Detroit, 1975-79; mem. Old Newsboys Goodfellow Fund Detroit, 1969—, bd. dirs. 1975-78. 1st lt. AUS, 1947-53. Recipient Algernon Sydney Sullivan Medallion U. Ky., 1957. Mem. ABA, Mich. Bar Assn., Fed. Bar Assn., Genesee County Bar Assn. (bench and bar com. 1975-78), Am. Judicature Soc., Am. Arbitration Assn., Am. Def. Trial Counsel, Def. Rsch. Inst., U. Ky. Alumni Assn., U. Detroit Law Sch. Alumni Assn. (dir. 1970-77, pres. 1974-75), U. Detroit Alumni Assn., 6th Cir. Jud. Conf. (life), Pine Lake Country Club (bd. dirs. 1991—, pres. 1994-95). Roman Catholic. Avocations: golf, downhill skiing, carpentry. Home: 4052 Waterwheel Ln Bloomfield Hills MI 48302-1870 Office: Premiere Packaging 6220 Lehman Dr Flint MI 48507-4678

LEHMAN, (ISRAEL) ROBERT, biochemistry educator, consultant; b. Tauroggen, Lithuania, Oct. 5, 1924; came to U.S., 1927; s. Herman Bernard and Anne (Kahn) L.; m. Sandra Lee Teper, July 5, 1959; children: Ellen, Deborah, Samuel. AB, Johns Hopkins U., 1950, PhD, 1954; MD (hon.), U. Gothenberg, Sweden, 1987; DSc (hon.), U. Pierre et Marie Curie, Paris, 1992. Instr. biochemistry Washington U., St. Louis, 1957-59; asst. prof. Stanford (Calif.) U., 1959-61, assoc. prof., 1961-66, prof., 1966—; sci. adv. bd., dirs. U.S. Biochem. Corp., Cleve., 1984—; sci. adv. RPI, Boulder. Author: Principles of Biochemistry, 6th edit., 1978, 7th edit., 1984. Sgt. U.S. Army, 1943-46, ETO. Mem. NAS, Am. Acad. Arts and Scis., Am. Soc. Biol. Chemistry and Molecular Biology (Merck award 1995). Democrat. Jewish. Home: 895 Cedro Way Palo Alto CA 94305-1002 Office: Stanford U Dept Biochemistry Beckman Ctr Stanford CA 94305

LEHMAN, ROBERT NATHAN, ophthalmologist, educator; b. Lancaster, Pa., Oct. 22, 1911; s. Harry Nathan and Mable May (Shenk) L.; m. Clara May Hileman, Apr. 24, 1938; 1 dau., Mary Dorcas. B.S., Franklin and

Marshall Coll., 1933; M.D., Temple U., 1937. Intern Temple U. Hosp., 1937-39, resident, 1947-48; resident Walter Reed Hosp., Washington, 1948-50, Armed Forces Inst. Pathology, Washington, 1950-51; chief ophthalmology VA Hosp., Pitts., 1954-78; prof. ophthalmology U. Pitts. Med. Sch., 1954—, lectr. pathology, 1966—. Contbr. articles to profl. jours. Served with AUS, 1939-54. Decorated Bronze Star; Croix de Guerre (2) France). Mem. ACS, Am. Acad. Ophthalmology, Pitts. Ophthal. Soc., Ea. Ophthal. Pathology Soc., Univ. Club (Pitts.). Home: 1240 S Corning St # 101 Los Angeles CA 90035

LEHMANN, DORIS ELIZABETH, elementary education educator; b. Ramsey, N.J., Aug. 17, 1933; d. Alfred Harrison and Anna Elizabeth (Gerhold) Rockefeller; m. Victor S. Lehmann, June 25, 1955; children: Joanne E. Cathy Lynn, Victor A., Kristie Sue. BS in Edn. magna cum laude, Wagner Coll., 1955; student in edn., Columbia U., summers 1988-91, Jersey City State, 1990—, William Paterson, 1971. Elem. tchr. Sch. St. Sch. Ramsey, 1955-56; bedside instr. N. Bergen County schs., N.J., 1966-71; elem. tchr. Edith A. Bogert Sch., Upper Saddle River, N.J., 1971—. Author numerous poems; author: (with others) Curriculum for Values Education in New Jersey, 1991. Indian cons. Bergen County Mus. of Art and Sci., Paramus, N.J., 1983—. Recipient Fellowship of Life award Luth. Layman's Movement, 1955. Fellow Upper Saddle River Edn. Assn. (social sec. 1972-73, v.p. 1974-75, 84-85, liaison to USR hist. soc. 1986—) N.J. Edn. Assn., N.J. North Edn. Assn., Alpha Omicron Pi (life, treas. 1954, v.p. 1995). Republican. Lutheran. Office: Edith A Bogert Sch 395 W Saddle River Rd Saddle River NJ 07458-1622

LEHMANN, ERICH LEO, statistics educator; b. Strasbourg, France, Nov. 20, 1917; came to U.S., 1940, naturalized, 1945; s. Julius and Alma Rosa (Schuster) L.; m. Juliet Popper Shaffer; children: Stephen, Barbara, Fia. M.A., U. Calif. at Berkeley, 1943, Ph.D., 1946; D.Sc. (hon.), U. Leiden, 1985, U. Chgo., 1991. Asst. dept. math. U. Calif. at Berkeley, 1942-43, asso., 1943-46, instr., 1946-47, asst. prof., 1947-51, asso. prof., 1951-54, prof., 1954-55, prof. dept. statistics, 1955-88, emeritus, 1988—, chmn. dept. statistics, 1973-76; vis. assoc. prof. Columbia, 1950-51, Stanford, 1951-52; vis. lectr. Princeton, 1951. Author: Testing Statistical Hypotheses, 1959, 2d edit., 1986, (with J.L. Hodges, Jr.) Basic Concepts of Probability and Statistics, 1964, 2d edit, 1970, Nonparametrics: Statistical Methods Based on Ranks, 1975, Theory of Point Estimation, 1983. Recipient Fisher award Coms. of Pres. Stats. Socs. in N.Am., 1988; Guggenheim fellow, 1955, 66, 79; Miller research prof., 1962-63, 72-73. Fellow Inst. Math. Statistics, Am. Statis. Assn., Royal Statis. Soc. (hon.); mem. Internat. Statis. Inst., Am. Acad. Arts and Scis., Nat. Acad. Scis. Office: U Calif Dept Statistics Berkeley CA 94720

LEHMANN, FREDERICK GLIESSMANN, university administrator; b. Hinsdale, Ill., Nov. 1, 1930; s. Frederick William and Hermine Barbara (Gliessmann) L.; m. Betty Ann Ferguson, Sept 13, 1952 (div. 1984); children: Karl F., Pamela J., Karen L., Andrew W. SB, MIT, 1951. Cert. Inst. for Ednl. Mgmt., Harvard Bus. Sch., 1973. Adminstrv. staff member MIT, 1953-54; prodn. dept. mgr. Procter & Gamble Co., Kansas City, Kans., 1954-59; asst. sec. MIT Alumni Assn., Cambridge, Mass., 1959-62, sec., 1962-73; advanced to fin. v.p. MIT Alumni Assn., 1973-77; dir. devel. Boston U., 1977-79; exec. dir. devel. & pub. affairs The Rockefeller Univ., 1979-84; v.p. for instl. advancement N.Y. Med. Coll., Valhalla, 1984-89; dep. v.p. for devel. Columbia U., N.Y.C., 1989—; cons. Nat. Acad. Scis., Washington, 1982-84, devel. div. visiting com., Carnegie-Mellon Univ., Pittsburgh, 1965-68. Trustee, Boxford (Mass.) Town Life., 1969-78; mem. gov.'s adv. coun. on comprehensive health planning, Boston, 1971-77. 1st lt. USAF, 1951-53. Recipient, U.S. Steel Award 1978, Time/Life Award, 1977. Mem. AAAS, N.Y. Acad. Scis., Assn. am. Med. Colls./GIA (steering com. 1992-93), MIT Alumni Ctr. N.Y. (exec. com./govs. 1978—), Unnamed Soc., Harvard Club N.Y.C. Avocations: skiing, sailing, photography. Home: 541 W 113th St # 6E New York NY 10025-8039 Office: Columbia U Health Scis 100 Haven Ave New York NY 10032-2601

LEHMANN, HEINZ EDGAR, psychiatrist, consultant, researcher; b. Berlin, July 17, 1911; came to Can., 1937, naturalized, 1948; s. Richard and Emmy (Grönke) L.; m. Annette Joyal, July 28, 1940; 1 child, François. Abiturium, Mommsen Gymnasium, Berlin, 1929; M.D., U. Berlin, 1935; LL.D. (hon.), U. Calgary, Can., 1980. Clin. dir. Douglas Hosp., Montreal, Que., Can., 1947-66; dir. research Douglas Hosp., 1966-67; prof. psychiatry McGill U., Montreal, 1965—; emeritus prof. McGill U., 1981—, chmn. dept. psychiatry, 1970-74; cons. 4 Montreal hosps., 1976—; dep. commr. research N.Y. State Office Mental Health, Albany, 1980—. Contbr. over 300 articles to profl. jours., chpts. to books. Contbr. articles to profl. jours. and chpts. to books. Decorated officer Order of Can., 1975; recipient Albert Lasker award Lasker Found., 1957, Heinz Lehmann Rsch. award N.Y. State Office of Mental Health, 1990. Fellow Internat. Coll. Neuropsychopharmacology (pres. 1970-72), Can. Coll. Neuropsychopharmacology (Heinz Lehmann ann. award 1983), Que. Psychiat. Assn. (Heinz Lehmann ann. award 1986); mem. Am. Coll. Neuropsychopharmacology (pres. 1965-66, life), Am. Psychiat. Assn. (life), Royal Soc. Can. Avocations: gemology; astronomy; magic; skiing; scuba diving. Office: 1033 Pine Ave W, Montreal, PQ Canada H3A 1A1

LEHMANN, MICHAEL STEPHEN, film director; b. San Francisco, Mar. 30, 1957; s. Herbert and Minette L.; m. Holland Sutton; children: Alexander, Natalie. BA, Columbia U., 1978; MFA, U. So. Calif., 1985. Mgr. electronic cinema div. Zoetrope, Hollywood, Calif., 1981-83. Dir. (films) Heathers, 1989 (Best First Feature award Ind. Feature Project 1990), Meet the Applegates, 1991, Hudson Hawk, 1991, Airheads, 1994; exec. prodr. (film) Ed Wood, 1994.

LEHMANN, PHYLLIS WILLIAMS, archaeologist, educator; b. Bklyn., Nov. 30, 1912; d. James Barnes and Florence Lourene (Richmond) Williams; m. Karl Lehmann, Sept. 14, 1944 (dec. Dec. 1960). B.A., Wellesley Coll., 1934, L.H.D., 1976; Ph.D., NYU, 1943; Litt.D., Mt. Holyoke Coll., 1971; D.F.A., Coll. Holy Cross, 1973. Asst. charge classical collection Bklyn. Museum, 1934-36; part-time instr. history art Bennett Jr. Coll., 1936-39; mem. faculty Smith Coll., 1946—, prof. art, 1955-67, Jessie Wells Post prof. art, 1967-72, William R. Kenan, Jr. prof. art, 1972-78, prof. emeritus, 1978—, dean, 1965-70; asst. field dir. excavations conducted by Archaeol. Research Fund of NYU at Samothrace, 1948-60, acting dir., 1960-62, adv. dir., 1962—; research prof. Inst. Fine Arts, NYU, 1961-62; adj. prof. Inst. Fine Arts, N.Y. U., 1965—; Flexner lectr. Bryn Mawr Coll., 1977; Baldwin lectr. Oberlin Coll., 1982. Author: Statues on Coins of Southern Italy and Sicily in the Classical Period, 1946, Roman Wall Paintings from Boscoreale in the Metropolitan Museum of Art, 1953, The Pedimental Sculptures of the Hieron in Samothrace, 1962, Samothrace, vol. 3, 1969, (with Karl Lehmann) Samothracian Reflections. Aspects of the Revival of the Antique, 1973, Skopas in Samothrace, 1973, Cyriacus of Ancona's Egyptian Visit and Its Reflections in Gentile Bellini and Hieronymus Bosch, 1977, Samothrace, Vol. 5, 1982, contbr. Vol. 7, 1992; also articles in profl. jours.; Editor: (with Karl Lehmann) Samothrace, 1961—; asst. editor: Art Bull., 1945-47; book rev. editor, 1949-52. Named hon. citizen of Samothrace, 1968; recipient Wellesley Coll. Alumnae Assn. Achievement award, 1976; Gold medal Pan Samothracian Hearth of Athens, 1981; ho. mem. Pan Samothracian Hearth of Athens, 1979; Fulbright research grantee Italy, 1952-53; Guggenheim fellow, 1952-53; Bollingen fellow, 1960. Fellow Am. Acad. Arts and Scis.; mem. Archaeol. Inst. am. (trustee 1970-73), Coll. Art Assn. am., Am. Numis. Soc., Soc. Archtl. Historians (Alice D. Hitchcock award 1969), AAUW, Renaissance Soc. Am., Am. Sch. Classical Studies in Athens (research fellow fall 1970, 76, exec. com. 1970-75, publ. com. 1975-80, chmn. 1977-80), Williamsburg Hist. Soc., Phi Beta Kappa. Club: Cosmopolitan. Home: 127 Main St Haydenville MA 01039-9715 Office: Smith Coll Hillyer Hall Northampton MA 01063

LEHMANN, RUTH PRESTON MILLER, literature educator; b. Ithaca, N.Y., Feb. 18, 1912; d. Ernest Allen and Lillian Allen (Phillips) Miller; m. Winfred P. Lehmann, Oct. 12, 1940; children—Terry Jon, Sandra Lehmann Hargis. B.A., Cornell U., 1932, M.A., 1934; postgrad., Bryn Mawr Coll., 1935-36; Ph.D., U. Wis.-Madison, 1942. Teaching asst. U. Wis. Madison, 1938-42; editor lang. texts U.S. Armed Forces Inst., Washington, 1943-44; instr. George Washington U., Washington, 1944-46; lectr. Washington U., St. Louis, 1946-47; instr. Georgetown U. English Lang. Program, Ankara,

Turkey, 1955-56; asso. prof. English Huston Tillotson Coll., Austin, Tex., 1956-58; lectr. English U. Tex., Austin, 1960-67; asso. prof. U. Tex., 1967-72, prof., 1972-80, prof. emeritus, 1980—; delivered Rudolf Thurneysen Meml. lecture, U. Bonn., Fed. Rep. of Germany, 1985. Contbg. author: The Origins of Writing, 1989; editor: Fled Duin na nGed, 1964, (with W.P. Lehmann) Introduction to Old Irish, 1975, Early Irish Verse, 1982, Beowulf: Am Imitative Translation, 1988. Mem. MLA, Medieval Acad. Am., Early English Texts. Soc., Phi Beta Kappa (pres. Austin chpt. 1978-79), Phi Kappa Phi, Pi Lambda Theta. Democrat. Home: 3800 Eck Ln Austin TX 78734-1613 Office: U Tex Dept English Austin TX 78712 Happiness is a state of mind and more fun than boredom.

LEHMANN, WILLIAM LEONARDO, electrical engineer, educator; b. Milw., Dec. 17, 1924; s. William Christian and Johanna Alma (Schrumpf) L.; m. Barbara Taylor, June 29, 1948; children: Johanna, William, Katherine, Wendy, Christianne. AB, Haverford (Pa.) Coll., 1944; MS, Syracuse (N.Y.) U., 1948, PhD, 1953. Registered profl. engr.; Ohio. Prof. physics acting dean Air Force Inst. Tech., 1951-66; lectr. Ohio State U., 1957-60; dep. for labs. Office Asst. Sec. Air Force Research and Devel., 1966-74; dir. Air Force Office Sci. Research, 1974-78, Air Force Weapons Lab., Kirtland AFB, N.Mex., 1978-81; chief scientist Combat Devel. Experimentation Ctr. U.S. Army Sci. Support Lab, Ft. Ord, Calif., 1982-85; sr. sci. analyst N.Mex. Engring. Research Inst., 1985-93; prof. elec. engring. U. N.Mex., Albuquerque, 1988-93; sr. assoc. Ctr. for Occupational R & D, 1993—; vis. prof. U. N.Mex., 1981-82, also adv. bd. Coll. Engring.; Past mem. Gov. N.Mex. Tech. Excellence Com.; mem. USAF Scientific Adv. Bd., 1985-92. Mem. Beaver Creek (Ohio) Sch. Dist. Bd., 1965-66; trustee Lovelace Med. Found. Served with AUS, 1944-45. Recipient Air Force Exceptional Civilian Service medal with three oak leaf cluster, 1981, Ohio Engr.'s award, 1966, award Ohio Soc. Profl. Engrs., 1965. Fellow AAAS; Mem. Air Force Assn. (citation honor 1978), Assn. Soc. Engring. Edn., AIAA, Am. Def. Preparedness Assn., Sigma Xi, Sigma Pi Sigma, Tau Beta Pi. Republican. Episcopalian. Lodge: Rotary. Patentee solar orientation device. Home: PO Box 637 700 Island Retreat Rd Port Aransas TX 78373 Office: Port Arausas High Sch PO Box 1297 Port Aransas TX 78373-1297

LEHMANN, WINFRED PHILIPP, linguistics educator; b. Surprise, Nebr., June 23, 1916; s. Phillip Ludwig and Elenore Friederike (Grosnick) L.; m. Ruth Preston Miller, Oct. 12, 1940; children: Terry Jon, Sandra Jean. BA, Northwestern Coll., Watertown, Wis., 1936; MA, U. Wis., 1938, PhD, 1941; LittD (hon.), SUNY, Binghamton, 1985; DHL (hon.), U. Wis., 1995. From instr. to asst. prof. Wash. U., 1946-49; from assoc. prof. to prof. U. Tex., 1949-63, Ashbel Smith prof. linguistics, 1963-83, Louann and Larry Temple prof. humanities, 1983-86, prof. emeritus, 1986—, chmn. dept. germanic langs., 1953-65, chmn. dept. linguistics, 1965-72, dir. Linguistics Research Center, 1961—; Jawaharlal Nehru Meml. lectr., New Delhi, 1981; dir. Georgetown English lang. program, Ankara, Turkey, 1955-56; chmn. linguistics del. People's Republic of China, 1974, co-chmn. Social Sci./Humanities Planning Commn., 1981. Author: (with L. Faust) A Grammar of Formal Written Japanese, 1951, Proto-Indo-European Phonology, 1952, The Alliteration of Old Saxon Poetry, 1953, The Development of Germanic Verse Form, 1956, Historical Linguistics: an Introduction, 1962, 3d edit., 1992, Descriptive Linguistics: An Introduction, 1972, 2d edit., 1976, Proto-Indo-European Syntax, 1974, Linguistische Theorien der Moderne, 1981, Language: An Introduction, 1982, Gothic Etymological Dictionary, 1986, Die Gegenwärtige Richtung der Indogermanistischen Forschung, 1992, Theoretical Bases of Indo-European Linguistics, 1993; editor: Language and Linguistics in the People's Republic of China, 1974, (with R.P.M. Lehmann) An Introduction to Old Irish, 1975, Syntactic Typology, 1978, (wityhYakov Malkiel) Perspectives on Historical Linguistics, 1982, Language Typology, 1985, Language Typology: Systematic Balance in Language, 1987, (with H.J.J. Hewitt) Typological Models in Reconstruction, 1988; contbr. articles to profl. jours. Chmn. bd. dirs. Center for Applied Linguistics, 1973-78. 1st lt. Signal Corps AUS, 1942-46. Decorated Comdr.'s Cross, Order Merit Fed. Republic Germany, 1987; recipient Jakob Grimm prize, 1975, Pro bene Meritis award, U. Tex., 1987; fellow Fulbright Found., Norway, 1950-51, Guggenheim Found., 1972-73. Mem. MLA (exec. coun. 1977-80, pres. 1987), Linguistic Soc. Am. (pres. 1973), Am. Coun. Learned Socs. (sec. bd. 1977-86, Harry H. Ransom award teaching excellence 1989), Danish Acad. Scis. Lutheran. Home: 3800 Eck Ln Austin TX 78734-1613

LEHMANN-HAUPT, CHRISTOPHER CHARLES HERBERT, book reviewer; b. Edinburgh, Scotland, June 14, 1934; came to U.S. 1934; s. Hellmut Otto Emil and Letitia Jane H. (Grierson) Lehmann-H.; m. Natalie S. Robins, Oct. 3, 1965; children: Rachel Louise, Noah Christopher. B.A., Swarthmore Coll., 1956; M.F.A., Yale U., 1959. Editor A.S. Barnes & Co., Inc., N.Y.C., 1961-62, Holt, Rinehart & Winston, 1962-63; sr. editor Dial Press, 1963-65; mem. staff N.Y. Times Book Review, 1965-69; sr. book reviewer N.Y. Times, 1969—; asst. prof. lit. CUNY, 1973-75. Author: Me and Di Maggio, 1986, A Crooked Man, 1995. Club: Century. Office: New York Times 229 W 43rd St New York NY 10036-3959

LEHMBERG, ROBERT HENRY, research physicist; b. Phila., Dec. 4, 1937; s. Henry and Marguerite Elenore (Schock) L.; m. Norma Geder, Dec. 29, 1966; 1 child, Karl Robert. BSc, Pa. State U., 1959; MSc, U. Ariz., 1961; PhD, Brandeis U., 1968. Rsch. physicist Naval Air Devel. Ctr., Warminster, Pa., 1966-72, Naval Rsch. Lab., Washington, 1972—; chmn. program com. Conf. on Lasers and Electro-Optics, Washington, 1991. Contbr. articles to profl. jours.; patentee in field. Fellow Am. Phys. Soc. (Excellence in Plasma Physics Rsch. award 1993); mem. AAAS, IEEE, Sigma Xi. Office: Naval Rsch Lab Plasma Physics Div 4555 Overlook Ave SW Washington DC 20375-0001

LEHMBERG, STANFORD EUGENE, historian, educator; b. McPherson, Kans., Sept. 23, 1931; s. Willard Eugene and Helen (Stanford) L.; m. Phyllis Barton, July 23, 1962; 1 son, Derek Grantham. BA, U. Kans., 1953, MA, 1954; PhD, Cambridge (Eng.) U., 1956, DLitt, 1990. Mem. faculty U. Tex., Austin, 1956-69; mem. faculty U. Minn., 1969—, prof. history, 1967—, chmn. dept., 1979-85. Author: Sir Thomas Elyot, Tudor Humanist, 1960, Sir Walter Mildmay and Tudor Government, 1966, The Reformation Parliament, 1970, The Later Parliaments of Henry VIII, 1977, The Reformation of Cathedrals, 1988, The People of the British Isles to 1688, 1991; also articles, revs. Fulbright scholar, 1954-56; Guggenheim fellow, 1965-66, 85-86. Fellow Royal Hist. Soc.; mem. Am. Hist. Assn., Midwest Conf. Brit. Studies (pres. 1982-84), Renaissance Soc. Am., Am. Soc. Reformation Research. Episcopalian. Home: 2300 Willow Ln S Minneapolis MN 55416-3863 Office: U Minn Dept History Minneapolis MN 55455

LEHNER, GEORGE ALEXANDER, JR., lawyer; b. Cleve., Aug. 13, 1948; s. George Alexander and Phyllis More (Holbrook) L.; m. Diana Hill Day, May 29, 1971; children: Kristin, Alison. BA, Wesleyan U., Middletown, Conn., 1971; JD, U. Mich., 1976, M in Urban Regional Planning, 1977. Bar: D.C. 1979, Mich. 1977, U.S. Ct. Appeals (4th cir.) 1987, (D.C. cir.) 1988, (9th cir.) 1993, U.S. Dist. Ct. D.C. 1987. Atty., advisor U.S. Dept. State, Washington, 1977-80; assoc. Arent, Fox, Kintner, Plotkin & Kahn, Washington, 1981-87; ptnr. Sloan, Lehner & Ruiz, Washington, 1987-89, Pepper, Hamilton & Scheetz, Washington, 1989—; adj. prof. Georgetown U. Law Ctr., 1990—; gen. counsel Internat. Women's Media Found., 1990—. Co-author: Europe Without Frontiers: A Lawyer's Guide, 1989. Advisor foreign policy Mondale for Pres., 1984; Watson Fellow. Mem. ABA, Phi Beta Kappa. Avocations: sailing, photography. Home: 508 Woodland Ter Alexandria VA 22302-3317 Office: Pepper Hamilton & Scheetz 1300 19th St NW Washington DC 20036-1609

LEHNER, MARK, archaeologist, educator; b. Fargo, N.D., Apr. 2, 1950; s. Paul William and Ethel Lois (Davy) L.; m. Suzanne Ayad Massoud, July 12, 1975 (div. 1985); children: Ramsi, Luke. BA in Anthropology, Am. U., Cairo, 1975; PhD in Egyptology, Yale U., 1990. Field dir. Sphinx and Isis Temple project Am. Rsch. Ctr., Egypt, 1979-83, co-dir. Pyramids radiocarbon dating project, 1984; dir. Giza Plateau mapping project Am. Rsch. Ctr./Oriental Inst. U. Chgo., Egypt, 1984—; instr. Egyptian Archaeology Oriental Inst., U. Chgo., 1990-91, asst. prof., 1991—; bd. dirs. Ancient Egypt Rsch. Assocs. Inc; archtl. surveyor, draughtsman, area supervisor Nag Hammadi, Faw Qibli Expeditions Claremont Inst. Antiquity and Christianity, 1976-78; surveyor and dir. clearing ops. Sci. and Archaeology project, 1978; supr. mapping, photographer, draughtsman, various excava-

tions in the Sphinx area, 1978; mapper Bayt al-Razzaz project Am. Rsch. Ctr., 1978; surveyor, object restorer, artist, photographer various salvage excavations, 1979; area supr., mapper, photographer, Tell el-Amarna expedition, Egypt Exploration Soc., 1979-80, archtl. surveyor Tomb of Akhenaten epigraphic survey, 1980;surveyor Deir el-Ballas expedition, Mus. Fine arts, Boston, 1983; archtl. surveyor Tombe of Aperia project, Saqqara Ctr. National de Recherches Scientifiques, 1983-85, Abdyos Regional Site Survey, U. Pa., 1983, Nasr. Mohammed Mosque Restoration, The German Archaeological Inst., 1985; cons. Time-Life Books, 1986-87, Field Mus. Nat. History, Chgo., 1987-88, NAS Com. Sphinx conservation study, 1989, Getty Conservation Inst., 1989-90, The Jerde Partnership, 1989-90, Egyptian Antiquities Orgn. Symposium on Sphinx restoration, 1992, materials adv bd. Nat. Rsch. Coun. conservation Egyptian monuments study steering com., 1992; lectr. in field. TV appearnaces include PM Mag., 1982, LBS Mysteries of the Pyramids, 1988, National Geographic Explorer, 1992, Nova: Building a Pyramid, 1992; contbr. articles to profl. jours. Sterling Prize fellow Yale U., 1986; recipient William J. Horowitz prize Near Eastern Langs. and Civilizations, Yale U. 1991. Office: U Chgo Oriental Inst 1155 E 58th St Chicago IL 60637-1540

LEHNER, URBAN CHARLES, journalist; b. Grand Rapids, Mich., May 10, 1947; s. Urban Edward and Angeline Grace (Marcy) L.; m. Anne Marie Eding, May 2, 1969 (div. 1976); m. Nancy Ellen Leonard, June 28, 1980; 1 child, Alicia Ann. AB in history, U. Mich., 1969; JD, Georgetown U., 1979. Staff reporter The Wall Street Jour., N.Y.C., Phila., Chgo., Washington, 1969-80; bur. chief. The Wall Street Jour., Tokyo, 1980-83, Detroit, 1983-85; mng. editor The Wall Street Jour. Europe, Brussels, 1985-87; bur. chief The Wall Street Jour., The Asian Wall Street Jour., Tokyo, 1988-92; editor The Asian Wall Street Jour., Hong Kong, 1992—. Lt. (j.g.) USNR, 1970-72. Recipient Citation for Excellence with Alan Murray for Strained Alliance Overseas Press Club, 1991. Mem. Fgn. Corrs. Club Japan. Office: The Asian Wall St Jour, 2/F AIA Bldg CPO Box 9825, Hong Kong Hong Kong

LEHNERT, HERBERT HERMANN, foreign language educator; b. Luebeck, Germany, Jan. 19, 1925; came to U.S., 1958, naturalized, 1971; s. Bernhard Alfred and Elisabeth (Doemel) L.; m. Ingeborg Poth, Aug. 13, 1952; children—Bernard (dec.), Brigitte, Bettina. Ph.D., U. Kiel, Germany, 1952. Lectr. U. Western Ont., Can., 1957; faculty Rice U., 1958-68, prof. German, 1966-68; prof. German U. Kans., 1968-69; prof. German U. Calif., Irvine, 1969—, chmn. dept., 1974-76; vis. prof. Harvard, fall 1970. Author: Thomas Mann: Fiktion, Mythos, Religion, 1965, Struktur und Sprachmagie, 1966, Thomas Mann Forschung, 1969, Geschichte der deutschen Literatur: Vom Jugendstil zum Expressionismus, 1978, Nihilismus der Menschenfreundlichkeit: Thomas Manns Wandlung (with Eva Wessell), 1991; editor: Doctor Faustus: A Novel at the Margin of Modernism (with Peter C. Pfeiffer) 1991; contbr. articles to profl. jours. Nat. Endowment for Humanities fellow, 1973, 78; Guggenheim fellow, 1978-79. Mem. MLA, Am. Assn. Tchrs. German. Home: 8 Harvey Ct Irvine CA 92715-4033 Office: U Calif Dept German Irvine CA 92717-3150

LEHOCZKY, JOHN PAUL, statistics educator; b. Columbus, Ohio, June 29, 1943; s. Paul Nicholas and Thelma Marie (Heisterkamp) L.; m. Mary Louise Zimmerman, Sept. 10, 1966; children: Jennifer Lynne, Jessica Augusta. BA, Oberlin Coll., 1965; MS, Stanford U., 1967, PhD, 1969. Asst. prof. stats. Carnegie Mellon U., Pitts., 1969-73, assoc. prof., 1973-81, prof., 1981—, head dept., 1984-95; assoc. editor IEEE Trans. on Computers, 1995—; cons. in legal stats., statis. analysis and real-time computing. Dept. editor: Mgmt. Sci., 1981-86; assoc. editor Jour. Real-Time Systems, 1989—; contbr. over 80 research papers in various disciplines. Fellow Am. Statis. Assn. (statistician of yr. Pitts. chpt. 1987), Inst. Math. Stats.; mem. IEEE, AAAS, Assn. for Computing Machinery, Internat. Statis. Inst. Office: Carnegie Mellon Univ Dept Stat Pittsburgh PA 15213

LEHR, DENNIS JAMES, lawyer; b. N.Y.C., Feb. 7, 1932; s. Irwin Allen and Teeny (Scofield) L.; m. Enid J. Auerbach, June 10, 1956; children—Austin Windsor, Bryant Paul, Amy Lynn. BA, NYU, 1954, LLM, 1961; LLB, Yale U., 1957. Bar: N.Y. 1959, D.C. 1967. Atty. Allstate Ins. Co., N.Y.C., 1958-59; atty. Regional Office SEC, N.Y.C., 1959-61; assoc. Borden and Ball, N.Y.C., 1961-63; atty. Office Spl Counsel Investment Co. Act Matters SEC, N.Y.C., 1963-64; assoc. chief counsel Office Comptroller Currency U.S. Treasury Dept., N.Y.C., 1964-67; assoc. Hogan & Hartson, N.Y.C., 1967-69, ptnr., 1969-94, of counsel, 1994—; bd. advis. So. Meth. U. Grad. Sch. Banking; adj. prof. Georgetown Law Sch., 1964-68; legal adv. com. Nat. Ctr. on Fin. Svcs., U. Calif.; lectr. Practicing Law Inst.; adv. coun. Banking Law Inst.; pub. mem. Adminstrv. Conf. of the U.S. Bd. contbrs. Fin. Services Law Report. Contbr. articles to profl. jours. Mem. ABA (coun. mem. sect. bus. law, former chmn. com. on Long Range Issues Affecting Bus. Law Practice, former chmn., com. on devels. in investment svcs.). Office: Hogan and Hartson 555 13th St NW Washington DC 20004-1109

LEHR, JANET, art dealer, publisher, author; b. N.Y.C., June 7, 1937; d. Herbert Davis and Florence (Lustig) Cooperman; m. Lewis Lehr, Feb. 22, 1959 (div. 1984); children: Florence Rachel, Michael William, Samuel Joseph. Ba, NYU, 1955; JD, Bklyn. Law Sch., 1958. Pvt. practice art dealer 20th century Am. paintings N.Y.C., 1962-72; dir. Janet Lehr Inc., 19th and 20th Century Photographs, N.Y.C., 1972—; ptnr. Vered Gallery, paintings and sculptures by modern Am. masters, emerging artists and Am. rediscovery 1920-70, East Hampton, N.Y., 1988—; co-dir. Gallery 6M, N.Y.C., 1964-72; curator Landscape Photography, State Mus. Munich, 1979. Author: William Henry Jackson, Picture Maker of the American West, William Henry Fox Talbot and the Art of Photo Mechanical Illustration, 1978; exhbns. include Horatio Ross: Scottish Photographs 1850s Yale University, British Ctr. for the Arts, 1993, Masterworks of Photography, Art Gallery of New South Wales, Sydney, Australia, 1994; also 33 quar. issues on history photography, 1976-86. Mem. Assn. Internat. Photography Art Dealers (founding), Antiquarian Book Dealers Am., Internat. Book Dealers Assn. Home and Office: 891 Park Ave New York NY 10021-0326

LEHR, LEWIS WYLIE, diversified manufacturing company executive; b. Elgin, Nebr., Feb. 21, 1921; s. Lewis H. and Nancy (Wylie) L.; m. Doris Stauder, Oct. 13, 1944; children—Mary A. Lehr Makin, William L., Donald D., John M. B.S. in Chem. Engring. U. Nebr., 1947, Sc.D. (hon.), 1977. With 3M Co., St. Paul, 1947—; v.p. med. products div. 3M Co., 1960-72, health care products group, 1972-74, tape and allied products group, 1974-75, pres. U.S. ops., 1975-79, vice chmn., 1979-80, chmn., chief exec. officer, 1980-86; bd. dirs. Jack Eckerd Corp., Tampa, Fla., various IDS Funds, Mpls., Peregrine, Inc. Trustee U. Nebr. Found. Served with AUS, 1943-46, ETO. Recipient Alumni Achievement award U. Nebr. Alumni Assn., 1976. Mem. Am. Chem. Soc. Clubs: North Oaks Golf, White Bear Yacht, Minnesota. Address: Minn World Trade Ctr 30 7th St E Ste 3050 Saint Paul MN 55101-4901

LEHRER, JAMES CHARLES, television journalist; b. Wichita, Kans., May 19, 1934; s. Harry Frederick and Lois Catherine (Chapman) L.; m. Kate Staples, June 4, 1960; children: Jamie, Lucy, Amanda. A.A., Victoria Coll., 1954; B.J., U. Mo., 1956. Reporter Dallas Morning News, 1959-61; reporter, columnist, city editor Dallas Times Herald, 1961-70; exec. producer, corr. Sta. KERA-TV, Dallas, 1970-72; pub. affairs coordinator Public Broadcasting Service, Washington, 1972-73; corr. NPACT-WETA-TV, Washington, 1973—; now assoc. editor-co-anchor MacNeil/Lehrer Newshour; instr. creative writing Dallas Coll., So. Meth. U., 1967-68. Author: (fiction) Viva Max, 1966, We Were Dreamers, 1975, Kick the Can, 1988, Crown Oklahoma, 1980, The Sooner Spy, 1990, Lost and Found, 1991, Short List, 1992, A Bus of My Own, 1992, Blue Hearts, 1993, Fine Lines, 1994, (plays) Chili Queen, 1986, Church Key Charlies Blue, 1987, The Will and Bart Show, 1992. Served with USMC, 1956-59. Recipient Columbia-Dupont award; George Polk award; Peabody award; Emmy award. Mem. Am. Acad. Arts and Scis., Dramatists Guild, Authors Guild, Tex. Inst. Letters, Coun. on Fgn. Rels. Office: Sta WETA-TV PO Box 2626 Washington DC 20013-2626

LEHRER, JOEL FREDRIC, otolaryngologist; b. Bklyn., May 2, 1941; s. Isidore and Helen (Barach) L.; m. Nancy-Dean Murray, June 15, 1962; children: Brian, Hilary. AB, Cornell U., 1952; MD, SUNY, Bklyn.; 1956. Diplomate Am. Bd. Otolaryngology. Intern Kings Co. Hosp., Bklyn., 1956-

57, resident in otolaryngology, 1959-61; resident in otolaryngology Mt. Sinai Hosp., N.Y.C., 1961-63, fellow, 1963-64; pvt. practice N.Y.C., 1964-73, Teaneck, N.J., 1968—; chief dept. otolaryngology Bergen Pines Hosp., Paramus, N.J., 1977-83, Holy Name Hosp., Teaneck, 1979-85. Contbr. articles to med. jours. Patroller Nat. Ski Patrol, Haystacks Mountain, Vt., 1973-88. Capt. M.C. USAF, 1957-59. Fellow ACS, Am. Neurootology Soc.; mem. Med. Soc. N.J., Bergen County Soc. Otlaryngologists (pres. 1987-91, Lotos Club (N.Y.C., pres. 1987-91). Avocations: golf, tennis, skiing. Office: 315 Cedar Ln Teaneck NJ 07666

LEHRER, KENNETH EUGENE, real estate advisor, consultant, developer; b. N.Y.C., Apr. 17, 1946; s. Charles Carlton and Evelyn Estelle (Rosenfeld) L.; m. Myrna Sue Newman, Apr. 4, 1981 (div. 1988); m. Geraldine Trudy Fishman, Mar. 18, 1994. BS, NYU, 1967, MBA, 1969, MA, 1972, D in Pub. Adminstrn., 1980. Registered investment advisor; cert. real estate appraiser; cert. review appraiser; lic. real estate broker. Asst. treas. Bankers Trust Co., N.Y.C., 1970-73; dir. devel. Coventry Devel. Corp., N.Y.C., 1974-77; asst. v.p. Affiliated Capital Corp., Houston, 1977-80; dir. fin. Allison/ Walker Interests, Houston, 1980-82; mng. dir. Lehrer Fin. and Econ. Adv. Svcs., 1982—; prof. real estate fin. U. Houston Grad. Sch. Bus. Adminstrn., 1985—; chmn. bd. dirs. Acadia Savs. and Loan Assn., Crowley, La., French Market Homestead Savs. Assn., Metairie, La., Twin City Savs. Bank, West Monroe, La., 1st Savs. La., LaPlace, Integrated Resource Techs. Inc., 1992-95. Pres. Cornerstone Mcpl. Utilities Dist., 1978-85; bd. dirs. Ft. Bend County Mcpl. Utility Dist. #106, Houston Caliber Fin. Group, chmn., 1994—. Mem. Am. Horse Show Assn. (life), Nat. Steeplechase and Hunt Assn. (life), U.S. Tennis Assn. (life), Am. Real Estate and Urban Econs. Assn., Am. Real Estate Soc., Nat. Assn. Bus. Economists, NYU Money Marketeers, Nat. Forensic Ctr., Nat. Assn. Corp. Dirs., Am. Acad. Econ. and Fin. Experts, Internat. Coll. Real Estate Cons. Profls., Internat. Assn. Corp. Real Estate Execs., Nat. Assn. Forensic Economists, Am. Arbitration Assn., Houston Bus. Economists, Western Econ. Assn., Internat. Real Estate Inst. Fin. Club. NYC., Real Estate Educators Assn., Am. Econ. Assn., N.Am. Econs. and Fin. Assn., So. Econ. Assn., NYU Alumni Fedn. (bd. dirs. 1974-77), Tex. Rep. Assn., Rep. Senatorial Inner Cir. (life, Medal of Freedom 1994), Houston C. of C. (mem. govtl. relations com.), Atrium Club, NYU Club, Princeton Club N.Y., Jockey Club (Miami, Fla.), Capitol Hill Club (Washington). Episcopalian. Home: 5555 Del Monte Dr Apt 802 Houston TX 77056 Office: Lehrer Fin and Econ Adv Svcs 1775 St James Pl Ste 165 Houston TX 77056

LEHRER, LEONARD, artist, educator; b. Phila., Mar. 23, 1935; s. Abraham and Bessie Lehrer; m. Marilyn Bigard, May 29, 1977; 1 child, Anna-Katrina Picard; stepchildren: Tracy Peel, Janna Peel, John Peel, Jamye Pawlak. B.F.A., Phila. Coll. Art, 1956; M.F.A., U. Pa., 1960. Mem. faculty Phila. Coll. Art, 1956-70, co-dir. found. program, 1965-70; prof. art U. N.Mex., 1970-74, chmn. dept., 1970-73; prof. U. Tex., San Antonio, 1974-77; dir. div. art and design U. Tex., 1974-75; prof. dir. Sch. Art, Ariz. State U., Tempe, 1977-90; dir. Visual Art Rsch. Studios, 1984-91; prof., chair dept. art and art professions NYU, 1991—. One-man shows Utah Mus. Fine Arts, Salt Lake City, 1973, 82, Marian Locks Gallery, Phila., 1974, 77, 84, McNay Art Mus., San Antonio, 1975, Galerie Kühl, Hannover, Germany, 1976, 79, 82 , 91, Bomann Mus., Celle, Fed. Republic Germany, 1980, Marilyn Butler Fine Art, Scottsdale, Ariz., 1980, Assoc. Am. Artists, Phila., 1984, Am. Cultural Affairs Ctr., Madrid, 1984, numerous others; group shows include 14th Ljubljana Internat. Print Biennial, 1981, 4th Graphic Arts Biennial of the Ams., Cali, Colombia, 1981, 7th Brit. Internat. Print Biennial, Bradford, Eng., 1982, Internat. Printmaking Invitational, San Bernardino, Calif., 1983, XXXV Art Fair, Munich, 1992, XXIV Art Fair, Hannover, Germany, 1993; represented in permanent collections Met. Mus. Art, N.Y.C., Phila. Mus. Art, Nat. Gallery Art, Washington, Library of Congress, Mus. Modern Art, N.Y.C., Cleve. Mus. Art, Sprengel Mus. Art, Hannover, Germany, The Art of Leonard Lehrer, Pub. Quensen, Germany, 1986; curator Large Scale Am. Prints in "art multiple dusseldorf," Germany, 1992; authored introductory essay to The Art of the Book; contbr. articles to profl. jours. Bd. dirs. Internat. Print Ctr. N.Y., Inc. Recipient 1st prize 4th Miami Internat. Print Biennial, 1980; recipient Western States Art Found. Printmaking Fellowship award, 1979, Heitland Found. prize, Celle, 1980, Gold Medal award Ariz. chpt. Nat. Soc. Arts and Letters, 1981. Office: NYU Dept Art and Art Professions New York NY 10003

LEHRER, SANDER, lawyer; b. Bronx, N.Y., Aug. 21, 1942; s. Sigmund and Rose (Sand) L.; m. Maryanne Leon, Apr. 17, 1961; children: Jon, Risë, Marc. BA, U. Mich., 1963; LLB, Harvard U., 1966. Bar: N.Y. 1967, U.S. Dist. Ct. (so., ea. dists.) N.Y., 1968. Law clerk to Hon. Dudley B. Bonsal Dist. Ct. (so. dist.) N.Y., N.Y.C., 1966-68; assoc. Webster & Sheffield, N.Y.C., 1968-73, ptnr., 1974-76, counsel, ptnr., 1978-91; gen. counsel N.Y.C. Dept. Housing and Preservation Devel., N.Y.C., 1976, commr., 1977; ptnr. McDermott, Will & Emery, N.Y.C., 1991—; adj. assoc. prof. NYU Sch. Law, 1979-81. Sec., bd. dirs. Citizens Housing and Planning Coun. N.Y.C., 1978—. Mem. Bar Assn. City N.Y., N.Y. State Bar Assn. Office: McDermott Will & Emery 1211 Ave of the Americas New York NY 10036

LEHRER, STANLEY, magazine publisher, editorial director, corporate executive; b. Bklyn., Mar. 18, 1929; s. Martin and Rose L.; m. Laurel Francine Zang, June 8, 1952; children: Merrill Clark, Randee Hope. BS in Journalism, N.Y. U., 1950; postgrad. in edn, San Antonio Coll., 1952. Editor and pub. Crossroads mag., Valley Stream, N.Y., 1949-50; youth service editor Open Road mag., N.Y.C., 1950-51; mng. editor School & Society, N.Y.C., 1953-68, v.p., 1956-68; pub. School & Society Books, N.Y.C., 1963-86; pres., pub. School & Society mag., N.Y.C., 1968-72; pres., pub. Intellect mag. N.Y.C., 1972-78, editorial dir., 1974-78; pres., pub. editorial dir. USA Today mag., Valley Stream, N.Y., 1978—, Newsview newsletter, 1979—, Your Health newsletter, 1980—, The World of Sci. newsletter, 1980—; cons. Child Care Pubs., N.Y.C., 1955. Producer: (WBAI-FM radio program) Report on Eucation, N.Y.C., 1960-61; author: John Dewey: Master Educator, 1959, Countdown on Segregated Education, 1960, Religion, Government, and Education, 1961, A Century of Higher Education: Classical Citadel to Collegiate Colossus, 1962, Automation, Education, and Human Values, 1966, Conflict and Change on the Campus: The Response to Student Hyperactivism, 1970, Leaders, Teachers, and Learners in Academe: Partners in the Educational Process, 1970, Education and the Many Faces of the Disadvantaged: Cultural and Historical Perspectives, 1972; contbr. articles to nat. mags., newspapers and profl. jours.; exhibited Stanley Lehrer maritime collection as part of the Ocean Liner Mus. presentation of ship memorabilia at N.Y. Yacht Club, 1983, on Cunard Line's 150th anniversary at Forbes Mag. Galleries, N.Y.C., 1989-90, on French Line's Normandie at French Embassy, N.Y.C., 1992, and Bass Mus. Art, Miami, Fla., 1993, on Ships of State: The Great Transatlantic Liners, PaineWebber Art Gallery, N.Y.C., 1994, on the Wreck of the Titanic, Nat. Maritime Mus., London, 1994-95. V.p. Garden City Park (N.Y.) Civic Assn., 1961-63; treas. Citizens' Com. Edn. Garden City Park, 1962; mem. nat. jr. book awards com. Boys' Clubs Am., 1954; mem. nat. hon. com. for Richard H. Heindel Meml. Fund, Pa. State U., 1979-80. With Signal Corps, U.S. Army, 1951-53. Recipient non-fiction awards Midwestern Writers Conf., Chgo., 1948. Mem. New Hyde Park (N.Y.) C. of C. (dir. 1961-62), Titanic Hist. Soc., S.S. Hist. Soc. Am., Soc. Advancement of Edn. (treas. 1953—, trustee 1963—, pres. 1968—), Ocean Liner Mus. (N.Y.), Psi Chi Omega. Home: 82 Shelbourne Ln New Hyde Park NY 11040-1044 Office: USA Today 99 W Hawthorne Ave Valley Stream NY 11580-6101

LEHRMAN, IRVING, rabbi; b. Tiktin, Poland, June 15, 1911; came to U.S. 1916; s. Abraham and Rachel Minnie (Dinowitz) L.; m. Bella Goldfarb, May 21, 1935; children: David Lehrman, Rosalind Lehrman. DHL, Jewish Theol. Sem. of Am., N.Y.C., 1948, DD, 1969; DHL, St. Thomas U., Miami, Fla., 1989; DL, Barry U., Miami, 1992; DHL, Fla. Internat. U., 1992. Ordained rabbi, 1943. Student rabbi Temple Shomrei Emunah, Montclair, N.J., 1939-43; rabbi Temple Emanu-El of Greater Miami, Miami Beach, Fla., 1943-93; founding rabbi, dean Lehrman Day Sch., 1993—; vis. prof. Homiletics Jewish Theol. Sem. Am.; nat. pres. Synagogue Coun. Am.; chmn. United Jewish Appeal Nat. Rabbinic Cabinet; chmn. Greater Miami Combined Jewish Appeal; chmn. bd. govs. Greater Miami State of Israel Bonds; found. chmn. Jewish Nat. Fund; hon. pres. S.E. region Rabbinical Assembly of Am. Author: In the Name of God, collection of sermons, articles, 1979, L'Chaim, thoughts for Jewish living, 1985, Portraits in Charcoal, 1980. Mem. White House Commn. on Obscenity and Pornography, Aging, and Food, Nutrition and Health (co-chmn. religious task force); bd. dirs. Miami

Jewish Home and Hosp. for Aged, Internat. Synagogue at JFK Airport, N.Y.; nat. v.p. Zionist Orgn. Am.; adv. bd. St. Thomas U., Nat. Conf. Christians and Jews; former mem. exec. com. UNESCO, Greater Miami Community Rels. Bd. Recipient silver medal NCCJ, Prime Min.'s medal State of Israel, Albert Einstein Brotherhood award Technion U., Golda Meir Leadership award State of Israel Bonds, also others; Rabbi Irving Lehrman Park established in his honor by Miami Friends of Tel Aviv Found., Tel Aviv, 1988; Rabbi Irving & Belle Lehrman Recreation and Picnic Area established Jabotinsky Park, Shuni, Israel, 1992. Mem. Rabbinical Assn. Greater Miami (past pres.). Office: Temple Emanu-El 1701 Washington Ave Miami FL 33139-7513

LEHRMAN, MARGARET MCBRIDE, television news executive, producer; b. Spokane, Wash., Sept. 25, 1944; d. John P. and Ruth A. (Score) McBride; m. Michael Lloyd Lehrman, June 27, 1970. BA, U. Oreg., 1966; MS, Columbia U., 1970. Dir. coll. desk Peace Corps, Washington, 1966-69; asst. to exec. editor The Morning News Co., Washington, 1970-72; reporter Albright Communications, Washington, 1973-74; tv assignment editor ABC News, Washington, 1974; press asst. Senator Robert P. Griffin, Washington, 1975-79; researcher Today Show, NBC News, Washington, 1979, assoc. producer, 1979-83, Washington producer, 1983-89, dep. bur. chief, 1989-95, Washington producer, spec. coverage and events, 1995—. Trustee U. Oreg. Found., 1990—. Recipient George Hood award for diplomatic reporting (China) adv. bd. Internat. Women's Media Found. Office: NBC News 4001 Nebraska Ave NW Washington DC 20016-2795

LEHRMAN, NAT, magazine editor; b. Bklyn., Aug. 5, 1929; s. Louis and Lena (Goldfarb) L.; m. Kazuko Miyajima, Nov. 13, 1956; children: Jerome M., Cynthia H. B.A., Bklyn. Coll., 1953; M.A., NYU, 1961. Travel editor internat. travel dept. Am. Automobile Assn., 1955-57; editor Relax mag., 1958, Dude, also Gent mags., 1959-61; assoc. to sr. editor Playboy mag., Chgo., 1966-71; editor new pubs. Playboy Enterprises, 1972; editor, then assoc. pub. Oui mag., 1973-75; sr. v.p., assoc. pub. Playboy mag., 1976-85, dir. mag. divsn., 1980-85, pres. pub. div., 1982-85; pub.'s cons., 1985-87; dir. Essence mag.; tchr. fiction Columbia Coll., Chgo., 1967, chmn. journalism dept., 1987—. Author: Masters and Johnson Explained, 1970. Bd. dirs. Chgo. Chamber Musicians. With U.S. Army, 1953-55. Mem. Chgo. Classical Guitar Soc. (bd. dirs.). Club: Lincoln Park Tennis (pres.). Office: 600 S Michigan Ave Chicago IL 60605-1901

LEIBACH, DALE W., public relations executive. Reporter Kansas City Star; mgr. pub. affairs Ford Motor Co., Washington; handled internal and external comms. Taft-Hartley's Pension Funds; asst. press sec. White House, 1977-81; press sec. to U.S. senator Tom Harkin; sr. v.p., mng. dir. Powell Adams Y Rinehart (Ogilvy & Mather), Washington; sr. v.p. Powell Tate, Washington. Office: Powell Tate 700 13th St NE #1000 Washington DC 20005*

LEIBACHER, JOHN WILLIAM, astronomer; b. Chgo., May 28, 1941; s. George W. and Irene (Novotney) L.; m. Lise H. Ouvarard, Dec. 21, 1976. AB, Harvard U., 1963, PhD, 1971. Postdoctoral fellow U. Colo., Boulder, 1970-71; scientist Laboratoire de Physique Stellaire et Planetaire, Paris, 1972-74, Lockheed Rsch. Lab., Palo Alto, Calif., 1975-81; astronomer Nat. Solar Obs., Tucson, 1982—, dir., 1988-93; dir. Global Oscillation Network Group Project, Tucson, 1984—. Office: Nat Solar Observatory Sacramento Peak Sunspot NM 88349

LEIBENSPERGER, EDWARD PAUL, lawyer; b. Columbus, Ohio, Dec. 3, 1948; s. William P. and Ruth (Wylie) L.; m. Patricia Karns, Aug. 16, 1969; children—Kristen, Kenneth. B.A. magna cum laude, Muskingum Coll., 1970; J.D. summa cum laude, Ohio State U., 1974. Bar: Mass. 1974, U.S. Dist. Ct. Mass. 1974, U.S. Ct. Appeals (1st cir.) 1974; C.P.A., Ohio. Acct. Ernst & Whinney, Columbus, Ohio, 1970-71; ptnr. Nutter, McClennen & Fish, Boston, 1974—. Bd. dirs. Friends of Eye Research, Inc., Boston, 1984—. Mem. ABA (com. on corporate counsel 1982—), Boston Bar Assn. (spl. com. on profl. ethics 1984). Democrat. Unitarian. Home: 1454 Centre St Newton MA 02159-2445 Office: Nutter McClennen & Fish 1 International Pl Boston MA 02110-2699

LEIBER, GERSON AUGUST, artist; b. Bklyn., Nov. 12, 1921; s. William and Rebecca (Margulis) L.; m. Judith Maria Peto, Feb. 5, 1946. Student art, Art Students League, N.Y., 1947-52, Bklyn. Mus. Art Sch., 1952-53; DFA (hon.), Bar Ilan U., Israel, 1993. Instr. Newark Sch. Fine and Indsl. Arts; v.p. Judith Leiber, Inc., N.Y.C., 1963—. One-man shows, Oakland (Calif.) Mus., 1960, N.Y.C., 1961, 62, 63, 64, 68, 69, 72, 76, 85, Fine Arts Mus. Long Island (N.Y.), 1991; exhibited in numerous nat. and internat. group shows, prints and paintings represented in, pvt. and permanent collections. With AUS, 1942-47. Recipient numerous prizes including Bklyn. Mus. Purchase awards, 1953-66, 2d prize of $1,000, Assoc. Am. Artists Nat. Print Exhbn., 1959, Soc. Washington Printmakers prize, 1962, purchase award Hunterdon County Art Center 6th nat. print exhbn., 1962, Audubon medals of Honor for Graphics, 1963, 65, Sonia Watter award Am. Color Print Soc., 1968, 1000 Purchase award Assn. Am. Artists, 1968, John Taylor Arms Meml. prize NAD, 1971; Tiffany fellow, 1957, 60. Mem. NAD, Soc. Am. Graphic Artists (past pres.), Art Students League N.Y. Studio: 27 E 31st St New York NY 10016-4330 Studio: 27 E 31st St New York NY 10016-6804

LEIBER, JUDITH MARIA, designer, manufacturer; b. Budapest, Hungary, Jan. 11, 1921; came to U.S., 1947, naturalized, 1949. d. Emil and Helen (Spitzer) Peto; m. Gerson Leiber, Feb. 6, 1946. Student pvt. schs., Hungary and Eng.; DFA (hon.), Internat. Fine Arts Coll., 1993; PhD (hon.), Bar Ilan U., Israel, 1993, Internat. Fine Arts Coll., Miami, Fla., 1993. Master handbag maker Hungary, 1942; pattern maker, designer Nettie Rosenstein, N.Y.C., 1947-60, Koret, N.Y.C., 1960-61; owner, mgr. Judith Leiber, Inc., N.Y.C., 1963—. Author: Judith Leiber, The Artful Handbag, 1995; designs represented in 30-yr. retrospective F.I.T. Mus., N.Y., 1993-94. Recipient Swarovski award and Am. Handbag Designer award Leather Industries Am., 1970, Coty award Am. Fashion Critics, 1973, Neiman-Marcus award, 1980, Women Who Made a Difference award Fashion Group, 1986, Lifetime Achievement award Dallas Mart, 1991, Am. Acad. Achievement award, 1992, FAAB Lifetime Achievement award, 1992, Ellis Island Medal Honor, 1993, Lifetime Achievement award Coun. Fashion Designers Am., 1993, Fashion Hall of Fame award Shannon Rodgers & Jerry Silverman Sch. Fashion Design and Merchanidising, Kent State U., 1995; featured Retrospective of Work New Orleans Mus. Mem. Nat. Handbag Authority (dir. 1972—). Pioneering woman master handbag maker, Hungary; first woman patternmaker Am. handbag industry. Office: 20 W 33rd St New York NY 10001-3305

LEIBHOLZ, STEPHEN WOLFGANG, physicist, engineering company executive, entrepreneur; b. Berlin, Jan. 28, 1932; came to U.S., 1936; s. Ernest S. and Louise (Stern) L.; m. Ann Esther Greenberg, May 29, 1958; children: Judith, Robert, Daniel. BA in Physics, NYU, 1952. Prin. engr. Repub. Fairchild Co., Farmingdale, N.Y., 1957-60; mgr. systems design and analysis Auerbach Corp., Phila., 1960-67; founder, chmn. Analytics, Inc., Willow Grove, Pa., 1967-91; advisor, cons. scientist U.S. govt. agys., Washington, 1970—; founder, chmn., CEO Antares Tech. Inc. 1989—, Transport Maintenance Systems, Inc., 1989—, Chesapeake Tech Labs Inc., 1986—, ACS, Inc. 1987—; founder, CEO TechLabs Inc., 1990—. Author and editor 7 books; contbr. articles to profl. pubs. Bd. dirs. Jenkintown Music Sch., 1970-74, advisor Kansas City Camerata Chamber Orch. Cons. U. of Arts, Pa. Conv. Ctr. Mem. AAAS, IEEE, Mil. Ops. Rsch. Soc. (past bd. dirs.), Cosmos Club (Washington). Office: 6 Pheasant Run Newtown PA 18940

LEIBLER, KENNETH ROBERT, financial service executive; b. N.Y.C., Feb. 21, 1949; s. Max and Martha (Dales) L.; m. Marcia Kate Reiss, July 15, 1973; children: Jessica Hope, Andrew Ethan. B.A. magna cum laude, Syracuse U., 1971; postgrad., U. Pa., 1972. Mgr. options Lehman Bros., 1972-75; v.p. options Am. Stock Exchange, N.Y.C., 1975-79; sr. v.p. adminstrn. and fin. Am. Stock Exchange, 1979-81, exec. v.p. adminstrn. and fin., 1981-85, sr. exec. v.p., 1985-86, pres., 1986-90; pres. Liberty Fin. Cos., Boston, 1990—; instr. N.Y. Inst. Fin.; dir. Securities Industry Automation Corp.; chmn. Amex Commodities Corp. Contbg. author: Handbook of Financial Markets: Securities, Options Futures, 1981. Trustee Beth Israel Med. Ctr., Dr.'s Hosp.; bd. dirs. Am. Forum for Global Edn. Mem. Fin.

Execs. Inst., Securities Industry Assn., Boston Stock Exchange (bd. dir.), Phi Beta Kappa, Phi Kappa Phi. Office: Liberty Fin Cos 600 Atlanta Ave Boston MA 02110

LEIBMAN, RON, actor; b. N.Y.C., Oct. 11, 1937; s. Murray and Grace (Marks) L.; m. Linda Lavin, Sept. 7, 1969 (div.); m. Jessica Walter, June 26, 1983. Student, Ohio Wesleyan U., Actors Studio, N.Y.C. mem. Yale Repertory Co., 1967-68; acting tchr. Yale U. Sch. Drama, New Haven, 1967-68. Appearances include (theatre) debut in A View from the Bridge, 1959, Legend of Lovers, 1959, Dear Me, the Sky is Falling, 1963, We Bombed In New Haven (Theatre World award), Room Service, I Ought To Be in Pictures, 1981, Don Pasquale, 1983, Doubles, 1985, Rumors, 1988, Angels in America: Millenium Approaches, 1993 (Best Actor Tony award 1993), Angels in America: Peristroika, 1993, The Merchant of Venice, 1995; (films) Where's Poppa, 1970, Hot Rock, 1972, Slaughterhouse Five, 1972, Your Three Minutes Are Up, 1973, The Super Cops, 1974, Won Ton Ton, 1976, Norma Rae, 1979, Up the Academy, 1980, Zorro the Gay Blade, 1982, Romantic Comedy, 1983, Phar Lap, 1983, Rhinestone, 1984, Door to Door, 1984, Seven Hours to Judgment, 1988; (TV movies) Martinelli: Outside Man, Rivkin-Bounty Hunter, Christmas Eve, 1986 (Golden Globe nominee), Terrorist on Trial: The United States vs. Salim Ajami, 1988; (TV series) star in Kaz, 1978-79 (Emmy award). Recipient Drama Desk award for role in We Bombed in New Haven, Transfers, Obie award for role in Transfers. Office: Martin Hurwitz Assocs Inc 427 N Canon Dr Ste 215 Beverly Hills CA 90210*

LEIBOLD, ARTHUR WILLIAM, JR., lawyer; b. Ottawa, Ill., June 13, 1931; s. Arthur William and Helen (Cull) L.; m. Nora Collins, Nov. 30, 1957; children: Arthur William III, Alison Aubry, Peter Collins. AB, Haverford Coll., 1953; JD, U. Pa., 1956. Bar: Pa. 1957. With Dechert, Price & Rhoads, Phila., 1956-69, ptnr., 1965-69; ptnr. Dechert, Price & Rhoads, Washington, 1972—; gen. counsel Fed. Home Loan Bank Bd. and Fed. Savs. & Loan Ins. Corp., Washington, 1969-72, Fed. Home Loan Mortgage Corp., 1970-72; lectr. English St. Joseph's Coll., Phila., 1957-59. Contbr. articles to profl. publs. Mem. Pres. Kennedy's Lawyers Com. Civil Rights, 1963, Adminstrv. Conf. U.S., 1969-72; bd. dirs. Marymount Coll. Va., 1974-75; Mem. Phila. Com. 70, 1965-74, Fellowship Commn. Mem. ABA (mem. ho. of dels. 1967-69, 79-88, treas. 1979-83, mem. fin. com., mem. bd. govs. 1977-83), Fed. Bar Assn. (mem. nat. coun. 1971-80), D.C. Bar Assn., Phila. Bar Assn., Am. Bar Found. (treas. 1979-83), Am. Bar Ret. Assn. (dir. 1978-83), Am. Bar Endowment (bd. dirs. 1984—), Internat. Bar Assn., Phila. Country Club (Gladwyn, Pa.), Chester River Yacht and Country Club (Chestertown, Md.), Skating Club Phila., Orpheus Club (Phila.), Order of Coif, Phi Beta Kappa. Republican. Roman Catholic. Home: 2014 N Kenmore St Arlington VA 22207 Office: Dechert Price & Rhoads 1500 K St NW Ste 500 Washington DC 20005-1209

LEIBOVICH, SIDNEY, engineering educator; b. Memphis, Apr. 2, 1939; s. Harry and Rebecca (Palant) L.; m. Gail Barbara Colin, Nov. 24, 1962; children: Bradley Colin, Adam Keith. BS, Calif. Inst. Tech., Pasadena, 1961; PhD, Cornell U., 1965. NATO postdoctoral fellow U. Coll., London, 1965-66; asst. prof. thermal engring. Cornell U., Ithaca, N.Y., 1966-70, assoc. prof. thermal engring., 1970-78, prof. mech. and aerospace engring., 1978-89, Samuel B. Eckert prof. mech. and aerospace engring., 1989—. Editor: Nonlinear Waves, 1974; assoc. editor: Jour. Fluid Mechanics, 1982-93; co-editor: Acta Mechanica, 1986-92; mem. editorial bd. Ann. Revs. of Fluid Mechanics, 1989-93; gen. editor Cambridge U. Press Monographs on Mechanics, 1994—. Disting. lectr. Naval Ocean Rsch. Devel. Activity, 1983. Recipient MacPherson prize Calif. Inst. Tech., 1961. Fellow ASME (chmn. applied mechanics div. 1987-88), Am. Phys. Soc. (chmn. div. fluid dynamics 1987-88), Am. Acad. Arts and Scis., U.S. Nat. Com. for Theoretical and Applied Mechanics (chair 1990-92.), Nat. Acad. Engring. Office: Cornell U Upson Hall Ithaca NY 14853

LEIBOVITZ, ANNIE, photographer; b. Conn., Oct. 2, 1949. Student, San Francisco Art Inst. Chief photographer Rolling Stone, from 1973, photographer, 1970-83; photographer Vanity Fair, 1983—; photographer for advertisements, 1987—; proprietor Ann Leibovitz Studio, N.Y.C. Works exhibited various galleries; author: Photographs 1970-90, 1992. Recipient Innovation in Photography award Am. Soc. Mag. Photographers, 1987. Office: Annie Leibovitz Studio 55 Vandam St New York NY 10013-1104 also: Annie Leibovitz Studio 101 W 18th St New York NY 10011*

LEIBOVITZ, MITCHELL G., retail executive; b. Phila., May 11, 1945; s. Jacob A. and Doris (Schultz) L.; m. Joanne Lippman, Aug. 24, 1969; children—Dana Jill, Daniel Jay. B.A., Temple U., 1966, M.Ed., 1971, M.B.A., 1974. C.P.A. Pa. Audit sr., acct. Arthur Young & Co., Phila., 1973-76; audit prin. Seidman & Seidman, Phila., 1976-78; various positions Pep Boys-Manny Moe & Jack, Phila., 1978-90, bd. dirs., 1985—; pres., chief oper. officer Pep Boys, 1986, chief exec. officer, 1990; chmn. bd. dirs., 1994—. Bd. dirs. Police Athletic League, Phila., 1983—. Mem. Locust Club, Atlantic City Country Club, Green Valley Country Club (Lafayette Hill, Pa.), Squires Golf Club (Ambler, Pa.). Avocations: golf, sport fishing. Office: Pep Boys-Manny 3111 W Allegheny Ave Philadelphia PA 19132-1116

LEIBOW, RONALD LOUIS, lawyer; b. Santa Monica, Calif., Oct. 4, 1939; s. Norman and Jessica (Kellner) L.; m. Linda Bengelsdorf, June 11, 1961 (div. Dec. 1974); children: Jocelyn Elise, Jeffrey David, Joshua Aaron; m. Jacqueline Blatt, Apr. 6, 1986. AB, Calif. State U., Northridge, 1962; JD, UCLA, 1965. Bar: Calif. 1966, U.S. Dist. Ct. (cen. dist.) Calif. 1966, U.S. Dist. Ct. (no., so. and ea. dists.) Calif. 1971. Spl. asst. city atty. City of Burbank, Calif., 1966-67; assoc., then ptnr. Meyers, Stevens & Walters, L.A., 1967-71; ptnr. Karpf, Leibow & Warner, Beverly Hills, Calif., 1971-74, Volk, Newman Gralla & Karp, L.A., L.A., 1979-81, Spector & Leibow, L.A., 1982-84, Stroock & Stroock & Lavan, L.A., 1984-94, Kaye, Scholer, Fierman, Hays & Handler, L.A., 1994—; lectr. law UCLA, 1968-69; asst. prof. Calif. State U., Northridge, 1969-71. Contbr. articles to profl. jours. Pres. Jewish Community Ctr., Greater L.A., 1983-86; v.p. Jewish Community Ctr. Assn. N.Am., N.Y.C., 1988—, Jewish Fedn. Community, Greater L.A., 1988—. Mem. ABA (bus. bankruptcy com.), Phi Alpha Delta. Avocations: writing, tennis, skiing, travel. Office: Kaye Scholer Fierman Hays & Handler 1999 Ave of the Stars 16th Fl Los Angeles CA 90067

LEIBOWITZ, ANN GALPERIN, lawyer; b. Balt., Oct. 11, 1940; d. Harold Marcy and Dorothy Rebecca (Trivas) Galperin; m. Howard Marvin Leibowitz, July 3, 1960; children: Ellen Ann, Katherine Leibowitz Kotkin. AB, Goucher Coll., 1960; LLB, U. Md., 1964. Bar: Mass. 1964, U.S. Ct. Appeals (1st cir.) 1984. Patent atty. W.R. Grace & Co., Clarksville, Md., 1960-63; patent atty. Polaroid Corp., Cambridge, Mass., 1963-72, corporate atty., 1972-77, sr. corporate atty. and labor counsel, 1977—; lectr. Coun. Edn. in Mgmt., Walnut Creek, Calif., 1987—; mem. faculty Mass. Continuing Legal Edn., Boston, 1991—. Bd. trustees Goucher Coll., Towson, Md., 1983-89; chmn. fin. com. Town of Weston, 1989-91, active, 1984-91, chmn. bd. selectmen, 1993—, active, 1991—; mem. exec. adv. bd. Ctr. House, Boston, 1990—. Mem. ABA, Am. Corporate Counsel Assn. (bd. dirs. N.E. chpt. 1988-91), Mass. Bar Assn. (lectr. 1987—), Polaroid Corp. Bar Assn., Indsl. Rels. Rsch. Assn. Office: Polaroid Corp 575 Technology Sq Cambridge MA 02139

LEIBOWITZ, HERBERT AKIBA, English language educator, author; b. Staten Island, N.Y., Apr. 26, 1935; s. Morris and Rose (Rabinowitz) L.; m. Susan Yankowitz, May 3, 1978; 1 son, Gabriel. B.A., Bklyn. Coll., 1956; M.A., Brown U., 1958; Ph.D., Columbia U., 1966. Asst. prof. English Columbia U., 1967-70; asst. prof. humanities Richmond Coll., Staten Island, N.Y., 1971-73, assoc. prof.-73-76; assoc. prof. English Coll. S.I., 1976-81; prof. English Coll. Staten Island, CUNY and Grad. Ctr. CUNY, 1981—; prof. English emeritus, 1991—. Author: Hart Crane: An Introduction to the Poetry, 1968, Fabricating Lives, 1989; editor: Selected Music Criticism of Paul Rosenfeld, 1970, Parnassus: Poetry in Review, 1972, Parnassus: Twenty Years of Poetry in Review, 1994, Asphodel, That Greeny Flower and Other William Carlos Williams Love Poems, 1994. Recipient Fels award for editorial distinction Coordinating Coun. Lit. Mags., 1975; postdoctoral fellow U. Ill. Ctr. Advanced Study, 1968-69, Chamberlain fellow Columbia U., 1970, fellow N.Y. Inst. Humanities, 1987—; Mellon Seminar fellow NYU, 1988, Guggenheim fellow, 1991-92. Mem. PEN (Nora Magid award for disting. editing of lit. mag. 1995). Nat. Book Critics Circle (bd. dirs. 1988-94, pres. 1992-94). Jewish. Home: 205 W 89th St New York NY 10024-1828 Office: Poetry Rev Found 205 W 89th St 8F New York NY 10024

LEIBOWITZ, JACK RICHARD, physicist, educator; b. Bridgeport, Conn., July 21, 1929; BA, NYU, MS, 1955; PhD in Physics, Brown U., 1962; m. 1954; 2 children; m. 1989. Rsch. physicist MIT Lincoln Lab., 1956-61, Westinghouse Rsch. Labs., Pitts., 1961-64; asst. prof. U. Md., College Park, 1965-69; assoc. prof. physics Cath. U. Am., Washington, 1969-73, prof. physics, 1974—, assoc. dean for grad. studies, 1988-93, chmn. art dept., 1882-86, acad. senate; sci. cons. govt. agys., NBC-TV. Fellow Am. Phys. Soc., Washington Acad. Scis.; mem. Sigma Xi. Contbr. numerous rsch. articles to sci. jours. and books. Research in condensed matter physics: superconductivity, electron-phonon interaction, band structure. Office: Cath U of Am P O Box 256 Ashton MD 20861

LEIBRECHT, JOHN JOSEPH, bishop; b. Overland, Mo., Aug. 8, 1930. PhD, Cath. U., Washington. Ordained priest, Roman Cath. Ch., 1956. Supt. schs. St. Louis Archdiocese, 1962-81; bishop Springfield-Cape Girardeau, Mo., 1984—. Address: The Catholic Ctr 601 S Jefferson Ave Springfield MO 65806-3107*

LEIBSON, CHARLES M., state supreme court justice; b. Louisville, KY, June 30, 1929; m. Margaret Leibson. LLB cum laude, U. Louisville, 1952; LLM, U. Va., 1986. Bar: Ky. 1952. Pvt. practice law Louisville, 1954-76; judge Ky. Cir. Ct., Louisville, 1976-82; justice Ky. Supreme Ct., Louisville, 1983—; lectr. courtroom law U. Louisville Sch. Law, 1969-82; pres. Ky. Assn. Trial Attys., 1965. Chmn. bd. trustees Jefferson County Pub. Law Library, 1978-81. 1st lt. JAGC U.S. Army, 1952-54. Named Judge of Yr., Louisville Bar Assn., 1979, Ky.'s Outstanding Judge, Ky. Bar Assn., 1990; recipient Outstanding State Trial Judge award award Assn. Trial Lawyers Am., 1980, Outstanding Svc. award Ky. Pers. Bd., 1982, Disting. Alumni award U. Louisville Sch. Law, 1984, Outstanding Legal Scholarship award Brandeis Soc., 1984, Outstanding State Appellate Judge award, Assn. Trial Lawyers Am., 1985; fellow NEH, 1981. Fellow Internat. Acad. Trial Lawyers; mem. Louisville Bar Assn., Internat. Acad. Trial Judges, Inner Circle of Advs. Office: Ky Supreme Ct 245 Capitol Bldg Frankfort KY 40601

LEIBSON, IRVING, industrial executive; b. Wilkes Barre, Pa., Sept. 28, 1926; s. Henry and Sonia (Rose) L.; m. Lola Pavalow, Feb. 16, 1950; children: Russell, Sandra Eve. B.Chem. Engring. cum laude, U. Fla., 1945, M.S., 1947; M.S. Carnegie Inst. Tech., 1949; D.Sc., Carnegie Inst. Tech., 1952. Registered profl. engr., Calif., N.J., Tex., D.C. Chem. engr. to supr. Humble Oil and Refining Co., Baytown, Tex., 1952-56; process engring., 1961-63, tech. mgr., 1963-65, dir. R & D, 1965-67; gen. mgr. ABS div., 1967-68; v.p. Dart Industries Chem. Group, Paramus, N.J., 1969-74; asst. to sr. v.p., investment dept. Bechtel Corp., San Francisco, 1974-75; mgr. process and environment, v.p. C & I/Girdler Inc. (a Bechtel Co.), 1976-78; v.p., mgr. rsch. and engring. Bechtel Nat. Inc., 1978-79; sr. v.p. Bechtel Inc., 1979-81; sr. v.p., mgr. mktg. Bechtel Group Inc., 1981-85, sr. v.p., sr. tech. officer, 1985-87, exec. cons., 1987—; founder, pres. Bold Techs., 1987—; prin. AI Enterprises, FN Enterprises, 1989—; part-time prof. Rice U., 1957, U. Md., 1954. Contbr. articles to profl. jours. Dist. commr. E. Harris County dist. Boy Scouts Am., 1958-61; Vice chmn. Intersoc. Task Force Energy, 1973; assoc. World Coal Study, 1979-80; assoc. coal industry adv. bd. Internat. Energy Agy., 1980—; treas., vice chmn.. chmn. mem. exec. com. Council Alternate Fuels, 1982-87; mem. Nat. Coal Council, 1985—; chmn. Coal Policy Commn., 1987-91; mem. exec. com., 1987—; mem. adv. bd. Ctr. Chem. Process Safety Tech., 1985-88; mem. liquid fuels com. NRC, 1989-90. Served with AUS, 1953-54. Recipient Disting. Alumnus award U. Fla., 1988. Fellow Am. Inst. Chem. Engrs. (dir. 1967-69, v.p. 1973, pres. 1974, Publ. award S. Tex. chpt. 1957, Founders award 1976); mem. Am. Chem. Soc., Engrs. Joint Council (dir. 1969-78), Engrs. Manpower Commn., Coal and Slurry Tech. Assn. (chmn. 1986-89). Clubs: Round Hill Golf and Country (San Francisco), World Trade (San Francisco), Sailfish Point Golf (Stuart, Fla.), Ary (Stuart), Villa Taverna (San Francisco). Patentee in field. Home: 2920 SE Dune Dr Apt 410 Stuart FL 34996-1986

LEICHTER, FRANZ S., state senator; b. Vienna, Austria, Aug. 19, 1930; s. Otto and Kathe (Pick) L.; m. Nina Williams, July 3, 1958; children: Katherine, Joshua. BA, Swarthmore Coll., 1952; JD, Harvard U., 1957. Bar: N.Y. 1957, U.S. Dist. Ct. (so. and ea. dists.) N.Y. 1959, U.S. Ct. Appeals (2d cir.) 1961. Mem. N.Y. State Assembly, Albany, 1969-74; mem. N.Y. State Senate, Albany, 1975—; ranking mem. environ. conservation com., 1986—, ranking mem. judiciary com., 1991—; ptnr. Wachtell, Manheim & Grouf, N.Y.C., 1974-88; of counsel Walter, Conston, Alexander & Green, N.Y.C., 1988—; chair N.Y. State Senate Dem. Policy Com., 1983-90. Author various reports, 1979—. Del. Dem. Nat. Convention, 1964, 84, 88. Cpl. U.s. Army, 1953-55. Recipient award Austrian Govt., 1984. Mem. ACLU, Assn. of Bar of City of N.Y., N.Y. State Bar Assn., Am. Jewish Congress. Democrat. Jewish. Avocations: hiking, skiing, tennis, reading history works. Home: 448 Riverside Dr New York NY 10027-6818 Office: NY State Senate Albany NY 12247

LEICHTLING, MICHAEL ALFRED, lawyer; b. N.Y.C., Mar. 30, 1943; s. Stanley Arthur and Roslyn Priscilla (Fuhr) L.; m. Arlene Dorf, July 30, 1966; children: Julie Karen, Nina Anastasia, Noah James. BA, SUNY, Binghamton, 1963; JD, Northwestern U., 1966; postgrad., Columbia U., 1968. Bar: N.Y. 1969, U.S. Ct. Appeals (2d cir.) 1969. Assoc. Aranow Brodsky Bohlinger Einhorn & Dann, N.Y.C., 1966, Parker Chapin & Flattau, N.Y.C., 1969-77; ptnr. Parker Chapin Flattau & Klimpl, N.Y.C., 1977—, mem. exec. com., 1987-92; bd. dirs. H. Warshow & Sons Inc., N.Y.C. Editor Northwestern U. Law Rev., 1965-66, Equipment Leasing Jour., 1986—, Computer Leasing Today, 1989—. Bd. dirs. Friends of Israel Disabled War Vets., N.Y.C., 1986—. With U.S. Army, 1966-68; Vietnam. Decorated Bronze Star; Regents scholar, 1963, Newman scholar, 1963-66. Mem. N.Y. State Bar Assn. (corp. law sect.), N.Y. County Lawyers Assn. (banking law com., secured lending com.), Equipment Lending Assn. Am. (legal com., state legis. com.), Ea. Assn. Equipment Lessors (chmn. legal com., gen. counsel 1986—). Avocations: reading, painting, swimming, golf. Home: 148 Quinn Rd Briarcliff Manor NY 10510-2133 Office: Parker Chapin Flattau & Klimpl 1211 6th Ave New York NY 10036-8701

LEIDEN, CARL, political scientist, educator; b. Boone, Iowa, Feb. 6, 1922; s. Carl Eric and Christine Olivia (Bergstrom) L.; m. Mary Katherine Rood, Sept. 5, 1945; children: Lisa Ingrid, Derek Stefan. B.S., Iowa State Coll., 1945; M.P.A., Wayne U., 1947; Ph.D., State U. Iowa, 1949. Instr. State U. Iowa, Iowa City, 1946-49; asst. prof. to assoc. prof. Marshall Coll., Huntington, W.Va., 1949-59; assoc. prof. Am. U., Cairo, Egypt, 1959-61; assoc. prof. to prof. polit. sci. U. Tex., Austin, 1961-87, prof. emeritus, 1987—; Fulbright lectr. Peshawar U., Pakistan, 1952-53; vis. assoc. prof. U. Calif.-Berkeley, 1957; prof. Nat. War Coll., Washington, 1972-73. Author or co-author eight books on polit. sci. Volker Found. fellow, 1945-46; Fulbright teaching grantee, 1952-53, 1966; Earhart Found. grantee, 1970. Republican. Home: 3301 Stoneridge Rd Austin TX 78746-7715 Office: Univ Texas Austin TX 78712

LEIDEN, JEFFREY MARC, molecular biologist, cardiologist; b. Chgo., Oct. 12, 1955; s. Irving and Rosemary (Rebelsky) L.; m. Lisa Leyland, June 23, 1982; children: Benjamin Bradford, Alexander Dow. BA in Biol. Sci. with honors, U. Chgo., 1975, MD with honors, 1979, PhD, 1981. Diplomate Am. Bd. Internal Medicine, Am. Bd. Cardiovascular Diseases; lic. cardiologist, Mass., Mich., Ill. Intern Brigham and Women's Hosp. Harvard Med. Sch., Boston, 1981, resident in internal medicine, 1982-84, cardiology fellow, 1984-87; clin. fellow Dana-Farber Cancer Inst. Harvard Med. Sch., Boston, 1984-87; from asst. to assoc. investigator Howard Hughes Med. Inst., Ann Arbor, 1987-92; from asst. to assoc. prof. internal medicine div. cardiology U. Mich. Sch. Medicine, Ann Arbor, 1986-92, asst. prof. dept. microbiology, immunology, 1987-92, assoc. chief div. cardiology, dir. Cardiovascular Rsch. Ctr., 1990-92; prof. pathology U. Chgo., 1992—, prof. medicine, chief sect. cardiology, 1992—; faculty appointment grad. program in cellular and molecular biology U. Mich., Ann Arbor, 1988-92, com. on immunology, U. Chgo., 1992—, Cancer Ctr., 1992—; ad hoc reviewer allergy and immunology study sect. NIH, 1990-91, immunobiology study sect., 1991; reviewer Am. Jour. Physiology, New Biologist, Jour. Immunology, Internat. Immu-

nology, Molecular and Cellular Biology, Circulation, Am. Review of Respiratory Disease, Leukocyte Biology, Jour. clin. Investigation; cons. and lectr. in field. Contbr. articles to Immunogenetics, Jour. Virology, Jour. Immunology, Molecular and Cellular Biology, Jour. Biol. Chem., Circulation, Jour. Exptl. Medicine, Sci., Immunology Today. Chmn. molecular biology session Am. Heart Assn. Nat. Meeting, 1992, Katz Prize selection com., 1992-93. Grantee NIH, 1990—, VA Rsch. Career Devel. award, 1989-93; Jere W. Thompson Neuromuscular Disease Rsch. fellow Muscular Dystrophy Assn., 1990-93, Vical Inc., 1992—, Howard Hughes Med. Inst., 1987-93, Am. Heart Assn., 1991-93; Pfizer Postdoctoral fellow, 1984; recipient Ctrl. Soc. for clin. Rsch. Presdl. award, 1991, John Van Prohaska award, 1981. Mem. AAAS, Am. Fedn. for Clin. Rsch., Am. Heart Assn. Basic Sci. Coun., Am. Soc. Microbiology, Am. Soc. for Clin. Investigation, Assn. Prof. Cardiology, Phi Beta Kappa, Alpha Omega Alpha. Achievements include research in transcriptional regulation during T cell devel. and activation, structure, function, and regulation of cardiac and skeletal muscle troponin C, gene therapy approaches in cardiac and skeletal muscle. Home: 5639 S Drexel Ave Chicago IL 60637 Office: Univ Chicago BRH B608 MC6080 5841 S Maryland Ave Chicago IL 60637-1463

LEIDEN, WARREN ROBERT, law association executive; b. N.Y.C., Jan. 15, 1949; s. Walter John and Bernice (Hansen) L.; m. Cathy Jane Bierbach, Nov. 20, 1976; children: Conrad, Adam. BA in Philosophy, Johns Hopkins U., 1971; JD, Boston U., 1974. Bar: Mass. 1974, U.S. Dist. Ct. Mass. 1978, U.S. Ct. Appeals (1st cir.) 1980. Assoc. Leland, Lasker & Weinstein, Boston, 1974-75; pvt. practice Boston, 1975-77; ptnr. Reitmeyer & Leiden, Boston, 1977-80; dir. Nat. Immigration Project, Boston, 1980-82; exec. dir. Am. Immigration Lawyers Assn., Washington, 1982—; exec. v.p. Am. Immigration Law Found., Washington, 1987—; treas. Nat. Immigrant, Refugee and Citizenship Forum, Washington, 1986—; bd. advisors Nat. Immigration Law Ctr., L.A., 1986—; mem. adv. bd. UN High Commn. for Refugees, Washington, 1987-88; mem. U.S. Commn. Immigration Reform, 1992—. Mem. ABA, Internat. Bar Assn., Am. Soc. Assn. Execs. (legal sect.). Office: Am Immigration Lawyers Assn 1400 I St NW Ste 1200 Washington DC 20005-2208

LEIDER, GERALD J., motion picture and television company executive; b. Camden, N.J., May 28, 1931; s. Myer and Minnie Leider; m. Susan Trustman, Dec. 21, 1968; children: Matthew Trustman, Kenneth Harold. B.A., Syracuse U., 1953. Theater producer in N.Y.C., London, 1956-59; dir. spl. programs CBS-TV, 1960-61, dir. program sales, 1961-62; v.p. TV ops. Ashley Famous Agy., Inc., N.Y.C., 1962-69; pres. Warner Bros. TV, Burbank, Calif., 1969-74; exec. v.p. fgn. prodn. Warner Bros. Pictures, Rome, 1975-76; ind. producer motion pictures and TV GJL Prodns., Inc., Los Angeles, 1977-82; pres. ITC Prodns., Inc., Los Angeles, 1982-87; pres., chief exec. officer ITC Entertainment Group, Studio City, Calif., 1987—. Producer: Gielgud's Ages of Man, 1958-59; feature motion pictures include The Jazz Singer (with Neil Diamond), 1980, Trenchcoat, 1983; TV films include And I Alone Survived, 1978, Willa, 1979, The Hostage Tower, 1980, The Scarlet and the Black, Secrets of a Married Man, The Haunting Passion, Letting Go, A Time to Live, The Girl Who Spelled Freedom, Unnatural Causes, Poor Little Rich Girl. Mem. Bd. Visitors Coll. Visual and Performing Arts, Syracuse U. Recipient Arents Alumni medal Syracuse U., 1977; Fulbright fellow U. Bristol (Eng.), 1954. Mem. Acad. Motion Picture Arts and Scis., Acad. TV Arts and Scis., Am. Film Inst. (second decade council), Hollywood Radio and TV Soc. (pres. 1975-76); mem. steering com. The Caucus for Producers, Writers & Dirs. Office: ITC Entertainment Group 12711 Ventura Blvd Studio City CA 91604-2431

LEIDHEISER, HENRY, JR., retired chemistry educator, consultant; b. Union City, N.J., Apr. 18, 1920; s. Henry and Margaret Marie (Steinel) L.; m. Virginia Townsend, Feb. 21, 1944; children: Margaret Frances, Henry III. BS in Chemistry, U. Va., 1941, MS in Phys. Chemistry, 1943, PhD in Phys. Chemistry, 1946. Research associate U. Va., Charlottesville, 1946-49; research chemist, dir. Va. Inst. for Sci. Research, Richmond, 1949-68; prof. chemistry Lehigh U., Bethlehem, Pa., 1968-90, prof. emeritus, 1990—; cons. space science NASA, 1972-84; cons. numerous indsl. orgns. Author or editor of 8 books; 275 publs. in tech. lit.; 6 patents on crystal growth and metal surface treatment. NATO fellow to Cambridge U., England, 1969; recipient J. Shelton Horsley Rsch. award Va. Acad. Sci., 1948, Oak Ridge Inst. Nuclear Studies Rsch. award, 1949, Westinghouse Signal and Brake Award of Inst. Metal Finishing, 1954, Silver medal Am. Electroplaters' Soc., 1978, Arch T. Colwell award Soc. Automotive Engrs., 1979, Humboldt Sr. Scientist award, 1985, Tambour award 11th Congress Metal Finishing, 1984, Silver medal South African Corrosion Inst., 1986, Libsch Rsch. award Lehigh U., 1987, Mattiello Rsch. award Fedn. Soc. Coatings Tech., 1990. Fellow AAAS; mem. Am. Chem. Soc., Electrochem. Soc. (Young Author's award 1948, Rsch. award 1986, 91), Nat. Assn. Corrosion Engrs. (Whitney award 1983), Rotary. Republican. Presbyterian. Avocations: bridge, golf, collecting ceramics. Home: 822 Carnoustie Dr Venice FL 34293-4343

LEIDINGER, WILLIAM JOHN, clinic administrator; b. Chgo., Feb. 1, 1940; s. Arthur George and Anna (Choisek) L.; m. Karen Aldinger, Sept. 1, 1962; children: Michael, Steven. B.A., Loras Coll., Dubuque, Iowa, 1962; M.A., State U. Iowa, 1963. Adminstrv. asst. to city mgr. Park Forest, Ill., 1963-65; asst. to city mgr. Alexandria, Va., 1965-71; asst. city mgr. Richmond, Va., 1971-72; city mgr., 1972-78; v.p. Rolm/Atlantic Corp., 1979-81; exec. dir. McGuire Clinic, Richmond, 1981—; instr. Purdue U., No. Va. Community Coll.; guest lectr. U. Richmond, mem. bd. assos., Va. Commonwealth U. Bd. dirs., pres. Greater Richmond Transit Co., 1973-78; mem. Richmond City Planning Commn., 1971-78; bd. dirs. Richmond Eye Hosp., 1979—, St. Luke's Hosp, Richmond Cerebral Palsy Ctr; mem. Richmond City Council, 1980—; bd. dirs. Port of Richmond. Mem. Internat. City Mgmt. Assn. (chmn. labor/mgmt. relations com. 1974-75), Nat. League Cities, Va. Municipal League, Am. Soc. Pub. Adminstrn. Roman Catholic. Office: Office of the County Exec 12000 Government Center Pky Fairfax VA 22035-0001

LEIDNER, HAROLD EDWARD, lawyer; b. Cleve., Aug. 23, 1937; s. Nathan Nelson and Therese Loretta (Burdine) L.; children—Kenneth Jason, Andrew Mitchell. A.B., Cornell U., 1959; LL.B., Western Res. U., 1963. Bar: Ohio 1963. Since practiced in Cleve.; prin. Fuerst, Leidner, Dougherty & Kasdan Co., 1968-79; ptnr. firm Benesch, Friedlander, Coplan & Aronoff, 1984—. Law editor: Webster's New World Dictionary of the American Language, 1970. Mem. Am. Ohio, Cleve. bar assns.; Am. Arbitration Assn. Republican. Clubs: Cornell; Commerce (Cleve.); Curzon House (London, Eng.). Home: 2112 Acacia Park Dr Lyndhurst OH 44124-3852 Office: Benesch Friedlander Coplan 2300 BP America Bldg 200 Public Sq Cleveland OH 44114-2378

LEIES, JOHN ALEX, academic administrator, educator, clergyman; b. Chgo., Apr. 24, 1926. BS in Edn., U. Dayton, 1948; STB, U. Friborg, Switzerland, 1954, STL, 1956, STD, 1958. Asst. to provincial Soc. of Mary, St. Louis, 1961-64; regional superior Marianist Missions, Peru, 1964-68; prof. theology, dir. campus ministry St. Mary's U., San Antonio, 1974-81, chmn. grad. theology dept., 1980-81, acad. v.p., 1981-85, pres., 1985-88; grad. advisor theology dept. St. Mary's U., 1977-81, dir. Ctr. for Profl. Ethics, 1991—; dir. Cath. Charismatic Bible Inst., 1977-86, 91—; theologian mem. ethics com. Santa Rosa Hosp., 1978-81, 89—; mem. gen. rght. Soc. of Mary, 1966-67, 71, 76, 81, 86, 91; rsch. fellow cons. Pope John Med. Moral Rsch. Ctr., Braintree, Mass., 1988—; bd. trustees Tex. Ctr. for Legal Ethics and Professionalism, 1994-95. Mem. Lambda Chi Alpha, Rotary, Univ. Faculty for Life, Fellowship of Cath. Scholars. Avocation: reading. Address: St Mary's Univ of San Antonio 1 Camino Santa Maria St San Antonio TX 78228-5433

LEIFER, LARRY JOHN, mechanical engineering design educator, health science facility administrator; b. Ely, Nev., July 2, 1940; s. Lewis Carl and Nelle Nadine (Evasovic) L.; m. Aimee Dorr, Sept. 20, 1963 (div. Oct. 1973); 1 child, Simeon Kel; m. Ines Jenal, Aug. 26, 1976 (div. 1987); children: Tjarko Zuri, Sascha Bjorn, Kalani Kai. BS, Stanford U., 1962, MS, 1963, PhD, 1969. Staff scientist, human machine integration NASA Ames Research Ctr., Calif., 1969-73; scientist, man-vehicle lab MIT, Cambridge, 1972-73; asst. prof. Inst. Biomed. Systems Analysis Swiss Fed. Inst. Tech., Zurich, Switzerland, 1973-76, prof., 1976—; assoc. prof. mech. engring. Stanford (Calif.) U., 1978—; dir. rehab. research and devel. ctr. VA Med. Ctr., Palo

Alto, Calif., 1978-89; chief exec. officer, founder Tolfa Corp., 1989—; dir. Smart Product Design Lab., Stanford U., 1977—, Ctr. for Design Research, Stanford U., 1984—; prof. mech. engring. Stanford (Calif.) U., 1988—. Editor: Distribute Nerve Conduction Velocity, 1981; contbr. articles to profl. jours. NASA, VA, NSF, IBM grantee. Mem. AAAS, ASME, IEEE, Biomed. Engring. Soc., Assn. Computer Machinery, Artificial Intelligence Soc., Rehab. Engring. Soc. N.Am. Avocations: design theory and methodology, interactive robotics, rehab. engring. Office: Stanford U Dept Mech Engring Stanford CA 94305

LEIGH, HOYLE, psychiatrist, educator, writer; b. Seoul, Korea, Mar. 25, 1942; came to U.S., 1965; m. Vincenta Masciandaro, Sept. 16, 1967; 1 child, Alexander Hoyle. MA, Yale U., 1982; MD, Yonsei U, Seoul, 1965. Diplomate Am. Bd. Psychiatry and Neurology. Asst. prof. Yale U., New Haven, 1971-75, assoc. prof., 1975-80, prof., 1980-89, lectr. in psychiatry, 1989—; dir. Behavioral Medicine Clinic, Yale U., 1980-89; dir. psychiat. cons. svc. Yale-New Haven Hosp., 1971-89; chief psychiatry VA Med. Ctr., Fresno, Calif., 1989—; prof., vice chmn. dept. psychiatry U. Calif. San Francisco, 1989—; head dept. psychiatry U. Calif., San Francisco, Fresno, 1989—; cons. Am. Jour. Psychiatry, Archives Internal Medicine, Psychosomatic Medicine; gov. bd. Internat. Coll. Psychosomatic Medicine. Author: The Patient, 1980, 2d edit., 1985, 3d edit., 1992; editor: Psychiatry in the Practice of Medicine, 1983, Consultation-Liaison Psychiatry: 1990's & Beyond, 1994. Fellow Am. Psychiat. Assn., ACP, Internat. Coll. Psychosomatic Medicine (gov. bd.); mem. AMA, AAUP, World Psychiat. Assn. Avocations: reading, music, skiing. Office: U Calif Dept Psychiat 2615 E Clinton Ave Fresno CA 93703

LEIGH, JANET (JEANETTE HELEN MORRISON), actress; b. Merced, Calif., July 6, 1927; m. Tony Curtis, June 4, 1951 (div. 1962); children: Jamie Lee, Kelly; m. Robert Brandt, 1962. Student, Coll. Pacific. Actress: (films) Romance of Rosy Ridge, 1947, If Winter Comes, 1947, Hills of Home, 1948, Words and Music, 1948, Act of Violence, 1948, Little Women, 1949, That Forsythe Woman, 1949, The Red Danube, 1949, The Doctor and the Girl, 1949, Holiday Affair, 1949, Two Tickets to Broadway, 1951, Strictly Dishonorable, 1951, Angels in the Outfield, 1951, It's a Big Country, 1952, Scaramouche, 1952, Fearless Fagan, 1952, The Naked Spur, 1953, Houdini, 1953, Walking My Baby Back Home, 1953, Confidentially Connie, 1953, Prince Valiant, 1954, The Black Shield of Falworth, 1954, Rogue Cop, 1954, Living It Up!, 1954, My Sister Eileen, 1955, Pete Kelly's Blues, 1955, Just This Once, 1955, Touch of Evil, 1958, The Vikings, 1958, The Perfect Furlough, 1958, Psycho, 1960, Who Was That Lady?, 1960, The Manchurian Candidate, 1962, Bye Bye Birdie, 1963, Wives and Lovers, 1963, Grand Slam, Harper, 1966, Kid Rodello, 1966, Hello Down There, 1968, The Deadly Dream, 1971, One Is a Lonely Number, 1972, Night of the Lepus, 1972, Boardwalk, 1979, Fog, 1980, Other Realms, (TV movies) numerous including The World Series Murders, Death's Head, The Monk, 1969, Honeymoon with a Stranger, 1969, The House on Green Apple Road, 1970, The Chairman, Murdock's Gang, 1973, Telethon, 1977, Mirror, Mirror, 1979, Murder at the World Series, Murder She Wrote, Love Letters, 1991; author: (autobiography) There Really Was a Hollywood, 1984, (novel) House of Destiny, (stage) Murder Among Friends, 1976, Love Letters, 1991, (non-fiction) Psycho Revisited; rec. (album) Bye Bye, Birdie. Home: 1625 Summitridge Dr Beverly Hills CA 90210

LEIGH, JENNIFER JASON (JENNIFER LEIGH MORROW), actress; b. L.A., Feb. 5, 1962; d. Barbara Turner and Vic Morrow. Student, Lee Strasberg Inst. Appearances include (films) Eyes of a Stranger, 1980, Fast Times at Ridgemont High, 1982, Wrong is Right, 1982, Easy Money, 1983, Grandview U.S.A., 1984, Flesh + Blood, 1985, The Hitcher, 1986, The Men's Club, 1986, Sister, Sister, 1987, Under Cover, 1987, Heart of Midnight, 1988, The Big Picture, 1989, Last Exit to Brooklyn, 1989, Miami Blues, 1990, Crooked Hearts, 1991, Backdraft, 1991, Rush, 1992, Single White Female, 1992, Short Cuts, 1993, The Hudsucker Proxy, 1994, Mrs. Parker and the Vicious Circle, 1994, Dolores Claiborne, 1994; (TV movies) Angel City, 1980, The Killing of Randy Webster, 1981, The Best Little Girl in the World, 1981, The First Time, 1982, Girls of the White Orchid, 1983, Buried Alive, 1990. Office: ICM 8899 Beverly Blvd West Hollywood CA 90048-2412 also: care Elaine Rich 2400 Whitman Pl Los Angeles CA 90068*

LEIGH, MONROE, lawyer; b. South Boston, Va., July 15, 1919; s. Leander Faulkner and Elizabeth Edmunds (Monroe) L.; m. Mary Gallaher Leigh, Apr. 15, 1951; children: Edward Monroe, Parker McCollester, Elizabeth Faulkner. B.A., Hampden-Sydney Coll., 1940; LL.B., U. Va., 1947. Bar: Va. 1947, D.C. 1948, U.S. Supreme Ct 1950. Assoc. firm Covington, Burling, Rublee, Acheson & Shorb, 1947-51; mem. U.S. del. N. Atlantic Council, London and Paris, 1951-53; dep. asst. gen. counsel Dept. Def., 1953-55, asst. gen. counsel internat. affairs, 1955-59; ptnr. Steptoe and Johnson, Washington, 1961-75, 77—; legal adviser Dept. State, 1975-77; lectr. U. Va. Law Sch., 1964-75, 78-88; mem. Permanent Ct. of Arbitration, The Hague, 1975-80; mem. Adv. Com. Internat. Investment U.S. Trade Rep., 1984—; mem. Legal Adviser's Adv. Com. on Pub. Internat. Law, 1993—; mem. adv. com. Am. Law Inst. on Fgn. Rels. Law. Co-editor: National Treaty Law and Practice, 1995; contbr. articles to profl. jours. Trustee U. Va. Law Sch. Found. Capt. USAAF, 1943-46. Recipient Superior Honor award Sec. of State, 1977. Mem. ABA (Theberge award 1989, chmn. task force on war crimes in Bosnia 1993—), Internat. Law Assn., Am. Soc. Internat. Law (pres. 1981-82, hon. pres. 1990-92), Coun. Fgn. Rels., Washington Inst. Fgn. Affairs, Am. Law Inst., Colonnade Club, Cosmos Club, Met. Club, Chevy Chase Club. Episcopalian. Home: 5205 Westwood Dr Bethesda MD 20816-1838 Office: 1330 Connecticut Ave NW Washington DC 20036-1704

LEIGH, SHERREN, communications executive, editor, publisher; b. Cleve. Dec. 22, 1942; d. Walter Carl Maurushat and Treva Eldora (Burke) Morris; m. Norman J. Hickey Jr., Aug. 23, 1969 (div. 1985). BS, Ohio U., 1965. Communications dir. Metal Lath Assn., Cleve., 1965-67; creative dir. O'Toole Inc., Chgo., 1967-69; sr. v.p. RLC Inc., Chgo., 1969-77; pres. Leigh Communications Inc., Chgo., 1978—; chmn. Today's Chgo. Woman mag., 1982—; pres. Ill. Ambassadors, Chgo., 1985-86; bd. dirs. Chgo. Fin. Exchange, 1985-87. Author: How to Write a Winning Resume, How to Negotiate for Top Dollar, How to Find, Get and Keep the Job You Want. Bd. dirs. Midwest Women's Ctr., Chgo., 1984-86, Girl Scouts Chgo., 1985-87, Black Women's Hall of Fame Found., Chgo., 1986—, Apparel Industry Bd., Chgo., 1988. Recipient Corp. Leadership award YWCA Met. Chgo., 1979, Entrepreneurship award, 1988, Media Advocate of Yr. award U.S. SBA, 1994; named one of 10 Women of Achievement Midwest Women's Ctr., Chgo., 1987, Advt. Woman of Yr. Women's Advt. Club, Chgo., 1984, inducted City of Chgo. Women's Hall of Fame, 1988. Mem. Chgo. Network, Econ. Club Chgo., Execs. Club Chgo., Com. of 200 (founding mem.). Office: Leigh Communications 233 E Ontario St Ste 1300 Chicago IL 60611-3214

LEIGH, STEPHEN, industrial designer; b. N.Y.C., May 21, 1931; s. Herman Lerner and Rhea (Drinkhouse) L.; m. Barbara Lynn Haim, Feb. 14, 1984; children: Harvey Alan, Madeleine Beth. BFA, Cooper Union, 1951. Interior designer Robert Gruen Assocs., N.Y.C., 1951-55; designer, project dir. Michael Saphier Assocs., N.Y.C., 1955-59; pres. Stephen Leigh & Assocs. Inc., N.Y.C., 1959—; interior designers; cons. specializing in comml. usage, United Jewish Appeal, 1963, U.S. Pavilion, Venezuelan Pavilion, N.Y. World's Fair, 1964-65, Random House, 1969, Mitsubishi Internat. Corp., 1980, Rapid Am. Corp., 1982, Bowery Savs. Bank, 1986; lectr. NYU. Columnist Real Estate Weekly, 1963-65, The Office Mag. 1985—; one-man shows of sculpture at Cartier and East River Savings Bank; recent prin. works include Union Chelsea Nat. Bank, Faberge, Fino Restaurant, Il Menestrello Restaurant, Schenley, redesign of landmark facade at 111 8th Ave., 1989; sculpted permanent team trophy for Eisenhower Golf Tournament. Recipient AIA design award for Venezuelan Pavilion N.Y. World's Fair, 1964-65, Excellence award The Archtl. Woodwork Inst. 1988. Mem. Am. Soc. of Interior Designers (N.Y. chpt.), Charge des Missions of the Confrerie de la Chaine des Rotisseurs (Bronze Star of Excellence), Brotherhood of the Knights of the Vine. Avocations: sculpture, painting, cooking, travel, collecting Americana. Office: 157 E 57th St New York NY 10022

LEIGH-MANUELL, ROBERT ALLEN, training executive, educator; b. Bay Shore, N.Y., Oct. 4, 1942; s. Darrell B. and Rose A. (Sanders) L.-M.; m. Diane W. Frisbee, Mar. 28, 1964 (div. May 1982); children: Nancy D., Timothy J., Charles R.; m. Donna M. McGrath, Oct. 25, 1982; children: Michael N., David A. Student, Kans. State U., 1960-61; BS, SUNY, Oswego, 1964; postgrad., Hofstra U., 1965-66; MA, NYU, 1977. Cert. secondary sch. tchr., N.Y.; cert. sch. adminstr., N.Y. Tchr. Sachem Cen. Sch. Dist., Holtsville, N.Y., 1964-67; tng. mgr. Deutsch Relays, North Port, N.Y., 1967-68; instructional systems engr. Sperry Gyroscope, Great Neck, N.Y., 1968-74; cons. Mind, Inc., N.Y.C., 1974; tchr. Wantagh Sch. Dist., Wantagh, N.Y., 1974-76; adminstrv. intern Mamaroneck (N.Y.) Sch. Dist., 1976; adminstr. Westchester B.O.C.E.S., Port Chester, N.Y., 1976-79; tng. mgr. Data Communication, Farmingdale, N.Y., 1979-84; mgr. program devel. The Southland Corp., Dallas, 1984-92; ind. cons., owner Monarch Assocs., Dallas, Tex., 1992—; com. mem. Commr.'s Task Force for technology in edn. Tex. Edn. Agy., Austin, 1987-88. Mem. Huntington (N.Y.) Sch. Dist. Bd. Edn., 1973-79, pres., 1975-77; vol. fireman West Sayville (N.Y.) Fire Dept., 1960-70. Named an Outstanding Young Man in Am., Jaycees, 1974. Republican. Baptist. Avocations: fishing, hunting. Home: 3439 Meadow Creek Ln Sachse TX 75048-4181 Office: Monarch Assocs Ste 214 9319 Lyndon B Johnson Fwy Dallas TX 75243-3453

LEIGHTEN, EDWARD HENRY, publisher, consultant; b. Montclair, N.J., June 22, 1914; s. Jack and Mariette G. (Ackerman) L.; m. Alice Celia Bowne, Aug. 31, 1940; children: Judith (Mrs. Harvey L. Slade), Jeanne Elizabeth (Mrs. T.E. Card). B.S. in Optics, U. Rochester, 1937. Engr. Universal Camera Corp., N.Y.C., 1938-39; mem. editorial staff Photo Technique and Product Engring. mags. McGraw-Hill Pub. Co., N.Y.C., 1939-42; tech. editor U.S. Camera mag., N.Y.C., 1946-47; editor, pub. Photo Devels. (now Photo Mktg.) mag. Master Photo Dealers Assn.), Jackson, Mich., 1947-52; editor Flow mag., Flow Quar. mag. and Flow Directory, Indsl. Pub. Co., Cleve., 1952-56; exec. editor Flow mag., Flow Quar. mag. and Flow Directory, Indsl. Pub. Co., 1956-60; with Cahners Pub. Co., Boston, 1960-82; pub. Modern Materials Handling mag., 1960-81, v.p., 1966-80; v.p. group pub. Modern Materials Handling and Traffic Mgmt. mags., 1974-80; staff v.p. Modern Materials Handling and Traffic Mgmt. mags. (Boston div. corp.), 1981-82; pres. Cons. Services Group (communications, mktg., pub. relations); asso. prof. mktg. Cape Cod Community Coll. Mem. Westlake (Ohio) Sch. Bd., 1958-60, Westlake Library Bd., 1958-60; vol. J.N. (Ding) Darling Wildlife Refuge, Sanibel, Fla. Lt. USNR, 1942-46. Recipient Honor award for contbns. to materials handling edn. Internat. Material Mgmt. Soc. Mem. Material Handling Inst., Caster and Floor Truck Mfrs. Assn., Nat. Wooden Pallet and Container Assn., Internat. Material Mgmt. Soc. (cert. profl. in material handling and material mgmt.), Material Handling Equipment Dealers Assn., Nat. Council Phys. Distbn. Mgmt., Bus./Profl. Advt. Assn. (cert. bus. communicator), Theta Chi. Home and Office: 531 Riverview Dr Chatham MA 02633-1117 *Full, clear, and honest communication among people—in social, industrial, professional and commercial endeavors—is essential to our social, economic, and political growth, nationally and internationally. To be a good communicator is to be a catalyst for progress in all aspects of life. Opportunities for good communicators abound, but relatively few persons are aware of them early enough in their careers. Too many who have writing abilities or aspirations think only in terms of news or literary careers. Whatever profession, trade or technology a person may choose, training in communications will enhance his development and speed his progress.*

LEIGHTON, CHARLES MILTON, specialty consumer products executive; b. Portland, Maine, June 4, 1935; s. Wilbur F. and Elizabeth (Loveland) L.; AB, Bowdoin Coll., 1957, LLD (hon.), 1989; M.BA, Harvard U., 1960; children: Julia Loveland, Anne Throop; m. Roxanne Brooks McCormick, May 23, 1992. Produce line mgr. Mine Safety Appliances Co., Pitts., 1960-64; instr. Harvard Bus. Sch., 1964-65; group v.p. Bangor Punta Corp., Boston, 1965-69; chmn., CEO CML Group, Inc., Acton, Mass., 1969—; bd. dirs. New England Investment Co., Boston, New Eng. Mut. Life Ins. Co., Boston. Past pres. Alumni Harvard Bus. Sch., Cambridge, Mass.; past pres. of trustees Concord (Mass.) Acad. Republican. Episcopalian. Clubs: New York Yacht (commodore 1993-94); Chatham (Mass.) Yacht (commodore 1957); Harvard of N.Y.C. and Boston, Harvard Faculty Club, Tarratine, Internat. Golf Club, Ocean Forest Golf Club. Home: PO Box 247 Bolton MA 01740-0247 Office: CML Group Inc 524 Main St Acton MA 01720-3933

LEIGHTON, FRANCES SPATZ, writer, journalist; b. Geauga County, Ohio; m. Kendall King Hoyt, Feb. 1, 1984. Student, Ohio State U. Washington corr. Am. Weekly; corr. and Washington editor This Week Mag.; Washington corr. Met. Group Sunday Mags.; contbg. editor Family Weekly; free-lance journalist Metro Sunday Group, Washington; lectr. summer confs. Dellbrook-Shenandoah Coll., Georgetown U., Washington. Author over 30 books on hist. figures, celebrities, Hollywood, psychiatry, the White House and Capitol Hill, 1957—; (with Louise Pfister) I Married a Psychiatrist, 1961, (with Francois Rysovy) A Treasury of White House Cooking, 1968, (with Frank S. Caprio) How to Avoid a Nervous Breakdown, 1969, (with Mary B. Gallagher) My Life with Jacqueline Kennedy, 1969, (with Traphes Bryant) Dog Days at the White House, 1975, (with William Fishbait Miller) Fishbait—the Memoirs of the Congressional Doorkeeper, 1977, (with Lillian Rogers Parks) My 30 Years Backstairs at the White House (made into TV mini-series), 1979, (with Hugh Carter) Cousin Beedie, Cousin Hot—, My Life with the Carter Family of Plains, Georgia, 1978, (with Jerry Cammarata) The Fun Book of Fatherhood-or How the Animal Kingdom is Helping to Raise the Wild Kids at Our House, 1978, (with Natalie Golos) Coping with Your Allergies, 1979, (with Ken Hoyt) Drunk Before Noon—The Behind the Scenes Story of the Washington Press Corps, 1979, (with Louis Hurst) The Sweetest Little Club in the World, The Memoirs of the Senate Restaurateur, 1980, (with John M. Szostak) In the Footsteps of Pope John Paul II, 1980, (with Lillian Rogers Parks) The Roosevelts, a Family in Turmoil, 1981, (with June Allyson) June Allyson, 1982, (with Beverly Slater) Stranger in My Bed, 1985 (made into TV movie, 1987), (with Oscar Collier) How to Write and Sell Your First Novel, 1986, The Search for the Real Nancy Reagan, 1987, (with Oscar Collier) How To Write and Sell Your First Nonfiction Book, 1990, (with Stephen M. Bauer) At Ease at the White House, 1991; contbr. numerous feature stories on polit. social and govtl. personalities to various publs. Bd. dirs. Nat. Found., from 1963. Recipient Edgar award, 1961. Mem. Senate Periodical Corr. Assn., White House Corr. Assn., Am. News Women's Club, The Writers Club, Nat. Press Club, Writers League of Washington (pres.), Washington League Am. Pen Women (pres.), Smithsonian Assocs., Nat. Trust Historic Preservation, Lake Barcroft Woman's Club, Delta Phi Delta, Sigma Delta Chi. Unitarian. Office: Lake Barcroft 6336 Lakeview Dr Falls Church VA 22041

LEIGHTON, GEORGE NEVES, retired federal judge; b. New Bedford, Mass., Oct. 22, 1912; s. Antonio N. and Anna Sylvia (Garcia) Leitao; m. Virginia Berry Quivers, June 21, 1942; children: Virginia Anne, Barbara Elaine. AB, Howard U., 1940; LLB, Harvard U., 1946; LLD, Elmhurst Coll., 1964; LL.D. John Marshall Law Sch., 1973, Southeastern Mass. U., 1975, New Eng. U. Sch. Law, 1978; LLD, Loyola U., Chgo., 1989, R.I. Coll., 1992. Bar: Mass. 1946, Ill. 1947, U.S. Supreme Ct. 1958. Ther. Moore, Ming & Leighton, Chgo., 1951-59, McCoy, Ming & Leighton, Chgo., 1959-64; judge Circuit Ct. Cook County Ill., 1964-69, Appellate Ct. 1st Dist., 1969-76; U.S. dist. judge No. Dist. Ill., 1976-86; sr. dist. judge U.S. Dist. Ct., No. Dist. Ill., 1986-87; of counsel Earl L. Neal & Assocs., 1987—; adj. prof. John Marshall Law Sch., Chgo., 1965—; commr., mem. character and fitness com. for 1st Appellate Dist., Supreme Ct. Ill., 1955-63, chmn. character and fitness com., 1961-62; joint com. for revision Ill. Criminal Code, 1959-63; chmn. Ill. adv. com. U.S. Commn. on Civil Rights, 1964, mem. pub. rev. bd. UAW, AFL-CIO, 1961-70; Nat. atty. gen. State of Ill., 1950-51; pres. 3d Ward Regular Democratic Orgn., Cook County, Ill., 1951-53; v.p. 21st Ward, 1964. Contbr. articles to legal jours. Bd. dirs. United Ch. Bd. for Homeland Ministries, United Ch. of Christ, Grant Hosp., Chgo.; trustee U. Notre Dame, 1979-83, trustee emeritus, 1983—; bd. overseers Harvard Coll., 1983-89. Capt. inf. AUS, 1942-45. Decorated Bronze Star.; Recipient Civil Liberties award Ill. div. ACLU, 1961; named Chicagoan of Year in Law and Judiciary Jr. Assn. Commerce and Industry, 1964. Fellow ABA (chmn. council 1976, mem. council sect. legal edn. and admissions to bar); mem. Howard U. Chgo. Alumni Club (chmn. bd. dirs.), John Howard Assn. (dir.), Chgo., Ill. bar assns. (joint com. mem. for revision jud. article 1959-62), NAACP (chmn. legal redress com. Chgo. br.), Nat. Harvard Law

Sch. Assn. (council), Phi Beta Kappa. Office: Earl L Neal & Assocs 111 W Washington St Ste 1700 Chicago IL 60602-2711

LEIGHTON, JOSEPH, pathologist; b. N.Y.C., Dec. 13, 1921; m. Rosalind Weinberger, Dec. 15, 1946; children—Daniel A., Edith R. AB, Columbia U., 1942; MD, L.I. Coll. Medicine, Bklyn., 1946. Intern Mt. Sinai Hosp., N.Y.C., 1946-47; resident in pathology Mass. Gen. Hosp., Boston, 1948-49, USPHS Hosp., Balt., 1950; research pathologist Nat. Cancer Inst., Bethesda, Md., 1951-56; mem. faculty dept. pathology U. Pitts. Sch. Medicine, 1956-70; prof. pathology Med. Coll. Pa., Phila., 1971-89, chmn. dept. pathology, 1971-87; pathologist Peralta Cancer Rsch. Inst., 1989-92, Aeron Biotech. Inc., San Leandro, Calif., 1994—. Author: The Spread of Cancer, 1967; inventor radial histophysiologic gradient culture chamber. Served with USPHS, 1948-56. Eleanor Roosevelt Cancer Research fellow, 1970-71. Mem. Am. Assn. Cancer Research, Tissue Culture Assn., Am. Assn. Pathologists, Internat. Acad. Pathology. Home: 2324 Lakeshore Ave Apt 2 Oakland CA 94606-1056 Office: Aeron Biotech Inc 1933 Davis St San Leandro CA 94577-1260

LEIGHTON, LAWRENCE WARD, investment banker; b. N.Y.C., July 1, 1934; s. Sidney and Florence (Ward) L.; m. Mariana Stroock, June 21, 1959; children: Sandra L. Galvin, Michelle Stroock. BSE, Princeton U., 1956; MBA, Harvard U., 1962. Vice pres. Kuhn Loeb & Co., N.Y.C., 1962-69, v.p. Clark, Dodge & Co., Inc., N.Y.C., 1970-74; dir. Norton-Simon, Inc., N.Y.C., 1974-78, ltd. ptnr. Bear, Stearns & Co., N.Y.C., 1978-82; mng. dir. Chase Investment Bank, 1983-88; pres., chief exec. officer Union d'Etudes et d'Investissements Mcht. Bank of Credit Agricole, 1989-93; vice chmn. 2I, Inc., 1993-94, mng dir. LM Capital Corp., 1994—; dir. Corp. Renaissance Group, 1994—; chmn. Princeton Schs. Com. of N.Y., 1965-85. Mem. exec. com. Princeton U. Alumni Council, 1975-80; vice chmn. nat. schs. com. Princeton U., 1980—; chmn. Harvard Bus. Sch. Fund of N.Y., 1964-65; mem. nat. fin. com. Pete DuPont for Pres., 1986-88. Served to lt. (j.g.) USN, 1957-60. Clubs: Stanwich (Greenwich, Conn.); Princeton Club of N.Y. (scholarship com. 1970—, bd. govs. 1989—); Coral Beach and Tennis (Bermuda). Avocations: flying, golf. Home: 1088 Park Ave New York NY 10128-1132 Office: LM Capital Corp 152 W 57th ST New York NY 10019

LEIGHTON, PAUL JOE, lawyer; b. Manhattan, Kans., June 7, 1953; s. Paulson and Deloris (Salero) L.; m. Beverly B. Albright; children: Steven P., David R., Mark W., Michael B. BS, U. Nebr., 1975, JD, 1978; MBA, U. S.D., 1980. Bar: Iowa 1978. Gen. atty. Midwest Energy Co., Sioux City, Iowa, 1978-85, asst. sec., gen. atty., 1985-86, asst. sec., sr. atty., 1986-88, corp. sec., sr. atty., 1988-90; sec., asst. treas. Midwest Resources Inc., Des Moines, 1990-92, sec., asst. treas., mgr. corp. legal svcs., audit and ins., 1992-94, v.p., sec., asst. treas., mgr. corp. legal svcs., 1994—; instr. Internat. Right-of-Way Assn., L.A., 1984-85. Solicitor United Way of Siouxland, 1985-86; bd. dirs., treas. Iowa Hist. Found.; mem. Des Moines Contbns. Consortium. Mem. ABA, Iowa Bar Assn., Polk County Bar Assn., Am. Soc. Corp. Secs., Clive C. of C. (bd. dirs.). Republican. Presbyterian. Office: Midwest Resources Inc 666 Grand Ave PO Box 9244 Des Moines IA 50306-9244

LEIGHTON, ROBERT, film editor. Editor: (films) Delusion, 1981, (with Peter Thornton) Kill and Kill Again, 1981, Blood Tide, 1982, The House Where Death Lives, 1982, The Being, 1983, (with Mark Goldblatt) Wavelength, 1983, This Is Spinal Tap, 1984, The Sure Thing, 1985, Stand By Me, 1986, The Princess Bride, 1987, (with Adam Weiss) Bull Durham, 1988, When Harry Met Sally..., 1989, Blaze, 1989, Misery, 1990, A Few Good Men, 1992, Life with Mikey, 1993, North, 1994. Office: care Motion Picture Editors 7715 Sunset Blvd #220 Los Angeles CA 90046*

LEIJONHUFVUD, AXEL STIG BENGT, economics educator; b. Stockholm, Sweden, Sept. 6, 1933; came to U.S., 1960; s. Erik Gabriel and Helene Adelheid (Neovius) L.; m. Marta Elisabeth Ising, June 10, 1955 (div. 1977); m. Earlene Joyce Craver, June 18, 1977; children—Carl Axel, Gabriella Helene, Christina Elisabeth. Fil. kand., U. Lund, Sweden, 1960; M.A., U. Pitts., Pa., 1961; Ph.D., Northwestern U., 1967; Fil. Dr. (hon.), U. Lund, Sweden, 1983. Acting asst. prof. econs. UCLA, 1964-67, assoc. prof. econs., 1967-71, prof. econs., 1971—, chair dept. econs., 1980-83, 90-92; dir. Ctr. for Computable Econs., 1992—; prof. monetary theory and policy U. Trento, Italy, 1995—; co-dir. summer workshops Siena Internat. Sch. Econ. Rsch., 1987-91; participant numerous profl. confs.; cons., lectr., vis. prof. econs. various colls. and univs.; cons. Republic of Tatarstan, 1994. Author: On Keynesian Economics and the Economics of Keynes: A Study in Monetary Theory, 1968, Keynes and the Classics: Two Lectures, 1969, Information and Coordination: Essays in Macroeconomic Theory, 1981, (with D. Heyemann) High Inflation, 1995. Mem. econ. expert com. of pres. Kazakhstan, 1991-92. Brookings Instn. fellow, 1963-64; Marshall lectr. Cambridge U., Eng. 1974; Overseas fellow Churchill Coll., Cambridge, 1974; Inst. Advanced Study fellow, 1983-84. Mem. Am. Econ. Assn., Western Econ. Assn., History of Econs. Soc. Office: UCLA Dept Econs Los Angeles CA 90024

LEIKAM, DALE FRANCIS, agronomist; b. Hays, Kans., Dec. 28, 1951; s. Robert and Louise (Gross) L.; m. Patricia D. Gilmore, July 14, 1973; children Michelle, Marianne, Melissa. BS in Argl. Edn., Kans. State U., 1973, MS in Agronomy, 1977, PhD in Agronomy, 1980. Cert. profl. agronomist, profl. soil scientist, profl. crop scientist; cert. crop advisor, Kans., Mo. Agriculturist Nat. Fertilizer Devel. Ctr. TVA, Muscle Shoals, Ala., 1980-81; area dir. TVA, Urbana, Ill., 1981-82; agronomist agri-prodn. svcs. dept. CENEX, St. Paul, 1982-84; agronomist tech. svcs. dept. Farmland Industries, Inc., Kansas City, Mo., 1984—; numerous invited lectures; presenter in field to seminars, symposia, assns., and confs.; bd. dirs. Kans. Fertilizer and Chem. Inst., 1985-88; bd. dirs. Kans. Agrl. Edn. Found., 1988—, mem. sci. rev. bd., 1990—; mem. planning com. Gt. Plains Soil Fertility Workshop, 1984-92, chmn.-elect, 1992, chmn., 1994; mem. exam. and fin. coms. Kans. Cert. Crop Advisor Bd., 1992—, chmn. continuing edn., 1993—; mem. Nat. Cert. Crop Advisor Coun., 1993; past proposal reviewer Kans. Fertilizer Rsch. Fund. Contbr. numerous articles to profl. jours. and popular publs. Mem. Am. Soc. Agronomy (reviewer, presenter, Werner L. Nelson award for diagnosis of yield limiting factors 1993), Soil Sci. Soc. Am. (reviewer), Kans. Fertilizer and Chem. Assn. (bd. dirs. 1985—, dealer edn. com., pub. edn. com., program planning com., awards com., scholarship com., expn. planning com., conservation plan for pesticides and wildlife task force, agrl. speakers bur.), Gamma Sigma Delta, Alpha Tau Alpha. Avocations: fishing, hunting, camping. Home: 159 S Dartmouth Manhattan KS 66502 Office: Farmland Industries Inc PO Box 7305 Kansas City MO 64116

LEIKEN, EARL MURRAY, lawyer; b. Cleve., Jan. 19, 1942; s. Manny and Betty G. L.; m. Ellen Kay Miner, Mar. 26, 1970; children: Jonathan, Brian. BA magna cum laude, Harvard U., 1964, JD cum laude, 1967. Asst. dean, assoc. prof. law Case Western Res. U., Cleve., 1967-71; ptnr. Hahn, Loeser, Freedheim, Dean & Wellman, Cleve., 1971-86, Baker & Hostetler, Cleve., 1986—; adj. faculty, lectr. law Case Western Res. U., 1971-86. Pres. Shaker Heights (Ohio) Bd. Edn., 1986-88, Jewish Community Ctr., Cleve., 1988-91, Shaker Heights Family Ctr., 1994—. Named one of Greater Cleve.'s 10 Outstanding Young Leaders, Cleve. Jaycees, 1972; recipient Kane award Cleve. Jewish Community Fedn., 1982. Mem. ABA, Greater Cleve. Bar Assn. (chmn. labor law sect. 1978). Home: 20815 Colby Rd Cleveland OH 44122-1903 Office: Baker & Hostetler 3200 Nat City Ctr 1900 E 9th St Cleveland OH 44114-3303

LEIMAN, SID ZALMAN, Judaic studies educator; b. N.Y.C., Nov. 3, 1941; s. Harold Isaac and Harriet (Gross) L.; m. Rivkah Landesman, Nov. 25, 1969; children—Akiva, Rose Nechama, Yocheved, Naomi. B.A., Bklyn. Coll., 1964; Rabbi, Mirrer Yeshiva Central Inst., 1964; Ph.D., U. Pa., 1970. Lectr. in Jewish history and lit. Yale U., 1968-70, asst. prof., 1970-72, assoc. prof., 1972-78; vis. scholar in Jewish law and ethics Kennedy Inst. Ethics, Georgetown U., Washington, 1977-78; prof. Jewish history and lit., dean Bernard Revel Grad. Sch.; dir. grad. Jewish edn. Yeshiva U., N.Y.C., 1978-81; prof. Judaic studies Bklyn. Coll., 1981—, chmn. dept., 1981-87. Author: The Canonization of Hebrew Scripture: The Talmudic and Midrashic Evidence, 1976, 2d edit., 1991; editor: The Canon and Masorah of the Hebrew Bible: An Introductory Reader, 1974; contbr. to: Ency. Judaica, 1972, Ency. Brit, 1974, Ency. Biblica, 1981. Morse fellow, 1971-72; Nat. Endowment for Humanities grantee, 1974. Mem. Am. Acad. Religion, Am.

Schs. Oriental Research, Assn. for Jewish Studies, Soc. Bibl. Lit. Home: 14002 69th Ave Flushing NY 11367-1637 Office: Bklyn Coll Judaic Studies Brooklyn NY 11210

LEIMKUHLER, FERDINAND FRANCIS, industrial engineering educator; b. Balt., Dec. 31, 1928; s. Ferdinand Frank and Louise (Kimmel) L.; m. Natalie Therese Morin, July 4, 1956; children: Kristin, Margaret, Jeanne, Benedict, Thomas, Ernest. B.S. cum laude, Loyola Coll., Balt., 1950; B.Engring., Johns Hopkins U., 1952, D.Engring. with distinction, 1962. Mgmt. engr. E.I. DuPont de Nemours & Co., Inc., 1950-57; research engr. Johns Hopkins U., 1957-61; prof. indsl. engring. Purdue U., 1961—, head Sch. Indsl. Engring., 1969-74, 81-93, dir. tech. assistance program, 1993—; vis. prof. U. Calif., Berkeley, 1968-69, 90; vis. prof. (Fulbright-Hayes sr. lectr.), U. Ljubljana, Slovenia, 1974-75; cons. in field. Served with AUS, 1952-54. Mem. Am. Inst. Indsl. Engrs., Operations Research Soc. Am., Inst. Mgmt. Scis., Am. Soc. Engring. Edn., Sigma Xi, Alpha Sigma Nu, Tau Beta Pi. Office: Purdue U Rm G-175 1284 Civil Engineering Bldg West Lafayette IN 47907-1284

LEIMKUHLER, GERARD JOSEPH, JR., financial holding company executive; b. Phila., June 13, 1948; s. Gerard Joseph and Dorothy Joan (Gaffney) L.; m. Karen Roberta Hall, Oct. 13, 1973; 1 child, Courtney Hall. BBA, Temple U., 1970. Mem. Phila. Stock Exch., 1971-75; v.p. Oxford First Corp., Phila., 1975-82, sr. v.p., 1982-87, exec. v.p., 1987-93, vice chmn., 1993—; sr. v.p., sec. Oxford Communities, Inc., Oxford Fin. Cos. Inc., Phila., 1985-87, exec. v.p., sec., 1987-93; vice chmn. Oxford Communities, Inc., Oxford Fin. Cos. Inc., 1993—; pres. Gen. Acquistions Corp., Phila., 1977—, also bd. dirs.; dir. First Fin. Reality Inc., First Homesites, Inc., First So. Corp., Money Mgmt. Inc., Home Security Corp. Vice-chmn. Newtown Twp. Planning Commn., Delaware County, Pa., 1976-77, 84—, chmn., 1995—; chmn. investment adv. bd. Newtown Twp. Investment, 1987—. With U.S. Army, 1970-71. Mem. Internat. Found. for Timesharing (chmn. investment com.), Turnaround Mgmt. Assn. (bd. dirs., treas.), Urban Land Inst., Am. Resort Devel. Assn., Mensa, Aronimink Golf Club. Republican. Roman Catholic. Home: 170 Hunt Valley Cir Berwyn PA 19312-2302 Office: Oxford First Corp 7300 Old York Rd Philadelphia PA 19126-1825

LEIN, MALCOLM EMIL, architect; b. Havre, Mont., July 19, 1913; s. Emil A. and Ruth (Fredeen) L.; m. Miriam Balliet Bend, Apr. 13, 1939; children: Eric Manning, Kristin Anker, R. Kurt Harrison. Student, U. Wis., 1930; BArch, U. Minn., 1936; student, U.S. Army C.I. Sch., 1943, Command & Gen. Staff Sch., U.S. Army, 1943, Nat. War Coll., 1963. Asst. head constrn. dept. F.W. Woolworth Co., Dist. Office, Mpls., 1936-41; pvt. practice architecture and design St. Paul, 1946—; instr. Macalester Coll., St. Paul, 1947-50; dir. Minn. Mus. of Art, St. Paul, 1947-77, pres., 1973-79; pres., founder Design Cons., Inc., St. Paul, 1949—, Mid-West Credit Corp., St. Paul, 1959—, Desconi Corp.; founder, dir. Gallery St. Paul, The Commodore, St. Paul, 1981-85; founder, pres. Madeline Island Art Ctr., La Pointe, Wis., 1991—. Trustee, founder Benlei Found., Scottsdale, Ariz., 1988—. Served to col. C.E., AUS, 1935-66, WWII CBI. Mem. Am. Assn. Mus., Am. Fedn. Art, Archives Am. Art, Res. Officers Assn., Air Force Assn., Japan Am. Soc. Minn. (v.p. bd. dirs.), Smithsonian Assocs., Phoenix Art Mus., Asian Art Coun. of Mpls. Art Inst., Planned Parenthood of Cen. & No. Ariz. (chmn. endowment and planned giving com.). Club: University (St. Paul). Home: 6200 E Hummingbird Ln Paradise Vly AZ 85253-3651 Office: 361 Summit Ave Saint Paul MN 55102-2120 *Goals: Find challenging creative work without sacrificing principles. Welcome the help and guidance from so many and do as much for others. Appreciate beauty. Live in harmony with nature, God and neighbors. Learn throughout life, Keep an open mind. Acquire wisdom. Remain a free spirit. And "be prepared" to live forever or die tomorrow.*

LEINART, BONNIE KATHERINE, nursing administrator; b. Moline, Ill., Feb. 21, 1947; d. August Louis and Irene Ann (Bomelyn) Claeys; m. John H. Leinart III, June 14, 1969; children: Katherine, John, Michael, Anne-Marie. BSN, Marquette U., 1969; M. Nursing, No. Ill. U., 1978. Staff/charge RN Vanderbilt U. Hosp., Nashville, 1969-75, Moline Pub. Hosp., 1975-77; assoc. prof. Marycrest Coll., Davenport, Iowa, 1978-80; nurse practitioner Ob-Gyn Physician Office, Moline, 1980-82; nurse educator Luth. Hosp. Sch. Nursing, Moline, 1982-86; nurse adminstr. Luth. Hosp.-United Med. Ctr., Moline, 1986—. Nurse Traineeship grantee U.S. Govt., 1977-78. Mem. Am. Orgn. Nurse Execs., Ill. Orgn. Nurse Execs., ANA (bd. dirs., sec. 1976-78), Ill. Nurses Assn. (5th dist.). Roman Catholic.

LEINBACH, PHILIP EATON, librarian; b. Winston-Salem, N.C., Sept. 17, 1935; s. Gray Newton and Martha Elizabeth (Eaton) L.; m. Nancy Lee Yocom, July 27, 1957; children—Jonathan Eaton, David Timothy. A.B., Duke U., 1956; M.A. in History, Ind. U., 1963, M.L.S., 1964. Adminstrv. asst. Harvard U. Library, Cambridge, Mass., 1964-66; asst. librarian for acquisitions Harvard U., Cambridge, 1966-67, specialist in book selection, 1967-71, asst. univ. librarian, 1972-82; univ. librarian Tulane U., New Orleans, 1982—; acting chief libr. Harvard U. Div. Sch., Cambridge, 1978-79; dep. libr. Queen Mary Coll., London, 1970-71. Author: Handbook for Librarians, 1977, Personnel Administration in an Automated Environment, 1990. Served with USNR, 1957-61. Fellow Ind. U., 1963-64; UCLA Grad. Sch. Library and Info. Sci., 1982; NDEA modern lang fellow, 1962-63. Mem. ALA (council 1984-88), La. Library Assn., Omicron Delta Kappa, Beta Phi Mu, Pi Sigma Alpha. Home: 7530 Saint Charles Ave New Orleans LA 70118-3878 Office: Tulane U Howard-Tilton Memorial Library New Orleans LA 70118-5682

LEINEN, MARGARET SANDRA, oceanographic researcher; b. Chgo., Sept. 20, 1946; d. Earl John and Ester (Louis) Leinen; m. Denzel Earl Gleason, 1984; 1 child, Daniel Glenn Whaley. BS, U. Ill. 1969; MS, Oreg. State U., 1975; PhD, U. R.I., Kingston, 1980. Marine scientist U. R.I., Kingston, 1980-82, asst. rsch. prof., 1982-86, assoc. prof., 1986-88, prof., 1988—, assoc. dean, 1988-92, dean and vice provost, 1992—. Office: U RI Grad Sch Oceanography Narragansett RI 02882-1197

LEINENWEBER, HARRY D., federal judge; b. Joliet, Ill., June 3, 1937; s. Harry Dean and Emily (Lennon) L.; m. Lynn Morley Martin, Jan. 7, 1987; children: Jane Dunn Campeau, John Dunn, Thomas More, Stephen Beckett, Justin Lennon. AB cum laude, U. Notre Dame, 1959; JD, U. Chgo., 1962. Bar: Ill. 1962, U.S. Dist. Ct. (no. dist.) Ill. 1967. Assoc. Dunn, Stefanich, McGarry & Kennedy, Joliet, Ill., 1962-65, ptnr., 1965-79; city atty. City of Joliet, 1963-67; spl. counsel Village of Park Forest, Ill., 1967-74; spl. prosecutor County of Will, Ill., 1968-70; spl. counsel Village of Bolingbrook, Ill., 1975-77, Will County Forest Preserve, 1977; mem. Ill. Ho. of Reps., Springfield, 1973-83, chmn. judiciary I com., 1981-83; ptnr. Dunn, Leinenweber & Dunn, Joliet, 1979-86; fed. judge U.S. Dist. Ct. (no. dist.) Ill., Chgo., 1986—; bd. dirs. Will County Bar Assn., 1984-86, mem. jud. adv. coun., 1973-85, sec. 1975-76. Bd. dirs. Will County Legal Assistance Found., 1982-86, Good Shepard Manor, 1981—, Am. Cancer Soc., 1981-85, Joliet (Ill.) Montessori Schs., 1966-74; del. Rep. Nat. Conv., 1980; precinct committeeman, 1966-86. Recipient Environ. Legislator Golden award. Mem. Nat. Conf. Commrs. on Uniform State Laws (exec. com. 1991-93). Roman Catholic. Office: US Dist Ct 219 S Dearborn St # 1778 Chicago IL 60604-1706

LEINIEKS, VALDIS, classicist, educator; b. Liepaja, Latvia, Apr. 15, 1932; came to U.S., 1949, naturalized, 1954; s. Arvid Ansis and Valia Leontine (Brunaus) L. BA, Cornell U., 1955, MA, 1956; PhD, Princeton U., 1962. Instr. classics Cornell Coll., Mount Vernon, Iowa, 1959-62, asst. prof. classics, 1962-64; vis. prof. classics Ohio State U., 1964-66; assoc. prof. classics U. Nebr., Lincoln, 1966-71, prof. classics, 1971—, chmn. dept. classics, 1967—, chmn. program comparative lit., 1970-86, interim chmn. dept. modern langs., 1982-83. Author: Morphosyntax of the Homeric Greek Verb, 1964; The Structure of Latin, 1975; Index Nepotianus, 1976; The Plays of Sophokles, 1982. Contbr. articles to profl. jours. Mem. AAUP, Am. Classical League, Classical Assn. Middle West and South, Am. Philol. Assn. Republican. Home: 2505 A St Lincoln NE 68502-1841 Office: U Nebr Dept Classics Lincoln NE 68588-0337

LEININGER, MADELEINE MONICA, nurse, anthropologist, administrator, consultant, editor; b. Sutton, Nebr., July 13, 1925; d. George M. S.

and Irene (Sheedy) L. BS in Biology, Scholastic Coll., 1950, LHD, 1976; MS in Nursing, Cath. U. Am., 1953; PhD in Anthropology, U. Wash., 1965; DSc (hon., U. Indpls., 1990; PhDN (hon.), Ind. State U., 1990, U. Kuopio, Finland, 1991. RN; cert. transcultural nurse. Instr., mem. staff, head nurse med.-surg. unit, supr. psychiat. unit St. Joseph's Hosp., Omaha, 1950-54; assoc. prof. nursing, dir. grad. program in psychiat. nursing U. Cin. Coll. Nursing, 1954-60; research fellow Nat. League Nursing, Eastern Highlands of New Guinea, Papul 68, 78, 92; research assoc. U. Wash. Dept. Anthropology, Seattle, 1964-65; prof. nursing and anthropology, dir. nurse-scientist PhD program U. Colo., Boulder and Denver, 1966-69; dean sch. nursing, prof. nursing, lectr. anthropology U. Wash., Seattle, 1969-74; dean coll. nursing, prof. nursing and anthropology U. Utah, Salt Lake City, 1974-80; Anise J. Sorell prof. nursing Troy (Ala.) State U., 1981; prof. nursing, adj. prof. anthropology, dir. Ctr. for Health Research, dir. transcultural nursing offerings Wayne State U., Detroit, 1981—; adj. prof. anthropology U. Utah, 1974-81; disting. vis. prof. at 75 univs., U.S. and overseas, 1970—; cons. Saudi Arabia, Brazil, Europe, Japan, Thailand, Indonesia, Australia, South Africa, Finland, Sweden, The Netherlands, New Guinea, Australia, Jordan, Iran, Africa, 58 health instn.'s in U.S. Author: 25 books including Nursing and Anthropology: Two Worlds to Blend, 1970, Contemporary Issues in Mental Health Nursing, 1973, Caring: An Essential Human Need, 1981, Reference Sources for Transcultural Health and Nursing, 1984, Basic Psychiatric Concepts in Nursing, 1960, Care: The Essence of Nursing and Health, 1984, Qualitative Research Methods in Nursing, 1985, Care: Discovery and Clinical-Community Uses, 1988, Ethical and Moral Dimensions of Caring, 1990, Culture Care, Diversity and Universality: A Theory of Nursing, 1991, Care: The Compassionate Healer, 1991, Caring Imperative for Nursing Education, 1991, Transcultural Nursing, 1995; editor Jour. of Transcultural Nursing, 1989—; mem. editl. bd. 10 nat. and internat. jours.; editor or contbr. 200 articles to profl. jours., 47 chpts. to books. Recipient Outstanding Alumni award Cath. U. Am., 1969, Recognition award Am. Assn. Colls. of Nursing, 1976, Nurse of Yr. award Dist. 1 Utah Nurses Assn., 1976, Literary award Utah Nurses Assn., 1978, Trotter Disting. Pub. Lectr. award U. Tex., 1985, Disting. Faculty Teaching Recognition award Wayne State U., 1985, Outstanding Faculty Research Scholar award Wayne State U. and Gerontology Inst., 1985, Gershenson Rsch. award Wayne State U., 1985, Pace Inst. Rsch. award, 1992, Hewlett Packard Rsch. award, 1992, Award for acad. excellence AAUW-Detroit, 1986, Disting. award Bd. Govs., 1987, Pres. Excellence in Teaching award, 1988, Women of Sci. award U. Calif. at Fullerton, 1990; named Detroit Woman of Yr., AAUW, 1986; named Outstanding Researcher, Wayne State U., 1987; disting. vis. scholar 54 univs. U.S. and overseas. Fellow Am. Anthropol. Soc. for Applied Anthropology (exec. com. 1980-84), Am. Acad. Nursing, Am. Nurses Assn.; mem. MNA (Bertha Culp Human Rights award 1994). Am. Acad. Humanities, Am. Applied Anthropol. Soc., Ctrl. States Anthropology, Amnesty Internat., Transcultural Nursing Soc. (founder, bd. dirs., pres. 1974-80), Cultural Community Group Assn. (ethics, humanities heritage study group), Nat. Research Care Confs. (leader human care research), Internat. Assn. Human Caring (founder, pres., bd. dirs. 1978—), Nordic Caring Soc. Sweden (hon.), Sigma Xi, Pi Gamma Mu, Sigma Theta Tau (Lectr. of Yr. 1987—), Delta Kappa Gamma, Alpha Tau Delta. Office: Wayne State U 5557 Cass Ave Detroit MI 48202-3615

LEIPER, ROBERT DUNCAN, protective services official; b. Houston, July 22, 1953; s. William Harper Leiper and Frances Ann (Wright) Freeman; m. Glynna Dell Wilson, May 18, 1985; children: Kelsey Allison, Chad Wilson. AAS in Fire Protection, San Jacinto Coll., 1983; BA in Pub. Mgmt., U. Houston, 1988. Master fire fighter, Tex. Lt. Spring Br. Fire Dept., Houston, 1973-75; asst. svc. mgr. Archer Motor Sales, Houston, 1975-77; fire fighter Baytown (Tex.) Fire & Rescue, 1977-80, driver, 1980-83, lt., 1983-88, capt., 1988-92, fire chief, 1992—; instr. Tex. A & M U., College Station, 1988-92, Lamar U., Beaumont, Tex., 1990-92. Chmn. bd. Baycoast Med. Ctr., Baytown, Tex., 1994-95. Named Exec. Fire Officer, Nat. Fire Acad.; recipient Fire Fighter of Yr. award VFW, 1987, 90. Mem. Nat. Fire Protection Assn., Baytown Profl. Fire Fighters (v.p. 1982), Hispanic C. of C., Baytown C. of C., Kiwanis Club (pres. 1994, Rookie of Yr. award 1989). Avocations: wood working, camping, photography. Office: Baytown Fire and Rescue Svcs 201 E Wye Dr Baytown TX 77521

LEIPPER, DALE FREDERICK, physical oceanographer, educator; b. Salem, Ohio, Sept. 8, 1914; s. Robert and Myrtle (Cost) L.; m. Virginia Alma Harrison, May 14, 1942; children: Diane Louise, Janet Elizabeth, Bryan Robert, Anita Dale. BS in Edn., Wittenberg Coll., 1937, DSc (hon.), 1968; MA, Ohio State U., 1939; postgrad., UCLA, 1939-40; Ph.D., Scripps Instn. Oceanography, 1950. Tchr. city schs. San Diego, 1940-41; research oceanographer, tchr. Scripps Instn. Oceanography, U. Calif., 1945-49; mem. faculty dept. oceanography and meteorology Tex. A&M U., 1949-68, head dept., 1949-64, prof., 1964-68; prof., chmn. dept. oceanography Naval Postgrad. Sch., 1968-79; supr. rsch. program NSF, Internat. Geophys. Year, Office Naval Rsch.; mem. tech. panel oceanography, exec. vice chmn. meteorology panel U.S. Nat. Com. Internat. Geophys. Year; chmn. com. marine scis. Soc. Regional Edn. Bd., 1952-56; assoc. dir. Tex. A&M Rsch. Found., 1953-54. Contbr. articles on West Coast fog, oceanography, hurricane-ocean interaction, ocean currents to jours. in field. Served as maj. USAAF, 1941-45; weather officer, oceanographer. Mem. Am. Meteorol. Soc., Am. Geophys. Union, Am. Soc. Limnology and Oceanography (pres. 1957-58), Tex. Acad. Sci. (pres. 1955), Nat. Acad. Sci. (panel chmn. 1959-64), Marine Tech. Soc., Am. Soc. Oceanography (pres. 1967-68), U. Corp. for Atmospheric Rsch. (founding mem., bd. dirs.), The Oceanography Soc., Sigma Xi, Phi Kappa Phi. Club: Rotary (pres. Bryan, Tex. 1965-66). Home and Office: 716 Terra Ct Reno NV 89506-9606

LEIPZIG, ARTHUR, photographer, educator emeritus; b. Bklyn., Oct. 25, 1918; s. Julius M. and Esther Pearl (Rubin) L.; m. Mildred Levin, Mar. 21, 1942; children: Joel Myron, Judith Anne. Student, Photo League, 1942-43, Paul Strand Photo Workshop, 1946. Staff photographer PM newspaper, N.Y.C., 1942-46, Internat. News Photos, N.Y.C., 1946; freelance photographer East Meadow, N.Y., 1946—; prof. art, dir. photography C.W. Post Sch. of Arts, L.I. U., Greenvale, N.Y., 1968—. Contbr. photographs to Fortune, Look, Parade, Life, Natural History, Sunday Times, also indsl. mags.; guest editor Infinity Mag., N.Y.C., 1970, mem. editorial bd., 1973-75; interview and photographs included Life Documentary Photo Book, N.Y.C., 1972, 83; exhibited works Mus. Modern Art, 1946-51, 55-58, Met. Mus. Art, 1961, 62, Nassau Mus. Art, 1975, Queens Mus. Art, 1982, Transco Gallery, Houston, 1985, Daniel Wolf Gallery, N.Y.C., Houston Foto Fest, 1986, Photo Find Gallery, Woodstock, Coll. Art Gallery, New Paltz, N.Y., Smithsonian Mus., Washington, 1987, Mus. of the City of N.Y., Children's Games, 1988, Photofind Gallery, N.Y.C., 1990 Salena Gallery, Bklyn., JCP, 1992; one-man shows include Midtown Y Gallery, 1978, Henry St. Settlement, Arts for Living Ctr., 1986, Frumkin Adams Gallery, N.Y.C., 1990, 92, Photofind Gallery, 1990, Howard Greenberg Gallery, 1991, Salena Gallery, Bklyn., 1992, Port Washington Libr., 1994; represented in permanent collections Mus. Modern Art, Bklyn. Mus., Eastman House, Nat. Gallery Art, Nassau Mus. Art, Houston Mus. Fine Arts, Midtown Y Gallery, Visual Studies Workshop, Pablo Casals Mus., Internat. Ctr. Photography, Nat. Mus. Am. Art, Washington, Consol. Freightways, San Francisco, Bank of Am. Art Program, San Francisco, Bibliotheque Nationale, Paris, The Jewish Mus., N.Y.C., Mus. Folkwang, Essen, Germany, The Nat. Portrait Gallery, Washington, The Gilman Paper Co., Queens Coll., N.Y., Dreyfus, N.Y.C.; retrospective exhbn. Hillwood Gallery, Brookville, N.Y., 1989, Musée De La Civilisation, Quebec City, 1990; featured on World of Photography, Sta. WABC-TV; pub. Classic Photographs from the Brooklyn Museum Collection, 1987, Sarah's Daughters, 1988, Master Photographs Photography in Fine Arts Exhbt. Internat. Ctr. Photography, 1988, 92, The Nat. Portrait Gallery, 1992, High Mus., Altlanta, 1992. Adv. bd. Midtown Y Gallery, 1983; bd. dirs. Nassau Mus. Fine Art, 1973-75. Recipient Nat. Urban League award, 1962, ORT award, 1976, Nassau County Office Cultural Devel. award, 1982, David Newton Excellence in Teaching award, 1989, Award for Scholarly Achievement, L.I. U. Trustees, 1983, 89. Mem. Am. Soc. Mag. Photographers (bd. govs., trustee 1960-65, treas. 1965). Office: LI U CW Post Coll Northern Blvd Greenvale NY 11548-1207 For me, the most important thing is loving what I do. I love photography and I love to teach photography. Both photography and teaching came into my life by chance. My success in both areas is due to may passion for my work.

LEIS, HENRY PATRICK, JR., surgeon, educator; b. Saranac Lake, N.Y., Aug. 12, 1914; s. Henry P. and Mary A. (Disco) L.; m. Winogene Barnette,

Jan. 8, 1944; children—Henry Patrick III, Thomas Frederick. B.S. cum laude, Fordham U., 1936; M.D., N.Y. Med. Coll., 1941. Diplomate Am. Bd. Surgery. Intern Flower and Fifth Ave Hosps., N.Y.C., 1941-42, resident, 1943-44, 46-49, attending surgeon, chief breast service, 1982—; resident in surgery Kanawa Valley Hosp., Charleston, W.Va., 1942-43; attending surgeon, chief breast service Met. Hosp., N.Y.C., 1960-81, emeritus chief breast service, 1982—; attending surgeon Coler Meml. Hosp., N.Y.C., 1960-76; chief breast surgery Cabrini Hosp. Med. Ctr., 1978-85, cons. breast surgery, 1985—; emeritus surgeon Lenox Hill Hosp., N.Y.C., 1980-83, hon. surg. staff, 1984—; hon. surg. staff Drs. Hosp., N.Y.C., Grand Strand Gen. Hosp., Myrtle Beach, S.C., 1985—; liason officer Am. Coll. Surgeons Commn. on Cancer; attending surgeon Westchester County Med. Ctr., 1977-81, emeritus surgeon, 1982—; clin. prof. surgery U. S.C. Sch. Medicine, Breast Surg. Oncology, Columbia, 1985—; hon. dir. breast cancer ctr., cons. in breast surgery Winthrop Univ. Hosp., Mineola, 1971—; cons. in breast surgery VA Hosp., Columbia, S.C., 1985—; cons. in breast surgery St. Claires Hosp., N.Y.C., 1979; attending surg. staff Richland Meml. Hosp., Columbia, 1986-90; clin. prof. surgery, 1960-81, prof. emeritus, 1982—, co-dir. Inst. Breast Diseases, 1978-82, emeritus, 1982—; chief breast svc. N.Y. Med. Coll., 1960-81, emeritus, 1982—; cons. in breast surgery SUNY Div. Rehab., 1965—; Med. and Surg. Specialists Plan N.Y.; mem. Am. Joint Com. on Breast Cancer Staging and End Results; v.p. N.Y. Met. Breast Cancer Group, 1975-76, pres., 1977-79; cons. Med. Advs. Selective Svc. System, N.Y.C. Alumni trustee N.Y. Med. Coll., 1971-76; adv. coun. Fordham Coll. Pharmacy, 1968; bd. dirs. Hall Fame and Mus. Surg. History and Related Scis. Author: Diagnosis and Treatment of Breast Lesions: The Breast, 1970, Management of Breast Lesions, 1978, Breast Cancer: Conservative and Reconstructive Surgery, 1989, Breast Lesions: Diagnosis and Treatment, 1988; co-editor: Breast; hon. editor Internat. Surgery Jour.; mem. editorial bd. jour. Senolgia, 1982—, Breast: An Internat. Jour.; contbr. articles to profl. jours. Mem. Women's Cancer Task Force of S.C. Capt. M.C., AUS, 1944-46, PTO. Decorated knight Grand Cross Equestrian Order Holy Sepulchre Jerusalem, knight Mil., Order of Malta, Knight Noble Co. of the Rose; recipient award of Merit Am. Cancer Soc., 1969, 87, cert. and award for outstanding and devoted services to indigent sick City N.Y., 1965, Dr. George Hohman Meml. medal, 1936, N.Y. Apothecaries medal, 1936, Internat. cert. merit for disting. service to surgery, 1970, award of merit N.Y. Met. Breast Cancer Group, 1976, medal of Ambrogino (Italy), 1977, Service award of Honor N.Y. Med. Coll., 1969, medaille d'Honneur (France), medal of City of Paris, 1979. Fellow ACS (cancer liaison physician Surgeons commn. on Cancer 1987—, Peruvian Acad. Surgery (hon.), Am. Acad. Compensation Medicine, Am. Soc. Clin. Oncology, Am. Assn. Cancer Rsch., Am. Geriatrics Soc., Indsl. Med. Assn., Internat. Coll. Surgeons (1st v.p. 1973-74, pres. 1977-78, v.p., chmn. coun. examiners U.S. sect. 1962-68, pres. 1971, Svc. award of honor 1971), Internat. Paleopathology Assn. (founder), N.Y. Acad. Medicine, N.Y. Coun. Surgeons, Royal Soc. Health (Eng.); mem. AMA, AAAS, AAUP, Am. Cancer Soc. (com. breast cancer), Am. Med. Writers Assn., Am. Profl. Practice Assn., Assn. Am. Med. Colls., Am. Coll. Radiology (com. mammography and breast cancer), Assn. Mil. Surgeons U.S., Cath. Physicians Guild (pres. N.Y. 1970-78), Gerontol. Soc., Internat. Platform Assn., N.Y. Cancer Soc., N.Y. County Med. Soc., N.Y. Surg. Soc., Pan Am Med. Assn. (v.p. N.Am. sect. on cancer 1967—), Pan Pacific Surg. Assn. (v.p. 1980, Res. Officers Assn. U.S., Soc. Acad. Achievement (editorial bd. 1969—), Nat. nsortium Breast Ctrs. (bd. dris. 1991—), Soc. Med. Jurisprudence, Soc. Nuclear Medicine Surg. Soc. N.Y. Med. Coll., WHO, World Med. Assn., Alumni assn. N.Y. Med. Coll. (gov. 1960—, pres. 1971), Assn. Mil. Surgeons U.S., Catholic War Vets Assn., VFW, Hollywood Acad. Medicine (hon.), Alpha Omega Alpha, Phi Chi; hon. mem. Argentine Soc. Mammary Pathology, Argentina Cardiac and Thoracic Surg. Soc., Ecuador Med. Assn., Mo. Surg. Soc., Venezuela Surg. Soc., Italian Surg. Soc., S.C. Oncology Soc., So. Med. Assn. Club: Ocean Dunes, Surf. Lodge: K.C. (4th deg.).

LEIS, PHILIP EDWARD, anthropologist; b. Newburgh, N.Y., Oct. 19, 1931; s. Louis and Sarah (Cohen) L.; children—Mark Samuel, Rachel Beth, Micela Sophia, Kiyara Judith. B.A., Antioch Coll., 1954; Ph.D., Northwestern U., 1962. Lectr. anthropology Nat. Coll. Edn., Evanston, Ill., summer 1960; instr., then asst. prof. Iowa State U., Ames, 1960-62; successively asst. prof., assoc. prof., prof. Brown U., Providence, 1962—; dir. anthropology Brown U., 1967-70, chmn. dept., 1970-76, 92—, chmn. faculty, 1986-87. Author: Enculturation and Socialization in an Ijaw Village, 1972; co-editor: Ethnic Encounters, 1977, (co-author) Becoming Nigerian in Ijo Society, 1989. Fulbright sr. scholar, Zimbabwe. Mem. African Studies Assn., Am. Ethnol. Soc., Am. Anthrop. Assn., Royal Anthrop. Inst. Home: 16 Irving Ave Providence RI 02906-4109 Office: Brown U Dept Anthropology Providence RI 02912

LEISECA, SERGIO A. JR., lawyer; b. La Habana, Cuba, Oct. 12, 1946. BA, Tulane U., 1968, JD, 1971. Bar: Ill. 1971. Ptnr. Baker & McKenzie, Caracas, Venezuela, 1974-78, Chgo. Office: Baker & McKenzie 1 Prudential Plz 130 E Randolph St Chicago IL 60601

LEISER, BURTON MYRON, philosophy and law educator; b. Denver, Dec. 12, 1930; s. Nathan and Eva Mae (Newman) L.; m. Janet A. Johnson, Aug. 12, 1984; children: Shoshana, Illana, Phillip, stepdaughter Sheri Johnson. BA, U. Chgo., 1951; MHL, Yeshiva U., 1956; PhD, Brown U., 1968; JD, Drake U., 1981. Bar: Iowa 1982, N.Y. 1985, U.S. Dist. Ct. (so. dist.) N.Y. 1986, U.S. Supreme Ct. 1986. Instr. Fort Lewis Coll., Durango, Colo., 1963-65; asst. prof. SUNY, Buffalo, 1965-68, assoc. prof., 1968-70; assoc. prof. Sir George Williams U., Montreal, Can., 1969-72; prof., chmn. Drake U., Des Moines, 1972-83; E.J. Mortola prof. philosophy, adj. prof. law Pace U., N.Y.C., 1983-88, disting. prof. philosophy, 1988—; del. UN for Am. Profs. for Peace in the Middle East, 1988-91. Author: Custom, Law and Morality, 1969, Values in Conflict, 1981, Liberty, Justice and Morals, 1986. Chmn. bd. trustees Congregation Bet Am Shalom, White Plains, N.Y., 1990-92. Brown U. fellow 1959-62, NYU fellow 1955-57; grantee NEH, Exxon Ednl. Found. Mem. Am. Profs. for Peace in the Middle East (nat. sec. 1983-89), Am. Soc. Value Inquiry (pres. 1978-80). Republican. Jewish. Avocations: bird watching, music. Office: Pace U Briarcliff Manor NY 10510 If God hadn't wanted us to stick our necks out, he wouldn't have given us necks.

LEISER, ERNEST STERN, journalist; b. Phila., Feb. 26, 1921; s. Monroe Felsenthal and Gertrude (Stern) L.; m. Caroline Thomas Camp, Oct. 26, 1946; children: Nancy, Shelley, Nicholas. AB, U. Chgo., 1941. Reporter City News Bur. Chgo., 1941; asst. picture editor Chgo. Herald-Am., 1941-42, 46; corr. Overseas News Agy., 1947-52; successively corr., producer, dir. TV news, exec. producer CBS News, N.Y.C., 1953-72; sr. producer, producer bicentennial coverage, spl. reports CBS News, 1975-79, v.p. spl. events and polit. coverage, 1979-81, v.p., dep. dir. news, 1981-85; exec. producer ABC News, N.Y.C., 1972-75; sr. fellow Gannett Ctr. for Media Studies, 1987-88. Author: This is Germany, 1950; contbr. articles to mags. Served with AUS, 1942-46. Decorated Bronze Star, Croix de Guerre; recipient Sigma Delta Chi award for TV reporting, 1956, Peabody awards for TV reporting and producing, 1956, 77, Ohio State awards, 1969, 77, Nat. Acad. TV Arts and Scis. award, 1968-71. Home: College Ave Nyack NY 10960-4208

LEISH, KENNETH WILLIAM, publishing company executive; b. Cambridge, Mass., Dec. 31, 1936; s. Frank and Lillian (Kargir) L.; m. Barbara Lynn Ackerman, Nov. 27, 1966; children: Matthew, Emily, Adam. A.B. magna cum laude, Harvard U., 1958; M.S. in Journalism, Columbia U., 1959. Interviewer Oral History Office, Columbia, 1960; free lance drama reviewer Variety, 1961-66; editor Am. Heritage Pub. Co., Inc., N.Y.C., 1961-69; v.p.; gen. mgr. book div. Am. Heritage Pub. Co., Inc., 1971-77; editor-in-chief Am. Heritage Press, 1970-71; mgr. large-format paperbacks Bantam Books Inc., N.Y.C., 1977-81; editor-in-chief Grolier Inc. Project Editorial Group, 1981-87; v.p. dir. product devel. Grolier Internat., Inc., Danbury, Conn., 1988-91; v.p. new product devel. Grolier Inc., Danbury, Conn., 1992—. Author: The White House, 1972, A History of the Cinema, 1974. Served with AUS, 1959-60. Home: 3 Vermont Ave White Plains NY 10606-3507 Office: Grolier Inc Sherman Turnpike Danbury CT 06816

LEISSA, ARTHUR WILLIAM, mechanical engineering educator; b. Wilmington, Del., Nov. 16, 1931; s. Arthur Max and Marcella E. (Smith) L.; m. Gertrud E. Achenbach, Apr. 11, 1974; children: Celia Lynn, Bradley Glenn. BME, Ohio State U., 1954, MS, 1954, PhD, 1958. Engr., Sperry

Gyroscope Co., Great Neck, N.Y., 1954-55; rsch. assoc. Ohio State U., 1955-56, instr. engring. mechanics, 1956-58, asst. prof., 1958-61, assoc. prof., 1961-64, prof., 1964—; vis. prof. Eidgenossische Technische Hochschule, Zurich, Switzerland, 1972-73, USAF Acad., Colorado Springs, Colo., 1985-86; Plenary lectr. 2nd Internat. Conf. on Recent Advances in Structural Dynamics, Southampton, Eng., 1984, 4th Internat. Conf. on Composite Structures, Paisley, Scotland, 1987, Dynamics and Design Conf., Japan Soc. Mech. Engrs., Kawasaki, 1990, Energy Sources and Tech. Conf., ASME, Houston, 1992; cons. in field. Performer Columbus Symphony Orch. Operas, 1971-79; author: Vibration of Plates, 1969, Vibration of Shells, 1973, Buckling of Laminated Composite Plates and Shell Panels, 1985; assoc. editor Applied Mechanics Revs., 1985-93, editor-in-chief, 1993—; assoc. editor Jour. Vibration and Acoustics, 1990-93; mem. editorial bd. Jour. Sound and Vibration, 1971—, Internat. Jour. Mech. Sci., 1971—, Composite Structures, 1982—, Applied Mechanics Revs., 1988-93; contbr. over 150 articles to profl. jours. Gen. chmn. Pan Am. Congress Applied Mechanics, Rio de Janeiro, 1989; leader Ohio State U. Mt. McKinley Expdn., 1978. Recipient Recognition plaque Inst. de Mecanica Applicada, Argentina, 1977, Centennial cert., Am. Soc. Engring. Edn., 1993. Fellow ASME, Am. Acad. Mechanics (pres. 1987-88), Japan Soc. for Promotion Sci.; mem. Am. Soc. for Engring. Edn. (Centennial Cert. 1993), Am. Alpine Club. Home: 1294 Fountaine Dr Columbus OH 43221-1520 Office: 155 W Woodruff Ave Columbus OH 43210-1181

LEISTEN, ARTHUR GAYNOR, lawyer; b. Chgo., Oct. 17, 1941; s. Arthur Edward Leisten and Mary (Francis) Gaynor; m. Florence T. Kelly, May 11, 1968; children: Thomas, Hillary. AB magna cum laude, Loyola U., Chgo., 1963; JD, Harvard U., 1966; grad. exec. mgmt. program, Northwestern U., Chgo., 1983 and 1986, Pa. State U., 1985. Bar: Ill. 1966, U.S. Dist. Ct. (no. dist.) Ill. 1967, U.S. Ct. Appeals 1967. Assoc. prof. Sch. Law Loyola U., 1966-69; assoc. Chadwell & Kayser, Ltd., Chgo. 1969-74; staff atty. Texaco, Inc., Chgo., 1974-75; atty. USG Corp., Chgo., 1975-78, sr. atty., 1978-82, sr. gen. atty., 1982-85, assoc. gen. counsel, 1985, v.p., assoc. gen. counsel, 1985-86, v.p., gen. counsel, 1986-90, sr. v.p., gen. counsel, 1990-93, sr. v.p., gen. counsel, sec., 1993—. Mem. ABA (corp. counsel com.), Chgo. Bar Assn., Am. Corp. Counsel Assn., Univ. Club, Law Club (Chgo.), Mich. Shores Club (Wilmette, Ill.), Westmoreland Country Club. Office: USG Corp 125 S Franklin St Chicago IL 60606-4678

LEISURE, GEORGE STANLEY, JR., lawyer; b. N.Y.C., Sept. 16, 1924; s. George S. and Lucille E. (Pelouze) L.; m. Joan Casey, June 22, 1949; children: Constance, Timothy, Matthew, George III. B.A., Yale U., 1948; LL.B., Harvard U., 1951. Bar: N.Y. 1953, U.S. Supreme Ct. 1966. Asst. U.S. atty. So. Dist. N.Y., 1954-56; trial atty. antitrust div. Dept. Justice, N.Y.C., 1956-57; partner firm Donovan Leisure Newton & Irvine, N.Y.C., 1957—; spl. counsel to Gen. William Westmoreland in Westmoreland vs. CBS, 1984-85. Served with USN, 1943-46; served to lt. USNR, 1951-53. Fellow Am. Coll. Trial Lawyers (chmn. N.Y. downstate com. 1975-77); mem. Fed. Bar Council (pres. 1976-78), Assn. Bar City N.Y. (exec. com. 1962-66), Fed. Bar Assn., ABA, N.Y. State Bar Assn., N.Y. County Lawyers Assn. Home: Cottage 467 PO Box 30221 Sea Island GA 31561 Office: Donovan Leisure et al 30 Rockefeller Plz New York NY 10112-0002

LEISURE, PETER KEETON, federal judge; b. N.Y.C., Mar. 21, 1929; s. George S. and Lucille E. (Pelouze) L.; m. Kathleen Blair; Feb. 27, 1960; children: Lucille K. (dec.), Mary Blair, Kathleen K. B.A., Yale U., 1952; LL.B., U. Va., 1958. Bar: N.Y. 1959, U.S. Supreme Ct. 1966, D.C. 1979, U.S. Dist. Ct. Conn. 1981. Assoc. Breed, Abbott & Morgan, 1958-61; asst. U.S. atty. So. Dist. N.Y., 1962-66; partner firm Curtis, Mallet-Prevost, Colt & Mosle, 1967-78; ptnr. Whitman & Ransom, N.Y.C., 1978-84; judge U.S. District Court Southern New York, New York, NY, 1984—. Bd. dirs. Retarded Infants Svcs., 1968-78, pres., 1971-75; bd. dirs. Community Coun. of Greater N.Y., 1972-79, Youth Consultation Svcs., 1971-78; trustee Ch. Club of N.Y., 1973-81, 87-90; mem. jud. ethics com. Jud. Conf., 1990-93, fin disclosure com. Fellow Am. Bar Found., Am. Coll. Trial Lawyers; mem. ABA, Am. Law Inst., Am. Judges Assn., D.C. Bar Assn., Fed. Bar Coun. (trustee, v.p. 1973-78), Bar Assn. City of N.Y., Nat. Lawyers Club (hon.). Office: US Dist Ct 608 US Courthouse Foley Sq New York NY 10007

LEITCH, VINCENT BARRY, literary studies educator; b. Hempstead, N.Y., Sept. 18, 1944; s. Eugene Vincent and Lucile Jean (Amplo) L.; m. Jill Robin Berman, May 20, 1970 (div. May 1987); children: Kristin M., Rory G. BA, Hofstra U., 1966; MA, Villanova U., 1967; PhD, U. Fla., 1972. Postdoctoral fellow Sch. Criticism and Theory, U. Calif., Irvine, 1978; interim asst. prof. U. Fla., Gainesville, 1972-73; from asst. prof. to prof. English Mercer U., Macon, Ga., 1973-86; prof. English Purdue U., West Lafayette, Ind., 1986—, co-dir. English and philosophy doctoral program, 1986-93; sr. Fulbright lectr. U. Tampere, Finland, 1979; reviewer NEH, 1985-88; bd. dirs. Purdue U. Press, 1988-90; Moss chair of excellence U. Memphis, 1991; mem. adv. bd. Modern Fiction Studies, 1992—. Author: Deconstructive Criticism, 1983, American Literary Criticism from the 1930s to the 1980s, 1988, Cultural Criticism, Literary Theory, Poststructuralism, 1992; mem. editorial bd. lit. and film series Fla. State U. Press, 1983—; mem. staff Abstracts of English Studies, 1972-75; mem. editorial bd. South Atlantic Rev., 1985-87. Recipient Outstanding Acad. Book award Assn. Coll. and Rsch. Librs., 1988; Am. Philos. Soc. grantee, 1974; fellow NEH, 1980, Mellon Found., 1981, Am. Coun. Learned Socs., 1985-86, Ctr. for Humanistic Studies, Purdue U., 1989. Mem. MLA (pubs. com. 1990-93, assembly del. 1990-92, 93-95, chair organizing com. 1995, exec. com. lit. criticism div. 1994—), Soc. for Critical Exch. (bd. dirs. 1978-83), PEN Am. Ctr., Internat. Assn. for Philosophy and Lit. Office: Purdue U Dept English West Lafayette IN 47907

LEITE, CARLOS ALBERTO, physician, medical educator; b. Rio de Janeiro, Feb. 2, 1939; s. Indayassu and Munira (Raed) L. BSc, Coleg. Ext. Sao Jose, Rio de Janeiro, 1956; MD, U. Brazil, Rio de Janeiro, 1962, PhD, 1972. Intern Rochester (N.Y.) Gen. Hosp., 1963-64; resident Henry Ford Hosp., Detroit, 1964-65; resident, fellow, researcher Jackson Meml. Hosp. and U. Miami, Fla., 1965-68; ltd. practice Nanticoke Meml. Hosp., Seaford, Del., 1968; prof. medicine U. Fed. Rio de Janeiro, 1972—; emeritus prof. medicine Faculty Medicine Soc. Ens. Sup. Nova Iguacu, Rio de Janeiro, 1986—; dir. Hosp. de Nova Iguacu-Posse, Rio de Janeiro, 1991; instr. medicine Fac. Nac. Med., U. Fed. Rio de Janeiro, 1963-72; chief in-patient ward Santa Casa da Misericordia Hosp., Rio de Janeiro, 1968-72, chief out-patient dept., 1968-76, cons. physician surg. unit, 1969—; chercheur visitant temporaire Inst. Pasteur, Paris, 1988; prof. U. Fed. Rio de Janeiro, Brazil, 1993; prof. medicine Univ. Federal Fluminense, 1994, cons. Embratel 1994, Med. writer Today's Medicine/Jour. Commerce, 1975—; editor: Metabolic Aspects of 95% Pancreatic Resection, 1971, Medicine, Logique and Reasoning, 1992, Limited Abduction of the Thumb-A New Physical Sign, 1992, Signs and Manoevers in Physical Diagnosis, 1992; editor: Crural Hernias, 1993; contbr. articles to profl. jours. 2d lt. Brazilian Army, 1961-62. Recipient Carlos Chagas medal State of Guanabara, 1972, Pedro Americo medal, 1993; prize Argentine Meeting of Gastroenterology, 1971. Fellow ACP, Colegio Interamericano de Medicos y Cirurjanos; mem. N.Y. Acad. Scis., Am. Venereal Disease. Brazilian Coll. Surgeons, Clube Monte Libano (counsel mem. 1972—). Home: 70 Rua Redentor Apt 101, Ipanema, 22421 Rio de Janeiro Brazil Office: Ste 302, 595 Rua Visconde de Piraja, 22420 Rio de Janeiro Brazil

LEITE, EDUARDO CERQUEIRA, lawyer; b. Montevideo, Uruguay, Aug. 7, 1950; came to U.S., 1988; s. Eduardo C. and Amanda E. (Mendez) L.; m. Yolanda Amaral C., Feb. 26, 1977; children: Juliana, Natalia. Bachelor, Inst. O. y Llerena, Salto, Uruguay, 1970; JD, U. Sao Paulo, 1978; Masters, NYU, 1980. Law clk. Dr. Maria C. Cebrian, Sao Paul, 1973-74, Dr. Benedito A.P. D'Olival, Sao Paulo, 1974-75; assoc. Stroeter, Trench e Veirano, Sao Paulo, 1975-79, Baker & McKenzie, Chgo., 1980-81; assoc. Stroeter, Trench E Veirano, Sao Paulo, 1981-86, ptnr., 1986-88; ptnr. Baker & McKenzie, Miami, 1988—. Sec. Fellowship Community Ch., Sao Paulo, 1982-86, pres., 1986-88. Recipient Medal Jose Bonifacio Soc. Bras. de Heraldica, Medal CArlosGomes Lodge Carlos Gomes 1598, 1988. Mem. Brazilian Bar Assn., Am. Soc. C. of C. (legal com. 1982-88), French C. of C. (legal com. 1987-88), Coral Gables C. of C. (internat. bus. com. 1988-93). Presbyterian. Home: 701 Brickell Ave Ste 1600 Miami FL 33131-2852 Office: Baker & McKenzie 701 Brickell Ave Ste 1600 Miami FL 33131-2827

LEITER, DONALD EUGENE, religious organization executive; b. Ashland, Ohio, Feb. 5, 1932; s. Harold Lewis and Sadie Helena (Watson) L.; m. Crystal Dianne Berkey, June 15, 1957; children: David Alan, Donald Eugene Jr., Dianne Elizabeth, Daniel Scott. BA, Manchester Coll., 1954; MDiv, Bethany Theol. Seminary, 1958; postgrad., Garret Theol. Seminary and Northwestern U., 1972, Carnegie-Melon U., 1993. Ordained to ministry Ch. of the Brethren, 1956. Min. West Side Christian Parish, Chgo., 1954-58; pastor Ch. of the Brethren, Everett, Pa., 1958-59, Germantown Ch. of the Brethren, Phila., 1959-61; pastor, organizer Immanuel Ch. of the Brethren, Paoli, Pa., 1959-66; assoc. pastor Washington City Ch. of the Brethren, 1966-72; coord. Capitol Hill Group Ministry, Washington, 1968-72; exec. dir. Delmarva Ecumenical Agy., Wilmington, Del., 1972-81; pastor, organizer Christ Ch. of the Brethren, Carol Stream, Ill., 1981-84; exec. dir. Ga. Christian Coun., Macon, 1984-90, Christian Assocs. Southwest Pa., Pitts., 1991—. Scoutmaster, agy. rep. Boy Scouts Am., 1963-72; co-chmn. Upper Main Line Com. Conscience, 1965-66; mem. Neighborhood Planning Coun., Washington, 1967-72, Leadership Pitts., Citizens League S.W. Pa., Interfaith/Impact for Justice and Peace, Pitts. Points of Light Leadership Coun., Nat. Conf. Christians and Jews, 1973-81, Habitat for Humanity, Ctr. Dem. Renewal. Mem. Nat. Assn. Ecumenical Staff, Nat. Coun. Chs., Ecumenical Networks. Office: Christian Assocs SW Pa 239 4th Ave Ste 1817 Pittsburgh PA 15222-1712 *To keep perspective in our contemporary periods of charismatic enthusiasm, fundamentalist challenges and liberal causes I rely upon the biblical foundation of my early study of each occurrence in the Bible of the word "Spirit" in the context of who made reference to the Spirit, why was the Spirit invoked and what was the immediate context as well as the overall context within biblical literature.*

LEITER, ELLIOT, urologist; b. Bklyn., May 24, 1933; s. David and Freda (Pearlman) L.; m. Renee Anita Epstein, June 9, 1963; children: Ariane L., Karen R., Michael E. AB, Columbia U., 1954; MD, NYU, 1957. Diplomate Nat. Bd. Med. Examiners, Am. Bd. Urology. Intern Johns Hopkins Hosp., Balt., 1957-58, resident in surgery, 1958-59; resident in surgery NYU Hosp., 1959-60; resident in urology Bellevue Hosp., N.Y.C., 1960-63; asst. in urology Johns Hopkins Hosp., Balt., 1958-59; asst. in urology NYU, N.Y.C., 1960-63, instr. in urology, 1963; instr. in urology Columbia U., N.Y.C., 1966-67; asst. prof. Mt. Sinai Sch. Medicine, N.Y.C., 1966-69, assoc. prof., 1969-78, prof., 1978-89; clin. prof. urology, 1989—; acting chmn. urology Mt. Sinai Sch. Medicine, N.Y.C., 1982-84; dir. urology Beth Israel Med. Ctr., N.Y.C., 1978-85; attending urologist, dir. pediatric urology Mt. Sinai Hosp., 1976-78; pres. Metro-Litho, Inc., N.Y.C., 1988-91, bd. dirs., 1991—. Contbr. articles to profl. publs., chpts. to books. Pres. Emerald Marine Ltd. Wilmington, Del., 1981; bd. dirs. Brith Milah Bd., 1970. Fellow Am. Urolog. Assn. (com. mem., 1st prize N.Y. sect. 1963, 64, pres. 1985-86), N.Y. Acad. Medicine (chmn. judicial com. urolog. sect. 1976, ACS; mem. Soc. Univ. Urologists, Royal Soc. Health, Soc. Pediatric Urology, Am. Acad. Pediatrics, Internat. Coll. Surgeons, N.Y. Met. Lithotriptor Assn. (pres. 1987), N.Y. Met. Biliary Lithotriptor Assn. (pres. 1989), Saugatuck Harbor Yacht Club, Seven Ses Cruising Assn. Republican. Jewish. Avocations: sailing, skiing, reading, music. Home: 181 Hawks Way Sequim WA 98382 Office: 109 E 38th St New York NY 10016-2601

LEITER, RICHARD ALLEN, law educator, law librarian; b. Sacramento, Mar. 21, 1952; s. Lionel and Lois Rose Leiter; m. Wendy Ellin Werges, Dec. 30, 1978; children: Madeline Rose, Anna Joy, Rebecca Hope. BA in Anthropology and Religious Studies with honors, U. Calif., Santa Cruz, 1976; JD, Southwestern U., 1981; M of Libr. and Info. Sci., U. Tex., 1986. Libr. asst. Irell & Manella, L.A., 1977-78; libr. Hopkins, Mitchell & Carley, San Jose, Calif., 1982-84; head of reference Law Sch., U. Tex., Austin, 1984-86; pub. svcs. libr. Law Sch., U. Nebr., Lincoln, 1986-88; head libr. Littler, Mendelson, Fastiff & Tichy, San Francisco, 1988-91; dir. law libr., assoc. prof. law Regent U. Sch. Law, Virginia Beach, Va., 1991-94, Howard U. Sch. Law, A.M. Daniels Law Libr., Washington, 1994—; mem. Westlaw Acad. Adv. Bd., 1990-93; sec. bd. dirs. StoneBridge Sch., 1993-94; mem. adv. bd. Oceana Publs., Inc., 1994—. Editor: (book sect.) Yellow Pads to Computers, 1986, 91; author: (bibliography) New Frontiers of Forensic & Demonstrative Evidence, 1985; editor: Automatome, 1987-89, The Spirit of Law Librarianship, 1991, National Survey of State Laws, 1993; editor Southwestern U. Law Review; contbr. articles to profl. jours. Mem. adv. com. StoneBridge Ednl. Found. Mem. ABA, Am. Assn. Law Librs. (so. chpt., automation and sci. devel. spl. interest sect. 1986—, chair 1989-90, indexing of periodical lit. adv. com. 1990-91, chair 1990-91, mem. spl. com. to promote development of resources for legal info. cmty. 1994—), San Francisco Pvt. Law Librs. (steering com. 1989), Consortium Southeast Law Librs. (vice chair), Scribes. Avocations: bicycling, reading, backpacking. Home: 2830 Woodlawn Ave Falls Church VA 22042 Office: Howard U Daniel Law Libr 2900 Van Ness St NW Washington DC 20008

LEITER, ROBERT ALLEN, journalist, magazine editor; b. Phila., Apr. 21, 1949; s. Samuel Simon and Beverly (Agins) L.; m. Barbara Ann Field, May 6, 1973; children: Lauren, James, Rebecca. BA in English and Creative Writing with honors, U. Iowa, 1970. Freelance writer short stories, book revs., feature articles The Nation, The New Republic, Redbook, Am. Scholar, N.Y. Times, Partisan Rev., The Forward, others, 1973—; mng. editor, book columnist Inside mag., Phila., 1983-87; gen. reporter, book editor Jewish Exponent, Phila., 1987—; co-editor Friday, lit. supplement newspaper Jewish Exponent, Phila., 1983-87, mng. editor Jewish Exponent 100th Anniversary edit., 1987, editor Extra Extra, weekly mag. sect., 1987-94; news editor Jewish Exponent, 1991—; contbr. editor Am. Poetry Rev., Phila., 1987—; instr. writing Am. Lit., theater Cheltenham (Pa.) Adult Sch., 1983-87. Author: (with others) Jewish Profiles, 1992. Asst. to vice chmn. U.S. Commn. on Civil Rights, Washington, 1987-88. Recipient Smolar award for excellence in N.Am. Jewish journalism for articles series, 1989, Simon Rockower awards, 1990, Rockower award, 1993, Keystone Press award, 1994. Mem. Phi Beta Kappa. Republican. Jewish. Avocation: collecting books, antique furniture and paintings. Home: 1002 Prospect Ave Melrose Park PA 19027 Office: Phila Jewish Exponent 226 S 16th St Philadelphia PA 19102-3348

LEITER, WILLIAM C., banking executive, controller; b. Akron, Ohio, May 16, 1939; s. Clarence Dailey and Lucille E. (Knecht) L.; m. Sue J. Sullivan, Nov. 5, 1965; children: Brian Robert, Sonja Lou. BS in Bus. Adminstrn., Kent State U., 1961. CPA, Pa. Various positions Coopers & Lybrand, Pitts., 1961-75; fin. v.p. Wendy's Internat. Inc., Dublin, Ohio, 1975-81; sr. v.p., controller Banc One Corp., Columbus, Ohio, 1981—. Mem. Am. Inst. CPAs, Fin. Execs. Inst. (past pres., bd. dirs. 1981—), Assn. Bank Holding Cos. (chmn. acctg. com. 1982—). Republican. Presbyterian. Club: Capital (Columbus). Avocations: fishing, reading, swimming. Office: Banc One Corp 100 E Broad St Columbus OH 43215-3607

LEITH, CECIL ELDON, JR., retired physicist; b. Boston, Jan. 31, 1923; s. Cecil Eldon and Elizabeth (Benedict) L.; m. Mary Louise Henry, July 18, 1942; children: Ann, John, Paul. A.B., U. Calif. at Berkeley, 1943, Ph.D. 1957. Exptl. physicist Lawrence Radiation Lab., Berkeley, 1946-52; theoretical physicist Lawrence Radiation Lab., Livermore, Calif., 1952-68; sr. scientist Nat. Center for Atmospheric Research, Boulder, Colo., 1968-83; div. dir. Nat. Center for Atmospheric Research, 1977-81; physicist Lawrence Livermore Nat. Lab. (Calif.), 1983-90; Symons Meml. lectr. Royal Meteorol. Soc., London, 1978; chmn. com. on atmospheric scis. NRC, 1978-80, sci. program evaluation com. Univ. Corp. for Atmospheric Rsch., 1991—; mem. joint sci. com. world climate research program World Meteorol. Organ. and Internat. Council Sci. Unions, 1976-83; mem. program adv. com. Office Advanced Sci. Computing, NSF, 1984-85. Served with AUS, 1944-46. Fellow Am. Phys. Soc., Am. Meteorol. Soc. (Meisinger award 1967, Rossby research medal 1982). Home: 627 Carla St Livermore CA 94550-2316 Office: Lawrence Livermore Nat Lab PO Box 808 Livermore CA 94551-0808

LEITH, EMMETT NORMAN, electrical engineer, educator; b. Detroit, Mar. 12, 1927; s. Albert Donald and Dorothy Marie (Emmett) L.; m. Lois June Neswold, Feb. 17, 1956; children: Kim Ellen, Pam Elizabeth. B.S., Wayne State U., 1950, M.S., 1952, Ph.D., 1978. Mem. research staff U. Mich., 1952—, prof. elec. engring., 1968—; cons. several indsl. corps. Contbr. articles to profl. jours. Served with USNR, 1945-46. Recipient Gordon Meml. award S.P.I.E., 1965; citation Am. Soc. Mag. Photographers, 1966; Achievement award U.S. Camera and Travel mag., 1967; Excellence of Paper award Soc. Motion Picture and TV Engrs., 1967; Daedalion award,

1968; Stuart Ballantine medal Franklin Inst., 1969; Distinguished Faculty Achievement award U. Mich., 1973; Alumni award Wayne State U., 1974; cited by Nobel Prize Commn. for contbns. to holography, 1971; Holley medal ASME, 1976; named Man of Year Indsl. Research mag., 1966; Nat. medal of Sci., 1979; Russel lecture award U. Mich., 1981; recipient Dennis Gabor medal Soc. Photo-Instrumentation Engrs., 1983, Gold medal, 1990; Mich. Sci. Trailblazer award, 1986. Fellow Optical Soc. Am. (Wood medal 1975, Herbert Ives medal 1985), IEEE (Liebmann award 1967, Inventor of Year award 1976), Engring. Soc. Detroit (hon.); mem. Nat. Acad. Engring., Sigma Xi, Sigma Pi Sigma. Patentee in field. First demonstrated (with colleague) capability of holography to turn high-quality 3-dimensional image. Home: 51325 Murray Hill Dr Canton MI 48187-1030 Office: Univ Mich Inst Sci and Tech PO Box 618 Ann Arbor MI 48106-0618

LEITH, JAMES CLARK, economics educator; b. Brandon, Man., Can., Dec. 9, 1937; s. James Scott and Bertha Miriam (Clark) L.; m. Carole Ann Mason, Aug. 29, 1964; children: James Douglas, Deborah Ann, Jonathan Gregory. B.A., U. Toronto, 1959; M.S., U. Wis., 1960, Ph.D., 1967. Fgn. service officer Trade Commn. Service-Govt. of Can., 1960-67, Santo Domingo, Dominican Republic, 1961-64, Chgo., 1965; asst. prof. econs. U. Western Ont., 1967-71, assoc. prof., 1971-78, prof., 1978—, chmn. dept. econs., 1972-76, v.p. acad. provost, 1980-86; econ. cons. Ministry Fin. and Devel. Planning, Gaborone, Botswana, 1986-88; dir. rsch. Bank of Botswana, 1993-95, policy advisor, 1995—; vis. lectr. U. Ghana, Legon, 1969-71; sr. research assoc. Nat. Bur. Econ. Research, 1971-75; vis. researcher Inst. Internat. Econ. Studies, Stockholm, 1976-77; vis. prof. Catholic U., Lima, Peru, 1979; vis. scholar Harvard Inst. Internat. Devel., Cambridge, Mass., 1992-93. Author: Foreign Trade Regimes..., Ghana, 1974; co-author: (with P.T. Ellsworth) The International Economy, 1975, 84; co-editor: (with D. Patinkin) Keynes, Cambridge and the General Theory, 1977; contbr. articles to econ. jours. Mem. United Ch. of Can.

LEITH, JOHN HADDON, clergyman, theology educator; b. Due West, S.C., Sept. 10, 1919; s. William H. and Lucy Ann (Haddon) L.; m. Ann Caroline White, Sept. 2, 1943; children—Henry White, Caroline Haddon. A.B., Erskine Coll., 1940, D.D. (hon.), 1972; B.D., Columbia Theol. Sem., 1943; M.A., Vanderbilt U., 1946; Ph.D., Yale U., 1949; D.D. (hon.), Davidson Coll., 1978; D.Litt. (hon.), Presbyn. Coll., 1990. Ordained to ministry Presbyterian Ch. 1943. Pastor chs. in Nashville and Auburn, Ala., 1944-59; Pemberton prof. theology Union Theol. Sem., Richmond, Va., 1959-90; vis. prof. Columbia Theol. Sem., Eckerd Coll., New Coll. at U. Edinburgh; adj. prof. Va. Commonwealth U.; mem. ad interim com. to revise book of ch. order Presbyn. Ch. U.S., 1955-61, mem. com. to write brief statement of faith, 1960-62, mem. com. to prepare brief statement of reformed faith, 1984-91; chmn. com. revision of chpt. 3 of Confession of Faith, 1959-60, mem. permanent nominating com. gen. assembly, 1972-75; chmn. bd. Presbyn. Survey, 1961-70; bd. dirs. Presbyn. Outlook Mag., 1962—; moderator Presbyn. Synod N.C., 1977-78; mem. Gov.'s Commn. on Seasonal and Migrant Farm Workers, 1982-94; mem. adv. coun. Ctr. of Theol. Inquiry, Princeton, N.J., 1989-94. Author: Creeds of the Churches, 1963, 3d. rev. edit., 1982, The Church, A Believing Fellowship, 1965, rev. 1980, Assembly at Westminster, 1973, Greenville Church, The Story of a People, 1973, The Reformed Tradition, A Way of Being the Christian Community, 2d edit., 1981, John Calvin, the Christian Life, 1984, The Reformed Imperative, 1988, John Calvin's Doctrine of the Christian Life, 1989; editor: Guides to Reformed Theology, The Reformed Imperative, 1988, From Generation to Generation, 1990, Basic Christian Doctrine, 1993; editor (with Stacy Johnson) A Reformed Reader, A Source Book for Christian Theology, 1993. Trustee Erskine Coll.; bd. dirs. Inst. Religion and Democracy, 1985-93; mem. Richmond City com. Dem. Party, 1973-93. Kent fellow, 1946-48; Folger Library fellow, 1964; grantee Advanced Religious Studies Found., 1974. Mem. Calvin Studies Soc. (pres. 1980-83). Home: 3311 Suffolk Rd Richmond VA 23227-4724

LEITMANN, GEORGE, mechanical engineering educator; b. Vienna, Austria, May 24, 1925; s. Josef and Stella (Fischer) L.; m. Nancy Lloyd, Jan. 28, 1955; children: Josef Lloyd, Elaine Michèle. BS, Columbia U., 1949, MA, 1950; PhD, U. Calif., Berkeley, 1956; D Engring. honoris causa, Tech. U. Vienna, 1988; D honoris causa, U. Paris, 1989, Tech. U. Darmstadt, 1990. Physicist, head aeroballistics sect. U.S. Naval Ordnance Sta., China Lake, 1950-57; mem. faculty U. Calif., Berkeley, 1957—, prof. engring. sci., 1963—, assoc. dean acad. affairs, 1981-90, assoc. dean rsch., 1990-94, acting dean, 1988, choir of the faculty, 1994—; cons. to aerospace industry and govt. Author: An Introduction to Optimal Control, 1966, Quantitative and Qualitative Games, 1969, The Calculus of Variations and Optimal Control, 1981, others; contbr. articles to profl. jours. Served with AUS, 1944-46, ETO. Decorated Croix de Guerre France, Fourragere Belgium; recipient Pendray Aerospace Lit. award, 1979, Von Humboldt U.S. sr. scientist award, 1980, Levy medal, 1981, Mechanics and Control of Flight award, 1984, Berkeley citation, 1991, von Humboldt medal, 1991; named Miller Research prof. 1966. Mem. NAE, Acad. Sci. Bologna, Internat. Acad. Astronautics, Argentine Nat. Acad. Engring, Russian Acad. Natural Sci., Georgian Acad. Engring., A.V. Humboldt Assn. Am. (pres. 1994), Bavarian Acad. Scis. Office: U Calif Coll Engring Berkeley CA 94720

LEITNER, ALFRED, mathematical physicist, educator, educational film producer; b. Vienna, Austria, Nov. 3, 1921; came to U.S. 1938, naturalized, 1944; s. Philipp and Lona (Machlup) L.; m. Marzia O'Neil, Nov. 24, 1948; children: Kathleen Adams, Deborah Matulis, David. B.A., U. Buffalo, 1944; M.S., Yale U., 1945, Ph.D., 1948. Research assoc. Courant Inst. Math. Scis. N.Y. U., 1947-51; from asst. prof. to prof. physics Mich. State U., 1951-67; prof. physics Rensselaer Poly. Inst., 1967-88, prof. emeritus, 1988—; research assoc. Harvard U., 1965-66; cons. Harvard project physics, 1966-68; vis. prof. U.S. Mil. Acad., West Point, 1983-85. Author papers on theory spl. functions, boundary value problems, antennas, history of sci., teaching.; Films Liquid Helium, 1963, Superconductivity, 1966, Project Physics, 1965-68; Dispersion, 1973, Fraunhofer (2 films), 1974, A Story of Research, 1981; (videotapes) Our Favorite Physics Demonstrations, 1987. Guggenheim fellow, 1958-59; Deutscher Akademischer Austauschdienst fellow, 1977. Fellow Am. Phys. Soc.; mem. Assn. Physics Tchrs., Am. Assn. Univ. Profs., Phi Beta Kappa, Sigma Xi. Home: 1201 8th Ter N Naples FL 33940-5411

LEITNER, PAUL R., lawyer; b. Winnsboro, S.C., Nov. 11, 1928; s. W. Walker and Irene (Lewis) L.; m. Jeannette C. Card, Mar. 16, 1985; children by previous marriage: David, Douglas, Gregory, Reid, Cheryl. AB, Duke U., 1950; LLB, McKenzie Coll., 1954. Bar: Tenn. 1954. Pvt. practice law Chattanooga, 1954; assoc. firm Leitner, Warner, Moffitt, Williams, Dooley, Carpenter & Napolitan and predecessor firms, 1952-57, ptnr., 1957—; Tenn. chmn. Def. Resch. Inst., 1978-89. Bd. dirs. Family Service Agy., 1957-63, Chattanooga Symphony and Opera Assn., 1986-89, sec., 1987-89; mem. Chattanooga-Hamilton County Community Action Bd.; mem. Juvenile Ct. Commn., Hamilton Country, 1955-61, chmn., 1958-59; chmn. Citizens Com. for Better Schs.; mem. Met. Govt. Charter Commn. Served with U.S. Army, 1946-47. Named Young Man of Yr. Chattanooga Area, 1957. Fellow Am. Coll. Trial Lawyers, Tenn. Bar. Found, Chattanooga Bar Found. (founding); mem. ABA, Tenn. Bar Assn., Jaycees (Chattanooga, pres. 1956-57), Fed. Ins. Corp. Counsel, Internat. Assn. Def. Coun, Trial Attys. Am., Tenn. Def. Lawyers Assn. (pres. 1975-76), Am. Bd. Trial Advs. (advocate), U.S. Sixth Cir. Jud. Conf. (life). Methodist. Home: Augusta Dr Lookout Mountain TN 37350

LEITZELL, TERRY LEE, lawyer; b. Williamsport, Pa., Apr. 15, 1942; s. Ernest Richard and Inez Mae (Taylor) L.; m. Lucy Acker Emmerich, June 18, 1966; children: Thomas Addison, Charles Taylor, Robert Davies. A.B., Cornell U., 1964; J.D., U. Pa., 1967. Bar: D.C. bar 1967. Consular officer Dept. State, Bombay, India, 1968-70; atty.-adv. for oceans affairs Dept. State, Washington, 1970-77; chief U.S. negotiator UN law of sea negotiations Dept. State, Geneva, also N.Y.C., 1974-77; asst. adminstr. for fisheries med. and dir. Nat. Marine Fisheries Service, NOAA, Dept. Commerce, Washington 1978-81; practice law Washington, 1982-92, Seattle, 1992—. mem. ABA, Mem. D.C. Bar Assn., Am. Soc. Internat. Law. Democrat. Home: 3150 W Laurelhurst Dr NE Seattle WA 98105-5346 Office: Bogle & Gates 2 Union St Seattle WA 98101-2023

LEIWEKE, TIMOTHY, sales executive, marketing professional; b. St. Louis, Apr. 21, 1957; s. John Robert and Helen (Caicuey) L.; m. Pamela

Leiweke, Nov. 1, 1984. Grad. high sch., St. Louis. Salesperson New Eng. Mut. Life Ins. Co., St. Louis, 1976-79; asst. gen. mgr. St. Louis Steamers/ MISL, 1979-80; gen. mgr. Balt. Blast/MISL, 1980-81; v.p., gen. mgr. Kansas City (Mo.) Comets/MISL, 1981-84; v.p. Leiweke and Co., Kansas City, 1984-85; pres. Kansas City Comets/MISL, 1986-88; v.p. sales and mktg. div. Minn. Timberwolves, Mpls., 1988-91; sr. v.p. of bus. ops. Denver Nuggets, Denver, 1991-92; pres. Denver Nuggets, Denver, CO, 1992—. Bd. dirs. Kidney Found., Minn., 1989—, Spl. Olympics, Minn., 1989—, Timberwolves Community Found., Minn., 1989—. Named Rookie of the Yr., Mo. Life Underwriters, 1976, Kansas Citian of the Yr., Kansas City Press Club, 1983; recipient William Brownfield award U.S. Jaycees, 1978, William Brownfield award Mo. Jaycees, 1978, Excalibur award Am. Cancer Soc., 1987. Mem. Kansas City Mktg. and Sales Execs., Mpls. Club. Avocations: running, golf, cross-country skiing, soccer, basketball. Home: 1635 Clay St Denver CO 80204-1799 Office: Denver Nuggets McNichols Sports Arena 1635 Clay St Denver CO 80204

LEIZEAR, CHARLES WILLIAM, retired information services executive; b. Balt., Dec. 15, 1922; s. Charles R. and Nellie Beyer L.; m. Jean Smith, Nov. 26, 1947; children: Robin DeBarry, Kathy King. Charles R. II. B.S. cum laude, Loyola Coll., Balt., 1949. With Burroughs Co., 1949-71; v.p. mktg. data systems Singer Co., N.Y.C., 1972-76; group v.p. cash mgmt. services Nat. Data Corp., Atlanta, 1976-81, exec. v.p. fin. service and systems, 1981-83, exec. v.p. ops., 1983-85, exec. v.p retail systems, 1984, sr. v.p., 1985-88; mktg. and quality process cons. Charles Assocs., Atlanta, 1989—. Served with U.S. Army, 1942-45. Recipient Susan Anthony award for highest acad. achievement Loyola U., 1947.

LEJEUNE, DENNIS EDWARD, investment counsel; b. Chgo., Feb. 25, 1942; s. Edward George and Eileen Marie (Donnellan) L.; m. Barbara Katharine Benson, July 24, 1965; children: Angela Marie, Katharine Kelly, Amy Eileen. B.B.A., U. Notre Dame; postgrad., Northwestern U. Internat. banking officer Provident Nat. Bank, Phila., 1971-73; fgn. exch. trader Harris Trust & Savs. Bank, Chgo., 1966-71, asst. v.p., 1973-74, v.p., mgr. IMM div., 1974-80, sr. v.p., mgr. investment dept., 1980-81, exec. v.p., 1981-88; dir. internat. fin. svcs. Stotler & Co., Chgo., 1986-88; pvt. investment counsel Traverse City, Mich., 1988—. Tchr. St. Faith, Hope & Chairty Ch., Winnetka, Ill., 1977-81; trustee Glen Arbor Twp., 1992; pres. Glen Lake Assn., 1992-93, bd. dirs., 1989-95. Mem. Forex Assn. N.Am. (sec. 1976-80), Pub. Securities Assn. (dir. 1983-85), Bond Club Chgo. (dir., pres. 1988), Rotary. Republican. Roman Catholic. Clubs: Univ. (Chgo.), Glen Lake Yacht, Traverse City Golf and Country. Avocations: sailing, golf, swimming, ancestry. Home: 7366 S Glen Lake Rd Glen Arbor MI 49636 Office: Investment Counsel 12935 W Bay Shore Dr Traverse City MI 49684-5470

LE JEUNE, FRANCIS ERNEST, JR., otolaryngologist; b. New Orleans, Jan. 3, 1929; s. Francis Ernest and Anna Lynne (Dodds) LeJ.; m. Ena Kay Hudson, Dec. 21, 1963; children: Francis III, Baltzer, Katherine, Ann. B.S., Tulane U., 1950, M.D., 1953. Intern Charity Hosp., La., New Orleans, 1953-54; resident U. Iowa Hosps., Iowa City, 1954-57; mem. staff dept. otolaryngology Ochsner Clinic, New Orleans, 1959—, chmn. dept. otolaryngology, 1963-89; clin. prof. dept. otolaryngology Tulane U. Sch. Medicine, New Orleans, 1977—. Served with USAF, 1957-59. Mem. ACS, Am. Laryngol. Assn., Am. Laryngol., Rhinol. and Otol. Soc., Am. Broncho-Esophagol. Soc., Am. Soc. Head and Neck Surgery, Am. Acad. Otolaryngology, Head and Neck Surgery, La.-Miss. Ophthalmol. and Otolaryngol. Soc. (pres. 1993-94), So. Yacht Club, Boston Club. Home: 334 Garden Rd New Orleans LA 70123-2004 Office: 1514 Jefferson Hwy New Orleans LA 70121-2483

LEKAS, MARY DESPINA, otolaryngologist; b. Worcester, Mass., May 13, 1930; d. Spyridon Peter and Merciny S. (Manoliou) L.; m. Harold William Picozzi. BA, Clark U., 1949; MD, Athens (Greece) U., 1957; MA, Brown U., 1986; student, Boston U. Diplomate Am. Bd. Otolaryngology. Sci. instr. Hahnemann Hosp. Sch. Nursing; rotating intern Meml. Hosp., Worcester, 1957-58; resident in otolaryngology R.I. Hosp., Providence, 1958-62; resident in otolaryngology and otorhinolaryngology U. Pa. Grad. Sch. Medicine, 1960; surgeon in chief, dept. otolaryngology R.I. Hosp., 1984—; pvt. practice Providence, 1962—; chmn. dept. otolaryngology Brown U., Providence, 1984—; cons. Cleft Palate Clin. and Craniofacial of R.I. Hosp., 1964—, VA Hosp., Providence, 1967—, St. Joseph Hosp., Providence, 1983—, Miriam Hosp., Providence, 1984—; lectr. profl. orgns. Europe, U.S. Mem. editorial bd. Am. Jour. Rhinology, 1987—; contbr. articles to profl. jours. Mem. alumni coun. Clark U. Clark V./Jonas Clark fellow; named R.I. Woman Physician of Yr., 1992. Fellow ACS, Soc. Univ. Otolaryngologists-Head and Neck Surgeons, Triological Soc. (ea. sect. sec., Presdl. Citation 1993), Am. Acad. Otolaryngology-Head and Neck Surgeons, Am. Acad. Facial Plastic and Reconstructive Surgeons, Am. Acad. Broncho-Escophalogy (treas., v.p. 1990); mem. AMA, Assn. Acad. Dept. Otolaryngology-Head and Neck Surgery, Deafness Rsch. Found., Am. Cleft Palate Assn., Am. Med. Women's Assn. (R.I. Woman Physician of Yr. 1992), Centurian Club, New Eng. Otolaryng. Soc. (pres. 1987-88). Greek Orthodox. Avocations: cycling, swimming, church choir. Home: 129 Terrace Ave Riverside RI 02915-4726 Office: Physicians Office Bldg 110 Lockwood St Providence RI 02903-4801

LELAND, DAVID D., timber company executive; b. Austin, Minn., July 26, 1935; s. P.C. and Leona (Christensen) L.; m. Maralee Brown (div.); children: D. Mark, Todd D., Reid H.; m. Leslie S. Gibbs, Aug. 21, 1987. BS in Forestry, U. Wash., 1958. Various positions Simpson Timber Co., Shelton, Wash., 1959-71, v.p. Calif. ops., 1971-76; sr. v.p. S.W. Forest Industries, Phoenix, 1976-77, exec. v.p. bldg. products, 1977-83; pres., chief exec. officer Plum Creek Timber Co., Seattle, 1983-93, chmn., pres., CEO, 1993—, chmn., 1994—; bd. dirs. Plum Creek Mgmt. Co., Seattle. Mem. Nat. Forest Products Assn. (bd. dirs., chmn. 1st vice chmn., 2d vice chmn., treas. 1989-92), Am. Plywood Assn. (trustee 1986-93), Am. Forest & Paper Assn. (bd. dirs. 1993), World Forestry Ctr. (bd. dirs. 1988—), Rainier Club, Seattle Yacht Club, Seattle Golf Club. Office: Plum Creek Timber Co LP 999 3rd Ave Ste 2300 Seattle WA 98104-4096

LELAND, HAROLD ROBERT, research and development corporation executive, electronics engineer; b. Eau Claire, Wis., Apr. 18, 1931; s. Harold F. and Julia E. (Porter) L.; m. Lorraine M. Weiss, Feb. 5, 1958; children: Jane Valorie, Robert William. BEE, U. Wis. 1954, MS, PhD, 1958. Registered profl. engr., N.Y. With Calspan Corp., Buffalo, 1958—, pres., 1983—; v.p. Arvin Industries, Inc., Columbus, Ind., 1984—; Vice chmn., dir. Calspan SUNY Buffalo Research Ctr., 1983—, The U. Tenn. Calspan Ctr. for Aerospace Research, 1985—. Served to capt. USAF, 1954-56. Recipient Alumni award U. Wis., 1981, Dean's award SUNY at Buffalo, 1987. Mem. AIAA, IEEE, Assn. Old Crows (Washington, Buffalo, N.Y.), Air Force Assn. (pres. sec. 1978—), Assn. U.S. Army, Am. Defense Preparedness Assn., Niagara Frontier Assn. (sec. 1974—), Sigma Xi, Tau Beta Pi, Sigma Phi (sec. 1952—). Unitarian. Office: Calspan Corp 4455 Genesee St Buffalo NY 14225

LELAND, HENRY, psychology educator; b. N.Y.C., Feb. 13, 1923; s. Ida (Miller) L.; m. Helen D. Faitos (div. 1979); children: Colombe, David Jean, Daniel Louis; m. Sherrie Lynn Ireland, Dec. 7, 1980. AB, San Jose State Coll., 1948; PhD, Université de Paris (Sorbonne), 1952. Lic. psychologist, Ohio. Clin. psychologist with Dr. Jean Biro, Paris, 1949-52; sr. clin. psychologist N.Y. State Mental Health Commn., Syracuse, 1952-54; dir. dept. psychol. svc. Muscatatuck State Sch., Butlerville, Ind., 1954-57; chief clin. psychologist Parsons (Kans.) State Hosp. and Tng. Ctr., 1957-63; coord. profl. tng., edn. and demonstration Parsons (Kans.) State Hosp. and Tng. Ctg., 1963-70; assoc. in child rsch. Kansas U. Bur. child Rsch., Lawrence, 1961-70; prof. psychology Ohio State U., Columbus, 1970-72; prof. Ohio State U., 1972-93, prof. emeritus, 1993—; chief psychology Herschel W. Nisonger Ctr., Columbus, 1970-93; teaching asst. Ind. U. Extension Svc., 1956-57; assoc. prof. Kansas State Coll. 1958-70; dist. vis. lectr. U. So. Calif., L.A., 1969; prin. investigator Adaptive Behavior Project, Ohio Dept. Mental Health and Mental Retardation, 1972-75; cons., 1972-75; bd. examiner State Bd. Psychology for Ohio, 1987-88, 1993-94, bd. sec. 1988-89, pres. 1989-90, 94—, active, 1986—; cons. Cen. Ohio Psychiat. Hosp., 1986-93; mem. com. on acad. misconduct. Ohio State Univ., 1990-93. Author: (wih D. Smith) Play Therapy with Mentally Subnormal Children, 1965, (with others) Brain Damage and Mental Retardation, 1967, (with others)

Handbuch der Kinderpsychotherapie, Vol. II, Germany, 1968, (with others) Social Perceptual Training Kit for Community Living, 1968, Impairment in Adaptive Behavior: A Community Dimension, Tracks, Vols. II, 12, 1960-67, (with others) Social Inference Training of Retarded Adolescents at the Pre-Vocational Level, 1968, (with others) Mental Health Services for the Mentally Retarded, 1972, (with others) Sociobehavioral Studies in Mental Retardation, 1973, (with others) Mental Retardation: Current and Future Perspectives, 1974, (with others) Research to Practice in Mental Retardation and Education and Training, II, 1977, (with others) International Encyclopedia of Psychiatry, Psychology, Psychoanalysis and Neurology, II, 1977, (wth others) Psychological Management of Pediatric Problems, 1978, (with Deutsch)Abnormal Behavior, 1980, (with others) Pscychoeducational Assessment of Preschool and Primary Age Children, 1982, (with others) Comprehensive Handbook of Mental Retardation, 1983, (with others) The Foundations of Clinical Neuropsychology, 1983, (with others) Institutions for the Mentally Retarded: A Changing Role in Changing Times, 1986; cons. editor Am. Jour. Mental Deficiency, 1965-70, Profl. Psychology, 1977—, Mental Retardatin, 1980-84; contbr. articles to profl. jours. Sgt. U.S. Army, 1942-45, ETO. Recipient Disting. Svc. in Mental Deficiency award, Am. Assn. on Mental Deficiency, 1985. Fellow AAAS, APA (councilor 1986-90, Edgar A. Doll Meml. award div. 33 1990), Am. Assn. on Mental Retardation (councilor 1964-68), Ohio Psychol. Assn., Soc. for Pediatric Psychology. Democrat. Jewish. Avocations: stamp collecting, gourmet cooking. Home: 2120 Iuka Ave Columbus OH 43201-1322 Office: Ohio State U Nisonger Ctr 1581 Dodd Dr Columbus OH 43210-1257

LELAND, JOY HANSON, anthropologist, alcohol research specialist; b. Glendale, Calif., July 29, 1927; d. David Emmett and Florence (Sockerson) Hanson; m. David A. Riegert, Nov. 14, 1993. B.A. in English Lit., Pomona Coll., Claremont, Calif., 1949; M.B.A., Stanford U., 1960; M.A. in Anthropology, U. Nev., 1972; Ph.D. in Anthropology, U. Calif., Irvine, 1975. With Desert Research Inst., U. Nev., 1961—; asst. research prof., 1975-77, assoc. research prof., 1977-79, rsch. prof., 1979-89, rsch. prof. emerita, 1990—. Author: monograph Firewater Myths, Frederick West Lander-A Biographical Sketch; contbg. author: Smithsonian Handbook of North American Indians; also articles, book chpts. Bd. dirs. Desert Rsch. Inst. Found. NIMH grantee, 1972-73; Nat. Inst. Alcohol Abuse and Alcoholism grantee, 1974-75, 79-81. Mem. Am. Anthrop. Assn., Southwestern Anthrop. Assn., Soc. Applied Anthropology, Soc. Med. Anthropology, Gt. Basin Anthrop. Conf., Phi Kappa Phi. Office: Desert Rsch Inst U Nev System PO Box 60220 7010 Dandini Blvd Reno NV 89512-3901

LELAND, LAWRENCE, insurance executive; b. C., Can., Nov. 13, 1915. A.B., Earlham Coll. C.L.U. Asst. supt. agys. Am. United Life Ins. Co., 1948-58, agy. v.p., 1958-67, dir., 1962-67; sr. v.p., mem. operating com. Nat. Life Ins. Co., Montpelier, Vt., 1967-72; exec. v.p. Nat. Life Ins. Co., 1972-80, ret., 1980; dir. Nat. Life Investment Mgmt. Co., Inc.; pres., dir. Equity Service, Inc., Adminstrv. Services, Inc.; exec. com. Audit Nat. Life Ins. Co. Trustee Earlham Coll., 1958-67, acting pres., 1984-85, hon. life trustee, 1985—; mem. Vt. Employment Security Bd.; bd. visitors Guilford Coll., 1980-85. Mem. Gen. Agts. and Mgrs. Assn., Central Vt. Life Underwriters Assn., Lafayette (Ind.) Life Underwriters Assn. (past pres.), Ind. Leaders Club. Club: Meridian Hills Country. Lodge: Masons. Home: 12 Westwood Dr Montpelier VT 05602-4211

LELAND, MARC ERNEST, trust advisor, lawyer; b. San Francisco, Apr. 20, 1938; s. Herbert and Sarah Betty (Robinson) L.; m. Elisabeth Gustava De Rothschild, July 7, 1970 (div. Sept. 1980); children: Natasha Hanna, Olivia Mitzi; m. Jacqueline de Botton, 1989. AB in Govt., Harvard U., 1959; MA in Law, St. John's Coll.-Oxford U., Eng., 1961; JD, U. Calif.-Berkeley, 1963. Ford Found. fellow Inst. Comparative Law-U., Paris, 1963-64; assoc. Cerf Robinson & Leland, San Francisco, 1964-68, ptnr., 1972-76; faculty fellow Harvard U. Law Sch., Boston, 1968-70; gen. counsel Peace Corps, Washington, 1970-71, ACTION, Washington, 1971-72; asst.sec. mem. AP Force Reduction Talks, Vienna, Austria, 1976-78; resident ptnr. Proskauer Rose Goetz & Mendelsohn, London, 1978-81; asst. sec. internat. affairs Dept. Treasury, Washington, 1981-84; sr. adv. Gordon P. Getty Trust, Washington, 1984—. Republican. Jewish. Office: 1001 19th St N Ste 1700 Arlington VA 22209

LELAND, PAULA SUSAN, educational administrator, educator; b. Duluth, Minn., Feb. 10, 1953; d. Clarence Henry and Agnes Gudrun (Feiring) L. BS in Elem. Edn. and Music with honors, U. Minn., Duluth, 1975, BS in English, Lang. Arts and Sec. Edn. with honors, 1979; MS in Edn. Adminstrn. and Edn. summa cum laude, U. Wis., Superior, 1982, MEd in Profl. Devel., English and Language Arts summa cum laude, 1984; Spl. degree in Edn. Adminstrn. summa cum laude, 1988, postgrad., 1988—; postgrad., U. St. Thomas, 1989, U. Minn., Mpls. Tchr. elem. gifted children U. Minn., Mpls., 1980; tchr. Hermantown (Minn.) Cmty. Schs. Dist. 700, 1975—, substitute adminstr., 1982-92; mem. staff devel. com. Hermantown (Minn.) Cmty. Schs. Dist. 700, Hermantown, 1987—; dist. coord. and chairperson, planning, evaluating and reporting com., adminstrv. rep. State Dept. of Edn. for Minn. #700, Hermantown, 1984-86; supr. student tchrs. U. Wis., Superior, 1977—, adminstr. practicum, 1981-82; supr. student tchrs. U. Minn., Duluth, 1977—; mem. faculty community adv. com. for student tchrs., 1985—; Coll. St. Scholastica, 1977—; supr. tchr. aides, parent vols. and interpreters, 1980—; fgn. exch. tchr. host, 1982-83; profl. edn. tutor, 1989-90; mem. textbook com. Hermantown Schs., 1977—; writer, reporter Hermantown Star, 1978. Curriculum writer Hermantown Community Schs.; music arranger, composer, lyricist. Mem. Dem. Nat. Conv. supporter, Dem. Party Local Affiliation, Duluth, 1972—; Lake Superior Ctr. Non-Profit Orgn.; choir dir., dir. music Zion Luth. Ch., 1980—, dir./coord. music and handbell, 1983—, asst. dir. 1976-79, co-chair music and co-author music tape for Centennial Celebration, 1988, mem. nominating and worship coms. chairperson, 1992-94, recorder, sec. and choir sec., pastor-selected com. for assoc. in ministry, 1980—, vocalist, 1967—, Sunday Sch. tchr., Bible sch. tchr. 1968-75, substitute asst. dir., 1976-80, coun. mem. 1992—, v.p. 1993-94, pres. 1994—, chair call com. pastor-elect, 1994—, found. bd. dirs. 1994—; supporter Reading is Fundamental, 1975—, United Way of Greater Duluth, 1975—; mem. Dairy Coun., Hermantown Arts Coun.; active Goodwill Industries, Salvation Army, Clean Water Action, Minn. Dept. Natural Resource-Wildlife, U. Minn. Legis. Network, 1992—; Archtl. Planner Ednl. Facilities and Creative Activity, 1984; bd. dirs. Duluth Fed. Employees Credit Union, 1994-95. Named to The Nat. Women's Hall of Fame, 1995; Alworth scholar, 1971-75, Denfeld scholar, 1968-71. Mem. AAUW, NAFE, Am. Mus. Nat. Hist., Assn. Lutheran Ch. Musicians (invited), Future Tchrs. Orgn., Red Cross Club (assoc., former v.p., svc. award), Sons of Norway (Viking Ship Project), N.Am. Assn. for Environ. Edn., Norwegian Am. Heritage Fund, Minn. Valley Nat. Wildlife Refuge, N.D. Parks and Recreation, Friends of Deep Portage, Arrowhead Reading Coun., Minn. Reading Assn., Hermantown Fedn. Tchrs., Hermantown Sch. Dist. Cont. Edn. (co-chair, former sec., cert. of appreciation 1990), Hermantown Fedn. Tchrs., Minn. Hist. Soc., Midwest Fed. Banking Consortium, U. Minn.-Duluth Alumni Assn., U. Wis.-Superior Alumni Assn., Minn. Naturalists Assn., Tweed Mus. Art, Mpls. Soc. of the Arts, Mpls. Soc. of Fine Arts, Minn. Inst. Art, Internat. Platform Assn., Smithsonian Nat. Assocs., Smithsonian Inst., Charles F. Menninger Soc., Laura Ingalls Wilder Meml. Soc., Midwesterners Club, Alpine Club, Zoofari Club, Queen Mary and Spruce Goose Voyager Club, Kappa Delta Pi, Sigma Alpha Iota, Phi Kappa Phi, Phi Delta Kappa, Delta Kappa Gamma, Beta Sigma Phi, Alpha Delta Kappa. Home: 2237 W 11th St Hermantown MN 55806-1201 Office: 4289 Ugstad Rd Hermantown MN 55811-3615

LELAND, RICHARD G., lawyer; b. Oceanside, N.Y., Jan. 25, 1949; s. Arnold Joseph and Eunice (Himlyn) L.; children: Jennifer Mara, David Jarett. BS, Cornell U., 1971; JD with distinction, Hofstra U., 1974. Bar: N.Y. 1975, U.S. CT. Appeals (2nd cir.) 1975, U.S. Dist. Ct. (so. and ea. dists.) N.Y. 1976, U.S. Supreme Ct. 1979. Assoc. Winer, Neuburger & Siw, N.Y.C., 1974-76; law sec. to justice Supreme Ct. N.Y. Nassau County, Mineola, 1976-79; assoc. Ruskin, Schlissel, Moscou & Evans, P.C. Mineola, 1979-82, ptnr., 1982-89; ptnr. Rosenman & Colin, N.Y.C., 1989—; faculty dir. Cambridge Inst., Vienna, Va., 1990-91; adj. prof. environ. law Hofstra U., Hempstead, N.Y., 1991—. Contbr. articles to profl. jours. Mem. ABA, N.Y. state Bar Assn., Nassau County Bar Assn. (chmn. com.). Office: Rosenman & Colin 575 Madison Ave New York NY 10022-2511

LELAND, SARA, ballet dancer; b. Melrose, Mass., Sept. 2, 1941; m. Arthur Kevorkian. Student with, E. Virginia Williams, Melrose, Mass. Dancer New England Civic Ballet, Joffrey Ballet, 1959-60; dancer N.Y.C. Ballet, 1960-83, asst. ballet mistress, 1983—. Dancer: (ballets) Les Biches, 1960, Don Quixote, Jewels, 1967, Symphony in Three Movements, 1972, Union Jack, 1976, Vienna Waltzers, Dances at a Gathering, 1969, The Golberg Variations, 1971, Illuminations, The Concert, 1971, Gaspardet de la Nuit, 1973, Lost Sonata, 1972, Choral Variations on Bach's Von Himmel Hoch, 1972, Scherzo Fantastique, 1972; ballet master staged works for the Joffrey Ballet, Boston Ballet, the Dance Theater of Harlem. Office: NYC Ballet Inc NY State Theater Lincoln Ctr Plz New York NY 10023*

LELAND, TIMOTHY, newspaper executive; b. Boston, Sept. 24, 1937; s. Oliver Stevens and Frances Chamberlain (Ayres) L.; m. Natasha Bourso, Sept. 26, 1964 (div. 1981); children: Christian Bourso, London Chamberlain; m. Julie S. Hatfield, Nov. 23, 1984. A.B. cum laude, Harvard U., 1960; M.S. with honors, Columbia Sch. Journalism, 1961. Med. editor Boston Herald, 1963-64; sci. editor Boston Globe, 1965-66, State House bur. chief, 1966-67, asst. city editor, 1968-69, investigative reporter, 1970-71, asst. mng. editor, 1972, mng. editor (Sunday), 1976-81, mng. editor (daily), 1981-82, now asst. to pub.; v.p. parent co. Affiliated Publs., Inc. Bd. dirs. Boys and Girls Clubs of Boston, World Affairs Coun. of Boston. Recipient Am. Polit. Sci. award, 1968; Pulitzer Prize for investigative reporting, 1972; Sigma Delta Chi award for civic service (reporting), 1972; award for pub. service A.P. Mng. Editors, 1974; Sevellon Brown award, 1974; U.S.-South African Leader Exchange Program traveling grantee, 1969; Internat. fellow Columbia, 1961. Mem. Am. Assn. Sunday and Feature Editors (past pres.), Harvard Club. Office: Boston Globe 135 Morrissey Blvd Dorchester MA 02107

LELCHUK, ALAN, author, educator; b. Bklyn., Sept. 15, 1938; s. Harry and Belle (Simon) L.; married; 2 children. B.A., Bklyn. Coll., 1960; M.A., Stanford, 1963; Ph.D., Stanford U., 1965; student, U. London, 1963-64. Writer-in-residence Brandeis U., 1966-81; vis. writer Amherst Coll., 1982-84; guest Mishkenot Sha'Aanim, Jerusalem, 1976-77; adj. prof. Dartmouth Coll., 1985—; writer-in-residence Haifa U., Israel, 1986-87; vis. writer CCNY, fall 1991. Author: American Mischief, 1973, Miriam at Thirty-four, 1974, Shrinking, 1978, Miriam in Her Forties, 1985, (young adult novel) On Home Ground, 1987, Brooklyn Boy, 1990, Playing the Game, 1995; assoc. editor Modern Occasions, 1970-72; editor: Eight Great Hebrew Short Novels, 1983, co-founder Steerforth Press, 1993; manuscript collection Mugar Meml. Libr., Boston U.; contbr. fiction, criticism to lit. mags. Yaddo and MacDowell Colony fellow, 1968-69; Guggenheim fellow, 1976-77; Fulbright grantee, 1986-87. Mem. Authors Guild, P.E.N. Home: RR 2 Canaan NH 03741-9802 Office: care Georges Borchardt 136 E 57th St New York NY 10022-2707

LELE, PADMAKAR PRATAP, physician, educator; b. Chanda, India, Nov. 9, 1927; came to U.S., 1958; s. Pratap Vasudev and Indira (Prabhudesai) L.; m. Carla Maria Tophoff, Jan. 23, 1959; children: Martin, Malcolm. M.D., Seth G.S. Med. Coll., 1950; D.Phil., Oxford (Eng.) U., 1955. Intern K.E.M. Hosp., Bombay, India, 1950-51; resident K.E.M. Hosp., 1951-52; lectr. Oxford U., 1952-57; vis. scientist NIH, Bethesda, Md., 1958-59; tech. dir. med. acoustics research group and asst. neurophysiologist Mass. Gen. Hosp., Boston, 1959-69; assoc. in neurosurgery Harvard Med. Sch.; assoc. prof. medicine MIT, Cambridge, 1969-71; prof. MIT, 1972-94, prof. emeritus, sr. lectr., 1994—; prof. Harvard-MIT Div. Health Scis. and Tech, also prof. exptl. medicine and dir. Hyperthermia Ctr.; cons. NIH. Mem. editl. bd. Ultrasound in Medicine and Biology, 1973-94, In Vivo, 1985—; contbr. articles to med. jours. Recipient History Med. Ultrasound Pioneer award World Fedn. Ultrasound in Medicine and Biology, 1988. Fellow Acoustical Soc. Am., Am. Inst. Ultrasound in Medicine (governing bd. 1973-76, Joseph H. Holmes Pioneer award 1988); mem. IEEE, Am. Soc. Clin. Hyperthermic Oncology, European Soc. for Hyperthermic Oncology, N.Am. Hyperthermia Group, Am. Assn. Physicists in Medicine, Bioelectromagnetics Soc. (charter). Home: 5820 Ravenswood Rd La Jolla CA 92037-7419 Office: MIT 5820 Ravenswood Rd La Jolla CA 92037-7419

LELLO, DAVID JOSEPH, special education educator; b. Taylor, Pa., Aug. 19, 1940; s. Dave M. and Mary C. (Merlino) L. BS in edn., Marywood Coll., 1972; M in Spl. Edn., Trenton U., 1976; spl. edn. supr. cert., Bloomsburg U., 1977. Cert. spl. edn. tchr.; elem. edn. tchr., Pa. Pers. mgr. Inst. Computer Tech., Trenton, N.J., 1967-69; sales mgr. Johnson-DeWalt Co., Flourtown, Pa., 1969-71; founder and tchr. Lifelong Learning Ctr., Abington, Pa., 1982-86; spl. edn. tchr. Abington (Pa.) Sch. Dist., 1972—; co-founder, facilitator self-esteem/self-awareness support group Bucks County Learning Disabilities Assn., 1985-90. Contbr. articles to profl. jours. Com. mem. The State Spl. Adv. Bd. Dist. 153, Glenside, Pa., 1989-90. With USAF, 1959-63. Recipient Disting. Svc. award Bucks County Learning Disabilities Assn. Mem. NEA, Pa. State Edn. Assn., Learning Disabilities Assn. (bd. mem. 1985—), Abington Edn. Assn. (v.p. membership 1993—), PACE com.), Glenside Kiwanis Club, Builders Club (advisor 1985—). Avocations: family genealogy research, travel, cooking, physical fitness. Office: Abington Sch Dist Abington Jr H S Susquehanna St Abington PA 19001

LELYVELD, ARTHUR JOSEPH, rabbi; b. N.Y.C., Feb. 6, 1913; s. Edward Joseph and Dora (Cohen) L.; m. Toby Bookholtz, Dec. 26, 1933 (div.); children: Joseph Salem, David Simon, Michael Stephen; m. 2d, Teela Stovsky, Dec. 5, 1964; children: Benjamin (dec.), Robin Beth. AB, Columbia U., 1933; M Hebrew Letters, Hebrew Union Coll., Cin., 1939; DD honoris caua, Hebrew Union Coll.-Jewish Inst. Religion, 1955; LittD (hon.), Cleve. Coll. Jewish Studies. 1986. Rabbi Congregation B'nai Israel, Hamilton, Ohio, 1939-41, Temple Israel, Omaha, 1941-44; pres. Jewish Peace Fellowship, 1941-43; exec. dir. Com. Unity for Palestine, 1944-46, nat. vice chmn., 1944-48; assoc. nat. dir. B'nai B'rith Hillel Founds., N.Y.C., 1946-47; nat. dir. B'nai B'rith Hillel Founds., 1948-56; exec. v.p. Am.-Israel Cultural Found., 1956-58; rabbi Fairmount Temple, Cleve., 1958-86, sr. rabbi emeritus, 1986—; interim rabbi Temple Emanu-El, Honolulu, 1994-95; founder, bd. dirs. Am. Jewish Soc. for Service, 1941; mem. adv. bd. Pastoral Psychology Inst., Case Western Res. U. Sch. Medicine; B.G. Rudolph lectr. in Judaic Studies, Syracuse U., 1984; lectr. So. African Union for Prog. Judaism, 1985; vis. scholar Oxford Ctr. for Postgrad. Hebrew Studies, Oxford, Eng.; adj. prof. religion Case Western Res. U., 1979-80; Bernard Rich Hollander lectr. in Jewish Thought, John Carroll U., 1980—; Walter and Mary Tuohy chair in Interreligious Studies, John Carroll U., 1989; sr. teaching fellow Cleve. Coll. Jewish Studies, 1986—; sec. Joint Rabbinical Com. Conscientious Objectors, 1941-46; Am. vice chmn. World U. Service, 1955-65; nat. pres. Am. Jewish Congress, 1966-72, hon. pres., 1972—; Goldenson lectr. Hebrew Union Coll.-Jewish Inst. Religion, 1973. Author: Atheism is Dead, 1968, paperback edit., 1970, 2d edit., 1985), The Steadfast Stream, 1995; contbg. author: Religion in the State University, Jewish Heritage Reader, Censorship: For or Against, Punishment: For or Against, Population Control: For or Against; contbr. Universal Jewish Ency., periodicals. Am. chmn. Omaha Fair Employment Practice Coun., 1942-44; pub. panel chmn. WLB 1944; exec. com. Nat. Hillel commn.; gen. chmn. Cleve. Jewish Welfare Fund, 1963; bd. advisors Martin Luther King Ctr. for Social Change. Edward L. Heinsheimer fellow, 1939-41; recipient Centennial medal John Carroll U., 1986; recipient award Western Res. Hist. Soc., 1992. Mem. Commn. on Social Action of Reform Judaism (hon. life), NAACP (hon. exec. com. Cleve. br.), Cen. Conf. Am. Rabbis (exec. bd., nat. v.p. 1973-75, pres. 1975-77), Synagogue Council Am. (nat. v.p. 1975-79, nat. pres. 1979-81), Am. Jewish League Israel (nat. v.p. 1962-84, hon. pres. 1984—), Nacoms, Phi Beta Kappa, Beta Sigma Rho. Lodge: B'nai B'rith. Office: Fairmount Temple 23737 Fairmount Blvd Cleveland OH 44122-2296 *In his late years, Teilhard de Chardin seemed obsessed with the goal of 'ending well.' What he meant is made clear in his life and work and in his letters. Ending well is actually the secure knowledge that one has made meaningful contributions to the welfare of humanity. Hence, 'ending well' means 'living well.'*

LELYVELD, JOSEPH SALEM, newspaper editor, educator; b. Cin., Apr. 5, 1937; s. Arthur Joseph and Toby (Bookholz) L.; m. Carolyn Fox, June 14, 1958; children: Amy, Nita. BA summa cum laude, Harvard U., 1958, MA, 1959; MS in Journalism, Columbia U., 1960. Reporter, editor N.Y. Times, 1963—; fgn. corr., Johannesburg, New Delhi, Hong Kong, London, 1965-86, columnist mag., staff writer, 1977, 84-85, fgn. editor, 1987-

89, mng. editor, 1990-94; exec. editor, 1994—. Author: Move Your Shadow, 1985 (Pulitzer prize, L.A. Times Book prize, Sidney Hillman award, Cornelius P. Ryan award, all 1986). Recipient George Polk Meml. award, 1972, 84; Guggenheim fellow, 1984. Mem. The Century Assn. Office: The NY Times 229 W 43rd St New York NY 10036-3913

LEM, RICHARD DOUGLAS, painter; b. L.A., Nov. 24, 1933; s. Walter Wing and Betty (Wong) L.; B.A., UCLA, 1958; M.A., Calif. State U.-Los Angeles, 1963; m. Patricia Ann Soohoo, May 10, 1958; 1 son, Stephen Vincent. Exhibited in one-man shows at Gallery 818, Los Angeles, 1965; group shows at Lynn Kottler Galleries, N.Y.C., 1973, Palos Verdes Art Gallery, 1968, Galerie Mouffe, Paris, France, 1976, Le Salon des Nations, Paris, 1984, numerous others; represented in permanent collections; writer, illustrator: Mile's Journey, 1983; cover illustrator: The Hermit, 1990, The Hermit's Journey, 1993. Served with AUS, 1958-60. Mem. UCLA Alumni Assn. Address: 1861 Webster Ave Los Angeles CA 90026-1229 *Personal philosophy: It requires a great deal of inner strength to pursue your personal vision with single mindedness - it's a challenge that justifies my existence.*

LEMAIRE, JACQUES, professional hockey coach; b. Lasalle, Que., Can., Sept. 7, 1945. Player Montreal Canadiens, 1967-79, head coach, 1983-85; head coach, player Sierre Hockey Club, Switzerland, 1979-81; asst. coach SUNY Coll., Plattsburgh, 1981-82; coach Longueuil Chevaliers, maj. jr. league, Que., 1982-83; dir. of hockey pers. Montreal Canadiens, 1985-87, asst. to mng. dir., 1987-93; head coach N.J. Devils, 1993—. Office: NJ Devils PO Box 504 East Rutherford NJ 07073-0504*

LEMAIRE, JEAN HENRI, actuarial science educator; b. Ixelles, Belgium, Apr. 10, 1947; came to U.S., 1987; s. Henri Lemaire and Odette Putman; m. Denyse Ronveaux, Oct. 27, 1971; children: Pierre, Francoise, Laurence. MD in Math., Free U., Brussels, 1969, MD in Actuarial Sci., 1972, PhD in Math., 1973. Assoc. prof. Free U. of Brussels, 1969-83; mng. dir. La Prevoyance Sociale Ins., Brussels, 1983-87; prof. U. Pa., Phila., 1987—; vis. prof. U. Calif., Berkeley, 1980, Universite Nationale du Zaire, 1973-76; chmn. automobile tchr. commn. Profl. Union Ins. Cos., 1986-87, various coms., 1985-87; mem. exec. com. Ins. Devel. Bur., 1984-87; bd. dirs. P.S. Societe Coop. d'Assurances, P.S.R. Reassurances, P.S. Caisse Commune, P.S.A.S.B.L. Oeuvres Sociales, CAST-TIB Caisse d'Assurance Sociales. Author: Automobile Insurance, 1985, 83. Recipient 1st prize Royal Belge 125th Anniv., 1980, 1st prize Boleslaw Monic reinsurance competition, 1981, Ernst Meyer Internat. prize Geneva Assn., 1986, Clarence Arthur Kelp Meml. award Am. Risk and Ins. Assn., 1987, Internat. Ins. prize Italian Acad. Scis., 1988. Mem. Actuarial Studies in Non-Life Ins. (pres. 1984-90, treas. 1981—), Internat. Actuarial Assn. (editor-in-chief 1984—). Office: U Pa Wharton Sch Ctr Rsch Risk & Ins 3641 Locust Walk # 306 Philadelphia PA 19104-6218

LE MAISTRE, CHARLES AUBREY, university official, physician; b. Lockhart, Ala., Feb. 10, 1924; s. John Wesley and Edith (McLeod) LeM.; m. Joyce Trapp, June 3, 1952; children: Charles Frederick, William Sidney, Joyce Anne, Helen Jean. BA, U. Ala., 1943, LLD (hon.), 1971; MD, Cornell U., 1947; LLD (hon.), Austin Coll., 1970; DSc (hon.), U. Dallas, 1978, Southwestern U., 1981; D honoris causa, U. Guadalajara (Mex.), 1989. Intern, then resident medicine N.Y. Hosp., 1947-49; research fellow infectious diseases Cornell U. Med. Coll., 1949-51, mem. faculty, 1951-54, asst. prof. medicine, 1953-54; mem. faculty Emory U. Sch. Medicine, 1954-59, prof. preventive medicine, chmn. dept., 1957-59; prof. medicine U. Tex. Southwestern Med. Sch., 1959-78, assoc. dean, 1965-66; vice chancellor health affairs U. Tex. System, Austin, 1966-68; exec. vice chancellor U. Tex. System, 1968-69, dep. chancellor, 1969-70, chancellor, 1971-78, prof. medicine, 1978—; pres., internist U. Tex. M.D. Anderson Cancer Ctr., 1978—; cons. epidemiology Communicable Disease Center, USPHS, 1953—; cons. medicine VA, 1954-59; area med. cons. VA (Atlanta area), 1958-59; vis. staff physician Grady Meml. Hosp., Atlanta, 1954-59, Emory U. Hosp., 1954-59; sr. attending staff mem. Parkland Meml. Hosp., Dallas, 1959-66; med. dir. chest div. Woodlawn Hosp., Dallas, 1959-65; mem. Surgeon Gen.'s Adv. Com. Smoking and Health, 1963-64, AMA-Edn. Research Found. com. research tobacco and health, 1964-66; chmn. Gov. Tex. Tb Eradication, 1963-64; cons. internal medicine Baylor U. Med. Center, Dallas, 1962-66, St. Paul Hosp., Dallas, 1966; cons. div. hosp. and med. facilities USPHS, 1966; mem. N.Y.C. Task Force on Tb, 1967; cons. Bur. Physician Adminstrn., 1977-80; mem. Tex. Legislature Dept. Health, Edn. and Welfare, 1967, Tex. Legislature Com. on Organ Transplantation, 1968, Carnegie Commn. on Non-Traditional Study, 1971-73; mem. bd. commrs. Nat. Commn. on Accrediting, 1973-76; mem. joint task force on continuing competence in pharmacy Am. Pharm. Assn.-Am. Assn. Coll. in Pharmacy, 1973-74; mem. exec. com. Legis. Task Force on Cancer in Tex., 1984-86; adv. bd. 6th World Conf. on Smoking and Health. Contbr. med. jours.; contbg. author: A Textbook of Medicine, 10 and 11th edits, 1963, Pharmacology in Medicine, 1958; Translating author: The Tubercle Bacillus, 1955; mem. editorial bd. Am. Rev. Respiratory Diseases, 1955-58. Mem. President's Commn. White House Fellows, 1971; chmn. subcom. on diversity and pluralism Nat. Council on Ednl. Research, 1973-75; bd. dirs. Assn. Tex. Colls. and Univs., 1974-75; mem. devel. council United Negro Coll. Fund, 1974-78; mem. nat. adv. council Inst. for Services to Edn., 1974-78; mem. exec. com. Assn. Am. Univs., 1975-77; mem. Project HOPE com. on Health Policy, 1977; chmn. steering com. Project HOPE com. on Health Policy, 1977; chmn. steering com. Project. Physicians for Fgn. Missions, 1960-62; mem. Ministers Cons. Clinic, Dallas, 1960-62; trustee Austin Coll., 1979-83, Stillman Coll., 1978-84; bd. dirs. Ga. Tb Assn., 1955-59; bd. dirs. Damon Runyon-Walter Winchell Cancer Fund, 1976-85, chmn. exec. com., v.p. 1991, pres., 1979-83; trustee Biol. Humanics Found., Dallas, 1973-82; chmn. health manpower com. Assn. Am. Univs., 1975-78; sec. Council So. Univs., Inc., 1976-78, pres., 1977-78; hon. life trustee Menninger Found.; Host com. Houston Econ. Summit, 1990. Recipient Cornell Univ. Alumni of Distinction award, 1978, Disting. Alumnus award U. Alabama Sch. Medicine, 1982, Pres'. award Am. Lung Assn., 1987, Gibson D. Lewis award for Excellence in Cancer Control Tex. Cancer Coun., 1988, award of Honor Am. Soc. Hosp. Pharmacists, 1988, Svc. to Mankind award Leukemia Soc. Am. Tex. Gulf Coast chpt., 1991, People of Vision award Tex. Soc. to Prevent Blindness, 1991, Outstanding Tex. Leader award 7th Ann. John Ben Shepperd Pub. Leadership Forum, 1991; named Houstonian of Yr. Houston Sch. for Deaf Children, 1987. Mem. AMA, NASA, NIH (chair Joint adv. com. Behavioral rsch. 1992), Am. Thoracic Soc. (past v.p.), So. Thoracic Soc. (past pres.), Nat. TB Assn., Tex. Med. Assn., Ga. Med. Assn., So. Assn. Oncology (bd. dirs.), Am. Cancer Soc. (Tex. bd. dirs. 1977-89, med. and sci. com. 1974, chmn. study com. on tobacco and cancer 1976—, pub. edn. com. 1976-87, chmn., mem. various nat. com.s, v.p., pres. 1986, med. dir.-at-large 1977-89), Houston C. of C. (dir. 1979-89), Philos. Soc. Tex. (pres. 1980-81), Greater Houston Ptnrship (bd. dirs. 1989—), Alpha Omega Alpha. Presbyterian. Home: 5316 Grand Lake St Bellaire TX 77401-4928 Office: U Tex M D Anderson Cancer Ctr 1515 Holcombe Blvd Houston TX 77030-4009

LE MAISTRE, CHRISTOPHER WILLIAM, educational director; b. Moradabad, India, Aug. 20, 1938; came to U.S., 1978; s. Archibald William and Kathleen Mary (Minas) L.; m. Patricia Margaret Briggs, May 18, 1963; children: Anne Louise, Nicole Marie. B of Applied Sci. in Metallurgy, U. Adelaide, Australia, 1962; PhD, Rensselaer Poly. Inst., 1971. Cert. materials engr. Trainee in metallurgy A. Simpson & Son., Ltd., Adelaide, 1957-60; cadet def. sci. Australian Dept. Supply, Adelaide, 1961-64; exptl. officer Weapons Rsch. Establishment, Adelaide, 1964-68, sr. rsch. scientist, 1971-74; R&D attache Australian High Commn., London, Eng., 1974-77; acting head lab. program Australian Def. Dept., Canberra, 1977-78; assoc. dir. mfg. ctr. Rensselaer Poly. Inst., Troy, N.Y., 1978-84, dir. ctr. for indsl. innovation, 1984—; cons. Xerox Corp., Nortons, Exxon, Bendix Corp., U. Ariz., N.J. State U., 1975—; chmn. peer rev. panel NJ Commn. on Sci. and Tech., Newark, 1987; bd. dirs. tech. adv. com. Hudson Valley Community Coll. Troy, 1988. Author: Computer Integrated Manufacturing, 1987, Technical Innovations and Economic Growth, 1987; editor: Industrial Innovation Productivity and Employment, 1986. Mem. Am. Soc. Metals (chmn. 1983), Am. Ceramic Soc. (chmn. 1984), Am. Soc. Engring. Edn. (chmn. St. Lawrence sect. 1991-92). Avocation: photography. Home: Joseph St Troy NY 12180 Office: Rensselaer Poly Inst Ctr for Indsl Innovation Troy NY 12180

LEMAN, EUGENE D., meat industry executive; b. Peoria, Ill., Dec. 1, 1942; s. Vernon L. and Viola L. (Beer) L.; m. Carolyn Leman, June 14, 1964; children—Jill C., Jennifer A. B.S., U. Ill., 1964. Dir. various depts. Wilson Foods, Oklahoma City, 1964-78, v.p. fresh and processed pork, 1978-80, v.p. fresh meat group, 1980-81; group v.p. IBP, Inc., Dakota City, Nebr., 1981-86, exec. v.p., 1986—, also bd. dirs. Mem. Am. Meat Inst. (chmn. pork com. 1980-81), Nat. Pork Producers Council (packer rep. Pork Value Task Force 1981-82, 88, pork export com. 1985). Republican. Club: Sioux City Country (Iowa). Office: IBP Inc Hwy 35 # 515 Dakota City NE 68731

LEMAN, LOREN DWIGHT, civil engineer; b. Pomona, Calif., Dec. 2, 1950; s. Nick and Marian (Broady) L.; m. Carolyn Rae Bratvold, June 17, 1978; children: Joseph, Rachel, Nicole. BSCE, Oreg. State U., 1972; MS in Civil, Environ. Engring., Stanford U., 1973. Registered profl. engr., Alaska. Project mgr. CH2M Hill, San Francisco, 1973, Reston, Va., 1973-74, Ketchikan, Alaska, 1974-75, Anchorage, 1975-87; state rep. State of Alaska, 1989-93, state senator, 1993—; owner Loren Leman, P.E. Anchorage, 1987—; mem. Anchorage Hazardous Materials Commn., Local Emergency Planning Com., 1989-93. Contbr. articles to profl. jours. Mem. Breakthrough Com., Anchorage, 1978; del. to conv. Rep. Party of Alaska, 1976-90; basketball coach Grace Christian Sch., Anchorage, 1985-88; commr. Pacific States Marine Fisheries Commn.; del. Pacific Fisheries Legis. Task Force. Mem. ASCE, Alaska Water Mgmt. Assn., The Nature Conservancy, Am. Legis. Exch. Coun., Water Environment Fedn., Toastmasters (pres.). Republican. Avocations: reading, fishing, biking, music, basketball. Home: 2699 Nathaniel Ct Anchorage AK 99517-1016 Office: Alaska State Legis 716 W 4th Ave #540 Anchorage AK 99501

LEMANN, THOMAS BERTHELOT, lawyer; b. New Orleans, Jan. 3, 1926; s. Monte M. and Nettie E. (Hyman) L.; m. Barbara M. London, Apr. 14, 1951; children: Nicholas B., Nancy E. A.B. summa cum laude, Harvard U., 1949, LL.B., 1952; M.C.L., Tulane U., 1953. Bar: La. 1953. Since practiced in New Orleans; assoc. Monroe & Lemann, New Orleans, 1953-58, ptnr., 1958—; bd. dirs. B. Lemann & Bro., Mermentau Mineral & Land Co., Riviana Foods Inc. Contbr. articles to profl. publs. Mem. council La. State Law Inst., sec. trust adv. com.; chmn. Mayor's Cultural Resources Com., 1970-75; pres. Arts Council Greater New Orleans, 1975-80; mem. vis. com. art museums Harvard U., 1974-80; trustee Metairie Park Country Day Sch., 1956-71, pres., 1967-70, New Orleans Philharmonic Symphony Soc., 1956-78, Flint-Goodridge Hosp., 1960-70, La. Civil Service League, pres., 1974-76, New Orleans Mus. Art, 1986-92; bd. dirs. Longue Vue Found., Zemurray Found., Arts Coun. New Orleans, Azby Fund, Musica da Camera. Served with AUS, 1944-46, PTO. Mem. ABA, La. Bar Assn. (bd. govs. 1977-78), New Orleans Bar Assn., Assn. Bar City N.Y., Am. Law Inst., Soc. Bartolus, Phi Beta Kappa. Jewish. Clubs: New Orleans Country, Wyvern (New Orleans); Harvard (N.Y.C.). Home: 6020 Garfield St New Orleans LA 70118-6039 Office: Monroe & Lemann 201 St Charles Ave New Orleans LA 70170-3300

LEMANSKI, LARRY FREDRICK, medical educator; b. Madison, Wis., June 5, 1943; s. Fredrick Everett and Marjery Ulila (Hill) L.; m. Sharon Lee Wulf, Aug. 6, 1966; children: Scott Fredrick, Jennifer Lee. BS, U. Wis., Platteville, 1966; MS, Ariz. State U., 1968, PhD, 1971. Asst. prof. U. Calif., San Francisco, 1975-77; assoc. prof. U. Wis., Madison, 1977-79, prof., 1979-83; prof., chmn. dept. anatomy and cell biology SUNY, Syracuse, 1983—; dir. cell and molecular biology doctoral tng. program and consortium, 1987—; rsch. prof. biology Syracuse U., 1988—; mem. ad hoc rev. panel NIH. Adult leader for Boy Scouts Am.; mem. nat. staff Boy Scout Jamboree 1989, coun. tng. chmn., 1992—. Officer USAR, 1965-69. Recipient Pres.' award Rsch. SUNY HSC, 1987, Disting. Alumnus award U. Wis., 1990, Profl. Excellence award N.Y. State/United Univ. Professions, 1990; NIH fellow, 1968-71, 71-73, Muscular Dystrophy fellow, 1973-75; grantee NIH, 1975—. Mem. AAAS, Am. Heart Assn. (Wis. affiliate rsch. com. 1982-83, Louis N. Katz Rsch. prize 1978, Outstanding Rsch. award 1982, Established Investigator award 1976-81), Electron Microscopy Soc. Am., Am. Assn. Anatomists, Am. Soc. Cell Biology (congrl. liaison com. 1993—), Soc. Devel. Biology, Am. Assn. Anatomy Chmn., N.Y. Acad. Scis., Masons (3d degree master), Sigma Xi, Beta Beta Beta. Methodist. Avocations: gardening, fishing, boating, camping, music. Home: 4163 Coye Rd Jamesville NY 13078-9780 Office: SUNY Coll Medicine Dept Anatomy Cell Biol Syracuse NY 13210

LEMARI, KUNIO DAVID, federal official; b. Jabor, Jaluit, Marshall Islands, Nov. 29, 1942; s. David Lemari and Tujo Lebje; m. Helisa A. Kaious, June 21, 1967 (div. Feb. 1985); children: Wesley, Ranny, Hearids, Evangeline, Diane, Kimberlynn, Dickson; m. Christina Maryrose Myazoe, Apr. 24, 1987; 1 child, Lyla. Degree in Theology, Bethel Bible Inst., Manila, 1967. Gen. supt. Micronesian Assemblies, Marshall Islands, 1976-80; coord. food svcs. Ministry of Social Svc., Marshall Islands, 1980-82; asst. hosp. adminstr. Ministry of Health Svc., Marshall Islands, 1982-83; officer pub. works adminstrn. Ministry of Pub. Works, Marshall Islands, 1983-84; senator Parliament of Marshall Islands, 1984-86; min. justice Govt. of Marshall Islands, 1986-87, min. transp. and comm., 1987—. Avocations: reading, fishing, baseball, bowling. Home: PO Box 648 Majuro MH 96960

LE MASTER, DENNIS CLYDE, forest economics and policy educator; b. Startup, Wash., Apr. 22, 1939; s. Franklin Clyde and Delores Irene (Schwartz) Le M.; m. Kathleen Ruth Dennis, Apr. 4, 1961; children: Paul, Matthew. BA, Wash. State U., 1961, MA, 1970, PhD, 1974. Asst. prof. dept. forestry and range mgmt. Wash. State U., Pullman, 1972-74, assoc. prof., 1978-80, prof., chair dept., 1980-88; prof., head dept. forestry and natural resources Purdue U., West Lafayette, Ind., 1988—; dir. resource policy Soc. Am. Foresters, Bethesda, Md., 1974-76; staff counsel subcom. on forests Ho. of Reps., Washington, 1977-78; cons. USDA Forest Svc., Washington, 1978, Com. on Agr., Ho. of Reps., 1979-80, Forest History Soc., Durham, N.C., 1979-83, Office Tech. Assessment, Washington, 1989-91. Author: Decade of Change, 1984; co-editor 8 books; contbr. articles to profl. jours. Bd. dirs. Pinchot Inst. for Conservation. Mem. AAAS, Soc. Am. Foresters (coun. 1988, chair house of soc. dels. 1982), Inland Empire Soc. of Soc. Am. Foresters (chair 1980-81, Forester of Yr. award 1982), Soc. for Range Mgmt., Forest Products Soc., Omicron Delta Epsilon, Beta Gamma Sigma, Xi Sigma Pi. Democrat. Episcopalian. Avocation: fishing. Home: 824 Lazy Ln Lafayette IN 47904-2722 Office: Purdue U Dept Foresty And Resou West Lafayette IN 47907

LEMASTERS, JOHN N., III, management and marketing consultant; b. Aug. 3, 1933. Student, Ga. Inst. Tech., 1958. With Harris Corp., Melbourne, Fla., 1958-84, engr., program mgmt. mgr., 1958-87, v.p. communications sector, 1978-84; pres., chief exec. officer Am. Satellite Co., Rockville, Md., 1984-85; pres., chief exec. officer Continental Telecom Inc., Atlanta, 1985-87, also bd. dirs., ret., 1987; prin., mgmt. and mktg. cons. Lemasters & Assocs., Inc., Atlanta, 1987—; mem., chief exec. officer Computer Products, Inc., Pompano Beach, Fla., 1988-91; chmn., chief exec. officer Computer Products, Inc., Boca Raton, Fla., 1991—; bd. dirs. AUGAT Inc., 1988—. Home: 45 Fairway Dr Lake Toxaway NC 28747-9629 Office: Computer Products Inc 7900 Glades Rd Ste 500 Boca Raton FL 33434-4105

LEMAY, JACQUES, lawyer; b. Quebec City, Can., July 10, 1940; s. Gerard and Jacqueline (Lachance) LeM. B.A., Que. Sem., 1959; LL.L., Laval U., 1962; postgrad., U. Toronto, 1964; D.E.S., 1965. Bar: Que. 1963. Practice in Quebec City, 1964—; mem. firm Prevost, Gagne, Flynn, Chouinard & Jacques, 1964-67; ptnr. Flynn, Rivard, Jacques, Cimon, Lessard & LeMay, 1968-86, Flynn, Rivard, 1986—; legal adviser Societe des Ajusteurs d'Assurance, 1969; bd. dirs. Can. Energy Corp. Mem. Societe des Etudes Juridiques (pres. 1969). Club: Cercle de la Garnison (Que.). Home: 2342 Marie-Victorin, Sillery, PQ Canada G1T 2W5 Office: 70 Dalhousie, Bureau 500, Quebec, PQ Canada G1K 7A6

LEMBERG, LOUIS, cardiologist, educator; b. Chgo., Dec. 27, 1916; s. Morris and Frances Lemberg; m. Dorothy Feinstein, 1940 (dec. 1969); children: Gerald, Laura Bott, Paula saltzman; m. Miriam Mayer, Jan. 29, 1971. B.S., U. Ill.-Chgo., 1938, M.D., 1940. Intern Mt. Sinai Hosp., Chgo., 1940-41, resident, 1945-48; asst. prof. med. 1955-58; assoc. prof. med. 1958-70; prof. clin. cardiology U. Miami Sch. Medicine (Fla.), 1970—; dir. coronary care unit, 1965-75; chief cardiology Mercy Hosp.; chief staff Nat. Children's Cardiac Hosp., 1959-66; cons. cardiology VA Hosp., Miami, 1953-64; dir. Cardiology Dade County Hosp., 1953-64, dir. Electrocardiology, U. Miami Jackson Meml. Med. Ctr., 1952-75, program dir. Courses in Coronary Care for Practicing Physician, 1970—, Master Approach to Cardiovascular Problems, 1972-82, Cardiology Update for Intensive Care Nurses, 1978-92, Cardiology Update, 1987—. Served to maj. AUS, 1941-55; ETO. Recipient U. St. Torres (Phillipines) Luis Guerrero hon. lectr. award, 1977; Recognition award U. Miami Sch. Medicine; Key to City of Miami Beach, Fla. Fellow ACP, Am. Coll. Cardiology (editorial bd. jour.); mem. Heart Assn. Greater Miami (pres.), Fla. Heart Assn. (pres.), Am. Heart Assn. (fellow Council Clin. Cardiology), AMA (Physician's Recognition award 1970-86, 1986-94). Democrat. Jewish. Clubs: Palm Bay, Westview Country (Miami), Williams Island. Author: Vectorcardiography, 1969, (1975 2d edit.); Electrophysiology of Pacing and Cardioversion, 1969. Editor-in-chief Current Concepts in Cardiovascular Disorders, 1984-86. Contbr. to med. publs. Pioneer in devel. Demand Pacemaker, 1964, a chair in Cardiology established at the U. Miami Sch. of Medicine entitled The Louis Lemberg Professor of Cardiology, 1990. Home: 720 NE 69 Ct Apt 18 South Miami FL 33138-5706 Office: Mercy Hosp Professional Office Bldg 3661 S Miami Ave Ste 606 Miami FL 33133-4214

LEMBERGER, AUGUST PAUL, university dean, pharmacy educator; b. Milw., Jan. 25, 1926; s. Max N. and Celia (Gehl) L.; m. Charlyne A. Young, June 30, 1947; children: Michael, Mary, Thomas, Terrence, Ann, Kathryn, Peter. B.S., U. Wis., 1948, P.h.D., 1952. Sr. chemist Merck & Co. Inc., Rahway, N.J., 1952-53; asst. prof. U. Wis. Sch. Pharmacy, 1953-57, asso. prof., 1957-63, prof. pharmacy, 1963-69; prof. pharmacy, dean U. Ill. Coll. Pharmacy, Chgo., 1969-80; prof. pharmacy, dean U. Wis.-Madison Sch. Pharmacy, 1980-91, ret., 1991; sec. Wis. Pharmacy Internship Bd., 1965-69; conf. dir. Nat. Indsl. Pharm. Research Conf., 1966-69; mem. Am. Council on Pharm. Edn., 1978-84, v.p., 1986-90. Served to 1st lt. AUS, 1944-46. Recipient Kiekhofer Meml. Teaching award U. Wis., 1957, citation of merit, 1977, Disting. Pharmacist award Wis. Pharm. Assn., 1969, Higuchi Lecture award Acad. Pharm. Sci. and Tech., Japan, 1989, Pres.' award Wis. Soc. Hosp. Pharmacists, 1991, Alumnus of Yr. award Pharmacy Alumni Assn., 1991. Fellow AAAS, Am. Found. for Pharm. Edn. (Disting. Svc. Profile award 1990), Acad. Pharm. Scis., Am. Assn. Pharm. Scientists; mem. Am. Soc. Hosp. Pharmacists, Am. Assn. Colls. of Pharmacy (past com. chmn., exec. com. 1971-74, chmn. coun. deans 1975-77, chmn. sect. tchrs. of pharmacy Conf. Tchrs., hon. pres. 1993-94), Acad. Pharm. Scis. (v.p. 1976-77, pres. 1983-84), Am. Pharm. Assn. (jud. bd. 1976-79, trustee 1985-88, treas. 1989-90), Wis. Pharm. Assn., Sigma Xi, Rho Chi (v.p. 1979-81). Home: 7439 Cedar Crk Trl Madison WI 53717-1538 Office: 425 N Charter St Madison WI 53706-1515

LEMBERGER, LOUIS, pharmacologist, physician; b. Monticello, N.Y., May 8, 1937; s. Max and Ida (Siegal) L.; m. Myrna Sue Diamond, 1959; children: Harriet Felice Schor, Margo Beth. B.S. magna cum laude, Bklyn. Coll. Pharmacy, L.I.U., 1960; P.h.D. in Pharmacology, Albert Einstein Coll. Medicine, 1964, M.D., 1968; Doctorate (hon.), L.I. U., 1994. Pharmacy intern VA Regional Office, Newark, summer 1960; postdoctoral fellow Albert Einstein Coll. Medicine, 1964-68; intern in medicine Mt. Hosp. Center, N.Y. Med. Coll., N.Y.C., 1968-69; rsch. assoc. NIH, Bethesda, Md., 1969-71; clin. pharmacologist Lilly Lab. for Clin. Rsch., Eli Lilly & Co., Indpls., 1971-75; chief clin. pharmacology Lilly Lab. for Clin. Rsch., Eli Lilly & Co., 1975-78, dir. clin. pharmacology, 1978-89, clin. rsch. fellow, 1982-93; asst. prof. pharmacology Ind. U., 1972-73, asst. prof. medicine, 1972-73, assoc. prof. pharmacology 1973-77, assoc. prof. medicine, 1973-77, prof. pharmacology, 1977—, prof. medicine, prof. psychiatry, 1977—, mem. grad. faculty, 1975—; adj. prof. clin. pharmacology Ohio State U., 1975-86; physician Wishard Meml. Hosp., 1976—; cons. U.S. Nat. Commn. on Marijuana and Drug Abuse, 1971-73, Can. Commn. Inquiry into Non-Med. Use of Drugs, 1971-73; mem. Pharm. Mfrs. Assn. Commn. on Medicines for Drug Dependence and Abuse, 1990-93, Ind. Optometric Legend Drug Adv. Com., 1991—; guest lectr. various univs., 1968—; lectr. U. Minn., 1993—; mem. adv. com. Faseb Life Scis. Rsch. Office, 1993—. Author: (with A. Rubin) Physiologic Disposition of Drugs of Abuse, 1976; contbr. numerous articles on biochemistry and pharmacology to sci. jours.; editorial bd.: Excerpta Medica, 1972—, Clin. Pharmacology and Therapeutics, 1976—, Communications in Psychopharmacology, 1975-81, Pharmacology, Internat. Jour. Exptl. and Clin. Pharmacology, 1978—, Drug and Alcohol Abuse Research, 1979-86, Drug Devel. Research, 1980-87, Trends in Pharmacol. Scis, 1989-85. Post adviser Crossroads of Am. council Boy Scouts Am., 1972-77. Served with USPHS, 1969-71. Recipient Disting. Alumnus award Albert Einstein Coll. Medicine, 1989, Disting. Alumnus award L.I. U., 1990. Fellow ACP, AAAS, Am. Coll. Neuropsychopharmacology (chmn. credentials com. 1993) , Am. Coll. Clin. Pharmacology; mem. Am. Soc. Pharmacology and Exptl. Therapeutics (com. div. clin. pharmacology 1972-78, chmn. com. 1978-83, coun. 1980-83, chmn. long-range planning com. 1984-86, pres. 1987-88, ASPET award in Therapeutics, 1985, Harry Gold award for rsch. and teaching excellence in clin. pharmacology 1993), Am. Soc. Clin. Pharmacology and Therapeutics (chmn. sect. neuropsychopharmacology 1973-80, chmn. fin. com. 1976-83, 89-92, v.p. 1981-82, pres. 1983-84, dir. 1975-81, 84-87, Rawls-Palmer award 1986, Henry Elliot Disting. Svc. award 1992), Am. Soc. Clin. Investigation, Collegiate Internat. Neuro-Psychopharmacologicum, Am. Fedn. Clin. Rsch. Ctrl. Soc. Clin. Rsch., Soc. Neuroscis., Sigma Xi, Alpha Omega Alpha, Rho Chi. Jewish. Home: 3315 Walnut Creek Dr N Carmel IN 46032-9038 Office: Ind Univ Sch Medicine Dept Pharmacology and Medicine Indianapolis IN 46202

LE MEHAUTE, BERNARD JEAN, marine physics educator; b. St. Brieuc, Bretagne, France, Mar. 29, 1927; m. Marie-Josseline Roy; children by previous marriage: Anne, Patrick. Licence es Scis., U. Toulouse, France, 1951, D in Engring., 1951; D in Advanced Study, U. Paris, 1953; PhD, U. Grenoble, France, 1957. Hydraulic engr. Sogreah, Grenoble, 1953-57; asst. prof. Ecole Polytechnique, Montreal, Can., 1957-61; dir. geomarine div. Nat. Engring. Sch. Cy., Pasadena, Calif., 1963-66; v.p. sr. v.p., corp. chief engr. TeTraTech. Inc., Pasadena, 1966-78, bd. dirs., 1966-81; chmn. ocean engring dept. Rosenstiel Sch. Marine and Atmospheric Scis., Miami, Fla., 1978-85; prof. applied marine physics U. Miami, 1985-92, prof. emeritus, 1992—. Author: Hydrodynamic and Water Waves, 1976, Ocean Engineering Science, 2 vols., 1990. Mem. nat. sea grant adv. bd. NOAA, 1971-78; mem. Coastal Engring. Rsch. Bd., C.E., U.S. Army, 1982-88. Mem. ASCE, NAE, Am. Shore and Beach Preservation Assn. (bd. dirs. 1966-93, dir. emeritus 1993—), Nat. Ac Eng. Republican. Roman Catholic. Office: Univ of Miami Dept of Ocean Engring 4600 Rickenbacker Cswy Miami FL 33149-1031

LEMEIN, GREGG D., lawyer; b. Chgo., Feb. 2, 1950. BS with high honors, U. Ill., 1972; MM with distinction, Northwestern U., 1976, JD magna cum laude, 1976. Bar: Ill. 1976, U.S. Claims Ct. 1978, U.S. Tax Ct. 1979. Ptnr. Baker & McKenzie, Chgo. Office: Baker & McKenzie 1 Prudential Plz 130 E Randolph Dr Chicago IL 60601-6206

LEMELLE, TILDEN JOHN, political science educator, editor, college official; b. New Iberia, La., Feb. 6, 1929; s. Eloi Sabas and Therese Marie (Francis) LeM.; m. Margaret Louraine Guillion, Aug. 29, 1959; children—Joyce, Stephanie, Therese. A.B., Xavier U., New Orleans, 1953, M.A., 1957; Ph.D., U. Denver, 1965. Prof. English, Grambling U., La., 1957-63; prof. polit. sci. No. Ill. U., Chgo., 1965-66, Fordham U., N.Y.C., 1966-69, Inst. Race Relations, U. Denver, 1969-71; prof. Hunter Coll., CUNY, N.Y.C., 1971—; provost, v.p. from 1984, interim pres., 1988—; pres. Univ. District of Columbia; now pres./chancellor Community Coll. of the Allegheny, North, Pittsburgh, Pa. Author: The Black College, 1969; editor: Race Among Nations, 1971; editor monograph series: Studies in Race and Nations, 1972-76; editor, pub. Africa Today, 1967—; contbr. articles on Africa and U.S. fgn. policy to profl. jours. Pres. Am. Com. on Africa, N.Y.C., 1984-87; trustee New Rochelle Bd. Edn., N.Y., 1976-81, Africa Fund, N.Y.C., 1979—, Social Sci. Found., Denver, 1979—, Ednl. Fund, N.Y.C., 1984-86; chmn. bd. trustees Africa Fund, 1987—; Internat. Fund for Peace. Recipient Community Leadership award NAACP, New Rochelle, N.Y., 1981; named hon. consul Govt. Senegal, 1969-71; fellow Social Sci. Found., 1963-65, John Hay Whitney, 1964-65; Ford Found. grantee, 1965. Fellow African Inst. Human Values; mem. African Heritage Studies Assn. (bd. dirs. 1969—), Council Fgn. Relations; Disting. Alumnus award U. Denver. Democrat. Roman Catholic. Avocations: tennis; swimming. Office: Community Coll of the Allegheny Office of the President 1130 Perry Hwy Pittsburgh PA 15237-2132

LEMEN, RICHARD ALAN, epidemiologist, medical administrator; b. Paola, Kans., July 23, 1943; s. Warren S. and Blanche (Hirt) L.; m. Kimble M. Varner; children: Monica D. (dec.), Wendy L., Tyler M. B.A., Central Meth. Coll., 1967; M.S., U. Mo., 1969; PhD, U. Cin., 1992. Dist. sanitarian Mo. Div. Health, Macon, 1966-67; epidemiologist Nat. Inst. Occupational Safety and Health, USPHS, Cin., 1970-73; biometry br. chief Nat. Inst. Occupational Safety and Health, USPHS, 1974-76, asst. chief industry wide studies br., 1978-80, dir. div. standards devel. and tech. transfer, 1980-88, dir. Washington office, asst. dir. Nat. Inst. Occupational Safety and Health, 1988-91, dep. dir., 1991—, acting dir., 1993-94; asst. surgeon gen. USPHS, 1995—; assoc. prof. divsn. environ. and occupational health Emory U., Atlanta, 1993—; bd. govs. Tri-State Air Com., 1974-76; mem. working group Internat. Agy. Research on Cancer, WHO; mem. VA adv. com. on herbicides, 1979-80; mem. Asbestos Sch. Hazards Safety Task Force, U.S. Dept. Edn., 1980-82; vice chmn. subcom. Risk Assessment of Com. to Coordinate Environ. and Health Related Programs, USPHS; chmn. asbestos ingestion task force, interagy. coordination com. for environ. research USPHS; chair Nat. Symposium on Prevention of Leading Work-Related Diseases and Injuries, Occupational Cancer, 1985, Disorders of Reproduction, 1986, Assn. Schs. Pub. Health and Nat. Inst. Occupational Safety and Health, USPHS; mem. expert panel on Occupational Health, WHO, 1993—; vol. assoc. profl dept. Environ. Helath U. Cin., 1994—. Author: Workplace Exposure to Asbestos, 1980; editor: Dust and Disease, 1979; contbr. chpts. to profl. books. Served with U.S. Army, 1967-69; served to rear adm. USPHS, 1970—. Decorated Army Commendation medal, others; recipient Meritorious Svc. medal USPHS, 1988, Commendation medal, 1981, 85, Disting. Svc. medal, 1991, Surgeon Gen's Exemplary Svc. medal, 1993; recipient Disting. Alumni award Cirl. Meth. Coll., 1989, I.W. Abel award for pub. svc. AFL-CIO, 1994, Alice Hamilton sci. award for occupational safety and health, 1993. Fellow Collegium Ramazzini; mem. Soc. Occupational and Environ. Health (dir. 1980-82, bd. dirs. 1992—), Mil. Surgeons U.S., Commd. Officers Assn. of USPHS, Beta Beta Beta. Office: Nat Inst Occupational Safety & Health 1600 Clifton Rd Atlanta GA 30333

LE MENAGER, LOIS M., incentive merchandise and travel company executive; b. Cleve., Apr. 25, 1934; d. Lawrence M. and Lillian C. (Simicek) Stanek; m. Charles J. Blabolil (dec. 1982); children—Sherry L., Richard A.; m. Spencer H. Le Menager, Mar. 23, 1984. Grad. high sch., Cleve. Bank teller, sec. to v.p., Peoples Savs. and Loan, Cleve., 1951-56; travel counselor Mktg. Innovators, Rosemont, Ill., 1978-80, mktg. dir., 1980-82, chmn., chief exec. officer, owner, 1982—; dir. Northwest Commerce Bank, Rosemont. Mem. Am. Inst. Entrepreneurs (Entrepreneur of Yr. 1988), Am. Mktg. Assn., Internat. Soc. Mktg. Planners, Mktg. Planners Internat., Soc. Incentive Travel Execs., Am. Soc. Travel Agents, Nat. Fedn. Ind. Bus., Nat. Assn. Women Bus. Owners, Nat. Assn. Female Execs., Des Plaines C. of C., Rosemont C. of C., Czechoslovak Soc. Am. Republican. Congregationalist. Club: Executive (Chgo). Office: Mktg Innovators Internat Inc 9701 W Higgins Rd Des Plaines IL 60018-4703

LE MENER, GEORGES PHILIPPE, hotel executive; b. Paris, Feb. 7, 1948; came to U.S. 1983; m. Annie Desmont, 1972; children: Sophie, Loic. BA in Hotel Mgmt., Paris, 1966. Gen. mgr. Novotel Siem, Eury, France, 1969-72, regional mgr., 1972-77, exec. v.p. ops. and human rels., 1977-83; pres. Accor N.Am. and Pacific, Scarsdale, N.Y., 1983—. Home: 2 Overhill Rd # 420 Scarsdale NY 10583-5316 Office: Accor N Am Corp 1500 Broadway New York NY 10036-4015

LEMER, ANDREW CHARLES, engineer, economist; b. Maxwell Field, Ala., Dec. 25, 1944; s. Samuel Theodore and Carol (Oppenheimer) L.; m. Patricia Spear, Aug. 1967 (div. Dec. 1981); m. Jane Felsten, Aug. 1992; children: Elizabeth Catherine, Daniel Evan. SB, MIT, 1967, SM, 1968, PhD, 1971. Assoc. Alan M. Voorhees & Assoc., Inc., McLean, Va., 1971-76; sr. assoc. PRC Planning & Econs., Inc., McLean, 1976-80; chief planner PRC (Nigeria) Ltd., Lagos, 1980-82; div. v.p. PRC Engring., Inc., McLean, 1982-85; pres. Matrix Group, Inc., Washington, 1985—; dir. bldg. rsch. bd. Nat. Acad. Scis., Washington, 1988-94; cons. Fed. Rail Adminstrn., Washington, 1975, FAA, Washington, 1986—, World Bank, Washington, 1980—, Abell Found., Balt., 1993—, Transp. Rsch. Bd., Washington, 1993—. Prin. author: In Our Own Back Yard: Principles for Improving the Nation's Infrastructure, 1993, Toward Infrastructure Improvement: A Research Agenda, 1994; contbr. articles to profl. jours.; editl. adv. bd. Jour. Infrastructure Sys., Constrn. Bus. Rev., Constrn. Mgmt. and Econs. Mem. ednl. coun. MIT, Washington, 1974—. Loeb fellow Harvard U., 1992-93. Mem. ASCE, Am. Inst. Cert. Planners, Am. Soc. for Macro-Engring. (sec. D.C. chpt. 1985—), Cosmos Club (Washington). Office: 4701 Keswick Rd Baltimore MD 21210

LEMERT, CHARLES CLAY, sociology educator; b. Cin., Sept. 21, 1937; s. Charles Clay and Helen (Radojits) L.; m. Phyllis Bonekemper LeMaire, Aug. 29, 1967 (div. Jan. 1985); children—Matthew C., Noah C. B.A., Miami U., Oxford, Ohio, 1959; B.D., Andover Newton Theol. Sch., 1963; Ph.D., Harvard U., 1972; M.A. ad eundem grandum (hon.), Wesleyan U., Middletown, Conn., 1982. Assoc. minister Congl. Ch., Needham, Mass., 1963-69; minister Unitarian Ch., Needham, Mass., 1969-71; assoc. prof. sociology So. Ill. U., Carbondale, 1971-81; prof. sociology Wesleyan U., Middletown, Conn., 1981-87, chmn. sociology dept., 1982-88, dean social scis., 1986-88; dir. etudes Ecole des Hautes Etudes en Scis. Sociales, Paris, 1984-85; vis. assoc. prof. psychiatry Harvard U. Med. Sch., 1979-80, 84-85; prof. Bard Coll., Nat. Endowment Humanities Inst. on Social Scis., summer 1983. Author: Sociology and the Twilight of Man, 1980, French Sociology, 1981; (with G. Gillan) Michel Foucault, 1983, Intellectuals and Politics, 1990. Sr. editor Theory and Society, 1980—. Contbr. articles to profl. jours.; assoc. editor: Theoretical Sociology. Research fellow Joint Ctr. for Urban Studies, Harvard U., 1969-70; faculty research fellow So. Ill. U., summers 1972, 73, 75; grantee Nat. Endowment Humanities, U. Paris, 1974. Mem. Am. Sociol. Assn. (chmn. theory sect.), Internat. Sociol. Assn., Phi Beta Kappa. Democrat. Mem. United Ch. of Christ. Home: 186 Cross St Middletown CT 06457-3161 Office: Wesleyan U Dept Sociology Middletown CT 06457

LEMERT, JAMES BOLTON, journalist, educator; b. Sangerfield, N.Y., Nov. 5, 1935; s. Jesse Raymond and Caroline Elizabeth (Brown) L.; m. Rosalie Martha Bassett, Mar. 23, 1972. A.B., U. Calif.-Berkeley, 1957, M.J., 1959; Ph.D., Mich. State U., 1964. Newspaper reporter Oakland Tribune, Calif., 1955-56; Newspaper reporter Chico Enterprise-Record, Calif., 1957, 58-60; asst. prof. journalism So. Ill. U., Carbondale, 1964-67, U. Oreg., Eugene, 1967-69; assoc. prof. U. Oreg., 1969-76, 1976—, dir. div. communication rsch., 1967—, dir. grad. program Sch. Journalism, 1983-86, 88-93; chair U. Oreg. Task Force to Revise Faculty Governance, 1983-84; mem. senate U. Oreg., 1981-83, 86-88, 93-94, chmn. senate rules com., 1987-88, chmn. intercollegiate athletics com., 1986-89, pres.'s adv. coun., 1990-91, chair, 1991-92, mem. grad. coun., 1984-86, 89-90, 94—, chair, 1993-94, chair task force on rsch. and grad. edn., 1990-91, mem. rsch. com., 1994-95. Prodr., on-air host Old Grooves show, KWAX-FM, 1977-80, 82-84; author: Does Mass Communication Change Public Opinion After All? A New Approach to Effects Analysis, 1981, Criticizing the Media: Empirical Approaches, 1989, News Verdicts, The Debates and Presidential Campaigns, 1991, Politics of Disenchantment: Bush, Clinton, Perot and the Press, 1995; editor Daily Californian, 1957; contbr. articles to profl. jours. Mem. Oreg. Alcohol and Drug Edn. Adv. Com., 1968-69; pres. South Hills Neighborhood Assn., 1976-77, bd. dirs., 1982-84, 86-88; bd. dirs. Traditional Jazz Soc. Oreg., 1981-83, 87; v.p. Met. Cable Access Corp., 1983-84; mem. exec. bd. AAUP, 1975-76, 91-94; mem. state coun., head chpt. Assn. Oreg. Faculties, 1981-83, 85-87, state v.p., 1987-89, del. to Oreg. Faculties Polit. Action Com., 1983-89. Recipient Outstanding Journalist award Sigma Delta Chi, 1957, Donald M. McGammon Communication Rsch. Ctr. critical rsch. grantee, 1988-89, Allen Family Found. grantee; NSF fellow, 1963, 64; Calif. Newspaper Pubs. fellow, 1957; Butte County Alumni scholar, 1953-54. Mem. Assn. Edn. Journalism, Am. Assn. Pub. Opinion Rsch., Am. Polit. Sci. Assn., Speech Comm. Assn., Phi Beta Kappa (membership chmn. 1985-86, v.p., pres. 1989-91). Home: 10 E 40th Ave Eugene OR 97405-3487 *Journalism is one of the more tradition-bound crafts. A constant underlying theme in the research and writing I do is that the research might help journalism redefine itself. There certainly is much need for change in long-held journalistic practices. Habit and "we've always done it this way" are no longer good enough reasons— if they ever were.*

LEMESH, NICHOLAS THOMAS, designer, filmmaker; b. McKees Rocks, Pa., May 21, 1946; s. Nicholas and Sophie (Nowak) L. B.F.A. with honors, Carnegie-Mellon U., 1968; M.F.A., NYU, 1971. Asst. program dir. Kingsley Assn., Pitts., 1968-70; art dir. William Sloane House YMCA, N.Y.C., 1969-71; graphic designer Kahn Assos., N.Y.C., 1971; adminstrv. asst. Grad. Inst. Film and TV, NYU, 1971-72; v.p. film producer Grey Advt., N.Y.C., 1972—. Youth rep. League of Red Cross Socs. to UN; nat. gov. Nat. ARC, 1970-77, chmn. hist. resources com., Washington, bd. dirs. N.Y. chpt.; U.S. rep. Internat. Red Cross Conf., Geneva, 1969. Recipient Internat. Disting. Service award for humanitarian service Macalester Coll., 1970; CLIO award for comml. excellence, 1984, 86; Andy One Show Houston Film Festival award. Mem. Nat. Inst. Social Scis., Broadcast Advt. Producers Soc. Am. Democrat. Mem. Byzantine Cath. Ch. Home: 240 E 35th St New York NY 10016-4282 Office: 777 3d Ave New York NY 10017

LEMESSURIER, WILLIAM JAMES, structural engineer; b. Pontiac, Mich., June 12, 1926; s. William James and Bertha Emma (Sherman) LeM.; m. Dorothy Wright Judd, June 20, 1953; children: Claire Elizabeth, Irene Louise, Peter Wright. AB cum laude, Harvard U., 1947, postgrad., 1948; SM, MIT, 1953. Registered profl. engr., Mass., D.C., N.Y., Tenn., Colo. Ptnr. Goldberg, LeMessurier Assoc., Boston, 1952-61; pres. LeMessurier Assocs. Inc., Boston and Cambridge, 1961-73; chmn. Sippican Cons. Internat. Inc., Cambridge, 1973-85, LeMessurier Cons. Inc., Cambridge, 1985—; instr. dept. bldg. constrn. and engring. MIT, 1951-52, asst. prof., 1952-56, assoc. prof. dept. architecture, 1964-67, sr. lectr. dept. civil engring., 1976-77, lectr., 1983-86; assoc. prof. grad. sch. design Harvard U., 1956-61, adj. prof., 1973—; vis. lectr. Yale U., U. Mich., U. Ill., Chgo., Rice U., Washington U. St. Louis, Northeastern U., R.I. Sch. Design, Cornell U., U. Pa., Roger Williams Coll., U. Calif., Berkeley, U. Tex., austin; speaker Assn. Collegiate Sch. of Architecture Constrn. Materials and Tech. Inst., Harvard U.; mem. sci. adv. com. Nat. Ctr. Earthquake Engring. Research. Co-author: Structural Engineering Handbook, 1968, 2d edit., 1979; prin. works include New Boston City Hall, Shawmut Bank Boston, 1st Nat. Bank Boston, Fed. Res. Bank Boston, Citicorp Ctr., N.Y.C., Dallas-Ft. Worth Airport Terminal Bldgs., Ralston Purina Hdqrs., St. Louis, Nat. Air and Space Mus., Washington, Am. Inst. Architects Hdqrs., Washington, One Post Office Sq., Boston, Bank Southwest Tower, Houston, InterFirst Plaza Dallas Main Ctr., Treasury Bldg., Singapore, King Khalid Mil. City, Al Batin, Saudi Arabia, TVA Hdqrs., Chattanooga, Lafayette Place Hotel, Boston, academic bldgs. at Harvard U., Princeton U., Amherst Coll., Bowdoin Coll., Williams Coll., U. Mass., U. Wis., U. Ill., Colby Coll., U. N.H., Northeastern U., Kirkland Coll., Cornell U. Mem. Cambridge Experimentation Rev. Bd., 1977; juror Capitol area archtl. and planning bd. State Capitol Bldg. Extension, St. Paul, 1977, Am. Inst. Architects Regional Awards Program, No. Vt., 1980, Progressive Architecutre mag., Portland Cement Assn. Awards, 1986, Fazlur Rahman Kahn Internat. Fellowship, N.Y.C., 1987; tech. advisor to jury Boston Archtl. Ctr. Competition. Recipient Am. Inst. Architects' Allied Professions medal, 1968, Profl. Service award Engring. News-Record, 1978, Prestressed Concrete Inst. award, 1984. Fellow ASCE (hon.), Am. Concrete Inst., Am. Inst. Archs. (hon.); mem. NAE, Boston Soc. Archs. (hon.), Boston Soc. Civil Engrs. (hon.), Boston Assn. Structural Engrs. (past pres.), Am. Inst. Steel Constrn. (specifications adv. com. 1961—, Award of Excellence 1962, 66, 70, 77, 79, Spl. award 1972), VA (adv. bd. div. constrn.), Nat. Com. on Housing Tech., Structural Clay Products Inst. (bldg. code com.), Seismic Safety Coun. (task com.), Bldg. Code Com., Internat. Masonry Inst. (rsch. coun.), Tau Beta Pi. Episcopalian. Club: Met. (N.Y.C.), St. Botolph, Boston. Developed Mah-LeMessurier high-rise housing system; conceived and developed Staggered Truss System for use in high-rise steel structures; conceived, developed and applied Tuned Mass Damper System to reduce tall bldg. motion. Avocation: music. Office: LeMessurier Cons 1033 Massachusetts Ave Cambridge MA 02138-5319

LEMIEUX, ANNETTE ROSE, artist; b. Norfolk, Va., Oct. 11, 1957; d. Joseph and Margaret (Merci) L. BFA, Hartford Art Sch., 1980. One-person shows include U. Hartford, 1980, Artists Space, N.Y.C., 1984, Cash/Newhouse, N.Y.C., 1984, 86, 87, Josh Baer Gallery, N.Y.C., 1987, 89, Daniel Weinberg Gallery, L.A., 1987, Lisson Gallery, London, 1988, Wadsworth Atheneum, 1988, Rhona Hoffman Gallery, Chgo., 1988, John and Mable Ringling Mus., 1989, Ctr. for Fine Arts, Miami, 1989, Rhona Hoffman Gallery, 1990, Monika Spruth Galerie, Cologne, Germany, 1990, Galerie Montenay, Paris, 1991, Stichting de Appel, Amsterdam, 1991; exhibited in numerous group shows, 1979—; represented in permanent collections Mus. Modern Art, N.Y.C., Mus. Fine Arts, Boston, Wadsworth Atheneum, Hartford, Conn., Whitney Mus. Am. Art, N.Y.C., Okla. Art Mus., Oklahoma City, Israel Mus., Jerusalem. Trustee Hartford Art Sch., 1989—; mem. bd. overseers Inst. Contemporary Art, Boston. N.Y. fellow, 1987, others.

LEMIEUX, CLAUDE, professional hockey player; b. Buckingham, Que., July 16, 1965. Right wing Montreal Canadiens, 1983-90, N.J. Devils, 1990—. Named to Que. Major Jr. Hockey League All-Star second team, 1983-83, first team, 1984-85; recipient Guy Lafleur trophy, 1985, Conn Smythe trophy for most valuable player in playoffs, 1995. Office: New Jersey Devils PO Box 504 East Rutherford NJ 07073*

LEMIEUX, JOSEPH HENRY, manufacturing company executive; b. Providence, Mar. 2, 1931; s. Mildred L. Lemieux; m. Frances Joanne Schmidt, Aug. 11, 1956; children: Gerald Joseph, Craig Joseph, Kimberly Mae Lemieux Wolff, Allison Jo. Student, Stonehill Coll., 1949-50, U. R.I., 1950-51; BBA summa cum laude, Bryant Coll., 1957. With Owens-Ill., Toledo, 1957—, various positions with glass container div. and closure and metal container group; exec. v.p. Owens-Ill., Toledo, 1984, pres. pkg. ops., 1984, pres., chief oper. officer, 1986-90, pres., chief exec. officer, 1990-91, chmn. bd., chief exec. officer, 1991—, also bd. dirs. Ohio Citizens Bank, Toledo, Nat. City Corp., Cleve. Vice chmn. bd. govs. Edison Indsl. Systems Ctr. U. Toledo, 1986. Served to staff sgt. USAF, 1951-55. Named one of Outstanding Young Men Am., Jaycees, 1965. Mem. Glass Packaging Inst. (chmn. 1984-86), Inverness Club (Toledo). Roman Catholic. Avocations: golf, tennis. Office: Owens-Illinois Inc 1 SeaGate Toledo OH 43666*

LEMIEUX, LINDA DAILEY, museum director; b. Cleve., Sept. 6, 1953; d. Leslie Leo LeMieux Jr. and Mildred Edna (Dailey) Tutt. BA, Beloit Coll., 1975; MA, U. Mich., 1979; assoc. cert., Mus. Mgmt. Program, Boulder, Colo., 1987. Asst. curator Old Salem, Inc., Winston-Salem, N.C., 1979-82; curator Clarke House, Chgo., 1982-84; curator Western Mus. Mining and Industry, Colorado Springs, Colo., 1985-86, dir., 1987—. Author: Prairie Avenue Guidebook, 1985; editor: The Golden Years--Mines in the Cripple Creek District, 1987; contbr. articles to mags. and newspapers. Fellow Hist. Deerfield, Mass., 1974—. Research grantee Early Am. Industries Assn., 1978. Mem. Am. Assn. Mus., Am. Assn. State and Local History, Colo.-Wyo. Mus. Assn., Colo. Mining Assn., Nev. Mining Assn., Mountain Plains Assn. Mus., Women in Mining. Republican. Presbyterian. Home: 1337 Hermosa Way Colorado Springs CO 80906-3050 Office: Western Mus of Mining & Industry 1025 N Gate Rd Colorado Springs CO 80921-3018

LEMIEUX, MARIO, professional hockey player; b. Montreal, P.Q., Can., Oct. 5, 1965; m. Nathalie Asselin, June 26, 1993; 1 child, Lauren. With Pitts. Penguins, 1984—; mem. NHL All-Star team, 1987-88, 88-89, 92-93, Stanley Cup Championship team, 1991, 92; player NHL All-Star game, 1992-93. Recipient Hart Meml. trophy for most valuable player, 1988, 89, Conn Smythe trophy for most valuable player in playoff, 1991, Art Ross Meml. trophy 1987-88, 88-89, 91-92, 92-93, Dodge Performance of the Year award, 1987-88, 88-89, Dodge Ram Tough award, 1988-89, Michel Briere trophy, 1983-84, Jean Beliveau trophy, 1983-84, Michael Bossy trophy, 1983-84, Guy LaFleur trophy, 1983-84, Calder Meml. trophy, 1984-85, Lester B. Pearson award, 1985-86, 87-88, 92-93, Pro Set NHL Player of the Year, 1991-92, Bill Masterson Meml. trophy, 1992-93; named Sporting News All-Star team, 1987-88, 88-89, 92-93, Player of the Year Canadian hockey League, 1983-84, All-Star game MVP, 1985, 88, 90, Player of the Year NHL, 1992-93. Office: Pittsburgh Penguins Civic Arena Gate # 7 Pittsburgh PA 15219*

LEMIEUX, RAYMOND URGEL, chemistry educator; b. Lac La Biche, Alta., Can., June 16, 1920; s. Octave L.; m. Virginia Marie McConaghie,

1948; children: 1 son, 5 daus. BS with honors, U. Alta., 1943; PhD in Chemistry, McGill U., 1946; DSc (hon.), U. N.B., 1967, Laval U., Quebec, 1970, U. Ottawa, 1975, U. Waterloo, 1980, Meml. U., Nfld., 1981, Université du Quebec, 1982, Queen's U., Kingston, 1983, McGill U., Montreal, 1984; Dr. honoris causa, Université de Provence, Marseille, France, 1972; LLD (hon.), U. Calgary, 1979, U. Sask., 1993; DSc (hon.), Université de Sherbrooke, 1986, McMaster U., 1986, U. Alta., 1991; PhD (hon.), U. Stockholm, 1988. Postdoctoral fellow Ohio State U., Columbus, 1946-47; asst. prof. U. Sask., Saskatoon, Can., 1947-49; sr. rsch. officer NRC of Can., Saskatoon, 1949-54; prof., chmn. chemistry dept. U. Ottawa, Can., 1954-61; vice dean, faculty of pure and applied sci. U. Ottawa, 1954-61; prof. organic chemistry U. Alta., Edmonton, Can., 1961-81, Univ. prof., 1981-85, prof. emeritus, 1985—. Author 243 published articles in sci. field. Decorated companion Order of Can.; recipient Louis Pariseau medal, Association Canadienne Francaise pour l'Advancement des Sciences, 1961, Centennial of Can. medal, 1968, award of achievement Province of Alta., 1980, diplome d'Honneur Le Groupe Francais des Glucides, Lyon, France, 1981, Izzak Walton Killam award The Can. Coun., 1981, rsch. prize U. Alta., 1982, Sir Frederick Haultain prize, Govt. Alta., 1982, Tishler award lectr. Harvard U., 1983, Gairdner Foun. Internat. award, 1985, Rhone-Poulenc award Royal Soc. Chemistry, Eng., 1989, King Faisal Internat. prize in sci., 1990, Gold medal Nat. Scis. and Engring. Rsch. Coun. Can., 1991, Manning award of distinction, 1992, PMAC Health Rsch. Found. Medal of Honor, 1992, Albert Einstein award World Cultural Coun., 1992, Gt. Can. award, 1993, Alta. Pioneer award Alta. Sci. and Tech. Found., 1993; inauguration of The Lemieux Lectures, U. Ottawa, 1972; inauguration of The Raymond U. Lemieux Lectures on Biotechnology, U. Alta., 1987; inauguration of The R.U. Lemieux Award for Organic Chemistry, Can. Soc. for Chemistry, 1992; inducted into Alta. Order of Excellence, 1990. Fellow Chem. Inst. Can. (hon., 1st div. award div. organic chemistry 1954, Palladium medal, 1964) Royal Soc. Can., Royal Soc. London, Am. Chem. Soc. (C.S. Hudson award 1966), The Chem. Soc. (Haworth medal 1978), medal of hon. Can. Med. Assn., 1985). Home: 7602 119th St, Edmonton, AB Canada T6G 1W3 Office: U Alta, Dept Chemistry, Edmonton, AB Canada T6G 2G2

LEMISH, DONALD LEE, university athletics director; b. Auburn, Ind., Oct. 4, 1943; s. Anthony G. and Dorothy (Palmer) L.; m. Sue Ann Schwartz, June 26, 1965; children: Michael Lee, Kyle Patrick. BS in Edn., Ball State U., 1965, MA, 1968; postgrad. cert., Harvard U., 1986. Assoc. and asst. dir. alumni and devel. programs Ball State U., Muncie, Ind., 1968-74, dir. devel., 1974-77; asst. v.p. devel. U. Ala., Birmingham, 1977-79; vice chancellor advancement and planning East Carolina U., Greenville, N.C., 1979-82; v.p. advancement Longwood Coll., Farmville, Va., 1982-87; v.p. univ. advancement James Madison U., Harrisonburg, Va., 1987-94; pres. James Madison U. Found., Harrisonburg, 1987-94; dir. athletics James Madison U., Harrisonburg, Va., 1994—; tchr. journalism Elmhurst High Sch., Fort Wayne, Ind., 1965-68. Author: Establishing a University Foundation, 1989, The Foundation Handbook, 1981. Treas. Constn. Bicentennial Commn., Prince Edward Co., Va., 1985-87; chmn. adv. coun. Harrisonburg Police Citizens, 1994; chair Harrisonburg/Rockingham County Crime Solvers, 1994—. Recipient CASE Alumni Giving Incentive award Coun. Advancement of Support Edn., 1975-81, 84-85. Mem. Bus. Edn. Assistance Corp. (dir., sec. 1991-92), Harrisonburg C. of C. (bd. dirs. 1990—, v.p. 1994—), Farmville C of C. (pres. 1986-87, dir. 1983-87), Rotary Club, Elks. Roman Catholic. Avocations: athletic officiating, collecting baseball memorabilia. Home: 523 Paul St Harrisonburg VA 22801-3229 Office: James Madison U Godwin Hall 206 Harrisonburg VA 22807

LEMKE, JAMES UNDERWOOD, physicist; b. Grand Rapids, Mich., Dec. 26, 1929; s. Andrew Bertram and Frances (Underwood) L.; m. Ann Stickley, Aug. 1, 1953; children: Catherine, Susan, Michael. BS in Physics, Ill. Inst. Tech., 1959; MS in Physics, Northwestern U., 1960; PhD in Physics, U. Calif., Santa Barbara, 1966. From assoc. to tech. v.p. Armour Rsch. Found., Chgo., 1957-60; dir. Bell & Howell Rsch. Labs., Pasadena, Calif., 1960-68; pres. Spin Physics, Inc. subs. Eastman Kodak, San Diego, 1968-82; fellow rsch. labs. Eastman Kodak, Rochester, N.Y., 1982-86; pres. Rec. Physics, Inc., San Diego, 1986—; founder, dir. Visqus Corp., 1989; adj. prof. U. Calif. at San Diego, LaJolla, 1982—. Contbr. numerous sci. and tech. articles to phys. jours.; patentee in field. Bd. dirs. San Diego Aero-Space Mus., 1982—. Recipient Revelle medal U. Calif. San Diego. Mem. NAE, Am. Phys. Soc., AAAS, Magnetic Soc. IEEE. Democrat. Avocation: airplane pilot.

LEMKE, JUDITH A., lawyer; b. New Rochelle, N.Y., Sept. 28, 1952; d. Thomas Francis and Sara Jane (Blish) Fanelli; m. W. Frederick Lemke, Apr. 1, 1980; 1 child, Morgan Frederick. Student, Manhattanville Coll., Purchase, N.Y., 1970-72; BA, Case Western Res. U., Cleve., 1974, MA, 1975, JD, 1978. Sr. cert. pub. acct. Price Waterhouse, Cleve., 1978-81; assoc. Benesch Friedlander Coplan & Aronoff, Cleve., 1981-85; adjunct faculty Cleve. Marshall Coll. Law, 1982-86; ptnr. Benesch Friedlander Coplan & Aronoff, Cleve., 1986-94; with Kahn Kleinman Yanowitz & Arnson Co., Cleve., 1994—; adj. faculty Case Western Res. U. Sch. of Law, 1993—. Recipient Elijah Watt Sells award for highest distinction AICPA, N.Y.C. 1979. Mem. ABA, Ohio State Bar Assn., Cuyahoga County Bar Assn., Cleve. Bar Assn., Cleve. Tax Club, Internat. Fiscal Assn., Nat. Assn. Stock Plan Profls., Case Western Res. U. Undergrad. Alumni Assn. (exec. com. 1987—, trustee 1987—, chmn. spl. events com. 1989-90, pres. 1990-92, v.p. 1993-94). Avocations: kayaking, wilderness canoe camping, guitar. Home: 36050 Pepper Dr Solon OH 44139 Office: Kahn Kleinman Yanowitz & Arnson Co The Tower at Erieview 1301 E 9th St Ste 2600 Cleveland OH 44114-1824

LEMKE, PAUL ARENZ, botany educator; b. New Orleans, July 14, 1937; s. Paul A. and Glory Ann (Schellinger) L.; m. Joy Faye Owens, 1963 (div. 1982); children: Paul Arenz, Anne Wellesley. B.S., Tulane U., 1960; M.A., U. Toronto, 1962; Ph.D., Harvard U., 1966. Instr. Tulane U., New Orleans, 1962-63; sr. scientist Eli Lilly & Co., Indpls., 1966-72; assoc. prof. Carnegie-Mellon U., Pitts., 1972-79, sr. fellow, 1972-79; prof. Auburn (Ala.) U., 1979—; head dept. botany, plant pathology and microbiology Auburn U., 1979-85; cons. Marcel Dekker Pub., 1974—, E.R. Squibb & Sons, 1975-76, Schering Corp., 1987-90; dir. Am. Genetics, Inc., Denver, 1982-86. Editor: Viruses and Plasmids in Fungi, 1979, Applied and Environmental Microbiology, 1982, Applied Microbiology and Biotechnology, 1985, The Mycota, 1994; author: (with others) Plasmids of Eukaryotes, 1986; patentee in field. Recipient award Humboldt Found., 1978; Woodrow Wilson fellow, 1960. Fellow Am. Acad. Microbiology; mem. Soc. for Indsl. Microbiology (pres. 1979-80, Charles Porter award 1982, Charles Thom award 1994), Mycol. Soc. Am. (ann. lectr. 1993), Gordon Rsch. Conf. (coun. 1980), Am. Inst. Biol. Sci. (governing bd.), Am. Soc. Microbiology (chmn. fermentation and biotech. div. 1982), Univ. Club, Lions, Phi Beta Kappa. Republican. Roman Catholic. Home: 161 Lee Rd 989 Opelika AL 36801 Office: Auburn U Dept Botany & Microbiology 101 Life Scis Bldg Auburn AL 36849-5407

LEMLE, ROBERT SPENCER, lawyer; b. N.Y.C., Mar. 6, 1953; s. Leo Karl and Gertrude (Bander) L.; m. Roni Sue Kohen, Sept. 5, 1976; children: Zachary, Joanna. AB, Oberlin Coll., 1975; JD, NYU, 1978. Bar: N.Y. 1979. Assoc. Cravath, Swaine & Moore, N.Y.C., 1978-82; assoc. gen. counsel Cablevision Systems Corp., Woodbury, N.Y., 1982-84, v.p., gen. counsel, 1984-86, sr. v.p., gen. counsel, sec., 1986-94, exec. v.p., gen. counsel, sec., 1994—; bd. editors Cable TV and New Media Law and Fin., N.Y.C., 1983—; bd. dirs. Cablevision Systems Corp., 1988—. Bd. trustees L.I. Children's Mus., 1990—. Mem. ABA, N.Y. State Bar Assn. Avocation: real estate. Home: 7 Grace Dr Old Westbury NY 11568-1228 Office: Cablevision Systems Corp 1 Media Crossway Dr Woodbury NY 11797

LEMLEY, BARBARA WINK, business educator; b. Gettysburg, Pa., Mar. 26, 1930; d. Howard Lamar and Anna Beamer (Tawney) Wink; m. Leo Wayne Lemley, Mar. 2, 1963; children: Susan Lee, Mark Christopher. BA, Pa. State U., 1951, MS, 1955; EdS, George Washington U., 1978, EdD, 1981. Tchr. high sch. N.J., Pa. and Mo., 1951-63; asst. prof. bus. U. D.C., Washington, 1971-82, assoc. prof., 1982-86; prof., 1986—, dept. chmn. 1985-88, assoc. dean, 1988-91; prof., 1986-94; pres. Lemley Assocs., Potomac, 1994—. Contbr. articles to profl. jours. Co-founder fundraiser Columbia Lighthouse for Blind, Washington, 1985, mem. adv. bd., 1986—; pres. devel. bd. De Sales Sch. Theology, 1992—; vol. at White House, 1990—; co-chmn. antiques show Our Lady of Mercy Ch., Potomac, Md., 1983, 84; mem. bd. dirs. Pub. Mems. Assn. of the Fgn. Svc., 1995—; mem. selection bd. U.S.

Dept. State, 1994—. Rsch. grantee Cheasapeake and Potomac Tel. Co., Washington, 1984, U. D.C., 1984. Mem. D.C. Bus. Edn. Assn. (pres.), Nat. Bus. Edn. Assn., Ea. Bus. Edn. Assn., Assn. Bus. Communication, Phi Delta Kappa, Delta Pi Epsilon. Republican. Roman Catholic. Avocations: travel, reading, volunteer work, fundraising. Home: 8326 Turnberry Ct Potomac MD 20854 Office: Lemley Assocs 8326 Turnberry Ct Potomac MD 20854

LEMLEY, STEVEN SMITH, academic administrator; b. Oakland, Calif., Jan. 7, 1945; married, 1967; 3 children. BA, Pepperdine U., 1966, MA, 1970; PhD in speech, communication, Ohio State U., 1972. Asst. prof. communication Pepperdine U., L.A., 1972-78, assoc. dean student life, 1972-76, dean student life, 1976-78; assoc. prof. speech, dean Lubbock (Tex.) Christian U., 1978-82, now pres. Office: Lubbock Christian U Office of Pres 5601 19th St Lubbock TX 79407-2099

LEMLY, THOMAS ADGER, lawyer; b. Dayton, Ohio, Jan. 31, 1943; s. Thomas Moore and Elizabeth (Adger) L.; m. Kathleen Brame, Nov. 24, 1984; children: Elizabeth Hayden, Joanna Marsden, Isabelle Stafford, Kate Brame. BA, Duke U., 1970; JD with honors, U. N.C., 1973. Bar: Wash. 1973, U.S. Dist. Ct. (we. dist.) Wash. 1973, U.S. Ct. Appeals (9th cir.) 1975, U.S. Supreme Ct. 1980. Assoc. Davis Wright Tremaine, Seattle, 1973-79, ptnr., 1979—. Contbg. editor Employment Discrimination Law, 1984-87, 94—; editor Wash., Oreg., Alaska and Calif. Employment Law Deskbooks, 1987—. Chmn. Pacific Coast Labor Conf., Seattle, 1983; trustee Plymouth Congregational Ch., 1980-84, Seattle Opera Assn., 1991—. Mem. ABA (labor employment law sect. 1975—, subcom. chmn. 1984-90, liaison com. 1982-89), Seattle-King County Bar Assn. (chmn. labor sect.), Assn. Wash. Bus. (trustee 1992—, chmn. human resources coun. 1993—, chmn. employment law task force 1987-93), U. N.C. Bar Found. (bd. dirs. 1973-76), Seattle Duke Alumni Assn. (pres. 1979-84), Order of Coif, Wash. Athletic Club (Seattle), Rotary. Republican. Congregationalist. Home: 1614 7th Ave W Seattle WA 98119-2919 Office: Davis Wright Tremaine 2600 Century Sq 1501 4th Ave Seattle WA 98101-1662

LEMMON, GEORGE COLBORNE, bishop; b. St. John, N.B., Can., Mar. 20, 1932; m. Lois Jean Foster, June 7, 1957; children: Paul, Marilu, Robert. BA, U. N.B., 1959; Licentiate in Theology, Wycliffe Coll., Toronto, Can., 1962, BD, 1964, DD (hon.), 1991; DD (hon.), King's Coll., Halifax, N.S., Can., 1990. Ordained deacon Anglican Ch. Can., 1962, priest, 1963. Consecrated bishop Diocese of Fredericton (N.B.), Anglican Ch. Can., 1989—; linotype operator, 10 yrs.; mem. nat. exec. com., nat. stewardship com. Anglican Ch. Can. Columnist The Daily Gleaner, 1986—. Active Mayor's Adv. Com. on Econ. Devel. Fredericton, 1991; sec. Crake Found. Inc.; founding mem. Cons for Christ, Fredericton. Mem. Irenaeus Fellowship. Office: Diocese of Fredericton, 115 Church St, Fredericton, NB Canada E3B 4C8

LEMMON, JACK (JOHN UHLER LEMMON, III), actor; b. Boston, Feb. 8, 1925; s. John Uhler, Jr. and Mildred LaRue (Noel) L.; m. Cynthia Boyd Stone, May 7, 1950; 1 child, Christopher; m. Felicia Farr, Aug. 17, 1962; 1 child, Courtney. Grad., Phillips Andover Acad., 1943; B.S., B.A., Harvard U., 1947. Pres. Jalem Prodns., N.Y.C., 1952—. Appeared in summer stock, 1940-48, radio, TV shows, 1948-52; including TV series That Wonderful Guy, 1950; summer replacement: Toni Twin Time, 1950; appeared in TV series: The Adlibbers, 1951, Couple Next Door, 1951-52, Heaven for Betsy, 1952; appeared on Broadway in: Room Service, 1953, Face of A Hero, 1960, Tribute, 1979 (Broadway Drama Guild award); other stage appearances Idiot's Delight, 1970, Juno and the Paycock, 1975, Long Day's Journey Into Night, 1986; appeared in films: Mister Roberts (Acad. award best supporting actor), It Happened to Jane, You Can't Run Away From It, Fire Down Below, Cowboy, Operation Madball, Bell Book and Candle, Miss Casy Jones, Some Like It Hot, The Apartment, The Wackiest Ship in the Army, Notorious Landlady, Irma La Douce, Under The Yum Yum Tree, Days of Wine and Roses, Good Neighbor Sam, How to Murder Your Wife, The Great Race, The Fortune Cookie, Luv, The Odd Couple, The April Fools, The Out-of-Towners, The War Between Men and Women, 1972, Avanti, 1972, Save the Tiger, 1973 (Acad. award best actor), The Front Page, 1974, The Prisoner of 2d Avenue, 1975, Alex & the Gypsy, 1976, Airport, 1977, The Gentleman Tramp, 1977, The China Syndrome, 1978 (Best Actor Cannes Film Festival), Tribute, 1980, Buddy Buddy, 1981, Missing, 1981 (Best Actor Cannes Film Festival), Mass Appeal, 1984, Macaroni, 1985, That's Life, 1986, Dad, 1989, JFK, 1990, The Player, 1992, Glengarry Glen Ross, 1992, Short Cuts, 1993, Grumpy Old Men, 1993, Getting Away with Murder, 1995, The Grass Harp, 1995; TV appearances include: The Entertainer, 1975 (Emmy award nomination), 'S Wonderful, 'S Marvelous, 'S Gershwin, 1972 (Emmyaward), The Murder of Mary Phagan, 1988, A Life in the Theatre, 1993, For Richer, For Poorer, 1992. Served as ensign USNR, 1945-46. Recipient Lifetime Achievement award, Am. Film Inst., 1988, D.W. Griffith award, 1987. Clubs: Hasty Pudding (pres. 1945-46), Delphic (v.p. 1945-46), Dramatic (v.p. 1945) (Harvard U.); Players (N.Y.C.). Office: Creative Artists Agy 9830 Wilshire Blvd Beverly Hills CA 90212-1825*

LEMMON, JEAN MARIE, editor-in-chief; b. Duluth, Minn., Nov. 11, 1932; d. Lawrence Howard and Marie Julien (Gunderson) H.; m. Richard LuVerne LemMon, Apr. 17, 1965 (div. 1976); 1 child, Rebecca Jean. BA, U. Minn., 1954. Editor Better Homes and Gardens Mag., Des Moines, 1961-63, dept. head crafts, 1985-86, editor-in-chief, 1993—; women's editor Successful Farming, Des Moines, 1963-68; pres. Jean LemMon & Assocs., Des Moines, 1968-84; project editor Meredith Pub. Svcs., Des Moines, 1984-85; editor-in-chief Country Home Mag., Des Moines, 1986-93; adv. bd. Drake U. Journalism Sch., 1991—. Mem. ASCAP, Mensa Internat., Am. Soc. Interior Designers. Office: Better Homes and Gardens 1716 Locust St Des Moines IA 50309*

LEMMOND, JOSEPH SHAWN, state legislator, insurance agent; b. Ft. Thomas-Kentfield, Ky., May 4, 1958; s. David Rea and Joyce Francis (Kinard) L.; m. Karen Alicia Flynt, May 9, 1987; stepchildren: Jason Anthony Mullis, Kenneth Allen Mullis. Degree in econs., U. N.C. Inside salesperson Robert E. Mason Assocs., Charlotte, N.C.; mayor Town of Matthews, 1987-91; ins. agt. Dean, Heckle, Hill, Inc., Matthews, N.C.; rep. N.C. State Ho. of Reps., 1992—. Mem. city coun., police com. Town of Matthews, 1983-87. With USN, 1976-82. Republican. Roman Catholic. Avocations: sailing, backpacking. Office: NC State Ho of Reps Legislative Blvd Rm 1317 Raleigh NC 27603

LEMOINE, PAMELA ALLYSON, assistant principal; b. Mansura, La., Sept. 6, 1945; d. Levy Paul and Iva Rae (Paul) L. BA in English, Libr. Sci., Nicholls State U., 1967; MEd in Ednl. Tech., McNeese State U., 1976; postgrad., Pepperdine U., 1978-80, Boston U., 1980-82. Libr. Evergreen Jr. High Sch., Houma, La., 1967-69, Zukiran Elem. Sch., Okinawa, Japan, 1969-70, Goose Bay High Sch., Labrador, Can., 1970-72, Matthew Perry Sch., Iwakuni, Japan, 1972-76; head libr., audio-visual specialist Kubasaki High Sch., Okinawa, 1978-80; libr. Bamberg (Germany) Am. High Sch., 1980-82; tchr. Evergreen Jr. High Sch., Houma, 1982-83; libr. Lisa Park Elem. Sch., Houma, 1983-84; audio-visual specialist H.L. Bourgeois High Sch., Houma, 1984-85; asst. prin. Lisa Park Elem. Sch., Houma, 1985—; cons. librarian Dept. Def. Schs., Bamberg, 1980-82. Contbr. articles to mags. Pres. Friends of the Libr., Houma, 1988, Houma-Terrebonne Arts and Humanities Coun., 1992-93, treas., 1989-91; bd. dirs. Terrebonne Libr. Bd. Control., Houma, 1990—. Named Outstanding Tchr. of Yr. Dept. Def. Schs., 1979, 81. Mem. NEA, Terrebonne Prin.'s Assn. (corr. sec. 1991), Phi Delta Kappa, Delta Kappa Gamma. Avocations: gardening, sewing, crafts, writing. Home: 116 Westview Dr Houma LA 70364-2534 Office: Lisa Park Sch 1900 Willie Lou Ave Houma LA 70364-2599

LEMOLE, GERALD MICHAEL, surgeon; b. S.I., N.Y., Dec. 17, 1936; s. Joseph Michael and Mary (Boylan) L.; B.S. in Biology, Villanova U., 1958; M.D., Temple U., 1962; m. Emily Jane Asplundh, Dec. 8, 1962; children—Lisa Jane, Laura Leigh, Emily Anne, Gerald Michael, Samantha Mary, Christopher Robin. Intern, S.I. Hosp., 1962-63; resident in gen. surgery Temple U., Phila., 1963-67; resident in thoracic surgery Baylor Affiliated Hosps., Houston, 1967-69; practice medicine specializing in cardio thoracic surgery, Phila., 1969—; Browns Mills, N.J., 1972-84; chief sect. cardiac and thoracic surgery Temple U. Hosp., Phila., 1970-77; prof. surgery Temple U. Health Scis. Ctr., 1975-77; chmn. dept. surgery Deborah Heart and Lung Ctr., Phila., 1972-84; chief sect. cardiovascular surgery Med. Ctr.

Del.; vis. prof. cardiac surgery U. Dublin (Ireland), 1974, U. Istanbul, Turkey, 1982, Mil. Med. Coll., Ankara, Turkey, 1985, Beijing Heart Inst., 1991; clin. prof. surgery U. Pa., 1979, Rutgers Med. Sch. Diplomate Am. Bd. Surgery, Am. Bd. Thoracic Surgery. Recipient Disting. Alumnus award VIIlanova U., 1987. Fellow ACS, Am. Coll. Cardiology, Am. Coll. Chest Physicians (cardiovascular com. 1974—); mem. Phila. Coll. Physicians, Am. Assn. Thoracic Surgery, Am. Fedn. Clin. Research, Am., Pan Am. thoracic socs., Internat., Cardiovascular Soc., Denton A. Cooley Cardiovascular Surg. Soc., Am. Coll. Angiology, Pa., Phila. County med. socs., Phila. Acad. Surgery, Phila. Acad. Cardiology (pres. 1976-79, chmn. exec. com. 1976—), Assn. Acad. Surgeons, Soc. Vascular Surgery, Pa. Assn. Thoracic Surgeons, AMA, Am. Heart Assn. (cardiovascular council 1973—, pres. Del. chpt. 1991, chmn. bd. dirs. 1992), Pa. Assn. Thoracic Surgery (program chmn. 1975—). Contbr. numerous articles on cardiovascular surgery and disease to med. jours.; research in cardiovascular physiology. Home: 404 Tomlinson Rd Huntingdon Valley PA 19006-4818 Office: Med Ctr Del 4745 Ogletown Stanton Rd 20 Newark DE 19713

LEMON, ERIC V., lawyer; b. Man., Can., 1942. AB, Princeton U., 1964; JD, U. Mich., 1968. Bar: Mo. 1968. Ptnr. Bryan Cave, St. Louis. Mem. ABA.

LEMON, HENRY MARTYN, physician, educator; b. Chgo., Dec. 23, 1915; s. Harvey Brace and Louise (Birkhoff) L.; m. Harriet Tuxbury Qua, May 3, 1941 (dec. Jan. 1976); children—Elizabeth Anne Lemon Carr, Harvey Brace, Stanley Moncrief, David Tuxbury, Jennifer Jane Lemon Dewitt; m. Dorothy Campbell, May 28, 1976. B.S., U. Chgo., 1938; M.D. cum laude, Harvard U., 1940. Diplomate: Am. Bd. Internal Medicine, Am. Bd. Med. Oncology. Intern Billings Hosp., Chgo., 1940-41; asst. resident medicine Billings Hosp., 1941-42; asst. dept. medicine U. Chgo., 1942-43; chief med. resident Univ. Hosp., Boston, 1946-48; instr. medicine Boston U., 1946-48, asst. prof. medicine, 1948-54, assoc. prof., 1954-61; dir. Eugene C. Eppley Cancer Inst. U. Nebr. Coll. Medicine, Omaha, 1961-68, prof. internal Medicine, 1961-86, emeritus prof., 1986—; cons. internal medicine VA, Boston, Omaha, 1950-86; bd. dirs. Mass., Nebr. divs. Am. Cancer Soc. Served to capt. M.C. U.S. Army, 1943-46; col. USAR; ret. Recipient Disting. Service award U. Chgo. Med. Alumni, 1952, awards of merit AMA Sci. Exhibits, 1957, 1962, 1965, Disting. Teaching award U. Nebr. Med. Center, 1976, Meritorious Service award, 1980, Margaret Hay Edwards medal Am. Assn. Cancer Edn., 1989. Fellow ACP; mem. AMA, Am. Assn. Cancer Research, Am. Soc. Clin. Oncology, Endocrine Soc., Soc. Surg. Oncology, Central Soc. Clin. Research, Planned Parenthood Omaha and Council Bluffs (pres. 1990), Res. Officers Assn., Phi Beta Kappa, Phi Beta Kappa Assocs. Omaha (pres. 1985-87), Sigma Xi (Disting. Research award U. Nebr. chpt. 1985), Alpha Omega Alpha. Unitarian. Club: Rotary. Rsch. in air-borne infection, Cytodiagnosis Pancreatic cancer, transplantation human cancer to hamsters, estrogen imbalance in breast cancer, endocrine and chemotherapy cancer, reduction toxicity in cancer chemotherapy, estriol prevention breast cancer, carcinogenesis breast, leukemia and lymphoma. Home: 10805 Poppleton Ave Omaha NE 68144-1843 Office: U Nebr Dept Internal Medicine Omaha NE 68198-3330 *My medical life in service, education and research has taken place during the golden age of American medicine, a period of unprecedented growth in our ability to diagnose and treat most diseases. My work has received inestimable benefit from those who were my teachers, and I have found my own greatest reward in attempting to illuminate the paths of my students; this fact and the privilege of serving my patients have been my chief professional guides along the way.*

LEMON, LESLIE GENE, consumer products and services company executive, lawyer; b. Davenport, Iowa, June 14, 1940. BS, U. Ill., 1962, LLB, 1964. Bar: Ill. 1964, Ariz. 1972. Asst. gen. counsel Am. Farm Bur. Fedn., Chgo., 1964-69; sr. atty. Armour and Co., Chgo., 1969-71; with The Dial Corp (formerly Greyhound Corp.), Phoenix, 1971—, sr. asst. gen. counsel, 1975-77, gen. counsel, 1977—, v.p., 1979—; bd. dirs. FINOVA Group. Vestryman All Saints Episcopal Ch., Phoenix, 1975-81; trustee Phoenix Art Mus., 1985—; bd. dirs. Phoenix Children's Hosp., 1985-86; br. head Naval U. Calif. Med. Sch., Davis, 1983—. Mem. ABA, Assn. Gen. Counsel, Maricopa County Bar Assn., State Bar Ariz., Phoenix C. of C. (bd. dirs. 1989—). Home: 1136 W Butler Dr Phoenix AZ 85021-4428 Office: The Dial Corp Dial Tower 1850 N Central Ave Phoenix AZ 85077-0001

LEMOND, GREGORY JAMES, former professional bicycle racer; b. L.A., June 26, 1961; m. Kathy Morris, 1980; children: Geoffrey James, Scott, Simone. Mem. Renault Team, 1980-83, La Vie Claire Team, 1983-89, Team Z, 1989-95; ptnr. Tour de France restaurant, Edina, Minn., 1990—. Winner Tour de France, 1986, 89, 90, profl. road racing championships, Altersheim, Switzerland, 1983, 89; named Sportsman of Yr., 1989; winner Tour Du Pont, 1992. Office: care Pat Stahl Cycle Goods 2801 Hennepin Ave Minneapolis MN 55408-1907*

LE MONE, ARCHIE, religious organization administrator; b. N.Y.C., Sept. 30, 1938; s. Archie and Christine (Webb) Le M.; m. Anita Joyce Colvin, June 18, 1966; children: Adae Ronald, Amani Philip (dec.). AB in History, Morgan State U., 1962; MDiv, Crozer Theol. Sem., 1965. Asst. pastor White Rock Bapt., Phila., 1962-66; divsn. asst. Am. Bapt. Convn., Valley Forge, Pa., 1965-66; mem. exec. staff World Coun. Chs., Geneva, 1966-75, Caribbean Conf. Chs., West Indies, 1975-80, Cleve. Coun. Chs., 1981-83; exec. dir. Home Mission Bd. Progressive Bapt. Conv., Washington, 1983—; bd. dirs. Nat. Coun. Chs., N.Y.C., 1983—, Washington Office on Africa, 1983—. Editor: RISK Study Series, 1973; contbr. articles to profl. jours. Mem. monitoring com. Montgomery County (Md.) Pub. Schs., 1994. Mem. Alpha Phi Alpha (chaplain 1993—). Avocations: foreign languages, reading, swimming. Office: Prog Nat Baptist Conv Inc 601 50th St NE Washington DC 20019-5499

LEMONICK, AARON, physicist, educator; b. Phila., Feb. 2, 1923; s. Samuel and Mary (Ferman) L.; m. Eleanor Leah Drutt, Feb. 12, 1950; children—Michael Drutt, David Morris. B.A., U. Pa., 1950; M.A., Princeton U., 1952, Ph.D., 1954. Asst. prof. physics Haverford Coll., Pa., 1954-57, assoc. prof., 1957-61; assoc. prof. Princeton U., N.J., 1961-64, prof., 1964-94, assoc. chmn. dept. physics, 1967-69, dean grad. sch., 1969-73, dean faculty, 1973-89, dean of faculty emeritus, 1989—; assoc. dir. Princeton-Pa. Accelerator, 1961-67; prof. emeritus Princeton U., N.J., 1994—; v.p. Princeton U. Press, 1973—; dep. dir. Princeton Plasma Physics Lab., 1989-90. Trustee Bryn Mawr Coll., 1988—. Fellow AAAS, Am. Phys. Soc.; mem. AAUP, Am. Assn. Physics Tchrs., Phi Beta Kappa, Sigma Xi. Office: Princeton U Dept Physics Princeton NJ 08544

LEMOS, RAMON MARCELINO, philosophy educator; b. Mobile, Ala., July 7, 1927; s. Marcelino and Marie Louise (Moore) L.; m. Mamie Loy McCrory, Dec. 26, 1951 (dec. Apr. 1990); children: Noah Marcelino, William Ramon, Christopher Tait, John Paul; m. Anne Craft, Aug. 7, 1994. B.A., U. Ala., 1951; M.A., Duke, 1953, Ph.D., 1955; Fulbright scholar, U. London, Eng., 1955-56. Mem. faculty U. Miami, 1956—; prof. philosophy, 1967—, chmn. dept., 1971-84. Author: Experience, Mind and Value, 1969, Rousseau's Political Philosophy, 1977, Hobbes and Locke: Power and Consent, 1978, Rights, Goods, and Democracy, 1986, Metaphysical Investigations, 1988, The Nature of Value: Axiological Investigations, 1995. Served with USMC, 1945-49. Named Outstanding Tchr. U. Miami, 1968. Mem. Am. Philos. Assn. (program chmn. Eastern div. meeting 1983), Fla. Philos. Assn. (pres. 1963), Phi Beta Kappa, Phi Kappa Phi, Omicron Delta Kappa. Home: 6960 SW 82nd Ct Miami FL 33143-2509 Office: U Miami Dept Philosophy Coral Gables FL 33124

LEMOYNE, IRVE CHARLES, career officer; b. Brownsville, Tex., June 28, 1939; s. McPherson and Doris (Grimm) LeM.; m. Elizabeth Gzeckowicz, June 11, 1961; children: Irve Charles Jr., Elizabeth Christian. BS in Indsl. Mgmt., Ga. Inst. Tech., 1961; MS in Mgmt., Naval Postgrad Sch. Monterey, Calif., 1972. Commd. ensign USN, 1961, advanced through grades to rear adm., 1991; div. officer USS Massey (DD 778), Mayport, Fla. 1961-62; student underwater demolition team tng. U.S. Naval Amphibious Base, Little Creek, Va., 1962-66, ops. officer Underwater Demolition Team 22, 1963 -66; exec. officer Seal Team 1 U.S. Naval Amphibious Base, Coronado, Calif., 1966-69; commdg. officer Underwater Demolition Team 11, Coronado, Calif., 1969-71; student Naval Postgrad. Sch., Monterey, 1971-72; spl. warfare project officer Naval Sea Systems Command, Wash-

ington, 1972-75; asst. to spl. warfare mission and resource officer OPNAV Staff, The Pentagon, Washington, 1975-77; student Nat. War Coll., Washington, 1977-78; commdg. officer Inshore Undersea Warfare Group One, Coronado, 1978-79; chief staff officer Naval Spl. Warfare Group 1, Coronado, 1979-81; spl. asst. Dep. chief Naval Material for Resources Mgmt., Arlington, Va., 1981-82, chief ops. div., 1982-83; comdr Naval Sp. Warfare Group 1, Coronado, 1983-85; fellow Chief Naval Ops. Strategic Study Group, Naval War Coll., Newport, R.I., 1985-86; br. head Naval Spl. Warfare Plans and Policy Dep. Chief Naval Ops. for Plans, Policy and Ops., Washington, 1986-87; comdr. Naval Spl. Warfare Command, Naval Amphibious Base, Coronado, 1987-89; dir. resources U.S. Spl. Ops. Command, MacDill AFB, Fla., 1989-93, dep. commander-in-chief, 1993—. Decorated Legion of Merit with two gold stars, Bronze Star with gold star and Combat V, Meritorious Svc. medal with two gold stars. Mem. U.S. Naval Inst. Episcopalian. Avocations: beekeeping, windsurfing. Office: US Spl Ops Command Dep Comdr in Chief Mac Dill AFB FL 33621-5323

LEMPERT, RICHARD OWEN, lawyer, educator; b. Hartford, Conn., June 2, 1942; s. Philip Leonard and Mary (Steinberg) L.; m. Cynthia Ruth Willey, Sept. 10, 1967; 1 child, Leah Rose. A.B., Oberlin Coll., 1964; J.D., U. Mich., 1968, Ph.D. in Sociology, 1971. Bar: Mich. 1978. Asst. prof. law U. Mich., Ann Arbor, 1968-72, assoc. prof., 1972-74, prof. law, 1974—, prof. sociology, 1985—, Francis A. Allen collegiate prof. law, 1990—, acting chair dept. sociology, 1993-94; Mason Ladd disting. vis. prof. U. Iowa Law Sch., 1981; vis. fellow Centre for Socio-Legal Rsch., Wolfson Coll., Oxford (Eng.) U., 1982; mem. adv. panel for law and social sci. div. NSF, 1976-79, mem. exec. com. adv. com. for social sci., 1979; mem. com. law enforcement and adminstrn. of justice NRC, vice chmn., 1984-87, chmn., 1987-89; mem. adv. panel NSF program on Human Dimensions of Global Change, 1989, 92—; mem. com. on DNA technology in forensic sci. NRC, 1989-92, com. on drug testing in workplace, 1991-93. Author: (with Stephen Saltzburg) A Modern Approach to Evidence, 1977, 2d edit., 1983; (with Joseph Sanders) An Invitation to Law and Social Science, 1986, Under the Influence, 1993; editor: (with Jacques Normand and Charles O'Brien) Under the Influence? Drugs and the American Work Force, 1994; editorial bd. Law and Soc. Rev, 1972-77, 89—, editor, 1982-85; editorial bd. Evaluation Rev, 1979-82, Violence and Victims, 1985—, Jour. Law and Human Behavior, 1980-82; contbr. articles to profl. jours. Fellow Ctr. for Advanced Study in Behavioral Scis., 1994-95. Fellow Am. Acad. Arts and Scis.; mem. Am. Sociol. Assn. (chair sect. sociology of law 1994-95), Law and Society Assn. (trustee 1977-80, 90-93, exec. com. 1979-80, 82-87), Soc. Am. Law Tchrs., Order of Coif, Phi Beta Kappa, Phi Kappa Phi. Office: U Mich Law Sch 625 S State St Ann Arbor MI 48109-1215

LENAHAN, WALTER CLAIR, retired foreign service officer; b. Everett, Wash., Apr. 20, 1934; s. James Harold and Doris Anne (Larson) L.; m. Patricia Anne Casey, July 6, 1957; children—Karen Diane, Desiree, Lorelei, Casey James. B.A., U. Oreg., 1960. Commd. fgn. service officer Dept. State, 1961; officer Dept. State, Washington, 1961-72, U.S. Embassy, Beijing, People's Republic of China, 1979-81, Dept. Commerce, Washington, 1981-86; dep. asst. sec. for textiles and apparel Dept. Commerce, 1982-86; v.p. Am.-Philippine Fiber Industry, Inc., Manila, 1972-76; pres. Internat. Bus. and Econ. Research Corp., Washington, 1986—. Served to sgt. U.S. Army, 1953-56. Recipient Sr. Fgn. Service Presdl. award Dept. State, 1984. Lutheran. Avocations: tennis; contract bridge. Office: Internat Bus and Econ Rsch Corp 2121 K St NW Washington DC 20037-1801

LENARD, MICHAEL BARRY, merchant banker, lawyer; b. Chgo., May 20, 1955; s. Henry Madart and Jacqueline Jo Anne (Silver) L.; m. Amy Jeanne Rifenbergh, Oct. 10, 1987; children: Madeline M., Nicholas X. BBA, U. Wis., 1977; postgrad., NYU, 1981-82; JD, U. So. Calif., 1982. Assoc. Whitman & Ransom, N.Y.C., 1982-83; assoc. Latham & Watkins, L.A., 1984-91, ptnr., 1992-93; mng. dir., counsellor William E. Simon & Sons, L.A., 1993—; bd. dirs. William E. Simon & Sons (Asia), Hong Kong. With So. Calif. Law Rev. mag., 1980-81. V.p. U.S. Olympic Com., 1989—, mem. exec. com., bd. dirs., 1985—, mem. athletes' adv. coun., 1981-89, vice chmn. athletes' adv. coun., 1985-89; named to Internat. Coun. for Arbitration of Sport, Internat. Olympic Com., 1994—; bd. dirs. L.A. Sports Coun., 1988—, Atlanta Com. for Olympic Games, 1990—. Named semi-finalist Outstanding Undergrad. Achievement award, 1977; recipient Harry A. Bullis scholarship, 1977; named USA Team Handball Athlete of the Yr., 1985, USOC Olympian Mag. Team Handball SportsMan of the Yr., 1985; mem. 1984 Olympic Team, U.S. Nat. Team, 1977-85 (capt. 1985). Mem. Order of the Coif, Phi Kappa Phi, Beta Gamma Sigma, Beta Alpha Psi, Phi Eta Sigma. Home: 1433 El Bosque Ct Pacific Palisades CA 90272-3313 Office: William E Simon & Sons 10990 Wilshire Blvd Ste 1750 Los Angeles CA 90024

LENARDIC, KENNETH RALPH, systems architect, consultant; b. Cleve., May 18, 1945; s. Ralph and Dolores (Klish) L.; m. Karen Lynn Pierce, Sept. 21, 1968; children: Janis, Kerri. Student, Internat. Data Processing Inst, Cleve., 1966, Kent State U., Euclid, Ohio, 1969. Ops. supr. Towmotor Corp., Cleve., 1969-70; sr. systems analyst Caterpillar Indsl. Inc., Mentor, Ohio, 1978-83, mktg. systems engr., 1983-92; instr. Lakeland C.C., Mentor, 1988-89; systems architect Mitsubishi-Caterpillar Forklift, Mentor, 1992—; computer cons., Concord, Ohio, 1988-92; pres. Micro Systems Architects, Mentor, 1994—; guest speaker in field. Contbr. articles to profl. jours. Republican. Roman Catholic. Avocations: music, photography, physical fitness. Home: 10265 Cherry Hill Dr Concord OH 44077-1515 Office: Micro Systems Architects 10265 Cherry Hill Dr Concord OH 44077-1515

LENARDON, ROBERT JOSEPH, classics educator; b. Fort William, Ont., Can., Sept. 8, 1928; came to U.S., 1949; s. Louis and Nina (Boffa) L. BA with honors in Latin, U. B.C., Can., 1949; MA in Classics, U. Cin., 1950, PhD, 1954. Instr. Greek and Latin Columbia, 1954-57; asst. prof. classics U. Wash., Seattle, 1957-59; mem. faculty dept. classics Ohio State U., Columbus, 1959—; assoc. prof. Ohio State U., 1963-69, prof., dir. grad. studies, 1969-84, prof. emeritus, 1984-92; prof., head dept. classics Siena Coll., 1992—; vis. prof. U. B.C., summers 1960-61, 66, NYU, 1973, 91-92. Author: (with Mark P.O. Morford) Classical Mythology, 1971, 2d edit., 1977, 3d edit., 1985, 4th edit., 1991, 5th edit., 1994, The Saga of Themistocles, 1977; book rev. editor: Classical Jour., 1961-68. Taft scholar and fellow, 1950-54; vis. fellow Corpus Christi Coll., Cambridge (Eng.) U., 1971. Mem. Am. Philol. Assn., Archeol. Inst. Am., Classical Assn. Atlantic States. Home: 62 Willett St Albany NY 12210-1140

LENCEK, RADO L., Slavic languages educator; b. Mirna, Slovenia, Oct. 3, 1921; came to U.S., 1956; s. Ludovik Ivan and Kati (Jaksa) L.; m. Nina A. Lovrencic, May 4, 1946; children: Bibi-Alice, Lena-Maria. Studied Slavic philology, U. Ljubljana, Slovenia, 1940-45, U. Padova, Italy, 1946-47; teaching diploma, Istituto Magistrale, Gorizia, Italy, 1947; M.A. in Linguistics, U. Chgo., 1959; Ph.D. in Slavic Langs., Harvard U., 1962. Asst. prof. Istituto Magistrale Sloveno, Gorizia-Trieste, Italy, 1944-55; editor USIS-Trieste, Italy, 1951-54; asst. prof. U. Ill., Urbana, 1962-65; asst. prof. Slavic langs. Columbia U., N.Y.C., 1965-69, assoc. prof. 1969-74, prof., 1974-92, prof. emeritus, 1992—; assoc. Averell Harriman Inst. for Advanced Study of the Soviet Union; mem. Inst. on East Cen. Europe; vis. assoc. prof. NYU, 1969-72; vis. prof. Yale U., 1974, U. Ill., Urbana, 1977; coord. Nat. Com. Serbo-Croatian Teaching Materials, 1982—; U.S. coord. for Cooperation Project on Slavistics, 1983—; active U.S.-USSR Commn. on the Humanities and Social Scis., Inst. East Ctrl. Europe; participant Internat. Congs. of Slavists Prague, 1968, Warsaw, 1973, Zagreb-Ljubljana, 1978, Kiev, 1983, Sofia, 1988, Bratislava, 1993; coord. Columbia U. Program in Slavic Cultures, organized symposia Columbia U., 1974, 84, Prato di Resia, Italy, 1979, Northwestern U., 1980, U. Chgo., 1984, Acad. of Scis. USSR, Moscow, 1987, Am. Assn. Tchrs. of Slavic and East European Langs. Annual Convention, San Francisco, 1991, Toronto, Can., 1993; mem. adv. bd. Slovenski jezik-Slovene Linguistic Studies, 1994—. Author: Ob Jadranu, Ethnographic Studies, 1947, The Verb Pattern of Contemporary Slovene, 1966, A Bibliographical Guide to Slavic Civilizations, 1966, An Outline of the Course on Slavic Civilizations, 1970, 2d edit., 1978, The Structure and History of Slovene Language, 1982, Slovenes, The Eastern Alpine Slavs, and Their Cultural Heritage, 1989, The Correspondence Between Jan Baudoin de Courtenay (1845-1929) and Vatroslav Oblak (1864-96), 1992; editor: (with others) Xenia Slavica, Gojko Ruzicic Festschrift, 1975, The Dilemma of the Melting Pot: The Case of the South Slavic Languages, 1976, To Honor Jernej

Kopitar, 1780-1980, 1982, A Bibliography of Recent Literature on Macedonian, Serbo-Croatian and Slovene Languages, 1990; co-editor: Who's Who of Slovene Descent in the United States, 1992, 2d edit. 1995; editor U.S. Info. Svcs. Bull., Trieste, Italy, 1951-54; editor (series) Papers in Slovene Studies, 1975-76, editl. com., editor book revs. Slovene Studies, 1979—; editl. com. Folia Slavica, 1976-89, Nationalities Papers, 1979, Geschichte, Kultur und Geisteswelt der Slowenen, Munich, 1982-91, Beiträge zur Kenntnis Südosteuropas, Munich, 1983-91, Münchner Zeitschrift für Balkankunde, 1983-91, Geschichte, Kultur und Geisteswelt der Südslaven, Munich, 1990; mem. coun. jours. Slavisticna revija, 1991—; contbr. articles in field of Slavic linguistics and cultures to scholarly jours. and proceedings of internat. confs., symposiums. Recipient Fulbright fellow, 1986; named Ambassador of the Rep. of Slovenia for Sci. Ministry for Sci. and Tech. of the Rep. of Slovenia, 1995; grantee NSF, 1974, 79, Japan Soc. for Promotion Sci., 1989, Internat. Rsch. Exchgs. Bd., 1971, 72, 83, 85, 94. Fellow Am. Coun. Learned Socs., Bulgarian Acad. Scis.; me. Slovenska Kulturna Akcija (Buenos Aire), Slavists' Assn. Slovenia (hon. Ljubljana chpt. 1989—), Linguistic Soc. Am., Linguistic Circle of N.Y., Am. Assn. Advancement Slavic Studies, Am. Assn. Tchrs. Slavic and East European Langs. (Disting. Scholarly Career award in recognition of outstanding achievement in scholarship 1994), Soc. Slovene Studies (founder, pres. 1973-83, editor newsletter 1973-77, editor Letter 1978-83, dir. Ctr. for Rsch. and Documentation 1988—), Inst. on East Ctrl. Europe; mem. N.Y. Acad. Scis., Slovene Acad. Scis. and Arts, Fulbright Assn., Am. Slovene Cong. (rognl. com. 1993-94, acad. advisor to the coun. on acad. activities 1994—). Home: 560 Riverside Dr New York NY 10027-3202 Office: Columbia U 420 W 118th St New York NY 10027-7213

LENCI, GORDON KENT, headmaster; b. Summit, N.J., Dec. 12, 1933; s. Thomas A. and Louise (Dexter) L.; m. Janet Richardson, July 24, 1971 (dec. June 1980); 1 child, Kent Sterling. BA, Dartmouth Coll.; MEd, Springfield Coll. Dir. admissions, tchr. Pingry Sch., Elizabeth, N.J., 1961-68; headmaster, tchr. Barstow Sch., Kansas City, Mo., 1968-75; headmaster Roland Park County Sch., Balt., 1975-83; exec. dir. Pastoral Counseling Ctr. Balt., 1987-91; headmaster Lincoln Sch., Providence, 1991-92; trustee Coun. Religion in Ind. Schs., Washington, 1961—; pvt. cons. Balt. and Providence, 1988—. Dir. Charles Pettinos Found., N.Y.C., 1961—; trustee Greater Balt. YMCA, 1978-83; docent New Bedford (Mass.) Whaling Mus., 1983-85. Building dedicated in his name, Roland Park County Sch., Balt., 1983. Mem. Country Day Sch. Headmasters Assn. USA. Avocations: sailing, scuba, music. Home: 282 Smith Neck Rd South Dartmouth MA 02748

LENDARIS, GEORGE GREGORY, electrical educator; b. Helper, Utah, Apr. 2, 1935; s. Gregory George and Argie (Xenakis) L.; m. Irene Kokinos, June 26, 1958 (dec. July 1988); children: Miriam, Dorothy. BSEE cum laude., U. Calif., Berkeley, 1957, MSEE, 1958; PhD in Electrical Engring., 1961. Registered profl. engr., Calif., Oreg. Sr. rsch. engr., program mgr. Gen. Motors Corp., Defense Rsch. Labs., Santa Barbara, Calif., 1961-69; assoc. prof. systems sci., chmn. faculty Oreg. Grad. Ctr. for Rsch., Beaverton, 1969-71; prof. systems sci., electrical engring. Portland State U. Systems Sci. PhD Program, Oregon, 1971—; with Accurate Automation Corp., Chattanooga, 1993—; cons. various bus.; editorial bd. Internat. Jour. of Gen. Systems (Gordon & Breach), 1974—, Systems Rsch. Jour. 1985—; IEEE Transactions on Neural Networks, 1991—; chmn. gen. Internat. Joint Conf. on Neural Networks, Oreg., 1991-93; bd. dirs. Accurate Automation Corp. Author jour. article Diffraction Pattern Sampling, 1970, selected reprints book IEEE, 1978, chpt. in book Conceptual Graphs & Neural Networks, 1992, numerous conf. articles. Choir dir. local chs. Greek Orthodox Ch., Santa Barbara, Portland, 1962-73, pres., chmn. various coms., 1962—, mem. justice and human rights com. local ch., Portland, 1974—; mem. Gov.'s Tech. Adv. Com., Oreg., 1970-72, oreg. State Senate Task Force on Econ. Devel., 1972-73; mem. adv. panel Portland Energy Commn., 1980. NAS fellow, 1974. Fellow IEEE; mem. Systems, Man & Cybernetics Soc., Internat. Neural Network Soc., Internat. Soc. Knowledge Engrs., AAAS, Am. Helenic Edn. Progressive Assn., Sigma Xi, Tau Beta Pi, Eta Kappa Nu. Avocations: woodworking, Greek folk dancing instructor, church choir singing. Office: Portland State U Sys Sci PhD Program PO Box 751 Portland OR 97207-0751 *People often consider the statement, "Peace on Earth, good will toward men," as descriptive of some future time. I consider it a dictum—for today.*

LENDER, ADAM, electrical engineer; b. Gleiwitz, Germany, Sept. 15, 1921; s. Joseph and Regina (Waksberg) L.; m. Lilia Sadowski, Aug. 10, 1945; children: James, Richard. BSEE, Columbia U., 1954, MSEE, 1956; PhDEE, Stanford U., 1972. Mem. tech. staff Bell Telephone Labs., Murray Hill, N.J., 1954-60; project engr. Internat. Tel. & Tel. Labs., Nutley, N.J., 1960-61; head advanced devel. GTE Lenkurt, Inc., San Carlos, Calif., 1961-84; sr. cons. scientist, sr. mem. Lockheed Rsch. Labs., Palo Alto, Calif., 1984-93; adj. prof. grad. sch. elec. engring. U. Santa Clara (Calif.), 1976-87. Author: (with others) Digital Communications, 1981; contbr. articles to profl. jours.; inventor correlative techniques applied in digital communications and magnetic tape recordings, patentee in field. Recipient Stuart Ballantine medal Franklin Inst., 1984. Fellow IEEE (editor in chief Transactions in Comm. 1978-84, sr. tech. editor Comm. Mag. 1987—; Donald J. McLellan award 1983, centennial medal 1984), AIAA (assoc.); mem. Comm. Soc. IEEE (bd. govs. 1977-79, 82-84), Columbia U. Alumni Assn. (N.Y.C.), Stanford U. Alumni Assn., Tau Beta Pi, Eta Kappa Nu. Avocations: music, history. Home: 4124 Briarwood Way Palo Alto CA 94306-4609

LENDER, HERMAN JOSEPH, reinsurance company executive; b. Irvington, N.J., Sept. 2, 1923; s. Herman Joseph and Monica (Martesteck) L.; m. Janet Harriet Van Wert, June 15, 1945; children: Mark, Jonathan, David, Paul. Student, NYU, 1941-43, Rutgers U., 1943-45. Underwriter, br. office Am. Surety Co., Newark, 1940-49; supervising underwriter Fidelity & Casualty Co., N.Y.C., 1949-58; v.p. bonding Excess and Treaty Mgmt. Co., N.Y.C., 1958-67; v.p. mktg. Gen. Reins. Corp., Greenwich, Conn., 1967-85; reins. cons., 1986—; instr. Coll. Ins., N.Y.C., 1949-55. Pres., trustee Mt. Tabor Free Library Assn., N.J., 1962-71; lay leader United Meth. Ch., 1955-71, chmn. edn. com., New Canaan, 1971-85; chmn. council of ministries United Meth. Ch., Mt. Tabor, N.J. Mem. Soc. C.P.C.U.s (chmn. edn. com. H.Y. chpt. 1951-53). Home and Office: 39 Strowbridge Ave Mount Tabor NJ 07878

LENEHAN, ART, newspaper editor. Picture editor The Star-Ledger, Newark. Office: Newark Morning Ledger Co One Star Ledger Plz Newark NJ 07102-1200*

LENESS, GEORGE CRAWFORD, lawyer; b. N.Y.C., Oct. 10, 1936; s. George John and Christine (Gibbs) L. AB magna cum laude, Harvard U., 1958; LLB, Columbia U., 1961. Bar: N.Y. 1962, D.C. 1972. Assoc. Simpson Thacher & Bartlett, N.Y.C., 1961-66; assoc. Hale Russell & Gray, N.Y.C., 1966-69, ptnr., 1969-85; ptnr. Winthrop, Stimson, Putnam & Roberts, N.Y.C., 1985-92, sr. counsel, 1992—. Sgt. USAR, 1954-60. Mem. N.Y.C. Bar Assn., Harvard Club N.Y.C., Westchester Country Club (Harrison, N.Y.). Republican. Office: Winthrop Stimson Putnam et al 1 Battery Park Plz New York NY 10004

LENFANT, CLAUDE JEAN-MARIE, physician; b. Paris, Oct. 12, 1928; came to U.S., 1960, naturalized, 1965; s. Robert and Jeanine (Leclerc) L.; children: Philipe, Bernard, Martine Lenfant Wayman, Brigitte Lenfant Martin, Christine. B.S., U. Rennes, France, 1948; M.D., U. Paris, 1956; D.Sc. (hon.), SUNY, 1988. Asst. prof. physiology U. Lille, France, 1959-60; from clin. instr. to prof. medicine physiology and biophysics U. Wash. Med. Sch., 1961-72; assoc. dir. lung programs Nat. Heart, Lung and Blood Inst. NIH, Bethesda, Md., 1970-72; dir. div. lung diseases Nat. Heart, Lung and Blood Inst. NIH, 1972-80; dir. Fogarty Internat. Center NIH, 1980-82, assoc. dir. internat. research, 1980-82; dir. Nat. Heart, Lung and Blood Inst., 1982—. Assoc. editor: Jour. Applied Physiology, 1976-82, Am. Jour. Medicine, 1979-91 ; mem. editorial bd.: Undersea Biomed. Research, 1973-75, Respiration Physiology, 1971-78, Am. Jour. Physiology and Jour. Applied Physiology, 1970-76, Am. Rev. Respiratory Disease, 1973-79; editor-in-chief: Lung Biology in Health and Disease. Fellow Royal Coll. Physicians; mem. Assn. Am. Physicians, Am. Soc. Clin. Investigation, French Physiol. Soc., Am. Physiol. Soc., N.Y. Acad. Scis., Undersea Med. Soc., Inst. of Medicine of Nat. Acad. Sci., USSR Acad. Med. Scis., French Nat. Acad. Medicine. Home: 13201 Glen Rd Gaithersburg MD 20878-8855 Office: Nat Heart Lung & Blood Inst Bldg 31A Rm 5A52 Bethesda MD 20892

LENFEST, HAROLD FITZ GERALD, cable television executive, lawyer; b. Jacksonville, Fla., May 29, 1930; s. Harold Churchill and Rena (FitzGerald) L.; m. Marguerite Brooks, July 9, 1955; children: Diane, H. Chase, Brook. AB, Washington and Lee U., 1953; LLB, Columbia U., 1958. Bar: N.Y. 1959. Assoc. Davis Polk & Wardwell, N.Y.C., 1958-65; assoc. counsel Triangle Publs., Phila., 1965-70; mng. dir. communications div. Triangle Publs., N.Y.C., 1970-74; editorial dir. pub. Seventeen mag., N.Y.C., 1970-74; pres. Suburban Cable TV Co., 1970—, Empire State Cable TV Co., 1970-74, Lenfest Communications, Inc., 1974—; bd. dirs. TCI West, Inc., Seattle, Liberty Media Corp., Cable Advt. Bur., Vidéopole (France), Australis Media Ltd. (Australia), Voice FX, Inc.; chmn. Video JukeBox, Inc.; chief exec. officer Cable AdNet, Inc., 1981-92, StarNet, Inc., 1989—, TelVue, Inc., 1990—. Bd. dirs., v.p. Columbia U. Sch. Law, N.Y.C., 1960-65, 74-78, mem. exec. com., 1992—; trustee Walter Kaitz Found., Oakland, Calif., 1986-88; trustee, nat. campaign chmn. Washington and Lee U., 1988—; mem. bd. regents Mercersburg Acad., 1989—, pres., 1994—; mem. James Madison Coun. Libr. of Congress, 1989—; bd. dirs. Phila. Mus. Art, 1993—; trustee Chesapeake Bay Found., 1995—. Capt. USNR, 1953-76, active duty, 1953-56, 62, ret. Named Man of Yr. Phila. Area Easter Seal Soc., 1992. Mem. Pa. Cable TV Assn. (bd. dirs., officer 1976-79), Assn. of Bar of City of N.Y., The Mayflower Soc., Soc. of Colonial Wars. Home: 2445 Oaks Cir Huntingdon Valley PA 19006-5621 Office: The Lenfest Group 202 Shoemaker Rd Pottstown PA 19464-6420

LENG, SHAO CHUAN, political science educator; b. Chengtu, China, Feb. 14, 1921; came to U.S., 1945, naturalized, 1953; s. Yin Tung and Nan (Chen) L.; m. Alice Li, Dec. 12, 1944 (dec. 1968); 1 child, David; m. Nora Yen, June 14, 1970. B.A., Nat. Central U. China, 1943; M.A., Yale, 1948; Ph.D., U. Pa., 1950. Lectr. U. Pa., 1949-50; from lectr. to prof. U. Va., Charlottesville, 1950-72; Doherty Found. prof. U. Va., 1972-85, D. Compton prof. govt. and fgn. affairs, 1985-92, Compton prof. emeritus, chmn. com. Asian studies 1965-68, 74-92; Fulbright lectr. Doshisha (Japan) U., 1956-57; adviser Union Research Inst., Hong Kong, 1961; vis. scholar Harvard, 1962; research asso. Duke U. Rule of Law Research Center, 1964-66; Cons. Research Analysis Corp., 1968-71, HEW, 1978; research asso. Harvard Law Sch., 1968-69. Author: Japan and Communist China, 1959, (with Norman D. Palmer) Sun Yat-sen and Communism, 1961, (with others) Sovereignty within the Law, 1965, Justice in Communist China, 1968, Criminal Justice System in Post-Mao China, 1985. Editor: (with Hungdah Chiu) Law in Chinese Foreign Policy, 1972, Post-Mao China and U.S.-China Trade, 1977, (with Hungdah Chiu) China: 70 Years After the 1911 Revolution, 1984, Changes in China: Party, State, and Society, 1989, Coping with Crisis: How Governments Deal with Emergencies, 1990, Chiang Ching-Kuo's Leadership in the Development of the Republic of China on Taiwan, 1992, Reform and Development in Deng's China, 1994; cons. editor: Asian Forum, 1974-81, Asian Affairs, 1983—, Asia Pacific Rev., 1989—, Jour. Chinese Studies, 1984—, World Affairs, 1975-84. Social Sci. Research Council grantee, 1956; research fellow Social Sci. Research Council-Am. Council Learned Socs., 1961-62, 68-69; Fulbright Research scholar Hong Kong and Taiwan, 1977; vis. scholar Wilson Center, 1980; research fellow Inst. for Study of World Politics, 1984; chmn. bd. dirs. U.S.-Asia Research Inst., 1983—. Mem. Am. Polit. Sci. Assn., Am. Soc. Internat. Law, Assn. Asian Studies, Assn. Chinese Social Scientists in N.Am. (pres. 1989-91). Home: 217 Highview Ln Charlottesville VA 22901-1017

LENGA, J. THOMAS, lawyer; b. Toledo, Dec. 16, 1942; s. Casimir M. and Rose C. (Sturniolo) L.; children by previous marriage: Christina M., John Thomas Jr., Peter M. BA, U. Toledo, 1965, JD, 1968. Bar: Mich. 1968, Ohio 1968. Ptnr. Dykema Gossett, Detroit, 1972—; mem. com. on std. jury instrns. Mich. Supreme Ct.; adv. Am. Bd. of Trial Advs. Capt. JAGC, U.S. Army, 1968-72. Named Disting. Alumnus, Coll. Law, U. Toledo, 1987. Fellow Am. Coll. Trial Lawyers; mem. ABA, Detroit Bar Assn. (pres. 1989-90), State Bar Mich. (bd. commrs. 1992—), Internat. Assn. Def. Counsel. Office: Dykema Gossett 400 Renaissance Ctr Fl 35 Detroit MI 48243

LENGEL, DAVID LEE, electronics manufacturing executive; b. Anderson, S.C., Sept. 13, 1951; s. Russell Gene and Lois Anne (Oswald) L.; m. Suzanne Allen, June 10, 1973 (div.); children: James Russell, Scott Allen; m. Leslie Ann Deitrich. BS, U.S. Naval Acad., 1973; MBA, Harvard U., 1980. Variuos mktg. & staff positions Bendix Avionics Divsn., Ft. Lauderdale, Fla., 1980-84; mgr. bus. devel. Bendix Aerospace Sector, Arlington, Va., 1984-86; plant mgr. Bendix/King Avionics, Paola, Kans., 1986, Bendix Electric Power Divsn., Orangeburg, S.C., 1988; dir. ops. Bendix/King Avionics, Olathe, Kans., 1989-92; v.p. ops. Miltope Corp., Melville, N.Y., 1992; pres., CEO Miltope Group Inc., Melville, 1992—. Bd. dirs. AFCEA Ednl. Found., Fairfax, Va., 1993-94; mem. adv. bd. Poly. U., Farmingdale, N.Y., 1993-94. Lt. USN, 1973-78. Mem. Armed Forces Comms. & Electronics Assn., Assn. of U.S. Navy, Navy League, U.S. Naval Inst. Avocation: horseback riding. Office: Miltope Group Inc 1770 Walt Whitman Rd Melville NY 11747-3068

LENGEMANN, FREDERICK WILLIAM, physiology educator, scientist; b. N.Y.C., Apr. 8, 1925; s. Peter and Dorathea Johanna (Wolter) L.; m. J. Joan Doremus, Dec. 23, 1950; children—Frederick William Jr., David Munson. Student, N.Y. State Sch. Agr., Farmingdale, 1942-43; B.S. with distinction, Cornell U., 1950, M.Nutrition Sci., 1951; Ph.D., U. Wis., 1954. Research asso. U. Tenn.-AEC Agrl. Research Program, Oak Ridge, 1954-55; asst. prof. dept. chemistry U. Tenn. Med. Sch., Memphis, 1955-59; prof. dept. physiology N.Y. State Coll. Vet. Medicine, Cornell U., 1959-88, prof. physiology emeritus, 1988—; biochemist div. biology and medicine AEC, 1962-63; cons. FAO-IAEA, Vienna, Austria, 1966-67, 76-77, Fed. Radiation Council, 1964-65, NRC, 1970-73, Nat. Com. on Radiation Protection, 1970-73, 79, 82; IAEA expert U. Nacional Agraria, Peru, 1978; lectr., dir. tng. courses. Contbr. articles to profl. jours. Mem. planning bd. Town of Dryden, N.Y., 1963-68. Served with USNR, 1943-46. Decorated Air medal with 3 stars. Fellow AAAS; mem. Council Agrl. Sci. and Tech., Am. Dairy Sci. Assn., Am. Nutrition Soc., Fed. Am. Socs. for Exptl. Biology, Nat., N.Y. State Christmas tree growers assns., Sigma Xi, Phi Kappa Phi. Home: PO Box 161 Rome PA 18837-0161 Office: Cornell U NY State Coll Vet Medicine Dept Physiology Ithaca NY 14853

L'ENGLE, MADELEINE (MRS. HUGH FRANKLIN), author; b. N.Y.C., Nov. 29, 1918; d. Charles Wadsworth and Madeleine (Barnett) Camp; m. Hugh Franklin, Jan. 26, 1946; children: Josephine Franklin Jones, Maria Franklin Rooney, Bion. A.B., Smith Coll., 1941; postgrad., New Sch., 1941-42, Columbia U., 1960-61; holder 19 hon. degrees. Tchr. St. Hilda's and St. Hugh's Sch., 1960—; mem. faculty U. Ind., 1965-66, 71; writer-in-residence Ohio State U., 1970, U. Rochester, 1972, Wheaton Coll., 1976—; Cathedral St. John the Divine, N.Y.C., 1965—. Author: The Small Rain, 1945, Ilsa, 1946, Camilla Dickinson, 1951, A Winter's Love, 1957, And Both Were Young, 1949, Meet the Austins, 1960, A Wrinkle in Time, 1962, The Moon by Night, 1963, The 24 Days Before Christmas, 1964, The Arm of the Starfish, 1965, The Love Letters, 1966, The Journey with Jonah, 1968, The Young Unicorns, 1968, Dance in the Desert, 1969, Lines Scribbled on an Envelope, 1969, The Other Side of the Sun, 1971, A Circle of Quiet, 1972, A Wind in the Door, 1973, The Summer of the Great-Grandmother, 1974, Dragons in the Waters, 1976, The Irrational Season, 1977, A Swiftly Tilting Planet, 1978, The Weather of the Heart, 1978, Ladder of Angels, 1980, A Ring of Endless Light, 1980, Walking on Water, 1980, A Severed Wasp, 1982, And I You Go, Based, 1983, A House Like a Lotus, 1984, Trailing Clouds of Glory, 1985, A Stone for a Pillow, 1986, Many Waters, 1986, Two-Part Invention, 1988, A Cry Like a Bell, 1987, Sold Into Egypt, 1989, From This Day Forward, 1988, An Acceptable Time, 1989, The Glorious Impossible, 1990, Certain Women, 1992, The Rock That Is Higher: Story As Truth, 1993, Anytime Prayers, 1994, Troubling a Star, 1994. Pres. Crosswicks Found. Recipient Newbery medal, 1963, Sequoyah award, 1965, runner-up Hans Christian Andersen Internat. award, 1964, Lewis Carroll Shelf award, 1965, Austrian State Lit. award, 1969, Bishop's Cross, 1970, U. South Miss. medal, 1978, Regina medal, 1985, Alan award Nat. Coun. Tchrs. English, 1986, Kerlan award, 1990; collection of papers at Wheaton Coll. Mem. Authors Guild (pres., mem. council, mem. membership com.), Authors League (mem. council), Writers Guild Am., Colonial Dames. Episcopalian. Home: 924 West End Ave New York NY 10025 Office: care Farrar Straus & Giroux Inc 19 Union Sq W New York NY 10003-3304 *Over the years I've worked out a philosophy of failure which I find extraordinarily liberating. If I'm not free to fail, I'm not free to take risks, and everything in life that's worth doing involves a willingness to take a risk and involves the risk of failure. Each time I start a new book I am risking failure. Although I have had over 40 books published, there are at least 6 full unpublished books which have failed, but which have been necessary for the book which then gets published. The same thing is true in all human relationships. Unless I'm willing to open myself up to risk and to being hurt, then I'm closing myself off to love and friendship.*

LENGYEL, ALFONZ, art history, archeology and museology educator; b. Godollo, Hungary, Oct. 21, 1921; came to U.S., 1957; s. Aurel and Margit (Furedy) L.; m. Hongying Liu. Terminal degree in Law and Polit. Sci., Miskolc Law Acad., Budapest, Hungary, 1944; M.A., San Jose State Coll., 1959; Ph.D., U. Paris, 1964; LL.D., London Inst. Applied Research, 1973. Asst. prof. San Jose State Coll. (Calif.), 1961-63; faculty U. Md. European Div., Paris and Heidelberg, Germany, 1963-68; intern museology Ecole du Louvre, Paris, 1965-66; prof. Wayne State U., Detroit, 1968-72, No. Ky. U., Highland Heights, 1972-77; dean, prof. Inst. Mediterranean Art and Archaeology, Cin., 1977-82; coord. art history Rosemont Coll. (Pa.), 1982-86; research prof. art history, dir. Goebel's Print Collection, 1986-88; pres. Fudan Mus. Found., 1988—; adj. curator Detroit Inst. Arts, 1968-72; cons. Paris Am. Acad., 1963—; dir. UPAO, Washington, 1983—; adv. prof. Fudan U., Shanghai, Peoples Republic of China; cons. prof. Xian Jiaotong U., Xian, Peoples Republic of China, founder Sino-Am. Summer Field Sch. Archaeology. Author: Archaeology for Museologists, 1993, Chinese Chronological History, 1993; co-author: The Archaeology of Roman Pannonia, 1980; contbr. numerous articles to profl. jours. Bd. dirs. Hungarian-Am. Fedn., Cleve., 1983-91, exec. v.p., Ft. Laudedale, Fla., 1951—; mem. Republican Presdl. Task Force, Washington, 1982—; mem. adv. bd. U.S. Dept. Interior Nat. Park Service, 1987-91. Rockefeller Found. grantee U. Vienna, 1957; Govt. of France grantee U. Paris, 1962-63; S. H. Kress Found. lectureship Denison U. (Ohio), 1967-68; Smithsonian Instn. grantee, 1968; NEH grantee, 1971, 76. Fellow Internat. Acad. Sci. and Lettres, Arpad Acad. (pres. 1982—), Szechenyi Acad., Am. Assn. Museums (bd. dirs.), mem. Internat. Coun. Mus., Renaissance Soc Am., Coll. Art Assn. Am., Archaeol. Inst. Am., Nat. Fedn. Hungarian-Ams., Soc. Architectural Historians, N.Y. Acad. Scis., Mich. Acad. Scis. and Letters, Soc. Profl. Archaeologists, Christopher Giest Hist. Soc., Detroit Classical Assn. Republican. Roman Catholic. Home: 1522 School House Rd Ambler PA 19002-1939 Office: Fudan Mus Found Ambler PA 19002

LENGYEL, CORNEL ADAM (CORNEL ADAM), author; b. Fairfield, Conn., Jan. 1, 1915; s. Elmer Alexander and Mary Elizabeth (Bismarck) L.; m. Teresa Delaney Murphy, July 10, 1933; children: Jerome Benedict, Paul Joel, Michael Sebastian, Cornelia (Mrs. Charles Burke). LittD (hon.), World Acad. of Arts and Culture, Taiwan, 1991. Editor, supt. Fed. Research Project, San Francisco, 1938-41; music critic The Coast, San Francisco, 1937-41; shipwright, personnel officer Kaiser Shipyard, Richmond, Calif., 1942-44; mgr. Forty-Nine Theatre, Georgetown, Calif., 1946-50; editor W.H. Freeman Co., San Francisco, 1952-54; founder, exec. editor Dragon's Teeth Press, Georgetown, 1969—; vis. prof., lectr. English lit. Sacramento State Coll., 1962-63; writer-in-residence Hamline U., St. Paul, 1968-69; guest lectr. MIT, 1969; transl. from Hungarian; editorial cons. HEW; ednl. dir. ILGWU. Author: (history) American Testament: The Story of the Promised Land, 1956, Four Days in July, 1958, I, Benedict Arnold: The Anatomy of Treason, 1960, Presidents of the U.S.A., 1961, Ethan Allen and the Green Mountain Boys, 1961, Jesus the Galilean, 1966, The Declaration of Independence, 1969; (poetry) Thirty Pieces, 1933, First Psalms, 1950, Fifty Poems, 1965, Four Dozen Songs, 1970, The Lookout's Letter, 1971, Late News from Adam's Acres, 1983, El Dorado Forest: Selected Poems, 1986; (plays) The World's My Village, 1935, Jonah Fugitive, 1936; The Giant's Trap, 1938, The Atom Clock, 1951, Eden, Inc., 1954, rev. edit. Omega, 1963, Will of Stratford, 1964, Three Plays, 1964, The Case of Benedict Arnold, 1975, Doctor Franklin, 1976, The Shadow Trap, 1977, The Second Coming, 1985, Mengele's Passover, 1987, A Clockmaker's Boy: Part One, 1987; (essays) The Creative Self, 1971; contbr. to anthologies The Golden Year, 1960, Interpretation in Our Time, 1966, The Britannica Library of Great American Writing, 1961, The Menorah Treasury, 1964, Interpretation for Our Time, 1966, The Courage to Grow Old, 1988, From These Hills, 1990, Blood to Remember, 1991, Anthology of Contemporary Poets, 1992, World Poetry, 1993, We Speak for Peace, 1993, also Poet Lore, The Coast, The Argonaut, Saturday Rev., Menorah Jour., others. Served with U.S. Merchant Marine, 1944-45. Recipient Albert M. Bender award in lit., 1945; recipient 1st prize Maritime Poetry Awards, 1945, 1st prize Poetry Soc. Va., 1951, Maxwell Anderson award drama, 1950, Di Castagnola award Poetry Soc. Am., 1971, Internat. Who's Who in Poetry award, 1972; Huntington Hartford Found. resident fellow, 1951, 64; MacDowell Colony resident fellow, 1967; Ossabaw Island Found. fellow, 1968; Nat. Endowment for Arts fellow, 1976-77. Mem. MLA, AAUP, PEN, Poetry Soc. Am., Poetry Soc. Eng., Authors Guild. Address: Adam's Acres Georgetown CA 95634 *What would a writer convey through his work? His vision of life, his response to the oddity, terror, humor, beauty, pathos, or grandeur of experience. He would never our original sense of wonder at the mystery of things and speak in a human voice fittingly of man's mortal adventures amid the immortal dance of the elements . . . To endure, a book must stir a variety of men in any generation. Though all that we do may prove perishable, we must proceed as if . . . Do one thing well enough to endure, we tell ourselves. A thing done well is well done for all time.*

LENGYEL, ISTVÁN, chemist, educator; b. Kaposvar, Hungary, July 12, 1931; came to the U.S., 1958; s. István and Margit (Palásthy) L. Diploma in chemistry, Eotvos Lorand U., 1955; PhD in Organic Chemistry, MIT, 1964. Rsch. chemist G. Richter Pharm. Works, Inc., Budapest, 1953-55; chemist State Geophys. Inst., Budapest, 1955-56; rsch. chemist Biochemie GmbH, Kundl, Austria, 1957-58; rsch. asst. Johns Hopkins Med. Sch., Balt., 1958-59; predoctoral fellow MIT, Cambridge, 1959-63, postdoctoral fellow, 1964; NIH postdoctoral fellow Techn. U., Munich, 1964-65; rsch. assoc. MIT, Cambridge, 1965-67; prof. chemistry St. John's U., Jamaica, N.Y., 1967—, chmn. dept. chemistry, 1985-91; vis. scholar U.S. Nat. Acad. Sci. and Hungarian Acad. Scis., 1973. Recipient award Alexander von Humboldt Found., 1973. Avocations: swimming, travel. Home: 84-01 169th St Jamaica NY 11432 Office: Saint Johns U 8000 Utopia Pky Jamaica NY 11439

LENGYEL, PETER EMERY, banker; b. N.Y.C., May 17, 1940; s. Emil and Livia (Delej) L.; m. Gretchen Hunicke; children: Monica, Kristin, Roger. B.I.E., NYU, 1962; M.B.A., Dartmouth Coll., 1964. Vice pres. Chase Manhattan Bank, N.Y.C., 1969-74, sr. v.p., 1974-79; sr. v.p. Bankers Trust Co., N.Y.C., from 1979, now exec. v.p. Office: Bankers Trust Co 280 Park Ave New York NY 10017-1216

LENHARDT, ALFONSO EMANUAL, army officer; b. N.Y.C., Oct. 29, 1943; s. Mary Katherine (Fields) Mackey; m. Jacqueline Odell Hill, Oct. 2, 1965; children: Robin Ann, Tracey Danielle, Kimberly Michelle. BA in Criminal Justice, U. Nebr., 1972; MS in Adminstrn. of Justice, Wichita (Kans.) State U., 1976; MA in Pub. Adminstrn., Cen. Mich. State U., 1976. Commd. 2d lt. U.S. Army, 1966, advanced through grades to brig. gen., 1990; platoon leader 199th Inf. Brigade, Vietnam, 1967; field officer U.S. Army Criminal Investigation Div., Ft. Meade, Md., 1973-76; bn. exec. officer Ft. Dix, N.J., 1976-78; co. tactical officer U.S. Army Mil. Acad., West Point, N.Y., 1978-81; bn. comdr. Kornwestheim, Fed. Republic Germany, 1981-84; mil. asst. Office Sec. Def., Washington, 1984-85; exec. officer Strategic Def. Initiative Orgn., Washington, 1985-86; brigade comdr. U.S. Army Europe, Frankfurt, Fed. Republic Germany, 1986-89; dep. comdg. gen. U.S. Army Recruiting Command, Ft. Sheridan, Ill., 1989—. Episcopalian. Avocations: golf, jogging, computer science, reading. Office: Hdqrs Army Recruiting Command Bldg 48A Fort Sheridan IL 60037

LENHART, CYNTHIA RAE, conservation organization executive; b. Cheverly, Md., Nov. 3, 1957; d. Donald Edward and Vesta Jean (Morris) L.; m. John Charles Doyle Jr., Oct. 24, 1987. BS in Environ. Studies, Coll. William & Mary, 1979; MS in Environ. Sci., SUNY, Syracuse, 1983. Asst. to pres. Environ. Policy Inst., Washington, 1979-81; wildlife policy analyst Nat. Audubon Soc., Washington, 1984-90; exec. dir. Hawk Mountain Sanctuary, Kempton, Pa., 1990—; bd. dirs. Am. Bird Conservancy, Washington. Contbr. chpts. to Audubon Wildlife Report, 1985, 87, 88, 89. Chair Everglades Coalition, Washington, 1986-88. Mem. NAFE. Office: Hawk Mountain Sanctuary RR 2 Box 191 Kempton PA 19529

LENHART, JAMES THOMAS, lawyer; b. Cambridge, Mass., Nov. 3, 1946; s. James Wills and Martha Agnes (Everly) L.; m. Lynn Dexter Stevens, June 21, 1969; children—Amanda Brooks, James Edward, Abigail Ames. Cert. in History, U. Edinburgh, Scotland, 1967; A.B., Columbia U., 1968, J.D., 1972. Bar: N.Y. 1973, D.C. 1974. Clk. to judge U.S. Dist. Ct. (so. dist.) N.Y., 1972-73; assoc. Shaw, Pittman, Potts & Trowbridge, Washington, 1973-79, ptnr., 1980—; adj. prof. Cornell Law Sch., 1992-93; instr. Washington Coll. Law of Am. U., Washington, 1976-78. Chair exec. com. Westmoreland Congregational Ch., Washington, 1989, bd. dirs. 1978-79, 83-84. Harlan Fiske Stone scholar Columbia U., 1968-69, 71-72. Mem. Am. Law Inst., D.C. Def. Lawyers Assn., ABA, D.C. Bar Assn., Fed. City Club. Democrat. Mem. United Ch. of Christ. Office: Shaw Pittman Potts & Trowbridge 2300 N St NW Washington DC 20037-1122

LENHART, LOWELL CORDELL, hospital administrator, consultant; b. Oklahoma City, Jan. 19, 1940; s. Herbert William and Helen Nancy Lenhart; m. Sharen Annette Gambill, Jan. 21, 1961; 1 child, Lance Christian. B.S., Central State U., 1963; M.S., Okla. State U., 1967; Ph.D., Okla. U., 1976. Tech. dir. service outcome measurement project Div. Rehab. Services, Oklahoma City, 1968-70; research utilization supr. Dept. Pub. Welfare, Oklahoma City, 1970-72; program evaluation supr. Dept. Instns., Oklahoma City, 1972-74; coordinator dept. mgmt. services Dept. Human Services, Oklahoma City, 1974-79; dep. adminstr. O'Donoghue Rehab. Inst., Oklahoma City, 1979-81, adminstr., 1981—; cons. in field. Contbr. articles to profl. jours. Pres. Okla. Ptnrs. of Americas, 1981-82; mem. Oklahoma City Alliance for Safer Cities, 1975-76; cons. Community Workshop, 1978-79. Mem. Am. Coll. Hosp. Adminstrs., Am. Hosp. Assn., Okla. Hosp. Assn., Nat. Rehab. Assn. Okla. Rehab. Assn. (bd. dirs.). Democrat. Lodge: Rotary. Avocations: renovation of historic homes; snow skiing; gardening; writing. Home: PO Box 54444 Oklahoma City OK 73154-1444 Office: Chisholm Trail Mental Health Ctr PO Box 851290 Yukon OK 73085

LENHERR, FREDERICK KEITH, neurophysiologist, computer scientist; b. N.Y.C., Feb. 4, 1943; s. Frederick Joseph and Thelma Frances (DeFrehn) L. A.B., Harvard U., 1965; M.S., U. Mass., 1973, Ph.D., 1975. Instr. biology and physics Taft Sch., Watertown, Conn., 1965-66; rsch. and devel. engr. No. Rsch. & Engring., Cambridge, Mass., 1966-69; turbine engr. Gen. Electric Co., Lynn, Mass., 1969-70; neurophysiologist, computer scientist Ctr. Systems Neurosci., U. Mass., Amherst, 1974-77; dir. Berkeley Brain Ctr., 1977-80; pres. New Salem (Mass.) Rsch., 1981—; sr. engr. Visual Intelligence, Amherst, Mass., 1982-85; project scientist Harvard U., Cambridge, Mass., 1986-87; microcomputer faculty Holyoke Community Coll., 1991-92; sr. engr. App. Comp. Sys. Inst. Mass., 1993—. Founding editor: Brain Theory Newsletter, 1975-77. Democrat. Lutheran. Home and Office: W Main St New Salem MA 01355

LENHOFF, HOWARD MAER, biological sciences educator, academic administrator, activist; b. North Adams, Mass., Jan. 27, 1929; s. Charles and Goldie Sarah (Rubin) L.; m. Sylvia Grossman, June 20, 1954; children: Gloria, Bernard. B.A., Coe Coll., 1950, D.Sc. (hon.), 1976; Ph.D., Johns Hopkins U., 1955. USPHS fellow Loomis Lab., Greenwich, Conn., 1954-56; vis. lectr. Howard U., Washington, 1957-58; rsch. assoc. George Washington U., Washington, 1957-58; postdoctoral fellow Carnegie Instn., Washington, 1958; investigator Howard Hughes Med. Inst., Miami, 1958-63; prof. biology, dir. Lab. for Quantitative Biology U. Miami, Coral Gables, 1963-69; prof. biol. scis. U. Calif., Irvine, 1969-92, prof. polit. sci., 1986-92, assoc. dean biol. scis., 1969-71, dean grad. div., 1971-73, faculty asst. to vice chancellor of student affairs, 1986-87, 90—, chair faculty senate, 1988-90, prof. emeritus, rsch. prof., 1993—, faculty asst. to dir. fin. aid; vis. scientist, Louis Lipsky fellow Weizmann Inst. Sci., Rehovot, Israel, 1968-69; vis. prof. chem. engring., Rothschild fellow Israel Inst. Tech., 1973-74; vis. prof. Hebrew U., Jerusalem, spring 1970, fall 1971, 77-78; Hubert Humphrey Inst. fellow Ben Gurion U., Beersheva, Israel, 1981; sr. rsch. fellow Jesus Coll., U. Oxford, 1988; dir. Nelson Rsch. & Devel. Co., Irvine, 1971-73; bd. dirs. BioProbe Internat., Inc., Tustin, Calif., 1983-89, chmn. bd., 1983-86. Editor/author: Biology of Hydra, 1961, Hydra, 1969, Experimental Coelenterate Biology, 1972, Coelenterate Biology—Review and Perspectives, 1974, Hydra: Research Methods, 1983, Enzyme Immunoassay, 1985, From Trembley's Polyps to New Directions in Research on Hydra, 1985, Hydra and the Birth of Experimental Biology, 1986, Biology of Nematocysts, Conception to Birth, 1988; mem. editorial bd. Jour. Solid Phase Biochemistry, 1976-80. Vice chmn. So. Calif. div. Am. Assn. Profs. for Peace in Middle East, 1972-80; bd. dirs. Am. Assn. for Ethiopian Jews, 1974-93, pres., 1978-82; bd. govs. Israel Bonds Orange County, Calif., 1974-80, Dade County Heart Assn., Miami, 1958-61, So. Calif. Technion Soc., 1976; pres. Hillel Coun. of Orange County, 1976-78; nat. chmn. faculty div. State of Israel Bonds, 1976; mem. sci. adv. bd. Am. Friends of Weizman Inst. Sci., 1980-84; bd. dirs. Hi Hopes Identity Discovery Found., Anaheim, Calif., 1982-87, pres. bd. govs., 1983-85, William Syndrome Found., trustee, 1992, pres., bd. dirs., 1993-95, exec. v.p., 1995—; v.p. edn. Williams Syndrome Assn., 1994, bd. dirs., 1993-94. 1st lt. USAF, 1956-58. Recipient Career Development award USPHS, 1965-69; Disting. fellow Iowa Acad. Sci., 1986. Fellow AAAS; mem. Soc. Physics and Natural History of Swiss Acad. Scis. (hon.), Am. Chem. Soc., Am. Biophys. Soc., Am. Soc. Zoologists, History of Sci. Soc., Am. Soc. Cell Biologists, Am. Soc. Biol. Chemists, Biophysics Soc., Soc. Gen. Physiologists, Soc. Growth and Devel. Home: 304 Robinhood Ln Costa Mesa CA 92627-2134 Office: U Calif Sch Biol Scis 320 UT Irvine CA 92717

LENKE, JOANNE MARIE, publishing executive; b. Chgo., Aug. 27, 1938; d. August Julian and Dorothy Anna (Gold) L.; B.S., Purdue U., 1960; M.S., Syracuse U., 1964, Ph.D., 1968. Tchr. pub. schs., Evanston, Ill., 1960-63; editor Test Dept., Harcourt, Brace & World, Inc., N.Y.C., 1967-70; research psychologist Harcourt Brace Jovanovich, Inc., N.Y.C., 1970-73, exec. editor, 1973-75; asst. dir. ednl. measurement div. The Psychol. Corp., N.Y.C., 1975-83, dir. ednl. measurement and psychometrics, Cleve., 1983-85, San Antonio, 1986, v.p., dir. Measurement div., 1986-88, sr. v.p. 1988-91, exec. v.p., 1991—; field reader U.S. Office Edn., 1972, NSF grantee, 1963-64. Mem. Nat. Council on Measurement in Edn., Am. Psychol. Assn., Am. Ednl. Research Assn. Adv. editor Jour. of Ednl. Measurement, 1974-78. Home: 1311 Vista Del Monte San Antonio TX 78216-2229 Office: The Psychol Corp 555 Academic Ct San Antonio TX 78204-2455

LENKER, MAX V., consumer products company executive; b. 1946. Pres. Racetrac Petroleum Inc., Smyrna, Ga., 1975—. Office: Racetrac Petroleum Inc 300 Technology Ct Smyrna GA 30082-5246

LENKOSKI, LEO DOUGLAS, psychiatrist, educator; b. Northampton, Mass., May 13, 1925; s. Leo L. and Mary Agnes (Lee) L.; m. Jeannette Teare, July 12, 1952; children—Jan Ellen, Mark Teare, Lisa Marie, Joanne Lee. A.B., Harvard, 1948, spl. student, 1948-49; M.D., Western Res. U., 1953; grad., Cleve. Psychoanalytic Inst., 1964. Intern Univ. Hosps., Cleve., 1953-54, resident in psychiatry, 1956-57, dir. psychiatry, 1970-86, chief of staff, 1982-90; dir. profl. services Horizon Ctr. Hosp., 1980; asst. resident in psychiatry Yale U., New Haven, 1954-56; teaching fellow Case Western Res. U., Cleve., 1957-60, from instr. to prof. psychiatry, 1960-93; prof. emeritus, 1993—; assoc. dean Sch. Medicine Case Western Res. U., Cleve., 1982-93, dir. Substance Abuse Ctr., 1990-93; cons. Cleve. Ctr. on Alcoholism, DePaul Maternity and Infant Home, St. Ann's Hosp., Def. Dept., Cleve. VA Hosp., Psychiat. Edn. for NIMH; mem. Cuyahoga County Mental Health and Retardation Bd., 1967-73, 94—, Health Planning and Devel. Commn., 1967-73, Ohio Mental Health and Retardation Commn., 1976-78. Contbr. articles to profl. jours. Bd. dirs. Hough-Norwood Health Ctr., Hitchcock Ctr., Hopewell Inn. 1st lt. USAAF, 1943-46. Decorated D.F.C., Air medal with oak leaf cluster.; Career Tchr. grantee NIMH, 1958-60. Fellow Am. Psychiat. Assn. (life), Am. Coll. Psychiatrists, Am. Coll. Psychoanalysts (pres. 1988-89); mem. AMA, AAAS, Ohio Psychiat. Assn. (pres. 1974—), Am. Psychoanalytic Assn., Assn. Am. Med. Colls., Cleve. Acad. Medicine (bd. dirs. 1987-90), Ohio Med. Assn., Pasteur Club, Am. Assn. Chairmen Depts. Psychiatry (pres. 1978-79), Alpha Omega Alpha. Home: 1 Bratenahl Pl Apt 1010 Cleveland OH 44108-1155 Office: 11000 Euclid Ave Cleveland OH 44106-2602

LENMAN, BRUCE PHILIP, historian, educator; b. Aberdeen, Scotland, Apr. 9, 1938; s. Jacob Philip and May (Wishart) L. MA in History with 1st class honors, Aberdeen U., 1960; MLitt, U. Cambridge, 1965, LittD, 1986.

LENN 2472 WHO'S WHO IN AMERICA

Asst. prof. U. Victoria, B.C., Can., 1963; lectr. Queen's Coll., Dundee, Scotland, 1963-67, U. Dundee, 1967-72; lectr. U. St. Andrews, Scotland, 1972-78, sr. lectr., 1978-83, reader, 1983-92, prof. of modern history, 1992—; James Pinckney Harrison prof. history Coll. William and Mary, Williamsburg, Va., 1988-89; mem. econs. and bus. studies panel Scottish Edn. Dept., Ediburgh, 1979-81, humanities sub.-com. Council for Nat. Acad. Awards, London, 1985-87. Author: From Esk to Tweed, 1975, Economic History of Modern Scotland, 1977 (Scottish Arts Coun. award 1977), The Jacobite Risings 1689-1746, 1980 (Scottish Arts Coun. award 1980), Scotland 1746-1832, 1981, The Jacobite Clans of the Great Glen, 1984, The Jacobite Clause, 1986, The Eclipse of Parliament, 1992; co-author: (with John S. Gibson) The Jacobite Threat, 1990; editor: Chambers Dictionary of World History, 1993. Brit. Acad.-Newberry Library fellow, 1982, John Carter Brown Library fellow, 1984, Mellon fellow U. Tex. Hist. Soc., 1990. Fellow Royal Hist. Soc.; mem. Am. Soc. for 18th Century Scottish Studies, Am. Soc. for 18th Century Studies, Soc. for History of Discoveries, Hakluyt Soc. Clubs: Royal Commonwealth (London); New Golf (St. Andrews). Avocations: golf, hill walking, squash, badminton, swimming. Office: U St Andrews Dept Modern History, St Katherine Lodge, Saint Andrews KY16 9AL, Scotland

LENN, STEPHEN ANDREW, lawyer; b. Ft. Lauderdale, Fla., Jan. 6, 1946; s. Joseph A. and Ruth (Kreis) L.; 1 child, Daniel Lenn. BA, Tufts U., 1967; JD, Columbia U., 1970. Assoc. Kronish, Lieb, Shainswit, Weiner & Hellman, N.Y.C., 1970-72, Shereff, Friedman, Hoffman & Goodman, N.Y.C., 1972-75; exec. v.p., gen. counsel Union Commerce Bank, Union Commerce Corp., Cleve., 1975-83; ptnr., mng. ptnr. Porter, Wright, Morris & Arthur, Cleve., 1983-88; ptnr. Baker & Hostetler, Cleve., 1988—. Trustee North Coast Harbor, Gt. Lakes Mus. Mem. ABA (com. on devel. in investment svcs.), Ohio Bar Assn., Cleve. Bar Assn., N.Y.C. Bar Assn., Calif. Bar Assn., Union Club, Oakwood Club. Office: Baker & Hostetler 3200 Nat City Ctr 1900 E 9th St Cleveland OH 44114

LENNARD, GERALD, metal products executive; b. 1930; married. Grad., Syracuse U., 1950. With Inter-Continental Metal Corp., N.Y.C., 1953-60, pres., 1960-62; pres. Gerald Inc., N.Y.C., 1962—. With U.S. Army, 1951-53. Office: Gerald Inc 6 High Ridge Park Stamford CT 06905 also: Gerald Inc 19 Rector St New York NY 10006

LENNARZ, WILLIAM JOSEPH, research biologist, educator; b. N.Y.C., Sept. 28, 1934; s. William and Louise (Richter) L.; m. Roberta S. Lozensky, June 16, 1956 (div. June 1973); children: William, Matthew, David; m. Sheila Jackson, July 13, 1973. B.S., Pa. State U., 1956; Ph.D., U. Ill., 1959; research fellow, Harvard, 1959-62. Mem. faculty Johns Hopkins Sch. Medicine, 1962-83, assoc. prof. biochemistry, 1966-70, prof., 1971-83; R.A. Welch prof. and chmn. dept. biochemistry and molecular biology U. Tex. Cancer Ctr., M.D. Anderson Hosp., Houston, 1983-89; leading prof., chmn. dept. biochemistry and cell biology SUNY, Stony Brook, 1989—; cons. NIH. Editorial bd.: Biochem. Biophys. Research Commn., Biosci. Reports. Clayton Found. scholar, 1962-64; Lederle Faculty awardee, 1965-67; recipient Distinguished Young Scientist award Md., 1967. Mem. NAS, Am. Chem. Soc., Am. Soc. Biol. Chemists and Molecular Biologists (pres. 1989-90), Am. Soc. Microbiology, Am. Soc. Cell Biology, Assn. Med. Grad. Sch. Dept. Biochemistry (pres. 1993), Soc. Complex Carbohydrates (pres. 1993), Sigma Xi, Phi Kappa Phi, Alpha Chi Sigma. Rsch. biochemistry of cell surface molecules and of fertilization. Home: 43 Erland Rd Stony Brook NY 11790-1124 Office: SUNY at Stony Brook 450 Life Scis Stony Brook NY 11790

LENNES, GREGORY, manufacturing and financing company executive; b. Chgo., Aug. 5, 1947; s. Lawrence Dominic and Genevieve (Karoll) L.; m. Maryann Meskers, July 27, 1968; children: Robert, Sandra, Ryan. BA, U. Ill., 1969, MA, 1971, postgrad., 1971-73. Corp. archivist Navistar Internat. Corp. (formerly Internat. Harvester Co.), Chgo., 1973-80, records mgr., 1980—, asst. sec., 1980—; sec. Navistar Fin. Corp., Schaumburg, Ill., 1980—, Navistar Internat. Transportation Corp., 1987—. Editor: Historical Records in the Farm Equipment Industry, 1977. Mem. Am. Soc. Corp Secs., Assn. Records Mgrs. and Adminstrs., Soc. Am. Archivists, Midwest Archives Conf., Assn. Info. and Image Mgmt. Home: 19641 Schoolhouse Rd Mokena IL 60448 Office: Navistar Internat Corp 455 N Cityfront Plaza Dr Chicago IL 60611-5503

LENNETTE, EDWIN HERMAN, virologist; b. Pitts., Sept. 11, 1908; s. John and Natalie Frances (LeManek) L.; m. Elizabeth Hubenthal, Sept. 2, 1930 (dec. Apr. 1981); children: Edwin Paul, David Alan. BS, U. Chgo., 1931, PhD, 1935, MD, 1936. Diplomate Am. Bd. Preventive Medicine, Am. Bd. Med. Microbiology. Instr. pathology Wash. U. Med. Sch., St. Louis, 1938-39; staff mem. internat. health div. Rockefeller Found., N.Y.C., 1939-46; dir. virus lab. Calif. Dept Health Services, Berkeley, 1947-78; cons. WHO, Geneva, 1952-78, Dept. of Army, Washington, 1948-78, NIH, 1951; pres. Armed Forces Epidemiol. Bd., Dept. of Army, 1973-76, Virion (U.S.), Inc., 1985—. Contbr. numerous articles to sci. and med. jours. Pres. Calif. Pub. Health Found., Berkeley, 1980—; bd. dirs. Rush Med. Coll., Chgo., 1970-74, Peralta Cancer Research Inst., Oakland, Calif., 1978—, pres., 1985—. Recipient Bronfman award Am. Pub. Health Assn., 1969, Profl. Achievement award U. Chgo., 1981. Mem. Am. Assn. Immunologists (pres. 1966-67), Fedn. Am. Socs. Exptl. Biology (pres. 1968-69), Tissue Culture Assn. (pres. 1976-78), Am. Soc. Microbiology (pres. 1978, Wyeth award 1976, Wellcome Diagnostics award 1986). Republican. Home: 6605 Ascot Dr Piedmont CA 94611-1710 Office: Calif Pub Health Found 2001 Addison St Ste 210 Berkeley CA 94704-1103

LENNON, A. MAX, food products company executive; b. Columbus County, N.C., Sept. 27, 1940; m. Ruth Carter; children—Daniel Ray, Robin LuRay. AA, Mars Hill Coll., 1960; BS, N.C. State U., 1962, PhD, 1970. Owner, operator crop and livestock farm, 1962-66; grad. assist. N.C. State U., Raleigh, 1966-70; asst. prof. animal sci. Tex. Tech U., Lubbock, 1970-72, assoc. prof., 1972, prof., chmn. dept. animal sci., 1974-77; asst. dean, dir. rsch. Coll. Agrl. Scis., Tex. Tech U., 1977-79, assoc. dean, dir. rsch., 1979; sr. swine nutritionist Central Soya Co., Decatur, Ind., 1973; dir. swine feeds rsch. Cen. Soya Co., Decatur, Ind., 1974; chairperson dept. animal husbandry U. Mo.-Columbia, 1980, dir. agrl. experiment sta., dean coll. agr., 1980-83; v.p. for agrl. adminstrn., exec. dean for agr., home econs. and natural resources Ohio State U., Columbus, 1983-86; pres. Clemson (S.C.) U., 1986-94; pres., CEO Ea. Foods Inc., Atlanta, 1994—; Seaman A. Knapp lectr. Dallas, 1988; past co-chmn. Ohio Gov.'s Commn. on Agr.; past chmn. N. Cen. region Coun. of Adminstrv. Heads of Agr.; bd. dirs. First Union Corp., Clemson (S.C.), Duke Woodside Industries, Inc., Duke Power Co., Escuela Agricola de la Region Tropical Humeda, Baptist Med. Ctr. Found.; past bd. govs. Am. Royal; E.T. York Disting. lectr. Auburn U., 1991. Contbr. articles to profl. jour. Mem. S.E. regional adv. bd. Inst. Internat. Edn.; adv. com. for task force on agriculture devel. and cooperation, Internat. Devel. Agy.; co-chair policy adv. com. Competitive Rsch. Grants; bd. dirs. Farm Found., Nat. Dropout Prevention Fund Devel. Coun., Greenville Tech. Coll. Fed. Devel. Coun., Fellowship Christian Farmers Internat. State Panel, S.C. Women in Higher Edn.; mem. Dept. Def. Clothing & Textile Bd., Adv. Com. for Task Force on Agrl. Devel. and Cooperation; trustee Palmetto Partnership, Found. for Drug Abuse Prevention, adv. bd. McDonald's Initiative, So. Assn. Coll. and Schs. Com. on Intercollegiate Athletics, Internat. Assn. of Agbus; mem. Congl. Office Tech. Assessment Coun., So. Assn. Colls. and Schs., Commn. on Colls. Class of 1994, rep. S.C.'s Exec. Coun.; bd. dirs. Bapt. Med. Ctr. Found. Recipient Disting. Alumnus award Coll. Agr. and Life Scis., N.C. State U., 1989, Nat. 4-H Alumni award, 1989, Thomas Green Clemson medallion Clemson U., 1991. Mem. AAAS, Am. Soc. Animal Sci., Internat. Assn. Agribus., Coun. for Agrl. Sci. and Tech., Farm House Assn., Internat. Devel. Agy., Alpha Zeta, Phi Sigma, Phi Kappa Phi, Gamma Sigma Delta. Office: Eastern Foods Inc 1000 Naturally Fresh Blvd Atlanta GA 30349

LENNON, DONALD RAY, archivist, historian; b. Brunswick County, N.C., Oct. 6, 1938; s. George William and Eula Lee (Rowell) L.; m. Billie Mae Royall, Dec. 20, 1969; children: William Christopher, Mark Whitfield. BS, East Carolina U., 1960, MA, 1962. Cert. archivist Am. Soc. Cert. Archivists. Archivist II N.C. Divsn. Archives and History, Raleigh, 1964-67; dir. manuscript collection East Carolina U., Greenville, N.C., 1967—; coord. spl. collections East Carolina U., Greenville, 1987—; mem. state hist. records adv. bd., Raleigh, 1975-85; mem. Hist. Bath (N.C.)

Commn., 1982-88. Co-author: A Quest for Glory, 1991 (Society Cup award 1992); co-editor: The Wilmington Town Book, 1743-1778 (Clarendon Cup award 1974), Harnett, Hooper and Howe, 1979, Politics, Bar and Bench, 1980. Bd. dirs. N.C. Preservation Consortium, Durham, 1989-93. With U.S. Army, 1962-64. Mem. Soc. Am. Archivists, Hist. Soc. N.C. (pres. 1992-93), Soc. N.C. Archivists. Democrat. Baptist. Home: 201 Cherrywood Dr Greenville NC 27858-8611 Office: East Carolina U Joyner Libr Special Collections Department Greenville NC 27858

LENNON, ELIZABETH M., retired educator; b. Chgo., Apr. 29; d. John Joseph and Johanna Amelia (Pfaff) L. AB, Ind. U., 1941; postgrad., Butler U., 1946, N.C. State U., 1956, San Francisco State U., 1960; MA in Edn. of Physically Handicapped, Columbia U., 1947. Elem. tchr., typing tchr. Ind. Sch. for the Blind, 1944-51; lower sch. tchr. Perkins Sch. for the Blind, 1951-53; tchr., insvc. coord. Gov. Morehead Sch., Raleigh, N.C., 1953-54; staff devel. specialist N.C. Commn. for the Blind, 1964-67; asst. prof. blind rehab. Western Mich. State U., Kalamazoo, 1967-78, part-time asst. prof. blind rehab., 1978-81, 88. Author publs. in field. Bd. dirs. Nat. Accreditation Coun. for Agys. Serving the Blind and Visually Impaired, 1976-83; vice chair Mich. Commn. for the Blind, 1978-84; vice chair bd. dirs Shepherd's Ctr. of Greater Kalamazoo, 1989-90, chmn., 1990—; sec. Affiliated Leadership League of and for the Blind of Am., 1978-91; bd. dirs. Southcentral Mich. Commn. on Aging, 1978-91, sec., 1986-88; sec. Am. Coun. of the Blind, 1988-90; bd. dirs. Voluntary Action Ctr. of Greater Kalamazoo, 1986—; bd. dirs., mem. com., founder Kalamazoo Ctr. for Ind. Living, 1980—; pres. Coun. of Citizens with Low Vision, 1985-88. Recipient Robert D. Mahoney award for Outstanding Svc. to Visually Impaired of Mich., Mich. Assn. of Blind and Visually Impaired, 1978, Clare Lynch award Kalamazoo Coun. of the Blind, 1981, George Card award for Outstanding Svc. to Visually Imparied Nationwide, Am. Coun. of the Blind, 1983, Spl. Tribute, State of Mich., 1984, Lifetime Achievement award Kalamazoo Ctr. for Ind. Living, 1987, Outstanding Svc. to the Older Citizens of S.W. Mich., Mich. Legislature, 1990, Jim Neubacher Lifetime Achievement award Kalamazoo Ctr. for Ind. Living, 1991, Golden Bell award J.C. Penney, 1992. Mem. Assn. for Edn. and Rehab. of the Blind and Visually Impaired (mem. various coms. on state and nat. levels), Coun. for Exceptional Children, Mich. Assn. of Transcribers for the Visually Impaired (past pres., editor newletter, bd. dirs., founding mem.). Avocations: reading, music, travel. Home: 1400 N Drake Rd # 218 Kalamazoo MI 49006

LENNON, FRANK M., retail executive; b. Boston, Jan. 13, 1938; s. Michael J. and Mary A. (MacDonald) L.; m. Christina J. Barron, Jan. 19, 1970; children: Raymond, Lorraine. BA, St. Paul's Coll., 1963; MS, Ariz. U., 1982. Tchr. City of Boston, 1963-67; personnel mgr. Stop and Shop Cos., Boston, 1967-72; v.p. adminstrn. Value House, Lewiston, Maine, 1972-79; sr. v.p. adminstrn. Golub Corp., Schenectady, N.Y., 1979—; adj. prof. Russell Sage Grad. Sch. Bus., Albany, N.Y., 1985—. Trustee LaSalle Acad., Troy, N.Y., 1988—. Mem. Orgn. Devel. Network, Am. Soc. Personnel Adminstrn., Shaker Ridge Country Club, Cobleskill Golf and Country Club, Elks. Avocations: golf, boating, stock market. Home: 62 Myers Rd Howes Cave NY 12092 Office: Golub Corp 501 Duanesburg Rd Schenectady NY 12306-1014

LENNON, GERARD PATRICK, civil engineering educator, researcher; b. N.Y.C., Nov. 15, 1951; s. Eugene Francis and Monica (Burghardt) L.; m. Linda More, June 5, 1976; children: Elizabeth, Brian, Marianne. BS, Drexel U., 1975; MS, Cornell U., 1977, PhD, 1980. Rsch. assoc. Cornell U., Ithaca, N.Y., 1978-80; asst. prof. Lehigh U., Bethlehem, Pa., 1980-86, assoc. prof., 1986-95; prof., 1995—; acting dir. Environ. Studies Ctr. Lehigh U., Bethlehem, Pa., 1989-91; cons. Woodward-Clyde Cons., Plymouth Meeting, Pa., 1985—. Editor Symposium on Groundwater, 1991; contbr. articles to profl. jours. including Jour. Hydraulic Engring., Marine Geology. Consistory 1st United Ch. of Christ, Hellertown, Pa., 1988-93, budget chmn., 1990-93. Mem. ASCE (tech. com. 1983-91). Republican. Achievements include design of (with Richard Weisman) fluidization systems for coastal applications; research in boundary element method for solving groundwater flow problems. Office: Lehigh U 13 E Packer Ave Bethlehem PA 18015-3101

LENNON, JOSEPH LUKE, college official, priest; b. Providence, Sept. 21, 1919; s. John Joseph and Marjorie (McCabe) L. AB, Providence Coll., 1940; STB, Immaculate Conception Coll., 1946; MA, U. Notre Dame, 1950, PhD, 1953; LLD, Bradford Durfee Coll. Tech., 1963; LittD (hon.), U. Southeastern Mass., 1975; DHL (hon.), Roger Williams Coll., 1980. Ordained priest Roman Cath. Ch., 1947; instr. U. Notre Dame, 1948-50; mem. edn. dept. Providence Coll., 1950-51, 53-56, asst. dean men, 1953, dean of men, 1954-56, dean of coll., 1956-68, v.p. community affairs, 1968-88, ret., 1988; dir. Tchrs. Guild of Thomistic Inst., 1953-56, Pennywise Shop; bd. trustees So. New Eng. Sch. of Law, 1994—. Author: The Role of Experience in the Acquisition of Scientific Knowledge, 1952, The Dean Speaks, 1958, College is for Knowledge, 1959; rev. as 30 Ways to Get Ahead at College, 1964. Mem. adv. council Citizens Ednl. Freedom; adv. bd. Perceptional Edn. and Research Center; co-chmn. Easter Seals, 1968; arbitrator R.I. Bd. Labor; adv. com. Mental Retardation, 1; chmn. Nat. Library Week, 1962; mem. R.I. Adv. Com. Vocational Edn.; ann. lectr. Psychology and Everyday Life, WJAR-TV, 1960-75; mem. Gov. R.I. Com. to Study R.I. State Inst. at, Howard; chmn. speaker's bur. United Fund Campaign, 1971; coordinator Civil Rights Affirmative Action Program, 1970-78; mem. Com. Future Jurisprudence in, R.I; com. clergy renewal Diocese Providence; mem. Com. for CROP-Community Hunger Appeal of Ch. World Service, 1974-75; mem. subcom. on family law Gov.'s Commn. on Jurisprudence of Future; mem. membership com. Cancer Control Bd., R.I, 1977; mem. Gov.'s Commn. on Consumer's Council, 1977, Gov.'s Leadership Conf. on Citizen Participation.; bd. dirs. Blue Cross and Blue Shield, Progress for Providence, R.I. Legal Services, Fed. Hill House, Pawtucket YMCA, The Samaritans, Handgun Alert, Vols. in R.I. Schs., Meeting St. Sch., Big Sisters, Big Bros. Assn. R.I., R.I. Easter Seal, Blackstone Valley Surgicare, R.I. Heart Assn.; chmn. 1975 Heart Fund campaign; trustee R.I. chpt. Leukemia Soc. Am.; adv. bd. Parents Without Partners; bd. govs. John E. Fogarty Found., Irish Scholarship Found.; bd. dirs., trustee Big Sisters Assn., R.I.; bd. dirs. Diabetes Assn.; adv. bd. St. Joseph's Merged Hosps.; mem. corp. R.I. Hosp.; trustee Emma Pendleton Bradley Hosp., 1984—, Southern New Eng. Sch. Law, 1994—; mem. adv. council Quirk Inst.; mem. Spl. Legis. Commn. Created on Catastrophic Health Ins., 1979—, Gov.'s Screening Com. for the Judiciary, 1980-89; mem. Save the Bay, 1986-88. Recipient Seal of Approval R.I. Automobile Dealers Assn., 1978. Mem. Nat. Cath. Edn. Assn., Am. Cath. Sociol. Soc., Nat. Soc. Study Edn., Am. Philosophers Edn. Assn., New Eng. Ednl. Assn., New Eng. Guidance and Personnel Assn., Greater Providence Epilepsy Assn., Nat. Soc. Study Edn., Am. Arbitration Assn., Alpha Epsilon Delta, Delta Epsilon Sigma (pres. 1966-69).

LENNON, MICHAEL T., public relations executive. COO MWW Strategic Comm. Co., Inc., River Edge, N.J. Office: MWW Strategic Comm Co Inc 70 Grand Ave River Edge NJ 07661*

LENNOX, ANNIE, rock musician; b. Aberdeen, Scotland, Dec. 25, 1954; m. Radha Raman, Mar. 1984 (div. 1985). Student, Royal Acad. Music, London. Mem. musical group Catch, Tourists, 1977-80; founding mem. Eurythmics. Albums: (with Eurythmics) In The Garden, 1980, Sweet Dreams, 1983, Touch, 1984, 1984 (For the Love of Big Brother), 1984, Be Yourself Tonight, 1985, Revenge, 1986, Savage, 1988, We Too Are One, 1989, Greatest Hits, 1991, Eurythmics Live, 1993; (solo) Diva, 1992; actress (film) Revolution. Office: RCA Records 1133 Ave Of The Americas New York NY 10036-6710*

LENNOX, DONALD D(UANE), automotive and housing components company executive; b. Pitts., Dec. 3, 1918; s. Edward George and Sarah B. (Knight) L.; m. Jane Armstrong, June 11, 1949; children: Donald D., J. Gordon. BS with honors, U. Pitts., 1947. CPA, Pa. With Ford Motor Co., 1950-69, Xerox Corp., 1969-80; corp. v.p. and sr. v.p. info. tech. group Xerox Corp., Rochester, N.Y., 1969-73, group v.p. and pres. info. tech. group, 1973-75, group v.p., pres. info. systems group, 1975-80; sr. v.p., sr. staff officer Xerox Internat. Corp., Stamford, Conn., 1973-74; sr. v.p., ops. staff Navistar Internat. Corp., Chgo., 1980-81, exec. v.p., 1981-82, pres., chief operating officer, 1982, chmn., chief exec. officer, 1983-87, also bd. dirs.; chmn., chief exec. officer Schlegel Corp., Rochester, N.Y., 1987-89; chmn. Internat. Imaging Materials, Inc., Amherst, N.Y., 1990—; also bd. dirs.

Internat. Imaging Materials, Inc., Amherst; bd. dirs. Prudential-Securities Mut. Funds, Gleason Corp. Served with AC USN, 1942-45. Decorated D.F.C. with 2 gold stars, Air medal with 4 gold stars. Mem. Rochester Area C. of C. (pres. 1979), Soc. Automotive Engrs., Country Club of Rochester, Genesee Valley Econ. Club, Chgo. Club, Order of Artus, Beta Gamma Sigma. Republican. *What modest success I have enjoyed is the result of hard work and dedication to the success of the organization public or private. Rarely is one's contribution to the success of the organization not recognized or rewarded.*

LENO, JAY (JAMES DOUGLAS MUIR LENO), comedian, writer; b. New Rochelle, N.Y., Apr. 28, 1950; s. Angelo and Cathryn Leno; m. Mavis Nicholson, 1980. Grad., Emerson Coll., 1973. Worked as Rolls-Royce auto mechanic and deliveryman. Stand-up comedian playing Carnegie Hall, Caesar's Palace, others; numerous appearances on Late Night with David Letterman; exclusive guest host The Tonight Show, NBC-TV, 1987-92, host, 1992—; host, prodr. Showtime Spl. Jay Leno and the American Dream, 1986, Saturday Night Live, 1986, Jay Leno's Family Comedy Hour (Writers Guild Am. nomination), 1987, Our Planet Tonight; film appearances include: The Silver Bears, Fun with Dick and Jane, 1977, American Hot Wax, 1978, Americathon, 1979, Collision Course, 1988, Dave, 1993. Avocations: antique motorcycles and automobiles. Office: PO Box 7885 Burbank CA 91510-7885

LENON, RICHARD ALLEN, chemical corporation executive; b. Lansing, Mich., Aug. 4, 1920; s. Theo and Elizabeth (Amon) L.; m. Helen Johnson, Sept. 13, 1941; children: Richard Allen, Pamela A., Lisa A. BA, Western Mich. Coll., 1941; postgrad., Northwestern U., 1941-42. Mgr. fin. div. Montgomery Ward & Co., Chgo., 1947-56; v.p. fin. Westinghouse Air Brake Co., 1963-67, treas., 1965-67; v.p., treas. Internat. Minerals & Chem. Corp., Skokie, Ill., 1956-63; group v.p. fin. and adminstrn. Internat. Minerals & Chem. Corp., 1967-68, exec. v.p., 1968-70, pres., 1970-78, chmn., 1977-86, chmn. exec. com., 1986-88; chmn. exec. com. IMC Global Inc., 1989—; bd. dirs. IMC Global Inc. Lt. comdr. USNR, 1942-47. Clubs: University (Chgo.); Glen View (Ill.). Home: 803 Solar Ln Glenview IL 60025-4464 Office: IMC Global Inc 2100 Sanders Rd Northbrook IL 60062-6139

LENOX, CHARLES N(EWTON), JR., newspaper editor; b. Tulsa, Aug. 16, 1938; s. Charles Newton and Helen Louise (Fortner) L.; m. Barbara Dever, Aug. 22, 1959 (div.); children: Jeff, Chris, Greg, Keith; m. Mary Kathleen Thibodeaux, Nov. 7, 1977 (div. 1989); stepchildren: Lynn, Susan, Julie; m. Chilah L. Nichols, Jan. 24, 1990; 1 adopted child, Trevor J. BS in Journalism, La. State U., 1961. Sports writer Lake Charles (La.) Am. Press, 1961-62; sports editor Lafayette (La.) Daily Advertiser, 1962-68, city editor, 1968-72, mng. editor, 1972-86, editor, 1986—. Bd. dirs. Lafayette chpt. ARC, 1983-86; bd. dirs. Lafayette Salvation Army, 1985-87. Mem. Lafayette C. of C. (v.p.), Lafayette Pvt. Industry Council (vice chmn. 1986), Vermilionville Hist. Found. (pres. 1995). Democrat. Roman Catholic. Home: 9 Audubon Oaks Blvd Lafayette LA 70506-2447 Office: Lafayette Daily Advertiser 221 Jefferson St Lafayette LA 70501-7061

LENOX, MARY FRANCES, academic dean; b. Chgo., July 19, 1944; d. Eleazar and Truesillia (Bryson) L. BS, Chgo. State U., 1966; MA, Rosary Coll., 1968; EdD, U. Mass., 1975; postdoctoral Inst. Ednl. Mgmt. Harvard U., 1990. Tchr., librarian Chgo. pub. schs., 1967-71; asst. reference librarian Ctr. for Inner City Studies, Northeastern Ill. U., Chgo., 1971-72; dir. ednl. materials ctr. Chgo. State U., 1971-72; mgr. circulation dept. learning resource ctr., faculty mem. Governors State U., Park Forest South, Ill., 1973-75; media specialist Chgo. Pub. Schs., 1975-78; mem. faculty Nat. Coll. Edn. Urban Campus, Chgo., 1977-78; assoc. prof. Sch. Library and Info. Sci., U. Mo.-Columbia, 1978-84, dean, 1984—; vis. prof. U. Denver, 1979, Stephens Coll., Columbia, 1980, 81; faculty-in-residence Chgo. Pub. Library, 1981; cons., evaluator Commn. on Instns. Higher Edn., N. Cen. Assn. Colls. & Schs., 1987—; evaluator Mo. Com. for Humanities, 1985—; project dir. Title II B HEA; libr. career tng. program sch. of libr. and info. sci. U. Mo., 1982-87, 90-91; cons., speaker in field. Contbr. articles to profl. jours. Bd. dirs. Halfway House Com., Inc., Chgo., 1977, New Wave Corp., Columbia, 1981-85; mem. bd. cons. The High-Low Report, N.Y.C., 1979-83; producer, moderator Black Women: African Past to Columbia Present Sta. KOPN-FM, Columbia, 1979; mem. editorial bd. Jour. of Youth Services. Named Outstanding Educator, Dist. II Chgo. Pub. Schs., 1977; Kellogg Nat. fellow, 1982-85. Mem. ALA (Grolier awards com. 1982), Am. Assn. Sch. Librarians (sch. media program of yr. awards com. 1979-80), Mo. Library Assn. (chmn. library educators 1978-82, outreach roundtable 1980-81), AAUW, Assn. Study Afro-Am. Life and History, Assn. Library and Info. Sci. Educators (chmn. Council of Deans and Dirs. 1987-88), Pi Lambda Theta, Delta Kappa Gamma, Kappa Delta Pi. Avocations: hiking, photography, floral designs, rock collecting, travel, environmental preservation. Office: U Missouri-Columbia Sch Libr & Info Sci 104 E Stewart Rd Columbia MO 65211-0001

LENSCHOW, WILLIAM, food products executive. Chmn., bd. dirs. Associated Milk Prodrs., San Antonio, Tex. Office: Associated Milk Producers Inc PO Box 790287 San Antonio TX 78279

LENSE, MARCIA, television anchor, producer, reporter; b. Evergreen Park, Ill., Mar. 12, 1960; d. Robert Fred and Beverly Jean (Mahoney) L.; m. Keith Vincent Judickas, Oct. 17, 1987; 1 child, Lauren Paige Judickas. BA, Western Ill. U., 1982. Reporter Sta. KCRG-AM, Cedar Rapids, Iowa, 1982-84, reporter, morning anchor, 1984-87; reporter Sta. WQAD-TV, Moline, Ill., 1987; anchor, prodr. Sta. KWQC-TV, Davenport, Iowa, 1988—. Prodr.: (documentaries) Bridge to Employment, 1993 (Soc. of Profl. Journalists award, 1994), It Takes a Village to Raise a Child, 1994 (AP award, 1995), Tornadoes-Fear and Fascination, 1994 (AP award 1994); co-prodr.: Road to Recovery-Flood of '93, 1993 (AP award 1994). Recipient Best Spot News Reporting award Women in Comm., 1986, Best Investigative News Reporting award AP, 1989, Sigma Delta Chi Pub. Svc. award Soc. Profl. Journalists, 1994, First Place farm reporting AP, 1995. Mem. Western Ill. U. Quad Cities Alumni Club (pres. 1993—). Lutheran. Avocations: boating, skiing, camping, cooking. Office: Sta KWQC-TV 805 Brady St Davenport IA 52803-5211

LENSING, LEO A., foreign language and humanities educator; b. Lake Providence, La., Sept. 28, 1948; s. Leo Alois and Elizabeth (Bauer) L.; m. Carolyn Jackson Sharp, June 10, 1989; 1 child, Dinah Rose. BA, U. Notre Dame, 1970; MA, Cornell U., 1974, PhD, 1976. Lectr. in German Wesleyan U., Middletown, Conn., 1974-76, asst. prof. German, 1976-81, assoc. prof. German and film studies, 1981-87, prof. German and film studies, 1987—; acting dean arts and humanities, 1992, dean arts and humanities, 1993—. Author: Narrative Structure and the Reader in William Raabe's Im Alten Eisen, 1977, (with Andrew Barker) Peter Altenberg, 1995; editor: (with H. W. Peter) Wilhelm Raabe: Studien zu seinem Leben und Werk, 1981, (with Michael Töteberg) R.W. Fassbinder, The Anarchy of the Imagination, 1992; mem. editorial adv. bd. Austrian Studies, U. Edinburgh, Scotland, 1990—; contbr. articles to profl. jours. Rsch. grantee German Acad. Exch. Svc., 1977, 83, 90, Am. Philos Soc., 1982; Coll. Tchr. fellow NEH, 1987-88; Eleanor M. Garvey fellow Houghton Libr., Harvard U., 1991-92. Mem. MLA, Am. Assn. Tchrs. German, North Am. Heine Soc., German Studies Assn., Sigmund Freud Soc. (Vienna), Internat. Arthur Schnitzler Rsch. Assn. Home: 2 Maple Shade Rd Middletown CT 06457 Office: Wesleyan U Dept German Middletown CT 06459-0400

LENT, JAMES A., analytical equipment company executive. Ceo Boehringer Mannheim Corp, Indpls., 1993—. Office: Boehringer Mannheim Corp 9115 Hague Rd Indianapolis IN 46256-1045

LENT, JOHN ANTHONY, journalist, educator; b. East Millsboro, Pa., Sept. 8, 1936; s. John and Rose (Marano) L.; remarried Rose Kueny, 1988; children: Laura, Andrea, John, Lisa, Shahnon. B.S., Ohio U., 1958, M.S., 1960; Ph.D., U. Iowa, 1972; cert., Press Inst. of India, Sophia U., Tokyo, Japan, U. Oslo, Guadalajara, Mex., Summer Sch. Dir. public relations, instr. English W.va. Tech., Montgomery, 1960-62; Newhouse research asst. and asst. to dir. communications research Syracuse (N.Y.) U., 1962-64; lectr. De La Salle Coll., Manila, 1964-65; asst. prof. W.Va. Tech., 1965-66; asst. prof. journalism U. Wis., Eau Claire, 1966-67; asst. prof. journalism and head tchrs.' journalism sequence Marshall U., Huntington, W.Va., 1967-69; vis. assoc. prof. U. Wyo., Laramie, 1969-70; asst. editor Internat. Comm. Bull., Iowa

City, 1970-72; coord. mass comm. U. Sains Malaysia, Penang, 1972-74; assoc. prof. comm. Temple U., Phila., 1974-76, profl., 1976—, Benedum vis. disting. prof., 1987. Author: Asian Newspapers Reluctant Revolution, 1971, Asian Mass Communications: A Comprehensive Bibliography, 1975, 78; Third World Mass Media and Their Search for Modernity, 1977, Broadcasting in Asia and Pacific, 1978, Topics in Third World Mass Media, 1979, Caribbean Mass Communications: A Comprehensive Bibliography, 1981, Asian Newspapers: Contemporary Trends and Problems, 1982, Videocassettes in the Third World, 1989, Asian Film Industry, 1990, Caribbean Popular Culture, 1990, Caribbean Mass Communications, 1990, Transnational Communications, 1991, Women and Mass Communications: An International Annotated Bibliography, 1991, Bibliographic Guide to Caribbean Mass Communication, 1992, Bibliography of Cuban Mass Communications, 1992, Cartoonometer, 1994, Animation, Caricature, and Gay and Political Cartoons in the U.S. and Canada: An International Bibliography, 1994, Comic Art of Europe: An International, Comprehensive Bibliography, 1994, Comic Books and Comic Strips in the United States: An International Bibliography, 1994, Comic Art of Africa, Asia, Australia, on Latin America: An International Bibliography, 1995, Asian Popular Culture, 1995, others; founding editor Berita, 1975—; founding mng. editor WittyWorld, 1987—; Editor: Westview Press Internat. Communication series, 1992—, Asian Cinema, 1994—. Awarded Chapel of Four Chaplains' Legion of Honor; Anchor Hocking scholar, 1954-58, U. Oslo scholar, 1962, Fulbright scholar Philippines, 1964-65; recipient Benedum award, 1968, Broadcast Preceptor awards (2), 1979, Paul Eberman Outstanding Rsch. award, 1988, Ray and Pat Browne Nat. Book award, 1988. Mem. Malaysia/Singapore/Brunei Studies Group (founding chmn. 1975-82), L.Am. Studies Assn., Caribbean Studies Assn., Asian Studies, Internat. Assn. Mass. Comm. Rsch. (visual and comic art organizer, chair), Asian Cinema Studies Soc. (chmn. 1994—), Sigma Delta Chi, Sigma Tau Delta, Kappa Tau Alpha, Phi Alpha Theta. Home: 669 Ferne Blvd Drexel Hill PA 19026-3110 Office: Temple U Philadelphia PA 19122 *I have cherished the principles of hard work over long hours, accuracy, comprehensiveness, and honesty in my intellectual and scholarly endeavors. I have considered it important to set and meet goals, to share my work with others, to remain untainted by organizations or individuals who, I feel, are not working for the good of mankind. I also cherish, and protect and use, my right to speak out on those issues which I feel are offensive to the public; the result has been that my writings have incurred the wrath of government ministers in at least two countries.*

LENT, NORMAN FREDERICK, JR., former congressman; b. Oceanside, N.Y., Mar. 23, 1931; s. Norman Frederick and Ellen (Bain) L.; m. Barbara Ann Morris, Aug. 4, 1979; children from previous marriage: Norman Frederick 3d, Barbara Anne, Thomas Benjamin. BA, Hofstra U., 1952; LLB, Cornell U., 1957; LLD (hon.), Kyung Hee U., Seoul, Republic of Korea, 1975, Molloy Coll., 1985, Hofstra Coll., 1988. Bar: N.Y. 1957, Fla. 1976. Assoc. police judge East Rockaway, N.Y., 1958-60; confidential law sec. to N.Y. State Supreme Ct., 1960-62; mem. N.Y. State Senate, 1963-70, chmn. joint legislative com. public health, 1966-70; mem. 92nd Congress 5th Dist. N.Y., 1971-73; mem. 93rd-102d Congresses 4th Dist. N.Y., 1973-93; vice chmn. Energy and Commerce com. 100th-102nd Congresses U.S. Ho. Reps., 1986-93, vice chmn. Mcht. Marine subcom., 1987-93; cons. Lent & Scrivner, Washington, 1993—; Rep. exec. leader, East Rockaway, N.Y., 1968-70. Mem. bd. visitors U.S. Mcht. Marine Acad., Kings Point, N.Y. With USNR, 1952-54. Recipient George Estabrook Disting. Service award Hofstra U., 1967, Israeli Prime Minister's medal, 1977, Disting. Achievement medal N.Y.C. Holland Soc., 1987, Tree of Life award Jewish Nat. Fund., 1987, Anatoly Sharansky Freedom award L.I. Com. for Soviet Jewry, 1983. Mem. ABA, Nassau County Bar Assn., Fla. Bar Assn. Office: Lent & Scrivner 555 13th St NW Ste 305 E Washington DC 20004-1109

LENTHALL, FRANKLYN, theatre historian; b. Nanticoke, Pa., July 14, 1919; s. Samuel Franklyn and Lena (Fraunfelter) L. Student, Cornell U., 1942-44, Am. Acad. Dramatic Arts, 1946. Curator Boothbay Theatre Mus.; Mem. faculty Am. Acad. Dramatic Arts, 1949-54, Am. Theatre Wing, 1958-59; acting curator, cons. theatre Mus. of City of N.Y., 1983-86; regional auditioner Am. Acad. Dramtic Arts, N.Y.C. and Pasadena, Calif., 1995—; Former mem. exec. bd. Theatre Library Assn., Lincoln Center, N.Y.C., 1966-70; mem. Maine Commn. on Arts and Humanities, 1966-73; theatre cons., 1968-69, lectr. on theatre, theatre historian. Appeared in profl. theatre, 1937-51; featured in: movies, including Naked City; producer, dir. with movies, including, Lenthall Players, 1951-58, producer, owner, dir. Boothbay (Maine) Playhouse and Theatre Mus., 1957-74; dir.: off-Broadway prodn. Hello and Goodby (Athol Fugard), N.Y.C., 1977, Oblomova, 1984. Contbr. articles on theatre to various pubs; contbg. author: Autographs and Manuscripts: A Collector's Manuel, 1978, Theatre and Performing Arts Collection, Playbill Mag., 1981; curator exhbns. The Old Met: A Memory of Opera On Broadway, N.Y.C. Operas First Forty Years. Served with CIC AUS, 1942-44. Recipient Disting. Service award in recognition of dedicated service to theatre Wyo. Sem., 1979. Mem. Drama League N.Y. (adv. bd. 1959—, bd. dirs. 1983-88), Lincoln County Cultural and Hist. Assn. (trustee 1973-77), Polish Theatre Inst. (bd. dirs. 1984-88), Boothbay C. of C. (dir. 1963-70). Methodist (lay Preacher). Home and Office: 3-A Signal Point Village Sea St Boothbay Harbor ME 04538 *Only in recent years have I learned to really appreciate and understand William Blake's lines from his poem ETERNITY: "He who binds to himself a joy Does the winged life destroy; But he who kisses the joy as it flies Lives in eternity's sunrise." Every day of my life I am more fully aware of the importance of the ARTS AND THE HUMANITIES in the lives of all of us. .in the life of this great country. For too long they have been neglected. I am in complete agreement with Tolstoy who wrote "When someone sees or feels something, and expresses it in such a form that he who listens, reads, or sees his work feels, sees, and hears the same thing in the same way as the artist, that is art.".*

LENTINI, JAMES SALVATORE, school librarian, fraternity executive; b. N.Y.C., Dec. 19, 1961; s. Pasquale J. and Gloria D. (Carniglia) L. BA in Social Studies, St. Francis Coll., Bklyn., 1984. Asst. archivist James Kelly Hist. Studies Inst., Bklyn., 1981-84; prodn. asst. Courier Life Publs., Bklyn., 1984; rsch. clk. libr. div. Morgan Stanley and Co., N.Y.C., 1984-85; tchr. Pub. Sch. 167, Bklyn., 1985-92; substitute tchr. Capital Sch. Dist., Dover, Del., 1992-94; libr. Holy Cross Sch., Dover, 1994—. Mem. Rep. Nat. Com. 1986—, Mem. Frat. Execs. Assn., Christian Coalition, Alpha Phi Delta (regional dist. gov. Bklyn. 1986-92, expansion chmn. 1988-92, exec. v.p. 1991-92, exec. sec. Dover 1992—, editor, main author Ecce Signum: Alpha Phi Delta Handbook 1991—). Roman Catholic. Avocations: computers, political and history books, movies, comics of 1930s, 40s and 50s. Home: 56 Greenway Sq Apt L-12 Dover DE 19904

LENTS, DON GLAUDE, lawyer; b. Kansas City, Mo., Nov. 4, 1949; s. Donald Victor and Helen Maxine (Draper) L.; m. Peggy Lynn Iglauer, Aug. 27, 1972; children: Stacie Lee, Kelsey Lynn. BA magna cum laude, Harvard U., 1971, JD magna cum laude, 1974. Bar: Mo. 1974, U.S. Dist. Ct. (ea. dist.) Mo. 1975, U.S. Ct. Appeals (8th cir.) 1975. Jr. ptnr. Bryan Cave, St. Louis, 1974-81, ptnr., 1982, 84—; ptnr. Bryan Cave, London, 1982-84; mgr. internat. dept. Bryan Cave, St. Louis, 1984-88, mgr. corp. and bus. dept., mem. exec. com., 1988—; instr. law Washington U., 1979-80. Co-author: Missouri Corporate Law and Practice, 1989, 91 and ann. supplements. Bd. dirs. Leadership St. Louis, Inc., 1978-81, 86-91, pres., 1989-91; bd. dirs. Coro Found., St. Louis, 1986-91, gen. counsel, sec., 1988-90; bd. dirs., vol. St. Louis Lawyers and Accts. for Arts, 1988-93, v.p., 1990-92, pres. 1991-92; bd. dirs. Brit. Am. Project, 1989-94, pres., 1993-94; bd. dirs. Confluence St. Louis, 1995—. Sheldon fellow Harvard U., 1974-75. Mem. ABA, Mo. Bar Assn. (coun. corp. and bus. law sect. 1987-93, vice chmn. 1988-92), Met. St. Louis Bar Assn. (sec. bus. law sect. 1980-81), Harvard Alumni Assn. (regional dir. 1993—), Hasty Pudding Club, Harvard Club (exec. com. St. Louis Club 1978-82, v.p. 1987-92, pres. 1992-93). Office: Bryan Cave 1 Metropolitan Sq 211 S Broadway Saint Louis MO 63102-2750

LENTZ, THOMAS LAWRENCE, biomedical educator, dean, researcher; b. Toledo, Mar. 25, 1939; s. Lawrence Raymond and Kathryn (Heath) L.; m. Judith Ellen Pernaa, June 17, 1961; children: Stephen, Christopher, Sarah. Student, Cornell U., 1957-60; MD, Yale U., 1964. Instr. in anatomy Yale U. Sch. Medicine, New Haven, 1964-66, asst. prof. of anatomy, 1966-69, assoc. prof. of cytology, 1969-74, assoc. prof. of cell biology, 1974-85, prof. of cell biology, 1985—, asst. dean for admissions, 1976—, vice chmn. cell biology, 1992—, chmn., 1980-86; mem. cellular and molecular neurobiology panel NSF, 1987-88, mem. cellular neurosci. panel, 1988-90. Author:

The Cell Biology of Hydra, 1966, Primitive Nervous Systems, 1968, Cell Fine Structure, 1971; contbr. over 90 articles to sci. publs. Chmn. Planning & Zoning Commn., Killingworth, Conn., 1979—; vice chmn. Killingworth Hist. Soc. Grantee NSF, 1968-92, Dept. Army, 1986, NIH, 1987—; fellow Trumbull Coll., Yale U.; recipient svc. award Conn. Fedn. Planning & Zoning Agys., 1995. Mem. AAAS, Am. Soc. Cell Biology, Soc. for Neurosci., N.Y. Acad. Scis., Appalachian Mtn. Club (trails com.). Killingworth Lions Club (citizen of yr. 1993), Alpha Omega Alpha. Republican. Mem. United Ch. of Christ. Achievements include study of primitive nervous systems, identification of neurotoxin binding site on the acetylcholine receptor, identification of cellular receptor for rabies virus. Office: U Sch Medicine Dept Cell Biol 333 Cedar St PO Box 208002 New Haven CT 06520-8002

LENZ, EDWARD ARNOLD, trade association executive, lawyer; b. White Plains, N.Y., Sept. 28, 1942; s. Frederick and Hildegarde (Bunzel) L.; m. Anna Maria Bartusiak, Mar. 21, 1987; children: Scott, Eric. BA, Bucknell U., 1964; JD, Boston Coll., 1967; LLM, NYU, 1968. Bar: N.Y. 1968, D.C. 1973, Mich. 1982. Trial atty. U.S. Dept. Justice, Washington, 1970-72; assoc. gen. counsel U.S. Cost of Living Coun., Washington, 1973; assoc. Miller & Chevalier, Washington, 1973-80; counsel Health Ins. Assn. Am., Washington, 1980-82; v.p., asst. gen. counsel Kelly Svcs. Inc., Troy, Mich., 1982-89; chmn. legis. com. Nat. Assn. Temp. & Staffing Svcs., Alexandria, Va., 1985-89; sr. v.p., gen. counsel Nat. Assn. Temp. Svcs., Alexandria, Va., 1989-93, sr. v.p. legal and govt. affairs, 1993—. Author: Co-employment—Employer Liability Issues in Staffing Services Arrangements, 1994. Capt. U.S. Army, 1968-70, Vietnam. Decorated Bronze Star. Mem. ABA, N.Y. Bar Assn., D.C. Bar Assn., Am. Corp. Counsel Assn., Pi Sigma Alpha, Sigma Alpha Epsilon. Home: 818 S Lee St Alexandria VA 22314-4334 Office: Nat Assn Temp & Staffing Svcs 119 S St Asaph St Alexandria VA 22314-3119

LENZ, HENRY PAUL, management consultant; b. N.Y.C., Nov. 24, 1925; s. Ernest and Margaret (Schick) L.; m. Norma M. Kull, Jan. 25, 1958; children: Susan, Scott, Theresa. A.B., U. N.C., 1946; M.B.A., Coll. Ins. 1974. Underwriter U.S. Casualty Co., N.Y.C., 1948-55; underwriting mgr. Mass. Bonding & Ins. Co., N.Y.C., 1955-60; with Home Ins. Co., N.Y.C., 1960-85; sr. v.p. Home Ins. Co., 1972-75, exec. v.p., dir., 1975-85; chmn. bd. Lenz Enterprises Ltd., Chatham, NJ, 1985—; former pres., dir. Home Indemnity Co.; pres., dir. Home Ins. Co. Ind., Home Ins Co. Ill., City Ins. Co., Home Group Risk Mgmt.; chmn. bd. Home Reins. Co., Scott Wetzel Services Inc.; chmn., pres. Cityvest Reins. Ltd., City Ins. Co. (U.K.) Ltd.; trustee Am. Inst. Property and Liability Underwriters, Ins. Inst. Am. Served with USNR, 1944-47, 52-53. Decorated Army Commendation medal. Mem. Soc. CPCU's, Phi Beta Kappa, Sigma Nu. Office: Lenz Enterprises Ltd 42 Edgehill Ave Chatham NJ 07928-1937

LENZ, RANDOLPH W., manufacturing company executive; b. 1947. BA, U. Wis. Pres. Ranmar Enterprises Inc., Milw., 1968-73, Network Investment Real Estate Corp., Brookfield, Wis., 1973-80; chmn. FWD Corp., Clintonville, Wis., 1981—; pres. Corsta Corp., Westport, Ct., 1981—, KCS Industry Inc., Westport, Ct., 1983—; chmn. Northwest Engring. Co., Green Bay, Wis., 1983-88; chmn. bd., pres., CEO Terex Corp., Green Bay, 1988—. With USMC, 1963-65. Office: Fruehauf Trailer Corporation 450 E 9 Mile Rd Ferndale MI 48220-1774*

LENZ, ROBERT WILLIAM, polymer chemistry educator; b. N.Y.C., Apr. 28, 1926; s. Henry B. and Olga A. (Grote) L.; m. Madeleine Leblanc, June 6, 1953; children: Kathleen, Douglas, Cynthia, Suzanne. BSChemE, Lehigh U., 1949; PhD, SUNY, Syracuse, 1956. Rsch. chemist Chicopee Mfg. Co., Chicopee Falls, Mass., 1951-53; rsch. chemist Dow Chem. Co., Midland, Mich., 1955-61, Framingham, Mass., 1961-63; asst. dir. FRL Inc., Dedham, Mass., 1963-66; prof. U. Mass., Amherst, 1966—; cons. many cos. in the chem. industry, 1966—; dist. faculty lectr. U. Mass., 1994. Author: Organic Chemistry of Synthetic High Polymers, 1967; assoc. editor Macromolecules, 1982-94, editor-in-chief, 1995—; contbr. over 375 articles to publs. Mem. adv. bd. Petroleum Rsch. Fund, 1989-93, Greve Found., 1985-94; bd. dirs. Cult Awareness Network, Chgo., 1989-91. Recipient Sr. Humboldt Prize, Humboldt Found., Bonn, Fed. Republic of Germany, 1979, Polymer Chemistry award Am. Chem. Soc., 1992; faculty fellow U. Mass., 1984. Achievements include 16 patents in field. Home: 43 Aubinwood Rd Amherst MA 01002-1623 Office: U Mass Polymer Sci Engring Dept Amherst MA 01003

LENZI, MARK, Olympic athlete, springboard diver. Olympic springboard diver Barcelona, Spain, 1992; nat. spokesperson Learn To Fly program Nat. Air Transp. Assn. Recipient Gold medal springboard diving Olympics, Barcelona, 1992, 17 internat. titles, 7 nat. titles, 2 World Cups. Achievements include first person to score over 100 points on a single dive; first American to complete a forward 4 1/2 somersault in national competition. Office: c/o US Olympic Com 1750 E Boulder St Colorado Springs CO 80909

LENZIE, CHARLES ALBERT, utility company executive; b. South Wilmington, Ill., Sept. 5, 1937; s. Charles and Dorothy Rosita (Fritz) L.; children: Ann Marie, Michael Charles, Jody Ann. Student Ill. State Normal U., 1955-58; BS in Acctg., U. Ill., 1960. CPA, Ill. Audit Mgr Arthur Andersen & Co., Chgo., 1960-70, U.S.A., 1970-74; v.p. fin. Nev. Power Co., Las Vegas, 1974-78, sr. v.p., 1978-83, pres., 1983-89, chmn. bd., chief exec. officer, 1989—, also bd. dirs. Bd. dirs. Las Vegas YMCA, Nev. Taxpayers' Assn., Nev. Devel. Authority. Mem. Rotary. Cpl. U.S. Army, 1961-63. Office: Nevada Power Co 6226 W Sahara Ave Las Vegas NV 89151-0002

LEO, JACQUELINE M., publishing company executive. Feature writer Singapore Herald, AP; sr. editor Modern Bride; co-founder Child, N.Y.C., 1986, editor-in-chief, 1987-88; editor-in-chief Family Circle, N.Y.C., 1988-94; editl. dir. women's mags. group N.Y. Times Co., N.Y.C., 1994, dir. mag. and media devel., 1994—. Author: New Woman's Guide To Getting Married; mem. editl. bd. The Scis., NAS. Bd. dirs. Nat. Com. To Prevent Child Abuse, Women's Commn. for Refugee Women and Children, Child Care Action Campaign; mem. environ. adv. com. Wal-Mart. Recipient Matrix award Women in Comm., 1993. Mem. Am. Soc. Mag. Editors (bd. dirs.), Overseas Press Club (bd. dirs.). Office: NY Times Co 1120 6th Ave New York NY 10036

LEO, KAREN ANN, library administrator; b. Akron, Ohio, June 5, 1945; d. Ellsworth John and Flonnie Ada (Dykes) Hunter; m. Louis J. Leo, May 23, 1970. BA, Baldwin-Wallace Coll., 1967; AM in Libr. Sci., U. Mich., 1968. Fiction libr. Cleve. Pub. Libr., 1968-69; ref. libr. San Jose State Coll., Calif., 1969-70; head ref. libr., asst. to county libr. Stanislaus County Free Libr., Modesto, Calif., 1970-77; asst. city libr. Pomona Pub. Libr., Calif., 1977-81; head cen. libr. Riverside City & County Pub. Libr., Calif., 1981-85; libr. dir Orange (Calif.) Pub. Libr., 1985-92, libr. dir. Corona Pub. Libr., Calif., 1992—. Community adviser Jr. League of Riverside, 1984-85. Mem. community video adv. bd., Orange, 1985-92. Mem. ALA (membership com.), AAUW, Calif. Libr. Assn. (community rels. com., Calif. Inst. Librs.), Pub. Libr. Execs. So. Calif. Democrat. Methodist. Office: Corona Public Libr 650 S Main St Corona CA 91720-0090

LEO, MALCOLM, producer, director, writer; b. N.Y.C., Oct. 9, 1944; s. Mack Leo and Gladys (Kaufman). BA, U. Calif., Santa Barbara, 1966. Ind. writer, producer, dir. Los Angeles, 1978-94; co-owner Solt/Leo Inc, Los Angeles, 1978-94; owner Malcolm Leo Prodns., Los Angeles, 1984—. Producer, dir., writer (TV spl.) Heroes of Rock & Roll, 1979; producer, dir. (TV spl.) Rolling Stone: 20 Years of Rock & Roll, 1987; exec. producer, dir. (cable spl.) Will Rogers: Look Back in Laughter, 1987 (Writers Guild award); producer, dir., writer (feature film) This Is Elvis, 1981; producer (TV spl.) Cole Porter-Red, Hot & Blue, 1990; producer, dir. (home video) Crosby, Stills & Nash: Long Time Comin', 1990; producer, dir. (feature film) The Beach Boys: An American Band, 1985; producer, dir. Happy Days Reunion, 1990, 92; Best of Hollywood Palace I, II, 1991-93; Bradymania-Very Brady Special, 1993; Rock'n Roll Fantasy Camp, 1994, Laverne & Shirley Reunion, 1995. Mem. Acad. Motion Picture Arts and Scis., Dirs. Guild Am., Writers Guild Am. Avocations: modern art, surfing, music, British literature. Office: 6536 Sunset Blvd Los Angeles CA 90028-7202

LEO, PETER ANDREW, newspaper columnist; b. Teaneck, N.J., Aug. 3, 1943; s. Maurice Matthew and Mary (Trincellita) L.; m. Sylvia Weed, July 26, 1970; children: Jane. A.B., U. Toronto, 1966; M.A., NYU, 1967. High sch. tchr. Peace Corps, Nairobi, Kenya, 1968-69; reporter AP, N.Y.C., 1970, Greensboro Record (N.C.), 1971-72, Wilmington News-Jour. (Del.), 1973-78; reporter, asst. city editor, columnist Pitts. Post-Gazette, 1978—. Recipient Headliners award Atlantic City Press Club, 1972, Golden Quill award Pitts. Press Club, 1980, Keystone award Pa. Newspaper Pubs. and Editors Assn., 1984. Home: 5266 Beelermont Pl Pittsburgh PA 15217-1010 Office: PG Pub Co 34 Blvd Of The Allies Pittsburgh PA 15222

LEOGRANDE, WILLIAM MARK, political science educator, writer; b. Utica, N.Y., July 1, 1949; s. John James and Patricia Ann (Ryan) LeoG; m. Martha J. Langelan. AB, Syracuse U., 1971, MA, 1973, PhD, 1976. Asst. prof. Hamilton Coll., Clinton, N.Y., 1976-78; dir. polit. sci. Am. U., Washington, 1980-82, asst. prof. polit. sci., 1978-83, assoc. prof., 1984-89, prof., 1989—; mem. profl. staff U.S. Senate, 1982-83, cons., 1984-85. Author: Cuba's Policy in Africa, 1980; editor: (with Morris Blachman) Confronting Revolution: Security Through Diplomacy in Central America, 1986, (with Louis Goodman) Political Parties and Democracy in Central America; dir. Latin Am. Research Rev., 1982-86, World Policy Jour., 1983—. Dir. svc. com. Unitarian-Universalist Ch., Boston, 1983-86; mem. staff John Anderson Presdl. Campaign, 1980, Michael Dukakis Presdl. Campaign, 1988. Council Fgn. Relation Internat. Affairs fellow, 1982-83. Mem. Coun. Fgn. Rels., Am. Polit. Sci. Assn., Latin Am. Studies Assn. (exec. council 1984-87). Democrat. Home: 7215 Chestnut St Bethesda MD 20815-4051 Office: Am U Sch Pub Affairs Ward Circle Washington DC 20016

LEON, ARTHUR SOL, research cardiologist, exercise physiologist; b. Bklyn., Apr. 26, 1931; s. Alex and Anne (Schrek) L.; m. Gloria Rakita, Dec. 23, 1956; children: Denise, Harmon, Michelle. BS in Chemistry with high honors, U. Fla., 1952; MS in Biochemistry, U. Wis., 1954, MD, 1957. Intern Henry Ford Hosp., Detroit, 1957-58; fellow in internal medicine Lahey Clinic, Boston, 1958-60; fellow in cardiology Jackson Meml. Hosp.-U. Miami (Fla.) Med. Sch., 1960-61; dir. clin. pharmacology research unit Hoffmann-La Roche Inc.-Newark Beth Israel Med. Ctr., 1969-73; from instr. to assoc. prof. medicine Coll. Medicine and Dentistry N.J., Newark, 1967-73; from assoc. prof. to prof. div. epidemiology U. Minn., Mpls., 1973—, H.L. Taylor prof. exercise sci. and health enhancement, dir. lab. physiol. hygiene and exercise sci., div. kinesiology, Coll. Edn., 1991—; dir. applied physiology and nutrition, 1973-91; mem. med. eval. team Gemini and Apollo projects NASA, 1964-67. Assoc. editor Surgeon Gen.'s Report on Health Benefits of Exercise, 1994-96; contbr. numerous articles to profl. publs. Trustee Vinland Nat. Sports Health Ctr. for Disabled, 1978—; mem. gov.'s coun. physical fitness sports, 1979—. Served as officer M.C. U.S. Army, 1961-67, 90-91, col. Res. 1978-92, ret. Recipient Anderson award AAHPER, 1981; Am. Heart Assn. fellow, 1960-61. Fellow Am. Coll. Cardiology, Am. Coll. Chest Physicians, Am. Coll. Clin. Pharmacology, N.Y. Acad. Scis., Am. Coll. Sports Medicine (trustee 1976-78, 82-83, v.p. 1977-79, pres. Northland chpt. 1975-76, Citation award 1995), Am. Assn. Cardiovasc. and Pulmonary Rehab. (trustee 1989-90), Am. Acad. Kinesiology and Phys. Edn.; mem. Am. Physiol. Soc., Am. Soc. Pharmacology and Exptl. Therapeutics, Am. Inst. Nutrition, Am. Heart Assn. (v.p. Hennepin County divsn. 1980-81, pres. 1982-83), Am. Coll. Nutrition, Am. Fedn. Clin. Rsch., Minn. Lung Assn. (trustee 1978-81), Phi Beta Kappa, Phi Kappa Phi. Jewish. Home: 5628 Glen Ave Hopkins MN 55345-6610 Office: U Minn Sch Kinesiology & Leisure Studies 110 Cooke Hall Minneapolis MN 55455-0136

LEON, BENJAMIN JOSEPH, electrical engineering educator, consultant; b. Austin, Tex., Mar. 20, 1932; s. Harry Joshua and Ernestine (Franklin) L.; m. Maxine Murphy, Jan. 26, 1954; children: Nathaniel J., Victoria R., Jennifer A., Theresa S. BS, U. Tex., 1954; SM, MIT, 1957, ScD, 1959. Registered profl. engr., Ky., La. Mem. tech. staff Lincoln Lab. MIT, Lexington, 1954-59; mem. tech staff Hughes Rsch. Labs., Malibu, Calif., 1959-62; assoc. prof. Purdue U., West Lafayette, Ind., 1962-64; prof. Purdue U., West Lafayette, 1964-80; chmn. dept. elec. engring U. Ky., Lexington, 1980-84, prof. elec. engring., 1980-88; sr. staff officer NRC, Washington, 1988-90; prof., coord. grad. telecommunications studies, dept. elect. and computer engring. U. Southwestern La., Lafayette, 1990—; vis. prof. Cornell U., Ithaca, N.Y., 1968-69; electronics engr. Def. Commn. Agy., Reston, Va., 1975-76; communications cons. Westinghouse Corp., Pitts., 1980; vis. prof. So. Meth. U., Dallas, 1986-87. Author: Lumped Systems, 1968, Basic linear Networks, 1970; editor IEEE Trans on Circuits, 1967-68, IEEE Impact, 1980-85, IEEE Profl. Perspective, 1985; patentee in field. Recipient Profs. Meml. Soc., Lafayette, 1963-68; sec. Wabash Vol. Fire Fighters, West Lafayette, 1978-79. Fellow IEEE (v.p. 1979-80), IEEE Cirs. and Sys. Soc. (pres. 1970-71), AAAS (coun. del. 1994-96); mem. NSPE. Unitarian. Home: 200 Cherry St Lafayette LA 70506-3626 Office: Univ Southwestern La Dept Elec and Computer Engring USL Box 43890 Lafayette LA 70504-3890

LEON, BRUNO, architect, educator; b. Van Houten, N.Mex., Feb. 18, 1924; s. Giovanni and Rose (Cunico) L.; m. Louise Dal-Bo, Sept. 4, 1948 (dec. 1974); m. Bonnie Bertram, Sept. 12, 1976; children: Mark Jon, John Anthony, Lisa Rose. Student, Wayne State U., 1942, U. Detroit, 1945-48; LHD (hon.), U. Detroit, 1984; BArch, N.C. State Coll., 1953. Registered architect, Mich., N.C., Mass., N.Y., N.Mex., Fla. Head design staff Fuller Research Found., Raleigh, N.C., 1954-55; archtl. designer I.M. Pei & Assos., N.Y.C., 1955-56; instr. Mass. Inst. Tech., 1956-59; designer Catalano & Belluschi (architects), Cambridge, Mass., 1958-59; asst. prof. U. Ill. at Urbana, 1959-61; dean Sch. Architecture, U. Detroit, 1961-93, dean emeritus, 1993; pvt. practice architecture, 1956—. Served with USAAF, 1942-45. Fellow AIA (dir. Detroit 1963-64); mem. Alpha Sigma Nu (hon.), Phi Kappa Phi. Home: 9 Redondo Ct Santa Fe NM 87505-8757 *I believe the integral quality of the human spirit to be the ability to dream rather than to rationalize.*

LEON, DENNIS, sculptor; b. London, July 27, 1933; came to U.S. 1951, naturalized, 1956; s. Ralph and Rebecca (Stone) L.; m. Joan Schaefer, Mar. 20, 1964 (div.); children: Ann, Susan; m. Christin Ann Nelson, 1985. BFA, Temple U., 1956, BS in Edn, 1956, MFA, 1957; Doctor (hon.), Calif. Coll. Arts and Crafts, 1993. Head dept. fine arts Phila. Coll. Art, 1965-67, chmn. dept. sculpture, 1967-70; prof. sculpture Calif. Coll. Arts and Crafts, Oakland, 1972-93, prof. emeritus, 1993—. Exhibited in numerous one-man shows including Kraushaar Gallery, N.Y.C., 1966, 68, 70, Hansen Fuller Goldeen Gallery, 1985, San Francisco, 1977, 79, 81-82, 84-85, Galleria D'Arte del Cavallino, Venice, Italy, 1978, San Jose Mus. Art, 1981, Jewish Mus. San Francisco, 1986, Goldeen Gallery, L.A., 1988, 89, 90, 92, Calif. State U., Fresno, 1990, Chemeketa Coll., Salem, Oreg., 1991, Anne Reid Gallery, Ketchum, Idaho, 1991, Cheryl Haines Gallery, San Francisco, 1991, 93, Butters Gallery, Portland, Oreg., 1991, Dorthy Goldeen Gallery, Santa Monica, Calif., 1991, Anne Reed Gallery, Ketchum, Idaho, 1991, Chemeketa Coll. Sale, 1991; exhibited in group shows including U. Calif. at Davis, 1974, Phila. Mus. Art, 1976, San Francisco Mus. Art, 1977, Newport Harbor Mus., 1981, Oakland (Calif.) Mus., 1989, Hudson River Mus. N.Y., 1990; represented in permanent collections Phila. Mus. Art, Oakland Mus. Art, San Francisco Mus. Modern Art, Storm King Art Ctr., N.Y., Bank of Ams., Phillip Morris Collection, Corcoran Mus. Art., Rutgers Archive; work commd. by Chevron Oil Co., 1986. Cons. La State Bd. Regents, 1980. Served with U.S. Army, 1957-59. Recipient Nat. Inst. Arts and Letters award, 1967; fellow Guggenheim Found., 1967, Macdowell Found., 1981, Djerassi Found., 1983-84; grantee San Francisco Mus. Modern Art, 1978, Nat. Endowment for Arts, 1979. Home: 1254 E 12th St Oakland CA 94606-4325

LEON, DONALD FRANCIS, university dean, medical educator; b. Washington, Aug. 19, 1932; s. Frank A. and Madeline (Wildman) L.; children: Anne, James, John, Sharon. AB, Georgetown U., 1953, MD, 1957. Diplomate Am. Bd. Internal Medicine, Subspecialty Bds. in Cardiovascular Diseases. Instr. medicine U. Pitts., 1965-67, asst. prof. medicine, 1967-70, assoc. prof., 1971-75, vice chmn. medicine, 1971-75, assoc. prof., 1975-77, exec. assoc. dean, 1975-79, prof. medicine, 1977—, pres. Univ. Health Ctr., 1979-83, dean Sch. Medicine, 1979-84; dean clin. affairs Georgetown U. Hosp., Washington, 1989-94, prof. medicine divsn. cardiology, 1994—; bd. dirs. Blue Cross Western Pa. Co-editor: Pericardial Disease, 1982, Am. Heart Assn. Monograph, 1975. Served to capt. USAF, 1961-63. Am. Heart Assn. scholar, 1968-73. Fellow ACP, Council on Clin. Cardiology, Am.

Heart Assn. (fellow Coun. on Circulation), Am. Coll. Cardiology (bd. dirs.); mem. Am. Fedn. for Clin. Rsch., Cen. Soc. for Clin. Rsch. Office: Georgetown Univ Hosp 3800 Reservoir NW Washington DC 20007

LEON, RICHARD J., lawyer, former government official; b. South Natick, Mass., Dec. 3, 1949; s. Silvano B. and Rita (O'Rorke) L.; m. M-Christine Costa; Nicholas Cavanagh. AB, Holy Cross Coll., 1971; JD cum laude, Suffolk Law Sch., 1974; LLM, Harvard U., 1981. Bar: R.I. 1975, U.S. Ct. Appeals (2d cir.) 1977, U.S. Dist. Ct. R.I. 1976, U.S. Supreme Ct. 1984, D.C. 1991, U.S. Dist. Ct. D.C. 1991, U.S.C. Ct. Appeals (D.C. cir.) 1991. Law clk. to justices Superior Ct. Mass., 1974-75, to justice R.I. Supreme Ct., 1975-76; spl. asst. U.S. atty. U.S. Attys. Office (so. dist.) N.Y., 1977-78; asst. prof. law St. John's U. Law Sch., 1979-83; sr. trial atty., criminal sect., tax div. U.S. Dept. Justice, Washington, 1983-87, dep. asst. atty. gen. environment and natural resources divsn., 1988-89; ptnr. Baker & Hostetler, Washington, 1989—; dep. chief minority counsel House Select Iran-Contra Com., 1987; active Jud. Conf. D.C. cir., 1991—, Pres. Commn. on White House Fellowships, 1990-93; chief minority counsel House Fgn. Affairs Com. 'October Surprise' Task Force, 1992. Author: Environmental Crime, Lawyers' Desk Book on White Collar Crime, 1991; contrb. articles to legal jours. Bd. trustees Suffolk U., 1990—. Mem. ABA, Am. Portuguese Soc., Order of Barristers, R.I. Bar Assn., Fed. Bar Council, Suffolk Law Sch. Assn. Met. N.Y. (past pres.), Suffolk Law Sch. Assn. Met. Washington (past pres.). Clubs: Harvard of N.Y.C., Harvard of Boston, University (Washington). Republican. Roman Catholic. Office: Baker & Hostetler 1050 Connecticut Ave NW Ste 1100 Washington DC 20008

LEON, ROBERT LEONARD, psychiatrist, educator; b. Denver, Jan. 18, 1925; s. Louis and Rae (Brown) L.; m. Willena Lee, Sept. 14, 1947; children: Alexis Kay, Mark Robert, Jeffrey Clayton, Stacy Lee. MD, U. Colo., 1948. Diplomate Am. Bd. Psychiatry and Neurology. Intern U. Mich. Hosp., Ann Arbor, 1948-49; resident in psychiatry U. Colo. Med. Ctr., Denver, 1949-52, child psychiatry fellow, 1951-52; child psychiatry fellow Bur. Mental Hygiene, New Haven, Conn. Dept. Health/Student Health Svc., Yale U., 1952-53; asst. dir., acting dir. child psychiatry Greater Kansas City Mental Health Found., 1953-54; instr. psychiatry U. Kans. Sch. Medicine, Kansas City, 1956-57; asst. prof. psychiatry U. Tex. Health Sci. Ctr. at Dallas, Southwestern Med. Sch., 1957-61, assoc. prof., 1961-65, prof., 1965-67; prof., chmn. dept. psychiatry Sch. Medicine U. Tex. Health Sci. Ctr. at San Antonio, 1967—; Ashbel Smith prof. U. Tex. Health Sci. Ctr., San Antonio, 1990—; chief psychiatry Univ. Health System, Bexar County, San Antonio, 1967—; cons. psychiatry Audie Murphy Vet.'s Hosp., 1973—; cons. Mental Health Orgn., region VI, HEW, 1957-73; mem. Psychiat. Tng. Rev. NIMH, Rockville, Md., 1970-74. Author: Psychiatric Interviewing: A Primer, 1982, 2d edit., 1989; contrb. articles to profl. jours. Sr. surgeon USPHS, 1954-57. Fellow ACP (pres. 1987-88), Am. Psychiat. Assn. (life), Am. Orthopsychiat. Assn. (life), Am. Acad. Child and Adolescent Psychiatry, Am. Assn. Social Psychiatry (pres. 1990-92); mem. Am. Assn. Chairmen Depts. Psychiatry (pres. 1982-83), Benjamin Rush Soc., World Assn. for Social Psychiatry. Home: 6866 Stonykirk St San Antonio TX 78240-2743 Office: U Tex Health Sci Ctr 7703 Floyd Curl Dr San Antonio TX 78284-7792

LEÓN, TANIA JUSTINA, composer, music director, pianist; b. Havana, Cuba, May 14, 1943; came to U.S., 1967; d. Oscar and Dora (Ferran) L. BA in Piano and Theory, Peyrellade Conservatory Music, Havana, 1963; MA in Music Edn., Nat. Conservatory Music, Havana, 1964; BA in Acctg., U. Havana, 1965; BS Music Edn., NYU, 1973, BS in Music Edn., 1973, MA in Composition, 1975. Prof. Bklyn. Coll. Conservatory of Music, 1994—; vis. prof. Yale U., New Haven, 1993; vis. lectr. Harvard U., Cambridge, Mass., 1994; resident composer Lincoln Ctr. Inst., 1985, teaching artist, 1982-88; composer in residence Nat. Black Music Festival, 1990, Cabrillo Music Festival, 1990, Yaddo, 1991, Ravinia Festival, 1991, Cleve. Inst., 1992, Bellagio Ctr., Italy, 1992, Cornish Coll., Seattle, 1993, Billings Symphony, 1993, Carnegie Mellon U., Pitts., 1993, Harvard Coll., Cambridge, Mass., 1993, Voices of Change, Dallas, 1993; panelist N.Y. State Council on the Arts, 1980, 81, 86, NEA composing program, 1980-82, recording program, 1985-87; mem. adv. bd. Bklyn. Coll. Conservatory, 1982-84, Meet the Composer, 1983—, Children TV Workshop; artistic dir. Composers Forum Inc., N.Y.C., 1987—; assoc. prof. composition Bklyn. Coll., 1987—; bd. dirs. Am. Music Ctr., N.Y. Found. for Arts; with Cin. Symphony Orch., 1991—, Revson Composer fellow N.Y. Philharmonic, 1993—; U.S. rep. U.S.-Mex. Fund for Culture, 1994. Piano soloist, Cuba, 1964-67; piano soloist, N.Y. Coll. of Music Orch., N.Y.C., 1967, NYU Orch., N.Y.C., 1969, Buffalo Symphony Orch., 1973; staff pianist, condr. Dance Theatre of Harlem, N.Y.C., 1968—; assoc. condr., 1973—; music dir., 1968-79; founder, Dance Theatre of Harlem Orch., 1975; concert series Meet the Performer, 1977; music dir. concert series Dance in Am. Spl., Sta. WNET-TV; guest condr. concert series, Genova (Italy) Symphony Orch., 1972, Juilliard Orch., Festival Two Worlds, Spoleto, Italy, Symphony New World, 1974, Royal Ballet Orch., 1974, 76, BBC Orch., 1974, 76, Halle Orch., 1974, Buffalo Philharm. Orch., 1975, Concert Orch. of L.I. 1979, Sadler's Wells Orch., 1979, London Universal Symphony, 1979, Composer's Forum, 1979, Lincoln Ctr. Outdoor Festival, 1980, Bklyn. Coll. Symphony, 1981, J. F. Kennedy Ctr. Opera House Orch., 1981, 82, Radio City Music Hall, 1982, Spoleto Festival, Charleston, 1983, Orch. of Our Time, N.Y., N.Y. Grand Opera, Colonne Orch., Paris, Mich. Opera, Human Comedy, Royale Theatre, Broadway, Pasadena Orch., P.R. Symphony, Met. Opera Orch., Phoenix Symphony, Columbus Symphony Orch., Fund. Latinoamericana Musica Contemporanea P.R., Am. Women Comst./Composer Symposium, Eugene, Oreg., New Music Am., Houston, New Music in Am., 1989 and Concert in the Pk., 1990 both with Bklyn. Philharm., Cabrillo Festival, 1990, Nat. Black Arts Festival, Atlanta, 1990, La Crosse Symphony, Wis., 1991, Dance Theatre of Harlem, 1991, 92, 93, 25th Anniversary Season-94, Celebrate Bklyn. Festival, 1991, Bklyn. Philharm., 1991, New World Symphony, Miami, Fla., 1991, 94, Cosmopolitan Symphony Orch., N.Y.C., 1991, Beethovenhalle Symphony Orch., Bonn, Germany, 1992, Opera Orch. of Johannesburg, 1992, Nat. Symphony Orch., Johannesburg, 1992, Louisville Symphony, 1992, RIAS Orch., Berlin, 1992, Billings Symphony, 1993, Dance Theater of Harlem, 1993, 94, Carnegie Mellon Orch., 1993, Alvin Ailey 35th Anniversary Season, 1993, Am. Composers Orch. Chamber Ensemble, 1994, Munich Biennale, 1994, others; royal command performer concert series, London Palladium, 1974, 76, Concert Orch. L.I., 1976, concert pianist, Sta. WNYC-FM, 1968-70; conductor coord.: concert series Music by Black Composers Series, Bklyn. Philharmonia, 1978-79; music dir., condr. Bklyn. Philharm. Community Concert Series, 1977—; mus. dir., condr. The Wiz, Broadway Theatre, 1978; music dir. Death, Destruction and Detroit, 1979, Alvin Ailey Am. Dance Theatre, 1983—, Whitney Mus. Contemporary Music Concert Series, 1986, 87; mus. dir.: composer: Maggie Magalita, J.F. Kennedy Ctr. Performing Arts, 1980, TWindows, 1982; apptd. music dir. concert series, Intar Theatre, N.Y.C.; condr., mus. dir. concert series Godspell, NYU, 1978, Carmencita, 1978; composer (ballet music) Haiku, 1974, (piano concerto) Tones, 1970, Sailor's Boat, (score for musical) Dougla, 1974, (African ballet) La Ramera de la Cueva, 1974, (score for musical) Namiac Poems, 1974, (for voice, chorus and orch.) Spiritual Suite, 1975, (2 sopranos, chorus and mixed ensemble with narrator), Concerto Criollo, 1976, (concerto for piano, 8 timpanies and orch.) Pet's Suite, 1979, (for flute and piano) I Got Ovah, 1980, (for soprano, piano and percussion, based on poems by Carolyn M. Rodgers) Concerto Criollo, 1980, Four Pieces for Cello, 1981, De-Orishas, 1982, Ascend, Fanfare for Brass and Percussion, 1983, (for solo piano) Momentum, 1984, Bata, 1985, Permutation Seven, 1985, A La Par, 1986, Ritual, 1987, Pueblo Mulato, 1987, Heart of Ours, a piece, 1988, Parajota Delaté, 1988, Kabiosile, 1988, Latin File, 1988, Indigena for instrumental ensemble, 1991, Solisti Chamber Orch N.Y., 1991, Carabali for orch., 1992, Crossings for brass ensemble, 1992, Arenas d'un Tempo for clarinet, cello and piano, 1992, Son Sonora for flute and guitar, 1993, Scourge of Hyacinths: chamber opera, 1994, Para Viola y Orquesta for viola and orch., 1994, Sin Normas Ajenas for chamber orch., 1994; records on CRI, WesternWind, Albany Records, Newport Classics, Leonarda Records. Bd. dirs. Am. Composers Orch. Recipient Young Composers prize Nat. Council Arts, Havana, 1966, Alvin Johnson award Am. Council Emigres in the Profession, 1971, Cintas award in composition, 1974-75, 78-79, Achievement award Nat. Council Women of U.S., 1980, Byrd Hoffman Found. award, 1981, Key to City of Detroit, 1982, Queens Council on Arts award, 1983, Meet The Composer awards, 1978-94, Manhattan Arts award, 1985, Dean Dixon Achievement award, 1985, N.Y. State Coun. on Arts award, 1988, Mayor's citation, City of N.Y., 1989, Celebrate Bklyn. Achievement award, 1990,

award in music Am. Acad. and Inst. of Arts and Letters, 1991; Nat. Endowment for Arts fellow, 1975. Mem. ASCAP (Composers award 1978-94), French Soc. Composers, Am. Acad. Poets (bd. dirs.), Am. Composers Orch. (bd. dirs.), Am. Fedn. Musicians, Ctr. New Music, Am. Music Ctr. (bd. dirs. 1985—), Internat. Artists Alliance, Am. Women Composers, AFL-CIO. *

LEON, TOMAS CARLOS, foreign exchange broker; b. Mexico City, July 20, 1951; came to U.S., 1983; s. Richard C. and Manuela (Santacruz) de Leon; m. Maria Sofia Cardenas, Nov. 1, 1979; children: Sofia, Tomas. BBA, Anahuac U., Mexico City, 1973; MBA, U. Tex., 1978. Account exec. Securities Banco Nacional de Mex., S.A., Mexico City, 1973-77; retail div. mgr. Casa de Bolsa Banamex, S.A. de C.V., Mexico City, 1979-80, mgr. securities rsch., 1981-82; dir. capital markets group Valores Finamex, S.A. de C.V., Mexico City, 1982-83; vice chmn., dir. Trans-Tex. Holdings Corp., Austin, 1983—; chief operating officer, dir. PSI Techs. Corp., Austin, 1986-87; chmn., chief exec. officer Impex Trading Corp., Austin, 1987-89; chmn., chief exec. officer, dir. Internat. Forex Corp., Austin, 1989—, Tex. Paymaster Corp., Austin, 1991—. Patentee investment and loan instruments indexed to inflation. Mem. Univ. Club de Mex. A.C., Austin Internat. Club, KC, U. Tex. Ex-Students Assn., Asociacion de Ex-Alumnos de la Universidad Anahuac. Roman Catholic. Office: Internat Forex Corp Ste 202 1001 Capital Of Tex Hwy S Austin TX 78746

LEONARD, SISTER ANNE C., superintendent, education director; b. N.Y.C., Dec. 22, 1936; d. Patrick A. and Mary T. (McAlpin) L. BS in Edn. and Social Sci., Fordham U., 1962, MA, 1965; CAGS, Boston U., 1972; postgrad., Hunter Coll., U. San Francisco, U. Northern Ill., Notre Dame U. Cert. tchr. K-12, adminstr. N.Y. Tchr., asst. prin., prin. Notre Dame Acad., Staten Island, N.Y., 1957-68; prin. Maternity B.V.M. Sch., Bourbonnais, Ill., 1968-69, St. Jude the Apostle Sch., South Holland, Ill., 1969-78; dir. Cath. Elem. Schs. Archdiocese of Chgo., 1978-83, dir. ednl. svcs., mem. Cardinal Bernadin's cabinet, 1983-90, exec. officer commn. ednl. svcs., 1983-90; supt. schs., dir. edn. Archdiocese of Okla. City, 1990—; chair edn. divisn. Cath. Conf. Ill., 1988-90; del. gen. chpt. Congregation Notre Dame, mem. provincial coun.; mem. edn. com. U.S. Cath. Conf. Bishops, Washington, 1985-88; speaker in field; lectr., presenter workshops; mem. Fortune 500 panel edn. and bus.; devel. mission statement, just principles compensation, new models compensation for prins., 1987-91; initiated, organized Dirs. Edn. Wis., Ill., Ind., Ohio, Mich.; attended symposia in field; mem. com. prep. Office of Cath. Edn. Conciliation Process; exec. officer local sch. bds.; initiated individually guided edn. program St. Jude Sch. Cons. textbooks William H. Sadlier, Inc.; contbr. articles to profl. jours. Trustee DePaul U., 1986—, bd. dirs. chair acad. affairs com.; bd. dirs. Jr. Achievement, Chgo., 1984-90, Okla. City, 1991—; mem. NCCJ, 1992—, Gov. Ill. adv. com. on non-pub. schs., Springfield, 1978-82, planning com. Big Shoulders Project. Mem. Nat. Cath. Ednl. Assn. (pres. chief adminstrs. Cath. edn. 1991—), v.p. 1989-91, vice chair bd. 1991—, task force 1990-91, Educator of Yr. award 1990, supervision, pers., curriculum), Archdiocesan Prins. Assn. (pres. 1973-78), Chgo. Coun. Fgn. Rels., Assn. Supervision and Curriculum Devel., Phi Delta Kappa (Educator of Yr. 1984). Avocations: reading, swimming, traveling. Home: 10804 Greystone Ave Oklahoma City OK 73120-3218 Office: Archdiocese Okla City PO Box 32184 Oklahoma City OK 73123-0384

LEONARD, BARBARA M, former secretary of state, federal agency administrator, state agency administrator. Grad., Brown U.; PhD (hon.), Johnson & Wales U. Cert. tchr. R.I., Ohio. Owner, CEO H & H Screw Products Mfg. Co., Lincoln, R.I.; regional adminstr. region 1 Gen. Svcs. Adminstrn. New England; dir. of devel. for child care ctrs. for federal employees throughout U.S.; sec. of state R.I., 1993-94. Pres. R.I Philharmonic Orch.; trustee emerita Brown U., Bryant Coll.; bd. dirs., sec. United Way; bd. dirs. Nat. Conf. Christians and Jews. Recipient R.I. Woman Bus. Advocate of Yr. award, 1983, Nat. Humanitarian award, 1983, Rhode Islander of Yr. award, 1984. Republican. Baptist. Office: State House Rm 218 Providence RI 02903

LEONARD, CLAIRE OFFUTT, pediatric geneticist educator; b. Rochester, N.Y., Apr. 1, 1945; d. Edward Preble and Virginia Leoma (Williams) Offutt; divorced; children: Christopher Edward, Kathleen. BA, Mount Holyoke Coll., 1967; MD, John Hopkins U., 1971. Diplomate Am. Bd. Pediatrics, Am. Bd. Genetics. Intern and resident in pediat. U. Colo., 1971-74, fellow in genetics and birth defects, 1974-75; fellow in genetics Johns Hopkins Hosp., Balt., 1978-80; asst. prof. pediatrics John Hopkins U., Balt., 1980-81; asst. prof. pediatrics U. Utah, Salt Lake City, 1981-87, assoc. prof. pediatrics, 1987—. Mem. Am. Soc. Human Genetics, Am. Acad. Pediatrics, Am. Coll. Human Genetics, Soc. Inherited Metabolic Disorders. Mem. Soc. of Friends. Avocations hiking, cooking, camping. Office: U Utah Dept Peds 50 N Medical Dr Salt Lake City UT 84112

LEONARD, DAVID ARTHUR, hospital executive emeritus; b. Red Oak, Iowa, June 3, 1928; s. Morris Condit and Wynona Loveland (Farquhar) L.; m. Elizabeth Harvey Berry; children: Deborah Anne Leonard Kotarski, Thomas Berry, Jane Elizabeth Leonard Shellum. AB, Grinnell Coll., 1949; MA, U. Minn., 1950. Pers. assoc. Mayo Clinic, Rochester, Minn., 1950-61, adminstrv. asst., 1962-75, chmn. div. pers. svcs., 1976-81, chmn. div. adminstrv. svcs., 1982-86; adminstr. St. Marys Hosp., Rochester, 1987-90, pres., trustee, 1974-82. Trustee Mayo Found., Rochester, 1988-90, Rochester Meth. Hosp., 1987-90; bd. dirs. Minn. Conf. Cath. Healthcare Facilities, St. Paul, 1988-90; chmn. adv. com. City Coun. Orgn., Rochester, 1978-80, Total Community Devel. Project, Rochester, 1966-68; councilman City of Rochester, 1961-64. Recipient Outstanding Young Man award Rochester Jaycees, 1962. Republican. Episcopalian. Office: Mayo Clinic Emeritus Office 200 1st St SW Rochester MN 55905

LEONARD, DAVID MORSE, lawyer; b. Akron, Ohio, Dec. 4, 1949; s. Frank O. and Barbara J. (Morse) L.; m. Sharon Elaine Quati, May 7, 1977; children: Michael Morse, Lindsey Marie. BS in Chem. Engring., Purdue U., 1972; JD, Emory U., 1975. Bar: Ga. 1975, U.S. Ct. Appeals (4th, 5th and 11th cirs.), U.S. Dist. Ct. (no., mid. and so. dist.) Ga., U.S. Dist. Ct. (so. dist.) Ala., U.S. Dist. Ct. (we. dist.) La.; cert. mediator. Assoc. Montet & Smith, Atlanta, 1975-79; assoc. Hurt, Richardson, Garner, Todd & Cadenhead, Atlanta, 1979-83, ptnr., 1983-85; of counsel Lord, Bissell & Brook, Atlanta, 1985-87, ptnr., 1987—. Mem. ABA (litigation sect., tort and ins. practice sect.), Atlanta Lawyers Club, Atlanta C. of C. Home: 4152 Club Dr NE Atlanta GA 30319-1116 Office: Lord Bissell & Brook Ste 3700 1201 W Peachtree St NW Atlanta GA 30309-3421

LEONARD, EDWARD F., chemical engineer, educator; b. Paterson, N.J., July 6, 1932; s. Edward F. and Adelyn (Minder) L.; children—Mary, Edward F., Gerald, Louise, Joseph. S.B. in Chem. Engring., M.I.T., 1953; M.S. in Chem. Engring. U. Pa., 1955, Ph.D., 1960. Mem. faculty Columbia U., 1958—, prof. chem. engring., 1968—, also founder seminar on biomaterials.; dir. Artificial Organs Rsch. Lab., chmn. bioengring. program, 1990—. Author articles in field. Fellow Am. Inst. Chem. Engrs. (William H. Walker award), Am. Inst. Med. and Biol. Engring. Found.; mem. Am. Soc. Artificial Internal Organs (pres. 1972-73), Biomed. Engring. Soc. (adv. bd.), N.Y. Acad. Medicine. Home: 29 Rossmore Ave Bronxville NY 10708-5615 Office: Columbia Univ 814B Mudd Bldg New York NY 10027

LEONARD, EDWARD PAUL, naval officer, dentist, educator; b. Greenfield, Mass., Dec. 29, 1935; s. Laurence Francis and Hilda Mae (Coutu) L.; m. Lola Jeanne Ahern, Sept. 6, 1958; children: Lisa Ann, Jeffrey Torbert, Julie Marie, Laurence Edward. Student, St. Joseph's Sem., 1953-56, St. Anselm's Coll., 1956, U. Mass., 1956-58; DDS, Georgetown U., 1962; MS, U. Md., 1968, PhD, 1970; attended, Marymount U., 1990-92. Commd. lt. USN, 1962, advanced through grades to capt., 1979; asst. dental officer Subic Bay Naval Sta. USN, The Philippines, 1970-72; assoc. histopathologist dental rsch. inst. USN, Great Lakes Naval Base, Ill., 1972-76, chief histopathology dental rsch. inst., 1976-80; program mgr. Naval Med. R & D USN Bethesda, Md., 1980-83; quality assurance officer Office Dir. Naval Med. USN, Washington, 1983-84, dental care analyst Office Dir. Naval Med., 1984-86; exec. officer Naval Dental Clin. USN, Parris Island, S.C., 1986-88; comdg. officer Naval Dental Clin. USN, Charleston, S.C., 1988—; mem. exec. coun. Mgmt. Devel. Adv. Bd. Navy Surgeon Gen., Washington, 1983-86; grant reviewer div. rsch. grants NIH, Washington, 1981-83; tchr. biology,

ecology Hargrave Mil. Acad., asst. basketball coach, sailing club sponsor, astronomy club sponsor; evaluator Va. Ind. Schs. Assn. Contbr. articles to profl. jours. Vol. coach Vienna (Va.) Youth League, 1983-84; coach McLean (Va.) Youth League, 1984. Recipient Carl A. Schlack Rsch. award Assn. Mil. Surgeons of U.S., 1989. Fellow Internat. Coll. Dentists, Am. Coll. Dentists; mem. Internat. Assn. Dental Rsch., Am. Assn. Dental Rsch., Am. Assn. Pub. Health Dentistry, Nat. Assn. Biology Tchrs. Democrat. Roman Catholic. Avocations: sailing, astronomy, historic preservation. Home: 9085 Wexford Dr Vienna VA 22182-2152

LEONARD, EDWIN DEANE, lawyer; b. Oakland, Calif., Apr. 22, 1929; s. Edwin Stanley and Gladys Eugenia (Lee) L.; m. Judith Swatland, July 10, 1954; children: Garrick Hillman, Susanna Leonard Hill, Rebecca, Ethan York. BA, The Principia, 1950; LLB, Harvard U., 1953; LLM, George Washington U., 1956. Bar: D.C. 1953, Ill. 1953, N.Y. 1957. Assoc. Davis Polk Wardwell Sunderland & Kiendl, N.Y.C., 1956-61; ptnr. Davis Polk & Wardwell, N.Y.C., 1961—. Trustee the Brearley Sch., N.Y.C., 1980-90. Served to 1st lt. JAGC, 1953-56. Mem. ABA, N.Y. Bar Assn., N.Y. County Bar Assn., Assn. of Bar of City of N.Y. (chmn. various coms.), Millbrook Equestrian Ctr. (pres.). Home: 1148 5th Ave New York NY 10128-0807 Office: Davis Polk & Wardwell 450 Lexington Ave New York NY 10017-3911

LEONARD, ELMORE JOHN, novelist, screenwriter; b. New Orleans, Oct. 11, 1925; s. Elmore John and Flora Amelia (Revé) L.; m. Beverly Claire Cline, Aug. 30, 1949 (div. 1977); children: Jane, Peter, Christopher, William, Katherine; m. Joan Leanne Lancaster, Sept. 15, 1979 (dec. 1993); m. Christine Kent, Aug. 19, 1993. PhB, U. Detroit, 1950. Author 30 novels including Hombre, 1961, City Primeval, 1980, Split Images, 1982, Cat Chaser, 1982, La Brava, 1983, Stick, 1983, Glitz, 1985, Bandits, 1987, Touch, 1987, Freaky Deaky, 1988, Killshot, 1989, Get Shorty, 1990, Maximum Bob, 1991, Rum Punch, 1992, Pronto, 1993, Riding the Rap, 1995. With USN, 1943-46. Recipient Mystery Writers of Am. Grand Master award, 1992. Mem. Writers Guild of Am., Authors Guild, Mystery Writers of Am., Western Writers of Am. Roman Catholic. Office: 2192 Yarmouth Bloomfield Hills MI 48301

LEONARD, EUGENE ALBERT, banker; b. St. Louis, Aug. 27, 1935; s. Albert Hiram and Mary (Crowson) L.; m. Mary Ann Sampson, Aug. 31, 1956 (div. 1994); children: Charles, James, Susan; m. Constance Anne Deschamps, June 3, 1995. BS, U. Mo., 1957, MS, 1958, PhD, 1962; postgrad., Stonier Grad. Sch. Banking, Rutgers U., 1964-66. Instr. agrl. econs. U. Mo. at Columbia, 1959-60; with Fed. Res. Bank St. Louis, 1961-77; v.p.; mgr. Fed. Res. Bank St. Louis (Memphis br.), 1967-70, sr. v.p., 1970-71, 1st v.p., 1971-77; on loan to bd. govs. FRS as asst. sec., Washington, 1970-71; sr. v.p. Merc. Bancorp. Inc., St. Louis, 1977-87; pres. Corp. for Fin. Risk Mgmt., St. Louis, 1987—; instr. econs. Central States Sch. Banking, 1962-69, Ill. Bankers Sch., 1962-74, Sch. Banking South, 1970-83, Stonier Grad. Sch. Banking, 1975-80, bd. regents, 1978-81; adj. assoc. prof. econs. Memphis State U., 1969-70. Bd. dirs. Logos Sch., St. Louis, 1977-85, chmn., 1985; bd. dirs. Repertory Theater of St. Louis, 1981-87. Mem. Mo. Bankers Assn. (treas. 1984-85, pres. 1986-87), U. Mo. Columbia Alumni Assn. (nat. pres. 1980-81, bd. dirs. devel. fund 1981-89, Faculty Alumni award 1986), Gamma Sigma Delta, Kappa Sigma. Unitarian. Home: 30 Portland Pl Saint Louis MO 63108-1204 Office: Corp for Fin Risk Mgmt 8675 Olive Blvd Saint Louis MO 63132-2503

LEONARD, GEORGE EDMUND, real estate, bank, and consulting executive; b. Phoenix, Nov. 20, 1940; s. George Edmund and Marion Elizabeth (Fink) L.; m. Gloria Jean Henry, Mar. 26, 1965 (div. Feb. 1980); children: Tracy Lynn, Amy Theresa, Kristin Jean; m. Mary C. Short, Sept. 22, 1990. Student, Ariz. State U., 1958-60; BS, U.S. Naval Acad., 1964; postgrad., Pa. State U., 1969-70; MBA, U. Chgo., 1973. Commd. ensign, USN, 1964, advanced through grades to lt. comdr., 1975; v.p. 1st Nat. Bank Chgo., 1970-75; exec. v.p., chief banking, chief fin. and chief lending officer Mera Bank, Phoenix, 1975-90, also bd. dirs., 1982-90; pres., chief exec. officer Cen. Savs., San Diego, 1985-87; chmn., CEO AmBank Holding Co. of Colo., Scottsdale, Ariz., 1990-91; pres., CEO Diversified Mgmt. Svcs., Inc., Phoenix, 1991—, GEL Mgmt. Inc., Phoenix, 1991—; bd. dirs. Beverly Hills (Calif.) Savs., Am. Nat. Bank of Scottsdale, Bank of Santa Fe, 1990-91, 1st Am. Bank of Colo. Springs. Active Phoenix Thunderbirds, 1979—; bd. dirs. Maricopa Community Colls. Found.; treas., 2d v.p., 1991-93, 1st v.p., 1993-94, pres. 1994-95, Camelback Charitable Trust, 1991-92, Samaritan Charitable Trust, 1993—, chmn. fin. com., 1994—. Mem. Phoenix Met. C. of C. (bd. dirs. 1975-82), Inst. Fin. Edn. (bd. dirs. 1980-87, nat. chmn. 1985-86), Ariz. State U. Coll. of Bus. Deans Coun. of 100, Paradise Valley Country Club (bd. dirs. 1991—, treas. 1992-95, pres. 1995—), Univ. Club (San Diego), Kiwanis. Republican. Roman Catholic. Home: 3064 E Stella Ln Phoenix AZ 85016-2244 Office: Diversified Mgmt Svcs Inc 3001 E Camelback Rd Ste 140 Phoenix AZ 85016-4427

LEONARD, GEORGE JAY, author; b. Bklyn., Jan. 13, 1946; s. L. Charles and Adele Leonard; m. Simei Du, 1987; 1 child, Andrew Charles. BA, Columbia U., 1967, MA, 1968, PhD with distinction, 1972. Gen. ptnr. George Leonard Prodns., N.Y.C., 1969—; asst. prof. English Yale U., New Haven, Conn., 1972-73; guest lectr. U. Calif., Irvine, 1973-74; screenwriter Gillwood Prodns., N.Y.C., 1976-80; writer-in-residence Scripps Coll., Claremont, Calif., 1977-80; head story dept. D.A. Prodns., N.Y.C., 1978-81; asst. prof. interdisciplinary humanities San Francisco State U., San Francisco, 1986-88, assoc. prof. interdisciplinary humanities, 1989-93, prof. interdisciplinary humanities, 1993—; cons. Keats-Shelley Meml. House, Rome, 1977-82; participant Inst. of Am. Studies, Beijing, Peoples Republic of China, 1988; appeared on various radio and TV programs, 1976—. Books include: From the Island (McGraw Hill First Novel Series award), 1967, Beyond Control, 1975, The Ice Cathedral, 1984, Into the Light of Things: The Art of the Commonplace from Wordsworth to John Cage (selected as one of Outstanding Books of Yr. 1994 by ALA), 1994; author, prodr., dir. (feature film) The Evil Weed, 1971; conception/choreography Sha Na Na rock and roll act, 1969; appeared in film Woodstock, 1969; mem. Nat. Book Critics' Cir., 1991—; contbr. books rev., articles to L.A. Times. Activist for bioethics, 1971-82, activist for ethnic brotherhood, 1983—; mem. adv. bd. U.S. Pacific Council, Bel Air, Calif., 1989-93; humanities cons. Korean-Am. Coalition and Japanese Village Plaza, Los Angeles, 1983-86; dir. mus. com. Anthony Duquette Found., Los Angeles, 1984-85. Fellow Huntington Library, San Marino, Calif., 1974-75. Mem. MLA, Nat. Assn. Asian-Am. Studies, Population Inst., Common Cause. Avocations: swimming, nature studies. Office: San Francisco State U Dept Interdisciplinary Humanities 530 Humanities San Francisco CA 94132

LEONARD, GILBERT STANLEY, oil company executive; b. Kingsport, Tenn., Sept. 3, 1941; s. Robert Spencer and Hope (Palmer) L.; m. Barbara Ann Bell, June 12, 1965 (div. 1982); m. Linda Marie Gremillion, Oct. 27, 1984. BS in Indsl. Mgmt., Purdue U., 1964; MS in Bus., U. Kans., 1970. Summer trainee Tenn. Eastman Co., Kingsport, 1963, prodn. planner, 1966-68; mktg. analyst Exxon Co., USA, Houston, 1970-74, distbn. specialist, 1975-78, staff systems analyst, 1979-81, group supr. applications support, 1982-84, strategic systems planner, 1984-85, supr. applications devel., 1986-89, system supr. Exxon Card Ctr., 1990-94; supr. network & telecommunication divsn. Exxon Computing Svc. Corp., 1994—; instr., facilitator team leadership forum Exxon Co., USA, Houston, 1988, instr., facilitator quality forum, 1990; advisor, cons. Nat. Jr. Achievement, Houston, 1972-74. Lay reader Episc. Ch. Good Shepherd, Kingwood, Tex., 1975-82; treas. Forrest Lake Townhome Assn., Houston, 1987-88, pres., 1988-89. Lt. USNR, 1964-66. Recognized for excellence in Naval ROTC Chgo. Tribune, 1963. Mem. Quarterdeck Soc. (pres. 1962-63), Beta Gamma Sigma. Avocations: private pilot, golf, running. Home: 15515 Township Glen Ln Cypress TX 77429-5505 Office: Exxon Co USA PO Box 2180 Houston TX 77252-2180

LEONARD, GLEN M., museum administrator; b. Salt Lake City, Nov. 12, 1938; s. Burnham J. and Allene (Green) L.; m. Karen Wright, Mar. 15, 1968; children: Cory, Kyle, Keith. BA, U. Utah, 1964, MA, 1966, PhD, 1970. Mng. editor Utah State Hist. Soc., Salt Lake City, 1973-77; sr. rsch. assoc. history div. Ch. of Jesus Christ of Latter-day Saints, Salt Lake City, 1973-78; dir. Mus. Ch. History and Art, Salt Lake City, 1979—; mem. adv. bd. editors Utah Hist. Quarterly, Salt Lake City, 1973-88; assoc. editor Jour. Mormon History, Provo, Utah, 1974-80; bd. dirs. Western Studies Ctr.,

Brigham Young U., Provo. Co-author: The Story of the Latter-day Saints, 1976; contbr. articles to profl. publs. Mem. Hist. Preservation Commn., Farmington, Utah, 1986-92; mem. adv. coun. Mormon Pioneer Nat. Hist. Trail, Nat. Park Svc., 1980-86. Recipient Dale Morgan Article award Utah State Hist. Soc., 1973. Mem. Orgn. Am. Historians, Western History Assn., Am. Assn. Mus. (museum assessment program cons.), Assn. Utah Historians (bd. dirs. 1981-83), Utah Mus. Assn. (bd. dirs. 1980-83), Am. Assn. State and Local History. Avocations: photography, music, gardening. Office: Mus Ch History and Art 45 N West Temple Salt Lake City UT 84150

LEONARD, HERMAN BEUKEMA (DUTCH LEONARD), public finance and management educator; b. Carlisle Barracks, Pa., Dec. 26, 1952; s. Charles Frederick and Margery Alden (Beukema) L.; m. Kathryn Anne Angell, Oct. 9, 1983; children: Whitney Angell, Dana Angell. AB summa cum laude, Harvard U., 1974, AM, 1976, PhD, 1979. Asst. prof. pub. policy John F. Kennedy Sch. Govt., Harvard U., Cambridge, Mass., 1979-83, assoc. prof., 1983-86, George F. Baker prof. pub. mgmt., 1986—, acad. dean curriculum and instrn., 1992—; mem. Gov.'s Coun. Econ. Policy, Alaska, 1980-82; chmn. Gov.'s Task Force on Coll. Opportunity, Mass., 1987-88; bd. dirs. Mass. Health and Ednl. Facilities Authority, 1988—; mem. adv. bd. N.Y.C. Debt Mgmt., 1990-94. Co-author: Discrimination in Rural Housing, 1976; author: Checks Unbalanced: The Quiet Side of Public Spending, 1986, By Choice or By Chance? Tracking the Values in Massachusetts Public Spending, 1992; contbr. numerous articles on pub. fin. and mgmt. to jours. in field. Recipient grad. fellowship NSF, 1974; jr. fellow Soc. Fellows, Harvard U., 1976-79; Presdl. scholar, 1970. Mem. Phi Beta Kappa. Office: Harvard U John F Kennedy Sch Govt 79 John F Kennedy St Cambridge MA 02138-5800

LEONARD, HUGH (JOHN KEYES BYRNE), playwright; b. Dublin, Ireland, Nov. 9, 1926; s. Nicholas Keyes and Margaret (Doyle) Byrne; m. Paule Jacquet, 1955; 1 child. Student, Presentation Coll., Ireland, 1941-45. Civil servant Dublin, 1945-59; TV script editor Granada TV, Manchester, Eng., 1961-63; freelance writer London, 1963-70; lit. editor Abbey Theatre, Dublin, 1976-77. Author: (plays) The Italian Road, 1954, The Big Birthday, 1956, A Leap in the Dark, 1957, Madigan's Lock, 1958, A Walk on the Water, 1960, The Passion of Peter McGinty, 1961, Stephen D, 1962, Dublin One, 1963, The Poker Session, 1963, The Family Way, 1964, The Saints Go Cycling In, 1965, Mick and Nick, 1966, The Quick, and the Dead, 1967, The Late Arrival of the Incoming Aircraft, 1968, The Au Pair Man, 1968, The Barracks, 1969, The Patrick Pearce Motel, 1971, Da, 1973 (Tony award for best play 1978, N.Y. Drama Critics' Circle award for best play 1978, Drama Desk award for outstanding new play 1978, Outer Critics Circle award for outstanding play 1978), Thieves, 1973, Summer, 1974, Irishmen, 1975, Time Was, 1976, Some of My Best Friends Are Husbands, 1976, Liam Liar, 1976, A Life, 1979 (Harvey award), Moving Days, 1981, Kill, 1982, Pizzazz, 1982, Good Behaviour, 1983, O'Neill, 1983, The Mask of Moriarty, 1985, Moving, 1991, Senna for Sonny, 1994, The Lily Lally Show, 1994; (autobiographies) Home Before Night, 1979, Out After Dark, 1987; (essays) Leonard's Last Book, 1978, A Peculiar People and Other Foibles, 1979, Rover and Other Cats, 1992; (novels) Parnell and the Englishwoman, 1990, The Off-Off-Shore Island, 1993; (screenplays) Great Catherine, 1968, Interlude, 1968, Whirligig, 1970, Percy, 1971, Our Miss Fred, 1972, Herself Surprised, 1977, Da, 1988, Widow's Peak, 1994; (teleplays) The Irish Boys, 1962, A King of Kingdom, 1963, The Second Wall, 1964, A Triple Irish, 1964, Realm of Error, 1964, My One True Love, 1964, The Late Arrival of the Incoming Aircraft, 1964, Second Childhood, 1964, Do You Play Requests?, 1964, The View From the Obelisk, 1965, I Loved You Last Summer, 1965, Great Big Blond, 1965, The Lodger, 1966, The Judge, 1966, Insurrection, 1966, The Retreat, 1966, Silent Song, 1966 (Italia prize Internat. Concourse for Radio and TV 1967, Merit award Writers Guild of Gt. Britain 1967), A Time of Wolves and Tigers, 1967, Love Life, 1967, Great Expectations (Dickens), 1967, Wuthering Heights (Bronte), 1967, No Such Thing as a Vampire, 1968, The Egg on the Face of the Tiger, 1968, The Corpse Can't Play, 1968, A Man and His Mother-in-Law, 1968, Assassin, 1968, Nicholas Nickleby (Dickens), 1968, A Study in Scarlet, 1968, The Hound of the Baskerville (Doyle), 1968, Hunt the Peacock, 1969, Talk of Angels, 1969, The Possessed (Dostoevsky), 1969, Dombey and Son (Dickens), 1969, P and O (Maugham), 1969, Jane (Maugham), 1970, A Sentimental Education (Flaubert), 1970, White Walls and Olive Green Carpets, 1971, The Removal Person, 1971, Pandora, 1971, The Virgins, 1972, The Ghost of Christmas Present, 1972, The Trugh Game, 1972, The Moonstone (Collins), 1972, The Sullen Sisters, 1972, The Watercress Girl (Bates), 1972, The Higgler, 1973, High Kampf, 1973, Milo O'Shea, 1973, Stone Cold Sober, 1973, The Bitter Pill, 1973, Another Fine Mess, 1973, Judgement Day, 1973, The Travelling Woman, 1973, The Hammer of God, 1974, The Actor and the Alibi, 1974, The Eye of Apollo, 1974, The Forbidden Garden, 1974, The Three Tools of Death, 1974, The Quick One, 1974, London Belongs to Me, 1977, The Last Campaign, 1978, The Ring and the Rose, 1978, Strumpet City, 1979, The Little World of Don Camillo, 1980, Kill, 1982, Good Behaviour, 1982, O'Neill, 1983, Beyond the Pale, 1984, The Irish RM, 1985, Troubles, 1987, Hunted Down, 1989, Parnell and the Englishwoman, 1991, The Celadon Cup, 1993; (TV series) Saki, 1962, Jezebel Ex-UK, 1963, The Hidden Truth, 1964, Undermine, 1964, Blackmail, 1965, Public Eye, 1965, The Liars, 1966, The Informer, 1966, Out of the Unknown, 1966-67, The Sinners, 1970-71, Me Mammy, 1970-71, Tales from the Lazy Acre, 1972, Father Brown, 1974. Office: 6 Rossaun, Pilot View, Dalkey County Dublin, Ireland*

LEONARD, IRVIN ALAN, lawyer; b. Phila., Feb. 7, 1944; s. Sidney K. and Anne (Barmack) L.; m. Elin Leslie Fleischer, Aug. 19, 1967; children: Ethan Gabriel, Jessica Silver, Matthew David. BA, U. Pitts., 1964; JD, NYU, 1967. Bar: N.Y. 1967, Ohio 1969. Law clk. to judge US Dist. Ct. (so. Dist.) N.Y., N.Y.C., 1967, 68; assoc. Jones, Day, Reavis & Pogue, Cleve., 1969-75, ptnr., 1975—; alt. gov. San Jose Sharks', NHL, 1991—, dir., 1991—, San Jose Arean Mgmt. Corp., 1991—. Trustee Jewish Community Fedn., Cleve., 1976—, Bur. Jewish Edn., 1977—, Agnon Sch., Cleve., 1986—; bd. trustees Convention and Visitors Bur. of Greater Cleve., 1988—. Recipient Kane award Jewish Community Fedn., Cleve., 1976—. Mem. ABA, Cleve. Bar Assn., Order of Coif. Democrat. Office: Jones Day Reavis & Pogue N Point 901 Lakeside Ave Cleveland OH 44114

LEONARD, JAMES JOSEPH, physician, educator; b. Schenectady, June 17, 1924; s. James Joseph and Helena (Flood) L.; m. Helen Louise Mitchell, Oct. 24, 1953; children: James Joseph, W. Jeffrey, Paul Mitchell, Kathleen Marie. M.D. Georgetown U., 1950. Intern medicine Georgetown U. Hosp., 1950-51, jr. asst. resident, 1951-52, fellow cardiology, 1953-54; asst. resident medicine Boston City Hosp., 1952-53; resident pulmonary diseases D.C. Gen. Hosp., 1954-55, med. officer, 1955-56; instr. medicine Georgetown U. Med. Sch., 1955-56, Duke Med. Center, 1956-57; asst. prof. medicine, dir. div. cardiology Georgetown U. service D.C. Gen. Hosp., 1957-59; asst. prof. medicine U. Tex. Med. Br., Galveston, 1959-62; assoc. prof. medicine Ohio State U. Med. Sch., 1962-63; dir. div. cardiology U. Pitts. Med. Sch., 1963-70, asso. prof. medicine, 1963-67, prof. medicine, 1967-77, acting chmn. dept., 1970, chmn. dept., 1971-77; prof., chmn. dept. medicine Uniformed Services U. of Health Scis., 1977—. Mem. So. Soc. Clin. Investigation, Am. Clin. and Climatol. Assn., Central Soc. Clin. Research, Assn. Am. Physicians, Assn. Profs. Medicine, Assn. U. Cardiologists. Home: 3200 Farmington Dr Chevy Chase MD 20815-4827 Office: 4301 Jones Bridge Rd Bethesda MD 20814-4712

LEONARD, JOANNE, photographer, educator; b. Los Angeles, Sept. 8, 1940; 1 child, Julia Marjorie. BA, U. Calif., Berkeley, 1962; postgrad., San Francisco State U., 1963-64; Minor White workshop, 1973. Official photographer U.S Olympic team Sapporo, Japan, 1972; instr. photography San Francisco Art Inst., 1973-75, Mills Coll., Oakland, Calif., 1975-78; lectr., asst. prof. various colls. and art schs., 1970-78; asst. prof. U. Mich. Sch. Art, Ann Arbor, 1978-80, assoc prof., 1980-84, prof., 1985—. One-person shows include de Young Mus., San Francisco, 1968, Hopkins Ctr. Dartmouth Coll. 1968, Seligman Gallery, Seattle, 1969, Wall St. Gallery, Spokane, Wash., 1973, San Francisco Art Inst., 1974, Bristol (Eng.) Poly. Art Gallery, 1975, Laguna Gloria Art Mus., Austin, Tex., 1980, U. Mich. Mus. Art, 1980, Orange Coast Coll. Gallery, Costa Mesa, Calif., 1984, Jeremy Stone Gallery, San Francisco, 1985, 88, Art Mus. of U. Mich., Ann Arbor, 1992; 2-person show San Francisco Mus. Modern Art, 1981; group shows include Focus Gallery, San Francisco, 1967-74, George Eastman House, Rochester, N.Y., 1969-70, Oakland Mus., 1971, Pasadena Art Mus., 1970, Smith Anderson Gallery, Palo Alto, Calif., 1971, Mus. Contemporary Crafts, N.Y.C., 1971-

72, San Francisco Mus. Art, 1971 and 1975, Light Gallery, N.Y.C., 1972, Laguna Beach (Calif.) Mus. Art, 1973, Boston U., 1973, Hansen Fuller Gallery, San Francisco, 1974, Woods-Gerry Gallery, Providence, R.I., 1975, Neikrug Gallery, N.Y.C., 1975-76, Stanford U. Mus., 1976, 112 Green St. Gallery, N.Y.C., 1977, Gallery 115, Santa Cruz, Calif., 1977, downtown br. Whitney Mus. Art, N.Y.C., 1978, MIT, 1978, San Francisco Mus. Modern Art. 1981, 85, Franklin Inst., Phila., 1983, Gallery of Art and Sci., IBM, N.Y.C., 1984, Calif. Mus. of Photography, Riverside, 1984, Santa Barbara (Calif.) Mus. Art, 1986 (3 person) Detroit Inst. Art, 1989; represented in permanent collections, U.S. State Dept., Am. Arts Documentation Centre, Exeter, Eng., The Oakland Mus., San Francisco Mus. Art, Internat. Mus. Photography, Rochester, N.Y., U. Mass. Art Mus. Stanford U. Mus., Crocker Art Mus., Sacramento, Calif., also numerous pvt. Am. collections; represented in various mus. catalogs and books including Contemporary Photographers, 1983, Photography in California 1945-80, 1984, Janson's History of Art, 1986, American Women Artists, Past and Present, 1990, Gardner's Art Through the Ages, 9th edit., 1991. Recipient Phelan Prix award, 1971, Josephine Nevins Keal award U. Mich., 1981; photosurvey grantee Nat. Endowment for Arts, 1977; fellow Humanities Inst., U. Mich., 1993-94. Pioneering mem. of women and first photographers to be included in textbook Janson's History of Art, 3d edit., 1986, also in Gardner's Art Through the Ages, 9th edit., 1991. Office: U Mich Sch Art Ann Arbor MI 48109

LEONARD, JOHN HARRY, advertising executive; b. N.Y.C., June 28, 1922; s. Frederick H. and Florence (Kiechlin) L.; m. Marjorie Jane Haslun, Oct. 19, 1946; children—John Kiechlin, Janet Ann. B.S., N.Y. U., 1942, M.B.A., 1951. Advt. mgr. Autographic Register Co., 1946-47; promotion mgr. Macfadden Pub. Co., 1947-50; successively copywriter, account exec., v.p. and account supr. Batten, Barton, Durstine & Osborn, 1950-64; with DDB Needham Worldwide (formerly Doyle Dane Bernbach, Inc.), N.Y.C., 1964-87, group sr. v.p., 1972-87; lectr. Grad. Sch. Bus., N.Y. U., 1959-61. Bd. dirs., exec. com. Am. Bible Soc.; chmn. bd. dirs. Wartburg Home, Mt. Vernon, N.Y.; trustee NYU, 1978-84. With USAAF, 1943-46. Recipient Alumni Meritorious Service award N.Y. U., 1969. Mem. NYU Grad. Sch. Bus. Alumni Assn. (pres.), NYU Commerce Alumni Assn. (pres. 1979-80), Alpha Delta Sigma. Home: 310A Heritage Village Southbury CT 06488 Office: Wartburg Home Bradley Ave Mount Vernon NY 10552

LEONARD, JOHN WIRTH, English educator, retailer; b. Balt., July 23, 1946; s. John William and Margaret Mary (Wirth) L.; m. Ellen Louise Brooks, June 21, 1969 (div.); children—Cora Lee, John Joseph. B.S., Loyola Coll., 1968; M. equivalent Towson State U., 1977. Licensed pyrotechnist, Md. Instr. English, Baltimore County Bd. Edn., Towson, Md., 1968—; pres. Pyrotechnics Guild Inc., White Marsh, Md., 1973-76; owner, operator Sparkler City, U.S.A., Perry Hall, Md., 1983—; pyrotechnic operator Zambelli Fireworks, New Castle, Pa., 1979—. Designer fireworks ground display (Plaque for best display), 1975. Mem. Pyrotechnics Guild Internat., Inc. (pres. 1975-77). Democrat. Roman Catholic. Clubs: Crackerjacks; Fireworks (Wood Bridge, Va.) (pres. 1982—). Lodge: K.C. (warden 1978-79). Home: 8841 Satyr Hill Rd Baltimore MD 21234-2331 Office: Baltimore County Bd Edn 1000 S Morven Ave Baltimore MD 21201

LEONARD, KURT JOHN, plant pathologist, university program director; b. Holstein, Iowa, Dec. 6, 1939; s. Elvin Elsworth and Irene Marie (Helkenn) L.; m. Maren Jane Simonsen, May 28, 1961; children: Maria Catherine, Mary Alice, Benjamin Andrew. BS, Iowa State U., 1962; PhD, Cornell U., 1968. Plant pathologist Agrl. Rsch. Svc. USDA, Raleigh, N.C., 1968-88; dir. Cereal Rust Lab. U. Minn. USDA, St. Paul, 1988—. Author: (with others) Annual Review of Phytopathology, 1980; co-editor: Plant Disease Epidemiology, vol. 1, 1986, vol. 2, 1989; editor-in-chief Phytopathology, 1981-84, APS Press, 1994—; contbr. 76 articles to profl. jours. Fellow Am. Phytopathol. Soc. (coun. 1981-84, 94—); mem. Am. Mycol. Soc., Internat. Soc. Plant Pathology (councilor 1982-93), Brit. Soc. Plant Pathology, Phi Kappa Phi, Sigma Xi, Gamma Sigma Delta. Achievements include description of new species and genera of plant pathogenic fungi; research on spread of disease through crop mixtures, on relationships between virulence and fitness in plant pathogenic fungi. Office: U Minn Usda Ars Cereal Lab Saint Paul MN 55108

LEONARD, LAURENCE BARBERIE, JR., investment company executive; b. Boston, Apr. 29, 1930; s. Laurence Barberie and Barbara (Beardsell) L.; m. Joan Willenbrok, Dec. 3, 1960; children: George, Susan. B.A., Harvard U., 1952; M.B.A., Stanford U., 1957. With Mfrs. Hanover Bank, N.Y.C., 1957-61; v.p. Eaton & Howard, Boston, 1961-71; v.p. Mass. Fin. Services, Boston, 1971-85, sr. v.p., 1985—; pres. Mass. Income Devel. Fund, Boston, 1981-85, Mass. Investors Trust, Boston, 1985—; trustee Lynn Inst. Colonial Bank for Savs., Mass., 1975—. Trustee Lynn Hosp., 1965-75; mem. exec. bd. Lynn Family and Children's Service; bd. dirs. Marblehead Youth Soccer Assn., Mass. Served with U.S. Army, 1952-55. Mem. Beach (dir. pres., Swampscott, Mass.), Tedesco Country (dir., sec., Marblehead), Eastern Yacht Club (Marblehead). Republican. Home: 12 Flint St Marblehead MA 01945-3743 Office: Mass Investors Trust 500 Boylston St Boston MA 02116-3740

LEONARD, MICHAEL, federal official; b. Ft. Benning, Ga., June 14, 1941; s. Charles Frederick and Margery Alden (Beukema) L.; m. Mary Eleanor Baluss, May 26, 1973; children, Claire, Alan, Keith. BS, U.S. Mil. Acad., 1964; MA, Harvard U., 1970. Commd. 2d lt. U.S. Army, 1964, advanced through grades to capt., 1967; officer 24th Inf. Div. U.S. Army, Fed. Republic Germany, 1964-66, U.S. Mil. Assist. Command, Republic of Vietnam, 1966-67; officer 902d Mil. Intelligence Group, Washington, 1968, U.S. Mil. Assist. Command, Saigon, Republic of Vietnam, 1969; budget analyst Office of Mgmt. and Budget, Washington, 1970-71; opns. rsch. analyst Office Asst. Sec. Def. (Program Analysis and Evaluation), Washington, 1971-75, div. chief, 1975-80, Dep. Asst. Sec. Def., 1980-87, Prin. Dep. Asst. Sec. Def., 1987-92. Decorated Bronze Star; recipient Def. Disting. Civilian Svc. award, SES Meritorious rank, 1981, 87, Disting. rank, 1989. Avocations: reading, hiking, boating. Home: 2850 Arizona Terr Washington DC 20016 Office: The Pentagon Rm 38835 Dept Def Asst Sec Program Analysis Washington DC 20301

LEONARD, MICHAEL A., automotive executive; b. Cadillac, Mich., Aug. 3, 1937; s. Hugel A. and Mildred (Johnson) L.; m. Frances Erickson, June 18, 1960; children: Kristin, Anne. MA, Alma Coll., 1959; MBA, Wayne State U., 1964; MS, MIT, 1971. Exec. Chrysler Corp., Highland Park, Mich., 1959-75; group v.p. Bendix Corp., Southfield, Mich., 1975-83; v.p., group exec. Allied Signal Automotive, Bloomfield Hills, Mich., 1983-91; pres. Harman, Inc., Southfield, Mich., 1991-94; mng. ptnr. Exec. Resources Inc., Bloomfield Hills, Mich., 1994—; bd. dirs. Kalyani Brake Co., Pune, India, Bendix France, Paris, Bendix Italy, and fgn. subs. Trustee Alma (Mich.) Coll.; bd. dirs. Presbyn. Villages of Mich. Sloan fellow, MIT. Mem. Soc. Automotive Engrs., Delta Sigma Phi (pres. 1958-59). Presbyterian. Avocations: swimming, golf, boating. Home: 4375 Barchester Dr Bloomfield Hills MI 48302-2116 Office: Executive Resources Inc PO Box 625 Bloomfield Hills MI 48303-9999

LEONARD, MICHAEL STEVEN, industrial engineering educator; b. Salisbury, N.C., Feb. 2, 1947; s. Charles Thomas and Dorothy Francis (Loflin) L.; m. Mary Elizabeth Stewart, June 21, 1969; children: Dorothy Elizabeth, Amanda Brooke, Gabrielle Francis. B in Engring., U. Fla., 1970, M in Engring., 1972, PhD, 1973. Registered profl. engr., Mo., S.C. Asst. prof. health systems rsch. ctr. Georgia Tech, Atlanta, 1973-75; asst. prof. indsl. engring. U. Mo., Columbia, 1975-79, assoc. prof. indsl. engring. 1979-82, prof. indsl. engring., 1982-90, dept. chmn. indsl. engring., 1985-90; dept. head indsl. engring. Clemson (S.C.) U., 1990—; program evaluator accreditaton bd. engring. and tech. N.Y.C., 1988—. Editor Jour. Soc. for Health Systems, 1989-91; contbr. articles to profl. jours. evaluation adv. com. Am. Blood Commn., Washington, 1977-80; bd. dirs. Am. Cancer Soc. Boone County Mo. unit, Columbia, 1978-90. Mem. Soc. Health Systems (bd. dirs. 1989-94, pres. elect 1991-92, pres. 1992-93), Inst. Indsl. Engrs. (nat. dir. career guidance 1987—), Mo. Soc. Profl. Engrs. (cen. chpt. treas. 1988-89, v.p. 1989-90). Office: Clemson U Dept Indsl Engring Clemson SC 29634

LEONARD, NELSON JORDAN, chemistry educator; b. Newark, Sept. 1, 1916; s. Harvey Nelson and Olga Pauline (Jordan) L.; m. Louise Cornelie Vermey, May 10, 1947 (dec. 1987); children: Kenneth Jan, Marcia Louise, James Nelson, David Anthony; m. Margaret Taylor Phelps, Nov. 14, 1992. B.S. in Chemistry, Lehigh U., 1937, Sc.D., 1963; B.Sc., Oxford (Eng.) U., 1940, D.Sc., 1983; Ph.D., Columbia U., 1942; D.h.c., Adam Mickiewicz U., Poland, 1980; D.Sc. (hon.), U. Ill., 1988. Fellow and rsch. asst. chemistry U. Ill., Urbana, 1942-43, instr., 1943-44, assoc., 1944-45, 46-47, asst. prof., 1947-49, assoc. prof., 1949-52, prof. organic chemistry, 1952-73, head div. organic chemistry, 1954-63, prof. biochemistry, 1973-86, R.C. Fuson prof. chemistry, mem. Ctr. for Advanced Study, 1981-86, R.C. Fuson prof. emeritus, 1986—; investigator antimalarial program Com. Med. Research, OSRD, 1944-46; sci. cons. and spl. investigator Field Intelligence Agy. Tech., U.S. Army and Dept. Commerce, 1945-46; mem. Can. NRC, summer 1950; Swiss-Am. Found. lectr., 1953, 70; vis. lectr. UCLA, summer 1953; Reilly lectr. U. Notre Dame, 1962; Stieglitz lectr. Chgo. sect. Am. Chem. Soc., 1962; Robert A. Welch Found. lectr., 1964, 83; Disting. vis. lectr. U. Calif.-Davis, 1975; vis. lectr. Polish Acad. Scis., 1976; B.R. Baker Meml. lectr. U. Calif., Santa Barbara, 1976; Ritter Meml. lectr. Miami U., Oxford, Ohio; Werner E. Bachman Meml. lectr. U. Mich., Ann Arbor, 1977; vis. prof. Japan Soc. Promotion of Sci., 1978; Arapahoe lectr. U. Colo., 1979; Tanabe rsch. lectr. Scripps Rsch. Inst., La Jolla, Calif., 1993; mem. program com. in basic scis. Arthur P. Sloan, Jr. Found., 1961-66; Philips lectr. Haverford Coll., 1971; Backer lectr., Groningen, Netherlands, 1972; FMC lectr. Princeton U., 1973; plenary lectr. Laaxer Chemistry Conf., Laax, Switzerland, 1980, 82, 84, 88, 90, 92; Calbiochem-Behring Corp. U. Calif.-San Diego Found. lectr., 1981; Watkins vis. prof. Wichita State U. (Kans.), 1982; Ida Beam Disting. vis. prof. U. Iowa, 1983; Fogarty scholar-in-residence NIH, Bethesda, Md., 1989-90; Sherman Fairchild Disting. scholar Calif. Inst. Tech., 1991; Syntex. disting. lectr. U. Colo., 1992; faculty assoc. Calif. Inst. Tech., 1992—; mem. adv. com. Searle Scholars program Chgo. Community Trust, 1982-85; ednl. adv. bd. Guggenheim Found., 1969-88, mem. com. of selection, 1977-88. Editor: Organic Syntheses, 1951-58, mem. adv. bd., 1958—, bd. dirs., 1969—, v.p., 1976-80, pres., 1980-88; editorial bd. Jour. Organic Chemistry, 1957-61, Jour. Am. Chem. Soc, 1960-72; adv. bd. Biochemistry, 1973-78, Chemistry International, 1984-91, Pure and Applied Chemistry, 1984-91; contbr. articles to profl. jours. Recipient Am. Chem. Soc. award, 1963, medal Synthetic Organic Chem. Mfrs., 1970, Wheland award U. Chgo., 1991, Creativity award U. Oreg., 1994; named to Mt. Vernon High Sch. Hall of Fame, N.Y., 1985; Rockefeller Found. fellow, 1950, Guggenheim Meml. fellow, 1959, 67. Fellow Am. Acad. Arts and Scis. (v.p. 1991—); mem. NAS, AAAS, Polish Acad. Scis. (fgn.), Ill. Acad. Sci. (hon.), Am. Chem. Soc. (Edgar Fahs Smith award and lectureship Phila. sect. 1975, Centennial lectr. 1976, Roger Adams award 1981), Am. Soc. Biol. Chemists, Chem. Soc. London, Swiss Chem. Soc., Internat. Union Pure and Applied Chemistry (sec. organic chemistry div. 1989, v.p. 1989-91, pres. 1991-93), Pharm Soc. (hon.), Phi Beta Kappa, Phi Lambda Upsilon (hon.), Tau Beta Pi, Alpha Chi Sigma. Achievements include patents on synthesis of sparteine; esters of pyridine dicarboxylic acid as insect repellents; fluorescent derivatives of adenine- and cytosine-containing compounds. Home: 389 California Ter Pasadena CA 91105-2463

LEONARD, PAUL HARALSON, retired lawyer; b. Houston, Mar. 4, 1925; s. Paul Haralson and Dovie Lore (Shuler) L.; m. Barbara Ann Underwood, Nov. 26, 1948; children: Leslie Ann, Scott Paul. BA, Rice U., 1948; JD, South Tex. Coll. of Law, 1957. Bar: Tex. 1957, U.S. Patent and Trademark Office 1960, U.S. Ct. Appeals (10th cir.) 1963, U.S. Ct. Mil. Appeals 1965, U.S. Supreme Ct. 1965, U.S. Ct. Appeals (5th cir.) 1981, U.S. Ct. Appeals (Fed. cir.) 1982. Acct. Highland Oil Co., Houston, 1948-50; statis. acct. Union Oil and Gas Corp. of La., Houston, 1953-59; assoc. Hayden & Pravel, Houston, 1959-61; patent atty. Halliburton Co., Duncan, Okla., 1961-69; div. patent atty. Ethyl Corp., Baton Rouge, 1969-87; v.p. Cen. Foods, Inc., Baton Rouge, 1979-90, bd. dirs. V.p. Plato Dependent Sch. Dist., Duncan, Okla., 1966-67, pres., 1968. Served to lt. comdr., USNR, 1942-67. Mem. Tex. Bar Assn., Duncan Country Club, Elks, Shriners, Masons. Republican. Avocations: U.S. coins, stamp collecting. Home and Office: 10639 Rondo Ave Baton Rouge LA 70815-4847

LEONARD, R. MICHAEL, lawyer; b. Atlanta, Feb. 27, 1953; s. Charles C. and Catherine (Martin) L.; m. Margaret Ellen Mead, June 29, 1985 (div. 1993); 1 child, Sarah Marie. AB, U. N.C., 1975, JD with honors, 1978. Bar: Ala. 1978, N.C. 1987. Assoc. Cabaniss, Johnston, Gardner, Dumas & O'Neal, Birmingham, Ala., 1978-85, ptnr., 1985-86; assoc. Womble Carlyle Sandridge & Rice, Winston-Salem, N.C., 1986-88, ptnr., 1988—. Author: Trail and Naturalist's Guide to Oak Mountain State Park, Alabama, 1982. Bd. dirs. Ala. Conservancy, Birmingham, 1981-85, Piedmont Land Conservancy, Greensboro, N.C., 1989-91; bd. dirs. Ala. Trails Assn. Birmingham, 1985—, founder, pres., 1985-87; trustee N.C. Nat. Heritage Found., Raleigh, 1989-92, Nature Sci. Ctr., Winston-Salem, 1987-91, Ruffner Mountain Nature Ctr., Birmingham, 1982-86; mem. capital campaign com. Bethabara Historic Park, Winston-Salem, 1994-95; gov.'s appointee N.C. Natural Heritage Trust for Pub. Land, San Francisco, 1991—. Recipient Oak Leaf award Nature Conservancy, Washington, 1991, Sol Feinstone Environ. award Coll. Environ. Sci. & Forestry, SUNY, Rochester, 1991, Chpt. Svc. award N.C. Chpt. Sierra Club, 1990, Malcolm Stewart Conservationist of Yr. award Ala. Conservancy, Birmingham, 1983. Mem. Ala. Bar Assn., N.C. Bar Assn., Birmingham Bar Assn., Forsyth County Bar Assn., Carolina Club, Black Bear Club, Order of Coif, Phi Beta Kappa, Phi Eta Sigma. Democrat. Avocations: writing, hiking, mountain climbing, camping, turkey hunting. Office: Womble Carlyle Sandridge & Rice 200 W 2d St 1600 So Nat Fin Ctr Winston Salem NC 27101

LEONARD, RICHARD ALAN, newspaper editor; b. Beverly, Mass., Aug. 8, 1952; s. Philip E. nad Celia M. (Sikora) Boynton; m. Laura Jean Nowicki, Sept. 17, 1983; children: Matthew, Susan, Audrey. BA in History and Sociology, Holy Cross Coll., 1974; MS in Journalism, Columbia U., 1976. Reporter Westchester-Rockland Newspapers, White Plains, N.Y., 1977-80, metro editor, 1980-83; mng. editor The Journal News, West Nyack, N.Y., 1983-87; exec. editor Gannett Co. Inc., Arlington, Va., 1987-95. Mem. Am. Soc. Newspaper Editors. Office: Valley News Dispatch 210 4th Ave Tarentum PA 15084

LEONARD, RICHARD HART, journalist; b. N.Y.C., May 23, 1921; s. Richard Barstow and Stella Burnham (Hart) L.; m. Barbara Klausner, July 11, 1948; children: Laurie, Lisa. BA, U. Wis., 1947. Reporter Milw. Jour., 1947, picture editor, 1948, with Madison (Wis.) bur., 1949-50, state desk, 1951-52, state editor, 1953-62, mng. editor, 1962-66; editor, v.p. Milw. Jour. Co., 1967-85, v.p., 1967-77, sr. v.p., 1977-85, ret., 1986; editor-in-residence East-West Ctr., Honolulu, 1987; sr. fellow East-West Ctr., 1988-89; mem. Pulitzer Prize Bd., 1976-86; prof. journalism Marquette U., 1989—. With AUS, 1942-46. Recipient Carr Van Anda award Ohio U., 1972, East-West Ctr. Disting. Svc. award, Disting. Svc. award U. Wis. Mem. Am. Soc. Newspaper Editors, Internat. Press Inst. (chmn. 1984-86), Milw. Press Club (pres. 1965, elected Hall of Fame), Sigma Delta Chi (nat. pres. 1976), Phi Kappa Phi. Presbyterian. Home: 330 E Beaumont Ave Milwaukee WI 53217-4867

LEONARD, ROBERT DOUGHERTY, communications company executive; b. Chgo., Apr. 15, 1942; s. Robert D. and Ruth Janet (Tankersley) L.; m. Janet Catherine Link, May 10, 1969; children: James Richard, John Banks, Anne Catherine. BS in Gen. Engring., U. Ill., 1964, BS in Communications, 1965. Engr. Teletype Corp., Skokie, Ill., 1965-68, tech. pubs. engr., 1968-72, planning engr., 1972-77; engring. staff mgr. AT&T Network Svcs., Basking Ridge, N.J., 1977-80; staff mgr. AT&T Bus. Svcs., Basking Ridge, 1980-82; dep. chief AT&T Teletype Corp., Skokie, 1982-85; dist. mgr. printers AT&T Computer Systems, Skokie, 1985-87; regional mgr. gateways Mitek Systems Corp., Northfield, Ill., 1987-88; product mgr. broadcast transmission line products Andrew Corp., Orland Park, Ill., 1988—. Contbr. to profl. publs. Mem. Am. Mktg. Assn. (exec.), Numismatic Lit. Guild (life), Am. Numismatic Assn., Am. Numismatic Soc., Am. Israel Numismatic Assn., Token and Medal Soc. (treas. 1993—). Republican. Methodist. Avocations: numismatic research, writing, speaking. Home: 1065 Spruce St Winnetka IL 60093-2169 Office: Andrew Corp 10500 153rd St Orland Park IL 60462-3071

LEONARD, ROBERT SEAN, actor; b. N.J., Feb. 28, 1969; s. Robert Howard and Joyce (Peterson) L. Stage debut in Oliver; stage appearances include Coming of Age in Soho, Sally's Gone, She's Left Her Name, 1985, The Beach House, Brighton Beach Memoirs, 1986, Breaking the Code, 1987, When She Danced, Biloxi Blues (tour), Romeo and Juliet, The Speed of Darkness, Our Town, Candida, Arcadia; film appearances include The Manhattan Project, 1986, My Best Friend Is A Vampire, 1988, Dead Poets Society, 1989, Mr. & Mrs. Bridge, 1990, Married to It, 1993, Swing Kids, 1993, Much Ado About Nothing, 1993, The Age of Innocence, 1993, Safe Passage, 1994; TV movies include My Two Loves, 1986, Bluffing It, 1987. Office: William Morris Agency 151 El Camino Beverly Hills CA 90212*

LEONARD, ROY JUNIOR, civil engineering educator; b. Central Square, N.Y., Aug. 17, 1929; s. Roy Jackson and Margaret Elizabeth (Keller) L.; m. Edith Campbell Gilmore; children: Robert J., Constance J. BS, Clarkson Coll. Tech., 1952; MS, U. Conn., 1954; postgrad., Mich. State U., 1954-55; PhD, Iowa State U., 1958. Registered profl. engr., N.Y., Pa., Kans., Mo., Colo. Asst. prof. civil engring. U. Del., 1957-59; assoc. prof. Lehigh U., 1959-65; spl. projects engr. Dames and Moore (geotech. cons.), N.Y.C., 1965; prof. civil engring. U. Kans., Lawrence, 1965-95; pres. Alpha-Omega Geotech., Inc., Kansas City, Kans. NSF fellow, 1964-65. Fellow ASCE; mem. Assn. Engring. Geologists, U.S. Com. Large Dams, Soc. Mining Engrs., Am. Soc. Testing Materials, Profl. Engrs. in Pvt. Practice, Nat. Soc. Forensic Engrs., Nat. Soc. Profl. Engrs., Am. Concrete Inst., Am. Pub. Works Assn., Chi Epsilon. Episcopalian. Home: 25003 Mackey Rd Lawrence KS 66044-7340

LEONARD, SAMUEL WALLACE, oil company executive; b. Cumberland, R.I., Sept. 29, 1922; s. Samuel James and Hazel Della (Flagg) L.; m. Dorothy Wilma Carpenter, Oct. 15, 1949. BS in Acctg. and Fin., Bryant Coll., 1941; BA in Econs., Brown U., 1948; student, Harvard U., 1969. Internal auditor Conoco Inc., Ponca City, Okla., 1948-51; asst. dir. employee benefits Conoco Inc., Houston, 1952-54; pres., gen. mgr. Sahara Petroleum Co., Alexandria, Egypt, 1954-60; v.p., treas. Pasa Petroquimica Argentina, Buenos Aires, 1961-66; pres. Conoco Libya, Tripoli, 1966-71, Conoco Española, Madrid, Spain, 1971-72; exec. asst. pres. Conoco Inc., Stamford, Conn., 1972-76; v.p., gen. mgr. Dubai (United Arab Emirates) Petroleum, 1976-82; ret.; chmn. bd. dirs. Security Bank and Trust Co., Ponca City, 1992-93; bd. dirs. Bank IV Okla., Ponca City. Chmn. Little League, Tripoli, Libya, 1966-71; bd. dirs. Ponca City Libr., 1988—. Sgt. U.S. Army, 1942-45, U.S. and Europe. Decorated Purple Heart, Bronze Star. Mem. VFW, Am. Legion, Ponca City Country Club, Elks. Republican. Episcopal. Avocations: hunting, fishing, travel, gardening. Home and Office: PO Box 667 Ponca City OK 74602-0667

LEONARD, SHELDON, television producer, director; b. N.Y.C., Feb. 22, 1907; s. Frank and Anna (Levitt) Bershad; m. Frances Bober, June 28, 1931; children: Andrea, Stephen W. BA, Syracuse U., 1929. Pres. T. & L. Prodns.; ptnr. Mayberry Prodns.; ptnr., officer Calvada Prodns., Sheldon Leonard Enterprises; guest producer Syracuse U. Screenwriter: Checkmate, others, 1948-57; actor numerous Broadway plays, 1930-39; numerous motion picture appearances; radio roles with Jack Benny, Bob Hope, Phil Harris, others; producer, dir. TV shows: I Spy, Dick Van Dyke, Andy Griffith, Danny Thomas, others; star TV series: Big Eddie, 1975 (Emmy award 1957, 61, Best Comedy Producer, 1970, 74, Christopher award 1955, Golden Globe award 1972, Sylvania award 1973). Trustee Motion Picture Home. Recipient Man of Yr. awards Nat. Assn. Radio Announcers, Profl. Mgrs. Guild, B'nai B'rith; Arents medal Syracuse U., Spl. Achievement award NAACP, Spl. Tribute award Nat. Collegiate Athletic Assn., Letterman of Distinction award Varsity Club Syracuse U., Govs. award Cinematographers Guild; inducted TV Hall of Fame, 1992. Mem. Dirs. Guild (hon. life, nat. trustee, bd. govds., v.p. Aldrich award). Home: 1141 Loma Vista Dr Beverly Hills CA 90210-2622 Office: Sheldon Leonard Prodns 2121 Avenue Of The Stars Los Angeles CA 90067 A man must be at peace with himself.

LEONARD, STEWART J., dairy company executive; b. Norwalk, Conn., Dec. 1, 1929; s. Charles Leo and Anna (Stewart) L.; m. Marianne Guthman, Oct. 15, 1952; children—Stewart J. Jr., Thomas, Beth, Jill. Grad. in dairy mfg., U. Conn., 1951. Pres. Clover Farms Dairy, Norwalk, 1957-69; chmn. Stew Leonard's, Norwalk, 1969—. Patentee skee-trainer, 1975. Recipient Presdl. award for Entrepreneurial Excellence, Conn. Small Bus. Advocate, 1986. U.S. water ski champion, 1955. Office: 100 Westport Ave Norwalk CT 06851-3915

LEONARD, SUGAR RAY (RAY CHARLES LEONARD), retired professional boxer; b. Wilmington, N.C., May 17, 1956; s. Cicero and Getha L.; m. Juanita Wilkinson, Jan. 19, 1980 (div. 1990); children: Ray Charles, Jr., Jarrell Giulio. Profl. boxer, 1977-82, 84, 1987-91; pres. SRL Mgmt., Inc.; with Franklin Sports Industries, Inc. Commentator boxing broadcasts; exercise video: Boxout with Sugar Ray Leonard, 1993. Recipient Gold medal Olympic Games, 1976; winner World Boxing Coun. Welterweight Championship, 1979, World Boxing Assn. Championship Jr. Middleweight div., 1981, World Boxing Coun. Championship and World Boxing Assn. Welterweight Championship, 1981, World Boxing Coun. Middleweight Championship, 1987, World Boxing Coun. Light Heavyweight and Super Middleweight Championship, 1988. Office: care Mike Trainer 4922 Fairmont Ave Bethesda MD 20814-6020*

LEONARD, THOMAS ALOYSIUS, lawyer; b. Phila., Sept. 5, 1946; s. Thomas Aloysius and Mary Teresa (Kelly) L.; m. Kathleen Mary Duffy; children: Sarah, Mary Kate, Tom. BS, Drexel U., 1968; JD, Temple U., 1971. Bar: Pa., U.S. Supreme Ct., U.S. Ct. Appeals (3d cir.), U.S. Dist. Ct. (ea., mid., we. dists) Pa., U.S. Dist. Ct. (so. dist.) N.J., U.S. Dist. Ct. Utah, U.S. Dist. Ct. (so. dist.) N.Y. Assoc. Dilworth, Paxson, Kalish & Kauffman, Phila., 1972-76, ptnr., 1976-79, 83-87, sr. ptnr., mem. exec. com., 1987—; controller City of Phila., 1987-91; chmn. litigation dept., sr. ptnr., permanent mem. mgmt. com. Obermayer, Rebmann, Maxwell and Hippel, Phila., 1991—; bd. dirs. Fed. Nat. Mortgage Assn., Independence Blue Cross; vice chmn. Phila. Gas Commn., 1979-83; register of wills City of Phila., 1976-79; mem. disciplinary bd. Supreme Ct., Pa., 1991—. Mem. editorial bd. Amran's Pa. Practice, 1972; contbr. articles to profl. publs. Mem. Dem. Nat. Com., Washington, 1976-83, mem. fin. com., 1988, vice chair Pa., 1993, Pa. fin. chair, 1993—, bd. dirs.; del. Dem. Nat. Conv., 1976, 80, 92; chmn. Pa. fin. com. Clinton for Pres.; co-chair Rendell for Mayor; mem. coun. Phila. Orch., 1981-86; bd. dirs. Acad. Scis., Phila., 1981-85; pres. Pa. chpt. Irish Am. Partnership. Capt. U.S. Army, 1971-77. Recipient Man of Yr. award Emerald Soc., 1979, Korean-Am. Friendship Soc., 1982, Carmel Humanitarian award Haifa U., 1981, Merit award Chapel of Four Chaplains, 1983. Mem. ABA, Pa. Bar Assn., Phila. Bar Assn. (bd. govs. 1979-82), Union League, Phila. Racquet Club, Serra Club (past pres.). Roman Catholic. Office: Obermayer Rebmann Maxwell and Hippel Packard Building Fl 14 Philadelphia PA 19102

LEONARD, TIMOTHY DWIGHT, judge; b. Jan. 22, 1940; s. Dwight and Mary Evelyn Leonard; m. Nancy Louise Laughlin, July 15, 1967; children: Kirstin Dione, Ryan Timothy, Tyler Dwight. BA, U. Okla., 1962; JD, 1965; student Mil. Naval Justice Sch., 1966. Bar: Okla. 1965, U.S. Dist. Ct. (no. and we. dists) Okla. 1969, U.S. Ct. Appeals (10th cir.) 1969, U.S. Supreme Ct. 1970. Asst. atty. gen. State of Okla., 1968-70, senator, 1979-88; ptnr. Blankenship, Herrold, Russell et al, Oklahoma City, 1970-71, Trippet, Leonard & Kee, Beaver, 1971-88; of counsel Huckaby, Fleming, et al., Oklahoma City, 1988-89; U.S. atty. Western Dist. Okla., 1989-92; judge U.S. Dist. Ct. (we. dist.) Okla., 1992—; guest lectr., chmn. Oklahoma City U., 1988-89. Mem. U.S. Atty. Gen.'s Adv. Com., 1990-92, chmn. office mgmt. and budget subcom., 1990-92. Co-author: 4 Days, 40 Hours, 1970. Rep. H. st gov. candidate Okla.; minority leader Okla. State Senate, 1985-86; white ho. mil. aide, Washington, 1966-67. Lt. USN, 1965-68, Washington. Named Outstanding Legislator Okla. Sch. Bd. Assn., 1988. Mem. ABA, Okla. Bar Assn., Phi Alpha Delta, Beta Theta Pi. Republican. Methodist. Avocations: basketball, running, reading. Home: PO Box 54587 Oklahoma City OK 73154-1587 Office: 200 NW 4th St Bldg 5102 Oklahoma City OK 73102-3031

LEONARD, WALTER RAYMOND, retired biology educator; b. Scott County, Va., July 5, 1923; s. Homer Stanley and Minnie Eunice (Neal) L.; m. Alice Ann McCaskill, Sept. 1, 1951; children—Leslie Ann, Walter

Raymond. B.A., Tusculum Coll., Greeneville, Tenn., 1946; M.A., Vanderbilt U., 1947, Ph.D., 1949. Mem. faculty Wofford Coll., Spartanburg, S.C., 1949-93; John M. Reeves prof. biology Wofford Coll., 1954-87, William R. Kenan Jr. prof. biology, 1987-93, prof. emeritus, 1993—; instl. rev. bd. mem. Spartanburg Regional Med. Ctr., 1994—; faculty athletic rep. NCAA. Served with USAAF, 1942-43. Named to Sports Hall of Fame, Tusculum Coll., 1983; Walter Raymond Leonard scholarship created Wofford Coll., 1973; W. Ray Leonard award established Beta Beta Beta, 1993; W. Ray Leonard Retirement Fund established Former Students Wofford Coll., 1993. Mem. AAAS, S.C. Acad. Sci., Scabbard and Blade (hon.), Lambda Chi Alpha, Letterman's Club (hon.). Methodist. Rsch. on cell metabolism. Home: 110 Pinetree Cir Spartanburg SC 29307-2938 Office: Wofford Coll N Church St Spartanburg SC 29301

LEONARD, WILL ERNEST, JR., lawyer; b. Shreveport, La., Jan. 18, 1935; s. Will Ernest and Nellie (Kenner) L.; m. Maureen Laniak; children—Will Ernest III, Sherry Elizabeth, Robert Scott, Stephen Michael, Christopher Anthony, Colleen Mary, Leigh Alison. B.A., Tulane U., 1956, LL.B., 1958; LL.M., Harvard U., 1966. Bar: La. 1958, D.C. 1963, U.S Supreme Ct. 1963. Announcer sta. WVUE-TV, New Orleans, 1958-60; legislative asst. to U.S. Senator Russell B. Long, 1960-65; profl. staff mem. com. fin. U.S. Senate, 1966-68; mem. Internat. Trade Commn. (formerly U.S. Tariff Commn.), 1968-77, chmn., 1975-76; ptnr. Stroock & Stroock & Lavan, Washington, 1992—; Congl. staff fellow Am. Polit. Sci. Assn., 1965-66. Home: 7324 Bradley Blvd Bethesda MD 20817-2130 Office: Stroock & Stroock & Lavan 1150 17th St NW Ste 600 Washington DC 20036-4603

LEONARDICH, AGNES M., school system administrator. Supt. schs. Diocese of Monterey, Calif. Office: Dept Cath Schs PO Box 350 Monterey CA 93942-0350

LEONBERGER, FREDERICK JOHN, electrical engineer, photonics manager; b. Washington, Sept. 25, 1947; s. Melvin Fred and Mary Dorothy (Burchell) L.; m. Janet Marie Bueche, Aug. 8, 1970; children—Gregory, Katharine. B.S.E., U. Mich., 1969; S.M., MIT, 1971, E.E., 1972, Ph.D., 1975. Mem. staff MIT Lincoln Lab., Lexington, 1975-81; group leader MIT Lincoln Lab., 1981-84; mgr. photonics and applied physics United Tech. Rsch. Ctr., East Hartford, Conn., 1984-91; gen. mgr. United Tech. Photonics, 1991—. Contbr. articles to profl. jours.; patentee in field. Fellow IEEE (tech. program com. 1979—, assoc. editor Jour. Quantum Electronics 1983-87), Optical Soc. Am. (tech. program com. 1979—, assoc. editor Optics Letters 1988-91); mem. IEEE Lasers and Electrooptics Soc. (adminstrv. com. 1984-86, pres. 1988, Quantum Electronics award 1993), Sigma Xi, Tau Beta Pi, Eta Kappa Nu. Avocations: tennis, golf, hiking, classical music. Office: United Tech Photonics 1289 Blue Hills Ave Bloomfield CT 06002

LEONE, GEORGE FRANK, pharmaceutical executive; b. Astoria, N.Y., Aug. 1, 1926; s. George and Fannie K. (Teano) L.); m. Mary Louise Potts, Dec. 14, 1945; children: Pamela Ann, George Frank. BS, Wesleyan U., 1949; postgrad., NYU, 1951; grad. Advanced Mgmt. Program,, Harvard Bus. Sch., 1959; postgrad., U. Tex., 1977; DSc (hon.), Tex. Wesleyan U., 1990. Chemist, Lederle Labs., Pearl River, N.Y., 1949-50; with Alcon Labs., Inc., Ft. Worth, 1950—; med. sales rep. Alcon Labs., Inc., 1950-54, dist. sales mgr., 1954-58, regional sales mgr., 1958-63, nat. sales mgr., 1963-66, dir. mktg., 1966-69, gen. mgr. domestic, 1969-70, v.p. sci., tech., 1971-81, sr. v.p., 1981—, also dir.; Pres. Laksmi Corp., Fort Worth, 1989—; pres. Avicon, Inc., 1972-79. Pres., commr. Earth County Water Control and Improvement, Dist. 1, 1976-80; trustee Tex. Wesleyan U., fin. com., exec. com., 1985—; bd. dirs. Tex. Christian U. Rsch. Found., 1976-82; chmn. athletic com. Dan Danciger Jewish Community Ctr.; pres. Peninsula Pecan Growers Assn., 1980-85; mem. fin. com. Fort Worth Acad., 1984-88, bd. dirs., 1986-88. With USN, 1944-46. Named Disting. Alumnus Tex. Wesleyan Coll., 1994. Mem. Yoga Soc. N.Y. (pres., bd. dirs. 1978—), Am. Radio Relay League, Alpha Chi. Club: Fort Worth. Home: 4100 Hildring Dr E Fort Worth TX 76109-4714 Office: Laksmi Corp 6201 S Freeway PO Box 1959 Fort Worth TX 76134-2099 also: 321 Monika Pl Saint Augustine FL 32084-6441

LEONE, LOUIS J., marketing and communications executive; b. Union City, N.J., Mar. 17, 1936; s. Louis J. and Catherine (DeVercelly) L.; m. Susan I. Sawtelle, Aug. 3, 1957; children: Louis C., Marian K., Mark O. BA, U. Tampa, 1972; MA, Cen. Mich. U., 1979. Enlisted U.S. Army, 1959, advanced through grades to lt. col.; pub. affairs officer US Forces in Iran U.S. Army, Tehran, 1974-76; brigade advisor 56th Infantry, 28th Infantry U.S. Army, 1976-78; chief tng. br. U.S. Army Readiness Region II U.S. Army, Ft. Dix, N.J., 1978-79; chief civil liaison br. hdqrs. Dept. of Army U.S. Army, Washington, 1979-82; dir. pub. affairs U.S. Mil. Acad. U.S. Army, Westpoint, N.Y., 1982-84; ret. U.S. Army, 1984; dir. devel. Northeastern Assn. of Blind, Albany, N.Y., 1984-87; mil. liaison Regents Coll. USNY, Albany, 1989-93, dir. military affairs, 1990—. Mayor Greenwich Village, 1986—, trustee, 1985-86; dir. Tri-County Am. Heart Assn., Glens Falls, N.Y., 1987-89. Mem. VFW, Am. Legion, Greenwich C. of C. (bd. dirs. 1989—), Greenwich Village Bus. Assn. (bd. dirs. 1986-89), Am. Assn. Counseling and Devel., Mil. Edn. Counselors Assn., Assn. of U.S. Army, Ret. Officers Assn., Elks, Lions, Alpha Chi. Republican. Roman Catholic. Avocations: hunting, fishing. Home: 181 Main St Greenwich NY 12834-1009

LEONE, PETER R., lawyer; b. Medina, N.Y., Aug. 19, 1940. BA, Middlebury Coll., 1962; LLB, Suffolk U., 1966; LLM, Boston U., 1982. Bar: Mass. 1967. Asst. atty. gen. Commonwealth of Mass., Boston, 1967-69; gen. counsel Mass. Rate Setting Commn., Boston, 1971-81; ptnr. McDermott, Will & Emery, Boston. Mem. Health Care Fin. Mgmt. Assn. (Mass. chpt. bd. dirs. 1989-91). Office: McDermott Will & Emery 75 State St Ste 1700 Boston MA 02109-1812

LEONE, STEPHEN ROBERT, chemical physicist, educator; b. N.Y.C., May 19, 1948; s. Dominic and Annie Frances (Sappa) L. BA, Northwestern U., 1970; PhD, U. Calif., Berkeley, 1974. Asst. prof. U. So. Calif., L.A., 1974-76; physicist/fellow Nat. Inst. Standards and Tech., Boulder, Colo., 1976-94, acting chief Quantum Physics divsn., 1994—; adj. prof. U. Colo., Boulder, 1976—. Contbr. over 200 articles to profl. publs.; mem. editorial bd. Optics Letters, Jour. Chem. Physics, Chem. Revs., Jour. Phys. Chemistry, Molecular Physics, Chem. Physics Letters, Progress in Reaction Kinetics; patentee in field. Recipient silver and gold medals Dept. Commerce, 1980, 85, Coblentz award Coblentz Soc., 1984, Arthur S. Flemming award U.S Govt., 1986, Samuel Wesley Stratton award Nat. Inst. Standards and Tech., 1992; Alfred P. Sloan fellow Sloan Found., 1977-81, Guggenheim fellow, 1988. Fellow AAAS, Optical Soc. Am., Am. Phys. Soc. (chair div. chem. physics 1987-88, Herbert P. Broida prize 1989); mem. Am. Chem. Soc. (Pure Chemistry award 1982, Nobel Laureate Signature award 1983). Office: Joint Inst for Lab Astrophysics Univ of Colo Campus Box 440 University Of Colorado CO 80309

LEONE, WILLIAM CHARLES, retired manufacturing executive; b. Pitts., May 3, 1924; s. Joseph and Fortuna (Sammarco) L.; m. Sara Jane Hollenback, Aug. 26, 1950; children: William Charles, David M., Patricia Ann, Mary Jane. BS, Carnegie Inst. Tech., 1944, MS, 1948, DSc, 1952. Asst. prof. engring. Carnegie Inst. Tech., Pitts., 1946-53; mgr. indsl. Sys. divsn. Hughes Aircraft, L.A., 1953-59; v.p., gen. mgr., dir. Rheem Califone, L.A. 1960, Rheem Electronics, L.A., 1960-68; group v.p. Rheem Mfg. Co., 1968-71; exec. v.p Rheem Mfg. Co., N.Y.C., 1971-72; pres., 1972-76; also dir. Rheem Mfg. Co.; pres. City Investing Co. Internat., 1972-76; pres., dir. Farah Mfg. Co., El Paso, Tex., 1976-77; bus. cons., 1977-79; acting vice chmn. McCulloch Oil Corp. (MCO), L.A., 1979-80, also bd. dirs.; pres., dir. MAXXAM Inc. (formerly MCO Holdings, Inc.), 1980-90; vice chmn. MAXXAM Inc., 1990-92; chmn., CEO, dir. Pacific Lumber Co., 1986-90, Horizon Corp., 1984-89. Trustee Carnegie Mellon U., 1986-92. Mem. ASME, IEEE, Am. Inst. Aerospace and Aeronautics, Sigma Xi, Tau Beta Pi, Pi Tau Sigma, Theta Tau, Pi Mu Epsilon. Home: 2209 Chelsea Rd Palos Verdes Peninsula CA 90274-2603

LEONETT, ANTHONY ARTHUR, banker; b. Summit, N.J., Jan. 4, 1929; s. Joseph J. and Margaret (DiGuglielmo) L.; m. Ann Marino, Oct. 6, 1974; 1 son by previous marriage, Anthony Arthur. B.S., Seton Hall U., 1950; certificate, Am. Inst. Banking, 1956; postgrad., U. Wis., 1962. Mgr. First

Nat. Bank & Trust Co., Summit, 1950-56; sr. v.p., auditor Nat. State Bank, Elizabeth, N.J., 1956—; instr. principles of auditing and bank operations Am. Inst. Banking; faculty N.J. Data Processing Sch., Princeton, Bank Adminstrn. Sch. of U. Wis. Bd. dirs. N.J. affiliate Am. Heart Assn. Served with U.S. Army, 1951-53. Recipient Irving Grabiel award for outstanding leadership in banking, 1979. Mem. Am. Inst. Banking (dir. chpt.), Bank Adminstrn. Inst. (N.J. state dir. 1977-79, pres. N.J. chpt., dist. dir. 1979-81). Republican. Roman Catholic. Clubs: K.C., Minisink (Chatham). Home: 102 N Hillside Ave Chatham NJ 07928-2825 Office: 68 Broad St Elizabeth NJ 07201-2298

LEONETTI, MATTHEW FRANK, cinematographer. Films include: The Bat People, 1974, Mr. Billion, 1977, The Chicken Chronicle, 1977, Breaking Away, 1979, Raise the Titanic, 1980, Eyewitness, 1981, Poltergeist, 1982, Fast Times at Ridgemont High, 1982, The Buddy System, 1984, The Ice Pirates, 1984, Songwriter, 1984, Fast Forward, 1985, Weird Science, 1985, Jagged Edge, 1985, Commando, 1985, Jumpin' Jack Flash, 1986, Extreme Prejudice, 1987, Dragnet, 1987, Action Jackson, 1988, Red Heat, 1988, Johnny Handsome, 1989, Hard to Kill, 1990, Another 48 Hrs., 1990, Dead Again, 1991, Leap of Faith, 1992, Hot Shots! Part Deux, 1993, Angels in the Outfield, 1994. Office: c/o Innovative Artists 1999 Ave of the Stars Ste 2850 Los Angeles CA 90067

LEONG, JO-ANN CHING, microbiologist, educator; b. Honolulu, May 15, 1942; d. Raymond and Josephine Ching; m. Oren T.H. Leong; children: Kara Elise, Jonathan Raymond. BA in Zoology, U. Calif., Berkeley, 1964; PhD in Microbiology, San Francisco Sch. Medicine, 1971. Postdoctoral rsch. assoc. dept. biochemistry U. Calif., San Francisco, 1971-75, asst. rsch. virologist Cancer Rsch. Inst., 1975; asst. prof. Oreg. State U., Corvallis, 1975-80, assoc. prof., 1980-86, prof., 1986-92, disting. prof., 1992—; grant reviewer Sea Grant, NSF, CRIS, USDA, NIH; cons. Am. Microscan, 1986. Co-author: Retroviruses and Differentiation, 1982, Molecular Approaches to Bacteria and Viral Diseases of Fish, 1983, Fish Vaccination, 1988, Viral Vaccines for Aquaculture, 1993, Human Endogenous Retroviruses, 1994. Coord. Women in Sci. Career Workshop, Portland (Oreg.) State U., 1977. Recipient Dernham Rsch. Fellowship, Am. Cancer Soc., 1973-75, fellowship Giannini Found. for Med. Rsch., 1973, Rsch. award Sigma Xi, 1990; named NORCAS prof. Batelle NW Labs, 1976, Disting Prof. Oreg. State U. Alumni Assn., 1991. Fellow Am. Acad. Microbiology; mem. AAAS, AAUP (exec. bd. 1982), European Assn. of Fish Pathologists, Am. Soc. Microbiology, Am. Soc. Virology, Am. Fisheries soc. (fish health sect.), Assn. Women in Sci., Am. Assn. Cancer Rsch. Office: Oreg State U Dept Microbiology Corvallis OR 97331

LEONHARD, WILLIAM EDWARD, engineering and construction company executive; b. Middletown, Pa., Dec. 9, 1914; s. Charles Frank and Ruth Eva (Wagner) L.; m. Wyllis Mary Rocker, Feb. 8, 1940; children: William Edward, Richard W., D. Jeanne. BEE, Pa. State U., 1936; MSEE, Mass. Inst. Tech., 1940; LLD, Pepperdine U., 1987. Commd. 2d lt. U.S. Army, 1936; Commd. lt. col. USAF, 1950, advanced through grades to brig. gen. 1960; ret., 1964; with Ralph M. Parsons Co., Pasadena, Calif., 1966—; pres. Ralph M. Parsons Co., 1974—, gen. mgr., 1974-75, chief exec. officer, 1975—, also dir. chmn. bd.; pres., chmn., chief exec. officer The Parsons Corp., 1978—. Bd. visitors, bd. overseers UCLA; assoc. Calif. Inst. Tech.; mem. corp. vis. com. dept. civil engring. MIT; trustee Harvey Mudd Coll., 1986—. Decorated Bronze Star, Legion of Merit (3); recipient Corp. Leadership award M.I.T., 1977; named Chief Exec. of Yr. Fin. World, 1982, 83, 84, 85, Outstanding CEO Wall Street Transcript, 1981, 83; recipient Disting. Alumnus award Pa. State U., 1982, Golden Beaver award in mgmt., 1984. Mem. ASME (Newman award 1961), Nat. Acad. Engring., Council on Fgn. Relations, Los Angeles World Affairs Council. Clubs: California (Los Angeles); Marrakech Country (Palm Desert, Calif.); Annandale Golf (Pasadena), Pasadena Breakfast, Forum (Pasadena), Twilight (Pasadena).

LEONHARDT, FREDERICK WAYNE, lawyer; b. Daytona Beach, Fla., Oct. 26, 1949; s. Frederick Walter and Gaetane Laura L.; m. Victoria Ann Cook, Dec. 27, 1975; children: Ashley Victoria, Frederick Whitaker. BA, U. Fla. 1971, JD, 1974. Bar: Fla. 1974, N.C. 1984, D.C. 1985; cert. real estate lawyer, Fla., 1987. Gen. counsel com. on growth and energy Fla. Ho. of Reps., 1974-75; ptnr. Cobb & Cole, P.A., Daytona Beach, Fla., 1975-79; pres. Leonhardt & Upchurch, P.A., 1979-87; ptnr. Holland & Knight, Orlando, 1987-93; ptnr. Gray, Harris & Robinson, P.A., Orlando and Cocoa Beach, 1993—; mem. Orange County Charter Rev. Commn., 1991-92. Chmn. bd. dirs. Orlando/Orange County Compact, 1989-90; founder Leadership Daytona Beach; grad. participant Leadership Fla., Leadership Orlando, 1992; bd. dirs. Orlando Regional Med. Ctr. Found., 1992—; past chmn. Orlando Area Sports Commn. Mem. ABA (urban, state and local govt. law sect. sec., past editor sect. newsletter 1991-94), Orange and Volusia Counties Bar Assn., Greater Orlando C. of C. (chmn. 1991-92), Daytona Beach Area C. of C. (pres. 1985), Fla. C. of C. (bd. dirs. 1984-90, 93—, mgmt. corp. bd. 1990-92), Phi Alpha Delta, Delta Chi. Office: Gray Harris & Robinson PA PO Box 3068 201 E Pine St Ste 1200 Orlando FL 32802

LEONHARDT, THOMAS C., engineering company executive; b. 1938. Pres., ceo Rust Environment & Infrastructure, Greenville, S.C., 1971—. Office: Rust Environment & Infrastructure 15 Brendan Way Greenville SC 29615

LEONHARDT, THOMAS WILBURN, librarian, technical services director; b. Wilmington, N.C., Feb. 7, 1943; s. Thomas Beauregard and Rachel Virginia (Callicutt) L.; m. Margaret Ann Pullen, Sept. 19, 1966; children: Hilary, Thomas, Rebecca, Benjamin. AA, Pasadena (Calif.) City Coll., 1968; AB, U. Calif., Berkeley, 1970, MLS, 1973. Head gift and exch. div. Stanford (Calif.) U. Librs., 1973-76; head acquisition dept. Boise (Idaho) State U. Libr., 1976-79, Duke U. Libr., Durham, N.C., 1980-82; asst. univ. libr. U. Oreg., Eugene, 1982-87; dean librs. U. of the Pacific, Stockton, Calif., 1987-92; dir. tech. svcs. U. Okla. Librs., Norman, 1992—; editor RTSD Newsletter, Chgo., 1986-89, Info. Tech. & Librs., Chgo., 1990—. Editor Advances in Collection Development and Resource Management, JAI Press, 1994—; contbr. articles to profl. jours. Bd. dirs. No Regional Libr. Facility, Richmond, Calif., 1988-92, Feather River Inst. for Libr. Acquisitions, Blairsden, Calif. With U.S. Army, 1963-66. Mem. ALA, Assn. Coll. Rsch. Librs., Libr. and Info. Tech. Assn., Assn. for Libr. Collections and Tech. Svcs., Cen. Assn. Librs. (bd. dirs. Stockton chpt. 1987-92). Democrat. Avocations: trumpet, guitar. Home: 204 Terra Ct Norman OK 73069-8641

LEONIS, JOHN MICHAEL, aerospace executive; b. Whittier, Calif., Oct. 21, 1933; s. Michael Arthur and Minnie Augusta (Peterson) L.; m. Edith Ann Pattison, Aug. 30, 1958; children: Susan Elizabeth, Carolyn Ann, Linda Maria. BEE, U. Ariz., 1959. Past pres. Litton Guidance and Control Systems, Woodland Hills, Calif.; pres., CEO Litton Industries, Inc., Beverly Hills, Calif., 1994—. Mem. AIAA, Inst. Navigation, Air Force Assn., Assn. U.S. Army, Assn. Naval Aviation, Naval Helicopter Assn., Am. Electronics Assn. Office: Litton Industries Inc 360 N Crescent Dr Beverly Hills CA 90210

LEONSIS, THEODORE JOHN, publishing company executive; b. Vero Beach, Fla., Jan. 8, 1956. BA magna cum laude, Georgetown U., 1976; postgrad. Suffolk U. Law Sch., 1980. Copywriter, advt. mgr. Wang Labs., Inc., 1976-78, corp. publicity/pub. relations dir., 1978-81; dir. mktg. communications Harris Corp., Melbourne, Fla., 1981-83; exec. v.p Redgate Pub. Co., Vero Beach, Fla., 1983—, also dir.; pres. Redgate Communications Corp., 1986—; founder Collegiate Entrepreneurs Fund; dir. Preview Media Inc., Brevard Venture Fund. Chmn. United Fund campaign, Wang Labs. Inc., 1980; bd. dirs. Big Bros. Brevard County, 1981. Brevard Art Ctr. and Mus., Brevard Council of Arts, 1981, Juvenile Employment Project, Lowell, Mass., Merrimack Regional Theatre. Mem. Pub. Relations Soc. Am. (cert.), Publicity Club Boston, Bus. Profl. Advt. Adminstrs., Am. Mktg. Assn. Author: Software Master for the IBM PC, Mastering The IBM Assistant Series, Software Master for PFS, Blue Magic; pub. The Macintosh Buyer's Guide, Apple II Rev., The Apple IIGS Buyer's Guide, COMPAQ, FYI; The Harris Mag. for Info. Mgmt.; contbr. articles to profl. jours. Office: Redgate Communications Corp 660 Beachland Blvd Vero Beach FL 32963-1700

LEONTIEF, WASSILY, economist, educator; b. Leningrad, Russia, Aug. 5, 1906; s. Wassily and Eugenia (Bekker) L.; m. Estelle Helena Marks, Dec. 25,

1932; 1 child, Svetlana Eugenia Alpers. Student, U. Leningrad, 1921-25; grad. Learned Economist; PhD, U. Berlin, 1928; PhD honoris causa, U. Bruxelles, Belgium, 1962, U. York, Eng., 1967, U. Louvain, 1971, U. Paris, 1972, U. Pa., 1976, U. Lancaster, Eng., 1976; D honoris causa, Adelphi Coll., 1988; LHD (hon.), Rensselaer Poly. Inst., 1988; D honoris causa, U. Cordoba, 1990. Rsch. economist Inst. Weltwirtschaft U. Kiel, Germany, 1927-28, 30; econ. adviser to Chinese govt. Nanking, 1929; with Nat. Bur. Econ. Rsch., N.Y.C., 1931; instr. econs. Harvard U., Cambridge, Mass., 1932-33; asst. prof. Harvard U., Cambridge, 1933-39; assoc. prof. 1939-46, prof., 1946-75, dir. econ. project, 1948-72, Henry Lee prof. econs., 1953-75; prof. econs. NYU, 1975—, univ. prof., 1983—; founder Inst. Econ. Analysis, 1978-85, mem. rsch. staff, 1986; cons. Dept. Labor, 1941-47, OSS, 1943-45, UN, 1961-62, Dept. Commerce, 1966-82, EPA, 1975-80 , UN, 1980—. Author: The Structure of the American Economy, 1919-29, 2d edit., 1976, Studies in the Structure of the American Economy, 1953, 2d edit., 1977, Input-Output Economics, 1966, 2d edit., 1986, Collected Essays, 1966, Theories, Facts and Policies, 1977, The Future of the World Economy, 1977, (with Faye Duchin) The Future Impact of Automation on Workers, 1989, Contbr. articles to sci. jours. and periodicals U.S. and abroad. Mem. Commn. to Study Orgn. of Peace, 1978; trustee N.C. Sch. Sci. and Math., 1978; mem. issues com. Progressive Alliance, 1979; mem. Com. for Nat. Security, 1980. Decorated officer Order Cherubim U. Pisa; comdr. Order Arts and Letters, Legion of Honor (France); Order of Rising Sun (Japan); recipient Bernhard-Harms prize econs. Fed. Republic of Germany, 1970, Nobel prize in econs., 1973, Takemi Meml. award Inst. Seizon and Life Scis., Japan, 1991; Guggenheim fellow, 1940, 50. Fellow Soc. Fellows Harvard (sr. fellow, chmn. 1964-75), Econometric Soc., Royal Statis. Assn. (hon.), Inst. de France (corr.); mem. NAS, AAAS, Am. Philos. Soc., Internat. Statis. Inst., Am. Econ. Assn., Am. Statis. Assn., USSR Acad. Scis. (fgn.), 1988, Royal Econ. Soc., Japan Econ. Rsch. Ctr. (hon.), Brit. Acad. (corr.), French Acad. Scis. (corr.), Royal Irish Acad. (hon.), Brit. Assn. Advancement Sci. (pres. Sect. F 1976), USSR Acad. Scis. (fgn.), Soc. of the Optimate Italian Cultural Isnt., Century Club. Mem. Greek Orthodox Church. Office: NYU Dept Econs 269 Mercer St New York NY 10003-6633

LEOPOLD, ESTELLA BERGERE, botany and environmental studies educator; b. Madison, Wis., Jan. 8, 1927; d. Aldo and Estella (Bergere) L. Ph.B., U. Wis., 1948; M.S., U. Calif.-Berkeley, 1950; Ph.D., Yale U., 1955. Asst. physiology and embryology Genetics Expt. Sta., Smith Coll., 1951-52; asst. biologist, then asst. animal ecology Yale U., New Haven, 1952-54; botanist, paleontology and stratigraphy br. U.S. Geol. Survey, 1955-76; dir. quaternary rsch. ctr. U. Wash., Seattle, 1976-82, prof. botany and forest resources, 1976-89; adj. prof. biology U. Colo., 1967-76. Recipient (with others) Conservationist of Yr. award Colo. Wildlife Fedn., 1969, award Keep Colo. Beautiful Inc., 1976; travel grantee NSF, Spain, 1957, Poland, 1961, Eng., 1977. Fellow AAAS; mem. Nat. Acad. Scis. (environ. studies bd. 1976-79), Ecol. Soc. Am. (climate rsch. bd. 1979-80), Internat. Quaternary Assn., Am. Quaternary Assn. (pres.-elect 1980-82, pres. 1982-84), Bot. Soc. Am., Inst. Ecology (bd. dirs.). Home: 5608 17th Ave NE Seattle WA 98105-2508 Office: U Wash Dept Botany Environmental Scis Seattle WA 98195

LEOPOLD, LUNA BERGERE, geology educator; b. Albuquerque, Oct. 8, 1915; s. Aldo and Estella (Bergere) L.; m. Barbara Beck Nelson, 1973; children: Bruce Carl, Madelyn Dennette. BS, U. Wis., 1936, DSc (hon.), 1980; M.S., UCLA, 1944; Ph.D., Harvard, 1950; D Geography (hon.), U. Ottawa, 1969; DSc (hon.), Iowa Wesleyan Coll. 1971, St. Andrews U., 1981, U. Murcia, Spain, with Soil Conservation Service, 1938-41, U.S. Engrs. Office, 1941-42, U.S. Bur. Reclamation, 1946; head meteorologist Pineapple Research Inst. of Hawaii, 1946-49; hydraulic engr. U.S. Geol. Survey, 1950-71, chief hydrologist, 1957-66, sr. research hydrologist, 1966-71; prof. geology U. Calif. at Berkeley, 1973—. Author: (with Thomas Maddock, Jr.) The Flood Control Controversy, 1954, Fluvial Processes in Geomorphology, 1964, Water, 1974, (with Thomas Dunne) Water in Environmental Planning, 1978; also tech. papers. Served as capt. air weather service USAAF, 1942-46. Recipient Disting. Svc. award Dept. of Interior, 1958; Veth medal Royal Netherlands Geog. Soc., 1963; Cullum Geog. medal Am. Geog. Soc., 1968; Rockefeller Pub. Service award, 1971; Busk medal Royal Geog. Soc., 1983, Berkeley citation U. Calif., David Linton award British Geomorphol. Research Group, 1986, Linsley Award Am. Inst. Hydrology, 1989, Caulfield medal Am. Water Resources Assn., 1991, Nat. Medal Sci. NSF, 1991, Palladium medal Nat. Audubon Soc., 1994. Mem. NAS (Warren prize), ASCE (Julian Hinds award), Geol. Soc. Am. (Kirk Bryan award 1958, pres. 1972, Disting. Career award geomorphological group 1991, Penrose medal 1994), Am. Geophys. Union (Robert E. Horton medal 1993), Am. Acad. Arts and Scis., Am. Philos. Soc., Sigma Xi, Tau Beta Pi, Phi Kappa Phi, Chi Epsilon. Club: Cosmos (Washington). Home: 400 Vermont Ave Berkeley CA 94707-1722 Office: U Calif Dept Geology Berkeley CA 94720

LEPAGE, WILBUR REED, electrical engineering educator; b. Kearny, N.J., Nov. 16, 1911; s. Wilbur Nicholas and Gertrude Elizabeth (Reedt) LeP.; m. Eveline Marie Jacobsen, June 9, 1936; 1 dau., Margaret Ann. E.E., Cornell U. 1933, Ph.D., 1941; M.S. in Physics, U. Rochester, 1939. Instr. engring. U. Rochester, 1933-38; grad. student, teaching asst. Cornell U., 1939-41; mem. staff advanced devel. lab. RCA, 1941; physicist radiation lab. Johns Hopkins, 1942-45; sr. research engr. Stromberg Carlson Co., 1946; prof. elec. engring. Syracuse U., 1947—, chmn. dept., 1956-74; initiated ann. Sagamore Conf. Elec. Engring. Edn., 1952; cons. to Signal Corps. U.S. Army, 1953; edni. cons. UNESCO, 1967; guest lectr. Rumanian Assn. Scientists, 1977; mem. Nat. Com. on Elec. Engring. Films, 1964-71. Author: Analysis Alternating Current Circuits, 1952, (with S. Seely) General Network Analysis, 1952, Complex Variables and The Laplace Transform for Engineers, 1961, (with N. Balabanian) Electrical Science, Book I, 1970, Book II, 1972, Applied APL Programming, 1978. Recipient Gen. Electric award for teaching excellence, 1985. Fellow IEEE (chmn. com. basic scis. 1955-56), AAUP, N.Y. Acad. Scis., Sigma Xi. Home: 217 Dewitt Rd Syracuse NY 13214-2006 Office: Syracuse U Link Hall Syracuse NY 13244

LEPINE, JEAN, cinematographer. Cinematographer: (films) Vincent & Theo, 1990, The Player, 1992, Bob Roberts, 1992. Office: Doug Apatow Agency 10559 Blythe Ave Los Angeles CA 90064*

LEPKOWSKI, WIL (WILBERT CHARLES LEPKOWSKI), journalist; b. Salem, Mass., Sept. 3, 1934; s. Charles J. and Alice (Bartnicki) L.; m. Jane Littlefield, Oct. 28, 1961 (May 1975); children: David E., Rebecca A., Thomas M.C.; m. Helene Kay Hollander, Feb. 4, 1984; 1 child, Katherine Angela. BS in Chemistry, U. Mass., 1956; MS in Biochemistry, Ohio State U., 1961. Asst. chemist Doeskin Products Inc., Easthampton, Mass., 1956; asst. editor Chem. Abstracts Svcs., Columbus, Ohio, 1956-58; reporter UP Internat., Columbus, 1960, Providence Jour.-Bull., Westerly, R.I., 1961; sci. writer Johns Hopkins Med. Instns., Balt., 1961-63, Newhouse Newspapers, Washington, 1963-65; bur. head, S.E. Chem. & Engring. News, Washington, 1965-69, sr. corr., 1977—; sci. corr. Bus. Week, Washington, 1969-75; freelance writer, cons., 1975-77. Contbr. articles to jours. in field. Sloan/ Rockefeller fellow Advanced Sci. Writing Prgram, Columbia U. Grad. Sch. Journalism, 1959-60. Mem. Am. Sci. Affiliation, Latin Am. Parents Assn., U.S. Assn. for Club of Rome. Roman Catholic. Avocations: natural history, geography, poetry, spiritual reading, running. Office: Chem & Engring News 1155 16th St NW Washington DC 20036-4800 *Tell the truth.*

LEPLEY, WILLIAM, state education official. Dir. edn. dept. State of Iowa. Office: Edn Dept Grimes State Office Bldg E 14th & Grand Sts Des Moines IA 50319

LEPORE, MICHAEL JOSEPH, gastroenterologist, educator; b. N.Y.C., May 8, 1910; s. Joseph and Florence (Melucci) L.; m. Ardean Clough Everett, Sept. 18, 1937; 1 son, Frederick Everett. B.S., N.Y. U., 1929; M.S., U. Rochester, 1931, M.D. with honor, 1934. Diplomate: Am. Bd. Internal Medicine. Intern Duke Hosp.; asst. resident in medicine, 1934-37; fellow in medicine Yale U., 1935-36; asst. in medicine Columbia U., 1937-46, instr., 1946-52, assoc. in medicine, 1952-56, asst. clin. prof. medicine, 1956-63; practice medicine specializing in internal medicine and gastroenterology, 1937—; cons. in field; dir. Upjohn Gastrointestinal service Roosevelt Hosp., 1962-66, St. Vincent's Hosp. and Med. Center, 1966-75; mem. staffs Englewood (N.J.) Hosp., St. John's Riverside Hosp., Yonkers, N.Y.; attending physician St. Vincent's Hosp. and Med. Center, N.Y.C., Univ. Hosp., Bel-

levue Hosp. Center; assoc. prof. clin. medicine Sch. Medicine, N.Y. U., 1968-70, prof., 1971—; profl. cons. Tripler Gen. Hosp., Oahu; chief of medicine 148th Gen. Hosp., Saipan, Marianas Islands. Author: Death of the Clinician— Requiem or Reveille?, 1981; Contbr. articles to med. jours. Pres. Upjohn Gastrointestinal Found., 1962-79; mem. pres.'s leadership council U. Rochester. Served as lt. col. M.C. AUS, 1942-46. Decorated Army Commendation medal; Michael J. Lepore Professorship in Gastroenterology endowed in his honor U. Rochester Sch. Medicine, 1986; recipient St Vincent de Paul Disting. Physician award St. Vincent's Hosp./Med. Ctr. N.Y.C., 1990. Fellow A.C.P., N.Y. Acad. Scis., N.Y. Acad. Medicine; mem. AMA, Am. Gastroenterol. Assn., N.Y. Gastroenterol. Assn., Physiol. Soc. Phila., AAAS, Royal Soc. Medicine, Alpha Omega Alpha, Sigma Xi. Office: 36 7th Ave New York NY 10011-6609

LEPPARD, RAYMOND JOHN, conductor, harpsichordist; b. London, Aug. 11, 1927; came to U.S., 1976; s. Albert Victor and Bertha May (Beck) L. M.A., U. Cambridge, Eng., 1955; D.Litt. (hon.), U. Bath, Eng., 1973; hon. doctorate, U. Indpls., 1991, Purdue U., 1992. Fellow Trinity Coll., Cambridge; univ. lectr. in music U. Cambridge, 1958-68. Musical dir. English Chamber Orch., London, 1959-77; prin. condr. BBC Philharm., Manchester, Eng., 1972-80; condr. symphony orchs. in Am. and Europe, Met. Opera, N.Y.C., Santa Fe Opera, San Francisco Opera, Covent Garden, Glyndebourne, Paris Opera; prin. guest condr. St. Louis Symphony Orch., 1984-90, music dir. Indpls. Symphony Orch., 1987—; European Tour, 1993; rec. artist; composer numerous film scores; author: (books) Authenticity in Music, Raymond Leppard on Music/An Anthology of Critical and Personal Writings. Decorated Commendatore Della Republica Italiana; comdr. Order Brit. Empire. Office: M L Falcone Pub Rels 155 W 68th St Apt 1114 New York NY 10023-5817 also: Indpls Symphony Orch 45 Monument Cir Indianapolis IN 46204-2919

LEPPER, MARK ROGER, psychology educator; b. Washington, Dec. 5, 1944; s. Mark H. and Joyce M. (Sullivan) L.; m. Jeanne E. Wallace, Dec. 22, 1966; 1 child, Geoffrey William. BA, Stanford U., 1966; PhD, Yale U., 1970. Asst. prof. psychology Stanford (Calif.) U., 1971-76, assoc. prof., 1976-82, prof., 1982—; chmn., 1990-94; fellow Ctr. Advanced Study in Behavioral Scis., 1979-80; chmn. mental health behavioral scis. research rev. com. NIMH, 1982-84; mem. basic sociocultural research rev. com., 1980-82. Co-editor: The Hidden Costs of Reward, 1978; cons. editor Jour. Personality and Social Psychology, 1977-85, Child Devel., 1977-86, Jour. Ednl. Computing Research, 1983—, Social Cognition, 1981-84; contbr. articles to profl. jours. Woodrow Wilson fellow, 1966-67, NSF fellow, 1966-69, Sterling fellow, 1969-70, Mellon fellow, 1975, Stanford U. fellow, 1988-89; grantee NSF, 1978-82, 86-88, NIMH, 1978-86, 88—, NICHD, 1975-88, 90—, U.S. Office Edn., 1972-73; recipient Hoagland prize, 1990. Fellow APA, Soc. Personality and Social Psychology, Soc. Psychol. Study of Social Issues; mem. Am. Ednl. Rsch. Assn., Soc. Exptl. Social Psychology, Soc. Rsch. in Child Devel. Home: 1544 Dana Ave Palo Alto CA 94303-2813 Office: Stanford U Dept Psychology Stanford CA 94305

LEPPERT, RICHARD DAVID, humanities educator; b. Fargo, N.D., Aug. 28, 1943; s. Frederick W. and Eunice I. (Conlon) L. B.A., Moorhead State U., 1966, B.S., B.A., 1966; M.M., M.Ed., U., 1969, Ph.D., 1973. Asst. prof. humanities U. Minn.-Mpls., 1973-78, assoc. prof., 1978-82, prof., 1982—; chmn. humanities program, 1980-86, chmn. dept. cultural studies & comparative lit., 1993—. Author: Theme of Music in Flemish Paintings of 17th Century, 1977; Arcadia at Versailles, 1978; editor (with others): Music & Society: the Politics of Composition, Performance & Reception, 1987, Music and Image, 1988, The Sight and Sound: Music Representation & The History of the Body, 1993. Woodrow Wilson fellow, 1970-71; Fulbright fellow, 1970-72; Guggenheim fellow, 1979-80; Nat. Endowment Humanities sr. fellow, 1986-87. Office: U Minn Dept Cultural Studies & Comp Lit Folwell Hall 350 Minneapolis MN 55455

LEPPIK, MARGARET WHITE, state legislator; b. Newark, N.J., June 5, 1943; d. John Underhill and Laura Schaefer White; m. Ilo Elmar Leppik, June 18, 1967; children: Peter, David, Karina. BA, Smith Coll., 1965. Rsch. asst. Wistar Inst., U. Pa., Phila., 1967-68, U. Wis., Madison, 1968-69; mem. Minn. Ho. Reps., St. Paul, 1990, 92, 94. Commr. Golden Valley (Minn.) Planning Com., 1982-90; mem. Golden Valley Bd. Zoning Appeals, 1985-87. Recipient Citizen of Distinction award Hennepin County Human Svcs. Planning Bd., 1992. Mem. LWV (v.p., dir. 1984-90), Minn. Opera Assn. (pres. 1986-88), Rotary Internat., Optimists Internat. Republican. Avocations: gardening, hiking. Home: 7500 Western Ave Golden Valley MN 55427 Office: 393 State Office Bldg Saint Paul MN 55155

LEPRI, DANIEL B., light manufacturing executive; b. 1953. BA, Coll. of the Holy Cross, 1975; MBA, Rutgers, 1976. Sr. auditor Coopers & Lybrand, N.Y.C., 1976-79; v.p., contr. Thico Plan, Inc., N.Y.C., 1979-82; asst. contr. Rheem Mfg. Co., N.Y.C., 1982-84, v.p., contr., 1984, now v.p., CFO. Office: Rheem Mfg Co 405 Lexington Ave New York NY 10174-0001

LEPRINO, JAMES G., food products executive; b. 1937. With Leprino Foods Co., Denver, 1955—, now chmn. bd. Office: Leprino Foods Co 1830 W 38th Ave Denver CO 80211-2200

LEPS, THOMAS MACMASTER, civil engineer, consultant; b. Keyser, W.Va., Dec. 3, 1914; s. Thomas Davis and Grace (King) L.; m. Catherine Mary Sacksteder, June 22, 1940; 1 son, Timothy. B.A., Stanford U., 1936, M.S., MIT, 1939. Chief civil engr. So. Calif. Edison Co., Los Angeles, 1946-61; chief engr. Shannon & Wilson Co., Seattle, 1961-63; cons. civil engr. U.S. and abroad, Dinuba, Calif., 1963—; mem. over 90 bds. of cons. on hydro, steam and nuclear power projects. Contbr. articles to profl. jours., chpts. to engring books. Served to comdr. USN, 1943-46, with USNR, ret. Recipient certificate of Appreciation Calif. Dept. Water Resources, 1971. Mem. NAE (life mem., nominations com. for officers 1991), ASCE (life mem., cert. of appreciation 1961), U.S. Com. on Large Dams (life mem. vice-chmn. exec. com. 1980-81), Phi Beta Kappa, Tau Beta Pi. Presbyterian. Address: PO Box 217 Dinuba CA 93618-0217

LE QUESNE, PHILIP WILLIAM, chemistry educator, researcher; b. Auckland, New Zealand, Jan. 6, 1939; came to U.S., 1967; s. Ernest W. B. and Bettie A. (Colwill) Le Q.; m. Mary E. Kinloch, 1965 (dec. 1988); children: Elizabeth Ruth, Martin James. B.S., U. Auckland, 1960, M.S., 1961, Ph.D., 1964, D.Sc. (hon.), 1979. Asst. prof. U. Mich., Ann Arbor, 1967-72; assoc. prof. Northeastern U., Boston, 1973-78, prof., 1978—, chmn. dept. chemistry, 1979-87; assoc. dir. Barnett Inst. for Chem. analysis and Materials Sci., 1993—. Contbr. articles to chemistry to profl. jours. Sr. warden Ch. of the Advent, Boston, 1990—. Home: 17 Stafford Rd Newton Center MA 02159-1818 Office: Northeastern U Chemistry Dept 360 Huntington Ave Boston MA 02115-5096

LERACH, WILLIAM S., lawyer; b. Pitts., Mar. 14, 1946. BA, U. Pitts., 1967, JD magna cum laude, 1970. Bar: Pa. 1970, Calif. 1976. presenter numerous seminars, confs. Contbr. articles to profl. jours. Mem. ABA, Assn. Trial Lawyers Am., Pa. Bar Assn., State Bar Calif., Calif. Trial Lawyers Assn., San Diego Bar Assn., San Diego County Trial Lawyers Assn., Order of Coif. Office: Milberg Weiss Bershad Hynes & Lerach 1800 One Am Plz 600 W Broadway San Diego CA 92101-5050

LERCH, RICHARD HEAPHY, lawyer; b. Balt., Oct. 8, 1924; s. Charles Sebastian and Marguerite Mary (Mullen) L.; m. Marie Therese Logan, Feb. 11, 1950; children—Marie L., Elizabeth L., Ellen C. A.B. magna cum laude, Loyola Coll., Balt., 1947; LL.B., U. Md., 1949. Bar: Md. bar 1948. Sine practiced in Balt.; partner Lerch & Huesman, 1959—; Pres. Jr. Bar Assn. 1960. Served with AUS, 1944-46, 51-52. Mem. Am., Md., Balt. bar assns. Internat. Assn. Ins. Counsel. Democrat. Roman Catholic. Home: 5906 Meadowood Rd Baltimore MD 21212-2435 Office: 102 W Pennsylvania Ave Towson MD 21204

LERER, KENNETH, public relations executive. Pub. rels. exec. Robinson, Lake, Lerer & Montgomery. Office: Robinson Lake Lerer & Montgomery Bozell Public Relations 75 Rockefeller Plz New York NY 10019-6908*

LEREW, EVERETT DUANE, special education administrator; b. Faulkton, S.D., May 20, 1941; s. Buster E. and Cecile (Elliott) L.; m. Sandra L. Sebade, Feb. 4, 1962; children: Shari Lerew Schutte, Jolene, Brett. BA, Black Hills State U., 1971, MA, 1978; specialist cert., Kearney State Coll. 1989. Elem. tchr. Kadoka (S.D.) Pub. Schs., 1971-74; elem. tchr. Superior (Nebr.) Pub. Schs., 1974-87, head tchr., 1976-80; psychologist, dir. preschs. Ednl. Svc. Unit 7 Nebr. Dept. Edn., Columbus, 1987-89; dir. spl. edn. Valley (Nebr.) Pub. Schs., 1989—. Author: (textbooks) Superior Spelling I, 1986, Superior Spelling II, 1987. Active Parent-Tchr.-Student Orgn., pres., 1986. Sgt. USAF, 1960-67. Named Outstanding Educator, Jaycees, Kadoka, 1973, Disting. Educator, U. Nebr., 1986, Nebr. Tchr. of Yr., Nebr. Dept. Edn., Lincoln, 1987. Mem. NASP, Coun. for Exceptional Children, Coun. for Adminstrs. of Spl. Edn., Nebr. State Edn. Assn., Assn. of Childhood Edn. Internat., Assn. for Edn. of Young Children (pres. Superior chpt. 1981-85), Valley Edn. Assn. (chmn. grant com.), Superior Edn. Assn. (pres. 1985), Ednl. Svc. Unit 7 Edn. Assn. (pres. 1988). Democrat. Methodist. Avocations: writing, reading, painting, gardening, travel. Home: 710 S Mayne St Valley NE 68064-2012 Office: Valley Pub Schs 401 S Pine St Valley NE 68064-9720

LERITZ, LAWRENCE, actor, singer, dancer, producer, director, songwriter, choreographer; b. Alton, Ill., Sept. 26, 1952; s. Leonard Henry and Marcella Rose (Fravle) L. Student Harkness Ballet Sch., 1973-74; Sch. Am. Ballet, 1975-76. Debut: State Fair, St. Louis Muny Opera, 1969, appeared in Can Can, 1983; TV appearances include: Capitol, 1982, All My Children, 1981, Home Sweet, Homeless; Rodney Dangerfield: It's Lonely at the Top, HBO, 1992, various commls.; film debut: Stardust Memories, 1979; appeared in Easy Money, 1982; star Leritz and His Girls, 1983-85; Broadway appearances include: Fiddler On the Roof, 1981, Fonteyn and Nureyev on Broadway, 1975; appeared Met. Opera telecast of Manon Lescaut, 1980; choreographer feature film musical The Last Dragon, 1984; choreographer, co-star home video Treehouse Trolls Birthday Day, 1993; dancer with Harkness Ballet, Paris Opera, Hamburg Ballet, Chgo. Ballet, world wide guest star; dir., choreographer own co. Dance Celebration which represented U.S. at Internat. Choreographic Competitions, Paris, 1979; dir. mus. numbers for Shields and Yarnell; creator mus. indsls. for Lily of France, Bausch & Lomb, Christian Dior; pres. Leritz Prodns., Ltd., N.Y.C. and L.A., 1983—; rec. artist: It Takes Two to Tango, 1984, Crank It Up, 1989, Bright Light, 1992; song lyricist, composer; co-prodr. Day of Compassion, 1995. Full scholar Sch. Am. Ballet, Harkness Ballet Sch.; Lawrence R. Leritz Day declared, recipient Key to City, Wood River, Ill., 1983, Alton, Ill., 1987; appeared on cover Dance Pages mag., fall 1987, spring 1989; writer Muscular Devel. mag., Ironman mag., Men's Fitness mag., Muscle & Fitness mag.; creator, star of video Total Stretch! with Lawrence Leritz, 1992. Mem. AFTRA, ASCAP (Pop Music awards for songwriting 1985—), SAG, Actors Equity Assn., Am. Guild of Musical Artists (bd. govs. 1979-92, 94—, prodn. supr./choreographer 50th Anniversary Gala 1986, Life Membership award for disting. svc. 1991); choreographer, guest dancer Placido Domingo's L.A. Music Ctr. Opera, 1987. Office: 318 W 45th St Ste 3 New York NY 10036

LERMAN, LEONARD SOLOMON, science educator, scientist; b. Pitts., June 27, 1925; s. Meyer Louis and Freamah (Hoffman) L.; m. Claire Carol Lindegren, July 14, 1952 (div. Sept. 1973); children: Averil, Lisa, Alexander; m. Elizabeth Knox Taylor, May 11, 1974. BS, Carnegie Inst. Tech., 1945; PhD, Calif. Inst. Tech., 1950. Postdoctoral fellow U. Chgo., 1949-51; from asst. to assoc. prof. U. Colo., Denver, 1951-63, prof. biophysics, 1963-65; prof. molecular biology Vanderbilt U., Nashville, 1965-76; prof., chmn. biology SUNY, Albany, 1976-84; dir. diagnostics Genetics Inst., Cambridge, Mass., 1984-87; sr. lectr. MIT, Cambridge, 1987—; bd. dirs. United Agriseeds, Champaign, Ill., 1985-87; mem. panel Dept. Energy, Washington, 1986-93; mem. Health and Environ. Rsch. Adv. Com. Bd., Bd. Radiation Effects Rsch., NRC, 1988—. Editor: Molecular and Gen. Genetics jour., 1976-82; mem. editorial bd. Genomics; contbr. articles to profl. jours. Guggenheim Found. fellow, 1971-72. Mem. NAS, AAAS, Am. Acad. Arts & Scis., Am. Soc. Biol. Chemists, Human Genome Orgn., Am. Soc. Human Genetics. Home: 100 Memorial Dr Apt 11-6A Cambridge MA 02142-1332 Office: MIT Dept Biology Bldg 68 Rm 630 Cambridge MA 02139

LERNER, ABRAM, retired museum director, artist; b. N.Y.C., Apr. 11, 1913; s. Hyman and Sarah (Becker) L.; m. Pauline Hanenberg, Oct. 7, 1940; 1 child, Aline. B.A., NYU, 1935; student, Ednl. Alliance, Art Students League, Bklyn. Mus.; pvt. studies, Florence, Italy. Asso. dir. A.C.A. Gallery and Artist's Gallery, N.Y.C., 1945-57; curator Joseph H. Hirshhorn Collection, N.Y.C., 1957-66; dir. Hirshhorn Mus. and Sculpture Garden Hirshhorn Mus. and Sculpture Garden, Washington, 1967-85; founding dir. emeritus, ret. Joseph H. Hirshhorn Mus. and Sculpture Garden, Smithsonian Instn., Washington, 1985; Adv. bd. Archives Am. Art, 1970—. Author: Hirshhorn Museum and Sculpture Garden - Inaugural Book, 1974, Gregory Gillespie, 1977; contbr. to mags., mus. catalogues.; one man show, Davis Gallery, N.Y.C., 1958, group shows include, A.C.A. Gallery, Peridot Gallery, Bklyn.- Mus., Pa. Acad., Davis Gallery, represented in pvt. collections. Decorated commandeur in de Orde Van Oranje-Nassau (The Netherlands); chevalier dans L'Ordre des Arts et des Lettres (France). Home: 98 Lewis St Southampton NY 11968-5006

LERNER, ALAN BURTON, financial service executive, lawyer; b. N.Y.C., Nov. 17, 1930; s. Samuel A. and Helen (Zisfein) L.; m. Elisabeth Waltraud Bruttel, July 5, 1959; children: Raissa, Anthony, Jessica, James. BBA, CCNY, 1951; LLB, Yale U., 1954. Bar: N.Y. 1954, D.C. 1973. Assoc. Chadbourne, Parke, Whiteside & Wolff, N.Y.C., 1956-60; with legal dept. C.I.T. Fin. Corp., N.Y.C., 1960-81; gen. counsel, sec. C.I.T. Fin. Corp., 1976-81, v.p., 1977-81; sr. exec. v.p. Assocs. Corp. of N.Am., Dallas, 1981-93; sr. exec. v.p. corp. staff Assocs. Corp. of N.Am.; also sr. exec. v.p. Assocs First Capital Corp.; cons. Fed. Res. Bd., 1973, Nat. Conf. Commrs. on Uniform State Laws, 1966-68. mem. adv. coun. Sch. Mgmt. and Adminstrn., U. Tex., Dallas, 1981-87; mem. Fin. Commn. of State of Tex., 1983-89; mem. adv. bd. Salvation Army Dallas County, 1991—. Mem. ABA, D.C. Bar Assn., Assn. Bar City N.Y., Am. Fin. Svcs. Assn. (bd. dirs. 1983-88, 90—, vice chmn. 1991-92, chmn. 1992-93, chmn. exec. com. 1993-94). Office: Assocs Corp NAm PO Box 660237 Dallas TX 75266-0237 also: Assocs Corp NAm 250 Carpenter Fwy Irving TX 75062*

LERNER, ALFRED, real estate and financial executive; b. N.Y.C., May 8, 1933; s. Abraham and Clara (Abrahmson) L.; m. Norma Wokloff, Aug. 7, 1955; children: Nancy Faith, Randolph David. BA, Columbia U., 1955. Chmn. bd., chief exec. officer Multi-Amp Corp., Dallas, 1970-80, Realty Refund Trust, Cleve., 1971-90; pres., chief exec. officer Refund Advisers, Inc., 1971—, Town & Country Mgmt. Corp., 1979-93; chmn., dir. Equitable Bancorp., Balt., 1981-90; chmn., bd. dirs. Prog. Corp., Cleve., 1988—; chmn., CEO MBNA Corp., Newark, 1991—, Town & Country Trust, 1993—; chmn., bd. dir. MNC Corp., Balt. Chmn. bd. visitors Columbia Coll. 1st lt. USMCR, 1955-57. Mem. Young Pres. Orgn. Jewish. Clubs: Beechmont (Cleve.), Commerce (Cleve.); Harmonie (N.Y.C.). Home: 19000 S Park Blvd Cleveland OH 44122-1853 Office: 25875 Science Park Dr Beachwood OH 44122*

LERNER, ARNOLD STANLEY, radio station executive; b. Phila., Feb. 17, 1930; s. Joseph C. and Rose L. (Friedmann) L.; m. Maureen Ann Ireland, Aug. 7, 1972; children: Hilary R., Joseph C. BS in Econs., U. Pa., 1951; M in Liberal Studies, Boston U., 1974. Ptnr. Sta. KOMA, Oklahoma City, 1956-58, Sta. KITO, San Bernadino, Calif., 1959, Sta. WORC, Worcester, Mass., 1984-89, Sta. WNVE, Rochester, N.Y., 1986—, Sta. WJMN, Boston, 1987-94, Sta. WZOU, Gorham, Maine, 1988—, Sta. WQSS, Camden, Maine, 1988—; pres. Sta. WADK, Newport, R.I., 1966-77, Comm. Mgmt., Inc. Hollis, N.H., 1978-87; chmn., gen. mgr. Sta. WSSH, Lowell, Mass., 1963-86, Sta. WLLH, Lowell, 1963—; chmn. Stas. WLAM/WKZS, Lewiston, Maine, 1977—; dir. Sta. WKSZ, Media-Phila., 1984—; bd. dirs., exec. com. First Bank, Chelmsford, Mass., 1977-88; vice chmn. Enterprise Bank and Trust, Lowell, 1988—; bd. dirs. Courier Corp. Trustee St. Joseph's Hosp., Lowell, 1976-87, Applewild Sch. Fitchburg, Mass., 1979-92, pres., 1985-89; bd. dirs. Merrimack Valley Goodwill Industries, Lowell, 1972-86, chmn., 1976-78; bd. dirs. Merrimack Repertory Theatre, Lowell, 1988—, v.p., 1989-91, treas. 1992-94. Recipient Meritorious Svc. award Nat. Rehab. Assn., 1975. Mem. Nat. Assn. Broadcasters (bd. dir. 1977-81, chmn. radio bd. 1979-81), Mass. Broadcasters Assn. (bd. dir. 1968-87, pres. 1969-70), Vesper Country Club

(Tyngsboro, Mass.), Kiwanis (pres. 1968, Citizen of Yr. award 1979, Lowell). Jewish. Home and Office: 155 Pine Hill Rd Hollis NH 03049-5939

LERNER, HARRY, lawyer, consultant; b. Easton, Pa., Jan. 24, 1939; s. Albert I. and Shirley (Kraus) L.; m. Sherryl Adrienne Blumin, Nov. 18, 1962; 1 child, Michelle Hope. BA, Cornell U., 1960; JD, NYU, 1963. Bar: N.Y. State 1963, N.J. 1966. Assoc. Otterbourg, Steindler, Houston & Rosen, N.Y.C., 1964-65, Robert Greenberg, West New York, N.J., 1965-67; asst. house counsel Ronson Corp., Bridgewater, N.J., 1967-71; asst. to gen. counsel Ronson Corp., 1971-75, sec., corp. counsel, 1975-82; corp. law cons., 1982—; v.p. Investors and Lenders Ltd., 1988-89. Served with U.S. Army, 1963-64. Mem. N.J. Bar Assn., Zeta Beta Tau.

LERNER, HARRY JONAS, publishing company executive; b. Mpls., Mar. 5, 1932; s. Morris and Lena (Liederschneider) L.; m. Sharon Ruth Goldman, June 25, 1961 (dec. 1982); children: Adam Morris, Mia Carol, Daniel Aryeh, Leah Anne. Student, U. Mich., 1952, Hebrew U., Jerusalem, 1953-54; B.A. U. Minn., 1957. Founder Lerner Publs. Co., Mpls., 1959; pres., chief exec. officer, pub. Lerner Publs. Co., 1959—; founder Muscle Bound Bindery, Inc., 1967, chief exec. officer, 1967—; founder Carolrhoda Books, Inc., 1969; pres., gen. mgr. Interface Graphics Inc., 1969—, CEO, 1993—; bd. visitors U Minn. Press; del. White House Conf. on Libr. and Info. Svcs., 1979; chmn. North Loop Bus. Assn., Mpls., 1972-79, Minn. Book Pubs. Roundtable, 1974; bd. overseers Hill Monastic Manuscript Libr., St. John's U., Collegeville, Minn., 1986-89; bd. dirs., libr. dir. Jewish Community Ctr. Pres. Twin City chpt. Am. Jewish Com., 1980-85; bd. dirs. Fgn. Policy Assn. Minn., 1970-71; bd. dirs. Children's Book Coun., N.Y.C., 1991-94. Recipient Brotherhood award NCCJ, 1961, also numerous graphic arts awards. Mem. ACLU, Mpls. Inst. Art, Walker Art Ctr, St. Paul-Mpls. Com. on Fgn. Affairs, Ampersand Club, Daybreakers Breakfast Club (Mpls.). Home: 2215 Willow Ln N Minneapolis MN 55416-3862 Office: Lerner Pub Co 241 1st Ave N Minneapolis MN 55401-1607

LERNER, HERBERT J., accountant; b. Newark, Aug. 19, 1938; s. Morris David Lerner and Evelyn L. (Shapiro) Kaplan; m. Dianne Joan Prag, Aug. 23, 1959; children—Joy Ellen, Mark Allen. B.S., Rutgers U., 1959; LL.B., Georgetown U., 1963. Bar: D.C. 1964; C.P.A., D.C. With Ernst & Young, Washington, 1963—; ptnr. Ernst & Young, 1970-83, 83-89; vice chmn. tax Ernst & Young, Washington, 1990—; nat. dir. tax policy and standards Ernst & Young; mem. IRS Commrs. Adv. Group, 1982-83, CCH Tax Adv. Bd., 1983—; treas., trustee Am. Tax Policy Inst., 1990—; bd. dirs. Tax Coun., 1984—; Internat. Tax and Investment Ctr., 1993—; mem. tax adv. coun. United Jewish Appeal Fedn., Washington, 1982—. Author: (with others) Federal Income Taxation of Corporations Filing Consolidated Returns, 4 vols., 1975, with ann. supplement; ptnr. letter rulings column Jour. Taxation. Mem. AICPA (exec. com. tax divsn. 1979-82, 85, 89, past chmn., bd. dirs., co-chmn. nat. conf. lawyers and CPAs), ABA, Internat. Fiscal Assn., George Town Club.

LERNER, IRWIN, pharmaceutical company executive. Pres., chief exec. officer Hoffmann-LaRoche, Inc., Nutley, N.J. Office: Hoffmann-La Roche Inc 340 Kingsland St Nutley NJ 07110-1199

LERNER, LAURENCE DAVID, writer, educator; b. Cape Town, South Africa, Dec. 12, 1925; came to U.S., 1985; s. Israel and May (Harrison) L.; m. Natalie Winch, June 15, 1948; children: David, Edwin, Martin, Richard. BA, U. Cape Town, 1944, MA, 1945; BA, Cambridge U., 1949. Asst. lectr. U. Coll. of Gold Coast, 1949-53; lectr. Queens Univ., Belfast, Eng., 1953-62; lectr. U. Sussex, Brighton, Eng., 1962-66, reader, 1966-70, prof., 1970-83; Kenan prof. Vanderbilt U., Nashville, 1985—; vis. prof. Munich U., 1968-69, 74-75, Paris U., 1982, U. Ottawa, 1983. Author: (critical books) The Truest Poetry, 1960, The Truthtellers, 1967, The Uses of Nostalgia, 1972, An Introduction to English Poetry, 1979, Love and Marriage: Literature and Its Social Context, 1979 (South East Arts Lit. prize), The Literary Imagination, 1982, The Frontiers of Literature, 1988, (poetry) Domestic Interior & Other Poems, 1959 (Poetry Book Soc. recommendation), The Directions of Memory, 1964, Selves, 1969, A.R.T.H.U.R. & M.A.R.T.H.A.: The Loves of the Computers, 1980, The Man I Killed, 1980 (Poetry Book Soc. recommendation), Chapter & Verse: Bible Poems, 1984, Selected Poems, 1984, Rembrandt's Mirror, 1987, (fiction) The Englishmen, 1959, A Free Man, 1968, My Grandfather's Grandfather, 1985. Fellow Royal Soc. Lit. Mem. Soc. of Friends. Office: Vanderbilt U 401 24th Ave S Nashville TN 37235

LERNER, MARTIN, museum curator; b. N.Y.C., Nov. 14, 1936; s. Joseph and Rose (Kolberg) L.; m. Roberta M. Rubenstein, Feb. 26, 1968; children: Benjamin Louis, Seth Laurence, Jocelyn Ann. BA, Bklyn. Coll., 1959; postgrad., Inst. Fine Arts, NYU, 1961-65. Asst. prof. U. Calif., Santa Barbara, 1965-66; asst. curator Oriental art Cleve. Mus. Art, 1966-72; asst. prof. Case Western Res. U., 1968-72; vice chmn. charge Far Eastern art Met. Mus. Art, N.Y.C., 1972-75; curator Indian and S.E. Asian art Met. Mus. Art, 1978—; cons. in field; internat. lectr. Author: Bronze Sculptures from Asia, 1975, Blue and White: Early Japanese Export Ware, 1978, The Flame and the Lotus, 1984, (with W. Felten) Cambodian and Thai Sculpture: From the 6th to the 14th Century, 1989, Entdeckungen: Skulpturen der Khmer und Thai, 1989, (with S. Kossak), The Lotus Transcendent, 1991, Ancient Khmer Sculpture, 1994; contbr. articles to profl. jours. Served with U.S. Army, 1959-61. Clubs: East India; Devonshire (London). Home: Giglio Ct Croton-on-Hudson NY 10520 Office: Met Mus Art Fifth Ave at 82d St New York NY 10028

LERNER, NATHAN BERNARD, artist; b. Chgo., Mar. 15, 1913; s. Louis Alexander and Ida Lerner; m. Kiyoko Asai, July 1, 1968; children: Michael John, Amy Elizabeth. Student, Nat. Acad. Art, Chgo., 1931, Art Inst. Chgo., 1933-34; B.S., Sch. Design in Chgo., 1941. Head of photo workshop Sch. of Design in Chgo., 1941-43; head of product design workshop, dean of faculty and students Inst. of Design, Chgo., 1945-49; ednl. dir. Inst. of Design, 1946-47; prof. U. Ill., Chgo., 1967-72; pres. Lerner Design Assos., 1949-72. One man shows include Chgo. Mus. Sci. and Industry, 1974, Bauhaus Archives, Berlin, 1975, Pentax Gallery, Osaka, Japan, 1976, Harry Lunn Gallery, Washington, 1977, Frumkin Gallery, Chgo., 1977, G.R. Hawkins Gallery, Los Angeles, 1977, Chgo. Hist. Soc., 1983, Photog. Gallery Internat., Tokyo, 1984, Ill. State Mus., Springfield, Chgo. Cultural Ctr., Ind. State U., Terre Haute, 1974, Bradley U., Peoria, Ill., 1973, Frumkin Gallery, Chgo., 1975, New York, 1976, Inst. of Contemporary Art, Boston, 1978, Augustana Mus., Rockford, Ill., 1987, The Photographers Gallery, London, 1988, Valparaiso U. Mus., 1989, U. Iowa Mus., 1993, Milw. Mus. Fine Art, 1995; represented in permanent collections Art Inst. Chgo., Mus. Modern Art, N.Y.C., Met. Mus. Art, N.Y.C., Mus. Fine Arts, Houston, Mus. Modern Art, Paris, Bibliothèque National, Paris, Eastman House, Rochester, Bauhaus Archive, Berlin, Mpls. Art Inst., Mus. Contemporary Art, Chgo., Nihon U., Tokyo, Seattle Mus. Art, Monterey (Calif.), Inst. Art, Amon Carter Mus., Fort Worth Israel Mus., Jerusalem, Kyoto Mus. Art, Japan, San Francisco Mus. Art, Ill. State Mus. Art, Internat. Ctr. Photography, N.Y.C. Ctr. for Creative Photography, Tucson, Santa Fe Mus. Fine Arts, Milw. Art Mus., Smart Gallery, Chgo., Les Recontres D'Arles, France. Ill. Arts Council grantee 1977-78. Mem. Artists Guild Chgo., Art Inst. Chgo. Alumni Assn. Patentee in field. Address: 849 W Webster Ave Chicago IL 60614-3615

LERNER, RALPH, architect, university dean; b. N.Y.C., Oct. 17, 1949; s. Irvin Louis and Sonia (Levine) L.; m. Lisa Diana Fischetti, June 20, 1982; children: Sigmund Michael, Esther Diana. BArch, Cooper Union, 1974; MArch, Harvard U., 1975. Registered architect, N.Y., N.J., Mass. Asst. prof. U. Va., Charlottesville, 1975-79; sr. lectr. Poly. Cen. London, 1979-80; assoc. prof. Harvard U., Cambridge, Mass., 1980-83; lectr. Princeton (N.J.) U., 1983-87, assoc. prof., 1987-89, prof., dean Sch. Architecture, 1989—; George Dutton '27 prof. of architecture, 1994—; pvt. practice, Princeton, 1980—. Prin. works include Villa Vasone (Progressive Architecture award 1981), Indira Gandhi Nat. Centre for The Arts, New Delhi, 1986 (1st prize design competition 1986). Recipient 1st prize internat. design competition Epping Town Coun., Essex, Eng., 1984, 1st award Progressive Architecture, 1987, 1st prize Eva's Kitchen and Sheltering Svcs., 1994. Mem. AIA, N.J. Soc. Architects. Office: 306 Alexander St Princeton NJ 08540-7124

LERNER, RALPH E., lawyer; b. N.Y.C., Apr. 12, 1943. BS, Bucknell U., 1964; JD, Boston U., 1967; LLM, NYU, 1969. Bar: N.Y. 1968, U.S. Tax Ct. 1969, Fla. 1975. Ptnr. Sidley & Austin, N.Y.C.; adj. asst. prof. paralegal studies NYU, 1975—. Co-author: Art Law: The Guide for Collectors, Investors, Dealers and Artists, 1989. Mem. ABA (mem. sect. taxation), Internat. Bar Assn., Assn. Bar City N.Y., N.Y. State Bar Assn. (mem. sect. taxation). Office: Sidley & Austin 875 3rd Ave New York NY 10022-6225

LERNER, RICHARD ALAN, chemistry educator, scientist; b. Chgo., Aug. 26, 1938; s. Peter Alex and Lily (Orlinsky) L.; m. Diana Lynn Pritchett, June 1966 (div. 1977); children: Danica, Arik, Edward; m. Nicola Green, Sept. 1, 1979. Student, Northwestern U., 1956-59; BS, MD, Stanford U., 1964; MD (hon.), Karolinska Inst., 1990. Intern Palo Alto (Calif.) Stanford Hosp., 1964-65, rsch. fellow, 1965-68; assoc. mem. Wistar Inst., Phila., 1968-70; assoc. mem. dept. exptl. pathology Scripps Clinic and Rsch. Found., La Jolla, Calif., 1970-72, mem., 1972-74, mem. dept. immunopathology, 1974-82; chmn. and mem. dept. molecular biology Rsch. Inst. Scripps Clinic, La Jolla, 1982-87, dir. dept. chemistry, 1988—, dir., 1987—; pres. The Scripps Rsch. Inst., La Jolla, also CEO; cons. Johnson & Johnson, 1983—; PPG Industries, Inc., Pitts., 1987—; sci. advisor Igen Inc., Rockville, Md.; 1986—; spl. advisor Genex Corp., Gaithersburg, Md., 1988—; bd. dirs. Cytel Corp.; chmn. Internat. Symposium on Molecular Basis Cell-Cell Interaction, 1977, 78, 79, 80; mem. organizing com. for Modern Approaches to Vaccines, Cold Spring Harbor, 1983-89. Contbr. over 250 sci. papers; mem. editorial bd. Jour. Virology, Molecular Biology and Medicine, Protein Engring., Vaccine, In Vivo, Peptide Rsch. Mem. sci. policy adv. com. Uppsala U. (Sweden), sci. adv. bd. Econ. Devel. Bd., Singapore. Decorated Oficial de la Orden de San Carlos (Colombia); recipient NIH AID Career Devel. award, 1970, Parke Davis award, 1978, John A. Muntz Meml. award, 1990, San Marino prize, 1990, Burroughs Wellcome Fund and FASEB Wellcome Vis. Prof. award, 1990-91, College de France award, 1991, 10th Ann. Jeanette Piperno Meml. award, 1991, Arthur C. Cope scholar award in chemistry, 1991. Fellow ACS (screening com. Calif. div.); mem. NAS Inst. Med. (ad hoc com. new rsch. opportunities in immunology), Am. Soc. Virology (charter), Am. Soc. Nephrology, Am. Assn. Immunologists, Am. Soc. Exptl. Pathology, Am. Soc. Microbiology, N.Y. Acad. Scis., Biophys. Soc., Royal Swedish Acad. Sci, Nat. Cancer Inst. (cancer preclin. program project rev. com. 1985-88), Royal Swedish Acad. Scis. (fgn., Lita Annenberg Hazen prof. immunochemistry 1986), 1st Thursday Club, Phi Eta Sigma, Alpha Omega Alpha. Avocations: tennis, walking, skiing, polo. Home: 2630 Torrey Pines Rd Apt 21 La Jolla CA 92037-3443 Office: Scripps Rsch Inst 10666 N Torrey Pines Rd La Jolla CA 92037-1027*

LERNER, RICHARD M., special education director; b. Bklyn., Feb. 23, 1946; s. Max and Sara (Goldfarb) L.; m. Jacquelene Rose Verdirame, July 24, 1977; children: Justin, Blair, Jarrett. BA in Psychology with honors, Hunter Coll. of CUNY, 1966, MA, 1967, PhD, CUNY, 1971. Rsch. asst. dept. edn. Bklyn. Coll. of CUNY, 1966-67; sci. rsch. asst. dept. psychology Hunter Coll. of CUNY, 1966-67, lectr. dept. psychology, 1967-69; asst. to assoc. prof. psychology Ea. Mich. U., Ypsilanti, 1969-76; assoc. prof. child devel. Pa. State U., University Park, 1976-80, prof. child and adolescent devel., 1981-91; dir. Inst. Children, Youth and Families Mich. State U., East Lansing, 1991—, prof. family and child ecology, psychology, pediatrics and human devel., 1991—; vis. scientist Max-Planck-Institut für Bildungsforschung, Berlin, 1983; co-dir. Ctr. for Advanced Study in the Behavioral Scis. Stanford, Calif., 1984; dir. Ctr. for the Study of Child and Adolescent Devel. Pa. State U., 1984-89, prof.-in-charge Grad. Program in Human Devel. and Family Studies, 1985-87, coord. rsch. Carnegie Corp.-Pa. State U. Policy, Rsch. and Intervention for Devel. in Early Adolescence Program, 1990-91; Lansdowne vis. scholar U. Victoria, B.C., Can., 1989. Author: Concepts and Theories of Human Development, 1976, On the Nature of Human Plasticity, 1984, Final Solutions: Biology, Prejudice and Genocide, 1992; author (with G.B. Spanier) Adolescent Development: A Life-Span Perspective, 1980, (with D.F. Hultsch) Human Development: A Life-Span Perspective, 1983, (with J. Belsky and G.B. Spanier) The Child in the Family, 1984, (with F.W. Vondracek and J.E. Schulenberg) Career Development: A Life-Span Developmental Approach, 1986, (with D.H. Ford) Developmental Systems Theory: An Integrative Approach, 1992; author (with others) Psychology, 1986; editor Mich. Psychologist, 1971-74, Newsletter of the Assn. Aviation Psychologists, 1973-74, Jour. Rsch. on Adolescence, 1991—; assoc. editor Internat. Jour. Behavioral Devel., 1984-90; co-editor Life-Span Devel. and Behavior, 1986-93; mem. editorial bd. Child Devel., 1978-88, Devel. Psychology, 1985-90, Devel. Rev., 1986—, Jour. of Applied Devel. Psychology, 1986—, Human Devel., 1988—; contbr. chapters to books; contbr. articles to profl. jours.; pub. monographs. NDEA Title IV Grad. fellow CUNY, 1966-69, fellow Ctr. Advanced Study in the Behavioral Scis. 1980-81; recipient Outstanding Teaching award AMOCO Found., 1982, PhD Alumni Spl. Achievement award CUNY, 1989; named to Hunter Coll. Hall of Fame, 1981. Fellow AAAS, Am. Psychol. Soc. (charter), Am. Psychol. Assn. (divsn. 2, 7, and 9, disting. visitor program), Am. Assn. Applied and Preventive Psychology (charter), Soc. for the Psychol. Study of Social Issues; mem. Internat. Soc. for the Study of Behavioral Devel., Am. Ednl. Rsch. Assn., Am. Home Econs. Assn., Nat. Coun. Family Rels., Ea. Psychol. Assn., N.Y. Acad. Scis., Merrill-Palmer Soc. (charter), Soc. Rsch. on Adolescence, Soc. Rsch. in Child Devel., Soc. for the Study of Social Biology, Kappa Omicron Nu, Sigma Xi, Psi Chi. Office: Mich State U Inst Children Youth & Families Paolucci Bldg Unit # 2 East Lansing MI 48824

LERNER, SANDY RICHARD, art educator, art restorer, appraiser, painter, sculptor, lithographer; b. Pa., May 13; s. Jay N. and Sally Lerner; children: Sandra, Scott Richard. B.A. Lafayette Coll., Easton, Pa., 1933; J.D., N.Y. Law Sch., 1938; M.F.A., Pratt Inst., pupil Fred Conway, Diego Rivera, others. Commd. lt. USAF, 1940, advanced through grades to col., 1946; service in U.S., Europe, Far East; ret., 1964; asst. to dean, tchr. art restoration, orthographic projection, mech. drawing, chemistry paints and pigments Pratt Inst., 1974; adj. prof. art Parson Sch. Design, 1975, New Sch., 1975-78; exec. dir. Art Restoration Tech. Internat. N.Y.C., 1961—, Learning Through Drawing, 1970—; curator Salmagundi Club, 1970, Masonic Grand Lodge Library, 1966; chmn. jury Washington Sq. Art Show, 1960; appraiser Masonic Thrift, 1979, Navy and Coast Guard Art Collection; restorer Shrine of Guadalupe (Mex.), 1980, numerous others; lecturing asst. prof. West Palm Beach Coll. (Fla.); lectr. U. Palm Beach, West Palm Beach, 1987. Prin. works include portraits of Masonic Grand Master Wendell Walker, Grand Master A.J. Punt, Col. of the Regt. 7th Regt., Rainbow Div., Gen. B. Ehrlich, Col. Davis, Gen. Douglas MacArthur, Winston Churchill. Decorated D.F.C., Air medal; honored for restoration Trinity Cathedral; Col. Miss.; hon. dep. Sheriff Ariz.; recipient Lyle Gun, USCG. Mem. Am. Inst. Conservation, Internat. Inst. Conservation, Art Students League (life), Composers, Authors and Artists, DAV (life), VFW, Am. Legion. Republican. Clubs: Masons, Lions, Rotary. Author numerous articles in field. Address: 220 E 65th St Apt 6H New York NY 10021-6600 also: 101 Central Park W # 2C New York NY 10023-4204

LERNER, STEPHEN ALEXANDER, microbiologist, physician, educator; b. Chgo., Oct. 4, 1938; s. David G. and Florence (Trace) L.; m. June 6, 1963 (div. 1990); children: Deborah, Daniel, Susan; m. Aug. 18, 1991. AB magna cum laude, Harvard U., 1959, MD magna cum laude, 1963. Intern, then resident Peter Bent Brigham Hosp., 1963-65; rsch. assoc. NIH, 1965-68; postdoctoral fellow Stanford (Calif.) U., 1968-71; asst. prof. then assoc. prof. U. Chgo., 1971-86; prof. of medicine Wayne State U., Detroit, 1986—; convenor Soviet-Am. Symposium Antibiotics and Chemotherapy, Moscow, 1988. Editor: Aminoglycoside Ototoxicity, 1981; mem. editorial bd. Antimicrobial Agts. and Chemotherapy, 1981—, European Jour. Clin. Microbiology and Infectious Diseases, 1992—; contbr. articles to profl. jours. With USPHS, 1965-67. Recipient Borden Rsch. award, 1963. Fellow Infectious Disease Soc. Am., Am. Acad. Microbiology (com. on awards); mem. Am. Soc. for Microbiology (chmn. antimicrobial chemotherapy 1987-88, divsn. group rep. 1990-92, councillor 1990-92, chmn. confs. com. 1993—, internat. coordinating com. 1993—), Inter-Am. Soc. for Chemotherapy (pres. 1986-88, bd. dirs. 1988—, chmn. 1988-91), Internat. Soc. Chemotherapy (exec. com. 1987—), Phi Beta Kappa, Sigma Xi, Alpha Omega Alpha. Democrat. Jewish. Avocations: Russian language, collecting antique maps. Office: Harper Hosp Div Infectious Diseases 3990 John R Detroit MI 48201-2018

LERNER, WARREN, historian; b. Boston, July 16, 1929; s. Max and Rebecca (Rudnick) L.; m. Francine Sandra Pickow, Aug. 16, 1959; children:

Suzanne Rachel, Amy Florence, Daniel Joseph. B.S., Boston U., 1952; M.A. and cert. of Russian, Inst. Columbia U., 1954, Ph.D. (Am. Council Learned Socs.-Social Service Research Council fgn. area fellow), 1961. Asst. prof. history Roosevelt U., 1959-61; asst. prof. Duke U., 1961-65, assoc. prof., 1965-72, 1972—, chmn. dept., 1985-90; cons. NEH, 1974-80. Author: Karl Radek: The Last Internationalist, 1970, A History of Socialism and Communism in Modern Times, 1982, rev. edit., 1993; editor: The Development of Soviet Foreign Policy, 1973, (with Clifford M. Foust) The Soviet World in Flux, 1967; contbr. articles to profl. jours; mem. internat. editorial bd. Studies in Comparative Communism, 1973-91. Served with U.S. Army, 1954-56. Am. Philos. Soc. fellow, 1972, 82; NEH, 1974-75. Mem. Conf. Slavic and East European History (exec. council 1978-80, pres. 1986-87), Am. Assn. Advancement Slavic Studies, Am. Hist. Assn., So. Conf. Slavic Studies. Jewish. Office: Duke U Dept History PO Box 90719 Durham NC 27708-0719

LEROY, CLAUDE, physics educator, researcher; b. Charleroi, Hainaut, Belgium, Sept. 30, 1947; s. Bernard and Rénée (Jacobeus) L. Mathématique Spéciale, Faculté St. Louis, Brussels, 1967; Lic. en Sci., U. Louvain, Belgium, 1971, PhD, 1976. Rsch. assoc. McGill U., Montréal, 1977-80; attaché de rsch U. Montréal, 1978-80; rsch. assoc. Northwestern U., Evanston, Ill., 1980-81; chercheur du fonds du devel. scis. U. Louvain, 1981-83; rsch. scientist Inst. Particle Physics, Montréal, 1983-90; assoc. prof. physics McGill U., 1983-90; titular prof. physics U. Montréal, 1990—, dir. nuclear physics lab., 1991—; vis. rsch. fellow U. Southampton, Eng., 1976-77; sci. assoc. Ctr. European Rsch. Nuclear physics, Geneva, Switzerland, 1980—; hon. prof. Nat. U. Peru, 1994—. Contbr. over 200 sci. papers to profl. jours. Killam Rsch. fellow The Can. Coun., 1993—. Fellow Royal Soc. Can. (Rutherford Prize for Physics, 1988); mem. Inst. Particle Physics Can., Can. Assn. Physicists. Roman Catholic. Avocations: Egyptian Hieroglyphics, history, fishing. Home: 5155 Boulevard Lasalle, Verdun, PQ Canada H4G 2C1 Office: U Montréal Nuclear Physics Lab, CP 6128, succursale A, Montreal, PQ Canada H3C 3J7

LEROY, DAVID HENRY, lawyer, state and federal official; b. Seattle, Aug. 16, 1947; s. Harold David and Lela Fay (Palmer) L.; 2 children. B.S., U. Idaho, 1969, J.D., 1971; LL.M., NYU, 1972; JD (hon.), Lincoln Coll., 1993. Bar: Idaho 1971, N.Y. State 1973, U.S. Supreme Ct. 1976. Law clk. Idaho 4th Dist. Ct., Boise, 1969; legal asst. Boise Cascade Corp., 1970; asso. firm Rothblatt, Rothblatt, Seijas & Peskin, N.Y.C., 1971-73; dep. prosecutor Ada County Prosecutor's Office, Boise, 1973-74; pros. atty. Ada County Prosecutor's Office, 1974-78; atty. gen. State of Idaho, Boise, 1978-82, lt. gov., 1983-87; ptnr. Runft, Leroy Coffin & Matthews, 1983-88, Leroy Law Offices, 1988—; candidate for Gov. of Idaho, 1986, U.S. Congress, 1994; U.S. nuclear waste negotiator, 1990-93; U.S. Presdl. elector, 1992; lectr., cons. in field. Mem. State Task Force on Child Abuse, 1975; mem. Ada County Coun. on Alcoholism, 1976; del. Rep. Nat. Conv., 1976, 80, 84; chmn. Nat. Rep. Lt. Gov.'s Caucus, 1983-86; bd. dirs. United Fund, 1975-81; del. Am. Coun. Young Polit. Leaders, USSR, 1979, Am. Coun. for Free Asia, Taiwan, 1980, U.S./Taiwan Investment Forum, 1983; del. leader Friendship Force Tour USSR, 1984; legal counsel Young Reps., 1974-81; candidate for Gov. Idaho, 1986; presdl. elector, 1992; candidate U.S. Ho. Reps. 1st Dist, Idaho, 1994. Mem. Nat. Dist. Attys. Assn., Idaho Prosecutors Assn., Am. Trial Lawyers Assn., Idaho Trial Lawyers Assn., Nat. Assn. Attys. Gen. (chmn. energy subcom., exec. com., del to China 1981), Western Attys. Gen. Assn. (vice chmn. 1980-83, chmn. 1981), Nat. Lt. Govs. Assn. (exec. bd. 1983), Idaho Bar Assn., Sigma Alpha Epsilon. Presbyterian. Office: The Leroy Offices PO Box 193 Boise ID 83701-0193

LEROY, EDWARD CARWILE, rheumatologist; b. Elizabeth City, N.C., Jan. 19, 1933; s. J. Henry and Grace Brown (Carwile) LeR.; m. Garnette DeFord Hughes, June 11, 1960; children: Garnette DeFord, Edward Carwile. B.S. in Sci. summa cum laude, Wake Forest Coll., 1955; M.S. in Pathology, U. N.C., 1958, M.D. with honors, 1960. Med. intern Presbyn. Hosp., N.Y.C., 1960-61; resident Presbyn. Hosp., 1961-62; clin. asso. Nat. Heart Inst., Bethesda, Md., 1962-65; fellow in rheumatology Columbia U., 1965-67; dir. Edward Daniels Faulkner Arthritis Clinic; asso. attending physician Presbyn. Hosp., N.Y.C., 1970-75; assoc. prof. Columbia U. Coll. Phys. and Surg., 1970-75; prof. medicine, dir. div. rheumatology and immunology Med. U. S.C., Charleston, 1975—; bd. dirs. Arthritis Found. Contbr. articles med. jours. Mem. Am. Coll. Rheumatology (bd. dirs.), AAAS, Am. Fedn. Clin. Research, Harvey Soc., A.C.P., Am. Assn. Immunologists, Soc. Exptl. Biology and Medicine, Am. Soc. Clin. Investigation, Microvascular Soc., N.Y. Acad. Scis., So. Soc. Clin. Investigation, Assn. Am. Physicians, Orthopedic Research Soc. First Scots Presbyterian. Clubs: Yeamans Hall, Carolina Yacht. Office: Med Univ SC Arthritis Clin & Rsch Ctr 171 Ashley Ave Charleston SC 29425-0001

LEROY, G. PALMER, publishing executive; b. N.Y.C., July 15, 1929; s. John Minturn and Georgiana Kip (Palmer) LeR.; m. Kyra Hawkins, June 18, 1955; children: Kyra, Nina, Pamela. BA, Harvard U., 1951. With N.Y. Times, 1951-52, Frank Best & Co., N.Y.C., 1952-53, Kenyon & Eckhardt, Inc., N.Y.C., 1953-55, Inmont Corp., U.S. and Europe, 1955-83; v.p. sales Inmont Internat., Inc., N.Y.C., 1974-83; ptnr. Clinton R. Howell, Inc. Antiques, Pound Ridge, N.Y., 1984-85; mng. dir. Met. Opera Guild, Inc., N.Y.C., 1985-94; pub. Opera News, N.Y.C., 1985-94; mem. industry sector adv. com. chem. industry U.S. Commerce Dept., 1976-83. Pres. Friends of John Jay Homestead, Inc., Katonah, N.Y., 1977-95, chmn., 1995—; bd. dirs. The Bedford Assn., 1972-85, pres., 1975-80, bd. dirs. emeritus, 1986—; bd. dirs. Wildlife Preservation Trust Internat., Inc., Phila., 1983-94, pres., 1990-93, emeritus coun., 1994—; bd. dirs. N.Y. br. English Speaking Union, 1993—, chmn., 1994—; sr. warden St. Matthew's Ch., Bedford, 1985-89.

LEROY, JOY, model; b. Riverdale, Ill., Sept. 8, 1927; d. Gerald and Dorothea (Wingebach) Reasor. BS, Purdue U., 1949. Model, sales rep. Jacques, Lafayette, Ind., 1950; book dept. sales rep. Loebs, Lafayette, 1951-52; window trimmer Marshall Fields and Co., Evanston, Ill., 1952-53; sales and display rep. Emerald Ho., Evanston, 1954-55; model, narrator, designer J.L. Hudson Co., GM Corp., Coca Cola Co., Hoover Vacuum Co., Jam Handy Orgn., Am. Motors Corp., Speedway Petroleum Corp., Ford Motors Tractor & Implement Divsn.-The Sykes Co., Detroit, 1958-61; tour guide, model The Christian Sci. Publ. Soc., spl. events coord. Prudential Ins. Co., model Copley 7, Boston, 1962-70. Author: Puzz-its, 1986-94. Founding angel Asolo Theatre, Sarasota, 1960s; mem. Ft. Lauderdale Internat. Film Festival, 1990, Mus. of Art, 1978, Fla. Conservation Assn., Rep. Senatorial Com. Inner Circle, 1990, Congrl. Com., 1990, Nat. Trust for Hist. Preservation, 1986, Fla., Trust for Hist. Preservation, 1988; Nat. Wildflower Rsch. Ctr., 1992; Founding friend 1001 Friends of Fla., 1991; mem. Republican Presdl. Task Force, 1993. Mem. Purdue U. Gold Coast Club, Stratford Shakespearean Festival of Am., USS Constn. Mus. (charter mem., 1993), Purdue Alumni Assn., Walt Disney's Magic Kingdom Club Entertainment Nat., Maupin Alumni, Nat. & Fla. Wildlife Fedn., Ducks Unltd., Paddlewheel Steamboatin' Soc. Am., Internat. Marine Animal Trainers Assn., Cunard World Club, Skald Club, Yacht Club, The Crystal Soc., The Cousteau Soc., Corvette Club, Coastal Conservation Assn., Captain's Cir., Intravler Club, Zeta Tau Alpha. Avocation: travel. Home: 2100 S Ocean Ln Apt 2104 Fort Lauderdale FL 33316-3827

LE ROY, L. DAVID, journalist; b. Tignall, Ga., Jan. 2, 1920; s. Lansing Burrows and Glennie (David) LeR.; m. Mary Margaret Pridgeon, Sept. 2, 1945 (div.); children: David Charles, Gregory Alan; m. Ydoine B. Marholec, Apr. 30, 1988 (div.). A.B., U. Ga., 1941; student, Va. C C., Shenandoah Coll., 1980. Mng. editor Air Force Times, 1950-53; with U.S. News & World Report, 1953-70, news editor, 1953-64; mem. Capitol Hill staff, 1964-70; public. dir. Republican Congl. Com., 1970-74, pub. relations dir., 1974-76; exec. dir. Nat. Press Found., 1977-80. Author: Gerald Ford—Untold Story, 1974, The Outdoorsman's Guide to Government Surplus, 1978, World War II As I Knew It, 1994. Active local Boy Scouts Am. Served with AUS, 1941-46. Decorated Purple Heart. Mem. Nat. Press Club (pres. 1967, bd. govs., chmn. bd. govs.), Nat. Rifle Assn., Sigma Delta Chi. Lutheran. Home: PO Box 145 New Market VA 22844-0145

LEROY, PIERRE ELIE, manufacturing executive; b. Port-au-Prince, Haiti, June 10, 1948; s. Elie Pierre and Yolande (Thomas) L.; m. Sue Ellen Starcevich, Nov. 4, 1989. BA, U. Mich., 1970; MBA, U. Chgo., 1972. Rsch. liaison Goldman, Sachs & Company, Chgo., N.Y.C., 1972-74; fin.

planning dir. Gould Inc., Chgo., 1974-76; asst. mg. domestic fin. Deere & Company, Moline, Ill., 1976-77, mg. planning indsl. equipment div., 1977-79; mgr. planning spl. projects John Deere Intercontinental, Brussels, 1979-81, mgr. fin., 1981-83; asst. dir. pricing Deere & Company, Moline, Ill., 1983-84, asst. treas., 1984-85, treas., 1985-87, v.p., treas. 1987-94, sr. v.p., CFO, 1994—; bd. dirs. Norwest Bank Quad-Cities. Trustee Moline YMCA, Quad City Symphony Orch. Assn., Davenport, Iowa. Mem. Mfrs. Alliance for Productivity and Innovation (fin. coun. II), Nat. Assn. Corp. Treasurers. Avocations: tennis, chess, bridge, bicycling. Home: 9 Windy Pt Rock Island IL 61201-9219 Office: Deere & Co John Deere Rd Moline IL 61265

LERUD, JOANNE VAN ORNUM, library administrator; b. Jamestown, N.D., Nov. 21, 1949; d. Elbert Hiel and Dorothy Arlene (Littrick) Van Ornum; m. Gerd Heil Groenewold, Jan. 15, 1971 (div. Nov. 1978); 1 child, Gerd Heil Groenewold; m. Jeffrey Craig Lerud, Aug. 30, 1980; 1 child, Jesse Currier. BS in Geology, U. N.D., 1971, MS in Geology, 1979; MA in Librarianship and Info. Mgmt., U. Denver, 1979. Assoc. tech. info. specialist Marathon Oil Co., Littleton, Colo., 1980-86; libr. dir. Mont. Coll. Mineral Sci. and Tech., Butte, 1986-89, Colo. Sch. Mines, Golden, 1989—; report investigator in field. NSF grantee, 1970. Mem. Geosci. Info. Soc. (v.p. 1988, pres. 1989). Avocations: reading, needlework, antiques. Office: Colo Sch Mines Arthur Lakes Libr Golden CO 80401

LERUP, LARS G., architecture educator, college dean. Civil engring. diploma, Helsingborg Tech. Coll., Sweden, 1960; BArch, U. Calif., Berkeley, 1968; MArch in Urban Design, Harvard U., 1970. Asst. prof. architecture U. Calif., Berkeley, 1970-77, assoc. prof. architecture, 1977-87, prof. architecture, 1987-93; Harry K. and Albert K. Smith prof. and chair in architecture Rice U., Houston, 1993—, dean Sch. of Architecture, 1993—; counselor Assn. Collegiate Schs. Architecture, Western Region, 1972-73, 76-77, 77-78; teaching cons. CCNY Sch. of Architecture, 1974; assoc. dean, chair environ. design program U. Calif., Berkeley, 1978-79; vis. fellow Inst. Architecture and Urban Studies, N.Y.C., 1979-81, dir. ednl. programs, 1981; Andrew Carnegie vis. prof. Cooper Union, N.Y.C., 1980-81; vis. prof. Rice U. Sch. Architecture, Houston, 1983, Caudill vis. prof., 1987; vis. prof. Architecture Assn., London, 1985, So. Calif. Inst. Architecture, L.A. and Vico Morcote, Switzerland, 1985, 91-93, ednl. dir., 1990-93; vis. prof. architecture U. Grenoble, France, 1990; mem. numerous U. Calif., Berkeley, So. Calif. Inst. Architecture, Rice U.; supr. grad. students; lectr., rschr., guest critic in field. Author: Building the Unfinished: Architecture and Human Action, 1977, 3rd edit., 1983, Planned Assaults: Nofamily Hous. Love/House, Texas Zero, 1987, (with others) Fires and Human Behavior, 1980, Designer's Own Homes: Private Residences of Thirty of America's Leading Interior Designers, 1984, Architecture and Body, 1988, Architect's People, 1989, Visionary San Francisco, 1990; contbr. articles to profl. jours. and catalogs; prin. works include Folksam Ins. Co. Hdqrs., Farsta, Sweden, Ecole Maritime, La Rochelle, Bretagne, France, Cmty. Ctr., Eskilstuna, Sweden, Ch. Stora Tuna, Sweden, Bldg. Sci. Rm., U. Calif., also furniture design. Regents Tuition scholar U. Calif., 1966-67, 67-68; Arthur Lehman grantee Harvard U., 1969-70, Gulf Oil grantee, 1969-70; recipient citation for excellence Progressive Architecture Awards Program, 1976, citation Assn. Collegiate Schs. Architecture, 1986. Office: Rice U Sch of Architecture 6100 Main St Houston TX 77005

LESAR, HIRAM HENRY, lawyer, educator; b. Thebes, Ill., May 8, 1912; s. Jacob L. and Missouri Mabel (Keith) L.; m. Rosalee Berry, July 11, 1937 (dec. Oct. 1985); children: James Hiram, Albert Keith, Byron Lee; m. Barbara Thomas, Feb. 12, 1987. AB, U. Ill., 1934, JD, 1936; JSD, Yale U., 1938. Bar: Ill. 1936. Asst. prof. law U. Kans., 1937-40, assoc. prof., 1940-42; sr., prin. atty. bd. legal examiners U.S. CSC, 1942-44; assoc. prof. law U. Mo., 1946-48, prof., 1948-57; prof. law Washington U., St. Louis, 1957-72, dean Sch. Law, 1960-72; founding dean, prof. law So. Ill. U., Carbondale, 1972-80, interim pres. univ., 1974, acting pres., 1979-80, disting. service prof., 1980-82, prof. emeritus, 1982—, vis. disting. svc. prof., 1983—; disting. vis. prof. McGeorge Sch. Law, 1982-83; vis. prof. law U. Ill., summer 1947, Ind. U., summer 1952, U. So. Calif., summer 1959, U. N.C. summer 1961, NYU, summer 1965. Author: Landlord and Tenant, 1957; Contbr. to: Am. Law of Property, 1952, supplement, 1977, also, Dictionary Am. History, Ency. Brit. Bd. dirs. Legal Aid Soc., St. Louis and St. Louis County, 1960-72, pres., 1966-67; mem. Human Rels. Commn., University City, Mo., 1966-71, chmn., 1966, 67; bd. dirs. Land of Lincoln Legal Assistance Found., 1972-82, pres., 1982, vice chmn., 1988—; mem. Fed. Mediation and Conciliation Svc., other arbitration panels; bd. dirs. Bacone Coll., 1981-87; trustee Lincoln Acad. Ill., 1987—, Ill. Acad. Fine Arts, 1990—. Lt. comdr. USNR, 1944-46. Recipient Pres.' award Mo. Bar, 1968; named Laureate Lincoln Acad. of Ill., 1985. Fellow Am. Bar Found.; mem. ABA, AAUP, Am. Arbitration Assn., Am. Law Inst., Fed. Bar Assn., Ill. Bar Assn., Mo. Bar Assn., St. Louis Bar Assn., Am. Judicature Soc., Univ. Club St. Louis, Yale Club Chgo., Rotary Internat., Jackson Country Club, Masons, K.T., Shriners, Order of Coif, Phi Beta Kappa, Phi Kappa Phi, Phi Delta Phi (hon.). Baptist. Home: 11 Hillcrest Dr Carbondale IL 62901-2444

LESCAZE, LEE ADRIEN, editor; b. N.Y.C., Dec. 8, 1938; s. William Edmond and Mary (Hughes) L.; m. Rebecca Giraud Hughes, Mar. 25, 1967; children: Alexandra Hughes, Miranda Mary, Adrien William. A.B., Harvard, 1960. With Washington Post, 1963—, asst. fgn. editor, 1965-67, Saigon corr., 1967-68, Hong Kong corr., 1970-73, fgn. editor, 1973-74, nat. editor, 1975-77, N.Y. corr., 1977-80, White House corr., 1980-82, asst. mng. editor, 1982-92; weekend editor The Wall Street Jour., 1995—. Office: The Wall St Jour 200 Liberty St New York NY 10281*

LESCH, ANN MOSELY, political scientist, educator; b. Washington, Feb. 1, 1944; d. Philip Edward and Ruth (Bissell) Mosely; Ba, Swarthmore Coll., 1966; PhD, Columbia U., 1973. Rsch. assoc. Fgn. Policy Rsch. Inst., Phila., 1972-74; assoc. Middle East rep. Am. Friends Svc. Com, Jerusalem, 1974-77; Middle East program officer Ford Found., N.Y.C., 1977-80; program officer, Cairo, 1980-84; assoc. Univs. Field Staff Internat., 1984-87; prof. Villanova U., 1987—, assoc. dir. ctr. Arab and Islamic studies, 1992—. Author: The Politics of Palestinian Nationalism, 1973, Arab Politics in Palestine, 1979, Political Perceptions of the Palestinians on the West Bank and Gaza, 1980, (with Mark Tessler) Israel, Egypt and the Palestinians, 1989, Transition to Palestinian Self-Government, 1992; contbr. articles to profl. jours. Bd. dirs. Am. Near East Refugee Aid, 1980-86, Middle East Report, 1989—, Mid. East Watch, 1989—; co-founder Middle East Program Com., Am. Friends Svc. Com., 1989—; mem. Quaker UN Com., 1979-80, U.S. adv. com. Interns for Peace, 1978-82. Fellow Catherwood Found., 1965; NDFL fellow, 1967-71; Am. Rsch. Ctr. grant Egypt, 1988, U.S. Inst. of Peace Rsch. grant, 1990-91; Wilson Ctr. Guest scholar Smithsonian, 1990. Mem. Middle East Studies Assn. (bd. dirs. 1988-91, pres. 1993—), Middle East Inst., Am. Polit. Sci. Assn. Unitarian. Office: Villanova U Dept Polit Sci Villanova PA 19085

LESCH, MICHAEL, cardiologist; b. N.Y.C., June 30, 1939; s. Maurice and Rose (Linn) L.; m. H. Bella Samuels, June 25, 1961; children—Leah Deura, Ian Samuel. A.B., Columbia U., 1960; M.D., Johns Hopkins U., 1964. Diplomate: Am. Bd. Internal Medicine, Am. Bd. Cardiology. Intern, then resident in medicine Johns Hopkins Hosp., 1964-66; physician USPHS, 1966-68; chief resident physician, fellow cardiology, asst. prof., then assoc. prof. medicine Harvard U. Med. Sch.-Peter Bent Brigham Hosp., 1968-76; Magerstadt prof. medicine Northwestern U. Med. Sch., 1976-89; clin. prof. medicine, chmn. dept. medicine, Henry Ford Hosp. U. Mich. Detroit, 1989—; prof. Medicine Case Western U., Cleve., 1990—; mem. life scis. adv. com. NASA, 1980. Editor: Progress in Cardiovascular Diseases, 1971—; editorial bd. profl. jours. Fellow A.C.P., Am. Coll. Cardiology; mem. Am. Soc. Clin. Investigation, Am. Heart Assn. (gov. 1978-81), Chgo. Heart Assn. (pres. 1982-83). Office: Henry Ford Hosp 2799 W Grand Blvd Detroit MI 48202-2689

LESCH, MICHAEL OSCAR, lawyer; b. Berlin, May 28, 1938; came to U.S., 1940, naturalized, 1946; s. Adolf F. and Maria E. Leschnitzer; m. Judith Willis, Aug. 31, 1965; children—Sara, Benjamin. A.B., Columbia U., 1958; LL.B., Harvard U., 1961. Bar: N.Y. 1961, U.S. Dist. Ct. (so. dist.) N.Y. 1963, U.S. Dist. Ct. (ea. dist.) N.Y. 1965, U.S. Ct. Appeals (2d cir.) 1968, U.S. Supreme Ct. 1975, U.S. Ct. Appeals (3d cir.) 1979, U.S. Ct. Appeals (7th cir.) 1979. Assoc. Shea & Gould and predecessors, N.Y.C., 1961-69; ptnr. Shea & Gould and predecessors, 1970-94, LeBoeuf, Lamb, Greene & MacRae, N.Y.C., 1994—. Contbr. articles to profl. jours. Mem.

ABA, N.Y. State Bar Assn., Assn. Bar City N.Y., Fed. Bar Council, Am. Arbitration Assn. (panel of arbitrators). Office: LeBoeuf Lamb Greene & MacRae 125 W 55th St New York NY 10019-5369

LESE, WILLIAM G(EORGE), JR., government official; b. Cokeburg, Pa., Jan. 13, 1943; s. William G. and Blandina (Bonazzoli) L.; m. Nancy Lee Phillips, Jan. 13, 1964; children—Lori Lee, William Delmont. B.S., California U. of Pa., 1963; M.S. in Stats. and Computer Sci., U. Del.-Newark, 1968, Ph.D. in Stats., 1972; student nat. policy formulation Nat. War Coll., 1977-78. Math. tchr. Ft. Cherry High Sch., McDonald, Pa., 1963-64; scientist, engr. U.S. Army Ballistic Research Lab., also Army Materiel Systems Analysis Agy., Aberdeen, Md., 1964-74; sci. adviser Hdqrs. U.S. Army Europe, Heidelberg, Germany, 1974-77; ops. research analyst Sec. Def. Program Analysis and Evaluation, Washington, 1978-80, vice dir., sci. and tech. adviser Joint Analysis Directorate, Joint Chiefs of Staff, Washington, 1980—; adj. prof. Am. U., 1979-84, Georgetown U., 1984-85; assoc. prof. U. Del., Newark, 1968-74. Author pub. reports. Recipient Meritorious Presdl. Rank, 1983, Illustrious Calif. award, Calif. U. of Pa., 1981. Mem. Mil. Ops. Research Soc., Am. Statis. Soc., Inst. Math. Stats., California U. of Pa. Alumni Assn. (pres. Mid-Atlantic chpt. 1982-85). Club: Ft. Hunt Sportsman. Office: Orgn Joint Chiefs of Staff Joint Analysis Directorate Room 1D940 Pentagon Washington DC 20301

LESER, BERNARD H., publishing executive. Formerly pub. Vogue Australia; pres. Condé Nast Publs., N.Y.C., 1987-94; chmn. Pacific operations Condé Nast Publs. Office: Condé Nast Publs 350 Madison Ave New York NY 10017-3704

LESER, LAWRENCE A., broadcasting company executive; b. Cin., 1935; married. BS, Xavier U., 1957. With Haskins & Sells, 1957-68; with Scripps Howard, Cin., 1968—, former sec., treas., former v.p. fin., dir. corp devel., now pres., chief exec. officer, also bd. dirs.; mem. nat. adv. bd. Chem. Bank; bd. dirs. Newspaper Advt. Bur., Union Cen. Life Ins. Co., Heekin Can. Inc. Office: Scripps Howard 1100 Central Trust Towers Cincinnati OH 45202

LESESNE, JOAB MAULDIN, JR., college president; b. Greenville, S.C., June 21, 1937; s. Joab Mauldin and Henrietta (Fennell) L.; m. Ruth Osborne, Feb. 1, 1958; children: Julia Ruth, Maryrose Lyle, Joab Mauldin III, Henry Herbert. B.A., Erskine Coll., 1959; M.A., U. S.C., 1961, Ph.D., 1967; hon. degree, Lander Coll., 1991. Instr. U. S.C.-Coastal Carolina br., Conway, 1960-62; mem. faculty Wofford Coll., 1964—, dean coll., 1970-72, pres., 1972—; past pres. S.C. Assn. Colls. and Univs.; past chmn. S.C. Tuition Grants Commn., 1972; mem. S.C. Commn. on Archives and History.; pres. So. Univ. Conf.; bd. dirs. Am. Coun. on Edn.; chmn. bd. dirs. NationsBank, N.C. and S.C. Author: History of Erskine College, 1967. Bd. dirs. Spartanburg County Found., United Way, chmn., 1991. Mem. S.C. Hist. Assn. (past pres.), Nat. Assn. Ind. Colls. and Univs. (chmn. 1985-86). Methodist. Office: Wofford Coll Office of Pres 429 N Church St Spartanburg SC 29303

LESH, PHILIP CHAPMAN, musician, composer; b. Berkley, Calif., Mar. 15, 1940; s. Frank Hamilton and Barbara Jewel (Chapman) L.; m. Jill Winifred Johnson, Sep. 12, 1984; children: Graham Hamilton, Brian James. Student, Coll. San Mateo, 1958-61, Mills Coll., 1962. Co-founder, bass and vocals group Grateful Dead, 1965—. Albums include American Beauty, Grateful Dead, 1967, Anthem of the Sun, Aoxomoxoa, 1969, Live Dead, 1970, Workingman's Dead, 1970, The Grateful Dead, 1971, Bear's Choice: History of the Grateful Dead, Vol. 1, 1973, Skeletons From the Closet, 1974, What A Long Strange Trip It's Been: The Best of the Grateful Dead, 1977, Wake Of the Flood, 1973, From Mars Hotel, 1974, Blues for Allah, 1975, Steal Your Face, 1976, Terrapin Station, 1977, Shakedown Street, 1978, Built to Last, 1989, Dead Set, Europe, 1972, Reckoning, 1986, Go To Heaven, In the Dark, 1987, Without a Net, 1990, One From the Vault, Two From the Vault, and others; songwriter (with Robert Hunter) Box of Rain, 1970, (with Robert M. Petersen) New Potato Caboose, 1967, Unbroken Chain, 1974, Pride of Cucamonga, 1974; composer Foci for 4 orchs., 1963. Office: care Grateful Dead Prodns. PO Box 1073 San Rafael CA 94915*

LE SHANA, DAVID CHARLES, seminary president; b. Lucknow, India, Nov. 15, 1932; came to U.S. 1949; naturalized, 1958; s. Newman John and Gwendolyn Beatrice (White) Le S.; m. Rebecca Ann Swander, June 8, 1951; children: Deborah Lynn, James David, Catherine Ann, Christine Joy. AB, Taylor U., Upland, Ind., 1953; AM in Edn, Ball State U., 1959; PhD, U. So. Calif., 1967; LHD (hon.), George Fox Coll., 1982. Ordained to ministry Friends Ch., 1953; pastor Ypsilanti (Mich.) Friends Ch., 1953-54; dir. pub. relations, chaplain Taylor U., 1954-61; pastor 1st Friends Ch., Long Beach, Calif., 1961-67; mem. staff George Fox Coll., Newberg, Oreg., from 1967, pres., 1969-82; pres. Seattle Pacific U., 1982-91, pres. emeritus, 1991—; pres. Western Evang. Sem., Portland, Oreg., 1992—; min. Pacific N.W. Conf. of Free Meth. Ch.; bd. dirs. Coun. Ind. Colls., 1971-80, chmn., 1976-78; chmn. commn. higher edn. Nat. Assn. Evangelicals, 1973-79; chmn. Oreg. Ind. Colls. Assn., 1971-72, 81-82; mem. So. Calif. Radio and TV Commn., 1963-67; bd. dirs. Christian Coll. Consortium, chmn., 1984-86; mem. fact-finding group to Bangladesh, 1972; mem. adv. bd. Oriental Missionary Soc.; bd. advs. Latin Am. Mission, Friends Ctr., Azusa Pacific U. Author: Quakers in California, 1969; Rec.: album Songs of Discipleship, 1965. Bd. dirs. Oreg. Ind. Coll. Found. 1969-82, 92—, George Fox Coll. Found. 1971-82, Herbert Hoover Found., Oreg., 1975-82, Ind. Colls. of Wash. 1982-91, Wash. Friends of Higher Edn., 1982-91; bd. assocs. Pacific Sci. Ctr.; mem. Wash. Gives Leadership Coun., 1989-92, mem. edn. commn. States Task Force on State Policy and Ind. Higher Edn., 1986-89; trustee CRISTA Ministries, 1982-88, 90—, bd. dirs., 1982—; chmn. bd. Christian Coll. Coalition, 1991. Recipient Alumni Service award Taylor U., 1961, Chamber of Achievement award, 1978; Tchr. of Yr. award Ball State U., 1978. Mem. Nat. Assn. Evangs. (bd. adminstrn., chmn. theology com. 1992—), Portland Rotary Club. Address: 5737 Charles Cir Lake Oswego OR 97035-8714

LESHER, DONALD MILES, lawyer; b. Middleport, Ohio, May 29, 1915; s. Miles Mosser and Edith Katherine (McMaster) L.; m. Josephine Kirkmeyer, May 31, 1942; children: Donna J. Lesher Pinder, Karen A. Lesher Mariea, Lorraine C. Lesher Boyd; m. Barbara Jean Johnson, Feb. 20, 1963; m. Jimmie H. Queen, Mar. 22, 1981. B.A., Colo. U., 1937; LL.B. Okla. U., 1940. Bar: Colo. 1941. Since practiced in Denver; partner firm Knight & Lesher, 1953-58, Lesher, Schmidt & Van Cise, 1958-64, Lesher & Gregg, 1964-72, Knight & Lesher, P.C., 1981-87; pvt. practice law as Donald M. Lesher (P.C.), 1972-81, 87—; dir. First S & L Shares, Inc., Majestic Savs. & Loan Assn.; instr. real estate law Westminster Law Sch., Denver U., 1955-59. Mem. Colo. Gen. Assembly, 1943-44. Served with USN, 1940-41. Mem. ABA, Colo. Bar Assn. (trustee 1948-51, v.p. 1954-55, award of merit 1958, chmn. real estate sect. 1962-64), Denver Bar Assn. (hon. life), Sigma Chi. Republican. Roman Catholic. Club: Denver Athletic. Home: 7017 E Girard Ave Denver CO 80224-2903 Office: Donald M Lesher PC 4100 E Mississippi Ave Denver CO 80222-3048

LESHER, JOHN LEE, JR., consulting services company executive; b. Harrisburg, Pa., Feb. 7, 1934; s. John Lee and Mary Alice (Watkeys) L.; m. Nancy Smith, July 11, 1970; children by previous marriage: John David, James Elam, Andrew Gwynne. BA cum laude, Williams Coll., 1956; MBA, Harvard U., 1958. Budget dir., asst. sec. The Barden Corp., Danbury, Conn., 1958-63; mem. cons. Booz, Allen & Hamilton Inc., N.Y.C., 1962-64, assoc., 1964-66, v.p., 1966-76, pres., 1976-85; pres. Mars & Co. Cons. Inc., Greenwich, Conn., 1985-87, Home Group Fin. Services, N.Y.C., 1987-88; v.p. Cresap, McCormick & Paget, N.Y.C., 1988-89; mng. dir. Korn/Ferry Internat., N.Y.C., 1989-93; pres. Jack Lesher & Assocs., Greenwich, Conn., 1993—. Clubs: Harvard Bus. Sch., Watch Hill Yacht, Misquamicut (Watch Hill, R.I.), Round Hill (Greenwich, Conn.), River (N.Y.C.), Coral Beach (Bermuda)

LESHER, MARGARET LISCO, newspaper publisher, songwriter; b. San Antonio, Tex., May 4, 1932; d. Lloyd Elmo Lisco and Dovie Deona (Maynard) Lisco Welch; m. William Jarvis Ryan (dec.); children: Patricia Ryan Simmonds, Wendi Ryan Alves, Jill Ryan Heidt, Roxanne Ryan Gibson; m. Dean Stanley Lesher, Sr., Apr. 2, 1973 (dec.). Student Coalinga (Calif.) Jr. Coll. Dir. sales Chatmar, Inc., Concord, Calif., 1970-73; dir. cmty. svcs. Contra Costa Times Newspaper, Walnut Creek, Calif., 1973-94;

chmn. bd. Lesher Comm., Inc., Walnut Creek, 1974—, Calif. Delta Newspapers, Inc., Antioch, 1975—, No. Calif. Publs., Inc., Telegraph.-News Publs., Inc.; pres., ceo, dean Margaret Lesher Found. Composer, lyricist gospel song Margaret Lesher Album, 1976 (So. Calif. Motion Picture Coun. Bronze Halo award 1982); author 14 published poems. Pres., exec. dir. Dean and Margaret Lesher Found.; regent Holy Names Coll., Oakland, Calif., 1979-86; chief of protocol Contra Costa County, 1980—; dir. Bay Area Sports Hall of Fame, San Francisco, 1982—; bd. overseers U. Calif., San Francisco, 1983-90; bd. dirs. Yosemite Fund; mem. San Francisco Host Com., 1983—, Internat. Host Com. of Calif., 1983-86, Nat. Reading Initiative Coordinating Coun., 1988—; dir. emeritus Alameda-Contra Costa Regional Parks Found.; developed Contra Costa County Citizen Recognition Awards Program with County Police Chiefs Assn.; founded Contra Costa Literacy Alliance; commr. Port of Richmond, Calif., 1983-86; chmn. adv. bd. Crisis Nursery of Bay Area, Concord, 1983-86; adv. bd. Oakland A's Baseball Team, 1984-85, Battered Women, 1983—; pres. bd. dirs. Mt. Diablo Hosp. Found., 1980-81; bd. dirs. Contra Costa Council, 1984-90; mem. adv. bd. Las Trampas Sch. Mentally Retarded, chmn., 1984-90; trustee Oakland Symphony Orch., 1985-86; host Informed Viewer pub. svc. program Sta. KFCB-TV. Recipient Spl. Merit award State of Calif., 1982, Charles E. Scripps award Outstanding Contbr. in the Promotion of Literacy, 1988, 2 Internat. Silver Angel awards, 1st pl. for lit. program Calif. Newspaper Pub.'s Assn., 1988; named Calif. Assembly Woman of Yr. Mem. Am. Newspaper Pub. Assn. (ednl. svcs. com. 1988—), Gospel Music Assn., ASCAP, Nat. TV Acad. Arts & Scis., Calif. Cattlemen's Assn., Cancer of the Prostate Cure, Walnut Creek Rotary, Blackhawk Country Club. Republican. Christian. Avocation: horses. Office: Contra Costa Times Lesher Comm Inc 2640 Shadelands Dr Walnut Creek CA 94598-2513

LESHER, RICHARD LEE, association executive; b. Doylesburg, Pa., Oct. 28, 1933; s. Richard E. Lesher and Rosalie Orabelle (Meredith) Lesher Ehrhart; m. Agnes Marie Plocki, June 13, 1981; children by previous marriage: Douglas Allen, Laurie Lynn, Betsy Lee, Craig Collin. BBA, U. Pitts., 1958; MS, Pa. State U., 1960; DBA, Ind. U., 1963, LLD (hon.), 1979; D of Pub. Service (hon.), Ferris State Coll., 1981; DBA (hon.), Lawrence Inst. Tech., 1985. Asst. prof. Coll. Commerce and Adminstrn., Ohio State U., Columbus, 1963-64; cons. NASA, Washington, 1964-65; dep. asst. adminstr. NASA, 1965-66, asst. adminstr., 1966-69; bus. and mgmt. cons. Washington, 1969-71; pres. Nat. Ctr. for Resource Recovery, Washington, 1971-75, U.S. C. of C., Washington, 1975—; bd. dirs. SHL Systemhouse, Inc., G&L Realty Corp.; mem. bd. advs. CORDECOM, Norfolk So. Corp. Author: (book) Economic Progress...It's Everybody's Business, 1980, syndicated newspaper column; participant (weekly syndicated debate show) It's Your Business. Mem. bd. visitors Coll. Bus. Adminstrn. Pa. State U.; mem. Sch. Bus. Dean's Adv. Coun. Ind. U. With U.S. Army, 1954-56. Recipient Superior Achievement award NASA, 1968, Exceptional Svc. award, 1968, Alumni Achievement award Pa. State U., 1976, Acad. of Alumni Fellows award Ind. U., 1977, Religious Heritage award 1978, Horatio Alger award 1980, Bicentennial Medallian of Distinction U. Pitts., 1987, Golden Exec. medal Gen. C. of C. of Taiwan, 1988, Disting. Alumni fellow Pa. State U. 1990, Am. Soc. of Assn. Execs. Spl. Key award, 1992, Assn. of Yr. award Assn. Trends, 1994. Mem. Am. Soc. Assn. Execs., Washington Soc. Assn. Execs., Am. C. of C. Execs. (bd. dirs.), Phi Alpha Kappa, Beta Gamma Sigma (dir.'s Table, Nat. award 1977). Club: Congressional Country, Met. Avocations: golfing, fishing, horseback riding, tennis. Office: C of C of the USA 1615 H St NW Washington DC 20062-0001

LESHER, ROBERT OVERTON, lawyer; b. Phoenix, Apr. 6, 1921; s. Charles Zaner and Alice Marguerite (Heckman) L.; children: Stephen Harrison, Janet Kay. BA, U. Ariz., 1942, LLB, 1949. Bar: Ariz. 1949, Ill. 1949. Atty. A. T. & Santa Fe Ry., 1949-54; pvt. practice law Tucson, 1954—; ptnr. Lesher & Williams, Tucson, 1960—; adj. prof. Law Sch., U. Ariz., 1954-84; mem. Supreme Ct. Ariz., 1960. With AUS, 1942-46, 50-52. Fellow Am. Coll. Trial Lawyers; mem. Am. Law Inst., Am. Bd. Trial Advs. (diplomate), Internat. Assn. Ins. Counsel, Tucson Country Club. Home: 510 N Dodge Blvd Tucson AZ 85716-5102 Office: 3773 E Broadway Blvd Tucson AZ 85716-5409

LESHER, WILLIAM RICHARD, retired university president; b. Carlisle, Pa., Nov. 14, 1924; s. David Luther and Carrie LaVerne (Adams) L.; m. Veda E. Van Etten, June 16, 1946; children—Eileen Fern, Martha Zoe Lesher Keough. Th.B., Atlantic Union Coll., South Lancaster, Mass., 1946; M.A., Andrews U., 1964; Ph.D., NYU, 1970. Ordained to ministry Seventh-day Adventist Ch., 1951. Pastor No. New Eng. Conf. Seventh-day Adventists, 1946-56; pastor, mission dir. Delta sect. Nile Union Seventh-day Adventists, Alexandria, Egypt, 1957-58; prin. Nile Union Acad., Cairo, Egypt, 1959-61; sec. Middle East Div. Seventh-day Adventists Beirut, Lebanon, 1962-64; assoc. prof. religion, dir. summer sch., asst. to pres. Atlantic Union Coll., 1964-71; assoc. dir. Sabbath sch. dept. Gen. Conf. Seventh-day Adventists, Washington, 1971-79; dir. Bibl. Research Inst., Gen. Conf. Seventh-day Adventists, Washington, 1979-84; gen. v.p. Gen. Conf. Seventh-day Adventists, Washington, 1981-84; pres. Andrews U., Berrien Springs, Mich., 1984-95; ret., 1994. Author: Tips for Teachers, 1979; editor adult Sabbath Sch. lessons, 1971-79, studies in sanctuary and atonement, 1980-81; contbr. articles to religious jours. Recipient Founders Day award NYU, 1970. Home: 4703 Greenfield Dr Berrien Springs MI 49103-9566

LESHY, JOHN D., lawyer, legal educator; b. Winchester, Ohio, Oct. 17, 1944; s. John and Dolores (King) L.; m. Helen M. Sandalls, Dec. 15, 1973; 1 child, David Alexander. AB cum laude, Harvard U., 1966, JD magna cum laude, 1969. Trial atty. Civil Rights Divsn. Dept. Justice, Washington, 1969-72; atty. Natural Resources Def. Coun., Palo Alto, Calif., 1972-77; assoc. solicitor energy and resources Dept. Interior, Washington, 1977-80; prof. law Ariz. State U., Tempe, 1980—; spl. counsel to chair Natural Resources Com. U.S. Ho. Reps., Washington, 1992-93; solicitor Dept. Interior, 1993—; cons. Calif. State Land Commn., N.Mex. Atty. Gen., Western Govs. Assn., Congl. Rsch. Svc., Ford Found.; mem. com. Onshore Oil & Gas Leasing, NAS Nat. Rsch. Coun., 1989-90; vis. prof. Sch. Law U. San Diego, 1990. Author: The Mining Law: A Study in Perpetual Motion, 1987, The Arizona State Constitution, 1993; co-author Federal Public Land and Resources Law, 3d edit., 1992; contbr. articles, book chpts. to profl. jours., environ. jours. Bd. dirs. Ariz. Ctr. Law in Pub. Interest, 1981-86; mem. Gov.'s Task Force Recreation on Fed. Lands, 1985-86, Gov.'s Task Force Environ. Impact Assessment, 1990, City of Phoenix Environ. Quality Commn., 1987-90. Robinson Cox vis. fellow U. Western Australia Law Sch., Perth, 1985, rsch. fellow U. Southampton, Eng., 1986; Ford Found. grantee, Resources for the Future grantee. Democrat. Avocations: piano, hiking, whitewater rafting, photography. Office: Department of the Interior Solicitor 1849 C St NW Washington DC 20240

LESIKAR, RAYMOND VINCENT, business administration educator; b. Rogers, Tex., June 29, 1922; s. Vince E. and Albina J. (Stanislaw) L.; m. Lou Clay Allen, July 7, 1945 (dec. July 1993); children: Patricia Lesikar King, Raymond Vincent. B.B.A., U. Tex., 1947, M.B.A., 1948, Ph.D., 1954. With Douglas Aircraft Co., 1941-42, Sears, Roebuck & Co., 1947; instr. Tex. Christian U., 1948-49; asst. prof. U. Tex., 1949-54; faculty La. State U., Baton Rouge, 1954-77; prof. bus. adminstrn. La. State U., 1959—, chmn. dept. mgmt., 1959-77; dean La. State U. (Coll. Bus. Adminstrn.), 1963-64, 72-73, prof. emeritus, 1977—; adj. prof. U. Tex., Austin, 1977-79; prof., chmn. dept. mgmt. U. North Tex., Denton, 1979-88; guest prof. univs., People's Republic China, spring 1982, 83, 84; cons. in field. Author: Business Communication: Theory and Application, 1968, 7th edit., 1993, Report Writing for Business, 9th edit., 1994, Introduction to Business: A Societal Approach, 1972, 3rd rev. edit. 1979, Productive Business Writing, 1959, Business Report Writing, 1957, How to Write Reports, 1974, 2d rev. edit. 1984, Basic Business Communication, 1979, 6th rev. edit., 1993; contbr. articles to profl. jours. Served with AUS, 1943-46. Fellow Am. Bus. Communication Assn. (pres. 1961); mem. S.W. Social Sci. Assn. (pres. 1967), Acad. Mgmt. Internat. Communication Assn., Internat. Soc. Gen. Semantics, Horseshoe Bay Country Club, Beta Gamma Sigma, Phi Kappa Phi, Sigma Iota Epsilon. Home and Office: PO Box 7912 Horseshoe Bay TX 78654

LESKO, HARRY JOSEPH, transportation company executive; b. Cleve., Dec. 6, 1920; s. Theodore Prokop and Bertha Barbara (Trojack) L.; m. Evelyn Martha Culley, Feb. 3, 1945; children—Harry Richard, Larry J.,

Garry E., Mark J., John M. B.B.A., Cleve. State U., 1956. Schedule analyst Cleve. Ry. System, 1938-40; pres., dir. Greyhound Lines, Inc., Phoenix, 1940—; pres. Atlantic Greyhound Lines of Va., Inc.; v.p. Gelco Bus Leasing Co., 1979—; pres. Trailways Lines Inc., Dallas, 1979—; pres., dir. The Trailways Corp., Trailways, Inc.; dir. Trailways Lines Inc. (25 subs.), Southeastern Stages, Inc., Atlanta, N.Mex. Transp. Co., Roswell, KG Lines, Tulsa, Okla. Transp. Co., Lubbock, Tex., Jefferson Lines Inc., Mpls., Kerrville Bus. Co., Tex., Continental Lines, Amarillo, Tex., Service Coach Co., Jacksonville, Fla., Gen. Fire and Casualty Co. Served to capt. USMC, 1942-46. Mem. Am. Bus. Assn. (dir.). Republican. Roman Catholic. Club: Brookhaven Country.

LESKO, LEONARD HENRY, Egyptologist, educator; b. Chgo., Aug. 14, 1938; s. Matthew Edward and Josephine Bernice (Jaszczak) L.; m. Barbara Jadwiga Switalski, Dec. 29, 1966. B.A., Loyola U., Chgo., 1961, M.A., 1964; Ph.D., U. Chgo., 1969; M.A. ad eundem, Brown U., 1983. Tchr. Quigley Prep. Sem. South, Chgo., 1961-64; Egyptologist, epigrapher, epigraphic survey Oriental Inst., U. Chgo., Luxor, Egypt, 1964-65; acting instr. U. Calif. at Berkeley, 1966-67, acting asst. prof., 1967-68, asst. prof. 1968-72, asso. prof., 1972-77, prof. Egyptology, 1977-82, dir. Center Nr. Eastern Studies, 1973-75, chmn. dept., 1975-77, 79-81, chmn. grad. program in ancient history and archeology, 1978-79, chmn. humanities council, 1980-81; dir. Seila project, 1981; C.E. Wilbour prof. Egyptology, chmn. dept. Brown U., 1982—; chmn. faculty, faculty exec. com., 1992-93. Author: The Ancient Egyptian Book of Two Ways, 1972, Glossary of the Late Ramesside Letters, 1975, King Tut's Wine Cellar, 1977, Index of the Spells on Egyptian Middle Kingdom Coffins and Related Documents, 1979; co-author: Religion in Ancient Egypt, 1991, Pharoah's Workers: The Villagers of Deir el-Medina, 1994; editor: A Dictionary of Late Egyptian, vol. I, 1982, vol. II, 1984, vol. III, 1987, vol. IV, 1989, vol. V, 1990, Egyptological Studies in Honor of Richard A. Parker, 1986; contbr. articles to profl. publs. and encys. NEH fellow, 1970-71, grantee, 1975-79; FIAT faculty fellow U. Torino, 1990; recipient award computer oriented rsch. in humanities Am. Coun. Learned Socs., 1973. Mem. Am. Rsch. Ctr. for Egypt (gov. 1973-75), Am. Oriental Soc., Archeol. Inst. Am. (pres. San Francisco chpt. 1976-78, pres. Narragansett chpt. 1994—), Internat. Assn. Egyptologists, Egypt Exploration Soc., Found. Egyptologique Reine Elisabeth, Société Française d'Égyptologie, U.S. Lighthouse Soc., Lighthouse Preservation Soc., Explorers Club. Office: Brown U Dept Egyptology PO Box 1899 Providence RI 02912-1899

LESLIE, DONALD WILMOT, landscape architecture educator; b. Pitts., Dec. 29, 1942; s. Donald and Harriette Rebecca (Wilmot) L.; divorced; children: Robin Elizabeth, Kristen Bogar. BS in Landscape Architecture, Pa. State U., 1965; M Landscape Architecture, U. Mich., 1967. Registered landscape architect, Pa. Landscape architect Simonds & Simonds, Pitts., 1967-71; asst. prof. dept. landscape architecture Pa. State U., University Park, 1971-78, asso. prof., 1978—, asso. dean, 1991—; pvt. practice, State College, Pa., 1979—; cons. Comprehensive Design, State Coll., 1986—; master grader Coun. Landscape Archtl. Registration Bds., 1988-90. Contbg. author: Landscape Architectural Construction, 1985. Pres. coun. Trinity Luth. Ch., State College, 1987-88; pres. Forest Edge Townhouse Assn., State College, 1987—. Recipient Disting. Teaching award Pa. State U., 1975. Fellow Am. Soc. Landscape Architects (pres. Pa. chpt. 1984-85, nat. trustee 1986-89, nat. v.p. 1989-91, Disting. Svc. award Pa. chpt. 1987). Republican. Home: 1210 Westerly Pky State College PA 16801-4158 Office: Pa State U Coll Arts & Architecture 116 Arts Bldg University Park PA 16802

LESLIE, DOUGLAS L., law educator; b. 1942. BA, U. Iowa, 1964; JD, U. Mich., 1968. Bar: Ohio 1968, D.C. 1970, Mass. 1970. Atty. NLRB, 1969; pvt. practice D.C., 1970-73; assoc. prof. Ariz. State U., 1973-75; prof. Ariz. State U., Charlottesville, 1976-78; prof. U. Va., Charlottesville, 1978-85, Charles O. Gregory prof., 1985—; vis. prof. U. Mich., fall 1976, U. La., 1977, Stanford U., fall 1982. Guggenheim fellow, 1982-83. Mem. ABA (sec. labor and employment sect.). Office: U Va Sch Law Charlottesville VA 22901

LESLIE, GERRIE ALLEN, immunologist; b. Red Deer, Alta., Can., Nov. 19, 1941; s. John Allen and Lily Elizabeth (von Hollen) L.; m. Anna Magdalene Madsen Ladefogod, July 31, 1965; children: Kirsten, John Gerrie. BS in Pharmacy, U. Alta., 1962, MS in Microbiology, 1965; PhD, U. Hawaii, 1968. Postdoctoral fellow U. Fla., Gainesville, 1968-70; prof. Tulane U. Med. Sch., New Orleans, 1970-74, Oreg. Health Scis. U., Portland, 1974-86; pres., chief exec. officer Immunology Cons. Lab., Lake Oswego, Oreg., 1979—; sci. adviser Epitope Inc., Beaverton, Oreg., 1987-91, Ultra Diagnostics, Seattle, 1987-91; cons. to biotech. cos. S.Am., Thailand, U.S. Author and co-author 110 sci. articles. Grantee NIH,1968-86, NSF, 1970-85, Kroc Found., 1970-86, Cancer Found., Med. Rsch. Found., John Hartford Found., others. Mem. Am. Assn. Immunology, Oreg. Polled Hereford Assn. (bd. dirs. 1991-94). Lutheran. Avocations: stamp collection, coin collecting, fishing, farming.

LESLIE, HENRY ARTHUR, lawyer, retired banker; b. Troy, Ala., Oct. 15, 1921; s. James B. and Alice (Minchener) L.; m. Anita Doyle, Apr. 5, 1943; children: Anita Lucinda Leslie Bagby, Henry Arthur Jr. B.S., U. Ala., 1942, J.D., 1948; J.S.D., Yale U., 1959; grad., Sch. Banking, Rutgers U., 1964. Bar: Ala. 1948. Asst. prof. bus. law U. Ala., 1948-50, 52-54; prof. law, asst. dean U. Ala. (Sch. Law), 1954-59; v.p. trust officer Birmingham Trust Nat. Bank, Ala., 1959-64; sr. v.p., trust officer Union Bank & Trust Co., Montgomery, Ala., 1964-73; sr. v.p., sr. loan officer Union Bank & Trust Co., 1973-76, exec. v.p., 1976-78, pres., chief exec. officer, 1978-91, also bd. dirs.; ret., 1991; sole practice Montgomery, Ala., 1991—; mem. Ala. Oil and Gas Bd., 1984-85; dir. First Fin. Mgmt. Corp., 1981—. Pres. Downtown Unltd., 1983-84; mem. Ala. Bd. Bar Examiners, 1973-78, Bus. Com. for Arts, Inc.; chmn. bd. dirs. Ala. Bankers Found., 1971-77; trustee Ala. Assn. Ind. Colls. Capt. AUS, 1942-46; lt. col. JAGC Res. Decorated Bronze Star. Mem. ABA, Ala. Bar Assn., Montgomery Bar Assn. (Liberty Bell award 1989), Ala. Ind. Bankers (chmn. 1983-84), Ala. Bankers Assn. (trust div. pres. 1963-65), Ind. Bankers Assn. Am. (dir. 1983-90), Farrah Order Jurisprudence (pres. 1973), Order of Coif Alumni, Newcomen Soc. N.Am., Montgomery C. of C. (dir. 1983-84, pres. 1987-88), Maxwell Officers Club, Montgomery Country Club, Kiwanis, Delta Sigma Pi, Phi Delta Phi, Omicron Delta Kappa, Pi Kappa Phi. Episcopalian (past sr. warden). Home: 3332 Boxwood Dr Montgomery AL 36111-1702 Office: 456 S Court St Montgomery AL 36104-4102

LESLIE, JACQUES ROBERT, JR., journalist; b. L.A., Mar. 12, 1947; s. Jacques Robert and Aleen (Wetstein) L.; m. Leslie Wernick, June 21, 1980; 1 child, Sarah Alexandra. BA, Yale U., 1968. Tchr. New Asia Coll., Chinese U., Hong Kong, 1968-70; free-lance journalist Washington, 1970-71; fgn. corr. L.A. Times, Saigon, 1972-73, Phnom Penh, 1973, Washington, 1974; chief New Delhi (India) bur. L.A. Times, 1974-75, Madrid, 1975-76; chief Hong Kong bur. L.A. Times, 1976-77; freelance journalist, 1977—. Author: The Mark: A War Correspondent's Memoir of Vietnam and Cambodia. Recipient Best Fgn. Corr. award Sigma Delta Chi, 1973, citation reporting Overseas Press Club, 1973. Home: 124 Reed St Mill Valley CA 94941-3448

LESLIE, JAMES HILL, paper company executive; b. Mpls., Feb. 27, 1930; s. Frank Paul and Ruth (Hill) L.; m. Carol Van Camp, Mar. 23, 1972; children: Laura, Kate, James. B.A., Princeton U., 1952; postgrad., Sloan Sch., M.I.T., 1954-55. With Leslie Paper, Mpls., 1955—; v.p. Leslie Paper, 1960-66, pres., 1966-82, chmn., chief exec. officer, 1982—. Served to lt. USN, 1952-54. Mem. Minnetonka Yacht Club, Sarasota Yacht Club, Rotary. Office: Leslie Paper PO Box 1351 Minneapolis MN 55440-1351

LESLIE, JOHN HAMPTON, manufacturing executive; b. Evanston, Ill., June 28, 1914; s. John W. and Alma (Bertles) L.; m. Virginia Andersen, Aug. 5, 1950; children: James Woodworth, Victoria Hall. BS, Harvard U., 1937. Design engr. Signode Corp. (now Ill. Tool Works Inc.), Glenview, Ill., 1937-41, v.p. engring. and rsch., 1946-49, pres., 1949-62, chmn. bd., 1962-82, ret., 1982; chief engr. South Wind div. Stewart Warner Corp., 1941-46. Trustee Signode Found., Inc., 1943-83, Village of Winnetka, Ill., 1955-59, Skokie Valley Community Hosp., 1958-69 (now Rush North Shore Med. Ctr.), Northwestern U.; bd. dirs. Evanston Hosp., 1972-81; mem. Winnetka Bd. Edn., 1963-69. Mem. Comml. Club, Univ. Club, Indian Hill Club. Office: 1 Northfield Plz Northfield IL 60093

LESLIE, JOHN WALTER, development consultant; b. Norfolk, Va., Sept. 18, 1929; s. John Walter and Ella Arden (Squires) L.; m. Audrey May Munford, Apr. 9, 1957. B.A., Coll. William and Mary, 1952; student, Mich. State U., 1957-58, U. Oreg., 1962-64; M.A., Am. U., 1968. From copy boy to sports reporter Norfolk Virginian-Pilot, 1944-49; sports reporter Newport News (Va.) Daily Press, 1950-52, asst. sports editor, 1956-57; asst. news editor Mich. State U., 1957-58; asso. dir. Ketchum, Inc., 1958-60; dir. devel. and pub. relations Lewis and Clark Coll., 1960-63; exec. v.p. Am. Coll. Pub. Relations Assn., 1963-74; pres. Instl. Advancement Consultants, Inc., N.Y.C., 1974-80; sr. v.p. Brakeley, John Price Jones, Inc., N.Y.C., 1974-80; v.p. devel. U. Houston System, 1981-85; pres. John W. Leslie Inc., Potomac, Md., 1986—. Author: Focus on Understanding and Support: A Study in College Management, 1969, Seeking the Competitive Dollar, 1971; contbr. articles to profl. jours. Served to 1st It. USAF, 1952-56. Home: 8004 Grand Teton Dr Rockville MD 20854-4074

LESLIE, JOHN WEBSTER, JR., communications company executive; b. Milw., July 20, 1954; s. John and Joanne Marie (Chamberlain) L.; m. Laura Elizabeth Bafford, June 7, 1986; children: Finn Elizabeth, John Webster III. BS in Fgn. Service, Georgetown U., 1976. Legis. asst. Senator Edward Kennedy, Washington, 1976-80; campaign dir. northeast region Kennedy for Pres., Washington, 1980-81; polit. dir. Senator Edward Kennedy for U.S. Senate, Washington, 1981-82; exec. dir. Fund for Dem. Majority, Washington, 1982-83; pres. Sawyer/Miller Group, N.Y.C., 1983-93; ptnr. Robinson Lake Sawyer Miller, N.Y.C., 1993—; Bd. dirs. Internat. Policy Research, Inc., N.Y.C., Creative Media, Inc., N.Y.C. Contbr. articles to profl. jours.; speaker in field. Bd. dirs. Nat. Student Edn. Fund, Washington, 1977-79. Fellow Circumnavigators Found., Am. Assn. Polit. Cons. Roman Catholic. Club: N.Y. Athletic. Office: Robinson Lake/Sawyer Miller 75 Rockefeller Plz 5th fl New York NY 10019

LESLIE, JOHN WILLIAM, public relations and advertising executive; b. Indpls., Nov. 22, 1923; s. John Edward and Catherine (Harris) L.; m. Joan Williams, Dec. 26, 1970; 1 dau. by previous marriage, Catherine Alexandra. Student, U.S. Naval Acad., 1943-44, George Washington U., 1949, Indsl. Coll. Armed Forces, 1956. Dep. excise adminstr. Ind., 1946-47; pvt. pub. relations bus., 1947-49; dir. pub. relations Ind. Democratic State Central Com., 1948-49, Ind. Dept. Vets. Affairs, 1949; press officer Dept. Labor, 1949-51, acting asst. dir. info., 1951-52, asst. dir., 1952-56, dep. dir., 1956-59, dir., 1959-81; sr. assoc. Kamber Group, Washington, 1981-84; counselor Kamber Group, 1984-88, exec. v.p., COO, 1988—, also bd. dirs.; mem., dir. pub. D.C. Com. Employment Physically Handicapped, 1952-53; charter mem. U.S. Sr. Exec. Svc., 1979—. Author numerous articles in field. Advt. cons. Pres.'s Com. on Youth Employment, 1964-80; U.S. del Internat. Graphic Design Coun., Japan, 1973; trustee Washington chpt. Leukemia Soc. Am., 1996-82; chmn. Pub. Printers Adv. Com. on Printing and Publs, 1977-79. Served with USN and USNR, 1941-46. Recipient commendation President's Com. Employment Physically Handicapped, 1954; Disting. Service award Dept. Labor, 1962; citation outstanding service Navy Dept., 1964; Presdl. citation, 1966; Merit award Internat. Labor Press Assn., 1969; Disting. Career Service award Dept. Labor, 1973; Communications award Ga. chpt. Pub. Relations Soc. Am., 1972; Sec. Labor's Recognition award, 1974; Communicator of Yr. award Nat. Assn. Govt. Communicators, 1981. Mem. Am. Assn. Polit. Cons., Am. League Lobbyists, Nat. Press Club, English Speaking Union. Episcopalian. Home: 4290 Massachusetts Ave NW Washington DC 20016-5553 Office: Kamber Group 1920 L St NW # 700 Washington DC 20036-5004

LESLIE, JOSHUA ALLENSWORTH, mathematics educator; b. Savannah, La Mar, Jamaica, Feb. 18, 1933; came to U.S., 1936; s. George Augustus and Margaret Isadore (Allen) L.; m. Abiodun Omolara Ogundipe, 1970 (div. 1977); children: Rachel, Isis; m. Annie Ruth Johnson, 1977; children: Harold, Sophia, Jamilah, Nandi, Ewadele. BA, U. Chgo., 1954; PhD, U. Sorbonne, Paris, 1960. Asst. prof. U. Ibadan, Nigeria, 1960-62, assoc. prof., 1962-64, prof., 1965-70; mem. Inst. for Advanced Study, Princeton, N.J., 1969-70, 87-88; vis. prof. Northeastern U., Boston, 1969-70; prof. Northwestern U., Evanston, Ill., 1970-91; prof. of math. Howard U., Washington, 1990—; vis. prof. U. Calif., Berkeley, 1970-71. Contbr. articles to Topology, Jour. Differential Geometry, Jour. Negro History, others. Grantee NATO, 1959, NSF, 1987—. Mem. Am. Math. Soc., Math. Assn. Am., Nat. Assn. Mathematicians, N.Y. Acad. Scis. Office: Northwestern U Math Dept 633 Clark St Evanston IL 60208-0001

LESLIE, LOTTIE LYLE, retired secondary education educator; b. Huntsville, Ala., Aug. 5, 1930; d. James Peter and Amanda Lacy Burns; children: Thomas E. Lyle Jr., Theodore Christopher Leslie, DeMarcus Miller Leslie. BS, Ala. A and M U., 1953, student, 1960-83; training cert., Learning Ctrs. of Am., 1985. Cert. secondary tchr. Social studies, English, Music. Tchr. Madison County Bd. Edn., Huntsville, Ala. Author: Teaching the Importance of Character Through Poetry, 1968-69, Ways to Teach Language Composition and Literature, Versatility Versus Violence, Families and Foreign Relationships, Musical Instruments of the World From K-12 and Undergraduate to Graduate; contbr. poetry to profl jours. Recipient Miss Liberty trophy, 1986, Victory pin, 1987, Medal of Honor Commemorating Disting. Lifelong Achievements, 1993, cert. appreciation Indian Creek P.B. Ch., 1994. Mem. NEA, ASCD, Ala. Edn. Assn., Madison County Music Edn. Assn., Internat. Black Writers and Artists, Inc., N.Y. Poetry Soc., Am. Poetry Assn. (vol. IV no. 2 summer 1985). Con sponsor Ednl. Expo 2000. Home: 3207 Farris Dr NW Huntsville AL 35810-3342

LESLIE, MARVIN EARL, minister; b. Boonville, Ind., Aug. 22, 1938; s. Ora Thomas and Mary Lucille (Kapperman) L.; m. Jenann Demuth, July 3, 1962; children: Elizabeth, Brian. BA, Bethel Coll., 1964; MDIV, Memphis Theol. Sem., 1967; D of Ministry, Valderbilt U., 1977; postgrad., Memphis State & Murray State U. Ordained to ministry Presbyterian Ch., 1965. Pastor Cumberland Presby. Ch., Springfield, Mo., 1967-73, Mayfield, Ky., 1973-75; pastor, assoc. pastor Cumberland Presby. Ch., Marshall, Tex., 1975-89; campus dir. Cumberland Presby. Children's Home, Denton, Tex., 1989-91; exec. dir. Cumberland Presby. Children's Home, 1991—; sec. interch. rels. com. Cumberland Presbyn. Ch., 1969-75, moderator Tex. Synod, 1982-83, stated clk., 1986-89, moderator Mission Synod, 1990-91. Contbr. articles to profl. jours. Organizing chmn. Vol. Chaplains Assn., Marshall, 1979; pres. United Chs. Care Bd., Marshall, 1980, 81; chmn. Christmas in April Housing Project, Marshall, 1985. 1 st. chaplains corps, USNR, 1971-80. Mem. Southwest Assn. Child Care Adminstrs., Optimist (sec. Marshall chpt. 1977-78), Kiwanis. Office: Cumberland Presbyterian Church Drawer G Denton TX 76202

LESLIE, SEAVER, artist; b. Boston, Aug. 22, 1946; s. John Frederick and Joan (Warland) L.; m. Anne Cleland Rogers; children: Genevieve, Marion, Frances. BFA, RISD, 1969, MEd, 1970. Exhibited in shows at Hirschl & Adler Gallery, N.Y.C., 1981, Tatistcheff Gallery, N.Y.C., 1982, Decordova Mus., Lincoln, Mass., 1989, Maine Coast Artists, Rockport, 1993, Portland (Maine) Mus. of Art, 1993. Author: 12 Points: Putting the Case for Customary Measure, 1979, Why America Should Not Go Metric, 1993. Founder, Ams. for Customary Weight and Measure, N.Y.C., co-founder Maine Trans. Coalition, Wicasset. Office: Old Stone Farm Wiscasset ME 04578

LESLIE, SEYMOUR MARVIN, communications executive; b. N.Y.C., Dec. 16, 1922; s. Harry and Fay (Goldstein) L.; m. Barbara Miller, Mar. 30, 1947; children: Ellen, Jane, Carol. EE, Syracuse U., 1945; grad., Advanced Mgmt. Program, Harvard U., 1971; DHL, Hofstra U., 1974. Sales mgr. Voco, Inc., N.Y.C., 1946-52; founder Pickwick Internat., Inc., Woodbury, N.Y., 1953, chmn. bd., pres., 1953-77, N.Y.C.; Leslie Group, Inc., 1977—; pres. CBS Video Enterprises div. CBS, Inc., N.Y.C., 1980-82; chmn., pres., chief exec. officer MGM/UA Home Entertainment Group, Inc., 1982-87; co-chmn. Leslie/Linton Entertainment Corp., 1993—; bd. dirs. Shorewood Packaging Corp., Gametek Corp., Allied Digital Corp., Songwriters Hall of Fame, K-Tel Corp.; vis. disting. prof. Syracuse U. Sch. Music, 1984. Active Boy Scouts Am. 1947-50; mem. corp. adv. coun. Syracuse U.; mem. coun. Hofstra U.; bd. govs. Anti Defamation League, 1960—; v.p. Am. Med. Ctr., Denver; v.p. dir. T.J. Martell Found.; v.p. Friars Found. Sgt. U.S. Army, 1942-46, PTO. Recipient Presdl. award Nat. Assn. Record Merchandisers, 1976, Disting. Svc. award, 1977, Outstanding Arendts Alumnus award Syracuse U., 1978; named Man of Yr. Time Mag., 1987; named to Video Hall of Fame, 1987. Mem. ASCAP, N.Y. Coun. for Humanities, Record

Industry Assn. Am. (profl. group), B'nai B'rith, Friars Club, Harvard Club, Harvard Bus. Club. Office: Leslie Group Inc 1370 Ave Of The Americas New York NY 10019-4602

LESLIE, (ROBERT) TIM, state legislator; b. Ashland, Oreg., Feb. 4, 1942; s. Robert Tabor Leslie and Virginia (Hall) P.; m. Clydene Ann Fisher, June 15, 1962; children: Debbie, Scott. BA in Political Sci., Calif. State U., Long Beach, 1963; MPA, U. Southern Calif., L.A., 1969. Prin. analyst Sacramento County Exec. Office, Calif., 1965-69; cons. Assm. W. & M. Commn., Sacramento, 1965-72; prin. legislator rep. County Sups. Assn., Sacramento, 1972-80; founder bd. dirs. Comm. Act. Against Drg., Sacramento, 1975-83; v.p. Moss & Thompson, Inc., Sacramento, 1980-84; exec. v.p. Kuhl. Corp., Sacramento, 1984-86; assemblyman Calif. State Legislature, Sacramento, 1986-91, senator, 1991—; vice chmn. Appropriations Com., Judiciary Com.; mem. Health Com., Natural Resources Com. Recipient Hang Tough Award Nat. Tax Limitation Com., Calif., 1987; named Legislator of the Yr. Sacramento City Taxpayers League & Osteopathic Surgeons of Calif., 1990. Republican. Presbyterian. Home: 4081 State Capital Sacramento CA 95814 Office: District Office 1200 Melody Ln Ste 110 Roseville CA 95678-5189

LESLIE, WILLIAM BRUCE, history educator; b. Orange, N.Y., July 21, 1944; s. William and Annette (Riedell) L.; children: William Andrew, Sarah Acton. BA, Princeton U., 1966; PhD, Johns Hopkins U., 1971. Asst. prof. history SUNY, Brockport, 1970-79, assoc. prof., 1979—; vis. prof. Jordanhill Coll., 1972, dir. MA in History program, 1984-90; co-dir. SUNY Social Sci. Program, London, 1978-79, 82-83, 89; mem. editorial bd. Hist. of Higher Edn. Ann., 1991—. Author: Gentlemen and Scholars, 1993; contbr. articles and revs. to profl jours. Mem. Orgn. Am. Historians, Am. Historical Assn., History of Edn. Soc., Adirondack Mountain Club, We. Monroe Hist. Soc., Amnesty Internat., Princeton Club N.Y. Democrat. Avocations: camping, travel, gardening. Office: SUNY History Dept Brockport NY 14420-2956

LESLIE, WILLIAM CAIRNS, metallurgical engineering educator; b. Dundee, Scotland, Jan. 6, 1920; came to U.S., 1925, naturalized, 1940; m. Florence M. Hall, 1948; 1 dau. B.Metall. Engring., Ohio State U., 1947, M.Sc., 1948, Ph.D., 1949. Metallurgist U.S. Steel Research Lab., Kearny, N.J., 1949-53; assoc. dir. staff research and devel. Thompson Products, Inc., Cleve., 1953-54; with U.S. Steel Corp., Monroeville, Pa., 1954-73; mgr. phys. metallurgy E.C. Bain Lab. for Fundamental Research, 1963-73; prof. materials engring. U. Mich., 1973-85, prof. emeritus, 1985—; adj. prof. metallurgy Bklyn. Poly. Inst., 1952-53; Battelle vis. prof. metallurgy Ohio State U., 1964-65; vis. prof. U. Melbourne, Australia, 1979; Am. Soc. Metals and AIME rep. to EJC Metric Council and Am. Nat. Metric Council, 1971-80; mem. ship research com. NRC, 1978-81; Garofalo lectr. Northwestern U., 1977; U.S. rep. Internat. Conf. Strength of Metals and Alloys, 1970-82; mem. Charles Hatchett award panel Metals Soc. Gt. Britain, 1978-81; cons. in field; mem. adv. com. div. metals and ceramics Oak Ridge Nat. Lab., 1974-75; mem. com. on basic research, advisor to Army Research Office, Durham, N.C., 1973-78; mem. ad hoc com. on non-magnetic structural steels Nat. Materials Adv. Bd., 1973-74. Author: The Physical Metallurgy of Steels, 1981; Contbr. articles to profl. jours. Served to 1st lt. C.E. U.S. Army, 1943-46. Named Disting. Alumnus Ohio State U. Coll. Engring., 1967, Disting. Alumnus lectr., 1984. Fellow Am. Soc. Metals Internat. (chmn. publs. com. 1966-68, mem. metals sci. divsn. coun. 1970-75, Pitts. chpt. Andrew Carnegie lectr. 1970, Edward DeMille Campbell lectr. 1971, Phila. chpt. Albert Sauveur lectr. 1975, Cleve. chpt. Zay Jeffries lectr. 1975, hon. mem. 1986, Barrett medal Rocky Mtn. chpt. 1992, Gold medal 1995), Inst. Materials of Gt. Britain (fellow 1984), Metall. Soc. (chmn. Inst. Metals divsn. 1971-72, bd. dirs. 1971-72), Internat. Metallographic Soc. (Henry Clifton Sorby award 1991); mem. AIME (v.p., dir. 1975), Krumb lectr. 1967), Henry Marion Howe lectr. 1982), AAAS, Sigma Xi, Tau Beta Pi. Patentee in field. Home and Office: RR 7 Box 7416 Palmyra VA 22963-9510

LESLY, PHILIP, public relations counsel; b. Chgo., May 29, 1918; m. Ruth Edwards, Oct. 17, 1940 (div. 1971); 1 son, Craig.; m. Virginia Barnes, May 11, 1984. BS magna cum laude, Northwestern U., 1940. Asst. to news editor Chgo. Herald & Examiner, 1935-37; copywriter advt. dept. Sears, Roebuck & Co., Chgo., 1940-41; asst. dir. publicity Northwestern U., 1941-42; account exec. Theodore R. Sills & Co. (pub. rels.), Chgo., 1942; v.p. Theodore R. Sills & Co. (pub. rels.), 1943, exec. v.p., 1945; dir. pub. rels. Ziff-Davis Pub. Co., 1945-46; exec. v.p. Harry Coleman & Co. (pub. rels.), 1947-49; pres. Philip Lesly Co. (pub. rels.), Chgo., 1949—; lectr. pub. rels., pub. opinion to bus. and sch. groups. Co-author: Public Relations: Principles and Procedures, 1945, Everything and the Kitchen Sink, 1955; author: The People Factor, 1974, Selections from Managing the Human Climate, 1979, How We Discommunicate, 1979, Overcoming Opposition, 1984, Bonanzas and Fool's Gold, 1987; bimonthly Managing the Human Climate; editor: Public Relations in Action, 1974, Public Relations Handbook, 3d rev. edit., 1967, Lesly's Public Relations Handbook, 1971, rev. edit., 1978, 83, Lesly's Handbook of Public Relations and Communications, 1991; contbr. articles to bus. publs. Recipient Gold Anvil award Pub. Relations Soc. Am., 1979; voted leading active practitioner Pub. Relations Reporter Survey, 1978. Mem. Pub. Rels. Soc. Am., Phi Beta Kappa. Home and Office: 155 N Harbor Dr Apt 5311 Chicago IL 60601-7328 One should stand out by focusing on those talents and skills that others cannot demonstrate, rather than by competing with the crowd.

LESNICK, HOWARD, legal educator; b. N.Y.C., Apr. 22, 1931; s. George L. and Sadie (Rovner) L.; m. Carolyn M. Schodt, May 1, 1976; children—Alice, Caleb, Abigail. A.B., NYU, 1952; A.M., Columbia U., 1953, LL.B., 1958. Bar: N.Y. 1958. Pa. 1968. Law clk. to justice John M. Harlan, U.S. Supreme Ct., 1959-60; prof. law U. Pa., Phila., 1960-80, 88—; disting. prof. CUNY Law Sch. at Queens Coll., 1982-88; impartial umpire AFL-CIO Internal Disputes Plan; dir. Ctr. for Law and Human Values. Served as pfc. U.S. Army, 1953-55. Mem. Am. Law Inst. Author: Becoming a Lawyer: A Humanistic Perspective on Legal Education and Professionalism, 1981. Office: U Pa Law Sch 3400 Chestnut St Philadelphia PA 19104-6204

LESONSKY, RIEVA, editor in chief; b. N.Y.C., June 20, 1952; d. Gerald and Muriel (Cash) L. BJ, U. Mo., 1974. Researcher Doubleday & Co., N.Y.C., 1975-78; researcher Entrepreneur Mag., L.A., 1978-83, rsch. dir., 1983-84, mng. editor, 1985-86, exec. editor, 1986-87; editor Entrepreneur Mag., Irvine, Calif., 1987-90; editor-in-chief Entrepreneur Mag. Bus. Start-Ups Entrepreneur Group, Irvine, Calif., 1990—; rsch. dir. LFP Inc., L.A., 1980-82; speaker, lect. in field. Editor: 184 Businesses Anyone Can Start, 1990, Complete Guide to Owning a Home-based Business, 1990, 168 More Businesses Anyone Can Start, 1991, 111 Businesses You Can Start for Under $10,000, 1991; contbr. articles to mags. Apptd. SBA Nat. Adv. Coun., 1994-96. Named Dist. Media Advocate of Yr., Small Bus. Adminstrn., 1993, Dist. Women in Bus. Advocate, Small Bus. Adminstrn., 1995. Mem. Women's Network for Entrepreneurial Tng. (bd. dirs., advisor, nat. steeri. Avocations: books, magazines, baseball. Office: Entrepreneur Mag Group 2392 Morse Ave Irvine CA 92714-6234

LESOURD, LEONARD EARLE, publisher, editor; b. Columbus, Ohio, May 20, 1919; s. Howard Marion and Lucile (Leonard) LeS.; m. Evelyn Chester, Aug. 21, 1948 (div. Mar. 1959); m. Catherine Marshall, Nov. 14, 1959 (dec. Mar. 1983); m. Sandra Jean Simpson, June 22, 1985; children: Linda, Chester, Jeffrey. BA, Ohio Wesleyan U., 1941. Editor Guideposts mag., N.Y.C., 1946-74; pub. Chosen Books, Grand Rapids, Mich., 1974-92; chmn. Breakthrough, Inc., Lincoln, Va., 1980-94; elder First Presbyn. Ch., Delray Beach, Fla., 1968-77, New Covenant Presbyn. Ch., Pompono Beach, Fla., 1977-81; v.p. Prebyn. Reformed and Renewal Ministries, Oklahoma City, 1977. Author: Skybent, 1944, Strong Men, Weak Men, 1990, (with Catherine Marshall) My Personal Prayer Diary, 1978; editor: Touching the Heart of God, 1990. Pres. PTA, Carmel, N.Y., 1956. 1st lt. USSAC, 1945. Mem. Fellowship Christian Athletes (sec., bd. dirs. 1970-76). Republican. Home: Evergreen Farm Lincoln VA 22078 Office: Breakthrough Inc Catherine Marshall Ctr Lincoln VA 22078 I have discovered the key to achieving fulfillment in life is to be a servant. The more I serve others, the more God has blessed me with health, leadership roles and abundance.

LESS, ANTHONY ALBERT, retired naval officer; b. Salem, Ohio, Aug. 31, 1937; s. Joseph Anthony and Mildred Gertrude (Bair) L.; m. Leanne Carol Kuhl, Mar. 3, 1962; children: Robyn, Pamela, Theresa, Christina. BS in Chemistry, Heidelberg Coll., 1959. Cert. naval aviator. Commd. ensign

USN, 1960, advanced through grades to vice adm., 1991, ret., 1994; commdg. oficer USS Wichita (AOR-1), Pacific, 1979-81, exec. asst. to commdr. in chief, 1981-82; commdg. officer USS Ranger (CV-61), Pacific, 1982-83; chief of staff Commdr. 7th Fleet, Yokosuka, Japan, 1983-84; dir. Polit. Mil Br. JCS, Washington, 1985-87; commdr. Carrier Group One, Pacific, 1987-88, Mid. East Force, Manama, Bahrain, 1988-89; dir. Plans and Policy Navy Staff, Washington, 1989-91; comdr. Naval Air Force Atlantic Fleet, Norfolk, Va., 1991-94; pres. Assn. Naval Aviation, Washington, 1994—; cons. Kaman Aerospace, Bloomfield, Conn., 1994—. Mem. Assn. Naval Aviation (pres. 1994), Soc. Naval Engrs. Roman Catholic. Avocations: racquetball, farming, reading. Office: Assn of Naval Aviation Ste 200 5205 Leesburg Park Falls Church VA 22041

LESSARD, DONALD ROY, management educator; b. San Jose, Calif., July 14, 1943; s. Roy Beverly and Dorita Esther (Thomann) L.; m. Pauline Marie Olsen, May 29, 1965; children—Paul Roy, Edward Martin. B.A., Stanford U., 1965, M.B.A., 1969, Ph.D., 1970. Asst. prof. Amos Tuck Sch., Darmouth Coll., Hanover, N.H., 1969-73; asst. prof. Sloan Sch., MIT, Cambridge, 1973-76, assoc. prof., 1977-84, prof. mgmt., 1984—; vis. fellow Inst. Internat. Econs., 1985; vis. prof. Stanford U. Grad. Sch. Bus., 1985-86; cons. govts. and agys. and firms, including Bolivia, Can., Ecuador, Peru, Kuwait, World Bank, Marakon Assocs., San Francisco, Chem. Bank, Merck and Co. Author: Capital Flight: The Problem and Policy Responses, 1987; (with John Williamson) Financial Intermediation Beyond the Debt Crisis, 1985; contbr. articles on internat. corp. fin., competitive strategy, and fin. for developing countries to profl. jours. Fellow Acad. Internat. Bus.; mem. Am. Fin. Assn., Fin. Execs. Inst. Democrat. Avocation: Latin Am. affairs. Office: MIT Sloan Sch Mgmt Mit Bldg E52-551 Cambridge MA 02139

LESSARD, MICHEL M., finance company executive; b. Quebec City, Can., Aug. 31, 1939; s. Maurice and Jacqueline (Lacasse) L.; m. Doris Lamoureux; children: Eric, Christine. BA, Laval U., Quebec, 1958, B in Commerce, 1961, M in Commerce, 1962; MBA, Harvard U., 1967. With Can. Ingersoll Rand, Allied Chem. Can. DomGlass Ltd., Montreal, Que., Can.; with Credit Foncier, Montreal, 1970-86, asst. gen. mgr., treas., 1978-79, sr. asst. gen. mgr., 1979-80, exec. v.p., 1980-81, pres., dir., mem. exec. com., 1981-86, pres., chief exec. officer, 1984-86; pres. Sogexfi Inc., 1986—; pres. and CEO Immobiliere Natgen Inc., 1993-95; chmn. Mildev Real Estate Svcs.; v.p., bd. dirs. Sucana Investments Inc., Montreal; bd. dirs. Jonergin Inc., Montreal, Overseas Med. Ventures N.V. Mem. Pride Can. Inc. Fellow Trust Cos. Inst., Mt. Royal Club, Winchester Club, Club de Golf de la Vallég du Richelieu. Home: 279 Kenaston, Mount Royal, PQ Canada H3R 1M6

LESSARD, RAYMOND W., bishop; b. Grafton, N.D., Dec. 21, 1930. Student, St. Paul Sem., Am. Coll., Rome. Ordained priest Roman Catholic Ch. Mem. staff Congregation for Bishops, Roman Curia, 1964-73; consecrated bishop, 1973; bishop Diocese of Savannah Ga., 1973—. Office: Catholic Pastoral Ctr 601 E Liberty St Savannah GA 31401-5196

LESSEM, JAN NORBERT, medical director; b. Malmo, Sweden, Apr. 7, 1948; s. Slom and Frida (Marcus) L.; m. Eva K. Löfquist, July 11, 1976; children: Martin A., Sarah E. MD, U. Lund, 1974, PhD, 1982. Med. diplomate. Intern, then resident in cardiology; assoc. prof. U. Lund, Sweden, 1981-82; med. dir. Merck, Sharp & Dohme, Rahway, N.J., 1982-83, Bristol-Myers, Evansville, Ind., 1983-85; sect. head cardiology div. Syntex Research, Palo Alto, Calif., 1986-87, sr. dept. head cardiology div., 1987-90; dir. clin. investigation SB Pharma., Phila., 1991-95; med. dir. Takeda Am., 1995—. Contbr. over 150 articles to profl. jours. Bd. dirs. Am. Swedish Hist. Mus., Phila., 1992—. Fellow Am. Coll. Cardiology, Coll. of Physicians Phila., Swedish Soc. Cardiology, Royal Swedish Coll. Med. Jewish Youth. Club: Jewish (Malmo) (pres. 1966-73). Avocations: opera, art, books, tennis, travelling. Office: SB-Four Falls Corp Ctr Rt 23 and Woodmont Ave King Of Prussia PA 19406

LESSEN, LARRY LEE, federal judge; b. Lincoln, Ill., Dec. 25, 1939; s. William G. and Grace L. (Plunkett) L.; m. Susan Marian Vaughn, Dec. 5, 1964; children: Laura, Lynn, William. BA, U. Ill., 1960, JD, 1962. Bar: U.S. Bankruptcy Ct. 1964, U.S. Tax Ct. 1982, U.S. Ct. Appeals (7th cir.) 1981, U.S. Supreme Ct. 1981. Law clk. to presiding justice U.S. Dist. Ct., 1962-64; asst. state's atty. State of Ill., Danville, 1964-67; mng. ptnr. Sebat, Swanson, Banks and Lessen, Danville, 1967-85; judge U.S. Bankruptcy Ct., Danville, 1973-85, U.S. Magistrate, Danville, 1973-84; chief judge U.S. Bankruptcy Ct., Springfield, Ill., 1985-93; U.S. bankruptcy judge Springfield divsn., 1993—. Mem. ABA, Fed. Bar Assn., Sangamon County Bar Assn., Vermilion County Bar Assn., Nat. Conf. Bankruptcy Judges, Am. Bankruptcy Inst., Lincoln-Douglas Inn of Cts. Office: US Bankruptcy Ct PO Box 2438 600 E Monroe St Springfield IL 62705-2438

LESSEN, MARTIN, engineering educator, consulting engineer; b. N.Y.C., Sept. 6, 1920; s. Philip and Lena (Sukornik) L.; m. Elizabeth Scher, Aug. 27, 1948; children: Margot, Deborah, David. B.S.M.E., CCNY, 1940; M.M.E., NYU, 1942; Sc.D., MIT, 1948. Registered profl. engr. Mech. engr. Bklyn. Navy Yard, 1940-46; aero. research scientist NACA Cleve., 1948-49; prof. aero. engrng. Pa. State U., State College, 1949-53; prof. and chmn. applied mechanics U. Pa., Phila., 1953-60; prof., chmn. dept. mech. engring U. Rochester, N.Y., 1960-70; Yates Meml. prof. engring. U. Rochester, 1967-83, Yates Meml. prof. engring. emeritus, 1983—; liaison scientist Office Naval Research, London, 1976-79; cons. Gen. Electric Co., 1954-58, RCA Co., 1957-64, Bausch & Lomb, 1965-75, Eastman Kodak Co., 1964—, Energy div. ORNL 1984—; advisory com. Oak Ridge Nat. Lab., 1984-87. Author numerous papers in field; patentee in field. Sr. postdoctoral fellow NSF, Cambridge, Eng., 1966; Vollmer Fries hon. fellow Rensselaer Poly. Inst., Troy, N.Y., 1978; exchange lectr. Nat. Acad. Sci., USSR, 1967. Fellow ASME (founding chmn. energetics 1964), Am. Phys. Soc., AAAS. Club: Cosmos (Washington). Home and Office: 12 Country Club Dr Rochester NY 14618-3720

LESSENCO, GILBERT BARRY, lawyer; b. Balt., June 19, 1929; s. Jacob David and Sarah (Bank) L.; B.S., Johns Hopkins U., 1950; LL.B., Harvard U., 1953. m. Elaine Beitler, Sept. 3, 1952; children: Susan Donna, Amy Gail, Robert Howard. Admitted to D.C. bar, 1953; since practiced in Washington; with Wilner and Bergson, 1955-60; ptnr. Wilner & Scheiner, 1960-90, Semmes, Bowen & Semmes, 1990—, mng. ptnr., Washington, 1992—. Mem., treas. Democratic Central Com., Montgomery County, Md., 1970-74; chmn. Internat. Visitors Service Council, 1962; bd. dirs. Jewish Social Service Agy. of Greater Washington, 1978—, pres., 1984-86; bd. dirs. Mental Health Assn. of Montgomery County, 1980-84, pres., 1981-82; trustee Meridian House Found.; commr. Washington Suburban San. Commn., 1987-93, chmn., 1989-90; co-chmn., fundraiser St. Luke's House, 1989. Served to lt. USAF, 1953-55. Named Outstanding Young Lawyer of Yr., D.C. Jr. Bar, 1965. Mem. Phi Sigma Delta (v.p.). Home: 10731 Gloxinia Dr Rockville MD 20852-3442 Office: 1025 Connecticut Ave NW Ste 900 Washington DC 20036-5405

LESSER, EDWARD ARNOLD, banker; b. N.Y.C., Feb. 2, 1934; s. Arnold A. and Dorothy B. (Stillwell) L.; m. Mary M. Maxwell, June 9, 1956; children: James Edward, Elizabeth Ann, Carol Jean. B.S., U. Pa., 1955. With Bankers Trust Co., N.Y.C., 1957—, v.p. U.S. dept., 1967, sr. v.p. charge banking ops., computer system dept., 1971-74, exec. v.p., 1974-77, exec. v.p. fiduciary dept., 1977-82, mem. mgmt. com., now exec. v.p.; dir. Bankers Trust N.Y. Corp Co., 1982—. Office: Bankers Trust NY Corp 280 Park Ave New York NY 10017-1216

LESSER, FREDERICK ALAN, mining and chemical company executive; b. London, June 20, 1934; s. Frederick Adolfo and Maria Isabel (Yriberry) L.; m. Stella Mary Holmes, Sept. 11, 1961; children: Maria Isabel Lesser Orchard, Frederick Alan, Hugo John. MA in Econs., Cambridge (Eng.) U. Mgmt. trainee U.S. Borax & Chem. Corp., L.A., 1957-60, chmn., 1989—; asst. mgr. subcos. dept. Borax Consol. Ltd., London, 1960-62, European sales mgr., 1963-69, chmn., MD, 1984—; asst. to pres. Boroquimica S.A., Buenos Aires, 1962-63; European mktg. dir. Borax Holdings Ltd., London, 1969-74; mktg. dir. RTZ Borax Ltd., London, 1974-84; chief exec. officer RTZ Borax and Minerals Ltd., London, 1984—. Gov. Farleigh Sch., Basingstoke, Eng., 1980—. Lt. Brit. Army, 1953-54. Mem. Royal Automobile Club. Roman Catholic. Avocations: fishing, travel, theater, music. Home: Hatch House Farm, West Woodhay NR Newbury, Berkshire RG18 0BG,

England Office: Borax Consol Ltd, Borax House Carlisle Pl, London SW1P 1HT, England also: US Borax 26877 Tourney Rd Valencia CA 91355-1846

LESSER, JOAN L., lawyer; b. L.A.. BA, Brandeis U., 1969; JD, U. So. Calif., 1973. Bar: Calif. 1973, U.S. Dist. Ct. (cen. dist.) Calif. 1974. Assoc. Irell and Manella, L.A., 1973-80, ptnr., 1980—; mem. planning com. Ann. Real Property Inst., Continuing Edn. of Bar, Berkeley, 1990—; speaker at profl. confs. Trustee Windward Sch.; mem. Grad. Leadership, L.A., 1992. Mem. Orgn. Women Execs., Order of Coif. Office: Irell and Manella Ste 900 1800 Avenue of the Stars Los Angeles CA 90067-4211

LESSER, JOSEPH M., retired business executive, retail store executive; b. N.Y.C., July 27, 1928; s. Jacob and Sonia (Gustow) L.; m. Sonia Rabinowitz, Nov. 26, 1948; children: Brett Paul, Peter John. BS in Social Sci., CCNY, 1949; JD, Bklyn. Law Sch., 1953. With Allied Stores Corp., 1955—, personnel and labor relations advisor, 1955-58, dir. cen. services, 1960-68; asst. to pres., 1958-60; coordinator control and ops. divs. Allied Stores Corp., 1963-65, v.p. control and ops., electronic data processing divs., 1967-80, v.p. food services div., 1967-80, pres. Alcomp Electronic Data Systems div., 1968-75; sr. v.p., exec. group mgr. Allied Stores Corp., N.Y.C., 1980—; dir., sr. v.p. Allied Stores-Penn. Ohio-Inc., N.Y.C., 1981—, Allied Cen. Stores, Inc., N.Y.C., 1984-88; sr. v.p. Allied Stores III, Inc., N.Y.C., 1985-88; dir., exec. v.p. Allied Stores-East, Inc., N.Y.C., 1986-88, ret.; exec. v.p. Internat. Collectibles Inc., 1989-92; ret.; bd. govs. Allied Stores Assocs., 1991—. Pres. Briarcliff Schs., Briarcliff Manor, N.Y., 1973; bd. dirs. North-East Council Schs., N.Y.C., 1967; life trustee Indpls. Mus. Art. Mem. Nat. Retail Mchts. Assn. (bd. dirs. 1977-79), Marco Island Art League, U.S. Power Squadrons (lt.-cruise comdr.) USCG Aux. Flotilla, Marco Island Civic Assn., Princeton Club (N.Y.C.) Calif. Yacht Club, Island Country Club, Hideaway Club (chmn. archtl. rev. com. 1991-93). Office: 2000 Royal Marco Way #603 Marco Island FL 33937

LESSER, LAURENCE, music conservatory president, cellist, educator; b. Los Angeles, Oct. 28, 1938; s. Moses Aaron and Rosalyne Anne (Asner) L.; m. Masuko Ushioda, Dec. 23, 1971; children—Erika, Adam. AB, Harvard U., 1961; student of Gaspar Cassadó, Germany, 1961-62; student of Gregor Piatigorsky, 1963-66. Mem. faculty U. So. Calif., Los Angeles, 1963-70; mem. faculty Peabody Inst., Balt., 1970-74; mem. faculty New Eng. Conservatory Music, Boston, 1974—, pres., 1983—; former vis. prof. Eastman Sch. Music, Rochester, N.Y.; vis. prof. Toho Gakuen Sch. Music, Tokyo, 1973—; performed with New Japan Philharm., Boston Symphony, London Philharm., L.A. Philharm. and Marlboro, Spoleto, Casals, Santa Fe and Banff festivals; rec. artist; overseer Boston Symphony Orch. Trustee WGBH Ednl. Found.; mem. adv. coun. Chamber Music Am. Recipient prize Tchaikovsky Competition, Moscow, 1966; Fulbright scholar, 1961-62; Ford Found. grantee, 1972. Mem. Am. Acad. Arts and Scis., Harvard Mus. Assn., Tavern Club, Phi Beta Kappa, Pi Kappa Lambda, Sigma Alpha Iota. Jewish. Home: 65 Bellevue St Newton MA 02158-1918 Office: New Eng Conservatory Music 290 Huntington Ave Boston MA 02115-5000

LESSER, LAWRENCE J., advertising agency executive; b. Bklyn., June 1, 1939; m. Joanna Savarese, Aug. 26, 1962; children: Eileen, Kristin. AAS, N.Y.C Community Coll., 1959. Asst. acct. exec. Friend Reiss Advt., 1959-63; v.p., acct. supr. sr. v.p. L.W. Frohlich, 1963-72; sr. v.p Medicus Comm. Inc., N.Y.C., 1972-76, pres., CEO, 1976—; chmn., CEO Medicus Group Internat.; bd. dirs., mem. exec. com. D'Arcy Masius Benton & Bowles. Office: D'Arcy Masius Benton & Bowles Inc 1675 Broadway New York NY 10019-5865

LESSER, WENDY, literary magazine editor, writer, consultant; b. Santa Monica, Calif., Mar. 20, 1952; d. Murray Leon Lesser and Millicent (Gerson) Dillon; m. Richard Rizzo, Jan. 18, 1985; 1 stepchild, Dov Antonio; 1 child, Nicholas. BA, Harvard U., 1973; MA, Cambridge (Eng.) U., 1975; PhD, U. Calif., Berkeley, 1982. Founding ptnr. Lesser & Ogden Assocs., Berkeley, 1977-81; founding editor The Threepenny Rev., Berkeley, 1980—; vis. lectr. U. Calif., Santa Cruz, 1983, 84, 90; Bellagio resident Rockefeller Found., Italy, 1984. Author: The Life Below the Ground, 1987, His Other Half, 1991, Pictures at an Execution, 1994; editor: Hiding in Plain Sight, 1993. Fellow NEH, 1983, 92, Guggenheim fellow, 1988. Democrat. Office: The Threepenny Rev PO Box 9131 Berkeley CA 94709

LESSER, WILLIAM HENRI, marketing educator; b. N.Y.C, Dec. 19, 1946; s. Arthur and Ethel (Boissevain) L.; m. Susan Elizabeth Bailey, Dec. 27, 1975; children: Andrew, Jordan. BA in Geography, U. Wash., 1968; MS in Resource Econs., U. R.I., 1974; PhD in Agrl. Econ., U. Wis., 1978. From asst. to assoc. prof. mktg. Cornell U., Ithaca, N.Y., 1978-91, prof., 1991—; with Internat. Acad. Environ., Geneva, 1993-94, acting exec. dir. internat. svc. to acquisition of agri-biotech applications, 1994-95, dur. biodiversity/ biotechnology programme, 1993—; grad. field rep. Dept. Agrl. Econs., Ithaca, 1985-88; dir. Cornell Western Socs. Program, 1991-93; cons. World Bank, Washington, US/AID, Winrock Internat., Morrilton, Ark. Editor: Animal Patents: The Legal Economic and Social Issues, 1990; author: Equitable Patent Protection in the Developing World, 1991, Marketing Livestock and Meat, 1993. Zone capt. Dem. com. Town of Ithaca, 1985-90, mem. planning bd., 1987-93. Nat. fellow Kellogg Found., 1988-91. Mem. Am. Agrl. Econ. Assn., Patent & Trademark Office Soc. Avocations: gardening, painting, antique cars. Home: 406 Coddington Rd Ithaca NY 14850-6012 Office: Cornell U Dept Argl Econs 405 Warren Hall Ithaca NY 14853-7801

LESSIN, LAWRENCE STEPHEN, hematologist, oncologist, educator; b. Washington, Oct. 14, 1937; s. Maurice and Anna (Brodsky) L.; m. Judith Ann Lustok, Dec. 23, 1961; children: Jennifer Lynn, Jonathan Lustok, Martine Rose. Student, U. Mich., 1955-58; M.D., U. Chgo., 1962. Diplomate Am. Bd. Internal Medicine (assoc. mem. 1976-82). Intern, resident in internal medicine, chief resident, fellow in hematology Hosp. U. Pa., 1962-67; spl. fellow Nat. Heart Inst., Inst. for Cell Pathology, Paris, 1967-68; asst. prof. medicine Duke U., 1968-70; assoc. prof. medicine and pathology George Washington U., 1970-74, prof. medicine and pathology, dir. div. hematology and oncology, 1974—; dir. George Washington U. Cancer Ctr., Washington, 1991-93; med. dir. Washington Cancer Inst. Washington Hosp. Ctr., 1993—; vis. physician medicine br. Nat. Cancer Inst., 1971-74; cons. hematology Washington VA Hosp., 1971—; cons. ARC Blood Bank, 1972—, Nat. Naval Med. Ctr., Bethesda, Md., 1974—, Nat. Heart, Lung and Blood Inst., 1974; Walter Reed Army Med. Ctr., 1978—; ad hoc cons. Nat. Heart, Lung and Blood Inst., Study Sect. Program-Project Grants, 1977; mem. NASA Biomed. Rev. Panel, 1981-88; chmn. div. blood diseases and resources adv. com. Nat. Heart, Blood and Lung Inst., NIH, 1985-86; chmn., program dir. Assn. Hematology-Oncology, 1983-87. editorial reviewer: Annals of Internal Medicine, 1969—, Nouvelle Revue de Hematologie, 1970—, Blood, Jour. Hematology, 1971—, Archives of Internal Medicine, 1972—, Nature, 1973, Jour. Clin. Investigation, 1973—, New Eng. Jour. Medicine; mem. editorial Blood Cells, 1979—, Hematologic Pathology, 1985—; contbr. articles to profl. jours., chpts. to books. Served to capt. M.C. USAR, 1963-69. Named Intern of Year U. Pa. Hosp., 1963; nominee for Golden Apple award, 1975; Nat. Heart Inst. spl. fellow Paris, 1967-68. Fellow ACP, Internat. Soc. Hematology; mem. Am. Coll. Physicians (chair Hematology Med. Knowledge Self-Assessment program, 1992—), Am. Soc. Hematology, Am. Fedn. Clin. Research, Am. Soc. Clin. Oncology, Am. Blood Commn., Am. Soc. Internal Medicine, D.C. Med. Soc., Internat. Blood Cells Club, Am. Soc. Clin. Oncology, Sigma Xi, Alpha Omega Alpha. Club: Cosmos (Washington). Office: 2150 Pennsylvania Ave NW Washington DC 20037-2396

LESSIN, MICHAEL EDWARD, oral-maxillofacial surgeon; b. Chgo., Jan. 24, 1944; m. Cathy Irene Wilkinson, June 22, 1968; children: Amy Suzanne, Beth Michele. BDS, U. Ill., 1965; DDS, Ill. Coll. Dentistry, 1969. Diplomate Am. Bd. Oral Maxillofacial Surgery. Commd. 1st lt. U.S. Army, 1969, advanced through grades to Col., 1983, retired, 1989; resident in oral and maxillofacial surgery Letterman Army Med. Ctr., San Francisco, 1974-77; clin. assoc. prof. dept. Oral and Maxillofacial Surgery U. Tex., San Antonio, 1985-89; clin. assoc. prof. Surgery W.Va. U., Morgantown, 1990—; assoc. dept. Dental Medicine and Surgery, dept. Pediatrics Geisinger Med. Ctr., Danville, Pa., 1990—; clin. assoc. prof. Surgery Hahnemann Hosp./Med. Coll. Pa., 1995—; cons. ROK Ctrl. Army Hosp., Seoul, Korea, 1977-79, U.S. Army Dental Activity Gen. Practice Residency Program, Ft. Sill, Okla., 1985-86,

87, to surgeon gen., 1987-89, William Beaumont Army Med. Ctr., El Paso, Tex., 1990-91, Dwight D. Eisenhower Med. Ctr., Augusta, Ga., 1990, residency program, Ft. Campbell, Ky., 1992-93; lectr. in field. contbr. articles to profl. jours. Mem. AAA, Am. Trauma Soc., Pa. Dental Assn., Tri-county Dental Assn., 38th Parallel Dental Soc. Avocations: travel, golf. Office: Geisinger Med Ctr Academy Ave Danville PA 17822

LESSING, DORIS (MAY), writer; b. Kermanshah, Persia, Oct. 22, 1919; d. Alfred Cook Taylor and Emily Maude McVeach; m. Frank Charles Wisdom, 1939 (div. 1943); m. Gottfried Anton Nicholas Lessing, 1945 (div. 1949); children: John W. (dec.), Jean W., Peter L. Educated in, So. Rhodesia; hon. degree, Princeton, 1989. Author: (novels) The Grass is Singing, 1950, Five Short Novels, 1955, Retreat to Innocence, 1959, The Golden Notebook, 1962 (Prix Medicis Award for work translated into French, 1976), Children of Violence, 5 vols., 1964-69, Briefing For a Descent Into Hell, 1971, The Summer Before the Dark, 1973, The Memoirs of a Survivor, 1975, Shikasta, 1979, Marriages Between Zones Three, Four and Five, 1980, The Sirian Experiments, 1981 (Booker McConnell Prize nominee, 1981), The Making of the Representative for Planet 8, 1982, Documents Relating to the Sentimental Agents in the Volyen Empire, 1983, The Diaries of Jane Somers (Diary of a Good Neighbour, 1983, and If the Old Could…, 1984, pub. under pseudonym Jane Somers), The Good Terrorist, 1985 (W.H. Smith Lit. Award, 1976; Palermo Prize, 1987; Premio Internazionale Monello, 1987), The Fifth Child, 1988, The Libretto of the Making of the Representative for Planet 8, 1988, African Laughter: Four Visits to Zimbabwe, 1992; (nonfiction) Going Home, 1957, In Pursuit of the English, 1961, Particularly Cats, 1967, Prisons We Choose to Live Inside, 1986, The Wind Blows Away Our Words…and Other Documents Relating to the Afghan Resistance, 1987, Particularly Cats and More Cats, 1989; (autobiography) Under My Skin: Volume One of My Autobiography, to 1949, 1994; (short stories) This Was the Old Chief's Country, 1952, The Habit of Loving, 1958, A Man and Two Women, 1963, African Stories, 1965, The Temptation of Jack Orkney and Other Stories, 1972, The Story of a Non-Marrying Man, 1972, Collected African Stories, 1973, London Observed: Stories and Sketches, 1992, The Real Thing, 1992; (collections) Room 19 (Collected Stories Vol. 1), The Doris Lessing Reader, 1990; (play) Mr. Dollinger, 1958, Each in His Own Wilderness, 1958, The Truth About Billy Newton, 1961, Play with a Tiger, 1962; (essays) A Small Personal Voice, 1974; (poetry) Fourteen Poems, 1959; also newspaper reports. Recipient Somerset Maugham award, 1954; Austrian State Prize for European Lit., 1981; Shakespeare prize (Hamburg), 1982; Grinzane Cavour award (Italy), 1989; Disting. Fellow in Lit. Sch. English & Am. Studies U. East Anglia, Eng., 1991. Fellow MLA (hon.); mem. Nat. Inst. Arts and Letters, Am. Acad. Arts & Letters (assoc. mem. 1974), Inst. Cultural Research. Office: care Jonathan Clowes Ltd, 10 Iron Bridge House, Bridge Approach, London NW1 8BD, England

LESSITER, FRANK DONALD, magazine editor; b. Pontiac, Mich., Oct. 5, 1939; s. Milon John and Donalda Belle (Taylor) L.; m. Pamela Ann Fuzak, Nov. 23, 1963; children—Deborah, Susan, Michael, Kelly. B.S. in Dairy Sci, Mich. State U., 1961, postgrad. in Advt., 1962-65. Info. specialist Mich. Coop. Extension Service, East Lansing, 1962-65; exec. editor Agrl. Pubs., Milw., 1965-68; editor Nat. Livestock Producer mag., Chgo., 1969-72, No-Till Farmer, 1972—; v.p., editor Nat. Livestock Producer, 1974-78; editor Rural Builder, 1977-89; exec. v.p. Reiman Assocs., 1977-81; editor Farmer's Digest, 1988—; pres. Am. Farm Bldg. Services, Inc., 1981-89, No-Till Farmer, Inc., 1981—, Lessiter Publs., Brookfield, Wis., 1989—; editor Ridge Till Hotline, 1991—, Am. Farrier's Jour., 1992—. Author: (with Pamela Ann Fuzak Lessiter) Agricultural Travel Guide, 1971, Horsepower, 1977, 100 Most Common No-Tillage Questions, 1981; editor, pub. Am. Farriers Jour., 1992—; contbg. author: (with Pamela Ann Fuzak Lessiter) Commodity Yearbook, 1972, 75. Named Farm Mag. Editor of Year Dekalb AgResearch Program, 1972, Newsletter Editor of Year Newsletter Clearing House, 1973, Best Farm Mktg. Writer CIBA-Ceigy Awards Program, 1976, Farm Mag. Writer of Yr., 1977. Mem. Nat. Press Photographers Assn., Nat. Agrl. Mktg. Assn., Am. Agrl. Editors Assn. (Photographer of Year 1975). Home: 16000 Choctaw Trl Brookfield WI 53005-5504 Office: PO Box 624 Brookfield WI 53008-0624

LESSLER, RICHARD SIGMUND, advertising executive; b. Lynbrook, N.Y., Aug. 26, 1924; s. William S. and Minnie (Gold) L.; m. Evelyn Sobotka, Aug. 31, 1952; children: Michael Jay, Jonathan Peter, Daniel Stephen. B.A. in Exptl. Psychology, U. N.C., 1943; M.B.A., Columbia U., 1948; postgrad., NYU, 1948-52. Research assoc. CBS, 1948-49; with Dancer-Fitzgerald-Sample, Inc., 1949-55; with Grey Advt., Inc., 1955-72, chmn. bd., 1967-72; also dir., mem. exec. com., chmn. mgmt. com.; vice chmn. bd., chief operating officer U.S., chmn. exec. com. McCann-Erickson, Inc., N.Y.C., 1972-79; vice chmn. bd., chmn. ops. com. The Interpublic Group Cos., Inc., 1972-79, 1979-80; exec. cons. The Interpublic Group Cos., Inc., 1980-82; mktg., communications cons. Carpinteria, Calif., 1990—; mgr. Western region Canter, Achenbaum, Assocs., Inc., 1980-89; exclusive cons. Bozell, Inc., Dallas, 1989-93; cons. Temerlen McClain, Dallas, 1993-94; mktg. cons., prof. mktg. and advt. U. Ariz., 1980-83. Author: (with Brown and Weilbacher) Advertising Media, 1957, (with Nugent Wedding) Advertising Management, 1962. Served to lt. USNR, World War II. Mem. Phi Beta Kappa, Beta Gamma Sigma. Home: 1946 Paquita Dr Carpinteria CA 93013-3026

LESSY, ROY PAUL, JR., lawyer; b. Wallingford, Pa., Feb. 27, 1944; s. Roy Paul and Ruth W. Lessy; m. Ellen Mauck, Jan. 24, 1970; children: Rose-Ellen, Anne, Page. BA, Franklin & Marshall U., 1966; JD, George Washington U., 1969; postgrad., Harvard U., 1979. Bar: D.C. Atty.-advisor Office of Sec. U.S. Treasury Dept., Washington, 1969-72; dep. chief hearing counsel U.S. Nuclear Regulatory Commn., Washington, 1972-82; atty. and counsel Morgan, Lewis & Bockius, Washington, 1983-86; ptnr. Akin, Gump, Strauss, Hauer & Feld, Washington, 1986—; mem. lawyers steering com. Atomic Indsl. Forum, Washington, 1984—. Author: Casenote on Federal Jurisdiction, 1969. Mem. ABA (lectr. Am. Law Inst. 1984—), Fed. Energy Bar Assn., Phi Delta Phi. Home: 8605 Fenway Dr Bethesda MD 20817-2709 Office: Akin Gump Strauss Hauer & Feld Ste 400 1333 New Hampshire Ave NW Washington DC 20036-1511

LESTAGE, DANIEL BARFIELD, retired naval officer, physician; b. Jennings, La., July 7, 1939; s. Henry Oscar Jr. and Juliet Xavier (Barfield) L.; m. Helen Newcomer, Mar. 9, 1963; children: Juliet Lestage Hirsch, Diane Lestage Davis, Daniel B. Jr. Grad., La. State U., 1959, MD, 1963; grad. Naval Sch. Aviation, 1964; MPH, Tulane U., 1969; diploma, Indsl. Coll. Armed Forces, 1978. Diplomate Am. Bd. Preventive Medicine (trustee 1988-94), Am. Bd. Family Practice. Commd. ensign USN, 1962, advanced through grades to rear adm., 1986; rotating intern Charity Hosp., New Orleans, 1963-64; resident in family practice Lafayette (La.) Charity Hosp., 1964; student flight surgeon Naval Sch. Aviation Medicine, Pensacola, Fla., 1964; staff flight surgeon/med. officer Carrier Air Wing 16 USS Oriskany, NAS Lemoore, Calif., 1965-67; sr. med. officer Naval Med. Clinic, NAS New Orleans, 1967-68, USS John F. Kennedy, Norfolk, Va., 1971-73; resident in aerospace medicine Naval Aerospace Med. Inst., Pensacola, 1969-71; sr. med. officer Br. Clinic, Jacksonville NAS, 1973-77; chief preventive medicine dept. Naval Regional Med. Ctrs., Jacksonville, 1973-77; spl. asst. to surgeon gen. navy Bur. Medicine and Surgery Dept. Navy, Washington, 1978-81; head operational medicine br., aeromed. advisor Office of Chief Naval Ops., Washington, 1978-81; dir. clin. svcs., dir. med. edn., exec. officer Naval Regional Med. Ctr., Portsmouth, Va., 1981-83; commanding officer Naval Hosp., Millington, Tenn., 1983-84; comdr. U.S. Naval Med. Command, London, 1984-86; fleet med. officer U.S. Naval Forces Europe, 1984-86; fleet surgeon U.S. Atlantic Fleet, Norfolk, 1986-88; command surgeon U.S. Atlantic Command Supreme Allied Comdr., Norfolk, 1986-89; asst. dir. naval medicine Office of Chief Naval Ops., 1989; insp. gen. Navy Bur. Of Medicine and Surgery, 1989-90; comdg. officer Naval Hosp., Portsmouth, Va., 1990-92; corp. med. dir. Blue Cross/Blue Shield of Fla., Jacksonville, 1992—; asst. dean Ea. Va. Med. Sch., Norfolk, 1981-83, assoc. dean, 1990-92; del. AMA ho. of dels from Aerospace Med. Assn., 1993—. Dir. Blood Bank, Jacksonville, 1973-77; bd. dirs. Cath. Family Svcs., Portsmouth, 1981-83, Fraser-Millington Mental Health Ctr., Memphis, 1983-84. Decorated Legion of Merit with four oak leaf clusters, Meritorious Svc. medal, Air medal with oak leaf cluster, Navy Commendation medal; recipient Physician's Recognition award AMA, 1972, 75, 78, 81, 85, 88, 91, 94, 97. Fellow Am. Coll. Physicians, Am. Coll. Preventive Medicine, Am. Acad. Family Physicians, Aerospace Med. Assn. (pres. 1988-89); mem. AMA (del.

1983—) VFW, Am. Legion, Internat. Acad. Aviation and Space Medicine, Am./Fla. Coll. of Occupational and Environ. Medicine, Rotary, Elks. Roman Catholic. Avocations: travel, cooking. Home: 1782 Long Slough Walk Orange Park FL 32073-7033 Office: Blue Cross/Blue Shield Fla 8657 Baypine Rd Jacksonville FL 32256

LESTER, ANDREW WILLIAM, lawyer; b. Mpls., Feb. 17, 1956; s. Richard G. and Marion Louise (Kurtz) L.; m. Barbara Regina Schmitt, Nov. 22, 1978; 1 child, Susan Erika. Student, Ludwig-Maximilians Univ., Munich, 1975-76; BA, Duke U., 1977; MS in Fgn. Service, JD, Georgetown U., 1981. Bar: Okla. 1981, D.C. 1985, Tex. 1990, U.S. Supreme Ct. 1992. Cons. Dresser Industries, Inc., Washington, 1979-81; assoc. Conner & Winters, Tulsa, 1981-82; asst. atty. City of Enid, Okla., 1982-84; ptnr. Lester & Bryant, P.C. and predecessor firms, Oklahoma City, Tulsa and Enid, 1984—; adj. prof. Okla. City Univ. Sch. of Law; lectr. in field; U.S. magistrate judge Western Dist. Okla., 1988—; constl. law specialist Ctrl. and East European Law Initiative, ABA, Ukraine and Moldova, 1993. Author: Constitutional Law and Democracy, 1994; contbr. book revs. and articles to profl. jours. Intern Office of Senator Bob Dole, Washington, 1977-78; mem. transition team EEOC Office Pres.-Elect Reagan, Washington, 1980-81; chmn. Enid Police Civil Service Commn., 1985-87; bd. dirs. Enid Habitat for Humanity, 1986-88, Booker T. Washington Community Ctr., Enid, 1987-90; mem. Martin Luther King, Jr. Holiday Commn. of Enid, 1988-91. Fellow Okla. Bar Found.; mem. Okla. Bar Assn., D.C. Bar Assn., Tex. Bar Assn., Garfield County Bar Assn., Okla. Assn. Mcpl. Attys. (bd. dirs. 1987-91, gen. counsel 1987-88, pres. 1988-90), Defense Rsch. Inst. (govtl. liability com.), Federalist Soc. Republican. Baptist. Avocations: German language, cartography. Office: Lester & Bryant PC 119 N Robinson Ave Ste 820 Oklahoma City OK 73102-4625

LESTER, BARNETT BENJAMIN, editor, foreign affairs officer; b. Toronto, Can., Aug. 7, 1912; came to U.S., 1917; s. Louis and Lena (Rubenstein) L.; m. Rita Constance Hatcher, May 31, 1943 (dec.); m. Claudette Yvonne Gionet, Apr. 19, 1970. Student, Cleve. Coll., Western Res. U., 1933; AB (Miller Scholar), Oberlin Coll., 1934, (grad. scholar), 1934-35; grad. scholar, Nat. Inst. Pub. Affairs, Washington, 1935-36; scholar, Syracuse U., 1935-36, Acad. Internat. Law, The Hague, 1936; student, fellow, Fletcher Sch. Law and Diplomacy, 1935-36; student, Fgn. Service Inst., 1952, 56, Dep. Chiefs Mission Seminar, Dept. State, 1981. Mem. staff, corr. Cleve. Plain Dealer and Cleve. News, 1928-33; feature writer Boston Sunday Post, 1935-38; mng. editor, later editor Exclusive Features Syndicate, Boston, 1936-38; asso. editor The Writer mag., Boston, 1936-38; info. officer Dept. Justice, 1938-41; asst. dir. feature div. Office Inter-Am. Affairs, 1941-45; info. publicist Dept. State, 1945; pub. relations exec. Al Paul Lefton Co., Inc., Phila., 1945-46; info. specialist, chief motion pictures, acting chief audio-visual sect. USPHS, Office Surgeon Gen., 1947-48; info. specialist Fed. Security Agy., 1948-49; chief editorial and prodn. sect. Nat. Heart Inst. (info. specialist, sci. reports br. NIH), 1949-52; pub. info. chief NIH, 1950; review officer Dept. State, 1952-61, supervisory publs. editor, 1961-63, editor-writer, 1963-73, pub. info. officer, 1973-85; asso. editor Newsletter, 1977-81; assoc. editor State Mag., 1981-86, sr. editor, 1986-89, on contract, 1989; pub. affairs specialist, 1985-89; fgn. svc. res. officer, 1965-73, assigned to policy and pub. info. affairs program, 1962-67; assigned to policy and pub. info. affairs program Newsletter and Info. Office, Office Dir. Gen. Fgn. Svc., 1967-81, Office Pub. Affairs and State Mag., Office Dir. Gen. Fgn. Svc., 1981-89; Career counselor Oberlin Coll., 1940—; invited participant symposium The White House: The First 200 Years, White House Hist. Assn., 1992. Author: (with others) The Writer's Handbook, 1936. Recipient War Service award Coord. Inter-Am. Affairs, 1945, Meritorious Honor Group award Dept. State, 1967, 40 Year Service award, 1979, Spl. Achievement award, 1979, Superior Honor award, 1983, Superior Honor Group award, 1984; Loy W. Henderson—Joseph C. Satterthwaite award for pub. service, 1987; Bicentennial award Am. Revolution Bicentennial Adminstrn., 1977; award for excellence Soc. Tech. Communications, 1982; award for achievement Soc. Tech. Communications, 1985; 50 Yr. Pin, Fletcher Sch. Law and Diplomacy, 1986; 50 Yr. Svc. award, bronze plaque for 51 yrs. U.S. Govt. Svc., 1989; John Jacob Rogers award for outstanding career achievement, Dept. State, 1989; cert. commendation Dept. State, 1989. Mem. Am. Fgn. Svc. Assn., Am. Polit. Sci. Assn., Am. Acad. Polit. and Social Sci., Acad. Polit. and Social Sci.; Diplomatic and Consular Officers Ret., Fed. Editors Assn. (Blue Pencil award 1975), Nat. Assn. Govt. Communicators (Blue Pencil Pubs. award 1983), Consular Officers Assn., Marquis Libr. Assn. (adv. mem.), U.S. Diplomatic Courier Assn. (hon., Silver Diplomatic Courier medal and cert. appreciation 1990), Nat. Press Found. (charter), Nat. Trust for Hist. Preservation, U.S. Capitol Hist. Soc. (charter), Assn. for Diplomatic Studies and Tng., Civil War Trust (charter), Internat. Club (charter, honored as founding mem. 1989), Nat. Press Club, Silver Owl Club, Am. Fgn. Svc. Two suggestions adopted by U.S. Postal Service resulted in issuing Treaty of Paris stamp and Great Seal of U.S. embossed stamped envelope. Home: 2507 N Lincoln St Arlington VA 22207-5023

LESTER, CHARLES TURNER, JR., lawyer; b. Plainfield, N.J., Jan. 31, 1942; s. Charles Turner and Marlyn Elizabeth (Tate) L.; m. Nancy Hudmon Simmons, Aug. 19, 1967; children: Susan Hopson, Mary Elizabeth. B.A., Emory U., 1964, J.D., 1967. Bar: Ga. 1966, U.S. Dist. Ct. (no. dist.) Ga. 1967, D.C. 1970, U.S. Ct. Appeals (5th cir.) 1967, U.S. Ct. Appeals (11th cir.) 1982, U.S. Ct. Appeals (10th cir.) 1984. Assoc. Sutherland, Asbill & Brennan, Atlanta, 1970-77, ptnr., 1977—. Mem. Leadership Atlanta, 1980-81; pres. Atlanta Legal Aid Soc., 1979-80. Lt. JAGC, USNR, 1967-70. Fellow Am. Bar Found.; mem. ABA, State Bar of Ga. (pres. young lawyers sect. 1977-78, bd. govs. 1977-78, 80-84, chmn. formal adv. common bd. 1987-90, exec. com. 1977-78, 1987-93, pres. 1991-92), Atlanta Bar Assn., Am. Judicature Soc., Lawyers Club Atlanta (treas. 1982-83, exec. com. 1982-90, 2d v.p. 1986-87, 1st v.p. 1987-88, pres. 1988-89), D.C. Bar Assn., Ga. C. of C. (bd. dirs.). Democrat. Methodist. Home: 1955 Musket Ct Stone Mountain GA 30087-1703 Office: Sutherland Asbill & Brennan 999 Peachtree St NE Atlanta GA 30309-3996

LESTER, JAMES DUDLEY, classicist, educator; b. Fort Smith, Ark., Mar. 5, 1935; s. Kenneth R. and Essie Fae (Bailey) L.; m. Martha S. Lester, 1958; children: Jim, Mark. BA, East Cen. Okla. State U., 1957; MA, Okla. State U., 1963; PhD, Tulsa U., 1970. Dir. pub. rels. East Cen. Okla. U., Ada, 1957; aide to Sen. Robert S. Kerr U.S. Senate, Washington, 1958-59; tchr. Fort Smith (Ark.) High Sch., 1959-63; from instr. to asst. prof. Emporia (Kans.) State U., 1963-67; grad. asst. Tulsa U., 1967-70; from asst. prof. to prof. Austin Peay State U., Clarksville, Tenn., 1970—. Pub., editor: Cumberland Mag., 1976-80, Tenn. Monthly, 1980-82. F.B. Parriott scholar U. Tulsa, 1969-70. Mem. MLA, South Ctrl. MLA, Nat. Coun. Tchrs. English, Conf. Coll. Comm. and Composition. Democrat. Methodist. Home: 489 Pond Apple Rd Clarksville TN 37043-2208 Office: Austin Peay State U Clarksville TN 37044

LESTER, JULIUS B., author; b. St. Louis, Jan. 27, 1939; s. W.D. and Julia (Smith) L.; children: Jody Simone, Malcolm Coltrane, Elena Milad, David Julius. BA, Fisk U., 1960. Prof. Judaic studies U. Mass., Amherst, 1971—. Profl. musician and singer, recording for Vanguard Records, folklorist and writer, dir., Newport Folk Festival, 1966-68; author: (with Pete Seeger) The 12-String Guitar as Played by Leadbelly, 1965, Look Out, Whitey, Black Power's Gon' Get Your Mama, 1968, To Be a Slave, 1968 (Newberry Honor book 1968), Black Folktales, 1969, Revolutionary Notes, 1969, Search for the New Land, 1970, The Knee-High Man and Other Tales, 1972, Long Journey Home: Stories from Black History, 1972 (Nat. Book Award finalist 1972), Two Love Stories, 1972, Who I Am, 1974, All Is Well, 1976, This Strange New Feeling, 1982, Do Lord Remember Me, 1985, The Tales of Uncle Remus: The Adventures of Brer Rabbit, 1987, The Tales of Uncle Remus, The Further Adventures of Brer Rabbit, 1988, Lovesong: Becoming a Jew, 1988, How Many Spots Does A Leopard Have?, 1989, Further Tales of Uncle Remus, 1990, Falling Pieces of the Broken Sky, 1990, Last Tales of Uncle Remus, 1994, And All Our Wounds Forgiven, 1994, The Man Who Knew Too Much, 1994, John Henry, 1994, Othello: A Novel, 1995; editor: Seventh Son: The Thoughts and Writings of W.E.B. DuBois, vol. 1 and 2, 1971; assoc. editor: Sing Out, 1964-69; contbg. editor: Broadside of New York, 1964-70. Address: PO Box 9634 North Amherst MA 01059-9634 *The older I become, the greater the mystery of my life. I think I see my life as journey into mystery, in awe and fear, with joy and apprehension. Whatever my accomplishments, my life is more than and other than, and finally, best expressed by the silence of winter snow, prairie skies, or a feathered serpent.*

To be as true and eloquent as a drop of water hanging from a twig—that is my ideal.

LESTER, JUNE, library-information management educator; b. Sandersville, Ga., Aug. 25, 1942; d. Charles DuBose and Frances Irene (Cheney) L.; 1 child, Anna Elisabeth Engle. B.A., Emory U., 1963, M.Librarianship, 1971; D in Library Sci., Columbia U., 1987; cert. in advanced librarianship Columbia U., 1982. Asst. prof., cataloger U. Tenn. Library, Knoxville, 1971-73; librarian div. library and info. mgmt. Emory U., Atlanta, 1973-81, asst. prof. div. library and info. mgmt., 1976-80, assoc. prof., 1980-87; accreditation officer Am. Library Assn., 1987—. UCLA sr. fellow, 1987. Mem. ALA (council mem. 1987), Assn. for Library and Info. Sci. Edn. (bd. dirs. 1985-87), Ga. Library Assn., Phi Beta Kappa, Beta Phi Mu. Unitarian. Home: 1900 Highland Park Cir Denton TX 76205-6932 Office: Am Library Assn 50 E Huron St Chicago IL 60611-2795

LESTER, LANCE GARY, education educator, researcher; b. Wausau, Wis., Sept. 12, 1943; s. Lawrence Harold and Joanna Susan (Martin) L.; m. Rochelle Damson McDermott, Sept. 25, 1973 (div.); stepchildren: Barbara Ann McDermott, John Patrick McDermott. BA in English, St. John's U., 1965, MS in Secondary Edn., 1967; MA in Cinematography, NYU, 1969. Prof. football player N.Y. Jets/Titans, N.Y.C., 1960-61; educator Newtown High Sch., Elmhurst, N.Y., 1965—; mgr. B. S. Klein Real Estate, Bayside, N.Y., 1974—, track coach, 1973—; prof. film St. John's U., Jamaica, N.Y., 1981—; prof. White Magic Moving Pictures & Video, Glendale, N.Y., 1986—; lectr. N.Y. Jet Parking & Chowder Soc., N.Y.C., 1986, Queensborough Coll. Film Forum, Bayside, 1988—. Named N.Y.C. Track Coach of Yr., 1986. Mem. United Fedn. of Tchrs., N.Y.C. Coun. of English, Cinephiles. Roman Catholic. Avocations: Karate, track, travel agent. Office: Newtown High Sch 48-01 90th St Elmhurst NY 11373

LESTER, MALCOLM, historian, educator; b. Georgetown, Ga., Dec. 9, 1924; s. Malcolm Nicholson and Emmie (Bledsoe) L.; m. Pauline Hardeman Domingos, July 7, 1956; 1 dau., Pauline Malcolm (dec.). A.B., Mercer U., 1945; M.A., U. Va., 1946, Ph.D., 1954; Fulbright scholar, U. London (King's Coll.), 1949-50. Instr. history Mercer U., Macon, Ga., 1946-47, asst. prof., 1947-50, assoc. prof., 1950-54, prof., 1954-59, dean Coll. Liberal Arts, 1955-59; prof. history Davidson (N.C.) Coll., 1959-89, Charles A. Dana prof. history, 1977-89, prof. emeritus, 1989—, chmn. history dept., 1962-87; dir. Davidson summer program at Cambridge U., 1981-87. Author: Anthony Merry Redivivus: A Reappraisal of the British Minister to the United States, 1803-6, 1978; contbr. to American National Biography, Dictionary of National Biography; contbr. book revs. to various hist. jours. Elder Presbyn. Ch., 1964—; moderator Mecklenburg Presbytery, 1974; mem. internat. adv. coun. U. Buckingham, England, 1980—. Recipient Algernon Sydney Sullivan award Mercer U., 1945, Thomas Jefferson award Davidson Coll., 1982. Fellow Royal Hist. Soc. (Eng.); mem. Am. So. Hist. Assns., Orgn. Am. Historians, Nat. Trust (Eng.), Hist. Assn. (Eng.), Conf. Brit. Studies, AAUP, Nat. Assn. Scholars, Soc. Nautical Rsch. (Eng.), English Speaking Union, Raven Soc., Sons Confederate Vets., Colonnade Club (U. Va.), Phi Beta Kappa (sen. United chpts. 1976-82, com. qualifications 1978-82), Omicron Delta Kappa. Republican. Presbyterian. Home: 228 Roundway Down PO Box 548 Davidson NC 28036-0548

LESTER, RICHARD, film director; b. Phila., Jan. 19, 1932; s. Elliott and Ella (Young) L.; m. Deirdre Vivian Smith, 1956; 2 children. B.S., U. Pa. TV dir., CBS, 1951-54, dir., TV Goon Shows, 1956; directed: Running, Jumping and Standing Still Film (Acad. award nomination, 1st prize San Francisco Festival 1960); dir.: feature films It's Trad, Dad, 1962, Mouse on the Moon, 1963, A Hard Day's Night, 1964 (Grand Prix, Cannes Film Festival), Help, 1965 (Best Film award, Best Dir. award Rio de Janeiro Festival), A Funny Thing Happened on the Way to the Forum, 1966, How I Won the War, 1967, Petulia, 1968, The Bed-Sitting Room, 1969 (Ghandi Peace prize, Berlin Festival 1969), The Three Musketeers, 1973, Juggernaut, 1974 (Best Dir., Teheran Festival), The Four Musketeers, 1975, Royal Flash, 1975, Robin and Marian, 1976, The Ritz, 1976, Butch and Sundance—The Early Days, 1978, Cuba, 1979, Superman II, 1980, Superman III, 1982, Finders Keepers, 1984, Return of the Musketeers, 1989, Get Back, 1991. Office: Twickenham Film Studios, St Margarets, Middlesex England

LESTER, RICHARD ALLEN, economist, educator; b. Blasdell, N.Y., Mar. 1, 1908; s. Garra Kimble and Jessie Isabel (Holmes) L.; m. Doris Margaret Newhouse; children: Margaret Wing, Harriet Tarver, Robert A. PhB, Yale U., 1929; AM, Princeton (N.J.) U., 1930, PhD, 1936. With Princeton U., 1931-32, 34-38, prof., 1945-74, prof. emeritus, 1974—; assoc. dean Woodrow Wilson Sch., 1966-68; dean faculty Princeton U., 1968-73, rsch. assoc. indsl. Rels. sect., 1973—; asst. prof. U. Wash., Seattle, 1938-40; from asst. to assoc. prof. Duke U., Durham, N.C., 1940-45; br. chief War Prodn. Bd. and War Manpower Commn., Washington, 1941-42; manpower cons. Office of Sec. of War, Washington, 1943-44; chmn. N.J. Employment Security Coun., Trenton, 1954-64; N.J. chmn. Pub. Employer-Employee Rels. Study Commn., Trenton, 1974-75; trustee Tchrs. Ins. and Annuity Assn., N.Y.C., 1959-63; v.p. Princeton U. Press, 1969-72. Author: Monetary Experiments, 1939, As Unions Mature, 1958, Economics of Labor, 2d edit., 1964, Labor Arbitration, 1984, Wages, Benefits and Company Employment Systems, 1988. Elected mem. Princeton Borough Coun., 1958-61; trustee Ctr. for Analysis Pub. Issues, Princeton, 1970-83; vice chmn. Pres.'s Commn. on Status of Women, Washington, 1961-63. U.S. Dept. Labor Merit award, 1968. Mem. Indls. Rels. Rsch. Assn. (pres. 1956), Am. Econ. Assn. (exec. com. 1951-53, v.p. 1961), Nat. Acad. Social Ins. Democrat. Avocations: swimming, fishing. Home: Meadow Lakes Meadow Lks Apt 46-03U Hightstown NJ 08520-3332 Office: Princeton U Indsl Rels Sect Firestone Libr Princeton NJ 08544

LESTER, RICHARD GARRISON, radiologist, educator; b. N.Y.C., Oct. 24, 1925; s. L. I. and Pauline (Smolan) L.; m. Marion Louise Kurtz, Jan. 17, 1949; children: Elizabeth P., Andrew W. A.B., Princeton U., 1946; M.D., Columbia U., 1948. Intern N.Y.C. Hosp., 1948-49; asst. resident radiology Stanford Hosp., 1950-51, 53-54; from instr. to asso. prof. radiology U. Minn., 1954-61; prof. radiology, chmn. dept. Med. Coll. Va., 1961-65, Duke Sch. Medicine, 1965-76; prof. radiology U. Tex. Med. Sch., Houston, 1976-84; chmn. dept. U. Tex. Med. Sch., 1977-81; interim pres. Meharry Med. Coll., Nashville, 1981-82; dean Eastern Va. Med. Sch., Norfolk, 1984-89, prof. radiology, 1984-93, chmn. dept., 1989-91; prof. emeritus, 1993—; v.p. acad. affairs Med. Coll. of Hampton Roads, formerly Eastern Va. Med. Authority, Norfolk, 1984-89; trustee Meharry Med. Coll., 1975—. Author: (with others) Congenital Heart Disease, 1965, Exposure of the Pregnant Patient to Diagnostic Radiations, 1985; also numerous articles. Deacon Freemason St. Bapt. Ch. Capt. USAF, 1951-53. Fellow Am. Coll. Radiology, Am. Coll. Chest Physicians; mem. Assn. Univ. Radiologists, Am. Roentgen Ray Soc., Soc. Pediatric Radiology, Radiol. Soc. N.Am. (dir. 1976—, chmn. bd. 1981, pres. 1983). Home: 1362 De Bree Ave Norfolk VA 23517-2131 Office: Ea Va Med Sch PO Box 1980 Norfolk VA 23501-1980

LESTER, ROBERT CARLTON, religious studies educator; b. Lead, S.D., Feb. 1, 1933; s. Odell and Mary Olivia (Martin) L.; m. Donna Helene Larson, Apr. 15, 1954; children: Paul E., Charles F., R. Timothy. BA, U. Mont., 1955; BD, Yale U., 1958, MA, 1959, PhD, 1963. From asst. prof. to assoc. prof. Am. U., 1962-70; mem. faculty U. Colo., Boulder, 1970—, prof. religious studies, 1972—; vis. prof. Cornell U., 1968-69; vis. lectr. Dept. State., monthly, 1963-70; mem. faculty Humanities Inst, NEH, 1979. Author: Theravada Buddhism in Southeast Asia, 1973, Ramanuja on the Yoga, 1975, Srivacana Bhushana of Pillai Lokacharya, 1979, Buddhism: The Path to Nirvana, 1987. Ford. Found. fellow, 1960-62, Fulbright Hays fellow, 1967, 74-75, faculty fellow U. Colo., 1974-75, Am. Inst. of Indian Studies fellow, 1982-83, 88. Mem. Am. Acad. Religion, Assn. Asian Studies, Soc. Values in Higher Edn., Phi Kappa Phi. Office: U Colo Dept Religious Studies Boulder CO 80309

LESTER, ROBIN DALE, private school educator, author, former headmaster; b. Holdrege, Nebr., Mar. 1, 1939; s. Earl L. and Evelyn Grace (Robinson) L.; m. Helen Sargent Doughty, Aug. 26, 1967; children: Robin Debevoise, James Robinson. BA, Pepperdine U., 1962, MA, 1963; MAT, U. Chgo., 1966, PhD, 1971. Resident head, dean students office U. Chgo. 1964-72, Ferdinand Schevill fellow dept. history, 1966-68; asst. prof. history

Columbia Coll., Chgo., 1966-70; chmn. social scis. dept. Columbia Coll., 1970-72; chmn. history dept. Collegiate Sch., N.Y.C., 1972-75; headmaster Trinity Sch., N.Y.C., 1975-86, San Francisco U. Sch., 1986-88, Latin Sch. of Chgo., 1989-93; tchr. Francis W. Parker Sch., Chgo., 1994—; adj. prof. Columbia Coll., Chgo., 1992—. Author: Stagg's University, 1995, Wizzy, 1995; contbr. to Dictionary of Am. Biography, 1974, N.Y. Times, 1979, 80, 81, Jour. Am. History, 1980, 95, Chgo. Tribune, 1989, Jour. Sport History, 1991, History of Edn. Quar., 1995, U. Chgo. mag., 1995. Mem. Manhattan Borough Dem. Com., N.Y.C., 1977—; commr. Comn. on Ednl. Issues, 1980—; mem. edn. com. Chgo. Hist. Soc., 1991—; mem. Chicago-Prague Sister Cities Com., 1991; trustee, treas. St. Andrews U. Am. Found. 1985—. Lauder fellow Aspen Inst., 1985. Mem. Am. Hist. Assn., Am. Studies Assn., Orgn. Am. Historians, Headmaster's Assn., Country Day Sch. Headmaster's Assn., University Club (N.Y.C.), Quadrangle Club. Episcopalian. Home: 2230 N Lincoln Park W Chicago IL 60614-3814 Office: Francis W Parker Sch 330 W Webster Chicago IL 60614

LESTER, VIRGINIA LAUDANO, association executive; b. Phila., Jan. 5, 1931; d. Edmund Francis and Emily Beatrice (Downes) Laudano; children: Pamela Lester Golde, Valerie Lester. BA, Pa. State U., 1952; MEd, Temple U., 1955; PhD, Union Grad. Sch., 1972; JD, Stanford U. Law Sch., 1988. Tchr. pub. schs. Abington, Pa., 1952-55, Greenfield Center, N.Y., 1956; instr. edn. dept. Skidmore Coll., Saratoga Springs, N.Y., 1962-64; dir. ednl. research Skidmore Coll., 1967-72, asst. to the pres., 1968-72; asst. dir. Capitol Dist. Regional Supplementary Edn. Center, Albany, N.Y., 1966-67; assoc. dean, asst. prof. state-wide programs Empire State Coll., State U. N.Y., Saratoga Springs, 1973-75; sr. assoc. dean, assoc. prof. Empire State Coll., State U. N.Y., 1975-76, acting dean state-wide programs, 1976; pres., prof. interdisciplinary studies Mary Baldwin Coll., Staunton, Va., 1976-85; cons. to bd. trustees Mary Baldwin Coll., 1985-88; assoc. Hunton & Williams, Richmond, Va., 1988-90; interim pres. Friends World Coll., Huntington, N.Y., 1990-91; dir. presdl. search consultation svc. Assn. of Governing Bds. of Univs. and Colls., 1991-94; sr. mgmt. advisor office of exec. dir. Am. Assn. Retired Persons, 1994—; mem. cons. core faculty Union Grad. Sch., Union for Experimenting Colls. and Univs., Cin., 1975-82; vis. faculty fellow Harvard U. Grad. Sch. Edn., 1976; cons. in field; bd. dirs. So. Bankshares, So. Bank; bd. dirs. Council Advancement of Small Colls., 1977-81, Am. Council Edn., 1983-85. Mem. com. on criminal sexual assault Va. State Crime Commn., 1976; v.p. Costume Collection, Inc., 1971-73; v.p. Warren, Washington, Saratoga Counties Planned Parenthood, 1972-74, bd. dirs., 1970-74; mem. Saratoga Springs Housing Bd. Appeals, 1966-76, Commn. on Future of Va., 1984-87; bd. dirs. Nat. Urban League, 1979-86; pres. commn. NCAA, 1984-85. Mem. Am. Acad. Polit. and Social Scis., Va. Found. Ind. Colls. (trustee, exec. com.), Va. Council Ind. Colls., Am. Council on Edn. (commn. on women in higher edn. 1977-80), Nat. Assn. Ind. Colls. and Univs. (dir.), Assn. Va. Colls. (sec.-treas. 1978-79, pres. 1980-81, dir.), Assn. Ch. Related Colls. and Univs. of South (pres. 1983), Pi Lambda Theta, Pi Gamma Mu, Chimes. Mem. Soc. of Friends. *I believe, not unlike many successful women in my generation, that I accepted each new opportunity as a gift of which to make the most. Now, three decades later, I aspire to create my own opportunities.*

LESTER, WILLIAM ALEXANDER, JR., chemist, educator; b. Chgo., Apr. 24, 1937; s. William Alexander and Elizabeth Frances (Clark) L.; m. Rochelle Diane Reed, Dec. 27, 1959; children: William Alexander III, Allison Kimberleigh. B.S., U. Chgo., 1958, M.S., 1959; postgrad., Washington U., St. Louis, 1959-60; Ph.D., Cath. U. Am., 1964. Phys. chemist Nat. Bur. Standards, Washington, 1961-64; asst. dir. Theoretical Chemistry Inst. of U. Wis.-Madison, 1965-68; research staff mem. IBM Research Lab., San Jose, Calif., 1968-75; mgr., 1976-78; mem. tech. planning staff IBM T.J. Watson Research Center, Yorktown Heights, N.Y., 1975-76; dir. Nat. Resource for Computation in Chemistry, Lawrence Berkeley (Calif.) Lab., 1978-81, also assoc. dir., staff sr. scientist, 1978-81, faculty sr. scientist, 1981—; prof. chemistry U. Calif., Berkeley, 1981—, assoc. dean Coll. Chemistry, 1991—; lectr. chemistry U. Wis., 1966-68; cons. NSF, 1976-77, mem. chem. div. adv. panel, 1980-83, adv. com. Office Advanced Sci. Computing program, 1985-87, chmn., 1987; mem. U.S. nat. com. Internat. Union Pure and Applied Chemistry, 1976-79; mem. com. on recommendations for U.S. Army Basic Sci. Research NRC, 1984-87, mem. steering com., 1987-88; chemistry research evaluation panel AF Office Sci. Research, 1974-78; chmn. Gordon Conf. Atomic and Molecular Interactions, 1978; mem. NRC panel on chem. physics Nat. Bur. Standards, 1980-83; mem. com. to survey chem. scis. NRC, 1982-84, Fed. Networking Coun. Adv. Com., 1991—; mem. blue ribbon panel on high performance computing Nat. Sci. Found., 1993; mem. com. high performance computing and comm.: status of a major initiative NRC, 1994—; mem. NRC com. on math. challenges from computational chemistry, 1994—. Editor: Procs. of Conf. on Potential Energy Surfaces in Chemistry, 1971; Author: (with Brian L. Hammond and Peter J. Reynolds) Monte Carlo Methods in Ab Initio Quantum Chemistry, 1994; mem. editorial bd. Jour. Phys. Chemistry, 1979-87, Jour. Computational Chemistry, 1980-87, Computer Physics Communication, 1981-86; mem. adv. bd. Sci. Yr., 1989—. Recipient Alumni award in sci. Cath. U. Am., 1983. Fellow AAAS (com. on nominations 1988-91, nat. bd. dirs. 1993—), Am. Phys. Soc. (chmn. div. chem. physics 1986); mem. Am. Chem. Soc. (sec.-treas. Wis. sect. 1967-68, chmn. div. phys. chemistry 1979, treas. div. computers in chemistry 1974-77), Nat. Orgn. Black Chemists and Chem. Engrs. (Percy L. Julian award 1979, Outstanding Tchr. award 1986, exec. bd. 1984-87). Home: 4433 Briar Cliff Rd Oakland CA 94605-4624 Office: U Calif Dept Chemistry Berkeley CA 94720

LESTON, PATRICK JOHN, lawyer; b. Maywood, Ill., May 2, 1948; s. John R. and Lorraine (McQueen) L.; m. Kristine Brzezinski; children: Alison, Adam. BS in Communications, U. Ill., 1970; JD cum laude, Northwestern U., Chgo., 1973. Bar: Ill. 1973, U.S. Dist. Ct. (no. dist.) Ill. 1973, U.S. Ct. Appeals (7th cir.) 1973. Ptnr. Jacobs & Leston, Villa Park, Ill., 1973-79; pvt. practice Glen Ellyn, Ill., 1979-89; ptnr. Keck, Mahin & Cate, Oakbrook Terrace, Ill., 1989—; bd. dirs. Villa Park Trust and Savs. Bank, Edville Bancorp, Villa Park; presenter profl. confs. Editor Ill. State Bar Assn./Young Lawyers Divsn. Jour., 1983-85. Class rep. Northwestern U. Law Sch. Fund, 1982-88; organizer DuPage County (Ill.) Law Explorers. Fellow ABA (Ill. del. to ABA/Young Lawyers divsn. assembly 1982-85), Ill. State Bar Assn. (chmn. fellows 1991-92, mem. bd. govs. 1990—, chmn. young lawyers divsn. 1983, chmn. agenda com. 1986, del. to 18th jud. cir. assembly 1982-88), Ill. Bar Found. (charter), Am. Bar Found.; mem. Chgo. Bar Assn., DuPage County Bar Assn. (pres. 1987, bd. dirs. 1979-84, chmn. judiciary com. 1988, gen. counsel 1989), Lions Club, Chi Psi. Avocations: volleyball, skiing, scuba diving, travel. Office: Keck Mahin & Cate One Mid America Plz Ste 1000 Villa Park IL 60181

LESUER, KENNETH RAY, oil company executive; b. Shreveport, La., Dec. 31, 1935; s. Garland Guy and Margaret Virginia (Kitchings) LeS.; m. Kim Eng Lim, June 19, 1970; children: Karyn, Geoffrey. B of Petroleum Engring., Tex. A&M U., 1959. Engr. Halliburton Svcs., 1959-65; engr. Halliburton Svcs., Asia, Australia, 1965-70, divsn. mgr., 1971-74; divsn. mgr. Halliburton Svcs., Europe, Africa, 1975-79, gen. mgr., 1980-82; v.p. internat. Halliburton Svcs., 1982-87; pres., CEO Halliburton Svcs., Houston, 1990-92; pres. Halliburton Reservoir Svcs., 1989-90, Vann Systems, 1988-89. Mem. Nat. Ocean Industries Assn., Am. Petroleum Inst., AIME, Internat. Assn. Drilling Contractors, Petroleum Equipment Suppliers Assn., Soc. Petroleum Engrs. Office: Halliburton Svcs Ste 2000 2700 Post Oak Blvd Houston TX 77056-5075

LETAW, HARRY, JR., technology corporation executive; b. Miami, Fla., Aug. 7, 1926; s. Harry and Ninda (Cook) L.; m. Joyce Winston Brown, June 4, 1947; children: Anne Winston, Kaye Lynn, John Robert, Mary Jane, Amelia Elizabeth, James Brown. BS in Chemistry with high honors, U. Fla., 1949, MS, 1951, PhD, 1952. Resch. asst. prof. Elec. Engring. dept., U Ill., Urbana, 1952-55; mktg. mgr. Raytheon Co., Wayland, Mass., 1955-61; dir. advanced programs Elec. div. Martin Marietta, Middle River, Md., 1961-64; v.p., gen. mgr. Ea. Tech. Ctr., Inc. Bunker-Ramo Corp., 1964-65; pres. Severn Comms. Corp., Millersville, Md., 1965—; Logos Ltd., Arlington, Va., 1968-72; chmn., pres. Radiation Systems, Inc., McLean, Va., 1974-78; pres. Intellinet Corp., Millersville, 1983—; chmn., pres. CEO Essex Corp. Columbia, Md., 1988—, also bd. dirs.; bd. dirs. Marsh-McBirney Corp., Frederick, Md.; cons. Compagnie Internat. Pour L'Informatique, St. Germain-en-Laye, France, 1966-68. Contbr. articles to profl. jours; patentee in field. Bd. dirs. Econ. Opportunity Com., Anne Arundel County, 1969-71;

chmn. adv. com. on ednl. aspects of contemporary issues Md. State Dept. Edn., 1969-73; pres. Greater Severna Park Coun., 1972-73. Sgt. U.S. Army, 1944-47; 2d lt. USAR, 1948-50. Emory U. Alumni scholar, 1943-44; U. Fla. rsch. corp. fellow, 1950; U.S. AEC predoctoral fellow Oak Ridge Inst. for Nuclear Studies, 1950-52. Mem. IEEE (sr.), Am. Phys. Soc., Security Affairs Support Assn. (bd. dirs.), Phi Beta Kappa, Sigma Xi. Avocations: hiking, reading, public affairs. Office: Essex Corp 9150 Guilford Rd Columbia MD 21046

LETEY, JOHN JOSEPH, JR., soil scientist, educator; b. Carbondale, Colo., June 13, 1933; s. John Joseph and Rosine (Tisseur) L.; m. Patricia Kaye Fitzgerald, Sept. 19, 1992; children: Laura, Donald, Lisa. BS in Agronomy, Colo. State U., 1955; PhD in Soil Physics, U. Ill., 1959. Asst. prof. soil physics UCLA, 1959-61; asst. prof., assoc. prof., prof. U. Calif., Riverside, 1961—, chmn. dept. soil and environ. scis., 1975-80; assoc. dir. water and wetlands resources, 1993—; FAO cons. Bulgaria, 1973, Cen. Soil Salinity Rsch. Inst., Karnal, India, 1989; dir. Kearney Found., U. Calif., 1980-85; mem. Soil Sci. Delegation to People's Republic of China, 1983; keynote speaker Internat. Conf. Soil Salinity Under Irrigation-Processes and Mgmt., Israel, 1984; researcher in field. Author: (with Stahrl Edmunds) Environmental Administration, 1973; contbr. numerous chpts. to books, articles to profl. jours. Mem. Soil Sci. Soc. Am. (fellow 1972, past chmn. soil physics div., assoc. editor proceedings 1967-73), Am. Soc. Agronomy (soil sci. award 1970). Mormon. Avocation: oil painting. Home: 435 Campus View Riverside CA 92507-4837 Office: U Calif Dept Soil & Environ Scis Riverside CA 92521

LETHBRIDGE, FRANCIS DONALD, architect; b. Hackensack, N.J., Oct. 5, 1920; s. Berry B. and Florence A. (Lapham) L.; m. Mary Jane Christopher, June 21, 1947; children: Catherine B. (Mrs. Robert A. Grove), Mary P. (Mrs. Christopher G. Cromwell), Christopher B., Margaret F. (Mrs. Arsim Cejku). Student, Stevens Inst. Tech., 1937-40, Yale Sch. Architecture, 1945-46. Ptnr. archtl. firm Keyes, Smith, Satterlee & Lethbridge, Washington, 1951-55, Keyes, Lethbridge & Condon, Washington, 1956-75, Francis D. Lethbridge & Assocs., Washington, 1975-90; mem. fgn. bldgs. archtl. rev. panel U.S. State Dept., 1977-80; mem. archtl. adv. panel Fed. Res. Bd., 1979-83; mem. Potomac Planning Task Force, 1965-67; bd. advisers Nat. Trust for Hist. Preservation, 1969-71; mem. Joint Com. Landmarks Nat. Capital, 1964-79, chmn., 1964-73. Co-author: Guide to the Architecture of Washington, D.C; prin. works include Pine Spring Community, Fairfax County, Va., 1951-54, Potomac Overlook, 1955-58, U.S. Chancery, Lima, Peru, 1957, Forest Industries Bldg., Washington, 1961, Carderock Springs Community, Montgomery County, Md., 1963-65, Unitarian Ch, River Road, Md., 1964, master plan Arlington Nat. Cemetery, 1966-68, Ft. Lincoln New Town, 1968, Visitors Ctr., Arlington Nat. Cemetery, 1988. Trustee Nantucket Atheneum; advisor Nantucket Hist. Assn. Officer, pilot USNR, 1942-45. Decorated D.F.C.; Air medal; recipient Design Merit award AIA, 1955, 66, 1st honor award, 1966, Potomac Valley Chpt. archtl. award, 1956, 58, 60, 62, 64, 66, 68, 70, 72, 74, 76, joint award of honor AIA-Nat. Assn. Home Builders, 1960; award in architecture Washington Bd. Trade, 1953, 55, 61, 63, 65, 67, 69, 71, 73; Renchard prize for historic preservation, 1983. Fellow AIA (pres. Washington Met. chpt. 1964, v.p. 1969-70, pres. AIA found. 1971-73); mem. Soc. Archtl. Historians. Club: Cosmos (Washington). Home and Office: 48 Orange St Nantucket MA 02554-3937

LETICHE, JOHN MARION, economist, educator; b. Uman, Kiev, Russia, Nov. 11, 1918; came to U.S., 1941, naturalized, 1949; s. Leon and Mary (Grossman) L.; m. Emily Kuyper, Nov. 17, 1945; 1 son, Hugo K. BA, McGill U., 1940, MA, 1941; PhD in Econs, U. Chgo., 1951. Rockefeller fellow Council Fgn. Relations, N.Y.C., 1945-46; Smith-Mundt vis. prof. U. Aarhus and U. Copenhagen, Denmark, 1951-52; spl. tech. econ. adv. UN ECA, Africa, 1961-62; prof. U. Calif. at Berkeley, 1960—; cons. AID, U.S. Depts. State, Labor, HUD and Treasury, 1962—; emissary to Japan and Korea, Dept. State, 1971; cons. Econ. Coun. Can., 1972—, World Bank, 1981—, Bank of Eng., London, Bundesbank, Frankfurt, Fed. Republic of Germany; lectr. Stockholm, Paris, Uppsala, Hamburg, Kiel, Oxford (Eng.), 1973—, Vancouver, Toronto, Montreal, Zagreb, 1983, Frankfurt, Bonn, Moscow and Nakhodka Acad. Scis. USSR, 1986, Hong Kong, Shanghai, Wuhan, Beijing, London, Bonn, Frankfurt, De Hague, 1987, Bundesbank, 1992, 93, Peoples Republic China, Beijing, Shanghai, 1988, 90, 94, Acad. Scis., Taipei, 1989, joint session Calif. legis., 1975; ext. examiner adv. degrees U. Hong Kong, U. Calcutta, India. Author: Reciprocal Trade Agreements in the World Economy, 1948, in Japanese, 1951, System or Theory of the Trade of the World, 2d edit., 1957, Balance of Payments and Economic Growth, 2d edit., 1976, A History of Russian Economic Thought, 2d edit., 1977, The Key Problems of Economic Reconstruction and Development in Nigeria, 1970, Dependent Monetary Systems and Economic Development, 1974, Lessons of the Oil Crisis, 1977, Gains from Trade, 1979, Controlling Inflation, Recession, Federal Deficits and the Balance of Payments, 1980, The New Inflation and Its Urban Impact, 1980, Monetary Systems of Africa in the 1980s, 1981, International Economic Policies and Their Theoretical Foundations, 1982, 2d edit., 1992; Russian Statecraft: An Analysis and Translation of Iurii Krizhanich's Politika, 1985, Economics of the Pacific Rim, 1989; editor Royer Lectures, 1980-90, Toward a Market Economy in China, 1992, China's Emerging Monetary and Financial Markets, 1995; contbr. articles to encys., congl. coms. and profl. jours. Supervisory bd. Sch. Econs., St. Petersburg, Russia, 1994—. Recipient certificate merit Ency. Brit., certificate merit Inst. World Affairs, certificate merit Internat. Legal Center, U. Mich., U.S. Office Personnel Mgmt. Sr. Fed. Govt. Execs. and Mgrs., U. Calif-Berkeley; Adam Smith medal U. Verona, 1977; Guggenheim fellow, 1956-57. Mem. Am. Econ. Assn. (nominating com. 1968-69), Econometric Soc., Royal Econ. Soc., U.S.-Asian Econ. Com. (bd. dirs. 1983—), African Studies Assn., Am. Soc. Internat. Law (bd. 1969-72). Home: 968 Grizzly Peak Blvd Berkeley CA 94708-1549

LETO, JAMES J., artificial intelligence executive. Ceo, pres. PRC Inc., McLean, Va. Office: The Black & Decker Corp PRC Inc 1500 PRC Dr Mc Lean VA 22102

LETOURNEAU, DUANE JOHN, biochemist, educator; b. Stillwater, Minn., July 12, 1926; s. John Peter and Olga Margaret (Lange) LeTourneau; m. Phyllis Jean Kaercher, June 22, 1947; children: Bruce Duane, Diane Elaine, Keith George. B.S., U. Minn., 1948, M.S., 1951, Ph.D., 1954. Asst. prof., asst. agrl. chemist U. Idaho, Moscow, 1953-58; assoc. prof., assoc. agrl. chemist U. Idaho, 1958-63, prof., biochemist, 1963-91, asst. dept. head, 1988-89, sec. faculty, 1990-91, sec. faculty, prof. biochemistry emeritus, 1992—; vis. prof. botany U. Sheffield (Eng.), 1973; vis. scientist Nat. Research Council Can., Saskatoon, 1981; Bd. dirs. Idaho Inst. Christian Edn., 1958-62, 73-75, v.p. 1959-62. Author research publs. on plant biochemistry. Bd. dirs. U. Idaho Luth. Campus Coun., 1962-64, 73-75, chmn., 1963-64; trustee FarmHouse Internat. Found., 1974-80, chmn., 1976-80; trustee Gritman Meml. Hosp., 1969-82, v.p., 1977-80; bd. dirs. Gritman Med. Ctr., 1991—, Palouse Regional Health Corp., 1992—; bd. dirs. Latah County Hist. Soc., 1982-91; v.p., pres. bd. dirs., 1984-87; trustee Idaho Hist. Soc., 1992—. With USAAF, 1945. Recipient Outstanding Faculty award Asso. Students U. Idaho, 1960-62, 87, Coll. Agr. Outstanding Instr. award, 1962, R.M. Wade Excellence in Teaching award, 1968, 78, Disting. Faculty award, 1982, Prof. of Yr. award, 1983; Citation for Disting. Achievement, U. Idaho, 1984; Nat. Acad. Scis.-NRC sr. postdoctoral fellow, 1964-65. Fellow AAAS, Am. Inst. Chemists; mem. AAUP (v.p. U. Idaho chpt. 1959-60, sec. 1984-87), Am. Chem. Soc., Am. Soc. Plant Physiologists, Am. Inst. Biol. Scis., Am. Physiol. Soc., Idaho Acad. Sci. (v.p. 1985-86, pres. 1986-87, editor jour. 1983-89), Mycol. Soc. Am., Phytochem. Soc. N.Am., Am. Soc. Plant Physiologists, Iron Wedge, FarmHouse (dir. Idaho chpt. 1957-62, 72-75, 82-90, pres. 1957-62, 74, 82-85, 90; nat. dir. 1960-64, nat. v.p. 1962-64), Lions (bd. dirs. Moscow Central club 1971-74, 90-91, pres. 1973-74), Sigma Xi, Alpha Zeta, Gamma Alpha, Gamma Sigma Delta (pres. U. Idaho chpt. 1979-80), Phi Kappa Phi (v.p. U. Idaho chpt., pres. 1990-91), Phi Sigma (regional v.p. 1993—). Lutheran (chmn. ch. council and congregation, 1966-69). Home: 479 Ridge Rd Moscow ID 83843-2521

LETOURNEAU, JEAN-PAUL, business association executive and consultant; b. St.-Hyacinthe, Que., Can., May 4, 1930; s. Eugene and Antonia (Deslandes) L.; m. Claire Paquin, Sept. 26, 1956. Counsellor in Indsl. Relations, U. Montreal, Que., 1953; cert. c. of c. adminstrn., U. Syracuse, 1962;

cert. advanced mgmt. U.S. C. of C, 1965. Mcpl. sec. Mont St.-Hilaire, Que., 1950-53; personnel mgr. Dupuis Freres (mail order house), 1953; editor Jeune Commerce, weekly tabloid Fedn. Que. Jr. C's. of C., 1953; sec. gen. Montreal Jr. C. of C., 1953-56; asst. gen. mgr. Province Que. C. of C., Montreal, 1956-59, gen. mgr., 1959-71, exec. v.p., 1971-90. Author: Quebec, The Price of Independence, 1969, Report on Corporate Social Responsibilities, 1982. Mem. C. of C. Execs. Can. (pres. 1982-83, mem. coun. excellence 1986), Corp. Consellors in Indsl. Rels. of Que., Am. C. of C. Execs. (bd. dirs. 1982-83), Can. Exec. Svc. Orgns. (bd. dirs. 1991—, vice-chair 1993—), Office Persons Handicapped of Que. (bd. dirs. 1992—, exec. com. 1994—). Roman Catholic. Club: St.-Denis. Office: 165 Cote Ste-Catherine #202, Outremont, PQ Canada H2V 2A7 *Liberty is priceless; but liberty imposes responsibility, and if one is not responsible he will lose his liberty.*

LETOURNEAU, JOCELYN, history educator; b. Lauzon, PQ, Canada, Oct. 26, 1956; d. Robert and Jacqueline (Roy) L.; m. Esther Ross; children: Lavinia, Gaultier, Saskia, Nathaniel. BA, Laval U., Quebec City, 1978; MA, U. Toronto, Can., 1979; PhD, Laval U., 1985. Asst. prof. Dept. History Laval U., 1985-90, assoc. prof., 1990-94, dir. Célat, Faculty of Letters, 1990-94, prof., 1994—; fellow Zentrum Für Interdisziplinare Forschung U. Bielefeld, Germany, 1994-95; mem. editl. bd. (periodical) Social Discourse, Montreal, 1994—. Author: (book) Le Coffre à Outils du Chercheur de Sutant, 1989; editor: (book) La Question Identitaire au Canada Francois: Recits, Parcours, en Jeux, Hors-Lieux, 1994, La Condition du Quesec Enjeux et Horizons d'eure Societe en Devenir, 1994. Office: Laval U (CELAT), Pavillon Charles De Konick, Quebec, PQ Canada G1K 7P4 also: U Bielefeld, Wellenberg 1, Bielefeld, PQ Canada D-33615

LETOURNEAU, RICHARD HOWARD, retired college president; b. Stockton, Calif., Jan. 3, 1925; s. Robert G. and Evelyn (Peterson) LeT.; m. Louise Marion Jensen, Feb. 8, 1947; children: Robert Gilmore, Caleb Roy, Linda Louise, Liela Lynn. Student, Wheaton Coll., 1946, LeTourneau Coll., 1956; B.S., Tex. A&M U., 1958, M.S., 1961; Ph.D., Okla. State U., 1970. Gen. mgr. Miss. div. R.G. LeTourneau, Inc., Longview, Tex., 1949-52; v.p. prodn. R.G. LeTourneau, Inc., 1952-57, exec. v.p., 1966, pres., 1966-71; sr. v.p. Marathon Mfg. Co., Houston, 1971-72; dir. Marathon Mfg. Co., 1971-76; pres. Mosley Machinery Co., Waco, Tex., 1972-73; v.p. LeTourneau Found., 1973-75; prof. bus. mgmt. Belhaven Coll., Jackson, Miss., 1993—; mem. Tex. Indsl. Commn., 1959-66; adminstrv. v.p. LeTourneau Coll., 1958-62, pres., 1962-68, 75-85, chancellor, 1985-86, pres. emeritus, 1986—, chmn. bd. trustees, 1968-75; cons. to higher edn., 1986-93. Author: Management Plus, 1973, Keeping Your Cool in a World of Tension, 1975, Success Without Succeeding, 1976, Success Without Compromise, 1977, Democracy in Trouble, 1985, More Than Knowledge, 1985, Laws of Success for Christians, 1985, Finding Your Niche in Life, 1985. Past pres. LeTourneau Found. Served with C.E. AUS, 1944-46, PTO. Mem. Sigma Xi, Phi Kappa Phi, Tau Beta Pi, Alpha Pi Mu. Home and Office: 2724 Timberwood Trl Longview TX 75605-2140 *As a successful industrialist, educator and author, I have found that life is more than mind and body. Everyone, to have a joyous and truly successful life must also trust Jesus Christ as Lord for a spiritual dimension and overall balance in life. With this element missing, regardless of the profession followed, life will be hollow and meaningless, and an eternity of regret is certain.*

LETSINGER, ROBERT LEWIS, chemistry educator; b. Bloomfield, Ind., July 31, 1921; s. Reed A. and Etna (Phillips) L.; m. Dorothy C. Thompson, Feb. 6, 1943; children: Louise, Reed, Sue. Student, Ind. U., 1939-41; B.S., Mass. Inst. Tech., 1943, Ph.D., 1945; DSc (hon.), Acordia U., Can., 1993. Research assoc. MIT, 1945-46; research chemist Tenn. Eastman Corp., 1946; faculty Northwestern U., 1946—, prof. chemistry, 1959—, chmn. dept., 1972-75, joint prof. biochemistry and molecular biology, 1974—, Clare Hamilton Hall prof. chemistry, 1986-92, Clare Hamilton Hall prof. emeritus chemistry, 1992—; Mem. med. and organic chemistry fellowship panel NIH, 1966-69, medicinal chem. A study sect., 1971-75; bd. on chem. scis. and tech. Nat. Research Council, 1987-90. Mem. bd. editors Nucleic Acids Research, 1974-80; contbr. articles to profl. jours. Guggenheim fellow, 1956; JSPS fellow Japan, 1978; recipient Rosenstiel Medallion, 1985, Humboldt Sr. US Scientist award, 1988, NIH merit award, 1988, Arthur C. Cope scholar award, 1993. Fellow Am. Acad. Arts and Scis., Nat. Acad. Scis., Am. Assn. Arts and Scis.; mem. Am. Chem. Soc. (bd. editors 1969-72, bioconjugate chemistry 1992—, Arthur C. Cope scholar award 1993), Internat. Union Pure and Applied Chemistry, Sigma Xi, Phi Lambda Upsilon (hon. mem.). Home: 316 3d St Wilmette IL 60091 Office: Northwestern U Chemistry Dept 2145 Sheridan Rd Evanston IL 60208

LETT, PHILIP WOOD, JR., defense consultant; b. Newton, Ala., May 4, 1922; s. Philip Wood Sr. and Lily Octavia (Kennedy) L.; m. Katy Lee Howell, June 26, 1948; children: Kathy, Warren, Lisa. B MechE, Ala. Poly. Inst., 1943; MS in Engring., U. Ala., 1947; PhD MechE, U. Mich., 1950; MS in Indsl. Mgmt., MIT, 1960. Registered profl. engr., Mich. Lab. engr., engring. div. Chrysler Corp., 1950-52, project engr., def. engring. div., 1952-54, chief engr., def. engring. div., 1954-61, operating mgr., def. engring. div., 1961-73; head XM1 Tank task force Chrysler Corp., Sterling Heights, Mich., 1973-76; gen. mgr. Sterling Def. div. Chrysler Corp., 1976-79; v.p. engring. Chrysler Def. Inc., Center Line, Mich., 1980-82; v.p. research & engring. Gen. Dynamics Land Systems Div., Center Line, 1982-86, v.p., asst. to gen. mgr., 1986-87; pres. PWL Inc., 1987—; mem. U.S. delegation to NATO Indsl. Adv. Group. Contbr. articles to tech. jours. and to Internat. Def. Rev. Trustee Judson Ctr., 1989—. Capt. U.S. Army, 1943-46. Decorated Cheonsu medal Republic of Korea; awarded membership U.S. NAE, 1984; recipient Outstanding Engr. award Auburn U., 1984, Ben S. Gilmer award, 1991, Silver medal Am. Def. Preparedness Assn., 1989; named Disting. Engring. fellow U. Ala. Coll. Engring., 1992; named to Ala. Engring. Hall of Fame, 1992; Sloan fellow MIT, 1960-61. Mem. Orchard Lake Country Club. Baptist. Home: 1330 Oxford Rd Bloomfield Hills MI 48304 Office: PO Box 2074 Warren MI 48090-2074

LETTERMAN, DAVID, television personality, comedian, writer; b. Indpls., Apr. 12, 1947; s. Joseph and Dorothy L.; m. Michelle Cook, 1969 (div. 1977). Grad., Ball State U., 1969. Radio and TV announcer, Indpls.; performer The Comedy Store, Los Angeles, 1975—; appearances on TV include (variety series) Mary, CBS; frequent guest host The Tonight Show; host (morning comedy/variety program) David Letterman Show, NBC, 1980, Late Night with David Letterman, NBC, 1982-1993, The Late Show with David Letterman, CBS, 1993— (also writer); host, Academy Awards, 1995; writer for TV including Bob Hope Special, Good Times, Paul Lynde Comedy Hour, John Denver Special; author: (with others) The Late Night with David Letterman Book of Top Ten Lists, 1990, An Altogether New Book of Top Ten Lists, 1991; film appearances include: Cabin Boy, 1994. Recipient 6 Emmy awards, 1981-88. Avocations: baseball, basketball, auto racing, running. Office: Late Show with David Letterman CBS 530 W 57th St New York NY 10019*

LETTIERI, RICHARD JOSEPH, lawyer; b. Chelsea, Mass., May 29, 1947; s. Rosario and Genevieve Helen (Sokoloski) L. AB in History, Villanova U., 1969; JD, Boston Coll., 1974. Bar: Mass. 1975, U.S. Dist. Ct. Mass. 1975, U.S. Ct. Appeals (1st cir.) 1979, U.S. Ct. Appeals (D.C. cir.) 1985. Pvt. practice Boston, 1975-77; staff atty. Mass. Port Authority, Boston, 1977-81, chief legal counsel, 1981-86; assoc. Ropes & Gray, Boston, 1987-90, ptnr., 1990—. Mem. Boston Bar Assn., Justinian Law Soc. Office: Ropes & Gray 1 International Pl Boston MA 02110-2600

LETTMANN, JOHN WILLIAM, defense manufacturing company executive; b. St. Louis, July 5, 1942; s. Henry William and Josephine (Randazzo) L.; m. Vicky Hodges; children: Susan, Jason, Michael. BSBA, U. Kans., 1964; MBA, Ind. U., 1968. Sr. auditor Gen. Mills, Inc., Mpls., 1964-66, with product mgmt. dept., 1968-71; v.p. mktg. and sales Malt-O-Meal Co., Mpls. 1971-85, pres., chief exec. officer, 1985—; bd. dirs. Liberty Mutual Adv. Bd., Am. Mgmt. Assoc. Bd. Gov. Cos., Horton Mfg. Recipient Leadership award Bush Found., 1969. Mem. Am. Mgmt. Assn. (council 1987—), Grocery Mfrs. Assn., Mpls. Athletic Club, Interlachen Country Club. Avocations: handball, golf, skiing, tennis, coaching little league. Office: Malt-O-Meal Co 80 S 8th St Ste 2600 Minneapolis MN 55402

LETTON, ALVA HAMBLIN, surgeon, educator; b. Tampa, Fla., May 23, 1916; s. James Hervey and Minerva (Hamblin) L.; m. Roberta Rogers, Oct.

7, 1938; children: Robert Hamblin (dec.), Alice Roberta. Student, U. Tampa, 1933-35, U. Fla., 1935-37; MD, Emory U., 1941. Diplomate Am. Bd. Surgery. Intern Ga. Baptist Hosp., Atlanta, 1941-42; resident Ga. Baptist Hosp., 1942-43; pvt. practice medicine specializing gen. surgery (oncology) Atlanta, 1946—; chief staff, attending surgeon Ga. Bapt. Hosp., 1965-73; dir. breast cancer demonstration project Bapt. Med. Ctr., chmn. exec. com. oncology dept.; clin. prof. surgery Med. Coll. Ga.; A. Hamblin Letton chair surg. oncology Ga. Bapt. Med. Ctr., 1990—; assoc. dir. Cancer Ctr. Ga.; vis. prof. Egypt Cancer Inst., 1985, Med. and Dental Sch. N.J., 1986, Coll. Medicine, U. Ill., Peoria, 1990; cons. Cobb Gen., Grady Meml., Scottish Rite hosps.; chmn. cancer task force Ga. Regional Med. Program, 1966-71; mem. Ga. Sci. and Tech. Com. 1964-70; active Am. Cancer Soc., 1949—, nat. chmn. pub. edn., 1965-68, nat. chmn. service com., 1968-69, nat. chmn. med. and sci. com., 1969-70, v.p., nat. pres.-elect, 1970-71, nat. pres., 1971-72, hon. bd. dirs. for life, 1979—; pres. Atlanta Med. Center, 1965—, Atlanta Health Evaluation Center, 1973-82; mem. Gov.'s Sci. Adv. Council, 1972-75, U.S. nat. com. Nat. Acad. Scis., 1976-79; Roswell Park Meml. lectr., 1983; A. Hamblin Letton lectr. Southeastern Surg. Congress, 1985; bd. judges Criss Award; mem. Ethicon Gen. Surg. Adv. Panel, 1975-85; mem. cancer control rehab. adv. com. Nat. Cancer Inst., 1975-79; chmn. first. cancer postgrad. course USA/USSR/ Union Internationale Contre Cancer, Leningrad, USSR, 1989; mem. profl. edn. com. Union Internat. Contre Cancer, 1966-78, cons., Budapest, Hungary, 1986, cons. to exec. sec., 1972—. Mem. editorial bd. Internat. Advances in Surg. Oncology, Jour. Cancer Prevention and Detection, 1985—; chmn. editorial bd. Oncology Times, 1979-90; guest editor Seminars in Surg. Oncology; contbr. articles to profl. jours., films. Deacon Bapt. ch. With M.C. USNR, 1943-46. Recipient Presdl. citation, 1944, Aven Citizenship award Fulton County Med. Soc., 1960, Honor Alumnus award Emory U., 1973, Hardman award Med. Assn. Ga., 1973, highest award John Muir Med. Film Festival, 1978, Disting. Svc. award Am. Cancer Soc., 1980, Nat. Div. award Am. Cancer Soc., 1986, Vaughn award Ga. div. Am. Cancer Soc.1987. Fellow ACS, Southeastern Surg. Congress (hon. 1986—, sec.-dir. 1960-86, Disting. Svc. award 1982); mem. Soc. Surg. Oncology, So. Surg. Assn., Soc. Nuclear Medicine, Am. Thyroid Assn., Soc. Internat. de Chirugie, Capital City Club (Atlanta), Univ. Yacht Club (Flowery Branch, Ga.). Baptist. Home: 3384 Rilman Rd NW Atlanta GA 30327-1508 Office: 315 Boulevard NE Atlanta GA 30312-1200

LETTOW, CHARLES FREDERICK, lawyer; b. Iowa Falls, Iowa, Feb. 10, 1941; s. Carl Frederick and Catherine (Reisinger) L.; m. Sue Lettow, Apr. 20, 1963; children: Renee, Carl II, John, Paul. BS in Chem. Engring., Iowa State U., 1962; LLB, Stanford U., 1968. Bar: Calif. 1969, Iowa 1969, D.C. 1972, Md. 1991. Law clk. to Hon. Ben C Duniway U.S. Ct. Appeals (9th cir.), San Francisco, 1968-69; law clk. to Hon. Warren E. Burger U.S. Supreme Ct., Washington, 1969-70; counsel Council on Environ. Quality, Washington, 1970-73; assoc. Cleary, Gottlieb, Steen & Hamilton, Washington, 1973-76, ptnr., 1976—; pres. Busy Way Farms, Inc., 1989—. Contbr. articles to profl. jours. Trustee Potomac Sch., McLean, Va., 1983-90, chmn. bd. trustees, 1985-88. 1st lt. U.S. Army, 1963-65. mem. ABA, Am. Law Inst., D.C. Bar Assn., Iowa Bar Assn., Order of Coif. Club: University. Office: 1752 N St NW Washington DC 20036-2806

LETTS, J. SPENCER, federal judge; b. 1934. BA, Yale U., 1956; LLB, Harvard U., 1960. Commd. U.S. Army, 1956, advanced through grades to capt., resigned, 1965; pvt. practice law Fulbright & Jaworski, Houston, 1960-66, Troy, Malin, Loveland & Letts, L.A., 1973-74, Hedlund, Hunter & Lynch, L.A., 1978-82, Latham & Watkins, L.A., 1982-85; gen. counsel Teledyne, Inc., 1966-73, 75-78, legal cons., 1978-82; judge U.S. Dist. Ct. (cen. dist.) Calif., L.A., 1986—. Contbr. articles to profl. jours. Mem. ABA, Calif. State Bar, Tex. State Bar, L.A. Bar Assn., Houston Bar Assn. Office: US Dist Ct 312 N Spring St Los Angeles CA 90012

LETTVIN, THEODORE, concert pianist; b. Chgo., Oct. 29, 1926; s. Solomon and Fannie (Naktin) L.; m. Joan Rorimer; children: Rory, Ellen, David. Mus. B., Curtis Inst. Music, 1949; grad. U. Pa. Head piano dept. Cleve. Music Sch. Settlement, 1957-68; prof. piano New Eng. Conservatory Music, Boston, 1968-77; prof., dir. doctoral program in piano performance U. Mich. Sch. Music, Ann Arbor, 1977-87; disting. prof. dept. music Rutgers U., New Brunswick, N.J., 1987-92, dir. doctor of mus. arts and artist's diploma program, 1987-92, studio tchr., coach chamber music, 1992—; vis. lectr. U. Colo., 1956-57; tchr. master classes U. S.E. Mass., summer 1973, U. Calif., San Jose, 1992, 93; mem. faculty Chamber Music Sch., U. Maine, Orono. First appeared as concert pianist, 1931, solo debut with, Chgo. Symphony Orch., 1939, solo, orchestral appearances include, Boston Symphony Orch., N.Y. Philharmonic, Phila. Orch., Cleve. Orch., Chgo. Orch., Washington Nat. Symphony, Pitts. Symphony, Seattle Symphony, Mpls. Symphony, Atlanta Symphony, other Am. orchs., also European orchs.; radio appearance, Bell Telephone Hour, 1948, debut, Ravinia Festival, 1951, apprentice condr., William Steinberg, Buffalo Symphony Orch., 1950-51, concertized, throughout U.S., Can., Europe, Africa, 1952—, recent concert appearances, Pitts., Cin., Atlanta, Boston, N.Y.C., Phila., Chgo., Cleve., Mpls. and Chautauqua, Ravinia, Interlochen and New Coll., Town Hall, Alice Tully Hall concerts, in N.Y.C., Boston Symphony Orch; performances in concert with Bernard Greenhouse, cellist; concert tours, Europe, 1952, 55, 58, 60, 62—, Israel, 1973, Africa and Japan, 1974; also numerous performances with European orchs., summer festivals, 1972; asst. artist: Africa and Japan, Marlboro Music Festival, 1963. Recipient award Soc. Am. Musicians, 1933, Naumberg award, 1948, Michaels Meml. award, 1949, Laureate internat. piano competition Queen Elisabeth of Belgium. Mem. Am. Fedn. Musicians, Am. Guild Mus. Artists, AAUP (exec. com.), Music Tchrs. Nat. Assn., Am. Liszt Soc., Curtis Inst. Music Alumnae Assn. (bd. dirs.). Home: 2 Bernard Rd East Brunswick NJ 08816-1306 Office: Rutgers U Old Music Bldg Douglass Campus New Brunswick NJ 08903 also: RR 1 Box 305 Bradford NH 03221-9116

LETWIN, LEON, legal educator; b. Milw., Dec. 29, 1929; s. Lazar and Bessie (Rosenthal) L.; m. Alita Zurav, July 11, 1952; children—Michael, Daniel, David. Ph.D., U. Chgo., 1950; LL.B., U. Wis., 1952; LL.M., Harvard U., Iowa. Bar: Wis. 1952, Calif. 1959. Teaching fellow Harvard Law Sch., Boston, 1963-64; faculty Law Sch. UCLA, 1964—, prof., 1968—. Contbr. articles to profl. jours. Active ACLU. Mem. Conf. Critical Legal Studies, Nat. Lawyers Guild, State Bar Calif. Home: 2226 Manning Ave Los Angeles CA 90064 Office: UCLA Law Sch 405 Hilgard Ave Los Angeles CA 90024

LETZIG, BETTY JEAN, association executive; b. Hardin, Mo., Feb. 18, 1926; d. Robert H. and Alina Violet (Mayes) L. BA, Scarritt Coll., 1950, MA, 1968. Nurse staff The Methodist Ch., Ark., Okla. Tex., 1953-60; with Internat. Deaconess Exchange Program, London, 1961-62; staff exec. Nat. Div. United Meth. Ch., N.Y.C., 1962-95, ret. 1995; coord. Mission Pers. Support Svcs., 1984-88; exec. sec. Deaconess Program Office, 1989-95. Contbr. articles to profl. jours. Bd. dirs. Internat. Svcs. Assn. for Health, Inc., Atlanta, 1974-88, Vellore Christian Med. Coll., N.Y.C., 1984-94; mem. U.S. com. Internat. Coun. Social Welfare, Washington, 1983-89; active Nat. Interfaith Coalition on Aging, Athens, Ga. and Washington, 1972—, pres., 1981-85. Recipient Deaconess Exch. award Commn. Deaconess Work, 1961-62. Mem. Nat. Coun. Aging, Nat. Voluntary Orgns. Ind. Living for Aging (exec. com. 1978-84), Nat. Coun. Social Welfare, Older Women's League. United Methodist. Avocations: travel, beachcombing, photography, needlework. Home: 235 E 22d St Apt 1U New York NY 10010 Office: Nat Program Divsn Gen Bd Global Ministries 475 Riverside Dr Rm 300 New York NY 10115-0099

LEUBERT, ALFRED OTTO PAUL, international business consultant; b. N.Y.C., Dec. 7, 1922; s. Paul T. and Josephine (Haaga) L.; m. Celestine Capka, July 22, 1944 (div. 1977); children: Eloise Ann (Mrs. Kevin B. Cronin), Susan Beth; m. Hope Sherman Drapkin, June 4, 1978 (div. 1982). Student, Dartmouth Coll. 1943; BS, Fordham U., 1946; MBA, NYU, 1950. Account mgr. J.K. Lasser & Co., N.Y.C., 1948-52; controller Vision, Inc., N.Y.C., 1952-53; with Old Town Corp., 1953-58, controller, 1953-54, sec., controller, 1954-56, sec.-treas., 1956-57, v.p., treas., 1957-58; dir. subsidiaries Old Town Corp. (Old Town Internat. Corp., Old Town Ribbon & Carbon Co., Inc.), Mass. and Calif., 1955-58; v.p., controller Willcox & Gibbs, Inc., N.Y.C. 1958-59; v.p., treas. Willcox & Gibbs, Inc., 1959-65, pres., dir., chief exec. officer, 1966-76; founder, pub., pres. Leubert's

Compendium of Bus. (Fin. and Econ. Barometers), 1978-82; pres. Alfred O.P. Leubert Ltd., 1981-82, chmn. CEO, 1993—; chmn., chief exec. officer Solidyne, Inc., 1982; chmn. bd., pres., chief exec. officer, dir. Chyron Corp., 1983-91; dir. K & E Real Estate Ltd., China, 1994—; chmn. bd. CEO Leubert & Co. (H.K.) Ltd., 1994—; chmn. bd., CEO, bd. dirs. Chyron Group (U.K.) Ltd., 1985-89; chmn. bd., chief exec. officer, bd. dirs. CMX Corp.; bd. dirs. Aurora Systems, 1988-91; CEO, dir. CGS Units, Inc., 1988-90, chmn. bd., 1989-90; bd. dirs. Digital Svcs. Corp.; vice chmn. bd. dirs. CMX Laser Sys., Inc., 1988-93; instr. accountancy Pace Coll., 1955-57. Bd. dirs. United Fund of Manhasset, 1963-69, pres., 1964-65; bd. dirs. Actor's Studio, 1972-76; adv. bd. St. Anthony's Guidance Clinic, 1967-69. Served to 1st lt., inf. USMCR, 1943-46. Decorated Bronze Star; recipient Humanitarian award Hebrew Acad., N.Y.C., 1971. Mem. AICPA, N.Y. State Soc. CPAs, Fordham U. Alumni Assn. Roman Catholic. Club: N.Y. Athletic (N.Y.C.). Home and Office: 1 Lincoln Plz New York NY 10023-7129

LEUBSDORF, CARL PHILIPP, newspaper executive; b. N.Y.C., Mar. 17, 1938; s. Karl and Bertha (Boschwitz) L.; m. Carolyn Cleveland Stockmeyer, Mar. 26, 1963 (div. 1978); 1 child: Carl Philipp Jr.; stepchildren: Lorna Stockmeyer, E. William Stockmeyer Jr., C. Cleveland Stockmeyer, Claire C. Stockmeyer; m. Susan Page, May 23, 1982; children: Benjamin Page, William Page. BA in Govt., Cornell U., 1959; MS in Jour., Columbia U., 1960. Staff writer AP, New Orleans, 1960-63, Washington, 1963-75; corr. Balt. Sun, Washington, 1976-81; AME Washington bur. chief Dallas Morning News, Washington, 1981—. Mem. White House Corrs. Assn. (pres. 1995-96), Gridiron Club, National Press Club (Washington). Office: Dallas Morning News 1012 Nat Press Bldg Washington DC 20045

LEUKART, RICHARD HENRY, II, lawyer; b. Detroit, Mar. 15, 1942; s. Richard Henry and Marjorie Ruth (Smith) L.; m. Barbara Joan Gottfried, Oct. 7, 1977; children—Elisabeth, Jennifer, Kathleen, Richard Henry III, Brian. A.B., Dartmouth Coll., 1964; A.B., Amos Tuck Sch. Bus., 1964; J.D., U. Mich., 1967. Bar: Ohio 1967. Ptnr. Baker & Hostetler, Cleve., 1967—. Bd. trustees Hudson Heritage Assn., 1984—. Alfred P. Sloan Found. scholar, 1960-62; Daniel Webster scholar, 1963-64. Mem. ABA, Ohio Bar Assn., Cleve. Bar Assn. Republican. Presbyterian. Office: Baker & Hostetler 3200 Nat City Ctr 1900 E 9th St Cleveland OH 44114

LEUNG, FRANKIE FOOK-LUN, lawyer; b. Guangzhou, China, 1949; married; 1 child. BA in Psychology with honors, Hong Kong U. 1972; MS in Psychology, Birmingham U., Eng., 1974; BA, MA in Jurisprudence, Oxford U., Eng., 1976; JD, Coll. of Law, London, 1977. Bar: Calif. 1987. Barrister Eng. and Hong Kong, 1977—; lectr. Chinese law for businessmen Hong Kong U., 1984-85, 85-86; vis. scholar Harvard U. Law Sch., 1983; barrister, solicitor Supreme Ct. of Victoria, Australia, 1983—; Calif. Bar, 1987—; cons. prof. Chinese Law Diploma Program, U. East Asia, 1986-87; adj. prof. Loyola Law Sch., L.A., 1988—; Pepperdine U. Law Sch., 1989-90; lectr. Stanford U. Law Sch., 1995—. Contbr. numerous articles to profl. jours.; contbr. chpts. to 2 books. Bd. advisors Hong Kong Archives Hoover Instn.-Stanford U., 1988—. Mem. Calif. State Bar (mem. exec. com. internat. sect. 1989-92), Hong Kong Bar Assn., European Assn. for Chinese Law (mem. exec. coun. 1986—, country corr. 1986-), Am. Soc. of C. (chmn. subcom. on Chinese intellectual property law 1985-86), Am. Soc. Internat. Law (judge moot ct. 1984-86). Office: Lewis D'Amato 221 N Figueroa St Ste 1200 Los Angeles CA 90012-2601

LEUPP, EDYTHE PETERSON, retired educator, administrator; b. Mpls., Nov. 27, 1921; d. Reynold H. and Lillian (Aldridge) Peterson; m. Thomas A. Leupp, Jan. 29, 1944 (dec.); children: DeEtte (dec.), Patrice, Stacia, Roderick, Braden. BS, U. Oreg., 1947, MS, 1951, EdD, 1972. Tchr. various pub. schs. Idaho, 1941-45, Portland, Oreg., 1945-55; dir. tchr. edn. Northwest Nazarene Coll., Nampa, Idaho, 1955-61; sch. administr. Portland Pub. Schs., 1963-84; dir. tchr. edn. George Fox Coll., Newberg, Oreg., 1984-87; ret., 1987; vis. prof. So. Nazarene U., Bethany, Okla., 1988—; pres. Portland Assn. Pub. Sch. Adminstrs., 1973-75; dir.-at-large Nat. Coun. Adminstrv. Women in Edn., Washington, 1973-76; state chmn. Oreg. Sch. Prins. Spl. Project, 1978-79; chair Confdn. Oreg. Sch. Adminstrs. Ann. Conf.; rschr. 40 tchr. edn. programs in colls. and univs.; designer tchr. edn. program George Fox Coll. Author tchr. edn. materials. Pres. Idaho State Aux. Mcpl. League, 1957, Nampa PTA, 1958, Nampa unit AAUW, 1956; bd. dirs. Portland Fedn. Women's Clubs, 1963. Idea fellow Charles Kettering Found., 1978, 80, 87, 91, 92, 93, 94. Mem. ASCD, Am. Assn. Colls. Tchr. Edn., Delta Kappa Gamma (state pres. 1986-88, Golden Gift award 1984), Phi Delta Kappa, Pi Lambda Theta. Republican. Nazarene. Avocations: travel, crafts, photography. Home: 8100 SW 2nd Ave Portland OR 97219 Office: So Nazarene U Bethany OK 73008

LEUTE, WILLIAM RUSSELL, III, bank executive; b. Phila., Oct. 27, 1945; s. William Russell Jr. and Maverne (Muffitt) L.; m. Landa Braggiotti, June 26, 1976; children: William, Alexander Chadwick. BA in Fin., Lehigh U., 1967; MBA in Internat. Fin., Columbia U., 1971. With internat. div. Irving Trust Co., N.Y.C., 1971-77; regional rep. Irving Trust Co., Paris, 1978-82; exec. v.p., chief operating officer Midland Internat. Trade Services, N.Y.C., 1983—. With U.S. Army, 1969-70, Vietnam. Republican. Episcopalian. Avocation: polo. Home: 92 Mallard Dr Greenwich CT 06830-6747 Office: Midland Internat Trade Svcs Corp 560 Lexington Ave Fl 11 New York NY 10022-6828

LEUTHOLD, RAYMOND MARTIN, agricultural economics educator; b. Billings, Mont., Oct. 13, 1940; s. John Henry and Grace Irene L.; m. Jane Hornaday, Aug. 20, 1966; children—Kevin, Gregory. Student, Colo. U., 1958-59; B.S., Mont. State U., 1962; M.S., U. Wis., 1966, Ph.D., 1968. Faculty U. Ill., Urbana-Champaign, 1967—; now prof. dept. agrl. econs. U. Ill., T.A. Hieronymus disting. prof., dir. office futures and options rsch.; vis. scholar Stanford U., 1974, Chgo. Mercantile Exch., 1990, 91. Co-author: The Theory and Practice of Futures Markets, 1989; editor: Commodity Markets and Futures Prices, 1979; co-editor: Livestock Futures Research Symposium, 1980. Served with U.S. Army, 1962-64. Fulbright research scholar Institute de Gestion Internationale Agro-Alimentaire, Cergy, France, 1981. Mem. Am. Econ. Assn., Am. Agrl. Econs. Assn. (Disting. Policy award 1980, Outstanding Instr. award 1985, 90, 92, College Funk award 1993). Office: 305 Mumford Hall 1301 W Gregory Dr Urbana IL 61801-3608

LEUTZE, JAMES RICHARD, academic administrator, television producer and host; b. Charleston, S.C., Dec. 24, 1935; w. Willard Parker and Magdalene Mae (Seith) L.; m. Kathleen Shirley Erskine, Feb. 13, 1960; children—Magdalene Leigh, Jay Erskine, James Parker. B.A., U. Md., 1957; M.A., U. Miami, 1959; Ph.D., Duke U., 1968. Legis. asst. U.S. Senator Hubert Humphrey, Washington, 1963-64; prof. history U. N.C., Chapel Hill, 1968-87, chmn. curriculum peace, war, and def., 1979-87, Bowman and Gordon Gray prof., 1982, Dowd prof. Peace and War, 1976; TV host-producer N.C. Ctr. for Pub. TV, Chapel Hill, 1984—; pres. Hampden-Sydney (Va.) Coll., 1987-90; chancellor U. N.C. at Wilmington, 1990—. Author: Bargaining for Supremacy: Anglo-American Naval Collaboration, 1937-41, 1977 (Bernath prize 1978), A Different Kind of Victory: The Biography of Admiral Thomas C. Hart, 1981 (John Lyman Book award 1981); editor: London Journal Gen. Raymond E. Lee, 1972, The Role of the Military in a Democracy, 1974; contbr. articles to profl. jours. Served to capt. USAF, 1960-63. Recipient Standard Oil award for teaching U. N.C., 1971, Tanner award for teaching, 1978, Order of Golden Fleece award, 1983. Mem. Orgn. Am. Historians, Royal U.S. Inst. (London), Am. Hist. Assn., Univ. Club (N.D.), George C. Marshall Found., Phi Beta Kappa. Democrat. Episcopalian. Avocations: sportsman; hunting; fishing. Office: U NC 601 S College Rd Wilmington NC 28403-3201

LEUVER, ROBERT JOSEPH, former government official, association executive; b. Chgo., Feb. 2, 1927; s. Joseph Anthony and Helen Yolanda (Fornaciari) L.; m. Hilda Sanjuana Ortiz, July 29, 1950; 1 dau., Mary Ellen. A.B., Loyola U., Los Angeles, 1950; M.A., Cath. U. Am., 1954. Exec. v.p., treas. Claretians, Inc., Chgo., 1959-72; chief mgmt. analysis div. ACTION, Washington, 1972-74; chief treas. payroll div. Dept. Treasury, Washington, 1974-79; asst. dir. Bur. Engraving and Printing, Washington, 1979-82, dep. dir., 1982, dir., 1983-88; now exec. dir. Am. Numismatic Assn., Colorado Springs, Colo.; mem. Citizens Stamp Adv. Com. to Postmaster

Gen., U.S. Postal Service, 1983-88. Bd. dirs. Cath. Journalism Scholarship Fund, N.Y.C., 1967-72; v.p., dir. Southampton Assn., Arlington, Va., 1979-86. Recipient Best Editorial award Cath. Press Assn., 1964, Sr. Exec. award, 1980, 84, 85, Presdl. Meritorious Svc. award U.S. Pres., Washington, 1983, Presdl. Disting. Svc. award, 1986. Mem. Fed. Exec. Inst., Sr. Exec. Assn. Roman Catholic. Office: Am Numismatic Assn 818 N Cascade Ave Colorado Springs CO 80903

LEV, ALEXANDER SHULIM, mechanical engineer; b. Tselinograd, USSR, May 4, 1945; came to U.S., 1979; s. Borukh and Golda (Kopitman) L.; m. Polina Zhdanovskaja, Aug. 31, 1968; 1 child. Victoria. MSME, Lvov Polytech Inst., 1968. Project mgr. Glavspetsavtotrans, Lvov, USSR, 1968-78; sr. engr. Machine Plant, Lvov, USSR, 1978-79; metalurgist Ronson Metals Corp., Newark, N.J., 1980-82, foundry quality control mgr., 1982-83, reduction dept. mgr., 1986; project mgr. FMB Systems Inc., Harrison, N.J., 1986-94; v.p. Internat. Fair Share Inc., Rockaway, N.J., 1994—. Patentee in field. Mem. Am. Metals Soc., Metallurgical Soc. Avocations: reading, art, metal work, tennis. Home: 16 Princeton St Maplewood NJ 07040-3517

LEV, ALLEN P., lawyer; b. Chgo., Nov. 24, 1947. BA, U. Ill., 1968, JD with honors, 1971. Bar: Ill. 1971. Mng. ptnr. Holleb & Coff, Chgo., 1989—. V.p. bd. edn. Northbrook (Ill.) Sch. Dist., 1983-89. Mem. Chgo. Bar Assn. Office: Holleb & Coff 55 E Monroe St Ste 4100 Chicago IL 60603-5803

LEV, BARUCH ITAMAR, business administration educator, consultant; b. Tel Aviv, June 3, 1938; came to U.S., 1965; s. Simon and Mia (Whul) L.; m. Ilana Mark; children: Rachel. BA, Hebrew U., Israel, 1962; MBA, U. Chgo., 1967, PhD, 1968. CPA, Israel. Auditor, cons. J. Ronen and Co., CPAs, Tel Aviv, 1966-65; asst. prof. U. Chgo., 1968-69; prof., dean Sch. Business Tel Aviv U., 1970-82; mgr. investment banking Bank Hapoalim, Tel Aviv, 1983-84; prof., chair acctg. group Sch. Bus. U. Calif., Berkeley, 1986—; Author 3 books; contbr. articles to profl. jours. Mem. Am. Econ. Assn., Am. Acctg. Assn. (Disting. Internat. lectr. award 1979), Am. Fin. Assn. Office: U Calif Sch Bus Berkeley CA 94720

LEVA, JAMES ROBERT, electric utility company executive; b. Boonton, N.J., May 10, 1932; s. James and Rose (Cocci) L.; m. Marie Marinaro, Dec. 19, 1950; children: James, Daniel, Linda, Michael, Christopher. BSEE, magna cum laude, Fairleigh Dickinson U., 1960; JD, Seton Hall Law Sch., 1980. Lineman Jersey Central Power and Light Co., Morristown, N.J., 1952-60, elec. engring. and operating depts., 1960-62, personnel rep., 1962-68, mgr. employee relations, 1968-69, v.p. personnel and services, 1969-79, v.p. consumer affairs, 1979-82, dir., 1976-82; pres., COO, dir. Pa. Electric Co., Johnstown, 1982-86; pres., COO Jersey Cen. Power & Light Co., Morristown, N.J., 1986-92; chmn., pres., CEO Gen. Pub. Utilities, 1992—, also bd. dirs.; chmn., pres., CEO, bd. dirs. GPU Service Corp., Parsippany, N.J.; chmn. bd. dirs. GPU Nuc. Corp., Parsippany, N.J.; chmn. CEO, bd. dirs. Met. Edison Co., Reading, Pa., Pa. Electric Co., Johnstown, Pa., Utilities Mut. Ins. Co., N.J. Utilities Assn., Chemical Bank N.J.; chmn. St. Clares Health Care Found.; bd. overseers N.J. Inst. Tech.; trustee Tri-County Scholarship Fund, Fairleigh Dickinson U.; chmn. Sch. Planning & Pub. Policy Rutgers U. Served with USMC, 1949-51, Korea. Mem. N.J. Bar, N.J. Bar Assn. Roman Catholic. Club: Rumbeah (N.J.) Golf & Tennis. Office: Gen Pub Utilities 100 Interpace Pky Parsippany NJ 07054-1113

LEVA, MARX, lawyer; b. Selma, Ala., Apr. 4, 1915; s. Leo and Fannie Rose (Gusdorf) L.; m. Shirley Pearlman, Oct. 31, 1942; children: Leo Marx, Lloyd Leva Plaine. B.S., U. Ala., 1937, LL.D., 1978; LL.B., Harvard U., 1940. Bar: Ala. 1940, U.S. Supreme Ct. 1946, D.C. 1950. Law clk. to Justice Hugo Black, U.S. Supreme Ct., 1940; sr. atty. O.P.A., 1941; acting regional atty. for Mich. and Ohio WPB, 1942; counsel to fiscal dir. of Navy, 1946, spl. asst. to sec. of navy, 1947; spl. asst. and gen. counsel to Sec. Def., 1947-49; asst. sec of def. (legal and legis.), 1949-51; ptnr. Fowler, Leva, Hawes & Symington, 1951-67, Leva, Hawes, Symington, Martin & Oppenheimer, 1967-85, Leva, Hawes, Mason & Martin, 1985-90; of counsel Robins, Kaplan, Miller & Ciresi, 1990—; Chmn. civilian-mil. review panel for spl. com. U.S. Senate, 1957; mem. Pres.'s Commn. to Rev. Fgn. Aid, 1958-59, Pres.'s Com. on Def. Establishment, 1960-61. Note editor: Harvard Law Rev, 1939-40; overseer, 1950-55. Served with amphibious forces USNR, 1943-44, ETO. Decorated Bronze Star with combat disting. device; named Outstanding Young Man In Govt., Washington Jr. C. of C., 1949. Home: 7115 Bradley Blvd Bethesda MD 20817-2125 Office: 1801 K St NW Washington DC 20006-1301

LEVACK, ARTHUR PAUL, history educator emeritus; b. Boston, Dec. 16, 1909; s. Arthur Joseph and Marie Agnes (St Onge) L.; m. Helen Gertrude O'Brien, Aug. 28, 1939; children—Ann Marie, Brian Paul. B.A. magna cum laude, Harvard, 1932, M.A., 1934, Ph.D., 1941. Teaching fellow Amherst Coll., 1935-36; instr. Fordham U., 1936-42, asst. prof., 1942-47, assoc. prof., 1947-67, prof., 1967-79, emeritus, 1979—, chmn. dept. history, 1950-65, dean summer session, 1965-78. Author: (with R.J.S. Hoffman) Burke's Politics, 1949, (with A.I. Abell) A History of the United States, 1951; Contbr. to Ency. Americana also articles to profl. jours. Mem. Am. Hist. Assn., Am. Cath. Hist. Assn. (pres. 1951), U.S. Cath. Hist. Soc. (pres. 1952-53). Democrat. Roman Catholic.

LEVADA, WILLIAM JOSEPH, archbishop; b. Long Beach, Calif., June 15, 1936; s. Joseph and Lorraine (Nunez) L. B.A., St. John's Coll., Camarillo, Calif., 1958; S.T.L., Gregorian U., Rome, 1962, S.T.D., 1971. Ordained priest Roman Cath. Ch., 1961, consecrated bishop, 1983. Assoc. pastor Archdiocese of L.A., 1962-67; prof. theology St. John's Sem., Camarillo, Calif., 1970-76; ofcl. Doctrinal Congregation, Vatican City, Italy, 1976-82; exec. dir. Calif. Cath. Conf., Sacramento, 1982-84; aux. bishop, vicar for Santa Barbara County, 1983-86; archbishop Archdiocese of Portland in Oreg., 1986—. Trustee Cath. U. Am.; chmn. bd. dirs. Pope John XXIII Med.-Moral Rsch. and Edn. Ctr. Mem. Nat. Conf. Cath. Bishops (com. on doctrine), U.S. Cath. Conf., Cath. Theol. Soc. Am., Canon Law Soc. Am. Office: Archdiocese of Portland 2838 E Burnside St Portland OR 97214-1895

LEVAL, PIERRE NELSON, federal judge; b. N.Y.C., Sept. 4, 1936; s. Fernand and Beatrice (Reiter) L. B.A. cum laude, Harvard U., 1959, J.D. magna cum laude, 1963. Bar: N.Y. 1964, U.S. Ct. Appeals 2d Circuit 1964, U.S. Dist. Ct. So. Dist. N.Y 1966. Law clk. to Hon. Henry J. Friendly, U.S. Ct. Appeals, 1963-64; asst. U.S. atty. So. Dist. N.Y., 1964-68, chief appellate atty., 1967-68; assoc. firm Cleary, Gottlieb, Steen & Hamilton, N.Y.C., 1969-74; ptnr. firm, 1973-75; 1st asst. dist. atty. Office of Dist. Atty., N.Y. County, 1975-76; chief asst. dist. atty. Office of Dist. Atty., 1976-77; U.S. dist. judge So. Dist. N.Y., N.Y.C., 1977-93; judge U.S. Ct. of Appeals (2d cir.), N.Y.C., 1993—. Contbr. articles to profl. jours. Served with U.S. Army, 1959. Mem. Am. Law Inst. (council), Assn. Bar City N.Y., N.Y. County Lawyers Assn. Office: US Courthouse Foley Square New York NY 10007-1501*

LEVALIER, DOTIAN, harpist; b. Salem, Mass., June 2, 1943; d. Curtis Levitt and Audrey Lois (Sargent) Bushby; m. William Daniel Carter, Sept. 3, 1965 (div. 1986); children: Lisa Dianne, Janice Elizabeth. Diploma, Curtis Inst., Phila., 1964. Prin. harpist Phila. Lyric Opera, 1964-69, Phila. Chamber Orch., 1965-68, Pa. Ballet, Phila., 1965-69, Nat. Symphony Orch., Washington, 1969—; solo harpist Stern & Levalier, Flute and Harp Duo, Washington, 1982—. Episcopalian. Avocations: camping, sewing, gardening, hiking, travel. Office: Nat Symphony Orch JFK Ctr Performing Arts Washington DC 20566

LE VAN, DANIEL HAYDEN, gas industry executive; b. Savannah, Ga., Mar. 29, 1924; s. Daniel Hayden and Ruth (Harner) LeV. Grad., Middlesex Sch., 1943; BA, Harvard U., 1950; postgrad., Babson Inst., 1950-51. Underwriter Zurich Ins. Co., N.Y.C., 1951-52; co-owner, dir. Overseas Properties, Ltd., N.Y.C., 1970—; dir. Colonial Gas Co., Lowell, Mass., 1973—. With AUS, 1943-46. Mem. Harvard Club (N.Y.C. and Boston).

LEVANT, BRIAN, film director. films include: Problem Child II, 1991, Beethoven, 1992, The Flintstones, 1994. Office: Telvan Prodns 9528

Dalegrove Dr Beverly Hills CA 90210-1711 also: United Talent Agy 9560 Wilshire Blvd Fl 5 Beverly Hills CA 90212-2427*

LEVASSEUR, WILLIAM RYAN, lawyer; b. Fredericksburg, Va., June 10, 1935; s. George B. and Martha F. (Callegary) L.; m. Joanne Bowers, May 30, 1958; children: William Ryan Jr., John M., Michele Henzi. AA, U. Balt., 1958, JD, 1961. Bar: Md. 1962, U.S. Dist. Ct. Md. 1962, U.S. Supreme Ct. 1972, D.C. 1979, U.S. Ct. Appeals (4th cir.) 1979. Pvt. practice Balt., 1962-69; asst. atty. gen. Md. Atty. Gen.'s Office, Balt., 1969-71; assoc. Semmes, Bowen & Semmes, Balt., 1971-73, ptnr., 1974-94; ptnr. Howell, Gately, Whitney & Carter, Towson, Md., 1994—. Mem. adv. bd. U. Balt. Sch. Law, 1985-91, Villa Julie Coll., 1982—. With USAFR, 1955-59. Named Alumnus of the Yr. U. Balt. Alumni Assn., 1989. Mem. ABA (tort and ins. practice sect., mem. minority women and gen. membership involvement com. 1992—, co-chmn. family life com. 1991-93, mem. pub. rels. com. 1990-93, chmn. liaison jud. adminstrv. div. 1986-89, chmn. Profl. Issues, 1987-88, chmn. Scope and Correlation, 1988-89, chmn. workers' compensation and employers' liability commn. and chmn. nat. inst. 1985-86, program chmn. 1983-84, sr. vice chmn. 1987—), Fed. Bar Assn. (pres. Md. chpt. 1987-88, chair select com. bench bar 1993-94, cir. officer 4th cir. 1988-92, chair nat. membership com. 1991-93, mem. 1994—, nat. membership svcs. com. 1988-89, nat. nominating com. 1988, ops. rev. com., advisor Found. 1991-93, bd. dirs., pres. 1994—), Md. State Bar Assn. (sect. adminstrn., law, litigation, negligence and compensation, mem. fed. dist. ct. com.), D.C. Bar Assn. (litigation div.), Md. Assn. Def. Trial Counsel (workers compensation com.), Assn. Compensation Inst. Attys. (pres. 1982), Bar Assn. Balt. City (sec. 1993-94, v.p. 1990, 94—, treas. 1992, chmn. law sch. activities/funding com. 1983-90, judiciary com. 1989-94, chmn. 1991-92, chair legis. com. joint task force for injured workers rehabilitation 1987—, pres. elect. 1995), Balt. City Bar Found., U. Balt. Alumni Assn. (pres. 1983-85, sch. law adv. bd. 1985-91), KC. Democrat. Roman Catholic. Home: 1917 Knollton Rd Lutherville Timonium MD 21093-5248 Office: Howell Gately Whitney & Carter 401 Washington Ave 12th Fl Towson MD 21204

LEVE, ALAN DONALD, electronic materials manufacturing company owner, executive; b. Los Angeles, Dec. 15, 1927; s. Milton Lewis and Etta L.; m. Annette Einhorn, Sept. 3, 1962; children—Laura Michelle, Elise Deanne. BS, UCLA, 1951. CPA, Calif. Staff acct., mgr. Joseph S. Herbert & Co. (C.P.A.s), Los Angeles, 1951-57; ptnr. Joseph S. Herbert & Co. (C.P.A.s), 1957-63; fin. and adminstrv. v.p., sec./treas. Mica Corp., Culver City, Calif., 1963-82, also bd. dirs., 1963-82, chmn. bd., chief exec. officer, 1982-83; v.p., bd. dirs. Micaply Internat. Inc., 1968-1982; v.p. Micaply AG, Switzerland, 1972-83, also bd. dirs., chief exec. officer, also bd. dirs., 1982-83; v.p., bd. dirs. Micaply Internat., Ltd., U.K., 1971-82; chmn. bd., mng. dir., chief exec. officer Micaply Internat. Ltd., U.K., 1982-83; v.p., bd. dirs. Titan Chem. Corp., Edgecraft Corp., Culver Hydro-Press, Inc., L.A., 1963-75; chmn. bd., pres., chief exec. officer Ohmega Techs., Inc., Culver City, Calif., 1983—, Calif. Capital mgmt. Inc., Los Angeles, 1985-86, Ohmega Electronics, Inc., Culver City, 1986—, Planar Techs., Inc., Nev., 1986—. Served with USAAF, 1946-47. Home: 16430 Dorado Dr Encino CA 91436-4118 Office: 4031 Elenda St Culver City CA 90232-3723

LEVE, SAMUEL, scenic designer; b. USSR, Dec. 1, 1910; 1 child, Teri. Student, various art schs., N.Y.C. Yale U., Jewish Theol. Sem. Am. instr., lectr. CCNY, Baylor U., Waco, Tex., Yale U., NYU, Fla. State U., Tallahassee, YMHA. Designer over 100 Broadway prodns. for Shurberts, George Abbott, Theatre Guild, Rodgers and Hammerstein, Orson Welles, David Merrick, Saroyan, Met. Opera, Maurice Schwartz (Yiddish Theatre), Habimah, others; design Chanukah Festivals at Madison Square Garden, N.Y.C., McCormick Place, Chgo.; designer two synagogues N.Y.C., St. John the Divine Cathedral, and for five presidents. Address: 277 W End Ave New York NY 10023

LEVEE, JOHN HARRISON, artist, designer; b. Los Angeles, Apr. 10, 1924; s. Michael Charles and Roze L.; m. Claude Marie, Dec. 19, 1964. B.A., UCLA, 1948; postgrad., New Sch. Social Research, N.Y.C., 1949, Acad. Julian, 1950. vis. prof. art U. Ill., 1965, N.Y. U., 1967-68, U. So. Calif., 1971. One-man shows, Konig Galerie, Geneva, 1971, Andre Emmerich Gallery, N.Y.C., 1957-59, 62, 66, Gimpel Fils, London, 1958, 60, 66, Galerie de France, 1961, 62, 64, 69, Nora Gallery, Jerusalem, Haifa (Israel) Mus. Art, Moose Gallery, Toronto, 1963, Phoenix Mus. Art, 1964, U. Ill. Krannert Art Mus., 1965, Tel Aviv (Israel) Mus., 1969, Margo Leavin Gallery, Los Angeles, 1970, Galerie la Toabis, Paris, 1975, Palm Springs (Calif.) Mus., 1978, Mus. Nice, France, 1980, Galerie La Closerie des Lilacs, Paris, 1983, 86, Galerie 1900-2000, Paris, Galerie de Poche, Paris, 1990; one-man retrospective Galerie Le Gall, Paris, 1986, retrospective of the 1950's, Gallerie Callu, Paris, 1989, retrospective of the 1960's, 1989, retrospective 1953-93 Toulouse Mus., France; group shows, Salon de Mai, Paris, 1954-79, 95, Salon des Realités Nouvelles, 1954-92, Salon Comparison, 1978-92, Paris, Carnegie Internat., 1955, 58, Washington's Corcoran Gallery of Art, 1956, 58, Mus. Modern Art N.Y.C., 1957, Whitney Mus., 1957-59, 65, Arts Club Chgo., 1958, Guggenheim Mus., 1966, others, many archtl. projects, France, U.S.A. Served with USAAF, 1944-46. Recipient prizes including Watercolor Assn. Ann. 1955, 56, Commonwealth of Va. Biann. Purchase award 1966, grand prix Woolmark Found. 1974-75, gran prix Biennale de Paris 1969; Ford grantee, 1969; Tamarind fellow Los Angeles, 1969. Jewish. Home: 119 rue Notre Dame des, Champs, 6 Paris France *Most thinkers and artists are not historical geniuses who have broken with previous tradition, perceived relationships hitherto unnoticed, or even invented new relationships or had new visions thus transforming the categories in terms of which human beings think of their place in the universe. But for each historical period there are these men of genius and it is the moral imperative of us all to strive, to reach out in our own way and within our own limits, toward this end.

LEVEILLE, GILBERT ANTONIO, food products executive; b. Fall River, Mass., June 3, 1934; s. Isidore and Rose (Caron) L.; divorced; children: Michael, Kathleen, Edward; m. Carol A. Phillips, Aug. 7, 1981. B in Vocat. Agr., U. Mass. 1956; MS, Rutgers U., 1958, PhD, 1960. Prof. nutritional biochemistry U. Ill., Urbana, 1965-71; chmn. dept. food sci. and human nutrition Mich. State U., East Lansing, 1971-80; dir. nutrition and health sci. Gen. Foods Corp., Tarrytown, N.Y., 1980-86; v.p. for rsch. and tech. svcs. Nabisco Inc., East Hanover, N.J., 1986—. Author: The Set Point Diet, 1985 (N.Y. Times nonfiction bestseller); also over 300 articles. Served to 1st lt. U.S. Army, 1960-62. Recipient rsch. award Poultry Sci. Assn., 1965, Disting. Faculty award Mich. State U., 1980. Mem. AAAS, Am. Chem. Soc., Am. Inst. Nutrition (pres.-elect 1987-88, pres. 1988-89, Mead Johnson rsch. award 1971), Am. Soc. for Clin. Nutrition, Inst. Food Technologists (pres. 1983-84, fellow 1983, Carl Fellers award 1992). Office: Nabisco Inc PO Box 1944 East Hanover NJ 07936-1944

LEVEL, LEON JULES, information services executive; b. Detroit, Dec. 30, 1940; s. Leon and Madeline G. (Mayea) L.; m. Constance Kramer, June 25, 1966; children—Andrea, Aileen. B.B.A., U. Mich., 1962, M.B.A., 1963. CPA, Mich. Asst. accountant Deloitte Haskins & Sells, Detroit, 1963-66, sr. accountant, 1966-69, prin., 1969-71; asst. corp. controller Bendix Corp., Southfield, Mich., 1971-81; v.p. fin. planning Burroughs Corp., Detroit, 1981-82, v.p., treas., 1982-86; v.p., treas. Unisys Corp., Blue Bell, Pa., 1986-89; v.p., chief fin. officer Computer Scis. Corp., El Segundo, Calif., 1989—; mem. U. Mich. adv. bd., Ann Arbor, 1984-90; Providence Hosp. Adv. Bd., Southfield, Mich., 1984-86, Allendale Ins. Adv. Bd., Cleve., 1985-89; bd. dirs. F.A. Tucker Group, Inc. Trustee Walnut St. Theatre, Phila., 1988-89. Mem. Fin. Execs. Inst. (sec. Detroit chpt. 1983-85, v.p. 1985-86, pres. 1986-87), Am. Inst. C.P.A.s, Mich. Assn. C.P.A.s, Inst. Mgmt. Accts. Office: Computer Scis Corp 2100 E Grand Ave El Segundo CA 90245-5098

LEVELL, EDWARD, JR., city official; b. Jacksonville, Ala., Apr. 2, 1931; m. Rosa M. (Casellas) L. Aug. 3, 1951; children: Edward III (dec.), Ruben C., Kenneth W., Randy C., Raymond C., Cheryl D. Levell Rivera, Michael K. BS, Tuskegee Inst., 1953; MA in Urban Sociology, U. No. Colo., 1972; M in Mgmt., Indsl. Coll./Air War Coll., 1974. Commd. 2d lt. USAF, 1953, advanced through grades to col., 1978, various flight tng., air ops. and command positions, 1953-69; comdr. cadet group, then dep. commandant cadet wing USAF Acad., 1969-73; dep. comdr., wing comdr., vice comdr. 1st spl. ops. wing USAF, 1973-77, wing comdr. 58th tactical air command tng. wing, 1977-78, col., vice comdr., comdr. 20th air divsn., 1978-83, ret., 1983;

dep. commr. aviation City of Chgo. Dept. Aviation, 1983-89; dep. dir. aviation, fin. and adminstrn. City of New Orleans Dept. Aviation, 1989-90, dep. dir. aviation, ops. and maintenance, 1990-92, dir. aviation, 1992—. bd. dirs. Tourist & Conv. Commn., New Orleans; trustee Dryades YMCA, New Orleans; mem. transp. com. World Trade Ctr. Decorated Legion of Merit, D.F.C. (2), Meritorious Svc. Medal (2), Air Medal (8), Air Force Commendation Medal; recipient Disting. Svc. award Jacksonville, Ala., 1974, State of Fla. Commn. Human Rels. award for spl. recognition, 1977, Air Force Assn. Spl. Citation of Merit, 1977, Disting. Svc. award City of Chgo. Dept. Aviation, 1986, 87, 88; inducted in Tuskegee Univ. Hall of Fame, 1991. Mem. Airport Ops. Coun. Internat. (task force chmn. ann. conf. New Orleans 1991), Am. Assn. Airport Execs., Gulf Coast Internat. Hispanic C. of C. Home: 1500 W Esplanade Ave Apt 46F Kenner LA 70065-5346 Office: New Orleans Aviation Bd New Orleans Intl Airport Box 20007 New Orleans LA 70141

LEVELT SENGERS, JOHANNA MARIA HENRICA, research physicist; b. Amsterdam, The Netherlands, Mar. 4, 1929; came to U.S., 1963; d. Wilhelmus Henricus and Maria Antonia Josephine (Berger) Levelt; m. Jan V. Sengers, Feb. 21, 1963; children: Rachel Teresa, Adriaan Jan, Maarten Willem, Phoebe Josephine. BS, Municipal U., Amsterdam, 1950, MS, 1954, PhD in Physics, 1958; hon. doctorate, Delft U. Tech., 1992. Rsch. asst. Municipal U., Amsterdam, 1954-63; postdoctoral assoc. U. Wis., Madison, 1958-59; rsch. physicist Nat. Bur. Standards, Gaithersburg, Md., 1963—; group leader Nat. Bur. Standards, Gaithersburg, 1978-88; vis. prof. U. Louvain, Belgium, 1971; vis. scientist Municipal U., Amsterdam, 1974-75; Regent's prof. U. Calif., L.A., 1982; sr. fellow Nat. Inst. Standards and Tech., Gaithersburg, 1983—. Contbr. 12 chpts. to books and over 100 articles to profl. jours. Recipient DOC silver medal, 1972, DOC gold medal, 1978, WISE award U.S. Interagy. Com., Women in Sci. and Engring., Washington, 1985, A.V. Humboldt Rsch. award Ruhr-U., Bochum, Germany, 1991. Fellow Am. Phys. Soc.; mem. ASME (nat. del. rsch. com. water and steam 1988—), AIChE, AAAS, NAE, Royal Netherlands Acad. Scis. (corr.), Internat. Assn. Properties Water and Steam (v.p. 1988-90, pres. 1990-91, hon. fellow 1994), European Phys. Soc., Am. Chem. Soc. (divsn. phys. chemistry), Sigma Xi. Democrat. Avocations: gardening, hiking, swimming, traveling, reading. Home: 110 N Van Buren St Rockville MD 20850-1861 Office: Nat Inst Standards & Tech Gaithersburg MD 20899

LEVEN, ANN RUTH, arts administrator; b. Canton, Ohio, Nov. 1, 1940; d. Joseph J. and Bessie (Scharff) L. AB, Brown U., 1962; cert. with distinction in program in bus. adminstrn., Harvard-Radcliffe Univs., 1963; MBA, Harvard U., 1964. Product mgr. household products div. Colgate-Palmolive, N.Y.C., 1964-66; account exec. Grey Advt., N.Y.C., 1966-67; fin. asst. Met. Mus. Art, N.Y.C., 1967-69; asst. treas. Met. Mus. Art, 1970-72, treas., 1972-79; v.p., sr. corp. planning officer Chase Manhattan Bank, N.Y.C., 1979-83; pres. ARL Assocs., N.Y.C., 1983—; treas. Smithsonian Instn., 1984-90; dep. treas. Nat. Gallery Art, Washington, 1990-94, treas., 1994—; adj. asst. prof. grad. sch. Bus., Chicago, U., 1975-77, adj. assoc. prof., 1977-79, adj. prof. 1980-93; exec.-in-residence Amos Tuck Sch., Dartmouth Coll., winter 1976, spring 1984; dir. Alliance Capital Res., Inc., 1978-79, Short Term Asset Res., 1985-93, Oreg. Tax Free Trust, 1986—, Churchill Tax-Free Fund of Ky., 1987—, Cascades Cash Fund, 1989-94, Del. Group, 1989—; trustee Carnegie Corp. of N.Y., 1981-90. Artist (awarded prizes for painting and graphic arts); author articles on grad. bus. edn., mgmt. studies on the arts. Mem. exec. bd. new leadership div. Fedn. Jewish Philanthropies, 1968-70; mem. council N.Y. Public Library, mem. exec. com., 1976-79; mem. mus. adv. panel N.Y. State Council on Arts, 1977-79; bd. dirs. Camp Rainbow, 1970-84, v.p., 1976-78, treas., 1982-84; bd. overseers Amos Tuck Sch., 1978-84, chmn. ednl. affairs com., 1979-84; trustee Brown U., 1976—, also mem. fin. and budget com., student life com., devel. com., adv. and exec. coms.; bd. mem. Ctr. for Fgn. Policy Devel., 1989-94; trustee Artists' Choice Mus., 1979-87; bd. dirs. Reading Is Fundamental, 1987-91, adv. coun., 1991-94; mem. vis. com. Harvard U. Bus. Sch., 1979-84; trustee ARC Endowment Fund, 1985-90; bd. dirs. Am. Arts Alliance, 1990-92; bd. dirs. Twyla Tharp Dance Found., 1982-87; bd. overseers Hood Mus.-Hopkins Ctr. Dartmouth Coll., 1984-91, chmn., 1988-91; mem. staff Presdl. Task Force on Arts and Humanities, 1981. Recipient Young Leadership award Council Jewish Fedns. and Welfare Funds, 1968; named N.Y. State's Outstanding Young Woman, 1976. Mem. Harvard Bus. Sch. Alumni Assn. (exec. coun. 1976-79, v.p. 1978-79), Women's Fin. Assn., Women's Forum, Econ. Club of Washington, Cosmopolitan Club, Harvard Bus. Sch. Club, Radcliffe Club, Brown Club. Home: 785 Park Ave New York NY 10021 Office: Nat Gallery Art Washington DC 20565

LEVEN, CHARLES LOUIS, economics educator; b. Chgo., May 2, 1928; s. Elie H. and Ruth (Reinach) R.; m. Judith Danoff, 1950 (div. 1970); m. Dorothy Wish, 1970; children: Ronald L., Robert M., Carol E., Philip W., Alice S. Student, Ill. Inst. Tech., 1945-46, U. Ill., 1947; B.S., Northwestern U., 1950, M.A., 1957, Ph.D., 1958. Economist Fed. Res. Bank of Chgo., 1950-56; asst. prof. Iowa State U., 1957-59, U. Pa., 1959-62; asso. prof. U. Pitts., 1962-65; prof. econs. Washington U., St. Louis, 1965-71, chmn. dept. econs., 1975-80, prof. emeritus, 1991—; dir. Inst. Urban and Regional Studies, 1965-85; disting. prof. U. Mo., St. Louis, 1991—; cons. EEC, Ill. Auditor Gen., Polish Ministry of Planning and Constrn., St. Louis Sch. Bd., Ukrainian Ctr. for Markets and Entrepreneurship, European Inst. Comparative Urban Rsch. Author: Theory and Method of Income and Product Accounts for Metropolitan Areas, 1963, Development Benefits of Water Resource Investment, 1969, An Analytical Framework for Regional Development Policy, 1970, Neighborhood Change, 1976, The Mature Metropolis, 1978. Served with USNR, 1945-46. Ford Found. fellow, 1956; grantee Social Sci. Rsch. Coun., 1960; grantee Com. Urban Econ., 1965; grantee NSF, 1968, 73, Merc. Bancorp., 1976, HUD, 1978, NIH, 1985. Mem. Am. Econ. Assn., Regional Sci. Assn. (pres. 1964-65), Western Regional Sci. Assn. (pres. 1974-75), So. Regional Sci. Assn. (disting. fellow 1991). Home: 7042 Delmar Blvd Saint Louis MO 63130-4301 Office: Washington U Box 1208 1 Brookings Dr Saint Louis MO 63130-4862 also: U Mo 8001 Natural Bridge Rd Saint Louis MO 63121 *Achievement is satisfying, but especially so when one can win without others losing. At the same time, it appears unnecessary to be a failure to prove one's sincerity.*

LEVENDUSKY, PHILIP GEORGE, clinical psychologist, administrator; b. Lowell, Mass., Oct. 21, 1946; s. Harry George and Phyllis Mary (Gowgill) L.; 1 child, Jason Philip. BA magna cum laude, U. Mass, 1968; MS, Wash. State U., 1971, Wash. State U., 1973. Diplomate Am. Bd. Profl. Psychology. Asst. to dir. Human Rels. Ctr., Wash. State U., Pullman, 1971-73; asst. psychologist McLean Hosp., Belmont, Mass., 1974-82; assoc. psychologist, 1982-92; psychologist McLean Hosp., Belmont, 1992—, dir. cognitive behavior therapy unit, 1974-94, dir. ambulatory care, 1991-93, asst. gen. dir., 1993—, dir. ambulatory care svcs., 1994—; instr. psychiatry Harvard Med. Sch., 1974-88, asst. prof., 1989—; dir. Levendusky and Assocs., Arlington, Mass., 1980—; Bd. dirs. Pullman Mgmt., Manchester, Mass., 1976-80, Feeding Ourselves, 1980, Anorexia Bulemia Care, 1991-93; dir. Bank & Employee Consultation, Boston, 1987—; cons. Va Hosp., Boston, 1977-85, Boston Cardiovascular Health, 1983-85, Mass. Dept. Mental Health, 1987—; mem. Mass. Bd. Psychology, Boston, 1988-93. Contbr. articles to profl. jours., mags., newspapers; author book chpts.; guest numerous TV and Radio programs, Boston. Mem. Am. Psychol. Assn., Assn. Advancement Behavior Therapy, New Eng. Soc. of Behavior Analysis and Therapy (bd. dirs. 1991), Phi Beta Kappa. Republican. Roman Catholic. Avocations: skiing, jogging. Home: . Manchester by the Sea MA 01944-1405 Office: McLean Hosp 115 Mill St Belmont MA 02178-1048

LEVENFELD, MILTON ARTHUR, lawyer; b. Chgo., Mar. 18, 1927; s. Mitchell A. and Florence B. (Berman) L.; m. Iona R. Wishner, Dec. 18, 1949; children—Barry, David, Judith. Ph.B., U. Chgo., 1947, J.D., 1950. Bar: Ill. 1950. Ptnr. Altman, Levenfeld & Kanter, Chgo., 1961-64, Levenfeld and Kanter, Chgo., 1964-80, Levenfeld, Eisenberg, Janger, Glassberg & Halper, Chgo., 1980—; former dir. Bank of Chgo., Garfield Ridge Trust & Savs. Bank; lectr. in fed. taxation. Contbr. articles to profl. jours. Bd. dirs. Spertus Coll. Judaica, Jewish Fedn. Chgo., 1975-84, Am. Israel C. of C.; chmn. legacies and endowments com., 1982-84; co-gen. chmn. Chgo. Jewish United Fund, 1977, vice chmn. campaign, 1979; governing mem. Orchestral Assn. Chgo. Symphony Orch.; vis. com. U. Chgo. Law Sch., 1989-91; pres. Am. Israel C. of C. of Met. Chgo., 1993—. Served with USNR, 1944-45. Recipient Keter Shem Tov award Jewish Nat. Fund, 1978. Mem. ABA, Ill.

Bar Assn., Chgo. Bar Assn. Home: 866 Stonegate Dr Highland Park IL 60035-5145 Office: 33 W Monroe St Chicago IL 60603-5302

LEVENSON, ALAN IRA, psychiatrist, physician, educator; b. Boston, July 25, 1935; s. Jacob Maurice and Frances Ethel (Biller) L.; m. Myra Beatrice Katzen, June 12, 1960 (div. 1993); children: Jonathan, Nancy; m. Linda Ann Nadell, Jan. 30, 1994. AB, Harvard U., 1957, MD, 1961, MPH, 1965. Diplomate: Am. Bd. Psychiatry and Neurology. Intern U. Hosp., Ann Arbor, Mich., 1961-62; resident psychiatry Mass. Mental Health Center, Boston, 1962-65; staff psychiatrist NIMH, Chevy Chase, Md., 1965-66; dir. div. mental health service programs NIMH, 1967-69; prof. psychiatry U. Ariz. Coll. Medicine, Tucson, 1969—, head dept. psychiatry, 1969-89; chief exec. officer Palo Verde Mental Health Svcs., Tucson, 1971-91, chief med. officer, med. dir., 1991-93; chmn. bd. dirs., CEO Psychiatrists' Purchasing Group, 1991—; chmn. bd. dirs. Psychiatrists' Risk Retention Group, 1991—; mem. staff Tucson Med. Ctr., U. Med. Ctr., Tucson. Author: The Community Mental Health Center: Strategies and Programs, 1972; Contbr. papers and articles to psychiat. jours. Bd. dirs. Tucson Urban League, 1971-78, Pima Council on Aging, 1976-83. Served with USPHS, 1965-69. Fellow Am. Psychiat. Assn. (treas. 1986-90), Am. Coll. Psychiatrists (regent 1980-83, v.p 1983-85, pres.-elect 1985-86, pres. 1986-87), Am. Coll. Mental Health Adminstrn. (v.p. 1980-82, pres. 1982-83); mem. Group for Advancement Psychiatry, Harvard Alumni Assn. (bd. dirs. 1988-91). Office: 75 N Calle Resplendor Tucson AZ 85716-4937

LEVENSON, HARVEY STUART, manufacturing company executive; b. N.Y.C., May 1, 1940; s. Abraham and Lucile (Lichtenstein) L.; m. Merrilee Borenstein, Aug. 28, 1960; children: Lee Alan, Gary Scott. BA, Drake U., 1962, JD, 1963; LLM, Georgetown U., 1966. Bar: Iowa 1963, N.Y. 1964, Conn. 1968. Atty. IRS, Washington, 1964-68; assoc. Murtha, Cullina, Richter & Pinney, Hartford, Conn., 1968-69; ptnr. Murtha, Cullina, Richter & Pinney, Hartford, 1970-82; sr. v.p., chief fin. officer Kaman Corp., Bloomfield, Conn., 1982-90; pres., chief oper. officer Kaman Corp., Bloomfield, 1990—, bd. dirs.; lectr. U. Conn. Law Sch., Hartford, 1972-76; bd. dirs. Conn. Natural Gas Corp., and Security Conn. Corp.; adv. bd. dirs. Shawmut Bank; corporator St. Francis Hosp., Hartford Hosp., Inst. of Living. Co-author: Depreciation & The Investment Tax Credit, 1983; contbr. various articles on taxation to profl. jours.

LEVENSON, JACOB CLAVNER, English language educator; b. Boston, Oct. 1, 1922; s. Joseph Mayer and Frances (Hahn) L.; m. Charlotte Elizabeth Getz, June 6, 1946; children: Anne Berthe, Jill Mayer, Paul Getz. AB, Harvard U., 1943, PhD, 1951. Tutor in history and lit. Harvard, 1946-50, vis. lectr. English and gen. edn., 1951-52; instr. English U. Conn., 1950-54; asst. prof. to prof. English U. Minn., 1954-67; Edgar Allan Poe prof. English U. Va., Charlottesville, 1967—; chmn. dept. U. Va., 1971-74; faculty Salzburg (Austria) Seminar in Am. Studies, 1947, 49; Mem. Com. of Cons., Notable Am. Women, 1607-1950, 63-72. Author: The Mind and Art of Henry Adams, 1957, Hist. and Critical Introductions The Works of Stephen Crane, II-V, VII, 1969-76; editor: Stephen Crane: Prose and Poetry, 1984, Mark Twain Life on the Mississippi, 1967, Discussions of Hamlet, 1960, The Letters of Henry Adams I-III, 1982, IV-VI, 1988; mem. editorial bd.; Am. Quar., 1964-70, Va. Quar. Rev., 1968—, New Literary History, 1969—, Am. Lit., 1988-91; contbr. articles to profl. jours. Served with AUS, 1943-45. Decorated Bronze Star medal; Guggenheim fellow, 1958-59; Am. Council Learned Socs. fellow, 1961-62; Am. Philos. Soc. Penrose grantee, 1956; recipient E. Harris Harbison award for disting. teaching Danforth Found., 1966. Mem. MLA, Am. Studies Assn., Signet Soc., Phi Beta Kappa. Home: 1100 Free State Rd Charlottesville VA 22901-1819

LEVENSON, MARC DAVID, optics and lasers specialist, scientist; b. Phila., May 28, 1945; s. Donald William and Ethyl Jean (Sapper) L.; m. Naomi Francis Matsuda, Oct. 24, 1971. SB, MIT, 1967; MS, Stanford U., 1968, PhD, 1971. Rsch. fellow Harvard U., Cambridge, Mass., 1971-74; asst. prof. physics U. So. Calif., L.A., 1974-77, assoc. prof., 1977-79; mem. rsch. staff IBM Rsch. div., San Jose, Calif., 1979-93, head mgr. OSC, 1987, mgr. quantum metrology, 1990; v.p. Focused Rsch., Inc., Sunnyvale, Calif., 1993-95; propr., cons. Marc D. Levenson Optics, Saratoga, 1993—. Author: Introduction to Nonlinear Laser Spectroscopy, 1988; editor: Lasers, Spectroscopy, New Ideas, 1987, Resonances, 1991; West Coast editor Solid State Tech. mag., 1993—; contbr. articles to profl. jours. Alfred Sloan rsch. fellow, 1975. Fellow IEEE, Optical Soc. Am. (Adolph Lomb medal 1976), Am. Phys. Soc., Bay Area Chrome Users Soc./Soc. Photog. and Instrumentation Engrs. (award 1991). Avocations: gardening, reading.

LEVENSON, STANLEY RICHARD, public relations and advertising executive; b. Chi., Dec. 28, 1933; s. Irven Philip and Dorothy (Aftel) L.; m. Barbara Lind, July 23, 1962; children: Laura, Amy. B.A., U. Mich., 1956; postgrad., Am. U. S.W. sales and promotion mgr. DOT Records, Hollywood, Calif., 1959-62; S.W. sales and mktg. rep. Pickwick Internat. Co., 1963-65; pres., chmn. bd. Stan Levenson Assos., Dallas, 1966-76; exec. v.p., gen. mgr. public relations div. S.W., Bozell & Jacobs, Dallas, 1976-81; pres., CEO Levenson & Levenson, Dallas, 1981-83; CEO Levenson Pub. Rels., 1984—; dir. Fidelity Nat. Bank, Dallas; Trustee TACA, 1980, Dallas Alliance, 1988; adj. prof. in pub. relations mgmt. So. Meth. U., 1987-88. mem. adv. bd. Pub. Rels. sequence studies. Group leader comm. task force Dallas Police Dept.; assoc. mem. Dallas Assembly; bd. dirs. Dallas Arboretum, Vis. Nurses Assn., Family Place; mem. adv. bd. Crystal Charity Ball; co-chmn. Dallas Mayor's Task Force on Mktg.; mem. exec. com., bd. dirs. Ctrl. Downtown Assn., Dallas, 1993-94. With U.S. Army, 1956-58. Mem. Pub. Rels. Soc. Am. (accredited, North Tex. Sliver award), Soc. Profl. Journalists. Home: 4545 Mill Run Rd Dallas TX 75244-6432 Office: Plz Am S Tower 600 N Pearl St Ste 910 Dallas TX 75201

LEVENSTEIN, ALAN PETER, advertising executive; b. N.Y.C., May 25, 1936; s. Jules David and Mollie Jarvis Levenstein; m. Gail Susan Berman, Sept. 15, 1963; children: Miranda, Jessica, Antony. AB magna cum laude, Amherst Coll., 1956. Copywriter J. Walter Thompson Co., N.Y.C., 1959-60, The Marschalk Co., N.Y.C., 1961-62; with Kenyon & Eckhardt Advt. Inc., N.Y.C., 1964-79, v.p., 1967-79; freelance journalist and advt. cons. N.Y.C., 1979-85; with Bozell, Jacobs, Kenyon & Eckhardt (now Bozell Worldwide), N.Y.C., 1985—; vice chmn. Bozell Worldwide, 1991—. Bd. dirs. Planned Parenthood, N.Y.C., 1988—; mem. coun. Nat. Acad. Design, 1993—. Mem. Phi Beta Kappa, Century Assn. Club (N.Y.). Democrat. Jewish. Office: Bozell Worldwide Inc 40 W 23 St New York NY 10010

LEVENTHAL, BENNETT LEE, psychiatry and pediatrics educator, administrator; b. Chgo., July 6, 1949; s. Howard Leonard and Florence Ruth (Albert) L.; m. Celia G. Goodman, June 11, 1972; children: Matthew G., Andrew G., Julia G. Student, Emory U., 1967-68, La. State U., 1968-70; BS, La. State U., 1972, postgrad., 1970-74, MD, 1974. Diplomate Am. Bd. Psychiatry and Neurology in Psychiatry, Am. Bd. Psychiatry and Neurology, Child Psychiatry; lic. physician N.C., La., Ill., Va. Undergrad. rsch. assoc. Lab. Prof. William A. Pryor dept. chemistry, La. State U., 1968-70; house officer I Charity Hosp. at New Orleans, 1974; resident in psychiatry Duke U. Med. Ctr., Durham, N.C., 1974-78, chief fellow divsn. dept. psychiatry, 1976-77, chief resident dept. psychiatry, 1977-78, clin. assoc. dept. psychiatry, 1978-80; staff psychiatrist, head psychiatry dept. Joel T. Boone Clinic, Virginia Beach, Va., 1978-80; staff psychiatrist, supr. mem. dept. psychiatry Naval Regional Med. Ctr., Portsmouth, Va., 1978-80; asst. prof. psychiatry and pediats. U. Chgo., 1978-85, dir. Child Psychiatry Clinic, 1978-85, dir. Child and Adolescent Psychiatry Fellowship tng. program, 1979-88; psychiat. cons. Caledonia State Prison/Halifax Mental Health Ctr., Tillery, N.C., 1976-77, Fed. Correctional Inst., Butner, N.C., 1977-78; cons. Norfolk Cmty. Mental Health Ctr., 1978-80; adj. prof. psychology, biopsychology, and devel. psychology U. Chgo., 1990, adj. assoc. prof. dept. psychology and com. on biopsychology U. Chgo., 1987-90; med. dir. Child Life and Family Edn. program Wyler Children's Hosp. of U. Chgo., 1983—; dir. child and adolescent programs Chgo. Lakeshore Hosp., 1986—; Pfizer vis. prof. dept. psychiatry U. P.R., 1992; vis. prof. U. Ill. Sch. Medicine, 1984; examiner Am. Bd. Psychiatry and Neurology in Gen. Pscyhiatry and Child Psychiatry, 1982—; mem. Instnl. Rev. Bd., U. Chgo. 1983-87; mem. steering com. Harris Ctr. for Student Rsch. Studies, U. Chgo., 1983—; mem. com. on evaluation of GAPS project AMA, 1993—; treas. Chgo. Consortium for Psychiat. Rsch., 1994; pres. Ill. Coun. Child and Adolescent Psychiatry, 1992-94; mem. instnl. rev. bd. Ill. State Psychiat. Inst., 1992-94; mem. Gov.'s Panel on

Mental Health Svcs., 1993-94; presenter in field. Mem. editl. bd. Univ. Chgo. Better Health Letter, 1994—; cons. editor: Jour. Emotional and Behavioral Disorders, 1992-96; reviewer: Archives of Gen. Psychiatry, 1983—, Biol. Psychiatry, 1983—, Am. Jour. Psychiatry, 1983—, Jour. AMA, 1983—, Jour. Am. Acad. Child and Adolescent Psychiatry, 1983—, Sci., 1983—; book rev. editor Jour. Neuropsychiatry and Clin. Neuroscis., 1989-92, mem. editl. bd., 1989-92; contbr. articles to profl. jours. Lt. comdr. M.C., USNR, 1978-80. Recipient Crystal Plate award Little Friends, 1994, Individual Achievement award Autism Soc. Am., 1991, Merit award Duke U. Psychiat. Resident's Assn., 1976, Bick award La. Psychiat. Assn., 1974; Andrew W. Mellon Found. faculty fellow U. Chgo., 1983-84; John Dewey lectr. U. Chgo., 1982. Fellow Am. Acad. Child and Adolescent Psychiatry (Outstanding Mentor 1988, dep. chmn. program com. 1979—, chmn. arrangements com. 1979—, new rsch. subcom. for ann. meeting 1986—, mem. work group on rsch. 1989—), Am. Psychiat. Assn. (Falk fellow, mem. Ittleson Award Bd. 1994-97, mem. Am. Psychiat. Assn./Wisniewski Young Psychiatrists Rsch. Award Panel 1994—), Am. Acad. Pediats., Am. Orthopsychiat. Assn.; mem. AAAS, Am. Coll. Psychiatrists, Brain Rsch. Inst., Ill. Coun. Child and Adolescent Psychiatry, Ill. Psychiat. Soc., Soc. for Rsch. in Child Devel., Soc. of Profs. of Child and Adolescent Psychiatry, Soc. Biol. Psychiatry, Nat. Bd. Med. Examiners, Mental Health Assn. Ill. (profl. adv. bd. 1991—), Sigma Xi. Office: U of Chgo Pritzker Sch of Medicine 5841 S Maryland Ave Chicago IL 60637

LEVENTHAL, CARL M., neurologist, government official; b. N.Y.C., July 28, 1933; s. Isidor and Anna (Semmel) L.; m. Brigid Penelope Gray, Feb. 4, 1962 (wid. Feb. 1994); children: George Leon, Sarah Elizabeth Roark, Dinah Susan, James Gray. A.B. cum laude, Harvard U., 1954; M.D., U. Rochester (N.Y.), 1959. Diplomate: Am. Bd. Psychiatry and Neurology. Fellow in anatomy U. Rochester, 1956-57; intern, then asst. resident in medicine Johns Hopkins Hosp., 1959-61; asst. resident, then resident in neurology Mass. Gen. Hosp., Boston, 1961-64; commd. officer USPHS, 1963—, asst. surgeon gen., 1979-83; asso. neuropathologist Nat. Inst. Neurol. Diseases and Blindness, 1964-66; neurologist Nat. Cancer Inst., 1966-68; asst. to dep. dir. sci., 1968-73; acting dep. dir. sci. NIH, 1973-74; dep. dir. bur. drugs FDA, Rockville, Md., 1974-77; dep. dir. Nat. Inst. Arthritis, Diabetes and Digestive and Kidney Diseases, 1977-81; div. dir. Nat. Inst. Neurol. Disorders and Stroke, 1981—; sr. policy analyst for life scis. Office of Sci. and Tech. Policy, Exec. Office of Pres., 1983; asst. clin. prof. neurology Georgetown U. Med. Sch., 1966-76. Recipient Commendation medal USPHS, 1970, Meritorious Svc. medal, 1974, 77, 91, Outstanding Svc. medal, 1988, dir's. award NIH, 1992. Fellow Am. Acad. Neurology; mem. Am. Assn. Neuropathologists, Am. Neurol. Assn., Soc. for Exptl. Neuropathology (councillor), Alpha Omega Alpha. Home: 9254 Old Annapolis Rd Columbia MD 21045-1832 Office: Nat Inst Neur Disorders & Stroke Fed Building Rm 810 Bethesda MD 20892-9150

LEVENTHAL, KATHY NEISLOSS, magazine publisher. Pub. Vanity Fair, N.Y.C. Office: Vanity Fair 350 Madison Ave New York NY 10017-3704

LEVENTHAL, NATHAN, performing arts executive, lawyer; b. N.Y.C., Feb. 19, 1943; s. Harry and Fay (Bronstein) L.; m. Gretchen Dykstra, Feb. 12, 1993. B.A. in Pub. Affairs, Queens Coll., 1963; J.D. cum laude, Columbia U., 1966. Bar: N.Y. 1967. Commr. Rent and Housing Maintenance, N.Y.C., 1972-73; chief counsel U.S. Senate Subcom. Administrv. Practice and Procedure, Washington, 1973-74; assoc. and ptnr. Poletti, Freidin, Prashker, Feldman & Gartner, N.Y.C., 1974-78; commr. Housing Preservation and Devel., N.Y.C., 1978-79; dep. mayor ops. City of N.Y., 1979-84; pres. Lincoln Ctr. for Performing Arts, N.Y.C., 1984—; lectr. govt. housing policy New Sch. Social Research, N.Y.C., 1979; lectr. health care and pub. policy Columbia Law Sch., N.Y.C., 1971. Editor-in-chief: Columbia Law Rev., 1965-66. Bd. visitors City Univ. Law Sch., N.Y.C., 1983—; Columbia Law Sch., 1989—, The New Sch., N.Y.C., 1992—; chmn. Citizens Union, 1994—; active Council on Jud. Adminstrn., Bar Assn. N.Y. City, 1983-90; dir. Nat. Youth Service Corp. for N.Y.C., 1983-85; commr. N.Y.C. Charter Revision Commn., 1986-89, N.Y. State Commn. on Constl. Revision, 1993—; dir. Queen's Coll. Found., 1988—; chair David M. Dinkins Mayoral Transition Com., 1989-90. Harlan Fiske Stone scholar Columbia Law Sch., 1963-65, Jerome Michael scholar, 1965-66; Disting. Service award Citizens Housing and Planning Council, N.Y.C., 1984, Am. Soc. Pub. Adminstrn. outstanding pub. adminstr. award 1982, Columbia Univ. Medal for Excellence, 1985.

LEVENTHAL, ROBERT STANLEY, academic administrator; b. Cambridge, Mass., Jan. 8, 1927; s. Harold A. and Matilda (Goldwyn) L.; children by previous marriage: Jeffrey Nelson, Daniel Philip; m. Jean B. Viereck, Feb. 14, 1994. A.B., Harvard U., 1948, M.B.A., 1956. Commd. ensign USN, 1948, advanced through grades to comdr., 1964; supply officer Naval Support Activity, Da Nang, Vietnam, 1965-66; with Office of Sec. of Def., Washington, 1966-68; ret., 1968; exec. asst. to chmn., dir. supply and distbn. Amerada Hess Corp., Woodbridge, N.J., 1968-71; exec. v.p. Engelhard Industries, Murray Hill, N.J.; sr. v.p. Engelhard Minerals and Chems. Corp., N.Y.C., 1971-75, Beker Industries Corp., Greenwich, Conn., 1975-77; pres., chief exec. officer Publicker Industries Inc., Phila., 1977-81; also. dir. Publicker Industries Inc.; pres. Tele-Total, Inc., 1981-83; pres., chief exec. officer Communications Products Corp., 1983-84; chmn., pres. Western Union Corp., Upper Saddle River, N.J., 1984-87, chief exec. officer, 1984-88, pres. 1987-88; cons. Western Union Corp., Upper Saddle River, 1988-89; dean Sch. Bus. Adminstrv. U. Wash., Seattle, 1989-94. Decorated Legion of Merit with gold star.

LEVER, ALVIN, health science association administrator; b. St. Louis, Jan. 27, 1939; s. Jack I. and Sabina (Vogel) L.; m. Norine Sue Schwedt, Jan. 27, 1963; children: Daniel Jay, Michael Aaron. BS in Archtl. Scis., Washington U., St. Louis, 1961, B in Architecture, 1963; MA in Applied Psychology, U. Santa Monica, 1992. Registered architect, Mo., Ill. Project designer Sir Basil Spence, Architects, Edinburgh, Scotland, 1963-65; sr. project designer Hellmuth, Obata & Kassabaum, St. Louis, 1965-68, v.p., project mgr., 1968-72; v.p. facility devel. Michael Reese Med. Ctr., Chgo., 1972-74; v.p., gen. mgr. Apelco Internat., Ltd., Northbrook, Ill., 1974-90; dir. membership Am. Coll. Chest Physicians, Northbrook, 1990-92, exec. dir., 1992—. Mem. Am. Soc. Med. Soc. Execs., Am. Soc. Assn. Execs., Chgo. Soc. Assn. Execs., Congregation B'nai Tikvah (v.p. 1987-91, pres. 1993—). Avocations: scuba diving, bicycling. Office: Am College of Chest Physicians 3300 Dundee Rd Northbrook IL 60062-2348

LEVERE, RICHARD DAVID, physician, academic administrator, educator; b. Bklyn., Dec. 13, 1931; s. Samuel and Mae (Fain) L.; m. Diane L. Gonchar, Jan. 15, 1956; children: Elyssa C., Corinne G., Scott M. Student, NYU, 1949-52; MD, SUNY, N.Y.C. 1956. Intern Bellevue Hosp., N.Y.C., 1956-57, resident, 1957-58; resident Kings County Hosp., 1960-61; instr. prof. medicine SUNY Downstate Med. Center, 1965-69, assoc. prof., 1969-73, prof., 1973-77, vice-chmn. dept. medicine, 1975-77, chief hematology/oncology div., 1970-77; asst. prof. Rockefeller U., 1964-65; prof., chmn. dept. medicine N.Y. Med. Coll., 1977-93, vice dean, 1991-93; med. dir. Westchester County Med. Ctr., 1991-92, v.p. med affairs St Agnes Hosp., 1991-93; sr. v.p. The Bklyn. Hosp. Ctr., 1994—; assoc. dean, prof. medicine NYU Sch. Medicine, 1994—; adj. prof. Rockefeller U., 1973—. Contbr. in field. Bd. dirs.Leukemia Soc. Am., 1970-85, Am. Heart Assn., 1978 94, trustee Our Lady of Mercy Med. Ctr., 1993. NIH grantee, 1971-76, 65-86. Fellow ACP (Physician Recognition award 1986, gov.-elect N.Y. State, Downstate I 1989, gov. 1990-94, pres. N.Y. State chpt. 1992-93); mem. Harvey Soc., Am. Soc. Clin. Investigation, Soc. Study of Blood (pres. 1973-74), Soc. Devel. Biology, Am. Soc. Pharm. Exptl. Therapeutics (William Dock Tchg. award, Tinsley Harrison Rsch. award), Den Tiroler Adler-Orden of Austria, Alpha Omega Alpha. Home: 5 Seymour Pl W Armonk NY 10504-2516 Office: Bklyn Hosp Ctr 121 Dekalb Ave Brooklyn NY 11201-5493

LEVERETT, MILES CORRINGTON, retired nuclear power consultant; b. Danville, Ill., Dec. 18, 1910; s. Warren Hamilton and Mary Joanna (Carrington) L.; m. Nancy Walker, Oct. 18, 1938. B.S., Kans. State U., 1931; M.S.E., U. Okla., 1932; D.Sc., MIT, 1958. Registered nuclear engr., Calif. Asst. chemist Marathon Paper Mills, Menasha, Wis., 1932-33; asst. chemist Phillips Petroleum Co., Bartlesville, Okla., 1933-35; with Humble Oil and Refining Co., Houston, 1938-42, 48-49; tech. dir. Manhattan Project, Oak Ridge, 1942-48, Fairchild Engring. & Airplane Co., Oak Ridge, 1949-51;

sect. mgr. Gen. Electric Co., various locations, 1951-76; cons. nuclear power Monte Sereno, Calif., 1976-94; ret., 1994. Patentee in field of petroleum, nuclear power. Fellow Am. Nuclear Soc. (pres. 1960-61); mem. Am. Inst. Chem. Engrs. (Robert E. Wilson award 1976), Nat. Acad. Engring. Republican. Methodist. Avocations: golf; gardening; travel. Home: 800 Blossom Hill Rd Apt 240 Los Gatos CA 95032-3500

LEVERT, FRANCIS EDWARD, nuclear engineer; b. Tusculoosa, Ala., Mar. 28, 1940; s. John Clemins and Bessie Leona (Williams) LeV.; m. Faye Burnett, June 5, 1965; children: Francis Edward, Gerald Clemins, Lisa Ann. BSME, Tuskegee Inst., 1964; MS in Nuclear Engring., U. Mich., 1966; PhD in Nuclear Engring., Pa. State U., 1971. Registered profl. engr, Tenn. Assoc. prof., head mech. engring. dept. Tuskegee (Ala.) Inst., 1972-73; nuclear engr. Commonwealth Edison, Chgo., 1973-74, Argonne (Ill.) Nat. Lab., 1974-79; sr. scientist Tech. for Energy Corp., Knoxville, Tenn., 1979-85; v.p. K.E.M.P. Corp., Knoxville 1985—. Author: (book) Literature Review and Commercial Source Evaluation of AM.-261 (AEC-ORO-4333), 1973, (book) A Guide to Patent Applications, (Van Nostrand Reinhold 1993); contbr. over 60 articles to tech. pubs. AEC fellow, 1964-66, Def. Nat. Edn. Act fellow, 1968-70, Am. Soc. Engring. Edn. Ford Found. fellow, 1973-74. Mem. Am. Soc. Mech. Engrs. (exec. com. Plant Main div. 1989—). Achievements include 12 patents for Heat Flux Monitor, Slag Depositor Monitor, Level Gages, Solid State Neutron Sensor, Directional Sensitive Self-power Gamma Detectors. Home: 1909 Matthew Ln Knoxville TN 37923-1340 Office: KEMP Corp Knoxville TN 37917

LEVERT, JOHN BERTELS, JR., investment executive; b. Birmingham, Ala., Apr. 16, 1931; s. John Bertels Sr. and Jacqueline (Tutwiler) L.; m. Anne Barrington King, Dec. 27, 1954; children: John Bertels III, Anne Lee. BA, Tulane U., 1954. Salesperson Carl E. Woodward Constrn. Co., New Orleans, 1956-58; from salesperson to exec. v.p. Metal Bldg. Product Co., Inc., New Orleans, 1958-70; stockbroker Howard Weil LaBouisse Friedrichs, New Orleans, 1970-75, pres., chief exec. officer, 1975-86, chmn. chief exec. officer, 1986—. Pres. United Way of Greater New Orleans, 1979-80; chmn. Archbishops Community Appeal, New Orleans, 1984; chmn. bd. trustees Loyola U., New Orleans, 1986—; chmn. fin. svc. survey com. New Orleans New Bus. Initiative, 1989—. 1st lt. U.S. Army, 1954-56. Recipient Humanitarian award Arthritis Found., 1989. Mem. N.Y. Stock Exch. (allied, regional firms adv. com. 1983-86), So. Yacht (commodore 1987-89). Republican. Roman Catholic. Avocations: sailing, flying. Office: Howard Weil LaBouisse Friedrichs 1100 Poydras St Ste 900 New Orleans LA 70163-1109

LEVERTOV, DENISE, poet; b. Ilford, Essex, Eng., Oct. 24, 1923; came to U.S., 1948, naturalized, 1955; d. Paul Philip and Beatrice A. (Spooner-Jones) Levertoff m. Mitchell Goodman, Dec. 2, 1947 (div. 1975); 1 child, Nikolai. Ed. privately; Litt.D. (hon.), Colby Coll., 1970, U. Cin., 1973, St. Lawrence U., 1984, Bates Coll., 1984, Allegheny Coll., 1987, St. Michael's Coll., 1987, Mass. Coll. of Art, 1989, U. Santa Clara, 1993. Tchr. YMCA-YWCA Poetry Ctr., N.Y.C., 1964; vis. lectr. Drew U., Madison, N.J., 1965, CCNY, 1965, Vassar Coll., Poughkeepsie, N.Y., 1966-67, U. Calif., Berkeley, 1969; vis. prof. MIT, Cambridge, 1969-70; scholar Radcliffe Inst. Indst. Study, 1964-65, 66-67; artist-in-residence Kirkland Coll., Clinton, N.Y., 1970-71; Elliston lectr. U. Cin., spring 1973; prof. Tufts U., Medford, Mass., 1973-79, Stanford U., Calif., 1981—; poet-in-residence Brandeis U., Waltham, Mass., 1981-94; A.D. White Prof. at Large Cornell U., Ithaca, N.Y., 1993—. Author: The Double Image, 1946, Here and Now, 1957, Overland to the Islands, 1958, Five Poems, 1958, With Eyes at the Back of Our Heads, 1959, The Jacob's Ladder, 1961, O Taste and See, 1964, City Psalm, 1964, Psalm Concerning the Castle, 1966, The Sorrow Dance, 1967, A Tree Telling of Orpheus, 1968, A Marigold from North Vietnam, 1968, Three Poems, 1968, In the Night: A Story, 1968, The Cold Spring and Other Poems, 1969, Embroideries, 1969, Relearning the Alphabet, 1970, Summer Poems, 1969, A New Year's Garland for My Students, 1970, To Stay Alive, 1971, Footprints, 1972, The Poet in the World, 1974, The Freeing of the Dust, 1975, Chekov on the West Heath, 1977, Modulations for Solo Voice, 1977, Life in the Forest, 1978, Collected Earlier Poems 1940-60, 1979, Pig Dreams: Scenes from the Life of Sylvia, 1981, Wanderer's Daysong, 1981, Light Up the Cave, 1981, Candles in Babylon, 1982, Poems 1960-1967, 1983, Oblique Prayers, 1984, El Salvador: Requiem and Invocation, 1984, The Menaced World, 1984, Selected Poems, 1986, Poems 1968-1972, 1987, Breathing the Water, 1987, A Door in the Hive, 1989, Evening Train, 1992, New and Selected Essays, 1992, Tesserae, 1995; translator: Selected Poems of Guillevic, 1969, Poets of Bulgaria, 1985, Black Iris: Selected Poems of Jean Joubert, 1988; translator, editor: (with Edward C. Dimock, Jr.) In Praise of Krishna: Songs from the Bengali, 1967; editor: Out of the War Shadow: An Anthology of Current Poetry, 1967, (with Kenneth Rexroth and William Carlos Williams) Penguin Modern Poets 9, 1967. Recipient Bess Hokin prize Poetry mag. 1959, Longview award 1961, Harriet Monroe Meml. prize 1964, Inez Boulton prize Poetry mag. 1964, Morton Dauwen Zabel Meml. prize Poetry mag., 1965, Lenore Marshall Poetry prize 1976, Elmer Holmes Bobst award in poetry 1983, Shelley Meml. award Poetry Soc. of Am., 1984, Robert Frost medal, 1990, Lannan award, 1993; Am. Acad. and Inst. of Arts and Letters grantee, 1965; Guggenheim fellow, 1962; NEA Sr. Fellowship, 1990. Mem. Am. Inst. Arts and Letters, Academie Mallarmé (corr.). Office: care New Directions 80 8th Ave New York NY 10011-5126*

LEVESON, IRVING FREDERICK, economist; b. N.Y.C., June 28, 1939; s. Hyman Wolf and Minnie L.; m. Barbara Diane Wurtzelman, Jan. 28, 1961; children: Stephen Martin, Scott Owen. BA (N.Y. State Regents scholar), CCNY, 1960, MBA, 1963; PhD, Columbia U., 1968. Rsch. analyst, rsch. asst. Nat. Bur. Econ. Rsch., 1963-67; rsch. economist N.Y.C. Health Svcs. Adminstrn., 1967-68; economist RAND Corp., 1968-69; dir. rsch. Office Comprehensive Planning, N.Y.C., Planning Commn., 1969-71; asst. adminstr. health systems planning N.Y.C. Health Services Adminstrn., 1971-74; sr. profl. staff, dir. econ. studies Hudson Inst., Croton-on-Hudson, N.Y., 1974-84; sr. v.p., dir. rsch. Hudson Strategy Group, N.Y.C., 1984-90; pres. Leveson Cons., Marlboro, N.J., 1990—; mem. Gov. N.Y. Health Adv. Council, 1975-78; mem. health svcs. rsch. and devel. grants rev. com. Nat. Ctr. Health Svcs. Rsch., 1979-82; lectr., cons. in field. Author: The Future of the Financial Services Industry, 1982, American Challenges: Business and Government in the World of the 1990s, 1991; editor: Quantitative Explorations in Drug Abuse Policy, 1980; co-editor: Analysis of Urban Health Problems, 1976, Western Economies in Transition, 1980. Trustee Monmouth Heights Civic Assn., 1971-77. Mem. Bronx County Com. (1961); mem. Am. Econ. Assn., Nat. Assn. Bus. Economists, Met. Econ. Assn., Assn. Social Scis. in Health (exec. council 1973-82). Jewish. Home and Office: 23 Prescott Dr Marlboro NJ 07746-1351

LEVESQUE, LOUIS, bishop; b. Amqui, Que., Can., May 27, 1908; s. Philippe and Catherine (Beaulieu) L. B.A., Laval U., 1928, Ph.L., 1930, Th.D., 1932; S.S.L., Bib. Inst., Rome and Jerusalem, 1935. Ordained priest Roman Cath. Ch., 1932; tchr. holy scripture Rimouski, Que., 1936-51; bishop of Hearst, Ont., 1952-64; archbishop of Rimouski, 1964-73, retired archbishop, 1973—; Chmn. Canadian Cath. Conf., 1965-67; mem. Congregation Bishops, Rome, 1968-73. Mem. Cath. Bibl. Assn. Am. Home: 300 Ave du Rosaire, Rimouski, PQ Canada G5L 3E3

LEVESQUE, RENE JULES ALBERT, retired physicist; b. St. Alexis, Que., Can., Oct. 30, 1926; s. Albert and Elmina Louisa (Veuilleux) L.; m. Alice Farnsworth, Apr. 6, 1956 (div.); children: Marc, Michel, Andre; m. Michèle Robert, Feb., 1992. B.Sc., Sir George Williams U., 1952; Ph.D., Northwestern U., 1957. Research assoc. U. Md., 1957-59; asst. prof. U. Montreal, 1959-64, assoc. prof., 1964-67, 1967-87, dir. nuclear physics lab., 1965-69, chmn. dept. physics, 1968-73, vice dean arts and scis., 1973-75, dean, 1975-78, v.p. research, 1978-85, v.p. research and planning, 1985-87, prof. emeritus, 1987; mem. Atomic Energy Control Bd., Ottawa, Can., 1985-87, pres., 1987-93; ret., 1993; mem. adv. comi. ING project Atomic Energy of Can. Ltd., 1966-69; mem. adv. bd. physics NRC Can., 1972-74, pres. nuclear physics grant selection, 1973; mem. adv. bd. on TRIUMF, 1977-89; v.p. Commn. Higher Studies Que. Ministry Edn., 1976-77, Natural Scis. and Engring. Research Council Can., 1987-87; v.p. bd. dirs. Can.-France-Hawaii Telescope Corp., 1979-80, pres., 1980-81; pres. permanent research com. Conf. Rectors and Prins. Que. Univs., 1979-80; pres. Mouvement Laïc de Langue française, 1961. Mem. Can. Assn. Physicists (pres. 1976-77), U. Montreal Faculty Assn. (pres. 1971), Fedn. Que. Faculty Assn. (pres. 1971-

72), Interciencia Assn. (v.p. bd. dirs. 1979-80), Assn. Sci., Engring. and Technol. Community Can. (v.p. 1979-80, pres. 1980-81). Home: 190 Willowdale PH 1, Outremont, PQ Canada H3T 1G2

LEVESQUE, ROGER RAYMOND, trading company executive; b. Fall River, Mass., Oct. 27, 1955; s. Raymond David and Cecile Teresa (Lapointe) L. BA, Carleton Coll., 1977. V.p.r GE Trading Co., N.Y.C. Mem. Phi Beta Kappa. Office: GE Trading Co 570 Lexington Ave # 18 New York NY 10022-6824

LEVETOWN, ROBERT ALEXANDER, lawyer; b. Bklyn., July 20, 1935; s. Alfred A. and Corinne L. (Cohen) L.; m. Roberta S. Slobodkin, Oct. 18, 1959. Student, U. Munich, Fed. Republic Germany, 1954-55; AB, Princeton U., 1956; LLB, Harvard U., 1959. Bar: D.C. 1960, N.Y. 1982, Va. 1984, Pa. 1985. Assoc. Pierson, Ball & Dowd, Washington, 1960-62; asst. U.S. atty. Washington, 1962-63; atty. Chesapeake & Potomac Telephone Cos., Washington, 1963-66, gen. atty., 1966-68, gen. solicitor, 1968-73, v.p., gen. counsel, 1975-83; exec. v.p., gen. counsel Bell Atlantic, 1983-91, vice chmn., 1991-92, also bd. dirs., 1989-92; bd. dirs. Telecom NZ. Mem. ABA (vice chmn. comm. com., pub. utility law sect. 1986-93), Washington Met. Corp. Counsels' Assn. (bd. dirs. 1981-83), Nat. Legal Ctr. (legal adv. coun. 1986-92). Republican. Jewish.

LEVEY, BARRY, state senator; b. Cin., Aug. 7, 1930. Student, U. Mich., Northwestern U. Coll. Law; JD, Ohio State U. Coll. Law, 1954; LLD (hon.), Miami U., Oxford, Ohio, 1988. Bar: Ohio, U.S. Supreme Ct. Pvt. practice Middletown, Ohio, 39 yrs.; sr. ptnr. Frost and Jacobs, Cin.; mem. Ohio State Senate from 4th dist., 1987—, chmn. jud. com., fin. instns. and ins. com., mem. ways and means com., legis. ethics com., others; pres., chief exec. officer Manchester Inn, Middletown; bd. dirs. 1st Fin. Bancorp; consul from Grand Duchy of Luxembourg to U.S. for So. Ohio, Ky., W.Va. Past v.p. Mound Builders Area Coun. Boy Scouts Am.; past bd. dirs. Butler County Children's Home; mem. adv. com. Partnership Middletown, Leadership Middletown; fin. chmn. Arts in Middletown, 1986; mem. pres.'s club Miami U., Ohio State U.; mem. Ohio Ho. of Reps., 1962-70; mem. Butler County Rep. Cen. and Exec. Com.; Rep. candidate for atty. gen. Ohio, 1986; trustee Miami U., 1977—, sec. bd. trustees, 1979, chmn., 1980; bd. dirs Middletown Community Found. With JAGC, U.S. Army, 1954-56. Recipient Pub. Svc. recognition Am. Legion, Middletown Jr. C. of C., Citizen Recognition award Miami U., Middletown. Mem. ABA, Ohio State Bar Assn., Butler County Bar Assn., Cin. Bar Assn., Middletown Bar Assn. (past pres.), Middletown Area C. of C. (mem. presdl. task force on pvt. enterprise, dir., com. chmn., Blue Ribbon award 1990). Office: Ohio State Senate Statehouse Columbus OH 43215 Address: 6560 Bunker Ln Middletown OH 45042-9218

LEVEY, ROBERT FRANK, newspaper columnist; b. N.Y.C., June 2, 1945; s. Stanley Victor and Sylvia Rose (Frank) L.; m. Jane Ellen Freundel, May 17, 1980; children: Emily Susanna, Alexander Freundel. B.A., U. Chgo., 1966. Reporter Albuquerque Tribune, 1966-67; reporter, editor Washington Post, 1967-81, columnist, 1981—; vis lectr. Duke U., Durham, N.C., 1979—; adviser journalism Cath. U. Am., Washington, 1979-81. Talk show host Sta. WRC-AM, 1981-83, Sta. WTTG-TV, Washington, 1982-87, Sta. WBAL, 1988-92, Sta. WMAL, 1993—; commentator Sta. WASH-FM, 1983-84, Sta. WJLA-TV, 1984-86, Sta. WETA-FM, 1985-90. Woodrow Wilson fellow. Mem. Reporters Com. for Freedom of the Press, Newspaper Guild (chmn. Washington Post unit 1972-75), AFTRA, U. Chgo. Alumni Assn. (bd. govs 1992—), Sigma Delta Chi. Jewish. Office: Washington Post 1150 15th St NW Washington DC 20071-0002

LEVEY, SAMUEL, health care administration educator; b. Cape Town, South Africa, July 11, 1932; came to U.S., 1949, naturalized, 1954; s. Harry and Esther (Turecka) L.; m. Linda Anne Madison, Dec. 26, 1965; children: Eric B., Andrea E., Sara B. A.B., Bowdoin Coll., 1955; A.M., Columbia U., 1956; M.A., U. Iowa, 1959, Ph.D., 1961; M.S., Harvard U., 1963. Adminstrv. assoc. U. Iowa hosps. and Clinics, Iowa City, 1958-60; instr. U. Iowa, 1960-61, asst. prof., 1961-62; dir. div. Mass. Dept. Public Health, Boston, 1963-67; asst. dir. med. care planning Harvard Med. Sch., Boston, 1967-68; lectr. health service adminstrn. Harvard Sch. Public Health, 1967-69; asst. commr. Mass. Dept. Public Welfare, Boston, 1968-69; chmn. grad. program in health care adminstrn. CUNY, 1969-77; prof., adminstr. medicine Mt. Sinai Sch. Medicine, N.Y.C., 1973-77; G. Hartman prof. and head of grad. program in hosp. and health adminstrn. Ctr. for Health Services Research Coll. Medicine U. Iowa, Iowa City, 1977-91; G. Hartman prof. Coll. Medicine and Grad. Coll., U. Iowa, 1991—; hosp. and health cons. Author: (with N.P. Loomba) Health Care Administration: A Managerial Perspective, 1973, 2d edit., 1984, Health Care Administration: A Selected Bibliography, 1973, (with H. Rosen and J. Metsch) The Consumer and the Health Care System, 1977, (with N.P. Loomba) Long Term Care Administration, vols. 1, 11, 1977, (with T. McCarthy) Health Management for Tomorrow, 1980, Hospital Leadership and Accountability, 1992; sr. editor: Spectrum series on Heath Systems Management, 1974-86; editor: Hosp. and Health Services Adminstrn., 1987-92. Named Otho Ball fellow Am. Coll. Hosp. Adminstrs., 1958-59; Faculty fellow Found. Econ. Edn., 1962; HHS trainee, 1962-63. Mem. Assn. Univ. Programs in Health Adminstrn. (dir. 1979-80, chmn. bd. 1980-81), Am. Pub. Health Assn., Internat. Hosp. Fedn., Am. Coll. Healthcare Execs., Am. Hosp. Assn. Home: 336 Macbride Dr Iowa City IA 52246-1716 Office: U Iowa Steindler Bldg Iowa City IA 52242

LEVI, ARLO DANE, lawyer; b. Zeeland, N.D., May 4, 1933; s. Emmanuel and Christine L.; m. Constance Marie Irvin, Aug. 20, 1961; children: Todd, Julie. B.S. in Engring., S.D. State U., 1963; J.D., U. Mich., 1966. Bar: Minn. 1966. With 3M Co., St. Paul, 1966—; asso. counsel, then asso. gen. counsel 3M Co., 1975-81, corp. sec., 1976-85, v.p., sec., 1985—. Served with USAF, 1953-60. Mem. Minn. Bar Assn., Am. Soc. Corp. Secs. (bd. dirs. 1991-94, exec. steering com. 1993-94, pres. Twin Cities chpt. 1980-81). Republican. Office: 3M Center Saint Paul MN 55144-1000

LEVI, BARBARA GOSS, physicist, editor; b. Washington, May 5, 1943; d. Wilbur H. and Mildred C. (Wallin) Goss; m. Ilan M. Levi, Sept. 10, 1966; children: Daniel S., Sharon R. BA, Carleton Coll., 1965; MS, Stanford U., 1967, PhD, 1971. Assoc. editor Physics Today Am. Inst. Physics, N.Y.C., 1969-70, cons. editor Physics Today, 1970-89, assoc. editor Physics Today, 1987-88; sr. assoc. editor Physics Today, N.Y.C., 1989-93, sr. editor, 1993—; mem. tech. staff Bell Labs, Holmdel, N.J., 1982-83; mem. rsch. staff Ctr. for Energy and Environ. Studies Princeton U., 1981-82, 83-87; lectr. Ga. Tech., Atlanta, 1976-80, Fairleigh Dickinson U., Madison, N.J., 1970-75; vis. prof. Rutgers U., Piscataway, N.J., 1988-89; cons. U.S. Office Tech. Assessment, Washington, 1976-93. Editor: (with others) Energy Sources: Conservation and Renewables, 1985, The Future of Land-Based Strategic Missiles, 1989, Global Warming: Physics and Facts, 1992. Treas. LWV, Holmdel and Colts Neck, N.J., 1983-84. Fellow AAAS, Am. Phys.Soc. (edn. com. 1989-91, chmn. forum on physics and soc. 1988-89, forum councilor, 1992-95, mem. exec. bd. 1994-95); mem. AAUW (nuclear energy task force 1975-77), Fedn. Am. Scientists (gov. bd. 1985-89), Am. Assn. Physics Tchrs. Avocations: tennis, traveling, hiking, skiing.

LEVI, DAVID F., federal judge; b. 1951. BA, Harvard U., MA, 1973; JD, Stanford U. Bar: Calif. 1983. U.S. atty. ea. dist. State of Calif., Sacramento, 1986-90; judge U.S. Dist. Ct. (ea. dist.) Calif., 1990—; pres. Milton L. Schwartz Am. Inn. of Ct. Am. Law Inst; chair 9th Cir. task force on race, religion, and ethnic fairness; adv. com. civil rules. Adv. com. on Civil Rules, 1994-95; chair 9th cir. task force on Race, Religious and Ethnic Fairness, 1994-95. Office: 2504 Fed Bldg 650 Capitol Mall Sacramento CA 95814-4708

LEVI, EDWARD HIRSCH, former attorney general, university president emeritus; b. Chgo., June 26, 1911; s. Gerson B. and Elsa B. (Hirsch) L.; m. Kate Sulzberger, June 4, 1946; children: John, David, Michael. PhB, U. Chgo., 1932, JD, 1935; JSD (Sterling fellow 1935-36), Yale U., 1938; LLD, U. Mich., 1959, U. Calif. at Santa Cruz, 1968, Jewish Theol. Sem. Am., 1968, U. Iowa, 1968, Brandeis U., 1968, Lake Forest Coll., 1968, Dropsie U., 1968, Columbia U., 1968, Yeshiva U., 1968, U. Rochester, 1969, U. Toronto, 1971, Yale U., 1973, U. Notre Dame, 1974, Denison U., 1974, U. Pa., 1976, U. Nebr., U. Miami, Boston Coll., Brigham Young U., Duke U., Ripon Coll., Georgetown U., Benjamin N. Cardozo Sch. Law, Claremont Ctr. and

Grad. Sch., Ind. U.; LHD, Hebrew Union Coll., 1968, Loyola U., 1970, U. Chgo., Bard Coll., 1985, Beloit Coll., DePaul U., 1978; DCL, NYU. Bar: Ill. U.S. Supreme Ct. 1945. Asst. prof. U. Chgo. Law Sch., 1936-40, prof. law, 1945-75, dean, 1950-62; provost U. Chgo., 1962-68, univ. pres., 1968-75, pres. emeritus, 1975—; Karl Llewellyn Disting. Svc. prof. U. Chgo. Law Sch., 1975—, Glen A. Lloyd Disting. Svc. prof., 1975-77, Glen A. Lloyd Disting. Svc. prof. emeritus, 1985—; atty. gen. U.S., 1975-77; Thomas Guest prof. U. Colo., summer 1960; Herman Phleger vis. prof. Stanford Law Sch., 1978; lectr. Salzburg (Austria) Seminar in Am. Studies, 1980; spl. asst. to atty. gen. U.S., Washington, 1940-45; 1st asst. war div. Dept. Justice, 1943, 1st asst. antitrust div., 1944-45; chmn. interdeptl. com. on monopolies and cartels, 1944; counsel Fedn. Atomic Scientists with respect to Atomic Energy Act, 1946; counsel subcom. on monopoly power Judiciary Com., 81st Congress, 1950; trustee Aerospace Corp., 1978-80; Mem. rsch. adv. bd. Com. Econ. Devel., 1951-54; bd. Social Sci. Rsch. Coun., 1959-62, Coun. Legal Edn. and Profl. Responsibility, 1968-74; chmn. 1969-73; mem. Citizens Commn. Grad. Med. Edn., 1963-66, Commn. Founds. and Pvt. Philanthropy, 1969-70, Pres.'s Task Force Priorities in Higher Edn., 1970, Sloan Commn. Cable Comm., 1970, Nat. Commn. on Productivity, 1970-75, Nat. Council on Humanities, 1974-75, Nat. Coun. on Legal clinics, 1966-65; chmn. Coun. on Edn. in Profl. Responsibility, 1965-69. Author: Introduction to Legal Reasoning, 1949, Four Talks on Legal Education, 1952, Point of View, 1969; editor: (with J. W. Moore) Gilbert's Collier on Bankruptcy, 1936, Elements of the Law, (with R. S. Steffen), 1950. Hon. trustee U. Chgo.; trustee Internat. Legal Ctr., 1966-75, Woodrow Wilson Nat. Fellowship Found., 1972-75, 77-79, Inst. Psychoanalysis Chgo., 1961-75, Urban Inst., 1968-75, Mus. Sci. and Industry, 1971-75, Russell Sage Found., 1971-75, Aspen Inst. Humanistic Studies, 1970-75, 77-79, Inst. Internat. Edn. (hon.), 1969; public dir. Chgo. Bd. Trade, 1977-80; bd. overseers U Pa., 1978-82; chmn. bd. Nat. Humanities Ctr., 1979-83, life trustee, 1978—; bd. dirs. MacArthur Found., 1979-84, William Benton Found., 1980-92, Martin Luther King Jr. Fed. Holiday Commn., 1986; bd. of govts. U. Calif. Humanities Rsch. Inst., 1988-91; mem. bd. trustees Skadden Fellowship Found., 1988—. Decorated Legion of Honor (France); recipient Learned Hand medal Fed. Bar Coun. 2d cir., 1976, Fordham Stein prize Fordham U., 1977, Louis Dembitz Brandeis medal Brandeis U., 1979; named laureate of Lincoln Acad. of Ill., 1976. Fellow Am. Acad. Arts and Scis. (pres. 1986-89); mem. Am. Bar Found., Fed. Bar Assn. (Honor award 1975), Am. Philos. Soc. (v.p. 1991-94), ABA, Ill. Bar Assn. (award of honor 1983), Chgo. Bar Assn. (Centennial award 1975), Ill. Bar Found. (Disting. Svc. award 1990), Am. Law Inst. (coun.), Am. Judicature Soc., Supreme Ct. Hist. Soc., Constl. Rights Found. (Disting. Svc. award 1992), Chgo. Comml. Club, Quadrangle Club, Columbia Yacht Club, Order of Coif, Phi Beta Kappa. Office: U Chgo 1116 E 59th St Chicago IL 60637-1513

LEVI, HERBERT WALTER, biologist, educator; b. Frankfurt, Germany, Jan. 3, 1921; came to U.S., 1938, naturalized, 1945; s. Ludwig and Irma (Hochschild) L.; m. Lorna Rose, June 13, 1949; 1 child, Frances. Student, Art Students League, N.Y.C., 1938-39; BS, U. Conn., 1946; M.S., U. Wis., 1947, Ph.D., 1949; MA (hon.), Harvard U., 1970. Instr., then asst. prof. to asso. prof. zoology, extension div. U. Wis., 1949-56; asst. curator arachnology Mus. Comparative Zoology Harvard U., 1956-57, assoc. curator, 1957-66, curator, 1966-91, prof. biology, 1970-91, Agassiz prof. zoology, 1972-91, prof. emeritus, 1981—; sec. Rocky Mountain Biol. Lab., 1959-65; vis. prof. Hebrew U., Jerusalem, 1975; bd. govs. Nature Conservancy, 1956-62; taxonomic cons. Smithsonian projects, 1979; cons. Syntax, Cambridge, Mass., 1986. Author: (with L.R. Levi) Spiders and Their Kin, 1968, 69, Aranas y especies afines, 1971; also numerous articles; translator, editor: Invertebrate Zoology (Kaestner), 3 vols.; bd. reviewers Pacific Insects, 1980-85; bd. editors Psyche, 1957-92, Zoomorphology, 1980-85, Sci. Bull. de Mus., Paris, 1980—, (internat.) Anales Zoologici Warszawa Poland, 1993—, Memorias do Instituto Butantan, São Paulo, Brazil, 1994—. Fellow AAAS; mem. Am. Soc. Zoologists, Soc. Study Evolution, Soc. Systematic Zoology (councilor 1967-69), Am. Micros. Soc. (bd. reviewers 1973—), Am. Arachnol. Soc. (hon. mem., bd. editors 1974—, dir. 1975-83, pres. 1979-81), Am. Ecol. Soc., Am. Inst. Biological Scis., Wildlife Soc., Am. Ornithol. Union, Assn. Systematics Collections (council nat. systematic collections and resources 1975), British Arachnological Soc., Cambridge Entomology Club, Centre International de Documentation Arachnologique (v.p. 1965-68, pres. 1980-83), Japanese Arachnological Soc. (hon.), Soc. Systematic Biologists, Spider Club So. Africa (hon.), Wilson Ornithological Soc., Wilderness Soc. Home: 45 Wheeler Rd Pepperell MA 01463-1025 Office: Harvard U Mus Comparative Zoolog Cambridge MA 02138

LEVI, ILAN MOSCHE, computer and communications company executive; b. Haifa, Israel, July 17, 1943; came to U.S., 1956; s. Seligman P. and Ruth (Bril) L.; m. Barbara Goss, Sept. 10, 1966; children: Daniel Steven, Sharon Ruth. BSME, The Cooper Union, 1965; MS in Aeros. and Astronautics, Stanford U., 1966, PhD in Structural Mechanics, 1968. Research assoc. Dept. Aeros. and Astronautics, Stanford U., Calif., 1968-69; mem. tech. staff engring. mechanics and physics dept. Bell Labs., Whippany, N.J., 1969-71, supr., 1971-80, dept. head, 1980-85; dir. Bell Labs., Holmdel, N.J., 1985—; dir. bus. terminals devel. lab AT&T Labs., Holmdel, 1985-88; dir. customer systems devel. lab. AT&T Bell Labs., Middletown, N.J., 1988-94; terminal products tech. officer/dir. terminal products devel AT&T Global Bus. Communication Systems, 1994—; cons. Lawrence Radiation Lab., Livermore, Calif., 1968-69, N.J. Com. on Sci. and Industry, Trenton, 1985-86. Contbr. articles to profl. jours., chpts. to books. NSF fellow, 1965. Jewish. Avocations: tennis, backpacking, bicycling, photography. Home: 1616 La Vista del Oceano Santa Barbara CA 93109-1790 Office: AT&T Bell Labs 200 S Laurel Ave Middletown NJ 07748-4801

LEVI, ISAAC, philosophy educator; b. N.Y.C., June 30, 1930; s. Eliezer Asher and Eva (Lunenfeld) L.; m. Judith S. Rubins, Dec. 25, 1951; children: Jonathan Abram, David Isaer. B.A., NYU, 1951; student, Jewish Theol. Sem., 1947-52; M.A., Columbia, 1953, Ph.D., 1957; PhD honoris causa, Lund U., 1988. Part-time instr. Rutgers U., 1954-56; lectr. CCNY, 1956-57, asst. prof. philosophy, 1962-64; asst. prof. philosophy Western Res. U., 1957-62, assoc. prof., 1964-67, prof., 1967-70, chmn. dept., 1968-70; prof. philosophy Columbia U., 1970—, chmn. dept., 1973-76, 89-91; vis. scholar Corpus Christi Coll., Cambridge (Eng.) U., 1973, vis. fellow Darwin Coll., 1980; vis. rsch. fellow Australian Nat. U., 1987; vis. fellow All Souls Coll., Oxford (Eng.) U., 1988; vis. fellow Inst. Advanced Study, Hebrew U. Jerusalem, 1994. Author: Gambling with Truth, 1967, The Enterprise of Knowledge, 1980, Decisions and Revisions, 1984, Hard Choices, 1986, The Fixation of Belief and Its Undoing, 1991; also articles. Fulbright scholar, 1966-67; Guggenheim fellow, 1966-67; NEH fellow, 1979-80. Fellow Am. Acad. Arts and Scis.; mem. AAUP, Am. Philos.Assn., Philosophy of Sci. Assn., Brit. Soc. Philosophy of Sci., Phi Beta Kappa, Pi Mu Epsilon. Democrat. Home: 25 Claremont Ave New York NY 10027-6827

LEVI, JAMES HARRY, real estate executive, investment banker; b. Boston, Oct. 28, 1939; s. Robert Emmett and Doris (Cohen) L.; m. Constance Jo Adler, Dec. 30, 1967; children: James H. II, Andrew R., Deanne D., Constance Jo. AB, Harvard U., 1961, MBA, 1964. Past pres. Value Properties Inc., N.Y.C.; now pres. Levi Co., Larchmont, N.Y.; chmn. bd. dirs. New Millenium Energies, Inc., St. Louis; pres. Gt. Train Store Co., Dallas, others; prof. Bus. Sch. Columbia U., N.Y.C.; past pres. Oppenheimer Properties, Inc., N.Y.C.; exec. v.p., mem. exec. com. Oppenheimer & Co., Inc.; pres., chmn. bd. dirs. numerous affiliated cos. Mem. Bus. Sch. coun. Tulane U., N.Y.; mem. bd. govs. Hebrew Union Coll./Jewish Inst. Religion; mem. bd. overseers Sch. Architecture, Ill. Inst. Tech.; mem. exec. bd. Westchester Putnam coun. Boy Scouts Am.; mem. traffic commn. Village of Larchmont, N.Y.; mem. joint planning commn. Villages of Larchmont and Mamaroneck; trustee Larchmont Hist. Soc. Ensign USN, 1961-62. Named Man of Yr., St. Louis Rabbinical Coll., 1986. Mem. Real Estate Securities and Syndication Inst. (former gov.), Nat. Assn. Realtors, Nat. Assn. Rev. Appraisers (cert.), Soc. for Indsl. Archeology, Soc. Archtl. Historians, Nat. Assn. Security Dealers (registered prin.), Sheldrake Yacht Club (past treas.). Avocations: boating and sailing, collecting antiques, travelling, opera, kinetic sculpture. Home: 85 Larchmont Ave Larchmont NY 10538-3748 Office: Levi Co 85 Larchmont Ave Larchmont NY 10538

LEVI, JOHN G., lawyer; b. Chgo., Oct. 9, 1948; s. Edward H. and Kate (Sulzberger) L.; m. Jill Felsenthal, Oct. 7, 1979; children: Benjamin E., Daniel F., Sarah H. AB, U. Rochester, 1969; JD, Harvard U., 1972, LLM, 1973. Bar: Ill. 1973. Ptnr. Sidley & Austin, Chgo. Vice chmn. bd. Weiss

Mem. Hosp., Chgo.; trustee Francis W. Parker Sch., Chgo.; bd. dirs. Chgo. Child Care Sco.; vis. com. U. Chgo. Coll.; trustee vis. com. U. Rochester; active Citizens Com. Juvenile Ct., Chgo. Mem. ABA, Ill. Bar Assn., Chgo. Bar Assn., Law Club Chgo., Exec. Club Chgo. Office: Sidley & Austin 1 1st Nat Plz Chicago IL 60603

LEVI, JOSEF ALAN, artist; b. New York, Feb. 17, 1938; s. Jacob and Evelyn D. (Speizer) L. B.A., U. Conn., 1959; postgrad., Columbia U., 1960. Artist in residence Appalachian State U., N.C., 1969, vis. prof. art, Pa. State U., 1976. One-man shows of paintings include Stable include N.Y.C., 1966, 67, 68, 69, 70, Arts Club of Chgo., 1967, J.B. Speed Art Mus., Louisville, Ky., 1968, Appalachian State U., Boone, N.C., 1969, Lambert Gallery, Los Angeles, 1971, Gertrude Kasle Gallery, Detroit, 1971, Jacobs Ladder Gallery, Washington, 1972, Images Gallery, Toledo, Ohio, 1972, A.M. Sachs Gallery, N.Y.C., 1975, 76, 78, O.K. Harris Gallery, N.Y.C., 1983, 85, 87, 90, 92, 94, Adams-Middleton Gallery, Dallas, 1986; numerous group shows, 1965—, latest being, Balt. Mus. Art, 1975, Mus. Art, R.I. Sch. Design, 1976, Art Mus., U. N.C., Greensboro, 1977, Russell Sage Coll., Troy, N.Y., 1977, Washington U., St. Louis, 1977, Whitney Mus., N.Y.C., 1978-79, Meml. Art Gallery, U. Rochester, N.Y., 1979, Aldrich Mus. Contemporary Art, Ridgefield, Conn., 1980, Western Assn. Art Museums, 1981, Worcester (Mass.) Art Mus., 1981, Palace Theatre of Arts Gallery, Stamford, Conn., 1984, Randolph Macon Coll., Ashland, Va., 1985, Robert I. Kidd Galleries, Birmingham, Mich., 1985, Elaine Benson Gallery, Bridgehampton, N.Y., 1985; others; represented in numerous permanent collections including, Aldrich Mus. Contemporary Art, Albright-Knox Gallery, Buffalo, N.Y., Mus. Modern Art, N.Y.C., Krannert Art Mus., U. Ill., Urbana, Va. Mus. Fine Arts, Richmond, AT&T, N.Y.C., Corcoran Gallery, Washington, U. Md. College City, Chrysler Corp., Detroit., Spellman Coll., Atlanta, Exxon Corp., N.Y.C., Minolta Corp., N.Y.C., Des Moines Art Ctr., Newark Mus., Dartmouth Coll., Hanover, N.H., Storm King Art Ctr., Mountainville, N.Y., U. Notre Dame Art Gallery, South Bend, Ind., J. B. Speed Art Mus., Louisville, Bank of N.Y., N.Y.C., Lewis and Clark Coll., Portland, Oreg.. Technimetrics Inc., N.Y.C., Best Products Corp., Ashland, Va., Southland Corp., Dallas, TRW Corp., Cleve., Bklyn. Mus. Art, Worcester (Mass.) Art. Mus., Albion (Mich.) Coll.; Prudential Ins. Co. Am., Newark. Served to 1st. lt. Adj. Gen. Corps U.S. Army, 1959-60. Mem. N.Y. Artist Equity Assn.

LEVI, JULIAN HIRSCH, lawyer, educator; b. Chgo., July 25, 1909; s. Gerson Baruch and Elsa (Hirsch) L.; m. Marjorie Reynolds, Sept. 16, 1938; children: William Gerson, Kay Levi Pick. Ph.B. with honors, U. Chgo., 1929, J.D. cum laude, 1931; LL.D. (hon.), John Marshall Law Sch., Chgo., Lake Forest (Ill.) Coll., 1967. Bar: Ill. 1931. Ptnr. Wilhartz & Hirsch, Chgo., 1931-46; officer Reynolds Pen Co., also Reynolds Printasign Co., Chgo., 1946-52; exec. dir. S.E. Chgo. Commn., 1952-80; prof. urban studies U. Chgo., 1962-80; vis. prof. Hastings Coll. Law, U. Calif., San Francisco, 1978-79, 79-80; prof. Hastings Coll. Law, U. Calif., 1981—; founder, chmn. Pub. Law Rsch. Inst., 1984—; dir. Hyatt Corp., 1977-79, Elsinor Corp., 1979—; chmn. Chgo. Plan Commn., 1973-79; sec. Am. Council Edn., 1971-72; vice chmn. White House Task Force Cities, 1967; adv. to architect of Capitol, Washington, 1976—. Author: Municipal and Institution Relations in Boston, 1964, Financing Education and the Effect of Tax Laws, 1975; chmn. editorial adv. bd.: Urban Affairs Reporter, 1972-82. Trustee Michael Reese Hosp., Chgo., 1967-80, Calif. State Libr. Found., 1992—. Recipient Rockefeller Public Service award Princeton U., 1977, Alumni Svc. medal U. Chgo., 1989. Mem. ABA, Am. Law Inst., Am. Soc. Planning Ofcls., Chgo. Bar Assn., Order of Coif, Phi Beta Kappa. Jewish. Clubs: Tavern, Arts, Quadrangle (Chgo.). Office: U Calif Hastings Coll Law 200 Mcallister St San Francisco CA 94102-4907

LEVI, KURT, retired banker; b. Wiesbaden, Germany, May 20, 1910; came to U.S., 1937, naturalized, 1942; s. Josef and Martha (Kahn) L.; m. Ruth Neumann, Feb. 17, 1938; 1 son, Peter. LL.B., U. Frankfurt, Germany, 1931. Mdse. mgr. Consol. Retail Stores, Kansas City, Mo., 1937-55; with United Mo. Bank, Kansas City, 1956-80; sr. v.p. United Mo. Bank, 1971-80, Traders Bank, Kansas City, 1980-85; adj. prof. Park Coll., Parkville, Mo., 1984-85. Gen. and area chmn. Kansas City (Mo.) United campaign, 1962; chmn. finance com. Camp Fire Girls Am., 1968; chmn. Kansas City Mayor's Prayer Breakfast Club, 1968; gen. chmn. Greater Kansas City Bonds for Israel, 1959; chmn. Greater Kansas City Conf. Soviet Jewry, 1966; vice chmn., mem. exec. bd. Community Relations Bur., 1972; pres. Heart Am. chpt., Religious Zionists Am., 1971; bd. govs. Jewish Fedn. and Council Kansas City, 1972-88, div. chmn. Fedn. campaign, 1986; bd. govs. Kansas City chpt. Am. Jewish Com., nat. bd. dirs.; pres., chmn. bd. Kehilath Israel Synagogue, lifetime hon. Gabbi; bd. govs., ombudsman Temple Sholom, Pompano Beach, Fla., 1988-94. Mem. Kansas City C of C., B'nai B'rith (pres. Kansas City lodge 1984 1965, Greater Kansas City Coun. 1966, pres. Dist. II 1975-76, exec. v.p., bd. dirs., pres. Ft. Lauderdale 1990-92, pres. Kol Haverim lodge 1990-95), Kiwanis (v.p. Kansas City 1955), Legion of Honor, Playa del Sol Social Club (pres. 1989-90). Home: Playa del Sol 3500 Galt Ocean Dr Apt 2405 Fort Lauderdale FL 33308 also: The Sulgrave Apt 1205 121 W 48th St Kansas City MO 64112

LEVI, MAURICE DAVID, economics educator; b. London, Sept. 28, 1945; came to U.S., 1967; s. Karl and Louisa Hannah (Magson) L.; m. Kathleen Birkinshaw, Jan. 14, 1979; children—Adam Julian, Naomi Anne, Jonathan Karl. B.A. in Econs. with 1st class honors, U. Manchester, Eng., 1967; M.A., U. Chgo., 1968, Ph.D., 1972. Vis. prof. Hebrew U., Jerusalem, 1978; vis. assoc. prof. U. Calif-Berkeley, 1979; vis. scholar MIT, Cambridge, 1980; prof. business U. B.C., Vancouver, Can., 1972—; vis. prof. London Bus. Sch., 1985. Author: Economics Deciphered, 1981, Thinking Economically, 1985, International Finance, 2d edit., 1990, Economics and the Modern World, 1994; contbr. articles to profl. jours. Mem. Vancouver Mayor's Econ. Adv. Commn., 1983-84. Recipient Seagram award, 1978; grantee Ford Found., 1969-70, Can. Coun., 1978, 80, 85; Nomura fellow U. Exeter, 1990. Jewish. Avocations: astronomy; salmon fishing.

LEVI, PETER STEVEN, chamber of commerce executive, lawyer; b. Washington, June 3, 1944; s. Kurt and Ruth (Neumann) L.; m. Enid Goldberg, Jan. 26, 1969; children: Joshua, Jeff. BA, Northwestern U., 1966; JD, U. Mo., Kansas City, 1969, LLM in Urban Legal Affairs, 1971. Bar: Mo. 1969. Gen. counsel Mid Am. Regional Coun., Kansas City, 1971-77, exec. dir., 1977-90; pres. Greater Kansas City C of C, 1990—; mem. Mo. Commn. on Intergovtl. Cooperation; participant internat. local govt. mgmt. exch. program with Israel, Internat. City Mgmt. Assn., 1985-86. Author: Model Subdivision Regulations, 1975; contbr. numerous articles to legal and pub. adminstrn. jours. Bd. dirs. Starlight Theatre, Kansas City Area Devel. Coun., Downtown Coun., Kansas City region NCCJ, Full Employment Coun., City of Fountains, Project NEIGHBOR-H.O.O.D., Am. Royal Assn., Edn. Inc.; mem. policy adv. group Bus.-Edn. Expectations; cmty. advisor Jr. League; past pres. Kehilath Israel Synagogue. Recipient Pub. Adminstr. of Yr. award Am. Soc. Pub. Adminstrn., 1985, L.P. Cookingham Pub. Adminstrn. award, 1989; Walter Scheiber Regional Leadership award Nat. Assn. Regional Couns., 1990; fellow U.S. Dept. Transp., 1975. Mem. Assn. C.C. Execs., Rotary. Home: 3720 W 119th Ter Leawood KS 66209 Office: Greater Kans City C of C 911 Main St Ste 2600 Kansas City MO 64105-2049

LEVI, YOEL, orchestra conductor; b. Sotmar, Rumania, Israeli, Aug. 16, 1950; naturalized U.S. citizen, 1987; m. Jacqueline; 3 children. MA in Violin and Percussion, U. Tel Aviv, 1975; grad. degree, Jerusalem Acad. Music, 1976; studied with, Mendi Rodan; Diploma, Guildhall Sch. Music and Drama, London, 1978; studied with Franco Ferrara, Siena, Acad. Santa Cecilia, Rome and Kiril Kondrashin, Hilversum. Percussionist Israel Philharmonic Orch., 1975, conducting asst., 1978-80; resident condr. Cleve. Orch., 1980-84; music dir. Atlanta Symphony Orch., 1988—; guest condr. N.Am. and European orchs. Albums include The Artistry of Yoel Levi: The Telarc Collection, Vol. 8; recs. with Angel-EMI, Schwann, Telarc. Recipient 1st prize Condrs. Internat. Competition, Besancon, 1978. Office: Atlanta Symphony Orch 1293 Peachtree St NE Ste 300 Atlanta GA 30309-3552 also: Columbia Artists Mgmt Foster Divsn 165 W 57th St New York NY 10019*

LEVICH, CECILIA CORTES, psychiatrist; b. San Carlos, Philippines, Nov. 22, 1947; came to U.S. 1974; d. Ramon and Rosario (Mendoza) C.; m. Robert Joseph Levich, Dec. 1, 1947. B.S., U. Philippines, 1967, M.D., 1972. Resident in psychiatry Philippine Gen. Hosp., Manila, 1972-74, Nassau

County Med. Ctr., East Meadow, N.Y., 1974-75, North Shore Univ. Hosp., Manhasset, N.Y., 1975-77; fellow in psychosomatics Downstate Med. Ctr., Bklyn., 1977-78; staff psychiatrist Jersey City Med. Ctr., N.J., 1978-79; part-time psychiatrist Morristown Meml. Hosp., 1979-82; practice medicine specializing in psychiatry, Long Valley, N.J., 1979—. Mem. Am. Psychiat. Assn., AMA, U. Philippines Med. Alumni Soc. in Am. Home: 8 E Gate Rd Long Valley NJ 07853-3068

LEVICH, ROBERT ALAN, geologist; b. Bklyn., Apr. 16, 1941; s. Leonard Walter and Dinah (Cohen) L.; m. Stella Araba Nkrumah, June 10, 1964; children: Alexander Kwamina, Walter Abraham, Leo Augustine. BS in Geology, CUNY, Bklyn., 1963; MA in Geol. Scis., U. Tex., 1973. Cert. profl. geologist. Geologist Ghana Geol. Survey, Sunyani, 1969-72, U.S. Atomic Energy Commn., Austin., Tex., Spokane, Wash., 1973-81; regional mgr. Apache Energy & Minerals Co., Spokane, 1981-82; cons. expert East Africa Internat. Atomic Energy Agy., Vienna, Austria, 1982-83; geologist U.S. Dept. Energy, Argonne, Ill., Las Vegas, Nev., 1984-88; chief tech. analysis br. U.S. Dept. Energy/YMP, Las Vegas, 1988-89, internat. programs mgr., 1989—; U.S. rep. Internat. Stripa Project, Stockholm, 1989-92; lead, coord. U.S. del. OECD/Nuclear Energy Agy. Site Evaluation and Design Experiments, Paris, 1990—; U.S. Dept. Energy rep. OECD/NEA Alligator Rivers Analogue Project, Sydney, NSW, Australia, 1990-92; project dir. USDOE/Atomic Energy, Can. Ltd. Subsidiary Agreement, 1991—; tech. coord. USDOE/Switzerland Nat. Co-op. for Disposal Radioactive Waste Project Agreement, 1991—; project dir. USDOE/Swedish Nuclear Fuel & Waste Mgmt. Co-Project Agreement, 1993—. Author, co-author, editor reports. Fellow Geol. Soc. Am., Soc. Econ. Geologists; mem. Am. Nuclear Soc. (Internat. High Level Radioactive Waste Mgmt. Conf. program com., steering com.), Assn. Geoscientists for Internat. Devel., Am. Inst. Profl. Geologists (v.p. Nev. sect. 1993). Achievements include development of international radioactive waste natural analogue study. Office: US Dept Energy YMP 101 Convention Center Dr Las Vegas NV 89109-2001

LEVIE, HOWARD S(IDNEY), lawyer, educator, author; b. Wolverine, Mich., Dec. 19, 1907; s. J. Walter and Mina (Goldfarb) L.; m. S. Blanche Krim, July 24, 1934. A.B., Cornell U., 1928, J.D., 1930; LL.M., George Washington U., 1957. Bar: N.Y. 1931, Mo. 1965, U.S. Dist. Ct. (ea. dist.) N.Y. 1934, U.S. Dist. Ct. (so. dist.) N.Y. 1935, U.S. Supreme Ct. 1947, U.S. Ct. Appeals (D.C. cir.) 1949, U.S. Ct. Mil. Appeals 1953. Assoc. Weit & Goldman, N.Y.C., 1931-42; with JAGC, U.S. Army, 1942, advanced through grades to col., 1954; staff officer UN Command Armistice Del., Korea, 1951-52; chief internat. affairs div. Office of JAG, 1954-58; legal adviser U.S. European Command, Paris, 1959-61; ret. 1963; prof. law St. Louis U., 1963-77, prof. emeritus, 1977—; prof. U.S. Naval War Coll., Newport, R.I., 1971-72, Charles H. Stockton prof. internat. law, 1971-72; instr. internat. law Salve Regina Coll., Newport, R.I., 1984-88; adj. prof. Naval War Coll., 1991—. Author: Prisoners of War in International Armed Conflict (Internat. Soc. for Mil. Law and the Law of War Ciardi prize 1982) 1979, Documents on Prisoners of War, 1980, Protection of War Victims, 4 vols., 1979-81, The Status of Gibraltar, 1983, The Code of International Armed Conflict, 1986, The Law of Non-International Armed Conflict, 1987, The Law of War and Neutrality: A Selected English-Language Bibliography, 1988, Mine Warfare at Sea, 1992, Terrorism in War: The Law of War Crimes, 1993. Decorated Legion of Merit, Bronze Star; grantee Ctr. for Advanced Rsch., Naval War Coll., 1980-82, U.S. Inst. Peace, 1991; Howard S. Levie Mil. Chair of Operational Law established by U.S. Naval War Coll., 1994. Mem. ABA, Am. Soc. Internat. Law (exec. coun. 1969-70), Internat. Law Assn., Ret. Army Judge Advs. Assn., Internat. Soc. for Mil. Law and Law of War, Phi Beta Kappa. Democrat. Home and Office: 41 Sherman St Newport RI 02840-2959

LEVIE, JOSEPH HENRY, lawyer; b. N.Y.C.; s. Mortimer Joseph and Pearl (Seelig) L.; m. Hallie Ratzkin, Jan. 26, 1963; children: Matthew Benjamin, Jessica Ruth. AB, Columbia U., 1949, LLB, 1951. Bar: N.Y. 1952, U.S. Supreme Ct. 1954. Atty. Laporte & Meyers, N.Y.C., 1955-59, Loew Theatres Inc., N.Y.C., 1959-63, Rathheim, Hoffman, Kassel & Levie N.Y.C., 1964-81, Rogers & Wells, N.Y.C., 1982—; lectr. banking and related subjects to various profl. groups. Contbr. articles to profl. jours. With JAGC, U.S. Army, 1952-55. Fellow Am. Coll. Comml. Fin. Attys.; mem. Columbia Coll. Alumni (pres. class of 1949). Home: 131 Riverside Dr New York NY 10024-3713 Office: Roger & Wells 200 Park Ave New York NY 10166-0153

LE VIEN, JOHN DOUGLAS (JACK LE VIEN), motion picture and television producer, director; b. N.Y.C., July 18, 1918; s. Christopher Luke and Rose Jeanette Le V. Chmn. bd. TCA Travel Corp. Am., 1979—; chmn. bd. Electronic Pub. Co., London. Div. News editor: Pathé News, 1946-57; ind. motion picture and TV dir. and producer, 1958—; producer: (TV series) Valiant Years, 1959-60; exec. producer: (film) Black Fox, 1962 (Acad. award); producer and dir.: (films) Finest Hours, 1963-64, A King's Story, 1965, Churchill Centenary, 1974; (TV shows) Other World of Winston Churchill, 1964, The Gathering Storm, 1973, The Amazing Voyage of Daffodil and Daisy, 1974, Cicero, 1975, Where the Lotus Fell, 1976, Flames Over the Sahara, 1977, Children of the Lotus, 1978, Churchill and The Generals, 1980; pres., exec. producer TV movies, Le Vien Internat. Prodns. Ltd., N.Y.C., 1958—; chmn. bd., exec. producer TV shows, Le Vien Films Ltd., London, Eng., 1963—; author: The Valiant Years, 1961, The Finest Hours, 1964, (with Lady Mosley) The Duchess of Windsor, 1979, (with Barrie Pitt) Churchill and The Generals. Served to col. AUS, World War II, ETO; col. Res. Decorated Legion of Merit, Bronze Star; Legion of Honor; Croix de Guerre France). Mem. Brit. Acad. Film & Television Arts. Club: Overseas Press (N.Y.C.). Home: 15 Chesterfield Hill, London W1, England

LEVIN, A. LEO, law educator, retired government official; b. N.Y.C., Jan. 9, 1919; s. Isaachar and Minerva Hilda (Shapiro) L.; m. Doris Feder, Dec. 28, 1947; children—Allan, Jay Michael. BA, Yeshiva Coll., 1939; JD, U. Pa., 1942; LLD (hon.), Yeshiva U., 1960, NY Law Sch., 1980; PhD (hon.), Bar-Ilan U., Israel, 1990. Bar: N.Y. 1947, U.S. Supreme Ct. 1982. Instr. then asst. prof. law U. Pa., 1949-47; law faculty U. Pa., Phila., 1949-69, 70-89, Meltzer prof. law, 1987-89, Meltzer prof. emeritus, 1989—, vice provost, 1965-68; v.p. for acad. affairs Yeshiva U., N.Y.C., 1969-70; dir. Fed. Jud. Ctr., Washington, 1977-87; chmn. Pa. State Legis. Reapportionment Commn., 1971-73; founding dir. Nat. Inst. Trial Advocacy, 1971-73; conf. coord. Nat. Conf. on Causes of Popular Dissatisfaction with Adminstrn. of Justice (Pound Conf.); chmn. bd. cert. Circuit Execs., 1977-87; mem. adv. bd. Nat. Inst. Corrections, 1977-87. Author: (with Woolley) Dispatch and Delay: A Field Study of Judicial Administration in Pennsylvania, 1961; (with Cramer) Problems on Trial Advocacy, 1968; editor: (with Schuchman and Yablon) Cases on Civil Procedure, 1992. Hon. trustee Bar Ilan U., Ramat Gan, Israel, 1967—; hon. pres. (former pres.) Jewish Publ. Soc. Am. Served to 1st lt. USAF, 1942-46, ETO. Recipient Mordecai Ben David award Yeshiva U., 1967, Disting. Service award U. Pa. Law Sch. Alumni, 1974, Bernard Revel award Yeshiva Coll., 1963; White lectr. U. Va., 1970, Jeffords lectr., N.Y. Law Sch., 1980, Murrah lectr. So. Meth. U. Law Sch., 1986, Roberts lectr. U. Pa. Law Sch., 1989. Fellow Am. Acad. Arts and Scis.; mem. Am. Law Inst., Am. Judicature Soc. (pres. 1987-89), Order of Coif (nat. pres. 1967-70). Jewish. Office: U Pa Law Sch 3400 Chestnut St Philadelphia PA 19104-6204

LEVIN, AARON REUBEN, pediatrician, educator; b. Johannesburg, Transvaal, Republic of South Africa, Mar. 19, 1929; came to U.S., 1964; s. Louis and Fanny (Galgut) L.; m. Lenore Zhita Gladstone, Dec. 6, 1955; children: Sheryl Rina, Terry Larice, Serle Kevin. BS, Witwatersrand U., 1948, MB, BCh, 1953, MD, 1969. Diplomate Am. Bd. Pediatrics, Pediatric Cardiology. Intern Edenvale Hosp., Johannesburg, 1954-55; sr. med. officer Fever Hosp., Johannesburg, 1955-56; registrar in pediatrics Coronation Hosp., Johannesburg, 1956-61, Charing Cross Hosp., London, 1961-62; attending pediatrician Edenvale Hosp., Johannesburg, 1962-64; instr. in pediatrics Duke Univ. Med. Sch., Durham, N.C., 1964-66; asst.-assoc. prof. pediatrics Cornell Univ. Med. Coll., N.Y.C., 1966-73, prof. pediatrics, 1973-94; prof. pediatrics N.Y. Med. Coll., 1994—; attending pediatrician N.Y. Hosp. Cornell Med. Ctr., 1966-94, also dir. pediatric catheterization labs. 1966-94; cons. cardiologist Englewood (N.J.) Hosp., 1980—; assoc. attending pediatric cardiologist Westchester County Med. Ctr., 1994—. Contbr. articles and papers to profl. jours. Pres. Beth Emeth Synagogue, Larchmont, N.Y., 1973,

Pediatric Cardiology Soc. Greater N.Y., 1978. Fellow Am. Heart Assn., Am. Coll. Cardiology, N.Y. Heart Assn., Am. Angiology Soc., Royal Coll. Physicians (Edinburgh, Scotland). Avocations: stamp collecting, reading, gardening.. Home: 10 Hall Ave Larchmont NY 10538-2929 Office: New York Medical College 601 Munger Pavilion Valhalla NY 10595

LEVIN, ALAN M., television journalist; b. Bklyn., Feb. 28, 1926; s. Herman and Shirley (Levinstein) L.; m. Hannah Alexander, Oct. 30, 1948; children: Marc, Nicole, Danielle, Juliet. B.A., Washington U., Middletown, Conn., 1946. Reporter, columnist Plainfield (N.J.) Courier News, 1957-60; statehouse corr. AP, Trenton, N.J., 1960-61; writer N.Y. Post, 1961-63; press sec. Sen. Harrison Williams, Washington, 1963-64; news producer, writer WABC-TV, N.Y.C., 1965-67; owner Levin Mediaworks Inc., producers documentaries for comml. and pub. TV, N.Y.C. Documentary film maker, NET, 1968-69, documentary film maker, pub. affairs, news writer, dir., producer, WNET-TV, N.Y.C., 1969-82. Served with AUS, 1944-46. Recipient numerous awards including George Polk Meml. award, Dupont Columbia award, Emmy awards. Home: 88 Claremont Ave Maplewood NJ 07040-2024 Office: Levin Mediaworks Inc 142 W 26th St New York NY 10001-6814

LEVIN, ALAN SCOTT, pathologist, allergist, immunologist; b. Chgo., Jan. 12, 1938; s. John Bernhard and Betty Ruth (Margulis) L.; m. Vera S. Byers, June 15, 1971. BS in Chemistry, U. Ill., Champaign-Urbana, 1960; MS in Biochemistry, U. Ill., Chgo., 1963, MD, 1964; JD, Golden Gate U., 1995. Diplomate Am. Bd. Allergy and Immunology, Am. Bd. Pathology. Intern Children's Hosp. Med. Ctr., Boston, 1964-65; adj. instr. pediatrics U. Calif., San Francisco, 1971-72, asst. prof. immunology dept. dermatology, 1972-78, adj. assoc. prof., 1978-88; dir. lab. immunology U. Calif. & Kaiser Found. Rsch. Inst. Joint Program Project, San Francisco, 1971-74; attending physician dept. medicine Mt. Zion/U. Calif. San Francisco Hosps., 1971—; dir. div. immunology Western Labs., Oakland, Calif., 1974-77; med. dir. MML/Solano Labs. Div. Chemed-W.R. Grace, Inc., Berkeley, Calif., 1977-79; med. dir. Levin Clin. Labs., Inc., San Francisco, 1979-81; pvt. practice San Francisco, 1981—. Contbr. articles to profl. jours., chpts. to books. Lt. USN, 1966-69, Vietnam. Decorated Bronze Star, Silver Star, 4 Air medals; Harvard Med. Sch. traineeship grantee, 1964, USPHS hematology tng. grantee U. Calif., San Francisco Med. Ctr., 1969-71; recipient Faculty Rsch. award Am. Cancer Soc., 1970-74. Fellow Coll. Am. Pathologists, Am. Coll. Emergency Physicians, Am. Soc. Clin. Pathologists; mem. AMA, Am. Acad. Allergy and Immunology, Am. Coll. Allergy and Immunology, Am. Assn. Clin. Chemists, Am. Acad. Environ. Medicine, Calif. Med. Assn., San Francisco Med. Soc. Jewish. Office: Immunology Inc 500 Sutter # 512 San Francisco CA 94102-1114

LEVIN, BARTON JOHN, aviation products and services company executive; b. Sioux Falls, S.D., Mar. 3, 1944; s. Arthur Harold Levin and Shirley Thelma (Yonover) Osborn; m. Nancy Ellen MacDonald, Mar. 3, 1972; children—Meredith Ellen, Andrew David. A.B. in Econ., U. Calif., Berkeley, 1965; M.B.A., U. Chgo., 1969. C.P.A., Ill. Exec. Santa Fe Ry. Co., Chgo., 1968-71, 72-78; presdl. interchange exec. U.S. Dept. Transp., Washington, 1971-72; exec. AAR Corp., Elk Grove Village, Ill., 1978-79, v.p., 1979-85, pres., chief oper. officer, dir., 1985-89; pres., chief exec. officer Grabill Corp., Oak Forest, Ill., 1989; pres. Larry Doyle Enterprises, Inc., Fox Lake, Ill., 1991—; cons. AAR Corp., 1989-90. Club: Economic (Chgo.). Office: 701 S Monarch St Aspen CO 81611-1853

LEVIN, BERNARD, physician; b. Johannesburg, Republic of South Africa, Apr. 1, 1942; came to U.S. 1966, naturalized 1972; m. Ronelle DuBrow; children: Adam, Katherine. MD, U. Witwatersrand, 1964. Resident Presbyn. St. Lukes Hosp., Chgo., 1966-68; rsch. fellow U. Chgo., 1968-71; NIH fellow U. Chgo., 1971-72; instr. medicine U. Chgo., 1971-73, asst. prof. medicine, 1973-78, assoc. prof., 1979-84; prof. med., chmn. dept gastrointestinal oncology and digestive diseases, U. Tex. Med. Ctr. M.D. Anderson Hosp., Houston, 1984-94, Robert R. Herring prof., 1986-91, Ellen F. Knisely chair, 1991-94, v.p. for Cancer Prevention (ad interim), 1992-94, v.p. for Cancer Prevention, 1994—, Betty Marcus chair 1994—; mem. large bowel cancer working group Nat. Cancer Inst., 1984-85; cons. spl. study sect. Nat. Cancer Inst., 1976-84, chair nat. adv. com. on colorectal cancer, 1990—. Contbr. articles to profl. jours.; mem. editorial bd. Pancreas, Jour. Nat. Cancer Inst. J. Clin. Oncology USPHS grantee, 1976-80; Melamid Found. Gift, U. Chgo., 1978-83; NCI grantee, 1980-84, others. Fellow ACP, Am. Coll. Gastroenterology; mem. AAAS, Am. Assn. Cancer Rsch., Am. Gastroenterol. Assn., Am. Soc. Gastrointestinal Endoscopy, Am. Pancreatic Assn., Am. Soc. Preventative Oncology, Internat. Assn. Pancreatology, Am. Soc. Clin. Oncology, Am. Cancer Soc. (chair nat. adv. com. on colorectal cancer), Sigma Xi. Jewish. Office: UT M D Anderson Cancer Ctr 1515 Holcombe Blvd 203 Houston TX 77030-4095

LEVIN, BETSY, lawyer, educator, university dean; b. Balt., Dec. 25, 1935; d. M. Jastrow and Alexandra (Lee) L. AB, Bryn Mawr (Pa.) Coll., 1956; LLB, Yale U., 1966. Bar: D.C. 1967, Colo. 1982. Research geologist U.S. Geol. Survey, Washington, 1956-63; law clk. to judge U.S. Ct. Appeals (4th cir.), Balt., 1966-67; spl. asst. to U.S. Amb. to UN, Arthur J. Goldberg N.Y.C., 1967-68; dir. edn. studies Urban Inst., Washington, 1968-73; prof. law Duke U., Durham, N.C., 1973-80; gen. counsel U.S. Dept. Edn., Washington, 1980-81; dean, prof. law U. Colo., Boulder, 1981-87; exec. v.p. Assn. Am. Law Schs., Washington, 1987-92; prof. law T. Allen vis. disting. prof. law U. N.C. Sch. Law, Chapel Hill, 1993; vis. prof. law Am. U. Washington Coll. Law, 1994, Georgetown U. Law Ctr., Washington, 1994; disting. vis. prof. sch. law U. Balt., 1995; mem. Nat. Coun. Ednl. Rsch., 1978-79; mem. civil rights reviewing authority HEW, 1979-80. Co-author: Educational Policy and the Law, 2d edit., 1982, 3d edit., 1991; editor: Future Directions for School Finance Reform, 1975; co-editor: The Courts, Social Science and School Desegregation, 1977, School Desegregation: Lessons of the First 25 Years, 1979. White House fellow, 1968-69. Fellow Am. Bar Found., Colo. Bar Found.; mem. ABA, Nat. Assn. Women Judges (program com. 1985-92), Am. Law Inst. (coun.), Order of Coif. Office: U Balt Sch Law 1420 N Charles St Baltimore MD 21201

LEVIN, BRUCE ALAN, lawyer, real estate developer; b. Jersey City, Sept. 5, 1939; s. Julius and Toby (Sand) L.; m. Ann Singley, June 1963 (div. Sept. 1967); 1 child, Peter; m. Pamela Jo Dillow, Dec. 23, 1975; children: Sean, Brett, Annalee. Student, Rutgers U., 1957-58; BS in Econs., U. Pa., 1961; JD, Harvard U., 1964. Bar: Calif. 1965, Oreg. 1978, Nev. 1980. Ptnr. Glaser & Levin, L.A., 1968-70, Levin, Saphier & Rein, L.A., 1970-76; v.p. gen. counsel, asst. sec. Mirage Resorts Inc., Las Vegas, 1979—; ptnr. D&L Devel. Co., Las Vegas, 1984; pres. Sandpiper Homes Ltd.-Liability Co., 1992—. Co-founder, trustee Meadows Sch., Las Vegas, 1984. Mem. Nev. Bar Assn., Calif. Bar Assn. Office: Mirage Resorts Inc 3400 Las Vegas Blvd S Las Vegas NV 89109-8923

LEVIN, BURTON, diplomat; b. N.Y.C., Sept. 28, 1930; s. Benjamin and Ida (Geller) L.; m. Lily Lee, Jan. 4, 1960; children: Clifton, Alicia. BA, CUNY, 1952; M Internat. Affairs, Columbia U., 1954; postgrad., Harvard U., 1964; LLD (hon.), Carleton Coll., 1993. Commd. fgn. service officer Dept. State, 1954; counselor/econ. officer Am. Embassy, Taipei, Taiwan, 1954-56, polit. officer, 1969-74; intelligence research specialist Dept. State, Washington, 1956-58, dir. Republic China affairs, 1974-77; polit. officer Am. Embassy, Jakarta, Indonesia, 1959-63; polit. officer Am. Consulate Gen. Hong Kong, 1965-69, dep. chief mission, 1977-78, consul gen., 1981-86; dep. chief mission Am. Embassy, Bangkok, Thailand, 1978-81; amb. to Burma, 1987-90; dir. Asia Soc. Hong Kong Ctr., 1990—; vis. fellow Stanford U., 1974; vis. lectr. Harvard U., 1986, Carleton Coll., 1994; bd. dirs. Mansfield Found., China Fund, Yaohan Food Processing and Trading Co. Ltd.; mem. coun. Nanjing U. Ctr. for Chinese and Am. Studies John Hopkins U. Mem. Am. Fgn. Service Assn. Clubs: Am., Hong Kong Country. Home: 72 Audubon Rd Wellesley MA 02181-2828

LEVIN, CARL, senator; b. Detroit, June 28, 1934; m. Barbara Halpern, 1961; children: Kate, Laura, Erica. BA, Swarthmore Coll., 1956; JD, Harvard U., 1959. Ptnr. Grossman, Hyman & Grossman, Detroit, 1959-64; asst. atty. gen., gen. counsel Mich. CRC, 1964-67; chief appellate defender City of Detroit, 1968-69, mem. coun., 1970-73, pres. coun. 1974-77; ptnr. Schlussel, Lifton, Simon, Rands & Kaufman, 1971-73, Jaffe, Snider, Raitt, Garratt & Heuer, 1978-79; U.S. senator from Mich., 1979—; past instr.

Wayne State U., U. Detroit; mem. Armed Svcs. Com., Govtl. Affairs Com., Com. on Small Bus., Senate Dem. Steering & Coordination Com. Mem. Mich. Bar Assn., D.C. Bar. Democrat. Office: US Senate 459 Russell Senate Ofc Washington DC 20510*

LEVIN, CARL, public and government relations consultant; b. Ringgold, La.; m. Doris Wechsler; m. Sonia Atlas, Oct. 13, 1958; children: Judith Friedman, Richard (dec.), Virginia Vinick, Alan Schwartzbach. Student, CCNY, 1930-33. Corr. CCNY N.Y. Herald Tribune, 1930-34, staff reporter, 1934-43, Washington corr., 1943-45, 46-50; war and fgn. corr. N.Y. Herald Tribune, Europe, 1945-46; free lance mag. writer, 1942-50; Washington mgr. William H. Weintraub & Co. (advt. and pub. relations), 1950-52; charge Washington activities Schenley Industries, Inc., 1952-62, v.p., 1955-62; dir. pub. support Trade Expansion Act, White House, 1962; pres. Carl Levin Assos., Inc., 1962-68; v.p., gen. mgr. Burson-Marsteller, Washington, 1968-72; v.p., sr. cons. Burson-Marsteller, 1972-83, sr. v.p., 1983-87; mem. Nat. Small Bus. Adv. Coun., 1964-68; cons. in field. Collaborator books on journalism, postwar security investigations; contbr. to nat. mags. Active in founding Am.-Israel Pub. Affairs Soc.; bd. dirs. Interracial Council Bus. Opportunity, 1972-75; mem. bd. Com. Accuracy in Middle East Reporting in Am., 1985-91, Am. Gas Index Fund, 1990—; trustee Opera Soc. Washington, 1976-70, Fords Theater Soc., Washington, 1975-81; co-chmn. Citizens Com. Opera, 1963. Mem. Soc. Profl. Journalists, Internat. Club Washington (bd. govs. 1985-90), Lotos Club (N.Y.C.). Home: 5450 Whitley Park Ter Bethesda MD 20814

LEVIN, CHARLES EDWARD, lawyer; b. Chgo., Oct. 6, 1946; m. Barbara Serwer, Dec. 28, 1975. BA with high honor, DePaul U., 1968; JD cum laude, Northwestern U., Chgo., 1971. Bar: Ill. 1971. Asst. instr. legal writing and rsch. Northwestern U. Law Sch., 1970-71; assoc. D'Ancona & Pflaum, Chgo., 1971-76, ptnr., 1977-90; ptnr. Jenner & Block, Chgo., 1990—; mem. governing bd. Comml. Fin. Assn. Edn. Found., 1990—; asst. instr. legal writing, rsch. Northwestern U., Chgo., 1970-71. Bd. editors Northwestern U. Law Rev., 1970-71. Mem. aux. bd. Chgo. Architecture Found., 1989—; mem. governing bd. Comml. Fin. Assn. Edn. Found., N.Y. Mem. ABA (bus. sect. 1992—), Chgo. Bar Assn. (vice chmn. architecture and law com. 1974-75, vice chmn. divsn. D., mem. exec. com. fed. tax com. 1983-84, comml. fin. and trans. com. 1990—, Article 9 drafting subcom.), East Bank Club Chgo., 410 Club. Avocations: acquisition fine arts, support arts organizations, jogging. Office: Jenner & Block 1 IBM Plz Ste 4400 Chicago IL 60614

LEVIN, CHARLES LEONARD, state supreme court justice; b. Detroit, Apr. 28, 1926; s. Theodore and Rhoda (Katzin) L.; children: Arthur, Amy, Fredrick. B.A., U. Mich., 1946, LL.B., 1947; LL.D. (hon.), Detroit Coll. of Law, 1980. Bar: Mich. 1947, N.Y. 1949, U.S. Supreme Ct. 1953, D.C. 1954. Pvt. practice law N.Y.C., 1948-50, Detroit, 1950-66; ptnr. Levin, Levin, Garvett & Dill, Detroit, 1951-66; judge Mich. Ct. Appeals, Detroit, 1966-73; assoc. justice Mich. Supreme Ct., 1973—; mem. Mich. Law Revision Commn., 1966. Trustee Marygrove Coll., 1971-77, chmn., 1971-74; mem. vis. coms. to Law Schs., U. Mich., U. Chgo., 1977-80, Wayne State U. Mem. Am. Law Inst. Office: Mich Supreme Ct 500 Woodward Ave 20th Fl Detroit MI 48226

LEVIN, EDWARD JESSE, lawyer; b. Balt., Oct. 31, 1951; s. Cyril and Virginia Lee (Kremer) L.; m. Cheri Wyron, Feb. 18, 1973; children: Paul Clifford, Benjamin Lawrence. BA, Johns Hopkins U., 1973; JD, U. Va., 1976. Bar: Md. 1976, U.S. Supreme Ct. 1980. Assoc Piper & Marbury LLP, Balt., 1976-84; ptnr. Piper & Marbury, Balt., 1984—. Co-author: Maryland Real Estate Leasing Forms and Practice, 1988. 1st v.p. Balt. Bd. of Jewish Edn., 1987-89, pres., 1989-91. Fellow Am. Coll. Real Estate Lawyers (chmn. attys.' opinions com. 1992—); mem. Md. State Bar Assn. (chmn. sect. real property, planning and zoning 1988-90. co-chmn. spl. joint com. lawyers' opinions comml. transactions 1989—), Balt. City Bar Assn. (co-chmn. spl. joint com. lawyers' opinions comml. transactions 1989—). Democrat. Jewish. Office: Piper & Marbury LLP 36 S Charles St Baltimore MD 21201-3018

LEVIN, EZRA GURION, lawyer; b. Bklyn., Feb. 10, 1934; s. Harry and Bertha (Lebendiger) L.; m. Batya Ann Schaefr, June 19, 1960; children: Zachary Abraham, Ayala Deborah Levin Kruss. AB, Columbia U., 1955; postgrad., U. Chgo., 1955-56; LLB, Columbia U., 1959. Bar: N.Y. 1961. Assoc., then ptnr. Marshall, Bratter, Greene, Allison & Tucker, N.Y.C., 1961-79; ptnr. Kramer, Levin, Naftalis, Nessen, Kamin & Frankel, N.Y.C., 1979—; bd. dirs. Federated Devel. Co., Houston, Kaiser Aluminum Corp., Oakland, Calif., United Mizrahi Bank and Trust Co., N.Y.C., MAXXAM, Inc., Houston; adj. prof. sociology Columbia U., 1973-77, 87, 93—; adj. faculty U. Conn. Law Sch., 1970-73, U. Wis. Law Sch., 1967. Contbr. articles to profl. jours. Mem.-at-large Jewish Cmty. Rels. Coun., N.Y.C., 1983—, v.p., 1994—; vice chmn. Coalition for Soviet Jewry, N.Y.C., 1984-93, co-chair, 1994—; counsel Am. Friends Sarah Herzog Meml. Hosp.-Jerusalem, Inc., N.Y.C., 1975—; sec., bd. dirs. Scholarship, Edn. and Def. Fund for Racial Equality, N.Y.C., 1961-70; chair, trustee Solomon Schechter High Sch. of N.Y., 1992—. Mem. ABA, Law and Soc. Assn. Mem. Columbia Coll. Alumni Assn. (bd. dirs.). Avocation: tennis. Office: Kramer Levin Naftalis Nessen Kamin & Frankel 919 3d Ave New York NY 10022

LEVIN, FRANK S., physicist, educator; b. N.Y.C., Apr. 14, 1933; s. James J. and Celia (Aronovitch) L.; m. Madeline Carol McMurrough, Apr. 1973; 4 children. B.A., Johns Hopkins U., 1955; Ph.D., U. Md., 1961. Research assoc. Rice U., Houston, 1961-63, Brookhaven Nat. Lab., Upton, N.Y., 1963-66, U.K. Atomic Energy Authority, Harwell, Eng., 1965-67; mem. faculty Brown U., Providence, 1967—; prof. physics Brown U., 1977—. Fellow Am. Phys. Soc. (founder, 1st chmn. topical group on few body systems and multiparticle dynamics). Office: Brown U Physics Dept PO Box 1843 Dept Providence RI 02912-1843

LEVIN, GEOFFREY ARTHUR, botanist; b. Los Alamos, N.Mex., Dec. 7, 1955; s. Jules Samuel and Jane Walden (Settle) L.; m. Renée Patricia Papini, May 24, 1981; children: Tobias, Madeline. BA, Pomona Coll., 1977; MS, U. Calif., Davis, 1980, PhD, 1984. Asst. prof. Ripon (Wis.) Coll., 1982-84; curator, chmn. botany dept. San Diego Natural History Mus., 1984-93; lectr. U. San Diego, 1984-90; asst. profl. scientist Ill. Natural History Survey, Champaign, 1994—; adj. prof. San Diego State U., 1985-94; dept. affiliate Dept. Plant Biology, U. Ill., 1995—; rsch. assoc. Mo. Bot. Garden, 1994—. Contbr. articles to jours. in field. Bd. dirs. Fond du Lac Audubon Soc., 1983-84, San Diego Audubon Soc., 1986-87; pres. Summit Unitarian Universalist Fellowship, El Cajon, Calif., 1989-91. Recipient Jesse M. Greenman award. Mo. Bot. Garden, 1987; NSF grad. fellow, 1977-81. Mem. Am. Inst. Biol. Scis., Am. Soc. Plant Taxonomists, Bot. Soc. Am., Calif. Bot. Soc. (bd. editors 1992-95), Phi Beta Kappa, Sigma Xi. Democrat. Office: Ill Natural History Survey Ctr for Biodiversity 607 E Peabody Dr Champaign IL 61820

LEVIN, GERALD MANUEL, media and entertainment company executive; b. Phila., May 6, 1939; s. David and Pauline (Schantzer) L.; m. Carol S. Needleman, Aug. 30, 1959 (div. Aug. 1970); children: Laura, Leon, Jonathan; m. Barbara J. Riley, Oct. 11, 1970; children: Michael, Anna. BA, Haverford Coll., 1960; LLB, U. Pa., 1963; LLD (hon.), Tex. Coll., 1985; LLD (hon.), Middlebury Coll., 1994. Assoc. Simpson, Thacher & Bartlett, N.Y.C., 1963-67; gen. mgr., chief operating officer Devel. and Resources Corp., N.Y.C., 1967-71; rep. Internat. Basic Economy Corp., Tehran, Iran, 1971-72; v.p. programming Home Box Office, N.Y.C., 1972-73, pres., chief exec. officer, 1973-76, chmn., chief exec. officer, 1976-79; group v.p. video Time, Inc., N.Y.C., 1979-84, exec. v.p., 1984-88, vice chmn., dir, 1988-90; vice chmn., dir. Time Warner Inc., N.Y.C., 1990—, chief oper. officer, 1991-92, pres., co-chief exec. officer to chmn. and CEO, 1992—; bd. dirs. Turner Broadcasting Systems, Inc. Trustee Haverford Coll., 1983—, chmn. bd. dirs., 1990—; bd. dirs., treas. N.Y. Philharm., 1989. Recipient Nat. Disting. Achievement award Am. Jewish Com., 1984. Mem. Ctr. for Comm., The Aspen Inst., N.Y. City Partnership, Coun. on Fgn. Rels., Corp. Governance Task Force of the Bus. Roundtable, Internat. Radio and TV Soc., Phi Beta Kappa. Avocations: reading, jogging. Office: Time Warner Inc 75 Rockefeller Plz New York NY 10019

LEVIN, GILBERT VICTOR, health information, bioengineering and environmental control company executive; b. Balt., Apr. 23, 1924; s. Henry I. and Lillian R. (Richman) L.; m. Karen Salisbury, Oct. 25, 1953; children: Ron L., Henry L., Carol Y. BE, Johns Hopkins U., 1947, MS, 1948, PhD, 1963. Registered profl. engr., D.C., Md. With Md. State Dept. Health, 1948-50, Calif. Dept. Health, 1950-51, D.C. Dept. Pub. Health, 1951-55; v.p. Resources Research, Inc., Washington, 1955-63; dir. life systems div. Hazleton Labs., Inc., Reston, Va., 1963-67; chief exec. officer, chmn. bd. Biospherics Inc. Beltsville, Md., 1967—. Contbr. 100 articles to profl. jours.; mem. editorial bd. BioScience, 1960-63. Trustee John Hopkins U., 1982-85. Merchant Marine USCG, 1944-46. Recipient Pub. Service medal NASA, 1977, Whiting medal Johns Hopkins U., 1989. Fellow Am. Pub. Health Assn.; mem. ASCE, AAAS (Newcomb Cleveland prize 1977), Am. Water Works Assn., Water Pollution Control Fedn., Am. Soc. Microbiology, N.Y. Acad. Scis. Club: Cosmos. NASA experimenter Mariner 9 mission, 1971, Viking Mission Labeled Release Life Detection expt., 1976; mem. team Mars oxident expt. for Russian Mars lander 1996; patentee in field; inventor PhoStrip process for wastewater nutrient removal, microbial radiorespirometry, nonfattening sweeteners use of D-Tagatose as antihyperglycemic agent and in diabetes treatment; applications of firefly bioluminescent assay for adenosine triphosphate bioassays and biomass determination. Home: 3180 Harness Creek Rd Annapolis MD 21403-1614 Office: Biospherics Inc 12051 Indian Creek Ct Beltsville MD 20705-4223 *Man's ability to accumulate information through learning and to pass it on to his descendents frees his generations from endless repetition. He may hope to understand the universe and his place in it.*

LEVIN, HENRY MORDECAI, economist; b. N.Y.C., Dec. 7, 1938. B.S. cum laude, NYU, 1960; M.A., Rutgers U., 1962, Ph.D., 1967. assoc. research scientist, Grad. Sch. Pub. Adminstrn., NYU, 1965-66; research assoc. social econs. Econ. Studies div. Brookings Inst., Washington, 1966-68; asst. prof. edn. and econs. Stanford U., Calif., 1968-69, assoc. prof. econs., 1969-75, prof. econs. and edn., 1975—, David Jacks Prof. of Higher Edn. and Econs., 1992—, fellow Ctr. for Advanced Studies in Behavioral Scis., 1976-77, dir. Inst. Research on Ednl. Fin. and Governance, 1978-84. Office: Stanford U Ctr Edn Rsch Ceras Bldg 109 Stanford CA 94305

LEVIN, IRA, author, playwright; b. N.Y.C., Aug. 27, 1929; s. Charles and Beatrice (Schlansky) L.; m. Gabrielle Aronsohn, Aug. 20, 1960 (div. 1968); children: Adam, Jared, Nicholas; m. Phyllis Finkel, Aug. 26, 1979 (div. 1982). Student, Drake U., Des Moines, 1946-48; A.B., N.Y. U., 1950. Freelance writer, 1950—; author: A Kiss Before Dying, 1953, Rosemary's Baby, 1967, This Perfect Day, 1970, The Stepford Wives, 1972, The Boys from Brazil, 1976, Sliver, 1991; playwright: No Time for Sergeants, 1955, Interlock, 1958, Critic's Choice, 1960, General Seeger, 1962, Drat! the Cat, 1965, Dr. Cook's Garden, 1967, Veronica's Room, 1973, Deathtrap, 1978, Break a Leg, 1979, Cantorial, 1989. Served with U.S. Army, 1953-55. Recipient Edgar Allan Poe award, 1953, 80. Mem. Dramatists Guild (council mem. 1980—). Office: care Harold Ober Assocs 425 Madison Ave New York NY 10017-1110

LEVIN, JACK, physician, educator, biomedical investigator; b. Newark, Oct. 11, 1932; s. Joseph and Anna (Greengold) L.; m. Francine Courtney, Apr. 13, 1975. B.A. magna cum laude, Yale U., 1953, M.D. cum laude, 1957. Diplomate: Am. Bd. Internal Medicine. Intern in medicine Grace-New Haven Hosp., 1957-58, asst. resident in medicine, 1960-62; chief resident in medicine Yale-New Haven Med. Ctr., 1964-65; clin. assoc. Nat. Cancer Inst., Bethesda, Md., 1958-60; fellow in hematology Johns Hopkins U. Sch. Medicine and Hosp., Balt., 1962-64, mem. faculty, 1965-82, prof. medicine, 1978-82; prof. lab. medicine, prof. medicine U. Calif. Sch. Medicine, San Francisco, 1982—; dir. hematology lab. and blood bank San Francisco VA Med. Ctr., 1982-93, dir. flow cytometry facility, 1987-90; cons. in field. Author: (with P.D. Zieve) Disorders of Hemostasis, 1976; editor: (with E. Cohen and F.B. Bang) Biomedical Applications of the Horseshoe Crab (Limulidae), 1979, (with S.W. Watson and T.J. Novitsky) Endotoxins and Their Detection with the Limulus Amebocyte Lysate Test, 1982, Detection of Bacterial Endotoxins with The Limulus Amebocyte Lysate Test, 1987, (with others) Bacterial Endotoxins. Structure, Biomedical Significance, and Detection with the Limulus Amebocyte Lysate Test, 1985, Megakaryocyte Development and Function, 1986, Bacterial Endotoxins. Pathophysiological Effects, Clinical Significance, and Pharmacological Control, 1988, Molecular Biology and Differentiation of Megakaryocytes, 1990, Bacterial Endotoxins: Cytokine Mediators and New Therapies for Sepsis, 1991, Bacterial Endotoxin: Recognition and Effector Mechanisms, 1993, Bacterial Endotoxins: Basic Science to Anti-Sepsis Strategies, 1994; mem. editorial bd. Blood Cells, Jour. Endotoxin Rsch.; contbr. numerous articles to profl. jours; developer (with F.B. Bang) Limulus test for bacterial endotoxins. Mem. Yale Alumni Schs. Com. for Md., 1967-82, for San Francisco, 1986—; mem. sci. adv. bd. Nat. Aquarium, Balt., 1978-82; mem. corp. Marine Biol. Lab., 1965—; trustee Marine Biol. Lab., 1988-93. Served with USPHS, 1958-60. Markle scholar, 1968-73; recipient USPHS Rsch. Career Devel. award, 1970-75; Royal Soc. Medicine fellow Oxford (Eng.) U., 1972; Josiah Macy Jr. Found. faculty scholar, 1978-79; Fredrick B. Bang award for rsch. in bacterial endotoxins, 1986. Fellow ACP; mem. Am. Soc. Hematology, Am. Soc. Clin. Investigation, Internat. Soc. Hematology, Internat. Soc. Explt. Hematology, Am. Soc. Investigative Pathology, Am. Fedn. Clin. Rsch., Soc. Exptl. Biology and Medicine, Internat. Endotoxin Soc., So. Soc. Clin. Investigation, Western Assn. Physicians, Soc. Invertebrate Pathology, Soc. Analytical Cytology, Cell Kinetics Socs., Calif. Acad. Medicine, Phi Beta Kappa, Sigma Xi. Clubs: 14 W Hamilton St, Tudor and Stuart; Yale (San Francisco).

LEVIN, JACK S., lawyer; b. Chgo., May 1, 1936; s. Frank J. and Judy G. (Skerball) L.; m. Sandra Sternberg, Aug. 24, 1958; children: Lisa, Laura, Leslie, Linda. B.S. summa cum laude, Northwestern U., 1958; LL.B. summa cum laude, Harvard U., 1961. Bar: Ill. 1961; C.P.A. (gold medalist), Ill., 1958. Law clk. to chief judge U.S. Ct. of Appeals 2d Circuit, N.Y.C., 1961-62; asst. for tax matters to Solicitor Gen. of U.S., Washington, 1965-67; assoc. law firm Kirkland & Ellis, Chgo., 1962-65, ptnr., 1967—; frequent lectr. on legal aspects of venture capital transactions, mergers, acquisitions, and workouts, fed. income tax matters; vis. com. Harvard Law Sch., 1987-93; lectr. Law Sch., U. Chgo., 1988—. Author book on structuring venture capital, pvt. equity and entrepreneurial transactions; co-author multi-volume work on mergers, acquisitions and buyouts; case editor Harvard Law Rev., 1959-61; contbr. numerous articles to legal jours. and chpts. to law books. Parliamentarian Winnetka (Ill.) Town Meetings, 1974-83, 89, 93; chmn. nat. fund raising drive Harvard Law Sch., 1985-86, 90-91, chmn. lawyers' divsn. Jewish United Fund of Chgo., 1993-95. Mem. ABA (chmn. subcom. 1968-79), Fed. Bar Assn., Chgo. Bar Assn. (exec. com. 1985—), Am. Coll. Tax Counsel. Clubs: Chgo., Mid-Am. (Chgo.) bd. dirs. 1985-88); Birchwood (Highland Park, Ill.) (pres. 1980-82). Home: 1220 Sunset Rd Winnetka IL 60093-3628 Office: Kirkland & Ellis 200 E Randolph Dr Chicago IL 60601-6401

LEVIN, JACOB JOSEPH, mathematician, educator; b. N.Y.C., Dec. 21, 1926; s. David and Rose (Kaplan) L.; m. Avis Harriet Ofstrock, Sept. 7, 1952; children—Debra F., Kenneth E., Claire B. B.E.E., Coll. City N.Y., 1949; Ph.D., Mass. Inst. Tech., 1953. Instr. math. Purdue U., 1953-55; lectr. Mass. Inst. Tech., 1955-56; staff mem. Lincoln Lab. of Mass. Inst. Tech., 1956-63; prof. math. U. Wis., 1963—; vis. prof. U. B.C., Vancouver, Can., 1977-78. Contbr. articles to profl. jours. Served with AUS, 1945-46. NSF sr. postdoctoral fellow, 1970-71. Mem. Am. Math. Soc., Soc. Indsl. and Applied Math., Sigma Xi. Home: 1110 Frisch Rd Madison WI 53711-3120

LEVIN, JERRY WAYNE, cosmetics executive; b. San Antonio, Tex., Apr. 18, 1944; s. Bernard H. and Marion (Bromberg) L.; m. Carol Lee Motel, Dec. 18, 1966; children—Joshua, Abby. B.S.E.E., U. Mich., 1966, B.S.E. in Math., 1966; M.B.A., U. Chgo., 1968. With Tex. Instruments, Dallas, 1968-72; with Marsh & McLennan, Chgo., 1972-74; with The Pillsbury Co., Mpls., from 1974, exec. v.p. corporate devel., treas., from 1985, exec. v.p. corp. devel., chmn. Haagen-Dazs div., 1987-88; exec. v.p. corp. devel. and chmn. S&A Restaurant Corp., from 1988; chmn. Burger King Corp., 1988-89; exec. v.p. MacAndrews Forbes, N.Y.; pres., CEO Revlon Inc.; bd. dirs. Apogee Enterprises, Inc. Coleman, Ecolabs, Meridian. Bd. dirs. United Way, N.Y.; N.Y. Hillek, N.Y. Fedn., N.Y. Philharm. Fragrance Found., U. Mich. Engring. Sch. Mem. U. Chgo. Alumni Bd., Oak Ridge Country Club, Ventana Canyon Country Club, Minneapolis Club. Home: 15 E 70th St New York NY 10021 Office: Revlon Consumer Products Corp 625 Madison Ave New York NY 10022

LEVIN, MARTIN P., publishing executive, lawyer; b. Phila., Dec. 20, 1918; s. Harry and Sarah (Haimon) L.; m. Marcia Obrasky, Apr. 2, 1939; children: Jeremy Carl, Wendy, Hugh Lauter. B.S., Temple U., 1950, postgrad. (personnel Council fellow), 1950; J.D., N.Y. Law Sch., 1983. Adminstrv. officer U.S. War Dept., 1940-44, VA, 1945-50; sr. v.p. Grosset & Dunlap, Inc., N.Y.C., 1950-66; pres. book pub. div. Times Mirror Co., N.Y.C., 1966-83; cons. Times Mirror; counsel Cowan, Leibowitz and Latman, P.C.; adj. prof. Benjamin N. Cardozo Law Sch., N.Y. Law Sch., Stetson Law Sch., Pace U. Grad. Sch.; resident fellow pub. course Stanford U.; cons. Ford Found., India, 1957-58; mem. Pres.'s Working Com. on Books and Publs. Abroad; mem. exec. com. Ctr. for the Book, Libr. of Congress; trustee Harvard U. Press; mem. Assn. Am. Pubs. delegation to USSR, 1976, to People Republic of China, 1979; former chmn. Franklin Book Programs. Author: Be Your Own Agent, 1995. Trustee William Alanson White Inst.; chmn. Assn. Am. Book Pubs., 1982. With AUS, 1944-45. Recipient Pub. of Yr. award ADL, 1980, Friend of Jerusalem award, 1985. Mem. Assn. Am. Pubs. (chmn., dir. exec. com.), Pubs. Lunch Club (past pres.), Friars Club. Home: 221 Kirby Ln Rye NY 10580-4307 also: 9150 Blind Pass Rd Sarasota FL 34242-2978 Office: Cowan Leibowitz & Latman 605 3rd Ave New York NY 10158-0121

LEVIN, MARVIN EDGAR, physician; b. Terre Haute, Ind., Aug. 11, 1924; s. Benjamin A. and Bertha Levin; m. Barbara Yvonne Symes; 3 children. BA, Washington U., St. Louis, 1947, MD, 1951. Diplomate Am. Bd. Internal Medicine. Intern Barnes Hosp., St. Louis, 1951-52, asst. resident in internal medicine, 1952-53; Nat. Polio Found. fellow in metabolism and endocrinology Sch. Medicine, Washington U., St. Louis, 1953-55; prof. clin. medicine, assoc. dir. Metabolism Clinic Endocrine, Diabetes and Metabolism Clinic, Washington U., St. Louis; attending physician Barnes Hosp., Jewish Hosp. St. Louis; vis. prof. endocrinology and diabetes Internat. Sino-Am. Exch. Program, People's Republic China, 1982, Jakarta, Indonesia, Taipei, 1994; cons. endocrine panel U.S. Pharmacopeia: med. dir. Harry and Flora D. Freund Meml. Found. Co-editor: (with L.W. O'Neal and J. Bowker) The Diabetic Foot, 1973, 5th edit., 1993; contbr. numerous articles to profl. jours., book chpts. With U.S. Army, 1944-46. Fellow ACP, Soc. Vascular Medicine and Biology; mem. AMA, Am. Diabetes Assn. (nat. bd. dirs. 1984-86, chmn. publ. com. 1987-88, bd. dirs. Mo. chpt. 1987—, editor Clin. Diabetes 1988-93, co-editor Diabetes Spectrum 1988-93), St. Louis Clin. Diabetes Assn. (pres. 1965-66), Am. Thyroid Assn., Endocrine Soc., Am. Fedn. for Clin. Rsch. (emeritus), St. Louis Soc. Internal Medicine, St. Louis Internist Club (pres. 1972), Sigma Xi, Alpha Omega Alpha. Avocations: golf, collecting Belle Epoque French prints. Office: 732 Fairfield Lake Dr Chesterfield MO 63017-5928

LEVIN, MICHAEL DAVID, lawyer; b. Chgo., Oct. 11, 1942; s. Joseph F. and Libbie (Landman) L.; children: Victoria, David, Elizabeth; m. Carol A. MeErlean, Oct. 10, 1993. AB, U. Mich., 1964, JD, 1967. Bar: Ill. 1967. Assoc. Arnstein, Gluck, Weitzenfeld & Minow, Chgo., 1967-73, ptnr., 1973-81; ptnr. Latham & Watkins, Chgo., 1982—. Mem. ABA, Chgo. Bar Assn. (chmn. securities law 1982-83), Standard Club, Met. Club. Republican. Jewish. Office: Latham & Watkins Sears Towers Ste 5800 Chicago IL 60606

LEVIN, MICHAEL H(OWARD), environmental scientist, engineer; b. N.Y.C., Sept. 25, 1936; s. Irving and Bess (Ruderman) L.; m. Catherine Arnold Brown, Mar. 21, 1959 (div. 1976); 1 child, Eleanor Marie; m. Lorna MacDonald, Sept. 6, 1986. B.S., U. Vt., 1958; M.S., Rutgers U., 1960, Ph.D., 1964. Cert. sr. ecologist, 1981. Research assoc. N.Y. Bot. Garden, Bronx, 1964; asst. prof. biology U. Notre Dame, Ind., 1964-66, U. Man., Winnipeg, Can., 1966-68; asst. prof. land architecture and regional planning U. Pa., Phila., 1968-73; adj. prof. Del. State Coll., Dover, 1980—; dir. Environ. Research Assocs., Inc., Villanova, Pa., 1970—, Ambric Environ. Scis., Inc., Phila., 1980—. Contbr. articles to profl. jours. Served to 1st. lt. Med. Service Corps, USAR, 1961-67. Fellow AAAS; mem. Ecol. Soc. Am., Phila. Bot. Club, Am. Assn. Plant Taxonomy, Sigma Xi, Alpha Zeta. Jewish. Avocations: skiing; sailing; tennis; environmental history. Home: 414 Mill Rd Upper Darby PA 19083-3740 Office: 3502 Scotts Ln Philadelphia PA 19129-1506

LEVIN, MORTON D(AVID), artist, printmaker, educator; b. N.Y.C., Oct. 7, 1923; s. Louis and Martha (Berusch) L. B.S. in Art Edn, CCNY, 1948; student in painting, Andre LHote, Paris, 1950; in sculpture, Ossip Zadkine, 1950; etching and engraving, Federico Castellon, N.Y.C., 1948, Stanley W. Hayter, Paris, 1951; student in lithography, Pratt Graphic Art Center, N.Y.C., 1966. Founder, dir., instr. printmaking, painting Morton Levin Graphics Workshop, San Francisco, 1972-91. One-man shows include Galerie Breteau, Paris, 1952, Winston Gallery, San Francisco, 1972, 80, 83, 85-94; exhibited in group shows at Seattle Art Mus., 1946-49, Libr. of Congress, Washington, 1946, 49, Pa. Acad. Fine Arts, 1948, Mus. Modern Art, Paris, 1951, Pallazzo del Academia, Genoa, Italy, 1951; represented in permanent collections at N.Y. Pub. Libr., Libr. of Congress, History of Medicine Divsn., Nat. Libr. Medicine; work featured in Jour. Erotic Arts, Yellow Silk #34, 1990. Served with inf. U.S. Army, 1943-45. Recipient Bryan Meml. prize Villager Travel Exhbn., N.Y.C., 1964, 3d prize Washington Sq. Art Exhbn., 1964. *My goal has been to define our world and the primal forces of desire, love, procreation, death, and rebirth. To this end, I have created a universe in my art inhabited by the natural and fantastic. Humans, birds, and beasts, male and female, interact and strive on an elemental level. In a romantic expressionistic style, I have attempted to illuminate the human condition.*

LEVIN, MURRAY SIMON, lawyer; b. Phila., Feb. 8, 1943; s. Sidney Michael and Eva (Goldstein) L.; m. Jalond Marie Robinson, June 9, 1968; children—Adrianne Lesley, Alexandra Amber-Rose. BA, Haverford Coll., 1964; MA, Harvard U., 1968, LLB, 1968; cert., Hague Internat. Acad. Law, 1967. Bar: Pa. 1968, U.S. Dist. Ct. (ea. dist.) Pa. 1970, U.S. Ct. Appeals (3d cir.) 1970, U.S. Supreme Ct. 1979. Instr. English Harvard U., 1965-68; law clk. to U.S. Dist. Ct. Judge, 1968-70; instr. govt. Haverford Coll., 1970-71; litigation ptnr. Pepper, Hamilton & Scheetz, Phila., 1970—, mem. firm exec. com., 1993—; overseas lectr. U.K., Sweden, Germany, Senegal, Kenya, Cameroon, Morocco, 1988-94; law seminar speaker. Weekly commentator radio Sta. WCAU Dick Clayton Show, TV program Morningside, 1973-76; weekly host, interviewer Sta. WHYY, 1974-79; TV commentator O.J. Simpson trial, 1995; contbr. articles to profl. jours. Chmn. Phila. Coun. Expt. in Internat. Living, 1967-70; mem. Phila. Urban Coalition Housing Task Force, 1968-80; chmn. coll. divsn. Allied Jewish Appeal, 1968-70; pres. Ctrl. Phila. Reform Dems., 1973-74; bd. dirs. Grad. Hosp. Phila., 1975—; Friends Ctrl. Sch., 1988—, divsn. Fgn. Policy Rsch. Com. Mid. East Coun., 1992-94, Mid. East Forum, 1994—; Root-Tilden fellow, 1964. Mem. ABA, Pa. Bar Assn. (ho. of dels.), Phila. Bar Assn. (young lawyers exec. bd. 1973, bd. govs. 1985-88, zone del. 1988—, chmn. profl. guidance com. 1989-92, co-chmn. internat. human rights com. 1990-91), Phila. Trial Lawyers Assn., Assn. Internat. des Jeunes Avocats Brussels (bd. dirs. 1981-85, 1st Am. pres. 1985-88), Union Internationale des Avocats Paris (advisor to pres.; mem. exec. com. 1993—, pres.-elect Am. chpt. 1993-95, pres. Am. chpt. 1995—), Am. Law Inst., Am. Judicature Soc., Phi Beta Kappa. Office: Pepper Hamilton & Scheetz 3000 2 Logan Sq 18th & Arch Sts Philadelphia PA 19103-2799

LEVIN, NEIL D., bank executive. AB, Lafayette Coll., 1976; MBA, Long Island U., 1978; JD, Hofstra U., 1981. Legs. asst. for banking and housing U.S. Senator Alfonse D'Amato, 1981-83; with U.S. Senate Com. on Banking, Housing and Urban Affairs, 1983-85; v.p. Goldman, Sachs & Co, N.Y.C., 1985—; chmn. bd. Fed. Home Loan Bank of N.Y., N.Y.C.; adv. com. Fed. Home Loan Mortgage Corp., 1987—. Office: Federal Home Loan Bank 1 World Trade Ctr New York NY 10048-0001

LEVIN, PETER J., hospital administrator, public health professor; b. N.Y.C., Apr. 25, 1939; s. Sol and Kate (Gottlieb) L.; m. Judith S. Bolton, June 3, 1967; children: Edward, Gael, Karen. B.A., Harvard U., 1961; M.P.H., Yale U., 1965; Sc.D., Johns Hopkins U., 1969. Asso. exec. dir. Bronx (N.Y.) Municipal Hosp. Center, 1970-72; exec. dir. New Haven Health Care, Inc., 1972-74; assoc. administr. Dept. Health, 1974-77; assoc. v.p. med. affairs, exec. dir. Stanford U. Hosp., 1977-81; asst. clin. prof.

dept. epidemiology and pub. health Yale Med. Sch., 1973-75; assoc. clin. prof. dept. community health Albert Einstein Coll. Medicine, 1976-77; clin. assoc. prof. dept. family, community and preventive medicine Stanford U., 1978-81; dean Coll. Pub. Health, prof. health administrn. U. Okla. Oklahoma City, 1982-84; dean Coll. Pub. Health U. South Fla., Tampa, 1984-94, prof. pub. health, 1984—; vis. scholar Hoover Inst, Stanford U. 1994-95. Chmn. Hosp. Cost Containment Bd., State of Fla., 1985-88, Fla. HMO Quality Care Interagy. Task Force, 1987, Hillsborough County Health Care Adv. Bd., 1990-92; Served with USPHS, 1965-67. Fellow Am. Coll. Healthcare Execs., Am. Public Health Assn. Club: Fly (Cambridge, Mass.). Office: Destin Cmty Hosp Destin FL 32541 Home: 13922 Shady Shores Dr Tampa FL 33613-1900

LEVIN, RICHARD C., lawyer; b. Dallas, June 15, 1945; s. Paul Michael and Yetta Gail (Caplan) L.; m. Kay Robins, June 18, 1982; children: Edward C., Henry A. BA, Tulane U., 1967; JD, Georgetown U., 1970. Bar: Tex. 1975. Law clerk 5th cir. U.S. Ct. Appeals, 1970-71; assoc. Sulivan & Cromwell, N.Y.C., 1971-74; assoc. Akin, Gump, Strauss, Hauer & Feld L.L.P., Dallas, 1974-77, ptnr., 1978—; with Dallas Mgmt. com., 1989—; co-head litigation sect. Akin, Gump, Strauss, Hauer & Feld, head antitrust sect., internat. litigation sect.; spkr. in field. Contbr. articles to profl. jours. Former mem. exec. bd. Dallas Opera; former mem. bd. govs. Dallas Symphony; corp. com. Dallas Mus. Fine Arts; former mem., v.p. bd. trustees Hist. Preservation League; former mem. Landmark Com. City Dallas, bd. trustees Arts Magnet Sch.; former mem., dep. vice chmn., mgmt. com. Arts Dist. in Dallas; former chmn. Task Force Multi-Purpose Performing Arts Hall Dallas Opera, Dallas Ballet; bd. dirs. Dallas Opera, Salzburg Music Festival. Mem. Dallas Bar Assn. (coun. mem. Antitrust, Trade Regulation sect. 1987—, internat. law sect. 1990—). Jewish. Avocations: classical music, art, sports. Home: 4408 St Johns Dallas TX 75205 Office: Akin Gump Strauss Hauer & Feld 4100 First City Ctr 1700 Pacific Ave Dallas TX 75201-4618

LEVIN, RICHARD CHARLES, economist; b. San Francisco, Apr. 7, 1947; s. D. Derek and Phylys M. (Goldstein) L.; m. Jane Ellen Aries, June 24, 1968; children: Jon, Daniel, Sarah, Rebecca. BA, Stanford (Calif.) U., 1968; LittB, Oxford (Eng.) U., 1971; PhD, Yale U., 1974; LLD (hon.), Princeton U., 1993, Harvard U., 1994. With Yale U., New Haven, 1974—, pres., 1993—, chmn. econs. dept., 1987-92, Frederick William Beinecke prof. econs., 1992—, dean Grad. Sch., 1992-93; rsch. assoc. Nat. Bur. Econ. Rsch., Cambridge, Mass., 1985-90; program dir. Internat. Inst. Applied System Analysis, Vienna, Austria, 1990-92; cons. numerous law and bus. firms; exec. com. Consortium on Financing Higher Edn., bd. trustees Tanner Lectures on Human Values. Trustee Hopkins Sch., New Haven, 1988—, Yale-New Haven Hosp., 1993—, Univs. Rsch. Assn., 1994—. Mem. Am. Econ. Assn., Econometric Soc. Democrat. Jewish. Office: Yale U 105 Wall St New Haven CT 06520

LEVIN, RICHARD LOUIS, English language educator; b. Buffalo, Aug. 31, 1922; s. Bernard and Meta (Block) L.; m. Muriel Abrams, June 22, 1952; children: David, Daniel. B.A., U. Chgo., 1943, M.A., 1947, Ph.D., 1957. Mem. faculty U. Chgo., 1949-57, asst. prof. English, 1953-57; prof. English, SUNY at Stony Brook, 1957—, acting chmn. English dept., 1960-63, 65-66; mem. adv. bd. World Center for Shakespeare Studies; mem. acad. adv. council Shakespeare Globe Ctr.; Fulbright lectr., 1984-85. Author, cons. in field.; Editor: Tragedy: Plays, Theory and Criticism, 1960, The Question of Socrates, 1961, Tragedy Alternate, 1965, (by Thomas Middleton) Michaelmas Term, 1966, The Multiple Plot in English Renaissance Drama, 1971, New Readings vs Old Plays: Recent Trends in the Reinterpretation of English Renaissance Drama, 1979. Served to lt. (j.g.) USNR, 1943-46, ETO. Recipient Explicator award, 1971; Am. Council Learned Socs. fellow, 1963-64; research fellow State N.Y., 1961, 65-68, 71, 73; NEH sr. fellow, 1974; Guggenheim fellow, 1978-79, Nat. Humanities Ctr. fellow, 1987-88; SUNY faculty exchange scholar. Mem. MLA (mem. adv. com. publs., mem. del. assembly), Internat. Shakespeare Assn., Shakespeare Assn. Am. (trustee), N.Y. Shakespeare Soc., Malone Soc., Joseph Crabtree Found., Marlowe Soc. Am., Medieval and Renaissance Drama Soc. (mem. council), AAUP, Inst. for Renaissance Interdisciplinary Studies. Democrat. Jewish. Home: 26 Sparks St Melville NY 11747-1727 Office: SUNY Humanities Bldg Stony Brook NY 11794

LEVIN, ROBERT BARRY, motion picture company executive; b. Chgo., May 31, 1943; s. Albert Harold and Sally Ethel (Bloom) L.; children: Jordan, Leigh; m. Pamela Knussman, Dec. 2, 1990; 1 stepchild, Taylor Thompson. BS in Journalism and Comm, U. Ill., 1965. Copywriter Sears Roebuck and Co., Chgo., 1965-66; pub. relations Natural Gas Pipeline Co. Am., Chgo., 1966-69; accounts exect. Hurvis Binzer and Churchill, Chgo., 1969-70; with McCann-Erickson, Chgo., 1975-82, acct. supr., 1975-79; mgmt. supr. Needham Harper Worldwide, Chgo., 1982-85; pres. mktg. Walt Disney Co., Burbank, Calif., 1985-94, chief corp. mktg. and comm., 1994—.

LEVIN, ROBERT JOSEPH, retail grocery chain store executive; b. Everett, Mass., Mar. 19, 1928; s. Edward A. and Rose E. L.; m. Carrol Silverman, June 21, 1948; children: Richard J., Cathy Levin Shuman. B.A. cum laude, U. Wis., 1948. From dir. store ops. and purchasing to pres., treas. C.B. Perkins Tobacco Co., Boston, 1948-73; from dir. store ops. and purchasing to pres., treas. C.B. Perkins Tobacco Co. (co. merged with Stop & Shop), Boston, 1970; v.p., then pres. Medi Mart div. Stop & Shop, 1971-75; group v.p. Stop & Shop Cos., Inc., Boston, 1975-79; sr. v.p. Stop & Shop Cos., Inc., 1979-82, vice. chmn., 1982—; also dir.; bd. dirs. S.A.Y. Industries, Sterling Inc.; chmn. bd. S.A.Y. Packaging, 1988—. Bd. dirs. U. Wis. Found. Mem. Nat. Mass Retailing Inst. (dir.). Jewish. Home: 65 Grove St Apt 343 Wellesley MA 02181-7806 Office: 1776 Heritage Dr Quincy MA 02171-2101 also: PO Box 369 Boston MA 02101-0369

LEVIN, RONALD MARK, law educator; b. St. Louis, May 11, 1950; s. Marvin S. and Lois (Cohn) L.; m. Anne Carol Goldberg, July 29, 1989. BA magna cum laude, Yale U., 1972; JD, U. Chgo., 1975. Bar: Mo. 1975, D.C. 1977. Law clk. to Hon. John C. Godbold U.S. Ct. Appeals, 5th cir., 1975-76; assoc. Sutherland, Asbill & Brennan, Washington, 1976-79; asst. prof. law Washington St. Louis, 1979-80, assoc. prof. law, 1980-85, prof. law, 1985—, assoc. dean, 1990-93; cons. Administrv. Conf. U.S. 1979-81, 93-95. Co-author: Administrative Law & Process, 3d edit., 1990; mem. adv. bd. Administrv. Law Rev., 1985—. Chair senate coun. Washington U., 1988-90. Mem. ABA (coun. sect. administrv. law and regulatory practice 1986-89), Assn. Am. Law Sch. (chair sect. administrv. law 1993, chair sect. litigation 1995). Home: 7352 Kingsbury Saint Louis MO 63130 Office: Wash Univ Sch Law Campus Box 1120 Saint Louis MO 63130

LEVIN, SANDER M., congressman; b. Detroit, Sept. 6, 1931; s. Saul R. and Bess (Levinson) L.; m. Victoria Schlafer, 1957. B.A., U. Chgo., 1952; M.A., Columbia U., 1954; LL.B., Harvard U. 1957. Supr. Oakland County Bd. Suprs., Mich., 1961-64; mem. Mich. Senate, 1965-70; fellow Kennedy Sch. Govt., Inst. Politics, Harvard U., Cambridge, Mass., 1975; asst. administr. AID, Washington, 1977-81; mem. 98th-104th Congresses from 17th (now 12th) Mich dist., 1983—; mem. ways and means com., subcoms. oversight and human resources; adj. prof. law Wayne State U., Detroit, 1971-74. Chmn. Mich. Dem. Com., 1968-69; Dem. Candidate for Gov., 1970, 74. Office: US Ho of Reps 2230 Rayburn HOB Washington DC 20515-2212*

LEVIN, SIMON, lawyer; b. Newark, Aug. 4, 1942; m. Barbara Leslie Lasky, Dec. 21, 1989; children: David, Jennifer Menken, Yale, Michael, Jacob. BS cum laude, Lehigh U., 1964; JD, NYU, 1967, LLM in Taxation, 1974. Bar: N.J. 1967, U.S. Tax Ct. 1971, U.S. Ct. Claims 1972, N.Y. 1980. Assoc. Shanley & Fisher, Newark, 1970, Hannoch Weisman, Newark, 1970-73; ptnr. Robinson, Wayne, Levin, Riccio & La Sala, Newark, 1973-88; mem., co-chmn. tax sect. Sills Cummis Zuckerman Radin Tischman Epstein & Gross, Newark, 1988—; civilian aide to Sec. Army for N.J., 1992—. mem. N.J. Dept. Treasury Transition Team for Gov. Christine Todd Whitman, 1993-94; lectr., panelist numerous orgns. Co-author: Taxation Investors in Securities and Commodities, 1983, 2d edit., 1984, supplement, 1986, Estate Planning and Administration in New Jersey, 1987; contbr. articles to profl. jours. Trustee, mem. exec. com. Jewish Comty. Found., MetroWest, Whippany, N.J., pres., 1979-83; trustee, mem. exec. com. Israel Bond Campaign MetroWest, Livingston, N.J., 1988—, chmn., 1988-89; commr. N.J. Vietnam Vets. Meml. Commn., Princeton, 1994—. Capt. U.S. Army, 1968-69,

Vietnam. Recipient Cohn Leadership award Jewish Fedn. MetroWest, 1982, Endowment Achievement award Coun. Jewish Fedns., 1986. Fellow Am. Coll. Tax Counsel; mem. ABA, N.J. Bar Assn. (chmn. commodities sect. 1982-86), Essex County Bar Assn. (chmn. sect. taxation 1974-76), Monmouth County Bar Assn., Phi Delta Phi. Avocations: tennis, skiing, politics, opera, charitable activities. Office: Sills Cummis Zuckerman Radin Tischman Epstein & Gross 1 Riverfront Plz Newark NJ 07102-5401

LEVIN, SIMON ASHER, mathematician, ecologist, educator; b. Balt., Apr. 22, 1941; s. Theodore S. and Clara G. L.; m. Carole Lotte Leiffer, Aug. 4, 1964; children: Jacob, Rachel. BA in Math, Johns Hopkins U., 1961; PhD in Math. (NSF fellow), U. Md., 1964; DSc (hon.), Ea. Mich. U., 1990. Teaching asst. U. Md., 1961-62, research assoc., 1964, visitor, 1968; NSF fellow U. Calif., Berkeley, 1964-65; asst. prof. math. Cornell U., 1965-70, assoc. prof. applied math., ecology, theoretical and applied math., 1971-77, prof. applied math. and ecology, 1977-92, Charles A. Alexander prof. biology, 1985-92, adj. prof., 1992—, chmn. sect. ecology and systematics div. biol. scis., 1974-79, dir. Ecosystems Rsch. Ctr., 1980-87, dir. Ctr. for Environ. Rsch., 1987-90; George Moffett prof. biology Princeton U., 1992—, assoc. faculty mem. applied math., 1992—; vis. scholar U. Wash., 1973-74; vis. scientist Weizmann Inst., Rehovot, Israel, 1977, 80; hon. prof. U. B.C., 1979-80; Lansdowne lectr. U. Victoria, 1981; disting. vis. scientist SUNY, Stony Brook, 1984; vis. fellow All Souls Coll., U. Oxford, 1988; MacArthur award Ecol. Soc. of Am., 1988; co-chmn. Gordon Conf. on Theoretical Biology, 1970, chmn. Gordon Conf. on Theoretical Biology and Biomath. 1971; chmn. Am. Math. Soc./Soc. Indsl. and Applied Maths. Com. on Maths. in Life Scis., 1973-79; mem. core panel on math. in biol. scis., program com. Internat. Congress Mathematicians, 1977-78; co-convenor Biomath. Conf., Oberwolfach, W. Ger., 1978; co-dir. Internat. Ctr. for Theoretical Physics Autumn Course on Math. Ecology, Trieste, Italy, 1982, 86, 90; co-dir. Internat. Ctr. for Theoretical Physics Autumn Workshop on Math. Ecology, Trieste, Italy, 1988, 90, 92, 94; mem. adv. com. div. environ. scis. Oak Ridge Nat. Lab., 1978-81; vice chmn. math. Com. Concerned Scientists, N.Y.C., 1979—; mem. scientific panel Hudson River Found., 1982-86, chmn., 1985-86, bd. dirs. 1986—; mem. Commn. on Life Scis., NRC, 1983-89; mem. Health and Environ. Rsch. Adv. Com., Dept. of Energy, 1986-90; prin. lectr. Conf. Ed. on Math. Scis. course on math. ecology, 1985; mem. oversight rev. bd. U.S. Nat. Acid Precipitation Assessment Program; speaker commencement address Ea. Mich. U., 1990; Ostrom lectr. Wash. State U., Pullman, 1994; dir. Princeton Environ. Inst., Beijer Inst., Ctr. Environ. Sci. and Econs.; sci. bd. Santa Fe Inst. Editor: Lectures on Mathematics in the Life Sciences, vols. 7-12, 1974-79, Ecosystem Analysis and Prediction, 1974, (with R. H. Whittaker) Niche: Theory and Application, 1975, Studies in Mathematical Biology, 2 vols, 1978, New Perspectives in Ecotoxicology, 1983, Mathematical Population Biology, 1984, Mathematical Ecology, 1984, Math Ecology: An Introduction, 1986, (with others) Mathematical Ecology, 1988, (with others) Ecotoxicology: Problems and Approaches, 1989, (with others) Perspectives in Theoretical Ecology, 1989, (with T. Hallam and L. Gross) Applied Mathematical Ecology, 1989; (with T. Powell and John Steele) Patch Dynamics, 1993, Frontiers in Mathematical Biology, 1994; editor-in-chief Ecological Applications, 1988—; editor Ecology and Ecol. Monographs, 1975-77, Jour. Math. Biology, 1976—. mng. editor, 1979—, Biomath, 1976—, Lecture Notes in Biomath, 1973—; assoc. editor: Theoretical Population Biology, 1976-84; mem. editl. bd. Evolutionary Theory, 1976—, Discrete Applied Math, 1978-87, Internat. Jour. Math. and Computer Modelling, 1979—, Jour. Theoretical Biology; Princeton U. Press Complexity Series, 1992—; mng. editor Princeton U. Press Monographs in Population Biology, 1992—; also various other editl. positions. Recipient Disting. Statis. Ecologist award Internat. Assn. Ecology, 1994; Guggenheim fellow, 1979-80; Japanese Soc. for Promotion of Sci. fellow, 1983-84. Fellow AAAS (bd. dirs. 1994—), Am. Acad. Arts and Scis.; mem. Ecol. Soc. Am. (chmn. Mercer awards subcom. 1976, mem. coun. 1975-77, ad hoc com. to evaluate ecol. consequences of nuclear war 1982-83, pres.-elect 1989-90, prec. com. 1991-92), Soc. Indsl. and Applied Math. (mem. coun. 1977-79, coun. exec. com. 1978-79, coun. rep. to bd. trustees 1978-79, chmn. human rights com. 1980-83, mng. editor Jour. Applied Math. 1975-79), Am. Inst. Biol. Scis., Am. Math. Soc., (dir. short course on math. population biology 1983), Am. Soc. Naturalists, Soc. Math. Biology (pres. 1987-89), Brit. Ecol. Soc., Soc. Study Evolution, U.S. Com. for Israel Environment, Sigma Xi. Jewish. Home: 11 Beechtree Rd Princeton NJ 08540 Office: Princeton U Dept Ecology & Evolutionary Biology Eno Hall Princeton NJ 08544

LEVIN, SUSAN BASS, lawyer; b. Wilmington, Del., July 18, 1952; d. Max S. and Harriet C. (Rubin) Bass; children: Lisa, Amy. BA, U. of Rochester, 1972; JD, George Washington U., 1975. Bar: D.C. 1975, U.S. Ct. Claims 1975, N.J. 1976, Pa. 1981, U.S. Ct. Appeals (3d cir.) 1983, U.S. Supreme Ct. 1984. Law clk. to assoc. justice U.S. Ct. Claims, Washington, 1975-76; assoc. Covington & Burling, Washington, 1976-79; pvt. practice Cherry Hill, N.J., 1979-87; counsel Ballard, Spahr, Andrews & Ingersoll, Phila., Camden (N.J.), 1994—; mayor Cherry Hill, 1988—. Pres. Cherry Hill (N.J.) Twp. Council, 1986-88; trustee N.J. Coalition of Black Rel. Orgns., 1985-87; del. Dem. Presdl. Conv., 1992; chair Pam's List; trustee N.J. Alliance for Action, South Jersey Devel. Coun. Recipient Woman of Achievement award Camden County Girl Scouts, 1986. Mem. Tri County Women Lawyers (pres. 1984-85), N.J. Assn. Women Bus. Owners (state pres. 1984-85 named Woman of Yr. 1985). Office: Ballard Spahr Andrews & Ingersoll 1735 Market St Philadelphia PA 19135

LEVIN, THOMAS AUGUSTUS, health care corporation executive; b. Montgomery, Ala., Dec. 8, 1946; m. Carolyn Dahlgren; children: Daniel, Carey. BA, U. Ala., 1968; JD, U. N.C., 1971. Bar: N.C. 1971, D.C. 1972, N.Mex. 1974. Staff counsel N.Mex. Blue Cross & Blue Shield, Albuquerque, 1974-76, v.p. legal affairs, 1976-81, pres., chief exec. officer, 1981-86; chief exec. officer Rocky Mountain Health Care Corp., 1986—, Blue Cross and Blue Shield plans Colo., N.Mex., Nev.; bd. dirs. First Interstate Bank; bd. dirs., exec. com. Blue Cross and Blue Shield Assn.; chmn. bd. Health Plan Capital Svcs. Corp., Firstsource, HMO Colo., Inc., Rio Grande HMO, Rocky Mountain Life Ins. Co. Mem. policy rev. bd. U. Colo., Denver, The Pub. Edn. Coalition Steering Com. Served with U.S. Army, 1972-74. Mem. N.Mex. Bar Assn., Nat. Health Lawyers Assn., The Econ. Club Colo., Colo. Forum. Office: New Mexico Blue Cross 12800 Indian School Rd NE Albuquerque NM 87112

LEVIN, WILLIAM COHN, hematologist, former university president; b. Waco, Tex., Mar. 2, 1917; s. Samuel P. and Jeanette (Cohn) L.; m. Edna Seinsheimer, June 23, 1941; children: Gerry Lee Levin Hornstein, Carol Lynn Levin Cantini. B.A., U. Tex., 1938, M.D. 1941; M.D. (hon.), U. Montpellier, 1980. Diplomate: Am. Bd. Internal Medicine. Intern Michael Reese Hosp., Chgo., 1941-42; resident John Sealy Hosp., Galveston, Tex., 1942-44; mem. staff U. Tex. Med. Br. Hosps., Galveston, 1944—, assoc. prof. internal medicine, 1948-65, prof., 1965—; Warmoth prof. hematology U. Tex. Med. Br., 1966-86, Ashbel Smith prof., 1986—, pres., 1974-87; past chmn., past mem. cancer clin. investigation rev. com. Nat. Cancer Inst., past mem. Bd. Sci. Counselors. Exec. com., mem. nat. bd. Union Am. Hebrew Congregations; trustee Houston-Galveston Psychoanalytic Found., 1975-78, Menil Found., 1976-83. Recipient Nicholas and Katherine Leone award for administrv. excellence, 1977; decorated Palmes Académiques France. Fellow ACP, Internat. Soc. Hematology; mem. Am. Fedn. Clin. Research, Central Soc. Clin. Research, Am. Soc. Hematology, Phi Beta Kappa, Sigma Xi, Alpha Omega Alpha. Office: Am Indemnity Co PO Box 1259 Galveston TX 77553-1259

LEVINE, AARON, city planner; b. Phila., July 16, 1917; s. Harry and Sophia (Raditz) L.; m. Beatrice Blass, May 16, 1958; children—Karen Levine Porreca, Lisa, Dennys, Marc. Student, U. Pa., 1937-40, B.S. in Landscape Architecture, 1941; student, U. Calif., 1940-41; M.S. in Govt. Adminstrn, U. Pa., 1951. Sr. planner Phila. City Planning Commn., 1946-51; area planner Housing and Home Fin. Agy., Washington, 1952; exec. dir. Phila. Citizens Council on City Planning, 1952-62; pres. Oahu Devel. Conf., Honolulu, 1962-87; cons. and lectr. in field. Contbr. articles to profl. jours. Vice pres. Honolulu Symphony, 1966, Friends of Iolani Palace, 1966-74; bd. dirs. Hawaii Visitors Bur., 1970. Served with U.S. Army, 1943-45. Fellow Am. Soc. Landscape Architects; mem. AIA (hon.), Am. Soc. Planning Ofcls. (pres. 1967-68), Am. Planning Assn. Unitarian. Home: 290 Waverly St Apt 1 Honolulu HI 94025

LEVINE, ALAN J., entertainment company executive; b. L.A., Mar. 8, 1947; s. Phil and Shirley Ann (Lauber) L.; m. Judy B. Birnbaum, July 18, 1973; children: Andrea, Jay. BS in Bus., U. So. Calif., L.A., 1968, JD, 1971. Bar: Calif. 1972, U.S. Dist. Ct. (so. dist.) Calif. 1972. Ptnr. Pacht, Ross, Warne, Bernhard & Sears, L.A., 1971-78, Schiff, Hirsch & Schreiber, Beverly Hills, Calif., 1978-80, Armstrong, Hirsch & Levine, L.A., 1980-89; pres., COO, SONY Pictures Entertainment, Inc., Culver, Calif., 1989—; v.p. cinema circulus dept. cinema and TV, U. So. Calif., L.A., 1988-90, bd. councilors of dept., 1991—; bd. dirs. UCLA Entertainment Symposium, 1986-89. Chmn. cabinet entertainment div. United Jewish Fedn., L.A., 1990-93; bd. govs. Cedars-Sinai Med. Ctr., L.A., 1989—. Mem. Calif. State Bar Assn., L.A. County Bar Assn., Beverly Hills Bar Assn., Acad. Motion Picture Arts and Scis., Acad. TV Arts and Scis. Democrat. Office: SONY Pictures Entertainment Inc 10202 Washington Blvd Culver City CA 90232-3119*

LEVINE, ARNOLD JAY, molecular biology educator, researcher; b. Bklyn., July 30, 1939; s. Samuel and Marion (Wisot) L.; m. Linda Hirst, June 5, 1962; children—Samantha, Alison. B.A., Harper Coll. SUNY, 1961; Ph.D., U. Pa. 1966; Docteur Honoris Causa, Sorbonne, Paris, 1994. Postdoctoral fellow Calif. Inst. Tech., Pasadena, 1968; asst. prof. Princeton U., N.J., 1968-73, assoc. prof., 1973-76, prof. biochemistry, 1976-79; prof. dept. molecular biology, chmn. dept. SUNY, Stony Brook, 1979-83; Harry C. Wiess prof. molecular biology, chmn. dept. Princeton U., N.J., 1984—; mem. human cell biology panel NSF, 1971-72, mem. genetics and biology panel, 1972-73. Assoc. editor Jour. Cellular and Molecular Biology, 1984—; editor-in-chief Jour. Virology, 1984-94; editor Virology Jour., 1974-94; contbr. articles to profl. jours. Mem. cell biology panel Am. Heart Assn., 1978-80; mem. adv. com. virology and cell biology Am. Cancer Soc., 1974-78, vice chmn., 1976, chmn. 1977; mem. Nat. Bd. Med. Examiners. Dryfus fellow, recipient Lila Gruber Cancer Rsch. award, Am. Acad. of Dermatology, 1992, Charles Rodolphe Brupbacher award, Switzerland, 1993, Katherine Berkan Judd award, Memorial Sloan-Kettering Cancer Ctr., 1993, Joseph Steiner Prize, Switzerland, 1993, 17th Annual Bristol-Myers Squibb Disting. Cancer Rsch. award 1994. Mem. Am. Soc. Microbiology, AAAS, Nat. Acad. of Scis., 1991, Assn. Med. Sch. Microbiology (chmn. adv. and ednl. coms.), Sigma Xi. Office: Princeton U Dept Molecular Biology Princeton NJ 08544

LEVINE, ARTHUR ELLIOTT, academic administrator, educator; b. N.Y.C., June 16, 1948; s. Meyer and Katherine (Kalman) L.; m. Linda Christine Fentiman, Aug. 18, 1974; children: Jamie Sloan Fentiman, Rachel Elizabeth Fentiman. B.A. in Biology, Brandeis U., 1970; Ph.D., SUNY-Buffalo, 1976; LHD (hon.), U. Puget Sound, 1981. U. New Eng, Biddeford, Maine, 1983, Unity Coll., Maine, 1984, Greensboro Coll., N.C., 1988, Bradford Coll., 1989, Capital U., 1991, Taitung Tchrs. Coll., Taiwan, 1991, Albright Coll., 1993, William Jewell Coll., 1995, U. N.H., 1995. Sr. fellow Carnegie Council on Policy Studies in Higher Edn., Berkeley, Calif., 1975-80, Carnegie Found., Washington, 1980-82; pres. Bradford Coll., Mass., 1982-89; chmn. Inst. for Edn. Mgmt. Harvard U., Cambridge, Mass., 1989-94; pres. Tchrs. Coll., Columbia U., N.Y.C., 1994—; cons. to numerous colls., univs., U.S. Co-author: Reform of Undergraduate Education, 1973 (Am. Coun. on Edn. Book of Yr. award 1974), Quest for Common Learning, 1982, Opportunity in Adversity, 1985, Shaping Higher Education's Future, 1989, Higher Learning in America, 1993; author: Handbook on Undergraduate Curriculum, 1978, Why Innovation Fails, 1980, When Dreams and Heroes Died, 1980. Recipient Edn. Press Assn. Am. award, 1981, 89, 90, 93, 94; book named Book of Yr., Am. Coun. on Edn., 1974; Spencer fellow, 1979, 89, Guggenheim fellow, 1982. Office: Tchrs Coll Columbia U 525 W 120th St New York NY 10027

LEVINE, ARTHUR SAMUEL, physician, scientist; b. Cleve., Nov. 1, 1936; s. David Alvin and Sarah Ethel (Rubinstein) L.; m. Ruth Eleanor Rubin, Oct. 14, 1959; children: Amy Elizabeth, Raleigh Hannah, Jennifer Leah. AB, Columbia U., 1958; MD, Chgo. Med. Sch., 1964. Diplomate Am. Bd. Pediatrics, Am. Bd. Pediatric Hematology-Oncology. Intern in pediatrics U. Minn., Mpls., 1964-65, resident in pediatrics, 1965-66, USPHS fellow in hematology and genetics, 1966-67; capt. USPHS, 1967-92, rear adm., asst. surgeon gen., 1992—; clin. assoc. div. cancer treatment Nat. Cancer Inst., Bethesda, Md., 1967-69, sr. staff fellow, 1969-70, sr. investigator, 1970-73, head sect. infectious disease, pediatric oncology br., 1973-75, chief pediatric oncology br., 1975-82; sci. dir. Nat. Inst. Child Health and Human Devel., Bethesda, 1982—; clin. prof. medicine and pediatrics Georgetown U., Washington, 1975—; clin. prof. pediatrics Uniformed Svcs. U. Health Scis., Bethesda, 1983—; vis. prof. Cold Spring Harbor Lab., N.Y., 1973, Benares Hindu U., India, 1975, U. Minn., 1974, Hebrew U., Israel, 1981, U. Bologna, 1989, Northwestern U., 1992; Karon meml. lectr. U. So. Calif., 1983; Seham lectr. U. Minn., 1983. Author: Cancer in the Young, 1982; editor-in-chief The New Biologist, 1989-92; contbr. articles to profl. jours. Recipient Disting. Alumnus award Chgo. Med. Sch., 1972, NIH Dir.'s award, 1984, Meritorious Svc. award USPHS, 1987, Disting. Svc. award, 1991, Surgeon Gen.'s Exemplary Svc. award, 1993. Mem. Am. Soc. Clin. Investigation, Soc. Pediatric Research, Am. Assn. Cancer Research, Am. Soc. Hematology, Am. Soc. Clin. Oncology, Am. Fedn. Clin. Research, AAAS, Am. Soc. Microbiology, Am. Soc. Pediatric Hematology/Oncology. Office: NIH Bldg 31 Room 2A-50 Nat Inst Child Health and Human Devel 9000 Rockville Pike Bethesda MD 20892-2425

LEVINE, BERYL JOYCE, state supreme court justice; b. Winnipeg, Man., Can., Nov. 9, 1935; came to U.S., 1955; d. Maurice Jacob and Bella (Gutnik) Choslovsky; m. Leonard Levine, June 7, 1955; children: Susan Brauna, Marc Joseph, Sari Ruth, William Noah, David Karl. BA, U. Man., Winnipeg, 1965; JD with distinction, U. N.D., 1974. Assoc. Vogel, Branther, Kelly, Knutson, Weir & Bye, Ltd., Fargo, N.D., 1974-85; justice N.D. Supreme Ct., Bismarck, 1985—, chmn. jud. planning com. Bd. dirs. Fargo Youth Commn., 1974-77, Hospice of Red River Valley, Fargo; chmn. Gov.'s Commn. on Children at Risk, 1985. Named Outstanding Woman in N.D. Law, U. N.D. Law Women's Caucus, 1985. Mem. Cass County Bar Assn. (pres. 1984-85), N.D. State Bar Assn., Burleigh County Bar Assn., Order of Coif. Office: ND Supreme Ct State Capitol Judicial Wing 1st Fl 600 E Blvd Ave Bismarck ND 58504

LEVINE, CARL MORTON, motion picture exhibition, real estate executive; b. Bklyn., Sept. 24, 1931; s. Joseph M. and Frances Pearl (Smith) L.; m. Judith Ann Pollack, June 12, 1955 (div.); m. Miriam Scott Zeldman Duberstein, June 24, 1973; children: Jonathan Mark, Suzanne Beth; stepchildren: Debra Wiley-Hart, Douglas Reed Duberstein. BA, Bklyn. Coll., 1953; M in Dramatic Arts, Columbia U., 1955. Unit mgr., fl. and stage mgr., asst. dir., assoc. producer Sta. WRCA-TV NBC, N.Y.C., 1952-57; theatre mgr., asst. mgr. Forty Second St. Co. Lawbin Theatre Corp., Inc., N.Y.C., 1958-62, supr., 1963-65, gen. mgr. 1965-74; owner, mgr. Double L. Ranch, Adirondack Mountains, 1958-62; v.p., gen. mgr. Midtown Theatre Corp. Brandt Theatres, N.Y.C., 1974-86; gen. mgr., dir. theatre ops. Sameric Mgmt. Corp., Phila., 1986; comml. ops. mgr. Newmark & Co. Real Estate, Inc., N.Y.C., 1987-88; mng. dir. Loews 84th St. Sixplex Theater, N.Y.C., 1988-89; dir. ops. Eugene M. Grant & Co., N.Y.C., 1989—; founder, producer, v.p., treas. Mirca Prodns. Ltd., N.Y.C., 1981-88; bd. dirs. Variety Club, N.Y.C., 1981-86, entertainment div. UJA-Fedn., N.Y.C., 1989—; mem. Nat. Commn. Anti-Defamation League, 1965-86; v.p. Queens Coun. on Arts, 1977-80, pres., 1980-81. Chmn. producer Vets. Com. Variety Shows, VA Hosp., 1968-71; mem. adv. bd. Nassau County Fine Arts Mus., 1981-83. Mem. Acad. TV Arts and Scis., Variety Internat., Motion Picture Pioneer (life), Ind. Theatre Owner's Assn. (v.p. 1967-85), League N.Y. Theatres and Producers (labor negotiation com. 1980-83), Cinema B'nai B'rith (pres. 1969-72). Republican. Jewish. Office: 277 Park Ave New York NY 10172-0002

LEVINE, CHARLES MICHAEL, publishing company executive, consultant; b. Buffalo, Dec. 19, 1942; s. Abraham and Rose (Ackman) L.; 1 child, Gabriel Lee. B.A., Columbia U., 1963; M.A., Ind. U., 1966. With Peace Corps, 1967-69; editor McGraw Hill F.E.P., Singapore, 1972-75; mng. dir. APA Pubis., Singapore, 1976-78; former dir. gen. ref. and sci. Macmillan Pub. Co. Inc., N.Y.C., from 1978; formerly with Simon & Schuster; v.p., exec. pub. John Wiley & Sons, N.Y.C.; with Random House Inc., N.Y.C., 1994—. Mem. Phi Beta Kappa. Office: Random House Reference & Elec Pub 201 E 50th StSt New York NY 10022

LEVINE, DANIEL BLANK, classical studies educator; b. Cin., July 22, 1953; s. Joseph and Elizabeth (Blank) L.; m. Judith Robinson, Aug. 14, 1984; children: Sarah Ruth, Amy Elizabeth. Student, Am. Sch. Classical Studies, Athens, 1974, 78-89; BA in Greek and Latin magna cum laude, U. Minn., 1975; PhD in Classics, U. Cin., 1980. Seymour fellow Am. Sch. Classical Studies, 1978-79; asst. prof. U. Ark., 1980-84, assoc. prof., 1984—; dir. Summer Session Am. Sch. Classical Studies, Athens, 1987, 95; dir. study tour in Greece Vergilian Soc., 1990; referee Classical Jour., 1984-88, Helios, 1984-88, Cornell U. Press, 1988-89, 91—, Classical Outlook, 1988-89; panelist NEH, Washington, 1986; co-dir., instr. gifted and talented H.S. students summer program State of Ark. Dept. Edn. Grant, 1988; mem. mng. com. Am. Sch. Classical Studies Athens, 1991—. Contbr. articles to profl. jours. Recipient Fulbright Coll. Master Tchr. award, 1995; grantee NEH, 1981, 82, 83, 84, 92. Mem. Am. Philological Assn. (Excellence in Tchg. Classics award 1992), Am. Classical League, Classical Assn. Mid. West and South (v.p. com. promotion Latin Ark. 1980-86, 91—, chmn. regional rep. com. for promotion Latin, Outstanding State V.P. for 1982-83), U. Ark. Tchg. Acad., Phi Beta Kappa. Home: 904 Park Ave Fayetteville AR 72701-2027 Office: U Arkansas Dept Fgn Langs 425 Kimpel Hall Fayetteville AR 72701

LEVINE, DAVID, artist; b. Bklyn., Dec. 20, 1926; s. Harry L.; children: Matthew, Eve. B.F.A., Temple U., 1949, B.S. in Edn, 1949; postgrad., Hans Hoffman Sch. Paintings, 1950. One-man shows Forum Gallery, N.Y.C., 1966—, Ga. Mus. Art, 1968, Calif. Palace Legion of Honor, 1968-69, 71-72, 83, Wesleyan U., 1970, Bklyn. Mus., 1971, Princeton U., 1972, Galerie Yves Lambert, Paris, 1972, Yale U., 1973, Hirshhorn Mus. and Sculpture Garden, Washington, 1976, Galerie Claude Bernard, 1979, Phillips Gallery, 1980, Pierpont Morgan Library, 1981, Santa Fe East Gallery, 1983, Ash Molean Mus., Meredith Long, Houston, 1984; represented by Forum Gallery; author: The Man From M.A.L.I.C.E. 1966, Pens and Needles, 1969, No Known Survivors, 1970, The Arts of David Levine, 1978, Aesop's Fables. Served with U.S. Army, 1945-46. Recipient Tiffany award, 1955, Isaac N. Maynard prize, 1958, Julius Halligarten prize, 1960, Thomas B. Clark prize, 1962, George Polk award, 1965, Childe Hassam Purchase prize 1972, Benjamin Altman prize, 1973, Gold medal for Graphic Work, Am. Acad. Inst. Arts and Letters, 1992, Thomas Nast award, 1995; Guggenheim fellow, 1967. Mem. AAAL, Century Assn. Address: care Forum Gallery 745 Fifth Ave New York NY 10151-0002

LEVINE, DAVID LAWRENCE, social work educator; b. N.Y.C., Aug. 30, 1919; s. Harold D. and Caroline (Leibowitz) L.; m. Laura Ann Kaplan, June 5, 1942; children: Edwin Alfred, Deborah Janet, Elizabeth Phylis, Helen Dorothy. B.S. in Social Scis., CCNY, 1941; M.S.W., U. Pa., 1943; Ph.D., U. Minn., 1953. Lic. clin. social worker, Ga. Visitor, intake worker Assn. Jewish Children, Phila., 1943-45; asst. to dir. Bklyn. Jewish Child Care Council, 1945-47; supr. children's services Jewish Family and Children's Services, Mpls., 1947-51; instr. family life edn. U. Minn., 1949-53, instr. Sch. Social Work, 1952-53; from asst. prof. to prof. Sch. Social Welfare, Fla. State U., 1953-67, chmn. dept. social work, 1965-67; asso. dean Sch. Social Work, Syracuse U., 1967-69; prof. social work Faculty Gerontology, U. Ga., Athens, 1968-90, prof. emeritus, 1990—; clin. prof. Dept. Psychiatry and Health Behavior Med. Coll. Ga., 1987—; rsch. assoc. cmty. mental health Harvard Sch. Pub. Health, 1959-60; cons. Operation Headstart, 1965-67, Geriatric Clinic, U. Miami, Fla., 1955; chmn. NE Ga. Cmty. Svc. Mental Health Bd., Mental Retardation; hon. bd. dirs. Athens Cmty. Coun. Aging, 1995; del. White House Conf. on Aging, 1995. Pres. Leon County (Fla.) Mental Health Assn., 1961-63; chmn. Leon County Community Action Com., 1966; mem. bd. Fla. Assn. Mental Health, 1965-67; chmn. Twin Cities group Vocat. Guidance Assn., 1951; chmn. community planning and devel. com. Athens Community Council on Aging, 1969-86, pres. bd. dirs. 1992-93; cons. Ga. State Commn. on Aging, 1969-70; chmn. Univ. Council on Gerontology, 1970-74; Ga. del. White House Conf. on Aging, 1971; v.p. Nat. Inter-Faith Coalition on Aging, 1972-73; chmn. edn. and research com., mem. research team Social Work Manpower Study; pres. Athens-Clarke County Community Coordinated Child Care, 1973; cons. Inst. for Creative Devel., Union Am. Hebrew Congregations, 1974-77; chmn. com. on licensing Ga. State Conf. on Social Welfare, 1975-76; chmn. Title XX Planning Council, Dist. 10, Ga. Dept. Human Resources, 1976-85 , State 1st v.p., 1979-80; co-dir. Livingston Found. Seminars on Humanistic Mgmt. in Health Care, U. Ga.; mem. univ. council U. Ga., 1981-82; mem. tech. com., nat. del. White House Conf. on Aging, 1981; mem. Ga. Council Aging, 1982—, chmn., 1985-87. Fellow Am. Orthopsychiat. Assn., Gerontol. Soc. (Elsie Alvis Disting. Svc. award Ga. chpt. 1981); mem. Acad. Cert. Social Workers, Nat. Assn. Social Workers (Ga. coun. 1975-76, Frankie V. Adams disting. career award 1981), Nat. Assn. Social Workers (diplomate in Clinical Work), 1993. Address: 189 Colonial Dr Athens GA 30606-4015

LEVINE, DAVID M., newspaper editor; b. Newark, Oct. 2, 1949; s. Seymour I. and Fay D. Levine; m. Arleen Weintraub, Apr. 5, 1987. BA, Montclair State Coll., 1971; MS, Columbia U., 1973. Reporter, state house corr. Herald-News, Passaic, N.J., 1971-74; editorial writer Phila. Bull., 1974-79; night mng. editor Trenton (N.J.) Times, 1979-83; exec. fin. editor Washington Times, 1983-85; exec. editor Lebhar-Friedman Co., N.Y.C., 1985-86; editor Daily Jour., Elizabeth, N.J., 1986-87, Hudson Dispatch, Union City, N.J., 1987-91, The Daily Jour., Elizabeth, N.J., 1990-92; editor, v.p. The Herald-News, Passaic, N.J., 1992—; adj. instr. English dept. Rutgers U., Newark, 1967—; prin. Jour. Publs., Trenton, 1971—, Levine Publ., Trenton, 1974—. Author: Editorial Style, 1974. Office: The North Jersey Herald & News 988 Main Ave Passaic NJ 07055-8619

LEVINE, DONALD NATHAN, sociologist, educator; b. New Castle, Pa., June 16, 1931; s. Abe and Rose (Gusky) L.; m. Joanna Bull, Nov. 6, 1955 (div. 1967); children: Theodore, William; m. Ruth Weinstein, Aug. 26, 1967; 1 child, Rachel. AB, U. Chgo., 1950, MA, 1954, PhD, 1957; postgrad., U. Frankfurt, Germany, 1952-53. Asst. prof. sociology U. Chgo., 1962-65, assoc. prof., 1965-73, prof., 1973-86, dean of Coll., 1982-87, Peter B. Ritzma prof., 1986—. Author: Wax and Gold: Tradition and Innovation in Ethiopian Culture, 1965, Georg Simmel on Individuality and Social Forms, 1971, Greater Ethiopia: The Evolution of a Multiethnic Society, 1974, Simmel and Parsons: Two Approaches to the Study of Society, 1980, The Flight from Ambiguity: Essays in Social and Cultural Theory, 1985, Visions of the Sociological Tradition, 1995; editor: The Heritage of Sociology series, 1988—. Recipient Quantrell award U. Chgo., 1971; Guggenheim fellow, 1980; fellow Center for Advanced Study in Behavioral Scis., 1980-81. Mem. Internat. Soc. Comparative Study Civilization, Am. Sociol. Assn. Jewish. Office: U Chgo 1126 E 59th St Chicago IL 60637-1580

LEVINE, DOUGLAS GARY, music industry executive; b. N.Y.C., Sept. 1, 1954; s. Edward Charles and Rhoda Evelyn (Polstein) L.; m. Susan Levitin, June 5, 1982; children: Zachary, Valorie. BS in Acctg., N.Y.U., 1976. Licensed prin. Nat. Assn. Securities Dealers. Jr. acct. J.K. Lasser & Co., N.Y.C., 1976; sec. OCG Tech. Inc., N.Y.C., 1977—; pres. Masterdisk Corp., N.Y.C., 1978—; chmn. bd. Masterdisk Corp., N.Y.C., 1984— Chapter chief NSA, 1975—. Democratic. Nichiren Shoshu Buddhist. Club: Hampshire Country (Mamaroneck, N.Y.). Office: Masterdisk Corp 16 W 61st St New York NY 10023-7606

LE VINE, DUANE GILBERT, petroleum company executive; b. Balt., July 5, 1933; s. Harry B. and Frances Annette (Culleton) LeV.; m. Patricia J. Allman, Aug. 10, 1957; children: Duane Gilbert, Michele P., William A., James D., Erin A., Megan K. B.S. in Chem. Engring., Johns Hopkins U., 1956, M.S., 1958. With Exxon Research & Engring. Co., 1959—; dir. fuels products research lab. Exxon Research & Engring. Co., Linden, N.J., 1971-74; mgr. gasoline and lube processes div. Exxon Research & Engring. Co., Florham Park, N.J., 1974-76; gen. mgr. Baytown (Tex.) research and devel. site, 1976-78, exec. dir. corp. research sci. labs., 1979-84; mgr. worldwide environ. affairs Exxon Corp., N.Y.C., 1984-90; mgr. sci. and strategy devel. Exxon Corp., Dallas, 1990—; mem. Nat. Air Pollution Rsch. Adv. Com. 1971-74, Tex. Energy and Natural Resources Adv. Coun. 1976-78; mem. com. energy tech. assessment NASA, 1974; participant UN/industry-sponsored conf. on environ. mgmt., Versailles, France, 1984; chmn. Rene Dubos Internat. Forum on Mng. Hazardous Materials, N.Y.C., 1988, Rene Dubos Internat. Forum on Global Urbanization, N.Y.C., 1989; mem. adv. com. Calif. Inst. Tech., Johns Hopkins U., Rene Dubos Ctr.; chmn. Internat. Petroleum Industry Global Climate Change Symposium, Rome, 1992. Author: (with Upton) Management of Hazardous Agents, 1992, The City as

a Human Environment, 1994; patentee, author combustion, electrochemistry, environ. petroleum/synthetic fuels. Fellow Am. Inst. Chemists; mem. AIChE, Internat. Combustion Inst., Am. Chem. Soc., Am. Petroleum Inst., AAAS, N.Y. Acad. Scis., Internat. Petroleum Industry Environ. Conservation Assn. (exec. com. 1984—, vice chmn. 1994—), Sigma Xi, Tau Beta Pi, Phi Lambda Upsilon. Achievements include research on automotive emission control catalyst systems, on evaporative loss control devices, on exhaust recycle systems for NOx control, on catalytic coal gasification, on donor solvent coal liquifaction, and on direct synthesis of hydrocarbon liquids from CO/H2. Office: Exxon Corp 225 E John W Carpenter Fwy Irving TX 75062

LEVINE, EDWARD LESLIE, lawyer; b. Sheboygan, Wis., June 11, 1927; s. Joseph and Rose (Nemschoff) L.; m. Rosalie Bernstein, July 5, 1953; children: Carol Lovseth, Alex H., James L. BS, U. Wis., 1950, LLB, 1952. Counsel Comptroller of the Currency, Washington, 1952-56; assoc. Cole & Deitz, N.Y.C., 1956-62; ptnr. Winston & Strawn and predecessor firms, N.Y.C., 1962—; counsel N.Y. Legis., State Com. to Revise Banking Law, Albany, 1967-68; cons. UN Devel. Program to Draft Banking Law for Federated States of Micronesia; bd. dirs. Nat. Westminster Bancorp Inc., Coutts Trust Holdings Ltd.; mem. Com. of Counsel, N.Y. Clearing House Assn.. Bd. visitors U. Wis. Law Sch., Madison, 1989—; mem. Gov.'s Coun. on Fin. Svcs., N.Y.C., 1986-88. With USAF, 1945-47. Mem. ABA (banking law com.), Assn. of Bar of City of N.Y. (banking law com. 1987-90). Democrat. Jewish. Avocations: tennis, bridge. Office: Winston & Strawn 175 Water St New York NY 10038-4918

LEVINE, EDWIN BURTON, retired classics educator; b. Chgo., Nov. 11, 1920; s. Benjamin and Bertha (Kauffman) L.; m. Myra Estrin, Apr. 22, 1944; children—William Alan, Patricia Ann. A.B., U. Chgo., 1949, A.M., 1950, Ph.D., 1953. Instr. classics U. Nebr., 1951-52; instr., then asst. prof. Wayne State U., Detroit, 1955-60; instr. Detroit Bd. Edn., 1960-61, New Trier High Sch., Winnetka, Ill., 1962-64; vis. lectr. U. Ill. at Chgo. Circle, 1964-65, mem. faculty, 1965—, prof. classics, 1968-87, prof. emeritus, 1987—, founder and 1st head dept., 1969-74. Author: Introduction to Classical Greek, 1968; prin. compiler: Follett World-Wide Latin-English Dictionary, 1968, Hippocrates, 1971, Landor's Latin Poetry, 1968. Served with AUS, 1943-46. Fellow AAAS; mem. Am. Philol. Assn., Soc. for History of Medicine, Archaeol. Inst. Am., Chgo. Classical Club (pres. 1967-69). Home: 701 Forum Sq Apt 509 Glenview IL 60025-3866

LEVINE, ELLEN R., magazine editor; b. N.Y.C., Feb. 19, 1943; d. Eugene Jack and Jean (Zuckman) Jacobson; m. Richard V. Levine, Dec. 21, 1964; children: Daniel, Peter. Student, Wellesley Coll. Reporter The Record, Hackensack, N.J., 1964-70; editor Cosmopolitan mag., N.Y.C., 1976-82; editor in chief Cosmopolitan Living mag., N.Y.C., 1980-81, Woman's Day mag., N.Y.C., 1982-91, Redbook mag., N.Y.C., 1991-94, Good Housekeeping, N.Y.C., 1994—; dir. N.J. Bell, Newark; commr. U.S. Atty. Gen.'s Commn. on Pornography, 1985-86. Author: Planning Your Wedding, Waiting for Baby, Rooms That Grow With Your Child. Mem. exec. com. Senator Bill Bradley, 1984—. Named to Writers Hall of Fame, 1981, Acad. Women Achievers, YWCA, 1982; recipient Outstanding Profl. Achievement award N.J. coun. Girl Scouts U.S., 1984, Woman of Achievement award N.J. Fedn. Women's Clubs, 1984, Matrix award N.Y. Women in Communications, Inc., 1989, honor award Birmigham So. Coll., 1991. Office: Good Housekeeping 959 Eighth Ave New York NY 10019*

LEVINE, GEORGE LEWIS, English language educator, literature critic; b. N.Y.C., Aug. 27, 1931; s. Harris Julius and Dorothy Sara (Podolsky) L.; m. Margaret Bloom, Aug. 19, 1956; children: David Michael, Rachel Susan. B.A., NYU, 1952; M.A., U. Minn., 1953, Ph.D., 1958. Instr. Ind. U., Bloomington, 1959-62, asst. prof., 1962-65, assoc. prof., 1965-68; prof. English Rutgers U., New Brunswick, N.J., 1968—, chmn. dept., 1979-83; Kenneth Burke prof. Rutgers U., New Brunswick, 1985—; vis. prof. U. Calif.-Berkeley, 1968, Stanford U., Calif., 1974-75; vis. research fellow Girton Coll., Cambridge U., Eng., 1983; dir. Ctr. for Critical Analysis of Contemp. Culture. Author: Boundaries of Fiction, 1968, The Endurance of Frankenstein, 1975, The Realistic Imagination, 1981, One Culture, 1987, Darwin and the Novelists, 1988, Lifebirds, 1995; author: editor: The Art of Victorian Prose, 1968, Mindful Pleasures, 1975, Constructions of the Self, 1992, Realism and Representation, 1993, Aesthetics and Ideology, 1994; editor: Victorian Studies, 1959-68. Served with U.S. Army, 1953-55. Guggenheim Found. fellow, 1971-72; NEH fellow, 1978-79; Rockefeller Found. fellow, 1983. Mem. MLA, AAUP. Democrat. Jewish. Home: 419 Lincoln Ave Highland Park NJ 08904-2728 Office: Rutgers U Ctr Crit Analysis Cont New Brunswick NJ 08903

LEVINE, GEORGE RICHARD, English language educator; b. Boston, Aug. 5, 1929; s. Jacob U. and Rose Lillian (Margolis) L.; m. Joan Adler, June 8, 1958 (div. 1977); children—David, Michael; m. Linda Rashman, Apr. 17, 1977. B.A., Tufts Coll., Medford, Mass., 1951; M.A., Columbia, 1952, Ph.D., 1961. Lectr. English Columbia, 1956-58; instr. Northwestern U., 1959-63; mem. faculty State U N.Y., Buffalo, 1963—; prof. English State U. N.Y., 1970—, dean faculty arts and letters, 1975-81. Author: Henry Fielding and The Dry Mock, 1967; editor: Harp on the Shore: Thoreau and the Sea, 1985, Jonathan Swift: A Modest Proposal and Other Satires, 1995; contbr. articles to profl. jours. Chmn. bd. dirs. Youth Orch. Found., Buffalo, 1974-75; trustee Buffalo Chamber Music Soc., Arts Devel. Svcs.; bd. dirs. Buffalo Philharm. Orch. With AUS, 1952-54. Univ. fellow Columbia U., 1959-59; Faculty Research fellow SUNY, 1966, 67; Fulbright lectr W. Ger., 1969-70; recipient Chancellor's award excellence in teaching SUNY, Buffalo, 1973-74. Mem. MLA, Am. Soc. 18th Century Studies, Internat. Assn. Univ. Profs. English. Jewish. Clubs: Adirondack Mountain. Home: 388 Parker Ave Buffalo NY 14216-2146 Office: SUNY Dept English 306 Clemens Hall Buffalo NY 14260

LEVINE, GERALD RICHARD, investment banker, financial advisor, estate planning and philanthropy specialist; b. N.Y.C., Nov. 7, 1936; s. Irving Arthur and Lillian (Kronstadt) L.; m. Linda L. Paige, May 17, 1991; children from previous marriage: Jodi Levine Avergun, Debby Levine Rifkin, James H. AB, Brown U., 1958; MBA, GM Inst. Tech., Flint, Mich., 1960; postgrad., Pohs Inst. Ins., N.Y.C., 1978, Securities Tng. Inst., N.Y.C., 1981; postgrad. real estate, NYU, 1993. Pres. Town and Country Motors (Div. KLZ Corp.), Woodmere, N.Y., 1959-78, TAR Brokerage Corp., 1977—; nat. mktg. dir. Performance Dynamics Inc., N.Y.C., 1978-81; v.p. Oppenheimer & Co., N.Y.C., 1981-84; sr. v.p. Twenty-First Securities Corp., N.Y.C., 1984-89; assoc. nat. dir. corp. and instl. investment programs Devel. Corp. for Israel, N.Y.C., 1989-91; assoc. dir. estate planning div. Prudential Securities/Ins., N.Y.C., 1991-92; dir. corp. philanthropy Anti-Defamation League, N.Y.C., 1992-93; dir. Sealy Hoffman & Sheehan Inc., 1993-94; mng. dir. Investment Adv. Group, N.Y.C., 1994—. Pres. 5 Towns div. Salvation Army, Woodmere, 1968-85; mem. exec. com., adv. bd. commerce and industry div. State of Israel Bonds, N.Y.C., 1988-89; mem. exec. com. Brown Ann. Fund, Providence, 1987-89, 92-94, Brown Corp. Com. on Devel., 1987-89, 92-94, major gifts chmn. 30th Reunion, 1988, 35th Reunion, 1993, N.Y.C. Brown Reg. Devel. Com., 1988-93; advisor Brown U. Sports Found., 1987—; bd. dirs. Brown U. Football Assn., Providence, 1988-92; bd. dir. Head Marshall Alumni Divsn. 1983-84, 88-89, head class agt. 1978-88, treas. class of 1958, 1988-93, pres. class of '58, 1993—, Alumni Marshall, 1993. Recipient Disting. Alumni Svc. award Brown U., 1988. Mem. Brown U. Alumni Assn. (exec. bd. assn. class officers 1994—), Brown U. Club N.Y. (pres. 1990-92, v.p., exec. dir. 1989-90), K.P. (mem. at large), Princeton Club, Nat. Arts Club. Republican. Jewish. Avocations: golf, fishing, antique car restorations, woodworking, chess. Office: Investment Adv Group 30th Fl 521 5th Ave New York NY 10175

LEVINE, HAROLD, lawyer; b. Newark, Apr. 30, 1931; s. Rubin and Gussie (Lifshitz) L.; children: Brenda Sue, Linda Ellen Levine Gersen, Louise Abby, Jill Anne Levine Zuvanich, Charles A. Cristina Gussie, Harold Rubin II; m. Cristina Cervera, Aug. 29, 1980. B.S. in Engring., Purdue U., 1954; J.D. with distinction, George Washington U., 1958. Bar: D.C. 1958, Va., 1958, Mass. 1960, Tex. 1972, U.S. Patent Office, 1958. Naval architect, marine engr. U.S. Navy Dept., 1954-55; patent examiner U.S. Patent Office, 1955-58; with Tex. Instruments Inc., Attleboro, Mass., 1959-77, asst. sec., Dallas, 1969-72, asst. v.p. and gen. patent counsel, 1977-77; ptnr. Sigalos & Levine, Dallas, 1977-93; prin. Levine & Majorie LLP, 1994—; chmn. bd. Vanguard Security, Inc., Houston, 1977—; chmn. Tex. Am. Realty, Dallas,

1977—; lectr. assns., socs.; del. Geneva and Lausanne (Switzerland) Intergovtl. Conf. on Revision, Paris Pat. Conv., 1975-76. Mem. U.S. State Dept. Adv. Panel on Internat. Tech. Transfer, 1977. Mem. ABA (chmn. com. 407 taxation pats. and trdmks. 1971-72), Am. Patent Law Assn., Dallas Bar Assn., Assn. Corp. Pat. Csl. (sec.-treas. 1971-73), Dallas-Fort Worth Patent Law Assn., Pacific Indsl. Property Assn. (pres. 1975-77), Electronic Industries Assn. (pres. pat. com. 1972), NAM, Southwestern Legal Inst. on Patent Law (planning com. 1971-74), U.S. C. of C., Dallas C. of C., Alpha Epsilon Pi, Phi Alpha Delta. Republican. Jewish. Club: Kiwanis. Contbr. chpt. to book, articles to profl. jours. Editor: George Washington U. Law Rev., 1956-57; mem. adv. bd. editors Bur. Nat. Affairs, Pat., Trdmk. and Copyright Jour., 1979-87. Office: Levine and Majorie LLP 12750 Merit Dr Ste 1000 Dallas TX 75251-1243

LEVINE, HENRY DAVID, lawyer; b. N.Y.C., June 7, 1951; s. Harold Abraham and Joan Sarah (Price) L.; m. Barbara Wolgel, Aug. 28, 1976; children: David, Rachel, Daniel. AB, Yale U., 1972; JD, M in Pub. Policy, Harvard U., 1976. Bar: N.Y. 1977, D.C. 1978, U.S. Supreme Ct. 1980. Assoc. Wilmer, Cutler & Pickering, Washington, 1976-80; assoc. Morrison & Foerster, Washington, 1981-83, ptnr., 1983-92; ptnr. Levine, Blaszak, Block & Boothby, Washington, 1993—; cons. to GSA on FTS2000 Successor System, 1994—. Editor Telematics, 1984-89. Mem. Nat. Rsch. Coun. Com. on High Tech. Bldgs., 1985-88. Mem. ABA, Fed. Communication Bar Assn. Home: 5208 Edgemoor Ln Bethesda MD 20814-2342 Office: Levine Blaszak Block & Boothby 1300 Connecticut Ave NW # 500 Washington DC 20036

LEVINE, HERBERT SAMUEL, economics educator, research consultant; b. N.Y.C., Dec. 12, 1928; s. Hyman and Bertha (Shalit) L.; m. Helene Jaffe, Jan. 25, 1953; children: Jonathan (dec.), Jan, Judith. AB in Econs., Harvard U., 1950, AM in Russian Studies, 1952, PhD in Econs., 1961. Teaching fellow Harvard U., Cambridge, Mass., 1956-57; assoc. Russian Rsch. Ctr., 1956-60; asst. prof., assoc. prof. econs. U. Pa., Phila., 1960-69, prof., 1969—, chmn. grad. group in econs., 1970-73, mem. exec. com. Ctr. for Soviet and East European Studies, 1985-94, mem. internat. studies grad. group Lauder Inst., 1985-94, co-dir. Inst., 1987-94; cons. RAND Corp., 1957, World Bank, 1992—; vis. asst. prof. Princeton U., 1962; vis. lectr. econs., rsch. fellow Russian Rsch. Ctr., Harvard U., 1963-64; vis. assoc. prof. Columbia U., 1965, 66, vis. rsch. fellow, 1973-74; vis. prof. U. Calif., Berkeley, 1966, London Sch. Econs., 1968-69; vis. scholar World Bank, 1993; chmn. bd. dirs. PlanEcon, Inc., 1985—; sr. rsch. cons. SRI Internat., 1973-82; trustee Nat. Coun. for Soviet and East European Rsch., 1977-89, mem. exec. com., 1977-89, chmn. bd. trustees, 1980-84; numerous others, v.p., pres. elect Am. Assn. for Advancement of Slavic Studies, 1989-90, pres., 1991; commr. Internat. Baltic Econ. Commn. Hundson Inst., 1991-93; mem. fgn. experts com. Russian Sci. Found., 1994—. Mem. editorial bd. Soviet Economy, 1984—; contbr. numerous articles to profl. jours. Recipient David A. Wells prize Harvard U., 1963, Linback Found. award for disting. teaching U. Pa., 1965, Irving B. Kravis prize for distinction in undergrad. teaching, 1988, 91; fellow Ford Found., 1958-59, Harvard U. Russian Rsch. Ctr., 1963-64, Fulbright-Hays Found. 1968-69, Am. Coun. Learned Socs., 1969. Mem. Assn. for Study Soviet-Type Economies (exec. sec. 1962-63), Assn. for Comparative Econs. (exec. com. 1970-73), Am. Econ. Assn., Phi Beta Kappa. Office: U Pa Dept Econs Philadelphia PA 19104

LEVINE, HOWARD HARRIS, health facility executive; b. Bklyn., Sept. 30, 1949; s. Roy and Lucille Levine. MPH in Hosp. Administrn., UCLA, 1974; BBA in Mktg., Baruch Coll., 1972. Adminstrv. resident Inter-Community Hosp., Covina, Calif., 1973-74; adminstrv. asst. to exec. dir. John F. Kennedy Med. Ctr., Edison, N.J., 1974-75; assoc. exec. dir. John F. Kennedy Med. Ctr., Edison, 1975-78; adminstr. Robert Wood Johnson Jr. Rehab. Inst., Edison, 1975-78; asst. dir. Beth Israel Med. Ctr., N.Y.C., 1978-81, assoc. dir., 1981-84, sr. assoc. dir. for ops., 1984-87; v.p. Staten Island Univ. Hosp., 1988, sr. v.p., chief oper. officer, 1988-91; exec. dir. Chapman Gen. Hosp., Orange, Calif., 1992—; v.p. OrNda Health Corp., 1994—; adj. lectr. dept. health care adminstrn. Bernard M. Baruch Coll./Mt. Sinai Sch. Medicine, N.Y.C., 1982—; Health Profl. adv. com. March of Dimes, 1992—; joint com. patient svcs. Calif. Hosp. Assn., 1992—; guest lectr. NYU Grad. Sch. Pub. Adminstrn., 1984-86; mem. mental health and substance abuse com. Greater N.Y. Health Adminstrn., 1988-91, profl. affairs and hosp. ops. com., 1989-91, chmn. com. on utilization rev., 1988-91; exec. and planning com. Hosp. Coun. So. Calif., 1992—; coun. on profl. practices N.J. Hosp. Assn., Princeton, 1977-78, dist. bd. Health Svcs. Adminstrn., N.Y.C., 1979-80. Mem. editorial adv. bd. The Malpractice Reporter, N.Y.C., 1980-88. Mem. ins. profl. adv. com. Fedn. Jewish Philanthropies Ins., 1981-87; mem. tech. adv. panel N.J. State Health Coordinating Coun., Princeton, 1976-78; bd. dirs. Meals-on-Wheels Program, Metuchen, Edison and Woodbridge, N.J., 1974-76; mem. budget com. United Crusade L.A., 1973-74. Fellow Am. Coll. Healthcare Execs.; mem. Coun. Hosp. Adminstrs. (pres. 1986-87) Met. Health Adminstrs. Assn. (pres. 1980-82), Am. Coll. Healthcare Mktg., Hosp. Adminstrs. Discussion Group. Home: 309 Bay Hill Dr Newport Beach CA 92660-5235 Office: OrNda Health Corp 2601 E Chapman Ave Orange CA 92669-9999

LEVINE, IRVING RASKIN, news commentator, author, lecturer; b. Pawtucket, R.I.; s. Joseph and Emma (Raskin) L.; m. Nancy Cartmell Jones, July 12, 1957; children—Jeffrey Claybourne Bond, Daniel Rome, Jennifer Jones. BS, Brown U., 1944, LHD (hon.), 1969; MS, Columbia, 1947; LHd (hon.), Bryant Coll., 1974; D.Journalism (hon.), Roger Williams Coll., 1985; LLD (hon.), U. R.I., 1988; LHD (hon.), Lynn U., 1992; LLD (hon.), Northeastern U., 1993. Writer obits. Providence Jour., 1940-43; fgn. news editor Internat. News Service, 1947-48; chief Vienna (Austria) bur., 1948-50; with NBC, 1950—; war corr. NBC, Korea, 1950-52; chief corr. NBC, Moscow, 1955-59, Rome, 1959-67, 68-70, London, 1967-68; chief econs. corr. NBC, Washington, 1971—; commentator Consumer News and Bus. Channel Cable TV affiliate svc. NBC Tv News; spl. writer London Times, 1955-59; covered assignments in, Can., China, Czechoslovakia, Bulgaria, Poland, Japan, Viet Nam, Formosa, Thailand, Eng., France, Germany, Switzerland, Algeria, Congo, Israel, Turkey, Tunisia, Greece, Yugoslavia, Union of S.Africa, Denmark, Sweden, Ireland, lectr., 1953—. Author: Main Street, USSR, 1959, Travel Guide to Russia, 1960, Main Street, Italy, 1963, The New Worker in Soviet Russia, 1973; contbr. articles to nat. mags.; guest on numerous TV shows including Murphy Brown, 1989, David Letterman Show, 1990, Jay Leno Show, 1990. Served with Signal Corps, U.S. Army, 1944-47. Recipient award for best radio-TV reporting from abroad Overseas Press Club, 1956, award for outstanding radio network broadcasting Nat. Headliners Club, 1957, 50th Anniversary award Columbia Sch. Journalism, 1963, Emmy citation 1966, Martin R. Gainsburgh award for best econ. reporting, 1978, William Rogers award Brown U., 1988, Silver Circle award Nat. Acad. TV Arts and Scis., 1990, 93; named one of 10 Outstanding Young Men, U.S. Jaycees, 1966; named to R.I. Hall of Fame, 1972, Pawtucket Hall of Fame, 1986; honoree Loyola Coll.'s Beta Gamma Sigma, 1994. Mem. Coun. on Fgn. Rels. (fellowship 1952-53), Cosmos, Phi Beta Kappa, Beta Gamma Sigma. Office: 4001 Nebraska Ave NW Washington DC 20016-2733

LEVINE, ISRAEL E., writer; b. N.Y.C., Aug. 30, 1923; s. Albert Ely and Sonia (Silver) L.; m. Joy Elaine Menuad, June 23, 1946; children: David, Carol. BS, CCNY, 1946. Asst. dir. pub. rels. CCNY, 1946-54, dir., 1954-77, editor Alumnus Mag., 1952-74, 87-89; editor Health Care Week, 1977-79, William H. White Publs., 1979-81; dir. communications Am. Jewish Congress, 1981-87; COO Richard Cohen Assocs., N.Y.C., 1987—. Author: (with A. Lateiner) The Techniques of Supervision, 1954; The Discoverer of Insulin: Dr. Frederick G. Banting, 1959, Conqueror of Smallpox: Dr. Edward Jenner, 1960, Behind the Silken Curtain: The Story of Townsend Harris, 1961, Inventive Wizard: George Westinghouse, 1962, Champion of World Peace: Dag Hammarskjold, 1962, Miracle Man of Printing: Ottmar Mergenthaler, 1963, Electronics Pioneer: Lee DeForest, 1964, Young Man in the White House: John Fitzgerald Kennedy, 1964, 91, Oliver Cromwell, 1966, Spokesman for the Free World: Adlai Stevenson, 1967, Lenin: The Man Who Made a Revolution, 1969, The Many Faces of Slavery, 1975; contbr. over 200 articles to mags. mem. exec. Com. for Pub. Higher Edn., N.Y.C., 1987—. 2d lt. USAAF, 1943-45, ETO. Recipient 125th Anniversary medal CCNY, 1972, Svc. medal CCNY Alumni Assn., 1974. Mem. the Authors Guild, Authors League Am., Soc. of the Silurians. Jewish. Avocation: gardening. Address: Richard Cohen Assocs 30 E 60th St Ste 1207 New York NY 10022-1008

LEVINE, JACK ANTON, lawyer; b. Monticello, N.Y., Dec. 23, 1946; s. Milton and Sara (Sacks) L.; m. Eileen A. Garsh, Sept. 7, 1974; children: Matthew Aaron, Dara Esther. BS with honors, SUNY, Binghamton, 1968; JD with honors, U. Fla., 1975, LLM in Taxation, 1976. Bar: Fla. 1975, U.S. Ct. Appeals (11th cir.) 1981, U.S. Tax Ct., 1982. Tax atty. legis. and regulations divsn. Office chief counsel IRS, Washington, 1977-81; assoc. Holland & Knight, Tampa, Fla., 1981-83, ptnr., 1984—; lectr. in field. Contbr. articles to profl. jours. Mem. ABA, Fla. Bar Assn. (sect. taxation exec. coun. 1984—, chmn. ptnrship. com. 1985-88, chmn. taxation regulated public utilities com. 1988-92, co-chmn. corps. and tax-exempt orgns. com. 1992—, bd. cert. in tax law 1984—), Carrollwood Village Golf & Tennis Club, Harbour Island Athletic Club. Democrat. Jewish. Avocations: basketball, golf, softball, reading, travelling. Home: 10905 Carrollwood Dr Tampa FL 33618-3903 Office: Holland & Knight 400 N Ashley Dr Ste 2300 Tampa FL 33602-4322

LEVINE, JAMES, conductor, pianist, artistic director; b. Cin., June 23, 1943; s. Lawrence M. and Helen (Goldstein) L. Studied piano with Rosina Lhevinne and Rudolf Serkin, studied conducting with Jean Morel, Fausto Cleva and Max Rudolf, studied theory and interpretation with Walter Levin; student, Juilliard Sch. Music; hon. degree, U. Cin., New Eng. Cons. Northwestern U. Music dir. Ravinia Festival, 1973-93; artistic dir. Met. Opera, 1986—; guest lectr. Sarah Lawrence Coll., Harvard U., Yale U. Piano debut with Cin. Symphony, 1953; conducting debut at Aspen Music Festival, 1961; Met. Opera debut, 1971; Chgo. Symphony debut at Ravinia Festival, 1971; regularly appears throughout U.S. and Europe as condr. and pianist, including Vienna Philharm., Berlin Philharm., Chgo. Symphony, Phila. Orch., Boston Symphony, N.Y. Philharm., Dresden Staatskapelle, Philharmonia Orch., Israel Philharmonic, Wagner Festival at Bayreuth; made Bayreuth debut in new prodn. of Parsifal, 1982; condr. Salzburg Festival, 1975—; Salzburg premiers include Schönberg's Moses and Aron, 1987, Offenbach's Tales of Hoffman, Mahler's Seventh Symphony, Mendelssohn's Elijah; condr. Met. premier prodns. of Verdi's I Vespri Siciliani, Stiffelio, I Lombardi, Weill's The Rise and Fall of the City of Mahogonny, Stravinsky's Oedipus Rex, Berg's Lulu, Mozart's Idomeneo and La Clemenza di Tito, Gershwin's Porgy and Bess, world premier Corigliano/Hoffman The Ghosts of Versailles; subject of documentary for PBS; artistic dir. Met. Opera. Recipient Smetana medal, 1987, 8 Grammy awards. Office: Met Opera Assn Inc Met Opera House Lincoln Ctr New York NY 10023

LEVINE, JEROME, psychiatrist, educator; b. N.Y.C., July 10, 1934; s. Abraham and Sadie (Glowatz) L.; children: Ross W., Lynn R., Andrew R. B.A., U. Buffalo, 1954, M.D., 1958. Intern, then psychiat. resident E.J. Meyer Meml. Hosp., Buffalo, 1958-61; sr. psychiat. resident St. Elizabeth's Hosp., Washington, 1961-62; staff psychiatrist USPHS Hosp., Lexington, Ky., 1962-64; research psychiatrist, asst. chief psychopharmacology research br. NIMH, 1964-67, chief of br., 1967-81, chief pharmacologic and somatic treatments research br., 1981-84; research prof. psychiatry U. Md. Sch. Medicine, Balt., 1985-94; dep. dir. Nathan Kline Inst. for Psychiat. Rsch., Orangeburg, N.Y., 1994—; rsch. prof. psychiatry NYU, 1994—; instr. psychiatry Johns Hopkins Med. Sch., 1964-72; vis. prof. U. Pisa, Italy, 1977. Author books and papers on psychopharmacology, clin. trial methodology, somatic treatment assessment for psychiat. disorders. Mem. Soc. Clin. Trials, Am. Psychiat. Assn. (Hofheimer Research prize 1970), Am. Coll. Neuropsychopharmacology, Collegium Internationale Neuropsychopharmacologicum, Am. Soc. Clin. Pharmacology and Therapeutics. Home: 15 Stony Hollow Chappaqua NY 10514 Office: Nathan Kline Inst Bldg 37 Orangeburg NY 10962

LE VINE, JEROME EDWARD, retired ophthalmologist, educator; b. Pitts., Mar. 23, 1923; s. Harry Robert and Marian Dorothy (Finesilver) L.; m. Marilyn Tobey Hiedovitz, Apr. 14, 1957; children: Loren Robert, Beau Jay, Janice Lynn. B.S., U. Pitts., 1944; M.D., Hahnemann Med. Sch., Phila., 1949; postgrad. in ophthalmology U. Pa., 1951-52. Diplomate Am. Bd. Disability Cons. Intern, St. Francis Hosp., Pitts., 1949-50; resident in ophthalmology Jefferson U. Med. Sch. Hosp., Phila., 1952-54; ophthalmologist Leech Farm VA Hosp., Pitts., 1955-59; chief eye dept. Stanocola Clinic, Baton Rouge, 1959-64; sole practice medicine specializing in ophthalmology, Baton Rouge, 1959-86; cons. La. State U., East La. State Hosp. Infirmary, Villa Feliciana Geriatric Hosp., disability dept. Social Security Adminstrn., div. blind La. State Pub. Welfare dept., VA outpatient clinic; mem. staff Our Lady of the Lake Hosp., Baton Rouge Gen. Hosp., Women's Hosp.; instr. spl. edn. U. Southeastern La., 1971. Mem. Am. Bd. Quality Assurance and Utilization Rev., 1990. Served with MC, AUS, 1942-44. Fellow Am. Geriatric Soc., Royal Soc. Health; mem. AMA, La. State Med. Soc., East Baton Rouge Parish Med. Soc., 6th Dist. Med. Soc., New Orleans Acad. Ophthalmology, Inst. Glaucoma Research, So. Med. Assn., Internat. Med. Assn., Indsl. Medicine Assn., La. Med. Soc., Baton Rouge Parish Med. Soc., Pi Lambda Phi, Phi Delta Epsilon. Democrat. Jewish. Office: PO Box 66787 Baton Rouge LA 70896-6787

LEVINE, JOHN DAVID, lawyer; b. Winona, Minn., June 9, 1936; s. Jerry R. and Marian S. (Shoresman) L.; m. Marcia Weinstein, June 24, 1962; children: James Scott, Karen Sue. BA, Carleton Coll., 1958; JD, Yale U., 1961. Assoc. Dorsey & Whitney, Mpls., 1961-67, ptnr., 1967-93, of counsel, 1994—, chair trial dept., 1978-86, group head trial and adminstrn. group, 1986-93; mem. Legal Advice Clinics, Ltd., Mpls., 1965—; vice chmn., 1981-86, chmn. Lawyers Profl. Responsibility Bd., St. Paul, 1986-89. Chmn. St. Louis Park (Minn.) Referendum Com., 1979; vice chmn. bd. visitors U. Minn. Law Sch., 1987-89, chmn., 1989-91; trustee Carleton Coll., Northfield, Minn., 1979-92; bd. dirs. Walker Art Ctr., Mpls., 1983-89. Recipient Leadership scholarship Edward John Noble Found., N.Y., 1958. Fellow Am. Coll. Trial Lawyers, Am. Bar Found.; mem. ABA, Minn. Bar Assn. (chmn. long range planning com. 1975-76), Hennepin County Bar Assn. (Disting. Svc. award for Pro-Bono Svc. During Career), Minn. State Bar Found. (past bd. dirs., past pres.), Hennepin County Bar Found. (past bd. dirs., past officer 1970-72). Office: Dorsey & Whitney 220 S 6th St Minneapolis MN 55402

LEVINE, JOSEPH MANNEY, lawyer; b. Bklyn., Jan. 6, 1948; s. Albert A. and Frances D. (Toorock) L.; m. Sheila R. Gluck, July 31, 1969; children: Adam J., Matthew J. BA, Syracuse U., 1968; JD, Columbia U., 1972. Bar: N.Y. 1972. Assoc. Norton, Sacks, Mollineaux & Pastore, N.Y.C., 1972; atty. advisor Office of Gen. Counsel, U.S. Dept. Commerce, Washington, 1972-79, dep. asst. gen. counsel for adminstrn., 1979-84; chief counsel Washington, 1984-88, 1988-94; sr. counsel Office Gen. Counsel, 1994—; 1st vice chairperson, bd. dirs. Dept. of Commerce, Fed. Credit Union, Washington, 1981—. Pres. Aspen Hill Park Community Assn., Rockville, Md., 1976-77, bd. dirs. 1975-78. Office: Office Gen Counsel Rm 6087B US Dept Commerce Washington DC 20230

LEVINE, LAINIE See KAZAN, LAINIE

LEVINE, LAURENCE BRANDT, investment banker; b. N.Y.C., Dec. 17, 1941; s. Martin and Beulah (Brandt) L.; m. Laura Lynn Vitale; 1 child, Blair Brandt. BA (Francis Biddle prize 1961), Princeton U., 1964; LLB, Stanford U., 1967. V.p., voting shareholder Drexel Burnham Lambert, N.Y.C., 1968-71; corp. planning officer Office of Chmn., Ogden Corp., N.Y.C., 1971-73; pres. Investment Research Assocs., West Chester, Pa., 1973-80; sr. v.p., dir. investment banking Kramer Capital Cons., Inc., N.Y.C., 1981; exec. v.p. Henry Ansbacher Inc., N.Y. and London, 1982-84; sr. v.p. Rothschild Inc., N.Y., 1984-86; exec. v.p. and dir. corp. fin. Smith New Ct. Inc., N.Y. and London, 1986-90; chmn. Blair Corp., N.Y. and London, 1990—, dir. First Internat. Fin. Group, Hamburg, London and Bermuda, Landmark Funds Svcs., Inc., N.Y.C.; dir., vice chmn. Signature Fin. Group, Boston; Bd. visitors Stanford U. Law Sch., 1968-71, exec. com., 1970; dir. Musica Sacra, N.Y., 1981-86, Concert Artists Guild, N.Y., 1989-92, Ballet Fla., 1992—, Palm Beach Performing Arts Sch., 1992—; adv. bd. Kravis Ctr., 1991—. With USMCR, 1961-65. Mem. City Athletic Club, Harmonie Club, St. James Club (London), Princeton Club (N.Y.), Gentlemen of the Garden (Palm Beach), Mar-a-Lago (Palm Beach), Old Oaks Country Club (Purchase, N.Y.), Loch Lomond Club (Scotland). Office: 250 Royal Palm Way Ste 205 Palm Beach FL 33480

LEVINE, LAURENCE HARVEY, lawyer; b. Cleve., Aug. 23, 1946; s. Theodore and Celia (Chaikin) Levine; m. Mary M. Conway, May 13, 1978;

---

children: Abigail, Adam, Sarah. BA cum laude, Case Western Res. U., 1968; JD, Northwestern U., 1971. Bar: Ill. 1971, U.S. Dist. Ct. (no. dist.) Ill. 1972, U.S. Ct. Appeals (6th, 7th, 10th and D.C. cirs.). Law clk. to presiding judge U.S. Ct. Appeals (6th cir.), Detroit, 1971-72; assoc. Kirkland & Ellis, Chgo., 1972-76; ptnr. Latham & Watkins, Chgo., 1976—. Bd. editors Northwestern Law Rev., 1968-71. Mem. ABA, Chgo. Bar Assn., Mid-Am. Club. Office: Latham & Watkins Sears Tower Ste 5800 Chicago IL 60606

LEVINE, LAURENCE WILLIAM, lawyer; b. N.Y.C., Apr. 9, 1931; s. Robert L. and Molly (Brunner) L. B.A., Union Coll., 1952; LL.B., Harvard U., 1955. Bar: N.Y. 1958. Teaching fellow Def. Studies Program, Harvard U., 1955-56; aide to Adlai Stevenson N.Y.C., 1956-57; office mgr. N.Y. com. Stevenson, Kefauver, Wagner, 1956; sec. N.Y. com. for Dem. Voters, 1962-66; ptnr. Walsh & Levine (merged with Bigham Englar Jones & Houston 1990), N.Y.C., 1958—; sec.-treas. Kabuki Japanese Restaurant, N.Y.C., 1958-80; counsel Northeast Airlines, N.Y.C., 1958-67, Brit. Eagle Airlines, 1963-69, Aerolineas Argentinas, 1960—, Banco de la Nacion Argentina, N.Y.C., 1972-79, Banco de Intercambio Regional Argentina, 1977-80; ptnr. San Francisco Mdse. Mart, 1964-84, Holiday Inn-Union Sq., 1969-89, Kaanapoli Hotel, Hawaii, Hilton Hotel, Pasadena, Calif., 1969-88, Gray Lines, Inc., San Francisco, 1980—, Investco Mortgage Co. of Boston, 1975—, Southern Cone Pub. Co., 1980-86, Arion Press, San Francisco, 1979—, Calix and Corolla; dir. Alaska Airline, 1966-68, Stanley Aviation Corp., 1966-73, Foothill Group, 1972-80, Security Nat. Bank, 1983-84, Pan Australian Fund, 1972-74, N.Y. Venture Fund., Venture Income Plus, R.P. F. Funds of Am., 1984—; liquidator Transcontinental Airlines, 1960-63; chmn. creditors com. Am. Hydrofoil Co., 1965-68, Imperial 400 Motels, 1967-74, Harvard Industries; treas., co-owner Games Mag., 1980-81; sec., dir. Games Mag., 1978-80; pub. mem. Blue Cross/Blue Shield, Downtown Eye and Ear Hosp. N.Y.C., 1978-93; sec. Sale Tilney (N.A.), Inc., 1987-90. Author: Gullibles Travels Thru Harvard, 1955, U.S.-China Relations, 1972; contbr. to: East-Europe mag., 1969, Cambio Mag., Argentina, Harvard Law Sch. Bull, N.Y. Times; Argentine newspapers Rev. of River Plate. Treas. Citizens for McCarthy, 1968; mem. Coun. on State Priorities State N.Y., 1982; trustee Bklyn. Poly. Prep. Country Day Sch., 1992. Mem. Assn. of Bar of City of N.Y., N.Y. County Lawyers Assn., Argentine-Am. C. of C. (pres. 1985-87, bd. dirs. 1994—), Downtown Assn., Georgetown Club, Harvard Club. Home: 245 Everglades Ave Palm Beach FL 33480 Office: Bigham Englar Jones & Houston 14 Wall St Fl 21 New York NY 10005-2101

LEVINE, LAWRENCE STEVEN, lawyer; b. Bklyn., Mar. 30, 1934; s. Harry and Bess (Feiner) L.; m. Linda Robbins, June 16, 1957; children: Lauren Victoria, Audrey Elizabeth, Hilary Anne. AB, Colgate U., 1955; LLB, Yale U., 1958. Bar: N.Y. 1958, U.S. Supreme Ct. 1973. Asst. U.S. Atty. Ea. Dist. N.Y. U.S. Dept. Justice, N.Y.C., 1958-62; assoc. firm Kronish & Lieb, N.Y.C., 1962-63; ptnr. Beldock Levine & Hoffman, N.Y.C., 1964—; vis. instr. Harvard Law Sch., 1991. Bd. dirs. Jewish Fund for Justice, 1984—, chair, 1988—; mem. nat. bd. New Jewish Agenda, 1980-89, New Outlook Mag., 1982-90; trustee YM-YWHA's Greater N.Y., Harry Levine Meml. Found., 1965—, Riverdale Coutnry Sch., 1979-89. Mem. Fed. Bar Assn., N.Y. County Lawyers Assn., N.Y. State Dist. Attys. Assn., N.Y. Civil Liberties Union (cooperating counsel), Yale Club. Democrat. Home: 122 E 76th St New York NY 10021-2833 Office: Beldock Levine & Hoffman 99 Park Ave New York NY 10016-1503

LEVINE, LEON, retail executive; b. 1937; married. Student, Wingate Coll., U. Miami. V.p. Hub Dept. Store Inc., Rockingham, N.C., 1954-57; pres. Union Craft Co. Inc., Wingate, N.C., 1957-59; with Family Dollar Stores, Matthews, N.C., 1959—, pres., chief exec. officer, now chmn., treas., also bd. dirs. Office: Family Dollar Stores Inc PO Box 1017 Charlotte NC 28201-1017

LEVINE, LOUIS DAVID, museum director, archaeologist; b. N.Y.C., June 4, 1940; s. Moe Wolf and Jeanne (Greenwald) L.; m. Dorothy Abrams, Dec. 30, 1962 (div. 1991); children: Sarra L., Samuel E. Student, Brandeis U., 1960; BA with honors, U. Pa., 1962, PhD with distinction, 1969. Instr. of Hebrew U. Pa., Phila., 1966-69; asst. curator Royal Ont. Mus., Toronto, Can., 1969-75, assoc. curator, 1975-80, curator, 1981, assoc. dir., 1987-90; asst. commr. dir. N.Y. State Mus., Albany, 1990—; vis. sr. lectr. Hebrew U., Jerusalem, 1975-76; vis. prof. U. Copenhagen, 1985; asst. prof. U. Toronto, 1969-74, assoc. prof. U. Toronto, 1974-81, prof., 1981-90; dir. Seh Gabi Expdn., western Iran, 1971-73, dir. Mahidasht Project, western Iran, 1975-79. Author: Two Stelae from Iran, 1972, The Neo-Assyrian Zagros, 1974; editor: Mountains and Lowlands, 1977; contbr. articles to profl. jours. NDEA fellow U. Pa., 1962-65, Fulbright fellow, 1965, W.F. Albright fellow, Am. Schs. of Oriental Rsch., 1966, fellow Inst. for Advanced Studies, Hebrew U. Mem. Brit. Inst. of Persian Studies, Brit. Sch. of Archaeology in Iraq, Am. Assn. Mus., Am. Oriental Soc. Jewish. Avocations: woodworking, music. Office: NY State Mus Cultural Edn Ctr Rm 3099 Albany NY 12230

LEVINE, MADELINE GELTMAN, Slavic literatures educator, translator; b. N.Y.C., Feb. 23, 1942; d. Herman and Nettie (Kritman) Geltman; m. Steven I. Levine; children: Elaine, Daniel. B.A., Brandeis U., 1962; M.A., Harvard U., 1964, Ph.D., 1971. Asst. prof. Grad Sch. CUNY, N.Y.C., 1971-74; assoc. prof. U. N.C., Chapel Hill, 1974-80, prof., 1980-94, Wm. R. Kenan, Jr. prof. Slavic lits., 1994—, chmn. dept. Slavic langs., 1979-87, 94—; chmn. joint com. on Ea. Europe, Am. Coun. Learned Socs.-Social Sci. Rsch. Coun., 1989-92. Translator: A Memoir of the Warsaw Uprising (Miron Bialoszewski), 1977, 2d edit. 1991, The Poetry of Osip Mandelstam: God's Grateful Guest (Ryszard Przybylski), 1987, Beginning With My Streets: Essays and Recollections (Czeslaw Milosz), 1992, A Year of the Hunter (Czeslaw Milosz), 1994; translator with Francine Prose: A Scrap of Time and Other Stories (Ida Fink), 1986, 2d edit., 1995; author: Contemporary Polish Poetry, 1925-75, 1981. NEH fellow, 1984; recipient (with Francine Prose) award for lit. translation PEN-America, 1988. Mem. Am. Assn. for Advancement of Slavic Studies, Polish Inst. of Arts and Scis. Am., Am. Assn. Tchrs. of Slavic and East European Langs., Am. Literary Translators Assn., Pen-Am. Home: 5001 Whitehorse Rd Hillsborough NC 27278-9399 Office: U NC 421 Dey Hall CB # 3165 Chapel Hill NC 27599

LEVINE, MARK LEONARD, lawyer; b. Bath, Maine, Mar. 6, 1945; s. Saul and Sophie Gertrude (Greenblatt) L.; m. Stephanie M. von Hirschberg, Nov. 9, 1989. AB, Columbia U., 1966, MS in Journalism, 1979; JD, NYU, 1969. Bar: N.Y. 1969, U.S. Dist. Ct. (so. and ea. dists.) N.Y. 1971. Assoc. White & Case, N.Y.C., 1969-78; pub. Scarf Press, N.Y.C., 1979-85; pvt. practice law N.Y.C., 1981-85; of counsel Sullivan & Worcester, N.Y.C., 1985-88, ptnr., 1988—. Author: Negotiating a Book Contract: A Guide for Authors, Agents and Lawyers, 1988; co-editor: The Tales of Hoffman, 1970, The Complete Book of Bible Quotations, 1986; contbg. editor Small Press Mag., 1986; contbr. articles to profl. jours. Campaign coord. McCarthy for Pres., Marshfield, Wis., 1968; dep. campaign mgr. Perrotta for Comptr./Com. to Re-elect John Lindsay Mayor, N.Y.C., 1969; cons. McGovern for Pres. Com., Albany, N.Y., 1972. Recipient Citation of Appreciation Laymen's Nat. Bible Com., 1979. Mem. Assn. of Bar of City N.Y., Authors Guild, Am. Book Producers Assn. (bd. dirs. 1984-87, v.p. 1986-87), B'nai B'rith Youth Orgn. (internat. v.p. 1963-64). Democrat. Jewish. Avocations: reading, chess, movies. Office: Sullivan & Worcester 767 3rd Ave New York NY 10017-2023

LEVINE, MARTIN DAVID, computer science and electrical engineering educator; b. Montreal, Que., Can. Mar. 30, 1938; s. Max and Ethel (Tauber) L.; m. Deborah Tiger (dec.), June 6, 1961; children: Jonathan, Barbara. B.Eng., McGill U., Montreal, 1960, M.Eng., 1963; Ph.D., Imperial Coll., U. London, 1965, also diploma. Part-time lectr. Imperial Coll., 1963-64; mem. faculty McGill U., 1965—, prof., 1977—; mem. tech. staff Jet Propulsion Lab., Pasadena, Calif., 1972-73; vis. prof. Hebrew U., Jerusalem, 1979-80; PRECARN/Can. Inst. Advanced Rsch. assoc., 1990; pres. Internat. Assn. Pattern Recognition, 1988-90; cons. computer vision, biomed. image processing, robotics; dir. McGill Rsch. Ctr. for Intelligent Machines, 1986—. Author: Vision in Man and Machine, 1985; co-author: (P. Noble) Computer-Assisted Analyses of Cell Locomotion and Chemotaxis; contbr. articles to profl. jours.; Assoc. editor Computer Vision, Graphics and Image Processing, Image Understanding; gen. editor Advances in Computer Vision

---

and Machine Intelligence. Fellow Am. Soc. Engring. Edn. Ford Found., 1972-73. Fellow IEEE, Internat. Assn. Pattern Recognition; mem. Computer Soc. of IEEE (assoc. editor Trans. on Pattern Analysis and Machine Intelligence), Pattern Recognition Soc. (assoc. editor Pattern Recognition), Order Engrs. Que., Can. Image Processing and Pattern Recognition Soc. (past founding pres.), Internat. Assn. Pattern Recognition (past pres.). Jewish. Office: McGill U Rsch Ctr for Intelligent, 3480 University St, Montreal, PQ Canada H3A 2A7

LEVINE, MARTIN ROBERT, executive search and recruiting company executive; b. Bklyn., Sept. 10, 1943; s. Jack and Minna (Fisher) L.; m. Hilda Lichtenstein, Jan. 28, 1968; 1 child, Jill. BA, Mich. State U., 1965; MA, NYU, 1969. Assoc. dir. placement office NYU, N.Y.C., 1966-69; dir. human resources J.K. Lasser and Co., N.Y.C., 1970-77; mgr. human resources Touche Ross and Co., N.Y.C., 1977-79; exec. v.p., pres. Earley Kielty and Assocs., N.Y.C., 1980—. Bd. dirs. L.I. Regional Am. Jewish Commn., Woodbury, N.Y., 1987-88, Student Aid Fund, Great Neck, N.Y., 1984-86; v.p. Temple Beth-El, Great Neck, 1987—. With U.S. N.G., 1966-71. Office: Earley Kielty & Assocs Inc 2 Pennsylvania Plz Ste 1990 New York NY 10121

LEVINE, MELDON EDISES, lawyer, former congressman; b. Los Angeles, June 7, 1943; s. Sid B. and Shirley B. (Blum) L.; children: Adam Paul, Jacob Caplan, Cara Emily. AB, U. Calif., Berkeley, 1964; MPA, Princeton U., 1966; JD, Harvard U., 1969. Bar: Calif. 1970, D.C. 1972. Assoc. Wyman, Bautzer, Rothman & Kuchel, 1969-71; legis. asst. U.S. Senate, Washington, 1971-73; ptnr. Levine Krom & Unger, Beverly Hills, Calif., 1973-77; mem. Calif. Assembly, Sacramento, 1977-82, 98th-102d Congresses from 27th Calif. dist., Washington, 1983-93; ptnr. Gibson, Dunn & Crutcher, L.A., 1993—. Author: The Private Sector and the Common Market, 1968; contbr. articles to various publs. Mem. governing bd. So. Calif. chpt. Anti-Defamation League, So. Calif. chpt. Am. Jewish Com., So. Calif. chpt. Am. Jewish Congress, So. Calif. chpt. NAACP Legal Def. Fund, U. Judaism, City of Hope, U. Calif. Alumni Council; mem. amateur baseball team Hollywood Stars, 1971—. Mem. Calif. Bar Assn., Los Angeles Bar Assn.

LEVINE, MICHAEL, public relations executive, author; b. N.Y.C., Apr. 17, 1954; s. Arthur and Virginia (Gaylor) L. Student, Rutgers U., 1972-77. Owner, operator TV News Mag., Los Angeles, 1977-83; owner Michael Levine Pub. Rels. (now Levine/Schnieder Pub. Rels.), Los Angeles, 1982—; mem. Gov.'s adv. bd. State Calif., Sacramento, 1980-82; pres., owner Aurora Pub., L.A., 1986—; moderator Thought Forum; lectr. in field. Author: The Address Book: How to Reach Anyone Who's Anyone, 1984, The New Address Book, 1986, The Corporate Address Book, 1987, The Music Address Book, 1989, Environmental Address Book, 1991, Kid's Address Book, 1991, Guerrilla P.R., Lessons at Halfway Point, Take It From Me; pub., writer For Consideration newsletter. Mem. Ronald Reagan Pres.'s Libr.; founder The Actor's Conf., Aurora Charity, 1987; bd. dirs. Felice Found., Micah Ctr.; adv. bd. Dare America. Mem. TV Acad. Arts and Scis., Entertainment Industries Coun. (Musician's Assistance Program), West Hollywood C. of C. (bd. dirs. 1980-82). Jewish. Office: 8730 Sunset Blvd Fl 6 West Hollywood CA 90069-2210

LEVINE, MURRAY, psychology educator; b. Bklyn., Feb. 24, 1928; s. Israel and Birdie (Cutler) L.; m. Adeline Gordon, June 15, 1952; children: David Israel, Zachary Howard. BS, CCNY, 1949; MA in Psychology, U. Pa., 1951, PhD in Psychology, 1954; JD, SUNY, Buffalo, 1983. Bar: N.Y. 1984; lic. psychologist N.Y.; diplomate in clin. psychology Am. Bd. Profl. Psychology. Psychologist VA, Phila., 1949-57, Deveraux Schs., Devon, Pa., 1957-63; from asst. to assoc. prof. psychology Yale U., New Haven, 1963-68; prof. SUNY, Buffalo, 1968—. Author: Community Psychology, 1987, Helping Children, 1992, 7 others; contbr. over 150 articles to profl. jours. Chmn. bd. dirs. Citizens Cleaning House Hazardous Wastes, Falls Church, Va., 1983—; U.S. adv. bd. Child Abuse and Neglect. Mem. APA (fellow sects. 12, 27, 41, disting. contbns. award div. 27, 1987, teaching and mentoring award div. 41, 1992), APHA. Home: 74 Colonial Circle Buffalo NY 14213 Office: SUNY Rsch Ctr Children Youth 228 Park Hall Buffalo NY 14260

LEVINE, NAOMI BRONHEIM, university administrator; b. N.Y.C., Apr. 15, 1923; d. Nathan and Malvina (Mermelstein) Bronheim; m. Leonard Levine, Apr. 11, 1948; 1 dau., Joan. B.A., Hunter Coll., 1944; LL.B., Columbia, 1946, J.D., 1970. Bar: N.Y. bar 1946. With firm Scaadrett, Tuttle & Chalaire, N.Y.C., 1946-48, Charles Gottleib, N.Y.C., 1948-50; with Am. Jewish Congress, 1950-78, exec. dir., 1972-78; v.p. sr. v.p. external affairs NYU, 1978—; asst. prof. law and police sci. John Jay Coll., N.Y.C., 1969-73, L.I. U., 1965-69. Author: Schools in Crisis, 1969, The Jewish Poor-an American Awakening, 1974, Politics, Religion and Love, 1990; mem. editorial staff Columbia Law Rev., 1945-46. Bd. dirs. Interracial Council Bus. Opportunities, Am. Women's Econ. Devel. Council; trustee N.Y. UJA-Fedn. Recipient Constl. Law prize Hunter Coll., 1944; named to Hall of Fame, 1972. Office: 70 Washington Sq S New York NY 10012-1091

LEVINE, NORMAN GENE, insurance company executive; b. N.Y.C., Sept. 14, 1926; s. Harris J. and Dorothy S. (Podolsky) L.; m. Sandra Leibow, Dec. 11, 1969; children—Linda, Daniel, Donald. Student, U. Wis.-Madison, 1943-48. Agt. Aetna Life Ins. Co., N.Y.C., 1948-56; supr. Aetna Life Ins. Co., 1956-59, gen. agt., 1959-75; mng. gen. agt. Mut. Benefit Life Ins. Co. in No. Calif., San Francisco, 1975-91; br. mgr. Sun Life of Can., 1991—; pres. Levine Fin. Group, 1975—; internat. speaker in field; past div. v.p. Million Dollar Round Table; nat. chmn. Life Underwriters Tng. Council, 1983-84; nat. pres. Gen. Agts. and Mgrs. Conf., 1986-87. Author: How To Build a $100,000,000 Agency in Five Years or Less, Yes You Can, Life Insurance to Diversification; editor: bi-weekly news report Probe; contbr. numerous articles to profl. jours.; author tapes on ins., mgmt., photography, Americanism. Past mem. bd. dirs. Calif. Law Enforcement Needs Com. Served with AUS, 1944-46, ETO. Recipient Julian Myrick award, 1969, John Newton Russell Meml. award, 1986; named to Hall of Fame Gen. Agts. and Mgrs. Conf., 1982. Mem. N.Y.C. Assn. Life Underwriters (pres. 1967-68), N.Y. State Assn. Life Underwriters (pres. 1968-69), Nat. Assn. Life Underwriters (pres. 1974-75, dir. polit. action com. 1967-69), N.Y.C. Life Mgrs. Assn. (pres. 1974-75), Assn. Advanced Life Underwriters, Am. Soc. C.L.U.s, San Francisco Gen. Agts. and Mgrs. Assn. (pres. 1983), Golden Key Soc., Linnaean Soc., San Francisco C. of C., Audubon Soc., Am. Israel Friendship League (trustee). Mem. Order B'nai Zion (pres. 1964-67). Home: 251 Crest Rd Woodside CA 94062-2310 Office: 1 California St San Francisco CA 94111-5401 Profit and concern for people are not mutually exclusive and, in fact, people working in a synergistic relationship produce greater profit and general well-being. Democracy with all its problems is still clearly the best of all available methods of government; capitalism and free enterprise create the competition and reward that best challenge the human mind and body; and freedom to "stand tall" with faith, integrity and dignity are the basis for one's conscience and a guide for society's morality.

LEVINE, PAMELA GAIL, business owner; b. Alameda, Calif., Nov. 20, 1942; d. Carl B. and Lucille N. (Lua) Leverenz; m. George David Barth (div. 1974); children; Claudia Anne, Shanette Michelle; m. Leonard Stuart Levine; children: Leslie, Julie, Susan, Stuart Carl. BA in Archtl. Design/Fine Arts, U. Calif., Berkeley, 1965. Designer Trude of Calif., San Francisco, 1965-66; tchr. TWA, Kansas City, Mo., 1966-69; ptnr., owner, archtl. designer Leverenz of N.Y., 1970—; owner, designer Ressco, Katonah, N.Y., 1974—; cons. archtl. design and real estate devel.; founder, owner Sintec-Internat. Bus. Opportunities, 1989—. Designer of Sets/Costumes, Chappaqua Drama Group, 1973—. Devel. com. Mount Holyoke Coll., S. Hadley, Mass., 1987—; co-founder Looking Glass Players, Mt. Kisco, N.Y., 1985—; active Jr. League, Caramoor, Katonah Mus. Mem. No. Westchester Ctr. for the Arts (bd. dirs. devel. com., co-chmn. bldg. com.), Chappaqua Drama Group (bd. dirs.). Republican. Avocations: painter, costume design, set design, doll design, artist. Home: RR 6 Katonah NY 10536-9805 Office: Real Estate Support Svcs PO Box 574 Katonah NY 10536-0574

LEVINE, PAUL MICHAEL, paper industry executive, consultant; b. Bklyn., Apr. 15, 1937; s. Isaac Bert and Jessie Sue (Pelavsky) L.; m. Lois Jaffin, June 11, 1954 (div.); children: Daniella Sarah, Julie Ann, Carl Joseph; m. 2d Noelle Tenedou, July 14, 1974; children: Simone Allana, Alexander

Owen. A.B. in Econs., Harvard Coll., 1954; A.M. in Internat. Econs., Fletcher Sch. Internat. Law and Diplomacy, 1955. Sales mgr. U.S. Industries, Stamford, Conn., 1956-61; chief exec. officer subs. cos. Parsons and Whittemore-Black Clawson, N.Y.C., 1962-69; dep. adminstr. City of N.Y., 1970-72; v.p. S&S Corrugated Paper Machinery Co., Bklyn., 1973-76, Continental Group, Stamford, Conn., 1977-83; chmn. New Lehigh Corrugated Products, Farmingdale, N.Y., United Container Corp., Phila.; lectr., fellow Yale U., U. Conn., Fordham U. 1979-90; bd. dirs. Seidman, Friant, Levine Ltd., N.Y.C.; chmn. Windsor Mktg., Inc., Tulsa, Okla., Internat. Creative Data Industries, Inc., Bethel, Conn., Neeltran Inc., New Milford, Conn. Author: Proceedings 6th World Forestry Congress, 1966; editor: Study of Peoria County Model Program, 1970, Practical Exporting, 1962, The Role of Venture Capital in Europe and the World. Trustee Hartman Regional Theatre, Stamford, 1981-82; bd. dirs. Ridgefield Orch., 1978-83, Bklyn. Arts and Culture Assn., 1973-92. Mem. Turnaround Mgmt. Assn., Explorers Club. Democrat. Jewish. Office: Paul M Levine & Assocs 466 Ridgebury Rd Ridgefield CT 06877-1228 Creativity, innovation and laughter are the glories of the world.

LEVINE, PETER HUGHES, physician, health facility administrator; b. Everett, Mass., Nov. 13, 1938; s. Louis and Helen (Hughes) L.; m. Catherine Brooks Holst, Aug. 26, 1962; children: Thomas H., William H., James L. BS, Tufts U., 1960; MD, Tufts U., Boston, 1964. Diplomate Am. Bd. Internal Medicine, Am. Bd. Hematology. Hematology fellow Tufts - N.E. Med. Ctr., Boston, 1967-69; hematologist Andrews AFB Referral Hosp., Washington, 1969-71; dir. blood coagulation lab. and hemophilia ctr. Tufts - N.E. Med. Ctr., Boston, 1971-75; chmn. dept. medicine Worcester (Mass.) Meml. Hosp., 1975-90, dir. Blood Rsch. Lab., 1975—; pres., chief exec. officer Med. Ctr. of Cen. Mass., Worcester, 1990—; asst. prof. medicine Tufts U. Sch. Medicine, Boston, 1971-75; prof. medicine U. Mass. Med. Sch., Worcester, 1975—. Contbr. 164 articles to med. jours., 131 published abstracts in area of hematology. Med. dir. Nat. Hemophilia Found., N.Y.C., 1983-87; pres. Worcester County Music Assn., 1989-92; trustee Worcester Poly. Inst., 1990—, Mass. Biotech. Rsch. Inst., 1990—, Worcester Bus. Devel. Com., 1992—, United Way Ctrl. Mass., 1993—; trustee and exec. com. mem. Mass. Hosp. Assn., 1992—. Maj. USAF, 1969-71. Recipient Disting. Tchr. award Tufts U. Sch. Medicine, Boston, 1973, 75, Outstanding Med. Educator, U. Mass. Med. Sch., Worcester, 1981, 85, 86, 88, 89, 91, House Staff Disting. Tchr., Worcester Meml. Hosp., 1980, 87, 88, Murray Thelin Award for Rsch. Nat. Hemophilia Found., 1987. Fellow ACP; mem. Am. Soc. Hematology, Am. Fedn. Clin. Rsch. Achievements include patent pending on cure of hemophilia by gene therapy; development of model program for home therapy of hemophilia; research on production and effects of leukocyte-generated oxidants, on omega-3 fatty acids, prostanoids, and platelet and leukocyte function. Office: Med Ctr Ctrl Mass 119 Belmont St Worcester MA 01605-2903

LEVINE, PHILIP, classics educator; b. Lawrence, Mass., Sept. 8, 1922; s. Samuel and Jennie (Derdak) L.; m. Dinnie Moseson, June 19, 1955; children—Jared Elliott, Harlan Alcon. A.B., Harvard, 1944, A.M., 1948, Ph.D., 1952; DHL (hon.), U. Judaism, 1986. Instr., asst. prof. classics Harvard, 1952-59; assoc. prof. classical langs. U. Tex. at Austin, 1959-61; assoc prof., prof. classics UCLA, 1961-91, prof. emeritus, 1991—; dean div. humanities U. Calif. at Los Angeles, 1965-83; Biggs resident lectr. Washington U., 1993. Author: Lo Scriptorium Vercellese da S. Eusueblo ad Attone, 1958, St. Augustine, City of God, Books 12-15, 1966; editor: Latin lt. sect. Twayne World Author Series, 1964—; adv. editor, U. Calif. Pubis. in Classical Studies, 1963-72; assoc. editor, contbr. to U. Calif. Studies in Classical Antiquity, 1967-75, sr. co-editor, 1975-78; mem. editorial bd. Classical Antiquity, 1986-93. Mem. rev. com., sr. fellowship program Nat. Endowment for Humanities, 1966-70; bd. govs. U. Judaism, 1968-90; coun. visitors, 1990-94, acad. adv. coun., 1994—. With AUS, 1943-46. Sheldon fellow Italy; Guggenheim fellow; Fulbright Research grantee; recipient Bromberg Humanities award; decorated Cavaliere dell' Ordine al Merito della Repubblica Italiana. Mem. Am. Philol. Assn. (dir. 1968-70), Mediaeval Acad. Am. (exec. council 1969-72), Renaissance Soc., Am. Philol. Assn., Pacific Coast (chmn. gen. lit. 1964-65), Phi Beta Kappa. Home: 224 S Almont Dr Beverly Hills CA 90211-2507 Office: U Calif Dept Classics Los Angeles CA 90024

LEVINE, PHILIP, poet, educator; b. Detroit, Jan. 10, 1928; s. A. Harry and Esther Gertrude (Priscol) L.; m. Frances Artley, July 12, 1954; children: Mark, John, Teddy. B.A., Wayne State U., 1950, A.M., 1955; M.F.A., U. Iowa, 1957, studied with John Berryman, 1954. Instr. U. Iowa, 1955-57; instr. Calif. State U., Fresno, 1958—; prof. English Calif. State U. 1969-92, Tufts U.; tchr. Princeton U., Columbia U., U. Calif., Berkeley.; Elliston lectr. poetry U. Cin.; poet-in-residence Vassar Coll., Nat. U. Australia; chmn. lit. panel Nat. Endowment Arts, 1985; adj. prof. NYU, Spring, 1984; Univ. prof. Brown U., spring 1985; tchr. NYU, U. Iowa, Vanderbilt U. Author: On the Edge, 1961, Silent in America: Vivas for Those Who Failed, 1965, Not This Pig, 1968, 5 Detroits, 1970, Thistles, 1970, Pili's Wall, 1971, Red Dust, 1971, They Feed They Lion, 1972, 1933, 1974, On The Edge & Over, 1976, The Names of the Lost, 1976 (Lenore Marshall award Best Am. Book Poems 1976), 7 Years from Somewhere, 1979 (Nat. Book Critics Circle prize 1979, Notable Book award Am. Libr. Assn. 1979), Ashes, 1979 (Nat. Book Critics Circle prize 1979, Nat. Book award 1979), Don't Ask, 1979, One for the Rose, 1981, Selected Poems, 1984, Sweet Will, 1985, A Walk with Tom Jefferson, 1988 (Bay Area Book Reviewers award), What Work Is, 1991 (L.A. Times Book Prize 1991, Nat. Book award for poetry, 1991), New Selected Poems, 1991, Earth, Stars, and Writers, 1992, The Bread of Time: Toward an Autobiography, 1994, Simple Truth, 1994 (Pulitzer Prize for poetry 1995); editor: (with Henri Coulette) Character and Crisis, 1966, (with E. Trejo) The Selected Poems of Jaime Sabines, (with Ada Long) Off the Map, The Selected Poems of Gloria Fuertes, 1984, (with D. Wojahn and B. Henderson) The Pushcart Prize XI, 1986, The Essential Keats, 1987. Active anti-Vietnam war movement. Recipient Joseph Henry Jackson award San Francisco Found., 1961, The Chaplebrook Found. award, 1968, Frank O'Hara Meml. prize, 1973; Amer. Academy of Arts and Letters Award of Merit, 1974; Levinson Prize, 1974; Harriet Monroe Meml. prize for poetry, 1976; Golden Rose award New Eng. Poetry Soc., 1985, Ruth Lilly Poetry Prize, Modern Poetry Assn. and Am. Council Arts, 1987, Elmer Bost award NYU, 1990, Lit. Lion New York Public Library 1993; named outstanding lectr. Calif. State U., Fresno, 1971, outstanding prof. Calif. State U. System, 1972; Stanford U. poetry fellow, 1957, Nat. Inst. Arts and Letters grantee, 1973, Guggenheim fellow, 1973-74, 80; Nat. Endowment for Arts grantee, 1969, 70 (refused), 76, 81, 87. Home: 4549 N Van Ness Blvd Fresno CA 93704-3727 My hope is to write poetry for people for whom there are no poems.

LEVINE, RACHMIEL, physician; b. Poland, Aug. 26, 1910; came to U.S., 1936, naturalized, 1944; s. Solomon and Bessie (Benzion) L.; m. Anne Gussack, Mar. 4, 1943; children—Judith Ann, Daniel Saul. B.A., McGill U., 1932, M.D., 1936. Intern, then resident Michael Reese Hosp., Chgo., 1936-38; research fellow Michael Reese Hosp., 1939, dir. dept. metabolism, 1942-60, chmn. dept. medicine, 1952-60, dir. med. edn., 1952-60; professorial lectr. physiology U. Chgo., 1945-60; prof., chmn. dept. medicine N.Y. Med. Coll., 1960-71; exec. med. dir. City of Hope Med. Center, Duarte, Calif., 1971-78; dir. research City of Hope Med. Center, 1978—; Active United Jewish Appeal, Chgo., 1959-60; Com. NSF, 1956-59, mem. bd. found. fund psychiat. research, 1958-61; Jakobaeus lectr. Karolinska Inst., Stockholm, 1963. Contbr. numerous articles to profl. jours. Fellow Am. Acad. Arts and Scis.; mem. Am. Physiol. Soc., Nat. Acad. Scis., Endocrine Soc. (Upjohn award 1957), A.C.P., Assn. Am. Physicians, N.Y. Acad. Medicine, Chgo. Inst. Medicine, Am. Diabetes Assn. (Banting medal 1961, council 1958, pres. 1964-65), Internat. Diabetes Assn. (pres. 1967-70, hon. pres. 1970—), Harvey Soc. (pres. 1967-68, Gairdner award 1971, Joslin medal 1972). Home: 2024 Canyon Rd Arcadia CA 91006-1503 Office: City of Hope Med Ctr Duarte CA 91010

LEVINE, RAPHAEL DAVID, chemistry educator; b. Alexandria, Egypt, Mar. 29, 1938; brought to U.S., 1939; s. Chaim S. and Sofia (Greenberg) L.; m. Gillah T. Ephraty, June 13, 1962; 1 child, Ornah T. Msc, Hebrew U., Jerusalem, 1959; PhD, Nottingham (Eng.) U., 1964; DPhil, Oxford (Eng.) U., 1966; PhD honoris causa, U. Liege, Belgium, 1991. Vis. asst. prof. U. Wis., 1966-68; prof. theoretical chemistry Hebrew U., Jerusalem, 1969—; chmn. research ctr. molecular dynamics, 1981—; Max Born prof. natural philosophy, 1985—; Battelle prof. chemistry and math. Ohio State U.,

Columbus, 1970-74; Brittingham vis. prof. U. Wis., 1973; adj. prof. U. Tex., Austin, 1974-80, MIT, 1980-88, UCLA, 1989—; Arthur D. Little lectr. MIT, 1978; Miller rsch. prof. U. Calif., Berkeley, 1989, A.D. White prof. at large Cornell U., 1989—. Author: Quantum Mechanics of Molecular Rate Processes, 1969, Molecular Reaction Dynamics, 1974, Lasers and Chemical Change, 1981, Molecular Reaction Dynamics and Chemical Reactivity, 1986, Algebraic Theory of Molecules, 1995; mem. editorial bds. several well known scientific jours.; contbr. articles to profl. jours. Served with AUS, 1960-62. Recipient Ann. award Internat. Acad. Quantum Molecular Sci., 1968, Landau prize, 1972, Israel prize in Exact Scis., 1974, Weizman prize, 1979, Rothschild prize, 1992; co-recipient Chemistry prize Wolf Found., 1988; Ramsay Meml. fellow, 1964-66, Alfred P. Sloan fellow, 1970-72. Fellow Am. Phys. Soc.; mem. Israel Chem. Soc., Israel Acad. Scis., Max Planck Soc. (fgn. mem.), Academia Europaea (fgn. mem.), Am. Acad. Arts and Scis. (fgn. hon. mem.). Office: UCLA Dept Of Chemistry Los Angeles CA 90024 also: Hebrew U Jerusalem, 91904 Jerusalem Israel

LEVINE, RHEA JOY COTTLER, anatomy educator; b. N.Y.C., Nov. 26, 1939; d. Zachary Robert Cottler and Hildreth (Abramson) Cottler Rosenfeld; m. Stephen Maxwell Levine, June 16, 1960; children: Elizabeth, Michael Gordon, Zachary Thomas. AB summa cum laude, Smith Coll., 1960; MS, NYU, 1963, PhD, 1966. Lab. instr. NYU Sch. Commerce, N.Y.C., 1963-64; postdoctoral fellow, instr. histology Yale U. Sch. Medicine, New Haven, 1966-68; rsch. assoc. U. Pa. Sch. Medicine, Phila., 1968-69; asst. prof. anatomy Med. Coll. Pa., Phila., 1969-74, assoc. prof. anatomy, 1974-80, prof. anatomy, 1980—, vice chmn., 1988-89; manuscript reviewer numerous sci. journals, Washington and N.Y.C., 1975—; reviewer grant proposals NSF, Washington, 1975—, mem. NIH Study Sect., 1980-84. Contbr. sci. articles to profl. jours. Trustee Stockton State Coll., Pomona, N.J., 1983—, chmn. bd. trustees, 1991-94; bd. dirs. The Hollybush Festival, Glassboro, N.J., 1987-91, Smith Coll. Friends of Libr., Northampton, Mass., 1968-72. NYU Sch. Medicine summer rsch. fellow, 1960, NSF grad. fellow, 1960-65, A.H. Robins rsch. fellow, 1966, USPHS fellow, 1966-68; grantee Women's and Program project NIH, NSF, 1973—; recipient Founder's Day award NYU, 1966, Smith Coll. medal, 1994. Mem. AAAS, Coalition Jewish Profl. Women South N.J. (steering coun.), Am. Assn. Anatomists, Am. Soc. Cell Biology, Biophys. Soc. (coun. 1991-94, chair pub. sci. policy com. 1992-94), Histochem. Soc., Soc. Gen. Physiology, Wilderness Med. Soc., N.Y. Acad. Scis., Smith Coll. Club, Woodcrest Country Club (house chair 1983-84), Phi Beta Kappa, Sigma Xi. Jewish. Office: Med Coll Pa Dept Anatomy Neurobiology EPPI Divsn 3200 Henry Ave Philadelphia PA 19129-1187

LEVINE, RICHARD E., lawyer; b. Flushing, N.Y., Aug. 6, 1950; s. Sol and Betty (Broad) L.; m. Lori A. Balter, Oct. 28, 1979; 1 child, Jamie Balter. BS in Mech. Engring., Bucknell U., 1972; JD, U. Md., 1975; LL.M. in Taxation, Georgetown U., 1978. Bar: Md. 1975, U.S. Tax Ct. 1979, D.C. 1980, U.S. Supreme Ct. 1983, U.S. Ct. Appeals (4th cir.) 1984. Assoc. Miles & Stockbridge, Balt., 1978-83, prin., 1983—; adj. prof. U. Md. Law Sch., Balt., 1988. Contbr. articles to profl. jours. Bd. dirs. Har Sinai West Sr. Citizens Housing, Balt., 1983-92. Fellow Am. Coll. Tax Counsel; mem. ABA (tax sect., chair partnerships 1990-92), Md. State Bar Assn. (tax sect. coun. 1983-86), The Center Club (house com. 1990—). Avocations: golf, music. Office: Miles & Stockbridge 10 Light St Baltimore MD 21202-1435

LEVINE, RICHARD JAMES, publishing executive; b. N.Y.C., Jan. 24, 1942; s. Irving Joseph and Dorothy Joyce (Thome) L.; m. Neil Ann Stuckey, June 1, 1963; children: Jonathan Donald, Russell Neilan. BS, Cornell U., 1962; MS with high honors, Columbia U., 1963. Gen. assignment reporter Wall St. Jour., Washington, 1966-67, labor corr., 1967-70, mil. writer, 1970-75, chief econ. writer, outlook columnist, 1975-80; editl. dir./data base pub. Dow Jones & Co., Princeton, N.J., 1980-87, v.p. Info. Svcs. Group, 1987-89, v.p. and editl. dir. info. svcs. group, mem. mgmt. com., 1989-92, v.p., mng. editor Info. Svcs. segment, Dow Jones & Co., N.Y.C.; v.p. News Svcs. Dow Jones & Co., N.Y.C., Mem. mgmt. com. 1995—; pres. Dow Jones AER Co., Inc., 1994—; pres. Econ. Rsch. Co. Inc., 1994—; bd. dirs. Internat. Electronic Pub. Rsch. Ctr. Author: (with others) The Wall Street Journal Views America Tomorrow, 1977. 1st lt. U.S. Army, 1964-66. Columbia U. Pulitzer fellow, 1963-64. Mem. Cornell U. Tower Club, Cornell Mag. Com., Soc. Profl. Journalists, Cornell Club (N.Y.C.), Princeton Indoor Tennis Ctr. Home: 108 Parkside Dr Princeton NJ 08540-4815 Office: World Fin Ctr 200 Liberty St New York NY 10281-1003

LEVINE, ROBERT ARTHUR, economist, policy analyst; b. Bklyn., July 7, 1930; s. Isaac Bert and Jessie Sue (Palevsky) L.; m. Esther Carol Knudsen, Mar. 2, 1953; children: David Knudsen, Peter Kemmerer, Joseph Karl. BA, Harvard U., 1950, MA, 1951; PhD, Yale U., 1957. Economist Rand Corp., 1957-61, sr. economist, 1962-65, 69-73, 87—; research assoc. Harvard U. Center Internat. Affairs, 1961-62; asst. dir. for research, plans, programs and evaluation OEO, Washington, 1966-69; pres. N.Y.C.-Rand Inst., 1973-75; dep. dir. Congl. Budget Office, Washington, 1975-79; v.p. System Devel. Corp., Santa Monica, Calif., 1979-85; pres. Canyon Analysts, 1985—; sr. fellow Nat. Security Studies Program, UCLA, 1964-65; vis. prof. public policy Stanford U. Grad. Sch. Bus., 1972; adj. prof. econs. Pepperdine U. Sch. Bus. and Mgmt., 1984. Author: The Arms Debate, 1963, The Poor Ye Need Not Have With You, 1971, Public Planning: Failure and Redirection, 1972, Evaluation Research and Practice, 1981, Still the Arms Debate, 1990, Turmoil and Transition in the Atlantic Alliance, 1991. With USN, 1951-54. Ford Found. grantee, 1969, 85; German Marshall Fund grantee, 1979; Carnegie Corp. grantee, 1986. Mem. Am. Econ. Assn., Inst. Strategic Studies. Club: Beverly Glen Democratic. Home and Office: 10321 Chrysanthemum Ln Los Angeles CA 90077-2812

LEVINE, ROBERT JAY, lawyer; b. Hackensack, N.J., Aug. 7, 1950; s. Nathan R. and Naomi (Bendel) L.; m. Joan Beth Mirviss, Aug. 10, 1975. AB, Brown U., 1972; JD, U. Pa., 1975. Bar: N.Y. 1976, U.S. Dist. (so. and ea. dist.) N.Y. 1976. Assoc. Davis Polk & Wardwell, N.Y.C., 1975-82, ptnr., 1983—; pres. and dir. Sylvan Winds, Inc. Mem. ABA, N.Y. State Bar Assn., Assn. of Bar of City of N.Y., Phi Beta Kappa. Democrat. Jewish. Club: Brown of N.Y. Avocations: golf, travel, cooking, film. Home: 115 Central Park W New York NY 10023-4153 Office: Davis Polk & Wardwell 450 Lexington Ave New York NY 10023

LEVINE, ROBERT JOHN, physician, educator; b. N.Y.C., Dec. 29, 1934; s. Benjamin Bernard and Ruth Florence (Schwartz) L.; m. Jeralea Fooshee Hesse, Nov. 28, 1987; children from previous marriage: John Graham, Elizabeth Hurt. Student, Duke U., 1951-54; MD with distinction, George Washington U., 1958. Diplomate Am. Bd. Internal Medicine. Med. house officer Peter Bent Brigham Hosp., Boston, 1958-59, asst. resident in medicine, 1959-60; clin. assoc. Nat. Heart Inst., Bethesda, Md., 1960-62, investigator, 1963-64; chief med. resident VA Hosp., West Haven, Conn., 1962-63; mem. faculty depts. medicine and pharmacology Yale U., New Haven, 1964-73, chief sect. clin. pharmacology, 1966-74, prof. medicine, lectr. pharmacology, 1973—; mem. med. staff Yale-New Haven Med. Ctr., 1964-68, attending physician, 1968—; mem. Conn. Adv. Com. on Foods and Drugs, 1967-82, sec., 1969-71, chmn., 1971-73; mem. adv. com. AIDS program U.S. HHS, 1989—; cons. Nat. Common. Protection of Human Subjects of Biomed. and Behavioral Rsch., 1974-78; bd. dirs. Medicine in the Pub. Interest, Inc., 1976—, sec., 1983—. Author: Ethics and Regulation of Clinical Research, 1981, 2d edit., 1986; co-editor: Ethics and Research on Human Subjects: International Guidelines, 1993; editor Clin. Rsch., 1971-76, IRB: Rev. Human Subjects Rsch., 1978—; contbr. numerous articles to profl. jours. Mem. Conn. Humanities Coun., 1983-89, chmn., 1988-89, Coun. Internat. Orgn. Med. Scis., co-chmn. steering com. revision internat. ethical guidelines for biomed. rsch. involving human subjects, 1991-93; bd. dirs. Pub. Responsibility in Ethics and Medicine, 1986—. With USPHS, 1960-64. Multiple rsch. grantee. Fellow ACP, Am. Coll. Cardiology, The Hastings Ctr.; mem. AAAS (coun. del. 1987-91), Am. Soc. Clin. Investigation, Am. Soc. Clin. Pharmacology and Therapeutics (dir. 1981-85), Am. Fedn. Clin. Rsch. (nat. coun. 1967-76, exec. com. 1971-76), Am. Soc. Pharmacology and Exptl. Therapeutics (exec. com. 1974-77), Am. Soc. Law, Medicine and Ethics (bd. dirs. 1986—, pres. 1989-90, pres. 1994-95), Soc. for Bioethics Consultation (bd. dirs. 1988—), Sigma Xi, Alpha Omega Alpha. Office: Yale U Sch Medicine 333 Cedar St New Haven CT 06520-8010

LEVINE, ROBERT SIDNEY, chemical engineer; b. Des Moines, June 4, 1921; s. George Julius and Betty (Dennen) L.; m. Sharon Lorraine White;

children: George, Gail, Tamara, Michelle, James. B.S. in Chem. Engring. Iowa State U., 1943; S.M. (Standard Oil Co. Ohio fellow 1947-48), M.I.T., 1946, Sc.D., 1949. With Rocketdyne div. Rockwell Internat. Co., 1948-66; assoc. research dir. NASA, 1966-74; chief liquid rocket tech. Nat. Bur. Standards, Washington, 1974—; chief fire dynamics Nat. Bur. Standards (now Nat. Inst. Standards and Tech.), Washington, 1975—; mem. faculty UCLA, 1970-74, George Washington U., 1977; pres. Combustion Inst., 1974-78. Author papers in field. Named Engr. of Year Los Angeles sect. Am. Inst. Chem. Engrs., 1961. Mem. Am. Chem. Soc., AIAA, Nat. Fire Prevention Assn., Soc. Fire Protection Engrs. Home: 19017 Threshing Pl Gaithersburg MD 20879-2150 Office: Nat Inst Standards & Tech Gaithersburg MD 20899

LEVINE, RONALD H., physician, state official; b. N.Y.C., Mar. 30, 1935; m. Elizabeth P. Kanof; children—Mitchell, Rebecca Ann. BS, Union Coll., Schenectady, N.Y., 1955, DSc (hon.), 1990; MD, SUNY-Bklyn., 1959; MPH, U. N.C., 1967. Officer USPHS, Raleigh, N.C., 1963-65; chief communicable disease br. N.C. State Bd. Health, Raleigh, 1965-67, chief community health sect., 1968-73; asst. state bd. health. Raleigh, 1974-81, state health dir., 1981—. Recipient Stevens award N.C. Assn. Local Health Dirs., 1982. Fellow Am. Acad. Pediatrics, Am. Pub. Health Assn., Am. Coll. Preventive Medicine, mem. N.C. Pub. Health Assn. (pres. 1974-75, Reynolds award 1973), Wake County Med. Soc. (pres. 1978), N.C. Med. Soc. Office: Dept Environ Health & Natural Resources PO box 27687 512 N Salisbury St Raleigh NC 27604-1118

LEVINE, RONALD JAY, lawyer; b. Bklyn., June 23, 1953; s. Louis Leon and Marilyn Priscilla (Markovich) L.; m. Cindy Beth Israel, Nov. 18, 1979; children: Merisa, Alisha. BA summa cum laude, Princeton U., 1974; JD cum laude, Harvard U., 1977. Bar: N.Y. 1978, U.S. Dist. Ct. (so. and ea. dists.) N.Y. 1978, D.C. 1980, N.J. 1987, U.S. Supreme Ct. 1982, U.S. Ct. Appeals (2d cir.) 1983, N.J. 1987, U.S. Dist. Ct. N.J. 1987, U.S. Dist. Ct. (we. dist.) N.Y. 1991, U.S. Ct. Appeals (3d Cir.) 1991. Assoc. Phillips, Nizer, Benjamin, Krim & Ballon, N.Y.C., 1977-80, Debevoise & Plimpton, N.Y.C., 1980-84; assoc. Herrick, Feinstein, N.Y.C., 1984-85, ptnr., 1985—; gen. counsel Greater N.Y. Safety Council, N.Y.C., 1979-81; arbitrator Small Claims Ct. of Civil Ct. of City of N.Y., 1983-85. Mem. Site Plan Rev. Adv. Bd., West Windsor, N.J., 1986, planning bd., 1987. Mem. ABA (litigation sect.), N.Y. State Bar Assn. (chmn. com. on legal edn. and bar admission 1982-92, com. on profl. discipline 1989-90), N.J. State Bar Assn. (product liability com. 1991—, profl. responsibility com. 1992—), Assn. of Bar of City of N.Y. (coun. jud. adminstrn. 1994—, com. on profl. responsibility 1980-83, com. on legal assistance 1983-86, product liability com. 1987-91, trustee career devel. awards 1989-90), Phi Beta Kappa. Home: 6 Arnold Dr Princeton Junction NJ 08550-1521 Office: Herrick Feinstein 2 Park Ave New York NY 10016-5603

LEVINE, RUTH ROTHENBERG, biomedical science educator; b. N.Y.C.; d. Jacob and Jeannette (Bandel) Rothenberg; m. Martin J. Levine, June 21, 1953. B.A. magna cum laude, Hunter Coll., 1938; M.A., Columbia U., 1939; Ph.D., Tufts U., 1955. Asst. prof. sch. medicine Tufts U., 1955-58; asst. prof. pharmacology sch. medicine Boston U., 1958-61, assoc. prof. sch. medicine, 1961-65, prof. sch. medicine, 1965—, univ. prof., 1972—; chmn. grad. div. med. and dental scis. Boston U. Sch. Medicine, 1964-89, assoc. dean grad. biomed. scis., 1981-89, assoc. dean emeritus, 1989—; mem. sci. adv. bd. U.S. EPA, 1976-82, Internat. Joint Commn., State Dept., 1983-89. Author: Pharmacology, Drug Actions and Reactions, 1973, 4th edit., 1990; coord. internat. symposia of subtypes of muscarinic receptors. Fellow AAAS; mem. Am. Soc. Pharmacology and Exptl. Therapeutics (sec.-treas. 1975-76), Biophys. Soc., Am. Chem. Soc., Am. Pharm. Assn., Acad. Scis., Phi Beta Kappa, Sigma Xi. Home: 212 Crafts Rd Chestnut Hill MA 02167-1452 Office: Boston U Sch Medicine Div Med and Dental Scis Boston MA 02118

LEVINE, SARAH LOEWENBERG, developmental psychologist, school director; m. Randolph H. Levine, June 21, 1970; children: Seth Jason, Johanna Beth. BA, Sarah Lawrence Coll., 1968; EdM, Harvard U., 1977, EdD, 1980. Cert. tchr., adminstr., Mass. Grade head Shady Hill Sch., Cambridge, Mass., 1969-72; coord. career edn. Roxbury-Harvard Sch. Program, Cambridge, 1977-78; teaching fellow Grad. Sch. Edn. Harvard U., Cambridge, 1978-80; prin. dir. Prins.'s Ctr. Principals' Ctr. Harvard U., Cambridge, 1983-89; dir. prins.'s cert., admstr. edn. Harvard U., Cambridge, 1984-89; lectr. Lesley Coll., Cambridge, 1980; rsch. assoc. Edn. Devel. Ctr., Newton, Mass., 1980-83; sch. head Belmont (Mass.) Day Sch., 1989—; cons. in field. Author: Promoting Adult and Growth in Schools, 1989; contbr. articles to profl. jours. Mem. APA, ASCD, Nat. Staff Devel. Coun. (editorial bd. 1985—), NAt. Assn. Ind. Schs., Assn. Ind. Schs. New England. Avocations: exercise, reading, movies. Office: Belmont Day Sch 55 Day School Ln Belmont MA 02178-2030

LEVINE, SOL, sociologist; b. Greenwood, Miss., Apr. 3, 1922; s. Samuel and Gussie (Kozlove) L.; m. Alice S. Gordon, July 15, 1963; children: Andrea, Pamela, Joshua. BA, Queens Coll., CUNY, 1942; MA, NYU, 1948, PhD, 1953. Instr. dept. sociology Univ. Heights Coll., NYU, 1951-53; from asst. to assoc. prof. social psychology Harvard U. Sch. Pub. Health, Cambridge, Mass., 1956-63, dir. social sci. program, 1963-66; prof. social rels. Johns Hopkins U., 1966-67; prof., dir. div. behavioral scis. Johns Hopkins U. Sch. Hygiene and Pub. Health, 1966-67, prof., chmn. dept. behavioral scis., 1967-72; univ. prof., prof. sociology, prof. pub. health Boston U., 1973-88, dir. univ. profs. program, 1973-76, chmn. dept. sociology, 1976-79, adj. univ. prof., adj. prof. sociology, adj. prof. pub. health, 1988—; v.p. Henry J. Kaiser Family Found., Palo Alto, Calif., 1988-90; prof. health and social behavior, prof. health policy Harvard Sch. Pub. Health, 1990—, interim chair dept. health & social behavior, 1993-95; dir. joint program in society and health New Eng. Med. Ctr., Boston, 1990-95, sr. scientist, 1990—; nat. program dir. awards health policy rsch. Robert Wood Johnson Found., 1994—; mem. study vol. agys. Rockefeller Found., 1957; mem. health services research study sect. NIH, 1964-68; mem. Sec.'s adv. com. on health protection and disease prevention HEW, 1969; chmn. alcohol research rev. com. Nat. Inst. on Alcohol Abuse and Alcoholism, 1976-77, mem., 1973-77; bd. dirs. Robert Wood Johnson Clin. Scholars Program, 1978-89. Author: (with others) Ency. Sociology, 1991; co-author: (with Odin Anderson and Gerald Gordon) Non-Group Enrollment for Health Insurance: A Study of Adminstrative Approaches of Blue Cross Plans, 1957, (with Sydney H. Croog) The Heart Patient Recovers, 1978, Life After a Heart Attack, 1982; co-editor: (with Howard E. Freeman and Leo G. Reeder) Handbook of Medical Sociology, 1963, 2d edit., 1972, 3d edit., 1978, (with Howard E. Freeman) 4th edit., 1989, (with Freeman, Orville Brim and Norman Scotch) The Dying Patient, 1970, (with Scotch) Social Stress, 1970, (with Abraham Lilienfeld) Epidemiology and Health Policy, 1986. Mem. research com. Nat. Acad. Social. Assn. (nat. med. soc. sect. 1968-69, Leo G. Reeder award 1986), Inst. Medicine-Nat. Acad. Scis. Home: 30 Powell St Brookline MA 02146-3921 Office: The Health Inst New Eng Med Ctr 750 Washington St # 345 Boston MA 02111-1533

LEVINE, SOLOMON BERNARD, business and economics educator; b. Boston, Aug. 10, 1920; s. Isaac William and Sybil (Mannis) l.; m. Elizabeth Jane Billett, Dec. 24, 1943; children: Janet Ruth Levine Thal, Michael Alan, Samuel Billett, Elliott Mannis. AB magna cum laude, Harvard Coll., 1942; cert. Japanese Lang., U. Colo., 1944; MBA with honors, Sch. Bus. Adminstrn., Harvard U., 1947; postgrad., MIT, 1947-49, Ph.D. in Indsl. Econs., 1951. Teaching asst. dept. econs. and social sci. MIT, 1947-49; faculty U. Ill., 1949-69, prof. labor and indsl. relations and Asian studies, 1964-69; prof. bus. and econs. U. Wis.-Madison, 1969-89, prof. emeritus, 1989—, mem. East Asian Studies Program, chmn., 1968-77, co-chmn., 1982-88, dir. Nat. Resource Ctr. for East Asian Studies, 1985-87, participating faculty mem. Indsl. Relations Research Inst.; Fulbright rsch. prof. Keio U., Tokyo, 1959; vis. prof. dept. econs. Pa. State U., 1960; vis. prof. labor relations dept. econs. MIT, 1962-63; vis. prof. econs. U. Singapore, 1968; vis. lectr. and research scholar various univs., Indonesia, 1973, Australia, 1973, N.Z., 1973, vis. scholar univs., Japan, 1978, Australia, 1978, N.Z., 1978, Singapore, 1978, South Korea, 1978; vis. prof., sr. scholar Monash U., Australia and Japan, 1981-82, vis. research scholar Macquarie U., Australia, 1985; vis. prof. Internat. U. Japan, 1984; vis. prof. Nanzan U., Nagoya, Japan, 1989-91, U. Hawaii, Manoa, 1991; vis. fellow Swinburne Inst. Tech.,

Australia, 1992; vis. scholar Japan Ctr. for Mich. Univ., Japan, 1994. labor arbitrator. Author: Industrial Relations in Postwar Japan, 1958, Japanese transl., 1959, (with Hishashi Kawada) Human Resources in Japanese Industrial Development, 1980; co-editor, co-author: chpts. and preface Workers and Employers in Japan: The Japanese Employment Relations System, 1973; contbr. to sect. Ency. Americana; chpts. to books, articles to publs. Treas. Stevenson for Pres. Campaign, Champaign-Urbana, Ill., 1952; mem. Community Integration Council, 1965-69. Sheldon traveling fellow Harvard U., Mex., 1942; Social Sci. Rsch. Coun. ing. fellow, 1948-49; Fulbright rsch. scholar and Ford Found. rsch. fellow Hitotsubashi U., Tokyo, 1953-54; Social Sci. rsch. Coun. fellow Carnegie Inst. Tech., 1957; life fellow Found. Keio U., 1961; Fulbright-Hays faculty rsch. scholar 1968, 73, 78, Singapore, 1968, 78, Australia, 1978; Fulbright-Hays faculty scholar N.Z., 1978; Japan Found. scholar, 1978; hon. Fulbright sr. scholar Australia, 1981. Mem. Indsl. Rels. Rsch. Assn., Am. Econ. Assn., Assn. for Asian Studies, Midwest Conf. of Asian Affairs (pres. 1961), Japan Soc., Internat. House of Japan, Internat. Indls. Rels. Assn., Japan Illini Club (hon. life), Wis. Alumni Assn. Japan (pres. 1990), Phi Beta Kappa, Beta Gamma Sigma. Home: 916 Van Buren St Madison WI 53711-2167

LEVINE, STUART GEORGE, editor, English literature educator, author; b. N.Y.C., May 25, 1932; s. Max and Jean (Berens) L.; m. Susan F. Matthews, June 6, 1962; children: Rebecca, Aaron, Allen. A.B. Harvard U., 1954; M.A., Brown U., 1956, Ph.D, 1958. Teaching fellow Brown U., 1956-57; instr. in English U. Kans., Lawrence, 1958-61; asst. prof. U. Kans., 1961-64, assoc. prof. Am. studies, 1964-66, prof., 1966—, founder, chmn. dept. Am. Studies, 1963-70, prof. English, 1976-92, Exxon intra-univ. vis. prof. dept. music history, 1981-82, prof. emeritus, 1992—; Fulbright disting. lectr., Naples chair U. Naples, Italy, 1994-95; Fulbright prof. U. La Plata (Argentina), 1962, U. Costa Rica, 1965, 67, Nat. Autonomous U. Mexico, 1973, several univs. in Chile, 1985; exchange professorship U. West Indies, 1988; scholar-in-residence U. Ariz., 1972-73; profl. concert musician, 1955-58, 73—, also artist; dir. Nat. Endowment Humanities Summer Seminar for Coll. Tchrs., 1978; also cons. panels. Regional chmn. Harvard Coll. Found.; vis. prof. various univs. Author: (with N. O. Lurie) The American Indian Today, 1968, Caffin's The Story of American Painting, 1970, Edgar Poe: Seer and Craftsman, 1972, (fiction) The Monday-Wednesday-Friday Girl and Other Stories (Gross-Wordley competition winner 1994); also author short stories pub. in various mags.; editor in chief Am. Studies, 1960-89, founding editor, 1989—; editor (with Susan F. Levine) The Short Fiction of Edgar Allan Poe: An Annotated Edition, 1976, 1990; one-man shows include Regents Ctr. Gallery, Kansas City, 1983, Lawrence Arts Ctr., 1984, French horn player, Lawrence Woodwind Quintet, Lawrence Symphony Orch., Lawrence Mcpl. Band. Recipient Anisfield Wolf award (with others) Saturday Rev., 1968, citation NCCJ, 1969; grantee Kans. Com. for Humanities, 1982-83, 83-84. Mem. Am. Studies Assn. (exec. com. nat. meeting 1965-66, publs. com. nat. meeting 1965-66, Gabriel and Bode prize coms. 1983, chmn. both coms. 1984-85), Mid-Am. Am. Studies Assn. (exec. and editorial bds. 1960—), MLA, Am. Fedn. Musicians. Home: 1644 University Dr Lawrence KS 66044-3150 *Open exchange of ideas, I believe, has been the strongest cause of benign revolution in the recent past. For changes to be benign, however, the quality of the ideas must be high. I worry that our nation is allowing the quality of its ideas to deteriorate. We need to insist on highest standards early in its citizens' education. Ill-paid overworked schoolteachers, many themselves clumsy of thought and of expression, ignorant of history and of culture, and frightened of science and mathematics cannot train the bright creators of ideas which our nation and the interlocked world need. Our best people, our best effort, should be engaged in doing better.*

LEVINE, SUMNER NORTON, industrial engineer, educator, editor, author, financial consultant; b. Boston, Sept. 5, 1923; s. Frank and Lillian (Gold) L.; m. Caroline Gassner, Nov. 27, 1952; 1 dau., Joanne. B.S., Brown U., 1946; Ph.D., U. Wis., 1949; postgrad., M.I.T., 1956. Instr. U. Chgo., 1949-50; sr. research fellow Columbia, 1950-54; dir. research labs. VA, East Orange, N.J., 1954-56; adv. scientist comml. atom power div. Westinghouse Electric Co., Pitts., 1956; dir. chemistry Metallurgy and Materials Labs.; also staff adv. engr. Gen. Engring. Labs., Am. Machine & Foundry Co., Greenwich, Conn., 1956-58; sect. head, materials and advanced electronic devices RCA, 1958-61; chmn. materials scis. dept., prof. engring., also prof., dir. grad. program in indsl. adminstrn. SUNY, Stony Brook, 1961-91; dir. urban research, vis. prof. CUNY Grad. Center, 1967-68; Danforth vis. lectr., 1968-69; vis. prof. Yale Sch. Orgn. and Mgmt., 1976; prof. fin. Coll. Urban and Policy Scis., SUNY, Stony Brook, 1978—; cons. to industry; bd. dirs. Norteck Assocs.; editorial adviser Ocean Engring. Author textbooks, profl. articles; editor: Financial Analysts Handbook, 1975, 2d edit., 1987, Investment Manager's Handbook, Dow Jones-Irwin Bus.and Investment Almanac, 1976—, Acquisition Manual, 1990, Turnaround and Bankruptcy Investing, 1991, Handbook of Global Investing, 1992, Internat. Bus. and Investment Almanac, 1992—; editor-in-chief Jour. Biomed. Materials Rsch., 1966-78, Jour. Socio-Econ. Planning Scis., 1966, Advances in Biomed. Engring. and Med. Physics, 1966. Recipient award for distinguished contbn. to biomed. materials research, 1973. Mem. IEEE, World Conf. Planning Scis., Am. Chem. Soc., Am. Soc. Metals, Electrochem. Soc., Ops. Research Soc. Am., Inst. Mgmt. Scis., Fgn. Policy Assn., N.Y. Acad. Scis. (chmn. conf. materials in biomed. engring. 1966, chmn. colloquia socioecon. planning 1966-68), Soc. for Biomaterials (dir. 1974-76), N.Y. Soc. Security Analysts (chmn. edn. and seminar coms., Vols. award 1984), Mus. Modern Art, Met. Mus. of Art, Princeton Club N.Y., Brown U. Club, Sigma Xi. Office: PO Box 2118 Setauket NY 11733-0883

LEVINE, SUZANNE BRAUN, magazine editor; b. N.Y.C., June 21, 1941; d. Imre and Esther (Bernson) Braun; m. Robert F. Levine, Apr. 2, 1967; children: Joshua, Joanna. BA with honors, Radcliffe Coll., 1963. Reporter Seattle mag., 1963-65; reporter, researcher Time/Life Books, N.Y.C., 1965-67; features editor Mademoiselle, N.Y.C., 1967-68, McCalls mag., N.Y.C., 1968-69; free-lance writer, 1970; mng. editor Sexual Behavior mag., 1971-72, MS. mag., N.Y.C., 1972-88; editor Columbia Journalism Rev., N.Y.C., 1989—; adj. prof. Columbia Grad. Sch. Journalism. Co-editor: The Decade of Women, A Ms History of the Seventies, 1980; exec. producer: Ms. HBO TV spl., 1981, She's Nobody's Baby, TV documentary, 1981 (Peabody award). Woodrow Wilson guest lectr. coord. Chautauqua Conf. on Families. Mem. Am. Soc. Mag. Editors (exec. com.), Women's Media Group. Office: Columbia U Columbia Journalism Rev 700 Journalism Bldg New York NY 10027

LEVINE, THEODORE A., lawyer; b. Bronx, N.Y., Nov. 8, 1944. BA, Rutgers U., 1966; JD, George Washington U., 1969. Bar: Va. 1969, D.C. 1970. Assoc. dir. divsn. enforcement SEC, 1979-84; mem. Wilmer, Cutler & Pickering, Washington. Office: Wilmer Cutler & Pickering 2445 M St NW Washington DC 20037-1435

LEVINE, THOMAS JEFFREY PELLO, lawyer; b. Santa Monica, Calif., Mar. 6, 1952; s. Allan Lester and Shirley Elaine (Pello) L.; m. Margaret Louise Adlon, Aug. 27, 1977; children: Marissa, Matthew, Molly. Student, U. Denver, 1970-71, Calif. State U. Northridge, 1971-73; BA, Calif. State U., Sacramento, 1974; JD, Southwestern U., 1977. Bar: Calif. 1977, U.S. Dist. Ct. (cen. dist.) Calif. 1978. Partner Levine & Levine, L.A., 1977-83; staff atty. Fed. Deposit Ins. Corp., Newport Beach, Calif., 1983-85; v.p., assoc. counsel Imperial Bank, Inglewood, Calif., 1985-88; v.p., counsel Community Bank, Pasadena, Calif., 1988; gen. counsel, sr. v.p., sec. Calif. Commerce Bank, Banamex USA Bancorp, L.A., 1988—; legal affairs com. mem. Calif. Bankers Assn., San Francisco, 1990—; Am. Bankers Assn. Bank Counsel Com. 1993—. Author: (course materials) Bank Counsel Symposium, 1991. Dir. Angelino Heights Historic Preservation Assn., L.A., 1985; sec., dir. Carroll Ave. Restoration Found. L.A., 1979-87; dir. Wilshire C. of C., L.A., 1982. Mem. L.A. County Bar Assn. Jewish. Avocations: running, golf, historic preservation, raising children. Office: Banamex USA Bancorp 811 Wilshire Blvd Los Angeles CA 90017

LE VINE, VICTOR THEODORE, political science educator; b. Berlin, Dec. 6, 1928; came to U.S., 1938; s. Maurice and Hildegard (Hirschberg) LeV.; m. Nathalie Jeanne Christian, July 19, 1958; children: Theodore, Nicole. BA, UCLA, 1950, MA, 1958, PhD, 1961. Research assoc. UCLA, 1958-60; prof., head dept. polit. sci. U. Ghana, Legon, 1969-71; vis. prof. Hebrew U., Jerusalem, 1978, U. Tex., Austin, 1980; Fulbright prof. U.

Yaounde, Cameroon, 1981-82; prof. polit. sci. Washington U., St. Louis 1961—; cons. U.S. Dept. State, Dept. Def., 1971—; lectr. USIA, 1981—; mem. U.S. Nat. Cmemn. UNESCO, 1964; dir. Office Internat. Studies, Washington U., 1975-76; vis. lectr. Fudan U., U. Nanjing (China), 1987, Ibn Saud and King Abdulazziz Univs., Saudi Arabia, 1990; mem. Carter Ctr. Internat. monitoring team to Ghana nat. elections, 1992. Author: Cameroons: Mandate to Independence, 1964, 70, Cameroon Federal Republic, 1971, Political Corruption: Ghana, 1975, (with Timothy Luke) Arab-African Connection, 1979; (with Heidenhimer and Johnston) Political Corruption: A Handbook, 1990. Mem., dir. UN Assn., St. Louis, 1964-74; mem. Coun. on World Affairs, 1969—; pres. Ctr. for Internat. Understanding, 1988—. With U.S. Army, 1951-54. Ford. Found. fellow Cameroon, 1960-61; Hoover Instn. fellow, 1974; Lester Martin fellow Truman Instn., Jerusalem, 1978; Fulbright lectr. U.S. Fulbright Commn., Yaounde, Cameroon, 1981-82. Mem. Am. Polit. Sci. Assn., African Studies Assn., Mideast Studies Assn., Midwest Polit. Sci. Assn., Mo. Polit. Sci. Assn. Office: Washington U Dept Polit Sci Saint Louis MO 63130

LEVINE, WILLIAM SILVER, electrical engineering educator; b. Bklyn., Nov. 19, 1941; s. Louis Nathan and Gertrude (Silver) L.; m. Shirley Johannesen, Feb. 14, 1963; children: Bruce Jonathan, Eleanor Joan. BEE, MIT, 1962, MEE, 1965, PhD in Elec. Engring., 1969. Project engr. Data Tech. Inc., Cambridge, Mass., 1962-64; grad. asst. MIT, Cambridge, 1964-69; asst. prof. U. Md., College Park, 1969-73, assoc. prof., 1973-81, prof., 1981—; cons. IBM Fed. System Div., Gaithersburg, Md., 1972-75, Computational Engring. Inc., Laurel, Md., 1980-90. Co-author: Using MATLAB to Nalayse and Design Control Systems, 1992, 3d edit., 1995; contbr. articles to profl. jours. Recipient numerous rsch. grants, 1969—. Fellow IEEE, IEEE Control Systems Soc. (pres. 1990, disting. mem. 1990); mem. IEEE Medicine and Biology Soc. (disting. sect. 1991), Soc. for Indsl. and Applied Math. Office: U Md Dept Elec Engring College Park MD 20742

LEVINGER, BERYL BETH, development specialist, organization administrator; b. N.Y.C., July 31, 1947; d. Adolph Seymour Schapira and Beatrice Glickman Lemeshnik; m. Samuel Levinger, June 17, 1967; children: Lisa, Andrea. BS, Cornell U., 1968; MA, U. Ala., 1974, PhD, 1977. Vol. U.S. Peace Corps, Colombia, 1967-69; assoc. dir U.S. Peace Corps, Bogota, Colombia, 1974-75; tchr., adminstr. Am. Schs. Abroad, Honduras and Colombia, 1970-74; edn. advisor AID, Bogota, 1975-77; spl. asst. to pres. Save the Children, Westport, Conn., 1977-79; dep. dir. tech. svcs. unit World Edn., N.Y.C., 1979-81; sr. rsch. assoc., adj. asst. prof. Columbia U., N.Y.C., 1981-84; sr. v.p. CARE, N.Y.C., 1984-89; pres. AFS Intercultural Programs, N.Y.C., 1989-93; disting. prof. nonprofit mgmt. Monterey (Calif.) Inst. Internat. Studies, 1992—; sr. dir. for internat. programs Edn. Devel. Ctr., Newton, Mass., 1992—; cons. in field. Mem. Cornell Club. Democrat. Jewish. Avocations: hiking, boating, cross-country skiing, music. Home: 17 Woods Grove Rd Westport CT 06880-2427

LEVINGER, JOSEPH SOLOMON, physicist, educator; b. N.Y.C., Nov. 14, 1921; s. Lee J. and Elma (Ehrlich) L.; m. Gloria Edwards, Aug. 14, 1943; children—Sam, Laurie, Louis, Joe. B.S., U. Chgo., 1941, M.S., 1944; Ph.D, Cornell U., 1948. Physicist Metall. Lab., U. Chgo., 1942-44, Franklin Inst., Phila., 1945; instr. Cornell U., 1948-51, vis. prof., 1961-64; from asst. prof. to prof. La. State U., 1951-61; prof. physics Rensselaer Poly. Inst., 1964-92, prof. emeritus, 1992—; Fulbright fellow, assoc. prof. U. Paris—Sud, 1972-73. Author: Nuclear Photo-disintegration, 1961, Secrets of the Nucleus, 1967, The Two and Three Body Problem, 1974. Guggenheim fellow, 1957-58. Fellow Am. Phys. Soc. Home: Red Mill Rd Rensselaer NY 12144-3010 Office: Rensselaer Poly Inst Physics Dept Troy NY 12180

LEVINS, ILYSSA, public relations executive; b. New Hyde Park, N.Y., Dec. 3, 1958; d. Jack and Marlene (Newman) L. BA, NYU, 1980. Asst. account exec. Gross, Townsend, Frank, Hoffman, Inc., N.Y.C., 1982, account exec., 1983, sr. account exec., 1984, account supr., 1985, group account supr., 1986, v.p., dir. pub. rels., 1987-88, sr. v.p., dir. pub. rels., 1988-90, pres. pub. rels. divsn., 1990-94; mng. dir., 1994—. Mem. Pub. Rels. Soc. Am., Am. Soc. for Hosp. Mktg. and Pub. Rels., Women in Communications, Pharm. Advt. Coun., Food and Drug Law Inst., Am. Med. Writer's Assn., Am. Soc. for Health Care Mktg. and Pub. Rels. Jewish. Avocations: poetry, biking, swimming. Office: Gross Townsend Frank Hoffman Inc 114 Fifth Ave New York NY 10011-5604

LEVINS, JOHN RAYMOND, investment advisor, management consultant, educator; b. Jersey City, Aug. 4, 1944; s. Raymond Thomas and Catherine (Kelly) L. BS in Acctg., U. N.H., 1973; MBA, U. N.H., Plymouth, 1976. Registered investment advisor; cert. mgmt. cons., enrolled to practice IRS; cert. licensing instr.; cert. real estate and multiple lines ins. broker, comml. arbitration panelist; accredited tax advisor. Mgmt. risk analyst Express Treaty Mgmt. Corp., N.Y.C., 1962-67; asst. risk mgr. Bigelow-Sanford, Inc., N.Y.C., 1967-71; cons., broker BYSE, Inc., Laconia, N.Y., 1971-74; asst. prof. Nathaniel Hawthorne Coll., Antrim, N.H., 1975-82, Keene (N.H.) State Coll., 1982—; prin. Levins & Assocs., Concord, N.H., 1986—; investment advisor Reality Techs., Internat. Fin., Concord, 1991—; dir. Small Bus. Inst. Keene State Coll., 1982-86; exec. seminar leader Strategic Mgmt Group, Inc., 1986—, Boston U., 1986—, Worcester Doly Tech. Inst., 1992; gen. securities rep. H.D. Vest Fin. Svcs., 1990; mem. bd. advisors Am. Biog. Inst.; pvt. practice real estate, ins. cons., Concord, 1981; panelist securities arbitration Nat. Assn. Security Dealers, Am. Stock Exchange; mortgage banker; comml. financing broker; mem. SEC, speaker, seminar leader in field. Author: Finance and Accounting, 1979 (Excellence award 1980), Financial Analysis, 1981 (Excellence award 1980), Managing Cash Flow, 1988 (Excellence award 1988), Finance and Management, 1989. Incorporator Spaulding Youth Ctr., Tilton, N.H., 1990; colleague Found. for Acctg. Edn., assoc., profl. standing, 1988; mem. Nat. Consortium Edn. and Tng., Madison, Wis., 1989. With USN, 1969-71, S.E. Asia. Named Outstanding Support Leader U.S. Small Bus. Adminstrn., Concord, 1985, Outstanding Svc. Leader Community Leaders Am., N.H., 1990, One of Outstanding Young Men Am. U.S. Jaycees Bd. Adv.'s, 1983. Mem. AICPA (mem. Profl. Devel. Inst., sponsor trainer 1988-89), Investment Co. Inst. (assoc., nat. standing 1987), Inst. Mgmt. Cons. (assoc., nat. standing 1985), Nat. Soc. Pub. Accts. (del., profl. standing 1985), Nat. Soc. Non-Profit Orgns. (svc. provider 1989, colleague), Accreditation Coun. for Accountancy (fed. taxation accreditation 1987, colleague). Avocations: boating, teaching, community service, athletics. Home and Office: Levins & Assocs PO Box 442 624 Alton Woods Dr Concord NH 03302-0442

LEVINS, RICHARD, science educator; b. N.Y.C., N.Y., June 1, 1930; s. Ruben and Ruth (Sackman) L.; m. Rosario Morales, June 10, 1950; children: Aurora, Ricardo, Alejandro. A.B., Cornell U., 1951; Ph.D., Columbia U., 1965. Farmer, P.R., 1951-56; research assoc. U. Rochester, N.Y., 1960-61; assoc. prof. biology U. P.R., 1961-66; assoc. prof. biology and math. biology U. Chgo., 1967-68, prof., 1969-75; John Rock prof. population sci. Harvard Sch. Pub. Health, 1975—; mem. sci. adv. council natural resources P.R. Dept. Pub. Works, 1970-72; mem. adv. bd. N.Y. Marxist Sch. Author: Evolution in Changing Environments, 1968; co-author: (with R.C. Lewontin) The Dialectical Biologist, (with C. Puccia) Qualitative Modeling of Complex Systems, (with Yrjo Haila) Humanity and Nature, 1992; editorial bd.: La Escalera, 1965-72, Am. Naturalist, 1968-71, Theoretical Population Biology, 1970—, Coffee region organizer P.R. Communist party, 1952-54; mem. Partido Socialista Puertorriqueño; bd. dirs. Concilio Hispano, 1986—, Oxfam Am., 1988—. Mem. Am. Acad. Arts and Sci., New World Agr. and Ecol. Group, Sci. for Vietnam, Nat. Organic Farmers Assn., Cuban Botanical Assn. (corr. mem.). Home: 107 Amory St Cambridge MA 02139-1229 *Understand the world in order to change it, and in changing it get to understand it better.*

LEVINSKY, NORMAN GEORGE, physician, educator; b. Boston, Apr. 27, 1929; s. Harry and Gertrude (Kipperman) L.; m. Elena Sartori, June 17, 1956; children—Harold, Andrew, Nancy. A.B. summa cum laude, Harvard U., 1950, M.D. cum laude, 1954. Diplomate Am. Bd. Internal Medicine. Intern Beth Israel Hosp., Boston, 1954-55; resident Beth Israel Hosp., 1955-56; commd. med. officer USPHS., 1956; clin. assoc. Nat. Heart Inst., Bethesda, Md., 1956-58; NIH fellow Boston U. Med. Center, 1958-60; practice medicine, specializing in internal medicine and nephrology Boston, 1960—; chief of medicine Boston City Hosp., 1968-72, 93—; physician-in-chief, dir. Evans dept. clin. research Univ. Hosp., Boston, 1972—; asst. prof.,

then assoc. prof. medicine Boston U., 1960-68, Wesselhoeft prof., 1968-72, Wade prof. medicine, 1972—, chmn. dept. medicine, 1972—; mem. drug efficacy panel NRC; mem. nephrology test com.-Am. Bd. Internal Medicine, 1971-76: mem. gen. medicine B rev. group NIH; mem. comprehensive test com. Nat. Bd. Med. Examiners, 1986-89; chmn. com. to study end-stage renal disease program Nat. Acad. Scis./Inst. Medicine, 1988-90, chmn. com. on Xenografts, 1995. Editor (with R.W. Wilkins) Medicine: Essentials of Clinical Practice, 3d edit., 1983, (with R. Rettig) Kidney Disease and the Federal Government, 1991; contbr. chpts. to books, sci. articles to med. jours. Recipient Distinguished Teacher awd. Am. Coll. of Physicians, 1992. Master ACP; mem. AAAS, Am. Fedn. Clin. Rsch., Am. Soc. Clin. Investigation, Am. Heart Assn., Assn. Am. Physicians, Am. Physiol. Soc., Assn. Profs. Medicine (sec., treas. 1984-87, pres.-elect 1987-88, pres. 1988-89), Am. Soc. Nephrology, Inst. Medicine NAS, Interurban Clin. Club (pres. 1985-86), Phi Beta Kappa, Alpha Omega Alpha. Home: 20 Kenwood Ave Newton MA 02159-1439 Office: Boston U Med Ctr 75 E Newton St Boston MA 02118-2340

LEVINSON, ARTHUR DAVID, molecular biologist; b. Seattle, Mar. 31, 1950; s. Sol and Malvina (Lindsay) L.; m. Rita May Liff, Dec. 17, 1978; children: Jesse, Anya. BS, U. Wash., 1972; PhD, Princeton U., 1977. Postdoctoral fellow U. Calif., San Francisco, 1977-80; sr. scientist Genentech, South San Francisco, 1980-84, staff scientist, 1984—, dir. cell genetics dept., 1988-89, v.p. rsch., 1990-93, sr. v.p. rcsh. and devel., 1993—. Mem. editorial bd. Virology, 1984-87, Molecular Biology and Medicine, 1986-90, Molecular and Cellular Biology, 1987—, Jour. of Virology, 1988-91. Mem. Am. Soc. Microbiology, Am. Soc. Biochemistry and Molecular Biology. Office: Genentech Inc 460 Point San Bruno Blvd South San Francisco CA 94080-4990

LEVINSON, BARRY L., film director; b. Balt., Apr. 6, 1942. Ed., Am. U., Washington. film writer, actor: Silent Movie, 1976, High Anxiety, 1978; writer: ...And Justice for All, 1979, Inside Moves, 1980, Best Friends, 1982, Unfaithfully Yours, 1984; dir.: The Natural, 1984, Young Sherlock Holmes, 1985, Good Morning Vietnam, 1987, Rain Man, 1988 (Academy award 1989, Dirs. Guild Am. award 1989); screenwriter, dir.: Diner, 1982, Tin Men, 1987, Avalon, 1990 (Writers Guild Am. award 1990); co-prodr., dir. Bugsy, 1991, Disclosure, 1994; co-writer, dir., prodr. Toys, 1992, Jimmy Hollywood, 1994 (also actor); actor: Quiz Show, 1994; dir. (TV) Homicide: Life on the Street, 1993 (Emmy award, Outstanding Individual Achievement in Directing in a Drama Series, 1993, Peabody award 1993). Mem. Dirs. Guild Am., Writers Guild Am. Address: c/o Michael Ovitz 9830 Wilshire Blvd Beverly Hills CA 90212*

LEVINSON, DANIEL RONALD, lawyer; b. Bklyn., Mar. 24, 1949; s. Gerald Sam and Risha Rose (Waxer) L.; m. Luna Frances Lambert, Sept. 13, 1980; children: Luna Claire, Hannah Louise. AB, U. So. Calif., 1971; JD, Georgetown U., 1974; LLM, George Washington U., 1977. Bar: N.Y. 1975, Calif. 1976, D.C. 1976, U.S. Supreme Ct. 1978. Law clk. appellate divsn. N.Y. Supreme Ct. Bklyn., 1974-76; assoc. McGuiness & Williams, Washington, 1977-81, ptnr., 1982-83; dep. gen. counsel U.S. Office Personnel Mgmt., Washington, 1983-85; gen. counsel U.S. Consumer Product Safety Commn., Washington, 1985-86; chmn. U.S. Merit Sys. Protection Bd., Washington, 1986-93; of counsel Shaw Bransford & O'Rourke, Washington, 1993-94; chief of staff U.S. Rep. from Ga. Bob Barr, Washington, 1995—; adj. lectr. Am. U., Washington, 1981-82, Cath. U. Am., Washington, 1982. Notes and comments editor Am. Criminal Law Rev., 1973-74; contbr. articles to profl. jours. Bd. dirs. Washington Hebrew Congregation; prin. Coun. for Excellence in Govt., 1993-94. Mem. ABA, Adminstrv. Conf. U.S. (govt. mem. 1984-93), Phi Beta Kappa. Republican. Home: 3529 Woodbine St Chevy Chase MD 20815-4047 Office: 1607 Longworth Ho Offc Bldg Washington DC 20515

LEVINSON, DAVID MAYNARD, music critic; b. Gary, Ind., Oct. 30, 1929; s. George Irving and Mary Francine (Cohn) L.; m. Arlene Frances Jaskulski, Oct. 14, 1956 (div. June 1971); m. Dorothy Joyce Korber, Feb. 10, 1978; children: Noah, Nathan. BA, U. Chgo., 1951; MA, Ind. U., 1953. Reporter Record-Searchlight, Redding, Calif., 1957-63, mng. editor, 1963-69; music critic Plain Dealer, Cleve., 1969-74, Press-Telegram, Long Beach, Calif., 1975—. Author: Introduction to the Dance, 1977; contbr. articles to profl. jours.; author newspaper col. on computer software. Mem. Am. Musicol. Soc., Music critics Assn. Democrat. Avocation: computer programming. Office: Press-Telegram 604 Pine Ave Long Beach CA 90844

LEVINSON, GARY HOWARD, real estate investor; b. Mpls., May 30, 1945; s. Sidney B. and Ruth F. L.; m. Susan Lynn Austrian, Dec. 15, 1968 (div. 1982); children: Bradley Ross, Todd Matthew. BA, U. Minn., 1967, JD cum laude, 1970. Bar: Minn., U.S.Ct. Appeals (8th cir.), U.S. Dist. Ct. Minn., Minn. Supreme Ct. Ptnr. Robins, Kaplan, Miller & Ciresi, Mpls., 1970-81; prin. Bradley Todd Group, Mpls., 1981-84; mng. ptnr., sr. v.p. Phila. region Lincoln Property Co., Dallas, 1985-92; investor, 1992—. Mem. Mayor's Non-Partisan Coord. Com. Criminal Justice Ctr., Phila., 1990-91; exec. com., dir. Friends of Rittenhouse Square, Phila., 1986—, chmn., 1991-92, pres., 1987-90; bd. govs. mid. east coun. Fgn. Policy Rsch. Inst., 1993-95; steering com. Phila. Ctr. City Concerned Citizens, 1989—; exec. com., dir. Anti-Defamation League, 1992—. Recipient award for excellence Pa. Soc. Cons. Engrs., 1991. Mem. Nat. Apt. Assn., Nat. Home Builders Assn., Nat. Assn. Real Estate Investment Trusts, Pa. Apt. Assn. (Planet Earth award 1992), Nat. Multi Housing Coun. (fin. com. 1993-94), Pa. Builders Assn., Order of Coif. Avocations: music, travel, ballet, film. Office: 580 W Germantown Pike Ste 202 Plymouth Meeting PA 19462

LEVINSON, HARRY, psychologist, educator; b. Port Jervis, N.Y., Jan. 16, 1922; s. David and Gussie (Nudell) L.; m. Roberta Freiman, Jan. 11, 1946 (div. June 1972); children—Marc Richard, Kathy, Anne, Brian Thomas; m. Miriam Lewis, Nov. 23, 1990. BS, Emporia (Kans.) State U., 1943, MS, 1946; PhD, U. Kans., 1952. Coordinator edn. Topeka State Hosp., 1950-53, psychologist, 1954-55; dir. div. indsl. mental health Menninger Found., Topeka, 1955-68; visiting prof. MIT, 1961-62, U. Kans. Bus. Sch., 1967, Texas A&M U., 1976; Thomas Henry Carroll-Ford Found. distinguished vis. prof. Harvard Grad. Sch. Bus., Boston, 1968-72; adj. prof. Coll. Bus. Administrn., Boston U., 1972-74; lectr. Harvard Med. Sch., 1972-85; adj. prof. Pace U., 1972-83; clin. prof. psychology Harvard Med. Sch., 1985-92, emeritus prof., 1992—; head sect. orgnl. mental health Mass. Mental Health Ctr., 1983-92; pres. The Levinson Inst., 1968—; chmn. bd., 1991—; mem. Am. Bd. Profl. Psychology, 1972-80, chmn., 1978-80; Ford Found. inst. Mathur Inst., Jaipur India, 1974; conducted internat. course on social psychiatry Finnish Govt. Inst., 1979. Author: Emotional Health In the World of Work, 1964, Executive Stress, 1970, The Exceptional Executive (McKinsey Found. and Acad. Mgmt. awards), 1968 (James A. Hamilton Hosp. Adminstrs. Book award), Organizational Diagnosis, 1971, The Great Jackass Fallacy, 1973, Psychological Man, 1976, Casebook for Psychological Man; (with S. Rosenthal) CEO: Corporate Leadership in Action (Am. Coll. Health Care Adminstrs. Book award 1986), 1984, Ready, Fire, Aim, 1986, Designing and Managing Your Career, 1989, Career Mastery, 1992. Chmn. Kans. adv. com. U.S. Civil Rights Commn., 1962-68; chmn. Topeka Human Relations Commn., 1967-68. Served with F.A. AUS, 1944-46. Recipient Perry Rohrer Cons. Psychology Practice award, 1984, Career award Mass. Psychol. Assn., 1985, First award Soc. Psychologists in Mgmt.; Eminent scholar in bus. Fla. Atlantic U., 1995. Fellow Am. Psychol. Assn. (award for disting. profl. contbn. to knowledge 1992); mem. AAAS, Acad. Mgmt., Authors Guild, Am. Psychol. Found. Home: 225 Brattle St Cambridge MA 02138-4623

LEVINSON, HERBERT SHERMAN, civil and transportation engineer; b. Chgo., Sept. 25, 1924; s. Israel and Tillie (Gash) L.; m. Sally Farver, July 3, 1977. BSCE, Ill. Inst. Tech., 1949; cert. in hwy. traffic, Yale U., 1952. Jr. traffic engr. Chgo. Park Dist., 1949-51; from assoc. to sr. v.p. Wilbur Smith & Assocs., New Haven, 1952-80; prin. Herbert S. Levinson Transp. Cons., New Haven, 1980—; prof. civil engring. U. Conn., Storrs, 1980-86; prof. transp. Poly. Inst. of N.Y., N.Y.C., 1986-88, rsch. prof., 1988—; vis. lectr. Yale U., New Haven, 1961-80; transp. cons. Author: Transportation and Parking for Tomorrow's Cities, 1966, (with D. Votaw) Elementary Sampling for Traffic Engrs., 1961, (with R. Weant) Urban Transportation Perspectives and Prospects, 1983, Parking, 1990; contbr. numerous articles to profl. jours. Served as cpl. USAF, 1943-46. Recipient Presdl. Design award Nat.

Endowment for the Arts, 1988. Fellow Am. Soc. Civil Engrs. (Benjamin Wright award, 1993), Inst. Transp. Engrs. (Transp. Engr. of Yr. 1976, Tech. Council award 1982); mem. Transp. Research Bd., Am. Planning Assn. Conn. Acad. Sci. and Engring., Nat Acad. Engring.

LEVINSON, JOHN MILTON, obstetrician-gynecologist; b. Atlantic City, Aug. 17, 1927; m. Elizabeth Carl Bell; children: Patricia Anne, John Carl, Mark Jay. BA, Lafayette Coll., Easton, Pa., 1949; MD, Thomas Jefferson U., 1953. Diplomate Am. Bd. Ob-Gyn. Intern Atlantic City Hosp., 1953-54; Am. Cancer Soc. clin. fellow Jefferson Med. Coll. Hosp., Phila., 1954-55; resident in ob-gyn. Del. Hosp., Wilmington, 1955-57; pvt. practice ob-gyn. Wilmington, 1957-85; prof. dept. ob-gyn. Jefferson Med. Coll., Thomas Jefferson U., Phila., hon. clin. prof., 1990—; sr. attending physician emeritus Med. Ctr. Del., Wilmington, 1986—; attending chief dept. ob-gyn. St. Francis Hosp., Wilmington, chief emeritus, 1982-92; founder, pres. Aid for Internat. Medicine, Inc., 1966—; med. dir., chief surgeon Quark Expeditions, 1991; cons. Riverside Hosp., 1972-86, Wilmington, Pa. Blue Shield, 1982—; cons. gynecology U.S. VA, 1974-85; founding mem., treas. bd. dirs. Physicians Health Svcs. Del., Ltd., 1985-87; vis. prof., cons., ship's surgeon, practicing physician various organizations in Africa, Antarctic, Arctic regions, Cen. Am., Europe, S.E. Asia, S.W. Asia, 1963—; bd. dirs. Del. Savs. Bank; lectr. in field; internat. med. cons. to Senator Edward M. Kennedy, 1967—; chmn. Antarctic expdns. study group to advise NSF, 1992—; cochmn. Com. for Safety in Arctic and Antarctic Frontier Expeditions, 1992—. Author: Shorebirds: The Birds, the Hunters, the Decoys, 1991; contbr. articles to profl. jours., book chpts. Bd. dirs. Del. com. Project H.O.P.E., 1965-75, ARC, 1968-70, Charles A. Lindbergh Fund, Inc., 1985-90; trustee Blue Cross/Blue Shield Del., Inc., 1968-86, Brandywine Coll., 1972-77; bd. dirs. Nat. Assn. Blue Shield Plans, , 1971-77 mem. adv. com. Trinity Alcohol and Drug Program, 1978-85; mem. Del. Gov.'s Commn. on Health Care Cost Mgmt., 1985-87; bd. dirs. founding mem. World Affairs Coun. Wilminton Inc., v.p., 1981-86; pres. Rockland Mills Community Assn. 1992—. With USN, 1945-47; col. M.C., USAFR, 1984-87. Recipient Brandywine award Brandywine Coll., 1968, cert. of appreciation for med. svcs. Ministry of Health, Republic of Vietnam, 1963-66, commendation Pres. of U.S., 1971, The Eisenhower award People to People Internat., 1986, Commemorative medal Charles A. Lindbergh Fund, 1987, Phila. Explorers award 1987, Citation for Outstanding Contbn. to People of Del., Med. Soc. Del., 1992. Fellow Am. Coll. Obstetricians and Gynecologists, Royal Geog. Soc. London; mem. AMA, Am. Assn. Gyn. Laproscopists (founding), Del. Obstet. Soc. (pres. 1980-82), Phila. Obstet. Soc., Med. Soc. Del. (Citation of Merit award 1992), New Castle County Med. Soc., Soc. Ob-Gyn. Vietnam (hon.), Ducks Unltd. (sponsor, mem. Del. com. 1980-92), Explorers Club (fellow 1966—, chmn. Phila. chpt. 1983-85, bd. dirs. 1981-88, pres. N.Y.C. 1985-87), Univ. and Whist Club Wilmington (life, bd. govs. 1961-64), Rotary (Disting. Svc. award Wilmington club 1988, bd. dirs. 1991—), Theta Chi (past pres. 1945), Phi Beta Pi (past pres. 1952) Kappa Beta Phi (past pres. 1952). Avocations: hunting, swimming, sailing, collecting shore bird decoys. Home: 55 Millstone Ln Rockland DE 19732

LEVINSON, LAWRENCE EDWARD, lawyer, corporation executive; b. N.Y.C., Aug. 25, 1930; s. Samuel Keever and Sara Lee (Tarvin) L.; m. Margaret Ann Bishop, Aug. 20, 1989; children: Elizabeth, Suzanne, Lucia. B.A. magna cum laude, Syracuse U., 1952; LL.B. Harvard U., 1955. Bar: N.Y. 1957, U.S. Supreme Ct. 1958. Atty. Office Sec. Air Force, Washington, 1957-63; spl. assignments Office Sec. Def., Washington, 1963-65; dep. counsel to Pres. U.S., Washington, 1965-69; sr. v.p. Paramount Communications, Inc., N.Y.C., 1969-94; sr. Washington counsel VIACOM Internat. 1994—; mem. Nat. Council on Health Planning and Devel., Washington, 1978-84; host pub. affairs TV program Capital Notebook, 1991—. Bd. visitors Syracuse U. Coll. Arts and Scis., 1981—. Served with Judge Adv. Div. U.S. Army, 1955-57. Mem. Am. Pubs. (bd. dirs. 1989—), Phi Beta Kappa. Home: 5715 Little Falls Rd Arlington VA 22207-1554

LEVINSON, L(ESLIE) HAROLD, lawyer, educator; b. Bournemouth, Eng., Oct. 17, 1929; s. Abraham and Ada (Bloomberg) L.; m. Joan Gluck, Mar. 28, 1965; children: Laura, Lara. BBA, 1957; LLB, U. Miami, 1962; LLM, NYU, 1964; JSD, Columbia U., 1974. Bar: Fla. 1962, N.Y. 1964; CPA. Ptnr. acctg. firm Miami, Fla., 1958-62; instr. acctg. NYU, 1962-64; lectr. on devel. financing UN, N.Y.C. and Geneva, summers 1963-65; asst. to legal dir. ACLU, N.Y.C., summers 1964-65; asst. prof. U. Fla., 1966-67, assoc. prof., 1967-70, prof., 1970-73; vis. prof. Vanderbilt U. Sch. Law, Nashville, 1973-74, prof., 1974—; mem. Fla. Law Rev. Coun., 1972-74; cons. Adminstrv. Conf. U.S. 1976-86; reporter 1981 Revision Model State Adminstrv. Proc. Act., Nat. Conf. Commrs. Uniform State Laws, 1978-81; vis. prof. NYU Sch. Law, 1994. Mem. ABA, Am. Law Inst., Am. Inst. CPA's. Office: Vanderbilt U Sch Law 21st Ave S Nashville TN 37240

LEVINSON, RASCHA, psychotherapist; b. N.Y.C., Nov. 27, 1930; d. Frank Alfred and Goldye Dena (Preiser) Cohen; m. Monroe Louis Levinson, Oct. 6, 1955 (div. 1973); 1 child, Nadia Levinson Fogel. BA, NYU, 1960; MSW, Columbia U., 1962; Tng. in Hypnosis, Milton Erickson Soc., 1992-93. Lic. social worker, N.Y. Pvt. practice N.Y.C., 1970—; psychotherapist Washington Square Inst., N.Y.C., 1973-74; intake therapist Women's Psychotherapy Referral Svcs., N.Y.C., 1973-77; supr. psychotherapy Mid-Hudson Cons. Ctr., Wappinger Falls, N.Y., 1974-83; workshop leader New Sch. Social Rsch., N.Y.C., 1980-87. Fellow Soc. Clin. Social Workers (pres. Westchester chpt. 1986-88); mem. Assn. for Women in Psychology, N.Y.C. Coalition for Women's Mental Health (bd. dirs. 1986-89), Advanced Feminist Therapy Inst. (editor newsletter 1990-92). Avocations: writing, motorcycle riding, reading, movies. Office: 55 Central Park W # 1B New York NY 10023-6003

LEVINSON, ROBERT ALAN, textile company executive; b. Balt., July 26, 1925; s. Louis and Frieda (Kellert) L.; m. Patricia S. Schulte, Apr. 23, 1954; children: Margot, Andrew, John. AB, Dartmouth Coll., 1946, MBA, 1946; postgrad., London Sch. Econs., 1946-47. With Burlington Industries, N.Y.C., 1949-51; v.p., dir. Bangor Punta, Inc., N.Y.C., 1964-68; chmn. bd. Duplan Corp., N.Y.C., 1968-79; chmn. Andrex Industries Corp., N.Y.C.; cons. Dillon Yarn Corp.; chmn., pres. Pantepec Internat.; dir., chmn., mem. exec. com. Belding Heminway Corp. Trustee Bklyn. Mus., chmn., 1972-84; chmn. Harlem Sch. of Arts, Nat. Dance Inst.; bd. dirs., exec. com., vice chmn. Nat. Commn. on U.S.-China Relations. With USNR, 1943-45, S2-84. Home: 1035 Fifth Ave New York NY 10028-0135 Office: 1071 6th Ave New York NY 10018-3704

LEVINSON, SANFORD VICTOR, legal educator; b. Hendersonville, N.C., June 17, 1941; s. Meyer Mayer and Shirley (Achler) L.; m. Cynthia Yenkin, June 8, 1966; children: Meira, Rachel. BA, Duke U., 1962; PhD, Harvard U., 1969; JD, Stanford U., 1973. Bar: Calif. 1973, U.S. Supreme Ct. 1981. Asst. prof. dept. polit. sci. Ohio State U., 1968-70; law clk. to judge U.S. Dist. Ct., Charlotte, N.C., 1973-74; staff atty. Children's Def. Fund., Cambridge, Mass., 1974-75; asst. prof. dept. politics Princeton (N.J.) U., 1975-79; prof. Dept. Govt. and Law Sch. U. Tex., Austin; vis. prof. Hebrew U., 1984, Harvard Law Sch., 1991-92; mem. Inst. Advanced Studies, Princeton, 1986-87; fellow program in ethics and the professions Harvard U., 1991-92. Author: Constitutional Faith, 1988; co-editor: Power and Community, 1971, Processes of Constitutional Decisionmaking, 1983, 92, Interpreting Law and Literature: A Hermeneutic Reader, 1988. Woodrow Wilson fellow, 1962, Kent fellow, 1966, Russell Sage fellow, 1970. Mem. Am. Law Inst., Conf. on Critical Legal Studies, Phi Beta Kappa. Democrat. Jewish. Home: 3410 Windsor Rd Austin TX 78703-2248 Office: U Tex Law Sch 727 E 26th St Austin TX 78705-3224

LEVINSON, WARREN MITCHELL, broadcast journalist; b. Bklyn., Feb. 23, 1953; s. Abraham and Roslyn Anne (Bell) L.; m. Debra Lynn Galant, Sept. 1, 1985; children: Margot, Noah. BA, Duke U., 1975. Reporter Sta. WCHL Radio, Chapel Hill, N.C., 1974-77; news dir. Sta. WBLG/WKQQ Radio, Lexington, Ky., 1977-78; newswriter AP, N.Y.C., 1979-82; corr. AP Radio, N.Y.C., 1982—. Co-host (radio talk program) Newsweek on Air, 1985—. Recipient Silver medal for News Mag. Internat. Radio T.V. Soc., 1989. Avocations: bicycling, poetry. Office: AP 50 Rockefeller Plz New York NY 10020

LEVINTHAL, ELLIOTT CHARLES, physicist, educator; b. Bklyn., Apr. 13, 1922; s. Fred and Rose (Raiben) L.; m. Rhoda Arons, June 4, 1944; children—David, Judith, Michael, Daniel. B.A., Columbia Coll., 1942; M.S., Mass. Inst. Tech., 1943; Ph.D., Stanford U., 1949. Project engr. Sperry Gyroscope Co., N.Y.C., 1943-46; research assoc. nuclear physics Stanford (Calif.) U., 1946-48, sr. scientist dept. genetics Sch. Medicine, 1961-74, dir. Instrumentation Research Lab., 1961-80, assoc. dean for research affairs, 1970-73, adj. prof. genetics Sch. Medicine, 1974-80, research prof. mech. engring., dir. Inst. Mfg. and Automation Sch. Engring., 1983-90, assoc. dean for research Sch. Engring., 1986-90, assoc. dean spl. programs, 1990-91, prof. emeritus, 1991—; research physicist Varian Assocs., Palo Alto, Calif., 1949-50, dir. research, 1950-52; chief engr. Century Electronics, Palo Alto, 1952-53; pres. Levinthal Electronics, Palo Alto, 1953-61; dir. def. scis. office Def. Advanced Projects Agy., Dept. Def., Arlington, Va., 1980-83; mem. NASA Adv. Coun., 1980-84, space studies bd., NRC, 1989-91, mem. human exploration, 1991-92, army sci. bd., 1989-91; cons. HEW. Recipient NASA Public Service medal, 1977. Mem. AAAS, IEEE, Am. Phys. Soc., Optical Soc. Am., Biomed. Engring. Soc., Sigma Xi. Democrat. Jewish. Office: Stanford U Sch of Engring 530 Duena St Rm 104 Stanford CA 94305-3030

LEVINTON, JEFFREY S., biology educator, oceanographer; b. N.Y.C., Mar. 20, 1946; s. Nathan and Lillian (Moshman) L.; m. Joan Miyeko Miyazaki, Mar. 30, 1979; children: Nathan Toshi, Andrew Koji. BS, CCNY, 1966; M in Philosophy, Yale U., 1969, PhD, 1971. Asst. prof. biology SUNY, Stony Brook, 1970-75, assoc. prof., 1975-83, prof., 1983—, head dept., 1984-90, 91-93; vis. prof. U. Arhus, Denmark, 1966-67, Uppsala (Sweden) U., 1981, U. Cambridge, England, 1983; chmn. panel Hudson River Found, 1986-90. Author: Marine Ecology, 1982, Genetics, Paleontology, and Macroevolution, 1988, Marine Biology, 1995; reviewer, contbr. over 100 articles to profl. jours. Mem. Environ. Policy Com. Conn., 1969. NSF fellow, 1969, Sterling hon. fellow, 1969, John Simon Guggenheim fellow, 1983. Mem. Ecol. Soc. Am. (editor 1986-93), Am. Soc. Naturalists (editor 1974-79). Democrat. Office: SUNY Ecology and Evolution Dept Stony Brook NY 11794-5245

LEVIS, DONALD JAMES, psychologist, educator; b. Cleve., Sept. 19, 1936; s. William and Antoinette (Stejskal) L.; children: Brian, Katie. Ph.D., Emory U., 1964. Postdoctoral fellow clin. psychology Lafayette Clinic, Detroit, 1964-65; asst. prof. psychology U. Iowa, Iowa City, 1966-70, assoc. prof., dir. research and tng. clinic, 1970-72; prof. SUNY-Binghamton, 1972—. Author: Learning Approaches to Therapeutic Behavior Modification, 1970, Implosive Therapy, 1973; cons. editor: Jour. Abnormal Psychology, 1974-80, Jour. Exptl. Psychology, 1976-77, Behavior Moedifications, 1977-81, Behavior Therapy, 1974-76, Clin. Behavior Therapy Rev., 1978—; contbr. articles to profl. jours. Served to capt. AUSR, 1958-66. Fellow Behavior and Therapy Research Soc. (charter, clin.), Am. Psychol. Assn.; mem. Assn. Advancement Behavior Therapy (publ. bd. 1979-82), AAAS, Psychonomic Soc., N.Y. State Psychol. Assn., Sigma Xi. Home: 48 Riverside Dr Binghamton NY 13905-4402 Office: SUNY Dept Psychology Binghamton NY 13901

LEVI-SETTI, RICCARDO, physicist, director; b. Milan, Italy, July 11, 1927; married, 1959; 2 children. Doctor Degree in Physics, U. Pavia, Italy, 1949; Libera Docenza in Physics, U. Rome, 1955. Asst. prof. U. Pavia, Italy, 1949-51; rsch. mem. Nat. Inst. for Nuclear Rsch. U. Milan, Italy, 1951-56; rsch. assoc. Enrico Fermi Inst. U. Chgo., 1956-57, asst. prof., 1957-62, assoc. prof., 1962-65, prof. physics, 1965—, dir. Enrico Fermi Inst., 1992—; Guggenheim fellow CERN, Geneva, 1963; hon. rsch. assoc. Field Mus. Natural History, Chgo., 1976—. John Simon Guggenheim fellow, 1963, Angelo della Riccia fellow Italian Phys. Soc., 1954. Fellow Am. Phys. Soc.; mem. Phi Beta Kappa. Office: U Chgo Enrico Fermi Inst 5640 S Ellis Ave Chicago IL 60637-1433

LEVISON, HAROLD GEORGE, lawyer; b. Englewood, N.J., Dec. 27, 1947; s. Nathaniel and Sylvia (Kunin) L.; m. Ilyse Roberta Leshinsky, June 7, 1970; children: Michael, Zachary. BA, Rutgers U., 1969; JD cum laude, Bklyn. Law Sch., 1972. Bar: N.Y. 1973, U.S. Dist. Ct. (so. and ea. dists.) 1973, U.S. Ct. Appeals (2d cir.) 1973, U.S. Supreme Ct. 1978, D.C., 1981, N.J., 1987, U.S. Dist. Ct. N.J., 1987, U.S. Ct. Appeals (5th cir.) 1988, U.S. Dist. Ct. (no. dist.) N.Y. 1988. Assoc. atty. Mudge, Rose, Guthrie, Alexancer & Ferdon, N.Y.C., 1972-80, ptnr., 1981—; arbitrator and neutral evaluator U.S. Dist. Ct. (ea. dist.) N.Y., Bklyn., 1994; arbitrator Nat. Assn. Securities Dealers, Inc. 1992—. Bd. dirs. Glen Rock (N.J.) Bd. Edn., 1987-89. Mem. ABA, N.Y. State Bar Assn., N.J. State Bar Assn. Office: Mudge Rose Guthrie Alexancer & Ferdon 180 Maiden Ln New York NY 10038-4925 also: Morris Corp Ctr Two 1 Upper Pond Rd Bldg D Parsippany NJ 07054-1050

LEVIT, EDITHE JUDITH, physician, medical association administrator; b. Wilkes-Barre, Pa., Nov. 29, 1926; m. Samuel M. Levit, Mar. 2, 1952; children: Harry M., David B. BS in Biology, Bucknell U., 1946; MD, Woman's Med. Coll. of Pa., 1951; DMS (hon.), Med. Coll. Pa., 1978; DSc (hon.), Wilkes U., 1990. Grad. asst. in psychology Bucknell U., 1946-47; intern Phila. Gen. Hosp., 1951-52, fellow in endocrinology, 1952-53, clin. instr., assoc. in endocrinology, 1953-57, dir. med. edn., 1957-61, cons. med. edn., 1961-65; asst. dir. Nat. Bd. Med. Examiners, Phila., 1961-67; assoc. dir., sec. bd. Nat. Bd. Med. Examiners, 1967-75, v.p., sec. bd., 1975-77, pres., chief exec. officer, 1977-86, pres. emeritus, life mem. bd., 1987—; cons. in field, 1964—; mem. coun. Coll. Physicians of Phila., 1986—, adv. coun. Inst. for Nuclear Power Ops., Atlanta, 1988-93; bd. dirs. Phila. Electric Co., Germantown Savs. Bank, Phila. Contbr. articles to profl. jours. Bd. dirs. Phila. Gen. Hosp. Found., 1964-70; bd. dirs. Phila. Council for Internat. Visitors, 1966-72; bd. sci. counselors Nat. Library Medicine, 1981-85. Recipient award for outstanding contbns. in field of med. edn. Commonwealth Com. of Woman's Med. Coll., 1970; Alumni award Bucknell U., 1978; Disting. Dau. of Pa. award, 1981; Spl. Recognition award Assn. Am. Med. Colls., 1986; Disting. Service award Fedn. State Med. Bds., 1987; Master A.C.P. Fellow Coll. Physicians of Phila.; mem. Inst. Medicine of Nat. Acad. Scis., AMA, Pa. Phila. County med. socs., Assn. Am. Med. Colls., Phi Beta Kappa, Alpha Omega Alpha, Phi Sigma. Home: The Rittenhouse 210 W Rittenhouse Sq Philadelphia PA 19103

LEVIT, JAY J(OSEPH), lawyer; b. Phila., Feb. 20, 1934; s. Albert and Mary Levit; m. Heloise Bertman, July 14, 1962; children: Richard Bertman, Robert Edward, Darcy Francine. AB, Case Western Res. U., 1955; JD, U. Richmond, 1958; LLM, Harvard U., 1959. Bar: Va. 1958, D.C. 1961, U.S. Supreme Ct. 1961. Trial atty. U.S. Dept. Justice, Washington, 1960-64; sr. atty. Gen. Dynamics Corp., Rochester, N.Y., 1965-67; ptnr. Stallard & Levit, Richmond, Va., 1968-77, Levit & Mann, Richmond, 1978—; instr. U. Mich. Law Sch., Ann Arbor, 1964-65; adj. assoc. prof. U. Richmond Law Sch., 1974-77; adj. lectr. Va. Commonwealth U., Richmond, 1970-85; lectr. in field. Contbg editor The Developing Labor Law-Bur. Nat. Affairs, 1974—. Mem. ABA (labor com.), Va. Bar Assn. (labor com.), Fed. Bar Assn. (labor com.). Avocations: art collecting, jogging, swimming, travel. Home: 1608 Harborough Rd Richmond VA 23233-4720 Office: Levit & Mann Hamilton Pl #100 1301 N Hamilton St Richmond VA 23230

LEVIT, LOUIS WILLIAM, lawyer; b. Chgo., Aug. 31, 1923; m. Ellen Goodyear Levit; children: Alan, Robert. BS, U. Chgo., 1943, JD, 1946. Bar: Ill. 1947, Supreme Ct. Ill. 1947, U.S. Dist. Ct. (no. dist.) Ill. 1948, U.S. Supreme Ct., 1965, U.S. Ct. Appeals (7th cir.) 1969, U.S. Dist. Ct. (ea. dist.) Wis. 1991; CPA. With Legis. Reference Bur., Springfield, Ill., 1947-48; pvt. practice Chgo., 1948-71; founder, prin. Levit & Mason Ltd., Chgo., 1971-89; atty. Ross & Hardies, Chgo., 1990—; lectr. in field. Author in field. Active Ill. Inst. Continuing Legal Edn. Fellow Am. Coll. Bankruptcy (bd. regents 1993—, mem. coun. insol internat. 1990-94); mem. ABA (sect. corp. banking and bus. law, com. business bankruptcy, chair subcom. sects. 1985-89), Insol Internat. (exec. coun. 1990-95), Chgo. Bar Assn. (treas. 1985-87, bd. mgrs. 1978-80, com. Bankruptcy and Reorganization, 1959—, chair 1966-67) Chgo. Bar Found. (dir. 1987-90, commercial code com. 1964-74, chair 1972-73, com. assn. mtgs. 1975-85, chair 1976-78, com. evaluation candidates 1980-83, profl. responsibility 1983-88, fin. 1984-88, chair 1985-87, 88-89, com. judiciary 1987—, long-range planning com. 1987-89), Ill. State Bar Assn. (coun. sect. commercial banking and bankruptcy law 1962-72, sec. 1968-70, chair 1970-71, chair com. corp. bankruptcy 1969-70), Ill. Bankers Assn. (com. Bank counsel 1988-90), Commercial Law League Am. (chair bankruptcy com. 1973-75, chair spl. jud. com. 1975-77, edn. com. 1970-71,

assoc. editor commercial law jour. 1967-85, contbg. editor 1985—, chair bankruptcy insolvency sect. 1988—), Bar Assn. Seventh Fed. cir. (chair com. bankruptcy and insolvency 1982—), Ill. State Bar Assn., Commercial Law League Am., Nat. Conf. Bankruptcy Judges, others. Office: Ross & Hardies 150 N Michigan Ave Chicago IL 60601-7508

LEVIT, MAX, food service executive. Pres. Grocers Supply Co., Houston. Office: Grocers Supply Co 3131 E Holcombe Blvd Houston TX 77021-2199

LEVIT, MILTON, grocery supply company executive; b. 1924; married. Grad., U. Tex., 1946. With Grocers Supply Co. Inc., Houston, 1946—, v.p., 1947-75, pres., 1975—, also chmn. bd., dir. Served with USN. Office: Grocers Supply Co Inc 3131 Holcombe Blvd Houston TX 77021-2116*

LEVIT, VICTOR BERT, lawyer, foreign representative, civic worker; b. Singapore, Apr. 21, 1930; s. Bert W. and Thelma (Clumeck) L.; m. Sherry Lynn Chamove, Feb. 25, 1962; children: Carson, Victoria. A.B. in Polit. Sci. with great distinction, Stanford, 1950; LL.B., Stanford U., 1952. Bar: Calif. 1953. Assoc. Long & Levit, San Francisco and Los Angeles, 1953-55, ptnr., 1955-83; mng. ptnr. Long & Levit, San Francisco and L.A., 1971-83; ptnr. Barger & Wolen, San Francisco, L.A. and Newport Beach, 1983—; assoc. and gen. legal counsel U.S. Jaycees, 1959-61; legal counsel for consul gen. Ethiopia for San Francisco, 1964-71; hon. consul for Ethiopia for San Francisco, Ethiopia, 1971-76; guest lectr. Stanford U. Law Sch., 1958—, Haile Selassie I Univ. Law Sch., 1972-76; mem. com. group ins. programs State Bar Calif., 1980—; Mem. Los Angeles Consular Corps, 1971-77; mem. San Francisco Consular Corps, 1971-77, vice dean, 1975-76; Grader Calif. Bar Exam., 1956-61; dir. San Francisco Mcpl. Conf., 1955-63, vice chmn., 1960, chmn., 1961-63. Author: Legal Malpractice in California, 1974, Legal Malpractice, 1977, 2d edit., 1983; Note editor: Stanford Law Rev, 1952-53; legal editor: Underwriters' Report, 1963—; Contbr. articles to legal jours. Campaign chmn. San Francisco Aid Retarded Children, 1960; mem. nat. com. Stanford Law Sch. Fund, 1959—; mem. Mayor's Osaka-San Francisco Affiliation Com., 1959-65, Mayor's Com. for Mcpl. Mgmt., 1961-64; mem. San Francisco Rep. Country Cen. Com., 1956-63; assoc. mem. Calif. Rep. Cen. Com., 1963-63, 70-72; campaign chmn. San Francisco Assemblyman John Busterud, 1960; bd. dirs. San Francisco Comml. Club, 1967-70, San Francisco Planning and Urban Renewal Assn., 1959-60, San Francisco Planning and Urban Renewal Assn. Nat. Found. Infantile Paralysis, 1958, Red Shield Youth Assn., Salvation Army, San Francisco, 1960-70, bd. dirs. NCCJ, San Francisco, 1959—, chmn., No. Calif., 1962-64, 68-70; mem. nat. bd. dirs., 1964-75; bd. dirs. San Francisco Tb and Health Assn., 1962-70, treas., 1964, pres., 1965-67; bd. dirs. San Francisco Assn. Mental Health, 1964-73, pres., 1968-71; mem. com. Nat. Assn. Mental Health, 1969-71; trustee United Bay Area Crusade, 1966-74; mem. In. Forum San Francisco; bd. visitors Stanford Law Sch., 1969-75; mem. adv. bd. Jr. League San Francisco, 1971-75. Named Outstanding Young Man San Francisco mng. editors San Francisco newspapers, 1960, One of Five Outstanding Young Men Calif., 1961. Fellow ABA (chmn. profl. liability com. for gen. practice sect. 1979-81, council gen. practice sect. 1982-86, sec.-treas. gen. practice sect. 1986-87); mem. San Francisco Bar Assn. (chmn. ins. com. 1962, 73, chmn. charter flight com. 1962-66), State Bar Calif. (com. on group ins. programs 1980—, chmn. gen. practice sect. 1988—), Consular Law Soc., Am. Arbitration Assn. (arbitrator), World Assn. Lawyers (chmn. parliamentary law com. 1976—), Am. Law Inst. (adviser restatement of law governing lawyers 1985—), Internat. Bar Assn., San Francisco Jr. C. of C. (dir. 1959, pres. 1958), U.S Jaycees (exec. com. 1959-61), Jaycees Internat. (life, senator), Calif. Scholarship Fedn., U.S.C. of C. (labor com. 1974-76), San Francisco C. of C. (dir.), Phi Beta Kappa, Order of Coif, Pi Sigma Alpha. Clubs: Commercial (San Francisco) (dir.); Commonwealth (quar. chmn.), California Tennis; World Trade; Bankers. Home: 45 Beach Rd Belvedere Tiburon CA 94920-2364 Office: Barger & Wolen 101 California St Ste 4725 San Francisco CA 94111-5875

LEVIT, WILLIAM HAROLD, JR., lawyer; b. San Francisco, Feb. 8, 1938; s. William Harold and Barbara Janis (Kaiser) L.; m. Mary Elizabeth Webster, Feb. 13, 1971; children: Alison Jones, Alexandra Bradley, Laura Elizabeth Fletcher, Amalia Elizabeth Webster, William Harold, III. B.A. magna cum laude, Yale U., 1960; postgrad. (Ford Found. fellow), U. Pa., 1961-62; M.A. (NDEA fellow), U. Calif., Berkeley, 1962; LL.B., Harvard U., 1967. Bar: N.Y. 1968, Calif. 1974, Wis. 1979. Fgn. service officer Dept. State, 1962-64; assoc. firm Davis Polk & Wardwell, N.Y.C., 1967-73; assoc. then ptnr. firm Hughes Hubbard & Reed, N.Y.C. and Los Angeles, 1973-79; sec., gen. counsel Rexnord Inc., Milw., 1979-83; ptnr., dir. Godfrey & Kahn, Milw., 1983—; substitute arbitrator Iran-U.S. Claims Tribunal, The Hague, 1984-88; lectr. Practicing Law Inst., ABA, Calif. Continuing Edn. of Bar, State Bar of Wis. Contbr. to: Mergers and the Private Antitrust Suit: The Private Enforcement of Section 7 of the Clayton Act, 1977. Bd. dirs. Wis. Humane Soc., 1980-90, pres., 1986-88; bd. dirs. Vis. Nurse Corp., Milw., 1980-90, chmn., 1985-87; bd. dirs. Vis. Nurse Found., 1986—, chmn., 1989-91; bd. dirs. Aurora Health Care Inc., 1988-93, Wis. Soc. to Prevent Blindness, 1981-91, Columbia Coll. Nursing, 1992—, Aurora Health Care Ventures, 1993—; rep. Assn. Yale Alumni, 1976-79, 81-84, 90-93; pres. Yale Club So. Calif., 1977-79; mem. neutral advisor panel CPR Inst. for Dispute Resolution, 1993—. Mem. Am. Soc. Corp. Secs. (pres. Wis. chpt. 1982-83, dir. 1981-92), Am. Arbitration Assn. (panel arbitrators 1977—), ABA (com. on corp. counsel, litigation sect.), Assn. of Bar of City of N.Y., State Bar Calif. (com. on continuing edn. of bar 1977-79), Los Angeles County Bar Assn. (ethics com. 1976-79), State Bar Wis. (dir. internat. bus. transactions sect. 1985-92, dist. 2 bd. attys. profl. responsibility com. 1985-94, chmn. 1993-94), Bar Assn. 7th Cir., Am. Branch Internat. Law Assn., Nat. Assn. Security Dealers (bd. arbitrators 1987—), N.Y. Stock Exch. (panel arbitrators 1988—), N.Am. Coun. London Court of Internat. Arbitration, Chartered Inst. Arbitrators (assoc. 1995—, London), Am. Soc. Internat. Law, Inst. Jud. Adminstrn., Milw. Club, Milw. Univ. Club, Town Club, Phi Beta Kappa. Office: 780 N Water St Ste 1500 Milwaukee WI 53202-3512

LEVITAN, DAN, investment banker; b. N.Y.C., May 13, 1957; s. Milton B. and Minna (Osinoff) L. BA magna cum laude, Duke U., 1979; MBA, Harvard U., 1983. Jr. exec. trainee Merrill Lynch & Co., N.Y.C., 1979-81; assoc. Wertheim Schroder & Co., Inc., N.Y.C., 1983-86, v.p., 1987-88, 1st v.p., 1989, assoc. mng. dir., 1989-90, dir. corp. fin. west coast Wertheim Schroder & Co., Inc., L.A., 1990-91, mng. dir., head investment banking West Coast, 1991-93; head bus. devel. Wertheim Schroder & Co., Inc., N.Y.C., 1993—. Bd. trustees Pilchuck Glass Sch.; mem. Duke Univ. N.Y.C. Exec. Leadership Bd. Mem. Harvard Club of N.Y., Beta Theta Pi. Office: Wertheim Schroder & Co 787 7th Ave New York NY 10019

LEVITAN, DAVID M(AURICE), lawyer, educator; b. Tver, Lithuania, Dec. 25, 1915; (parents Am. citizens); m. Judith Morley; children: Barbara Lane Levitan, Stuart Dean Levitan. B.S., Northwestern U., 1936, M.A., 1937; Ph.D., U. Chgo., 1940; J.D., Columbia U., 1948. Bar: N.Y. 1948, U.S. Supreme Ct. 1953. Various U.S. Govt. adminstrv. and advisory positions with Nat. Youth Adminstrn., Office Price Adminstrn., War Prodn. Bd., Fgn. Econ. Adminstrn. Supreme Hdqrs. Allied Expeditionary Force, and Cen. European div. Dept. State, 1940-46; cons., sec. joint-com. of 5th and 6th coms., 2d Gen. Assembly, dir. com. of experts for establishing adminstrv. tribunal UN, 1946-47; cons. pub. affairs dept., producer series of pub. affairs programs on TV and radio ABC, 1946-53; pvt. practice N.Y.C., 1948-66; ptnr. Hahn & Hessen, N.Y.C., 1966-86, counsel, 1986—; adj. prof. public law Columbia U., 1946-63; adj. prof. John Jay Coll. Criminal Justice, CUNY, 1966-75; adj. prof. polit. sci. Post Coll., 1964-66; adj. prof. law Cardozo Sch. Law, 1978-82; asst. to Ill. state adminstr. Nat. Youth Adminstrn. chief budget sect., Washington, 1940-41; mgmt. analyst Office of Price Adminstrn., 1941; spl. asst. to chmn. War Prodn. Bd., 1942-43; chief property control div. Foreign Econ. Adminstrn., Washington, 1944-45; with U.S. Group of Control Coun. for Germany at SHAEF, London, 1944; European and Cen. European Div. U.S. Dept. of State, 1945; cons. UN, 1946-47; Sect. Joint Com. 5th and 6th Coms., 1946-47, 2nd Gen. Assembly, 1946-47; dir. Com. of Experts on Establishment of Adminstrn. Tribunal, 1946-47; cons. pub. affairs dept. ABC, 1946-53. Contbr. articles to legal jours. Mem. Nassau County (N.Y.) Welfare Bd., 1965-69; chmn. Planning Bd., Village of Roslyn Harbor, N.Y., 1965-66; chmn. Bd. of Zoning Appeals, Village Roslyn Harbor, 1967—. Recipient Demobilization award Social Sci. Rsch. Coun., 1946-48. Fellow Am. Coll. Trust and Estate Counsel; mem. ABA,

Am. Polit. Sci. Assn., Am. Soc. Internat. Law, Am. Law Inst., N.Y. State Bar Assn., Assn. Bar City N.Y. Home: 250 Scudders Ln Roslyn NY 11576-1021 Office: 350 Fifth Ave New York NY 10118-0110

LEVITAN, IRWIN BARRY, neuroscience educator, academic administrator; b. Jan. 13, 1947; came to U.S., permanent resident; married; two children. BSc in Biochemistry with first class honors, McGill U., Montreal, 1967, MSc in Biochemistry, 1968, PhD in Biochemistry, 1970. Rschr. in lab. of Dr. T. E. Webb, cancer rsch. unit McGill U., 1967-70; rschr. in lab of prof. H. Hyden, Inst. Neurobiology U. Goteborg, Sweden, 1970-72; rschr. in lab. of Dr. S. H. Barondes, dept. psychiatry U. Calif. San Diego, 1972-74; permanent staff and group leader Friedrich Miescher Institut, Basel, Switzerland, 1974-82; assoc. prof. biochemistry Brandeis U., Waltham, Mass., 1982-85, prof. biochemistry, 1985—, Nancy Lurie Marks Prof. neuroscience, 1992—; dir. biochemical seminar McGill U., 1969-70; instr. neurochemistry U. Calif. San Diego, 1972-73; coord. and instr. introductory neurobiology Friedrich Miescher Institut, 1975-77, mem. exec. com., 1975-78; instr. introductory neurobiology Biozentrum, U. Basel, 1975-82; instr. introductory and advanced neurobiology Brandeis U., 1983—, coord. and dir. neuroscience program, 1983—, dir. ctr. complex systems, 1989—; vis. prof. cellular neurology MIT, 1987-93; co-dir. summer course in neurobiology Marine Biolog. Lab., Woods Hole, Mass., 1990—; chmn. Gordon Conf. on Ion Channels, 1986; mem. adv. bd. Whitney Lab. Marine Biology-U. Fla., nominating com. Dana Found. Awards in Health, selection com. Bristol Myers Squibb Award for Disting. Achievement in Neuroscience. Author: (with L. K. Kaczmarek) Neuromodulation: the Biochemical Control of Neuronal Excitability, 1987, (with L. K. Kaczmarek) The Neuron: Cell and Molecular Biology, 1991; editor (with P. D. Evans) Ion Channels and Receptors, 1986; mem. editorial bd. Jour. Neuroscience, Jour. Molecular Biology, Jour. Exptl. Biology, Neuron; contbr. numerous articles to profl. jours. and chapters to books. Mem. adv. bd. Cystic Fibrosis Rsch. Ctr.-U. Ala. Woodrow Wilson fellow 1967; Centennial fellow Med. Rsch. Coun. Can., 1970-73; Quebec scholar, 1968, 69; scholar McGill U., 1963, 66, 67; bursar Nat. Rsch. Coun. Can., 1967, studentship, 1968, 69; named Helen Wendler Deane Disting. lectr. Wellesley Coll., 1988, J. H. Quastel Disting. Vis. prof. McGill U., 1989, Rushton lectr. Fla. State U., 1991, Cooper lectr. Yale U., 1992, Disting. Vis. prof. in Pharmacology and Neurobiology, Duke U., 1993; recipient Jacob Javits Neuroscience Investigator award NIH, 1985, 1992. Office: Brandeis Univ Nat Ctr Complex Systems 415 South St Waltham MA 02154-2700

LEVITAN, JAMES A., lawyer; b. N.Y.C., Mar. 24, 1925; s. Leo and Della (Brody) L.; m. Ruth Terry White, Jan. 30, 1951; children—Deborah A., Judith T., Susan J. B.S. in Chem. Engring, M.I.T., 1948; LL.B. (mem. bd. Law Rev. 1950-51), Columbia U., 1951. Bar: N.Y. bar 1951. Since practiced in N.Y.C.; ptnr. Skadden, Arps, Slate, Meagher & Flom, 1965-95, of counsel, 1995—; mem. MIT Corp., Cambridge, Mass., 1990—, chmn. audit com., 1994—; regional chmn. N.Y.C. MIT Ednl. Coun., 1974-90; lectr. in field of tax. Served with USNR, 1944-46. Stone scholar, 1948-51; Kent scholar, 1950. Mem. N.Y. State Bar Assn., Assn. Bar City N.Y., Tau Beta Pi. Home: 26 Wake Robin Ln Stamford CT 06903-4611 Office: Skadden Arps Slate Meagher & Flom 919 Third Ave New York NY 10022-3903

LEVITAN, LAURENCE, lawyer, former state senator; b. Washington, Oct. 22, 1933; s. Maurice Land Nathlie (Rosenthal) L.; BS, Washington and Lee U., 1955; JD, George Washington U., 1958; m. Barbara E. Levin, 1957; children: Jennifer, Michelle, Lisa. Admitted to Md. bar, 1964; with Levitan, Cramer & Weinstein, 1959-72, Levitan Ezrin, West & Kenxton, 1973-85, Beckett Cromwell & Myers, 1985-90, Frank Bernstein Conaway & Goldman, 1990-92; of counsel Baker & Hostetler, 1992-95, Rifkin Livingston and Silver, LLC, Annapolis, Md., 1995—; mem. Md. Ho. of Dels., 1971-74; mem. Md. Senate, 1975-94, chmn. budget and taxation com., policy com., spending affordability com., mem. joint com. on mgmt. pub. funds., legis. com. on budget and audit, gov.'s commn. to rev. state taxes & taxes structure, joint legis. com. on tax reform, govtl. commn. to revise annotated code of Md., joint subcom. on program open space, chmn. drunk and drugged driving task force, chmn. joint com. on ins. tax reform; mem. Montgomery County Exec.'s Commn. for Higher Edn. in High Tech.; past mem. Gov.'s Commn. To Study Unification of Circuit Ct., Gov.'s Commn. to Study Condominium Laws, Gov.'s Commn. Law Enforcement and Adminstrn. Justice, Gov.'s Subcom. on Revenue Structure of Task Force to Study State-Local Relationships; mem. Gov.'s Commn. To Study Feasibility of Biennial Budget, Gov.'s Task Force on Real Property Closing Costs, Task Force To Study Md. Tax Ct., Gov.'s Commn. Sch. Funding, Joint Task Force on Md.'s Procurement Law. Mem. ABA, D.C. Bar Assn., Md. Bar Assn., Nat. Conf. State Legislatures (mem. subcom. on fed. budget and taxation com., fiscal affairs govt. oversight com.), So. Legis. Conf. (chmn. fiscal affairs and govt. ops. steering com. 1992-93), Am. Legis. Exch. Coun. (tax task force). Democrat. Jewish. Office: 163 Conduit St Annapolis MD 21401 also: 11426 Georgetown Dr Potomac MD 20854

LEVITAN, VALERIE FASSLER, fraternal organization executive; b. Phila., Aug. 18, 1932; d. Joseph Lionel and Regina (Sekler) Fassler; m. Peter Wallfield Levitan, Dec. 20, 1950 (div. Nov. 1972); children: Daniel, Regine. BEd, U. Pa., 1954, postgrad, 1954, 65-66. Co-owner, adminstr. Levitan Sch., Phila., 1950-69; exec. dir. Soroptimist Internat. Am., Phila., 1970-79, Zonta Internat., Chgo., 1979—; dir. pubs. various orgn. manuals; author, presenter Category I status application Econ. and Social Org. UN, 1985. Pres. Cong. Kol Ami, Chgo., 1986-87, pres., 1987. Recipient Merit award Alumnae Assn. Phila. High Sch. for Girls, 1970, Achievement award, Zonta Internat., 1985, Am.'s Citizen Vol. award, U.S. Savs. Bond, 1982. Mem. AAUW, Am. Soc. Assn. Execs., Am. Assn. World Health (bd. dirs. 1986—), UN Assn. (bd. dirs. 1986—, pres. USA Ill., 1988, sec. greater Chgo. area), Nat. Vol. Orgn. for Ind. Living of Aging (grantee 1976-77, chmn. 1986-86), Nat. Council Aging (bd. dirs. 1984-86), League of Women Voters. Democrat. Jewish. Lodge: Zonta Chgo. Waterfront. Avocations: reading, painting, cooking, visiting museums. Office: Zonta Internat 557 W Randolph St Chicago IL 60661-2206

LEVITAS, ELLIOTT HARRIS, lawyer; b. Atlanta, Dec. 26, 1930; s. Louis and Ida (Goldstein) L.; m. Barbara Hillman; children: Karin, Susan, Kevin. AB, Emory U., 1952, JD, 1956; MA, Oxford U., 1954; postgrad., U. Mich., 1954-55. Bar: Ga. 1955, D.C. 1984, U.S. Supreme Ct. 1955. Atty. Arnall Golden & Gregory, Atlanta, 1955-56, ptnr., 1958-75; mem. Ga. Ho. of Reps., Atlanta, 1966-75, U.S. Ho. of Reps., Washington, 1975-85; ptnr. Kilpatrick & Cody, Atlanta, 1985—. Contbr. articles to profl. jours. Commr. Nat. Commn. Fin. Reform, Recovery & Enforcement, Washington, 1991-93; chmn. Ga. Hazardous Waste Authority, 1991-93, Anti-Defamation League S.E. Region, Atlanta, Civil Rights Commn., 1993-94; bd. dirs. Ga. Conservancy, Atlanta, Nat. Bldg. Mus., Washington, Chatham House Found., Inc., IBM External Environ. Adv. Com. Rhodes scholar, 1952-54; named One of 10 Most Effective Legislators, Ga. Ho. of Reps., Atlanta, One of 100 Most Influential People in Ga., Ga. Trend Mag., 1991, Conservationist of Yr., Ga. Wildlife Fedn., Alumni of the Yr. Emory Law Sch., 1994. Mem. Nat. Dem. Club, The Standard Club, The Commerce Club. Jewish. Home: 829 Castle Falls Dr NE Atlanta GA 30329-4113 Office: Kilpatrick & Cody 700 13th St NW Ste 800 Washington DC 20005-3960 also: Kilpatrick & Cody 1100 Peachtree St Ste 2800 Atlanta GA 30309

LEVITAS, MITCHEL RAMSEY, editor; b. N.Y.C., Dec. 1, 1929; s. Samuel M. and Fira (Zilboorg) L.; m. Gloria Barach, Dec. 24, 1950; children: Anthony, Daniel. AB, Bklyn. Coll., 1951. With Dept. State, 1951-53; reporter N.Y. Post, 1953-60; asst. editor Time mag., 1960-64; editor, writer N.Y. Times Mag., 1965-70; editor Metropolitan, 1976; editor Week in Rev. N.Y. Times, from 1977; editor Sunday Book Rev., 1983-89; sr. editor weekends N.Y. Times, 1989—; editor Op-Ed page N.Y. Times, 1990-95, asst. foreign editor, 1995—; vis. scholar Woodrow Wilson Found., 1979—. Author: America in Crisis. Recipient George Polk award investigative reporting, 1957; Woodrow Wilson fellow, 1951, Nieman fellow, 1958. Mem. Century Assn., Coun. Fgn. Rels. Office: NY Times Co 229 W 43rd St New York NY 10036-3959*

LEVITCH, JOSEPH See LEWIS, JERRY

LEVITON, ALAN EDWARD, museum curator; b. N.Y.C., Jan. 11, 1930; s. David and Charlotte (Weber) L.; m. Gladys Ann Robertson, June 30, 1952;

children: David A., Charlotte A. AB, Stanford U., 1949, MA, 1953, PhD, 1960; student, Columbia U., summers 1947, 48, 53, NYU, 1948, U. Nebr. 1954. Asst. curator herpetology Calif. Acad. Scis., San Francisco, 1957-60, assoc. curator, 1960-61, chmn. curator, 1962-82, 89-92, curator, 1983-88, 93—; chmn. computer svcs. Calif. Acad. Scis., 1983-92; editor Sci. Publs., 1994—; assoc. curator zool. collections Stanford, 1962-63; lectr. biol. sci., 1963-70; professional lectr. Golden Gate U., 1953-63; adj. prof. biol. sci. San Francisco State U., 1967—. Author: North American Amphibians and Reptiles, 1972; Amphibians and Reptiles of the Middle East, 1992; contbr. numerous articles to sci. and profl. jours. Am. Philos. Soc. grantee, 1960, NSF grantee, 1960-61, 77-79, 80, 83-86, 86-89, 91-93, Belvedere Sci. Fund grantee, 1958-59, 62. Fellow AAAS (coun. 1976—, com. coun. affairs 1983-85, sec.-treas. PAcific divsn. 1975-79, exec. dir. 1980—), Calif. Acad. Scis., Geol. Soc. Am. (vice chmn. history geology divsn. 1989-90, chmn. 1990-91); mem. Am. Soc. Ichthyologists and Herpetologists (bd. govs. 1960-84), Soc. Systematic Zoology (sec.-treas. Pacific sect. 1970-72), Forum Historians of Sci. Am. (coord. com. 1986-88, sec.-treas. 1988-90), Herpetologists League (pres. 1961-62), Hist. of Sci. Soc. Home: 571 Kingsley Ave Palo Alto CA 94301-3225 Office: Calif Acad Scis Golden Gate Park San Francisco CA 94118

LEVITSKY, MELVYN, ambassador; b. Sioux City, Iowa, Mar. 19, 1938; s. David and Mollie (Schwartz) L.; m. Joan Daskovsky, Aug. 12, 1962; children: Adam, Ross Josh. BA, U. Mich., 1960; MA, U. Iowa, 1963. Polit. officer U.S. Embassy, Moscow, 1972-75; officer-in-charge Soviet-U.S. bilateral relations Dept. State, Washington, 1975-78, dep. dir. UN polit. affairs, 1978-80, dir. UN polit. affairs, 1980-82, dep. asst. sec. for human rights and humanitarian affairs, 1982-83; dep. dir. Voice of Am., Washington, 1983-84; dep. assoc. dir. broadcasting USIA, Washington, 1983-84; U.S. amb. to Bulgaria, 1984-87; exec. sec., spl. asst. to sec. Dept. State, Washington, 1987-89, asst. sec. state internat. narcotics matters, 1989-94; U.S. amb. to Brazil, 1994—. Recipient Meritorious Honor award Dept. State, 1968, Superior Honor award Dept. State, 1975, 82, Presdl. Meritorious Svc. awards, 1986-91. Mem. Am. Fgn. Service Assn.

LEVITT, JERRY DAVID, medical educator; b. Phila., Apr. 11, 1941; s. Abraham and Nettie (Dash) L.; m. Julie Meranze,k June 2, 1967; children: Rachel, Daniel, Gabriel. BA, U. Pa., 1962, MD, 1966. Diplomate Am. Bd. Anesthesiology; lic. physician, Pa. Intern Mt. Sinai Hosp., N.Y.C., 1966-67; resident in anesthesia U. Pa. Hosp., Phila., 1967-69, rsch. fellow, 1971-72; instr. anesthesia U. Pa., phila., 1972-73, asst. prof. anesthesia, 1973-82; assoc. prof. anesthesiology Hahnemann U., Phila., 1982—. Author: (with others) Basic Pharmacology in Medicine, 1990; contbr. articles to profl. jours. With USPHS, 1969-71. Avocations: photography, hiking, music. Office: Hahnemann U Med Coll Pa Broad & Vine Sts Philadelphia PA 19102

LEVITT, LEROY PAUL, psychiatrist, psychoanalyst; b. Wilkes-Barre, PA, Jan. 8, 1918; s. Samuel and Paula (Goldstein) L.; divorced; children: Steven C., Susan M., Jeremy W., Sara H.; m. Jane A. Glaim, Apr. 7, 1971. B.S., Pa. State U., 1939; M.D., Chgo. Med. Sch., 1943; postgrad., Inst. Psychoanalysis, Chgo., 1950-59. Diplomate: Am. Bd. Psychiatry and Neurology. Intern Beth David Hosp., N.Y.C., 1943; resident Elgin (Ill.) State Hosp., 1947-49; pvt. practice, specializing in psychiatry and psychoanalysis Chgo., 1949—; prof. psychiatry Chgo. Med. Sch., 1949-76, dean, 1966-73; dir. Ill. Dept. Mental Health, 1973-76; v.p. Mt. Sinai Hosp. Med. Ctr., Chgo., 1976-82, chmn. dept. psychiatry, 1982-87, dir. med. edn., 1987-88; prof. psychiatry Rush Med. Coll., 1977-89, prof. emeritus, 1989—; mem. staff Naples Community Hosp., 1989—; cons. Blue Cross-Blue Shield, 1977-80, Nat. Council Aging, Ill. Psychiat. Inst.; mem. Mayor's Commn. on Aging, 1955-60. Pres. Chgo. Bd. Health, 1979-83; bd. dirs. Med. Ctr. YMCA, Med. Careers Council; bd. govs. Inst. of Medicine of Chgo. Med. Soc. Served to capt. M.C. AUS, 1944-46. Named Prof. of Year Chgo. Med. Sch., 1964, Tchr. of Year Ill. Psychiat. Inst., 1966, Chicagoan of Yr. in Medicine, 1970; WHO fellow Europe, 1970; recipient Sinai Health Service award, 1986. Fellow Am. Psychiat. Assn. (life), Am. Acad. Psychoanalysis, Am., Internat. psychoanalytic assns., Ill. Psychiat. Soc. (pres.), Chgo. Inst. Medicine, Am. Coll. Psychiatrists, Am. Coll. Psychoanalysts (pres. 1983, Laughlin award 1985), Sigma Xi, Alpha Omega Alpha, Phi Lambda Kappa (Gold medal sci. award). Home: 222 Harbour Dr Naples FL 33940-4022 Office: Health Ctr David Lawrence Mental Naples FL 33999

LEVITT, BRIAN MICHAEL, consumer products and services company executive, lawyer; b. Montreal, Que., Can., July 26, 1947; s. Eric and Rya Levitt; m. Claire Gohier, Jan. 25, 1992; children: Marie-Anne, Katherine. BASc, U. Toronto, Ont., Can., 1969, LLB, 1973. Spl. asst. to provost U. Toronto, 1969-73; dir. interpretation Anti-Inflation Bd. Govt. Can., Ottawa, 1975-76; assoc. Osler, Hoskins & Harcourt, Toronto, 1976-79, ptnr., 1979-91; pres. Imasco Ltd. Montreal, 1991—, COO, 1993—; also bd. dirs.; bd. dirs. First Fed. Savs. & Loan Assn., Rochester, N.Y., CT Fin. Svcs., Inc., Westbury Can. Life Ins. Co.; mem. adv. bd. faculty of mgmt. McGill U., Montreal. Contbr. articles to profl. jours. Bd. dirs. Montcrest Schs.; mem. adv. coun. Soc. Ednl. Visits and Exchanges in Can. Mem. ABA (bus. law subsect.), Can. Bar Assn., Law Soc. Upper Can., Caledonia Ski, Toronto Club. Avocation: skiing, skating, sailing. Office: Imasco Ltd, 600 Boul De Maisonneuve O #190, Montreal, PQ Canada H3A 3K7

LEVITT, GEORGE, retired chemist; b. Newburg, N.Y., Feb. 19, 1925; m. Julie Zeto; children: Barbara Klein, Jeffery, David, Gregory. BS, Duquesne U., 1950, MS, 1952; PhD, Mich. State U., 1957. Rsch. chemist Exptl. Sta. E.I. du Pont de Nemours & Co., Inc., 1956-63, rsch. chemist Stine Lab., 1963-66, rsch. chemist Exptl. Sta., 1966-68, sr. rsch. chemist, 1968-80, rsch. assoc., 1981-86; instr. Del. Tech. and C.C., 1975-80. Recipient Quadrennial award Swiss Soc. Chem. Industries, 1982, Nat. Agrl. award Nat. Agrl. Mktg. Assn., 1987, 88, Nat. Medal of Tech. NSF, 1993. Mem. AAAS, Am. Chem. Soc. (Creative Invention award 1989, Kenneth Spencer award 1991), Internat. Union Pure & Applied Chemistry, Sigma Xi. Achievements include research in organic syntheses, herbicides, fungicides, medicinals, pesticides, heterocyclic compounds, synthesis, characterization and identification of novel organic compounds for biological evaluation, developed programs to define and optimize chemical structure- biological activity relationships, sulfonylurea herbicides, heteroyclics, exploratory process research. Home: 110 Downs Dr Greenville DE 19807-2556*

LEVITT, GERALD STEVEN, natural gas company executive; b. Bronx, N.Y., Mar. 21, 1944; s. Charles and Beatrice (Janet) L.; m. Natalie Lillian Hoppen; children: Mark, Roy. B in Mgmt. Engring., Rensselaer Poly. Inst., 1965; MBA, DePaul U., 1972. Registered profl. engr., Ill. Tech. rep. Worthington Air Conditioning Co., Ampere, N.J., 1965-67; indsl. sales engr. Peoples Gas Light & Coke Co., Chgo., 1967-71; planning specialist Peoples Gas Co., Chgo., 1971-72; v.p. Stone & Webster Mgmt. Cons., Inc., N.Y.C., 1972-82; exec. v.p., chief staff officer South Jersey Gas Co., Folsom, N.J., 1982—; v.p., CFO South Jersey Industries, Inc., Folsom, N.J., 1987—. Bd. dirs. Camden County coun. Boy Scouts Am., West Collingswood, N.J., Rowan Coll. Found. Mem. Am. Gas Assn., Greater Atlantic City C. of C. (past bd. dirs.), N.J. State C. of C. (bd. dirs.). Office: S Jersey Gas Co 1 S Jersey Plz Rte 54 Hammonton NJ 08037

LEVITT, IRVING FRANCIS, investment company executive; b. Braddock, Pa., July 3, 1915; s. Charles and Frances (Goretsky) L.; m. Florence Chaikin, Oct. 10, 1937; children: Robert Bruce, Linda Ann (Mrs. Stanley L. Ehrenpreis). B.S. (hon.) in journalism, U. Mich., 1936. Advt. mgr. feature writer Braddock (Pa.) Free Press, 1936-37; advt. mgr. Levitt Bros. Furniture Stores, 1936-38; partner, exec. adminstr. stores in Levitt Bros. Furniture Stores, Braddock, Vandergrift and New Kensington, Pa., 1938-55; exec. asst., v.p Levinson Steel Co., Pitts., 1942-44; real estate, indsl. devel., 1938-82; pres. Lepar, Inc., 1950-80; pres., chmn. bd. Union Screw & Mfg. Co., Pitts.; chmn. bd. Investment Capital Corp., Pitts., 1955—, Radix Orgn., Inc., N.Y., Radix Real Estate, Inc., RRE Enterprises, Inc.; pres. Kirwan Heights Land Co., King Land Co., Ind., Blawnox Realty Co.; chmn. bd. Apollo Industries, Inc., 1959-68; chmn. bd., dir. Apollo Internat. Corp.; pres., dir. Apollo-Peru S.A., Oakland Investment Corp., Pitts.; v.p., dir. Apollo Indsl., Inc., Apollo Investment Co., Pitts.; sr. v.p. Parker-Levitt Corp., Sarasota, Fla., Marble Island, Inc., Vt.; ptnr. Oliver-Smithfield Venture, Pitts., Nineteen Hundred Group Ltd., Sarasota, Fla.; bd. dirs. Comml. Bank & Trust Co., Pitts., Nuclear Materials & Equipment Corp., Ednl. Audio Visual, Inc., N.Y., London, Radix Ventures, N.C., N.Y.; chmn. bd., dir. Lido Beach Devel. Co., Inc., Sarasota, Fla.; partner One Hundred Kennedy Ltd., Tampa, Fla., SMP, Ltd., Pine Run Devel., Inc., Sarasota; mem. Pitts. Bd. Realtors, New Kensington Indsl. Devel. Corp., Smaller Mfrs. Coun. Bd. dirs. Massanutten Mil. Acad., Woodstock, Va., United Jewish Fedn. Finance, Pitts., Irene Kaufman Settlement Bd.; trustee Levitt Found. Pitts., Rodef Shalom Temple, Pitts. Mem. Nat. Sales Execs. Club (dir. 1952-82), Am. Jewish Com., Chautauqua Soc., Am. Arbitration Assn. (panel of arbitrators), Nat. Assn. Securities Dealers (bd. arbitrators). Clubs: Westmoreland Country (Export, Pa.) (v.p 1948-83); Metropolis Country (White Plains, N.Y.); Longboat Key Country; Marco Polo (N.Y.C.); Standard (Pitts.) (dir. Pitts. Athletic Assn. Pitts.); Belfry New Century (London); Univ. (Sarasota). Office: 1800 2nd St Ste 808 Sarasota FL 34236-5904 also: 230 Park Ave Ste 630 New York NY 10169-0004

LEVITT, ISRAEL MONROE, astronomer; b. Phila., Dec. 19, 1908; s. Joseph and Jennie (Marriner) L.; m. Alice Gross, July 3, 1937; children: Peter Leighton, Nancy Bambino. B.S. in Mech. Engring., Drexel U., 1932,

D.Sc., 1958; M.A., U. Pa., 1937, Ph.D., 1948; D.Sc., Temple U., 1958, Phila. Coll. Pharmacy and Sci., 1963. Astronomer, Fels Planetarium of The Franklin Inst., Phila., 1934-39; asst. assoc. dir. Fels Planetarium of The Franklin Inst., 1939-49, dir., 1949-72, v.p. inst., 1970-72; exec. dir. Phila. Mayor's Sci. and Tech. Adv. Council, 1972-93; sr. lectr. astronomy U. Pa., 1977; astronomer The Flower Obs., 1946-48; dir. (Sci. Council), 1953—; sci. cons. to City of Phila., 1956-63; chmn. Air Pollution Control Bd. Phila., 1965—. Author: Precision Laboratory Manual, 1932, (with Roy K. Marshall) Star Maps for Beginners, 1942, Space Traveler's Guide to Mars, 1956, Target for Tomorrow, 1959, Exploring The Secrets of Space, 1963, (with Dandridge M. Cole) Beyond the Known Universe, 1974; developer NASA Spacemobile; inventor oxygen mask, pulse counting photoelectric photometer (with William Blitzstein); contbr. articles in jours., mags. on sci. subjects; author: internationally syndicated Space column for Gen. Features. Recipient USN Ordnance Devel. award, 1945; Henry Grier Bryant gold medal Geog. Soc. Phila., 1962; Joseph Priestley award Spring Garden Inst., Phila., 1963; Writing award Aviation/Space Writers Assn., 1965; Samuel S. Fels Medal award, 1970; cert. of recognition NASA, 1977. Fellow AAAS, Am. Astronautical Soc., Brit. Interplanetary Soc.; mem. AIAA, Am. Astron. Soc., Rittenhouse Astron. Soc. (past pres.), Acad. Scis. Phila. (v.p. 1993), Nat. Assn. Sci. Writers, Aviation Writers Assn., Explorers Club, Pi Tau Sigma. Home: 3900 Ford Rd Apt 19D Philadelphia PA 19131-2036 Office: 1515 Market St Fl 17 Philadelphia PA 19102-1921

LEVITT, MIRIAM, pediatrician; b. Lampertheim, Germany, June 10, 1946; came to U.S., 1948; d. Eli and Esther (Kingston) L.; m. Harvey Flisser, June 25, 1967; children: Adam, Elizabeth, Eric. AB, NYU, 1967; MD, Albert Einstein Coll. Medicine, Yeshiva U., 1971. Diplomate Am. Bd. Pediatrics. Intern Montefiore Med. Ctr., Bronx, N.Y., 1970-71, resident in pediatrics, 1971-73, attending pediatrician, 1975—; dir. outpatient svcs. pediatrics Bronx-Lebanon Hosp., N.Y.C., 1973-77; instr. pediatrics Albert Einstein Coll. Medicine, N.Y.C., 1973-76, asst. prof. clin., 1976—; med. staff Lawrence Hosp., Bronxville, N.Y., 1978—; dir. pediatrics, 1988—; sch. physician Bronxville Bd. Edn., 1983—. Fellow Am. Acad. Pediatrics; mem. Westchester County Med. Soc. Office: 1 Pondfield Rd Bronxville NY 10708-3706

LEVITT, MITCHELL ALAN, management consultant; b. N.Y.C., June 20, 1944; s. Ben and Rhea (Brody) L. BA, CUNY, 1967; MA, Temple U., 1969. Sr. ptnr., pres. Klein Consultants, N.Y.C., 1979—; bd. dirs. Hyde Products, Cleve. Mem. Am. Psychol. Assn., Inst. Mgmt. Cons. Home: 1675 York Ave New York NY 10128-6752 Office: Klein Cons 38 E 29th St New York NY 10016-7911

LEVITT, RAYMOND ELLIOT, civil engineering educator; b. Johannesburg, Republic of South Africa, Aug. 7, 1949; came to U.S., 1972; s. Barnard and Riva Eleanor (Lazarus) L.; m. Kathleen Adele Sullivan, Nov. 26, 1976; children: Benjamin John, Joanna Maurine, Zoë Ellen. BSCE, U. Witwatersrand, Johannesburg, 1971; MSCE, Stanford U., 1973, PhDCE, 1975. Project engr. Christiani & Neilsen, Cape Town, Republic of South Africa, 1971-72; asst. prof. civil engring. MIT, Cambridge, 1975-79, assoc. prof., 1979-80; assoc. prof. Stanford (Calif.) U., 1980-88, prof., 1988—; assoc. dir. Ctr. for Integrated Facility Engring.; chmn. bd. Design Power, Inc., Cupertino, Calif.; advisor U.S. Dept. Labor, Washington, 1976-77, Calif. Pub. Utilities Commn., San Francisco, 1982-84. Co-author: Union and Open-Shop Construction, 1978, Construction Safety Management, 1987, 2d edit., 1993, Knowledge-Based Systems in Engineering, 1990. Pres. Stanford Homeowners Assn., 1981-83. Recipient Marksman award Engring. News Record, N.Y.C., 1985, Commitment to Life award Nat. Safe Workplace Inst., 1987. Mem. ASCE (Huber Prize award 1982), Am. Assn. Artificial Intelligence, Project Mgmt. Inst. Unitarian. Avocations: swimming, trout fishing, tennis, music. Office: Stanford U Dept Civil Engring # 4020 Stanford CA 94305

LEVITT, SEYMOUR HERBERT, physician, radiology educator; b. Chgo., July 18, 1928; s. Nathan E. Levitt and Margaret (Chizever) D.; m. Phillis Jeanne Martin, Oct. 31, 1952 (div. Oct. 1981); children: Mary Jeanne, Jennifer Gaye, Scott Hayden; m. Solveig I. Ostberg, Feb. 6, 1983. B.A., U. Colo., 1950, M.D., 1954. Diplomate: Am. Bd. Radiology (trustee). Intern Phila. Gen. Hosp., 1954-55; resident in radiology U. Calif. at San Francisco Med. Center, 1957-61; instr. radiation therapy U. Mich., Ann Arbor, 1961-62, U. Rochester, N.Y., 1962-63; asso. prof. radiology U. Okla., Oklahoma City, 1963-66; prof. radiology, chmn. div. radiotherapy Med. Coll. Va., Richmond, 1966-70; prof., head dept. therapeutic radiology U. Minn., Mpls., 1970—; cons. in field. Exec. bd. Am. Joint Com. for End Result Reporting and Cancer Staging; com. radiation oncology studies Nat. Cancer Inst. Bd. dirs., mem. exec. com. Am. Cancer Soc., 1990—. Served with M.C., AUS, 1955-57. Recipient Disting. Service award U. Colo., 1988. Fellow Am. Coll. Radiology (bd. chancellors, Gold medal 1995), Royal Coll. Radiology (hon.); mem. Am. Radium Soc. (sec. 1981-83, pres. 1983-84), Janeway medal 1989), Radiol. Soc. N.Am., Am. Assn. Cancer Research, Am. Cancer Soc. (pres. Minn. div. 1979-80, nat. bd., exec. com.), Am. Roentgen Ray Soc. Soc. Chairmen of Acad. Radiation Oncology Programs (pres. 1974-76), Internat. Soc. Radiation Oncology (pres. 1981-85), Soc. Nuclear Medicine, Am. Soc. Clin. Oncology, Am. Soc. Therapeutic Radiologists (exec. bd. 74-78, pres. 1978-79, chmn. bd. 1979-80, Gold medal 1991), Deutsche Rontgengesellschaft Gesellschaft fur Medizinische Radiologie E.V. (hon.), Phi Beta Kappa, Sigma Xi, Alpha Omega Alpha. Home: 6413 Cherokee Trl Minneapolis MN 55439-1106 Office: U Minn PO Box 436 Minneapolis MN 55455

LEVITZ, PAUL ELLIOT, publishing executive; b. Bklyn., Oct. 21, 1956; s. Alfred Lazarus and Hannah (Brenner) L.; m. Jeanette Francine Cusimano, Nov. 2, 1980; children: Nicole, Philip, Garret. Student, N.Y. U., 1973-76. Editor, pub. The Comic Reader, Bklyn., 1971-73; writer, asst. editor Nat. Periodical Publs., Inc., N.Y.C., 1973-76; editor, editorial coordinator, writer DC Comics, N.Y.C., 1976-80, mgr. bus. affairs, 1980-82, v.p. ops., 1982-84, exec. v.p., 1984-89, exec. v.p., pubs., 1989—; exec. v.p., pub. MAD mag. 1993—. Jewish. Home: 23 Stony Hollow Chappaqua NY 10514 Office: DC Comics 1700 Broadway New York NY 10019

LEVMORE, SAUL, law educator; b. 1953. BA, Columbia Coll., 1973, PhD, 1978; JD, Yale U., 1980. Bar: Va. 1983. Dean Jonathan Edwards Coll. Yale U., 1979-80; asst. prof. U. Va., Charlottesville, 1980-84, prof., 1984—; Brokaw prof. of law; lectr. in econs. Yale U., 1976-80, vis. prof., 1986-87; vis. prof. U. Chgo., 1993. Office: U Va Sch Law Sch Law Charlottesville VA 22905-1789

LEVOVITZ, PESACH ZECHARIAH, rabbi; b. Poland, Sept. 15, 1922; came to U.S., 1923; s. Reuben and Leah Zlate (Kustanowitz) L.; m. Bluma D. Feder, Feb. 5, 1945 (dec. 1970); children: Sivya, Yaakov; m. Eleanore Herman Klugmann, 1972 (dec. Nov. 1980); children: Maurice, Danny, Renee, Jackie; m. Frayde Twersky Perlow, Dec. 18, 1989; stepchildren: Yitzchok, Faige, Joseph. B.A., Yeshivah U., 1942. Rabbi Mesivtha Tifereth Jerusalem Rabbinical Sem., 1943, Congregation Sons of Israel, Lakewood, N.J., 1944—; founder, 1945; since dean Bezalel Day Sch.; Pres. Rabbinical Council Am., 1966-68, chmn. commn. on internat. affairs, 1972; asso. chmn. Soviet Jewry commn., 1980; mem. exec. com. Synagogue Council Am., 1953—; standing com. Conf. European Rabbis and Asso. Rabbis, 1964—; steering com. World Conf. Ashkenazi and Sephardi Synagogues; Co chmn. rabbinic cabinet Bonds for Israel, 1972; chaplain Lakewood Police Dept., 1950—; vis. chaplain Naval Air Sta., Lakehurst, N.J., 1945—; nat. chmn. ann. conv. Rabbinical Council of Am., 1971; v.p. Religious Zionists Am., 1974; nat. chmn. Vaad Haroshi Religious Zionists Am., 1975; pres. Beth Din of Am., 1986. Mem. adv. bd. Lakewood Housing Council, Nat. Community Relations Adv. Council, United Jewish Appeal; chmn. bd. Sons of Israel Sr. Citizens Housing Inc., 1980; mem. N.J. Drug Utilization Council.; chmn. adv. council on protection kosher legislation to Atty. Gen., State of N.J.; mem. exec. Ocean County Jewish Fedn., 1988; co-chmn. BLue Ribbon Panel Lakewood Twp., 1992—. Recipient Revel Meml. award in religion and religious edn. Yeshivah Coll. Alumni Assn., 1967; award for outstanding rabbinic leadership Union of Orthodox Jewish Congregations Am., 1969; Nat. Assn. Hebrew Day Schs., 1980; chief Rabbi Issas Halevi Herzog Torah Fellowship award Religious Zionists Am., 1972; chmn. nat. conv., 1974; named Rabbi of Yr.; Israel Bond Orgn., 1991. Mem. Conf. Presidents Nat. Jewish Orgns., Am. Conf. Soviet Jewry. Home: 631 8th St Lakewood NJ 08701-2609 Office: Congregation Sons of Israel Madison Ave Lakewood NJ 08701

LEVOY, MYRON, author; b. N.Y.C., Jan. 30, 1930; s. Bernard and Elsie (Schwartz) L.; m. Beatrice Fleischer, Jan. 27, 1952; children: David, Deborah. BS in Chem. Engring., CCNY, 1952; MS in Chem. Engring., Purdue U., 1953. Engr. Pratt & Whitney Aircraft Co., East Hartford, Conn., 1953-56; project engr. Reaction Motors Inc., Rockaway, N.J., 1956-67; engr. specialist Polytech. Design, Livingston, N.J., 1973-81; writer, 1955—. Author: (novel) A Necktie in Greenwich Village, 1968; Penny Tunes and Princesses, 1972, The Witch of Fourth Street and Other Stories, 1972 (Book World Honor Book 1972), Children's Book Showcase award 1973), Alan and Naomi, 1977 (Boston Globe-Horn Book award, Honor Book 1978, Jane Addams Honor Book award 1978, Am. Book award finalist 1980, Silver Pencil award The Netherlands 1981, Austrian State prize for children's lit 1981, German State prize for young adult lit. 1982, Buxtenhuder Bulle award Fed. Republic Germany 1982), A Shadow Like a Leopard, 1981 (ALA Best Book for Young Adults 1981), Three Friends, 1984, The Hanukkah of Great-Uncle Otto, 1984, Pictures of Adam, 1986 (ALA Best Book for young adults 1986, Internat. Reading Assn. young adult choice 1986), The Magic Hat of Mortimer Wintergreen, 1988 (Jr. Lit. Guild selection 1988), Kelly 'N' Me, 1992, also poetry and plays; contrb. articles to profl. jours. Mem. PEN, The Authors Guild, The Dramatists Guild. Jewish. Avocations: tennis, cross-country skiing, swimming, museums, films. Office: Writers House Inc 21 W 26th St New York NY 10010

LEVY, ALAIN M., record company executive; b. France, Dec. 19, 1946. Grad., Ecole des Mines, France; MBA, U. Pa. Asst. to the pres. CBS Internat., N.Y.C., 1972-73; v.p. mktg. for Europe CBS Internat., Paris, 1973, v.p. of creative ops. for Europe; also mgr. CBS/Italy, 1978; mng. dir. CBS Disques, France, 1979; chief exec. officer PolyGram France, 1984; exec. v.p. PolyGram group, France and Fed. Republic of Germany, 1988; mgr. U.S. ops. PolyGram group, 1990—; pres., chief exec. officer, mem. bd. mgrs. PolyGram USA, 1991—; apptd. to group mgmt. com. Phillips Electronics, majority shareholder of PolyGram USA, 1991—. Office: PolyGram Records Inc 825 8th Ave New York NY 10019-7416 also: 30 Berkeley Sq, London W1X 5HA, England*

LEVY, ALAN JOSEPH, editor, journalist, writer; b. N.Y.C., Feb. 10, 1932; s. Meyer and Frances (Shield) L.; m. Valerie Wladaver, Aug. 7, 1956; children—Monica, Erika. A.B., Brown U., 1952; M.S. in Journalism, Columbia U., 1953. Reporter Louisville Courier-Jour., 1953-60; free-lance contbr. Life, Sat. Eve. Post, N.Y. Times, others, 1960-91; investigator Carnegie Commn. Ednl. TV, Boston, 1966-67; fgn. corr. Life, N.Y. Times mags., Prague, Czechoslovakia, 1967-71; dramaturg Vienna's English Theatre, Austria, 1977-82; free-lance author, dramatist, corr. Vienna, 1971-90; founding editor in chief The Prague Post (Eng. language weekly newspaper), 1991—; lectr. on theatre Salzburg Seminar in Am. Studies, Austria, 1981; adj. prof. lit. and journalism Webster U., Vienna, 1983—; lectr.-in-residence Gritti Palace, Venice, Italy, 1987; prof. non-fiction Ctrl. European U. Summer Writer's Workshop, Prague, 1994. Author: Draftee's Confidential Guide, 1957, 2d edit., 1966, Operation Elvis, 1960, The Elizabeth Taylor Story, 1961, Wanted: Nazi Criminals at Large, 1962, Interpret Your Dreams, 1962, 2d edit., 1975, Kind-Hearted Tiger, 1964, The Culture Vultures, 1968, God Bless You Real Good, 1969, Rowboat to Prague, 1972, 2d edit. titled So Many Heroes, 1980, Good Men Still Live, 1974, The Bluebird of Happiness, 1976, Forever, Sophia, 1979, 2d edit., 1986, Treasures of the Vatican Collections, 1983, Ezra Pound: the Voice of Silence, 1983, W.H. Auden: In the Autumn of the Age of Anxiety, 1983, Vladimir Nabokov: The Velvet Butterfly, 1984, Ezra Pound: A Jewish View, 1988, The Wiesenthal File, U.K. edit. 1993, U.S. edit. 1994 (U.S. Author of the Year Soc. of Journ. and Authors, 1995); dramatist The World of Ruth Draper, 1982; librettist Just an Accident?, 1983 (Ernst Krenek prize City of Vienna, 1986). Trustee Thomas Nast Found., Landau, Germany, 1978—, Saving Our Heritage Assn., Oberdorf, Switzerland, 1994—. Served with U.S. Army, 1953-55. Recipient New Republic Younger Writer award, 1958, Best Enterprise Reporting award Sigma Delta Chi, 1959; Bernard De Voto fellow Middlebury Coll., 1963; golden Johann Strauss medal City of Vienna, 1981; travel writing awards Pacific Area Travel Assn., 1978, Govt. of Malta, 1985. mem. Am. Soc. Journalists and Authors, Authors Guild and Dramatists Guild of Authors League of Am., Overseas Press Club Am., PEN, Fgn. Press assns. Vienna, Prague, Austrian Soc. Authors, Composers and Music Pubs., Czech Union Journalists. Democrat. Jewish. Office: Wallace Literary Agency 177 E 70 St New York NY 10021 Address: The Prague Post, Na Porici 12, CZ-11530 Prague 1, Czech Republic

LEVY, ARNOLD S(TUART), real estate company executive; b. Chgo., Mar. 15, 1941; s. Roy and Esther (Scheff) L.; m. Eva Cichosz, Aug. 8, 1976; children: Adam, Rachel, Deborah. BS, U. Wis., 1963; MPA, Roosevelt U., 1970. Dir. Neighborhood Youth Corps, Chgo., 1966-68; v.p. Social Planning Assn., Chgo., 1968-70; planning dir. Office of Mayor Chgo., 1970-74; dep. dir. Mayor's Office Manpower, Chgo., 1974-75; sr. v.p. Urban Investment & Devel. Co., Chgo., 1975-93; pres., CEO Stone-Levy, LLC, Chgo., 1994—;mem. Stone-Levy Hospitality Group, LLC, 1995—; pres. JMB/ Urban Hotels, Hotel and Resort Devel. Group, JMB/Urban Devel. Co., 1985-93; ptnr. Pierce and Co., 1994—; bd. dirs. Hostmark Mgmt. Group, Inc.; mem. Urban Land Inst. Pres. Ark, Chgo., 1970-72, Parental Stress Svcs., Chgo., 1978-79; past lectr. DePaul U., Roosevelt U., Loyola U.; v.p. Inst. Urban Life, Chgo., 1983—. Co-editor: The Professionals' Guide to Commercial Property Development, 1988. Bd. dirs. Mus. Broadcast Communications, Chgo. Coun. of Urban Affairs, Am Shalom, pres. Ill. Humane Soc., Hostmark Mgmt. Group, Inc.; steering com. Radio Hall of Fame; chmn. Spertus Coll. of Judaica, Glencoe Plan Commn., Carlton Club (Chgo.), SL Hospitality Group LLC, Twin Orchard Club. Home: 535 Park Ave Glencoe IL 60022-1501 Office: Stone-Levy & Co LLC 8700 W Bryn Mawr Ave Ste 900 Chicago IL 60631-3507

LEVY, ARTHUR JAMES, public relations executive, writer; b. Bklyn., Dec. 23, 1947; s. Bernard and Bernice (Lipner) L.; m. Andrea Susan Hall, May 11, 1980; children: Zoe Jess, Jake Benjamin. BA, Brandeis U., 1969.

Account exec., disc jockey Sta. WBUS-FM, Miami Beach, Fla., 1971; pop music critic Magic Bus Newspaper, Miami Beach, 1971; sr. editor, writer Zoo World mag., Ft. Lauderdale, Fla., 1971-74; chief writer Atlantic Records, N.Y.C., 1975-78; assoc. dir. Press and Pub. Info. dept. Columbia Records, N.Y.C., 1978-88, nat. dir. media services, publicity dept., 1988-93; v.p. Sony Music Entertainment Comms. Dept., N.Y.C., 1993—; so. regional v.p. Rock Writers of the World, 1973-74; seminar panelist United Jazz Coalition, N.Y.C., 1983—, CMJ Folk, 1987—, New Music Seminar Folk, 1989—. Writer, researcher album and video liner notes for Rolling Stones, Blue Öyster Cult, Eric Andersen, Johnny Cash, Herbie Mann, Taj Mahal, Al Kooper, Robert Johnson, Jan Hammer, Julio Iglesias, Boomtown Rats, Jimmy Webb, Pete Seeger, Montreux Festival '77, Elvis Presley: Golden Celebration, 1985 (Grammy nomination), Songs of the Civil War; appeared on album session (Finnadar Records) Idil Biret's New Line Piano, 1978, (Columbia) Jaroslav Jakubovic's Checkin' In, 1978. Named Publicist of Yr. Columbia Records, 1982, 87, Media Man of Yr. Record World mag., N.Y.C., 1981. Mem. NARAS (gov. N.Y. chpt., Grammy voting com., crafts com.), Rock and Roll Hall of Fame (nominating com., mus. experts com.), Nat. Acad. Popular Music. Avocation: record collecting.

LEVY, BENJAMIN, artist; b. Tel-Aviv, Feb. 28, 1940; s. Ovadia and Bat-Sheva (Mizrachi) Nahum-Levy; student Meirovitch and Yaskil Art Sch., Haifa, Israel, 1957-58, Ecole DeMont Parnass, Paris, 1959, Pratt Graphic Art Center, 1966-67; m. Hanna Vroman, Oct. 10, 1962; children: Ofer, Bat-Sheva, Amnon, Jhonathan; came to U.S., 1965, naturalized, 1970. Exhibited one-man shows Dugit Gallery, Tel-Aviv, 1961, Tchermerinsky Gallery, Tel-Aviv, 1964, Israeli Art Gallery, N.Y.C., 1966, Morris Gallery, Woodstock, N.Y., 1966, Everyman Gallery, N.Y.C., 1968, 71, Morris Gallery, N.Y.C., 1969, New Haven Jewish Center, 1970, Aleph Gallery, Mexico City, 1971, Miami Mus. Modern Art, 1971, Graphic Art Gallery, Tel-Aviv, 1971, Galerias Del Centro Deportivo, Mexico City, 1972, Nat. Mus. Panama, 1973, Carol Halsband Gallery, N.Y.C., 1973, Israel Art Gallery, N.Y.C., 1973, Gallery T, Amsterdam, 1975, 76, Tel-Aviv Mus., 1976, Delson Richter Galleries, Jaffa and Jerusalem, 1976, La Cadre Gallery, Toronto, Ont., Can., 1976, Mus. Modern Art, Utrecht, Holland, 1978, Galerij 565, Aalst, Belgium, 1978, 79, 80, Wetering Gallery, Amsterdam, Holland, 1978, 79, Palm Springs (Calif.) Mus., 1978, Ordan Gallery, Israel, 1979, L'Affiche Galerie, N.Y.C., 1979, Mus. of S.C. Columbia, 1979, U. S.C., Columbia, 1979, JAS Gallery, Utrecht, 1980, Nat. Print Center for Graphics, Kasterlee, Belgium, 1980, Kaneda Gallery, Tokyo, 1980, Marquis Gallery, Flisingen, Netherlands, 1980, D Cercle, Oostende, Belgium, 1981, Montjoi Gallery, Brussels, 1981, McKissik Mus., Columbia, S.C., 1982, Holdsworth Galleries, Australia, 1983, Galerie Fabien Boulakia, Paris, 1985, Sander Fine Arts Gallery, Daytona Beach, Fla., Goldman Fine Arts Mus., Washington, 1985, Roslyn Fine Art Mus., N.J., 1990, Sailor Gallery, Phila., 1991, Union League, N.Y.C., 1991, Yeshiva U. Mus., N.Y.C., 1991, Geneva Art Fair, 1992, Gallery Guy Marain, Geneva, 1993, Nat. Jewish Mus., Washington, Nahan Gallery, N.Y.C., 1994, New Orleans, 1994, St. Mary's Coll., Md., 1994, Nat. Arts Club, N.Y.C., 1995; group shows: Georgetown Gallery, Washington, 1969, Mus. Modern Art, Utrecht, Holland, 1972, Mus. Tel-Aviv, 1973, Cabinet, São Paulo, Brazil, 1977, Mus. Israel, 1978, Malmo (Sweden) Mus., 1978, UN, N.Y.C., 1979, Museo Vial, Venezuela, 1982, Museo Sefardi, Toledo, Spain, Am. Acad. and Inst. Arts and Letters, 1983-84, musee suquemart Andre Paris, 1992, numerous others; represented in permanent collections: Haifa Mus. Modern Art, Pub. Library N.Y.C., Mus. Detroit, Miami Mus. Modern Art, Utrecht Mus. Modern Art, Nat. Mus. Panama, Joseph Hirshhorn Mus., Stedelejke Mus., Amsterdam, Skirball Mus., Calif., McKissic Mus., Columbia, S.C., Jewish Mus., N.Y.C., Mus. Contemporary Art, Caracas, Venezuela, Transito Mus., Toledo, Spain, Mus. Art, New Orleans, other prt. and public collections. Illustrator children's books Bobbs Merrill Co.; illustrator yearly UN envelope, also lithographs, 1976; artist jacket for jazz record Garry Burton and Pat Mathini-Reunion, 1990. Recipient prizes Young Israeli Artists, 1965, Helena Rubenstein Norman Fund, 1966, Audubon Artists, 1969, Nat. Arts Club award, 1995. Address: 317 W 89th St New York NY 10024

LEVY, BURTON See LANE, BURTON

LEVY, DALE PENNEYS, lawyer; b. Phila., Sept. 10, 1940; d. Harry M. and Rosalind (Fried) Penneys; m. Richard D. Levy, Dec. 12, 1970; children: Jonathan D., Michael Z. BA, Wellesley Coll., 1962; JD, U. Pa., 1967. Bar: Pa. 1967, U.S. Ct. Appeals (3rd cir.) 1971. Assoc. Blank, Rome, Comisky & McCauley, Phila., 1967-76, ptnr., 1976—; bd. dirs. Phila. Sch., Phila. Indsl. Devel. Corp. Contbr. articles to profl. jours. Bd. dirs., chair Women in Transition 1983-85, active adv. bd., 1985—; chair Women's Rights Com., 1978; bd. dirs. Phila. Sr. Ctr., 1994—. Mem. ABA, Pa. Bar Assn., Phila. Bar Assn. (past chair women's rights com.). Mem. ABA (real property, probate and trust law sect., vice chairperson com. on pub.-pvt. ventures/privatization internat. law and practice sect.), Phila. Bar Assn. (real estate, corp., banking and bus. law sect., women's rights com.). Office: Blank Rome Comisky & McCauley 4 Penn Center Plz Philadelphia PA 19103-2521

LEVY, DAVID, lawyer, insurance company executive; b. Bridgeport, Conn., Aug. 3, 1932; s. Aaron and Rachel (Goldman) L. BS in Econs., U. Pa., 1954; JD, Yale U., 1957. Bar: Conn. 1958, U.S. Supreme Ct. 1963, D.C. 1964, Mass. 1965, N.Y. 1971, Pa. 1972; CPA, Conn. Acct. Arthur Andersen & Co., N.Y.C., 1957-59; sole practice Bridgeport, 1959-60; specialist tax law IRS, Washington, 1960-64; counsel State Mut. Life Ins. Co., Worcester, Mass., 1964-70; assoc. gen. counsel taxation Penn Mut. Life Ins. Co., Phila., 1971-81; sole practice Washington, 1982-87; v.p., tax counsel Pacific Mut. Life Ins. Co., Newport Beach, Calif., 1987—. Author: (with others) Life Insurance Company Tax Series, Bureau National Affairs Tax Management Income Tax, 1970-71. Mem. adv. bd. Tax Mgmt., Washington, 1975-90, Hartford Inst. on Ins. Taxation, 1990—; bd. dirs. Citizens Plan E Orgn., Worcester, 1966-70. With AUS, 1957. Mem. ABA (vice-chmn. employee benefits com. 1980-86, ins. com. 1984-86, torts and ins. practice sect., subcom. chair ins. cos. com. tax sect. 1994—), Assn. Life Ins. Counsel, AICPA, Beta Alpha Psi. Jewish.

LEVY, DAVID, broadcasting executive; b. Phila.; s. Benjamin and Lillian (Potash) L.; m. Lucile Alva Wilds, July 25, 1941 (div. 1970); children: Lance, Linda; m. Victoria Robertson, Apr. 23, 1987; 1 stepchild, Kate Jolson. BS in Econs., U. Pa., 1934, MBA, 1935. With Young & Rubicam, Inc., N.Y.C., 1938-59, v.p., assoc. dir. radio-TV dept.; v.p. charge network programs and talent NBC, N.Y.C., 1959-61; exec. producer Filmways, L.A., 1964-68, Goodson-Todman Prodns., West Coast, 1968-69; exec. v.p. Golden Orange Broadcasting Co., Anaheim, Calif., 1969-88, bd. dirs.; exec. v.p. charge TV activities Four Star Internat., Inc., Beverly Hills, Calif., 1970-72; pres. Wilshire Prodns. Inc., Beverly Hills, 1972—; mem. faculty Calif. State U., Northridge, 1973-77; TV adviser Citizens for Eisenhower, 1952, 56, Haig for Pres., 1988; dir. radio and TV for Citizens for Eisenhower-Nixon, 1956; prodr., writer 3-network program for closing Rep. campaign broadcast Four More Years, 1956; writer, co-prodr. closing program election eve Behalf of Wendell Willkie, 1940; cons. Sec. Treasury, 1944-46; chief radio sect. war fin. divsn. Treasury Dept. Exec. producer Double Life of Henry Phyffe, 1965; exec. producer, creator TV series Addams Family, 1964-66, The Pruitts of Southampton ABC-TV, 1966-67; producer world premier Sarge, also exec. producer, creator TV series Universal Studios NBC, 1971-72; creator Hollywood Screen Test, Bat Masterson, Appointment with Adventure, Outlaws, The Americans, Real West, The Kate Smith Daytime Hour, others; launched Maverick, Shirley Temple, National Velvet, Father Knows Best, Godfrey's Talent Scouts, People's Choice, I Married Joan, Life of Riley, Dr. Kildare, Bonanza, Hitchcock Presents, Thriller, Saturday Night at the Movies, Walt Disney's Wonderful World of Color, Robert Taylor and The Detectives, The Deputy (starring Henry Fonda), Car 54, 1st Bob Newhart Show, 1st Phil Silver's Show, Goodyear TV Playhouse, Peter Pan (starring Mary Martin), What's My Line, Make the Connection, Say When; others; producer Paramount TV, 1972-73, Hanna Barbera Prodns. NBC, 1973-74; creative cons. The Addams Family, Name That Tune, Ralph Edwards Prodns., 1974-81, new series You Asked for It; TV cons. Mark Goodson Prodns., 1989—; co-creator, exec. producer Face the Music TV series, 1980-81; author (novels) The Chameleons, 1964, The Network Jungle, 1976, The Gods of Foxcroft, 1970, Potomac Jungle, 1990; contbr. short stories to popular mags. Lt. USN, 1944-46. Recipient Treasury medal and disting. svc. citation U.S. Treasury Dept., 1946. Mem. ASCAP, TV Acad., Writers Guild Am., Prodrs. Guild Am. (sec., bd. dirs.), Hollywood Radio-TV Soc. (pres. 1969-70, award 1970), Caucus for Prodrs., Writers and Dirs. (sec., steering com.,

exec. dir. 1974—; Disting. Svc. award 1985, Spl. award of merit for 20 yrs. svc. 1994). Republican. Jewish. Avocation: writing. Office: 210 S Spalding Dr Beverly Hills CA 90212

LEVY, DAVID, lawyer; b. Atlanta, July 7, 1937; s. Meyer and Elsie (Reisman) L.; m. Diane L. Lerner; children: Jeffrey Marc, Robert William, Danielle Beth, Margo Shaw; stepchildren: Mitchell S. Haber, Cort A. Haber. B.A., Emory U., 1959, LL.B., 1961; LL.M., Georgetown U., 1964. Bar: Ga. 1961. Atty. SEC, Washington, 1961-65; assoc., partner Arnstein, Gluck, Weitzenfeld & Minow, Chgo., 1965-71; partner Kaler, Karesh & Frankel, Atlanta, 1971-73; exec. v.p administrn., counsel, dir. Nat. Svc. Industries, Inc., Atlanta, 1973—; also bd. dirs. Nat. Service Industries Inc., Atlanta. Mem. Am., Ga. bar assns. Home: 2005 Monterey Pky Atlanta GA 30350-6806 Office: Nat Svc Industries Inc 1420 Peachtree St NE Atlanta GA 30309-3002

LEVY, DAVID ALFRED, immunology educator, physician, scientist; b. Washington, Aug. 27, 1930; s. Stanley A. and Blanche B. (Berman) L.; m. Annette Levy-Badoux; children: Jill, William, Stanley. BS, U. Md., 1952, MD, 1954. Diplomate Am. Bd. Internal Medicine, Am. Bd. Allergy and Immunology. Intern, resident in medicine U. Hosp., Balt., 1954-59; physician VA Hosp., Balt., 1961-62; fellow dept. microbiology Sch. Medicine Johns Hopkins U., 1962-66, asst. prof. radiol. sci. Sch. Hygiene and Pub. Health, Sch. Medicine, 1966-68, assoc. prof. Sch. Hgiene and Pub. Health, Sch. Medicine, 1968-71, prof. radiol. sci. and epidemiology Sch. Hygiene and Pub. Health, Sch. Medicine, 1972-73, prof. biochemistry Sch. Hygiene and Pub. Health, Sch. Medicine, 1973-82, with joint appointments in epidemiology and medicine Sch. Medicine, 1973-82, in pathobiology Sch. Medicine, 1980-82, prof. immunology and infectious diseases Sch. Medicine, 1982-86; mem. FDA Panel on Rev. of Allergenic Extracts, 1975-83; mem. allergy and immunology rev. com. Nat. Inst. Allergy and Infectious Diseases, 1975-77; adj. dir. Centre d'Immunologie et de Biologie, Pierre Fabre, S.A., 1985-90; cons. to pharm. industry, 1990—. Editorial bd. Clin. Immunology and Immunopathology, 1971-76, Revue d'Allergologie Française; contbr. articles to med. jours. and books. Sci. dir. Centre d'Allergie, Hopital Rothschild, Paris, 1991—. With U.S. Army, 1959-61. Fellow Am. Acad. Allergy and Immunology; mem. Internat. Union Immunol. Socs. (vice-chmn. allergen standardization subcom. 1980-83), Am. Assn. Immunologists, Md. Soc. Allergy, French Soc. Immunology, French Soc. Allergology, Sigma Xi.

LEVY, DAVID CORCOS, museum director; b. N.Y.C., Apr. 10, 1938; s. Edgar Wolf and Lucille (Corcos) L.; m. Janet Meyer, June 7, 1959 (div.); children: Jessica Anne, Thomas William; m. Carole L. Feld, May 19, 1992. BA, Columbia U., 1960; MA, NYU, 1969, PhD, 1979; DFA (hon.), New Sch. for Social Rsch., 1989. Asst. dir. admissions Parson Sch. Design, N.Y.C., 1961-62, dir. admissions, 1962-67, v.p., 1967-70, dean, chief adminstrv. officer, 1970-79, exec. dean, chief adminstrv. officer, 1979-89; chancellor New Sch. for Social Rsch., N.Y.C., 1989-90; pres., dir. The Corcoran Gallery of Art, Washington, D.C., 1991—. Photographer of works exhibited in Guggenheim Mus., Mus. Modern Art; art dir. jours., books, posters; contbr. articles to jours. and newspapers. Decorated Chevalier des Arts et des Lettres (France). Home: 2556 Massachusetts Ave NW Washington DC 20008 Office: Corcoran Gallery of Art 500 17th St NW Washington DC 20006

LEVY, DAVID FRANKLIN, sales and marketing executive; b. Sao Paulo, Brazil, Apr. 12, 1945; came to U.S., 1975; s. Benjamin Teodoro and Lydia (Defez) L.; m. Luciene Souhami, Feb. 15, 1973; 1 child, Tatiana Souhami. BS in Mech. Engring., Pontifical U. Catolica, Rio de Janeiro, 1969; MBA, John F. Kennedy U., 1979. Prodn. mgr. Bloch Pub., Rio de Janeiro, 1969-71; v.p. ops. Sedegra, Inc., Rio de Janeiro, 1971-75; mfg. mgr. Signetics Corp., Sunnyvale, Calif., 1978-82; v.p. sales and mktg. Micro Air Systems, Sunnyvale, 1982-85, Dexon, Inc., Mpls., 1985-88; pres., chief exec. officer SubMicron Systems Inc., Mpls., 1988—. Avocations: tennis, racquetball, skiing, bicycling. Office: 11728 Welters Way Eden Prairie MN 55347-2837

LEVY, DAVID MATTHEW, lawyer; b. Boston, Feb. 13, 1954; s. Harold and Lillian (Kruger) L.; m. Keily Downey, June 14, 1986. BA, Cornell U., 1975; JD, U. Mich., 1979. Bar: D.C. 1979, U.S. Ct. Appeals (3rd cir.) 1980, U.S. Ct. Appeals (3rd cir.) 1982, U.S. Ct. Appeals (9th cir.) 1986, U.S. Supreme Ct. 1989. Assoc. Sidley & Austin, Washington, 1979-86, ptnr., 1986—. Contbr. articles to profl. jours. Mem. ABA (vice-chair postal matters com. adminstrv. law sect. 1991-92, 1992-95). Office: Sidley & Austin 1722 I St NW Washington DC 20006-3705

LEVY, DONALD HARRIS, chemistry educator; b. Youngstown, Ohio, June 30, 1939; s. Gabriel and Minnie (Lerner) L.; m. Susan Louise Miller, June 14, 1964; children—Jonathan G., Michael A., Alexander B. B.A., Harvard U., 1961; Ph.D., U. Calif.-Berkeley, 1965. Asst. prof. chemistry U. Chgo., 1967-74, assoc. prof., 1974-78, prof., 1978—, chmn. dept. chemistry, 1983-85, Ralph and Mary Otis Isham prof.; mem. chemistry adv. com. NSF. Assoc. editor Jour. Chem. Physics, 1983—. Fellow Am. Phys. Soc., AAAS; mem. Am. Chem. Soc., Optical Soc. Am., Am. Acad. Arts and Scis., Nat. Acad. Scis. Office: U Chgo Dept Chemistry 5640 S Ellis Ave Chicago IL 60637-1433

LEVY, EDWARD CHARLES, JR., manufacturing company executive; b. Detroit, Nov. 14, 1931; s. Edward Charles and Pauline (Birndorf) L.; m. Julie Ruth Honigman, July 11, 1955; 2 children. S.B., MIT, 1952. With Edward C. Levy Co. Detroit, 1952—; v.p. ops. and engring. Edward C. Levy Co., 1957-63, exec. v.p., 1963-70, pres., 1970—; bd. dirs. Tecumseh (Mich.) Products Co. Bd. dirs. Edward C. Levy Found., Mich. Cancer Found., Detroit Round Table of Christians and Jews; trustee Children's Hosp. of Mich., Citizen's Rsch. Coun. of Mich., Wash. Ist. for Near East policy; gov. Jewish Welfare Fedn. Detroit; officer Am. Israel Pub. Affairs Com. Mem. Am. Concrete Inst., ASTM, Engring. Soc. Detroit. Jewish. Clubs: Detroit, Renaissance (Detroit); Franklin Hills Country (Franklin, Mich.). Office: Edward C Levy Co Inc 8800 Dix St Detroit MI 48209-1093

LEVY, EUGENE, actor, director, screenwriter; b. Hamilton, Ont., Can. Appearances include (films) Cannibal Girls, 1972, Running, 1979, Nothing Personal, 1980, Heavy Metal, 1981, Strange Brew, 1983, Going Berserk, 1983, National Lampoon's Vacation, 1983, Splash, 1984, Armed and Dangerous, 1986, The Canadian Conspiracy, 1986, Club Paradise, 1986, Speed Zone, 1989, Father of the Bride, 1991, Once Upon A Crime, 1992, Stay Tuned, 1992, I Love Trouble, 1994; (TV) The Lovebirds, 1979, From Cleveland, 1980, George Burn's Comedy Week, 1985, Dave Thomas: The Incredible Time Travels of Henry Osgood, 1986, Billy Crystal-Don't Get Me Started, 1986, Bride of Boogedy, 1987, Ray Bradbury Theatre, 1988; actor, dir.: (TV) Second City TV, 1977-81, SCTV Network, 1981-83, The Last Polka, 1985, Autobiographies: The Enigma of Bobby Bittman, 1988; dir.: (TV) Second City's 50th Anniversary Special, 1988, Partners in Love, 1992, Sodbusters, 1994. Office: William Morris Agy 151 S El Camino Dr Beverly Hills CA 90212-2704*

LEVY, EUGENE HOWARD, planetary sciences educator, researcher; b. N.Y.C., May 6, 1944; s. Isaac Philip and Anita Harriet (Guttman) L.; m. Margaret Lyle Rader, Oct. 13, 1967; children: Roger P., Jonathan S., Benjamin H. AB in Physics with high honors, Rutgers U., 1966; PhD in Physics, U. Chgo., 1971. Teaching asst. dept. physics U. Chgo., 1966-69, rsch. asst. Enrico Fermi Inst., 1969-71; postdoctoral fellow dept. physics and astronomy U. Md., 1971-73; asst. prof. physics and astrophysics Bartol Rsch. Found., Franklin Inst., Swarthmore, Pa., 1973-75; asst., then assoc. prof. U. Ariz., Tucson, 1975-83, prof. planetary scis., 1983—, mem. faculty applied math. program, 1981—, head dept. planetary scis., dir. lunar and planetary lab., 1983-94, mem. theoretical astrophysics program, 1985—; dean coll. of sci. U. Ariz., 1993—; dir. NASA-Ariz. Spacegrant Coll. Consortium U. Ariz., Tucson, 1989—; mem. com. on planetary and lunar exploration of space sci. bd. Nat. Acad. Scis., 1976-79, chmn., 1979-82, co-chair Space Sci. Bd. Study on Exploration Primitive Solar-System Bodies, 1978, mem. Space Sci. Bd., 1979-82, head U.S. del., co-chair Nat. Acad. Scis.-European Sci. Found. Joint Working Group on Cooperation in Planetary Exploration, 1982-84, mem. steering group com. on major directions for space sci. 1995-2015, 1984-86, chair adv. com. on internat. cooperation for Mars sample return, 1986-88; mem. Comet Halley Sci. Working Group, NASA, 1977, mem. spacelab phys. sci. rev. panel space sci. steering com., 1979, mem. rev. panel on origin plasmas in Earth's neighborhood, 1980, mem. solar system exploration com. of Adv. Coun., 1980-83, mem. Ames Rsch. Ctr. Planetary Detection Study, 1983, Solar System Exploration Mgmt. Coun., 1983-87, mem. com. on future space-sta. sci. projects, 1985, mem. Space Sta. Sci. Users' Working Group, 1985-86, Space and Earth Sci. Adv. Com., 1985-88, chair Comet Rendevous and Asteroid Flyby Rev. Panel, 1986, mem. Mars Exploration Strategy Adv. Group, 1986, Mars Rover Sample Return Sci. Working Group, 1987—; sci. cons. Rockwell Internat. Corp., 1980; mem. COSPAR Internat. Tech. Panel on Comets, 1980-82; U.S.-NASA del. to discussions on internat. cooperation investigations of Comet Halley, Padua, Italy, 1981, to U.S.-USSR Joint Working Group on Near-Earth Space, the Moon and Planets, 1981; mem. program adv. bd. Internat. Conf. on Cometary Exploration, Budapest, Hungary, 1982; mem. exec. univs.' space sci. working group Assn. Am. Univs., 1982-86; study panel U.S.-Soviet cooperation in space sci. U.S. Cong. Office of Tech. Assessment, 1984; chair planetary exploration panel Pacific Rim Nations Internat. Space Yr. Conf., Kona, Hawaii, 1987; mem. working group planetary systems sci. NASA, 1988—, rev. panel lunar and planetary, 1988-90, rev. panel origins solar systems programs, 1990-91; mem. astronomy and astrophysics survey com., sci. opportunities panel NAS, 1989-90; mem. study panel on robotic exploration of Moon and Mars, U.S. Cong. Office Tech. Assessment, 1991; chmn. coun. of instns., bd. dirs. U.S. Space Rsch. Assn., 1991—, vice-chmn. bd. dirs. 1993—; chmn. NASA Origins of Solar Syss. Planet Formation and Defection Rev. Panel, 1993-95, Internat. Sci Found. Astronomy Rev. Panel, 1993-94, NASA Origins of Solar Syss. Mgmt. Ops. Working Group, 1994—, Am. Astron. Soc. Com. on Pub. Edn., 1994; cons. and lectr. in field. Editor: Protostars and Planets III, 1993; contbr., author articles for gen. pub., adv. reports for Congl. Record, abstracts, book revs., others. Recipient Disting. Pub. Svc. medal NASA, 1983, Alexander von Humboldt-Stiftung Sr. Scientist award Fed. Republic Germany, 1989; Disting. vis. scientist Jet Propulsion Lab., Calif. Inst. Tech., 1985-91; NASA predoctoral fellow U. Chgo., 1966-69, fellow Ctr. for Theoretical Physics, U. Md., 1971-73; rsch. grantee NASA, NSF. Mem. AAAS, Am. Astron. Soc. (com. on pub. edn., 1994-95), Am. Geophys. Union, Am. Phys. Soc., Internat. Astron. Union, Univs. Space Rsch. Assn. (1991—), Coun. Instns. (pres. 1991-92, vice chmn. bd. dirs. 1993-94), NASA Origins of Solar Syss. Mgmt. Working Group (chair 1993—), Phi Beta Kappa, Sigma Xi. Achievements include research in theoretical cosmical physics, planetary geophysics, magnetohydrodynamics, space and solar physics, magnetic field generation, physical processes associated with the formation of stars and planetary systems. Office: U Ariz Lunar And Planetary La Tucson AZ 85721

LEVY, EUGENE PFEIFER, architect; b. Little Rock, Dec. 14, 1936; s. Emmanuel Gabe and Elizabeth (Pfeifer) L.; m. Gertrude Watkins Cromwell, June 24, 1959; children: Edwin Cromwell, Andrew Stewart, Charles Pfeifer. B.Arch., U. Va., 1959. Registered architect, Ark., Calif., Ga., Tex. Apprentice Erhart, Eichenbaum, Rauch & Blass, Little Rock, 1959-60; architect, pres. Cromwell, Truemper, Levy, Thompson & Woodsmall, Inc., Little Rock, 1962—. Bd. dirs. Little Rock Boys' Club, 1973—; bd. dirs. Temple B'nai Israel, Little Rock, 1975-78, Little Rock chpt. NCCJ, 1984, Ark. chpt. ARC, 1989. Capt. U.S. Army, 1960-62. Recipient numerous awards including: U.S. Corps. of Engrs. 1985 Design award for Resident Office and Visitors Ctr., Greers Ferry Lake, Ark., USAG 1985 First Honor award for commissary, Camp Foster, Okinawa, Japan, AIA 1980 Design award for Master Plan and First Phase Design for Multi Agy. Office Bldg., State of Ark. Capitol Ground, Little Rock, AIA Honorable Mention award for Systematics, Inc., Corp. Hdqrs., 1982, AIA Design award for Winthrop Rockefeller Meml. Gallery Ark. Arts Ctr., Little Rock, 1982, AIA Design for Commissary, USAF Acad., Colo., 1983, Little Rock Riverfront Belvedere, AIA Design award, 1987, AIA Design award for Itzkowitz residence, Little Rock, 1991. Fellow AIA (Design award Commissary USAF; mem. Greater Little Rock C. of C. (com. 1983-84). Clubs: Little Rock Country, Little Rock Athletic. Home: 5415 Sherwood Rd Little Rock AR 72207-5333 Office: Cromwell Truemper Levy Thompson Woodsall Inc 101 S Spring St Little Rock AR 72201-2428

LEVY, FRANKLIN L., mail order food service company executive; b. 1944; married. BS, L.I. U., 1965. With Julian J. Studley Inc., 1965-68; mgmt. agt. Investors Funding, 1969-70; asst. dir. real estate Horn & Hardart Co., Las Vegas, Nev., 1970-71, dir. real estate, 1971-73, v.p. real estate, 1973-82, exec. v.p., 1982—. Office: Horn & Hardart Co 101 Convention Center Dr Las Vegas NV 89109-2001

LEVY, GERARD G., industrial gases executive; b. 1939. With L'Air Liquide, SA, Paris, France, 1961—; chrm. bd. Bigg Three Industries Inc., Houston, 1988—. Office: Big Three Industries Inc 3535 W 12th St Houston TX 77008-6098

LEVY, H. RICHARD, biochemistry educator; b. Leipzig, Germany, Oct. 22, 1929; came to U.S., 1946; s. Berthold and Charlotte Agnes Hedwig (Frank) L.; m. Betty Louise Samuels, June 12, 1960; 1 child, Karen. BSc in Chemistry, Rutgers U., 1950; PhD in Biochemistry, U. Chgo., 1956. Instr. Ben May Lab. for Cancer Rsch., U. Chgo., 1959-61, asst. prof., 1961-63; asst. prof. dept. bacteriology and botany Syracuse (N.Y.) U., 1963-66, assoc. prof. dept. bacteriology and botany, 1966-70, assoc. prof. dept. biology, 1970-71, prof. of biochemistry, 1971—; chmn. dept. biology, 1993—. Contbr. over 70 articles, revs. to profl. publs. Grantee NIH, NSF, 1963—. Mem. AAAS, AAUP, Am. Chem. Soc., Am. Soc. for Biochemistry and Molecular Biology, Protein Soc. Home: 144 Lewis Ave Syracuse NY 13224-2232 Office: Syracuse U Biology Dept 130 College Pl Syracuse NY 13244-1220

LEVY, IRVIN L., diversified company executive; b. Dallas, 1929. BBA, So. Meth. U., 1950. With NCH Corp. (formerly Nat. Chemsearch Corp.), Irving, Tex., 1950—, now pres., CEO, 1965—, also bd. dirs. Office: NCH Corp 2727 Chemsearch Blvd Irving TX 75062-6454*

LEVY, JACQUES, educator, theater director, lyricist, writer; b. N.Y.C., July 29, 1935; s. Milton and Jean (Brandler) L.; m. Claudia Carr, Apr. 27, 1980; children: Maya, Julien. BA, CCNY, 1956; MA, Mich. State U., 1958, PhD, 1961; postgrad., Kansas U., 1964-65. Moderator dirs./playwrights unit The Actors Studio; co-dir. Open Theater Workshop, Bklyn.; tchr. play analysis, lyric writing New Sch. Social Rsch.; tchr. acting, directing, playwriting Hunter Coll., N.Y.C.; tchr. directing Tisch Sch Arts NYU, Grad. Dept. Theater Columbia U., Sch. Drama Yale U.; head univ. theater program Colgate U., Hamilton, N.Y., tchr. acting, directing, playwriting, prof. Eng. Dir., writer (Broadway plays) Oh! Calcutta!, Almost an Eagle; dir., writer (Broadway play) Doonesbury; dir.: (off-Broadway, regional, European plays) Turtlenecks, Back Country; dir.: (off-Broadway, regional, European plays) America Hurrah, Scuba Duba, Red Cross (Obie award for disting. direction), La Turista, Geography of a Horse Dreamer, Rock Garden, Where Has Tommy Flowers Gone?, American Days, Sleep, Mensch Meyer, dir., lyricist: (off-Broadway, regional European plays) The Golden Land, The Potsdam Quartet, The Bed Was Full, Green Pants, K2, The Glass Menagerie, Exact Change, Blood Wedding, A Chekhov Concert, The Beggar's Opera, The Rolling Thunder Review; playwright, lyricist: Miami Lights, Berchtesgaden, Back Country, Just a Season, (adaptation) Alcestis, Eyes in the Heat, Tell the Rain; lycricist: (Byrds'albums) Byrdmaniax, Untitled, (Roger McGuinn's solo album) Thunderbyrd, (Bob Dylan's album) Desire, Fame...the Musical. Recipient Obie award group achievement as co-dir. Open Theater, Drama Desk directing award nominations, Outer Critics Circle directing award nominations, Grammy award lyricist nominations; BMI grantee (5). Office: Colgate U Univ Theater 13 Oak Dr Hamilton NY 13346

LEVY, JAMES PETER, publishing company executive; b. Oak Park, Ill., June 17, 1940; s. Andrew and Anna (Solsrud) L.; m. Loretta Constance Puglia; children: Elyssa, Andrew, Adam, Gina. Ed.B., U. Ill., 1962, B.A. in Edn., 1963. Sales rep. Prentice-Hall Inc., Englewood Cliffs, N.J., 1963-66; engring. editor Prentice-Hall Pubs., Englewood, N.J., 1966-67; co-founder, exec. v.p. Goodyear Pub., Santa Monica, Calif., 1967-78; sr. v.p. gen. mgr. Scott, Foresman & Co., Glenview, Ill., 1978-88, bd. dirs.; pres. Higher Edn. Div. McGraw-Hill, N.Y.C., 1988-89; pres., CEO Merrill Pub. Co., Columbus, Ohio, 1989-90, Macmillan/McGraw-Hill, N.Y.C., 1990-92, Harcourt Brace Ednl. Pub., Chestnut Hill, Mass., 1992—. Mem. Assn. Am.

Pubs. (chmn.. higher edn. div. 1982-84). Home: 24 Partridge Ln Weston CT 06883-2440 Office: Harcourt Brace Ednl Pub Chestnut Hill MA 02167

LEVY, JEAN, cosmetics company executive. Pres., chief exec. officer Cosmair, Inc., Clark, N.J. Office: Cosmair Inc 30 Terminal Ave Clark NJ 07066-1397

LEVY, JOEL N., financial executive; b. N.Y.C., Aug. 17, 1941; s. Louis N. and Rena Levy; m. Rona Levy, July 8, 1973; children: Marcy, Jeremy. BA, Am. U., 1963. Formerly mgr. Leveraged Acquisition Fund Resource Holdings Capital Group, N.Y.C., 1985-90; dir. Levy/Schulte, Carl Mark & Co., N.Y.C., 1992—. Home: 14 Saint George Rd Great Neck NY 11021

LEVY, JOSEPH, lawyer; b. N.Y.C., June 9, 1928; s. Morris Joseph and Dora (Cohen) L.; m. Gertrud C. Roeder, Jan. 20, 1967; children—Diana N., Susan R. BBA cum laude, Coll. City N.Y., 1950; JD cum laude, N.Y. U., 1954. Bar: N.Y. 1955, D.C. 1968. Asso. Parker, Chapin and Flattau, N.Y.C., 1954-62; ptnr. firm Rivkin, Sherman & Levy (and predecessors), N.Y.C., 1962-84; Schnader, Harrison, Segal & Lewis, 1984-93; sec., dir. Horizons Comms. Corp., 1970-78, Quad Typographers, Inc., 1965-79; sec. Savin Bus. Machines Corp., 1959-84, On-Line Systems, Inc., 1968-78, Lambda Tech., Inc., 1970-78, Programming Methods, Inc., 1969-72, Kreisler Mfg. Cor., 1969-72, Peck & Peck, 1970-73, v.p., sec., dir. Trecom Bus. Systems, Inc., 1985—. Served to capt. AUS, 1951-53. Home: 254 University Way Paramus NJ 07652-5516 Office: 330 Madison Ave New York NY 10017-5001

LEVY, JOSEPH WILLIAM, department stores executive; b. Fresno, Calif., 1932; m. Sharon Sorokin; children: Felicia, Jody, Bret. BS, U. So. Calif., 1954. Asst. merchandising mgr., then mgr. Gottschalks, Inc., Fresno, 1956-72, exec. v.p., 1972-82, chmn., chief exec. officer, 1982—; chmn. exec. com. Frederick Atkins Inc., N.Y.C., 1992—, also bd. dirs. Chmn. Fresno Econ. Devel. Corp., 1982-83; mem. Calif. Transp. Commn., 1983-91, chmn., 1986-87; sec. City of Fresno Equipment Corp.; mem. bus. adv. coun. Sch. Bus. and Adminstrv. Scis., Calif. State U., Fresno; trustee Community Hosps. Cen. Calif. With USNR, 1950-58. Mem. Calif. C. of C. (bd. dirs.), Fresno County and City C. of C. (transp. com.), U. So. Calif. Sch. Bus. Alumni Assn., San Joaquin Country Club, U. Sequoia-Sunnyside Country Club, Downtown Club (Fresno). Home: 6475 N Sequoia Dr Fresno CA 93711-1232 Office: Gottschalks Inc PO Box 28920 Fresno CA 93729-8920

LEVY, KENNETH, music educator; b. N.Y.C., Feb. 26, 1927; s. Meyer and Sylvia (Licht) L.; m. Clara Brooks Emmons, Jan. 25, 1956; children: Robert Brooks, Helen Gardner. A.B., Queens Coll., 1947; M.F.A., Princeton U., 1949, Ph.D., 1956. Instr. music Princeton (N.J.) U., 1952-54; from asst. prof. to Fredrick R. Mann. prof. Brandeis U., Waltham, Mass., 1954-66; prof. music Princeton U., 1966—, chmn. dept. music., 1967-70, 88, Scheide prof. music history, 1988—. Author: Music: A Listener's Introduction, 1983; assoc. editor: Anthologie de la Chanson Parisienne au Seizieme Siecle, 1953; mem. editorial bd. Monumenta Musicae Byzantinae, 1968—, Grove's Dictionary, 6th edit, Early Music History, 1980—; contbr. articles to profl. jours. With USNR, 1945-46. Recipient Fulbright award Italy, 1962-63, Howard T. Behrman award for disting. achievements in humanities, 1983, Deems Taylor award ASCAP, 1989; Guggenheim fellow, 1955-56, Am. Coun. Learned Socs. fellow, 1970-71, sr. fellow Dumbarton Oaks, Harvard U., 1992—; vis. fellow Cambridge U., 1995. Fellow Medieval Acad. Am.; mem. Am. Philos. Soc. Office: Princeton U Dept Music Woolworth Ctr Mus Studies Princeton NJ 08544

LEVY, KENNETH JAMES, advertising executive; b. Cleve., June 15, 1949; s. Morton Leonard and Joan (Beitman) L.; m. Carol Wallisa, Sept. 7, 1974; children: Michael, Allison. BSBA, Ohio State U., 1971, MBA, 1973. Asst. account exec. Ketchum Advt., Pitts., 1973-75, account exec., 1975-77, account supr., 1977-78; account exec. Grey Advt., N.Y.C., 1978-79, account supr., 1979-80, v.p., mgmt. supr., 1980-84, v.p., group mgmt. supr., 1984-87, sr. v.p., 1987-94; exec. v.p., 1994—. Advisor Jr. Achievement Pitts., 1979. Mem. Ohio State U. Alumni Assn., Whippoorwill Country Club (Armonk, N.Y.). Avocations: golf, physical fitness, biographical reading. Home: 3 Carolyn Pl Armonk NY 10504-1101

LEVY, KENNETH JAY, psychology educator, academic administrator; b. Dallas, Sept. 18, 1946; s. Reuben and Ruth (Okon) L.; children: Ryan S., Scott D. BA, U. Tex., 1968, MA, 1969; PhD, Purdue, 1972. Asst. prof. psychology SUNY, Buffalo, 1972-75, assoc. prof., 1976-78, prof., 1979—, chmn. dept. psychology, 1976-78, dean social scis., 1978-82, various adminstrv. positions, 1985—, assoc. provost, 1987—. Contbr. numerous articles to profl. jours.; editorial cons. Psychometrika. Home: 39 Shire Dr S East Amherst NY 14051-1816 Office: SUNY Capen Hall Buffalo NY 14260

LEVY, LEAH GARRIGAN, federal official; b. Miami, Fla., Apr. 29, 1947; d. Thomas Leo and Mary (Flaherty) Garrigan; m. Roger N. Levy, May 2, 1977; children: Philip, Aaron. Student, George Mason U. Mem. legis. staff U.S. Ho. Reps., 1973-75; mem. scheduling staff U.S. Senate, 1975-77, mem. administrv. scheduling staff, 1977-81; staff asst. pub. liaison The White House, 1982-84; spl. asst. U.S Dept. Transport, Washington, 1984-89, U.S. Dept. Housing, Washington, 1989—; scheduling asst. Empower Am., Washington, 1993-94; scheduler majority leader Dick Armey U.S. Ho. of Reps., Washington, 1995—. Contbr. to Rep. Nat. Com., Washington. Contbr. Rep. Nat. Conv. Va. Rep. Party, Washington; del. Va. State GOP Conv., Richmond, 1994. Roman Catholic. Avocations: tennis, golf, reading (nonfiction).

LEVY, LEON, investment company executive; b. N.Y.C., Sept. 13, 1925; s. Jerome and Sadie (Samuelson) L.; m. Roxanne Wruble, Dec. 13, 1959 (div.); m. Shelby White, Aug. 12, 1983. BSS, City Coll., 1948. Security analyst Hirsch & Co., N.Y.C., 1948-51; gen. ptnr. Odyssey Ptnrs. (formerly Oppenheimer & Co.), N.Y.C., 1951—; chmn. bd. dirs. Oppenheimer Mutual Funds; chmn. bd. dirs. Avatar Holdings, Inc.; bd. dirs. United Kingdom Fund, Electra Investment Trust P.L.C., Mercury Assets Mgmt., Ltd.; lectr. CCNY, 1952-59. Trustee Bard Coll., Inst. Fine Arts, NYU, Inst. Advanced Studies, Rockefeller U.; pres. Jerome Levy Inst. for Econ. Rsch., N.Y.C.; bd. dirs. Internat. Found. Art Rsch., John Simon Guggenheim Found. Office: Odyssey Ptnrs LP 31 W 52d St New York NY 10019

LEVY, LEONARD WILLIAMS, history educator, author; b. Toronto, Ont., Can., Apr. 9, 1923; s. Albert and Rae (Williams) L.; m. Elyse Gitlow, Oct. 21, 1944; children: Wendy Ellen, Leslie Anne. BS, Columbia U., 1947, MA, 1948, PhD (Univ. fellow), 1951; LHD, Brandeis U., 1987; DHL (hon.), Claremont Grad. Sch., 1991. Research asst. Columbia U., 1950-51; instr., asst. prof., asso. prof., prof. Brandeis U., Waltham, Mass., 1951-70, first incumbent Earl Warren chair constl. history, 1957-70, dean Grad. Sch. Arts and Scis., 1958-63, dean faculty arts and scis., 1963-66; Andrew W. Mellon prof. humanities, history, chmn. grad. faculty history Claremont (Calif.) Grad. Sch., 1970-90, prof. emeritus, 1990—; Disting. scholar in residence So. Oreg. State Coll., 1990—; Reiser lectr. U. Chgo. Law Sch., 1964; Gaspar Bacon lectr. Boston U., 1972; Elliott lectr. U. So. Calif. Law Sch., 1972; Hugo Black lectr. U. Ala., 1976; Bicentennial lectr., City of St. Louis, 1976; disting. lectr. U. Cin., 1978. Author: The Law of the Commonwealth and Chief Justice Shaw, 1957, Legacy of Suppression; Freedom of Speech and Press in Early American History, 1960, Jefferson and Civil Liberties; The Darker Side, 1963, Origins of the Fifth Amendment, 1968 (Pulitzer Prize in history 1969), Judgments: Essays on American Constitutional History, 1972, Against The Law: The Nixon Court and Criminal Justice, 1974, Treason Against God: History of the Offense of Blasphemy, 1981, Emergence of a Free Press, 1985, Constitutional Opinions, 1986, The Establishment Clause, 1986, Original Intent and the Framers' Constitution, 1988, Blasphemy: Verbal Offense Against the Sacred, 1993, Seasoned Judgments, 1994, A License to Steal: The Forfeiture of Property, 1995; editor: Major Crises in American History, 1962, The American Political Process, 1963, The Presidency, 1964, The Congress, 1964, The Judiciary, 1964, Parties and Pressure Groups, 1964, Freedom of the Press from Zenger to Jefferson, 1966, American Constitutional Law, 1966, Judicial Review and the Supreme Court, 1967, Freedom and Reform, 1967, Essays on The Making of the Constitution, 1969, rev. edit. 1987, The Fourteenth Amendment and the Bill of Rights, 1970, The Supreme Court Under Earl Warren, 1972, Jim Crow in

Boston, 1974, Essays on the Early Republic, 1974, Blasphemy in Massachusetts, 1974, The Framing and Ratification of the Constitution, 1987, The American Founding, 1988, American Constitutional History, 1989; co-editor: Ency. Am. Presidency, 4 vols., 1993; gen. editor: Am. Heritage Series, 60 vols., Harper Documentary History of Western Civilization, 40 vols.; editor-in-chief Ency. Am. Constn., 4 vols., 1986, supplement, 1991; gen. editor: Bicentennial History of the American Revolution; adv. bd.: Revs. in Am. History, John Marshall Papers, Salmon P. Chase Papers; contbr. articles to profl. jours. Mem. nat. bd. Commn. on Law and Social Action, Am. Jewish Congress; mem. U.S. Bicentennial Commn. Am. Revolution, 1966-68; mem. exec. council Inst. for Early Am. History and Culture; mem. nat. adv. council ACLU, Pulitzer prize juror, chmn. biog. jury, 1974, history jury, 1976. With AUS, 1943-46. Recipient Sigma Delta Chi prize for journalism history, 1961, 86; Frank Luther Mott prize Kappa Tau Kappa, 1961; Pulitzer prize for history, 1969; Commonwealth Club prize for nonfiction, 1975; Oboler Meml. Prize of Am. Library Assn. for Intellectual Freedom, 1986; Cert. Merit ABA, 1986; Henry L. Mencken award Free Press Assn., 1986; Dartmouth Medal Am. Library Assn., 1987, 95; Guggenheim fellow, 1957-58; Center For Study Liberty in Am. fellow Harvard, 1961-62; Am. Bar Found. sr. merit fellow, 1973-74; Am. Coun. Learned Socs. fellow, 1973; NEH sr. fellow, 1974. Mem. Am. Hist. Assn. (Littleton-Griswold com. legal history), Orgn. Am. Historians, Am. Soc. Legal History (dir.), Am. Antiquarian Soc., Soc. Am. Historians, Inst. Early Am. History and Culture (exec. coun.), Mass. Hist. Soc., Kappa Delta Pi. Democrat. Home: 1025 Timberline Ter Ashland OR 975-3436

LEVY, LESTER A., sanitation company executive; b. Dallas, 1922; married. Grad. in law, U. Tex., 1945. With NCH Corp. (formerly Nat. Chemsearch Corp.), Irving, Tex., 1946—, now chmn., also bd. dirs. Office: NCH Corp 2727 Chemsearch Blvd Irving TX 75062-6454

LEVY, LOUIS, chess master; b. N.Y.C., Feb. 10, 1921; s. Victor and Sarah (Caffina) L.; m. Gloria Alice Cressy, Jan. 21, 1972. B.S., N.Y. U., 1941. Engaged in car washing business, 1947-66, chess and bridge player, 1939—; Bd. dirs. N.J. Bridge League, 1969-73. Served with USAAF, 1942-46. Named U.S. Internat. Master Am. Contract Bridge League, 1972. Mem. Marshall, Manhattan chess clubs, Am. Contract Bridge League. U.S. Nat. Open chess co-champion, 1972; Empire City chess champion, 1968; U.S. Sr. Open chess champion, 1984. Address: 12317 Ridge Circle Los Angeles CA 90049

LEVY, LOUIS EDWARD, retired accounting firm executive; b. Cleve., Nov. 16, 1932; s. Jerome and Bessie (Goldberg) L.; m. Sandra Harris, Mar. 4, 1956; children: Jerold, Richard, Lawrence. BBA, Case Western Res. U., 1956. CPA, N.Y. Agt. IRS, Cleve., 1956; ptnr., vice chmn. KPMG Peat Marwick, N.Y.C., 1958-90; bd. dirs. Household Internat. Inc., Kimberly-Clark Corp., Alex Brown Group Mutual Funds; former mem. emerging issues task force Fin. Acctg. Standards Bd.; mem. bd. advisors Morin Ctr. for Banking Law Studies, Boston U. Sch. Law. Chmn. emeritus Nat. Multiple Sclerosis Soc., N.Y.C., 1978—; fellow Brandeis U., Boston, 1981—; Recipient Braden award Weatherhead Sch. Mgmt. Case Western Res. U., 1984, Community Svc. award Brandeis U., 1980. Mem. AICPA, Ohio Soc. CPA's, Maplewood Country Club (N.J.), Sky Club. Republican. Jewish. Avocations: tennis, boating.

LEVY, MARK ALLAN, lawyer; b. Cambridge, Mass., May 31, 1939; s. Robert A. and Muriel (Goldman) L.; m. Ellen Grob, Oct. 2, 1966; children: Abigail R., Eric V.R. AB, Harvard U., 1961; LLB, Columbia U., 1964, MBA, 1965. Bar: N.Y. 1964, Mass. 1965. Assoc. Parker, Chapin, Flattau & Klimpl, N.Y.C., 1965-68; sr. ptnr. Stroock & Stroock & Lavan, N.Y.C., 1968—. Contbr. articles to profl. jours. Former mem. Planning Bd. Town of Greenburgh, N.Y. Mem. N.Y. State Bar Assn., Columbia Law Sch. Alumni Assn. (dir.). Home: 60 Highridge Rd Hartsdale NY 10530-3605 Office: Stroock & Stroock & Lavan 7 Hanover Sq New York NY 10004-2616

LEVY, MARK IRVING, lawyer; b. Chgo., June 28, 1949; s. Kenneth Warren and Arleen (Langhaus) L.; m. Judith Jarrell Levy, Sept. 8, 1979; children: Elizabeth Sara, Mitchell Bennett. BA summa cum laude/hons. ex. distinction, Yale U., 1971, JD, 1975. Bar: D.C. 1976, U.S. Dist. Ct. D.C. 1977, U.S. Supreme Ct. 1980, Ill. 1986, U.S. Ct. Appeals (D.C. cir.) 1990, U.S. Ct. Appeals (6th, 7th and 8th cirs.) 1990, U.S. Tax Ct. 1990, U.S. Ct. Appeals (9th cir.) 1993, U.S. Ct. Appeals (2d, 4th and 10th cirs.) 1994. Law clk. Judge Gerhard A. Gesell, Washington, 1975-76; assoc. Covington & Burling, Washington, 1976-79, 81-83; asst. to solicitor gen. U.S. Dept. Justice, Washington, 1979-81, 83-86; ptnr. Mayer, Brown & Platt, Chgo., 1987-93; dep. asst. atty. gen. Civil Div. U.S. Dept. Justice, Washington, 1993—. Exec. editor Yale Law Jour., 1974-75. Recipient Israel H. Peres prize Yale Law Sch., 1975. Mem. Law Club of Chgo., Mich. Shores Club, Yale Law Sch. Alumni Assn. (former treas., exec. com. mem. 1987-90), Phi Beta Kappa. Home: 7609 Winterberry Pl Bethesda MD 20817 Office: US Dept Justice Civil Div Rm 3139 Tenth and Pennsylvania Ave Washington DC 20530

LEVY, MARK RAY, lawyer; b. Denver, Mar. 2, 1946; s. Richard C. and Hilde (Lindauer) L.; m. Patricia Loeb, June 13, 1971; children: Betsy, Robert. BA, U. Colo., 1968, JD, 1972. Bar: Colo. 1972, U.S. Dist. Ct. Colo. 1972. Assoc. Holland & Hart, Denver, 1972-78; ptnr. Holland & Hart, 1978—; adj. prof. the lawyering process U. Denver Law Sch., 1990-93. Author: (with others) Colorado Corporations Manual, 1987, Colorado Corporation Law and Practice, 1990. Trustee Congregation Emanuel, Denver, 1984-90, mem. legal com., 1989-93; chmn. Denver Alumni Phonathon U. Colo. Law Sch. 1989-90; mem. alumni bd. U. Colo. Law Sch., 1992—, chmn., 1994-95. Mem. ABA, Colo. Bar Assn. (mem. Blue Sky Law task force 1980-81, co-chmn. Colo. securities law rev. com. 1988-91), Denver Bar Assn., Am. Soc. Corp. Secs. Office: Holland and Hart Ste 3200 555 17th St Denver CO 80202

LEVY, MARVIN DANIEL, professional football coach, sports team executive; b. Chgo., Aug. 3, 1929. BA, Coe Coll., 1950; MA, Harvard U., 1951. High sch. coach St. Louis, 1951-52; asst. football coach Coe Coll., Cedar Rapids, Iowa, 1953-55; asst. coach, then head coach U. N.Mex., 1956-59; head coach U. Calif., Berkeley, 1960-63, Coll. William & Mary, Williamsburg, Va., 1964-68; asst. coach Phila. Eagles, NFL, 1969, Los Angeles Rams, NFL, 1970, Washington Redskins, NFL, 1971-72; head coach Montreal (Que., Can.) Alouettes, Can. Football League, 1973-77, Kansas City (Mo.) Chiefs, NFL, 1978-82, Chgo. Blitz, U.S. Football League, 1984, head coach Buffalo Bills, NFL, 1986—, v.p. 1995—. Office: Buffalo Bills 1 Bills Dr Orchard Park NY 14127-2237*

LEVY, MARVIN DAVID, composer; b. Passaic, N.J., Aug. 2, 1932; s. Benjamin and Bertha (Tramberg) L. BA, N.Y. U., 1954; M.A., Columbia U., 1956; pupil, Philip James, Otto Luening. Asst. dir. Am. Opera Soc., 1952-61; music critic Mus. Am. Herald Tribune, 1952-58; assoc. prof. of music Bklyn. Coll., 1974-76. Composer: orchestral Caramoor Festival Overture, 1958, Symphony, 1960, Kyros, 1961, One Person, 1962, Piano Concerto, 1970, Trialogus, 1972, In Memoriam: W.H. Auden, 1974, Canto de los Maranos, 1978, Pascua Florida, 1987, Arrows of Time, 1988; oratorios For The Time Being, 1959, Sacred Service, 1964, Masada (Nat. Symphony commn.); operas Mourning Becomes Electra (Met. Opera commn.), 1967, Escorial, 1958, Sotoba Komachi, 1957, The Tower, 1956; musical The Grand Balcony, 1990, 95; film theater scores; chamber music; artistic dir. Ft. Lauderdale Opera, 1989-94. Recipient Prix de Rome, 1962, 65, N.Y.C. Scroll award for Disting. and Exceptional Svc., 1967; Guggenheim grantee, 1960, 64, Ford Found. grantee, 1965, Damrosch grantee, 1961, NEA grantee, 1974, 78. Mem. ASCAP. Office: care Sheldon Soffer Mgmt 130 W 56th St New York NY 10019-3818*

LEVY, MICHAEL B., federal official; b. Balt., July 12, 1947; m. Bonny B. Wolf; 1 child. BA, Brown U., 1969; PhD, Rutgers U., 1979. Tchr. social studies, coach Loyola High Sch., Balt., Md., 1973-76; teaching asst. Rutgers U., New Brunswick, N.J., 1977-78, instr., 1978-84; asst. prof. Tex. A&M Univ., College Sta., 1978-84, assoc. prof. polit. sci., 1984-85; economist joint econ. com. U.S. Congress, Washington, 1985-87; adminstrv. asst. to Sen. Lloyd Bentsen U.S. Senate, Washington, 1987-93; asst. sec. legis. affairs U.S. Dept. Treasury, Washington, 1993—; adj. instr. Georgetown Univ., Washington, 1986-93. Editor: Political Thought in America, 1981, 87, (with Philip

Abbot) The Liberal Future in America: Essays in Renewal, 1985, (with Edward Portis) Handbook of Political Theory and Policy Sciences, 1989; contbr. articles to profl. jours. Bevier fellow Rutgers U., 1979; R.J. Reynolds fellow for So. High Sch. Tchrs. Office: Dept Treasury Legis Affairs Rm 3134 15th & Pennsylvania Ave NW Washington DC 20220

LEVY, MICHAEL RICHARD, publishing executive; b. Dallas, May 17, 1946; s. Harry Aaron and Florence (Friedman) L.; m. Rebecca Gloria Schulman, Jan. 19, 1969 (div. 1993); children: Anne Rachel, Tobin Janel and Mara Elizabeth (twins). BS, U. Pa., 1968; JD, U. Tex., 1972. Bar: Tex. 1972. Pres. Mediatex Communications Corp., Austin, Tex., 1972—; founder, pub. Tex. Monthly mag., 1973—. Mem. bd. visitors U. Tex. Sch. Law, M.D. Anderson Hosp.; bd. trustees Capital of Tex. Pub. Telecomms. Coun., Austin; trustee St. Stephen's Episc. Sch., Austin; mem. comty. adv. bd. Jr. League of Austin; mem. Austin EMS Quality Assurance Com. Named One of Outstanding Amss. under 40, Esquire mag., 1984; recipient Excellence in Media award Susan G. Komen Found., 1989, Disting. Alumnus award St. Mark's Sch. Tex., 1994. Mem. State Bar Tex., Mag. Pubs. Assn. Am. (bd. dirs.), Young Pres.' Orgn., Met. Club, Rockefeller Ctr. Club, Crescent Club, Westwood Country Club, Headliners Club. Home: PO Box 146 Austin TX 78767-0146 Office: Texas Monthly PO Box 1569 Austin TX 78767-1569

LEVY, NELSON LOUIS, physician, scientist, corporate executive; b. Somerville, N.J., June 19, 1941; s. Myron L. and Sylvia (Cohen) L.; m. Joanne Barnett, Dec. 21, 1963 (div. 1972); children: Scott, Erik, Jonathan; m. Louisa Douglas Stiles, Dec. 21, 1974; children: Michael, Andrew, David. BA/BS summa cum laude, Yale U., 1963; MD, Columbia U., 1967; PhD, Duke U., 1972. Diplomate Am. Bd. Allergy and Immunology. Intern, U. Colo. Med. Ctr., Denver, 1967-68; resident Duke U. Med Ctr., Durham, N.C., 1970-73; rsch. assoc. NIH, Bethesda, Md., 1968-70; asst. prof. immunology Duke U. Med. Ctr., 1972-75, assoc. prof. immunology and neurology, 1975-80, prof., 1980-81; dir. biol. rsch. Abbott Labs., Abbott Park, Ill., 1981, v.p. rsch., 1981-84; pres. Nelson L. Levy Assocs., Inc., 1984-87; chief exec. officer The CoreTechs Corp., Lake Forest, Ill., 1987-92; pres., Fujisawa Pharm., Deerfield, Ill., 1992-93; CEO Ill. Tech. Devel. Corp., 1993—; cons. Upjohn Co., Inc., Kalamazoo, 1976-77, G.D. Searle Inc., Skokie, Ill., 1984-87, Erbamont Inc., Stamford, Conn., 1984-90, Eastman Kodak, Rochester, N.Y., LyphoMed, Inc., Rosemont, Ill., 1985-89, The Nutrasweet Co., Skokie, Ill., 1985-88, Bayer AG, 1987-89, Fujisawa Pharm. Co., 1988-92, Alcide Corp., 1991—, Ameritech, 1993—, several venture cos.; bd. dirs. Intek Diagnostics, Inc., Helis, Inc., Bionica Pty, Ltd., Software Care Mgmt. Systems, Inc., Heybach Enterprises, Inc., Saniguard Products Corp., MedVac, Inc., Anthra Pharms., Inc., Myotech Corp., ChemBridge Corp. Editor several books; contbr. articles to profl. publs., chpts. to books. Coach Little League, Am. Youth Soccer Orgn.; bd. Family Svc. of South Lake County, 1991—. Surgeon USPHS, 1968-70. Grantee Am. Cancer Soc., 1970-75, NIH, 1971-81, Nat. Mult Sclerosis Soc., 1974-81, Ill. Dept. Commerce and Cmty. Affairs, 1993—. Mem. Am. Assn. Immunologists, Am. Assn. Cancer Rsch., Licensing Execs. Soc., Rotary, Phi Beta Kappa, Sigma Xi, Alpha Omega Alpha, Phi Gamma Delta. Avocations: triathlons, tennis, biking, sailing. Office: 1391 Concord Dr Lake Forest IL 60045

LEVY, NORMAN, motion picture company executive; b. Bronx, N.Y., Jan. 3, 1935; s. Irving and Helen (Saunders) L.; m. Hirsch, Nov. 11, 1962; children—Jordan, Brian, Matthew. BA, CCNY. Salesman Universal Pictures, 1957-67, Nat. Gen. Pictures, 1967-74; gen. sales mgr. Columbia Pictures, Burbank, Calif., 1974-75; exec. v.p. in charge domestic sales Columbia Pictures, 1975-77, exec. v.p. mktg. 1977-78, pres. domestic distbn., 1978-80, pres. Twentieth Century Fox Entertainment Group, 1980-81, vice chmn., 1981-85; mktg., distbn. cons., 1985—; chmn. New Century/Vista Film Co. L.A., 1985-91; chmn., chief exec. officer Domino Entertainment, L.A., 1991-92; pres., CEO Creative Film Enterprises, L.A., 1992—. Served with U.S. Army, 1955-57. Office: Creative Film Enterprises Ste 1201 1801 Avenue of the Stars Los Angeles CA 90067

LEVY, NORMAN S., psychiatrist, educator; b. N.Y.C., 1931; s. Barnett Theodore and Lena (Gulnick) L.; m. Lya Weiss (dec.); children: Karen, Susan, Joanne; m. Carol Lois Spiegel, 1 son, Robert Barnett. B.A. cum laude, NYU, 1952; M.D., SUNY. Diplomate: Am. Bd. Psychiatry and Neurology (examiner). Intern Maimonides Med. Center, Bklyn.; resident physician in medicine U. Pitts.-Presbyn. Hosp.; resident in psychiatry Kings County Hosp. Center, Bklyn.; instr. psychiatry State U. N.Y. Downstate Med. Center Coll. Medicine, Bklyn.; asst. prof. State U. N.Y. Downstate Med. Center Coll. Medicine, asso. prof., prof.; presiding officer faculty State U. N.Y. Downstate Med. Center Coll. Medicine (Medicine), assoc. dir. med-psychiat. liaison service; prof. psychiatry, medicine, surgery and coordinator psychiat. liaison services N.Y. Med. Coll.; dir. liaison psychiatry Westchester County Med. Center, mem. exec. com. of med. staff, 1981-85, 89-92; vis. prof. psychiatry and medicine So. Ill. U. Sch. Medicine; vis. prof. psychiatry John A. Burns Sch. Medicine, U. Hawaii, 1981; coordinator 1st Internat. Conf. Psychol. Factors in Hemodialysis and Transplantation, 1978, 2d-9th Internat. Confs. on Psychonephrology; cons. NIMH.; chief med. services USAF Hosp., Ashiya, Japan. Author: (with others), editor: Living or Dying: Adaptation to Hemodialysis, 1974, Psychonephrology I: Psychological Factors in Hemodialysis and Transplantation, 1981, Men in Transition: Theory and Therapy, 1982, Psychonephrology II: Psychological Problems in Kidney Failure and their Treatment, 1983; contbr. articles to jours., chpts. to textbooks in field.; assoc. editor: Gen. Hosp. Psychiatry, 1978-82, sect. editor, 1982—; sect. editor: Internat. Jour. Psychiatry in Medicine, 1977-78; mem. editorial bd., book rev. editor Jour. Dialysis and Transplantation, 1979—; mem. editorial bd. Resident and Staff Physician, 1981-91, Internat. Jour. Artificial Internal. Organs, 1983-93, Geriatric Nephrology and Urology, 1990—, Kidney: A Current Survey of World Literature, 1990—. Served to capt. M.C., USAF. Served to capt. M.C., USAF. Recipient Willaim A. Console Master Tchr. award, SUNY, Brooklyn, 1991; Thomas P. Hackett award Acad. Psychosomatic med., 1993. Fellow ACP, Am. Coll. Psychiatrists, Am. Psychiat. Assn. (pres. Kings County dist. br. 1981-82), Internat. Coll. Psychosomatic Medicine, Acad. Psychosomatic Medicine; mem. AAAS, Am. Psychosomatic Soc. (coun. 1994—), N.Y. Acad. Scis., Psychonephrology Found. (pres. 1978—), Assn. Acad. Psychiatry, Internat. Soc. Nephrology, Am. Soc. Nephrology, Am. Assn. Artificial Internal Organs, Soc. Liaison Psychiatry (bd. dirs. 1979-80, sec. 1980-81, pres. elect 1991-92, pres. 1992-94), Phi Beta Kappa, Sigma Xi. Home: 169 Westminster Rd Brooklyn NY 11218-3445 Office: NY Med Coll Dept Psychiatry Valhalla NY 10595

LEVY, NORMAN JAY, investment banker, financial consultant; b. N.Y.C., Aug. 14, 1942; s. Benjamin and Sophie (London) L.; m. Rene S. Cohen; children—Ellen, David. B.B.A., U. Cin., 1964; M.B.A., Columbia U., 1966. Assoc., v.p. Salomon Bros., N.Y.C., 1966-77, spl. ptnr., 1977-79, gen. ptnr., 1979-81; sr. v.p. Wertheim & Co., N.Y.C., 1982; mng. dir. L.F. Rothschild, Unterberg, Towbin, N.Y.C., 1983-84; private practice investment cons. Tenafly, N.J., 1985—. Mem. Securities Industry Assn. (com. on acctg. 1977-79). Home: 40 Mayflower Dr Tenafly NJ 07670-3130

LEVY, PETER, cinematographer. Cinematographer: (films) A Nightmare on Elm Street Part 5: The Dream Child, 1989, Dangerous Game, 1989, Predator 2, 1990, Ricochet, 1992, Judgment Night, 1993, Blown Away, 1994. Office: The Gersh Agency 232 N Canon Dr Beverly Hills CA 90210*

LEVY, RALPH, engineering executive, consultant; b. London, Apr. 12, 1932; came to U.S., 1967, naturalized, 1978; s. Alfred and Esther L.; m. Barbara Dent, Dec. 12, 1959; children: Sharon E., Mark S. B.A., Cambridge U., 1953, M.A., 1957; Ph.D., Queen Mary Coll. U. London, 1966. Mem. sci. staff GEC, Stanmore, Middlesex, Eng., 1953-59; mem. sci. staff Mullard Research Labs., Redhill, Eng., 1959-64; lectr. dept. elec. and electronic engring. U. Leeds, 1964-67; v.p. research Microwave Devel. Labs., Inc., Natick, Mass., 1967-84; v.p. engring. KW Engring., San Diego, 1984-88; v.p. research Remec Inc., San Diego 1988-89; R. Levy Assocs., 1989—. Author: (with J.O. Scanlan) Circuit Theory, 1970, 2d vol., 1973; contbr. articles in field. Fellow IEEE (editor Transactions on Microwave Theory and Techniques 1986-88); mem. Instn. Elec. Engrs. (London). Patentee in field. Office: 1897 Caminito Velasco La Jolla CA 92037-5725

LEVY, REYNOLD, communication company executive; b. Apr. 27, 1945. BA, Hobart Coll. 1966; MA, U. Va., 1968, PhD, 1973; JD, Columbia

U., 1973. Sr. staff officer gen. counsel's office N.Y.C. Health & Hosp. Corp., 1973-74; dir., exec. asst. Jewish Bd. Guardians, N.Y.C., 1974-75; asst. dir., Pluralism and the Commonwealth project The Aspen Inst. Humanistic Studies, N.Y.C., 1975; staff dir., task force on N.Y.C. crisis Community Council Greater N.Y., 1976-77; exec. dir. 92nd St. YMCA, N.Y.C., 1977-84; pres. AT&T Found., N.Y.C., 1984—; corp. v.p. AT&T, N.Y.C., 1986—; cons. Charles R. Bronfman Found., Montreal, Ont., Can., 1985, Nat. Jewish Welfare Bd., 1983, Corp. Contributions, Inc., Princeton, N.J., 1982-84; panelist Nat. Endowment Arts, Arts Ctrs. & Festivals Challenge, Washington, 1979-84. Author: Nearing The Crossroads: Contending Approaches to Contemporary Foreign Policy, 1975. Bd. dirs. Consortium for Advancement Higher Edn., 1984—, Mcpl. Arts Soc., 1985—, Independent Sector, 1985—, Am. Council Arts, 1986—; mem. fedn. Jewish philanthropies com. Public Programs and Policy, N.Y.C., 1977-81; mem. task force N.Y.C. crisis, 1977-81; mem. Mayor's task force on foster care services, N.Y.C., 1979; mem. United Way Corp. Assocs., N.Y.C., 1984-86. U. Chgo. full tuition fellow, 1966-67, DuPont grad. fellow, 1969-70, Woodrow Wilson dissertation fellow, 1969-70, New Sch. Soc. Research-Presdl. sr. fellow, 1987. Mem. Pi Gamma Mu (chpt. pres. 1965-66). Office: AT&T Foundation 1301 Ave of the Americas New York NY 10019

LEVY, RICHARD HERBERT, lawyer; b. Chgo., Sept. 15, 1943; s. Milton David and Sophie (Lippert) L.; children: Joshua, Rachel. BS, So. Ill. U., 1966; JD magna cum laude, DePaul U., 1976. Bar: Ill. 1976. Ptnr. Felwell, Galper & Lasky, Chgo., 1976, Rudnick & Wolfe, Chgo., 1983-88, Vedder, Price, Kaufman & Kammholz, Chgo., 1992—; counsel to exec. bd. Home Builders Chgo., Oak Brook, Ill., 1986—. Mem. ABA, Chgo. Vol. Lawyers Soc., Practising Law Inst. (real estate law adv. com.). Home: 1205 Wincanton Deerfield IL 60035 Office: Vedder Price Kaufman & Kammholz 222 N La Salle St Chicago IL 60601-1003

LEVY, RICHARD PHILIP, physician, educator; b. Hempstead, N.Y., Nov. 3, 1923; s. Edward I. and Elma (Nathan) L.; m. Barbara Quint, Sept. 15, 1945; children: Donald Martin, Ellen Susan, Charles Edward. B.S., Yale U., 1944, M.D., 1947. Intern, resident Univ. Hosps. of Cleve., 1947-53; faculty Case Western Res. Med. Sch., Cleve., 1953—, prof. medicine, 1977-78, clin. prof. medicine, 1978—, prof. internal medicine, 1978—, chmn. dept. internal medicine, 1983-89; prof. internal medicine endocrinology Coll. Medicine Northeastern Ohio U., Akron, Ohio, 1978—; svc. chief endocrinology St. Thomas Med. Ctr., Akron, 1985-92; med. editor Webster's New World Dictionary, 1970. Contbr. articles to profl. jours. Served with USNR, 1949-51. Fellow ACP; mem. Thyroid Assn., Endocrine Soc., Am. Diabetes Assn., Am. Coll. Clin. Endocrinology, Ohio Med. Assn., Summit County Med. Soc., Sigma Xi. Office: 444 N Main St Akron OH 44310-3110

LEVY, ROBERT EDWARD, biotechnology company executive; b. Cin., May 23, 1939; s. Aaron F. and Elizabeth W. (Hirsch) L.; m. Candace Ann Wolfe, June 20, 1970; children: Brian D., Jessica A. BChemE, Cornell U., 1962; PhDChemE, U. Calif. at Berkeley, 1967. Various positions, including mgr. synthetic fuels devel., rsch. and engring. Exxon Co., Florham Park, N.J., 1967-80, 84-86; mgr. tech. dept. Lago Oil & Transport Co., Esso Interam. div. Exxon Co., Aruba, Netherlands Antilles, 1980-84; v.p., dir. tech. devel. M.W. Kellogg Co., Houston, 1987-93; v.p. new bus. devel. Energy Biosystems Corp., The Woodlands, Tex., 1993—; cons. in field. Patentee in field. Indsl. mem. Comm. for Prevention of Shoreline Pollution by Oil, Aruba, 1982-84. Mem. AIChE (mem. long range planning com.), Indsl. Rsch. Inst. (mem. bd. editors 1992—), Sigma Xi (pres. Kellogg chpt. 1991-92). Avocations: tennis, jogging, sailing. Office: Energy Biosystems Corp 4200 Rsch Forest Dr The Woodlands TX 77381

LEVY, ROBERT ISAAC, physician, educator, research director; b. Bronx, N.Y., May 3, 1937; s. George Gerson and Sarah (Levinson) L.; m. Ellen Marie Feis, 1958; children: Andrew, Joanne, Karen, Patricia. B.A. with high honors and distinction, Cornell U., 1957; M.D. cum laude, Yale U., 1961. Intern, then asst. resident in medicine Yale-New Haven Med. Ctr., 1961-63; clin. assoc. molecular diseases Nat. Heart, Lung and Blood Inst., Bethesda, Md., 1963-66, chief resident, 1965-66, attending physician molecular disease br., 1965-80, head sect. lipoproteins, 1966-80, dep. clin. dir. inst., 1968-69, chief clin. services molecular diseases br., 1969-73, chief lipid metabolism br., 1970-74, dir. div. heart and vascular diseases, 1973-75, dir. inst., 1975-81; v.p. health scis., dean Sch. Medicine Tufts U., Boston, 1981-83, prof. medicine, 1981-83; v.p. health scis. Columbia U., N.Y.C., 1983-84, prof., 1983-88, sr. asst. v.p. health scis., 1985-87; pres. Sandoz Research Inst., East Hanover, N.J., 1988-92; pres. Wyeth-Ayerst Rsch. Wyeth-Ayerst Labs div. Am. Home Products, Phila., 1992—; attending physician Georgetown U. med. div. D.C. Gen. Hosp., 1966-68; spl. cons. anti-lipid drugs FDA. Editor: Jour. Lipid Rsch., 1972-80, Circulation, 1974-76, Am. Heart Jour., 1980-90; contbr. articles to profl. jours. Served as surgeon USPHS, 1963-66. Recipient Kees Thesis prize Yale U., 1961; Arthur S. Flemming award, 1975; Superior Service award HEW, 1975; Rsch. award and Van Slyke award Am. Soc. Clin. Chemists, 1980; Roger J. Williams award, 1985; award Humana Heart Found., 1988. Mem. Am. Heart Assn. (mem.-at-large exec. com. council basic sci., mem. exec. council on atherosclerosis), Am. Inst. Nutrition, Am. Fedn. Clin. Research, N.Y. Acad. Scis., Am. Soc. Clin. Nutrition, Am. Soc. Clin. Investigation, Am. Coll. Cardiology, Inst. Medicine of Nat. Acad. Scis., Am. Soc. Clin. Pharmacology and Therapeutics, Assn. Am. Physicians, Phi Beta Kappa, Sigma Xi, Alpha Omega Alpha, Alpha Epsilon Delta, Phi Kappa Phi. Office: Wyeth-Ayerst Rsch PO Box 8299 Philadelphia PA 19101-0082

LEVY, ROBERT JOSEPH, lawyer, educator; b. Phila., June 27, 1931; m. Roberta Kaplan; children: Valerie R. Levy Rennert, Jonathan B., Joshua M. B.A., Kenyon Coll., 1952; J.D., U. Pa., 1957. Bar: D.C. bar 1957, Minn. bar 1966. Trial atty. Dept. Justice, Washington, 1957-59; prof. law U. Minn., Mpls., 1959-89, Dorsey & Whitney prof. law, 1989—; Ida Beam prof. law U. Iowa, 1978; fellow Center Advanced Study in the Behavioral Scis., 1967-68. Author: (with Caleb Foote and Frank Sander) Cases and Materials on Family Law, 1966, rev. edit., 1976, 3d. edit., 1985, (with Thomas Lewis and Peter Martin) Cases on Social Welfare and the Individual, 1970, (with Caleb Foote) Cases and Materials on the Criminal Justice Process, 1981. Office: U Minn Sch Law Minneapolis MN 55422

LEVY, ROCHELLE FELDMAN, artist; b. N.Y.C., Aug. 4, 1937; d. S. Harry and Eva (Krause) Feldman; m. Robert Paley Levy, June 4, 1955; children: Kathryn Tracey, Wendy Paige, Robert Paley, Angela Brooke, Michael Tyler. Student Barnard Coll., 1954-55, U. Pa., 1955-56; BFA, Moore Coll. Art, 1979. Mgmt. cons. Woodlyne Sch., Rosemont, Pa., 1983-84; sr. ptnr. DRT Interiors, Phila., 1983—; ptnr. Phila. Phillies, 1981-94. One-woman shows: Watson Gallery, Wheaton Coll., Norton, Mass., 1977, U. Pa., 1977, Med. Coll. Pa., Phila., 1982, Aqueduct Race Track, Long Island, N.Y., 1982, 68, Phila. Art Alliance, 1983, Moore Coll. Art, Phila., 1984, Phila. Art Alliance, 1994. Pres., League of Children's Hosp., Phila., 1969-70; chmn. bd. trustees Moore Coll. Art, 1988—; bd. overseers Ctr. for Judaic Studies U. Pa., 1993—. Recipient G. Allen Smith Prize, Woodmere Art Gallery, Chestnut Hill, Pa., 1979; Woman honoree Samuel Paley Day Care Ctr., Phila., 1990, Jefferson Bank Declaration award, 1991, Nat. Philanthropy honoree The Nat. Soc. of Fund Raising Execs. Greater Phila. chpt., 1994. Trustee Moore Coll. Art, 1988—, chmn. bd. trustee, 1990—; mem. selections and acquisitions com. Pa. Acad. Fine Arts, 1979—; bd. mgrs., 1975—, chmn. exec. com., 1982—, bd. trustee, 1990—. Mem. Allied Artists Am., Artist's Equity, Phila. Art Alliance, Phila. Print Club. Office: 2 Logan Sq Ste 2525 Philadelphia PA 19103

LEVY, RONALD, medical educator, researcher; b. Carmel, Calif., B.S. Harvard U.; M.D. Stanford U., 1968. Diplomate Am. Bd. Internal Medicine. Intern Mass. Gen. Hosp., Boston, 1968-69; researcher Mass. Gen. Hosp., 1969-70; Helen Hay Whitney Found. fellow in dept. chem. immunology Weizmann Inst. Sci., Rehovot, Israel, 1973-75; mem. faculty Stanford U., Calif., 1975—, now assoc. prof. dept. medicine-oncology. Co-recipient (with G. Telford) 1st award for cancer research Armand Hammer Found. Mem. ACP, Am. Soc. Clin. Oncology. Office: Stanford U Dept Medicine-Oncology 300 Pasteur Dr Stanford CA 94305

LEVY, S. WILLIAM, dermatologist; b. San Francisco, Sept. 28, 1920; s. Joseph and Dora (Taylor) L.; m. Elisabeth Rachlin, Mar. 17, 1974; children: David Lewis, Ann Louise. BS, U. Calif., San Francisco, 1943, MD, 1949.

Practice medicine specializing in dermatology San Francisco; research dermatologist Biomechanics Lab., U. Calif., San Francisco; mem. staff Children's Hosp., Mt. Zion Hosp. and Med. Center; cons. to Letterman Army Hosp.; central med. adv. Calif. Blue Shield, San Francisco; clin. prof. dermatology U. Calif.; cons. in field. Author: Skin Problems of the Amputee, 1983; co-author: The Skin in Diabetes, 1986, Dermatology, 3rd edit., 1992, Dermatology in General Medicine, 4th edit., 1993, Atlas of Limb Prosthetics, 2d edit., 1992, Cutis, 1995. Served with USN, 1943-46. Recipient Lehn and Fink Gold Medal award. Fellow Am. Acad. Dermatology (Gold medal); mem. San Francisco Dermatol. Soc. (pres.), Pacific Dermatologic Assn. (v.p.), AMA, Calif. Med. Assn. (sci. council 1977-84), San Francisco Med. Soc. Office: Ste 203 599 Sir Francis Drake Blvd Greenbrae CA 94904

LEVY, SALOMON, mechanical engineer; b. Jerusalem, Apr. 4, 1926; came to U.S., 1945; s. Abraham Isaac and Sultana Claire (Elyachar) L.; m. Eileen Dolores Jaques, Oct. 14, 1951; children: Marshall Douglas, Linda C. BSME, U. Calif., Berkeley, 1949, MME, 1951, PhD in Mech. Engring., 1953. Engr. Gen. Electric Co., Schenectady, N.Y. and San Jose, Calif., 1953-59; mgr. heat transfer Gen. Electric Co., San Jose, 1959-66, mgr. systems engring., 1966-68, mgr. design engring., 1968-71, gen. mgr., 1971-75, gen. mgr. boiling water reactor ops., 1975-77; chmn. S. Levy Inc., Campbell, Calif., 1977—; adj. prof. UCLA, 1986-87; Springer prof. U. Calif., Berkeley, 1979-80; bd. dirs. IES Industries, Inc., Cedar Rapids. Patentee in field. Fellow ASME (chmn. heat transfer divsn. 1964-65, heat transfer meml. award 1966, heat transfer conf. award 1963, 50th Ann. Heat Transfer Divsn. award 1988), Am. Nuclear Soc. (chmn. thermal hydraulics divsn. 1985-86, Thermal Hydraulics Divsn. Achievement award 1987, Power Divsn. Walter H. Zinn award 1989); mem. NAE, AIChE (Donald Kern award 1993), Inst. Nuclear Power Ops. (adv. coun.). Democrat. Mem. Unitarian Ch. Avocations: racquetball, golf. Home: 1829 Dry Creek Rd San Jose CA 95124-1002 Office: Levy and Assocs Ste 112 3880 S Bascom Ave San Jose CA 95124

LEVY, SAM, consumer products company executive. Pres. Schwegmann Giant Super Markets, New Orleans, La., 1962—. Office: Schwegmann Giant Super Markets 5300 Gentilly Rd New Orleans LA 70126

LEVY, SAM MALCOLM, advertising executive; b. Henderson, Ky., Nov. 26, 1901; s. Mike Meyer and Hattie Belle (Wile) L.; m. Isabel Helen Cone, Apr. 22, 1929; 1 child, Sue Levy Klau. Student, U. Mo., 1919-21; PhB, U. Chgo., 1921-23; postgrad., Harvard Coll., 1926. Exec. McCann Erickson, N.Y.C., 1923-30; adv. dir. News & Record, Greensborough, N.C., 1930-31; v.p. dir. Keelor & Stites, Cin., 1931-46; lectr. speech U. Cin., 1940-44; pres. Assoc. Adv. Agy., Cin., 1946-71; sr. v.p. Sive Inc. - A Div. Young & Rubicam, 1971-89; ret. Sive Inc.-A Div. Young & Rubicam, 1989; life trustee Clean Cin. Inc., bd. gov. Big Bros. Assn., Glen Manor-Home For Aged, 1963—; instr. adv. speech evening coll. U. Cin., 1945-48. Editor: Sociony Monthly Mag., 1925-27. Active Friend of Serengeti Aftrica; mem. Cin. Art Mus. Named to Hon. Order of Ky. Cols., 1984; donated Glass Gallery to Cin. Art Mus., 1980, Floral Clock to Cin. Park Bd., 1988; recipient Key to the City of Cin., 1988, Emerald award, 1993. Mem. Advts. Club Cin., Black Friars Club Chgo., Bankers Club, Losanti Ville Country Club Cin., Founders Soc., Cin. Symphony Orch., Thomas Schippers Soc., Zeta Beta Tau (pres., grad club). Republican. Home: 2444 Madison Rd Cincinnati OH 45208-1256

LEVY, STANLEY HERBERT, lawyer; b. Phila., Apr. 11, 1922; s. Max and Rose (Cohen) L.; m. Gloria Kamber, Dec. 20, 1953; children: Steven M., Peter B. B.A., Cornell U., 1943; LL.B., Harvard U., 1949, J.D., 1968. Bar: N.Y. 1949, U.S. Dist. Ct. (ea. and so. dists.) N.Y., U.S. Treasury 1949, U.S. Supreme Ct. 1949. Practiced in N.Y.C., 1949—. Mem. Republican Town Com., Scarsdale, 1963-65, Temple Emanu-el, Westchester, N.Y. Served to 1st lt. F.A., AUS, 1943-47. Mem. Assn. Bar City N.Y., Confrérie des Chevaliers du Tastevin (officier commandeur), Commanderie de Boreaux (comdr.), Harvard Club, Yale Club, Century Country Club (Purchase, N.Y.), Westchester Flying Club (White Plains, N.Y.), Mashomack Fish and Game Preserve (Pine Plains, N.Y.). Home: 3 Richbell Rd Scarsdale NY 10583-4421 Office: 521 5th Ave New York NY 10175-0001

LEVY, STEPHEN RAYMOND, diversified high technology company executive; b. Everett, Mass., May 4, 1940; s. Robert George and Lillian (Berfield) L.; m. Sandra Helen Rosen, Aug. 26, 1961; children: Phillip, Susan. B.B.A., U. Mass., 1961. Chmn., dir. Bolt Beranek and Newman Inc., Cambridge, Mass.; mem. policy adv. com. on trade U.S. Dept. Def. Mem. Fov.'s coun. Econ. Growth and Tech. (chmn. com. telecomms. devel.); bd. dir.s Mass. Telecomms. Coun., Mass. High Teh. Coun.; bd. overseer Boston Symphony Orch. Served with AUS, 1963-66. Decorated Army Commendation medal. Mem. Am. Bus. Conf., Am. Electronics Assn. (chmn. 1986), Mass. High Tech. Coun. (chmn. 1987-89). Home: 300 Boylston St Apt 1204 Boston MA 02116-3923 Office: Bolt Beranek & Newman Inc 150 Cambridge Park Dr Cambridge MA 02140

LEVY, SY, advertising and direct marketing executive; b. Bklyn., Apr. 24, 1929; s. Benjamin and Hattie (Imerman) L.; m. Suzanne Newman, Feb. 2, 1949; children: Jeffrey, Benjamin, Honor. Student, NYU, 1947-50. Freelance radio writer N.Y.C., 1948-54; research asst. Buchanan Advt., N.Y.C., 1954-55; advt. dir. Hudson Pulp & Paper Corp., N.Y.C., 1955-59; v.p. Beekman, Ciangio & Packard Advt., N.Y.C., 1959-60, Blackstone Advt., N.Y.C., 1960-78; chmn. bd. March Direct Mktg., N.Y.C., 1978-80; chmn. bd., exec. v.p. McCann Erikson Direct div. Inter Pub. Group Cos., 1980-83; pres. Rosenfeld Sirowitz & Lawson, Direct, 1983-85; exec. v.p. Rosenfeld, Sirowitz & Lawson, 1983-85; owner Sy Levy Direct Mktg. Cons., Housatonic, Mass., 1985—; pres. Bumper Crop, Inc., 1991—. Contbr. chpts. to books in field. Bd. dirs. Louise Wise Services, N.Y.C., 1970-80. Mem. Direct Mktg. Assn. (chmn. Direct Mktg. Day in N.Y. 1978, vice chmn. mktg. council 1980-82, chmn. 1982-84), League Advt. Agys. (v.p. 1975-80). Jewish. Home and Office: 2 Samantha Ln Housatonic MA 01236-9710

LEVY, WALTER JAMES, oil consultant; b. Hamburg, Germany, Mar. 21, 1911; s. Moses and Bertha (Lindenberger) L.; m. Augusta Sondheimer, Apr. 11, 1942 (dec.); children: Robert Alan (dec.), Susan Clementine. Student, U. Heidelberg, 1929-30, U. Berlin, 1930-31, U. Kiel, 1931-32. Asst. to editor Petroleum Press Bur., London, Eng., 1936-41; free lance economist N.Y.C., 1941-42; chief petroleum sect. OSS, Washington, 1942-45; asst. office intelligence research Dept. State, 1945-48, cons., also Pres. com. fgn. aid, 1948; chief oil br. ECA, 1948-49, cons., 1949-51; econ. cons., 1949—, NSRB, 1950; pres. Materials Policy Commn., 1951; cons. policy planning staff Dept. State, 1952-53, ICA, 1956-57; cons. office Under Sec. and Asst. Secs., 1960-80, Office Civil and Def. Moblzn., 1960, European Econ. Community, 1970; fgn. econ. adviser Socony-Vacuum Oil Co., 1948; adviser to Mr. Harriman on mission to Iran, 1951; Petroleum adviser U.S. del. Council Fgn. Ministers meeting, 1947; mem. U.S. del. of Austrian Treaty Commn., 1947, State Dept. del. for oil discussions with U.K., 1946, U.S. del. trade discussion with Sweden, 1945, U.S. world programming group on petroleum, 1945; mem. enemy oil com. Joint Chiefs Staff, 1943-45; oil adviser to spl. emissary of Pres. Kennedy to Pres. of Indonesia, 1963; Mem. adv. council to Sch. Advanced Internat. Studies Johns Hopkins U. Author (Oil Strategy and Politics, 1941-81 1982); Contbr. articles to profl. publs. Recipient spl. plaque in grateful appreciation for invaluable contbr. to welfare U.S., Sec. State, 1968; decorated Dato Setia haila Jasa Sultan Brunei, 1968; Order of Taj Iran, 1969; hon. companion Order St. Michael and St. George, Eng.; insignia of comdr.'s cross Order of Merit Fed. Republic of Ger., 1979; President's certificate of merit. Mem. Council on Fgn. Relations. Home: 300 Central Park W New York NY 10024-1513

LEVY, WALTER KAHN, management consultant executive; s. Benn Barnet and Beatrice (Kahn) L.; m. Anita von Bachelle, July 23, 1955; children: Gregg W., Evonne A. BA, Washington & Jefferson Coll., 1952; MS in Retail, NYU, 1966. Cert. mgmt. cons. Mgmt. trainee Burlington Mills, N.Y.C., 1952; buyer, merchandiser Bloomindale Bros., N.Y.C., 1953-65; cons. Cresap, McCormack & Padget, N.Y.C., 1965-68; v.p. ops. Bonwit Teller, N.Y.C., 1968-71; cons., chmn. Walter K. Levy & Robert E. Kerson Assocs., Inc., N.Y.C., 1971—. Trustee Washington & Jefferson Coll., Washington, Pa., 1980—; bd. dirs. Sch. Bd. Selection Com., Larchmont, N.Y., 1973-76. Sgt. USAR, 1954-62. Mem. Japan Soc., Larchmont Yacht

Club. Avocations: history, reading, travel, tennis. Home: 35 Ellsworth Rd Larchmont NY 10538 Office: Walter K Levy & Robert E Kerson Assocs Inc 633 3d Ave New York NY 10017

LEW, GINGER, lawyer; b. San Mateo, Calif., Nov. 3, 1948; d. Bing and Suey Bow (Ng) L.; m. Carl Lennart Ehn, Feb. 2, 1984; children: Melissa, Jeremy. BS, UCLA, 1970; JD, U. Calif.-Berkeley, 1974. Bar: Calif. 1974, D.C. 1980. Dep. city atty. City of Los Angeles, 1974-75; asst. regional counsel Dept. Energy, San Francisco, 1975-77, dep. regional counsel, 1977-78, chief counsel, 1978-80; dep. asst. sec. of state for East Asia, Dept. of State, Washington, 1980-81, spl. adviser, 1981-82; ptnr. Stovall, Spradlin, Armstrong & Israel, Washington, 1983-86, Arthur Young Co., Washington, 1986-93; gen. counsel U.S. Dept. Commerce, Washington, 1993—. Recipient Outstanding Achievement award Dept. of State, 1980, Meritorious Svc. award, 1981. Mem. ABA, Asian Pacific Am. Bar Assn. (bd. dirs. 1981-83), Women's Bar Assn., Orgn. of Chinese-Americans, Pi Sigma Alpha. Clubs: Commonwealth (San Francisco); Nat. Lawyers. Office: US Dept Commerce Office Gen Counsel 14th & Constitution Ave NW Washington DC 20230

LEW, ROGER ALAN, manufacturing company executive; b. N.Y.C., Mar. 16, 1941; s. Louis Arthur and Estelle Bebe (Marcus) L.; m. Marilyn Drourr, May 29, 1962; children—William, Jeffrey, Richard. B.S. in Fin, NYU, 1963. With Franklin Nat. Bank, N.Y.C., 1963-66; sr. v.p. Security Nat. Bank, N.Y.C., 1966-75; v.p. NVF Co., N.Y.C., 1975-78; sr. v.p. NVF Co., 1978-81, treas., 1979-81; pres., bd. dirs. Wormuth Bros. Foundry, Inc., Athens, N.Y., 1981—; pres., bd. dirs. Mirage Fin., Inc., 1985—, transmission Gear Sales, Inc., 1985—, Hudson Valley Buyers, Inc., 1985—; former sr. v.p., treas. Sharon Steel Corp., Pa. Engring. Corp., DWG Co., Southeastern Pub. Svc. Co.; former sr. v.p., treas., bd. dirs. Wilson Bros.; former mem. small bus. and agr. adv. coun. to N.Y. Fed. Res. Bank. Trustee, former exec. v.p. Universal Housing & Devel. Co.; former v.p. Security Mgmt. Corp. Served with U.S. Army, 1959-60. Mem. Am. Iron and Steel Inst. Clubs: Colonie Country (Voorhees, N.Y.); Sag Harbor (N.Y.) Yacht. Office: Howard Hall Rd RR 1 Athens NY 12015

LEW, RONALD S. W., federal judge; b. L.A., 1941; m. Mamie Wong; 4 children. BA in Polit. Sci., Loyola U., L.A., 1964; JD, Southwestern U., 1971. Bar: Calif. 1972. Dep. city atty. L.A. City Atty's. Office, 1972-74; ptnr. Avans & Lew, L.A., 1974-82; commr. fire and police pension City of L.A., 1976-82; mcpl. ct. judge County of L.A., 1982-84, superior ct. judge, 1984-87; judge U.S. Dist. Ct. (cen. dist.) Calif., L.A., 1987—; Bar: Calif. 1971. Mem. World Affairs Council of L.A., 1976—, Christian Businessmen's Com. of L.A., 1982—. 1st lt. U.S. Army, 1967-69. Recipient Vol. award United Way of L.A., 1979, cert. of merit L.A. Human Relations Commn., 1977, 82. Mem. Am. Judicature Soc., Calif. Assn. of Judges, So. Calif. Chinese Lawyer's Assn. (charter mem. 1976, pres. 1979), Chinese Am. Citizens Alliance, San Fernando Valley Chinese Cultural Assn., Delta Theta Phi. Office: US Dist Ct 312 N Spring St Los Angeles CA 90012-4701

LEWANDOWSKI, THEODORE CHARLES, psychology educator; b. Phila., Apr. 26, 1945; s. Theodore A. and Teresa M. Lewandowski; m. Regina F. Blake, Sept. 21, 1968; children: Michael T., Joan T. BA, Villanova U., 1967, MS, 1969; CAGS, Temple U., 1979. Lic. psychologist, Pa. Lectr. Villanova (Pa.) U., 1974-79; prof. Delaware County Coll., Media, Pa., 1969—; lectr. Thomas Jefferson U., Phila., 1981—; credential evaluator Pa. State Bd. Psychology, Harrisburg, 1987—, vice-chairperson, 1980-86; mem. Pa. Drug, Device and Cosmetic Bd., Harrisburg, 1987-92. Author: Abnormal Psychology Case Interviews, 1971; co-author: Instructor's Manual to accompany Understanding Abnormal Behavior, 1971. Emergency coord. for Ea. Pa. Am. Radio Relay League, Newington, Conn., 1989-92. Mem. APA (state liaison 1970-72), Am. Ednl. Rsch. Assn., Ea. Psychol. Assn., Pa. Psychol. Assn. (standards com. 1973-74), Pa. Ednl. Rsch. Assn. Office: Delaware County College 901 S Media Line Rd Media PA 19063-1094

LEWARK, CAROL ANN, special education educator; b. Fort Wayne, Ind., Mar. 8, 1935; d. Lloyd L. and Elizabeth J. (Arthur) Meads; m. Paul N. Lewark, Aug. 20, 1955; children: David P., Laura, Beth, Daniel A. BA, St. mary of Woods, 1978; MS, Ind. U., 1981. Cert. elem. educator, spl. educator mentally retarded K-12, learning disabilities K-12, Ind.; cert. home tng. specialist, Wis. Home tng. specialist Madison Wis. ARC, Madison, 1968-70; nursery sch. cons. Allen County ARC, Ft. Wayne, Ind., 1971-73; early childhood spl. edn. dir. Allen County ARC, Ft. Wayne, 1973—; cons. in field; presenter in field; apptd. by Ind. Gov. to State Interagy. Coordinating Coun. for Infants and Toddlers, 1992-95; apptd. to Higher Ed Coun. for Early Childhood and Spl. Edn. Contbr. articles to profl. jours. Apptd. to Leadership Ft. Wayne, 1994. Named Model Project Site 99-457 Early Intervention Ind. State Dept. Mental Health, 1987; Tech. Assistance grantee Georgetown U., 1991-93. Mem. Ind. Coun. for Exceptional Children (sec. 1990-94), First Steps of Allen County (facilitator 1989—), Leadership Fort Wayne. Avocations: painting, music, needle work, travel. Home: 910 Kensington Blvd Fort Wayne IN 46805-5312 Office: ARC of Allen County 2542 Thompson Ave Fort Wayne IN 46807-1099

LEWCOCK, RONALD BENTLEY, architect, educator; b. Brisbane, Australia, Sept. 27, 1929; s. Harry Kingsley and Ena (Orrock) L.; m. Barbara Sansoni, Aug. 8, 1981. Student, U. Queensland, 1947-49; BArch, Capetown U., South Africa, 1951; PhD, U. Cape Town, South Africa, 1961; MA, Cambridge U., Eng., 1970; Eliza Brown vis. fellowship, Columbia U., 1963. Pvt. practice architecture, 1951—; Whitehead research fellow Clare Hall, Cambridge U., Eng., 1970-72, offl. fellow, 1976-84; research officer Middle East Centre, Cambridge, 1973-80; Aga Khan prof. architecture for Islamic culture, dir. program in architecture for Islamic socs. MIT, Cambridge, 1984-91; chmn. Aga Khan program for Islamic architecture MIT and Harvard U., 1985-87; prof. architecture Ga. Inst. Tech., Atlanta, 1991—; cons. UNESCO, Habitat, World Bank, British Coun., Am. Rsch. Cen., Egypt, 1976—; lectr. U. Natal, 1952-57, sr. lectr., 1958-69; lectr., examiner Cambridge U., 1973-85; unit leader design in developing world Archtl. Assn., London, 1977-81; lectr. Archtl. Assocs. Sch., London, 1971-82; vis. prof. grad. sch. architecture Ga. Inst. Tech., 1979-84, Harvard, 1984, Louvain U., 1984; vis. Aga Khan prof., MIT, 1991-93. Author: Early 19th Century Architecture in South Africa, 1963, Traditional Architecture in Kuwait and the Northern Gulf, 1978, 2d edit. 81, Wadi Hadramawt and the Walled City of Shibam, 1986, The Old World City of San'a', 1986; editor: (with R.B. Serjeant) San'a' an Arabian Islamic City, 1983; contbr. articles to profl. jours., Architecture in the Islamic World, 1976, New Grove Dictionary of Music and Musicians, 1980. Mem. coun. Inst. History and Archaeology East Africa, London, 1976-86, Middle East Centre, Cambridge, Eng., 1981-88, British Sch. Archaeology in Jerusalem, London, 1981—; tech. coord. Internat. Campaign for the Conservation of Sana's in Yemen Arab Rep. and Shibam and Wadi Hadramant in Peoples Dem. Rep. of Yemen, 1978—, UNESCO/UNDP Campaign for Conservation of Monuments and Cities in Uzbekistan, 1994—; steering com. mem. Aga Khan award, 1990-93, Aga Khan Trust for Culture, Geneva, 1993—. Mem. Royal Inst. British Architects (assoc.). Avocations: reading, writing, music, sailing. Office: Georgia Institute of Technology Atlanta GA 30332

LEWELL, PETER A., international technology executive, researcher; b. St. John, N.B., Can.. Exec. dir. N.B. Rsch. and Productivity Coun., Fredericton, N.B., Can.; bd. dirs. Brunswick Ltd., N.B. Mfg. Tech. Ctr., Ctr. Nuclear Energy Rsch. Office: NB Rsch & Productivity Coun, 921 ch College Hill Rd, Fredericton, NB Canada E3B 6Z9

LEWELLEN, WILBUR GARRETT, management educator, consultant; b. Charleroi, Pa., Jan. 21, 1938; s. Anthony Garrett and Cozie Harriett (Watson) L.; m. Jean Carolyn Vanderlip, Dec. 8, 1962 (div. 1982); children—Stephen G., Jocelyn A., Jonathan W., Robyn E.; m. Eloise Evelyn Vincent, Mar. 5, 1983. B.S., Pa. State U., University Park, 1959; M.S., MIT, Cambridge, 1961, Ph.D. 1967. Asst. prof. mgmt. Purdue U., West Lafayette, Ind., 1964-68, assoc. prof. mgmt., 1968-72, prof., 1972-83, Loeb prof. mgmt., 1983-88; Krannert disting. prof. mgmt. Purdue U., 1988—; dir. exec. edn. programs Purdue U., West Lafayette, Ind., 1985—; cons. Bank Am., San Francisco, 1975—, Ind. Bell tel. Co., Indpls., 1976—, Am. Water Works Co., Wilmington, Del., 1978—, Indpls. Power and Light Co., 1993—; bd. dirs. USF & G Corp. Author: Executive Compensation in Large Industrial Corporations, 1968, Ownership Income of Management, 1971, The Cost of Capital, 1981. Recipient Salgo-Noren award as Outstanding Tchr. in

Grad. Profl. Programs, Salgo-Noren Found., 1973, 77, 79, 84. Mem. Fin. Mgmt. Assn. (v.p. 1973-74), Am. Fin. Assn., Strategic Mgmt. Soc., AAUP, Western Fin. Assn., Lafayette Country Club, Ford's Colony Country Club. Methodist. Home: 3809 W Capilano Dr West Lafayette IN 47906-8881 Office: Purdue Univ Grad Sch Mgmt West Lafayette IN 47907

LEWENT, JUDY C., pharmaceutical executive; b. Jan. 13, 1949. BA, Goucher Coll., 1970; MS in Mgmt., MIT, 1972. With corp. fin. dept. E.F. Hutton & Co., Inc., 1972-74; asst. v.p. for strategic planning Bankers Trust Co., 1974-75; sr. fin. analyst corp. planning Norton Simon, 1975-76; div. contr. Pfizer, Inc., 1976-80; dir. acquisitions and capital analysis Merck & Co., 1980-83; asst. contr. Merck & Co., Inc., Whitehouse Station, N.J., 1983-85; exec. dir. fin. evaluation and analysis, 1985-87; v.p., treas. Merck & Co., Inc., Whitehouse Station, N.J., 1987-90, v.p. fin., CFO, 1990-92, sr. v.p., CFO, 1993—. Office: Merck & Co Inc PO Box 100 One Merck Dr Whitehouse Station NJ 08889-0100

LEWIN, ANN WHITE, museum director, educator; b. Boston, Dec. 19, 1939; d. Albert and Florence (Levy) White; m. Lawrence S. Lewin, June 5, 1960 (div. July 1978); 1 child, Daniel. AB, Bryn Mawr Coll., 1960. Tchr., adminstr. Montessori Sch., Annandale, Va., 1965-69; staff devel. Nat. Child Research Ctr., Washington, 1969-70; acting dir. Community Learning Ctr., Washington, 1970-71; founder, adminstr. Parkmont Sch., Washington, 1970-75; exec. dir., founder Capital Children's Mus., Washington, 1975-95; founder, pres. The Nat. Learning Ctr., Wasington, 1983-95; cons. Arlington County Pub. Schs., Va., 1970-75, Edufax, Washington, 1969-70, George Washington U., Washington, 1970-71. Contbr. articles to profl. jours. Named Washingtonian of Yr., Washingtonian mag., 1979. Mem. Am. Assn. Mus., Cultural Alliance, Assn. Sci. and Tech. Ctrs. (bd. dirs. 1982), Nat. Assn. Edn. Young Children, Assn. Childhood Edn. Internat. Home: 1577 Cherry Park Dr Memphis TN 38120

LEWIN, DAVID, management educator; b. Nov. 9, 1943. BS in Acctg., Calif. State U., L.A., 1965; MBA, UCLA, 1967, PhD in Bus. Adminstrn., 1971. Staff acct. Alexander Grant & Co., L.A., 1965-66; assoc. in bus. Columbia U., N.Y.C., 1970-71, asst. prof., 1971-74, assoc. prof., 1974-80, prof., 1980-90; prof. mgmt. UCLA, 1990—, dir. Insl. Indsl. Rels., 1990—, vice dean, faculty dir. MBA program Anderson Grad. Sch. Mgmt.; vis. prof. UCLA, 1988; mem. adv. coun. N.Y. State Sch. Indsl. and Labor Rels. Cornell U., 1987-91; active U.S. Dept. Labor Com on Labor-Mgmt. Cooperation, 1988—, Econ. Policy Coun. Com. on Labor-Mgmt. Cooperation, 1989—; mediator, factfinder labor disputes N.Y. State, 1977-90; participant IBM Human Resources Forum, Armonk, N.Y., 1993; cons. U.S. Dept. Labor, State of Ill., County of L.A., City of L.A., U.S. Office Personnel Mgmt., N.Y. State Gov. Office Employee Rels., U. Calif., numerous others; prin. investigator, co-investigator numerous grants; attendee numerous confs. on human resources and cmty. rels.; lectr. in field. Author (with others): The Urban Labor Market: Institutions, Information, Linkages, 1974, Collective Bargaining and Manpower Utilization in Big City Governments, 1979, The Labor Sector, 1980, Advances in Industrial and Labor Relations, vol. 3, 1986, vol. 4, 1987, vol. 5, 1991, vol. 6, 1994, Public Sector Labor Relations: Analysis and Readings, 1988, The Modern Grievance Procedure in the United States, 1988 (Outstanding Book in Indsl. Rels., Princeton U. 1988), Research Frontiers in Industrial Relations and Human Resources, 1992 (Outstanding Book in Indsl. Rels., Princeton U. 1993), International Perspectives and Challenges in Human Resource Management, 1994, Human Resource Management: An Economic Approach, 1994; author chpts. to books; co-editor Advances in Indsl. and Labor Rels., 1986—; mem. editl. bd. Indsl. Rels., 1988-92, 94—, Calif. Mgmt. Rev., 1990—; referee numerous profl. jours.; contbr. articles to profl. jours. Ford Found. grantee, 1982. Mem. AAAS, Am. Econ. Assn., Indsl. Rels. Rsch. Assn. (chmn. subcom. on rels. with other scholarly and profl. orgns. 1985-89, mem. program com. 1986-88, mem. exec. bd. 1987-90, mem. task force on programs and ann. and semiann. meetings 1987-88, mem. task force on rsch. and publs. 1987-88, So. Calif. chpt. exec. bd. 1990—), Acad. Mgmt., Internat. Indsl. Rels. Assn., Inst. Indsl. Rels. Assn. (mem. exec. bd. 1990—), Nat. Acad. Human Resource Mgmt. (founding dir. 1992-94), Univ. Coun. Indsl. Rels. and Human Resource Programs (pres. 1994—), Beta Gamma Sigma. Appeared on local and nat. television and radio news and spl. reports on human resource mgmt., labor and employee rels. Office: UCLA Rm 5315 Anderson Grad Sch Mgmt Los Angeles CA 90024

LEWIN, GEORGE FOREST, former insurance company executive; b. Plainfield, N.H., Oct. 25, 1916; s. George Forest and Maude (Welch) L.; m. Barbara DeFord, May 26, 1943. A.B., Middlebury Coll., 1940; LL.B., J.D., Georgetown U., 1951. Claims adjuster Liberty Mut. Ins. Co., 1940-41; exec. trainee Provident Mut. Life Ins. Co., 1941-43; asst. Washington rep. Anthracite Coal Industry, 1943-45; asst. traffic mgr. Aircraft Industries Assn., 1945-47; with Govt. Employees Ins. Co., Washington, 1947-73; v.p., sec. Govt. Employees Ins. Co., 1963-70, sr. v.p., 1970-73; v.p. Govt. Employees Life Ins. Co., Govt. Employees Ins. Co., Govt. Employees Financial Corp., 1974-76; sec. Criterion Ins. Co., 1964-70, exec. v.p., 1973-74, pres., 1974-81, also former dir.; ret., 1981. Trustee Kimball Union Acad., Meriden, N.H., 1977-82. Mem. Am., Va. bar assns., Newcomen Soc., Phi Alpha Delta, Kappa Delta Rho. Republican. Methodist. Home: 5225 Connecticut Ave NW Washington DC 20015-1845

LEWIN, KLAUS J., pathologist, educator; b. Jerusalem, Israel, Aug. 10, 1936; came to U.S., 1968; s. Bruno and Charlotte (Nawratzki) L.; m. Patricia Coutts Milne, Sept. 25, 1964; children: David, Nicola, Brumo. Attended, King's Coll. U. London, 1954-55; MB, BS, Westminster Med. Sch. London, Eng., 1959; MD, U. London, 1966. Diplomate Am. Bd. Pathology, Royal Coll. Pathologists (London), lic. Calif. Casualty officer Westminster Med. Hosp., 1960; resident Westminster Hosp. Med. Sch., London, 1960-68; pediatric house physician Westminster Hosp. Med. Sch., Westminster Children's Hosp., 1961; house physician St. James Hosp., Balham, London, 1961; asst. prof. pathology Stanford (Calif.) U., 1970-76; assoc. prof. pathology UCLA, L.A., 1977-80; attending physician Dept. Medicine Gastroenterology divsn. UCLA, Wadsworth, Va., 1978—; prof. pathology UCLA Med. Sch., L.A., 1980—, prof. dept. medicine divsn. gastroenterology, 1986—; chief divsn. surg. pathology UCLA Ctr. Health Scis.; resident pathologist clinical chemistry, bacteriology, hematology, blood transfusion, serology, Westminster Hosp. Med. Sch., 1961-62, registrar dept. morbid anatomy, 1962-64, rotating sr. registrar morbid anatomy, Royal Devon, Exeter Hosp., 1964-68; vis. asst. prof. pathology, Stanford U. Med. Sch., 1968-70; vice chmn. pathology UCLA, L.A., 1979-86; pres. L.A Soc. Pathologists Inc., 1985-86; mem. curriculum com. U. Calif. Riverside, 1977-84; cons. Wadsworth VA Hosp., L.A., carcinoma of esophagus intervention study, Polyp Prevention study, Nat. Cancer Inst., Cancer Preservation Studies br., Bethesda, Md., Sepulveda VA Hosp.; mem. various coms. UCLA in field; rschr. structure, function, pathologic disorders of gastrointestinal tract and liver. Author: (with Riddel R., Weinstein W.) Gastrointestinal Pathology and Its Clinical Implications, 1992; edit. bd. Human Pathology, 1986—, Am. Jour. Surg. Pathology, 1990—; reviewer Gastroenterology and Archives of Pathology; contbr. papers, abstracts, review articles to profl. jours., chpts. in books; lectr., presenter in field. Dir. diagnostic Immunohistochemistry Lab.; mem. diagnostic surg. Pathology svc. Recipient Chesterfield medal Inst. Dermatology, London, 1966; named Arris and Gale lectr. Royal Coll. Surgeons, London, 1968; Welcome Trust Rsch. grantee, 1968; fellow Found. Promotion Cancer Rsch., Tokyo, 1992. Fellow Royal Coll. Pathologists (Eng.); mem. Pathological Soc. Great Britain, Am. Gastroenterology Soc., Gastrointestinal Pathology Soc. (founder, pres. 1985-86, exec. com., edn. com. 1990—), U.S. Acad. Pathology, Can. Acad. Pathology, Assn. Clin. Pathologists, Pathological and Bacteriological Soc. Great Britain, Internat. Acad. Pathology, L.A. Pathology Soc. (bd. dirs.), Calif. Soc. Pathology (edn. com. 1983—), So. Calif. Soc. Gastrointestinal Endoscopy, Arthur Purdy Stout Soc., Gastrointestinal Pathology Soc. (pres., by-laws com., chmn. edn. com., exec. com.). Avocations: internat. travel, geographic pathology, hiking, swimming. Home: 333 N Las Casas Ave Pacific Palisades CA 90272-3307 Office: UCLA Sch Medicine Dept Pathology 10833 Le Conte Ave Los Angeles CA 90024-1722

LEWIN, MARTIN J., lawyer; b. Trenton, N.J., Apr. 18, 1949. BS in Econs., U. Pa., 1970, JD, 1973. Bar: D.C. 1973, U.S. Ct. Internat. Trade, U.S. Ct. Customs and Patent Appeals. Advisor U.S. Gen. Acctg. Office, Washington, 1974-78; investigator subcom. on internat. orgns. U.S. House

Reps., Washington, 1978-79; legal advisor U.S. Internat. Trade Commr., Washington, 1979-80; assoc. Daniels Houlihan & Palmeter, Washington, 1980-82; prin. Daniels Houlihan & Palmeter, 1983-84; ptnr. Mudge Rose Guthrie Alexander, Washington, 1984—; bd. dirs., gen. counsel Am. Import Shippers Assn., 1988—; counsel U.S. Assn. Importers of Textiles and Apparel, 1987—. Office: Mudge Rose Guthrie Alexander 1709 N St NW Washington DC 20036-2801 also: Mudge Rose Guthrie Alexander 180 Maiden Ln New York NY 10038-4925

LEWIN, MOSHE, historian, educator; b. Wilno, Poland, Nov. 6, 1921; came to U.S., 1978; s. Leo J. and Fima L. (Koltunova) L. B.A., Tel Aviv U., 1961; Ph.D. Sorbonne, Paris, 1964. Dir. study Ecole des Hautes Etudes, Paris, 1965-66; sr. fellow Columbia U., N.Y.C., 1967-68; research prof. Birmingham U., Eng., 1968-78; prof. history U. Pa., Phila., 1978—; mem. acad. council Kennan Inst. for Russian Studies, Washington, 1981-84. Author: Russian Peasant and Soviet Power, 1968, Lenin's Last Struggle, 1968, Political Undercurrents in Soviet Economic Debates, 1974, 2d edit., The Making of the Soviet System, 1985, The Gorbachev Phenomenon, 1988, expanded edit., 1991, Stalinism and the Roots of Reform, 1991, Russia-USSR-Russia, 1995. Fellow Inst. for Advanced Studies, Princeton, N.J., 1972-73, Wilson Kennan Ctr., Washington, 1976-77, John Simon Guggenhein Found., 1995. Mem. AAUP, AAAS, Am. Hist. Assn., Inst. d'Etudes Slaves, Paris. Home: 309 S 25th St Philadelphia PA 19103-6403 Office: U Pa Coll Hall Dept History Philadelphia PA 19104

LEWIN, RALPH ARNOLD, biologist; b. London, Apr. 30, 1921; came to U.S., 1947; s. Maurice and Ethel Lewin; m. Joyce Mary Chismore, June, 1950 (div. 1965); m. Cheng Lanna, June 3, 1969. BA, Cambridge U., Eng., 1942, MA, 1946; PhD, Yale U., 1950; ScD, Cambridge U., Eng., 1973. Instr. Yale U., New Haven, Conn., 1951-52; sci. officer Nat. Research Council, Halifax, N.S., Can., 1952-55; inst. investigator NIH, Woods Hole, Mass., 1956-59; assoc. prof., now prof. U. Calif., La Jolla, 1960—. Editor: Physiology and Biochemistry of Algae, 1962, Genetics of Algae, 1976, Biology of Algae, 1979, Biology of Women, 1981, Origins of Plastids, 1993; co-editor: Prochloron, a microbial enigma, 1989; transl. Winnie-La-Pu (Esperanto), 1972, La Dektri Horlogoj, 1993. Served with British Army, 1943-46. Mem. Phycological Soc. Am. (pres. 1970-71, Darbaker prize 1963). Avocations: Esperanto, recorders, badminton. Home: 8481 Paseo Del Ocaso La Jolla CA 92037-3024 Office: U Calif San Diego Scripps Inst Oceanogra # 0202 La Jolla CA 92093

LEWIN, SEYMOUR ZALMAN, chemistry educator, consultant; b. N.Y.C., Aug. 16, 1921; s. Charles and Ida (Lazaroff) L.; m. Pearl Goldman, Oct. 17, 1943; children: David, Jonathan. BS, CCNY, 1941; MS, U. Mich., 1942, PhD, 1950; Prof. (hon.), Instituto Quimico de Sarria, Spain, 1961. Lectr. U. Mich., Ann Arbor, 1947-48, rsch. fellow, 1948-50; instr. NYU, N.Y.C., 1950-51, asst. prof., 1951-54, assoc. prof., 1954-59, prof. chemistry, 1959-91, emeritus, 1991—; cons. in field; vis. prof. Internat. Ctr. Conservation, Venice, Italy, 1974—. Author: Earth, Air, Fire, Water and DNA, 1970; Editor: Chemists' Dictionary, 1963; Funk & Wagnall Ency., 1972-77. Patentee in field. With U.S. Army, 1943-45. Recipient K. Fajans prize U. Mich., 1954, Golden Dozen Teaching Excellence awards NYU, 1960, 89, Oscar Foster prize N.Y. Chemistry Tchrs. Soc., 1973; Belgian-Am. Found. fellow, 1962. Fellow N.Y. Acad. Scis. (Cressy Morisson prize 1958), Am. Inst. Chemists; mem. Am. Chem. Soc. (chmn. analytical group N.Y. sect. 1973-74, tour speaker of yr. 1970-71), Am. Assn. Cereal Chemists, Sigma Xi (pres. NYU chpt. 1965-66), Inst. Food Technologists. Home: 4231 N Walnut Ave Arlington Heights IL 60004-1302

LEWIN, TED BERT, writer, illustrator; b. Buffalo, N.Y., May 6, 1935; s. Sidney Walter and Berenece (Klehn) L.; m. Betsy Reilly, 1963. BFA, Pratt Inst., 1956. Author: I Was a Teenage Professional Wrestler, 1993 (ALA Notable award 1993); illustrator: Island of the Blue Dolphins, 1990, Bird Watch, 1990 (ALA Notable award), Herds of Thunder Manes of Gold, 1989, National Velvet, 1985, The Day of Ahmed's Secret, 1990 (ALA Notable award), I Wonder if I'll See a Whale?, 1991, The Potato Man, 1991, Faithful Elephants, 1988, Brother Francis and the Friendly Beasts, 1991, Sami and the Time of the Troubles, 1992, Matthew's Meadow, 1992, Matthew Wheelock's Wall, 1992, The Great Pumpkin Switch, 1992, Cowboy Country, 1993, The Always Prayer Shawl, 1993, Pepe the Lamplighter, 1993 (Caldecott Honor award 1994), Just in Time for Christmas, 1994, Lost Moose, 1994; author, illustrator: Tiger Trek, 1990, When the Rivers Go Home, 1992, Amazon Boy, 1993, The Reindeer People, 1994. Home and Office: 152 Willoughby Ave Brooklyn NY 11205

LEWIN, WALTER H. G., physics educator; b. The Hague, The Netherlands, 1936; came to U.S., 1966; s. Walter S. and Pieternella J. (v.d Tang) L.; children: Pauline, Emanuel, Yakob, Emma. Doctorate, Tech U. Delft, The Netherlands. Tchr. Libanon Lyceum, Rotterdam, The Netherlands, 1960-66; rsch. fellow U. Delft, 1960-66; asst. prof. physics MIT, Cambridge, 1966-68, assoc. prof., 1968-74, prof., 1974—. Editor 5 books; contbr. over 250 articles on astrophysics to sci. jours. Recipient award for exceptional sci. work NASA, 1978, Alexander von Humboldt award, 1984, 91, prize for excellence in teaching MIT Sci. Coun., 1984, Buechner teaching prize, 1988; Guggenheim fellow, 1984. Mem. Am. Astron. Soc., Am. Phys. Soc., Internat. Astron. Union, Dutch Acad. Scis. (elected 1993). Office: MIT 37-627 77 Massachusetts Ave Cambridge MA 02139-3594

LEWINE, ROBERT F., broadcasting company executive; b. N.Y.C., Apr. 16, 1913; s. Irving I. and Jane (Weinberg) L.; m. Lucille Litwin, May 18, 1938; 1 child, Robert W. B.A., Swarthmore Coll., 1934; L.H.D., Columbia Coll., 1975. V.p. ops. Cine-TV Studios, Inc., 1945-47; dir. radio and TV Hirshon-Garfield, Inc., 1949-52; dir. programs Ea. div. ABC, 1953-54, nat. dir. programs, 1954-55, v.p. programming and talent, 1955-56; v.p. night time programs NBC TV, 1957; v.p. nat. programs NBC, 1958-59; v.p. in charge programs CBS Films, Inc., 1959-62; v.p. programs Hollywood, CBS TV Network, 1962-64; exec. v.p. Creative Mgmt. Assocs., Ltd., 1964-65; v.p. charge Warner Bros. TV, Burbank, Calif., 1965-68; pres., chief exec. officer Nat. Acad. TV Arts and Scis., Beverly Hills, Calif., 1970-76; sr. cons. NBC-TV Network, Burbank, 1977—; chmn. bd. Riverside Broadcasting Co., Los Angeles, 1977—; vis. prof. Calif. State U.-Northridge, 1979—, U. So. Calif., 1979—, UCLA, 1979—; mktg. cons. A.M.E. & Co., 1988—. Trustee Am. Women in Radio and TV Soc. Found., Columbia Coll., Los Angeles; pres. Acad. TV Arts and Scis. Found., 1965-85, Film and TV Study Center, Los Angeles; bd. dirs. Paw Soc.; mem. internat. adv. council Population Inst. Served as lt. USNR, 1942-45. Recipient Nat. Acad. of Television Arts & Scis. Founders award, 1992. Mem. Nat. Acad. TV Arts and Scis. (pres. N.Y. chpt. 1958-59, 1st nat. v.p. 1958-59, gov. 1954-62, pres. 1961-63, pres. 1970-77, chmn. membership com. 1960). Clubs: Quaker Ridge (N.Y.); Golf (dir. 1953-55). Home: 9360 Readcrest Dr Beverly Hills CA 90210-2533

LEWINS, STEVEN, security analyst, investment advisor, corporate officer; b. N.Y.C., Jan. 22, 1943; s. Bruno and Kaethe (Czhoeck) L.; m. Rayna Lee Kornreich, July 4, 1968 (div. 1991); children: Shani Nicole, Scott Asher. BA, Queens Coll., CUNY 1964, MA in Diplomatic-Econ. History, 1966, postgrad. in bus. adminstrn., 1969-72; postgrad. cert. in public adminstrn. NYCSC, SUNY, 1967. Park ranger-historian Nat. Park Svc., Statue of Liberty, N.Y.C., 1964-66; traffic asst. AT&T, White Plains, N.Y., 1966; adminstrv. intern N.Y. State, Albany, 1966-67; asst. to commr. N.Y. State Narcotics Addiction Control Commn., N.Y.C., 1967-69; security analyst Value Line Investment Survey, N.Y.C., 1969-71, assoc. rsch. dir., 1971-74, rsch. dir., directing editor Value Line Investment Survey, 1974-80, v.p. Value Line Data Svcs., 1975-80 (created Value Line Financial Data Base, 1974); v.p. Arnold Bernhard & Co., 1975-80, dir., 1976-80, mem. exec. com., 1977-80; ptnr. Ray-Lux Products, 1978-80; pres. RayLux Assocs., 1980-81, dir., 1980-86; founder RayLux Fin. Svc., 1980 (1st SEC-registered electronic investment adv. svc.); v.p., unit head investment div. Citibank N.A., 1981-86, v.p. Citicorp Investment Mgmt., Inc., 1986-88; v.p. transp. and aerospace investment mgmt. Chancellor Capital Mgmt., 1988-92; mng. dir., rsch. dir., head of equity First Capital Advisers/F.C. Fin. Svcs., N.Y.C., 1992-93; v.p. Investment Rsch. Gruntal & Co., Inc., 1994—; adv. corp. disclosure com. SEC, 1977-78, ICC, 1982-92, Dept. Transp., 1982-92, Dept. Justice, 1982-92, Dept. State, 1986-92. Participant U.S.-USSR Emigration/Jackson Vanek, 1984-91, U.S.-USSR Pan Am-Aeroflot Aviation Agreement, 1985, USSR Student Exchg., 1985-86, U.S.-USSR Anti-Internat. Terrorism, 1985-91, U.S.-USSR Rights of Terrorists, 1985, U.S.-USSR Trans-Siberian-CSX Corp.

Initiative, 1989, TRW, Inc-Energia N.P.O. Look Down Satellite Agreement, 1989-90, U.S.-USSR Orbital Space Coop., 1989-90, U.S.- USSR Def. Conv. Projects, 1990-93, Reagan-Gorbachev Summit Preparations, 1986, 87, 88, Bush-Gorbachev Summit Preparation, 1990, U.S.-USSR AMR Corp.-Aeroflot Bilateral Discussion, 1989, U.S.-USSR Spl. Mission /Secure Info. Negotiation, 1983-92; sponsor U.S.-USSR Pace U., rsch. exch., 1990; Citicorp liaison USSR mission to UN, 1982-88, Inst. U.S. and Can., Acad. Scis. USSR, 1985-88, econs. dept. Acad. Scis. USSR, 1988; liaison Chancellor Capital Mgmt., USSR, 1988-92; overseas fact-finding visits include Saudi Arabia, Egypt, Jordan, Israel, 1979, Peoples Republic of China, Japan, Hong Kong, 1981, USSR, 1985, 86, 89, 90, Georgia SSR, 1985, Uzbekistan SSR, 1986, Baykhal, Irkutsk, Olha, Siberia, 1989, Kazakhstan SSR, Republic of Georgia, Baykonour-Soyuz Launch Ctr., 1990. Acting col. S.I.M., USAF, M.A.C., 1990. Recipient Commendation award U.S. Dept. of Justice for spl. assistance in pursuit of U.S-USSR rels., 1990, U.S. Commendation award for Gulf War, 1992. Mem. Croton-on-Hudson Narcotics Guidance Coun., 1972-75, Cortland Indsl. Com., 1975-77; dist. leader Dem. Party, 1979-83; founding mem. Challenger Found., 1987. Fellow Fin. Analyst Fedn. Mem. N.Y. Soc. Security Analysts (sr. security analyst, membership com., computer applications symposium, airline splinter group, motor carrier splinter group, aerospace splinter group), Bus. Economists Coun., Washington Transp. Roundtable, Assn. Computer Users, Internat. Platform Assn., N.Y. Assn. Bus. Economists, Nat. Assn Bus. Economists, Nat. Planetary Soc., Nat. Space Soc., Nat. Air and Space Mus., Tau Delta Phi (pres. 1963, 64, undergrad. of yr. 1963, spl. student senate recognition 1964, Coll. Distinction medal French 1964). Democrat. Author: Fashoda Crisis of 1898, 1966, Knowing Your Common Stocks, 1979, The Social Overhaul of the USSR, 1986, Economics Can Bind U.S.-USSR, 1986, Ecomonic Reform in the U.S.S.R., 1990, USA: 21st Century World Transportation Crossroads, 1994, U.S. Needs World-Class Transportation System, 1994; co-author: (with Bogdanov) US-USSR Anti-International Terrorit Protocol, 1989, Rights of Terrorist, 1990, (with Semenov) U.S.-USSR Space Cooperation, 1990; editor: Megatrends, 1980, Witch Doctor of Wall Street, 1990. Speaker security analysis, econs., transp., aerospace, def., corp. disclosure, deregulation, air traffic control and safety, fin. data svcs., U.S. megatrends, USSR Glastnost and Perestroika. Home: 66 Grand St Croton On Hudson NY 10520-2519 Office: Gruntal & Co Inc 14 Wall St 15th Fl New York NY 10005

LEWINTON, CHRISTOPHER, business executive; b. London, Jan. 6, 1932; came to U.S.A., 1960; s. Joseph and Elizabeth (Gee) L.; m. Jennifer A. Alcock, 1957 (div. 1973); children: Stephen, Peter; m. Louise H. Tidd, July 26, 1978. Grad. in mech. engring., London U., 1958. Sr. devel. engr. Wilkinson Sword Ltd., London, 1955-58; mktg. dir. Graviner Ltd., London, 1958-60; pres., chief exec. officer Wilkinson Sword Inc., N.J., 1960-70; mng. dir. Wilkinson Sword Ltd., London, 1970-78; exec. v.p., dir. Allegheny Internat., Pitts., 1978—; chmn. internat. group Allegheny Internat., London, 1978—; dir. Rowenta, Frankfort, W. Ger., Wilkinson Sword Group, London, Sunbeam Internat., London. Mem. council World Wildlife Fund, London. Served to capt. Brit. Army, 1953-55, Egypt. Fellow Inst. Mech. Engrs. (charter mem.). Office: TI Group Inc 375 Park Ave 2 New York NY 10152

LEWIS, A. DUFF, JR., investment executive; b. Pitts., May 3, 1939; s. A. Duff and Helen Radey (Woolford) L.; m. Nancy Bastian, May 3, 1969; children: Amie D., Jennifer E., Katherine E., Jonathan K. BSME, Grove City Coll., 1962; MS, Purdue U., 1965. Chartered fin. analyst. Project engr. Bailey Meter Co., Wickliffe, Ohio, 1962-64; from fin. analyst mfg. to fin. analyst corp. Eastman Kodak Co., Rochester, N.Y., 1965-82, pension investment coord., 1982-91; mng. dir. Rogers, Casey & Assocs., Darien, Conn., 1992—. Mem. Inst. Chartered Fin. Analysts, Fin. Analysts Fed., Rochester Soc. Security Analysts, Mill Creek Community Club, Inc. (cofounder, treas.). Republican. Lutheran. Home: 1231 Stockbridge Rd Webster NY 14580-9145 Office: Rogers Casey & Assocs 1 Parklands Dr Darien CT 06820-1460

LEWIS, A. JEFFERSON, III, botanical garden administrator; b. McCormick, S.C., Dec. 4, 1945; s. Archie J. Jr. and Frances (Schumpert) L.; m. Judith Sheppard, Dec. 22, 1973; children: Andrew P., Frances E. BS, Clemson U., 1967, MS, 1970, PhD, 1975. Instr. Clemson (S.C.) U., 1972-75; asst. prof. Va. Poly. Inst. and State U., Blacksburg, 1976-82; assoc. prof. U. Ga., Athens, 1983-88, prof., 1989; dir. The State Bot. Garden of Ga., Athens, 1989—. Contbr. articles to profl. jours. Chmn. Athens-Clarke County Clean and Beautiful Commn., 1992-93. 1st lt. USAF, 1970-72. Mem. Am. Soc. Hort. Sci. (so. region), Am. Assn. Bot. Gardens and Arboreta, So. Assn. Agrl. Scientists, Ga. Hort. Soc. Office: The State Bot Garden Ga 2450 S Milledge Ave Athens GA 30605-1624

LEWIS, ALAN JAMES, pharmaceutical executive, pharmacologist; b. Newport Gwent, UK. BSc, Southampton U., Hampshire, 1967; PhD in Pharmacology, U. Wales, Cardiff, 1970. Postdoctoral fellow biomedical sci. U. Guelph, Ont., Can., 1970-72; rsch. assoc. lung rsch. ctr. Yale U., 1972-73; sr. pharmacologist Organon Labs., Ltd., Lanarkshire, Scotland, 1973-79; rsch. mgr. immunoinflammation Am. home products Wyeth-Ayerst Rsch., Princeton, N.J., 1979-82, assoc. dir. exptl. therapeutics, 1982-85, dir., 1985-87, asst. v.p., 1987-89, v.p. rsch., 1989-93; pres. Signal Pharms. Inc., San Diego, 1994—. Editor allergy sect. Agents & Actions & Internat. Archives Pharmacodynamics Therapy; reviewer Jour. Pharmacology Exptl. Therapy, Biochemical Pharmacology, Can. Jour. Physiol. Pharmacology, European Jour. Pharmacology, Jour. Pharm. Sci. Mem. Am. Soc. Pharmacology and Exptl. Therapeutics, Am. Rheumatism Assn., Mid-Atlantic Pharmacology Soc. (v.p. 1991-93, pres. 1993-94), Pulmonary Rsch. Assn., Inflammation Rsch. Assn. (pres. 1986-88), Pharm. Mfrs. Assn., Internat. Assn. Inflammation Socs. (pres. 1990—). Achievements include research in mechanisms and treatment of inflammatory diseases including arthritis and asthma, cardiovascular pharmacology, metabolic disorders, central nervous system pharmacology, osteoporosis and viral diseases. Office: Signal Pharms Inc 5555 Oberlin Dr # 100 San Diego CA 92121

LEWIS, ALEXANDER, JR., oil company executive; b. Danville, Pa., July 21, 1916; s. Alexander and Elizabeth (Mason) L.; m. Alice Kabakjian, May 1, 1942; children—Alexander III, Dennis James, Brady Mason. B.S., Ursinus Coll., 1938; M.S., U. Pa., 1940; Ph.D., U. Pitts., 1951. Chemist refinery tech. div. Gulf Oil Corp., Phila., 1938-42; chief product devel. engr. Gulf Oil Corp., Pitts., 1951-54; mgr. chem. mktg. Gulf Oil Corp., USA-58, mgr. petrochems. dept., 1958—, v.p., 1960-64, sr. v.p., 1964-78; pres. Internat. Trade and Tech., 1978—; dir. Tri Century Ins. Corp. 1985—; mem. Pa. Gov.'s Sci. Adv. Com., 1965-75, Pa. State Com. for Nuclear Energy Devel. and Radiation Control, 1969-79, Pa. State Bd. Edn., 1969-77; pres. Gulf Oil Found., 1973-78; v.p. World Petroleum Congresses, London, 1975-79. Trustee Ursinus Coll., 1972, Point Park Coll., 1973; bd. regents Georgetown U.; bd. dirs. St. Clair Meml. Hosp., Pitts., Internat. Mgmt. and Devel. Inst., Washington. Served to lt. USNR, 1942-46. Fellow Mellon Inst. Indsl. Research, 1946-51. Mem. Am. Chem. Soc., Am. Petroleum Inst., Soc. Automotive Engrs., AAAS, Pitts. Chemists Club, Explorers Club, Duquesne Club, Univ. Club (Pitts.), Downtown Club (Pitts.), Longue Vue Club, Frosty Valley Country Club (Danville, Pa.), Sigma Psi, Phi Lambda Upsilon.

LEWIS, ALEXANDER INGERSOLL, III, lawyer; b. Detroit, Apr. 10, 1946; s. Alexander Ingersoll Jr. and Marie T. (Fuger) L.; m. Gretchen Elsa Lundgren, Aug. 8, 1970; children: Jennifer L., Katherine F., Elisabeth M., Alexander Ingersoll IV. BA with honors, Johns Hopkins U., 1968; JD cum laude, U. Pa., 1971. Bar: Md. 1972, U.S. Dist. Ct. Md. 1972, U.S. Ct. Appeals (4th cir.) 1975, U.S. Supreme Ct. 1976, D.C. 1982. Assoc. Venable, Baetjer & Howard, LLP, Balt., 1972-75, 78-80; ptnr. Venable, Baetjer & Howard, L.L.P., Balt., 1981—; head estate and trust practice group Venable, Baetjer & Howard, Balt., 1993—; asst. atty. gen. State of Md., Balt., 1975-77; cons. subcom. on probate rules, standing com. on rules and procedures Md. Ct. Appeals, 1976—; mem. Md. Gov.'s Task Force to Study Revision of Inheritance and Estate Tax Laws, 1987-88; lectr. Md. Inst. Continuing Profl. Edn. Lawyers, 1978—, Nat. Bus. Inst. 1986-87, 92—, Cambridge Inst. 1986-90, Nat. Law Found., 1988—. Contbr. articles to legal jours. Vice chmn. Md. Gov.'s Task Force on Long-Term Fin. Planning for Disabled Individuals, 1990-94. 1st lt. U.S. Army, 1972. Fellow Am. Coll. Trust and Estate Counsel; mem. ABA, Md. Bar Assn. (chmn. probate reform and simplification com. estates and trusts coun. 1984-86, sec. 1987-88, chmn. 1989-90, com. on laws 1994—), Bar Assn. City Balt., D.C. Bar Assn., Am.

Immigration Lawyers Assn., Balt. Estate Planning Coun., Johns Hopkins Club. Republican. Roman Catholic. Avocations: canoeing, camping, tennis. Home: Venable Baetjer Howard LLP 922 Army Rd Ruxton MD 21204-6703 Office: Venable Baetjer & Howard 1800 Two Hopkins Plz Baltimore MD 21201

LEWIS, ALLAN, conductor, ballet company music director. Former asst. artistic dir. The Joffrey Ballet, N.Y.C.; now music dir. The Joffrey Ballet. Office: Joffrey Ballet 130 W 56th St New York NY 10019-3818*

LEWIS, ANDRE LEON, associate artistic director; b. Hull, Que., Can., Jan. 16, 1955; s. Raymond Lincoln and Therese L.; m. Sarah May Slipper, Sept. 1, 1990. Student, Classical Ballet Studio, Ottawa, Royal Winnipeg (Man.) Ballet Sch., 1975; studies with David Moroni, Arnold Spohr, Rudi van Dantzig, Jiri Kylian, Peter Wright, Hans van Manen, and Alicia Markova, among others. Mem. corps de ballet Royal Winnipeg (Man.) Ballet, 1979-82, soloist, artistic coord., 1984-89, interim artistic dir., 1989-90, assoc. artistic dir., 1990—. Dancer, soloist (ballets) Song of a Wayfarer, Fall River Legend, Nuages Pas de deux, Lento A Tempo E Appassionatto, Nutcracker, Four Last Songs, Romeo and Juliet, Belong Pas de deux, Ectasy of Rita Joe, (TV and films) Fall River Legend, Giselle, Heartland, Romeo and Juliet, The Big Top, Firebird, Belong Pas De Deux; performed at many events including the opening Gala performance of the Internat. Ballet competition in Jackson, Miss., Le Don Des Etoiles, Montreal, a spl. gala honoring Queen Beatrix of Holland and at a Gala performance in Tchaikovsky Hall, Moscow; appeared as a guest artist throughout N.Am., the Orient and USSR. Avocation: listening to opera. Office: Royal Winnipeg Ballet, 380 Graham Ave, Winnipeg, MB Canada R3C 4K2

LEWIS, ANDREW LINDSAY, JR. (DREW LEWIS), transportation and natural resources executive; b. Phila., Nov. 3, 1931; s. Andrew Lindsay and Lucille (Bricker) L.; m. Marilyn S. Stoughton, June 1, 1950; children: Karen Lewis Sacks, Russell Shepherd, Andrew Lindsay IV. BS, Haverford (Pa.) Coll., 1953; MBA, Harvard U., 1955; postgrad., MIT, 1968. With Henkels & McCoy, Inc., Blue Bell, Pa., 1955-60, Am. Olean Tile Co., Inc., Lansdale, Pa., 1960-68, Nat. Gypsum Co., Buffalo, 1960-70; chmn. Simplex Wire & Cable Co., Boston, 1970-74, chief exec. officer, 1972-74; pres., chief exec. officer Snelling & Snelling, Inc., Boston, 1972-74; fin. and mgmt. cons. Lewis & Assocs., Plymouth Meeting, Pa., 1974-81; sec. U.S. Dept. Transp., Washington, 1981-83; chmn. Warner Amex Cable Communications Inc., N.Y.C., 1983-86; chmn., chief exec. officer Union Pacific R.R., Omaha, 1986; pres. Union Pacific Corp., N.Y.C., 1986-87; chmn., CEO Union Pacific Corp., Bethlehem, Pa., 1987—; bd. dirs. Am. Express, Ford Motor Co., AT&T, FPL Group Inc., Gulfstream Aerospace Corp.; trustee Com. for Econ. Devel. Rep. candidate for gov., Pa., 1974; mem. Rep. Nat. Com., 1976-90, dep. chmn., 1980; dep. polit. dir. Reagan-Bush Campaign Com., 1980; cochmn. Nat. Econ. Commn., 1988-89; chmn. The Bus. Roundtable, 1990-92; mem. nat. exec. bd. Boy Scouts of Am. Mem. Phila. Club, Sunnybrook Golf Club (Plymouth Meeting, Pa.), Saucon Valley Country Club (Bethlehem, Pa.), Bohemian Club (San Francisco). Office: Union Pacific Corp Martin Tower 8th & Eaton Ave Bethlehem PA 18018

LEWIS, ANN FRANK, social welfare association executive, columnist; b. Jersey City, Dec. 19, 1937; d. Samuel and Elsie (Golush) Frank; student Radcliffe Coll., 1954-55; m. Myron Sponder, 1989; children from previous marriage: Patricia Fay, Beth Ellen, Susan Jane. Asst. to mayor of Boston, 1968-75; dep. campaign mgr. Bayh for President, 1975-76; adminstrv. asst. to cong. Stan Lundine, 1976-81; adminstrv. asst. to Congresswoman Barbara Mikulski, 1978-81; polit. dir. Dem. Nat. Com., 1981-85; nat. dir. Ams. for Dem. Action, 1985-87; nat. affairs columnist MS mag., 1988-92; analyst Monitor Radio and WHDH TV 1992; v.p. for pub. policy Planned Parenthood Fedn. Am.; pres. Politics, Inc. Co-chair Back to Bus. com., 1994. Inst. Politics of Kennedy Sch. Govt. fellow Harvard U., 1989. Office: 1120 Connecticut Ave # 461 Washington DC 20036-5004

LEWIS, ANNE MCCUTCHEON, architect; b. New Orleans, Oct. 15, 1943; d. John Tinney and Susan (Dart) McCutcheon; m. Ronald Burton Lewis, Oct. 2, 1971; children: Matthew, Oliver. BA magna cum laude, Radcliffe Coll., 1965; MArch, Harvard U., 1970. Registered architect, D.C. Designer and planner Skidmore, Owings & Merrill, Washington, 1969-72, Keyes, Lethbridge & Condon, Washington, 1972-75; prin. Anne McCutcheon Lewis AIA, Washington, 1976-81; ptnr. McCartney Lewis Architects, Washington, 1981—. Mem. Harvard U. Grad. Sch. Design Alumni Coun., Cambridge, Mass., 1979-82; bd. dirs. Friends Non-Profit Housing, Washington, 1981—Washington Humane Soc., 1990—. Fellow AIA (Design awards 1979, 83, 89, 90, 91, 92, 93, dir.-at-large Washington chpt. 1982-84). Mem. Soc. of Friends. Office: McCartney Lewis Architects 1503 Connecticut Ave NW Washington DC 20036-1103

LEWIS, ANTHONY, newspaper columnist; b. N.Y.C., Mar. 27, 1927; s. Kassel and Sylvia (Surut) L.; m. Linda Rannells, July 8, 1951 (div.); children: Eliza, David, Mia; m. Margaret H. Marshall, Sept. 23, 1984. A.B., Harvard U., 1948. Deskman Sunday dept. N.Y. Times, 1948-52; staff Democratic Nat. Com., 1952; reporter Washington Daily News, 1952-55, Washington bur. N.Y. Times, 1955-64; chief London bur. N.Y. Times, 1965-72; editorial columnist, 1969—; lectr. on law Harvard U., 1974-89; James Madison vis. prof. Columbia U., 1983—. Author: Gideon's Trumpet, 1964 (award as best fact-crime book Mystery Writers Am.), Portrait of a Decade: The Second American Revolution, 1964, Make No Law: The Sullivan Case and the First Amendment, 1991; contbr. articles to profl. jours. Recipient Heywood Broun award, 1955, Pulitzer prize for nat. reporting, 1955, 63; Nieman fellow, 1956-57. Mem. Am. Acad. Arts and Scis., Tavern Club. Office: NY Times 2 Faneuil Hall Marketplace Boston MA 02109

LEWIS, ARTHUR DEE, corporation executive; b. Greenville, Tex., Sept. 13, 1918; s. Carl Hamilton and Maxie (Curtis) L.; m. Hildegard Bair, Dec. 7, 1946; children: Gregory Scott, Kimberly Kealani. Student, U. Tex., 1935-41, Advanced Mgmt. Program, Harvard, 1952; Sc.D., Clarkson Coll. Tech. With Am. Airlines, 1941-55, beginning as cargo research analyst, successively supr. spl. projects, mgr. econ. analysis fit. div. econ. planning div., 1941-54, asst. v.p. planning 1954-55; exec. v.p. Hawaiian Airlines, 1955, pres., dir., chief exec. officer, 1955-64; sr. v.p., gen. mgr., dir. Eastern Air Lines, 1964-67, pres., chief operating officer, dir., 1967-69; gen. partner F. S. Smithers & Co., 1969—; chmn., pres., chief exec. officer F. Smithers & Co., 1969-73; chmn., chief exec. officer U.S. Ry. Assn., 1977-78; pres., chief exec. officer Am. Bus Assn., 1977-82; chmn., chief exec. officer U.S. Africa Airways, 1990-94, bd. dirs., chmn. emeritus, chmn. bd. Airline Media Assocs., Inc.; organizer Consol. Ry. Corp.; organizer Nat. Ry. Passenger Corp.; dir. Riegel Paper Corp., Rexham Corp., Bankers Security Life Ins. Soc., Bank of Commerce, Iroquois Brands Ltd., C. Brewer & Co., Bishop Trust Co., Internat. Bank; chmn. Mid Pacific Airlines, Honolulu; cons. airline moblzn., transp. div. Nat. Security Resources Bd., Korean War; cons. Def. Air Transp. Adminstrn., 1951-55, Dept. Transp., 1969. Bd. regents U. Hawaii; bd. govs. Pacific and Asian Affairs Council, Iolani Sch. Boys; bd. dirs. Hawaii Visitors Bur.; trustee, chmn. emeritus Clarkson Coll. Tech. Mem. Am. Mgmt. Assn. (dir., mem. exec. com.), Honolulu C. of C. (dir. 1958-59), Young Presidents Organ., World Bus. Council (pres., dir. 1973-80), Conquistadores del Cielo (dir.). Club: Burning Tree (Bethesda, Md.). Office: 4th fl 11180 Sunrise Valley Dr Reston VA 22019-1606

LEWIS, AUDREY GERSH, financial marketing consultant; b. Phila., Dec. 1, 1933; d. Benjamin and Augusta (Fine) Gersh; divorced; children: Jamie Lewis Keith, Ruth-Ellen. Student, Temple U., 1951-53. Asst. mgr. accounts payable/receivable Turner Constrn. Co., Louisville, 1953-55; rep. sales, mktg., fin. depts. Benjamin Gersh Wholesaler Jeweler, Wyncote, Pa., 1955-69; registered rep. Seaboard Planning Corp. (formerly B.C. Morton Broker Del.), Greenwich, Conn. and Wyncote, 1969-72; placement counselor sales and mktg. dept. Greyhound Permanent Pers. subs. Greyhound Corp., Stamford, Conn., 1974-77; asst. v.p. Am. Investors Corp., Greenwich, 1977-85; founder, pres. Audrey Gersh Lewis Cons. Ltd., Greenwich, 1985—. Chair Cancer Fund, Wyncote, United Fund Leadership Award, Wyncote; asst. treas. Republican Town Com., Greenwich, 1981-82; mem. Greenwich Town Alarm Appeals Bd., 1985—. Mem. Assn. Corp. Growth (bd. dirs., v.p. mktg. and pub. rels. N.Y. chpt. 1989-92, mem. nat. meeting planning com. 1992, 93, 94), Fin. Women's Assn., Women's Econ. Round Table, Greenwich C. of C. (mem. pub. rels. com. 1990—, corp. devel. com. 1991—),

Centre for the Study of the Presidency (nat. adv. coun.), N.Y. Hong Kong Assn., Am. C. of C. in Hong Kong, World Trade Centres in Can. Avocations: antiquing, walking, reading. Office: Audrey Gersh Lewis Cons Ltd PO Box 4644 Greenwich CT 06830-8644

LEWIS, BERNARD, Near Eastern studies educator; b. London, May 31, 1916; s. H. Lewis; m. Ruth Helene Oppenhejm, 1947 (div. 1974); 2 children. BA, U. London, PhD; postgrad., univs. of London and Paris; hon. doctorate, Hebrew U., Jerusalem, 1974, Tel Aviv U., 1979, SUNY, Binghamton, 1987, U. Pa., 1987, Hebrew Union Coll., 1987, Yeshiva U., 1991; Haifa U., 1991, Bar-Ilan U., 1992, Brandeis U., 1993. Asst. lectr. in Islamic history Sch. Oriental Studies U. London, 1938, prof. history Near and Middle East, Sch. Oriental and African Studies, 1949-74, hon. fellow, 1986; Cleveland E. Dodge prof. nr. ea. studies Princeton U., 1974-86, prof. emeritus, 1986—; A.D. White prof. at large Cornell U., 1984-90; dir. Annenberg Rsch. Inst., Phila., 1986-90; Ataturk prof. (hon.) Princeton (N.J.) U., 1992-93; vis. prof. history UCLA, 1955-56, Columbia U., 1960, Ind. U., 1963; vis. prof. College de France, 1980, Ecole des Hautes Etudes, Paris, 1983-86; Class of 1932 lectr. Princeton U., 1964; vis. mem. Inst. for Advanced Study, Princeton, N.J., 1969, long-term mem., 1974-86; Gottesman lectr. Yeshiva U., 1974; Jefferson lectr. NEH, 1990; Tanner lectr. Oxford U., 1990; Weizmann lectr. in Humanities, 1991; Henry M. Jackson meml. lectr.; 1992; Siemens Stiftung lectr., Munich, 1993; Merle-Curti lectr., Madison, Wis., 1993; lectr. N.Y. Pub. Libr., 1993. Author: The Origins of Ismailism, 1940, Turkey Today, 1940, British Contributions to Arabic Studies, 1941, Handbook of Diplomatic and Political Arabic, 1947, The Arabs in History, 1950, new edit., 1993, Notes and Documents from the Turkish Archives, 1952, The Emergence of Modern Turkey, 1961, rev. edit., 1968, (transl. from Ibn Gabirol) The Kingly Crown, 1961, Istanbul and the Civilization of the Ottoman Empire, 1963, The Middle East and the West, 1964, The Assassins, 1967, Race and Color in Islam, 1971, Islam in History, 1973, new edit., 1993, Islam to 1453, 1974, Islam from the Prophet Muhammad to the Capture of Constantinople, 2 vols., 1974, History Remembered, Recovered, Invented, 1975, Studies in Classical and Ottoman Islam, 7th-16th centuries, 1976, The Muslim Discovery of Europe, 1982, The Jews of Islam, 1984, Semites and Anti-Semites, 1986, The Political Language of Islam, 1988, Race and Slavery in Islam, 1990, Islam and the West, 1993, The Shaping of the Modern Middle East, 1994, Cultures in Conflict: Christians, Muslims and Jews in the Age of Discovery, 1995; (with Amnon Cohen) Population and Revenue in the Towns of Palestine in the Sixteenth Century, 1978; author, editor: Land of Enchanters, 1948, The World of Islam: Faith, People, Culture, 1976; author, co-editor: Historians of the Middle East, 1962, Ency. of Islam, 1956-87; editor: (with others) The Cambridge History of Islam, vols. 1-11, 1971; co-editor: Musulmans en Europe, 1992, Religionsgespräche im Mittelalter, 1992; also articles. Served with Royal Armoured Corps and Intelligence Corps, Brit. Army, 1940-41; with dept. Fgn. Office, 1941-45. Recipient Cert. of Merit for svcs. to Turkish culture, Turkish Govt., 1973, Harvey prize, 1978; Univ. Coll. of London fellow, 1976. Fellow Brit. Acad., Royal Hist. Soc., Turkish Hist. Soc. (hon.), Sch. of Oriental and African Studies (hon.); mem. Am. Acad. Arts and Scis., Am. Philos. Soc., Am. hist. Assn., Soc. Asiatique (hon.), Inst. d'Egypte (Cairo, assoc.), AthenaeumClub (coord. Inst. de France 1995). Office: Princeton U Near Ea Studies Ea Dept Princeton NJ 08544

LEWIS, BERNARD LEROY, electronic scientist, consultant; b. Storm Lake, Iowa, Dec. 19, 1923; s. Lee Leroy and Francis Mae (Cutchael) L.; m. Dorothy Louise Simoneaux, Feb. 16, 1946 (dec. Feb. 1985); children: David Leroy, Michael Peter, Patrick Daniel, Timothy Mark; m. Marilyn W. McCullum, Oct. 10, 1990. BS in Physics, Tulane U., 1947, MS in Physics, 1948; postgrad., U. Md., 1953-56. Sect. head Naval Rsch. Lab., Washington, 1948-57; cons. Systems Inc., Orlando, Fla., 1957-60; prin. engr. Radiation Inc., Orlando, 1960-61; design engr. Martin Marietta Co., Orlando, 1961; chief engr. Airtronics, Washington, 1961-63; prin. engr. Harris Intertype, Melbourne, Fla., 1963-69; bus. ptnr. McDowell Assocs., Melbourne, 1969-72; sr. scientist Naval Rsch. Lab., Washington, 1972-84; radar cons. Bernard L. Lewis Assocs., Melbourne, Fla., 1984—; cons. Sperry Rand, Great Neck, N.Y., 1984-87, Naval Rsch. Lab., Washington, 1987-88; adj. prof. Fla. Inst. Tech., Melbourne, Fla., 1984-89. Author: Aspects of Radar Signal Processing; contbr. over 72 tech. papers to profl. jours.; patentee in field. Lt. USN, 1957. Recipient Disting. Civilian Svc. award USN Rsch. Lab., 1981, 5 times Best Paper of the Yr. award Naval Rsch. Lab., 1972-82, Outstanding Alumnus award Tulane U., 1984. Fellow IEEE. Democrat. Roman Catholic. Avocations: physics theory, bridge, golf, dancing. Home and Office: 817 Villa Dr Melbourne FL 32940-7037

LEWIS, BOYD DE WOLF, publisher,editor, writer; b. Boston, Aug. 18, 1905; s. Harry Braddock and Margaret De Wolf (Wade) L.; m. Hazel Riviere Bestick, Sept. 1, 1929; children: David De Wolf, Patricia Ann. Student, Boston U., 1923-27. Reporter, editor and bur. mgr. UP Assns., 1927-45; war corr. with Canadian, Brit. and Am. forces, 1944-45; 1 of 3 Am. press reps. at German surrender Rheims, France, 1945; European news mgr. UP, 1945; exec. editor Newspaper Enterprise Assn., N.Y.C., 1945—; v.p. Newspaper Enterprise Assn., 1949-63, pres., 1963-72; v.p. pub. info. Nat. Safety Council, 1949-57; pub. The World Almanac, 1966-72; Sec. bd. Wolf Trap Found., 1975-76; trustee Cooper Inst., Naples, Fla.; cons. editor and columnist Maturity News Service, 1987—. Author: autobiography Not Always a Spectator, 1981. Mem. Mayflower Descs. Am. Address: 9319 Old Court House Rd Vienna VA 22182

LEWIS, BRIAN KREGLOW, computer consultant; b. Durban, Republic of South Africa, Sept. 2, 1932; s. Arthur Armington and Isabel (Kreglow) L.; m. Mary Helen Kidwell, July 14, 1953; children: Brian E., James A., Charles A., Carol J., Robert E., Sharon H. BS, Ohio State U., 1954; PhD, Tufts U., 1971. Biology tchr. Lincoln-Sudbury (Mass.) Regional High Sch., 1965-66; rsch. assoc. May Inst. for Med. Rsch., Cin., 1971-75; from asst. to assoc. prof. health sci. Grand Valley State U., Allendale, Mich., 1975-81; prin. Lewis Assocs., Sarasota, Fla., 1984—; adj. asst. prof. physiology Cin. Coll. Medicine, 1972-75; assoc. prof. Ponce (Puerto Rico) Sch. Medicine, 1981-84, prof., chmn. physiology, 1987-91. Contbr. revs. and articles to Computer Shopper, Proceedings Soc. Exptl. Biology Medicine, Am. Heart Jour., Atherosclerosis; developer business and edit. software. Cubmaster, scoutmaster Boy Scouts Am., 1963-78; mem. fin. com., ch. choir St. Andrew Ch., Sarasota, 1984—; bd. dirs. Sarasota chpt. Soc. Promotion and Encouragement Barbershop Quartet Singing in Am., 1994—, active, 1993—; active Village Voices, Greenhills, Ohio, 1972-75. Lt. USN, 1954-62. NIH fellow, 1965-71. Mem. Endocrine Soc., Soc. for Study Reproduction, Soc. for Study Fertility, Sarasota IBM PC Users Group (spreadsheet SIG leader 1993-94, software reviewer 1992—). Office: 6423 Caracara St Sarasota FL 34241

LEWIS, C. A., church administrator. Exec. sec. Ch. of the Living God Exec. Bd. Office: Church of The Living God 1360 N Boston Oklahoma City OK 73111

LEWIS, CALVIN FRED, architect, educator; b. Chgo., Mar. 27, 1946; s. Howard George and Fern Teresa (Voelsch) L.; m. L. Diane Johnson, Aug. 24, 1968; children: Nathan, Miller, Cooper, Wilson. B of Architecture, Iowa State U., 1969. Architect Charles Herbert and Assocs., Des Moines, 1970-86; prin. Herbert Lewis Kruse Blunck Architecture, Des Moines, 1987—; arch., lectr. Inter Market Sq., Mpls., 1985, Nat. Tile Conf., L.A., 1987, Am. Soc. Landscape Archs., 1988, Iowa State U., 1985, 89; awards juror Dallas AIA, Kans. AIA, Nebr. AIA. Projects published in profl. jours. Chmn. profl. adv. bd. Iowa State U. Recipient Best in Design award Time Mag., 1982; named one of Top Young Architects in Country, Met. Home mag., 1983. Mem. AIA (nat., regional and state chpts., 47 design awards 1972—, nat. fellowship 1995—). Avocations: sports, photography. Office: Herbert Lewis Kruse Blunk Architecture 202 Fleming Building Bldg Des Moines IA 50309-4081

LEWIS, CARL, Olympic track and field athlete; b. Birmingham, Ala., July 1, 1961; s. Bill and Evelyn (Lawler) L. Student, U. Houston. Competed in Europe and U.S.; track meets include: Nat. Collegiate Athletic Assn. indoor championships, Baton Rouge, La., 1981, Nat. Outdoor Championships, Knoxville, Tenn., 1982, Nat. Sports Festival, 1982, Athletic Congress Outdoor Championships, Indpls., World Championships, Helsinki, 1983, Millrose Games, N.Y., 1984, Summer Olympics, L.A., 1984; recorded album Break it Up, 1986. Recipient James E. Sullivan award best amateur athlete,

1981, Jesse Ownes award, 1982, Athlete of Yr. award Assoc. Press Sports, 1983; winner 3 Gold medals World Championships, 1983, 4 Gold medals Olympics, 1984, Long Jump competition IAAF World Track and Field Championships, 1987, 100 Meter Dash Olympic Games, 1988; named to U.S. Olympic Hall of Fame, 1985; Gold medal, Long Jump competition, Olympics, 1992. Office: care Tom Tellez U Houston Athletic Dept 4800 Calhoun Rd Houston TX 77004-2610*

LEWIS, CEYLON SMITH, JR., physician; b. Muskogee, Okla., July 19, 1920; s. Ceylon Smith and Glenn (Ellis) L.; m. Marguerite Dearmont, Dec. 20, 1943; children: Sarah Lee Lewis Lorenz, Ceylon Smith III, Carol D. Lewis Kast. B.A., Washington U., 1942, M.D., 1945. Diplomate: Am. Bd. Internal Medicine, bd. govs., 1976-82. Intern Salt Lake Gen. Hosp., Salt Lake City, 1945-46; fellow in cardiovascular disease Salt Lake Gen. Hosp., 1950-51; resident in internal medicine VA Hosp., Salt Lake City, 1948-50; practice medicine specializing in internal medicine and cardiology Tulsa, 1951—; mem. staff St. John's Hosp., Tulsa, 1952—; chief of staff St. John's Hosp., 1963, chmn. dept. medicine, 1970-71, mem. teaching staff, 1952—; cons. in internal medicine and cardiology Indian Health Svc., Claremore (Okla.) Indian Hosp., 1956—, USAID for Czeck Republic, Slovak Republic; vis. staff Hillcrest Med. Ctr., Tulsa, 1953—, St. Francis Hosp., Tulsa, 1963—, Univ. Hosp., Oklahoma City, 1973—; med. dir. St. John's Med. Ctr., Tulsa, 1976-78; asst. clin. prof. medicine Okla. U., 1970-74, assoc. clin. prof., 1975-76; clin. prof. U. Okla. Coll. of Medicine, Tulsa, 1976—; dir. Internat. Studies in Medicine, 1990—; adj. clin. prof. med. scis. U. Tulsa Coll. Nursing, 1978—; mem. Okla. Phsician Manpower Tng. Commn.; cons. USAID Czeck Rep., Slovak Rep., 1993—. Contbr. articles to profl. jours. Trustee Coll. Ozarks, 1962-72, chmn., 1964-66; bd. dirs. United Way, Tulsa, 1973-81, St. John Med. Ctr., 1974-84, Okla. Found. Peer Rev., 1973-79, treas., 1973—; bd. dirs. Med. Benevolence Found., 1993—; pres. Tulsa Med. Edn. Found., Inc., 1973-77, 82-84, Presbyn. Med. Mission Fund, Inc., Woodville, Tex., 1973-77, 82-84, bd. dirs. 1972-89; elder 1st Presbyn. Ch., Tulsa, 1959—; chmn. joint com. on health affairs United Presbyn. Ch. in U.S.A., 1969-72. With M.C. AUS, 1946-48. Fellow Royal Australian Coll. of Physicians, 1986; recipient Heart of Yr. award Okla. Heart Assn., 1974, Disting. Svc. award Am. Heart Assn., 1976. Fellow ACP (chmn. bd. govs. 1978-79, bd. regents 1980—, treas. 1983-85, pres.-elect 1985-86, pres. 1986-87, immediate past pres 1987-88, pres. emeritus 1988—), Am. Coll. Cardiology, Am. Coll. Chest Physicians, Royal Australasian Coll. Physicians (hon.); mem. Tulsa County Med. Soc. (pres. 1971), Am. Clin. and Climatological Assn., Okla. Med. Assn. (pres. 1977-78), Inst. Medicine Nat. Acad. Scis. (1984—), AMA, Am. Fedn. Clin. Research, Okla. Soc. Internal Medicine (pres. 1971-72), Am. Soc. Internal Medicine, Tulsa County Heart Assn. (dir. 1952-74, pres. 1956-57), Okla. Heart Assn. (dir. 1952—, pres. 1959-60), Am. Heart Assn. (fellow council clin. cardiology, v.p. 1974-75), Royal Soc. Medicine (London), Action in Internat. Medicine (v.p. 1991—), So. Hills Country Club. Office: 1725 E 19th St Tulsa OK 74104-5424

LEWIS, CHARLES A., investment company executive; b. Orange, N.J., Oct. 23, 1942; s. F. Donald and Edna H. L.; m. Gretchen Smith, July 1967 (div.); m. Penny Bender Sebring, June 9, 1984. BA, Amherst Coll., 1964; MBA, U.Pa., 1966. Asst. to pres. Computer Tech., Inc., Skokie, Ill., 1969-70; 1st v.p. White, Weld, & Co., 1970-78; vice chmn. investment banking Merrill Lynch & Co., Chgo., 1978—. Trustee Amherst Coll., 1989—, Chgo. Symphony Orch., 1989—; assoc. Northwestern U., 1989—; life dir. Juv. Diabetes Found. Internat., Met. Chgo. Mem. Chgo.Club, Glen View Club, Econ. Club Chgo. Office: Merrill Lynch & Co 5500 Sears Tower Chicago IL 60606

LEWIS, CHARLES ARLEN, financial services company executive; b. Columbus, Ga., Nov. 7, 1943; s. Harlin B. and Dorothy A. (Elliott) L.; m. Linda L. McDowell, Dec. 5,1964; 1 child, Bryan A. Security trader White & Co. Investments, St. Louis, 1964-67; dist. sales mgr. Horizon Corp., Overland Park, Kans., 1967-73; mgr. U.S. Realty & Investment Co., St. Louis, 1973-75; fin. cons. Profesco, Inc., St. Louis, 1975-77; pres., CEO Am. Econ. Svcs., Ltd., St. Louis, 1977-82, Nat. Investment Corp., St. Louis, 1982-88; pres., CEO Le Bryan Corp., Washington, 1988—, bd. dirs.; bd. dirs. Grimm Fin. Resources Inc., McLean, Va., Elliott, McDowell & Davis, Ltd., St. Louis. Adv. bd. mem. Child Find Internat., St. Louis, 1987-88; chmn. bd. World Practical Taekwondo Fedn., Hong Kong, 1986—. 2d lt. U.S. Army, 1961-64. Recipient Disting. Svc. award Hong Kong Taekwondo Assn., 1982, Outstanding Svc. award World Practical Taekwondo Fedn., 1984, 87. Avocations: flying, golf.

LEWIS, CHARLES D., insurance executive, rancher; b. Denver, June 22, 1936; s. Harry Thompson and Margretta (Borrmann) L.; m. Penelope Hall, June 18, 1956; children: C. Randel, Christina, Vanda H. Student, Dartmouth Coll., 1954-55; BSBA, U. Denver, 1959, MBA, 1961. Tax mgr. Arthur Andersen & Co., Denver, 1959-64; exec. v.p., treas. Vail (Colo.) Assocs., Inc., 1964-67, Writer Constrn. Corp., Denver, 1967-69; pres., chief exec. officer, founder Copper Mountain (Colo.), Inc., 1969-82; gen. ptnr. W.F.R. Ltd., Kremmling, Colo., 1979—; gen. ptnr., dir. Boettcher & Co., Denver, 1982-85; pres. L.W.P. Svcs., Inc., Golden, Colo., 1985—; pres. Arlberg Holding Co., 1990—, Arlberg Ins. Co., 1990—; bd. dirs. Eire County Investment Co. Chmn. Copper Mountain Water & Sanitation Dist., 1972-82, Copper Mountain Met. Dist., 1972-82; mem. Colo. Passenger Tramway Bd., 1974-82, chmn., 1976-82. Recipient Industry and Environ. award Rocky Mountain Ctr. on Environment, 1974; named Outstanding Design, Ski Mag., 1975, Colo. Ski Hall of Fame, 1989. Mem. Colo. Soc. CPAs, AICPAs, Nat. Ski Areas Assn. (chmn. 1981-83), Colo. Ski Country USA (chmn. 1978-79), Am. Ski Fedn. (vice chmn. 1980-82), Am. Arbitration Assn., Denver Club. Republican. Episcopalian. Avocations: climbing, fishing. Home: 19752 US Hwy 40 Kremmling CO 80459-9603 Office: LWP Svcs Inc 350 Indiana St Golden CO 80401-5050

LEWIS, CHARLES EDWIN, physician, educator; b. Kansas City, Dec. 28, 1928; s. Claude Herbert and Maudie Friels (Holaday) L.; m. Mary Ann Gurera, Dec. 27, 1963; children—Kevin Neil, David Bradford, Matthew Clinton, Karen Carleen. Student, U. Kans., 1948-49; M.D., Harvard, 1953; M.S., U. Cin., 1957, Sc.D., 1959. Diplomate Am. Bd. Occupational Medicine. Intern, resident U. Kans. Hosp., 1953-54; trainee USPHS, 1956-58; fellow occupational health Eastman Kodak Co., 1958-59; asst. clin. prof. epidemiology Baylor U. Sch. Medicine, 1960-61; assoc. prof. medicine U. Kans. Med. Sch., 1961-62, prof., chmn. dept. preventive medicine, 1962-69; coordinator Kan. Regional Med. Program, 1967-69; prof. social medicine Harvard Med. Sch., 1969-70; prof. pub. health, head div. health adminstrn. UCLA Med. Sch., 1970-72, prof. medicine, div. head, 1972-90, prof. nursing Sch. Nursing, 1973—, head div. preventive and occupational medicine, 1991—; dir. Health Svcs. Rsch. Ctr., 1991-93, UCLA Ctr. Health Promotion and Disease Prevention, 1991—; cons. Getty Trust, Walt Disney Prodns.; mem. Nat. Bd. Med. Examiners, 1964-68, 80-83; health services research study sect. USPHS, 1968-76; commr. joint com. accreditation Health Care Org., 1990—; vis. scholar Annenberg Sch. Communications, U. So. Calif., 1980-81; mem. adv. bd. Hosp. Research and Edn. Trust, 1972-75. Contbr. articles to profl. Jours. Served to capt. USAF, 1954-56. Recipient Ginsberg prize medicine U. Kans., 1954, Glasier award Soc. Gen. Internal Medicine, 1988. Fellow Am. Pub. Health Assn., Acad. Occupational Medicine; mem. Internat. Epidemiology Soc., Assn. Tchrs. Preventive Medicine (pres. 1969-70), Inst. of Medicine of Nat. Acad. Scis. (governing council 1977-80), Am. Assn. Physicians, ACP (regent 1988—, Rosenthal award 1980). Home: 221 S Burlingame Ave Los Angeles CA 90049-3702

LEWIS, CHARLES JOSEPH, journalist; b. Bozeman, Mont., July 10, 1940; s. Vern Edward James and Mary (Brooke) L.; m. Sarah Winters; children: Peter, Patrick, Barbara. BS in Humanities with Honors, Loyola U., Chgo., 1962; JD, Columbia U., 1965. Bar: Ill. 1965. Atty. McDermott, Will & Emery, Chgo., 1965-67; reporter City News Bur., Chgo., 1967-68; reporter, editor Chgo. Sun-Times, 1968-73; with AP, 1974-89; reporter, editor, Washington, 1974-78, reporter, editor, L.A., 1978-80, personnel mgr., N.Y.C., 1981-83, bur. chief, Hartford, Conn., 1980-81, bur. chief Washington, 1984-89; bur. chief Hearst Newspapers, Washington, 1989—. Bd. dirs. Nat. Press Found., Washington, 1985—, treas., 1987-88, vice chmn., 1988-90, chmn., 1990-92; dir. Reporters Com. for Freedom of the Press, 1993—. Lance cpl. USMCR, 1963-67. Mem. Gridiron Club, Sigma Delta Chi (v.p. Washington chpt. 1988-89). Office: Hearst Newspapers 1701 Pennsylvania Ave NW Washington DC 20006-5801

LEWIS, CHARLES LEONARD, psychologist; b. Wellsville, Ohio, Jan. 6, 1926; s. Cleo L. and Charlotte (Hahn) L.; m. Charlotte J. Wynn, Sept. 8, 1948 (dec. Mar. 1987); children: Stephen C., Janet J., Judith A.; m. Jane E. McCormick, Oct. 1, 1988. B.S. in Edn. with honors, Ohio U., 1949; M.A., U. Minn., 1953, Ph.D., 1955. Assoc. dir. activities U. Minn., 1950-55; dean student affairs, assoc. prof. psychology U. N.D., 1955-62; exec. dean, assoc. prof. ednl. psychology U. Tenn., 1962-67; v.p. student affairs Pa. State U., 1967-72; exec. dir. Am. Personnel and Guidance Assn., Washington, 1972-74, exec. v.p., 1974-83, exec. v.p. emeritus 1984—; pres. Charles L. Lewis & Assocs., Annandale, Va., 1983-85, Chuck Lewis et al, Annandale, 1985—; guest prof. U. Md., 1973; mem. Nat. Adv. Com. for Devel. Guidance Components-Career Edn., 1972-76. Editor: Jour. Coll. Students Personnel, 1958-64; mem. editorial bd.: Personnel and Guidance Jour., 1954-57. Mem. Pres.'s Com. for Handicapped, 1972-80; bd. dirs. Ctr. Cmty. Hosps., Bellefonte, Pa. With U.S. Army, 1944-47. Recipient George Hill Disting. Alumni award Ohio U., 1981, Outstanding Alumnus Coll. Edn. Ohio U., 1988. Mem. APA, AAUP, Am. Assn. Higher Edn., Am. Coll. Pers. Assn. (pres. 1968-69), Nat. Assn. Student Pers. Adminstrs., Nat. Assn. Woman Deans and Counselors, Am. Pers. and Guidance Assn. (dir. 1967-70), Am. Assn. Univ. Adminstrs. (dir. 1973), Coun. Advancement of Stds. (bd. dirs.), Ohio U. Alumni Soc. and Friends Coll. Edn. (coun. 1985-92, bd. dirs. 1986-92), Psi Chi, Kappa Delta Pi, Beta Theta Pi, Chi Sigma Iota (founding dir. 1984-90). Episcopalian.

LEWIS, CHRISTOPHER ALAN, lawyer; b. Phila., Sept. 16, 1955; s. Charles Edward and Florence (Scott) L.; m. Sheilah Diane Vance, Oct. 18, 1986. BA magna cum laude, Harvard U., 1975; JD magna cum laude, U. Mich., 1978. Bar: Pa. 1979, U.S. Dist. Ct. (ea. dist.) Pa. 1979, U.S. Ct. Appeals (3d cir.) 1979. Law clk. to judge U.S. Dist. Ct. (ea. dist) Pa., Phila., 1978-80; assoc. Dilworth, Paxson, Kalish & Kauffman, Phila., 1980-85, ptnr., 1986-87; exec. dep. gen. counsel Commonwealth of Pa., Harrisburg, 1987-89; sec., 1988-91; ptnr. firm Blank, Rome, Comisky & McCauley, Phila., 1991—. Mem. steering com. 21st Century Inst. for Polit. Action, 1985—, Com. on Seventy; bd. dirs. Pub. Interest Law Ctr. of Phila., 1984-87, Crime Prevention Assn., 1986-87. Mem. ABA, Fed. Bar Assn., Phila. Bar Assn., Barristers' Assn. Phila., Kappa Alpha Psi (treas. alumni chapt. 1981-83), Sigma Pi Phi. Democrat. Episcopalian. Avocation: sailing. Home: 6425 Wayne Ave Philadelphia PA 19119-3630 Office: Blank Rome Comisky McCauley 1200 Four Penn Ctr Plz Philadelphia PA 19103

LEWIS, CLAUDE, JR., retired shoe company executive; b. Jefferson City, Mo., Aug. 21, 1924; s. Claude and Opal Mae (Fowler) L.; m. Aletha Avonell Harrison, Oct. 16, 1943; 1 child, Gregory Lee. A.B., Central Meth. Coll., Fayette, Mo., 1949; postgrad., U. Mo., 1949-50. Office mgr. Brown Shoe Co., Moberly, Mo., 1950; dept. supr. Brown Shoe Co., St. Louis, 1954-58; asst. gen. supt. Kinney Shoe Corp., Carlisle, Pa., 1959-62; gen. supt. Kinney Shoe Corp., 1962-65, dir. purchasing, 1965-68, v.p mfg. div., 1968, pres. mfg. div., 1969-74, corp. exec. v.p., 1974-86. Trustee Carlisle YMCA. Officer CIC, U.S. Army, 1942-46, SO-52. Mem. SAR. Republican. Methodist. Clubs: Carlisle (Pa.) Country; Officers (Army War Coll.) (Carlisle); Officers (Army War Coll. Lodge: Masons (32 degree). Home: 121 Strayer Dr Carlisle PA 17013-4408

LEWIS, CLAUDE AUBREY, columnist; b. N.Y.C., Dec. 14, 1936; s. Robert George Lewis and Hazel (Perkinson) Gray; m. Beverly McKelvey, Oct. 18, 1953; children: Pamela, Bryan, Craig, Beverley. AB in English, CCNY, 1958; LHD (hon.), Thomas Jefferson U., 1986. From editorial asst. to asst. editor Newsweek, N.Y.C., 1953-64; reporter N.Y. Herald Tribune, N.Y.C., 1964-65, NBC, Phila., 1965-67; assoc. editor, columnist Phila. Bull., 1967-82; editor, pub. Nat. Leader, Phila., 1982-84; columnist, mem. editorial bd. Phila. Inquirer, 1984—. Author: Muhammad Ali, 1962, Adam Clayton Powell, 1965, Benjamin Banneker, 1968; co-author: New York City in Crisis, 1966. Bd. dirs. Valley Forge Med. Ctr., Phila., Met. Hosp., Phila., Djonge McNair Health Fund, Phila. Recipient Gold Typewriter award Schaefer, 1964, 67; 1st pl. award Phila. Med. Soc., 1967, Martin Luther King Jr. award Nat. Orgn. of Unions, 1967. Mem. Nat. Assn. Black Journalists (founder). Avocations: photography, reading. Office: Phila Inquirer 400 N Broad St Philadelphia PA 19130-4099

LEWIS, CRAIG GRAHAM DAVID, public relations executive; b. Dearborn, Mich., Jan. 25, 1930; s. Floyd B. and Elizabeth (Hickey) L. AB, UCLA, 1951; m. Karen Kerns, Oct. 23, 1954; children: Mark, Kern, Arden, Robin. Corr., McGraw-Hill, Inc., Washington, 1952-56; bur. mgr. Aviation Week mag., Dallas, 1957-59, Washington news editor, 1959-61; dept. dir. pub. affairs FAA, Washington, 1961-63; v.p. pub. rels. Air Transport Assn. Washington, 1963-64; dir. pub. rels. Martin Marietta Corp., N.Y.C., 1964-67; assoc. Earl Newsom & Co., N.Y.C., 1967—, 1968—, pres., 1975—, chmn., 1982—; exec. v.p. Adams & Rinehart, Inc., N.Y.C., 1983—, vice chmn., 1986—; vice-chmn. Ogilvy Pub. Rels. Group, 1988—, Ogilvy Adams & Rinehart, 1992—. Mem. Aviation/Space Writers Assn., Am. Inst. Aero-Astro, Nat. Press Club. Home: PO Box 1052 Ojai CA 93024-1052 Office: Ogilvy Adams & Rinehart 11766 Wilshire Blvd Los Angeles CA 90025

LEWIS, DALE KENTON, retired lawyer; b. Goodland, Kans., June 20, 1937; s. W. Homer and L. (Fern) L.; m. Constance L. Coover, Dec. 27, 1958; children—James W., Bari Lynn, Brad Kenton. B.A., State U. Iowa, 1959; J.D., Colo. U., 1962. Bar: Colo. 1962, Ind. 1968. Mem. firm Lewis & Ausenhus, Loveland, Colo., 1962-67; with Eli Lilly and Co., 1967-90; counsel Elanco Products Co., 1969-77; gen. counsel, sec. Elizabeth Arden, Inc., 1977-81, corp. asst. sec. and assoc. gen. counsel, 1981-83, corp. asst. sec., dep. gen. counsel, 1983-86, sec., dep. gen. counsel, 1986-89; v.p., sec., gen. counsel DowElanco, Indpls., 1989-95; ret., 1995. Mem. Am. Corp. Counsel Assn., Order of Coif. Episcopalian. Office: 9330 Zionsville Rd Indianapolis IN 46268

LEWIS, DAN ALBERT, education educator; b. Chgo., Feb. 14, 1946; s. Milton and Diane (Sabath) L.; m. Stephanie Riger, Jan. 3, 1982; children: Matthew, Jake. BA cum laude, Stanford U., 1968; PhD, U. Calif., Santa Cruz, 1980. Rsch. assoc. Arthur Bolton Assocs., Sacramento, 1969-70; survey contr. Sci. Analysis Corp., San Francisco, 1971; dir. Stanford Workshops on Polit. and Social Issues Stanford (Calif.) U., 1971-74; projects adminstr. Ctr. Urban Affairs and Policy Rsch., Northwestern U., Evanston, Ill., 1975-80, asst. prof. edn., 1980-86, assoc. prof. edn., 1986-90, assoc. dir., chair grad. program human devel./social policy, 1987-90, prof. edn., 1990—; vis. scholar Sch. Edn., Stanford U., 1990-91; mem. task force on restructuring mental health svcs. Chgo. Dept. Health, 1982; mem. human rights authority Ill. Guardianship and Advocacy Commn., 1980-82; adv. mem. com. on planning and inter-agy. coordination Commn. Mental Health and Devel. Disabilities, 1979; interim adv. com. on mental health City of Chgo., 1978; adv. mem. Gov.'s Commn. to Revise Mental Health Code Ill., 1975-77; presenter at profl. consts.; presenter workshops. Editor: Reactions to Crime, 1981; co-author: Fear of Crime: Incivility and the Production of a Social Problem, 1986, The Social Construction of Reform: Crime Prevention and Community Organizations, 1988, The Worlds of the Mentally Ill, 1991, The State Mental Patient and Urban Life, 1994, Race and Educational Reform, 1995; contbr. articles, book revs. to profl. publs. Bd. dirs. Designs for Change, Ill. Mental Health Assn.; rsch. adv. com. Chgo. Urban League, Chgo. Panel Pub. Sch. Finances, 1989-91; needs assessment tech. com. United Way Chgo., 1989-90; ednl. coun. Francis W. Parker Sch., Chgo., 1988-90; task force on restructuring mental health svcs. Chgo. Dept. Health, 1982; com. on mentally disabled Ill. State Bar Assn., 1983-89; rsch. policy com. Ill. Dept. Mental Health, 1978; bd. dirs. Mental Health Assn. Greater Chgo., 1977-84, v.p. pub. policy, 1979-83. Office: Northwestern Univ 2040 Sheridan Rd Evanston IL 60208-0855

LEWIS, DANA KENNETH, marketing company executive, consultant; b. L.A., Aug. 24, 1945; s. Kenneth Robert and Ouida Jo (Norris) L.; m. Yoko Koshio, Sept. 12, 1969; 1 child, Michelle Cynthia. BA, Friends World Coll., Huntington, N.Y., 1976; MA, Goddard Coll., Plainfield, Vt., 1980. Cons. to pres. Emile, Inc., Osaka, Japan, 1976-77; residential houseparent Bethany Children's Home, Womelsdorf, Pa., 1977-78; cottage life supr., 1978-86, dir. home life, adminstr., 1986-94; co-founder, pres. Lewis Mktg., Inc. (formerly Pacific Rim Enterprises, Inc.), Fleetwood, Pa., 1989—; founder The Metalog Group, Fleetwood, Pa., 1993—; instr. Pa. State U., 1981-83, Family Life Devel., Cornell U., 1982-85; presenter Treischman Conf., Boston, 1989. Author: Working with Children, 1981; author, speaker, audio cassettes Child Care and Communications, 1979—; mem. editorial bd. Jour. 1984; book reviewer, 1988; contbr. articles to profl. jours. Lectr. various local facilities, 1978—. Served as staff sgt., USAF. Mem. Child Care Assn. of Pa. (trainer, presenter 1979-87, keynote speaker Regional Confs. 1986, Dedicated Service award 1986). Avocations: computers, reading, poetry, writing, travelling. Home: 22 Bick Rd Fleetwood PA 19522-9611 Office: Lewis Mktg Inc 22 Bick Rd Fleetwood PA 19522-9611

LEWIS, DARRELL L., retail executive; b. Mason City, Iowa, Nov. 20, 1931; s. Milton Loren and Blanche Ione (Wilson) L.; m. Mary Jo Bahnsen, Oct. 22, 1950; children—John L., Lonnette Ann, Sherri Jo. Grad. high sch. With Osco Drug, Inc. subsidiary Jewel Cos., Inc., 1949-62; with Jewel Turn-Style, 1962; pres. Turn-Style Family Centers, Franklin Park, Ill., 1967-74; head Jewel Hypermarket Turn-Style Family Centers, 1974; pres. Osco Drug, Inc., 1974-75, v.p. store and sales devel., 1976-77; pres. D.L. Lewis Drug Co. Inc., Bensenville, Ill., 1978—, chmn. bd., 1987—. Home: 12338 Sunset Shore Three Rivers MI 49093-9500 Office: DL Lewis Drug Co 1325 W Irving Park Rd Bensenville IL 60106-1758

LEWIS, DAVID, association executive; b. Carmel, Calif., Aug. 18, 1944; s. Chester Allen and Harriet E. (Minster) L. BA, Calif. State U., Sacramento, 1967. Cert. Assn. Exec., FAAO. Assoc. dir. Jr. Statesman Found., Palo Alto, 1970; dir. govt. affairs Calif. Optometric Assn., Sacramento, 1971-75; various positions Am. Optometric Assn., Washington, 1975-86; exec. dir. Am. Acad. Optometry, Bethesda, Md., 1986—, Am. Soc. Adolescent Psychiatry, Bethesda, Md., 1987-93; sr. acct. exec. PAI Mgmt., Bethesda, Md., 1986—; 1st vice chmn. Nat. Vol. Orgns. for Ind. Living for Aging, Washington, 1986-89, chmn., 1989-90; cons. Internat. Coun. Prison Med. Svcs., Washington and Paris, 1987-92. Co-author: Community and Public Health Optometry, 1989. Officer, trustee Jr. Statesmen Found., Palo Alto, 1967-70, 71-76, hon. trustee, 1976; sr. warden St. Paul's Episc. Ch., Washington, 1991-92. Sgt. U.S. Army, 1968-70, Vietnam. Recipient Bronze star, Air medal, U.S Army, Vietnam, 1969. Fellow Am. Acad. Optometry; mem. Am. Soc. Assn. Execs., Internat. Assn. Optometric Execs., Calif. Optometric Assn. (hon.). Office: PAI Mgmt 4330 E West Hwy # 1117 Bethesda MD 20814

LEWIS, DAVID CARLETON, medical educator, university center director; b. Hartford, Conn., May 19, 1935; s. Theodore and Lillian (Levin) L.; m. Eleanor Grace Levinson, Aug. 23, 1959; children: Deborah, Steven. AB magna cum laude, Brown U., 1957; MD, Harvard U., 1961. Intern Beth Israel Hosp., Boston, 1961-62, jr. resident, 1962-63, chief med. resident, 1966-67, dir. emergency unit and med. outpatient dept, 1969-71; sr. resident U. Hosps. Cleve., 1963-64, Parkland Meml. Hosp., Dallas, 1964-66; fellow U. Tex. Southwestern Med. Hosp., Dallas, 1964-66; Sloan Found. fellow Harvard Med. Sch., Boston, 1971-72; med. dir. Washingtonian Ctr. for Addictions, Boston, 1972-77; dir. div. alcohol and substance abuse Roger Williams Gen. Hosp., Providence, 1976—; dir. program in alcoholism and drug abuse Brown U., Providence, 1976-82, prof. medicine and community health, 1982—, Donald G. Millar prof. alcohol and addiction studies, 1987—, chmn. dept. community health, 1981-86, dir. Ctr. Alcohol and Addiction Studies, 1982—; mem. nat. adv. coun. Nat. Alcohol Inst., Rockville, Md., 1981-85, cons. to dir., 1985—; mem. sci. adv. bd. Children of Alcoholics Found., N.Y.C., 1985—; cons. WHO, 1986—; mem. cocaine global adv. com., 1992—; chair Physician Consortium on Substance Abuse Edn., 1989—; mem. Carnegie Substance Abuse com., 1989-92; scholar-in-residence Nat. Inst. Med., 1991-92. Author: The Drug Experience: Data for Decision Making, 1970; editor: Providing Care for Children of Alcoholics, 1986; editor Brown U. Digest of Addiction Theory and Application, 1986—; exec. editor Substance Abuse jour., 1984—; contbr. numerous articles to profl. jours. Med. dir. Beacon Hill Free Clinic, Boston, 1968-71; chmn. Mayor's Coun. on Drug Abuse, Boston, 1972-80. Grantee Nat. Alcohol and Drug Insts., 1986—, Edward John Noble fellow Harvard U. Med. Sch., 1957-91. Fellow ACP; mem. NAS, Inst. Medicine Study on Treatment Alcohol Problems, Assn. MEd. Edn. and Rsch. in Substance Abuse (pres. 1983-88, Excellence in Med. Edn. award 1986), Am. Soc. Addiction Medicine (chair core curriculum com. 1989—, chair sect. on internal medicine 1990—), Brown Med. Alumni Assn. (pres. 1974-76), Phi Beta Kappa, Sigma Xi. Avocations: choral singing, sailing, photography. Office: Brown Univ Ctr Alcohol & Addiction Studies Box G Providence RI 02912

LEWIS, DAVID ELDRIDGE, airport development executive; b. Washington, Mar. 10, 1924; s. S. Lawrence and Ruth (Eldridge) L.; m. Anne Hutchison Reppert, Aug. 19, 1949; children: David Eldridge, Charles Adams, Laura Peter. B.A., Yale U., 1945; postgrad., Harvard U., 1946-47. Sales rep. J.W. Valentine Co., Inc., N.Y.C., 1948-53; asst. to sales mgr. Wellington Sears Co., N.Y.C., 1953-58; mgr. converted fabrics div. Wellington Sears Co., 1958-59, mgr. converted apparel fabrics, 1959-60, v.p., 1960-66; v.p. mktg. West Point Pepperell, N.Y.C., 1966-70; v.p., gen. mgr. Nonwoven Fabrics div. Internat. Paper Co., N.Y.C. 1970-75; with Blessings Corp., N.Y.C., 1975-89, exec. v.p., 1976-77, pres., dir. mem. exec. com., 1975-76, 76-89, chief exec. officer, 1978-87, vice chmn., 1988; asst. sec. U.S. Dept Vets. Affairs, 1989-92; mng. dir. KACI Internat., 1992—; dir. J.L. Prescott Co., Internat. Barrier Corp. Bd. dirs. Inst. Infant Services, 1982-84. Served to ensign U.S. Navy, 1944-46; lt. 1950-51. Mem. Nat. Trust Hist. Preservation (mem. coun. Decatur House 1993—), Nat. Policy Forum (mem. policy coun. on entrepreneurial and small bus. 1994—). Republican. Presbyterian. Clubs: Coral Beach and Tennis (Bermuda); Army and Navy (Washington). Home: 4994 Glenbrook Rd NW Washington DC 20016-3223 Office: 4005 64th St Bethesda MD 20816

LEWIS, DAVID JOHN, lawyer; b. Zanesville, Ohio, Feb. 4, 1948; s. David Griff and Barbara Ann (Hoy) L.; m. Susan G. Smith; 1 child, Ann Elizabeth. BS in Fin., U. Ill., 1970, JD, 1973. Bar: Ill. 1973, D.C. 1974. Law clk. to Judge Philip W. Tone U.S. Dist. Ct. For North Dist. Ill., Chgo., 1973-74; assoc. Sidley & Austin, Washington, 1974-80, ptnr., 1980—. Mem. ABA. Office: Sidley & Austin 1722 I St NW Washington DC 20006-3705

LEWIS, DAVID KELLOGG, philosopher, educator; b. Oberlin, Ohio, Sept. 28, 1941; s. John Donald and Ewart (Kellogg) L.; m. Stephanie Robinson, Sept. 5, 1965. BA, Swarthmore Coll., 1962; MA, Harvard U., 1964, PhD, 1967. Asst. prof. philosophy UCLA, 1966-70; mem. faculty Princeton U., 1970—, prof. philosophy, 1973—; cons. Hudson Inst., 1962-75; Fulbright lectr., Australia, 1971; Locke lectr. Oxford U., 1984.; Kant lectr. Stanford U., 1988. Author: Convention: A Philosophical Study, 1969, Counterfactuals, 1973; On the Plurality of Worlds, 1986, Philosophical Papers, vol. I, 1983, vol. II, 1986, Parts of Classes, 1991. Fulbright rsch. fellow N.Z., 1976, Santayana fellow Harvard U., 1988; Recipient Matchette prize for philos. writing, 1972. Mem. AAAS, AAUP, NAS, Brit. Acad., Australian Acad. Humanities. Office: Princeton U Dept Philosophy Princeton NJ 08544

LEWIS, DAVID LEVERING, history educator; b. Little Rock, May 25, 1936; s. John Henry and Alice Urnestine (Bell) L.; m. Sharon Lynn Siskind, 1965 (div. Oct. 1988); children: Eric, Allison, Jason; m. Ruth Ann Stewart, Apr. 15, 1994; 1 child, Allegra. BA in History/Philosophy, Fisk U., 1956; MA in U.S. History, Columbia U., 1959; PhD in Modern Europe/France, London Sch. Econs. & Polit. Sci., 1962. Lectr. European history U. Ghana, Legon, 1963-64; lectr. history Howard U., Washington, 1964-65; from asst. to assoc. prof. Morgan State U., Balt., 1966-70; from assoc. prof. to prof. U. D.C., 1970-80; prof. U. Calif. San Diego, La Jolla, 1981-85; M.L. King, Jr. prof. Rutgers U., New Brunswick, N.J., 1985—; lectr. overseas edn. program U. Md., U.K., Germany, 1961, 62; vis. asst. prof. U. Notre Dame, South Bend, Ind., 1965-66; mem. final rsch. fellowships panel NEH, 1978-82; author, cons. Joint Ctr. Polit. Studies, Inc., Washington, 1982; co-organizer We Shall Overcome: A Retrospective on the Civil Rights Movement of the 1960s cont. U. Calif.San Diego, 1987; mem. grad. dean search com. Rutgers U., 1985-86, mem. adv. com. appointment v.p. acad. rsch., 1985-86; mem. com. humanities Yale U. Coun., 1988-92; commr. Nat. Portrait Gallery, Smithsonian Instn., Washington, 1989-94; mem. Rutgers U. Press Coun., 1989-94; mem. Overseers' Com. to Visit Harvard U. Libr., 1990-93; mem. selection com. fellowships Nat. Humanities Ctr., Research Triangle Park, N.C., 1994, bd. dirs.; cons. Atlanta History Ctr. Atlanta Hist. Soc., 1994—; presenter in field. Author: King: A Biography, 1970, Prisoners of Honor: The Dreyfus Affair, 1974, District of Columbia: A Bicentennial History, 1976, When Harlem Was in Vogue, 1981, The Race to Fashoda: European Colonialism and African Resistance in the Scramble for Africa,

1988, W.E.B. DuBois: Biography of A Race, 1868-1919, Vol. I, 1993 (Pulitzer Prize for history 1994), (with others) Black Leaders of the Twentieth Century, 1982, Jews in Black Perspectives: A Dialogue, 1984, The Civil Rights Movement in America, 1986, Harlem Renaissance: Black Art of America, 1987, Bridges and Boundaries: African Americans and American Jews, 1992; contbr. foreword to Living Black in White America, 1971; contbr. introduction to Black Reconstruction in America, 1992; contbr. articles and revs. to profl. jours. Founding mem. Com. Policy Racial Justice, 1982—; bd. dirs. D.C. Humanities Coun., 1979-80. With M.C., U.S. Army, 1962-63. Recipient Bancroft prize, 1994, Francis Parkman prize, 1994; rsch. grantee Am. Philos. Soc., 1967, Social Sci. Rsch. Coun., 1967, Am. Coun. Learned Socs., 1971; fellow Drug Abuse Coun. Inc., Ford. Found., 1972-73, Woodrow Wilson Internat. Ctr. Scholars, Smithsonian Instn., 1977-78, 90-91, Ctr. Advanced Study Behavioral Scis., 1980-81, Nat. Humanities Ctr., 1983-84, John Simon Guggenheim Meml. Found., 1986-87. Mem. AAUP, Am. Hist. Assn. (mem. Alexis de Tocqueville prize com. 1979, 89), African Studies Assn., Orgn. Am. Historians (mem. nominating com. 1989-90), Soc. French Hist. Studies, So. Hist. Assn., Century Club, Phi Beta Kappa (chmn. Am. Scholar com. 1991-93, senator united chpts. 1991—). Avocations: traveling, cycling. Office: Rutgers U Dept History Van Dyck Hall New Brunswick NJ 08903*

LEWIS, DELANO EUGENE, broadcast executive; b. Arkansas City, Kans., Nov. 12, 1938; s. Raymond Ernest and Enna (Wordlow) L.; m. Gayle Carolyn Jones; children: Delano Jr., Brian, Geoffrey, Phillip. BA, U. Kansas, 1960; JD, Washburn U., 1963; LHD (hon.), Marymount U., 1988; D of Humane Letters, Bowie State U., 1992; D of Pub. Svc., George Washington U., 1991. bd. dirs. Eugene & Agnes Meyer Found., GEICO Co., Colgate-Palmolive Co. Staff atty. U.S. Dept. of Justice, Washington, 1963-65, EEOC, Washington, 1965-66; assoc. dir., country dir. U.S. Peace Corps, Nigeria, Uganda, 1966-69; legis. asst. Sen. Edward Brooke Mass., Washington, 1969-71; adminstrv. asst. Congressman Walter Fauntroy, Washington, 1971-73; mgr. pub. affairs Chesapeake & Potomac Telephone Co., Washington, 1973-76, asst. v.p., 1976-83, v.p., 1983-88, pres., 1988-93; pres., CEO Nat. Public Radio, Washington, 1993—; bd. dirs. Eugene & Agnes Meyer Found., Psychiat. Inst., GEICO, Chase Manhattan Corp., Apple Computer, Guest Svcs., Inc., Black Entertainment Television. Pres. Greater Washington Bd. Trade, 1988; chmn. Mayor's Transition Com., 1978, D.C. Youth Employment Adv. Coun., 1992; co-chair D.C. Vocational Edn. and Career Opportunities Com., 1991, NPR Found.; mem. emeritus bd. Washington Performing Arts Soc., 1990—, Nat. Bd. AFRICARE, 1990—; bd. dirs. Lincoln Theatre. Named Washingtonian of Yr. Washingtonian mag. 1978, Man of Yr., Greater Washington bd. trustees, 1992; recipient Pres. medal Cath. U., Washington, 1978, Tree of Life award NCCJ, 1989, Social Responsibility award George Washington U. Sch. Bus., 1990, Spl. award Women of Washington, Disting. Alumni Citation U. Kans. Mem. Kansas Bar Assn., D.C. Bar of Assn., City Club, Georgetown Club, Club at Franklin Sq. Democrat. Roman Catholic. Avocations: jogging, tennis, racquetball. Office: Nat Public Radio 635 Massachusetts Ave NW Washington DC 20001-3753*

LEWIS, DONALD EMERSON, banker; b. Orange, N.J., Apr. 3, 1950; s. Donald Emerson Lewis and Marie (Gannon) Slaght; m. Suzanne Kimm, Oct. 12, 1974; children: Andrew Gannon, Meredith Marie, Carolyn Ann. AB, Villanova U., 1972; MBA, Boston Coll., 1974. V.p. Citibank N.A., N.Y.C., 1974-85, Boston Safe Deposit & Trust Co., N.Y.C., 1985-87; sr. v.p. United Jersey Banks, Princeton, N.J., 1987-91; v.p. Nat. Westminster Bank, Jersey City, 1991—. Republican. Roman Catholic. Club: Canoe Brook Country. Avocations: golf, platform tennis. Office: Nat Westminster Bank 1125 Rte 22 W Bridgewater NJ 08807

LEWIS, DONALD JOHN, mathematics educator; b. Adrian, Minn., Jan. 25, 1926; s. William J. and Ellanora (Masgai) L.; m. Carolyn Dana Hauf, Dec. 28, 1953. BS, Coll. St. Thomas, 1946; PhD, U. Mich., 1950. Instr. Ohio State U., Columbus, 1950-52; asst. prof. U. Notre Dame (Ind.), 1953-57, assoc. prof., 1977-61; assoc. prof. U. Mich., Ann Arbor, 1961-63, prof. maths., 1963—, dept. chair, 1983-94; dir. Divsn. Math. Scis. Nat. Sci. Found., 1995—; mem. Inst. for Adv. Study, 1952-53, 90-91; vis. scientist U. Manchester (Eng.), 1959-61, Cambridge (Eng.), 1960-61; vis. fellow Trinity Coll., Cambridge, 1965, 69, Japanese Soc. for Promotion of Sci., Tokyo, 1974; adv. bd. math. sci. NSF, 1983-86, adv. bd. Math. Panel, 1993-95. Author: Introduction to Algebra, 1965, Calculus and Linear Algebra, 1970; editor: Proceedings of Symposia in Pure Math., 1971; contbr. 55 articles on number theory to profl. jours. Recipient Humboldt Preis award Alexander von Humboldt Soc., Germany, 1980, Disting. Svc. award Am. Math. Soc., 1995; fellow NSF, 1952-53, 59-61. Roman Catholic. Avocations: gardening. Home: 2250 Glendaloch Rd Ann Arbor MI 48104-2832 Office: Math Dept U Mich Ann Arbor MI 48109-1003

LEWIS, DOUGLAS, art historian; b. Centreville, Miss., Apr. 30, 1938; s. Charles Douglas and Beatrice Fenwick (Steward) L. B.A. in History; B.A. in History of Art, Yale U., 1960, M.A., 1963, Ph.D., 1967; B.A. in Fine Arts, Clare Coll., Cambridge (Eng.) U., 1962, M.A., 1966. Asst. in instrn. Yale U., 1962-64; asst. prof. art Bryn Mawr Coll., 1967-68; vis. lectr. U. Calif., Berkeley, spring 1970, fall 1979; adj. prof. Johns Hopkins U., 1973-77; curator sculpture and decorative arts Nat. Gallery Art, Washington, 1968—; professorial lectr. Georgetown U., 1980-93; adj. prof. U. Md., 1989-91, 93—; mem. art adv. coms. Mt. Holyoke Coll. Art Mus., Lawrenceville Sch.; vis. com. Smith Coll. Mus. Art; vice-chmn. nat. citizens stamp adv. com. U.S. Postal Svc.; adv. bd. Centro Palladiano, Vicenza, Italy. Author: The Late Baroque Churches of Venice, 1979, The Drawings of Andrea Palladio, 1981, intro. to Renaissance Master Bronzes, 1986. Mem. Am. fellowship com., Belgian-Am. Ednl. Found.; bd. dirs. Bauman Found. Recipient Copley medal Nat. Portrait Gallery, 1981; Chester Dale fellow; David E. Finley fellow Nat. Gallery Art, 1964-67; Rome Prize fellow Am. Acad. Rome, 1964-66. Mem. Coll. Art Assn. Am., Soc. Archtl. Historians, Nat. Trust Historic Preservation, Washington Collegium for the Humanities (adv. bd.), Manuscript Soc. Episcopalian. Clubs: Yale (N.Y.C.); Falcons (Cambridge U.). Office: Nat Gallery Art Washington DC 20565-0001

LEWIS, DOUGLAS GRINSLADE, Canadian minister, parliament member; b. Toronto, Ont., Can., Apr. 17, 1938; s. Horace Grinslade and Brenda Hazeldine Reynolds; m. Linda Diane Haggans, July 14, 1962; children: Justin, Matthew, Penny, Gillian, Susan. Grad. Chartered Acct., 1962; JD, Osgoode Hall Law Sch., 1967. Bar: Ont. 1969. Assoc. Crawford Lewis Worling Ewart & MacKenzie, Orillia, Ont., 1969-79; mem. Ho. of Commons, 1979—, mem. parliament from Simcoe North, Ont., parliamentary sec. to minister supply and services, 1979-80, spokesman for housing, 1980, dep. opposition house leader, interim opposition house leader, 1983, chmn. pub. accounts com., chmn. fed. Ont. Prog. Conservative Caucus, 1983-84, parliamentary sec. to pres. treasury bd., 1984-85, parliamentary sec. to pres. Queen's privy council for Can., 1985-86, parliamentary sec. to dep. prime minister and govt. house leader, 1986-87, minister of state dep. house leader, minister of state treasury bd., 1987-88, minister of justice and atty. gen. Can., govt. house leader, 1989-90, minister of transport, 1990-91; solicitor gen. of Can., 1991—, minister designate of public security, 1993—. Past pres. Toronto Jr. Bd. Trade, Ont. Jaycees, Can. Jaycees; active various polit. campaigns, 1971-79. Named Queen's counsel, 1984; sworn to Privy Coun., 1987. Fellow Inst. Chartered Accts. Conservative. Mem. United Ch. Office: Solicitor General Canada, 340 Laurier Ave West, Ottawa, ON Canada K1A 0P8 also: 41 Peter St N, Orillia, ON Canada L3V 4Y9 also: 517 Dominion Ave, Midland, ON Canada L4R 1P7

LEWIS, E. GREY, lawyer; b. Altlantic City, N.J., Sept. 27, 1937; s. John Connell and Ella P. (Grey) L.; m. Carolyn Groves; children: Amy, Leslie, Peter, Sarah. AB, Princeton U., 1959; LLB, U. Pa., 1964, D.C. 1964, U.S. Supreme Ct. 1968. Asst. atty. U.S. Atty.'s Office, Washington, 1966-68; dept. asst. atty. gen. civil div. U.S. Dept. Justice, Washington, 1971-73; gen. counsel USN, Washington, 1973-77; ptnr. McDermott, Will & Emery, Washington, 1977—. Recipient Disting. Civillian Svc. award U.S. Navy, 1977. Office: McDermott Will & Emery 1850 K St NW Ste 500 Washington DC 20006-2296

LEWIS, EDWARD ALAN, religious organization adminstrator; b. Brazil, Ind., July 22, 1946; s. Edward and Ruth Margaret (Eberwein) L. B in Music Edn., Grace Coll., 1969; M in Divinity, Grace Sem., 1973. Asst. to pastor, youth dir. Grace Brethren Ch., Winona Lake, Ind., 1969-73; nat. dir. youth ministries Grace Brethren Ch. Christian Edn., Winona Lake, 1973-85; dir. candidate personnel Grace Brethren Fgn. Missions, Winona Lake, 1982-88; exec. dir. Grace Brethren Ch. Christian Edn., Winona Lake, 1989—. Mem. Grace Brethren Ch., Winona Lake, 1969—, exec. mem. denominational youth com., 1984—; moderator Nat. Fellowship of Grace Brethren Chs., 1994—. Mem. Grace Sem. Alumni Assn. (pres. 1984-85), Ind. Dist. Ministerium, Nat. Ministerium Assn. Avocations: music, piano, singing, jogging, travel. Home and Office: PO Box 365 Winona Lake IN 46590-0365

LEWIS, EDWARD B., biology educator; b. Wilkes-Barre, Pa., May 20, 1918; s. Edward B. and Laura (Histed) L.; m. Pamela Harrah, Sept. 26, 1946; children: Hugh, Glenn (dec.), Keith. B.A., U. Minn., 1939; Ph.D., Calif. Inst. Tech., 1942; Phil.D., U. Umea, Sweden, 1982; DSc, U. Minn., 1993. Instr. biology Calif. Inst. Tech., Pasadena, 1944-48, asst. prof., 1949-56, prof., 1956-66, Thomas Hunt Morgan prof., 1966-88, prof. emeritus, 1988—; Rockefeller Found. fellow Sch. Botany, Cambridge U., Eng., 1948-49; mem. Nat. Adv. Com. Radiation, 1958-61; vis. prof. U. Copenhagen, 1975-76, 82; researcher in developmental genetics, somatic effects of radiation. Editor: Genetics and Evolution, 1961. Served to capt. USAAF, 1942-46. Recipient Gairdner Found. Internat. award, 1987, Wolf Found. prize in medicine, 1989, Rosenstiel award, 1990, Nat. Medal of Sci. NSF, 1990, Albert Lasker Basic Med. Rsch. award, 1991, Louisa Gross Horowitz prize Columbia U., 1992. Fellow AAAS; mem. NAS, Genetics Soc. Am. (sec. 1962-64, pres. 1967-69, Thomas Hunt Morgan medal), Am. Acad. Arts and Scis., Royal Soc. (London) (fgn. mem.), Am. Philos. Soc., Genetical Soc. Great Britian (hon.). Home: 805 Winthrop Rd San Marino CA 91108-1709 Office: Calif Inst Tech Div Biology 1201 E California Blvd Pasadena CA 91125-0001

LEWIS, EDWARD SHELDON, chemistry educator; b. Berkeley, Calif., May 7, 1920; s. Gilbert Newton and Mary (Sheldon) L.; m. Fofo Catsinas, Dec. 21, 1955; children—Richard Peter, Gregory Gilbert. B.S., U. Calif., Berkeley, 1940; M.A., Harvard U., 1947, Ph.D., 1947. NRC postdoctoral fellow UCLA, 1947-48; from asst. prof. to prof. chemistry Rice U., Houston, 1948-90, prof. emeritus, 1990—, chmn. dept. chemistry, 1963-67, 80-85; Vis. prof. U. Southampton, Eng., 1957, Phys. Chem. Lab., Oxford (Eng.) U., 1967-68, U. Kent, Canterbury, Eng., 1977, H.C. Ørsted Inst. , U. Copenhagen, 1980. Contbr. articles to profl. jours.; Editor: Investigation of Rates and Mechanisms of Reactions, 1974. Served with USNR, 1944-46. Guggenheim fellow, 1968. Fellow AAAS, Royal Irish Acad.; mem. Am. Chem. Soc. (S.W. regional award 1987), Royal Soc. of Chemistry, Phi Beta Kappa, Sigma Xi, Phi Lambda Upsilon. Home: 5651 Chevy Chase Dr Houston TX 77056-4004

LEWIS, EDWIN A., communications company executive; b. Bronx, N.Y., Oct. 28, 1942. BBA, Baruch Coll., 1964. CPA, N.Y. Acctg. surp. Pall Corp., Sea Cliff, N.Y., 1964-65; various staff positions Deloitte Haskins & Sells, N.Y.C., 1965-75; ptnr. Deloitte Haskins & Sells, 1975-82; with Hearst Corp., N.Y.C., 1983—; v.p., treas. Hearst Corp., 1984—. Mem. Am. Inst. CPA's, N.Y. State Soc. CPA's, Fin. Execs. Inst. Avocation: antique collecting. Office: Hearst Corp 959 8th Ave New York NY 10019-3737

LEWIS, EDWIN REYNOLDS, biomedical engineering educator; b. Los Angeles, July 14, 1934; s. Edwin McMurtry and Sally Newman (Reynolds) L.; m. Elizabeth Louise McLean, June 11, 1960; children: Edwin McLean, Sarah Elizabeth. AB in Biol. Sci., Stanford U., 1956, MSEE, 1957, Engr., 1959, PhD in Elec. Engring., 1962. With research staff Librascope div. Gen. Precision Inc., Glendale, Calif., 1961-67; mem. faculty dept. elec. engring. and computer sci. U. Calif., Berkeley, 1967—, dir. bioengring. tng. program, 1969-77, prof. elec. engring. and computer sci., 1971-94, prof. grad. sch., 1994—, assoc. dean grad. div., 1977-82, assoc. dean interdisciplinary studies coll. engring., 1988—; chair joint program bioengring. U. Calif., Berkeley and San Francisco, 1988-91. Author: Network Models in Population Biology, 1977, (with others) Neural Modeling, 1977, The Vertebrate Inner Ear, 1985, also numerous articles. Grantee NSF, NASA, 1984, 87, Office Naval Rsch., 1990-93, NIH, 1975—; Neurosci. Rsch. Program fellow, 1966, 69; recipient Disting. Teaching Citation U. Calif., 1972; Jacob Javits neurosci. investigator NIH, 1984-91. Fellow IEEE, Acoustical Soc. Am.; mem. AAAS, Assn. Rsch. in Otolaryngology, Soc. Neurosci., Toastmasters (area lt. gov. 1966-67), Sigma Xi. Office: U Calif Dept Elec Engring & Computer Scis Berkeley CA 94720

LEWIS, ELMA I., cultural organization artistic director; b. Boston, Sept. 15, 1921; d. Clairmont McDonald and Edwardine (Jordan) L. B in Literary Interpretation, Emerson Coll., 1943; MEd, Boston U., 1944; HHD (hon.), Emerson Coll., 1968, Anna Maria Coll., 1968, Boston Coll., 1971, Bridgewater State Coll., 1976, Stonehill Coll., 1979; DFA (hon.), Bates Coll., 1971, Colby Coll., 1971, Regis Coll., 1973, Smith Coll., 1976, Brown U., 1982, Mass. Coll. Art, 1985; ArtsD (hon.), Harvard U., 1972, Merrimac Coll., 1973, Clark U., 1973; D in Pedagogy (hon.), R.I. Coll., 1976; MusD (hon.), New Eng. Conservatory Music, 1977; LittD (hon.), Franklin Pierce Coll., 1977, Northeastern U., 1979; LHD (hon.), Framingham State Coll., 1982, New Eng. Conservatory, 1982; D in Fine and Performing Arts (hon.), Southeastern Mass. U., 1985. Dance tchr. Doris Jones Sch. Dance (name now Jones Haywood Ballet, Washington), Boston, 1935-41; English, speech tchr. Roxbury Meml. High Sch. Girls, Boston, 1942-43; speech therapy tchr. Woodward Inst., Quincy, Mass., 1942-43, Habit Clinics of Boston Mental Health, 1942-43; fine arts worker Harriet Tubman House, Boston, 1945-49, League of Women for Community Service, Boston, 1943-45; dir., choreographer Robert Gould Shaw House Chorus, Boston, 1946-68; ballet mistess, drama instr. Elma Lewis Sch. Fine Arts, Boston, 1950-71; founder, artistic dir. Nat. Ctr. Afro-Am. Artists, Boston, 1969—; cons. Boston Pub. Schs. Program Devel. Office, 1966-67, Nat. Inst. Edn., Washington, Nat. Endowment for Arts. Contbr. articles to profl. jours. Trustee Mass. Coll. Art, Sta. WGBH Ednl. Soc., Boston Zool. Soc.; mem. bd. overseers Mus. Fine Arts; mem. vis. com. Mus. Fine Arts; bd. dirs. NAACP, Boston, Greater Boston Diabetes Found.; mem. corp. Northeastern U., Joslin Diabetes Found.; mem. U.S. Pres.'s Com. on Arts and Humanities. Recipient Mayor's citation, 1972,74,75, Gov.'s citation 1973-75, City Council citation 1973-75, Disting. Citizen award Am. Soc. Pub. Adminstrs., 1972, U.S. HEW citation, 1971, Mass. State Legislature citation, 1975, Gold Key award Boston Coll., 1976, Boston Jaycees cert. appreciation, 1978, Outstanding Ednl. Contribution citation Black Educators Alliance Mass., 1981, McArthur Prize Fellows award, 1987, Distinguished Service award Nat. Alumni Council, Silver medal Boston U., 1982, Presdl. Citation Pres.'s Com. on the Arts and Humanities, Washington, 1983, Humanitarian award Mass. Assn. Psychologists, 1985, Monarch award Nat. Inst. Culture and Art, 1986; named into Acad. Disting. Bostonians, Greater Boston C. of C., 1985; recipient of 100 other citations and awards. Fellow Am. Acad. Arts Scis.; mem. Boston U. Nat. Alumni Council (Disting Service award 1982). Subject of several hundred newspaper, mag. articles and TV productions. Home: 15 Homestead St Dorchester MA 02121-1405 Office: Nat Ctr Afro Am Artists Inc 122 Elm Hill Ave Dorchester MA 02121-2923

LEWIS, EMANUEL RAYMOND, historian, librarian, psychologist; b. Oakland, Calif., Nov. 30, 1928; s. Jacob A. and Rose (Grossman) L.; m. Joan R. Wilson, Feb. 7, 1954; 1 son, Joseph J.; m. Eleanor M. Gamarsh, Aug. 24, 1967. B.A., U. Calif., Berkeley, 1951, M.A., 1953; Ph.D., U. Oreg., 1962. Asst. prof. psychology Oreg. Coll. Edn., 1961-62, Oreg. State U., 1962-67; project mgr. System Devel. Corp., Falls Church, Va., 1968-69; vis. postdoctoral research asso. in Am. history Smithsonian Instn., Washington, 1969-70; chief historian, dir. research Contract Archeology, Alexandria, Va., 1971-73; librarian U.S. Ho. of Reps., Washington, 1973-95. Author: Seacoast Fortifications of the United States, 1970, 2d edit. 1979, 3d edit. 1993; editor: The Educational Information Center, 1969. Served with M.I. U.S. Army, 1954-56. NIMH research fellow, 1960. Office: B-18 Cannon House Office Bldg Washington DC 20515

LEWIS, FELICE FLANERY, lawyer, educator; b. Plaquemine, La., Oct. 5, 1920; d. Lowell Baird and E. Elizabeth (Lee) Flanery; m. Francis Russell Lewis, Dec. 22, 1944. BA, U. Wash., 1947; PhD, NYU, 1974; JD, Georgetown U., 1981. Bar: N.Y. 1982. Dean L.I. Univ., Liberal Arts & Scis., Bklyn., 1974-78; assoc. Harry G. English, Bklyn., 1983-85, 91—; adj. prof. polit. sci. L.I. Univ., Bklyn., 1983—. Author: Literature, Obscenity and Law, 1976; co-editor: Henry Miller, Years of Trial & Triumph, 1962-64,

1978. Home: 28 Whitney Cir Glen Cove NY 11542-1316 Office: Harry G English 7219 3rd Ave Brooklyn NY 11209-2131

LEWIS, FLORA, journalist; b. Los Angeles; d. Benjamin and Pauline (Kallin) L.; m. Sydney Gruson, Aug. 17, 1945 (div.); children—Kerry, Sheila, Lindsey. B.A., UCLA, 1941; M.S., Columbia U., 1942, LHD (hon.), 1984; LL.D., Princeton U., 1981; hon. doctorate, Mt. Holyoke Coll., Bucknell U., Muhlenberg Coll., Manhattan Marymount. Reporter Los Angeles Times, 1941, A.P., N.Y., Washington, London, 1942-46; free lance or contract for N.Y. Times Mag., London, Warsaw, Berlin, Hague, Mexico City, Tel Aviv, 1946-54, Prague, Warsaw, 1956-58; editor McGraw-Hill, N.Y.C., 1955; bur. chief Washington Post, Bonn, London, N.Y.C., 1958-66; syndicated columnist Newsday, Paris, N.Y.C., 1967-72; bur. chief N.Y. Times, Paris, 1972-80; European diplomatic corr. N.Y. Times, 1976-80, fgn. affairs columnist 1980-90, sr. columnist, 1990—. Author: Case History of Hope, 1958, Red Pawn, 1964, One of Our H-Bombs is Missing, 1967, Europe: A Tapestry of Nations, 1987, Europe: A Road to Unity, 1992; contbr. to anthologies, books, mags. Arthur D. Morse fellow in communications and society Aspen Inst. for Humanistic Studies, 1977; decorated chevalier Legion d'Honneur; recipient awards for best interpretation fgn. affairs, 1956, best reporting fgn. affairs, 1960; Overseas Press Club award; Columbia Journalism Sch. 50th Anniversary Honor award, 1963; award for disting. diplomatic reporting George Washington U. Sch. Fgn. Service, 1978, Carr Van Anda award Ohio State U. Sch. Communications, 1982, Fourth Estate award Nat. Press Club, 1985, Matrix award for Newspapers N.Y. Women in Communications Inc., 1985, Elmer Holmes Bobst award in Arts and Letters NYU, 1987, Internat. House award, 1990; named hon. fellow UCLA Coll. Arts and Scis. Mem. Coun. on Fgn. Rels., Internat. Inst. for Strategic Studies (coun.), Inst. for East-West Security Studies, Phi Beta Kappa. Office: Am University in Paris, 34 Ave de New York, 75014 Paris 75116, France

LEWIS, FLOYD WALLACE, former electric utility executive; b. Lincoln County, Miss., Sept. 23, 1925; s. Thomas Cassidy and Lizzie (Lofton) L.; m. Jimmie Etoile Slawson, Dec. 27, 1949; children: Floyd Wallace, Gail, Julie, Ann, Carol, Michael Paul. B.B.A., Tulane U., 1945, LL.B., 1949. Bar: La. 1949. With New Orleans Pub. Service Inc., 1949-62, v.p. chief fin. officer, 1960-62; v.p. Ark. Power & Light Co., Little Rock, 1962-63; sr. v.p. Ark. Power & Light Co., 1963-67; exec. v.p., dir. La. Power & Light Co., New Orleans, 1967-68; pres. La. Power & Light Co., 1968-70, chief exec. officer, 1968-71, chmn. bd., 1970-72; pres. Middle South Utilities, Inc., 1970-79, 80-85, chmn. bd., 1979-85, also dir., chief exec. officer, 1972-85; pres., dir. Middle South Services, Inc., New Orleans, 1970-75, chmn., 1975-85, chief exec. officer, 1972-79; pres., dir. Middle South Energy, Inc., 1974-85; chmn. bd. System Fuels, Inc., 1972-85; dir. New Orleans br. Fed. Res. Bank, 1974-75, chmn., 1975; past dir. Fed. Res. Bank of Atlanta, Breeder Reactor Corp., New Orleans Pub. Service Inc., Ark. Power and Light Co., La. Power & Light Co., Miss. Power and Light Co., U.S. Chamber Commerce; mem. adv. com. Elec. Cos. Advt. Program, 1969-72, chmn., 1970-71; mem. electric utility adv. com. to Fed. Energy Adminstrn., 1975-76; chmn. Edison Electric Inst., 1976-77, mem. exec. com., 1974-78; mem. exec. com. Assn. Edison Illuminating Cos., 1973-80; dir. Electric Power Research Inst., 1977-82, chmn., 1979-81; dir. Am. Nuclear Energy Council, 1982-86. Mem. exec. bd. New Orleans area council Boy Scouts Am., 1967-80, v.p., 1970-74, pres., 1975-76, mem. regional exec. com., 1968-80; v.p. Com. for a Better La., 1975-76, sr. v.p., 1976-77, pres., 1977-78; bd. dirs. La. World Expn. Inc., 1976-89, chmn., 1980-81, 83-89, pres., 1981-83; chmn. Utility Nuclear Power Oversight Com., 1979-81; vice chmn. campaign United Fund, New Orleans, 1970, chmn., 1971; bd. dirs. New Orleans Symphony Soc., 1974-75, Atomic Indsl. Forum, 1982-86, vice chmn., 1985-86; bd. dirs. Pub. Affairs Research Council of La.; pres. New Orleans Bapt. Sem. Found., 1973-76, 91-92; trustee La. Coll., 1984-90; New Orleans Baptist Theol. Sem., 1954-62, 1968-78, v.p., 1970-78; bd. adminstrs. Tulane U., 1973-88, bd. visitors, 1968-71; bd. govs. Med. Center, 1969-73, vice chmn., 1969-71; chmn. alumni adv. council Grad. Sch. Bus., 1970-73; bd. dirs. U.S. Com. Energy Awareness, 1982-85, vice-chmn., 1983-84, chmn., 1985; v.p. Internat. House, 1970; trustee Com. Econ. Devel., 1972-87; mem. bd. Ochsner Med. Found., 1976-95, mem. exec. com., 1977-95; 1st chmn. Parents Council, Furman U., mem. Parents Council, Wake Forest U., 1980-81. Served to ensign USNR, 1945-46. Recipient Silver Beaver, Silver Antelope Boy Scouts Am.; Oliver Townsend medal Atomic Indsl. Forum; Outstanding Alumni award Grad. Sch. Bus., 1970; Disting. Alumnus award Tulane U., 1983. Mem. Tulane Alumni Assn. (exec. com., treas. 1970), Order of Coif, Beta Gamma Sigma, Omicron Delta Kappa, Beta Theta Pi, Phi Delta Phi. Baptist (deacon). Office: 4480 Gen DeGaulle Dr New Orleans LA 70131

LEWIS, FORBES DOWNER, computer science educator, researcher; b. New Haven, Apr. 15, 1942; s. Taylor Downer Lewis and Clara (Bartholow) Hall. B.S., Cornell U., 1967, M.S., 1969, Ph.D., 1970. Asst. prof. Harvard U., Cambridge, Mass., 1970-75; assoc. prof. SUNY-Albany, 1975-78; assoc. prof. U. Ky., Lexington, 1978-83, prof. computer sci., 1983—. Contbr. articles to profl. jours. Served with U.S. Army, 1960-63. Mem. Assn. for Computing Machinery, Assn. for Symbolic Logis, Soc. for Indsl. Applied Math., IEEE. Office: National Sci Found 1800 G St NW Washington DC 20550-0001

LEWIS, FRANCES AARONSON, retail company executive; b. Bklyn., June 27, 1922; d. Nathaniel Bernard L. and Lillian (Beller) Aaronson; m. Sydney Lewis, Sept. 3, 1942; children: Sydney, Andrew M., Susan Lewis Butler. B.A., U. Mich., 1942; D.H.L. hon., Va. Union U., 1977; H.H.D. hon., Va. Commonwealth U., 1983. Cert. diamond evaluator and appraiser Gemological Inst. Am. Entrepreneur, founder Best Products Co., Inc., Richmond, Va., 1957—; now exec. v.p., vice chmn. bd. Best Products Co., Inc. Trustee Va. Environ. Endowment, Richmond, 1978—, Va. Mus. Fine Arts, 1990—, Cir. City Found.; mem. Richmond Pub. Sch. Bd., 1980—; mem. legis. affairs com. C. of C. Richmond, 1981—; mem. exhbns. com. Va. Mus. Fine Art, Richmond, 1982—; mem. Va. State Fedn. Block Grant com. City of Richmond, 1983; mem. Va. State Bd. Edn., 1983—, vocational ednl. policy com., 1987—, chmn. curriculum and instructions and profl. edn. 1987—; tchr. edn. com., 1986—; bd. trustees Washington & Lee U., 1984—; bd. dirs. Circuit City Found. 1987; mem. capital funds bd. United Way, 1985—; judaic culture adv. com. Va. Commonwealth U., 1987—; adv. bd. Garfield F. Childs Meml. Fund, 1987—; Recipient Disting. Virginian award State of Va., 1972; recipient ann. award Federated Arts Council, Richmond, 1976, Jackson Davis award for Disting. Service to High Edn. Va., 1978, Thomas Jefferson award State of Va., 1978, Pres.'s Nat. Medal of Arts, 1987, Gov. award for Arts in Va., 1985. Mem. Va. Retail Mchts. Assn. (award for Retailer of Yr. 1982), Beta Gamma Sigma, DAR (Medal of Honor 1983). Democrat. Jewish. Office: Best Products Co Inc PO Box 26303 1400 Best Plz Richmond VA 23285-0046

LEWIS, FRANK HARLAN, botanist, educator; b. Redlands, Calif., Jan. 8, 1919; s. Frank Hooker and Mary Elizabeth (Smith) L.; m. Margaret Ruth Ensign, Aug. 2, 1945 and Aug. 2, 1984; children: Donald Austin, Frank Murray; m. Ann Gibbons, Dec. 23, 1968 (dec. 1983). AA, San Bernardino Valley Coll., 1939; BA, UCLA, 1941, MA, 1942, PhD, 1946; postgrad., Calif. Inst. Tech., 1942-44. Mem. faculty UCLA, 1946-82, prof. botany, 1956-82, prof.emeritus, 1982—, systematist supt. sta., 1956-62, chmn. dept., 1959-62, dean of life scis., 1962-82, dean emeritus, 1982—; Cons. genetics NSF, 1958-61, specialized biol. facilities, 1963-68. Bd. editors: Evolution, 1951-53; editor, 1972-74; bd. editors: Am. Jour. Botany, 1964-66, Am. Naturalist, 1965-67, 77-79; chmn. bd. editors U. Calif. publs. in botany, 1958-62. Trustee Graeme Joseph Revolving Scholarship Fund, 1968-86. NRC fellow John Innes Hort. Instn., London, 1947-48; Guggenheim fellow, 1954-55. Fellow AAAS (council mem. 1974-76), Calif. Acad. Sci.; mem. Bot. Soc. Am. (pres. Pacific div. 1959, Merit award 1972), Soc. Study Evolution (pres. 1961), Internat. Orgn. Plant Biosystematists (exec. com. 1961-81, v.p. 1964-69, pres. 1969-75), Am. Soc. Naturalists (pres. 1971), Am. Soc. Plant Taxonomists (pres. 1969), Internat. Soc. Plant Taxonomists, Phi Beta Kappa, Sigma Xi. Home: 14280 W Sunset Blvd Pacific Palisades CA 90272-3933

LEWIS, GARY, trucking executive; b. 1953. Pres. Schneider National Carriers, Green Bay, Wis., 1979—. Office: Schneider National Carriers 3101 South Packerland Dr Green Bay WI 54304

LEWIS, GENE DALE, historian, educator; b. Globe, Ariz., Feb. 20, 1931; s. Abner E. and May J. (Hyatt) L.; m. Dottie Ladd Bidlingmeyer, Aug. 3, 1963. BA, Ariz. State U., 1951, MA, 1952; PhD, U. Ill., 1957. Lectr. Ariz. State U., 1953, So. Ill. U., 1957-58; vis. assoc. prof. history U. Ill., Urbana, 1965, Case Western Res. U., Cleve., 1966; prof. history U. Cin., 1958—; acting head dept., 1981-82, dir. grad. studies, 1989, head dept., 1989—; sr. v.p., provost, 1973-76. Author: Charles Ellet Jr., Engineer as Individualist, 1968; editor: New Historical Perspectives: Essays on the Black Experience in Antebellum America, 1984; co-editor Greater Cincinnati Bicentennial History Series, 1988—. Recipient Barbour award for excellence U. Cin., 1969, Nat. award Omicron Delta Kappa, 1968. Mem. AAUP, So. Hist. Assn., Am. Hist. Assn., Orgn. Am. Historians. Home: 444 Rawson Woods Ln Cincinnati OH 45220-1142 Office: U Cin Dept History Cincinnati OH 45221

LEWIS, GENE EVANS, retired medical equipment company executive; b. Terrell, Tex., May 17, 1928; s. John Evans and Helen Elizabeth (Paterson) L.; m. Sonya Dolishny, Jan. 21, 1950; children: Robert, Melissa. BSEE, Tex. A&M U., 1949. Sales, mktg. and engring. mgr. GE, Schenectady, Dallas, Pittsfield, Holyoke, Lynn, 1950-68; gen. mgr. various bus. GE, Milw., 1970-77; group product mgr. Picker X-Ray, Cleve., 1968-70; pres. sci. instruments div. Am. Optical Corp., Southbridge, Mass., 1977-78; pres. internat. div. Am. Optical Corp., 1978-79, pres., 1979-84; pres. Baker Instruments Corp., Allentown, Pa., 1985-88; chmn., CEO Novecon Technologies, 1994—; bd. dirs. EDITEK, Inc., Gaitscan, Alpine Group, Inc., Am. Drug Co.; mem. adv. bd. The Holly Inn; sr. adv. bd. Novecon Corp. With Signal Corps U.S. Army, 1949. Mem. Calibogue Club, Sea Pines Country Club. Home: 25 Spartina Cres Hilton Head Island SC 29928-2925 Office: Novecon Technologies Ste 300 12030 Sunrise Valley Dr Reston VA 22091

LEWIS, GEORGE RALPH, consumer goods company executive; b. Burgess, Va., Mar. 7, 1941; s. Spencer Harcum and Edith Pauline (Toulson) L.; m. Lillian Charlotte Glenn, Oct. 11, 1963. BSBA, Hampton U., 1963; MBA, Iona Coll., 1968. Product analyst Gen. Foods Corp., White Plains, N.Y., 1963-66; fin. analyst W.R. Grace, N.Y.C., 1966-67; corp. analyst Philip Morris Inc., N.Y.C., 1967-69, sr. planning analyst, 1969-70, mgr. fin. rels., 1970-72, mgr. fin. svcs., 1972-73, asst. treas., 1973-75; v.p. fin. and planning, treas. Philip Morris Indsl., Milw., 1975-82; v.p., treas. Philip Morris Cos., Inc., N.Y.C., 1984—; v.p. fin. The Seven Up Co., St. Louis, 1982-84; bd. dirs. Ctrl. Fidelity Bank, Richmond, Va., Kemper Nat. Ins. Cos., Ceridian Corp.; nat. adv. com. Profl. Golfers' Assn. Am. Trustee Hampton (Va.) U.; bd. dirs. Nat. Urban League, N.Y.C. Recipient Arthur A. Loftus Achievement award in Fin., Iona Coll., 1981, Outstanding Twenty Yr. Alumnus award Hampton U., 1983. Mem. Nat. Corp. Treas. Assn., Nat. Bankers Assn. (corp. adv. bd.), Omega Psi Phi, Sigma Pi Phi. Office: Philip Morris Cos Inc 120 Park Ave New York NY 10017-5523

LEWIS, GEORGE RAYMOND, clinical social worker; b. Bridgeton, N.J., July 7, 1944; s. Raymond and Evelyn Rhoda (Mitchell) L.; m. Tenelia Kay Boykin, Sept. 3, 1966. BA, U. N.Mex., 1966; MSW, Our Lady of the Lake Coll., 1971. Cert. social worker; lic. ind. social worker. With N.Mex. Health and Social Services Dept., 1971-92; dist. rsng. officer N.Mex. Health and Social Services Dept., Roswell, 1972-73, field office mgr., 1973-75, social worker cons., 1975-84, dist. ops. mgr., 1984-92; clin. dir. Assurance Home Inc., 1992—; behavioral sci. specialist Cmty. Guidance Ctr., San Antonio, 1971; adj. instr. N.Mex. State U. Las Cruces, 1971, 83, 85, 94, Ea. N.Mex. U., Roswell, 1973-76, 92; clin. dir. Chaves County 1st Offender Program, Roswell, 1974-77; field instr. Tex. Tech. U., Lubbock, 1981; bd. dirs. Assurance Home Inc., Roswell; mem. N.Mex. Bd. Social Work Examiners, 1989-93; N.Mex. del. to am. Assn. State Social Work Bd., 1990-93. Bd. dirs. Chaves County Home Health Agy. Inc., Roswell, 1973-76, Parents Anonymous of N.Mex. Inc., 1978-79; mem. State N.Mex. Acupuncture Bd., 1994-95. Named an Outstanding Young Man of Am., U.S. Jaycees, 1978, 81. Mem. Nat. Assn. Social Workers (New Mexico Rose Praisner award, 1992), Acad. Cert. Social Workers, Order of the Arrow, Blue Key. Democrat. Baptist. Avocations: greenhouse gardening, camping, fishing, hunting. Home: 1018 N Plains Park Dr Roswell NM 88201-2516 Office: Assurance Home Inc 100 E 18th St Roswell NM 88201

LEWIS, GEORGE WITHROW, business executive; b. Berwyn, Ill., May 13, 1929; s. George Edward and Katherine (Withrow) L.; m. Ellen Freer Baker, Sept. 14, 1963 (div. Apr. 1987); children: George Baker, Martha Freer; m. Elizabeth Morgan Williams, Dec. 26, 1992. A.B., Princeton, 1951; M.B.A., Harvard, 1955. With Ford Motor Co., 1955-62; cons. McKinsey & Co., N.Y.C., 1962-64; mng. dir. Rolls-Royce Motors Internat. Div., 1964-83. Vice-pres. fin. Eisenhower Exchange Fellowships, 1985-92. 1st lt., arty. AUS, 1952-53, Korea. Mem. Harvard Bus. Sch. Club of Phila. (past pres.). Episcopalian (vestryman). Home: 1325 Lombard St Philadelphia PA 19147-1003

LEWIS, GOLDY SARAH, real estate developer, corporation executive; b. West Selkirk, Man., Can., June 15, 1921; d. David and Rose (Dwor) Kimmel; m. Ralph Milton Lewis, June 12, 1941; children: Richard Alan, Robert Edward, Roger Gordon, Randall Wayne. B.S., UCLA, 1943; postgrad., U. So. Calif., 1944-45. Pvt. practice acctg. L.A., 1945-57, law office mgr., 1953-55; dir., exec. v.p. Lewis Homes, Upland, Calif., 1955—, Lewis Construction Co. Inc., Upland, 1959—, Lewis Bldg. Co. Inc., Las Vegas, 1960—, Republic Sales Co., Inc., 1956—, Kimmel Enterprises, Inc. 1959—; mng. partner Lewis Homes of Calif., 1973—; mng. ptnr. Lewis Homes of Nev., 1972—, Western Properties, 1972—, Foothill Investment Co., 1971—, Republic Mgmt. Co., 1978—. Contbr. articles to mags., jours. Mem. Dean's Coun. UCLA Grad. Sch. Architecture and Urban Planning; mem. UCLA Found., Chancellor's Assocs.; endowed Ralph and Goldy Lewis Ctr. for Regional Policy at UCLA, 1989, Ralph and Goldy Lewis Hall of Planning and Devel. at U. S.C., 1989, others. Recipient 1st award of distinction Am. Builder mag., 1963, Homer Briggs Svc. to Youth award West End YMCA, 1990, Spirit of Life award City of Hope, 1993; co-recipient Builder of Yr. award Profl. Builder Mag., 1988, Housing Person of Yr. award Nat. Housing Conf., 1990, Entrepreneur of Yr. award Inland Empire, 1990; Ralph and Goldy Lewis Sports Ctr. named in their honor City of Rancho Cucamonga, 1988, also several other parks and sports fields including Lewis Park in Claremont.; named one of Woman of Yr. Calif. 25th Senate Dist., 1989, (with husband Ralph M. Lewis) Disting. Chief Exec. Officer, Calif. State U., San Bernadino, 1991, Mgmt. Leaders of the Yr. Univ. Calif. Riverside, 1993. Mem. Nat. Assn. Home Builders, Bldg. Industry Assn. So. Calif. (Builder of Yr. award Baldy View chpt. 1988), Internat. Coun. Shopping Ctrs., Urban Land Inst. Office: Lewis Homes PO Box 670 Upland CA 91785-0670

LEWIS, GORDON GILMER, golf course architect; b. Shawnee, Okla., Sept. 7, 1950; s. Ted Eugene and Janet Garvin (Panner) L.; m. Karen Louise McKenzie, June 2, 1973 (div. Dec. 1981); children: Melanie Marie Lewis-Lehr, Katie McKenzie Lewis-Lehr; m. Susette Mamie London, June 11, 1988; children: London Marshall, Sarah June Victoria. B of Landscape Architecture, Kans. State U., 1974. Registered landscape architect, Ala., Kans., Fla. Golf course architect David Gill, St. Charles, Ill., 1974-75, Charles M. Graves Orgn., Atlanta, 1975-78, Gordon G. Lewis, Naples, Fla., 1978—. Prin. works include Meadowbrook Links, Rapid City, S.D. (Top 50 Pub. Courses in U.S.), The Hulman Links at Los Creek, Terre Haute, Ind. (Top 50 Pub. Courses in U.S.), Lagoon Park, Montgomery, Ala. (Top 75 Pub. Courses in U.S.), The Forest, Ft. Myers, Fla. (Top 50 Courses in Fla.), The Vines, Estero, Fla. (Golf Digest One of Top New Courses 1986), Worthington, Bonita Springs, Fla., Tsai-Hsing, Taipei, Taiwan, others. Republican. Presbyterian. Avocation: golf. Home: 5098 2nd Ave SW Naples FL 33999-2528

LEWIS, GRANT STEPHEN, lawyer; b. N.Y.C., Apr. 27, 1942; s. Arnold R. and Gladys F.; m. Shari J. Gruhn, Sept. 15, 1974; 1 dau., Carrie Ann. A.B., Bates Coll., 1962; J.D., Harvard U., 1965. Bar: N.Y. 1966, U.S. Supreme Ct. 1975, all fed. cir. cts., various fed. dist. cts. With firm LeBoeuf, Lamb, Greene & MacRae (formerly LeBoeuf, Lamb, Leiby & MacRae), N.Y.C., 1966—, ptnr., 1973—. Mem. ABA, Assn. Bar City N.Y. Clubs: University, Harvard (N.Y.C.). Contbr. articles to profl. jours. Office: LeBoeuf Lamb Greene & MacRae 125 W 55th St New York NY 10019-5369

LEWIS, GREEN PRYOR, JR., community service administrator; b. Columbus, Ga., Apr. 27, 1945; s. Green Pryor Sr. and Minnie Mae (Jones)

L.; m. Christine McGhee, Aug. 22, 1945; children: Raquel Leneise Lewis Davis, Green Pryor III, LeKeisha Shanquata. BS, Ft. Valley State Coll., 1966; cert., George Meany Inst., U. Ala., So. Labor Sch., U. Fla. Labor Inst. Asst. mgr. Am. toy co. Gaylord's Dept. Store, Columbus, 1966-67; tchr. sci., coach Muscogee County Sch. Sys., Columbus, 1966-69; field rep. region 5 AFL-CIO, Atlanta, 1969-81; asst. regional dir., coord. Houston orgn. program AFL-CIO, Houston, 1981-83; asst. nat. dir. orgn. and field svcs. AFL-CIO, Washington, 1984-93; dir. region V, asst. nat. dir. AFL-CIO, Washington and Atlanta, 1987-88; dir. dept. comty. svcs. AFL-CIO, Washington, 1993—; advisor Frontlash, AFL-CIO, Washington, 1984—. Editor-in-chief: (h.s. ann.) Tigonian, 1963. Pres. Proud Neighbor of South DeKalb, DeKalb County, Ga.; vice chmn. precinct South DeKalb Dem. Ctrl. Com., DeKalb County; labor liaison to Mayor M. Jackson, Atlanta Labor Coun., AFL-CIO, Atlanta; labor liaison to Congressman Andrew Young, Ga. AFL-CIO/Atlanta Labor Coun., Ga. 5th Congl. Dist.; trustee, pres. sanctuary choir Seaton AME Ch.; exec. bd. del. Enterprise Estates P.G.; mem. Coalition Labor Women; bd. govs. United Way Am. Recipient Histadrut Menorah award Nt. Com. for Labor, Israel-Histadrut, 1989, Keeper of the Flame award NAACP, 1992. Mem. Svc. Employees Internat. Union (# 80), A. Philip Randolph Inst. (exec. com. Achievement award 1992). Avocations: woodwork, modern dance, bicycling, singing, reading. Home: 11412 Bayard Dr Mitchellville MD 20721 Office: AFL-CIO Dept Cmty Svcs 815-16th St NW Washington DC 20006

LEWIS, GREGORY SCOTT, lawyer; b. Larchmont, N.Y., Mar. 13, 1951; s. Arthur Dee and Hildegard (Bair) L.; m. Susan Hall, Sept. 7, 1974; children: Kip, Marc, Trevor. BA in Polit. Sci., Amherst Coll., 1975; JD, Duke U., 1978. Bar: D.C. 1978. Assoc. Morgan, Lewis & Bockius, Washington, 1978-86, ptnr., 1986—; assoc. tennis profl. New Canaan (Conn.) Field Club, summers 1973-76. Contbr. articles to legal jours. Pres. Choral Arts Soc. Washington, 1981-84, bd. dirs., 1989—; bd. dirs. Soc. for Edn. in Performing Arts. Mem. ABA (chmn. labor and employment law com. pub. utility law sect.), D.C. Bar, Washington Revels. Office: Morgan Lewis & Bockius 1800 M St NW Washington DC 20036-5869

LEWIS, GREGORY WILLIAMS, scientist; b. Seattle, Mar. 3, 1940; s. Delbert Srofe and Eileen Juliann (Williams) L.; m. Stephanie Marie Schwab, Sept. 18, 1966; children: Jeffrey Williams, Garrick Peterson. BS, Wash. State U., 1962, MA, 1965, PhD, 1970. Tchr., rsch. asst. Wash. State U., Pullman, 1965-69; prin. investigator U.S. Army Med. Rsch. Lab., Ft. Knox, Ky., 1970-74; prin. investigator USN Pers. R & D Ctr., San Diego, 1974—, head neurosci. lab., 1980—, leader security systems, 1981-83, head neurosci. projects office, 1987-89, div. head neuroscis., 1989-95, sr. prin. scientist, 1995—; cons. in field. Contbr. articles to profl. jours. Bd. dirs., pres. Mesa View Homeowners Assn., Calif., 1980-82; bd. dirs. Santa Fe Hills Homeowners Assn., Calif., 1994—. Capt. U.S. Army, 1967-74. Fellow Internat. Orgn. Psychophysiology; mem. AAAS, Soc. Neurosci., Internat. Brain Rsch. Orgn., N.Y. Acad. Scis., Soc. Psychophysiol. Rsch., Sigma Xi, Alpha Kappa Delta, Delta Chi, Psi Chi. Achievements include research in ophthalmic ultrasonography; neuroelectric research and development of brain activity and variability for improving the evaluation of education and training materials, personnel assessment, and prediction of job performance; physiological correlates of performance; psychophysiology of individual differences; neuromagnetic research directed toward individual differences and personnel performance; neuroelectric and neuromagnetic data acquisition and analysis; patent issued for development of neuroelectric and neuromagnetic method and system for individual identification and impairment of function using artificial neural network analyses; developing personnel performance models for use in rapid prototyping of system designs. Avocations: music, electronics, working on timber land and vacation log home. Home: 410 Santa Cecelia Solana Beach CA 92075-1505 Office: US Navy Pers R&D Ctr 53335 Ryne Rd San Diego CA 92152

LEWIS, HARRIET GERBERT, plumbing fixtures manufacturing company executive; b. Chgo., Nov. 30, 1919; d. Max and Lottie (Schiffman) Gerber; m. Maurice L. Lewis, Oct. 12, 1940; children—Ila J., Nancy G., Alan G. B.A., Northwestern U., 1941. With Gerber Plumbing Fixtures Corp., Chgo., 1953—, chmn. bd. dirs., pres., chief exec. officer, 1983—. Trustee Northshore Congregation Israel. Named Woman of Yr., Am.-Israel C. of C., 1983, Hon. Dir., Women's div. Jewish United Fund, 1985. Mem. Com. of 200. Office: Gerber Plumbing Fixtures Corp 4656 W Touhy Ave Chicago IL 60646-1699

LEWIS, HENRY RAFALSKY, manufacturing company executive; b. Yonkers, N.Y., Nov. 19, 1925; s. Jasper R. and Freda (Rafalsky) L.; m. Barbara Connolly, June 15, 1957; children—Peter, Susan, Abigail. A.B. Harvard U., 1949, M.A., 1951, P.h.D., 1957. Group head Ops. Evaluation Group, Washington, 1955-57; mem. staff Electronic Rsch. Lab. RCA, Princeton, N.J., 1957-66, dir., 1966-70; v.p. rsch./devel. Itek Corp., Lexington, Mass., 1970-74; pres. Optel Corp., Princeton, N.J., 1974; sr. v.p. Dennison Mfg. Co., Waltham, Mass., 1974-85, vice chmn., 1986-91, also bd. dirs.; cons., 1991—; chmn. bd. dirs. Delphax Sys., Randolph, Mass.; bd. dirs. Cenzyme Corp., Cambridge, Mass., Protein Engring. Corp., Cambridge. Contbr. articles to profl. jours. Chmn. investment com. Powers (Mass.) Music Sch., 1978-90; mem. Harvard Grad. Soc. Coun., 1992—. With U.S. Army, 1944-46. Mem. IEEE, Am. Phys. Soc., Phi Beta Kappa, Sigma Xi. Club: Harvard. Home: 35 Clover St Belmont MA 02178-2410 Office: Delphax Systems Canton Tech Ctr 5 Campanelli Circle Canton MA 02021

LEWIS, HENRY WILKINS, university administrator, lawyer, educator; b. Jackson, N.C., Nov. 7, 1916; s. Edmund Wilkins and Jane Crichton (Williams) L. A.B., U. N.C., 1937; J.D., Harvard, 1940. Bar: N.C. bar 1940. Practice in Jackson, 1940-41; mem. staff Inst. of Govt., U. N.C., 1946-51, research prof. pub. law and govt., 1951-57, prof., 1957-73; acting v.p. U N.C., 1968-69; dir. Inst. Govt., 1973-78, Kenan prof. pub. law and govt., 1975-78, emeritus, 1978—; v.p. bd. dirs. Wilkins Texas Corp., 1967-92. Author: Property Tax Collection in North Carolina, 1951, rev. edit., 1957, The General Assembly of North Carolina: Organization and Procedure, 1952, Legislative Committees in North Carolina, 1952, Basic Legal Problems in the Taxation of Property, 1958, (with Robert G. Byrd) In Rem Property Tax Foreclosure, 1959, An Introduction to County Government, 1963, rev. edit., 1968, Primary and General Election Law and Procedure, 11 edits., latest, 1968, Property Tax Exemptions and Classifications, 1970, The Property Tax: An Introduction, 1972, rev. edits., 1975, 78, Northampton Parishes, 1951, The Doctor and Mrs. Lewis, 1980, More Taste Than Prudence: A Study of John Evans Johnson (1815-1870), 1983, Compelled to Wander, 1987; contbr. articles to profl. jours. Counsel N.C. Elections Laws Commn., 1967; counsel N.C. Commn. for Study Local and Ad Valorem Tax Structure, 1970, N.C. Commn. for Study Property Tax Exemptions and Classifications, 1973; mem. N.C. Criminal Justice Tng. and Standards Council, 1973-78, N.C. Criminal Justice Edn. and Tng. System Council, 1973-78, N.C. Commn. on Productivity in State Govt., 1976-77; mem. adv. bd. N.C. State Art Soc., 1962-63; mem. Com. for Restoration St. John's Ch., Williamsboro, N.C., 1950-79; mem. adv. bd. Ackland Art Center, U. N.C., 1957-78, mem. vis. com. 1987—; trustee Va. Episcopal Sch. 1974-80, U. N.C. Center for Public TV, 1980-88; bd. dirs. N.C. Pub. TV Found., 1987-88. Served to capt. AUS, 1941-46. Mem. Lincoln's Inn, N.C. Bar Assn., N.C. Lit. and Hist. Assn. (v.p. 1972-75), N.C. Collectors (pres. 1965-66), N.C. Soc. (dir.) Roanoke-Chowan Group (convenor 1962-65), Nat. Sporting Libr. (hon. life), Va. Hist. Soc., Jamestowne Soc., Order of Gimghouls, Phi Beta Kappa, Alpha Tau Omega. Episcopalian (parish conv. del. intermittently 1948—; mem. diocesan standing com. intermittently 1957-91, com. on constitution and canons 1973—; dep. Gen. Conv. 1967, 69, 70, 76, 79, 82, 85). Home: 386 Fearrington Post Pittsboro NC 27312-8518

LEWIS, HERBERT SAMUEL, anthropologist, educator; b. Jersey City, May 8, 1934; s. Frederic and Estelle (Sachs) L.; m. Marcia Barbash, June 23, 1957; children—Tamar Anne, Paula Miriam, Joshua Daniel. A.B., Brandeis U., 1955; Ph.D., Columbia U., 1963. Instr. Northwestern U., Evanston, Ill., 1961-63; lectr. anthropology Columbia U., N.Y.C., 1961; from asst. to full prof. anthropology U. Wis., Madison, 1963-73, prof., 1973—; dir. African studies program, 1993-95; vis. prof. Hebrew U., Jerusalem, 1969-70; cons. AID, Africare, 1981-84. Author: A Galla Monarchy, 1965, After the Eagles Landed: The Yemenite Jews of Israel, 1989, (monograph) Leaders and Followers: Anthropological Perspectives, 1974, The Origins of the Galla and Somali; contbr. articles to profl. jours. Research grantee Ford Found., Ethiopia, 1958-60, NSF, Ethiopia, 1965-66, Israel, 1975-77; Fulbright

research grantee, 1987. Fellow Am. Anthropol. Assn., Royal Anthropol. Inst. of Gt. Britain and Ireland, African Studies Assn. Home: 1009 Tumalo Trl Madison WI 53711-3024 Office: U Wis Dept Anthropology Social Sci Bldg Madison WI 53706

LEWIS, HUEY (HUGH ANTHONY CREGG, III), singer, composer, bandleader; b. N.Y.C., July 5, 1951; s. Hugh Anthony II and Magda Cregg; m. Sidney Conroy, 1983; children: Kelly, Austin. Student, Cornell U. Mem. Clover, 1972-77; singer, composer leader Huey Lewis and the News, 1978—. Rec. artist: (with Clover) Clover, 1977, Unavailable, 1977, Love on the Wire, 1977, (with Huey Lewis and the News) Huey Lewis and the News, 1980, Picture This, 1982, Sports, 1983, Fore, 1986, Small World, 1988, Hard at Play, 1991, Best of Huey Lewis and the News, 1992, Four Chords and Several Years Ago, 1994; hit singles include Do You Believe in Love?, Workin' for a Living, I Want a New Drug, The Heart of Rock 'n' Roll, Heart and Soul, Walking on a Thin Line, Hip To Be Square, I Know What I Like, (single from Back to the Future soundtrack) The Power of Love; contbr. (single and video) We Are the World, 1984; appeared in films: Back to the Future, 1985, Short Cuts, 1993. Office: care Capito-EMI Records 1750 Vine St Hollywood CA 90028-5247*

LEWIS, HUNTER, financial advisor, publisher; b. Dayton, Ohio, Oct. 13, 1947; s. Welbourne Walker and Emily (Spivey) L.; m. Elizabeth Sidamon-Eristoff, July 3, 1993. AB magna cum laude, Harvard U., 1969. Asst. to office of pres. Boston Co., 1970, v.p., 1972-73; pres. Boston Co. Fin. Strategies, Inc., 1971-72; co-founder Cambridge Assocs. Inc. and Cambridge Capital Advisors, Inc., formerly Lewis, Bailey Assocs., Washington, 1973—; former dir., chmn. bd. Shelburne Farms Inc. Former trustee, chmn. fin. com. Groton Sch.; former chmn. adv. bd. Dumbarton Oaks, affiliate of Harvard U.; pres., trustee Am. Sch. Classical Studies at Athens; former mem. pension fin. com. World Bank; bd. dirs., treas. World Wildlife Fund; former dir. Worldwide Fund for Nature; dir. Worldwatch Inst.; chmn. fin. com., trustee Pierpont Morgan Libr., N.Y.C.; trustee Thomas Jefferson Found.; Monticello; chmn.; bd. dirs. Trearne Found. With USMC, 1969-70. Author: The Real World War, 1982, A Question of Values, 1990; contbr. articles to N.Y. Times, Atlantic Monthly, Washington Post, other mags. and newspapers; author monographs on specialized fin. subjects. Mem. Univ. Club (N.Y.C.), Knickerbocker Club (N.Y.C.), Union Boat Club (Boston), Met. Club (Washington). Office: 4301 Fairfax Dr # 800 Arlington VA 22203-1627

LEWIS, HYLAN GARNET, sociologist, educator; b. Washington, Apr. 4, 1911; s. Harry Wythe and Ella (Wells) L.; A.B., Va. Union U., 1932; A.M. (Social Sci. Research Council fellow 1932, Rosenwald Found. fellow 1939-41), U. Chgo., 1936, Ph.D., 1951; m. Leighla Whipper, Oct. 4, 1935 (div. May 1945); 1 dau., Carole Ione Lewis Bovoso; m. Audrey Carter, Nov. 2, 1946; 1 son, Guy Edward. Instr. sociology Howard U., Washington, 1934-41, prof. sociology, 1964-67; prof. social sci. Talladega (Ala.) Coll., 1941-42; info. specialist OWI, 1942-45; asso. prof. Hampton Inst., 1945-48; asso. prof. sociology Atlanta U., 1948-55, prof., 1955-57; asso. dir. community services Unitarian Service Com., Inc., Boston, 1957-59; dir. child rearing study Health and Welfare Council, Washington, 1959-64; mem. delinquency grants rev. com. NIMH, 1963-67, mem. social problems research rev. com., 1969-73; mem. devel. behavioral scis. study sect. NIH, 1974-76; prof. sociology Bklyn. Coll. 1967-77, prof. emeritus, 1977—; vis. prof. Grad. Center, CUNY, 1977—; Michael Harrington prof. Queens Coll. CUNY, 1990-91, vis. prof. sociology, 1991-92; sr. cons. Clark, Phipps, Clark & Harris, Inc., 1975-85; sr. assoc. Kenneth B. Clark & Assocs., 1985—; sr. v.p. Met. Applied Research Center, Inc., 1967-75; vis. scholar Russell Sage Found., 1974-75. Research asso. Inst. for Research in Social Sci., U. N.C., 1947-48; cons. Volta River Project Preparatory Commn., Gold Coast, 1954; Ashmore project Fund for Advancement Edn., 1953, So. Regional Council, 1954-58, Commn. on Race and Housing, 1956-57; cons. disaster study com. NRC, 1955-56; mem. adv. com. grants program U.S. Children's Bur., 1962-66; mem. adv. panel small grants program U.S. Dept. Labor, 1963-83; chief cons. family panel White House Conf. Civil Rights Planning, 1965; mem. rev. panel U.S. Office Edn., 1965-67; mem. Head Start research adv. com. Office Econ. Opportunity, 1965-67; mem. grants adv. com. Nat. Endowment for the Humanities, Nat. Found. Arts and Humanities, 1967-68, others. Fund for Advancement Edn. fellow, 1955-56. Fellow AAAS; mem. Am. Sociol. Assn. (DuBois-Johnson-Frazier award 1976), African Studies Assn., Soc. Applied Anthropology, Eastern Sociol. Soc. (merit award 1979), Alpha Phi Alpha. Author: Blackways of Kent, 1955. Home: 372 Central Park W New York NY 10025-8201

LEWIS, JACK (CECIL PAUL LEWIS), publishing executive, editor; b. North English, Iowa, Nov. 13, 1924; s. Cecil Howell and Winifred (Warner) L.; children—Dana Claudia, Brandon Paul, Scott Jay, Suzanne Marie. B.A., State U. Iowa, 1949. Publicist savs. bonds U.S. Treasury Dept., Des Moines, 1948-49; reporter Santa Ana (Calif.) Register, 1949-50; motion picture writer Monogram Pictures, 1950; reporter Daily Pilot, Costa Mesa, Calif., 1956-57; editor Challenge Pub., North Hollywood, Calif., 1957-60; pres. Gallant/Charger Publs. Inc, Capistrano Beach, Calif., 1960—; editor, pub. Gun World, 1960—. Author 8 novels, 22 other books, 11 TV shows, 7 motion pictures; pub. mags. Bow and Arrow Hunting, Horse and Horseman; editor 23 books; contbr. articles to mags. Served to lt. col. USMCR, 1942-46, 50-56, 58, 70. Decorated Bronze Star, Air medal (3), Meritorious Service medal, Navy Commendation medal. Mem. Writers Guild Am., U.S. Marine Corps Combat Corrs. Assn. (pres. 1970-71, 73-74, 80-81, chmn. bd. 1972-78), Sigma Nu, Sigma Delta Chi. Republican. Home: 405 Avenida Teresa San Clemente CA 92672-2234 Office: Gallant Charger Publs 34249 Camino Capistrano Capistrano Beach CA 92624

LEWIS, JAMES BERTON, law educator; b. Lenox, Tenn., Oct. 29, 1911; s. Oscar and Maude (Kirby) L.; m. Irene Fogt, Dec. 9, 1961; children: Edward K., Robert L. Student, Centralia (Wash.) Jr. Coll., 1929-31, Wash. State Coll., 1931; LLB, Columbus U., Washington, 1940. Bar: D.C. 1942, N.Y. 1954. With Treasury Dept., 1931-34, IRS, 1934-42, 45-48; atty. Office Tax Legis. Counsel, Treasury Dept., 1948-52; spl. asst. to chief counsel IRS, 1952-53; assoc. firm Paul, Weiss, Rifkind, Wharton & Garrison, N.Y.C., 1953-55; partner Paul, Weiss, Rifkind, Wharton & Garrison, 1955-82, of counsel, 1982—; adj. prof. NYU Law Sch., 1962-83; prof. Benjamin N. Cardozo Sch. Law, 1983—; cons. Am. Law Inst. estate and gift tax, income tax projects; mem. adv. group to commr. IRS, 1976, 87. Author: The Estate Tax, 4th edit, 1979, The Marital Deduction, 1984. Served with USNR, 1942-45. Mem. ABA (vice chmn. publns., sect. taxation 1980-83, chmn. 1984-85), Am. Law Inst., N.Y. State Bar Assn., N.Y. County Lawyers Assn., Assn. Bar City N.Y., D.C. Bar Assn. Democrat. Presbyterian. Club: Masons. Home: 320 E 72nd St New York NY 10021-4769 Office: Benjamin N Cardozo Law Sch 55 5th Ave New York NY 10003-4301

LEWIS, JAMES EARL, investment banker; b. Chgo., Aug. 1, 1939; s. J. Earl and Elsie L. (Danneberg) L.; m. Patricia Ann Martin, Jan. 19, 1980. BA, DePauw U., 1961; MBA, U. Chgo., 1966. Analyst Harris Trust & Savs. Bank, Chgo., 1966-68; v.p. Paine, Webber, Jackson & Curtis, Boston, 1968-70; mgr. corp. loan component Gen. Electric Credit Corp., Stamford, Conn., 1971-77; v.p. Rauscher Pierce Refsnes Inc., Dallas, 1978-82; sr. v.p., mgr. corp. fin. dept. First Oklahoma Bancorp. Inc., Dallas and Oklahoma City, 1982-84; v.p., mgr. corp. fin. group PNC Mcht. Banking Co., Phila. 1984-87; v.p., dir. corp. fin. Ferris & Co., Inc., Washington, 1987-88; v.p. Washington Sq. Capital Markets Inc., Bala Cynwyd, Pa., 1988-90; pres., founder Mid. Atlantic Capital, Wayne, Pa., 1990—; founder, dir. Phila. Factors, Inc., 1993—; bd. dirs. Phila. Factors. With U.S. Army, 1962-64. Mem. Phila. Fin. Assn., Delaware Valley Venture Group, Orpheus Club. Home: 852 Briarwood Rd Newtown Square PA 19073-2620 Office: Ste 1 175 Stafford Ave Wayne PA 19087

LEWIS, JAMES ELDON, health care executive; b. Pontiac, Mich., Jan. 5, 1938; s. Wilbur Arthur and Mary Helen (Eatwell) L.; m. Anita L. Koplan, Sept. 28, 1988; children from previous marriage: James Eldon, Sara Ann. BA in Geography, Ea. Mich. U., 1961; MS in Urban and Econ. Geography, U. Ga., 1963, PhD in Urban and Econ. Geography, 1966. Urban geographer Gulf South Rsch. Inst., Baton Rouge, 1966-69; asst. prof. La. State U., 1966-69, U. Va., 1969-73; v.p. dir. Enviro-Med Inc., Washington, 1973-74; sr. profl. assoc. Inst. Medicine, NAS, 1974-77; interim dean, then dean Med. Coll. U. Okla., Tulsa, 1977-78; dir. Health Sci. Ctr. U.

Okla., Washington, 1978-89; v.p., then sr. v.p. CDP Assocs. Inc., Rockville, Md., 1979-83; pres. Health Resources Devel. Group, 1979-83; sr. exec. officer, prof. dept. medicine, U. Ala., Birmingham, 1983-95, spl. asst. to pres., 1994—; cons. in field. Pres. Lupus Found. Am., 1987-88. Alumni Found. fellow U. Ga., 1964-66. Mem. Adminstrs. Internal Medicine (pres. 1990-91). Office: Office of Pres U Ala Birmingham AL 35294

LEWIS, JAMES HISTED, retired foreign service officer; b. Carbondale, Pa., Dec. 18, 1912; s. Edward Butts and Laura (Histed) L.; m. Betty Prater, Dec. 12, 1943; children—Jane, Marie, David, Jon. AB., George Washington U., 1935, A.M., 1939. Asst. in polit. sci. George Washington U., Washington, 1934-36; mem. staff div. trade agreements U.S. Dept. State, Washington, 1936-42; fgn. service aux. officer, spl. asst. amb. Am. Embassy, London, 1942-44; economist div. comml. policy U.S. Dept. State, Washington, 1944-45, sec. Sec. State's Staff Com., 1945-46, advisor econs. U.S. Del. of Paris Peace Conf. and Council Fgn. Ministers, 1946, chief Brit. Commonwealth br. div. comml. policy, 1947-49, with Office Brit. Commonwealth and No. European Affairs, 1949-54; mem. U.S. del. GATT trade negotiations, Annecy, France, 1949; head negotiator GATT trade negotiations, Torquay, England, 1950-51, Geneva, 1956, 61; commd. fgn. service officer U.S. Dept. State, Washington, 1954, 1st sec. Am. embassy and consul in London, 1954-57, counselor econ. affairs Am. embassy in Copenhagen, 1957-61, chief div. trade agreements, 1961-62, chief div. comml. policy and treaties, 1962-63, dep. dir. Office Internat. Trade, 1963-65, minister-counselor for econ. affairs U.S. mission to Geneva, also dep. head U.S. del. Kennedy round trade negotiations, 1965-67, dep. dir. gen. with personal rank of ambassador GATT Secretariat in Geneva, 1967-69, counselor Am. embassy in Bonn, Fed. Republic Germany, 1969-70, dep. amb. Am. embassy in Helsinki, 1970-73, ret., 1973; cons. multilateral trade matters, 1975—. Mem. Am. Fgn. Service Assn., Pi Gamma Mu, Delta Phi Epsilon. Presbyterian. Home: 8800 Clifford Ave Bethesda MD 20815-4745

LEWIS, JAMES LEE, JR., actuary; b. Toungoo, Burma, June 11, 1930; s. James Lee and Lilly (Ryden) L.; m. Tamra Dell Johns, June 30, 1954; children: James Lee III, David Alexander, Stephen John, Susan Kim, Michael Ryden. BA, U. Mich., 1952, MA, 1956. Actuary Lincoln Nat. Life Ins. Co., Ft. Wayne, Ind., 1956-74; sr. v.p. Mutual Security Life Ins. Co., Ft. Wayne, 1974-83; v.p., actuary Montlife Corp., Itaska, Ill., 1983-84; v.p., sr. actuary Covenant Life Ins. Co., Phila., 1984-94; actuary provident Mut. Life Ins. Co., Phila., 1994—. Pres. Associated Chs., Ft. Wayne., 1982; chmn. Project Commitment, Ft. Wayne, 1969. With U.S. Army, 1952-54. Fellow Soc. of Actuaries (com. chair 1988-91); mem. Am. Acad. of Actuaries (charter), Phila. Actuaries Club. Baptist. Avocations: racquetball, barbershop singing.

LEWIS, JEROME A., petroleum company executive, investment banker; b. Wichita, Kans., 1927; married. BA in Engring., U. Okla. Geologist Shell Oil Co., 1950-51; pres. Lewmont Drilling, Inc., 1951-65, Border Exploration Co., 1965-68; pres., chmn. bd., chief exec. officer Petro-Lewis Corp., 1968-87; pres. Princeps Ptnrs., Inc., 1987—; also dir. DenverAmerican Petrol. 1991—. Bd. dirs. Denver Leadership Found., Trinity Forum, Downing St. Found. Mem. Ind. Petroleum Assn. Am., Oil Investment Inst. (founding gov.), World Pres.' Orgn., Am. Assn. Petroleum Geologists, Am. Petroleum Inst., Chief Execs. Orgn. Office: Princeps Ptnrs Inc 1775 Sherman St #1450 Denver CO 80203-1100

LEWIS, JERROLD See BOCK, JERRY

LEWIS, JERRY (JOSEPH LEVITCH), comedian; b. Newark, Mar. 16, 1926; s. Danny and Mona Levitch; m. Patti Palmer, 1944 (div.); children: Gary, Ron, Scott, Chris, Anthony, Joseph; m. Sandra Pitnick, 1983. Edn., Irvington (N.J.) High Sch.; DHL (hon.), Mercy Coll., 1987. Prof. cinema U. So. Calif.; pres. JAS Prodns., Inc., P.J. Prodns., Inc. Began as entertainer with record routine at Catskill (N.Y.) hotel; formed comedy team with Dean Martin, 1946-56; performed as a single, 1956—; formed Jerry Lewis Prodns. Inc., prod., dir., writer, star, 1956; films include: My Friend Irma, 1949, My Friend Irma Goes West, 1950, At War with the Army, 1950, That's My Boy, 1950, Sailor Beware, 1951, The Stooge, 1952, Jumping Jacks, 1952, Scared Stiff, 1953, The Caddy, 1953, Money From Home, 1953, Three Ring Circus, 1954, Living it Up, 1954, You're Never Too Young, 1955, Artists and Models, 1955, Partners, 1956, Hollywood or Bust, 1956, The Delicate Delinquent, 1957, The Sad Sack, 1957, The Geisha Boy, 1958, Rockabye Baby, 1958, Don't Give Up the Ship, 1959, Li'l Abner, 1959, Visit to a Small Planet, 1960, The Bellboy, 1960, Cinderfella, 1960, The Ladies Man, 1961, It's Only Money, 1962, The Errand Boy, 1962, It's a Mad, Mad, Mad, Mad World, 1963, The Nutty Professor, 1963, Who's Minding The Store, 1963, The Patsy, 1964, The Disorderly Orderly, 1964, The Family Jewels, 1965, Boeing-Boeing, 1965, Three On A Couch, 1965, Way ... Way ... Out, 1966, The Big Mouth, 1967, Don't Raise the Bridge, Lower the Water, 1968, Hook, Line and Sinker, 1969, One More Time, 1969, Which Way To the Front?, 1970, Hardly Working, 1981, King of Comedy, 1983, Smorgasbord, 1983, Slapstick, 1984, To Catch A Cop, 1984, How Did You Get In?, 1985, Cookie, 1989, Arrowtooth Waltz, 1991, Mr. Saturday Night, 1992; author: The Total Film-Maker, 1971, Jerry Lewis in Person, 1982; principal TV appearances include master of ceremonies ann. Labor Day Muscular Dystrophy Telethon, 1966—. Comdr. Order of Arts & Letters, France, 1984; nat. chmn. Muscular Dystrophy Assn. Recipient most promising male star in TV award Motion Picture Daily's 2nd Ann. TV poll, 1950, (as team), one of TV's 10 money making stars award Motion Picture Herald - Fame poll, 1951, 53-54, 57, best comedy team award Motion Picture Daily's 16th annual radio poll, 1951-53, Nobel Peace Prize nomination, 1978. Mem. Screen Producers Guild, Screen Dirs. Guild, Screen Writers Guild. Office: Jerry Lewis Films Inc 3160 W Sahara Ave # 16C Las Vegas NV 89102-6003 also: William Morris Agy Inc 151 El Camino Beverly Hills CA 90212

LEWIS, JERRY, congressman; b. Oct. 21, 1934. BA, UCLA, 1956. Former underwriter life ins. underwriter; field rep. for former U.S. Rep. Jerry Pettis; mem. Calif. State Assembly, 1968-78; vice chmn. rules com., chmn. subcom. on air quality; mem. 96th-103rd Congresses from 35th (now 40th) Calif. dist., 1979—; chmn. appropriation com. Va.-HUD subcom., mem. defense subcom., select com. on intelligence, chmn. subcom. on human intelligence. Presbyterian. Office: 2112 Rayburn Bldg Washington DC 20515

LEWIS, JERRY LEE, country-rock singer, musician; b. Ferriday, La., Sept. 29, 1935; s. Elmo and Mary Ethel L.; m. Kerrie Lee; children: Phoebe, Jerry Lee Jr. Student, Waxahachie (Tex.) Bible Inst. Rock and roll performer, recs. on Sun Records label, Whole Lotta Shakin' Goin' On, 1957, Great Balls of Fire, Mercury/Phonogram, 1963-78, Elektra Records, 1978-81; shifted to country and rock repertoire: recs. include Golden Hits, Odd Man In, Country Class, Roll Over Beethoven, High Heel Sneakers, Jerry Lee Lewis, Southern Roots, Good Rockin' Tonight, Taste of Country, Sunday After Church, Rural Route #1, Drinkin Wine Spo Dee O Dee, Golden Cream of Country, Monsters, Old Tyme Country Music, Rockin with From the Vaults of Sun; appeared in films American Hot Wax, Disc Jockey Jamboree, High School Confidential; albums include Sold Gold, 1986, The Killer Rocks On, 1987, Rocket, 1988, 1992, Killer: The Mercury Years Vol. One, Vol. Two, Vol. Three, 1989, Great Balls of Fire, 1989, Whole Lotta Shakin' Goin' On, 1992, Rockin' My Life Away, 1992, Heartbreak, 1992, All Killer, No Filler: The Anthology, 1993. Named to Rock and Roll Hall of Fame, 1986. Office: care RCA Records 1133 Ave Of The Americas New York NY 10036-6710

LEWIS, JERRY M., psychiatrist, educator; b. Utica, N.Y., Aug. 18, 1924; s. Jerry M. and Margaret (Miller) L.; m. Patsy Ruth Price, Sept. 24, 1949; children: Jerry M., Cynthia Lewis-Reynolds, Nancy Minns, Tom. MD, Southwestern Med. Sch., Dallas, 1951. Diplomate Am. Bd. Psychiatry and Neurology. Staff psychiatrist Timberlawn Psychiat. Hosp., Dallas, 1957-63, chief women's svc., 1963-66, chief adolescent svcs., 1966-70, dir. profl. edn., 1970-79, psychiatrist-in-chief, 1979-88, dir. rsch., 1988-93; dir. rsch. and tng. Timberlawn Psychiat. Rsch. Found., Dallas, 1967-88; dir. rsch. psychiatrist, 1988—; clin. prof. psychiatry, family practice and cmty. medicine Southwestern Med. Sch.; cons. in psychiatry Baylor U. Med. Ctr., Dallas. Author: No Single Thread, 1976, How's Your Family, 1978, To Be A Therapist, 1979, The Long Struggle, 1983, Swimming Upstream: Integrating Psychotherapy in a Biological Era, 1991. Served with USN, 1943-45. Fellow Am. Coll. Psychiatrists (pres. 1985), Am. Psychiat. Assn., So. Psychiat. Assn. (pres. 1979); mem. Group for Advancement of Psychiatry (pres. 1987), Benjamin Rush

Soc. (pres. 1994-95), AMA, Tex. Med. Assn. Home: PO Box 270789 Dallas TX 75227-0789

LEWIS, JESSICA HELEN (MRS. JACK D. MYERS), physician, educator; b. Harpswell, Maine, Oct. 26, 1917; d. Warren Harmon and Margaret (Reed) L.; m. Jack D. Myers, Aug. 31, 1946; children—Judith Duane (dec.), John Lewis, Jessica Read, Elizabeth Reed, Margaret Anne. A.B. Goucher Coll., 1938; M.D., Johns Hopkins U., 1942. USPHS Research fellow U. N.C., 1947-48, research assoc. dept. physiology, 1948-55; assoc. dept. medicine Duke Med. Sch., 1951-55; research assoc. dept. medicine U. Pitts., 1955-58, faculty, 1958—, research assoc. prof., 1965-70, prof. medicine, 1970-92, prof. medicine emeritus, 1992—; dir. research Central Blood Bank Pitts., 1969-74, v.p., 1974-85, med. dir. and sr. v.p., 1985-89, sci. dir., 1985-92, sr. v.p., med. and sci. dir. emeritus, 1992—; dir. Hemophilia Center Western Pa., 1973-81. Mem. Am. Physiol. Soc., Am. Soc. Clin. Investigation, Am. Fedn. Clin. Research, Soc. for Exptl. Biol. Medicine, Internat. Soc. Hematology, Am. Soc. Hematology, Sigma Xi. Rsch. on mechanism blood coagulation, fibrinolysis, hemorrhagic and thrombotic diseases and comparative vertebrate coagulation. Home: Dithridge House 220 N Dithridge St # 900 Pittsburgh PA 15213 Office: Central Blood Bank Pitts 812 Fifth Ave Pittsburgh PA 15219

LEWIS, JOHN BRUCE, lawyer; b. Poplar Bluff, Mo., Aug. 12, 1947; s. Evan Bruce and Hilda Kathryn (Kassebaum) L.; m. Diane F. Grossman, July 23, 1977; children: Samantha Brooking, Ashley Denning. BA, U. Mo., 1969, JD, 1972; LLM in Labor and Employment Law, Columbia U., 1978; diploma, Nat. Inst. Trial Advocacy, 1982. Bar: Mo. 1972, U.S. Ct. Appeals (8th cir.) 1973, U.S. Dist. Ct. (ea. dist.) Mo. 1974, U.S. Dist. Ct. (no. dist.) Ohio 1979, Ohio 1980, U.S. Ct. Appeals (6th cir.) 1982, U.S. Dist. Ct. (ea. dist.) Mich. 1983, U.S. Ct. Appeals (3d cir.) 1987, U.S. Supreme Ct. 1987, U.S. Dist. Ct. (no. dist.) Calif. 1987, U.S. Ct. Appeals (7th cir.) 1990. Assoc. Millar, Schaefer & Ebling, St. Louis, 1972-77, Squire, Sanders & Dempsey, Cleve., 1979-85; ptnr. Arter & Hadden, Cleve., 1985—; chair Labor and Employment Law Practice Group, 1987—; lectr. in field. Contbr. articles to legal jours. Mem. Cleve. Council on World Affairs. Mem. ABA (sec. labor and employment law, com. EEO law, comm. law forum), Ohio State Bar Assn. (sec. labor and employment law), Greater Cleve. Bar Assn. (sec. labor law), St. Louis Met. Bar Assn., Am. Law Inst., Def. Rsch. Inst., Selden Soc., Ohio C. of C. (labor adv. com.). Office: Arter & Hadden 925 Euclid Ave Cleveland OH 44115-1475

LEWIS, JOHN CLARK, JR., manufacturing company executive; b. Livingston, Mont., Oct. 15, 1935; s. John Clark and Louise A. (Anderson) L.; m. Carolyn Jean Keesling, Sept. 4, 1960; children: Robert, Anne, James. BS, Fresno (Calif.) State U., 1957. With Service Bur. Corp., El Segundo, Calif., 1960-70, Computer Scis. Corp., 1970; with Xerox Corp., El Segundo, 1970-77, pres. bus. systems div., 1977; pres. Amdahl Corp., Sunnyvale, Calif., 1983-87, chief exec. officer, 1983—, chmn., 1987—. Served with USNR, 1957-60. Roman Catholic. Office: Amdahl Corp PO Box 3470 1250 E Arques Ave Sunnyvale CA 94086-4730

LEWIS, JOHN D., financial services company executive; b. 1941. Mng. ptnr. Arthur Anderson and Co., N.C., S.C., 1978-90; mng. ptnr., CFO Arthur Anderson and Co., 1990-93; mng. ptnr. Arthur Anderson and Co. Societe Coop., 1993—. Office: Arthur Anderson & Co 69 W Washington Chicago IL 60602-3004

LEWIS, JOHN FRANCIS, lawyer; b. Oberlin, & Ohio, Oct. 25, 1932; s. Ben W. and Gertrude D. Lewis; m. Catharine Monroe, June 15, 1957; children: Ben M., Ian A., Catharine G., William H. B.A., Amherst Coll., 1955; J.D., U. Mich., 1958. Bar: Ohio 1958, U.S. Dist. Ct. (no dist.) Ohio 1959, U.S. Supreme Ct. 1973. Assoc. firm Squire, Sanders & Dempsey, Cleve., 1958-67; ptnr. Squire, Sanders & Dempsey, 1967—, mng. ptnr. Cleve. office, 1985—. Co-author: Baldwin's Ohio School Law, 1980-91, Ohio Collective Bargaining Law, 1983. Trustee Playhouse Sq. Found., chmn., 1980-85; mem. Cleve. Tomorrow; trustee, chmn. Case Western Res. U.; mem. exec. com. chmn. Univ. Circle, Inc., New Cleve. Campaign; trustee Cleve. Commn. on Higher Edn., Musical Arts Assn.; hon. chmn. Found. for Sch. Bus. Mgmt., Leadership Cleve., 1977-78. Recipient Malcolm Daisley Labor-Mgmt. Rels. award, 1991, Tree of Life award Jewish Nat. Fund, 1993. Mem. Cleve. Bar Assn., Ohio Bar Assn., ABA (com. pub. edn.), Nat. Sch. Bd. Assn., Nat. Orgn. Legal Problems (past pres.), Ohio Assn. Sch. Bus. Ofcls. (hon. life), Fifty Club of Cleve., Ohio Council Sch. Bd. Attys. Episcopalian. Home: 2001 Chestnut Hills Dr Cleveland OH 44106-4601 Office: Squire Sanders & Dempsey 4900 Society Tower 127 Public Sq Cleveland OH 44114-1304

LEWIS, JOHN FURMAN, lawyer, oil company executive; b. Fort Worth, Apr. 24, 1934; s. Ben B. and Minnie W. (Field) L.; children from previous marriage: Joyce Ann, George Field, William Patrick; m. Virginia Edmonds Kingsley. Student, Tex. Christian U., summer 1955; B.A. in Econs., Rice U., 1956; J.D. with honors, U. Tex., 1962; postgrad., Princeton U., 1965-66; M.B.A., Bowling Green State U., 1971. Bar: Tex. 1962, U.S. Dist. Ct. 1965, U.S. Supreme Ct. 1967, Ohio 1968, U.S. Ct. Mil. Appeals 1971, Okla. 1987. Atty. Atlantic Richfield Co., 1962-67; with Marathon Oil Co., Findlay, Ohio, 1967-86, gen. atty., 1978, sr. atty., 1978-81, assoc. gen. counsel, 1981-83, v.p., gen. counsel, 1983-84, v.p., gen. counsel, sec., 1984-86; sr. v.p., gen. counsel The Williams Cos., Tulsa, 1986—; mem. adv. bd. Internat. Oil and Gas Ednl. Ctr. of Southwestern Legal Found. Contbr. articles to profl. jours. Mem. exec. com., trustee United Way of Hancock County, Findlay, Ohio, 1984-86; bd. dirs. No-We-Oh coun. Camp Fire, Inc., Findlay, 1974-86, Okla. Green Country coun., Tulsa, 1987-89; mem. Arts. and Humanities Coun., Tulsa, 1991—. Served to lt. (j.g.) USN, 1956-59. Mem. ABA (subcom. chmn. 1984-85), Tex. Bar Assn., Am. Petroleum Inst. (lawyer-adviser mktg. com. 1982-84, gen. law com. 1983—), Ohio Bar Assn., Okla. Bar Assn., Tulsa County Bar Assn., U. Tex. Law Sch. Alumni Sch. Assn. (bd. dirs. 1994—). Republican. Avocations: jogging, tennis, golf. Office: Williams Cos 1 Williams Ctr PO Box 2400 Tulsa OK 74172-2400

LEWIS, JOHN HARDY, JR., lawyer; b. East Orange, N.J., Oct. 31, 1936; s. John Hardy and Sarah (Ripley) L.; m. Mary Ann Spurgeon, June 25, 1960; children: Peter, David, Mark. AB magna cum laude, Princeton U., 1958; JD cum laude, Harvard U., 1961. Bar: Pa. 1962. Assoc. Morgan, Lewis & Bockius, Phila., 1965-69, ptnr., 1969—. trustee Blair Acad., Blairstown, N.J.; rector's warden All Saints' Ch., Wynnewood, Pa. Served to major USAF, 1962-65. Fellow Am. Coll. Trial Lawyers. Home: 1000 Green Valley Rd Bryn Mawr PA 19010-1912 Office: Morgan Lewis & Bockius 2000 One Logan Sq Philadelphia PA 19103

LEWIS, JOHN LEEMAN, JR., obstetrician, gynecologist; b. San Antonio, June 5, 1929; s. John Leeman and Lois Black (Perry) L.; student U. Tex. at Austin, spring, 1948; B.A., Harvard, 1952, M.D. (Frederick Sheldon Traveling fellow 1952-53, Nat. scholar 1953-57), 1957; m. Jane Darling Davis, July 30, 1955 (div. 1976); children—Anne Darling, Elizabeth Perry, Katherine Folsom; m. Susan Vere Paris, Oct. 16, 1976 (div. 1981); m. Patricia Ann Mazzola, May 8, 1984 (div. 1994). Diplomate Am. Bd. Ob-Gyn (dir. 1971—, cert. spl. competence gynecologic oncology). Intern Mass. Gen. Hosp., Boston, 1957-58, resident, 1958-59, 61-62; clin. asso. endocrinology Nat. Cancer Inst., Bethesda, Md., 1965-67; resident Boston Lying-in Hosp., 1962-65, Free Hosp. for Women, Brookline, 1962-65; sr. investigator surgery br. Nat. Cancer Inst., Bethesda, Md., 1965-67; assoc. attending obstetrician and gynecologist Presbyn. Hosp., N.Y.C. July-Dec. 1967, also asso. prof. obstetrics and gynecology Coll. Phys. and Surgs. Columbia; pvt. practice medicine, specializing in obstetrics and gynecology, N.Y.C., 1967—; chief gynecology service Meml. Hosp. for Cancer and Allied Diseases, N.Y.C., 1968-90, attending surgeon, 1990—; chmn. instl. rev. bd., 1984—; assoc. prof. Cornell U. Med. Coll. at N.Y.C., 1968-71, prof., 1971—; assoc. attending obstetrician and gynecology N.Y. Lying-in Hosp., N.Y.C., 1968-71, attending obstetrician and gynecologist, 1971—; mem. Sloan Kettering Inst. Cancer Rsch., 1971—; v.p. internat. Gynecologic Cancer Soc., 1993—; chmn. Gynecologic Cancer Found., 1994—; mem. editorial bd. Jour. Am. Coll. Surgeons, 1994—. Served with USPHS, 1959-67. Recipient Alumni award Harvard Med. Sch., 1957. Mem. Harvard Med. Alumni Assn. (councilor 1969-70). Democrat. Episcopalian. Clubs: Griffis Faculty (N.Y.C.), Englewood Field Club (N.J.); Harvard (N.Y.C.). Assoc. editor Obstetrical and Gynecological Survey. Contbr. articles to profl. jours. Home:

1175 York Ave New York NY 10021-7169 Office: 1275 York Ave New York NY 10021-6007

LEWIS, JOHN MILTON, cable television company executive; b. nr. Slocomb, Ala., Mar. 29, 1931; s. Phil Truman and Vermell Beatrice (Avery) L.; grad. high sch.; m. Mary Lee Robledo, June 9, 1951; children: Janet Lee, Lee Michael. With Gulf Power Co., Panama City, Fla., 1949-56; self employed vehicle svc. co., Panama City, 1956-58; v.p., bd. dir., Burnup & Sims of Fla., Inc., West Palm Beach, 1958-70; pres., bd. dir. Wometco Cable Corp., Miami, Fla., 1970-94; pres., CEO SPI Holding, Inc., Richardson, Tex., 1988-89, also bd. dirs.; CEO Spectradyne, Inc., Richardson, 1988-89; pres. Key Capital Group, Inc., Miami, 1995—; bd. dirs. Allied Waste Mgmt., Phoenix; cons. in field. Recipient Tower Club award So. TV Assn. Mem. Cable TV Pioneers, Masons. Republican. Office: Key Capital Group Inc PO Box 561009 9500 S Dadeland Blvd Ste 603 Miami FL 33156

LEWIS, JOHN P., bank executive; b. 1936. With Interfirst Bank, Dallas; mng. dir. Mason-Best Co., Dallas, 1985-87; with Ameri Serv, Dallas, 1987—, now CEO. Office: AmeriServ 13355 Noel Rd Ste 2225 Dallas TX 75240-6657

LEWIS, JOHN R., congressman; b. Pike County, Ala., Feb. 21, 1940; m. Lillian Miles, 1968; 1 child, John-Miles. BA, Am. Bapt. Theol. Sem., Nashville, 1961, Fisk U., 1963. Mem. City Coun., Atlanta, 1982-86, 100th-104th Congresses from 5th Ga. dist., Washington, 1986—; former chief dep. majority whip. Civil rights leader; mem. Martin Luther King Ctr. for Social Change, African Am. Inst., Robert F. Kennedy Meml. Office: US Ho of Reps 329 Cannon Washington DC 20515

LEWIS, JOHN ROBERT, zoo administrator; b. Ironton, Mo., Aug. 17, 1952; s. Bob G. Lewis and Joan (Burlingame) Shank; m. Deborah June Holley, Jan. 15, 1972; children: Jill Elizabeth, Ian James. BS in Animal Sci., NE La. U., 1974, postgrad., 1974-77; postgrad., St. Thomas Coll., 1981-84. Primate supr. La. Purchase Garden and Zoo, Monroe, 1974-76, zoo supr., 1976-77; curator Minn. Zoo, Apple Valley, 1977-80, sr. curator, 1980-83, asst. dir., 1983-86; dir. John Ball Zoo, Grand Rapids, Mich., 1986—. Author: Clouded Leopard Studbook, 1982, vol. II, 1987; several TV appearances. Mem. Internat. Union for Conservation Nature and Natural Resources (cat specialist group 1984—). Avocations: photography, fly-tying and fishing, gardening. Office: John Ball Zoo 201 Market Ave SW Grand Rapids MI 49503-4090 also: John Ball Zoological Garden 1300 W Fulton St NW Grand Rapids MI 49504-6100

LEWIS, JOHN WILSON, political science educator; b. King County, Wash., Nov. 16, 1930; s. Albert Lloyd and Clara (Lewis) Seeman; m. Jacquelyn Clark, June 19, 1954; children: Cynthia, Stephen, Amy. Student, Deep Springs Coll., 1947-49; AB with honors, UCLA, 1953, MA, 1958, PhD, 1962; hon. degree, Morningside Coll., 1969, Lawrence U., 1986. Asst. prof. govt. Cornell U., 1961-64, assoc. prof., 1964-68; prof. polit. sci. Stanford U., 1968—; William Haas prof. Chinese politics, 1972—, co-dir. arms control and disarmament program, 1971-83, co-dir. NE Asia U.S. Forum on Internat. Policy, 1980-90, co-dir. Ctr. for Internat. Security and Arms Control, 1983-91, sr. fellow, 1991—, dir. Project on Peace and Cooperation in the Asian-Pacific Region; chmn. Internat. Strategic Inst., 1983-89; chmn. joint com. on contemporary China Social Sci. Rsch. Coun. Am. Coun. Learned Socs., 1976-79; former vice chmn. and bd. dirs. Nat. Com. on U.S.-China Relations; cons. Senate Select Com. on Intelligence, 1977-81, Lawrence Livermore Nat. Lab., Dept. of Defense; mem. Def. Policy Bd.; chmn. com. advanced study in China Com. Scholarly Communication with People's Republic of China, 1979-82; mem. com. on internat. security and arms control Nat. Acad. Scis., 1980-83; organizer first univ. discussion arms control and internat. security matters Chinese People's Inst. Fgn. Affairs, 1978, first academic exchange agreement Dem. People's Rep. of Korea, 1988; negotiator first univ. tng. and exchange agreement People's Rep. of China, 1978. Author: Leadership in Communist China, 1963, Major Doctrines of Communist China, 1964, Policy Networks and the Chinese Policy Process, 1986; co-author: The United States in Vietnam, 1967, Modernization by Design, 1969, China Builds the Bomb, 1988, Uncertain Partners: Stalin, Mao, and the Korean War, 1993, China's Strategic Seapower: The Politics of Force Modernization in the Nuclear Era, 1994; editor: The City in Communist China, 1971, Party Leadership and Revolutionary Power in China, 1970, Peasant Rebellion and Communist Revolution in Asia, 1974, Uncertain Partners: Stalin, Mao and the Korean War, 1993, China's Strategic Seapower: The Politics of Force Modernization in the Nuclear Era, 1994; contbr.: Congress and Arms Control, 1978, China's Quest for Independence, 1979, others.; mem. editorial bd.: Chinese Law and Govt, China Quar., Survey, The Pacific Rev. Served with USN, 1954-57. Mem. Assn. Asian Studies, Am. Polit. Sci. Assn., Coun. Fgn. Rels. Home: 541 San Juan St Palo Alto CA 94305-8432 Office: Stanford U 320 Galvez St Palo Alto CA 94305-6105

LEWIS, JORDAN DAVID, management consultant, author, international speaker, educator; b. Chgo., Aug. 9, 1937; s. Murray Robert and Ruth (Weinstein) L.; m. Lynn Lopata, Sept. 20, 1964; children: Matthew Michael, Katherine Anne. B.S.Engring. in Physics., U. Mich., 1960, B.S. Engring. in Math, 1960, M.S. Engring. in Instrumentation (fellow), 1963, M.S. Engring. in Nuclear Engring., 1963, Ph.D. in Thermonuclear Physics, 1966. Instr. physics U. Mich. at Dearborn, 1962-64, research asst., 1964-66; with Battelle Devel. Corp., Columbus, Ohio, 1966-72; asst. mgr. devel. dept. Battelle Devel. Corp., 1968-70, mgr. gen. operations, 1970-72; dir. applied tech. programs Batelle Columbus Labs., Columbus, 1972; dir. presdl. tech. and econ. policy program Nat. Bur. Standards, Washington, 1973-77; exec. dir. A.T. Internat., Washington, 1977-79; mgmt. cons., 1979—; sr. lectr. Wharton Sch., U. Pa.; U.S. del. to OECD, Paris; advisor strategic alliance to nat. govts. and internat. corps.; fellow World Econ. Forum, Geneva, 1993; chmn. Fed. Task Force on Energy Intensive Products, 1975. Author: Partnerships for Profit: Structuring and Managing Strategic Alliances, 1990, The Connected Corporation: Managing Customer-Supplier Alliances, 1995; editor: (with Lynn L. Lewis) Industrial Approaches to Urban Problems, 1972; guest columnist Wall St. Jour., N.Y. Times; contbr. articles to newspapers and profl. jours. Co-chmn. Columbus Outdoor Summer Concerts, 1968-70; chmn. bd. dirs. Columbus Inner-City Econ. Devel. Corp., 1969-71. AEC fellow, 1964-66. Fellow AAAS (mem. council; chmn. indsl. sci. sect. 1975); mem. Am. Econs. Assn., Sigma Xi. Home: 3707 33rd Pl NW Washington DC 20008-3201

LEWIS, JUDITH A., nursing educator, women's health nurse; b. Everett, Mass., Jan. 19, 1945; d. Edward and Miriam (Goldsmith) Kaden; m. Arthur R. Lewis, Jan. 1, 1970; 1 child, Jonathan. AB, Brandeis U., 1966, PhD, 1985; BS, Boston U., 1968; MS, U. Calif., San Francisco, 1977. RN, Mass., Va.; cert. ob-gyn. nurse practitioner. Assoc. dean acad. affairs U. Mass., Boston, 1985-88; assoc. prof. MGH Inst. Health Professions, Boston, 1988-93; assoc. prof. and chair maternal/child nursing Va. Commonwealth U., Richmond, 1993—. Author: Perinatal Regionalization in MA: Process, Product & Potential Politics, Policy Making, and Nursing, Joint Efforts between Education and the Community, Effect of Previous Infertility on Maternal-Fetal Attachment, Coping Styles and Attachment During Pregnancy. Lt. USN, 1967-70. Named Disting. Practitioner Nat. Acad. Practice in Nursing. Fellow Am. Acad. Nursing; mem. ANA, Assn. of Women's Health, Obstetric and Neonatal Nurses, Nat. League Nursing, Am. Fertility Soc., Sigma Theta Tau. Home: 13705 Milbranch Ct Richmond VA 23233-7638

LEWIS, JULIETTE, actress; b. Fernando Valley, Calif., June 21, 1973; d. Geoffrey and Glenis Batley L. TV appearances include Homefires (Showtime miniseries), I Married Dora, 1988, A Family For Joe, 1990; TV Movies include Too Young To Die, 1989; films include My Stepmother is an Alien, 1988, Meet the Hollowheads, 1989, National Lampoons Christmas Vacation, 1989, Cape Fear, 1991 (Academy Award nomination best supporting actress 1991), Crooked Hearts, 1991, Husbands and Wives, 1992, Kalifornia, 1993, That Night, 1993, What's Eating Gilbert Grape, 1993, Romeo is Bleeding, 1994, Natural Born Killers, 1994, Mixed Nuts, 1994, Strange Days, 1995. Office: William Morris Agy 151 El Camino Blvd Beverly Hills CA 80212

LEWIS, JULIUS, lawyer; b. Omaha, Nov. 29, 1931; s. Aaron and Dorothy (Gendler) L. B.A., U. Chgo., 1950, M.A., 1954; LL.B., Yale U., 1957. Bar:

Ill. 1957. Assoc. Sonnenschein Nath & Rosenthal, Chgo., 1957-65, ptnr., 1965—; bd. dirs. Juno Lighting, Inc., Des Plaines, Ill., The Fremont Found., O.L. and Hazel Rhoades Fund. Trustee Art Ist. Chgo.; pres., bd. dirs. Alliance Française de Chgo., 1983—. Mem. Chgo. Bar Assn., Legal Club of Chgo., Law Club of Chgo., Casino Club, Racquet Club, Yale Club. Democrat. Office: Sonnenschein Nath 233 S Wacker Dr Ste 8000 Chicago IL 60606

LEWIS, KATHRYN HUXTABLE, pediatrician; b. Lakewood, Ohio, July 23, 1934; d. Harold Stafford and Otillie Louise (May) H.; m. Samuel T. Lewis III, Apr. 8, 1967 (dec. Sept. 1994); children: Samuel T. IV, Tirone A., Anne E. Student, Cornell U., 1952-55; MD, Yale U., 1959; MPH, Johns Hopkins U., 1964. Diplomate Nat. Bd. Med. Examiners, Am. Bd. Pediatrics. Intern Univ. Hosps., Cleve., 1959-60, resident in pediatrics, 1961-62, chief resident in pediatrics, 1962-63; resident in pediatrict Children's Hosp. of Phila., 1960-61, Cleve. Met. Gen. Hosp., 1961-62; tchg. fellow in pediatrics Western Res. U., Cleve., 1962-63, sr. instr. dept. pediatrics, 1965-67, sr. clin. instr. dept. preventive medicine, 1965-66, sr. instr. dept. preventive medicine, 1966-67; tchg. fellow in pediatrics Johns Hopkins U., Balt., 1963-64; rsch. assoc. Sch. Hygiene and Pub. Health Johns Hopkins U., Lahore, Pakistan, 1964-65; tchg. assoc. Ford Found., Lahore, 1964-75; dir. pediatric clinics ambulatory svcs. Cleve. Met. Gen. Hosp., 1966-67; cons. in field.; sch. physician Tyrone Area Bd. Edn., 1976—; dir. Pediatric Outpatient Ctr. Tyrone Hosp., 1975-92, Pediatric Outpatient Ctr. Geisinger Tyrone divsn., 1992—. Contbr. articles to profl. jours. Recipient Disting. Alumni award in sci. Lakewood H.S., 1993. Fellow Am. Acad. Pediatrics, APHA ; mem. Pa. Med. Soc., Assn. for Ambulatory Pediatric Svcs., Phi Beta Kappa. Office: Geisinger Med Group 1 Hospital Dr Tyrone PA 16686

LEWIS, KENNETH D., banker; b. 1947. BA, Ga. State U., 1969. Pres. NCNB Nat. Bank Fla., 1986-88, NCNB Tex., Dallas, N.C., 1988-90, Gen. Bank NationsBank, Atlanta, Ga., 1991-93, NationsBank Corp., Charlotte, N.C., 1993—. Office: NationsBank Corp Nationsbank Corp Ctr Charlotte NC 28255

LEWIS, LARRY LYNN, college official, minister, denominational official; b. Mexico, Mo., Jan. 27, 1935; s. Artie Francis and Mary Lue (Whiteside) L.; m. Betty Jo Cockerell, Feb. 28, 1964; children—Janet Lynn, Christy Ann, Mark Ray. A.A., Hannibal-LaGrange Coll., 1954; B.A., U. Mo., 1956; B.D. Southwestern Bapt. Sem., 1960, M.R.E., 1960; D.Ministry, Luther Rice Sem., 1978. Ordained to ministry Southern Bapt. Conv., 1954; pastor Parsons Bapt. Ch., Columbus, Ohio, 1961-66, Delaware Valley Bapt. Ch., Willingboro, N.J., 1966-71; dir. religious edn. Bapt. Conv. Pa./South Jersey, Harrisburg, Pa., 1971-74; pastor Tower Grove Bapt. Ch., St. Louis, 1974-81; pres. Hannibal-LaGrange Coll., Hannibal, Mo., 1981-87, pres. Home Mission Bd. off So. Bapt. Conv., 1987—; minister edn. youth Tri-Village Bapt. Ch., Columbus, 1961-62; pub. sch. tchr. Columbus Pub. Sch., 1962-63; ch. growth cons. Bapt. Sunday Sch. Bd., Nashville, 1971-74; pres. Tower Grove Christian Sch., 1978-81; pres. Mo. Bapt. Pastors Conf., 1979; v.p. Southern Bapt. Pastors Conf., Southern Bapt. Conv., 1980. Bd. dirs Hannibal YMCA. Author: The Bus Ministry, 1971, The Church Planter's Handbook, 1992; (with others) Outreach with Church Buses, 1973; Organize to Evangelize, 1980. Editor: Walking with God, 1972. Contbr. articles to various ch. mags. Mem. Mo. Edn. Assn., Hist. Hannibal Assn., Hannibal C. of C. (pres. 1985). Lodge: Hannibal Rotary. Avocation: farming. Home: 319 Nimblewill Way SW Lilburn GA 30247-6517 Office: So Bapt Home Mission Bd 1350 Spring St NW Atlanta GA 30367

LEWIS, LOIDA NICOLAS, food products holding company executive; b. The Philippines, 1942; m. Reginald Lewis (dec. 1993); children: Leslie, Christina. BA, St. Theresa's Coll., 1963; LLB, U. Philippines, 1967. Immigration atty. N.Y.C.; with Immigration and Naturalization Svc.; chmn., CEO TLC Beatrice Internat. Ptnrs. L.P., N.Y.C., 1994—. Author: How the Filipino Veteran of World War II Can Become a U.S. Citizen (According to the Immigration Act of 1990), 1991, One Hundred One Legal Ways to Stay in the U.S.A.; or, How to Get a Green Card According to the Immigration Act of 1990, 1992, How to Get a Green Card: Legal Ways to Stay in the U.S.A., 1993. Office: TLC Beatrice Internat Ptnrs LP 9 W 57th St 48th Fl New York NY 10019*

LEWIS, LOIS A., health services administrator; b. Tuskegee, Ala.; d. Arthur J. and Katie (Cephus) Long; m. Charles Lewis; children: Robin Jordan, Michelle Allen. BSN, U. Conn., 1959, MS, 1974; PhD, Columbia Pacific, 1989. CNAA. Community health nurse Hartford VNA, Conn., 1967-68, 70-71; sch. nurse Clark County Schs., Las Vegas, 1968-70; dir. job corps. Community Renewal Team, Hartford, 1971-72; sr. nurse Cap. Reg. Mental Health, Hartford, 1974-75; exec. dir. Manchester (Conn.) VNA, 1975-87; br. dir. Vis. Nurse and Home Care, Inc., Hartford, 1987-88; dir. community nursing and home health State Dept. Health, Hartford, 1988—; chairperson Cedarcrest Hosp., Newington, Conn., 1980—; mem. adv. bd. dirs. U. Ct. Health Ctr., Farmington, 1982—; Hartford Hosp., 1992—. Contbr. articles to profl. jours. Bd. dirs. ARC, Farmington, Conn., 1989—; mentor Career Beginnings, Hartford, 1989, 90. With USN, 1959-61. Mem. Nat. Assn. for Home Care (bd. dirs. 1980-83, 85-88), Conn. League for Nursing, Conn. Pub. Health Assn., Am. Pub. Health Assn., Sigma Theta Tau, Chi Eta Phi. Democrat. Methodist. Avocations: swimming, reading, knitting. Office: Conn State Dept Health 150 Washington St Hartford CT 06103

LEWIS, MARILYN WARE, water company executive; b. 1943. Former pres. Solanco Pub. Co.; vice chmn. Am. Water Works Co., Inc., Voorhees, N.J., now chmn., also bd. dirs.; bd. dirs. South Jersey Industries, Inc., Penn Fuel Gas Co., Cigna Corp. Office: Am Water Works Co Inc 1025 Laurel Oak Rd PO Box 1770 Voorhees NJ 08043

LEWIS, MARTIN R., paper company executive; b. N.Y.C., Feb. 14, 1929; s. William and Ida (Goldman) L.; m. Renee Raines, Aug. 13, 1950 (div.); children—Jeffrey, Wendy, Lisa; m. Diane Carol Brandt, July 4, 1975. B.A., NYU, 1949, LL.B., 1951; LL.M., U. Mich., 1952. CEO Williamhouse-Regency, Inc., N.Y.C., 1955—, exec. v.p., 1967-69. Bd. dirs. McBurney br. YMCA, N.Y.C. Mem. Envelope Mfg. Assn., Paper Club N.Y., N.Y. Jewish.

LEWIS, MELVIN, psychiatrist, pediatrician, psychoanalyst; b. London, May 18, 1926; came to U.S., 1956; s. Abraham George and Kitty (Merrick) L.; m. Dorothy S. Otnow, May 30, 1963; children: Gillian Io, Eric Anthony. M.B., B.S., Guy's Hosp. Med. Sch., London, 1950; D.C.H., 1954; M.A. (hon.), Yale U., 1972. Diplomate Am. Bd. Psychiatry and Neurology, Am. Bd. Child Psychiatry; cert. in psychoanalysis, child psychoanalysis. Intern Lambeth Hosp., 1950, Fulham Hosp., 1951 (both Eng); resident in pediatrics Yale U. Sch. Medicine, 1956-57, resident in psychiatry and child psychiatry, 1957-61; instr. psychiatry Yale U. Child Study Center, New Haven, 1961-63; assoc. prof. pediatrics and psychiatry Yale U. Child Study Center, 1963-67, assoc. prof., 1967-70, prof., 1971—, dir. med. studies 1970—. Author: Clinical Aspects of Child and Adolescent Development, 1971, 3d edit., 1991; editor: Jour. Am. Acad. Child & Adolescent Psychiatry, 1975-87, Child and Adolescent Psychiatry, A Comprehensive Textbook, 1991; cons. editor: Child and Adolescent Psychiatric Clinics of North America, 1991—. Served with M.C. Royal Army, 1951-53. Fellow Am. Acad. Child and Adolescent Psychiatry, Am. Psychiat. Assn.; Royal Coll. Psychiatrists; mem. Royal Soc. Medicine, Am. Pediatric Soc., Am. Psychoanalytic Assn. Home: 10 St Ronan Ter New Haven CT 06511-2315 Office: Yale U Child Study Ctr 333 Cedar St New Haven CT 06510-3289

LEWIS, MICHAEL, small business owner; b. St. Thomas, Ont., Can., Dec. 18, 1950; m. Krystyna Katherine Ballantyne; 2 children: Shannon, Jessica. BS, Queen's U., Kingston, Ont., Can., 1973; MBA, York (Can.) U., 1977. Sr. cons. CLC Can. Mktg. Assn. Ltd, Toronto, Ont., Can., 1981-85; v.p. No Frills Divsn. Loblaws Supermarkets Ltd., 1985-89; pres. Willson Stationers, Mississauga, Ont., Can., 1989-92, Manchu Wok, Markham, Ont., Can., 1993—; bd. dirs. Kennedy Marchant Shields Inc., Toronto, 1991—. Mem. Young Pres.'s Orgn., Toronto Crikst and Skating Club. Home: 115 Melrose Ave Toronto, ON Canada M5M 1Y8 Office: Manchu Wok, 500 Hood Rd, Markham, ON Canada L3R 0P6

LEWIS, MO, professional football player; b. Atlanta, Ga., Oct. 21, 1969. Student, U. Georgia. With N.Y. Jets, 1991—. Office: New York Jets 1000 Fulton Ave Hempstead NY 11550-1099*

LEWIS, NATHAN SAUL, chemistry educator; b. L.A., Oct. 20, 1955. BS in Chemistry with highest honors, MS in Chemistry, Calif. Inst. Tech., 1977; PhD in Chemistry, MIT, 1981. Asst. prof. chemistry Stanford (Calif.) U. 1981-86, assoc. prof., 1986-88; assoc. prof. Calif. Inst. Tech., 1988-90, prof., 1990—; cons. Lawrence Livermore (Calif.) Nat. Lab., 1977-81, 84-88, Solar Energy Rsch. Assocs., Santa Clara, Calif., 1981-85, Am. Hosp. Supply, Irvine, Calif., 1983-85, Molecular Devices, Palo Alto, Calif., 1983-88; mem. U.S. Japan Joint Conf. Photochemistry and Photoconversion, 1983, Chem. Revs. Adv. Bd., 1989-92, long range planning com. Electrochem. Soc., 1991-94, Adv. Bd. Progress Inorganic Chemistry, 1992-94; vis. com. dept. applied sci. Brookhaven Nat. Lab., 1993—. Divisional editor Jour. Electrochemical Soc., 1984-90; mem. editorial adv. bd. Accounts Chem. Rsch., 1993—. Recipient Presdl. Young Investigator award, 1984-88, Fresenius award Phi Lambda Upsilon, 1990, Pure Chemistry award Am. Chem. Soc., 1991; Achievement Rewards Coll. Scientists Found. scholar Calif. Inst. Tech., 1975-77, Calif. State scholar, 1976-77, Carnation Co. Acad. Merit scholar, 1976-77, Camille and Henry Dreyfus Tchr. scholar, 1985-90; Fannie and John Hertz Found. fellow MIT, 1977-81, Alfred P. Sloan Rsch. fellow, 1985-87. Office: Calif Inst Tech Dept Chem 127-72 Pasadena CA 91125

LEWIS, NORMAN, English language educator, writer; b. N.Y.C., Dec. 30, 1912; s. Herman and Deborah (Nevins) L.; m. Mary Goldstein, July 28, 1934; children—Margery, Debra. B.A., CUNY, 1939; M.A., Columbia U., 1941. Instr. lectr CUNY, N.Y.C., 1943-52; assoc. prof. English NYU, N.Y.C., 1955-64; instr. Compton Coll., Calif., summers 1962-64, UCLA, 1962-69; prof. English Rio Hondo Coll., Whittier, Calif., 1964-91, chmn. communications dept., 1964-75. Author: (with others) Journeys Through Wordland, 1941, Lessons in Vocabulary and Spelling, 1941, (with Wilfred Funk) Thirty Days to a More Powerful Vocabulary, 1942, rev. edit., 1970, Power with Words, 1943, How to Read Better and Faster, 1944, rev. edit., 1978, The Lewis English Refresher and Vocabulary Builder, 1945, How to Speak Better English, 1948, Word Power Made Easy, 1949, rev. edit., 1978, The Rapid Vocabulary Builder, 1951, rev. edit., 1980, 3d edit., 1988, How to Get More Out of Your Reading, 1951, Twenty Days to Better Spelling, 1953, The Comprehensive Word Guide, 1958, Dictionary of Correct Spelling, 1962, Correct Spelling Made Easy, 1963, rev. edit. 1987, Dictionary of Modern Pronunciation, 1963, New Guide to Word Power, 1963, The New Power with Words, 1964, Thirty Days to Better English, 1964, The Modern Thesaurus of Synonyms, 1965, RSVP-Reading, Spelling, Vocabulary, Pronunciation (books I-III), 1966, 77, See, Say, and Write! (books I and II), 1973, Instant Spelling Power, 1976, R.S.V.P. for College English Power (books I-III), 1977-79, R.S.V.P. with Etymology (books I and II), 1980-81, Instant Word Power, 1980, New American Dictionary of Good English, 1987; editor: New Roget's Thesaurus of the English Language in Dictionary Form, 1961; also numerous articles in nat. mags.

LEWIS, NORMAN G., academic administrator, researcher, consultant; b. Irvine, Ayrshire, Scotland, Sept. 16, 1949; Came to U.S., 1985; s. William F. and Agnes H. O. L.; m. Christine I. (div. Oct. 1994); children: Fiona, Kathryn. BSc in Chemistry with honors, U. Strathclyde, Scotland, 1973; PhD in Chemistry 1st class, U. B.C., 1977. NRC postdoctoral fellow U. Cambridge, Can., 1978-80; rsch. assoc. chemistry dept. Nat. Rsch. Coun., Can., 1980; asst. scientist fundamental rsch. divsn. Pulp and Paper Rsch. Inst. Can., Montreal, 1980-82, group leader chemistry and biochemistry of woody plants, grad. rsch. chemistry divsn., 1982-85; assoc. prof. wood sci. and biochemistry Va. Poly. Inst. and State U., Blacksburg, 1985-90; dir. Inst. Biol. Chemistry, Wash. State U., Pullman, 1990—; Eisig-Tode disting. prof.; Cons. NASA, DOE, USDA, NIH, NSF, other industries, 1985—. Mem. editl. bd. Holzforschung, 1986, TAPPI, 1986, 89, Jour. Wood Chemistry and Tech., 1987—, Phytochemistry, 1992—, Polyphenols Actualities, 1992—; author or co-author more than 94 publs., books, articles to profl. jours. Hon. mem. Russian Assn. Space and Mankind. Recipient ICI Merit awards Imperial Chem. Industries, 1968-69, 69-70, 70-71, 71-72, ICI scholar, 1971-73; recipient Chemistry awards Kilmarnock Coll., 1969-70, 70-71; NATO/SRC scholar U. B.C., 1974-77; named Arthur M. and Kate Tode Disting. Prof. Mem. Am. Chem. Soc. (at-large cellulose divsn., organizer symposia, programme subcom. cellulose, paper and textile divsn. 1987-90, editorial bd.), Am. Soc. Plant Physiologists, Am. Soc. Gravitational and Space Biology, Phytochemical Soc. N.A. (phytochemical bank com. 1989—), Chem. Inst. Can. (treas. Montreal divsn. 1982-84, Am. Inst. Chemists and Chem. Inst. Can. Montreal conf. 1982-84), Can. Pulp and Paper Assn., Tech. Assn. of Pulp and Paper Industry, Societe de Groupe Polyphenole, Gordon Rsch. Conf. (vice-chmn. raenewable resources com. 1993—). Presbyterian. Achievements include 2 patents in field. Home: 1710 NE Upper Dr Pullman WA 99163-4624 Office: Washington State U Inst Biol Chemistry Clark Hall Pullman WA 99164

LEWIS, ORME, JR., real estate company executive, land use adviser; b. Phoenix, Apr. 26, 1935; s. Orme and Barbara (Smith) L.; m. Elizabeth Bruening, Oct. 17, 1964; children: Joseph Orme, Elizabeth Blaise. BS, U. Ariz., 1958. Assoc. Coldwell Banker, Phoenix, 1959-64; v.p. Braggiotti Constrn., Phoenix, 1964-65; pvt. practice investment brokerage Phoenix, 1966-69; dep. asst. sec. Dept. Interior, Washington, 1969-73; dir. devel. Ariz. Biltmore Estates, 1973-76; exec. World Resources Co., Phoenix and McLean, Va., 1978-91; mng. mem. Applewhite Laflin & Lewis, Phoenix, 1979—; gen. ptnr. Equity Interests, Phoenix, 1982—; co-chmn. U.S. Adv. Com. on Mining and Mineral Rsch., Washington, 1982-94; mem. U.S. Emergency Minerals Administrn., 1987—, Gov.'s Regulatory Rev. Coun., 1992-95, State Plant Site Transmission Line Com., Phoenix, 1974-85. Mem. Ariz. Senate, 1955-59; chmn. Phoenix Children's Hosp., 1981—; mem. governing bd. Polycystic Kidney Rsch. Found., Kansas City, Mo., 1983—, Ariz. Cmty. Found., 1986-91, Ariz.-N.Mex. Parks and Conservation Coun., 1985—, Ariz. State U. Found., Tempe, 1981—, Ariz. Hist. Found., 1984—, Desert Bot. Garden, 1987-89, Men's Art Coun., 1983-85. Mem. Ariz. C. of C., Met. Club (Washington), Ariz. Valley Field Riding and Polo Club, Paradise Valley Country Club, Rotary. Republican. Home: 4325 E Palo Verde Dr Phoenix AZ 85018-1127 Office: Applewhite Laflin & Lewis 4250 E Camelback Rd Ste 175K Phoenix AZ 85018-2784

LEWIS, PAUL LE ROY, pathology educator; b. Tamaqua, Pa., Aug. 30, 1925; s. Harry Earl and Rose Estella (Brobst) L.; m. Betty Jane Bixby, June 2, 1953; 1 child, Robert Harry. AB magna cum laude, Syracuse U., 1950; MD, SUNY, Syracuse, 1953. Diplomate Am. Bd. Pathology. Intern Temple U. Hosp., Phila., 1953-54; resident in pathology Hosp. of U. Pa., Phila., 1954-58, asst. instr., 1957-58; instr. pathology Thomas Jefferson U. Coll. Medicine, Phila., 1958-62, asst. prof., 1962-65, assoc. prof., 1965-75, prof., 1975—; pathologist Thomas Jefferson U. Hosp., 1958-92; attending pathologist Meth. Hosp., Phila., 1975-93, dir. clin. labs., chmn. dept. pathology, 1975-92, cons. pathologist, 1993—; pvt. practice Phila., 1993—; pres. Penndel Labs. Inc., Ardmore, Pa., 1974-85; cons. VA Hosp., Coatesville, Pa., 1976-85; mem. med. adv. com. ARC Blood Bank, Phila., 1978—. Contbg. author: Atlas of Gastrointestinal Cytology, 1983; contbr. articles to med. jours. 2d lt. USAAF, 1943-46. Fellow Am. Soc. Clin. Pathologists, Coll. Am. Pathologists; mem. AMA, Pa. Med. Soc., Philadelphia County Med. Soc., Internat. Acad. Pathology, Am. Soc. Cytology, Masons, Phi Beta Kappa, Alpha Omega Alpha, Nu Sigma Nu. Republican. Methodist. Avocations: photography, hiking. Home and office: 521 Baird Rd Merion Station PA 19066-1301 Office: Methodist Hosp Dept Path 2301 S Broad St Philadelphia PA 19148-3594

LEWIS, PEIRCE FEE, geographer, educator; b. Detroit, Oct. 26, 1927; s. Peirce and Amy Lois (Fee) L.; m. Flecia Louise Stegeman, Feb. 2, 1952; 1 child, Hugh Gilchrist. BA summa cum laude, Albion Coll., 1950; MA, U. Mich., 1953, PhD, 1957. Geographer, U.S. Army Forces, Tokyo, 1953-55; lectr. U. Mich., Ann Arbor, 1958; NSF fellow, U. Wash., Seattle, 1957-58; vis. prof. U. Calif., Berkeley, 1976-77; asst. prof. Pa. State U., University Park, 1958-62, prof. geography, 1962—; John Hannah prof. Integrative Studies, Mich. State U., E. Lansing, 1992; cons., author Smithsonian Instn., Washington, 1974-77, Smithsonian Instn. Books, 1989-90, Ency. Britannica, Chgo., 1973-74, 81-83, 89-90, Pa. Pub. TV, 1982-83; cons. Nat. Geog. Soc., 1981—. Nat. Mus. Am. History, Washington, 1990—, Nat. Rural Studies Com., 1991, So. Living Mag.; cons. Strong Mus., Rochester, N.Y., Newberry Libr., Chgo.; mem. steering com. Pioneer Am. Soc. vols. on Nat. Rd. Author: New Orleans: Making An Urban Landscape, 1976; editor: Visual Blight in America, 1973; contbr. articles to profl. jours. Mem. Borough Planning Commn., State College, Pa., 1967-76, mem. traffic commn., 1968-70; bd. dirs. Pa. Roadside Council, 1969-74. Served with U.S. Army, 1945-47. Recipient First Prize essay Internat. Geog. Congress, Stockholm, 1960; Lindback Teaching award Pa. State U., 1981; Disting. Teaching award Nat. Council for Geog. Edn., 1982; Nat. Honors award Assn. Am. Geographers, 1977, Trustee of Am. award Ctr. for Hist. Preservation, Mary Washington Coll., 1987, Disting. Geographer award Pa. Geog. Soc., 1991; rsch. assoc. U. Calif., Berkeley, 1986; John Simon Guggenheim Fellow, 1986-87, Woodrow Wilson fellow Woodrow Wilson Internat. Ctr. for Scholars, Smithsonian Inst., 1988, John Bracken fellow Pa. State U., 1993—. Mem. Am. Geographers (pres. 1983-84, nat. councillor 1981-82, 84-85, vis. geog. scientist, chmn. J.B. Jackson prize com.), Am. Geog. Soc., Nat. Council for Geog. Edn., Phi Beta Kappa. Democrat. Club: State College Literary. Avocation: travel. Home: 1377 Penfield Rd State College PA 16801-6420 Office: Pa State Univ Dept Geography 307 Walker Bldg University Park PA 16802

LEWIS, PERRY JOSHUA, investment banker; b. San Antonio, Feb. 11, 1938; s. Perry Joshua and Zelime L. L.; m. Memrie Taylor Mosier, May 12, 1962 (div. 1994); children—Perry Joshua, IV, Memrie Fraser. B.A., Princeton U., 1959. Registered rep. Lee Higginson Corp., N.Y.C., 1960-63; comml. project mgr. Parsons & Whittemore, Inc., N.Y.C., 1964-67; sr. v.p., mgr. corp. fin. div. Smith Barney, Harris Upham & Co. Inc., N.Y.C., 1967-79; pres. MacKay-Lewis Inc., N.Y.C., 1980-81; ptnr. Morgan Lewis Githens & Ahn, Conn., N.Y.C., 1982—; bd. dirs. Aon Corp., Chgo., Tyler Corp., Dallas, Broadcasting Ptnrs., Inc., Haynes Internat., Quaker Fabric Corp. ITI Techs., Inc., North St. Paul, Stuart Entertainment, Inc. With U.S. Army, 1959-60, 61-62. Served with U.S. Army, 1959-60, 61-62. Clubs: Knickerbocker of N.Y., Doubles N.Y., Field (Greenwich, Conn.). Office: Morgan Lewis Githens & Ahn 2 Greenwich Plz Greenwich CT 06830

LEWIS, PETER BENJAMIN, insurance company executive; b. Cleve., Nov. 11, 1933; s. Joseph M. and Helen (Rosenfeld) L.; married, June 19, 1955 (div. 1980); children: Ivy, Jonathan, Adam. A.B., Princeton U., 1955. With Progressive Ins. Cos., 1955—; pres., CEO Progressive Casualty Ins. Co., The Progressive Corp., Ohio, 1965-94; pres., CEO Mayfield Village, 1965-94, chmn. bd., 1993—. Mem. Soc. C.P.C.U. Clubs: Ceve. Racquet, Oakwood, Union. Office: Progressive Corp 6300 Wilson Mills Rd Mayfield Heights OH 44124

LEWIS, PHILIP, educational and technical consultant; b. Chgo., Oct. 23, 1913; s. Solomon and Fannie (Margolis) L.; m. Geraldine Gisela Lawenda, Sept. 1, 1947; 1 child, Linda Susan. BS, DePaul U., Chgo., 1937, MA, 1939; EdD, Columbia Tchrs. Coll., 1951. Chmn. dept. edn. Chgo. Tchrs. Coll.; also asst. prin., tchr. South Shore High Sch., Chgo., 1940-51; prin. Herman Felsenthal Elementary Sch., Chgo., 1955-57; dir. Bur. Instructional Materials, Chgo. Pub. Schs., 1957-63, Bur. Research Devel. and Spl. Projects, 1963-67; pres. Instructional Dynamics Inc., Chgo., 1967-89, ret., 1989; ednl. and tech. cons., 1991—; nat. cons. TV and instructional techniques, 1955—; ednl. cons. to accrediting bur. Health Edn. Schs., 1971-89; chmn. adv. com. U.S. Office Edn., Title VII, 1966-71. Author: Educational Television Guidebook for Electronics Industries Association, 1961, also numerous articles.; mem. editorial bd. Nation's Schs. and Colls; multimedia tech. editor: Tech. Horizons in Edn; cons.: Jour. Ednl. Tech. and Communications; producer ednl., multimedia, tng. and mental health and human devel. materials. Served to lt. comdr. USNR, 1942-45. Mem. Soc. Programmed and Automated Learning (pres. 1960-65), NEA (v.p. dept. audiovisual instrn., chmn. commn. on tech. standards dept. audiovisual instrn. 1965-85), Nat. Assn. Ednl. Broadcasters, Am. Legion, Council for Ednl. Facilities Planners (editorial adv. bd. 1972-80) Ill. C. of C. (elem. com. 1970-77), Chgo. Assn. Commerce and Industry (elem. com. 1970-80), Nat. Audio-Visual Assn. (profl. devel. bd. 1969-76, chmn), Chgo. Press Club, Masons, Shriners, Rotary, Phi Delta Kappa. Home: 2 E Oak St Apt 3201 Chicago IL 60611-1216

LEWIS, PHILLIP HAROLD, museum curator; b. Chgo., July 31, 1922; s. Bernard and Sonia (Pimstein) L.; m. Sally Leah Rappaport, Aug. 25, 1949; children—David Bernard, Betty Alice and Emily Ruth (twins). B.F.A., Art Inst. Chgo., 1947; M.A., U. Chgo., 1953, Ph.D., 1966; postgrad. (Fulbright ednl. grant), Australian Nat. U., Canberra, 1953-54. Conducted field research projects on art and soc. of New Ireland, 1953-54, 70, 81; asst. curator primitive art Field Mus. Natural History, Chgo., 1957-59; assoc. curator Field Mus. Natural History, 1960, curator, 1961-67, curator primitive art and Melanesian ethnology, 1968-92, ret., 1992, chmn. dept. anthropology, 1975-79, co-chmn. dept., 1980-81, acting chmn. dept., 1987; curator emeritus, 1994—. Served with USAAF, 1942-45. Fellow Royal Anthrop. Inst. Gt. Britain and Ireland, Am. Anthrop. Assn. Home: 1118 Main St Evanston IL 60202-1649 Office: Field Mus Natural History Roosevelt Dr Chicago IL 60607

LEWIS, RALPH MILTON, real estate developer; b. Johnstown, Pa., Nov. 9, 1919; s. Morris and Sarah (Galfond) L.; m. Goldy Sarah Kimmel, June 12, 1941; children: Richard Alan, Robert Edward, Roger Gordon, Randall Wayne. AA, Los Angeles City Coll., 1939; BS, UCLA, 1941; postgrad., U. So. Calif., 1945-48. Bar: Calif. 1952. Pvt. practice acctg. Los Angeles, 1945-55, pvt. practice law, 1953-55; founder Lewis Homes, 1957; chmn. bd. Lewis Construction Co., Inc., Upland, Calif., 1959—, Lewis Bldg. Co., Inc., Las Vegas, 1960—, Republic Sales Co. Inc.; dir., v.p. Kimmel Enterprises, Inc., 1959—; mng. partner Lewis Homes of Calif., 1973—, Lewis Homes of Nev., 1972—, Western Properties, Upland, 1972—, Foothill Investment Co., Las Vegas, 1971—, Republic Mgmt. Co., Upland, 1978-86; dir. Gen. Telephone Co. Calif. 1981-86; mem. adv. bd. Inland divsn. Bank of Am.; instr. U. Soc. Calif., UCLA, L.A. City Coll., 1948-54, Dooley Law Rev. Course, 1953-54; guest lectr. numerous colls., univs. Author: Land Buying Checklist, 1981, 85, 88, 90; contbr. articles to mags., jours. Mem., com. chmn. Calif. Commn. of Housing and Community Devel., 1965-67; mem. Calif. Gov.'s Task Force on the Home Bldg. and Construction Industry, 1967; pres. Bd. of Edn. Citrus Community Coll. Dist., Azusa, Calif., 1969, 73, mem., 1967-73; mem. Citizens Planning Council, Los Angeles County Regional Planning Commn., 1972-73, UCLA Found., Chancellor's Assoc.; mem. dean's council UCLA Grad. Sch. Architecture and Urban Planning; trustee U. Calif. Riverside Found.; bd. dirs. Regional Research Inst. So. Calif., 1983-84; chmn. land use and planning com. Citizens' Adv. Council, Calif. Senate Housing Com., 1983-84; founding mem. Rancho Cucamonga Community Found., 1987-88; donated $5 million to Lewis Ctr. for Regional Policy Studies Grad. Sch. UCLA, 1989, $5 million to the Ralph and Goldy Lewis Hall of Planning and Devel. Sch. Urban and Regional Planning U. So. Calif., 1989; funded Goldy & Ralph Lewis Edn. Ctr. Temple Beth Israel, Pomona, Calif.; land donor to City of Claremont, Calif., City of Rancho Cucamonga, Calif., City of Ontario, Calif.; bd. dirs. Calif. Community Colls., 1992—. Recipient Profl. Achievement commendation Calif. State Assembly, 1977, Humanitarian award NCCJ, 1979, Builder of Year award Bldg. Industry Assn. So. Calif., 1970; named as U. So. Calif.'s 1st Developer in Residence, 1988 at Lusk Ctr. for Real Estate Devel., (with wife Goldy) Entrepreneur of Yr., Inland Empire, 1990, 92, Housing Person of Yr. Nat. Housing Conf., 1990; recipient Good Scout award Old Baldy council Boy Scouts Am., 1984, (with wife) Builder of Yr. award Profl. Builder mag., 1987, Disting. chief exec. officer award Calif. State U., San Bernardino, 1992, Calif. State Legis. recognition Outstanding Leadership in the Bus. World, 1991, Spirit of Life award City of Hope, 1993, Mgmt. Leaders of Yr. award U. Calif., Riverside, 1993; inducted Nat. Housing Ctr.'s Hall of Fame, Washington, 1988; named Builder of Century, U. Calif., Irvine and Sumigarden Group, 1991. Mem. Am. Bar Assn., Calif. Soc. C.P.A.'s, Nat. Assn. Home Builders (dir.), Calif. Bldg. Industry Assn. (dir., chmn. affordable housing task force 1978-80, named to Hall of Fame 1987), Bldg. Industry Assn. So. Calif. (past treas., pres., dir., Bldg. Industry Assn. Medal of Honor, 1986, Builder of Yr. 1988).). Office: Lewis Homes 1156 N Mountain Ave Upland CA 91786-3633

LEWIS, RAMSEY EMANUEL, JR., pianist, composer; b. Chgo., May 27, 1935; s. Ramsey Emanuel and Pauline (Richards) L.; m. Geraldine Taylor, Apr. 7, 1954 (div. Mar. 1989); children—Vita Denise, Ramsey Emanuel III, Marcus Kevin, Dawn, Kendall, Frayne, Robert; m. Janet Tamillow, June 10,

1990. Student, Chgo. Music Coll., 1947-54, U. Ill., 1953-54, De Paul U., 1954-55; DHL (hon.), De Paul U., 1993. Mgr. record dept. Hudson-Ross, Inc., Chgo., 1954-56. Organizer Ramsey Lewis Trio, 1956; now solo artist; 1st profl. appearance, Chgo. 1957, appeared N.Y.C., 1958—, San Francisco, 1962, played Randall's Island Jazz Festival, N.Y.C., 1959, Saugatuck (Mich.) Jazz Festival, 1960, Newport (R.I.) Jazz Festival, 1961, 63, numerous jazz concerts at various festivals and univs. since 1961; toured with New Sounds of 1963; appeared in film Save the Children, 1973; recipient Grammy awards for The In Crowd 1965, Hold It Right There 1966, Hang on Sloopy 1973]; albums include Another Voyage, 1970, The Piano Player, 1970, Them Changes, 1970, Back To The Roots, 1971, Upendo Ni Pamoja, 1972, Funky Serenity, 1973, Legacy, 1978, Best of Ramsey Lewis, 1981, Salongo, 1976, Sun Goddess, 1974, Tequila Mockingbird, 1977, Ramsey, 1979, Routes, 1980, (with Nancy Wilson) The Two of Us, 1984, Fantasy, 1985, Keys to the City, 1987, A Classic Encounter (with London Philharm. Orch.), 1988, Urban Renewal, 1989, We Meet Again (with Billy Taylor), 1989, The Electric Collection, 1991, Ivory Pyramid, 1992, Sky Island, 1993, Maiden Voyage, 1994; composer: Sound of Spring, Fantasia for Drums, Look-a-Here, Sound of Christmas; organizer, Rams' L Prodns., Inc., Chgo., 1966, Ramsel Pub. Co., Chgo., 1966; host weekly jazz TV show, Sta. B.E.T. (cable TV) Bet on Jazz With Ramsey Lewis, 1990—; host weekly jazz radio show The Ramsey Lewis Show, 1990—, Sta. WNUA, Chgo., syndicated in various cities throughout the U.S.; artistic dir. Jazz in June series at Ravinia Festival Chgo., 1993—; numerous TV appearances; lectr. various univs. Address: 180 N LaSalle St # 2200 Chicago IL 60601*

LEWIS, RICHARD, actor, comedian; b. Bklyn., June 29, 1948; s. Bill and Blanche L. Student, Ohio State U., 1970. Head copywriter N.J. advt. agency, 1970-71; appearances include Greenwich Village club, The Improv, The Tonight Show. Co-writer: (TV special) Diary of a Young Comic; actor (TV series) Harry, 1987, King of the Building, 1987, Anything But Love, 1990-92, Daddy Dearest, 1993, over 40 appearances on Late Night With David Letterman, 1982; appeared in (cable special) I'm In Pain, 1985, I'm Exhausted, 1988 (ACE award nomination 1988), All-Star Toast to the Improv; 1988, I'm Doomed, 1990; films include The Wrong Guys, 1988, That's Adequate, 1989, Once Upon a Crime, 1992, Robin Hood: Men in Tights, 1993, Wagons East, 1994. Office: Michelle Marx Inc 8756 Holloway Dr West Hollywood CA 90069-2327 also: ICM 8942 Wilshire Blvd Beverly Hills CA 90211*

LEWIS, RICHARD, SR., securities broker, consultant; b. Macon, Ga., Jan. 18, 1930; s. William Chapman and Florida (Zelius) L.; m. Iris Joy Clements, Sept. 10, 1949; children: Richard Jr., Linda Lee. Cert. investments securities broker, pistol and rifle instr. State trooper Fla. Hwy. Patrol, various cities, 1951-72; pres. Gateway Shooters Supply, Inc., Jacksonville, Fla., 1972-82; broker Global Investments Securities Inc., Miami, 1985-86, Investacorp, Inc., Miami Lakes, Fla., 1986-89. Lobbyist Fla. Assn. of State Troopers, Tallahassee, 1988-89. With U.S. Army, 1952-54. Recipient cert. of appreciation, State of Fla., Tallahassee, 1972; Demolay Cross of Honor, Internat. Coun., Kansas City, Mo., 1973; cert. of commendation, State of Fla., 1972. Mem. NRA (life), Fla. Assn. State Troopers (legis. chmn. retirees 1987), V.F.W., Jacksonville Pistol Club (pres. 1968-72), Marion Dunn Masonic Lodge, Elks, Sons Am. Revolution, Sons Confederate Vets., Mil. Order Stars and Bars, Fraternal Order Police, Scottish Rite, Nobles Mistic Shrine (Ambassador-at-large). Republican. Methodist. Avocations: fishing, photography, competitive pistol shooting. Home: 130 Cypress Cir Lake Helen FL 32744-3100 also: PO Box 502 Cleveland GA 30528

LEWIS, RICHARD ALLAN, financial planner; b. Pitts., Feb. 25, 1952; s. Harry C. and Vera E. (Williams) L. BS in Econs., Allegheny Coll., 1974; MBA in Fin., U. Pitts., 1978. CFP. Trainee Mellon Bank, Pitts., 1974-75, various positions with, 1975-84, v.p. N.Am. ops., 1984-86; pres., COO WorkWell, Pitts., 1987-89; sr. fin. planner The Acacia Group, Pitts., 1989—. Mem. Nat. Automated Clearing House Assn. (bd. dirs. 1981-86), Tri-State Automated Clearing House Assn. (pres. 1984-86, treas. 1980-83, v.p. 1984-85), Masons, Blue Lodge, Phi Beta Kappa, Delta Tau Delta (pres. house corp. 1976—). Republican. Methodist. Avocations: skiing, jogging, travel, gourmet cooking. Home: 106 Fairway Landings Dr Canonsburg PA 15317-9567 Office: Acacia Group Acacia Bldg Pittsburgh PA 15220

LEWIS, RICHARD HAYES, lawyer, former state legislator; b. Hopkinsville, Ky., Dec. 3, 1937; s. Fred Theodore and Nola Angeline (Hayes) L.; m. Martha Jane Cunningham, June 24, 1961; children: Laura Elizabeth, Cynthia Jane, Katherine Hayes. BS, Murray (Ky.) State U., 1960; JD, U. Ky., 1965. Bar: Ky. 1965, U.S. Dist. Ct. (we. dist.) Ky. 1965, U.S. Ct. Appeals (6th cir.) 1983, U.S. Ct. Appeals (fed. cir.) 1986, U.S. Supreme Ct. 1983. Assoc. Lovett & Lovett, Benton, Ky., 1965-69, Lovett & Lewis, Benton, 1969-76; CEO to Gov. Julian Carroll Frankfort & Ky., Frankfort, 1975-76, mem. worker's compensation bd., 1976-78; prin. Law Office of Richard Lewis, Benton, 1976-93; ptnr. Lewis & Telle P.S.C., Benton, 1993—; mem. Ky. Ho. of Reps., Frankfort, 1970-75, 89-94, commr. Ky. alcoholic beverage control com., 1980-82. Sec. Marshall County C. of C., 1974; pres. Lions, Benton, 1974. Capt. U.S. Army, 1960-62. Mem. Marshall County Bar (pres.), Ky. Bar Assn., Ky. Trial Lawyers Assn., Nat. Bd. Trial Advocacy (cert. civil trial advocate 1994). Democrat. Baptist. Home: RR 8 Box 508 Benton KY 42025-8864 Office: Lewis & Telle PSC PO Box 430 1100 Main St Benton KY 42025-1450

LEWIS, RICHARD JAY, marketing educator, university dean; b. Marion, Ohio, July 14, 1933; s. Harley Franklin and Christina Mary (Anderson) L.; m. Patricia Ruth Montgomery, Sept. 17, 1955; children: Pamela Kay, Gregory Carl, Scott Alan. BS, Miami U., Oxford, Ohio, 1957, MBA, 1959; DBA, Mich. State U., 1964. Mem. faculty Mich. State U., East Lansing, 1964-93, prof. mktg., 1970-93, dean Coll. Bus., 1975-93; dean Faculty of Bus. U. Nigeria, Enugu, 1966-67; mem. faculty, dean Coll. Mgmt., N.C. State U., Raleigh, 1993—; bd. dirs. First of Mich. Corp., Detroit, First of Mich. Capital Corp., Am. Assembly Collegiate Schs. Bus. Author: Logistical Information System for Marketing Analysis, 1970, (with R. von H. Gilmer) Industrial and Organizational Psychology, 1971. Bd. dirs. Edward W. Sparrow Hosp., 1985—. Served with U.S. Army, 1953-55. Decorated Commendation medal. Mem. Am. Mktg. Assn., Lansing Regional C. of C. (bd. dirs. 1980-83), Am. Assembly Collegiate Schs. Bus. (pres. elect 1990, pres. 1991), Golden Key, Sigma Xi, Beta Gamma Sigma (dist. govs. 1976-82, nat. pres. 1980-82), Sigma Beta Delta (exec. coun.), Omicron Delta Epsilon. Home: 6100 Heatherstone Dr Raleigh NC 27606 Office: NC State U Coll Mgmt Raleigh NC 27606-8614

LEWIS, RICHARD KNOX, assitant city manager; b. Auburn, N.Y., June 25, 1946; s. Harry C. and Jean E. (Knox) L.; m. Barbara, Dec. 28, 1968; children: Wendy, Adam. AA, Auburn Community Coll., 1968; BA, U. Miss., 1970, MA, 1972. Project planner Mo. Dept. Community Affairs, Jefferson City, Mo., 1971-73; planning dir. City of Ocala, Fla., 1973-79; asst. city mgr., airport mgr. City of Ocala, 1979—. Past pres. Vol. Svc. Bur. Bd., Ocala, 1991, United Way of Marion County, Ocala, 1984-85, past campaign chmn., 1981-82; chmn. United Way Fla., 1995-96. Recipient Community Svc. award Marion County Jaycees, 1986. Mem. CFDSP (vice chmn.), Am. Planning Assn., Am. Inst. Cert. Planners, Assn. Urban Planners, Fla. Airport Mgrs. Assn., Am. Assn. Airport Execs., Fla. Cit. Episcopalian. Office: City of Ocala 151 SE Osceola Ave Ocala FL 34471-2148

LEWIS, RICHARD PHELPS, physician, educator; b. Portland, Oreg., Oct. 26, 1936; s. Howard Phelps and Wava Irene (Brown) L.; m. Penny A. Brown, Oct. 12, 1982; children: richard Phelps, Heather Brown. BA, Yale U., 1957; MD, U. Oreg., 1961. Intern Peter Bent Brigham Hosp., Boston, 1961-62, resident, 1962-63; Howard Irwin fellow in cardiology U. Oreg., Portland, 1963-65; sr. resident Stanford U., 1965-66, instr. dept. medicine, 1968-69; asst. chief cardiology Madigan Gen. Hosp., Tacoma, 1966-68; asst. prof. medicine div. cardiology Ohio State U., 1969-71, assoc. prof., 1971-75, prof., 1975—, dir. Divsn. Cardiology, 1972-86, dir., 1972-86, assoc. chmn. for hosp. and clin. affairs, 1980-86; mem. cardiovascular sect. Am. Bd. Internal Medicine, 1984-87, critical care medicine, 1988-92. Contbr. articles to profl. jours. Served with M.C. U.S. Army, 1966-68, col. res. Decorated Army Commendation medal. Fellow ACP (gov. Ohio chpt. 1976-80, chmn. MKSAP cardiovascular sect. 1980-82), Am. Heart Assn. (coun. on clin. cardiology), Am. Coll. Cardiology (Ohio gov. 1988-91, chmn. bd. govs. 1990-91, trustee 1991—, chmn. self assessment program, v.p. 1994-95, pres.-

elect 1995—), Am. Clin. and Climatological Assn.; mem. Am. Fedn. Clin. Rsch., Cen. Soc. Clin. Rsch., Laennec Soc., Am. Heart Assn., Assn. U. Cardiologists, Am. Soc. Internal Medicine, Alpha Omega Alpha. Republican. Home: 5088 Stratford Ave Powell OH 43065-8771 Office: 466 W 10th Ave Columbus OH 43210-1240

LEWIS, RICHARD STANLEY, author, former editor; b. Pitts., Jan. 8, 1916; s. S. Morton and Mary L. (Lefstein) L.; m. Louise G. Silberstein, June 8, 1938; children: Jonathan, David. B.A., Pa. State U., 1937. Reporter Cleve. Press, 1937-38; rewrite man, drama critic Indpls. Times, 1938-43, reporter, city editor, 1946-49; reporter St. Louis Star-Times, 1949-51; mem. staff Chgo. Sun-Times, 1951-68, sci. editor, 1967-68; mng. editor Bull. Atomic Scientists, Chgo., 1968-70; editor Bull. Atomic Scientists, 1971-74; writing cons. earth sci. curriculum project NSF, summers 1964-65. Author: The Other Child, 1951, (rev. edit, 1964), A Continent for Science, 1965, Appointment on The Moon, 1968, rev. edit., 1969, The Nuclear Power Rebellion, 1972, The Voyages of Apollo, 1974, From Vinland to Mars: 1000 Years of Exploration, 1976, The Other Child Grows Up, 1977, The Voyages of Columbia, 1984, Challenger: The Final Voyage, 1987, Space in the 21st Century, 1990; prin. author: The New Illustrated Encyclopedia of Space Exploration; editor: Man on the Moon, 1969, Alamogordo Plus 25 Years, 1970, Frozen Future, 1972, The Energy Crisis, 1972, The Environmental Revolution, 1973. Mem. Indialantic Town Council, 1980-82, apptd. dep. mayor, 1980. Served with AUS, 1943-46, ETO. Fellow Brit. Interplanetary Soc. (London); Mem. Authors Guild, Authors League Am. Club: Nat. Press (Washington); Canaveral Press (Cocoa Beach, Fla.) (pres. 1985). Home: 1401 S Magnolia Ave Indialantic FL 32903-3510

LEWIS, RITA HOFFMAN, plastic products manufacturing company executive; b. Phila., Aug. 6, 1947; d. Robert John and Helen Anna (Dugan) Hoffman; 1 child, Stephanie Blake. Student Jefferson Med. Coll. Sch. Nursing, 1965-67, Gloucester County Coll., 1993—; Gen. mgr. Sheets & Co., Inc. (now Flower World, Inc.), Woodbury, N.J., 1968-72; dir., exec. v.p., treas. Hoffman Precision Plastics, Inc., Blackwood, N.J., 1973—; ptnr. Timber Assocs.; commr. N.J. Expressway Authority, 1990—, sec., 1990-91, treas., 1991—, chmn. pers., 1991—; apptd. mem. N.J. Senate Forum on Budget and Revenue Alternatives, 1991; guest speaker various civic groups, 1974; poetry editor SPOTLIGHTER Innovative Singles Mag. Author: That Part of Me I Never Really Meant to Share, 1979; In Retrospect: Caught Between Running and Loving; columnist Innovative Singles mag., 1989—. Mem. Com. for Citizens of Glen Oaks (N.J.), 1979—; Gloucester Twp. Econ. Devel. Com., 1981—; Gloucester Twp. Day Scholarship Com., 1984—; chairperson Gloucester Twp. Day Scholarship Found., 1985—; bd. dirs Diane Hull Dance Co. Recipient Winning Edge award, 1982, Mayor's award for Womens' Achievement, 1987, Outstanding Community Service award Mayor, Council and Com., 1987. Mem. NAFE, Sales Assn. Chem. Industry, Blackwood Businessmen's Assn., Soc. Plastic Engrs. Roman Catholic.

LEWIS, ROBERT, periodical editor, journalist; b. Montreal, Que., Can., Aug. 19, 1943; s. Leon R. and Margaret (Horan) L.; m. Sara Lewis, May 27, 1967; children: Christopher Robert, Timothy O'Neill. BA, Loyola Coll. 1964. Gen. reporter Montreal Star, 1964-65, Ottawa corr., 1965-66; chief Montreal bur. Time mag., 1967-68, Ottawa corr., 1968-70, Boston corr., 1970-72, chief Toronto bur., 1972-74; chief Ottawa bur. Maclean's Mag., 1975-82, mng. editor, 1982-93, editor, 1993—. Home: 31 Brooke Ave, Toronto, ON Canada M5M 2J5 Office: Maclean's Mag, 777 Bay St, Toronto, ON Canada M5W 1A7

LEWIS, ROBERT ALAN, biologist, physiologist, environmental scientist, researcher, educator, administrator, author; b. Chillicothe, Ohio, Apr. 23, 1933; s. Clarence Albert and Ethel (Hamm) L.; m. Carolyn Jane Weber, Dec. 22, 1960; 1 child, Cynthia Anne. B.Sc., Ohio State U., 1959; M.Sc., Rutgers U., 1963; Ph.D., U. Wash., 1971. Asst. curator vertebrate collections Ohio Hist. Mus., Columbus, 1958-60; field rep. for vet. pub. health N.J. Dept. Health, Trenton, 1960-61; acting chmn. dept. biology Monroe Coll., Rochester, N.Y., 1963; zoologist Avian Physiology Lab., U. Wash., Seattle, 1966-73, research assoc. dept. zoology, 1973-74, sr. research assoc. dept. zoology, 1974-77; sr. scientist, environ. physiologist Nat. Ecol. Research Lab., Corvallis, Oreg., 1973-77; gen. ecologist, program mgr. Office Health and Environ. Research U.S. Dept. Energy, Washington, 1977-81; prof., dir. Inst. Biogeography U.-Saarland, Saarbruecken, Fed. Republic Germany, 1982, prof. Sch. Biogeography, 1982-91; adj. prof. Grad. Sch., Hood Coll., Frederick, Md., 1978-93; cons. toxicology, environmental and biol. monitoring, biotech., risk mgmt., 1991-93; sr. scientist, program dir. Waste Policy Inst., Washington; mem. Pres.'s Water Policy Study; mem. Internag. Com. on Health and Environ. Effects of Advanced Energy Tech.; mem. Working Group on Western Range Mgmt. of Commn. on Food and Renewable Resources, Fed. Coordinating Council for Sci., Engring. and Tech.; bd. examiners Banares U., India; dir. Mont. Coal-fired power Plant Study, 1973-77; lectr. in field; advisor to govts., facilitator coop. activities between U.S. and West German agys.; ofcl. liaison between Man and the Biosphere Program of U.S. Dept. State and Fed. Republic Germany, 1986—; evaluated and recommended system of Nat. Ecol. Research Parks which were then established by Fed. Republic Germany; mem. sci. adv. coun. environ. assessment program Christian-Albrechts U., Kiel, Fed. Republic Germany; participant Expert Colloquium on Integrated Environ. Assessment, Berlin; chmn. cost efficient acquisition and utilization of data in mgmt. of hazardous waste sites Internat. Conf., Herndon, Va., 1994; participant White House Conf. Tech. for Sustainable Future, 1994; chmn. Internat. Conf. Challenge and Innovation in Mgmt of Hazardous Waste, Washington, 1995. Author, editor: Guidelines for the Establishment of an Environmental Specimen Bank in the Federal Republic of Germany: Ecological Foundations, 1985; editor: Environmental Specimen Banking and Monitoring as Related to Banking, 1984, Challenges and Innovations in the Management of Hazardous Waste, 1995; mem. editl. bd. Toxicology and Environmental Chemistry; contbr. numerous articles to profl. jours., books chpts.; editor: Cost Efficient Acquisition and Utilization of Data in the Management of Hazardous Waste Sites, 1994; co-inventor zonal air pollution system. Served with U.S. Army, 1955-58. Grantee in field. Mem. AAAS, Air and Waste Mgmt. Assn., Delattinia, Internat. Statis. Program, Soc. Environ. Toxicology and Chem., Wheaton Club of Ohio, Sigma Xi. Republican. Avocations: hiking; bicycling; camping; natural history. Established research field station; co-designer remote, computerized air quality monitoring and micrometeorological network; tested and applied state-of-the-art controlled environment system; developed new remote sensing application in assessment of chronic pollution effects; active in development environmentally safe energy techs., environ. toxicology, risk assessment. Led the team that selected the Nat. Ecological Rsch. Parks for Fed. Republic Germany. Home: 7213 James Dr Frederick MD 21701-6266

LEWIS, ROBERT CHARLES, lawyer; b. Des Moines, Oct. 21, 1943; s. Raymond and Gwenn L.; B.A., U. Md., 1965; J.D., George Washington U., 1968. Bar: D.C. 1968. Dep. dir. div. market regulation SEC, Washington, 1968-76; ptnr. Shearman & Sterling, N.Y.C., 1976—; lectr. securities law confs. Mem. ABA. Office: Shearman & Sterling 599 Lexington Ave Fl 2C New York NY 10022-6030 also: 4 Embarcadero Ctr San Francisco CA 94111-4106 also: 1001 30th St NW Washington DC 20007-3883

LEWIS, ROBERT EDWIN, JR., pathology immunology educator, researcher; b. Meridian, Miss., Mar. 11, 1947. BA in Biology and Chemistry, U. Miss., 1969, MS in Microbiology, 1973, PhD in Pathology, 1976; specialty tng., Barnes Hosp., U. Miami Med. Ctr., U. Tenn. Ctr. for Health Scis., City of Memphis Hosps., St. Jude Children's Research Hosp. Instr. pathology, anesthesiology U. Miss. Med. Ctr., Jackson, 1976-77, asst. prof. pathology, 1977-84, asst. prof. anesthesiology, 1977-85, asst. dir. clin. immnuopathology lab., 1978-81, assoc. dir. tissue typing lab., 1980-84, dir. paternity testing lab., 1981—, assoc. dir. clin. immunopathology lab., 1981-84, asst. prof. nurse anesthesiology, 1981-85, assoc. prof. pathology, 1984-91, prof., 1991—, co-dir. clin. immunology, tissue typing lab., 1984—, mem. grad. council, 1981—; co-dir. clin. immunology, tissue typing lab., 1984—; prof. U. Miss. Med. Ctr., Jackson, 1991—. Co-author: Illustrated Dictionary of Immunology, 1985-91, (with J. M. Cruse) Concepts in Immunopathology, Vols. 1-8, 1985-91, The Year in Immunology-1984-85, 1985, The Year in Immunology-1985-86, 1986, The Year in Immunology-1986-87, 1987, The Year in Immunology-1988, 1989, The Year in Immunology-1989-90, 1990, Progress in Experimental Tumor Research, Vol. 32, 1987, Con-

tributions to Microbiology and Immunology, Vol. 8, 1986, Vol. 9, 1987, Vol. 10, 1989, Vol. 11, 1989, The Year in Immunopathology, 1987, Complement Profiles, Vol. 1, 1992; sr. editor Pathology and Immunopathology Research, 1982-90, Immunologic Research, 1981—, Transgenics, 1993—; series editor Concepts in Immunopathology, The Year in Immunology, Contributions to Microbiology and Immunology; vol. editor Progress in Experimental Tumor Research; immunology editor Dorland's Illustrated Medical Dictionary 26th and 27th edits.; dep. editor-in-chief Pathobiology, 1990—; contbr. chpts. to books. Grantee Am. Cancer Soc., NIH, Wilson Found., 1990-95. Fellow Royal Soc. Health; mem. AAAS, Am. Assn. Pathologists, Am. Assn. Immunologists, Clin. Immunology Soc., Can. Soc. Immunology, Reticuloendothelial Soc., Am. Soc. for Microbiology, Am. Soc. for Histocompatibility and Immunogenetics (co-chmn. publications com.), Exptl. Biology and Medicine, N. Y. Acad. Scis., Miss. Acad. Scis., Sigma Xi. Office: U Miss Med Ctr Pathology Dept 2500 N State St Jackson MS 39216-4505

LEWIS, ROBERT ENZER, lexicographer, educator; b. Windber, Pa., Aug. 12, 1934; s. Robert Enzer and Katharine Torrence (Blair) L.; m. Julie Fatt Cureton, May 14, 1977; children: Perrin Lewis Rubin, Torrence Evans Lewis; stepchildren: Sarah Cureton Kaufman, James S. Cureton. BA, Princeton U., 1959; MA, U. Pa., 1962, PhD, 1964. Tchr. English Mercersburg (Pa.) Acad., 1959-60; teaching fellow U. Pa., Phila., 1961-63; lectr. Ind. U., Bloomington, 1963-64, asst. prof., 1964-68, assoc. prof., 1968-75, prof. English, 1975-82; prof. English U. Mich., Ann Arbor, 1982—. Author: (with A. McIntosh) Descriptive Guide to the Manuscripts of the Prick of Conscience, 1982, (with others) Index of Printed Middle English Prose, 1985; editor: De Miseria Condicionis Humane (Lotario dei Segni), 1978; co-editor: Middle English Dictionary, 1982-83, editor-in-chief: vols. 8, 9, 10, 11, 1983—; gen. editor: Chaucer Libr., 1970—, chmn. editorial com., 1978-89; mem. editorial bd. New Oxford English Dictionary, 1984—. Bd. regents Mercersburg Acad., 1975-87. U.S. Army, 1954-56. Vis. rsch. fellow Inst. Advanced Studies in the Humanities, U. Edinburgh, 1973-74; Am. Coun. Learned Socs. fellow, 1979-80. Mem. Medieval Acad. Am. (mem. publs. com. 1987-92), Dictionary Soc. N.Am., New Chaucer Soc. Episcopalian. Office: Middle English Dictionary 555 S Forest Ave Ann Arbor MI 48109-2531

LEWIS, ROBERT J., secondary education educator. Tchr. sci. Downers Grove (Ill.) High Sch. North. Recipient James Bryant Conant award Am. Chem. Soc., 1995. Office: Downers Grove High School N 4436 Main St Downers Grove IL 60515*

LEWIS, ROBERT KAY, JR., fundraising executive; b. Danville, Ky., Aug. 10, 1935; s. Robert K. and Mona (Hyden) L.; m. Wendy Gardiner, June 18, 1960; children: Mary Elizabeth, Mona Hyden, Robert K. III. BA, Ctr. Coll., Danville, 1957; MS, George Washington U., 1972. Advanced through ranks to lt. U.S. Navy, 1958-63; alumni/annual giving dir. Ctr. Coll., 1963-67; served to capt. U.S. Navy, 1967-81; alumni/pub. affairs dir. Ctr. Coll., 1981-83; pub. affairs dir. Va. Tech., Blacksburg, 1983-87; sr. v.p. Host Comm., Lexington, 1987-89; pres. Ky. C. of C., Frankfort, 1990, Global Advancement, Lexington, Ky., 1991—. Trustee Severn Sch., Severna Park, Md., 1979-83; bd. visitors McCallie Sch., Chattanooga, 1983-86; bd. dirs. Ky. Advocates for Higher Edn., Lexington, 1990—. Mem. Nat. Soc. Fund Raising Execs. (bd. dirs. Lexington chpt. 1991—), Henry Clay Found. (bd. dirs. Lexington, 1994—), Nat. Press Club, Coun. Advancement and Support of Edn. (Ky. bd. dirs. 1991—). Presbyterian. Home: Forest Hill Farm 2667 Lexington Rd Danville KY 40422 Office: Global Advancement 333 W Vine St Ste 300 Lexington KY 40507-1626

LEWIS, ROBERT LAWRENCE, lawyer, educator; b. N.Y.C., Sept. 25, 1919; s. Isador and Sadie (Holzinger) L.; m. Frieda Friedman, Nov. 24, 1940 (dec. 1961); children—Brian S., Paul E., David N.; m. Joanne Marcia Waxman, June 16, 1963; children—Pavia S., Eraclea S. A.B., Hamilton Coll., 1940; LL.B., Case Western Res. U., 1948. With firm Ulmer & Berne, Cleve., 1948-64, ptnr., 1956-64; ret., 1964; prof. law, dir. grad. div. Cleve.-Marshall Law Sch. (now Cleve. State U.), 1948-53; bd. dirs. Banner Industries, Inc., Cleve.; scholar-in-residence, prof. classics Cuayhoga C.C.; adj. prof. nonprofit governance Case Western Res. U., Cleve. Author: Five Angry Women, 1990, Agatharcus, 1993. Cons., evaluator North Central Assn. Colls. and Schs., Middle States Assn. Mem. Cleve. Area Arts Council, 1971-73; pres. Fairmount Center for Creative and Performing Arts, 1973-75; trustee, chmn. bd. Cuyahoga Community Coll.; trustee Cuyahoga Community Coll. Found., Playhouse Sq. Found., Cleve., Cleve. Commn. Higher Edn., Lake Erie Coll., Council for Interinstnl. Leadership, Pace Assn., New Orgn. for Visual Arts; bd. dirs. Assn. Governing Bds. Univs. and Colls.; bd. advisers Cleve. Ballet; trustee, v.p. New Cleve. Opera Co. Served to 1st lt., arty. and ordnance corps AUS, 1942-46, NATOUSA. Decorated Legion of Merit, Purple Heart. Mem. Exec. Order Ohio Commodore, Phi Beta Kappa. Home: 2425 N Park Blvd Apt 4 Cleveland OH 44106-3154 Office: 900 Bond Ct Bldg Cleveland OH 44114 *There is neither a standard nor a uniform set of qualities which best fits one to be a member of society, and anyone who contends to the contrary, may be equated with the infamous and mythical Procrustes. I for one prefer the preservation of individuality. No one of us should be fitted to the bed of Procrustes. I prefer that we shall all survive, and each of us shall then be the richer for the survival of the other.*

LEWIS, ROGER KUTNOW, architect, educator, author; b. Houston, Jan. 9, 1941; s. Nathan D. and Betty (Kutnow) L.; m. Eleanor Draper Roberts, June 24, 1967; 1 child, Kevin Michael. BArch, MIT, 1964, MArch, 1967. Registered architect, D.C., Va., Md. Vol. architect Peace Corps, Nabeul, Tunisia, 1964-66; designer Wilkes & Faulkner, Washington, 1967-68; ptnr. Chavarria/Lewis Assocs., Washington, 1968-71; prin. Roger K. Lewis AIA & Assocs., Washington, 1971-80; pres. Pecla Corp., Washington, 1971-81; ptnr. Chesapeake Design Group, Balt., 1980-81; prin. Roger K. Lewis FAIA Architect & Planner, Washington, 1981—; prof. U. Md. Sch. Arch., 1968—; mem. D.C. Com. on Design Arts, Washington, 1988-92. Author: Architect? A Candid Guide to the Profession, 1985, Shaping the City, 1987; co-author Growth Management Handbook, 1989; author articles in jours.and periodicals, chpts. in books, encys.; columnist The Washington Post, 1984—. Recipient Fed. Design Achievement award Nat. Endowment for the Arts, Washington, 1988, numerous awards Am. Planning Assn., AAUW, 1985—. Fellow AIA (numerous design awards 1973—); mem. Washington Area Architecture Group (co-founder), Faberge Arts Found. (bd. advs.), Cosmos Club, Lambda Alpha. Home: 5034 1/2 Dana Pl NW Washington DC 20016-3441 Office: Univ Md Sch Architecture College Park MD 20742

LEWIS, RON, congressman; b. Greenup County, Ky., Sept. 14, 1946; m. Kayi Gambill, 1966; children: Ronald Brent, Allison Faye. Student, Morehead State U.; BA in History and Polit. Sci. U. Ky., 1969; MA in Higher Edn., Morehead State U., 1981; student, USN Officer Candidate Sch. Ordained to ministry Bapt. Ch. With Ky. Hwy. Dept., Ea. State Hosp.; with sales various cos.; tchr. Watterson Coll., 1980-85; pastor White Mills Bapt. Ch.; owner small bus. Elizabethtown, Ky.; mem. 103d-104th Congresses from 2d Ky. Dist., 1994—; mem. mil. procurement and mil. pers. subcoms., nat. security com., mem. risk mgmt. and splty. crops and resource conservation, rsch. and forestry subcoms., agr. com. Past pres. Hardin and Larue County Jail Ministry. Named Guardian of Srs.' Rights, Tax Fairness Srs.; honoree U.S. Term Limits, Citizens for Property Rights, Coun. Citizens Against Govt. Waste, Nat. Fed. Ind. Bus. Mem. Severus Valley Ministerial Assn., Elizabethtown C. of C. Office: US House Representatives 2333 Rayburn House Office Bldg Washington DC 20515-1702

LEWIS, ROY ROOSEVELT, physicist; b. Richmond, Va., Mar. 4, 1935; s. Jesse NMN and Elizabeth (Lewis) L.; m. Debra Blondell, Sept. 21, 1968 (div. Aug. 1974); 1 child, Roy Jr.; m. Linda Eleanor, Dec. 19, 1985. BS, Va. Union U., Richmond, 1958; MS, Howard U., 1962, UCLA, 1969; PhD, UCLA, 1972. Member. tech. staff Hughes Rsch. Labs., Malibu, Calif., 1972-75, Aerospace Corp., El Segundo, Calif., 1977-81, TRW, Redondo Beach, Calif., 1981-82; dir. minority engring. Calif. State U., Long Beach, 1982-83; assoc. prof. Calif. State U., 1982-86, Calif. State Polytech. U., Pomona, Calif., 1986-89; faculty fellow Jet Propulsion Lab. Cal. Inst. Tech., Pasadena, Calif., 1987-89; mem. tech. staff Jet Propulsion Lab. Cal. Inst. Tech., 1989-93; pres. Roy Lewis & Assocs., a sci. cons. firm, Inglewood, Calif., 1993—. Author: LewLearns, Science Lessons For Children, 1977; contbr. articles to profl. jours. Mem. Am. Soc. Engring. Edn., Nat. Soc. Black Physicists, L.A.

Coun. Black Engrs., IEEE, Inglewood Dem. Club, Sigma Xi, Alpha Phi Alpha, Sigma Phi Sigma. Episcopalian. Home: 1401 Overhill Dr Inglewood CA 90302-1346

LEWIS, RUSSELL T., newspaper publishing executive. Pres., gen. mgr. The N.Y. Times, N.Y.C., 1993—. Office: NY Times 229 W 43rd St New York NY 10036-3913

LEWIS, SAMELLA SANDERS, artist, educator; b. New Orleans, Feb. 27, 1924; d. Samuel and Rachel (Taylor) Sanders; m. Paul Gad Lewis, Dec. 22, 1948; children—Alan Stephen, Claude Anthony. Student, Dillard U., 1941-43; BS, Hampton Inst., 1945; MA, Ohio State U., 1947, PhD, 1951; postgrad., U. So. Calif., 1964-66; LHD (hon.), Chapman Coll., 1976, U. Cin., 1993; DHL (hon.), Hampton U., 1990. Asst. prof. Hampton (Va.) Inst., 1945-47; asso. prof. at Morgan State Coll., 1950-52; chmn. dept. art, prof. Fla. A&M U., 1953-58; prof. SUNY, Plattsburgh, 1958-67; coordinator edn. Los Angeles County Mus. Art, 1968-69; prof. Asian, African, Afro-Am. Art History Scripps Coll., Claremont, Calif., 1970-84; prof. emerita Scripps Coll., 1984—. Author: Art, African American Textbook, 1978, The Art of Elizabeth Catlett, 1984, African American Art for Young People, 1991, African American Art and Artists Textbook, 1993; producer five films on Black Am. artists; founder Mus. African Am. Art, Los Angeles, 1976; founder, dir., The Gallery, Los Angeles, 1969-79, Asanti Gallery, Pomona, Calif., 1980; Art editor Internat. Rev. African Am. Art, 1976—; One woman shows, Clark Mus., Claremont, Calif., 1979, Univ. Union Gallery, 1980, Delta Art Ctr., Winston-Salem, N.C., 1989, Bennett Coll., Greensboro, N.C., 1994; group shows include, Huntsville (Ala.) Mus., 1979, Smithsonian Instn. travelling exhbn., 1980-81, Vorpal Gallery, San Francisco, 1989, Hampton (Va.) U. Mus., 1990, Am. Fedn. Arts, 1993—, Bomani Gallery, San Francisco, 1994; curator Masters Exhbn., Salvador, Bahia, Brazil, 1988, curator Two Sculptures Two Eras-Richmond Barthé and Richard Hunt, travel to mus. 1992—; solo: James E. Kemp Gallery, Baltimore, Dallas, Tex., 1995; represented in permanent collections, Balt. Mus. Art, Oakland Mus. Art, High Mus., Atlanta, Palm Springs Mus., Va. Mus. Art. Recipient Faculty Recognition award Scripps Coll., 1984, Disting. Alumni award Ohio State U., 1986, Honor award for outstanding achievement in visual arts Women's Caucus for Art, 1989, Legends in Our Time award Essence Mag., 1990, James Van Der Lee Lifetime Svc. to Arts award Brandywine Workshop, Phila., 1992, Lifetime Achievement award Brandywine Workshop, 1992; Fulbright fellow, 1962, NDEA postdoctoral fellow, 1964-66; Ford Found. grantee, 1965, 81. Mem. Assn. Asian Studies, Nat. Conf. Artists, So. Calif. Art History Assn., Coll. Art Assn. Am. (bd. dirs. 1990—). Home: 1237 Masselin Ave Los Angeles CA 90019-2544

LEWIS, SAMUEL WINFIELD, retired government official, former ambassador; b. Houston, Oct. 1, 1930; s. Samuel Winfield and Sue Roselle (Hurley) L.; m. Sallie Kate Smoot, June 20, 1953; children: Pamela Gracelle, Richard Winfield. BA magna cum laude, Yale U., 1952; MA, Johns Hopkins U., 1954; PhD (hon.), Tel Aviv U., 1985, Hebrew U. Jerusalem, 1985, Weizman Inst. Sci., 1985; DHL (hon.), Hebrew Union Coll., 1986, Balt. Hebrew U., 1988; LLD (hon.), Salem-Teikyo U., 1991. Exec. asst. Am. Trucking Assn., Washington., 1953-54; fgn. svc. officer Dept. State, Washington, 1954-85; consular officer Naples, Italy, 1954-55; consul Florence, Italy, 1955-59; officer-in-charge Italian affairs Washington, 1959-61, spl. asst. to undersec. state, 1961-63; dep. asst. dir. US AID Mission to Brazil, Rio de Janeiro, 1964-65; exec. officer embassy, Rio de Janeiro, 1965-67; dep. dir. Office Brazil Affairs, Washington, 1967-68; sr. staff mem. for Latin Am. Affairs Nat. Security Council, White House, Washington, 1968-69; spl. asst. for policy planning Bur. Inter-Am. Affairs, Washington, 1969; spl. asst. to dir. gen. Fgn. Svc., 1970-71; dep. chief mission and counselor embassy Kabul, Afghanistan, 1971-74; dep. dir. policy planning staff Dept. State, 1974-75, asst. sec. state for internat. orgn., 1975-77; U.S. ambassador to Israel, 1977-85; lectr., diplomat-in-residence Johns Hopkins Fgn. Policy Inst., Washington, 1985-86; pres. U.S. Inst. of Peace, Washington, 1987-93; dir. policy planning staff U.S. Dept. State, Washington, 1993-94; cons. U.S. Dept. State, 1994-95; sr. internat. fellow The Dayan Ctr., Tel Aviv U., 1986-87; chmn. bd. overseers Harry S. Truman Rsch. Inst. for Advancement of Peace and Hebrew U., Jerusalem, 1986-91; guest scholar The Brookings Inst., Washington, 1987; mem. bd. advisors Washington Inst. Near East Policy, 1986-93, counselor, 1995—; adv. com. Initiative for Peace and Cooperation in the Middle East, Washington, 1994—; vis. prof. Hamilton Coll., spring 1995. Author: Making Peace Among Arabs and Israelis, 1991; contbg. author: The Middle East: Ten Years After Camp David, 1988, Soviet-Arms Competition in the Middle East, 1988, Israel: The Peres Era, 1987; contbr. articles to profl. jours. and The N.Y. Times, The Washington Post. Bd. dirs. Inst. for Study of Diplomacy, Georgetown U., 1994—. Recipient William A. Jump award for outstanding service in pub. adminstrn., 1967, Meritorious Honor award Dept. State, 1967, Meritorious Honor award AID, 1967, Pres.' Mgmt. Improvement cert., 1971, Distinguished Honor award Dept. State, 1977, 85, Disting. Alumnus award Johns Hopkins U., 1980, Wilbur J. Carr award Dept. State, 1985; vis. fellow Princeton U., 1994. Mem. Am. Acad. Diplomacy, UN Assn., Coun. on Fgn. Rels., Middle East Inst., Cousteau Soc., Sierra Club, Phi Beta Kappa. Episcopalian.

LEWIS, SHARI, puppeteer, entertainer; b. N.Y.C., Jan. 17, 1934; d. Abraham B. and Ann (Ritz) Hurwitz; m. Jeremy Tarcher, Mar. 15, 1958; 1 child, Mallory. Star weekly NBC-TV show The Shari Lewis Show, 1960-63, weekly syndicated series Lambchop's Play-Along (named TV Guide's Best of Best for Children), 1975-77, weekly TV show BBC, London, 1969-75, weekly TV show for intl. network in Gt. Britain, 1970, daily TV show PBS, 1992—; writer, producer, star NBC spl. A Picture of Us, 1971; condr. over 100 symphonies in U.S., Can., Japan, 1977—; command performances, London, 1970, 73, 78; author 59 pub. books including 15 One Minute Bedtime Stories (bestselling series); 18 home video cassettes: including 101 Things for Kids to do Shari's Christmas Concert, Don't Wake Your Mom, 1992, Let's Make Music, 1994. Past mem. nat. bd. dirs. Girl Scouts U.S.; past internat. bd. dirs. Boy Scouts Am.; past pres. Am. Ctr. Films for Children; past hon. chmn. bd. trustees Internat. Reading Found.; trustee Greater L.A. Zoo Assn. Recipient 10 Emmy awards, including award for best program and outstanding female personality, 1989, for outstanding performer in a children's program, 1992, outstanding writing in children's series, 1993, outstanding performer in a children's series, 1993, 94; Peabody award, 1960, 50th Anniversary Dir.'s award Ohio State U award Com., 1988, Monte Carlo Internat. TV award, 1963, Radio-TV Mirror award, 1960, Kennedy Ctr. award for excellence in arts for young people, 1986, Video Choice award, 1988, Parents Choice award, 1992, Calif. Media award, 1992, Dir. Choice Recognition award, 1992, Assn. Visual Communicators Gold Cindy award, 1992, Parents Mag. prize, 1993, Gemini award for LambChop's Play Along, 1994; TV Guide Top Ten Children's Shows, 1993. Office: care Jim Golden 3128 Cavendish Dr Los Angeles CA 90064-4743*

LEWIS, SHELDON NOAH, technology consultant; b. Chgo., July 1, 1934; s. Jacob Joseph and Evelyn (Mendelsohn) Iglowitz; m. Suzanne Joyce Goldberg, June 17, 1957; children: Sara Lynn, Matthew David, Rachel Ann. BA with honors, Northwestern U., 1956, MS (Univ. fellow), 1956; PhD (Eastman Kodak fellow), UCLA, 1959; postgrad. (NSF fellow), U. Basel, Switzerland, 1959-60; postgrad. cert. in research mgmt, Indsl. Research Inst., Harvard U., 1973. With Rohm & Haas Co., 1960-78, head lab., 1963-68, research supr., 1968-73, dir. splty. chem. research, 1973-74; gen. mgr. DCL Lab. AG subs., Zurich, Switzerland, 1974-75; dir. European Labs. Valbonne, France, 1975-76; corp. dir. research and devel. worldwide for polymers, resins and monomers Spring House, Pa., 1976-78; with The Clorox Co., Oakland, Calif., 1978-91, v.p. R&D, 1978, group v.p., 1978-84, exec. v.p., 1984-91, also bd. dirs.; pres. SNL Inc., Lafayette, Calif., 1991—; mem. indsl. panel on sci. and tech. NSF. Referee: Jour. Organic Chemistry; patentee in field; contbr. articles to profl. pubs. Mem. Calif. Inst. Adv. Bd., World Affairs Council, UCLA Chemistry Adv. Council, Bay Area Sci. Fair Adv. Bd., Mills Coll. Adv. Council for Sci. and Math. Recipient cert. in patent law Phila. Patent Law Assn., 1962, Roon award for coatings research Fedn. Socs. Coatings Tech., 1966, cert. of service Wayne State U. Polymer Conf. Series, 1967, cert. in mgmt. by objectives Am. Mgmt. Research, Inc., 1972. Mem. Soap and Detergent Assn. (bd. dirs.), Chem. Ind. Inst. of Toxicology (bd. dirs.), Indsl. Rsch. Inst., Am. Chem. Soc. (chmn. Phila. polymer sect. 1970-71), Sci. Rsch. Industry London, Sigma Xi. Jewish. Office: SNL Inc 3711 Rose Ct Lafayette CA 94549-3030

LEWIS, SHERMAN RICHARD, JR., investment banker; b. Ottawa, Ill., Dec. 11, 1936; s. Sherman Richard and Julia Audrey (Rusteen) L.; m. Dorothy Marie Downie, Sept. 9, 1967; children: Thomas, Catherine, Elizabeth, Michael. AB, Northwestern U., 1958; MBA, U. Chgo., 1964. With investment dept. Am. Nat. Bank & Trust Co., Chgo., 1961-64; v.p. Halsey, Stuart & Co., N.Y.C., 1964-70, v.p. in charge corp. fin. dept., 1970-73; v.p. C.J. Lawrence & Sons, N.Y.C., 1970; ptnr. Loeb, Rhoades & Co., N.Y.C., 1973-76, ptnr. in charge corp. fin. dept., 1975-76, exec. v.p. bd. dirs., 1976-77, pres., co-chief exec. officer, 1977-78; vice chmn., co-chief exec. officer Loeb Rhoades, Hornblower & Co., N.Y.C., 1978-79; pres. Shearson/Am. Express Inc., N.Y.C., 1979-82, vice chmn., 1983-84; vice chmn. Shearson Lehman/Am. Express Inc., 1984-85, Shearson Lehman Bros. Inc., 1985-87, Shearson Lehman Hutton Inc., 1988-89; co-chief exec. officer, vice chmn., chmn. exec. com. Lehman Bros., 1990; vice chmn. Shearson Lehman Bros. Holdings, Inc., N.Y.C., 1990-93, Lehman Bros. Holdings, Inc., Lehman Bros., Inc., 1993—. Mem. Pres.'s Commn. on Housing, 1981-82, Pres.'s Coun. on Internat. Youth Exch., 1982-88; trustee Northwestern U., 1992—, regent, 1990—; mem. vis. com. Coll. Arts and Scis., Northwestern U., 1981—, chmn., 1990—; mem. coun. Grad. Sch. Bus., U. Chgo., 1991—; bd. dirs. The Korea Soc., U.S.-Greek Bus. Coun. Commd. officer USMC, 1958-61. Mem. N.Y. Soc. Security Analysts, The Pilgrims, Bond Club, Ridgewood Country Club, Univ. Club, Quogue Field Club. Office: Lehman Bros Inc 3 World Financial Ctr New York NY 10285

LEWIS, STEPHEN RICHMOND, JR., economist, academic administrator; b. Englewood, N.J., Feb. 11, 1939; s. Stephen Richmond and Esther (Magan) L.; m. Gayle Elizabeth Foster, June 24, 1961 (div. 1994); children: Virginia Rebecca, Deborah Elizabeth, Mark Stephen. B.A., Williams Coll., 1960, LLD, 1987; M.A., Stanford U., 1962, Ph.D., 1963; LHD, Doshisha U., 1993. Instr. Stanford U., 1962-63; research advisor Pakistan Inst. Devel. Econs., Karachi, 1963-65; asst. prof. econs. Harvard U., 1965-66; asst. prof. econs. Williams Coll., 1966-68, assoc. prof., 1968-73, prof., 1973-76, Herbert H. Lehman prof., 1976-87, provost of coll., 1969-71, 73-77, spl. asst. to pres., 1979-80, dir. Williams-Botswana Project, 1982-88, chmn. dept. econs., 1984-86; vis. sr. research fellow Inst. Devel. Studies, Nairobi, Kenya, 1971-73; econ. cons. to Ministry of Finance and Devel. Planning, Govt. of Botswana, 1977—; vis. fellow Inst. Devel. Studies, Sussex, Eng., 1986-87; pres., prof. econs. Carleton Coll., Northfield, Minn., 1987—; cons. econs. Ford Found., Edna McConnell Clark Found., World Bank, Orgn. Econ. Coop. and Devel., Govts. of Kenya, Philippines, Botswana; trustee Carnegie Endowment for Internat. Peace, 1988—. Author: (with others) Relative Price Changes and Industrialization in Pakistan, 1969, Economic Policy and Industrial Growth in Pakistan, 1969, Pakistan: Industrialization and Trade Policy, 1970, Williams in the Eighties, 1980, Taxation for Development, 1983, South Africa: Has Time Run Out?, 1986, Policy Choice and Development Performance in Botswana, 1989, The Economics of Apartheid, 1989; editorial bd. Jour. Econ. Lit., 1985-87. Contbr. chpts. to books, articles to profl. jours. Exec. com. Indianhead coun. Boy Scouts Am., 1989—. Decorated Presdl. Order of Meritorious Svc. (Botswana), 1983; Danforth Found. fellow, 1960-63; Ford Found. dissertation fellow, 1962-63; recipient Disting. Eagle Scout award, 1993. Mem. Council on Fgn. Relations, Nat. Tax Assn., Am. Econ. Assn., Phi Beta Kappa. Office: Carleton Coll Office Pres 1 N College St Northfield MN 55057-4001*

LEWIS, STEVE, Olympic athlete, track and field. Olympic track and field participant Seoul, Korea, 1988, Barcelona, Spain, 1992. Recipient 400m Track and Field Gold medal Olympics, Seoul, 1988, 400m Track and Field Silver medal Olympics, Barcelona, 1992, 4x400m relay Gold medal Olympics, Seoul, 1988, Barcelona, 1992. Office: US Olympic Com 1750 E Boulder St Colorado Springs CO 80909*

LEWIS, SYDNEY, retail company executive; b. Richmond, Va., Oct. 24, 1919; s. Julius Beryl and Dora (Lewis) L.; m. Frances Aaronson, Sept. 3, 1942; children: Sydney Jr., Andrew Marc, Susan (Mrs. Dixon Butler). B.A., Washington and Lee U., 1940, postgrad. in law, 1940-42; postgrad. bus. adminstrn., Harvard, 1942-43; in law, George Washington U., 1946; H.H.D., Va. Commonwealth U., 1983; hon. patron of arts degree, Va. Mus. Fine Arts. Bar: Va. 1942, D.C. 1947. V.p-v New Standard Pub. Co. Inc., Richmond, 1947-58; pres. New Standard Pub. Co. Inc., 1958—; also dir.; founding pres., chmn. Best Products Inc. Inc., Richmond, 1951—; also dir. Best Products Co. Inc. Pres. Richmond Jewish Community Council, 1953—, Va. Mus., 1986—; trustee Washington and Lee U., Lexington, Va., Va. Union Univ., Richmond; trustee Hirshorn Mus., Washington, 1976—, chmn., 1985, pres., 1985—; trustee Inst. Contemporary Art, Phila., 1975—, Sch. Visual Arts, Boston U., 1976—, Va. Environ. Endowment Fund, Va. Found. for Humanities and Public Policy, Hebrew Union Coll., Cin., Hirshorn Mus., 1985—, Bklyn. Acad. Music, N.Y., 1985—; mem. bd. assocs. U. Richmond.; trustee Va. Mus. Fine Arts, 1980—, pres., 1986—; trustee Council of Nat. Gallery Art, Washington, 1983; dir. bus. Jobs for Va. Grads., Commonwealth of Va., 1985. Recipient Disting. Virginian award, 1972, nat. honoree award Beta Gamma Sigma, 1976, ann. award Federated Arts Council of Richmond, 1976, Jackson Davis award for disting. service to higher edn. in Va., 1978, Thomas Jefferson award for pub. service, 1978, Retailer of Yr. award Va. Retail Mchts. Assn., 1982, Medal of Honor Nat. DAR, 1983, Hon. Degree Dr. of Humanities, Va. Commonwealth U., 1983, Gov.'s awards Arts of Va., 1985, Disting. Retailers award Retail Mchts. Assn. Greater Richmond, 1985, Archtl. Medal for Va. Service award Va. Soc. AIA, 1986, Pres.'s Nat. Medal of Arts award, 1987, Skowhegan Gertrude Vanderbilt Whitney award, 1990, William P. Robinson Sr. Dem. award, 1989, Detocqueville Soc. Greater Richmon award, 1990, ABG Disting. Svc. award, 1991, Va. Cultural Laureate award, 1992, Bernard Glasser Meml. award Anti-Defamation League of B'nai B'rith; named to Richmond Bus. Hall Fame, 1989. Club: Lakeside Country. Home: 2601 Monument Ave Richmond VA 23220-2620 Office: Best Products Co Inc PO Box 26303 Richmond VA 23260-6303

LEWIS, SYLVIA DAVIDSON, association executive; b. Akron, Ohio, Apr. 28, 1927; d. Harri I. and Helen E. (Stein) Davidson; m. Allen D. Lewis, Oct. 12, 1947; children: Pamela Lewis Kanfer, Randy, Daniel, Cynthia. Student. U. Mich., 1945-47, U. Akron, 1961-62. Editor Akron Jewish News, 1948-50; tchr. Revere Rd. Congregation, Akron, 1964-70; office mgr. Acme Lumber & Fence Co., Akron, 1970-85; nat. pres. Movement of Working Women & Vols., N.Y.C., 1947—. Founding mem. Govt. Affairs Com., Columbus, Ohio, 1981—, exec. com., 1988-89; v.p. Akron Jewish Cmty. Fedn., 1988-94, pres. Women's Div., Akron, 1987-90. Recipient Golden Rule award J.C. Penney, 1994, Vol. of Yr. award Lippman Cmty. Day Sch., 1992, Commendation of Honor award Ohio Gen. Assembly, 1993. Mem. Planned Parenthood Summit County (bd. dirs. 1994—). Democrat. Jewish. Avocations: reading, writing, travel, grandchildren. Home: 277 Keith Ave Akron OH 44313 Office: NA'AMAT USA 200 Madison Ave New York NY 10016

LEWIS, SYLVIA GAIL, journalist; b. N.Y.C., Apr. 8, 1945; d. Ben and Clara Lewis. BA, Cornell U., 1967; MA, U. Wash., Seattle, 1968; MS in Journalism, Northwestern U., 1974. Reporter Seattle-Post Intelligencer, 1968-69; asst. editor Cowles Book Co., N.Y.C., 1969-70; with Am. Planning Assn., Chgo., 1974—, mng. editor Planning mag., 1975-77, dir. pubs., editor, assoc. pub. Planning mag., 1977—. Contbr. articles to profl. jours. Mem. Soc. Profl. Journalists, Chgo. Headline Club (pres. 1992-93), Soc. Nat. Assn. Publs. (pres. Chgo. chpt. 1986-87, nat. bd. dirs. 1989-91), Northwestern U. Alumni Assn., Cornell Club of Chgo, Phi Beta Kappa. Office: Am Planning Assn 1313 E 60th St Chicago IL 60637-2830

LEWIS, THOMAS B., specialty chemical company executive; b. Cleve.; s. Bryn H. and Margaret (Connaughton) L.; m. Mary C. Lewis; children: Mark, Mary-Margaret, Maureen. B.S., John Carroll U., M.S.; Ph.D., MIT; postdoctoral fellow, Cornell U.; postgrad. Exec. Program, Stanford U., 1983. With Monsanto Co., St. Louis, 1966-88, sr. rsch. chemist, rsch. group leader, project mgr.; mgr. comml. devel., dir. corp. rsch. labs. & R&D, gen. mgr. Rubber chem. divsn.; corp. v.p. Celgene Corp., Warren, N.J., 1988-92; pres., CEO Chiral Techs. Inc., Exton, Pa., 1992—; pres. Akron Polymer Lecture Group, 1977-78. Mem. AAAS, Am. Chem. Soc., Am. Phys. Soc., Soc. Chem. Industries, N.Y. Acad. Sci., Sigma Xi. Roman Catholic. Office: Chiral Techs Inc PO Box 564 Exton PA 19341-0564

LEWIS, THOMAS JOHN, III, hospital administrator; b. Pitts., Mar. 26, 1952; s. Thomas John and Nancy (Hoser) L.; m. Kathleen Dalrymple, Sept.

4, 1983; children: Benjamin Stephen, Jeffrey Thomas. BA in Biology, Bucknell U., 1974; MHA, Duke U., 1976. Adminstrv. resident Thomas Jefferson U. Hosp., Phila., 1976-77, acting dir. quality assurance and MR, 1977-79, mgr. care program, 1979-82, asst. exec. dir., 1982-85, dir., 1984-85, assoc. exec. dir., 1985-89, exec. dir., chief oper. officer, 1989-90, sr. v.p., chief exec. officer, 1990—. Bd. dirs. Phila. Healthh Acad., 1989—, Welcon of Delaware Valley, Phila., 1990—. Mem. Am. Coll. Health Care Execs. (nominee), Delaware Valley Hosp. Coun., Hosp. Assn. Pa. Home: 123 W End Ave Haddonfield NJ 08033-2617 Office: Thomas Jefferson U Hosp Walnut 11th St Philadelphia PA 19107

LEWIS, THOMAS PROCTOR, legal educator; b. Ashland, Ky., Mar. 26, 1930; s. Blaine and Hallie Maud (Heal) L.; m. Nancy Ann Magruder, Sept. 27, 1949; children: Jean, Catherine, Jennifer, Blaine. A.B., U. Ky., 1959, LL.B., 1954; S.J.D., Harvard U., 1964. Asst. prof. law U. Ky., 1957-59, assoc. prof., 1959-60, prof., 1961-65, acad. asst. to pres., 1966-65, dean Coll. of Law, 1976-82, prof., 1982—; prof. law U. Minn., 1965-72, Boston U., 1972-76; of counsel Wyatt, Tarrant & Combs, 1982-86 ; vis. prof. U. Chgo., 1962, U. Wash., 1963-64; labor arbitrator, 1965—. Author: (with R. Levy, P. Martin) Social Welfare and the Individual, 1971; contbr. articles to law jours. Served with USNR, 1954-57. Mem. Ky., Mass. bar assns., Nat. Acad. Arbitrators, Am. Law Inst., Am. Arbitration Assn. Office: U Ky Coll of Law Lexington KY 40506

LEWIS, TIMOTHY K., federal judge; b. 1954. BA, Tufts U., 1976; JD, Duquesne U., 1980. Asst. dist. atty. Allegheny County Dist. Attys. Office, Pa., 1980-83; asst. U.S. atty. U.S. Attys. Office (we. dist.) Pa., 1983-91; fed. judge U.S. Dist. Ct. (we. dist.) Pa., 1991-92, U.S. Ct. Appeals (3d cir.), Pitts., 1992—; vis. com. mem. U. Chgo. Law Sch., 1993-96. Former bd. dirs. Ctr. Victims Violent Crime; former mem. Aid Citizen Enterprise. Mem. Pa. Bar Assn. (del. to PBA ho. of dels. 1989-91), Allegheny County Bar Assn. (mem. jud. com. 1988-90, mem. profl. ethics com., mem. planning com., chmn. subcom. minorities in law of planning com., mem. nominating com., mem. fin. com., mem. minorities mentor program, mem. women in law com., fed. ct. sect.), Homer S. Brown Bar Assn., The Boule, Alpha House (former bd. dirs.). Office: US Ct of Appeals 3rd Cir 1014 US Courthouse 7th Ave And Grant St Pittsburgh PA 15219*

LEWIS, TOLA ETHRIDGE, JR., state agency administrator, martial arts instructor; b. Columbia, S.C., July 7, 1945; s. Tola Ethridge and Hettie (Willets) L.; m. Frances Rebecca Coggins, July 10, 1965 (div. Jan., 1978); m. Martha E. Cartwright, Mar. 24, 1978: children: Toby Isaac, Charles Andrew. AB, East Carolina U., 1972. Dist. vets. svc. officer N.C. Div. Vets. Affairs, Elizabeth City, 1972—; instr. karate. Contbr. articles to martial arts jours. With USN, 1964-66, retired USNR, 1989. Mem. Am. Legion (comdr. dist., chmn. oratorical contest), Nat. Karate and Jujitsu Union (dir. 1989—). Republican. Baptist. Avocation: Karate (7th degree black belt). Home: PO Box 1331 Elizabeth City NC 27906-1331 Office: NC Div Vets Affairs 1023 US 17 S Ste 2 Elizabeth City NC 27909-3542

LEWIS, W. WALKER, cosmetics executive; b. Middletown, Ohio, Sept. 15, 1944; s. W. Walker and Emily (Spivey) L.; m. Ellen Anschuetz, March 30, 1970; children: Walker G., Alexandra D., Morgan D. AB, Harvard Coll, 1967. Asst. to exec. v.p. Ohio U., 1968-70; with Boston Consulting Group, 1970-72; founder Strategic Planning Assocs., 1972-89; chmn., CEO Mercer Mgmt. Consulting, Inc., 1989-92, Avon Products, Inc., 1989-92; exec. v.p. and pres. Avon U.S., 1992—. Address: Avon Prod Inc 638 Otis Pl NW Washington DC 20010-1702*

LEWIS, WALTER DAVID, historian; b. Towanda, Pa., June 24, 1931; s. Gordon Cleon and Eleanor Esther (Tobias) L.; m. Carolyn Wyatt Brown, June 12, 1954 (div. 1980); children: Daniel Kent, Virginia Lorraine, Nancy Ellyn; m. Patricia L. Freeman, Apr. 26, 1986. BA cum laude, Pa. State U., 1952, MA, 1954; PhD, Cornell U., 1961. Instr. pub. speaking Hamilton Coll., Clinton, N.Y., 1954-57; fellowship coordinator Eleutherian Mills-Hagley Found., Wilmington, Del.; also lectr. History U. Del., 1959-65; assoc. prof. history SUNY, Buffalo, 1965-71, prof., 1971; Hudson prof. history and engring. Auburn (Ala.) U., 1971-95, disting. Univ. prof., 1994—; dir. univ. project tech., human values and so. future, 1974-79; sr. fellow in Am. civilization Cornell U., 1958-59; vis. prof. history U. Tex.-Dallas, summer 1982, 83, 84; pres., dir. conf. on history of civil and comml. aviation (ICCA 92), Swiss Transport Mus., Lucerne, Switzerland, 1992; Charles A. Lindbergh prof. of aerospace history Nat. Air and Space Mus., 1993-94. Exec. co-producer (documentary film): About Us: A Deep South Portrait, 1977; author: From Newgate to Dannemora: The Rise of the Penitentiary in New York, 1965, Iron and Steel in America, 1976, Sloss Furnaces and the Rise of the Birmingham District: An Industrial Epic, 1994; co-author: Delta: The History of an Airline, 1979, Hopewell Furnace, 1983, The Airway to Everywhere: A History of All American Aviations, 1937-53, 1988; contbg. author: The Professions in America, 1965, Technology in Western Civilization, 1967, The Development of an American Culture, 1969, Notable American Women, 1971, Great Engineers and Pioneers in Technology, 1981, Technology in America, 2d edit., 1990, Science-Technology Relationships, 1993; co-editor: Economic Change in the Civil War Era, 1965, The Southern Mystique: Technology and Human Values in Changing Region, 1977; gen. editor Procs. of the Internat. Conf. on the History of Civil and Commercial Aviation, 1995; contbr. articles to profl. jours. Grantee NEH, 1973-79, 80—, Delta Airlines Found. 1973-79, Eleutherian Mills Hist. Libr. 1970-73, 80; postdoctoral fellow Nat. Humanities Inst., U. Chgo., 1977-78, Mellon fellow Va. Hist. Soc., 1988, 89, 92; recipient Leonardo da Vinci medal, (Soc. for the Hist. of Tech., 1993). Mem. Soc. History Tech., Lexington Group Transp. Historians, Phi Beta Kappa. Episcopalian. Home: 210 Lee Dr Auburn AL 36830-6722 Office: Auburn U Dept History 310 Thach Hall Auburn AL 36849-3501

LEWIS, WAYNE H., investment company executive; b. N.Y.C., July 8, 1931; s. Harry Wayne and Eleanor (Diegoli) L.; m. Mary Jane Durnford, June 18, 1956; 1 child, Laura Alane. AB, Harvard U., 1953. Sales, instr. Exxon Corp., Boston, 1956-59; sales Conn. Gen. Life Ins. Co., Hartford, Conn., 1959-62; mgr. Mass. Gen. Life Ins. Co., Boston, 1962-67; v.p. sales Integon Corp., Winston-Salem, N.C., 1967-69, Lionel D. Edie & Co., N.Y.C., 1969-72; v.p. fin. planning 1st Pa. Bank, Phila., 1970-72; pres., owner Investor Svcs. Ltd., Villanova, Pa., 1972—. Chmn., bd. trustees Anthony Wayne Found., Paoli, 1991—; pres. Wayne Family Orgn., Paoli, 1988-92; mem., oper. com. Wayne Mus., Paoli, 1984—. Mem. Union League Pa. (life), Merion Cricket Club. Desert Mountain Club, Chaine des Rotisseurs (officer exec. com. 1982—). Avocations: aerobics, off road driving & hiking, exploring nat. and state parks. Home: 200 S Ithan Ave Villanova PA 19085-1432 Office: Investor Svcs Ltd PO Box 310 Villanova PA 19085

LEWIS, WELBOURNE WALKER, JR., lawyer; b. Lewisburg, Tenn., Jan. 11, 1915; s. Welbourne Walker and Jessie (Culbertson) L.; m. Esther Phillips, July 26, 1975; children by previous marriage—Welbourne Walker III, H. Hunter, Berton B. A.B., Dartmouth, 1936; J.D., Harvard U., 1939. Bar: Ohio 1939. Since practiced in Dayton; asso. Smith, Schnacke & Compton, 1939-45; mem. Smith & Schnacke, 1945-75; chmn. Master Consol., Inc., 1950-67; sec. Mead Corp., Dayton, 1952-64, gen. counsel, 1958-75, dir., 1959-75. Former mem. bd. dirs. Dayton dept. ARC; former trustee Dayton Pvt. Sch. Found. Mem. Phi Beta Kappa, Delta Tau Delta, Delta Sigma Rho. Episcopalian (former trustee, mem. planning com. Diocese So. Ohio, former mem. diocesan standing com., former sr. warden). Club: Dartmouth (Dayton). Home: 3720 Ridgeleigh Rd Dayton OH 45429-1252

LEWIS, WILBUR CURTIS, surgeon; b. Okmulgee, Okla., Sept. 10, 1930; s. Charles D. and Eula Alice (Cole) L.; m. Gladys Sherman, Jan. 28, 1955; children: Karen Kay, Mark David, Leanne Gwynneth, Cristen Sue. BS, Okla. Bapt. U., 1952; MD, Okla. U., 1955. Diplomate Am. Bd. Family Practice (charter); ordained to ministry Bapt. Ch. as pastor, 1953. Intern Harris Hosp., Ft. Worth. 1955-56; resident in surgery VA Hosp., Dallas, 1956-57, Univ. Hosp. Oklahoma City, 1965-67; med. missionary So. Bapt. Conv., Costa Rica and Paraguay, 1959-70; prvt. practice medicine specializing in surgery, Oklahoma City, 1970—; leader med. disaster relief team, Honduras, 1975, Guatemala, 1976, Dominican Republic, 1977; surgeon, lectr. Maraciabo, Venezuela, 1989, Taxila, Pakistan, 1990, Bangalore, India, 1990, Guito, Ecuador, 1991, Signatepeque and Teguigalpa, Honduras, 1993; mem. staff Bapt. Hosp., Deaconess Hosp., Mercy Hosp., St. Anthony Hosp.,

Oklahoma City Hosp.; deacon, mem. meml. trust com. 1st Bapt. Ch., Oklahoma City; former chmn. deacons and social ministries com.; former pastor various chs., Okla. and Paraguay; co-founder, former pres. Baptist Med. Dental Fellowship; lectr. on surgery and burn care topics in Venezuela, Pakistan, India and Equador and Honduras. Past pres. Midwest City C. of C. Capt. USAF, 1957-59. Decorated knight Knights of Malta. Fellow ACS, Internat. Coll. Surgeons; mem. AMA, Internat. Fedn. Surgical Colls., Okla. State Med. Assn. (former del. and alt. del.), Christian Med. and Dental Soc. (former del.), Oklahoma City Surg. Soc., Am. Burn Assn., Internat. Soc. Burn Injuries (burn care com.), Oklahoma City Clin. Soc. Democrat. Home: 14501 N Western Ave Edmond OK 73013-1828 Office: 3141 NW Expressway St Oklahoma City OK 73112-4143

LEWIS, WILBUR H., educational management consultant; b. Belmont, Ohio, Sept. 16, 1930; s. Charles W. and Lily B. (Dunfee) L.; m. Jean E. Lewis, Aug. 23, 1958; children—David, Deretta, Denise, Dawn, Darrin. Student, Miami U., Oxford, Ohio, 1948-51; B.S.B.A., Ohio State U., 1953; M.Ed., Ohio U., 1961, Ph.D., 1964. Tchr. pub. schs Scioto County, Ohio, 1957; tchr., adminstr. public schs. Belmont County, Ohio, 1958-60; grad. asst. Ohio U., 1960-61; prin. high sch., adminstrv. asst. to supt. public schs. Athens, Ohio, 1961-64; asst. prof., adviser to Govt. of Nigeria, 1964-66; asst. supt. pub. schs. Athens, Ohio, 1966-67; prin. high sch. public schs. Wilmington, Ohio, 1967-68; with Parma (Ohio) City Schs., 1968-77, asst. to supt., 1968-70, asst. supt., 1970-72, assoc. supt., 1972-75, supt., 1975-77; supt. Tucson Unified Sch. Dist., 1977-79; cons. ednl. mgmt. Tucson, 1979—; vice chmn. nat. adv. council Edn. Disadvantaged Children, 1972-80. Planning divsn. United Way, Tucson, 1978-80; bd. dirs. Jr. Achievement, 1978-80; interim supt. Ariz. State Schs. for Deaf and Blind, 1994-95. With U.S. Army, 1954-56. Recipient numerous civic awards for community service; Kettering Found. fellow, 1970. Mem. Am. Assn. Sch. Adminstrs., Buckeye Assn. Sch. Adminstrs., Masons, Shriners, Rotary Internat. (v.p. Tucson 1987—, past pres., dist. gov.'s rep. group study exch. dist. 9120 Nigeria, dist. 550 1990, chmn. group study exch. dist. 5490 1991-93), Phi Delta Kappa, Lambda Chi Alpha, Sigma Phi Epsilon. Rsch. in orgnl. devel., adminstrv. behavior patterns, tchr. job satisfaction, student achievement. Home: PO Box 31690 Tucson AZ 85751 To achieve one must aspire. To aspire one must dream. But if dreams and aspirations are to become achievements one must persevere. The perseverance necessary to turn dreams and aspirations into achievements has always been made easier for me knowing that children and youth were the benefactors of my efforts.

LEWIS, WILLIAM HENRY, JR., lawyer; b. Durham, N.C., Nov. 12, 1942; s. William Henry Sr. and Phyllis Lucille (Phillips) L.; m. Jo Ann Whitsett, Apr. 17, 1965 (div. Sept. 1982); 1 child, Kimberly N.; m. Peyton Cockrill Davis, Nov. 28, 1987. Student, N.C. State U., 1960-63; AB in Polit. Sci., U. N.C., 1965, JD with honors, 1969. Bar: Calif., D.C., U.S. Dist. Ct. (cen. dist.) Calif., U.S. Ct. Appeals (D.C. cir., 2nd and 5th cirs.), U.S. Supreme Ct. Assoc. Latham & Watkins, Los Angeles, 1969-74; exec. officer Calif. Air Resources Bd., Los Angeles and Sacramento, Calif., 1975-78; dir. Nat. Com. on Air Quality, Washington, 1978-81; counsel Wilmer, Cutler & Pickering, Washington, 1981-84; ptnr. Morgan, Lewis & Bockius, Washington, 1984—; spl. advisor on environ. policy State of Calif., Los Angeles and Sacramento, 1975; lectr. in law U. Va. Law Sch., 1993—. Bd. dirs. For Love of Children, Inc., Washington, 1985—, pres., 1987-91; bd. dirs. Advs. for Families, Washington, 1985-87, Hillandale Homeowners Assn., Washington, 1986-87, Anthony Bowen Landmark Bldg. Trust, Washington, 1989—. Mem. ABA. Home: 3900 Georgetown Ct NW Washington DC 20007-2127 Office: Morgan Lewis & Bockius 1800 M St NW Washington DC 20036-5869

LEWIS, WILLIAM LEONARD, food products executive; b. Providence, Apr. 8, 1946; s. George Dawson and Margaret Eleanor (Cuddigan) L.; m. Barbara Jane Fournier, July 20, 1968; children: Hillary, Megan. BBA, Gonzaga U., 1973; MBA, Dartmouth Coll., 1975. With product mgmt. dept. Frito-Lay div. Pepsico, Dallas, 1975-80; product mgr. grocery products div. Ralston-Purina Co., St. Louis, 1981-83, brand dir., 1983-84, group dir., 1985-86, dir. mktg., 1986-87; exec. v.p. grocery products div. Ralston-Purina Can., Inc., Mississauga, Ont., 1987-89, pres. grocery products div., 1989-90, pres. parent co., 1990—. With U.S. Army, 1968-71. Office: Ralston Purina Can Inc, 2500 Royal Windsor Ave, Mississauga, ON Canada L5J 1K8

LEWIS, WILLIAM SCHEER, electrical engineer; b. Mt. Vernon, N.Y., Feb. 7, 1927; s. Perley Linwood and Nellie Cora (Scheer) L.; m. Jane Alexander, Feb. 4, 1950 (div. 1972); children: Christopher J., Pamela Scheer Shaw, David Robert; m. Barbara Johnson, June 24, 1972. BS, MIT, 1950, SM, 1950. Registered profl. engr. Mass., N.Y. Sales engr. Gen. Electric Co., Erie, Pa., 1950-53, Morrissey Tractor Co., Burlington, Mass., 1953-56, Hubbs Engine Co., Cambridge, Mass., 1956-57; mgr. contract div. Payne Elevator Co., Cambridge, 1957-69; sales mgr. diversified systems Otis Elevator Co., N.Y.C., 1969-72, mktg. analyst/gen. sales, 1972-73; mgr. vertical transp. Jaros, Baum & Bolles, N.Y.C., 1973-91, ptnr., 1978-91, ret., 1991—. Author: (handbooks) Materials Handling, Freight Elevators, 1985, Building Structural Design-Vertical Transportation, 1987; editor: (monograph) Tall Buildings—Vertical and Horizontal Transportation, 1978. Mem. Wayland (Mass.) Bd. Assessors, 1954-69, chmn., 1963-69. Recipient 1st prize award N.Y. Assn. Consulting Engrs., 1987, Honor award Am. Consulting Engrs. Council, 1987. Mem. ASME. Republican. Unitarian. Avocations: white water canoeing, hunting, fishing, photography. Home: The Chase House RR2 Box 909 Cornish NH 03745-9743 Office: Jaros Baum & Bolles Cons Engrs 345 Park Ave New York NY 10154-0004

LEWIS, WILLIAM WALKER, management consultant; b. Roanoke, Va., Mar. 29, 1942; s. William Walker and Nancy Katherine (Phipps) L.; m. Jutta Maria Schwarzkopf, Dec. 27, 1966; children: Christopher William, Monica Gisela. BS in Physics with honors, Va. Poly. Inst. and State U., 1963; PhD in Theoretical Physics, Oxford U., 1966. Mem. staff Office of Asst. Sec. for Systems Analysis, Dept. Def., Washington, 1966-69; asso. provost for resource planning, lectr. public and internat. affairs Princeton U., 1969-71; dir. office of analytical studies U. Calif., Berkeley, 1971-73; sr. ops. officer World Bank, 1973-77; prin. dep. asst. sec. for program analysis and evaluation Dept. Def., Washington, 1977-79; asst. sec. policy and evaluation Dept. Energy, Washington, 1979-81; pres. Dist. Heat and Power, Inc., Washington, 1981-82; ptnr. McKinsey & Co., Inc., Washington, 1982—; dir. McKinsey Global Inst., Washington, 1990—. Trustee George C. Marshall Found. Rhodes scholar, 1963-66. Office: 1101 Pennsylvania Ave NW Washington DC 20004-2504

LEWIS, WINIFRED P., nursing administrator; b. Guyana, July 21, 1954; d. Stanley A. and Winifred I. (Pemberton) L.; m. Roger J. AbiNader, Oct. 14, 1989. AAS, Bronx Community Coll., 1974; BSN, L.I. U., 1980; MA in Nursing Adminstrn., Columbia U., 1985. RN, N.Y.; cert. nurse advanced adminstrn. Staff nurse Meml. Sloan Kettering Cancer Ctr., N.Y.C., head nurse, asst. dir. nursing, dir. nursing practice. Mem. N.Y. Nurses Assn., AONE, ONS.

LEWISON, EDWARD FREDERICK, surgeon; b. Chgo., Feb. 11, 1913; s. Maurice and Julia (Trockey) L.; m. Elizabeth Oppenheim, July 24, 1938 (wid. 1947); 1 child, John Edward; m. Betty Fleischmann, Mar. 21, 1948; children: Edward M., Robert S., Richard J. BS, U. Chgo., 1932; MD, Johns Hopkins U., 1936. Lic. MD Ill., Md., Fla.; diplomate Am. Bd. Surgery. Chief, Breast Clin. Johns Hopkins Hosp., Balt., 1948-72; asst. prof. surgery Johns Hopkins U. Sch. Med., Balt., 1954-69, assoc. prof. surgery, 1969-80, assoc. prof. surgery, emeritus, 1980—; vice-chmn. breast cancer comm., WHO, Geneva, 1968-70; chmn. nat. conf. breast cancer, Am. Cancer Soc., Washington, 1969, Swiss Cancer League, Lucerne, 1976; mem. H.S. Nat. Comm. of the Nat. Rsch. Coun., Washington, 1983-87. Author: Breast Cancer and Its Diagnosis and Treatment, 1955; editor: Breast Cancer, 1977, Conference on Spontaneous Regression of Cancer, 1974; co-author: Diagnosis and Treatment of Breast Cancer, 1981. Bd. dirs. United Way of Md., Balt., 1986-94. Recipient Humanitarian of the Yr., Wyman Guild, Balt., 1990; named Disting. Citizen, Gov., State of Md., 1980, others. Fellow AMA, Royal Soc. Medicine, Am. Coll. Surgeons; mem. Am. Cancer Soc. (hon. life, Vol. Leadership award 1984, Premier award 1995), N.Y. Acad. Scis. Achievements include invention of rayable gauze for surgery.

LEWIS-WHITE, LINDA BETH, elementary school educator; b. Fresno, Calif., June 30, 1950; d. Lloyd Ernest and Anne Grace (Barkman) Lewis; m. Francis Everett White, Feb. 15, 1975; children: Anna Justine, Christopher Andrew Arthur. BA in Home Econs., Calif. State U., Sacramento, 1972, MA in Social Scis., 1973; postgrad., Tex. Women's U., 1976-79; PhD in Reading, East Tex. State U., 1994. Cert. bilingual and elem. edn. tchr., Tex. Tchr. bilingual Arlington Sch. Dist., 1977—; PhD, 1994; adj. prof. reading Tex. Women's U., Denton, 1989, adj. prof. ESL East Tex. State U., 1993; mem. tchr. trainer cadre, Dallas Ind. Sch. Dist., 1985-92; freelance cons., 1987—; presenter TESOL Internat. Conf., San Antonio, 1989. Cons., writer (book) Ciencias-Silver Burdett, 1988. Troop leader Girl Scouts U.I.S., Dallas, 1980-82. Mem. Nat. Reading Conf., Nat. Writing Project, Internat. Reading Assn., Tchrs. of English to Spkrs. of Other Langs. (nominating com. 1990-91), TEXTESOL V (chair elem. edn. com. 1989-91), Tex. Assn. Bilingual Edn., Phi Delta Kappa, Pi Mu. Mem. Christian Ch. Avocations: sewing, knitting, quilting, reading, gourmet cooking. Office: Thornton Elem Sch 4301 E Park Row Arlington TX 76010

LEWITT, SOL, artist; b. Hartford, Conn., 1928. B.F.A., Syracuse U., 1949. Instr. Mus. Modern Art Sch., 1964-67, Cooper Union, 1967, Sch. Visual Arts, N.Y.C., 1969-70, NYU, 1970. Contbr. articles on sculpture, drawing, conceptual art to jours., mags.; one-man shows include Guggenheim Mus., 1971, Mus. Modern Art, N.Y.C., 1971, Walker Art Center, Mpls., 1972, Mus. Modern Art, Oxford, Eng., 1973, Stedelijk Mus., Amsterdam, The Netherlands, 1974, Visual Arts Mus., N.Y.C., 1976, San Francisco Mus. Art, 1975, Wadsworth Atheneum, Hartford, Conn., 1981, Musee d'Art Contemporain, Bordeaux, France, 1983, retrospective travelling exhbn., Mus. Modern Art, N.Y.C., Mus. Contemporary Art, Montreal, Krannert Mus., Champaign, Ill., Mus. Contemporary Art, Chgo., La Jolla (Calif.) Mus., 1978-79, Stedelijk Mus., Amsterdam, 1984, Stedelijk Van Abbe Mus., Eindhoven, 1984, Musee d'Art Moderne de la ville de Paris, 1987, Tate Gallery, 1986, Walker Art Ctr., Mpls., 1988, Kunstlalle Bern, Switzerland, 1989, Touko Mus., 1990, Porticus, Frankfort, Fed. Republic Germany, 1990, Drawings 1958-92 Haags Gemeentemus., The Hague and tour, Structures 1962-93 Mus. Modern Art, Oxford and tour, 25 Years of Wall Drawings 1968-93 Addison Gallery, Phillips Acad., Andover, Mass.; group exhbns. include Sculpture Ann, Whitney Mus. Am. Art, N.Y.C., 1967, Minimal Art, The Hague, 1968, Documenta, Kassel, W. Ger., 1968, 72, 77, 82, Prospect, 1968, Dusseldorf, 1968, Stadtische Kunsthalle, Dusseldorf, 1969, La Jolla Mus. Contemp. Art, 1970, Tokyo Biennale, 1970, Guggenheim Internat., N.Y.C., 1971, Whitney Biennial, Whitney Mus. Am. Art, N.Y.C., 1979, Hayward Gallery, London, 1980, Internat. Sculpture exhbn., Basel, Switzerland, 1980, Westkunst, Cologne, Fed. Republic Germany, 1981, Musee Nat. d'Art Moderne, Paris, 1981, Art Inst. Chgo., 1982, Mus. Modern Art, N.Y.C., 1983, Mus. Contemporary Art, Los Angeles, 1986, Whitney Biennial, 1987, Skultitur Projekk, Münster, Fed. Republic Germany, 1987, Venice (Italy) Biennale, 1988, Zeitlos, Hamburg, Fed. Republic Germany; represented in permanent collections, Stedelijk Mus., Albright-Knox Art Gallery, Buffalo, Art Gallery Ont., Toronto, Los Angeles County Mus. Art, Los Angeles, Mus. Modern Art, N.Y.C., Tate Gallery, London, Centre Georges Pompidou, Paris, Whitney Mus. Am. Art, N.Y.C., Met. Mus. Art, N.Y.C., Art Inst. Chgo.; work also in German, Swiss, Australian, Dutch, Belgian and Am. mus. Office: care Susanna Singer 50 Riverside Dr New York NY 10024-6508

LEWITZKY, BELLA, choreographer; b. Los Angeles, Jan. 13, 1916; d. Joseph and Nina (Ossman) L.; m. Newell Taylor Reynolds, June 22, 1940; 1 child, Nora Elizabeth. Student, San Bernardino Valley (Calif.) Jr. Coll., 1933-34; hon. doctorate, Calif. Inst. Arts, 1981; PhD (hon.), Occidental Coll., 1984, Otis Parsons Coll., 1989, Juilliard Sch., 1993; DFA, Santa Clara U., 1995. Chmn. dance dept., chmn. adv. panel U. So. Calif. Idyllwild, 1956-74; founder Sch. Dance, Calif. Inst. Arts, 1969, dean, 1969-74; vice chmn. dance adv. panel Nat. Endowment Arts, 1974-77, mem. artists-in-schs. adv. panel, 1974-75; mem. Nat. Adv. Bd. Young Audiences, 1974—; Joint Commn. Dance and Theater Accreditation, 1979; com. mem. Am. chpt. Internat. Dance Coun. of UNESCO, 1974—; bd. dirs. Am. Arts Alliance, 1974-88; trustee Nat. Found. Advancement Arts, 1982-90, 92-95, Calif. Arts Coun., 1983-86; trustee Calif. Assn. Dance Cos., 1976—; Idyllwild Sch. music and Arts, 1986—, Dance/USA, 1988—, Calif. State Summer Sch. of Arts, 1988—; cons. the dance project WNET, 1987—. Co-founder, co-dir., Dance Theatre, Los Angeles, 1946-50; founder, dir., Dance Assocs., Los Angeles, 1951-55; founder 1966, since artistic dir., Lewitzky Dance Co., Los Angeles; choreographer, 1948—; founder, former artistic dir. The Dance Gallery, Los Angeles; contbr. articles in field. Works choreographed include Trio for Saki, 1967, Orrenda, 1969, Kinaesonata, 1971, Pietas, 1971, Ceremony For Three, 1972, Game Plan, 1973, Five, 1974, Spaces Between, 1975, Jigsaw, 1975, Inscape, 1976, Pas de Bach, 1977, Suite Satie, 1980, Changes and Choices, 1981, Confines, 1982, Continuum, 1982, Walking/Falling, 1982, 1990, The Song of the Woman, 1983, Nos Duraturi, 1984, 8 Dancers/8 Lights, 1985, Facets, 1986, Impressions #1, 1987, Impresssions #2, 1988, Agitime, 1989, Impressions #3, 1989, Episode #1, 1990, Glass Canyons, 1991, Episode #2, 1992, Episode #3, 1992, Episode #4, 1993. Mem. adv. com. Actors' Fund of Am., 1986—, Women's Bldg. Adv. Council, 1985-91, Calif. Arts Council, 1983-86, City of Los Angeles Task Force on the Arts, 1986—; mem. artistic adv. bd. Interlochen Ctr. for Arts, 1988—. Recipient Mayoral Proclamation, City of L.A., 1976, 1982, ann. award Dance mag., 1978, Dir.'s award Calif. Dance Educators Assn., 1978, Plaudit Award, Nat. Dance Assn., 1979, Labor's Award of Honor for Community Svc., L.A. County AFL-CIO, 1979, L.A. Area Dance Alliance and L.A. Junior C. of C. Honoree, 1980, City of L.A. Resolution, 1980, Distguished Artist Award, City of L.A. and Music Ctr., 1982, Silver Achievement award YWCA, 1982, California State Senate Resolution, 1982, 1984, Award of Recognition, Olympic Black Dance Festival, 1984, Distinguished Women's Award, Northwood Inst., 1984, California State U. Distinguished Artist, 1984, Vesta Award, Woman's Bldg, L.A., 1985, L.A. City Council Honors for Outstanding Contributions, 1985, Woman of the Year, Palm Springs Desert Museum, Women's Committee, 1986, Disting. Svc. award Western Alliance Arts Adminstrs., 1987, Woman of Achievement award, 1988, Am. Dance Guild Ann. award, 1989, So. Calif. Libr. for Social Studies & Rsch. award, 1990, Am. Soc. Journalists & Authors Open Book award, 1990, Internat. Soc. Performing Arts Adminstrs. Tiffany award, 1990, Burning Bush award U. of Judaism, 1991, 1st recipient Calif. Gov.'s award in arts for individual lifetime achievement, 1989; honoree L.A. Arts Coun., 1989, Heritage honoree, Nat. Dance Assn., 1991, Vaslav Nijinsky award, 1991, Hugh M. Hefner First Amendment award, 1991, Artistic Excellence award Ctr. Performing Arts U. Calif., 1992, Lester Horton Lifetime Achievement award Dance Resource Ctr. of L.A., 1992, Occidental Coll. Founders' award, 1992, Dance/USA honor, 1992, Visual Arts Freedom of Expression award Andy Warhol Found., 1993, Artist of Yr. award L.A. County High Sch. Arts, 1993, Freedom of Expression honor Andy Warhol Found. Visual Arts, 1993; Calif. Alliance Edn. award, 1994; grantee Mellon Found., 1975, 81,ggenheim Found., 1977-78, NEA, 1969-94. Mem. Am. Arts Alliance (bd. dirs. 1977), Internat. Dance Alliance (adv. council 1984—), Dance/USA (bd. dirs. 1988). Office: Lewitzky Dance Co 1055 Wilshire Blvd Ste 1140 Los Angeles CA 90017 Dance is communicative of personal, emotive knowledge-- of sensory information common to all. The feel of the wind, the exhilaration of clear space, the headiness of an enormous height, the marvel of human power, one's personal worth-- can take shape and be illuminated in dance. How wonderful to work at something you love! How remarkable to be given the opportunity to utilize one's whole being, one's physical knowledge, intellectual capacity, imagination and creativity in a single persuit. How good to practice dance and know that it will not engage you in mass murders of warfare; it will not destroy our environment. It is capable of healing, celebrating, and sharing human resources. My philosophy is predicated on the belief that choreography is the taskmaster of us all. In each work, I attempt to discover again the truth of that statement.

LEWY, JOHN EDWIN, pediatric nephrologist; b. Chgo., Apr. 22, 1935; s. Stanley B. and Lucile (Mayer) L.; m. Rosaline Portnoy, June 9, 1963; children—Karen, Steven. B.A., U. Mich. 1956; M.D., Tulane U., 1960. Diplomate Am. Bd. Pediatrics (oral examiner 1985-89, oral examination com. 1987-91, certifying examination com. on clin. problems 1989—), Am. Bd. Pediatric Nephrology (credentials com. 1981-83). Intern Michael Reese Hosp. Med. Center, Northwestern U., 1960-61, resident in pediatrics, 1961-62; resident in pediatrics Michael Reese Hosp. Med. Center, 1963-64, chief resident, 1964, pediatric nephrology fellow, 1965, dir. sect. pediatric nephrology, 1967-70; fellow dept. pediatrics Cornell U. Med. Coll., 1966,

research fellow physiology, 1966-67, asst. prof. pediatrics, 1970-71, asso. prof., 1971-75, prof., 1975-78, dir. div. pediatric nephrology, 1970-78; prof., chmn. dept. pediatrics Tulane U. Hosp., New Orleans, 1978—; physician-in-chief Tulane Hosp. for Children, New Orleans, 1993—; mem. staff Children's Hosp., Med. Ctr. La.; pediatrician La. Handicapped Children's Program; bd. dirs., sci. adv. com. La. End Stage Renal Disease Council. Assoc. editor Jour. Dialysis, 1978—, Jour. Pediatric Nephrology, 1979—; contbr. over 200 articles and abstracts to profl. jours. Mem. profl. adv. com. Nat. Found. March of Dimes; sci. adv. com. U.S. Renal Data System, HHS, 1990—. Served with M.C., USAF, 1962-63. Named Intern of Year Michael Reese Hosp. Med. Center, 1961; recipient award La. Pediatric Soc., 1960. Mem. Inst. Medicine (end stage renal disease com. 1989-91), Am. Acad. Pediatrics, Soc. Pediatric Research, Am. Pediatric Soc., Am. Soc. Pediatric Nephrology (sec.-treas. 1974-80, pres. 1980-81, pub. policy com. 1991—), Am. Soc. Nephrology, Internat. Soc. Nephrology, Midwest Soc. Pediatric Research, AAAS, Salt and Water Club, N.Y. Acad. Scis., Internat. Pediatric Nephrology Assn. (asst. sec. gen. 1977-78), La. State Med. Soc., Assn. Med. Sch. Pediatric Dept. Chairmen, Am. Soc. Artificial Internal Organs, Orleans Parish Med. Soc., Greater New Orleans Pediatric Soc., Nat. Kidney Found. (health and sci. affairs com. 1989—), So. Soc. Pediatric Research, Kidney Found. La. (bd. dirs., med. adv. bd. 1981—, sci. adv. bd. 1982—), Tulane Clin. Sci. Council (chmn. 1980-90, Tulane senate com. on honors 1982-83, senator 1987-90), Alpha Omega Alpha. Home: 700 S Peters St New Orleans LA 70130 Office: 1430 Tulane Ave New Orleans LA 70112-2699

LEWY, RALPH I., hotel executive; b. Leiwen, Trier, Germany, May 28, 1931; s. Rudolf Reuben and Isabella (Haas) L.; m. Doris J. Laser, Apr. 12, 1964; children: Reuben Mark, Gary Daniel. B.S. in Commerce, Roosevelt U., 1953. C.P.A., Ill. Partner, Katz, Wagner & Co. (C.P.A.s), Chgo.; Partner Grant Thornton (C.P.A.s), Chgo., 1970-76; sr. v.p. Americana Hotels Corp., Chgo., 1976-87; pres. Ralph Lewy Ltd., Chgo., 1987—. Sec., treas., dir. Albert Pick Jr. Fund; v.p. Emanuel Congregation, Chgo.; v.p. dir. Lois and Leonard Laser Charitable Found. Mem. Am. Inst. C.P.A.s. Jewish. Office: Ralph Lewy Ltd 180 N La Salle St Ste 2401 Chicago IL 60601-2704

LEWYN, THOMAS MARK, lawyer; b. N.Y.C., July 2, 1930; s. Oswald and Agnes (Maas) L.; m. Ann Salfeld, July 15, 1955; children—Alfred Thomas, Mark Henry. B.A., Stanford, 1952, postgrad., 1952-54; LL.B., Columbia, 1955. Bar: N.Y. 1957. Since practiced in N.Y.C.; assoc. Simpson, Thacher & Bartlett, N.Y.C., 1957-64, ptnr., 1965-75, sr. ptnr., 1976-90, of counsel, 1991—; bd. dirs. Metro-Goldwyn-Mayer, Inc. Contbr. articles to profl. jours. Served to 1st lt., F.A. AUS, 1955-57. Mem. ABA, Assn. of Bar of City of N.Y., N.Y. State Bar Assn. Home: 911 Park Ave New York NY 10021-0337 Office: Simpson Thacher & Bartlett 425 Lexington Ave New York NY 10017-3903

LEY, ANDREW JAMES, lawyer; b. Boston, May 18, 1945; s. Douglas Leo and Ruth Hadley (Schauweker) L.; m. Susan Belle Wilde, Sept. 1, 1968 (div. Jan. 1985); children: Morgan B., Brooke A., Whitney B., Haven D. AB, Dartmouth Coll., 1967; JD, Boston U., 1975. Bar: Mass. 1975, U.S. Dist. Ct. Mass. 1975. Assoc. Tyler, Reynolds & Craig, Boston, 1975-78, Goodwin, Procter & Hoar, Boston, 1978-85; ptnr. McDermott, Will & Emery, Boston, 1985—. Alumni interviewer Dartmouth Coll., Hanover, N.H., 1973—; alumni fund agent, 1975—; pres. Chi-Heorot Assn., Boston, 1978—; cub scout leader Boy Scouts Am., Wellesley, Mass., 1979-81. Col. USMCR, 1967-91. Mem. Mass. Bar Assn., Boston Bar Assn., Mass. Conveyancer's Assn., Marine Corps Hist. Found., Naval Aviation Mus. Found., Marine Corps Res. Officers Assn., Marine Corps Aviation Assn. Avocations: flying, fishing, squash, tennis, rugby. Home: 686 Webster St Needham MA 02192-3120 Office: McDermott Will & Emery 75 State St Boston MA 02109-1807

LEY, HERBERT LEONARD, JR., retired epidemiologist; b. Columbus, Ohio, Sept. 7, 1923; s. Herbert Leonard and Laura (Spencer) L. M.D., Harvard U., 1946, M.P.H., 1951. Commd. 1st lt. M.C., U.S. Army, 1947, advanced through grades to lt. col., 1955; resigned, 1958; prof. microbiology George Washington U. Sch. Medicine, 1958-61; civil service with U.S. Army Research Office, 1961-63; asso. prof. epidemiology and microbiology Harvard Sch. Pub. Health, 1963-66; dir. Bur. Medicine, FDA, 1966-68, commr. food and drugs, 1968-69; cons. to food and drug industry, 1969-93. Contbr. sci. articles to profl. jours., chpts to med. texts. Decorated Bronze Star. Fellow Am. Coll. Preventive Medicine; mem. Am. Acad. Microbiology. Office: 4816 Camelot St Rockville MD 20853

LEY, RONALD, psychologist, educator; b. Buffalo, N.Y., Oct. 19, 1929; s. August Andreas and Marie (Jerge) L.; m. Carmen De Brito, Jan. 16, 1965; 1 child, Jessica Elizabeth. BA, U. Buffalo, 1951; PhD, Syracuse U., 1963. Rsch. dir. Madison Area Project, Syracuse, 1962-63; asst. prof. psychology No. Ill. U., DeKalb, 1963-64, Grad. Faculty, New Sch. for Social Rsch., N.Y.C., 1964-66; prof. psychology and stats. SUNY, Albany, 1966—; cons. Nat. Inst. for Occupational Safety and Health; vis. prof. psychology U. P.R., 1969, cardiac dept., Charing Cross Hosp., London, 1988. Author: A Whisper of Espionage, 1990; editor: Behavioral and Psychological Approaches to Breathing Disorders, 1993; editorial bd. Jour. Behavior Therapy and Exptl. Psychiatry, 1983—; guest editor: Biofeedback and Self-Regulation, 1994; contbr. numerous articles to profl. jours. Bd. dirs. Father's Assn. of the Albany Acad. for Girls, 1981-84. SUNY rsch. fellow, 1967, 68, 70, 74, 76, 78, 91; SUNY rsch. grantee, 1967-68, 69-70, 71-72, 74-75, 76, 78, 87-88, 91-92, Nat. Inst. Occupational Safety and Health grantee, 1982-83, 87, 88, others. Mem. APA, Am. Psychol. Soc., Assn. for Advancement Behavior Therapy, Assn. for Applied Psychophysiology and Biofeedback, Authors Guild, Authors League Am., Behavior Therapy and Rsch. Soc., Ea. Psychol. Assn., Internat. Soc. Advancement of Respiratory Psychophysiology (pres. 1993-95), New Eng. Soc. Behavior Analysis and Therapy, Psychol. Assn. Northeastern N.Y. (sec. 1967-68, pres. 1983-84), Soc. for Psychophysiol. Rsch., Psychonomic Soc., Sigma Xi. Home: 22 Marion Ave Albany NY 12203-1823 Office: SUNY 1400 Washington Ave Albany NY 12222-0001

LEYDEN, DONALD ELLIOTT, chemist, researcher; b. Gadsden, Ala., June 26, 1938; s. Elliott Hampton and Vivian Ione (Buckner) L.; m. Alice Jane Trowbridge, June 10, 1961; children: Mary Dawn, Sean Michael. BS, Kent State U., Ohio, 1960; MS, Emory U., 1961, Ph.D., 1964. Faculty U. Ga., Athens, 1965-76; Phillipson prof. environ. and mining chemistry U. Denver, 1976-81; prof. chemistry Colo. State U., Ft. Collins, 1981-88; assoc. prin. scientist Philip Morris USA, Richmond, Va., 1988—. Mem. editorial adv. bd. Analytica Chimica Acta, 1977-89, Internat. Jour. Environ. Analytical Chemistry, 1977-91, Mikrochimica Atca, X-Ray Spectrom, 1987-91; editor Chemically Modified Surfaces, 1985-90; contbr. articles to profl. jours. NIH grantee, 1965-68; NSF grantee, 1970-88; Philip Morris Tobacco Co. grantee, 1973-74. Mem. Am. Chem. Soc. (dir. for Applied Spectroscopy. Home: 502 Rivers Bend Cir Chester VA 23831-2570 Office: Philip Morris USA PO Box 26583 Richmond VA 23261-6583

LEYDEN, EDWARD E., secondary school principal. Prin. Bishop Lynch High Sch., Dallas. Recipient Blue Ribbon Sch. award U.S. Dept. Edn. 1990-91. Office: Bishop Lynch High Sch 9750 Ferguson Rd Dallas TX 75228

LEYDEN, NORMAN, conductor; m. Alice Leyden; children: Robert, Constance. Grad., Yale U. 1938; MA, Columbia U., PhD, 1970. Bass clarinetist New Haven Symphony; arranger Glenn Miller Air Force Band, Eng., France; chief arranger Glenn Miller Orch., 1946-49; freelance arranger N.Y.C.; mus. dir. RCA Victor Records, Arthur Godfrey, 1956-59; with Oreg. Symphony, 1970—; assoc. conductor, 1974—; music dir. Seattle Symphony Pops, 1975-93; tchr. Columbia U.; guest condr. over 30 Am. symphony orchs. including Boston Pops, Minn. Orch., Pitts. Symphony, St. Louis Symphony, San Diego Symphony, San Francisco Symphony, Nat. Symphony, Utah Symphony; condr. Army Air Force. Author: The Big Band Style: A Guide for Performers. Office: Oreg Symphony Orch 711 SW Alder Ste 200 Portland OR 97205

LEYDET, FRANÇOIS GUILLAUME, writer; b. Neuilly-sur-Seine, France, Aug. 26, 1927; came to U.S., 1940, naturalized, 1956; s. Bruno and Dorothy (Lindsey) L. AB, Harvard, 1947, postgrad. Bus. Sch., 1952; postgrad. Johns

Hopkins Sch. Advanced Internat. Studies, 1952-53; Bachelier-es-lettres-philosophie, U. Paris (France), 1945; m. Patience Abbe, June 17, 1955 (div.); step-children: Catherine Abbe Geissler, Lisa Amanda O'Mahony; m. Roslyn Carney, June 14, 1970; step-children: Walter E. Robb IV, Rachel R. Avery, Holly H. Prunty, Mary-Peck Peters. Bd. advisers Am. Wilderness Alliance; past dir. Marin County Planned Parenthood Assn., Planned Parenthood Center Tucson; docent Ariz.-Sonora Desert Mus. 1st lt. French Army, 1947-48. Mem. Nat. Parks Assn., Wilderness Soc., Sierra Club, Nat. Audubon Soc., World Wildlife Fund, Am. Mus. Natural History, Environ. Def. Fund, Friends of the Earth, Ariz.-Sonora Desert Mus., Ariz. Hist. Soc., LWV, Ariz. Opera League, Western Writers Assn., Commonwealth Club. Author: The Last Redwoods, 1963, Time and the River Flowing: Grand Canyon, 1964, The Coyote: Defiant Songdog of the West, 1977; editor: Tomorrow's Wilderness, 1963; contbr. to Nat. Geog. mag. Home: 5165 N Camino Real Tucson AZ 85718-5026

LEYDON, JOSEPH PATRICK, film critic, journalist; b. New Orleans, Aug. 22, 1952; s. Michael and Beverly (Garvey) L.; m. Anne Sarsonas, Aug. 26, 1976; 1 child, George Michael. Student, U. New Orleans, 1969-72; BA in Journalism, Loyola U., New Orleans, 1974. Staff writer Dallas Morning News, 1979-82; contbg. editor Dallas Observer, 1982-91; film critic Houston Post, 1982—; corr. Variety, N.Y.C., 1990—; film critic New Orleans Mag., 1980-83; film series advisor Media Ctr. Rice U., Houston, 1984—, film class instr. div. continuing studies, 1987-89; selection com. advisor Houston Internat. Film Festival, 1984-91. Recipient Critical Rev. award New Orleans Press Club, 1976, 81, 82, Newspaper Commentary award Houston Press Club, 1985, 86, Mag. Feature award, 1988, Comment and Criticism award AP Mng. Editors of Tex., 1986, 90, 93, 95. Democrat. Roman Catholic. Office: Houston Post 4747 Southwest Fwy Houston TX 77027-6901

LEYDORF, FREDERICK LEROY, lawyer; b. Toledo, June 13, 1930; s. Loftin Herman and Dorothy DeRoyal (Cramer) L.; m. Mary MacKenzie Malcolm, Mar. 28, 1953; children—Robert Malcolm, William Frederick, Katherine Ann, Thomas Richard, Deborah Mary. Student, U. Toledo, 1948-49; B.B.A., U. Mich., 1953; J.D., UCLA, 1958. Bar: Calif. 1959. Assoc. Hammack & Pugh, L.A., 1959-61; ptnr. Willis, Butler, Scheifly, Leydorf & Grant, L.A., 1961-81, Pepper, Hamilton & Scheetz, L.A., 1981-83, Hufstedler & Kaus, L.A., 1983-95; lectr., cons. Calif. Continuing Edn. of Bar, 1965-92; mem. planning com. Probate and Trust Conf., U. So. Calif., 1984-92. Contbg. author: California Non-Profit Corporations, 1969; contbr. articles to profl. jours. Chmn. pub. adminstr.-pub. guardian adv. comm. Los Angeles County Bd. Suprs., 1972-73; bd. dirs. J.W. and Ida M. Jameson Found., 1967—, Western Ctr. on Law and Poverty, Inc., 1980-82, L.A. Heart Inst., 1988-90; mem. legal com. Music Ctr. Found., 1980-95; mem. lawyers adv. coun. Constl. Rights Found., 1987-90; mem. devel. adv. bd. U. Mich. Sch. Bus. Adminstrn., 1984-90; mem. adv. bd. UCLA-CEB Estate Planning Inst., 1979-91. Lt. USNR, 1953-55. Mem. ABA, L.A. County Bar Assn. (bd. trustees 1973-75), State Bar Calif. (chmn. conf. dels. 1977, Alumnus of Yr. award, conf. of dels. 1983, mem. exec. com. estate planning, trust and probate law sect. 1979-80), L.A. County Bar Found. (pres. 1977-79, bd. dirs. 1975-87), Am. Coll. Trust and Estate Counsel, Internat. Acad. Estate and Trust Law (v.p. N.Am. 1978-82), Life Ins. and Trust Coun. L.A. (pres. 1983-84), UCLA Law Alumni Assn. (pres. 1982), L.A. World Affairs Coun., Chancery Club (pres. 1991-92), Jonathan Club (L.A.), Annandale Golf Club, Phi Delta Phi, Phi Delta Theta. Republican. Lutheran. Home: 3078-D Via Serena S Laguna Hills CA 92653-2771

LEYH, GEORGE FRANCIS, association executive; b. Utica, N.Y., Oct. 1, 1931; s. George Robert and Mary Kathleen (Haley) L.; m. Mary Alice Mosher, Sept. 17, 1955; children—Timothy George, Kristin Ann. B.C.E., Cornell U., 1954; M.S. (Univ. fellow), 1956. Structural engr. Eckerlin and Klepper, Syracuse, N.Y., 1956-59; asso. dir. engring. Martin Marietta Corp., Chgo., 1959-63; structural engr. Portland Cement Assn., Chgo., 1963-67; dir. mktg. Concrete Reinforcing Steel Inst., Chgo., 1967-75; exec. v.p. Am. Concrete Inst., Detroit, 1975—; editor jour. Am. Concrete Inst., 1975—. Mem. Planning Commn., Streamwood, Ill., 1960-68; chmn. Lake Bluff (Ill.) Citizens Com. for Conservation, 1972. Recipient Bloem Disting. Service award Am. Concrete Inst., 1972. Mem. ASCE, Am. Soc. Assn. Execs. (chmn. key profl. assns. com. 1989-90), Nat. Inst. Bldg. Scis., Am. Ry. Engring. Assn., Am. Nat. Standards Inst. (bd. dirs. 1986—), Am. Soc. for Concrete Constrn. (bd. dirs. 1984—), Phi Kappa Phi. Clubs: North Cape Yacht, Lake Bluff Yacht (dir. 1969-74, commodore 1973). Home: 1327 Lone Pine Rd Bloomfield Hills MI 48302-2756 Office: Am Concrete Inst PO Box 19150 22400 W 7 Mile Rd Detroit MI 48219-1849

LEYH, RICHARD EDMUND, SR., retired investment executive; b. Union City, N.J., Mar. 25, 1930; s. Louis Anthony and Grace Agnes (Barringer) L.; m. Patricia Ann Ryan, Apr. 18, 1949; children: Gail, Gloria, Anne, Teresa, Richard, Elizabeth, David. Student, Rutgers U., 1948-49. Sr. clk. Jersey Cen. Power and Light Co., Asbury Park, N.J., 1949-52; dist. mgr. N.J. Natural Gas Co., Asbury Park, 1952-56; methods analyst Univac, Newark, 1957-60; adv. systems engr. IBM, N.Y.C., 1960-65; mgr. real time systems N.Y. Stock Exchange, N.Y.C., 1965-66; prt. ops. Carlisle DeCoppet and Co., N.Y.C., 1967-76; exec. v.p., chief ops. officer Securities Industry Automation Corp., N.Y.C., 1976-91. Mem. Am. Mgmt. Assn., Inst. for Certification Computer Profls. Democrat. Roman Catholic. Avocations: bridge, golf, swimming. Home: 407 Mercer Ave Spring Lake NJ 07762-1228 Office: Securities Industry Automation Corp Two MetroTech Ctr Brooklyn NY 11201

LEYLAND, JAMES RICHARD, professional baseball team manager; b. Toledo, Dec. 15, 1944; m. Katie Leyland. Player various minor league teams Detroit Tigers, 1964-69, coach minor league system, 1970-71, mgr. minor league system, 1971-81; coach Chgo. White Sox, 1981-85, mgr. Pitts. Pirates, 1985—. Christmas chmn. Salvation Army, 1990-91. Named Nat. League Mgr. of Yr. Baseball Writer's Assn. Am., 1988, 90, Sporting News, 1990, Man of Yr. Arthritis Found., 1989, Epilepsy Found., 1991. Office: Pitts Pirates 600 Stadium Cir Pittsburgh PA 15212-5731*

LEYLEGIAN, JACK H., II, investment management company executive; b. Providence, Oct. 26, 1935; m. Dorothy Patricia Aprahamian, July 21, 1957; children: George A., Debra A. BSBA, Boston U., 1957; MBA, U. So. Calif., 1960. Vice pres. No. Trust Co., Chgo., 1966-71; pres. Dreyfus Mgmt. Inc., N.Y.C., 1971-77, Bank Am. Investment Mgmt. Co., San Francisco, 1977-81, Leylegian Investment Mgmt. Inc., Menlo Park, Calif., 1981-; bd. dirs. Imperial Bank, Los Angeles. Mem. Chartered Fin. Analysts Soc., San Francisco Security Analysts Soc. Office: Leylegian Investment Mgmt 601 Gateway Blvd Ste 700 South San Francisco CA 94080-7007

LEYMASTER, GLEN R., former medical association executive; b. Aurora, Nebr., Aug. 17, 1915; s. Leslie and Frances (Wertman) L.; m. Margaret Hendricks, June 20, 1942; children: Mark H., Mary Beth, Lynn F. A.B., U. Nebr., 1938; M.D., Harvard, 1942; M.P.H., Johns Hopkins U., 1950. Intern, asst. resident, resident Harvard Med. Service, Boston City Hosp., 1942-44; mem. faculty Johns Hopkins Med. Sch., 1944-48; instr., asst. prof. bacteriology Sch. Pub. Health and Hygiene, 1946-48; asso. prof. pub. health, instr. medicine U. Utah Sch. Medicine, 1948-50, prof., head dept., preventive medicine, asst. prof. medicine, also dir. univ. health service, 1950-60; adviser med. edn.- preventive medicine ICA, Bangkok, Thailand, 1956-58; asso. sec. council med. edn. and hosps. AMA, Chgo., 1960-63; pres., dean Women's Med. Coll. Pa., 1964-70; dir. dept. undergrad. med. edn. AMA, 1970-75; exec. dir. Am. Bd. Med. Spltys., Evanston, Ill., 1975-81; ret. exec. dir., 1981. Contbr. articles to profl. jours. Mem. AMA, Ill. Med. Assn., Inst. Medicine Chgo., Phi Beta Kappa, Sigma Xi, Alpha Omega Alpha. Home: 154 Kendal at Longwood Kennett Square PA 19348

L'HEUREUX, JOHN CLARKE, English language educator; b. South Hadley, Mass., Oct. 26, 1934; s. Wilfred Joseph and Mildred (Clarke) L'H.; m. Joan Ann Polston, June 26, 1971. AB, Weston Coll., 1959, Licentiate in Philosophy, 1960; MA, Boston Coll., 1963; Licentiate in Sacred Theology, Woodstock Coll., 1967; postgrad., Harvard U., 1967-68. Ordained priest Roman Catholic Ch., 1966, laicized, 1971; writer in residence Georgetown U., 1964-65, Regis Coll., 1968-69; staff editor The Atlantic, 1968-69, contbg. editor, 1969-83; vis. prof. Am. lit. Hamline U., 1971, Tufts Coll., 1972; vis. asst. prof. Harvard U., 1973; asst. prof. Stanford U., 1973-79, assoc. prof., 1979-81, prof., 1981—, Lane prof. humanities, 1985-90, dir. creative

writing program, 1976-89. Author: Quick as Dandelions, 1964, Rubrics for a Revolution, 1967, Picnic in Babylon, 1967, One Eye and a Measuring Rod, 1968, No Place for Hiding, 1971, Tight White Collar, 1972, The Clang Birds, 1972, Family Affairs, 1974, Jessica Fayer, 1976, Desires, 1981, A Woman Run Mad, 1988, Comedians, 1990, An Honorable Profession, 1991, The Shrine at Altamira, 1992. Office: Stanford U Dept English Stanford CA 94305

L'HEUREUX, WILLARD JOHN, real estate lawyer, diversified company executive; b. Ottawa, Ont., Can., May 25, 1947; s. Willard Joseph and Viola L'Heureux; m. Janet Elizabeth Button, 1973; children: Willard John, Jocelyn Marie, Robert Malcolm. BA, U. Western Ont., 1968; LLB, U. Toronto, 1971. Bar: Ont. 1973; called to Queen's Counsel 1983. Read law with Tory, Tory, DesLauriers & Binnington, 1972-73, assoc., 1973-79, ptnr., 1979-83; mng. ptnr. fin. svcs. Hees Internat. Bancorp., Toronto, 1983-88, pres., mng. ptnr., 1988-93; pres., CEO Carena-Bancorp Inc., Toronto, 1985-93, Trizec Corp. Ltd., Calgary, Alta., Can., 1993—; bd. dirs. Astral Comm., Noranda Inc., Trizec Corp. Ltd., Hees Internat. Bancorp Inc. Chmn., pres. Can. Spl. Olympics; hon. chmn. Intercollegiate Hockey Championships, Univ. Cup, 1994; mem. governing coun. U. Toronto; mem. adv. coun. Can. Canoe Mus. Mem. Royal Can. Yacht Club, Queen's Tennis Club, Calgary C. of C. (mem. pres. coun.). Office: Trizec Corp Ltd, 855 2nd St SW Ste 1700, Calgary, AB Canada T2P 4J7*

L'HEUREUX-DUBE, CLAIRE, judge; b. Quebec City, Que., Can., Sept. 7, 1927; d. Paul H. and Marguerite (Dion) L'H.; m. Arthur Dubé (dec. 1978); children: Louise Dubé, Pierre Dubé (dec. 1994). BA magna cum laude, Coll. Notre-Dame de Bellevue, Que., 1946; LLL cum laude, Laval U., Que., 1951, LLD (hon.), 1984; LLD (hon.), Dalhousie U., 1981, Montreal U., 1983, Ottawa U., 1988, U. Que., 1989, U. Toronto, 1994. Bar: Que. 1952. Ptnr. Bard, L'Heureux & Philippon, 1952-73; sr. ptnr. L'Heureux, Philippon, Garneau, Tourigny, St.-Arnaud & Assocs., from 1969; Puisne judge Superior Ct. Que., 1973-79, Ct. Appeal of Que., 1979-87, Supreme Ct. Can., Ottawa, 1987—; commr. Part II Inquiries Act Dept. Manpower and Immigration, Montreal, 1973; del. Gen. Council Bar of Que., 1968-70, com. on adminstrn. justice, 1968-73, others; pres. family law com., Family Ct. com. Que. Civil Code Revision Office, 1972-76; pres. Can. sect. Internat. Commn. Jurists, 1981-83; participant Internat. Invitational Conf. on Matrimonial and Child Support, Inst. Law Research and Reform, Edmonton, Alta., 1981; adminstr., mem. Que. founding com. of Judges' Conf., 1982-83; lectr. in family law. Editor: (with Rosalie S. Abella) Family Law - Dimensions of Justice, 1983; chmn. editorial bd. Can. Bar Rev., 1985-88; author articles, conf. proc., book chpt. Bd. dirs. YWCA, Que., 1969-73, Ctr. des Loisirs St. Sacrement, 1969-73, Ctr. Jeunesse de Tilly-Ctr. des Jeunes, 1971-77; v.p. Can. Consumers Council, 1970-73; v.p. Vanier Inst. of the Family, 1972-73; lifetime gov. Fondation Univ. Laval, 1980, bd. dirs., 1984-85; mem. Comité des grandes orientations de l'Univ. Laval, 1971-72; mem. nat. council Can. Human Rights Found., 1980-82, 82-84; mem. Can. del. to Peoples Republic China on Status of Women, 1981; pres. Can. sect. Internat. Commn. Jurists, 1981-83, v.p. internat. bd., 1992—. Apptd. Queen's Counsel, 1969; recipient Medal of the Alumni, U. Laval, 1986, Medaille du Barreau de Que., 1987. Mem. Can. Bar Assn., Can. Inst. Adminstrn. Justice, Internat. Soc. Family Law (bd. dirs. 1977-88, v.p. 1981-88), Internat. Fedn. Woman Lawyers, Fedn. Internat. des Femme Juristes, L'Assn. des Femmes Diplômées d'Univ., Assn. Québécoise pour l'Étude Comparative du Droit (pres. 1984-90), Internat. Commn. Jurists (pres. Can. sect., 1981-83, v.p. internat. bd. 1992—), Phi Beta Phi. Roman Catholic. Office: Supreme Ct Can, Wellington St, Ottawa, ON Canada K1A 0J1

LHEVINE, DAVE BERNARD, radiologist, educator; b. Tulsa, May 20, 1922; s. Morris Boise and Sarah Fannie (Piatt) L.; m. Mary Helen Orr, Dec. 19, 1963 (div. July 1986); children: Rhonda Dean, Paul Morris; m. Catherine Marie Garvey, Mar. 28, 1992. BA, Okla. U., 1943, MD, 1945. Diplomate Am. Bd. Radiology. Intern U.S. Naval Hosp., Bklyn., 1945-46; resident in radiology St. Louis City Hosp., Bklyn., 1948-51, 1948-51; dir. dept. radiology Hillcrest Med. Ctr., Tulsa, 1951-83, dir. dept. radiation therapy, 1983-86; clin. prof. dept. radiation oncology Okla. U., Okla. City, 1987-94; vice chmn. dept. radiology Okla. U. Sch. Medicine Tulsa Med. Coll., 1978—; corp. sec. Sterling Oil Co. of Okla., Tulsa, 1987-94. Active Tulsa County Dem. politics. Elected chmn. Tulsa County Dem. Com., 1995. Lt. (j.g.) USN, 1942-47. Fellow Am. Coll. Radiology (hon., emeritus); mem. AMA, Radiol. Soc. of N.Am., Okla. State Radiol. Soc. (pres. 1958). Democrat. Avocations: sailing, painting, photography, computers. Home: 2716 E 26th Pl Tulsa OK 74114-4308 Office: Okla Sch Medicine NE 13th Oklahoma City OK 73125

LHOTA, WILLIAM J., electric company executive. Exec. v.p. Am. Electric Power Svc. Corp., Columbus, Ohio. Office: Am Electric Power Svc Corp 1 Riverside Plz Columbus OH 43215-2355

L'HUILLIER, PETER (PETER), archbishop; b. Paris, Dec. 3, 1926; came to U.S., 1980; s. Eugene Henry and Emilienne (Haslin) L'H. Diploma, Inst. St. Denys, Paris, 1949; License of Theology, Moscow Theol. Acad., 1962, D of Canon Law, 1985. Ordained priest Russian Orthodox Ch. in Western Europe, 1954. Lectr. St. Denys Inst., Paris, 1949-50, Three Hierarchs Sem., Villemoisson, France, 1952-62; priest Russian Ch., Paris, 1954-68; prof. Cath. U., Paris, 1966-78; bishop of Chersonese, Diocese of France Russian Ch., Paris, 1968-79, archbishop of Chersonese, 1979; aux. bishop of Bklyn. Orthodox Ch. in Am., N.Y.C., 1979-81; bishop N.Y. and N.J. Orthodox Ch. in am., 1981-89; archbishop of N.Y. and N.J. Orthodox Ch. in Am., N.Y.C., 1990—; chmn. dept. external affairs Orthodox Ch. in Am., Syosset, N.Y., 1990—; adj. prof. St. Vladimir's Orthodox Sem., Crestwood, N.Y. 1980—; canonical advisor, chmn. theol. edn. commn. Standing Conf. Canonical Orthodox Bishops in Am., N.Y.C. 1990—. Office: Orthodox Ch in Am 33 Hewitt Ave Bronxville NY 10708-2333

LI, CHING-CHUNG, electrical engineering, computer science educator; b. Changshu, Kiangsu, China, Mar. 30, 1932; came to U.S., 1954, naturalized, 1972; s. Lung-Han and Lien-Tseng (Hwa) L.; m. Hanna Wu, June 10, 1961; children: William Wei-Lin, Vincent Wei-Tsin. B.S.E.E., Nat. Taiwan U., 1954; M.S.E.E., Northwestern U., 1956, Ph.D., 1961. Jr. engr. analytical dept. Westinghouse Electric Corp., East Pittsburgh, Pa., 1957; inst. fellow Northwestern U., Evanston, Ill., 1957-59; asst. prof. elec. engring. U. Pitts., 1959-62, assoc. prof., 1962-67; vis. assoc. prof. elec. engring. U. Calif.-Berkeley, 1964; vis. prin. scientist Alza Corp., Palo Alto, Calif. 1970; faculty rsch. participant Pitts. Energy Tech. Ctr., Dept. Energy, Pitts., 1982, 83, 85, 88, 89; prof. elec. engring. U. Pitts., 1967—, prof. computer sci., 1977—; mem. Ctr. Multivariate Analysis, 1982-87, Ctr. for Parallel and Distributed Intelligent Systems, 1986—; sabbatical leave Lab. for Info. and Decision Systems, MIT, 1988. Guest editor Jour. Cybernetics and Info. Sci., 1979, Computerized Med. Imaging and Graphics, 1991; assoc. editor Pattern Recognition, 1985—; contbr. articles to profl. jours. Co-recipient cert. of merit Radiol. Soc. N.Am., 1979; rsch. grantee NSF, 1975, 85-87, Pa. Dept. Health, 1977-79, We. Pa. Advanced Tech. Ctr., 1983-84, 86-88, Health Rsch. and Svc. Found., 1985-86, Air Force Office Sci. Rsch., 1990-93. Fellow IEEE (tech. com., com. chmn. 1967—); mem. Biomed. Engring. Soc., AAAS, N.Y. Acad. Sci., Pattern Recognition Soc., Sigma Xi, Eta Kappa Nu. Home: 2130 Garrick Dr Pittsburgh PA 15235-5033 Office: U Pitts Dept Elec Engring Pittsburgh PA 15261

LI, CHU-TSING, art history educator; b. Canton, China, 1920; came to U.S., 1947; m. Yao-wen; children: Ulysses, Amy. B.A., U. Nanking, 1943; M.A. in English Lit., U. Iowa, 1949, Ph.D. in Art History, 1955. Instr. U. Iowa, 1954-55, 56-58, asst. prof., 1958-62, assoc. prof., 1962-65, prof., 1965-66; prof. art history U. Kans., Lawrence, 1966-78, dept. chmn., 1972-78, Judith Harris Murphy Disting. prof., 1978-90, prof. emeritus, 1990—, dir. NEH summer seminar on Chinese art history, 1975, 78, coordinator Mellon faculty seminar, 1979; acting asst. prof. Oberlin Coll., 1955-56; asst. prof. Ind. U., summer 1956; coordinator N.Y. state faculty seminar on Chinese Art History, SUNY, 1965; research curator Nelson Gallery of Art, Kansas City, 1966—; vis. prof. fine arts Chinese U., Hong Kong, 1972-73, summer 1971, leader China visit group, 1973; vis. prof. Grad. Inst. Art History, Nat. Taiwan U., 1990; dir. NEH Summer Inst. on Modern Chinese Art and Culture, 1991; participant Internat. Symposiums on Chinese Painting, Nat. Palace Mus., Taipei, 1970, on Chinese Painting, Cleve. Mus. Art, 1981, Huangshan Sch. Painters, Hefei, Anhui, Rep. of China, 1984, on Words and

Images in Chinese Painting, Met. Mus. Art, N.Y.C., 1985, on the Elegant Brush: Chinese Painting under the Qianlong Emperor, Phoenix Art Mus., 1985, to celebrate 60th anniversary Nat. Palace Mus., Taipei, Taiwan, 1985, on History of Yuan Dynasty, Nanjing U., People's Republic of China, 1986, on art of Badashanren (Chu Ta), Nanchang, People's Republic of China, 1986; on Dunhuang Grottoes, Dunhuang, People's Republic of China, 1987; on the Four Monk Painters, Shanghai Mus., 1987; on the art of Chang Daichien, Nat. Mus. History, Taipei, 1988; Symposium on the Contemporary Artistic Development, Nanjing, 1988; Symposium on Chinese Painting of the Ming Dynasty, Chinese U. Hong Kong, 1988; Symposium on Chinese Painting of the Ming and Qing Dynasties from the Forbidden City, Cleve. Mus. Art, 1989, Symposium on Hist. Studies, since 1911, Nat. Taiwan U., Taipei, 1989, Symposium on the 40th Anniversary of the Founding of Liaoning Provincial Mus., Shenyang, People's Republic China, 1989, Symposium on Painting of Wu Sch., Palace Mus., Beijing, 1990; Internat. Colloquium on Chinese Art History, Nat. Palace Mus. Taipei, 1991, Internat. Symposium on Art of Four Wangs, Shanghai, 1992, VIIème Colloque Internat. de Sinologie, Chantilly, France, 1992, Symposium Painting at Close Qing Empire, Phoenix, 1992; spl. cons. Chinese U., Hong Kong, 1971, Symposium on Painting and Calligraphy by Ming Loyalists, Early Ch'ing Period, 1975. Author: books and exhbn. catalogues including The Autumn Colors on the Ch'iao and Hua Mountains, A Painting by Chao Meng-fu, 1254-1322, 1965, Liu Kuo-sung: The Development of a Modern Chinese Artist, 1970, A Thousand Peaks and Myriad Ravines: Chinese Paintings in the Charles A. Drenowatz Collection, 2 vols., 1974, Trends in Modern Chinese Painting, 1979; co-editor, contbr. Chinese Scholar's Studio: Artistic Life in Late Ming, Asia Soc., N.Y.C., 1987; editor, contbr.: Artists and Patrons: Some Social and Economic Aspects of Chinese Painting, 1990; contbr. articles to books and catalogues. Ford Found. Fgn. Area Tng. fellow, 1959-60; grantee Am. Council Learned Socs. and Social Sci. Research Council, 1963-64, NEH, 1975, 78, 91, Com. for Scholarly Communication with People's Republic of China Nat. Acad. Scis., 1979, Am. Council Learned Socs., 1980, Asian Cultural Council, N.Y., 1981, Kans. U., summers 1966-80; U. Iowa research prof., 1963-64; Fulbright-Hayes faculty fellow, 1968-69. Mem. Coll. Art Assn. Am., Assn. for Asian Studies, Midwest Art History Soc., Internat. House of Japan, Min-chiu Soc. Hong Kong, Phi Tau Phi, Phi Beta Kappa (hon.), Phi Beta Delta. Home: 1108 Avalon Rd Lawrence KS 66044-2506 Office: Univ Kans Kress Found Dept Art History Lawrence KS 66045

LI, DAVID WEN-CHUNG, television company executive; b. Yun-Nan, China; came to U.S. 1977; BA, Nat. Taiwan U., 1951. Editor, reporter, dep. city editor Hsin Sheng Daily News, Taipei, Taiwan, 1951-62; news analyst Broadcasting Corp. of China, Taipei, Taiwan, 1959-62; reporter, news anchor, news dept. dir., news commentator Taiwan TV Ent., Taipei, 1962-77; spl. corres. TTV, San Francisco, 1977-85; pres., gen. mgr. Pan Pacific TV, Inc./KPST-TV, San Francisco, 1985—; news commentator BBC London, San francisco, 1992. Author/editor news mag.: This Year, 1971-72; author: News Commentaries, 1974, Viewing the World From San Francisco, 1992, 94 ; author pamphlet: Ten Great Constructions, 1975. Sec.-gen. Chinese Youth Anti-Communist League, Taipei, 1950-51; founder, dir. Chinese Acupuncture Sci. Rsch. Found., Taipei, 1972—. Recipient Best TV News Program award GIO Taiwan, 1973, Internat. Preceptor award San Francisco State U., 1974. Avocation: golf. Home: 9 Jasmine Ct Millbrae CA 94030-1701 Office: Pan Pacific TV 475 El Camino Real # 308 Millbrae CA 94030-2627

LI, GERALD, architect, film producer; b. Washington, Mar. 4, 1942; s. Chen Sheng and Gloria (Mark) L.; m. Annemarie van Kersen, Oct. 31, 1972 (div. 1990); children: Alexis, Madison. BS, Rensselaer Poly. Inst., 1963, BArch, 1965. Architect Edward Larabee Barnes, N.Y.C., 1965-67; with Romaldo Guirgola, N.Y.C., 1967-68, Brown-Daltas, Rome, 1969-70, Conklin-Rossant, N.Y.C., 1970-72; chief designer Odell Assocs., Charlotte, N.C., 1972-73; prin. Clark Tribble Harris and Li, Charlotte, N.C., 1973-86; chmn., CEO Tribble Harris Li, Inc., Charlotte, N.C., 1986-90; dir. Young Pres'. Orgn., N.Y.C., L.A., 1988-90, Covell Matthews Wheatley, PLC, London, 1987-90, THL, Inc., Delaware, 1986-90. Principal works include Saatchi-Saatchi World Hdqs., Georgetown Park shopping mall, Northwest Mutual Office Bldg., Milw., Ritz Carlton Hotel, Aspen, Bank of Spain, N.Y.C. Recipient Young Profls. Design award Building Design Construction Mag., 1980. Fellow AIA (award Hist. Preservation for Market House 1981, Honor award for Discovery Place Mus. 1984); mem. Nat. Coun. Archtl. Registration Bds. Home: 929 E 2d St Ste 202 Los Angeles CA 90012

LI, NORMAN N., chemicals executive; b. Shanghai, China, Jan. 14, 1933; came to U.S.; naturalized, 1969.; s. Lieh-wen and Amy H. Li; m. Jane C. Li, Aug. 17, 1963; children: Rebecca H., David H. BSin Chem. Engring., Nat. Taiwan U., Taipei, 1955; MS, Wayne State U., 1957; PhD, Stevens Inst. Tech., 1963. Sr. scientist Exxon Rsch. and Engring. Co., Linden, N.J., 1963-81; dir. separation sci. and tech. UOP, Des Plaines, Ill., 1981-88; dir. engineered products and process tech. Allied-Signal Inc., Des Plaines, Ill., 1988-92, dir. rsch. and tech., 1993—; mem. NRC, 1985-89; lectr. Am. Inst. Chem. Engrs., 1975-86. Editor 13 books on separation sci. and tech.; contbr. articles to jours. in field; patentee in field. Fellow AICE (dir. divsn. food, pharms. and bioengring. 1988-91, Alpha Chi Sigma rsch. award 1988, bd dirs 1992-94, Ernest Thiele award 1995); mem. NAE, Am. Chem. soc. (Seperation Sci. and Tech. award 1988), N.Am. Membrane Soc. (pres. 1991-93). Home: 620 Rolling Ln Arlington Heights IL 60004-5820 Office: Allied-Signal Rsch Ctr PO Box 5016 Des Plaines IL 60017-5016

LI, PETER WAI-KWONG, mathematics educator; b. Hong Kong, Apr. 18, 1952; came to U.S., 1971; s. Chun Tat and Lai Mui (Sum) L.; m. Glenna Marie Seaver, Oct. 30, 1982; children: Tiana, Natasha, Talia. BA, Calif. State U., 1974; MA, U. Calif., Berkeley, 1977, PhD, 1979. Rsch. mem. Inst. for Advanced Study, Princeton, N.J., 1979-80; asst. prof. Stanford (Calif.) U., 1980-83; assoc. prof. Purdue U., West Lafayette, Ind., 1983-85; prof. U. Utah, Salt Lake City, 1985-89, U. Ariz., Tucson, 1989-91, U. Calif., Irvine, 1991—; chair math. dept. U. Calif., 1993—. Editor Rocky Mountain Jour. Math., 1989-91, Procs. of Am. Math. Soc., 1991—; Editor-in-Chief Comm. in Analysis and Geometry, 1992—. Grantee NSF, 1980—; fellowship Sloan, 1982-83, Guggenheim, 1989-90. Mem. Am. Math. Soc., Phi Beta Kappa. Avocations: swimming, skiing, cooking, wine-tasting. Office: U Calif Irvine Dept Math Irvine CA 92717

LI, PUI-PUI, interior and graphic designer; b. Hong Kong, Nov. 21, 1954; came to U.S., 1975; d. Hung Tong and Choi Gee Lee; m. Eric M. Jones, Nov. 22, 1979. BFA, Art Ctr. Coll. Design, Pasadena, Calif., 1979. Creative dir. Atelier Internat. Ltd. IDCNY, L.I., N.Y., 1987-92; 1980—; v.p. design Internat. Contract Furnishings, N.Y.C., 1994—, 1994; creative dir. Cassina USA, Inc., Flos Inc., 1995—; creative dir. Cassina USA, Inc., Flos Inc., 1995—. Prin. works include Artists and Poets of Hong Kong, Art Ctr. Coll. of Design Gallery, Sundance Film Festival, 1987, Design Industry Found. for AIDS, Sotheby's, N.Y., 1989, Murray Feldman Gallery, L.A. 1990, Cooper-Hewitt Gallery, L.A., 1990, Nat. Bldg. Mus., Washington, 1991, Notes from Underground, 1995. Recipient Creativity award Art Direction mag., 1985, 87, 89, Product Lit. award Interiors Mag. 1988, Small Showroom award Am. Soc. Interior Designers, 1988, 92, Neocon Product Display award AIA, 1988, Strathmore Cert. of Silver, 1993, Packaging Design award I.D. mag., 1993. Office: Jones Studio Ltd PO Box 140402 Staten Island NY 10314

LI, STEVEN SHOEI-LUNG, geneticist, educator; b. Pingtang, Taiwan, Republic of China, Oct. 20, 1938; came to the U.S., 1964; s. Ai (Chen) L.; m. Pearl Y-J.C. Li, July 25, 1967; children: Michael, Nancy. BS, Nat. Taiwan U., 1961, MS, 1963; PhD, U. Mo., 1968. Postdoctoral fellow U. Tex., Austin, 1968-70; rsch. assoc. Stanford (Calif.) U., 1970-74; assoc. prof. Mount Sinai Sch. Medicine, N.Y.C., 1974-77; rsch. geneticist Nat. Inst. Environ. Health Scis., NIH, Research Triangle Park, N.C., 1977—; adj. prof. biochemistry and chemistry U. N.C., Chapel Hill, 1977—. Contbr. more than 100 rsch. papers to profl. jours.; mem. editl. bd. Jour. Genetics and Molecular Biology, 1990—. NIH grantee, 1975-77. Mem. Genetics Soc. Am., AAAS, Am. Soc. for Biochemistry and Molecular Biology, Am. Soc. Microbiology. Achievements include research in organization and regulation of mammalian genes, structure and function of proteins, molecular evolution.

Office: Nat Inst Environ Health Sci NIH Lab Genetics 111 TW Alexander Dr Research Triangle Park NC 27709

LI, TINGYE, electrical engineer; b. Nanking, China, July 7, 1931; came to U.S., 1953, naturalized, 1963; s. Chao and Lily Wei-peng (Sie) L.; m. Edith Hsiu-hwei Wu, June 9, 1956; children: Deborah Chunroh, Kathryn Dairoh. B.Sc. in Elec. Engring. U. Witwatersrand, South Africa, 1953; M.S., Northwestern U., Evanston, Ill., 1955, Ph.D., 1958; Dr. Engring. (hon.), Nat. Chiao Tung U., Hsinchu, Republic of China, 1991. Mem. tech. staff AT&T Bell Labs., Holmdel, N.J., 1957-67; dept. head repeater techniques research dept. Bell Labs., 1967-76, lightwave media research dept., 1976-84, lightwave systems research dept., 1984—. Assoc. editor Optics Letters, 1977-78, topical editor, 1989-91; assoc. editor Jour. of Lightwave Tech., 1983-86; editor book series: Optical Fiber Communications; mem. editorial bd. Procs. IEEE, 1974-83, Microwave and Optical Tech. Letters, 1987—; Internat. Jour. High Speed Electronics, 1990—; contbr. articles on microwave antennas and propagation, lasers, coherent optics, optical communications, optical-fiber transmission to sci. jours., chpts. in books. Recipient Alumni Merit award Northwestern U., 1981 John Tyndall Awd., 1995, Optical Soc. Am.; named hon. prof. Tsinghua U., Shanghai Jiao Tong U., Beijing U. Posts and Comms., U. Electronic Sci. and Tech. of China, Qufu Normal U., No. Jiao Tong U. Fellow IEEE (W.R.G. Baker prize 1975, David Sarnoff award 1979), AAAS, Photonics Soc. Chinese-Ams., Optical Soc. Am. (chmn. optical comms. tech. group 1979-80, bd. dirs. 1985-87, chmn. internat. activities com. 1988-90, chmn. photonics divsn. 1991-92, pres. 1995, John Tyndall award 1995); mem. NAE, Chinese Inst. Engrs. U.S.A. (bd. dirs. 1974-78, Achievement award 1978), Academia Sinica (Taiwan), Chinese Am. Acad. and Profl. Assn. (bd. dirs. 1985-89, Achievement award 1983), Electromagnetics Acad., F.F. Fraternity Club, Sigma Xi, Eta Kappa Nu, Phi Tau Phi (pres. East Am. chpt. 1991-93). Club: F.F. Fraternity. Patentee in field. Office: AT&T Bell Labs PO Box 400 Holmdel NJ 07733

LI, TZE-CHUNG, lawyer, educator; b. Shanghai, China, Feb. 17, 1927; came to U.S., 1956; s. Ken-hsiang Li and Yun-hsien (Chang) Li; m. Dorothy In-lan Wang, Oct. 21, 1961; children—Lily, Rose. LL.B., Soochow U., Shanghai, 1948; Diploma, Nat. Chengchi U., Nanking, 1949, China Research Inst. of Land Econs., Taipei, 1952; M.C.L., So. Meth. U., Dallas, 1956; LL.M., Harvard U., Cambridge, 1958; M.S., Columbia U., N.Y.C., 1965; Ph.D., New Sch. for Social Research, N.Y.C., 1963. Judge Hwa-lien Dist. Ct., Hwa-lien, Taiwan, Republic of China, 1949-51; dist. atty. Ministry of Justice, Tapei, 1951-52; chief law sect. Ministry of Nat. Def., Tapei, 1952-56; asst. prof. library sci. Ill. State U., Normal, 1965-66; asst. prof. polit. sci., library sci. Rosary Coll., River Forest, Ill., 1966-69, assoc. prof. library sci., 1969-70, 72-74, prof. library sci., 1974-82, dean, prof. Grad. Sch. Library and Info. Sci., 1982-88, prof., 1988—; vis. assoc. prof. law Nat. Taiwan U., 1969; vis. assoc. prof. polit. sci. Soochow U., Taipei, 1969; dir. Nat. Central Library, Taipei, 1970-72; chmn. Grad. Inst. Library Sci., Nat. Central Library, Taipei, 1971-72; commr. Ministry of Examination, Examination Yuan, Taipei, 1971; chmn. com. on library standards, Ministry of Edn., Taipei, 1972; library cons. Soochow U., Nat. Chengchi U., Dr. Sun Yat-sen Meml. Library; mem. library adv. com. Ency. Britannica, 1982—; hon. prof. library and info. sci. Jiangxi U., People's Republic of China, 1985—; vis. prof. law Suzhou U., Peking U., Nat. Taiwan U., 1991; hon. cons. univ. library, 1985—; hon. cons. Jiangxi Med. Coll., 1985—; adv. prof. East China Normal U., 1987—; cons. Nova U., 1987-88; mem. ad hoc adv. com. Chgo. Pub. Library Bldg. Planning, 1987-88. Author books including: Social Science Reference Sources, 1980, 2d edit., 1990, Mah Jong, 1982, 2d edit., 1991, An Introduction to Online Searching, 1985; also numerous articles in profl., scholarly jours.; founding editor Jour. Library and Info. Sci., 1975-80, mem. editorial bd. 1986-90; founding chmn., mem. editorial bd. Internat. Jour. of Revs., 1984-89. Pres. Chinese Am. Ednl. Found., Chgo., 1968-70; chmn. Com. for Chinatown Library, Chgo., 1966-67; advisor Friends of Soochow, Los Angeles, 1974-87; bd. dirs. Asian Human Services, Inc., Chgo., 1978; co-chmn. Com. for Expansion of Chinatown Library, Chgo., 1984-86; pres. China Council on Cultural Renaissance, Midwest chpt., 1974-85. Recipient Govt. Citation Republic of China, 1956, 1972, Philip D. Sang Excellence in Teaching award Rosary Coll., 1971, Disting. Service award Phi Tau Phi, Chgo., 1982, Service award HUD, Chgo. region, 1985, Disting. Service award Chinese Am. Librarians Assn., 1988. Mem. ALA1 Am. Soc. Info. Sci., Assn. for Asian Studies, Assn. Coll. and Research Libraries, Assn. Library ad Info. Sci. Edn., Chinese Am. Librarians Assn. (founding pres. 1976-80), Library Assn. China (Taipei), Spl. Library Assn., Phi Tau Phi (pres. 1985-87). Republican. Roman Catholic. Home: PO Box 444 Oak Park IL 60303-0444 Office: Rosary Coll 7900 Division St River Forest IL 60305-1099

LI, WEIYE, ophthalmologist, biochemist, educator; b. Zhejiang, China, Oct. 10, 1946; came to U.S., 1990; s. Zhao-ji Li and Qin Yue; m. Xinru Liu, Apr. 12, 1986; 1 child, Yafeng. MD, Peking Second Med. Coll., China, 1970; postgrad., Acad. Med. Scis., China, 1978-80; PhD, U. Pa., 1984. Intern Chao Young Hosp., Peking, 1970-71, resident ophthalmology, 1971-78; rsch. fellow dept. ophthalmology and biochem. grad. sch. Sch. Medicine U. Pa., Phila., 1981-84, postdoctor, asst. prof. dept. ophthalmology Scheie Eye Inst. Sch. Medicine, 1984-85; asst. prof., attending physician ophthalmology Peking Union Med. Coll. Hosp., 1985-86, assoc. prof. ophthalmology, 1986-88, prof. ophthalmology, 1988-93, chmn. dept. ophthalmology, 1989-93; prof. ophthalmology, dir. rsch. dept. ophthalmology, prof. pathology, mem. faculty interdepartmental program molecular biology and biotech. Hahnemann U., Phila., 1990—. Recipient Rsch. award Internat. Juvenile Diabetes Found., 1984-86, 1st Class Sci. and Tech. Advances prize Chinese Ministry Pub. Health, 1988; grantee NIH, 1981-82, 86—, Fight for Sight, Inc., 1982-83, Am. Diabetes Assn., 1990—, Frank E. Snider Trust Fund, 1990—; Postdoctoral fellow Internat. Juvenile Diabetes Found., 1982-84. Mem. Assn. Rsch. in Vision and Ophthalmology, Assn. Chinese Ophthal. Soc. Avocations: table tennis, bicycling, classical music. Office: Hahnemann U Dept Ophthalmology MS 209 Broad and Vine Sts Philadelphia PA 19102-1192

LIACOS, PAUL JULIAN, state supreme judicial court chief justice; b. Peabody, Mass., Nov. 20, 1929; s. James A. and Pitsa K. (Karis) L.; m. Maureen G. McKean, Oct. 6, 1954; children: James P., Diana M., Mark C., Gregory A. AB magna cum laude, Boston U. Coll. Liberal Arts, 1950; LLB magna cum laude, Boston U., 1952; LLM, Harvard U., 1953; diploma, Air Command and Staff Sch., 1954; LLD (hon.), Suffolk U., 1984, New Eng. Sch. Law, 1985; LHD (hon.), Salem State Coll., 1988; LLD (hon.), Northeastern U., 1991. Bar: Mass. 1952, U.S. Dist. Ct. Mass. 1954, U.S. Ct. Mil. Appeals 1955, U.S. Ct. Appeals (1st cir.) 1971, U.S. Supreme Ct. 1980. Ptnr. firm Liacos and Liacos, Peabody, Mass., 1952-76; prof. law Boston U., 1952-76, adj. prof. law, 1976-89; assoc. justice Mass. Supreme Jud. Ct., 1976-89, chief justice, 1989—; Distinguished lectr. on law U.S. Mil. Acad., West Point, N.Y., 1972; lectr. Suffolk U. Law Sch., 1978-79; U.S. Constn. Bicentennial lectr. Boston Pub. Library, 1987; cons. to atty. gen. Mass. on staffing and personnel, 1974-75; lectr. on criminal evidence Boston Police Acad., 1963-64; reporter New Eng. Conf. on Def. of the Indigent, Harvard Law Sch., 1963; reader and cons. on legal manuscripts Little, Brown & Co., Boston, 1968-76; editorial cons. Warren, Gorham & Lamont, 1968-84; steering com. Lawyers Com. for Civil Rights under Law, Boston, 1969-72; chmn. com. on discrimination in the cts. Conf. of Chief Justices, 1993—. Author: Handbook of Massachusetts Evidence, 1981,6th edit., 1993; contbr. articles in field to legal jours.; book rev. editor: Boston U. Law Rev, 1952. Trustee Suffolk U., Boston, 1993—; trustee, mem. exec. com. Chamberlayne Sch. and Jr. Coll., Boston, 1972-74; trustee Anatolia Coll., Salonika, Greece, 1980—, exec. com., 1986-89; hon. trustee Deree-Pierce Colls., Athens, 1976—; corp. mem. MIT, 1989. With USAF, 1953-56. Named Man of Year Boston U. Law Sch., 1952; recipient Man of Year award Alpha Omega, 1977; named mem. Colleguum Distinguished Alumni Boston U. Coll. Liberal Arts, 1974; recipient Disting. Public Service award Boston U. Alumni, 1980, Allied Profl. award Mass. Psychol. Assn., 1987, Man of Vision award Nat. Soc. to Prevent Blindness, 1988, State Bill of Rights award Nat. Assn. Criminal Def. Lawyers, 1988, Good Neighbor award Mishkan Tefila Brotherhood, 1990, Founders' award Lawyers Com. for Civil Rights under the Law, Boston Bar Assn., 1993. Mem. ABA, Mass. Bar Assn. (criminal law com. 1964-66), Essex County Bar Assn., Peabody Bar Assn., assn. Trial Lawyers Am. (editor 1968-73, Outstanding State Appellate Judge 1982), Harvard Law Sch Assn., Boston U. Law Sch. Alumni Assn. (Silver Shingle award 1977), Phi Beta Kappa. Democrat. Mem. Greek Orthodox Ch. Of-

fice: Mass Supreme Jud Ct Pemberton Sq 1300 New Courthouse Boston MA 02108

LIANG, EDISON PARKTAK, astrophysicist, educator, researcher; b. Canton, Republic of China, July 22, 1947; came to U.S.; 1964; s. Chi-Sen and Siu-Fong (Law) L.; m. Lily K. Yuen, Aug. 7, 1971; children: Olivia, James, Justin. BA, U. Calif., Berkeley, 1967, PhD, 1971. Rsch. scientist U. Tex., Austin, 1971-73; assoc. instr. U. Utah, Salt Lake City, 1973-75; asst. prof. Mich. State U., East Lansing, Mich., 1975-76, Stanford (Calif.) U., 1976-79; physicist, group leader Lawrence Livermore Nat. Lab., Livermore, Calif., 1980-88; assoc. div. leader Lawrence Livermore Nat. Lab., Livermore, 1988-91; prof. Rice U., Houston, Tex., 1991—; mem. NASA Rev. Panels, Washington, 1988. Editor: (book) Gamma Ray Bursts, 1986. Named Sci. fellow and Anthony scholar U. Calif., Berkeley, 1967-69. Fellow Am. Physical Soc.; mem. Am. Astron. Soc., Internat. Astron. Union, Phi Beta Kappa, Sigma Xi. Office: Rice U PO Box 1892 Houston TX 77251-1892

LIANG, JASON CHIA, research chemist; b. Beijing, Peoples Republic China, Feb. 24, 1935; came to U.S., 1978, naturalized 1984; s. Tsang Truan and Shulin (Tang) L.; m. Juan Chorng Chen, June 11, 1960; children: Cheryl, Chuck. BS in Pharm. Chemistry, U. Beijing, 1957; postgrad., Pharm. Research Instn., Beijing, 1961; MS in Organic Chemistry, U. Oreg., 1980. Chemist Beijing Chem. Factory, 1961-71; rsch. chemist Beijing Pharm. Factory, 1971-78; rsch. chemist Tektronix Inc., Beaverton, Oreg., 1980-85, sr. rsch. chemist, 1985-88; sr. rsch. chemist Kalama (Wash.) Chem. Inc., 1988—; rschr. in flavor and fragrance chemistry. Contbr. articles to profl. jours.; patentee in field. Fellow Am. Inst. Chemists; mem. Am. Chem. Soc. (organic chemistry divsn., paper presenter 1984-95), Internat. Union Pure and Applied Chemistry (affiliate). Office: Kalama Chem Inc 1296 NW 3D St Kalama WA 98625

LIANG, JEFFREY DER-SHING, retired electrical engineer, civil worker, diplomat; b. Chungking, China, Oct. 25, 1915; came to U.S., 1944, naturalized, 1971; s. Tze-hsiang and Sou-yi (Wang) L.; m. Eva Yin Hwa Tang, Jan. 2, 1941; 1 child, Shouyu. BA, Nat. Chengchih U., Chungking, 1940; BAS, U. B.C., Vancouver, 1960. Office asst. Ministry of Fgn. Affairs, Chungking, 1940-43; vice consul, Chinese consulate Ministry of Fgn. Affairs, Seattle, 1944-50; consulate-gen. Ministry of Fgn. Affairs, San Francisco, 1950-53; consul, Chinese consulate-gen. Ministry of Fgn. Affairs, Vancouver, 1953-56; engr.-in-tng. Can. Broadcasting Corp., Vancouver, 1960-65; assoc. engr. Boeing Co., Seattle, 1965-67, rsch. engr., 1967-70, engr., 1970-73, sr. engr., 1973-75, specialist engr., 1975-78; cons. Seattle, 1979-81. Mem. chancelor's cir. Wesbrook Soc. U. B.C., Vancouver, 1986—, Seattle-King County Adv. Coun. on Aging, 1984-88, Gov.'s State Coun. on Aging, Olympia, 1986-88, Pres. Coun., Rep. Nat. Com.; permanent mem. Rep. Nat. Senatorial Com., Washington State Rep. Party, Seattle Art Mus.; life mem. Am. Assn. Individual Investors, Rep. Presdl. Task Force; sustaining mem. Rep. Nat. Congl. Com., Rep. Presdl. Adv. Com.. Mem. IEEE (life), Heritage Found., Hwa Sheng Chinese Music Club (v.p. 1978-79, chmn. nomination com. 1981-88, 90-94). Republican. Mem. Christian Ch. Avocations: Chinese calligraphy, opera, poetry, physical fitness. Home: 1750 152d Ave NE Apt 302 Bellevue WA 98007-4270

LIANG, JUNXIANG, aeronautics and astronautics engineer, educator; b. Hangzhou, Zhejiang, China, Aug. 17, 1932; s. Yigao and Yunruo (Yu) L.; m. Junxian Sun, Jan. 27, 1960; 1 child, Song Liang. Grad., Harbin Inst. Tech., 1960. Head control dept. Shenyang (Liaoning, China) Jet Engine R&D Inst., 1960-70, China Gas Turbine Establishment, Jiangyou, Sichuan, China, 1970-78; assoc. chief engr. China Gas Turbine Establishment, Jiangyou, 1978-83; vis. scientist MIT, Cambridge, Mass., 1984-86; prof. China Aerospace Inst. Systems Engring., Beijing, China, 1986—; grads. supr. Beijing U. Aero-Astronautics, Beijing, 1986—; chief engr. Full Authority Digital Elec. Engine Control China Aerospace Industry Ministry, Beijing, 1986-93; mem. China Aerospace Sci. and Tech. Com., Beijing, 1983-94, Aero-engine R&D Adv. Bd., Beijing, 1991-95; bd. dirs. China Aviation Ency. Editl. Bd., Beijing, 1991-95; tech. support supr., mgmt. info. svc. mgr. Am. PC, Inc., Union City, Calif., 1993—. Author: Nonlinear Control System Oscillation, 1964; contbr. articles to Jour. Aeronautics and Astronautics, Jour. Propulsion Tech., Internat. Aviation, Acta Aeronautica et Astronautica Sinica. Recipient Nat. Sci. and Tech. 2d award, China Nat. Sci. and Tech. Com., Beijing, 1965, Sic. and Tech. Progress award, China Aerospace Industry Ministry, 1991, Nat. Outstanding Sci. and Tech. Contbn. award, 1992. Mem. AIAA, Chinese Soc. of Aeronautical, Astronautical Engine Control (mem. commn. 1987—). Achievements include solution of oscillation problem on nonlinear control system; formulation of overall strategy, study and control of High Thrust/Weight Engine Rsch. Program. Office: China Aerospace Inst Sys Engring, Beiyuan-Dayuan # 2 An-Wai, Beijing 100012, China

LIANG, MATTHEW H., medical director; b. Santa Monica, Calif., May 24, 1944. AB in Philosophy and Chemistry, Johns Hopkins U., 1965; BMS, Dartmouth U., 1967; MD, Harvard U., 1969, MPH, 1972. Diplomate Am. Bd. Internal Medicine. Intern in medicine U. Minn. Hosps., Mpls., 1969-70, resident in medicine, 1970-71; resident in medicine Harvard Med. Svc., Boston City Hosp., 1972-73; physician People's Riverside Free Clinic, Mpls., 1969-71, Cambridgeport Free Clinic, Cambridge, Mass., 1971-73; interist Family Health Ctr. Boston City Hosp., 1972-73, assoc. med. dir. Nursing Home Telemedicine, 1972-73; with med. corps Office Gen. Surgeon, U.S. Army, Ft. Belvoir, Va., 1973-74; asst. chief med. clinic Walter Reed Army Med. Ctr., Washington, 1974-75, mem. attending staff, 1974-75; clin. instr. Sch. Medicine, Georgetown U., Washington, 1974-75; mem. attending staff Georgetown Med. Svc., D.C. Gen. Hosp., Washington, 1974-75; asst. prof. medicine dept. rheumatology and immunology Harvard Med. Sch., Brigham Women's Hosp., Boston, 1977-86, assoc. prof. medicine, 1986; lectr. dept. health svcs. Sch. Pub. Health, Harvard U., 1977-79, lectr. dept. health policy and mgmt., 1979; mem. staff Peter Bent Brigham Hosp., Boston, 1977-79, Robert B. Brigham Hosp., Boston, 1977-79, The Hosp. at Parker Hill, Boston, 1979-82, Brigham and Women's Hosp., Boston, 1979—, Brockton (Mass.) VA Hosp., 1980-82, Dana-Farber Cancer Inst., Boston, 1984-86; assoc. dir. Robert B. Brigham Multipurpose Arthritis Ctr., Boston, 1979-80, dir., 1980—; med. dir. rehab. svcs. Brigham and Women's Hosp., Boston, 1982—, med. dir. acute rehab. program, 1984-86; mem. exec. com. Mass. chpt. Arthritis Found., 1979-81, mem. govtl. affairs com., 1981-82, co-chmn., 1984, bd. trustees 1982—, mem. med. and sci. com. 1982—, chmn. grants subcom. 1990—, mem. rsch. com. 1991—, chmn. Mass. chpt. 1993; mem. arthritis interagency coordinating com., data systems subcom. NIH, 1979, mem. spl. rev. com., 1980-81, mem. nat. arthritis adv. bd. 1985-88, co-chmn. adv. com. on rehab., 1990; mem. adv. panel on allergy, immunology and connective tissue disease U.S. Pharmacopoa Conv., Inc., 1980-82; mem. musculoskeletal panel Social Security Adminstrn., 1985; mem. med. adv. com. Blue Shield Bd. Dirs., Boston, 1986-89; mem. adv. com. Maternal and Child Health Improvement Project, Boston, 1986; chmn. statewide adv. com. on vocat. rehab. 1986; mem. musculoskeletal and skin disease task force on lupus in high risk populations Nat. Inst. Arthritis, 1988—, chmn. health svcs., behavioural and ednl. rsch. steering com. 1990; mem. rsch. grants rev. com. Scleroderma Found., 1989-90; mem. practice guidline panel on low back dysfunction Agy. Health Care Policy and Rsch., 1991—, mem. health svcs. rsch. tng adv. com. 1992; mem. hip fracture and replacement patient outcomes Assessment Rsch. Team Nat. Adv. Bd., 1991—; mem. steering com. assessment program on low back pain L'Institute de recherche en Sante et en Securite du travail du Quebec, 1989-92; chmn. external monitoring com. Multicenter Clin. Trial Hydroxychloroquine in Early Rheumatoid Arthritis, 1989—; mem. grants rev. com. Med. Found., 1990—, mem. clin. rsch. com., 1993, mem. community health and edn. com., 1993; Kellogg Fellowship lectr., 1986—; Kare Bergling lectr. in Rheumatology U. Lund, Sweden, 1990; A.S.B. Bank vis. prof. in Rheumatology/Rehab., Auckland, New Zealand, 1990; Highton Oration lectr., Queenstown, New Zealand, 1990; Matilda G. Irving Meml. lectr.; Providence, 1991; Kovacs vis. prof. Royal Soc. Medicine, London, 1994; active Quebec Taskforce on Whiplash Injuries; med. cons. Internat. Grenfell Mission, Newfoundland, 1971. Editor Rheumatology Rev., 1990—, Jour. Orthopaedic Rheumatology, 1990-92; assoc. editor Arthritis and Rheumatism, also mem. editorial bd., 1983-88; mem. editorial bd. Annals of the Rheumatic Diseases, 1989—, Brit. Jour. Rheumatology, 1989—, Lupus, 1990—; mem. adv. bd. Current Med. Lit., 1982-87, Arthritis Info. Mag., 1986, Spine, low in clin. cardiology Royal Postgrad. Sch., Hammersmith Hosp., London, 1969, Clin. fellow in rheumatology Stanford (Calif.) U. Sch. Medicine, 1975-77, Travelling fellow

WHO, 1977, 83, Med. Found. fellow, 1979-81; Robert Wood Johnson Clin. scholar, Stanford (Calif.) U. Med. Ctr., 1975-77. Mem. APHA, ACP, Am. Fedn. Clin. Rsch., Am. Coll. Rheumatology (mem. glossary com. 1979-89, mem. com. on health svcs. and health tech. 1980—, mem. orthopaedic coun. 1982-83, chmn. adv. com. med. info. system 1981-83, mem. program com. 1983-84, mem. coun. rehab. rheumatology 1984—, mem. subcom. revision of criteria for classification rheumatoid arthritis 1984-85, councilor northeast region 1984, chmn. subsect. health svcs. rsch. program com. 1985, mem. sr. rheumatology scholar award com. 1985, mem. ad hoc com. for rheumatologic tng. 1986, mem. subcom. on synovial fluid analyses cert. 1989, mem. subcom. on disease activity in systemic lupus eythematosus 1989, mem. allied health profl. assn. rsch. com. 1989-91, mem. com. health care rsch. 1990, mem. coun. rsch. 1992), Mass. Pub. Health Assn., New Eng. Rheumatism Soc., Can. Arthritis Soc. (mem. epidemiology health scis. panel 1990-92, chmn. 1992—), Arthritis Health Professions Assn., Soc. Rsch. and Edn. in Primary Care Internal Medicine, Heberden Soc., Ankylosing Spondylitis Assn. (mem. med. adv. bd. 1986—), Newton Choral Soc. (mem. adv. bd. 1983—), N.Am. Spine Soc. (mem. outcome com. 1991—). Office: Brigham Multipurpose Arthritis Ctr 75 Francis St Boston MA 02115-6195

LIAO, MEI-JUNE, biopharmaceutical company executive; came to U.S., 1974; BS, Nat. Tsing-Hua U. Taiwan, 1973; MPh, Yale U., 1977, PhD, 1980. Tchg. asst. Nat. Taiwan U., 1973-74, Temple U., Phila., 1974-75; tchg. asst. Yale U., New Haven, 1975-76, rsch. asst., 1976-79; postdoctoral assoc. MIT, Cambridge, 1980-83; sr. scientist Interferon Scis., Inc., New Brunswick, N.J., 1983-84; group leader Interferon Scis. Inc., New Brunswick, N.J., 1984-85, dir. cell biology, 1985-87; dir. R&D Interferon Scis., Inc., New Brunswick, N.J., 1987-94, v.p. rsch. & deve., 1995—. Contbr. articles to profl. jours.; inventor in field. Mem. Am. Soc. Biochemistry and Molecular Biology, Internat. Soc. Interferon and Cytokine Rsch., Soc. Chinese Bioscientists in Am. Office: Interferon Sci Inc 783 Jersey Ave New Brunswick NJ 08901-3605

LIAO, PAUL FOO-HUNG, communications research company executive, physicist; b. Phila., Nov. 10, 1944; s. Tseng Wu and Tung Mei (Lin) L.; m. Karen Ann Pravetz, Aug. 31, 1968; children: Teresa S., Joanna S. BS, MIT, 1966; PhD, Columbia U., 1973. Rsch. assoc. Columbia U., N.Y.C., 1972-73; mem. tech. staff Bell Labs., Holmdel, N.J., 1973-80, dept. head., 1980-83; div. mgr. Bell Communications Rsch., Red Bank, N.J., 1984-89, asst. v.p., 1989-93, gen. mgr., 1993—. Co-editor: Academic Press Quantum Electronics Book Series; contbr. over 75 articles to profl. jours.; holder over 12 patents in field. Fellow IEEE, Optical Soc. Am. (editor jour.), Am. Phys. Soc.; mem. Lasers and Electro Optic Soc. of IEEE (pres. 1987). Office: Bell Communications Rsch Rm 1A209A 331 Newman Springs Rd Red Bank NJ 07701-5657

LIAO, SHUTSUNG, biochemist; b. Tainan, Taiwan, Jan. 1, 1931; s. Chi-Chun Liao and Chin-Shen Lin; m. Shuching Liao, Mar. 19, 1960; children: Jane, Tzufen, Tzuming, May. BS in Agrl. Chemistry, Nat. Taiwan U., 1953, MS in Biochemistry, 1956; PhD in Biochemistry, U. Chgo., 1961. Rsch. assoc., 1960-63; asst. prof. U. Chgo., 1964-69; assoc. prof. dept. biochemistry Ben May Lab. Cancer Rsch., U. Chgo., 1969-71; prof. depts. biochemistry and cancer biology Ben May Inst., 1972—; cons. various nation and internat. confs., agys., founds., and workshops; bd. dirs. NiOptics Corp., TBS Inc. Mem. editorial bd. Jour. Steroid Biochemistry and Molecular Biology, The Prostate, and Receptors; assoc. editor Cancer Research, 1982-89; contbr. over 200 articles to profl jours. V.p. Chgo. Formosan Fed. Credit Union, 1977-79; trustee Taiwanese United Fund in U.S., 1981—; mem. adv. com. Taiwan-U.S. Cultural Exch. Ctr., 1984—. Recipient Sci-Tech. Achievement prize Taiwanese-Am. Found., 1983, Pfizer Lecture fellow award Clin. Rsch. Inst. Montreal, 1972, Gregory Pincus medal and award Worcester Found. for Exptl. Biology, 1992, Tzongming Tu award Formosan Med. Assn., 1993, C.H. Li Meml. Lecture award, 1994; NIH grantee, 1962—; Am. Cancer Soc. grantee, 1971-81. Mem. Am. Soc. Biochemistry and Molecular Biology, Am. Assn. Cancer Rsch., Endocrine Soc., N.Am.-Taiwanese Profs. Assn. (pres. 1980-81, exec. dir. 1981—), Academia Sinica. Achievements include discovery of androgen activation mechanism and androgen receptors; cloning and structural determination of androgen receptors and other novel nuclear receptors, and their genes, and receptor gene mutation in hereditary abnormalities and cancers; rsch. on regulation of hormone-dependent gene expression and cell growth on molecular bases and therapeutic agents for treatment of androgen-sensitive and insensitive abnormal growth and diseases. Home: 5632 S Woodlawn Ave Chicago IL 60637-1623 Office: U Chgo Ben May Inst 5841 S Maryland Ave Chicago IL 60637-1463

LIARD, JEAN-FRANCOIS, cardiovascular physiologist, researcher, educator; b. Pompaples, Vaud, Switzerland, Dec. 20, 1943; came to U.S., 1983; s. Heli Albert and Jeanne (Meystre) L.; m. Fanny Suzanne Klaiber, July 9, 1966; children: Monique Florence, Gisele Catherine. MD, U. Lausanne, Switzerland, 1968. Rsch. asst. Dept. Pharmacology, Lausanne, 1968-71; rsch. fellow dept. physiology Sch. Medicine, Jackson, Miss., 1971-73; rsch. fellow Cleve. Clinic, 1973-74; assoc. prof. INSERM U. Paris, 1974-77; prof. Inst. Rsch. Cardio-Angiology, Fribourg, Switzerland, 1977-83; prof. dept. physiology Med. Coll. Wis., Milw., 1983-93; dir. office scientific affairs Otsuka Am. Pharm., Rockville, Md., 1993—. Contbr. articles to Circulation Rsch., Am. Jour. Physiology. Recipient Marc Dufour award U. Lausanne, 1973, ann. award Swiss Soc. Cardiology, 1975, rsch. grant Swiss Nat. Sci. Found., 1977-83, NIH, 1983-93. Fellow High Blood Pressure Coun.; mem. Internat. Soc. Hypertension, Am. Physiol. Soc. Achievements include research on role of sodium excretion in reversal of renal hypertension, on models of cardiogenic hypertension in dogs, on role of renal innervation in spontaneously hypertensive rats, on role of vasopressin in cardiovascular control and cardiac output regulation, on extrarenal vasopressin V2 receptors, on the use of allosteric effectors of hemoglobin, on the clinical use of vaspressin antagonists. Office: Otsuka America Pharm 2440 Research Blvd Rockville MD 20850

LIBA, PETER MICHAEL, communications executive; b. Winnipeg, Man., Can., May 10, 1940; s. Theodore and Rose Liba; m. Shirley Ann Collett, May 4, 1963; children: Jennifer, Jeffrey, Christopher. Reporter, news editor The Daily Graphic, Portage la Prairie, Man., 1957-59; reporter The Winnipeg Tribune, 1959-67, city editor, 1967-68; ind. communications cons. Winnipeg, 1968-73; v.p. pub. affairs CanWest Broadcasting Ltd., Winnipeg, 1974-75, exec. v.p., 1979—; asst. gen. mgr. Sta. CKND-TV, Winnipeg, 1975-79, mgr., 1980-87, gen. mgr., 1987-92; pres., chief exec. officer Sta. CKND TV Inc./SaskWest Television Inc., Winnipeg, 1988-94; exec. v.p. CanWest Global Comm. Corp., Winnipeg, 1993—; bd. dirs. CanWest Comm. Corp., Winnipeg, Global Comm. Ltd., Toronto, CanWest Broadcasting Ltd., Winnipeg, CanWest TV Inc., Winnipeg, CanWest Prodns., Ltd. Winnipeg, CanWest Maritime TV Inc., Halifax, LaRed, Chile, TV 3 Network, New Zealand, Networ Ten, Australia. Trustee Transcona-Springfield Sch. div., Winnipeg, 1964-67; bd. dirs. Conv. Ctr. Corp., Winnipeg 1976-86, Atomic Energy of Can., Ltd., Ottawa, Ont., Can., 1981-86, St. Boniface Gen. Hosp., Winnipeg, 1987—, chmn. bd., 1992—. Recipient Presdl. Citation Variety Clubs Internat., 1983, Order of Can. Gov.-Gen. of Can., 1984, Internat. Media award Variety Clubs Internat., 1986, commemorative medal 125th anniversary Can., 1992, named Manitoban of Month Mid-Can. Commerce mag., 1982; designated Mem. of Can. by Gov.-Gen. of Can. Mem. Broadcasters Assn. Man. (pres. 1981-82), Western Assn. Broadcasters (pres. 1984-85, Broadcaster of Yr. award 1991, Broadcaster of Decade award 1994), Can. Assn. Broadcasters (chmn. bd. 1990-92), St. Charles Cluntry Club, Man. Club, Variety Club Man. (chief barker 1984-85). Office: CanWest Global Comm Corp, 31st Fl TD Centre, 201 Portage Ave, Winnipeg, MB Canada R3B 3L7

LIBASSI, FRANK PETER, lawyer, dean; b. N.Y.C., Apr. 20, 1930; s. Frank G. and Mary (Marino) L.; m. Mary Frances Steen, July 10, 1954; children: Thomas, Timothy, Jennifer. B.A. cum laude with honors in Polit. Sci, Colgate U., 1951; LL.B. Yale U., 1954. Bar: N.Y. 1955, Conn. 1960. Enforcement atty. N.Y. State Housing and Rent Commn., 1954-56; regional dir. N.Y. State Commn. on Human Rights, Albany, 1956-62; dep. staff dir. U.S. Commn. on Civil Rights, 1962-66; spl. asst. to sec., dir. office for civil rights HEW, Washington, 1966-68; exec. v.p. The Urban Coalition, Washington, 1968-71; v.v. Aita City Corp., Columbia, Md., 1971-72; pres., chief exec. officer Greater Hartford Process Inc. (Greater Hartford Community Devel. Corp.), 1971-77; gen. counsel HEW, Washington, 1977-79; partner firm Verner, Liipfert, Bernhard and McPherson, Washington, 1979-82; sr.

v.p. Travelers Corp., Hartford, Conn., 1982-93; of counsel Verner, Liipfert, Bernhard & McPherson, Washington, 1993—; dean Barney Sch. of Bus. and Pub. Adminstrn., U. Hartford, West Hartford, Conn., 1993—; bd. dirs. Forstmann Corp., 1994—; vis. lectr. Anderson Coll., chatham Coll., Goddard Coll., Ohio Wesleyan U., 1974-76; adj. faculty Grad. Sch. Bus. and Pub. Adminstrn. U. hartford, 1976-77; mem. Urban Land Inst., 1971-77; adv. bd. Bur. Nat. Affairs Housing and Cmty. Devel. Reporter, 1972-77. Author: The Negro in the Armed Forces, 1963, Family Housing and the Negro Serviceman, 1963, Equal Opportunity in Farm Programs, 1965, Revitalizing Central City Investment, 1977. Bd. dirs. legis. com. Am. Coun. Life Ins., 1987-90; bd. dirs., exec. com. Ins. Inst. of Hwy. Safety, 1984-88; mem. pub. relations policy com. Health Ins. Assn. Am., 1988-93; incorporator Inst. Living, 1973—, Hartford Hosp., 1973—, St. Francis Hosp., 1990—, Hartford Seminary, 1993-95; mem. adv. com. Dem. Nat. Com., 1974-77; chmn. Ct. Community Care, Inc., 1980-86; mem. Mt. Sinai Hosp., 1982-90; mem. com. on aging soc. Nat. Acad. Scis., 1982-86; mem. exec. com. Downtown Council Hartford, 1983-86, Greater Hartford Arts Council, 1985-86; chmn. Gov.'s Commn. on Financing Long Term Care, 1986-87; mem. nat. consumer adv. com. Am. Health Care Assn., 1985-86; mem. Sec. Bowen's Task Force on Long-term Health Care Policies of Health Care Financing Adminstrn., 1986-87; bd. dirs. Alliance for Aging Research, 1988-96; mem. Nat. Retirees Vol. Ctr., 1988-90; mem. Pew Commn. on future of health profls., 1990-93; mem. United Srs. Health Cooperative, 1990-91; mem. health adv. coun. Johns Hopkins U., 1990—, mem. com. predicting future diseases Inst. Medicine, 1991-93, bd. advisors Nat. Acad. on Aging, 1992-95; trustee Com. Pub. Expenditure Coun., 1991-95; mem. adv. com. on health care reform The Commonwealth Fund, 1993—; mem. Children's Fund of Conn., 1993—, Duncaster Cmty., 1993—. Recipient Superior Performance award U.S. Commn. on Civil Rights, 1963, Meritorious Svc. award, 1965; Sec.'s spl. citation, 1967; Disting. Svc. award HEW, 1968, Friend of La Casa de Puerto Rico, Hartford award, 1992; Woodrow Wilson sr. fellow, 1973-77. Mem. ABA, Fed. Bar Assn., N.Y. State Bar Assn., Conn. Bar Assn., Am. Assn. Retired Persons (nat. steering com. for new roles in soc. 1987-90), Greater Hartford C. of C. (bd. dirs. 1985-93, exec. com.). Club: Hartford. Home: 580 J Mountain Rd West Hartford CT 06117-1827 Office: Barney Sch Bus/Pub Adminstn U Hartford 200 Bloomfield Ave West Hartford CT 06117-1599

LIBBEY, ROBERT DAVID, television producer; b. Bangor, Maine, Feb. 28, 1962; s. Fred Harold and Alice Virginia (Keirstead) L.; m. Denise Marie O'Connel, Oct. 8, 1988. BA in Theatre and Broadcasting, U. Maine, 1984. Videographer Community Broadcasting Svc., Bangor, 1985-87; TV producer Maine Pub. Broadcasting Network, Bangor, 1987—; bd. dirs. Bangor Community Theatre, 1988—. Producer TV shows Painting in Maine, 1989-90, The Air We Breathe, 1990. Democrat. Avocations: tennis, dance, acting. Office: Maine Pub Broadcasting 65 Texas Ave Bangor ME 04401-4324

LIBBIN, ANNE EDNA, lawyer; b. Phila., Aug. 25, 1950; d. Edwin M. and Marianne (Herz) L.; m. Christopher J. Cannon, July 20, 1985; children: Abigail Libbin Cannon, Rebecca Libbin Cannon. AB, Radcliffe Coll., 1971; JD, Harvard U., 1975. Bar: Calif. 1975, U.S. Dist. Ct. (cen. dist.) Calif 1977, U.S. Dist. Ct. (no. dist.) Calif. 1979, U.S. Dist. Ct. (ea. dist.) Calif. 1985, U.S. Ct. Appeals (2d cir.) 1977, U.S. Ct. Appeals (5th cir.) 1982, U.S. Ct. Appeals (7th cir.) 1976, U.S. Ct. Appeals (9th cir.) 1976, U.S. Ct. Appeals (D.C. cir.) 1978. Appellate atty. NLRB, Washington, 1975-78; assoc. Pillsbury, Madison & Sutro, San Francisco, 1978-83, ptnr., 1984—; dir. Alumnae Resources, San Francisco. Mem. ABA (labor and employment sect.), State Bar Calif. (labor law sect.), Bar Assn. San Francisco (labor law sect.), Nat. Women's Health Network, No. Calif. Field Hockey Assn., Radcliffe Club (San Francisco). Office: Pillsbury Madison & Sutro 235 Montgomery St San Francisco CA 94104-2902

LIBBY, GARY RUSSELL, museum director; b. Boston, June 7, 1944; s. Charles W. and Sylvia P. L. B.A., U. Fla., 1967, M.A. (NDEA fellow 1967-71), 1968; M.A., Tulane U., 1972. Instr. English, Tulane U., 1968-71; asst. prof. Stetson U., Deland, Fla., 1972-77, vis. prof., 1977-86; dir. Mus. Arts and Scis., Daytona Beach, Fla., 1977—; reviewer Inst. Mus. Svcs., mem. panel Mus. Assessment Program; reviewer Accreditation Commn. of Am. Assn. of Mus. Editor Mus. mag.; Internat. Fine Art Collector mag., The Splendor of American Ceramic Art, Alexander Archipenko: Themes and Variations, A Treasury of Indian Miniature Painting, Form From Fire, 100 Years of Jewelry and Gems: The Levine Collection, 100 Years of Florida Painting: The Vickers Collection, Introduction; contbr. articles to profl. jours. Trustee Cuban Found.; mem. visual arts panel, youth and children's mus. panel, sci. mus. panel, A.D.A. statewide panel Fla. Arts Coun.; panelist Cultural Instns. Program; mem. hist. mus. grants panel Fla. Divsn. History. Mem. Am. Assn. Mus., Fla. Art Mus. Dirs. Assn., Fla. Mus. Assn. Home: 419 Jessamine Blvd Daytona Beach FL 32118-3740 Office: Mus of Arts & Scis 1040 Museum Blvd Daytona Beach FL 32114-4597

LIBBY, JOHN KELWAY, financial services company executive; b. Washington, June 13, 1926; s. John H.and Violet K. (Bamber) L.; m. Mary Seymour Kindel, Dec. 30, 1960; children: Carolyn K., Anne K., Virginia K. BA, Haverford Coll., 1945; postgrad., Harvard U., 1946. With U.S. Dept. State, Washington, 1947-48, Capital Airlines Inc., 1949-51, S.G. Warburg & Co., London, 1954; assoc. and v.p. Kuhn Loeb & Co., N.Y.C., 1955-66, gen. ptnr., 1967-77; mng. dir. Lehman Bros. Kuhn Loeb, Inc., N.Y.C., 1977-80, adv. dir., 1981-84; gen. ptnr. K.L. Assocs., N.Y.C., 1985—; adviser Cen. Bank Venezuela, 1974-75; bd. dirs. various corps. Trustee Brearley Sch., N.Y.C., 1977-85. Lt. USN, 1944-46, PTO, 1951-53. Office: K L Assocs 450 Park Ave New York NY 10022-2605

LIBBY, LAUREN DEAN, foundation president; b. Smith Center, Kans., Jan. 9, 1951; s. Dean L. and Elizabeth V. (Hansen) L.; m. June Ellen Hofer, Apr. 29, 1979; 1 child, Grant Lauren. BS in Agrl. Econs., Kans. State U., 1973; MBA, Regis U., 1988. Radio sta. employee, 1968-72; asst. program dir. info. br. Kans. State Extension Svc., Manhattan, 1969-73; economist Howard Houk Assocs., Chgo., 1973-75; asst. to pres. The Navigators, Colorado Springs, Colo., 1975-78, ministry devel. coord., 1979-86, dir. min. advancement, 1986-90, v.p., 1990—; pres. New Horizons Found., Colorado Springs, 1990—; bd. dirs. Navigators, Colorado Springs 1993—; founding bd. dirs. Sta. KTLF-FM/Ednl. Comms. of Colorado Springs, 1987—; cons. 6 listener-supported radio stas., 1989—. Contbr. articles to mags. Mem. Nat. Soc. Fundraising Execs. Avocation: amateur radio. Home: 6166 Del Paz Dr Colorado Springs CO 80918-3004 Office: The Navigators 3820 N 30th St Colorado Springs CO 80904-5001

LIBBY, PETER, cardiologist, medical researcher; b. Berkeley, Calif., Feb. 13, 1947; s. Henry and Vivian (Green) L.; m. Beryl Rica Benacerraf, Nov. 22, 1975; children: Oliver, Brigitte. BA, U. Calif., Berkeley, 1969; MD, U. Calif., San Diego, 1973. Diplomate Am. Bd. Internal Medicine and Cardiovascular Disease. Intern Peter Bent Brigham Hosp., Boston, 1973-74, resident, 1974-76; fellow Harvard Med. Sch., Boston, 1976-79, Brigham & Women's Hosp., Boston, 1979-80; asst. Prof. Tufts U. Sch. Sch. Medicine, Boston, 1980-86, assoc., 1986-90; asst. physician New Eng. Med. Ctr., Boston 1980-87, physician, 1987-90; dir. vascular medicine and atherosclerosis unit Brigham and Women's Hosp., Boston, 1990—, physician, 1990—; assoc. prof. medicine Harvard Med. Sch., Boston, 1990—; mem. ad hoc peer rev. com. NIH, Bethesda, Md., mem. pathology A study sect., 1988-92; mem. advisor W.W. Smith Charitable Trust, Phila., 1985-88; mem. peer rev. com. Am. Heart Assn., Mass., 1982-88, chmn., 1992-94, chmn. rsch. com., 1994—. Recipient Established Investigator award Am. Heart Assn., 1986-91; MERIT award Nat. Heart, Lung, Blood Inst., 1993—; S.A. Levine fellow Am. Heart Assn., Mass., 1976-77, Med. Found., Inc. fellow, Boston, 1980-82, fellow Council Arteriosclerosis, Am. Heart Assn. and Coun. on Circulation. Fellow Am. Coll. Cardiology; mem. Am. Soc. Clin. Investigation, Am. Physiological Soc., Am. Soc. Cell Biology. Home: 111 Perkins St Jamaica Plain MA 02130 Office: Brigham & Women's Hosp 221 Longwood Ave Boston MA 02115-5817

LIBBY, RONALD THEODORE, political science educator, consultant, researcher; b. L.A., Nov. 20, 1941; s. Theodore Harold and Patricia Mildred (Griswold) L.; m. Kathleen Christina Jacobson, June 3, 1972; children: Kathleen Elizabeth Libby, Erin Kristin Shoaf. BA, Wash. State U., 1965;

MA, U. Wash., 1966, PhD, 1975. Lectr. U. Bostwana, Lesotho and Swaziland, 1973-75, U. Malawi, Zomba, 1975-76, U. Zambia, Lusaka, 1976-79; asst. prof. U. Notre Dame, South Bend, Ind., 1981-83; sr. lectr. U. West Indies, Kingston, Jamaica, 1983-85; assoc. prof. Northwestern U., Evanston, Ill., 1985-86; sr. rsch. fellow Australian Nat. U., Darwin, 1986-87; sr. lectr. Victoria U., Wellington, New Zealand, 1987-89; prof. S.W. State U., Marshall, Minn., 1989—; treas New Zealand Polit. Sci. Assn., Wellington, 1988-89. Author: Towards an Africanized U.S. Policy for Southern Africa, 1980, The Politics of Economic Power in Southern Africa, 1987, Hawke's Law, 1989 (Choice award 1991), Protecting Markets: U.S. Policy and the World Grain Trade, 1992; contbr. articles to profl. jours. With U.S. Army, 1962-64. Rsch. grantee Carnegie Endowment, 1971. Mem. Am. Polit. Sci. Assn., Internat. Studies Assn., Australian Polit. Sci. Assn. Roman Catholic. Avocations: tennis, handball, piano, singing. Home: 100 Circle Dr Marshall MN 56258-2510 Office: SW State U Dept Polit Sci Marshall MN 56258 *Through the many travails of life the one abiding principle that has guided me is intellectual honesty and integrity.*

LIBCHABER, ALBERT JOSEPH, physics educator; b. Paris, Oct. 23, 1934; came to U.S., 1983; s. Charles and Cyrla (Markowska) L.; m. Irene Gelman, Sept. 11, 1955; children—Jacques, Remy, David. B.S., U. Paris, 1956; M.S., U. Ill., 1959; Ph.D., Ecole Normale Superieure, Paris, 1965. Matre de Recherche CNRS, Ecole Normale, Paris, 1967-74, dir. research, 1974-83; prof. physics U. Chgo., 1983-91, Paul Snowden Disting. Svc. prof., 1987—; prof Dept. Physics Princeton (N.J.) U., 1991—. Served as officer French Army, 1959-61. Recipient Wolf prize Wolf Found., Herzlia, Israel, 1986, MacArthur Found. Fellow, 1986-91. Fellow NEC Rsch. Inst. Princeton; mem. Am. Phys. Soc., French Phys. Soc. (Silver medal 1971, prix Ricard 1979), Am. Acad. Arts and Scis. Jewish. Home: 1640 E 50th St Chicago IL 60615-3161 Office: Princeton U Dept Physics PO Box 708 Princeton NJ 08544 Office: NEC Rsch Inst Inc 4 Independence Way Cranbury NJ 08512*

LIBEN, MICHAEL PAUL, magazine publisher; b. Lakewood, N.J., Sept. 6, 1954; s. Norman and Sylvia (Schneider) L.; m. Jo Ann Allison Krohn, July 13, 1986; children: Matthew Aaron, Hannah Rose. BS in Chemistry, SUNY, Buffalo, 1975. Catalog researcher Standard Motors Products, Inc., L.I. City, N.Y., 1976; free-lance photographer N.Y.C., 1977-78; photo editor Whizbang Publications, Inc., N.Y.C., 1978-79; prodn. mgr. Platinum Publications, Inc., N.Y.C., 1979-82; ptnr. Guitarchitect Enterprises, N.Y.C., 1982-83; publisher, v.p., gen. mgr. Sterling/Macfadden Partnership, N.Y.C., 1983-93; pres., CEO Emmelle Pub. Co., Millburn, N.J., 1993-94; v.p. MagazineCapital Divsn. Am. Factors Group, Princeton, N.J., 1994—. Avocations: pvt. pilot, audio electronics, tennis, handyman, photography. Office: Mag Capital Divsn Am Factors Group 457 N Harrison St Princeton NJ 08540

LIBERATI, MARIA THERESA, fashion production company executive; b. Phila., July 16, 1965; d. Edward Michael and Anna Maria (Santpolo) L. Student, Laval U., Que., Can., 1984; BS in Fgn. Lang. Edn., Temple U., 1986. Pres., bd. dirs. Sierra Ctr., Feasterville, Pa., 1988—; pres. M.T.L. Prodns., Phila., 1989—; spokesperson Compassion for Animals, Phila., 1988—. Author: Fashion, Fun and Fitness, 1989; editor mab. Better Nutrition for Today's Living, 1990—. Named Miss Pa., 1980, Miss World, 1982; recipient Merit award Actors & Artists Assn., Rome. Mem. AFTRA, NAFE (adv. bd. 1988—). Avocations: reading, cooking. Office: Sierra Ctr divsn MTL Prodns PO Box 322 Feasterville PA 19053

LIBERATORE, NICHOLAS ALFRED, business consultant; b. N.Y.C., June 19, 1916; s. Alexander and Angelina (Laspagnoletta) L.; m. Jean Talbot MacAdam, June 6, 1943 (div.); children: Virginia, George, Nicholas, Elliott, Mark; m. Marianne Westpalm van Hoorn Jewett, Feb. 10, 1973. B, NYU; M.A., Fairfield U. Vice pres. Ebasco Internat. Co., N.Y.C., 1956-58; pres. Raymond Concrete Pile Co. Am., N.Y.C., 1958-59; chmn. operating com. Brown-Raymond-Walsh, Madrid, Spain, 1959-62; v.p. Raymond Internat. Inc., N.Y.C., 1962-65; sr. v.p., pres. internat. Group Lone Star Industries, Inc., Greenwich, Conn., 1965-74; sr. v.p. Ebasco Services Inc., N.Y.C., 1974-77; exec. v.p. Genstar Ltd., San Francisco, 1977-83; cons. Royal Bank of Can., Toronto, 1983-90; bd. dirs. Internat. Mining Corp. Bd. dirs. Fgn. Trade Coun. Served to capt. C.E., AUS, 1943-46. Decorated Bronze Star medal, Army Commendation medal; Cross of Isabel the Catholic, (Spain). Mem. Internat. Coun. (conf. bd.), Brazilian-Am. C. of C. (founder), Pan Am. Soc. (pres.), Argentine-Am. C. of C. (pres.), Chile-U.S.C. of C. (pres.). St. Francis Yacht Club, Econ. Club N.Y., Bankers' Club San Francisco, Recess Club. Home: 4 Mayflower Ln Weston CT 06883-2632

LIBERMAN, ALEXANDER, artist, editor; b. Kiev, Russia, Sept. 4, 1912; came to U.S., 1941, naturalized, 1946; s. Simon and Henriette (Pascar) L.; m. Tatiana Yacovleff Du Plessix, Nov. 4, 1942 (dec. Apr. 1991); 1 stepdau., Francine Du Plessix Gray; m. Melinda Pechangco, Dec., 1992. Student in architecture, Ecole des Beaux Arts, Paris, 1930; DFA (hon.), R.I. Sch. Design, 1980. Art dir., mng. editor Vu Paris, 1931-36, Vogue mag., Conde Nast Publs., N.Y.C., 1941-43; art dir. Vogue mag., Conde Nast Publs., 1943-62; editorial dir. Conde Nast Publs., 1962-94; deputy chmn.-editorial Conde Nast Publs., 1994—. Exhibited photographs Mus. Modern Art, N.Y.C., 1959, retrospective painting and sculpture exhibit, Corcoran Gallery Art, Washington, 1970; sculptor works: Covenant, U. Pa., 1975, Symbol, Rockford, Ill., 1978, On High, New Haven, 1979, Windward, Miami, 1983, Stargazer, San Diego, 1983, Olympic Iliad, Seattle, 1984, Galaxy, Oklahoma City, 1984, Venture, Dallas, 1985, Beyond, Cleve., 1985, Aura, Palm Beach, 1986, Faith, Jerusalem, 1987, Ulysses, L.A., 1988, Vice-Versa-Korea I, Kyongju, 1991, Lightweb, N.Y., 1991; painting and sculpture in permanent collection Mus. Modern Art; author: The Artist in His Studio, 1960, 2nd edit., 1968, rev. and expanded edit., 1988, Greece, Gods and Art, 1968, Marlene: An Intimate Photographic Memoir, 1992, Campidoglio: Michelangelo's Roman Capitol, 1994. Decorated chevalier Legion of Honor, France; recipient Henry Johnson Fisher award, 1994, 95. Subject of book Alexander Liberman (Barbara Rose), 1981, Alex: The Life of Alexander Liberman (Dodie Kazanjian and Calvin Tomkins), 1993. Office: Conde Nast Publs Inc 350 Madison Ave New York NY 10017-3704 Gallery: Andre Emmerich 41 E 57th St New York NY 10022-1908

LIBERMAN, ALVIN MEYER, psychology educator; b. St. Joseph, Mo., May 10, 1917; s. Max and Lotte (Korbholz) L.; m. Isabelle Yoffe, June 1, 1941; children—Mark Yoffe, Michael Charles, Sarah Ivy. A.B., U. Mo., 1938, M.A., 1939; Ph.D., Yale U., 1942. Mem. faculty U. Conn., Storrs, 1949—, prof. psychology, 1950-87, Alumni Assn. Disting. prof., 1979—; adj. prof. linguistics Yale U., 1968-87; pres., dir. rsch. Haskins Labs., New Haven, 1975-86, sr. v.p., 1986—. Contbr. articles to profl. jours. Guggenheim fellow, 1964-65. Fellow Am. Acad. Arts and Scis.; mem. Nat. Acad. Scis., Soc. Exptl. Psychologists (Warren medal 1975), Acoustical Soc. Am., Am. Psychol. Assn. (Disting. Sci. Contbn. award 1980, F.O. Schmitt medal and prize in neuroscience 1988). Address: 614 Storrs Rd Mansfield Center CT 06250

LIBERMAN, GAIL JEANNE, editor; b. Neptune, N.J., Feb. 26, 1951; d. Si and Dorothy (Gold) L.; m. Alan Lavine, Dec. 20, 1991. BA, Rutgers U., 1972. Youth editor AP, N.Y.C., 1972-73; writer United Feature Syndicate, N.Y.C., 1973; reporter, broadcast editor UPI, Phila. and Hartford, Conn., 1973-75; reporter Courier-Post, Camden, N.J., 1976-80, Bank Advt. News, North Palm Beach, Fla., 1981-82; editor Bank Rate Monitor, North Palm Beach, 1982—. Author: Improving Your Credit and Reducing Your Debt, 1994.

LIBERMAN, IRA L., real estate broker; b. Richmond, Va., June 21, 1926; s. Morris Joseph and Dora (Sharove) L.; m. Frances Sour, Sept. 26, 1953; children—Barbara Janet, Lynn Dora, Leslie Ann. B.S., U. Va., 1949. With Richmond Tomato Repacking Co., Va., 1949; with Duke City Lumber Co., Inc., Albuquerque, 1949-85; pres., chmn., chief exec. officer Duke City Lumber Co., Inc., 1974-85; assoc. real estate broker Vaughan and Co., 1985-91, Berger Briggs Real Estate & Ins., Albuquerque, 1991—; nat. chmn. Western Wood Products Assn., 1985-86. Bd. dirs. Albuquerque Indsl. Devel., Albuquerque Symphony Orch., State Girl Scout Council. Served with USAF, 1944-46. Mem. Albuquerque Bd. Realtors, S.W. Pine Assn. (past pres.), Fed. Timber Purchasers Assn. (past pres.), Nat. Forest Products Assn. (dir.). Clubs: Four Hills Country, Crossroads Flying. Lodge: Masons.

Home: 2601 Schell Ct NE Albuquerque NM 87106-2532 Office: Berger Briggs Real Estate & Ins Inc 275 3rd St SW Albuquerque NM 87102-3311 also: PO Box 27754 Albuquerque NM 87125-7754

LIBERMAN, LEE MARVIN, utility executive; b. Salt Lake City, July 12, 1921; s. Benjamin L. and Sylvia (Goldfarb) L.; m. Jeanne Hirsch, Oct. 19, 1946; children: Alise, James, Celia; m. Ann Medler, Aug. 21, 1982. BSChemE, Yale U., 1942. Registered profl. engr., Mo. With Laclede Gas Co., St. Louis, 1945—, exec. v.p., 1968-70, pres., 1970-89, CEO, 1974-91, chmn., 1976-94, chmn. emeritus, 1994—, also bd. dirs.; bd. dirs. Boatmen's Bancshares, Angelica Corp., Falcon Products Co., Interco. Inc., D7 Industries, Instituform Mid-Am. Inc., CPI Corp. Mem. Civic Progress, Inc.; past pres. Family and Children's Svc. of St. Louis; past chmn. St. Louis Symphony Soc., Regional Commerce and Growth Assn.; vice chmn. bd. trustees Washington U.; chmn. campaign United Way, 1987; past chmn. bd. Jewish Hosp. With USAAF, 1944-45. Named St. Louis Man of Yr., 1986. Mem. NSPE. Office: Laclede Gas Co 720 Olive St Saint Louis MO 63101-2337

LIBERMAN, ROBERT PAUL, psychiatry educator, researcher, writer; b. Newark, Aug. 16, 1937; s. Harry and Gertrude (Galowitz) L.; m. Janet Marilyn Brown, Feb. 16, 1973; children: Peter, Sarah, Danica, Nathaniel, Annalisa. AB summa cum laude, Dartmouth Coll., 1959, diploma in medicine with honors, 1960; MS in Pharmacology, U. Calif.-San Francisco, 1961; MD, Johns Hopkins U., 1963. Diplomate Nat. Bd. Med. Examiners, Am. Bd. Psychiatry and Neurology. Intern Bronx (N.Y.) Mcpl. Hosp.-Einstein Coll. Medicine, 1963-64; resident in psychiatry Mass. Mental Health Ctr., Boston, 1964-68; postdoctoral fellow in social psychiatry Harvard U., 1966-68, teaching fellow in psychiatry, 1964-68; mem. faculty group psychotherapy tng. program Washington Sch. Psychiatry, 1968-70; with Nat. Ctr. Mental Health Svc., Tng. and Rsch., St. Elizabeths Hosp., also mem. NIMH Clin. and Rsch. Assocs. Tng. Program, Washington, 1968-70; asst. clin. prof. psychiatry UCLA, 1970-72, assoc. clin. prof., 1972-73, assoc. rsch. psychiatrist, 1973-76, rsch. prof. psychiatry, 1976-77, prof. psychiatry, 1977—; dir. Camarillo-UCLA Clin. Rsch. Unit, 1970—, UCLA Clin. Rsch. Ctr. Schizophrenia and Psychiat. Rehab., 1977—; chief Rehab. Medicine Svc., West L.A. VA Med. Ctr., Brentwood divsn., 1980-92; cons. div. mental health and behavioral scis. edn. Sepulveda (Calif.) VA Hosp., 1975-80; practice medicine specializing in psychiatry, Reston, Va., 1968-70, Thousand Oaks, Calif., 1977—; staff psychiatrist Ventura County Gen. Hosp.; mem. med. staff UCLA Neuropsychiatric Inst. and Hosp., Ventura Gen. Hosp., Camarillo State Hosp., West Los Angeles VA Med. Ctr.; dir. Rehab. Rsch. and Tng. Ctr. Mental Illness, 1980-85. Bd. dirs. Lake Sherwood Community Assn., 1978—, pres., 1979-81, 90-92, v.p., 1992-95; mem. Conejo Valley Citizens Adv. Bd., 1979-81. Served as surgeon USPHS, 1964-68. Recipient Noyes award for Rsch. in Schizophrenia, 1992, Kolb award in Schizophrenia, 1994. Research grantee NIMH, SSA, NIDA, VA, 1972—. Mem. Assn. Advancement Behavior Therapy (exec. com. 1970-72, dir. 1972-79), Am. Psychiat. Assn. (Hibbs and Van Ameringen awards), Assn. Clin. Psychosocial Research (exec. com. 1985—), Phi Beta Kappa. Author: (with King, DeRisi and McCann) Personal Effectiveness: Guiding People to Assert Their Feelings and Improve Their Social Skills, 1975; A Guide to Behavioral Analysis and Therapy, 1972; (with Wheeler, DeVisser, Kuehnel and Kuehnel) Handbook of Marital Therapy: An Educational Approach to Treating Troubled Relationships, 1980, Psychiatric Rehabilitation of Chronic Mental Patients, 1987, (with De Risi and Mueser) Social Skills Training for Psychiatric Patients, 1989, (with Kuehnel, Rose and Storzbach) Resource Book for Psychiatric Rehabilitation, 1990, (with Yager) Handbook of Psychiatric Rehabilitation, 1992, Stress in Psychiatric Disorders, 1993, (with Corrigan) Behavior Therapy in Psychiatric Hospitals, 1994; mem. editorial bd. Jour. Applied Behavior Analysis, 1972-78, Jour. Marriage and Family Counseling, 1974-78, Jour. Behavior Therapy and Exptl. Psychiatry, 1975—, Behavior Therapy, 1979-84, Assessment and Invervention in Devel. Disabilities, 1980-85; assoc. editor Jour. Applied Behavior Analysis, 1976-78, Schizophrenia Bull., 1981-87; Internat. Rev. Jour. Psychiatry, 1988—, Psychiatry, 1993—; contbr. over 300 articles to profl. jours., chpts. to books. Home: 528 Lake Sherwood Dr Thousand Oaks CA 91361 Office: Cmty & Rehab W LA Psychiatry VA Med Ctr 116 AR 11301 Wilshire Blvd Los Angeles CA 90073

LIBERT, DONALD JOSEPH, lawyer; b. Sioux Falls, S.D., Mar. 23, 1928; s. Bernard Joseph and Eleanor Monica (Sutton) L.; m. Jo Anne Murray, May 16, 1953; children: Cathleen, Thomas, Kevin, Richard, Stephanie. B.S. magna cum laude in Social Scis., Georgetown U., 1950, LL.B., 1956. Bar: Ohio. From assoc. to ptnr. Manchester, Bennett, Powers & Ullman, Youngstown, Ohio, 1956-65; various positions to v.p., gen. counsel and sec. Youngstown Sheet & Tube Co., 1965-78; assoc. group counsel LTV Corp., Youngstown and Pitts., 1979; v.p. and gen. counsel Anchor Hocking Corp., Lancaster, Ohio, 1979-87. Served to lt. (j.g.) USN, 1951-54. Mem. Ohio Bar Assn. (chmn. sr. lawyers com.), Columbus Bar Assn., Fairfield County Bar Assn., Lancaster Country Club, Rotary. Republican. Roman Catholic. Office: 127 W Wheeling St Lancaster OH 43130-3737

LIBERTI, PAUL ALFONSO, biotechnology executive, inventor, entrepreneur, consultant; b. Lyndhurst, N.J., Mar. 18, 1936; s. Paul Frank and Rose (Pollara) L.; m. Rae Francis, July 1, 1961; children: Paul P., Theodore L. Roseanne, Joseph F. AB, Columbia U., 1959; postgrad., Loyola U., Chgo., 1959-61; PhD, Stevens Inst. Tech., Hoboken, N.J., 1966. Prof. biotechnology, immunology Jefferson Med. Coll., Phila., 1968-83, adj. prof., 1984—; pres., founder Immunochem. Assocs., 1981—; pres., founder Immunicon Corp., Huntingdon Valley, Pa., 1984-91, dir. R & D, 1991—; vis. scientist Inst. for Med. Rsch., London, 1976-77; mem. adv. bd. Ben Franklin Partnership; mem. study sect. NIH/NSF U.S. Army Breast Cancer Program. Mem. adv. bd. Jour. Immunology, Molecular Immunology; contbr. more than 60 articles to profl. jours. Founder, speaker Anti-Drug Program, Bucks County, Pa., 1981-83. Recipient Rsch. Career award NIH, 1971-77. Mem. Am. Assn. Immunologists, Am. Soc. Hematologists, Internat. Soc. Hematopoetic Graft Engring. Achievements include 16 patents for biotechnology, which include high gradient magnetic separation technology and biocompatible magnetic liquids and their use as contrast agents for magnetic resonance imaging liver tumor agent, blood pool agent, automated immunoassays, in purging bone marrow of tumor cells (oncology therapy), in the analysis of rare cells for diagnostic purposes (genetic disorders, viral insertions circulating tumor cells); discovery of Immunoglobulin and Clq structure and function, of antigenicity of polypeptides. Home: 1503 Grasshopper Rd Huntingdon Valley PA 19006-5807 Office: Immunicon Corp 1310 Masons Mill Business Park Huntingdon Valley PA 19006-3515

LIBERTO, JOSEPH SALVATORE, banker; b. Balt., Apr. 26, 1929; s. Cosimo and Anna (Serio) L.; m. Mary Jane Colandro, May 20, 1962; children—Joseph G. Grace Ann. Student, Balt. City Coll., 1945-47; certificate accounting, Balt. Coll. Commerce, 1949; grad., Nat. Assn. Bank Auditors, and Comptrollers Sch. Banking, U. Wis., 1968. With Signet Bank, Md., Balt., 1954—; auditor Union Trust Co. Md., 1963—, asst. v.p., security officer, 1979—. Served with AUS, 1951-53, Japan. Mem. Bank Adminstrn. Inst. (past Balt. 1968—), Inst. Internal Auditors. Home: 5609 Biddison Ave Baltimore MD 21206-3442 Office: Signet Bank Baltimore St Baltimore MD 21202-1603

LIBIN, JEROME B., lawyer; b. Chgo., Oct. 27, 1936; s. Mitchell and Charlotte Libin; m. June Austin, Apr. 12, 1965; 1 child, Nancy Crawford. B.S., Northwestern U., 1956; J.D., U. Mich., 1959. Bar: D.C. 1961, Ill. 1961. Law clk. U.S. Supreme Ct. Justice Charles E. Whittaker, 1959-60; assoc. Sutherland, Asbill & Brennan, Washington, 1961-66, ptnr., 1966—; professorial lectr. in law George Washington U. 1974-80; cons. Am. Law Inst. Internat. Tax Study Project 1982-86. Contbr. articles to profl. jours. Mem. D.C. Tax Revision Commn., 1976-78; mem. Mayor's Revenue Policy Com., 1980-82; counsel Lawyers' Com. for Civil Rights Under Law, 1980—; mem. com. Visitors U. Mich. Law Sch.; trustee Fed. City Coun. and Greater Washington Rsch. Ctr. Served with USAFR. Fellow Am. Coll. Tax Counsel, Am. Bar Found.; mem. ABA (coun., Tax sec.), J. Edgar Murdock Am. Inn of Ct. (master of the bench), D.C. Bar Assn. (chmn. taxation div. 1975-77), Am. Law Inst., Internat. Fiscal Assn. (v.p. U.S. br.). Home: 3022 P St NW Washington DC 20007-3052 Office: Sutherland Asbill & Brennan 1275 Pennsylvania Ave NW Washington DC 20004-2404

LIBIN, PAUL, theatre executive, producer; b. Chgo., Dec. 12, 1930; m. Florence Rowe, Sept. 25, 1956; children: Charles, Claire, Andrea. Student, U. Ill.; B.F.A., Columbia U., 1956. Producing dir., v.p. Jujamcyn Theatres, N.Y.C., 1990—. Producer (plays) including The Crucible, 1958, Six Characters in Search of an Author, 1963, Royal Hunt of the Sun, 1965, Circle in the Sq. Theatre, N.Y.C., 1965-90; co-producer (plays) Uncle Vanya, 1973, The Iceman Cometh, 1973, Death of a Salesman, 1975, The Lady from the Sea, 1976, The Night of the Iguana, 1976, The Club, 1976, Tartuffe, 1977, The Inspector General, Man and Superman, Spokesong, Loose Ends, 1978, Major Barbara, Past Tense, The Man Who Came to Dinner, 1979, The Bacchae, John Gabriel Borkman, The Father, Scenes and Revelations, 1980, Candida, Macbeth, Eminent Domain, 1981, Present Laughter, The Queen and the Rebels, The Misanthrope, 1982, The Caine Mutiny Court-Martial, Heartbreak House, Awake and Sing, 1983, Design for Living, 1984, Arms and the Man, Marriage of Figaro, 1985, You Never Can Tell, 1986, Coastal Disturbances, 1987, A Streetcar Named Desire, Juno and the Paycock, 1988, The Night of the Iguana, 1988, The Devil's Disciple, 1988, Ghetto, 1989, Sweeney Todd, 1989, Zoya's Apartment, 1990, The Miser, 1990; producing dir. plays I Hate Hamlet, 1991, Secret Garden, 1991, La Bete, 1991, Two Trains Running, 1992, Jelly's Last Jam, 1992, Tommy, 1993, Angels in America, 1993, My Fair Lady, 1993, Grease, 1994. Served with U.S. Army, 1953-55. Recipient Obie award The Club, Village Voice, 1977, Tony award, 1976. Mem. 2d League Off Broadway Theatres and Producers (pres. emeritus), 1st League Am. Theatres and Producers (officer, exec. com., bd. govs.). Office: Jujamcyn Theatres St James Theatre 246 W 44th St New York NY 10036-3971 also: Circle in the Sq Theatre 1633 Broadway New York NY 10019-6708

LIBMAN, STEVEN BRADLEY, performing arts administrator; b. Providence, Oct. 5, 1959; s. Herman and Marilyn Kayla (Zettel) L.; m. Keitha Ann Grace, Aug. 17, 1980; 1 child, Tracy. B.A. magna cum laude, R.I. Coll., 1980; Asst. mng. dir. R.I. Coll., Providence, 1978-80; box office mgr. Trinity Sq. Repertory Co., Providence, 1980-81; mng. dir. Auburn Civic Theatre, N.Y., 1981-83, Fulton Opera House, Lancaster, Pa., 1983-86; devel. dir. Pitts. Ballet Theatre, 1987-91, exec. dir., 1991—; guest lectr. Non-Profit Mgmt. U., Pitts. Trustee Citizens for Arts in Pa., Harrisburg, 1984—; Regent Theatre, 1993—, Dance/USA, 1994—; mem. theatre panel Pa. Council on the Arts, 1986-88; mem. adv. com. arts mgmt. program Carnegie Mellon U., Pitts., 1993— . Recipient Theatre Mgmt. award R.I. Coll., 1979. Mem. Am. Council for Arts, Theatre Comm. Group. Avocation. Home: 716 Kewanna Ave Pittsburgh PA 15234 Office: Pitts Ballet Theatre 2900 Liberty Ave Pittsburgh PA 15201

LIBOFF, RICHARD LAWRENCE, physicist, educator; b. N.Y.C., Dec. 30, 1931; s. William and Sarah (Mell) L.; m. Myra Blatt, July 4, 1954; children: David, Lisa. A.B., Bklyn. Coll., 1953; Ph.D., NYU, 1961. Asst. prof. physics NYU, 1961-63; prof. applied physics, applied math. and elec. engring. Cornell U., 1964—; prin. investigator Air Force Office Sci. Research, 1978-83, Army Research Office, 1984—; cons. Batelle Columbus Lab. Author: Introduction to the Theory of Kinetic Equations, 1969, 79, Russian edit., 1974, Introductory Quantum Mechanics, 1980, 2d edit., 1991, Korean edit., 1993, Waveguides, Transmission Lines and Smith Charts, 1984, Kinetic Theory: Classical, Quantum and Relativistic Descriptions, 1990. Served with Chem. Corps U.S. Army, 1953-55. Recipient Founders Day cert. N.Y. U., 1961; Solvay fellow, 1972; Fulbright scholar, 1984. Fellow Am. Phys. Soc.; mem. IEEE (sr.), Sigma Xi. Office: Cornell U Phillips Hall Ithaca NY 14853

LIBONATI, MICHAEL ERNEST, lawyer, educator, writer; b. Chgo., May 25, 1944; s. Roland V. and Jeannette K. (van Hanxleden) L.; m. Yvonne M. Barber, Sept. 30, 1967; children: Michael, Emma. LLB, Yale U., 1967, LLM, 1969. Bar: D.C. 1968, Ill. 1975, Pa. 1976. Prof. law Temple U., Phila., 1972-90, Carnell prof. law, 1990—; cons. U.S. Adv. Commn. Intergovernmental Rels.; vis. prof. law U. Ala., Tuscaloosa, summer 1976, Cornell U., Ithaca, N.Y., spring 1977, Coll. William and Mary, Williamsburg, Va., fall 1987. Author: (with Sands and Martinez) Local Government Law, 4 vols., 1981-82, (with Hetzel and Williams) Legislative Law and Process, 2d edit., 1993, Local Government Autonomy, 1993; asst. editor articles Am. Jour. Legal History, 1971-82. Recipient Williams prize for Excellence in Teaching, 1985, 90; named Hon. Editor Temple U. Law Quarterly, vol. 59, 1986. Mem. NAS (nat. rsch. bd., highway law project adv. commn.), ABA (coun. urban state and local govt. law sect. 1979-83), Am. Law Inst., Nat. Assn. Atty's Gen. (state constitution law project adv. bd.). Office: Temple U Sch Law 1719 N Broad St Philadelphia PA 19122-2504

LIBOUS, THOMAS WILLIAM, state senator; b. Binghamton, N.Y., Apr. 16, 1953; s. William Abraham and Kathrine (Haddad) L.; m. Frances Pianella, Sept. 27, 1975; children: Matthew, Nicholas. AAS in Mktg., Broome Community Coll., 1973; BS in Mktg. and Fin., SUNY, Utica, 1975. Dir. mktg. Chase Lincoln First Bank, Binghamton, 1975-83; v.p. mktg. Johnson City Pub. Co., Binghamton, 1983-88; senator N.Y. State Legislature, Albany, 1989—. Minority leader Binghamton City Coun., 1985-88; pres. N.Y. State Assn. City Counc., 1988; chmn. Binghamton City Rep. Com., 1980-87, vice chmn. Broome County Rep. Com., 1987-88; mem. Broome County chpt. ARC. Named Outstanding Rgional Pres. Binghamton JayCees, 1977. Mem. Rotary, Sons of Italy, KC. Republican. Roman Catholic. Office: 1607 State Office Bldg 44 Hawley St Binghamton NY 13901-3315

LIBOVE, CHARLES, mechanical and aerospace engineering educator; b. N.Y.C., Nov. 7, 1923; s. Meyer and Anna (Steinberg) L.; m. Rosa Greenspan, July 12, 1951; children: Joel, Fred. BCE, CCNY, 1944; M in Applied Mechanics, U. Va., 1952; PhD in ME, Syracuse (N.Y.) U., 1962. Aero. rsch. scientist Nat. Adv. Com. for Aeronautics, Hampton, Va., 1944-53; assoc. prof. aero. engring. Tri-State Coll., Angola, Ind., 1955-58; applied mathematician Brush Labs. Co., Cleve., 1953-55; from instr. to prof. mech. and aerospace engring. Syracuse U., 1958—; pvt. practice cons., Syracuse, 1958—. Contbr. numerous articles to profl. jours. Recipient Outstanding Tchr. awards Syracuse U., 1967-89, numerous grants. Fellow ASME, AIAA (assoc. fellow); mem. ASCE, AAUP, Am. Acad. Mechs., Structural Stability Rsch. Coun. (mem.-at-large). Home: 209 Locksley Rd Syracuse NY 13224-1826 Office: Syracuse U Dept Mech Aerospace and Mfg Engring Syracuse NY 13244

LIBRIZZI, ROSE MARIE MEOLA, library administrator, counselor; b. Newark, Apr. 15, 1940; d. Salvatore J. and Marie (Consoli) Meola; m. Vincent F. LiBrizzi, June 25, 1965 (div. 1983); children: Vincent, Steve. BA in History and Pre-law magna cum laude, Bloomfield (N.J.) Coll., 1965; MLS, Rutgers U., 1967; JD, Seton Hall U., 1989; MA in Counseling, MontclairState U., 1992. Cert. tchr., N.J.; cert. sch. libr.; profl libr. cert. Acting children's libr. Newark Pub. Libr., 1965-66; head children's svcs. Belleville (N.J.) Pub. Libr., 1966-68; asst. dir. Kearny (N.J.) Pub. Libr., 1969; mem. adj. faculty Kean Coll., Union, N.J., 1969-73; supr. children's svcs. Jersey City Pub. Libr., 1973-87, asst. dir., 1987-90, 91-, dir. 1990-91. Mem. ABA, ALA, N.J. Libr. Assn. (v.p. 1988, mem.-at-large 1982, sec. 1981, pres. and founder administr. sect. 1978, chairperson pers. administrn. com., chairperson resolutions, nominations and honor and awards coms., chairperson NJLA Centennial Celebration com. 1984-89, Administrn. section award), Hudson County Libr. Dirs. Assn. (pres. 1990—), Exxex-Hudson Region Exec. Bd. (mem-at-large, sec. 1990—, chairperson continuing edn. com. 1986-88), Rutgers Alumni Assn. (pres., senator, mem. alumni fedn. bd. 1990—). Home: 5 Squier Ct Livingston NJ 07039 Office: Jersey City Pub Libr 472 Jersey Ave Jersey City NJ 07302-3499

LIBURD, ALMANDO LEANDO, senator; b. Cruz Bay, St. John, V.I., Jan. 12, 1953; s. Hugo O. and Catherine M. Liburd; m. Faye Liburd, Oct. 31, 1985; 1 child, Alana. BA in Spanish, Inter-Am. U., Hato Rey, P.R., 1978, postgrad.; postgrad., U. V.I. Tchr. Dept. Edn., St. Thomas, V.I., 1974-90; senator V.I. Legislature, St. John, Thomas, 1991—. V.p. Coral Bay Community Orgn., St. John, 1987-90; bd. dirs. representing St. John, Pvt. Industry Coun., 1979-84. Mem. Ind. Citizens Movement Party. Office: VI Legislature PO Box 1690 Saint Thomas VI 08801

LICARI, JOSEPH, real estate company executive. With Helmsley Enterprises Inc., N.Y.C., 1965-71, sr. v.p. 1971—. Office: Helmsley Enterprises Inc 60 E 42nd St Fl 53 New York NY 10165-0001

LICATA, ARTHUR FRANK, lawyer; b. N.Y.C., June 16, 1947; s. Arthur A. and Anne Licata. BA in English, Le Moyne Coll., 1969; postgrad., SUNY, Binghampton, 1969-71; JD cum laude, Suffolk U., 1976. Bar: Mass. 1977, U.S. Ct. Appeals (1st cir.) 1977, N.Y. 1985; cert. Nat. Bd. Trial Advocacy. Assoc. Parker, Coulter, Daley & White, Boston, 1977-82; pvt. practice Arthur F. Licata P.C., Boston, 1982—; prin. Ardcon Internat. Import-Export Co.; lectr. Mass. Continuing Legal Edn., Boston, 1982-90, mem. faculty, legal seminars, 1984—, adv. com., 1985-88; mem. working group on drinking and drunk driving Harvard Sch. Pub. Health Ctr. for Health Communications, 1986; speaker conv. Nat. Fedn. Paralegal Assns., Boston, 1987; del. U.S.-China Joint Session on Trade, Investment and Econ. Law, Beijing, 1987; co-sponsor Estonian legal delegation visit to Mass., N.H. correctional instns., 1990; Boston host former Soviet legal delegation visit, 1989; U.S. legal advisor Czech-Anglo American Bus. Inst., Prague, Czech Republic, 1990—, Russian Children's Fund, 1992-94, Estonia Acad. for Pub. Safety, 1990—; del. White House conf. on trade and investment in ctrl. and ea. Europe, Cleve., 1995. Panel mem. sta. WBZ TV, Boston; contbr. articles to profl. jours. U.S. Del. 6th People to People Juvenile Justice Del. to USSR, 1989; mem. state coordinating com. MADD, Mass., 1984-86, legal advisor Plymouth County (Mass.) chpt., 1984-87; mem. State Adv. Com. Med. Malpractice, Boston, 1985; bd. dirs. Boston Ctr. for the Arts, 1990-94; mem. profl. adv. bd. Mass. Epilepsy Assn., 1986-94; registrant seminar sponsored by Czechoslovakian TV in Prague Mass Media and the Electorial Process, 1991; judge N.E. Regional Jessup Competition, 1992; mem. internat. adv. group Legal Resource Ctr. Ford Found., Prague, Czech Republic, 1994—. Recipient Outstanding Citizen award Mothers Against Drunk Driving, 1986. Fellow Mass. Bar Found.; mem. ABA, Mass. Bar Assn. (bd. dirs. young lawyers sect. 1979-80, 21st Century Club 1984), Assn. Trial Lawyers Am. (diplomat), Nat. Bd. Trial Advocacy (cert. 1992—), Mass. Acad. Trial Attys. (mem. faculty, legal seminars, bd. govs. 1990—). Avocation: travel, reading. Office: Ste 1010 20 Custom House St Boston MA 02110-3526

LICH, GLEN ERNST, regional studies educator, ethnographer, government consultant, writer; b. Fredericksburg, Tex., Nov. 5, 1948; s. Ernst Perry and Thelma Olive (Woolfley) L.; m. Lera Patrick Tyler, Sept. 5, 1970; children: James Ernst Lich-Tyler, Stephen Woolfley Lich-Tyler, Elizabeth Erin Lich-Tyler. Student, U. Vienna, Austria, 1969-70; BA, Southwestern U., 1971; MA, U. Tex., 1976; MA, S.W. Tex. State U., 1978; PhD, Tex. Christian U., 1984; grad., U.S. Army Command and Gen. Staff Coll., 1984. Instr. U. New Orleans, 1979-80; asst. prof. Schreiner Coll., 1980-87; assoc. prof. and dir. regional studies Baylor U., 1987-90; prof. and chair U. of Winnipeg, 1990-93; exec. dir. Hill Country Inst., 1992—; dir. World Heritage Tours, 1978—; adj. faculty U.S. Army Command and Gen. Staff Coll., 1987—; vis. fellow Yale U., 1987, German Fgn. Ministry, 1983; rsch. fellow Mosher Inst. Internat. Policy Studies, Tex. A & M U., 1988-93; sr. rsch. fellow Ctr. Socioeconomic Rsch. U. Coahuila, Mexico, 1990—; coord. Standing Conf. Ethnic Chairs and Professorships in Can., 1991-92; cons. in field. Author: The German Texans, 1981, The Humanities and Public Issues, 1990, Fred Gipson at Work, 1990, The Women of Viscri, 1995; editor: (with Dona Reeves-Marquardt) Retrospect and Retrieval: The German Element in Review: Essays on Cultural Preservation, 1978, German Culture in Texas: A Free Earth, 1980, The Cabin Book, 1985, (with Dona Reeves-Marquardt) Texas Country: The Changing Rural Scene, 1986, (with Joseph A. McKinney) Region North America: Canada, United States, Mexico, 1990, Regional Studies: The Interplay of Land and People, 1992; assoc. editor Jour. German-Am. Studies, 1977-80, Yearbook of German-Am. Studies, 1981-93; editor: Jour. Am. Studies Assn. Tex., 1988-90; contbr. articles to profl. publs. Served with U.S. Army, 1972-75, lt. col USAR, 1985—; asst. attache to Portugal, 1987-92, asst. attache to Germany, 1992-94; chief mil. liaison mission U.S. Embassy, Bucharest, Romania, 1993, Ljubljana, Slovenia, 1993-94; dir. internat. programs Adj. Gen.'s Dept. of State of Tex., 1994—. NEH rsch. grantee, 1978, 86-87; Fed. Republic Germany, 1983, 87; Swiss Humanities Acad., 1988; Tex. Com. Humanities, 1988, 89; Am. Coun. of Learned Socs., 1988; Embassy of Can., 1988; Max Kade Found., 1989-92; Joint Econ. Com. of U.S. Congress, 1989-91; Ministry of Multiculturalism and Citizenship of Can., 1991-92; Soc. Scis. and Humanities Rsch. Coun. Can., 1991-92; Mem. MLA, Am. Studies Assn., Assn. Am. Geographers, Am. Folklore Assn., Am. Assn. Tchrs. German, Nat. Coun. Tchrs. English, Soc. for Romanian Studies, Assn. for Can. Studies in U. S., Can. Ethnic Studies Assn., Oral History Assn., Tex. Folklore Soc., Tex. State Hist. Assn., German Studies Assn., Pi Kappa Alpha. Office: Hill Country Inst PO Box 1850 Kerrville TX 78029-1850

LICHT, PAUL, zoologist, educator; b. St. Louis, Mar. 12, 1938; s. Harry and Betty L.; m. Barbara Margaret Morrison, June 30, 1963; children: Andrew Stephen, Rachael Margaret, Carolyn Ann. BA, Washington U., St. Louis, 1959; PhD, U. Mich., 1964. Asst. prof. zoology U. Calif., Berkeley, 1964-68; asso. prof. U. Calif., 1968-72, prof., 1972—, chmn. dept. zoology 1977-82; dean divsn. biol. scis. U. Calif., Berkeley, 1994—. Numerous publs. in field, 1961—; editor McGraw Hill Book Series, 1976-78; mem. editorial bds. Gen. Comparative Endocrinology, 1978—, Jour. Exptl. Zoology, 1990—; author/owner microcomputer bibliographic programm REFMENU. Recipient Grace Pickford medal Soc. Comparative Endocrinology, 1980. Fellow AAAS, Calif. Acad. Sci.; mem. Am. Soc. Zoology (chmn. divsn. comparative endocrinology 1992-93). Office: U Calif Dept Zoology Berkeley CA 94720

LICHT, RICHARD A., lawyer; b. Providence, Mar. 25, 1948; s. Julius M. Licht and Irene (Lash) Olson; m. Roanne Sragow; children: Jordan David, Jeremy Michael, Jaclyn Rose. AB cum laude, Harvard U., 1968, JD cum laude, 1972; LLM in Taxation, Boston U., 1975. Law clk. to chief justice R.I. Supreme Ct., Providence, 1973-74; ptnr. Letts, Quinn & Licht, Providence, 1974-84; mem. R.I. Senate, Providence, 1975-84, chmn. judiciary com. and rules com., 1984; lt. gov. State of R.I., Providence, 1985-89; ptnr. Licht & Semonoff, Providence, 1989—; former chmn. R.I. Commn. on Racial, Religious and Ethnic Harrassment, Dr. Martin Luther King Jr. Holiday Commn., State Energy and Tech. Study Commn. rules com.; chmn. Coun. of State Govt., Intergovtl. Affairs Com., Nat. Focus Team, Bd. Gov. Higher Edn.; bd. regents Elem. and Secondary Edn.; mem. Pub. Telecom. Authority R.I., Univ. R.I. Found., Community Coll. R.I. Found. Bd. dirs. Roger Williams Hosp.; advisor Community Prep. Sch.; corporator Roger Williams Hosp.; trustee Save the Bay, Inc., Emma Pendleton Bradley Hosp.; bd. dirs. Temple Emanuel, Providence, Jewish Fedn. R.I., Samaritans; chmn. Small Bus. Adv. Council, Task Force on Teenage Suicide Prevention, CD Civil Preparedness Adv. Council, Urban League R.I. 1980-82, John Hope Settlement House, 1976-81; chair Am. Cancer Soc. Ball, 1989, Jewish Fedn. R.I. Passage to Freedom, 1989; chair R.I. chpt. Anti-Defamation League; mem. Meeting St. Sch. steering com. for capital fund drive, 1989-92; mem. Women and Infants Corp., Dorcas Place, PARI, UNITAM, NCLG task force of Youth Suicide Prevention, Jewish Home for the Aged of R.I., bd. govs. for the handicapped; active YWCA of Greater R.I., Vols. in Action, Inc., Big Sister Assn. of R.I., Big Bros. R.I.; coordinator vols. gubernatorial campaigns Frank Licht, 1968, 70; active Jewish Community Ctr., Providence, 1975-83, E. Side Sr. Citizens Ctr., 1975-76, R.I. Youth Guidance Ctr., Inc., 1987, Block Island Conservancy, Inc., Notre Dame Health Care Corp., 1987; Dem. candidate for U.S. Senate, 1988; ann. campaign chair Meeting St. Sch., 1990-91. Named an Outstanding Young Man of R.I., R.I. Jaycees, 1979; recipient David Ben Gurion award State of Israel Bonds, 1977, Outstanding Pub. Service award Temple Torat Yisrael, 1985, Disting. Services to the Hispanic Community award Casa Puerto Rico, 1985, Hon. Pub. Service award Meeting St. Sch., 1986, Recognition award R.I. Day Care Dirs. Assn., 1986, award of Appreciation Child Care/Human Services, 1986, Govtl. services award Ocean State Residences for the Retarded, 1987. Mem. R.I. Bar Assn., Corp. Womens' and Infants' Hosp., Corp. Roger Williams Hosp., Vols. in Action, Inc. Democrat. Office: Licht & Semonoff One Park Row Providence RI 02903

LICHTBLAU, JOHN H., economist; b. Vienna, Austria, June 26, 1921; came to U.S., 1939; s. Ernst and Alice (Fischer) Lichtblau-Lind; m. Charlotte M. Adelberg, Apr. 12, 1944; 1 child, Claudia L. Payne. B in Social Sci., CCNY, 1949; postgrad., NYU, 1950-53. Economist U.S. Dept. Labor, Washington, 1951-53, Conf. Bd., N.Y.C., 1953-54, Walter J. Levy Assocs., N.Y.C., 1955-56; research dir. Petroleum Ind. Research Found. Inc., N.Y.C., 1956-61, exec. dir., 1961-72, pres., 1972—; chmn. Petroleum Ind. Research Assocs. Inc., N.Y.C., 1977—; bd. dirs. Snyder Oil Co., Ft. Worth. Mem. editorial bd. Energy Policy (London), 1987—; contbr. articles to profl. jours., book chpts. Served with U.S. Army, 1944-47, ETO. Mem. Am. Petroleum Inst., Nat. Petroleum Council, Am. Econ. Assn., Internat. Assn. Energy Economists (5th Ann. award for outstanding contbns. 1986), Council on Fgn. Relations. Office: Petroleum Industry Rsch Found 122 E 42nd St New York NY 10168-0001

LICHTBLAU, MYRON IVOR, language educator; b. N.Y.C., Oct. 10, 1925; s. Samuel and Sadonia (Weinberg) L.; m. Bernice Glanz, June 23, 1956; children: Mark (dec.), Anita, Eric. BA, CCNY, 1947; MA, U. Nacional Mex., 1948; PhD, Columbia U., 1957; diploma (hon.), U. de Nuevo Leon, Mex., 1964. Tchr. spanish secondary schs., N.Y.C., 1948-57; instr. Ind. U., Bloomington, 1957-59; prof. Syracuse U., N.Y., 1959—, chmn. dept. fgn. langs., 1967-74, 86-88; vis. prof. Colgate U., Hamilton, N.Y., 1970, SUNY-Binghamton, 1975; coordinator language program Peace Corps, 1966. Author: The Argentine Novel in the Nineteenth Century, 1959, El Arte estilistico de Eduardo Mallea, 1967, Manuel Galvez, 1972, A Practical Reference Guide to Reading Spanish, 1977, Rayuela y la creatividad artistica, 1989; editor: Manuel Galvez: Las dos vidas del Pobre Napoleon, 1963, E. Caballero Calderon: Manuel Pacho, 1980, Eduardo Mallea Ante La Critica, 1985, Emigration and Exile in Twentieth-Century Hispanic Literature, 1988, Mario Vargas Llosa: A Writer's Reality, 1990, Manuel Galvez: La maestra normal, 1991; editor Symposium, 1995—; translator: Eduardo Mallea: History of an Argentine Passion, 1983; book rev. editor Symposium, 1966-94, Hispania, 1974-83; mem. editorial bd. Critica Hispánica, 1985—. Bd. dirs. Syracuse Jewish Community Ctr., 1973; pres. Rabbi Jacob Epstein Sch. Jewish Studies, 1981-83; trustee Temple Beth Sholom, 1987-88. With U.S. Army, 1944-46. Mem. AAUP, MLA, Am. Assn. Tchrs. of Spanish and Portuguese (assoc. editor 1974-83), Inst. Internat. de Lit. Iberoamericana (exec. sec. 1959-63), Internat. Assn. Hispanistas. Jewish. Avocation: tennis. Office: Syracuse U Dept Fgn Langs Syracuse NY 13210

LICHTENBERG, BYRON K., futurist, manufacturing executive, space flight consultant; b. Stroudsburg, Pa., Feb. 19, 1948; s. Glenn John and Georgianna (Bierei) L.; m. Lee Lombard, July 25, 1970 (divorced); children—Kristin, Kimberly. Sc.B., Brown U., 1969; M.S., MIT, 1975, Sc.D., 1979. Rsch. scientist MIT, Cambridge, 1978-84; pres. Payload Systems, Inc., Cambridge, 1984-89, chief scientist, 1989-91; pres., chief exec. officer Omega Aerospace Inc., Virginia Beach, Va., 1991—. Contbg. author NASA Payload Specialist, 1979-92, Flew on Space Shuttle Mission #9, #45; contbr. articles to profl. jours. Served to lt. col. USAF, Mass. Air N.G., 1969-93. Recipient NASA Space Flight award, 1983, 92, Spaceflight award VFW, 1983, Haley Spaceflight award AIAA, 1983. Mem. Tau Beta Pi, Sigma Xi. Avocations: golf; racquetball; windsurfing; skiing. Office: Omega Aerospace Inc 728 Wolfsnare Cres Virginia Beach VA 23454

LICHTENBERG, MARGARET KLEE, publishing company executive; b. N.Y.C., Nov. 19, 1941; d. Lawrence and Shirley Jane (Wicksman) Klee; m. James Lester Lichtenberg, Mar. 31, 1963 (div. 1982); children: Gregory Lawrence, Amanda Zoe. BA, U. Mich., 1963; postgrad., Harvard U., 1963. Book rev. editor New Woman mag., 1972-73; assoc. editor children's books Parents Mag. Press, 1974; editor, rights dir. Books for Young People, Frederick Warne & Co., N.Y.C., 1975-78; sr. editor Simon & Schuster, N.Y.C., 1979-80; dir. sales promotion Grosset & Dunlap, N.Y.C., 1980-81; edni. sales mgr. Bantam Books, N.Y.C., 1982-84; dir. mktg. and sales Grove Press, N.Y.C., 1984-86; dir. of sales Grove Press, 1986-87; dir. sales Weidenfeld & Nicolson, N.Y.C., 1986-87; mktg. dir. Beacon Press, Boston, 1988-95; cons. Book Mktg. and Literary Svcs., 1995—; writer, freelance critic, 1961—. Contbr. articles, essays, stories, poetry, revs. to mags., newspapers and anthologies. Bd. dirs. Children's Book Council, 1978. Recipient 2 Avery Hopwood awards in drama and fiction, 1962, 2 in drama and poetry, 1963; coll. fiction contest award Mademoiselle mag., 1963; Woodrow Wilson fellow, 1963. Mem. Women's Nat. Book Assn. (past pres. N.Y. chpt.). Home and Office: 130 Appleton St Apt 5D Boston MA 02116-6045

LICHTENBERGER, HORST WILLIAM, chemical company executive; b. Yugoslavia, Nov. 5, 1935; came to U.S., 1950, naturalized, 1955; s. Andrew W. and Hella L.; m. Patricia Ann Thomas, June 15, 1957; children: Erich, Lisa. B.A., U. Iowa, 1957, B.S. in Chem. Engring., 1959; M.B.A., SUNY, Buffalo, 1962. With Union Carbide Corp., 1959—; bus. mgr. Union Carbide Corp., N.Y.C., 1972-75; v.p., gen. mgr. Linde div. Union Carbide Corp., Geneva, 1975-80; v.p. mktg. Union Carbide Corp., N.Y.C., 1980-82; v.p. gen. mgr. gas products Union Carbide Corp., 1982-85, pres. Solvents and Coatings div., from 1985, pres. Chemicals and Plastics group, 1986-92; pres., CEO Praxair Inc., 1992—; also chmn. Praxair Inc., Danbury, C.T. Mem. Iowa N.G., 1954-62. Mem. Am. Iron and Steel Inst., Chem. Mfg. Assn., Soc. of Chem. Industry. Republican. Achievements include patentee storage cryogenic fluids. Office: Praxair Inc 39 Old Ridgebury Rd Danbury CT 06817 *Progress is best achieved by encouraging people to innovate and to take prudent risks.*

LICHTENSTEIN, ELISSA CHARLENE, legal association executive; b. Trenton, N.J., Oct. 23, 1954; d. Mark and Rita (Field) L. AB cum laude, Smith Coll., Northampton, Mass., 1976; JD, George Washington U., 1979. Bar: D.C. 1980, U.S. Dist. Ct. (D.C. dist.) 1980, U.S. Ct. Appeals (D.C. cir.) 1980. Law clk. U.S. EPA, Washington, 1978-79; staff dir. ABA, Washington, 1979—, assoc. dir. pub. svcs. div., 1981-85, dir., 1985—. Editor, contbr.: Common Boundary/Common Problems: The Environmental Consequences of Energy Production, 1982, Exit Polls and Early Election Projections, 1984, The Global Environment: Challenges, Choices and Will, 1986, (newsletter) Environ. Law; co-editor, contbr. The Environ. Network; co-editor: Determining Competency in Guardianship Proceedings, 1990, Due Process Protections for Juveniles in Civil Commitment Proceedings, 1991, Environmental Regulation in Pacific Rim Nations, 1993, The Role of Law in the 1992 UN Conference on Environment and Development, 1992, Trade and the Environment in Pacific Rim Nations, 1994, Public Participation in Environmental Decisionmaking, 1994, Endangered Species Act Reauthorization: A Biocentric Approach. Mem. Nat. Trust for Hist. Preservation. Named Outstanding Young Woman of Am., 1982. Mem. ABA, NAFE, Am. Soc. Assn. Execs., Washington Coun. Lawyers, Women in Communications, Inc., Environ. Law Inst. (assoc.), Met. Washington Environ. Profls. (bd. dirs., pres.), D.C. Bar Assn. Democrat. Jewish. Office: ABA Div Pub Svcs 1800 M St NW Washington DC 20036-5801

LICHTENSTEIN, HARVEY, performing arts executive; b. Bklyn., Apr. 9, 1929; s. Samuel and Jennie (Meiner) L.; m. Phyllis Holbrook, Nov. 14, 1971; children: Saul, John. BA, Bklyn. Coll., 1951, LHD (hon.), 1986; postgrad., Bennington (Vt.) Coll., 1953; ArtsD (hon.), L.I. U., 1989; MusD (hon.), Mannes Coll. Music, 1989; LHD (hon.), Pratt Inst., 1993. Subscription and group sales mgr. N.Y.C. Ballet, also N.Y.C. Opera, 1965-67; pres., exec. producer Bklyn. Acad. Music, 1967—; exec. producer Bklyn. Philharm. Symphonic Orch., 1989—; Am. dir. Spoleto (Italy) Festival, 1971-73. Mem. Century Assn. (N.Y.C.). Office: Bklyn Acad Music 30 Lafayette Ave Brooklyn NY 11217-1486

LICHTENSTEIN, LAWRENCE JAY, lawyer; b. Phila., June 22, 1929; s. Leo and Harriet (Herbach) L.; m. Barbara Eberhardt, June 13, 1987. AB, Dickinson Coll., 1951; LLB, U. Pa., 1954. Bar: Pa. 1954, U.S. Dist. Ct. Pa. 1954, U.S. Ct. Appeals (3d cir.) 1991. Ptnr., chair bankruptcy dept. Mesirov, Gelman, Jaffe, Cramer & Jamieson, Phila., 1983-91; shareholder Buchanan Ingersoll P.C., Phila., 1991—. Mem. ABA (bus. bankruptcy com., comml. fin. svcs. com., co-chair chpt. II subcom. task force on mediation in bankruptcy), Phila. Bar Assn. (v.p. exec. com. bus. law sect., pres.-elect consumer bankruptcy assistance project eastern dist. bankruptcy conf.). Office: Buchanan Ingersoll PC 1200 Two Logan Sq Philadelphia PA 19103

LICHTENSTEIN, LAWRENCE MARK, allergy, immunology educator, physician; b. Washington, May 31, 1934; s. Samuel and Lillian (Colodny) L.; m. Carolyn Eggert, June 15, 1956; children: Elizabeth, Joshua, Rebekah. MD, U. Chgo., 1960; PhD, Johns Hopkins U., 1965. Diplomate: Am. Bd. Allergy and Immunology. Intern, Johns Hopkins Hosp., 1960-61, resident in medicine, 1965-66; asst. prof. medicine Johns Hopkins U. Sch. Medicine, 1966-70, assoc. prof., 1970-75, prof., 1975—; dir. Johns Hopkins Asthma and Allergy Ctr.; mem. Nat. Adv. Allergy and Infectious Diseases Coun. Mem. editorial bd.: Clin. Immunology and Pathology, Immunology, Pulmonary, Allergy; editor 11 books; contbr. articles to profl. jours. Fellow ACP; mem. Am. Assn. Immunology (sec., treas.), Am. Fedn. Clin. Rsch.,

Am. Soc. Clin. Investigation, Am. Acad. Allergy and Immunology (pres.), Am. Soc. Exptl. Pathology, Collegium Internat. Allergologicum (pres. elect), ASPET, Assn. Am. Physicians. Democrat. Jewish. Home: 1600 The Terraces Baltimore MD 21209-3637 Office: John Hopkins Asthma & Allergy Ctr 5501 Hopkins Bayview Cir Baltimore MD 21224-6819

LICHTENSTEIN, ROBERT JAY, lawyer; b. Phila., Jan. 23, 1948; s. Irving M. and Marjorie J. (Weiss) L.; m. Sandra Paley, Aug. 14, 1971; children: David P., Kate. BS in Econs., U. Pa., 1969; JD, U. Pitts., 1973; LLM in Taxation, NYU, 1974. Bar: Pa. 1974, U.S. Tax Ct. 1978, U.S. Dist. Ct. (ea. dist.) Pa. 1979, U.S. Ct. Appeals (3rd cir.) 1982, U.S. Ct. Appeals (4th cir.) 1987. Ptnr. Saul, Ewing, Remick & Saul, 1978-88; assoc. Morgan, Lewis & Bockius, Phila., 1974-78, ptnr., 1988—; instr. Main Line Paralegal Inst., Wayne, Pa., 1984-87, Paralegal Inst., Phila., 1987-90; adj. prof. law Villanova U. Sch. Law, 1991—. Trustee Temple Brith Achim, King of Prussia, Pa., 1986-91. Mem. ABA, Pa. Bar Assn., Phila. Assn., Locust Club. Democrat. Avocations: skiing, tennis, reading. Office: Morgan Lewis & Bockius 2000 One Logan Sq Philadelphia PA 19103

LICHTENSTEIN, ROY, artist; b. N.Y.C., Oct. 27, 1923; s. Milton and Beatrice (Werner) L.; m. Isabel Wilson, June 12, 1949 (div.); children: David, Mitchell; m. Dorothy Herzka, Nov. 1, 1968. BFA, Ohio State U., 1946, MFA, 1949; DFA (hon.), Calif. Inst. Arts., 1977, Ohio State U., 1988, Bard Coll., 1989. Instr. Ohio State U. 1946-51; asst. prof. SUNY-Oswego, 1957-60, Douglass Coll., Rutgers U., 1960-63. Pop art and other themes derived from comic strip techniques; one-man shows include Leo Castelli Gallery, N.Y.C., 1962, 63, 65, 67, 71, 72, 73, 74, 75, 77, 79, 81, 83, 85, 86, 87, 89, 92, Galerie Ileana Sonnabend, Paris, 1963, 65, 70, 75, Pasadena (Calif.) Art Mus., 1967, Walker Art Ctr., Mpls., 1967, Stedelijk Mus., Amsterdam, 1967, Tate Gallery, London, 1968, Guggenheim Mus., N.Y.C., 1969, Nelson Gallery, Kansas City, Mo., 1969, Mus. Contemporary Art, Chgo., 1970, Centre National D'Arte Contemporain, Paris, 1975, and traveling to: Nationalgalerie Staatliche Museum Kulterbesitz, Berlin, Seattle Art Mus., 1976, Inst. Contemporary Art, Boston, 1979, Portland Ctr. for Visual Arts, 1980, St. Louis Art Mus., 1981, Fundacion Juan March, Madrid, 1982, Walker Art Ctr., Mpls., 1986, 'The Drawings of Roy Lichtenstein', Mus. Modern Art, N.Y.C., 1987, and traveling to: Mus. Overholland, Amsterdam, 1987, Tel Aviv Mus. Israel, 1987, Schirn Kunsthalle, Frankfurt, 1988, Mus. Modern Art, Oxford, Eng., 1988, Corcoran Gallery of Art, Washington, 1988; group shows include Whitney Mus. Am. Art, N.Y.C., 1966, 67, 68, 70, 72, 73, 74, 75 (Downtown), 77, 78, 80, 82, 83, 84, 85, 87, Mus. Modern Art, N.Y.C., 1966, 67, 68, 74, 76, 80, 85, 88, Solomon R. Guggenheim Mus., N.Y.C., 1965,76, Venice Biennale, 1966, Corcoran Gallery Art 36th Biennale, Washington, D.C., 1978, Solomon R. Guggenheim MUs., N.Y.C., 1965, 76, Hirschorn Mus., Washington, 1980, Bklyn. Mus. Art, N.Y.C., 1981, Nat. Mus. Am. Art, Smithsonian Inst., Washington, 1984, Palacio Velazquez, Madrid, Spain, 1991, Galerie Martine Queval, Paris, 1992, Galerie Joachim Becker, Paris, 1992; represented in permanent collections: Mus. Modern Art, N.Y.C., Whitney Mus. Am. Art, N.Y.C., Corcoran Gallery Art, Washington, Hirschorn Mus. and Sculpture Garden, Washington, Libr. Congress, Washington, Nat. Gallery Art, Washington, Chgo. Art Inst., Smithsonian Inst., Washington, Victoria and Albert Mus., London, Seibu Art Mus., Tokyo, Ludwig Mus., Cologne, Stedelijk Mus., Amsterdam, Norton Simon Mus., Pasadena, Yale U., New Haven, Walker Art Ctr., Mpls., San Francisco Mus. Modern Art, Albright Knox Gallery, Buffalo; created outside wall for Circarama, N.Y. State Pavillion, N.Y. State World's Fair, 1963, large Painting for Expo '67, Montreal, 1967, Brushstroke Murals for Dusseldorf U. Med. Ctr., 1970, 'Mermaid' (NEA grantee), pub. sculpture for Theatre Performing Arts in Miami Beach, Fla., 1979, 'Brushstrokes in Flight', Port Columbus Airport, Columbus, Ohio, 1984, 'Mural with Blue Brushstroke', Equitable Life Assurance Bldg. with Whitney Mus. Art, 1985, 'Coups de Pinceau', Caisse des Depots and Consignations, Paris, 1988, Tel Aviv Mus. Art, Tel Aviv, 1989. With AUS, 1943-46. Recipient Skowhegan medal for painting, 1977. Mem. Am. Acad. and Inst. Arts and Letters.

LICHTENSTEIN, SEYMOUR, clothing manufacturing company executive; b. N.Y.C., 1927. With Garan Inc. and predecessors, N.Y.C., 1942—, salesman, exec. v.p., sec., 1957-65, pres., 1965-81, chief exec. officer, 1965—, chmn. exec. com., from 1981, also chmn., dir. Office: Garan Inc 350 Fifth Ave New York NY 10118-0100

LICHTER, EDWARD ARTHUR, physician, educator; b. Chgo., June 5, 1928; s. Joseph and Eva (Wise) L.; m. Charlotte Sells, Sept. 7, 1952; children: Michael, Jay. PhB, U. Chgo., 1947; BS, Roosevelt U., 1949; MS, U. Ill., 1951, MD, 1955. Intern Fitzsimons Army Hosp., Denver, 1955-56; resident internal medicine U. Ill., Chgo., 1958-61, assoc. prof. preventive medicine and community health Med. Ctr., 1966-69, prof., dept. head preventive medicine and community health, 1969-86, prof., dept. head health care svcs., 1972-79, prof. community health scis., 1979—, prof. internal medicine, assoc. chief Sect. of Gen. Internal Medicine, 1986—, mem. exec. com., 1990—; mem. exec. com. Univ. Senates Conf., 1992-95; practice medicine specializing in internal medicine and preventive medicine Chgo., 1966—; fellow in immunology NIH, 1961-63, USPHS officer, mem. staff immunology, 1963-66. Served with AUS, 1955-58. Fellow ACP, APHA, Am. Coll. Preventive Medicine; mem. Am. Coll. Epidemiology, Cen. Soc. for Clin. Rsch., Assn. Tchrs, Preventive Medicine, Chgo. Heart Assn., Alpha Omega Alpha. Home: 1310 Maple Ave Evanston IL 60201-4325 Office: 840 S Wood St Chicago IL 60612-7317

LICHTER, PAUL RICHARD, ophthalmology educator; b. Detroit, Mar. 7, 1939; s. Max D. and Buena (Epstein) L.; m. Carolyn Goode, 1960; children: Laurie, Susan. BA, U. Mich., 1960, MD, 1964, MS, 1968. Diplomate Am. Bd. Ophthalmology. Asst. to assoc. prof. ophthalmology U. Mich., Ann Arbor, 1971-78, prof., chmn. dept. ophthalmology, 1978—; intern. Am. Bd. Ophthalmology, 1987. Editor-in-chief Ophthalmology jour., 1986-94. Served to lt. comdr. USN, 1969-71. Fellow Am. Acad. Ophthalmology (bd. dirs. 1981—, pres.-elect 1995, sr. honor award 1986); mem. AMA, Pan Am. Assn. Ophthalmology (bd. dirs. 1988—, sec.-treas. English speaking countries 1991-95), Mich. State Med. Soc., Washtenaw County Med. Soc., Mich. Ophthalmol. Soc. (pres. 1993-95), Assn. Univ. Profs. Ophthalmology (trustee 1986-93, pres. 1991-92), Alpha Omega Alpha. Office: U Mich Med Sch Kellogg Eye Ctr 1000 Wall St Ann Arbor MI 48105-1912

LICHTERMAN, MARTIN, history educator; b. N.Y.C., July 18, 1918; s. Joseph Aaron and Esther S. (Schacknowitz) L.; m. Charlotte Rottenberg, Oct. 7, 1945; children: Joshua David, Andrew Marc. B.S., Harvard U., 1939, A.M., 1947; Ph.D., Columbia U., 1952. Instr. Rutgers U., Newark, 1948-51; instr., lectr. Princeton U., 1953-55; mem. research staff Princeton U. (Center for Research on World Polit. Instns.), 1951-53; asst. prof. M.I.T. 1955-60; dir. research to gov. Mass., 1959-60; exec. sec., dir. New Eng. Bd. Higher Edn., Winchester, Mass., 1961-66; dean Center Humanities and Social Scis. Union Coll., Schenectady, 1966-71; acting dean faculty Union Coll., 1971-72, dean faculty, 1972-76; prof. history Center Humanities and Social Scis. Union Coll., Schenectady, distinguished prof. history and higher edn., 1976-78; dean Empire State Coll., 1978-82, prof. history, 1982-83, prof. emeritus, 1983—; pres. Alternative Lifelong Learning, Berkeley, Calif., 1989-91; cons. 20th Century Fund, N.Y.C., 1955-57, Friends World Coll., 1984-86; mem. Mass. Bd. Collegiate Authority, 1961-66. Author: To the Yalu and Back, 1963; co-author: Political Community in the North Atlantic Area, 1957; contbr. articles to profl. jours. Vice chmn. bd. Mass. Com. Children and Youth, 1963-66, mem. exec. bd., 1961-66; adv. bd. Civil Liberties Mass., 1963-66; chmn. bd. New Eng. Council Advancement Sch. Adminstrn., 1961-63; vice chmn. Capital Dist. Civil Liberties Union, 1966-67; chmn. Freedom Forum, Inc., 1970-71, Schnectady Renewals, Inc., 1972-76; bd. dirs. Suffolk County chpt. N.Y. Civil Liberties Union, 1981-87; bd. dirs. Della Corte Internat., Inc., 1983-88. Mem. Am. Hist. Assn., Orgn. Am. Historians. Home: 2587 Hilgard Ave Berkeley CA 94709-1104

LICHTIN, (JUDAH) LEON, pharmacist; b. Phila., Mar. 5, 1924; s. Aaron and Rosa (Rosenberg) L.; m. Beverly I. Cohen, Aug. 6, 1950; children—Benjamin Lloyd, Alan Eli. B.S. in Pharmacy, Phila. Coll. Pharmacy and Sci., 1944, M.S. in Pharmacy, 1947; Ph.D. in Pharmacy, Ohio State U., 1950. Asst. prof. pharmacy U. Cin., 1950-51, assoc. prof., 1951-64, prof., 1964—, Andrew Jergens prof. pharmacy, 1971-91, Andrew Jergens prof. pharmacy emeritus, 1991—; cons. in cosmetic sci. Contbr. articles to pharm. jours.; composer string music, vocal music. Past pres. No. Hills Synagogue,

Cin. Fellow AAAS, Soc. Cosmetic Chemists; mem. Am. Colls. of Pharmacy Assn., Sigma Xi, Rho Chi. Achievements include patents in field. Home: 801 Cloverview Ave Cincinnati OH 45231-6017

LICHTIN, NORMAN NAHUM, chemistry educator; b. Newark, Aug. 10, 1922; s. James Jechiel and Clara (Greenspan) L.; m. Phyllis Selma Wasserman, May 30, 1947; children—Harold Hirsh, Sara Marjorie, Daniel Albert. B.S., Antioch Coll., 1944; M.S., Purdue U., 1945; Ph.D., Harvard U., 1948. Faculty Boston U., 1947-93, prof. chemistry, 1961-93, prof. emeritus, 1993—, Univ. prof., 1973-93, chmn. dept. chemistry, 1973-84, dir. Div. Engring. and Applied Sci., 1983-87; chief scientist Synlize, Inc., 1987-90; chief scientist, sec. corp. Project Sunrise Inc., 1990-92; chief scientist ClearFlow Inc., 1993-94, Photox Corp., Boston, 1993—; vis. chemist Brookhaven Nat. Lab., Upton, N.Y., 1957-58, research collaborator, 1958-70; guest scientist Weizmann Inst. Sci., Rehovoth, Israel, 1962-63; vis. prof. Inst. Phys. and Chem. Research, Wako, Japan, 1980, Hebrew U., Jerusalem, 1962-63, 70-71, 75, 76, 80; Coochbehar lectr. Indian Assn. Cultivation of Sci., Calcutta, 1980. Assoc. editor Solar Energy, 1976-93; rsch. and publs. on mechanisms of chem. reactions including reaction of atomic nitrogen with organic compounds, influence of high energy radiation on organic compounds and photoredox reactions of dyes; photochem. conversion solar energy, ionization processes and ionic reactions in solutions in liquid sulfur dioxide, photo assisted solid-catalysis; catalytic and photocatalytic decomposition of organic and inorganic pollutants of air and water. NSF fellow, 1962-63. Fellow AAAS; mem. Am. Chem. Soc., Inter-Am. Photochem. Soc., Internat. Solar Energy Soc., Sigma Xi, Phi Beta Kappa (hon.). Home: 195 Morton St Newton MA 02159-1522 Office: 590 Commonwealth Ave Boston MA 02215-2507

LICHTMAN, DAVID MICHAEL, military officer, health care administrator, orthopedist, educator; b. Bkyln., Jan. 14, 1942; s. Harry S. and Frances (Rubin) L.; m. Frances Lubin; children: James Matthew, Elisabeth Jill. Student, Tufts Coll., 1962; MD, SUNY, Bklyn., 1966. Diplomate: Am. Bd. Orthopaedic Surgery. Intern U. Minn. Hosp., 1966-67, Naval Aerospace Med. Inst., Pensacola, Fla., 1967; commd. lt. USN, 1967, advanced through grades to rear adm., 1988, flight surgeon Air Wing 3, 1968-69; mem. staff orthopaedic svc. Nat. Naval Med. Ctr., Bethesda, Md., 1974-77, chmn. dept. orthopaedic surgery head, hand surgery svc., dir. orthopaedic residency program, 1984-87, asst. chmn. dept. orthopaedic surgery, 1975-77, chmn. dept. orthopaedic surgery, head hand surgery svc., dir. orthopaedic residency program, 1984-87; chmn. dept. orthopaedic surgery and rehab., dir. orhopaedic residency program, dir. navy hand fellowship, head, hand and microsurgery svc. Naval Hosp., Oakland, Calif., 1977-83, mem. staff orthopaedic surgery, sr. hand/microsurgery cons., 1988-91, commanding officer, 1989-91; comdr. San Francisco Med. Command, Oakland, 1988-91; promoted to Rear Adm. (lower half), 1989, Rear Adm. (upper half), 1991; retired USN, 1994; John Dunn prof. orthopaedic hand surgery Baylor Coll. Medicine, Houston, 1994—; cons. orthopaedic surgery assc. sec. def. for health affairs Dept. Def., Washington, 1988-94; specialty advisor naval surgeon gen. for orthopaedic surgery and hand surgery Bur. Medicine and Surgery Dept. Navy, Washington, 1983-86; prof. surgery and head divsn. orthopaedic surgery Uniformed Svcs. U. of Health Scis., Bethesda, 1984-94, ex-officio mem. bd. regents, 1991-94. Editor: The Wrist and Its Disorders, 1988, Hand and Wrist Sect. Current Opinion in Orthopaedics.; contbr. articles to profl. jours. mem. ACS (bd. govs.), Am. Acad. Orthopaedic Surgeons, Am. Soc. for Surgery of the Hand Assn., Am. Orthopaedic Assn. (hon.), Mil. Surgeons U.S (Philip Hench award 1982), Soc. Naval Flight Surgeons, Soc. Mil. Orthopaedic Surgeons (bd. dirs.). Home: 45 Briar Hollow #11 Houston TX 77028 Office: Dept Orthopedic Surgery Baylor Coll Medicine 6550 Fannin Ste 2525 Houston TX 77030

LICHTMAN, MARSHALL ALBERT, medical educator, physician, scientist; b. N.Y.C., June 23, 1934; s. Samuel and Vera L.; m. Alice Jo Maisel, June 23, 1957; children—Susan, Joanne, Pamela. AB, Cornell U., 1955; MD, U. Buffalo, 1960. Diplomate Am. Bd. Internal Medicine. Resident in medicine Strong Meml. Hosp., 1960-63; surgeon USPHS and postdoctoral research assoc. Sch. Pub. Health, U. N.C., 1963-65; chief resident and instr. medicine Strong Meml. Hosp., 1965-66; sr. instr. medicine, research trainee in hematology U. Rochester Sch. Medicine, N.Y., 1966-67, asst. prof. medicine, spl. postdoctoral research fellow in hematology, 1968-70, assoc. prof. medicine and radiation biology and biophysics, 1971-74, prof. medicine and radiation biology and biophysics, 1974—, chief hematology unit dept. medicine, 1975-77, co. chief, 1977-89; sr. assoc. dean for acad. affairs and research, 1979—, dean Sch. of Medicine and Dentistry, 1990—; vis. prof. univs.; lectr. in field. Leukemia Soc. Am. scholar, 1969-74; recipient contracts U.S. Army Research, 1972-78, U.S. Dept. Energy, 1972-80; USPHS grantee, 1971—. Editor: Abnormalities of Granulocytes and Monocytes, 1975, Hematology for Practitioners, 1978, Hematology and Oncology, 1980, (with W.J. William, E. Beutler, A.J. Erslev) Hematology, 3d edit., 1983, 4th edit., 1990, 5th edit., 1995; (with H.J. Meiselman and P.L. LaCelle) White Cell Mechanics: Basic Science and Clinical Aspects, 1984. Contbr. articles to profl. jours. Master ACP; mem. NIH (hematology study sect., 1982-86), Am. Fedn. Clin. Research, AAAS, Am. Soc. Hematology (pres. 1989), Internat. Soc. Hematology, N.Y. Acad. Scis., Am. Soc. Clin. Investigation, Assn. Am. Physicians, Am. Assn. for Cancer Research, Am. Physiol. Soc., Reticuloendothelial Soc., Soc. Exptl. Biology and Medicine, Am. Soc. Cell Biology. Home: 64 Woodbury Pl Rochester NY 14618-3445 Office: U Rochester Sch Medicine/Dentistry Box 706 601 Elmwood Ave Rochester NY 14642-9999

LICHTWARDT, ROBERT WILLIAM, mycologist; b. Rio de Janeiro, Nov. 27, 1924; s. Henry Herman and Ruth Moyer Lichtwardt; m. Elizabeth Thomas, Jan. 27, 1951; children: Ruth Elizabeth, Robert Thomas. AB, Oberlin Coll., 1949; MS, U. Ill., 1951, PhD, 1954. Postdoctoral fellow NSF, Panama, Brazil, 1954-55; postdoctoral rsch. assoc. Iowa State U., Ames, 1955-57; asst. prof. U. Kans., Lawrence, 1957-60, assoc. prof., 1960-65; sr. postdoctoral fellow NSF, Hawaii, Japan, 1963-64; prof. U. Kans., Lawrence, 1965—. Author: The Trichomycetes, Fungal Associates of Arthropods, 1986; contbr. 95 articles to profl. jours. Mem. Mycological Soc. Am. (life, pres. 1971-72, editor-in-chief 1965-70, William H. Weston award for teaching excellence in mycology 1982, Disting. Mycologist award 1991), Brit. Mycological Soc., Japan Mycological Soc. Office: U Kans Dept Of Botany Lawrence KS 66045

LICK, DALE WESLEY, academic administrator; b. Marlette, Mich., Jan. 7, 1938; s. John R. and Florence M. (Baxter) L.; m. Marilyn Kay Foster, Sept. 15, 1956; children: Lynette (dec.), Kitty, Diana, Ronald. BS with honors, Mich. State U., 1958, MS in Math, 1959; PhD in Math, U. Calif., Riverside, 1965. Research asst. physics Mich. State U., East Lansing, 1958; teaching asst. math. Mich. State U., 1959; instr., chmn. dept. math. Port Huron (Mich.) Jr. Coll., 1959-60; asst. to comptroller Mich. Bell Telephone Co. Detroit, 1961; instr. U. Redlands, 1961-63; teaching asst. math. U. Calif. Riverside, 1964-65; asst. prof. math. U. Tenn., Knoxville, 1965-67; postdoctoral fellow Brookhaven Nat. Lab., Upton, N.Y., 1967-68; assoc. prof. U. Tenn., 1968-69; assoc. prof., head dept. math. Drexel U., Phila., 1969-72; adj. assoc. prof. dept. pharmacology Med. Sch., Temple U., Phila., 1969-72; v.p. acad. affairs Russell Sage Coll., Troy, N.Y., 1972-74; prof. math. and computing scis. Old Dominion U., Norfolk, Va., 1974-78; also dean Old Dominion U. (Sch. Scis. and Health Professions); pres., prof. math. and computer sci. Ga. So. Coll., Statesboro, 1978-86; pres., prof. math. U. Maine, Orono, 1986-91; pres., prof. math. Fla. State U., Tallahassee, 1991-93, univ. prof., 1993—; textbook and manuscript reviewer for Appleton-Century Crofts, Bogden and Quigley, Macmillan and Prentice-Hall, 1966-90; cons. Va. Health Planning and Resources Devel. Agy., 1976-78, Norfolk State U., Va., 1977, U. Central Fla., 1977; proposal reviewer divs. higher edn. in sci. and public understanding of sci. NSF, 1972-76; appeared in interviews, discussions and spl. topic presentations various radio and TV programs, 1974—, mem. faculty 7 day tng. programs series in health adminstrn., 1977-79, guest lectr. various conf. and symposia on health care and interinstnl. cooperation, 1975-80; bd. dirs. Blue Cross/Blue Shield, 1987-88. Author: Fundamentals of Algebra, 1970; contbr. articles to profl. jours. Bd. dirs. Statesboro/Coll. Symphony, 1978-86, Statewide Health Coordinating Coun. Va., 1976-78; chmn. higher edn. adv. bd. Reorganized Ch. of Jesus Christ of Latter Day Sts., 1986—; mem. planning com. Bulloch Meml. Hosp., 1979-86; active Coastal Empire coun. Boy Scouts Am., 1982-86, Katalidin coun., 1986-91; bd. dirs. Health Care Ctrs. Am., Virginia Beach, Va., 1978, Ea. Va. Health Systems Agy., 1976-78; chmn., bd. dirs. Assembly

Against Hunger and Malnutrition, 1977-78, pres., 1977-78. Mem. AAUP, AAAS, Am. Math. Soc., Math. Assn. Am., Am. Assn. Univ. Adminstrs., Am. Soc. Allied Health Professions, Am. Assn. State Colls. and Univs. (chmn. com. agr. resources and rural devel. 1981-86), Am. Assn. Higher Edn., Sigma Xi, Phi Kappa Phi, Pi Mu Epsilon (governing coun. 1972-77), Beta Gamma Sigma, Pi Sigma Epsilon. Mem., high priest Reorganized LDS Ch. Lodge: Rotary. Office: Learning Systems Inst 205 Dodd Hall Tallahassee FL 32306-4041

LICK, WILBERT JAMES, mechanical engineering educator; b. Cleve., June 12, 1933; s. Fred and Hulda (Sunntag) L.; children—James, Sarah. B.A.E., Rensselaer Poly. Inst., 1955, M.A.E., 1957, Ph.D., 1958. Asst. prof. Harvard, 1959-66; sr. research fellow Calif. Inst. Tech., 1966-67; mem. faculty Case Western Res. U., 1967-79, prof. earth scis., 1970-79, chmn. dept., 1973-76; prof. mech. engring. U. Calif.-Santa Barbara, 1979—, chmn. dept., 1982-84. Home: 1236 Camino Meleno Santa Barbara CA 93111-1007 Office: U Calif Dept Mech and Environ Engring Santa Barbara CA 93106

LICKHALTER, MERLIN EUGENE, architect; b. St. Louis, May 4, 1934; s. Frank E. and Sophia (Geller) L.; m. Harriet Braen, June 9, 1957; children: Debra, Barbara. BArch, MIT, 1957. Registered arch., Mo., Ill., Calif., Fla. Mich., Wis., Nev., Tex., Ala., Nev., Va. Ptnr. Drake Partnership, Architects, St. Louis, 1961-77; pres. JRB Architects, Inc., St. Louis, 1977-81; sr. v.p., mng. dir. Stone, Marraccini & Patterson, St. Louis, 1981-93; sr. v.p. Cannon, 1993—; also bd. dirs.; owner, pres. mgmt. program Harvard U. Bus. Sch., 1992; cons. Dept. Def., Washington, 1977-78; lectr. Washington U. Sch. Medicine, 1989—. Trustee United Hebrew Cong., St. Louis, 1980-88, 93—; exec. com. bd. dirs. Arts & Edn. Coun. St. Louis, 1991—. Capt. U.S. Army, 1957-59. Recipient Renovation Design award St. Louis Producers Coun., 1976, USAF Europe Design Award, 1990. Mem. AIA (nat. acad. architect for health, chmn. 1993), Am. Hosp. Assn., Am. Assn. for Health Planning, St. Louis Regional Growth Assn., Hawthorn Found., St. Louis Club, St. Louis Ambs., Frontenac Racquet Club, Masons. Jewish. Home: 2 Warson Ln Ladue MO 63124-1251 Office: Cannon One City Ctr Saint Louis MO 63101

LIDDELL, DONALD MACY, JR., retired investment counsellor; b. Elizabeth, N.J., Mar. 11, 1907; s. Donald M. and Edith (Stabler) L.; m. Jane Hawley Hawkes, Mar. 30, 1940; children: Jane Liddell Bass, Donald Roger Brooke. B.S., Princeton U., 1928; grad. student, Am. Inst. Banking, N.Y. U. Statistician Banker's Trust Co., N.Y.C., 1928-29, White, Weld & Co., 1929-33; security analyst Fidelity Union Trust Co., Newark, 1935-40; v.p., dir. Templeton, Dobbrow & Vance, Inc., 1946-51, exec. v.p., 1951-60, chmn. bd., 1960-74; dir. 930 Park Ave. Corp., Nat. State Bank of Elizabeth, 1950-88; dir. N.Y. Sch. Interior; dir., fin. adviser Smoke, Fire and Burn Inst., 1990—, cons., 1983—. Contbr. articles to profl. publs. Bd. dirs., fin. adviser Youth Found., 1985—. Res. officer U.S. Army, 1933-35; lt. col. AUS, 1940-45; fin. officer Ea. Def. Command, 1944-45. Mem. Soc. Colonial Wars (treas.-gen. 1969-78, gov. N.J. Soc. 1986-88), Mil. Order Loyal Legion (comdr.-in-chief 1961-62), Sons of Revolution, Mil. Order Fgn. Wars, Order Colonial Lords of Manors in Am. (treas. 1969-88, pres. 1972-75), Lords of Md. Manors, Conf. Patriotic and Hist. Socs. (treas 1974-84), Pilgrims of U.S., Colonial Order of the Acorn, Down Town Assn., Union Club, Badminton Club, Univ. Club, Ch. Club (all N.Y.C.), Nassau Club (Princeton, N.J.). Republican. Episcopalian. Home: 930 Park Ave New York NY 10028-0209

LIDDELL, JANE HAWLEY HAWKES, civic worker; b. Newark, Dec. 8, 1907; d. Edward Zeh and Mary Everett (Hawley) Hawkes; AB, Smith Coll., 1931; postgrad. in art history, Harvard U., 1933-35; MA, Columbia U., 1940; Carnegie fellow Sorbonne, Paris, 1937; m. Donald M. Liddell, Jr., Mar. 30, 1940; children: Jane Boyer, D. Roger Brooke. Pres., Planned Parenthood Essex County (N.J.), 1947-50; trustee Prospect Hill Sch. Girls, Newark, 1946-50; mem. adv. bd., publicity and public relations chmn. N.J. State Mus., Trenton, 1952-60; sec., then v.p. women's br. N.J. Hist. Soc.; women's aux. prodn. chmn. Englewood (N.J.) Hosp., 1959-61; pres. Dwight Sch. Girls Parents Assn., 1955-57; v.p. Englewood Sch. Boys Parents Assn., 1958-60; mem. Altar Guild, women's aux. bd., rector's adv. council St. Paul's Episcopal Ch., Englewood, 1954-59; bd. dir. N.Y. State Soc. of Nat. Soc. Colonial Dames, 1961-67, rep. conf. Patriotic and Hist. Socs., 1964—; bd. dirs. Huguenot Soc. Am., 1979-86, regional v.p.; 1979-82, historian, 1983-84, co-chmn. Tercentennial Book, 1983-85; bd. dirs. Soc. Daus. Holland Dames, 1965-82; nat. jr. v.p. Dames of Loyal Legion, USA; bd. dirs., mem. publs. com. Daus. Cin., 1966-72; bd. dirs. Ch. Women's League Patriotic Service, 1962—, pres., 1968-70, 72-74; bd. dirs., chmn. grants coun. Youth Found., N.Y.C., 1974—; chmn. for Newark, Smith Coll. 75th Ann. Fund, 1948-50; pres. North N.J. Smith Club, 1956-58; pres. Smith Coll. Class 1931, 1946-51, 76-81, editor 50th anniversary book, 1980-81. Author: (with others) Huguenot Refugees in the Settling of Colonial America, 1982-85; contbr. The Dutch Contribution to the Development of Early Manhattan, 1969. Recipient various commendation awards. Republican. Mem. Colonial Dames Am. (N.Y.C. chpt.). Clubs: Colony, City Gardens, Church (N.Y.C.); Jr. League (N.Y.); N.Y. Jr. League; Needle and Bobbin, Nat. Farm and Garden . Editor: Maine Echoes, 1961; research and editor asst., Wartime Writings of American Revolution Officers, 1972-75.

LIDDELL, LEON MORRIS, librarian, educator; b. Gainesville, Tex., July 21, 1914; s. Thomas Leon and Minnie Mae (Morris) L. B.A., U. Tex., 1937, J.D., 1937; B.L.S., U. Chgo., 1946; postgrad., Columbia U., 1948. Bar: Tex. bar 1937. Practiced in Gainesville, 1938-39; with claims dept. Hartford Accident & Indemnity Co., 1937-38, Pacific Mut. Life Ins. Co., 1939-41; asst. prof. law, law librarian U. Conn., 1946-47; asst. prof. law U. Minn., 1949-50, assoc. prof., 1950-54, prof. law, 1954-60, law librarian, 1949-60; prof. law, law librarian U. Chgo., 1960-74, prof. law, law librarian emeritus, 1974—; prof. law, law librarian Northwestern U. Law Sch., 1974-80. Maj. AUS, 1941-46; lt. col. USAR, 1946-62. Mem. Am. Bar Assn., Am. Assn. Law Libraries, Chgo Assn. Law Libraries (past pres.), Spl. Libraries Assn. Club: Mason. Home: 4718 Hallmark Dr Apt 504 Houston TX 77056-3911

LIDDELL, W. KIRK, specialty contracting and distribution company executive, lawyer; b. Lancaster, Pa., July 24, 1949; m. Pamela E. Trow; four children. AB in Econs. magna cum laude, Princeton U., 1971; MBA, U. Chgo., 1976, JD, 1976. Assoc. Covington & Burling, Washington, 1976-80; gen. counsel, v.p. AC and S Inc/Irex Corp., Lancaster, 1980-83; pres., chief exec. officer Irex Corp. 1984—; bd. dirs. High Industries Inc.; exec. com., bd. dirs. Cove States Hamilton Bank; Chmn. Lancaster City Ptnrship., 1986; chmn. Lancaster County Ct. of C. & Industry, 1991; bd. dirs. Econ. Devel. Co. Industry; bd. dirs. The Lancaster Alliance; bd. dirs. Econ. Devel. Co. Lancaster County; Nat. Football Found. Served as lt. USAR, 1971-73. Leon Carol Marshall scholar U. Chgo. Grad. Sch. Bus., 1974-76. Office: Irex Corp 120 N Lime St Lancaster PA 17602-5015

LIDDICOAT, RICHARD THOMAS, JR., association executive; b. Kearsarge, Mich., Mar. 2, 1918; s. Richard Thomas and Carmen (Williams) L.; m. Mary Imogene Hibbard, Sept. 21, 1939. BS in Geology, U. Mich., 1939, MS in Mineralogy, 1940; grad. gemologist, Gemological Inst. Am., 1941; MS in Meteorology, Calif. Inst. Tech., 1944. Cert. gemologist (hon.). With Gemological Inst. Am., L.A., 1940-42, 46—; dir. edn. Gemological Inst. Am., 1942, 46-49, asst. dir., 1950-52, exec. dir., 1952-83, pres., 1970-83, chmn. bd., 1983—, also author courses; editor Gem and Gemology, 1952—; hon. mem. rsch. staff L.A. Mus. Natural History, 1968—; U.S. dep. to Internat. Gem Conf., 1960, 64, 66, 68, 70, 72, 75, 77, 79, 81, 83, 85, 89; del. Pres.'d Conf. on Small Bus., 1957. Author: Handbook of Gem Identification, 12th edit, 1987, (with others) The Diamond Dictionary, 1960, 2d edit., 1977, (with Copeland) Jewelers Manual, 2d edit, 1967; numerous articles.; contbr. to Ency. Britannica Jr., Ency. Americana, McGraw-Hill Ency. of Sci. and Tech. Trustee Nat. Home Study Coun., 1948-88. Recipient Lifetime Achievement award Modern Jeweler's mag., 1985, award Internat. Soc. Appraisers, 1985, Spl. award internat. Colored Stone Assn., 1984, Lifetime Achievement award Morris B. Zale, 1987; named Man of Yr., Consol. Jewelers Assn. Greater N.Y., 1984; named to Nat. Home Study Coun. Hall of Fame, 1991; Liddicoatite species of tourmaline group named for him. Fellow Mineral. Soc. Am., Am. Geol. Soc. Am., Geochem. Assn. Gt. Britain (hon.); mem. AAAS, Am. Gem Soc. (supr. ednl. sessions ann. conclaves 1948-83, Shipley award 1976), Am. Gem Trade Assn. (hon.), Gem Assn. Australia (hon. v.p.), Gem Testing Lab. Gt. Britain (1st hon. life mem.), Bel Air Country Club (bd. dirs. 1980-83, Twenty-Four Karat Club (N.Y.C. and So.

Calif.), Sigma Xi, Sigma Gamma Epsilon. Developer system of diamond grading. Home: 1484 Allenford Ave Los Angeles CA 90049-3614 Office: Gemological Inst Am 1660 Stewart St Santa Monica CA 90404-4088

LIDDLE, ALAN CURTIS, architect; b. Tacoma, Mar. 10, 1922; s. Abram Dix and Myrtle (Maytum) L. B.Arch., U. Wash., 1948; postgrad., Eidgenoissche Technische Hochschule, Zurich, Switzerland, 1950-51. Asst. prof. architecture U. Wash., 1954-55; prin. Liddle & Jones, Tacoma, 1957-67, Alan Liddle & Jacklin, Tacoma, 1967-90, Liddle & Jacklin, Tacoma, 1990—. Architect oceanography bldgs, U. Wash., 1967, Tacoma Art Mus., 1971, Charles Wright Acad., Tacoma, 1962, Pacific Nat. Bank Wash., Auburn, 1965. Pres. bd. Allied Arts Tacoma, 1963-64, Civic Arts Commn. Tacoma-Pierce County, 1969; commr. Wash. Arts Commn., 1971; Bd. dirs. Tacoma Art Mus., Tacoma Zool. Soc., Tacoma Philharmonic, Inc. Served with AUS, 1943-46. Fellow A.I.A. (pres. S.W. Wash. chpt. 1967-68); mem. Wash. Hist. Soc., U. Wash. Alumni Assn. (all life). Home: 12735 Gravelly Lake Dr SW Tacoma WA 98499-1459 Office: 703 Pacific Ave Tacoma WA 98402-5207

LIDDY, EDWARD M., manufacturing company executive; b. 1945; married. Student, Cath. U., 1968; MBA, George Washington U., 1968. With Internat. Harvester Co., Ford Motor Co., Ryder Systems Inc., 1968-79; sr. v.p. G.D. Searle & Co., Skokie, Ill., 1979-85; with ADT Inc., N.Y.C., 1985—, now chief fin. officer, exec. v.p., dir. Office: Sears Roebuck & Co Sears Towers Chicago IL 60684

LIDDY, RICHARD A., insurance company executive; b. 1935. BS, Iowa State U., 1957. V.p. ops. Conn. Gen. Life, Hartford, 1957-82; exec. v.p. Continental Corp., 1982-88; pres., COO, now pres., CEO Gen. Am. Life Ins. Co., St. Louis, 1988—. Office: Gen Am Life Ins Co 700 Market St Saint Louis MO 63101-1829 also: Repertory Theatre St Louis PO Box 191730 Saint Louis MO 63119

LIDICKER, WILLIAM ZANDER, JR., zoologist, educator; b. Evanston, Ill., Aug. 19, 1932; s. William Zander and Frida (Schroeter) L.; m. Naomi Ishino, Aug. 18, 1956 (div. Oct., 1982); children: Jeffrey Roger, Kenneth Paul; m. Louise N. DeLonzor, June 5, 1989. B.S., Cornell U., 1953; M.S., U. Ill., 1954, Ph.D., 1957. Instr. zoology, asst. curator mammals U. Calif., Berkeley, 1957-59; asst. prof., asst. curator U. Calif., 1959-65, assoc. prof., assoc. curator, 1965-69; assoc. dir. Mus. Vertebrate Zoology, 1968-81, acting dir., 1974-75, prof. zoology, curator mammals, 1969-89, prof. integrative biology, curator of mammals, 1989—. Contbr. articles to profl. jours. Bd. dirs. No. Calif. Com. for Environ. Info., 1971-77; bd. trustees BIOSIS, 1987-92, chmn., 1992; N.Am. rep. steering com., sect. Mammalogy IUBS, UNESCO, 1978-89; chmn. rodent specialist group Species Survival Commn., IUCN, 1980-89; mem. sci. adv. bd. Marine World Found. at Marine World Africa USA, 1984—; pres. Dehnel-Petrusewicz Meml. Fund, 1985—. Fellow AAAS, Calif. Acad. Scis.; mem. Am. Soc. Mammalogists (dir., 2d v.p. 1974-76, pres. 1976-78, C.H. Merriam award 1986), Am. Soc. Naturalists, Berkeley Folk Dancers Club (pres. 1969, tchr. 1984—), others. Office: U Calif Mus Vertebrate Zoology Berkeley CA 94720

LIDOW, ERIC, electrical parts manufacturing company executive; b. Vilnius, Lithuania, Dec. 22, 1912; came to U.S., 1937, naturalized, 1941; s. Leon and Rachel (Schwartz) L.; m. Judith Margolis, July 2, 1939 (div. 1952); 1 son, Alan; m. Elizabeth Hay, Oct. 1952; children: Derek Balfour, Alexander. M. Elec. Engring., Technische Hochschule, Berlin, Germany, 1937. Elec. engr. Super Electric Co., Berlin, Germany, 1937; elec. devel. engr. Emby Products Cal., 1939-41; co-founder, v.p. Selenium Corp. Am., 1941-46; with Internat. Rectifier Corp., El Segundo, Calif., 1946—, now pres., chmn. bd., also dir. corp. and domestic and fgn. subsidiaries; Mem. Assos. Calif. Inst. Tech. Bd. dirs. Univ. Judea Found.; trustee City of Hope, Los Angeles County Mus. Art. Sr. mem. IEEE; mem. Am. Technion Soc. (v.p.). Achievements include patents in semiconductors. Home: 454 Cuesta Way Los Angeles CA 90077-3434 Office: Internat Rectifier Corp 233 Kansas St El Segundo CA 90245-4316

LIDTKE, DORIS KEEFE, computer science educator; b. Bottineau County, N.D., Dec. 6, 1929; d. Michael J. and Josephine (McDaniels) Keefe; m. Vernon L. Lidtke, Apr. 21, 1951. BS, U. Oreg., 1952; MEd cum laude, Johns Hopkins U., 1974; PhD, U. Oreg., 1979. Programmer analyst Shell Devel. Co., Emeryville, Calif., 1955-59, U. Calif., Berkeley, 1960-62; asst. prof. Lansing (Mich.) Community Coll., 1963-68; ednl. specialist Johns Hopkins U., Balt., 1968; assoc. program mgr. NSF, Washington, 1984-85; program dir., 1992-93; sr. mem. tech. staff Software Productivity Consortium, Reston, Va., 1987-88; asst. prof. Towson State U., Balt., 1968-80, assoc. prof., 1980-90, prof. computer sci., 1990—. Named Outstanding Educator, Assn. for Ednl. Data Systems, 1986. Mem. Assn. for Computing Machinery (coun. 1984-86, 94—, spl. interest group bd. 1985—, edn. bd. 1980—, chair 1994—, recognition Svc. award 1978, 83, 85, 86, 90, 91), Computer Soc. of IEEE (Outstanding Contbn. award 1986, 92), Nat. Edl. Computer Conf. (steering com., chmn. 1985-89, vice chmn. 1983-85, recognition award 1988, 92), Computing Scis. Accreditation Bd. (v.p. 1993—). Home: 4806 Wilmslow Rd Baltimore MD 21210-2328 Office: Towson State U Computer & Info Scis Baltimore MD 21204

LIDTKE, VERNON LEROY, history educator; b. Avon, S.D., May 4, 1930; s. Albert William and Aganeta (Boese) L.; m. Doris Eileen Keefe, Apr. 21, 1951. B.A., U. Oreg., 1952, M.A., 1955; Ph.D., U. Calif., Berkeley, 1962. Tchr. high sch. Riddle, Oreg., 1953-55; instr. social sci. U. Calif., Berkeley, 1960-62; asst. prof. history Mich. State U., 1962-66, asso. prof., 1966-68; vis. asst. prof. U. Calif., Berkeley, 1963; asso. prof. Johns Hopkins U., 1968-73, prof., 1973—, chmn. dept. history, 1975-79; chair Friends of the German Historical Inst., Washington, 1991-94; chair Modern European Sect., Am. Hist. Assn., 1992. Author: The Outlawed Party: Social Democracy in Germany, 1878-1890, 1966, The Alternative Culture: Socialist Labor in Imperial Germany, 1985; editorial bd.: Jour. Modern History, 1973-76, Central European History, 1982-89, Internat. Labor and Working Class History, 1984-89; contbr. articles to profl. jours. Fulbright research fellow, 1959-60, 66-67; Nat. Endowment Humanities fellow, 1969-70; fellow Wissenschaftekolleg zu Berlin, 1987-88. Mem. AAUP, Am. Hist. Assn., Conf. Group for Cen. European History (v.p. 1985, pres. 1986), Conf. Group German Politics (officer 1975-83), Johns Hopkins Club. Home: 4806 Wilmslow Rd Baltimore MD 21210-2328 Office: Johns Hopkins U Dept History Baltimore MD 21218

LIDZ, CHARLES WILMANNS, sociologist; b. Balt., Feb. 1, 1946; s. Theodore and Ruth (Wilmanns) L.; m. Christine MacDougall, June 18, 1967 (div. 1978); m. Lynn C. Brown, May 26, 1979; children: James H. Carwile, Heather M. Carwile, Molly E.M. Lidz. BA, Yale U., 1967; MA, Harvard U., 1968, PhD, 1974. Asst. prof. psychiatry and sociology U. Pitts., 1974-80, assoc. prof., 1980-86, prof., 1986—, assoc. dir. Ctr. for Med. Ethics, 1987—. Editor, Qualitative Sociology, 1987-91; co-author: Connections: Notes from the Heroin World, 1974, Heroin, Deviance and Morality, 1980, Informed Consent: A Study..., 1984, Informed Consent: Legal Theory and Clinical Practice, 1987, The Erosion of Autonomy in Long-Term Care, 1992. Co-founder New Haven Half-Way House, 1967; bd. dirs. Am. Chronic Pain Assn., Rocklin, Calif., 1982—, pres., 1987, 89; bd. dirs. Transitional Svcs., Inc., Pitts., 1986-93, 95—, v.p., 1991-92. Grantee NIMH, 1976-79, 85-94, Pres. Commn. on Bioethics, 1981-82, Retirement Rsch. Found., 1987-89, MacArthur Found., 1990—. Mem. Soc. for Study of Social Problems, Am. Sociol. Assn. Office: WPIC/U of Pitts 3811 O'Hara St Pittsburgh PA 15213-2593

LIEB, ELLIOTT HERSHEL, physicist, mathematician, educator; b. Boston, July 31, 1932; s. Sinclair M. and Clara (Rosenstein) L.; m. Christiane Fellbaum; children: Alexander, Gregory. BSc, MIT, 1953; PhD, U. Birmingham, Eng., 1956; DSc (hon.), U. Copenhagen, 1979; Dr. (hon.), Ecole Poly. Fed. Lausanne, Switzerland, 1995. With IBM Corp., 1960-63; sr. lectr. Fourah Bay Coll., Sierra Leone, 1961; mem. faculty Yeshiva U., 1963-66, Northeastern U., 1966-68; mem. faculty MIT, Cambridge, 1968-75, prof. physics, 1963-68, prof. math., 1968-73, prof. math. and physics, 1973-; prof. math. and physics Princeton (N.J.) U., 1975—. Author: (with D.C. Mattis) Mathematical Physics in One Dimension, 1966, (with B. Simon and A. Wightman) Studies in Mathematical Physics; also articles. Recipient Boris Pregel award chem. physics N.Y. Acad. Scis., 1970; Dannie Heineman

prize for mathematical physics Am. Inst. Physics and Am. Phys. Soc., 1978; Prix Scientifique, Union des Assurances de Paris, 1985; Birkhoff prize Am. Math. Soc. and Soc. Indsl. Applied Math., 1988; Max-Planck medal German Phys. Soc., 1992; Guggenheim Found. fellow, 1972, 78. Fellow Am. Phys. Soc.; mem. NAS, Austrian Acad. Scis., Danish Royal Acad., Am. Acad. Arts and Scis., Internat. Assn. Math. Physics (pres. 1982-84). Office: Princeton U Jadwin Hall-Physics Dept PO Box 708 Princeton NJ 08544-0708

LIEB, MICHAEL, English educator, humanities educator. AB in Eng. Lit., Rutgers U., 1962, AM in Eng. Lit., 1964, PhD in Eng. Lit., 1967; student, U. Iowa, 1962-63, U. Chgo. Divinity Sch., 1974-75, Spertus Coll. of Judaica, 1987-92. Asst. prof. Eng. Coll. of William and Mary, Williamsburg, Va., 1967-70; assoc. prof. Eng. U. Ill., Chgo., 1970-75, prof. Eng., 1975-88, rsch. prof. humanities, prof. Eng., 1988—; vis. professorial lectr. U. Chgo. Divinity Sch., 1979; bd. dirs. Friends of Milton's Cottage; mem. exec. com. U. Chgo. Renaissance Seminar, 1977—; mem. exec. com. Divsn. 17th Century Eng. Lit. MLA, 1982-86, Divsn. Religious Approaches to Lit., 1987-91; mem. exec. com. Ctr. Renaissance Studies Newberry Libr., 1979—, mem. com. Brit. Acad. Fellowships, 1982-83, mem. search com. for dir., 1984; mem. adv. com. 2d Internat. Milton Symposium, 1983, 4th, 1990; campus rep. Woodrow Wilson Found., 1982-83; mem. numerous coms. U. Ill. Author: The Dialectics of Creation: Patterns of Birth and Regeneration in Paradise Lost, 1970, Poetics of the Holy: A Reading of Paradise Lost, 1981 (James Holly Hanford award Milton Soc. Am.), The Sinews of Ulysses: Form and Convention in Milton's Works, 1989, The Visionary Mode: Biblical Prophecy, Hermeneutics and Cultural Change, 1991, Milton and the Culture of Violence, 1994; co-editor, contbg. author: Achievements of the Left Hand: Essays on the Prose of John Milton, 1974, Eyes Fast Fixt: Current Perspectives in Milton Methodology, 1975, Literary Milton: Text, Pretext, Context, 1994; contbr. articles to profl. jours.; symposia speaker in field; panelist; invited speaker; cons. edit. bds., univ. presses, profl. jours., lib"s., depts. Eng., Comparative Lit., Divinity. Pres., co-founder Oak Park Housing Ctr., 1971-73, Advocate award 1992; mem. hon. com. Ill. Humanities Coun., 1986; mem. Am. Jewish Com. Academicians Seminar, Israel, 1986. NEH U. Tchrs. fellow, 1991-92, John Simon Guggenheim Meml. Found. fellow 1987-88, U. Ill. Chgo. Inst. for Humanities sr. fellow 1983, Newberry Libr. Nat. Endowment for Humanities sr. fellow 1981-82, NEH Younger Humanist Study fellow 1974-75; recipient Am. Coun. Learned Societies Grant-in-Aid, 1985, Am. Philosophical Soc. Grant-in-Aid, 1983, Folger Shakespeare Libr. fellow, 1970, 74; Honors Coll. U. Ill. Chgo. fellow 1986—; others. Mem. Milton Soc. Am. (chair James Holly Hanford awards com. 1991-93, treas. 1973-77, v.p. 1980, pres. 1981, honored scholar 1992), Modern Lang. Assn., Milton Soc. of Japan, Southeastern Renaissance Conf., Renaissance Soc. of Am., Calif. Renaissance Conf., Northeastern Modern Lang. Assn., Newberry Libr. Milton Seminar (co-founder, co-chair 1986—), Newberry Libr. Dante Lectures. Home: 212 S Ridgeland Ave Oak Park IL 60302-3226 Office: U Ill Chgo Dept Eng M/c 162 Chicago IL 60607

LIEBELER, SUSAN WITTENBERG, lawyer; b. New Castle, Pa., July 3, 1942; d. Sherman K. and Eleanor (Klivans) Levine; BA, U. Mich., 1963, postgrad. U. Mich., 1963-64; LLB (Stein scholar), UCLA, 1966; m. Wesley J. Liebeler, Oct. 21, 1971; 1 child, Jennifer. Bar: Calif. 1967, Vt. 1972, D.C. 1988. Law clk. Calif. Ct. of Appeals, 1966-67; assoc. Gang, Tyre & Brown, 1967-68, Greenberg, Bernhard, Weiss & Karma, L.A., 1968-70; assoc. gen. counsel Rep. Corp., L.A., 1970-72; gen. counsel Verit Industries, L.A., 1972-73; prof. of law law sch. Loyola U., L.A., 1973-84; spl. counsel, chmn. John S. R. Shad, SEC, Washington, 1981-82; commr. U.S. Internat. Trade Commn. Washington, 1984-88, vice chmn., 1984-86, chmn., 1986-88; ptnr. Irell & Manella, L.A., 1988-94; sr. v.p. Legal Rsch. Network, Inc., L.A., 1994; vis. prof. U. Tex., summer 1982; cons. Office of Policy Coordination, office of Pres.-elect, 1981-82; cons. U.S. Ry. Assn., 1975, U.S. EPA, 1974, U.S. Price Commn., 1972; mem. Administrv. Conf. U.S., 1986-88. Mem. editorial adv. bd. Regulation mag. CATO Inst. 1984-, ABA, State Bar Calif. (treas., vice chair, chair exec. com. internat. law sect.), L.A. County Bar Assn., D.C. Bar Assn., Practicing Law Inst. (internat. law adv. com.), ITC Trial Lawyers Assn., Washington Legal Found. (acad. adv. bd.), bd. dirs. Century City Hosp., adv. bd. U. Calif. Orientation in U.S.A. Law, Order of Coif. Jewish. Sr. editor UCLA Law Review, 1965-66; contbr. articles to legal publ.

LIEBELER, WESLEY J., law educator, lawyer; b. 1931. B.A., Macalester Coll., 1953; J.D., U. Chgo., 1957. Bar: N.Y. 1958. Assoc. Carter, Ledyard & Milburn, N.Y.C., 1958-64; prof. UCLA Sch. Law, 1965—; dir. Office Policy Planning FTC, Washington, 1974-75; cons. in field; asst. counsel Pres.'s Commn. on Assassination Pres. Kennedy, 1964. Served with U.S. Army. Mem. Western Econ. Assn. Mem. Order of Coif. Past articles editor U. Chgo. Law Rev. Office: UCLA Law Sch 405 Hilgard Ave Los Angeles CA 90024-1301

LIEBENSON, HERBERT, economist, trade association executive; b. Chgo., July 26, 1920; s. Michael and Evelyn (Zimmerman) L.; m. Gloria Rachel Krasnow, Mar. 11, 1944; children: Lauren Ward, Lynn Green. B.A., Roosevelt U., 1948; postgrad., U. Chgo., 1948, Am. U., 1949-52. Research assoc. United Mineworkers Pension and Welfare Fund, Washington, 1948-52; employee benefit/labor relations analyst C. of C. U.S., Washington, 1952-58; with Nat. Small Bus. Assn., Washington, 1958—; v.p. Nat. Small Bus. Assn., 1958-80, pres., 1980-86, sr. cons., 1986—; exec. dir. Small Bus. Legis. Council, 1980-86, chmn. tech. for new products and jobs, 1986—; mem. exec. com., chmn. com. on taxation SBA Nat. Adv. Council, 1982-86; pres. del. White House Conf. on Small Bus., 1986; mem. Sec. Labor's mgmt. adv. com. on Landrum-Griffin Act, U.S. Employment Service Adv. Com.; mem. adv. com. on jobs Dept. Commerce Com. on Product Standards; alt. mem. Presdl. Pay Bd., 1973-74; mem. steering com. Nat. Com. to Preserve Family Bus., 1981; mem. nat. com. Am. Energy Week, 1981. Served with USAAF, 1942-46. Mem. Indsl. Relations Research Assn. (pres. chpt. 1961-62), Bus. Adv. Council Fed. Reports (bd. govrs. 1970-85), Am. Soc. Assn. Execs. Jewish. Club: Internat. Home: 2703 Unicorn Ln NW Washington DC 20015-2233

LIEBER, CHARLES DONALD, publisher; b. Scheveningen, The Netherlands, Jan. 30, 1921; came to U.S., 1941, naturalized, 1944; s. Edmund Z. and Gabrielle (Lifczis) L.; m. Miriam Levin, July 17, 1960; children: John Nathan, James Edmund, George Theodore, Anne Gabrielle. Student, U. Brussels, 1938-40; B.A., New Sch. for Social Research, 1948. With H. Bittner & Co. (Pubs.), N.Y.C., 1947-49; with Alfred A. Knopf, Inc., 1949-52; dir. coll. dept. Random House, N.Y.C., 1952-64; pub. Atherton Press, N.Y.C., 1964-67; pres. Atherton Press, Inc., N.Y.C., 1967-70; v.p. Aldine-Atherton, Inc., N.Y.C., Chgo., 1971-72; pres. Lieber-Atherton, Inc., N.Y.C., 1972—; gen. mgr. Hebrew Pub. Co., 1980-85, pres., 1985—; pres. Lieber Publs., Inc., N.Y.C., 1981—. Author: (with A.D. Murphy) Great Events of World History, 1964; chmn. nat. editorial bd. Reconstructionist mag., 1983—. Chmn. West Side Jewish Community Council, Manhattan, 1978-82, mem. at large, 1977—; exec. bd. Jewish Reconstrn. Found., 1978-83, vice chmn., 1979-80, chmn., 1980-83, nat. bd. dirs., 1983-92; trustee Std. Ann's Sch., 1983-89; trustee Soc. for the Advancement Judaism, 1974-90, treas., 1976-79, co-chmn., 1979-81; bd. dirs. Hebrew Arts Sch., 1974-82. Fedn. Reconstructionist Congregations, 1983-91. Lt. AUS, 1942-46, CBI. Recipient Mordecai M. Kaplan award Jewish Reconstructionist Found., 1988. Mem. Coll. Pubs. Group (chmn. 1965-66), Assn. Jewish Book Pubs. (pres. 1988-90). Office: Hebrew Publishing Co PO Box 222 Spencertown NY 12165

LIEBER, CHARLES SAUL, physician, educator; b. Antwerp, Belgium, Feb. 13, 1931; came to U.S., 1958, naturalized, 1966; s. Isaac and Lea (Maj) L.; m. M. A. Leo; children: Colette, Daniel, Leah, Samuel, Sarah. Candidate in natural and med. sci., U. Brussels, 1951; M.D., 1955. Intern, resident U. Hosp., Brugmann, Brussels, Belgium, 1954-56; research fellow med. found. Queen Elizabeth, 1956-58; research fellow Thorndike Meml. Lab., Harvard Med. Sch., 1958-60, instr., 1961, assoc., 1962; assoc. prof. medicine Cornell U., 1963-68; prof. liver disease and nutrition unit Bellevue Hosp., N.Y.C., 1963-68; chief sect. liver disease, nutrition and GI-Liver Tng. Program VA Hosp., Bronx, N.Y., 1968—; prof. medicine Mt. Sinai Sch. Medicine, 1969—; prof. pathology, 1976—; dir. Alcohol Research and Treatment Ctr., 1977—; assoc. vis. physician Cornell Med. div. Bellevue, Meml., James Ewing hosps., 1964-69; Am. Coll. Gastroenterology disting. lectr., 1978, Henry Baker lectr., 1979. Recipient award of Belgian Govt. for rsch. on gastric secretion,

1956, Rsch. Career Devel. award NIH, USPHS, 1964-68, E.M. Jellinek Meml. award, 1976, A. Boudreau award Laval U., 1977, W.S. Middleton award, 1977, Leahy Rsch. award, highest honor for med. rsch. Dept. Vets. Affairs, 1994. Fellow AAAS; mem. Assn. Am. Physicians, N.Y. Gastroent. Assn. (pres. 1974-75), Am. Soc. Biochemistry and Molecular Biology, ACP, Am. Inst. Nutrition, Am. Soc. Addictive Medicine (pres. 1974-77, Sci. Achievement award 1989), Assn. Clin. Biochemists (Kone award 1994), Am. Soc. Clin. Nutrition (McCollum award 1973, pres. 1975-76, Robert H. Herman Memorial award 1993), Am. Coll. Nutrition (Outstanding Achievement award, 1990), Am. Soc. Clin. Investigation, Am. Soc. Pharmacol. Exptl. Therapy, Am. Gastroent. Assn. (Disting. Achievement award 1973, Hugh R. Butt award for liver/nutrition 1992), Research Soc. on Alcoholism (pres. 1977-79, Sci. Excellence award 1980, Disting. Svc. award 1992), Am. Coll. Nutrition (Outstanding Achievement award 1990, Am. Assn. Study Liver Diseases. Home: 6 Innes Ave Englewood Cliffs NJ 07632-2107 Office: 130 W Kingsbridge Rd Bronx NY 10468-3904

LIEBER, DAVID LEO, university president; b. Stryj, Poland, Feb. 20, 1925; came to U.S., 1927, naturalized, 1936; s. Max and Gussie (Jarmush) L.; m. Esther Kobre, June 10, 1945; children—Michael, Daniel, Deborah, Susan. B.A., CCNY, 1944; B.Hebrew Lit., Jewish Theol. Sem. Am., 1944, M.Hebrew Lit., 1948, D. Hebrew Lit., 1951; M.A., Columbia, 1947; postgrad., U. Wash., 1954-55, UCLA, 1961-63; L.D.H. hon., Hebrew Union Coll., 1982—. Ordained rabbi, 1948. Rabbi, 1948, Sinai Temple, Los Angeles, 1950-54; dir. (B'nai B'rith Hillel), Seattle, Cambridge, 1954-56; dean students U. Judaism, Los Angeles, 1956-63; Samuel A. Fryer prof. Bible, pres. U. Judaism, 1963-92, Skovron Disting. Svc. prof. Bibl. lit., 1990—, pres. emeritus, 1992—; pres. emeritus U. Judaism, L.A., 1992—; lectr. Hebrew UCLA, 1957-90; vice chancellor Jewish Theol. Sem., 1972-92; mem. exec. coun. Rabbinical Assembly, 1966-69, v.p., 1994—; vice chmn. Am. Jewish Com., L.A., 1972-75; bd. dirs. Jewish Fedn. Coun., L.A., 1980-86, bd. govs., 1986—. Mem. editorial bd.: Conservative Judaism, 1968-70. Served as chaplain USAF, 1951-53. Mem. Assn. Profs. Jewish Studies (dir. 1970-71), Phi Beta Kappa. Office: U Judaism 15600 Mulholland Dr Los Angeles CA 90077-1519

LIEBER, DAVID LESLIE, journalist; b. Gastonia, N.C., June 26, 1957; s. Stanley J. and Denise (Berwald) L.; m. Karen Pasciutti, Feb. 18, 1995; stepchildren: Maddie Lauren, Jonathan Lawrence. BA in Am. Civilization, U. Pa., 1979. Feature writer, media columnist Ft. Myers (Fla.) News-Press, 1980-81; statehouse reporter Charleston (W.Va.) Gazette, 1981-83; staff writer Phila. Inquirer, 1983-93; metro columnist Ft. Worth (Tex.) Star-Telegram, 1993—. Named Outstanding Journalist W.va. Trial Lawyers Assn, 1982-83; recipient Smolar award Coun. Jewish Fedns., 1989. Mem. Investigative Reporters and Editors, Soc. Profl. Journalists, Pen and Pencil, Nat. Soc. Newspaper Columnists, Lonesome Dove Cemetery Assn. Avocation: political memorabilia collector. Office: Ft Worth Star-Telegram 3201 Airport Fwy Bedford TX 76021-6036

LIEBER, EDWARD JOSEPH, lawyer; b. L.A., May 6, 1921; s. John and Margaret (Gotto) L.; m. Mary Louise Connelly, Aug. 5, 1945; children: Mary, Maureen, Edward, Elaine, Michael, Arthur. BBA, Loyola U., L.A., 1947, LLB, 1959. Bar: Calif. 1960, U.S. Dist. Ct. (all distrs.) Calif. 1960. Assoc. counsel Calif. Dept. Ins., L.A., 1947-62; ptnr. Luckham, Fenton and Lieber, L.A., 1962-74; sec., gen. counsel Fremont Gen. Corp., Glendale, Calif., 1974—. 1st lt. USAF, 1943-45, ETO. Mem. ABA, State Bar Calif., Los Angeles County Bar Assn. Republican. Roman Catholic. Office: Fremont Gen Corp 500 N Brand Blvd Glendale CA 91203

LIEBER, ROBERT J., political science educator, writer; b. Chgo., Sept. 29, 1941; m. Nancy Isaksen; 2 children. BA with High Honors in Polit. Sci., U. Wis., 1963; postgrad. in Polit. Sci., U. Chgo., 1963-64; PhD in Govt., Harvard U., 1968; postgrad. St. Antony's Coll., Oxford (Eng.) U., 1969-70. Asst. prof. Polit. Sci. U. Calif., Davis, 1968-72, assoc. prof., 1972-77, chmn. dept. Polit. Sci., 1975-76, 77-80, prof., 1977-81; prof. Georgetown U., Washington, 1982—, chmn. dept. govt., 1990-96; vis. prof. Oxford U., 1969, Fudan U., Shanghai, China, 1988; rsch. assoc. Ctr. Internat. Affairs, Harvard U., 1974-75; cons. U.S. Dept. State and Dept. Def., 1975—; presdl. and strategic study groups on U.S. Mid East policy Washington Inst. Near East Policy, 1987-88, 90-92; com. peace and security in the Gulf, 1991. Author: British Politics and European Unity, 1970, Theory and World Politics, 1972, Oil and the Middle East War: Europe in the Energy Crisis, 1976, The Oil Decade: Conflict and Cooperation in the West, 1983, No Common Power: Understanding International Relations, 1988, 2d edit., 3d edit., 1995; co-author: Contemporary Politics: Europe, 1976; e tor, contbg. author: Eagle Entangled: U.S. Foreign Policy in a Complex World, 1979, Eagle Defiant: U.S. Foreign Policy in the 1980s, 1983, Will Europe Fight for Oil?, 1983, Eagle Resurgent? The Reagan Era in American Foreign Policy, 1987; co-editor, contbg. author: Eagle in a New World: American Grand Strategy in the Post-Cold War Era, 1992; contbr. articles to Harper's, Politique Etrangere, New York Times, Washington Post, Christian Science Monitor, others; contbr. articles to profl. jours.; TV appearances include Nightline, Good Morning America, This Week with David Brinkley, Crossfire, others. Advanceman nat. campaign staff McCarthy for Pres.; 1968; fgn. policy advisor presdl. campaigns of Sen. Edward Kennedy, 1979-80, Walter Mondale. 1984, Bill Clinton, 1991-92; coord. Mid. East Issues presdl. campaign Michael Dukakis, 1988. Woodrow Wilson fellow, 1963, fellow NDEA, 1963-64, Harvard U., 1964-68, Social Sci. Rsch. Coun., 1969-70, Coun. Fgn. Rels., 1972-73, Guggenheim Found., 1973-74, Rockefeller Found., 1978-79, Wilson Ctr. Smithsonian Inst., 1980-81, Ford Found., 1981; vis. fellow Atlantic Inst. Internat. Affairs, Paris, 1978-79; guest scholar Brookings Inst., 1981. Mem. Coun. on Fgn. Rels., Internat. Inst. for Strategic Studies, Phi Beta Kappa. Office: Georgetown U Dept of Government Washington DC 20057

LIEBER, STANLEY MARTIN See LEE, STAN

LIEBERMAN, ARCHIE, photographer, writer; b. Chgo., July 17, 1926; s. Sol and Rose (Schiff) L.; m. Esther Kraus, Jan. 11, 1948; children—Eric Joseph, Robert David Vories, Kurt Murrow. Student, Inst. Design, Chgo., 1946-48. Contract photographer Time Mag., Chgo., 1950-51; staff photographer Black Star Pub. Co., N.Y.C., 1951-61; adj. prof. Photog. Sem., 1976-74; instr. Columbia Coll., Chgo., 1968-74. One man shows include Presbyn.-St. Luke's Hosp., Chgo., Chapel Hill Shopping Ctr., Akron, Ohio Mchts. Assn., Flint, Mich., Arie Crown Theater, Chgo., Carson Pirie Scott & Co., Chgo., Prudential Bldg., Chgo. Agr. U.S.A., Soviet Union, U. Ill., Lake Forest Coll., Kodak Gallery, Grand Central Sta., N.Y.C., Rizzoli Gallery, Chgo., U. Dubuque (retrospective), 1987, Dubuque Mus. Art, Lands End Gallery, Dodgeville, Wis., 1991, Ford Ctr. Fine Art-Knox Coll., 1993, Elveahjem Mus., Madison, Wis., 1994, Freeport Art Mus., 1994, Lake Forest Coll., 1995; group shows include Jewish Mus., N.Y.C., Tower Gallery, Chgo., Garrett Bible Inst., Evanston, Met. Mus. Art, N.Y.C., Expo '67, Montreal, Art Inst. Chgo., 1986, Photography in Fine Arts, N.Y.C., San Diego Mus. Photographic Arts, 1986, Mitchell Mus., Mt. Vernon, Ill., 1987, 88, The Art Inst. of Chgo., 1986, 92, numerous others; author, photographer: The Israelis, 1965 (One of Best 50 Books award), Farm Boy (Friends of Lit. award), Neighbors, 1993; photographer books: Shalom, A Solitary Life, The Future of Religions, The Eternal Life, Holy Holy Land, The Story of Israel, Chicago In Color, Chicago, God Make Me Brave For Life, (with Ray Bradbury) The Mummies of Guanajuato, Chicago: A Celebration, 1990; photojournalist for mags. including: Look, Life, Saturday Evening Post, Collier's, Ladies Home Jour., Fortune, London Illustrated, Redbook, Farm Jour., Pageant, Parade, Bus. Week, Am. Weekly, Venture, U.S. News & World Report, Newsweek, Paris Match, Chgo. Mag.; indsl. photographer for corps. including Inland Steel, Acme Steel, Lands' End, Harvester, Gould Inc., McDonald's, Motorola, Grumman Corp., Internat. Minerals & Chem. Corp.; advt. photographs for: Allstate Ins., Phillip Morris, Schlitz, United Airlines, Jack Daniel, others. Recipient Peter Lisagor award Headline Club of Sigma Delta Chi, 1980; Sinai Health Service award Mt. Sinai Hosp. Med. ctr., Chgo., 1985; various award U. Mo. Sch. Photog. Clubs: Arts of Chgo., Chgo. Press Photog. Office: PO Box 61 Scales Mound IL 61075-0061

LIEBERMAN, CAROL COOPER, healthcare marketing communications consultant, city planning administrator; b. St. Louis, June 14, 1938; d. Norman Leonard and Ethel (Silver) Mistachkin; m. Malcolm P. Cooper, Aug. 25, 1962 (div. June 1977); children: Lawrence, Edward, Marcus; m.

Edward Lieberman, Apr. 1992. BS, U. Wis., 1959; MA, N.Y. Inst. Tech., 1992. Media buyer Lennen and Newell, Los Angeles, 1959-61; advt. mgr. Hartfield-Zodys, Los Angeles, 1961-62, Haggarty's, L.A., 1962-63; sales rep. Abbott Labs., Bklyn., 1974-75; edn. dir. N.Y. and N.J. Regional Transp. Program, N.Y.C., 1975-78; account exec. Med. Edn. Dynamics, Woodbridge, N.J., 1978-79; dir. program devel. Kallir, Phillips & Ross Info. Media, N.Y.C., 1979-81; exec. v.p. sales and mktg. Audio Visual Med. Mktg., N.Y.C., 1981-85; exec. v.p. Park Row Pubs./John Wiley & Sons Med. Div. N.Y.C., 1985-88; pres., prin. Park Row Pubs., N.Y.C., 1988-91; healthcare mktg. communications cons., Southampton, N.Y., 1991—; cons., prof. comms. and speech N.Y. Inst. Tech., 1991—; exec. dir. Bus. Improvement Dist., Riverhead, N.Y., 1994—; cons. Am. Acad. Physician Assts., Washington, 1986-87, Am. Soc. Anesthesiologists, Chgo., 1986-88, Am. Acad. Family Physicians, 1987-91, Am. Psychiat. Assn., 1988, Am. Coll. Gen. Practitioners, 1988, N.Am. Soc. Pacing and Electrophysiology, 1988-91. Editor pub. med. papers, med. films, med. jours. for pharmaceutical cos. Mem. Am. Women in Radio and TV, Soc. Tchrs. Family Medicine (cons.), Pharm. Advt. Council, Nat. Council Jewish Women, Hadassah. Avocations: tennis, writing fiction, classical piano. Home and Office: 41 Barkers Island Rd Southampton NY 11968

LIEBERMAN, CHARLES, economist; b. Landsburg, Bavaria, Germany, July 25, 1948; s. Leo and Tola (Melcer) L.; m. Anne Rosenberg, Aug. 26, 1972; children: David, Michael, Jeremy. BS, MIT, 1970; AM in Econs., U. Pa., 1972, PhD in Econs., 1974. Asst. prof. U. Md., College Park, 1974-79; vis. assoc. prof. Northwestern U., Evanston, Ill., 1978-79; economist Fed. Res. Bank N.Y., N.Y.C., 1979-81; sr. economist Morgan Stanley, N.Y.C., 1981-83; v.p., sr. economist Shearson Lehman Bros., N.Y.C., 1983-86; mng. dir., dir. fin. market rsch. Chem. Securities Inc./Mfrs. Hanover Securities Corp., N.Y.C., 1986—; econs. commentator CNBC. Author: (newsletter) Market Commentary; contbr. articles to profl. jours. Sgt. U.S. Army Res., 1970-76. Stonier fellow, 1973, Fellow NSF, 1971. Mem. Forecasters Club N.Y. (treas. 1987-89, v.p. 1990-91, pres. 1991-92), Money Marketeers NYU (bd. govs., v.p., pres. 1992-93). Jewish. Avocations: tennis, skiing, classical music. Office: Chemical Securites 270 Park Ave New York NY 10017-2014 *Work hard, play hard, and enjoy life.*

LIEBERMAN, DAVID, law educator; b. Canton, Ohio, May 21, 1953; s. George Bernard and Sylvia (Klein) L.; m. Carol Louise Brownstein, Dec. 20, 1987; 1 child, George. BA with honors, Cambridge U., Eng., 1974, MA, 1978; PhD, U. London, Eng., 1980. Rsch. fellow St. Catharines Coll., Cambridge, Eng., 1978-82; fellow, lectr. Christ's Coll., Cambridge, Eng., 1982-83; acting prof. U. Calif., Berkeley, 1984-89, prof. law sch., 1989—. Author: Province of Legislation Determined, 1989. Rsch. fellow Am. Bar Found., 1978-79, Inst. Hist. Rsch., 1977-78; hon. rsch. fellow U. Coll. London U., 1986. Mem. Am. Soc. for Legal History, Internat. Soc. for Utilitarian Studies. Office: U Calif Sch Law Boalt Hall Berkeley CA 94720

LIEBERMAN, DAVID IRA, mathematician, administrator; b. Newark, Aug. 8, 1941; s. Milton M. and Jeannette (Feierstein) ; m. Marcia H. Israelite, Aug. 30, 1964; children: Lisa, Benjamin. AB in Math., Harvard U., 1963; PhD in Math., MIT, 1966. Mem. Inst. for Advanced Study, Princeton, N.J., 1966-68; prof. math. Brandeis U., Waltham, Mass., 1968-77; dep. dir. Communications Research Div. Inst. for Def. Analyses, Princeton, 1977-85; dir. Inst. for Def. Analyses, Princeton, 1985-91, mem. rsch. staff, 1991—; vis. faculty Princeton U., 1967-69, 81-82, Harvard U., Cambridge, Mass., 1973, Purdue U., Lafayette, Ind., 1973, Inst. des Hautes Etudes Scientifiques, 1975-76; founder Ctr. for Comms. Rsch., LaJolla. Mem. editorial bd. Advances in Applied Math., 1985—; contbr. articles to math. jours.; achievements include research in analysis of qualitative behavior of solutions of large systems of algebraic and differential equations; dynamical systems on Kahler manifolds and algebraic varieties; invariants of and deformations of algebraic cycles and the theory of intermediate Jacobians. Treas. Jewish Ctr., Princeton, 1984-85, trustee, 1989-90. Recipient fellowship NSF, 1963-66, 66-68, Sloan Found., 1972-73. Mem. IEEE, Am. Math. Soc., Math. Assn. Am., Harvard Club of N.J. (schs. com. 1977-92, v.p. 1991), Ctrl. N.J. Squash Racquet Assn., Phi Beta Kappa, Sigma Xi. Avocations: music, squash, cross-country skiing. Home: 15 Woodhollow Rd Lawrenceville NJ 08648-4910 Office: Ctr for Comms Rsch Thanet Rd Princeton NJ 08540

LIEBERMAN, EDWARD JAY, lawyer; b. Evansville, Ind., Apr. 8, 1946; s. Heiman George and Anna Sharp (Blacker) L.; m. Ellen Ackerman Wequsen, June 1, 1969; 1 child: Laura Amy. BSBA, Washington U., St. Louis, 1968, JD, 1971. Bar: Mo. 1971. Jr. ptnr. Bryan Cave, St. Louis, 1972-76; assoc. counsel 1st Nat. Bank in St. Louis, 1976-80; ptnr. Lowenhaupt, Chasnoff, Armstrong & Mellitz, St. Louis, 1980-84, Husch & Eppenberger, St. Louis, 1984—. Mem. ABA, Mo. Bar, Bar Assn. Met. St. Louis, Am. Coll. Mortgage Attys. Office: Husch & Eppenberger 100 N Broadway Ste 1300 Saint Louis MO 63102

LIEBERMAN, FREDRIC, ethnomusicologist, educator; b. N.Y.C., Mar. 1, 1940; s. Stanley and Bryna (Mason L.). MusB, U. Rochester, 1962; MA in Ethnomusicology, U. Hawaii, 1965; PhD in Music, UCLA, 1971; diploma in Electronics, Cleve. Inst. Electronics, 1973; cert. Inst. for Ednl. Mgmt., Harvard U., 1984. Asst. prof. music Brown U., Providence, 1968-75; assoc. prof. U. Wash., Seattle, 1975-83, chmn. dir. ethnomusicology, 1977-80, dir. sch. music, 1981-83; prof. U. Calif., Santa Cruz, 1983—, dir. dept. arts, 1983-85, provost Porter Coll., 1983-85; chmn. Bd. of Studies in Music, 1988-92; fieldworker Taiwan and Japan, 1963-64, Sikkim, winter 1970, Madras, India, winters 1977, 78, 82, 83; mem. folk arts panel Nat. Endowment for Arts, 1977-80, internat. panel, 1979-80; panelist basic rsch. divsn. NEH, 1982-84, Calif. Arts Coun., 1993; fieldworker, presenter Smithsonian Instn. Festival Am. Folklife, 1978-82; reviewer Ctr. for Scholarly Communication with People's Republic China, 1979—; exchange lectr. U. Warsaw, Poland, spring 1980; co-dir. summer seminar for coll. tchrs. NEH, 1977; dir. Am. Musical Heritage Found., 1991—. Author: Chinese Music: An Annotated Bibliography, 1970, 2d edit., 1979, A Chinese Zither Tutor: The Mei-An Ch'in-P'u, 1983, (with Mickey Hart) Drumming at the Edge of Magic, 1990, Planet Drum: A Celebration of Percussion and Rhythm, 1991; editor (with Fritz A. Kuttner) Perspectives on Asian Music: Essays in Honor of Lawrence Picken, 1975; gen. editor Garland Bibliographies in Ethnomusicology, 1980-86; mem. editorial bd. Musica Asiatica, 1984—; contbr. numerous articles and revs. to profl. publs.; composer: Suite for Piano, 1964, Sonatina for Piano, 1964, Two Short String Quartets, 1966, Leaves of Brass (for brass quartet), 1967, Psalm 137; By the Rivers of Babylon (for chorus), 1971; records include China I: String Instruments, 1969, China II: Amoy Music, 1971, Music of Sikkim, 1975; ethnomusicology cons. 360 Degrees Prodns., 1988—; filmer, editor (with Michael Moore) Traditional Music and Dance of Sikkim, Parts I and II, 1976; producer, dir., editor videotape Documenting Traditional Performance, 1978. Mem. exec. bd. Pub. Radio Sta. KRAB-FM, Seattle, 1977-78; mem. King County Arts Commn., Seattle, 1977-80. Grantee Nat. Endowment for the Arts, NEH, 1978, 80; N.Y. State Regents fellow, 1958-62, East-West Ctr. fellow and travel grantee, 1962-65, UCLA Chancellor's teaching fellow, 1965-69, John D. Rockefeller 3d Fund research fellow, 1970-71. Mem. NARAS, Soc. for Ethnomusicology (editor Ethnomusicology 1977-81, nat. coun. 1970-72, 74-76, 78-81, 83-86), Soc. for Asian Music (editorial bd. Asian Music 1968-77, editor publs. series 1968—), Coll. Music Soc. (nat. coun. 1973-75, exec. bd. 1974-75, 76-77), Conf. on Chinese Oral and Performing Lit. (exec. bd. 1971-74, 78-80), ASCAP, Internat. Coun. Traditional Music, Am. Musical Heritage Found. (treas. 1991—), Phi Mu Alpha Sinfonia. Avocations: amateur radio, photography. Office: U Calif Porter Coll Santa Cruz CA 95064

LIEBERMAN, GAIL FORMAN, financial executive; b. Phila., May 26, 1943; d. Joseph and Rita (Groder) Forman. BA in Physics and Math., Temple U., 1964, MBA in Fin., 1977. Dir. internat. fin. Standard Brands Inc., N.Y.C., 1977-79; staff v.p. fin. and capital planning RCA Corp., 1979-82; CFO, exec. v.p. Scali McCabe Sloves, Inc., 1982-93; v.p. finance, CFO, mng. dir. Moody's Investors Svc., N.Y.C., 1994—; bd. dirs. Allied Devices, Inc. Bd. dirs. Vineyard Theater Group, N.Y.C. Mem. Fin. Execs. Inst. Office: Moody's Investor Svcs 99 Church St New York NY 10007-2701

LIEBERMAN, GERALD J., statistics educator; b. N.Y.C., Dec. 31, 1925; s. Joseph and Ida (Margolis) L.; m. Helen Herbert, Oct. 27, 1950; children—Janet, Joanne, Michael, Diana. B.S. in Mech. Engring., Cooper Union, 1948; A.M. in Math. Stats., Columbia U., 1949; Ph.D., Stanford U., 1953. Math. statistician Nat. Bur. Standards, 1949-50; mem. faculty Stanford U., 1953—, prof. statistics and indsl. engring., 1959-67, prof. statistics and operations research, 1967—, chmn. dept. operations research, 1967-75, assoc. dean Sch. Humanities and Scis., 1975-77, acting v.p. and provost, 1979, vice provost, 1977-85, dean research, 1977-80, dean grad. studies and research, 1980-85, provost, 1992-93; cons. to govt. and industry, 1953—. Author: (with A.H. Bowker) Engineering Statistics, 1959, 2d edit., 1972, (with F.S. Hillier) Introduction to Operations Research, 1967, 6th edit., 1995. Ctr. Advanced Studies in Behavioral Scis. fellow, 1985-86. Fellow Am. Statis. Assn., Inst. Math. Statistics, Am. Soc. Quality Control (Shewhart medal 1972), AAAS; mem. Nat. Acad. Engring., Inst. Mgmt. Sci. (pres. 1980-81), Ops. Research Soc. Am., Sigma Xi, Pi Tau Sigma. Home: 811 San Francisco Ter Stanford CA 94305-1021

LIEBERMAN, JAMES, federal agency administrator; b. Providence, Nov. 24, 1945. BSME, U. R.I., 1967; MS in Thermal Engring., Cornell U., 1969; JD with honors, George Washington U., 1974. Bar: Va. 1974, D.C. 1976. Engr. Combustion Engring. Co., Windsor, Conn., 1967; devel. engr. Eastman Kodak Co., Rochester, N.Y., 1968-71; legal asst. Berlin, Roisman & Kessler, Washington, 1973; law clk. McKean, Whitehead & Wilson, Washington, 1973-74; atty. Office of Exec. Legal Dir. NRC, Washington, 1974-81, dir. enforcement staff Office Inspection and Enforcement, 1982, chief counsel for regional ops. and enforcement, 1982-86, asst. gen. for enforcement, chief counsel regional ops., 1986-87, dir. Office of Enforcement, 1987—. Contbr. articles to profl. publs. John McMullen fellow, 1967-69. Office: NRC Office of Enforcement Washington DC 20555

LIEBERMAN, JOSEPH I., senator; b. Stamford, Conn., Feb. 24, 1942; s. Henry and Marcia (Manger) L.; m. Hadassah Freilich, Mar. 20, 1983; children: Matthew, Rebecca, Ethan, Hana. B.A., Yale U., 1964, J.D., 1967. Bar: Conn. 1967. Mem. Conn. Senate, 1971-81, Senate majority leader, 1975-81; ptnr. Lieberman, Segaloff & Wolfson, New Haven, 1972-83; atty. gen. State of Conn., Hartford, 1983-89; U.S. Senator from Conn., 1989—. Author: The Power Broker, 1966, The Scorpion and the Tarantula, 1970, The Legacy, 1981, Child Support in America, 1986. Democrat. Jewish. Office: 316 Hart Senate Office Bldg Washington DC 20510

LIEBERMAN, LAURENCE, poet, educator; b. Detroit, Feb. 16, 1935; s. Nathan and Anita (Cohen) L.; m. Bernice Clair Braun, June 17, 1956; children—Carla, Deborah, Isaac. BA, U. Mich., 1956, MA in English, 1958; postgrad., U. Calif.-Berkeley. Prof. English Coll. V.I., 1964-68; prof. English and creative writing U. Ill., Urbana, 1968—; U. Ill. Ctr. for Advanced Study Creative Writing fellow, Japan, 1971-72. Author: The Unblinding, 1968, The Achievement of James Dickey, 969, The Osprey Suicides, 1973, Unassigned Frequencies: American Poetry in Review (1964-77), 1977, God's Measurements, 1980, Eros at the World Kite Pageant: Poems (1979-82), 1983, The Mural of Wakeful Sleep, 1985, (poems) The Creole Mephistopheles, 1989, The Best American Poetry, 1991 (award), New and Selected Poems (1962-92), 1993, (poems) The St. Kitts Monkey Feuds, 1995, Beyond the Muse of Memory: Essays on Contemporary Poets, 1995; poetry editor poetry books program U. Ill. Press, 1970—; contbr. poetry to lit. jours., popular mags. Recipient award for Best Poems of 1968, Nat. Endowment for Arts, 1969, Jerome P. Shestack award Am. Poetry Rev., 1986; creative writing fellow U. Ill. Ctr. for Advanced Study, Nat. Endowment Arts, 1986-87. Office: U Ill English Dept Urbana IL 61801

LIEBERMAN, LEONARD, retired supermarket executive; b. Elizabeth, N.J., Jan. 23, 1929; s. Joseph Harry and Bessie (Bernstein) L.; m. Arlene Ginsberg; children: Elizabeth Susan, Nancy Ellen, Anne Judith. B.A., Yale U., 1950; J.D., Columbia U., 1953; grad., Advanced Mgmt. Program, Harvard U., 1970. Bar: N.J. bar 1954. Assoc., then partner firms in Newark and Orange, 1954-65; v.p., gen. counsel, dir. Supermarkets Operating Co., Union, N.J., 1966-66; v.p., gen. counsel Supermarkets Gen. Corp., Woodbridge, N.J., 1966-69, sr. v.p., 1969-81, chmn. Pathmark div., 1977-79, exec. asst. to pres., 1979-80, chief adminstrv. and fin. officer, 1980-82, exec. v.p., 1981-82, pres., 1982-87, chief exec. officer, 1983-87, chmn., 1986-87; bd. dirs. Outlet Comm., Inc., Celestial Seasonings, Inc., Republic N.Y. Corp., La Petite Academy, Inc., Sonic Industries; instr. Am. Inst. Banking, 1954-55; co-chmn. joint industry com. on uniform comm. sys. for the grocery industry, 1978-81, com. to improve shipping container design, 1984-86; co-chmn. Gov. Florio's task force on local partnerships, 1991-92. Trustee Jewish Counseling and Svc. Agy. Essex County, 1968-73, Fund for N.J., 1987—, Ctr. for Analysis of Pub. Issues, 1987— (chmn. 1990-92), Boys & Girls Clubs of Newark, 1987—; trustee Newark Beth Israel Med. Center, Newark, 1971-82, treas., 1972-73, pres., 1973-78, hon. pres., 1982—; bd. dirs. Newark Performing Arts Corp., 1987-91; commr. N.J. Public Broadcasting Authority, 1982-86, 1st v.p., 1983-86; chmn. N.J. Acad for Aquatic Scis., 1989-92; mem. coun. for N.J. affairs, Princeton U., 1988—; bd. regents Seton Hall U., 1989-90, trustee, mem. exec. com.; trustee N.J. Ctr. for Performing Arts, 1989—; mem. N.J. com. Regional Plan Assn., 1982—; task force chmn. Gov.'s Mgmt Improvement Program, 1982-83; mem. Partnership for N.J., 1983—; assoc. gov. Hebrew U., 1983-84, bd. govs., 1984-90; bd. dirs. Ctr. Excellence in Govt., 1981-83; trustee Victim Svc. Agy., 1986—; mem. N.J. State Planning Commn., 1986-90. Recipient Justice Louis D. Brandeis Humanitarian award N.J. region Zionist Orgn. Am., 1977. Mem. Food Mktg. Inst. (dir. exec. com. 1983-87), Regional Plan Assn. (dir. 1985-95). Office: One Gateway Ctr Ste 532 Newark NJ 07102

LIEBERMAN, LESTER ZANE, engineering company executive; b. Newark, N.J., May 4, 1930; s. Herman P. and Cecile A. (Ashenfeld) L.; m. Judith Mazor, Aug. 11, 1957; children—Susan, Jane. BS in Mech. Engring., Newark Coll. Engring., 1951, postgrad., 1953-58; DHL (hon.), Clarkson U., 1991. Registered profl. engr., N.J., Pa. Pres. Crest Engring. Inc., Newark, 1955-60; chmn., pres. Atmos Engring. Co. Inc., Kenilworth, N.J., 1960-78; pres., chief exec. officer Clarkson Industries, Inc., N.Y.C., 1978-90; mem. N.J. State Investment Coun., 1991—. Bd. trustees Clarkson U., Potsdam, N.Y.; chmn. Beth Israel Med. Ctr., Newark, 1970—; chair Irvington Gen. Hosp., 1991—; bd. dirs. Lazard Funds, 1991—. Served with USCG, 1951-53. Named Alumnus of Yr., Newark Coll. Engring., 1980. Mem. ASHRAE (pres. 1964-65), Nat. Soc. Profl. Engrs., N.J. Soc. Profl. Engrs., Assn. Energy Engrs., Am. Acad. Environ. Engrs. (diplomate), Tau Beta Pi (Key award 1982). Jewish. Lodge: Masons. Avocations: skiing, sailing, tennis, golf. Home: Spring Valley Rd Morristown NJ 07960-7011 Office: 25 Vreeland Rd Florham Park NJ 07932-1907

LIEBERMAN, LOUIS (KARL LIEBERMAN), artist; b. Bklyn., May 7, 1944; s. Abraham and Jeannette (Feinberg) L. BFA, R.I. Sch. Design, 1969; cert., Bklyn. Mus. Art Sch., 1964; BA, Bklyn. Coll., 1966. Adj. lectr. Bklyn. Coll., 1971-78, Lehman Coll., Bronx, N.Y., 1972-75; vis. artist Ill. State U., Normal, 1978, Hamilton Coll., Clinton, N.Y., 1982. One-man shows include Vancouver Art Gallery, B.C., Can., 1969, James Yu Gallery, N.Y.C., 1973, 74, Nina Freudenheim Gallery, Buffalo, 1976, Root Art Ctr., Hamilton Coll., Clinton, N.Y., 1980, Harm Bouckaert Gallery, N.Y.C., 1981, John Davis Gallery, Akron, Ohio, 1983, 85, Columbus Mus. Art, Ohio, 1983, John Davis Gallery, N.Y.C., 1986; group shows include Aldrich Mus. Contemporary Art, Ridgefield, Conn., 1973, 74, Johnson Mus. Art, Ithaca, N.Y., 1981, Fine Arts Mus. L.I., Hempstead, N.Y., 1982, Cleve. Inst. Art, 1982, Met. Mus. Art, N.Y.C., 1983, Byer Mus. Art, Evanston, Ill., 1982, Visual Arts Ctr., Beer-Sheva, Israel, 1985, Kunsthauses, Zurich, Switzerland, McNay Art Mus., San Antonio, Phila. Mus. of Art, 1988, Erie (Pa.) Art Mus., 1988, Art Mus. of Santa Cruz, Calif., 1988, Hunter Mus., Chattanooga, 1989, others; represented in permanent collections include Kenan Ctr., Lockport, N.Y., Aldridge Mus. Contemporary Art, Ridgefield, Conn., Met. Mus. Art, N.Y.C., Phila. Mus. Art, Stamford (Conn.) Mus., Bklyn. Mus., Mus. Fine Arts, Budapest, Hungary, Istvan Kiraly Mus., Budapest; art critic N.Y. Arts Jour., 1978-79. Recipient Sculpture award Creative Artist Pub. Service Found., 1971-72, Graphics award Creative Artist Pub. Svc. Found., 1980-81, Graphics award N.Y. Found. Arts, 1984-85; visual arts fellow Nat. Endowment for Arts, 1979-80; Pollack-Krasner Found. fellow, 1987; Adolf and Esther Gottlieb Found. grantee, 1989.

LIEBERMAN, MELVYN, biology educator; b. Bklyn., Feb. 4, 1938; married; 2 children. BA in Zoology, Cornell U., 1959; PhD in physiology, SUNY Downstate Med. Ctr., 1965. Lectr., lab in instr., dept. biology Queens Coll., CUNY, 1960, 63-64; teaching asst. dept. physiology SUNY Downstate Med. Ctr., Bklyn., 1960-64; postdoctoral fellow dept. embryology Carnegie Inst. Washington, Balt., 1964-65, Inst. de Biofisica, U. Federal do Rio de Janeiro, Brazil, 1965-67; postdoctoral fellow div. biomed. engring. Duke U., Durham, N.C., 1967, rsch. assoc. dept. physiology and pharmacology, 1967-68; asst. prof. Duke U. Med. Ctr., Durham, N.C., 1968-73, assoc. prof. 1973-78, prof. dept. physiology, 1978-88, dir. dept. grad. studies, 1977-80, prof. dept. cell biology, 1988—, dir. grad. studies, 1988-90, assoc. prof. dept. medicine, mem. integrated toxicology program, 1989—; spl. asst. to exec. v.p., 1990—, exec. com. grad. sch., 1991—; mem. Heart Ctr. Duke U. Med. Ctr., Durham, N.C., 1988—; dir. univ. assocs. program Duke U. Med. Ctr., Durham, N.C., 1992-94; prof. dept. biomed. engring., 1993—; Internat. Affairs Commn., 1994—; coordinator U.S-Japan Coop. Sci. Program Conf., Tokyo, 1974, 88, U.S.-Brazil Coop. Sci. Program Conf., Rio de Janeiro, 1980, Gordon Conf.-Muscle, 1979; vis. investigator Jan Seammerdam Inst., U. Amsterdam, Netherlands, 1975; cons. Macy Found., 1970, NIH, 1972—; physiology study sect., 1980-84, Rsch. Tng. Rev. Comm., 1990-94, NSF, 1974—, others; mem. research rev. com. N.Y. Heart Assn., 1980-85; mem. cardiovascular research study com. Am. Heart Assn., 1987-90; Howard Hughes Predoctorate Fellowhip Evaluation, 1994—; participant numerous sci. symposia; mem. basic Sci. coun. Am. Heart Assn., 1963, established investigator, 1971-76, pub. rev. com., 1989-93, Rsch. Program and Evaluation Commn., 1995—; rsch. rev. subcom. N.C. Heart Assn., 1972-75, chmn. 1975-76, pub. affairs com., 1988-91, rsch. com., 1993—; microstructure com., N.C. Bd. Sci. and Tech., 1989—, Task Force on Intellectual property and licensing govt. univ. industry rsch. roundtable, 1991-93, Indsl. Liaison program, Rsch. Triangle Univs., 1991—93; acad. adv. coun. Indsl. Rsch. Inst., 1994—, Pres.'s adv. coun., Houston Advanced Rsch. Ctr., 1995—. Co-editor: Development and Physiological Correlates of Cardiac Muscle, 1975, Excitable Cells in Tissue Culture, 1981, Normal and Abnormal Conduction of the Heart, 1982, Electrogenic Transport: Fundamental Principles and Physiological Implications, 1984; assoc. editor Am. Jour. Physiology, Cell, 1981—; mem. editorial adv. bd. Experientia, 1982-90, Physiol. Revs., 1985-91, Molecular Cell Biochemistry, 1991—; editorial cons. contbr. numerous articles to profl. jours. Recipient founders award, 1975, achievement award N.C. Heart Assn., 1984, Cecil Hall award Electron Microscopy Soc. Am., 1989. Mem. AAAS, AAUP, Am. Heart Assn., Am. Physiol. Soc. (Porter devel. com. 1974-77, ednl. materials rev. bd. 1975-77, internat. physiol. com. 1993, chmn. 1994—, councillor cell and gen. physiol. sect. 1984-87, chmn. 1987-88, 91—, sect. adv. com. 1992—), Am. Soc. Cell Biology, Biophys. Soc., Cardiac Muscle Soc., Internat. Soc. Heart Rsch. (councillor 1993—), N.Y. Acad. Sci., N.C. Heart Assn., Physiol. Soc., Soc. Gen. Physiologists (sec. 1969-71, rep. NRS 1971-74, pres. 1981-82, publs. com. 1982-85), Physiol. Soc. (U.K.), Sigma Xi. Home: 1110 Woodburn Rd Durham NC 27705-5738 Office: Duke U Med Ctr Dept Cell Biology Box 3709 Div Physiology Durham NC 27710

LIEBERMAN, MYRON, lawyer; b. Chgo., Feb. 14, 1931; s. Louis and Ethel (Shulman) L.; m. Eleanor Levy, July 22, 1954; children: Elizabeth Lieberman Keller, Peter Harold. BS, Stanford U., 1952; LLB, Northwestern U., Chgo., 1954. Bar: Ill. 1954. Assoc. Law Office of Bernard Mamet, Chgo., 1954-55, Law Office of Swiren & Heineman, Chgo., 1955-57; ptnr. Lieberman, Levy, Baron & Stone, Chgo., 1958-80; sr. ptnr. Altheimer & Gray, Chgo., 1980—; dir. Columbia Nat. Bank of Chgo., Montgomery Ward & Co., Inc., Chgo., Mid-Town Bank & Trust Co., Chgo. Bd. dirs. Anti-Defamation League, Chgo., 1991—. Mem. Standard Club. Home: 360 N Deere Park Dr E Highland Park IL 60035 Office: Altheimer & Gray 10 S Wacker Dr Chicago IL 60606

LIEBERMAN, MYRON, educational consulting firm executive; b. St. Paul, Apr. 30, 1919. BS in Law, U. Minn., 1941, BS in Edn., 1948; MA, U. Ill., 1950, PhD, 1952. Rsch. analyst civil intelligence sect. Dept. War, Tokyo, 1946-47; tchr. Humboldt High Sch., St. Paul, 1948-49; teaching asst. U. Ill., 1949-52; asst. prof. U. Okla., 1953-56; chmn. dept. edn. Yeshiva U., N.Y.C., 1956-59; dir. basic rsch. Ednl. Rsch. Coun. Greater Cleve., 1959-60; cons. Rand McNally Co., Skokie, Ill., 1961; prof. edn. Hofstra U., N.Y.C., 1962-63; prof. R.I. Coll., 1963-69, asst. dean for profl. studies, 1963-64, dir. edn. R&D, 1965-67; prof. edn. CUNY, 1969-75; Disting. prof. edn. U. So. Calif., L.A., 1975-77; pres. Ednl. Employment Svcs., Washington, 1976—; Disting. prof. Va. Consortium on Higher Edn., 1975; vis. prof. edn. Ohio U., 1984-86, U. Pa., 1986-88; vis. scholar Social Philosophy and Policy Ctr., Bowling Green (Ohio) State U., 1990-91; cons. William C. Norris Inst., 1988-89, Office Sec. Edn., Washington, 1987, Dept. Edn., 1988; invited lectr. numerous colls. and univs. in U.S. and Can.; guest speaker convs. of maj. nat. ednl. orgns. Author or co-author: Education as a Profession, 1956, The Future of Public Education, 1960, Language and Concepts in Education, 1961, Social Forces Influencing American Education, 1961, Collective Negotiations for Teachers, 1966, Readings in Collective Negotiations for Teachers, 1967, Bargaining: Before, During, After, 1979, Public Sector Bargaining: A Policy Reappraisal, 1980, NLRA Precedent in ALRB Decisions, 1982, Beyond Public Education, 1986, Privatization and Educational Choice, 1989, Public School Choice, 1990, Public Education: An Autopsy, 1993; also monographs; contbr. articles to profl. jours. Staff sgt. U.S. Army, 1942-46. Recipient Herman Meml. trophy, 1937, Disting. Alumnus award Coll. Edn. U. Ill., 1965. Holder 25 jr., adult and sr. tennis championships. Home and Office: 4600 Connecticut Ave NW # 823 Washington DC 20008

LIEBERMAN, PAUL, aeronautical engineer, engineering research company executive; b. Bklyn., Dec. 25, 1932; s. Benjamin and Frances (Firestone) L.; children by previous marriage—Naomi Ruth, Leah, Micah Benjamin. B.S. in Aero. Engring., NYU, 1954; M.S. in Aero. Engring., Princeton U., 1956; Ph.D. in Applied Mechanics, Ill. Inst. Tech., 1964. Engr. Bell Aircraft Corp., Buffalo, 1954; sr. scientist Ill. Inst. Tech. Research Inst., Chgo., 1957-69, project engr. devel. of instrumentation; sr. project mgr. TRW, Redondo Beach, Calif., 1969-81; v.p. systems engring. Nat. Tech. Systems, Saugus, Calif., 1981—. Contbr. numerous articles on thermodynamics, applied mechanics, optics and air force systems to profl. jours. Author reports in field. Served to 1st lt. USAF, 1955-57. Guggenheim fellow, 1954-55. Mem. Sigma Xi. Jewish. Home: 19815 Mildred Ave Torrance CA 90503-1121 Office: Nat Tech Systems 26525 Golden Valley Rd Santa Clarita CA 91350-2622

LIEBERMAN, PHILLIP LOUIS, allergist, educator; b. Memphis, Mar. 20, 1940; m. Barbara; children: Ryan, Lee, Jay. Student, London Sch. Econs., 1961; BA in Sociology, Tulane U., 1962; MD, U. Tenn., 1965. Intern City of Memphis Hosp. U. Tenn., 1965-66, asst. resident internal medicine, 1966-67, assoc. resident internal medicine, 1967-68, chief resident, 1968-69; fellow in allergy, immunology Northwestern U., Evanston, Ill., 1969-71; asst. prof., chief div. allergy, immunology U. Tenn., 1971-74, assoc. prof., chief div. allergy, immunology, 1974-79, prof., chief div. allergy, immunology, 1979—; instr. internal medicine U. Tenn., 1968-69; mem. exec. bd. Joint Coun. of Allergy & Immunology, 1985-90, AAAI rep., 1990; AAAI rep. Mothers for Asthmatics, 1990. Co-editor: Asthma Edition: Abstract-a-Card System, 1991—; contbr. numerous articles, abstracts to profl. publs.; author numerous presentations in field, book chpts., revs. Exec. bd. dirs. Asthma and Allergy Found. of Am., 1990—, mem. med. scientific coun., 1987, chmn., 1990—. Served to cpt. USAR, 1965-71. Mem. Am. Acad. Allergy (com. on alternative forms of therapy, 1980—), Am. Acad. Allergy and Immunology (exec. com. 1983-91, constitution and by-laws com. 1984-87, also chmn. 1985, undergraduate com. 1985, pres.-elect. 1987-88, pres. 1988-89, nominating com. 1987, also chmn. 1989, program com. 1987), Am. Coll. Allergists, Am. Assn. Allergists (sec. 1985), Am. Assn. Certified Allergists (2d v.p. 1986-87, pres. 1989-90), Am. Bd. Allergy and Immunology. Office: U Tenn 300 Walnut Bend Rd S Memphis TN 38018 also: Allergy Assocs 920 Madison Ave # 909N Memphis TN 38103-3438

LIEBERMAN, SEYMOUR, biochemistry educator emeritus; b. N.Y.C., Dec. 1, 1916; s. Samuel D. and Sadie (Levin) L.; m. Sandra Spar, June 5, 1944; 1 child, Paul B. B.S., Bklyn. Coll., 1936; M.S., U. Ill., 1937; Ph.D. (Rockefeller scholar 1939-41), Stanford U., 1941; Traveling fellow, U. Basle, Switzerland, Eidgenoess. Tech. Hochschule, Zurich, Switzerland, 1946-47. Chemist Schering Corp., 1938-39; spl. research assoc. Harvard U., 1941-45; assoc. mem. Sloan-Kettering Inst., 1945-50; mem. faculty Columbia Coll. Physicians and Surgeons, N.Y.C., 1950—; prof. biochemistry Columbia Coll. Physicians and Surgeons 1950-87, prof. emeritus, 1987—; assoc. dean Inst. Health Scis. St. Luke's Roosevelt Hosp. Center, 1984-90, pres., 1981—, vice provost, 1991; assoc. dir. office sci. & tech. Columbia U., N.Y.C., 1991—; Pfizer traveling fellow McGill U., 1968; Syntex lectr. Mexican Endocrine

Soc., 1970; mem. Am. Cancer Soc. panel steroids, 1945-49, hormones, 1949-50, mem. com. pathogenesis of cancer, 1957-60; mem. endocrine study sect. NIH, 1959-63, chmn., 1963-65, mem. gen. clin. research centers, 1967-71; mem. med. adv. com. Population Council, 1961-73; mem. endocrinology panel Cancer Chemotherapy Nat. Service Center, 1958-62; cons. WHO human reprodn. unit, 1972-74, Ford Found., 1974-77. Editor Jour. Clin. Endocrinology and Metabolism, 1963-67, editorial bd., 1958-63, 68-70, Jour. Biol. Chemistry, 1975-80; contbr. articles to profl. jours. Recipient Disting. Alumnus award Bklyn. Coll., 1971, Disting. Svc. award Columbus U., 1991. Fellow N.Y. Acad. Scis., NAS; mem. Am. Soc. Biol. Chemists, Am. Chem. Soc., Internat. Soc. Endocrinology (U.S. del. central com.). Endocrine Soc. (Ciba award 1952, Koch award 1970, council 1970-73, pres. 1974-75, Roussel prize 1984, Dale medal 1986, Boehringer-Mannheim award lectr. 1992), Harvey Soc. Home: 515 E 72nd St New York NY 10021-4032 Office: 432 W 58th St New York NY 10019-1102

LIEBERMANN, LOWELL, composer, pianist, conductor; b. N.Y.C., Feb. 22, 1961. D in Musical Arts, Juilliard Sch.; studied with David Diamond, Vincent Persichetti, Jacob Lateiner, Laszlo Halasz. Composer (orchestra) War Songs for Bass Voice and Orch. Op. 7, 1981, Concertino for Cello and Chamber Orch. Op. 8, 1982, Symphony No. 1 Op. 9 (BMI award, 1st prize Juilliard Orch. Competition 1987), 1982, Three Poems of Stephen Crane Op. 11 for baritone, string orch., two horns, harp (Devora Nadworney award Nat. Fed. Music Clubs 1986) 1983, Concerto No. 1 for Piano and Orch. Op. 12, 1983, Sechs Gesaenge Nach Gedichten Von Nelly Sachs Op. 18 for soprano and orch., 1986, The Domain of Arnheim Op. 33, 1990, Concerto No. 2 for Piano and Orch. Op. 36, 1992, Flute Concerto Op. 39, 1992; (chorus) Two Choral Elegies Op. 2 for SATB a capella (Fred Waring Choral award Nat. Fed. Music 1978), 1977, Missa Brevis Op. 15 for SATB chorus, tenor and baritone solos, organ (3d prize Ch. and Artist Composers Competition 1987), 1985; (piano solo) Piano Sonata Op. 1 (Outstanding Composition award Yamaha Music Found. 1982, 1st prize Nat. Composition Contest Music Tchrs. Nat. Assn. 1978), 1977, Piano Sonata No. 2 Sonata Notturna Op. 10, 1983, Variations on a Theme by Anton Bruckner Op. 19, 1987, Nocturne No. 1 Op. 20, 1987, Four Apparitions Op. 17, 1987, others; (chamber music) Sonata for Violoncello and Piano Op. 3, 1978, Two Pieces for Violin and Viola Op. 4, 1978, Sonata for Viola and Piano Op. 13 (1st Place Victor Herbert/ASCAP awards Nat. Fed. Music Clubs 1986, Brian Israel prize Soc. for New Music 1986), 1984, Sonata for Contrabass and Piano Op. 24, 1987, Fantasy on a Fugue by J.S. Bach Op. 27 for flute, oboe, clarinet, horn, bassoon, piano, 1989, Quintet for Piano and Strings Op. 34 for piano and string quartet, 1989, others; also organ music, voice and piano. Mem. ASCAP, Corp. Yaddo (dir.). Democrat. Office: 155 West 68th St Apt 315 New York NY 10023

LIEBERSON, STANLEY, sociologist, educator; b. Montreal, Que., Can., Apr. 20, 1933; s. Jack and Ida (Cohen) L.; m. Patricia Ellen Beard, 1960; children—Rebecca, David, Miriam, Rachel. Student, Bklyn. Coll., 1950-52; MA, U. Chgo., 1958, PhD, 1960; MA (hon.), Harvard U., 1988; LHD (hon.), U. Ariz., 1993. Asso. dir. Iowa Urban Community Research Center, U. Iowa, 1959-61, instr., asst. prof. sociology, 1959-61; asst. prof. sociology U. Wis., 1961-63, asso. prof., 1963-66, prof., 1966-67; prof. sociology U. Wash., 1967-71, dir. Center Studies Demography and Ecology, 1968-71; prof. sociology U. Chgo., 1971-74, assoc. dir. Population Research Center, 1971-74; prof. sociology U. Ariz., Tucson, 1974-83, head dept., 1976-79; prof. sociology U. Calif., Berkeley, 1983-88; prof. sociology Harvard U., 1988-91, Abbott Lawrence Lowell prof. sociology, 1991—; vis. prof. Stanford U., summer 1970; Claude Bissell disting. vis. prof. U. Toronto, 1979-80; mem. com. on sociolinguistics Social Sci. Research Council, 1964-70; mem. sociology panel NSF, 1978-81. Author: (with others) Metropolis and Region, 1960, Ethnic Patterns in American Cities, 1963; editor: Explorations in Sociolinguistics, 1967, (with Beverly Duncan) Metropolis and Region in Transition, 1970, Language and Ethnic Relations in Canada, 1970, A Piece of the Pie, 1980, Language Diversity and Language Contact, 1981, Making It Count, 1985, (with Mary C. Waters) From Many Strands, 1988; assoc. editor: Social Problems, 1965-67, Sociol. Methods and Research, 1971—; editorial cons. Sociol. Inquiry, 1965-67; adv. editor: Am. Jour. Sociology, 1969-74; editorial bd. Lang. in Society, 1972-74, Internat. Jour. Sociology of Lang, 1974—, Canadian Jour. Sociology, 1975—, Social Forces, 1980-83; adv. council Sociol. Abstracts, 1972-73, Language Problems and Language Planning, 1984-87; mem. editorial com. Ann. Rev. Sociology, 1992—. Recipient Colver Rosenberger Ednl. prize, 1960; Guggenheim fellow, 1972-73. Fellow NAS, Am. Acad. Arts and Scis.; mem. Am. Sociol. Assn. (coun. mem. 1985-87, pres. 1990-91, Disting. Contbn. to Scholarship award 1982), Am. Sociol. Found. (trustee 1992—), Population Assn. Am. (dir. 1969-72), Internat. Population Union, Pacific Sociol. Assn. (v.p. 1984-85, pres. 1986-87), Sociol. Rsch. Assn. (exec. com. 1976-81, pres. 1981), Am. Name Soc., Oakland Sch. Sociology. Home: 5 Mystic Lake Dr Arlington MA 02174-2305 Office: Harvard U Dept Sociology William James Hall Cambridge MA 02138

LIEBERT, ARTHUR EDGAR, hospital administrator; b. Milw., Nov. 18, 1930; married. B, Lake Forest Coll; MHA, Northwestern U. Adminstrv. resident Rochester (N.Y.) Gen. Hosp., 1953-54, adminstrv. asst., 1954, asst. adminstr., 1957-65, assoc. dir., 1965-70, admitting dir., 1970-73, pres., 1973-93; pres., CEO Rochester Health Care Inc., 1993—. Mem. Am. Hosp. Assn. (del.), Hosp. Assn. N.Y. (del.). Home: 611 Dewitt Rd Webster NY 14580-1333 Office: Greater Rochester Health Sys Inc 1415 Portland Ave Rochester NY 14621-3022

LIEBES, RAQUEL, import/export company executive, educator; b. San Salvador, El Salvador, Aug. 28, 1938; came to the U.S., 1952, naturalized, 1964; d. Ernesto Martin and Alice (Philip) L.; m. Richard Paisley Kinkade, June 2, 1962 (div. 1977); children: Kathleen Paisley, Richard Paisley Jr., Scott Philip. BA, Sarah Lawrence Coll., 1960; MEd, Harvard U., 1961; MA, Yale U., 1965, postgrad., 1991; PhD in English, Oxford (Eng.) U., 1994. Teaching fellow in Spanish Sarah Lawrence Coll., Bronxville, N.Y., 1958-60; econ. teaching fellow Yale U., New Haven, 1964-65, instr. Spanish, 1964-66; exec. stockholder Import Export Co., San Salvador, 1968—, also bd. dirs.; adj. prof. Am. U., Washington, 1989-91; instr. dept. fgn. lang. and linguistics, dept. fgn. studies Georgetown U., Washington, 1989-93. Contbr. glossary of Spanish med. terms. Hon. consul Govt. of El Salvador, 1977-80; docent High Mus. of Art, Atlanta, 1972-77; vol. Grady Hosp., Atlanta, 1966-71; instr. Spanish for med. drs. Tucson Med. Ctr., 1966-71; chmn. Atlanta Coun. for Internat. Visitors, 1966-71; mem. Outreach Group on Latin Am., Washington, 1982-86; founding mem. John Kennedy Ctr. for Performing Arts, 1980—; mem. Folger/Shakespeare Libr., Smithsonian Inst., Agape, El Salvador. Econ. fellow Yale U., 1964-65; fellow Corcoran Mus. of Art, 1984-85. Mem. MLA, Am. Biog. Inst. Rsch. Assn. (hon. consul of El Salvador, dep. gov. 1978-80, bd. advisors 1994), Jr. League of Washington, Harvard Club, Yale Club. Republican. Avocations: comparative literature, languages, international business, English literature, Shakespeare. Home: 700 New Hampshire Ave NW Washington DC 20037-2406

LIEBIG, RICHARD ARTHUR, retired manufacturing company executive; b. Quincy, Ill., Sept. 2, 1923; s. Arthur William and Florence Ann (Parrott) L.; m. Peggy O. Shiley, Aug. 4, 1946; children: Lynn Margaret, Ann Kay. BS, U. Ill., 1949; LLD (hon.), Culver-Stockton Coll., 1989. With Moorman Mfg. Co., Quincy, 1949-93, credit mgr., 1958-60, mgr. fin. adminstrn., 1960-64, treas., 1960-76, v.p. fin. adminstrn., 1964-75, sec., mem. exec. com., 1971-75, exec. v.p. fin., 1975-76, pres., COO, 1976-77, pres., CEO, 1977-84, chmn. bd., CEO, 1984-87, chmn. bd., 1987-88; sec. Quincy Soybean Co., 1961-76, v.p., 1968-76, mem. exec. com., 1964-93, past chmn. bd. dirs.; v.p. Moorman Co. Fund, 1960-75; mem. exec. com. Moorman Found., 1969-90, 1st v.p., 1972-80, pres., 1980-90; pres., mem. exec. com. CFM Found., 1990—, also bd. dirs.; mem. St. Louis adv. bd. Liberty Mut. Ins. Co., 1980, 93; mem. adv. coun. Coll. Commerce and Bus. Adminstrn. U. Ill., Urbana, 1974—; mem. exec. com. Convocom, 1983—, sec., 1990—, also bd. dirs. Mem. adv. coun. Culver-Stockton Coll., Canton, Mo., 1972-82, trustee, 1983—, mem. exec. com., chmn. bd. trustees, 1989—; vice chmn. Profit Sharing Coun. Am., 1979, bd. dirs., 1972-82; mem. Sch. Dist. 172 Bd. Edn., 1963-69, pres., 1969; trustee Quincy Found. for Quality Edn. 1989—; bd. dirs., treas., ednl. revolving fund Blessing Hosp., Quincy, 1963-85; mem. adv. bd. YWCA, 1984—; bd. dirs. Inst. Human Studies, 1985—. With AUS, 1943-47. Paul Harris fellow, 1987. Mem. Fin. Execs. Instl. Mem. MFrs. Assn. (bd. dirs. 1982-88), Ill. State C of C. (bd. dirs. 1980-86), Indsl. Assn. Quincy (2nd v.p., mem. exec. com. 1969-71, 75-88, trustee Profit Sharing Rsch.

Found. 1986-92), Rotary (bd. dirs. Quincy chpt.). Methodist. Home: 2311 Vermont St Quincy IL 62301

LIEBLING, JEROME, photographer, educator; b. N.Y.C., Apr. 16, 1924; s. Maurice and Sarah (Goodman) L.; married, Nov. 11, 1949 (div. 1969); children: Madeline, Tina, Adam, Daniella, Rachel Jane. Student, Bklyn. Coll., 1942, 46, 48, New Sch. for Social Research, N.Y.C., 1948-49; LLD (hon.), Portland (Maine) Sch. Art, 1989. Prof. photography U. Minn., Mpls., 1949-69; prof. SUNY-New Paltz, 1957-58, Yale U., New Haven, 1976-77, Hampshire Coll., Amherst, Mass., 1970—. Author, photographer: Jerome Liebling Photographs (Best of Yr. 1982), Aperture, N.Y.C., 1988, The People Yes, The Photographs of Jerome Liebling, Aperture, 1995; editor: Photography-Current Perspective, 1977. Served with U.S. Army, 1942-45, ETO, Africa. Fellow Mass. Arts Found., 1975; fellow Nat. Endowman Arts, 1979, Guggenheim, 1977, 81. Mem. Soc. Photog. Edn. Home: 39 Dana St Amherst MA 01002-2208 Office: Hampshire Coll West St Amherst MA 01002-2954

LIEBMAN, HOWARD MARK, lawyer; b. L.A., Dec. 20, 1952; s. Martin Irving and Frances (Weiner) L.; m. Alena Bekova, Aug. 16, 1975 (div. Dec. 17, 1990); 1 child, Peter. AB, Colgate U., 1974, AM, 1975; JD, Harvard Law Sch., 1977. Cons. Office of Tax Analysis, U.S. Treasury Dept., Washington, 1975; assoc. Paul, Weiss, Rifkind, Wharton & Garrison, N.Y.C., 1976, Covington & Burling, Washington, 1977-79; ptnr. Oppenheimer, Wolff & Donnelly, Brussels, 1979-94, Morgan, Lewis & Bockius, Brussels, 1994—; mem. div. coun. on fin. and banking Mgmt. Ctr. Europe, Brussels, 1984—; adv. mem. BNA Direct Investment in N.Am., Washington, 1988—. Co-author: Business Operations in the European Union; contbg. editor Tax Planning Internat. Rev., 1982—, Jour. Strategy in Internat. Taxation, 1984-86. Bd. dirs. Harvard Club of Belgium, Brussels, 1989—, pres., 1993-95; co-chmn. Dukakis for Pres. Belgian Campaign. Recipient Fulbright fellowship Fulbright Commn., 1979. Mem. ABA, Am. C. of C. in Belgium asbl. Democrat. Home: 30 Ave de Boetendael, 1180 Brussels Belgium Office: Morgan Lewis & Bockius, rue Guimard 7, 1040 Brussels Belgium

LIEBMAN, JUDITH RAE STENZEL, operations research educator; b. Denver, July 2, 1936; d. Raymond Oscar and Mary Madelyn (Gallory) Stenzel; m. Jon Charles Liebman, Dec. 27, 1958; children: Christopher Brian, Rebecca Anne, Michael Jon. BA in Physics, U. Colo., Boulder, 1958; PhD in Ops. Rsch., Johns Hopkins U., 1971. Successively asst. prof., head indsl. systems, assoc. prof. U. Ill., Urbana, 1972-84, prof., 1984—, chmn. bd. Ill. Resource Network, 1987-90, acting vice chancellor for rsch., 1986-87, vice chancellor for rsch., 1987-92, acting dean Grad. Coll., 1987-92, dean, 1987-92, prof. ops. rsch., 1992—; vis. prof. Tianjin (China) U., 1985; charter mem. Ill. Gov.'s Sci. Adv. Com., Ill. Exec. Com., 1989-92; mem. adv. com. for engring. NSF, 1988-92, chmn., 1991-92. Author: Modeling and Optimization with GINO, 1986; author numerous articles in field. Bd. dirs. United Way, Champaign, Ill., 1986-91; bd. dirs. East Cen. Ill. Health Systems Agy., Champaign, 1977-82, pres., 1980-82. Mem. Ops. Rsch. Soc. Am. (pres. 1987-88), Nat. Assn. State Univs. and Land Grant Colls. (exec. bd. 1990-92), Rotary, Sigma Xi, Sigma Pi Sigma, Alpha Pi Mu, Phi Kappa Phi. Home: 110 W Whitehall Ct Urbana IL 61801-6664 Office: U Ill 1206 W Green St Urbana IL 61801

LIEBMAN, LANCE MALCOLM, dean, lawyer; b. Newark, Sept. 11, 1941; s. Roy and Barbara (Trilinsky) L.; m. Carol Bensinger, June 28, 1964; children: Jeffrey, Benjamin. B.A., Yale U., 1962; M.A., Cambridge U., 1964; LL.B., Harvard U., 1967. Bar: D.C. 1968, Mass. 1976. Asst. to Mayor Lindsay, N.Y.C., 1968-70; asst. prof. law Harvard U., 1970-76, prof., 1976-91, assoc. dean, 1981-84; dean, Lucy G. Moses prof. law Columbia U. Sch. Law, N.Y.C., 1991—. Successor trustee Yale Corp., 1971-83. Office: Columbia U Sch Law 435 W 116th St New York NY 10027-7201

LIEBMAN, PAUL ARNO, biophysicist, educator; b. Pitts., Aug. 1, 1933; s. Arno Jack and M. Josephine (Schurr) L.; m. Elizabeth Loeffler, Nov. 6, 1982; 1 child, Erica. BS in Chemistry, U. Pitts., 1954; MD, Johns Hopkins U., 1958. Intern in medicine Barnes Hosp., St. Louis, 1958-59; postdoctoral fellow Johnson Rsch. Found., Phila., 1959-63; asst. prof. physiology U. Pa. Sch. Medicine, Phila., 1963-67, assoc. prof. anatomy, 1967-76, prof. anatomy, 1976-92, prof. ophthalmology, 1982—, prof. neurosci., prof. biophysics/biochemistry, 1992—; dir. U. Pa. Vision Rsch. Ctr., Phila., 1976—. Contbr. numerous articles to Jour. Biol. Chemistry, Science, Nature, others. Grantee NIH, 1962—. Mem. Biophys. Soc. for Neurosci., Assn. for Rsch. in Vision and Ophthalmology, Phila. Canoe Club (hon. life mem.). Achievements include invention of UV-VIS microspectrophotometers, ultrasensitive pH recording instruments; discovered color vision pigments, biochemical mechanism of visual transduction, membrane protein lateral diffusion. Office: U Pa Vision Rsch Ctr 36th & Hamilton Walk Philadelphia PA 19104*

LIEBMAN, RONALD STANLEY, lawyer; b. Balt., Oct. 11, 1943; s. Harry Martin and Martha (Altgenug) L.; m. Simma Liebman, Jan. 8, 1972; children: Shana, Margot. BA, Western Md. Coll., Westminster, 1966; JD, U. Md., 1969. Bar: Md. 1969, D.C. 1977, U.S. Dist. Ct. (ea. dist.) Va. 1970, U.S. Dist. Ct. Md. 1970, U.S. Dist. Ct. D.C. 1982, U.S. Dist. Ct. (no. dist.) Calif. 1994, U.S. Ct. Appeals (4th cir.) 1972, U.S. Ct. Appeals (D.C. cir.) 1982, U.S. Ct. Appeals (5th cir.) 1985. Law clk. to chief judge U.S. Dist. Ct. Md., 1969-70; assoc. Melnicove, Kaufman & Weiner, Balt., 1970-72; asst. U.S. atty. Office of U.S. Atty., Dept. Justice, Balt., 1972-78; ptnr. Sachs, Greenebaum & Tayler, Washington, 1978-82, Patton & Boggs LLP, Washington, 1982—. Author: Grand Jury, 1983; co-editor: Testimonial Privileges, 1983. Recipient spl. commendation award U.S. Dept. Justice, 1978. Mem. ABA, D.C. Bar Assn., Md. Bar Assn. Club: Sergeants Inn (Balt.). Office: Patton & Boggs LLP 2550 M St NW Washington DC 20037-1301

LIEBMAN, THEODORE, architect; b. Newark, May 7, 1939; s. Edward and Miriam (Applebaum) L.; m. Nina Roskin, Oct. 27, 1968; children—Sophie, Hanna, Tessa. B.Arch., Pratt Inst., 1962; M.Arch., Harvard U., 1963. Registered architect, Mass., N.Y., Colo., Ind. Fla. Project design officer Boston Redevel. Authority, Mass., 1963-64; project dir. David A. Crane, Architect, Phila., 1966-69; chief architect N.Y. State Urban Devel. Corp., N.Y.C., 1969-75; prin. urban design and archtl. adviser Harvard Inst. Internat. Devel., Tehran, Iran, 1975-77; pres. HAUS Internat., Inc., N.Y.C., 1977-79, The Liebman Melting Partnership, Architects and Planners, N.Y.C., 1979—; bd. advisers Internat. Urban Design, N.Y.C., 1980-84; assoc. prof. urban design Pratt Inst., Bklyn., 1983-88. Mem. editorial bd. Metropolis, N.Y.C., 1981-88. Contbr. articles to mags. Fellow Am. Acad. in Rome, 1966; Wheelwright travelling fellow Harvard U., 1971. Fellow AIA (pres. N.Y. chpt. 1983-84); mem. Urban Land Inst. Home: 105 Montague St Brooklyn NY 11201-3459 Office: The Liebman Melting Partnership 330 W 42nd St New York NY 10036-6902

LIEBMANN, GEORGE WILLIAM, lawyer; b. N.Y.C., June 20, 1939; s. William Liebmann and Margaret (Hirschman) Cook; m. Anne-Lise Grimstad, Apr. 29, 1967; children: Pamela Dione, George William, Franklin Alexander. AB, Dartmouth Coll., 1960; JD, U. Chgo., 1963. Bar: Md. 1964, Ill. 1964. With Chaucer Head Book Shop Inc., N.Y.C., 1958-59; law clk. to chief judge Ct. Appeals Md., 1963-64; with Frank, Bernstein, Conaway and Goldman, Balt., 1964-79; asst. atty. gen. State of Md., Balt., 1967-69; exec. asst. to Gov. Md., Annapolis, 1979-80; sole practice Balt., 1980—; lectr. U. Md. Law Sch., 1977-78, Johns Hopkins U., 1992; asst. reporter Md. Commn. on Criminal Law and Procedure, 1965-70; mem. Gov.'s Commn. to Revise Annotated Code Md., 1974-83; alt. mem. State Planning Coun. on Radioactive Waste Mgmt., 1980-82; chmn. Gov.'s Task Force on Local Govt. Antitrust Liability, 1983-84; gen. coun. Md. Econs. Devel. Corp., 1985—. Author: Maryland District Court Law and Practice, 2 vols., 1976, Maryland Civil Practice Forms, 2 vols., 1984, The Little Platoons: Sub-Local Governments in Modern History, 1995; mng. editor U. Cho. Law Rev., 1962-63; mem. adv. bd. Accessory Housing, 1990—; contbr. articles to law jours. Sec. Coalition Against the SST, Washington, 1969; trustee Hist. Annapolis Found., 1991—. Simon indsl. and profl. fellow U. Manchester, Eng., 1993-94. Mem. Am. Law Inst., Fed. Jud. Conf. 4th Cir., Libr. Co. Balt. Bar (bd. dirs. 1967—, pres. 1975-77), Engring. Soc. Md. (assoc.). Office: 8 W Hamilton St Baltimore MD 21201-5031

LIEBMANN, SEYMOUR W., construction consultant; b. N.Y.C., Nov. 1, 1928; s. Isidor W. and Etta (Waltzer) L.; m. Hinda Adam, Sept. 20, 1959; children: Peter Adam, David W. BSME, Clarkson U. (formerly Clarkson Coll. Tech.), 1948; grad. Indsl. Coll. Armed Forces, 1963, U.S. Army Command and Gen. Staff Coll., 1966, U.S. Army War Coll., 1971. Registered profl. engr., N.Y., Mass., Ga. Area engr. constrn. div. E.I. DuPont de Nemours & Co., Inc., 1952-54; constrn. planner Lummus Co., 1954-56; prin. mech. engr. Perini Corp., 1956-62; v.p. Boston Based Contractors, 1962-66; v.p. A.R. Abrams, Inc., Atlanta, 1967-74, pres., 1974-78, also bd. dirs.; founder Liebmann Assocs., Inc., Atlanta, 1979—; mem. nat. adv. bd. Am. Security Council. Author: Military Engineer Field Notes, 1953, Prestressing Miter Gate Diagonals, 1960; contbr. articles to publs. Mem. USO Council, Atlanta, 1968—, v.p., 1978, mem. exec. com., 1975-79; mem. Nat. UN Day Com., 1975; sr. army coord., judge Sci. Fair, Atlanta Pub. Schs. annually 1979-88, 92-95; asst. scoutmaster troop 298 Atlanta area council Boy Scouts Am., 1980-87, Explorer advisor, 1982-86, unit commr., 1985, dist. commr. North Atlanta Dist., Atlanta Area Council, 1988-90, asst. coun. commr., 1990—, mem. faculty Commrs. Coll., 1985-88, 92; mem. alumni adv. com. Clarkson Coll. Tech., 1981—, alumni bd. govs., 1983—, Disting. Alumni Golden Knight award, 1983; mem. exec. com., zoning chmn. neighbor planning unit City of Atlanta, 1982—, chmn., 1988, 95, vice-chmn., 1989; pres. West Paces/Northside Neighborhood Assn., 1991—; apptd. civil engr. mem. to City of Atlanta Water and Sewer Appeals Bd., 1992—. Col. AUS Ret. Corps Engrs., 1948-52, Korea, Germany. Decorated Legion of Merit, Meritorious Service medal, U.S. Army Res. medal, 1975; elected to Old Guard of Gate City Guard, 1979; recipient cert. of Achievement Dept. Army, 1978, USO Recognition award, 1979, Order of Arrow award Boy Scouts Am., 1983, 87, Scouters Key Boy Scouts Am., 1988, North Atlanta Dist. Merit award Boy Scouts Am., 1989, Silver Beaver award, 1991, Disting. Commn. award, 1991, Engring. Profl. award Am. Inst. Plant Engrs., 1987; named Met. Atlanta Engr. of Yr. in Pvt. Practice Ga., 1991, Engr. of Yr. in Pvt. Practice, 1991. Fellow Soc. Am. Mil. Engrs. (bd. dirs. 1986—, chmn. readiness com. 1986-88, program chmn. Atlanta post 1980-81, v.p. 1982, pres. 1983, program chmn. 1988 nat. meeting, asst. regional v.p. for readiness So. region 1991—, Nat. award of Merit 1982-83, Atlanta post Leadership award 1988, life dir. Atlanta Post, 1994, elected nat. dir. 1994, James Lucas Chair Atlanta Post, 1994, life mem.); mem. ASTM, NSPE, Am. Cons. Engrs. Coun. (state and nat. pub. rels. coms., nat. ethics com., state legis. liaison com.), Am. Concrete Inst., Soc. 1st U.S. Inf., Res. Officers Assn. (life mem.), U.S. Army War Coll. Found. (life mem.), Nat. Def. Univ. Found., U.S. Army War Coll. Alumni Assn. (life), Ga. Soc. Profl. Engrs. (bd. dirs. Buckhead chpt., state ethics com.), Engrs. Club Boston, Assn. U.S. Army, Am. Def. Preparedness Assn., Am. Arbitration Assn. (panel arbitrators 1979—, constrn. adv. com. 1984—), Cobb C. of C., Downtown Atlanta Kiwanis, Mil. Order World Wars, Order of Engr., Army Engrs. Assn. (life), Appalachian Trail Conf., Benyton Mackaye Trail Assn., Ga. Conservancy, Atlanta Hist. Soc., NRA. Republican. Jewish. Clubs: Ft. McPherson Officers; Ga. Appalachian Trail. Lodges: Masons (32 deg.) Shriners, Nat. Sojourners, Elks, Civitan. Home: 3260 Rilman Dr NW Atlanta GA 30327-2224 Office: Ste 700 210 Interstate North Pky NW Atlanta GA 30339-2120

LIEBOWITZ, HAROLD, aeronautical engineering educator, dean emeritus; b. Bklyn., June 25, 1924; s. Samuel and Sarah (Kaplan) L.; m. Marilyn Iris Lampert, June 24, 1951; children: Alisa Lynn, Jay, Jill Denice. B. in Aero. Engring., Poly. Inst. Bklyn., 1944, M. in Aero. Engring., 1946, D. in Aero. Engring., 1948. With Office Naval Research, 1948-60; asst. dean Grad. Sch., exec. dir. engring. expt. sta. U. Colo., Boulder, 1960-61; also vis. prof. aero. engring. U. Colo.; head structural mechs. br. Office Naval Research, 1961-68, dir. Navy programs in solid propellant mechanics, 1962-68; dean Sch. Engring. and Applied Sci., George Washington U., Washington, 1968-90; L. Stanley Crane endowed prof., 1990—; rsch. prof., endowed prof. Cath. U., Washington, 1962-68; cons. AERDCO, 1970—, Office Naval Rsch., 1970—, Pratt & Whitney Aircraft Co., 1981-82, Pergamon Press, 1968—, Acad. Press, 1968—; mem. Israeli-Am. Materials Adv. Group, 1970—; sci. adviser Congl. Ad Hoc Com. on Environ. Quality, 1969—; co-dir. Joint Inst. for Advancement Flight Scis. NASA-Langley Rsch. Ctr., Hampton, Va., 1971—. Editor: Advanced Treatise on Fracture, 7 vols., 1969-72; founder, editor-in-chief Internat. Jour. Computers and Structures, 1971—; founder, editor Internat. Jour. Engring. Fracture Mechanics, 1968—; founder computer series jours., 1968—; contbr. articles to profl. jours. Bd. govs. U. Denver, 1987—. Recipient Outstanding award Office Naval Research, 1961, Research Accomplishment Superior award, 1961; Superior Civilian Service award USN, 1965, 67; Commendation Outstanding Contbns. sec. navy, 1966; Wash. Soc. Engrs. award, Ednl. Service award, Wash. Soc. Engrs., Fundacion Gran Mariscal de Avacucho, Service cert. Tech. Contbns. to Structures and Materials Panel, NATO, Disting. Alumnus award Polytechnic Inst. Bklyn., Tech. Achievement cert. Washington sect. ASME, Civilian Service award USN, Albert Einstein prize, 1991, Washington Acad. of Scis. award for Disting. career in Sci., 1990. Fellow AAAS, AIAA, Am. Soc. Metals; mem. Soc. Engring. Scis. (past pres.), Sci. Rsch. Soc. Am., Am. Technion Soc. (dir.), Am. Acad. Mechanics (founder, pres.), Internat. Coop. Fracture Inst. (founder, v.p.), Engrs. Coun. for Profl. Devel., nat. Acad. Engring. (home sec.), Engring. Acad. Japan, Argentina NAS, Hungarian Acad. Scis., Sigma Xi, Tau Beta Pi, Sigma Gamma Tau, Omega Rho, Pi Tau Sigma, Sigma Tau. Office: George Washington U Sch Engring & Applied Sci Dept Civil/Mech/Environ Eng Washington DC 20052

LIEBOWITZ, LEO, oil company executive; b. 1926. Former pres. Leemilts Petroleum Inc., L.I., N.Y., from 1961; now pres., chief exec. officer Getty Petroleum Co., Jericho, N.Y. Served with U.S. Army, 1943-46. Office: Getty Petroleum Corp 125 Jericho Tpke Jericho NY 11753-1016

LIEBTAG, BENFORD GUSTAV, III (BEN LIEBTAG), engineer, consultant; b. Pitts., Sept. 20, 1941; s. Benford Gustav and Alice Mildred (Hunt) L.; m. Cynthia Taylor Creighton, Aug. 22, 1964; children: Cindy, Ben. BSEE, U. Pitts., 1964. Sr. heating and air-conditioning engr. Duquesne Light Co., Pitts., 1964-79; dir. energy mgmt. Van Wagenen and Searcy, Inc., Jacksonville, Fla., 1979-80, v.p., 1980-81; pres. Liebtag, Robinson, and Wingfield, Inc., Jacksonville and Gainesville, Fla., 1981. Mem. ASHRAE (Merit award, Disting. Service award), Assn. Energy Engrs., Soc. Am. Mil. Engrs. Methodist. Lodges: Masons, Kiwanis. Home: 4134 Old Mill Cove Trl E Jacksonville FL 32211-1594 Office: 4811 Beach Blvd Ste 400 Jacksonville FL 32207-4871

LIECHTY, ERIC, church administrator. Youth dir. The Missionary Church, Fort Wayne, Ind. Office: The Missionary Ch PO Box 9127 3811 Vanguard Dr Fort Wayne IN 46809-3304

LIEDERMAN, DAVID SAMUEL, child welfare administrator; b. Malden, Mass., Apr. 26, 1935; s. Harry A. Liederman; married; children: Wendy, Keith, Larry. BA, U. Mass., 1957; MEd, Springfield Coll., 1958; MSW, U. Pitts., 1962. Teenage supr. Youngstown (Ohio) Jewish Community Ctr., 1958-62; dir. extension services Roxbury (Mass.) Neighborhood Assn., 1962-64; asst. dir. Roxbury Fedn. Neighborhood Ctrs., 1964-66; dir. family relocation United South End Settlements, Boston, 1966-69; state rep. Mass. Ho. Reps., Boston, 1969-73; dir. Mass. State Office for Children, Boston, 1973-75; chief of staff Mass. Gov. Michael S. Dukakis, Boston, 1975-79; exec. dir. pub. affairs Fedn. Jewish Philanthropies, N.Y.C., 1979-84; exec. dir. Child Welfare League Am., Washington and Los Angeles, 1984—. Contbr. numerous articles to profl. jours. Bd. dirs. Nat. Assembly, Washington, 1984—; mem. United Way Am. Leadership 18, Alexandria, Va., 1984—; chair Nat. Collaboration for Youth, 1990-94; co-chair Generations United, 1987—. Recipient Disting. Alumni award U. Pitts., 1975. Office: Child Welfare League Am 440 1st St NW Washington DC 20001-2028

LIEDTKE, JOHN HUGH, petroleum company executive; b. Tulsa, Feb. 10, 1922; m. Betty Lyn; children: Karen, Kristin, John Hugh, Blake, Kathryn. B.A., Amherst Coll., 1942; postgrad., Harvard Grad. Sch., Bus. Adminstrn., 1943; LL.B., U. Tex., 1947. Pres. Zapata Petroleum Corp., 1953-62; pres., chief exec. officer Pennzoil Co., Houston, 1962-68, chmn., 1968-88, chief exec. officer, dir., 1988—, also bd. dirs. Trustee Kinkaid Sch., Houston, Baylor Coll. Medicine, U.S. Naval Acad. Found.; council overseers Jesse H. Jones Grad. Sch. Adminstrn. Rice U. Served to lt. USN, 1942-45. Mem. Tex. Mid-Continent Oil and Gas Assn. (dir.), Am. Petroleum Inst. (dir.), Nat. Petroleum Council (dir.), Nat. Petroleum Refiners Assn. (bd. dirs.), Ind. Petroleum Assn. Am. (bd. dirs.), Penn Grade Assn. (bd. dirs.),

Houston C. of C. (dir.), Beta Theta Pi, Phi Alpha Delta. Clubs: Houston Country, Ramada, Petroleum; Rolling Rock (Ligonier, Pa.); Racquet (Midland, Tex.); Calgary (Alta., Can.). Office: Pennzoil Co 700 Milam Pennzoil Plz Houston TX 77252-2967

LIEF, HAROLD ISAIAH, psychiatrist; b. N.Y.C., Dec. 29, 1917; s. Jacob F. and Mollie (Filler) L.; m. Myrtis A. Brumfield, Mar. 3, 1961; Caleb B., Frederick V., Oliver F.; children from previous marriage: Polly Lief Goldberg, Jonathan F. BA, U. Mich., 1938; MD, N.Y. U., 1942; cert. in psychoanalysis, Columbia Coll. Physicians and Surgeons, 1950; MA (hon.), U. Pa., 1971. Intern Queens Gen. Hosp., Jamaica, N.Y., 1942-43; resident psychiatry L.I. Coll. Medicine, 1946-48; pvt. practice psychiatry N.Y.C., 1948-51; asst. physician Presbyn. Hosp., N.Y.C., 1949-51; asst. prof. Tulane U., New Orleans, 1951-54, asso. prof., 1954-60, prof. psychiatry, 1960-67; prof. psychiatry U. Pa., Phila., 1967-82, prof. emeritus, 1982—; dir. div. family study U. Pa., 1967-81; dir. Marriage Council of Phila., 1969-81, Ctr. for Study of Sex. Edn. in Medicine, 1968-82; mem. staff U. Pa. Hosp., 1967-81, Pa. Hosp., 1981—; clin. prof. psychiatry Jefferson Med. U., 1994—. Author: (with Daniel and William Thompson) The Eighth Generation, 1960; Editor: (with Victor and Nina Lief) Psychological Basis of Medical Practice, 1963, Medical Aspects of Human Sexuality, 1976, (with Arno Karlen) Sex Education in Medicine, 1976, Sexual Problems in Medical Practice, 1981, (with Zwi Hoch) Sexology: Sexual Biology, Behavior and Therapy, 1982, (with Zwi Hoch) International Research in Sexology, 1983, Human Sexuality With Respect to AIDS and HIV Infection, 1989; contbr. numerous articles to pubis. Bd. dirs. Ctr. for Sexuality and Religion; mem. La. State Commn. Civil Rights, 1958-67. Maj. M.C. U.S. Army, 1943-46. Commonwealth Fund fellow, 1963-64; recipient Gold Medal award Mt. Airy Hosp., 1977, Lifetime Achievement award Phila. Psychiat. Soc., 1992. Fellow Phila. Coll. Physicians, Am. Psychiat. Assn. (life), N.Y. Acad. Scis., AAAS, Am. Acad. Psychoanalysis (charter, past pres.), Am. Coll. Psychiatrists (founding), Am. Coll. Psychoanalysts (charter); mem. Am. Assn. Marriage and Family Therapists, Sex Info. and Edn. Council U.S. (past pres.), Group Advancement Psychiatry (life), Am. Soc. Adolescent Psychiatry, Am. Psychosomatic Soc., Assn. Psychoanalytic Medicine (life), Internat. Acad. Sex Rsch., Soc. Sci. Study of Sex, Am. Soc. Sex Educators, Counselors and Therapists, Soc. Sex Therapists and Researchers, World Assn. Sexology (past v.p.), Soc. Exploration of Psychotherapy Integration (adv. bd.), Columbia Club, Mich. Club of Greater Phila., Penn Club of N.Y., Sigma Xi, Alpha Omega Alpha, Phi Eta Sigma, Phi Kappa Phi. Home: 101 S Buck Ln Haverford PA 19041-1104 Office: 700 Spruce St Fl 503 Philadelphia PA 19106-4027 *The conflict between individual gratification and the needs of society, between competition and cooperation, appears to me to be the most fundamental issue confronting mankind. My goal in life has been to steer a course that fosters service to others and to society without undue sacrifice of individual aspirations.*

LIEF, THOMAS PARRISH, sociologist, educator; b. N.Y.C., Oct. 4, 1931; s. Alfred and Zola Nina (Vogel) L. BA, U. N.Mex., 1955, MA, 1961; PhD, Tulane U., 1970. Cert. substance abuse counselor, La. Counselor, archaeology asst. U. N.Mex., Albuquerque, 1959-60, 60-61; teaching asst. dept. sociology Tualen U., New Orleans, 1961-64; instr. to asst. prof. dept. sociology Loyola U., New Orleans, 1964-69; assoc. prof. to prof. dept. sociology So. U., New Orleans, 1968—; cons. on curriculum devel. Tuskegee Inst. Drug Abuse Human Svcs. Manpower Devel. Tng., 1973-78; adj. prof. sociology, assoc. grad. faculty mem. U. New Orleans, 1975-76; cons. various orgns., 1981-82; vis. prof. dept. sociology Tulane U., New Orleans, 1986; rev. com. mem. Alcohol, Drug Abuse & Mental Health Adminstrn. Office, 1987—; bd. dirs. Nat. Assn. Alcoholism and Drug Abuse Counselors, 1990-91; pres. La. Assn. Substance Abuse Counselor and Trainers, 1990-91; adv. bd. Michael Halbrook Recovery Ctr. East Lake Hosp., 1990-92; mem. La. State Bd. Certification for Substance Abuse Counselors, 1988-92, Adv. Com. for Historically Black Colls. and Univs. Program for Substance Abuse Tng., 1987-89; tng. cons. Am. Indian Tng. Inst., Sacramento, Calif., 1985—; mem. La. Commn. on Alcohol and Drug Abuse, 1984-91; mem. La. Drug Control and Violent Crime Policy Bd., 1993—; contract cons. Ctr. for Substance Abuse Treatment, 1994—; founder, bd. dirs. Accreditation Coun.: Alcohol and Drug Counselor Program in Higher Edn.; cons. in field. Contbr. numerous articles to profl. jours.; mem. editl. rev. com. Counselor, 1986-92; co-author: Academic Linkages Resource Manual. Co-chair La. State-Wide Taskforce Counselor Manpower, 1984-90; pres., founder Nat. Assn. Substance Abuse Trainers and Educators, 1983—; bd. dirs. Nat. Commn. on Accreditation of Alcoholism and Drug Abuse Counselors, 1982-90, Certification Reciprocity Consortium/Alcohol and Other Drug Abuse, Inc., 1981-82; pres., founder La. Cert. Examining Bd. of La. Assn. Substance Abuse Counselor & Trainers, 1978-82; mem. Child Abuse Com. Dist. Atty.'s Office, 1976-80; co-dir. Insight House Adv. Bd., 1976-80. Mem. Am. Sociol. Assn., Am. Acad. Polit. and Social Scis., La. Assn. Substance Abuse Counselors and Trainers, La. Alcohol and Drug Abuse Assn., Nat. Assn. Alcoholism and Substance Abuse Counselors, Nat. Assn. Substance Abuse Trainers and Educators, Soc. for Applied Anthropology, Soc. for Study of Social Problems, So. Sociol. Soc., Substance Abuse Counselor Orgn., Nat. Commn. on Accreditation of Alcoholism and Drug Abuse Counselors Credentialing Bodies. Office: 6400 Press Dr New Orleans LA 70126-1009

LIEGL, JOSEPH LESLIE, lawyer; b. Fond du Lac, Wis., Jan. 20, 1948; s. Melvin Theodore and Verna Lavinia (Jagdfeld) L.; m. Janet L. Meyer, Feb. 1, 1969; children: Matthew, Jeremy. BA with distinction, U. Wis., 1970, JD cum laude, 1973. Bar: Wis. 1973, U.S. Supreme Ct. 1976, Ohio 1978, U.S. Dist. Ct. (no. dist.) Ohio 1978, U.S. Tax Ct. 1978. Assoc. Muchin & Muchin S.C., Manitowoc, Wis., 1973-74; trial atty. U.S. Dept. Justice, Washington, 1974-78; assoc. Jones, Day, Reavis & Pogue, Cleve., 1978-83, prin., 1983—. mem. ABA (taxation sect.), Cleve. Bar Assn. (chmn. tax sect. 1987-88), Cleve. Tax Inst. (chmn. 1994), Cleve. Tax Club (v.p. 1993—, past bd. dirs.), Order of Coif, Phi Eta Sigma, Phi Kappa Phi. Avocation: music. Home: 16824 Holbrook Rd Cleveland OH 44120-3446 Office: Jones Day Reavis & Pogue 901 Lakeside Ave E Cleveland OH 44114-1116

LIEGL, PETER J., company executive; b. Petoskey, Mich., Apr. 30, 1944; s. Frederick J. Kathlyn (Foltz) L.; m. Sharon Chamnorlin Ą JUne 29, 1968; 1 child, Lisa. BA, Northern Mich. U., 1968; MBA, Western Mich. U., 1971. Regional mktg. mgr. Clark Equipment Corp., Bachanan, Mich., 1970-74; gen. mgr. Morrison Equipment Co., Kalamazoo, Mich., 1974-76; sales rep. Coachmen Ind., Middlebury, Ind., 1976-77; sales mgr., gen.mgr. Coachmen Ind., Leola, Pa.; pres. Coachmen Ind. Midas, Elkhart, Ind., 1982-83, Coachmen Ind., Shasta Ind. Ind., 1983-85; pres., owner prin. Van Am., Cobra, Goshen, Ind., 1985—, former pres., former owner, now bd. dirs. Mem. Elks. Republican. Roman Catholic. Home: 54061 Hampton Rd Elkhart IN 46514-4825 Office: Cobra Industries Inc 2766 College Ave Goshen IN 46526*

LIEM, KAREL FREDERIK, biologist, educator; b. Jogya, Java, Indonesia, Nov. 24, 1935; came to U.S., 1964; s. Soen Ging and Maria Carolina (Bader) L.; m. Hetty Khouw, Sept. 4, 1965; children—Karel Frederik, Erika Elise. B.Sc., U. Indonesia, 1957, M.Sc. cum laude, 1958; Ph.D., U. Ill., 1961; A.M. (hon.), Harvard, 1972. Asst. prof. U. Leiden, Netherlands, 1962-64; asst. prof., then asso. prof. U. Ill., Urbana, 1964-72; asst. curator, then asso. curator of anatomy Field Museum Natural History, Chgo., 1966-72; Henry Bryant Bigelow prof. biology, curator ichthyology Harvard, 1972—; Mem. vis. com. New Eng. Aquarium; trustee Cohasset (Mass.) Marine Biol. Lab.; mem. com. Latimeria, Nat. Acad. Scis. Editor: Copeia, 1974; asso. editor jour. morphology, 1974—. Guggenheim fellow, 1970. Fellow Linnean Soc.; mem. Am. Soc. Ichthyologists and Herpetologists, Am. Soc. Zoologists, Zool. Soc. London (sci. fellow), Soc. Study Evolution. Home: 935 Memorial Dr Cambridge MA 02138-6114 Office: Harvard U Museum of Comparative Zoology Cambridge MA 02138

LIEM, KHIAN KIOE, medical entomologist; b. Semarang, Java, Indonesia, Jan. 11, 1942; came to U.S., 1969; s. Coen Ing T and Marie Soei-Nio (Goei) L.; m. Anita Tumewu, Apr. 3, 1980; children: Brian Dexter, Tiffany Marie, Jennifer Amanda, Ashley Elizabeth. BS, Bandung Inst. Tech., Bandung, Indonesia, 1964; MS, Bandung Inst. Tech., 1966, Eastern Ill. U., 1970; PhD, U. Ill., 1975. Registered profl. entomologist, vector ecologist. Grad. teaching asst. Bandung Inst. Tech., 1964-66, grad. instr., 1966-68; grad. rsch./teaching asst. Eastern Ill. U., 1969-70; grad. teaching asst. U. Ill.,

1970-74; med. entomologist South Cook County Mosquito Abatement Dist., Harvey, Ill., 1974-76; mgr./dir.-med. entomologist South Cook County Mosquito Abatement Dist., Harvey, 1977--; cons. U.S. AID, Washington, 1979--. Recipient Community Svc. award Asian Am. Coalition, 1993. Mem. Am. Mosquito Control Assn. (chmn. resolution com. 1977-78, mem. editorial bd. 1980-83, mem. worldwide com. 1987—), Ill. Mosquito Control Assn. (pres. 1979-81), Entomol. Soc. Am. (com. on book revs.), Am. Tropical Medicine and Hygiene Assn., Am. Registry of Profl. Entomologists, Scientists Inst. Pub. Info., Soc. Vector Ecology, Sigma Xi, Phi Sigma. Roman Catholic. Avocations: soccer, tennis, martial arts, camping, classical music. Home: 8012 W Binford Dr Orland Park IL 60462 Office: Mosquito Abatement Dist 15440 Dixie Hwy Harvey IL 60426-3402

LIEN, BRUCE HAWKINS, minerals and oil company executive; b. Waubay, S.D., Apr. 7, 1927; s. Peter Calmer and LaRece Catherine (Holm) L.; m. Deanna Jean Browning, May 4, 1978. BS in Bus., Wyo. U., 1953. Chmn. bd. Pete Lien & Sons, Inc., Rapid City, S.D., 1944-84, bd. chmn., 1984—. Chmn. Community Chest, Rapid City, S.D., 1956; pres., nat. council Boys Club Am., Rapid City, S.D., N.Y.C., 1968; commr. Presdl. Scholars Commn., Washington, 1982; pres. U. Wyo. Found., 1989-90. Served to 1st lt. U.S. Army, 1945-47, 50-53. Recipient Disting. Service award S.D. Sch. Mines, Rapid City, 1972, Disting. Service award Cosmopolitan Internat., Rapid City, 1983; named Disting. Alumnus, Wyo. U., Laramie, 1982. Mem. Internat. Lime Assn. (pres. 1973-75), Nat. Lime Assn. (pres. 1973-75, Merit award 1973, bd. dirs.), VFW. Republican. Lutheran. Club: Cosmopolitan (Rapid City, S.D.). Lodges: Masons, Elks. Home: PO Box 440 Rapid City SD 57709-0440 Office: Pete Lien & Sons Inc I 90 & Deadwood Ave PO Box 440 Rapid City SD 57709-0440

LIEN, ERIC JUNG-CHI, pharmacist, educator; b. Kaohsiung, Taiwan, Nov. 30, 1937; came to U.S., 1963, naturalized, 1973; m. Linda L. Chen, Oct. 2, 1965; children: Raymond, Andrew. B.S. in Pharmacy (Frank Shu China Sci. scholar), Nat. Taiwan U., 1960; Ph.D. in Pharm. Chemistry, U. Calif., San Francisco, 1966; postdoctoral fellow in bio-organic chemistry, Pomona Coll., Claremont, Calif., 1967-68. Hosp. pharmacist 862 Hosp. of Republic of China, 1960-61; asst. prof. pharmaceutics and biomedicinal chemistry U. So. Calif., L.A., 1968-72; assoc. prof. U. So. Calif., 1972-76, prof., 1976—, coord. sects. biomedicinal chemistry and pharms., 1975-78, coord. sect. biomedicinal chemistry, 1975-84; cons. Internat. Medication Sys., Ltd., 1978, NIH, 1971, 82-87, 92, 94, Inst. Drug Design, Inc., Calif., 1971-73, Allergan Pharms., Inc., 1971-72, EPA, 1985, 89, Ariz. Disease Control Rsch. Commn., 1986—; sci. adv. nat. labs. Dept. Health, Foods and Drugs, Exec. Yuan, China, Dept. Health, Taipei, Taiwan; referee Jour. Pharmacokinetics and Biopharmaceutics, Jour. Medicinal Chemistry, Jour. Food Agr. Chemistry, Jour. Pharm. Sci., Pesticide Biochemistry and Physiology, Chem. Resv., Jour. Organic Chemistry, Pharm. Rsch., Internat. Jour. Oriental Medicine, Am. Jour. Pharm. Edn. Author 3 books; mem. editorial bd. Jour. Clin. Pharmacy and Therapeutics, 1979—, Internat. Jour. Oriental Medicine, Med. Chem. Rsch., 1991—, Chinese Pharm. Jour., 1991-93, Acta Pharmaceutica, 1992—; contbr. numerous articles to profl. jours. Grantee Merck, 1970, Abbott, 1971-72, NSF, 1972-74, 76-77, IMS, 1979, H & L Found., 1989-95. Fellow AAPS, AAAS, Louis Pasteur Found.; mem. Am. Assn. Cancer Rsch., Acad. Pharm. Scis., Am. Chem. Soc., Am. Assn. Pharm. Scientist, Internat. Union Pure and Applied Chemistry, Sigma Xi, Rho Chi, Phi Kappa Phi. Office: U So Calif Sch Pharmacy 1985 Zonal Ave Los Angeles CA 90033-1058

LIENHARD, JOHN HENRY, mechanical engineering educator; b. St. Paul, Aug. 17, 1930; s. John Henry and Catherine Edith Lienhard; m. Carol Ann Bratton, June 20, 1959; children—John Henry V, Andrew Joseph. A.S., Multnomah Jr. Coll., 1949; B.S., Oreg. State Coll., 1951; M.S. in M.E., U. Wash.-Seattle, 1953; Ph.D. in Mech. Engring., U. Calif.-Berkeley, 1961. Assoc. prof. mech. engring. Wash. State U., Pullman, 1961-67; prof. mech. engring. dept. U. Ky., Lexington, 1967-80; Clyde chair prof. U. Utah, Salt Lake City, summer 1981; prof. mech. engring. U. Houston, 1980-89; M.D. Anderson prof. mech. engring. and history, 1989—. Recipient Portrait award Am. Women in Radio and TV, 1990. Fellow ASME (heat transfer meml. award, Charles Russ Richards award, Ralph Coats Roe medal). Episcopalian. Author 4 books; author/host of program on Pub. Radio, The Engines of Our Ingenuity, also numerous articles in profl. jours. Home: 3719 Durhill St Houston TX 77025 Office: U Houston Dept Mech Engring Houston TX 77204-4792

LIENHART, DAVID ARTHUR, geologist, consultant, laboratory director; b. Cin., Sept. 28, 1939; s. Arthur C. and Grace H.J. (Burger) L.; m. Donna Paula Klosterman, June 12, 1964; children—Devin Scott, Dana Ann. B.A., U. Cin., 1961, M.S., 1964. Cert. profl. geologist, Ind.; registered geologist, Del.; lic. profl. geologist, N.C. Petrographer Ohio River Div. Lab., Cin., 1964-70, geologist, 1970-76; geologist, lab. dir. Ohio River Div. Lab., 1976-90; hydrologist geotech. HTRW div. U.S. Army Corps Engrs., 1990-95; cons. constrn. rock properties and evaluation of rock for erosion control, 1995—; agy. chmn. Combined Fed. Campaign, 1989, 82-84; guest spkr. internat. tech. seminars. Contbr. articles to profl. jours.; author and editor tech. pubis. U. Cin. Dept. Army fellow, 1986-87; recipient Outstanding Pub. Svc. award, Cin., 1972-94. Fellow Geol. Soc. Am., Geol. Soc. London; mem. ASCE, ASTM (Excellence in Symposium and Publ. Mgmt. 1995), Assn. Engring. Geologists, Nat. Ground Water Assn., Geol. Soc. Ky., Internat. Soc. Engring. Geologists, Sigma Xi. Methodist. Avocations: fishing, music. Office: US Army Corps Engrs Geotech HTRW Div PO Box 1159 Cincinnati OH 45201-1159

LIENHART, JAMES LEE, graphic designer; b. Chambers, Nebr., Aug. 4, 1935. BFA in Design, Kansas City Art Inst. and Sch. of Design, 1957; postgrad., Drake U. Promotion designer Better Homes and Gardens Mag., 1958-60; promotion designer Look Mag., 1960-61; designer with Whitaker Guernsey Studio, Chgo., 1961-65; dir. design Unimark Internat. Chgo. 1965-69; v.p., dir. design RVI Corp., Chgo., 1969-71; v.p., art dir. Vertical Mktg. Inc., 1971-72; ptnr., creative dir. Murrie Lienhart Rysner & Assocs., Chgo., 1972—; co-founder, prin. creative dir. Calif. Dreamers Inc., Chgo., 1981-86; founder, creative dir. James Lienhart Design, Chgo., 1978-88; founder, pres., creative dir. Wild Oats Prodns., Chgo., 1989—; Taught and lectured in field. Recipient numerous awards Am. Inst. Graphic Arts, others, 345 design awards.

LIEPMANN, HANS WOLFGANG, physicist, educator; b. Berlin, Germany, July 3, 1914; came to U.S. 1939, naturalized, 1945; s. Wilhelm and Emma (Leser) L.; m. Kate Kaschinsky, June 19, 1939 (div.); m. Dietlind Wegener Goldschmidt, 1954; 2 children. Student, U. Istanbul, 1933-35, U. Prague, 1935; Ph.D., U. Zurich, 1938; Dr. Engring. (hon.), Tech. U. Aachen, 1985. Research fellow U. Zurich, 1938-39; mem. faculty Calif. Inst. Tech., Pasadena, 1939, prof. aeronautics, 1949—, dir. Grad. Aeronautical Labs., 1972-85, Charles Lee Powell prof. fluid mechanics and thermodynamics, 1976-83, Theodore von Kármán prof. aeronautics, 1983-85, Theodore von Kármán prof. aeronautics emeritus, 1985—; mem. research and tech. adv. com. on basic research NASA. Co-author: (with A.E. Puckett) Aerodynamics of a Compressible Fluid, 1947; (with A. Roshko) Elements of Gas-dynamics, 1957. Contbr. articles to profl. jours. Recipient Physics prize U. Zurich, 1939, Prandtl Ring, German Soc. Aeros. and Astronautics, 1968, Worcester Reed Warner medal ASME, 1969, Nat. Medal of Sci., 1986, Guggenheim medal, 1986, Nat. Medal of Tech., 1993. Fellow AIAA (Fluid and Plasmadynamics award 1990), Am. Acad. Arts and Scis., Am. Phys. Soc. (Fluid Dynamics prize 1980, Otto Laporte award 1985); hon. fellow Indian Acad. Scis., 1985; fgn. fellow Max-Planck Institut, 1988; mem. NAS (award 1971), NAE (award 1965), AAAS, ASME (hon.), Internat. Acad. Astronautics, Sigma Xi (Monie A. Ferst award 1978). Address: Calif Inst Tech Dept Aeronautics Pasadena CA 91125

LIES, RICHARD LORENZ, JR., cosmetics executive; b. Newark, N.J., Sept. 1, 1945; s. Richard L. and Madelon (Thompson) L.; m. Susan Dorothy Nielsen, July 1, 1967; 1 child, Richard L. III. BA in Econs., Northwestern U., 1967; MBA in Finance, U. Chgo., 1978; postgrad., Cleve. Inst. Electronics, 1980. Maintenance supt. Johnson and Johnson, Chgo., 1972-76; maintenance and mfg. mgr. Dial Corp. formerly Armour-Dial, Inc., Montgomery, Ill., 1976-78, plant mgr., 1978-81, sr. v.p., gen. mgr. personal care div. Dial Corp., Phoenix, 1986—; bd. dirs. CCVI Investment, Chgo., 1981-86. Bd. dirs. Ill. Safety Council, Chgo., 1981-86, United Way, Aurora,

Ill., 1983-84; pres. YMCA, Aurora, 1982-83. Capt. USAF, 1967-72. Decorated Vietnam Service medal; recipient Nat. Sci. medal Bausch and Lomb Co., 1963. Avocations: snow skiing, scuba diving, golf. Office: Dial Corp Greyhound Towers # 702 Phoenix AZ 85077

LIETZKE, MILTON HENRY, chemistry educator; b. Syracuse, N.Y., Nov. 23, 1920; s. Henry Robert and Emma (Gutknecht) L.; m. Marjorie Helen Padrutt, May 31, 1943; children: Kathryn Ann, Milton Henry, Carol Lynn; m. Eleanor Jean Hawkins, May 29, 1965; adopted children: Susan Lucinda, Mary Lindl. B.A., Colgate U., 1942; M.S., U. Wis., 1944, Ph.D., 1949. Lab. supr. Tenn. Eastman Corp., Oak Ridge, 1944-47; group leader chemistry div. Oak Ridge Nat. Lab., 1949-74, sr. scientist, 1978-83; prof. chemistry U. Tenn., Knoxville, 1964-90, prof. emeritus, 1990—. Contbr. numerous articles and reports to profl. jours. Bd. dirs. Oak Rige Festival, 1962-64. Fellow Am. Inst. Chemists, N.Y. Acad. Scis.; mem. Am. Chem. Soc. (D.A. Shirley award East Tenn. sect. 1991), Sci. Research Soc. Am., Tenn. Acad. Sci., Alpha Chi Sigma. Home: 7600 Twining Dr Knoxville TN 37919-7127 Office: U Tenn Dept Chemistry Knoxville TN 37916

LIEW, FAH POW, mechanical engineer; b. Kuala Lumpur, Selangor, Malaysia, Sept. 30, 1960; s. Yeam Shoon and Park Yuen (Yong) L. BA in Computer Sci., SUNY, Buffalo, 1983; BS in Aerospace Engring., SUNY, 1983, MS in Mech. Engring., 1987. Teaching asst. SUNY, Buffalo, 1983-85; research asst. SUNY, 1985-87; engr. E.I. DuPont de Nemours & Co., Buffalo, 1988—. Mem. AIAA, ASME (assoc.), N.Y. Soc. Profl. Engrs., S.E. Asian Student Assn. (pres. 1980-81). Office: EI DuPont de Nemours Sheridan Dr At River Rd Buffalo NY 14207

LIFFERS, WILLIAM ALBERT, retired chemical company executive; b. Union City, N.J., Jan. 12, 1929; s. William F. and Gertrude (Wildemann) L.; m. Mary Rafferty, Sept. 5, 1953; children—Steven, Linda, Wendy. B.S. in Bus. Adminstrn, Seton Hall U., 1953. With Am. Cyanamid Co., Wayne, N.J., 1953—; v.p. Cyanamid Internat., 1972-74; pres. Cyanamid Internat. (Cyanamid Americas/Far East), 1974-76, corp. v.p., 1976-77, sr. v.p., dir., 1977-78, vice chmn., 1978-93; ret., 1993; sr. advisor UN Devel. Programme, 1994. Bd. dirs. Nat. Fgn. Trade Council, Tax Found., U.S. Council Internat. Bus., N.J. Inst. Tech., Ireland-U.S. Council Commerce and Industry, Council U.S. and Italy, Pub. Affairs Research Inst. N.J. Served with Finance Corps U.S. Army, 1951-53. Mem. Nat. Planning Assn. (trustee), Brit.-N. Am. Com., Council on Fgn. Relations.

LIFKA, MARY LAURANNE, history educator; b. Oak Park, Ill., Oct. 31, 1937; d. Aloysius William and Loretta Catherine (Juric) L. B.A., Mundelein Coll., 1960; M.A., Loyola U., Los Angeles, 1965; Ph.D., U. Mich., 1974; postdoctoral student London U., 1975. Life teaching cert. Prof. history Mundelein Coll., Chgo., 1976-84, coordinator acad. computer, 1983-84, prof. history Coll. St. Teresa, Winona, Minn., 1984-89, Lewis U., Romeoville, Ill., 1989—; chief reader in history Ednl. Testing Service, Princeton, N.J., 1980-84; cons. world history project Longman, Inc., 1983—; cons. in European history Coll. Bd., Evanston, Ill., 1983—; mem. Com. on History in the Classroom. Author: Instructor's Guide to European History, 1983; contbr. articles to publs. Mem. Am. Hist. Assn., Ednl. Testing Service Devel. Com. of History. Democrat. Roman Catholic. Office: Lewis U RR 53 Romeoville IL 60441

LIFLAND, JOHN C., federal judge; b. 1933. BA, Yale U., 1954; LLB, Harvard U., 1957. Pvt. practice law, 1957-59; law sec. to Hon. Thomas F. Meaney U.S. Dist. Ct. N.J., 1959-61; mem. firm Stryker, Tams & Dill, 1961-88; dist. judge U.S. Dist. Ct. N.J., Newark, 1988—; mem. N.J. State Bd. Bar Examiners, 1968-77. 1st lt. U.S. Army, 1958. Fellow Am. Bar Found., Assn. Fed. Bar (v.p. 1986—), N.J. State Bar Assn., Essex County Bar Assn.; mem. ABA (antitrust sect. publs. com., books editor/co-editor Antitrust Law Jour. 1981-87), Clearwater Seim Club, Essex Club, Harvard Law Sch. Assn. Office: US Dist Ct M L King Fed Bldg & Cthouse PO Box 999 Newark NJ 07101-0999

LIFLAND, WILLIAM THOMAS, lawyer; b. Jersey City, Nov. 15, 1928; s. Charles and Carolyn (Francks) L.; m. Nancy Moffat, May 29, 1954; children—Carol M., Charles C., J. Kerin, David T. BS, Yale U., 1949; J.D., Harvard U., 1952. Bar: D.C. 1954, N.Y. 1955, N.J. 1965. Law clk. to Justice John M. Harlan U.S. Supreme Ct., 1954-55; assoc. Cahill Gordon & Reindel, N.Y.C., 1955-58, Paris, 1958-60; ptnr. Cahill Gordon & Reindel, N.Y.C., 1965—; adj. prof. Fordham Law Sch., N.Y.C.; dir Commodities Corp., Princeton, N.J. Served as lt. USAF, 1952-54. Mem. ABA, N.Y. State Bar Assn., N.J. Bar Assn., D.C. Bar Assn., N.Y. County Lawyers Assn., Assn. Bar City N.Y. Clubs: India House (N.Y.C.), Nassau Club (Princeton, N.J.). Office: Cahill Gordon & Reindel 80 Pine St New York NY 10005-1702

LIFSON, KALMAN ALAN, management consultant, retail executive; b. Mpls., Oct. 15, 1926; s. Maurice Kalman and Gertrude (Shulkin) L.; m. Irene Londer, June 17, 1950 (dec. July 1968); m. Judith Abrams, Sept. 3, 1969; children: Valerie Leftwich, Kipp, Ione Spear, Stacey Dorfman, Grant Dorfman. BS in Naval Tech., U. Minn., 1946, MABA, 1949; PhD in Psychology, Purdue U., 1951. Commd. ensign USN, 1945, lt. (j.g), 1952; engring. officer Panama Canal Zone, 1945-46; supr. indsl. engring. Temco Aircraft, Dallas, 1951-52; mgmt. engring. officer USN, Washington, 1953-54, resigned; prin. Lifson, Wilson, Ferguson & Winick, Dallas, 1954-94, Pers. Decisions, Inc., Dallas, 1995—; chmn. Harris'Dept. Stores, San Bernadino, Calif., 1980-94, Tex. Rsch. and Electronic Corp. and successors, Dallas, 1962-94, Electronic Mgmt. Info. Sys., 1970-94; chmn. emeritus B.R. Blackmarr & Assocs., Dallas, 1986—; chmn. Fed. Home Loan Bank of 9th Dist., Little Rock, 1979-80; bd. dirs. Bioseparations Inc., Tucson, Ariz., Century Univ., Albuquerque; speaker in fields of psychology, retailing, banking, ops. rsch. Contbr. articles to profl. jours. Chmn. Congl. Commn. on Guaranteed Student Loans, Washington, 1975, Commn. on Orgn. of U.S. Dept. Labor, Washington, 1976; mem. Tex. Commn. on State Employee Productivity, Austin, Tex., 1985; bd. dirs. Century U., Albuquerque, 1989—. Mem. Am. Psychol. Assn., World Pres. Orgn., Columbian Club (treas. 1950—), Crescent Club, Republican. Jewish. Office: Pers Decisions Inc 480 Williams Tower 5215 N O'Connor Blvd Dallas TX 75039-2260 *"Winners" are those who can make the big play, who can turn the game around, who can conceive and institute dramatic changes. Those few of us who have been so endowed and developed must use our winnership to effect significant improvements to the well-being of those within our spheres of influence.*

LIFTIN, JOHN MATTHEW, lawyer; b. Washington, June 25, 1943; children: Eric, Hilary. AB, U. Pa., 1964; LLB, Columbia U., 1967. Bar: N.Y. 1967, D.C. 1974, U.S. Dist. Ct. D.C. 1975, U.S. Ct. Appeals (D.C. cir.) 1975, U.S. Supreme Ct. 1980. Assoc. Sullivan & Cromwell, N.Y.C., 1967-71; spl. counsel to chmn. SEC, Washington, 1971-72, assoc. dir. market reg. div., 1972-74; ptnr. Rogers & Wells, Washington, 1974-85; pres. Quadrex Securities Corp., N.Y.C., 1985-87; sr. v.p., gen. counsel Kidder, Peabody Group Inc., N.Y.C., 1987—; mem. adv. bd. securities regulation and law reports Bur. Nat. Affairs, Inc., Washington, 1971—. Contbr. articles on securities law to profl. jours. Mem. ABA (chmn.-elect com. on fed. regulation securities), Univ. Club. Office: Kidder Peabody & Co Inc 10 Hanover Sq Fl 21 New York NY 10005

LIFTON, ROBERT JAY, psychiatrist, author; b. N.Y.C., May 16, 1926; s. Harold A. and Ciel (Roth) L.; m. Betty Jean Kirschner, Mar. 1, 1952; children: Kenneth Jay, Natasha Karen. Student, Cornell U., 1942-44; MD, N.Y. Med. Coll., 1948, DHL, 1977; DSc (hon.), Lawrence U., 1971, Merrimack Coll., 1973; DHL (hon.), Wilmington Coll., 1975, N.Y. Med. Coll., 1977, Marlboro Coll., 1983, Maryville Coll., 1983, Iona Coll., 1984; DSc (hon.), U. Vt., 1984, Amerika Institut Der Universitat, Munich, 1989; DHL (hon.), U. New Haven, 1986. Intern Jewish Hosp. Bklyn., 1948-49; resident psychiatry State U. N.Y. Downstate Med. Center, 1949-51; mem. faculty Washington Sch. Psychiatry, 1954-55; research assoc. psychiatry, also assoc. East Asian studies Harvard U., 1956-61; Found.'s Fund for research psychiatry assoc. prof. Yale Med. Sch., 1961-67, research prof., 1967—; disting. prof. psychiatry and psychology, dir. Ctr. on Violence and Human Survival John Jay Coll. Criminal Justice, the Grad Sch. and Univ. Ctr. and Mt. Sinai Sch. Medicine, CUNY, 1985—; cons. behavioral scis. study sect. NIMH, 1962-64; com. invasion of privacy N.Y. State Bar Assn., 1963-64, various law firms, Columbia seminars modern Japan and Oriental thought and religion,

1965-70; Peter B. Lewis lectr., Princeton U., 1988; Gay lectr. Harvard Med. Sch., 1976, Messenger lectr. Cornell U., 1980. Author: Thought Reform and the Psychology of Totalism: A Study of Brainwashing in China, 1961, 1989, Revolutionary Immorality: Mao Tse-Tung and the Chinese Cultural Revolution, 1968, Death in Life: Survivors of Hiroshima (Nat. Book award), 1969, 1991, (Van Wyck Brooks award), History and Human Survival, 1970, Boundaries: Psychological Man in Revolution, 1970, Home from the War: Vietnam Veterans—Neither Victims Nor Executioners, 1973 (Nat. Book award nominee), (with Eric Olson) Living and Dying, 1974, The Life of the Self, 1976, (with Shuichi Kato and Michael Reich) Six Lives/Six Deaths: Portraits from Modern Japan, 1979, The Broken Connection: On Death and the Continuity of Life, 1979, (with Richard A. Falk) Indefensible Weapons: The Political and Psychological Case Against Nuclearism, 1982, 1991; humorous cartoons Birds, 1969, PsychoBirds, 1979, (with Nicholas Humphrey) In a Dark Time, 1984 (Brit. edit. selected Top Twenty Nat. Peace Book Week, Martin Luther King award, Eng.), The Nazi Doctors: Medical Killing and Psychology of Genocide, 1986 (Nat. Jewish Book award, Los Angeles Times Book prize for history 1987 and Lisl and Leo Eitinger award, Oslo, Norway, 1988), German edit. 1988, The Future of Immortality and Other Essays for a Nuclear Age, 1987; (with Eric Markusen) The Genocidal Mentality: Nazi Holocaust and Nuclear Threat, 1990, The Protean Self: Human Resilience in an Age of Fragmentation, 1993, (with G. Mitchell) Hiroshima in America: Fifty Years of Denial, 1995; editor: Woman in America, 1965, America and the Asian Revolutions, 1970, (with R.A. Falk and G. Kolko) Crimes of War, 1971, (with Eric Olson) Explorations in Psychohistory: The Wellfleet Papers, 1975, (with Eric Chivian, Suzanna Chivian, John E. Mack) Last Aid: Medical Dimensions of Nuclear War, 1982, The Genocidal Mentality: Nazi Doctor and Nuclear Threat, 1990. Organizer redress group opposing Vietnam War IAEA, Vienna, 1975. Served to capt. USAF, 1951-53. Recipient Pub. Service award N.Y. Soc. Clin. Psychologists, Alumni medal N.Y. Med. Coll., 1970, Karen Horney lectr. award, 1972, Distinguished Service award Soc. Adolescent Psychiatry, 1972, Mt. Airy Found. Gold medal, 1973, Hiroshima gold medal, 1975, Gandhi Peace award, 1984, Bertrand Russell Soc. award, 1985, Holocaust Meml. award, 1986, 1st Ann. Nuc. Psychology Rsch. award Harvard U., 1986, Bird Hadorot Covenant of Generations award,1987, Max A. Hayman award Am. Orthopsychiat. Assn., 1992, Nat. Living Treasure award Psychiatric Inst., 1994. Fellow Am. Acad. Arts and Scis., Am. Psychiat. Assn. (Oskar Pfister award 1987); mem. Am. Scientists, Soc. Psychol. Study of Social Issues. Office: John Jay Coll Criminal Justice 899 10th Ave New York NY 10019-1029

LIFTON, ROBERT KENNETH, diversified companies executive; b. N.Y.C., Jan. 9, 1928; s. Benjamin and Anna (Pike) L.; m. Loretta J. Silver, Sept. 5, 1954; children: Elizabeth Gail Lifton Hooper, Karen Grace Lifton Healy. BBA magna cum laude, CCNY, 1948; LLB, Yale U., 1951; doctorate (hon.), Bar Ilan U., Israel, 1993. Bar: N.Y. 1952. Assoc. Kaye, Scholer, Fierman, Hays & Handler, N.Y.C., 1955-56; asst. to pres. Glickman Corp., N.Y.C., 1956-57; pres. Robert K. Lifton, Inc. N.Y.C., 1957-61; chmn. bd. Terminal Tower Co., Inc., Cleve., 1959-63; pres. Transcontinental Investing Corp., N.Y.C., 1961-72, chmn. bd., 1969-72; ptnr. Venture Assocs., 1972-89; pres. Preferred Health Care Ltd., 1983-88; chmn. bd. dirs. Marcade Group, Inc., 1986-91, Medis El, 1993—, Cell Diagnostics, Inc., 1992—, Medis Inc., 1992—; treas. Consol. Accessories Corp., 1980-88, Caron's Connection, Inc., 1985-89; bd. dirs. Bank Leumi Trust co., N.Y.C.; mem. faculty Columbia U. Law Sch., 1973-78, Yale U. Law Sch., 1972-75; guest lectr. Practicing Law Inst., Yale Law Sch., Pace Inst., NYU; founder Nat. Exec. Conf., Washington, Inc.; chmn. oversight com. for Masters Degree, NYU Real Estate Inst., 1987-88. Author: Practical Real Estate: Legal Tax and Business Strategies, 1978; contbr. articles to profl. jours. and handbooks. Mem. McGovern econ. adv. com., 1972-73; chmn. parents com. Barnard Coll., 1976-78; mem. com. of the collection Whitney Mus., 1976-79; trustee Yale U. Sch. Fund, 1974-77, NYU Real Estate Inst., 1983-89; chmn., bd. dirs. Fund for Religious Liberty, 1987-88; pres. Am. Jewish Congress, 1988-94; chmn. Internat. Bd. U.S. Mid. East Project coun. fgn. rels., 1994—; pres. Israel Policy Forum, 1994—; bd. dirs. Builders for Peace, 1993—; vice-chmn. NJCRAC, 1994—; exec. com. AIPAC, 1993—. Lt. (j.g.) USN, 1952-55. Recipient Achievement award Sch. Bus. Alumni Soc. CCNY, James Madison award Fund for Religious Liberty, 1987, Stephen S. Wise award Am. Jewish Congress, 1993. Mem. Order of Coif. Home: 983 Park Ave New York NY 10028-0808 Office: 805 3d Ave New York NY 10022

LIFTON, WALTER M., psychology and education consultant; b. Bklyn., Nov. 2, 1918; s. Samuel S. and Sarah G. (Berman) L.; m. Ruth S. Knoppow, Oct. 1, 1940; children: Hazel Miriam Kroesser Palmer, Robert William. B.A., Bklyn. Coll., 1942; M.A., NYU, 1947, Ph.D., 1950. Sr. vocat. appraiser Vets. Guidance Center, Hunter Coll., 1946-48; psychologist, research div. NYU, 1948-50; assoc. prof. edn. guidance and counseling U. Ill., 1950-59; dir. guidance public. and services Sci. Research Assocs., Chgo. 1959-63; coordinator pupil personnel services Rochester City Sch. Dist., N.Y., 1964-70; prof. edn. dept. counseling psychology and student devel. SUNY-Albany, 1970-82, prof. emeritus, 1982—; edn. and psychology cons., 1982—; disting. vis. prof. Coll. Grad. Studies, W.Va., 1985-86; vis. prof. lectr. guidance and counseling 34 colls. and univs.; cons. in field. Author: Keys to Vocational Decisions, 1964, Working With Groups, 2d edit, 1966, Educating for Tomorrow—The Role of Media, Career Devel. and Society, 1970, Groups—Facilitating Individual Growth and Societal Change, 1972; film Just Like a Family, 1979; contbr. articles to profl. jours. Mem. White House Conf. on Children and Youth, 1969-70; cons. Title III ESEA project, Knox County, Tenn., 1967; interim dir. Action for a Better Community, Rochester, 1964-65, Center for Coop. Action in Urban Edn., 1966; apptd. to Durham County Youth Svcs. Bd., 1994. Served with AUS, 1942-46. Fellow Assn. for Specialists in Group Work (sec. 1976—, pres. 1980-81, Eminent Career award 1986); mem. Nat. Assn. Pupil Personnel Adminstrs. (pres. 1970), Nat. Vocat. Guidance Assn. Home and Office: Apt 3036 2701 Pickett Rd Durham NC 27705-5654 *As a person in the mental health field my focus has been increasingly concerned with prevention rather than remediation, and with helping people shape their environments not just adjust to the status quo.*

LIGARE, KATHLEEN MEREDITH, strategy and marketing executive; b. Providence, Aug. 29, 1950; d. Kenneth MacAllister and Carol (Smith) Ligare. BA, Carleton Coll., 1972; MS, Yale U., 1976; MBA, Northwestern U., 1982. Sr. assoc. Booz, Allen & Hamilton, Chgo. 1978-82; mgr. mktg. and product devel. GE Capital Corp., Barrington, Ill., 1982-83, planning mgr., 1983-84, region mgr., 1984-85; sr. v.p. sales and mktg. Gen. Electric Capital Corp., Barrington, Ill., 1992-93, region mgr., 1984-85, sr. v.p. sales and mktg., 1992-93, sr. v.p. internat., 1993—; prin. KML Enterprises, Inc., Chgo., 1985-92. Author: Illinois Women's Directory, 1977. Bd. dirs. Midwest Women's Ctr., Chgo., 1978-89; chair, bd. dirs. alumni ann. fund Carleton Coll., 1990-93, bd. dirs., 1987-94, mem. alumni bd., 1989, trustee, 1993—. Mem. Chgo. Fin. Exch. Office: Gen Electric Capital Corp 600 Hart Rd Barrington IL 60010

LIGETT, WALDO BUFORD, chemist; b. Middletown, Ohio, Nov. 2, 1916; s. Waldo Buford and Mabel Louise (Berkley) L.; m. Ann Elizabeth Hartwell, Aug. 29, 1940; children: Robert A., John D., Michael T., Steven D., Daniel L. B.S., Antioch Coll., 1939; M.S., Purdue U., 1941, Ph.D., 1944, D.Sc. (hon.), 1965; grad., Advanced Mgmt. Program, Harvard U., 1967. Chemist Eastman Kodak Co., Rochester, N.Y., 1935-38; research supr. Ethyl Corp., Detroit, 1944-51; asst. dir. chem. Ethyl Corp., 1951-52, asso. dir. chem., 1952-62, dir. research and devel., 1962-63; v.p. Celanese Chem. Co., Corpus Christi, Tex., 1963-64; v.p. tech. and mfg. Celanese Chem. Co., 1964-66; tech. dir. Celanese Corp., N.Y.C., 1966-67; v.p. Celanese Corp., 1967-72, Franklin Inst., Phila., 1973-81; pres. Franklin Inst. Research Labs., 1975-81; dir. Franklin-Hahnemann Inst., 1974-81. Fellow Am. Inst. Chemists; mem. Am. Chem. Soc., AAAS, Indsl. Research Inst., Research Soc. Am., N.Y. Assn. Research Dirs., Am. Nuclear Soc., Atomic Indsl. Forum. Patentee in field. Home: 485 Hickorynut Ave Oldsmar FL 34677

LIGGETT, HIRAM SHAW, JR., retired diversified industry financial executive; b. St. Louis, Jan. 12, 1932; s. Hiram Shaw and Lucille (Gardner) L.; m. Margaret McGinness, Jan. 21, 1961; children: Lucille Gardner, Frances Shelby. BA, Colo. Coll., 1953; LLD (hon.), Maryville U., 1991. Cashier Brown Group, Inc., St. Louis, 1957-64, asst. treas., 1964-68, treas., 1968—, v.p., 1983—; bd. dirs. Roosevelt Fed. Savs. and Loan, St. Louis. Past

trustee, vice chmn. bd. dirs. McKendree Coll., Lebanon, Ill., 1980-88; trustee, past chmn. bd. trustees Maryville U., St. Louis, 1982-91; past chmn. Provident Counseling, 1983; past v.p., bd. dirs. Jr. Achievement Miss. Valley, 1983; past dir. bi-state chpt. ARC, 1983; bd. dirs., pres. Cardinal Ritter Inst.; bd. dirs., chmn. devel. bd. Paraquad. Capt. USNR, 1953-79. Mem. Fin. Execs. Inst. (pres., dir. 1983—), St. Louis Coun. Navy League (bd. councilors 1982), Univ. Club (St. Louis, chmn. house com. 1975-78), Strathalbyn Farms Club (chmn. house com, bd. mem.), Alpha Kappa Psi, Tau Kappa Alpha. Republican. Presbyterian. Home: 64 Chesterfield Lakes Rd Chesterfield MO 63005-5400

LIGGETT, LAWRENCE MELVIN, vacuum equipment manufacturing company executive; b. Denver, June 22, 1917; s. Thomas Harrison and Mary Deacon (Taylor) L.; m. Edith Irene Harris, June 20, 1943; children: Pamela Jane Liggett Schwartz, Betty Sue Liggett Brooks El Gammal. A.B., Central Coll., Pella, Iowa, 1938; Ph.D. in Chemistry, Iowa State Coll., 1943. Research chemist NDRC, Iowa State Coll., 1941-43; plant mgr. Cardox Corp., Claremore, Okla., 1943-48; dir. inorganic research Wyandotte Chems. Corp., 1948-55; dir. research, v.p. tech. dir. Airco Speer div. Airco, Inc., 1955-70, pres. Airco Electronics div., 1970-75; pres. Airco Temescal div. BOC Group, Berkeley, Calif., 1975-82; cons. bus. and tech., 1982—. Author. Mem. Am. Chem. Soc., Electronic Industries Assn. Republican. Patentee in field. Home: 1856 Piedras Cir Danville CA 94526-1329

LIGGETT, LEE BROWN, lawyer. BS, U. Nebr., 1968, JD, 1971. Bar: U.S. Supreme Ct., Vt., Va., Nebr., U.S. Ct. Appeals (4th cir.), U.S. Dist. Ct. (we. and ea. dists.) Va., U.S. Dist. Ct. Nebr., U.S. Dist. Ct. Vt., U.S. Ct. Mil. Appeals. Assoc. Anderson, Storms and Strasburger, Holdrege, Nebr., 1975-77; gen. counsel, exec. asst. to pres., atty. to rector and bd. visitors Va. Poly. Inst. and State U., Blacksburg, 1977-80; gen. counsel U. Vt. and State Agrl. Coll., Burlington, 1980—; Presenter confs. and profl. meetings. Capt. JAGC, U.S. Army, 1972-75. Mem. ABA, Nat. Assn. Coll. and Univ. Attys. (chmn. com. continuing legal edn. 1982-83, bd. dirs. 1985-87, treas. 1986—, chmn. fin. com. 1986—), Nat. Orgn. Legal Problems in Edn., Va. State Bar Assn., Vt. State Bar Assn., Nebr. State Bar Assn., Phi Kappa Psi. Home: 200 Summit St Burlington VT 05401-3928 Office: U Vt Gen Counsel Waterman Bldg Rm 349 Burlington VT 05405

LIGGETT, THOMAS JACKSON, retired seminary president; b. Nashville, May 27, 1919; s. Thomas Jackson and Lola Cleveland (Ballentine) L.; m. Virginia Corrine Moore, Aug. 12, 1941; children: Thomas Milton, Margaret Ann Liggett Herod. A.B., Transylvania U., 1940; M.Div., Lexington Theol. Sem., 1944; postgrad., Union Theol. Sem. and Columbia U., 1950-52; LL.D., Interam. U., 1965, Culver-Stockton Coll., 1959, Butler U., 1975; D.H.L., Transylvania U., 1969; D.D., Eureka Coll., 1971, Phillips U., 1989. Ordained to ministry Christian Ch., 1940; pastor in Danville, Ky., 1943-45; missionary Argentina, 1946-57; prof. Union Theol. Sem., Buenos Aires, 1948-57; pres. Evang. Sem. of P.R., 1957-65; exec. sec. for Latin Am. Christian Ch., 1965-67, chmn. div. world mission, 1967-68; pres. United Christian Missionary Soc., 1968-74; pres. Christian Theol. Sem., Indpls., 1974-86, ret., 1986; del. World Council Chs. assembly in Uppsala, 1968, adviser assembly, Nairobi, Kenya, 1975; mem. governing bd. Nat. Council Chs., 1969-75, 85-87; moderator Disciples of Christ, 1985-87. Author: Where Tomorrow Struggles to be Born, 1970; Editor: Cuadernos Teologicos, 1954-55. Cochmn. McGovern Task Force on Fgn. Policy in Latin Am., 1972, Democratic precinct committeeman, 1970-72. Mem. Disciples of Christ Hist. Soc. (life), Theta Phi. Home: 647 W Harrison Ave Claremont CA 91711-4537

LIGGETT, TWILA MARIE CHRISTENSEN, public television company executive, academic administrator; b. Pipestone, Minn., Mar. 25, 1944; d. Donald L. Christensen and Irene E. (Zweigle) Christensen Flesher. BS, Union Coll., Lincoln, Nebr., 1966; MA, U. Nebr., 1971, PhD, 1977. Dir. vocal and instrumental music Sprague (Nebr.)-Martell Pub. Sch., 1966-67; tchr. vocal music, pub. schs., Syracuse, Nebr., 1967-69; tchr. Norris Pub. Sch., Firth, Nebr., 1969-71; cons. fed. reading project, pub. schs., Lincoln, 1971-72; curriculum coord. Westside Community Schs., Omaha, 1972-74; dir. State program Right-to-Read, Nebr. Dept. Edn., 1974-76; asst. dir. Nebr. Commn. on Status of Women, 1976-80; asst. dir. project adminstrn./devel. Great Plains Nat. Instructional TV Libr., U. Nebr., Lincoln, 1980—; exec. prodr. Reading Rainbow, PBS nat. children's series, 1980— (8 Emmy awards 1990-94); cons. U.S. Dept. Edn., 1981; Far West Regional Lab., San Francisco, 1979-80; panelist, presenter AAAS, NEA, NEH, NSF, Corp. Pub. Broadcasting, Internat. Reading Assn., Blue Ribbon panelist, Acad. TV Arts & Scis., 1991-95, final judge Nat. Cable Programming Awards, 1991-92. Author: Reading Rainbow's Guide to Children's Books: The 101 Best Titles, 1994. Bd. dirs. Planned Parenthood, Lincoln, 1979-81. Recipient Grand award N.Y. Internat. Film and TV Festival, 1993. Mem. NATAS, Internat. Reading Assn. (Spl. award Continental Worldwide Literacy 1992), Am. Women in Film and TV,Phi Delta Kappa. Presbyterian. Home: 649 S 18th St Lincoln NE 68508-2681 Home: 301 E 79th St Apt 23P New York NY 10021-0944 Office: PO Box 80669 Lincoln NE 68501-0669 Office: Reading Rainbow 301 E 79th St Apt 23P New York NY 10021-0944

LIGGINS, GEORGE LAWSON, microbiologist-diagnostic company executive; b. Roanoke, Va., June 19, 1937; m. Joyce Preston Liggins, Sept. 3, 1966; 1 child, George Lawson Jr. BA, Hampton U., 1962; cert. med. technician, Meharry Med. Sch., 1963; MPH, U. N.C., 1969; PhD, U. Va., Charlottesville, 1975. Med. technician Vets. Hosp., Hampton, Va., 1963-66; rsch. technician U. N.C. Med. Sch., Chapel Hill, 1966-69; postdoctoral fellow Scripps Clinic, La Jolla, Calif., 1975-76, Salk Inst., La Jolla, 1976-77; rsch. mgr. Hyland div. Baxter, Costa Mesa, Calif., 1977-78; R & D dir. diagnostics div. Baxter, Roundlake, Ill., 1978-83; pres., COO Internat. Immunology, Murrieta, Calif., 1983-86; chmn., CEO Bacton Assay Systems, Inc., San Marcos, Calif., 1986—; cons. Beckman Instruments, Inc., Brea, Calif., 1987-90, Paramax divsn. Baxter, Irvine, Calif., 1988-90, Scantibodies Lab., Santee, Calif., 1990-92; presenter in field; mem. virology study Cold Spring Harbor Lab., L.I., N.Y., 1974. Contbr. articles to profl. jours. Fellow NIH, 1975, Am. Cancer Soc., 1976. Mem. Am. Soc. Microbiology, Am. Assn. Clin. Chemistry, Van Slyke Soc. of Am. Assn. Clin. Chemistry, Am. Heart Assn., Nat. Hampton Alumni, Inc. (pres. 1991—), Omega Psi Phi. Republican. Methodist. Avocations: music, golf, tennis, literature. Office: Bacton Assay Systems Inc 772-A N Twin Oaks Valley Rd San Marcos CA 92069

LIGGIO, CARL DONALD, lawyer; b. N.Y.C., Sept. 5, 1943. AB, Georgetown U., 1963; JD, NYU, 1967. Bar: N.Y. 1967, D.C. 1967, Wis. 1983. Cons. Arent, Fox, Kintner, Plotkin & Kahn, Washington, 1968-69; assoc. White & Case, N.Y.C., 1969-72; gen. counsel Arthur Young & Co., N.Y.C., 1972-89, Ernst & Young, N.Y.C., 1989-94. Contbr. articles to legal and bus. jours. Trustee Fordham Prep. Sch. Mem. ABA, N.Y. State Bar Assn., D.C. Bar Assn., Assn. of Bar of City of N.Y., Am. Corp. Counsel Assn. (chmn. bd. dirs. 1984, mem. exec. com. 1982—), Am. Judicature Soc. (bd. dirs. 1988-92). Home: 11 E 86th St New York NY 10028

LIGGIO, JEAN VINCENZA, adult education educator, artist; b. N.Y.C., Nov. 5, 1927; d. Vincenzo and Bernada (Terrusa) Verro; m. John Liggio, June 6, 1948; children: Jean Constance, Joan Bernadette. Student, N.Y. Inst. Photography, 1965, Elizabeth Seton Coll., 1984, Parsons Sch. of Design, 1985. Hairdresser Beauty Shoppe, N.Y.C., 1947-65; freelance oil colors and portraits N.Y.C., 1958-75; instr. watercolor N.Y. Dept. Pks., Recreation and Conservation, Yonkers, 1985-89, Bronxville (N.Y.) Adult Sch., 1989—; substitute tchr. cosmetology Yonkers Bd. Edn., 1988-89. Paintings pub. by Donald Art Co., C.R. Gibson Greeting Card Co.; 12 watercolor paintings for Avon Calendar, Avon Cosmetics Co., 1994. Recipient numerous awards. Mem. Mt. Vernon Art Assn. (pres. membership com. 1983—), Mamaroneck Artist's Guild, Hudson River Contemporary Artist's, Scarsdale Art Assn. (publicity chmn. 1984-89), New Rochelle (N.Y.) Art Assn. Avocation: collect antiques. Home and Office: 166 Helena Ave Yonkers NY 10710-2524

LIGHT, ALFRED ROBERT, lawyer, political scientist; b. Atlanta, Dec. 14, 1949; s. Alfred M. Jr. and Margaret Francis (Asbury) L.; m. Mollie Sue Hall, May 25, 1977; children: Joseph Robert, Gregory Andrew. Student Ga. Inst. Tech., 1967-69; BA with highest honors, Johns Hopkins U., 1971; PhD, U. N.C., 1976; JD cum laude, Harvard U., 1981. Bar: D.C. 1981, Va. 1982. Tax clk. IRS, 1967; lab. technician Custom Farm Services Soils Testing Lab.,

1968; warehouse asst. State of Ga. Mines, Mining and Geology, 1970; clk.-typist systems mgmt. div., def. contract adminstrv. services Def. Supply Agy., Atlanta, 1971, research and teaching asst. dept. polit. sci. U. N.C., Chapel Hill, 1971-74; research asst. Inst. Research in Social Sci., 1975-77; program analyst Office of Sec. Def., 1974; asst. prof. polit. sci., research scientist Ctr. Energy Research, Tex. Tech U., Lubbock, 1977-78; research asst. grad. sch. edn., Harvard U., 1978-79; assoc. Butler, Binion, Rice, Cook & Knapp, Houston, summer 1980, Bracewell & Patterson, Washington, summer 1980, Hunton & Williams, Richmond, Va., 1981-89, of counsel, 1989-93—; assoc. prof. St. Thomas U. Sch. Law, Miami, Fla., 1989-93, prof., 1993—, interim dean, 1993—. Bd. advisors Toxics Law Reporter, Bur. Nat. Affairs, Washington, 1987—; contbr. articles to profl. jours. Charter mem. West Broward Community Ch. Capt. USAR, 1971-85. Grantee NSF, Inst. Evaluation Research, U. Mass., Ctr. Energy Research, Tex. Tech U., 1977-78; recipient Julius Turner award Johns Hopkins U., 1971, William Anderson award Am. Polit. Sci. Assn., 1977. Mem. ABA (vice-chmn. tort and ins. practice sect. 1988—), Fed. Bar Assn., Va. Bar Assn., Richmond Bar Assn., Phi Beta Kappa, Phi Eta Sigma. Democrat. Home: 1042 Woodfall Ct Fort Lauderdale FL 33326-2832 Office: St Thomas U Sch Law 16400 NE 32nd Ave Miami FL 33160

LIGHT, ARTHUR HEATH, bishop; s. Alexander Heath and Mary Watkins (Nelson) L.; m. Sarah Ann Jones, June 12, 1954; children: William Alexander, Philip Nelson, John Page, Sarah Heath. BA, Hampden-Sydney Coll., 1951, DD, 1987; M.Div., Va. Theol. Sem., 1954, DD, 1970; DD, St. Paul's Coll., 1979. Ordained priest Episcopal Ch., 1955. Rector West Mecklenburg Cure, Boydton, Va., 1954-58, Christ Ch. Elizabeth City, N.C., 1958-63, St. Marys Ch., Kinston, N.C., 1963-67, Christ and St. Luke's Ch., Norfolk, Va., 1967-79; bishop Diocese of Southwestern Va., Roanoke, 1979—; pres. Province III Espiscopal Ch., 1984-93; mem. adv. coun. to presiding bishop, 1985-93. Author: God, The Gift, The Giver, 1984. Bd. dirs. United Communities Fund, 1969-79, Norfolk Seamen's Friends Soc., 1969-79, Tidewater Assembly on Family Life, 1970-79, Friends of Juvenile Ct., 1975-79, Va. Inst. Pastoral Care, 1971-72; bd. dirs., mem. exec. com. Va. Coun. Chs., 1979—; bd. dirs. Roanoke Valley Coun. of Community Svcs., 1980-83, Virginians Organized for Informed Community Effort (VOICE), 1981—; bd. dirs. Appalachian People's Svc. Orgn., 1981-91, pres., 1981-85, v.p., 1989-91; mem. bio-med. ethics com. Ea. Va. Med. Sch., 1973-79, Lewis Gale Hosp., Salem, 1988—, Community Hosp. Roanoke Valley, 1990-94; trustee Va. Episc. Sch., Lynchburg, 1979—, Episc. High Sch., Alexandria, 1979—, Boys' Home, Covington, 1979—, Stuart Hall Sch., Staunton, 1979—, St. Paul's Coll., Lawrenceville, 1979-88; chmn. com. on continuing edn. Va. Theol. Sem., Alexandria, 1985—, v.p. bd. trustees, 1987—; bd. dirs., co-chair rural residency program Appalachian Ministries Edn. Resource Ctr., Berea, Ky., 1985-87; mem. coordinating cabinet, Va. Council. Churches, 1988—, chair com. on church and society, 1989-92; mem. Am. com. Kiyosato Ednl. Experiment Project, 1990—, v.p., 1991—; mem. Gen. Conv. Standing Com. on World Mission, 1988-94, chair, 1991-94; trustee Kanuga Conf. Ctr., 1991—. Named Young Man of Yr., Jaycees, 1961, 63; fellow St. George's Coll., Jerusalem, 1978, 89, fellow in biomed. ethics U. Va., 1989. Democrat. Office: PO Box 2068 1000 1st St SW Roanoke VA 24009

LIGHT, BETTY JENSEN PRITCHETT, former college dean; b. Omaha, Sept. 14, 1924; d. Lars Peter and Ruth (Norby) Jensen; m. Morgan S. Pritchett, June 27, 1944 (dec. 1982); children: Randall Wayne, Robin Kay Pritchett Church, Royce Marie Pritchett Creech; m. Kenneth F. Light, Nov. 23, 1985. B.S., Portland State U., 1965; M.B.A., U. Oreg., 1966; Ed.D. Oreg. State U., 1973. Buyer Rodgers Stores, Inc., Portland, Oreg., 1947-62; chmn. bus. div. Mt. Hood Community Coll., Gresham, Oreg., 1966-70, dir. evening coll., 1970-71, assoc. dean instn., 1972-77, dean humanities and behavioral scis., 1977-79, dean devel. and spl. programs, 1979-83; dean communication arts, humanities and social scis. Mt. Hood Community Coll., 1983-86; mem. state com. for articulation between community colls. and higher edn., 1976-78; mem. Gov.'s Council on Career and Vocat. Edn., 1977-86. Author: Values and Perceptions of Community College Professional Staff in Oregon, 1973; contbg. author: (case study) The Pritchett Study in Retailing, An Economic View, 1969. Mem. Gresham City Council, 1983-86. Mem. Oreg. Bus. Edn. Assn., Am. Assn. Higher Edn., Nat. Assn. Staff and Oreg. Devel., Oreg. Women's Polit. Caucus, Am. Vocat. Assn., Oreg. Vocat Assn., Danish Heritage Soc. Club: Soroptimist (pres. 1974-75, 81-82). Home: 1635 NE Country Club Ave Gresham OR 97030-4432

LIGHT, CHRISTOPHER UPJOHN, writer, computer musician; b. Kalamazoo, Jan. 4, 1937; s. Richard and Rachel Mary (Upjohn) L.; m. Lilykate Victoria Wenner, June 22, 1963 (div. 1986); children: Victoria Mary, Christopher Upjohn Jr.; m. Margo Ruth Bosker, Jan. 2, 1994. AB, Carleton Coll., 1958; MS, Columbia U., 1962; MBA, We. Mich. U., 1967; PhD, Washington U., 1971. Editor, pub. The Kalamazoo mag., 1963-66; pres. Mich. Outdoor Pub. Co., Kalamazoo, 1965-68; product planner The Upjohn Co., Kalamazoo, 1967-68; asst. prof. U. Utah, Salt Lake City, 1971-72; assoc. prof., chmn. fin. dept. Roosevelt U., Chgo., 1975-78; vis. prof. fin. No. Ill. U., 1978-79; freelance writer, computer musician, 1979—; editor Charles Dickens' Village Coquettes, 1992; mgr. spl. projects Sarasota Music Archive, 1992—. Trustee Harold and Grace Upjohn Found., 1965-85, 94—, pres. 6 yrs.; trustee Kalamazoo Symphony Orch. Assn., 1990—, Sarasota Music Archive, 1990—, Kalamazoo Coll., 1991-93, Am. Symphony Orch. League, 1992—. Recipient ann. press award Mich. Welfare League, 1967. Mem. ASCAP, NARAS (voting com.), Fin. Mgmt. Assn., Soc. Profl. Journalists, Computer Music Assn. Contbr. articles to profl. and microcomputer jours.; music compositions include Ten Polyrhythmic Etudes 1991, Piano Sonata # 1, 1992, record albums include Apple Compote, 1983, One-Man Band, 1985, Ultimate Music Box, Vol. I, 1988, Vol. II, 1993. Mem. U. Club Chicago, Park Club, Gull Lake Country Club. Office: 136 E Michigan Ave Kalamazoo MI 49007-3947

LIGHT, DOROTHY KAPLAN, lawyer, insurance executive; b. Alden, Iowa, May 20, 1937; d. Edward T. and Bessie (Nachazel) Kaplan; m. Ernest Isaac Light, Dec. 28, 1959; children: Christina, William, Samuel, David (twins). B.A., U. Iowa, 1959, J.D., 1961, hon. degree Georgian Ct. Coll., 1991. Bar: Iowa 1961, N.J. 1973; C.P.C.U., CLU. Pvt. practice, Marshalltown, Iowa, 1962-63, Iowa City, 1963-71; with U.S. Army, N.J., 1972-74; asst. gen. counsel Prudential Property & Casualty Ins. Co., Holmdel, N.J., 1974-77, assoc. gen. counsel, dir. corp. services, 1977-82, dir. pub. affairs mktg. dept., 1979-82, dir. pub. affairs, 1982-83, v.p. govt. affairs, 1982-87; v.p. The Prudential Ins. Co. Am., Newark, 1987-90, v.p. and corp. sec., 1990—; chmn. Prudential Found.; bd. dirs. Ctr. for N.J. Resources, trustee N.J. Ctr. Analysis of Public Issues, N.J. Supreme Ct. adv. comm. Profl. ethics; Mem. N.J. gov's. transition team, N.J. econ. master plan commn., N.J. econ. devel. task force, Am. Soc. Corp. Secs. Republican. Roman Catholic. Office: Prudential Ins Co Am 751 Broad St Newark NJ 07102-3777

LIGHT, HAROLD L., health care facility executive; b. Perth Amboy, N.J., Apr. 21, 1929; s. Samuel and Augustia (Schmeir) L.; m. Marilyn Weintraub, Aug. 19, 1951; children: Julie, Jeffrey. BA, Brooklyn Coll., 1950; MSS, NYU, 1959. Adminstr. Gouverneur Ambulary Care Program, N.Y.C., 1962-67; spl. asst. ambulatory care planning N.Y.C. Dept. of Health, 1967-87; asst. adminstr. St. Vincent Hosp., N.Y.C., 1968-70; sr. v.p. adminstrn. L.I. Jewish Med. Ctr., North Hyde Park, N.Y., 1970-77; pres. L.I. Coll. Hosp., Bklyn., 1977—. Trustee Bklyn. Botanic Garden, 1983—. With U.S. Army 1951-53. Fellow Am. Coll. Health Care Execs., Am. Pub. Health Assn.; mem. Greater N.Y. Hosp. Assn. (bd. govs. 1977—, chmn.), Hosp. Assn. N.Y.C. (chmn.), League of Voluntary Hosps. (bd. trustees 1979—). Home: 18442 Tudor Rd Jamaica NY 11432-1512 Office: L I Coll Hosp 340 Henry St Brooklyn NY 11201-5525

LIGHT, JAMES FOREST, English educator; b. Memphis, Nov. 5, 1921; s. Luther and Lois Ginevra (Smith) L.; m. Norma Rowena Neal, Mar. 8, 1948 (dec. 1959); children—Sheldon Neal, Matthew Forest, Jama Rowena; m. Amy Marcella Wolf, Dec. 20, 1959. B.A., U. Chgo., 1945, M.A., 1947, Ph.D., Syracuse U., 1953. Instr. U. Ky., 1947-48, Syracuse U., 1948-53; assoc. Radford Coll., 1953-56; asst. prof. Ind. State U., 1956-59, assoc., 1959-61, prof., 1961-65; Bernhard prof., chmn. dept. English U. Bridgeport, 1965-71; dean Sch. of Humanities of Calif. State U.-Fresno, 1971-72; dean of faculties Lehman Coll., CUNY, 1972-73, provost, 1973-79; dean Coll. Liberal Arts, So. Ill. U., Carbondale, 1979-85, prof. English, 1979-88; Fulbright prof. Keele U., Eng., 1963-64; vis. prof. CUNY, summers 1966-69; Fulbright prof. Canterbury U., N.Z., 1986. Author: Nathanael West: an Interpretive Study, rev. edit, 1971, John William DeForest, 1965, J.D. Salinger, 1967; editor The Modern Age, 4th rev. edit, 1981, Studies in All the Kings Men, 1971; contbr. articles to profl. jours. Fellow Found. Econ. Edn., Yaddo Writers and Artists Colony; mem. MLA, AAUP, Nat. Council Tchrs. English, Ind. Coll. English Assn. (pres. 1962-63), New Eng. Coll. English Assn. (dir. 1969-71). Democrat. Office: 47 Dogwood Dr Apt 301 Nashua NH 03062-4413

LIGHT, JOHN CALDWELL, chemistry educator; b. Mt. Vernon, N.Y., Nov. 24, 1934; s. Robert Fredrich and Alice (Caldwell) L.; m. Phyllis M. Kittel, Dec. 17, 1978; children: David C., Robert S., Erik G. B.A., Oberlin Coll., 1956; Ph.D., Harvard U., 1960. Postdoctoral rsch. assoc. U. Libre de Bruxelles, 1959-61; instr. U. Chgo., 1962-63, asst. prof., 1963-66, assoc. prof., 1966-70, prof. chemistry, 1970—, chmn. dept. chemistry, 1980-82; mem. adv. bd. Petroleum Rsch. Fund, 1981-86; cons. Inst. Def. Analyses, 1962-65, IBM Rsch Labs., San Jose, 1975, Lawrence Livermore Lab., 1979—; adv. com. Army Rsch. Office, Durham, N.C., 1966-72; vis. prof. Yale U., New Haven, 1968; vice chmn. Theoretical Chemistry Conf., Boulder, 1978, chmn., 1981; vis. scientist JILA, U. Colo., Boulder, 1976-77, others. Editor: Jour. Chem. Physics, 1983—. NSF predoctoral/postdoctoral fellow, 1956-61; Alfred P. Sloan Found. fellow. Fellow AAAS, Am. Phys. Soc., Am. Chem. Soc.; mem. Internat. Acad. Quantum Molecular Sci. Home: 1034 E 49th St Chicago IL 60615-1814 Office: 5640 S Ellis Ave Chicago IL 60637-1433

LIGHT, JOHN ROBERT, lawyer; b. Kansas City, Mo., Feb. 13, 1941; s. Robert Ralph and Marcia Ruth (Springer) L.; m. Sharon Dietrich Koch, Dec. 27, 1966; children: Allison, Robert. BA, U. Kans., 1963, JD with highest distinction, 1967. Bar: Calif., U.S. Dist. Ct. (cen., no., so., ea. dists.) Calif., U.S. Ct. Appeals (9th cir.). Assoc. Latham & Watkins, L.A., 1967-73, ptnr., 1973—. Mem. Soc. of Fellows of Huntington Mus. mem. ABA (chmn. Sherman Act com. antitrust sect. 1982-84), Calif. Bar Assn., U. Kans. Chancellor's Club. Republican. Episcopalian. Avocations: golf, swimming, art collecting. Office: Latham & Watkins 633 W 5th St Ste 4000 Los Angeles CA 90071-2005

LIGHT, KEN, photojournalist, educator; b. N.Y.C., Mar. 16, 1951; s. Stanley and Dorothea (Gottfried) L.; m. Carmen Lising, June 1976 (div. Aug. 1985); children: Stephen, Allison Rose; m. Melanie Hastings, Aug. 1, 1992. BGS, Ohio U., 1973. Instr. Contra. Costa Coll., San Pablo, Calif., 1974-84; photographer Labor Occ. Health Program, Berkeley, Calif., 1975-81; mem. staff Alameda Neighborhood Arts Program, Oakland, Calif., 1975-81; instr. Grad. Sch. Journalism U. Calif., Berkeley, 1986-89; cons. photographer Libr. Congress Folklife Ctr., 1989-90; faculty San Francisco Acad. Art Coll., 1977—; lectr. Berkeley Grad. Sch. Journalism, 1983—; founder Fund Documentary Photog., 1988—. Author: To the Promised Land, 1988, With These Hands, 1986, In the Fields, 1984, Delta Time, 1994. Recipient Meritorious Achievement award Media Alliance, 1990, Thomas More Storke Internat. Journalism award World Affairs Coun., 1989; nominnee Pulitzer Prize Feature Photography, 1993; grantee Am. Film Inst., 1979; NEA fellow, 1982, 86, Dorothea Lange fellow. Mem. Soc. Photog. Edn., ASMP, fellow Erna and Victor Hasselblad Found. Home: 3107 Deakin St Berkeley CA 94705-1950

LIGHT, KENNETH BENJAMIN, manufacturing company executive; b. N.Y.C., June 2, 1932; s. Max and Mollie (Schein) Lichtenholtz; m. Judith Klein, May 18, 1961; children: Corey, Randi Beth, Allison. B.S., NYU, 1954, LL.B. cum laude, 1957; M.B.A., U. Chgo., 1976. Bar: N.Y. 1957. Partner firm Light & Light, 1959-61; asst. sec. Gen. Bronze Corp., Garden City, N.Y., 1961-69; sec., gen. counsel Allied Products Corp., Chgo., 1969-76; v.p., gen. counsel Allied Products Corp., 1976-79, sr. v.p., 1979-83, exec. v.p., 1983-93; dir. Allied Products Corp., Chgo., 1993—; exec. v.p., CFO Allied Products Corp., 1995—; pres. Midwest Steel Processing, Inc., 1982-84; dir. Aurora Corp. Ill., Chgo.; vice chmn. Family Res. Ctr., Chgo., 1989-94, chmn., 1994—; v.p., dir. Verson Corp., Bush Hog Corp. Mem. Chgo. Bar Assn., N.Y.C. Subcontractors Assn. (v.p. 1967-69), Am. Subcontractors Assn. (dir. 1967-68), Chgo. Assn. Commerce and Industry. Home: 1825 Cavell Ave Highland Park IL 60035-2202 Office: Allied Products Corp 10 S Riverside Plz Chicago IL 60606-3708

LIGHT, KENNETH FREEMAN, college administrator; b. Detroit, Jan. 22, 1922; s. Delbert Bertram and Hilma (Stolt) L.; m. Shirley Claire Bower, Jan. 7, 1944 (dec. 1984); children—Karen Christine, Kevin Harold, Brian Curtis; m. Betty Jensen Pritchett, Nov. 23, 1985. B.S., U. Ill., 1949; M.A., Mich. State U., 1952, Ph.D., 1967. Instr. mech. engring. dept. Mich. Tech. U., 1956-60, assoc. prof., coord. for tech. edn., 1960-65; vice chancellor for acad. affairs, v.p. for acad. affairs Lake Superior State Coll., Sault Ste. Marie, Mich., 1965-76; pres. Lake Superior State Coll., 1982-86, Oreg. Inst. Tech., Klamath Falls, 1976-82. Pres. Upper Peninsula Health Edn. Corp., 1975-76; mem. Mich. Manpower Commn., 1973-74, Vocat. Edn. Adv. Council, 1973-76, Oreg. Career and Vocat. Adv. Council, 1977-82, Oreg. Manpower Commn., 1978-80; mem. Econ. Devel. Corp. Chippewa County, 1982-86. Served with USAF, 1942-45, to maj., USAFR. Mem. AAUP, Am. Soc. Engring. Edn., Am. Soc. Mil. Engrs., Air Force Assn., Phi Delta Kappa. Home: 1635 NE Country Club Ave Gresham OR 97030-4432 Home (summer): 6 Partridge Ave Kincheloe MI 49788

LIGHT, MURRAY BENJAMIN, newspaper editor; b. Bklyn., Oct. 14, 1926; s. Paul and Rose (Liatsk) L.; m. Joan M. Cottrell; children: Lee Light Monier, Laura Light Arbogast, Jeffrey Eugene. B.S., Bklyn. Coll., 1948; M.S. in Journalism, Northwestern U., 1949. Copy editor New York World-Telegram, 1949; with Buffalo Evening News, 1949—, news editor, 1962-69, mng. editor for news, 1969-79, editor, v.p., 1979—, sr. v.p., 1983—; mem. Temporary State Commn. on Constl. Revision, 1993—; mem. arts adv. coun. SUNY, Buffalo, 1987—, N.Y. State Jud. Screening Com. for 4th Dept., 1983-93; mem. nominating jury for journalism Pulitzer Prize, 1990, 91. Mem. adv. coun. to pres. on journalism St. Bonaventure U., 1980—; mem. cmty. adv. coun. SUNY, Buffalo, 1979—; steering com. State Citizen Bee, 1990—, Wiht AUS, WWII. Mem. N.Y. State Soc. Newspaper Editors (pres. 1977), Am. Soc. Newspaper Editors, A.P. Mng. Editors Assn., N.Y. Fair Trial Free Press Conf. (past chmn.). Office: Buffalo News PO Box 100 1 News Plz Buffalo NY 14203-2994

LIGHT, RICHARD JAY, statistician, education educator; b. N.Y.C., Sept. 10, 1942; s. Solomon Julius and Muriel (Szwarcman) L.; m. Patricia Kahn, June 27, 1965; children: Jennifer Susan, Sarah Elizabeth. BS, U. Pa., 1962, AM; PhD, Harvard U., 1969; LLD (hon.), U. Winnipeg, Can., 1991. Mem. faculty Harvard U., Cambridge, Mass., 1969—, prof. stats., 1975—; dir. faculty studies John F. Kennedy Inst. Politics, 1971-76; mem. panel children's and family policy Nat. Acad. Scis., 1977—; mem. panel on evaluation, 1982; panel program evaluation Social Sci. Research Council, 1977—; bd. dirs Huron Inst., Cambridge, Mass., 1971—; cons. World Bank, 1975—; dir. Harvard Assessment Seminar, Cambridge, 1986—. Co-author: Data for Decisions, 1982, Summing Up, 1984, By Design, 1990, Metaanalysis for Explanation, 1992; editor: Learning from Experience, 1982, Evaluation Studies Rev., 1983. Trustee Buckingham, Browne and Nichols Sch., Cambridge, 1977—; mem. policy adv. group Mass. Office of Children, 1977—; bd. dirs Fund for Improvement Post-Secondary Edn., 1992-95. N.Y. State Advanced Coll. Teaching fellow, 1965; vis. fellow Ctr. Analysis Health Practices, Harvard U. Sch. Pub. Health, 1977-78; Sr. Research award Spencer Found., Chgo., 1978-84; research fellow Ford Found., N.Y.C., 1981; recipient Paul Lazarsfeld award for contbns. to sci., 1992. Mem. Am. Assn. Higher Edn. Assn., Am. Edstl. Rsch. Assn., Am. Sociol. Assn., Am. Evaluation Assn. (pres. 1986), Coun. Applied Social Rsch., Evaluation Rsch. Soc. (Paul Lazarsfeld award 1991), Am. Assn. for Higher Edn. (nat. bd.), Fund for Improvement Postsecondary Edn. (nat. bd.). Home: 31 Dunbarton Rd Belmont MA 02178-2458 Office: John F Kennedy Sch Govt Harvard U Cambridge MA 02138

LIGHT, RICHARD WAYNE, medical educator; b. Steamboat Springs, Colo., Feb. 9, 1942; s. Roland Wayne and Helen Marie (Long) L.;m. Linda Dawson, June 8, 1963 (div. Dec. 1992); children: Mark, Sandra. BS in Engring. Applied Math., U. Colo., 1964; MD, Johns Hopkins U. Med. Sch., 1968; postgrad., Johns Hopkins Hosp. Intern Osler Svc., 1968-69; resident Johns Hopkins Hosp., Balt., 1969-70; asst. prof. medicine La. State U.,

Shreveport, 1974-77, assoc. prof. medicine, 1977-78; assoc. prof. medicine U. Calif., Irvine, 1978-84, prof. medicine, 1984—, asst. dean rsch., 1985-93; attending pulmonologist La. State U. Med. Ctr., Shreveport, 1974-78; chief pulmonary diseases VA Med. Ctr., Long Beach, Calif., 1978-86, acting chief staff rsch. and devel., 1984-85, assoc. chief staff, 1985-93, chief pulmonary exercise lab., 1983—. Contbr. articles to profl. jours. Maj. U.S. Army, 1972-94. Fellow Johns Hopkins U. Sch. Medicine, 1970-71, 71-72; Boettcher scholar U. Colo., 1960-64; VA grantee, 1978-80, 80-85, 85-88, 83-88, 87-89, 89-92, 92-95. Fellow Am. Coll. Chest Physicians (program sel. com. 1981, 82, 83, 84); mem. Am. Thoracic Soc. (program sel. com. 1976, 78, 81, 82, 85, 87, 89, rep. counselor clin. problems assembly 1980-81, sec.-treas. clin. problems assembly 1981-82, liaison 1985-88), Am. Soc. Clin. Rsch., So. Soc. Clin. Investigation. Avocations: tennis, travel, sailing, wine. Home: 6302 Mariam Pacific S Long Beach CA 90803 Office: VA Med Ctr 5901 E 7th St Long Beach CA 90822

LIGHT, ROBERT M., broadcasting association executive; b. Denver, June 23, 1911; s. Louis and Sally (Conn) L.; m. Margaret Colville Dodgson, Oct. 2, 1943; 1 child, Robert Louis; m. Julie Fraser Giguere, Dec. 10, 1953; children: Jonathan Fraser, Lisa Light Piscitelli. Student, pub. schs., Denver and N.Y.C. Actor theater, radio, TV NBC, N.Y.C., 1934-39; contract player Warner Studios, Hollywood, Calif., 1935-37; writer, dir., radio programs ABC, NBC, Los Angeles, 1939-42; tchr., exec. dir. refresher course AFRA, Los Angeles, 1946-49; writer Alan Ladd Radio Show Abbott Kimbal Co. Advt., Los Angeles, 1949-53; dir. promotion and advt. western div. RKO Gen., Los Angeles, 1953-59; pres. So. Calif. Broadcasters Assn., Hollywood, 1959-89; pres. emeritus, 1989—; lectr., tchr. UCLA, U. So. Calif., Los Angeles City Coll., London U. Mem. Los Angeles County Hwy. Safety Commn.; mem. adv. council So. Calif. Assn. Govts.; bd. dirs. Pacific Pioneer Broadcasters, mem. PPB Diamond Circle. Lt. col. Armed Forces Radio, 1942-46, ETO. Decorated Bronze Star; recipient honor Los Angeles County Bd. Suprs., Los Angeles City Council. Mem. So. Calif. Theater Assn. (v.p.). Home: 3272 Longridge Ave Sherman Oaks CA 91423-4910

LIGHT, TIMOTHY, linguistics, religious and Asian studies educator, academic administrator; b. Kalamazoo, Nov. 5, 1938; s. Richard Upjohn Light and Mary (Upjohn) Meader; m. Joy Chi-yan Cheng, June 12, 1964; children: Ann, Claire. BA, Yale U., 1960; MDiv., Union Theol. Sem., 1965; MA, Columbia U., 1966; PhD, Cornell U., 1974. Tutor, lectr. English New Asia Coll. Chinese U., Hong Kong, 1960-62, 66-70; sr. rep. Yale-China Assn., Hong Kong, 1970-71; from asst. to assoc. prof. oriental studies U. Ariz., Tucson, 1974-80; prof., chmn. Ea. Asian langs. Ohio State U., Columbus, 1980-86; prof. linguistics and Asian studies, provost Kalamazoo Coll., 1986-89, acting pres., 1989-90; pres. Middlebury (Vt.) Coll., 1990-91; prof. religion Western Mich. U., Kalamazoo, 1992—; vis. prof. Beijing Lang. Inst., 1981; dir. Union Theol. Sem., N.Y.C., 1981—; Disting. vis. prof. Western Mich. U., 1991-92. Author: Xiandai Waiyu Jiaoxuefa, 1987; co-author: The Character Book, 1985; co-editor: Contributions to Sino-Tibetan Studies, 1986. Mem. Ohio Trade Coun., Columbus, 1984-86, Mich. Coun. on Humanities; bd. dirs. WorldPaper; trustee Kal Inst. Arts. Grantee NEH, 1977, 82. Mem. Chinese Lang. Tchrs. Assn. (exec. com., editor 1978-82, pres. 1993-94), Linguistics Soc. Am., Coun. Fgn. Rels., Internat. Assn. for Teaching Chinese (v.p. 1993—), Yale Club (N.Y.C.). Democrat. Episcopalian. Office: Western Mich U Office of Pres Kalamazoo MI 49008

LIGHT, WALTER FREDERICK, telecommunications executive; b. Cobalt, Ont., Can., June 24, 1923; s. Herbert and Rosetta Elizabeth (Hoffman) L.; m. Margaret Anne Wylie Miller, July 8, 1950; children: Elizabeth Jean, Janice Catherine. BS with honours, Queen's U., 1949, LLD (hon.), 1981; LLD (hon.), Concordia U., 1980, Dalhousie U., 1985; D in Applied Sci. (hon.), U. Ottawa, 1981; DSc (hon.), Laurentian U., 1984; DEng (hon.), U. Waterloo, 1985. Exec. v.p. ops. Bell Can., Montreal, Que., 1970-74; pres., dir. No. Telecom Ltd., Montreal, 1974-79, pres., chief exec. officer, 1979-82, chmn., chief exec. officer, 1982-84, chmn., 1984-85; bd. dirs. Rockcliffe Rsch. and Tech. Inc., Transtream Inc. Mem. Assos. Carleton U.; fellow Montreal Mus. Fine Arts. Served with RCAF, 1942-45. Decorated Officer, Order of Can., 1986, Order of Ont., 1988. Fellow Engring. Inst. Can., Ca. Acad. Engring.; mem. Corp. Engrs. Que., Assn. Proff. Engrs. Ont., Mount Royal Club, York Club. Office: Bell Trinity Sq, South Tower 10th Fl, Toronto, ON Canada M5G 2E1

LIGHTELL, KENNETH RAY, education educator; b. Oak Park, Ill., Nov. 13, 1944; s. Ray and Mildred (Miller) L.; m. Charlotte Hawkins, Aug. 3, 1989. BA, North Ctrl. Coll., Naperville, Ill., 1966; grad. studies in edn., U. Mo., 1969; grad. studies in computers, Depaul U., 1983; MLA, Houston Bapt. U., 1995. Tchr., coach Roycemore Sch., Evanston, Ill., 1966-68; dir. middle sch. Bklyn. Friends Sch., 1969-81; dir. Olympia (Wash.) Ind. Sch., 1982-83; tchr., coach The Lexington (Ky.) Sch., 1984-88; prin. Charles Wright Acad., Tacoma, 1988-89; dir. of mid. sch. John Cooper Sch., Woodlands, Tex., 1989-92; headmaster St. James Episcopal Sch., Houston, 1993-94; owner, dir. Washinee Woods Camp, Taconic, Conn., 1975-81, Wilderness Adventures, Bklyn., 1970-75; pres., CEO S.L.K. Inc., N.Y.C., 1975-83. Editor: N.C.C. Spectrum, 1966; dir. Festival of the Arts, 1986. Pres. NCC Young Rep., Naperville, Ill., 1964-65. Mem. B.P.O.E. Elks, Nat. Mid. Sch. Assn., Alpha Sigma Lambda. Avocations: sailing, wooden boat building, photography, travel. Home: 25830 Overlake Dr Spring TX 77380

LIGHTFOOT, DAVID WILLIAM, linguistics educator; b. Looe, Eng., Feb. 10, 1945; s. William Richard and Peggy May (Stevens) L.; m. Sarah Elizabeth Hairs, Feb. 7, 1946 (div. 1980); children: Kirsten, Heidi; m. Sari Ruth Hornstein, Nov. 24, 1955; children: Eric, Alexander. BA with honors, U. London, 1966; MA, U. Mich., 1968, PhD, 1971. Asst. prof. McGill U., Montreal, Que., Can., 1970-75; assoc. prof. McGill U., Montreal, Que., 1975-78; prof. U. Utrecht, The Netherlands, 1978-83, U. Md., College Park, 1983—. Author: Natural Logic and Greek Moods, 1975, Principles of Diachronic Syntax, 1979, Explanation in Linguistics, 1981, The Language Lottery, 1982, How to Set Parameters, 1991, Verb Movement, 1994. Mem. Linguistic Soc. Am., Linguistic Assn. Gt. Britain. Home: 7208 Heatherhill Rd Bethesda MD 20817-4657 Office: Univ Md Dept Linguistics College Park MD 20472

LIGHTFOOT, EDWIN NIBLOCK, JR., chemical engineering ecuator; b. Milw., Aug. 25, 1925; married 1949, 5 children. BS, Cornell U., 1947, PhD in chem. engr., 1951. Asst prof., prof. biochem engr. U. Wis-Madison, 1953-80, prof. chem. engr., 1980—; vis. prof. Tech. U. Norway, 1962, Stanford U. 1971, U. Canterbury, New Zealand , 1972. Recipient William H. Walker award Am. Inst. Chem. Engrs, 1975, Food, Pharm. and Bioeng award, 1979, Warren K. Lewis award 1991. Mem. Nat. Acad. Engr., Royal Norweg Soc. Sci. & Letter, Am. Inst. Chem. Engr., Am. Chem. Soc. (E V Murphree award, 1994). Physical separation tech. mass transfer, biomedical engring. author of 14 books and tech. articles. Office: U Wis Dept Chem Engring 1415 Johnson Dr Madison WI 53706-1691*

LIGHTFOOT, GORDON MEREDITH, singer, songwriter; b. Orillia, Ont., Can., Nov. 17, 1938; s. Gordon Meredith and Jessie Vick (Trill) L.; divorced; children: Fred, Ingrid; m. Elizabeth Moon; children: Eric, Miles. Student, Westlake Coll. Music, Los Angeles, 1958. Singer, songwriter, 1959—; compositions include Early Morning Rain, 1965, Canadian Railroad Trilogy, 1967, If You Could Read My Mind, 1970, Sundown, 1974, Carefree Highway, 1974, The Wreck of the Edmund Fitzgerald, 1976, Race Among the Ruins, 1976; album Lightfoot, 1966, Way I Feel, 1967, Did She Mention My Name, 1968, Back Here On Earth, 1969, Early Lightfoot, 1969, Sunday Concert, 1969, Summerside of Life, 1971, Don Quixote, 1972, Old Dan's Records, 1972, Cold On Shoulder, 1975, Gord's Gold, 1975, Summertime Dream, 1976, Endless Wire, 1978, Dream Street Rose, 1980, Salute, 1983, Gord's Gold, Vol. II, 1989, East of Midnight, Songbook, 1986, Best of Gordon Lightfoot, 1991, The United Artists Collection, 1993, Waiting For You, 1993. Decorated Order Can., 1970; recipient Vanier award Canadian Jaycees, 1977, Juno Hall of Fame award, 1986, Juno Gold Leaf awards, 1965-66, 68-69, 73-77, Pop Record of Yr. award Music Operators Am., 1974; named Top Folksinger, 1965-66, 68-69, 73-77, Top Male Vocalist, 1967, 70-72, 74, Composer of Yr., 1972, 76, Can. Male Rec. Artist of Decade, 1980; recipient awards for songs ASCAP, 1971, 74, 76, 77; numerous Gold albums in Can., U.S. Australia; numerous Platinum albums including Sundown, Summertime Dream, Gord's Gold. Mem. Order of Ont. Address: care ICM 40 W 57th St New York NY 10019*

LIGHTFOOT, JAMES ROSS, congressman; b. Sioux City, Iowa, Sept. 27, 1938; s. Elmer and Altha Lightfoot; m. Nancy Lightfoot; children: Terri, Jamie, Allison, James. Police officer City of Tulsa, 1959-61; broadcaster, 1961-70; Mgr. farm equipment plant Corsicana, Tex., 1970-76; small bus. owner, 1981—; mem. 99th-104th Congress from 5th (now 3rd) Iowa dist., 1985—, appropriations com., chmn. treas., postal svc. and gen. govt. subcom., fgn. ops. appropriations subcom., sub. appropriations, trans. Farm editor Sta. KMA-Radio, Shenandoah, Iowa, 1976-84. Served with U.S. Army, then USAR, 1956-64. Mem. FAA (outstanding service award, vol. safety counselor), Farm Bur., U.S. Feed Grains Council, Soybean Assn., Nat. Agr. Mktng. Assn. (agr. spokesman of the year award), Iowa Park Prodrs. Assn., Iowa Cattleman's Assn. (broadcasting award); participant numerous world confs. to promote agr. Office: US House of Reps 2161 Rayburn Washington DC 20515

LIGHTHIZER, ROBERT E., lawyer; b. Ashtabula, Ohio, 1947. BA, Georgetown U., 1969, JD, 1973. Bar: D.C. 1973. Ptnr. Skadden, Arps, Slate, Meagher & Flom, N.Y.C.; chief of staff U.S. Senate Com. Fin., 1981-83; dep. U.S. Trade Rep. rank of amb. Mem. Internat. Bar Assn. Office: Skadden Arps Slate Meagher & Flom 1440 New York Ave NW Washington DC 20005-2111

LIGHTMAN, ALAN PAIGE, physicist, writer; b. Memphis, Nov. 28, 1948; s. Richard Lovis and Jeanne (Garretson) L.; m. Jean Greenblatt, Nov. 28, 1976; children: Elyse, Kara. AB, Princeton U., 1970; PhD in Physics, Calif. Inst. Tech., 1974. Postdoctoral fellow Cornell U., Ithaca, N.Y., 1974-76; asst. prof. Harvard U., Cambridge, Mass., 1976-79; staff scientist Smithsonian Astrophys. Obs., Cambridge, 1979-88; prof. sci. and writing MIT, Cambridge, 1988—. Author: Problem Book in Relativity and Gravitation, 1974, Radiative Processes in Astrophysics, 1976, Time Travel and Papa Joe's Pipe, 1984, A Modern Day Yankee in Connecticut Court, 1986, Origins: The Lives and Worlds of Modern Cosmologists, 1990 (Most Oustanding Sci. Book in Phys. Sci. award Assn. Am. Pubs.), Ancient Light, 1992, Great Ideas in Physics, 1992, Time for the Stars, 1992, Einstein's Dreams, 1993, Good Benito, 1995. Fellow AAAS, Am. Phys. Soc.; mem. Am. Astron. Soc. (chmn. high energy astrophysics div. 1991). Achievements include proof of Schiff Conjecture for relativistic gravitation theories; discovery of secular instabilities in accretion disks; pioneering development of theory of relativistic plasmas in astrophysics. Office: MIT 77 Massachusetts Ave Cambridge MA 02139-3594

LIGHTSTONE, RONALD, lawyer; b. N.Y.C., Oct. 4, 1938; s. Charles and Pearl (Weisberg) L.; m. Nancy Lehrer, May 17, 1973; 1 child, Dana. AB, Columbia U., 1959; JD, NYU, 1962. Atty. CBS, N.Y.C., 1967-69; assoc. dir. bus. affairs CBS News, N.Y.C., 1969-70; atty. NBC, N.Y.C, 1970; assoc. gen. counsel Viacom Internat. Inc., N.Y.C., 1970-75; v.p., gen. counsel, sec. Viacom Internat. Inc., 1976-80; v.p. bus. affairs Viacom Entertainment Group Viacom Internat., Inc., 1980-82; v.p. corp. affairs, 1982-84, sr. v.p. corp. and legal affairs, 1984-87; exec. v.p. Spelling Entertainment Inc., L.A., 1988-91, COO, 1991-93; chmn. Multimedia Labs. Inc., 1994—; bd. dirs. Starsight Telecast, Inc. Served to lt. USN, 1962-66. Mem. ABA (chmn. TV, cable and radio com.), Assn. Bar City N.Y., Fed. Communications Bar Assn.

LIGOMENIDES, PANOS ARISTIDES, electrical and computer engineering educator, consultant; b. Pireaus, Greece, Apr. 3, 1928; came to U.S., 1955; s. Aristides P. and Sonia (Akritides) L.; m. Danae J. Tsarmaklis, Dec. 29, 1973;children: Katerina, Christina. BSc in Physics with high honors, U. Athens, 1951, MSc in Radio Engring 1952; MSc in Elec. Engring., Stanford U., 1956, PhD in Elec. Engring. and Physics, 1958. Registered profl. engr. Research engr. IBM, Poughkeepsie, N.Y., 1958-59, San Jose, Calif., 1959-64; asst. prof. elec. engring. UCLA, 1964-69; adj. prof. elec. engring Stanford U., Calif., 1969-71, Fulbright prof., 1970-71; disting. vis. prof. U. Md., College Park, 1971-72, prof. elec. engring., 1971-93, prof. emeritus, 1993—, chmn. computer engring. elec. engring. dept., 1972-76; prof. U. Patras, Greece, 1993—; pres., Computer Engring. Cons., Lanham, Md., 1976-80; dir. Cybernetics Rsch. Lab., 1982—; v.p. Caelum Rsch. Corp., 1988-93; cons. to various industries and govt. orgns.; elected chair of informatics, Acad. of Athens, Greece, 1993. Author: Information Processing Machines, 1969, Notions, Measures of Probability, 1978, Axiomatic Probability Theory, 1979, Computer Application in Industry and Management, 1981, Management and Office Information Systems, 1984, Visual Languages, 1986, Uncertainty in Knowledge-Based Systems, 1987; assoc. editor sci. jours.; contbr. over 140 articles to sci. and engring. books, jours., conf. proceedings; patentee pathfinder algorithm. Lt. Greek Navy, 1952-54. OECD fellow, 1965, 74; Ford Found. fellow, 1966-68; Salzburg Seminar fellow, 1971; recipient grants and contracts for rsch. in computers and artificial intelligence. Mem. IEEE (life, sr.), N.Y. Acad. Sci. Home: 39 Bakoyianni St, 15235 Athens Greece Office: Acad Athens, 28 Panepistimiore Ave, 10679 Athens Greece

LIGON, WILLIAM AUSTIN, consumer products company executive; b. Trinidad, Colo., Jan. 27, 1951; s. William Hastings and Rosalie (Ferguson) L.; m. Samornmitr Lamsam; children: Aaron Ng, Nisha Ferguson, Nina Rujiraporn. BA with honors, U. Tex., 1973, MA in Econs., 1978; M of Pub. and Pvt. Mgmt., Yale U., 1980. Economist U. Tex. Med. Sch., San Antonio, 1976-78; sr. cons. Boston Cons. Group, London, 1980-82; pres. Liglam Devel. Ltd., Bangkok, 1983-84; dir. corp. planning Marriott Corp., Washington, 1984-86, v.p. mktg. Big Boy div., 1986-87, v.p., gen. mgr. Allie's Restaurant divsn., 1987-89; sr. v.p. hotel planning Marriott Hotels, 1989-90; sr. v.p., exec. officer corp. planning Cir. City Stores, Inc., Richmond, Va., 1990—. Named one of Top 50 Corp. Execs. under 35, Bus. Week Mag., 1976. Mem. Phi Beta Kappa. Clubs: Yale (N.Y.C.); Royal Bangkok Sports. Avocations: hiking, squash. Home: 4304 Sulgrave Rd Richmond VA 23221-3257 Office: Cir City Stores Inc 9950 Mayland Dr Richmond VA 23233-1463

LIGUORI, FRANK NICKOLAS, temporary personnel company executive; b. Bklyn., July 2, 1946; s. August and Mary (Perotto) L.; m. JoAnn Scioscia, July 7, 1968; children: Frank Jr., Mark. BS in Acctg., St. Francis Coll., Bklyn., 1964. CPA, N.Y. Sr. auditor Coopers & Lybrand, N.Y.C., 1964-71; successively controller, treas., sr. v.p., exec. v.p., pres., CEO, chmn. Olsten Corp., Westbury, N.Y., 1971—, also bd. dirs.; bd. dirs. WLIW 21, Plainview, N.Y. Mem. Am. Inst. CPAs, N.Y. State Soc. CPAs, Nat. Assn. Temporary Services (bd. dirs.). Home: 2 Talisman Ct Huntington Station NY 11746-5320*

LIJINSKY, WILLIAM, biochemist; b. Dublin, Ireland, Oct. 19, 1928; came to U.S., 1951; s. Morris and Rebecca (Hershman) L.; m. Rosalie K. Elespuru, June 10, 1973; 1 dau. Catherine Elizabeth; 1 dau. by previous marriage, Sharon Anne. B.Sc. with honours, U. Liverpool, Eng., 1949, Ph.D., 1951. Asst. prof., then assoc. prof. Chgo. Med. Sch., 1955-68; prof. biochemistry U. Nebr. Med. Sch., Omaha, 1968-71; group leader carcinogenesis program Oak Ridge Nat. Lab., 1971-76; expert Nat. Inst. Environ. Health Scis., N.C., 1991-92. Author research papers, revs. Mem. Biochem. Soc., Am. Chem. Soc., Am. Assn. Cancer Research, Am. Soc. Biol. Chemists, Environmental Mutagen Soc., Soc. Occupational and Environ. Health, Sigma Xi. Home: 11398 High Hay Dr Columbia MD 21044

LIKENS, GENE ELDEN, ecologist; b. Pierceton, Ind., Jan. 6, 1935; s. Colonel Benjamin and Josephine (Garner) L.; m. Phyllis Craig; children: Kathy, Gregory, Leslie. BS, Manchester (Ind.) Coll., 1957, DSc (hon.), 1979; MS, U. Wis., 1959, PhD, 1962; DSc (hon.), Rutgers U., 1985, Plymouth State Coll., U. N.H., 1989, Miami U., 1990; LHD (hon.), Union Coll., 1991; DSc (hon.). U. Bodenkultur, Vienna, Austria, 1993, Marist Coll. 1993. Asst. zoology Manchester Coll. 1955-57; grad. teaching asst. U. Wis. 1957-59, vis. lectr. 1963; instr. zoology Dartmouth Coll., 1961, instr. biol. scis., 1963, asst. prof., then assoc. prof. 1963-69; mem. faculty Cornell U., 1969-83, prof. ecology 1972-83, Charles A. Alexander prof. biol. scis., 1983, adj. prof., 1983—; v.p. N.Y. Botanical Garden, 1983-93; dir. Inst. Ecosystem Studies, Millbrook, N.Y., 1983—, pres., 1993—; dir. Mary Flagler Cary Arboretum, 1983—; prof. biology Yale U., 1984—; prof. grad. field of ecology Rutgers U., 1985—; vis. prof. Ctr. Advanced Rsch., also dept. environ. scis. U. Va., Charlottesville, 1978-79; lectr. Williams Summer Inst.

Coll. Tchrs., 1966, 67, Drew Summer Inst. Coll. Tchrs., 1968, Cornell U. Alumni Assn., 1978; Paul C. Lemon ecology lectr. SUNY, Albany, 1978; chmn. New Eng. div. task force conservation aquatic ecosystems U.S. Internat. Biol. Program, 1966-67; vis. assoc. ecologist Brookhaven Nat. Lab., 1968; C.P. Snow lectr. Ithaca Coll., 1979, 89; Robert S. Campbell lectr. U. Mo., 1980; A.E. Waller lectr. Ohio State U., 1990; Disting. Ecologist lectr. N.C. State U., 1980; Henry J. Oosting lectr. Duke U., 1985; Rilett vis. scholar Ill. State U., 1985; vis. scholar James Madison U., 1988; Class of 1960 vis. scholar, Williams Coll., Williamstown, Mass., 1988; Jack R. Hargis lectr. U. Minn., Duluth, 1988; Robert H. Woodworth lectr. in sci. Bennington (Vt.) Coll., 1988; mem. Nat. Commn. on Environment, 1987; Olin lectr. Environ. Fairfield U., 1990; lectr. Golden Series, Universität für Bodenkultur, 1991; William V. Kaesar Meml. scholar U. Wis., Madison, 1991; disting. scientist lecture series Bard Coll., 1991; Donnell Foster Hewett Lecture series Lehigh U., 1992; Miles C. Horton spl. lect. Va. Polytech. Inst., State U., 1993, Marine Biological Lab. Fri. evening lecture series Woods Hole, 1993; Granville Sewell disting. lectr. Columbia U., 1994; vis. disting. ecdologist, Colo. State U., 1994; lectr. in field; cons. in field; mem. numerous govt. and sci. panels, participant numerous confs. Author 11 books and more than 325 sci. jour. publs. Recipient Conservation award Am. Motors Corp., 1969, 75th Anniversary award U.S. Forest Svc., 1980, Disting. Achievement award Lab. Biomed. and Environ. Studies, UCLA, 1982, Regents medal of excellence SUNY, 1984, award N.Y. Acad. Scis., 1984, Internat. ECI prize for Limnetic Ecology, 1989, Disting. Svc. award N.Y. Bot. Garden, 1989, Disting. Svc. award Am. Inst. Biol. Scis., 1990, The Garden Club of America Spl. Citation, 1992, The Tyler Prize, U. Southern California, 1993, World Prize for Environment, 1993, Australia Prize, 1994; NATO sr. fellow, 1969, Guggenheim fellow, 1972-73; grantee NSF, EPA, Dept. Energy, USDA Forest Svc., NOAA. Fellow AAAS; mem. NAS (chmn. sect. 27 1986-89), Ecol. Soc. Am. (chmn. study com. 1971-74, v.p. 1978-79, pres. 1981-82), Am. Soc. Limnology and Oceanography (pres. 1976-77, 1st G.E. Hutchinson award for excellence in research 1982), Royal Swedish Acad. Scis., Am. Acad. Arts and Scis., Am. Polar Soc., Explorers Club, Freshwater Biol. Assn., Internat. Assn. Gt. Lakes Research, Internat. Water Resources Assn. (charter), Soc. Internat. Limnologiae (nat. rep.), Australian Soc. Limnology, Am. Water Resources Assn. (hon.), British Ecological Soc. (hon.), Am. Inst. Biol. Scis., Danish Acad. Sci., Sigma Xi, Gamma Alpha, Phi Sigma. Methodist. Office: Inst Ecosystem Studies Box AB Millbrook NY 12545

LIKENS, JAMES DEAN, economics educator; b. Bakersfield, Calif., Sept. 12, 1937; s. Ernest LeRoy and Monnie Jewel (Thomas) L.; m. Janet Sue Pelton, Dec. 18, 1965 (div.); m. Karel Carnohan, June 4, 1988 (div.); children: John David, Janet Elizabeth. BA in Econs., U. Calif., Berkeley, 1960, MBA, 1961; PhD in Econs., U. Minn., 1970. Analyst Del Monte Corp., San Francisco, 1963; economist 3M Co., Mpls., 1968-71; asst. prof. econs. Pomona Coll., 1969-75, assoc. prof. econs., 1975-83, prof. econs., 1983-85, Morris B. Pendleton prof. econs., 1989—; vis. asst. prof. econs. U. Minn., 1970, 71, vis. assoc. prof. econs., 1976-77; pres., dean Western CUNA Mgmt. Sch., Pomona Coll., 1975—; chmn. bd. 1st City Savs. Fed. Credit Union, 1978—; coord. So. Calif. Rsch. Coun., L.A., 1980-81, 84-85; mem. adv. coun. Western Corp. Fed. Credit Union; mem. bd. Health Plan Am., 1983-85; cons. in field. Author: (with Joseph LaDou) Medicine and Money, 1976, Mexico and Southern California: Toward A New Partnership, 1981, Financing Quality Education in Southern California, 1985; contbr. articles to profl. jours. Served with USCGR, 1961-67. Rsch. grantee HUD-DOT, Haynes Found., Filene Rsch. Inst. Mem. ABA, Am. Econ. Assn., Western Econ. Assn. Home: 725 W 10th St Claremont CA 91711-3719 Office: Pomona Coll Dept Econs Claremont CA 91711

LIKINS, PETER WILLIAM, university president; b. Tracy, Calif., July 4, 1936; s. Ennis Blaine and Dorothy Louise (Medlin) L.; m. Patricia Ruth Kitsmiller, Dec. 18, 1955; children: Teresa, Lora, Paul, Linda, Krista, John. BCE, Stanford U., 1957, PhD in Engring. Mechanics, 1965; MCE, MIT, 1958; hon. doctorates, Lafayette Coll., 1983, Moravian Coll., 1984, Med. Coll. Pa., 1990, Lehigh U., 1991, Allentown St. Francis de Sales, 1993; hon. doctorate, Czech Tech U., 1993. Devel. engr. Jet Propulsion Lab., Pasadena, Calif., 1958-60; asst. prof. engring. UCLA, 1964-69, assoc. prof. 1969-72, prof., 1972-76, asst. dean, 1974-75, assoc. dean, 1975-76; dean engring. and applied sci. Columbia U., N.Y.C., 1976-80, provost, 1980-82; Lehigh U., Bethlehem, Pa., 1982—; engring. cons. U.S. and fgn. corps. and govt. agys., 1965—. Author: Elements of Engineering Mechanics, 1973, Spacecraft Dynamics, 1982; Contbr. articles to profl. jours. Mem. U.S. Pres.'s Coun. Advisers Sci. and Tech., 1990-93. Ford Found. fellow, 1970-72; named to Nat. Wrestling Hall of Fame. Fellow AIAA; mem. Nat. Acad. Engring., Phi Beta Kappa, Sigma Xi, Tau Beta Pi. Office: Lehigh U 27 Memorial Dr W Bethlehem PA 18015-3089

LILES, JACK S., construction company executive; b. High Point, N.C., Jan. 26, 1928; s. Sherwood E. and Emma W. Liles; m. Ruth Padgett, Aug. 9, 1952; children: Jenna, Jack Jr., Richard, Laura. BCE, Clemson U., 1949. Field engr. Tidewater Constrn. Co., Norfolk, Va., 1949-53, supt., 1953-59, mgr., 1959-70, v.p., 1970-84, pres., 1984—; bd. dirs. Liberty Mut. Adv. Bd., Va. Mem. devel. council Clemson U., S.C., 1986—. Mem. Hampton Rds. Engring. Club, Tech. Assn. Pulp and Paper Industry, Va. Rd. and Trasp. Builders Assn. (bd. dirs. 87—), N.C. Pulp and Paper Found. (bd. dirs. 1985—). Clubs: Princess Anne Country (Virginia Beach, Va.), Broad Bay Country. Office: Tidewater Constrn Corp PO Box 57 Norfolk VA 23501-0057

LILEY, PETER EDWARD, mechanical engineering educator; b. Barnstaple, North Devon, Eng., Apr. 2, 1927; came to U.S., 1957; s. Stanley E. and Rosa (Ellery) L.; m. Elaine Elizabeth Kull, Aug. 16, 1963; children: Elizabeth Ellen, Rebecca Ann. B.Sc., Imperial Coll., U. London, 1951, Ph.D. in Physics, 1957, D.I.C., 1957. With Brit. Oxygen Engring., London, 1955-57; asst. prof. mech. engring. Purdue U., West Lafayette, Ind., 1957-61, assoc. prof., 1961-72; assoc. sr. researcher Thermophys. Properties Research Ctr., Purdue U., West Lafayette, Ind., 1961-72, prof. mech. engring., 1972—; sr. rschr. Ctr. for Info. and Numerical Data Analysis and Synthesis, Purdue U., West Lafayette, Ind., 1972-92; cons. in field. Author: Sect. 3 Perry's Chemical Engineers Handbook, 4th edit., 1963, 5th edit., 1972, 6th edit., 1985; (with Hartnett et al.) Handbook of Heat Transfer Fundamentals, 2nd edit., 1985; (with others) Marks Mechanical Engineers Handbook, 9th edit., 1987, Schaums 2000 Solved Problems in Mechanical Engineering Thermodynamics, Tables and Charts for Thermodynamics, 1995, Kutz Mechanical Engineers Handbook, 1986; co-author: Steam and Gas Tables with Computer Equations, 1985, Thermal Conductivity of Nonmetallic Liquids and Gases, 1970, Properties of Nonmetallic Fluid Elements, 1981, Properties of Inorganic and Organic Fluids, 1988; editor, mem. editl. bd. Internat. Jour. Thermophysics, 1980-86; contbr. chpts. to handbooks in field; contbr. articles to profl. jours.; reviewer profl. jours. Served with Royal Corps Signals, Brit. Army, 1945-48. Lutheran. Home: 3608 Mulberry Dr Lafayette IN 47905-3937 Office: Purdue U Dept Mech Engring West Lafayette IN 47907

LILIEN, MARK IRA, publishing, retailing and systems executive; b. Kew Gardens, N.Y., Sept. 7, 1953; s. Robert Samuel and Annette Audrey (London) L. BS in Labor Relations, Cornell U., 1974; MBA in Entrepreneurial Mktg., U. Pa., 1976. Buyer, mdse. controller Korvettes Dept. Stores, N.Y.C., 1976-79; div. mdse. adminstrn. Walden Books, Stamford, Conn., 1979-84, U.S. Retail div. Genesco, Nashville, 1984-85; sr. assoc. Booz Allen & Hamilton, N.Y.C., 1985-86; v.p. Penguin USA, N.Y.C., 1986-89, Barnes & Noble Bookstores, N.Y.C., 1989-92, Lechters, 1992-94, McGraw-Hill, N.Y.C., 1994—. Mem. editorial bd. Retail Systems Alert Newsletter, 1991-94. Schirer fellow Wharton Sch. Bus. U. Pa., 1975-76. Mem. Book Industry Systems Adv. Com. (vice chmn. 1983-84, chmn. 1988-89), Book Industry Study Group, Assn. Am. Pubs. (bus. mgrs. com., Pubnet com. 1986-89), Nat. Retail Fedn. (chmn. SpecNet com. 1990-92). Avocations: theatre, films. Home: 350 Bleecker St Apt 3E New York NY 10014-2631

LILIENFIELD, LAWRENCE SPENCER, physiology and biophysics educator; b. Bklyn., May 5, 1927; s. Henry Jacob and Lee (Markman) L.; m. Eleanor Marion Russ, Oct. 22, 1950; children: Jan, Adele, Lisa. BS, Villanova (Pa.) U., 1945; MD, Georgetown U., 1949. MS, 1954, PhD, 1956. Diplomate Nat. Bd. Med. Examiners, Am. Bd. Internal Medicine. Intern Georgetown U. Hosp., Washington, 1949-59, 1949-50, resident in internal

medicine, 1950, 52-54, rsch. fellow, 1954-55; instr. medicine Sch. Medicine Georgetown U., Washington, 1955-56, asst. chief cardiovascular rsch. lab., dept. mediicne, 1956-63, asst. chief cardiovascular rsch. lab. dept. medicine, 1956-63, assoc. prof. physiology, biophysics and medicine Sch. Medicine, 1961-64, prof. physiology and biophysics Sch. Medicine, 1964—61, prof., chmn. dept. physiology and biophysics Sch. Medicine, 1963-93; attending physician VA Hosp., Washington, 1956-70; cons. USPHS, 1964-69, NASA, 1964-70, U.S. Dept. State, 1967-74; established investigator Am. Heart Assn., 1958; vis. prof. faculty of medicine U. Saigon, Republic of Korea, 1965-74. Contbr. numerous articles to profl. jours. Bd. dirs. Washington Heart Assn., 1962-67, chmn., 1966. With USN, 1945; capt. USAF, 1950-52. Recipient Established Investigator award Am. Heart Assn., 1958; Rsch. Career Devel. award USPHS, 1963, Rsch. Career award, 1963, Kaiser-Permanente Teaching award, 1987; USPHS rsch. and rsch. tng. grantee, 1987. Fellow ACP; mem. Am. Soc. for Clin. Investigation, Am. Physiol. Soc., Soc. for Exptl. Biology and Medicine, Am. Fedn. for Clin. Rsch. (chair ea. sect. 1965-66). Avocations: computers in education. Office: Georgetown U Sch Medicine 3900 Reservoir Rd NW Washington DC 20007-2187

LILIENSTERN, O. CLAYTON, lawyer; b. Houston, Nov. 13, 1943; s. Oscar C. and Suzanne (Haughton) L.; m. Helen A. Andronis, Jan. 14, 1979; children: Robert, Susan, Kelli, Melanie. AB, U. Ala., 1965; JD, U. Houston, 1968, MBA, 1992; LLM, George Washington U., 1972. Bar: Tex. 1968, U.S. Dist. Ct. (so. dist.) Tex. 1973, U.S. Tax Ct. 1975, U.S. Supreme Ct. 1976, U.S. Dist. Ct. (we. dist.) Tex. 1978, U.S. Dist. Ct. (ea. dist.) Tex. 1987, U.S. Dist. Ct. (no. dist.) Tex. 1988, U.S. Ct. Appeals (5th, 9th, 11th and fed. cirs.); cert. civil trial law Tex. Bd. Legal Specialization; Assoc. Andrews & Kurth, Houston, 1972-79, ptnr., 1979—; adv. dir. 1st City Bank, Bellaire, 1985-91; bd. dirs. Houston Law Review, Inc. Bd. Dirs. U. Houston Law Found., chmn. bd. dirs., 1991-94. Bd., Vocat. Guidance Svc., Inc.; pres. bd. dirs. Annunciation Orthodox Sch., 1991-94, Leadership Houston, 1989—. Capt. JAGC, U.S. Army, 1968-72. Decorated Joint Svc. Commendation medal. Fellow Tex. Bar Found., Houston Bar Found.; mem. ABA, State Bar Tex. (chair com. on coordination with other profl. groups), Houston Bar Assn., Century Club and Ezekiel Cullen Soc. U. Houston, A.A. White Soc. U. Houston Law Ctr., U. Houston Law Alumni Assn. (pres. 1982-83, life mem.), Houston Law Rev. Alumni Assn. (pres. 1991-92), Jasons Soc., The Houston Forum, The Houston Club, The Briar Club, Delta Tau Delta, Omicron Delta Kappa, Phi Alpha Delta. Home: 4821 Maple St Bellaire TX 77401-5728 Office: Andrews & Kurth 4200 Tex Commerce Tower Houston TX 77002

LILIENTHAL, ALFRED M(ORTON), author, historian, editor; b. N.Y.C., Dec. 25, 1913; s. Herbert and Lottye (Kohn) L. BA, Cornell U., Ithaca, N.Y., 1934; LLB, Columbia U., 1938, JD, 1969. Bar: N.Y. 1938. With Bennett, House & Couts, N.Y.C., 1939-41, State Dept., 1942-43, 45-48; cons. U.S. del. UN San Francisco Conf., 1945; adminstrv. practice, 1947-50; counsel Am.-Arab Assn. Commerce & Industry, 1960-65; editor, pub. Middle East Perspective (monthly newsletter), 1967-85; lectr. on Middle East at numerous colls. and clubs throughout U.S. and fgn. countries, 1951-93, frequent guest TV and radio news commentator on Middle East devels., 1951-91; lectr. cultural symposium United Arab Emirates, Libya, Lebanon, Vienna, Baghdad, Prague; polit. columnist daily Al Qabas, Kuwait, 1976-77; accredited corr. to UN; chmn. Am. Coun. on the Middle East; cons. UN Internat. Conf. on Question Palestine, Geneva, 1983; participant Model Internat. Conf. on Middle East, Prague, 1988; 27 Middle East trips including West Bank and Gaza, 1953-94. Author: Which Way to World Government, 1949, What Price Israel?, 1954, There Goes the Middle East, 1957, Studies in Twentieth Century Diplomacy, 1959, The Other Side of the Coin, 1965, The Zionist Connection, 1978, The Zionist Connection II, 1982, rev. Czechoslovakian edit., 1989, Japanese edit., 1991, This I Do Believe, 1994; contbr. to: book Zionism-The Dream and the Reality, 1974; monthly commentaries Washington Report on Middle East Affairs, 1988—; also numerous mag. articles and syndicated newspieces. Pres. Rep. First Voters League, 1940; Fusion Party candidate for N.Y.C. Coun., 1941; leader fight against Communist controlled Am. Youth Congress, 1941. With AUS, 1943-45. Papers housed in archives of Hoover Instn., Stanford, Calif. Mem. Nat. Rep. Club, Univ. Club, Capitol Hill Club, Nat. Press Club, Cornell Club Washington. Home and office: 800-25th St NW Washington DC 20037

LILJEGREN, FRANK SIGFRID, artist, art association official; b. N.Y.C., Feb. 23, 1930; s. Josef Sigfrid and Ester (Davidsson) L.; m. Donna Kathryn Hallam, Oct. 12, 1957. Student, Art Students League, N.Y.C., 1950-55. Instr. painting, drawing, composition Westchester County Center, White Plains, N.Y., 1967-77, Art Students League, N.Y.C., 1974-75, Wassenberg Art Center, Van Wert, Ohio, 1978-80, Wright State U. Br. Western Ohio Campus, Celina, Ohio, 1981—; corr. sec. Allied Artists Am., N.Y.C., 1967, exhbn. chmn., 1968—, pres., 1970-72, also dir. Exhibited at: Suffolk Mus., Stonybrook, N.Y., Springfield (Mass.) Mus., Marion Kugler McNay Art Inst., San Antonio, Philbrook Mus., Tulsa, N.A.D., N.Y.C., New Britain (Conn.) Mus. Am. Art, Ft. Wayne (Ind.) Mus. Art; represented in permanent collections, Art Students League, Manhattan Savs. Bank, N.Y.C., Am. Ednl. Pubs. Inst., N.Y.C., New Britain Mus. Am. Art; (Recipient numerous awards for still life oil paintings. Served with AUS, 1951. Mem. Fine Arts fedn. N.Y. Art Students League (life), Acad. Artists Assn., Coun. Am. Artists Socs., Artists Fellowship, Salmagundi. Office: 203 S Cherry St Van Wert OH 45891-2006 *The best advice I could give young artists is to first learn their craft to the fullest so that they can then be free to express themselves in what ever style and medium they then choose to work. Last but not least, they should have self-respect and great love for what they are doing.*

LILLARD, JOHN FRANKLIN, III, lawyer; b. Cheverly, Md., Aug. 2, 1947; s. John Franklin, Jr. and Madeline Virginia (Berg) L.; m. Shannon Leslie Oliver, June 1, 1991; 1 child, John F. Lillard IV. B.A., Washington and Lee U., 1969, J.D., 1971. Bar: N.Y. 1972, D.C. 1974, Md. 1975. Assoc. Donovan, Leisure, Newton & Irvine, N.Y.C., 1971-74, Pierson, Ball & Dowd (merged into Reed, Smith, Shaw & McClay), Washington, 1974-76; trial atty. civil div. Dept. Justice, Washington, 1976-77; ptnr. Lillard & Lillard, Washington, 1977—. Vice chair Village Council of Friendship Heights, Chevy Chase, Md., 1975-77; candidate U.S. Congress from 5th dist. Md., 1981; chair Am. Solar Energy Assn.; founding mem. Nat. Adv. Coun. Ctr. for the Study of The Presidency, 1970—, Md. State Adv. Bd. on Spl. Tax Dists., 1976-77, alcoholic beverage adv. bd. Montgomery County, 1977-79; chair Eisenhower Centennial Meml. Com., 1990—. Served to 1st lt. USAF Aux., 1973-77. Recipient Eastman award Am. Arbitration Assn., 1971. Mem. Md. Bar Assn., Prince George's County Bar Assn., Anne Arundel County Bar Assn. Republican. Episcopalian. Clubs: Metropolitan (Washington); Tred Avon Yacht (Oxford, Md.); Marlborough Hunt (Upper Marlboro, Md.). Office: Lillard & Lillard 1518 K St NW # 201 Washington DC 20005-1203

LILLARD, MARK HILL, III, computer consulting executive, former air force officer; b. Jacksonville, Fla., Sept. 1, 1943; s. Mark Hill Jr. and Cornelia Kingman (Callaway) L.; m. Marie-Jacques Le Guyader, June 3, 1972; children: Mark Hill IV, Michael Robert. BA, Bowling Green U., 1965; MS, St. Mary's U., San Antonio, 1976; MBA, Auburn U., 1977. Commd. 2d lt. USAF, 1965, advanced through grades to brig. gen., 1991; dir. spl. actions Combined Forces Command, Republic of Korea, 1980-83; comdr. 596 BMS, Barksdale AFB, La., 1983-85; dep. comdr. OPS, 2 BMS, Barksdale AFB, La., 1985; chief force mgmt. Strategic Air Command Hdqrs, Offutt, Nebr., 1985-87; comdr. 64 ABG, Reese AFB, Tex., 1987, 64 FTW, Reese AFB, Tex., 1987-88; exec. to chief of staff SHAPE (NATO), Mons, Belgium, 1988-91; comdr. 57th Air Div., Minot AFB, N.D., 1991; ret., 1991; exec. v.p. Pilot Rsch. Assocs., Inc., Vienna, Va., 1991—, also bd. dirs. Author: Simulation, 1976. Decorated Legion of Merit, Def. Superior Svc. medal, Def. Meritorious Svc. medal; Samil medal (Republic of Korea). Mem. Air Force Assn., Lions, Kiwanis, Phi Delta Theta. Republican. Avocations: tennis, golf. Home: 9516 Locust Hill Dr Great Falls VA 22066-2021 Office: Pilot Rsch Assocs Inc 1953 Gallows Rd Ste 350 Vienna VA 22182-3934

LILLEGRAVEN, JASON ARTHUR, paleontologist, educator; b. Mankato, Minn., Oct. 11, 1938; s. Arthur Oscar and Agnes Mae (Eaton) L.; m. Bernice Ann Hines, Sept. 5, 1964 (div. Feb. 1983); children: Brita Anna, Ture Andrew; m. Linda Elizabeth Thompson, June 5, 1983. BA, Long Beach State Coll., 1962; MS, S.D. Sch. Mines and Tech., 1964; PhD, U. Kans., 1968.

Professional geologist, Wyo. Postdoctoral fellow Dept. Paleontology U. Calif., Berkeley, 1968-69; from asst. prof. to prof. zoology San Diego State U., 1969-75; from assoc. prof. to prof. geology and zoology U. Wyo., Laramie, 1975—; program dir. NSF Systematic Biology, Washington, 1977-78; assoc. dean U. Wyo. Coll. Arts and Scis., 1984-85, temporary joint appointment Dept. Geography, 1986-87; U.S. sr. scientist Inst. for Paleontology Free U., Berlin, 1988-89. Author, editor: Mesozoic Mammals the First Two Thirds of Mammalian History, 1979, Vertebrates, Phylogeny and Philosophy, 1986; editorial bds. of Research and Exploration (Nat. Geographic Soc.), Jour. of Mammalian Evolution, Jour. of Vertebrate Paleontology; contbr. articles to profl. jours. Recipient numerous rsch. grants NSF, 1970-95, Humboldt prize. Mem. Am. Soc. Mammalogists, Am. Assn. Petroleum Geologists, Paleontol. Soc., Soc. Vertebrate Paleontology (pres. 1985-86), Linnean Soc. London, Soc. Mammalian Evolution, Sigma Xi. Avocations: computer graphics, outdoor activities. Office: U Wyo Dept Geology and Geophysics Laramie WY 80271-3006

LILLEHEI, CLARENCE WALTON, surgeon; b. Mpls., Oct. 23, 1918; s. Clarence Ingewald and Elizabeth Lillian (Walton) L.; m. Katherine Ruth Lindberg, Dec. 31, 1946; children—Kimberle Rae (Mrs. Allen Loken), Craig Walton, Kevin Owen, Clark William. B.S., U. Minn., 1939, M.D., 1942, M.S. in Physiology, 1951, Ph.D. in Surgery, 1951; Dr. Medicinae h.c., U. Oslo, 1976; hon. degree, Faculte De Medecinae De Montpellier, France, 1977; Dr. honoris causa, Sorbonne U., Paris, 1986, U. Rome, 1991; LHD (hon.), Oklahoma City U., 1987; DSc, W.Va. U., 1993. Diplomate: Am. Bd. Surgery, 1951, Am. Bd. Thoracic Surgery, 1954. Pvt. practice medicine, 1942—, specializing gen., thoracic and cardiovascular surgery, 1945—; instr. dept. surgery U. Minn. Med. Sch., 1949-51, asso. prof. surgery, 1951-56, prof. surgery, 1956-67, clin. prof. surgery, 1967—; dir. med. affairs St. Jude Med. Sch., St. Paul, 1979—; chmn. dept. surgery Cornell U. Med. Center, N.Y.C., 1967-74, Lewis Atterbury Stimson prof. surgery Med. Coll., 1967-74; surgeon-in chief N.Y. Hosp., N.Y.C., 1967-70; bd. dirs. Getz Bros. Med., Tokyo. Served lt. col. M.C., AUS, 1942-46. Decorated Bronze Star; officer Order of Leopold (Belgium); recipient Theobald-Smith award AAAS, 1951, Ida. B. Gould award, 1957; 1st prize Am. Coll. Coll. Chest Physicians, 1952; Lasker award, 1955; Hektoen Gold medal AMA, 1957; Oscar B. Hunter award Am. Therapeutic Soc., 1958; Purdue Frederick Med. Achievement Travel award Internat. Consul for Health, 1958; Malcom F. Rogers Meml. award Wis. Heart Assn., 1962; Cummings Humanitarian Award Am. Coll. Cardiology, 1963; Gairdner Found. Internat. award, 1963; Honor award Stevens Inst. Tech., 1967; Gold Plate award Am. Acad. Achievement, 1968; Bio-Med. Tech. Innovative Contbn. award Congl. Inst. for Space, Sci., and Tech., 1985; Outstanding Achievement award Bd. of Regents, U. Minn., 1991, Markowitz award Acad. Surgical Rsch., 1994; Lillehei Endowed Chair in thoracic and cardiovascular surgery named in his honor U. Minn. Med. Sch., 1988, Lillehei Libr. named in his honor, 1991; named to Minn. Inventors Hall of Fame, 1993. Fellow A.C.S., Am. Coll. Chest Physicians, Am. Coll. Cardiology (pres. 1966-67), Am. Coll. Angiology, Am. Heart Assn., Halsted Soc., Internat. Soc. Surgery, Allen O. Whipple Surg. Soc., Pan Am. Med. Soc., Royal Soc. Medicine (Gt. Britain), Soc. Thoracic Surgery; mem. AMA (Billings silver medal 1972), Am. Surg. Assn., Acad. Surg. Rsch., Am. Assn. Thoracic Surgery, Soc. U. Surgeons, Soc. Exptl. Biology and Medicine, AAAS, Internat. Cardiovascular Soc., Soc. Vascular Surgery, Sigma Xi. Home: 73 Otis Ln Saint Paul MN 55104-5645

LILLESTOL, JANE MARIE, academic administrator; b. Jamestown, N.D., July 20, 1936; d. Harper J. and Doris (Mikkelson) Brush; m. Harvey Lillestol, Sept. 29, 1956; children: Kim, Kevin, Erik. BS, U. Minn., 1969, MS, 1973, PhD, 1977; grad. Inst. Ednl. Mgmt., Harvard U., 1984. Dir. placement, asst. to dean U. Minn., St. Paul, 1975-77; assoc. dean, dir. student acad. affairs N.D. State U., Fargo, 1977-80; dean Coll. Human Devel. Syracuse (N.Y.) U., 1980-89, v.p. for alumni rels., 1989—, project dir. IBM Computer Aided Design Lab., 1989-92; charter mem. Mayor's Commn. on Women, 1986-90; NAFTA White House Conf. for Women Leaders, 1993. Co-author: Textile Fabrics and Their Selection, 9th edit. Bd. dirs. Univ. Hill Corp. Syracuse, 1983-93; mem. steering com. Consortium for Cultural Founds. of Medicine, 1980-89; trustee Pebble Hill Sch., 1990-94, N.D. State U., Archbold Theatre. Recipient award U.S. Consumer Product Safety Commn., 1983, Woman of Yr. award AAUW, 1984, svc. award Syracuse U., 1992. Roman Catholic. Office: Syracuse U Office Alumni Rels 820 Comstock Ave Syracuse NY 13244-5040

LILLEVANG, OMAR JOHANSEN, civil engineer; b. Los Angeles, Sept. 8, 1914; s. Gunnar Johansen and Nina (Christiansen) L.; m. D. Miriam Guest, Sept. 10, 1939 (dec. Sept. 1990); children—Ralph Glen, Carol Ellen. A.A., Los Angeles Jr. Coll., 1935; B.S., U. Calif., Berkeley, 1937, postgrad., 1950-51. Registered profl. engr., Alaska, Calif., Hawaii, N.J., Oreg., Utah, Wash., Wis. Topographic surveyor Calif. Hwy. Commn., 1937; asst. engr. Coachella Valley County (Calif.) Water and Stormwater Dist., 1938; harbor constrn. engr., 1939-40, cantonment design and constrn. engr., 1941, constrn. engr. dams, aqueduct, tunnel, pump plants, 1942, water resources analyst, 1943; with Leeds, Hill, Barnard and Jewett (Cons. Engrs., and successors), Los Angeles, 1938-43, 46-61; supervising engr. Leeds, Hill, Barnard and Jewett (Cons. Engrs., and successors), 1950-61; v.p., dir. Leeds, Hill & Jewett Inc. (Cons. Engrs.), Los Angeles, 1961-64; cons. civil engring., especially for harbors, rivers, lakes, seas, coastal processes L.A., Whittier, 1964—; mem. advisory panel for shore erosion protection U.S. Army Chief Engrs. Contbr.: articles to profl. jours. including Shore & Beach mag. Trustee, chmn. bldg. com. Plymouth Congregational Ch. of Whittier, Calif. Served with USN, 1943-46. Fellow ASCE (mem. task groups, John G. Moffatt-Frank E. Nichol Meml. award 1981); mem. Am. Shore Beach Preservation Assn., Permanent Internat. Assn. Navigation Congresses, U.S. Power Squadrons. Club: Rotary Internat. Home: 14318 Eastridge Dr Whittier CA 90602-2721 Office: PO Box 4382 Whittier CA 90607-4382

LILLEY, ALBERT FREDERICK, lawyer; b. Harrisburg, Pa., Dec. 21, 1932; s. Frederick Anthony and Jane Sander (Ingham) L.; m. Judith Carter Pennock, Sept. 1, 1956; children: Kirk Anthony, Kristin Sander, James Alexander. A.B., Bowdoin Coll., 1954; LL.B., U. Va., 1959. Assoc. Milbank, Tweed, Hadley & McCloy, N.Y.C., 1959-67, ptnr., 1967—. Trustee No. Highlands Regional H.S., Allendale, N.J., 1964-65; mem. Allendale Bd. Zoning Adjustment, 1965-66; bd. overseers Bowdoin Coll., 1976-88, overseer emeritus, 1988—; trustee Valley Hosp., Ridgewood, N.J., 1978-92, vice chmn. bd., 1985-89, chmn. bd., 1989-92; bd. dirs. Valley Care Corp., 1992—, Valley Home and Cmty. Health Care, Inc., 1992—; mem. alumni coun. U. Va. Law Sch., 1991-94, U.S. Can. Law Project Adv. Bd. 1st lt. U.S. Army, 1954-56. Mem. ABA, Am. Law Inst., N.Y. State Bar Assn., Assn. of Bar of City of N.Y.,, U. Va. Law Sch. Alumni Assn. (fund class mgr.). Home: 180 Lincoln Ave Ridgewood NJ 07450-4106 Office: Milbank Tweed Hadley & McCloy 1 Chase Manhattan Plz New York NY 10005-1401

LILLEY, JAMES RODERICK, foreign relations expert, former federal government official; b. Tsingtao, China, Jan. 15, 1928; s. Frank Walder and Inez (Bush) L.; m. Sally Booth, May 1, 1954; children: Douglas, Michael, Jeffrey. BA, Yale U., 1951; MA, George Washington U., 1972. Fgn. affairs officer U.S. State Dept., various East Asian posts, 1958-75; dep. asst. sec. of state U.S. State Dept., Washington, 1985-86; nat. intelligence officer CIA, Washington, 1975-78; sr. East Asian specialist NSC, Washington, 1981; dir. Am. Inst. in Taiwan, 1982-84; ambassador U.S. Embassy, Seoul, Korea, 1986-89, Beijing, People's Republic of China, 1989-91; asst. sec. Dept. Defense, Washington, 1991-93; resident fellow Am. Enterprise Inst., Washington, 1993—; cons. Hunt/Sedco Oil Co., Dallas, 1979-81, United Techs., Hartford, Ct., 1979-80, Otis Elevator, Farmington, Ct., 1984-85, Westinghouse, Balt., 1984. Author: Beyond MFN, 1994. With U.S. Army, 1946-47; 1st lt. USAFR, 1950-67. Recipient Disting. Intelligence medal, CIA, 1979, Kang Hua medal Republic of Korea. Mem. Met. Club (Washington), Royal Bangkok Sports Club. Republican. Home: 7301 Maple Ave Chevy Chase MD 20815-5107 Office: 1150 17th St NW Fl 11 Washington DC 20036-4603

LILLEY, JOHN MARK, university provost and dean; b. Converse, La., Mar. 24, 1939; s. Ernest Franklin and Sibyl Arrena (Geoghagan) L.; children: Sibyl Elizabeth, Myles Durham; m. Geraldine Murphy; stepchildren: Benjamin Murphy, Jason Murphy. B in Music Edn., Baylor U., 1961, MusB, 1962, MusM, 1964; D of Musical Arts, U. So. Calif., 1971. Mem.

faculty Claremont McKenna, Harvey Mudd, Pitzer and Scripps Colls., Claremont, Calif., 1966-76; asst. dean faculty Scripps Coll., 1973-76; asst. dean arts and scis. Kans. State U., Manhattan, 1976-80; provost, dean Pa. State U., Erie, 1980—; bd. dirs. Erie Conf., 1980—, Erie Plastics Corp., 1994—; mem. N.W. Pa. Indsl. Resource Ctr., 1987—. Condr. 1st performances Kubik, 1972, 76, Ives, 1974, (recording) Kubik, 1974. Bd. dirs., v.p. So. Calif. Choral Music Assn., L.A., 1971-76; mem. Archtl. Commn., Claremont, 1974-76; bd. dirs. Erie Philharm., 1980-86, United Way, Erie County, 1981—, Sta. WQLN Pub. Broadcasting of N.W. Pa., 1992—; mem. Regents Commn. on Nursing Edn., Kansas City, Kans., 1978-79; pres. Pacific S.W. Intercollegiate Choral Assn., L.A., 1969-70. NEH grantee, 1978. Mem. Am. Assn. Higher Edn., Coll. Music Soc., Am. Choral Dirs. Assn., Am. Assn. of State Coll. and Univs. (vice chair confs. and profl. devel. com. 1989, chair 1990), Erie Club, Kahkwa Club, Rotary (bd. dirs. Manhattan club 1979-80, Erie club, 1981-88), Phi Mu Alpha Sinfonia, Omicron Delta Kappa. Republican. Presbyterian. Avocation: golf. Home: 601 Pasadena Dr Erie PA 16505-1038 Office: Pa State U Behrend Coll Station Rd Erie PA 16563

LILLEY, THEODORE ROBERT, financial executive; b. Paterson, N.J., Jan. 11, 1923; s. Ernest Raymond and Antoinette Eleanor (Hartmann) L.; m. Marguerite Anne Gallman, Jan. 27, 1951; children—Cheryl Anne, Wayne Robert, Ross Warren. B.A. cum laude, N.Y. U., 1946; M.B.A., Columbia U., 1948. Chartered financial analyst. With Standard Oil Co., N.J., 1948-64; investment mgr. Standard Oil Co., 1956-62, fin. mgr., 1962-64; asst. treas. Esso Internat. Inc., 1964-69; v.p. Tchr. Ins. and Annuity Assn. and Coll. Retirement Equities Fund, 1969-72; exec. dir. Fin. Analysts Fedn., N.Y.C., 1972-73; pres. Fin. Analysts Fedn., 1973-81, T.R. Lilley Assocs., 1981—; mem. advisory council Fin. Acctg. Standards Bd., 1976-80. Mem. bd. nat. missions United Presbyn. Ch. U.S.A., 1966-72; mem. United Presbyn. Found., 1972-81; trustee Englewood Hosp., 1979-85; bd. dirs. Near East Found., 1970—; trustee Ramapo Coll., 1977—, chmn. bd., 1980-82. Served to 1st lt. inf. AUS, 1943-46, ETO. Decorated Bronze Star, Purple Heart. Mem. Phi Beta Kappa, Phi Lambda Upsilon, Beta Gamma Sigma. Office: TR Lilley Assos PO Box 426 Tenafly NJ 07670-0426

LILLEY, WILLIAM, III, communications business consultant; b. Phila., Jan. 14, 1938; s. William, Jr. and Ida Weaver (Macklin) L.; m. Eve Auchincloss, Mar. 12, 1977; children—Buchanan Morgan, Brooke Carole, Whitman Elisa, Justin Weaver. B.A. magna cum laude, U. Pa., 1959; M.A., Yale U., 1961, Ph.D., 1965. Asst. prof. history Yale U., New Haven, 1962-69; prof. govt. U. Va., Charlottesville, 1977; co-founder, editor Nat. Jour., Washington, 1969-73; dep. asst. sec. HUD, Washington, 1973-75; dep., then dir. Council Wage and Price Stability, Washington, 1975-77; staff dir. Com. on Budget, Ho. of Reps., Washington, 1977-78; v.p. CBS, Inc., Washington, 1980-81; v.p. corporate affairs CBS, Inc., N.Y.C., 1981-84, sr. v.p. corporate affairs, 1985-86; pres. Am. Bus. Conf., 1986-88, Policy Communications Inc., Washington, 1988—; chmn., chief exec. officer InContext, Inc., Washington, 1992—; bd. dirs. Ply Gem Industries, Inc., Econ. and Social Rsch. Inst., Madison Ctr. for Ednl. Affairs. Co-author: New Technologies Affecting Broadcasting, 1981, Economic and Social Impacts of Media Advertising, 1989, Impact of Advertising on the Competitive Structure of the Media, 1990, Impact of Media Advertising on International Competitiveness, 1991, Geographic Distribution of U.S. Businesses which Advertise Heavily, 1991, Almanac of State Legislatures, 1994; contbr. articles to profl. jours. Recipient U.S. Govt. Disting. Svc. award 1975, 76; Samuel F.B. Morse Rsch. fellowship, 1967-68; George Washington Eggleston prize; Most Disting. PhD Dissertation, humanities divsn., Yale U., 1965; Woodrow Wilson Fellowship, 1959-61. Mem. Yale Club, Merion Cricket, Cosmos, River Club, Chevy Chase, Met. Club. Clubs: Yale, Merion Cricket, Cosmos, River, Chevy Chase. Office: Policy Communications Inc 1615 L St NW Washington DC 20036-5610

LILLIBRIDGE, JOHN LEE, retired airline executive; b. Dover, Okla., Nov. 3, 1924; s. John Lee and Myra Ina (Munger) L.; m. Audrey Rae Hart, Aug. 22, 1948; 1 son, John Lee III. B.S. in Mech. Engring., Okla. A&M Coll., 1950; B.S. in Civil Engring., Tex. A&M Coll., 1956. Enlisted in U.S. Army, 1943, advanced through grades to col., 1970, ret., 1973—; officer Corps of Engrs., 1950-73; v.p. Eastern Airlines, Miami, Fla., 1973-86. Democrat.

LILLICH, ALICE LOUISE, retired secondary education educator; b. East Cleveland, Ohio, Aug. 18, 1940; d. Robert Earl and Charlotte Louise (Stewart) L. BS in Home Econs. Edn., Ohio U., 1968. Cert. tchr., Ohio. Quality control Stouffer's Frozen Foods, Cleve., 1961-67; head home econs. dept. Wellston (Ohio) City Schs., 1969-94; Ohio reference person Wagons West tours of Afton, Wyo. Vol. Willoughby Hills United Meth. Ch. Mem. AAUW (2d vice chair 77-80, publicity chair 1985-86, issue chair 1987-90), Ohio Ret. Tchrs. Assn. (Lake County chpt.), Cleve. Audubon Soc., Republican Optimist Club (flag chair 1987-88, 2d v.p. 1989-90), Phi Delta Kappa (found. rep. 1986-87), Delta Kappa Gamma (Iota chpt. Lake County v.p. 1992—, pres. 1994). Methodist. Avocations: hiking, travel, reading, photography. Home: 37570 Milann Dr Willoughby OH 44094

LILLICH, RICHARD B., law educator; b. 1933. AB, Oberlin Coll., 1954; LLB, Cornell U., 1957; LLM, JSD, NYU, 1960. Bar: N.Y. 1957, D.C. 1980. Pvt. practice N.Y.C., 1957-60; vis. asst. prof. Ind. U., 1960; asst. prof. Syracuse U., 1960-63, assoc. prof., 1963-67, prof., 1967-69; prof. U. Va., 1969—; legal cons. U.S. Naval War Coll., 1964-78, chair internat. law, 1968-69; vis. prof. NYU, 1977, FSU, 1992, Ga. U., 1994. Ford fellow, Eng., 1963, Guggenheim fellow, Eng., 1966-67, Sr. fellow NEH, Eng., 1974-75, Thomas Jefferson vis. fellow Downing Coll., Eng., 1980-81, vis. fellow All Souls Coll., Eng., 1987, vis. fellow Max Planck Inst., Heidelberg, 1993. Mem. Internat. Law Assn. (exec. coun., chmn. internat. com. on human rights law and practice), Am. Soc. Internat. Law (exec. coun. 1966-72, 73-76, 82-85), Procedural Aspects of Internat. Law Inst. (pres.). Office: U Va Sch Law Charlottesville VA 22903

LILLIE, CHARISSE RANIELLE, lawyer, educator; b. Houston, Apr. 7, 1952; d. Richard Lysander and Vernell Audrey (Watson) L.; m. Thomas L. McGill, Jr., Dec. 4, 1982. B.A. cum laude, Conn. Wesleyan U., 1973; J.D., Temple U., 1976; LL.M., Yale U., 1982. Bar: Pa. 1976, U.S. Dist. Ct. (ea. dist.) Pa. 1977, U.S. Ct. Appeals (3d cir.) 1980. Law clk. U.S. Dist. Ct. (ea. dist.) Pa., Phila., 1976-78; trial atty., honors program, civil rights div. Dept. Justice, Washington, 1978-80; dep. dir. Community Legal Services, Phila., 1980-81; asst. prof. law Villanova U. Law Sch., Pa., 1982-83, assoc. prof., 1983-84, prof. 1984-85; asst. U.S. atty. U.S. Dist. Ct. (ea. dist.) Pa., 1985-88; gen. counsel Redevel. Authority City of Phila., 1988-90; city solicitor Law Dept. City of Phila., 1990-92; ptnr. litigation dept. Ballard, Spahr, Andrew and Ingersoll, 1992—, exec. com. bd. dirs., 1994—; mem. 3d Cir. Lawyers Adv. Com., 1982-85, legal counsel Pa. Coalition of 100 Black Women, Phila., 1983-88; bd. dirs. Juvenile Law Center, Phila., 1982—, Pa. Intergovernmental Coop. Authority, 1992—; commr. Phila. Ind. City Charter Commn. 1991-94; trustee Women's Law Project, Phila., 1984—; mem. Mayor's Commn. on May 13 MOVE Incident, 1985—. Bd. dirs. Women's Way, Phila. Davenport fellow, 1973; Yale Law Sch. fellow, 1981; recipient Equal Justice award Community Legal Svcs., Inc, 1991, J. Austin Norris award Barristers Assn., 1991, Outstanding Alumna award Wesleyan U., 1993, Elizabeth Dole Glass Ceiling award ARC, Phila. chpt., 1994; named One of the Top Three Phila. Labor Mgmt. Attys. Phila. Mag., 1994. Mem. ABA, Nat. Bar Assn., Fed. Bar Assn. (1st v.p. Phila. chpt. 1982-84, pres. Phila. chpt.1984-86, 3rd cir. rep. 1991—), Nat. Conf. Black Lawyers (pres. 1976-78, Outstanding Service award 1978), Am. Law Inst., Phila. Bar Assn. (vice chair bd. govs. 1994, chair, bd. of govs., 1995—), Hist. Soc. U.S. Dist. Ct. (ea. dist.) Pa. (dir. 1983—), Barristers Assn. (J. Austin Norris award 1991). Home: 7000 Emlen St Philadelphia PA 19119-2601 Office: Ballard Spahr Andrews Ingersoll 1735 Market St 51st Fl Philadelphia PA 19103-7599

LILLIE, JAMES WOODRUFF, JR., lawyer; b. Toms River, N.J., Oct. 10, 1931; s. James Woodruff and Madeleine (Pendergast) L.; m. Barbara markoe Scott, Jan. 10, 1953 (div. Oct. 1983); children: Lydia, Christopher, James III, Derek; m. Inger Irene Andersson, June 27, 1987. BA, U. Pa., 1953, JD, 1959. Bar: N.Y., U.S. Dist. Ct., U.S. Ct. Appeals. Ptnr. N.Y.C., 1959-85; ptnr. sr. resident Bryan, Cave, McPheeters & McRoberts, N.Y.C., 1985—; mem. mgmt. bd. Internat. Tennis Fedn., London, 1978—. Served to lt. USNR, 1953-56. Mem. ABA, N.Y. State Bar Assn., Assn. of the Bar of the

City of N.Y., Internat. Bar Assn., Order of Barrister. Clubs: Board Room, Rockefeller Ctr. (N.Y.C.). Avocations: sailing, equestrian. Office: Morgan Lewis & Bockus 101 Park Ave New York NY 10178

LILLIE, JOHN MITCHELL, transportation company executive; b. Chgo., Feb. 2, 1937; s. Walter Theodore and Mary Ann (Hatch) L.; m. Daryl Lee Harvey, Aug. 23, 1987; children: Alissa Ann, Theodore Perry. BS, Stanford U., 1959, MS, MBA, 1962-64. Various positions including dir. systems devel., also asst. to pres. Boise Cascade Corp., 1964-68; v.p., chief financial officer Arcata Nat. Corp., Menlo Park, Calif., 1968-70; exec. v.p., chief operating officer Arcata Nat. Corp., 1970-72; pres., chief exec. officer Leslie Salt Co., Newark, Calif., 1972-79; exec. v.p. Lucky Stores Inc., Dublin, Calif., 1979-81, pres., 1981-86, chmn., chief exec. officer, 1986-89; gen. ptnr. Sequoia Assocs., Menlo Park, Calif., 1989-90; pres., COO, Am. Pres. Cos., Ltd., Oakland, Calif., 1990-91, chmn., pres., CEO, 1991—; bd. dirs. Am. Pres. Co., Gap Inc. Trustee Stanford (Calif.) U., 1988—; bd. dirs. Am. Pres. Co. Mem. Beta Theta Pi, Tau Beta Pi. Office: Am Pres Cos 1111 Broadway Oakland CA 94607-4021*

LILLY, EDWARD GUERRANT, JR., retired utility company executive; b. Lexington, Ky., Oct. 29, 1925; s. Edward Guerrant and Elisabeth Read (Frazer) L.; m. Nancy Estes Cobb, Nov. 25, 1961; children: Penelope Read, Edward Guerrant III, Collier Cobb (dec.), Steven Clay. B.S., Davidson Coll., 1948; M.B.A., U. Pa., 1949. Credit analyst Citizens and So. Nat. Bank, Charleston, S.C., 1949-50; asst. v.p. Wachovia Bank and Trust Co., Charlotte, 1952-55, v.p., 1956; v.p., loan adminstrv. officer Wachovia Bank and Trust Co., Wilmington, N.C., 1956-60; sr. v.p., area exec. Wachovia Bank and Trust Co., Kinston, N.C., 1961-62, Durham, N.C., 1963-70; sr. v.p., mgr. trust investment svcs. dept. Wachovia Bank and Trust Co., Winston-Salem, N.C., 1970-71, also bd. dirs., 1971-88; sr. v.p., group exec. Carolina Power and Light Co., Raleigh, N.C., 1971-76, sr. v.p., chief fin. officer, 1976-81; exec. v.p., chief fin. officer Carolina Power and Light Co., Raleigh, 1981-90; also bd. dirs. Carolina Power and Light Co., Raleigh, N.C.; bd. dirs. CSC Industries, N.C. Enterprise Corp. Mem. U. N.C. bd. visitors, 1974-87; bd. dirs. Rsch. Triangle Found., Research Triangle Park; trustee Davidson Coll., 1976-88, Union Theol. Seminary. Served to lt. USNR, 1950-52. Mem. Edison Electric Inst. (chmn. fin. group 1979). Presbyterian. Lodge: Rotary (Raleigh).

LILLY, FRANK, oncogenetic biomedical researcher; b. Charleston, W.Va., Aug. 28, 1930; s. Frank Otho and E. Verna (Zimmerman) L.; 1 child, Matthew T. PhD, U. Paris, 1959, Cornell U., 1965. Asst. prof. dept. genetics Albert Einstein Coll. Medicine, Bronx, N.Y., 1967-70, assoc. prof. 1970-74, prof., 1974—, chmn. dept., 1976-89; Am. Cancer Soc. rsch. prof. oncogenetics Albert Einstein Coll. Medicine, Bronx, 1989—; mem. bd. scientific overseers Jackson Lab., Bar Harbor, Maine, 1989-94; mem. scientific adv. coun. Cancer Rsch. Inst., N.Y.C., 1975-94; mem. scientific adv. com. Wistar Inst., Phila., 1979-93. Contbr. 150 scientific articles to profl. publs. Mem. Presdl. Commn. on the HIV Epidemic, Washington, 1987-88. With U.S. Army, 1952-53. Fellow N.Y. Acad. Scis.; mem. NAS (mem. Com. on a Nat. AIDS Strategy 1986-87), Am. Assn. for Cancer Rsch. Achievements include research in genetics of susceptibility and resistance to carcinogens and to retroviruses. Office: Albert Einstein Coll of Med Genetics Dept 1300 Morris Park Ave Bronx NY 10461-1975

LILLY, GRAHAM C., law educator; b. 1938. BS, Va. Poly. Inst., 1960; LLB, U. Va., 1963. Bar: Va. 1963, D.C. 1966. Assoc. Covington and Burling, D.C., 1963-64; asst. prof. U. Va., Charlottesville, 1967-69, assoc. prof., 1969-71, asst. dean, 1970-73, prof., 1971—; exec. dir. Law Sch. Fdn. U. Va., 1973-76, assoc. dean acad. affairs, 1986-89, U. Assoc. Provost, 1989-90. Mem. Raven Soc., Omicron Delta Kappa, Phi Kappa Phi. Office: U Va Sch Law Charlottesville VA 22901

LILLY, JOHN CUNNINGHAM, medical scientist, author; b. St. Paul, Jan. 6, 1915; s. Richard Coyle and Rachel (Cunningham) L.; m. Antonietta Ficorotta, 1975 (dec. Jan. 1986); children—John, Charles, Cynthia, Pamela, Nina, Lisa, Barbara Jane. B.Sc., Calif. Inst. Tech., 1938; student, Dartmouth Med. Sch.; M.D., U. Pa., 1942; postgrad. in Gnosiology, Institute de Gnosolia, Arica, Chile, 1970-71. Mem. faculty U. Pa., 1942-56; fellow in biophysics E. R. Johnson Found. Med. Physics, 1942-46, assoc. 1946-49, asst. prof. biophysics, 1949-52, assoc. prof. med. physics, 1952-56; also assoc. prof. exptl. neurology dept. neurology and E. R. Johnson Found. Med. Physics (Grad. Sch. Medicine), 1952-56; chief cortical integration sect. Lab. of Neurophysiology NIMH and Nat. Inst. Neurol. Disease and Blindness, 1953-58; established Communication Research Inst., St. Thomas, V.I., 1959, revived in Calif., 1988; chmn. neurol. div. Md. Psychiat. Research Center, 1968; Hixon lectr. Calif. Inst. Tech., 1952; Mayo Found. lectr., 1952; Colloquium lectr. Harvard U., 1954; John Kershman Meml. lectr., 1961; prof. medicine U. Miami Med. Sch., 1960; also lectr. numerous univs., learned socs.; Condr. war research for com. on med. research OSRD-USAF, 1942-46; fellowship bd. Nat. Inst. Mental Health, 1954-57; sci. adv. com. for grad. schs. NIH, 1954; mem. bioscis. adv. panel Office Sci. Research, USAF Research and Devel. Command, 1958, 61, sci. adv. bd., 1958-63, Peace in Space Inst. adv. bd.; bd. dirs. Internat. Tank Assn., U.S. Floatation Tank Assn., 1985—. Author: Man and Dolphin, 1961, The Mind of the Dolphin, 1967, Programming and Metaprogramming in the Human Biocomputer, Theory and Experiments, 1972, 1987, The Center of the Cyclone, 1972, 1987, Simulations of God: the Science of Belief, 1974, The Deep Self: Isolation Tank Relaxation, 1976, The Scientist: a Novel; autobiography, 1978, 2nd edit., 1988, Communication Between Man and Dolphin: The Possibility of Talking with Other Species, 1978, 1988, also sci. papers pub. in jours.; co-author: The Dolphin in History, 1963, (with Antoinette Lilly) The Dyadic Cyclone; inventor isolation/floatation tank, 1954; bd. dirs. Albert Hofman Meml. Library, 1988—. Recipient John Clark Research prize, 1943; Effective Service award OSRD-USAF, 1945; Humanities award Lompuc Prison, 1987; grantees NIH, 1946-69; grantees Office Naval Research; grantees NSF; grantees NASA, 1962-68; fellow Center for Advanced Study Behavioral Scis., 1969-70; resident asso. Esalen Inst., 1969-71. Fellow AAAS, N.Y. Acad. Scis.; mem. Am. Physiol. Soc. (steering com. on neurophysiology 1953-56), Cal. Tech. Alumni Assn. (life mem. Plus 50 Yr. Club), Biophys. Soc. (charter), Phila. Assn. of Psychoanalysis (assoc. 1949), Sigma Xi. Office: Human/Dolphin Found 11930 Oceanaire Ln Malibu CA 90265 *My life is devoted to exploration of inner and outer realities; this means a thorough self-review frequently, conducted with candor and discipline derived from medical, scientific, psychoanalytic and research training over the years.*

LILLY, JOHN RUSSELL, surgeon, educator; b. Milw., May 23, 1929; s. John J. and Hazel (Boyer) L.; m. Roberta J. Hall, 1990; children: John Richard, Megan Beth, Grace Eudora. BS, U. Wis., 1951, MD, 1954. Diplomate Am. Bd. Surgery, Am. Bd. Thoracic Surgery, Am. Bd. Pediatric Surgery. Postgrad. fellow pediatric surgery Hosp. for Sick Children, London, 1963-64; chief resident pediatric surgery Children's Hosp. D.C., Washington, 1964-65, dir. surg. rsch. Rsch. Found. of hosp., surg. dir. surg. rsch. Clin. Rsch. Ctr.; fellow in transplantation U. Colo. Health Scis. Ctr., Denver, 1969-70, prof., chief pediatric surgery, 1973—, acting chmn. dept. surgery, 1980-84; chmn. dept. pediatric surgery The Children's Hosp., Denver, 1990—; surg. dir. Pediatric Liver Ctr. U. Colo., 1985—; mem. admissions com. U. Colo. Sch. Medicine, 1987-92; chmn. session adv. bd. chronic liver disease Nat. Inst. Diabetes and Digestive and Kidney Diseases, 1988. Guest editor issue on pediatric surgery World Jour. Surgery, 1984. Recipient Disting. Surgeon award Hodgen Soc., 1980, Disting. Faculty award U. Colo. Sch. Medicine, 1988, Outstanding Tchr. Surgery award, 1989, Disting. Citation, Wis. Med. Alumni Assn., 1991. Mem. ACS, Am. Acad. Pediats. (sects. on surg., oncology/hematology), Am. Surg. Assn., Am. Pediat. Surg. Assn. Office: The Children's Hosp Ctr 1950 Ogden St # 323B Denver CO 80218-1022

LILLY, MARTIN STEPHEN, university dean; b. New Albany, Ind., Aug. 31, 1944; s. Raymond John and Amy Elizabeth (Peake) L.; m. Marilyn Ann MacDougall, Jan. 8, 1966; children—Matthew William, Mark Christopher, Rachel Marie, Martin Stephen, Jason Wood. B.A., Bellarmine Coll., Louisville, 1966; M.A., Peabody Coll., Nashville, 1967, Ed.D., 1969. Instr. dept. spl. edn. Peabody Coll., 1967-69; asst. prof. edn. U. Oreg., 1969-71; research coordinator N.W. Regional Spl. Edn. Instructional Materials Center, 1969-71; research coordinator div. research Bur. Edn. for Handicapped U.S. Office Edn., 1971-72; assoc. prof. dept. spl. edn. U. Minn., Duluth, 1972-75; assoc.

prof., chmn. dept. spl. edn. U. Ill., Urbana-Champaign, 1975-79, prof., chmn., 1979-81, assoc. dean grad. studies Coll. Edn., 1981-84; dean Coll. Edn. Wash. State U., Pullman, 1984-90, Calif. State U. San Marcos, 1990—; cons. in field. U.S. Office Edn. fellow, 1966-69. Author: Children with Exceptional Needs: A Survey of Special Education, 1979, (with C.S. Blankenship) Mainstreaming Students With Learning and Behavior Problems, 1981; assoc. editor: Exceptional Children, 1969-79; cons. editor: Edn. Unltd, 1979-81; reviewer: Jour. Tchr. Edn, 1980—; mem. editorial bd. Tchr. Edn. and Spl. Edn, 1980-83, co-editor, 1983-84; contbr. chpts. to books, articles to profl. jours. Mem. Coun. for Exceptional Children, Assn. Tchr. Educators, Am. Assn. Colls. Tchr. Edn., Phi Delta Kappa. Democrat. Roman Catholic. Office: Calif State U San Marcos CA 92096-0001

LILLY, MICHAEL ALEXANDER, lawyer; b. Honolulu, May 21, 1946; s. Percy Anthony Jr. and Virginia (Craig) L.; m. Kathryn I. Collins, Aug. 10, 1991; children: Michael A. Jr., Cary J., Laura B., Claire F., Winston W. AA, Menlo Coll., Menlo Park, Calif., 1966; BA, U. Calif., Santa Cruz, 1968; JD with honors, U. of Pacific, 1974. Bar: Calif. 1974, U.S. Dist. Ct. (no., so. and ea. dists.) Calif. 1974, U.S. Ct. Appeals (9th cir.) 1974, Hawaii 1975, U.S. Dist. Ct. Hawaii 1975, U.S. Ct. Appeals (D.C. cir.) 1975, U.S. Supreme Ct. 1978, U.S. Ct. Appeals (7th cir.) 1979. Atty. Pacific Legal Found., Sacramento, 1974-75; dep. atty. gen. State of Hawaii, Honolulu, 1975-79, 1st dep. atty. gen., 1981-84, atty. gen., 1984-85; ptnr. Feeley & Lilly, San Jose, Calif., 1979-81, Ning, Lilly & Jones, Honolulu, 1985—. Author: If You Die Tomorrow-A Layman's Guide to Estate Planning. Bd. dirs. Diamond Head Theatre; Lt. USN, 1968-71, Vietnam; capt. USNR. Named hon. Ky. col. Mem. Nat. Assn. Attys. Gen., Hawaii Law Enforcement Ofcls. Assn., Navy Res. Assn. (pres. 14th dist. 1986-89), Navy League (nat. dir., contbg. editor Fore 'N Aft mag., pres., dept. judge adv. to bd. Honolulu coun.), Outrigger Canoe Club. Home: 2769 Laniloa Rd Honolulu HI 96813-1041 Office: Ning Lilly & Jones 707 Richards St Ste 700 Honolulu HI 96813-4623 *Personal philosophy: Always do what you are afraid to do. Never give up. Forgive your enemies.*

LILLY, PETER BYRON, coal company executive; b. Beckley, W.Va., Sept. 26, 1948; s. Wallace Byron and Mabel Elizabeth (Dodson) L.; m. Brenda Jean Ernst, June 20, 1970; children: Lauren E., Peter E. BS in Engring., U.S. Mil. Acad., 1970; MBA, Harvard U., 1977. Commd. 2d lt. U.S. Army, 1970, advanced through grades to capt., served in Vietnam, resigned, 1975; mgmt. cons. Emory Ayers Assocs., N.Y.C., 1977-80; mgr. maintenance Kerr-McGee Coal Corp., Okla. City, 1980-81, dir. adminstrn., 1981-83; gen. mgr. Galatia Mine Kerr-McGee Coal Corp., Galatia, Ill., 1983-88; v.p. mktg. and planning Kerr-McGee Coal Corp., Oklahoma City, 1988-89, pres., 1989-91; sr. v.p. Kerr-McGee Corp., Oklahoma City, 1989-91; pres. Ea. Associated Coal Corp., Charleston, W.Va., 1991—. Decorated Bronze Star, Purple Heart; Cross of Gallantry (South Vietnam). Mem. Nat. Coal Assn. (bd. dirs. 1989—), Am. Mining Congress (bd. dirs. 1989-91), Nat. Coal Coun. Office: Coal Properties Corp 800 Laidley Tower Charleston WV 25301-2145

LILLY, SHANNON JEANNE, dancer; b. Alexandria, Va., Feb. 18, 1966; d. John Howard Lilly and Barbara Lynn (Root) Graham. Student, Contra Costa Ballet Centre, San Francisco Ballet Sch. Dancer Phoenix Ballet Co., 1985-86; mem. of Corps de Ballet San Francisco Ballet, 1986-88, soloist, 1988-91, prin. dancer, 1991-94; prin. dancer Northern Ballet Theatre, Birmingham, England, 1994—; Performed with San Francisco Opera, 1993; performed at the Reykjavik Arts Festival, Iceland, 1990. Performed with Jean Charles Gil and Friends, Paris, 1988, Tanantella, 1989, In the Middle Somewhat Elevated, 1990, Rubies, 1991, Bagaku, 1991, Sleeping Beauty, 1991; ballets include New Sleep, Connotations, Narcisse, Interplay, The Concert, Handel-a Celebration, Ballet d'Isoline, Menuetto, Giuliani: Variations on a Theme, Contredanses, Concerto in d: Poulenc, Con Brio, Intimate Voices, Calcium Light Night, Krazy Kat, Serenade, Swan Lake, Flower Festival at Genzano, Dark Elegies, Who Cares?, Theme and Variations, Airs de Ballet, Pulcinella, The Wanderer Fantasy, The Sons of Horus, Ballo Della Regina, The Theme Variations, Dreams of Harmony, Nutcracker, La Fille mal gardee, Rodeo, La Sylphide, The Sleeping Beauty, Meistens Mozart, Bugaju, Rubies, Symphony in C, The Four Temperaments, Star and Stripes, In the middle, somewhat elevated, Seeing Stars, Company B, La Pavane Rouge, Job, Harvest Moon, Tagore, Romeo and Juliet, Il Distratto, Divertissement d'Auber, Sinfonia, Scarlatti, Portfolio, The Comfort Zone, Dreams of Harmony, The End, Forgotten Land, Napoli. Episcopalian. Avocations: swimming, reading, movies, family, cooking. Office: Northern Ballet Company, Spring Hall Huddersfield Rd, Halifax HX3 0AQ, England*

LILLY, THOMAS GERALD, lawyer; b. Belzoni, Miss., Sept. 17, 1933; s. Sale Trice and Margaret Evelyn (Butt) L.; m. Constance Ray Holland, Dec. 29, 1962; children: Thomas Gerald Jr., William Holland, Carolyn Ray. BBA, Tulane U., 1955; LLB, U. Miss., 1960, JD, 1968. Bar: Miss. 1960. Assoc. firm Stovall & Price, Corinth, Miss., 1960-62; asst. U.S. atty. No. Dist. Miss., Oxford, 1962-66; assoc. firm Wise Carter Child & Caraway (and predecessor), Jackson, Miss., 1966-67; ptnr. Wise Carter Child & Caraway (and predecessor), 1967-94, Lilly & Wise, Jackson, 1994—. Served with USNR, 1955-58; rear adm. Res. ret. Decorated Legion of Merit, Navy Commendation medal. Mem. ABA, Fed. Bar Assn. (nat. coun. 1972—, rec. sec. 1975-76, gen. sec. 1976-77, 2d v.p. 1977-78, pres.-elect 1978-79, pres. 1979-80), Hinds County (Miss.) Bar Assn., Miss. State Bar, Miss. Bar Found., Miss. Def. Lawyers Assn., Inter-Am. Bar Assn., Internat. Bar Assn., Am. Counsel Assn., Res. Officers Assn. (pres. Miss. dept. 1982-83), Naval Res. Assn., Naval Order of U.S., Navy Supply Corps Assn., Navy League (pres. Cirit. Miss. Coun. 1993), Mil. Order World Wars, Southeastern Legal Found. (legal adv. bd. 1988—), Lamar Order, Newcomen Soc., English-Speaking Union, Omicron Delta Kappa, Phi Delta Phi, Sigma Nu. Office: Lilly & Wise 2180 Deposit Guaranty Plz 210 E Capitol St Jackson MS 39201

LILLY, WILLIAM ELDRIDGE, government official; b. Liberty, Tex., Aug. 25, 1921; s. Lawrence C. and Maude (McKinney) L.; m. Blanche Elizabeth Bromert, Jan. 18, 1944; children—Lizbeth Kristine, William Michael. A.B., U. Calif. at Berkeley, 1950, grad. student, 1950-51. Program analyst Naval Ordnance Test Sta., China Lake, Calif., 1950-52; head estimates and analysis Naval Bur. Ordnance, Washington, 1952-54; dep. budget officer Nat. Bur. Standards, 1954-56; asst. dir. plans and programs Navy Polaris program, 1956-60; with NASA, 1960—; asst. adminstr. for adminstrn., 1967-72, comptroller, 1972-82, cons., 1982—. Pres. Arlington County (Va.) Youth Orgn., 1966-69. Served with USN, 1940-46. Recipient Exceptional Service medal NASA, 1966, 69, Disting. Service medal, 1973, 81; Career Service award Nat. Civil Service League, 1978; presdl. rank of Disting. Exec., 1980. Mem. Phi Beta Kappa, Pi Sigma Alpha. Home: PO Box 2028 Arlington VA 22202-0028 Office: P100 L'Enfant Plz N SW Washington DC 20024

LILLYA, CLIFFORD PETER, musician, educator; b. Joliet, Ill., Jan. 20, 1910; s. Arthur Henning and Anna Wilhelmina (Lindstrum) L.; m. Helen Tait Keltie, Dec. 27, 1931; children: Clifford Peter, Sarah Ann. MusB, VanderCook Coll. Music, 1931; MusM, Northwestern U., 1944; MusD (hon.), VanderCook Coll. Music, 1990. Instrumental music tchr. Chgo. Public Schs., 1931-47; faculty U. Mich., Ann Arbor, 1947-80; prof. music (trumpet) U. Mich., 1947-80, chmn. wind and percussion dept., 1970-80, Earl V. Moore prof. music (trumpet), 1974-80, Earl V. Moore prof. emeritus, 1980—; prof. trumpet U. Kans., summer 1936; instr. trumpet U. Mich., summers 1937-40, Nat. Music Camp, Interlochen, Mich., summers 1945-50. Freelance musician trumpet, 1928-33; author: Lillya Method for Cornet and Trumpet, vol. I, 1937, vol. II, 1940, Trumpet Technic, 1952; composer: (with Merle J. Isaac) Concert Overture in G minor, 1942; for symphonic band A Childhood Fantasy, 1935, A Christmas Fantasy, 1937; transcription for band (choral prelude by J.S. Bach) A Mighty Fortress Is Our God, 1948; (with Harold Bachman) edition for band Ariane Overture by Louis Boyer, 1935; editor: Thirty Trios for 3 cornets (by Wilhelm Wurm), 1985. Recipient Edwin Franco Goldman Meml. citation Am. Bandmaster's Assn., 1989. Mem. Internat. Trumpet Guild (dir. 1977-81, v.p 1975-77), Mich. Sch. Band and Orch. Assn., Kappa Kappa Psi, Pi Kappa Lambda. Internationally known authority on trumpet pedagogy. Address: 1212 Henry St Ann Arbor MI 48104-4341

LILLYMAN, WILLIAM JOHN, German language educator; b. Sydney, Australia, Apr. 17, 1937; came to U.S. 1963, naturalized, 1974; s. John and Christina Mary (Munro) L.; m. Ingeborg Wolz, Sept. 14, 1962; children: Gregory, Christina. AB, U. Sydney, 1959; PhD, Stanford U., 1964. Asst.

prof. Stanford (Calif.) U., 1964-67; assoc. prof. U. Calif., Santa Cruz, 1967-72; prof. German U. Calif., Irvine, 1972—, dean humanities, 1973-81, vice chancellor acad. affairs, 1981-82, exec. vice chancellor, 1982-88. Author: Otto Ludwig's Zwischen Himmel und Erde, 1967, Otto Ludwig: Romane und Romanstudien, 1977, Reality's Dark Dream The Narrative Fiction of Ludwig Tieck, 1979, Goethe's Narrative Fiction, 1991; co-editor; Probleme der Moderne, 1983, Horizonte Festschrift für H. Lehnert, 1990, Critical Architecture and Contemporary Culture, 1994. Mem. MLA, Am. Assn. Tchrs. German. Office: U Calif Dept German Irvine CA 92717

LIM, ALEXANDER RUFASTA, neurologist, clinical investigator, educator; b. Manila, Philippines, Feb. 20, 1942; s. Benito P. and Maria Lourdes (Cuyegkeng) L.; m. Norma Sue Hanks, June 1, 1968; children: Jeffrey Allen, Gregory Brian, Kevin Alexander, Melissa Gail. AA, U. Santo Tomas, Manila, Philippines, 1959, MD, 1964. Intern Bon Secours Hosp., Balt., 1964-65; resident internal medicine Scott and White Clinic, Temple, Tex., 1965-67; resident in neurology Cleve. Clinic, 1967-69, chief resident in neurology, 1969-70, fellow clin. neurophysiology, 1970-71, clin. assoc. neurologist, 1971-72; neurologist, co-founder, co-mng. ptnr. Neurol. Clinic, Corpus Christi, Tex., 1972—; pres., CEO Neurology, P.A., Corpus Christi, 1972-92; chief neurology Meml. Med. Ctr., Corpus Christi, 1975-90, Spohn Hosp., Corpus Christi, 1974-90, Reynolds Army Hosp., Ft. Sill, Okla., 1990-91; clin. assoc. prof. Sch. Medicine U. Tex. Health Sci. Ctr., San Antonio. Mem. editorial bd. Coastal Bend Medicine, 1988—. Lt. col. Med. Corps, 1990-91. Recipient Army Commendation medal, 1991, Nat. Def. medal U.S. Army, 1991. Mem. AMA, Tex. Med. Assn. (chmn. neurology 1985-86), Tex. Neurol. Soc. (sec. 1986-88, pres. 1989-90), Am. Acad. Neurology, Am. Epilepsy Soc., Am. Acad. Clin. Neurophysiology, Am. Electroencephalographic Soc., So. Electroencephalographic Soc., Am. Acad. Pain Mgmt., Physician Com. Responsible Medicine, Am. Legion, Internat. Platform Assn., KC. Republican. Roman Catholic. Avocations: tennis, philately, travel, snow skiing, bonsai. Home: 4821 Augusta Cir Corpus Christi TX 78413-2711 Office: The Neurological Clinic 3006 S Alameda St Corpus Christi TX 78404-2601

LIM, DANIEL VAN, microbiology educator; b. Houston, Apr. 15, 1948; s. Don H. and Lucy (Toy) L.; m. Carol Lee, Sept. 2, 1973. BA in Biology, Rice U., 1970; PhD in Microbiology, Tex. A&M U., 1973. Postdoctoral fellow Baylor Coll. Medicine, 1973-76; asst. prof. U South Fla., Tampa, 1976-81, assoc. prof. microbiology, 1981-87, chmn. dept. biology, 1983-85, prof. 1987—; pres. Micro Concepts Rsch. Corp; dir. Inst. Biomolecular Sci., 1988-93; cons. in field. Author: Microbiology, 1989, Introduction to Microbiology, 1995; inventor bacteriological broth. Recipient Outstanding Ph.D. Dissertation in U.S. award Phi Sigma, 1974, Outstanding Contbn. in Sci. and Tech. award Fla. Gov. Fellow Am. Acad. Microbiology; mem. Inter-Am. Soc. Chemotherapy (v.p. 1983-88), Am. Soc. Microbiology (pres. southeastern br. 1990-91, Carski award com. 1983-86, Margaret Green Outstanding Tchr. award). Office: U South Fla 4202 E Fowler Ave LIF 136 Tampa FL 33620-5150

LIM, DAVID JONG-JAI, otolaryngology educator, researcher; b. Seoul, Republic of Korea, Nov. 27, 1935; came to U.S., 1964; s. Yang Sup Lim and Cha Nang Yoo; m. Young Sook Hahn, May 14, 1966; children: Michael, Robert. AB, Yonsei U., Seoul, 1955, MD, 1960. Research fellow in otolaryngology Mass. Eye & Ear Infirmary, Boston, 1965-66; research assoc. dept. otolaryngology Ohio State U. Coll. Medicine, Columbus, 1966-67, asst. prof., 1967-71, assoc. prof., 1971-76, prof. dept. otolaryngology, 1976-91, dir. otological research labs., 1967-91, prof. cell biology, neurobiology and anatomy, 1977-91, prof. emeritus, 1992—; dir. intramural rsch. program Nat. Inst. on Deaf and Other Communication Disorders, NIH, Bethesda, Md., 1992-94, chief lab cellular biology, 1993—; mem. nat. adv. neurol. and communicative disorders and stroke coun. NIH, Bethesda, Md., 1979-83; mem. adv. bd. Nat. Inst. Deafness and Other Communication Disorders, 1989-91; cons., bd. dirs. Rsch. Fund Am. Otol. Soc., 1982-87; mem. adv. bd. Cen. Inst. for Deaf, 1989-91. Contbr. articles to profl. jours., chpts. to textbooks. Pres. Korean Assn. in Columbus, 1970; chmn. bd. dirs. Cen. Ohio Korean Lang. Sch., Columbus, 1986; bd. dirs. Deafness Rsch. Found., N.Y.C., 1980—. Fogarty Internat. fellow Karolinska Inst., Stockholm, 1982; recipient Disting. Scholar award Ohio State U., 1985, Javits award NIH, 1985, Guyot prize U. Groningen, 1994; grantee various orgns., 1969-91. Fellow Am. Acad. Otolaryngology (Gold award 1972); mem. Assn. for Research in Otolaryngology (sec./treas. 1973-75, pres. 1976-77, editor-historian 1980-93, historian, 1993—, Merit award 1993), Am. Laryngol. Rhinol. and Otol. Soc., Collegium Oto-rhino-laryngologicum Amicitiae Sacrum (Shambaugh prize 1993), Am. Otol. Soc., Soc. Neurosci., Am. Soc. Cell Biology, Histochem. Soc., Soc. for Mucosal Immunology, Aspen Hill Racquet and Fitness Club (Silver Spring, Md.). Methodist. Avocations: tennis, skiing. Home: 227 Midsummer Cir Gaithersburg MD 20878 Office: NIDCD NIH 5 Research Ctr Rockville MD 20850

LIM, JOHN K., state senator, business executive; b. Yeoju, South Korea, Dec. 23, 1935; came to U.S., 1966, naturalized, 1976; s. Eun Kyu and Seu Nyu (Chung) L.; m. Grace Young-Hee Park, Dec. 9, 1963; children: Peter, Billy, Gloria. BA in Religion, Seoul Theol. Coll., 1964; MDiv, Western Evang. Sem., Portland, Oreg., 1970. Founder, chmn. Am. Royal Jelly Co., 1972—; founder, pres. ARJ Co., 1973—; pres. Realty Resources, 1981-91; mem. Oreg. State Senate, 1993—; chair Senate Trade and Econ. Devel. Com., 1995; vice chair Senate Bus. and Consumer Affairs Com., 1995; mem. Govs. Adv. Com. on DUII, 1993—; mem. sheriffs forum Multnomah County, Oreg., 1994; asst. majority leader Oreg. State Senate, 1995. Pub.: World Korean Conference Journal, 1989; editor, pub.: (directory) World Korean C of C., 1990, The World Korean Soc. Directory, 1989. Oreg. Gubernatorial Candidate, 1990; nat. chair Asian Am. Voters Coalition, 1990-91; bd. dirs. Rep. Nat. Com. Asian Adv., 1992; mem. exec. com. Billy Graham Crusade, Portland, Oreg., 1992; mem. Oreg.-Korea Econ. Coop., 1986-88; mem. Cmty. Bd. Mt. Hood Med. Ctr., 1993—; bd. mem. Western Evang. Sem., 1995—. Mem. Korean Am. Soc. U.S.A., Korean Soc. Oreg. (pres. 1986), Oreg. Royal Rosarian Soc., Portland Rose Soc. Republican. Avocations: golf, fishing, skiing. Office: 3630 SE Division Portland OR 97202

LIM, ROBERT CHEONG, JR., surgeon, educator; b. San Francisco, Aug. 27, 1933; s. Robert Cheong and Helen (Ho) L.; m. Carolee Yee, Aug. 23, 1959; children: Gregory Matthew, Jonathan Robert. A.B., U. Calif., Berkeley, 1956; M.D., U. Calif., San Francisco, 1960. Diplomate: Am. Bd. Surgery. Intern U. Calif., San Francisco, 1960-61; asst. resident in surgery U. Calif., 1963-64, VA Hosp., San Francisco, 1961-63; chief resident VA Hosp., 1964-65, NIH fellow in vascular surgery, 1965-66; practice medicine specializing in gen. trauma and vascular surgery San Francisco; asst. prof. U. Calif., San Francisco, 1968-74; assoc. prof. U. Calif., 1974-78, prof., 1978—; mem. staffs U. Calif. Hosps., San Francisco Gen. Hosp. Contbr. articles on surgery to profl. jours. Mem. ACS (gov.), Am. Burn Assn., Am. Assn. Surgery of Trauma, Am. Surg. Assn., Am. Trauma Soc., Internat. Cardiovascular Soc., Calif. Med. Assn., Assn. Acad. Surgery, Howard C. Naffziger Surg. Soc. (pres. 1995), Pacific Coast Surg. Assn., Pan Pacific Surg. Assn., San Francisco Surg. Soc. (past pres.), Soc. Univ. Surgeons, Soc. Vascular Surgery, Western Surg. Assn., Western Vascular Soc., Alpha Omega Alpha. Presbyterian. Office: U Calif PO Box 780 # U San Francisco CA 94143

LIM, SONIA YII, minister; b. China, Jan. 1, 1924; arrived in The Philippines; d. Edward C. and King Hua (Co) Yii; m. Teddy T. Lim, Jan. 3, 1943; children: Dorothy, DoraMay Cantada, Sally Jane, Teddy Jr., Nellie Ann L. Tan, Raymond, Roger. AB, Am. Bordner Sch., Manila, 1944; postgrad., St. Thomas U., Manila, 1948, Cornell U., 1972; DD (hon.), Am. Fellowship Ch., Monterey, Calif., 1982; D of Prayer Tech., World Inst., Manila, 1989. Ordained to ministry Full Gospel Ch., 1981. Min. Internat. Fellowship of Clergy, Alta Vista, Calif., 1980-84; founder, pres. Dove Found. Internat. Inc., 1982—; min. Gospel Crusade Ministerial Fellowship Inc., Bradenton, Fla., 1983—; underwriter Insular Life Ins., Pasay, The Philippines, 1991—; Bishop, first lady in Asia, Christian Ch. Fellowship Internat., amb. of goodwill to all nations; conductor ann. Nat. Week of Prayer, Philippines; chmn. Golden Mother's Day and Golden Father's Day celebrations; group dir. Giorelli Internat., 1992; condr. tng. seminars. Bd. dirs. Consumers Union of The Philippines, 1971—; chaplain, chmn. internat. rels. Mother's Day and Father's Day Coun., Manila, 1988—. Recipient Angel award Religion in Media, 1984, Golden Leadership award Humanitarian Ctr. The Philippines, 1988, Appreciation award Armed Forces of The

Philippines, 1988, award Internat. Cops for Christ Inc., 1990, Grand Achievement award Young Achiever's Found., 1995, Key to City of Detroit, Flint, Mich., Jacksonville, Fla., Covina, Calif., Wilson, N.C., Las Vegas, Ft. Worth, Corsicana, Tex., Manila, Mandaluyong, Baguio, Davao, Quezon City, Olongapo, Subic Bay; named Mother of Yr., Gintong Ina Found., 1988, hon. mayor Oklahoma City. Mem. Philippine Bible Soc. (life), Info. and Referral Svcs. The Philippines (life), Makati C. of C. and Industry (bd. dirs. 1968-72), Manila Bay Breakfast Club (bd. dirs. 1976—), Makati Breakfast Club (chaplain 1988—), Manila Overseas Press Club (assoc.), Consumers Union Philippines (chmn. award com.), Nat. Prestige Club. Mem. Movers Party. Office: Dove Found Internat Sunset View Towers, 2230 Roxas Blvd, Ste 402, Pasay City Metro Manila, The Philippines

LIMA, LUIS EDUARDO, tenor; b. Cordoba, Argentina, Sept. 12, 1950; s. Horacio and Yayi (Junyent) L.; m. Caterin de Virgilio, Feb. 18, 1979; children: Rodrigo, Camila, Martin-Geronimo Leandro. B.A. in Music, Teatro Colon, Argentina, 1971; student voice, Carlo Guichandut, Buenos Aires, Gina Cigna, Italy. Am. debut Carnegie Hall, 1976; appeared in maj. opera houses throughout the world, including La Scala, Milan, Italy, 1978, N.Y.C. Opera, 1978-79, Met. Opera, N.Y.C., 1978, 84-85, San Francisco Opera, 1980, 83-91, Covent Garden, London, 1984-91, Vienna State Opera, 1988-93; performances at maj. festivals; author: Poems, 1982; recs.: Donizetti: Gemma di Vergy, Le Roi de Laohr, La Traviata, Requiem; appeared in films: Cossi fan Tutte, Carmen, Don Carlo. Mem. Am. Guild Musicians. Roman Catholic. Avocations: painting; horseback riding. Office: 1950 Redondela Dr Rancho Palos Verdes CA 90732 also: ICM Artists Inc 40 W 57th St New York NY 10019*

LIMA, ROBERT, Hispanic studies and comparative literature educator; b. Havana, Cuba, Nov. 7, 1935; came to U.S., 1945; BA in English and Philosophy, Villanova U., 1957, MA in Theatre Arts and Drama, 1961; PhD in Romance Lits., NYU, 1968. Prof. Spanish and comparative lits. Pa. State U., University Park, 1965—; fellow Inst. for Arts and Humanistic Studies Pa. State U., 1986—; vis. prof. comparative lit. Pontificia Universidad Católica del Peru; poet-in-residence Universidad Nacional Mayor de San Marcos, Peru, 1976-77; lectr. Romance langs. and lits. Hunter Coll. CUNY, 1962-65, USIA lectr., Peru, Cameroon, Equatorial Guinea. Author: The Theatre of Garcia Lorca, 1963, An Annotated Bibliography of Ramon del Valle-Inclan, 1972, (poetry) Fathoms, 1981, The Olde Ground, 1985, (biography) Valle-Inclan, The Theatre of His Life, 1988, (poetry Mayaland), 1992, Park Prisms Occultism in Hispanic Drama, 1995, The International Annotated Bibliography of Ramon del Valle-Inclan, Valle-Inclan El Teatro De Su Vida, 1995; co-author: Dos ensayos sobre teatro espanol de los viente, 1984; editor/translator: Borges the Labyrinth Maker (A.M. Barrenechea), 1965, Valle-Inclan: Autobiography, Aesthetics, Aphorism, 1966; editor, contbr. Borges and ther Esoteric, 1993; translator: TheLamp of Marvels. Aesthetic Mediatations (Ramon del Valle-Inclan), 1986, Savage Acts: Four Plays (Ramon del Valle-Inclan), 1993; co-editorL the aReaders Encyclopedia of American Literature, 1962; contbr. numerous articles, essays, book revs., poetry, plays and poetry translations to profl. publs.; producer/cons. TV and radio programs Centro de Estudios de Television de la Universidad Catolica, Lima, Peru, 1976-77, Voice of Am., N.Y.C., 1961-62, Pendulum Prodns., 1960-61. Bd. dirs. Pa. Ctr. for Book. Recipient Founders Day award NYU, 1968, Play Translation prize Modern Internat. Drama, cert. of merit Writer's Digest Mag., 1982; Rsch. grantee Fund for Rsch. Pa. State U., Inst. for Arts and Humanistic Studies; Cintas Found. fellow in poetry Inst. Internat. Edn., 1971-72, fellow Commonwealth Speakers Program Pa. Humanities Coun., Sr. Fulbright fellow Coun. Internat. Exch. Scholars, 1976-77; others. Fellow Inst. for Arts and Humanistic Studies, Phi Kappa Phi (hon.), Phi Sigma Iota (hon.); mem. Internat. PEN, Poetry Soc. Am., Am. Assn. Tchrs. Spanish and Portuguese, Archaeol. Inst. Am., Am. Comparative Lit. Assn., Internat. Comparative Lit. Assn., Galician Studies Assn., Internat. Assn. Valleinclanistas, Am. Name Soc., Am. Soc. Sephardic Studies, Poets and Writers, Hermetic Text Soc., Beast Fable Soc., Pa. Humanities Coun., N.Am. Acad. Spanish Lang., Fulbright Alumni Assn., Alpha Psi Omega. Home: 485 Orlando Ave State College PA 16803-3477 Office: Pa State U N-346 Burrowes Bldg University Park PA 16802

LIMAN, ARTHUR LAWRENCE, lawyer; b. N.Y.C., Nov. 5, 1932; s. Harry K. and Celia L.; m. Ellen Fogelson, Sept. 20, 1959; children: Lewis, Emily, Douglas. A.B., Harvard U., 1954; LL.B., Yale U., 1957. Bar: N.Y. bar 1958. Asst. U.S. atty. So. Dist. N.Y., 1961-63, spl. asst. U.S. atty., 1965; with firm Paul, Weiss, Rifkind, Wharton & Garrison, N.Y.C., 1957-61, 63—; ptnr. Paul, Weiss, Rifkind, Wharton & Garrison, 1966—; chief counsel N.Y. State Spl. Commn. on Attica, 1972; chmn. Legal Action Center, N.Y.C., 1975; v.p. Legal Aid Soc., N.Y.C., 1973; pres. Legal Aid Soc., 1983-85; chmn. Gov. N.Y. Adv. Commn. Adminstrn. Justice in N.Y. State, 1981-83; mem. N.Y. State Exec. Adv. Com. Sentencing, 1977; adv. com. civil rules U.S. Jud. Conf., 1980-85; mem. commn. on reduction costs and delay U.S. 2d Circuit, 1976-80; bd. dirs. Continental Grain Co., Equitable Life Assurance Soc. U.S., Harvard U., Capital Defender's Office; chief counsel U.S. Senate select com. on Secret Mil. Assistance to Iran and the Nicaraguan Opposition, Washington, 1987; chmn. Mayor's Com. on Appts., 1990-93. Contbr. articles to legal jours.; bd. editors: Nat. Law Jour, 1979—. Bd. overseers Harvard U., 1988-94. Fellow Am. Coll. Trial Lawyers, Am. Bar Found.; mem. Am. Bar Assn., N.Y. State Bar Assn., Bar Assn. City N.Y. (exec. com.), Lawyers Com. Civil Rights Under Bd. Overseers Harvard U. 1988—. Home: 1060 Fifth Ave New York NY 10128-0104 Office: Paul Weiss Rifkind Wharton & Garrison 1285 Avenue Of The Americas New York NY 10019-6064

LIMARZI, JOSEPH, artist; b. Chgo., Sept. 15, 1907; s. Joseph and Mary Della (Guardia) LiM. With Mus. Fine Arts, Springfield, Mass.; instr. painting High Sch. Art & Design, N.Y., 1952-73. Commn. works include HIst. Fed. Govt., Fed. Bldg., Wapokeneta, Ohio, 1937, Fed. Govt., Staten Island, N.Y., 1942; Royal Scarlet Foods, N.Y., 1951; Gen. Cables, Inc., N.Y., 1952; exhibits include Art Inst. Chgo., Bklyn. Mus. Nat., Pa. Acad. Fine Arts; one man shows include Comtemporary Arts, N.Y.; Simon's Rock, Mass. & Lehman Gallery, Red Rock, N.Y., 1975; Cleve. Art Inst., Mus. Modern Art. N.Y.; liberal Arts Ctr., Newport, N.H., Berkshire Mus., Pittsfield, Mass., Spencertown Acad., N.Y. Recipient Hon. award Fed. Govt., 1937. Mem. Painters and Sculptors Soc. N.J., Audubon Artists of N.Y., Am. Soc. Contemporary Artists. Avocations: classical, jazz and folk music, history Jefferson and Lincoln. Home: PO Box 144 East Chatham NY 12060-0144 Office: Ella Lerner Gallery 17 Franklin St Lenox MA 01240-2303

LIMATO, EDWARD FRANK, talent agent; b. Mt. Vernon, N.Y., July 10, 1936; s. Frank and Angelina (Lacerra) L. Grad. high sch., Mt. Vernon. With Ashley Famous, 1966, I.F.A., N.Y.C., William Morris Agy., L.A.; talent agt. Internat. Creative Mgmt., N.Y.C., L.A. Mem. Acad. Motion Picture Arts & Scis. (assoc.). Republican. Roman Catholic. Office: Internat Creative Mgmt 8899 Beverly Blvd Los Angeles CA 90048*

LIMBACH, WALTER F., construction company executive; b. Pitts., June 17, 1924; s. Emil and Sarah (Zuckerman) L.; m. Sarah Z. Minard, June 16, 1976; children by previous marriage: Elsa, Kurt. B.S., Lehigh U., 1947. With Limbach Co., Pitts., 1947-80; v.p. Limbach Co., 1955-57, pres. 1957-81, dir., 1955-84; chmn., chief exec. officer, dir. Limbach Inc., Pitts., 1980-86; chmn., chief-exec.-officer, dir. Limbach Holdings, Inc., Pitts., 1986-88; dir. Contractors Mut. Assn., Washington, 1971-84; vice chmn. Contractors Mut. Assn., 1973-78, chmn., 1977-84. Bd. dirs. Hill House Assn., Pitts., v.p. 1968-73, 75-80; bd. dirs. Vocat. Rehab. Ctr., Pitts., 1975—, chmn. 1991-93; bd. dirs. Nat. Constrn. Employers Coun., Washington, 1979-84; bd. dirs. Neighborhood Ctrs. Assn., Pitts., 1989—, treas. 1990—. Served with USNR, 1943-46. Mem. Sheet Metal and Air Conditioning Contractors Nat. Assn. (pres. 1958-59), ASME. Home: 123 Beechmont Rd Pittsburgh PA 15206-4513

LIMBACK, E(DNA) REBECCA, vocational education educator; b. Higginsville, Mo., Mar. 23, 1945; d. Henry Shobe and Martha Pauline Rebecca (Willard) Ernstmeyer; m. Duane Paul Limback, Nov. 9, 1963; children: Lisa Christine, Derek Duane. BE, Cen. Mo. State U., 1968, MEd, 1969, EdS, 1976; EdD, U Mo., 1981. Cert. bus., English and vocat. tchr. Supervising tchr. Lab. Sch. Cen. Mo. State U., Warrensburg, 1969-76, asst. to grad.

dean, 1977-79, asst. prof., asst. to bus. dean, 1981-83, assoc. prof. computer and office info. systems, 1984—; mem. manual editing/revision staff State of Mo., Jefferson City, 1989-90; textbook reviewer Prentice-Hall, Englewood Cliffs, N.J., 1990-91. Author various curriculum guides; mem. editl. bd. Cen. Mo. State U. Rsch. 1982-92. Active Warrensburg Band Aides, 1989-93. Grantee RightSoft Corp., 1988. Mem. DAR, Nat. Bus. Edn. Assn. (mem. conf. profl. opportunities com. 1989, info. processing editor Bus. Edn. Forum 1991), Am. Vocat. Assn., North Cen. Bus. Edn. Assn. (Mo. rep., Collegiate Disting. Svc. award 1993), Mo. Bus. Edn. Assn. (all-chpt. pres. 1988-89, Postsecondary Tchr. of Yr. 1992), Assn. Bus. Comms., Warrensburg Athletic Booster Club, Phi Delta Kappa (all-chpt. pres. 1985), Delta Pi Epsilon (rsch. rep. 1989-92, nat. publs. com. 1993—). Lutheran. Avocations: archaeology, oil painting. Home: 1102 Tyler Ave Warrensburg MO 64093-2049 Office: Dockery 200-I/COIS Dept Cen Mo State U Warrensburg MO 64093

LIMBAUGH, RONALD HADLEY, history educator, history center director; b. Emmett, Idaho, Jan. 22, 1938; s. John Hadley and Evelyn E. (Mortimore) L.; m. Marilyn Kay Rice, June 16, 1963; 1 child, Sally Ann. BA, Coll. Idaho, 1960; MA, U. Idaho, 1962, PhD, 1967. Hist. libr. Idaho State Hist. Soc., Boise, 1963-66; instr. Boise Coll., 1964-66; asst. prof. history U. of the Pacific, Stockton, Calif., 1966-71; archivist, curator U. of the Pacific, Stockton, 1968-87, prof. history, 1977—; Rockwell Hunt chair of Calif. history Rockwell Hunt, 1989—; dir. Holt-Atherton Ctr., U. of the Pacific, Stockton, 1984-87; exec. dir. Conf. of Calif. Hist. Socs., Stockton, 1973-76, 77-78, 82-86, 90—; dir. John Muir Ctr. for Regional Studies, U. of Pacific, Stockton, 1989—; cons., evaluator NEH, 1983, 86. Author: Rocky Mountain Carpetbaggers, 1982; co-editor (microform) John Muir Papers, 1986; (book) Guide to Muir Papers, 1986; contbr. articles to profl. jours. With U.S. Army, 1955-56. NDEA fellow, 1960; grantee Calif. Coun. Humanities, 1976, Nat. Hist. Publs. and Records Commn., 1980-82, NEH, 1983, Inst. European Studies, 1989. Mem. AAUP, Western History Assn., Orgn. Am. Historians, Phi Kappa Phi (pres. UOP chpt. 1988), Mining History Assn. Christian Humanist. Avocations: hiking, golf. Office: Univ Pacific 3601 Pacific Ave Stockton CA 95211-0197

LIMBAUGH, RUSH HUDSON, radio and talk show host; b. Cape Girardeau, Mo., 1951; s. Rush Hudson Limbaugh Jr., Millie Limbaugh; m. Marta Fitzgerald, May 27, 1994. Various disc jockey positions, 1960-88; host The Rush Limbaugh Show on 480 radio stations nationwide, 1988—. Author: The Way Things Ought To Be, 1992, See, I Told You So, 1993; TV syndicated show The Rush Limbaugh Show, 1992—; publisher, monthly newsletter, The Limbaugh Letter, 1995—. Office: Sta WABC 125 W End Ave # 6 New York NY 10023-6345*

LIMBAUGH, STEPHEN NATHANIEL, federal judge; b. Cape Girardeau, Mo., Nov. 17, 1927; s. Rush Hudson and Bea (Seabaugh) L.; m. DeVaughn Anne Mesplay, Dec. 27, 1950; children—Stephen Nathaniel Jr., James Pennington, Andrew Thomas. B.A., S.E. Mo. State U., Cape Girardeau, 1950; J.D., U. Mo., Columbia, 1951. Bar: Mo. Prosecuting atty. Cape Girardeau County, Mo., 1954-58; judge U.S. Dist. Ct. (ea. and we. dists.) Mo., St. Louis, 1983—. Served with USN, 1945-46. Recipient Citation of Merit for Outstanding Achievement and Meritorious Service in Law, U. Mo., 1982. Fellow Am. Coll. Probate Counsel, Am. Bar Found.; mem. ABA (ho. of dels. 1987-90), Mo. Bar Assn. (pres. 1982-83). Republican. Methodist. Office: US Dist Ct 1114 Market St Rm 315 Saint Louis MO 63101-2038

LIMBAUGH, STEPHEN NATHANIEL, JR., judge; b. Cape Girardeau, Mo., Jan. 25, 1952; s. Stephen N. and Anne (Mesplay) L.; m. Marsha Dee Moore, July 21, 1973; children: Stephen III, Christopher K. BA, So. Meth. U., 1973, JD, 1976. Bar: Tex. 1977, Mo. 1977. Assoc. Limbaugh, Limbaugh & Russell, Cape Girardeau, 1977-78; pros. atty. Cape Girardeau County, Cape Girardeau, 1979-82; shareholder, ptnr. Limbaugh, Limbaugh, Russell & Syler, Cape Girardeau, 1983-87; cir. judge 32d Jud. Cir., Cape Girardeau, 1987-92; judge Supreme Ct. Mo., Jefferson City, 1992—. Mem. ABA, State Bar Tex., Mo. Bar. Office: Supreme Ct Mo 207 W High St Jefferson City MO 65101

LIMERICK, PATRICIA NELSON, history educator; b. Banning, Calif., Apr. 17, 1951. BA, U. Calif., Santa Cruz, 1972; PhD, Yale, 1980. Prof. history dept. U. Colo., Boulder; chmn. bd. dirs. Ctr. Am. West. Author: (books) Desert Passages: Encounters With the American Deserts, 1985, The Legacy of Conquest: The Unbroken Past of the American West, 1987. MacArthur fellow, 1995. Office: Univ CO Boulder Dept History Box 234 Boulder CO 80309*

LI MIN HUA See CREW, LOUIE

LIMON, LAVINIA, social services administrator; b. Compton, Calif., Mar. 5, 1950; d. Peter T. and Marie W. Limon; m. Mohamed Hanon. BA in Sociology, U. Calif., Berkeley, 1972. Asst. dir., office mgr. Ch. World Svc., N.Y.C., 1975-77; chief Vietnamese refugee sect. Internat. Rescue Com., N.Y.C., 1977-79; dir. Internat. Rescue Com., L.A., 1983-86, 1983-86; asst. dir. ops. Am. Coun. for Nationalities Svcs., L.A., 1979-83; exec. dir. Internat. Inst. L.A., Washington, 1986-93; dir. office refugee resettlement and office family assistance Adminstrn. for Children and Families Dept. HHS, Washington, 1993—; bd. dirs. Am. Coun. for Nationalities Svc., 1992, chair standing com. of profl. coun., 1992; organizer U.S. refugee conf. Am. Coun. Vol. Agys., Manila, 1982; cons. Dept. of State, 1979, 80. Mem. bd. human rels. hate violence response alliance City of L.A., 1992; chair corp. coun. execs. United Way of L.A., 1992, mem. task force fund on devel., 1990; mem. citizen's adv. com. Eastside Neighborhoods Revitalazation Study, 1992; mem. steering com. Coalition for Humane Immigration Rights of L.A., 1992; mem. steering com. Jerusalem Coop. Cities Project, 1991; chair Refugee Forum L.A. County, 1984-85, chair vol. agy. com., 1983-84; treas. Calif. Refugee Forum 1985-86. Democrat. Home: 4508 Flintstone Rd Alexandria VA 22306 Office: Refugee Resettlement Office 370 L'Enfant Promenade SW Washington DC 20447

LIMPERT, JOHN ARTHUR, editor; b. Appleton, Wis., Mar. 15, 1934; s. John Adam and Olga Charlotte (Lindstrom) L.; m. Jocelyn Roberta Minarik, 1957 (div. 1971); 1 child, John; m. Jean Ann Vincent, July 3, 1975; children—Ann, Jean. B.S., U. Wis., Madison, 1959; student, Stanford U. Law Sch., 1959-60. Reporter UPI, Minn., 1960-61; regional exec. UPI, St. Louis, 1961-63, Detroit, 1963-64; editor Warren Progress, Mich., 1964-65; mng. editor San Jose Sunpapers, Calif., 1965-67; editor DC Examiner, 1967-68, The Washingtonian, Washington, 1969—. Recipient Disting. Reporting of Pub. Affairs award Am. Political Sci. Assn., 1970, Life Achievement award City and Regional Mag. Assn., 1991; Congl. fellow Am. Political Sci. Assn., 1968. Mem. Am. Editors, Soc. Profl. Journalists. Office: Washingtonian 1828 L St NW Ste 200 Washington DC 20036-5169

LIMPITLAW, JOHN DONALD, retired publishing executive, clergyman; b. N.Y.C., Jan. 4, 1935; s. Robert and Olga (Lang) L.; m. Susan Elizabeth Glover, May 21, 1960; children: Alison, Amy Elizabeth. BA, Trinity Coll., Hartford, Conn., 1956; MA in Religion, Yale U., 1992. With Marine Midland Bank Trust Co. N.Y., N.Y.C., 1956-61, Celanese Corp., N.Y.C., 1961-63; mgr. personnel Westvaco Corp., N.Y.C., 1963-69; v.p. Warnaco Inc., Bridgeport, Conn., 1969-77, Macmillan Inc., N.Y.C., 1977-89; vicar Parish of Christ's Ch., Easton, Conn., 1992—; dir. St. Mark's Day Care Ctr., Easton, 1995—; seminarian Yale Divinity Sch., New Haven, Conn., 1989-92; trustee Episcopal Investment Funds; bd. dirs. Inter-Ch. Residences, 3030 Park, Inc. Democrat. Episcopalian. Avocations: sailing; skiing. Home: 120 Chelsea St Fairfield CT 06430-4904

LIN, CHIN-CHU, physician, educator, researcher; b. Taichung, Taiwan, Oct. 24, 1935; came to U.S., 1969; naturalized, 1977; s. Kung Yen and Nung (Chiang) L.; m. Sue S. Hsu; children: Jim, John, Juliet. BS, Nat. Taiwan U., 1956, MD, 1961. Diplomate Am. Bd. Ob-Gyn., Am. Bd. Maternal-Fetal Medicine (bd. examiners 1986-89). Rsch. fellow SUNY Downstate Med. Ctr., N.Y.C., 1969-71; resident in ob-gyn Columbia U., N.Y.C., 1972-74; fellow in maternal-fetal medicine Albert Einstein Med. Coll., 1974-76; lectr. staff Nat. Taiwan U. Hosp., Taipei, 1966-69, 1971-72; staff, assoc. prof. U. Chgo., 1976-80, assoc. prof., 1980-87, prof., 1987—; maternal-child health adv. com. Dept. of Health, Chgo., 1985-88; frequent keynote speaker numerous internat. confs. including 12th Asian and Oceanic Congress on

Ob-Gyn., 1989; vis. prof. univs. in U.S., Japan, People's Republic of China, Republic of China, 1981—; keynote speaker, prof. S.J. Chiu Meml. lectures, Taiwaan, 1989. Author: Interauterine Growth Retardation, 1984, The High Risk Fetus, 1993; editor in chief Taiwan Tribune Med. Issues, 1986-89; contbr. over 80 articles to profl. jours., 17 chpts. to books; reviewer for Am. Jour. Ob-Gyn., Jour. Perinatal Medicine, Obstetrics and Gynecology, Jour. Maternal-Fetal Medicine, Jour. Fromosan Med. Assn.; pres. 10th ann. meeting N. Am. Taiwanese Profs. Assn., Taiwan, 1990. People to People Ob-Gyn del. to USSR, 1987; bd. dirs. Taiwanese United Fund, 1980—, pres. 1984-85. Selected candidate semifinalist dean of med. sch. Nat. Taiwan U., 1993; disting. scholar lectr. award Formosa Med. Assn., 1981, Kenote Speaker award Asia-Oceanic Congress Perinatology, 1986, 94, 2d Internat. Symposium on Obstetrics and Perinatal Medicine, Beijing, 1988, 28th Sci. Meeting Assn. Ob-gyn., Taiwan, 1988, 12th Asian Oceanic Congress on Obstetrics and Gynecology, 1989, 33d Ann. Meeting Assn. Ob-gyn., Taiwan, 1993, 5th World Congress Ultrasound in Ob-gyn., Japan, 1995. Mem. Am. Coll. Ob.-Gyn. (jour. reviewer 1982—, Purdue Frederick award 1978), N.Am. Taiwanese Profs. Assn. (bd. dirs. 1988-91, bull. editor 1980—, v.p. 1988-89, pres. 1989-90, pres. 10th ann. meeting Taiwan 1990) N.Am. Taiwanese Med. Assn. (chmn. ednl. com. 1984-88, bd. dirs. 1991-93, chmn. scientific program 1994), Taiwanese United Fund (bd. dirs. 1980—, pres. 1984-85), Cen. Assn. Ob.-Gyn., Soc. Perinatal Obstetricians, Internat. Soc. Study Hypertension in Pregnancy, Am. Inst. Ultrasound in Medicine, Chgo. Gynecol. Soc. Avocations: tennis, swimming. Home: 500 Devon Dr Burr Ridge IL 60521 Office: U Chgo Dept Ob-Gyn 5841 S Maryland Ave Chicago IL 60637-1470

LIN, JAMES CHIH-I, biomedical and electrical engineer, educator; b. Dec. 29, 1942; m. Mei Fei, Mar. 21, 1970; children: Janet, Theodore, Erik. BS, U. Wash., 1966, MS, 1968, PhD, 1971. Asst. prof. U. Wash., Seattle, 1971-74; prof. Wayne State U., Detroit, 1974-80; prof. U. Ill.-Chgo., 1980—, head dept. bioengring., 1980-92, dir. robotics and automation lab., 1982-89, dir. spl. projects Coll. Engring., 1992-94, NSC chair prof., 1993-94; vis. prof. in Beijing, Rome, Shan Dong, Taiwan Univs.; lectr. of short courses, 1974—; cons. Battelle Meml. Inst., Columbus, Ohio, 1973-75, SRI Internat., Palo Alto, Calif., 1978-79, Arthur D. Little, Inc., Cambridge, Mass., 1980-83, Ga. Tech. Rsch. Inst., Atlanta, 1984-86, Walter Reed Army Inst. Rsch., 1973, 87, 88, Naval Aerospace Med. Rsch. Labs., Pensacola, 1982-83, U.R.S. Corp., San Francisco, 1985-87, CBS, Inc., N.Y., 1988, U. Va., 1991-92, ACS, Inc., Santa Clara, Calif., 1989-90, Luxtron Corp, Mountainview, Calif., 1991-92, Commonwealth Edison, Chgo., 1991-93; program chmn. Frontiers of Engring. and Computing Conf., Chgo., 1985; chmn., convener URSI Joint Symposium Electromagnetic Waves in Biol. Systems, Tel-Aviv, 1987, Internat. Conf. on Sci. and Tech., 1989-91; chmn. Chinese-Am. Acad. and Profl. Conv., 1993; mem Congrl. Health Care Adv. Coun., 13th dist. Ill., 1987—; mem. citizen's adv. coun. Hinsdale Cen. High Sch., 1988-93. Author: Microwave Auditory Effects and Applications, 1978, Biological Effects and Health Implications of Radiofrequency Radiation, 1987, Electromagnetic Interaction with Biological Systems, 1989; assoc. editor Jour. Microwave Power and Electromagnetic Energy, 1988-90; editor Advances in Electromagnetic Fields in Living Systems; also numerous papers. Panelist NSF Presdl. Young Investigator award com., Washington, 1984, 89, mem. NIH diagnostic radiology, 1981-85, chmn. SBIR study sect., 1986-94; mem. U.S. Nat. Commn. for URSI, NAS, 1980-82, chair Commn. K, 1990—; mem. Pres. Com. Nat. Medal of Sci., 1992-93; mem. Nat. Coun. Radiation Protection and Measurement, 1992—. Recipient IEEE Transaction Best Paper award, 1975; Nat. Rsch. Svcs. award, 1982, Disting. Svc. award, Outstanding Leadership award Chinese Am. Acad. and Profl. Assn. MidAm., 1989 (pres. 1991-92). Fellow AAAS, AIMBE, IEEE (tech. policy coun. 1990-91, chmn. com. on man and radiation 1990-91, assoc. and guest editor transactions on biomed. engring., guest editor transactions on microwave theory and techniques, disting. lectr. engring. in medicine and biology 1991-93); mem. NSPE, Biomed. Engring. Soc. (sr. mem.), Robotics Internat. (sr. mem.), Am. Soc. Engring. Edn., Bioelectromagnetics Soc. (charter, pres.-elect 1993-94, pres 1994-95, chmn. ann. meeting 1994), Electromagnetics Acad., Golden Key, Sigma Xi, Phi Tau Phi (v.p.), Tau Beta Pi. Office: U Ill Coll Engring 1030 SEO MC/154 851 S Morgan St Chicago IL 60607

LIN, JOSEPH PEN-TZE, neuroradiologist, clinical administrator, educator; b. Foochow, China, Nov. 25, 1932; came to U.S., 1959, naturalized, 1974; s. Tai Shui and Chin Sien Lin; m. Lillian Y. Hsu, Dec. 23, 1959; children: James S., Carol W., Julia W. MD, Nat. Taiwan U., 1957. Diplomate Am. Bd. Radiology. Rotating intern Robert B. Green Meml. Hosp., San Antonio, 1959-60; resident in radiology Santa Rosa Med. Center, San Antonio, 1960-61, Bellevue Hosp. Center, N.Y.C., 1961-63; fellow in neuroradiology NYU Med. Ctr., N.Y.C., 1963-65; instr. radiology NYU Med. Ctr., 1965-67, asst. prof., 1967-70, assoc. prof., 1970-74, prof., 1974—; dir. neuroradiology sect. Univ. Hosp., N.Y.C., 1974—; cons. Manhattan VA Hosp., N.Y.C., 1974—, Booth Meml. Hosp., N.Y.C., 1978-84, St. Vincent's Hosp., S.I., N.Y., 1978-85, New Rochelle (N.Y.) Hosp., 1978-85. Contbr. articles on neuroradiology to med. jours. Fellow Am. Coll. Radiology, Am. Heart Assn. (stroke coun.); mem. Am. Chinese Med. Soc. (pres. 1978), Am. Soc. Neuroradiology, Radiol. Soc. N.Am., Assn. Univ. Radiologists. Home: 15 Oxford Rd New Rochelle NY 10804-3712 Office: NYU Med Ctr 550 1st Ave New York NY 10016-6497

LIN, KEH-MING, psychiatrist, researcher; b. Taiwan, China, Feb. 1, 1946; came to U.S.; s. An-Kuo and Pi-Luang (Huang) L.; m. Wen-Ling Sung, July 31, 1974; 1 child, Jseeica S. BM, National Taiwan U., 1971; MPH, U. Wash., 1979. Head physician Psychiat. Inpatient Svcs., Torrance, Calif., 1979-81; coordinator Minority Mental Health Svcs.-Coastal Reg., L.A., 1982-86; founder Long Beach (Calif.) Asian Pacific Mental Health Ctr., 1986; founder, dir. Coastal Asian Pacific Mental Health Clinic, Gardena, Calif., 1984-86; dir. Schizophrenia Clinic, Torrance, 1990; dir. Rsch. Ctr. of Psychobiol. Ethnicity NIMH/Harbor-UCLA, Torrance, 1990—. Fellow Am. Assn. Social Psychiatry; mem. Am. Coll. Psychiatrists, Am. Soc. Clin. Psychopharmacology, Chinese Soc. Neurology and Psychiatry, Pacific Rim Assn. for Clin. Pharmacogenetics, Pacific Rim Coll. Psychiatrists. Democrat. Office: Rsch Ctr on Psychobiolog Ethnicity 1124 W Carson St B4-South Torrance CA 90502

LIN, MING-CHANG, physical chemistry educator, researcher; b. Hsinpu, Hsinchu, Taiwan, Oct. 24, 1936; came to U.S., 1967, naturalized, 1975; s. Fushin and Tao May (Hsu) L.; m. Juh-Huey Chern, June 26, 1965; children: Karen, Linus H., Ellena J. BSc, Taiwan Normal U., Taipei, 1959; PhD, U. Ottawa, Ont., Can., 1966. Postdoctoral rsch. fellow U. Ottawa, 1965-67; postdoctoral rsch. assoc. Cornell U., Ithaca, N.Y., 1967-69; rsch. chemist Naval Rsch. Lab., Washington, 1970-74, supervisory rsch. chemist, head chem. kinetics sect., 1974-82, sr. scientist for chem. kinetics, 1982-88; Robert W. Woodruff prof. phys. chemistry Emory U., Atlanta, 1988—; mem. adv. bd. Internat. Jour. Chem. Kinetics, 1990-93, Chemistry, World Sci. Pub. Co., Singapore, 1991—; Inst. Atomic and Molecular Sci., Taipei, 1991—; mem. young presdl. award com. NSF, Washington, 1990. Contbr. over 270 articles to profl. jours. 2d lt. Taiwan ROTC, 1960-62. Recipient Civilian Meritorious award USN, 1979, Humboldt award Humboldt Found., 1982, prize in sci. tech. Taiwanese-Am. Found., 1989; Guggenheim fellow, 1982. Mem. Am. Chem. Soc. (Hillebrand prize 1975), Combustion Inst., Am. Vacuum Soc., Materials Rsch. Soc., N.Am. Taiwanese Profs. Assn., Sigma Xi (Pure Sci. award 1976 Naval Rsch. Lab. chpt.). Achievements include discovery of numerous chemical lasers, use of lasers to elucidate mechanisms of combustion, propulsion and gas-surface reactions; first use of lasers to ionize nonfluorescing radicals and to probe for radicals formed in heterogeneous catalytic reactions. Office: Emory Univ Dept Of Chemistry Atlanta GA 30322

LIN, PEN-MIN, electrical engineer, educator; b. Liaoning, China, Oct. 17, 1928; came to U.S.; 1954; s. Tai-sui and Tse-san (Tang) L.; m. Louise Shou Yuen Lee, Dec. 29, 1962; children: Marian, Margaret, Janice. B.S.E.E., Taiwan U., 1950; M.S.E.E., N.C. State U., 1956; Ph.D. in Elec. Engring., Purdue U., 1960. Asst. prof. Purdue U., West Lafayette, Ind., 1961-66, assoc. prof., 1966-74, prof. elec. engring., 1974-94, prof. emeritus, 1994—. Author: (with L.O. Chua) Computer Aided Analysis of Electronic Circuits, 1975, Symbolic Network Analysis, 1991, (with R.A. DeCarlo) Linear Circuit Analysis, 1995. Fellow IEEE. Home: 3029 Covington St West Lafayette IN 47906-1107 Office: Purdue Univ Sch Of Elec Engring West Lafayette IN 47907

LIN, SHIN, biophysics educator; b. Hong Kong, Feb. 14, 1945; s. Wilhoit Y.M. and Mary (Lew) L.; m. Diane Chang, June 21, 1969; children: Howe Lin, Payton Lin. BS in Chemistry, U. Calif., Davis, 1965; MS in Chemistry, San Diego State U., 1967; PhD in Biol. Chemistry, UCLA, 1971. Postdoctoral fellow, dept. biochemistry and biophysics U. Calif., San Francisco, 1971-74; asst. prof. Johns Hopkins U., Balt., Md., 1974-79; assoc. prof. Johns Hopkins U., Balt., 1979-82, prof. biophysics, 1982—, chmn. biophys., 1983—, prof. biology, 1985—; assoc. dean for rsch. and grad. studies Sch. Arts and Scis., Johns Hopkins U., Balt., 1992—. Cons. editor in biophysics McGraw-Hill Encyclopedia of Science and Technology, 1992—. Recipient Research Career Devel. award NIH, 1976-81. Fellow AAAS; mem. Am. Soc. Biol. Chemists Mol. Biologists, Am. Soc. Cell Biology, Biophys. Soc. Office: Johns Hopkins U Dept of Biophysics 3400 N Charles St Baltimore MD 21218-2608

LIN, SHU-FANG HSIA, librarian; b. Kweiling, China, Jan. 7, 1939; came to U.S., 1962; s. Chien-cheng and Yu-chia (Sun) Hsia; m. George Chwen-Chen Lin, Sept. 11, 1931; children: Michael, Lawrence. BA, Tunghai U., 1961; MA, Vanderbilt U., 1963, St. John's U., 1981. Internat. law diplomate. Contbr. articles to profl. jours. Mem. AAUP, ALA, Cath. Libr. Assn., Chinese Am. Librs. Assn., Metro Govt. Docs. Interest Group. Avocations: travel, movies, opera, reading. Office: St John's U Libr 8000 Utopia Pkwy Jamaica NY 11439

LIN, TUNG HUA, civil engineering educator; b. Chungkin, China, May 26, 1911; s. Yao-Ching and Yue (Kuo) L.; m Susan Z. Chiang, Mar. 15, 1939; children: Rita P., Lin Chiou, Robert P., James P. B.S., Tangshan Coll., Chiaotung U., 1933; S.M., MIT, 1936; D.Sc., U. Mich., 1953. Prof. Tsing Hua U., China, 1937-39; chief engr. Chinese 2d Aircraft Co., Nancheun, Szechuan, 1939-44; prodn. mgr. Mfg. Factory, China, 1940-44; mem. tech. mission in charge of jet aircraft design, 1945-49; prof. aero. engring. U. Detroit, 1949-55; prof. engring. and applied scis. UCLA, 1955-78, prof. emeritus, 1978—; cons.N.Am. Aviation, N.Am. Rockwell, L.A., 1964-74, Atomic Internat., Canoga Park, Calif., 1965-68, ARA Inc., Industry City, Calif., 1964-94. Author: Theory of Inelastic Structure, 1968; contbr. articles to profl. jours.; mem. editorial bd.: Jour. Composite Materials, 1966-75; patentee in field. Chinese Nat. fellow Tsing-Hua U., 1933; recipient medal for Design of 1st Chinese twin-engine airplane, 1944, Disting. Svc. award Applied Mechanics Rev. ASME, 1966, NSF grantee, 1954-78; named prin. investigator Office Naval Rsch., 1985-93, Air Force Office of Sci. Rsch., 1988—. Fellow ASME, Am. Acad. Mechanics; mem. ASCE (life, gen. chmn. engring. mechanics conf. 1965, Theodore von Karman award 1988); mem. NAE. Home: 906 Las Pulgas Rd Pacific Palisades CA 90272-2441 Office: UCLA Dept Civil Engring 405 Hilgard Ave Los Angeles CA 90024-1301

LIN, TUNG YEN, civil engineer, educator; b. Foochow, China, Nov. 14, 1911; came to U.S., 1946, naturalized, 1951; s. Ting Chang and Feng Yi (Kuo) L.; m. Margaret Kao, July 20, 1941; children: Paul, Verna. BS in Civil Engring., Chiaotung U., Tangshan, Republic of China, 1931; MS, U. Calif., Berkeley, 1933; LLD, Chinese U. Hong Kong, 1972, Golden Gate U., San Francisco, 1982, Tongji U., Shanghai, 1987, Chiaotung U., Taiwan, 1987. Chief bridge engr., chief design engr. Chinese Govt. Rys., 1933-46; asst., then assoc. prof. U. Calif., 1946-55, prof., 1955-76, chmn. div. structural engring., 1960-63, dir. structural lab., 1960-63; chmn. bd. T.Y. Lin Internat., 1953-87, hon. chmn. bd., 1987-92; pres. Inter-Continental Peace Bridge, Inc., 1968—; cons. to State of Calif., Def. Dept., also to industry; chmn. World Conf. Prestressed Concrete, 1957, Western Conf. Prestressed Concrete Bldgs., 1960; chmn. bd. Lin Tung Yen, China, 1993—. Author: Design of Prestressed Concrete Structures, 1955, rev. edit., 1963, 3d edit. (with N.H. Burns), 1981, (with B. Bresler, Jack Scalzi) Design of Steel Structures, rev. edit., 1968, (with S.D. Statesbury) Structural Concepts and Systems, 1981, 2d edit., 1988; contbr. articles to profl. jours. Recipient Berkeley citation award, 1976, NRC Quarter Century award, 1977, AIA Honor award, 1984, Pres.'s Nat. Med. of Sci., 1986, Merit award Am. Cons. Engrs., Coun., 1987, John A. Roebling medal Bridge Engring., 1990, Am. Segmental Bridge Inst. Leadership award, 1992, Outstanding Paper of Yr. award Internat. Assn. Bridge and Structural Engring., 1993, Lifetime Achievement award Asian Am. Archs. and Engring. Assn., 1993, Outstanding Achievement award AAAE Assn. of Southern Calif.; named Outstanding Alumni of Yr., U. Calif. Engring. Alumni Assn., 1984, U. Calif Alumnus of the Year award, 1994, Hon. Prof., Chiaotung U., 1982, Hon. Prof., Tongji U., 1984, Hon. Prof., Shanghai Chiaotung U., 1985; fellow U. Calif. at Berkeley. Mem. ASCE (hon., life, Wellington award, Howard medal), Nat. Acad. Engring., Academia Sinica, Internat. Fedn. Prestressing (Freyssinet medal), Am. Concrete Inst. (hon.), Prestressed Concrete Inst. (medal of honor). Home: 8701 Don Carol Dr El Cerrito CA 94530-2734 Office: 315 Bay St San Francisco CA 94133 *Fear incites fear; complex breeds complex. If one learns to control one's own fear and complex, and at the same time understands those of others, one will have gone a long way toward success and happiness.*

LIN, WILLIAM WEN-RONG, economist; b. Pintung, Taiwan, Sept. 5, 1942; came to U.S., 1967; naturalized, 1976; s. Ming-Lay and Shyr-Mey (Chow) L.; m. Kimy Kuei-mei Juan, Oct. 5, 1964; children: Susan, George, Roger. BS, Chung-Hsing U., Taichung, Taiwan, 1969; MS, U. Calif.-Davis, 1969, PhD, 1973. Economist Oak Ridge Nat. Labs., Tenn., 1974-76; agrl. economist U.S. Dept. Agriculture, Washington, 1976-80, sect. head Econ. Rsch. Svc., 1982-92; sr. agrl. economist, 1992—; economist U.S. Dept. Energy, Washington, 1980-81, U.S. Dept. Interior, 1981-82; leader livestock feed del. to China, 1991, OECD, 1991; cons. in field. Contbr. articles to profl. jours. Mem. Taiwanese Am. Assn., 1976-86; legis. affairs com. Saratoga Cmty. Assn., Springfield, Va., 1983; pres. Chinese-Am. Profl. Assn. Met. Washington, 1995. U. Calif. fellow, 1967-68, Disting. scholar, 1969-71; Merit award U.S. Dept. Agr., 1979, 85, 90, 92. Mem. Am. Agrl. Econ. Assn. (productivity com. 1978-80, lectr. 1977), Am. Econs. Assn., Chinese-Am. Profls. Assn. (bd. dirs. 1994), Western Agrl. Econ. Assn. (lectr. 1979), Southern Agrl. Econ. Assn. Home: 9404 Crosstimber Ct Fairfax Station VA 22039-3175 Office: USDA Econ Rsch Svc 1301 New York Ave NW Rm 1034 Washington DC 20005-4788

LIN, WUU-LONG, senior economist; b. Taiwan, Apr. 28, 1939; came to U.S., 1966, naturalized, 1977; s. Yeu-Chung and Lu-Jing (Lu) L.; m. Ai-Ai Anna Kuo, Dec. 26, 1970; children: Joel, Pansy. BS, Nat. Taiwan U., 1965; MS (Ford Found. fellow 1966), Kans. State U., 1968; PhD (Univ. fellow 1968-72), Stanford U., 1972. Tchr. Taipei Chuang-San Sch., 1958-61; rsch. assoc. Kans. State U., 1968, Harvard U., 1970; vis. economist Chinese-Am. Joint Commn. Rural Reconstrn., Taipei, 1971; rsch. economist, vis. scholar Stanford U., 1972-75; econometrician FAO, Rome, 1974-78; chief dub. enterprise mgmt., UN, N.Y.C., 1979—; adj. econometrics prof. Baruch Coll. CUNY, 1989—; lectr. econ. info. systems and population and devel. UN Mission to China, 1983, 85, Africa, Asia, USSR, macroecons. at Peking U., 1987; cons./advisor Coun. of Agr., Taiwan, 1990, external aid, 1991—; econ. adviser to Devel. Rsch. Ctr. for State of China, 1992; cons. in field. Author: Planning and Control of Public Current Expenditure: Lessons of Country Experience, 1987, Guidelines for Development Planning, English and French version, 1987, also papers, reports in global devel., info. mgmt. and country planning. Officer Chinese Army, 1965. Recipient 1st pl. stats. award Republic of China, 1962, Disting. Achievement award Hsin-chu Normal Coll., Republic of China, 1990; grantee NSF, 1971-72. Mem. Am. Econ. Assn., Am. Agrl. Econs. Assn., Stanford U. Alumni Assn. (life), Phi Kappa Phi. Democrat. Home: 61 Old Knollwood Rd White Plains NY 10607-1827 Office: UN PO Box 20 Rm Dc1-946 New York NY 10163-0020

LIN, Y. K., engineer, educator; b. Foochow, Fukien, China, Oct. 30, 1923; came to U.S., 1954, naturalized, 1964; s. Fa Been and Chi Ying (Cheng) L.; m. Ying-yuh June Wang, Mar. 29, 1952; children: Jane, Della, Lucia, Winifred. BS, Amoy U., 1946; MS, Stanford U., 1955, PhD, 1957; Dr. Engring. honoris causa, U. Waterloo, Can., 1994. Tchr. Amoy U., China, 1946-48, Imperial Coll. Engring, Ethiopia, 1957-58; engr. Vertol Aircraft Corp., Morton, Pa., 1956-57; research engr. Boeing Co., Renton, Wash., 1958-60; asst. prof. U. Ill., Urbana, 1960-62, assoc. prof., 1962-65, prof. aero. and astron. engring., 1965-83; Charles E. Schmidt Eminent scholar chair Coll. Engring., dir. Ctr. for Applied Stochastics Rsch. Fla. Atlantic U., Boca Raton, 1984—; vis. prof. mech. engring. M.I.T., 1967-68; sr. vis. fellow Inst. Sound and Vibration Research, U. Southampton, Eng., 1976; cons. Gen.

Motors Corp., Boeing Co., Gen. Dynamics Corp., TRW Corp., Brookhaven Nat. Lab. Author: Probabilistic Theory of Structural Dynamics, 1967, Stochastic Structural Mechanics, 1987, Stochastic Approaches in Earthquake Engineering, 1987, Stochastic Structural Dynamics, 1990, Probabilistic Structural Dynamics: Advanced Theory and Applications, 1995; contbr. articles to profl. jours. Sr. postdoctoral fellow NSF, 1967-68. Fellow ASCE (Alfred M. Freudenthal medal 1984), Am. Acad. Mechs., Acoustical Soc. Am., AIAA (assoc.); mem. Sigma Xi (Internat. Assn. for Structural Safety and Reliability award, 1993). Home: 2684 NW 27th Ter Boca Raton FL 33434-6001 Office: Fla Atlantic U Coll Engring Boca Raton FL 33431

LINANE, WILLIAM EDWARD, corporate real estate executive; b. Chgo., Apr. 15, 1928; s. Francis John and Eva (Knott) L.; m. Elaine Ruth Linstead, Oct. 22, 1948 (div. Jan. 1957); children: James Richard, Judith Linane Healey. Am. Park Coll., 1948; BS, Northwestern U., 1952; MBA, U. Chgo., 1964. Various positions Eastern Weighing & Insp. Bur., Chgo., 1948-52; with freight sales div. Michan Navigation Co., Chgo., 1952-55, Ill. Calif. Express, Chgo., 1955-61; exec. dir. Am. Soc. Traffic & Transp., Chgo., 1961-69; v.p. William Kritt & Co., Chgo., 1969-74; pres. Linane & Co., Inc., Rosemont, Ill., 1974—; midwest regional advisor N.Am. Property Assn., Coeur D Alene, Idaho, 1988—. Author: Encyclopedia of Professional Management, 1979. Mem. Coun. of Logistics Mgmt. (pres. Ill. chpt. 1984-85). Avocations: aviation, golf, skiing, scuba diving, reading.

LINCE, JOHN ALAN, pharmacist; b. Cleve., Sept. 15, 1940; s. John Alexander and Isabelle Stella (Wirbalas) Lincewicz; m. Katherine Ann Hudson, Sept. 9, 1961 (div. Aug., 1984); children: John Jr., Karen, Mark; m. Shirley Ann Baker, Jan. 18, 1985. BS in Pharmacy, Ohio State U., 1964. Registered pharmacist, Ohio. Pharmacist, owner Hill & Dale Pharmacy, Columbus, Ohio, 1964-75, Franklin Park Med. Pharmacy, Columbus, 1975—. Pharmacy Mktg. award Johnson & Johnson, N.J., 1964. Mem. Coop. of Ohio Pharmacies (charter mem., pres. 1991—), Am. Pharm. Assn., Nat. Assn. Retail Druggists, Ohio Pharmacists Assn., Acad. Pharmacy Ctrl. Ohio (trustee 1994-95, pres.-elect 1995—), Ohio State Alumni Assn., Ohio State U. Coll. of Pharmacy Alumni Assn. (charter), Mid-Ohio Combat Shooters Assn. (pres. 1985-88), Rho Chi. Avocations: photography, woodworking, target shooting. Home: 4645 Meekison Dr Columbus OH 43220-3038 Office: Franklin Park Med Pharmacy 1829 E Long St Columbus OH 43203-2066

LINCHITZ, RICHARD MICHAEL, psychiatrist, physician; b. Bklyn., Mar. 29, 1947; m. Rita A. Colao, Sept. 22, 1973; children: Elise Ann, Michael Benjamin, Jonathan Adam. BA cum laude in Psychology, Cornell U., 1967, MD, 1973; student L.I. Univ., 1967-68, U. Lausanne Med. Sch., 1968-71. Diplomate Am. Bd. Psychiatry and Neurology, Am. Acad. Pain Mgmt., AM. Bd. Pain Medicine. Intern, Moffit Hosp., San Francisco, 1973-74; resident in psychiatry Langley Porter Neuropsychiat. Inst., San Francisco, 1974-77; practice medicine specializing in treatment of chronic pain conditions and psychiatry, Carle Place, N.Y., 1978—; med. dir. Roslyn Mental Health Ctr. (N.Y.), 1978—, Pain Alleviation Center, Carle Place, 1978-93. Recipient letter of commendation White House, 1977; Nathan Seligman award Cornell U. Med. Coll., 1973; Nat. Psychiat. Endowment Fund award Langley Porter Neuropsychiat. Inst., 1977; Langley Porter Youth Service award, 1977. Fellow Am. Coll. Pain Medicine; mem. Am. Psychiat. Assn., Acad. Pain Research, Am. Pain Soc., Nassau Psychiat. Soc., Am. Acad. of Pain Medicine, Am. Acad. Pain Mgmt. (cert.), Alpha Omega Alpha. Author: Life Without Pain, 1987. Office: 179 Westbury Ave Carle Place NY 11514-1227

LINCICOME, BERNARD WESLEY, journalist; b. Zanesville, Ohio, Sept. 13, 1941; s. Robert Parr and Mary Edith Lincicome; m. Jaye Slaughter, Sept. 21, 1963; children: Romey, David. B.s in Edn., Ohio State U., 1963. Staff writer Sun-Sentinel, Ft. Lauderdale, Fla., 1968-70, sports editor, 1970-73; sports editor Ft. Lauderdale News, 1973-83; columnist Chgo. Tribune, 1983—. Served with USAF, 1958-61. Recipient Best Sports Column award Fla. Press Club, 1981; Column writing award AP Sports Editors, 1982, 85, 88; Best Sports Column award AP, 1984; Peter Lisagor award, 1985, 87. Mem. Fla. Sportswriters Assn. (pres. 1977, Sportswriter of Yr. award 1973, 75, 79, 81).

LINCICOME, DAVID RICHARD, biomedical and animal scientist; b. Champaign, Ill., Jan. 17, 1914; s. David Rosebery and Olive Iola (Casper) L.; m. Dorothy Lucile Van Cleave, Sept. 1, 1941 (dec. Nov. 1952); children: David Van Cleave, Judith Ann; m. Margaret Stirewalt, Dec. 29, 1953. BS, MS with high honors, U. Ill., 1937; PhD, Tulane U., 1941. Diplomate (emeritus) Am. Bd. Microbiology; cert. animal scientist Am. Registry Profl. Animal Scientists. Asst. instr. U. Ill., 1937; asst. instr. tropical medicine Tulane U. Med. Sch., 1937-41; asst. prof. parasitology U. Ky., 1941-47; sr. rsch. parasitologist Du Pont Co., 1949-53; from asst. prof. to full prof. biol. Scis. Howard U., 1953-70; vis. sci. NIH, 1965-66; registrar, Jacob Sheep Conservancy, 1989—, bd. dirs., 1990—; vis. scholar Nat. Agrl. Libr. USDA, 1990-92; guest scientist USDA Exp. Sta., Beltsville, Md., 1978—, Naval Med. Rsch. Inst., 1954-62. Founder, editor Exptl. Parasitology, 1949-76; editor Transactions of the Ky. Acad. Sci., 1946-49, Transactions of the Am. Microscopical Soc., 1970-71, Internat. Rev. Tropical Medicine, 1953-63; founder Virology, 1950, Advances in Vet. Sci., 1952. Lt. col. Med. Svc. Corps, U.S. Army, World War II, PTO. Recipient Anniversary award Helminthological Soc., 1975; rsch. grantee NIH, 1958-68. Fellow AAAS, Explorers Club (nat., N.Y.); mem. Helminthological Soc. (pres. 1958, emeritus), Am. Physiol. Soc. (emeritus), Soc. Invertebrate Zoology (emeritus), Am. Soc. Zoologists (emeritus), Am. Soc. Parasitologists, Am. Microscopical Soc. (emeritus), Royal Soc. Tropical Medicine (emeritus), Am. Soc. Tropical Medicine (emeritus), Am. Goat Soc. (bd. dirs. 1992—), Am. Dairy Goat Assn. (founder, 1st sec. rsch. found. 1979, bd. dirs. 1972-87), Nat. Pygmy Goat Assn. (bd. dirs. 1976-92, pres. 1979), Natural Colored Wool Growers Assn. (bd. dirs. 1988-94), Jacob Sheep Breeders Assn., Jacob Sheep Soc. (Eng.), Nat. Tunis Sheep Registry (bd. dirs. 1991-93, sec. 1991-92), Greater Washington D.C. Area Soft-Coated Wheaten Terrier Club (founder, pres. 1991-92, mem. rescue com. 1993—), Am. Livestock Breeds Conservancy (bd. dirs. 1994—), Midwestern Conf. Parasitologists (founder, 1st sec. 1949), Phi Beta Kappa, Sigma Xi (assoc. mem. 1936, mem. 1941, pres. Howard U. chpt. 1962). Achievements include breeding of two rare and endangered breeds of sheep, Jacob and Tunis; founder and first sec. The Rsch. Found. of the Am. Dairy Goat Assn.; founder Midwestern Conf. of Parasitologists. Home: Frogmoor Farm 3032 Courtney Sch House Rd Midland VA 22728-9748 also: PO Box 13 4419 Cambria Ave Garrett Park MD 20896 Office: USDA BARC East Rm 207 Bldg 467 Beltsville MD 20705

LINCOLN, ABBEY (ANNA MARIE WOOLRIDGE, GABY LEE, AMINATA MOSEKA), jazz singer, actress; b. Chicago, IL, Aug. 6, 1930; m. Max Roach, 1962 (div. 1970). Albums include: Affair: A Story of a Girl in Love, 1956, That's Him, 1957, It's Magic, 1958, Abbey is Blue, 1959, We Insist: Freedom Now Suite, 1960, Straight Ahead, 1961, It's Time, 1962, People in Me, 1979, Golden Lady, 1981, Talking to the Sun, 1984, Abbey Sings Billie, 1987, The World is Falling Down (with Stan Getz), 1990, You Gotta Pay the Band, 1991, Abbey Sings Billie, Volume 2, 1992, Devil's Got Your Tongue, 1993, Talking To The Sun, 1993, Lincoln on Paris, 1993, When There Is Love (with Hank Jones), 1994; film appearances include: The Girl Can't Help It, 1956, Nothing But a Man, 1964, For the Love of Ivy, 1968, A Short Walk to Daylight, 1972, Mo' Better Blues, 1990; wrote, directed and produced play, A Pig in a Poke, 1975. inducted into Black Filmakers Hall of Fame, 1975. Office: care Verve 825 8th Ave New York NY 10019-7416*

LINCOLN, (CHARLES) ERIC, sociologist, educator, author; b. Athens, Ala., June 23, 1924; s. Less and Mattie (Sowell) L.; m. Lucy Cook, July 1, 1961; children: Hilary Anne, Less Charles II; children by previous marriage: Cecil Eric, Joyce Elaine. AB, Lemoyne Coll., 1947; AM, Fisk U., 1954; student law, U. Chgo., 1948-49, BD, 1956; MEd, Boston U., 1960, PhD, 1960; LLD (hon.), Carlton Coll., 1968; LHD (hon.), St. Michael's, 1970, Lane Coll., 1982, Clark Coll., 1983, Boston U., 1991; DCL (hon.), Shaw Div. Sch., 1988; DD (hon.), Interdenominational Theol. Ctr., 1991, Emory U., 1993; LHD, Clark U., 1993. Pastor John Calvin Presbyn. Ch., Nashville, 1953-54; asst. personnel dean Fisk U., Nashville, 1953-54; asst. prof. religion and philosophy Clark Coll., 1954-60, asso. prof. social philosophy, 1960-61, prof. social relations, 1961-65, asst. to pres., 1960-63; prof. sociology Portland (Ore.) State U., 1965-67; prof. sociology and religion Union Theol. Sem., N.Y.C., 1965-73; adj. prof. sociology Vassar Coll., 1969-70; adj. prof. religion Columbia U., 1965-73; prof. sociology and religion, chmn. dept. religious studies Fisk U., Nashville, 1973-76; prof. religion Duke U., Durham, N.C., 1976—; William Rand Kenan Jr. Disting. prof. emeritus religion and culture, 1991—; lectr. in residence Dartmouth, 1962, vis. prof. social relations, 1963; intern in coll. adminstrn. Brown U., 1964-65; resident fellow Hope Coll., Brown U., 1964-65; resident chaplain Sch. Theology, Boston U., 1958-59; dir. Sch. Theology, Boston U. (Panel of Americans), 1958-60; adj. prof. Sch. Theology, Boston U. (Human Relations Center), 1963-65; lectr. Harvard, Yale, univs. Madrid (Spain), Oslo (Norway), Edinburgh (Scotland), London (Eng.) Sch. Econs., Shiraz, Abu Dhabi and Oman, 1964; others; external assessor univs. of, Ghana, 1975; cons. research Office Edn.; rep. Dept. State at internat. seminar on Am. Negro Freedom Movement, Paris, France, 1965; participant Internat. Conf. on Color, Copenhagen, Denmark, 1965; founding pres. Black Acad. Arts and Letters; vis. prof. Queens Coll., 1972; E. Franklin Frazier vis. prof. history, sociology, Clark U., 1992-93. Author: The Black Muslims in America, 1961, 2d edit., 1973; 1961, My Face is Black, 1964, The Negro Pilgrimage in America, 1967, Sounds of the Struggle, 1967, Is Anybody Listening?, 1968, The Black Americans, 1969, A Profile of Martin Luther King, 1969, rev. edit., 1985, The Black Experience in Religion, 1974, The Black Church since Frazier, 1974, Race, Religion and the Continuing American Dilemma, 1984, (collected poems) This Road Since Freedom, 1990; fiction: The Avenue, Clayton City, 1987; (with L.H. Mamiya) The Black Church in the African American Experience, 1990; gen. editor: C. Eric Lincoln Series in Black Religion; contbr. articles N.Y. Times, books, periodicals. Former trustee Boston U. Clark U.; former assoc. dir. Am. Forum for African Study; bd. dirs. African Student Aid Fund. Served with USNR, 1944-45. Named Howard Johnson Disting. tchr. Duke U., 1988; Crusade fellow, 1957; John Hay Whitney fellow, 1957-58; Eli Lilly fellow, 1958; Human Relations fellow, 1959, 60; Fund for Advancement Edn. grantee, 1964; Lilly Endowment grantee, 1976, 78-85; Ford Found. grantee, 1986. Fellow Am. Acad. Arts and Scis.; mem. Soc. of Psychol. Study Social Issues, AAUP, N.Y. Acad. Scis., Nat. Social Sci. Assn., Assn. for Study Negro Life and History, Am., So. sociol. assns., Am. Psychol. Assn., Am. Assn. Sci. Study Religion NAACP (life), Masons (33 deg.), Kappa Alpha Psi (life), Sigma Pi Phi. Home: 2507 Tanglewood Dr Durham NC 27705-5580 Office: Duke U 324 Gray Ave Durham NC 27701-2426

LINCOLN, EDMOND LYNCH, investment banker; b. Wilmington, Del., Aug. 3, 1949; s. Edmond Earl and Mary Margaret (Lynch) L.; B.A. magna cum laude, Harvard U., 1971, M.B.A., with distinction, 1974; m. Pamela Wick, Sept. 3, 1977; children: Lucy Arms, Emily Lord. Acting care book librarian Henry Francis duPont Winterthur Mus. (Del.), 1971-72; with Kidder Peabody & Co., Inc., N.Y.C., 1974-94, assoc. v.p., 1977-79, v.p. 1979-91, sr. v.p., 1991-94, mgr. govt. agy. fin., 1984-86, transp. group, 1986-94; mng. dir. PaineWebber Inc., N.Y.C., 1994—; pub. interest dir. Fed. Home Loan Bank of N.Y., 1987-89. Recipient Washburn History prize, Harvard U., 1971. Treas., Fed. Hall Meml. Assocs., 1981-87; mem. vis. com. Harvard Coll. Library, 1981-86, 88-94; exec. com. Friends of Harvard U. Track, 1972—, sec., 1976-87. Mem. Investment Assn. N.Y., Friends of Winterthur (trustee 1976-81, 87-93, sec. 1978-81, Winterthur Mus. acad. affairs com. 1992—), Assn. Internationale de Bibliophilie, Assn. of Fellows, The Pierpont Morgan Library, Club of Odd Volumes, Bond Club of N.Y., Grolier Club, Harvard Club (N.Y.C.), India House, Wilmington Club, Wilmington Country Club, Phi Beta Kappa. Republican. Roman Catholic. Home: 161 E 79th St New York NY 10021-0433 Office: PaineWebber Inc 1285 Ave of the Americas New York NY 10019

LINCOLN, LUCIAN ABRAHAM, coal company executive; b. Evanston, Ill., Nov. 29, 1926; s. Lucian Abraham and Ruth (Nelson) L.; m. Marie Teresa Mantello, 1957 (dec. 1979); 1 child by previous marriage, Deborah Lynn; children: Laurel Marie, Christopher Lucian; m. Mary Lynn Levanti, Dec. 21, 1984. JD, DePaul U., 1951. Bar: Ill. 1951, U.S. Dist. Ct. (no. dist.) Ill. 1958. Pvt. practice Chgo., 1955-70; pres. Great Lakes Towing Co., Cleve., 1970-72; chmn., chief exec. officer Freeman United Coal Mining Co., 1973-92, Freeman Energy Corp., Marion, Ill., 1992—. Bd. dirs. United Charities, Chgo., 1979. Served with USN, 1943-46. Mem. Franklin County Country Club (West Frankfort, Ill.). Avocations: fishing, hunting, golf. Office: Freeman Energy Corp 111 Airway Dr PO Box 220 Marion IL 62959

LINCOLN, RAYNARD C., JR., utility company executive; b. Jackson, Mich., Sept. 15, 1934; s. Raynard C. Sr. and Harriette (Nichols) L.; m. Marilyn Jean Summers (dec. Dec. 1979); children: Chris Allen, Margaret Ann, Mary Catherine, Julia Ann, Mark Joseph, Kristin Louise, Ann Therese, Andrew John; m. Barbara Louise Bartell, Aug. 1, 1981. BS, Purdue U., 1959. With Consumers Power Co., Jackson, 1959—, v.p. gen. svcs., 1974-84, v.p. dist. ops., 1984-87, sr. v.p. energy distbn., 1987—; bd. dirs. CMS Utility Svcs., Inc., Jackson. Mem. adv. bd. Cen. Mich. U., Mt. Pleasant, 1988; bd. dirs. Jackson Edn. Fund, 1988—United Way Mich., 1989—, United Way Jackson, 1978—, Cascades Health Group, 1988—, Jackson Alliance Bus. Devel., 1987—. With U.S. Army, 1957-59. Roman Catholic. Avocation: antique toys. Office: Consumers Power Co 212 W Michigan Ave Jackson MI 49201-2236

LINCOLN, SANDY, investment management executive; b. Des Moines, Sept. 19, 1945; s. Seamon Andrew and Marjorie Helen (Falls) L.; children: Laura Michelle, Darcy Ann. BA, Valparaiso U., 1967; MBA, Loyola U., 1973. Trust officer Continental Ill. Nat. Bank, Chgo., 1967-73; v.p. A.G. Becker, Chgo., 1973-79; mng. dir. William M. Mercer, Chgo., 1979-89; chief investment officer Kemper Corp., Chgo., 1989—. Contbg. author: S&P Inclusion Effect, Fixed Income Active Trading Strategies, Performance Measurement-Time Horizon Implication. Chmn. planning com. Lake Forest (Ill.) Sch. Bd., 1987-90; rep. Everett Park Commn., Lake Forest, 1989; annexation rep. for Lake Forest; bd. dirs. Catalyst Inst.; dir. Internat. Found. Mem. Pension Real Estate Assn., Chgo. Assn. Commerce and Industry (bd. dirs.), Mid-Day Club. Home: 1230 Harlan Ln Lake Forest IL 60045-3893 Office: Kemper Fin Cos 120 S La Salle St Chicago IL 60603-3402

LIND, CARL BRADLEY, retired museum director; b. Bethel, Vt., Apr. 22, 1929; s. Carl Olaf and Signe Alfield (Anderson) L.; m. Barbara Ann Eskridge, Oct. 22, 1951; children: Carl Garrett, Susan Ann, Craig Era. BA, Norwich U., 1951; cert., Command and Gen. Staff Coll., Fort Leavenworth, Kans., 1960; MA, Columbia U., 1963; cert., NATO Def. Coll., Rome, 1976. Commd. 2d lt. U.S. Army, advanced through grades to col., 1968; asst. prof. U.S. Mil. Acad., West Point N.Y., 1961-64; comdr. 1st Squadron 3d Armored Cavalry Regt. U.S. Army, Fed. Republic Germany, 1965-67; sr. advisor Vietnamese Nat. Mil. Acad. U.S. Army, Dalat, Vietnam, 1967-68; chief Congl. Inquiry Div., Office Sec. of the Army U.S. Army, Washington, 1968-71; area comdr. 2d ROTC Region U.S. Army, Fort Knox, Ky., 1973-75; exec. for interoperability to SACEUR, SHAPE NATO, Mons, Belgium, 1977-79; exec. v.p. Evans Llewellyn Securities, Bellevue, Wash., 1979-81; dep. dir. Mus. of History and Industry, Seattle, 1984-88, exec. dir., 1988-91; bd. dirs. Museum of History and Industry, Seattle, Coast Guard Mus. of Northwest, Seattle. Contbr. articles to jours. in field. Neighborhood commr. Boys Scouts Am., Baumholder, Fed. Rep. Germany, 1965-66; pres. PTA, Baumholder, 1965-66; commr. King County (Wash.) Landmarks & Heritage Commn., 1992—, Wash. State Heritage Caucus, 1990—; bd. dirs. Hydroplane and Antique Race Boat Mus., Seattle, 1993—; exec. bd. Bigelow House Preservation Assn., Olympia, Wash., 1993—. Decorated Bronze star, Dept. Def. Superior Svc. medal. Legion of Merit, Meritorious Svc. medal. Mem. VFW (comdr. Mercer Island, Wash. post 5760 1984-85), Assn. of U.S. Army, U.S. Army Armor Assn., Ret. Officer Assn., Am. Assn. State and Local History, Lions, Rotary. Home: 3023 Country Club Rd NW Olympia WA 98502-3738

LIND, GREGORY ALAN, nurse; b. Mpls., July 15, 1953; s. Raymond Pernal and Barbara (Haddad) L.; m. Diane Nancy Erpenbach, Dec. 28, 1974; children: Brienne Jo, Kacie Barbara. BS in Nursing, Viterbo Coll., 1976; MS in Nursing, U. Mo., 1980; PhD in Nursing, U. Kans., 1988. Staff nurse Truman Vet.'s Hosp., Columbia, Mo., 1976-78; family nurse practitioner Callaway Family Clinic, Fulton, Mo., 1979-83; prin. Family Nurse Practitioner Care, Unlimited, Columbia, 1983-87; asst. prof. Sch. Nursing U.

Mo., Columbia, 1986-87; assoc., advanced nurse practitioner Primary Health Care Assocs., Seattle, 1988-89; asst. prof. dept. cmty. health care, primary health care pathway Sch. Nursing, U. Wash., Seattle, 1988-89; pres., owner, practitioner Lake Serene Walk-In Clinic, Lynwood, Wash., L&Y Inc., P.S., L&Y Investments. Contbr. to profl. publs.; health columnist, local newspaper, 1982-87. Sec.-treas., Cedar Lake homeowners Assn., Columbia, 1982-86; mem. Corrections Health Task Force, Jefferson City, Mo., 1986; mem. Columbia City/County Bd. Health, 1986. Mem. Am. Nurses Assn. (exec. mem. cabinet 1988—, mem. exec. coun. 1986-88), Wash. State Nurses Assn., King County Nurses Assn., Sigma Theta Tau. Roman Catholic. Avocations: weight lifting, running. Home: 6526 St Andrews Dr Mukilteo WA 98275-4848 Office: 3501 Shelby Rd Ste B Lynnewood WA 98037

LIND, JAMES FOREST, surgeon, educator; b. Fillmore, Sask., Can., Nov. 22, 1925; s. James Forest and Isabella (Pringle) L.; m. Dorothy Anne Berlette, Aug. 23, 1950; children: Heather, James, Scott, Robert, Gregory. M.D., C.M., Queen's U., 1951. Intern Hamilton (Ont.) Gen. Hosp., 1951-52, resident in pathology, 1952-53; fellow in anatomy Queen's U., 1953-54, fellow in medicine, 1954-55; fellow in surgery, 1955-56; registrar in surgery Liverpool, 1956-58; fellow in physiology Mayo Found., 1958-60; lectr. in surgery U. Man., 1960-62, asst. prof. surgery, 1962-64, assoc. prof., 1964-66, prof., 1966-72, head dept. surgery, 1969-72; prof., chmn. dept. surgery McMaster U., 1972-79, Eastern Va. Med. Sch., 1979-94; retired, 1994; dir. surgery Med. Center Hosps., Norfolk, Va., 1979—; chief surgery Sentara Hosps., 1979—; hon. cons. attending staff Norfolk Gen. Hosp., Leigh Meml. Hosp., Norfolk, De Paul Hosp., Norfolk; practice medicine specializing in surgery Norfolk, 1979—; vis. prof. U. B.C., 1966, U. Alta., 1967, U. Sask., 1968, Royal Victoria Hosp., 1969, McGill U., 1969, U. Calgary, 1969, Meml. U., Newfoundland, 1973, Harvard U., 1972, numerous others. Contbr. numerous articles to med. jours. Served with RCAF, 1943-45; lt. comdr. RCN(R), 1948—. John S. McEashern fellow Can. Cancer Soc., 1956-57; recipient George Christian Hoffman award Queen's U., 1957-58; John and Mary Markle scholar, 1960; other honors. Mem. Royal Coll. Phys. and Surg. Can., Can. Assn. Clin. Surgeons, Can. Assn Gastroenterology (pres. 1972), Can. Soc. Clin. Investigation, Am. Surg. Assn., Central Surg. Assn., Mayo Alumni Assn., Soc. Surg. Chmn., Soc. Univ. Surgeons, Soc. Surgery Alimentary Tract, A.C.S., AMA, Va. Med. Soc., Va. Surg. Soc., Southeastern Surg. Congress, Soc. Am. Gastrointestinal Endoscopic Surgeons (pres. 1986), Am. Motility Soc., Assn. Acad. Surgery, Norfolk Medicine Acad., Esophageal Club. Home: 4044 Sherwood Ln Virginia Beach VA 23455-5613 Office: 825 Fairfax Ave Norfolk VA 23507-1912

LIND, JON ROBERT, lawyer; b. Evanston, Ill., July 4, 1935; s. Robert A. and Ruth (Anderson) L.; m. Jane Langfitt, Aug. 29, 1959; children: Jon Robert Jr., Elizabeth Neal, Susan Porter. AB, Harvard U., 1957, LLB, 1960; diploma in comparative law, Cambridge (Eng.) U., 1961. Bar: Ill. 1961. Assoc. Isham, Lincoln & Beale, Chgo., 1961-68, ptnr., 1968-88; ptnr. McDermott, Will & Emery, Chgo., 1988—. Atty. Winnetka (Ill.) Park Dist., 1973-78; bd. dirs. Swedish-Am. Mus. Ctr., 1988—. Mem. ABA, Chgo. Bar Assn., Harvard U. Alumni Assn. (sec. 1970-73), Econ. Club of Chgo., Legal Club of Chgo. Home: 644 Walden Rd Winnetka IL 60093-2035 Office: McDermott Will & Emery 227 W Monroe St Chicago IL 60606-5096

LIND, MARSHALL L., academic administrator. Dean Sch. Extended and Grad. Studies U. Alaska, Juneau, until 1987, chancellor, 1987—. Office: U of Alaska Southeast Office of Chancellor 11120 Glacier Hwy Juneau AK 99801-8625

LIND, NIELS CHRISTIAN, civil engineering educator; b. Copenhagen, Mar. 10, 1930; s. Axel Holger and Karen (Larsen) L.; m. Veronica Claire Hummel, Nov. 29, 1957 (div. 1979); children: Julie Wilhelmina, Peter Christian, Adam Conrad; m. Virginia Patricia Cano Reynoso, Jan. 26, 1985; 1 child, Andreas Manuel. M.Sc., Tech. U. Denmark, 1953; Ph.D., U. Ill., 1959. Design engr. Dominia Ltd., Copenhagen, 1953-54; engr. I Bell Telephone Co., Montreal, 1954-55; field engr. Drake-Merritt, Labrador, Nfld., 1955; asst. prof. U. Ill., Urbana, 1959-60; assoc. prof. civil engring. U. Waterloo, Ont., 1960-62, prof., 1962-91, disting. prof. emeritus, 1992, dir. Inst. Risk Research, 1982-88; adj. prof. U. Victoria, B.C., 1991-. Recipient Ostenfeld gold medal, 1978; recipient Cancam award Can. Congress Applied Mechanics, 1981. Fellow Royal Soc. Can., Can. Acad. Eng., Am. Acad. Mechanics (pres. 1972-73); mem. Soc. Risk Analysis. Home: 504-640 Montreal St, Victoria, BC Canada V8V 1Z8 Office: U Victoria, Dept Mech Engring, Victoria, BC Canada V8W 3P6

LIND, THOMAS OTTO, barge transportation company executive; b. New Orleans, Apr. 24, 1937; s. Henry Carl Lind and Elinor (Rooney) Messersmith; m. Eugenia Niehaus, June 8, 1963; children: Elinor Ashley, Elizabeth Kelly. BS in MechE, Tulane U., 1959, LLB, 1965. Cert. mech. engr., 1959. Assoc. Jones, Walker, Waechter, Poitevent, Carrere and Denegre, New Orleans, 1965-66; v.p.; sec., counsel Ingram Corp., New Orleans, 1966-84; v.p. Gulf Fleet Marine Corp., New Orleans, 1984-85; v.p., regulatory counsel, sec. and asst. treas. New Orleans Pub. Svc., Inc. and La. Power and Light Co., 1985-92; regional counsel for La. Entergy Svcs., Inc., 1993-94; risk mgr. Canal Barge Co., Inc., New Orleans, 1994—. Trustee Metairie Park Country Day Sch., 1991—; mem. bd. govs. Trinity Sch., New Orleans, 1982-85; vestryman Trinity Ch., New Orleans, 1987-91; active Family of Community and Utility Supporters, New Orleans, 1987-94. Served to lt. (j.g.) USN, 1959-62; comdr. USNR, 1962-79. Mem. ABA, La. State Bar Assn. (bd. dirs. corp. law sect. 1973-75), New Orleans Bar Assn. (exec. com. 1989—, 2d v.p. 1989-90, sec. 1992-93, 1st v.p. 1993-94, pres.-elect 1994—), La. Orgn. for Jud. Excellence (bd. dirs. 1989—), New Orleans Lawn Tennis Club (pres. 1986-88). Republican. Episcopalian. Avocations: tennis, jogging, numismatics. Home: 1126 Octavia St New Orleans LA 70115-3129 Office: Canal Barge Co Inc 835 Union St New Orleans LA 70112

LINDA, GERALD, advertising and marketing executive; b. Boston, Nov. 25, 1946; s. Edward Linda and Anne Beatrice (Lipofsky) Coburn; m. Claudia Wollack, Sept. 24, 1978; children—Jonathan Daniel Rezny, Jessica Simone. BS in Bus. Adminstrn., Northeastern U., 1969, MBA, 1971; postgrad., U. Mich., 1971-75. Faculty U. Ky., Lexington, 1975-77; ptnr. Tatham-Laird & Kudner, Chgo., 1977-80; v.p. Marsteller, Chgo., 1980-84; sr. v.p. HCM, Chgo., 1984-86; pres. Gerald Linda & Assocs., Chgo., 1986-89; prin. Kurtzman/Slavin/Linda, Inc., Chgo., 1990-93, Kapuler Mkgt. Rsch., Chgo., 1993-94; pres. Gerald Linda & Assocs., Glenview, Ill., 1994—. Mem. editorial review bd. Jour. Current Issues and Rsch. in Advt., 1984—. Mem. Am. Mktg. Assn. (exec.), Assn. for Consumer Rsch., Bus. Mktg. Assn., Am. Acad. Advt.

LINDAHL, HERBERT WINFRED, appliance manufacturing executive; b. Malvern, Ark., Nov. 25, 1927; s. Herbert Winfred and Helen Ester (VanDusen) L.; m. Mary Evalyn Nenon, Feb. 27, 1954; children: Evalyn Nenon, Eric VanDusen. BA, Vanderbilt U., 1950. With State Industries, Inc., Nashville, 1946—, v.p., 1955-68, pres., Ashland City, 1968—. Republican. Clubs: City, Hillwood (Nashville). Avocations: tennis, wine, poetry. Office: State Holdings Co 500 By Pass Rd Ashland City TN 37015-1234

LINDAMOOD, JOHN BEYER, lawyer; b. Columbus, Ohio, Jan. 18, 1941; s. H. Ray and Betty C. (Beyer) L.; m. Barbara L. Fordyce, Dec. 28, 1985; children: Jennifer, J. Brad. AB, DePauw U., 1963; JD, Western Res. U., 1966. Bar: Ohio 1966, U.S. Dist. Ct. (no. dist.) Ohio 1968, U.S. Ct. Appeals (6th cir.) 1984, U.S. Supreme Ct. 1986. Assoc. Carson, Vogelsang & Sheehan, Canton, Ohio, 1966-71; ptnr. Vogelsang, Howes & Lindamood, Canton, 1971-79. Editor Western Res. Law Rev., 1965-66. Pres. Canton Exch. Club, 1970; v.p. Canton Jaycees, 1970-71; pres. Stark County Bar Assn., Canton, 1989-90. Fellow Ohio State Bar Found.; mem. ABA, Def. Rsch. Inst., Ohio State Bar Assn. (exec. com. 1982-85), Ohio Assn. Civil Trial Attys. Office: Vogelsang Howes Lindamood & Brunn 400 Tuscarawas St W Canton OH 44702-2018

LINDARS, LAURENCE EDWARD, retired health care products executive; b. N.Y.C., Oct. 14, 1922; s. Arthur John and Florence Vera (Cunard) L.; m. Mary Gibson Grandy, Jan. 22, 1972; children—John L., William A. Nancy E. Student, Dartmouth Coll., 1943-44; B.S., Columbia U. 1947. Sr. auditor Arthur Young & Co., N.Y.C., 1947-51; chief acct. Deering, Milliken & Co. 1951-53; treas., dir. Poloron Products, Inc., New Rochelle, N.Y., 1953-58;

controller Atlas Gen., Inc., N.Y.C., 1958-59; controller, treas., dir. fin. planning Pepperidge Farm, Inc., Norwalk, Conn., 1959-67; with C.R. Bard, Inc., Murray Hill, N.J., 1967-88; dir. C.R. Bard, Inc., 1972-92, vice chmn., 1983-88; mem. adv. bd. of Summit Trust Co., 1970-84. Trustee Overlook Hosp., 1973-79, Found. 1988-91, treas., 1989-90; trustee Epilepsy Found. N.J., 1985-90, pres., 1986-87, chmn., 1988-90. Lt. (j.g.) USNR, 1943-46. Mem. Fin. Execs. Inst., Canoe Brook Country Club, Harbour Ridge Yacht and Country Club, Delta Upsilon. Presbyterian.

LINDAU, JAMES H., grain exchange executive; b. Red Wing, Minn., May 21, 1933; s. Gottfrid and Stasia J. (Holmstrom) L.; m. Barbara Ann Marie Braaten, June 12, 1955; 1 child, James H. Jr. BA, Grinnell Coll. 1955. Mgmt. trainee The Glidden Co., Indpls., 1955-56; adminstrv. asst. Honeywell, Mpls., 1959-60; commodity merchandising v.p. The Pillsbury Co., Fresno, Mpls., 1960-83; mayor City of Bloomington, Minn., 1977-88; pres. Mpls. Grain Exch., 1988—; bd. dirs. Nat. Futures Assn., Chgo., 1988—, Nat. Grain Trade Coun., Washington, 1988—; owner francise Burger King Restaurant, Burnsville, 1983—; mem. agrl. tech. adv. com. Depts. of Agriculture and Trade, 1990—. Mem. Bloomington Bd. Edn., 1972-75, chmn., 1973-75; mem. Hennepin County Vo-Tech. Sch. Bd., Mpls., 1972-75, Hennepin Parks Found., 1990-92; candidate for lt. gov. Minn. (Rep., primary), 1982; candidate for gov. Minn. (Rep., primary), 1986; pres. Bloomington Minn. Port Authority, 1982-87. Capt. USAF, 1956-59. George F. Baker scholar Grinnell Coll., 1951-55; recipient Outstanding Leader award City of Bloomington, 1986, Good Neighbor award WCCO Radio, Mpls., 1987. Mem. Grand Nat. Quail Club (Enid, Okla., treas. 1986), Am. Swedish Inst., Svenska Sallskapet (Mpls.), Swedish Am. C. of C. (pres. Minn. chpt. 1990—). Lutheran. Avocations: hunting, fishing, golfing, cooking, politics. Office: Mpls Grain Exch 400 Grain Exchange Minneapolis MN 55415-1411

LINDAUER, JOHN HOWARD, II, newspaper publisher; b. Montclair, N.J., Nov. 20, 1937; s. John Howard and Louise (Platts) L.; m. Jacqueline Shelly, Sept. 2, 1960 (dec. 1992); children: Susan, John Howard. BS, Ariz. State U., 1960; PhD in Econs., Okla. State U., 1964. Asst. prof. econs. Occidental Coll., L.A., 1964-66; assoc. prof. Claremont (Calif.) Men's Coll. and Grad Sch., 1966-70, prof., chmn. econs., 1970-74; dean Coll. Bus. Murray (Ky.) State U., 1974-76; chancellor U. Alaska, Anchorage, 1976-78; commr. Alaska Pipeline, Anchorage, 1978; pres., chief exec. officer Alaska Industry and Energy Corp., Anchorage, 1978—; mem. Alaska Ho. of Reps., 1983-84; Rep. candidate for gov., 1990; bd. dirs. various cos.; owner various newspapers and radio sta.; cons. econ. policy and devel. U.S. Congress; cons. econs. U.S. corps; mem. AF Adv. Bd. Author: Macroeconomics, 1968, 71, 76, Economics: The Modern View, 1977, Land Taxation and the Indian Economic Development, 1979; editor Macroeconomic Readings; contbr. articles to profl. jours. Co-founder, vice chmn. Group against Smog Pollution, 1968; pres. So. Calif. Econ. Assn., 1974. With Army U.S., 1955-57. Fulbright prof., India, 1972; vis. prof. U. Sussex, Eng., 1972-73. Home: 3933 Geneva Pl Anchorage AK 99508-5055

LINDBERG, CHARLES DAVID, lawyer; b. Moline, Ill., Sept. 11, 1928; s. Victor Samuel and Alice Christine (Johnson) L.; m. Marian J. Wagner, June 14, 1953; children: Christine, Breta, John, Eric. AB, Augustana Coll., Rock Island, Ill., 1950; LLB, Yale U., 1953. Bar: Ohio 1954. Assoc. Taft, Stettinius & Hollister, Cin., 1953-61, ptnr., 1961-85; mng. ptnr. Taft, Stettinius & Hollister, 1985—; dir. Cin. Bengals Profl. Football Team, Gibson Greetings, Inc., Arga Co., Schonstedt Instrument Co. Editor Nat. Law Jour., 1979-90. Sec. Good Samaritan Hosp., Cin.; bd. dirs. Taft Broadcasting Co., Cin., 1973-87, Dayton Walther Corp., 1986-87; bd. dirs. Augustana Coll., 1978-87, 91—, sec., 1981-82, vice-chmn., 1982-83, chmn., 1983-86; pres. Cin. Bd. Edn., 1971, 74, Zion Luth. Ch., Cin., 1966-69; chmn. policy com. Hamilton County Rep. Com., 1981-90; mem. exec. com. Ohio Rep. Fin. Com., 1989-90; trustee Greater Cin. Ctr. Econ. Edn., 1976-91, pres. 1987-89; chmn. 1989-91; chmn. law firm div. Cin. United Appeal, 1976; chmn. law firm div. Fine Arts Fund, 1985; trustee Pub. Libr. of Cin. and Hamilton County, 1982—, pres. 1989-, v.p. 1995; exec. com. Ohio Rep. Fin. Com., 1989. Mem. ABA, Chgo. Bar Assn., Cin. Bar Assn., Greater Cin. C. of C. (trustee 1985, exec. com., vice chmn. govt. and community affairs com. 1989-91), Ohio Libr. Trustees Assn. (bd. dirs. 1986-87), Ohio C. of C. (bd. dirs. 1988-89), Queen City Club (sec. 1989-91), Commonwealth Club, Comml. Club, Cin. Country Club, Optimists. Office: Taft Stettinius & Hollister 1800 Star Bank Ctr 425 Walnut St Cincinnati OH 45202-3957

LINDBERG, DONALD ALLAN BROR, library administrator, pathologist, educator; b. N.Y.C., Sept. 21, 1933; s. Harry B. and Frances Seeley (Little) L.; m. Mary Musick, June 8, 1957; children: Donald Allan Bror, Christopher Charles Seeley, Jonathan Edward Moyer. AB, Amherst Coll., 1954, ScD (hon.), 1979; MD, Columbia U., 1958; ScD (hon.), SUNY, 1987; LLD (hon.), U. Mo., Columbia, 1990. Diplomate Am. Bd. Pathology, Am. Bd. Med. Examiners (exec. bd. 1987-91). Rsch. asst. Amherst Coll., 1954-55; intern in pathology Columbia-Presbyn. Med. Ctr., 1958-59, asst. resident in pathology, 1959-60; asst. in pathology Coll. Physician and Surgeons Columbia U., N.Y.C., 1958-60; instr. pathology Sch. of Medicine U. Mo., 1962-63, asst. prof. Sch. of Medicine, 1963-66, assoc. prof. Sch. of Medicine, 1966-69, prof. Sch. of Medicine, 1969-84, dir. Diagnostic Microbiology Lab. Sch. of Medicine, 1960-63, dir. Med. Ctr. Computer Program Sch. of Medicine, 1962-70, staff physician, 1965; dir. for health affairs Sch. of Medicine, 1968-70, prof., chmn. dept. info. sci. Sch. of Medicine, 1969-71; dir. Nat. Libr. of Medicine, Bethesda, Md., 1984—; adj. prof. pathology U. Md. Sch. Med., 1988—, clin. prof. pathology U. Va., 19922—; dir. Nat. Coord. Office for High Performance Computing and Comms., exec. office of Pres., Office Sci. & Tech. Policy, 1992—; mem. computer sci./engring. bd. Nat. Acad. Sci., 1971-74, chmn. Nat. Adv. Com. Artificial Intelligence in Medicine, Stanford U., 1975-84; U.S. rep. to Internat. Med. Info. Assn./Internat. Fedn. Info. Processing, 1975-84; bd. dirs. Am. Med. Info. Assn., 1992—; adv. coun. Inst. Medicine, 92—. Author: The Computer and Medical Care, 1968; The Growth of Medical Information Systems in the United States, 1979; editor: (with W. Siler) Computers in Life Science Research, 1975; (with others) Computer Applications in Medical Care, 1982; editor Methods of Info. in Medicine, 1970-83, assoc. editor, 1983—; editor Jour. Med. Systems, 1976—; Med. Informatics Jour., 1976—; chief editor procs. 3d World Conf. on Med. Informatics, 1980; editorial bd. Jour. of AMA, 1991—; contbr. articles to jours. Recipient Silver Core award Internat. Fedn. for Info. Processing, 1980, Walter C. Alvarez award Am. Med. Writers Assn., 1989, PHS Surgeon Gen.'s medallion, 1989, Nathan Davis award AMA, 1989, Presdl. Disting. Exec. Rank award Sr. Exec. Svc., Outstanding Svc. medal Uniformed Svcs. U. of the Health Scis., 1992, Computers in Healthcare Pioneer award 1993; Simpson fellow Amherst Coll., 1954-55; Markle scholar in acad. medciine, 1964-69. Mem. Inst. Medicine of NAS, Coll. Am. Pathologists (commn. on computer policy and coordination 1981-84), Mo. State Med. Assn., Assn. for Computing Machines, Salutis Unitas (Am. v.p. 1981-91), Am. Assn. for Med. Systems and Informatics (internat. com. 1982-89, bd. dirs. 1982, editor conf. procs. 1983, 84), Gorgas Meml. Inst. Tropical and Preventive Medicine (bd. dirs. 1987—), Am. Med. Informatics Assn. (pres. 1988-91), Sigma Xi. Democrat. Club: Cosmos (Washington). Avocations: photography; riding. Home: 13601 Esworthy Rd Germantown MD 20874-3319 Office: Nat Libr of Medicine 8600 Rockville Pike Bethesda MD 20894-0001

LINDBERG, DUANE R., minister. Presiding pastor The Am. Assn. Luth. Chs., Waterloo, Iowa. Office: Amer Assn of Lutheran Churches PO Box 416 Waterloo IA 50701

LINDBERG, GEORGE W., federal judge; b. Crystal Lake, Ill., June 21, 1932; s. Alger Victor and Rilla (Wakem) L. BS, Northwestern U., 1954, JD, 1957. V.p., legal counsel John E. Reid & Assocs., Chgo., 1955-68; ptnr. Franz, Franz, Wardell & Lindberg, Crystal Lake, 1968-73; comptr. State of Ill., Springfield, 1973-77; dep. atty. gen. State of Ill., Chgo., 1977-78; justice Ill. Appellate Ct., Elgin, 1978-89; fed. judge U.S. Dist. Ct. (no. dist.) Ill., Chgo., 1989—; chmn. Ill. House Com. on Judiciary, Com. on Ethics, Springfield, 1970-73. Holder numerous govt. offices, 1966—. Office: US Dist Ct 219 S Dearborn St Chicago IL 60604-1702

LINDBERG, HELGE, aviation consultant; b. London, Sept. 17, 1926; arrived in Norway, 1936; s. Carl Andreas and Sigrid Kristine (Bay) L.; m. Kerstin Hildegard Sjunnesson, Oct. 23, 1970; children by previous marriage: Sigrid Kristine, Carl Andreas. Grad. Treiders Handelsskole, Oslo, 1944.

With Scandinavian Airlines System, 1946-91; dist. mgr. Scandinavian Airlines System, Arabian Gulf, 1958; asst. regional mgr. Scandinavian Airlines System, Middle East, 1959-60; traffic sales mgr., dep. mng. dir. Scanair Charter Co. subs. Scandinavian Airlines System, Copenhagen, 1961-68; div. mgr. Scandinavian Airlines System, Finland and Eastern Europe, 1969-72; v.p. industry assn. affairs Scandinavian Airlines System, Stockholm, 1973-75, v.p. passenger mktg., 1976-78, exec. v.p. comml., 1979-83, chief oper. officer, 1983-86; dep. pres. Scandinavian Airlines System Group, Stockholm, 1986-91; chmn. Scanavia Aviation Cons., Stockholm, Sweden, 1993—; chmn. Scandinavian Air Tour Prodn., Stockholm, 1976-79, AMADEUS Global Travel distbn., Madrid, 1988-91; bd. dirs. Nymann & Schultz Travel Agy., Stockholm, 1976-91, Widerøe's Airline, 1986—, Oslo, Diners Nordic A/S, 1986-94, Bennett Scandinavia Travel Bur., Oslo, 1988-91; mem. traffic com. Internat. Air Traffic Assn., Geneva, 1973-74, chmn., 1975-76; mem. European Pratt & Whitney Adv. Bd., Paris, 1993—; chmn. Scanavia Aviation Cons., Oslo, 1994—. Bd. dirs. World Wildlife Fund, 1986-92. Mem. Assn. European Airlines (chmn. comml. and air polit. com. 1981-83), Scandinavian Multi Access System for Travel Agts. (chmn. 1983-85). Home: Lappstigen 3, 165 72 Hasselby Sweden Office: Scanavia Baltzar von Platen, Gata 9, 112 42 Stockholm Sweden

LINDBERG, LAWRENCE V., lawyer; b. Youngstown, Ohio, Dec. 21, 1947. BA, Coll. Wooster, 1970; JD, NYU, 1973. Bar: Ohio 1973. Ptnr. Baker & Hostetler, Cleve. Office: Baker & Hostetler 3200 Nat City Ctr 1900 E 9th St Cleveland OH 44114

LINDBERG, STANLEY WILLIAM, English language educator, editor; b. Warren, Pa., Nov. 18, 1939; s. Carl Leander and Leah Lucille (Henderson) L.; m. Jeanne Grace Heller, June 26, 1965; children: Kristin Anne, Eric Heller, Carl Muir. A.B. Dickinson Coll., 1961; M.A., U. Pa., 1967, Ph.D., 1969. Asst. prof. English Ohio U., Athens, 1969-75, assoc. prof., 1975-77; prof. humanities U. Ga., Athens, 1977-83, prof. English, 1983—; cons. editor Pushcart Prize Anthology, N.Y.C., 1978—; bd. advisors N.Y. State Lit. Ctr., Rochester, 1982—. Author: The Annotated McGuffey, 1976, The Legacy of Erskine Caldwell, 1989; co-author: Van Nostrand's Plain English Handbook, 1980, The Nature of Copyright, 1991; editor: The Plays of Frederick Reynolds (3 vols.), 1983; co-editor: Necessary Fictions, 1986, Keener Sounds, 1987, Inland Boat Poetry Series (10 vols.), 1980, The Ohio Rev., Athens, 1971-77; editor: The Ga. Rev., Athens, 1977—. Served to 1st lt. U.S. Army, 1962-64. Recipient Ga. Gov.'s award in the humanities, 1986, Nat. Mag. award fiction, 1986. Mem. MLA, Am. Soc. Mag. Editors, Conf. Editors of Learned Jours. (exec. com. 1980—), Phi Beta Kappa (pres. Alpha Ga. 1986-88), Omicron Delta Kappa. Home: 195 Maple Cir Athens GA 30606-4813 Office: U Ga Ga Rev Main Libr Athens GA 30602-9009

LINDBERGH, ANNE SPENCER MORROW (MRS. CHARLES AUGUSTUS LINDBERGH), author; b. Englewood, N.J., 1906; d. Dwight Whitney and Elizabeth Reeve (Cutter) Morrow; m. Charles Augustus Lindbergh, May 27, 1929 (dec. 1974); children: Charles Augustus (dec.), Jon Morrow, Land Morrow, Anne Spencer, Scott Morrow, Reeve Morrow. G-rad., Miss Chapin's Sch., N.Y.C., Smith Coll., Northampton, Mass., 1928; MA (hon.), Smith Coll., Northampton, Mass., 1935; LLD (hon.), Amherst Coll., 1939, Univ. Rochester, 1939. Author: North to the Orient, 1935, Listen! The Wind, 1938, The Wave of the Future, 1940, The Steep Ascent, 1944, Gift from the Sea, 1955, The Unicorn and Other Poems, 1935-1955, 1956, Dearly Beloved, 1962, Earth Shine, 1969, Christmas in Mexico: 1972, 1971, Bring Me a Unicorn: Diaries and Letters of Anne Morrow Lindbergh, 1972, Hour of Gold, Hour of Lead: Diaries and Letters of Anne Morrow Lindbergh, 1929-2932, 1973, Locked Rooms and Open Doors: Diaries and Letters of Anne Morrow Lindbergh, 1932-1935, 1974, The Flower and the Nettle: Diaries and Letters of Anne Morrow Lindbergh, 1936-1939, 1976, War Within and Without: Diaries and Letters of Anne Morrow Lindbergh, 1939-1944, 1980, The People in Pineapple Place, 1982, Bailey's Window, 1984, The Worry Week, 1985, The Hunky-Dory Diary, 1986, The Shadow on the Dial, 1987, Nobody's Orphan, 1987, The Prisoner of Pineapple Place, 1988, Next Time, Take Care, 1988, Tidy Lady, 1989, Travel Far, Pay No Fare, 1992, Three Lives to Live, 1992, Nick of Time, 1994. Recipient two prizes for lit. work Smith Coll.; cross of honor (for part in survey of trans-Atlantic air route) U.S. Flag Assn., 1933; Hubbard gold medal (for work as co-pilot and radio operator in flight of 40,000 miles over five continents) Nat. Geog. Soc., 1934. *

LINDBLAD, RICHARD ARTHUR, health services administrator, drug abuse epidemiologist; b. Atlantic, Iowa, July 15, 1937; s. Clifford Robert and Emma Ruth (Dunham) L.; children: Julie, Richard, Mark. B.S., San Jose State Coll., 1961; M.S., U. Colo., 1965; M.P.H., Johns Hopkins U., 1971, Dr.P.H., 1974. Capt. USPHS, 1961, col., 1975, ret. capt., 1961-94; various assignments including adminstrn., epidemiology, research and prevention of substance abuse disorders Fed. Drug Abuse Treatment Hosp., Ft. Worth, Denver; now dir. internat. programs Nat. Inst. on Drug Abuse, Rockville, Md.; cons. in drug abuse epidemiology WHO, UN; designed and supervised devel. of UN Internat. Drug Abuse Assessment System; cons. on drug abuse rsch. and program devel. Designed and supervised devel. of the International Visiting Scientist and Technical Exchange program of the dept. of Health and Human Svcs.; Contbr. articles to profl. jours. Mem. Am. Public Health Assn., Md. Public Health Assn., Commd. Officers Assn. USPHS, Nat. Assn. Uniformed Services. Home: PO Box 179 Libertytown MD 21762-0179

LINDBLOM, MARJORIE PRESS, lawyer; b. Chgo., Mar. 17, 1950; d. John E. and Betty (Grage) P.; m. Lance E. Lindblom, June 13, 1971; children: Derek, Ian. AB cum laude, Radcliffe Coll., 1971; JD with honors, U. Chgo., 1978. Bar: Ill. 1978, U.S. Dist. Ct. (no. dist.) Ill. 1978, U.S. Ct. Appeals (7th cir.) 1978, U.S. Ct. Appeals (10th cir.) 1983, U.S. Supreme Ct. 1983, U.S. Ct. Appeals (5th cir.) 1984, N.Y. 1995, U.S. Dist. Ct. (so. dist.) N.Y. 1995. Assoc. Kirkland & Ellis, Chgo., 1978-84, ptnr., 1984-94; N.Y.C. 1994—; asst. dir. fiscal affairs Ill. Bd. Higher Edn., 1973-75; budget analyst Ill. Bur. Budget, Office of Gov., 1972-73; admissions officer Princeton U., 1971-72; adj. prof. Northwestern U., Evanston, Ill., 1994. Comment editor U. Chgo. Law Rev., 1977-78. Bd. dirs. Chgo. Lawyers Com. for Civil Rights Under Law, 1989-94, Pub. Interest Law Initiative, 1989-94. Mem. ABA, Chgo. Coun. Lawyers (bd. govs. 1987-91, legal counsel 1986-87), 7th Cir. Bar Assn., Women's Bar Assn. of Ill. Office: Kirkland & Ellis Citicorp Ctr 153 East 53rd St New York NY 10022

LINDE, HANS ARTHUR, state supreme court justice; b. Berlin, Germany, Apr. 15, 1924; came to U.S., 1939, naturalized, 1943; s. Bruno C. and Luise (Rosenhain) L.; m. Helen Tucker, Aug. 13, 1945; children: Lisa, David Tucker. BA, Reed Coll., 1947; JD, U. Calif., Berkeley, 1950. Bar: Oreg. 1951. Law clk. U.S. Supreme Ct. Justice William O. Douglas, 1950-51; atty. Office of Legal Adviser, Dept. State, 1951-53; pvt. practice Portland, Oreg., 1953-54; legis. asst. U.S. Sen. Richard L. Neuberger, 1955-58; from assoc. prof. to prof. U. Oreg. Law Sch., 1959-76; justice Oreg. Supreme Ct., Salem, 1977-90, sr. judge, 1990—; Fulbright lectr. Freiburg U., 1967-68, Hamburg U., 1975-76; cons. U.S. ACDA, Dept. Def., 1962-76; mem. Adminstrv. Conf. U.S., 1978-82. Author: (with George Bunn) Legislative and Administrative Processes, 1976. Mem. Oreg. Constl. Revision Commn., 1961-62, Oreg. Commn. on Pub. Broadcasting, 1990-93. With U.S. Army, 1943-46. Fellow Am. Acad. Arts and Scis.; mem. Am. Law Inst. (council), Order of Coif, Phi Beta Kappa.

LINDE, MAXINE HELEN, lawyer, business executive, private investor; b. Chgo., Sept. 2, 1939; d. Jack and Lottie (Kroll) Stern; B.A. summa cum laude, UCLA, 1961; J.D., Stanford U., 1967; m. Ronald K. Linde, June 12, 1960. Bar: Calif. 1968. Applied mathematician, research engr. Jet Propulsion Lab., Pasadena, Calif., 1961-64; law clk. U.S. Dist. Ct. No. Calif., 1967-68; mem. firm Long & Levit, San Francisco, 1968-69, Swerdlow, Glikbarg & Shimer, Beverly Hills, Calif., 1969-72; sec., gen. counsel Envirodyne Industries, Inc., Chgo., 1972-89; pres. The Ronald and Maxine Linde Found., 1989—; vice chmn. bd., gen. counsel Titan Fin. Group, LLC, Chgo., 1994—. Mem. bd. visitors Stanford Law Sch., 1989-92, law and bus. adv. coun., 1991-94, dean's adv. coun. 1992-94. Mem. Order of Coif, Phi Beta Kappa, Pi Mu Epsilon, Alpha Lambda Delta.

LINDE, ROBERT HERMANN, economics educator; b. Schlewecke, Fed. Republic Germany, July 22, 1944; s. Robert and Emma (Lohmann) L.; m.

Sabine Rinck, Mar. 12, 1976 (div. 1985); children: Niels Christian, Johanne Cornelia; m. Ingrid Windus, June 30, 1987. Diploma in Econs., U. Gottingen, Fed. Republic Germany, 1969, D in Polit. Sci., 1977, D in Habilitation, 1981. Asst. U. Gottingen, 1976-81, lectr., 1981-86, prof. econs., 1986-87; prof. econs. U. Luneburg, Fed. Republic Germany, 1987—. Author: Theory of Product Quality, 1977, Pay and Performance, 1984, Introduction to Microeconomics, 2d edit., 1992; co-author: Production Theory, 1976. Mem. Am. Econ. Assn., Verein für Socialpolitik, European Econ. Assn. Office: U Lüneburg, Scharnhorststrasse 1 Haus 4, 21332 Lüneburg Germany

LINDE, RONALD KEITH, corporate executive, private investor; b. L.A., Jan. 31, 1940; s. Morris and Sonia Doreen (Hayman) L.; m. Maxine Helen Stern, June 12, 1960. BS with honors, UCLA, 1961; MS (Inst. scholar), Calif. Inst. Tech., 1962, PhD (ARCS scholar, Rutherford scholar), 1964. Cons. Litton Industries, L.A., 1961-63; materials scientist Poulter Labs., Stanford Rsch. Inst., Menlo Park, Calif., 1964; head solid state rsch. Stanford Rsch. Inst., Menlo Park, Calif., 1965-67; chmn. shock wave physics dept., mgr. tech. svcs. Poulter Labs., 1967, dir. shock and high pressure physics div., 1967-68, chief exec. labs., 1968-69; dir. phys. scis. Stanford Rsch. Inst., 1968-69; chmn. bd., CEO Envirodyne Industries, Inc., Chgo., 1969-89; chmn. bd. The Ronald and Maxine Linde Found., Chgo., 1989—; co-chmn. bd. Titan Fin. Group, LLC, Chgo., 1994—; law and bus. adv. coun. Stanford Law Sch., 1991-94, dean's adv. coun. 1992-94. Contbr. articles to various publs.; patentee in field. Mem. adv. bd. ARCS Found., Chgo., 1993—; mem. Northwestern U. Assocs., 1987—; trustee Calif. Inst. Tech., 1989—, Harvey Mudd Coll., 1989—, vice chmn., bd. trustees, 1993—. Mem. Sigma Xi, Tau Beta Pi, Phi Eta Sigma. Office: Linde Found Unit 5801 180 E Pearson St Chicago IL 60611-2115

LINDEGREN, JACK KENNETH, elementary and secondary education educator; b. Fresno, Calif., Feb. 9, 1931; s. Henry Jack and Katherine (Metzler) L.; m. Betty Jo Rowland, Dec. 1960 (div. Apr. 1963); m. Elaine Finnegan, Apr. 27, 1963; children: Susan Carol, Karen Ann. BA, Fresno State Coll., 1954; MA, Calif. State U., Fresno, 1976. Educator, adminstr. Fresno County, Firebaugh, Calif., 1954-5; educator Calaveras County Schs., San Andreas, Calif., 1964-66, Kings County Schs., Corcoran, Calif., 1966-80, Kern County Schs., Bakersfield, Calif., 1985-87, L.A. Unified Schs., 1985—; educator L.A. Unified Schs., 1977-92; instr. ARC, Hanford, Calif., 1974-79-; instr. County Sci. Insvc., 1985. Inventor electroanalysis device Chrysler award., 1965. Participant Desert Opera, Palmdale, Calif., 1986-88; bd. mem., chmn. ARC, Hanford, 1973-78. Sgt. U.S. Army, 1955-57. Mem. NAS, AAAS, NEA, Nat. Assn. Legions of Honor, Nat. Space Soc., Tehran Shrine, Fresno East/West Game Corcoran Band Club, Santa Clara U. Alumni Assn., N.Y. Acad. Scis., Internat. DeMolay Alumni Assn. (life), Assn. Calif. Sch. Adminstrs., Calif. State U. of Fresno Alumni Assn. (life), Scottish Rite (life), Corcoran/Tulare Masons (life, Bethel guardian 1978-80, Pin 1980), Odd Fellows (30 Yr. Mem. award 1991), Mensa (elder, deacon bushop, 10 v.p. Membership award). Presbyterian. Avocations: reading, science and religious literature (Mensa spl. interest groups in religion).

LINDELL, EDWARD ALBERT, former college president, religious organization administrator; b. Denver, Nov. 30, 1928; s. Edward Gustaf and Estelle (Lundin) L.; m. Patricia Clare Eckert, Sept. 2, 1965; children—Edward Paul, Erik Adam. B.A., U. Denver, 1950, M.A., 1956, Ed.D., 1960, L.H.D. (hon.), 1975; Litt.D. (hon.), Tusculum Coll., 1979; D.H.L. (hon.), Roanoke Coll., 1981; Litt.D (hon.), Christ Coll., Irvine, 1992. Tchr. N. Denver High Sch., 1952-61; asst. dean Coll. Arts and Scis., U. Denver, 1961-65, dean, 1965-75; pres. Gustavus Adolphus Coll., St. Peter, Minn., 1975-80, Luth. Brotherhood Mut. Funds, Mpls., Minn., 1980—; v.p. Lutheran Brotherhood Found., 1980—, exec. dir. Mem. exec. bd. Rocky Mountain Synod Lutheran Ch. Am., 1968—, also pres. bd. coll. edn. and ch. vocations.; Trustee Midland Luth. Coll., Fremont, Nebr., Kans. Wesleyan U., Colo. Assn. Ind. Colls. and Univs., Luth. Med. Center, Wheatridge, Colo. Luth. Sch. Theology, Chgo., 1975—, St. John's U., Minn., 1978—; bd. dirs. Pacific Luth. Theol. Sem., 1978-80, Loretto Heights Coll., Colo., 1978-86, Swedish Council Am., 1978—, Gettysburg Theol. Sem., 1981-83; exec. bd. Luth. Council U.S.A., v.p., 1975—; mem. adv. bd. Royal Swedish Acad. Scis., 1980; v.p. Am.-Swedish Inst., 1980; exec. v.p. for external affairs Luth. Brotherhood, 1981—; pres. Nat. Fraternal Congress Am., 1988—; bd. dirs. Wittenberg U., 1988, Bethany Coll., 1991—, Minn. Orch., 1983—, Am. Scandinavian Found., 1982—, Fairview Hosp., 1982—, U.S. Swedish Found. Internat. Sci. Rsch., 1981— (v.p. 1986—), Habitat for Humanity Internat., 1992—. Named Outstanding Faculty Mem. Coll. Arts and Scis., U. Denver, 1964; decorated knight King of Sweden, 1976; recipient Suomi Disting. Svc. award, 1989. Mem. Swedish Pioneer Hist. Soc. (dir. 1979—), U. Denver Alumni Assn. (Career Alumni Achievement award 1994), Phi Beta Kappa. Office: Luth Brotherhood Mut Funds 625 4th Ave S Minneapolis MN 55415-1624

LINDEMANN, DONALD LEE, utility executive; b. Indpls., Oct. 1, 1936; s. Paul Alexander and Pearl Ann (Raybern) L.; m. Lou Anne Nerge, Dec. 27, 1957; children: Bradford Allen, Dawn Marie. B.S. in Acctg., Butler U., 1958; M.S. in Acctg., St. Louis U., 1961; M.B.A., Harvard U., 1964. C.P.A. Ind. Mgmt. cons. Peat-Marwick-Mitchell, 1964-65; dir. systems and audit Citizens Gas & Coke, Indpls., 1965-66, controller, 1967-78, sr. v.p., 1978-79, exec. v.p., 1979-80, exec. v.p., chief operating officer, 1981-86, pres., chief exec. officer, 1986—. Bd. dirs. Cmty. Hosp. Indpls., 1994—. 1st lt. USAF, 1959-62. Mem. AICPA, Ind. Assn. CPAs, Am. Gas Assn., Midwest Gas Assn. Republican. Presbyterian. Home: 8612 Emerald Ln Indianapolis IN 46260-1751 Office: Citizens Gas & Coke Utility 2020 N Meridian St Indianapolis IN 46202-1306

LINDEMER, LAWRENCE BOYD, lawyer, former utility executive, former state justice; b. Syracuse, N.Y., Aug. 21, 1921; s. George F. and Altamae (Reimers) L.; children—Lawrence Boyd, David G. Student, Taft Sch., 1939, Hamilton Coll., 1939-41; A.B., U. Mich., 1943, LL.B., 1948. Bar: Mich. 1948. Asst. pros. atty. Ingham County, 1949-51; asst., commn. on orgn. Exec. Br. Govt., Hoover Comm., 1953-55; partner Foster, Lindemer, Swift & Collins (and predecessor firm), 1955-75; justice Mich. Supreme Ct., Lansing, 1975-76; sr. v.p., gen. counsel Consumers Power Co., 1977-86. Mem. Mich. Ho. of Reps., 1951-52; Republican state chmn., 1957-61; mem. Rep. Nat. Com., 1957-61; Rep. candidate atty. gen. Mich., 1966; bd. regents U. Mich., 1968-75; trustee Gerald R. Ford Found., 1985—. Served with USAAF, 1943-45. Mem. ABA, State Bar Mich. (commr. 1963-70), Mich. State Bd. Ethics, U. Mich. Alumni Assn. (pres. 1983-85), Am. Automobile Assn. (bd. dirs 1987—, chmn. 1993-95), Auto Club Mich. (bd. dirs., chmn. bd. 1985-87). Presbyterian (elder). Home: PO Box 667 Stockbridge MI 49285-0667 Office: Foster Swift Collins & Smith PC 313 Washington Sq S Lansing MI 48933-2114

LINDEN, BARNARD JAY, electrical engineer; b. Bklyn., May 18, 1943; s. Abraham and Beatrice (Westler) L.; m. Janet Sigrid Jaffe, Sept. 12, 1965; 1 child, Michelle. BS, Monmouth Coll., 1965; postgrad., Adelphi U., 1966, N.Y. Inst. Tech., 1970-71; MA, SUNY, 1995. Registered profl. engr., N.Y., N.J. Electronics engr. Grumman Aerospace, Bethpage, N.Y., 1965-72; sr. electronics engr. Litton Industries, Melville, N.Y., 1972-73; elec. engr. N.Y.C. Bd. Edn., 1973-75; chief elec. engr. N.Y. State Div. Housing, N.Y.C., 1975—; chmn. Profl. Engrs. in Govt., 1992-95; cons. in field, N.Y. Vol. Spl. Olympics, Patchogue, N.Y., 1991, Hauppage, Stony Brook, 1992. Mem. N.Y. State Soc. Profl. Engrs. (legis. chmn. 1986-88, chair membership 1988-90, treas. 1990-91, chair profl. engrs. in govt. 1992-95), Nat. Soc. Profl. Engrs., Suffolk County Radio Club (pres. 1994-95), Sigma Pi Sigma. Jewish. Avocations: skiing, amateur radio, golf, classical music. Office: NY State Div Housing One Fordham Plz Bronx NY 10458

LINDEN, CAROL MARIE, special education educator; b. Pitts., Dec. 24, 1953; d. Enio P. and Mary C. (Santillo) Cardone; m. Frank J. Miller Jr., Dec. 21, 1974 (div. 1989); children: Emily, Karl, Richard; m. James Anthony Linden, Dec. 9, 1989; children: Shiloh, Shane, Shasta, Shelby (dec.). BS, California (Pa.) State U., 1974; MS, Youngstown State U., 1981. Cert. moderate, severe, profoundly retarded, educable mentally retarded, learning disabled/behavior disordered, speech and hearing. Tchr. multi-handicapped Youngstown (Ohio) City Schs., 1987—; tchr. multihandicapped Trumbull County Bd. Edn., Lordstown, Ohio, 1986-87; spl. vocat. edn. coord. Trumbull County Joint Vocat. Sch., Warren, Ohio, 1985-86; lang. devel. specialist Fairhaven Sheltered Workshop, Niles and Champion, Ohio, 1976-

85. Grantee N.E. Ohio Spl. Edn. Resource Ctr., 1989-92, Ohio Bell and Ameritech Impact II, 1991, 92, 95, Consumer/Econ. grantee, 1989-95; Wolves Club Carapolis scholar, 1971. Mem. Ohio Speech and Hearing Assn., Coun. for Exceptional Children, Nat. Soc. for Autistic Citizens (sec. 1986-87). Roman Catholic/Baptist. Avocations: reading, crafts, camping. Home: 432 Hunter Ave Niles OH 44446-1625

LINDEN, HAL, actor, singer; b. Bronx, N.Y., Mar. 20, 1931; s. Charles and Frances (Rosen) Lipshitz; m. Frances Martin, Apr. 13, 1958; children: Amelia Christine, Jennifer Dru, Nora Kathryn, Ian Martin. BBA, CCNY, 1952; student, Am. Theatre Wing, N.Y.C., 1954-55; student acting, Paul Mann, 1956-60, Lloyd Richards, 1962-63; student voice, Lou McCollogh, 1953-56, John Mace, 1958-64. Saxophone player and singer; played with bands of Sammy Kaye, Bobby Sherwood and, Boyd Raeburn; stage debut in Wonderful Town, Cape Cod Melody Tent, Hyannis, Mass., 1955; N.Y. stage debut as understudy to Sydney Chaplain in Bells are Ringing, 1956, then took over lead; other stage appearances include The Rothschilds (Tony award 1971), Three Men on a Horse, Anything Goes, Pajama Game, I'm Not Rappaport, 1987, The Sisters Rosensweig, 1993; appeared in film Bells are Ringing, 1959, When You Comin' Back, Red Ryder?, 1979, A New Life, 1988; TV series Barney Miller, 1975-82, Blacke's Magic, 1985-86, Jack's Place, 1992-93, The Boys are Back, 1994-95; host: children's series Animals Animals Animals; informational series FYI, ABC-TV, 1980; narrator: series Saga of the Western World, 1963-64; film When You Comin' Back, Red Ryder?, 1979, A New Life, 1988; TV films include Mr. Inside, Mr. Outside, 1973, The Love Boat, 1976, How to Break a Happy Divorce, 1976, Father Figure, 1980, Starflight, the Plane That Couldn't Land, 1983, The Other Woman, 1983, My Wicked, Wicked Ways: The Legend of Errol Flynn, 1985, The O'Connors, Dream Breakers, 1989; appeared with L.A. Philharm. Orch., Hollywood Bowl, 1984. Served in U.S. Army, 1952-54. Mem. Actors Equity, Screen Actors Guild, AFTRA, AGVA, Am. Fedn. Musicians. Office: William Morris Agy 151 El Camino Beverly Hills CA 90212*

LINDEN, HENRY ROBERT, chemical engineering research executive; b. Vienna, Austria, Feb. 21, 1922; came to U.S., 1939, naturalized, 1945; s. Fred and Edith (Lermer) L.; m. Natalie Govedarica, 1967; children by previous marriage: Robert, Debra. BS, Ga. Inst. Tech., 1944; MChemE, Poly. U., 1947; PhD, Ill. Inst. Tech., 1952. Chem. engr. Socony Vacuum Labs., 1944-47; with Inst. of Gas Tech., 1947-78, various rsch. mgmt. positions, 1947-61, dir., 1961-69, exec. v.p., dir., 1969-74, pres., trustee, 1974-78; various acad. appointments Ill. Inst. Tech., Chgo., 1954-86, Frank W. Gunsaulus Disting. Prof. chem. engring., 1987-90, McGraw prof. energy and power engring. and mgmt., 1990—, interim pres., CEO, 1989-90, interim chmn., CEO Ill. Inst. Tech. Rsch. Inst., 1989-90; COO Gas Devel. Corp. (name now GDC, Inc.) subs. Inst. of Gas Tech., Chgo., 1965-73, CEO, 1973-78, also bd. dirs.; pres., dir. Gas Rsch. Inst., Chgo., 1976-87, exec. advisor, 1987—; bd. dirs. Larimer & Co., AES Corp., Resources for the Future Inc. Author tech. articles; holder U.S. and fgn. patents in fuel tech. Recipient award of merit oper. sect. Am. Gas Assn., 1956, Disting. Svc. award 1974, gas industry rsch. award, 1982; Walton Clark medal Franklin Inst., 1972, Bunsen-Pettenkofer-Ehrentafel medal Deutscher Verein Gas und Wasserfaches, 1978, R & D award Nat. Energy Resources Orgn., 1986, Homer H. Lowry award for excellence in fossil energy rsch. U.S. Dept. Energy, 1991, award U.S. Energy Assn., 1993; named to Ill. Inst. Tech. Hall of Fame, 1982. Fellow AIChE, Inst. Energy; mem. NAE, Am. Chem. Soc. (recipient H.H. Storch award, chmn. divsn. fuel chemistry 1967, councilor 1969-77), So. Gas Assn. (hon. life). Office: Ill Inst Tech 10 W 33rd St PH 135 Chicago IL 60616 also: Gas Rsch Inst 8600 W Bryn Mawr Ave Chicago IL 60631-3505

LINDENBAUM, SANDFORD RICHARD, lawyer; b. N.Y.C., July 6, 1948; s. Sidney Lewis and Ruth Jane (Krauskopf) L.; m. Leslie Sircus, Jan. 19, 1982; children: Dara, David. BA, Franklin & Marshall Coll., 1970; JD with honors, George Washington U., 1973. Bar: N.Y. 1974, U.S. Dist. Ct. (so. dist.) N.Y. 1975, U.S. Dist. Ct. (no. dist.) N.Y. 1985. Asst. dist. atty. County of Westchester, White Plains, N.Y., 1973-78; from assoc. to ptnr. Bower & Gardner, N.Y.C., 1978-94; ptnr. Garbarini & Scher, N.Y.C., 1994—. Mem. ABA, N.Y. State Bar Assn. Office: Garbarini and Scher 1114 Ave of the Americas New York NY 10036

LINDENBERG, STEVEN PHILLIP, counselor, consultant; b. Lancaster, Pa., Dec. 6, 1945; s. Sidney David and Ruth Lillian (Levine) L.; m. Linda Kathleen Young, Aug. 26, 1967; children: Sara Michelle, Karen Rebecca, Elisabeth Claudine. BS, Millersville U., 1968; MEd, Shippensburg State U., 1974; PhD, U. Ga., 1977. Cert. clin. mental health counselor, Nat. Acad. Cert. Clin. Health Counseling, cert. counselor Nat. Bd. Cert. Counselors, cert. sch. psychologist, Pa. Jr. high sci. tchr. Chambersburg (Pa.) Area Sch. Dist., 1972-74; grad. asst. dept. counseling edn. Univ. Ga., Athens, 1974-77; ptnr., cert. clin. mental health counselor Hershey (Pa.) Psychiat. Assocs., 1977-93; founder Lindenberg Inst. for Therapy, 1993—; co-founder, 1st vice-chair Nat. Acad. Cert. Clin. Mental Health Counselors, Falls Church, Va., 1978-80; founder Lindenberg & David, Assocs., Hershey, 1990—. Mem. editorial bd.: Jour. Mental Health Counseling, 1991-94, author: Group Psychotherapy with People Who Are Dying, 1983; contbr. articles to profl. jours. Founding bd. mem. Hospice of En. Pa., Enola, 1978-87, past pres., mem. bereavement com. 1978-93; mem. profl. devel. com. Am. Cancer Soc., Harrisburg, Pa., 1986-87; past pres., mem. bd. sch. dirs. No. Lebanon Sch. Dist., Fredericksburg, Pa., 1988-93. Decorated Am. Spirit of Honor medal Citizens Com. for Army, Navy and Air Force, Inc., Lackland AFB, Tex., 1968. Mem. AACD (bd. dirs. 1979-80), Am. Mental Health Counselors Assn. (pres. 1979-80, profl. recognition awards 1981, 89, charter mem.), Pa. Mental Health Counselors Assn. (treas. 1993-95, pres. 1995—, eminent practitioner 1988), Dauphin Co. Bar Assn. (task force mem. 1994—), Phi Kappa Phi, Kappa Delta Pi. Avocations: real estate investment, writing, music composition and performance, gardening. Office: Lindenberg Inst Therapy 218 West Governor Rd Hershey PA 17033

LINDENBERGER, HERBERT SAMUEL, writer, literature educator; b. Los Angeles, Apr. 4, 1929; s. Hermann and Celia (Weinkrantz) L.; m. Claire Flaherty, June 14, 1961; children: Michael James, Elizabeth Celia. BA, Antioch Coll., Yellow Springs, Ohio, 1951; PhD, U. Wash., Seattle, 1955. From instr. to prof. English and comparative lit. U. Calif., Riverside, 1954-66; prof. German and English, chmn. program comparative lit. Washington U., St. Louis, 1966-69; Avalon prof. humanities Stanford U., 1969—, chmn. program comparative lit., 1969-82; dir. Stanford Humanities Ctr., 1991-92. Author: On Wordsworth's Prelude, 1963, Georg Büchner, 1964, (play) Lear and Cordelia at Home, 1968, Georg Trakl, 1971, Historical Drama: The Relation of Literature and Reality, 1975, Saul's Fall: A Critical Fiction, 1979, Opera: The Extravagant Art, 1984, The History in Literature: On Value, Genre, Institutions, 1990; contbr. articles to profl. jours. Fulbright scholar Austria, 1952-53; Guggenheim fellow, 1968-69; Nat. Endowment Humanities fellow, 1975-76, 82-83; Stanford U. Humanities Center Fellow, 1982-83. Mem. MLA (2d v.p., pres. 1995—), Am. Comparative Lit. Assn. Office: Stanford U Dept Comparative Lit Stanford CA 94305

LINDENFELD, PETER, physics educator; b. Vienna, Austria, Mar. 10, 1925; came to U.S., 1940, naturalized, 1957; s. Bela and Elda (Lachs) L.; m. Lore Kadden, May 31,1953; children: Thomas, Naomi. Student, U. Man., Can., 1942-43; B.A.Sc., U.B.C., Can., 1946, M.A. Sc., 1948; Ph.D., Columbia U., 1954. Vis. lectr. Drew U., Madison, N.J., 1952-53; instr. Rutgers U., 1953-55, asst. prof. physics, 1955-61, asso. prof., 1961-66, prof., 1966—; cons. summer inst. AID, Tirupati, India, 1965; regional counselor N.J. Am. Inst. Physics, 1963-71; dir. NSF In-svc. Insts. High Sch. Tchrs., 1964-66; Rutgers Rsch. Coun. fellow and guest scientist Faculte de Scis., U. Paris-Sud, Orsay, France, 1970-71; vis. scholar Kyoto U., Japan, 1982. Contbr. articles to profl. jours. Recipient Warren I. Susman award for excellence in teaching, 1988, Robert A. Millikan Lecture award and medal Am. Assn. Physics Tchrs., 1989. Fellow Am. Phys. Soc.; mem. AAUP, Am. Assn. Physics Tchrs. (hon. mem. N.J. sect.). Home: 121 Harris Rd Princeton NJ 08540-3375 Office: Rutgers U Dept Physics and Astronomy Piscataway NJ 08855-0849

LINDER, BERTRAM NORMAN, foundation administrator, horse-breeder, actor; b. N.Y.C., Nov. 24, 1915; s. Albert Aaron and Bess (Newman) L.; m. Eleanor Jones (dec.); children: Robert Allan (dec.), Denise J.; m. Mary Ellen Smith. BA, Williams Coll., 1936; postgrad., Yale U., 1937-38, Columbia U.,

1938-39. V.p. Linder Bros., Inc., Scranton, Pa., 1940-65, pres., treas., 1965-80; pres., treas. Albert A. & Bertram N. Linder Found., Inc., N.Y.C., 1965—; owner Hickory Hill Farm, Dalton, Pa., 1947—. Author: Songs to the Night, 1941. Pres. Jewish Fedn., Scranton, 1949-52; pres., co-founder Child Guidance & Psychiatry Ctr., Lackawanna County, Pa.; chmn. adv. bd. Salvation Army, Scranton, 1947-50; pres. United Way, Lackawanna County, 1960-63. 1st lt. inf. U.S. Army, 1943-46, ETO. Recipient Community Svc. award Scranton C. of C., 1949, Salvation Army, 1950, Citizenship award AFL-CIO, 1962, 65, Americanism award B'nai B'rith, 1965. Mem. AFTRA, Screen Actors Guild, Thoroughbred Owner's and Breeders Assn., Thoroughbred of Am. Club (Lexington, Ky.), B'nai B'rith, Phi Beta Kappa. Republican. Jewish. Avocations: fishing, travel. Home: Hickory Hill Farm W Main St Dalton PA 18414-9522 Office: Linder Found Inc 305 E 40th St New York NY 10016-2189

LINDER, FANNIE RUTH, psychotherapist, concert soprano; b. Hartwell, Ga., Mar. 14, 1934; d. Marion Taylor and Nobie (Gaines) Barnes; m. Raymond Linder, Jan. 30, 1953; children: Raymond T., Michael C. BA, SUNY, Binghamton, 1986; MA, Liberty U., 1990. Tchr. Romulus (N.Y.) Ctrl. Schs., 1969-70; owner, prodr. ISHI Rec. Studio, Apalachin, N.Y., 1981—; pvt. psychotherapist Apalachin, 1984—; bd. dirs. The Stewart W. and Willma C. Hoyt Found., Binghamton; bd. mem. So. Tier Inst. for Arts in Edn., Binghamton, 1993—, Eckelberger Towers, Binghamton, 1993—; mem. ethics com. United Health Hosps., Binghamton, 1993—; lectr. in field. Concert soprano worldwide, 1968—. Spokesperson, chair Police/Community Group, Binghamton, 1987-93. Named Outstanding Young Women of Am., 1965; recipient Appreciation award Gen. Commn. on Chaplains and Armed Forces Pers., Romulus, 1970. Mem. Assn. for Psychol. Type, Personality Inst. (bd. chmn., founder). Avocations: reading, research, music. Home: 21 W Glann Rd Apalachin NY 13732

LINDER, JOHN E, congressman, dentist; b. Deer River, Minn., Sept. 2, 1942; s. Henry and Vera Elizabeth Davis L.; m. Lynne Leslee Peterson, 1963; children: Kristine Kerry, Matthew John. BS, U. Minn., 1963, DDS, 1967. Pvt. practice Atlanta, Ga., 1967-82; mem. Ga. Ho. of Reps., 1975-80, 82-90; pres. Linder Fin. Corp., 1977-92; mem. 103d-104th Congress from 4th Ga. Dist., 1993—; mem. Banks and Banking, Def. and Vet. Affairs, Legis. and Congl. Reapportionment coms. Ga. State Ho. of Reps.; mem. vets. affairs com., banking, fin. and urban affairs com., sci., space tech. com., com. on coms., hosps. and health care subcom., consumer credit and ins. subcom., fin. instns. supervision, regulation and deposit ins. subcom., house rules com., legis. process subcom., Rep. steering com. U.S. Ho. of Reps. Founder I Care, 1970. Capt. USAF, 1967-69. Mem. ADA, Ga. Dental Assn., No. Dist. Dental Soc., Rotary. Republican. Presbyterian. Office: US Ho of Reps 1318 Longworth Bldg Washington DC 20515

LINDER, STU, film editor. Editor: (films) The Fortune, 1975, (with Susan Martin) First Family, 1980, My Bodyguard, 1980, Six Weeks, 1982, Diner, 1982, The Natural, 1984, Young Sherlock Holmes, 1985, Code Name: Emerald, 1985, Good Morning, Vietnam, 1987, Tin Men, 1987, Rain Man, 1988 (Academy award nomination best film editing 1988), Avalon, 1990, Bugsy, 1991, Toys, 1992, Quiz Show, 1994. Office: care Motion Picture Editors 7715 Sunset Blvd #220 Los Angeles CA 90046*

LINDERMAN, DEAN, data processing services company executive; b. 1943. BS, U. Vt., 1961. Sr. v.p. Electronic Data Systems Corp., Plano, Tex., 1986—, also bd. dirs. Office: Electronic Data Systems Corp 5400 Legacy Dr Plano TX 75024-3105

LINDERMAN, JEANNE HERRON, priest; b. Erie, Pa., Nov. 14, 1931; d. Robert Leslie and Ella Marie (Stearns) Herron; m. James Stephens Linderman; children: Mary Susan, John Randolph, Richard Webster, Craig Stephens, Mark Herron, Elizabeth Stewart. BS in Indsl. and Labor Rels., Cornell U., 1953; MDiv magna cum laude, Lancaster Theol. Sem., 1981; postgrad., clin. pastoral edn., Del. State Hosp., New Castle, 1981. Ordained priest, Episcopal Ch. Mem. pers. staff Hengerer Co., Buffalo, 1953-55; chaplain Cathedral Ch. St. John, Wilmington, Del., 1981-82; priest-in-charge Christ Episcopal Ch., Delaware City, Del., 1982-87; vicar Christ Episcopal Ch., 1987-91; assoc. rector St. Andrew's Episcopal Ch., Wilmington, Del., 1991-95, priest in charge, 1995—; chair human sexuality task force, Diocese of Del., 1981-82, mem. clergy compensation com. and diocesan coun., 1982-86, pres. standing com., 1991—, com. on constitution and canons, 1989. Author, editor hist. study papers. Bd. dirs. St. Michael's Day Nursery, Wilmington, 1985-88; mem. secondary schs. com. Cornell U.; bd. dirs., chmn. pers. com. Geriatrics Svcs. of Del., 1989—, sec. bd., 1993—. Mem. Episcopal Women's Caucus, Del. Episcopal Clergy Assn., Nat. Assn. Episcopal Clergy, DAR, Mayflower (elder, surgeon 1983—), Dutch Colonial Soc. Del., Stoney Run Questers (pres.), Cornell Women's Club Del. (pres. 1966), Women of St. James the Less (pres. 1972-73), Women's Witnessing Community at Lambeth, Patriotic Soc. in Del. (sec.-treas. coun. 1965-68), Chi Omega. Republican. Avocations: history, genealogy, travel. Home: 307 Springhouse Ln Hockessin DE 19707-9691 Office: St Andrews's Episcopal Ch Eighth And Shipley St Wilmington DE 19801

LINDFORS, VIVECA, actress; b. Uppsala, Sweden; came to U.S., 1946, naturalized, 1950; d. Torsten and Karin (Dymling) L.; m. George Tabori, July 4, 1954; children: John, Lena, Kristoffer. Grad., Gymnasium, Stockholm. Founder Berkshire Festival; dir. Sch. Visual Arts; tchr. acting workshop Sarah Lawrence Coll., Poetry Workshop, N.Y.C., Lehurden Coll., NYU, New Sch. Gene Frankel Theatre Workshop, others. Joined, Royal Drama Sch. and Theatre, Sweden, 1938; appeared in plays in Sweden including: Anne Sophe Hedvig, 1937, French Without Tears, 1940, Green Pastures, 1941, Blood Wedding, 1943, Twelfth Night, 1945, Anna, 1984; Swedish films include: Think if I Marry the Minister, 1940, Anna Lans, 1941, The Two Brothers, 1941, In Death's Waiting Room, 1942, Appasionata, 1983, others; plays in the U.S. include: I've Got Sixpence, 1952, Anastasia, 1954 (Drama League award), King Lear, 1956, Miss Julie, 1956, The Stronger, 1956, The Rose Tatoo, 1956, The Golden Six, 1956, I Rise in Flame, Cried the Phoenix, 1959, Brouhaha, 1960, Brecht on Brecht, 1962, Pal Joey, 1963, A Far Country, 1962-63, Postmark Zero, 1965, Merchant of Venice, Strolling Players: Sernora Carrar, Cuba Si, Three Bands and A Passion, 1966, The Cretan Woman, 1966, Nigger Lovers, 1967, Mother Courage, 1970, Dance of Death, 1971, I Am A Woman (co-producer, co-arranger, actress), 1974, Touring, 1973, My Mother, My Son, 1978-80, Richard III, 1980, Three Boards and a Passion, 1981, Kathe Kollwitz, 1982, I Am A Woman, 1982, Anna (actress, writer), 1983-93 (N.Y., San Francisco, Uppsala, Sweden); film appearances: Night Unto Night, 1947, The Adventures of Don Juan, 1947, No Sad Songs for You, 1948, Four Men in a Jeep, 1948 (Berlin Film Festival award), Run for Cover, 1953, Captain Dreyfus, 1956, I Accuse!, 1958, Weddings and Babies, 1956, No Exit (Berlin Festival Silver Bear award 1960), The Damned, 1960, Affair of the Skin, 1962, Sylvia, 1964, Brainstorm, 1965, Coming Apart, 1969, Puzzle of a Downfall Child, 1971, The Way We Were, 1973, The Stronger, The Jewish Wife, An Actor Works, 1974, Tabu, 1976, Welcome to LA, 1977, A Wedding, 1978, Girlfriends, 1978, Voices, 1979, Natural Enemies, 1979, Linus, 1979, Creepshow, 1981, Divorce Wars, 1981, Silent Madness, 1983, Yellow Pages, 1985, The Sure Thing, 1985, (writer, dir.) Unfinished Business, 1986, Rachel River, 1986 (spl. jury award Sundance Festival, jury award best actress Sundance Festival 1986), Lady Beware, 1986, Misplaced, 1989, Luba, 1990, The Exorcist III, 1990, Zandalee, 1991, North of Pittsburgh, 1991 (Genie Award nomination), A House in the Hamptons, 1993, Stargate, 1993; TV appearances include: The Bridge of San Luis Rey, 1958, The Idiot, 1958, Defenders, 1963, Naked City, 1963, Ben Casey, 1964, The Nurses, 1964, F.B.I., Medical Center, The Detectives, Marilyn, All My Children, Trapper John, A Doctor's Story, Hotel, Before Winter Arrives, 1979, Playing for Time, 1980, Best Little Girl in the World, 1980, For Ladies Only, 1980, Inside the Third Reich, Passions, 1985, Billy Grier, 1985, Life Goes On, 1990 (Emmy award 1990), Last Dance, 1990; European TV appearances: Frankenstein's Aunt, 1995; theatre prodns. I Am A Woman, My Mother, My Son; prod. for coll. tours: Strolling Players, 1966-69; artistic dir., founder, Berkshire Theatre Festival; author: Viveka . . . Viveca, An Actress, A Woman, A Life, 1981, I Am A Woman..., 1986; author, director: (film) Unfinished Business, 1985, (play) I, Clara, 1986, Anna, the Gypsy Speaks, 1986, In Search of Strindberg, 1992. Recipient Vasaorden, King of Sweden, Best Actress award Berlin Film Festival; named Best Actress of Yr., Internat. Film Awards, Actors Studio award, Emmy Best Actress (guest) in series Life Goes On, 1990.

LINDGREN, A. BRUCE, church administrator; m. Carole Coonce; children: Stacy, Michael, David (dec.). BS in Sociology, Mich. State U., 1970; MDiv, St. Paul Sch. Theology, 1975. Ordained high priest. Dir. ministerial edn. Temple Sch.; exec. min., World Ch. sec., exec. asst. to 1st presidency Reorganized Ch. of Jesus Christ of Latter Day Saints, 1992—; dir. devel. basic leadership curriculum Temple Sch. Editor: Leaders Handbook. Office: Reorganized Ch of Jesus Christ PO Box 1059 Independence MO 64051-0559

LINDGREN, D(ERBIN) KENNETH, JR., lawyer; b. Mpls., Aug. 25, 1932; s. Derbin Kenneth and Margaret (Anderson) L.; m. Patricia Ann Ransier, Dec. 17, 1955; children—Christian Kenneth, Carol Ann, Charles Derbin. B.S., U. Minn., 1954, J.D., 1958. Bar: Minn. 1958, U.S. Supreme Ct. 1968, U.S. Tax Ct. 1959, U.S. Ct. Appeals (D.C. cir.) 1981. Gen. practice law Mpls., 1958—; mem. Larkin, Hoffman, Daly & Lindgren, Ltd., Mpls., 1960—. Contbr. articles to profl. jours. Mem. Ind. Sch. Dist. 274 Bd. Edn., Hopkins, Minn., 1970-76, chmn., 1972-76; mem. Ind. Sch. Dist. 287 Bd. Edn. (Area Vocat. Tech. Coll.), 1979-83; trustee Mpls. Soc. Fine Arts, 1982-88, Minn. Landscape Arboretum Found., 1989—, pres. 1993—; bd. overseers Mpls. Inst. Art, 1986-88, Mpls. Coll. Art and Design, 1980-86, vice chmn., 1982-83, chmn., 1983-86, trustee, 1988—; mem. Gov.'s Commn. on Reform of Govt., 1983. Lt. USAF, 1955-57. Fellow Am. Coll. Trust and Estate Counsel; mem. ABA, Minn. Bar Assn., Hennepin County Bar Assn., Alpha Delta Phi, Phi Delta Phi. Congregationalist. Clubs: Mpls. Athletic; Interlachen Country. Home: 225 Hawthorne Rd Hopkins MN 55343-8511 Office: 1500 Norwest Financial Ctr 7900 Xerxes Ave S Minneapolis MN 55431-1106

LINDGREN, JOHN RALPH, philosophy educator; b. Oak Park, Ill., Oct. 8, 1933; s. Francis L. and Leona (Toussaint) Nichols; m. Shirley Ann Tryon, Dec. 27, 1958; children: J. Thomas, Michael B., David J., Timothy P., Kathryn A. B.S in Bus. Adminstrn., Northwestern U., 1959; M.A. in Philosophy, Marquette U., 1961, Ph.D. in Philosophy, 1963. Instr. dept. philosophy Holy Cross Coll., Worcester, Mass., 1962-64, asst. prof., 1964-65; asst. prof. Lehigh U., Bethlehem, Pa., 1965-69, assoc. prof., 1969-79, chmn. dept. philosophy, 1973-85, dir. law and legal instns. program, 1978-94, prof., 1979—, William Wilson Selfridge prof., 1985-88, Clara H. Stewardson prof., 1989—; vis. scholar Oxford U., 1986, U. Pa. Law Sch., Phila., 1977-78. Author: Social Philosophy of Adam Smith, 1973, Sex Discrimination in Higher Education, 1984, The Law of Sex Discrimination, 1988, 2d edit., 1993; editor: Early Writing of Adam Smith, 1967, Horizons of Justice, 1995. Mem. adv. bd. Alternatives to Violence Project University-City Sci. Ctr., Phila., 1980-83. Served with U.S. Army, 1953-55. Mem. Am. Philos. Assn., Internat. Soc. for Philosophy of Law (exec. bd. dirs. 1981-83), Soc. for Philosophy and Pub. Affairs (exec. bd. 1987—). Democrat. Office: Lehigh U Dept Philosophy 15 University Dr Bethlehem PA 18015

LINDGREN, TIMOTHY JOSEPH, supply company executive; b. N.Y.C., Dec. 7, 1937; s. Carl Herbert and Ruth Elizabeth (Pickering) L.; m. Barbara Fiorini, Feb. 7, 1957; children: Sharon, Mark, Susan. AA, Pierce Coll., Woodland Hills, Calif., 1959; BS in Prodn. Mgmt., Calif. State U., Northridge, 1961; MBA in Indsl. Relations, UCLA, 1962. Registered profl. engr., Calif. cert. tchr., Calif. Systems analyst, methods acct. Pacific Tel. & Tel., Van Nuys, Calif., 1964-65; dir. mfg. Olga Co., Van Nuys, 1965-69; dir. prodn. Calif. Almond Orchards, Bakersfield, 1972-73, gen. mgr., 1972-73; pres. United Wholesale Lumber Co., Montebello, Calif., 1973-77; pres., chief exec. officer Fruit Growers Supply Co., Sherman Oaks, Calif., 1978—. Mem. Calif. C. of C. (chair com. on natural resources). Office: Fruit Growers Supply Co 14130 Riverside Dr Sherman Oaks CA 91423-2313

LINDGREN, WILLIAM DALE, librarian; b. Peoria, Ill., Mar. 8, 1936; s. Hugh Gottfried and Olive Kathryn (Myer) L. BA, Bradley U., 1958, MA, 1959; MSLS, U. Ill., 1967. Tchr. Limestone High Sch., Bartonville, Ill., 1960-68; asst. dir. Learning Resources Ctr. Ill. Cen. Coll., East Peoria, 1968-73, dir., 1973—; mem. transition bd. merger of four systems, 1993-94; bd. dirs. Alliance Libr. Sys., 1994—. Chmn. East Peoria Oral History Com., 1983-84, Resource Sharing Alliance West Cntrl. Ill. Adv. Coun., 1985—; v.p. Ill. Valley Libr. System, pres. bd., 1988, 90—, treas., 1989, bd. dirs., 1990—; bd. dirs. Alliance Libr. System, 1993—. Mem. ALA, Ill. Libr. Assn. (cochair cracker barrels program ann. conf. 1989, 90, 91), Assn. Ednl. Media Tech., Assn. Ednl. Media and Tech. Ill., Coun. Libr. Tech., Creve Coeur Club (Peoria). Office: Ill Cen Coll One College Dr Peoria IL 61635-0001

LINDH, ALLAN GODDARD, seismologist; b. Mason City, Wash., Mar. 18, 1943; s. Quentin Willis and Helma (Beagle) L.; m. Julie Gunda Pulver, Mar. 21, 1971; children: Briana Christine, Quentin William. BA in Geology and Physics, U. Calif., Santa Cruz, 1972; MS, Stanford U., 1974, PhD, 1980. Geophysicist U.S. Geol. Survey, Menlo Park, Calif., 1972—; chief scientist Parkfield prediction experiment, 1986—. Avocation: prevention of nuclear war. Office: US Geol Survey 345 Middlefield Rd MS 977 Menlo Park CA 94025

LINDH, PATRICIA SULLIVAN, banker, former government official; b. Toledo, Oct. 2, 1928; d. Lawrence Walsh and Lillian Winifred (Devlin) Sullivan; m. H. Robert Lindh Jr., Nov. 12, 1955; children: Sheila, Deborah, Robert. B.A., Trinity Coll., Washington, 1950, LL.D., 1975; LL.D., Walsh Coll., Canton, Ohio, 1975, U. Jacksonville, 1975. Adoption case worker Cath. Charities, Chgo., 1954-55; editor Singapore Am. Newspaper, 1957-62; spl. asst. to counsellor to Pres., 1974, spl. asst. to Pres., 1975-76; dep. asst. sec. state for ednl. and cultural affairs Dept. State, 1976-77; v.p., dir. corp. communications Bank Am., Los Angeles, 1978-84, World Banking P.R. Bank Am., San Francisco, 1985—. Trustee La. Arts and Sci. Center, 1970-73, Calif. Hosp. Med. Ctr., 1979-84; bd. dirs. Jr. League of Baton Rouge, 1969, Children's Bur. Los Angeles, 1979, 84, USO Northern Calif.; Rep. state vice chairwoman La., 1970-74; Rep. nat. committeewoman, La., 1974; mem. pub. affairs com. San Francisco World Affairs Coun., 1985; adv. bd. Jr. League Los Angeles, 1980-84; bd. visitors Southwestern U. Sch. Law. Roman Catholic. Home: 850 Powell St San Francisco CA 94108-2051

LINDHEIM, JAMES BRUCE, public relations executive; b. Cleve., Nov. 26, 1945; s. John Arthur and Lois (Reinitz) L.; m. Barbara Levitz, June 6, 1970 (div. May 1978). BA, Williams Coll., 1967; MS in Pub. Affairs, Princeton U., 1970. Asst. dean Woodrow Wilson Sch. Pub. and Internat. Affairs Princeton (N.J.) U., 1971-73; rsch. assoc. Mathematica, Inc., Princeton, 1973-75; dir. corp. priorities svc. Yankolovich, Skelly and White, N.Y.C., 1975-80; pres., v.p., dir. pub. affairs Burson-Marsteller, N.Y.C., 1981-88; dir. corp. svcs. Europe Burson-Marsteller, London, 1989; dir. corp. svcs. Europe Burson-Marsteller, Paris, 1990—, vice-chmn., 1990-92; chmn. Burson-Marsteller, Europe, Paris, 1992-94, Burson-Marsteller, N.Y.C., 1994—. Home: 15 W 53rd St New York NY 10019 Office: Burson-Marsteller 230 Park Ave S New York NY 10003

LINDHEIM, RICHARD DAVID, television company executive; b. N.Y.C., May 28, 1939; s. Gilbert R. and Pearl (Gruskin) L.; m. Elaine Lavis, Dec. 22, 1963; children: Susan Patricia, David Howard. B.S., U. Redlands, 1961; postgrad, U. So. Calif., 1963. Adminstrv. asst. story dept. CBS, L.A., 1962-64; project dir. entertainment testing ASI Market Rsch., L.A., 1964-69; v.p. program research NBC, L.A., 1969-78, v.p. dramatic programs, 1978-79; producer Universal TV, L.A., 1979-81, v.p. current programs, 1981-85, sr. v.p. series programming, 1986-87, exec. v.p. creative affairs, 1987-91; exec. v.p. program strategy MCA TV Group, 1992; exec. v.p. Paramount TV Group, 1992—; asst. prof. Calif. State U.; sr. lectr. U. So. Calif.; lectr. UCLA; reviewer NEH; bd. dirs. AFS Intercultural Program-USA. Author: (with Richard Blum) Primetime: Network Television Programming, 1987, Inside Television Producing, 1991; contbr. articles to profl. jours. Mem. Acad. TV Arts and Scis., Producers Guild Am., Writers Guild Am. Democrat. Jewish. Avocations: model railroading, photography, music, traveling. Office: Universal Studios 100 Universal City Plz Universal City CA 91608 *In this sophisticated society there are huge employment opportunities for the individual. Technology has made most tasks too complex for one man. As a result the ability to work with other people and to provide leadership and management to groups of people has become vital. The key ingredients are communication, respect for others, and a feeling of belonging, while working in a relaxed, casual environment, where the leader is responsible and receptive.*

LINDHOLM, CLIFFORD FALSTROM, II, engineering executive, mayor; b. Passaic, N.J., Dec. 8, 1930; s. Albert William and Edith (Neandross) L.; m. Margery Nye (div.); children: Clifford, Elizabeth, John; m. Karen Cooper, Oct. 7, 1989. BS in Engring., Princeton U., 1953; M in Engring., Stevens Inst. Tech., 1957. Supr. prodn. GM, Linden, N.J., 1953-56; pres. Falstrom Co., Passaic, N.J., 1956—; bd. dirs. N.J. Mfg. Ins. Co., Trenton. Mayor Twp. Montclair, N.J., 1988-92; pres. Montclair Bd. Edn., 1968-72; bd. dirs. Albert Payson Terhune Found., N.J., 1976—. Mem. N.J. Bus. and Industry Assn. (bd. dirs. 1977—), Princeton Club N.Y., Upper Montclair Golf Club, Mantoloking Yacht Club. Republican. Mem. Ch. of Christ. Home: 10 Mountainside Park Ter Montclair NJ 07043-1209 Office: Falstrom Co 3 Falstrom Ct Passaic NJ 07055

LINDHOLM, DWIGHT HENRY, lawyer; b. Blackduck, Minn., May 27, 1930; s. Henry Nathanial and Viola Eudora (Gummert) L.; m. Loretta Catherine Brown, Aug. 29, 1958; children: Douglas Dwight, Dionne Louise, Jeanne Marie, Philip Clayton, Kathleen Anne. Student, Macalester Coll., 1948-49; BBA, U. Minn., 1951, LLB, 1954; postgrad., Mexico City Coll. (now U. of Ams.), 1956-57. Bar: Minn. 1954, Calif. 1958. Sole practice Los Angeles, 1958-65, 72-81, 84—; ptnr. Lindholm & Johnson, Los Angeles, 1965-69, Cotter, Lindholm & Johnson, Los Angeles, 1969-72; sole practice Los Angeles, 1972-81; of counsel Bolton, Dunn & Moore, Los Angeles, 1981-84. Mem. Calif. Republican Central Com., 1962-66, Los Angeles Republican County Central Com., 1962-66; bd. dirs. Family Service Los Angeles, 1964-70, v.p., 1968-70; bd. dirs. Wilshire YMCA, 1976-77; trustee Westlake Girls Sch., 1978-81; hon. presenter Nat. Charity League Coronet Debutante Ball, 1984; bd. dirs. Calif. State U.-Northridge Trust Fund, 1989-93; bd. dirs. Queen of Angeles/Hollywood Presbyn. Med. Ctr., 1990—. Served as capt. JAG Corps USAF, 1954-56. Recipient Presdl. award Los Angeles Jr. C. of C., 1959. Mem. ABA, Calif. Bar Assn., L.A. County Bar Assn., Wilshire Bar Assn. (bd. govs. 1989-91), Internat. Genealogy Fellowship of Rotarians (founding pres. 1979-86), Calif. Club, Ocean Cruising Club Eng. (Newport Harbor port officer), Rotary (dir. 1975-78), Delta Sigma Pi, Delta Sigma Rho, Delta Theta Phi (state chancellor 1972-73). Presbyterian. Avocations: sailing, offshore cruising. Home: 5 S Rossmore Ave Los Angeles CA 90004-3738 Office: 3580 Wilshire Blvd Fl 17 Los Angeles CA 90010-2501

LINDHOLM, FREDRIK ARTHUR, electrical engineering educator, researcher; b. Tacoma, Wash., Feb. 26, 1936; s. George Fred and Evelyn Blanche (Faul) L.; m. Susanne Shroad Howry, Aug. 22, 1959 (div. July 1966); m. Merle Elizabeth Flannery, Dec. 20, 1969. BS, Stanford U., 1958, MS, 1960; PhD, U. Ariz., 1963. Sr. engr. Motorola Corp., Phoenix, 1963-66; asst. prof. U. Ariz., Tucson, 1963-64, assoc. prof., 1964-66; prof. U. Fla., Gainesville, 1966—; vis. prof. U. Leuven, Belgium, 1973-74; gen. chmn. Internat. Electron Devices Meeting Conf., Washington, 1974; program chmn. Internat. Photovoltaics Specialists Conf., Washington, 1978; cons. Jet Propulsion Lab., Pasadena, Calif., 1978-87, Los Alamos (N.Mex.) Nat. Lab., 1981-86. Author: Principles and Applications of Semiconductor Device Modeling, 1971; contbr. numerous articles to profl. jours.; patentee high-low emitter solar cell. Recipient Best Paper award Internat. Solid-State Cirs. Conf., 1963, 65, Outstanding Engring. Faculty award U. Fla., 1975, univ. tchr.-scholar, 1988. Fellow IEEE; mem. Am. Phys. Soc. Home: 4406 SW 17th Ter Gainesville FL 32608-3910

LINDHOLM, JOHN VICTOR, business executive; b. Kane, Pa., Dec. 29, 1934; s. John Edwin and Mary (Nord) L.; m. Ann Christine Lundquist, Apr. 27, 1957; children: Scott Benjamin, Kristine Ann, John Edwin. BBA, Upsala Coll., 1956; postgrad., NYU, 1960-66. Loan officer Irving Trust Co., N.Y.C., 1960-61, coord. spl. svcs., 1969-72, exec. dir., 1972-74; pres., exec. dir. EOPI, 1974—; dir. fin. Guideposts Assocs., Inc., 1975-91; chief fin. officer, exec. dir., 1991; pres. Econ. Svcs., Inc., 1992—; dir. fin. and support svcs. Christian Children's Fund, Richmond, Va.; bd. dirs. Naromi Land Trust, Sherman, Conn., County Bank, Carmel, N.Y.; chmn. bd. dirs. County Bank, Carmel, 1988-93; pres. Putnam Alliance, 1980-82. Treas. Putnam Alliance, 1978-80; trustee Bethel Meth. Home, 1978-85, 87—; dir. fin. Christian Children's Fund, Inc., 1992—. Lt. USNR, 1956-59. Home: 6400 Buckhill Rd Richmond VA 23225 Office: Christian Children's Fund 2821 Emerywood Pkwy Richmond VA 23294

LINDHOLM, ULRIC SVANTE, engineering research institute executive, retired; b. Washington, Sept. 11, 1931; s. Svante Godfred and Hedwig (Krueger) L.; m. Laura Ann Carranza, July 6, 1962; children: Karl, Kirsten, Jon, Siri. BS, Mich. State U., 1953, MS, 1955, PhD, 1960. Rsch. instr. Mich. State U., East Lansing, 1959-60; sr. engr., mgr., dir., v.p. Southwest Rsch. Inst., San Antonio, 1960-94, ret., 1994; lectr. St. Mary's U., San Antonio, 1961-62. Assoc. editor Soc. Exptl. Stress Analysis Exptl. Mechanics, 1979-82; contbr. numerous articles to profl. jours.; patentee in field. Chmn. bd. dirs. Healy-Murphy Ctr., San Antonio, 1970-81. With USN, 1955-57. Fellow ASME (assoc. editor Jour. Applied Mechanics 1981-83), AAAS; mem. Am. Soc. Metals. Democrat. Avocations: woodworking, antiques. Home: 110 Honey Bee Ln San Antonio TX 78231-1205

LINDLEY, DAVID MORRISON, lawyer; b. Montclair, N.J., June 17, 1949; s. Dwight Newton and Janie (Morrison) L.; m. Jane Cowan von der Heyde, June 12, 1971; children: Camilla von der Heyde, Carolyn Field. AB, Columbia Coll., 1971; JD, Harvard U., 1974. Bar: N.J. 1974, U.S. Dist. Ct. N.J. 1974, N.Y. 1976,U.S. Dist. Ct. (so. and ea. dists.) N.Y. 1977, U.S. Ct. Appeals (1st cir.) 1983, U.S. Ct. Appeals (2d cir.) 1991. Assoc. McCarter & English, Newark, 1974-77; assoc. Hale Russell & Gray, N.Y.C., 1977-82, ptnr., 1983-85; ptnr. Winthrop Stimson Putnam & Roberts, N.Y.C., 1985—. Mem. ABA (chair internat. law and practice sect., internat. cts. com.), Assn. of Bar of City of N.Y., N.Y. State Bar Assn. Episcopalian. Home: 6 W 77th St New York NY 10024-5125 Office: Winthrop Stimson Putnam & Roberts 1 Battery Park Plz New York NY 10004-1403

LINDLEY, JAMES GUNN, bank executive; b. Greensboro, N.C., June 13, 1931; s. Paul Cameron and Helen Marie (Gunn) L.; m. Jane Kennedy, Dec. 3, 1954; children: James Gunn, Patricia Van, Julia Anne. BS in Bus. Adminstrn., U. N.C., 1953; MBA in Fin., NYU, 1960. Sr. v.p. Mfrs. Hanover Trust Co., N.Y.C., 1953-75; pres., chief exec. officer Bankshares of N.C. and Bank of N.C., N.A., Raleigh, 1975-79; chief exec. officer S.C. Nat. Bank, Columbia, 1979—, pres., 1979-92, now also chmn., chmn., chief exec. officer, 1981—; pres. S.C. Nat. Corp., Columbia, 1979-92; vice chmn. Wachovia Corp., Winston-Salem, N.C., 1991—. Served to capt. USNR, 1953-57. Office: SC Nat Corp 1426 Main St Columbia SC 29226-0001

LINDLEY, JOHN, cinematographer. Cinematographer: (TV movies) The Demon Murder Case, 1983, Girls of the White Orchid Death Ride to Osaka, 1983, (films) The Goodbye People, 1983, Lily in Love, 1985, Home of the Brave, 1986, Killer Party, 1986, The Stepfather, 1987, In the Mood, 1987, Shakedown, 1988, The Serpent and the Rainbow, 1988, True Believer, 1989, Field of Dreams, 1989, Immediate Family, 1989, Vital Signs, 1990, Sleeping with the Enemy, 1991, Sneakers, 1992, Father of the Bride, 1992, The Good Son, 1993, I Love Trouble, 1994. Office: care Spyros Skouras Sanford Skouras Gross & Assocs 1015 Gayley Ave 3rd Fl Los Angeles CA 90024*

LINDLEY, THOMAS ERNEST, environmental lawyer, law educator; b. Danville, Ill., July 15, 1948; s. Oscar Ernest and Helen (Milewski) L. BA, U. Ill., 1970; postgrad., U. Tex., 1970-71; JD, Vanderbilt U., 1977. Bar: Ill. 1977, U.S. Dist. Ct. (no. dist.) Ill. 1978, U.S. Dist. Ct. (cen. dist.) Ill. 1983, U.S. Ct. Appeals (7th cir.) 1978, U.S. Supreme Ct. 1982, Oreg. 1985, U.S. Dist. Ct. Oreg. 1985, Trial Bar No. Dist. Ill. 1985, U.S. Ct. Appeals (9th cir.) 1985, Wash. 1987, U.S. Dist. Ct. (we. dist.) Wash. 1987, U.S. Dist. Ct. (ea. dist.) Wash. 1988. Asst. dir. div. EMS Tenn. Dept. Health, Nashville, 1972-74; law clk. Gullet, Steele, Stanford, Robinson and Merritt, Nashville, 1975; lawyer Jenner & Block, Chgo., 1977-83, Balbach, Fehr & Lindley, Urbana, Ill., 1983-84, Miller, Nash, Wiener, Hager & Carlsen, Portland, Oreg., 1985—; adj. prof. Lewis & Clark Northwestern Sch. Law, Portland, 1991—; lectr. ITT-Kent Coll. Law, Chgo., 1981-83; extern Supreme Ct. Tenn. Nashville, 1976-77; co-chair and author 7th Ann. EPA/Lewis & Clark Hazardous Waste Law & Mgmt. Conf., 1990, 8th Ann. Conf., 1991; chair Assoc. Oreg. Industries' Environ. Crimes Task Force, 1993; chair Assn. Oreg. Industries, Water Resources Com., 1995—. Author: Contracting for Environmental Services, 1991, Reducing Lender Liability, 1994; co-author: Oregon's Environmental Audit Privilege: Traveling the Path to Consensus:

Preventive Law Reporter, 1994, Oregon Environmental Law--Crimes and Contracting, 1994, Environmental Audit Privilege: BNA, 1993; editor: Oregon Environmental Law--Insurance Coverage, 1991. Bd. dirs. Oreg. Environ. Tech. Assn., 1993—, sec., 1994—, United Way Columbia-Willamette, Oreg., 1990-91, United Cerebral Palsy, Oreg., 1987-90, 95—, mem., 1987—, Mental Health Svcs. West, Oreg., 1985, Ill. Pub. Action Coun., 19880-83; chmn. Adv. Bd. CANPAC, 1981; coord. counsel Kennedy for Pres., Ill., 1979-80; vol. Cook County Spl. Bail Project, Ill., 1978-79; candidate U.S. Congress, Ill., 1983-84. Mem. ABA (natural resource sect., torts and ins. sect., litigation sect.), Wash. State Bar Assn. (land use and environ. law sect.), Oreg. State Bar (environ. law sect.). Avocations: backpacking, cross country skiing, theater, politics. Office: Miller Nash Wiener et al 3500 US Bancorp Tower 111 SW Fifth Ave Portland OR 97204

LINDLY, DOUGLAS DEAN, elementary school educator, administrator; b. San Diego, Aug. 22, 1941; s. George A. and Jessie V. L.; m. Brenda J., Oct. 22, 1971; children: Elizabeth, David. MA in Curriculum, Pepperdine U., 1967, student, 1975; credential edn., USC, 1971; student, U. Oreg., 1981-85, Oreg. State U., 1981-85; credential adminstrn., Calif. State U., Fullerton, 1991; cert. in spl. edn., Calif. State U., L.A., 1994. Cert. in profl. adminstrv. svcs., Calif., gen. teaching, Calif., standard designated adult edn., Calif., standard elem. teaching, Oreg., standard adminstrv., Oreg.; cert. lang. devel. specialist, Calif., Learning Handicapped and Resource Specialist Aid. Supervising tchr. Imperial Schs., Pasadena, Calif., 1965-70; tchr. Charter Oak Unified Sch. Dist., Covina, Calif., 1970-78, Sweet Home (Oreg.) Unified Sch. Dist., 1978-81, Rialto (Calif.) Unified Sch. Dist., 1989-90; prin. Lewis and Clark Sch. Dist., Astoria, Oreg., 1981-86, Barstow (Calif.) Unified Sch. Dist., 1986-88; spl. edn. dir. River Delta Unified Sch. Dist., Walnut Grove, Calif., 1988-89; tchr. and coord. gifted Los Angeles Unified Sch. Dist., South Gate, 1990—; tchr. motivational program Great Kids Club, 1982—. Author: A Handbook for Parents, 1967, Summer Education Handbook, 1970; contbr. numerous articles on ednl. programs to newspapers and mags., 1970-89. Vol. ARC, Pasadena/Covina, 1970-78; cubmaster Boy Scouts Am., Astoria and Barstow, 1982-88 (Outstanding Svc. award 1988); coach Little League, Astoria, 1985; leader youth group Ch. of God, 1975-81. Grantee Adventures in Success, 1976-78; scholar Future Tchrs. Am. and Eugene Tchrs. Assn., 1959; named San Gabriel Valley Outstanding Educator, San Gabriel Valley Endl. Consortium, 1977; recipient Outstanding Speaker award Toastmasters Internat., 1986, Outstanding Svc. award PTA, 1988. Mem. NEA, ASCD, Calif. Assn. Gifted, Calif. Tchrs. Assn., Assn. Calif. Sch. Adminstrs. (assoc.), Kappa Delta Pi. Avocations: family physical fitness, reading, travel. Home: PO Box 1058 962 E Mountain View Ave Glendora CA 91741-2871

LINDMARK, RONALD DORANCE, retired federal agency administrator; b. Clearwater County, Minn., May 3, 1933; s. John G. and Aaste L. (Torgerson) L.; m. Lynette C. Larson, Dec. 16, 1961; children: Eric Karl, Kirstin Sigrid. BS in Forestry, U. Minn., 1961, MS, 1963; PhD in Agrl. Econs., Ohio State U., 1971. Forestry aide No. Pacific Rwy., Seattle, 1959-60; rsch. asst. U. Minn., St. Paul, 1961-63; scientist Ctrl. State Forest Experiment Sta., Columbus, Ohio, 1963-66, No. Ctrl. Forest Experiment Sta., Duluth, Minn., 1966-69; scientist, project leader No. Ctrl. Forest Experiment Sta., Carbondale, Ill., 1969-74; asst. dir. Intermountain Forest Experiment Sta., Ogden, Utah, 1974-77; staff asst. dep. chief Forest Svc. Rsch., Washington, 1977-81; dir. Forest Environ. Rsch., Washington, 1982-87, No. Ctrl. Forest Experiment Sta., St. Paul, 1987-93; ret., 1993. Contbr. articles to profl. jours. With USN, 1951-56. Avocations: travel, photography, outdoor recreation, woodcraft. Home: 1140 Amble Dr Arden Hills MN 55112-5713

LINDNER, CARL HENRY, JR., financial holding company executive; b. Dayton, Ohio, Apr. 22, 1919; s. Carl Henry and Clara (Serrer) L.; m. Edith Bailey, Dec. 31, 1953; children: Carl Henry III, Stephen Craig, Keith Edward. Co-founder United Dairy Farmers, 1940; pres. Am. Fin. Corp., Cin., 1959-84, chmn., 1959—, chief exec. officer, 1984—; chmn., chief exec. officer, chmn. exec. com. United Brands Co. (now Chiquita Brands Internat. Inc.), N.Y.C., 1984—; chmn. Penn Cen. Corp. (now American Premier Underwriters), Cin., 1983—, chief exec. officer, 1987—, also bd. dirs.; chmn., chief exec. officer Gt. Am. Communications Co., Cin., 1987—; bd. dirs. Mission Ins. bd. advs. Bus. Adminstrn. Coll., U. Cin. Republican. Baptist. Office: Charter Co 1 W Charter Plz Jacksonville FL 32202-3105*

LINDNER, JAMES D., computer company executive; b. 1941. With IBM; v.p. Exxon Office Systems; pres., CEO Philips Data Systems, Ontro Advanced Systems Corp.; v.p. mergers and acquisitions Olivetti Group, 1986-91; pres. Bunker Ramo Corp., 1986-91; chmn., CEO ISC Bunker Ramo Corp., 1986-91; exec. v.p. Memorex Telex Corp., Irving, Tex., 1991—. Office: Memorex Telex Corp 545 E John Carpenter Fwy Irving TX 75062

LINDNER, JOSEPH, JR., physician, medical administrator; b. Cin., Apr. 5, 1929; s. Joseph and Mary (Apger) L.; m. Doris G. Beatty, July 29, 1961; children: Laura Lynn, Karen Leslie. AB, Dartmouth Coll., 1951; MD, U. Cin., 1955; MPH, Harvard U., 1977. Intern Cin. Gen. Hosp., 1955-56, resident in medicine, 1958-60, fellow in cardiology, 1960-61; mem. faculty dept. medicine U. Cin. Coll. Medicine, 1961-79, prof., 1975-79; sr. assoc. v.p. U. Cin., 1975-79; sr. assoc. dir., 1977-79; pres., chief exec. officer St. Barnabas Med. Ctr., Livingston, N.J., 1979-89; Trimark Corp., West Orange, N.J.; ptnr. Cons. Assocs., Inc., 1991-92; pres. J. Lindner, Inc., Morristown, N.J., 1992—. Trustee Mt. St. Joseph Coll., 1972-76. With USN, 1956-58. Fellow ACPE; mem. N.J. Med. Soc., Commonwealth Club, Univ. Country Club, Baltusrol Golf Club, Country Club Hilton Head, Bear Creek Golf Club, Cartmouth Club of N.Y., Short Hills Club, Morristown Club. Home: 8 Cross Gates Short Hills NJ 07078-2106 Office: 55 Madison Ave Ste 200 Morristown NJ 07960-7397

LINDNER, KEITH E., food company executive. Formerly sr. exec. v.p. United Brands Co., Cincinnati; now pres., chief oper. officer Chiquita Brands Internat. Inc. (formerly United Brands Co.), Cincinnati. Office: Chiquita Brands Internat Inc 250 E 5th St Cincinnati OH 45202-4103

LINDNER, KENNETH EDWARD, academic administrator and chemistry educator emeritus; b. LaCrosse, Wis., Nov. 29, 1922; s. Henry B. and Cora (Ward) L.; m. Ila M. Jacobson, Feb. 28, 1947 (div.); children: Diane, Charles, Barbara, Nancy, John, Sara; m. Marcia A Lee, March 17, 1990. B.S., Wis. State U., 1949; M.A., U. Iowa, 1953, Ph.D., 1966; HHD (hon.), Tex. Chirpractic Coll., 1994. High sch. chemistry tchr. Black River Falls, Wis., 1949-55; prof. chemistry Wis. State U., LaCrosse, 1956-67; head acad. affairs Wis. State U. System, Madison, 1967-70; chancellor U. Wis.-LaCrosse, 1971-79, chancellor emeritus, Disting. prof., 1983—; chmn. Council Chancellors U. Wis. System, 1978-79; sec. Wis. State Dept. Adminstrn., 1979-82; chmn. bd. Digicators Systems, Inc., 1985-90; adv. bd. Deli Corp., 1980-90; v.p. adminstrn.-provost Tex. Chiropractic Coll., Pasadena, Tex., 1993-94, advisor to pres., 1994—; cons. N.Y. Chiropractic Coll., 1994-95; cons. for closure Coll. St. Teresa, Winona, Minn., 1988-90; cons.-examiner North Ctrl. Assn. Colls. and Secondary Schs., 1972-79, commr., 1976-79; cons. data processing Sentry Ins. Co., 1983, govt. relations Gateway Foods, Inc., LaCrosse, Wis.; cons. radiation chemistry Dairyland Power Coop., LaCrosse Boiling Water Reactor, 1966-67; cons. radiation safety Gunderson Clinic, Luth. Hosp., LaCrosse, 1966-67. Chmn. bd. trustees Coll. St. Teresa, Winona, Minn., 1986-88. Served with AUS, 1942-45. Mem. Internat. Radiation Protection Soc., Am. Chem. Soc., Health Physics Soc. Home: 301 Ashley Way Pharr TX 78577

LINDNER, PATRICIA REID, state representative, lawyer. BS in Speech, Northwestern U., 1961; MS in Polit. Sci., U. Colo., 1966; JD, No. Ill. U., 1980. Bar: Ill. 1981, Fed. Trial Bar, 1981. Asst. pub. defender Kane County, Ill., 1981-84; ct. apptd. atty. Kane County, 1984-86; pvt. practice Aurora, Ill., 1986—; state rep. State of Ill., Springfield. Bd. dirs. Aurora Found., Gary Wheaton Bank of Fox Valley, YWCA, chair pers. com., Community Div. for Capital Campaign, Legal Aid Vol., co-chair Women of Distinction Luncheon, 1991; active Rep. Women's Club and numerous coms. Mem. Ill. State Bar Assn., LaCrosse, Wis., Kane County Bar Assn. (chair legis. com.), Women in Mgmt., Kane County Family Law Com. Home: PO Box 661 Densmore Rd Aurora IL 60506

LINDNER, ROBERT DAVID, finance company executive; b. Dayton, Ohio, Aug. 5, 1920; s. Carl Henry and Clara (Serrer) L.; m. Betty Ruth Johnston, Mar. 29, 1947; children—Robert David, Jeffrey Scott, Alan

Bradford, David Clark. Grad. high sch. Chmn. bd. United Dairy Farmers, Cin., 1940—; With Am. Financial Corp., Cin., 1950—, former v.p., vice chmn. bd., now vice chmn. bd. dirs. Trustee No. Bapt. Theol. Sem. Served with U.S. Army, 1942-45. Mem. Masons (33 degree). Home: 6950 Given Rd Cincinnati OH 45243-2840 Office: United Dairy Farmers 3955 Montgomery Rd Cincinnati OH 45212-3798 also: American Financial Corp 1 E 4th St Cincinnati OH 45202

LINDO, J. TREVOR, psychiatrist, consultant; b. Boston, Feb. 12, 1925; s. Edwin and Ruby Ianty (Peterson) L.; m. Thelma Elaine Thompson, Sept. 22, 1962. BA, NYU, 1946; cert. in pre-clin. studies, U. Freibourg, Switzerland, 1953; MD, U. Lausanne, Switzerland, 1957. Lic. psychiatrist, N.Y., Conn. Clin. instr. Columbia U., N.Y.C., 1965-75, asst. clin. prof., 1975-82, assoc. clin. prof., 1982-85; attending psychiatrist Bedford-Stuyvesant Community Mental Health Clinic, Bklyn., 1976-86, med. dir., 1986—; attending psychiatrist Harlem Hosp. Ctr., N.Y.C., 1964-75; vis. psychiatrist Interfaith Hosp. Bklyn., 1976-85; psychiat. cons. Bklyn. Bur. Community Svc., 1980, Marcus Garvey Manor, Bklyn., 1982-86. Co-chairperson com. Dr. Thomas Matthew, N.Y.C., 1974. With U.S. Mcht. Marine, 1947-51. Fellow Am. Coll. Internal Physicians; mem. Nat. Med. Assn., Am. Psychiat. Assn., Provident Clin. Soc. (v.p. 1980-82, parliamentarian 1982—), Bklyn. Psychiat. Soc., Black Psychiatrists of Am. Avocations: travel, African art, sailing, swimming. Office: 1265 President St Brooklyn NY 11213-4237 also: Bedford Stuyvesant Community Mental Health Ctr 1406 Fulton St Brooklyn NY 11216

LINDOW, DONALD AUGUST, insurance company executive; b. Detroit, Apr. 23, 1916; s. Wesley Frederick and Ida Anna (Oetjen) L.; m. Helen Nielson, June 14, 1941; children: Marcia Lindow Stevens, Judy Lindow Adams, Donald A., Nancy Lindow Wolf. A.B., Wayne State U., 1938. CPCU. With Mich. Mut. Ins. Co., Detroit, 1935—, pres., chief exec. officer, 1978-81, chmn. bd., 1981-85, dir., cons. corporate affairs, 1985—. Dir. Civic Searchlight, Inc.; mem. adv. council Detroit Hist. Soc.; bd. dirs. Detroit Exec. Service Corps. Lt. USN, 1942-46. Mem. Soc. CPCUs. Clubs: Detroit Athletic, Country Club of Detroit, Crescent Sail Yacht, Gowanie Golf. Home: 804 N Brys Dr Grosse Pointe MI 48236-1202 Office: Mich Mut Ins Co 28 W Adams Ave Detroit MI 48226-1617

LINDOW, JOHN WESLEY, banker, corporate executive; b. Detroit, June 28, 1910; s. Wesley and Ida Anna (Oetjen) L.; m. Eleanor Niemetta, Aug. 2, 1940; children: John Frederick, Eric Anthony. A.B., Wayne State U., 1931; M.A., George Washington U., 1940. Economist, FCA, 1934; economist U.S. Treasury, 1934-47, asst. dir. research and statistics, 1944-47; with Irving Trust Co., N.Y.C., 1947-75; v.p. charge econs. dept. Irving Trust Co., 1947-55, v.p., head investment adminstrn. div., 1955-68, sec., 1959-70, sr. v.p., 1961-66; exec. v.p. Irving Bank Corp., 1966-70, vice chmn., 1970-72, pres., 1972-75, also bd. dir.; chmn. bd. Nat. Thrift News, Inc., 1976—; chmn. Dorset Group, 1980—; former mem. faculty Stonier Grad. Sch. Banking, Rutgers U.; com. tax policies econ. growth Nat. Bur. Econ. Research; mem. adv. com. to supt. banks N.Y. State, 1973-74; bd. dirs., former mem. exec. com., chmn. research com. Assn. Bank Holding Cos.; occasional cons. Fed. Home Loan Bank Bd. and Sec. of Treasury. Author: Inside the Money Market, 1972; co-author: Determining the Business Outlook, 1954; author articles in banking and finance. Recipient Alumni award Wayne State U., 1953. Mem. Phi Beta Kappa. Home: 23 Bellows Ln Manhasset NY 11030-2606

LINDQUIST, CLAUDE S., electrical and computer engineering educator; b. Des Moines, Mar. 13, 1940; s. Claude R. and Eva E. (Cox) L.; children: Todd, Tad. BA, U. Redlands, 1963; BSEE, Stanford U., 1963; MSEE, Oreg. State U., 1964, PhD, 1968. Design engr. Collins Radio, Newport Beach, Calif., 1968-71; prof. Calif. State U. Long Beach, 1971-84; prof. elec. and computer engring. U. Miami, Fla., 1984—; cons. Phoenix Data, Computer Automation, Edwards Pacemaker Systems, Bournes, KVB Equipment Systems, Vega Electronics, Datanetics, 1973-81, SHAPE Tech. Ctr.; pres. E&H Electronics, Long Beach, 1979-84; vis. prof. U. Calif., Irvine, 1983-84. Author: Active Network Design, 1977, Adaptive and Digital Signal Processing, 1989; contbr. 100 tech. papers. Mem. IEEE (sr.), CAS Soc., AASP Soc., Omicron Delta Kappa, Phi Beta Delta, Alpha Epsilon Lambda. Republican. Mem. Assemblies of God Ch. Avocations: church out-reach programs, boating. Office: U Miami Elec and Computer Engring Dept PO Box 24-8294 Miami FL 33124

LINDQUIST, EVAN, artist, educator; b. Salina, Kans., May 23, 1936; s. E.L. and Linnette Rosalie (Shogren) L. B.S.E., Emporia State U., 1958; M.F.A., U. Iowa, 1963; m. Sharon Frances Huenergardt, June 8, 1958; children: Eric, Carl. One man shows include Mo. Arts Council, 1973-75, Albrecht Art Mus., St. Joseph, Mo., 1975, 89, S.E. Mo. State U., 1977, Sandzen Gallery, Lindsborg, Kans., 1978, Galerie V. Kunstverlag Wolfbrum, Vienna, 1979, Poplar Bluff, Mo., 1987, Gallery V, Kans. City, Mo., 1988, Northwest Mo. State U., 1991; group shows include Benjamin Galleries, Chgo., 1976, City of Venice, 1977, Boston Printmakers, 1971-87, Visual Arts Ctr. of Alaska, Anchorage, 1979, Western Carolina U., 1980, Pa. State U., 1980, Kans. State U., 1980, U. N.D., 1981 & 92, Ariz. State U., 1981, 93, Barcelona, Cadaques, Girona, 1990, 93, 94, Tulsa, 1982, Jay Gallery, N.Y.C., 1983, Artists Books, German Dem. Republic, 1984, U. Tenn.-Knoxville, 1985, Memphis State U., 1985, Ark. Ctr., 1983-83, Miss. State U., 1986, Hunterdon Art Ctr., Clinton, N.J., 1986-87, 94, Washington, 1988, Soc. of Am. Graphic Artists/Printmakers, 1988-94, Boston, 1989-94, John Szoke Gallery, 1989, Woodstock, N.Y., 1990, 92, Silvermine Guild Galleries, New Canaan, Conn., 1992, 93, Woodstock Artists Assn., Littman Gallery, Portland State U., Galeria Brita Prinz Madrid, Spain, 1992, U. Nebraska, 1992, Parkside National, Kenosha, Wis., 1993, 95, Minot, N.D., 1994, Fla. Community Coll., Jacksonville, Fla., 1995, Stonemetal Press, San Antonio, Tex., 1995; represented in permanent collections Albertina, Vienna, Art Inst. Chgo., Nelson-Atkins, Kansas City, Phoenix Art Mus., Uffizi Gallery, Florence, Municipal Gallery, Dublin, San Francisco Art Mus., Whitney Mus. Am. Art, N.Y.C., St. Louis Art Mus., Museo Reina Sofia, Madrid, others; staff artist Emporia State U., 1958-60; prof. Ark. State U., 1963—, pres.'s fellow, 1981-82, 84-85. Mem. Soc. Am. Gr. Artists, Coll. Art Assn. Am., MidAm. Coll. Art Assn., Visual Artists and Galleries Assn. Office: PO Box 2782 State University AR 72467-2782

LINDQUIST, MARK ALVIN, artist; b. Oakland, Calif., May 16, 1949; s. Melvin Benjamin and Helen Margaret (Lilly) L.; m. Kathleen Bowes Bragg, June 8, 1968; children: Benjamin, Joshua. BA, New Eng. Coll., Henniker, N.H., 1971; postgrad., Pratt Inst., Bklyn., 1971; MFA, Fla. State U., 1990. Tchr. New Eng. Coll., 1971; head dept. woodworking Worcester (Mass.) Craft Ctr., 1977-78; tchr. Haystack Mountain Sch. Arts and Crafts, Deer Isle, Maine, 1979, Arrowmont Sch. Arts and Crafts, Gatlinburg, Tenn., 1981-82; vis. assoc. prof. Fla. A&M U., Tallahassee, 1988-89. Exhibited in mus. collections including The White House, Washington, Met. Mus. Art, N.Y.C., Nat. Mus. Am. Art, Smithsonian Inst., Washington, Am. Craft Mus., N.Y.C., Boston Mus. Fine Arts, Dallas Mus. Art, Phila. Mus. Art, High Mus. Art, Atlanta, Greenville County (S.C.) Mus. Art, Fine Arts Mus. of South, Mobile, Ala., Brockton (Mass.) Art Mus., Schenectady (N.Y.) Mus.; author: Sculpting Wood, 1986; contbr. articles to profl. jours. Fellow MacDowell Colony; mem. Am. Crafts Council, Internat. Sculpture Ctr., Phi Kappa Phi. Home: RR 2 Box 247 Quincy FL 32351-9625

LINDQUIST, RAYMOND IRVING, clergyman; b. Sumner, Nebr., Apr. 14, 1907; s. Rev. Elmer H. and Esther (Nyberg) L.; m. Ella Sofield, Sept. 16, 1930; children: Ray Irving, Ruth Elizabeth Lindquist McCalmont. Student, Kearney State Coll., 1925; A.B., Wheaton Coll., Ill., 1929; student, Columbia U. Law Sch., 1929-30; A.M., Princeton U., 1933; Th.B. (Hugh Davies prize homiletics); Erdman prize Bible; Zwemer fellow Comparative Religions; Princeton Sem., 1933; D.D., Cumberland U., 1939, Ursinus Coll., 1980; LL.D., Bloomfield Coll., N.J., 1957, Eastern Coll., 1977; L.H.D., Calif. Coll. Medicine, 1963. Ordained to ministry Presbyn. Ch., 1934; dir. religious edn. Third Presbyn. Ch., Newark, 1931-34; minister Old First Presbyn. Ch., Orange, N.J., 1934-53, Hollywood First Presbyn. Ch., 1953-71; vis. prof. homiletics Bloomfield Sem., N.J., 1945-53; lectr. Princeton Sem., Pittcairn-Crabbe, Pitts., USAF, Israel, Germany, Johnston Island; lectr. UCLA, U. So. Calif.; lectr. Pentagon, Northwestern U.; Pres. bd. mat. missions United Presbyn. Ch., 1955-62, gen. council, 1955-62; v.p. Templeton Found. Author: Notes for Living. Bd. dirs. Covenant Life (formerly Presbyn.

Ministers Fund), Phila., chmn. bd., 1980—; bd. dirs. Presbyn. Med. Center, Hollywood, Calif., 1954—, Met. YMCA, Los Angeles; trustee Princeton Theol. Sem., So. Calif. Presbyn. Homes., Olmstead Trust, Hollywood, Calif., 1954—. Recipient Gold medal Religious Heritage Am., 1984. Mem. Phi Kappa Delta. Clubs: Rotary (Los Angeles) (bd. dirs.), Los Angeles Country (Los Angeles); Symposium (Princeton); Glen Lake (Sparta, N.J.), Sunset Rock (Sparta, N.J.); Shadow Mountain (Palm Desert, Calif.). Home: 568 Avenida Sevilla # B Laguna Hills CA 92653-4075 also: 3 Christiansted St Toms River NJ 08757-4244 also: 568 Avenida Sevilla # B Laguna Hills CA 92653-4075 Faith is not jumping to conclusions: it is concluding to jump...The thought of God swings the world like a rock on a rope.

LINDQUIST, SUSAN PRATZNER, museum executive; b. San Francisco, Dec. 20, 1940; d. Carleton Edward Pratzner and Edith Crane (Johnson) Cox; m. Philip George Lindquist, Oct. 27, 1962; children: Tucker D., Travis C. BS in Edn., Lesley Coll., 1962; MEd, Northeastern U., Boston, 1979; postgrad., U. Calif. Berkeley, 1994. Tchr. local sch. Marshfield, Mass. 1962-63, Peabody, Mass., 1963-66; coord. early intervention Dept. Mental Health, Hyannis, Mass., 1976-79; supr. Dept. Social Svcs., Hyannis, 1981; program dir. Latham Sch., Brewster, Mass., 1982-85; vol. coord. Cape Cod Mus. Natural History, Brewster, 1986—, assoc. dir., 1987, pres., 1987—; corporator Cape Cod Five Bank, 1994, trustee. Bd. dirs. Cape Cod C. of C., 1993, Mus. Inst. for Teaching Sci., Boston; trustee Cape Cod Acad., 1994; mem. Brewster Bd. Appeals, 1977-87. Avocations: world travel, gardening. Office: Cape Cod Mus Natural History PO Box 1710 Rte 6A Brewster MA 02631

LINDROS, ERIC BRYAN, professional hockey player; b. London, Ont., Can., Feb. 28, 1973; s. Carl and Bonnie L. Student, York U., Toronto. With Detroit Compuware, 1989—, Phila. Flyers, 1992—; mem. Canadian Olympic Team, 1992, Cup All-Star team, 1989-90, OHL All-Star team 1990-91, NHL All-Star team, 1992-93; player NHL All-Star game, 1992-93. Recipient Plus/Minus award Canadian Hockey League, 1990-91, Red Tilson trophym 1990-91, Eddie Powers Meml. trophy, 1990-91; named Most Valuable Player World Jr. Hockey Championships, 1990, Most Valuable Player Ont. Jr. Hockey Assn., 1991, Player of the Year Canadian Hockey League, 1990-91. Office: care Rick Curran PO Box 735 Devon PA 19333*

LINDSAY, BRUCE GEORGE, statistics educator; b. The Dalles, Oreg., Mar. 7, 1947; s. George Speers and Geneva Elizabeth (Davis) L.; m. Teresa Ann Goff, Aug. 23, 1969 (sep.); children: Dylan Brantley, Camden James. BA, U. Oreg., 1969; PhD, U. Wash., 1978. Postdoctoral fellow Imperial Coll., London, 1978-79; asst. prof. Pa. State U., University Park, 1979-85, assoc. prof., 1985-87, prof. stats., 1987-91, disting. prof. stats., 1992—. Assoc. editor Annals Stats., 1985-91, 93—, Annals Stat. Math., 1987—, Math. Methods Stats., 1992—; contbr. articles to profl. jours. Scoutmaster Boy Scouts Am., State College, Pa., 1988-89. With USCG, 1970-74. Recipient Humboldt Sr. scientist award, 1990. Fellow Inst. Math. Stats.; mem. Am. Statis. Assn., Math. Assn. Am., Internat. Statis. Inst. Democrat. Avocations: running, hiking, reading. Office: Pa State U Dept Stats 326 Classroom Bldg University Park PA 16802

LINDSAY, BRYAN EUGENE, humanities educator, musician, writer; b. Bklyn., Sept. 19, 1931; s. Eugene Fenton and Evelyn (Moore) L.; m. Mary Ray Moore; children: Eric Evan, Alyson, Christy, Tracey, Jason Moore. AA, Syracuse U., 1952; BA, Troy (Ala.) State Coll., 1956; MA, George Peabody Coll. Tchrs., 1962, PhD, 1966. Choral and stage band dir. Choctawatchee High Sch., Shalimar, Fla., 1956-61; chmn. dept. humanities, dir. music Okaloosa-Walton Jr. Coll., Valparaiso, Fla., 1965-69; chmn. gen. studies humanities program, prof. humanities Eastern Ky. U., Richmond, 1969-72; mem. staff Center Humanities, Converse Coll., Spartanburg, S.C., 1972-76; assoc. prof. U. S.C. Spartanburg, 1976-82, prof., 1982—; specialist, workshop gifted and talented, gifted program devel. sect. Ill. Dept. Edn., 1970—; cons. Project EQ Coll. Bd., 1986—; chmn. creative writing sub-com. S.C. ABC Project, 1993; chmn. tchr. edn. com. SCMEA, 1994—. Author poems.; composer music. Served with USAF, 1951-54. NDEA fellow, 1961-64; Guidance and Counseling Inst. fellow, 1960. Mem. ASCAP (Composers award 1963, 64, 65), Nat. Acad. Rec. Arts and Scis., Internat. Assn. Jazz Educators (div. coord. 1972-74, S.C. chpt. pres.-elect 1993), Nat. Assn. Humanities Edn. (exec. bd. dirs. sec. 1978-87). Home: 109 Greenbriar Rd Spartanburg SC 29302-2128 Office: Tomorrow Ltd PO Box 6366 Spartanburg SC 29304-6366

LINDSAY, CAROL FRANCES STOCKTON, dean; b. Haileyville, Okla., Dec. 25, 1940; d. Buel Benjamin and Natalie Frances (Bailey) Stockton; m. Robert Carr Lindsay, Oct. 15, 1961; children: Matthew Robert, Mark Stockton, Michael George. AA, Stockton Coll., 1960; BA, Calif. State U., Sacramento, 1970; MEd, U. Nev., 1982, EdS, 1990. Cert. tchr., adminstr., Calif. Tchr. 2d grade Taft Elem. Sch., Stockton, Calif., 1966-67; tchr. 2d and 3rd grades Dry Creek Joint Elem. Sch., Roseville, Calif., 1967-69; tchr. 1st-5th grades Chartville Elem. Sch., Fallon, Calif., 1970-77; tchr. 1st and 5th-8th grades Northside Elem. sch., Fallon, Nev., 1977-80; tchr. 3rd grade West End Elem. Sch., Fallon, 1980-83; tchr. 7th-8th grades Roosevelt Roads Midd./High Sch., Ceiba, P.R., 1983-85, fine arts dept. coord., 1984-85; student svcs. coord., tchr. Stead Elem. Sch., Reno, 1986-89; student svcs. coord. Silver Lake Elem. Sch., Reno, 1989-93, dean students, 1993-94; art specialist Clark County Sch. Dist., 1994-95; sch. rep. Antilles Consolidated Sch. System Curriculum Coun., Ceiba, P.R. 1983-85. Co-author: Art Goals and Objectives, 1989; author: Site Based Management, 1990. Co-chairperson Muscular Dystrophy Telethon, Fallon, 1980-82; neighborhood supr. Am. Heart Assn., Reno, 1985-86; mem. PTA. Named one of Outstanding Tchr. of Am., 1972. Mem. AAUW, ASCD, Linden Edn. Assn. (bldg. rep., exec. bd. dirs 1970-77), Churchill Edn. Assn. (bldg. rep., exec. bd. dirs. 1980-83), Nev. Assn. Sch. Adminstrs., Internat. Reading Assn., Washoe County Tchrs. Assn. (Disting. Svc. award 1988, Dedicated Svc. award 1992, bldg. rep. 1989-92), Clark County Classroom Tchrs. Assn., Nat. Art Edn. Assn. Avocations: art, music, golfing.

LINDSAY, CHARLES JOSEPH, banker; b. Bklyn., Mar. 21, 1922; s. George Patrick and Evelyn (Roth) L.; m. Marie A. Faraone, Jan. 19, 1947; children—George, Charles, Mary Ann. Student, U. Mo., 1943; grad., Am. Savs. and Loan Inst., 1947, Savs. and Loan Grad. Sch., Ind. U.; Profl. Studies in Bus. Adminstrn; Degree with high distinction, Pace U., 1973. With Nassau Fed. Savs. formerly Serial Fed. Savs. & Loan Assn., N.Y.C., 1947—, successively teller, supr., asst. v.p., asst. sec., sec., v.p. and sec., sr. v.p. and dir., pres., 1965—; ret. as pres. Nassau Fed. Savs., 1986, bd. dirs.; mem. faculty, bd. govs. Savs. and Loan Inst.; gov. for N.Y. State, Nat. League Savs. Assns. Mem. pres.'s adv. council Fairfield U., Pace U. Served with USAAF, World War II. Decorated Air medal with cluster; recipient Alumnus of Year award Pace U., 1975. Mem. N.Y. Fin. Advertisers, State League Savs. Assn. (dir.), Nat. League Savs. Assns. (exec. com., dir.), Alumni Assn. Pace U. (pres.*). Club: Aspetuck Country (Weston, Conn.). Home: Winter Leaves 4 Lilac Ln Weston CT 06883-3008 also: 100 Worth Ave Palm Beach FL 33480

LINDSAY, DALE RICHARD, research administrator; b. Bunker Hill, Kans., Aug. 9, 1913; s. Charles Edwin and Iva (Missimer) L.; m. Sybil Anne McCoy, June 6, 1937; children—Martha Lou Lindsay Cover, Judith Anne Lindsay Clapp, Patricia Dale. A.B., U. Kans., 1937, M.A., 1938; Ph.D., Iowa State Coll., 1943. Entomologist Dept. Agr., summers 1937-39; teaching fellow, instr. research assoc. Iowa State Coll., 1938-43; commd. officer USPHS, 1943—; scientist dir., 1955; assigned malaria control in war areas, 1943-45; entomologist charge operations Communicable Disease Center Activies, Pharr, Tex. 1945-48; chief Thomasville (Ga.) field sta., 1948-53; chief program evaluation sect., div. research grants NIH, 1953-55, asst. chief div., 1955-60, chief div., 1960-63; dep. to gen. dir. Mass. Gen. Hosp., Boston, 1963-65; spl. asst. to chancellor health scis. U. Calif. at Davis, 1965-67, asst. chancellor research and health scis., 1968-69; asso. commr. sci. FDA, 1969-71; asso. dir. med. and allied health edn. Duke U., 1971-75; asst. dir. for sci. coordination Nat. Center for Toxicol. Research, Jefferson, Ark., 1975-76; adj. prof. medicine U. Ark. Med. Sch., 1975-76; asso. dept. family and community medicine U. Ariz., 1977-82; Agrl. bd. Nat. Acad. Sci.-NRC, 1970-73; mem. exec. com., public trustee Nutrition Found., 1972-76, Environ. and Agrl. Found., 1974-79; chmn. sci. adv. bd. Nat. Center for Toxicol. Research, 1972-74. Fellow AAAS, Am. Public Health Assn.; mem. Entomol. Soc. Am. (gov. bd. 1958-62), Commd. Officer Assn.

USPHS (treas. nat. exec. com. 1959-61) , Sigma Xi, Phi Kappa Phi, Gamma Sigma Delta.

LINDSAY, DAVID BREED, JR., aircraft company executive, former editor and publisher; b. Fayetteville, N.C., Dec. 25, 1922; s. David Breed and Helen Carter (Dodson) L.; m. Elizabeth Hotchkiss Girvin, June 19, 1944; children: David G.B., Robert A., Ann C., Edward H. B.S., Purdue U., 1947. Reporter/photographer Marion (Ind.) Chronicle, 1947-48; editor, gen. mgr. Sarasota (Fla.) Herald Tribune, 1948-55, editor, pres., 1955-82; pres. Cavalier Aircraft Corp., 1955-70, Lindair, Inc., 1971—; designer, test pilot Enforcer Aircraft; cons. Piper Aircraft Corp. Founder, trustee New Coll., Sarasota, 1950-75. Served with U.S. Army, 1943-46. Decorated Army Commendation medal. Mem. Am. Newspaper Pubs. Assn. (dir.), Am. Newspaper Pubs. Assn. Found. (pres.), Inter Am. Press Assn. (dir.), Soc. Exptl. Test Pilots., Sigma Delta Chi. Episcopalian. Clubs: Met. (Washington); Old Capital (Monterey, Calif.); Univ. (Sarasota). Inventor various aircraft systems, including Enforcer Aircraft. Office: PO Box 13367 Sarasota FL 34278

LINDSAY, DIANNA MARIE, educational administrator; b. Boston, Dec. 7, 1948; d. Albert Joseph and June Hazelton (Mitchell) Raggi; m. James William Lindsay III, Feb. 14, 1981. BA in Anthropology, Ea. Nazarene Coll., 1971; MEd in Curriculum and Instrn., Wright State U., 1973, MEd in Social Studies Edn., 1974, MEd in Edn. Adminstrn., 1977; EdD in Edn. Adminstrn., Ball State U., 1976. Supr. social edn. Ohio Dept. Edn., Columbus, 1976-77; asst. prin. Orange City Schs., Pepper Pike, Ohio, 1977-79; prin. North Olmsted (Ohio) Jr. High Sch., 1979-81; dir. secondary edn. North Olmsted City SChs., 1981-82; supt. Copley (Ohio)-Fairlawn City Schs., 1982-85; prin. North Olmsted High Sch., 1985-89, New Trier High Sch., Winnetka, Ill., 1989—; bd. dirs. Harvard Prins. Ctr., Cambridge, Mass. Contbr. articles to profl. jours. Bd. dirs. Nat. PTA, Chgo., 1987-89 (Educator of Yr. 1989). Named Prin. of Yr. Ohio Art Tchrs., 1989, one of 100 Up and Coming Educators, Exec. Educator Mag., 1988; recipient John Vaughn Achievements in Edn. North Cen. Assn., 1988. Mem. AAUW, Ill. Tchrs. Fgn. Lang., Rotary Internat., Phi Delta Kappa. Methodist. Avocations: stained glass, reading, travel, biking, snorkling. Office: New Trier High Sch 385 Winnetka Ave Winnetka IL 60093-4295

LINDSAY, DONALD PARKER, former savings bank executive; b. Spokane, Aug. 31, 1915; s. Alexander John and Alice Maude (Kelly) L.; m. Patricia Lally, Oct. 2, 1940; children: Karen, Bridget, Monica. Student, U. Wash., 1934-35. With Lincoln Mut. Savs. Bank, Spokane, 1935-85; pres. Lincoln Mut. Savs. Bank, 1962-80, chief exec. officer, 1969-80, chmn., 1978-85; past dir. First Nat. Bank, Spokane; cons. AID Mission to Iran, 1964. Chmn. United Red Feather drive, Spokane, 1952; past pres. Spokane Philharmonic; trustee Spokane Unltd.; past trustee Mcpl. League Spokane; past chmn. Champagne Ball Charities; chmn. adv. com. on bond issues Spokane Sch. Bd., 1978; mem. bus. adv. com. Wash. State U. Coll. Bus. and Econs., 1979—; mem. North Am. Savs. League, 1976-85, chmn., 1984-85. Served from pvt. to 1st lt. USAAF, 1942-46. Mem. Wash. Savs. League (pres. 1961-62), Nat. Assn. Mut. Savs. Banks (past dir.), Savs. and Loan Found. (past mem. nat. bd.), Mut. Savs. Bank Assn. Wash. (pres. 1979), U.S. League Savs. Assns. (mut. instns. com.), Nat. League Insured Savs. Assn. (mem. bd. govs. 1966-76, mem. exec. com. 1974-76), Soc. Residential Appraisers (pres. Spokane chpt. 1952), Spokane C. of C. (trustee, exec. com. 1970-72, 78-82, sec.-treas. 1979, vice chmn. 1980-81, chmn. 1981-82). Clubs: University (past pres.), Spokane Country (past pres.), Spokane, Manito Golf and Country, Empire, Prosperity, Spokane. Office: 905 W Riverside Ave Spokane WA 99201-1099

LINDSAY, FRANKLIN ANTHONY, business executive, author; b. Kenton, Ohio, Mar. 12, 1916; s. Harry Wyatt and Ruth (Andrews) L.; m. Margot Coffin, Dec. 17, 1948; children: Catherine, Alison (dec.), John Franklin. A.B., Stanford U., 1938; postgrad., Harvard U., 1946. With Columbia div. U.S. Steel Corp., 1938-39; exec. asst. to Bernard Baruch, U.S. del. UN Atomic Energy Commn., 1946; cons. Ho. of Reps. Select (Herter) Com. on Fgn. Aid, 1947-48, ECA, Paris; rep. to exec. com. OEEC, 1948-49; with CIA, 1949-53; with pub. affairs program Ford Found., 1953-56; pres. McKinsey & Co., Inc., N.Y.C., 1956-61; exec. v.p. dir. Itek Corp., Lexington, Mass., 1961-62, pres., 1962-75, chmn. bd., 1975-81, chmn. exec. com., 1981-83; chmn. Engenics, Inc., Menlo Park, Calif., 1983-85; rsch. assoc. Inst. Politics, Harvard U., 1967-71; cons. 2d Hoover Commn., 1954, The White House, 1955; mem. Rockefeller Spl. Studies Panel Econ. Policy, 1956, Gaither Com. Nat. Security Policy, 1957; asst. staff dir. President's Com. World Econ. Policy, 1958; mem. President Elect's Task Force on Disarmament, 1960; dir. Com. for Nat. Trade Policy, 1956-71; adv. coun. dept. econs. Princeton U., 1961-64; mem. Wilson Ctr. adv. coun. Smithsonian Instn., 1980-94; trustee Bennington Coll., 1963-73; chmn. bd. trustees Edn. Devel. Ctr., 1967-73; mem. vis. com. dept. econs. Harvard U., 1976-80; mem. President's Adv. Com. on Trade Negotiations, 1976-79; bd. dirs. Nat. Bur. Econ. Rsch., 1976-93, mem. exec. com., 1980—, chmn., 1983-86; mem. adv. coun. Gas Rsch. Inst., 1977-83; vice chmn. energy and raw materials, bus. and industry advisory com. OECD, 1977-82; bd. dirs. Corp. Pub./Pvt. Ventures, 1978-82, chmn., 1980; mem. advisory bd. Pub. Agenda Found., 1978-84; mem. NRC Commn. Engring. Systems, 1978-84, panel on balancing nat. interest NAS, 1985-87; bd. dirs. Resources for the Future, 1978-86; assoc. Ctr. for Internat. Affairs, Harvard U., 1988—; vis. scholar Woodrow Wilson Ctr. for Scholars, Washington, 1987-88, 90; adj. prof. Internat. Mgmt. Inst., Kiev, Ukraine, 1993—. Author: New Techniques of Management Decision Making, 1958, Beacons in the Night: War and Revolution in Yugoslavia 1941-45, 1993; contbg. author: Preparing Tomorrow's Business Leaders Today, The Conscience of the City, Removing Obstacles to Economic Growth; contbr. articles on nat. and fgn. policy to profl. jours. Vis. scholar Woodrow Wilson Ctr. for Scholars, Washington, 1987-88, 90. Lt. col. AUS, 1940-45; with guerrilla forces 1944-45, Europe (OSS); chief U.S. Mil. Mission to Yugoslavia, 1945. Decorated Legion of Merit. Mem. Nat. Planning Assn. (vice chmn. com. arms control 1959-62), Coun. Fgn. Rels., Inst. Strategic Studies (London), Com. for Econ. Devel. (trustee 1967—, vice chmn. 1974-88, mem. rsch. and policy com. 1968—), Can.-Am. Com., Hudson Inst. (pub. mem.), Saturday Club (Boston), Century Club (N.Y.), Phi Beta Kappa, Tau Beta Pi.

LINDSAY, GEORGE CARROLL, former museum director; b. Cochranville, Pa., Sept. 28, 1928; s. J. George and M. Elizabeth (Copeland) L.; m. Mary-Edythe Shelley, June 27, 1953. BA, Franklin and Marshall Coll., 1950; student, Dickinson Sch. Law, 1950-53; M.A. (Winterthur fellow early Am. culture 1953-55), U. Del., 1955. Asst. to dir. Henry Francis du Pont Winterthur Mus., Del., 1955-56; asst. curator ethnology Smithsonian Instn., 1956-57, asso. curator cultural history, 1957-58, curator mus. service, 1958-66; dir. mus. services N.Y. State Mus., 1966-81, dir., 1981-83, dir. planning and program devel., 1983-86; exec. dir. Vanderbilt Mus., 1986-89; lectr. early Am. decorative arts and architecture; cons. in field; v.p. Alexandria Mars., Va., 1961-62, pres., 1962-63, bd. dirs., 1963-66; bd. dirs. Greater Washington Ednl. TV Assn., 1964-66, mem. programming com., 1965-66; bd. dirs. No. Va. Fine Arts Assn., 1964-66, Mus. Audio-Visual Applications Group, 1962-70, mem. furnishing ofcl. reception room State Dept., 1960-75. Bd. dirs. Menands (N.Y.) Pub. Libr. 1970-86, Albany Symphony Orch., 1969-72, Albany Area chpt. ARC, 1977-86; mem. Strasburg (Pa.) Borough Coun., 1992—, pres., 1994-95; trustee Octoraro United Presbyn. Ch., 1993—. Mem. Am. Assn. Mus. (coun. 1969-72, v.p. 1970-71, chmn. profl. rels. com. 1974-80), N.Y. State Assn. Mus. (sec. 1968-77, pres. 1977-79, coun. 1985-89), N.E. Mus. Conf. (bd. govs. 1982-85, chmn. long range planning com. 1983-85), St. Andrew's Soc. (pres. Albany 1983-85), St. Andrew's Soc. Phila. Mem. Soc. of Friends. Address: 255 Wallingford Rd Strasburg PA 17579

LINDSAY, GEORGE EDMUND, museum director; b. Pomona, Calif., Aug. 17, 1916; s. Charles Wesley and Alice (Foster) L.; m. Geraldine Kendrick Morris, 1972. Student, San Diego State Coll., 1936-39; B.A., Stanford U., 1951, Ph.D., 1956. Dir. Desert Bot. Gardes, Phoenix, 1939-40, San Diego Natural History Mus., 1956-63; Dir. Calif. Acad. Scis, San Francisco, 1963-82, dir. emeritus, 1982—. Served to capt. USAAF, 1943-46. Decorated Air medal with 3 clusters, Bronze Star. Fellow San Diego Soc. Natural History, Zool. Soc. San Diego, Calif. Acad. Scis., A.A.A.S. (Cactus and Succulent Soc. Spl. rsch. taxonomy desert plants, Cactaceae of Baja Calif., Mex. Home: 87 Barbaree Way Tiburon CA 94920 Office: Calif Acad Scis San Francisco CA 94118

LINDSAY, GEORGE NELSON, lawyer; b. N.Y.C., Oct. 20, 1919; m. Mary Sloan Dickey, Apr. 13, 1946; children: George Nelson Jr., Louise Dickey, Stephen Whitney, Peter Vliet. BA, Yale U., 1941, LLB, 1947. Bar: N.Y. 1947. Assoc. Debevoise & Plimpton and predecessors, N.Y.C., 1947-54; ptnr. Debevoise & Plimpton (and predecessor firms), N.Y.C., 1955-90; presiding ptnr. Debevoise & Plimpton and predecessors, N.Y.C., 1980-87, of counsel, 1991-93; resident ptnr. Debevoise & Plimpton and predecessors, London, 1989-90; mem. adv. coun. of Africa, Dept. State, 1964-68; mem. exec. com. Lawyers Com. for Civil Rights Under Law, 1969—, co-chmn. 1969-71. Mem. urban design coun. City of N.Y., 1969-75; bd. dirs. African-Am. Inst., 1969—, chmn. bd. dirs., 1981-84; trustee, mem. coun. Yale U., 1973-78, 81-86, v.p., 1976-78, 81-86; bd. dirs. Planned Parenthood-World Population, 1965-68, chmn. bd. dirs., 1965-66; trustee Carnegie Endowment for Internat. Peace, 1981-91, vice chmn., 1986-89, hon. trustee, 1991—; bd. dirs. The Ogilvy Group, Inc., 1962-89, Am. Ditchley Found., 1985—. Recipient Whitney North Seymour award for civil right, 1988. Fellow Am. Bar Found., N.Y. Bar Found.; mem. ABA, N.Y. State Bar Assn., Assn. of Bar of City of N.Y. (mem. exec. com. 1973-77, chmn. exec. com. 1976-77, v.p. 1977), Am. Judicature Soc., Am. Assn. Internat. Commn. Jurists (bd. dirs. 1969—, chmn. bd. dirs. 1983-88), Coun. Fgn. Rels., Overseas Devel. Coun. Home: 16 Sutton Pl New York NY 10022-3057

LINDSAY, GEORGE PETER, lawyer; b. Bklyn., Feb. 22, 1948; s. Charles Joseph and Marie Antionette (Faraone) L.; m. Sharon Winnett, Sept. 8, 1973; children: William Charles, Kimberly Michelle. BA, Columbia U., 1969; JD, Harvard U., 1973. Bar: N.Y. 1974, Mass. 1975, U.S. Dist. Ct. (so. dist.) N.Y. 1974, U.S. Ct. Appeals (2d cir.) 1975. Assoc. White & Case, N.Y.C., 1973-82; ptnr. Miller, Wrubel & Dubroff, N.Y.C., 1982-83, Sullivan & Worcester, N.Y.C., 1983—. Mem. ABA, Assn. Bar City of N.Y., N.Y. State Bar Assn. Office: Sullivan & Worcester 767 3d Ave New York NY 10017

LINDSAY, JAMES WILEY, agricultural company executive; b. Des Moines, Sept. 13, 1934; s. Worthington U. Lindsay and Marsha E. (Wiley) Asher; m. Shirley L. Shutt, July 2, 1953 (div. May 1985, dec. 1990); children: Elizabeth Lindsay Foster, James W. II, Jennifer, Lindsay; m. Jean M. Baumann, Aug. 2, 1986; 1 child, Amanda Marie. Student, Drake U., 1954-60. Mgr. ops. Archer, Daniels, Midland, Fredonia, Kans., 1968-70, Lincoln, Nebr., 1970-72; mgr. export Archer, Daniels, Midland, Decatur, Ill., 1972-74; v.p. western region Archer, Daniels, Midland, Lincoln, 1974-76; v.p. ops. Archer, Daniels, Midland, Cedar Rapids, Iowa, 1979-80; ops. mgr. Archer, Daniels, Midland, Decatur, 1980-83; pres. Brazil ops. T.V.P., Inc., Campinas, Brazil, 1976-79; chief exec. officer AG Processing Inc., Omaha, 1983—; bd. dirs. ABC Ins., Des Moines, Firster Bank, Omaha. Mem. Nat. Soybean Processors Assn. (chmn. 1987-91), Jaycees (pres. Fredonia chpt. 1963-64, bd. dirs. Des Moines chpt. 1960). Republican. Roman Catholic. Lodge: Masons. Avocations: singing, guitar, acting. Office: AG Processing Inc PO Box 2047 Omaha NE 68103-2047

LINDSAY, JOHN VLIET, former mayor, former congressman, author, lawyer; b. N.Y.C., Nov. 24, 1921; s. George Nelson and Eleanor (Vliet) L.; m. Mary Harrison, June 18, 1949; children—Katharine, Margaret, Anne, John Vliet. Grad., St. Paul's Sch., Concord, N.H., 1940; B.A., Yale U., 1944, LL.B., 1948; LL.D. (hon.), Harvard U., 1969, Williams Coll., 1968. Bar: N.Y. State 1949, N.Y. Dist. Ct. (so. dist.) N.Y 1950, U.S. Supreme Ct. 1955, D.C. 1958. Mem. firm Webster & Sheffield, N.Y.C., 1953-60, 74-91, presiding ptnr., 1989-91; of counsel Mudge Rose Guthrie Alexander & Ferdon, N.Y.C., 1991-94, ret., 1994; exec. asst. to U.S. atty. gen., 1955-56; mem. 86th-89th Congresses from 17th Dist. N.Y.; mayor N.Y.C., 1965-73; Commentator on TV. Author: Journey Into Politics, 1966, The City, 1970, The Edge, 1976. Bd. mem. emeritus Lincoln Ctr. for Performing Arts; chmn. emeritus bd. dirs. Lincoln Ctr. Theatre Co. Lt. USNR, 1943-46. Mem. Assn. of Bar of City of N.Y. (com. exec. 1956-60), ABA, N.Y. State Bar Assn., Assn. Former Mems. Congress (pres. 1987-88). Episcopalian. Democrat.

LINDSAY, LESLIE, packaging engineer; b. Amsterdam, N.Y., Oct. 30, 1960; d. R. Gardner and Dorothy (Loucks) L. BA in Advt., Mich. State U., 1981, BS in Package Engring., 1982. Cert. profl. engr. in packaging. Constrn. inspector N.Y. State Dept. Transp., Albany, 1983; sr. package design engr. Wang Labs., Inc., Lowell, Mass., 1983-90; packaging engr. Apple Computer, Inc., Santa Clara, Calif., 1990—; conf. speaker Internat. Safe Transit Assn., 1994. N.Y. State Regents scholar, 1977; recipient Silver Ameristar award for electronics packaging, 1993. Mem. Soc. Packaging Profls., Inst. Packaging Profls. (mem. reduction, reuse, and recycling of protective packaging task group), Boston Women's Rugby Club (tour chmn. 1985), Wang Ultimate Frisbee (social chmn. 1986-89). Home: 239 Erie Way # 5 Campbell CA 95008-1630 Office: Apple Computer Inc 20730 Valley Green Dr Cupertino CA 95014-1704

LINDSAY, NATHAN JAMES, aerospace company executive, retired career officer; b. Monroe, Wis., May 24, 1936; s. Ralph Allen and Gertrude (Wartenweiler) L.; m. Shirley Rae Montgomery, Feb. 2, 1958; children: Lori E. Lindsay Smith, Anne, Nathan J. Jr., Susan E. BS in Mech. Engring., U.Wis., 1958, MS in Mech. Engring., 1965; MS in Systems Mgmt., U. So. Calif., L.A., 1976. Commd. 2d lt. USAF, 1958, advanced through grades to maj. gen., 1988; munitions officer USAF Weapons Ctr., Tripoli, Libya, 1959-61; weapons logistics officer USAF Europe, Wiesbaden, Germany, 1961-63; Titan III propulsion officer USAF Space Systems Divsn., L.A., 1965-69; aircraft guns devel. officer Air Force Armament Lab., Fla., 1969-70; grad. Armed Forces Staff Coll., Norfolk, Va., 1970; mgmt. auditor Air Force Systems Command, Andrews AFB, Md., 1971-73; grad. Def. Systems Mgmt. Coll., Ft. Belvoir, Va., 1973; space systems policy officer Air Force Office Special Projects, L.A., 1973-74, launch systems integration mgr., 1974-78; dir. policy and adminstrn. Air Force Office Space Systems, Pentagon, Washington, 1978-80; dir. space ops. support Air Force Space Divsn., L.A., 1980-82, program mgr. launch and control systems, 1982-84; comdr. Ea. Space and Missile Ctr., Patrick AFB, Fla., 1985-86; dep. comdr. for space launch and control systems Air Force Space Divsn., L.A., 1986-87; dir. office spl. projects Office Sec. of Air Force, L.A., 1987-92; v.p. Mission Success and Product Assurance Martin Marietta Astrospace; mem. investigation task force NASA Challenger Accident, Kennedy Space Ctr., 1986. Co-chmn. Brevard County, Fla. Civilian-Mil. Affairs Coun., Cocoa Beach, 1984-86; elder Presbyn. Ch. Decorated D.S.M., Def. Superior Svc. medal, Legion of Merit with one oak leaf cluster, Meritorious Svc. medal with one oak leaf cluster, Joint Svc. Commendation medal, Air Force Commendation medal with one oak leaf cluster, Def. Disting. Svc. medal, NASA Disting. Svc. medal, Gen. Thomas White USAF Space trophy, 1992, AAS Mil. Astronautics award, 1993. Mem. AIAA, Am. Astronautical Soc., Air Force Assn. (Bernard A. Shriever Space award 1989), Nat. Space Club (bd. dirs. 1992-94), U. Wis. Alumni Assn., Am. Legion. Avocations: hiking, traveling, fishing, reading. Home: 48 Madison Dr Plainsboro NJ 08536-2318

LINDSAY, REGINALD CARL, lawyer; b. Birmingham, Ala., Mar. 19, 1945; s. Richard and Louise (Crosier) L.; A.B., Morehouse Coll., 1967; cert. U. Valencia (Spain), 1966; J.D., Harvard U., 1970; m. Cheryl E. Hartgrove, Aug. 15, 1970. Admitted to Mass. bar, 1970; assoc. firm Hill & Barlow, 1970-75, 78-79, partner, 1979—; commr. Mass. Dept. Pub. Utilities, Boston, 1975-77; pres. adv. bd. Mus. of Nat. Center of Afro-Am. Artists, 1975-81, v.p., 1981—; trustee Thompson Islands Edn. Center, Boston, 1975-81; bd. dirs. Morgan Meml. Goodwill Industries, Boston, 1992—; mem. Nat. Consumer Law Ctr. (bd. dirs.), Mass. Commn. on Jud. Conduct. Mem. Am., Nat., Mass., Boston (council 1977—) bar assns., Pi Sigma Alpha. Democrat.

LINDSAY, ROBERT VAN CLEEF, trust company executive; b. N.Y.C., Jan. 1, 1926; s. George N. and Eleanor (Vliet) L.; m. Nancy A. Dalley, Apr. 29, 1950; children: Cameron, Dorothy A., Robert D. BA, Yale U., 1949. With J.P. Morgan & Co., 1949-86, asst. treas., asst. v.p., 1949-60; v.p. Morgan Guaranty Trust Co., 1960-69, sr. v.p., 1969-76, exec. v.p., 1976-79, chmn. exec. com., 1978-79, pres., 1980-86, chmn. internat. coun., 1987-89; bd. dirs. Fluor Corp., Chubb Corp., Russell Reynolds Assocs., Inc., United Meridian Corp., Fishkill Nat. Corp., Lomas Fin. Corp., J.P. Morgan (Suisse) S.A.; sr. advisor Unibank Danmark A/S. Bd. dirs. N.Y. Philharm. Symphony Soc., 1966-73, 77-85; trustee Cooper Union, 1967-73; trustee John Simon Guggenheim Meml. Found., 1983—, chmn., 1991—; bd. dirs. Ctr. for Interam. Relations, 1980-86, Ams. Soc., 1982-86. Served with U.S. Mcht.

Marine, 1943-45. Mem. Soc. for Prevention Cruelty to Animals (bd. mgrs. 1962-72), L.I. Biol. Assn. (bd. dirs. 1953-73), Fgn. Policy Assn. (chmn. 1986-90), Coun. on Fgn. Rels., Phi Beta Kappa, Chi Psi. Episcopalian. Clubs: Links, Leash. Home: Rural Rte 3 Box 219 Altamont Rd Millbrook NY 12545 Office: Morgan Guaranty Trust Co 15 Broad St New York NY 10005-1908

LINDSAY, ROGER ALEXANDER, investment executive; b. Dundee, Scotland, Feb. 18, 1941; s. Archibald Carswell Lindsay and Edith Paterson Bissett. Student, The Morgan Acad., Dundee, Queen's Coll. U. St. Andrews, Scotland. Asst. acct., office mgr. Andrew G. Kidd Ltd., Dundee, 1964; head office acct. Associated British Foods Ltd., London, 1966; sec., treas. Wittington Investments, Ltd., Toronto, Ont., Can., 1971; exec. v.p. Wittington Investments Ltd., Toronto, Ont., Can., 1981; bd. dirs. Loblaw Cos. Ltd., Intercon Security Ltd., Laser Guest Corp., United World Coll. Internat. of Can., Inc., The W. Garfield Weston Found.; pres. Fort House Investments Ltd. Trustee Presbyn. Ch. of Can. Knight, comdr. The Sov. Order of St. John. Fellow Inst. Mgmt., Inst. Dirs., Soc. of Antiquaries of Scotland; mem. Inst. Chartered Accts. Scotland; mem. Royal Overseas League, The Nat. Club (dir. Toronto), Royal Can. Yacht Club, Coral Beach Club (Bermuda). Avocations: heraldry, antique silver. Office: Wittington Investments Ltd, 22 St Clair Ave East, Toronto, ON Canada M4T 2S3

LINDSAY, W. DOUGLAS, JR., historic site administrator. Supt. Saratoga National Historical Park, Stillwater, N.Y. Office: Saratoga Nat Hist Pk 648 Route 32 Stillwater NY 12170-1604*

LINDSAY, WILLIAM KERR, surgeon; b. Vancouver, BC, Can., Sept. 3, 1920; s. James Arthur and Lottie Mary (Early) L.; m. Frances Beatrice Ferris, Feb. 15, 1945; children—William Arthur, Barbara Susanne, Katherine Mary, Anne Louise. M.D. U. Toronto, 1945, BS in Medicine, 1949, M.S., 1959. Intern Toronto Gen. Hosp., 1945-46; resident Toronto Gen. Hosp. and Hosp. Sick Children, 1948-51, Montreal Gen. Hosp., 1951-52, Baylor U. Hosp., 1952-53; practice medicine, specializing in plastic surgery Toronto 1953—; staff surgeon to head divsn. plastic surgery Hosp. for Sick Children, 1953-86, cons., 1986—; project dir. Research Inst., 1954-85; faculty dept. surgery U. Toronto Faculty of Medicine, 1953-86, prof., 1968-86, chmn. interhospital com. for plastic surgery, 1965-86, prof. emeritus, 1986—; Chmn. med. dental staff com. Ont. Hugh MacMillan Treatment Ctr. (formerly Crippled Childrens Ctr.), 1958-63. Trustee McLaughlin Found., 1986—. With M.C., Royal Can. Army, 1943-46; surg. lt. Royal Can. Navy, 1946-47. Hon. head burn and plastic surg. dept. Ganso Provincial People's Hosp., Lanzhou City, China, 1994—. Fellow ACS, Royal Coll. Surgeons Can.; mem. Am. Assn. Plastic Surgeons (pres. 1970-71), Can. Soc. Plastic Surgeons (pres. 1963), Easter Seal Soc. Ont. (chmn. med. adv. com. 1957-65, cons. 1952—, mem. rsch. inst. 1979—), Am. Soc. Plastic and Reconstructive Surgeons (Spl. Achievement award 1979), Am. Soc. Surgery of Hand, Am. Cleft Palate Assn., Brit. Soc. Surgery of Hand. Home: 44 Clarendon Ave, Toronto, ON Canada M4V 1J1 Office: 555 University Ave, Toronto, ON Canada M5G 1X8

LINDSELL, HAROLD, clergyman, educator, editor; b. N.Y.C., Dec. 22, 1913; s. Leonard Anthony and Ella Briggs (Harris) L.; B.S., Wheaton Coll., 1938; M.A., U. Calif., 1939, Ph.D., N.Y. U., 1942; D.D., Fuller Theol. Sem., 1964; m. Marion Joanne Bolinder, June 12, 1943; children: Judith Ann (Mrs. William C. Wood), Joanne (Mrs. Robert Webber), Nancy J. (Mrs. Daniel Sharp), John H. Prof. history, missions, registrar Columbia Bible Coll., 1942-44; ordained to ministry Baptist Ch., 1944; prof. missions, assoc. prof. ch. history No. Bapt. Theol. Sem., 1944-47, prof., 1947-51, registrar, 1947-50, dean, 1950-51; dean faculty, prof. missions Fuller Theol. Sem., 1951-61, v.p., prof. missions, 1961-64; associate editor Christianity Today, 1964-67, editor, pub., 1968-78; prof. Bible, Wheaton (Ill.) Coll., 1967-68; prof. apologetics Simon Greenleaf Sch. Law, 1983-89, dir. M.A. program, 1984-89. Mem. exec. com. Internat. Congress on World Evangelization. Trustee emeritus Westmont Coll., Wheaton Coll.; chmn. emeritus Gordon Conwell Theol. Sem., Outreach, Christianity Today. Mem. Tournament Roses, Nat. Assn. Bible Instrs., Am. Hist. Assn., Am. Soc. Ch. History, Nat., Greater Washington (pres. 1966-67) assns. evangelicals, NEA, Am. Acad. Polit. and Social Scis., Evang. Theol. Soc. (pres. 1970-71), Pi Gamma Mu, Pi Kappa Delta, Alpha Gamma Omega. Republican. Clubs: Nat. Press, Cosmos (Washington). Author: Abundantly Above, 1944; The Thing Appointed, 1949; A Christian Philosophy of Missions, 1949; Park Street Prophet, 1951; (with C.J. Woodbridge) Handbook of Christian Truth, 1953; Missionary Principles and Practice, 1955; The Morning Altar, 1956; Daily Bible Readings from the Revised Standard Version, 1957; Christianity and the Cults, 1963; Harper Study Bible (rev. standard version), 1964, 91; When You Pray, 1969; The World, The Flesh and The Devil, 1974; The Battle for the Bible, 1976; God's Incomparable Word, 1978; The Bible in the Balance, 1979; The Lindsell Study Bible in the Living Bible, 1980; The Gathering Storm, 1980; Free Enterprise: a Judeo-Christian Defense, 1982; The Holy Spirit in the Latter Days, 1983; Armageddon Spectre, 1984, The People's Study Bible in King James and Living Bible, 1986, The New Paganism, 1987; also articles; editor: The Church's Worldwide Mission, 1966, Harper Study Bible (New Am. Standard Version), 1985, The Everyday Pocket Bible, 1988, Tyndale Words of God for Every Day, 1989, New Harper Study Bible (New Rev. Standard Version), 1991. Home: 23442 El Toro Rd E344 Lake Forest CA 92630

LINDSETH, RICHARD EMIL, orthopedic surgeon; b. Denver, Apr. 3, 1935; s. Emil Victor and Audrey Madera (Yeo) L.; m. Marilyn Martha Miller, July 7, 1959; children: Erik Lars, Ellen Sue. BA, Dartmouth Coll., 1957; MD, Harvard U., 1960. Diplomate Am. Bd. Orthopaedic Surgery. Intern, then resident in surgery SUNY, Syracuse, 1960-62, resident in orthopaedic surgery, 1964-67; prof. orthopaedic surgery Ind. U., Indpls., 1975—, acting chmn. dept. orthopaedic surgery, 1984-86; pres. Assoc. Orthopaedic Surgeons, Inc., Indpls., 1983-86. Mem. editorial bd. Jour. Pediatric Orthopaedics; contbr. articles to profl. jours. Fellow ACS, Am. Acad. Orthopaedic Surgeons, Am. Acad. Pediatrics, Scoliosis Rsch. Soc., Am. Orthopaedic Assn.; mem. Pediatric Orthopaedic Soc. N.Am. (pres. 1986-87), European Pediatric Orthopaedic Soc., Internat. Soc. for Rsch. into Hydrocephalus and Spina Bifida, Spina Bifida Assn. Am. (profl. adv. coun. 1978-88, chmn. 1987-88). Methodist. Office: Ind U Med Ctr Riley Hosp 702 Barnhill Dr Indianapolis IN 46202-5128

LINDSEY, CASIMIR CHARLES, zoologist; b. Toronto, Ont., Can., Mar. 22, 1923; s. Charles Bethune and Wanda Casimira (Gzowski) L.; m. Shelagh Pauline Lindsey, May 29, 1948. B.A., U. Toronto, 1948; M.A., U. B.C., Vancouver, 1950; Ph.D., Cambridge (Eng.) U., 1952. Div. biologist B.C. Game Dept., 1952-57; with Inst. Fisheries, also dept. zoology U. B.C., 1953-66; prof. zoology U. Man., Winnipeg, 1966-79; dir. Inst. Animal Resource Ecology, U. B.C., 1980-85; mem. Fisheries and Oceans Adv. Council, 1981-86; prof. emeritus U. B.C., 1988—; bd. govs. Vancouver Public Aquarium, 1956-66, 80-95; external assessor univs. S ingapore and Nanyang, 1979-81; cons. in field. Author papers in field. Served with Can. Army, 1943-45. Recipient Publ. award Wildlife Soc., 1972; Sanderson award for excellence in teaching U. Man., 1977; Rh Inst. award, 1979; Nuffield Found. grantee, 1973; Killam sr. fellow, 1985-86. Fellow Royal Soc. Can.; mem. Can. Soc. Zoologists (pres. 1977-78), Can. Soc. Environ. Biologists (v.p. 1974-75), Am. Soc. Ichthyologists and Herpetologists (gov.). Office: U BC Dept of Zoology, 6270 University Blvd, Vancouver, BC Canada V6T 1Z4

LINDSEY, D. RUTH, physical education educator; b. Kingfisher, Okla. Oct. 26, 1926; d. Lewis Howard and Kenyon (King) L. BS, Okla. State U., 1948; MS, U. Wis., 1954; PEd, Ind. U., 1965. Cert. kinesiotherapist, 1970. Instr. Okla. State U., Stillwater, 1948-50, Monticello Coll., Alton, Ill., 1951-54, DePauw U., Greencastle, Ind., 1954-56; prof. Okla. State U., Stillwater, 1956-75; vis. prof. U. Utah, Salt Lake City, 1975-76; prof. phys. edn. Calif. State U., Long Beach, 1976-88; prof. emeritus phys. edn. Calif. State U. 1988—; freelance author, cons. Westminster, Calif. Co-author: Fitness for the Health of It, 6th edit., 1989, Concepts of Physical Fitness, 8th edit., 1993, Fitness for Life, 4th edit., 1992, Concepts of Physical Fitness and Wellness, 1993, The Ultimate Fitness Book, 1984, Survival Kit for Those Who Sit, 1989; editor: Perspectives: Jour. of Western Soc. for Phys. Edn. Coll. Women, 1988—. Amy Morris Homans scholar, 1964; recipient Disting. and Meritorious Svc. Honor award Okla. Assn. Health, Phys. Edn. and Recreation, 1970, Meritorious Performance award Calif. State U., 1987, Julian Vogel Meml. award Am. Kinesiotherapy Assn., 1988. Fellow AAH-

PERD, Am. Kinesiotherapy Assn., Calif. Assn. Health, Phys. Edn., Recreation and Dance, Nat. Coun. Against Health Fraud, Orange County Nutrition Coun., Tex and Acad. Authors Assn., Phi Kappa Phi. Republican. Baptist. Avocations: golf, travel, writing.

LINDSEY, DAVID HOSFORD, lawyer; b. Kingsville, Tex., July 25, 1950; s. Ernest Truman and Helen Elizabeth (Hosford) L.; m. Marilyn Kay Williams, June 8, 1974; children: Seth Williams, Brooks Daniel. BS in Bus. Adminstrn., U. Mo., 1972; JD, Washburn U., 1975. Bar: Mo. 1975. With trust dept. Commerce Bank, Kansas City, Mo., 1974-75, asst. v.p., 1979-83, v.p., 1983-85, sr. v.p., 1985-94, chief credit officer, 1989—; mgr., sales dept. Pioneer Pallet, Inc., North Kansas City, Mo., 1976; asst. cashier Nat. Bank, North Kansas City, 1977, asst. v.p., 1977-78, v.p., 1978-79. Vice chmn. planning and zoning com. City of Liberty, Mo., 1981-93; bd. dirs. Kansas City Met. YMCA (treas., mem. exec. com.). Mem. Mo. Bar Assn., Lawyers Assn. Kansas City, Kansas City Met. Bar Assn., Robert Morris Assn. (bd. dirs. Kansas City chpt.), Kansas City C. of C., Kansas City Alumni Assn. (bd. dirs.), Clayview Country Club, Phi Gamma Delta. Baptist. Home: 602 Camelot Dr Liberty MO 64068-1176 Office: Commerce Bank 1000 Walnut St Kansas City MO 64106

LINDSEY, JACK LEE, curator; b. June 7, 1958; s. Charles Edward and Ruth Jacquelyn (Hensley) L. BA in Am. Social and Cultural History with honors, BA in Studio Art with honors, Guilford Coll., 1980; MA in Am. Civilization and Curatorial Studies, U. Pa., 1986, postgrad., 1986—. Asst. curator exhibitions Guilford Coll., Greensboro, N.C., 1978-80; chmn. dept. art and history Atlantic Friends Sch., Northfield, N.J., 1981-85; field rschr., archivist U. Pa., Phila., 1986-87; instr. Am. civilization and folklore Guilford Coll., 1986-89; asst. curator Am. decorative arts Phila. Mus. Art, 1986-88, assoc. curator Am. decorative arts, 1988-89, curator Am. decorative arts, 1990—; chmn. adv. bd. Phila. Folklore Project, 1989-91; lectr. in field. Contbr. articles to profl. jours. Recipient Outstanding Educators award Friends Coun. in Edn., 1984, 85; Newlin Grad. History scholar Guilford Coll., 1980; Rotary Internat. Edn. scholar, 1980-81; rsch. grantee NEA, 1980; Edward Maverick fellow Attingham Trust, 1987. Mem. Am. Folklore Soc. (vice chmn. adv. bd. 1989-90). Office: Phila Mus Art 26th And The Pky Philadelphia PA 19130

LINDSEY, JOHN HORACE, insurance executive, museum official; b. Waxahachie, Tex., July 28, 1922; s. Harry E. and Marie (Smith) L.; m. Sara Houstoun, Aug. 30, 1946; children: Edwin (dec.), David C. BA, Tex. A&M U., 1944. Propr. Lindsey Ins. Agy., Houston, 1953—; bd. of regents Texas A&M U System. Former v.p. Houston Mus. Fine Arts; former pres. Alley Theatre; bd. dirs. South Tex. Coll. Law, Tex. A&M Rsch. Found., College Station; pres. Tex. A&M U. Alumni, 1964; vice chmn. bd. visitors U.S. Mil. Acad.; bd. dirs. George Bush Presdl. Libr. Found. Recipient Disting. Alumni award Tex. A&M U. Home: 3640 Willowick Rd Houston TX 77019-1114 Office: Tex Am Bldg 921 Main St Ste 625 Houston TX 77002-6422

LINDSEY, JONATHAN ASMEL, development executive, educator; b. Bulloch County, Ga., June 9, 1937; s. Joel Wesley and Ethel Iora (Stickland) L.; m. Edythe Annette Lowner, Apr. 3, 1965; children—Julianna Elizabeth, Jonathan Edward. A.B., George Washington U., 1961; B.D., So. Bapt. Sem., Louisville, 1964; Ph.D., So. Bapt. Sem., 1968; M.S.L.S., U. Ala., 1975. Assoc. prof., librarian Judson Coll., Marion, Ala., 1967-77; assoc. dean, librarian Meredith Coll., Raleigh, N.C., 1977-83; librarian Baylor U., Waco, Tex., 1983-89, dir. found. devel., 1989—. Author: (monographs) Free To Be, 1975, Change and Challenge, 1978, (with others) Professional Ethics and Librarians, 1985, Performance Evaluation: A Management Basic, 1986; editor: N.C. Libraries (H.W. Wilson award 1981), 1979-83, Publications in Librarianship, 1988-93; contbr. articles and book revs. to profl. jours. Mem. Waco Peace Alliance, PTA. Mem. ALA, Tex. Libr. Assn., NSFRE, CASE. Home: 8265 Mosswood Dr Waco TX 76712-2407 Office: Baylor U PO Box 97026 Waco TX 76798-7026

LINDSEY, LAWRENCE BENJAMIN, economist, federal official; b. Peekskill, N.Y., July 18, 1954; s. Merritt Hunt and Helen Ruth (Hissam) L.; m. Susan Ann McGrath, Aug. 28, 1982; 2 children. AB magna cum laude, Bowdoin Coll., Brunswick, Maine, 1976; MA, Harvard U., 1981, PhD, 1985; JD (hon.), Bowdoin Coll., 1993. Economist Coun. Econ. Advisers, Washington, 1981-84; from asst. prof. to assoc. prof. Harvard U., Cambridge, Mass., 1984-90; faculty rsch. fellow Nat. Bur. Econ. Rsch., Cambridge, 1984-89; from assoc. dir. to spl. asst. to Pres., Office of Policy Devel., The White House, Washington, 1989-91; gov. Fed. Res. Bd., Washington, 1991—. Author: The Growth Experiment, 1990; contbr. articles to profl. jours. Recipient Walter Wriston award Manhattan Inst., 1988. Mem. Phi Beta Kappa. Office: Fed Res Bd 20th & C Sts NW Washington DC 20551

LINDSEY, LOWELL L., library director. Dir. N.E. Tex. Libr. System, Garland. Office: Nicholson Meml Libr 625 Austin St Garland TX 75040-6304

LINDSEY, SETH MARK, lawyer, federal agency administrator; b. L.A., Oct. 18, 1947; s. Seth Rankin and Lela Belle (Johnson) L.; m. Susan Adelaide Badger, June 29, 1968; 1 child, Samantha. BA, U. So. Calif., A.A., 1968; JD, Yale U., 1971. Bar: Calif. 1972, U.S. Supreme Ct. 1984. Honors atty. Housing and Urban Devel., Washington, 1971-72, atty., 1972-76; asst. chief counsel Fed. Railroad Adminstrn., Washington, 1976-86, chief counsel, 1986—, acting adminstr., 1993; spl. counsel for Conrail and Union Sta. Redevel. Fed. Railroad Adminstrn., 1984-86. Recipient Silver medal Dept. Transp., 1977, 83, Gold medal, 1984. Republican. Baptist. Office: Dept Transp Fed RR Adminstrn Adminstrn 400 7th St SW Ste 8201 Washington DC 20590

LINDSEY, SUSAN LYNDAKER, zoologist; b. Valley Forge, Pa., Aug. 23, 1956; d. Howard Paul and Lillian Irene (Whitman) Lyndaker; m. Kevin Arthur Lindsey, July 17, 1982. BS in Biology, St. Lawrence U., 1978; MA in Zoology, So. Ill. U., Carbondale, 1980; PhD in Zoology, Colo. State U., 1987. Rschr. St. Lawrence U., Kenya, East Africa, 1974; rschr. mammal dept. Dallas Zoo, 1988-93; exec. dir. Wild Canid Survival and Rsch. Ctr., Eureka, Mo., 1993—; adj. prof. Cedar Valley Coll., 1992-93; propagation group mem. Red Wolf Species Survival Plan, Tacoma, Wash., 1994—, Mexican Gray Wolf Species Survival Plan, Albuquerque, 1993—. Contbr. articles to profl. jours. Docent Denver Zool. Found., Denver Zoo, 1985-88. Mem. Am. Zoo and Aquarium Assn., Am. Behavior Soc., Am. Soc. of Mammalogists, Beta Beta Beta, Phi Beta Kappa, Psi Chi. Avocations: horseback riding, canoeing, gardening, photography, travel. Office: Wild Canid Survival Rsch Ctr Wash U PO Box 760 Eureka MO 63025

LINDSKOG, DAVID RICHARD, lawyer; b. New Haven, Aug. 4, 1936; s. Gustaf Elmer and Charlotte (Birely) L.; m. Elisabeth Lagg, Jan. 28, 1978; 1 child, Stefanie. B.A., Yale U., 1958; LL.B., U. Va., 1965. Bar: N.Y. 1966, conseil juridique France 1978, avocat 1992. Assoc., Curtis, Mallet-Prevost, Colt & Mosle, N.Y.C., 1965-72, ptnr., 1973—. Served to lt. USNR, 1958-62. Mem. Internat. Bar Assn. Episcopalian. Club: Yale (N.Y.C.). Home: 22 Shore Acre Dr Old Greenwich CT 06870-2130 Office: Curtis Mallet-Prevost Colt & Mosle 101 Park Ave New York NY 10178-0061

LINDSLEY, DONALD BENJAMIN, physiological psychologist, educator; b. Brownhelm, Ohio, Dec. 23, 1907; s. Benjamin Kent and Mattie Elizabeth (Jenne) L.; m. Ellen Ford, Aug. 16, 1933; children: David Ford, Margaret, Robert Kent, Sara Ellen. A.B., Wittenberg Coll. (now Univ.), 1929, D.Sc. (hon.), 1959; A.M., U. Iowa, 1930, Ph.D., 1932; Sc.D. (hon.), Brown U., 1958, Trinity Coll., Hartford, Conn., 1965; D.Sc. (hon.), Loyola U. Chgo., 1969; Ph.D. (hon.), Johannes Gutenberg U., Mainz, W.Ger., 1977. Instr. psychology U. Ill., 1932-33; NRC fellow Harvard U. Med. Sch., 1933-35; research assoc. Western Res. U. Med. Sch., 1935-38; asst. prof. psychology Brown U.; also dir. psychol. and neurophysiol. lab. Bradley Hosp., 1938-46; dir. war research project on radar operation Yale, OSRD, Nat. Def. Research Com., Camp Murphy and Boca Raton AFB, Fla., 1943-45; prof. psychology Northwestern U., 1946-51; prof. psychology, physiology, psychiatry and pediatrics UCLA, 1951-77, prof. emeritus, 1977—, mem. Brain Research Inst., 1961—, chmn. dept. psychology, 1959-62; William James lectr. Harvard, 1958; Univ. Research lectr. U. Calif. at Los Angeles,

1960; Phillips lectr. Haverford Coll., 1961; Walter B. Pillsbury lectr. psychology Cornell U., 1963; vis. lectr. Kansas State U., 1966, Tex. A & M U., 1980; Mem. sci. adv. bd. USAF, 1947-49; undersea warfare com. NRC, 1951-64; cons. NSF, 1952-54; mem. mental health study sect. NIMH, 1953-57; neurol. study sect. Nat. Inst. Neurol. Diseases and Blindness, 1958-62; cons. Guggenheim Found., 1963-70, mem. editorial adv. bd., 1970-78; chmn. behavioral scis. tng. com. Nat. Inst. Gen. Med. Scis., 1966-69; mem. behavioral biology adv. panel AIBS-NASA, 1966-71; mem. space sci. bd. NAS, 1967-70; mem. com. space medicine, 1969-71; mem. Calif. Legis. Assembly Sci. and Tech. Coun., 1970-71. Cons. editor Jour. Exptl. Psychology, 1947-68, Jour. Comparative and Physiol. Psychology, 1952-62, Jour. Personality, 1958-62; mem. editorial bd. Internat. Jour. Physiology and Behavior, 1965-77, Exptl. Brain Rsch., 1965-76, Developmental Psychobiology, 1968-82, Neurosci. and Behavioral Physiology, 1976—; contbr. numerous articles on physiol. psychology, neurosci., brain and behavior to sci. jours., also numerous chpts. in books. Trustee Grass Found., 1958—. Awarded Presdl. Cert. of Merit (for war work), 1948; recipient Disting. Sci. Achievement award Calif. Psychol. Assn., 1977, Disting. Sci. Contbn. award Soc. Psychophysiol. Rsch., 1984, Disting. Grad. award Dept Psychology U. Iowa, 1987, Disting. Alumnus award for Achievement U. Iowa, 1988, Gerard prize (with H.W. Magoun) Soc. Neurosci., 1988, Gold Medal award Am. Psychol. Found., 1989, Hon. Life Mem. award Dept. Psychobiology, U. Calif., Irvine, 1989; Guggenheim fellow Europe, 1959, hon. fellow UCLA Sch. Medicine, 1986. Mem. Nat. Acad. Scis. (chmn. com. long duration missions in space 1967-72, mem. space sci. board); Am. Psychol. Assn. (Distinguished Sci. Contbn. award 1959), Am. Physiol. Soc., Soc. Exptl. Psychologists, Am. Electroencephalographic Soc. (pres. 1964-65, hon. mem. 1980—, Herbert Jasper award 1994), AAAS (v.p. 1954, chmn. sect. J 1977), Midwest Psychol. Assn. (pres. 1952), Am. Acad. Cerebral Palsy, Western Soc. Electroencephalography (hon. mem. with great distinction, pres. 1957), Western Psychol. Assn. (pres. 1959-60), Am. Acad. Arts and Scis., Internat. Brain Research Orgn. (treas. 1967-71), Soc. Neuroscis. (Donald B. Lindsley prize in behavioral neurosci. established in his name), Finnish Acad. of Sci. and Letters (fgn. mem.), Sigma Xi, Alpha Omega Alpha, Gamma Alpha, Phi Gamma Delta. Conglist. Home: 471 23d St Santa Monica CA 90402-3125 Office: U Calif Dept Psychology Los Angeles CA 90024-1583

LINDSLEY, JAMES BRUCE, sales and marketing executive; b. Alliance, Ohio, Feb. 28, 1941; s. George Graham and Ruth May (Wilcox) Lindsley; m. Betty Jane Cooper, Aug. 29, 1965. BS in Chemistry, Mt. Union Coll., Alliance, 1964. Lab. technician Hanna Chem. Coatings, Columbus, Ohio, 1965-68; group leader Wm. Armstrong Smith Co., East Point, Ga., 1968-72; chief chemist Progress Paint Mfg. Co., Louisville, 1972-76; product mgr. Freeman Chem. Corp., Port Washington, Wis., 1976-86; sales mgr. Akzo Nobel Resins, East St. Louis, Ill., 1986-91; dir. sales and mktg. Akzo Resins, East St. Louis, Ill., 1991—. Mem. Nat. Paint and Coatings Assn., Fedn. of Socs. for Coating Tech., Honorable Order of Ky. Cols. Avocations: world travel; collecting French crystal, old clocks and model trains. Office: Akzo Nobel Resins 2904 Missouri Ave East Saint Louis IL 62205-1123

LINDSTEDT-SIVA, (KAREN) JUNE, marine biologist, oil company executive; b. Mpls., Sept. 24, 1941; d. Stanley L. and Lila (Mills) Lindstedt; m. Ernest Howard Siva, Dec. 20, 1969. Student, U. Calif.-Santa Barbara, 1959-60, U. Calif.-Davis, 1960-62; B.A., U. So. Calif., 1963, M.S., 1967, Ph.D., 1971. Asst. coordinator Office Sea Grant Programs U. So. Calif., 1971; environ. specialist So. Calif. Edison Co., Rosemead, 1971-72; asst. prof. biology Calif. Luth. U., 1972-73; sci. advisor Atlantic Richfield Co., Los Angeles, 1973-77, sr. sci. advisor, 1977-81, mgr. environ. scis., 1981-86, mgr. environ. protection, 1986—; mem. Nat. Sci. Bd., 1994-96; mem. panels on environ. issues Nat. Rsch. Coun.; mem. Polar Rsch. Bd., 1994—; mem. EPA Panel on Environ. Risk Reduction, 1992-94; mem. NAS Alaska Panel; mem. biology adv. coun. Calif. State U.-Long Beach, 1980-92; bd. dirs. So. Calif. Acad. Scis., 1983-93, pres., 1990-92; mem. Marine Scis.; adv. coun. U. So. Calif. Inst. Coastal and Marine Scis.; trustee Bermuda Biol. Sta. for Rsch.; chmn. Oil Spill Conf., San Antonio, 1989, API Oil Spills Com. Contbr. articles to profl. jours. Recipient Calif. Mus. Sci. and Industry Achievement award, 1976, Trident award for Marine Scis., 11th Ann. Rev. Underwater Activites, Italy, 1970, Achievement award for Advancing Career Opportunities for Women, Career Planning Council, 1978; research grantee; disting. scholar biology Calif. Lut. U. Colloquium Scholars, 1988. Fellow AAAS, ASTM (award of merit 1990), So. Calif. Acad. Scis.; mem. Soc. Petroleum Industry Biologists (pres. 1976-80), Marine Tech. Soc., Calif. Native Plant Soc., Am. Inst. Biol. Sci., Phi Beta Kappa, Sigma Xi, Phi Kappa Phi. Office: Atlantic Richfield Co 515 S Flower St Los Angeles CA 90071-2200

LINDSTROM, CHARLES CLIFFORD, hospital administrator; b. Sauk Center, Minn., Apr. 15, 1928; married;. BA, U. Minn., 1952, MA, 1960. Asst. exec. dir. Twin City Regional Hosp. Coun., St. Paul, 1955-57; administr. rsch. St. John's Hosp., St. Paul, 1957-58, Abbott Hosp., Mpls., 1959-60; asst. administr. Mpls. Gen. Hosp., 1960-63; administr. Hennepin County Med. Ctr., Mpls., 1963-64, Fairview Southdale Hosp., Mpls., 1964-66; CEO St. Luke's Health Sys., Kansas City, 1966—. Mem. ACHE (com. svc.), AHA (com. svc.), Kans. Hosp. Assn. (bd. dirs., com. svc.). Office: St Luke's Hosp PO Box 119000 Kansas City MO 64111-5001*

LINDSTROM, DONALD FREDRICK, JR., priest; b. Atlanta, July 18, 1943; s. Donald Fredrick Sr. and Elizabeth (Haynes) L.; m. Marcia Pace, Dec. 30, 1983; children: Christopher, Eric, Ashley, Ellison. ABJ, U. Ga., 1966; MDiv, Va. Theol. Sem., 1969; JD, Woodrow Wilson Coll. Law, 1977; postgrad., U. West Fla., 1984. Lic. marriage and family therapist. Broadcast journalist radio and TV Atlanta and N.Y.C., 1961-68; priest Episcopal ch., 1969—; rector Episcopal Ch. Mediator, Meridian, Miss., 1991—; pvt. practice as marriage and family therapist, Pensacola, Fla., 1983-91; ecumenical officer Diocese of Cen. Gulf Coast, 1989-91, Miss., 1993; bd. visitors Kanuga Conf. Ctr., 1993—; guest chaplain U.S. Ho. of Reps., nat. prayer breakfast, 1994; mem. ecumenical staff gen. conv., Episcopal Ch., 1994. Writer, producer The Cry for Help, The Autumn Years. Chaplain Atlanta Police Dept., 1975-78; pres. N.W. Fla. chpt. Nat. Kidney Found., 1987-88; mem. Leadership Atlanta, 1975; trustee Fla. Trust for Hist. Preservation. Mem. Am. Assn. for Marriage and Family Therapy (clin.), Mental Health Assn. (life, bd. dirs. Pensacola 1986-88), Navy League, Order of Holy Cross (assoc.), Bailli (pres.), Confrerie de la Chaine des Rotisseurs, Balliage de Meridian, Alpha Tau Omega, Sigma Delta Chi, Delta Gamma Kappa. Avocations: music, photography, art and wine collector, gourmet, fly fishing. Office: Episcopal Ch Mediator 3825 35th Ave Meridian MS 39305-3617

LINDSTROM, EUGENE SHIPMAN, biologist, academic administrator; b. Ames, Iowa, Jan. 12, 1923; s. Ernest Walter and Achsah Cornelia (Anderson) L.; m. Eleanor Eastman Joys, Sept. 8, 1949; children: Karen, Mark, Jon, Scott. Student, Swarthmore Coll., 1940-42, U. Iowa, 1942-43; BA, U. Wis., 1947, MS, 1948, PhD, 1951. Postdoctoral fellow enzyme inst. U. Wis., Madison, 1951-52; from asst. prof. to prof. bacteriology Pa. State U., University Park, 1952-66, from asst. dean to assoc. dean coll. sci., 1966-77, head biology dept., 1977-88, prof. emeritus, 1988—. Served as corp. USAAF, 1943-45, ETO. NSF postdoctoral fellow U. Minn., 1960. Fellow Am. Acad. Microbiology; mem. Am. Soc. for Microbiology, Am. Soc. for Biochemistry and Molecular Biology. Episcopalian. Office: Pa State U Dept Biology 208 Mueller Lab University Park PA 16802-5301

LINDULA, PAMELA O'HARA, lawyer; b. St. Cloud, Minn., Dec. 7, 1962; d. Cecil Alvin and Delores Evelyn (Henry) O'Hara; m. Mark Elvin Lindula, May 4, 1993; 1 child, Katherine Anna. BS, Coll. St. Benedict, St. Joseph, Minn., 1984; JD, U. Minn., 1988. Bar: Minn. 1988. Law clk. Court of Appeals, State of Minn., St. Paul, 1988-89; sr. atty. Bankers Systems, St. Cloud, Minn., 1989—. Mem. NOW. Office: Bankers Systems Inc PO Box 1457 Saint Cloud MN 55302

LINDZEN, RICHARD SIEGMUND, meteorologist, educator; b. Webster, Mass., Feb. 8, 1940; s. Abe and Sara (Blachman) L.; m. Nadine Lucie Kalougine, Apr. 7, 1965; children: Eric, Nathaniel. A.B., Harvard U., 1960, S.M., 1961, Ph.D., 1964. Research assoc. U. Wash., Seattle, 1964-65; Research assoc. U. Oslo, 1965-66; with Nat. Center Atmospheric Research, Boulder, Colo., 1966-68; mem. faculty U. Chgo., 1968-72; prof. meteorology Harvard U., 1972-83, dir. Center for Earth and Planetary Physics, 1980-83; Alfred P. Sloan prof. meteorology MIT, 1983—; Lady Davis vis. prof. Hebrew U., 1979; Sackler prof. Tel Aviv U., 1992; Vikram Sarabhai prof.

Phys. Rsch. Lab. Ahmedabad, India, 1985; Lansdowne lectr. U. Victoria, 1993; cons. NASA, Jet Propulsion Lab., others; mem. bd. on atmospheric scis. and climate NRC, corr. mem. com. on human rights NAS. Author: Dynamics in Atmospheric Physics; co-author: Atmospheric Tides; contbr. to profl. jours. Recipient Macelwane award Am. Geophys. Union, 1968. Fellow NAS, AAAS, Am. Geophys. Union, Am. Meteorol. Soc. (Meisinger award 1969, councillor 1972-75, Charney award 1985), Am. Acad. Arts and Scis., Norwegian Acad. Scis. and Letters; mem. Internat. Commn. Dynamic Meteorology, Woods Hole Oceanographic Instn. (corp.), Institut Mondial des Scis. (founding mem.). Jewish. Office: MIT 54 1720 Cambridge MA 02139

LINDZEY, GARDNER, psychologist, educator; b. Wilmington, Del., Nov. 27, 1920; s. James and Marguerite (Shotwell) L.; m. Andrea Lewis, Nov. 28, 1944; children: Jeffrey, Leslie, Gardner, David, Jonathan. AB, Pa. State U., 1943, MS, 1945; PhD, Harvard U., 1949; LHD (hon.), U. Colo., 1990; DSc (hon.), Rutgers U., 1992. Research analyst OSRD, 1944-45; instr. psychology Pa. State U., 1945-46; teaching fellow Harvard U., Cambridge, Mass., 1946-47, research fellow, 1947-49, research assoc., asst. prof., 1949-53, lectr., chmn. psychol. clinic staff, 1953-56, prof., chmn. dept., 1972-73; prof. psychology Syracuse (N.Y.) U., 1956-57, U. Minn., 1957-64; prof. psychology U. Tex., 1964-72, chmn., 1964-68, v.p. acad. affairs, 1968-70, v.p. ad interim, 1971, v.p., dean Grad. Studies, prof. psychology, 1973-75; dir. Ctr. for Advanced Study in Behavioral Scis., Stanford (Calif.) U., 1975-89, dir. emeritus, 1989—; mem. psychopharmacology study sect. NIMH, 1958-62, mem. program-project com., 1963-67, mem. adv. com. on extramural research, 1968-71; mem. com. faculty research fellowships Social Sci. Research Council, 1960-63, bd. dirs., 1962-76, mem. com. problems and policy, 1963-70, 72-76, chmn., 1965-70, mem. exec. com., 1970-75, chmn., 1971-75, mem. com. genetics and behavior, 1961-67, chmn., 1961-65; mem. com. biol. bases social behavior, 1967—; mem. com. work and personality in middle years, 1972-77; mem. sociology and social psychology panel NSF, 1965-68, mem. spl. commn. social scis., 1968-69, mem. adv. com. research, 1974—, mem. Waterman award com., 1976-79; mem. exec. com., assembly behavioral and social sci. NAS-NRC, 1970—, mem. com. life sci. and pub. policy, 1968-74, mem. panel nat. needs for biomed. and behavioral research personnel, 1974—, mem. com. social sci. in NSF, 1975—, mem. Inst. Medicine, 1975—; mem. com. on drug abuse Office Sci. and Tech., 1962-63; mem. Presdl. Com. Nat. Medal Sci., 1966-69; bd. dirs. Found.'s Fund Research in Psychiatry, 1967-70; bd. dirs. Am. Psychol. Found., 1968-76, v.p., 1971-73, pres., 1974-76. Author: (with Hall) Theories of Personality, 1957, 70, 78; (with Allport and Vernon) Study of Values, 1951, 60; Projective Techniques and Cross-Cultural Research, 1961; (with J.C. Loehlin and J.N. Spuhler) Race Differences in Intelligence, 1975; (with C.S. Hall and R.F. Thompson) Psychology, 1975; also articles; editor: Handbook of Social Psychology, Vols. 1 and 2, 1954, Vols. 1-5, 1969, Assessment of Human Motives, 1958, Contemporary Psychology, 1967-73, History of Psychology in Autobiography, Vol. 6, 1974, vol. 7, 1980, vol. 8, 1989; assoc. editor Psychol. Abstracts, 1960-62, Ency. Social Scis., 1962-67; co-editor Century Psychology Series, 1960-74, Theories of Personality: Primary Sources and Research, 1965, History of Psychology in Autobiography, Vol. V, 1968, Behavioral Genetics: Methods and Research, 1969, Contributions to Behavior-Genetic Analysis, 1970. Fellow Ctr. Advanced Study Behavioral Scis., Stanford, 1955-56, 63-64, 71-72, Inst. Medicine, 1975—. Fellow Am. Psychol. Assn. (bd. dirs. 1962-68, 70-74, mem. publs. bd., 1956-59, 70-73, chmn. 1958-59, mem. council of reps. 1965-67, 68-74, pres. divsn. social and personality psychology 1963-64, mem. policy and planning 1975, 78, pres. assn. 1966-67, mem. council of editors 1968-73, chmn. com. sci. award 1968-69, pres. divsn. gen. psychology 1970-71), Am. Acad. Arts and Scis., Am. Philos. Soc., Inst. Medicine, NAS, AAAS; mem. Am. Eugenics Soc. (bd. dirs. 1962-70), Soc. Social Biology (bd. dirs. 1972—, pres. 1978—), Am. Psychol. Assn. (dir. ins. trust 1973—), Univs. Research Assn. (bd. dirs. 1973-75). Home: 109 Peter Coutts Cir Palo Alto CA 94305-2517

LINEBERGER, WILLIAM CARL, chemistry educator; b. Hamlet, N.C., Dec. 5, 1939; s. Caleb Henry and Evelyn (Cooper) L.; m. Katharine Wyman Edwards, July 31, 1979. BS, Ga. Inst. Tech., 1961, MSEE, 1963, PhD, 1965. Research physicist U.S. Army Ballistic Research Labs., Aberdeen, Md., 1967-68; postdoctoral assoc. Joint Inst. for Lab. Astrophysics U. Colo., Boulder, 1968-70, from asst. prof. to prof. chemistry, 1970-83, E.U. Condon prof. chemistry, 1983—; Phi Beta Kappa nat. lectr., 1989. Served to capt. U.S. Army, 1965-67. Fellow AAAS, Joint Inst. for Lab. Physics, Am. Phys. Soc. (H.P. Broida prize 1981, Bomen Michelson prize 1987, Optical Sci. Am. Meggers prize 1988, Plyler prize 1992); mem. NAS, Am. Chem. Soc., Am. Acad. Arts and Scis., Sigma Xi. Office: U Colo Joint Inst Lab Astrophysics CB 440 Boulder CO 80309-0440

LINEBERRY, PAUL F., JR., music educator; b. Waynesville, N.C., Aug. 6, 1944; s. Paul F. and Elmorene L. Lineberry; m. Jane Bulla, Aug. 27, 1966; children: Scott Eric, Brittnay Anne. MusB Edn., East Carolina U., 1966, MusM Edn., 1967. Cert. music tchr. K-12, Pa., supvr. pub. sch. music, Pa. Adj. graduate faculty Music Dept., Trenton State Coll., N.J.; dist. coord. music edn. Coun. Rock Sch. Dist., Richboro, Pa.; instrumental music instr. Coun. Rock H.S., Newtown, Pa., 1991—, chairperson music dept., 1993—; dir. sch. bands in performance in U.S. and Western Europe; cons. pub. sch. music programs, Bucks County, Pa.; lectr. in field. Curriculum devel. com. Coun. Rock Sch. Dist., Richboro, Bucks County Int. Unit Task Force on Music Edn., 1991—; mem. Pa. State Profl. Stds. Com. in Music Edn., 1990—. Recipient graduate study grant HEW Dept. Mem. NEA, ASCD, Music Educators Nat. Conf., Pa. Music Educators Assn. (com. chmn., Citation of Excellence in Teaching award 1991), Bucks County Music Edn. Assn. (past pres. and com. chmn.), Coun. Rock Edn. Asns., Pa. Edn. Assn., Phi Mu Alpha, Phi Beta Mu. Home: 197 Fletcher Dr Morrisville PA 19067-5968

LINEHAN, PATRICK FRANCIS, JR., financial planner; b. Jefferson Heights, N.Y., July 31, 1945; s. Patrick Francis and Dorothy Frances (Rowland) L.; m. Jane Elizabeth Uftring, Nov. 18, 1967; children: Patrick Francis III, Colleen Elizabeth, Erin Kathleen. BS in Edn., St. John's U., Jamaica, N.Y., 1966, MS in Edn., 1970. CFP; registered fin. cons.; cert. investment specialist. Math tchr. Bellmore (N.Y.)-Merrick Sch. Dist., 1967-85; fin. planner Amityville, N.Y., 1984—; ocean lifeguard Jones Beach-State Park, Babylon, N.Y., 1965-86; speaker Estate Planning and Seminars, Coll. Fin. Plan Seminars, Tchr. Retirement Seminars. Editor (quar. newsletter) Think About It, 1967—. Mem. Inst. of CFP, Internat. Assn. of Fin. Planners, Internat. Assn. Profl. Fin. Cons., Elks, K.C. Roman Catholic. Avocations: reading, music, golf, swimming. Home: 142 Richmond Ave Amityville NY 11701-4209 Office: Planning for Life 142 Richmond Ave Amityville NY 11701-4209

LINEMEYER, DAVID LEE, molecular biologist; b. Denver, Apr. 19, 1949; s. Clarence Brockman and Frances Pauline (Whitlock) L. BS with highest distinction, Colo. State U., 1971; MS, U. Wash., 1973, PhD, 1977. Staff fellow Nat. Cancer Inst., Bethesda, Md., 1977-80, sr. staff fellow, 1980-81; rsch. fellow Merck Rsch. Labs., Rahway, N.J., 1981-89, assoc. dir., 1989—. Contbr. articles to sci. jours.; patentee mutant acidic fibroblast growth factor field. Scholar Colo. State U., 1967-71. Mem. AAAS, Am. Soc. for Biochemistry and Molecular Biology, Am. Soc. for Microbiology, Phi Kappa Phi. Office: Merck Res Lab 126 E Lincoln Ave Rahway NJ 07065

LINEVSKY, MILTON JOSHUA, physical chemist; b. Glen Cove, N.Y., Apr. 20, 1928; s. David I. and Tillie (Ain) L.; m. Barbara Jody Rutenberg, June 29, 1958; children: Joanne, Richard. BS in Chemistry, Rensselaer Poly. Inst., 1949; MS, Pa. State U., 1950, PhD, 1953. Phys. chemist GE, King of Prussia, Pa., 1957-79, Johns Hopkins Applied Physics Lab., Laurel, Md., 1979—; with NSF, Washington, 1993—. With U.S. Army, 1955-57. Gotshall Powel scholar, 1946. Mem. Am. Chem. Soc. Achievements include invention and development of technique for matrix isolation applied to high-temperature materials, development of first flame laser using chemical pumping reactions. Home: 700 Hermleigh Rd Silver Spring MD 20902-1647 Office: Johns Hopkins Applied Physics Lab Johns Hopkins Rd Laurel MD 20723 also: NSF 1800 G St NW Washington DC 20550-0001

LINFANTE, CHARLES VINCENT, dental, medical, optical products company executive; b. Bklyn., Oct. 21, 1939; s. Vincent J. and Lea (Rossi) L.; m. Joan Mary Kulha, Jan. 20, 1962; children: Michele, Gene, Kristen,

Robert. BS in Acctg., Fairleigh Dickinson U., 1962. CPA, N.Y. Staff acct. Price Waterhouse & Co., N.Y.C., 1962-66, sr. acct., 1966-70, mgr., 1970-72; internal audit dir. IPCO Corp., White Plains, N.Y., 1972, div. controller, 1972-73, corp. controller, 1973-76, v.p., controller, 1976-80, v.p., chief fin. officer, 1980-82, exec. v.p., chief fin. officer, 1982-84, pres., chief fin. officer, 1984—; also bd. dirs. Chmn. Westchester C. of C., White Plains, 1979-80, Westchester Multiple Sclerosis Soc., White Plains, 1984-87; pres. Vis. Nurse Services of Westchester, 1986-87. Mem. Am. Inst. CPA's, N.Y. State Soc. CPA's. Avocation: marathon running.

LINFORD, LAURANCE DEE, cultural organization administrator; b. Cheyenne, Wyo., Mar. 2, 1951; s. Dee Verl and Helen Grace L.; m. Karen Page Stephens, Nov. 23, 1971; children: Justin, Micah. BA, U. N.Mex., 1973; MA, U. Ariz., 1978. Archaeologist Sch. Am. Research, Santa Fe, 1967-75, Ariz. State Mus., Tucson, 1975-77, Nat. Park Service, Tucson, 1977-78, Navajo Nation, Window Rock, Ariz., 1978-82; exec. dir. Inter-Tribal Indian Ceremonial Assn., Gallup, N.Mex., 1982—; bd. dirs. St. Michaels (Ariz.) Hist. Mus., 1979-86. Author: A Measure of Excellence, 1992; author, editor: The Pinon Project, 1982; editor: The Caremonial Mag., 1986-89, Inter-tribal Am. Mag. 1990-92. Pres. Indian Country Tourism Coun., 1982-86; mem. tourism com. Gallup McKinley County Chamber, 1985-86; bd. dirs. Gallup Conv. and Visitors Bur., 1987-89, 91—. Mem. N.Mex. Assn. Execs. Democrat. Avocations: cabinetry, woodwork, research of Am. frontier. Office: Inter-Tribal Indian Ceremonial Assn PO Box 1 Church Rock NM 87311-0001

LINFORD, MARY SUZANNE (SUE LINFORD), food distibrution executive; b. Indpls., Apr. 15, 1935; d. Robert William and Mary Catherine (Madden) Schmutte; widowed; children: Christopher, Douglas, Mark, Paul, Julie. Student, U. Alaska, 1959-80. Lic. real estate agt., Alaska. Various positions Indpls. and Anchorage, 1949-1973; acct., treas., gen. mgr., pres. Linford of Alaska Wholesale Food Distbr., Anchorage, 1973-83; pres., gen. mgr. Linford of Alaska, Anchorage, 1985—; exec. dir. Common Sense for Alaska, Anchorage, 1984-86; property mgr. Sue Linford Investments, Anchorage, 1983—; pvt. practice real estate, Anchorage, 1985—. Editor State PTA Bulletin, 1969-71. Mem. Alaska Blue Ribbon Commn., 1979-80, various city commns. City of Anchorage, 1979-92, budget commr., 1988-89; commr. Port of Anchorage, 1989-92; chmn. libr. bds. City of Anchorage, Greater Anchorage Borough and Municipality of Anchorage, 1969-77; founding mem., officer Anchorage Arts Coun., 1971-74; bd. dirs. Anchorage Symphony, 1990—, Alaska Zoo, 1989—; vice chmn., mem. Archdiocesan Fin. Coun.; pres. Anchorage Sch. Bd., 1974-77; active Anchorage PTA; mem. Anchorage Concert Chorus, 1981—. Mem. Alaska C. of C., Anchorage C. of C. (sec.-treas., v.p., bd. dirs. 1977-81, treas., bd. dirs 1992—, Outstanding Cmty. Svc. Gold Pan award 1981), Ruralcap (cert. of appreciation 1981, outstanding contbn. award 1985), Chaine des Rotisseurs, Bailliage U.S.A., Petroleum Club Anchorage, San Francisco Tennis Club (life), Capt. Cook Athletic Club, Zonta (bd. dirs. 1968-80), Rotary. Avocations: singing, cross country skiing, swimming. Office: Linford of Alaska Inc 135 Cordova St Anchorage AK 99501

LINFORD, RULON KESLER, physicist, engineer; b. Cambridge, Mass., Jan. 31, 1943; s. Leon Blood and Imogene (Kesler) L.; m. Cecile Tadje, Apr. 2, 1965; children: Rulon Scott, Laura, Hilary, Philip Leon. BSEE, U. Utah, 1966; MS in ElecE, Mass. Inst. Tech., 1969, PhD in ElecE, 1973. Staff CTR-7 Los Alamos (N.Mex) Nat. Lab., 1973-75, asst. group leader CTR-7, 1975-77, group leader CTR-11, 1977-79, program mgr., group leader compact toroid CTR-11, 1979-80, program mgr., asst. div. leader compact toroid CTR divsn., 1980-81, assoc. CTR divsn. leader, 1981-86, program dir. magnetic fusion energy, 1986-89, program dir., div. leader CTR div. office, 1989-91, program dir. nuclear sys., 1991-93; staff LER, 1993-94, U. Calif. coord. sci. and tech., 1994—. Contbr. articles to profl. jours. Recipient E. O. Lawrence award Dept. of Energy, Washington, 1991. Fellow Am. Physical Soc. (exec. com. 1982, 90-91, program com. 1982, 85, award selection com. 1983, 84, fellowship com. 1986); mem. Sigma Xi. Office: Los Alamos Nat Lab PO Box 1663 MS F673 Los Alamos NM 87545

LING, DEIRDRE ANN, headmistress; b. N.Y.C., Feb. 11, 1944; d. Frank Hayes and Annette Anna (Larned) L.; m. Edward H. Russell, July 11, 1981. BA, U. Rochester, N.Y., 1965; MA, U. R.I., 1968; PhD, Tufts U., 1976. Advt. copywriter Harper & Row Pubs., N.Y.C., 1965-66; admissions counselor Western Mich. U., Kalamazoo, 1973-74; asst. dir. admissions SUNY, Stony Brook, 1974-78; dir. freshman admissions U. Mass., Amherst, 1978-79, dean admissions, 1979-81, dean acad. support svcs., 1981-82, asst. chancellor, 1982-83, vice chancellor univ. rels. and devel., 1983-90; headmistress Middlesex Sch., Concord, Mass., 1990—; adj. lectr. women's studies program U. Mass., 1980-90. Recipient Disting. Svc. award SUNY, Stony Brook, 1983; Nat. Assn. Coll. Admissions Counselors grantee, 1979.

LING, DWIGHT L., college administrator, history educator; b. Johnstown, Pa., Oct. 9, 1923; s. Leroy Victor and Nellie Grace (Cypher) L.; m. Phyllis Cooper, June 8, 1946; children—Douglas, Gregory, Angela. B.A., Pa. State U., 1948, M.A., 1949; Ph.D., U. Ill., 1955. Cert. tchr., Pa. Asst. prof. history Centre Coll., Danville, Ky., 1949-52; teaching asst. U. Ill.-Champaign-Urbana, 1952-55; prof. history DePauw U., Greencastle, Ind., 1955-72; provost Rollins Coll., Winter Park, Fla., 1972-79; dean, provost Marietta Coll., Ohio, 1979-86, prof. history, 1986—, emeritus prof. history, 1989—; counselor, examiner North Central Assn., Chgo., 1965-70. Author: Tunisia: From Protectorate to Republic, 1967; Morocco and Tunisia: A Comparative History, 1979. Mem. adv. bd. Glenridge Jr. High Sch., Winter Park, Fla., 1977-79; mem. adv. com. Marietta Pub. Schs., 1985. Served with U.S. Army, 1943-46. Rockefeller fellow, 1952-53; Tunisian Govt. fellow, 1963; Am. Philos. Soc. fellow, 1963; Fulbright scholar, Netherlands, 1976. Mem. Am. Assn. Higher Edn., Fulbright Alumni Assn. Democrat. Clubs: Marietta Reading (pres. 1985—), Econ. Roundtable. Lodge: Rotary. Avocations: tennis; traveling; reading; North African history. Home: 107 Rathbone Rd Marietta OH 45750-1438 Office: Marietta Coll Marietta OH 45750

LING, JAHJA WANG-CHIEH, conductor; b. Jakarta, Indonesia, Oct. 25, 1951; came to U.S., 1970; s. Bok-Som and Eng-Nio (Kwee) L.; m. Jane Yuan, May 8, 1976; children: Gabriel En-Wei, Daniel En-Hao. BMus, Julliard Sch., 1974, MMus, 1975; DMus Arts, Yale U., 1980. Asst. conductor San Francisco Symphony, 1981-83, assoc. conductor, 1983-84; assoc. conductor Cleve. Orch., 1984-85, resident conductor, 1985—; music dir. Fla. Orch., Tampa, 1988—; founding music dir. San Francisco Symphony Youth Orch., 1981-84, Cleve. Orch. Youth Orch., 1986—; music dir. San Francisco Conservatory Orch., 1981-84; co-dir. Tanglewood (Mass.) Young Artists Orch., 1983-84; guest conductor Boston Symphony, Phila. Orch., Minn. Orch., Nat. Symphony in D.C. Recipient Bronze medal Artur Rubinstein Internat. Piano Competition, 1977, Seaver/NEA Conductors award, 1988; Leonard Bernstein fellow Tanglewood Music Ctr., 1980, Exxon/Arts Endowment conductor Affiliate Artists, 1981-84. Office: Fla Orch Inc 101 E Kennedy Blvd Ste 1530 Tampa FL 33602-5147

LING, JOSEPH TSO-TI, manufacturing company executive, environmental engineer; b. Peking, China, June 10, 1919; came to U.S., 1948, naturalized, 1963; s. Ping Sun and Chong Hung (Lee) L.; m. Rose Hsu, Feb. 1, 1944; children: Lois Ling Olson, Rosa-Mai Ling Ahlgren, Louis, Lorraine. B.C.E. Hangchow Christian Coll., Shanghai, China, 1944; M.S. in Civil Engring. U. Minn., 1950, Ph.D. in San. Engring. 1952. Registered profl. engr., Minn., Ala., N.J., Okla., W.Va., N.Y., Ill., Ind., Pa., Mich. Civil engr. Nanking-Shanghai R.R. System, 1944-47; research asst. san. engring. U. Minn., 1948-52; sr. staff san. engr. Gen. Mills, Inc., Mpls., 1953-55; dir. dept. san. engring. research Ministry Municipal Constrn., Peking, 1956-57; prof. civil engring. Bapt. U., Hong Kong, 1958-59; head dept. water and san. engring. Minn. Mining & Mfg. Co., St. Paul, 1960-66, mgr. environ. and civil engring., 1967-70, dir. environ. engring. and pollution control, 1970-74, v.p. environ. engring. and pollution control, 1975-84, community service exec., 1985—; adv. mem. on air pollution Minn. Bd. Health, 1964-66; mem. Minn. Gov.'s Adv. Com. on Air Resources, 1966-67; mem. adv. panel on environ. pollution U.S. C. of C., 1966-71; mem. chem. indsl. com., adv. to Ohio River Valley Water Sanitation Commn., 1962-76; mem. environ. quality panel Electronic Industries Assn., 1971-80; mem. environ. quality com. NAM, 1965-84; mem. Pres.'s Adv. Bd. on Air Quality, 1974-75; vice chmn. environ. com. U.S. Bus. and Industry Adv. Com. to OECD, 1975-84; mem. adv.

subcom. on environ., health and safety regulations Pres.'s Domestic Policy Rev. of Indsl. Innovation, 1978-79; adv. panel indsl. innovation and health, safety and environ. regulation Office Tech. Assessment of U.S. Congress, 1978-80; exec. com. engring. assembly NRC, 1977-80; also environ. studies bd. Commn. Natural Resources, 1977-82; mem. staff svcs. subcom. of environ. com. Bus. Roundtable, 1975-84; vice chmn. environ. com. U.S. Coun., Internat. C. of C., 1978-89; adv. com. on rsch. applications policy NSF, 1976-80; mem. Sci. Adv. Bd. EPA, 1984-88, selection com. Pres.' Environment and Conservation Challenge Award, 1991-93. Contbr. articles to profl. jours. Trustee Belwin Outdoor Lab., St. Paul, 1970—; bd. dirs. Fresh Water Found., 1974—, Northwest Area Found., 1970-87, St. Paul Area YMCA, 1974-80, Midwest China Study Center, Minn. Environ. Sci. Found., 1970-78, Nat. Water Alliance, 1983-88, World Environ. Ctr., 1984—, Woodrow Wilson Sr. fellow, 1975—; recipient numerous awards, including Joan Hodges Queneau award Am. Assn. Engring. Socs., 1990; named Laureate, Global 500 Honor Role UN Environ. Program, 1990. Fellow ASCE; mem. NAE, Am. Acad. Environ. Engrs. (diplomate, chmn. examination update com. 1981-83), Minn. Assn. Commerce and Industry, Am. Water Works Assn. (life), Air and Waste Mgmt. Assn. (dir.), Chem. Mfg. Assn. Club: Rainbow (Mpls.). Home: 2090 Arcade St Saint Paul MN 55109-2564 *There must be a goal in any stage of one's life. It must be high enough to offer a challenge. One should not wait for the opportunity but create the opportunity to achieve that goal.*

LING, ROBERT MALCOLM, banker, publishing executive; b. Akron, Ohio, July 6, 1931; s. Howard George and Catherine Zola (Smith) L.; m. Lois Claire Fisher Ling, Nov. 1, 1992; children: Shelly, Robert Jr., Amy, Beth, Patricia. BA in Journalism, Mich. State U., 1952. Asst. pres. Dike-O-Seal, Inc., Chgo., 1955-56; gen. mgr. Vollwerth Marquette (Mich.) Co., 1956-58, pres., 1958-75; pres. Vandco Incorp., Marquette, 1975-85, Cable Americal Corp., Rancho Cordova, Calif., 1985-89, Romali Holdings, Inc., Rancho Cordova, Calif., 1989—; chmn. Gold River Bank, Fair Oaks, Calif., 1990-92; publisher Grapevine-Independent newspaper, Rancho Cordova, Calif. Mayor City of Marquette, 1980-83, City of Rancho Cordova, Calif., 1986-87. Capt. U.S. Army, 1952-55. Republican. Home: 6032 Puerto Dr Rncho Murieta CA 95683-9313 Office: Romali Holdings Inc 3338 Mather Field Rd Rancho Cordova CA 95670-5966

LING, SUILIN, management consultant; b. Shanghai, China, Oct. 13, 1930; s. Chunchen and Maisan (Dunn) L.; came to U.S., 1949, naturalized, 1963. BS, U. Mich., 1952; PhD, Columbia U., 1961; m. Avril Marjorie Kathleen Button, Apr. 4, 1964; children: Christopher Charles, Charmian Avril. Mech. engr. Ebasco Services, Inc., 1953-54; with research div. Foster Wheeler Corp., 1954-64; mgmt. cons. The Emerson Cons., Inc., 1964-65; sr. economist Communications Satellite Corp., 1965-67; chief economist Northrop-Page Communication Engrs., Inc., 1967-70; founder-dir., chief economist Teleconsult, Inc., Washington, 1970-82; founder, pres. Communications Devel. Corp., 1982-87; lead scientist, Mitre Corp., 1987-91; sen. advisor internat. affairs Nat. Regulatory Rsch. Inst. Ohio State U., 1992-95; prin. Booz, Allen & Hamilton Inc., 1995—. lectr. econs. Bernard M. Baruch Sch. Bus. and Pub. Adminstrn., CCNY. Mem. Am. Mgmt. Assn., Am. Econ. Assn., Am. Soc. M.E., Am. Acad. Polit. and Social Sci. Author: Economies of Scale in the Steam-Electric Power Generating Industry, 1964. Home: 2735 Unicorn Ln NW Washington DC 20015-2233 Office: 8283 Greensboro Dr Mc Lean VA 22102-3838

LINGAFELTER, EDWARD CLAY, JR., chemistry educator; b. Toledo, Mar. 28, 1914; s. Edward Clay and Winifred (Jordan) L.; m. Roberta Crowe Kneedler, Apr. 30, 1938; children—Robert Edward, Thomas Edward, James Edward, Richard Edward, Daniel Edward. B.S., U. Calif.-Berkeley, 1935, Ph.D., 1939. Mem. faculty U. Wash., Seattle, 1939—; prof. chemistry U. Wash., 1952-84, prof. emeritus, 1984—, assoc. dean Grad. Sch., 1960-68. Contbr. articles to profl. jours. Mem. Am. Chem. Soc., Am. Crystallographic Assn. (pres. 1974), Assn. Italian Cristallografia. Rsch. on solutions, molecular structures of paraffin-chain and coordination compounds. Home: 5323 27th Ave NE Seattle WA 98105-3105 Office: U Washington Seattle WA 98195

LINGAMNENI, JAGANMOHAN RAO, criminology educator; b. Dondapadu, India, Mar. 15, 1942; came to U.S., 1967, naturalized, 1974; s. Satyanarayana and Satyavathi Settipalli L.; m. Uma Uppaluri, Feb. 26, 1967; children: Santhisri, Pragathisri. B.S., A.P. Agrl. Coll, India, 1962; M.S., A.P. Agrl. U., 1965; Ph.D., Mich. State U., 1972; M.S. in Criminal Justice, U. Ala.-Birmingham, 1979. Research asst. A.P. State Dept. Agr., 1964-65; instr. A.P. Agrl. U., 1965-66; research asst. Mich. State U., Nat. Inst. Community Devel. Diffusion Project, Hyderabad, India, 1966-67; teaching asst., grad. research asst., diffusion research fellow Mich. State U., East Lansing, 1967-70; lectr. Mich. State U.-AID Communication Workshops, 1969-75; asst. prof. sociology W. Ga. Coll, 1970-75; assoc. prof. W. Ga. Coll., 1975-80, dir. grad. program, 1973-75, 76-80; vice chmn. dept. sociology W. Ga. Coll., 1973-74; prof. human justice Governors State U., University Park, Ill., 1979-83, univ. prof. criminal justice, 1983-85, 91—; coord. criminal justice program, 1992—, univ. prof. pub. adminstrn., 1985-91, chmn. div. communications and human services, 1982-83; mem. adj. faculty Emory U., Atlanta, 1976-80, Union Inst., Cin., 1986—; sec., chmn., trustee Telugu Found. (N. Am.), 1981-90. Author: Status Inconsistency, Communication Behavior and Modernization, 1972; assoc. editor, So. Jour. Criminal Justice, 1977-81, Jour. Communication Therapy; contbr. articles to profl. jours. Diffusion research fellow Mich. State U., 1967-68. Mem. Am. Soc. Criminology (life mem., adv. internat. liason com. 1978—), Acad. Criminal Justice Scis. (life mem., com. internat. criminology and criminal justice 1978—), Internat. Communication Assn., Midwestern Criminal Justice Educators Assn., Ill. Criminal Justice Educators Assn. (v.p. 1981-83, pres. 1989—), Am. Sociol. Assn., So. Sociol Soc. (racial and ethnic minorities com. 1978-80), So. Assn. Criminal Justice Educators (sec.-treas. 1978-80), Alpha Kappa Delta, Lambda Alpha Epsilon. Hindu. Home: 77 Graymoor Ln Olympia Fields IL 60461-1215 Office: Govs State U Coll Arts and Scis Div Humanities and Social Sci University Park IL 60466 *In my life, I always strove to be an ethical individual and maintained standards of excellence for myself that I and others around me could be proud of. As a naturalized citizen, I have been a true believer of the melting-pot of American ethnicity in providing equal opportunities for all to achieve success. Although my belief in the fundamental fairness of the American System has diluted somewhat, my obligation and commitment to contribute toward that broader goal continues to persist.*

LINGEMAN, RICHARD ROBERTS, editor, writer; b. Crawfordsville, Ind., Jan. 2, 1931; s. Byron Newton and Vera Frances (Spencer) L.; m. Anthea Judy Nicholson, Apr. 3, 1965; 1 child, Jenifer Kate. B.A., Haverford Coll., 1953; postgrad., Yale U. Law Sch., 1956-58, Columbia U. Grad. Sch. Comparative Lit., 1958-60. Exec. editor Monocle mag., N.Y.C., 1960-69; assoc. editor, columnist N.Y. Times Book Review, 1969-78; exec. editor The Nation, N.Y.C., 1978—; Bd. dirs. Small Town Inst., Center Middletown Studies. Author: Drugs from A to Z, 1969, Don't You Know There's A War On?, 1971, Small Town America, 1980, Theodore Dreiser: At the Gates of the City 1871-1907, 1986, Theodore Dreiser: An American Journey, 1908-1945, 1990 (Chgo. Sun-Times Book of Yr.). Served with U.S. Army, 1953-56. Mem. Authors Guild, PEN, Nat. Book Critics Circle, N.Y. Hist. Soc., Soc. Am. Historians, Phi Beta Kappa. Office: 72 Fifth Ave New York NY 10011-8004

LINGENFELTER, SHERWOOD GALEN, university provost, anthropology educator; b. Hollidaysburg, Pa., Nov. 18, 1941; s. Galen Miller and Kathern Margaretta (Rogers) L.; m. Judith Elaine Beaumont, Aug. 10, 1962; children: Jennifer Elaine, Joel Sherwood. BA, Wheaton Coll., 1963; PhD, U. Pitts., 1971. Dir. acad. advising U. Pitts., 1964-66; instr. SUNY, Brockport, N.Y., 1966-67; asst. prof SUNY, Brockport, 1969-74, assoc. prof., 1974-82, prof. anthropology, 1982-83; NIH predoctoral fellow U. Pitts., 1967-69; prof. Biola U., La Mirada, Calif., 1983-88, provost, sr. v.p., 1988—; cons. in anthropology Summer Inst. Linguistics, Dallas, 1977-94; tng. cons. Liebenzell Mission of Am., Schooleys Mountain, N.J., 1981-89; evaluating cons. Trust Terr. of the Pacific Islands, Saipan, Mariana Islands, 1969-74. Author: Yap: Political Leadership, 1975, The Deni of Western Brazil, 1980, Ministering Cross-Culturally, 1986, Transforming Culture, 1992; editor: Political Development in Micronesia, 1974, Social Organization of Sabah Societies, 1990. Bd. dirs. Christian Scholars Rev., 1989—, Grace Brethren

Internat. Missions, 1994—. Recipient Disting. Teaching award Biola U., 1987-88; grantee NSF, 1967-69, 79-81, SUNY Rsch. Found., 1970. Fellow Am. Anthrop. Assn., Soc. for Applied Anthropology, Am. Ethnol. Soc.; mem. Assn. Social Anthropology Oceania, Am. Conf. Acad. Deans. Democrat. Mem. Grace Brethren Ch. Office: Biola U Office of Provost 13800 Biola Ave La Mirada CA 90639-0001

LINGL, FRIEDRICH ALBERT, psychiatrist; b. Munich, Germany, Apr. 4, 1927; came to U.S., 1957, naturalized, 1962; s. Friedrich Hugo and Marie Luise (Lindner) L.; m. Leonore E. Trautner, Nov. 15, 1955; children—Herbert F., Angelika M. M.D., Ludwig-Maxim U., Munich, 1952. Diplomate Am. Bd. Psychiatry and Neurology, Am. Bd. Med. Psychotherapists (fellow); cert. mental health adminstr. Intern Edward W. Sparrow Hosp., 1957-58; resident internal medicine City Hosp., Augsburg, Germany, 1953-54; resident psychiatry Columbus (Ohio) State Hosp., 1958-61; supt. Hawthornden State Hosp., Northfield, Ohio, 1963-66; dir. Cleve. Psychiat. Inst., 1966-72; pvt. practice, 1972-94; dir. Windsor Hosp., 1976-92, med. dir. emeritus, 1992—; asst. clin. prof. Case Western Res. U., Cleve., 1970—. Contbr. articles to med. jours. Fellow Am. Psychiat. Assn. (life); mem. AMA, Ohio Med. Assn., Ohio Psychiat. Assn., Am. Assn. Psychiat. Adminstrs., N.Y. Acad. Scis., Cleve. Psychiat. Soc. Address: 40 Farwood Dr Chagrin Falls OH 44022-6848

LINGLE, SARAH ELIZABETH, research scientist; b. Woodland, Calif., July 22, 1955; d. John Clayton and Dorothy Adelaide (Dubois) L.; m. Thomas Pratt Washington IV, May 20, 1989. BS, U. Calif., Davis, 1977; MS, U. Nebr., 1978; PhD, Washington State U., 1982. Lab. asst. U. Calif., Davis, 1975-77; rsch. asst. U. Nebr., Lincoln, 1977-78; teaching asst. Wash. State U., Pullman, 1979-82; rsch. assoc. Agrl. Rsch. Svc., USDA, Fargo, N.D., 1982-84; supr. plant physiologist USDA, Weslaco, Tex., 1984—, acting rsch. leader, 1991-92. Assoc. editor Crop Sci.; contbr. articles to profl. jours. Mem. AAAS, Am. Soc. of Plant Physiologists, Am. Soc. Agronomy, Crop Sci. Soc. of Am., Sigma Xi. Episcopalian. Achievements include research in biochemistry and physiology of sugar deposition in sucrose-storing plant tissues. Office: USDA Agrl Rsch Svc 2413 E Us Hwy 83 Weslaco TX 78596-8344

LINGNAU, LUTZ, pharmaceutical executive; b. 1943; came to the U.S., 1989; With Schering Berlin, Inc., Germany, 1965-89; pres., CEO Schering Berlin, Inc., Cedar Knolls, N.J., 1989—. Office: Schering Berlin Inc 110 E Hanover Ave Cedar Knolls NJ 07927-2007

LINHARDT, ROBERT JOHN, medicinal chemistry educator; b. Passaic, N.J., Oct. 18, 1953; s. Robert J. and Barbara A. (Kelley) L.; m. Kathryn F. Burns, May 31, 1975; children: Kelley, Barbara. BS in Chemistry, Marquette U., 1975; MA in Chemistry, Johns Hopkins U., 1977, PhD in Organic Chemistry, 1979; postgrad., Mass. Inst. Tech., 1979-82. Rsch. assoc. Mass. Inst. Tech., Cambridge, 1979-82; asst. prof. U. Iowa, Iowa City, 1982-86, assoc. prof., 1986-90, prof. medicinal and natural products chemistry, 1990—; cons. in field.; interacad. exchange scientist to USSR NAS, 1988. Mem. editorial bd. Applied Biochemistry and Biotech., 1985—, Carbohydrate Rsch., 1990—, Analytical Biochemistry, 1991—; Jour. Biol. Chem.; contbr. numerous articles to profl. jours. Johnson and Johnson fellow MIT, 1981; NIH grantee, 1982-91. Mem. AAAS, Am. Chem. Soc., Soc. for Glycobiology. Office: U Iowa Coll of Pharmacy Phar # 303A Iowa City IA 52240

LINHART, LETTY LEMON, columnist; b. Pittsburg, Kans., Sept. 22, 1933; d. Robert Sheldon and Lois (Wise) Lemon; m. Robert Spayde Kennedy, June 8, 1955 (div. 1978); children: Carole Shea, Nancy Schrimpf, Nina Kennedy; m. Daniel Julian Linhart, June 9, 1986. BS, BA in English and Journalism, U.Kans., 1955; MS in Journalism, Boston U., 1977. Reporter Leavenworth (Kans.) Times, 1954; editor Human Resources Rsch. Office George Washington U., Washington, 1955-56; editor Behavior Rsch. Lab. Harvard Med. Sch., Boston, 1956-58; instr. Boston YMCA, 1960-64; freelance writer and columnist, 1975—; editor Somerville (Mass.) Times, 1975-77; pub. rels. dir. Lettermen of Lexington, Mass., 1978; instr. English Rollins Coll., Winter Park, Fla., 1978-79, Valencia Community Coll., Orlando, Fla., 1978-82, U. Cen. Fla., Orlando, 1979-82; tech. writer Kerchman Software, Altamonte Springs, Mass., 1980-81, Dynamic Control Software, Winter Park, Fla., 1981-82; editor Fla. Specifier, Winter Park, 1982-85, Mobile Home News, Maitland, Fla., 1985-86; instr. English Seminole C.C., Sanford, Fla., 1986-94; Elderhostel instr. Canterbury Rsch. Ctr., 1994—; editor Oviedo (Fla.) Voice, 1994-95, staff writer, 1995—. Author: Are These Extravagant Promises, 1989; contbr. articles to profl. jours. Pres. MIT Dames Boston, 1958-59, Boston Alumnae of Delta Delta Delta, 1959-62; dist. pres Delta Delta Delta, Tex., 1962-65; mem. Friends of Cornell Mus., Winter Park, Fla. Named Outstanding Collegiate Delta Delta Delta, 1955. Mem. NAFE, Ctrl. Fla. Jazz Soc. (bd. dirs. 1983-93), Internat. Platform Soc., Soc. of Women Execs., Altrusa Club (publicity com. 1980-83), Univ. Club of Winter Park, Mortar Bd., Phi Beta Kappa (Belmont, Mass. pres. 1965-78), Theta Sigma Phi, Sigma Delta Chi, Delta Sigma Rho. Avocations: swimming, guitar, singing, jazz. Home: PO Box 1131 Oviedo FL 32765-1131

LINICK, ANDREW S., marketing executive; b. 1945. PhD in Indsl. Psychology, NYU, 1972. Chmn. bd. dirs. Linick Group Inc., Middle Island, N.Y. Office: Linick Group Inc PO Box 102 Middle Island NY 11953*

LINK, ARTHUR STANLEY, history educator, editor; b. New Market, Va., Aug. 8, 1920; s. John William and Helen Elizabeth (Link) L.; m. Margaret McDowell Douglas, June 2, 1945; children: Arthur Stanley, James Douglas, Margaret McDowell, William Allen. A.B. with highest honors, U. N.C. 1941, Ph.D., 1945; postgrad., Columbia U., 1944-45; M.A., Oxford (Eng.) U., 1958; Litt.D., Bucknell U., 1961, Bethany Coll., 1994; U. N.C., Washington and Lee U., 1965; L.H.D., Washington Coll., 1962, Eastern Ill. U., 1983, Northwestern U., 1984, Monmouth Coll., N.J., 1993; H.H.D. (hon.), Davidson Coll., 1965; Westminster Coll. (Pa.), 1984. Instr. N.C. State Coll., 1943-44; instr. Princeton U., 1945-48, asst. prof., 1948-49; mem. (Inst. Advanced Study), Princeton, 1949, 54-55; assoc. prof. Northwestern U., 1949-54, prof., 1954-60; prof. Princeton U., 1960-65, Edwards prof. Am. history, 1965-76, George H. Davis '86 prof. Am. history, 1976-91, prof. emeritus, 1991—; Disting. adj. prof. Am. history U. N.C., Greensboro, 1992—; lectr. history of medicine Bowman Gray Sch. Medicine, 1993—; Albert Shaw lectr. Johns Hopkins, 1956; Harmsworth prof. Am. history Oxford U., 1958-59; Commonwealth Fund lectr. U. London, 1977; mem. Nat. Hist. Publs. Commn., 1968-72; pres. Nat. Commn. on Social Studies in Schs., 1987-90. Author: Wilson: The Road to the White House, 1947, (with R. W. Leopold and Stanley Coben) Problems in American History, 1972, Woodrow Wilson and the Progressive Era, 1954, 63, 88, (with William B. Catton and William A. Link) American Epoch, 2 vols., 1986, Wilson: The New Freedom, 1956, Wilson the Diplomatist, 1957, Wilson: The Struggle for Neutrality, 1914-15, 1960, La Política de los Estados Unidas en América Latina, 1960, (with D.S. Muzzey) Our American Republic, 1963, Our Country's History, 1964, Woodrow Wilson, A Brief Biography, 1963, Wilson: Confusions and Crises, 1915-1916, 1964, Wilson: Campaigns for Progressivism and Peace, 1916-17, 1965; editor: (with R.W. Patrick) Writing Southern History, 1967, The Growth of American Democracy, 1968, Woodrow Wilson, A Profile, 1968, The Impact of World War I, 1969, (with W.M. Leary, Jr.) The Diplomacy of World Power: The United States, 1889-1920, 1970, (with Stanley Coben) The Democratic Heritage: A History of the United States, 1971, The Higher Realism of Woodrow Wilson and Other Essays, 1970, (with William M. Leary, Jr.) The Progressive Era and the Great War, 1978, Woodrow Wilson: Revolution, War, and Peace, 1979, Woodrow Wilson and a Revolutionary World, 1913-1921, 1982, (with Richard L. McCormick) Progressivism, 1983, (with W.A. Link) The Twentieth Century: An American History, 1991, Brother Woodrow: A Memoir of Woodrow Wilson (Stockton Axson), 1993; editor: Papers of Woodrow Wilson, 69 vols., 1966-94; editor, sr. writer: A Concise History of the American People, 1984, The American People: A History, 1987; translator, editor: Paul Mantoux, The Deliberations of the Council of Four, 2 vols., 1992; mem. bd. editors Jour. So. History, 1955-58, 63-66, Jour. Am. History, 1967-70; contbr. articles to popular and profl. jours. Trustee Westminster (Pa.) Coll., 1971-82, Warren Wilson Coll., 1993—. Recipient Bancroft prize for biography, 1957, 61; Guggenheim fellow, 1950-51; hon. fellow Jagiellonian U., Cracow, Poland. Fellow Am. Acad. Arts and Scis., Soc. Am. Historians; mem. Am. Philos. Soc. (Thomas Jefferson medal 1994), Am. Hist. Assn.

(pres.-elect 1983-84, pres. 1984), So. Hist. Assn. (v.p. 1967-68, pres. 1968-69), Orgn. Am. Historians (pres.-elect 1983-84, pres. 1984-85), Nat. Coun. Chs. (v.p. 1963-66), Mass. Hist. Soc. (corr.), Assn. Documentary Editors (pres. 1978-79), Soc. Colonial Wars, Phi Beta Kappa. *I have no thoughts on life that do not stem from my Christian faith. I believe that God created me to be a loving, caring person to do His work in the world. I also believe that He called me to my vocation of teacher and scholar.*

LINK, CHARLES DALE, air force officer; b. Cleve., Sept. 15, 1939; s. Norbert C. and Evelyn (Humphery) L.; m. Elisabeth Kloth, Mar. 5, 1960; children: Mary E., Frank J., Ruth A., Michael A. BS, Troy State U., 1975. Enlisted USAF, 1957, commd. 2d lt., 1963, advanced through grades to maj. gen., 1990; flight comdr., then squadron ops. officer 23 Tactical Fighter Squadron, Spangdahlem Air Base, Fed. Republic Germany, 1970-73; student Air Command and Staff Coll., Maxwell AFB, Ala., 1975; dir. combat ops. 603d Tactical Air Control Ctr., 314th Air Div., Osan Air Base, Republic of Korea, 1980; dep. comdr. for ops. 51st Composite Wing, Osan Air Base; comdr. 51st Combat Support Group, Osan Air Base; student Nat. War Coll., Washington, 1983; comdr. 51st Tactical Fighter Wing, Osan Air Base, 1983; asst. dir. joint and nat. security coun. matters Office Dep. Chief of Staff for Plans and Ops., USAF, Washington, 1985, dir., 1986; asst. dep. dir. for politico-mil. affairs, Orgn. of Joint Chiefs of Staff, Washington, 1987, dep. dir., 1988; comdr. Air Command and Staff Coll., Maxwell AFB, 1989, Air War Coll.; vice comdr. Air U., Maxwell AFB, 1990; comdr. Third Air Force, RAF Mildenhall, Eng., 1991—. Mem. Air Force Assn., Air War Coll. Assn., Daedalians. Roman Catholic. Address: USAF 3 AF USAFE APO AE 09459 *A key to a successful life is to remember that there is no scarcity of people who wish to be in charge, and there is no surplus of people who wish to be responsible.*

LINK, DAVID M., medical products consultant; b. N.Y.C., Feb. 5, 1930; s. Frederick George and Eleanore Sarah (Merrill) L.; m. Shirley G. Crane, Jan. 21, 1956; children: Susan C., David F. BS, MIT, 1952; MS, U. Ill., 1953; MBA, Harvard U., 1960. With Melpar Inc., Boston, 1957-58, Hewlett Packard Corp., Palo Alto, Calif., 1960-61, Gen. Tech. Corp., Torrance, Calif., 1961-63, Hewlett Packard Corp., Waltham, Mass., 1963-69, Sterling Inst., Boston, 1969-70, FDA, Rockville, Md., 1970-80; dir. Bur. Med. Devices, Rockville, 1974-80; dir. corp. mktg. Millipore Corp., Bedford, Mass., 1980-82; v.p. corp. devel. Mentor O&O Inc., Hingham, Mass., 1982-86; v.p. corp. product assurance Cordis Corp., Miami, Fla., 1986-91; v.p. Expertech Assoc., Inc., Concord, Mass., 1991—; instr. Boston Coll. Grad. Sch. Bus. Adminstrn., 1970. Served with USAF, 1952-57. Mem. Assn. Advancement Med. Instrumentation, Sigma Xi. Office: Expertech Assoc Inc 111 Silver Hill Rd Concord MA 01742

LINK, ELEANOR ANN, elementary education educator; b. Salisbury, N.C., May 5, 1943; d. Rufus Edward and Alma Eleanor (Jordan) Scruggs; m. John Barry Link, Dec. 24, 1964; children: Leigh Ann Link Cross, John Edward. AB in Elem. Edn. and Home Econs., Catawba Coll., 1965. Cert. elem. tchr., N.C. Tchr. 3d grade Davidson County Sch. System, Lexington, N.C., 1965-66; tchr. asst. Guilford County Sch. System, Greensboro, N.C., 1984-88, tchr. 1st grade, 1988—; mem. Sch. Improvement Team. Recipient Evon Dean Svc. award to Children, Guilford County PTA. Mem. NEA, N.C. Edn. Assn., Internat. Reading Assn., Greater Greensboro Reading Coun., N.C. Ctr. Advancement of Teaching. Democrat. Methodist. Avocations: reading, cross stitch, traveling, church work. Home: 8757 Snow Camp Rd Snow Camp NC 27349-9726 Office: Nathanael Greene Elem Sch 2717 Nc Highway 62 E Liberty NC 27298-9119

LINK, GEORGE HAMILTON, lawyer; b. Sacramento, Calif., Mar. 26, 1939; s. Hoyle and Corrie Elizabeth (Evans) L.; m. Betsy Leland; children—Thomas Hamilton, Christopher Leland. AB, U. Calif., Berkeley, 1961; LLB, Harvard U., 1964. Bar: Calif. 1965, U.S. Ct. (no., ca., ctrl and so dists.) Calif. 1965, U.S. Ct. Appeals (9th cir.) 1965. Assoc. Brobeck, Phleger & Harrison, San Francisco, 1964-69, ptnr., 1970—; mng. ptnr. Brobeck, Phleger & Harrison, L.A., 1973-93; mng. ptnr. firmwide Brobeck Phleger & Harrison, 1993—; chmn. Pacific Rim Adv. Coun., 1992—. Bd. regents U. Calif., 1971-74; trustee Berkeley Found., Jr. Statesmen Am.; bd. govs. United Way, 1991; trustee, v.p. Calif. Hist. Soc., 1987—. Fellow Am. Bar Found.; mem. ABA, Calif. Bar Assn., L.A. Bar Assn., U. Calif. Alumni Assn. (pres. 1972-75), Calif. Club, Bohemian Club, Jonathan Club. Republican. Methodist. Home: 315 N Carmelina Ave Los Angeles CA 90049-2701 Office: Brobeck Phleger & Harrison 550 S Hope St Los Angeles CA 90071

LINK, MAE MILLS (MRS. S. GORDDEN LINK), space medicine historian and consultant; b. Corbin, Ky., May 14, 1915; d. William Speed and Florence (Estes) Mills; m. S. Gordden Link, Jan. 11, 1936. B.S., George Peabody Coll. for Tchrs., Vanderbilt U., 1936; M.A., Vanderbilt U., 1937; Ph.D., Am. U., 1951; grad., Air War Coll., 1965. Instr. social sci. Oglethorpe U., 1938-39; instr. English Drury Coll., 1940-41; assoc. dir. edn. Ga. Warm Springs Found., 1941-42; mil. historian Hdqrs. Army Air Forces, 1943-45, Office Mil. History, Dept. of Army, 1945-51; spl. asst. to surgeon gen., sr. med. historian U.S. Air Force, Washington, 1951-62; cons. in documentation and space medicine historian NASA, Washington, 1962-64; coord. documentation, life scis. historian NASA, 1964-70; rsch. assoc. Ohio State U. Found., 1970-72. Author: Medical Support of the Army Air Forces in World War II, 1955, Annual Reports of the U.S. Air Force Medical Service, 1949-62, Space Medicine in Project Mercury, 1965; (with others) USA/USSR Joint Publ. Foundations of Space Biology and Medicine, 1976; Editor: U.S. Air Force Med. Service Digest, 1957-62; contbr. to Collier's Ency., Ency. Brit., Funk and Wagnall's New Ency., profl. jours. Recipient Meritorious Service award U.S. Air Force, 1955, Ann. Outstanding Performance awards, 1956-62, Outstanding Alumna award Sue Bennett Coll., 1977. Fellow Am. Med. Writers Assn. (past pres. Middle Atlantic region); mem. Aerospace Med. Assn., Air Force Hist. Found. (charter), Internat. Congress History Medicine, Societe Internat. d'Histoire de la Medecine, Planetary Soc. (charter). Episcopalian. *The desire to reconcile scientific and philosophical truth led to my formal education in the discipline of historical research and writing. The challenge of man's oldest dream—to learn the secret of the universe—led me to concentrate upon aerospace medical research and the related Space sciences. Perhaps our children's children or theirs will ultimately glimpse the truths that thus far have eluded earthbound man.*

LINK, PETER KARL, geologist; b. Batavia, Java, Indonesia, Nov. 7, 1930; s. Walter Karl Peter L. and Miriam Magdalene (Wollaeger) Wilcox; m. June 1, 1957 (div. Feb. 1987); children: Bennett Karl, Hillary Leslie; m. Lucille R. Morrell, May 29, 1990. BS, U. Wis., 1953, MS, 1955, PhD, 1965. Field party chief Esso Std. (Libya) Inc., Tripoli, 1957-61; regional geologist Humble Oil and Refining Co., Ardmore, Okla., 1961-63; sr. rsch. geophysicist Atlantic Richfield Co., Dallas, 1965-68, 68-70; sr. rsch. scientist Amoco Prodn. Co., Tulsa, Okla., 1970-73; geol. cons. Tulsa, 1973-90; staff instr. Oil and Gas Cons. Internat., Tulsa, 1979—; geol. cons. Evergreen, Colo., 1990—; adj. prof. structural geology U. Tulsa, 1975-77; cons. Placid Oil, Shell Oil, Petrocons., Pogo Producing, 1973—; rsch. petroleum geologist, Asia, Europe, U.S., Can., S.Am., 1973—; instr. structural and petroleum geology worldwide, 1979—. Author: Basic Petroleum Geology, 1982, 2nd ed. 1987; contbr. articles to profl. jours. 1st lt. U.S. Army, 1955-57, Korea. Fellow Geol. Soc. Am.; mem. Am. Assn. Petroleum Geologists, Rocky Mountain Assn. Geologists, Sigma Xi. Avocations: pilot flight instr., skiing, hiking, basketball, tennis. Home and Office: 7637 S Centaur Dr Evergreen CO 80439-6434

LINK, RAYMOND ARTHUR, construction company executive; b. Buffalo, Mar. 27, 1954; s. Charles and Norma (Steinwachs) L.; m. Marianne Cassetta, July 8, 1977; children: Charles, Raymond. BS, SUNY-Buffalo, 1975, MBA, U. Pa., 1980. CPA, Fla.; cert. mgmt. acct. Staff acct. Price Waterhouse Buffalo, Phila., 1975-79; mgr. corp. fin. Harris Corp., Melbourne, Fla., 1980-87; v.p. fin. Hubbard Constrn. Co. Orlando, Fla., 1987—. Contbr. articles to profl. jours. Councilman, City of Matiland, Fla., 1990—; bd. dirs. treas. Fla. Symphony Orch., Orlando, 1987-90. Named Up and Comer of the Yr., Orlando Bus. Jour., 1988. Mem. Fin. Execs. Inst., University Club. Republican. Roman Catholic. Avocation: sports. Home: 181 White Oak Cir Maitland FL 32751-6111 Office: Hubbard Constrn Co 1936 Lee Rd Winter Park FL 32789-7201

LINK, ROBERT ALLEN, lawyer, financial company executive; b. Detroit, July 2, 1932; s. Raymond Henry and Helen Emily (Grassley) L.; m. Cynthia Louise Krans, June 15, 1957; children: Charles Nicholas, Frederick Allen. B.S., Wayne State U., 1954; J.D., U. Mich., 1957. Bar: Mich. 1958, U.S. Dist. Ct. (ea. dist.) Mich. 1958, U.S. Ct. Appeals (6th cir.) 1960. Assoc. firm Darden & Bonk, Detroit, 1958-61; pvt. practice Detroit, 1961-63; assoc. firm Manikoff & Munde, Pontiac, Mich., 1963-64; atty. Chrysler Fin. Corp., Detroit, 1964-67; sr. atty. Chrysler Fin. Corp., Southfield, Mich., 1967-70; sec. Chrysler Fin. Corp., Troy and Southfield, Mich., 1970—. Mem. ABA, State Bar Mich., Detroit Bar Assn. Home: 945 Harmon St Birmingham MI 48009-3818 Office: Chrysler Fin Corp 27777 Franklin Rd Southfield MI 48034-2337

LINK, WILLIAM P., insurance company executive. Exec. v. pres. Prudential Ins. of Am. Inc., Newark, 1990—. Office: Prudential Ins. of Am. Inc. 751 Broad St. Newark NJ 07102

LINK, WILLIAM THEODORE, television writer, producer; b. Phila., Dec. 15, 1933; s. William Theodore and Elsie (Roerecke) L.; m. Margery Nelson, Sept. 5, 1980. B.S., U. Pa., 1956. bd. govs. The TV Acad., 1976. Writer, creator, producer (with ptnr. Richard Levinson) TV series Columbo, Mannix, McCloud, Murder, She Wrote, also others; writer, producer: made-for-TV movies The Storyteller; My Sweet Charlie, That Certain Summer, The Execution of Private Slovik, The Gun, Crisis at Central High, The U.S. vs. Salim Ajami, The Boys, The Bill Cosby Mysteries; Author: Fineman, 1973, Stay Tuned, 1981, The Playhouse, 1985, Off-Camera, 1986. Served with SIgnal Corps U.S. Army, 1956-58. Recipient Emmy awards Acad. TV Arts and Scis., 1970, 72, Golden Globe awards Hollywood Fgn. Press Assn., 1972 (2), Peabody award, Edgar Allan Poe award Mystery Writers Am., 1980, 81, 83, 84; Paddy Chayefsky Laurel award, 1986, Ellery Queen Lifetime Achievement award, 1989, Bouchercon Performnance in the Arts award, 1989. Mem. Writers Guild Am., Dramatists Guild, Mystery Writers Am., Screen Actors Guild.

LINKLATER, ISABELLE STANISLAWA YAROSH-GALAZKA (LEE LINKLATER), secondary education educator; b. Chgo., Sept. 15, 1939; d. Baron Stanislaw and Isabelle Lydia (Yarosh) Galazka. BE, Chgo. State U., 1959. Cert. secondary tchr., Ill. Pub. rels. coord. Kelling Co., Chgo., 1955-57; tchr. Chg. Bd. Edn., 1957-89, coord. computer lab., 1989—; founder, pres., exec. dir. Assisi Animal Found. Edn. writer, coord. Elsa Internat. Wild Animal Appeal, Ill., 1985—; writer Lakeland Press, 1992. Bd. dirs. Townsquare Players, Woodstock (Ill.) Opera House, 1989-91. Recipient Outstanding Citizen award CBS Broadcasting, 1992. Mem. McHenry County Defenders (bd. dirs. 1989-91), East African Wildlife Soc. (U.S. rep.). Avocations: travel, music, theater. Office: Assisi Animal Found PO Box 143 Crystal Lake IL 60039-0143

LINKLATER, WILLIAM JOSEPH, lawyer; b. Chgo., June 3, 1942; s. William John and Jean (Connell) L.; m. Dorothea D. Ash, Apr. 4, 1986; children: Erin, Emily. BA, U. Notre Dame, 1964; JD, Loyola U., 1968. Bar: Ill. 1968, Calif. 1981, U.S. Dist. Ct. (no. dist.) Ill. 1968, U.S. Ct. Appeals (7th cir.) 1971, U.S. Supreme Ct. 1971, U.S. Ct. Appeals (6th cir.) 1990, U.S. Ct. Appeals Washington 1978, Calif. 1981, U.S. Dist. Ct. (cen. dist.) Calif. 1981, U.S. Tax Ct. 1982, U.S. Ct. (no. dist.) Calif. 1983, U.S. Dist. Ct. (ea. dist.) Mich. 1989, U.S. Dist. Ct., Colo. 1990, U.S. Dist. Ct. Hawaii, 1992. Attr. Fed. Defender Project, Chgo.; assoc. Baker & McKenzie, Chgo., 1968-75, ptnr., 1975—. Contbr. articles to profl. jours. Mem. ABA (past co-chmn. com. on internat. criminal law criminal justice sect., mem. criminal practice and procedure com. antitrust sect.), FBA, Ill. Bar Assn., 7th Cir. Bar Assn., Chgo. Bar Assn. (past v.p. jud. candidates evaluation com., v.p. large law firm com.), Internat. Inst. (mem. adv. bd.), Calif. Bar Assn., Colo. Bar Assn., Am. Coll. Trial Lawyers, Am. Bd. Criminal Lawyers, Chgo. Inn of Ct., Wong Sun. Soc. San Francisco (internat. proctor), Alpha Sigma Nu. Office: Baker & McKenzie 1 Prudential Plz Ste 3000 Chicago IL 60601

LINKLETTER, ARTHUR GORDON, radio and television broadcaster; b. Moose Jaw, Sask., Can., July 17, 1912; s. Fulton John and Mary (Metzler) L.; m. Lois Foerster, Nov. 25, 1935; children: Jack, Dawn, Robert (dec.), Sharon, Diane (dec.). A.B., San Diego State Coll., 1934. Program dir. Sta. KGB, San Diego, 1934; program dir. Calif. Internat. Expn., San Diego, 1935; radio dir. Tex. Centennial Expn., Dallas, 1936; San Francisco World's Fair, 1937-39; pres. Linkletter Prodns.; ptnr., co-owner John Guedel Radio Prodns.; chmn. bd. Linkletter Enterprises; owner Art Linkletter Oil Enterprises. Author: theme spectacle Cavalcade of Golden West, 1940; author and co-producer: theme spectacle Cavalcade of Am, 1941; writer, producer, star in West Coast radio shows, 1940-55; former star, writer: People Are Funny, NBC-TV and radio, Art Linkletter's House Party, CBS-TV and radio; Author: People Are Funny, 1953, Kids Say The Darndest Things, 1957, The Secret World of Kids, 1959, Confessions of a Happy Man, 1961, Kids Still Say The Darndest Things, 1961, A Child's Garden of Misinformation, 1965, I Wish I'd Said That, 1968, Linkletter Down Under, 1969, Oops, 1969, Drugs at My Door Step, 1973, Women Are My Favorite People, 1974, How to be a Super Salesman, 1974, Yes, You Can!, 1979, I Didn't Do It Alone, 1979, Public Speaking for Private People, 1980, Linkletter on Dynamic Selling, 1982, Old Age is not for Sissies, 1988; lectr. convs. and univs. Nat. bd. dirs. Goodwill Industries; commr. gen. to U.S. Exhibit at Brisbane Expo 88, Australia, 1987; amb. to The 200th Anniversary Celebration, Australia, 1987—; bd. regents Pepperdine U.; bd. advisors Ctr. On Aging UCLA; ch. bd. French Fn for Alzheimers Rsch. Recipient numerous awards. Address: 8484 Wilshire Blvd Ste 205 Beverly Hills CA 90211-3220

LINKOUS, WILLIAM JOSEPH, JR., lawyer; b. Roanoke, Va., July 17, 1929; s. William Joseph and Mary Virginia (Lester) L.; m. Anita Marie Stedronsky, Oct. 15, 1960; children—William Joseph III, Brian Keith. BA, Roanoke Coll., Salem, Va., 1951; MA in Econs., U. Va., 1954, JD, 1956. Bar: Va. 1956, Ga. 1957. Assoc. Powell, Goldstein, Frazer & Murphy, Atlanta, 1956-62, ptnr., 1962-79, 85—; mng. ptnr., 1979-85. Trustee Holy Innocents Episcopal Sch., Atlanta, 1974-80, Roanoke Coll., 1980—. Fellow Am. Coll. Trust and Estate Counsel, Am. Bar Found.; mem. State Bar Ga. (past chmn. fiduciary sect., co-chmn. Ga. trust law revision com. 1988-91, chmn. Ga. probate code revision com. 1991—), Va. State Bar, Am. Law Inst., Internat. Acad. Estate and Trust Law, Atlanta Estate Planning Coun. (pres. 1983-84). Avocation: tennis. Home: 730 Langford Ln NW Atlanta GA 30327-4732 Office: Powell Goldstein Frazer & Murphy 191 Peachtree St NE Ste 16 Atlanta GA 30303-1741

LINMAN, JAMES WILLIAM, retired physician, educator; b. Monmouth, Ill., Aug. 30, 1924; s. Chester E. and Ruth L. (Pearson) L.; m. Frances Firth, Aug. 31, 1946; children—John, Jean, James, Jeffrey. B.S., U. Ill., 1945, M.D., 1947. Intern, resident internal medicine Med. Sch., U. Mich., Ann Arbor, 1947-51, fellow in hematology, 1951-52, 54-56, asst. prof. internal medicine, 1955-56; chief hematology sect. VA Research Hosp. Chgo.; assoc. prof. medicine Med. Sch., Northwestern U., Evanston, Ill., 1956-65; prof. internal medicine Mayo Grad. Sch. Medicine, U. Minn., Mpls.; cons. hematology and head spl. hematology sect. Mayo Clinic-Found., Rochester, Minn., 1965-72; prof. medicine, dir. Osgood Leukemia Ctr., Health Sci. Ctr., U. Oreg., Portland, 1972-79, head hematology div., 1974-78; prof. medicine John A. Burns Sch. Medicine, U. Hawaii, Honolulu, 1979-92; emeritus prof., 1992—; chmn. admissions com. John A. Burns Sch. Medicine, U. Hawaii, Honolulu, 1983-92, asst. dean for admissions, 1988-92; chmn. State of Hawaii Adv. Commn. on Drug Abuse and Controlled Substances, 1986-88; dir. med. edn. The Queen's Med. Ctr., Honolulu, 1987-88. Author: Principles of Hematology, 1966, Factors Controlling Erythropoiesis, 1960, The Leukemias, 1971, Hematology, 1975; Contbr. articles to profl. jours. Served with USAF, 1952-54. Recipient Tchr. of Year award Mayo Fellows Assn., 1970, Tchr. of Year award U. Hawaii, 1980, 81. Mem. Am. Soc. Clin. Investigation, Central Soc. Clin. Research, Am., Internat. socs. hematology, A.C.P., Western Assn. Physicians, Western Soc. Clin. Research, Pacific Interurban Clin. Club, Alpha Omega Alpha, Phi Kappa Phi. Club: Oahu Country. Home: 2130 Pililani Pl Honolulu HI 96822-2513

LINN, EDWARD ALLEN, writer; b. Boston, Nov. 14, 1922; s. Hyman and Gertrude (Ober) L.; m. Ruth Goldberg, June 12, 1949; children: Michael, David, Hildy. B.S. in Journalism, Boston U., 1949. With USIS, Washington, 1951-52; asst. editor Macfadden Publs., 1952-53; contbg. writer Sat.

Eve. Post, 1964-68. Free-lance writer, 1953-63; author: The Eternal Kid, 1961, Veeck-as in Wreck, 1962, The Last Loud Roar, 1964, The Hustler's Handbook, 1965, Koufax, 1966, Masque of Honor, 1969, Thirty Tons a Day, 1972, The Adversaries, 1973, Big Julie of Vegas, 1974, Out of the Fire, 1975, Nice Guys Finish Last, 1975, Where The Money Was, 1976, Inside the Yankees, The Championship Season, 1978, Steinbrenner's Yankees, 1982, A Great Connection, 1988, The Great Rivalry, 1991, Hitter, 1993, The Life and Turmoils of Ted Williams. Named Mag. Sportswriter of Year, Nat. Sportscasters and Sportswriters Assn., 1963; recipient Oppie award, 1975. Address: 1150 Anchorage Ln San Diego CA 92106

LINN, GARY DEAN, golf course architect; b. Wichita, Kans., May 11, 1955; s. Richard W. and Marilyn (Hanson) L.; m. Vicki Duncan, Aug. 6, 1977; children: Rachel, Jason, Nathan. B of Landscape Architecture, Kans. State U., 1978. Registered landscape architect Kans., 1979. Mem. Am. Soc. Landscape Architects, Am. Soc. Golf Course Architects. Avocations: family, golf, sports cards, sports. Office: 705 Forest Ave Palo Alto CA 94301-2102

LINN, JAMES HERBERT, retired banker; b. Jacksonville, Fla., Nov. 22, 1925; s. Herbert P. and Evelyn Lucile (Gore) L.; m. Betty J. Thatcher, Oct. 22, 1949; children: David, Donald, Charles, Craig, Jill. BA in Liberal Arts, U. Mo., Kansas City, 1948. With various commerce cos., 1948; vice-chmn. Commerce Bancshares, Inc., Kansas City, 1970-90; ret., 1993—; bd. dirs. Commerce Bank NA, Hays, Manhattan, El Dorado, Lenexa and Leavenworth, Kans. Dir. Eye Found. of Kansas City. Mem. Robert Morris Assos. Home: 10261 Rosewood Dr Overland Park KS 66207-3456

LINN, MARCIA CYROG, educator; b. Milw., May 27, 1943; d. George W. and Frances (Vanderhoof) Cyrog; m. Stuart Michael Linn, 1967 (div. 1979); children: Matthew, Allison; m. Curtis Bruce Tarter, 1987. BA in Psychology and Stats., Stanford U., 1965, MA in Ednl. Psychology, 1967, PhD in Ednl. Psychology, 1970. Prin. investigator Lawrence Hall Sci. U. Calif., 1970-87, prin. investigator Sch. Edn., 1985—, asst. dean Sch. Edn., 1983-85, prof., 1989—; Fulbright prof. Weizmann Inst., Israel, 1983; exec. dir. seminars U. Calif., 1985-86, dir. instdl. tech. program, 1988—; cons. Apple Computer, 1983—; mem. adv. com. on social edn. NSF, 1978—, Ednl. Testing Svc., 1986—, Smithsonian Instn., 1986—, Fulbright Program, 1983-86, Grad. Record Exam. Bd., 1990-94; chair Cognitive Studes Bd. McDonell Found., 1994—. Author: Education and the Challenge of Technology, 1987; co-author: The Psychology of Gender—Advances through Meta Analysis, 1986—, Designing Pascal Solutions, 1992—; also articles. Sci. advisor Parents Club, Lafayette, Calif., 1984-87; mem. Internat. Women's Forum, Women's Forum West, 1992—. Recipient fellow Ctr. for Adv. Study in Behav. Scis., 1995—. Fellow AAAS, APA, Am. Psychol. Soc.; mem. AAAS (at large), Nat. Assn. Rsch. in Sci. and Teaching (bd. dirs. 1983-86, assoc. editor jour., Outstanding Paper award 1978, Outstanding Jour. Article award 1975, 83, Disting. Contributions to Sci. Edn. through Rsch. award 1994), Am. Ednl. Rsch. Assn. (chmn. rsch. on women and edn. 1983-85, Women Educators Rsch. award 1982, 88, edn. in sci. and tech. 1989-90, annual mtg. program com. 1996, Willystine Goodsell award 1991), Nat. Sci. Tchrs. Assn. (mem. rsch. agenda com. 1987-90, task force 1993-94), Soc. for Rsch. in Child Devel. (editorial bd. 1984-89), Soc. Rsch. Adolescence, Sierra Club. Avocations: skiing, hiking. Office: U Calif Sch Edn 4611 Tolman Hall Berkeley CA 94720

LINN, STUART MICHAEL, biochemist, educator; b. Chgo., Dec. 16, 1940; s. Maurice S. and Pauline L.; m. Priscilla K. Cooper; children: Matthew S., Allison D., Meagan S. B.S. with honors in Chemistry, Calif. Inst. Tech., 1962; Ph.D. in Biochemistry, Stanford U. 1967. Asst. prof. biochemistry U. Calif., Berkeley, 1968-72, assoc. prof., 1972-75, prof., 1975-87, head div. biochemistry and molecular biology, 1987-90, 95—. Mem. editorial bd. Nucleic Acids Rsch., 1974—, Jour. Biol. Chemistry, 1975-80, Molecular and Cellular Biology, 1987-91; contbr. articles to profl. jours., chpts. to books. Helen Hay Whitney fellow, 1966-68; John Simon Guggenheim fellow, 1974-75; recipient USPHS Merit Grant award, 1988—. Mem. AAAS, Am. Soc. Biol. Chemists (coun.), Am. Soc. Microbiologists. Office: U Calif Divsn Biochem & Mo Bio Barker Hall Berkeley CA 94720

LINNA, TIMO JUHANI, immunologist, researcher, educator; b. Tavastkyro, Finland, Mar. 16, 1937; came to U.S., 1968, naturalized, 1981; foster s. Gustaf Lennart and Anne-Marie (Forsstrom) Ackell; m. Rhoda Margareta Popova, May 20, 1961; children: Alexander, Fredrik, Maria. MB, U. Uppsala, Sweden, 1959, MD, 1965, PhD, 1967. Intern, resident hosps. Sweden, pvt. practice medicine hosps. and clinic; asst. prof. histology U. Uppsala, 1967-71; asst. prof. microbiology and immunology Temple U., Phila., 1970-71; dir. lab. clin. immunology hosps. Temple U., 1970-72, adviser clin. immunology, 1972-80; assoc. prof. microbiology, immunology Temple U., Phila., 1971-78; prof. Temple U., 1978-80, research prof. 1980-90; group leader immunology central research and devel. dept. E.I. duPont de Nemours & Co., Wilmington, Del., 1980-84, research supr., 1984-85, mgr. med. research,med. products dept., 1986-87, assoc. med. dir., 1987-90; sr. dir. cellular immunology Applied Immune Scis., Inc., Menlo Park, Calif., 1990-91; sr. assoc. med. dir. inst. clin. immunology and infectious diseases, devel. rsch., Syntex (USA) Inc., Palo Alto, Calif., 1992-94, dir. med. rsch., 1994—; immunology cons. UNDP/World Bank/WHO Spl. Program for Research and Tng. in Tropical Diseases, WHO, Geneva, 1978-79; mem. sci. adv. council Internat. Inst. Immunology Tng. and Research, Amsterdam, Netherlands, 1975-81. Author books; contbr. articles to profl. publs. USPHS Internat. postdoctoral research fellow, 1968-70; spl. research fellow U. Minn., 1970; Eleanor Roosevelt Am. Cancer Soc. fellow, 1976; grantee Swedish Med. Research Council, 1969-71; grantee NIH, 1972-80. Mem. Am. Assn. Cancer Research, Am. Assn. Immunologists (chmn. edn. com. 1975-80), Am. Assn. Pathologists, Am. Soc. Microbiology, Internat. Soc. Exptl. Hematology, Internat. Soc. Lymphology, N.Y. Acad. Scis. Reticuloendothelial Soc., Royal Lymphatic Soc. Uppsala, Scandinavian Soc. Immunology, Soc. Swedish Physicians, Swedish Med. Assn. Lutheran. Home: 260 Highland Ave San Carlos CA 94070-1911 Office: PO Box 10850 3401 Hillview Ave Palo Alto CA 94303

LINNELL, ROBERT HARTLEY, environment, safety consultant; b. Kalkaska, Mich., Aug. 15, 1922; s. Earl Dean and Constance (Hartley) L.; m. Myrle Elizabeth Talbot, June 17, 1950; children: Charlene LeGro, Lloyd Robert, Randa Ruth, Dean Maxfield. B.S., U. N.H., 1944, M.S., 1948; Ph.D., U. Rochester, 1950. Asst. instr. U. N.H., 1942-44, instr., 1947; asst. prof. chemistry Am. U., Beirut, 1950-52; assoc. prof., chmn. chemistry dept. Am. U., 1952-55; v.p. Tizon Chem. Corp., Flemington, N.J., 1955-58; assoc. prof. chemistry U. Vt., 1958-61; dir. Scott Research Labs., Plumsteadville, Pa., 1961-62; program dir. phys. chemistry NSF, 1962-65, planning assoc., 1965-67, program mgr. departmental sci. devel., 1967-69; dean Coll. Letters, Arts and Scis., U. So. Calif., Los Angeles, 1969-70; dir. Office Instl. Studies U. So. Calif., 1970-82, chmn. safety sci. dept., 1982-85, prof. emeritus, 1985—; pres. Harmony Inst., 1985-92; cons. Reheis Corp., 1958-61, Coll. Chemistry Cons. Service, 1970-76, EPA, 1973-73, Lake Erie Environment Program, 1971-73. Author: Graduate Student Support and Manpower Resources in Graduate Science Education, 1968, Air Pollution, 1973, Hydrogen Bonding, 1971, Dollars and Scholars, 1982, Meeting The Needs of The Non-Smoking Traveler, 1986, Ignition Interlock Devices: An Assessment of Their Application to Reducing DUI, 1991; contbr. articles to profl. jours. Mem. traffic adv. com. Auto Club So. Calif., 1985-93. Served with USNR, 1944-46. Recipient Outstanding Achievement award Coll. Tech., U. N.H., 1969. Fellow AAAS; mem. AAUP, Am. Chem. Soc. (program chmn. Washington 1968, divsn. chem. edn. 1971), Am. Assn. Higher Edn., Assn. Instl. Rsch., Am. Soc. Safety Engrs., Nat. Safety Mgmt. Soc., Am. Assn. Univ. Adminstrs., Am. Lung Assn. (bd. dirs. 1986, pres. 1991-92), Upper Valley Habitat for Humanity (bd. dirs. 1993-95), Rotary. Patentee in chemistry field. Home: 255 Kings Hwy W White River Junction VT 05001

LINNEMEYER-BUSCH, ANNIE, library director; b. Joplin, Mo., Jan. 6, 1947; d. George Lee and Margaret Eleanor (Williams) Chancellor; 1 child, William Andrew Keller. BA, Mo. U., 1969, MA, 1976. Br. mgr. St. Charles (Mo.) City Coun. Libr., 1977-84; br. mgr. Springfield/Greene County (Mo.) Libr., 1985-89, exec. dir., 1989—; exec. bd. Mo. Libr. Network Corp., St. Louis, 1991—. Mem. adv. bd. Springfield Pub. Sch. Found., 1992-94; pres. Ozarks Regional Info. On-Line Network, Springfield, 1993—; mem. Gov.'s Commn. on Informational Tech.; mem. exec. bd. Mo. Rsch. and Edn. Network; bd. dirs. Ozarks Pub. TV, 1994—; mem. task force Mo. Goals

2000, 1995. Mem. ALA, Mo. Libr. Assn. (pres. 1993-94, exec. bd. 1990-94), Forum, Pub. Libr. Assn., Rotary (treas. Springfield Club 1994). Office: Springfield-Greene Cty Libr 620 W Republic Rd Springfield MO 65807-5818

LINNERT, TERRENCE GREGORY, lawyer; b. Cleve., Oct. 16, 1946; s. Ralph Marshall and Mary Gertrude (Gessner) L.; m. Susan Kay Chesnes, Jan 25, 1969; children: Michael, Patrick, Terrence, Timothy. BSEE, U. Notre Dame, 1968; JD, Cleve. State U., 1975. Bar: Ohio 1975. Engr. Cleve. Electric Illuminating, 1968-77, corp. counsel, 1977-84, sr. corp. counsel, 1984-86; sr. corp. counsel Centerior Energy Corp., Independence, Ohio, 1986-87; prin. counsel Centerior Service Co., Independence, Ohio, 1987; asst. gen. counsel Centerior Svc. Co., Independence, Ohio, 1988-89; gen. counsel Centerior Energy Corp., Independence, 1989-92, v.p., legal & govtl. affairs, 1992—. Mem. Citizens' League, Cleve; pres. St. Gabriel's Parents' Assn. Concord, Ohio, 1984-85, v.p. parish coun., 1986-87; pres. Lake Cath. Edn. Commn., Mentor, Ohio, 1991-92. Roman Catholic. Home: 7260 Winchester Pl Painesville OH 44077-2226 Office: Centerior Energy Corp 6200 Oak Tree Blvd Independence OH 44131

LINNEY, BEVERLY See HALLAM, BEVERLY

LINNEY, ROMULUS, author, educator; b. U.S., 1930. BA, Oberlin Coll., 1953, LittD (hon.), 1995; MFA, Yale U., 1958. Prof. arts Sch. Arts Columbia U., N.Y.C.; lectr. U. N.C., Chapel Hill, Raleigh, U. Pa., Bklyn. Coll., Conn. Coll., Princeton U., Hunter Coll. Author: (novels) Heathen Valley, 1962, Slowly, By Thy Hand Unfurled, 1965, Jesus Tales 1980, (plays) The Sorrows of Frederick, 1968, Democracy and Esther, and The Love Suicide at Schofield Barracks, 1973, Holy Ghosts, and The Sorrows of Frederick, 1977, Old Man Joseph and His Family, 1978, The Captivity of Pixie Shedman, 1981, Tennessee, 1981, Childe Byron, 1981, The Death of King Philip, 1983, Laughing Stock, 1984, Sand Mountain, 1985, A Woman Without a Name, 1986, Pops, 1987, Juliet, Yancy and April Snow, 1989, Three Poets, 1989, Unchanging Love, 1990, '2', 1990, Ambrosio, 1991, Spain, 1993. Grantee NEA, Guggenheim Found., Rockefeller Found., others; recipient Lit. award Am. Acad., 1984, Obie awards, 1980, 90. Address: 35 Claremont Ave 9N New York NY 10027

LINOWES, DAVID FRANCIS, political economist, educator, corporate executive; b. N.J., Mar. 16, 1917; m. Dorothy Lee Wolf, Mar. 25, 1946; children: Joanne Linowes Alinsky, Richard Gary, Susan Linowes Allen (dec.), Jonathan Scott. BS with honors, U. Ill., 1941. Founder, ptnr. Leopold & Linowes (name now BDO Siedman), Washington, 1946-62; cons. sr. ptnr. Leopold & Linowes, 1962-82; nat. founding ptnr. Laventhol & Horwath, 1965-76; chmn. bd, chief exec. officer Mickleberry Comm. Corp., 1970-73; chmn., CEO Perpetual Investment Co., Inc., 1950-88; dir. Horn & Hardart Co., 1971-77, Piper Aircraft, 1972-77, Saturday Rev./World Mag., Inc., 1972-77, Chris Craft Industries, Inc., 1958—, Work in Am. Inst., Inc.; prof. polit. economy, pub. policy, bus. adminstrn. U. Ill., Urbana, 1976—; Boeschenstein prof. emeritus, 1987—; cons. DATA Internat. Assistance Corps., 1962-68, U.S. Dept. State, UN, Sec. HEW, Dept. Interior; chmn. Fed. Privacy Protection Commn., Washington, 1975-77, U.S. Commn. Fair Market Value Policy for Fed. Coal Leasing, 1983-84, Pres.'s Commn. on Fiscal Accountability of Nation's Energy Resources, 1981-82; chmn. Pres.' Commn. on Privatization, 1987-88; mem. Council on Fgn. Relations; cons. panel GAO; adj. prof. mgmt. NYU, 1965-73; Disting. Arthur Young Prof. U. Ill., 1973-74; emeritus chmn. internat. adv. com. Tel Aviv U.; headed U.S. State Dept. Mission to Turkey, 1967, to India, 1970, to Pakistan, 1968, to Greece, 1971, to Yugoslavia, 1991; U.S. rep. on privacy to Orgn. Econ. Devel. Intergovtl. Bur. for Informatics, 1977-81, cons., N.Y.C., 1977-81; U.S. State Dept. mission to Chile, Argentina and Uruguay, July, 1988, Yugoslavia, May, 1991. Author: Managing Growth Through Acquisition, Strategies for Survival, Corporate Conscience; commn. report Personal Privacy in Information Society, Fiscal Accountability of Nation's Energy Resources, The Privacy Crisis In Our Time; editor: The Impact of the Communcation and Computer Revolution on Society, Privacy in America, 1989; contbr. articles to profl. jours. Trustee Boy's Club Greater Washington, 1955-62, Am. Inst. Found., 1962-68; assoc. YM-YWHA's Greater N.Y., 1970-76; chmn. Charities Adv. Com. of D.C., 1958-62; emeritus bd. dirs. Religion in Am. Life, Inc.; former chmn. U.S. People for UN; chmn. citizens com. Combat Charity Rackets, 1953-58. Served to 1st lt. Signal Corps, AUS, 1942-46. Recipient 1970 Human Relations award Am. Jewish Com., U.S. Pub. Service award, 1982, Alumni Achievement award U. Ill., 1989, CPA Distinguished Pub. Svc. award, Washington, 1989. Mem. AICPA (v.p. 1962-63), U. Ill. Found. (emeritus bd. dirs. 1), Coun. Fgn. Rels., Cosmos Club (Washington), Phi Kappa Phi (nat. bd. dirs.), Beta Gamma Sigma. Home: 803 Fairway Dr Champaign IL 61820-6325 Office: U Ill 308 Lincoln Hall Urbana IL 61801 also: 9 Wayside Ln Scarsdale NY 10583-2907

LINOWES, HARRY MICHAEL, accountant; b. Trenton, N.J., Feb. 4, 1928; s. Joseph and Rose (Oglensky) Linowitz; m. Judith Barbara Bierman, July 6, 1952; children: Jeffrey A., Ronni J. Savran, Gary J., Steven D. BS in Bus. Adminstrn., Rutgers U., 1948. Mng. ptnr. Leopold and Linowes, CPA's, Washington, 1963-86, sr. ptnr. BDO Seidman, Accts. and Cons. (merger Leopold & Linowes, CPA's and BDO Seidman 1986), 1986—. Treas. Greater Washington Bd. of Trade, 1985, also bd. dirs., pres. Washington Performing Arts Soc., 1984-86; pres. Jewish Community Ctrs. Greater Washington, 1978-80, also bd. dirs.; adv. com. Boys and Girls Clubs Greater Washington, 1983—; former pres. Young Jewish Leadership Coun. of Greater Washington, Nat. Children's Ctr. for Retardation; bd. dirs. Cultural Alliance of Greater Washington, 1985, v.p., 1987, pres. 1988-89; exec. com. D.C. Pvt. Industry Coun., 1991—; bd. dirs. B'nai Brith Nat. Jewish Mus.; exec. com. Michael D. Dingman Ctr. for Entrepreneurship U. Md., 1990—, bd. dirs. Md. Citizens for the Arts, 1992—; chmn. community adv. bd. Pub. Radio Sta. 88.5-FM, 1985; pres. D.C. Estate Planning Council, 1990-91; bd. dirs. United Arts Orgn. Washington, 1993—; mem. editorial adv. bd. The Practical Accountant mag. With U.S. Army, 1950-52. Recipient Ottenstein award for leadership in social welfare Greater Washington Jewish Social Service Agy.; Nat. Gulick award Camp Fire Girls; Bronze Stone award Boys Clubs of Am. for outstanding svc. to Boys Clubs movement; Golden Links award Greater Washington Bd. Trade, 1990, Washingtonian of Yr. award, 1990. Mem. D.C. Inst. C.P.A.s (pres. 1967-68), Am. Inst. C.P.A.s (council mem. 1967-68, 84-86; pub. service award 1982, pub. svc. com. 1987-90), C.P.A. Assocs. (chmn. exec. com. 1975-76), Jr. C. of C. (recipient several ann. awards for leadership to orgn. and community). Home: 6220 Clearwood Rd Bethesda MD 20817-5633 Office: BDO Seidman 1707 L St NW Fl 8 Washington DC 20036-4201

LINOWITZ, SOL MYRON, lawyer; b. Trenton, N.J., Dec. 7, 1913; s. Joseph and Rose (Oglenskye) L.; m. Evelyn Zimmerman, Sept. 3, 1939; children: Anne, June, Jan, Ronni. AB, Hamilton Coll., 1935; JD, Cornell U., 1938; LLD (hon.), Allegheny Coll., Amherst Coll., Bucknell U., Babson Inst., Brandeis U., Colgate U., Curry Coll., Dartmouth Coll., Elmira Coll., Georgetown U., Hamilton Coll., Hebrew Union Coll., Ithaca Coll., Marietta Coll., John Hopkins U., Oberlin Coll., St. John Fisher Coll., St. Lawrence U., Jewish Theol. Sem., Washington U., St. Louis, U. Miami, Muskingum Coll., Notre Dame U., U. Pacific, U. Pa., Rutgers U., Pratt Inst., Rider Coll., Roosevelt U., Chapman Coll., U. Mich., Govs. State U., U. Mo., Syracuse U.; LHD (hon.), Am. U., Loyola U., U. Rochester, Yeshiva U.; U. Judaism, Wooster Coll.; PhD (hon.), U. Haifa. Bar: N.Y. 1938. Asst. gen. counsel OPA, Washington, 1942-44; ptnr. Sutherland, Linowitz & Williams, 1946-58, Harris, Beach, Keating, Wilcox & Linowitz, Rochester, N.Y., 1958-66; chmn. Nat. Urban Coalition, 1970-76; chmn. bd. dirs., chmn. exec. com., gen. counsel Xerox Corp., 1958-66; chmn. bd. dirs. Xerox Internat., 1966; sr. ptnr. Coudert Bros., 1969-84, sr. counsel, 1984-94; ambassador to OAS, 1966-69; hon. chmn. Acad. Ednl. Devel., Washington, 1992—; co-negotiation Panama Canal treaties, 1977-78; spl. Middle East negotiator for Pres. Carter, 1979-81; chmn. Am. Acad. of Diplomacy, 1984-89; co-chmn. Inter-Am. Dialogue, 1981-92; vice chmn. Acad. for Ednl. Devel., 1986-92; pres. Fed. City Coun., 1974-78; chmn. Pres. Commn. World Hunger, 1978-79; bd. dirs., co-founder Internat. Exec. Svc. Corps; chmn. State Dept. Adv. Com. on Internat. Orgns., 1963-66. Author: The Betrayed Profession, 1994, (memoir) The Making of a Public Man, 1985, This Troubled Urban World, 1974; contbr. articles to profl. jours. Trustee Hamilton Coll., Cornell U., Johns Hopkins U., Am. Assembly; chmn. bd. overseers, bd. dirs. Jewish Theol. Sem., 1971-79. Lt. USNR, 1944-46. Fellow Am. Acad. Arts and

Scis.; mem. Am. Assn. for UN (pres. N.Y. State), Rochester Assn. for UN (pres. 1952), Rochester C. of C. (pres. 1958), ABA, N.Y. Bar Assn. Rochester Bar Assn. (v.p. 1949-50), Am. Assn. UN (bd. dirs.), Council on Fgn. Relations, Order of Coif, Phi Beta Kappa, Phi Kappa Phi. Office: Acad for Ednl Devel 1875 Connecticut Ave NW Washington DC 20009-5728

LINSCOTT, JACQUELINE C., elementary school educator, consultant; b. Franklin, N.C., Feb. 26, 1941; d. Clyde W. and Katherine (Ray) Clark; m. Leonard Lee Linscott, Aug. 16, 1964; 1 child, Laura Leigh Linscott Bledsoe. BS in Edn., U. N.C., 1964; M in Elem. Edn., Adminstrn. Supr., Stetson U., 1980. Edn. Cert., Fla. Tchr. Riverview Elem. Sch., Titusville, Fla., 1964-66, Jackson Middle Sch., Titusville, Fla., 1966-67, Coquina Elem. Sch., Titusville, Fla., 1967-86; tchr. Challenger 7 Elem. Sch., Cocoa, Fla., 1986-89, PRIME specialist, 1989-91, YRE coord., 1991—; cons. Yr. Round Edn. Dept. Edn., Tallahassee, 1992—. Author: Blue-Bell Paper Weights and Other Bells, 1990, rev. edit., 1992. Grantee PAC-MAN Reading Program Brevard Pub. Schs., Melbourne, Fla., 1982, Caring Adults Reading with Elem. Students, Brevard Pub. Schs., 1990. Mem. Assn. Sch. Curriculum and Devel., Nat. Assn. Yr. Round Edn. (presenter confs. 1993-95), Fla. Assn. Yr. Round Edn. (presenter conf. 1991—, sec.), Alpha Delta Kappa. Avocations: antique collecting, reading, crafts. Home: 3557 Nicklaus Dr Titusville FL 32780-5356 Office: Challenger 7 Elem School 6135 Rena Ave Cocoa FL 32927-8260

LINSCOTT, JERRY R., lawyer; b. Falls City, Nebr., July 21, 1941; s. Judd M. and Viola M. (Apel) L.; m. Dona L. Friesen (div. 1980); m. Linda S. Paintieri (div. 1985); children: Mark, Todd; m. Theresa Watkins, May 17, 1986; 1 child, Palmer Jarvis. BS, U. Nebr., 1963, LLB, 1966. Bar: Mo. 1966, U.S. Dist. Ct. (mid. dist.) Mo. 1967, Fla. 1972, U.S. Dist. Ct. (mid. dist.) Fla. 1972, U.S. Ct. Appeals (11th cir.) 1990. Mem. firm Linde, Thomson, Langworthy, Van Dyke & Kohn, Kansas City, Mo., 1966-72; ptnr. Young, Turnbull & Linscott, Orlando, Fla., 1972-79, Baker & Hostetler, Orlando, 1979—. Mem. ABA (state leader litigation sect. 1990—). Office: Baker & Hostetler 200 S Orange Ave Ste 2300 Orlando FL 32801-3439

LINSENMEYER, JOHN MICHAEL, lawyer; b. Columbus, Ohio, June 20, 1940; s. John Cyril and Ruth Theresa (Motz) L.; m. Barbara Panish, Aug. 12, 1961; children: Ann Elizabeth Linsenmeyer Nelson, Thomas More, Barbara Mary Linsenmeyer Malone. AB, Georgetown U., 1961, JD, 1964. Bar: Va. 1964, N.Y. 1965, U.S. Supreme Ct.1967, D.C. 1975. Assoc. Cravath, Swaine & Moore, N.Y.C., 1966-75; ptnr. Forsyth, Decker, Murray & Broderick, N.Y.C., 1975-80, Morgan, Lewis & Bockius, N.Y.C., 1980—. Columnist Southern Conn. Newspapers, Greenwich, 1984—; contbr. articles to profl. jours. Police officer, sgt. Greenwich Police Dept. Special Div., 1966-87; cons. firearms Presdl. Commn. on the Causes and Prevention of Violence, 1968-69; bd. dirs. Fairfield County Fish and Game Agy., Newtown, Conn., 1973-77. Mem. N.Y. State Bar Assn., N.Y.C. Fed. Cts. Com., N.Y.C. Fed. Bar Coun. Republican. Roman Catholic. Clubs: University (N.Y.C.) Squadron A (N.Y.C.), Rocky Point (Old Greenwich, Conn.), Royal Can. Milit. (Toronto). Avocations: hunting, shooting, horses, military history. Home: 9 Hendrie Ave Riverside CT 06878-1808 Office: Morgan Lewis & Bockius 101 Park Ave New York NY 10178-0060

LINSEY, NATHANIEL L., bishop; b. Atlanta, July 24, 1926; s. Samuel and L. E. (Forney) L.; m. Mae Cannon Mills, June 8, 1951; children: Nathaniel Jr., Ricarldo Mills, Julius Wayne, Angela Elise. BS, Paine Coll., 1948, LLD (hon.), 1990; BD, Howard U., 1951; MA in Evangelism, Scarritt Coll., 1974; DD (hon.), Miles Coll., 1975, Tex. Coll., 1985. Ordained to ministry Christian M.E.Ch., 1948. Nat. dir. youth Christian M.E.Ch., 1951-52; pastor Rock of Ages Christian M.E.Ch., 1952-53; presiding elder Columbia (S.C.) dist. Christian M.E.Ch., 1953-55; pastor Vanderhorst Christian M.E.Ch., 1955-56, Mattie E. Coleman Christian M.E.Ch., 1956-62, Thirgood Christian M.E.Ch., 1962-66; gen. sec. evangelism Christian M.E.Ch., 1966-78, chmn. bd. lay activities, 1978-82, chmn. fin. com., 1982-86, elected 39th bishop, 1978—; sr. bishop, CEO, presiding bishop 2d dist., 1994, founder Congress on Evangelism, chmn. dept. fin., 1982-86, bd. evangelism, missions and human concerns, chmn. Coll. of Bishops, 1980, 92; v.p. Interfaith Christian Coun., Washington, 1979-82; mem. presidium World Meth. Coun.; regional sec. N.Am. sect. world evangelism com. World Methodist Coun. Pres. local chpt. NAACP, Knoxville, Tenn., 1957; trustee Miles Coll., Birmingham, Ala. Recipient Disting. Alumni award Paine Coll., 1978, Presdl. citation Nat. Assn. for Equal Opportunities in Higher Edn., 1979, Disting. Svc. award Govt. D.C., 1984, Pub. Svc. award Tex. Coll., 1984, Disting. Missionary award Calif. conf. M.E.Ch., 1985; chieftancy of Obong Uwanna Ibibio Tribe, Nigeria, 1992—. Mem. World Meth. Coun., So. Calif. Ecumenical Coun. Chs. (pres. L.A. chpt. 1984). Democrat. Home: 6322 Elwynne Dr Cincinnati OH 45236

LINSK, MICHAEL STEPHEN, real estate executive; b. L.A., Apr. 20, 1940; s. Abe P. and Helen Linsk; BS in Adminstrn., U. So. Calif., 1965, MBA, 1969; m. Wilma M. Stahl, Aug. 11, 1979; children by previous marriage: Cari E., Steven D. CFO Larwin Group, Inc., Encino, Calif., 1970-75; v.p. fin. dir. Donald L. Bren Co., Los Angeles, 1976-78; v.p. CFO, treas., dir. Wilshire Mortgage/Wilshire Diversified, Burbank, Calif., 1980-81, pres., dir. subs. Wilshire Mortgage Corp., Burbank, 1981-84; pres., dir. Wilshire Realty Investments, Burbank, 1981-84, Glenfed Investments Inc., subs. Glendale Fed. Savs., 1982-84; pres. Eastern Pacific Fin. Group, Los Angeles, 1984-85; sr. v.p. Leisure Tech., Inc., Los Angeles, 1985-87, CEO, Investec Realty Group, Inc., Encino, Calif., 1987-88; sr. v.p. L.A. Land Co., 1988-91, dir. real estate consulting Price Waterhouse, 1992—; dir. Presdl. Savs. Bank, dir. Jewel City Ins., Glendale, Verdugo Services, Inc., Glendale. Treas. Temple Judea, Tarzana, Calif., 1982-83, trustee, 1981-83; treas., bd. dirs. Am. Theater Arts; bd. dirs. North Hollywood Cultural Ctr., Inc. Mem. Bldg. Industry Assn. (dir. Los Angeles chpt. 1981-88), AICPA, Calif. Soc. CPAs, Beta Gamma Sigma. Office: Price Waterhouse 400 S Hope St Los Angeles CA 90071

LINSLEY, ROBERT MARTIN, retired geology educator; b. Chgo., Feb. 19, 1930; s. Robert Martin and Mary (Morgan) L.; m. JoAnn Hoehler (div.); children: David, Barbara, Christopher. B.S., U. Mich., 1952, M.S., 1953, Ph.D., 1960. Ford teaching intern Colgate U., Hamilton, N.Y., 1954-55; mem. faculty Colgate U., 1955—, Whitnall prof. geology, chmn. dept. geology, 1955-92, ret., 1992. Contbr. articles to profl. jours. Office: Colgate U Dept Geology Hamilton NY 13346

LINSTROTH, TOD B., lawyer; b. Racine, Wis., Feb. 19, 1947; s. Eugene and Gloria L.; m. Jane Kathryn Zedler, June 23, 1972; children: Kathryn, Krista, Kassandre, Kyle. BBA in Acctg., U. Wis., 1970, JD, 1973. Bar: Wis. Assoc. Michael, Best & Friedrich, Madison, Wis., 1973-79, ptnr., 1980—. Mem. Madison Plan Commn., 1978-82; mem. Gov.'s Task Force Am. Motors Corp., Madison, 1986; mem. bus. alumni bd. U. Wis., Madison, 1991—; mem. Gov.'s Sci. and Tech. Coun., Madison, 1993—. 1st lt. USAR, 1970-78. Mem. Madison Club. Republican. Avocation: sailing. Office: Michael Best & Friedrich 1 S Pinckney St # 900 Madison WI 53703-2808

LINTHICUM, GARY REX, construction company executive; b. Tulsa, Mar. 3, 1940; s. Rex R. and Theo Murtle (Mace) L.; m. Dianne Davis, May 28, 1960; children: David, Dana, Eric. BS in Engring. and Constrn., Ariz. State U., 1964; postgrad., U. Ariz., 1974, Stanford U., 1980. Field engr. Craig & Keithline Emgrs., Tulsa, 1960-61; project engr. Kitchell Contractors, Phoenix, 1964, estimator, project mgr., ops. mgr., exec. v.p., pres., 1980-84; pres. Linthicum Constructors Inc., Scottsdale, Ariz., 1984—. Named Mgr. of Yr. City of Scottsdale, 1986. Mem. Associated Gen. Contractors (special contracting methods com. 1980-82, bd. dirs. 1982-83, collective bargaining com. 1983, contract documents coordinating com. 1983, spl. contracting methods com. 1983, chmn. edn. com. Ariz. chpt. 1980-82, bd. dirs. 1982-83, chmn. collective bargaining com. 1983, 2d v.p. 1987, 1st v.p. 1988, pres. Ariz. chpt. 1989), Ariz. State Alumni Assn. (bd. dirs. 1983-85). Republican. Methodist. Office: Linthicum Constructors Inc 9322 N 94th Way Ste 102 Scottsdale AZ 85258-5522

LINTON, FRED ERNEST JULIUS, mathematics educator; b. Genova, Italy, Apr. 8, 1938; s. Martin and Melitta (Joel) L.. BA, Yale U., 1958; MA, Columbia U., 1959, PhD, 1963; MA (hon.), Wesleyan U., Middletown, Conn., 1972. Asst. prof. Wesleyan U., Middletown, 1963-68; assoc. prof

Wesleyan U., 1968-72, prof. math., 1972—, chmn. math. dept., 1975. Mem. Am. Math. Soc., Math. Assn. Am. Home: 36 Everit St New Haven CT 06511-2208 Office: Wesleyan U Dept Math Middletown CT 06459

LINTON, FREDERICK M., strategic planning consultant; b. Stanton, Mich., 1932; m. Peggy Jensen, May 27, 1954; children: Michael, Melinda, Margaret. B.A., Mich. State U., 1959, M.A., 1960. Tchr. San Diego, 1960-66; with AMCORD, Inc., 1966-69, Peat, Marwick & Mitchell, Los Angeles, 1969-70; sr. v.p. Shareholders Capital Corp., Los Angeles, 1970-72; pres., chief exec. officer Boyden Assos. Inc., N.Y.C. and Los Angeles, 1972-74; pres., chmn. Delta Group Inc., Laguna Beach, Calif., 1974—; pres. Universal Paper Goods, 1983-85; dir Irvine Indsl. League. Bd. dirs. U. Calif. at Irvine Indsl. Assn. Mem. Calif. Council Econ. Edn. (pres., trustee), Newcomen Soc. N.Am., Town Hall Calif., World Affairs Council, World Bus. Council. Home: 26851 Salazar Dr Mission Viejo CA 92691-5011 Office: 23276 Del Lago Dr Laguna Hills CA 92653

LINTON, JACK ARTHUR, lawyer; b. N.Y.C., May 29, 1936; s. Paul Phillip and Helen (Feller) L.; m. Nancy A., Sept. 1, 1957; children: Ann Deborah Linton Wilmot, James Paul, John Michael. BA, Albright Coll., 1958; JD, NYU, 1961, LLM in Taxation, 1966. Bar: Pa. 1962, N.Y. 1963, U.S. Dist. Ct. (ea. dist.) Pa. 1978, U.S. Ct. Appeals 1984. Assoc. DeLong, Dry & Binder, Reading, Pa., 1961-63; asst. ho. counsel Bob Banner Assocs., Inc., N.Y.C., 1963-66; ptnr. DeLong, Dry, Cianci & Linton, Reading, 1967-70, Williamson, Miller, Murray & Linton, Reading, 1970-72, Gerber & Linton, P.C., Reading, 1972-88, Linton & Giannascoli, P.C., Reading, 1989—; solicitor Reading Parking Authority, 1967-76, City of Reading, 1980—; bd. dirs. The Group, Inc., Small Bus. Coun. Am., Inc., chmn. polit. action com., 1988—; numerous med. profl. corps., Reading area; lectr. nat. seminars on tax problems for small bus.; co-founder, mem. Estate Planning Coun. Berks County, 1978—. Editor Tax Law Rev., 1965-67; contbr. articles to profl. jours. Pres. Berks County Mental Health Assn., 1968-69, Reading Jewish Community Ctr., 1980-82; mem. Mental Health/Mental Retardation Bd. Berks County, 1974-80; treas., bd. dirs. Reading-Berks Youth Soccer League, 1982-85; bd. dirs. Gov. Mifflin Sch. Dist., Shillington, 1985-93. Kenneson fellow NYU Sch. Law, 1965-67. Mem. ABA (mem. personal svc. orgn. com., tax sect. 1981—; chairperson task force for repeal top-heavy rules 1987-89, vice chmn. personal svc. orgn. com. 1992-94, chmn. personal svc. orgn. com. 1992-94), Pa. Bar Assn., Berks County Bar Assn. (treas. 1969-72), Berks County C. of C. (mem. nat. affairs com.). Democrat. Jewish. Avocations: sports, photography, horticulture. Office: Linton & Giannascoli PC PO Box 461 1720 Mineral Spring Rd Reading PA 19603

LINTON, ROY NATHAN, graphic arts company executive; b. Jamestown, Ohio, Jan. 22, 1918; s. Lindley Vanniman and Pearl Candice (Jackson) L.; m. Joyce Sandra Phillips, Dec. 11, 1945; children—Michael, Philip. A.B., Cedarville Coll., 1938; postgrad., Ohio State U., 1938-40. Tchr. math. Blanchester (Ohio) High Sch., 1938-41; with Standard Register Co., Dayton, 1947-83; v.p. ops. Standard Register Co., 1971-72, exec. v.p., 1972-77, pres., 1977-83, chief exec. officer, 1981-83, also dir. Past trustee Miami Valley Hosp., Dayton. Maj. field arty. AUS, 1941-46. Republican. Clubs: Masons (Jamestown), Rotary (San Diego). Office: 5969 Madra Ave San Diego CA 92120-3954

LINTZ, PAUL RODGERS, physicist, engineer, patent examiner; b. Dallas, Feb. 8, 1941; s. Norman Edmund and Sarah Kathleen (Powers) L.; m. Mary Grace Caggiano, Nov. 27, 1965; children: Matthew Thomas, Eileen Sarita, Jerome Peter, Elizabeth Irene. BA cum laude, U. Dallas, 1963; MS, Cath. U. Am., 1965, PhD, 1977. Mem. tech. staff Tex. Instruments, Dallas, 1965-67; rsch. physicist Teledyne Geotech. Co., Alexandria, Va., 1967-74; specialist Planning Systems Inc., McLean, Va., 1974-76; prin. investigator Sci. Applications Internat. Corp., McLean, 1976-84; systems engr. Mitre Corp., McLean, 1984-87; ind. cons. Vienna, Va., 1987-92; patent examiner U.S. Patent and Trademark Office, Washington, 1992—. Mem. Providence Dist. Dem. Com., Vienna, 1985; com. mem. Vienna area Boy Scouts Am., 1986-90; pres. Tysons Woods Civic Assn., Vienna, 1991. Mem. IEEE, Patent and Trademark Office, Internat. Platform Assn., Sigma Xi. Roman Catholic. Achievements include development of digital signal processing techniques for defense purposes in seismic detection of underground nuclear blasts, submarine sonar signal processing, passive bistatic radar signal processing, detection, tracking. Home: 2222 Craigo Ct Vienna VA 22182 Office: US Dept Commerce Patent and Trademark Office ART Unit 2307 Box 13 Washington DC 20231

LINTZ, ROBERT CARROLL, financial holding company executive; b. Cin., Oct. 2, 1933; s. Frank George and Carolyn Martha (Dickhaus) L.; m. Mary Agnes Mott, Feb. 1, 1964; children—Lesa, Robert, Laura, Michael. B.B.A., U. Cin., 1956. Staff accountant Alexander Grant, Cin., 1958-60; dist. mgr. Uniroyal, Memphis, 1960-65; v.p. Am. Fin. Corp., Cin., 1965—; dir. Rapid-American Corp., McGregor Corp., Faberge Inc., all N.Y.C., H.R.T. Industries Inc. Los Angeles. Fisher Foods Inc., Cleve., Am. Agronomics, Tampa, Fla. Trustee, St. Francis-St. George Hosp., Cin., 1974-81. Served to capt. U.S. Army, 1956-58, 61-62. Republican. Roman Catholic. Home: 5524 Palisades Dr Cincinnati OH 45238-5620 Office: Am Fin Corp 1 E 4th St Cincinnati OH 45202-3717

LINVILL, JOHN GRIMES, engineering educator; b. Kansas City, Mo., Aug. 8, 1919; s. Thomas G. and Emma (Crayne) L.; m. Marjorie Webber, Dec. 28, 1943; children: Gregory Thomas, Candace Sue. A.B., William Jewell Coll., 1941; S.B., Mass. Inst. Tech., 1943, S.M., 1945, Sc.D., 1949; Dr. Applied Sci., U. Louvain, Belgium, 1966; DSc, William Jewell Coll., 1992. Asst. prof. elec. engring. Mass. Inst. Tech., 1949-51; mem. tech. staff Bell Telephone Labs., 1951-55; assoc. prof. elec. engring. Stanford U., 1955-57, prof., dir. solid-state electronics lab., 1957-64, prof., chmn. dept. elec. engring., 1964-80, prof., dir. Center for Integrated Systems, 1980-90—, Canon USA prof. engring., 1988-89, prof. emeritus, 1989—; co-founder, ptnr., chmn. bd. Tele Sensory Corp.; dir. Read-Rite Corp. Author: Transistors and Active Circuits, 1961, Models of Transistors and Diodes, 1963; inventor Optacon reading aid for the blind. Recipient citation for achievement William Jewell Coll., 1963, John Scott award for devel. of Optacon, City of Phila., 1980, Medal of Achievement Am. Electronics Assn., 1983, Louis Braille Prize Deutscher Blindenverband, 1984. Fellow IEEE (Edn. medal 1976), AAAS; mem. Nat. Acad. of Engring., Am. Acad. of Arts and Scis. Home: 30 Holden Ct Portola Vally CA 94028-7913 Office: Stanford U Dept Elec Engring Stanford CA 94305

LINXWILER, LOUIS MAJOR, JR., retired finance company executive; b. Blackwell, Okla., Mar. 7, 1931; s. Louis Major and Flora Mae (Horton) L.; m. Susan Buchanan, July 27, 1963; children: Louis Major III, Robert William. BS, Okla. State U., 1954. Mgr. credit dept. Valley Nat. Bank, Tucson, 1957-60; sales rep. Vega Industries, Syracuse, N.Y., 1960-62; program dir. Am. Cancer Soc., Phoenix, 1962-67; v.p., mgr. credit dept. United Bank Ariz., Phoenix, 1967-76; dean adm. Am. Inst. Banking, Phoenix, 1976-80; cons. Phoenix 1980-81, United Student Aid Funds Inc., Phoenix, 1981-82; founder, pres., chief exec. officer Ariz. Student Loan Fin. Corp., Phoenix, 1982-88, also bd. dirs.; founder, chmn., chief exec. officer Western Loan Mktg. Assn., Phoenix, 1984-90, also bd. dirs. Editor: Money and Banking, 1978. Pres. City Commn. Sister Cities, Phoenix, 1986-87, Am. Inst. Banking, Phoenix, 1973-74, Phoenix YMCA Bd. Dirs., 1974-75; v.p. North Mountain Behavioral Inst., Phoenix, 1975-77. Served to 1st lt. U.S. Army, 1954-56. Mem. Shriners, Hiram Club, Rotary (bd. dirs. 1982-83, 93-94), Beta Theta Pi. Republican. Presbyterian. Avocations: restoring automobiles, World War II history, travel. Home: 3311 E Georgia Ave Phoenix AZ 85018-1424

LINZ, WERNER MARK, publishing executive; b. Cologne, Germany, Apr. 6, 1935; came to U.S. 1957, naturalized, 1976; s. George A. and Catherine B. (Wegener) L.; m. Helen Ruth Baumler, July 27, 1959; children: Julia, Alice. Student, U. Frankfurt, Germany, 1954-57, NYU, 1958. Successively treas., mktg. v.p., exec. v.p. Herder & Herder Pub. Co., N.Y.C., 1958-71; pub., gen. mgr. Herder div. McGraw-Hill Book Co., 1971-73; pres., chief exec. officer Seabury Press, N.Y.C., 1973-80; founder, chmn., CEO Continuum Pub. Co. and Crossroad Pub. Co., N.Y.C., 1980; chmn., CEO Continuum Pub. Group, 1992—; adj. prof. mktg. NYU, City U., Pace U. Charter mem. nat. adv. com. Ctr. for the Book Libr. of Congress; mem. Nat. Com. on Higher Edn. and Libr. Programs; bd. dirs. Peterson's, Princeton, N.J., Aperture Found., Wainwright House Found., Rye, N.Y., Temple of

Understanding, Soundwaters, Stamford, Conn. Mem. Assn. Am. Pubs. (bd. dirs., chmn. edn. com.), Soc. Scholarly Pub. (charter). Clubs: University (N.Y.C.); Am. Yacht (Rye, N.Y.). Home: 230 Stuyvesant Ave Rye NY 10580-3115 Office: Continuum Pub Group 370 Lexington Ave New York NY 10017-6503

LION, PAUL MICHEL, III, transportation engineer, executive; b. Washington, Dec. 7, 1934; s. Paul Miller and Anna Louise (Chandler) L.; m. Jane Sanford, June 16, 1956; children: David, James, Thomas, William. BS, U.S. Mil. Acad., 1956; MA, MSE in Aero. Engring., Princeton U., 1963, PhD, 1965. Engr. Applied Physics Lab., Silver Spring, Md., 1960-61; rsch. asst. Princeton (N.J.) U., 1961, postdoctoral fellow, 1965-66, asst. prof. transp., 1966-70, assoc. prof., 1970-74, prof., 1974-79; dir. ops. and cost analysis U.S. Ry. Assn., Washington, 1977-81; v.p. ALK, Washington, 1981—; cons. Snavely King, Harris, Washington, 1981-83, Tech. Resource Ctr., Arthur D. Little, 1983-94; v.p. ALK, Washington. Contbr. articles to profl. publs. With arty. U.S. Army, 1956-59. Mem. IEEE, Ops. Rsch. Soc. Am., Cosmos Club. Home: 7012 Hamel Hill Ct Mc Lean VA 22101-4307 Office: ALK 888 16th St NW Ste 700 Washington DC 20006

LIONAKIS, GEORGE, architect; b. West Hiawatha, Utah, Sept. 5, 1924; s. Pete and Andriani (Protopapadakis) L.; student Carbon Jr. Coll., 1942-43, 46-47; BArch., U. Oreg., 1951; m. Iva Oree Braddock, Dec. 30, 1951; 1 dau., Deborah Jo. With Corps Engrs., Walla Walla, Wash., 1951-54; architect Liske, Lionakis, Beaumont & Engberg, Sacramento, 1954-86, Lionakis-Beaumont Design Group, 1986—. Mem. Sacramento County Bd. Appeals, 1967—, chmn., 1969, 75, 76; pres. Sacramento Builders Exchange, 1976. Served with USAAF, 1943-46. Mem. AIA (pres. Central Valley chpt., 1972—), Constrn. Specifications Inst. (pres. Sacramento chpt., 1962; nat. awards, 1962, 63, 65), Sacramento C of C (code com., 1970—). Club: North Ridge Country (pres. 1987). Lodge: Rotarian (pres. East Sacramento 1978-79). Prin. works include Stockton (Calif.) Telephone Bldg., 1968, Chico (Calif.) Main Telephone Bldg., 1970, Mather AFB Exchange Complex Sacramento, 1970, Base Chapel Mather AFB, Sacramento, 1970, Woodridge Elementary Sch., Sacramento, 1970, Pacific Telephone Co. Operating Center Modesto, Calif., 1968, Sacramento, 1969, Marysville, Calif., 1970, Red Bluff, Calif., 1971, Wells Fargo Banks, Sacramento, 1968, Corning, Calif., 1969, Anderson, 1970, Beale AFB Exchange Complex, Marysville, 1971, Cosumnes River Coll., Sacramento, 1971, base exchanges at Bergstrom AFB, Austin, Tex., Sheppard AFB, Wichita Falls, Tex., Chanute AFB, Rantoul, Ill., McChord AFB, Tacoma, Wash., health center Chico State U., Sacramento County Adminstrn. Center, Sacramento Bee Newspaper Plant. Home: 160 Breckenwood Way Sacramento CA 95864-6968 Office: Lionakis Beaumont Design Group 1919 19th St Sacramento CA 95814-6714

LIONBERGER, RICHARD LEE, lawyer; b. Terre Haute, Ind., June 20, 1950; s. Paul Henry and Lois Pauline (Wells) L.; m. Margaret Lamond Chance, Dec. 20, 1975; children: Janet, Sarah, Douglas. BS in Petroleum Engring., Tex. A&M U., 1972; JD, U. Tex., 1979. Bar: Tex. 1980. Petroleum engr. Pennzoil Co., Houston, 1972-75; drilling engr. Continental Oil Co., Houston, 1975-77; v.p. legal div. Diamond M Co., Houston, 1980-84; atty. Kaneb Services Inc., Houston, 1984-85; with Lionberger & Assocs., 1985-92; v.p. gen. counsel Diamond Offshore Drilling, Inc., 1992—. Bd. dirs. Ft. Bend Office of Early Childhood Devel., Richmond, Tex., 1985-91, pres. 1990-91. Mem. Am. Corp. Counsel Assn., Maritime Law Assn. U.S., Tex. State Bar Assn., Houston Bar Assn., Soc. Petroleum Engrs., Internat. Bar Assn., Internat. Assn. Drilling Contractors (bd. dirs. 1994—). Republican. Methodist. Lodge: Optimist (Sugarland) (pres. 1984-85). Office: Diamond Offshore Drilling Inc 15415 Katy Fwy Ste 400 Houston TX 77094

LIONNI, LEONARD, author, artist; b. Amsterdam, Holland, May 5, 1910; came to U.S., 1939, naturalized, 1945.; s. Louis and Elizabeth (Grossouw) L.; m. Nora Maffi, Dec. 23, 1931; children: Louis, Paolo. Student, U. Zurich, Switzerland, 1928-30; ArtsD (hon.), Cooper Union, 1991. Freelance writer, designer, painter, 1930-39; art dir. N. W. Ayer & Sons, Inc., Phila., 1939-47, Fortune mag., 1949-62; design dir. Olivetti Corp. Am., San Francisco, 1949-59; dept. head Parsons Sch. Design, N.Y.C., 1952-54. Exhibited Norlyst Gallery, N.Y., 1947, Print Club Phila., 1948, Mus. Modern Art, N.Y.C., 1954, Bratislava Biennale, 1967, Venice Biennale, 1972; one-man show Worcester (Mass.) Mus., 1958, Portland Mus., Phila. Art Alliance, 1959, Naviglio, Milan, Italy, 1963, Obelisco, Rome, 1964, Galleria dell'Ariete, Milan, 1966, Galleria del Milione, Milan, 1972, I Portici, Turin, Italy, Biennale de Venezia, Linea 70, Verona, Italy, 1973, Il Vicolo, Genoa, Italy, 1973, Klingspor Mus., Offenbach, Fed. Republic Germany, 1974, Baukunst Galerie, Cologne, Fed. Republic Germany, 1974, 78, Galleria CIAK, Rome, 1975, Galleria dell'Oca, Rome, 1976, Staempfli Gallery, N.Y.C., 1977, 79, Mus. Castelvecchio, Verona, 1978, Frankfurter Galerie, Frankfurt, Fed. Republic Germany, 1979, Galleria Giulia, Rome, 1987, 91, Lehman Coll. Art Gallery, N.Y., 1990; retrospective Mus. Modern Ar, Bologna, 1990; author, illustrator: Little Blue and Little Yellow, 1959, (N.Y. Times Best Illustrated Book award 1959), Design for the Printed Page, 1960, Inch by Inch, 1960 (Caldecott Honor Book 1960, Lewis Carroll Shelf award 1962, Children's Book Prize Germany 1963), On My Beach There Are Many Pebbles, 1961, Swimmy, 1963 (N.Y. Times Best Illustrated Book award 1963, Caldecott Honor Book 1964, ALA Notable Book citation 1964, German Govt. Illustrated Book award 1965, Bratislava Biennale Golden Apple 1967), Tico and the Golden Wings, 1964, Frederick, 1967, (N.Y. Times Best Illustrated Book award 1967, Caldecott Honor Book 1968, ALA Notable Book citation 1968), The Alphabet Tree, 1968, The Biggest House in the World, 1968 (Spring Book Festival Picture Book honor 1968), Alexander and the Wind-up Mouse, 1969, (Caldecott Honor Book 1970, ALA Notable Book citation 1970, Christopher Book award 1970), Fish Is Fish, 1970, (ALA Notable Book citation 1970), Theodore and the Talking Mushroom, 1971, Il Taccuino di Leo Lionni, 1972, The Greentail Mouse, 1973, In the Rabbitgarden, 1975, A Colour of His Own, 1975, Pezzettino, 1975, La Botanica Parallela, 1976, A Flea Story: I Want To Stay Here! I Want To Go There!, 1977, Geraldine, the Music-Mouse, 1979, Let's Make Rabbits: A Fable, 1982, Cornelius, 1983, Frederick's Fables, 1985, It's Mine!, 1986, Nicolas, Where Have You Been?, 1987 (Jane Addams Children's Book award 1988), Six Crows, 1988, Tillie and the Wall, 1989, Frederick and His Friends, 1989, Matthew's Dream, 1991, A Busy Year, 1992, Mr. McMouse, 1992, Let's Make Rabbits, 1993, A Color of His Own, 1993, An Extraordinary Egg, 1994; "Pictures to Talk About" series: Who?, 1983, What?, 1983, Where?, 1983, When?, 1983; "Colors, Letters, Numbers and Words To Talk About" series: Colors to Talk About, 1985, Letters to Talk About, 1985, Numbers to Talk About, 1985, Words to Talk About, 1985; illustrator: (books) Mouse Days: A Book of Seasons, 1981, Come With Us, 1982; editor: Print, 1955-57, Panorama, 1964-65. Named Art Dir. of Yr. Nat. Soc. Art Dirs., 1955; named to Art Dir.'s Hall of Fame, 1974; recipient Gold medal Archtl. League, 1956, 5 Manor awards for 2 animated films Teheran Film Festival, 1970, George G. Stone Ctr. Children's Book award for body of work, 1976, Gold medal Am. Inst. Graphic Arts, 1984; George Miller lect. Ill., 1967. Office: care Alfred A Knopf Inc 201 E 50th St New York NY 10022-7703*

LIOTTA, LANCE ALLEN, pathologist; b. Cleve., July 12, 1947; married; 2 children. BA in Gen. Sci. and Biology, Hiram Coll., 1969; PhD in Biomed. Engring. and Biomath., Case Western U., 1974, MD, 1976. Cert. basic life support Am. Heart Assn., advanced life support Am. Heart Assn. Instr. pathology for inhalation therapists dept. pathology St. Luke's Hosp., Cleve., 1972-74; sr. instr. pulmonary pathology Phase I and Phase II, Sch. Medicine Case Western Reserve U., 1973-74; USPHS resident physician Lab. Pathology, Nat. Cancer Inst. NIH, Bethesda, Md., 1976-78, pathologist, expert/cons. Lab. Pathophysiology, Nat. Cancer Inst., 1978-80, sr. investigator, pub. health svc. officer Lab. Pathophysiology and Pathology, Nat. Cancer Inst., 1980-82, chief tumor invasion and metastases sect. Lab. Pathology and Lab. Pathology, Nat. Cancer Inst., 1982—, dir. anatomic pathology residency program Lab. Pathology, Nat. Cancer Inst., 1982—, dep. dir. intramural rsch., 1992-93; adj. clin. prof. pathology Sch. Medicine George Wash. U.; mem. adj. faculty Sch. Medicine Georgetown U.; invited faculty mem. Rockefeller U., 1979; speaker in field. Author: (with others) Cancer Invasion and Metastasis, 1977, Pulmonary Metastasis, 1978, Metastatic Tumor Growth, 1980, Bone Metastasis, 1981, Cell Biology of Breast Cancer, 1980, New Trends in Basement Membrane Research, 1982, Tumor Invasion and Metastasis, 1982, Progress in Clinical and Biological Research, 1982, Growth of Cells in Hormonally Defined Media, 1982, Understanding Breast Cancer: Clinical and Laboratory Concepts, 1983, The Role of Ex-

tracellular Matrix in Development, 1984, Basic Mechanisms and Clinical Treatment of Tumor Metastasis, 1985, Hemostatic Mechanisms and Metastasis, 1984, Biological Responses in Cancer, vol. 4, 1985, The Cell in Contact: Adhesions and Junctions as Morphogenetic Determinants, 1985, Rheumatology, vol. 10, 1986, Progress in Neuropathology, vol. 6, 1986, Cancer Metastasis: Experimental and Clinical Strategies, 1986, Biochemistry and Molecular Genetics of Cancer Metastasis, 1986, Basement Membranes, 1985, 1986 Year Book of Cancer, New Concepts in Neoplasia as Applied to Diagnostic Pathology, 1986, Head and Neck Management of the Cancer Patient, 1986, Cancer Metastasis: Biological and Biochemical Mechanisms and Clinical Aspects, 1988, Important Advances in Oncology, 1988, Breast Cancer: Cellular and Molecular Biology, 1988, Cancer: Principles and Practice of Oncology, vol. 1, 3d edit., 1989, Molecular Mechanisms in Cellular Growth and Differentiation, 1991, Peptide Growth Factors and Their Receptors, 1990, Molecuar Genetics in Cancer Diagnosis, 1990, Cancer Surveys-Advances & Prospects in Clinical, Epidemiological and Laboratory Oncology, vol. 7, no. 4, 1988, Genetic Mechanisms in Carcinogenesis and Tumor Progression, 1990, Molecular and Cellular Biology, Host Immune Responses and Perspectives for Treatment, 1989, Origins of Human Cancer: A Comprehensive Review, 1991, Cancer and Metastasis Reviews, vol. 9, 1990, Comprehensive Textbook of Oncology, 1991, Textbook of Internal Medicine, 2d edit., vol. 2, 1992, Molecular Foundations in Oncology, 1991, Genes, Oncogenes, and Hormones: Advances in Cellular and Molecular Biology of Breast Cancer, 1991, Cell Motility Factors, 1991, Oncogenes and Tumor Suppressor Genes in Human Malignancies, 1993, Principles and Practice of Gnecologic Oncology, 1992, Cancer Medicine, 3d edit., 1993; contbr. articles to profl. jours. NIH Pre-doctoral fellow; recipient Arthur S. Flemming award, 1983, Flow award lectureship Soc. Cell Biology, 1983, Nat. award and lectureship Am. Assn. Clin. Chemistry, 1987, Rsch. award Susan G. Komen Found., 1987, Disting. Lectr. award Rush Cancer Ctr., 1987, George Hoyt Whipple award and lectureship Sch. Medicine U. Rochester, 1988, Karen Grunebaum Symposium award lectureship Hubert H. Humphrey Cancer Rsch. Ctr., 1988, Cancer Rsch. award Milken Family Med. Found., 1988, William M. Shelly Meml. award and lectureship Centennial Johns HopkinMed. Inst., 1989, Josef Steiner Cancer Found. prize, 1989, Basic Rsch. award Am. Soc. Cytology, 1989, Officer's Recognition award Equal Employment Opportunity, 1990, John W. Cline Cancer Rsch. award and lectureship U. Calif., 1990, Herman Pinkus award lectureship Am. Soc. Dermatology, 1991, Simon M. Shubitz award U. Chgo. Cancer Ctr., 1991, Stanley Gore Rsch. award, 1991, Lila Gruber Cancer Rsch. award Am. Acad. Dermatology, 1991, Am.-Italian Found. Cancer Rsch. award, 1992. Mem. Am. Assn. Cancer Rsch. (bd. dirs., 6th Ann. Rhoads Meml. award 1985), Am. Assn. Pathologists (Warner-Lambert/Parke-Davis award 1984), Am. Soc. Cell Biology, Am. Soc. Clin. Investigation, Internat. Acad. Pathology, Internat. Assn. Metastasis Rsch. (pres.-elect 1990), Sigma Xi, Phi Beta Kappa. Achievements include patents for method and device for determining the concentration of a material in a liquid, method for isolating bacterial colonies, test method for separating and/or isolating bacteria and tissue cells, divice and method for detecting phenothiazine-type drugs in urine, in vitro assay for cell invasiveness, enzyme immunoasessay with two-zoned device having bound antigens, metalloproteinase peptides, matrix receptors role in diagnosis and therapy of cancer, genetic method for predicting tumor aggressiveness, therapeutic application of an anti-invasive compound; patents pending for role of tumor motility factors in cancer diagnosis, role of tumor metalloproteinases in cancer diagnosis, peptide inhibitor of metalloproteinases, protein inhibitors of metalloproteinases, autotaxin motility stimulating proteins diagnosis and therapy, motility receptor protein and gene diagnosis and therapy. Office: Lab of Pathology Nat Cancer Inst 9000 Rockville Pike Bethesda MD 20892-0001

LIOTTA, RAY, actor; b. Newark, NJ, Dec. 18, 1955; s. Alfred and Mary L. Grad., U. Miami. TV appearances: Another World, NBC, 1978-80, Hardhat & Legs, CBS movie, 1980, Crazy Times, ABC pilot, 1981, Casablanca, NBC, 1983, Our Family Honor, NBC, 1985-86, Women Men = In Love There are no Rules, 1991.; films: The Lonely Lady, 1983, Something Wild, 1986, Arena Brains, 1987, Dominick and Eugene, 1988, Field of Dreams, 1989, Goodfellas, 1990, Article 99, 1992, Unlawful Entry, 1992, No Escape, 1994, Corrina, Corrina, 1994, Operation Dumbo Drop, 1995. mem. SAG, AFTRA. Office: Creative Artists Agy Inc 9830 Wilshire Blvd Beverly Hills CA 90212-1825*

LIOU, MING-LEI, electrical engineer; b. Tinghai, Chekiang, China, Jan. 6, 1935; came to U.S., 1958, naturalized, 1971; s. Ih-Min and Hsiao-Pao (Cheng) L.; m. Pearl B. Shen; children—Michael, Christopher, Derek. B.S.E.E., Nat. Taiwan U., 1956; M.S.E.E., Drexel U., 1961; Ph.D. E.E., Stanford U., 1964. Communications engr. Chinese Govt. Radio Adminstrn., Taiwan, 1957-58; instr. dept. elec. engring. Drexel U., Phila., 1958-61; research asst. Stanford Electronics Labs., Stanford U., 1961-63; mem. tech. staff Bell Labs., North Andover, Mass., 1963-66; supr. AT&T Bell Labs., 1966-84; dir. Bell Communications Research, Red Bank, N.J., 1984-92; prof. Hong Kong U. Sci. and Tech., 1992—; dir. Hong Kong Telecom. Inst. Info. Tech., 1993—. Contbr. chpts. to engring. books. Served to 2d lt. ROTC Chinese Air Force, 1956-57, Taiwan. Fellow IEEE, Hong Kong Inst. Engrs.; mem. IEEE Cirs. and Sys, Soc. (chmn. publs. bd. 1981-85, co-chmn. awards com. 1981-83, exec. v.p. 1986, pres. 1988, edit. Trans. on Cirs. and Sys. for video tech. 1991—, spl. prize paper award 1973, Darlington prize paper award 1977, Disting. Svc. award 1991), Hong Kong Inst. Sci., Sigma Xi, Eta Kappa Nu. Office: The Hong Kong U Sci and Tech, Dept EEE, Clear Water Bay, Kowloon Hong Kong

LIOY, PAUL JAMES, environmental health scientist; b. Passaic, N.J., May 27, 1947; s. Nicholas Paul and Jean Elizabeth (Licurse) L.; m. Mary Jean Yonone, June 13, 1971; 1 child, Jason. BA in Physics and Edn., Montclair State Coll., 1969; MS in Physics and Applied Math., Auburn U., 1971; MS in Environ. Sci., Rutgers U., 1973, PhD in Environ. Sci., 1975. Sr. engr. air pollution Interstate Sanitation Commn., N.Y.C., 1975-78; asst. to assoc. prof. Inst. Environ. Medicine/NYU Med. Ctr., N.Y.C., 1978-85; dep. dir. lab. of aerosol rsch. Inst. Environ. Medicine/NYU Med. Ctr., 1982-85; assoc. prof. to prof. Robert Wood Johnson Med. Sch. U. Medicine and dentistry of N.J., Piscataway, N.J., 1985—; dir. exposure measurement and assessment divsn. Environ. and Occupational Health Scis. Inst. (EOHSI), Piscataway, 1986-94; dep. dir. Environ. and Occupational Health Scis. Inst. (EOHSI), 1994—; mem. grad. faculty Rutgers U., 1986—, admissions chair in environ. scis., 1993—; cons. bd. environ. studies and toxicology, Nat. Rsch. Coun., NAS, Washington, 1989-92, mem. numerous coms. 1984—; chmn. Clean Air Coun., N.J. Dept. Environ. Protection, Trenton, 1981—; mem. Internat. Air Quality Bd., Internat. Joint Commn., USA-Can., 1991—; mem. sci. adv. bd. U.S. Environ. Protection Agy, 1991—; adj. asst. prof. Brooklyn Coll., 1977-78. Author 140 scientific publs., 1975—, chpts. in 6 books; author: (book) Toxic Air Pollution, 1987, co-editor: (with M.J. Yonone-Lioy) Air Sampling Instruments, 1985; exec. editor: Atmospheric Environment jour., 1989-94; assoc. editor: Environ. Rsch., 1995—; patentee, 1994. Chair Cranford (N.J.) Environ. Commn., 1978; treas. Cranford Little League, 1984-85. Rsch. grantee EPA, NIH, CDC, ATSDR, N.J. Dept. Environ. Protection, API, DOE, 1978—. Mem. Air Waste Mgmt. Assn. (chmn. editorial bd. 1978-80), Am. Conf. Gov. Indsl. Hygiene (chmn. air sample inst. com. 1984-87), Am. Assn. Aerosol Rsch. (editorial bd. 1990-93), Internat. Soc. Environ. Epidemiology (bd. councilors 1988-89), Internat. Soc. Exposure Analysis (pres. 1993-94, treas. 1990-91, exec. com. 1989—); Soc. of Risk Analysis. Avocations: restoration of houses, tennis, automobiles. Office: Environ/Occupational Health Scis Inst 3d Flr 681 Frelinghuysen Rd Piscataway NJ 08855

LIOZ, LAWRENCE STEPHEN, lawyer, accountant; b. N.Y.C., Sept. 24, 1945; s. William and Irma (Berksohn) L.; m. Carol Renee Skolnik, Nov. 20, 1971; children: Adam Russell, Randall Eric. BS, SUNY, Albany, 1967; JD, SUNY, Buffalo, 1970; LLM in Taxation, NYU, 1975. Bar: N.Y.; CPA, N.Y. Mgr. Ernst & Whinney, N.Y.C., 1970-79; dir. tax affairs Azcon Corp., N.Y.C., 1979-82; mgr. Deloitte Haskins & Sells, N.Y.C., 1982-83, ptnr., 1983-84; ptnr. Deloitte Haskins & Sells, Woodbury, N.Y., 1984-87, Margolin, Winer & Evens, Garden City, N.Y., 1987—; speaker various tax seminars 1986—. Contbr. articles on tax to profl. jours. Pres. Rolling Wood Civic Assn., Roslyn, N.Y., 1985—; trustee Flower Hill (N.Y.) Assn., 1985-87, Village of Flower Hill, 1987-92; treas. Roslyn Sch. Dist., 1986—. Mem. ABA, AICPA, N.J. State Bar Assn., N.Y. State Soc. CPAs (chmn. fed. tax com. Nassau chpt. 1989-92, exec. bd. 1992—), L.I. Assn. (Advancement for Commerce and Industry (dir.), L.I. Housing Partnership (dir.), Internat.

Assn. of Corp. Real Estate Execs. (v.p.). Jewish. Avocations: skiing, tennis, golf. Home: 84 Knollwood W Roslyn NY 11576-1319 Office: Margolin Winer & Evens 400 Garden City Plz Garden City NY 11530-3336

LIPELES, MAXINE INA, lawyer; b. N.Y.C., Sept. 26, 1953; d. David Arthur and Pauline (Cooper) L.; m. Joel Kramer Goldstein, Aug. 31, 1980; children: Rachel, Joshua. AB, Princeton U., 1975; JD, Harvard U., 1979. Bar: Mass. 1980, Mo. 1982, U.S. Dist. Ct. (ea. dist.) Mo. 1982, U.S. Dist. Ct. Mass., U.S. Ct. Appeals (1st cir.) 1980, U.S. Ct. Appeals (8th cir.) 1982. Law clk. U.S. Dist. Ct. (no. dist.) Calif., San Francisco, 1979-80; asst. atty. gen. State of Mass., Boston, 1980-82; assoc. Husch & Eppenberger, St. Louis, 1982-86, ptnr., 1986-94, of counsel, 1995—; part-time prof. environ. regulation and policy sch. engring. Washington U., St. Louis, 1990—. Co-author: Hazardous Waste, 1992, Water Pollution, 1993. Mem. ABA, Mo. Bar Assn., Bar Assn. Met. St. Louis (chmn. environ. law com. 1986-88). Office: Husch & Eppenberger 100 N Broadway Ste 1300 Saint Louis MO 63102-2706

LIPFORD, ROCQUE EDWARD, lawyer, corporate executive; b. Monroe, Mich., Aug. 16, 1938; s. Frank G. and Mary A. (Mastromarco) L.; m. Marcia A. Griffin, Aug. 5, 1966; children: Lisa, Rocque Edward, Jennifer, Katherine. BS, U. Mich., 1960, MS, 1961, JD with distinction, 1964. Bar: Mich. 1964, Ohio 1964. Instr. mech. engring. U. Mich., 1961-63; atty. Miller, Canfield, Paddock & Stone, Detroit, 1965-66; asst. gen. counsel Monroe Auto Equipment Co., 1966-70, gen. counsel, 1970-72, v.p., gen. counsel, 1973-77; v.p.; gen. counsel Tenneco Automotive, 1977-78; ptnr. firm Miller, Canfield, Paddock & Stone, Detroit, 1978—, mng. ptnr., 1988-91; bd. dirs. La-Z-Boy Chair Co., Monroe Bank & Trust, Kincaid Furniture Co., Q.E.D. Environ. Systems, Ferrous Environ. Recycling Corp. Mem. Mich. Bar Assn., Legatus, Knights of Malta, North Cape Yacht Club, Monroe Golf and Country Club, Otsego Ski Club, Tau Beta Pi, Pi Tau Sigma. Home: 1065 Hollywood Dr Monroe MI 48161-3045 Office: Miller Canfield Paddock & Stone 214 E Elm Ave Monroe MI 48161-2682

LIPINSKI, ANN MARIE, newspaper editor. Assoc. mng. editor for met. news. Chgo. Tribune, now dep. mng. editor. Recipient Pulitzer prize for series on politics and conflicts of interest Chgo. City Coun., 1988. Office: Chgo Tribune PO Box 25340 435 N Michigan Ave Chicago IL 60611*

LIPINSKI, WILLIAM OLIVER, congressman; b. Chgo., Dec. 22, 1937; s. Oliver and Madeline (Collins) L.; m. Rose Marie Lapinski, Aug. 29, 1962; children: Laura, Daniel. Student, Loras Coll., Dubuque, Iowa, 1957-58. Various positions to area supr. Chgo. Parks, 1958-75; alderman Chgo. City Coun., 1975-83; mem. 98th-104th Congresses from 5th (now 3rd) Dist. Ill., 1983—; ranking minority mem., mem. transp. and infrastructure subcom. on railroads. Dem. ward committeeman, Chgo., 1975—; del. Dem. Nat. Midterm Conv., 1974, Dem. Nat. Conv., 1976, 84, 88; pres. Greater Midway Econ. and Community Devel. Com.; mem. Chgo. Hist. Soc., Art Inst., Chgo., pres.'s coun. St. Xavier Coll.; mem. Congl. Competitive Caucus, Congl. Caucus for Women's Issues, Congl. Hispanic Caucus, Congl. Human Rights Caucus, Congl. Populist Caucus, Dem. Study Group, Export Task Force, Inst. for Ill., Maritime Caucus, N.E.-Midwest Congl. Coalition, Urban Caucus. Named Man of Yr. Chgo. Park Dist. 4, 1983; recipient Archer Heights Civic Assn. award 1979, 23d Ward Businessmen and Mchts. award Chgo., 1977, Garfield Ridge Hebrew Congregation award Chgo., 1975-77, Installing Officer award Vittum Park Civic Assn., 23d Ward Minuteman award, Friends of Vittum Park Polish award, Nathan Hale Grand award from S.W. Liberty Soc., S.W. Am. Edn. and Recreation program award, Sentry of Yr. award Stars & Stripes Soc., Ill. State Minuteman award 1991. Mem. Polish Nat. Alliance, Kiwanis (Disting. Svc. award, pres., Peace Through Strength Leadership award 1991). Democrat. Roman Catholic. Office: US Ho of Reps 1501 Longworth House Bldg Washington DC 20515-1303 also: 5832 S Archer Ave Chicago IL 60638*

LIPINSKY, EDWARD SOLOMON, chemist; b. Asheville, N.C., Nov. 15, 1929; s. Louis and Clara Louise (Nathan) L.; m. Sherry Dobrow, June 20, 1954; children—Edward Louis, Sarah Beth. B.S., MIT, 1952; M.A., Harvard U., 1954. Research assoc. Ohio State U., 1957-59; research economist Battelle Columbus Div., Ohio, 1959-79; sr. research leader biomass techs. Battelle Columbus Labs., Ohio, 1979-85, research leader organic/polymer chemistry, 1985—; chmn. Gov.'s Task Force on Gasohol; advisor Internat. Energy Agy. Greenhouse Gas Programme. Contbr. articles to profl. jours. Fellow AAAS; mem. TAPPI, Am. Chem. Soc., Am. Inst. Chem. Engrs., Commrl. Devel. Assn., Sigma Xi. Office: Battelle Columbus Div 505 King Ave Columbus OH 43201-2681

LIPKA, DAVID H., food company executive; b. Bklyn., Nov. 14, 1929; s. Charles and Leonie Viola L.; m. Lillian Wissner, Feb. 14, 1954; children: Andrew, Wendy, Suzanne. B.A., Bklyn. Coll., 1954; student, N.Y. U. Sch. Bus. With DCA Food Industries, 1955—, v.p. ops., 1969-72, pres., 1972—, COO, 1978-82, 1982—; pres., CEO DCA Food Industries, N.Y.C., 1978—; dir. Allied-Lyons PLC, N. Am. Cos., J. Lyons Inc. Pres. bd. dirs. Karen Horney Clinic. Served with U.S. Army, 1951-53. Mem. Am. Baking Assn. (Privy Council), Inst. Food Technologists, Am. Inst. Baking (dir.), Am. Mgmt. Assn., Nat. Indsl. Conf. Bd. Club: Mill River (Upper Brookville, Oyster Bay, N.Y.). Patentee food processing. Home: 19 Oakwood Cir Roslyn NY 11576-1428 Office: D C A Food Industries Inc 1501 Franklin Ave Garden City NY 11530

LIPKIN, DAVID, chemist; b. Phila., Jan. 30, 1913; s. William and Ida (Zipin) L.; m. Silvia Stantic Alvarez, Nov. 10, 1973; children—Jeffrey Alan, Edward Walter. B.S., U. Pa., 1934; PhD., U. Calif., Berkeley, 1939. Research chemist Atlantic Refining Co., Phila., 1934-36; research fellow U. Calif., Berkeley, 1939-42; research chemist Manhattan Project, Berkeley, 1942-43; research chemist, group leader Los Alamos Sci. Lab., 1943-46; mem. faculty Washington U., St. Louis, 1946—; prof. chemistry Washington U., 1948-66, chmn. dept., 1964-70, William Greenleaf Eliot prof., 1966-81, emeritus, 1981—; sr. vis. fellow Agrl. Research Council, Cambridge, Eng., 1960; vis. research scientist John Innes Inst., Norwich, Eng., 1971, 78; trustee Argonne Univs. Assn., 1969-71; cons. in field. Author: Guggenheim fellow, 1955-56. Mem. Am. Chem. Soc. (St. Louis award 1970), AAUP, Sigma Xi, Tau Beta Pi, Phi Mu Epsilon. Patentee in field. Office: Washington Univ Chemistry Dept Saint Louis MO 63130

LIPKIN, EDWARD B., real estate developer; b. Phila., Aug. 15, 1945; s. Al and Sophie (Feldman) L.; children: Theodore, Jeremy. B.S. in Fin., Temple U., 1967; D.B.A. (hon.), Spring Garden Coll., 1984. Sr. tax assoc. Shearson Hayden Stone, Phila., 1975-76; pres. Nat. Property Analysts (name now EBL&S Inc.), Phila., 1976—. Pres. Friends of Rittenhouse Sq. (bd. dirs.), Phila., 1983—; mem. exec. com. of Senator Bill Bradley, N.J., 1978—; Served with U.S. Army, 1967-73. Mem. Internat. Council Shopping Ctrs. (bd. trustee 1986). Republican. Jewish. Clubs: Cat Cay (Bahamas), Locust (Phila.). Office: EBLTS Inc 230 S Broad St Philadelphia PA 19102-4121

LIPKIN, JEFFREY ALAN, lawyer; b. Los Alamos, N.Mex., Mar. 18, 1946; s. David and Shirley (Douthitt) l.; m. Kathleen Anderson, Aug. 5, 1974; 1 child, Andrew. BA, Harvard U., 1968, JD, 1974. Bar: N.Y. 1975, D.C. 1982, Calif. 1985, U.S. Dist. Ct. (so. dist.) N.Y. 1975, U.S. Ct. Appeals (2d cir.) 1975. Assoc. Cahill, Gordon & Reindel, N.Y.C., 1974-80; dep. gen. counsel U.S. Synthetic Fuels Corp., Washington, 1981-84; ptnr. Gaston & Snow, San Francisco, 1984—. With USMC, 1969-71. Mem. ABA, Calif. State Bar Assn. Office: Gaston & Snow 101 California St Ste 3000 San Francisco CA 94111-5869

LIPKIN, MARTIN, physician, scientist; b. N.Y.C., Apr. 30, 1926; s. Samuel S. and Celia (Greenfield) L.; m. Joan Schulein, Feb. 16, 1958; children—Richard Martin, Steven Monroe. A.B., NYU, 1946, M.D., 1950. Diplomate: Nat. Bd. Med. Examiners. Practice medicine specializing in internal medicine, gastroenterology and neoplastic diseases N.Y.; mem. staff N.Y. Hosp., Meml. Hosp. for Cancer and Allied Diseases; prof. medicine Cornell U. Med. Coll., 1978—, prof. Grad. Sch. Med. Scis., 1978—; mem. and attending physician Meml. Sloan-Kettering Cancer Ctr., 1985—; vis. physician Rockefeller U. Hosp., 1981—; hon. lectr. Israel Med. Assn. and Gastroenterology Soc., 1982; nominator Nobel Prize for Physiology and Medicine, 1982; bd. dirs., officer Med. Ednl. and Sci. Found. of N.Y.; chmn.

bd. Irving Weinstein Found. Mem. editorial bd. Cancer Epidemiology, Biomarkers and Prevention, Cancer Rsch., Cancer Letters, Internat. Jour. Oncology; editor: Gastrointestinal Tract Cancer, 1978, Inhibition of Tumor Induction and Development, 1981, Gastrointestinal Cancer: Endogenous Factors, 1981, Calcium, Vitamin D and Prevention of Colon Cancer, 1991, Cancer Chemoprevention, 1992; contbr. articles to profl. jours. Served as officer USN, 1953-55. Recipient NIH career devel. award, 1962-71; Albert F.R. Andresen ann. award and lectureship N.Y. State Med. Soc., 1971. Fellow ACP, Am. Coll. Gastroenterology; mem. Med. Soc. State of N.Y. (chmn. sci. program com. 1990-91, chmn. edn. com. 1991—), Digestive Diseases Soc. (founder), Internat. Soc. Investigative Gastroenterology (founder), Am. Soc. Clin. Investigation, Am. Physiol. Soc., Am. Assn. Cancer Rsch., Am. Gastroenterol. Assn., Soc. for Exptl. Biology and Medicine, Harvey Soc. Office: 1275 York Ave New York NY 10021-6094

LIPKIN, SEYMOUR, pianist, conductor, educator; b. Detroit, May 14, 1927; s. Ezra and Leah (Vidaver) L.; m. Catherine Lee Bing, Dec. 27, 1961 (div. 1983); 1 son, Jonathan Michael. Mus. B., Curtis Inst. Music, 1947; studied piano with, David Saperton, 1938-41, Rudolf Serkin, Mieczyslaw Horszowski, 1941-47; conducting with, Serge Koussevitzky, Berkshire Music Center, 1946, 48, 49. Piano tchr. Juilliard Sch. Music, N.Y.C., 1961—; mem. faculty Manhattan Sch. Music, 1965-70, 72-86, NYU, 1980-86; mem. piano faculty Curtis Inst. Music, 1969—, New Eng. Conservatory, 1984-86, faculty music dept. Marymount Coll., Tarrytown, N.Y., 1963-72, chmn. music dept. 1968-71. Condr. Bklyn. Coll. Orch., 1973-74; Ford Found. commn. to perform concerto by Harold Shapero, 1959; debut with Detroit Civic Orch., 1937; apprentice condr. to George Szell, Cleve. Orch., 1947-48; appearances as pianist other U.S. orchs. including Boston Symphony in Tanglewood; ann. tours including soloist, Buffalo and Nat. Symphony, soloist, asst. condr. N.Y. Philharm. tour, Europe and Russia, 1959; conducting debut Detroit Symphony, 1944; recitalist, 92d St YMHA, N.Y.C., 1981, 83, soloist N.Y. Philharm., N.Y.C., 1983, participant in chamber music, Spoleto Festivals, 1982, 83, co-condr. Curtis Inst. Orch., 1952-53, asst. condr. Goldovsky Opera Co. on tour, 1953, condr. N.Y.C. Opera Co., 1958, 1 of 3 asst. condrs. New York Philharm., 1959-60; mus. dir. Teaneck Symphony, N.J., 1961-70, L.I. Symphony, 1963-79, Scarboro Chamber Orch., N.Y., 1964-65, Joffrey Ballet, N.Y. City Center, 1966-68, 1972-79, prin. guest condr., 1968-72; artistic dir. Kneisel Hall Summer Chamber Music Sch. and Festival, 1987—(performed cycle of 32 Beethoven Sonatas 1988-90); appearances as opera condr. Curtis Inst., Teatro Petruzzelli, Bari, Italy, 1986-87; participant in chamber music Norfolk Fest., 1984-85, Marlboro Fest., 1986; recorded Stravinsky Piano Concerto with N.Y. Philharm., Grieg, Saint-Saens, Strauss sonatas with Aaron Rosand (violin), Grieg, Dohnanyi, Weiner sonatas with Oscar Shumsky (violin), Franck Sonata, Chausson Concerto with Rosand, Hindemith Sonata with Rafael Hillyer (Viola), Beethoven Sonatas op106 and 109 (solo), Schubert Works and Weber Sonatas with Arnold Steinhardt (violin); artistic dir. internat. piano festival and William Kapell competition U. Md., 1988-92. Recipient 1st prize Rachmaninoff Piano Competition, 1948. Mem. Am. Guild Mus. Artists, Am. Fedn. Musicians. Home: 420 W End Ave New York NY 10024-5708 Office: Earl Blackburn Assocs 67-26 Exeter St Forest Hills NY 11375 Address: care Louis Scott Mgmt Inc PO Box 140 Closter NJ 07624

LIPMAN, BERNARD, internist, cardiologist; b. St. Joseph, Mo., June 14, 1920; s. Harry and Sarah K. (Kross) L.; m. Leslie Joy Garber, Apr. 23, 1949; children: Lawrence Alan, Robert Bruce, Bradford Craig, William Lloyd. A.B., Washington U., 1941, M.D., 1944. Diplomate: Am. Bd. Internal Medicine, Am. Bd. Cardiology. Intern Barnes Hosp., St. Louis, Newington Hosp.-Yale Med. Sch.; resident in medicine Barnes Hosp., 1947-49; teaching fellow U. Wash. Med. Sch., 1949-50; mem. faculty Emory U. Sch. Medicine, Atlanta, 1950—; clin. prof. medicine Emory U. Sch. Medicine, 1978-83, clin. prof. emeritus, 1983—; mem. staff St. Joseph Hosp., Grady Hosp., Piedmont Hosp., Emory U. Hosp., West Paces Ferry Hosp.; dir. heart sta. St. Joseph Hosp.; co-dir. Giddings Heart Clinic. Co-author Lipman-Massie Clinical Electrocardiography, 8th edit., 1989, ECG Pocket Guide, 1987; contbr. articles to med. jours. Co-trustee Albert Steiner Found. Served to capt. M.C. AUS, 1945-47. Fellow A.C.P., Am. Coll. Cardiology (emeritus); mem. Am. Heart Assn. (mem. council clin. cardiology), Am. Fedn. Clin. Research, Am. Soc. Internal Medicine, Phi Beta Kappa, Sigma Xi, Alpha Omega Alpha. Home: 2652 Brookdale Dr NW Atlanta GA 30305-3504

LIPMAN, DAVID, multimedia company executive; b. Springfield, Mo., Feb. 13, 1931; s. Benjamin and Rose (Mack) L.; m. Marilyn Lee Vittert, Dec. 10, 1961; children: Gay Ilene, Benjamin Alan. BJ, U. Mo., 1953. Sports editor Jefferson City (Mo.) Post-Tribune, 1953, Springfield Daily News, 1953-54; gen. assignment reporter Springfield Leader and Press, 1956-57; reporter, copy editor Kansas City (Mo.) Star, 1957-60; sports reporter St. Louis Post-Dispatch, 1960-66, asst. sports editor, 1966-68, news editor, 1968-71, asst. mng. editor, 1971-78, mng. editor, 1979-92; chmn. Pulitzer 2000 Pulitzer Pub. Co., 1992—; bd. dirs. Pulitzer Charitable, RXL Pulitzer; chmn. oper. com. Ptnrs. Affiliated for Exploring Tech., 1994—; guest lectr. Am. Press Inst., Columbia Journalism Sch., 1967-70; chmn. bd. advisors U. Mo. Sch. Journalism, chmn. bd. dirs. multi-cultgural mgmt. program, 1995—; bd. dirs. New Directions for News; bd. dirs. Columbia Missourian. Author: Maybe I'll Pitch Forever, The Autobiography of LeRoy (Satchel) Paige, 1962, reissued, 1993, Mr. Baseball, The Story of Branch Rickey, 1966, Ken Boyer, 1967, Joe Namath, 1968; co-author: The Speed King, The Story of Bob Hayes, 1971, Bob Gibson Pitching Ace, 1975, Jim Hart Underrated Quarterback, 1977. Bd. dirs. Mid-Am. Press Inst., 1973—, chmn., 1975-77; trustee United Hebrew Congregation, 1975-77; chmn. com. 21st Century, U. Mo., 1993-94; vice chair Mo. Gov.'s Commn. on Info. Tech., 1994-95. 1st lt. USAF, 1954-56. Recipient Univ. Mo. Faculty and Alumni award, 1988, Univ. Mo. Disting. Svc. in Journalism award, 1989, St. Louis Jermiah award, 1991. Mem. Am. Soc. Newspaper Editors, Newspaper Assn. Am. Industry (devel. standing com. 1994—), Interactive Svcs. Assn. (bd. dirs. 1994—), Football Writers Assn. Am. (bd. dirs. 1968), Mo. Editors and Pubs. Assn. (pres. 1990-91), Mo. Soc. Newspaper Editors (bd. dirs. 1990—, vice chmn. 1992-93, chmn. 1993), Mo. Press Assn. (v.p. 1994—), AP Mng. Editors Assn., U. Mo. Sch. Journalism Nat. Alumni Assn. (chmn. 1980-83), Press Club of St. Louis (chmn. 1987-94), Sigma Delta Chi Pres. St. Louis chpt. 1976-77), Kappa Tau Alpha, Omicron Delta Kappa. Jewish. Office: Pulitzer Pub Co 900 N Tucker Blvd Saint Louis MO 63101-1069

LIPMAN, FREDERICK D., lawyer; b. Phila., Nov. 16, 1935; s. Charles S. and Beatrice (Sanderow) L.; m. Gail Heller, July 25, 1965; children—L. Keith, Darren A. AB, Temple U.; LLB, Harvard Law Sch. Bar: Pa. 1960. Sole practice, 1960-62; corp. counsel AEL Industries, Inc., Colmar, Pa., 1962-69; ptnr. Blank, Rome, Comisky & McCauley, Phila., 1972—; dir. KTI Corp., Monrovia, Calif., 1985-88; lectr. law sch. U. Pa., 1989—, law sch. Temple U., 1989—. Author: Going Public, 1994. Bd. dirs. Penjerdel, 1995, Phila. Geriatric Ctr.; pres. Phila. Ch. of Bezalel, 1989-91, audit coms., 1995. Harvard Law Sch. scholar, 1957; Temple U. scholar, 1953. Mem. Phila. Bar Assn. (bd. govs. 1985), Greater Phila. C. of C. (bd. dirs., mem. exec. com. 1980-90, chmn. tech. council 1983-85), Harvard Law Sch. Assn. Greater Phila. (pres. 1988-89). Democrat. Jewish. Lodge: Masons. Avocation: tennis. Office: Blank Rome Comisky & McCauley 4 Penn Center Plz Philadelphia PA 19103-2521

LIPMAN, IRA ACKERMAN, security service company executive; b. Little Rock, Nov. 15, 1940; s. Mark and Belle (Ackerman) L.; m. Barbara Ellen Kelly Couch, July 5, 1970; children: Gustave K., Joshua S, M Benjamin. Student, Ohio Wesleyan U., 1958-60; LLD (hon.), John Marshall U., Atlanta, 1970. Salesman, exec. Mark Lipman Svcs. Inc., Memphis, 1960-63; v.p. Guardsmark, Inc., Memphis, 1963-66; pres. Guardsmark, Inc., 1966—, chief exec. officer, 1968—, chmn. bd., 1968—; bd. dirs. Nat. Coun. Crime and Delinquency, 1975, chmn. exec. com., 1986, chmn. fin. com., treas., 1978-79, vice chmn. bd., 1982-86—, exec. com. 1976—, chmn. emeritus, 1995—; bd. dirs. Greater Memphis Coun. Crime and Delinquency, 1976-78, entrepreneurial fellow Memphis State U., 1976; mem. environ. security com., pvt. security adv. council Law Enforcement Assistance Adminstrn., 1975-76; mem. nat. conf. planning com. 2d Nat. Law Enforcement Explorer Conf., 1980; chmn. bd. dirs. Nat. Coun. Crime and Deliquency, 1993—, chmn. emeritus, 1995—. Author: How to Protect Yourself From Crime, 1975, 3d edit., 1989; contbr. numerous articles to profl. jours., mags. and newspapers. Bd. dirs. Memphis Jewish Community Center, 1974, Memphis Shelby County unit Am. Cancer Soc., 1980-81, Memphis Orches-

tral Soc., 1980-81, Memphis Jewish Fedn., 1974-83; chmn. Shelby County com. U.S. Savs. Bonds, 1976; mem. president's coun. Memphis State U., 1975-79;, mem. visual arts coun., 1980-82; Memphis met. chmn. Nat. Alliance Businessmen, 1970-71; mem. task force Reform Jewish Outreach, Union Am. Hebrew Congregations, 1979-83; mem. young leadership cabinet United Jewish Appeal, 1973-78, mem. S.E. regional campaign cabinet, 1980; exec. bd. Chickasaw council Boy Scouts Am., 1978-81; bd. dirs., exec. com. Tenn. Ind. Coll. Fund, 1979; trustee Memphis Acad. Arts, 1977-81; mem. president's club Christian Bros. Coll., 1979; bd. dirs. Future Memphis, 1980-83, 83-86; nat. trustee NCCJ, 1980-92, exec. com., 1981-92, nat. Jewish co-chmn., 1985-88, nat. chmn., 1988-92, hon. chmn., past nat. chmn. nat. conf. Christians and Jews, 1992—; bd. dirs. Memphis chpt., 1980-85, life bd. dirs. Memphis chpt. 1985—; group II chmn. for 1982 campaign United Way Greater Memphis, 1981; v.p. exec. com. Internat. Coun. Christians and Jews, 1992-94; bd. govs. United Way of Am., 1992—, bd. gov.'s liaison, 1991-92, chmn. ethics com., 1992—; mem. exec. com., 1992—, co-chmn. vol. involvement com., 1992—; mem. Alexis de Tocqueville Soc. Nat. Leadership Coun., 1992—, mem. Second Century Initiative Vol. Involvement com., 1987-91; chair Task Force on Critical Markets, 1987-91, mem. exec. cabinet, 1990-91; trustee Memphis Brooks Mus. Art, 1980-83, Yeshiva U.; trustee Simon Wiesenthal Ctr., 1982—, chmn. campaign com., 1983—, mem. fin. and audit com., 1993—; bd. dirs. Nat. Alliance against Violence, 1983-85, Nat. Ctr. Learning Disabilities, 1989-94, United Way of Greater Memphis, 1984-85, gen. campaign chmn., 1985-86; founder, bd. overseers B'nai Brith, 1980; bd. dirs. Tenn. Gov.'s Jobs for High Sch. Grads. Program, 1980-83; trustee Ohio Wesleyan U., 1988—; vice chmn. spl. task force on endowment growth Ohio Wesleyan U., 1990—; mem. bd. overseers Wharton Sch., U. Pa., 1991—; assoc. trustee U. Pa., 1991—; mem. exec. com. Am. Israel Pub. Affairs Com., 1991—;. Recipient Humanitarian of Yr. award NCCJ, 1985, Outstanding Community Sales award Sales and Mktg. Execs. Memphis, 1987, Jr. Achievement Master Free Enterprise award, 1987; one of 10 cited as Best Corp. Chief Exec. of Achievement, Gallagher Pres.'s Report, 1974. Mem. Internat. Assn. Chiefs Police, Am. Soc. Criminology, Internat. Soc. Criminology, Am. Soc. Indsl. Security (cert. protection profl.), 100 Club, B'nai B'rith, Ridgeway Country Club, Racquet Club, Summit Club, Econ. Club (bd. dirs. 1980-85, v.p. 1983-84, pres. 1984-85, chmn. exec. com. 1984-85), Internat. Club (Washington). Republican.

LIPNER, HARRY, physiologist, educator; b. N.Y.C., Aug. 26, 1922; s. Samuel and Sarah L.; m. Ethel Lapis, Nov. 11, 1949 (dec. Nov. 1979); children—Laura Jean, Sandra Lea, William F., Michael A.; m. Janet C.A. Mauney, July 10, 1981. B.S., L.I. U., 1942; M.S., U. Chgo., 1947; Ph.D., U. Iowa, 1952. Instr. Chgo. Med. Sch., 1954-55; asst. prof. physiology and endocrinology Fla. State U., Tallahassee, 1955-60; asso. prof. Fla. State U., 1960-67, 1967-89, prof. emeritus, 1990—; vis. prof. Harvard U. Med. Sch., 1969-70 mem. rev. panel regulatory biology program NSF, 1984-87. Mem. editorial bd.: Endocrinology, 1968-74; contbr. chpts. to textbooks, articles to profl. jours. NIH fellow, 1952-55; Spl. postdoctoral fellow, 1969-70; Fulbright lectr. India, 1974-75. Mem. AAAS, Am. Physiol. Soc., Endocrine Soc., Sigma Xi. Office: Fla State U Dept Biol Sci Tallahassee FL 32306

LIPNER, WILLIAM E., information systems executive; b. 1947. BSEE, U. Toledo, 1968, BBA, 1971. With Honeywell Corp., 1971-74, NFO Rsch. Inc. and predecessor cos., Greenwich, Conn., 1974—; pres, pres. NFO Rsch. Inc., Greenwich. Office: NFO Rsch Inc PO Box 315 Toledo OH 43654

LIPOWSKI, ZBIGNIEW JERZY, psychiatrist, educator; b. Warsaw, Poland, Oct. 26, 1924; emigrated to Can., 1955, naturalized, 1960; s. Jerzy Ignacy and Zofia (Szeliski) L.; m. Ingrid Thiessen, Nov. 27, 1978; children: Christopher John, Anna Christina. M.B., B.Ch., U. Coll., Dublin, 1954; Diploma in Psychiatry, McGill U., 1959; M.D. (hon.), U. Helsinki, 1981; M.A. (hon.), Dartmouth Coll., 1981. Resident in psychiatry Allan Meml. Inst., Montreal, Que., Can., 1955-58, Mass. Gen. Hosp., Boston, 1958-59; teaching fellow in psychiatry Harvard U., Boston, 1958-59; demonstrator in psychiatry McGill U., Montreal, 1959-62; lectr. McGill U., 1962-65, asst. prof., 1965-67, assoc. prof., 1967-71; dir. psychiat. cons. service Royal Victoria Hosp., Montreal, 1959-71; prof. psychiatry Dartmouth Med. Sch., Hanover, N.H., 1971-83; prof. psychiatry U. Toronto, Ont., Can., 1983-90, prof. emeritus psychiatry, 1990—; cons. psychiatrist Montreal Neurol. Inst., 1968-71; vis. prof. psychiatry Med. U. S.C., Charleston, 1977-78. Author: Delirium: Acute Brain Failure in Man, 1980, Psychosomatic Medicine and Liaison Psychiatry. Selected Papers, 1985, Delirium: Acute Confusional States, 1990; mem. editorial bd.: Gen. Hosp. Psychiatry, 1978—, Jour. Psychosomatic Research, 1981—; Advances in Psychosomatic Medicine, 1968— ; editor: Psychosocial Aspects of Physical Illness, 1973, (with D.R. Lipsitt and P.C. Whybrow) Psychosomatic Medicine: Current Trends and Clinical Applications, 1977, (with E. Kurstak and P.V. Morozov) Viruses, Immunity and Mental Disorders, 1987; contbr. numerous articles to profl. jours. Recipient Lapinlahti medal Finland, 1980; Mona Shenkman Bronfman fellow, 1958-59. Fellow Royal Coll. Physicians Can., Am. Psychiatric Assn. (life, task force on nomenclature 1975-79, Spl. Presdl. Commendation 1987), Acad. Psychosomatic Medicine; mem. Am. Psychosomatic Soc., Polish Inst. Arts and Scis. in Am. Office: 170 St George St, Toronto, ON Canada M5R 2M8

LIPP, ROBERT I., bank holding company executive; b. 1938; married. Grad., Williams Coll.; grad. in bus., Harvard U.; JD, NYU, 1969. With Chem. Bank, N.Y.C., 1963-86, sr. trainee, 1963-65, office asst. control div., 1965-66, asst. controller, 1966-67, asst. v.p. corp. planning, 1967-69, corp. sr. v.p., dep. head ops., 1972-74, exec. v.p., head ops. div., 1974-77, exec. v.p., head met. div., 1977-79, corp. sr. exec. v.p., head met. div., 1979, sr. exec. v.p., 1979-83, pres., 1983-86; v.p. corp. planning, treas. Chem. N.Y. Corp., 1969-70, dep. mgr ops. div., 1970-72; exec. v.p. for consumer fin. services group Comml. Credit Co., Balt., 1986-89, chmn. consumer fin. svcs., 1989—; exec. v.p. consumer fin. Primerica Corp. (parent co.), N.Y.C., 1988—; bd. dirs. Greater N.Y. Fund; mem. mgmt. team Comml. Credit Corp., San Antonio. Trustee Jackie Robinson Found. Office: The Phoenix Ins Co 1 Tower Sq Hartford CT 06183

LIPPARD, STEPHEN JAMES, chemist, educator; b. Pittsburgh, Pa., Oct. 12, 1940; s. Alvin I. and Ruth (Green) L.; m. Judith Ann Drezner, Aug. 16, 1964; children: Andrew (dec.), Joshua, Alexander. BA, Haverford Coll. 1962; PhD, MIT, 1965. Postdoctoral research fellow chemistry MIT, Cambridge, 1965-66, prof. chemistry, 1983-89, Arthur Amos Noyes prof. chemistry, 1989—; asst. prof. chemistry Columbia U. N.Y.C., 1966-69; asso. prof. Columbia U., 1969-72, prof., 1972-82; dept. head MIT, Cambridge, 1995—; mem. study sect. medicinal chemistry NIH, 1973-77. Editor: Progress in Inorganic Chemistry, 1967-92; mem. editorial bd. Inorganic Chemistry, 1981-83, 89-91, assoc. editor, 1983-88; mem. editorial bd. Account Chem. Res., 1986-88; contbr. articles to profl. jours. Coach Demarest Borough Soccer Team, 1975-82, league adminstr., 1979-82. NSF fellow, 1962-66; Alfred P. Sloan fellow, 1968-70; Guggenheim fellow, 1972; recipient Tchr.-Scholar award Camille and Henry Dreyfus Found., 1971-76, Henry J. Albert award Internat. Precious Metals Inst., 1985, Alexander von Humboldt U.S. Sr. Scientist award, 1988; sr. internat. fellow John E. Fogarty Internat. Center, 1979. Fellow AAAS; mem. NAS, Am. Acad. Arts and Sci., Nat. Inst. Medicine, Am. Chem. Soc. (chmn. bioinorganic subdiv. 1987-88, Inorganic Chemistry award 1987, Remson award 1987, Mallinckrodt Disting. Svc. award 1994, Nichol's medal 1995, assoc. editor jour. 1989—, chmn. inorganic div., chmn. 1992), Am. Crystallographic Assn., Am. Soc. Biol. Chemists, Nat. Inst. Medicine, Chem. Soc. (London), Biophys. Soc., Phi Beta Kappa. Home: 450 Memorial Dr Cambridge MA 02139-4306 Office: MIT 77 Massachusetts Ave Cambridge MA 02139-3594

LIPPE, MELVIN KARL, lawyer; b. Chgo., Oct. 21, 1933; s. Melvin M. and Myrtle (Karlsberg) L.; children: Suzanne, Michael S., Deanna; m. Sandra M. Bauer, Jan. 5, 1974. B.S., Northwestern U., 1955, J.D., 1958; grad. cert., Grad. Sch. Banking, U. Wis., 1965; cert., Sr. Bank Officers Seminar, Harvard U., 1966. Bar: Ill. 1958. C.P.A. Assoc. D'Ancona, Pflaum, Wyatt & Riskind, Chgo., 1958-61; asst. to chmn. bd. Exchange Nat. Bank of Chgo., 1961-62, asst. v.p., 1962-64, v.p., 1964-66, sr. v.p., asst. to bd. dirs., 1966-69, exec. v.p. dir., 1969-74, vice chmn. bd., 1974-76, also dir.; dir. Am.-Israel Bank, Ltd., 1974-76; ptnr. Antonow & Fink, Chgo., 1977-88, Altheimer and Gray, Chgo., 1988—; instr. Ill. Inst. Tech., 1960-63. Bd. dirs. Jewish Cmty. Ctrs. Chgo., 1972—, pres.; 1980-82; bd. dirs. Chgo. chpt. Am. Jewish Com.,

1974-78; life bd. dirs. Jewish Coun. for Youth Svcs., Chgo., pres., 1971; bd. dirs. Family Focus, 1992—. With Ill. N.G., 1959. Mem. Am., Ill., Chgo. bar assns., Am. Jewish Com., Phi Epsilon Pi, Beta Gamma Sigma. Jewish. Club: Standard (Chgo.). Office: Altheimer & Gray 10 S Wacker Dr Chicago IL 60606-7407

LIPPE, PHILIPP MARIA, neurosurgeon, educator; b. Vienna, Austria, May 17, 1929; s. Philipp and Maria (Goth) L.; came to U.S., 1938, naturalized, 1945; m. Virginia M. Wiltgen, 1953 (div. 1977); children: Patricia Ann Marie, Philip Eric Andrew, Laura Lynne Elizabeth, Kenneth Anthony Ernst; m. Gail B. Busch, Nov. 26, 1977. Student Loyola U., Chgo., 1947-50; BS in Medicine, U. Ill. Coll. Medicine, 1952, MD with high honors, 1954. Rotating intern St. Francis Hosp., Evanston, Ill., 1954-55; asst. resident gen. surgery VA Hosp., Hines, Ill., 1955, 58-59; asst. resident neurology and neurol. surgery Neuropsychiat. Inst., U. Ill. Rsch. and Ednl. Hosps., Chgo., 1959-60, chief resident, 1962-63, resident neuropathology, 1962, postgrad. trainee in electroencephalography, 1963; resident neurology and neurol. surgery Presbyn.-St. Luke's Hosp., Chgo., 1960-61; practice medicine, specializing in neurol. surgery, San Jose, Calif., 1963—; instr. neurology and neurol. surgery U. Ill., 1962-63; clin. instr. surgery and neurosurgery Stanford U., 1965-69, clin. asst. prof., 1969-74, clin. assoc. prof., 1974—; staff cons. in neurosurgery O'Connor Hosp., Santa Clara Valley Med. Ctr., San Jose Hosp., Los Gatos Cmty. Hosp., El Camino Hosp. (all San Jose area); chmn. divsn. neurosugery Good Samaritan Hosp., 1989—; founder, exec. dir. Bay Area Pain Rehab. Center, San Jose, 1979—; clin. advisor to Joint Commn. on Accreditation of Hosps.; mem. dist. med. quality rev. com. Calif. Bd. Med. Quality Assurance, 1976-87, chmn., 1976-77. Served to capt. USAF, 1956-58. Diplomate: Am. Bd. Neurol. Surgery, Nat. Bd. Med. Examiners. Fellow ACS, Am. Coll. Pain Medicine (pres. 1992-93, bd. dirs. 1991-94, v.p. 1991-92, pres. 1992-93, exec. v.p. 1994—); mem. AMA (Ho. of Dels. 1981—), Am. Coll. Physician Execs., Calif. Med. Assn. (Ho. of Dels. 1976-80, sci. bd. council 1979-87, sec. 1981-87, Outstanding Svc. award 1987), Santa Clara County Med. Soc. (coun. 1974-81, pres. 1978-79, Outstanding Contbn. award 1984, Benjamin J. Cory award 1987), Chgo. Med. Soc., Congress Neurol. Surgeons, Calif. Assn. Neurol. Surgeons (dir. 1974-82, v.p. 1975-76, pres. 1977-79), San Jose Surg. Soc., Am. Assn. Neurol. Surgeons (chm. sect. on pain 1987-90, dir. 1985-87, 87-90, Disting. Svc. award 1986, 90), Western Neurol. Soc., San Francisco Neurol. Soc., Santa Clara Valley Profl. Standards Rev. Orgn. (dir., v.p., dir. quality assurance 1975-83), Fedn. Western Scis. Neurol. Sci., Internat. Assn. for Study Pain, Am. Pain Soc. (founding mem.), Am. Acad. Pain Medicine (sec. 1983-86, pres. 1987-88, Philipp M. Lippe Disting. Svc. award, 1995), Am. Coll. Pain Medicine (bd. dir. 1991-94, v.p., 1991-92, pres. 1992-93), Am. Bd. Pain Medicine (exec. v.p., 1994—), Alpha Omega Alpha, Phi Kappa Phi. Assoc. editor Clin. Jour. of Pain; contbr. articles to profl. jours. Pioneered med. application centrifugal force using flight simulator. Office: 2100 Forest Ave Ste 106 San Jose CA 95128-1496

LIPPERT, ROBERT J., administrator and culinary arts educator, consultant; b. Alma, Mich., May 17, 1932; s. Ackley William Matthew and Myrtle (Boddy) L.; m. Marie Alphonsine Mantei, Apr. 2, 1956; children: Robert Jr., Jeffrey Paul, Mark Edward. BS, Ctrl. Mich. U., 1959, MA, 1965, EdS, 1977. Exec. chef Mt. Pleasant (Mich.) Country Club, 1983-86, Riverwood Golf Course, Mt. Pleasant, 1986-90, The Embers, Inc., Mt. Pleasant, 1957-67; instr. Mt. Pleasant Pub. Schs., 1959-67; dir./ culinary arts instr. Mt. Pleasant Tech. Ctr., 1968—; exec. banquet chef The Embers, Inc., 1967—; pres. Lippert Consulting and Svc. Mt. Pleasant, 1983—. Writer, editor, dir. TV program Ask The Chef, 1989-90; contbr. articles to profl. jours. Active ch. fund raisers, Mt. Pleasant, 1973—, State Spl. Olympics, 1982-87; chef banquets for sr. citizens. With USN, 1951-54, Korea. Mem. Internat. Food Svc. Execs. Assn., Am. Acad. Chefs (Svc. award 1990), Am. Culinary Fedn. (Ctrl. Regional Profl. Chef award 1990), Capitol Profl. Chefs (pres. 1985-89, chmn. of bd. 1990-91, Chef of Yr. award 1987), Food Svc. Tchrs. (pres. 1980, 81, 84, bd. dirs. 1979-89), Golden Toque, Mich. Restaurant Assn. (bd. dirs. 1980, 81, 82, 84, 85, 93, Food Tchr. of Yr. award 1981), Mich. Occupational Edn. Assn. (bd. dirs. 1980-87, Vocat. Tchr. of Yr. award 1986), Mich. Chefs (Jefferson medal 1986). Roman Catholic. Home: 1214 Glenwood Dr Mount Pleasant MI 48858-4328 Office: Mt Pleasant Area Tech Ctr 1155 S Elizabeth St Mount Pleasant MI 48858-3911

LIPPERT, ROBERT LAWRENCE, social services administrator; b. Detroit, Mar. 28, 1935; s. Lawrence and Isabel (Forman) L.; 1 child, David Alan. AB, San Francisco State, 1957; AM, U. Chgo., 1960. Lic. clin. social worker ACSW. Exec. dir. Boys and Girls Aid Soc., Spring Valley, Calif.; adminstr. Village of Childhelp, Beaumont, Calif. Mem. Am. Orthopsychiat. Assn., Am. Assn. Children's Residential Ctrs., NASW. Home: PO Box 1960 Idyllwild CA 92549-1960 Office: Village of Childhelp PO Box 247 14700 Manzanita Park Rd Beaumont CA 92223

LIPPES, GERALD SANFORD, lawyer, business executive; b. Buffalo, Mar. 23, 1940; s. Thomas and Ruth (Landsman) L.; m. Sandra Franger; children: Tracy E., David S., Adam F. Student, U. Mich., 1958-61; JD, U. Buffalo, 1964. Bar: N.Y. 1964. Sr. ptnr. Lippes, Silverstein, Mathias & Wexler, Buffalo, 1964—; sec., dir., gen. counsel Mark IV, Industries, Inc., Amherst, N.Y., 1969—; chmn. Del. Photographic Products, Buffalo, 1970-88, Ingram Software, Buffalo, 1982-86, Abels Bagels, Inc., Buffalo, 1972-75; bd. dirs. Mark IV Industries, Inc., Amherst, N.Y., Gilbraltar Steel Corp., Buffalo, Upgrade Corp. of Am., Buffalo, Carton-Craft Corp., Buffalo, Nat. Health Care Affiliates, Inc., Buffalo, Niagara Envelope. Bd. dirs. Buffalo Fine Arts Acad. Ctr. for Entrepreneurial Leadership SUNY, Children's Hosp. of Buffalo, vice-chmn.; bd. dirs. Greater Buffalo Partnership, Roswell Park Meml. Inst., Buffalo, Downtown Med. Ctr., Inc., Buffalo; chmn. U. Buffalo Law Sch., Found. Jewish Philanthropies, Inc., U. at Buffalo Found. Recipient Disting. Alumni award U. Buffalo Law Sch.; named Entrepreneur of Yr., 1993. Mem. N.Y. State Bar Assn., Erie County Bar Assn., Am. Soc. Corp. Secs. Office: Lippes Silverstein Mathias & Wexler 28 Church St Buffalo NY 14202

LIPPINCOTT, JAMES ANDREW, biochemistry and biological sciences educator; b. Cumberland County, Ill., Sept. 13, 1930; s. Marion Andrew and Esther Oral (Meeker) L.; m. Barbara Sue Barnes, June 2, 1956; children—Jeanne Marie, Thomas Russell, John James. A.B., Earlham Coll., 1954; A.M., Washington U., St. Louis, 1956, Ph.D., 1958. Lectr. botany Washington U., 1958-59; Jane Coffin Childs Meml. fellow Centre Nat. de la Recherche Scientifique, France, 1959-60; asst. prof. biol. scis. Northwestern U., Evanston, Ill., 1960-66; assoc. prof. Northwestern U., 1966-73, prof., 1973-81, prof. biochemistry, molecular biology and cell biology, 1981-93; prof. emeritus Northwestern U., Evanston, Ill., 1994—; assoc. dean biol. scis. Northwestern U., 1980-83. Contbr. articles to profl. jours. Grantee NIH, NSF, Am. Cancer Soc., USDA. Mem. Am. Soc. Biol. Chemists, Am. Soc. Plant Physiologists, Bot. Soc. Am., Am. Soc. Microbiology. Office: Dept Biochem Molecular Biol & Cell Biol Northwestern University Evanston IL 60208

LIPPINCOTT, JOSEPH P., photojournalist, educator; b. Somerset, Pa., Mar. 12, 1940; s. Joseph Britton and Louise Frances (Picking) L.; widowed; children: Douglas B., David S. BA in Journalism, U. Iowa, 1968. Staff photographer The Miami (Fla.) Herald, 1964-67; pub. rels. dir. Lock Haven (Pa.) State Coll., 1967-68; mag. editor Caterpillar Tractor Co., Peoria, Ill., 1968-69; photo editor, photographer The Detroit Free Press, 1969-75; photo advisor The State News Mich. State U., East Lansing, 1975-84; instr. Lansing C.C., 1977-84; photo editor The Detroit News, 1984-87, The Patriot Ledger, Quincy, Mass., 1988—; lectr. Boston U., 1990—. Author: An Introduction to Camera Maintenance, 1980. Mem. Nat. Press Photographers Assn. (chmn. nat. portfolio critique 1994—, Pictures of the Yr. awards), Boston Press Photographers Assn. Avocation: unique photographic equipment. Home: 148 Old Colony Ave # 291 Quincy MA 02170-3897 Office: The Patriot Ledger 400 Crown Colony Dr Quincy MA 02169-0930

LIPPINCOTT, PHILIP EDWARD, retired paper products company executive; b. Camden, N.J., Nov. 28, 1935; s. J. Edward and Marjorie Nix (Spooner) L.; m. Naomi Catherine Prindle, Aug. 22, 1959; children: Grant, Kevin, Kerry. BA, Dartmouth Coll., 1957; MBA with distinction, Mich. State U., 1964. With Scott Paper Co., Phila., 1959-94, staff v.p. corp. planning, 1971, div. v.p., consumer products mktg., 1971-72, corp. v.p., mktg., 1972-75, sr. v.p., mktg., 1975-77, v.p., group exec. packaged products div., 1977, dir., 1978-94, pres., COO, 1980-94, chief exec. officer, 1982-94, chmn., 1983-94; ret., 1994; bd. dirs. Campbell Soup Co., Exxon Corp., The Bus. Coun.; trustee Penn Mut. Life Ins. Co. Bd. overseers Wharton Sch. U. Pa., Dartmouth Inst.; bd. dirs. Fox Chase Cancer Ctr., Phila. Capt. U.S. Army, 1957-59. Mem. Riverton Country Club, Pine Valley Country Club, Stone Harbor Country Club, Kappa Kappa Kappa, Pi Sigma Epsilon, Beta Gamma Sigma. Mem. Society of Friends.

LIPPINCOTT, SARAH LEE, astronomer, graphologist; b. Phila., Oct. 26, 1920; d. George E. and Sarah (Evans) L.; m. Dave Garroway. Student, Swarthmore Coll., 1938-39, M.A., 1950; B.A., U. Pa., 1942; D.Sc. (hon.), Villanova U., 1973. Research asst. Sproul Obs., Swarthmore (Pa.) Coll., 1941-50, research asso., 1951-72, dir., 1972-81, prof., 1977-81, prof. and dir. emeritus, 1981—, research astronomer, 1981—; vis. assoc. in astronomy Calif. Inst. Tech., 1977. Author: (with Joseph M. Joseph) Point to the Stars, 1963, 3d edit., 1977, (with Laurence Lafore) Philadelphia, the Unexpected City, 1965; contbr. articles to profl. jours. Mem. Savoy Opera Co., Phila., 1947—; bd. mgrs. Societe de Bienfaisance de Philadelphie, 1966-69. Recipient achievement award Kappa Kappa Gamma, 1966; Disting. Daus. of Pa. award, 1976; Fulbright fellow Paris, 1953-54; Jessie Kovalenko scholar, 1953-54. Mem. Am. Soc. Profl. Graphologists (treas. 1988-93), Rittenhouse Astron. Soc. (sec. 1946-48), Am. Astron. Soc. (lectr. 1961-84), Internat. Astron. Union (v.p. commn. 26 1970-73, pres. 1971-73), Disting. Daus. Pa. (sec. 1988—). Home: 306 Bell Rd Cinnaminson NJ 08770

LIPPINCOTT, WALTER HEULINGS, JR., publishing executive; b. Phila., Jan. 16, 1939; s. Walter Heulings and Helen B. (Howe) L.; m. Caroline Seebohm, June 8, 1974 (div. June 1993); children: Sophie, Hugh. A.B., Princeton U., 1960. With Morgan Guaranty Trust Co., N.Y.C., 1960-63; coll. traveler Harper & Row Pubs., 1963-65, editor, 1965-70, editor-in-chief, coll. dept., 1970-74; editorial dir. Cambridge Univ. Press, N.Y.C., 1974-81; assoc. dir. Cornell Univ. Press, 1982, dir., 1983-86; dir. Princeton U. Press, N.J., 1986—. Club: Knickerbocker (N.Y.C.). Home: 1 River Knoll Dr Titusville NJ 08560-1308 Office: Princeton U Press 41 William St Princeton NJ 08540-5237

LIPPMAN, BARRY, publishing executive; b. N.Y.C., Sept. 9, 1949; s. Mark and Edythe Lippman. BA in English, SUNY, Buffalo, 1971; MFA, U. Montana, 1973. Editorial asst. New Am. Libr., N.Y.C., 1973-74, editor, 1974-78; sr. editor Doubleday & Co., N.Y.C., 1978-81; gen. mgr. paperbacks Little, Brown & Co., Boston, 1981-83; v.p., pub. Collier Books, Macmillan Pub. Co., N.Y.C. 1983-85, Macmillan & Collier Books, N.Y.C., 1985-87; pres., pub. adult trade amd trade sales divsn. Macmillan Pub. Co., 1988-93, acting pres., 1993—; chmn. bd. dirs. Keter Puub. Co., Israel, 1989-92. Named LMP Person of Yr., 1993. Mem. Assn. Am. Pubs. (exec. com.), Internat. Freedom to Publish Com.

LIPPMAN, MARC ESTES, pharmacology educator; b. Bklyn., Jan. 15, 1945. BA, Cornell U., 1964; MD, Yale U., 1968. Intern Osler med. svc. Johns Hopkins Hosp., Balt., 1968-69, asst. resident, 1969-70; clin. assoc. leukemia svc. Nat. Cancer Inst., NIH, Washington, 1970-71, clin. assoc. lab. biochemistry, 1971-73, sr. investigator med. br., 1974-88, head med. breast cancer sect., 1976-88; clin. prof. medicine & pharmacology, uniformed svc. U. Health Sci., 1978—; dir. Vincent T. Lombardi Cancer Ctr. Georgetown U., Washington, 1988—, prof. medicine & pharmacology, 1988—; mem. merit rev. bd. oncology Vet. Adminstrn. Med. Rsch. Svc., 1977-81, endocrine treatment com. Nat. Surg. Adjuvant Breast Project, 1977-86; cons. dept. pharmacology George Washington Sch. Medicine, 1978-89; co-chmn. Gordon Rsch. Conf. on Hormone Action, 1984, chmn., 1985; treas. Internat. Congress Hormones & Cancer, 1984—; mem. med. adv. bd. Nat. Alliance Breast Cancer Orgn., 1986—; mem. stage III monitoring com. Nat. Surg. Adjuvant Project Breast & Bowel Cancers, 1987-89; bd. trustees Am. Cancer Soc., Washington, 1989-92; mem. sci. adv. bd. Coordinated Coun. Cancer Rsch., 1989—; hon. dir. Y-ME, Nat. Orgn. Breast Cancer Info. & Support, 1990—; Woodward vis. prof., mem. Sloan-Kettering, 1990; Sidney Sachs Meml. lectr. Case Western Reserve, 1985, D.R. Edwards lectr. Tenovus Inst., Wales, 1985, Gosse lectr. Dalhousie U., Halifax, N.S., 1987, Transatlantic lectr. Brit. Endocrine Socs., 1989, Barofsky lectr. Howard U., 1990, Rose Kushner Meml. lectr. Long Beach Meml. Med. Ctr., 1990, Constance Wood Meml. lectr. Hammersmith Hosp., Eng., 1991. Endocrinology fellow Yale Med. Sch., 1973-74; recipient Mallinckrodt award Clin. Radioassay Soc., 1978, D.R. Edwards medal Tenovus Inst., 1985, Transatlantic medal Brit. Endocrine Socs., 1989, Tiffany award of Distinction, Komen Found., 1989. Fellow ACP, Am. Fedn. Clin. Rsch., Am. Soc. Cell Biology, Am. Assn. Cancer Rsch. (program com. 1986), Am. Soc. Clin. Oncology (program com. 1987-89, chmn. local organizing com. 1989-90), Endocrine Soc. (pub. affairs com. 1980-81, Edward B. Astwood lecture award 1991), Metastasis Rsch. Soc.; mem. Assn. Am. Physicians, Am. Soc. Clin. Investigators (program com. 1988), Am. Soc. Biol. Chemists. Achievements include research in growth regulation of cancer, breast cancer, cancer endocrinology, growth factor receptors. Office: Georgetown U Med Ctr Vincent T Lombardi Cancer Ctr 3800 Reservoir Rd NW Washington DC 20007*

LIPPMAN, SHARON ROCHELLE, cultural organization educator, director; b. N.Y.C., Apr. 9, 1950; d. Emanuel and Sara (Goldberg) L. Student, Mills Coll., 1968; BFA, New Sch. Social Rsch., 1970, CCNY, 1972; MA, NYU, 1976. Cert. secondary tchr., N.Y. Instr., dir. Sara Sch. of Creative Art, Sayville, N.Y., 1976-85; exec. dir., tchr Art Without Walls, Inc., Sayville and N.Y.C., 1985—. Author: Patterns, 1968, College Poetry Press Anthology, 1970; contbr. articles to profl. jours. Vol. Schneider Children's Hosp., New Hyde Park, N.Y., 1992, New Light-AIDS Patients, Smithtown, N.Y., 1993, Helen Keller Svcs. for the Blind, Hempstead, N.Y., 1993-94. Recipient Suffolk County News Inspiration award, 1990, Am. Artist Art Svc. award Am. Artists mag., 1993, Suffolk County Legislature proclamation, 1993, Newsday Leadership Vol. award Newsday newspaper, 1994. Mem. Orgn. Through Rehab. and Tng., Coll. Art Assn., Met. Mus. Art, Mus. Modern Art Univ. Film Assn. Avocations: fine art, books, cinema, political science, inventions. Office: Art Without Walls Inc PO Box 341 Sayville NY 11782

LIPPMAN, WILLIAM JENNINGS, investment company executive; b. N.Y.C., Feb. 13, 1925; s. Henry J. and Fanny (Schapira) L.; m. Doris Kaplan, July 11, 1948; children—Howard Mark, Deborah Ellen. B.B.A. cum laude, City N.Y., 1947; M.B.A., N.Y.U., 1957. Marketing mgr. Pavelle Color, Inc., N.Y.C., 1947-50; sales mgr. Terminal Home Sales Corp., N.Y.C., 1950-55; div. mgr. King Merritt & Co., Inc., Englewood, N.J., 1955-60; pres., dir. Pilgrim Distbrs. Inc., Ft. Lee, N.J., 1960-86; pres. L.F. Rothschild Managed Trust L.F. Rothschild Fund Mgmt. Inc., N.Y.C., 1986-88, also dir.; pres. Franklin Managed Trust, New York, 1988—; mem. faculty Fairleigh Dickinson U. Sch. Bus. Adminstrn., 1957-69; bd. govs. Investment Co. Inst. Contbg. author: Investment Dealer Digest. Mem. Nat. Assn. Securities Dealers (investment cos. com.). Home: 18 Daniel Dr Englewood NJ 07631-3736 Office: Franklin Managed Trust 1 Parker Plz Fort Lee NJ 07024-2937

LIPPOLD, RICHARD, sculptor; b. Milw., May 3, 1915; s. Adolph and Elsa (Schmidt) L.; m. Louise Greuel, Aug. 24, 1940; children—Lisa, Tiana, Ero. Student, U. Chgo., 1934-37; B.F.A., Art Inst. Chgo., 1937; D.F.A. (hon.), Ripon Coll., 1968. Tchr. Layton Sch. Art, Milw., 1940-41, U. Mich., 1941-44, Goddard Coll., 1945-47; head art sect. Trenton (N.J.) Jr. Coll., 1948-52; prof. Hunter Coll., N.Y.C., 1952-67. Works exhibited Inst. Arts, Detroit, 1946-47, St. Louis City Mus., 1946, Toronto (Ont.) Mus., 1947, Whitney Mus., N.Y.C., 1947, 49, 51-53, 76, Calif. Palace Legion of Honor, San Francisco, 1948, Fundacao de Arte Moderne, Sao Paulo, Brazil, 1948, Mus. Modern Art, N.Y.C., 1951-53, 63, Tate Gallery, London, 1953, Musée d'Art Moderne, Paris, 1955, Nat. Collection Fine Arts, Washington, 1976, Nat. Air and Space Mus., Washington, 1976, Biennale, Venice, 1988; one-man show Willard Gallery, N.Y.C., 1947-48, 50, 53, 62, 68, 73, Arts Club, Chgo., Layton Art Gallery, Milw., 1953, Haggerty Mus., Milw. 1990; represented in collections Addison Gallery Am. Art, Andover, Mass., Fogg Mus., Harvard U., Wadsworth Atheneum, Hartford, Mus. Modern Art, Whitney Mus., N.Y.C., Newark Mus., Met. Mus. Art, N.Y.C., Detroit Art Inst., Des Moines Art Inst., Brooks Gallery, Memphis, Mobile (Ala.) Art Mus., Musée de Vin, Pavillac, France, Munson-Williams-Proctor Inst., Utica, N.Y., Va. Mus. Fine Arts, Milw. Art Center, Yale U. Art Gallery, others,

also pvt. collections, U.S. and Europe; commns. include Harvard U., 1950, Inland Steel Bldg, Chgo., 1958, Four Seasons Restaurant, Seagram Bldg., N.Y.C., 1959, Stage Set, Spoleto, Italy, 1959; Portsmouth (R.I.) Priory Ch. 1960, Pan Am Bldg., N.Y.C., 1961, Avery Fisher Hall, Lincoln Center, N.Y.C., 1961, Jesse Jones Hall, Houston, 1965, St. Mary's Cathedral, San Francisco, 1967, Christian Sci. Center, Boston, 1974, Hyatt Regency Atlanta, 1975, Fairlane Plaza, Dearborn, Mich., 1975; 115 foot stainless steel sculpture on mall in front, Air and Space Mus., Washington, 1976; King's Retiring Room, Riyadh, Saudi Arabia, 1977, Columbia (S.C.) Mall, 1977, Kish Island, Iran, 1978, Hyatt Regency, Milw., 1980, Shiga Sacred Garden, Kyoto, Japan, 1981; 250 foot sculpture Park Ave Atrium Bldg., N.Y.C., 1981, One Fin. Ctr., Boston, 1984, Deutsche Bank, Frankfurt, W. Ger., 1985, First Interstate Bank, Seattle, 1985, Sohio Hdqrs., Cleve., 1986, 200 foot high outdoor sculpture, Seoul, South Korea, 1986, Atrium Sculpture for Crystal City, Va., 1986, Marina Square, Singapore, 1986, Orange County Ctr. for Performing Arts, Costa Mesa, Calif., 1987, Atrium Sculpture and Tapestry, Alexandria, Va., 1988, Atrium Sculpture, San Diego, 1990, 95, Haggerty Mus. Retrospective, Marquette U., Milw., 1991, Montrone Residence, La Jolla, 1992, Conv. Ctr., Charlotte, N.C., 1995. Recipient 3d prize Internat. Sculpture Competition, Inst. Contemporary Arts, London, 1953, Creative Arts award Brandeis U., 1958, Silver medal Archtl. League N.Y., 1960, Honor award Mcpl. Art Soc. N.Y., 1963, Fine Arts medal AIA, 1970. Mem. Nat. Inst. Arts and Letters (v.p. 1966). Address: PO Box 248 Locust Valley NY 11560-0248

LIPPS, JERE HENRY, paleontology educator; b. L.A., Aug. 28, 1939; s. Henry John and Margaret (Rosaltha) L.; m. Karen Elizabeth Loeblich, June 25, 1964 (div. 1971); m. Susannah McClintock, Sept. 28, 1973; children: Jeremy Christian, Jamison William. BA, UCLA, 1962, PhD, 1966. Asst. prof. U. Calif., Davis, 1967-70, assoc. prof., 1970-75, prof., 1975-88; prof. U. Calif., Berkeley, 1988—, prof. paleontology, 1988-89, prof. integrative biology, 1989—; dir. Mus. Paleontology, Berkeley, 1989—; dir. Inst. Ecology, U. Calif., Davis, 1972-73, chmn. dept. geology, 1971-72, 78-84, chmn. dept. integrative biology, Berkeley, 1991-94. Contbr. articles to sci. pubs. Fellow, dir. Cushman Found. Recipient U.S. Antarctic medal NSF, 1975; Lipps Island, Antarctica named in his honor, 1979. Fellow AAAS, Calif. Acad. Scis., Geol. Soc. Am., Cushman Found. Avocation: scuba diving. Office: Mus Paleontology U Calif 1101 Valley Life Scis Bldg Berkeley CA 94720

LIPPWE, ESIKIEL, broadcast specialist; b. Namoluk Island, Chuuk State, Dec. 12, 1936; m. Marigita C. Billy Lippwe, Aug. 3, 1957; children: Jacinta, Lucia, Amy, Bendery, Brenda, Rosalinda, Joeverly. Observer U.S. Weather Bur., 1958-62; program and news dir., broadcast mgr., announcer KVZA, 1959-62; from radio announcer to broadcast mgr. Truk Dist. Govt. Broadcast Sta., 1962-73; with Trust Territory Hdqrs., Saipan, Mariana Islands, 1973-80; broadcast officer Federated States Micronesia Nat. Govt., Ponape, broadcast adminstr., broadcast specialist; liaison with outside TV and radio as well as tng. instns., brief radio, TV and newspaper journalists; Trust Territory of Pacific Islands rep. to broadcasting unions. Bd. dirs. Pohnpei Cath. Sch.; mem. HIV Task Force, Ponape; mem. Namoluk Island Constl. Conv., 1991-92, Election Bd. Chuuk State, Pres. Inauguration Com. Mem. Pacific Islands Assn. of Libr. and Archives (planning com.), Chuukese Govt. Employees Assn. (pres.), Pacific Islands News Assn. (founder), Pacific Islands Broadcasting Assn. (founder, vice chmn.), Nat. Geog. Soc. (forum planning com.), PEACESTAT Satellite Conf. (chmn.). Roman Catholic. Avocations: fishing, playing music, reading, swimming. Home: Box 144, Pohnpei 96941, FM Office: Fed States of Micronesia Pub Info PO Box PS34 Palikir Ponape FM 96941

LIPSCHUTZ, ILSE HEMPEL, French and Franco-Spanish relations, painting and literature educator; b. Boennigheim, Wurttemberg, Germany, Aug. 19, 1923; came to U.S., 1946; d. Joseph Martin Paul and Fanny (Würzburger) Hempel; m. Lewis D. Lipschutz, Feb. 6, 1952; children: Elizabeth, Marion, Marc Hempel, Margaret Hempel. Diplôme Institut des Professeurs de Français à l'Etranger, Sorbonne U., Paris, 1942, Licence ès Lettres, 1943, Diplôme d'Etudes Supérieures Lettres, 1944; Diploma de Estudios Hispánicos, U. Complutense, Madrid, 1945; MA, Harvard U., 1949, PhD, 1958. Teaching fellow Radcliffe Coll. Harvard U., 1947-50; instr. Vassar Coll., Poughkeepsie, N.Y., 1951-58, asst. prof., 1958-63, assoc. prof., 1963-72, prof., 1972-92, Andrew W. Mellon prof. Humanities, 1981-92; prof. emerita Vassar Coll., 1992—, chair dept., 1975-82; cons. collaborator Spanish Ministry of Culture, Madrid, 1979; lectr. Frick Collection, N.Y.C., 1976, Prado Mus., Madrid, 1983, Met. Mus., N.Y.C., 1989, Universidad Internacional Menéndez Pelayo, Santander, Spain, 1990, Fundación Ramón Areces, Madrid, 1991; vis. prof. U. Complutense, Madrid, 1990; invited mem. Centre de Recherche sur les Origines de l'Espagne Contemporaine, Sorbonne, U. Paris, 1992. Author: Spanish Painting and the French Romantics, 1972, rev. Spanish edit., 1988, (with others) La Imagen romántica de España, 1981, Goya, nuevas visiones, 1987, Viajeros románticos a Andalucía, 1987; contbr. articles to profl. jours. Spanish Govt. fellow U. Madrid, 1945; N.Y. state fellow AAUW, 1950-51; Ann Radcliffe fellow Radcliffe Coll.-Harvard U., 1950-51; faculty fellow Vassar Coll., 1960-61, 67-68; research scholar U.S.-Spain Commn. on Edn., 1979-80; Sr. research fellow Fulbright-Hays Commn., 1983-84 (nat. fellowship com. 1972-75, 84-87); chevalier Palmes Académiques, 1984. Mem. AAUP, AAUW (nat. fellowship com. 1961-67), Soc. Théophile Gautier (bd. dirs. 1986—), Soc. Etudes Romantiques, Am. Soc. for Hispanic Art Studies, Am. Soc. for Spanish & Portuguese Hist. Studies. Home: 11 Park Ave Poughkeepsie NY 12603-3101 Office: Vassar College PO Box 394 Poughkeepsie NY 12601

LIPSCHUTZ, MICHAEL ELAZAR, chemistry educator, consultant, researcher; b. Phila., May 24, 1937; s. Maurice and Anna (Kaplan) L.; m. Linda Jane Lowenthal, June 21, 1959; children—Joshua Henry, Mark David, Jonathan Mayer. B.S., Pa. State U., 1958; S.M., U. Chgo., 1960, Ph.D, 1962. Gastdocent U. Bern, Switzerland, 1964-65; asst. prof. chemistry Purdue U., West Lafayette, Ind., 1965-68, assoc. prof., 1968-73, prof., 1973—, chmn. inorganic chemistry, 1978-82, assoc. head dept. of chemistry, 1993—; dir. chemistry ops. Purdue Rare Isotope Measurement Lab. (PRIME), 1990—; vis. assoc. prof. Tel Aviv U., 1971-72; vis. prof. Max-Planck Inst. fuer Chemie, Mainz, Fed. Republic Germany, 1987; mem. panel space sci. experts Com. on Space Rsch., Space Agy. Forum of the Internat. Space Yr., Internat. Coun. Sci. Unions, 1990-92; cons. in field. Assoc. editor 11th Lunar and Planetary Sci. Conf., 3 vols., 1980; fin. editor: Meteoritics, 1992—; contbr. numerous articles to profl. publs. Served to 1st lt. USAR, 1958-64. Recipient Cert. of Recognition, NASA, 1979, Cert. of Spl. Recognition, 1979, Group Achievement award, 1983, Cert. Appreciation, Nat. Commn. on Space, 1986; postdoctoral fellow NSF, 1964-65, NATO, 1964-65; Fulbright fellow, 1971-72. Fellow Meteoritical Soc. (treas. 1978-84, mem. joint com. on pubs. of Geochem. and Meteoritical Socs. 1985-93, fin. officer 1985-93, chmn. 1988-90); mem. AAAS, Am. Chem. Soc., Am. Geophys. Union, Planetary Soc., Internat. Astron. Union (U.S. rep. 1988), Sigma Xi. Minor planet named in honor of Lipschutz by Internat. Astronomical Union, 1987. Office: Purdue U Dept Chemistry West Lafayette IN 47907

LIPSCOMB, OSCAR HUGH, archbishop; b. Mobile, AL, Sept. 21, 1931; s. Oscar Hugh and Margaret (Saunders) L. S.T.L., Gregorian U., Rome, 1957; Ph.D., Cath. U. Am., 1963. Ordained priest Roman Cath. Ch., 1956; consecrated bishop Roman Cath. Ch., 1980. Asst. pastor Mobile, 1959-65; tchr. McGill Inst., Mobile, 1959-60, 61-62; vice chancellor Diocese of Mobile-Birmingham, 1963-66, chancellor, 1966-80; pastor St. Patrick Parish, Mobile, 1966-71; lectr. history Spring Hill Coll., Mobile, 1971-72; asst. pastor St. Matthew Parish, Mobile, 1971-79, Cathedral Immaculate Conception, Mobile, 1979-80; adminstr. sede vacante Diocese of Mobile, 1980, now archbishop; pres. Cath. Housing Mobile, Mobile Senate Priests, 1978-80; chmn. com. on doctrine Nat. Conf. Cath. Bishops, 1988-91. Author articles, papers in field. Pres. bd. dirs. Mobile Mus., 1966-76; trustee Ala. Dept. Archives and History, Cath. U. Am., Washington, 1983—, Spring Hill Coll., Mobile; chmn. NCCB Com. on Ecumenical and Interreligious Affairs; chmn. bd. govs. N.Am. Coll., Rome, 1982-85. Mem. Am. Cath. Hist. Assn., So. Hist. Assn., Ala. Hist. Assn. (pres. 1971-72, exec. com. 1981-88), Hist. Mobile Preservation Inc., Lions. Address: PO Box 1966 400 Government St Mobile AL 36602-2332

LIPSCOMB, PAUL ROGERS, orthopaedic surgeon, educator; b. Clio, S.C., Mar. 23, 1914; s. Paul Holmes and Mary Emma (Rogers) L.; m. Phyllis

M. Oesterreich, July 20, 1940; children—Susan L. Nachbaur, Paul Rogers. B.S., U. S.C., 1935; M.D., Med. U. S.C., 1938; M.S. in Orthopaedic Surgery, Mayo Found., U. Minn., 1942. Diplomate Am. Bd. Orthopaedic Surgery (sec. 1968-71, pres. 1971-73). Intern Cooper Hosp., Camden, N.J., 1938-39; resident in orthopaedic surgery Mayo Clinic, Rochester, Minn., 1939-43, asst. to staff orthopaedic surgery, 1941-43, staff surgery, 1943-69, v.p staff, 1963; cons. Methodist, St. Mary's hosps., 1943-69; mem. faculty Mayo Grad. Sch. U. Minn., 1944-69, prof. orthopaedic surgery, 1961-69; mem. univ. senate from U. Minn. (Mayo Grad. Sch.), 1963-67; past mem. grad. and admissions com. and joint com. Grad. Sch. U. Minn. and Mayo Grad. Sch.; prof., chmn. dept. orthopedic surgery (Sch. of Medicine, U. Calif.), Davis, 1969-81, prof. emeritus, 1981—; pres. staff Sacramento Med. Center, 1980-81; mem. staff Woodland Clinic, 1981-86; ret., 1992; v.p. Woodland Clinic Research and Edn. Found., 1982-84, pres., 1984-85; hon. vis. prof. orthopaedics U. Auckland, New Zealand, 1978; cons. Disability Evaluation Group, Sacramento, 1988-92. Contbr. numerous articles to profl. jours. Mem. Am. Acad. Orthopaedic Surgery (chmn. com. sci. investigation 1955-56, chmn. instrl. course com., editor instrl. course lectures 1961-63, chmn. com. on arthritis 1970), Orthopaedic Rsch. Soc. (chmn. membership com., mem. exec. com. 1956), AMA (chmn. orthopaedic sect. 1965), ACS, Am. Orthopaedic Assn. (pres. 1974-75), Western Orthopaedic Assn., Am. Soc. Surgery Hand, Clin. Orthopaedic Soc., Internat. Soc. Orthopaedic Surgery and Traumatology, Central, Internat. orthopaedic clubs, New Zealand Orthopaedic Assn. (corr.), Sacramento County, Yolo County med. socs., Sterling Bunnell Found. (trustee 1984—), Calif. Med. Assn., Sigma Xi, Alpha Omega Alpha. Presbyterian. Home: 749 Sycamore Ln Davis CA 95616-3432

LIPSCOMB, WILLIAM NUNN, JR., retired physical chemistry educator; b. Cleveland, Ohio, Dec. 9, 1919; s. William Nunn and Edna Patterson (Porter) L.; m. Mary Adele Sargent, May 20, 1944; children: Dorothy Jean, James Sargent; m. Jean Craig Evans, 1983. BS, U. Ky., 1941, DSc (hon.), 1963; PhD, Calif. Inst. Tech., 1946; DSc (hon.), U. Munich, 1976, L.I. U., 1977, Rutgers U., 1979, Gustavus Adolphus Coll., 1980, Marietta Coll., 1981, Miami U., 1983, U. Denver, 1985, Ohio State U., 1991; Transylvania U., 1992, Transylvania U., 1992. Phys. chemist Office of Sci. R&D, 1942-46; faculty U. Minn., Mpls., 1946-59, asst. prof., 1946-50, assoc. prof., 1950-54, acting chief phys. chemistry div., 1952-54, prof. and chief phys. chemistry div., 1954-59; prof. chemistry Harvard U., Cambridge, Mass., 1959-71, Abbott and James Lawrence prof., 1971-90, prof. emeritus, 1990—; mem. U.S. Nat. Commn. for Crystallography, 1954-59, 60-63, 65-67; chmn. program com. 4th Internat. Congress of crystallography, Montreal, 1957; mem. sci. adv. bd. Robert A. Welch Found.; mem. rsch. adv. bd. Mich. Molecular Biology Inst.; mem. adv. com. Inst. Amorphus Studies; mem. sci. adv. com. Nova Pharms., Daltex Med. Svc., Gensia Pharms., Binary Therapeutics. Author: The Boron Hydrides, 1963, (with G.R. Eaton) NMR Studies of Boron Hydrides and Related Compounds, 1969; assoc. editor: (with G.R. Eaton) Jour. Chemical Physics, 1955-57; contbr. articles to profl. jours.; clarinetist, mem.: Amateur Chamber Music Players. Guggenheim fellow Oxford U., Eng., 1954-55; Guggenheim fellow Cambridge U., Eng., 1972-73; NSF sr. postdoctoral fellow, 1965-66; Overseas fellow Churchill Coll., Cambridge, Eng., 1973; Robert Welch Found. lectr., 1966, 71; Howard U. distinguished lecture series, 1966; George Fisher Baker lectr. Cornell U., 1969; centenary lectr. Chem. Soc., London, 1972; lectr. Weizmann Inst., Rehovoth, Israel, 1974; Evans award lectr. Ohio State U., 1974; Gilbert Newton Lewis Meml. lectr. U. Calif., Berkeley, 1974; also lectureships Mich. State U., 1975, U. Iowa, 1975, Ill. Inst. Tech., 1976, numerous others; also speaker confs.; Recipient Harrison Howe award in Chemistry, 1958; Distinguished Alumni Centennial award U. Ky., 1965; Distinguished Service in advancement inorganic chemistry Am. Chem. Soc., 1968; George Ledlie prize Harvard, 1971; Nobel prize in chemistry, 1976; Disting. Alumni award Calif. Inst. Tech., 1977; sr. U.S. scientist award Alexander von Humboldt-Stiftung, 1979; award lecture Internat. Acad. Quantum Molecular Sci., 1980. Fellow Am. Acad. Arts and Scis., Am. Phys. Soc.; mem. NAS, Am. Chem. Soc. (Peter Debye award phys. chemistry 1973, chmn. Minn. sect. 1949-50), Am. Crystallographic Assn. (pres. 1955), The Netherlands Acad. Arts and Scis. (fgn.), Math. Assn. Bioinorganic Scientists (hon.), Academie Europeenne des Sciences des Arts et des Lettres, Royal Soc. Chemistry (hon.), Phi Beta Kappa, Sigma Xi, Alpha Chi Sigma, Phi Lambda Upsilon, Sigma Pi Sigma, Phi Mu Epsilon. Office: Harvard U Dept Chemistry 12 Oxford St Cambridge MA 02138-2902

LIPSCOMB-BROWN, EDRA EVADEAN, retired childhood educator; b. Marion, Ill., Aug. 3, 1919; d. Edgar and Anna Josephine (Wiesbrodt) Turnage; m. July 5, 1939 (div. Sept. 1950); 1 son, H. Alan; m. Mark S. Brown, 1981. B.S., So. Ill. U., 1955; M.A., U. Mich., 1955; Ed.D., Ind. U., 1962; postgrad., U. Minn. Tchr. Benton (Ill.) Elem. Schs., 1939-54, DeKalb (Ill.) Consol. Schs., 1955-56; mem. faculty No. Ill. U., DeKalb, 1956-81; prof. elem. edn. No. Ill. U., 1967-81, chmn. elem. and childhood edn., 1978-81, ret., 1981; ednl. cons. to various schs., No. Ill.; mem. vis. accreditation com. Nat. Council Accreditation Tchr. Edn., Kent State U., 1974, U. Wis.-Stout, 1975; co-author, director numerous projects sponsored by U.S. Office Spl. Edn., 1979-81. Author: Lipscomb Teacher Attitude Scale; Contbr. articles to profl. jours. Research grantee No. Ill. U., 1965, 73; Research grantee State of Ill., 1972-73. Mem. Internat. Reading Assn., Internat. Assn. Supervision and Curriculum Devel., NEA, Ill. Edn. Assn., Assn. Higher Edn., Am. Ednl. Research Assn., Pi Lambda Theta. Democrat. Throughout my life, I have striven toward professional achievement and personal happiness. I tried never to let disappointments become bitterness, life's traumas to become defeat or sadness to become self-pity.

LIPSET, SEYMOUR MARTIN, sociologist, political scientist, educator; b. N.Y.C., Mar. 18, 1922; s. Max and Lena (Lippman) L.; m. Elsie Braun, Dec. 26, 1944 (dec. Feb. 1987); children: David, Daniel, Carola; m. Sydnee Guyer, July 29, 1990. BS, CCNY, 1943; PhD, Columbia U., 1949; MA (hon.), Harvard U., 1966; LLD (hon.), Villanova U., 1973, Hebrew U., 1981, U. Buenos Aires, 1987, Free U., Brussels, 1990, U. Judaism, 1991, Hebrew Union Coll., 1993, Boston Hebrew Coll., 1993. Lectr. U. Toronto, 1946-48; asst. prof. U. Calif., Berkeley, 1948-50; asst., then assoc. prof. grad. faculty Columbia U., 1950-56, asst. dir. Bur. Applied Social Research, 1954-56; prof. sociology U. Calif., Berkeley, 1956-66, dir. Inst. Internat. Studies, 1962-66; vis. prof. social rels. and govt. Harvard U., 1966-66, prof. govt. and sociology, exec. com. Ctr. Internat. Affairs, 1966-75, George Markham prof. Ctr. Internat. Affairs, 1974-75; sr. fellow Hoover Inst. Stanford U., 1975; prof. polit. sci. and sociology, 1975-92, Caroline S.G. Munro prof., 1981-92; Hazel prof. pub. policy George Mason U., Fairfax, Va., 1990—; Henry Ford vis. research prof. Yale U., 1960-61; Paley lectr. Hebrew U., 1973; Fulbright program 40th Anniversary Disting. lectr., 1987; vis. scholar Russell Sage Found., New York, 1988-89. Author: Agrarian Socialism, 1950, (with others) Union Democracy, 1956, (with R. Bendix) Social Mobility in Industrial Society, 1959, expanded edit., 1991, Political Man, 1960, expanded edit., 1981, The First New Nation, 1963, expanded edit., 1979, Revolution and Counter Revolution, 1968, expanded edit., 1988, (with Earl Raab) The Politics of Unreason, 1970, expanded edit., 1978, Rebellion in the University, 1972, (with Everett Ladd) Academics and the 1972 Election, 1973, Professors, Unions and American Higher Education, 1973, The Divided Academy, 1975, (with David Riesman) Education and Politics at Harvard, 1975, (with I.L. Horowitz) Dialogues on American Politics, 1978, (with William Schneider) The Confidence Gap, 1983, expanded edit., 1987, Consensus and Conflict, 1987, Continental Divide: The Institutions and Values of the United States and Canada, 1990, The Educational Background of American Jews, 1990, American Exceptionalism; co-editor: Class, Status and Power, 1953, Labor and Trade Unionism, 1960, Sociology: The Progress of a Decade, 1961, Culture and Social Character, 1961, The Berkeley Student Revolt, 1965, Class, Status and Power in Comparative Perspective, 1966, Social Structure, Mobility and Economic Development, 1966, Elites in Latin America, 1967, Party Systems and Voter Alignments, 1967, Students in Revolt, 1969, Issues in Politics and Government, 1970, Failure of a Dream? Essays in the History of American Socialism, 1974, rev. edit., 1984; co-editor: Democracy in Developing Countries, 3 vols., Africa, Asia and Latin America, 1988, 89, Politics in Developing Countries, 1990; co-editor Public Opinion mag., 1977-89, Internat. Jour. Pub. Opinion Rsch. 1989—; editor: Students and Politics, 1967, Politics and Social Science, 1969, Emerging Coalitions in American Politics, 1978, The Third Century, 1979, Party Coalitions in the Eighties, 1981, Unions in Transition, 1986, American Pluralism and the Jewish Community, 1990; adv. editor: various jours. including Sci., Comparative Politics. Mem. Bd. Fgn. Scholarships, 1968-71; bd. dirs.

Aurora Found., 1985—; Nat. chmn. B'nai B'rith Hillel Found., 1975-79, chmn. nat. exec. com., 1979-84; assoc. pres. Am. Profs. for Peace in Middle East, 1976-77, nat. pres., 1977-81; co-chmn. exec. com. Internat. Ctr. Peace in Middle East, 1982-92; co-chmn. Com. for Effective UNESCO, 1976-81; chmn. Com. for UN Integrity, 1981-83; chmn. nat. faculty cabinet United Jewish Appeal, 1981-84; pres. Progressive Found., 1991—. Recipient Gunnar Myrdal prize, 1970, Townsend Harris medal, 1971, 125th Anniversary Alumni medal CCNY, 1963, M.B. Rawson award, 1986, No. Telecom. Gold Medal for Can. Studies, 1987, Marshall Sklare award Assn. Social Sci.tudy of Jewry, 1993; fellow Social Sci. Rsch. Coun., 1945-46, Ctr. Advanced Study Behavioral Sci. fellow, 1955-56, 72-73, Guggenheim Found. fellow, 1971-72. Fellow NAS, Am. Acad. Arts and Scis. (v.p. 1974-78), Nat. Acad. Edn., Am. Sociol. Assn. (coun. 1959-62, MacIver award 1962, pres. 1992-93), Japan Soc.; mem. AAAS (chmn. sect. on econ. and social sci. 1975-76), Am. Sociologists Assn. (pres. 1992-93), Sociol. Rsch. Assn. (exec. com. 1981-84, pres. 1985), Am. Polit. Sci. Assn. (coun. 1975-77, pres. 1981-82, Leon Epstein prize 1989), Internat. Polit. Sci. Assn. (coun. 1981-88, v.p. 1982-88), Internat. Soc. Polit. Psychology (pres. 1979-80), Internat. Sociol. Assn. (chmn. com. polit. sociology 1959-71), World Assn. Pub. Opinion Rsch. (v.p. and pres.-elect 1982-84, pres. 1984-86), Am. Philos. Soc., Finnish Acad. Sci. (hon.), Paul Lazarsfeld Gesellschaft. Office: George Mason U Inst of Policy Studies Pohick Module Fairfax VA 22030 also: Stanford U 213 Herbert Hoover Meml Bu Stanford CA 94305

LIPSEY, HOWARD IRWIN, lawyer; b. Providence, Jan. 24, 1936; s. Harry David and Anna (Gershman) L.; children: Lewis Robert, Bruce Stephen. AB, Providence Coll., 1957; JD, Georgetown U., 1960. Bar: R.I. 1960, U.S. Dist. Ct. R.I. 1961, U.S. Supreme Ct. 1972. Assoc. Edward I. Friedman, 1963-67, Kirshenbaum & Kirshenbaum, 1967-82; ptnr. Abedon, Michaelson, Stanzler, Biener, Skolnik & Lipsey, 1982-83; ptnr. Lipsey & Skolnik, Esquires, Ltd., Providence, 1983—; lectr. trial tactics Nat. Coll. Adv., 1986, U. Bridgeport Law Sch., Yale U., U. Denver Law Sch., Suffolk U. Law Sch., 1987—. Served to capt. JAGC, USAR, 1960-71. Fellow Am. Coll. Trial Lawyers, Am. Acad. Matrimonial Lawyers; mem. ABA (family law advocacy inst.), R.I. Bar Assn., Assn. Trial Lawyers Am. Clubs: B'nai B'rith (Anti-Defamation League). Contbg. author: Valuation and Distribution of Marital Property, 1984. Office: Lipsey & Skolnik 321 S Main St Ste 400 Providence RI 02903-7108

LIPSEY, JOHN C. (JACK LIPSEY), insurance company executive; b. Chgo., Oct. 1, 1930; s. Albert Ellis and Mae (Smikler) L.; m. Elise Sandra Gross, Apr. 15, 1956; children—William, Laura, Abby. Ph.B., U. Chgo., 1948; postgrad., NYU, 1949-50. C.L.U.; chartered fin. cons. Spl. agt. mgr., v.p. Prudential Co., Chgo. and N.Y.C., 1956-80; sr. v.p. Home Life Ins. Co., N.Y.C., 1980-82, exec. v.p., 1982-84; pres. HL Fin. Services of N.Y., N.Y.C., 1984-88; v.p. Personal Lines Ins. Co., 1988—. Bd. govs. Am. Jewish Com., Boca Raton, Fla., 1991—, v.p., 1992—. With Army N.G., 1950-52. Mem. Am. Soc. C.L.U.s, Internat. Assn. Fin. Planners, Nat. Assn. Life Underwriters, Round Table of N.Y., Mountain Ridge Country Club, Delaire Country Club. Republican. Jewish. Avocations: golf; travel. Office: Personal Lines Ins 7777 Glades Rd Ste 100 Boca Raton FL 33434-4150

LIPSEY, JOSEPH, JR., water bottling executive; retail and wholesale corporation executive; b. Selma, Ala., Sept. 12, 1934; s. Joseph and Anna (Bendersky) L.; m. Betty Fay Wellan, June 5, 1960; children: Debora, Joseph III, Elizabeth, Tami. BA, La. State U., 1955, LLB, 1957. Bar: La. 1957, U.S. Dist. Ct. La. 1957, Korea 1959, Ryukyu Island 1958. Ptnr., Howell & Lipsey, Baton Rouge, 1960-65; v.p. Steinberg Sports Ctrs., Baton Rouge, 1960-91; ptnr. IsraAm Venture Group, Tel Aviv; v.p. Lipsey's Wholesale, Baton Rouge, 1977—; bd. dirs. Baton Rouge Broadcasting, Transcontinental Broadcasting, Baton Rouge, 1989-94; pres. So. Media Rsch. Co., Monroe, La., 1984—; chmn. Composite Analysis Group, Inc., Alexandria, 1989—; CEO Lipsey Mountain Spring Water, Atlanta, 1990—, Nantahalla Spring Water Bottling Co., Highlands, N.C., 1994—; speaker OPM 10 Harvard U., 1985; lectr. La. State U. Law Sch., Baton Rouge, 1961-63; chmn. Fashion Mchts. Conf., N.Y.C., 1977-81; chmn., sec.-treas. EAS Pub. Co., Inc., 1994—. Mem. exec. com. Com. for a Better La., Baton Rouge, 1971-86; pres. La. State U Found., 1980-81. Inducted into La. State U. Law Sch. Hall of Fame, 1987. Capt. USAF, 1957-60. Mem. La. State C. of C. (pres. 1973-75), Alexandria C. of C. (pres. 1971-72), Rotary. Democrat. Jewish.

LIPSEY, RICHARD GEORGE, economist, educator; b. Victoria, B.C., Can., Aug. 28, 1928; s. Richard Andrew and Faith Thirell (Ledingham) L.; m. Diana Louise Smart, Mar. 17, 1960; children: Mark Alexander (stepson), Mathew Richard, Joanna Louise, Claudia Amanda. B.A. with honours, U. B.C., 1950; M.A., U. Toronto, 1953; Ph.D., London Sch. Econs., 1958; LL.D. (hon.), McMaster U., 1984, Victoria U., 1985, Carleton U., 1986, Qeens U., 1990; D.Sc. (hon), Toronto U., 1992; D.Litt., Guelph U., 1993; LL.D (hon.), U. Western Ont., 1994. Research asst. B.C. Dept. Trade and Industry, 1950-53; from asst. lectr. to prof. econs. London Sch. Econs., 1955-63; prof. econs., chmn. dept., dean Sch. Social Studies, U. Essex, Eng., 1965-69; vis. prof. U. B.C., 1969-70, U. Colo., 1973-74; Irving Fisher vis. prof. Yale U., 1979-80; Sir Edward Peacock prof. econs. Queens U., Kingston, Ont., 1970-87; prof. Simon Fraser U., Vancouver, B.C., 1989—; sr. rsch. advisor C.D. Howe Inst., 1983-89; dir. rsch. into growth in U.K. Nat. Econ. Devel. Coun. U.K., 1961-63; mem. coun. and planning com. Nat. Inst. Econ. and Social Rsch. U.K., 1962-69; mem. bd. Social Sci. Rsch. Coun. U.K., 1966-69. Author: An Introduction to Positive Economics, 8th edit, 1995, The Theory of Customs Unions: A General Equilibrium Analysis, 1971; co-author: An Introduction to a Mathematical Treatment of Economics, 3d edit, 1977, Economics, 11th edit., 1995, Mathematical Economics, 1976, An Introduction to the U.K. Economy, 1983, 4th edit., 1993, Common Ground for the Canadian Common Market, 1984, Canada's Trade Options in a Turbulent World, 1985, Global Imbalances, 1987, First Principles of Economics, 1988, 2d edit., 1992, Evaluating the Free Trade Deal, 1988, The NAFTA, What's In, What's Out, What Next; editor: Rev. Econ. Studies, 1962-64. Decorated officer Order of Can.; Can. Inst. for Advanced Rsch. fellow, 1989—. Fellow Econometric Soc., Royal Soc. Can.; mem. Royal Econ. Soc. (council 1967-71), Econ. Study Soc. (chmn. 1965-69), Am. Econ. Assn., Can. Econ. Assn. (pres. 1980-81), Atlantic Econ. Soc. (chmn. 1986-87). Office: Simon Fraser U Harbour Centre, 515 W Hastings St, Vancouver, BC Canada V6B 5K3

LIPSEY, ROBERT EDWARD, economist, educator; b. N.Y.C., Aug. 14, 1926; s. Meyer Aaron and Anna (Weinstein) L.; m. Sally Irene Ruthstein, Nov. 24, 1948; children: Marion (Mrs. William Greenlee), Carol (Mrs. William Hersh), Eleanor (Mrs. William Ho). B.A., Columbia, 1944, M.A., 1946, Ph.D., 1961. Research asst. Nat. Bur. Econ. Research, N.Y.C., 1945-53; research assoc. Nat. Bur. Econ. Research, 1953-60, sr. research staff, 1960—, v.p. research, 1970-75, dir. internat. studies, 1975-78, dir. N.Y. Office., 1978—; lectr. econs. Columbia U., 1961-64; prof. econs. Queens Coll. and Grad. Ctr., CUNY, 1967—; cons. Dept. Commerce, Fed. Res. Bd., UN World Bank; mem. President's Adv. Bd. on Internat. Investment, 1977-78; bd. dirs. Rsch. Found. CUNY, 1994—. Author: Price and Quantity Trends in the Foreign Trade of the U.S, 1963, (with Raymond W. Goldsmith) Studies in the National Balance Sheet of the U.S, 1963, (with Doris Preston) Source Book of Statistics Relating to Construction, 1966, (with Irving B. Kravis) Price Competitiveness in World Trade, 1971, (with Phillip Cagan) Financial Effects of Inflation, 1978, (with Irving B. Kravis) Saving and Economic Growth: Is the U.S. Really Falling Behind, 1987; editor: (with Helen Stone Tice) The Measurement of Saving, Investment and Wealth, 1989, (with Magnus Blomström and Lennart Ohlsson) Economic Relations Between the U.S. and Sweden, 1989; assoc. editor Rev. of Econs. and Stats., 1989-92; mem. editorial bd. Rev. of Income and Wealth, 1992—; contbr. articles to profl. jours. Fellow Am. Statis. Assn.; mem. Acad. Internat. Bus., Nat. Assn. bus. Economists, Am. Econ. Assn., Internat. Assn. for Rsch. in Income and Wealth, N.Y. Acad Sci., Conf. on Rsch. in Income and Wealth, Econometric Soc. Home: 70 E 10th St New York NY 10003-5102 Office: 269 Mercer St New York NY 10003-6633

LIPSHIE, JOSEPH, apparel manufacturing company executive; b. Bklyn., Sept. 16, 1911; s. Arthur and Rose Hannah (Knopfer) L.; m. Mildred Lee Wright, Mar. 5, 1942; children—Arthur Bruce, Mary Jane, Samuel David. AB, Syracuse (N.Y.) U., 1932. With Salant Corp., N.Y.C., 1935-76; pres., chief exec. officer Salant Corp., 1965-74, chmn. bd., 1974-75, chmn. exec. com., 1976-80; dir. Internat. Health Found., Inc., Jackson, Tenn. Bd.

dirs. West Tenn. council Boy Scouts Am. Served with USCGR, 1942-45. Mem. Am. Apparel Edn. Found. (pres. emeritus), Tau Epsilon Phi. Jewish. Club: Shriners. Home: 647 Russell Rd Jackson TN 38301-3444

LIPSHUTZ, ROBERT JEROME, lawyer, former government official; b. Atlanta, Dec. 27, 1921; s. Allen A. and Edith (Gavronski) L.; m. Barbara Sorelle Levin, Feb. 16, 1950 (dec.); children: Randall M., Judith Ann, Wendy Jean, Debbie Sue; m. Betty Beck Rosenberg, Feb. 10, 1973; stepchildren: Robert, Nancy Fay. J.D., U. Ga., 1943. Bar: Ga. 1943, D.C. 1980. Practice in Atlanta, 1947-77, 79—; ptnr. firm Lipshutz, Greenblatt & King, 1979—; counsel to Pres. U.S., Washington, 1977-79. Past vice chmn. Ga. Bd. Human Resources; treas., legal counsel Jimmy Carter Presdl. campaign com., 1976; trustee The Carter Ctr., Americans United for Separation of Ch. and State. Capt. AUS, 1944-46. Mem. Am., Ga., Atlanta, D.C. bar assns. Atlanta Lawyers Club, Atlanta., B'nai B'rith (past pres.). Jewish (past pres. The Temple). Office: Lipshutz Greenblatt & King Harris Tower Peachtree Ctr Ste 2300 Atlanta GA 30343

LIPSIG, ETHAN, lawyer; b. N.Y.C., Dec. 11, 1948; s. Daniel Allen and Haddassah (Adler) L. BA, Pomona Coll., 1969; postgrad., Oxford U., 1969-70; JD, UCLA, 1974. Bar: U.S. Dist. Ct. (cen. dist.) Calif. 1974, U.S. Ct. Appeals (9th cir.) 1974, U.S Tax Ct. 1978. Author: (book) Individual Retirement Arrangements, 1980. Mem. ABA (tax and labor rels. sect.), Western Pension and Benefits Conf., Calif. C. of C., Order of Coif, Ctrl. City Assn., Soc. of Fellows of Huntington Libr., Calif. Club. Avocations: travel, horticulture, wine, music, art. Home: 280 California Ter Pasadena CA 91105-1515 Office: Paul Hastings Janofsky & Walker 555 S Flower St Fl 23 Los Angeles CA 90071-2300

LIPSITT, LEWIS PAEFF, psychology educator; b. New Bedford, Mass., June 28, 1929; s. Joseph and Anna Naomi (Paeff) L.; m. Edna Brill Duchin, June 8, 1952; children: Mark, Ann. BA, U. Chgo., 1950; MS, U. Mass., 1952; PhD, U. Iowa, 1957. Instr. dept. psychology Brown U., Providence, 1957; asst. prof. Brown U., 1958-61, assoc. prof., 1961-66, prof., 1966—, dir. Child Study Ctr., 1967-92, Wriston Lectr., 1993—; mem. Gov.'s Adv. Commn. on Mental Retardation, 1963-66; cons. NIH; mem. edn. task force Model Cities Program, Providence, 1969-71; fellow Stanford Ctr. for Advanced Study in Behavioral Scis., 1979-80; vis. scientist NIMH, 1986-87. Co-author: Child Development, 1979; founder, editor: Infant Behavior and Devel., 1978-82; founding co-editor: Advances in Child Development and Behavior, 1963-70, 78-82; co-editor: Research Readings in Child Psychology, 1963, Experimental Child Psychology, 1971, Advances in Infancy Research, Self-regulatory Behavior and Risk Taking, 1991; contbr. articles to profl. jours. Bd. dirs. Providence Child Guidance Clinic, 1960-63; trustee Butler Hosp., Providence, 1965-84; mem. bd. sci. counselor Nat. Inst. Child Health and Human Devel., 1984-88; nat. co-dir. Lee Salk Family Ctr., Kidspeace, Allentown, Pa., 1993—. USPHS Spl. Rsch. fellow, 1966, Guggenheim fellow, 1972-73, USPHS fellow, 1973; recipient Profl. Achievement citation U. Chgo., 1995. Fellow AAAS (Lifetime Mentor award 1994), APA (exec. com. divsn. devel. psychology 1967-70, pres.-elect divsn. devel. psychology 1979-80, pres. divsn. devel. psychology 1980-81, bd. sci. affairs 1985-89, exec. dir. for sci. 1990-91, sci. officer 1991-92, Nicholas Hobbs award 1990); mem. AAUP, Soc. Rsch. in Child Devel., Internat. Soc. Study of Behavioral Devel. (membership sec. 1981-83, exec. com. 1984-89), Am. Psychol. Soc. (founding mem., charter fellow, bd. dirs. 1989-90).

LIPSKI, DONALD G., sculptor; b. Chgo., May 21, 1947. BA in History, U. Wis.; MFA, Cranbrook Acad. Art, 1973. Asst. prof. U. Okla., Norman, 1973-77. Solo exhns. include Mus. Modern Art, N.Y.C., 1979, Ft. Worth Art Mus., 1980, Neuberger Mus., Purchase, N.Y., 1981, Am. Acad. Inst. Arts and Letters, N.Y.C., 1983, New Mus. Contemporary Art, N.Y.C., 1984, Bklyn. Mus., 1985, Walker Art Ctr., Mpls., 1988; travelling exhbn. Tex., Mich., Fla., 1984; represented in permanent collections Met. Mus. Art, N.Y.C., Walker Art Ctr., Boston Mus. Fine Arts, San Antonio Art Mus. Recipient Visual Arts award, 1984, N.Y. Found. Arts award, 1986, Acad. award in art Am. Acad. Arts and Letters, 1993; Nat. Endowment Arts fellow 1978, 84, Guggenheim fellow 1988. Office: RR 7 Box 569G Cleveland TX 77327-8501

LIPSKY, JANICE GWYNNE, nursing administrator; b. Spartanburg, S.C.; d. Vernon David and Betty Lou (Ragan) Gwynne; children: Jessica Erin, Emma Leigh. BSN, Fla. State U., 1976; MSN, U. Fla., 1986. Cert. nurse adminstr. Staff nurse critical care Bapt. Med. Ctr., Jacksonville, Fla.; cardiovascular clin. practice instr. St. Vincent's Med. Ctr., Jacksonville, dir. cardiovascular nursing, dept. dir. critical care and mental health. Contbr. articles to profl. jours. Mem. Fla. Nurses Assn. (chmn. coun. on adminstrn., bd. dirs. dist. 2, Nurse Recognition award).

LIPSKY, MICHAEL, political science educator; b. N.Y.C., Apr. 13, 1940. BA, Oberlin Coll., 1961; MA in Pub. Affairs, Princeton U., 1964, MA in Politics, 1964, PhD in Politics, 1967. Predoctoral research fellow Brookings Instn., 1965-66; asst., Pub. Affairs program Ford Found., 1965; asst. prof. polit. sci. U. Wis., Madison, 1966-69; spl. asst. to Chancellor for Equal Opportunity Programs, 1968-69; staff assoc. Inst. for Rsch. for Poverty, 1966-69; prof. polit. sci. MIT, Cambridge, Mass., 1969—; lectr. Harvard U. Grad. Sch. Edn., Cambridge, Mass., 1983—. Author: Protest in City Politics: Rent Strikes, Housing and the Power of the Poor, 1970, Theoretical Perspectives on Urban Politics, 1976, Commission Politics: The Processing of Racial Crisis in America, 1977, Street-Level Bureaucracy: Dilemmas of the Individual in Public Services, 1980 (C. Wright Mills award 1981, Gladys E. Kammerer award 1981); also articles. cons. Dept. Pub. Welfare, Mass., 1983-88, Dept. Social Svcs., N.Y., 1984, 86-88; rsch. on Temp. Emergency Food Assistance Program and submissions to Select Com. on Hunger, U.S. Ho. of Reps., Washington, 1984; mem. com. om status Black Ams. NRC/NAS, 1985-89. Guggenheim fellow, 1984-85. Office: MIT Dept Polit Sci Cambridge MA 02139

LIPSKY, STEPHEN EDWARD, engineering executive, electronic warfare engineer; b. N.Y.C., Jan. 18, 1932; s. Arthur Arnold and Sophie (Malsbrook) L.; m. Laura Roher, May 11, 1958 (div. 1978); children—Janice, Sharon, David; m. Hyla Schaffer, Apr. 7, 1979. B.E.E., NYU, 1953, M.E.E., 1962; PhD in Elec. Engring., Drexel U., 1993. Project engr. Fisher Radio Corp; div. mgr., staff scientist Loral Electronics, Yonkers, N.Y., 1958-63; corp. v.p. Polarad-Radiometrics, Lake Success, N.Y., 1963-70; dir. advanced systems Gen. Inst. Corp.; Hicksville, N.Y., 1970-79; chief tech. officer, sr. v.p. Am. Electronic Labs., Lansdale, Pa., 1979-93; founder, chief tech. officer Bynetics Corp., Jenkintown, Pa., 1993—; adj. univ. prof. elec. engring. Drexel U., Phila. Author: Microwave Passive Direction Finding, 1987; patentee; contbr. articles to profl. jours. Served to lt. U.S Army, 1953-55. Decorated Bronze AFCEA medal. Fellow IEEE, IEE (London/assoc.); mem. Assn. Old Crows (charter mem., bd. dirs. 1972-74, sr. Gold cert. merit 1990), Am. Radio Relay League, Masons, Navy League, Army Assn. Republican. Avocations: radio amateur, color photography, stamp collecting, antique radios.

LIPSON, LEON, law educator, lawyer; b. 1921. A.B., Harvard U., 1941, M.A., 1943, LL.B., 1950. Bar: N.Y. 1951, D.C. 1951. Assoc. Cleary, Gottlieb et al., Washington, 1950-56; assoc. prof. Yale U. Law Sch., 1957-60, prof. 1960-79, Henry R. Luce prof., 1979-92, assoc. provost, 1965-68, Taal Professorial lectr., 1992—; advisor U.S. del. UN Mission, 1959; cons. RAND Corp., 1956-70; bd. dirs. Social Sci. Research Council, 1969—, chmn., 1974-76, chmn. exec. com., 1976-78; bd. dirs. Internat. Research and Exchanges Bd., 1973-75; mem. acad. adv. bd. RAND Grad. Inst., 1977—, chmn. 1992—. Am. Council Learned Socs. exchange scholar Acad. Sci. USSR, 1963; fellow Ctr. Advanced Study in Behavioral Scis., 1968-69; Rockefeller Found. scholar, Bellagio, Italy, 1978. Mem. Am. Assn. Advancement Slavic Studies (v.p. 1967-70, 81-82, pres. 1982-83). Author: (with N. Katzenbach) Report on the Law of Outer Space, 1961; editor: (with V. N. Chalidze) Papers on Soviet Law, vol. 1, 1977, vol. 2, 1979, (with Stanton Wheeler) Law and the Social Scis., 1987; past note editor Harvard Law Rev. Office: Yale U Law Sch PO Box 401A New Haven CT 06520-7397

LIPSON, LESLIE MICHAEL, political science educator; b. London, Nov. 14, 1912; came to U.S., 1947, naturalized, 1953; s. Alexander and Caroline Rachel (Goodman) L.; m. Helen M. Fruchtman, Oct. 2, 1980; 1 son by previous marriage, David Roger. B.A., Oxford U., 1935, M.A., 1945; Ph.D., U. Chgo., 1938. Prof. polit. sci. and dir. Sch. Public Adminstrn., Victoria

U., Wellington, N.Z., 1939-46; prof. polit. sci. Swarthmore (Pa.) Coll. 1947-49, U. Calif., Berkeley, 1950-83; chmn. undergrad. program dept. polit. sci. U. Calif., 1977-80, prof. emeritus, 1980—; mem. faculty Fromm Inst. for Lifelong Learning, San Francisco, 1983—; acad. advisor, 1989—; civilian guest lectr. Nat. War Coll., Washington, 1948-75, Air War Coll., Montgomery, Ala., 1954-86; prof. polit. sci. UN Program of Tech. Assistance in Latin Am., Fundacao Getulio Vargas, Rio de Janeiro, Brazil, 1953; vis. prof. Columbia U., 1961, Stanford U., 1963, polit. sci. U. Copenhagen, 1970-71; others; vis. lectr. Oxford U. Inst. Commonwealth Studies, London, Institut Universitaire de Hautes Etudes Internationales, Geneva, U. Pavia, U. Zagrebb, others; panelist, reporter Brit. Press on PBS program "World Press" at Sta. KQED-TV, San Francisco, 1963-75; seminar leader Danforth Assocs. Conf., Estes Park, Colo., 1970; panelist World Affairs Coun., Weekly radio program, 1986-87; cons. in field. Author: The American Governor, 1939, reprinted, 1968, The Politics of Equality, 1948, The Great Issues of Politics, 1954, 9th edit., 1993, The Democratic Civilization, 1964, The Ethical Crises of Civilization, 1993, (with Elizabeth M. Drews) Values and Humanity, 1971, I Do Not Itch to Etch, Views in Verse, 1987; contbr. articles to profl. jours. and Ency. Brit. Trustee World Affairs Council No. Calif., 1979-87. Served with Home Guard, 1941-44, N.Z. Commonwealth Fund fellow Harkness Found., 1935-38; Rockefeller fellow, 1955-56, 59-60, grantee, 1967. Mem. NOW, UN Assn. (bd. dirs. San Francisco chpt. 1988-92). Democrat. Jewish. Home: 25 Stoddard Way Berkeley CA 94708 Office: U Calif Dept Polit Sci Berkeley CA 94720

LIPSON, MELVIN ALAN, technology and business management consultant; b. Providence, R.I., June 1, 1936; s. Nathan and Esta (Blumenthal) L.; m. Jacqueline Ann Barclay, July 2, 1961; children: Donna, Robert, Michelle, Judith. BS, ICI R.I., 1957; PhD, Syracuse U., 1963. Chemist ICI Organics, Providence, 1963, Philip A. Hunt Chem. Co., Lincoln, R.I., 1964-67; rsch. mgr. Philip A. Hunt Chem. Co., Lincoln, 1967-69; tech. dir. Dynachem div. Morton Thiokol Inc., Tustin, Calif., 1969-72; v.p. Morton Thiokol Inc., Tustin, 1979-82, sr. v.p., 1972-82, 1982-85, exec. v.p., 1985-86, pres., 1986-89; v.p. tech devel. Morton Internat. Inc., Chgo., 1989-92; pres. Lipson Assocs., Newport Beach, Calif., 1992—. Home and Office: 1715 Plaza Del Sur Newport Beach CA 92661-1417

LIPSTEIN, ROBERT A., lawyer; b. Wilmington, Del., Dec. 6, 1954; s. Eugene Joseph and Leona (Feld) L.; m. Cheryl A. Artibee-Wedlake, July 30, 1978; children: Rebecca Lynn, Matthew Wedlake. BA in Econs., Stanford U., 1975, JD, 1978. Bar: D.C. 1978, U.S. Dist. Ct. D.C. 1979, U.S. Ct. Appeals (D.C. dir.) 1980, U.S. Ct. Internat. Trade, 1984, U.S. Ct. Appeals (fed. cir.), U.S. Supreme Ct. 1990. Assoc. Morgan, Lewis & Bockius, Washington, 1978-84, Coudert Bros., Washington, 1984-86; ptnr. Coudert Bros., 1987-94; mng. ptnr. Lipstein, Jaffe & Lawson, 1994—. Mem. ABA (antitrust sect.), D.C. Bar Assn., Phi Beta Kappa. Avocations: golf, wood working, Tae Kwan Do (black belt). Home: 511 Stonington Rd Silver Spring MD 20902-1545 Office: Lipstein Jaffe & Lawson 1615 M St NW ste 710 Washington DC 20036

LIPSTONE, HOWARD HAROLD, television production executive; b. Chgo., Apr. 28, 1928; s. Lewis R. and Ruth B. (Fischer) L.; m. Jane A. Nudelman, Apr. 7, 1957; children—Lewis, Gregory. BA in Cinema, U. So. Calif., 1950. Asst. to gen. mgr. Sta. KTLA, Los Angeles, 1950-54; program dir. Sta. KABC-TV, Los Angeles, 1955-61, film and program dir., 1961-63; exec. asst. to pres., exec. producer Selmur Prodns., Inc. subs. ABC-TV, Los Angeles, 1963-69; exec. v.p. Ivan Tors Films and Studios, Inc., 1969-70; pres. Alan Landsburg Prodns., Inc., Los Angeles, 1970-85; pres., chief oper. officer The Landsburg Co., Los Angeles, 1985—. Mem. NATAS, Soc. Motion Picture and TV Engrs., Motion Picture Acad. Arts and Scis., Radio Club Am. Office: The Landsburg Co 11811 W Olympic Blvd Los Angeles CA 90064-1113

LIPTAK, IRENE FRANCES, retired business executive; b. Clifton, N.J., Feb. 22, 1926; d. George J. and Anna J. (Strelec) L. Student, U. Newark, 1944-45; BS, Rutgers U., 1950, MBA, 1955, EdM, 1964; postgrad., Montclair State Coll., 1960-61, Fairleigh Dickinson U., 1963-64. Exec. sec., adminstrv. asst. to pres. and chmn. bd. Botany Mills, Inc., Passaic, N.J., 1942-53; treas., sec. Rowland-Johnson Co., 1953-80; exec. sec. to chief exec. officer Edison Parking Corp., Newark, 1983; bldg. adminstr. Hippodrome Bldg., N.Y.C., 1984; office mgr. Decor Structure, Inc., Carlstadt, N.J., 1984-85. Editor: Ch. News, 1958-68. Mem. conf. planning com. N.J. Commn. on Women, 1972; treas. Slovak Nat. Cath. Cathedral, Passaic, 1976-77; sec., dir., trustee Charles Jr. and Dorothy Johnson Found., 1957-80. Mem. AAUW (life, corr. sec. Nutley br. 1972-74, treas. 1974-76, pres. 1979-81, dir. N.J. divsn. 1975-76), Grad. Sch. Edn. Alumni Assn. Rutgers, Rutgers U. Coll. Honor Soc. (life), Rutgers U. Coll. Alumni Assn. (life, mem. ctrl. coun. 1971-74, v.p. Paterson regional coun. 1986-94), Am. Soc. Notaries (life), Am. Friends Arts, S.W. Bergen Stroke and Disabled Club (founder, pres. 1987-88), Phi Chi Theta (nat. conv. 1972). Republican. Home: 106 Ridge Rd Rutherford NJ 07070-2422

LIPTAY, LYNNE MIRIAM, pediatrician; b. Panama, C.Z., Nov. 3, 1947; d. Thomas Emil and Lea Miriam (Maki) Oakland; m. John Stephen Liptay, Dec. 30, 1972; children—Thomas John, Steven Robert. B.A., Swarthmore Coll., 1969; M.D., Yale U., 1973. Diplomate Am. Bd. Pediatrics. Intern in pediatrics Montefiore Hosp. and Med. Ctr., N.Y.C., 1973-74, resident in pediatrics, 1974-76; practice medicine specializing in pediatrics, Hyde Park, N.Y., 1976—; mem. staff No. Dutchess Hosp., Rhinebeck, N.Y., 1976—. Co-author: Talk & Toddle, 1983. Fellow Am. Acad. Pediatrics. Office: 104 Fulton Ave Poughkeepsie NY 12603

LIPTON, ALLAN, medical educator; b. N.Y.C., Dec. 29, 1938; s. Murray and Ruth (Goldberg) L.; m. Nancy E. Whitcomb; children: Samuel, Joshua, Sarah Jan. AB, Amherst Coll., 1959; MD, NYU, 1963. Intern then resident in medicine Bellevue Hosp., N.Y.C., 1963-65; research assoc. NIH, Bethesda, Md., 1965-67; hematology, oncology fellow Meml. Hosp., N.Y.C., 1967-69; research fellow Salk Inst., San Diego, Calif., 1969-71; prof. medicine dept. oncology Coll. Medicine, Pa. State U., Hershey, 1971—; staff mem. Hershey Med. Ctr., 1971—. Served as lt. comdr. USPHS, 1965-67. Fellow ACP; mem. Am. Soc. Clin. Oncology, Am. Assn. Cancer Research. Office: Hershey Med Ctr Hershey PA 17033

LIPTON, ALLEN DAVID, retail executive; b. Bklyn., Aug. 10, 1940; s. Moses Meyer and Pearl (Schiff) L.; m. Nanci Mayer, Feb. 24, 1963 (div. 1991); children: Dawn Natalie, Lori Roberta, Paige Heather. AAAS, N.Y.C. Community Coll., 1961. Salesman Bakers Shoe Store, N.Y.C., 1961, Fabrex, N.Y.C., 1962-63, Sporteens, N.Y.C., 1963; asst. buyer Hammacher & Schlemmer, N.Y.C., 1961-62, Gimbels Dept. Store, N.Y.C., 1963-65; area mgr. Gimbels Dept. Store, Paramus, N.J., 1965-69; corp. buyer Stone & Thomas Dept. Store, Charleston, W.Va., 1969—; seminar spokesperson Draperies & Window Coverings Mag., N. Palm Beach, Fla., 1984; chmn. steering com. Fredrick Atkins Wholesale Buying Office. Author: Drapery and Curtain Department Store Training Manual, 1972, Buying Curtains and Draperies, 1987, Buying Carpet, Broadloom and Orential Rugs, 1991. Firefighter, Parsippany-Troy Hills (N.J.) Vol. Fire Assn., 1966-69. With N.Y. Nat. Guard, 1962-68. Recipient Leadership award Kirsch Co., 1983. Mem. Kanawha Valley Aquarium Soc. (pres. 1972, v.p. 1973, treas. 1975), Phi Kappa Rho (sec. 1960). Democrat. Jewish. Avocations: fishing, collecting and breeding tropical fish, collecting stamps and fish coins. Home: 1619 Quarrier St Apt A Charleston WV 25311 Office: Stone & Thomas Dept Store Lee at Dickinson Charleston WV 25326

LIPTON, ALVIN ELLIOTT, lawyer; b. Hackensack, N.J., Jan. 5, 1945; s. Irving and Goldie (Blickstein) L. BA, U. Rochester, 1966; JD, Boston U., 1969; LLM in Taxation, NYU, 1970. Bar: N.Y. 1972, U.S. Tax Ct. 1972, Conn. 1973, U.S. Ct. Claims 1977, U.S. Supreme Ct. 1977, Calif. 1983. Internat. tax analyst Price, Waterhouse & Co., N.Y.C., 1969-70; tax analyst Arthur Young & Co., N.Y.C., 1970; tax assoc. Weiss, Bronston, Rosenthal, Heller & Schwartzman, N.Y.C., 1971; tax atty. Conn. Gen. Life Ins. Co., Hartford, 1971-76; tax counsel Owens-Corning Fiberglas Corp., Toledo, 1976-80, Crown Zellerbach Corp., San Francisco, 1981-87; pvt. practice, San Francisco, 1988—. Mem. San Francisco Choral, Instrumental & Theatrical for Youth, 1985-92; bd. dirs. San Francisco Chanticleer, vice chmn. 1987-89; citizens amb. to People's Republic of China, 1987. Mem. ABA (tax sect. 1972—), Tax Execs. Inst., Calif. Bar Assn., San Francisco Bar Assn.

(tax sect. 1982—). Avocations: reading, hiking, snorkling, choral and solo singing. Home: 1800 Franklin St San Francisco CA 94109-3481 Office: 1 Sansome St Ste 2000 San Francisco CA 94104

LIPTON, BARBARA, museum director, curator; b. Newark, N.J.; m. Milton Lipton; children: Joshua, Sara, Beth. BA, U. Iowa; MA, U. Mich.; MLS, Rutgers U. Library director. Newark Mus., 1970-75, spl. projects cons.; 1975-82; asst. dir. Castle Gallery Coll. of New Rochelle, N.Y., 1982-83; guest curator Dept. Indian and No. Officers, Ottawa, Ont., Can., 1983-85; dir. Jacques Marchais Mus. Tibetan Art, S.I., N.Y., 1985—; tchr., lectr. various schs. and mus. including Mus. Natural History, Smithsonian Inst., Washington, 1976—; former guest curator many mus. Author: (catalogs) Survival Art Life of the Alaskan Eskimo, 1976, Arctic Vision, 1984, Treasures of Tibetan Art, 1995; (bibliography) Westerners in Tibet, 1972; exec. producer, writer documentary film: Village of No River, 1981. Grantee NEH, 1976, 79, 80, 87, 91. Mem. Am. Assn. Museums. Avocation: photography. Office: Jacques Marchais Mus Tibetan Art PO Box 060198 Staten Island NY 10306

LIPTON, BRONNA JANE, marketing communications executive; b. Newark, May 10, 1951; d. Julius and Arlene (Davis) L.; m. Sheldon Robert Lipton, Sept. 23, 1984. BA in Spanish, Northwestern U., 1973. Tchr. Spanish Livingston (N.J.) High Sch., 1973-78; profl. dancer Broadway theater, film, TV, N.Y.C., 1978-82; v.p., mgr. Hispanic mktg. svcs. Burson-Marsteller Pub. Rels., N.Y.C., 1982-89; exec. v.p. Lipton Communications Group, Inc., N.Y.C., 1989—; mem. minority initiatives task force Am. Diabetes Assn., Alexandria, Va., 1987-90, mem. pub. rels. com., 1990-91, mem. visibility and image task force, 1991-92, bd. dirs. N.Y. Downstate affiliate, chmn. visibility and image com., 1992-93. Mem. rev. panel Hispanic Designers, Inc. Recipient Pinnacle award Am. Women in Radio and TV (N.Y. Chpt.), 1984, Value Added awards Burson-Marsteller, N.Y.C., 1982, 83, 84. Mem. Hispanic Pub. Rels. Assn. Avocations: ballet, jazz dance, tennis, fgn. travel, birding. Home: 1402 Chapel Hill Mountainside NJ 07092

LIPTON, CHARLES, public relations executive; b. N.Y.C., May 11, 1928; s. Jack B. and Bertha (Lesser) L.; m. Audrey Williams, Nov. 11, 1951; children—Susan, Jack. AB, Harvard U., 1948. Market researcher Cecil & Presbury, Inc., N.Y.C., 1948-49; spl. events dir. 20th Century Fox Film Corp., N.Y.C., 1949-52; account exec. Ruder & Finn, Inc., N.Y.C., 1953-58; v.p. Ruder & Finn, Inc., 1958-63, sr. v.p., 1963-69, vice-chmn.; 1969—; also bd. dirs.; guest lectr. Boston U., 1967-68. Mem. coun. Ctr. for Vocat. Arts, Norwalk, Conn., 1966-74; trustee Norwalk Jewish Ctr., 1966-70; treas., mem. exec. com. Norwalk Symphony Soc., 1972-85; chmn. parent's counsel Washington U., St. Louis, 1976-77, trustee, 1977—. Mem. Am. Soc. Colon and Rectal Surgeons (trustee), Internat. Pub. Rels. Assn., USIA (pub. rels., pvt. sector com. 1988—), Nat. Emphysema Soc. (trustee), Nat. Investor Rels. Inst., Harvard Club, Harvard Varsity Club. Home: 18 Douglas Dr Norwalk CT 06850-1730 Office: Ruder Finn Inc 301 E 57th St 3rd Fl New York NY 10022

LIPTON, CHARLES JULES, lawyer; b. N.Y.C., Oct. 26, 1931; m. Alice Garretson; children: Leah Jane, Emma Ely. AB, Syracuse (N.Y.) U., 1951; LLB, Yale U., 1954; LLM in Internat. Law, NYU, 1966. Bar: N.Y., U.S. Supreme Ct. Assoc. Hughes, Hubbard and Reed, N.Y.C., 1954-55; trial atty. before Armed Svcs. Bd. Contract Appeals U.S. Dept. of Air Force, Washington, 1955-57; assoc. Breed, Abbott and Morgan, N.Y.C., 1957-62; counsel Freeport Minerals Co., N.Y.C., 1962-69; interregional advisor UN, N.Y.C., 1969-74; sr. cons. UN Centre on Transnational Corps., N.Y.C., 1976-90, chief legal adviser, 1991-92; legal advisor to govts. of 59 countries and 21 groups of indigenous peoples; spl. counsel Am. Indian Coun. Energy Resource Tribes, Denver, 1978-84; bd. dirs. Havelock Asbestos Mines (Swaziland) Ltd., Sun Internat. of Lesotho Pby, Ltd., Dokolwayo Diamond Mines Ltd., Emaswati Coal Pty, Ltd.; cons. U.S. Commr. of Edn., 1965, also numerous internat. orgns.; comml. legal advisor to Kings of Swaziland, 1969—; adj. prof. law NYU, 1975-87; vis. prof. law U. Swaziland, 1977—, Nat. U. Lesotho, 1984—; vis. lectr. in law U. Calif., Berkeley, 1974-82; vis. fellow U. New South Wales, Sydney, 1987; lectr. in field, participant numerous workshops. Contbr. articles to profl. jours. Ctp. USAF. Mem. Am. Soc. Internat. Law, Am. Fgn. Law Assn., ABA (chmn. African law com. sect. on internat. and comparative law 1964-67), Assn. of Bar of City of N.Y., African Law Assn. in Am. (bd. dirs. 1969-72. Home: 1136 Fifth Ave New York NY 10128-0122

LIPTON, CLIFFORD CARWOOD, retired glass company executive; b. Huntington, W.Va., Jan. 30, 1920; s. Clifford Carwood and Zerelda (Adkins) L.; m. Alyce Jo Anne Eckley, Jan. 3, 1943 (dec. July 1975); children: Clifford Carwood III, Thomas Denton, Michael Forrester; m. Marie Hope Mahoney, May 26, 1976. B in Engring. Sci., Marshall U., 1948. Staff engr. Owens-Ill. Inc., Huntington, 1948-52; supr. engring. Owens-Ill. Inc., Toledo, 1952-55; chief engr. divsn. Owens-Ill. Inc., Toledo, 1955-66; gen. mgr. Giralt Laporta SA, Madrid, 1966-71; dir. mfg. United Glass Ltd., London, 1971-74; mfg. and tech. dir. Owens-Ill. Internat., Geneva, 1974-82; dir. internat. devel. Owens-Ill. Inc., Toledo, 1982-83; ret., 1983; cons. Owens-Ill., Inc., China, Greece and U.S., 1983-85, Internat. Exec. Svc. Corps., 1986—. Mem. sch. bd. Am. Sch., Barcelona, Spain, 1966-67, Madrid, 1967-70; pres. Highland Trails Homeowners Assn., Southern Pines, N.C., 1987-93. 1st lt. Parachute Inf., U.S. Army, 1942-45. Mem. Benevolent and Protective Order Elks, 101st Airborne Divsn. Assn. Republican. Presbyterian. Avocations: travel, golf, reading, music, model engineering. Home: 104 Selkirk Trl Southern Pines NC 28387-7230

LIPTON, DANIEL BERNARD, conductor; b. Paris; s. Gerald David and Germaine (Chaison) L.; m. Olga Lucia Gaviria, Mar. 7, 1983 (div. Oct. 1985). BS in Music, Julliard Sch., 1963, Mannes Coll., 1965; postgrad. Accademia Chigiana, Siena, Italy, 1965, 67, Ecole Normale Superieure, Paris, 1967. Artistic dir. Opera Hamilton, Ont., Can.; prof. McMaster U., Hamilton, 1988. Condr. Am. Ballet Theater, 1968, Denver Symphony Orch., 1969-70, Teatro Comunale, Firenze, Italy, 1970-71, Teatro Comunale, Bologna, Italy, 1972, Opernhaus Zürich, 1973-75, Teatro del Liceo, Barcelona, Spain, 1979-82, Grand Theatre, Dijon, France, 1980-81, 83, Theatre de l'Opera, Nice, 1982-83, 87, Châtelet, Paris, Teatro de la Zarzuela, Madrid, Teatro La Fenice, Venezia, 1982, Utah Opera, 1983-85, Orch. de l'Opera de Paris, 1986, Bayerische Staatsoper, München, Germany, 1986-87, National theater Mannheim, 1988, 90, Teatro Regio di Parma, Teatro San Carlo, Napoli, Opera in Seoul, Republic of Korea, 1988, Il Giorno di Nozze, Oper Dortmund, Festival in Jesi, Italy, Opera Buffalo, Oper Köln; artistic dir. Orquesta Sinfonica de Colombia, Opera de Colombia, 1975-83, Opera Hamilton, 1986—, San Antonio Internat. Festival of Arts, 1986-89, dir. music Houston Grand Opera, 1984-85, Spoleto Festival, 1991, Deutsche Oper, Berlin, 1992; gen. music dir. Dessau, Germany, 1992; music dir., prin. conductor Anhaltische Philharmonie, Germany. Decorated Cruz de Boyaca (Colombia); recipient award Italian Govt.; Besançon conducting grantee, Fulbright grantee. Office: Opera Hamilton, 100 King St W, Hamilton, ON Canada L8P 1A2

LIPTON, ERIC, reporter. With Hartford Courant; now county govt. reporter The Washington Post, Fairfax, Va. Recipient Pulitzer Prize for explanatory journalism, 1992. Office: The Washington Post Fairfax County Bureau 4020 University Dr Ste 220 Fairfax VA 22030*

LIPTON, JOAN ELAINE, advertising executive; b. N.Y.C., July 12; 1 child, David Dean. B.A., Barnard Coll. With Young & Rubicam Inc., N.Y.C., 1949-52, Robert W. Orr & Assocs., N.Y.C., 1952-57, Benton & Bowles, Inc., N.Y.C., 1957-64; asso. dir. Benton & Bowles, Ltd., London, Eng., 1964-68; with McCann-Erickson, Inc. (advt. agy.), N.Y.C., 1968-85; v.p. McCann-Erickson, Inc. (creative dir., 1970-79, sr. v.p., creative dir., 1979-85; pres. Martin & Lipton Advt. Inc., 1985—. Chmn. bd. trustees Film/Video Arts, Inc., 1983—, pres., 1994—; mem. Bus. Coun. for the UN Decade for Women, 1977-78; bd. disitors PhD program in bus. CUNY, 1986—. Named Woman of Yr. am. Advt. Fedn., 1974; recipient Honors award Ohio U. Sch. Journalism, 1976; Matrix award, 1979; YWCA award for women achievers, 1979; named Advt. Woman of Yr., 1984. Mem. Advt. Women N.Y. (1st v.p. 1975-76, v.p. Found. 1977-78), Women's Forum (bd. dirs. 1988-90), Women in Communications (pres. N.Y. chpt. 1974-76, named Nat. Headliner 1976). Office: 163 E 62d St New York NY 10021

LIPTON, LEAH, art historian, educator, museum curator; b. Kearny, N.J., Mar. 22, 1928; d. Abraham and Rose (Berman) Shneyer; m. Herbert Lipton, Sep. 19, 1951 (dec. 1979); children: David, Ivan, Rachel. BA, Douglass Coll. Rutgers U., New Brunswick, N.J., 1949; MA, Harvard U., Cambridge, Mass., 1950; postgrad., Harvard U., 1973-74, Wellesley Coll., 1970-73. Photo, library researcher Mus. Fine Arts, Boston, 1950-53, lectr., division edn., 1965-70; instr. Boston Coll., 1968-69; faculty, half prof. Framingham State Coll., Mass., 1969-94; ret., 1994; interim dir. Danforth Mus. Art, 1994-95; mem. bd. trustees Danforth Mus. Art, Framingham Mass., 1975—; curator Art at Danforth Mus. Art, Framingham Mass., 1994—; chair exhibitions Com.; Collections Com. Danforth Mus., Framingham Mass., 1988, guest curator Nat. Portrait, Wash., 1985. Author: Book, 1985, Exhibition Catalogues, 1988-94; contbr. articles to profl. jours., 1981—. Co-Founder Danforth Mus. Art., Mass. 1973-75. Recipient Distinguished Service award Framingham State Coll., Mass. 1978, 87. Mem. Coll. Art Assn., Am. Studies Assn. Office: Danforth Mus of Art 123 Union Ave Framingham MA 01701

LIPTON, LOIS JEAN, lawyer; b. Chgo., Jan. 14, 1946; d. Harold Lypski and Bernice (Reiter) Farber L.; m. Bertram Kraft, June 13, 1968 (div. 1977); 1 child, Rachel; m. R. Peter Carey, May 30, 1978; 1 child, Sara. B.A., U. Mich., 1966; J.D. summa cum laude, DePaul Coll. Law, Chgo., 1974; postgrad. Sheffield U., Eng., 1966. Bar: Ky. 1974, U.S. Dist. Ct. (we. dist.) Ky. 1974, U.S. Ct. Appeals (6th cir.) 1974, Ill. 1975, U.S. Dist. Ct. (no. dist.) Ill., 1975, U.S. Ct. Appeals (7th cir.) 1976. Staff counsel Roger Baldwin Found. of ACLU, Inc., Chgo., 1975-79; dir. reproductive rights project, 1979-83; atty. McDermott, Will & Emery, Chgo., 1984-86, G.D. Searle, Skokie, Ill., 1988-90; sr. atty. AT&T, Chgo., 1990—. Del White House Conf. on Families, Mpls., 1980. Recipient Durfee award, 1984. Mem. Am. Judicature Soc., ACLU (bd. dirs. Ill.), Chgo. Bar Assn., Chgo. Council Lawyers. Office: AT&T 227 W Monroe St Chicago IL 60606

LIPTON, MARTIN, lawyer; b. N.J., June 22, 1931; s. Samuel D. and Fannie L.; m. Susan Lytle, Feb. 17, 1982; children: James, Margaret, Katherine, Samantha. BS in Econs., U. Pa., 1952; LLB, NYU, 1955. Bar: N.Y. 1956. Ptnr. Wachtell Lipton Rosen & Katz, N.Y.C., 1965—; mem. coun. Am Law Inst. Trustee NYU; pres. bd. trustees NYU Law Sch.; hon. chmn. Jerusalem Found.; chmn. bd. dirs. Prep for Prep; dir. Inst. Jud. Adminstrn. Office: Wachtell Lipton Rosen & Katz 51 W 52nd St New York NY 10019-6618

LIPTON, RICHARD M., lawyer; b. Youngstown, Ohio, Feb. 25, 1952; s. Sanford Y. Lipton and Sarah (Kentor) Goldman; m. Jane Brennan, May 24, 1981; children—Thomas, Anne, Martin, Patricia. B.A., Amherst Coll., 1974; J.D., U. Chgo., 1977. Bar: Ill. 1977, D.C. 1978, U.S. Dist. Ct. (no. dist.) Ill. 1979, U.S. Ct. Appeals (D.C. and 7th cirs.) 1979, U.S. Tax Ct. 1977, U.S. Ct. Claims 1979. Law clk. to judge Hall, U.S. Tax Ct., Washington, 1977-79; assoc. Isham, Lincoln & Beale, Chgo., 1979-83; ptnr. Ross & Hardies, Chgo., 1983-86; v.p. Pegasus Broadcasting, Chgo., 1986-88; ptnr. Sonnenschein Nath & Rosenthal, Chgo., 1988—. Contbr. articles to profl. jours. Recipient Order of Coif award U. Chgo. Law Sch., 1977. Fellow Am. Coll. Tax Counsel; mem. ABA (coun. dir. 1990-93, vice chair taxation sect. 1993—), Chgo. Bar Assn. (subcom. chair, chair fed. taxation com. 1991-92). Republican. Club: Union League, Mich. Shores, Geneva Nat. Office: Sonnenschein Nath Rosenthal 233 S Wacker Dr Ste 8000 Chicago IL 60606

LIPTON, ROBERT STEVEN, lawyer; b. N.Y.C., May 12, 1946; s. Max and Mildred (Goodman) L.; m. Stephanie F. Kass, Aug. 8, 1971. BA, NYU, 1967, JD, 1971. Bar: N.Y. 1972, U.S. Ct. Appeals (2d cir.) 1972, U.S. Dist. Ct. (so. dist.) N.Y. 1973, U.S. Supreme Ct. 1975. Assoc. Curtis, Mallet-Prevost, Colt & Mosle, N.Y.C., 1971-80, ptnr., 1980—. Editor NYU Law Rev., 1969-71. Mem. ABA, Fed. Bar Council, N.Y. State Bar Assn., Assn. of Bar of City of N.Y., Phi Beta Kappa. Club: India House (N.Y.C.). Office: Curtis Mallet-Prevost Colt & Mosle 101 Park Ave New York NY 10178-0002

LIPTON, STUART ARTHUR, neuroscientist; b. Danbury, Conn., Jan. 11, 1950; s. Harold and Evelyn Ruth (Stein) L.; m. Elisabeth Kay Ament, Aug. 10, 1980; children: Jennifer Ann, Jeffrey Harris. BA, Cornell U., 1971; MD, U. Pa., 1977, PhD, 1977; postgrad. Cornell U., 1971, U. Oxford (Eng.) 1972, Harvard U., 1974-76. Diplomate Am. Bd. Psychiatry and Neurology. Intern Beth Israel Hosp. and Harvard Med. Sch., Boston, 1977-78; resident in neurology Beth Israel, Brigham and Women's, Children's Hosp., Boston, 1978-80; chief neurology resident Beth Israel, Brigham and Women's Children's Hosp., Boston, 1980-81; research fellow in neurobiology Harvard Med. Sch., Boston, 1980-83, instr. in neurology, 1981-83, asst. prof. neurology and neurosci., 1983-87, assoc. prof. neurology and neurosci., 1987—; dir. cellular and molecular neurosci. Children's Hosp., Harvard Med. Sch.; neurologist Mass. Gen. Hosp., Brigham and Women's Hosp., Beth Israel Hosp., Children's Hosp., Boston. Contbr. articles to profl. jours.; patentee in field; composer of popular songs including one that sold 1.5 million copies, 1968. Established investigator Am. Heart Assn., 1988-93. Hartford Found. fellow, 1981, 82, 83, 84, NIH fellow, 1984, 85, 86, 87, 88, 89; NIH grantee, 1984—; Rhodes scholar Oxford (Eng.) U., 1971-72; recipient Pattison award, 1989. Mem. AAAS, Am. Acad. Neurology, Am. Neurol. Assn., Soc. for Neurosci., Assn. for Rsch. in Vision and Opthalmology, Biophys. Soc., Phi Beta Kappa, Alpha Omega Alpha. Avocations: musical composition, soccer. Office: Childrens Hosp & Harvard Med Sch 300 Longwood Ave Boston MA 02115-5737

LIPTON, SUSAN LYTLE, investment banker, lawyer; b. Ft. Warren, Wyo., Oct. 23, 1945; d. James and Bette Lytle; m. Martin Lipton, Feb. 17, 1982. AB, U. Miami, 1967, JD, 1970; LLM, Harvard U., 1971. Bar: Fla. 1970, N.Y. 1984. From assoc. to ptnr. Greenberg Traurig Askew, Miami, Fla., 1970-77; from assoc. to v.p. Goldman Sachs & Co., N.Y.C., 1977-81; from v.p. to mng. dir. L.F. Rothschild, Unterberg, Towbin, N.Y.C., 1981-86; trustee Jewish Mus., 1986—, Brearley Sch., 1991—, Wildlife Conservation Soc., 1991—; trustee, pres. Jewish Communal Fund, 1992—.

LIPTON, WILLIAM JAMES, accountant, lawyer; b. N.Y.C., July 11, 1947; s. Irvin Edward and Evelyn Deborah (Morris) L.; m. Carol Anne Miller, Jan. 3, 1982; children: Michael Jon, Bradley Scott, Marissa Kate. BS in Acctg., U. Pa., 1969; JD, St. John's U., N.Y.C., 1973; LLM, N.Y.U, 1977. Bar: N.Y. 1974; CPA, N.Y. Tax assoc. Ernst & Whinney, N.Y.C., 1973-80, ptnr., 1980-87; ptnr.-in-charge of tax Ernst & Whinney, Phila., 1987-89; dir. tax Ernst & Young, Stamford, Conn., 1989-91; mng. ptnr. Ernst & Whinney, Stamford, Conn., 1991-93; assoc. editor St. John's Law Rev., 1972; contbr. articles to profl. jours. Mem. ABA, N.Y. State Bar Assn., Phila. Bar Assn., AICPA, N.Y. State Soc. CPAs (chmn. partnership com 1985-87), Conn. State Soc. CPAs. Home: 255 Marvin Ridge Rd New Canaan CT 06840-6910 Office: Ernst & Young 787 7th Ave New York NY 10019

LIPTZIN, BENJAMIN, psychiatrist; b. N.Y.C., Sept. 17, 1945; s. David Murray and Mollie (Brody) L.; m. Sharon Leslie Rothstein, June 10, 1968; children: Shoshanna, Daniel, Deborah. BA, Yale U., 1966; MD, U. Rochester, N.Y., 1971. Diplomate Am. Bd. Psychiatry and Neurology. Resident in psychiatry U. Va. Hosp., Charlottesville, 1971-74; med. officer NIMH, Rockville, Md., 1974-78; dir. geriatric psychiatry McLean Hosp., Belmont, Mass., 1978-89, asst. gen. dir., 1989-90; chief dept. psychiatry Baystate Med. Ctr., Springfield, Mass., 1990—; prof., dep. chmn. dept. psychiatry Tufts U. Sch. Medicine, 1990—. Contbr. articles to profl. jours. With USPHS, 1972-78. Recipient Acad. award NIMH, 1983. Fellow Am. Psychiat. Assn. (trustee-at-large 1992-95), Gerontological Soc. Am.; mem. AMA, Am. Geriatrics Soc. Democrat. Jewish. Office: Baystate Med Ctr Dept Psychiatry 140 High St Springfield MA 01199-1000

LIQUORI, MARTIN WILLIAM, JR., athlete, business executive, television commentator; b. Montclair, N.J., Sept. 11, 1949; s. Martin William and Sara Ann (Tosone) L.; divorced; 1 child, Michael. BS, Villanova U., 1972; postgrad., U. Fla., 1973-75. Master of ceremonies International Track Association ProTrack, Los Angeles, 1971-73; commentator ABC-TV, N.Y.C. 1971—; commentator ESPN, 1984—, host Running and Racing, 1986-91, exec. producer Running and Racing, 1991—; host Sundance G.P. of Cycling, 1988; pres. Athletic Attic, Inc., Gainesville, Fla., 1972—; designer, pres. Marty Liquori Prodn. Inc.; cons. Turn Tec Sport Shoes, Nutri Products,

Bruder Health Care; v.p. Athletic Lady; spokesman Precor, 1987-88, Frelonic, 1989; bd. dirs. Nat. Sporting Goods Assn. Author: (with Skip Myslenski) On the Run; (with John Parker) Marty Liquori's Guide to the Elite Runner; Working Out at Home; contbg. editor Runners World Mag., 1979—. Mem. Pres.'s Coun. on Phys. Fitness, 1968-72; bd. mem. Stop! Children's Cancer; nat. spokesperson Nat. Leukemia Soc., 1992. Milrose Games mile champion, 1969, 70, 71; Pan Am. games champion, 1971; recipient Vitalis award for sports excellence, 1982; Am. holder in 5000 meters; ranked No. 1 in World for 1 mile, NCAA mile champion, 1969, 70, 71; mem. 1968 Olympic team; inducted into Italian-Am. Sports Hall of Fame, 1990. Home: 2915 NW 58th Blvd Gainesville FL 32606-8517 Office: PO Box 14503 Gainesville FL 32604-2503 *Lucky is the man who discovers his talents early in life—more fortunate is he who has the maturity to develop those talents.*

LIS, ANTHONY STANLEY, business administration educator; b. Eastampton, Mass., Aug. 11, 1918; s. Anthony Stanley and Anna Barbara (Kaczmarczyk) L.; m. Jane Ann Mikus, June 25, 1951 (dec.); children: Anthony, Judith A., Sandra J.; m. Sophie A. Pobieglo, June 24, 1983. B.S., Mass. State Coll., Salem, 1950; M.S., Okla. State U., 1951; Ph.D., U. Minn., 1961. Asst. prof. Okla. State U., Stillwater, 1951-55; assoc. prof. U. Tulsa, 1956-62; mem. faculty U. Okla., Norman, 1962-86, prof. bus. adminstrn., 1967-86, prof. emeritus, 1986—; vis. prof. Central Sch. Planning/Stats., Warsaw, Poland, 1984; del. II Congress Scholars of Polish Descent, Warsaw, 1979, III Congress, 1989 ; cons. to numerous bus. and govtl. agys. Served with U.S. Army, 1937-40, 1942-46. Decorated Bronze Star; recipient Superior Profl. and Univ. Service award U. Okla., 1981; Summer fellow Found. Econ. Edn., 1954. Mem. Am. Bus. Communication Assn., Polish Am. Hist. Assn., Am. Assn. Advancement Slavic Studies, Adminstrv. Mgmt. Soc., Southwestern Social Sci. Assn., Delta Pi Epsilon, Beta Gamma Sigma, Delta Sigma Pi. Roman Catholic. Lodge: Lions. Home: 1827 Peter Pan St Norman OK 73072-5837 Office: U Okla Coll Bus Adminstrn Norman OK 73019

LIS, EDWARD FRANCIS, pediatrician, consultant; b. Chgo., Apr. 1, 1918; s. Stephen and Stephanie L.; m. Sonne Nadine Kowalsen, Apr. 3, 1944; children—Jeffrey Warren, James Bryan. Student, DePaul U., 1936-37; B.S. MD., U. Ill. Pvt. practice Park Forest, Ill., 1949-51; faculty U. Ill. Coll. Medicine, 1951-90, prof. pediatrics, also dir. div. services crippled children, 1959-90, prof. emeritus, 1990—; dir. center handicapped children Univ. Hosp., U. Ill., 1955-90; cons. in field. Contbr. to profl. jours. Chmn. research adv. com. Children's Bur., HEW, 1964-67; mem. Ill. Commn. Children. Served to capt. AUS, 1944-46. Fellow Am. Acad. Pediatrics, Am. Pub. Health Assn.; mem. Sigma Xi. Home: 3003 Balmoral Cres Flossmoor IL 60422-1404

LISA, ISABELLE O'NEILL, mergers and acquisitions executive, law firm administrator; b. Phila., Mar. 12, 1934; d. Thomas Daniel and Margaret Marie (Hayes) O'Neill; m. Donald Julius Lisa, June 15, 1957; children: Richard Allan, Steven Gregory. Student, Harper Community Coll., Rolling Meadows, Ill., 1976, Scottsdale Community Coll., 1980, Ariz. State U., 1981-82. Cost control clk. Curtis Pub. Co., Phila., 1952-56; sec. United Ins. Co., Annapolis, Md., 1956-57; firm adminstr., legal sec. Law Offices Donald J. Lisa, Bloomingdale, Ill., 1987; legal sec. Lisa & Kubida, P.C., Phoenix, 1987-88, firm adminstr., 1987-89; firm adminstr. Lisa & Assocs., Phoenix, 1989-90, Lisa & Lisa, Phoenix, 1990-91, Lisa & Assocs., 1991—; v.p. adminstrn. Lisa & Co., Phoenix, 1987—. Den mother Cub Scouts Am., Millburn, N.J., 1965; founder, pres. Pro-Tem Rutgers U. Law Wives Assn., 1962-63; bd. advisors Am. Inst., Phoenix, 1991—. Mem. NAFE, Maricopa County Bar Assn. (legal adminstrs. sect. 1992—), Internat. Platform Assn., Rotary. Republican Roman Catholic. Avocations: painting, drawing, photography. Home: # 215 8989 E Via Linda Scottsdale AZ 85258-5409

LISANBY, JAMES WALKER, retired naval officer; b. Princeton, Ky., Jan. 31, 1928; s. Alvin and Rebecca L.; m. Gladys Elnora Kemp, Nov. 18, 1951; children: Elizabeth Ann, Sarah Hollingsworth. B.S. in Elec. Engring. U.S. Naval Acad., 1950; Engrs. Degree in Naval Architecture, MIT, 1953-56; student, Program for Mgmt. Devel., Harvard U., 1967. Commd. ensign U.S. Navy, 1950, advanced through grades to rear adm., 1977; ship supt. Charleston Naval Shipyard, 1956-59; main propulsion asst. U.S.S. Antietam (CVS 36), 1959-61; asst. for ship materials, staff, comdr.-in-chief Atlantic Fleet, 1961-63; asst. for new constrn. cruisers and destroyers Naval Ship Systems Command, Dept. Navy, Washington, 1963-65; head procurement and prodn. br.; fast deployment logistic ship project office Naval Ship Systems Command, Dept. Navy, 1965-68, exec. asst. to comdr., 1969-70; dir. indsl. engring. office of asst. sec. of navy, installations and logistics, 1968-69; supr. shipbldg. Pascagoula, Miss., 1970-73; asst. for ship design, office chief naval ops., 1973-74, project mgr. LHA class amphibious assault ships, 1974-77; comdr. Naval Ship Engring. Center Navy Dept., Washington, 1977-79; dep. comdr. ship design and integration Naval Sea Systems Command, Dept. Navy, Washington, 1979-81; prin. dep. acquisition Naval Sea Systems Command, Dept. Navy, 1981-83, ret., 1983; founder, pres. Naval Services Internat. Inc., Washington, 1983—, pres., chief exec. officer. Recipient Engr. of Yr. award Soc. Mfg. Engrs., 1979; decorated Legion of Merit. Mem. Am. Soc. Naval Engrs. (nat. v.p. 1979-81), Soc. Naval Architects and Marine Engrs., Sigma Xi, Tau Beta Pi. Office: PO Box 15515 Arlington VA 22215-0515

LISCHER, LUDWIG FREDERICK, consultant, former utility company executive; b. Darmstadt, Germany, Mar. 1, 1915; came to U.S., 1923, naturalized, 1933; s. Ludwig J. and Paula (Stahlecker) L.; m. Helen Lucille Rentz, Oct. 1, 1938; 1 dau., Linda Sue. B.S. in Elec. Engring., Purdue U., 1937, D.Eng. (hon.), 1976. With Commonwealth Edison Co., Chgo., 1937-80; v.p. charge engring., research and tech. activities Commonwealth Edison Co., 1964-80; ret., 1980; cons. and mem. adv. com. to engring. tech. div. Oak Ridge Nat. Lab., 1980-84; cons. energy and electric utility fields; past chmn. various tech. adv. coms. to fed. agys.; past chmn. and adv. to Edison Electric Inst.; past chmn. rsch. adv. com. Electric Power Rsch. Inst. Contbr. articles to profl. jours. Past bd. dirs. Chgo. Engring. and Sci. Center; former trustee Ill. Inst. Tech. Served to lt. col. AUS and USAAF, 1941-45. Fellow IEEE; mem. ASME, Nat. Acad. Engring., Am. Nuclear Soc., Tau Beta Pi, Eta Kappa Nu. Home: 441 N Park Blvd Apt 5A Glen Ellyn IL 60137-4646

LISENBEE, ALVIS LEE, structural geologist, educator; b. Lamesa, Tex., Dec. 3, 1940; s. Alvis and Geneva (Hancock) L.; divorced; stepchildren: Dana Richart, Jason Armstrong. BS, U. New Mex.-Albuquerque, 1963, MS, 1967; PhD, Pa. State U.-State College, 1972. Asst. geologist Ark-La. Gas Co., Shreveport, La., 1964; geologist Climax Molybdenun Corp., Golden, Colo., 1967, Noranda Mining Co., Reno, Nev., 1972-73; chief geologist Posora Mining Co., Ltd., Esfahan, Iran, 1974-76; asst. prof. geol. engring. S.D. Sch. Mines and Tech., Rapid City, 1972-76, assoc. prof., 1976-78, prof., 1978—, head dept., 1979-85; cons. Armco Steel Corp., Denver, 1979-80, Gulf Oil Co., Casper, Wyo., 1981-82, S.D. Geol. Survey, 1982-83, Exxon Corp., Denver, 1982-83, Turkish Petroleum Corp., Ankara, 1985-90, Yates Petroleum Corp., Artesia, N.Mex., 1991-95, Homestake Minig Corp., Reno, 1993-95. Fulbright scholar U.S. Commn. for Ednl. Exchange, Turkey, 1983-84. Mem. Geol. Soc. Am., Wyo. Geol. Soc., Darton Geol. Soc., Nev. Petroleum Soc. Republican. Office: SD Sch Mines and Tech Dept Geology & Geol Engring Rapid City SD 57701

LISH, GORDON, author, educator, editor; b. Hewlett, N.Y., Feb. 11, 1934; s. Philip and Regina (Deutsch) L.; m. Loretta Frances Fokes, Nov. 7, 1956 (div. May 1967); children: Jennifer, Rebecca, Ethan; m. Barbara Works, May 30, 1969; 1 son, Atticus. LittD (hon.), SUNY, 1993. Editorial dir. Genesis West, 1961-65; editor in chief, dir. linguistic studies Behavioral Research Labs., Menlo Park, Calif., 1963-66; with Ednl. Devel. Corp., Palo Alto, 1966-69; fiction editor Esquire mag., N.Y.C., 1969-77; with Alfred A. Knopf, Inc., 1977-95; lectr. Yale U., 1970-74, guest fellow, 1974-80; tchr. fiction writing Columbia U., 1980—; prof. NYU Coll. Arts and Scis. Author: fiction and non-fiction under several pen-names: English Grammar, 1964, The Gabbernot, 1965, Why Work, 1966, A Man's Work, 1967, New Sounds in American Fiction, 1969; (short stories) What I Know So Far, 1981, 84, Mourner at The Door, 1988; (novels) Dear Mr. Capote, 1983, Peru, 1986, Extravaganza, 1989, My Romance, 1991, Zimzum, 1993; editor: The Secret of Life of Our Times, 1973, All Our Secrets Are the Same, 1976; editor in chief The Quarterly; editor 1987—, Chrysalis Rev., 1959-61. Pres. Chrysalis

West Found., 1962—. Office: Ste 2600 650 Madison Ave New York NY 10022

LISHNER, LAURENCE H., lawyer; b. L.A., May 6, 1947; s. Theodore Samuel and Yetta Lishner; m. Annette, Sept. 10, 1978. BA, Calif. State U., L.A., 1968; JD, U. of the Pacific, 1971. Bar:Calif. 1972, U.S. Dist. Ct. (cen. dist.) Calif. 1973, U.S. Dist. Ct. (ea. dist.) Calif. 1989. Pvt. practice Calif. 1972—; judge pro tempore; guest lectr. UCLA ext. Mem. ABA, L.A. County Bar Assn., Landlords Trial Lawyers Assn., Lawyers Club (bd. dirs. 1990, past pres., chmn. state bar conv. del. 1995). Office: 3000 S Robertson Blvd Ste 215 Los Angeles CA 90034-3158

LISIMACHIO, JEAN LOUIS, book publishing executive; b. Nice, France, 1946. Mng. dir. book group Grolier Inc., 1982-91, chmn. bd. dirs., 1991—. Office: Grolier Inc Sherman Tpke Danbury CT 06816

LISIO, DONALD JOHN, historian, educator; b. Oak Park, Ill., May 27, 1934; s. Anthony and Dorothy (LoCelso) L.; m. Susanne Marie Swanson, Apr. 22, 1958; children: Denise Anne, Stephen Anthony. B.A., Knox Coll., 1956; M.A., Ohio U., 1958; Ph.D., U. Wis., 1965. Mem. faculty overseas div. U. Md., 1958-60; asst. prof. history Coe Coll., Cedar Rapids, Iowa, 1964-69, assoc. prof., 1969-74, prof., 1974—, chmn. dept., 1973-81, Henrietta Arnold prof. history, 1980—. Author: The President and Protest: Hoover, Conspiracy, and the Bonus Riot, 1974, Hoover, Blacks, and Lily-Whites: A Study of Southern Strategies, 1985; contbg. author: The War Generation, 1975; contbr. articles to hist. jours. Mem. exec. com. Cedar Rapids Com. Hist. Preservation, 1975-77. Served with U.S. Army, 1958-60. Recipient Outstanding Tchr. award Coe Coll., 1969, Charles J. Lynch Outstanding Teaching award Coe Coll., 1991; William F. Vilas rsch. fellow U. Wis., 1963-64; NEH fellow, 1969-70, rsch. fellow, 1984-85; Am. Coun. Learned Socs. grantee, 1971-72, fellow, 1977-78; U.S. Inst. of Peace rsch. grantee, 1990. Mem. Orgn. Am. Historians, Am. Hist. Assn., AAUP, ACLU. Roman Catholic. Home: 4203 Twin Ridge Ct SE Cedar Rapids IA 52403-3950 Office: Coe Coll Cedar Rapids IA 52402

LISK, PAMELA KONIECZKA, lawyer; b. Chgo., Oct. 8, 1959; m. Thomas Joseph Lisk; 1 child, Sarah. BA, Northwestern U., 1980; M of Pub. Policy, JD, Harvard U., 1984. Staff atty. SEC, Washington, 1984-86; assoc. Lord, Bissell & Brook, Chgo., 1986-89; sr. atty. Sundstrand Corp., Rockford, Ill., 1989—. Mem. Ill. Bar Assn., Phi Beta Kappa.

LISKA, GEORGE, political science educator, author; b. Pardubice, Czechoslovakia, June 30, 1922; came to U.S., 1949, naturalized, 1957; s. Bedrich and Karla (Slezakova) L.; m. Suzy Colombier, June 30, 1962; children: Ian Pierre, Anne Fernande. Dr.Jr., Charles U., Prague, Czechoslovakia, 1948; Ph.D. in Polit. Sci, Harvard U., 1955. Sec. to sec. gen. Czechoslovak Ministry Fgn. Affairs, 1946-48; exec. asst. Council Free Czechoslovakia, Washington, 1949-52; asst. prof. polit. sci. U. Chgo., 1958-61; prof. polit. sci. Johns Hopkins U. and Sch. Advanced Internat. Studies, Washington; also research assoc. Johns Hopkins' Washington Ctr. Fgn. Policy Research (succeeded by Fgn. Policy Inst.), 1964—. Author: International Equilibrium, 1957, The New Statecraft, 1960, Nations in Alliance, 1972, Europe Ascendant, 1964, Imperial America, 1967, War and Order, 1968, States in Evolution, 1973, Beyond Kinninger, 1975, Quest for Equilibrium, 1977, Career of Empire, 1978, Russia and World Order, 1980, Russia and the Road to Appeasement, 1982, Rethinking U.S.-Soviet Relations, 1987, Ways of Power, 1990, Fallen Dominions, 1990, The State and Foreign Policy, 1992, Return to the Heartland and Rebirth of the Old Order, 1994. Recipient Sumner prize Harvard U., 1955. Office: 1740 Massachusetts Ave NW Washington DC 20036-1984 also: Johns Hopkins U Dept Polit Sci Baltimore MD 21218 *The impetus behind my efforts as a writer on and academic teacher of international relations has been the effort to convert the impossibility of actual participation—due to the loss of an official role in my native Czechoslovakia—into a deepened insight into the processes ultimately responsible for my expatriation.*

LISKAMM, WILLIAM HUGO, architect, urban planner, educator; b. N.Y.C., Sept. 10, 1931; s. William J. and Johanne (Herz) L.; m. Karen Elizabeth Nunn, May 1979; children: Amanda Nunn, Mason Nunn; children by previous marriage—Erika, Thea, Fiona. B.Arch., Pratt Inst., 1954; Fulbright scholar, Technische Hochschule, Stuttgart, Germany, 1954-55; M.Arch., Harvard, 1956. Project architect maj. archtl. and urban planning programs Calif. and N.Y., 1958-63; exec. v.p. Okamoto & Liskamm, Inc. (planners and architects), San Francisco, 1963-71; ind. archtl. and urban planning cons., 1971-74; pres. William H. Liskamm, AIA, AIP, Inc., 1974—; dir. planning Woodward-Clyde Consultants, San Francisco, 1978-79; dir. campus planning office U. Calif., Berkeley, 1984-90; asst. prof. dept. architecture Coll. Environ. Design, U. Calif. at Berkeley, 1963-69, vice chmn., 1965-67, vis. sr. lectr. U. Coll., London, 1967-68; chmn. bd. Archtl. Found. No. Calif.; chmn. design rev. bd. San Francisco Bay Conservation and Devel. Commn., State of Calif., 1970-80; chmn. archtl. adv. com. Golden Gate Bridge Hwy. and Transp. Dist., 1980-81; prof., advisor major planning and design competitions Nat. Endowment for the Arts. Author: Appearance and Design Element, California Coastal Plan, 1974. Served to 1st lt. C.E. AUS, 1956-58. Recipient awards for profl. projects HUD; Am. Inst. Planners award for San Francisco Urban Design Plan, 1972; Wheelwright fellow Harvard, 1967-68; Nat. Endowment for Arts grantee. Mem. AIA (coll. of fellows).

LISKER, DEBORAH J(ANE), lawyer; b. Providence, Oct. 30, 1950; d. Hyman and Lilyan Davis (Toretsky) L.; m. Edward Milton Chernoff, Oct. 14, 1984; children: Hilary Isiner Chernoff, Benjamin Isiner Chernoff. AB, Brown U., 1972; JD, U. Chgo., 1975. Bar: Pa. 1975. Assoc. Dechert, Price & Rhoads, Phila., 1975-81; fin. and corp. counsel Geothermal Resources Internat., Inc., Phila., 1981-83; assoc. counsel Campbell Soup Co., Camden, N.J., 1983-89, corp. counsel, 1989-92; sr. counsel Ind. Blue Cross, Phila., 1993—. Mem. Phila. Bar Assn. Avocation: tennis. Office: Ind Blue Cross 1901 Market St Philadelphia PA 19103

LISKOV, BARBARA HUBERMAN, software engineering educator; b. Los Angeles, Nov. 7, 1939. BA in Math., U. Calif., Berkeley, 1961; MS in Computer Sci., Stanford U., 1965, PhD, 1968. With applications programming sect. Mitre Corp., Bedford, Mass., 1961-62, mem. tech. staff, 1968-72; with Harvard U., Cambridge, Mass., 1962-63; grad. research asst. dept. computer sci. Stanford U., Palo Alto, Calif., 1963-68; prof. computer sci. and engring. MIT, Cambridge, 1972—; NEC prof. software sci. and engring., 1984—. Author: (with others) CLU Reference Manual, Lecture Notes in Computer Science 114, 1981; (with J. Guttag) Abstraction and Specification in Program Development, 1986; assoc. editor Transactions on Programming Langs. and Systems; contbr. articles to profl. jours. Mem. IEEE, Am. Acad. Arts and Scis., Assn. Computing Machinery (spl. interest groups on databases, oper. systems and programming langs.), Nat. Acad. Engring.

LISLE, JANET TAYLOR, writer; b. Englewood, N.J., Feb. 13, 1947; d. Alden Mygatt and Janet Roberton (MacColl) Taylor; m. Richard Waterman Lisle, Oct. 17, 1976; 1 child, Elizabeth. BA, Smith Coll., 1969; cert. in journalism, Ga. State U., 1971. Author: (books) The Dancing Cats of Applesap, 1984, 93, Sirens and Spies, 1985, 90 (Booklist Best of the 80's 1990, Notable Children's Book ALA 1985, Best Book for Young Adults, Booklist Editor's Choice), The Great Dimpole Oak, 1987 (Golden Kite Honor award, Booklist Editor's Choice), Afternoon of the Elves, 1989, 91, (Newbery Honor award Children's Lit., 1990, Best Book of the Yr. Sch. Libr. Jour., Notable Children's Book ALA, Booklist Editor's Choice), Forest, 1993 (Best Book of the Yr. Sch. Libr. Jour., Am. Bookseller Pick of the Lists), The Gold Dust Letters, 1994 (Jr. Libr. Guild Selection), Looking For Juliette, 1994 (anthologized short stories) Those in Peril on the Sea, 1992, The Face in the Rafters, 1993. Mem. Author's Guild, Soc. Children's Book Writers. Avocations: choral activities, tennis, writing group. Office: care Orchard Books 95 Madison Ave New York NY 10016

LISOTA, GARY MARTIN, business executive, retired naval officer; b. Milw., Nov. 22, 1949; s. Martin Gerard and Shirley Rose (Francke) L.; m.

Judith Ann Winnicki, May 25, 1970 (div. July 1986); 1 child, Mark Joseph; m. Karen Janelle Bennett, May 13, 1989. Student, Ill. Inst. Tech., 1967-68; BSEE, Purdue U., 1974. Commd. 2d lt. USN, 1969, advanced through grades to lt. comdr., ret., 1980; program mgr. SEACOR, Alexandria, Va., 1980-81; dir. corp. mktg. AMSEC, Arlington, Va., 1981-83, ops. ctr. mgr., 1983-87; v.p. Washington div. SAIC-AMSEC, Arlington, 1987-88; v.p. bus. devel. SAIC-AMSEC, Virginia Beach, Va., 1988-90, COO, 1990—, also bd. dirs. Mem. Am. Soc. Naval Engrs., Purdue Alumni Assn., Tau Beta Pi, Eta Kappa Nu. Roman Catholic. Office: SAIC-AMSEC 2829 Guardian Ln Virginia Beach VA 23452

LISS, HERBERT MYRON, newspaper publisher, communications company executive; b. Mpls., Mar. 23, 1931; s. Joseph Milton and Libby Diane (Kramer) L.; m. Barbara Lipson, Sept. 19, 1954; children: Lori-Ellen, Kenneth Allen, Michael David. BS in Econs., U. Pa., 1952. With mktg. mgmt. Procter & Gamble Co., Cin., 1954-63, Procter & Gamble Internat., various countries, 1963-74; gen. mgr. Procter & Gamble Comml. Co., San Juan, P.R., 1974-78; v.p., mgr. internat. ops. InterAm. Orange Crush Co. subs. Procter & Gamble Co., Cin., 1981-84; pres. River Cities (Ohio) Communications Inc, 1985—; pub. The Downtowner newspaper, Cin. Health and Fitness, others, Cin., 1985—. Bd. dirs. Charter Com., Cin., 1958-63, Promotion and Mktg. Assn. U.S., 1978-81, Jr. Achievement, Cin., 1980-87; bd. dirs. Downtown Coun., Cin., 1985—, treas., 1991-92; mem. mktg. com. Downtown Cin. Inc./Downtown Coun., 1994—. Mem. Manila Yacht Club, Manila Polo, Equitación De Somos Aguas, Rotary (Cin. club), Cin. Racquet Club. Home: 8564 Wyoming Club Dr Cincinnati OH 45215-4243 Office: The Downtowner Newspaper 128 E 6th St Cincinnati OH 45202-3208

LISSACK, MICHAEL ROBERT, investment banker; b. Lynn, Mass., Aug. 5, 1958; s. Kenneth B. and Carol A. (Goldstein) L. BA, Williams Coll., 1979; M in Pub. and Pvt. Mgmt., Yale U., 1981. Assoc. Lewin & Assocs., Washington, 1980; assoc. Smith Barney, N.Y.C., 1981-83, 2d v.p., 1984, v.p., 1985-87; mng. dir. Smith Barney Inc., N.Y.C., 1987—; adj. prof. econs. Williams Coll., 1995—. Office: Smith Barney Inc Pub Fin 2d Fl 388 Greenwich St New York NY 10013

LISSENDEN, CAROLKAY, pediatrician; b. Newark, Aug. 22, 1937; d. George Cyrus Sr. and Irene Elizabeth (Hempel) L.; m. Bart Albert Barré, June 13, 1964; children: Lisa Kim Barré-Quick, Bart Christopher Barré. BA, U. Pa., 1959; MD, Med. Coll. Pa., 1964. Pediat. intern St. Luke's Hosp., N.Y.C., 1964-65; pediat. resident Columbia-Presbyn. Hosp., N.Y.C., 1965-67; pvt. practice Mountainside, N.J., 1967—. Fellow Am. Acad. Pediats.; mem. AMA, N.J. Med. Assn., Union County Med. Assn. Republican. Presbyterian. Avocations: gardening, roller skating, sewing. Home and Office: 135 Wild Hedge Ln Mountainside NJ 07092

LISSMAN, BARRY ALAN, veterinarian; b. N.Y.C., June 13, 1952; s. George Joseph and Helene Anna (Freilich) L.; m. Wendy Louise Cooper, June 8, 1975; children: Erica Beth, Rachel Danielle. BS, Cornell U., 1974, DVM, 1977. Lic. veterinarian N.Y., Mass., N.J., Fla. Pvt. practice L.I., N.Y., 1977—; owner, dir. Sachem Animal Hosp. and L.I. Mobile Vet. Clinics, Holbrook, N.Y., 1981—, Animal Med. Clinic, Centereach, N.Y. Contbr. to vet. text books, profl. jours. Mem. AVMA (Practitioner Rsch. award 1989), N.Y. State Vet. Med. Assn. (outstanding svc. to vet. medicine award 1992), L.I. Vet. Med. Assn. (Merit award 1994), Assn. Avian Veterinarians, Am. Assn. House Call Veterinarians (v.p.). Discoverer 1st clin. cases Rocky Mountain spotted fever in dogs, 1979, Lyme disease in dogs, 1983. Home: 15 Quaker Hill Rd Stony Brook NY 11790-1546 Office: Sachem Animal Hosp 227 Union Ave Holbrook NY 11741-1806

LIST, CHARLES EDWARD, management and organization development consultant; b. Chgo., May 9, 1941; s. Kermit Paul and Johanna Emma (Staat) L.; B.A., Valparaiso U., 1963; M.A., St. Marys Coll., Winona, Minn., 1980; Ph.D. in Orgn. Devel., Union Coll., Cin., 1984; m. Susan Mary Nelson, July 20, 1968; children—Andrea Sarang, Darcy Young. Mem. personnel staff Control Data Corp., Mpls., 1965-72; mgr. human resource center Supervalu Stores, Mpls., 1973-74; dir. personnel Internat. Dairy Queen, Mpls., 1974-77; mgr. mgmt. and orgn. devel. Cardiac Pacemakers Inc., St. Paul, 1977-82; adj. faculty instr. U. St. Thomas, Cardinal Stritch Coll.; instr. Met. State U., St. Paul, 1972—. Served with USMC, 1963-64. Recipient Instr. Recognition award Met. State U., 1975, 80, 86. Mem. Am. Soc. Personnel Adminstrn., Am. Soc. Tng. and Devel. Episcopalian. Contbr. articles to profl. jours. Home: 4940 Winterset Dr Minnetonka MN 55343-8726

LIST, DAVID PATTON, lawyer; b. Belvidere, Ill., Feb. 4, 1920; s. Raymond Ford and Marguerite (Patton) L.; m. Patricia Porter, Jan. 7, 1949 (dec. 1978); children—John, Victoria, David Patton; m. Annette Kahlmorgan, 1979. A.B., Dartmouth Coll., 1942; LL.B., Harvard U., 1948. Bar: Ill. 1948. Since practiced in Chgo.; partner firm Sidley & Austin (and predecessors), 1955-85, of counsel, 1985—. Served with USAAF, 1942-45. Fellow Am. Coll. Trial Lawyers; mem. Am. Bar Assn., Ill. Bar Assn., Chgo. Bar Assn., Legal Club Chgo., Law Club Chgo. Republican. Episcopalian. Clubs: Westmoreland Country, U. Chgo. Office: Sidley & Austin 1 First National Plz Chicago IL 60603

LIST, ERICSON JOHN, environmental engineering science educator, engineering consultant; b. Whakatane, New Zealand, Mar. 27, 1939; came to U.S., 1962; s. Ericson Bayliss and Freda Helen (Sunkel) L.; m. Olive Amoore, Feb. 3, 1962; children: Brooke Meredith, Antonia Michael. B.E. with honors, U. Auckland, N.Z., 1961, M.E., 1962, Ph.D., 1968; Calif. Inst. Tech., 1965. Registered profl. engr., Calif. Sr. lectr. U. Auckland, 1966-69; asst. prof. Calif. Inst. Tech., Pasadena, 1969-72; assoc. prof., 1972-78, prof. environ. engring. sci., 1978—, exec. officer, 1980-85; dir. Fluid Kinetics Corp., Ventura, Calif., 1972-82; bd. chmn. Flow Sci. Inc., Pasadena, 1983—; cons. So. Calif. Edison, Rosemead, Calif., 1973—; City and County of San Francisco, 1974—. Author: (with Hugo B. Fischer) Mixing in Inland and Coastal Waters, 1979, (with W. Rodi) Turbulent Jets and Plumes, 1982. Mem. Blue Ribbon Commn. City of Pasadena, 1976-78. Recipient Spl. Creativity award NSF, 1982. Republican. Club: Athenaeum (Pasadena) (chmn. wine com. 1981-83). Office: Calif Inst Tech 1201 E California Blvd Pasadena CA 91125-0001

LIST, RAYMOND EDWARD, engineering and construction executive, management consultant; b. Bklyn., Apr. 9, 1944; s. Raymond William and Mildred Patricia (Maroney) L.; m. Susan Gladys McKenna ; children: Raymond McKenna, Julia McKenna. BCE, Union Coll., Schenectady, N.Y., 1966; M in Engring., Manhattan Coll., 1967; MBA with honors, Harvard U., 1977. Registered profl. engr., Calif., Nev., Mass., Pa. Project mgr. Kaiser Engrs., Inc., Oakland, Calif., 1967-78; exec. asst. Perini Corp., San Francisco, 1977-78; v.p. Arthur D. Little Inc., Washington, 1978-80; v.p., gen. mgr. Planning Rsch. Corp., McLean, Va., 1980-82; pres. List and Assocs. Inc., Washington, 1982-86; chmn. Am. Venture Investments Inc., Fairfax, Va., 1986—, also bd. dirs.; chmn. ICF Tech. Inc., Fairfax, 1987-89; pres. Kaiser Engrs. Group Inc., Oakland, 1988-89, ICF Kaiser Engrs. Group Inc., Oakland, 1989—; also bd. dirs. ICF-Kaiser Engrs. Group Inc., Oakland; bd. dirs. ICF Corp. Internat. Inc., Am. Capital and Rsch. Inc. Fellow Pub. Health Soc., 1967. Mem. ASCE, AIME, Am. Mining Congress, Harvard Club of N.Y.C., Harvard Bus. Sch. Club of Washington. Lutheran. Avocations: running, swimming, fishing. Office: ICF Kaiser Engrs Group Inc PO Box 23210 1800 Harrison St Oakland CA 94623*

LIST, ROLAND, physicist, educator, former UN official; b. Frauenfeld, Thurgau, Switzerland, Feb. 21, 1929; s. August Joseph and Anna (Kaufmann) L.; m. Gertrud K. Egli, Apr. 14, 1956; children: Beat R., Claudia G. List Woolner. Diploma physics ETH, Swiss Fed. Inst. Tech., 1952, Dr. Sci. Nat., 1960. Head hail sect. Swiss Fed. Inst. for Snow and Avalance Rsch., Davos, Switzerland, 1952-63; prof. dept. physics U. Toronto, Ont., Can., 1963-82, prof.—, assoc. chmn. dept. physics, 1968-73; dep. sec.-gen. World Meteorol. Orgn., Geneva, 1982-84; chmn. World Meteorol. Orgn.-EC Panels on Cloud Physics/Weather Modification, 1969-82, Italian Sci. Com. for Rain Enhancement, 1990—; vis. prof. Swiss Fed. Inst. for Tech., Zurich, Switzerland, 1974; bd. dirs. Univ. Corp.for Atmospheric Rsch., Boulder, Colo., 1974-77; mem. Sci. Coun. Space Shuttle Program, 1979-82. Author more than 200 papers in atmospheric and classical physics. Recipient Sesquicentennial medal St. Petersburg U., Russia, 1970, Patterson medal Can. Meteorol. Soc., 1979, Recognition plaque Govt.

of Thailand, 1986. Fellow Can. Acad. Sci./Royal Soc. Can., Royal Meteorol. Soc. (U.K.), Am. Meteorol. Soc.; mem. Can. Meteorol. Oceanic Soc., Am. Geophysics Soc., Am. Physics Soc., European Geophys. Soc., Swiss Phys. Soc., Swiss Acad. Natural Scis., Rotary. Home: 58 Olsen Dr, Toronto, ON Canada M3A 3J3 Office: U Toronto, Dept Physics, Toronto, ON Canada M5S 1A7

LISTACH, PATRICK ALAN, professional baseball player; b. Natchitoches, La., Sept. 12, 1967. Student, Ariz. State U. Baseball players Milwaukee Brewers, 1988—. Named Am. League Rookie of the Year, 1992. Office: Milw Brewers County Stadium PO Box 3099 Milwaukee WI 53201-3099*

LISTER, DIANNE ELIZABETH, foundation administrator; b. Toronto, Ont., Can., Dec. 21, 1952; d. Edwin and Ella Jeanne Marie (Norton) Lister; m. Ron Weinberger, June 14; children: Jason, Sarah. BA with honors, Trent U., Peterborough, Ont., 1976; LLB, Osgoode Hall Law Sch., Toronto, 1980. Proprietor, lawyer Toronto, 1983-84, atty., 1984-87; found. administr. CCAS Found., Toronto, 1987-89; sr. fundraising coord. Toronto, 1989-91; exec. v.p. Hosp. for Sick Children Found., Toronto, 1991-92, COO, 1992-93, pres., CEO, 1993—; dir. vice chmn. Safe Kids Can., 1992—. Mem. Nat. Assn. Fund Raising Execs. (dir., pres.-elect 1994—), Can. Assn. Gift Planners, Assn. Healthcare Philanthropy, Law Soc. Upper Can. Avocations: photography, creative writing. Office: Hospital for Sick Children Found, 555 University Ave, Toronto, ON Canada M5G 1X8

LISTER, EARLE EDWARD, animal science consultant; b. Harvey, N.B., Can., Apr. 14, 1934; s. Earle Edward and Elizabeth Hazel (Coburn) L.; m. Teresa Ann Moore, June 4, 1983. BSc in Agriculture, McGill U., Montreal, Can., 1955, MSc in Animal Nutrition, 1957; PhD in Animal Nutrition, Cornell U., 1960. Feed nutritionist Ogilvie Flour Mills, Montreal, 1960-65; rsch. scientist rsch. br. Animal Rsch. Ctr. Agriculture Can., Ottawa, 1965-74, dep. dir. rsch. br. Animal Rsch. Ctr., 1974-78, program specialist ctrl. region rsch. br., 1978-80; dir. gen. Atlantic region rsch. br. Agriculture Can., Halifax, N.S., 1980-85; dir. gen. plant health and plant products and pesticides, food prodn. and inspection br. Agriculture Can., Ottawa, 1985-87, dir. rsch. br. Animal Rsch. Ctr., 1987-91; dir. Ctr. Food and Animal Rsch., 1991-92; cons., 1992—; former mem. Ont. Agrl. Rsch. and Svc. Coms.; former chmn. Beef Rsch. Com.; invited presenter Atlantic Livestock Conf., 1968, Ea. CSAS meeting, 1969, Can. Com. Animal Nutrition, 1976, CSAS Symposium Laval U., 1974, Guelph Nutrition Conf., 1973, 74, Asst. Dep. Minister Dairy Rev. meeting, Toronto, 1985, U. Guelph ethics conf., 1991, Can. Consumers Assn., Saskatchewan, 1991. Contbr. 54 articles to profl. jours. co-chmn. United Way/Health Ptnrs. for Agriculture Can., Ottawa, 1991; former dir. N.S. Inst. Agrologists. McGill U. scholar, 1953-55; recipient Nat. Rsch. Coun. Post Grad. Spl. scholarship Cornell U., 1957-59. Mem. Am. Soc. Animal Sci., Am. Dairy Sci. Assn. Advancement Sci. in Can., Agrl. Inst. Can., Can. Soc. Animal Sci. (former dir.), Ont. Inst. Agrologists. Achievements include research in the determination of nutrient requirements of beef cows during winter pregnancy, determination of protein and energy levels and appropriate sources of nutrients for young dairy calves for optimal growth; development of intensive feeding system for raising high quality beef from Holstein male calves. Home: 390 Hinton Ave, Ottawa, ON Canada K1Y 1B1 Office: Ctr for Food and Animal Rsch, NCC Driveway Bldg #55, Ottawa, ON Canada K1A 0C6

LISTER, HARRY JOSEPH, financial company executive, consultant; b. Teaneck, N.J., Jan. 27, 1936; s. Harry and Arline Audrey (Pinera) L.; m. Erika Anna Maria Englisch, Sept. 3, 1960; children: Harry Joseph Jr., Karen P. Lister Lawson, Leslie M. Lister Fidler, Andrea A. Lister Lytle, Michael P. BS in Fin. and Econs., Lehigh U., 1958. Security analyst Calvin Bullock, Ltd., N.Y.C., 1959-61, assoc. dir. estate planning, 1961-65, dir. estate planning., 1965-72, asst. v.p., 1969-72; v.p. N.Y. Venture Fund, Inc., N.Y.C., 1970-72; registered rep. Johnston, Lemon & Co., Inc., Washington, 1972—, dir., 1978-90, v.p., 1983-88, corp. sec., 1978-85, sr. v.p., 1984-90; v.p. Wash. Mgmt. Corp., 1972-81, corp. sec., 1978-81, exec. v.p., 1981-85, pres., 1985—, dir., 1978—; pres. JL Fin. Svcs., Inc., Washington, 1975-90; v.p. Washington Mut. Investors Fund, Inc., Washington, 1972-81, corp. sec., 1978-81, exec. v.p., 1981-85, pres., dir., 1985—; pres. The Growth Fund of Washington, Inc., 1985—, also bd. dirs.; registered prin., bd. dirs. Washington Funds Distbrs., Inc., 1985-93, pres., 1992-93; pres., trustee The Tax Exempt Fund of Md., 1986—, The Tax Exempt Fund of Va., 1986—; chmn., bd. dirs. Washington Investment Advisors, Inc., 1991—; cons. Capital Group, Inc., L.A., 1972—; regent Coll. for Fin. Planning, Denver, 1979-84, mem. exec. com., 1980-84, chmn. bd. regents, 1981-83; bd. dirs. Internat. Bd. Standards and Practices for Cert. Fin. Planners, 1985-86. Author: Your Guide to IRAs and 14 Other Retirement Plans, 1985. Bd. dirs. cen. Bergen chpt. ARC, Hackensack, N.J., 1968-72, chmn. exec. com. 1970-72; bd. dirs. Westwood, N.J. Planning Bd., 1969-72, vice-chmn., 1970-72; bd. dirs. Westwood N.J. Zoning Bd. Adjustment, 1970-72. Mem. Investment Co. Inst. (pension com., chmn. 1976-81, tax com., rsch. com.), Nat. Assn. Securities Dealers, Inc. (investment cos. com. 1984-87, bd. arbitrators 1987-93), Met. Club, Univ. Club. Home: Spinnaker Ct Reston VA 22091 Office: 1101 Vermont Ave NW Washington DC 20005-3521

LISTER, KEITH FENIMORE, publishing executive; b. Clio, Iowa, Aug. 29, 1917; s. W. Frank and Maude (Fenimore) L.; m. Margaret Boman, Sept. 1, 1941; children: Janet, Priscilla. Student, Drake U., 1936-41. Pres. Lister Investment Co., San Diego, 1955-61, Southcoast Capital Co., San Diego, 1961-65, City Bank San Diego, 1965-69; pub. San Diego Daily Transcript, 1972-94. Mem. San Diego Yacht Club, Univ. Club. Presbyterian. Avocation: sailing.

LISTER, SARA ELISABETH, lawyer; b. St. Paul, May 10, 1940; d. Joseph H. and Elisabeth R. Ball; m. Charles E. Lister, June 23, 1961; children—Penny Margaret, Jennifer Mary. A.B., Radcliffe Coll., 1961; M.A. in Polit. Sci., George Washington U., 1966, J.D., 1974. Bar: D.C. Ct. Appeals 1974, U.S. Dist. Ct. 1975, U.S. Cir. Ct. Appeals 1979, U.S. Supreme Ct. 1980. Assoc. Leva, Hawes, Symington, Martin & Oppenheimer, Washington, 1974-77; dep. gen. counsel U.S. Navy, Washington, 1977-79; dep. spl. asst. to sec. def. U.S. Dept. Def., Washington, 1979; gen. counsel U.S. Army, Washington, 1979-81; ptnr. Patterson Belknap Webb & Tyler, 1982-85; gen. counsel Washington Met. Area Transit Authority, 1985—. Editor George Washington Law Rev., 1974; contbr. articles to profl. jours. Mem. ABA, D.C. Bar Assn. Office: 600 5th St NW Washington DC 20001-2651

LISTER, THOMAS MOSIE, composer, lyricist, publishing company executive, minister; b. Empire, Ga., Sept. 8, 1921; s. Willis Waller and Orena Pearl (Holl) L.; m. Jewel Wylene Whitten, June 2, 1946; children—Brenda (Mrs. James Milton Vann), Barbara (Mrs. David Miller Williams). Attended, Rennsalaer Poly. Inst., 1944-45, Middle Ga. Coll., 1945-46, U. South Fla., 1968; studied privately at, Tampa U., 1958-63. Founder, pres. Mosie Lister Publs., Atlanta, 1952-56, Tampa, 1956—; affiliate for performance and synchronization rights SESAC, Inc., 1955—; affiliate Lillenas Pub. Co., Kansas City, Mo., 1969—; also cons. and dir.; ordained to ministry Baptist Ch., 1975; choral dir. Composer, lyricist numerous gospel songs, 1940—; singer, Tampa, Fla., and Atlanta, 1941, 46-47; Compiler song. collections, hymnbooks, and others; arranger religious music for choral groups and ensembles; songs include I'm Feeling Fine, Where No One Stands Alone, His Hand in Mine; contbg. arranger profl. singing groups. Served with USNR, 1942-45. Named Bapt. Layman of Year for Tampa, 1971; inducted into Gospel Hall of Fame, 1976; recipient Humanist award Sesac, Inc., 1976; Mosie Lister Day named in his honor Tampa, 1974. Mem. Gospel Music Assn. (dir. 1970-71), Fla. Bapt. Ministers of Music Assn. (hon. life). Democrat. Address: 17008 Winners Circle Odessa FL 33556

LISTERUD, MARK BOYD, retired surgeon; b. Wolf Point, Mont., Nov. 19, 1924; s. Morris B. and Grace (Montgomery) L.; m. Sarah C. Mooney, May 26, 1946; children: John, Mathew, Ann, Mark, Sarah, Richard. BA magna cum laude, U. Minn., 1949, BS, 1950, MB, 1952, MD, 1953. Diplomate Am. Bd. Surgery. Intern King County Hosp., 1952-53; resident in surgery U. Wash., Seattle, 1953-57; practice medicine specializing in surgery Wolf Point, 1958-93; mem. admission com. U. Wash. Med. Sch., Seattle, 1983-88; instr. Dept. Rural and Community Health, U. N.D. Med. Sch., 1991. Contbr. articles to med. jours. Mem. Mont. State Health Coordinating Council, 1983, chmn. 1986—; bd. dirs. Blue Shield, Mont., 1985-87. Served with USN, 1943-46. Fellow Am. Coll. Surgeons, Royal

Soc. Medicine; mem. N.E. Mont. Med. Soc. (pres.), Mont. Med. Assn. (pres. 1968-69), AMA (alt. del., del. 1970-84). Clubs: Montana, Elks. Avocations: fishing, hunting. Home: Rodeo Rd Wolf Point MT 59201 Office: 100 Main St Wolf Point MT 59201-1530

LISTGARTEN, MAX ALBERT, periodontics educator; b. Paris, May 14, 1935; came to U.S., 1968; s. Samuel and Etla (Weber) L.; m. Eileen Anne Gregory, July 3, 1963; children: Karen, Sheralyn, Michael. DDS, U. Toronto, 1959; cert. in periodontics, Harvard U., 1963; MA (hon.), U. Pa., 1971; PhD (hon.), U. Athens, 1993. Research assoc. Harvard U., Boston, 1963-64; asst. prof. periodontics U. Toronto, Can., 1964-67, assoc. prof., 1967-68; assoc. prof. U. Pa., Phila., 1968-71, prof., 1971—; vis. prof. U. Gothenburg, Sweden, 1976-77, U. Berne, 1988-89; cons. Nat. Inst. Dental Research, Bethesda, Md., 1979-88, FDA, Rockville, Md., 1992—; cons. in field. Author textbooks and numerous articles on various aspects of periodontal anatomy, microbiology, histopathology, and diagnosis. Recipient Periodontology award William J. Gies Found., 1981; named Disting. Alumnus, Harvard U., 1986, U. Pa., 1994. Fellow AAAS, Am. Acad. Periodontology (Clin. Rsch. award 1987); mem. ADA, Am. Assn. for Dental Rsch. (pres. 1991-92), Internat. Assn. Dental Rsch. (award for basic rsch. in periodontology 1973). Jewish. Avocations: swimming, skiing, hiking, photography. Office: U Penn-School of Dental Medicine Dept of Periodontics 4001 Spruce St Philadelphia PA 19104

LISTON, AARON IRVING, botanist; b. Cleve., Dec. 2, 1959; s. Herbert Liston and Seema Beatrice Feinstein; m. Sara Noelle Meury, Nov. 11, 1990. BSc in Biology, The Hebrew Univ., Jerusalem, 1982, MSc cum laude in Botony, 1984; PhD in Botany, Claremont Grad. Sch., 1990. Herbarium asst. The Hebrew Univ., Jerusalem, 1982-86; rsch. asst. Rancho Santa Ana Botanic Garden, Claremont, Calif., 1987-89; postdoctoral rschr. dept. Genetics U. Calif., Davis, 1990; asst. prof., dir. herbarium, dept. botany & plant pathology Oreg. State U., Corvallis, 1991—. Contbr articles to profl. jours. Grantee Claremont Grad. Sch., 1986, 87, 89, Sigma Xi, 1988, NSF, 1988, 93, 94, Oreg. Dept. Agr., 1991, M.J. Murdock Charitable Trust, 1991-92, Hardman Found., 1993, 94, Hardman Found. and Hoover Trust, 1993, 94, NAS/Nat. Rsch. Coun., 1993; recipient G. Ledyard Stebbins award Calif. Native Plants Soc., 1987, The Nature Conservancy, 1994. Mem. AAAS, Am. Soc. Plant Taxonomists, Assn. Systematics Collections, Bot. Soc. Am., Soc. for Molecular Biology and Evolution, Soc. Systematic Biologists, Calif. Bot. Soc. Office: Oregon State University Cordley Hall 2082 Corvallis OR 97331

LISTON, ALAN A., lawyer; b. Hamilton, Ont., Oct. 11, 1946; s. Ambrose James and Kathleen Frances (Burns) L. BA, U. Western Ont., 1968, B. Laws, 1972. Solicitor Domgroup Ltd., Toronto, 1976-81, dir. legal svcs., 1981-82, gen. counsel, sec., 1982-84, v.p., gen. counsel, sec., 1984-85, sr. v.p., gen. counsel, sec., 1986-88, pres., 1988-92, also bd. dirs. Office: 29 Notley Pl, Toronto, ON Canada M4B 2M7 Office: Domgroup Ltd, 10 Toronto St, Toronto, ON Canada M5C 2B7

LISTON, MARY FRANCES, retired nursing educator; b. N.Y.C., Dec. 17, 1920; d. Michael Joseph and Ellen Theresa (Shaughnessy) L. BS, Coll. Mt. St. Vincent, 1944; MS, Catholic U. Am., 1945; EdD, Columbia, 1962; HHD (hon.), Allentown Coll., 1987. Dir. psychiat. nursing and edn. Nat. League for Nursing, N.Y.C., 1958-66; prof. Sch. Nursing, Cath. U. Am., Washington, 1966-78; dean Sch. Nursing, Cath. U. Am., 1966-73; prof. Marywood Coll., 1984-87; spl. assignment Imperial Med. Center, Tehran, Iran, 1975-78; dep. dir. for program affairs Nat. League for Nursing, N.Y.C., 1978-84. Mem. Sigma Theta Tau. Home: 182 Garth Rd Scarsdale NY 10583-3863

LISTROM, LINDA L., lawyer; b. Topeka, Kans., Mar. 17, 1952. BA magna cum laude, U. Houston, 1974; JD, Harvard U., 1977. Bar: Ill. 1977. Ptnr. Jenner & Block, Chgo. Bd. dirs. Cook County Court Watching Project, Inc., 1983-92. Mem. ABA. Office: Jenner & Block 1 IBM Plz Chicago IL 60611

LISZT, HOWARD PAUL, advertising executive; b. Mpls., Aug. 12, 1946; s. Melvin Sherman and Evalyn (Chapman) Schwartz; m. Roberta Jean Bregman, Feb. 14, 1970; children: Andrew Charles, Daniel Mark. BA, U. Minn., 1968, MBA, 1970. From market rsch. mgr. to sr. product mgr. Green Giant Co., Mpls., 1970-76; from. account exec. to exec. v.p., gen. mgr. Campbell-Mithun, Mpls., 1976-88, pres., chief oper. officer, 1988—; lectr. Augsburg Coll., Mpls., 1981-86. Bd. dirs. St. Paul Chamber Orch., 1984—, Minn. Children's Mus., St. Paul., 1979-86. Mem. Am. Mktg. Assn., Am. Assn. Advt. Agys. (mem. client svc. com.), Oakridge Club. Jewish. Avocations: golfing, traveling, theater. Office: CME KHBB Advt 222 S 9th St Minneapolis MN 55402-3389

LITAN, ROBERT ELI, lawyer, economist; b. Wichita, Kans., May 16, 1950; s. David and Shirley Hermine (Krischer) L.; BS in Econs. (Class of 1946 award, W. Gordon award 1972, Albert A. Berg award 1971, 72), Wharton Sch., U. Pa., 1972; MPhil in Econs., Yale U., 1976, JD (Felix S. Cohen award 1976), 1977, PhD in Econs., Yale U., 1987. Bar: D.C. 1980. m. Avivah D. Swirsky, Aug. 12, 1980. Res. asst. Brookings Instn., 1972-73; instr., then lectr. econs. Yale U., 1975-75; energy cons. Nat. Acad. Scis., 1975-77; regulation and energy specialist President's Council Econ. Advs., 1977-79; assoc. Arnold & Porter, Washington, 1979-82, assoc., then ptnr. and counsel, Powell, Goldstein, Frazer & Murphy, Washington, 1982-90; sr. fellow Brookings Instn., Washington, 1984-92; dir. Ctr. for Econ. Progress, Brookings Inst., 1987-93; dep. asst. atty. gen. U.S. Dept. Justice, 1993-95, assoc. dir. office of mgmt. and budget, 1995—; cons. Inst. Liberty and Democracy, Lima, Peru, 1985-88; visiting lectr., Yale U. Law Sch., 1985-86, 89-90, dir. Ctr. for law, econ. and politics; mem. Presdl. Congl. Commn. on Causes of the Savs. and Loan Crisis, 1991-92. Recipient Silver medal Royal Soc. Arts, 1972; Thouron fellow, Eng., 1972. Mem. ABA, Am. Econs. Assn. Democrat. Author or co-author: Energy Modeling for an Uncertain Future, 1978; Reforming Federal Regulation, 1983; Saving Free Trade: A Pragmatic Approach, 1986, What Should Banks Do?, 1987, Liability: Perspectives and Policy, 1988, American Living Standards: Threats and Challenges, 1988, Blueprint for Restructuring America's Financial Institutions, 1989, Banking Industry in Turmoil, 1990, The Revolution in U.S. Finance, 1991, The Liability Maze, 1991, The Revolution in U.S. Finance, 1991, Down in the Dumps: Adminstration of the Unfair Trade Laws, 1991, The Future of American Banking, 1992, Growth with Equity, 1993, Assessing Bank Reform, 1993, Verdict, 1993, Financial Regulation in a Global Economy, 1994, Footing the Bill for Superfund Cleanups, 1995; contbr. articles to profl. publs. Home: 3 Golden Crest Ct Rockville MD 20854-2982 Office: US Dept Justice 10th and Constitution Ave NW Washington DC 20530

LITCHFIELD, RUTH FRANCE, reading, literacy specialist; b. Cleve., Mar. 17, 1945; d. Edward Agnew and Elizabeth Ann (Way) France; m. Charles Frederick Litchfield, June 6, 1981; children: Katherine Ann, Charles Robert. AA, Christian Coll., Columbus, Mo., 1965; BS in Elem. Edn. and French, U. Mo., 1969; MEd in Reading, U. Hawaii, 1974; student CAGS, Boston, U. 1995. Cert. advanced grad. study, consulting tchr. of reading, French K-9, Mass. Elem. tchr. Claude O. Markoe Sch., Fredericsted, St. Croix, V.I., 1969-70; tchr. Ecole Active Bilingue, Paris, 1970-71; elem. tchr. Punahou Sch., Honolulu, 1971-74; nat. cons., asst. editor, editor, asst. to mng. editor The Economy Co.-McGraw Hill Divsn., Oklahoma City, 1974-81; pvt. cons., tutor U.S. Army, West Germany, 1981-84; tchr., substitute Community Nursery Sch., Lexington, Mass., 1985-89; substitute tchr. Lexington (Mass.) Pub. Schs., 1989-91; instrnl. aide Bridge Elem. Sch., Lexington, 1991-92, reading recovery trainee, 1992-93; reading recovery tchr. Davis Elem. Sch., Bedford, Mass., 1994, Bridge Elem. Sch., Lexington, 1992—; rsch. asst. Harvard U., 1993; workshop presenter in field; rsch. asst. Harvard U. Contbr. articles to profl. publs. Mem. ASCD, Internat. Reading Assn., New Eng. Reading Assn., Mass. Bilingual Edn., Reading Recovery Coun. North Am., Phi Delta Kappa, Pi Lambda Theta (Alpha Gamma chpt.). Republican. Avocations: reading, swimming, knitting, biking, sewing, crafts. Home: 6 Conestoga Rd Lexington MA 02173-6427 Office: 55 Middleby Rd Lexington MA 02173-6920

LITES, JAMES, professional hockey team executive; b. Pentwater, Mich.; m. Denise Lites; children: Brooke, Samuel. BA, U. Mich., 1975; JD, Wayne State U., 1978. Exec. v.p. Detroit Red Wings, 1982-93; v.p. Little Caesar's

Internat., Inc.; president Dallas Stars, 1993—; team rep. bd. govs. NHL. Office: Dallas Stars 211 Cowboys Pky Irving TX 75063

LITFIN, RICHARD ALBERT, retired news organization executive; b. The Dalles, Oreg., Sept. 9, 1918; s. Bernard R. and Alberta (Knappenberger) L.; m. Marie Foley, June 28, 1944; children: Maria Eschen, Mercedes Zingmark, Regina Dibble, Angela Provenzale, Thomas, Anthony. B.J., U. Mo., 1940. Bur. mgr. U.P.I., Olympia, Wash., 1946-47, Pacific Northwest bus. rep., 1946-52, San Francisco rep., 1953-54; bus. mgr. U.P.I. Pacific div., 1954-56, div. mgr., 1956-75, v.p. western region, 1976-79, sr. v.p., 1980-83; Former owner The Dalles, Oreg. Daily Chronicle. Bd. fellows U. Santa Clara. Midshipman Northwestern U., 1940, commd. ensign USNR, 1941, assigned Battleship Idaho, 1941, after flight tng., assigned Fighting 12, U.S.S. Saratoga, 1943, PTO; inactive status, 1946—. Decorated D.F.C., Air Medal with stars. Mem. SAR, Sigma Delta Chi, Alpha Delta Sigma, Sigma Alpha Epsilon. Republican. Roman Catholic. Home: 1790 Oak Ave Menlo Park CA 94025-5863

LITHERLAND, ALBERT EDWARD, physics educator; b. Wallasey, Eng., Mar. 12, 1928; emigrated to Can., 1953, naturalized, 1964; s. Albert and Ethel (Clement) L.; m. Anne Allen, May 12, 1956; children: Jane Elizabeth, Rosamund Mary. B.Sc., U. Liverpool, Eng., 1949, Ph.D., 1955. Rutherford scholar Atomic Energy of Can., Chalk River, Ont., 1953-55; sci. officer Atomic Energy of Can., 1955-66; prof. physics U. Toronto, 1966-79, Univ. prof., 1979-93, prof. emeritus, 1993—. Contbr. articles to profl. jours. Recipient Rutherford medal Inst. Physics, London, 1974, Silver medal for accelerator-based dating techniques Jour. Applied Radiation and Isotopes, 1980, Henry marshall Tory Medal, 1993, Royal Soc. Can.; Guggenheim fellowship, 1986-87. Fellow Royal Soc. Can. (Henry Marshall Tory medal 1993), Royal Soc. London, AAAS, Am. Phys. Soc.; mem. Can. Assn. Physicists (Gold medal for achievement in physics 1971). Home: 3 Hawthorn Gardens, Toronto, ON Canada M4W 1P4 Office: 60 Saint George St, Toronto, ON Canada M5S 1A7

LITHERLAND, KAY, hospital administrator; b. Champaign, Ill., Dec. 11, 1937. Diploma, Evanston Hosp., 1958; BS, Northwestern U., 1963; MA, U. Iowa, 1973. Asst. dir. div. nursing Am. Hosp. Assn., Chgo., Ill.; asst. instr. Coll. Nursing U. Iowa, Iowa City; dir. maternity, gynecol. nursing U. Chgo. Hosp. and Clinics; v.p. Luth. Gen. Hosp., Park Ridge, Ill., Rhode Island Hosp., Providence. Wharton fellow Mgmt. for Nursing Program. Mem. VNA of R.I. (bd. dirs.), Sigma Theta Tau.

LITHGOW, JOHN ARTHUR, actor, director; b. Rochester, N.Y., Oct. 19, 1945; s. Arthur and Sarah L.; m. Jean Taynton, Sept. 10, 1966 (div.); 1 child, Ian; m. Mary Yeager, 1981; children: Phoebe, Nathan. Grad. magna cum laude, Harvard U., 1967; postgrad., London Acad. Music and Dramatic Art, 1967-69. Printmaker, founder Lithgow Graphics. Appeared in plays: A Midsummer Night's Dream, 1953, The Prodigal Daughter, 1973, Patience, Beggar's Opera, La Perichole, Iolanthe, 1965, Pygmalion, Of Mice and Men, Troilus and Cressida, 1969-70, Roar of the Greasepaint, Hadrian VII, The Magistrate, 1970, The Changing Room, What Price Glory, Trelawny of the Wells, 1972; Broadway plays: The Changing Room, 1973, My Fat Friend, 1974, Beyond Therapy, 1982, Requiem For A Heavyweight, 1985, The Front Page, 1986, M. Butterfly, 1988; stock and regional theatre, 15 Shakespearean roles at Gt. Lakes Shakespeare Festival, Ohio, summers 1963-64; dir. plays: As You Like It, 1968, Much Ado About Nothing, 1969, The Way of the World, 1970, The Magistrate, Barefoot in the Park, 1970, Abduction from the Seraglio, 1970, Beaux' Stratagem, 1972, A Pagan Place, 1973; appeared in films: Dealing, 1972, Obsession, 1976, All That Jazz, 1979, Rich Kids, 1979, Mom, the Wolfman and Me, 1980, Blow Out, 1981, Kaufman at Large, 1981, The World According to Garp, 1982 (Acad. award nomination), The Twilight Zone, 1983, Terms of Endearment, 1983 (Acad. award nomination), Footloose, 1984, 2010, 1984, The Glitter Dome, 1984, The Adventures of Buckaroo Banzai: Across The 8th Dimension, 1984, Santa Claus, The Movie, 1985, Manhattan Project, 1986, Harry and the Hendersons, 1987, Distant Thunder, 1988, Memphis Belle, 1990; Out Cold, 1989, Ricochet, 1991, At Play in the Fields of the Lord, 1991, Raising Cain,1992, Cliffhanger, 1993, The Pelican Brief, 1993, A Good Man in Africa, 1994, Princess Caraboo, 1994, Silent Fall, 1994; appeared in TV show The Country Girl, 1974; TV film appearances include Not in Front of the Children, 1982, The Day After, 1983, Resting Place, 1986, Baby Girl Scott, 1987, Amazing Stories (Emmy award 1987), Mesmerized, The Traveling Man, The Last Elephant, 1990, The Boys, 1991, The Wrong Man, 1993, Love, Cheat and Steal, 1993, World War II: When Lions Roared, 1994; writer, producer, actor radio show Under the Gun, Sta. WBAI-FM, N.Y.C., 1972-73. Office: Creative Artists Agy 9830 Wilshire Blvd Beverly Hills CA 90212*

LITHWICK, NORMAN HARVEY, economics educator; b. Ottawa, Ont., Can., Oct. 10, 1938; s. Arnold and Rose Lillian (Esar) L.; m. Yvonne Kate Baher, Mar. 12, 1964; children: Alexander, Dahlia, Hillel. BA with honors, U. Western Ont., 1960; AM, Harvard U., 1962, PhD, 1963. Asst. prof. econs. Carleton U., Ottawa, 1963-67, assoc. prof. econs., 1967-71, prof. econs., 1971—, chmn. econs., 1974-77, prof. pub. adminstrn., 1981—, supr. devel. adminstrn., 1985-90; dir. Inst. Can. Studies Carleton U., 1972-73; vis. prof. econs. and geography Hebrew U., Jerusalem, 1977-78, 90-93; rsch. fellow Brookdale Instn., 1990—; vis. prof. Urban and Regional Econ. Devel. Beer Sheva, mng. dir. Negev Ctr. Regional Devel., asst. sec. Ministry Urban Affairs, Ottawa, 1970-71; advisor Prime Minister Can., Ottawa, 1984; cons. in field. Author: Economic Growth in Can., 1970, Urban Canada, 1970, Regional Policy in Can., 1978; contbr. articles to profl. jours. Mem. Jerusalem Can., 1981—; pres. Jewish Community Council, Ottawa, 1983-85; v.p. Nat. Budgeting Conf., Toronto, Ont., 1985—, Can. Jewish Congress, Montreal, Que., 1986-90; bd. dirs. Children's Hosp. Eastern Ont., Ottawa, 1982-85. Harvard U. grad. fellow, 1960-63, Lady Davis Trust fellow, 1977-78; Can. Mortgage/Housing research grantee, 1966, Can. Council research grantee, 1968. Mem. Can. Econs. Assn., Can. Regional Sci. Assn., Can. Assn. Studies in Devel. Office: Carleton U Sch Pub Adminstrn, Colonel By Dr, Ottawa, ON Canada K1S 5B6 also: PO Box 845, 85025 Metar Israel

LITKE, ARTHUR LUDWIG, business executive; b. Torrington, Conn., Apr. 4, 1922; s. Gustav and Julia (Weiman) L.; m. Stephanie Eleanore Lojewski, June 9, 1951; children: Arthur Lawrence, Suzanne Elizabeth. B.S. in Econs, Trinity Coll., 1944; M.B.A., U. Pa., 1947; grad., Advanced Mgmt. Program, Harvard U., 1961. C.P.A., N.C. With GAO, 1946-64, asso. dir. civil accounting and auditing div., 1963-64; chief accountant, chief Office Accounting and Fin., FPC (FERC), 1964-73; mem. Fin. Acctg. Standards Bd., 1973-78; asso. adminstr. econ. and regulatory adminstrn. Dept. Energy, Washington, 1978; cons. to comptroller gen. of U.S. GAO, 1978-81, 92—; sr. v.p. Zinder Assocs., 1981-93; v.p. and sec. Zinder Cos., 1985-89, sec., treas., 1990-92, vice chmn., 1993—; mem. teaching staff econs. dept. Cath. U. Am., 1966-67; professorial lectr. acctg. George Washington U., 1967-73; adj. prof. acctg. Georgetown U., 1981-83; pres. Internat. Consortium on Govtl. Fin. Mgmt., 1981-84. Contbr. articles to profl. jours. Bd. dirs. Potomac Swimming and Recreation Assn., 1958-72, McLean Citizens Assn., 1990—; adv. bd. Conn. State Opera Assn., 1973-78. Recipient Meritorious Service award GAO, 1959; Meritorious Service award FPC, 1969; Disting. Service award, 1973; Disting. Leadership award Assn. Govt. Accts., 1969; Robert W. King Meml. gold medal, 1975. Mem. AICPA (com. on auditing procedure 1967-70, ethics com. 1971-73), D.C. Inst. CPAs, Assn. Govt. Accts. (nat. pres. 1972-73, bd. dirs. Washington chpt. 1969-72), Am. Arbitration Assn., Am. Accts. Assn., Rotary, Pi Kappa Alpha. Lutheran (council). Home: 1422 Lady Bird Dr Mc Lean VA 22101-3227 Office: 1828 L St NW Washington DC 20036-5104

LITKE, DONALD PAUL, business executive, retired military officer; b. Denver, Nov. 7, 1934; s. Walter Monroe and Alice Vivian (Fowler) L.; m. Myrna Kay McDonald, July 1, 1956; children—Bradley, Susan, Lisa. B.S. in Econs., Colo. A&M U., 1956; MS in Internat. Affairs, George Washington U., 1966. Ops. and staff positions U.S. Air Force, 1956-79; vice compdr. Oklahoma City Air Logistics Ctr., 1979-81; dep. for logistics and security assistance U.S. European Command, Stuttgart, Germany, 1981-83; comdr. U.S. Logistics Group, Ankara, Turkey, 1983-85; dep. dir. Def. Logistics Agy., Alexandria, VA., 1985-86; pres. Bus. Devel. Internat., Alexandria and Niceville, Fla., 1986—. Contbr. articles to profl. jours. Mem. Air Force Assn. (Middle Mgr. of Yr. 1970, award of excellence 1977), Alpha Tau

Omega. Methodist. Avocations: automobile restoration; racquet sports. Home and Office: 2422 Edgewater Dr Niceville FL 32578

LITMAN, BERNARD, electrical engineer, consultant; b. N.Y.C., Oct. 26, 1920; s. Nathan and Gussie (Friedman) L.; m. Ellen Ann Kaufman, Feb. 27, 1949; children—Barbara, Richard. BS. in Elec. Engring, Columbia U., 1941, Ph.D., 1949; M.S., U. Pitts., 1943. Design engr. energy equipment Westinghouse Electric Co., Pitts., 1941-47; with AMBAC Industries div. United Tech. Corp., Garden City, N.Y., 1949-83; tech. dir. guidance equipment Atlas inter-continental missile AMBAC Industries div. United Tech. Corp., 1962-63; chief engr. systems devel. and research, 1964-83; dir. advanced tech. Gull Electronics Systems Div., Parker Hannifin Corp., 1983-93; tech. cons., 1994—; Westinghouse lectr. U. Pitts., 1944; lectr. Adelphi U., Garden City. Co-author: Gyroscopics, 1961. William Petit Trobridge fellow, 1948. Asso. fellow Am. Inst. Aeros. and Astronautics (Achievement award L.I. sect. 1966); mem. IEEE (sr.), Am. Automatic Control Council, N.Y.-N.J. Trail Conf., Sigma Xi. Jewish. Patentee rotary amplifiers, axial motors, gravity pendulums, inductors, 2 axis accellerometers, ballistic missile safety devices, gyro attenuators, thrust retainers. Home: 2857 Morgan Dr Wantagh NY 11793-1721

LITMAN, HARRY PETER, lawyer, educator; b. Pitts., May 4, 1958; s. s. David and Roslyn M. (Margolis) L. BA, Harvard U., 1981; JD, U. Calif. Berkeley, 1986. Bar: Calif. 1987, U.S. Ct. Appeals (D.C. cir.) 1987, Pa. 1988, U.S. Ct. Appeals (9th cir.) 1990, U.S. Dist. Ct. (so. dist.) Tex, 1992, D.C. 1989, U.S. Supreme Ct. 1992, U.S. Dist. Ct. (ea. and we. dist.) Pa. 1993. Prodn. asst. feature films N.Y.C., 1980-82; newsman, clk. baseball desk AP, N.Y.C., 1982-83; sports reporter AP, 1983-86; law clk. to Hon. Abner J. Mikva U.S. Ct. Appeals (D.C. cir.), 1986-87; law clk. to Hon. Thurgood Marshall U.S. Supreme Ct., Washington, 1987-88, law clk. to Hon. Anthony M. Kennedy, 1989; asst. U.S. atty., dep. chief appellate sect. Dept. Justice, San Francisco, 1990-92; dep. assoc. atty. gen. Dept. Justice, Washington, 1992-93, dep. asst. atty. gen., 1993—; adj. prof. Boalt Hall Sch. Law U. Calif. Berkeley, 1990-92. Editor-in-chief Calif. Law Rev. Vol. 73. Presdl. scholar, 1976. Mem. Pa. Bar Assn., State Bar Calif., D.C. Bar, Order of Coif. Office: Dept of Justice 10th & Constitution Ave NW Washington DC 20530-0001

LITMAN, HELENA D., lawyer; b. Wrocław, Poland, July 24, 1948; French citizen; came to U.S., 1968, permanent resident, 1968; d. Ignacy and Barbara (Katz) Dunica; children: Sacha, Benjamin. Student, NYU, 1971, JD, 1979. Bar: N.Y. Assoc. Kaye, Scholer, Fierman, Hayes & Handler, N.Y.C., 1979-83; assoc. counsel Citibank, N.A., N.Y.C., 1983—. Contbg. editor NYU Jour. Internat. Law, 1977-78. Woodrow Wilson Dissertation fellow, 1971. Mem. ABA, N.Y. State Bar Assn. Home: 350 Central Park West New York NY 10025

LITMAN, RAYMOND STEPHEN, financial services consultant; b. Kingston, Pa., Nov. 2, 1936; s. Stephen Vincent and Mary Helen (Wisnewski) L.; m. Ann Mae Kosik, Nov. 24, 1960; children: Raymond Stephen II, A. Christine. BS in Commerce, Wilkes Coll., 1961. Credit mgr. Sears Roebuck & Co., eastern div., 1961-66; banking officer Phila. Nat. Bank, 1966-69; dir. Decision Dynamics Corp., Marlton, N.J., 1969-71; asst. v.p. Bankers Trust Co., N.Y.C., 1971-75; sr. banking officer Girard Bank, Phila., 1975-77; pres. World Wide Cons. Svcs., Plymouth Meeting, Pa., 1977-78; asso. dir. bank card divsn. Am. Bankers Assn., 1978-80; mng. dir. Chemical Bank, N.Y.C., 1981-92, pres., chief oper. officer, ECC Mgmt. Svcs. Inc., King of Prussia, Pa., 1992-93; pres., CEO Litman Assocs., Inc. Fin. Svcs. Cons.; mem. adv. coun. Credit Rsch Ctr. Purdue U. Served with USN, 1954-57; ETO. Mem. Am. Bankers Assn. (mem. bank card div. exec. com.), Govt. Rels. Coun. and Banking Leadership, Internat. Assn. Credit Card Investigators (pres. Del. Valley chpt. 1976-77, dir. nat. chpt. 1976-77, life mem.), Montgomery County Police Chiefs Assn., Police Chiefs Assn. Southeast Pa., Plymouth Meeting Hist. Soc., VFW, Am. Legion, Frat. Order of Police. Republican. Roman Catholic. Home: 2057 Sierra Rd Plymouth Meeting PA 19462-1826

LITMAN, ROBERT BARRY, physician, author, television and radio commentator; b. Phila., Nov. 17, 1947; s. Benjamin Norman and Bette Etta (Saunders) L.; m. Niki Thomas, Apr. 21, 1985; children: Riva Belle, Nadya Beth, Caila Tess, Benjamin David. BS, Yale U., 1967, MD, 1970, MS in Chemistry, 1972, MPhil in Anatomy, 1972, postgrad. (Life Ins. Med. Rsch. Fund fellow) Yale U., Univ. Coll. Hosp., U. London, 1969-70; Am. Cancer Soc. postdoctoral rsch. fellow Yale U., 1970-73. Diplomate Am. Bd. Family Practice. Resident in gen. surgery Bryn Mawr (Pa.) Hosp., 1973-74; USPHS fellow Yale U. Sch. Medicine, 1974-75; pvt. practice medicine and surgery, Ogdensburg, N.Y., 1977-93, San Ramon, Calif., 1993—; mem. med. staff A. Barton Hepburn Hosp., 1977-93, John Muir Med. Ctr., 1993—, San Ramon (Calif.) Regional Med. Ctr., 1993—, also chmn. med. edn.; commentator Family Medicine Stas. WWNY-TV and WTNY-Radio, TCI Cablevision; clin. preceptor dept. family medicine State Univ. Health Sci. Ctr., Syracuse, 1978—. Author: Wynnefield and Limer, 1983, The Treblinka Virus, 1991, Allergy Shots, 1993; contbr. articles to numerous sci. publs. Pres. Am. Heart Assn. No. N.Y. chpt., 1980-84. Fellow Am. Coll. Allergy, Asthma and Immunology, Am. Acad. Family Physicians; mem. AMA (Physicians Recognition award 1970—), Calif. State Med. Assn., Alameda-Contra Costa County Med. Assn., Joint Coun. Allergy and Immunology, Nat. Assn. Physician Broadcasters (charter), Acad. Radio and TV Health Communicators, Book and Snake Soc., Gibbs Soc. of Yale U. (founder), Sigma Xi, Nu Sigma Nu, Alpha Chi Sigma. Home: PO Box 1857 San Ramon CA 94583-6857 Office: 3160 Crow Canyon Rd Ste 150 San Ramon CA 94583-1331

LITOW, JOEL DAVID, controller; b. N.Y.C., Feb. 10, 1947; s. Herbert and Jean (Zaller) L.; m. Lorraine Aziz; children: Jason, Jennifer. BChemE, CCNY, 1968; MBA, Rutgers U., 1973. Chem. engr. Airco, N.Y., 1968-69, fin. analyst, 1969-73; mgr. fin. analysis Bali Co., N.J., 1973-75; mgr. cost acctg. M&T Chems. Inc., Rahway, N.J., 1976-77, dir. control devel., 1978-79, controller, 1979-86, v.p. fin., controller, 1986—. Avocations: tennis, basketball, softball.

LITRELL, BARBARA, publishing executive. Sr. v.p., pub. McCall's mag., N.Y.C. Office: McCalls 110 Fifth Ave New York NY 10011*

LITROWNIK, ALAN JAY, psychologist, educator; b. Los Angeles, June 25, 1945; s. Irving and Mildred Mae (Rosin) L.; m. Hollis Merle, Aug. 20, 1967; children: Allison Brook, Jordan Michael. BA, UCLA, 1967; MA, U. Ill., Champaign-Urbana, 1969, PhD, 1971. Psychologist Ill. Dept. Mental Health, Decatur, 1970-71; asst. prof. psychology San Diego State U., 1971-75, assoc. prof., 1975-78, prof., 1978—, chmn. dept. psychology, 1981-87, assoc. dean for curriculum and acad. planning, North County Campus, 1987-88; co-dir. Ctr. for Behavioral and Community Health Studies, San Diego, 1989—; cons. San Diego County Dept. Edn. Program Evaluation, 1975-81; project dir. Self-Concept and Self-Regulatory Processes in Developmentally Disabled Children and Adolescents, 1975-78; co-dir. Child Abuse Interdisciplinary Tng. Program, 1987—; project dir. tobacco use prevention in youth orgns., 1989-92. Research. publs. in field. Contbr. chpts. to books. Mem. San Diego County Juvenile Justice Commn., 1989-92; mem. juvenile systems adv. group San Diego County Bd. Suprs., 1989-91. Grantee U.S. Office Edn., 1975-78, 80-81, Nat. Ctr. Child Abuse, 1987—, Calif. Dept. Health, 1989-92, U. Calif. Tobacco-Related Disease Rsch. Program, 1992-94. Office: Ctr Behavioral/Comm Health Studies 9245 Sky Park Ct San Diego CA 92123

LITSCHGI, A. BYRNE, lawyer; b. Charleston, S.C., Dec. 31, 1920; s. Albert William and Mary Catherine (Byrne) L.; m. Mary Elaine Herring, Sept. 13, 1952. B.B.A., U. Fla., 1941; J.D., Harvard U., 1948. Bar: Fla. 1948, D.C. 1950. Atty. Office Gen. Counsel, Treasury Dept., Washington, 1949-52; legis. asst. to U.S. senator, 1952; mem. firm Hedrick & Lane, Washington, 1953-60, Coles, Himes & Litschgi, Tampa, Fla., 1960-62, Shackleford, Farrior, Stallings & Evans, 1962-87, Dykema Gossett, Tampa, Fla., 1988-92; chmn. SL Industries, Inc., 1976-92; mem. firm Holland & Knight, Tampa, 1992—; incorporator, dir. Communications Satellite Corp., 1962-64; mem. Fla. Jud. Council, 1965-68, U.S. Internal Revenue Commn. Adv. Group, 1967-68. Mem. Harvard Law Sch. Assn. (nat. council 1956-61), ABA (chmn. excise and miscellaneous tax com. tax sect. 1956-59), Fla. Bar, Bar Assn. D.C. Home: PO Box 1288 Tampa FL 33601-1288 Office: Holland & Knight PO Box 1288 Tampa FL 33601-1288

LITSCHGI, RICHARD JOHN, computer manufacturing company executive; b. St. Louis, July 1, 1937; s. William J. and Mary F. (Eynatten) L.; m. Christine Ewert, Aug. 21, 1968. BS, St. Louis U., 1959; MS, U. Okla., 1964. Cert. meteorology St. Louis U./USAF. Supr., Bellcomm, Inc., Washington, 1964-67; mgr. Computer Scis., Brussels, 1967-68, Intranet Computing Co., L.A., 1968-71, Xerox Corp., El Segundo, Calif., 1971-76; dir. Honeywell, Inc., L.A., 1976-80, v.p., Phoenix, 1980-85, v.p. Mpls., 1985-87, v.p. Honeywell Bull Inc., 1987-88, v.p. Bull HN Inc., Boston, 1988-93; v.p. Vanguard Automation Inc., Tucson, 1993-94; ret., 1994. Bd. dirs. Arizonians for Cultural Devel., 1981-85; trustee Phoenix Art Mus., 1982-85 . Served to capt. USAF, 1959-62. Democrat. Home: 24 Tupelo Rd Falmouth MA 02540-1945

LITSTER, JAMES DAVID, physics educator, dean; b. Toronto, Ont., Can., June 19, 1938; s. James Creighton and Gladys May (Byers) L.; m. Cheryl Ella Schmidt, June 26, 1965; children: Robin Joyce, Heather Claire. B Engring., McMaster U., Hamilton, Ont., 1961; PhD, MIT, 1965. Instr. physics MIT, Cambridge, Mass., 1965-66, asst. prof. physics, 1966-71, assoc. prof. physics, 1971-75, prof. physics, 1975—, head div. atomic, condensed matter and plasma physics, dept. physics, 1979-83, dir. Ctr. for Materials Sci. and Engring., 1983-88, dir. Francis Bitter Nat. Magnet Lab., 1988-92, interim assoc. provost, v.p. for rsch., 1991, v.p., dean for rsch., 1991—, mem. rsch. staff Thomas J. Watson Rsch. Ctr. IBM, 1969, cons. to liquid crystal group Thomas J. Watson Rsch. Ctr., 1969-70; vis. prof. U. Paris (Orsay), 1971-72; lectr. in physics Harvard Med. Sch., 1974-75; mem. ad hoc oversight com., Solid State Chemistry, NSF, 1977-78; cons. N.Y. State Edn. Dept., 1978, vis. scientist Risø Nat. Lab., Denmark, 1978; mem. condensed matter scis. subcom. (chmn. 1980-81), materials rsch. adv. com. NSF, 1978-81; mem. solid state scis. panel, NRC (chmn. 1991-92), 1986—. Regional editor Molecular Crystals and Liquid Crystals, 1986—. Recipient Gold medal Assn. Profl. Engrs. Ont., 1961, Chancellor's Gold medal McMaster U., 1961, Irving Langmuir Chem. Physics prize Am. Chemical Soc., 1993; Kennecott Copper Co. fellow, 1964-65, John Simon Guggenheim Meml. fellow, 1971-72. Fellow Am. Phys. Soc., Am. Acad. Arts and Scis. Office: MIT 77 Massachusetts Ave Rm 3-240 Cambridge MA 02139-3594

LITT, IRIS FIGARSKY, pediatrics educator; b. N.Y.C., Dec. 25, 1940; d. Jacob and Bertha (Berson) Figarsky; m. Victor C. Vaughan, June 14, 1987; children from previous marriage: William M., Robert B. AB, Cornell U., 1961; MD, SUNY, Bklyn., 1965. Diplomate Am. Bd. Pediatrics (bd. dirs. 1989-94), sub-specialty bd. cert. in adolescent medicine. Intern, then resident in pediat. N.Y. Hosp., N.Y.C., 1965-68; assoc. prof. pediat. Stanford U. Sch. Medicine, Palo Alto, Calif., 1982-87, prof., 1987—, dir. divsn. adolescent medicine, 1976—, dir. Inst. for Rsch. on Women and Gender, 1990—; bd. dirs. Youth Law Ctr., San Francisco. Editor Jour. Adolescent Health. Mem. Soc. for Adolescent Medicine (charter), Am. Acad. Pediat. (award sect. on adolescent health), Western Soc. Pediat. Rsch., Soc. Pediat. Rsch., Am. Pediat. Soc. Office: Stanford U Sch of Medicine 300 Pasteur Dr Stanford CA 94305

LITT, MITCHELL, chemical engineer, educator, bioengineer; b. Bklyn., Oct. 11, 1932; s. Saul and Mollie (Steinbaum) L.; m. Zelda Sheila Levine, Sept. 6, 1955; children: Ellen Beth, Steven Eric. A.B., Columbia U., 1953, B.S. in Engring. 1954, M.S., 1956; D.Engring. Sci., Columbia, 1961. Research engr. Esso Research and Engring. Co., 1958-61; faculty U. Pa., 1961—, asso. prof. chem. engring., 1965-72, prof., 1972—, prof. bioengring., 1977—, chmn. dept. bioengring., 1981-90; vis. prof. environ. medicine Duke, 1971-72; vis. prof. Weizmann Inst., Israel, 1979; v.p. research and devel. KDL Med. Techs. Inc., 1984—. Co-editor: Rheology of Biological Systems, 1973; asso. editor: Biorheology; contbr. articles to profl. engrs. Mem. Am. Inst. Chem. Engrs., Am. Soc. Engring. Edn., IEEE (engring. in medicine and biology soc.), Am. Chem. Soc., Biomed. Engring. Soc., Internat. Soc. Biorheology, N.Am. Soc. Biorheology, Phi Beta Kappa, Sigma Xi, Tau Beta Pi, Phi Lambda Upsilon, Theta Tau. Spl. research biorheology transp. processes, chemically reacting systems, med. aspects engring. Home: 2420 Spruce St Philadelphia PA 19103-2114 Office: Univ Pa Philadelphia PA 19104

LITT, MORTON HERBERT, macromolecular science educator, researcher; b. N.Y.C., Apr. 10, 1926; s. Samuel Bernard and Minnie (Hertz) L.; m. Lola Natalie Abrahamson, July 7, 1957; children: Jonathan S., Jennifer A. B.S., CCNY, 1947; M.S., Bklyn. Poly. Inst., 1953, Ph.D., 1956. Turner and Newall fellow U. Manchester, Eng., 1956-57; sr. research fellow N.Y. State Coll. Forestry, Syracuse, N.Y., 1958-59; sr. scientist Allied Chem. Corp., Morristown, N.J., 1960-64, assoc. dir. research, 1965-67; assoc. prof. Case Western Res. U., Cleve., 1967-76, prof. macromolecular sci., 1976—; cons. Allied Corp., Morristown, N.J., 1967-93, Vistakon, Jacksonville, Fla., 1980—, Polaroid Corp., Cambridge, Mass., 1987-90. Patentee in field. Fellow AAAS, Am. Inst. Physics; mem. Am. Chem. Soc., Chem. Soc. London, J. Polymer Sci. Polymer Chem. (adv. bd.). Home: 2575 Charney Rd Cleveland OH 44118-4402 Office: Case Western Res U Olin Bldg Cleveland OH 44106

LITT, NAHUM, federal judge; b. Balt., Aug. 3, 1935; s. Harry and Reva L. (Naiman) L.; 1 child, Marcia; m. Jean F Greene, Aug. 17, 1987. AB, Cornell U., 1956; LLB, Columbia U., 1959. Bar: Md. 1959, D.C. 1969. Atty. office proceedings ICC, Washington, 1960-65; appellate trial lawyer Gen. Counsel's Office, 1965-70; hearing examiner Fed. Energy Regulatory Agy., 1970-77; chief adminstrv. law judge CAB, Washington, 1977-79, Dept. Labor, Washington, 1979—. Mem. Fed. Adminstrv. Law Judges Conf. (pres. 1977), ABA, Fed. Bar Assn. Club: Cosmos. Office: Dept Labor 800 K St NW Ste 400 Washington DC 20001-8002

LITTELL, FRANKLIN HAMLIN, theologian, educator; b. Syracuse, N.Y., June 20, 1917; s. Clair F. and Lena Augusta (Hamlin) L.; m. Harriet Davidson Lewis, June 15, 1939 (dec. 1978); children: Jennith, Karen, Miriam, Stephen; m. 2d Marcia S. Sachs, 1980. BA, Cornell Coll., 1937, DD, 1953; BD, Union Theol. Sem., 1940; PhD, Yale U., 1946; Dr. Theology (hon.), U. Marburg, 1957; ThD (hon.), Thiel Coll., 1968; other hon. degrees, Widener Coll., 1969, Hebrew Union Coll., 1975, Reconstructionist Rabbinical Coll., 1976, Gratz Coll., 1977, St. Joseph's U., 1988, Stockton State Coll., 1991. Dir. Lane Hall, U. Mich., 1944-49; chief protestant adviser to U.S. High Commr., other service in Germany, 1949-51, 53-58; prof. Chgo. Theol. Sem., 1962-69; pres. Iowa Wesleyan Coll., 1966-69; prof. religion Temple U., 1969-86; adj. prof. Inst. Comtemporary Jewry, Hebrew U., Israel, 1973-94; inaugural Ida E. King disting. vis. prof. Holocaust Studies Stockton (N.J.) State Coll., 1990, 91, Robert Foster Cherry disting. vis. prof. Baylor U., 1993-94, guest prof. numerous univs. Author numerous books including The Anabaptist View of the Church: an Introduction to Sectarian Protestantism (Brewer award Am. Soc. Ch. History), 1952, rev. edit., 1958, 64, From State Church to Pluralism, 1962, rev., 1970; (with Hubert Locke) The German Church Struggle and the Holocaust, 1974, 90; The Crucifixion of the Jews, 1975, 86, The Macmillan Atlas History of Christianity, 1976, German edit., 1976, 89 , (with Marcia Sachs Littell) A Pilgrim's Interfaith Guide to the Holy Land, 1981; A Half-Century of Religious Dialogue: Amsterdam 1939-1989; editor or assoc. editor numerous jours. including Jour. Ecumenical Studies, A Jour. of Ch. and State and Holocaust Genocide Studies; author weekly syndicated columns, also over 300 major articles or chpts. of books in field of modern religious history. cons. NCCJ, 1958-83; mem. exec. com. Notre Dame Colloquium, 1961-68; vice chmn. Ctr. for Reformation Research, 1964-77; nat. chmn. Inst. for Am. Democracy, 1966-69, sr. scholar, 1969-76; co-founder, officer Ann. Scholars' Conf. on Ch. Struggle and Holocaust, 1970—; pres. Christians Concerned for Israel, 1971-78, Nat. Christian Leadership Conf. for Israel, 1978-84, pres. emeritus 1985—; founder, chmn. ecumenical com. Deutscher Evangelischer Kirchentag, 1953-58; co-founder, cons. Assn. Coordination Univ. Religious Affairs, 1959—; mem. U.S. Holocaust Meml. Council, 1979-93; founder, pres. Nat. Inst. on Holocaust, Temple U., 1975-83, Anne Frank Inst., Phila., 1983-89; co-founder, pres. Phila. Ctr. on Holocaust, Genocide and Human Rights, 1989—; mem. exec. com. Remembering For The Future, Oxford and London, 1988, Berlin, 1994; named observer to Vatican II; mem. Internat. Bd. of Yad Vashem, Jerusalem, 1984—. Decorated Grosse Verdienstkreuz (Fed. Republic Germany); recipient Jabotinsky medal, Israel, Ladislaus Laszt Internat. Ecumenical award Ben Gurion U. of Negev, 1991. Mem. PEN, European Assn. Evang. Acads. (co-founder), Locust Club, Yale Club, Pen and Pencil Club, Phi Beta Kappa, Phi Beta Kappa Assocs. Home: PO Box 172 Merion Station PA 19066-0172

LITTIG, LAWRENCE WILLIAM, psychologist, educator; b. Madison, Wis., June 30, 1927; s. Lawrence Victor and Elsie Louise (Rosanske) L.; m. Iris Mark, June 15, 1957; children—Eve Alexandra, Amy Victoria, Sharon Elizabeth. B.S., U. Wis., 1950, M.S., 1955; Ph.D., U. Mich., 1959. Instr. dpet. psychology U. Mich., Ann Arbor, 1958-59; Asst. prof. psychology U. Buffalo, 1959-62; asst. program dir. instl. programs NSF, Washington, 1962-63; social psychologist W.E. Upjohn Inst. Employment Research, Washington, 1963-65; prof. emeritus social psychology Howard U., Washington, 1965—; prof. psychology Md. Inst. Coll. of Art, Balt., 1993—; Fulbright prof. U. Nottingham, 1961-62; vis. scholar U. London, 1971-72; cons. Brookings Instn., 1968-70, Dept. Labor, 1968-70; vis. prof. U. Wis., 1970. Cons. editor: Jour. Cross Cultural Psychology, 1969-74; contbr. articles to profl. jours. Port warden City of Annapolis. U.S. Office Edn. grantee, 1965-70; NIMH research grantee, 1968-69; NSF research grantee, 1961-62; Nat. Inst. Child Health and Human Devel. grantee, 1971-73. Fellow AAAS, Am. Psychol. Assn., Am. Psychol. Soc., Soc. for Personality and Social Psychology; mem. Psychonomic Soc., Brit. Psychol. Soc., Sigma Xi. Clubs: Cosmos (Washington); Md. Capital Yacht, Eastport Yacht (Annapolis, Md.); Amateur Fencing (London). Home: 2 Wells Lndg Annapolis MD 21403-2316 Office: Howard U Dept Psychology Washington DC 20059

LITTLE, ALAN BRIAN, obstetrician, gynecologist, educator; b. Montreal, Que., Can., Mar. 11, 1925; emigrated to U.S., 1951, naturalized, 1959; s. Herbert Melville and Mary Lizette (Campbell) L.; m. Nancy Alison Campbell, Aug. 20, 1949 (div.); children: Michael C. (dec.), Susan MacF. and Deborah MacF. (twins), Catherine E., Jane A., Mary L.; m. Bitten Stripp, Mar. 31, 1983. B.A., McGill U., 1948, M.D., C.M., 1950. Intern Montreal Gen. Hosp., 1950-51; resident Boston Lying-in and Free Hosp. for Women, 1951-55, asst. obstetrician, asso. obstetrician and gynecologist, 1955-65; teaching fellow, asst. prof. Harvard Med. Sch., 1952-65; prof. ob-gyn, then Arthur H. Bill prof. ob-gyn Case Western Res. U. Sch. Medicine, Cleve., 1965-82; chmn. dept. reproductive biology Case Western Res. U. Sch. Medicine, 1972-82; prof. gynecology McGill U., Montreal, 1983—, chmn. dept. ob-gyn., 1983-94; clin. prof. ob-gyn. U. Medicine and Dentistry N.J., Newark, 1994—; dir. dept. ob-gyn. Univ. Hosps., Cleve., to 1982, Royal Victoria Hosp., Montreal, 1983-94; mem. nat. adv. com. Nat. Inst. Child Health and Human Devel. Author: (with B. Tenney) Clinical Obstetrics, 1962; editor: (with others) Gynecology and Obstetrics-Health Care for Women, 1975, 2d edit., 1982; contbr. articles profl. jours. Served with RCAF, 1943-45. Fellow ACS, Royal Coll. Surgeons, Am. Coll. Obstetricians and Gynecologists; mem. AMA, Endocrine Soc., Am. Gynecol. and Obstet. Soc., Am., Central assns. ob-gyn., Assn. Profs. Ob-Gyn., Soc. Gynecol. Investigation, Soc. Ob-Gyn. Can. Office: 687 Pine Ave W, Montreal, PQ Canada H3A 1A1

LITTLE, ARTHUR DEHON, investment banker; b. Providence, Feb. 13, 1944; s. Royal and Augusta Willoughby (Ellis) L.; m. E. Janice Leeming, Sept. 6, 1974; children: Cameron Royal, Kimberley Murray. B.A. in History, Stanford U., 1966. With Narragansett Capital Corp., Providence, 1967—, asst. to pres., 1968-69, v.p., 1969-73, exec. v.p., treas., 1975-76, pres., treas., chief operating officer, dir., 1976-77, pres., treas., chief exec. officer, dir., 1977-80, pres., chief exec. officer, dir., 1980, chmn. bd., chief exec. officer, 1980-86; mng. dir. Narragansett Capital, Inc., Providence, 1986—; prin. The Little Investment Co., Boston, 1992—; bd. dirs. A.T. Wall Co., Quantun Internat., JDR Holdings, Inc., R.I. Zool. Soc., Lyford Cay Found., Nat. Am. Liver Found., New England Chpt. Am. Liver Found., Jr. Achievement No. New England, Jr. Achievement. Chmn. JDR Holdings, Inc. Mem. Lyford Cay Club, Somerset Club. Office: 33 Broad St 10th Fl Boston MA 02109

LITTLE, BRIAN F., oil company executive; b. Moncton, N.B., Can., Oct. 28, 1943; s. George E. and Marion M. (McCartney) L.; m. Dianne E. Rogers, Oct. 9, 1969; chldren: Michael William, Sara Elizabeth. BA, Am. Internat. Coll., 1966; LLB, Osgoode Hall Law Sch., 1974; LLM, London Sch. Econs., Eng., 1975. Indsl. devel. asst. Can. Nat., Moncton and Montreal, Can., 1967-71; articling student McMillan Binch, Toronto, Ont., Can., 1975-76, assoc., 1977-82, ptnr., 1982-83; v.p., gen. counsel Dome Petroleum, Calgary, Alta., Can., 1983-88; v.p. law and external affairs Amoco Can. Petroleum Co. Ltd., Calgary, 1988-89, sr. v.p. law, 1989-92, sr. v.p. law, gen. counsel, 1992—. Mem. Can. Bar Assn., Law Soc. Upper Can., Can. Petroleum Law Found. (bd. dirs.), Osgoode Hall Law Sch. Alumni Assn. (bd. dirs.). Office: Amoco Can Petroleum Co Ltd, 240 Fourth Ave SW, Calgary, AB Canada T2P 4H4

LITTLE, CARL MAURICE, performing arts administrator; b. Campbellton, N.B., Can., Mar. 17, 1924; s. George Everett and Ada (Boucher) L.; m. Frances R. Corner, Aug. 27, 1949; children—Christine, Jennifer, Geoffrey, Stephen; m. Barbara Wolfond, Dec. 8, 1978. B.Sc., Dalhousie U., Halifax, N.S., Can., 1945, Licentiate of Music, 1945, Diploma Engring., 1944; Assoc. Royal Coll. Music, London, 1952; Licentiate, Royal Acad. Music, London, 1952. Tchr. music public schs. Outremont, Que., Can., 1949-50; pvt. tchr. music Montreal, Que., 1946-59, Toronto, Ont., 1959-70; producer music CBC Radio, Montreal, 1952-59; producer music CBC Radio, Toronto, 1959-65, nat. network supr. serious music, 1965-75; mgr. Nat. Arts Centre Orch., Ottawa, 1975-78; co-founder, pres. Little Gallery of the arts, Ottawa, 1979-80; pres. Arts Connection, Victoria, B.C. 1980—; exec. dir., festival adminstr. Courtenay Youth Music Centre (B.C.) 1983; organist Holy Trinity Anglican Ch., Saanichton, B.C., 1984—. Pianist, 1945-52; juror for internat. music competitions including Scriabin Piano Competition, Oslo, Norway, Internat. String Quartet, Stockholm, Sweden, Let The Peoples Sing, Choir, London; jury chmn. Kathaumixw Internat. Choral Festival Powell River, B.C., Can. Mem. Royal Can. Coll. Organists (program chmn. 1985), Can. Conf. of Arts, Can. Music Council, Can. Amateur Musicians Assn. (dir.; co-founder), Ont. Choral Fedn., Nat. Arts Centre Orch. Assn. Instrumental in founding and adminstrn. of CBC competitions, CBC music projects and programs. Address: 2171-2600 Ferguson Rd, Saanichton, BC Canada V8M 2C1

LITTLE, CHARLES GORDON, geophysicist; b. Liuyang, Hunan, China, Nov. 4, 1924; s. Charles Deane and Caroline Joan (Crawford) L.; m. Mary Zughaib, Aug. 21, 1954; children: Deane, Joan, Katherine, Margaret, Patricia. BSc with honors in Physics, U. Manchester, Eng.; 1948; PhD in Radio Astronomy, U. Manchester, 1952. Jr. engr. Cosmos Mfg. Co. Ltd., Enfield, Middlesex, Eng., 1944-46; jr. physicist Ferranti Ltd., Manchester, Lancashire, Eng., 1946-47; asst. tchr. U. Manchester, 1952-53; prof. dept. geophysics U. Alaska, 1954-58, dep. dir. Geophys. Inst., 1954-58; cons. Ionosphere Radio Propagation Lab. U.S. Dept. Commerce Nat. Bur. Standards, Boulder, Colo., 1958-60, chief Upper Atmosphere and Space Physics divsn., 1960-62, dir. Central Radio Propagation Lab., 1962-65; dir. Inst. Telecommunication Sci. and Aeronomy, Environ. Sci. Services Adminstrn., Boulder, Colo., 1965-67; dir. Wave Propagation Lab. NOAA (formerly Environ. Sci. Services Adminstr.), Boulder, Colo., 1967-86; sr. UCAR fellow Naval Environ. Prediction Research Facility, Monterey, Calif., 1987-89; George J. Haltiner rsch. prof. Naval Postgrad. Sch., Monterey, 1989-90. Author numerous sci. articles. Recipient U.S. Dept. Commerce Gold medal, 1964, mgmt. and sci. research awards NOAA, 1969, 77, Presdl. Meritorious Exec. award, 1980. Fellow IEEE, Am. Meteorol. Soc. (Cleveland Abbe award 1984); mem. NAE, AIAA (R.M. Losey Atmos. Sci. award 1992). Address: 7175 Lookout Rd Longmont CO 80503

LITTLE, CHARLES LAWSON, judge, lawyer; b. Montgomery, Ala., Aug. 21, 1946; s. Horton Henry and Martha Roberta (Hogg) L.; m. Gloria Lane, Jan. 23, 1971; children: Jennifer Marie, Charles Lawson Jr. BS, Troy (Ala.) State U., 1969; JD, U. Ala., 1972. Bar: Ala. 1972, U.S. Dist. Ct. Ala. 1975, U.S. Ct. Appeals (11th cir.) 1975. Asst. atty. gen. State of Ala. Atty. Gen., Montgomery, 1974-79; chief asst. dist. atty. Houston and Henry Counties, Dothan, Ala., 1979-82; U.S. magistrate judge U.S. Dist. Ct., Mid. Dist. Ala., Dothan, 1986-92; pvt. practice Dothan, 1981-94; cir. judge 20th Jud. Cir., 1995—. Mem. Dothan Rescue Mission Bd., 1994; chmn. jud. govtl. and legis. com. Houston County Substance Abuse Bd., 1994. Sgt. Ala. NG, 1969-75. Mem. Houston County Bar Assn. (exec. com. 1991-92), Kiwanis Club (chmn. law and regulation com. 1988-90). Baptist. Avocation: guitar.

Home: 2802 Briarcliff Rd Dothan AL 36303-2121 Office: Houston County Courthouse Dothan AL 36301

LITTLE, CHARLES ORAN, agriculture director, animal scientist; b. Schulenburg, Tex., July 21, 1935; married 1955; 3 children. BS, U. Houston, 1957; MS, Iowa State U., 1959, PhD in Animal Nutrition, 1960. Rsch. asst. animal nutrition Iowa State U., Ames, 1957-60; from asst. to assoc. prof. U. Ky., Lexington, 1960-67, prof. animal sci., 1967-85, assoc. dean rsch., 1969-85, dean Coll. Agriculture, 1988—; vice chancellor rsch., dir. Exptl. Sta. La. State U., 1985-88, dir. Agrl. Exptl. Sta. & Coop. Extension, 1988—; assoc. dir. Ky. Agrl. Exptl. Sta., 1989—; mem., chmn. So. Regional Rsch. Com., 1972-75; mem. So. Rsch. Planning Com., 1973-75; chmn. So. Assn. Agrl. Exptl. Sta. Dirs., 1976-77; mem. Exptl. Sta. Com. on Policy, 1978—; Agrl. Rsch. Svc. grantee 1964-67; recipient Disting. Nutritionist award Nat. Distillers Feed Rsch. Coun., 1964, Outstanding Rsch. awards Thomas Poe Cooper & Ky. Rsch. Founds., 1967. Mem. AAAS, Am. Soc. Animal Sci., Am. Inst. Nutrition. Office: U Ky S-107 Agrl Sci Ctr Lexington KY 40506*

LITTLE, CHRISTOPHER MARK, publishing company executive, lawyer; b. Tazewell, Va., Mar. 11, 1941; s. Haskin Vincent and Janet Koe (Kessinger) L.; m. Virginia Elizabeth Silver, Dec. 27, 1963 (div. Oct. 1988); children: Timothy Mark, Margaret Elizabeth; m. Elizabeth Foster Anderson, Oct. 15, 1988. BA, Yale U., 1963; LLB, U. Tex., 1966. Bar: D.C. 1966. Assoc. Covington & Burling, Washington, 1966-68, 70-75; adminstrv. asst. to Congressman Bob Eckhardt, U.S. Ho. of Reps., Washington, 1968-70; asst. gen. counsel EPA, Washington, 1975-76; v.p., counsel The Washington Post, 1976-80; pres., pub. The Herald, Everett, Wash., 1980-84; sr. v.p. adminstrn. Newsweek, Inc., N.Y.C., 1984-86, pres., 1986-89; pres. Cowles Mags., Inc., Harrisburg, Pa., 1989-92; v.p. pub. dir. Meredith Corp., Des Moines, Iowa, 1992-94, pres. mag. group, 1994—. Internat. bd. trustees Am. Field Svc., N.Y.C., 1989-95, chmn., 1992-95. Mem. Mag. Pubs. Am. (chmn. govt. affairs coun. 1990—), Wakonda Club, Des Moines Club. Episcopalian. Avocations: landscape architecture, 18th century American history, classical music. Office: Meredith Corp. 1716 Locust St Des Moines IA 50309

LITTLE, DANIEL EASTMAN, philosophy educator, associate dean; b. Rock Island, Ill., Apr. 7, 1949; s. William Charles and Emma Lou (Eastman) L.; m. Ronnie Alice Friedland, Sept. 12, 1976; children: Joshua Friedland-Little, Rebecca Friedland-Little. BS in Math. with highest honors, AB in Philosophy with high honors, U. Ill., 1971; PhD in Philosophy, Harvard U., 1977. Asst. prof. U. Wis.-Parkside, Kenosha, 1976-79; vis. assoc. prof. Wellesley (Mass.) Coll., 1985-87; vis. scholar Ctr. Internat. Affairs Harvard U., 1989-91, assoc. Ctr. Internat. Affairs, 1991—; asst. prof. Colgate U., Hamilton, N.Y., 1979-85, assoc. prof., 1985-92, prof., 1992—, chmn. dept. philosophy and religion, 1992-93, assoc. dean faculty, 1993—; teaching fellow Harvard U., 1973-76; participant internat. confs. Ctr. Asian and Pacific Studies, U. Oreg., 1992, Social Sci. Rsch. Coun./MacArthur Found., U. Calif., San Diego, 1991, Budapest, Hungary, 1990, Morelos, Mex., 1989, Rockefeller Found., Bellagio, Italy, 1990, U. Manchester, Eng., 1986; mem. screening com. on internat. peace and security Social Sci. Rsch. Coun./MacArthur Found., 1991—; manuscript reviewer Yale U. Press, Cambridge U. Press, Princeton U. Press, Oxford U. Press, Westview Press, Harvard U. Press, Can. Jour. Philosophy, Philosophy Social Scis., Synthese, Am. Polit. Sci. Review; grant proposal reviewer NSF, Social Sci. Rsch. Coun., Nat. Endowment for Humanities; mem. adv. com. 1994 Internat. Devel. Ethics Assn.; tenure and promotion reviewer U. Tenn., Bowdoin Coll., Duke U. Author: The Scientific Marx, 1986, Understanding Peasant China: Case Studies in the Philosophy of Social Science, 1989, Varieties of Social Explanation: An Introduction to the Philosophy of Social Science, 1991 (Outstanding Book award Choice 1992), On the Reliability of Economic Models, 1995; contbr. articles to profl. jours., books. Social Sci. Rsch. Postdoctoral fellow MacArthur Found., 1989-91, Rsch. grantee NSF, 1987, Woodrow Wilson Grad. fellow, 1971-72. Mem. Am. Philos. Assn., Am. Soc. for Polit. & Legal Philosophy, Assn. Asian Studies, Internat. Assn. Philosophy of Law & Social Philosophy, Internat. Devel. Ethics Assn., Phi Beta Kappa. Office: Colgate U 13 Oak Way Hamilton NY 13346

LITTLE, DENNIS GAGE, diversified business executive; b. Cambridge, Mass., June 22, 1935; s. Thomas Wolcott and Margaret (deRongé) L.; m. Susan Gay Walker, May 11, 1957 (div.); children: Heather Gage, Jennifer Wolcott; m. Joanne Bowers, Oct. 1, 1983. A.B., Harvard U., 1956, M.B.A. with distinction, 1961. With J.P. Stevens & Co., Inc., 1961-67, asst. to fin. v.p., 1961-67; treas. GK Techs., Inc. (name formerly Gen. Cable Corp.), 1967-82, v.p., 1969-78, v.p. indsl. relations, 1975-78, sr. v.p., chief fin. officer, 1979-82, dir.; 1979-82; exec. v.p., chief fin. officer Avco Corp., Greenwich, Conn., 1982-85, also dir.; exec. v.p., chief fin. officer Textron Inc., 1985-92; bd. dirs. Winthrop Focus Funds, Russell Reynolds Assocs., Rhode Island Hosp. Trust Co., Taco, Inc., Cranston. Trustee Bryant Coll. Served with Supply Corps USNR, 1956-59. Mem. R.I. Country Club (Barrington), Agawam Hunt Club. Home: 28 Rumstick Dr Barrington RI 02806-4912 Office: 10th Fl Rm 1022 15 Westminister St Providence RI 02903-2525

LITTLE, ELBERT LUTHER, JR., botanist, dendrologist; b. Fort Smith, Ark., Oct. 15, 1907; s. Elbert L. and Josephine (Conner) L.; m. Ruby Rema Rice, Aug. 14, 1943; children: Gordon Rice, Melvin Weaver, Alice Conner. BA, U. Okla., 1927, BS, 1932; MS, PhD, U. Chgo., 1929; postgrad., U. Mich., 1927, Utah State U., 1928. Botanist Okla. Div. Forestry, 1930, 77-78; asst. prof. biology Southwestern Okla. State U., 1930-33; from asst. to asso. forest ecologist Forest Service, U.S. Dept. Agr., Tucson, 1934-42; dendrologist Forest Service, U.S. Dept. Agr., Washington, 1942-76; botanist Fgn. Econ. Adminstrn., Bogotá, Colombia, 1943-45; prodn. specialist U.S. Comml. Co., Mexico, 1945; prof. dendrology Universidad de Los Andes, Mérida, Venezuela, 1953-54, 60; botanist U. Md., Guyana, 1955; cons. UN Mission, Costa Rica, 1964-65, 67, Ecuador, 1965, 75, Nicaragua, 1971; cons. Peace Corps, Paraguay, 1984; vis. prof. biology Va. Poly. Inst. State U., 1966-67; prof. U. D.C., 1979; collaborator U.S. Nat. Mus. Natural History, Smithsonian Instn., 1965-76, research assoc., 1976—. Author: Checklist of U.S. Trees, Atlas of U.S. Trees, Audubon Society Field Guide to North American Trees, Common Fuelwood Crops, and tree books for Alaska, Hawaii, Puerto Rico and Virgin Islands, Southwest, Okla., Esmeraldas Ecuador, Paraguay; contbr. articles to tech. jours. Recipient Disting. Svc. award USDA, 1973. Fellow Soc. Am. Foresters (Barrington Moore award 1986), AAAS, Washington Acad. Scis., Okla. Acad. Sci., Explorers Club; mem. Am. Inst. Biol. Scis. (governing bd. 1956-60), Am. Forestry Assn. (Disting. Svc. award 1981), Bot. Soc. Am. Home: 924 20th St S Arlington VA 22202-2616 Office: Smithsonian Instn Dept Botany Washington DC 20560

LITTLE, EMILY BROWNING, architect; b. Austin, Tex., June 4, 1951; d. Betty (Browning) L. BA in Cultural Anthropology, U. Tex., 1973, MArch, 1979. Registered architect, Tex. Archtl. apprentice Austin Design Assocs., 1980-81; project mgr. Nutt, Wolters & Assocs., Austin, 1981-84; prin. Emily Little/Architect, Austin, 1984—. Prin. works include numerous residences, hist. restorations and comml. bldgs. Mem. citizens adv. com. Travis County Juvenile Ct., Austin, 1984-86; mem. adv. bd. Deborah Hay Dance Co., Austin, 1984—; chmn. Austin Design Commn., 1987-89. Recipient Archtl. Merit award Austin Bd. Realtors, 1989. Mem. AIA (comml. Austin chpt. 1987-88, Outstanding Young Architect of Tex. 1993), Tex. Soc. Architects (honors com. 1992), Austin Women in Architecture (pres. 1985-86), Nat. Trust for Hist. Preservation, Tex. Fine Arts Assn. (pres. 1990-92), Heritage Soc. Austin (bd. dirs. 1989—, pres.-elect 1994, Bldg. award 1988, 90, 92, 93). Democrat. Avocations: travel, swimming. Office: 1001 E 8th St Austin TX 78702-3248

LITTLE, F. A., JR., federal judge; b. 1936; m. Gail Little; children: Sophie, Sabrina. BA, Tulane U., 1958, LLB, 1961. Assoc. Chaffe, McCall, Phillips, Toler & Sarpy, New Orleans, 1961-65, Gold, Little, Simon, Weems & Bruser, Alexandria, La., 1965-69; pres. Gold, Little, Simon, Weems & Bruser, Alexandria, 1968-84; judge U.S. Dist. Ct. (we. dist.) La., Alexandria, 1984—. Office: US Dist Ct PO Box 1031 Alexandria LA 71309-1031

LITTLE, GEORGE DANIEL, clergyman; b. St. Louis, Dec. 18, 1929; s. Henry and Agathe Cox (Daniel) L.; m. Joan Phillips McCafferty, Aug. 22, 1953; children: Deborah Philips, Cynthia McCafferty (dec.), Alice Annette, Daniel Ross, Benjamin Harry. AB, Princeton U., 1951; MDiv, McCormick Theol. Sem., Chgo., 1954; LLD (hon.), Huron Coll., 1977. Ordained to ministry Presbyn. Ch., 1954; pastor East London Group Ministry, Presbyn. Ch. Eng., 1954-56, Friendship Presbyn. Ch., Pitts., 1956-62; assoc. dir. dept. urban ch., planning assoc. Bd. Nat. Missions, United Presbyterian Ch. U.S.A., N.Y.C., 1962-72; assoc. for budgeting Gen. Assembly Mission Council, 1973-76, exec. dir. council, 1976-84; pastor First Presbyn. Ch., Ithaca, N.Y., 1984-93; interim pres. McCormick Theol. Sem., Chgo., 1993-94, ret., 1995. Home: PO Box 4302 Ithaca NY 14852-4302

LITTLE, JACK EDWARD, oil company executive; b. Dallas, Sept. 9, 1938. BS, Tex. A&M U., 1960, MS, 1961, PhD, 1966. Dir. prodn. research and exploration research Bellaire Research Ctr., Shell Devel. Co., Houston, 1977; div. prodn. mgr. onshore div. So. region Shell Oil Co., New Orleans, 1978-79; gen. mgr. western exploration and prodn. region Shell Oil Co., Houston, 1979-80, gen. mgr. Pacific div. western exploration and prodn. ops., 1980-81, v.p. corp. planning, 1981-82, sr. v.p. adminstrn., 1985-86, exec. v.p. exploration and prodn., 1986-94, also bd. dirs.; head Southeast Asia div. Shell Internat. Petroleum Co., London, 1982-85; pres. Shell Energy Resources, Inc., Newark, Del.; pres., CEO Shell Exploration 7 Prodn. Co., 1995—; mem. equity adv. com. Gen. Electric Investment Corp., Stamford, Conn., 1987—; bd. dirs. Am. Petroleum Inst., Washington, 1986—. Trustee, mem. exec. com. United Way Tex. Gulf Coast, Houston, 1987—; mem. external adv. com. Tex. A&M Coll. Engring., 1988—. Mem. Soc. Petroleum Engrs. (chmn. nat. coms. on career guidance, investments and mgmt. and gen. interest 1967-81, nat. bd. dirs. 1977-78, bd. dirs. Bakersfield sect. 1970, bd. dirs. Houston sect. 1969), Nat. Ocean Industries Assn. (bd. dirs., mem. exec. com. 1986—), Mid-Continent Oil and Gas Assn. (exec. com. 1986—). Baptist. Clubs: Petroleum (bd. dirs. 1987-90), Forum of Houston (bd. govs. 1985—), Lakeside Country (Houston, bd. dirs. 1988-91). Avocation: golf. Office: Shell Oil Co PO Box 2463 Houston TX 77252-2463

LITTLE, JACK MERVILLE, lawyer; b. Harlingen, Tex., Nov. 14, 1934; s. Welton O. and Thelma Grace (Pierson) L.; m. Waldine Ann Peterson, Dec. 22, 1956 (div. 1980); m. Martha Louise Gaddy, June 21, 1981; children: Kathryn Anne, John Stephens, Jacqueline Marie, James McLean. BBA with honors, U. Tex., 1956, JD, 1959. With Thompson, Knight, Wright & Simmons, 1959—; sr. shareholder Thompson & Knight, Dallas, 1959—, sr. ptnr., 1971—; ptnr. Thompson, Knight, Simmons & Bullion, 1965; mgmt. com. Thompson, Knight, Simmons & Bullion, legal personnel com., recruiting com., audit com., centennial com. Editor Tex. Law Review. Curriculum com. Tex. Law Sch., 1980-85, dir. Alumni Assn., 1978-83; dir. Dallas Tex. Exes, 1980-85; chmn. bd. dirs. Dallas County Heritage Soc. (past chmn. community affairs, corp. fund raising coms., exec., fin., endowment coms.); adv. dir. Dallas Alliance Mentally Ill.; mem. Dallas Citizens Coun., 1981-84. Capt. U.S. Army 1956-57. Mem. ABA (corp. banking, bus. law sect., com. non-profit corps. 1964-78), State Bar Tex. (banking, bus. law sect., com. revision corp. laws 1973-82), Dallas Bar Assn. (task force mental illness legal system Dallas county), Phi Delta Phi, Phi Gamma Delta, Dallas Country Club (legal com.). Republican. Episcopalian. Avocations: golf, tennis, travel. Home: 4044 Glenwick Ln Dallas TX 75205 Office: Thompson & Knight 1700 Pacific Ave Dallas TX 75201

LITTLE, JAN NIELSEN, lawyer; b. Oakland, Calif., Jan. 20, 1958; d. Jack Harry and Patricia Ann (Holzknecht) N.; m. Rory K. Little, Mar. 19, 1983. AB, U. Calif., Berkeley, 1978; JD, Yale U., 1981. Bar: Calif. 1981, D.C. 1984. Law clk. to judge U.S. Dist. Ct. (no. dist.) Calif. San Francisco, 1981-82; trial atty. Dept. Justice, Washington, 1982-86; assoc. Keker & Brockett, San Francisco, 1986-88, ptnr., 1989—. Recipient Spl. Commendation award Dept. Justice, Washington, 1984. Mem. ABA, Calif. Bar Assn. D.C. Bar Assn. Home: 148 Bret Harte Rd San Rafael CA 94901-5249 Office: Keker & Brockett 710 Sansome St San Francisco CA 94111-1704

LITTLE, JOHN BERTRAM, physician, radiobiology educator, researcher; b. Boston, Oct. 5, 1929; s. Bertram Kimball and Nina (Fletcher) L.; m. Francoise Cottereau, Aug. 4, 1960; children—John Bertram, Frederic Fletcher. A.B. in Physics, Harvard U., 1951; M.D., Boston U., 1955. Diplomate Am. Bd. Radiology. Intern in medicine Johns Hopkins Hosp., Balt., 1955-56; resident in radiology Mass. Gen. Hosp., Boston, 1958-61; fellow Harvard U., Cambridge, Mass., 1961-63; from instr. to assoc. prof. radiobiology Harvard Sch. Pub. Health, Boston, 1963-75; prof. Harvard Sch. Pub. Health, 1975—, chmn. dept. physiology, 1980-83, James Stevens Simmons prof. radiobiology, 1987—; dir. Kresge Ctr. Environ. Health, Boston, 1982—; cons. radiology Mass. Gen. Hosp., Boston, 1968—; chmn. bd. sci. counsellors, Nat. Inst. Environ. Health Sci., 1982-84; bd. sci. counsellors Nat. Toxicology Program, 1988-92; mem. sci. coun. Radiation Effects Rsch. Found., Hiroshima, Japan, 1993—. Mem. editorial bd. numerous nat. and internat. jours.; contbr. chpts. to books and articles to profl. jours. Mem. coun. Nat. Coun. on Radiation Protection and Measurements, 1993—; trustee various hist. and cultural orgns. Capt. U.S. Army, 1956-58. Am. Cancer Soc. grantee, 1965-68; recipient numerous rsch. and grants NIH, 1968—; named one of Outstanding Investigator grantee Nat. Cancer Inst., 1988—. Mem. Radiation Rsch. Soc. N.Am. (pres.-elect 1985, pres. 1986-87), Am. Assn. Cancer Rsch., Am. Physiol. Soc., Health Physics Soc., Am. Soc. Photobiology, AAAS (coun. in med. scis. 1988-91). Avocations: music, architectural history. Office: Harvard U Dept Radiobiology 665 Huntington Ave Boston MA 02115-6021

LITTLE, JOHN DUTTON CONANT, management scientist, educator; b. Boston, Feb. 1, 1928; s. John Dutton and Margaret (Jones) L.; m. Elizabeth Davenport Alden, Sept. 12, 1953; children: John Norris, Sarah Alden, Thomas Dunham Conant, Ruel Davenport. SB in Physics, MIT, 1948, PhD, 1955; PhD (hon.), U. Liege, Belgium, 1992. Engr. Gen. Electric Co., Schenectady, 1949-50; asst. prof. ops. research Case-Western Res. U., 1957-60, assoc. prof., 1960-62; research asst. MIT, 1951-54, assoc. prof. mgmt., 1962-67, prof., 1967-78, George M. Bunker prof. mgmt., 1978-89, Inst. prof., 1989—; dir. Ops. Research Ctr., 1969-76, head mgmt. sci. group Sloan Sch. Mgmt., 1972-82, head behavioral and policy scis. area, 1982-88; pres. Mgmt. Decision Systems, Inc., 1967-80, chmn. bd. dirs., 1967-85; dir., advisor to bd. dirs. Info. Resources, Inc., 1985—; cons. ops. rsch. indsl. govtl. orgns., 1958—; vis. prof. mktg. European Inst. Bus. Adminstrn., Fontainebleau, France, fall 1988; researcher math. programming, queuing theory, mktg., traffic control, decision support systems. Assoc. editor: Mgmt. Sci, 1967-71; contbr. articles to profl. jours. Trustee Mktg. Sci. Inst., 1983-89. Served with AUS, 1955-56. Fellow AAAS; mem. NAE, Ops. Rsch. Soc. Am. (coun. 1970-73, pres. 1979-80), Inst. Mgmt. Scis. (v.p. 1976-79, pres. 1984-85), Inst. Ops. Rsch. and Mgmt. Scis. (pres. 1995), Am. Mktg. Assn., Sigma Xi. Home: 37 Conant Rd RR 3 Lincoln MA 01773 Office: MIT Sloan Sch Mgmt Cambridge MA 02142-1347

LITTLE, JOHN HADLEY, army officer; b. Wichita, Kans., Oct. 16, 1941; s. Walter Hadley and Mary Margaret (Howell) L.; m. Lorraine Torres, June 6, 1964; children: Leigh Ann, Christopher Garrett. AA, Wentworth Mil. Acad., Lexington, Mo., 1961; BS, Cen. Mo. State U., 1963; MBA, Tulane U., 1976. Commd. 2d lt. U.S. Army, 1963, advanced through grades to maj. gen., 1991; battery comdr. 6th Bn., 56th Air Def. Arty., Vietnam, 1966-67; student Command and Gen. Staff Coll., Ft. Leavenworth, Kans., 1972-73; ops. officer 1st Bn., 3d Air Def. Arty., 101st Airborne Div., Ft. Campbell, Ky., 1973-75; bn. comdr. 2d Bn., 5th Air Def. Arty., 2d Armored Div., Ft. Hood, Tex., 1978-79; staff officer Office Dep. Chief of Staff for Rsch., Devel. and Acquisition, Washington, 1979-82; student Air War Coll., Maxwell AFB, Ala., 1982-83; dir. combat devel. Air Def. Arty. Ctr., Ft. Bliss, Tex., 1983-87; comdr. 56th Air Def. Arty. Brigade, Ft. Bliss, 1987-88; asst. dept. chief of staff for combat devel. Hdqrs. Tng. and Doctrine Command, Ft. Monroe, Va., 1988-90; dep. comdg. gen. Air Def. Arty. Ctr., Ft. Bliss, 1990-91, comdg. gen., 1991—. Contbr. articles to mil. mags. Bd. dirs. Boys and Girls Clubs of El Paso, Tex., 1987-88, El Paso chpt. ARC, 1987-88, Armed Svcs. YMCA, Ft. Bliss, 1987-92. Decorated Legion of Merit with 4 oak leaf clusters, Bronze Star with 3 oak leaf clusters, Meritorious Svc. medal with 3 oak leaf clusters. Mem. Assn. U.S. Army, Air Def. Arty. Assn. Avocations: running, woodworking. Office: Department of the Army Chief of Public Affairs Office Washington DC 20310

LITTLE, JOHN WILLIAM, plastic surgeon, educator; b. Indpls., Mar. 12, 1944; s. John William Jr. and Naida (Jones) L.; m. Patricia Padgett Lea, May 26, 1969 (div. 1974); m. Teri Ann Tyson, Feb. 28, 1981 (div. 1982). AB, Dartmouth Coll., 1966. B. in Med. Scis., 1967; MD, Harvard

---

U., 1969. Diplomate Am. Bd. Med. Examiners, Am. Bd. Surgery, Am. Bd. Plastic Surgery. Intern affiliated hosps. Case Western Res. U., Cleve., 1969-70, resident in surgery, 1970-74, resident in plastic surgery, 1973-75; fellow in plastic surgery affiliated hosp. U. Miami, 1975-77; asst. prof. Georgetown U., Washington, 1977-82, assoc. prof., 1982-87, prof., 1987-92, clin. prof., 1992—, dir. div. plastic surgery, residency tng. program, plastic surgeon-in-chief univ. hosp., 1979-92; dir. Nat. Capital Tng. Program in Plastic Surgery affiliated hosps. Georgetown U. and Howard U., 1988-92; dir. Georgetown Plastic Surgery Fellowship in Breast and Aesthetic Surgery, 1990-92; chief plastic surgery Medlantic Ctr. for Ambulatory Surgery, Inc., 1993—; cons. Nat. Cancer Inst., NIH, Bethesda, Md., 1977-92, Washington VA Med. Ctr., 1981-92, Reach to Recovery program Nat. Capital chpt. Am. Cancer Soc., 1981—, RENU program in breast reconstrn., 1982; specialist site visitor plastic surgery residency rev. com. Accreditation Coun. for Grad. Med. Edn., 1982—; vis. lect. various insts. Contbr. numerous articles to profl. jours.; manuscript reviewer Plastic and Reconstructive Surgery, Annals of Plastic Surgery. Bd. dirs. triann. reconstructive surgery teams to Caribbean and S.Am., 1981—, Georgetown Tissue Bank, 1986-88, Operation Luz de Sol, 1992—, Reconstructive Surgeons Vol. Program, 1993—; trustee Washington Opera, 1993—, mem. artistic com., 1994—. Mem. AMA, ACS (council plastic surgery audiovisual program Ann. Clin. Congress 1988-90, 92-93, Met. Washington chpt. councillor 1985-94, chmn. sci. program com. 1990-91, v.p. 1991-92, pres. 1992-93), Nat. Capital Soc. Plastic Surgeons (sec. treas. 1982-83, pres. 1984-85), Am. Soc. Plastic and Reconstructive Surgeons (audiovisual program dir. ann. meeting 1984-86, strategic planning com. 1987-92, fin. com. 1989-94, conv. policy com. 1993—, mem. ops. com. 1994-95, chmn. 1995—; network spokesperson steering com. 1994—, bd. dirs. 1995—), Am. Assn. Plastic Surgeons (co-chmn. local arrangements com. 1985-86, sci. program com. 1986-87, award com.), Plastic Surgery Ednl. Found. (bd. dirs. 1985—, chmn. mktg. com. 1988-91, chmn. audiovisual com. 1984-86, commr. products and svcs. commn. 1987-91, 93-94, mng. com. 1986-87, 89-91, 93—, fin. com. 1989—, rep. to Coun. Plastic Surg. Orgns. 1989—, Parliamentarian 1992-93, v.p. 1993-94, devel. com. 1992—, endowment subcom. 1993—, presdl. adv. coun. 1993—, edn. com. 1994-95, commr. edn. com. 1995—, pres.-elect 1994-95), Med. Soc. D.C. (chmn. plastic surgery sect. 1985), D.R. Millard Surg. Soc. and Ednl. Found. (pres. 1985-87), Am. Cleft Palate Assn., Am. Soc. Maxillofacial Surgeons, Washington Acad. Surgeons (coun. 1988-90), Am. Soc. Aesthetic Plastic Surgery, NE Soc. Plastic Surgeons (chmn. sci. program com. 1988-89, v.p. 1991-92, pres. 1992-93, chmn. second decade fund trustees 1993-94, nominating com. 1993-94, chmn. second decade fund com. 1994—), Plastic Surgeons Assn. of the Ams., Internat. Soc. Aesthetic Plastic Surgery (chmn. bylaws com. 1990-93, parliamentarian 1990-93, chmn. membership com. 1993-95), Am. Alpine Workshop in Plastic Surgery (founder, vice chmn. 1990-91, chmn. 1991-92, historian 1995—), Internat. Fedn. Plastic Reconstructive and Aesthetic Surgery (com. quality assurance plastic surgery units 1994—), Internat. Plastic, Reconstructive, and Aesthetic Found (publs. and video lib. com. 1993—), Aesthetic Surgery Edn. and Rsch. Found., Nat. Endowment Plastic Surgery (bd. govs. 1995—). Republican. Presbyterian. Home: 4200 Massachusetts Ave NW Washington DC 20016-4744 Office: 1145 19th St NW Ste 802 Washington DC 20036-3701

LITTLE, LARRY CHATMON, head football coach; b. Groveland, Ga., Nov. 2, 1945; s. George Chatmon and Ida Mae (Haynes) L.; m. Rose DeJesus, Apr. 15, 1978; children: Damita, Learon. BS, Bethune-Cookman Coll., 1967; DSc, Biscayne Coll., 1972. Pro-football player San Diego Chargers, 1967-69, Miami Dolphins, 1969-80; athletic dir. Miami (Fla.) Edison High Sch., 1981-83; head football coach Bethune-Cookman Coll., Daytona Bch., Fla., 1983-92, Ohio Glory World League, Columbus, 1992, N.C. Ctrl. U., Durham, 1993—. Named All Pro, 1971, 72, 73, 74, 75, 76, Off Lineman of Yr. by NFL, 1971, 72, 73, Fla. Hall of Fame by Fla. Sports Writers, 1978, NFL Hall of Fame, 1993. Democrat. Baptist. Home: 5310 Lacy Rd Durham NC 27713-1626 Office: NC Ctrl U PO Box 19705 Durham NC 27707-0099

LITTLE, LESTER KNOX, historian, educator; b. Providence, Oct. 21, 1935; s. Arthur Foster and Edith Caroline (Hyde) L.; m. Lella Gandini, Apr. 7, 1972; stepchildren: Andrea Dell'Antonio, Ian Dell'Antonio. AB, Dartmouth Coll., 1957; MA, Princeton U., 1960, PhD, 1962. History instr. Princeton U., 1961-63; asst. prof. history U. Chgo., 1963-69, assoc. prof. 1969-71; assoc. professor history Smith Coll., Northampton, Mass., 1971-76, prof., 1976-82, Dwight W. Morrow prof. history, 1982—, chmn. dept. history, 1986-89; dir. Smith Coll. in Italy, 1989-91; vis. prof. history U. Calif., Berkeley, 1988, Yale U., 1995. Author: Religious Poverty and the Profit Economy in Medieval Europe, 1978, Liberty, Charity, Fraternity: Lay Religious Confraternities at Bergamo in the Age of the Commune, 1988, Benedictine Maledictions: Liturgical Cursing in Romanesque France, 1993; co-editor, translator: Nature, Man and Society in the Twelfth Century, 1968. Fellow Inst. Advanced Study, 1969-70, Am. Coun. Learned Socs., 1970-71, Guggenheim Found., 1983, NEH, 1992, resident fellow Am. Acad. in Rome, 1995; grantee Am. Philos. Soc., 1974-75, NEH, 1982. Mem. Am. Hist. Assn., Medieval Acad. Am., Societa Internazionale di Studi Francescani. Home: 33 Washington Ave Northampton MA 01060-2822 Office: Smith College Dept History Northampton MA 01063

LITTLE, LOREN EVERTON, musician, ophthalmologist; b. Sioux Falls, S.D., Oct. 28, 1941; s. Everton A. and Maxine V. (Alcorn) L.; m. Christy Gyles; 1 child, Nicole Moses; children from previous marriage: Laurie, Richard. BA, Macalester Coll., 1963; BS, U. S.D., 1965; D. Medicine, U. Wash., 1967. Prin. trumpeter Sioux Falls Mcpl. Band, 1956-65; trumpeter St. Paul Civic Orch., 1960-62; leader, owner Swinging Scots Band, St. Paul, 1960-63; trumpeter Edgewater Inn Show Room, Seattle, 1966-67, Jazztet-Arts Council, Sioux Falls, 1970-71, Lee Maxwell Shows, Washington, 1971-74; residency in ophthalmology Walter Reed Med. Ctr., Washington, 1974; co-leader, trumpeter El Paso (Tex.) All Stars, 1975; freelance trumpeter, soloist various casinos and hotels, Las Vegas, Nev., 1977—. Trumpeter (album) Journey by R. Romero Band, 1983; soloist for numerous entertainers including Tony Bennet, Burt Bacharach, Jack Jones, Sammy Davis Jr., Jerry Lewis Telethon, for video Star Salute to Live Music, 1989; with Stan Mark Band Nat. Pub. Radio Broadcast, 1994, 95. Trustee Nev. Sch. of the Arts, Las Vegas, 1983—. Served to lt. col. U.S. Army, 1968-76, Vietnam. Decorated Silver Star, Purple Heart, Bronze Star, Air medal; fellow Internat. Eye Found., 1974; Dewitt Wallace scholar Readers Digest, 1963-65. Fellow ACS, Am. Acad. Ophthalmology; mem. Am. Fedn. Musicians, Nat. Bd. Med. Examiners. Presbyterian. Avocations: history, music, medicine, sports, skiing.

LITTLE, LOYD HARRY, JR., author; b. Hickory, N.C., Sept. 12, 1940; s. Loyd Harry and Rebecca Lillian (Bailey) L.; m. Kris Petesch, 1993. BA in Journalism, U. N.C., 1962, postgrad., 1967-68. Editor Lumbee weekly newspaper, Pembroke, N.C., 1966; med. reporter Winston-Salem (N.C.) Jour., 1967-69; bus. editor Raleigh (N.C.) News and Observer, 1969; editor Carolina Fin. Times, Raleigh, 1970-75; spl. projects editor Durham (N.C.) Morning Herald, 1976-79; tchr. creative writing courses U. N.C., 1979-82; asst. city editor Greenville (S.C.) News, 1990-93; mng. editor Carteret County News-Times, Morehead City, N.C., 1993—. Author: Parthian Shot, 1975 (Ernest Hemingway award), In the Village of the Man, 1978, Smokehouse Jam, 1988. Chmn. Orange Grove Precinct Republican Com., 1972-73. With Green Berets U.S. Army, 1962-65. Decorated Commendation medal; Vietnamese Bronze Star medal; Hickory Daily Record scholar U. N.C., 1962. Mem. PEN, Chez Hickory Club. Home: 189 Hibbs Rd Newport NC 28570-9419

LITTLE, RICHARD CARUTHERS (RICH LITTLE), comedian, impressionist, actor; b. Ottawa, Ont., Can., Nov. 26, 1938; s. Lawrence Peniston and Elizabeth Maud (Wilson) L. Ed.: Lisgar Collegiate, Ottawa, 1953-57; student drama, Ottawa Little Theatre, 1950-60. First TV appearance in U.S. on Judy Garland Show, 1964; appearances films, TV, night clubs; host: TV series The Rich Little Show, 1975-76 (Winner Entertainer of Year award 1974), You Asked For It, 1981-83; appeared on TV series Love on a Rooftop, 1966-71, The John Davidson Show, 1969, ABC Comedy Hour, 1972, The Julie Andrews Hour, 1972-73; TV film appearance Dirty Tricks, 1981, Rich Little's Christmas Card, Rich Little's Washington Follies, Parade of Stars, The Christmas Raccoons, Rich Little and Friends in New Orleans; others; rec. albums include My Fellow Canadians, The First Family Rides Again; appeared in films Dirty Tricks, 1981, Happy Hour, 1987. Recipient

---

Maple Leaf Disting. Arts and Letters award, 1983. Office: William Morris Agy 151 El Camino Beverly Hills CA 90212

LITTLE, ROBERT ANDREWS, architect, designer, painter; b. Brookline, Mass., Sept. 9, 1915; s. Clarence Cook and Katherine Day (Andrews) L.; m. Ann Murphy Halle, Dec., 27, 1940; children: Sam Robertson, Revere (dec.). A.B. cum laude, Harvard U., 1937, M.Arch., 1939. Designer G.H. Perkins, Cambridge, Mass., 1939-41; architect U.S. Navy, Washington, 1941-43; ops. analyst Air Staff Intelligence, Washington, 1943-45; prin. Robert A. Little & Assos., Cleve., 1946-58, 67-69; partner Little & Dalton, Cleve., 1958-67; dir. design Dalton-Dalton-Little-Newport, Cleve., 1969-78; owner Robert A. Little, Design and Architecture, 1978—; tchr., lectr. Harvard, U. Pa., Carnegie Inst. Tech., U. Mich., Smith Coll., U. Notre Dame, Kent State U. Exhibited art and graphics in Cleve., Phila., Boston., since 1970; works include Air Force Mus., Dayton, Ohio, Supreme Ct. and Tower, Columbus, Ohio.; one-person shows in Ohio, Maine, Mass. Trustee Cleve. Mus. Sci., 1952-56, Cleve. Inst. Music, 1956-58; mem. Cleve. Fine Arts Com. Served with U.S. Army, 1940. Fellow AIA (pres. Cleve. chpt. 1966-68, nat. and state design awards), Harvard Sch. of Design Alumni Assn. (past pres., internat. dir. of devel). Home: 5 Pepper Ridge Rd Cleveland OH 44124-4904 Office: Robert A Little FAIA Design 5 Pepper Ridge Rd Cleveland OH 44124-4904 *As a child, I drew pictures all the time—and they were my current ideal—a face I thought pretty, a massive locomotive, a pine tree against the sea, or a castle in the sky. As an adult Designer and Artist, too, I have spent my whole life dreaming of beauty, and trying to create it—and, of course, never fully succeeding. But the great satisfaction has not been the results, but rather the breathless moments of the search itself, and the boundless horizons of the dream.*

LITTLE, ROBERT COLBY, physiologist, educator; b. Norwalk, Ohio, June 2, 1920; s. Edwin Robert and Eleanor Thresher (Colby) L.; m. Claire Campbell Means, Jan. 20, 1945; children—William C., Edwin C. A.B., Denison U., 1942; M.D., Western Res. U., 1944, M.S., 1948. Intern Grace Hosp., Detroit, 1944-45; USPHS postdoctoral research fellow Western Res. U., 1948-49; resident internal medicine Crile VA Hosp., Cleve., 1949-50; asst. prof. physiology, then assoc. prof. physiology and medicine U. Tenn. Sch. Medicine, 1950-54; rsch. participant Oak Ridge Inst. Nuclear Studies, 1952; dir. clin. research Mead Johnson & Co., 1954-57; lectr. medicine U. Louisville, 1955-57; dir. cardio pulmonary labs. Scott and White Clinic, Scott Sherwood and Brindley Found., Temple, Tex., 1957-59; prof. physiology, asst. prof. medicine Seton Hall Coll. Medicine and Dentistry, 1957-64, acting chmn. dept. physiology, 1961-63; prof. physiology, chmn. dept., also asst. prof. medicine Ohio State U. Sch. Medicine, 1964-73; prof. physiology, prof. medicine Med. Coll. Ga. Sch. Medicine, Augusta, 1973-89, chmn. dept. physiology, 1973-86, prof., chmn. emeritus, 1989—; cons. in field. Author: Physiology of the Heart and Circulation, 1977, 2d edit., 1981, 3d edit., 1985, 4th edit., 1989; editor: Physiology of Atrial Pacemakers and Conductive Tissues, 1980; contbr. articles to profl. jours. Served to capt. M.C. AUS, 1945-47. Member. Am. Physiol. Soc., So. Soc. Clin. Investigation, Am. Heart Assn., Soc. Exptl. Biology and Medicine, Am. Fedn. Clin. Research, Sigma Xi, Sigma Chi, Alpha Kappa Kappa, Alpha Omega Alpha. Home: 44 Plantation Hills Dr Evans GA 30809-9719

LITTLE, ROBERT DAVID, library science educator; b. Milw., July 11, 1937; s. Kenneth Edwin and Grace Elizabeth (Terwiliger) L. BA, U. Wis., Milw., 1959; MA, U. Wis., 1964, PhD, 1972. Tchr., sch. librarian Sevastapol Pub. Schs., Sturgeon Bay, Wis., 1959-62; sch. librarian Highland Park (Ill.) High Sch., 1962-63; supr. sch. libraries Sevastapol/Gilbraltor Pub. Sch., Sturgeon Bay, 1963-65; state sch. library supr. Wis. Dept. Pub. Instrn., Madison, 1965-69, program administr., 1969-70; asst. prof. libr. sci. U. Wis. Milw., 1970-71, acting dir. Sch. Libr. Sci., 1971; assoc. prof. libr. sci. Ind. State U., Terre Haute, 1971-77, prof., 1977—, chmn. dept., 1971-93; cons. Ind. Nat. Network Study, Terre Haute, 1978-79; cons., researcher Nat. Ctr. Edn. Stats., Washington, 1978-79; mem. Ind. State Libr. Adv. Coun., Indpls., 1981-91. Co-author: Public Library Users and Uses, 1988; editor: Cataloging, Processing, Administering AV Materials, 1972; contbr. articles to profl. jours. Pres. West Cen. Ind. chpt. Ind. Civil Liberties Union, 1988-92. Edn. Act fellow U. Wis., Madison, 1967, 68. Mem. ALA, Am. Assn. Sch. Librs., Assn. Ind. Media Educators (pres. 1981-82, Peggy Leach Pfeiffer Svc. award 1987), AAUP. Methodist. Avocations: reading, travel. Home: 376 Keane Ln Terre Haute IN 47803-2010 Office: Ind State U Ctr for Libr Sci Reeve Hall 336 Terre Haute IN 47809

LITTLE, ROBERT EUGENE, mechanical engineering educator, materials behavior researcher; b. Enfield, Ill., May 24, 1933; s. John Henry and Mary (Stephens) L.; m. Barbara Louina Farrell, Feb. 4, 1961; children: Susan Elizabeth, James Robert, Richard Roy, John William. BSME, U. Mich., 1959; MSME, Ohio State U., 1960; PhDME, U. Mich., 1963; MSME. Asst. prof. mech. engring. Okla. State U., Stillwater, 1963-65; assoc. prof. U. Mich., Dearborn, 1965-68, prof., 1968—. Author: Statistical Design of Fatigue Experiments, 1975, Probability and Statistics for Engineers, 1978. Mershon fellow Ohio State U., 1960. Mem. ASTM, Am. Statis. Assn., Rehab. Engring. Soc. N.Am. Home: 3230 Pine Lake Rd West Bloomfield MI 48324-1951 Office: U Mich 4901 Evergreen Rd Dearborn MI 48128-1491

LITTLE, SYLVIA FORD, oil industry executive. Student, So. Meth. U., Scottsdale Community Coll., Ariz. Owner, operator gas and oil properties San Juan Basin, N.Mex., 1977—; pres. Little Oil & Gas, Inc., San Juan Basin, N.Mex. Founder Farmington (N.Mex.) Totah Festival of Authentic Indian Art; chmn. residential com. Town Forum 2000, 1980; mem. exec. com., state ctrl. com. N.Mex. Rep. Com., 1984-86; bd. dirs. N.Mex. Fedn. Rep. Women, 1984-90, Farmington LWV; mem. industry adv. com. to N.Mex. Dept. Energy, 1993; mem. N.Mex. Bd. Econ. Devel. Commrs., 1994—. Mem. Ind. Petroleum Assn. N.Mex. (pres.-elect 1990, pres. 1991-93), N.Mex. Oil and Gas Assn. (exec. com. 1993—), Assn. Commerce and Industry N.Mex. (bd. dirs. 1988-92), Farmington C. of C. (redcoats amb. com., pres.-elect 1995), Rotary. Avocations: needlepoint, photography. Office: 2346 E 20th St Farmington NM 87401-8906

LITTLE, TED DAVID, lawyer; b. Andalusia, Ala., June 21, 1942; s. Grover Henry and Hester Jane (Brogden) L.; m. Jonnie Dee Riley (dec. Jan. 1988); children: Mollie Dora Little, Terre Su Little. BS, U. Ala., 1967, JD, 1967. Asst. prof. bus. Auburn (Ala.) U., 1968-74, adj. prof. bus., 1974-85, student legal advisor, 1972-74; sole practice Auburn, 1974—; mem. Ala. Legislature, 1974-86, 90-94; chmn. So. Legis. Conf., Atlanta, 1984-85; mem. exec. com. Coun. State Govts., Lexington, 1984-86; mem. exec. com. Nat. Conf. State Legis., Denver, 1985-86. Mem. ABA, Ala. Bar Assn., Kiwanis (pres. Greater Auburn Club 1970-71, 89-90). Democrat. Baptist. Office: PO Box 2366 Auburn AL 36831-2366

LITTLE, THOMAS MAYER, public relations executive; b. Columbus, Ohio, Dec. 21, 1935; s. John William and Eulalia Josephine (Mayer) L.; m. Susan Mulford, Sept. 29, 1959; children: Carin Andrea, Debora Mayer, Sharon Mulford, Patricia Anne. BS in Journalism, Northwestern U., 1958; postgrad., Bradley U., 1958. Account supr. Philip Lesly Co., Chgo., 1962-77; v.p., account supr. Burson-Marsteller, N.Y.C., 1977; v.p. Foote Cone & Belding, Inc., N.Y.C., 1977-78; pres. FCB Pub. Rels., N.Y.C., 1978-81, Bus. Orgn., Inc. div. Carl Byoir & Assocs., N.Y.C., 1982, Tracy-Locke/BBDO Pub. Rels., Dallas, 1983-85; exec. v.p., gen. mgr. Manning, Selvage & Lee, N.Y.C., 1986; pres. T.J. Ross & Assocs., N.Y.C., 1986-87; pres., gen. mgr. Golin/Harris Communication, N.Y.C. 1987-91; pub. rels. cons., 1992—. Bd. dirs. Damon Runyon-Walter Winchell Cancer Fund, N.Y.C. Lt. (j.g.) USN, 1959-62. Mem. Am. Mktg. Assn., Pub. Rels. Soc. Am. Publicity Club N.Y.C., Mt. Kisco (N.Y.) Country Club, Sea Pines Country Club (Hilton Head Island), Lotos Club (N.Y.C.), Sigma Alpha Epsilon. Roman Catholic. Home and Office: 2 Newhall Rd Hilton Head Island SC 29928-3112

LITTLE, THOMAS WARREN, broadcast executive; b. Portland, Oreg., June 24, 1939; s. Hollis R. and Bernice (Lesseg) L.; m. Ruth Brady, Aug. 31, 1958; children—Vincent Thomas, Elizabeth Ann. BA and MA in Radio-TV, UCLA. Stage mgr. Sta. KPIX-TV, San Francisco, 1969-61; producer, dir. Sta. KVCR-TV, San Bernardino, Calif., 1963-65; telecommunications prof. San Bernardino Valley Coll., 1965-75; gen. mgr. Sta. KVCR-TV, Sta. KVCR-FM, San Bernardino, 1975-77, dir. radio-TV, 1979—; dir. TV Sta. KVZK-TV, Pago Pago, Am. Samoa, 1977-79. Served with U.S. Army, 1961-63. Mem. Assn. Calif. Pub. TV Stations, Calif. Pub. Radio, Pub. Broadcasting

Service, Pacific Mountain Network. Democrat. Office: Sta KVCR-TV 701 S Mount Vernon Ave San Bernardino CA 92410-2705

LITTLE, WILLIAM A., foreign language educator, researcher; b. Boston, July 28, 1929; s. Wm. A. and Myrle A. (Holmes) L. BA, Tufts U., 1951; LTCL, Trinity Coll., London, 1952; MA, Harvard U., 1953, PhD, 1961. Asst. prof. Williams Coll., Williamstown, Mass., 1957-63; assoc. prof., chair Tufts U., Medford, Mass., 1963-66; chair U. Va., Charlottesville, 1966-72, prof., 1966-95, prof. German and music emeritus, 1995—; vis. prof. musicology U. Rochester, N.Y., 1995—. Author: G.A. Bürger, 1974; editor: Mendelssohn-Complete Organ Works, 5 vols., 1987-90; editor The German Quarterly, 1970-78; contbr. articles to profl. jours. Cpl. U.S. Army, 1953-55. Sesquicentennial fellow U. Va., 1972-73, 78-79, 88-89. Mem. MLA (chair comp. lit. 1970-72), Am. Assn. Tchrs. German (nat. exec. coun. 1968-78), Am. Guild Organists (registrar Mass. chpt. 1949-53, dean Charlottesville chpt. 1977-78, registrar, archivist Ctrl. Fla. chpt. 1995—, nat. com. profl. edn. 1993—), Am. Mus. Soc., Orgn. Hist. Soc. Home: 6853 S Atlantic Ave New Smyrna Beach FL 32169 also: Bonhoeffer Str 6, 99246 Weimar Germany

LITTLE, WILLIAM ARTHUR, physicist, educator; b. South Africa, Nov. 17, 1930; came to U.S., 1958, naturalized, 1964; s. William Henry and Margaret (Macleod) L.; m. Annie W. Smith, July 15, 1955; children—Lucy Claire, Linda Susan, Jonathan William. Ph.D., Rhodes U., S. Africa, 1953, Glasgow (Scotland) U., 1957. Faculty Stanford, 1958—, prof. physics, 1965—; cons. to industry, 1960—; co-founder, chmn. MMR Techs. Inc., 1980—. Recipient Deans award for disting. teaching Stanford U., 1975-76, Walter J. Gores award for excellence in teaching, Stanford U., 1979, IR-100 award Indsl. Rsch. and Devel., 1981; NRC Can. postdoctoral fellow Vancouver, Can., 1956-58, Sloan Found. fellow, 1959-63, John Simon Guggenheim fellow, 1964-65, NSF sr. postdoctoral fellow, 1970-71. Fellow Am. Phys. Soc. Spl. research low temperature physics, superconductivity, neural network theory cryogenics; holder 10 patents in area of cryogenics and med. instrumentation. Home: 15 Crescent Dr Palo Alto CA 94301-3106 Office: Stanford Univ Dept Physics Stanford CA 94305

LITTLEDALE, FREYA LOTA BROWN, writer, editor; b. N.Y.C.; d. David Milton and Dorothy (Passloff) Brown; 1 son, Glenn David. BS, Ithaca Coll., 1951; postgrad., NYU, 1952. Tchr. English Pub. Schs. Willsboro, N.Y., 1952-53; editor South Shore Record, L.I., N.Y., 1953-55; assoc. editor Maco Mag. Corp., N.Y.C., 1960-61, Rutledge Books and Ridge Press, N.Y.C., 1961-62; juvenile book editor Parents' Mag. Press, N.Y.C., 1962-65; free-lance writer-editor, 1965—; writer Silver Burdett div. Time-Life Corp., 1965; editor, anthologist Arrow Book Club div. Scholastic Book Services; adj. prof. Fairfield U., 1984, 86-92. Author: The Magic Fish, 1967, rev. edit., 1985; (with Harold Littledale) Timothy's Forest, 1969; King Fox and Other Old Tales, 1971; The Magic Tablecloth, The Magic Goat, and The Hitting Stick, 1972; The Boy Who Cried Wolf, 1975; The Elves and the Shoemaker, 1975; Seven at One Blow, 1976; The Brave Little Tailor, 1990; The Snow Child, 1978, rev. edit., 1989; The Magic Plum Tree, 1981, The Farmer in the Soup, 1987, Peter and the North Wind, 1988, The Twelve Dancing Princesses, 1988; editor: A Treasure Chest of Poetry, 1964; Fairy Tales by Hans Christian Andersen, 1964; Aesop's Fables, 1964; Grimm's Fairy Tales, 1964; 13 Ghostly Tales, 1966; Ghosts and Spirits of Many Lands, 1970; Ghosts, Witches, and Demons, 1971; Strange Tales from Many Lands, 1975; (poetry) I Was Thinking, 1979; (plays) The King and Queen Who Wouldn't Speak, 1975; Stop That Pancake, 1975; The Giant's Garden, 1975; The Magic Piper, 1978; adapter: Pinnochio, 1979; Snow White and the Seven Dwarfs, 1981; The Wizard of Oz, 1982; Frankenstein, 1983; The Sleeping Beauty, 1984; The Little Mermaid, 1986, The Twelve Dancing Princesses, 1988, King Midas and the Golden Touch, 1989, Rip Van Winkle, 1991; contbr. to Scribner's Anthology for Young People, 1976; A New Treasury of Children's Poetry, 1984. PEN, Mem. Soc. Children's Book Writers, Authors Guild. Address: care Curtis Brown Ltd 10 Astor Pl New York NY 10003-6935

LITTLEFIELD, EDMUND WATTIS, mining company executive; b. Ogden, Utah, Apr. 16, 1914; s. Edmond Arthur and Marguerite (Wattis) L.; m. Jeannik Mequet, June 14, 1945; children: Edmund Wattis, Jacques Mequet, Denise Renee. BA with great distinction, Stanford U., 1936, MBA, 1938. With Standard Oil Co. of Calif., 1938-41, Golden State Co., Ltd., 1946-50; v.p., treas. Utah Internat. Inc. (formerly Utah Constrn. & Mining Co.), San Francisco, 1951-56; exec. com., dir. Utah Internat. Inc. (formerly Utah Constrn. & Mining Co.), 1951—, exec. v.p., 1956, gen. mgr., 1958—, pres., 1961—, chmn. bd., 1971—, chief exec. officer, 1971-78, chmn. exec. com., dir., 1978-86; bd. dirs. SRI Internat., FMC Gold. Served as lt. (j.g.) USNR, 1941-43; spl. asst. to dep. adminstr. Petroleum Adminstrn. for War 1943-45. Recipient Ernest C. Arbuckle award Stanford Bus. Sch. Assn., 1970, Golden Beaver award, 1970, Bldg. Industry Achievement award, 1972, Harvard Bus. Statesman award, 1974, Internat. Achievement award World Trade Club, 1986; named to Nat. Mining Hall of Fame. Mem. San Francisco C. of C. (pres. 1956), Bus. Council (hon. mem., past chmn.), Conf. Bd., Phi Beta Kappa, Chi Psi. Clubs: Burlingame (Calif.) Country; Pacific Union, San Francisco Golf (San Francisco); Augusta National Golf, Eldorado Country; Bohemian, Cypress Point (Pebble Beach, Calif.); Vintage. Office: 550 California St San Francisco CA 94104-1006

LITTLEFIELD, JOHN WALLEY, physiology educator, geneticist, cell biologist, pediatrician; b. Providence, Dec. 3, 1925; s. Ivory and Mary Russell (Walley) L.; m. Elizabeth Legge, Nov. 11, 1950; children: Peter P., John W., Elizabeth L. M.D., Harvard U., 1947; MHS, Johns Hopkins U., 1992. Diplomate: Am. Bd. Internal Medicine. Intern Mass. Gen. Hosp., Boston, 1947-48; resident in medicine Mass. Gen. Hosp., 1948-50, staff, 1956-74, chief genetics unit children's service, 1966-73; asso. in medicine Harvard U. Med. Sch., 1956-62, asst. prof. medicine, 1962-66, asst. prof. pediatrics, 1966-69, prof. pediatrics, 1970-73; prof., chmn. dept. pediatrics Johns Hopkins U. Sch. Medicine, Balt., 1974-85, prof., chmn. dept. physiology, 1985-92; pediatrician-in-chief Johns Hopkins U. Hosp., 1974-85. Author: Variation, Senescence and Neoplasia in Cultured Somatic Cells, 1976. Served with USNR, 1952-54. Guggenheim fellow, 1965-66; Josiah Macy Jr. Found. fellow Oxford U. Mem. NAS, Am. Acad. Arts and Scis., Am. Soc. Biol. Chemists, Am. Soc. Clin. Investigation, Tissue Culture Assn., Soc. Pediatric Rsch., Am. Soc. Human Genetics, Am. Pediatric Soc., Assn. Am. Physicians, Phi Beta Kappa, Alpha Omega Alpha, Delta Omega. Home: 304 Golf Course Rd Owings Mills MD 21117-4114 Office: Johns Hopkins U Sch Medicine Dept Physiology Baltimore MD 21205

LITTLEFIELD, MARTIN (MARTIN KLEINWALD), book publishing executive; b. N.Y.C., 1940; m. Sheila Kleinwald; children: Susanne Camilleri, Lisa Wolf. Pres., CEO Vantage Press, Inc., N.Y.C. Office: Vantage Press Inc 516 W 34th St New York NY 10001

LITTLEFIELD, PAUL DAMON, management consultant; b. Cambridge, Mass., June 8, 1920; s. W. Joseph and Sally Pastorius (Damon) L.; m. Emmy Farnsworth Neiley, June 19, 1943 (dec. Apr. 9, 1982); children: Diane Neiley Littlefield Ritsher, Elizabeth Damon Littlefield Lehman, Paul Damon Jr.; m. Lucy Jean Boyd, Dec. 30, 1983. A.B., Harvard U., 1942, M.B.A. with distinction (Baker scholar), 1948. Assoc., Freeport Minerals Co., N.Y.C., 1948-50, 52-62, treas. 1956-62; v.p. finance, treas. Arthur D. Little, Inc., Cambridge, 1962-73; sr. v.p., chief fin. officer Arthur D. Little, Inc., 1973-85, cons., 1985—; pres. Brynmere Assoc., Inc., 1991-92; asst. to pres. Coty, Inc., 1950-52; bd. dirs. Cambridge Trust Co. Trustee Old Sturbridge Village, past chmn., Addison Gilbert Found., Gloucester, Mass., ESOP Arthur D. Little, Cambridge; bd. mgrs. Cape Ann Hist Assn. Inc. Served to lt. comdr. USNR, 1942-45. Mem. Fin. Execs. Inst., Harvard Bus. Sch. Assn. Boston (past pres.), Annisquam Yacht Club (past gov.), Leonard Club, Harvard Club of Boston and N.Y.C., Harvard U. Varsity Club, Treas.'s Club, Bass Rocks Golf Club, Cape Ann Paddle Tennis Club. Home: 15 Norwood Heights Annisquam Gloucester MA 01930 Office: Acorn Pk Cambridge MA 02140

LITTLEFIELD, VIVIAN MOORE, nursing educator, administrator; b. Princeton, Ky., Jan. 24, 1938; children: Darrell, Virginia. B.S. magna cum laude, Tex. Christian U., 1960; M.S., U. Colo., 1964; Ph.D., U. Denver, 1979. Staff nurse USPHS Hosp., Ft. Worth, Tex., 1960-61; instr. nursing Tex. Christian U., Ft. Worth, 1961-62; nursing supr. Colo. Gen. Hosp.,

Denver, 1964-65, pvt. patient practitioner, 1974-78; asst. prof. nursing U. Colo., Denver, 1965-69, asst. prof., clin. instr. 1971-74, asst. prof., 1974-76, acting asst. dean, assoc. prof. continuing edn., regional perinatal project, 1976-78; assoc. prof., chair dept. women's health care nursing U. Rochester Sch. Nursing, N.Y., 1979-84; clin. chief ob-gyn. nursing U. Rochester Strong Meml. Hosp., N.Y., 1979-84; prof., dean U. Wis. Sch. Nursing, Madison, 1984—; cons. and lectr. in field. Author: Maternity Nursing Today, 1973, 76, Health Education for Women: A guide for Nurses and Other Health Professionals, 1986; mem. editorial bd. Jour. Profl. Nursing; contbr. articles to profl. jours. Bur. Health Professions Fed. trainee, 1963-64; Nat. Sci. Service award, 1976-79. Mem. MAIN, AACN, NLN (bd. dirs.), Am. Acad. Nursing, Am. Nurses Assn., Consortium Prime Care Wis. (chair), Health Care for Women Internat., Midwest Nursing Research Soc., Sigma Theta Tau (pres. Beta Eta chpt., co-chair coun nursing practice and edn 1995). Avocations: golf, biking. Office: U Wis Sch Nursing 600 Highland Ave H6/150 Madison WI 53792-2455

LITTLEFIELD, WARREN, television executive; m. Theresa Littlefield; 2 children. Student, Am. U., Washington; grad. in psychology, Hobart Coll., Geneva, N.Y. With Westfall Prodns., N.Y.C.; dir. comedy devel. Warner Bros. TV, 1979; mgr. comedy devel. NBC, 1979-81, v.p. current comedy programs, 1981-85; sr. v.p. series spls. and varied programmings NBC Entertainment, 1985-87, exec. v.p. prime time programs, 1987-90, pres., 1990—. Office: NBC Entertainment 3000 W Alameda Ave Burbank CA 91523-0001*

LITTLEJOHN, BROADUS RICHARD, JR., retail supermarket chain executive; b. Spartanburg, S.C., Dec. 4, 1925; s. Broadus Richard and Evelyn (Hicks) L.; m. Margaret Poole; children—Broadus Richard III, Margaret Anne. B.A., The Citadel, 1949. Vice pres. Community Cash Stores, Spartanburg, S.C., 1949-76, chief exec. officer, pres., 1976—; bd. dirs Food Mktg. Inst., Washington. Trustee Converse Coll., North Greenville Coll.; mem. adv. bd. So. Bapt. Radio and TV Com., 1980—; bd. advisers Furman U.; charter mem. Food Industry Crusade Against Hunger; bd. dirs. Salvation Army, Piedmont Interstate Fair Assn., WSPA Radio and TV. Served with USN, 1943-46. Recipient Man of Yr. award Sertoma Club, Spartanburg, S.C., 1968. Mem. Spartanburg C. of C. (bd. dirs. 1978-82). Home: 395 Forest Ave Spartanburg SC 29302-3266 Office: Community Cash Stores Blackstock Rd Spartanburg SC 29301

LITTLEJOHN, BRUCE EVERY, film and television producer; b. Washington, Mar. 28, 1951; s. William F. and Barbara B. (Bairnsfather) L. BA in History, U. Va., 1973. Film distbr. United Artists Corp., Boston, 1975-78; media coord. Clements for Gov. campaign, Austin, Tex., 1978; exec. producer Klein & Co., L.A., 1979—. Assoc. producer (albums) Tom Scott Streamlines, 1987 (Grammy nomination), Flashpoint, 1988; exec. producer (TV series) Against the Odds, 1982. Recipient Album Art Direction award Art Dirs. Club N.Y., 1988, Clio award for TV music, 1985, Best of Broadcasting award New England Broadcasting Assn., 1985, Cine Golden Eagle award Coun. on Internat. Nontheatrical Events, 1982. Home: 155 Seven Hills Dr Boulder CO 80302-9786 Office: Klein & Co 1111 S Robertson Blvd Los Angeles CA 90035-1403

LITTLEJOHN, DAVID, journalism educator, writer; b. San Francisco, May 8, 1937; s. George Thomas and Josephine Mildred (Cullen) L.; m. Sheila Beatrice Hageman, June 10, 1963; children: Victoria Schoenke, Gregory David. BA, U. Calif., Berkeley, 1959; MA, Harvard U., 1961, PhD, 1963. Assoc. prof. English U. Calif., Berkeley, 1963-69, assoc. prof. journalism, 1969-76, prof., 1976—; chmn. com. ednl. policy, 1981-82, chmn. senate policy com., vice chmn. acad. senate, 1984-86, assoc. dean Grad. Sch. Journalism, 1974-78, 85-86, 87-89. Author: (novel) The Man Who Killed Mick Jagger, 1977, (novel) Going to California, 1981, Architect: The Life and Work of Charles W. Moore, 1984, The Ultimate Art: Essays around and about Opera, 1992, also 7 other books, over 200 articles and 200 TV programs; arts critic Sta. KQED-TV, San Francisco, 1965-75, PBS nationwide, 1971-72; critic and corr. London Times, 1975-89, Architecture mag., 1984-89, Wall St. Jour., 1990—. Fulbright lectr., Montpellier, France, 1966-67; Am. Coun. Learned Socs. rsch. fellow, London, 1972-73; NEH grantee 1976-77. Mem. Arts Club (Berkeley). Democrat. Roman Catholic. Home: 719 Coventry Rd Kensington CA 94707-1403 Office: U Calif Grad Sch Journalism Berkeley CA 94720

LITTLER, GENE ALEC, professional golfer; b. San Diego, Calif., July 21, 1930; s. Stanley Fred and Dorothy (Paul) L.; m. Shirley Mae Warren, Jan. 5, 1951; children: Curt Michael, Suzanne. Student, San Diego State Coll. Mem. U.S. Ryder Cup Team, 61, 63, 65, 67, 69, 71, 75. Served with USN, 1951-54. Winner 29 PGA tour events including Nat. Jr. Championship, 1948, Nat. Amateur Championship, 1953, U.S. Open, 1961, Canadian Open, 1965, Tournament of Champions, 1955, 56, 57, World Series of Golf, 1966, Taheiyo Masters, Japan, 1974, 75, Australian Masters, 15 sr. tour titles and Coca Cola Grand Slam, Japan, 1983, 87.

LITTLE RICHARD (RICHARD WAYNE PENNIMAN), recording artist, pianist, songwriter, minister; b. Macon, Ga., Dec. 5, 1932; s. Bud and Leva Mae Penniman; m. Ernestine Campbell, 1957 (div.). BA, Oakwood Coll. Sem., Huntsville, Ala., 1961. Ordained to ministry Seventh Day Adventist Ch., 1961. Began singing and dancing on streets of Macon, Ga., 1942; won talent shows in Atlanta, 1943 and 1951; toured with Dr. Hudson's Medicine Show and other shows, 1949-51; worked with own band doing dances and clubs, 1951-52, with Tempo Toppers in New Orleans, 1953-54; recording artist Peacock Records, Houston, 1953-54, Splty. Records, 1955-58, 64; toured in Big 10 Package shows, U.S. Australia and Gt. Brit., 1957-58; recording artist Veejay Records, 1964-65. Songs include Long Tall Sally, Tutti Frutti, Slippin' and Slidin', Rip it Up, Ready Teddy, Lucille, Send Me Some Lovin', Jenny, Jenny, Miss Ann, Keep A-Knockin', Good Golly Miss Molly, Baby Face, True Fine Mama, Kansas City, Bama Lama Bama Loo, Freedom Blues, Greenwood Mississippi; albums include Here's Little Richard, 1958, Little Richard 2, 1958, The Fabulous, 1959, Well Alright, 1959, Sings Gospel, 1964, Coming Home, 1964, Sings Freedom Songs, 1964, King of Gospel Songs, 1965, Wild & Frantic, 1965, The Explosive, 1967, The Explosive & Roy Orbison, 1970, The Rill Thing, 1971, King of Rock N Roll, 1971, Second Coming, 1971, All Time Hits, 1972, Rock Hard Rock Heavy, 1972, The Very Best Of, 1975, Georgia Peach, 1980, Get Down With It, 1982, Ooh! My Soul, 1983, Lucille, 1984, Shut Up, 1988, The Specialty Sessions, 1990, Greatest Songs, 1995, Mega-Mix, 1995; film appearances include The Girl Can't Help It, 1956, Don't Knock the Rock, 1957, She's Got It, 1957, Mr. Rock and Roll, 1957, Jimi Plays Berkeley, 1970, Let the Good Times Roll, 1973, Jimi Hendrix, 1973, Down and Out in Beverly Hills, 1985; TV appearances include Tonight Show, Merv Griffin Show, Mike Douglas Show, Smothers Brothers Show, American Bandstand, Glen Campbell Good Time Hour, Tom Jones Show, Midnight Special, Donny & Marie Show; stage appearances include Paramount Theatre, The Felt Forum, Wembley Stadium, Hollywood Paladium. Inducted Rock & Roll Hall of Fame. Office: PO Box 29 Hollywood CA 90028*

LITTLETON, CAROL, film editor. Editor: (films) The Mafu Cage, 1978, French Postcards, 1979, Roadie, 1980, Body Heat, 1981, E.T. The Extra-Terrestrial, 1982 (Academy award nomination best film editing 1982), The Big Chill, 1983, Places in the Heart, 1984, Silverado, 1985, Brighton Beach Memoirs, 1986, Swimming to Cambodia, 1987, The Accidental Tourist, 1988, Vibes, 1988, White Palace, 1990, Grand Canyon, 1991, Benny & Joon, 1993, China Moon, 1994, Wyatt Earp, 1994. Office: care United Talent 9560 Wilshire Blvd Ste 500 Beverly Hills CA 90212*

LITTLETON, CHRISTINE A., law educator; b. 1952. BS, Pa. State U., 1974; JD, HArvard U., 1982. Bar: Calif. 1982. Law clk. to Hon. Warren J. Ferguson U.S. Ct. Appeals, L.A., 1982-83; acting prof. UCLA, 1983-89, prof., 1989—; mng. editor Harvard U. Women's Law Jour. Bd. dirs. Calif. Women's Law Ctr., 1989—; mem. Feminist Critical Legal Scholars. Office: UCLA Sch Law 405 Hilgard Ave Los Angeles CA 90024-1476

LITTLETON, HARVEY KLINE, artist; b. Corning, N.Y., June 14, 1922; s. Jesse Talbot and Bessie (Cook) L.; m. Bess Toyo Tamura, Sept. 6, 1947; children—Carol Louise Littleton Shay, Thomas Harvey, Kathryn Tamara (dec.), Maurine Bess, John Christopher. Student, U. Mich., 1939-42, B.Design, 1947; M.F.A., Cranbrook Acad. Art, 1951; D.F.A., Phila. Coll.

Art. Instr. ceramics Toledo Mus. Art, 1949-51; prof. art U. Wis., Madison, 1951-77; chmn. dept. U. Wis., 1964-67, 69-71, prof. emeritus, 1977—. Author: Glass Blowing - A Search for Form, 1971; recent one- and two-man exhbns. include Lee Nordness Galleries, N.Y.C., 1969-70, Maison de Culture, Liege, Belgium, 1974, J & L Lobmeyr, Vienna, 1974, Brooks Meml. Art Gallery, Memphis, 1975, Contemporary Art Glass Gallery, N.Y.C., 1977, 78, 79, Habatat Gallery, Detroit, 1980, 81, Heller Gallery, N.Y.C., 1980, 81, 82, 83, 84, 85, Glasmuseum Ebeltoft, Sweden, 1989, Royal Copenhagen Gallery, 1989, Finnish Glasmusem, Riihimaki, Finland, 1989, Kunsthaus am Mus., Cologne, Germany, 1990, Immenhausen, Germany, 1990, Glasmuseum, Frauenau, Germany, 1992, Yokohama (Japan) Mus. Art, 1995, retrospective exhbn. originated by High Mus. Art, Atlanta, 1984, traveling to the Renwick Gallery, Am. Craft Mus., Iowa State U., Milw. Art Mus. and Portland (Maine) Mus. Art; represented in permanent collections, Victoria and Albert Mus., London, museums in Germany, Holland, Switzerland, Belgium, Austria and, Czechoslovakia; also, Met. Mus. Art, N.Y.C., Mus. Modern Art, N.Y.C., Am. Craft Mus., N.Y.C., L.A. County Mus. Art., L.A., Corning Mus. of Glass, Toledo Mus. Art, Detroit Art Inst., Milw. Art Center, Smithsonian Instn., Washington, High Mus. Art, Atlanta, Chrysler Mus., Norfolk, Va., U. Mich., U. Ill., Ohio State U., Phila. Mus. Art, The White House, Washington, numerous other pub. and pvt. collections. Bd. dirs. Penland Sch., N.C., pres. bd. dirs., 1986-88; pres., chmn. Littleton Co., Inc., Spruce Pine, N.C., 1981—. With Signal Corps U.S. Army, 1942-45, ETO. Recipient Fine Arts award Gov. of N.C., 1987; Toledo Mus. Art research grantee, 1962; Louis Comfort Tiffany Found. grantee, 1970-71; Corning Glass Works grantee, 1974; U. Wis. research grantee, 1954, 57, 62, 73, 75; Nat. Endowment for Arts grantee, 1978-79; Diploma of Honor, Glass Mus. Frauenau, Fed. Republic Germany. Fellow Am. Crafts Coun. (trustee 1957, 61-64, trustee emeritus, gold medal 1983), Corning Mus. Glass (Rakow award for excellence in art of glass); mem. Nat. Coun. for Edn. in Ceramic Arts (hon.), Glass Art Soc. (hon. life, lifetime achievement award 1993), Am. Ceramic Soc. (hon. life).

LITTLETON, ISAAC THOMAS, III, retired university library administrator, consultant; b. Hartsville, Tenn., Jan. 28, 1921; s. Isaac Thomas Jr. and Bessie (Lowe) L.; m. Dorothy Etta Young, Aug. 12, 1949; children—Sally Lowe Littleton Phillips, Thomas Young, Elizabeth Ann. B.A., U. N.C., Chapel Hill, 1943; M.A., U. Tenn., Knoxville, 1950; M.S.L.S., U. Ill., Champaign-Urbana, 1951, Ph.D., 1968. Circulation librarian, asst. librarian U. N.C., Chapel Hill, 1951-58; asst. dir. then dir. libraries N.C. State U., Raleigh, 1959-87; emeritus dir. libraries N.C. State U., 1987—; mem. N.C. Libr. Networking Steering Com., Raleigh, 1982-85; bd. dirs. Southeastern Libr. Network, Atlanta, 1973-74, 83-86, chmn., 1985-86; chmn. Assn. Southeastern Rsch. Librs., 1969-71; mem. com. Gov.'s Conf. on Libr. and Info. Svcs., 1990. Author: The Literature of Agricultural Economics, 1969, State Systems of Higher Education and Libraries, 1977, D.H. Hill Library: An Informal Historu, 1993; editor: N.C. Union List of Scientific Serials, 1967. Bd. dirs., treas. Theater in Park, Raleigh, 1982-85, Friends of Wake County Pub. Librs.; sec. N.C. State U. Friends of Libr., Raleigh, 1964-87, bd. dirs., 1990—; pres. Friends of N.C. Libr. for Blind and Physically Handicapped, 1989-93, bd. dirs., 1993—. Lt. (j.g.) USN, 1943-46, PTO. Council on Library Resources fellow, Washington, 1975-76. Mem. Southeastern Library Assn. (exec. bd. 1974-78), N.C. Library Assn. (exec. bd. 1969-71, hon. life). Mem. Community United Ch. of Christ. Club: Torch (pres. Raleigh, N.C. 1974-75). Avocations: theater; reading; concerts. Home: 4813 Brookhaven Dr Raleigh NC 27612-5706

LITTLETON, JESSE TALBOT, III, radiology educator; b. Corning, N.Y., Apr. 27, 1917; s. Jesse Talbot and Bessie (Cook) L.; m. Martha Louise Morrow, Apr. 17, 1943 (dec. 1994); children: Christine, Joanne, James, Robert, Denise; m. Mary Lou Durizch, Mar. 25, 1995. Student, Emory (Va.) and Henry Coll., 1934-35. Johns Hopkins U., 1935-39; MD, Syracuse U., 1939-43. Diplomate Am. Bd. Radiology, Intern Buffalo Gen. Hosp., 1943; resident in medicine, surgery and radiology Robert Packer Hosp., Sayre, Pa., 1946-51, assoc. radiologist, 1951-53, chmn. dept. radiology, 1953-76; prof. radiology U. South Ala., Mobile, 1976-87, prof. emeritus, 1987—; cons. in field. Author textbooks (3); contbr. chpts. to books and 100 articles to profl. jours., sci. exhibits to profl. confs. Served to capt. U.S. Army MC, 1944-46; Pacific. Fellow Am. Coll. Radiology; mem. AMA, Radiol. Soc. N.Am., Am. Roentgen Ray Soc., Ala. Acad. Radiology, Med. Assn. Ala., French Soc. Neuroradiology, Sigma Xi, Alpha Omega Alpha. Republican. Methodist. Club: Country of Mobile (Ala.). Research on conventional tomography, phys. principles, equipment devel. and testing and clin. applications; transp. and radiology of acutely ill and traumatized patient; angiography, devel. first sheet film serialograph; devel. of equipment for sectional radiographic anatomy. Home: 5504 Churchill Downs St Theodore AL 36582-9622 Office: U South Ala Med Ctr 2451 Fillingim St Mobile AL 36617-2238

LITTLETON, TAYLOR DOWE, humanities educator; b. Birmingham, Ala., Mar. 14, 1930; s. M. Taylor and Florence (Longcrier) L.; m. Lucy Williams, Aug. 7, 1954; children: Dowe, George, Franklin, Mary Wood. B.S., Fla. State U., 1951, M.A., 1952, Ph.D., 1960. Teaching fellow Fla. State U., Tallahassee, 1954-57; from instr. to prof. dept. English Auburn U., Ala., 1957—, dean undergrad. studies, 1968-71, v.p. for acad. affairs, 1972-83, W. Kelly Mosley prof. sci. and humanities, 1983—. Author: Advancing American Art: Painting, Politics, and Cultural Confrontation at Mid-century, 1989, Athletics and Academe: An Anatomy of Abuses and a Prescription for Reform, 1991; author, editor: To Prove A Villain: The Case of King Richard III, 1964, The Idea of Tragedy, 1965; editor: multi-vol. series The Franklin Lectures in Sci. and Humanities: Approaching the Benign Environment, 1970; The Shape of Likelihood, 1974, A Time To Hear and Answer, 1977, The Rights of Memory, 1985; assoc. editor So. Humanities Jour., 1967-70. Served with U.S. Army, 1952-54. Mem. So. Atlantic MLA, Phi Kappa Phi, Omicron Delta Kappa. Democrat. Episcopalian. Home: 415 Norman Cir Auburn AL 36830-6307 Office: Auburn U Haley 9030 Auburn AL 36830

LITTLETON, DOUGLAS BURDEN, business brokerage executive; b. Buffalo, Sept. 24, 1922; s. Frank and G. Joan (Burden) L.; m. Jevene Hope Baker, July 2, 1949; children—Douglas Baker, Dean Houston, Laurie Littlewood Vogelsang. B.S. in Mech. Engring. Rensselaer Poly. Inst., 1945; M.B.A., Harvard, 1947. Sales engr. Otis Elevator Co., 1948-49; asst. to sec. Nat Gypsum Co., Buffalo, 1949-52; sec. Nat Gypsum Co., 1952-67; investment banker Hornblower & Weeks, 1967-68; pres. Littlewood Assocs., Inc., Valuvest, Inc., 1968—. Past pres. Greater Niagara Frontier coun. Boy Scouts Am.; active Buffalo YMCA, United Fund; bd. dirs. Presbyn. Homes of Western N.Y.; bd. dirs., chmn. emeritus Salvation Army; v.p. N.E. region Boy Scouts Am. Served to lt. (j.g.) USNR, 1943-46. Recipient Silver Beaver, 1965; recipient Silver Antelope, 1978, Disting. Eagle, 1979. Mem. Country Club of Sebring, Buffalo Jr. C. of C. (past dir., chmn. bd.), Am. Soc. Corp. Secs., Buffalo Canoe Club (past commodore), Buffalo Country Club. Home: 1925 SE Lakeview Dr Sebring FL 33870-4938 Office: 22 Dawnbrook Ln Buffalo NY 14221-4930 *If you truly believe you are happy and successful then, and only then, you truly are.*

LITTLEWOOD, THOMAS BENJAMIN, journalism educator; b. Flint, Mich., Nov. 30, 1928; s. Thomas Nelson and Louise Engela (Grebenkemper) L.; m. Barbara E. Badger, June 9, 1951; children: Linda S. Johnson, Lisa L. Ratchford, Thomas S., Leah J. Hamrick. Student, DePauw U., 1948-51; BS, Northwestern U., 1952, MS, 1953. Reporter Chgo. Sun-Times, 1953-76, chief Springfield State Capital Bur., 1955-64, corr. Washington Bur., 1965-76; prof. journalism U. Ill. Urbana-Champaign, 1977—, head dept., 1977-87. Author: Bipartisan Coalition in Illinois, 1959, Horner of Illinois, 1969, The Politics of Population Control, 1977, Coals of Fire, 1988, Arch, 1990. John F. Kennedy Inst. Politics Harvard U. fellow, 1975. Mem. Soc. Profl. Journalists (SDX Nat. award 1988), Ill. State Hist. Soc., N.Am. Soc. Sports History, Sigma Delta Chi, Kappa Tau Alpha. Office: Univ Ill 119 Gregory Urbana IL 61801

LITTMAN, EARL, advertising and public relations executive; b. Bklyn., Jan. 29, 1927; s. David and Cele Littman; m. Natalie Carol Jacobson, Dec. 21, 1948; children: Erica Humphrey, Bonnie Likover, Michael L. Littman. BS, NYU, 1948. With George N. Kahn, N.Y.C., 1948-50; Jones & Brown, Pitts., 1950-52; chmn., CEO Goodwin, Dannenbaum, Littman & Wingfield Inc., Houston, 1952-92; pres. The Advertizing Firm, Inc., Two Nerds and A Suit, Inc. Chmn. Anti Defamation League, Tex. 1984; bd. dirs. Am. Heart

Assn., Houston, Glassell Sch.; active End Hunger Network, Houston, 1984, active NCCJ. With USN, 1944-45. Recipient Silver medal Am. Advt. Fedn., 1989, Outstanding Vol. award Savvy, 1990, Anti-Defamation League Popkin award, 1990, End Hunger Network award, 1992; Am. Heart Assn. honoree, 1988; Heritage award Am. Women in Radio and TV, 1992. Mem. Affiliated Advt. Agys. Internat. (pres. 1979-80), Am. Advt. Agy. Assn. (gov. Houston chpt. 1990, Paul Dudley White award 1991), Houston Advt. Fedn. (Living Legend award 1993), Winedale Hist. Assn. (pres.-elect), Tex. Entrepreneurial Soc. (bd. dirs.). Jewish.

LITTMAN, HOWARD, chemical engineer, educator; b. Bklyn., Apr. 22, 1927; s. Morris and Gertrude (Goldberg) L.; m. Arline F. Caruso, July 3, 1955; children—Susan Joy, Vicki Kim, Paul William. BChemE, Cornell U., 1951; PhD, Yale U., 1956. Asst., then assoc. prof. Syracuse U., 1955-65; on leave to Brookhaven Nat. Lab., summer 1957, Argonne Nat. Lab., 1957-59; faculty Rensselaer Poly. Inst., Troy, N.Y., 1965—; prof. chem. engring. Rensselaer Poly. Inst., 1967—, chmn. faculty council, 1975-76; vis. prof. Imperial Coll., London, Eng., 1971-72, Chonn'am Nat. U., Kwangju, Korea, 1988; Fulbright lectr. U. Belgrade, Yugoslavia, 1972; pres. Particle Systems Internat. Corp., 1990—. Patentee in field; contbr. articles to profl. jours. A founder Onondaga Hill Free Library, 1961, trustee, 1961-65, pres., 1965; a founder Onondaga Library System, 1962, trustee, 1962-65, v.p., 1965; trustee Capital Dist. Library Council, 1969-75, pres., 1970, 73. Served with USN, 1945-46. IREX grantee U. Belgrade, summer 1973; recipient Disting. Faculty award Rensselaer Poly. Inst., 1988. Mem. Am. Inst. Chem. Engrs., Am. Chem. Soc., Sigma Xi. Home: 7 Tulip Tree Ln Niskayuna NY 12309-1837 Office: Rensselaer Poly Inst Troy NY 12180-3590

LITTMAN, IRVING, forest products company executive; b. Denver, Apr. 21, 1940; s. Maurice Littman and Cecile P. Zohn.; m. Gertrude Pepper, Aug. 16, 1964; children: Margaret R., Michael J., Elizabeth B. BS in Engring. (Applied Math.), U. Colo., 1964; MBA, U. Chgo., 1966. Mgr. corp. systems Boise Cascade Corp., Idaho, 1966-68, corp. mgr. budgeting, 1968-71, asst. to pres., 1971-73; asst. controller realty group Boise Cascade Corp., Palo Alto, Calif., 1973-76; dir. investor relations Boise Cascade Corp., 1976-84, treas., 1984-86, v.p., treas., 1986—. Bd. dirs. Idaho Humanities Council, Boise, 1985-88, vice chair, 1987-88; trustee Boise High Sch. Band Scholarship Endowment, 1987—; referee US Soccer Fedn., 1982—; investment com. Idaho Community Found., 1989—, chmn. investment com., 1991— With U.S. Army, 1958-59. Mem. Bogus Basin Ski Area Assn. (bd. dirs. 1988—, treas. 1989-94, vice-chmn. 1991-94, chmn. 1994—), Treas. Club of San Francisco, Crane Creek Country Club, Arid Club (Boise). Office: Boise Cascade Corp 1 Jefferson Sq Boise ID 83728-0001

LITTMAN, RICHARD ANTON, psychologist, educator; b. N.Y.C., May 8, 1919; s. Joseph and Sarah (Feinberg) L.; m. Isabelle Cohen, Mar. 17, 1941; children—David, Barbara, Daniel, Rebecca. AB, George Washington U., 1943; postgrad., Ind. U., 1943- 44; PhD, Ohio State U., 1948. Faculty U. Oreg., 1948—, prof. psychology, 1959—, chmn. dept., 1963-68, vice provost acad. planning and resources, 1971-73; Vis. scientist Nat. Inst. Mental Health, 1958-59. Contbr. articles to profl. jours. Sr. postdoctoral fellow NSF, U. Paris, 1966-67; sr. fellow Nat. Endowment for Humanities, U. London, 1973-74; Ford Found. fellow, 1952-53; recipient U. Oreg. Charles H. Johnson Meml. award, 1980. Mem. Am., Western, psychol. assns., Soc. Research and Child Devel., Psychonomics Soc., Animal Behavior Soc., Soc. Psychol. Study of Social Issues, Internat. Soc. Developmental Psychobiology, History of Sci. Soc., Am. Philos. Assn., AAUP, Sigma Xi. Home: 3625 Glen Oak Dr Eugene OR 97405-4736 Office: U Oreg Dept Psychology Eugene OR 97403

LITTON, MARTIN, conservationist. Recipient John Muir award Sierra Club, 1993. Address: 180 Bear Gulch Dr Portola Valley CA 94028-7945*

LITVACK, SANFORD MARTIN, lawyer; b. Bklyn., Apr. 29, 1936; s. Murray and Lee M. (Korman) L.; m. Judith E. Goldenson, Dec. 30, 1956; children—Mark, Jonathan, Sharon, Daniel. BA, U. Conn., 1956; LLB, Georgetown U., 1959. Bar: N.Y. 1964, D.C. 1979. Trial atty. antitrust div. Dept. Justice, Washington, 1959-61; asst. atty. gen. Dept. Justice, 1980-81; asso. firm Donovan, Leisure, Newton & Irvine, N.Y.C., 1961-69; ptnr. Donovan, Leisure, Newton & Irvine, 1969-80, 81-86, Dewey, Ballantine, Bushby, Palmer & Wood, N.Y.C., 1987-91; sr. exec. v.p., chief of corp. ops., gen. counsel The Walt Disney Co., Burbank, Calif., 1991—. Bd. dirs. Bet Tzedek, L.A. Urban League. Fellow Am. Coll. Trial Lawyers; mem. ABA, Fed. Bar Coun., N.Y. State Bar Assn. (sec. antitrust sect. 1974-77, chmn. antitrust sect. 1985-86), Va. Bar Assn. Office: The Walt Disney Co Corp Legal Dept 500 S Buena Vista St Burbank CA 91521-1030

LITVACK, GERALD, biochemistry researcher, educator, administrator; b. Boston, Jan. 11, 1929; s. David and Edith Jean (Berkman) Lytell; m. Patricia Lynn Gorog, Feb., 1956 (div. 1973); 1 child, Claudia; m. Ellen Judith Schatz, Aug. 31, 1973; children: Geoffrey Sandor, Katherine Victoria. BA, Hobart Coll., 1949; MS, U. Wis., 1950, PhD, 1953. Postdoctoral fellow Biochem. Labs. U. Paris, 1953-54; asst. prof. Rutgers U., New Brunswick, N.J., 1954-60; assoc. prof. U. Pa., Phila., 1960-64; Carnell prof., dep. dir. Fels Inst., Sch. of Medicine Temple U., Phila., 1964-91; prof., chair dept. pharmacology Thomas Jefferson U., Phila., 1991—, also dep. dir. Jefferson Cancer Inst., 1991—; assoc. dir. for basic sci. Jefferson Cancer Ctr., Phila., 1992—; chmn. adv. com. Am. Cancer Soc., N.Y.C., 1977-80; mem adv. panel NSF, Washington, 1980-84; mem. ad hoc panels NIH, Bethesda, 1985, 89, Israel Cancer Rsch. Fund Sci. Rev. Panel, 1992-93, U.S. Army Breast Cancer Study Sect., 1994; councilor Soc. for Exptl. Biology and Medicine, N.Y.C., 1984-88; cons. Franklin Inst., 1976, Georgetown U., 1980, NIEHS, NIH, 1982; reviewer Haverford Coll., 1976, NIH, 1977, 84, 91; evaluator Roswell Park Meml. Inst., 1978; mem. sci. adv. bd. Norris Cotton Cancer Ctr. Dartmouth Med. Sch., 1984; Jefferson rep. U. Catania, Sicaly, 1994—. Author, co-author Experimental Biochemistry, 1960, Hormones, 1987; editor: Biochemical Actions of Hormones, Vol. XIV, 1970-87, Receptor Purification, 1990; editor-in-chief Vitamins and Hormones, 1992—, co-editor Actions of Hormones on Molecular Processes, 1964; mem. editorial bd. Chemtracts, Cancer Comm., Cancer Rsch., Endocrinology, Anticancer Rsch., Oncology Rsch., 1992—, Oncology Reports, 1993—, Critical Revs. in Eukaryotic Gene Expression, 1994; editor-in-chief Jour. Receptor, 1990. Recipient Pub. Svc. award Chapel of Four Chaplains, 1977, Faculty Rsch. award Temple U., 1987. Mem. Am. Assn. Cancer Rsch. (chair endocrinology task force 1995), Endocrine Soc. (program com. 1991-93, sci. and edn. com. 1992-93). Achievements include discovery and identification of the glucocorticoid receptor; co-discovery of ligandin (glutathione S-Transferase family) mechanism of glucocorticoid receptor activation, studies in apoptosis. Home: 380 E Montgomery Ave Wynnewood PA 19096 Office: Thomas Jefferson U 10th Locust St Philadelphia PA 19107

LITWACK, LEON FRANK, historian, educator; b. Santa Barbara, Calif., Dec. 2, 1929; s. Julius and Minnie (Nitkin) L.; m. Rhoda Lee Goldberg, July 5, 1952; children: John Michael, Ann Katherine. BA, U. Calif., Berkeley, 1951, MA, 1952, PhD, 1958. Asst. prof., then assoc. prof. history U. Wis., Madison, 1958-65; mem. faculty U. Calif., Berkeley, 1965—, prof. history, 1971—, Alexander F. and May T. Morrison prof. history, 1987—; dir. NDEA Inst. Am. History, summer 1965; vis. prof. U. S.C., 1975, Colo. Coll., Sept. 1974, 79, La. State U., 1985; Fulbright prof. Am. history U. Sydney, Australia, 1991, Moscow (USSR) State U., 1980; vis. lectr. Peking U., (China), 1982; Walter Lynwood Fleming lectr. La. State U., 1983; Wentworth scholar-in-residence U. Fla., Spring 1983; mem. Nat. Afro-Am. History and Culture Commn., 1981-83; mem. screening com. Fulbright Sr. Scholar Awards, 1983-86; bd. acad. advisors The American Experience Sta. WGBH-TV, 1986—; Ford Found. prof. So. studies U. Miss., 1989; mem. exec. com. of dels. Am. Coun. of Learned Socs., 1993—. Author: North of Slavery: The Negro in the Free States, 1790-1860, 1961, Been in the Storm So Long: The Aftermath of Slavery, 1979; (film) To Look for America, 1971; co-author: The United States, 1981, rev. edit., 1991; editor: American Labor Movement, 1962; co-editor: Reconstruction, 1969, Black Leaders in the Nineteenth Century, 1988. Mem. Bradley Commn. on History in Schs. 1987-90, Schomburg Commn. for the Preservation of Black Culture; trustee Nat. Coun. for History Edn., 1990—, mem. steering com. 1994 NAEP History Consensus Project. Served with AUS, 1953-55. Recipient Excellence in Teaching award U. Calif., Berkeley, 1967, Disting. Teaching award, 1971; Francis Parkman prize, 1980; Pulitzer prize history, 1980; Gold medal

Commonwealth Club Calif., 1980; Am. Book award in history, 1980; fellow Social Sci. Research Council, 1961-62; fellow Henry E. Huntington Library, summer 1964; fellow Guggenheim Found., 1967-68; fellow U. Calif., Berkeley, 1976, 80; fellow Rockefeller Found. Humanities, 1983; grantee Nat. Endowment Humanities, 1971; grantee NIMH, 1972-73. Mem. Orgn. Am. Historians (chmn. nominations bd. 1975-76, exec. bd. 1983-85, pres. 1986-87), Am. Hist. Assn. (chmn. program com. 1980-81), So. Hist. Assn., Soc. Am. Historians, Am. Acad. Arts and Scis., Am. Antiquarian Soc., U. Calif. Alumni Assn., Am. Studies Assn., PEN Am. Ctr. Office: U Calif Dept History Berkeley CA 94720

LITWEILER, JOHN BERKEY, writer, editor; b. South Bend, Ind., Feb. 21, 1940; s. John Ernest and Pauline Lucile (Yoder) L. BA, North Cen. Coll., Naperville, Ill., 1962. Indexer-researcher Urban Rsch. Corp., Chgo., 1970-74; editor Maher Pubs., Chgo., 1974-75, 79-81; instr. Am. Sch., Chgo., 1975-79; writer Ency. Brittanica, 1992—; free-lance writer, editor, jazz critic Chgo., 1981—; vis. instr. Sch. of Art Inst., Chgo., 1982. Author: The Freedom Principle, 1984, Ornette Coleman: A Harmolodic Life, 1993; contbr. numerous articles to Reader, Chgo. Tribune, N.Y. Times, Kulchur, Down Beat, other publs. Bd. dirs. Jazz Inst. of Chgo., 1977-88; com. mem. DeMichael Jazz Archives, 1977-88, Chgo. Jazz Festival, 1984-88, Jazz Criticism Inst. Music Critics Assn. fellow, 1974, NEH fellow, 1981. Home: 5633 S Kenwood Ave Chicago IL 60637-1760

LITWIN, BURTON HOWARD, lawyer; b. Chgo., July 26, 1944; s. Manuel and Rose (Boehm) L.; m. Nancy Iris Stein, Aug. 25, 1968; children: Robin Meredith, Keith Harris, Jill Stacy. BBA with honors, Roosevelt U., 1966; JD cum laude, Northwestern U., 1970. Bar: Ill. 1970, U.S. Dist. Ct. (no. dist.) Ill. 1970, U.S. Tax Ct. 1972, U.S. Claims Ct. 1983; CPA, 1966. Ptnr. Hopkins & Sutter, Chgo., 1970—. Author chpts. of books; contbr. articles to profl. jours. Recipient Gold Watch award Fin. Execs. Inst., Chgo., 1965. Mem. ABA (chmn. nonfiler task force for no. Ill. 1992-93), Fed. Bar Assn., Chgo. Bar Assn. (chmn. adminstrv. practice subcom., fed. taxation subcom. 1982-83), Rosarian-Am. Rose Soc. (cons.), Legal Club Chgo. Avocations: roses, painting, photography. Office: Hopkins & Sutter 3 First National Plz Chicago IL 60602

LITWIN, MARTIN STANLEY, surgeon; b. Florence, Ala., Jan. 8, 1930; s. Ben and Rose L.; m. Cheryl Denise Mason; children: Anna Marie, Rebecca, Benjamin, Martin. BS, U. Ala., 1951, MD, 1955. Diplomate Am. Bd. Surgery. Intern Michael Reese Hosp., Chgo., 1955-56; asst. in surgery to chief surg. resident Peter Bent Brigham Hosp., Boston, 1965-65; pvt. practice specializing in surgery New Orleans; asst. prof. to assoc. prof. surgery Tulane Med. Sch., New Orleans, 1966-75; prof. surgery Tulane Med. Sch., 1975—, assoc. dean, med. dir. faculty practice, 1976—, Robert and Viola Lobrano prof. surgery, 1977—; chmn. continuing edn., 1979-93; clin. investigator VA Hosp., West Roxbury, Mass., 1964-66; vis. surgeon Charity Hosp. of La., 1966; active staff Tulane Med. Ctr. Hosp., 1977—; univ. staff Touro Infirmary, 1967—. Contbr. articles to profl. jours.; assoc. editor Emergency Medicine, 1969-84. 1st lt. to col. USAR-MC, 1956-80. Fellow ACS; mem. Assn. Am. Med. Colls. (chmn. steering com. 1994—, Group on Faculty Practice), Am. Burn Assn., Am. Surg. Assn., Am. Assn. Surgery of Trauma, So. Surg. Assn., So. Med. Assn., Southeastern Surg. Congress, La. Med. Soc., New Orleans Surg. Soc. (pres. 1989), Orleans Parish Med. Soc. (mem. hosp. com. 1983), European Soc. Exptl. Surgery, Assn. Acad. Surgery, Soc. Surgeons of Alimentary Tract, Soc. Univ. Surgeons, Brigham Sur. Alumni Assn., Tulane Surg. Soc., others. Address: 5591 Bellaire Dr New Orleans LA 70124 Office: Tulane U Med Ctr 1415 Tulane Ave New Orleans LA 70112-2632

LITZ, ARTHUR WALTON, JR., English language educator; b. Nashville, Oct. 31, 1929; s. Arthur Walton and Lucile (Courtney) L.; m. Marian Ann Weller, Feb. 2, 1958; children: Katharine, Andrew, Victoria, Emily. AB, Princeton U., 1951; DPhil (Rhodes scholar) Oxford (Eng.) U., 1954. Instr. Princeton U., 1956-58; lectr. Columbia U., 1957-58; mem. faculty Princeton U., 1958—, prof. English lit., 1968—, chmn. English dept., 1974-81; Vis. prof. Bryn Mawr Coll., Swarthmore Coll., BreadLoaf Sch. of English, Temple U.; mem. editorial bd. Princeton U. Press, 1967-71. Author: The Art of James Joyce, 1961, Modern American Fiction: Essays in Criticism, 1963, Jane Austen, 1965, James Joyce, 1966, James Joyce's Dubliners, 1969, The Poetic Development of Wallace Stevens, 1972, Eliot in His Time, 1973, Scribner Quarto of Modern Literature, 1977, Major American Short Stories, 1980, rev. edit., 1994, Ezra Pound and Dorothy Shakespear: Their Letters, 1985, Collected Poems of William Carlos Williams, 1986, Personae: The Shorter Poems of Erza Pound, 1990, James Joyce: Poems and Shorter Writings, 1990, Ezra Pound's Poetry & Prose, 1992. With AUS, 1954-56. Recipient E. Harris Harbison award for gifted teaching Danforth Found., 1972; named Am. Coun. Learned Socs. fellow, 1960-61, NEH sr. fellow, 1974-75, Guggenheim fellow, 1982-83, Eastman prof. U. Oxford, 1989-90. Mem. Am. Philos. Soc. Home: 62 Western Way Princeton NJ 08540-7206

LITZSINGER, PAUL RICHARD, publishing company executive; b. Clayton, Mo., Jan. 8, 1932; s. Melvin Paul and Catherine (Mooney) L.; m. Dona Lucy Follett, July 10, 1954; children: Mark, Robin, Heidi, Shawn, Todd. BS, U. Mo., 1954. With Follett Corp., Chgo., 1957—; retail stores supr. Follett Corp., 1962-66, pres. retail stores div., 1966-76, pres., chief exec. officer corp., 1977—; bd. dirs. Continental Water Corp., Chgo. Area dir. United Crusade; bd. dirs Hinsdale Community House. Served with USAF, 1954-57. Mem. Nat. Assn. Coll. Stores (dir. 1971-73), Nat. Assn. Colls. Stores Corp. (pres. 1974-75, trustee), Am. Assn. Pubs., Fla. Assn. Coll. Stores, Nat. Assn. Aux. Enterprise Dirs., Nat. Assn. Bus. Mgrs., Nat. Assn. Coll. and Univ. Bus. Officers, Nat. Assn. Jr. Colls., Mgt. Assn. Ill. (bd. dirs 1992—). Presbyterian. Club: Knollwood Golf. Home: 1650 Green Bay Rd Lake Bluff IL 60044-2306 Office: Follett Corp 2233 N West St River Grove IL 60171-1817

LIU, ALICE YEE-CHANG, biology educator; b. Hunan, China, July 12, 1948; came to U.S., 1970; d. Tin-Kai and Te-Ming (Young) L.; m. Kuang Yu Chen, Aug. 26, 1978; children: Andrew T-H, Winston T-C. BS, Chinese U., Hong Kong, 1969; PhD, Mount Sinai Sch. Med., 1974. Postdoctoral fellow Yale U. Med. Sch., New Haven, Conn., 1974-77; asst. prof. Harvard Med. Sch., Boston, 1977-84; assoc. prof. Rutgers U., Piscataway, N.J., 1984-89, prof., 1989—; dir. grad. program in cell and devel. biology Rutgers U-U. Medicine-Dentistry N.J.-R.W. Johnson Med. Sch., 1994—; mem. pharmacological scis. rev. com. NIH, 1984-88; mem. cell biology panel NSF, 1989-93, 94-95; mem. basic rsch. adv. group N.J. Commn. on Cancer Rsch., 1989-93, 94—. Author: Receptors Again, 1985; editorial bd. Biol. Signals, 1991—. Recipient N.Y.C. Bd. of Higher Edn. award, 1972, Am. Cancer Soc. Scholar award, Boston, 1982-85; NIH postdoctoral fellow, 1974-77, Medical Found. fellow, Boston, 1977-79. Mem. Am. Soc. Biochemistry and Molecular Biology, Am. Soc. Pharmacology and Experimental Therapeutics. Home: 20 Woodlake Dr Piscataway NJ 08854-5148 Office: Rutgers U PO Box 1059 Nelson Biology Labs Piscataway NJ 08855-1059

LIU, BEDE, electrical engineering educator; b. Shanghai, China, Sept. 25, 1934; came to U.S., 1954, naturalized, 1960; s. Henry and Shan (Yao) L.; m. Maria Agatha Sang, Jan. 31, 1959; 1 dau., Beatrice Agatha. B.S. in Elec. Engring., Nat. Taiwan U. 1954; M.E.E., Poly. Inst. Bklyn., 1956, D.E.E. 1960. Equipment engr. Western Electric Co., N.Y.C., 1954-56; intermediate engr. A.B. DuMont Lab., Clifton, N.J., summer 1956; mem. tech. staff Bell Telephone Labs., Murray Hill, N.J., 1952-60; summers 1957, 58, 66; mem. faculty Princeton U., 1962—; prof. elec. engring., 1969—; vis. prof. Nat. Taiwan U., 1970-71, U. Calif., Berkeley, 1971, Shanghai Jiao Tong U., 1979. Co-author: Digital Signal Processing, 1976; editor: Digital Filters and the Fast Fourier Transform, 1975; patentee in field. Recipient Tech. Achievement award IEEE Acoustics Speech and Signal Processing Soc., 1985, Edn. award IEEE Cir. and Systems Soc, 1988; named Hon. Prof. Inst. Acoustics, Inst. Electronics, Academia Sinica, 1988. Fellow IEEE (bd. dirs. 1984-85, Centennial medal 1984); mem. IEEE Circuits and Systems Soc. (v.p. 1979, pres. 1982, Edn. award 1988). Home: 248 Hartley Ave Princeton NJ 08540-5656 Office: Princeton Univ Dept Elec Engring Princeton NJ 08540

LIU, BEN-CHIEH, economist; b. Chungking, China, Nov. 17, 1938; came to U.S., 1965, naturalized, 1973; s. Pei-juang and Chung-su L.; m. Jill Jyhhuey, Oct. 2, 1965; children—Tina Won-ting, Roger Won-jung, Milton Wonming. B.A., Nat. Taiwan U., 1961; M.A., Meml. U. Nfld., 1965, Wash-

ington U., St. Louis, 1968; Ph.D., Washington U., St. Louis, 1971. Economist Chinese Air Force and Central Customs, Taiwan, 1961-63; resource economist Canadian Land Inventory and Forest Services, Nfld., 1963-65; research project dir. St. Louis Regional Indsl. Devel. Corp., 1968-72; prin. econs. Midwest Research Inst., Kansas City, Mo., 1972-80; mgr. Energy and Environ. Systems Div., Argonne (Ill.) Nat. Lab., 1980-81; prof. econs., assoc. dir. rsch. Oklahoma City U., 1981-82; prof. mgmt., mktg. and info. systems Chgo. State U., 1982—; pres. Liu & Assocs., Inc., 1982—; vis. prof. econs. U. Mo., 1970-78, Nat. Taiwan U., 1991-92; cons. UN, NSF; mem. Gov. Thompson's Adv. Com. on Agrl. Export, 1985-87, Congressman Fawell's Adv. Com. on Sci. and Tech., 1985—; commr. Nat. Commn. on Librs. and Info. Svcs., 1991-94. Author: Interindustrial Structure Analysis: An Input-Output Study for St. Louis Region, 1968, The Quality of Life in the United States, 1970, Rating, Index and Statistics, 1973, Quality of Life Indicators in U.S. Metropolitan Areas, 1975, Physical and Economic Damage Functions for Air Pollutants by Receptors, 1976, Earthquake Risk and Damage Functions, An Integrated Model, 1981, Income, Energy and Quality of Life: An Information Systems Approach to Decisions, 1988; mem. editorial bd.: Internat. Jour. Math. Social Sci, Am. Jour. Econs. and Sociology, Hong Kong Jour. Bus. Mgmt.; contbr. articles to profl. jours. Recipient rsch. study award Am. Indsl. Devel. Coun., 1969—, Fulbright Scholar award, 1990-92, Faculty Meritorious award Chgo. State U., 1983, 86, 89, 90; U.S. Econ. Devel. Adminstrn. fellow, 1967-68; Korean Govt. scholar, 1963-65; Fulbright scholar Mgmt. Devel. Inst., Delhi U., 1992. Fellow Am. Statis. Assn. (com. mem.); mem. Am. Econ. Assn. (com. mem.), Econometric Soc., Royal Econ. Soc., Internat. Statis. Instn., Assn. for Social Econs. (com. mem.), Tax Inst. Am., Chinese Acad. and Profl. Assn. (pres. 1984-85), Chinese Econ. Assn. in N.Am. (pres. 1988-90). Home: 5360 Pennywood Dr Lisle IL 60532-2032 Office: Chgo State U Chicago IL 60628 The joy of living may temporarily rest on present or past glory, but it is the immersion in planning for the future—the living ahead of one's time—which ensures permanently the flourishing of the joy of life. In a commonwealth society, happiness does not come from doing what we like to do, but from liking what we have to do for the less-well-to-do-ones.

LIU, BENJAMIN YOUNG-HWAI, engineering educator; b. Shanghai, China, Aug. 15, 1934; s. Wilson Wan-su and Dorothy Pao-ning (Cheng) L.; m. Helen Hai-ling Cheng, June 14, 1958; 1 son, Lawrence A.S. Student, Nat. Taiwan U., 1951-54; B.S. in Mech. Engring., U. Nebr., 1956, Ph.D., U. Minn., 1960. Asso. engr. Honeywell Co., Mpls., 1956; research asst., instr. U. Minn., 1956-60, assst. prof. 1960-67, asso. prof., 1967-69, prof., 1969-93, regent's prof., 1993—, dir. Particle Tech. Lab., 1973—; vis. prof. U. Paris, 1968-69; patentee in field. Contbg. author: Aerosol Science, 1966; editor: Fine Particles, 1976, Application of Solar Energy for Heating and Cooling Buildings, 1977, Aerosols in the Mining and Industrial Work Environment, 1983, Aerosols: Science, Technology and Industrial Application of Airborne Particles, 1984; editor-in-chief: Aerosol Sci. and Tech., 1983-93; contbr. articles to Ency. Chem. Tech. Guggenheim fellow, 1968-69; recipient Sr. U.S. Scientist award Alexander von Humboldt Found., 1982-83. Mem. ASME, ASHRAE, Inst. of Environ. Scis. (v.p. 1993—), Air and Waste Mgmt. Assn., Am. Assn. for Aerosol Rsch. (pres. 1986-88), Chinese Am. Assn. Minn. (pres. 1971-72), Nat. Acad. Engring. Home: 1 N Deep Lake Rd North Oaks MN 55127-6504 Office: U Minn Particle Tech Lab 111 Church St SE Minneapolis MN 55455

LIU, BRIAN CHEONG-SENG, urology and oncology educator, researcher; b. Hong Kong, Jan. 15, 1959; came to U.S., 1980; s. Keh Ming and Yin Man (Au) L. BS in Microbiology summa cum laude, UCLA, 1980, PhD in Molecular Biology, 1984. Postdoctoral fellow in tumor immunology and tumor biology Sch. Medicine UCLA, 1984-88; instr. dept. urology Mt. Sinai Sch. Medicine, N.Y.C., 1988-89, asst. prof. dept. urology, dir. urologic rsch., 1989—; sr. rsch. fellow Jonsson Comprehensive Cancer Ctr., 1985-88; vis. investigator dept. pathology Henry Ford Hosp., Detroit, 1987-88. Contbr. articles to profl. jours. Recipient Edwin Beer award N.Y. Acad. Med., 1991-93, New Investigator award Am. Found. Urologic Diseases, 1994—, Cancer of the Prostate Rsch. award Capcure Found., 1995; Nat. Cancer Inst. grantee, 1991—. Mem. Am. Urologic Assn., Soc. Basic Urologic Rsch., Sigma Xi. Office: Mt Sinai Sch Med Dept Urology 1 Gustave L Levy Pl New York NY 10029-6574

LIU, CHAOQUN, staff scientist; b. Yizheng, Jiangsu, China, Apr. 8, 1945; came to U.S.; 1986; s. Jixiang and Guiying (Han) L.; m. Weilan Jin, Dec. 25, 1972; children: Haiyan, Haifeng. MS, Tsinghua U., Beijing, China, 1981; PhD, U. Colo., 1989. Asst. prof. Nanjing Aero. Inst., Nanjing, China, 1981-86; vis. scholar Miss. State U., 1986; rsch. asst. U. Colo., Denver, 1986-89; staff scientist Ecodynamics Rsch. Assocs., Inc., Denver, 1990—; asst. prof. adj. U. Colo., Denver, 1990-93, assoc. prof. adj., 1993—. Contbr. articles to profl. jours. Grantee USN, 1992-93, 95—, NASA, 90-93, 92-95, 93-94, 94-95, USAF, 1991, 95-97. Mem. AIAA, SIAM, Am. Phys. Soc. Office: Univ of Colorado Denver Computational Math Group Campus Box 170 Denver CO 80217

LIU, CHUNG-CHIUN, chemical engineering educator; b. Canton, Kwangtun, China, Oct. 8, 1936; came to U.S., 1961, naturalized, 1972; s. Pay-Yen and Chi-Wei (Chen) L.; m. Mary Lou Rice, Nov. 25, 1967; children: Peter S.H. Bs., Nat. Cheng-Kung U., Taiwan, 1959; M.S., Calif. Inst. Tech., 1962; Ph.D., Case Western Res. U., 1968. Grad. asst. Case Western Res. U., Cleve., 1963-68, postdoctoral fellow, 1968, prof. chem. engring., 1978—; asst. prof. chem. engring. U. Pitts., 1968-72, assoc. prof., 1972-76, prof., 1976-78; prof. chem. engring. Case Western Res. U., Cleve., 1978—; assoc. dir. Case Center for Electrochem. Scis., Cleve., 1982-86; dir. electronics design ctr. Case Center for Electrochem. Scis., 1986-89, Wallace R. Persons prof. sensor tech. and control, 1989—. Contbr. articles in field to profl. jours.; patentee in field. Mem. Electrochem. Soc. (summer fellowship award 1963, 66), Am. Inst. Chem. Engrs. Home: 2917 E Overlook Rd Cleveland OH 44118-2433 Office: Case Western Res U Dept Chem Engr 10900 Euclid Ave Cleveland OH 44106

LIU, DARRELL TEH YUNG, biochemist, researcher; b. Tainan, Taiwan, May 24, 1932; came to U.S., 1956; s. Chu-An and Chi-Li (Wu) L.; m. Sue C. Chen, Aug. 30, 1961; children: Cornelia Liu Trimble, J Rebecca, Daniel H. BS, Nat. Taiwan U., 1955; PhD, U. Pitts., 1961. Rsch. assoc. Rockefeller U., N.Y.C., 1961-64, asst. prof., 1964-67; from biochemist to sr. biochemist Brookhaven Nat. Lab., L.I., N.Y., 1967-73; sect. head NIH, Bethesda, Md., 1974-80; dep. dir. div. bacterial products FDA Ctr. Biologics Evaluation and Rsch., Bethesda, 1978-80, dir. div. biochem. biophysics, 1980-92, dir. divsn. allergenic products, parasitology, 1993—; hon. prof. Peking Union Med. Coll., Peking, China, 1989; vis. prof. Kyoto U., Japan, 1989; elected fellow St. John's Coll., Cambridge, Eng., 1989. Editor Jour. Biol. Chemistry, 1985-90, 91—; mem. editorial bd. Analytical Biochemistry, 1984-86. Mem. sr. exec. svcs. U.S. Civil Svc., Washington, 1984—. Recipient award Fed. Asian Pacific Am. Coun., 1987. Memm. Chinese Am. Med. and Health Assn. (pres. 1986), Am. Soc. Biol. Chemists, Phi Lambda Upsilon, Sigma Xi. Achievements include research on hydrolysis of protein and peptides with tolvenesulfonic acid, discovery of several proteins in Lymulus lysates, discovery of structure and function of human C-reactive protein. Office: FDA Divsn Allergenic Products 1401 Rockville Pike Rockville MD 20852-1448*

LIU, ERNEST K. H., international banking executive, international financial consultant; b. Hong Kong, Oct. 4, 1950; came to U.S., 1979; s. Sun-Ip and Mei-Choi (Man) L.; m. Lily Chan, Dec. 5, 1979; children—Aimee On-On, Alvin Lok-Tin. B.Social Sci., Hong Kong U., 1974; M.B.A. in Fin., NYU, 1986. Lending officer Bank of Am. NT and SA, Hong Kong, 1974-76; market officer Hong Kong Trade Devel. Council, Hong Kong, 1976-79; mgr. Hong Kong Trade Devel. Council, N.Y.C., 1979-82; asst. v.p. mktg. Honkong and Shanghi Banking Corp, N.Y.C., 1982-83; sr. account exec. Citibank, N.A., N.Y.C., 1984-88; asst. v.p. Merrill Lynch Internat. Pvt. Client Svcs., N.Y.C., 1988-91; dir. Asia-Pacific Internat. Trade Promotion Ltd., N.Y.C., 1991—.

LIU, GANG-YU, chemist, educator; b. Zhengzhou, Henan, China, Apr. 19, 1964; came to U.S., 1986; s. Zhen Kun and Quan xian (Guo) L.; m. Xiaoyuan Li, Dec. 1, 1987. BS, Peking (China) U., 1988; MS, Princeton U., 1990, PhD, 1992. Postdoctoral assoc. U. Calif., Berkeley, 1992-94; asst. prof. chemistry Wayne State U., Detroit, 1994—. Camille & Henry Dreyfus fellow, 1994—, Miller Rsch. fellow The Miller Inst. for Basic Rsch. in Sci., 1992-94, Harold W. Dodds Honorific fellow Princeton U., 1991-92, CGP fellow Ministry of Edn., China, 1986-87. Mem. AAAS, Am. Chem. Soc., Am. Phys. Soc., Am. Vacuum Soc. Office: Wayne St U Dept Chemistry Detroit MI 48202

LIU, KEH-FEI FRANK, physicist, educator; b. Beijing, Jan. 11, 1947; came to U.S., 1969; s. Hsien-Chang and Juihua (Wang) L.; m. Yao-Chin Ko, Apr. 6, 1974; children: Helen, Alexander. BS, Tunghai U., Taichung, Taiwan, 1968; MS, SUNY, Stony Brook, 1972, PhD, 1975. Vis. scientist C.E.N. Saclay France, Paris, 1974-76; from rsch. assoc. to adj. asst. prof. UCLA, 1976-80; assoc. prof. U. Ky., Lexington, 1980-86, prof. physics, 1986—; vis. prof. SUNY, Stony Brook, 1985-86, 1990; univ. rsch. prof. U. Ky., 1992. Editor: Chiral Solitons, 1987; assoc. editor World Scientific Pub. Co., Singapore, 1985—; contbr. articles to profl. jours. Recipient First Prize in Theoretical Physics Academia Sinica, China, 1987, Grand Challenge award DOE, 1988, 1989, Alexander Von Humboldt Sr. Scientist award Humboldt Found., Germany, 1990. Mem. Am. Phys. Soc., European Phys. Soc., Overseas Chinese Physicists Assn. (coord. 1991—). Office: U Ky Dept Physics & Astronomy Lexington KY 40506

LIU, PINGYU, physicist, educator; b. Shanghai, China, May 27, 1941; came to U.S., 1980; s. Shih-Tsan and Wen-Chang (Chen) L.; m. Jiagi Wang, Dec. 22, 1972 (dec. 1983); 1 child, Mei; m. Carolyn Hsu, Oct. 14, 1983; 1 child, Helen Wen. Diploma, Dalian (China) Poly. Inst., 1963; MS, U. Utah, 1982, PhD, 1984. Rsch. asst., postdoctoral rsch. assoc. U. Utah, Salt Lake City, 1981-85; devel. engr. Garrett AiResearch, L.A., 1985-86; sr. engr., engring. specialist, engr. III Allied-Signal Aero. Co., Tucson, Ariz., 1986-92; assoc. prof. imaging sci., dept. radiology Ind. U., Indpls., 1992—. Mem. IEEE, Am. Assn. Physicists in Medicine, Biomed. Optics Soc., SPIE. Achievements include patent on enhancement of fluoroscopically generated images. Office: Ind U Sch Medicine 541 Clinic Dr Indianapolis IN 46202

LIU, RAY HO, forensic science program director, educator; b. Taiwan, Apr. 3, 1942; s. Ku and Tsan (Hwang) L.; m. Hsiu-Lan Lin, Dec. 4, 1965; children: Yu-Ting, Eugene, Hubert. LLB, Cen. Police Coll., Taipei, Taiwan, 1965; PhD, So. Ill. U., 1976. Qualified as lab. dir., N.Y. State Dept. Health. Asst. prof. forensic sci. U. Ill., Chgo., 1976-80; mass spectrometrist Cen. Regional Lab, U.S. EPA, Chgo., 1980-82; ctr. mass spectrometrist Ea. Regional Rsch. Ctr. USDA, Phila., 1982-83; assoc. prof. forensic sci. U. Ala., Birmingham, 1984-89, prof., 1989—, dir. grad. program in forensic sci., 1991—; tech. dir. Environ. Health Rsch. and Testing, Birmingham, Ala., 1987-91, Environ. Chem. Corp., Birmingham, 1992-93; cons. in field; vis. prof. Taiwanese Nat. Sci. Coun., 1981, 1994; insp. Nat. Lab. Certification Program, Research Triangle Park, N.C., 1988—. Author: Approaches to Drug Sample Differentiation, 1982, Elements and Practice in Forensic Drug Urinalysis, 1994; editor-in-chief Forensic Sci. Rev., 1989—; contbr. numerous articles to profl. jours. Fellow Am. Acad. Forensic Scis.; mem. Am. Chem. Soc., Am. Assn. for Clin. Chemistists, Am. Soc. for Mass Spectrometry, Sigma Xi. Office: U Ala Dept Criminal Justice Birmingham AL 35294

LIU, VI-CHENG, aerospace engineering educator; b. Wu-ching, China, Sept. 1, 1917; came to U.S., 1946, naturalized, 1973; s. Bi-Ching and Shu-Fung (Keng) L.; m. Hsi-Yen Wang, Mar. 1, 1947. B.S., Chiao Tung U., 1940; M.S., U. Mich., 1947, Ph.D., 1951. Instr. Tsing-Hua U., Kunming, 1940-46; research engr. Engring. Research Inst., U. Mich., Ann Arbor, 1951-59; prof. aerospace engring. U. Mich., 1959-89, prof. emeritus, 1989—; vis. prof. Inst. of Mechanics, Chinese Acad. Sci., Peking, 1980—; ministry edn., vis. chair prof. Nanjing Aero. Inst., People's Republic China, 1989-91, hon. prof., 1991—; cons. NASA, 1964-65. Ministry of Edn. China research fellow, 1946-49; NASA research grantee, 1964-80, USAF Geophysical Rsch. grantee, 1958-64. Research and 100 sci. publs. in rarefied gas dynamics, ionospheric physics, space physics, geophys. fluid dynamics. Home: 2104 Vinewood Blvd Ann Arbor MI 48104-2762

LIU, WING KAM, mechanical and civil engineering educator; b. Hong Kong, May 15, 1952; came to U.S., 1973, naturalized, 1990; s. Yin Lam and Siu Lin (Chan) L.; m. Betty Hsia, Dec. 12, 1986; children: Melissa Margaret, Michael Kevin. BSc with highest honors, U. Ill., Chgo., 1976; MSc, Calif. Inst. Tech., 1977, PhD, 1981. Registered profl. engr., Ill. Asst. prof. mech. and civil engring. Northwestern U., Evanston, Ill., 1980-83, assoc. prof., 1983-88, prof., 1988—; prin. cons. reactor analysis and safety div. Argonne (Ill.) Nat. Labs., 1981—. Co-editor: Innovative Methods for Nonlinear Problems, 1984, Impact-Effects of Fasts Transient Loadings, 1988, Computational Mechanics of Probabilistic and Reliability Analysis, 1989. Recipient Thomas J. Jaeger prize Internat. Assn. for Structural Mechanics in Reactor Tech., 1989, Ralph R. Teetor award Soc. Automotive Engrs., 1983; grantee NSF, Army Rsch. Office, NASA, AFSOR. Fellow ASME (Meville medal 1979, Pi Tau Sigma gold medal 1985); mem. ASCE, Am. Acad. Mechanics. Office: Northwestern U Dept Mech Engring 2145 Sheridan Rd Evanston IL 60208-0002

LIU, YUAN HSIUNG, drafting and design educator; b. Tainan, Taiwan, Feb. 24, 1938; came to U.S., 1970; s. Chun Chang and Kong (Wong) L.; m. Ho Pe Tung, July 27, 1973; children: Joan Anshen, Joseph Pinyang. BEd, Nat. Taiwan Normal U., Taipei, 1961; MEd, Nat. Chengchi U., Taipei, 1967, U. Alta., Edmonton, 1970; PhD, Iowa State U., 1975. Cert. tchr. Tchr. indsl. arts and math. Nan Ning Jr. High Sch., Tainan, Taiwan, 1961-62, 63-64; tech. math. instr. Chung-Cheng Inst. Tech., Taipei, 1967-68; drafter Sundstrand Hydro-Transmission Corp., Ames, Iowa, 1973-75; assoc. prof. Fairmont (W.Va.) State Coll., 1975-80; per course instr. Sinclair Community Coll., Dayton, Ohio, 1985; assoc. prof. Miami U., Hamilton, Ohio, 1980-85, Southwest Mo. State U., Springfield, 1985—; cons. Monarch Industries Prevision Co., Springfield, 1986, Gen. Electric Co., Springfield, 1988, Fasco Industries, Inc., Ozark, Mo., 1989, Springfield Remfg. Corp., 1990, 92, Ctrl. States Indsl., Intercont Products, Inc., & L&W Industries, Inc., ZERCO Mfg. Co. 2d lt. R.O.C. Army, 1962-63. Recipient Excellent Teaching in Drafting award Charvoz-Carsen Corp., Fairfield, N.J., 1978. Mem. Am. Soc. Engring. Edn., Am. Design Drafting Assn. Avocations: walking, watching TV. Office: Southwest Mo State U Tech Dept 901 S National Ave Springfield MO 65804-0094

LIUKKONEN, KAREN ELAINE, financial company executive; b. Gardner, Mass., Oct. 30, 1958; d. Kaarlo and Helvi Helena (Manty) L. BS in Chemistry, Worcester Polytechnic Inst., 1980; MBA, Babson Coll., 1982. Credit analyst John Hancock Mut. Life, Boston, 1982-84, investment specialist, 1984-85, treas. officer, 1985-86; dir. money market ops. HHS, Boston, 1986-89; spl. asst. Dept. of Health and Human Svcs., Washington, 1989-90; pres. John Hancock Capital Corp., Boston, 1990—, gen. dir. portfolio mgmt. and investment svcs., 1991—; bd. dirs. John Hancock Corp. Republican. Avocation: traveling. Office: John Hancock Capital Corp PO Box 111 John Hancock Pl Boston MA 02117-0111

LIUZZI, ROBERT C., chemical company executive; b. Boston, 1944; married. AB, Coll. of Holy Cross, 1965; LLB, U. Va., 1968. V.p. gen. counsel U.S. Fin., Inc., 1969-74; with CF Industries, Long Grove, Ill., 1975—, exec. v.p., chief fin. officer, 1977-80, exec. v.p., operating officer, 1980-84, pres., chief exec. officer, 1985—; chmn. ad hoc com. Domestic Nitrogen Producers, Washington; bd. dirs. Can. Fertilizers Ltd., The Fertilizer Inst., Nat. Coun. Farmer Coops., Fla. Phosphate Coun., Tampa; co-chmn. Petrochem. Trade Group, Washington. Mem. coun. Internat. Exec. Svc. Corps, Stamford, Conn.; mem. bus. adv. coun. Law Sch. U. Va., Charlottesville. Mem. Ill. Bus. Roundtable, Northwestern U. Assocs., Coun. of 100, Tampa Fla. Office: CF Industries Inc One Salem Lake Dr Long Grove IL 60047-8402

LIUZZO, JOSEPH ANTHONY, food science educator; b. Tampa, Fla., Dec. 16, 1926; s. Joseph and Annie (Minardi) L.; m. Elaine Grammer, Nov. 30, 1951; children: Paul Arthur, Patricia Joyce, Jolaine Marie. BS, U. Fla., 1950, MS, 1955; postgrad., U. So. Calif., 1952-53; PhD, Mich. State U., 1958. Microbiologist Stokely-Van Camp Co., Tampa, 1950; head, div. microbiology Nutrilite Products, Inc., Buena Park, Calif., 1951-54; asst. prof. biochemistry La. State U., Baton Rouge, 1958-62; assoc. prof. food sci. La. State U., 1962-69, prof., 1969—, faculty chmn. athletics, 1979-83; Chmn. Am. Legion Baseball Program, 1976-82. Contbr. articles to profl. jours. With U.S. Army, 1945-46. Recipient Outstanding Alumnus award Food Sci. and Human Nutrition, Mich. State U., 1994. Fellow AAAS, Am. Inst.

Chemists, Inst. of Food Technologists; mem. Am. Inst. Nutrition, Am. chem. Soc., Kiwanis (pres. 1988-89, div. lt. gov. 1990-91), Sigma Xi, Phi Tau Sigma, Gamma Sigma Delta, Phi Sigma, Omicron Delta Kappa. Democrat. Mem. Ch. of Christ. Office: La State U Dept Food Science Baton Rouge LA 70803

LIVA, EDWARD LOUIS, eye surgeon; b. Lyndhurst, N.J., Aug. 30, 1925; s. Paul Francis and Lucy Agnes (Andreozzi) L.; m. Dorothea Lucille Carter, Aug. 29, 1946; children: Edward Jr., Bradford, Douglas, Jeffrey, Elaine. SB, Harvard U., 1946, MD, 1950. Diplomate Am. Bd. Ophthalmology. Internship Med. Coll. Va., Richmond; fellowship in eye pathology Mass. Eye and Ear, Boston, 1951; residency Brooklyn Eye and Ear, N.Y., 1952-53; chief ophthalmic examiner Workman's Compensation Bd., N.Y.C., 1957-63; sr. ophthalmic surgeon Hackensack (N.J.) Med. Ctr., 1957—, Valley Hosp., Ridgewood, N.J., 1963—; sr. ophthalmic surgeon, resident instr. oculoplastics Manhatten Eye, Ear and Throat, N.Y.C., 1957—; pres. Bergen Surg. Ctr., Paramus, N.J., 1991—, Eye Inst. of N.J., Paramus, 1987—. Author: Advances in Ophthalmic Plastic, 1983. Mem. Rep. Club, Ridgewood, 1960—. Capt. USAF, 1955-57. Fellow AMA, Am. Acad. Ophthalmology, Internat. Coll. of Surgeons, Am. Soc. of Ophtalmic Plastic and Reconstructive Surgery (chartered). Republican. Roman Catholic. Achievements include development new lid flaps oculoplastics, prototype of lid canal laceration repair, major modification of ptosis surgical procedures widely used, disproved Trichromatic theory of color vision in 1952. Home: 225 Sollas Ct Ridgewood NJ 07450 Office: Liva Eye Ctr One West Ridgewood Ave Paramus NJ 07652

LIVAS, EDUARDO, JR., milling company executive; b. 1945. PhD in Econs., U. Tex. With Gruma Mex. S.A., Monterrey, Mex., 1966-80; pres. Azteca Milling Co., Edinburg, Tex., 1990—. Office: Azteca Milling Co 501 W Chapin St Edinburg TX 78539-2412

LIVAUDAIS, MARCEL, JR., federal judge; b. New Orleans, Mar. 3, 1925; m. Carol Black; children: Julie, Marc, Durel. BA, Tulane U., 1945, JD, 1949. Bar: La. Assoc. Boswell & Loeb, New Orleans, 1949-50, 52-56; ptnr. Boswell Loeb & Livaudais, New Orleans, 1956-60, Loeb & Livaudais, 1960-67, 71-77, Loeb Dillon & Livaudais, 1967-71; U.S. magistrate, 1977-84; judge U.S. Dist. Ct. (ea. dist.) La., New Orleans, 1984—. Mem. Am. Judicature Soc. Office: US Dist Ct C-313 US Courthouse 500 Camp St New Orleans LA 70130-3313

LIVE, ISRAEL, microbiologist, educator; b. Zakrzewce, Austria, Apr. 26, 1907; came to U.S., 1928, naturalized, 1934; s. Herman and Rose (Nagelberg) L.; m. Anna Harris, Nov. 25, 1936; children—Theodore Ross, David Harris. V.M.D., U. Pa., 1934, A.M., 1936, Ph.D., 1940. Diplomate: Am. Bd. Microbiology. Faculty U. Pa., 1934—, successively asst. pathology, instr., assoc. asst. prof., asst. prof. bacteriology, assoc. prof., 1934-53, prof. microbiology, 1953-80, prof. emeritus, 1980—, chmn. dept., 1953-64; expert for com. on brucellosis WHO, UN; mem. com. on brucellosis research Nat. Acad. Scis.-NRC. Contbr. to: The Staphylococci, 1972. Fellow Am. Coll. Vet. Microbiololgy (charter), A.A.A.S., Am. Acad. Microbiology; mem. AVMA, Soc. Am. Bacteriologists, Am. Pub. Health Orgn., Am. Assn. Immunologists, U.S. Livestock San. Assn., Assn. Research Workers Animal Diseases in N. Am., World Assn. Vet. Microbiologists, Immunologists and Specialists in Infectious Diseases. Home: 3900 Ford Rd # 10 Philadelphia PA 19131

LIVELY, CAROL A., association executive; b. Chgo., Sept. 2, 1935; d. William Mann and Lillian (Juske) Haycock; m. E. Raymond Platig; children: Richard B., Laura Jean. L.P.N., Los Angeles Sch. Nursing, 1953; student, Columbia U., 1954, Boston U., 1956-57. Program dir. United Fund, Pittsfield, Mass., 1966-71; exec. dir. Western Mass. Health Council, 1971-74; asst. exec. dir. Genesse Health Council, Rochester, N.Y., 1974-76; dir. devel. Shimer Coll., Mt. Carroll, Ill., 1976-77; assoc. dir. Am. Hosp. Assn., Chgo., 1977-80; dir. health div., v.p. Smith Bucklin Assn., Washington, 1980—; mem. Achievement Rewards Coll. Scientists, Washington, 1980—; cons. Dept. Health Rep. Haiti, Washington, 1976—. Contbg. author: Politics of Health Planning, 1962; contbr. articles to profl. jours. Bd. dirs. Jacobs Pillow Dance Theatre, Pittsfield, 1968; bd. dirs. Albany Regional Med. Program, N.Y., 1971-74; active Jr. League, Washington, 1965—; mem. Commn. Drug Abuse Council, Boston, 1971-74. Recipient Woman of Yr. award Bus. and Profl. Women, 1971. Mem. New Eng. Pub. Health Assn., Mass. Council on Aging, Am. Soc. Hosp. Planning, Am. Pub. Health Assn. Home: 2138 California St NW Washington DC 20008-1876 Office: American Coll Nuclear Physicians 1200 19th St NW # 300 Washington DC 20036-4303

LIVELY, EDWIN LESTER, retired oil company executive; b. Bowie, Tex., June 16, 1930; s. L. D. and Lois E. Lively; m. G. Marie Bryan; 1 child, James E. B.B.A., Midwestern State U., Wichita Falls, Tex., 1951; postgrad. in Advanced Mgmt., Emory U., 1967. Adminstr. recruiting Conoco, Inc. (subs. E.I. du Pont de Nemours), Houston, 1967-68; Lake Charles coordinator Conoco, Inc., Lake Charles, La., 1968-75, Gulf Coast coordinator, 1975-79, regional coordinator, 1979-85, v.p. and regional coordinator so.western areas external affairs, 1985-86; gen. mgr. external affairs dept. State Affairs div. E.I. du Pont de Nemours & Co., 1987-88, retired. Served to sgt., U.S. Army, 1952-54. Avocations: golf; fishing.

LIVELY, EDWIN LOWE, sociology educator; b. Fairmont, W.Va., Aug. 14, 1920; s. E.L. and Lucy (Ross) L.; m. Virginia Isabelle Reed, Aug. 25, 1940; children: Lynellen, Gerianne (Mrs. Michael Green), Edwin L. II. A.B. in Edn, Fairmont State Coll., 1940; M.A. in Sociology, Ohio State U., 1946, Ph.D., 1959. Tchr. high sch. Farmington, W.Va., 1940-42; instr. Kent State U., 1947-53, asst. prof., 1953-58, assoc. prof., 1958-63; prof. sociology, chmn. dept. Akron U., 1963-68, dean grad. studies and research, 1968-75, prof. 1975-78; lectr. Labor and Edn. Service, Ohio State U., 1966-68; cons. Ohio Youth Commn., Akron Urban Renewal, Akron Community Action Council, Akron Community Relations Commn., Canton (Ohio) Bd. Edn. Contbg. editor: Dynamic Urban Sociology, 1954; guest editor: Sociol. Focus, 1970; co-author: (with V. Lively) Sexual Development of Young Children, 1990. Pres. Greater Akron Area Council Alcoholism, 1969-71; chmn. Akron Commn. Civil Disorders, 1968-69; pres. United Community Council, 1972-74; bd. dirs. Goals for Greater Akron Area, 1974-80. Served with USAAF, 1942-45. Decorated Air medal with five oak leaf clusters.; Swift fellow, 1963; grantee Esso Edn. Found., 1966; grantee div. adult and vocational research Dept. Health, Edn. and Welfare, 1967; grantee Ohio Bd. Regents, 1967; grantee Ohio Dept. Health, 1968. Fellow Am. Sociol. Assn.; mem. Ohio Valley Sociol. Soc. (bd. dirs. 1964-68), Nat. Council Family Relations, Summit County Mental Health Assn. (pres. 1965-67). Club: Mason. Home: 634 Brackenwood Cv West Palm Beach FL 33418-9001

LIVELY, H(OWARD) RANDOLPH, JR., retail company executive; b. Atlanta, Nov. 24, 1934; s. Howard R. Sr. and Nelle (Everett) L.; m. Barbara Fortun, June 3, 1958 (div. Apr. 1975); children—Bonnie, Dana, Andrea, Mindy, John; m. Fran Antone, Apr. 3, 1976. B.A., La. State U., 1957. Cert. consumer credit exec. With Sears Roebuck and Co., 1960-81, asst. credit mgr., New Orleans, 1960-63, statis. analyst, Atlanta, 1963-64, credit field supr., 1964-66, asst. gen. credit mgr., 1966-69, spl. research asst., Chgo., 1969-71, dir. public affairs, 1971-77, gen. credit mgr. Southwest Territory, Dallas, 1978-80, gen. credit mgr. Eastern Territory, Phila., 1981; pres. Jewelers Fin. Services Div., Zale Corp., Dallas, 1981-84, exec. v.p. Zale Corp., Dallas, 1984-85, ret., 1993; owner Via Real, Inc., 1987—, Kokopelli by Via Real, Dallas, Tex., Via Real, Irving, Tex.; pres., CEO Am. Fin. Svcs. Assn., Washington, 1994—. Chmn. Bd. Jr. Achievement Dallas, Inc., 1991-92, bd. dirs., 1989-95, CEO Fine Jewelers Guild div., 1986-91; chmn. bd. First Bank/Las Colinas, Irving, Tex.; pres. Merchants Research Council, Chgo., 1982-84. Contbr. articles in field to profl. pubs. Exec. advisor (indsl. film) A Day at the Fair 1975 (Best Indsl. Film Indsl. Film Producers Assn. 1977). Chmn., Zale PAC, 1983—; mem. legis. com. Am. Retail Fedn., 1972—; mem. Ill. State Electronic Funds Transfer Study Commn., 1976-77. Served to E-5 U.S. Army, 1957-59. Recipient Disting. Service to Retail Industry award Merchants Research Council, 1977; President's Cup Zale Corp., 1984. Mem. Credit Research Ctr. Purdue U. (exec. com. 1985—), mem. Columbia U. Fin. Services Mgmt. Program Alumni Assn., Nat. Retail Merchants Assn. (chmn. credit mgmt. div. 1984—, bd. dirs. 1985—), Internat. Credit Assn. (bd. dirs. 1982—). Republican. Methodist. Clubs: Las

Colinas Sports, La Cima (Irving, Tex.). Avocations: home computing; swimming.

LIVELY, PIERCE, federal judge; b. Louisville, Aug. 17, 1921; s. Henry Thad and Ruby Durrett (Keating) L.; m. Amelia Harrington, May 25, 1946; children: Susan, Katherine, Thad. AB, Centre Coll., Ky., 1943; LL.B., U. Va., 1948. Bar: Ky. 1948. Individual practice law Danville, Ky., 1949-57; mem. firm Lively and Rodes, Danville, 1957-72; judge U.S. Ct. Appeals (6th cir.), Cin., 1972—, chief judge, 1983-88; now sr. judge; Mem. Ky. Commn. on Economy and Efficiency in Govt., 1963-65, Ky. Jud. Advisory Com., 1972. Trustee Centre Coll. Served with USNR, 1943-46. Mem. ABA, Am. Judicature Soc., Order of Coif, Raven Soc., Phi Beta Kappa, Omicron Delta Kappa. Presbyterian. Office: US Ct Appeals PO Box 1226 Danville KY 40423-1226 also: US Courthouse Rm 418 Cincinnati OH 45202

LIVENGOOD, JOANNE DESLER, healthcare administrator; b. Omaha, Sept. 29, 1936; d. Arthur Frederick and Rosamond Christina (Knudsen) D.; m. Richard Vaughn Livengood, Aug. 11, 1962; children: Linda Renee, John David. BA, W.Va. State Coll.Inst., 1975; Diploma, Swedish Am. Hosp. Sch. Nursing, Rockford, Ill., 1961; MBA, Ea. Ill. U., Charleston, 1984. RN, Ill. DON Hoopeston (Ill.) Hosp. and Nursing Home, 1981-84; adminstr. Vermilion Manor Nursing Home, Danville, Ill., 1984-88; asst. adminstr. R.E. Thomason Hosp., El Paso, Tex., 1989-91; adminstr. Horizon Splty. Hosp., El Paso, Tex., 1992-93, Ill. Vets. Home at Anna, 1994—; cons. J.D. Williams Ins. Agy., El Paso, Tex., 1991-92, The Regional Clinic, Carterville, Ill., 1994. Mem. Danville (Ill.) Dist. 118 Sch. Bd., 1976-82. Fellow Am. Coll. Healthcare Execs.; mem. S.W. Healthcare Execs. (treas. 1989-93), Anna-Jonesboro Rotary Club. Home: 1810 Paula Ln Marion IL 62959 Office: Ill Vets Home at Anna 792 N Main St Anna IL 62906

LIVENGOOD, RICHARD VAUGHN, healthcare executive; b. Offerle, Kans., Mar. 24, 1934; s. Earl and Wynona Mae (Block) L.; m. D. Joanne Desler, Aug. 11, 1962; children: Linda Renee, John David. BS in Edn., Eastern Ill. U., 1956; student, Kings Fund Coll., London, 1972; MHA, Duke U., 1973. Instr., coach Rockford (Ill.) Sch. Bus. and Engring., 1959-64; asst. adminstr. Freeport (Ill.) Meml. Hosp., 1964-68; asst. adminstr. finance Manatee Meml. Hosp., Bradenton, Fla., 1968-71; v.p. Charleston (W.Va.) Area Med. Ctr., 1973-75; pres. Lakeview Med. Ctr., Danville, Ill., 1975-88; pres., CEO Providence Meml. Hosp., El Paso, 1988-92; COO Santa Rosa Health Care Corp., San Antonio, 1992-93; pres., CEO Marion (Ill.) Meml. Hosp., 1993—. Fellow Am. Coll. Healthcare Execs., Hosp. Fin. Mgmt. Assn., Ill. Hosp. Assn. (trustee 1981-88, chmn. 1987); mem. Tex. Hosp. Assn. (trustee 1989-91), Am. Hosp. Assn., S.W. Healthcare Execs. (pres. 1990-91), VHA S.W. (bd. dirs. 1988-91), Lakeview Meml. Found. (bd. dirs. 1979-87), El Paso Hosp. Coun. (bd. dirs. 1988-91). Methodist. Avocations: golf, tennis, travel. Home: 1810 Paula Ln Marion IL 62959-1425 Office: Marion Meml Hosp Marion IL 62959

LIVENGOOD, THOMAS CLAUDE, financial executive; b. Wichita, kans., July 7, 1955; s. Vern D. and Lois (Carson) L.; m. Cynthia D. Morrison, Jan. 4, 1974; children: Michelle, Scott, Mark, Brad. B., So. Meth. U., 1977. CPA, Tex. Mgr. Peat, Marwick, Mitchell & Co., Dallas, 1977-81; asst. gen. mgr. acctg. Tex. Oil and Gas Corp., Dallas, 1981-88; treas. Tenneco Gas, Houston, 1988-91, contr., 1991, v.p., CFO, 1991—. Mem. Fin. Execs. Inst., Petroleum Accts. Soc. (bd. dirs. 1982). Home: 8002 Hertfordshire Ct Spring TX 77379 Office: E Tennessee Nat Gas Co 1010 Milam St Houston TX 77002

LIVENGOOD, VICTORIA ANN, opera singer; b. Thomasville, N.C., Aug. 8, 1959; d. Gerald Winston and Carolyn Ann (Young) L. MusB in Voice, U. N.C., 1983; MusM in Opera, Boston Conservatory, 1985. tchr. master classes Pittsburg U., Kans., 1990, Temple U., Phila., 1993, U. N.C., Chapel Hill, 1994. Appeared as Queen Gertrude in Hamlet, Greater Miami (Fla.) Opera Co., 1987, Beauty in Beauty and the Beast, Opera Theater St. Louis, 1987, Mercy Kirke in Hazel Kirke, Lake George (N.Y.) Opera, 1987, Giulietta in Les Contes d'Hoffmann, Cleve. Opera Co., Charlotte in Werther, Seattle Opera Co., 1989, Dalila in Samson and Dalila, Lyne Opera, Kansas City, 1990, Dorabella in Cosi Jan Tutte, Hawaii Opera Theater, 1990, Carmen in Carmen, Conn. Opera Co., Hartford, 1990, Dalila in Samson and Dalila, Lyric Opera, Kansas City, 1990, Dorabella in Cosi Fan Tutti, Hawaii Opera Theater, 1990, Carmen in Carmen, Oper der Stadt Köln, Cologne, Germany, 1992, 94, Meg Page in Falstaff, Calgary (Can.) Opera Co., 1991, Idamante in Idomeneo, and Sesto in La Clemenza, L'Opera de Nice, France, 1991, Laura in Louisa Miller, Met. Opera Co., N.Y.C., 1991, Mrs. Grose in Turn of the Screw, Edmonton Opera, Can., 1993, Isolier in Il Conte Ory with Charleston's Spoleto Festival, 1993, Maddalena in Rigoletto, Oper der Stadt Köln and Edmonton Opera, 1994, Desideria in the Saint of Bleeker Street, Kansas City Lyric Opera, 1994, Lola in Cavalleria Rusticana, Met. Opera, 1994, Sonetka in Lady Macbeth of Mtsensk, Met. Opera, 1994, Dalila, Balt. Opera, 1995, Carmen, Edmonton Opera, Can., Giulietta in Les Contes d'Hoffmann, Santiago (Chile) Opera, 1995; soloist at J.F. Kennedy Ctr., Washington, 1986; performed with Am. Symphony Orch., Carnegie Hall, N.Y., 1986, N.C. Symphony Orch., Carnegie Hall, 1987, Nat. Symphony Orch., Washington, 1990, Atlanta Symphony Orch., 1991, Balt. Symphony Orch., 1991, Cologne Symphony, Germany, 1992, Minn. Symphony, 1992, Columbus Symphony, 1993, Buffalo Philharm., 1994, Northwest Chamber Mus. Soc., Portland, Oreg., 1994, others; solo recitalist in numerous locations including Boston, N.Y., N.C., Kans., Mo., others; EMI recs. include Oberon (soloist), 1992; subject of article Mus. Am. mag., 1986, Opera News Mag., 1987, 94, 95. Min. music Mills Home Bapt. Ch., Thomasville, 1980-81; recitalist Hosp. Guild, Thomasville 1980-82, 87, 92, Epilepsy Benefit, Kansas City, Mo., 1989, Aids Benefit-Buffalo Philharmonic N.Y., 1994. Recipient Nat. award Met. Opera Auditions, N.Y.C., 1985, Internat. award Rosa Ponselle Competition, N.Y.C., 1987, Luciano Pavarotti Competition, Phila., 1988, Key to City of Thomasville, 1992; grantee Sullivan Found., 1987, Nat. Inst. Music Theater, 1989. Avocations: crossstitch, swimming, floral arranging, dancing, movies. Office: care Herbert Barrett Mgmt 1776 Broadway Ste 1610 New York NY 10019-2002

LIVERGANT, HAROLD LEONARD, health services executive; b. Winnipeg, Man., Can., Nov. 10, 1924; m. Lynda Silverman; children—Bradley, Susan, Elyssa. B.S. in Acctg., U. Sask., 1945; D.H.A., U. Toronto, 1964. Acctg. cons. Dept. Health Sask. Govt., 1954-58; exec. dir. Northwest Regional Hosp. Council, North Battleford, Sask., Can., 1958-62; prin. hosp. cons. Thorne Group, Toronto, Ont., Can., 1964-66; exec. dir. Met. Toronto Hosp. Planning Council, 1966-68; chmn. pres. Extendicare Ltd., Toronto, 1968-80, pres., chief operating officer, 1980-83; pres., chief operating officer Crownx Inc., Toronto, 1983-84, vice chmn., 1984, also dir.; dir. Crown Life Ins. Co., Toronto. Contbr. articles to profl. jours. Bd. govs. Mt. Sinai Hosp. Fellow Am. Coll. Healthcare Execs., Can. Sch. Mgmt.; mem. Can. Coll. Health Svcs. Execs., Ontario Club, Primrose Club. Avocation: horse breeding. Home: 519 Spadina Rd, Toronto, ON Canada M5P 2W6 Office: Crownx Inc, 120 Bloor St E, Toronto, ON Canada M4W 1B8

LIVERMORE, JOSEPH MCMASTER, judge; b. Portland, Oreg., Feb. 5, 1937; s. Ernest R. and Frances (McMaster) L.; m. Elaine Dufort, Mar. 18, 1966; 1 son, Caleb. A.B., Dartmouth, 1958; LL.B., Stanford, 1961. Bar: Calif. 1962, Minn. 1968, Ariz. 1974. Assoc. Brobeck, Phleger & Harrison, San Francisco, 1961, 64-65; prof. law U. Minn., Mpls., 1965-73; asst. U.S. atty., Mpls., 1971-72; dean Coll. Law, U. Ariz., Tucson, 1973-77, prof., 1977-85; judge Ariz. Ct. Appeals, 1985—. Served with JAG Corps AUS, 1962-63. Mem. ABA, Ariz. Bar Assn., State Bar Calif., Order of Coif, Phi Beta Kappa. Home: 3208 E 3rd St Tucson AZ 85716-4232 Office: Ariz Ct Appeals 400 W Congress St Tucson AZ 85701-1352

LIVERSAGE, RICHARD ALBERT, cell biologist; b. Fitchburg, Mass., July 8, 1925; s. Rodney Marcellus and Hazel Mildred (Huntting) L.; m. June Patricia Krebs, June 19, 1954; children: John Walter, Robert Richard, James Keith, Ross Andrew. B.A., Marlboro Coll., 1951; A.M., Amherst Coll., 1953, Princeton U., 1957; Ph.D., Princeton U., 1958. Fellow Bowdoin Coll., Brunswick, Maine, 1953-54; instr. Amherst Coll., 1954-55, Princeton, 1958-60; mem. faculty U. Toronto, 1960—, prof. zoology, 1969—, grad. sec. dept., 1975-77, asso. chmn. grad. affairs dept., 1978-84, acting chmn., 1980-81; Investigator Huntsman Marine Lab., St. Andrews, N.B., Can., 1968-71. Author more than 82 rsch. publs. on role of nerves and endocrine secretions at the cellular-molecular levels in vertebrate appendage regeneration. Served as flight engr. USAAF, 1943-45. Recipient 5 decorations. Mem. Am. Soc. Zoologists, Soc. Devel. Biology, Can. Soc. Zoologists, Royal Can. Inst., Wound Healing Soc., Sigma Xi (exec. com., v.p., pres. U. Toronto chpt.). Home: 48 Ferndell Circle, Unionville, ON Canada L3R 3Y8 Office: U Toronto, Ramsay Wright Zool Lab, Toronto, ON Canada M5S 1A1

LIVESAY, THOMAS ANDREW, museum administrator, lecturer; b. Dallas, Feb. 1, 1945; s. Melvin Ewing Clay and Madge Almeda (Hall) L; m. Amanda Haralson, 1985; children: Heather Marie, Russell Lee. BFA, U. Tex., Austin, 1968, MFA, 1972; postgrad., Harvard U. Inst. Arts Adminstrn., 1978. Curator Elisabet Ney Mus., Austin, 1971-73; dir. Longview (Tex.) Mus. and Arts Center, 1973-75; curator of art Amarillo (Tex.) Art Center, 1975-77, dir. center, 1977-80; asst. dir. for adminstrn. Dallas Mus. Fine Arts, 1980-85; dir. Mus. of N.Mex., Santa Fe, 1985—; mem. touring panel Tex. Commn. Arts; mem. panel Nat. Endowment Arts, Inst. Mus. Services; adj. tchr. U. Okla., Coll. Liberal Studies, 1992—, U. N.Mex., 1992—. Author: Young Texas Artists Series, 1978, Made in Texas, 1979; editor: video tape American Images, 1979, Ruth Abrams, Paintings, 1940-85, NYU Press. Served with U.S. Army, 1969-71. Mem. Am. Assn. Mus. (coun. 1986-89, commn. on ethics 1992—, accreditation commn. 1994—), Tex. Assn. Mus. (v.p. 1981, pres. 1983), N.Mex. State Records and Archives Commn. (chmn. 1986—), Rotary. Methodist. Office: Mus of New Mexico PO Box 2087 Santa Fe NM 87504-2087

LIVICK, MALCOLM HARRIS, school administrator; b. Staunton, Va., Apr. 5, 1929; s. Arthur Crawford and Sallie (Harris) L; m. Linda Moorman Roller, July 21, 1956; children: Malcolm Harris, Charles Roller, Linda Lee, Todd Stephenson, Taylor Crawford (dec.). Student, Hampden Sydney Coll., 1947-48; B.S., U. Va., 1951; M.Ed., Madison Coll., 1965. Instr., coach Augusta Mil. Acad., 1955-56; instr. Norfolk (Va.) pub. schs., 1956-57; underwriter Mutual of N.Y., Norfolk, 1957-58; coach, asst. prin. Augusta Mil. Acad., Fort Defiance, Va., 1958-66; supt. Augusta Mil. Acad., 1966-83; dir. ednl. devel. Blue Ridge Community Coll., 1984-85, dir. continuing edn., 1986; dir. Blue Ridge Community Coll. Waynesboro Ctr., 1986—. Chmn. Upper Valley Regional Park Authority, 1969-78; Trustee King's Daus. Hosp., Staunton, Massanetta Springs. Served with USAF, 1951-55. Mem. Va. Mil. Schs. League (pres. 1966-68), Va. Assn. Prep. Schs. (exec. com. 1967-73, pres. 1971-72), Nat., Va. assns. secondary sch. prins. Presbyn. (deacon 1963-65, elder 1965—). Lodge: Kiwanis (pres. 1970-71, lt. gov. 1971, gov. 1979-80). Address: PO Box 22 Fort Defiance VA 24437-0022

LIVICK, STEPHEN, fine art photographer; b. Leeds, Yorkshire, Eng., Feb. 11, 1945; arrived in Can., 1947; Student, Sir George Williams U., Montreal, Can., 1963-66. Self employed artist, 1970—. One man shows include Centaur Gallery, Montreal, 1972, London Art Gallery, Ont., 1973, George Eastman House, Rochester, N.Y., 1975, David Mirvish Gallery, Toronto, 1976, 77, Photography Gallery, Bowmanville, Ont., 1976, 77, Balt. Mus. Art, 1978, Lunn Graphics, Washington D.C., 1978, Gallery Graphics, Ottawa, 1978, Jane Corkin Gallery, Toronto, 1979, 80, 81, U. Western Ont., London, 1981, George Dalsheimer Gallery, Balt., 1982, MacDonald Stewart Art Ctr., Guelph, 1983, New Brunswick Craft Sch., Fredericton, 1986, Winnipeg Photographers Group, 1987, Galerie Sequence, Quebec, 1988, U .Sherbrooke, 1990, Can. Mus. Contemporary Photography, Ottawa, 1992; travelling exhibitions include George Eastman House, 1978-81, London Regional Art Gallery, 1976-77, Nat. Film Bd., 1976-84, Art Gallery Ont., 1980, 81, Can. Mus. Contemporary Photography, 1986, 87; exhibited in group shows at Nat. Art Gallery, Ottawa, 1975, London Pub. Art Gallery, 1976, Nat. Film Bd., Ottawa, Can., 1977, Mendal Art Gallery, Saskatoon, Can., 1977, Neikrug Galleries, N.Y.C., 1978, Banff-London Exchange, Alberta, Can., 1978, Smithsonian Instn., Washington, 1981, Carpenter Ctr. Visual Arts, Cambridge, Mass., 1981, U. Calgary, 1982, Saidy Bronfman Mus., Montreal, 1984, Photographers Gallery, London, Eng., 1984, Presentation House, Vancouver, B.C., 1985, Photo Union Gallery, Hamilton, Ont., 1986, Film In The City, St. Paul, 1989, Corcoran Gallery Art, Washington, 1989, London (Can.) Regional Art Mus., 1990, Can. Mus. Contemporary Photography, Ottawa, 1992, others; represented in permanent collections Nat. Art Gallery Can., Can Mus. Contemporary Photography, Art Gallery Ont., Can. Art Bank, Nat. Archives Can., Mus. Modern Art, N.Y., George Eastman House, Rochester, N.Y., Carnegie Mus. Art, Pitts., Mus. Fine Arts, Houston, Fogg Art Mus., Cambridge, Mass., Balt. Mus. Art, George Washington U., Washington, Norton Gallery Art, West Palm Beach, Fla., Syracuse (N.Y.) U., Middlebury (Vt.) Coll., Hickory (N.C.) Mus. Art, U. Iowa Mus., U. No. Iowa, Art Gallery Hamilton, Can., High Mus. Art, Atlanta, Ga., London Regional Art Gallery, Corcoran Gallery Art, Washington, Queens U., Kingston, Can., Winnipeg (Can.) Art Gallery, Sarnia (Ont.) Art Gallery, U. Western Ont., London, Macdonald Stewart Art Ctr., Guelph, Ont., numerous pvt., corp. collections. B level grantee Can. Coun., Ottawa; sr. grantee Ont. Arts Coun., Toronto. Home and Office: 22A Maitland St Studio, London, ON Canada N6B 3L2

LIVINGOOD, CLARENCE S., dermatologist; b. Elverson, Pa., Aug. 7, 1911; s. Clarence A. and Eliza (Zerr) L.; m. Louise Sinclair Woelpper, Oct. 24, 1947; children: Wilson, Louise S., Clarence, Susan, Elizabeth. B.S., Ursinus Coll., 1932, D.Sc. (hon.), 1982; M.D., U. Pa., 1936. Diplomate Am. Bd. Dermatology (exec. dir. 1968-92, exec. cons. 1993—). Intern, then resident dermatology Hosp. U. Pa., 1936-41; asst. prof. dermatology U. Pa. Med. Sch., 1946-48, U. Pa. Med. Sch. (Grad. Sch.), 1946-49; chief dermatology Children's Hosp. Pa., 1946-48; prof., chmn. dept. dermatology Jefferson Med. Sch., Phila., 1948-49, U. Tex. Sch. Medicine, 1949-53; chmn. dermatology dept. Henry Ford Hosp., Detroit, 1953-76; chmn. emeritus Henry Ford Hosp., 1976—; team physician Detroit Tigers baseball club, 1967—; clin. prof. dermatology U. Mich. Sch. Medicine; mem. com. on cut. diseases AFEB, 1956-72; chief cons. dermatology VA, 1953-59; Sec.-gen. XII Internat. Congress of Dermatology, 1962; exec. com. Am. Bd. Med. Specialties, 1963-92, 19 Special award, 1993; mem. AMA residency rev. com. for dermatology, 1957-67; adv. com. Nat. Disease and Therapeutic Index, 1974—; bd. dirs., treas. Council Med. Splty. Socs., 1976-80, mem. liaison com. on grad. med. edn., 1978-83; mem. Accreditation Council for Grad. Med. Edn., 1977-83. Author: (with D.M. Pillsbury, M.B. Sulzberger) Manual of Dermatology. Mem. editorial bd.: (with D.M. Pillsbury, M.B. Sulzberger) Jour. Geriatrics. Contbr. articles to med. jours. Trustee Dermatology Found., 1965-71, ECFMG, 1975-79. Served to lt. col. M.C. AUS, 1942-46. decorated Bronze Star, Legion of Merit; recipient Profl. Achievement award Wayne County Med. Soc., 1993, Dermatology Fedn. Practitioner of Yr. award, 1993. Fellow Am. Acad. Dermatology (dir., past pres., Gold medal 1975, Masters in Dermatology 1985, Presdl. Citation 1987, C.S. Livingood Ann. Lectureship established 1993), ACP; mem. AMA (ho. of dels., chmn. sect. dermatology 1958, Disting. Svc. award 1990), Soc. Investigative Dermatology (past pres., Stephen Rothman award 1980), Am. Dermatol. Assn. (past pres., dir. 1964-68, named hon. mem. 1981), Am. Bd. Dermatology (diplomate, exec. dir. 1968-92, exec. cons. 1993—), Coll. Physicians Phila., Pacific Dermatol. Soc. (hon. mem.), Phila. Dermatol Soc., Detroit Dermatol. Soc. (past pres.), Mich. Med. Soc. (jud. council, ho. dels. 1974-80), Med. Cons. Soc. World War II, Assn. Mil. Dermatologists, Detroit Acad. Medicine, Assn. Maj. League Team Physicians, Assn. Dermatology Argentina (corr.) N.Y. Acad. Scis. (internat. congress dermatology), Danish Soc. (hon.), Indian Assn. Dermatologists (hon.), Brit. Dermatol. Soc. (hon.), Yugoslavian Dermatol. Soc. (hon.), Israel Dermatol. Soc. (hon.), N.Y. Dermatol. Soc. (hon. 1992), 18th World Congress Dermatology (hon. mem. 1992). Clubs: Grosse Pointe, Witenagemote. Home: 345 University Pl Grosse Pointe MI 48230-1635 Office: Henry Ford Hosp 2799 West Grand Blvd Detroit MI 48202

LIVINGSTON, ALAN WENDELL, communications executive; b. McDonald, Pa.; s. Maurice H. and Rose L. (Wachtel) L.; m. Nancy Olson, Sept. 1, 1962; children: Peter, Laura, Christopher. BS, U. Pa., 1940. Exec. v.p. Capitol Records, Inc., Hollywood, Calif., 1946-55, pres., chmn., 1960-68; v.p. programming NBC, Burbank, Calif., 1955-60; pres. Mediarts, Inc., Los Angeles, 1968-76; exec. v.p., pres. entertainment group 20th Century Fox Film Corp., Beverly Hills, Calif., 1976-80; pres. Pacific Rim Entertainment, Los Angeles, 1980—. Creator various children's books, records and Bozo the Clown, 1946—; writer: Ronnie Finklehof, Superstar, 1968; writer, producer (animated film) Sparky's Magic Piano, 1988. Bd. dirs. Ctr. Theater Group, Los Angeles. Served to 2d lt. inf. U.S. Army, 1943-46. Mem. ASCAP, Nat. Acad. Rec. Arts and Scis., Acad. TV Arts and Scis., Acad. Motion Picture Arts and Scis. Office: Pacific Rim Entertainment Inc 9229 W Sunset Blvd Los Angeles CA 90069

LIVINGSTON, DAVID MORSE, biomedical scientist, physician, internist; b. Cambridge, Mass., Mar. 29, 1941; s. Arthur Joshua and Phyllis Freda (Kanters) L.; m. Jacqueline Gutman, June 23, 1963 (div. 1983); m. Emily Rabb, Jan. 25, 1986; children: Catherine Ellen, Julie. AB cum laude, Harvard U., 1961; MD magna cum laude, Tufts U., 1965. Diplomate Nat. Bd. Med. Examiners, Am. Bd. Internal Medicine. Intern, resident Peter Bent Brigham Hosp., Boston, 1965-67; rsch. assoc., sr. staff fellow, sr. investigator NCI-NIH, Bethesda, Md., 1967-69, 71-73; rsch. fellow in biol. chemistry Harvard Med. Sch., Boston, 1969-71, asst. prof. medicine, 1973-76, assoc. prof. medicine, 1976-82, prof. medicine, 1982—; Emil Frei III prof. medicine Harvard Med. Sch., 1992—; v.p. Dana-Farber Cancer Inst., Boston, 1989-91; dir., physician-in-chief Harvard Med. Sch., Boston, 1991—, Emil Frei III prof. medicine, 1992—. Mem. editorial bd. Virology jour., 1989—; editor BBA Revs. on Cancer, 1988—; contbr. articles to profl. jours. Mem. sci. adv. com. Damon Runyan-Walter Winchell Cancer Fund, N.Y.C., 1988-92, chmn. sci. adv. com., 1989-90; mem. bd. dirs. Cancer Rsch. Fund, 1992—, exec. com., 1994—; vice chmn. sci. adv. com. Pezcoller Found., Trento, Italy, 1994—; mem. sci. adv. bd. Inst. Cancer Rsch., Fox Chase, Pa., 1991-94, Lineburger Comprehensive Cancer Ctr., U. N.C., Chapel Hill. Comdr. USPHS, 1967-73. Recipient Claire & Richard Morse award for Rsch., Dana-Farber Cancer Inst., 1991. Mem. Am. Soc. for Clin. Investigation, Assn. Am. Physicians, Am. Soc. Biol. Chemistry and Molecular Biology, Am. Soc. Microbiology, Am. Soc. Virology, Inst. Medicine of Nat. Acad. Scis., Met. Club Washington, Harvard Club (N.Y.C., Boston), Alpha Omega Alpha. Achievements include discovery of important aspects of the neoplastic transforming process and of the mechanisms governing control of the mammalian cell cycle. Office: Dana-Farber Cancer Inst 44 Binney St Boston MA 02115

LIVINGSTON, DONALD RAY, lawyer; b. Oak Ridge, Tenn., Jan. 11, 1952; s. Tally R. and Pansy L. (Heiskell) L.; m. Anne Davis, May 2, 1992; 1 child, John T. Livingston. AB in Econs., U. Ga., 1974, JD, 1977. Bar: Ga. 1977, U.S. Dist. Ct. (no. dist.) Ga. 1977, U.S. Dist. Ct. (mid. dist.) Ga. 1978, U.S. Dist. Ct. (no. dist.) Calif. 1984, U.S. Dist. Ct. (no. dist.) N.Y., U.S. Ct. Appeals (5th cir.) 1978, U.S. Ct. Appeals (4th and 11th cirs.) 1981, U.S. Ct. Appeals (6th cir.) 1984, U.S. Supreme Ct. 1983. Assoc. Adair, Goldthwaite, Stanford & Daniel, Atlanta, 1977-79; ptnr. Adair, Goldthwaite & Daniel, Atlanta, 1979-87; exec. asst. to gen. counsel EEOC, Washington, 1987-90, acting gen. counsel, 1990-91, gen. counsel, 1991-93; ptnr. Akin, Gump, Strauss, Hauer & Feld, Washington, 1993—; lectr. seminars on employment law, 1987—. Contbr. articles to profl. jours. Mem. ABA, Ga. Bar Assn. (chair Labor Law sect. 1985-86), Washington D.C. Bar Assn. Office: Akin Gump Strauss Hauer & Feld 1333 New Hampshire Ave NW Washington DC 20036-1500

LIVINGSTON, GROVER D., newspaper publishing executive. V.p. information management The Dallas Morning News, Tex. Office: The Dallas Morning News Communication Ctr Young & Houston Sts Dallas TX 75202*

LIVINGSTON, HOMER J., JR., stock exchange executive; b. Chgo., 1935. BA in Econs., Princeton U., 1957; JD, Chgo. Kent Coll. Law, 1966. Pres., CEO LaSalle Nat. Bank, Chgo., 1984-88; chmn., CEO Livingston & Co., Chgo., 1988-92; pres., CEO, Chgo. Stock Exch., 1993—; bd. dirs. Peoples Energy Corp., Am. Nat. Can Corp. Office: Chgo Stock Exch 440 S La Salle St Chicago IL 60605-1028

LIVINGSTON, JAMES DUANE, physicist, educator; b. Bklyn., June 23, 1930; s. James Duane and Florence (Boullee) L.; m. Nancy Lee Clark, June 27, 1953 (div. 1976); children: Joan, Susan, Barbara; m. Sharon Hood Penney, Mar. 30, 1985. B in Engring. Physics, Cornell U., 1952; PhD in Applied Physics, Harvard U., 1956. Physicist R & D GE, Schenectady, N.Y., 1956-89; sr. lectr. dept. material sci. and engring. MIT, Cambridge, 1989—. Author, co-author over 100 publications in field. Coolidge Fellow Gen. Electric Corp. R & D, 1987; recipient Disting. Career award Hudson-Mohawk chpt. AIME, 1986. Fellow Am. Soc. Metals, Am. Phys. Co.; mem. Nat. Acad. Engring., IEEE, AAAS, Materials Rsch. Soc., The Minerals, Metals and Materials Soc. Democrat. Unitarian. Achievements include 7 patents; advanced research in superconducting, ferromagnetic, and mechanical properties of materials. Home: 90 Albee Dr Braintree MA 02184-8252 Office: MIT 13 4066 Cambridge MA 02139

LIVINGSTON, JAMES EVERETTE, marine corps officer; b. Towns, Ga., Jan. 12, 1940; s. Myret Barrett and Ruth Leona (Browning) L.; m. Sara Craft, June 10, 1966; children: Kimberly Anne, Melissa Paige. BSCE, Auburn U., 1962; MA in Mgmt., Webster U., 1984. Commd. 2d lt. USMC, 1962, advanced through grades to maj. gen., 1991; platoon comdr. Co. A, Schs. Demonstration Troops, Quantico, Va., Co. H, 2d Tng. Bn., Officer Candidates Sch., Quantico, 1963, various units, 1963-65; stationed at MCAS, Cherry Point, N.C., 1965, MCRD, Parris Island, S.C., 1966; comdg. officer USMC detachment USS Wasp, 1966-67; comdg. officer Co. E, 2d Bn., 4th Marines, Republic of Vietnam, 1967-68; dir. div. schs. 1st Marine Div., Camp Pendleton, N.C., 1972-73; ops. officer 3d Bn., 7th Marines, 1973-75, 4th Marines, Okinawa, Japan, 1975; comdg. officer Marine Barracks, U.K., 1977-80; comdg. officer 3d Recruit Tng. Bn., then asst. chief of staff for ops. and tng. USMC Recruit Depot, Parris Island; asst. chief of staff for manpower, then for ops. and tng. 2d Marine Div.; comdg. officer 6th Marine Regiment, 2d Marine Div., Camp Lejeune, N.C., 1986-87; sr. Marine/joint plans and programs officer (chief) Joint U.S. Assistance Group, The Philippines, 1987-88; dep. dir. for ops. Nat. Mil. Command Ctr., Joint Staff, Washington, 1988-90; acting comdg. gen. USMC Air-Ground Combat Ctr., Twentynine Palms, Calif., 1990-91; comdg. gen. 1st Marine Expeditionary Brigade, Kaneohe Bay, Hawaii, 1991, 4th Marine Div. (Reinforced), New Orleans, 1991-92, Marine Res. Forces, USMCR, New Orleans, 1992—. Decorated Medal of Honor, Silver Star, Bronze Star with combat V, Purple Heart, Def. Superior Svc. Medal, Def. Meritorious Svc. Medal, Meritorious Svc. Medal with gold star, Combat Action Ribbon; Cross of Gallantry (Republic of Vietnam); named Man of Yr. Sigma Pi, 1990. Mem. Marine Corps Assn.; 3d Marine Div. Assn., 2d Bn. 4th Marine Regiment Assn., Medal of Honor Soc. Republican. Baptist. Home: 102 Constitution St New Orleans LA 70114-1532 Office: Marine Res Force FMF USMCR 4400 Dauphine St New Orleans LA 70146-5400

LIVINGSTON, JAY HAROLD, composer, lyricist; b. McDonald, Pa., Mar. 28, 1915; s. Maurice and Rose (Wachtel) L.; m. Lynne Gordon, Mar. 19, 1947; m. Shirley Mitchell, May 16, 1992; children from previous marriage: Travilyn, Tammy. B.A., U. Pa., 1937. With Paramount Pictures, 1945-55. Writer songs for over 100 motion pictures; songs, spl. material for Broadway shows Sons O' Fun, Hellzapoppin, also for Bob Hope, 1947-89, 90; scores for Broadway prodns. Oh Captain, 1958, Let It Ride, 1961; 2 songs in Sugar Babies, 1979; TV theme songs including Bonanza, Mister Ed, To Rome With Love; songs To Each His Own, Silver Bells, Tammy, Golden Earrings, Dear Heart, Never Let Me Go. Recipient 3 Acad. Awards for songs Buttons and Bows, Mona Lisa, Que Sera Sera, Star on Hollywood Blvd. Walk of Fame, 1995; named to Songwriters Hall of Fame, 1973. Mem. Acad. TV Arts and Scis., ASCAP, Acad. Motion Picture Arts and Scis. (exec. bd.), Nat. Acad. Rec. Arts and Scis. (gov.), Songwriters Guild (exec. com.), AFTRA, Dramatist's Guild. Office: care ASCAP 1 Lincoln Pla New York NY 10023

LIVINGSTON, JOHNSTON R., manufacturing executive; b. Foochow, China, Dec. 18, 1923; s. Henry Walter V and Alice (Moorehead) L.; m. Caroline Johnson, Aug. 17, 1946 (dec.); children: Henry, Ann, Jane, David; m. Patricia Karolchuck, Sept. 4, 1965. B.S. with honors in Engring., Yale U., 1947; M.B.A. with distinction (Baker scholar), Harvard U., 1949. With Mpls.-Honeywell Regulator Co., 1949-55; with Whirlpool Corp., 1956-66, v.p., until 1966; v.p. Redman Industries, Dallas, 1966-67; dir. Constm. Tech., Inc., Dallas, 1967—; chmn. bd., pres. Constrm. Tech., Inc., Denver, 1974-89; chmn. bd. Enmark Corp., Denver, 1979—; pres. Marcor Housing Syustems, Inc., Denver, 1971-74; bd. dirs. Rocky Mountain World Trade Assn. (past chmn.). Former mem. industry adv. com. Nat. Housing Ctr.; bd. dirs., past pres. Nat. Home Improvement Coun.; chmn. bd., pres. Denver Symphony Assn., 1977-81; dir., past chmn. Rocky Mountain Regional Inst. Internat. Edn.; bd. trustees Bonfils-Stanton Found., Denver, 1980—; hon. trustee Inst. Internat. Edn., N.Y. Mem. Sigma Xi, Tau Beta Pi. Clubs:

Denver Country. Home: 1649 Keystone Ranch Rd Dillon CO 80435-8384 Office: 5070 Oakland St Denver CO 80239-2724

LIVINGSTON, LOUIS BAYER, lawyer; b. N.Y.C., Dec. 12, 1941; s. Norman and Helen (Bayer) L.; m. Mari Livingston, Apr. 6, 1968; children: Diana, Alex, Ann. BA, Yale U., 1963; LLB, Harvard U., 1966. Bar: N.Y. 1967, Oreg. 1971. Atty. NLRB, Memphis, 1967-68, Poletti, Freidin et al., N.Y.C., 1968-71; ptnr. Miller, Nash, Wiener, Hager & Carlsen, Portland, Oreg., 1971—. Office: Miller Nash Wiener Hager & Carlsen 111 SW 5th Ave Portland OR 97204-3604

LIVINGSTON, MYRA COHN, poet, writer, educator; b. Omaha, Aug. 17, 1926; d. Mayer L. and Gertrude (Marks) Cohn; m. Richard Roland Livingston, Apr. 14, 1952 (dec. 1990); children: Joshua, Jonas Cohn, Jennie Marks. BA, Sarah Lawrence Coll., 1948. Profl. horn player, 1941-48; book reviewer Los Angeles Daily News, 1948-49, Los Angeles Mirror, 1949-50; asst. editor Campus Mag., 1949-50; various public relations positions and pvt. sec. to Hollywood (Calif.) personalities, 1950-52; tchr. creative writing Dallas (Tex.) public library and schs., 1958-63; poet-in-residence Beverly Hills (Calif.) Unified Sch. Dist., 1966-84; sr. instr. UCLA Extension, 1973—; cons. to various sch. dists., 1966-84, cons. poetry to publishers children's lit., 1975—. Author: Whispers and Other Poems, 1958, Wide Awake and Other Poems, 1959, I'm Hiding, 1961, See What I Found, 1962, I Talk to Elephants, 1962, I'm Not Me, 1963, Happy Birthday, 1964, The Moon and a Star and Other Poems, 1965, I'm Waiting, 1966, Old Mrs. Twindlytart and Other Rhymes, 1967, A Crazy Flight and Other Poems, 1968, The Malibu and Other Poems, 1972, When You Are Alone/It Keeps You Capone: An Approach to Creative Writing with Children, 1973, Come Away, 1974, The Way Things Are and Other Poems, 1974, 4-Way Stop and Other Poems, 1976, A Lollygag of Limericks, 1978, O Sliver of Liver and Other Poems, 1979, No Way of Knowing: Dallas Poems, 1980, A Circle of Seasons, 1982, How Pleasant to Know Mr. Lear!, 1982, Sky Songs, 1984, A Song I Sang to You, 1984, Monkey Puzzle, 1984, The Child as Poet: Myth or Reality?, 1984, Celebrations, 1985, Worlds I Know and Other Poems, 1985, Sea Songs, 1986, Earth Songs, 1986, 1987, Higgledy-Piggledy, 1986, Space Songs, 1988, There Was a Place and Other Poems, 1988, Up in the Air, 1989, Birthday Poems, 1989, Remembering and Other Poems, 1989, My Head Is Red and Other Riddle Rhymes, 1990, Climb Into the Bell Tower: Essays on Poetry, 1990, Poem-making: Ways to Begin Writing Poetry, 1991, Light and Shadow, 1992, I Never Told and Other Poems, 1992, Let Freedom Ring: A Ballad of Martin Luther King, Jr., 1992, Abraham Lincoln, A Man for All the People, 1993, Platero Y Yo/Platero and I (trans. 1994, Flights of Fancy and other poems, 1994, Keep on Singing: A Ballad of Marian Anderson, 1994; The Writing of Poetry, film strips; co-editor: The Scott-Foresman Anthology, 1984; editor 36 anthologies of poetry; contbr. articles on children's lit. to ednl. pubis., essays on lit. and reading in edn. to various books; mem. editorial adv. bd. The New Advocate, The Reading Teacher. Officer Beverly Hills PTA Council, 1966-75; pres. Friends of Beverly Hills Public Library, 1979-81; bd. dirs. Poetry Therapy Inst., 1975—, Reading is Fundamental of So. Calif., 1981—. Recipient honor award N.Y. Herald Tribune Spring Book Festival, 1958, excellence in poetry award Nat. Coun. Tchrs. of English, 1980, Commonwealth Club award, 1984, Nat. Jewish Book award, 1987, Kerlan award U. Minn., 1994, Transl. award Internat. Bd. on Books for Young People, 1994. Mem. Authors Guild, Internat. Reading Assn., Soc. Children's Book Writers (honor award 1975), Tex. Inst. Letters (awards 1961, 80), So. Calif. Council on Lit. for Children and Young People (Comprehensive Contribution award 1968, Notable Book award 1972, Poetry Quartet award 89), PEN. Address: 9308 Readcrest Dr Beverly Hills CA 90210-2533

LIVINGSTON, ROBERT GERALD, university official, political scientist; b. N.Y.C., Nov. 17, 1927; s. Robert Teviot and Geraldine (Gray) L.; m. Jeanne Andrée Nettel, May 12, 1955; children: Catherine Schuyler Livingston Fernandez, Robert Eric. AB, Harvard U., 1953, AM, 1953, PhD, 1959. Fgn. svc. officer U.S. Dept. State, Washington, 1956-74; v.p. German Marshall Fund U.S., Washington, 1974-77, pres., 1977-81; writer Washington, 1981-83; acting dir. Am. Inst. for Contemporary German Studies, Johns Hopkins U., Washington, 1983-87, dir. Am. Inst. for Contemporary German Studies, 1987-94, sr. devel. officer Am. Inst. for Contemporary German Studies, 1994—; commentator BBC German Svc., London, 1986—, Deutschlandfunk, Cologne, 1991—. Co-author, editor: The Federal Republic in the 1980s, 1983, West German Political Parties, 1986; contbr. over 200 articles to polit. jours. and newspapers. Sgt. U.S. Army, 1946-49. Mem. German Studies Assn. U.S., Harvard Grad. Soc. (coun.), Coun. on Fgn. Rels., N.Y. Soc. Sons of Cincinnati, Cosmos Club, Chevy Chase Club, Barnstable Yacht Club (Mass.), Phi Beta Kappa. Democrat. Episcopalian. Avocations: hiking, swimming, tennis. Office: Am Inst Contemporary German Studies 11 Dupont Cir NW Ste 350 Washington DC 20036

LIVINGSTON, ROBERT LINLITHGOW, JR. (BOB LIVINGSTON, JR.), congressman; b. Colorado Springs, Colo., Apr. 30, 1943; s. Robert L. and Dorothy (Godwin) L.; m. Bonnie Robichaux, Sept. 13, 1965; children: Robert Linlithgow, III, Richard Godwin, David Barkley; SuShan Alida. BA in Econs., Tulane U., 1967, JD, 1968; postgrad., Loyola Inst. Politics, 1973. Bar: La. 1968. Ptnr. Livingston & Powers, New Orleans, 1976-77; asst. U.S. atty., dep. chief criminals divsn. U.S. Attys. Office, 1970-73; chief spl. prosecutor, chief armed robbery divsn. Orleans Parish Dist. Atty.'s Office, 1974-75; chief prosecutor organized crime unit La. Atty. Gen.'s Office, 1975-76; mem. 95th-104th Congresses from 1st La. Dist., 1977—; Mem. nat. adv. bd. Young Ams. for Freedom. Served with USN, 1961-63. Named Outstanding Asst. U.S. Atty., 1973. Mem. ABA, Fed. Bar Assn., La. Bar Assn. New Orleans Bar Assn., Navy League, Am. Legion. Republican. Episcopalian. Clubs: Masons, Young Mens Business. Home: 111 Veterans Memorial Blvd Metairie LA 70005-3035 Office: US Ho of Reps 2406 Rayburn HOB Washington DC 20515

LIVINGSTON, SHARON HOLLANDER, advertising executive; b. Camden, N.J., Nov. 23, 1946; d. Samuel Alexander and Matilda (Rosner) Hollander; m. Glenn S. Livingston, Mar. 3, 1988. MS in Psychology, Fairleigh Dickinson U., 1976. Project dir. Comml. Analysts Co., N.Y.C., 1969-74; field dir. Grey Advt., N.Y.C., 1971-74; research analyst Gen. Foods, Westchester, N.Y., 1974, Warner Lambert Co., Morris Plains, N.J., 1975-77; pres. Exec. Solutions Inc., Locust Valley, N.Y., 1977—. Mem. Qualitative Rsch. Coun. Advt. Rsch. Found. (founder), Qualitative Rsch. Nat. Acad. Counselors and Family Therapists. Office: Exec Solutions 30 Lincoln Plz 30 W 63rd St/Ste 25 O New York NY 10023

LIVINGSTON, STANLEY C., architect. BArch, U. So. Calif., 1961; student, U. Calif. San Diego. Lic. architect Calif., N.Mex., Nev.; cert. Nat. Coun. Archtl. Registration. Prin. Salerno/Livingston Architects, San Diego; lectr. numerous insts. Archtl. projects include Residence Hall Tower & Multi Purpose Bldg. San Diego State U., Pacific Southwest Airlines Adminstrv. Offices & Hangar Facility, Fujitsu Microelectronics, Inc., Belden Village Low Income Sr. Housing Project, Atkinson Marine Corp. Hdqs. & Ship Repair Facility, Campbell Industries, Islandia Hotel Tower, Marlin Club, Sportfishing Facility and 500 Boat Marina, Branch Libr., Belmont Park Master Plan, Expert Witness Projects; other comml. projects include U.S. Fin. Office Bldg., Lake Murray Office Bldg., San Diego Fed. Branch Bank (5 locations), Nat. U. Office Bldg., Harbor Boat & Yacht Shipyard Renovation, Pacific Southwest Airlines Passenger Lounges & Gates (2 locations), and others. Symposia chmn. "Frank Lloyd Wright-Living in the Wright Century...An Evaluation" San Diego Archtl. Found./San Diego Mus. Art, 1990; mem. design competition adv. panel Balboa Park Organ Pavilion Parking Garage, 1990; mem. urban design com. San Diego Center City, 1982-86; founder Orchids and Onions Program, 1976, com. chmn. 1984, jury chmn. 1985; chmn. design adv. com. San Diego Center City Devel. Corp., 1980. Fellow AIA (San Diego chpt., past pres. 1978-79, chmn. urban design com. 1978-86, chmn. task force Balboa Pk. master plan); mem. Am. Planning Assn. (mem. bd. dirs. San Diego 1981-82), Soc. Mktg. Profl. Svcs. Am. Arbitration Assn. (mem. panel arbitrators 1988—), Urban Land Inst. (assoc.), Urban Design & Planning Com., Bldg. Industry Assn. (mem. construction quality com.), Community Assn. Inst., San Diego Archtl. Found. (bd. dirs.), SCARAB. Office: Salerno/Livingston Architects 363 5th Ave 3rd Fl San Diego CA 92101-6909

LIVINGSTON, THEODORE A., JR., lawyer; b. Cleve., July 21, 1946. BA summa cum laude, McPherson Coll., 1969; JD, U. Kans., 1973. Bar: Ill. 1973. Ptnr. Mayer, Brown & Platt, Chgo. Office: Mayer Brown & Platt 190 S La Salle St Chicago IL 60603-3441

LIVINGSTON, THOMAS MATHIAS, advertising agency executive, writer; b. White Plains, N.Y., July 18, 1935; s. Warren Putnam Livingston and Emily Celeste (Mathias) Beard; m. Christine Turpin, Feb. 21, 1964; children: Tracy Emilie, Terence Howard. AB, Stanford U., 1959. Freelance writer Europe, 1959-66; lectr. Rutgers U., New Brunswick, N.J., 1966-68, San Jose (Calif.) State U., 1969-73; v.p. Regis McKenna Advt., Palo Alto, Calif., 1973-76, exec. v.p., 1979-80, creative dir. 1973-76, 79-80; v.p. mktg. Saga Corp., Menlo Park, Calif., 1976-79; pres., chief exec. officer Livingston-Sirutis Advt., San Francisco 1980-. Author: (novel) Paper Walls of Innocence, 1964, The Tower Is Down, 1966; contbr. short stories to mags. Michael Karolyi Found. fellow, Vence, France, 1964; Music Corp. Am. fellow, 1966. Office: Livingston-Sirutis Advt 2 Embarcadero Ctr San Francisco CA 94111-3807

LIVINGSTON, WILLIAM SAMUEL, university administrator, political scientist; b. Ironton, Ohio, July 1, 1920; s. Samuel G. and Bata (Elkins) L.; m. Lana Sanor, July 10, 1943; children: Stephen Sanor, David Duncan. B.A., Ohio State U., 1943, M.A., 1943; Ph.D., Yale U., 1950. Asst. prof. U. Tex., Austin, 1949-54; asso. prof. U. Tex., 1954-61, prof. govt., 1961—, chmn. dept. govt., 1965-69, Jo Anne Christian centennial prof. Brit. studies, 1982—, asst. dean Grad. Sch., 1954-58, chmn. Grad. Assembly, 1965-68, chmn. faculty senate, 1973-79, chmn. comparative studies program, 1978-79; vice chancellor acad. programs U. Tex. System, 1969-71, v.p., dean grad. studies, 1979—, acting pres., 1992-93; vis. prof. Yale U., 1959-56, Duke U., 1960-61; sec.-treas. Assn. Grad. Schs., 1982-85; bd. dirs. Council Grad. Schs. in U.S., 1983-86. Author: Federalism and Constitutional Change, 1956; contbg. author: World Pressures on American Foreign Policy, 1962, Teaching Political Science, 1965, Federalism: Infinite Variety in Theory and Practice, 1968, Britain at the Polls 1979, 1981; editor: The Presidency and Congress: A Shifting Balance of Power, 1979; co-editor: Australia, New Zealand and the Pacific Islands Since the First World War, 1979; editor, contbr. author: Federalism in the Commonwealth, 1963, A Prospect of Liberal Democracy, 1979, The Legacy of the Constitition: an Assessment for the Third Century, 1987; book rev. editor: Jour. Politics, 1965-68; editor-in-chief, 1968-72; mem. editorial bd. Publius: Jour. of Federalism, 1971—; mem. bd. editors: P.S, 1976-78; chmn., 1978-82. Served to 1st lt. FA AUS, 1943-45. Decorated Bronze Star, Purple Heart.; Recipient Teaching Excellence award, 1959; Ford Found. fellow, 1952-53; Guggenheim fellow, 1959-60; USIS lectr. in U.K. and India, 1977. Mem. Am. Polit. Sci. Assn. (exec. council and adminstrv. com. 1972-74, chmn. nominating com. 1973-74, 78-79), So. Polit. Sci. Assn. (exec. council 1964-67, pres. 1974-75), Southwestern Polit. Sci. Assn. (pres. 1973-74), Brit. Polit. Sci. Assn., Canadian Polit. Sci. Assn., Hansard Soc. (London), Royal Commonwealth Soc. (London), Philos. Soc. Tex., Austin Soc. for Pub. Adminstrn. (pres. 1973-74), Southwestern Social Sci. Assn. (pres. 1977-78), Phi Beta Kappa, Omicron Delta Kappa, Phi Gamma Delta, Pi Sigma Alpha (nat. council 1976-84, nat. pres. 1980-82). Home: 3203 Greenlee Dr Austin TX 78703-1621 Office: Univ Tex Office Grad Studies Austin TX 78712

LIVINGSTONE, DANIEL ARCHIBALD, zoology educator; b. Detroit, Aug. 3, 1927; s. Harrison Lincoln and Elizabeth Agnes (Matheson) L.; m. Bertha Griffin Ross, June 17, 1952 (div.); children: Laura Ross, Mary Lisa, John Malcolm, Christina Ann, Elizabeth; m. Patricia Greene Palmer, June 3, 1989. BS, Dalhousie U., Halifax, N.S., Can., 1948, MSc, 1950; PhD, Yale U., 1953. Postdoctoral fellow Cambridge U., Eng., 1953-54, Dalhousie U., Halifax, 1954-55; asst. prof. zoology U. Md., College Park, 1955-56; asst. prof. zoology Duke U., Durham, N.C., 1956-59, assoc. prof., 1959-66, prof., 1966—, James B. Duke prof. zoology, 1980—; prof. geology Duke U., Durham, 1990—; limnogist U.S. Geol. Survey, Washington, summers 1956-58; mem. adv. panel Environ. Biology br. NSF, 1964-67, Tundra Biome Project, 1974-76, mem. human origins panel, 1978, mem. river-ocean interaction panel, 1978; mem. U.S. Nat. Com. for Internat. Hydrological Decade, 1964; mem. adv. council for systematic and environ. biology Fgn. Currency program, Smithsonian Instn., 1977-80; mem. external rev. com. U. Minn. Dept. Ecology and Behavioral Biology, 1979; collaborator Nat. Park Service U.S. Dept. Interior, 1974; cons. on geochemistry to A.D. Little Inc., 1972-73, on study on mineral cycling in Volta Lake, Ghana, Smithsonian Instn., 1973, to South-East Consortium for Internat. Devel., Kakamega, Kenya, 1985; convenor various workshop sessions. Mem. editorial bd. Limnology and Oceanography, 1969-72, Ecology, 1970-72, Ann. Rev. Ecology and Systematics, 1975-80, African Archaeol. Rev., 1985—; assoc. editor Paleobiology, 1974-79; mem. editorial adv. bd. Tropical Freshwater Biology, 1987—; contbr. articles to profl. jours. NRC fellow, 1953, 54-55; John Simon Guggenheim Meml. Found. fellow, 1960-61. Fellow AAAS; mem. Nova Scotian Inst. Sci., Internat. Union for Quaternary Research (U.S. nat. com. 1970-78, sub.-commn. for African stratigraphy 1973-82), Am. Quaternary Assn. (council 1982, counselor 1971-73, 81—), Am. Soc. Ichthyologists and Herpetologists, Ecol. Soc. Am. (council 1961-66, ecology study com. 1964, chmn. weather working group 1965-66), Am. Soc. for Limnology and Oceanography (G.E. Hutchinson medal 1989), N.C. Acad. Scis., Freshwater Biol. Assn. U.K., Hydrobiol. Soc. East Africa, Can. Quaternary Assn., Am. Assn. Stratigraphic Palynologists, Internat. Assn. for Fundamental and Applied Limnology, Limnological Soc. So. Africa, Assn. Pour l'Etude Taxonomique de la Flore d'Afrique Tropicale, Sigma Xi. Avocation: woodworking. Home: 2671 Davis St Raleigh NC 27608-2029 Office: Duke U Dept Zoology Durham NC 27706

LIVINGSTONE, FRANK BROWN, anthropologist, educator; b. Winchester, Mass., Dec. 8, 1928; s. Guy Philip and Margery Stuart (Brown) L.; m. Carol Southworth Ludington, Aug. 13, 1960; 1 dau., Amy Ferner. A.B., Harvard U., 1950; Ph.D., U. Mich., 1957. Research assoc. Liberian Inst. Tropical Medicine, 1955-56, 57-58; asst. prof. anthropology U. Mich., Ann Arbor, 1959-63; assoc. prof. U. Mich., 1963-68, prof., 1968—, chmn. dept. anthropology, 1983-86; cons. in field. Author: Abnormal Hemoglobins in Human Populations, 1967; Frequencies of Hemoglobin Variants, 1985; contbr. articles to profl. jours. Constable, Ann Arbor Twp., 1963-65. Served with U.S. Army, 1951-53. NSF fellow, 1957-59; Recipient Martin Luther King award So. Christian Leadership Conf., 1972. Mem. Am. Anthrop. Assn., Human Biology Council, Am. Assn. Phys. Anthropologists. Home: 471 Rock Creek Dr Ann Arbor MI 48104-1863 Office: Univ Mich Dept Anthropology Ann Arbor MI 48109

LIVINGSTONE, JOHN LESLIE, accountant, management consultant, business economist, educator; b. Johannesburg, Republic of South Africa, Aug. 29, 1932; m. Trudy Dorothy Zweig, Aug. 7, 1977; children: Roger Miles, Adrienne Jill, Graham Ross, Robert Edward. B in Commerce, U. Witwatersrand, South Africa, 1956; MBA, Stanford U., 1963, PhD, 1966. C.P.A., N.Y., Tex. Budget dir. Edgars Stores Ltd., South Africa, 1958-61; asso. prof. Ohio State U. Columbus, 1966-69; Arthur Young Disting. prof. Ohio State U. 1970-73; Fuller E. Callaway prof. Ga. Inst. Tech., Atlanta, 1973-78; mem. exec. bd. Ga. Inst. Tech. 1976-78; ptnr. Coopers & Lybrand, N.Y.C., 1978-81; prin., v.p. Mgmt. Analysis Center, Inc., Cambridge, Mass., 1975-90; prof., chmn. div. acctg. and law Babson Coll., 1985—; cons. FPC, SEC, HEW, also maj. corps. Author: 10 books including Accounting for Changing Prices: Replacement Cost and General Price Level Adjustments, 1976, Management Planning and Control, 1987, The Portable MBA: Finance and Accounting, 1992; contbr. numerous articles to profl. jours.; assoc. editor: Decision Scis., 1973-78; mem. editorial bd.: The Acctg. Rev., 1969-72, 76-78, Acctg. Orgns. and Soc., 1975-78, Jour. Acctg. and Pub. Policy, 1983—. Mem. AICPA, Fla. Inst. CPAs, N.Y. Soc. CPAs, Am. Acctg. Assn., Acad. of Experts, Nat. Assn. for Forensic Econs., Nat. Assn. Bus. Economists, Tex. Soc. CPAs, Am.Arbitration Assn., Palm Beach Nat. Golf and Country Club, Breakers Club (Palm Beach), Govs. Club (Palm Beach). Office: 2300 Palm Beach Lakes Blvd West Palm Beach FL 33409-3306

LIVINGSTONE, SUSAN MORRISEY, nonprofit administrator; b. Carthage, Mo., Jan. 13, 1946; d. Richard John II and Catherine Newell (Carmean) Morrisey; m. Neil C. Livingstone III, Aug. 30, 1968. AB, Coll. William and Mary, 1968; MA. U. Mont., 1973; postgrad., Tufts U., 1973, Fletcher Sch. Law and Diplomacy, 1973—. Researcher Senator Mark O. Hatfield, Washington, 1969-70; chief legis. and press asst. Congressman

Richard H. Ichord, Washington, 1973-75, adminstrv. asst., 1975-81; cons. Congressman Wendell Bailey, Washington, 1981; exec. asst. VA, Washington, 1981-85, assoc. dep. adminstr. logistics and mgmt., 1985-86, sr. procurement exec., 1985-89, assoc. dep. adminstr. logistics, 1986-89; asst. sec. Army Dept. of Def., Washington, 1989-93; v.p. health and safety svcs. ARC, Washington, 1993—; mem interagy. com. on women's bus. enterprise The White House, 1985-89; mem. Pres.'s Coun. on Mgmt. Improvement, 1985-86. NDEA fellow. Mem. Exec. Women in Govt., Procurement Round Table (bd. dirs. 1994), Assn. U.S. Army (bd. dirs. 1994—), Women in Internat. Security (adv. bd. 1994—). Republican. Episcopalian. Office: ARC 8111 Gatehouse Rd Falls Church VA 22042

LIVINGSTONE, WILLIAM EDWIN, III, lawyer; b. Fort Worth, May 22, 1935; s. William Edwin and Margaret (Hall) L.; m. Janice Ann Crow, Aug. 23, 1958; children—William Edwin IV, Carol Roth, Scott Louis. BBA, So. Meth. U., 1957, LLB, 1960. Bar: Tex. 1960. From assoc. to ptnr. Phinney, Hallman, Pulley & Livingstone, Dallas, 1960-73; gen. counsel Dallas Fed. Savs. and Loan Assn., 1973-86; of counsel Jackson, Walker, Winstead, Cantwell & Miller, Dallas, 1986—. Bd. dirs. Greater Dallas Crime Commn., 1980. Served to capt. Air and Army N.G., 1958-65. Mem. ABA, Tex. Bar Assn., Dallas Bar Assn., Tex. Savs. & Loan League (attys. com. 1986—), U.S. League Savs. Assn. (attys. com. 1977—). Office: Jackson Walker Winstead Cantwell & Miller 6000 Interfirst Plaza 901 Main St Dallas TX 75202-3707

LIVNAT, JOSHUA, accounting educator, consultant; b. Jerusalem, June 8, 1949; came to U.S., 1973; s. Hayim Livnat; m. Shoshana Livnat; children: Orit, Ofer, Shira. BSc in Math. & Stats., Hebrew U., 1973; MPhil, NYU, 1978, PhD in Acctg. and Quantitative Analysis, 1978. CPA, Tenn. Lectr. acctg. NYU, N.Y.C., 1978; asst. prof. Hebrew U., Jerusalem, 1979-81, 83, 84, assoc. prof., 1985; assoc. prof. acctg. NYU, 1988-90, chmn. dept. acctg., taxation and bus. law, 1990—; vis. lectr. U. Tex., Austin, 1979, 89, NYU, 1980, U. Wash., Seattle, 1981, U. Calif., Berkeley, 1982, Vanderbilt U., Nashville, 1983, J.L. Kellogg grad. sch. mgmt. Northwestern U., 1984-85, Chulalongkorn U., Thailand, 1987-88, U. Auckland, New Zealand, 1990-91; vis. assoc. prof. Vanderbilt U., 1986-87; acting dir. Ross Inst. Acctg. Rsch. NYU, 1994—; com. chair Acceptance of Books of Accounts; lectr., expert witness in field. Author: Financial Accounting, 1986, Managerial Accounting, 1992; co-author: Cash Flow and Security Analysis, 1992; mem. editorial bd. Acctg. Rev., 1984-87; contbr. questions to Uniform CPA Exams., Israel; contbr. articles to profl. jours. Mem. acctg. adv. bd. Nassau C.C., Garden City, N.Y., 1992—. Lt. Israeli Army, 1968-70. Recipient Best Article award Roeh Hahesbon, 1978, Best Presentation of Rsch. Paper award Berlin conf. Inst. Quantitative Investment Rsch., 1991; Price Waterhouse fellow NYU, 1975-77, Lady Davis Post Doctoral fellow Hebrew U., 1978. Mem. Am. Acctg. Assn. (doctoral consortium fellow ann. conv. 1977). Jewish. Avocations: swimming, traveling. Office: NYU Stern Sch Bus Dept Acctg 40 W 4th St New York NY 10012

LIVSEY, ROBERT CALLISTER, lawyer; b. Salt Lake City, Aug. 7, 1936; s. Robert Frances and Rosezella Ann (Callister) L.; m. Renate Karla Guertler, Sept. 10, 1962; children: Scott, Rachel, Daniel, Benjamin. BS, U. Utah, 1962, JD, 1965; LLM, NYU, 1967. Bar: Utah 1965, Calif. 1967. Prof. Haile Selassie U., Addis Abbaba, Ethiopia, 1965-66; spl. asst. to chief counsel IRS, Washington, 1977-79; assoc., then ptnr. Brobeck, Phleger & Harrison, San Francisco, 1967—; adj. prof. U. San Francisco Law Sch., 1970-77; mem. adv. com. IRS Dist. Dirs., 1986-89; mem. western region liason com IRS (chmn. 1989). Research editor U. Utah Law Rev., 1964-65; editor Tax Law Rev., 1966-67; contbr. articles to profl. jours. Bd. dirs. Gilead Group, 1986-88, East Bay Habitat for Humanity, 1987-88, Morning Song, 1992-94. Mem. ABA (chmn. subcom. real estate syndications 1981-84), State Bar Calif. (chmn. taxation sect. 1984-85), San Francisco Bar Assn. (chmn. taxation sect. 1982), Am. Coll. Tax Counsel, Am. Law Inst., Tax Litigation Club (pres. 1986-87), Order of Coif, Beta Gamma Sigma. Democrat. Mem. Evangelical Covenant Ch. Club: Commonwealth (San Francisco). Home: 128 La Salle Ave Piedmont CA 94610-1233 Office: Brobeck Phleger & Harrison 1 Market Plz San Francisco CA 94105-1019

LLAURADO, JOSEP G., nuclear medicine physician, scientist; b. Barcelona, Catalonia, Spain, Feb. 6, 1927; s. José and Rosa (Llaurado) Garcia; m. Deirdre Mooney, Nov. 9, 1966; children—Raymund, Wilfred, Mireya; m. Catherine D. Entwistle, June 28, 1958 (dec.); children—Thadd, Oleg, Montserrat. B.S., B.A., Balmes Inst., Barcelona, 1944; M.D., Barcelona U., 1950; Ph.D. in Pharmacology, 1960; M.Sc. Biomed. Engring., Drexel U., 1963. Diplomate: Am. Bd. Nuclear Medicine. Resident Royal Postgrad. Sch. Medicine, Hammersmith Hosp., London, 1952-54; fellow M.D. Anderson Hosp. and Tumor Inst., Houston, 1957-58, U. Utah Med. Coll., Salt Lake City, 1958-59; asst. prof. U. Otago Dunedin, N.Z., 1954-57; sr. endocrinologist Pfizer Med. Research Lab., Groton, Conn., 1959-60; assoc. prof. U. Pa., 1963-67; prof. Med. Coll. Wis., Milw., 1970-82, Marquette U., 1967-82; clin. dir. nuclear medicine service VA Med. Ctr., Milw., 1977-82; chief nuclear medicine service VA Hosp., Loma Linda, Calif., 1983—; prof. dept. radiation scis. Loma Linda U. Sch. Medicine, 1983—; U.S. rep. symposium on dynamic studies with radioisotopes in clin. medicine and research IAEA, Rotterdam, 1970, Knoxville, 1974. Editor: Internat. Jour. Biomed. Computing; dep. editor Environ. Mgmt. and Health; contbr. numerous articles to profl. jours. Merit badge counselor Boy Scouts Am., 1972—; pres. Hales Corners (Wis.) Hist. Soc., 1981-83. Recipient Commendation cert. Boy Scouts Am., 1980. Fellow Am. Coll. Nutrition; mem. Soc. Nuclear Medicine (computer and acad. councils), IEEE (sr.), IEEE in Medicine and Biology Soc. (nat. adminstrv. Com. 1986-89), Biomed. Engring. Soc. (charter), Am. Physiol. Soc., Am. Soc. Pharmacology and Exptl. Therapeutics, Soc. Math. Biology (founding), Endocrine Soc., Royal Soc. Health, Societat Catalana de Biologia, Casal dels Catalans de Calif. (pres. 1989-91), Catalan Med. Soc. adv. panel nuclear medicine 1983—). Office: Nuclear Med Svc #115 11201 Benton St Loma Linda CA 92357-0001

LL COOL J (JAMES TODD SMITH), rap singer, actor; b. Queens, N.Y., 1968; s. Jimmy Nunya. Albums: Radio, 1984, Bigger and Deffer, 1987, Walking with A Panther, 1989, Mama Said Knock You Out (Grammy award Best Rap Vocal), 1991; actor: (films) Krush Groove, 1984, The Hard Way, 1991, Toys, 1992; (TV series) In the House, 1995—. Grammy nomination (Best Rap Solo, 1994) for "Stand By Your Man". Office: Bad Boy Entertainment Inc 8-10 W 19th St New York NY 10011*

LLEWELLYN, CHARLES ELROY, JR., psychiatrist; b. Richmond, Va., Jan. 16, 1922; s. Charles Elroy and Pearl Ann (Shield) L.; m. Grace Eldridge, Sept. 25, 1948; children: Charles Elroy III, George E. (dec.), Richard S. BS, Hampden-Sydney Coll., 1943; MD, Med. Coll. Va., 1946; MS in Psychiatry, U. Colo., 1953. Diplomate Am. Bd. Psychiatry and Neurology; lic. marriage and family therapist, N.C. Intern psychiatry Tucker Hosp., Inc., Richmond, 1946-47, asst. to staff, 1948-50; intern gen. medicine Bellevue Hosp., N.Y.C., 1947-48; fellow psychiatry Colo. Psychopathic Hosp. and U. Colo. Med. Ctr., Denver, 1950-53; assoc. dept. psychiatry Duke U., Durham, N.C., 1955-56, asst. prof., 1956-63, assoc. prof., 1963-87, head div. community and social psychiatry, 1963-87; asst. dir. adult psychiat. outpatient clinic Duke U. Med. Ctr., Durham, 1955-56, head adult psychiat. outpatient div., 1956-76, acting head divsn. cmty. and social psychiatry, 1976-81, chief tng. divsn. cmty. and social psychiatry, 1976-85, head divsn. cmty. cmty. and social psychiatry, 1985-87; pvt. practice Durham, 1987—; psychiat. cons. supr., seminar dir. pastoral counseling tng. programs Duke U. Med. Ctr., 1965-87, dir. student mental health svc. Duke U., 1959-68; psychiat. cons. N.C. Divsn. Social Svcs., 1955-79, N.C. Medicaid Program, 1971-75, N.C. Med. Peer Rev. Found., Inc., 1975-79; sr. psychiat. cons. Family Cons. Svc., Durham, 1966-87; mem.-at-large N.C. Substance Abuse Profl. Ctr. Bd., 1984-89; part-time cons., med. dir. Durham Substance Abuse Treatment Ctr., 1968-88. Contbr. articles to profl. jours, chpts. to books. Mem. adv. bd. Durham County Drug Counseling and Evaluation Svc., 1972-79; bd. dirs. Family Counseling Svc. Durham, 1973-78, pres. 1975; bd. dirs. United Health Svcs., 1975-84; trustee Epworth United Meth. Ch., 1959-62, dir. cmty. ministries com., 1961-62; cubmaster Boy Scouts Am. 1960-66; mem. ch. campus reln. com. The Meth. Ctr., Duke U., 1964-66. Capt. U.S. Army, 1953-55. Recipient Outstanding Profl. Human Svcs. Am. Acad. Human Svcs., 1974-75; grantee U.S. Inst. Mental Health, 1967-71. Fellow Am. Psychiat. Assn. (life); mem. AMA (life), Am. Group Psychotherapy Assn., Pan Am. Med. Soc. (life), Am. Assn. Marriage and Family Therapy,

Carolinas Group Psychotherapy Soc. (treas. 1983-94), N.C. Med. Soc. (life), N.C. Assn. Marriage and Family Therapists, Mental Health Assn. N.C., Durham-Orange County Med. Soc. (life). Avocations: fishing, electronic gadgets, gardening. Office: 3308 Chapel Hill Blvd Ste 110 Durham NC 27707-2643

LLEWELLYN, J. BRUCE, food products executive. Chmn. Phila. Coca-Cola Bottling Co. Office: Phila Coca-Cola Bottling Co 725 E Erie & G St Philadelphia PA 19134*

LLEWELLYN, JOHN SCHOFIELD, JR., food company executive; b. Amsterdam, N.Y., Jan. 10, 1935; s. John S. and Dorothea (Breedon) L.; m. Mary Martha Pallotta, June 9, 1962; children: Mary M., John S. III, Robert J., James P., Timothy J. AB, Holy Cross Coll., 1956; MBA, Harvard U., 1961. With mktg. Gen. Foods Corp., White Plains, N.Y., 1961-69, Sunshine Biscuit div. Am. Brands, N.Y.C., 1973-77; exec. v.p. Morton Frozen Foods div. ITT Continental Baking Co., Charlottesville, Va., 1977-79; gen. mgr. Continental Kitchens ITT Continental Baking Co., Rye, 1980-81; sr. v.p. Ocean Spray Cranberries Inc., Plymouth, Mass., 1982-86; exec. v.p., chief operating officer Ocean Spray Cranberries Inc., Plymouth, 1986-87, pres., chief exec. officer, 1988—; bd. dirs. Dean Foods Co. Trustee Derby Acad., Hingham, Mass., 1984—, St. Sebastian's Country Day Sch., Needham, Mass., 1991—; bd. dirs. Mass. Environ. Trust, 1991—. Capt. USMC, 1957-63. Mem. Nat. Food Processors Assn. (bd. dirs., exec. com., vice chmn.), Grocery Mfrs. Am. (bd. dirs., fin. com., govt. affairs coun.). Roman Catholic. Home: Steamboat Ln Hingham MA 02043 Office: Ocean Spray Cranberries Inc 1 Ocean Spray Dr Middleboro MA 02349-1000*

LLEWELLYN, RALPH ALVIN, physics educator; b. Detroit, June 27, 1933; s. Ralph A. and Mary (Green) L.; m. Laura Diane Alsop, June 12, 1955; children: Mark Jeffrey, Rita Annette, Lisa Suzanne, Eric Matthew. B.S in Chem. Engring. with high honors, Rose-Hulman Inst. Tech., 1955; Ph.D. in Physics, Purdue U., 1962. Mem. faculty Rose-Hulman Inst. Tech., Terre Haute, Ind., 1961-70, assoc. prof. physics, 1964-68, prof., 1968-70, chmn. dept. physics, 1969-70; prof., chmn. dept. Ind. State U., Terre Haute, 1970-72, 74-80; dean Coll. of Arts and Scis. U. Cen. Fla. Orlando, 1980-84, prof., 1984—; exec. sec. Energy Bd., staff officer environmental Studies Bd. NAS/NRC, Washington, 1972-74; vis. prof. Rensselaer Poly. Inst., Troy, N.Y., 1964; cons. Commn. on Coll. Physics, 1987-89, NSF, 1965-66; mem. Ind. Lt. Gov.'s Sci. Adv. Coun., 1974-80; adv. bd. Ind. Gov.'s Energy Extension Svc., Fla. Solar Energy Ctr., policy coun. Fla. Inst. Govt., Fla. Radon Adv. Coun., 1988—; mem. environ. adv. com. Fla. Inst. Phosphate Rsch.; mem. grievance com. Fla. Bar, nat. adv. coun. Nat. Commn. on Higher Edn. Issues, 1982. Assoc. editor: Phys. Rev. Letters; contbr. articles to profl. jours.; producer instructional films and TV. Trustee Merom (Ind.) Inst. NSF Coop. fellow, 1959-60, Am. Coun. Edn. Acad. Adminstrn. Internship Program fellow. Fellow Ind. Acad. Sci. (chmn. physics divsn. 1969-70, Speaker of Yr. award 9175, pres.-elect 1980, Fla. State Univ. System TEaching Incentive award 1994), mem. AAAS, AAUP, Am. Phys. Soc., Am. Assn. Physics Tchrs. (pres. Ind.), N.Y. Acad. Scis., Fla. Acad. Scis. (endowment com.), Internat. Oceanographic Found., Ind. Acad. Sci., Sigma Xi, Tau Beta Pi. Home: 1463 Palomino Way Oviedo FL 32765-9304 Office: U Cen Fla Dept Physics Orlando FL 32816

LLOYD, ALBERT LAWRENCE, JR., German language educator; b. Evanston, Ill., Aug. 10, 1930; married; 1 child. A.B., George Washington U., 1951, M.A., 1954, Ph.D., 1957. Asso. in German, George Washington U., 1954-57; mem. faculty U. Pa., 1957—, prof. German, 1970—, chmn. dept., 1972-80; nat. adv. bd. Jr. Yr. in Munich and Freiburg Program, 1962-82. Author: The Manuscripts and Fragments of Notker's Psalter, 1958, Der Münchener Psalter des 14. Jahrhunderts: Eine Auswahl zusammen mit den entsprechenden Teilen von Notkers Psalter, 1969, Anatomy of the Verb: The Gothic Verb as a Model for a Unified Theory of Aspect, Actional Types, and Verbal Velocity, 1979; co-author: Deutsch und Deutschland heute, 1967, 2d edit., 1981, Etymologisches Wörterbuch der Althochdeutschen, Vol. I, 1988; also articles. Grantee Am. Philos. Soc., 1966; Nat. Endowment for Humanities grantee, 1978—. Mem. Inst. Deutsche Sprache, Linguistic Soc. Am., Am. Assn. Tchrs. of German, Mediaeval Acad. Am., Soc. for Germanic Philology, Phi Beta Kappa. Office: U Pa 745 Williams Hall Philadelphia PA 19104-6305

LLOYD, BOARDMAN, investment executive; b. Concord, N.H., Jan. 8, 1942; s. Francis Vernon and Elisabeth (Boardman) L.; m. Barbara Horwich, Mar. 20, 1966; children: Pamela, Amy, Emily. BA, Yale U., 1964; JD, U. Chgo., 1967. Bar: N.Y. 1968, Mass. 1971. Assoc. Casey, Lane & Mittendorf, N.Y.C., 1967-69; assoc. Choate, Hall & Stewart, Boston, 1969-76, ptnr., 1976-90; v.p. William Harris Investors Inc., Cambridge, Mass., 1991—. Chmn. Cambridge United Way, 1975-82, Yale U. Parents Com., 1989-90; bd. dirs. Greater Boston Legal Svcs, 1986—; trustee First Night, Boston, 1987-90, Shady Hill Sch., Cambridge, 1980-84. Mem. N.Y. Bar Assn., Boston Bar Assn. Office: Harris & Lloyd Inc 80 Trowbridge St Cambridge MA 02138-3102

LLOYD, CHRISTOPHER, actor; b. Stamford, Conn., Oct. 22, 1938; m. Carol Lloyd. Actor, Neighborhood Playhouse, N.Y.C.; actor: summer stock and off-Broadway, including title role in Kaspar, 1973 (Obie award, Drama Desk award); Broadway appearances include White and Maddox, Macbeth, N.Y. Shakespeare Festival; films include Butch and Sundance, 1969, Three Warriors, The Onion Field, 1979, The Black Marble, 1980, The Legend of the Lone Ranger, 1981, Mr. Mom, 1983, To Be or Not to Be, 1983, Star Trek III, 1984, Adventures of Buckaroo Banzai, 1984, Back to the Future, 1985, Clue, 1985, Who Framed Roger Rabbit, 1988, Walk Like a Man, 1987, Eight Men Out, 1988, Why Me, The Dream Team, 1989, Back to the Future, Part II, 1989, Back to the Future, Part III, 1990, The Addams Family, 1991, Suburban Commando, 1991, Dennis the Menace, 1993, Twenty Bucks, 1993, Addams Family Values, 1993, Angels in the Outfield, 1994, The Pagemaster, 1994, Camp Nowhere, 1994, The Radioland Murders, 1994, Things To Do in Denver When You're Dead, 1995; TV films include Lacy and the Mississippi Queen, 1978, The Word, 1978, Stunt Seven, 1979, Money on the Side, 1982, September Gun, 1983, Avonlea, 1991 (Emmy award, Best Actor in a Drama Series, 1992); appeared as regular in TV series Taxi, 1978-83, Back to the Future, 1991-92. Office: c/o Guild Mgmt Corp 9911 W Pico Blvd PH-A Los Angeles CA 90035-2733*

LLOYD, DAVID LIVINGSTONE, JR., lawyer; b. Butler, Pa., Aug. 28, 1952; s. David Livingstone and Jean Marie (Basher) L.; m. Dana L. Kadison, June 26, 1983; children: John Gabriel, Margaret Kadison. BS, AB, U. Pa., 1974, JD, 1977. Bar: N.Y. 1977. Assoc. Dewey Ballantine, N.Y.C., 1977-85, ptnr., 1986-93; sr. counsel Financing and transactions GE Aircraft Engines, Cin., 1993—. Office: GE Aircraft Engines 1 Newmann Way F17 Cincinnati OH 45215-6301

LLOYD, DOUGLAS GEORGE, watercolor artist, educator; b. Portsmouth, Hampshire, Eng., Jan. 8, 1918; came to U.S., 1946; s. John Albert and Jessie (Lavender) L.; m. Dorothy May Van Alphen, June 10, 1944 (dec. Apr. 1984); children: Ian Douglas (dec.), Lawrence Merrill, Robert Rodney, Jess Andrew, Robin Lee, Barbara Jeanne; m. Martha Clydesdale Amoia, June 21, 1986. Student, Portsmouth Jr. Tech., 1933-36; cert., Royal Naval Extension Coll., Dartmouth, Eng., 1944. Photography tchr. Boston Coll. Photography, 1946-47; photography editor Harvard Film Svc., Boston, 1947-48; microfilm specialist Hall & McChesney, Syracuse, N.Y., 1948-50; exec. v.p. Dakota So. Microfilm, Miami, Fla., 1950-54; microfilm cons. Miami, 1954-60, Oakland, Calif., 1961-67; microfilm specialist, special courses instr. Datagraphix Inc. San Diego, 1968-78; watercolor artist Las Vegas, Nev., 1978—; cons., Indio, Calif.; microfilm cons. Clk. of Cir. Ct., Deland, Fla., 1950-52, Bahamian Govt., Nassau, Bahamas, 1954. Author: (series of articles) Gremlins in the Computer Output Microfilm System, 1975 (monetary award 1975); artist: (series of ink drawings) The California Scene, 1981 (monetary award 1986). Alderman Hayling Island (Eng.) Coun., 1945; fire commr. City Fire Commn., Lake Helen, Fla., 1950-52; spl. dep. to Clk. of Cir. Ct., Deland, 1950-52; pilot and cadet commandant CAP, Miami, 1952-54; mem. Vols. in Police Program, City of Indio, Calif., 1993-95; apptd. to City of Indio Cultural Arts Commn., 1994—, chmn. spl. art show projects, 1994; treas. San Diego Watercolor Soc., 1980. With Royal Navy, 1936-45. Mem. Nev. Watercolor Soc. (signature award 1988), San Diego Watercolor Soc. (treas. 1982), Western Fedn. Watercolor Socs., Cochella Valley Watercolor Soc.,

Riverside Art Mus., 1993—. Republican. Episcopalian. Avocations: photography, deep sea fishing, creative art, travel, landscape designing. Home and Office: Douglas Lloyd Arts 81297 Avenida Gaviota Indio CA 92201-7812

LLOYD, DOUGLAS SEWARD, physician, public health administrator; b. Bklyn., Oct. 16, 1939; s. Heber Hughes and Virginia Seward (Chamberlin) L. A.B. in Chemistry, Duke U., 1961, M.D., 1971; postgrad., Old Dominion U., 1965-67; M.P.H. in Health Planning, U., 1971. Diplomate Am. Bd. Preventive Medicine. Intern in pediatrics Duke U., Durham, N.C., 1971-72; clin. scholar Duke U., 1972, resident in family practice, 1972-73; commr. health Conn. Dept. Health Services, 1973-87; assoc. med. dir. Nat. Med. Rsch. Corp., Hartford, Conn., 1987-89; pres. Doug Lloyd Assocs., Farmington, Conn., 1989-92; assoc. adminstr. Health Resources and Svcs. Adminstrn., Rockville, Md., 1992—; lectr. Yale U., Conn., 1973-87; chmn. bd. Pub. Health Found., 1984-87. Contbr. articles to profl. jours. Served to capt. USNR. Recipient Lange Publ. award, 1971, McCormick award for excellence in pub. health, 1987. Fellow Am. Coll. Preventive Medicine; mem. Am. Pub. Health Assn., Assn. State and Territorial Health Ofcls. (past pres.), AMA, Conn. Med. Soc., Hartford County Med. Assn. Home: 11410 Stonewood Ln Rockville MD 20852-4543 Office: Health Resources & Svcs Adminstrn 5600 Fishers Ln Rockville MD 20857-0001

LLOYD, EMILY (EMILY LLOYD PACK), actress; b. North London, England, Sept. 29, 1970; d. Roger Lloyd Pack. Grad. Italia Conti Sch. for Performing Arts. Films: Wish You Were Here, 1987, Cookie, 1989, In Country, 1989, Chicago Joe and the Showgirl, 1990, A River Runs Through It, 1992. Office: William Morris Agency Ltd 151 El Camino Beverly Hills CA 90212*

LLOYD, EUGENE WALTER, construction company executive; b. Bklyn., Apr. 9, 1943; s. Walter Vincent and Mary Regina (Conway) L.; m. Julia Ann Bain Menzies, May 6, 1967; children: Deborah Ann, Doreen Marie. AA in Constrn., N.Y. Tech. Coll., 1960-63. Estimator Stephen H. Falk & Assocs., Great Neck, N.Y., 1962-65, Builder's Estimating Service, N.Y.C., 1965-67, Humphreys & Harding, Inc., N.Y.C., 1967-68; chief estimator, corp. sec. Conforti & Eisele, Inc., N.Y.C., 1968-76; exec. v.p. Torcon, Inc., Westfield, N.J., 1976—. Served with U.S. Army, 1963-69. Republican. Roman Catholic. Avocation: working on old cars. Home: 242 W Central Ave Pearl River NY 10965-2119 Office: Torcon Inc Box 609 214 E Grove St Westfield NJ 07090-1657

LLOYD, HUGH ADAMS, lawyer; b. Pine Apple, Ala., Oct. 5, 1918; s. James Adams and Kate (Compton) L.; m. Lydia Douglas, Sept. 18, 1942; children: Kathryn Lloyd Allen, Sally Douglas (Mrs. Charles Proctor), Elizabeth Anne (Mrs. Thomas Goodman), Hugh Adams Jr. Student, Oglethorpe U., 1936-37; A.B., U. Ala., 1941, LL.B., 1942. Bar: Ala. 1942, U.S. Supreme Ct 1958. Adjudicator VA, Montgomery, Ala., 1946-47; partner firm Lloyd, Dinning, Boggs & Dinning, Demopolis, Ala., 1947-95, ret., 1995; chmn. bd. dirs., chief exec. officer Robertson Banking Co., Demopolis. Active Boy Scouts Am.; chmn. Demopolis Indsl. Devel. Com., 1970; mem. Regional Com. Juvenile Delinquency, 1970; chmn. Marengo County Devel. Bd., 1972-73; mem. Demopolis City Coun., 1974; chmn. Indsl. Devel. Bd. Marengo County, 1980; pres. Marengo County Port Authority, 1987, Demopolis City Schs. Found., Inc., 1994; trustee Judson Coll., Marion, Ala., 1981, vice-chmn. bd., 1989, chmn., 1991. With AUS, 1943-45. Decorated Bronze Star; recipient Silver Beaver award Boy Scouts Am., 1972. Mem. Am. Judicature Soc., ABA, Ala. Bar Assn., 17th Jud. Circuit Bar Assn. (pres.), Marengo County Hist. Soc. (v.p. 1980), Demopolis C. of C. (pres.), Ala. Law Inst. (coun.), Bus. Coun. Ala. (bd. dirs.), Ala. Safety Coun., Demopolis Country Club (pres. 1967-68), Kiwanis (dist. gov. 1967, chmn. internat. com. Key clubs 1969, internat. com. on boys and girls work 1972, dist. chmn. laws and regulations com. Ala. dist. 1979). Baptist (past chmn. ch. bd. deacons). Home: 1409 Colony Dr Demopolis AL 36732-3445 Office: PO Drawer Z 501 N Walnut Ave Demopolis AL 36732 also: Robertson Banking Co 216 N Walnut Ave Demopolis AL 36732

LLOYD, JAMES T., air carrier corporation executive, corporate lawyer; b. 1941. BA, kans. State U., 1963; LLB, So. Meth. U., 1966. Atty. Hydeman, Mason Burzio & Lloyd, 1967-85, Preston, Thorgrimson, Ellis & Holman, 1985-87; sr. v.p., gen. counsel USAIR Inc., 1987—; exec. v.p., gen. counsel USAIR Group Inc., 1990—. Office: USAIR Group Inc 2345 Crystal Dr Arlington VA 22227

LLOYD, JOHN KOONS, hospital administrator; b. Phila., Apr. 6, 1946. B, Princeton U., 1968; MHA, Temple U., 1973. Adminstrv. asst. Episcopal Hosp., Phila., 1973-74, v.p., 1974-80, exec. v.p., 1980-82; exec. v.p., exec. dir. Jersey Shore Med. Ctr., Neptune, 1982-83, pres., 1983—. Mem. Am. Coll. Healthcare Execs. Home: 2313 Orchard Crest Blvd Manasquan NJ 08736-4003 Office: Jersey Shore Med Ctr 1945 Rt 33 Neptune NJ 07754

LLOYD, JOHN RAYMOND, mechanical engineering educator; b. Mpls., Aug. 1, 1942; s. Raymond Joseph and Wilma Mable (Epple) L.; m. Mary Jane Whiteside, Dec. 20, 1963; children: Jay William, Stephanie Christine. BS in Engring., U. Minn., 1964, MSME, 1966, PhD in Mech. Engring., 1971. Devel. engr. Procter & Gamble Co., Cin., 1966-67; prof. mech. engring. U. Notre Dame, South Bend, Ind., 1970-83; Univ. Disting. prof. Mich. State U., East Lansing, 1983-92, chmn. dept. mech. engring., 1983-91, disting. prof., 1991—; cons. LeRoy Troyer & Assocs., Mishawaka, Ind., 1980-90, Azdel Inc., Shelby, N.C., 1987-90; advisor NSF, Washington, 1987-90; mem. Nat. Bur. Standards assessment panel NRC, Washington, 1987-93; mem. sci. coun. Internat. Ctr. Heat and Mass Transfer, Yugoslavia, 1986—; chmn. Midwest Energy Consortium, 1991—; adv. editor McGraw Hill, Inc., 1990—. Adv. editor Internat. Jour. Heat and Fluid Flow, 1985—, Jour. Engring. Physics and Thermodynamics, 1993—; contbr. over 90 articles to profl. jours., chpts. to books. Recipient Outstanding Faculty award U. Notre Dame, 1975, 82, Ralph R. Teetor Ednl. award Soc. Automotive Engrs., 1986. Fellow ASME (nat. bd. commn. 1983-90, rsch. and tech. devel. bd. 1985—, coun. on edn. 1991-93, critical techs. com. 1991—, editor Jour. Heat Transfer 1989-95, Outstanding Paper award 1977, Melville medal 1978, v.p. rsch. 1995—). Office: Mich State Univ Dept Mech Engring East Lansing MI 48824

LLOYD, JOSEPH WESLEY, physicist, researcher; b. N.Mex., Jan. 31, 1914; s. William Washington and Mattie May (Barber) L.; m. Lenora Lucille Hopkins, Jan. 24, 1944 (dec. June 1969); 3 children (dec.); m. Ruth Kathryn Newberry, Nov. 19, 1988; children: Kathryn Ruth Jordan, Mary Evelyn Jordan. Student, Pan Am. Coll., 1942. Plumber Pomona, Calif., 1951-57; plumber, pipefitter Marysville, Calif., 1957-79; ret., 1979; ind. researcher in physics and magnetism, Calif., 1944—. With CAP, 1944-45. Mem. AAAS, N.Y. Acad. Scis. Mem. Ch. of Christ.

LLOYD, KATE RAND, magazine editor; b. Mpls., Dec. 25, 1923; d. Rufus Randall and Helen Starkweather (Chase) Rand; m. John Davis Lloyd, Feb. 25, 1950; children:—Kate Angeline Lloyd Traverse, Ann Elizabeth Lloyd Ingrasci, John Rand. B.A. cum laude, Bryn Mawr Coll., 1945. Staff, feature writer Vogue Mag., N.Y.C., 1945-54, sr. feature editor, 1963-74, mng. editor, 1977-97; mng. editor Glamour Mag., N.Y.C., 1974-77; editor-in-chief Working Woman Mag. div. HAL Publs., N.Y.C., 1977-83, editor-at-large, 1983-92, also mem. speaker's bur.; adj. lectr. Columbia U. Sch. Journalism, N.Y.C., 1975-80, NYU Sch. Continuing Edn., 1982-83. Editor: Glamour Magazine Party Book, 1965, Vogue Beauty and Health Guide, 1975, 76; editorial supr.: Vogue's Book of Etiquette, rev. edit., 1969. Commr. Nat. Commn. on Working Women, Washington, 1979-90, N.Y. State Job-Tng. Ptnrship Council, 1986—, N.Y.C. Commn. on Status of Women, 1982—; bd. dirs. Planned Parenthood Fedn. Am., 1978-84, bd. advocates, 1984—; mem. adv. bd. Nat. Women's Polit. Caucus (Pres.'s Media award 1991), Cornell U.; bd. dirs. Alan Guttmacher Inst., N.Y.C., 1984-90, Coun. on Econ. Priorities, 1986—, Women's Equity Action League, 1986-90; charter mem. Women in Community Svcs., 1991—; bd. dirs. Child-Care Action Campaign, 1984—, v.p., 1990; trustee OEF Internat., 1987—; mem. Conf. Bd. Work and Family Rsch. Coun. Recipient Prix de Paris, Vogue, 1945, Women of Achievement award YWCA, 1978, Econ. award Women's Equity Action League, 1983, Outstanding Woman in Mag. Pub. award March of Dimes, 1983, Dr. Louis M. Spadaro award Fordham U. Sch. Bus., Disting. Woman award

Northwood Inst., 1991. Mem. AAUW, Am. Soc. Mag. Editors, Women in Communications (Woman of Yr. award 1989), Advt. Women N.Y. (bd. dirs. 1982-84, Advt. Woman of Yr. award 1987), Fin. Women's Assn., Women's Econ. Round Table, Nat. Coun. Women, Internat. Women's Forum Club (v.p. 1984-85, 87-89), Colony Club.

LLOYD, KENT, education policy research and public interest executive, educator; b. Grace, Idaho, Mar. 5, 1931; s. Wesley Parkinson and Lillie (Murdock) L.; m. Diane Ramsey, Sept. 15, 1973; children: Lorie, Jeralie, Kathie, Leslie, Susan, Donna, Kellie. BS in Psychology, Brigham Young U., 1955; MPA in Mgmt., Wayne State U., 1957; PhD in Polit. Sci., Stanford U., 1963. Asst. prof. pub. adminstrn. U. So. Calif., L.A., 1961-66; pres., co-founder Ctr. for Leadership Devel., L.A., 1967—; prof. bus. mgmt. Pepperdine U., 1970-74; presdl. appointee, dep. undersec. for mgmt. U.S. Dept. Edn., Washington, 1981-82; pres. Policy Mgmt. Assocs., Arlington, Va., 1983-86; chmn. Knowledge Revolution Network, Arlington, 1986—; cons. McCone Com. on L.A. Riot, 1966-67; vis. assoc. prof. polit. sci. U. Hawaii, 1967; chair exec. com. L.A. Alliance for Career Edn., 1973-74; mgmt. cons. EEOC, PBS, Washington, 1983-84; chmn. Parents-As-Educators Utah State Nat. Demonstration Project, 1992, Calif. Demonstration Project, 1994—; dir. nation leadership summit on world-class edn. for all Am.'s children, Washington, 1995. Author: Knowledge Revolution for All Americans: Empowering Public Schools, 1992; contbr. articles to profl. jours. Rep. candidate for Calif. State Treas., 1982, Dem. candidate for U.S. Congress 31st Congl. dist., 1968; bishop LDS Ch., 1963-66. Recipient Prof. of Yr. award Sch. Pub. Adminstrn., U. So. Calif., 1963, Disting. Svc. award Calif. State PTA, 1978; Danforth Found. fellow, 1956-61. Mem. Am. Edn. Rsch. Assn., Am. Mgmt. Assn., Brigham Young U. Mgmt. Soc. Washington (pres. 1987-90). Home: 4412 S Pershing Ct Arlington VA 22204 Office: Knowledge Revolution Network 4350 N Fairfax Dr Ste 740 Arlington VA 22203

LLOYD, LEWIS KEITH, JR., surgery and urology educator; b. Shreveport, La., Sept. 18, 1941; s. Lewis Keith Sr. and Cidney (Linxwiler) L.; m. Karen Hansen, June 9, 1970; children—Kristine Elizabeth, Lewis Keith III, Kevin Hansen. Student, Centenary Coll., 1959-62; M.D., Tulane Med. Sch., 1966. Diplomate Am. Bd. Urology. Intern USPHS Hosp., Norfolk, Va., 1966-67; resident in urology Tulane U. Med. Sch., New Orleans, 1970-74; from asst. to assoc. prof. surgery U. Ala., Birmingham, 1974-77, prof., 1981—; dir. Urol. Rehabilitation Rsch. Ctr., Birmingham, 1978—; chmn. exec. com. Univ. Hosp., 1988-90. Adminstrv. bd. Highlands Meth. Ch., Birmingham, 1983-90; trustee Ala. chpt. Multiple Sclerosis Soc., Birmingham, 1984-85, 92—; bd. dirs. Am. Spinal Injury Assn., 1986-92. Lt. comdr. USPHS, 1966-70, Vietnam. Mem. AMA (Billings Gold medal 1978), Am. Urol. Assn. (bd. dirs. Southeastern sect. 1991-94), Am. Spinal Injury Assn., Birmingham Urology Club (pres. 1981-82), Greystone Golf Club. Republican. Clubs: Birmingham Urology (pres. 1981-82), Mountain Brook Swim and Tennis, Summit Club. Office: U Ala Med Sch 606 MEB Birmingham AL 35294

LLOYD, LLYN ALLAN, association executive; b. Evergreen Park, Ill., Jan. 14, 1938; s. Russell Donald and Gladys Marie (Bladholm) L.; m. Helen Elizabeth Main, Mar. 22, 1959; children: Leanne, Douglas, Bradley. BS in Pharmacy, Ohio No. U., 1960; MA in Pub. Adminstrn., Boise State U., 1980. Lic. pharmacist, Ohio, Idaho, Ariz. With various pharmacies, Ohio and Idaho, 1960-63; pharmacist, owner Arco (Idaho) Drug, 1963-76; pharmacist City of Boise, Idaho, 1976-82; exec. dir. Idaho Bd. Pharmacy, Boise, 1982-86, Ariz. State Bd. Pharmacy, Phoenix, 1986—. Chmn. Butte County unit ARC, Arco, Idaho, 1968-74; mem. forest adv. com. Challis (Idaho) Nat. Forest, 1969-72. Recipient A.H. Robbins Bowl of Hygiene award Challis Nat. Forest, 1973. Mem. Nat. Assn. Bds. Pharmacy (exec. com. 1986—), Ariz. Pharmacy Assn., Ariz. Soc. Hosp. Pharmacists (Svc. to Pharmacy award 1988), Rotary, Lions, Masons. Avocations: woodworking, rose growing, travel, fishing, golf. Home: 3044 W Myrtle Ave Phoenix AZ 85051-7541 Office: Ariz State Bd Pharmacy 5060 N 19th Ave Phoenix AZ 85015-3210

LLOYD, MICHAEL JEFFREY, recording producer; b. N.Y.C., Nov. 3, 1948; s. John and Suzanne (Lloyd) Sutton; m. Patricia Ann Varble, Sept. 6, 1980; children: Michael, Christopher, Jeni, Deborah. Student, U. So. Calif. V.p. artists and repertoire MGM Records, Inc., 1969-73; ind. record producer, 1973—; pres. Heaven Prodns., 1975—, Michael Lloyd Prodns., 1979—, Taines-Lloyd Film Prodns., 1984-85; music dir. TV series Happy Days; music dir. Kidsongs, Living Proof, NBC-TV movie, Kidsongs Videos; prodr. Love Lines, NBC-TV movie Swimsuit; guest lectr. UCLA; judge Am. Song Festival. Composer: (music for feature films) Tough Enough, If You Could See What I Hear, Dirty Dancing, All Dogs Go to Heaven; composer music for 8 Movies of the Week, 9 TV spls., 28 TV Series and 32 feature motion pictures. Recipient 50 Gold Album awards, 24 Platinum Album awards, 26 Gold Single awards, 2 Platinum Single awards, 3 Grammy awards, 41 Chart Album awards, 100 Chart Single awards, 10 Broadcast Music Inc. awards, 1 Am. Music award, 1 Dove award, 2 NARM awards. Mem. ASCAP (12 awards), Am. Fedn. Musicians, Screen Actors Guild, Nat. Assn. Rec. Arts and Scis., AFTRA.

LLOYD, MICHAEL STUART, newspaper editor; b. Dickinson, N.D., Aug. 11, 1945; s. James William and Mary Marie (Ripley) L.; m. Judith Ann Baxter, May 24, 1966; children—Matthew James, Kristen Ann. B.Jour., U. Mo., 1967. Reporter Grand Rapids (Mich.) Press, 1967-72, asst. city editor, 1972-74, city editor, 1975-77, editor-in-chief, 1978—. Bd. dirs. Mary Free Bed Hosp., Grand Valley State Coll. Found., Celebration on Grand Com. Mem. Am. Soc. Newspaper Editors. Office: The Grand Rapids Press Booth Newspaper 155 Michigan St NW Grand Rapids MI 49503-2353*

LLOYD, PHILIP ARMOUR, lawyer; b. Youngstown, Ohio, Feb. 13, 1947; s. Robert Brill and Blanche (Butler) L.; m. Margaret McDowell, Aug. 9, 1969; children—Kimberly, Beatrice. B.A., Ohio Wesleyan U., 1969; J.D., U. Akron, 1972. Bar: Ohio 1972. Mem. firm Brouse & McDowell, Akron, 1972—, ptnr., 1977—. Trustee U. Akron Sch. Law Alumni Assn., Bd. Mental Retardation, Summit County, Ohio, Akron City Hosp. Found., Summit County Defenders Assn., Fairlawn West United Ch.; past trustee Old Trail Sch., Perkiomen Sch., Akron City Club, United Cerebral Palsy and Services for Handicapped; pres. United Cerebral Palsy and Services for Handicapped, 1982-83. Mem. Akron Bar Assn., Ohio Bar Assn., ABA. Republican. Mem. United Ch. of Christ. Avocations: skiing, flying. Office: Brouse & Mc Dowell 500 1st National Tower Akron OH 44308-1471*

LLOYD, ROBERT ANDREW, art educator; b. Boston, Mar. 10, 1934; s. Claude T. and Dorothy (Clarkson) L.; m. Susan M. McIntosh, Jan. 28, 1956; children: Benjamin, Seth, Thomas. Ba, Harvard U., 1956, MArch, 1959. Tchr. art Phillips Acad., Andover, Mass., 1962—, dean Visual Studies Inst., 1978-94; mem. accreditation com. Taft Acad., Stoneleigh-Burnham Acad., Deerfield Acad., Baylor Acad., Westminster Schs., coun. acad. affairs The Coll. Bd., 1978-81, steering com. 1996 Nat. Assessment Ednl. Progress Arts Edn. Consensus Project. Author: Images of Survival, 1973. Chmn. bldg. com. Bancroft Sch., Andover, 1965-70, Greater Lawrence (Mass.) Habitat for Humanity, 1991-94; mem. Andover Hist. Commn., 1982-85. Klingenstein fellow Columbia U., N.Y.C., 1981-82. Avocations: singing, writing, land conservation. Home: 49 Highland Rd Andover MA 01810

LLOYD, SUSAN ELAINE, middle school educator; b. Sioux Falls, S.D., Aug. 25, 1942; d. Travis Monroe and Lois Elaine (Herridge) Hetherington; m. Jerry Glynn Lloyd, Mar. 13, 1982; children: Joseph Sanders Rogers III, Melissa Elaine Rogers. BS in Edn., SW Tex. State U., 1965; MA, U. Tex., San Antonio, 1991; AA, Stephens Coll., 1962. Cert. reading specialist, supervisory, art (all levels), secondary English, elem. edn. Art tchr. South Park Ind. Sch. Dist., Beaumont, Tex., 1965-68; reading specialist John Jay High Sch., San Antonio, 1979-84; reading dept. coord. Sul Ross Mid. Sch., Northside Ind. Sch. Dist., San Antonio, 1984—; remedial reading tchr., 1990; developer reading curricula, cons.; advisor Scholastic TAB Book Club, 1992-94. Author: Reading Education in Texas, 1992, 93. Named Sul Ross Middle Sch. Tchr. of Yr., 1993, Trinity U. Disting. Educator, 1993. Mem. ASCD, Internat. Reading Assn. (hon. chmn. 14th ann. SW regional meeting, presenter 19th 1991, 20th 1992), Tex. Reading Coun., Alamo Reading Assn., Assn. Tex. Profl. Educators, San Antonio Watercolor Group. Home: 7614 Tippit Trl San Antonio TX 78240-3627 Office: Sul Ross Mid Sch 3630 Callaghan Rd San Antonio TX 78228-4323

LLOYD, TIMOTHY L., art educator; b. Canton, Ohio, May 31, 1937; s. Donald J. and Wilma A. (Little) L.; m. Susan J. Lloyd, Dec. 19, 1959; children: Timothy Jr., Stephen. BFA, Kent State U., 1960, postgrad, 1960; MFA, Rochester Inst. Tech., 1964. Prof. art Carleton Coll., Northfield, Minn., 1964—; instr. Haystack Mountain Sch. Crafts, Deer Isle, Maine, 1964; vis. artist Duncan of Jordanstone Coll. Art, Dundee, Scotland, 1978-79. One-man shows include Stubhahn Gallery, Salzburg, Austria, 1971, Duncan of Jordanstone Coll., Dundee, Scotland, 1979, Clark Gallery, Lincoln, Mass., 1987, Raymond Ave. Gallery, St. Paul, 1988, 91, others; exhibited in group shows at Canton (Ohio) Art Inst., 1959, Akron (Ohio) Art Inst., 1960, Wichita Art Assn., Kans., 1960, 85, Amerika Hause, Heidelberg, Germany, 1961, Mus. Contemporary Crafts, N.Y.C., 1962, Am. Fedn. Arts. Traveling Exhibit: Young Americans, 1962-63, Everhart Mus., Scranton, Pa., 1967, Brooks Art Gallery, Memphis, Tenn., 1967, Cedar Rapids (Iowa) Art Ctr., 1970, First Nat. Bank, Mpls., 1973, Minn. Mus. Art, St. Paul, 1974, Rochester Art Ctr. Gallery, 1977, U. Wis., River Falls Gallery, 1978, Zaner Gallery, Rochester, N.Y., 1982, Aaron Faber Gallery, 1985, Downey (Calif.) Nus. Art, 1985, Helen Drutt Gallery, Phila., 1985, Smithsonian Inst., Washington, 1986, Esther Saks Gallery, Navy Pier, Chgo., 1986, 87, Javier Puig Decorative Arts, Mpls., 1991, others; represented in permenent collectins including Smithsonian Inst. Nat. Air and Space Mus., Washington, Duncan of Jordanstone Coll. Art, Dundee, CRM Russell Mus., Great Falls, Mont., St. John's Abbey, Collegeville, Minn., Northwestern Nat. Life Inst., Mpls., Maud Hill Family Found., St. Paul, Minn., Carleton Coll., Northfield, Minn.; prin. works include Carleton Centennial Medal, 1966, communion vessels Nidaros Luth. Ch., Ashland Wis., 1966, communion vessels St. Andrew's Luth. Ch., Ames Iowa, 1966, communion vessels, processional cross, 1973, Minn. State Art Ctr. award sculpture, 1969, 73, Pres.'s Medal, St. John's Coll., 1972, gift from city of Northfield to Sidney Rand, Amb. to Norway, 1980, raised sterling vessel, Trustee award, Carleton Coll., 1980, Presdl. medal, 1987, William Carleton medal, 1992. Mem. Soc. N.Am. Goldsmiths, Am. Crafts Coun., Minn. Crafts Coun. (exec. bd. 1986-89). Avocations: fly fishing, kayaking, canoeing. Office: Carleton College 100 S College St Northfield MN 55057-4002

LLOYD, WALT, cinematographer. Cinematographer: (films) Dangerous Close, 1986, Down Twisted, 1987, The Wash, 1988, Sex, Lies, and Videotape, 1989, To Sleep with Anger, 1990, Pump Up the Volume, 1990, Kafka, 1992, Short Cuts, 1992, There Goes the Neighborhood, 1992, Amos & Andrew, 1993, (TV movies) Out On the Edge, 1989, Extreme Close-up, 1990. Office: Innovative Artists 1999 Ave of the Stars Ste 2850 Los Angeles CA 90067*

LLOYD, WILLIAM F., lawyer; b. Youngstown, Ohio, Dec. 27, 1947. AB magna cum laude, Brown U., 1969; JD cum laude, U. Chgo., 1975. Bar: Ill. 1975, U.S. Supreme Ct. 1980. Ptnr. Sidley & Austin, Chgo. Mem. ABA (mem. litigation and bus. sects.), ABA, Chgo. Bar Assn., Legal Club Chgo. Office: Sidley & Austin 1 First Nat Plz Chicago IL 60603

LLOYD-JONES, DONALD J., transportation executive; b. N.Y.C., May 25, 1931; s. Silas and Esther (McDonald) L.-J.; m. Beverly Louise Miller, June 12, 1954; children: Anne, Lisa, Susan, Donald. Ba, Swarthmore Coll., 1952; MBA, Columbia U., 1954, PhD, 1961. Sr. analyst Am. Airlines, N.Y.C., 1957-63, asst. v.p., 1963-66, v.p., 1966-69, chief fin. officer, 1969-72, chief oper. officer, 1972-82; pres. Air Fla., Miami, 1982-84; cons. Western Airlines, L.A., 1984-85, pres., 1985-87; pres. Am. Express Bank-Aviation Svcs., N.Y.C., 1987—; dir. SL Industries, Mt. Laurel, N.J., 1972-93. Bd. dirs. Aeronautics and Space Engring. Bd., Washington, 1985, Swarthmore (Pa.) Coll., 1972-84; councilor Am. Geog. Soc., 1992—. Republican. Episcopalian. Office: Am Express Aviation Svcs World Fin Ctr New York NY 10285

LLOYD WEBBER, SIR ANDREW, composer; b. London, Mar. 22, 1948; s. of late William Southcombe and Jean Hermione (Johnstone) Lloyd W.; m. Sarah Jane Tudor Hugill, July 24, 1971 (div. 1983); children: Imogen, Nicholas; m. Sarah Brightman, Mar. 1984 (div. 1990); m. Madeleine Astrid Gurdon, Feb. 1, 1991; children: Alastair Adam, William Richard. Ed., Westminster Sch., Magdalen Coll., Oxford U., Royal Coll. Music. Composer: (with lyrics by Timothy Rice) Joseph and The Amazing Technicolor Dreamcoat, 1968, rev., 73, 81 (Best Score Tony award nominee 1982), 91, Jesus Christ Superstar, 1971 (Drama Desk award 1971, Best Original Score Tony award nominee 1972), (with lyrics by Alan Ayckbourn) Jeeves, 1975, (with lyrics by Timothy Rice) Evita, 1978 (Best Score Tony award 1980, Drama Desk award 1980), (with lyrics by Don Black) Tell Me On A Sunday, 1979, Cats, 1982 (Best Musical and Best ScoreTony awards 1983, Drama Desk award 1983), (with lyrics by Richard Stilgoe) Starlight Express, 1984, (with lyrics by Don Black) Song and Dance, 1985 (Best Score Tony award nominee 1986), (with lyrics by Richard Stilgoe and Charles Hart) The Phantom of the Opera, 1986 (Ivor Novello award 1987, Drama Desk award 1988, Best Score Tony award nominee 1988), (with lyrics by Don Black and Charles Hart) Aspects of Love, 1989, (with lyrics by Don Black and book by Christopher Hampton) Sunset Boulevard, 1993; prodr.: Cats, 1981, Daisy Pulls It Off, 1983, The Hired Man, 1984, Starlight Express, 1984, On Your Toes, 1984, Shirley Valentine, 1986, Lend Me A Tenor, 1986, The Resistible Rise of Arturo Vi, 1987, Aspects of Love, 1989, Joseph and the Amazing Technicolor Dreamcoat, 1991, Sunset Boulevard, 1993; co-producer: Jeeves Takes Charge, 1975, Cats, 1981, Song and Dance, 1982, The Phantom of the Opera, 1986, GIE Puccini, 1986, La Bete, 1991; composer film scores: Gumshoe, 1971, The Odessa File, 1974; composer: Variations based on A Minor Caprice #24 by Paganini), 1977, symphonic version, 1986, Requiem Mass, 1985. Recording knight Order Brit. Empire; recipient Grammy awards, 1980, 83, 85, Triple Play award ASCAP, 1988, award City and Music Ctr. of L.A, 1991; named a Living Legend Grammy, 1989; named to Queen's Birthday List, 1992. Fellow Royal Coll. Music. Avocations: architecture, art. Office: 22 Tower St, London WC2H 9NS, England

LLUBIEN, JOSEPH HERMAN, psychotherapist, counselor; b. San Juan, PR, July 14, 1943; s. Herman LLubien-Torres and Guilliermina Diaz Vaquez-LLubien; m. Soccorro Cordova Duprey, Sept. 8, 1967 (div. 1983); m. Adelaida Colon, 1983 (div. 1985); children: Sandy Alexander, Jiang Lloyd; m. Lisa Seda, 1964 (div. 1967); children: Jose Lorenzo, Jill Ann Jo Quiñones-Llubien; m. Mary Elizabeth Smith, 1992; stepchildren: Shannon Raven Mitchell, Jonelle Mitchell. BA in Psychology and English, Fordham U., 1973; MA in Lit. and Creative Writing, CUNY, 1981; PhD, Sch. for Social Rsch., 1984, Walden U. Inst. for Advanced Studies, Mpls., 1995. Nat. adminstr., dir. counseling Employment Tng. Adminstrn. U.S. Labor Dept., Washington, 1970-82, nat. dir. counseling and tng. Community Employment Tng. Adminstrn./Employment Tng. Adminstrn., 1971-82; adjunct prof. English and Composition Malcolm King Coll., N.Y.C., 1984; substance abuse treatment counselor Alcohol Drug Addiction Svcs. Adminstrn. D.C. Gen. Hosp., Washington, 1989-90; psychotherapist, crisis counselor, bilingual guidance counselor, clin. mental health specialist JMC Assocs., Inc., Washington, 1990-91; bilingual guidance counselor D.C. Pub. Schs. Bancroft Elem. Sch., Washington, 1991-93; clin. mental health specialist, bilingual Dept. Human Svcs., Commn. on Mental Health, Washington, 1993; psychol. treatment counselor II Nat. Capital Systems, Inc. Methadone Therapy Treatment Ctr., Washington, 1993—; curriculum co-writer (with others) Substance Abuse Prevention Curriculum for pre-kindergarten and primary grades; helped develop a bilingual activity workbook for elem. schs. with U.S. Dept. Justice and Nat. Crime Prevention Coun., 1992. Author: (poetry) From the Belly of the Shark, 1978, For Neruda La Luz Que Llega, 1979, Black Yellow Red Indian Songs, 1993, Black Streams, 1993. Vol. counselor Apache reservation in southern Tex., 1986-87, Northern Cheyenne reservation, Lamedeer, Mont.; vol. trainer for guidance counselors D.C. elem. schs. in substance abuse prevention. With USAF, 1962-65, Vietnam, USAR, 1983-90. Furman fellow Am. Acad. Child and Adolescent Psychiatry, 1991, Doctoral fellow Walden U. Inst. Advanced Studies. Mem. NAACP, ACA, Washington Sch. of Psychiatry, Assn. of Sch. Counselors, La Raza Unida, U.S. Youth Coun., U.S. Karate Assn., Am. Karate Assn., U.S. Tai Chi Assn., Japan-USA Akeido Fedn., Internat. Kung Fu Assn., Akido Assn., Tai Chi Assn., Japan Akeido USA Fedn., All Japan Am. Akeido Fedn., Tai Chi Chinese Fedn., Tae Quan Do Am. Karate Fedn., Kung Fu Am. Fedn. Home: 4600 Duke St Alexandria VA 22304-2552

LO, KWOK-YUNG, astronomer; b. Nanking, Jiangsu, China, Oct. 19, 1947; came to U.S., 1965; s. Pao-Chi and Ju-Hwa (Hsu) Lu; m. Helen Bo Kwan

Chen Lo, Jan. 1, 1973; children: Jan Hsin, Derek. BS in Physics, MIT, 1969; PhD in Physics, MIT, MIT, 1974. Rsch. fellow Calif. Inst. Tech., Pasadena, 1974-76, sr. rsch. fellow, 1978-80, asst. prof., 1980-86; prof. U. Ill., Urbana, 1986—, assoc. Ctr. for Advanced Study, 1991-92; dept. chmn., 1995—; chmn. Vis. COm. to Haystack Obs., Westford, Mass., 1991-92; adv. panel Academia Sinica Inst. Astronomy and Astrophysics, Taipei, Rep. China. Contbr. articles to Astronomical Jour. Grantee NSF, 1977-95; Miller fellow U. Calif., Berkeley, 1976-78, James Clerk Maxwell Telescope fellow U. Hawaii, 1991; recipient Alexander von Humboldt award, Bonn, Germany, 1994. Mem. Am. Astron. Soc., Internat. Astron. Union. Achievements include studies of center of Galaxy and of star formation in galaxies. Office: U Ill Astronomy Dept 1002 E Green St Urbana IL 61801-3547

LO, ROBERT, process engineering company executive, computer support company executive. Pres., COO Xytel Corp., Mt. Prospect, Ill. Office: Xytel Corp 801 E Business Center Dr Mount Prospect IL 60056*

LO, RONALD PING WONG, banker, consultant; b. Hong Kong, Apr. 9, 1936; s. Robert Ka Fatt and Esther Ming Fung (Ching) L.; m. Carol Rosemary Dyason, June 11, 1965; children: Howard Brenden, Collin Harvard. B.C.S., Melbourne (Australia) U., 1961. Tchr. Chao Yang Chinese Sch., Singapore, 1955-56; accounts auditor Wilson, Bishop & Henderson, Melbourne, Australia, 1959; tchr. Niddrie high sch., Essenden, Australia, 1961-62; marketing mgr. Harper Gilfillan Ltd., Singapore and Malaysia, 1963-71; 1st sec. Singapore embassy, Washington, 1971-74; v.p., internat. dept. Republic Nat. Bank Dallas, 1974-79; v.p., group head for eastern hemisphere, internat. dept. Merc. Trust Co. (N.A.), St. Louis, 1979-81; v.p., group head for Asia and Pacific Am. Security Bank (N.A.), Washington, 1981-85; v.p. trade fin. Gulf Bank K.S.C., Kuwait, 1985-87; pres. G.L. Cons. Ptd Ltd., 1988; pres., chief exec. officer 1st Comml. Bank Phila. 1989-90; cons., sr. v.p. Calif. Nat. Bank, 1990-92; cons. Davis-Hold Capital Source, Inc., Dallas, 1994—; mem. banking and fin. com. Nat. Coun. for U.S.-China Trade, Washington, 1982-87; cons. mem. Internat. Rsch. Affiliates, Singapore, 1964; rep. Asia Pacific group of countries interim communications satellite com. INTELSAT, 1972, also bd. govs.; mem. World Affairs Coun., Washington, 1983-85. Mem. Banking Inst. Australasia, Kiwanis. Presbyterian. Home: 6 Redbud Ct Potomac MD 20854-3731 Office: 15150 Preston Rd Dallas TX 75248

LO, SHUI-YIN, physicist; b. Canton, Peoples Republic of China, Oct. 20, 1941; came to the U.S., 1959; s. Long tin and Ty-Fong (Chow) L.; m. Angela Kwok-Kie Lau, Dec. 18, 1969; children: Alpha Wei-min, Fiona Ai-ming, Hao-min. BS, U. Ill., 1962; PhD, U. Chgo., 1966. Rsch. assoc. Rutherford High Energy Lab., Chilton, United Kingdom, 1966-69, Glasgow (United Kingdom) U., 1969-72; sr. lectr. U. Melbourne, Australia, 1972-89; pres. Inst. for Boson Studies, Pasadena, Calif., 1986—; dir. Sinotronic Co., Hong Kong, 1980; dir. rsch. Am. Environ. Tech. Group, Monrovia, Calif., 1993—. Author: Scientific Studies of Chinese Character, 1986; author, editor: Geometrical Picture of Hadron Scattering, 1986; contbr. over 100 articles to profl. jours. Prin. Chinese Sch. of Chinese Fellowship Victoria, Australia, 1977-84. Fellow Australian Inst. Physics; mem. Am. Phys. Soc. Achievements include patents for Chinese computer and BASER.

LOACH, PAUL ALLEN, biochemist, biophysicist, educator; b. Findlay, Ohio, July 18, 1934; s. Leland Oris and Dorothy Elizabeth (Davis) L.; m. Patricia A. Johnson, Dec. 27, 1957; children: Mark, Eric, Jennifer; m. Pamela Sue Parkes, Apr. 19, 1986; children: Matthew, Sarah, Andrew. B.S., U. Akron, 1957; Ph.D. (NIH fellow), Yale, 1961. Research assoc. Nat. Acad. Scis.-NRC; postdoctoral fellow U. Calif. at Berkeley, 1961-63; asst. prof. chemistry Northwestern U., 1963-68, assoc. prof., 1968-73, prof., 1973-74, prof. biochemistry and molecular biology, and chemistry, 1974—; mem. BBCA study sect. NIH, 1978-82. Assoc. editor: Photochemistry and Photobiology, 1973-80, Biophysics of Structure and Mechanism, 1973-82; Contbr. articles, revs. to profl. jours. Recipient C.P. award U. Akron, 1957, Research Career Devel. award USPHS, 1971-76. Mem. Am. Soc. Biol. Chemists, Am. Chem. Soc., AAAS, Biophys. Soc., Am. Soc. Photobiology (pres. 1985-86). Congregationalist (Man of Year award 1969-71, chmn. ch. council 1974-75).

LOADER, JAY GORDON, retired utility company executive; b. Plainfield, N.J., Aug. 3, 1923; s. Carl and Madalyn (Wright) L.; m. Joan Merrell, Aug. 19, 1965; children: Patricia Kay, Michael Jay, Sandra Lee, Gigi Ann. B.S., U. Ala., 1951. C.P.A., Ga. Auditor Arthur Andersen & Co., Atlanta, 1951-55; with Fla. Power Corp., St. Petersburg, Fla., 1955-82; asst. sec., asst. treas. Fla. Power Corp., 1966-67, sec.-treas., 1967-82, v.p., 1980-89; v.p., sec. Fla. Progress Corp., St. Petersburg, 1983-89; ret., 1989. Served with AUS, 1943-44. Mem. Soc. CPAs, Am. Soc. Corporate Secs., Fin. Analysts Soc. Central Fla., U. Ala. Alumni Assn., Phi Eta Sigma, Beta Gamma Sigma, Beta Alpha Psi. Clubs: Redington Beach Bath; St. Petersburg Yacht; Treasure Island Tennis and Yacht. Home: 13325 108th Ave Largo FL 34644-4649

LOBANOV-ROSTOVSKY, OLEG, arts association executive; b. San Francisco, July 12, 1934; s. Andrei and Grace S. (Pope) L-R.; m. Susan Waters, Sept. 8, 1979; 1 child, Alexandra; children by previous marriage: Christopher, Nicholas. BA, U. Mich., 1956. Community concert rep. Columbia Artists Mgmt. Inc., 1958-59; mgr. Columbus (Ohio) Symphony Orch., 1959-62, Hartford (Conn.) Symphony Orch., 1962-65, Balt. Symphony, 1965-69; program officer div. humanities and arts Ford Found., 1969-75; exec. dir. Denver Symphony Orch., 1975-76; mng. dir. Nat. Symphony Orch., Washington, 1977-80; cons. Fed. Coun. on Arts, 1980-81; exec. dir. Del. Ctr. for Performing Arts, 1981-82; exec. v.p., mng. dir. Detroit Symphony Orch., 1982-83, pres., 1983-89; ind. cons., 1989-90; mng. ptnr. Middle Am. div. Jerold Panas, Young & Ptnrs. Inc., Chgo., 1990-91; pres. Calif. Ctr. for the Arts, Escondio, Calif., 1991—.

LOBB, MICHAEL LOUIS, psychologist; b. Pine Bluff, Ark., Feb. 16, 1942; s. Grady Boyd and Mary Elizabeth (Baldus) L.; m. Mary J. Ferebee, Oct. 14, 1972 (div. 1990); children: Susan Kathryn, George Chapman; m. Nancy Gale Love (div. 1971); 1 child, William Boyd; m. Helen Jeanette Greenwood, Nov. 23, 1990. BA, U. Tex., Arlington, 1968, MA, 1974, PhD, 1978. Licensed psychologist, Tex.; cert. profl. sch. psychologist (life), Tex. Ednl. Agy. Rsch. assoc., asst. prof. U. Tex., Arlington, 1977-87; dir. dept. psychol. svcs. Ind. Sch. Dist., Fort Worth, 1985-87; adj. prof. Tex. Wesleyan U., Fort Worth, 1986-90; dir. rsch. Applied Behavioral Scis., Austin, Tex., 1990—; clin. trainee Mental Health Clinic USAF Regional Hosp., Fort Worth, 1980-82; summer faculty rsch. fellow USAF Sch. Aerospace Medicine, San Antonio, 1982, rsch. assoc., 1983-84. Author: (test) Psycho Orthopedic Pain Screen, 1988; contbr. articles to Internat. Jour. Neuro Sci., Animal Learning and Behavior, Zool. Record; author: Native American Youth and Alcohol, 1987. Lt. col. USAFR, 1967-90. Decorated Bronze star; grantee U.S. DOD, 1982, Air Force Office Scientific Rsch., 1983. Mem. Am. Psychol. Assn., Am. Coll. Forensic Psychology, Vietnam Vets. Am., Beta Phi. Achievements include demonstration of oculomotor indices of altered states of consciousness, eyelid velocities predictive of decision errors, stomach ulcer prevention through sectioning adrenal splanchnic, behavioral sink effect in population density control mechanisms, evaluation of performance effects of atropine sulfate; Psycho Orthopedic Pain Screen and Patient Health History Test. Office: Applied Behavioral Scis PO Box 27467 Austin TX 78755-2467

LOBB, WILLIAM ATKINSON, financial services executive; b. Arlington, Pa., Apr. 21, 1951; s. Anthony William and Annamarie (Hilpert) L.; m. Maureen Veronique O'Hagan, July 7, 1977; children: William Atkinson III, Anthony Hagan. BS, Georgetown U., 1977. Account exec. Johnston Lemon, Washington, 1977-78; sr. account exec. Merrill Lynch, Alexandria, Va., 1979-83; asst. v.p. E.F. Hutton, Washington, 1983-85; mng. dir., ptnr.-in-charge Oppenheimer and Co., Inc., Atlanta, 1985—. Chmn. Atlanta Metro chpt. Am. Diabetes Assn. Mem. Ga. Rep. Found., Nat. Assn. Securities Dealers (bd. arbitrators), Nat. Securities Traders Assn., Ga. Securities Assn., Securities Industry Assn., Am. Arbitration Assn. Clubs: University, Army-Navy, Settindown Creek. Avocation: squash. Office: Oppenheimer & Co Inc 1200 Monach Plz 3414 Peachtree Rd NE Atlanta GA 30326

LOBBIA, JOHN E., utility company executive; b. 1941; married. BSEE, U. Detroit, 1964. With Detroit Edison Co., 1964—, asst. primary svc. engr. sales dept., 1964-68, acting asst. dist. mgr., dir. svc. planning, 1969-72, project mgr. constrn., 1972-74, dir. generation constrn. dept., 1974-75, mgr. Ann Arbor div., 1975-76, asst. mgr. Detroit div., 1976-78, mgr. Oakland div., 1978-80, asst. vice chmn., 1980-81, asst. v.p., mgr. fuel support, 1981-82, v.p. fin. svcs., 1982-87, exec. v.p., 1987-88, pres., chief operating officer, 1988—, also chmn., chief exec. officer, 1990—, also bd. dirs.; bd. dirs. Nat. Bank of Detroit, NBD Bancorp, Inc. Office: Detroit Edison Co 2000 2nd Ave Detroit MI 48226-1279*

LOBDELL, FRANK, artist; b. Kansas City, Mo., 1921; m. Ann Morency, 1952; children: Frank Saxton, Judson Earle. Studied, St. Paul Sch. Art, 1938-39, Calif. Sch. Fine Arts, 1947-50, Academie de la Grande Chaumiere, Paris, France, 1950-51. Tchr. Calif. Sch. Fine Arts, 1957-65; prof. art, Stanford, 1965—. One man shows, Lucien Labaudt Gallery, 1949, Martha Jackson Gallery, 1958, 60, 63, 72, 74, de Young Meml. Mus., San Francisco, 1959, Ferus Gallery, 1962, Pasadena Art Mus., 1961, San Francisco Mus. Art, 1969, Benador Gallerie, Geneva, Switzerland, 1964, Gallerie Anderson-Mayer, Paris, 1965, Smith-Anderson Gallery, San Francisco, 1982, Oscarsson Hood Gallery, N.Y.C., 1983, 84, 85, John Berggruen Gallery, San Francisco, 1987, Charles Campbell Gallery, San Francisco, 1988, 90, 92, Stanford Mus. Art, 1988, retrospective show, Pasadena Art Mus. and Stanford Mus., 1966, San Francisco Mus. Modern Art, 1983, Stanford Mus., 1993; exhibited group Shows, Salon du Mai, Paris, 1950, III Sao Paulo Biennial, 1955, Whitney Mus. Am. Art, 1962-63, 72, Guggenheim Mus., N.Y.C., 1964, Van Abbemuseum, Eindhoven, Holland, 1970, Corcoran Gallery Art, Washington, 1971, U. Ill., 1974; represented in permanent collections, San Francisco Mus. Art, Oakland Mus. Art, L.A. County Mus., Nat. Gallery Washington, others. Served with AUS, 1942-46. Recipient Nealie Sullivan award San Francisco Art Inst., 1960, award of merit AAAL, 1988. Home: 2754 Octavia St San Francisco CA 94123-4304

LOBDELL, ROBERT CHARLES, retired newspaper executive; b. Mankato, Minn., Jan. 1, 1926; s. Darwin Norman and Hilda Cecelia (Peterson) L.; m. Nancy Marion Lower, July 12, 1952; children: Teresa M., Robert John, William Scott, James Marston. A.B., Stanford U., 1948, LL.B., 1950. Bar: Calif. 1951, U.S. Supreme Ct 1964. Atty. legal dept. Bank of Am., Los Angeles, 1951-52; atty., corp. officer Youngstown Sheet and Tube Co., 1952-65; asst. gen. counsel, sec. Times Mirror Co., 1965-70, v.p., asst. sec., 1970-86; v.p., gen. counsel Los Angeles Times, 1970-86; bd. dirs. Embarcadero Pub. Co.; former sec., trustee Pfaffinger Found., Los Angeles Times Fund. Trustee, former pres. Long Beach Mus. of Art Found. Mem. Calif. Bar Assn., Beta Theta Pi. Home: 925 Hillside Dr Long Beach CA 90815-4720

LOBECK, CHARLES CHAMPLIN, JR., pediatrics educator; b. New Rochelle, N.Y., May 20, 1926; s. Charles Champlin and Jeanne (Weiss) L.; m. Isabelle Anne Emerson, Feb. 6, 1954; children: Charles III, Anne, Sarah, Jane. AB, Hobart Coll., 1948; MD, U. Rochester, 1952. Diplomate Am. Bd. Pediatrics. Instr. U. Rochester, N.Y., 1955-58; asst. prof. U. Wis., Madison, 1958-62, assoc. prof., 1962-66, chmn. dept. pediatrics, 1964-74, prof., 1966-75; dir. clin. affairs Univ. Hosp., Madison, 1970-75; dean U. Mo. Sch. Medicine, Columbia, 1975-83; assoc. dean U. Wis. Med. Sch., Madison, 1984-91, prof. emeritus, 1991—; mem. study sect. NIH, Bethesda, Md., 1968-72. Author: (with others) Metabolic Basis of Inherited Disease, 2d edit., 1965, 3d edit., 1972. V.P. Cystic Fibrosis Found., Rockville, Md., 1982-83. Sgt. USAAF, 1944-46, ETO. Recipient Rsch. Career Devel. award, NIH, 1962. Fellow Am. Acad. Pediatrics; mem. Soc. for Pediatric Rsch., Am. Pediatric Soc., Am. Coll. Physician Execs., Rotary, Am. Assn. Accreditation Lab Animal Care (chmn. bd. 1984-89, Bennet J. Cohen award 1990). Democrat. Avocations: fly-fishing, biking. Home: 5801 Woodcreek Ln Middleton WI 53562-1981 Office: Programs Health Mgmt 1300 University Ave Madison WI 53706

LO BELLO, JOSEPH DAVID, banking executive; b. Northampton, Mass., Feb. 5, 1940; s. Joseph Vincenzo and Marie (Mandella) Lo B; m. Karen Suzanne Martin, June 21, 1969; children: Mark, Kara, Kimberly. BS, Babson Coll., 1961; MBA, U. Mass., 1963; postgrad., Harvard Bus. Sch., 1987. Loan officer Third Nat. Bank Hampden County, Springfield, Mass., 1963-65, v.p., 1965-75, sr. v.p., 1975-81; exec. v.p. Bank of New Eng. West, N.A., Springfield, 1981-90; regional pres. Bank of New Eng. N.A., Springfield, 1990-92; pres., chief exec. officer Peoples Savs. Bank, Holyoke, Mass., 1992—. Dir. Mass. Indsl. Fin. Agy., Boston, 1987; treas., trustee Basketball Hall of Fame, Springfield, 1985; trustee Springfield Coll., 1984, Baystate Med. Ctr., Springfield, 1983. Mem. Rotary Club, Robert Morris Assn. Avocations: golf, hiking, theatre, travel. Home: 152 Meadowbrook Rd Longmeadow MA 01106-1341

LO BELLO, NINO, author, journalist; b. Bklyn., Sept. 8, 1921; s. Joseph and Rosalie (Moscarelli) Lo B.; m. Irene Helen Rooney, Feb. 22, 1948; children: Susan, Thomas. BA, Queens Coll., 1947; MA, NYU, 1948. Reporter and columnist Ridgewood (N.Y.) Times, 1946-50; instr. sociology U. Kans., 1950-55; Rome corr. Bus. Week mag., 1959-62, N.Y. Jour. Commerce, 1962-64; European editor corr. Opera Is My Hobby Syndicated Radio Show, 1960—; bus. news writer N.Y. Herald Tribune, 1964-66; Vienna corr. 103 U.S. and Can. dailies, 1966—; vis. prof. sociology Denison U., Ohio, spring 1956; vis. prof. journalism U. Alaska, summer 1974. Author: The Vatican Empire (N.Y. Times Best Seller List), 1968, The Vatican's Wealth, 1971, Vatican, U.S.A., 1972, European Detours, 1981, The Vatican Papers, 1982, Guide to Offbeat Europe, 1985, English Well Speeched Here, 1986, Guide to the Vatican, 1987, Der Vatikan, 1988, Vatikan Im Zwielicht, 1990, The Danube: Here And There, 1992, Travel Trivia Handbook of Oddball European Sights, 1992; contbr. articles to mags. and jours. With USAAF, 1942-46. Recipient Goldener Rathausmann award for Outstanding Fgn. Reporting, Vienna, 1974, Silver decoration (Austria), 1988, Gold plaque Austrian Nat. Tourist Office, 1988; named Alumnus of Yr., Grover Cleveland High Sch., Queens, N.Y., 1977. Mem. Overseas Press Club Am., Am. Soc. Journalists and Authors, Fgn. Press Club Vienna (bd. dirs.). Home: 78 Walnut St Winsted CT 06098-1721 Office: 8 Bankgasse, Vienna 1010, Austria *Work hard, play hard!.*

LOBIONDO, FRANK A., congressman; m. Jan Dwyer; children: Adina, Amy. BA in Bus. Adminstrn., St. Joseph's U., 1968. Ops. mgr. LoBiondo Bros. Motor Express, Inc., Rosenhayn, N.J., 1968-94; mem. Cumberland County Bd. Chosen Freeholders, 1985-88; chmn. Gen. Assembly Econ. and Cmty. Devel., Ar. and Tourism Com., 1992-94; mem. First Legis. Dist. N.J. Gen. Assembly, 1988-94; mem. U.S. House Reps., 1995—. Dir. YMCA, 1978-84, mem. bd. dirs., 1986-94; pres. Cumberland County Guidance Ctr., 1982-84; founder Cumberland County Environ. Health Task Force, 1987; chmn. Cumberland County chpt. Am. Heart Assn., 1989-90; hon. chmn. annual fund raising drive Cumberland County Hospice, 1992; mem. bd. dirs. Cape May County chpt. Lit. Vols. Am., 1991—, (hon. 1995—). Office: US House Reps 241 Cannon House Office Bldg Washington DC 20515-3002*

LOBITZ, WALTER CHARLES, JR., physician, educator; b. Cin., Dec. 13, 1911; s. Walter Charles and Elsa (Spangenberg) L.; m. Caroline Elizabeth Rockwell, July 11, 1942; children: Walter Charles III, John Rockwell, Susan Hastings. Student, Brown U., 1930-31; B.Sc., U. Cin., 1939, M.B., 1940, M.D., 1941; M.Sc., U. Minn., 1945; M.A. (hon.), Dartmouth, 1958; LL.D., Hokkaido U., 1976. Diplomate Am. Bd. Dermatology (bd. dirs. 1955-64, pres. 1962). Intern Cin. Gen. Hosp., 1940, resident medicine, 1941; fellow Mayo Found., 1942-45; 1st asst. Mayo Clinic, 1945-47; chmn. sect. dermatology Hitchcock Clinic, Hanover, N.H., 1947-59; bd. dirs Hitchcock Clinic, 1955; faculty Dartmouth Med. Sch., 1947-59, prof. dermatology, 1957-59; prof. dermatology, head div. U. Oreg. Med. Sch., 1959-69, chmn. dept., 1969-77; prof. Oreg. Health Scis. Univ., until 1980; emeritus prof. U. Oreg. Health Scis. Ctr., 1980—; area cons. VA, 1949-59; mem. commn. cutaneous diseases Armed Forces Epidemiologic Bd., 1955-75; cons., mem. gen. med. study sect. USPHS, 1961-65; mem. grant rev. com. United Health Found., 1964-65; cons. dermatology tng. grants com. Nat. Inst. Arthritis and Metabolic Diseases, 1966-70; cons. dermatology, 1953-54. Mem. Phys. 99-53; civilian cons. to surg. gen. USAF, 1969-79; U.S. Air Force-Nat. cons. to Surgeon Gen., 1970-80; Dohi Meml. lect. Japanese Dermatol. Assn., 1964; lectr. U. Copenhagen, Denmark, 1969, 74. Author numerous articles in field.; Co-editor: The Epidermis; editorial bd.: Jour. Investigative

Dermatology, 1958-61, Excerpta of Medicine, 1961-78, Clinics in Dermatology, 1982; mem. editorial bd.: Archives Dermatology, 1960-77, chief editor, 1963-68. Trustee Dermatology Found., Med. Research Found. Oreg., 1972, exec. com., 1977-80, v.p., 1975-76, pres., 1977-78; music adv. com. Oreg. Symphony Orch., 1970-73; mem. Oreg. Ballet Council, 1974; bd. govs. Hitchcock Hosp., 1955; trustee Hitchcock Found., 1958-59, exec. com., 1958-59. Recipient Outstanding Achievement award U. Minn., 1964, Disting. Alumni award U. Cin. Coll. Medicine, 1995; dedication of Lobitz-Jillson Libr., Dartmouth-Hitchcock Med. Ctr., 1992; decorated Japanese Order of the Sacred Treasure, Gold Rays with neck ribbon, Emperor of Japan, 1993. Fellow ACP, Am. Acad. Dermatology (hon., bd. dirs 1958-61, 66-69, pres. 1969, gold medal 1985, Master in Dermatology 1987), Phila. Coll. Physicians (hon.); mem. AMA, AAAS, Am. Dermatol. Assn. (bd. dirs. 1962-67, pres. 1972, hon. 1982), Soc. Investigative Dermatology (hon., v.p. 1952, bd. dirs. 1953-58, pres. 1957, Stephan Rothman medal for disting. achievement 1989), N.H., Multnomah County, Oreg. med. socs., N.Y. Acad. Scis., Pacific N.W. Dermatol. Assn. (pres. 1971), Pacific Dermatol. Assn., Israel Dermatol. Assn. (hon.), N.W. Soc. Clin. Rsch., Oreg. Dermatol. Soc. (pres. 1969), Portland Acad. Medicine, Am. Fedn. Clin. Rsch., Pacific Interurban Clin. Club (councilor 1971), Internat. Soc. Tropical Dermatology, Assn. Univ. Profs. Dermatology (founder, bd. dirs 1961-66, pres. 1965-66), Soc. Venezolana de Dermatologia & Leprologia (hon.), French Soc. Dermatology, Brit. Assn. Dermatology, Assn. parala Investigacion Dermatologica (Venezuela), Soc. Dermatol. Danicae, Italian, Japan, Hokkaido, Sapporo derm. socs., Sigma Xi, Pi Kappa Epsilon, alpha Omega Alpha. Presbyn. Home: 2211 SW 1st Ave Portland OR 97201-5060

LOBL, HERBERT MAX, lawyer; b. Vienna, Austria, Jan. 10, 1932; s. Walter Leo and Minnie (Neumann) L.; m. Dorothy Fullerton Hubbard, Sept. 12, 1960; children: Peter Walter, Michelle Alexandra. AB magna cum laude, Harvard U., 1953, LLB cum laude, 1959, Avocat honoraire, 1993. Bar: N.Y. 1960, U.S. Tax Ct. 1963, French Conseil Juridique 1973; French avocat. mem. Paris bar, 1992, avocat hon., 1993. Assoc. Davis, Polk & Wardwell, N.Y.C., 1959-60; assoc. counsel to Gov. Nelson Rockefeller, Albany, N.Y., 1960-62; assoc. Davis, Polk & Wardwell, N.Y. and Paris, 1963-69, ptnr., Paris, 1969-92, sr. counsel, 1993—; lectr. law Columbia U., N.Y.C., 1993—; supervisory bd. mem. CII-HB Internationale, Amsterdam, Holland, 1977-82. Gov. Am. Hosp. Paris, 1981-83, 88-93; trustee Am. Libr., Paris, 1969-81. Served to 1st lt. USAF, 1954-56, Berlin. Fulbright scholar U. Bonn, Germany, 1954. Mem. Am. C. of C. (bd. dirs. France 1988-90), Univ. Club, Harvard Club (N.Y.). Address: PO BOX 2488 Nantucket MA 02584 Home: 3 Weetamo Rd Nantucket MA 02554 also: 22 Water's Edge Rye NY 10580 also: Davis Polk & Wardwell 450 Lexington Ave New York NY 10017

LOBLEY, ALAN HAIGH, lawyer; b. Elkhart, Ind., Aug. 26, 1927; s. Frederick Askew and Eva May (Haigh) L.; m. Kathleen Covert Nolan, Mar. 2, 1957; children: James, Sarah. BSChemE, Purdue U., 1949; JD, Ind. U., 1952. Bar: Ind. 1952, U.S. Dist. Ct. (so. dist.) Ind. 1955, U.S. Ct. Appeals (6th cir.) 1979, U.S. Ct. Appeals (7th cir.) 1963, U.S. Supreme Ct. 1971. Assoc., then ptnr. Ice, Miller, Donadio & Ryan (formerly Ross, McCord, Ice & Miller), Indpls., 1955—. 1st lt. USAF, 1952-54. Mem. ABA, Ind. Bar Assn., Indpls. Bar Assn., Skyline Club, Indpls. Rowing Ctr. Democrat. Avocations: photography, music, sculling. Home: 4535 N Park Ave Indianapolis IN 46205-1836 Office: Ice Miller Donadio & Ryan 1 American Sq Indianapolis IN 46282-0001

LOBRON, BARBARA L., writer, editor, photographer; b. Phila., Mar. 19, 1944; d. Martin Aaron and Elizabeth (Gots) L.; student Pa. State U., 1962-63; B.A. cum laude, Temple U., Phila., 1966; student photography Harold Feinstein, N.Y.C., 1970, 79-80; student art therapy Erika Steinberger, N.Y.C., 1994—. Reporter, writer Camden (N.J.) Courier-Post, 1966-68; editorial asst. Med. Insight mag., N.Y.C., 1970-71; mng. editor Camera 35 mag., N.Y.C., 1971-75; also asso. editor photog. anns. for U.S. Camera/Camera 35, 1972, 73; freelance editor as Word Woman, N.Y.C., 1975-77, 79—; acct. exec. Bozell & Jacobs, N.Y.C., 1977-79; copy editor Camera Arts mag., N.Y.C., 1981-83; editorial coord. Center mag., Nat. Ctr. Health Edn., 1985; editorial coord. Popular Photography mag., 1986-95; assoc. editor Sony Style, 1995; contbg. editor Photograph; Photographs: group exhbns. include Internat. Women's Art Festival, N.Y.C., 1975, Rockefeller Ctr., N.Y.C., 1976, Photograph Gallery, N.Y.C., 1981; acrylic painting exhbns. at Tchrs. Coll., N.Y.C., 1994, Warwick Hotel, N.Y.C., 1995; represented in collection Library of Calif. Inst. Arts, Valencia. Tchr. Sch. Vol. Program, N.Y.C., 1994—. Recipient 1st pl. honors Dist. 1, Internat. Assn. Bus. Communicators, 1977. Copy editor: The Complete Guide to Cibachrome Printing, 1980, The Popular Photography Question and Answer Book, 1979, The Photography Catalog, 1976, Strand: Sixty Years of Photography, 1976, You and Your Lens, 1975; contbr. articles to comml. publs., chpts. to books. Dist. leader SGI-USA. Buddhist. Avocations: ceramics, reading, photography, singing, walking. Home: 85 Hicks St Apt 7 Brooklyn NY 11201-6825

LOBSENZ, HERBERT MUNTER, data base company executive; b. N.Y.C., June 10, 1932; s. Jacob Munter and Marjorie (Roset) L.; m. Viola Pedreira, Sept. 29, 1961 (div. 1975); children: Jonathan, Andrew; m. 2d Sheila Katharine Martin, Dec. 18, 1975; children: James, Elizabeth, Emily, Daniel. B.A., NYU, 1953; acad. diploma, Courtauld Inst. Art, U. London, 1959; cert. Spanish studies, U. Madrid, Spain, 1956; postgrad., U. Perugia, Italy, 1958. Sales promotion mgr. Remington Rand, N.Y.C., 1964-66, product planning mgr., 1966-67; long range planning mgr. Xerox Pub., Stamford, Conn., 1967-69; v.p. Houghton Mifflin, Boston, 1976-81; pres. Market Data Retrieval, Shelton, Conn., 1969—; exec. v.p. Dun & Bradstreet Bus. Mktg. Services, 1987; CEO D&B Receivables Mgmt. Svc., 1991. Author: Vangel Griffin, 1961 (Harper Prize 1961). Chmn. Bd. Edn., Westport, Conn., 1975-85, 89-93; mem. town com. Republican party, Westport, 1970-72. Served with U.S. Army, 1953-55. Mem. Assn. Media Producers (bd. dirs. 1972-78), Direct Mktg. Assn. Jewish. Office: Market Data Retrieval 16 Progress Dr Shelton CT 06484-6224

LOBSINGER, THOMAS, bishop; b. Ayton, Ont., Can., Nov. 17, 1927. Ordained priest Roman Cath. Ch., 1954, bishop, 1987. Bishop Whitehorse, Y.T., Can., 1987—. Home: 5119 5th Ave, Whitehorse, YK Canada Y1A 1L5

LOCALIO, S. ARTHUR, retired surgeon, educator; b. N.Y.C., Oct. 4, 1911; s. Joseph and Carmella (Franco) L.; m. Ruth Virginia Adkins, July 14, 1945; children: William Hale, Susan Emily, Arthur Russell, David Charles. A.B., Cornell U., 1932; M.D., U. Rochester, 1936; D.Sc., Columbia, 1942. Diplomate Am. Bd. Surgery. Intern pathology N.Y. U. Hosp., 1936-37, intern medicine, 1937-38, asst. resident in surgery, 1938-40, sr. resident, 1940-42, asst. surgeon, 1945-47, asst. attending surgeon, 1947-49, asso. attending surgeon, 1949-52, attending surgeon, 1952—; clin. asst. vis. surgeon 4th surg. div. Bellevue Hosp., N.Y.C., 1945-46; asst. vis. surgeon 4th surg. div. Bellevue Hosp., 1946-48, asso. vis. surgeon, 1948-52, vis. surgeon, 1952—; practice medicine specializing in surgery, N.Y.C., 1945—; instr. surgery Columbia Postgrad. Med. Sch., 1945-48; asst. prof. Columbia Postgrad. Med. Sch., 1948-49; asst. prof. surgery N.Y. U. Schs. Medicine, N.Y.C., 1949-50; asso. prof. N.Y. U. Schs. Medicine, 1950-53, prof., 1953—; Johnson and Johnson Disting. prof. surgery N.Y.U. Schs. Medicine, 1972-92, Johnson and Johnson Disting. prof. surgery emeritus, 1992—; cons. in surgery Riverview Hosp., Red Bank, N.J., 1952—, Monmouth Meml. Hosp., Long Branch, N.J., 1952—, St. Barnabas Hosp., N.Y.C., 1958—, VA Hosp., N.Y.C., Wyckoff Heights Hosp., Bklyn., N.Y. Infirmary, N.Y.C., Booth Meml. Hosp., Flushing, N.Y., Brookhaven Meml. Hosp., Patchogue, N.Y. Contbr. articles to med. jours. Trustee Deerfield (Mass.) Acad. Served from capt. to lt. col. M.C. AUS, 1942-45, PTO. Mem. Am. Gastroent. Assn., N.Y. Gastroent. Assn., ACS, AMA, Am. Assn. for Surgery of Trauma, Soc. for Surgery Alimentary Tract, N.Y. Acad. Medicine (trustee 1971-75), N.Y. Acad. Scis., N.Y. Cancer Soc., N.Y. Soc. Colon and Rectal Surgeons, Pan Am. Med. Soc. (N.Am. chmn. sect. gen. surgery 1972—), N.Y. County Med. Soc., N.Y. State Med. Soc. Sociedad Colombiana de Cirujanos, Société Internationale de Chirurgie, Collegium Internationale Chirurgie Digestivae, Royal Soc. Medicine, N.Y. Surg. Soc., B.C. Surg. Soc., Transplantation Soc., Am. Surg. Assn., Sigma Xi. Home: Mill Village Rd (147) Deerfield MA 01342 Office: NYU Sch Medicine 530 1st Ave New York NY 10016-6402

LOCASCIO, SALVADORE JOSEPH, horticulturist; b. Hammond, La., Oct. 29, 1933; s. John A. and Mary (Dantone) L.; m. Sybil Olivette Johnson, Nov. 21, 1954 (dec. May 1991); children: John David, Judy Lynn, Paul Anthony; m. Carol Smith Riggall, Dec. 29, 1993. BS, Southeastern La. Coll., 1955; MS, La. State U., 1956; PhD, Purdue U., 1959. Grad. asst. La. State U., 1955-56, Purdue U., 1956-59; asst. horticulturist U. Fla., Gainesville, 1959-65; assoc. prof. U. Fla., 1965-69, prof., 1969—. Contbr. articles to profl. publs. Recipient Am. Rsch. award Fla. Fruit and Vegetable Assn., 1993. Fellow Am. Soc. for Hort. Sci.; mem. Fla. State Hort. Soc. (v.p. vegetable sci. 1975-76, pres. 1994, Presdl. Gold medal 1978), Fla. Weed Sci. Soc. (Outstanding Weed Sci. of Yr. award 1989, pres.-elect 1989-90, pres. 1990-91). Democrat. Roman Catholic. Achievements include research in efficient use of fertilizer, polyethylene mulch, and water for the production of vegetable crops. Office: U Fla Dept Hort Scis 1245 Fifield Hall Gainesville FL 32611

LOCATELLI, PAUL LEO, university president; b. Santa Cruz, Calif., Sept. 16, 1938; s. Vincent Dino and Marie Josephine (Piccone) L. B.S. in Acctg., Santa Clara U., 1961; MDiv, Jesuit Sch. Theology, 1974; DBA, U. So. Calif., 1971. CPA, Calif. Ordained priest Roman Cath. Ch., 1974. Acct., Lautze & Lautze, San Jose, Calif., 1960-61, 1973-74; prof. acctg. Santa Clara (Calif.) U., 1974-86, assoc. dean Bus. Sch. and acad. v.p., 1978-86, pres., 1988—. bd dirs. Silicon Valley, Tech. Mus.; bd. govn., Inst. of Eur & Asian Studies; mem. Nat. Cath. Bishops and Pres.' Com., Acctg. Edn. Change Commn.; mem. adv. couns. Parents Helping Parents and Community Found.; past rector Jesuit Community at Loyola Marymount U. Trustee Regis U.; past trustee U. San Francisco, Seattle U., St. Louis U. and Loyola Marymount U.; past mem. Sr. Commn. of Western Assn. Schs. and Colls. Mem. AICPA, Calif. Soc. CPAs (Disting. Prof. of the Yr award, 1994), Am. Acctg. Assn., NCCJ (bd. dirs.), Assn. Jesuit Colls. and Univs. (chair), Ind. Colls. Calif., Am. Leadership Forum (bd. dirs.). Democrat. Office: Santa Clara U Office of Pres Santa Clara CA 95053

LOCHER, RICHARD EARL, editorial cartoonist; b. Dubuque, Iowa, June 4, 1929; s. Joseph John and Lucille (Jungk) L.; m. Mary Therese Cosgrove, June 15, 1957; children: Stephen Robert, John Joseph, Jana Lynne. Student, Loras Coll., 1948, Chgo. Acad. Fine Arts, 1949-51; BFA, Art Center, Los Angeles, 1954, postgrad., 1955-56; LHD (hon.), Ill. Benedictine Coll., 1992, LHD, 1992. founder, pres. Novamark Corp., Chgo., 1968-72; cons. McDonalds Corp., Oakbrook, Ill.; tchr. art at local high schs. and colls. Asst. writer, artist: Buck Rogers Comic Strip, 1954-57, Dick Tracy Comic Strip, 1957-61, Martin Aerospace Co., Denver, 1962-63; art dir. Hansen Co., Chgo., N.Y.C., 1963-68; editorial cartoonist Chgo. Tribune, 1972—; artist Dick Tracy Comic Strip, 1983—; author: Dick Locker Draws Fire, 1980, Send in the Clowns, 1982, (with Michael Kilian) Flying Can Be Fun, 1985; patentee Poker Face device to play poker without cards. Trustee Ill. Benedictine Coll., 1984—. Served with USAF, 1951-53. Recipient Dragonslayer award U.S. Indsl. Coun., 1976, 77, 78, 80, 81, 82, Disting. Health Journalism award, 1981, 82, 83, 84, 85, 92, Overseas Press Club award, 1983, 84, Pulitzer prize, 1983, Sigma Delta Chi award, 1985, World Population Inst. award, 1986, John Fischetti award, 1987, Peter Lisagor award, 1987, 89, 91; Named Ill. FBI Man of Yr., 1993. Mem. Assn. Am. Editorial Cartoonists. Office: Chgo Tribune Co 435 N Michigan Ave Rm 3200 Chicago IL 60611

LOCHIANO, ROCCO, natural gas company executive; b. Kansas City, Mo., Jan. 24, 1925; s. Anthony and Leona (Mangiarcina) LoC.; m. Sally Norman, Aug. 2, 1975; children: Steve, Mark, Nancy. B.S. in Mech. Engring, Iowa State U., 1944. Resident engr. Panhandle Eastern Pipeline Co., Kansas City, Mo., 1946-50; sr. engr. Trunk Line Gas Co., Houston, 1950-53; asst. chief engr. Interstate Gas Co., Houston, 1953-59; v.p. Gulf Interstate Engring. Co., Houston, 1959-64; with No. Natural Gas Co., Omaha, 1964—; v.p. engring. div. No. Natural Gas Co., 1966, group v.p. corp. engring. and research, 1975—; dir. subs.; dir. No. Petrochem. Co.; sr. v.p., chief tech. officer, mem. corp. exec. com. InterNorth, 1980—. Served with USNR, 1944-46. Mem. Am. Gas Assn. Home: 12023 Washington Plz Omaha NE 68137-4422

LOCHMILLER, KURTIS L., real estate entrepreneur; b. Sacramento, Dec. 30, 1952; s. Rodney Glen and Mary Margaret (Frauen) L.; m. Mariye Susan Mizuki, Nov. 9, 1951; children: Margaux Sian, Chase Jordan. BA in Econs. and Fin., U. Denver, 1975. Dist. sales mgr. Hertz Truck Div., Denver, 1975-76; drilling foreman Shell Oil, Alaska, Mont., Colo., 1976-79; pres., owner Kurtex Mortgage & Devel. Co., Denver, 1979—, Kurtex Properties Inc., Denver, 1980-86; pres., chief exec. officer Kurtex Inc., Denver, 1981—; Bankers Pacific Mortgage, Denver, 1980—, Bankers Fin. Escrow Corp., Denver, 1984—, Northwest Title & Escrow, Denver, 1984—; pres., chief exec. officer Steamboat Title, Steamboat Springs, Colo., 1985—, First Escrow, Denver, 1986—, Fidelity-Commonwealth-Continental Escrow, Denver, 1984—; pres. Colonnade Ltd., Denver, 1981-88; pres., bd. dirs. Breckridge (Colo.) Brewery. V.p., founder Colfax on the Hill, Denver, 1984; mediator, arbitrator Arbitrator/Mediation Assn., Denver, 1986; mem. Police Athletic League, Denver, 1988. Recipient Pres. Spl. Achievement/Founder award Colfax on the Hill, Denver, 1984, Spl. Mayor's award, City & County of Denver, 1985. Mem. Nat. Assn.of Real Estate Appraisers, Internat. Brotherhood of Teamsters, Colo. Mortgage Bankers Assn., Mortgage Banking Assn., Denver C. of C., Phi Beta Kappa, Omicron Delta Epsilon. Clubs: U.S. Karate Assn. (Phoenix) (3d degree Black Belt), Ferrari (Portland). Lodge: Internat. Supreme Council Order of Demolay. Avocations: collecting cars, karate, fishing, art collecting. Home: 1 Carriage Ln Littleton CO 80121-2010 Office: Bankers Fin Escrow Corp 1660 S Albion St Ste 518 Denver CO 80222-4021

LOCHNER, PHILIP RAYMOND, JR., lawyer, communications executive; b. New Rochelle, N.Y., Mar. 3, 1943; s. Philip Raymond and Maryl (Browning) L.; m. Sally Soth, June 23, 1973; children: Lauren Soth, John Philip. BA, Yale U., 1964, LLB, 1967; PhD, Stanford U., 1971. Bar: N.Y. 1972, D.C. 1991. Assoc. dean SUNY Law Sch., Amherst, 1971-73; assoc. Cravath, Swaine & Moore, N.Y.C., 1973-78; assoc. gen. counsel Time Inc., N.Y.C., 1978-80, corp. assoc. gen. counsel, 1980-84, sr. v.p., gen. counsel video, 1984-86, v.p., 1986-88, gen. cousel, sec., 1988-90; commr. SEC, Washington, 1990-91; sr. v.p. Time Warner Inc., N.Y.C., 1991—; bd. dirs. Bklyn. Bancorp., N.Y.C.; lectr. Practicing Law Inst., N.Y.C., 1980—; mem. legal adv. com. N.Y. Stock Exch., 1991-94; mem. corp. governance and fin. markets sub-coun. U.S. Competitiveness Policy Coun., 1992. Treas., Yale Class of 1964, 1979-84; bd. dirs. Henry St. Settlement, N.Y.C., 1991—, Canterbury Sch., New Milford, Conn., 1994—, Citizens Budget Commn., N.Y., 1994—. Fellow Am. Bar Found.; mem. N.Y. State Bar Assn. (chmn. corp. counsel sect. 1989-90), Internat. Bar Assn. (N.Am. adv. group bus. law sect. 1992—). Clubs: Greenwich Country. Office: Time Warner Inc 75 Rockefeller Plz New York NY 10019-6907

LOCIGNO, PAUL ROBERT, public affairs executive; b. Cleve., Sept. 1, 1948; s. Paul Robert and Anna May (Zingale) L.; m. Ku Oho Rim; children: Tammy, Robert. AA, Cuyahoga Community Coll., Parma, Ohio, 1974; BA, Case Western Res. U., 1976; postgrad., Cleve. State U., 1977-78. Part-time faculty Cuyahoga Community Coll., 1979-83; vice chmn. Presdl. Inaugural Labor Com., Washington, 1980-81; vice chmn. labor com. Presdl. Inaugural Com., Washington, 1984-85; legis. agt. Internat. Brotherhood of Teamsters, Washington, 1977-90, dir. govt. internat. affairs, 1983-89; dir. Asian/Pacific br. Internat. Brotherhood of Teamsters, Taipei, Taiwan, 1985-88; spl. rep. of chmn. Hill & Knowlton Pub. Affairs Worldwide, Washington, 1989-91; pres., founding ptnr. Rollins Internat. Ltd., Alexandria, Va., 1992—. mem. Nanjing Ya Dong Corp. Mem. Pres.'s Export Coun., 1988-89; mem. Asia adv. com. Bicentennial of U.S. Constitution, 1990; bd. govs. Am. League for Exports and Security Assistance, 1989; mem. Nat. Commn. for Employment Policy, Washington, 1981-86. With USMC, 1968-70, Vietnam. Republican. Roman Catholic. Avocations: archery, hunting, fishing. Home: 8203 Cherry Ridge Rd Fairfax VA 22039-3011 Office: Rollins Internat Ltd 510 King St Ste 302 Alexandria VA 22314

LOCK, GERALD SEYMOUR HUNTER, retired mechanical engineering educator; b. London, June 30, 1935; arrived in Can., 1962, naturalized, 1973; s. George and Mary (Hunter) L.; m. Edna Burness, Sept. 19, 1959; children: Graeme, Gareth, Grenville. B.Sc. with honors, U. Durham, Eng., 1959, Ph.D., 1962. Asst. prof. mech. engring. U. Alta. (Can.), Edmonton, 1962-64;

assoc. prof. U. Alta. (Can.), 1964-70, prof., 1970-93, dean interdisciplinary studies, 1976-81; cons. mech. engr., Edmonton, 1993—; chmn. Internat. Arctic Sci. Commn. Regional Bd., 1993—. Vice chmn. Alta. Manpower Adv. Coun., 1979-84, chmn., 1984-89; chmn. Salvation Army Red Shield Appeal, 1980-82; bd. govs. Alta. Coll., chmn., 1982-85; founding pres. Alta. Poetry Festival Soc., 1981. Recipient Queen Elizabeth II Silver Jubilee medal, 1977. Fellow Engring. Inst. Can., Can. Soc. Mech. Engring. (pres. 1977-78), ASME; mem. Sci. Coun. Can., Can. Can. Polar Commn. Mem. Progressive Conservative Party. Anglican. Home: 11711 83d Ave, Edmonton, AB Canada T6G 0V2 Office: U Alta, Edmonton, AB Canada T6G 2G3

LOCK, RICHARD WILLIAM, packaging company executive; b. N.Y.C., Oct. 5, 1931; s. Albert and Catherine Dorothy (Magnus) L.; m. Elizabeth Louise Kenney, Nov. 2, 1957; children—Albert William, Dorothy Louise Lock Kuhl, John David. B.S., Rutgers U., 1953; M.B.A., N.Y. U., 1958. Acct. Gen. Electric Co., 1953-54, Union Carbide Co., N.Y.C., 1956-58; div. controller St. Regis Paper Co., Houston, 1959-62; div. controller Owens-Illinois, Inc., Toledo, 1962-64; supr. programmer office methods and data processing, 1964-65, asst. mgr. data processing procedures, 1965-67, mgr. systems analysis and devel., 1967-68, mgr. corp. systems analysis and devel., 1968-70, dir. corp. systems and data processing, 1970-72, gen. mgr. electro/optical display, 1972-75, treas., 1975-80, v.p. dir. corp. planning, 1980-84, v.p. asst. chief fin. officer, treas., 1984-88; mng. dir. Magnus Assocs., 1989—. Mem. adv. bd. Toledo Salvation Army, 1973—, chmn., 1974-77; pres. Toledo Area Govtl. Research Assn., 1978-79; bd. dirs. Riverside Hosp. Found., Toledo, 1982—. Served with USAF, 1954-56. Mem. Fin. Execs. Inst., Am. Soc. Corp. Secs., Phi Beta Kappa. Republican. Lutheran. Club: Toledo. Home: 5831 Monroe St Apt 406 Sylvania OH 43560-2256

LOCKARD, JOHN ALLEN, naval officer; b. Mobile, Ala., July 30, 1944; s. John David and Mary Ethlyn (Wyatt) L.; m. Peggy Lee Cantrell, Apr. 25, 1970; children: Denise, Karen, John, Kelley. BS, U.S. Naval Postgrad. Sch., 1971. Commd. ensign USN, 1966, advanced through grades to rear adm., 1991; commanding officer Attack Squadron 25 USN, Lemoore, Calif., 1980-81, commanding officer Strike Fighter Squadron 125, 1983-84; exec. officer USS Coral Sea USN, Norfolk, Va., 1985-86; program mgr. F/A-18 Naval AIr Systems Command USN, Washington, 1986-90, asst. comdr. for systems engring., 1990-91, program exec. officer to sec. navy staff, 1991-95, commdr. naval air systems command, 1995—; chmn. retirement com., bd. dirs. Navy Fed. Credit Union, Merrifield, Va., 1991—. Mem. Assn. Naval Aviation. Office: 1421 Jefferson Davis Hwy Arlington VA 22201-1010

LOCKE, CARL EDWIN, JR., academic administrator, engineering educator; b. Palo Pinto County, Tex., Jan. 11, 1936; s. Carl Edwin Sr. and Caroline Jane (Brown) L.; m. Sammie Rhae Batchelor, Aug. 25, 1956; children: Stephen Curtis, Carlene Rhae. BSChemE, U. Tex., 1958, MSChemE, 1960, PhDChemE, 1972. Rsch. engr. Continental Oil Co., Ponca City, Okla., 1959-65; prodn. engr. R.L. Stone Co., Austin, Tex., 1965-66; prodn. rsch. engr. Tracor Inc., Austin, 1966-71; vis. assoc. prof. U. Tex., Austin, 1971-73; from asst. prof. to prof., dir. chem. engring. U. Okla., Norman, 1973-86; dean engring. U. Kans., Lawrence, 1986—; Co-author: Anodic Protection, 1981; contbr. articles to profl. jours. Disting. Engring. grad. U. Tex., 1993. Fellow Am. Inst. Chem. Engrs.; mem. ASTM, Nat. Assn. Corrosion Engrs. (regional chair 1988-89, Eben Junkin award South Cen. region 1990), Am. Soc. Engring. Edn., Lawrence C. of C., Rotary. Democrat. Presbyterian. Office: U Kans 2291 Irving Rd Lawrence KS 66044-7541

LOCKE, CHARLES STANLEY, manufacturing company executive, director; b. Laurel, Miss., Mar. 5, 1929; s. Richard C. and Florence (Parker) L.; m. NoraLou Fulkerson, Mar. 15, 1952; children: Cathy, Stanley, Lauren, Pamela. BBA, U. Miss., 1952, MS in Acctg., 1955. With audit staff Price Waterhouse & Co., New Orleans, 1955-58; with Comml. Analysis for Converting div. Westvaco, Inc., 1958-64; controller A.E. Staley Mfg. Co., 1964-69; v.p. fin., dir., mem. exec. com. Brown Co., Pasadena, Calif., 1969-73; sr. v.p., mem. exec. com. Allen Group Inc., Melville, N.Y., 1973-75; v.p. fin., dir. MortonNorwich, Chgo., 1975-80, pres., chief operating officer, dir., Mar. 1980, pres., chief exec. officer, dir., Apr. 1980, pres., chief exec. officer, chmn. bd., Aug. 1980; chmn. bd., chief exec. officer, dir. Morton Thiokol, Inc. (named changed 1982), Chgo., 1981-83, chmn. bd., chief exec. officer, pres., dir., 1983-84, chmn. bd., chief exec. officer, dir., from 1984, dir., 1989; chmn., chief exec. officer, dir. Morton Internat. (spin off Morton Thiokol 1989), 1989-94; ret.; bd. dirs. Thiokol Corp., Avon Products, Inc., NICOR, Inc., No. Ill. Gas Corp., Whitman Corp. Chmn. bd. trustees Mus. Sci. and Industry, Chgo. With U.S. Army, 1952-54. Mem. Chgo. Club, Rm. 100 Club, Mid-Am. Club, Sunset Ridge Country Club, Old Elm Country Club, Shoreacres Country Club, Beta Alpha Psi.

LOCKE, DAVID HENRY, state senator, lawyer; b. Boston, Aug. 4, 1927; s. Allen W. and Florence Elizabeth (Henry) L.; A.B., Harvard U., 1951, LL.B., 1954; m. Patricia Locke; children—David Byron, Jeffrey Allen, Jennifer, Amy Beth, John Adam. Admitted to Mass. bar, 1955; spl. asst. dist. atty. Norfolk County (Mass.), 1956-57; mem. firm Jameson, Locke & Fullerton, Wellesley, Mass.; mem. Wellesley Town Meeting, 1949—, Wellesley Republican Town Com., 1952—; selectman, Wellesley, 1959-62; mem. Mass. State Ho. of Reps., 1960-68; mem. Mass. State Senate, 1969—, mem. ins., state adminstrn., judiciary and rules coms., asst. minority leader, 1971—. Served with USMC, 1945-46. Mem. ABA, Mass. Bar Assn., Boston Bar Assn., Norfolk County Bar Assn., Trial Lawyers Assn. Republican. Roman Catholic. Office: Mass State Senate State Capital Boston MA 02133

LOCKE, EDWIN ALLEN, JR., investment banker; b. Boston, June 8, 1910; s. Edwin Allen and Elizabeth (Ferguson) L.; m. Dorothy Q. Clark, June 16, 1934 (div.); children: Elizabeth Eliane, Edwin Allen III, Benjamin Clark; m. Karin Marsh, 1952; 1 son, Jonathan Winston. Grad., Phillips Acad., Exeter, N.H., 1928; A.B. cum laude, Harvard U., 1932. Assoc. Chase Nat. Bank, N.Y.C., 1932-33, assoc. Paris br., 1933-35, assoc. London br., 1935-36, assoc., N.Y.C., 1936-40, v.p., 1947-51; Office Coordinator Purchases, adv. commn. to Council Nat. Def., 1940-41; asst. dep. dir. priorities div. Office Prodn. Mgmt., 1941; dep. chief staff officer Supply Priorities and Allocation Bd., 1941-42; asst. to chmn. WPB, 1942-44; exec. asst. to personal rep. of Pres., 1944-45, personal rep. of, 1945-47; also spl. asst. to pres., 1946-47; spl. rep. Sec. State; ambassador to Near East, 1951-53; exec. asst. to pres. Union Tank Car Co., Chgo., 1953-54, exec. v.p., 1954-55, pres., chief exec. officer, dir., 1955-63; pres., chief exec. officer Modern Homes Constrn. Co., Valdosta, Ga., 1963-67, Coastal Products Corp., Blountstown, Fla., 1964-67, Am. Paper Inst., N.Y.C., 1967-77, Econ. Club of N.Y., 1977-85; investment banker, 1985—; dir. Alusit Holdings, L.P., 1993—; chmn., dir. Fed. Home Loan Bank of Chgo., 1956-63; overseer Harvard U., 1958-64; trustee Century Power Corp. Ariz., 1989-91. Mem. Presdl. Survey Mission to Liberia and Tunisia, 1963; mem. adv. com. on internat. bus. problems Dept. State, 1962-67; trustee China Med. Bd., 1947-80, Radio Officers Union Benefit Plans, 1988-93. Mem. Racquet and Tennis Club (N.Y.C.), Metropolitan Club (Washington). Home and Office: PO Box 2568 Daytona Beach FL 32115

LOCKE, EDWIN ALLEN, III, psychologist, educator; b. N.Y.C., May 15, 1938; s. Edwin Allen and Dorothy (Clark) L.; m. Anne Hassard, June 13, 1968. B.A., Harvard U., 1960; M.A., Cornell U., 1962, Ph.D., 1964. Assoc. research scientist Am. Inst. Research, 1964-66, research scientist, 1966-70; asst. prof. Washington U. Md., College Park, 1967-69; assoc. prof. U. Md., 1969-70, assoc. prof. bus., mgmt. and psychology, 1970-73, prof., 1973—; chmn., faculty mgmt. and orgn. Coll. Bus. and Mgmt., College Park, 1986—. Author: A Guide to Effective Study, 1975; co-author: Goal Setting: A Motivational Technique That Works, 1984, A Theory of Goal Setting and Task Performance, 1990, The Essence of Leadership, 1991; editor: Generalizing from Laboratory to Field Settings, 1986; cons. editorial bd. Organizational Behavior and Human Decision Processes, J. Applied Psychology; contbr. articles to profl. jours. Office Naval Research grantee, 1964, 79; NIMH grantee, 1967; Army Rsch. Inst. grantee, 1993. Fellow APA, Acad. Mgmt., Am. Psychol. Soc., Soc. Indsl. and Orgnl. Psychology (Disting Scientific Contbn. award 1993). Home: 30 Old Mill Bottom Rd N Annapolis MD 21401-5448 Office: U Md Coll Bus and Mgmt College Park MD 20742 *The most important literary/philosophical influence in my life has been Ayn Rand. Her philosophy of Objectivism demonstrates that man's highest purpose is the achievement of his own happiness and that reason is*

his only means to achieve it. Her novels, which portray man as an heroic being, are an inspiration to every man to achieve the best within him.

LOCKE, MICHAEL, zoology educator; b. Nottingham, Eng., Feb. 14, 1929; came to U.S., 1961; s. R.H. and K.N. (Waite) L.; m. J. V. Collins; children by previous marriage, Vanessa , John, Timothy, Marius. B.A., Cambridge U., 1952, M.A., 1955, Ph.D., 1956, Sc.D., 1976. State scholar, found. scholar St. John's Coll., 1949-56; lectr. zoology Univ. Coll. W.I., 1956-61; guest investigator Rockefeller Inst., N.Y.C., 1960; assoc. prof. biology Case Western Res. U., Cleve., 1961-67, prof. biology, 1967-71; prof., chmn. dept. zoology U. Western Ont., London, Can., 1971-85; prof. zoology U. Western Ont., 1985—; Raman prof. U. Madras, India, 1969; vis. dir. rsch. Internat. Ctr. Insect Physiology and Ecology, Nairobi, Kenya, 1977-81. Editor Monographs on Ultrastructure, 1970—; mem. editorial bd. Tissue and Cell, 1968—, Jour. Insect Physiology, 1978—, Insect Sci. and Its Applications, 1979-89; former editor: Growth Soc. Symposia; contbr. over 200 articles to profl. jours. Served with RAF. Disting. Internat. award in Insect Morphology & Embryology, Gold medal, 1988; Killam fellow, 1988-90. Fellow Royal Soc. Can., AAAS; mem. Am. Soc. Cell Biology. Avocations: lapidary; gemologist. Office: Dept Zoology, U Western Ont, London, ON Canada N6A 5B7

LOCKE, NORTON, hotel management and construction company executive; b. Mpls., May 22, 1927; s. Ben and Harriet (Markus) L.; m. Peggy Jane Smith, Nov. 6, 1959; children: Alexandria, Jonina, Elizabeth, Victoria. B.S., U. Wis., 1951; M.B.A., Mich. State U., 1957, cert. food and beverage exec., 1984, cert. hotel adminstr., 1986, cert. food service profl., 1988. Corp. dir. food and beverage Kahler Corp., Rochester, Minn., 1970; gen. mgr., chief exec. officer Carolando Corp., Orlando, Fla., 1971-74; also dir.; gen. mgr. Radisson Muehlebach Hotel, Kansas City, Radisson Cadillac Hotel, Detroit, 1974-79; v.p. gen. mgr. White Co. Hospitality Div., Merrillville, Ind., 1979-80; dist. dir. I.D.M. Mgmt. Co., Chgo., 1980-83; v.p., gen. mgr. Skirvin Plaza Hotel, Oklahoma City, 1983-87; v.p., dir. ops. SBI Mgmt. Co., Oklahoma City, 1987-91; v.p., gen. mgr. Anaheim (Calif.) Plz. Hotel, 1991-93; corp. dir. Midwest Hospitality Mgmt., Anaheim, Calif., 1993—; faculty Vallencia Coll., 1971-74; adj. prof. Oklahoma City Community Coll., 1983-89; adj. prof. Century Coll., San Diego. Author: Hard Times Cook Book, World Without Milk Cookbook, Land of Milk and Honey, Heritage, A Taste of Tradition. Bd. dirs. U. Minn. Tech. Coll., 1970-75, Am. Hotel and Motel Assn. Sch., 1975-79, Detroit Conv. and Visitors Bur. Served with inf. AUS, 1944-46. Mem. Internat. Food Service Execs. Assn. (dir. 1971-74), Am. Hotel and Motel Assn. (cert.), Am. Chefs Assn., Mich. and Ind. Hotel Assn., Nat. Restaurant Assn., Hotel Sales Mgrs. Assn., Am. Fisheries Inst. (dir. 1970-71), Okla. State Hotel Assn. (Innkeeper of Yr. 1985, Bd. Mem. of Yr. 1986). Republican. Clubs: Masons (Scottish Rite 32 degree), Shriners, Rotary, SKAL Internat, Toastmasters Internat.

LOCKE, VIRGINIA OTIS, textbook editor, behavioral sciences writer; b. Tiffin, Ohio, Sept. 4, 1930; d. Charles Otis and Frances Virginia (Sherer) L. BA, Barnard Coll., 1953; MA in Psychology, Duke U., 1972, postgrad. Program officer, asst. corp. sec. Agrl. Devel. Coun., N.Y.C., 1954-66; staff psychologist St. Luke's-Roosevelt Med. Ctr., N.Y.C., 1973-75; freelance writer and editor N.Y.C., 1976-85; writer-editor Cornell U. Med. Coll./N.Y. Hosp. Med. Ctr., N.Y.C., 1986-89; sr. editor humanities and social scis. coll. divsn. Prentice Hall divsn. Simon & Schuster, Upper Saddle River, N.J., 1989—. Co-author: (coll. textbook) Introduction to Theories of Personality, 1985, The Agricultural Development Council: A History, 1989. Founder Help Our Neighbors Eat Year-round (H.O.N.E.Y.), Inc., N.Y.C., chmn., 1983-87, vol., 1987—; newsletter editor, 1992—; reader Recording for the Blind, N.Y.C., 1978-84; vol. Reach to Recovery program Am. Cancer soc., Bergen County, N.J., 1990—. Recipient Our Town Thanks You award, N.Y.C., 1984, Mayor's Vol. Svc. award, N.Y.C., 1986, Cert. of Appreciation for Community Svc. Manhattan Borough, 1986, Jefferson award Am. Ins. Pub. Svc., Washington, 1986.

LOCKE, WILLIAM, endocrinologist; b. Morden, Man., Can., Mar. 16, 1916; s. Corbet and Ruby Louise (Brown) L.; m. Katherine Elizabeth Acer, Sept. 29, 1945. MD, U. Man., Winnipeg, 1938; MS in Medicine, U. Minn., 1947. Diplomate Am. Bd. Internal Medicine. Intern Winnipeg (Man., Can.) Gen. Hosp., 1937-38; fellow in medicine Mayo Found., Rochester, Minn., 1938-40, 46-48; rsch. fellow Harvard U., Boston, 1948-50; mem. staff Ochsner Clinic, New Orleans, 1950—, sr. cons., 1987—; clin. prof. medicine Tulane U., New Orleans, 1968-86, prof. emeritus, 1986—; sec. Alton Ochsner Clinic, New Orleans, 1950—; pres. med. staff Ochsner Found. Hosp., New Orleans, 1954-55, trustee, 1978—. Author, editor: Hypothalmus and Pituitary in Health and Disease, 1972; contbr. numerous chpts. to books and articles to sci. jours. Lt. comdr. RCNVR, 1940-46. NIH grantee, 1958-62. Fellow ACP; mem. Am. Diabetes Assn., Endocrine Soc., Sigma Xi, others. Republican. Episcopalian. Home: 4815 Dryades St New Orleans LA 70115 Office: Ochsner Clinic 1514 Jefferson Hwy New Orleans LA 70121-2483

LOCKE, WILLIAM LOUIS, pharmacist; b. Reno, May 20, 1946; s. John William and Janice Elizabeth (Leavy) L.; m. Sarah Elizabeth Witherell, June 19, 1978 (div. Apr. 1983); children: Kate MacKenzie, Nicholas Kristopher; m. Katherine Ann Beach, Sept. 26, 1987. BS in Pharmacy, U. Pacific, 1969. Registered pharmacist. Treas. Nev. Pharmacists Assn., Reno, 1982-84, bd. dirs., 1984-87, pres., 1987—. With US Air N.G., 1969-75. Republican. Avocations: golfing, camping, fishing. Home: 4310 Elmwood Ln Reno NV 89509-5906 Office: Hales Drug Inc 975 Ryland St Reno NV 89502-1667

LOCKE, WILLIAM SWEET, manufacturing executive; b. Orange, N.J., Nov. 12, 1931; s. Walter James and Paulyne (Sweet) L.; m. Marianne Griffith, Nov. 24, 1957 (dec. May 1962); 1 child, Stephan James; m. Jane Ann Eytcheson, July 23, 1967; children: Jacinda Hope, Kyla Marie. Student, Lehigh U., 1949-53, U. Mich., 1968, Purdue U., 1970, U. Ky., 1974. Registered profl. engr., Ky., Ind. Mgr. engr. Internat. Harvester, Ft. Wayne, Ind., 1956-71; gen. mgr. Dura Corp., Paris, Ky., 1971-82; pres. Weaver Corp., Paris, 1982-83; v.p. engring. Knoll Internat., East Greenville, Pa., 1983-86; pres. Talbert Mfg. Corp., Rensselaer, Ind., 1986-92; gen. mgr., exec. v.p. CMI Corp., Oklahoma City, 1992—. Contbr. articles to Classic Car mag. and jour.; patentee vehicle suspension. With U.S. Army, 1953-55, Korea. Mem. Soc. Automotive Engrs. (exec. com., chmn. tech. session 1980), Truck Trail Mfr. Assn. (chair com. 1986, bd. dirs.), Soc. Automotive Historians, Music Box Soc., Classic Car Club Am. (life), Auburn Cord Duesenberg Club. Avocations: vintage automobiles, mechanical music machines. Home: 9916 Thompson Ave Yukon OK 73099-7928 Office: CMI Corp Box 1985 Oklahoma City OK 73101

LOCKER, J. GARY, university official, civil engineering educator; b. Kenora, Ont., Can., Nov. 19, 1937; s. Lorne John and Gladys Sarah (Kirk) L.; m. Elaine June Letawsky, May 25, 1963; children: Laura Lee, Tiffany Dawn. BSCE, U. Man., Winnipeg, Can., 1961; MS, U. Alta., Edmonton, Can., 1963, PhD, 1969. Registered profl engr., Ont. Lectr. dept. civil engring., Royal Mil. Coll., Kingston, Ont., 1963-66, asst. prof., 1968-71; assoc. prof. faculty engring. U. Regina, Sask., Can., 1971-73; chmn. dept. civil engring. Lakehead U., Thunder Bay, Ont., 1973-76, dir. Sch. Engring., 1976-94; dean Faculty Engring. Lakehead U., Thunder Bay, 1994—; mem. past chmn. Coun. Ont. Deans Engring., Nat. Coun. Deans Engring. and Applied Sci. Fellow Engring. Inst. Can.; mem. Can. Geotech. Inst., Profl. Engrs. Ont. (order of honor), Internat. Soc. Soil Mechanics and Found. Engring., Thunder Bay Fly Fishing Club. Geotech. engring. rsch. in organic soils and clay shales. Avocations: fly fishing and tying, gardening, trailer travel, cross-coutry skiing. Office: Lakehead U Faculty Engring, Oliver Rd, Thunder Bay, ON Canada P7B 5E1

LOCKER, RAYMOND DUNCAN, editor; b. Dunkirk, N.Y., Apr. 15, 1960; s. Robert Smith and Margaret Ellen (Duncan) L.; m. Debbie Elizabeth Long, July 2, 1988; 1 child, Margaret Katherine. BA in Political Sci., U. Cin. 1982; MS in Journalism, Ohio U., 1984. Reporter Lake Wales Highlander, Lake Wales, Fla., 1982-83, The Montgomery Advertiser, Montgomery, Ala., 1985-87; political reporter The Tampa Tribune, Tampa, Fla., 1987-89, Washington corr., 1989-91, political columnist, 1991-93, night metro editor, 1993-94, political editor, 1994—. Panelist Tampa Bay Week, WEDU-TV, 1993—, Bayside, WTOG-TV, 1994—. Roman Catholic. Office: The Tampa Tribune PO Box 191 Tampa FL 33601-0191

LOCKETT, BARBARA ANN, librarian; b. Northampton, Mass., Feb. 21, 1936; d. William M. and Anna A. (Vachula) Prabulos; m. Richard W. Rice, June 2, 1957 (div. Feb. 1966); 1 child, Annamarie Louise; m. Benjamin B. Lockett, June 7, 1985. BS, U. Mass., 1957; MLS, U. Calif., Berkeley, 1967. Documents librarian Knolls Atomic Power Lab., Schenectady, N.Y., 1968-74; coordinator bibliog. devel. SUNY, Albany, 1974-81; prin. librarian reference services N.Y. State Library, Albany, 1981-85; dir. libraries Rensselaer Poly. Inst., Troy, N.Y., 1985-94; cons. Office Mgmt. Svcs., Assn. Resch. Librs., Washington, 1981-86. Contbr. articles on collection devel., mgmt. and info. systems to profl. jours. Mem. ALA (cons. collection mgmt. and devel. com., Resources and Tech. Svcs. div. 1983-87), Assn. Coll. and Resch. Libs. (chmn. standards and accreditation com. 1988-90), N.Y. State Edn. and Resch. Network (chmn. info. resources com. 1988-89), N.Y. State Libr./ NYSERNet (joint planning team 1991-94, del. N.Y. State Gov.'s Conf. on Libraries, 1990), Sigma Xi, Phi Kappa Phi, Beta Phi Mu. Mem. Unitarian Ch. Avocations: tennis, gardening, accordion, travel. Home: 1772 Calle Poniente Santa Barbara CA 93101

LOCKETT, HAROLD JAMES, physician, psychiatrist; b. Wilmington, Del., July 17, 1924; s. Jesse and Annie Lessie (Colbert) L.; m. Betty Jean Griffin, June 11, 1950 (dec. Aug. 1980); 1 child, Chérie Robin. AB, Ind. U., 1948; MD, Meharry Med. Coll., 1952. Diplomate Am. Bd. Psychiatry and Neurology, Am. Bd. Child Psychiatry. Intern L.A. County Gen. Hosp., 1952-53; resident in psychiatry U. Mich. Med. Ctr., Ann Arbor, 1953-56; resident fellow in child psychiatry Hawthorn Ctr., Northville, Mich., 1956-58, staff psychiatrist, 1958-72, asst. dir., 1972-90, dir., 1990—; psychiatrist, 1958—; clin asst. prof. U. Mich. Med. Sch., Ann Arbor, Wayne State U. Med. Sch.; pvt. practice in psychiatry, Ann Arbor, 1958—; cons. to numerous sch. systems. Contbr. articles to profl. jours. Pres. Ann Asthma Bd. Edn., 1969-71, trustee, 1965-71; bd. dirs. Ann Arbor chpt. ACLU, Spaulding for Children, 1969—; mem. adv. bd. Mich. Theater Found. Fellow Am. Acad. Child Psychiatry, Am. Orthopsychiatric Assn.; mem. Am Psychiat. Assn., Nat. Med. Assn., Black Psychiatrists Am. Democrat. Avocations: tennis, art objects, paintings, African artifacts, skiing. Home: PO Box 608200 Chicago IL 60660 Office: Hawthorn Ctr 18471 Haggerty Rd Northville MI 48167-9575

LOCKETT, PIERRE, dancer; b. Mobile, Ala.. Scholarship student, The Joffrey Ballet Sch., 1980-82, Robert Joffrey Workshop, 1981. Dancer Dance Theater of Harlem, N.Y.C., 1982-88, Princeton Ballet, 1988-89, The Joffrey Ballet, N.Y.C., 1989—. Office: The Joffrey Ballet 130 W 56th St New York NY 10019-3818*

LOCKETT, TYLER CHARLES, state supreme court justice; b. Corpus Christi, Tex., Dec. 7, 1932; s. Tyler Coleman and Evelyn (Lemond) L.; m. Sue W. Lockett, Nov. 3, 1961; children: Charles, Patrick. AB, Washburn U., 1955, JD, 1962. Bar: Kans. 1962. Pvt. practice law Wichita, 1962—; judge Ct. Common Pleas, 1971-77, Kans. Dist. Ct. 18th Dist., 1977-83; justice Supreme Court Kans., Topeka, 1983—. Methodist. Office: Kans Supreme Ct Kans Jud Ctr 301 W 10th St Topeka KS 66612

LOCKEY, RICHARD FUNK, allergist, educator; b. Lancaster, Pa., Jan. 15, 1940; s. Stephen Daniel and Anna (Funk) L.; m. Carol Lee Madill, July 3, 1982; children—Brian Christopher, Keith Edward. B.S., Haverford Coll., 1961; M.D., Temple U., 1965; M.S., U. Mich., 1972. Diplomate Am. Bd. Internal Medicine, Am. Bd. Allergy and Immunology. Intern Temple U. Med. Sch., Phila., 1965-66; asst. resident internal medicine Univ. Hosp. U. Mich., Ann Arbor, 1966-67, resident, 1966-68, fellow in allergy and immunology, 1969-70; asst. prof. medicine U. South Fl. Coll. Medicine, Tampa, 1973-77, assoc. prof. medicine, 1977-83, asst. dir. div. allergy and immunology, 1979-82, dir. allergy and immunology, 1982—; prof. medicine, 1983—; prof. pediatrics, 1983, prof. pub. health, 1987—; asst. chief sect. allergy and immunology VA Hosp., Tampa, 1973-82, chief sect. allergy and immunology, 1983—; mem. allergenic adv. com. FDA, 1985-89. Editor: Allergy and Clinical Immunology, 1980; co-editor (with S.C. Bukantz) Fundamentals of Immunology and Allergy, 1987, (with S.C. Bukantz) Principals of Immunology and Allergy, 1987, JAMA Primer on Allergic and Immunologic Diseases, 1987, (with S.C. Bukantz) Allergen Immunotherapy, 1991; contbr. articles to profl. jours. and chpts. to books; author monographs. Served to maj. USAF, 1971-73. Named Outstanding Med. Specialist, Town and Country Mag., 1989, recipient Alumni Achievement award, Temple U. Sch. of Medicine Alumni Assn., 1990, hon. mem. The Soc. of Allergy and Immunolgy of Cordoba, Argentina, 1991, recipient Outstanding Leadership in Chapter Devel. and Patient Support, Nat. Asthma and Allergy Found. of Am. award, 1992, Cert. of Appreciation, Fla. Med. Assn., 1992; named Claude P. Brown Meml. lectr. Assn. of Clin. Scientists, ADA, 1981, Disting. Visitor Ann. Meeting of Coll. of Medicine, Republic of Costa Rica, 1979, special mem. The Internat. Scientific Bd. Pharmacia Allergy Resch. Found., 1992-93. Fellow ACP, Am. Coll. Chest Physicians, Am. Acad. Allergy and Immunology (chmn. com. on insects 1978-81, chmn undergrad. and grad. edn. com. 1982-88, com. on occupational lung disease 1982—, chmn. com. on standardization of allergenic extracts 1983-86, exec. com. mem. at large 1986-88, historian 1988-89, sec. 1989-90, treas. 1990-91, pres.-elect 1991-92, pres. 1992-93, Am. Bd. Allergy and Immunology (bd. dirs. 1993—), John M. Sheldon U. of Mich. Allergy Soc. (councilor 1977-80, pres. 1980-82), Fla. Allergy and Immunology Soc. (sec.-treas. 1979-80, pres. 1981-82), Southeastern Allergy Assn., AMA, Hillsborough County Med. Assn., Joint Coun. Allergy and Immunology, , Clin. Immunology Soc., AAAS, Fla. Thoracic Soc., Alpha Omega Alpha. Clubs: Carrollwood Village (Tampa), University. Avocations: antiques, hiking, back packing, photography. Home: 3909 Northampton Way Tampa FL 33624-4443 Office: U So Fla VA Hosp 13000 Bruce B Downs Blvd Tampa FL 33612-4799

LOCKHART, AILEENE SIMPSON, retired dance, kinesiology and physical education educator; b. Atlanta, Mar. 18, 1911; d. Thomas Ellis and Aileene Reeves (Simpson) L. B.S., Tex. Woman's U., 1932; M.S., U. Wis. 1937, Ph.D., 1942; D.Sc. (hon.), U. Nebr., 1967. Mem. faculty Mary Hardin Baylor Coll., Belton, Tex., 1933-42, U. Wis., 1941-42; asst. prof., then assoc. prof. phys. edn. and pharmacology U. Nebr., 1942-49; assoc. prof., then prof. U. So. Calif., 1949-73; dean Coll. Health, Phys. Edn., Recreation and Dance Tex. Woman's U., 1973-78, prof. dance and phys. edn., chmn. dept. dance, 1978-83, adj. prof., 1983-88; Clare Small lectr. U. Colo., 1975; Ethel Martus Lawther lectr. U. N.C., 1978; Amy Morris Homans lectr., Milw., 1976; Donna Mae Miller Humanities scholar/lectr. , U. Ariz., Tucson, 1989; vis. prof./lectr. Iowa State U., univs., Wash., Oreg., Wis., Mass.; N.H., Calif. State U., Long Beach, Springfield (Mass.) Coll., Smith Coll., Wellesley Coll., U. Maine-Presque Isle, Dunfermline Coll., Edinburgh, Scotland, U. Brazil, Brasilia; cons. editor William C. Brown Publishing Co., Dubuque, Iowa, 1954—. Author or co-author 12 books; contbr. numerous articles profl. jours.; cons. editor or editor over 200 books. Recipient Disting. Alumnae award Tex. Woman's U., 1971, Disting. Alumnae award U. Wis.-Madison, 1981, Cornaro award, 1980, Honor award Ministry Edn., Taiwan, 1981, Minnie Stevens Piper Found. award State of Tex., 1983, Nat. Dance Assn. Heritage award, 1985, Amy Morris Homans fellow, 1961-62; honra ao Merito Ministerio de Educato and Cultura Brazilia, Brazil, 1977; Nat. Dance Assn. scholar, 1986-87; Tex. Assn. Health, Phys. Edn., Recreation and Dance scholar, 1986. Fellow Am. Coll. Sports Medicine, Am. Alliance Health, Phys. Edn., Recreation and Dance (Honor award 1963, Luther Halsey Gulick award 1980), Am. Acad. Phys. Edn. (pres. 1980-81, Hetherington award 1992); mem. Nat. Assn. Girls and Women in Sports (honor award 1991), Nat. Dance Assn., So. Assn. Phys. Edn. Coll. Women, Nat. Assn. Phys. Edn. in Higher Edn., Phi Kappa Phi. Presbyterian. *That my students, many now well respected scholars, others eager neophytes in the journey of learning, exemplify some of the goals, ideals and visions, the high standards and high expectancies we have shared together is to me the most meaningful and fulfilling aspect in my life as an educator.*

LOCKHART, BROOKS JAVINS, retired college dean; b. Sandyville, W.Va., Feb. 8, 1920; s. Therman Allen and Erna Shirley (Javins) L.; m. Patricia Durrant, July 31, 1969; 1 son, Jonathan Joseph; children by previous marriage: Patricia (Mrs. Meldon Wolfgang), Lynn Allen. A.B., Marshall U., 1937; M.S., W.Va. U., 1940; Ph.D., U. Ill., 1943. Asst. instr. U. Ill., Urbana, 1940-43; instr. U. Mich., Ann Arbor, 1943-44, 46-48; asst. prof. math. Naval Postgrad. Sch., Monterey, Calif., 1948-51; assoc. prof. Naval Postgrad. Sch., 1951-55, prof., 1955-62, 77-79, dean, 1962-77; ret., 1979; governing bd. Monterey City Schs., 1954-69, pres., 1965-67; mem. governing bd. Monterey

Peninsula Coll., 1954-63, pres., 1960-63. Bd. dirs. Carmel Found., 1989-95. Lt. (j.g.) USNR, 1944-46. Bd. dirs. Carmel Found., 1989—. Served to lt. (j.g.) USNR, 1944-46. Mem. Math. Assn. Am. (pres. Calif. 1960, sec. 1961-63), Calif. Sch. Bds. Assn. (dir. 1963-70, pres. 1969), Sigma Xi, Chi Beta Phi, Kappa Delta Pi. Democrat. Methodist. Home: 157 Via Gayuba Monterey CA 93940-4320

LOCKHART, JAMES BICKNELL, III, investment banker; b. White Plains, N.Y., May 13, 1946; s. James Bicknell Jr. and Mary Ann (Riegel) L.; m. Carolyn Strahan Zoephel, June 17, 1972; children: James Bicknell IV, Grace Strahan. BA, Yale U., 1968; MBA, Harvard U., 1974. Asst. treas. Gulf Oil (E.H.), London, 1979-80; fin. dir. Gulf Oil Belgium, Brussels, 1980-81; sr. mgr. Gulf Oil Corp., Pitts., 1981-82, asst. treas., 1982-83; v.p., treas. Alexander and Alexander Services, N.Y.C., 1983-89; exec. dir. Pension Benefit Guaranty Corp., Washington, 1989-93; mng. dir., head pvt. fin. group Smith Barney, Inc., N.Y.C., 1993—. Contbr. articles to profl. jours. Treas. Reps. Abroad, London, 1978-80. Served to lt. (j.g.) USNR, 1969-72. Fellow Assn. Corp. Treas. (Eng.); mem. Assn. Pvt. Pension and Welfare Plans (bd. dirs.). Office: Smith Barney Inc 388 Greenwich St New York NY 10013

LOCKHART, JAMES BLAKELY, public affairs executive; b. N.Y.C., May 27, 1936; s. Edgar L. and Margaret Evelyn (Blakely) L.; m. Ruth Douglas, Oct. 30, 1976; children: Marc Blakely, Diallo Henry. BS, Boston U., 1956, JD, 1959. Bar: S.C. 1959, Ill. 1963. Sr. ptnr. Rivers, Lockhart, Clayter & Lawrence, Chgo., 1965-71; sr. v.p. legal affairs, sec., dir. Budget Rent-a-Car Corp., Chgo., 1972-79; v.p. public affairs Transam. Corp., San Francisco, 1979—; chmn. bd. Chgo. Community Ventures, Inc., 1975-79; bd. dir. Budget Rent-a-Car Internat., Inc. Mem. men's coun. Art Inst. of Chgo., 1970-72; bd. dirs., v.p., mem. exec. com. Bd. Episcopal charities Diocese of Chgo.; mem. Gov.'s Task Force on Civil Rights, Calif., 1980; past chmn. bd. dirs. Bay Area Urban League, Sta. KQED-TV, pub. broadcasting, also Sta. KQED-TV, KQED-FM; past chmn. St. Mary's Coll. Exec. Symposium; chmn. bus. coun., mem. exec. com., trustee emeritus Fine Arts Mus. San Francisco; bd. dirs., vice chmn. bd. dirs. Pub. Broadcasting Svcs.; commr., pres. Bd. of Port Commrs., Port of Oakland. Capt. JAGC, AUS, 1960-63. Recipient Sta. WBEE Radio Community Svc. award, 1973, Corp. Leadership award, 1973, Corp. Leadership award San Francisco Planning and Urban Resch. Assn., 1989, Cert. of Honor, San Francisco Bd. Suprs., 1989. Mem. Internat. Franchise Assn. (bd. dirs. 1973-77), Ill. Bar Assn., S.C. Bar Assn., Bay Area Coun. (liaison), Pub. Affairs Coun. (bd. dirs.), Calif. Bus. Roundtable (dep.), Downtown Assn. San Francisco (past pres., bd. dirs.), San Francisco C. of C. (bd. dirs., exec. com., chmn. pub. affairs com.), Bohemian Club, City Club (past pres.), Lakeview Club, Boulé, Sigma Pi Phi. Episcopalian. Home: 6037 Ridgemont Dr Oakland CA 94619-3721 Office: Transam Corp 600 Montgomery St San Francisco CA 94111-2702

LOCKHART, JOHN MALLERY, management consultant; b. Mellen, Wis., May 17, 1911; s. Carl Wright and Gladys (Gale) L.; m. Judith Anne Wood, Feb. 26, 1938 (dec. June 1991); children: Wood Alexander, Gale, Thomas; m. Frances Whittaker, Jan. 7, 1993. BS, Northwestern U., 1931; JD, IIT, 1938. CPA, Ill. Teaching fellow Northwestern U., 1931; asst. v.p. Welsh, Davis & Co. (investment bankers), Chgo., 1935-41; treas. Transcontinental & Western Air, Inc., Kansas City, Mo., 1941-47; exec. v.p., gen. mgr. TACA Airways, S.A., 1944-45; v.p., dir. The Kroger Co., 1947-71, exec. v.p., 1961-71; pres. Kroger Family Ctr. Stores, 1969-71, Lockhart Co. (mgmt. cons.), 1971—; v.p. corp. fin. Gradison & Co., 1973-86; chmn. bd. dirs., CEO Ohio Real Estate Investment Co., Ohio Real Estate Equity Corp., 1974-76; bd. dirs. Employers Mut. Cos., Des Moines, Witt Co.; chmn. bd. dirs. Autotronics Systems, Inc., 1976-78; bd. dirs. Vectra Internat., Inc. Chmn. Hamilton County Hosp. Commn., 1965-84; mem. adv. bd. Greater Cin. Airport, 1961-86. Mem. Comml. Club, Cin. Country Club, Conquistadores del Cielo Club. Home and Office: 2770 Walsh Rd Cincinnati OH 45208-3425

LOCKHART, KEITH ALAN, orchestra conductor, musician, teacher; b. Poughkeepsie, N.Y., Nov. 7, 1959; s. Newton Frederick and Marilyn Jean (Woodyard) L.; m. Ann Louise Heatherington, Aug. 22, 1981 (div. 1983). B.A. summa cum laude in German, Furman U., 1981, Mus.B. summa cum laude in Piano Performance, 1981; M.F.A. in Orch. Conducting, Carnegie-Mellon U., 1983. Instr. Carnegie-Mellon U., Pitts., 1982-84, assoc. dir. univ. orchs., 1983-86, dir. univ. orchs., 1986—; music dir. Carnegie-Mellon Repertory Theatre, 1982—; assoc. condr. Pitts. Civic Orch., 1982-87, music dir., 1987—; music dir. Akron (Ohio) Youth Symphony, 1988—; asst. condr. Akron Symphony Orch., 1988—. Author reviews for Clarinet mag. and Brit. jours., 1983. Co-editor, arranger performance edition opera John Gay: The Beggars' Opera, 1985; internat. tour with soprano Joan Merrigan, 1987. Quarter- finalist at Ernst Ansermet Internat. Conducting Competition, Geneva, Switzerland, 1984; quarter finalist Besancon Internat. Conducting Competition, France, 1987; grantee Kurt Weill Found. Music, 1985; participant Internat. Condrs. Masterclass, Hilversum, The Netherlands, 1988. Mem. Conductors' Guild Am., Symphony Orch. League, Am. Fedn. Musicians. Democrat. Avocations: reading; cooking; skiing; raquetball; outdoor sports. Home: 507 Western Ave Covington KY 41011-1041 Office: The Boston Pops Orchestra care Boston Symphony Orchestra Symphony Hall Boston MA 02115

LOCKHART, MICHAEL D., electric company executive; b. Muncie, Ind., Mar. 25, 1949; s. Roy Eugene and Marjorie Ilene (Thornburg) L.; children—Jennifer, Jessica, Kathleen Coleman. MBA, U. Chgo., 1975. Systems analyst Needham Harper & Steers, Chgo., 1969-74; v.p. Boston Consulting Group, Boston, 1975-81, GE Credit Corp., 1981-83, GE Corp. Exec. Office, Fairfield, Conn., 1984-85, GE Turbine Bus. Ops., Schenectady, N.Y., 1985-87, GE Aircraft Engines, Cin., 1987-88, GE Transp. Systems, Erie, Pa., 1989-91; v.p., gen. mgr. GE Aircraft Engines, Cin., 1992-94; pres. Gen. Signal Corp., Stamford, Conn., 1994—. Mem. Beta Gamma Sigma. Office: Gen Signal Corp PO Box 10010 High Ridge Park Stamford CT 06904

LOCKHEAD, GREGORY ROGER, psychology educator; b. Boston, Aug. 8, 1931; s. John Roger and Ester Mae (Bixby) L.; m. Jeanne Marie Hutchinson, June 9, 1957; children: Diane, Elaine, John. B.S., Tufts U., 1958; Ph.D., Johns Hopkins, 1965. Psychologist research staff IBM Research, Yorktown Heights, N.Y., 1958-61; research assoc., instr. Johns Hopkins, 1961-65; asst. prof. psychology Duke, 1965-68, assoc. prof., 1968-71, prof., 1971-91; chmn. dept. exptl. psychology Duke U., Durham, N.C., 1991—; scholar Stanford U.; research asso. U. Calif., Berkeley, 1971-72; fellow Wolfson Coll., Oxford (Eng.) U., 1980-81; scholar Fla. Atlantic U., 1981; Cons. in human engring. Cons. editor: Perception and Psychophysics, 1972-92; contbr. articles to profl. jours., co-author, editor chpts. in books. Served with USN, 1951-55. NSF grantee, 1966-69, 79-84, USPHS grantee, 1963-69, 70-79, Air Force Office Sci. Resch., 1983-91. Fellow Am. Psychol. Assn., Am. Psychol. Soc.; mem. Psychonomic Soc., Internat. Soc. Psychophysics, Sigma Xi, Phi Beta Kappa. Home: 2900 Montgomery St Durham NC 27705-5638 Office: Duke U Dept Exptl Psychology Durham NC 27708

LOCKLEAR, HEATHER, actress; b. L.A., Sept. 25, 1961; d. Bill and Diane L.; m. Tommy Lee, 1986 (div. 1994). m. Richie Sambora, 1994. Appeared in (TV series) Dynasty, 1981-89, T.J. Hooker, 1982-87, Going Places, 1990, Melrose Place, 1992—, (films) Firestarter, 1986, Return of the Swamp Thing, 1990, Wayne's World 2, 1993, (TV movies) Twil, 1981, City Killer, 1984, Blood Sport, 1986, Rich Men, Single Women, 1990, Texas Justice, 1995. Office: William Morris Agy 151 El Camino Blvd Beverly Hills CA 90212*

LOCKLIN, ALLEN CLEMENT, petroleum exploration geologist; b. Ballinger, Tex., Dec. 27, 1929; s. Clifford Griffith and Willie Eugenia (Long) L.; m. Nancy Lee Summers, Aug. 14, 1954; children: Chris Allen, Lee Ann Locklin Shaver. BS, U. Tex., Austin, 1954. Cert. geologist. Dist. geologist Humble Oil and Refinery Co., Tyler, Tex., 1959-60; ptnr. Ridley & Locklin Petroleum Geologists, Tyler, 1960-79; pres. Locklin Oil Co., Tyler 1981—. Precinct chmn. Rep. County Precinct, Tyler, 1963. With USN, 1948-49. Mem. East Tex. Geol. Soc., Am. Assn. of Petroleum Geologists, Nat. Vitiligo Found., Inc. (pres. 1985—). Achievements include inititating geological work up resulting in the discovery of several oil and gas fields. Office: Locklin Oil Co PO Box 6337 100 Independence Pl Ste 200 Tyler TX 75703

LOCKLIN, WILBERT EDWIN, management consultant; b. Washington, Apr. 2, 1920; s. Wilbert Edwin and Margaret Mae (Franklin) L.; m. Olga

Maria Osterwald, June 28, 1947; children: Kenneth, Patricia, Randall. B.S., Johns Hopkins U., 1942; LL.D., George Williams Coll., 1966. Vice-pres. Nat. Bur. Pvt. Schs., N.Y.C., 1947-49; account exec. Reuel Estill & Co., N.Y.C., 1949-51; asst. dir. admissions Johns Hopkins, 1945-47, asst. to pres., 1955-65; v.p. Johns Hopkins Fund, 1960-65; pres. Springfield (Mass.) Coll., 1965-85, Locklin Mgmt. Services, 1985—; chmn. bd. dirs., mem. exec. com., salary com., charitable funds com.; chmn. exec. com. Bay Bank Valley Trust Co., 1966-91; mem. exec. com. Assn. Ind. Colls. and Univs. in Mass., 1971-83; founding mem. Cooperating Colls. of Greater Springfield.; pres. Cooperating Colls. of Greater Springfield, 1982-83; mem. exec. com., bd. dirs. Business Friends of Arts. Bd. dirs. Springfield Symphony Orch., 1973-83. Served with USAAF, 1942-45. Decorated DFC, Air medal. Home: 225 Prynnwood Rd Longmeadow MA 01106-2754

LOCKMAN, STUART M., lawyer; b. Jersey City, July 18, 1949; s. Albert Korey and Edna Sally (Easton) L.; m. Deena Laurel Young, Dec. 27, 1970; children: Jeffrey, Susan, Karen. BA, U. Mich., 1971, JD, 1974. Bar: Mich. 1974, Fla. 1991. Ptnr. Honigman Miller Schwartz and Cohn, Detroit, 1974—. Office: Honigman Miller Schwartz & Cohn 2290 1st National Bldg Detroit MI 48226

LOCKMILLER, DAVID ALEXANDER, lawyer, educator; b. Athens, Tenn., Aug. 30, 1906; s. George Franklin and Lotta May (Ulrey) L.; m. Alma Elizabeth Russell, Sept. 23, 1930; children: Franklin Russell, Carlotta Elizabeth Lockmiller Minnis. B.Ph., Emory U., 1927, A.M., 1928, LL.D., 1954; J.D., Cumberland U., 1929, LL.D., 1940; Ph.D., U. N.C., 1935; postgrad. summers, Oxford U., Eng., 1937, U. Chgo., 1940, U. Paris, 1952; Litt.D., U. Chattanooga, 1960; L.H.D., Am. U., 1961; EdD, Tenn. Wesleyan Coll., 1962. Bar: Ohio, Mo., Okla., Ark., N.C., Tenn., Supreme Ct. U.S. Practiced in Monett, Mo., 1929-33; research asst. Inst. Research in Social Sci., U. N.C., 1934-35; instr. history and polit. sci. N.C. State U., 1935-36, asst. prof., 1936-38, assoc. prof., 1938-41, prof., head dept., 1940-42; pres. U. Chattanooga, 1942-59, Ohio Wesleyan U., 1959-61; exec. dir. Nat. Home Study Council, Washington, 1961-72; edn. cons., 1972—; vis. prof. Am. history Emory U., summer 1938, N.C. Coll., Durham, summer 1941; vis. prof. geography Meredith Coll., 1941-42; 1st vice chmn. Am. Council on Edn., 1952-53. Author: Magoon in Cuba, A History of the Second Intervention, 1906-09, 1938, 69, Sir William Blackstone, 1938, 70, History of N.C. State College of Agriculture and Engineering, 1889-1939, 1939, The Consolidation of the University of North Carolina, 1942, General Enoch H. Crowder: Father of Selective Service, 1955, Scholars on Parade: Academic Degrees and Costumes, 1969, 92; contbr. to hist., ednl. jours., encys. Mem. exec. com. N.C. Hist. Highway Markers, 1935-42, Nat. Mental Health Council USPHS; def. adv. com. edn. Armed Forces; mem. Pres.'s Commn. to Argentina Sesquicentennial, 1960; Past mem. U. Senate Meth. Ch. State dept. rep. to colls. and univs. Far East, 1953; hon. trustee U. Chattanooga Found., Rockefeller Found. Recipient Chattanooga Man of Yr. award, 1953, Hon. alumnus award N.C. State U., 1940, NTL Home Study Coun. Man of Yr. award, 1969, Disting. Svc. award United Schs. Bus., 1972, Spl. Achievement award Nat. Assn. Trade and Tech. Schs., 1972, Alumnus medal St. Andrew's Sch., 1980, Honor Leadership award Cleve. Inst. Electronics, 1982, Lifetime Achievement award Samford U., 1994; named to NTL Home Study Coun. Hall of Fame; Travel grantee to Brit. Univs., 1956. Fellow Am. Scandinavian Found.; mem. Assn. Am. Colls. and Univ. (pres. 1960-61), So. Univ. Conf. (exec. sec. 1956-59), Assn. Urban Univs. (past pres.), Internat. Conf. Correspondence Edn., Chattanooga Bar Assn., Chattanooga Exec. Club (ex-pres.), SAR, Am. Hist. Assn., Tenn. Coll. Assn. (pres. 1948-49, So. Assn. Colls. and Secondary Schs. (v.p. 1953), Am. Polit. Sci. Assn., So. Hist. Assn., Bar Assn. Ohio, Am. Mil. Inst., Conf. Latin Am. Studies, State Lit. and Hist. Assn. N.C., Newcomen Soc., Sovereign Order St. John of Jerusalem-Knights of Malta, Phi Beta Kappa, Phi Kappa Phi, Omicron Delta Kappa, Blue Key, Phi Delta Phi, Pi Gamma Mu, Pi Delta Epsilon, Tau Kappa Alpha, Sigma Chi, Alpha Pi Omega, Delta Sigma Rho, Alpha Beta Kappa (founder). Republican. Methodist. Clubs: Masons, KT, Shriners; Rotary (Washington) (past Chattanooga pres., dist. gov.), Kiwanis (Chattanooga) (hon.), Torch International (Washington), Cosmos (Washington). Home: McKendree Towers 4343 Lebanon Rd Apr 1711 Hermitage TN 37076

LOCKNER, VERA JOANNE, farmer, rancher, legislator; b. St. Lawrence, S.D., May 19, 1937; d. Leonard and Zona R. (Ford) Verdugt; m. Frank O. Lockner, Aug. 7, 1955; children: Dean M., Clifford A. Grad., St. Lawrence (S.D.) High Sch., 1955. Bank teller/bookkeeper First Nat. Bank, Miller, S.D., 1963-66, Bank of Wessington, S.D., 1966-74; farmer/rancher Wessington, 1955—. Sunday sch. tchr. Trinity Luth. Ch., Miller, 1968-72; treas. PTO, Wessington, 1969-70; treas., vice chmn., chmn., state com. woman Hand County Dems., Miller, 1978—. Named one of Outstanding Young Women of Am., Women's Study Club, Wessington, 1970. Mem. Order of Ea. Star (warder, marshall, chaplain 1970—). Avocations: oil painting, crafts, gardening, photography. Home and Office: RR 2 Box 102 Wessington SD 57381

LOCKSHIN, MICHAEL DAN, rheumatologist; b. Columbus, Ohio, Dec. 9, 1937; s. Samuel Dan and Florence (Levin) L.; m. Jane Toby Roberts, Sept. 2, 1965; 1 child, Amanda. AB, Harvard U., 1959, MD, 1963. Diplomate Am. Bd. Internal Medicine. From asst. prof. to prof. Cornell U. Med. Coll., N.Y.C., 1970-89; attending physician Hosp. for Spl. Surgery and N.Y. Hosp., N.Y.C., 1970-89; dir. extramural program Nat. Inst. Arthritis & Musculoskeletal Skin Diseases/NIH, Bethesda, Md., 1989—, acting dir., 1994—. Contbr. over 100 articles to jours., chpts. to books. Mem. Am. Rheumatism Assn. (2d v.p. 1984-85), La Sociedad Chilena de Reumatologica (hon.), Alpha Omega Alpha. Office: NIAMS/NIH Bldg 31 Rm 4 C32 Bethesda MD 20892

LOCKWOOD, BARBARA JORDAN, nurse administrator; b. Landshut, W. Ger., Aug. 23, 1948; d. Ernest Bob and Christa Barbara (Tilgner) Jordan (father Am. citizen); BS in Nursing with honors, U. Colo., 1970, MS in Med.-Surg. Nursing, 1973. Staff nurse Denver Gen. Hosp., 1970-72, Med. Personnel Pool, Denver, 1973; flight nurse St. Anthony Hosp. Systems, Denver, 1973-75, flight nurse supr., 1975-76, mgr. critical care services, 1976-79, systems dir. nursing services, 1979-81, asst. exec. dir. nursing services, 1981-86, v.p. patient care services, 1986—; pres. St. Anthony Home Health Services, Inc., 1985—; sec. Alina Health Systems, 1985—; tchr. Am. Assn. Operating Room Nurses, 1976, Am. Assn. Critical Care Nurses, 1977, 78, Chautauqua confs. Colo. Assn. Nurses, 1977, 78, 79, 80, 81, Colo. Student Nurses Assn., 1979; vol. nurse Comitis Crisis Ctr., Aurora, Colo., 1970-73; mem. sch. nursing alumni bd. U. Colo., 1986—. Cert. critical care practitioner ACS. Mem. Am. Assn. Critical Care Nurses, Denver Assn. Critical Care Nurses, Nat. League for Nursing, Colo. League for Nursing (sec. 1982-86), Sigma Theta Tau. Democrat. Lutheran. Contbr. chpt. on flight nursing to Critical Care Nursing, 1977; also articles. Office: St Anthony Hosp Systems 16th & Raleigh Sts Denver CO 80204

LOCKWOOD, DONALD A., retired insurance company executive; b. 1934. With U. Fed. Savings & Loan, Seattle, 1954-84; chmn. bd. Blue Cross of Washington and Alaska, Mountlake Ter., 1984—. Office: Blue Cross of Wash & Alaska 7001 220th St SW Mountlake Terrace WA 98043-2124

LOCKWOOD, FRANK JAMES, manufacturing company executive; b. San Bernadino, Calif., Oct. 30, 1931; s. John Ellis and Sarah Grace (Roberts) L.; children from previous marriage: Fay, Frank, Hedy, Jonnie, George, Katherine, Bill, Dena; m. 2d. Crystal Marie Miller, 1986. Student, Southeast City Coll., Chgo., 1955, Ill. Inst. Tech., 1963-64, Bogan Jr. Coll., Chgo., 1966. Foreman Hupp Aviation, Chgo., 1951-60; dept. head UARCO, Inc., Chgo., 1960-68; pres. XACT Machine & Engring., Chgo., 1968—; chmn. bd., pres., bd. dirs. Lockwood Engring., Inc., Chgo.; Ill. Nat. Corp. Chgo., and cons. engr., Chgo. Patentee printing equipment, beverage cans, gasoline pump dispenser "Super Pin", bus. forms equipment. Participant Forest Land Mgmt. Program; mem. Ill. Ambassadors; commr. Econ. Devel. Commn., Mt. Vernon, Ill., 1985; mem. bd. County of Jefferson, Ill., 1992—; mem. exec. com., legis. com. Ill. County Bds. Coun. Named Chgo. Ridge Father of the Yr., 1964. Mem. Ill. Divers' Assn. (pres. 1961-62). Lodge: Masons (32 degree), Shriners (past master 2). Home: RR 1 Texico IL 62889-9801 Office: 7011 W Archer Ave Chicago IL 60638-2201

LOCKWOOD, GARY LEE, lawyer; b. Woodstock, Ill., Dec. 3, 1946; s. Howard and Luella Mae (Behrens) L.; m. Cheryl Lynn Wittrock, Jan. 5, 1967; children: Jennifer, Lee, Cynthia. BA magna cum laude, Iowa Wesleyan Coll., 1969; student, Albert Ludwig U., Freiburg in Breisgau, Fed. Republic Germany, 1968-69; JD, Northwestern U., 1976. Bar: Ill. 1976, U.S. Dist. Ct. (no. dist.) Ill. 1976. Assoc. Lord, Bissell & Brook, Chgo., 1976-85, ptnr., 1985—. Bd. dirs. McHenry Sch. Dist. 15, Ill., 1974-85, pres., 1979-80. Served to sgt. U.S. Army, 1970-72. Mem. ABA (bus. and ins. com. 1985—). Methodist. Avocations: sports. Home: 175 N Harbor Dr Chicago IL 60601 Office: Lord Bissel & Brook 115 S La Salle St Ste 3600 Chicago IL 60603-3801

LOCKWOOD, GEORGE J., newspaper editor; b. Albany, N.Y., Aug. 19, 1931; s. James Daniel and Evelyn Eva (Weinstein) L.; m. Eileen Chamberlain, Sept. 3, 1955; children: Audrey, Cary, Noah, Jason. BA, Syracuse U., 1953; MA, U. Minn., 1957. Reporter The Milw. Jour., 1956-58, asst. picture editor, 1958-62, rotogravure editor, 1962-66, picture editor, 1966-69, mag. editor, 1969-72, asst. mng. editor, 1972-84, mng. editor, 1984-86; prof. journalism Marshall U., Huntington, W.Va., 1986-90; exec. editor News-Press, St. Joseph, Mo., 1990—. Author: The Cartoons of R.A. Lewis, 1968. With USN, 1953-55. Recipient Pulitzer Prize for Meritorious Pub. Svc., 1967, Silver Beaver award Boy Scouts of Am., 1969. Mem. Mo. AP, Inland Press Assn. (bd. dirs. 1980-87, pres. 1985-86)Mid-Am. Press Inst. (bd. dirs.), Boy Scouts of Am. Jewish. Avocation: cartoon historian, baseball, travelling. Home: 4614 Woodfield Dr Saint Joseph MO 64506-4011 Office: St Joseph News-Press 825 Edmond St Saint Joseph MO 64501-2737

LOCKWOOD, JOHN LEBARON, plant pathologist; b. Ann Arbor, Mich., May 28, 1924; s. George LeBaron and Mary Bonita (Leininger) L.; m. Jean Elizabeth Springborg, Mar. 21, 1959; children: James L., Laura A. student, Western Mich. Coll., 1941-43; BA, Mich. State Coll., 1948, MS, 1950; PhD, U. Wis., 1953. Asst. prof. Ohio Agri. Expt. Sta., Wooster, 1953-55; asst. prof. Mich. State U., East Lansing, 1955-61, assoc. prof., 1961-67, prof., 1967-90, prof. emeritus, 1990—. Served with U.S. Army, 1943-46. NSF research fellow, 1970-71. Fellow Am. Phytopathol. Soc. (pres. 1984-85). Home: 1931 Yuma Trl Okemos MI 48864-2744 Office: Mich State Univ Dept Botany And Pathol East Lansing MI 48824

LOCKWOOD, MOLLY ANN, communications company executive; b. London, Sept. 19, 1936; d. Warren Sewell and Ann Frances (Gleason) L.; BS, Pa. State U., 1958. With exec. tng. program Lord & Taylor, N.Y.C., 1958-60; assoc. merchandising director House & Garden Mag., N.Y.C., 1960-65; advt. dir. Status Mag., N.Y.C., 1965-70; merchandising dir. Holiday Mag., N.Y.C., 1970; account mgr. Ladies' Home Journal Mag., N.Y.C., 1970-72; adv. dir. Girl Talk Mag., N.Y.C., 1972-74; mktg. dir./assos. pub. East/West Network Mag., N.Y.C., 1974-77; pres., chief exec. officer, ptnr. Catalyst Communications, Inc., N.Y.C., 1977—; pres. Catalyst Pub. Inc., 1987—; sec. bd. 244 Madison Realty Corp., 1984—; mktg. and sales dir. Mus. Mag., 1979-83. Mem. Advt. Women N.Y., Am. Soc. Travel Agts., Rear Guard, Kappa Kappa Gamma Alumnae Assn. Home: 1133 Park Ave New York NY 10128-1246 Office: Catalyst Comm Inc 260 Madison Ave New York NY 10016-2401

LOCKWOOD, RHODES GREENE, retired lawyer; b. Buchanan, Va., Nov. 26, 1919; s. Rhodes G. and Violet (Bennett) L.; m. Mary Hitchcock, Jan. 22, 1949; children: Mary Howland, Rhodes G., Faith B., Rebecca Ingersoll. B.A., Williams Coll., 1941; postgrad, U. Va., 1941-42, Va. Poly. Inst. 1946-47; LL.B., Harvard U., 1949. Bar: Mass. bar 1949. Assoc. firm Choate, Hall & Stewart, Boston, 1949-59; ptnr. Choate, Hall & Stewart, 1959-92— Trustee Brigham and Women's Hosp.; sec., trustee Univ. Hosp.; vice chmn. Wellesley (Mass.) Sch. Com., 1966, chmn., 1967-69; mem. Wellesley Bd. Health. Served with USNR, 1942-52. Mem. Boston Bar Assn., Am. Law Inst., Am. Soc. Hosp. Attys., Mass. Hosp. Assn., Harvard U. Law Sch. Alumni Assn. Democrat. Home: 1 Edgewater Dr Wellesley MA 02181-1617 Office: Choate Hall & Stewart 53 State St Exchange Pl Boston MA 02109

LOCKWOOD, ROBERT PHILIP, publishing executive; b. Yonkers, N.Y., Dec. 21, 1949; s. Albert Francis and Evelyn (Toburn) L.; m. Christiana Lynn Nowels, July 21, 1973; children—Ryan Robert, Theresa Lynn. B.A. in History, Fairfield U., 1971. Assoc. editor Our Sunday Visitor, Huntington, Ind., 1971-77, dir. books, 1982-90, editor, 1977-85, dir., editor in chief, 1985-87, pub., 1987-90, pres., chief exec. officer, 1990—. Author: 70 Years of Our Sunday Visitor, 1982; columnist Catholic Jour.; contbr. articles to profl. jours., numerous periodicals. Chmn. St. Mary's Sch. Bd., Huntington, 1984-85; coach Huntington Cath. H.S. Tennis, 1983-85; bd. dirs. Cath. League for Religious and Civil Rights, 1994—; nat. adv. bd. Cath. Campaign for Am., 1993—. Mem. Cath. Press Assn. (editorial com. 1983—, Best Regular Column 1992). Avocations: writing; tennis. Home: 4919 Long Canon Pl Fort Wayne IN 46804

LOCKWOOD, ROBERT W., management consultant; b. Boise, Idaho, June 11, 1924; s. Walter Thomas and Elizabeth C. (Chamberlain) L.; m. Lois M. Minely, Feb. 19, 1945; children—Linda Kay Lockwood Johnson, Craig H. B.S., U. Calif., Berkeley, 1949, M.B.A., 1950; LL.D. (hon.), Northrop U., 1971. Civilian chief mgmt. Los Angeles procurement dist. U.S. Army, 1955-56; cons. Booz Allen and Hamilton, Los Angeles, 1956-58; v.p. United Calif. Bank, Los Angeles, 1958-75; v.p. acad. affairs Northrop U., 1975-76; asst. to pres. Bradston Hurricane, 1979-80; pres. Diversified Baby Products Internat., West Covina, Calif., 1980—; grad. prof. mgmt. Northrop U., Nat. U., San Diego. Served to 1st lt. USAR, 1942-45. Fellow Am. Inst. Indsl. Engrs. (pres. 1971-72). Club: Masons.

LOCKWOOD, THEODORE DAVIDGE, former academic administrator; b. Hanover, N.H., Dec. 5, 1924; s. Harold John and Elizabeth (Van Campen) L.; m. Elizabeth Anne White, Apr. 13, 1944 (dec. Feb. 1980); children: Tamara Jane Lockwood Quinn, Richard Davidge, Mavis Ferens, Serena Katherine; m. Lucille LaRose Abbot, Sept. 7, 1980. B.A., Trinity Coll., 1948, Litt.D. (hon.), 1981; M.A., Princeton, 1950, Ph.D., 1952; L.H.D., Concord Coll., 1968; LL.D., Union Coll., 1968, U. Hartford, 1969; L.H.D., Wesleyan U., Middletown, Conn., 1970. Instr. great issues Dartmouth, 1952-53; asst. prof. history Juniata Coll., Huntingdon, Pa., 1953-55, Mass. Inst. Tech., 1955-60; dean faculty Concord Coll., Athens, W.Va., 1960-64; provost, dean faculty Union Coll., Schenectady, 1964-68; pres. Trinity Coll., Hartford, Conn., 1968-81, Armand Hammer United World Coll. of Am. West, Montezuma, N.Mex., 1981-93; chmn. Greater Hartford Consortium for Higher Edn., 1972-81. Author: Mountaineers, 1945, Studies in European Socialism, 1960, Our Mutual Concern: The Role of the Independent College, 1968. Bd. dirs. World Affairs Ctr. Internat. 1965-85, chmn., 1966-71; Bd. fellows Trinity Coll., 1962-64, trustee, 1964-81; corporator Hartford Hosp., 1978-81, Hartford Pub. Libr., 1969-81; bd. dirs. Inst. for Living, 1981-89, Edn. Commn. of States, 1969-71, Am. Coun. on Edn., 1977-81; trustee Northwood Sch., Lake Placid, N.Y., 1969-78; dir. adv. coun. Audubon Soc. Expdn. Inst., 1978-90; bd. dirs. Harry Frank Guggenheim Found., 1979—, Nepal adv. com. World Wildlife Fund, 1985-95; dir. Ars Publica, 1989-95. With U.S. Army, 1943-45. Belgian-Am. Fellow, 1959. Mem. Am. Coll. (dir. 1973-78, chmn. 1976-77, mem. project on undergrad. edn. 1981-85), Greater Hartford C. of C. (dir. 1977-81), Phi Beta Kappa, Pi Gamma Mu. Unitarian.

LOCKWOOD, WILLARD ATKINSON, publisher; b. Washington, Mar. 4, 1924; s. Hanford Nichols and Anna Lillian Atkinson L.; m. Marie Louise Field, June 7, 1947 (div. 1979); children: Andree, Rachel, Winthrop; m. Eleanor Bloch, 1979. B.A., Wesleyan U., 1945; postgrad., Art Students League N.Y.C. 1949-50. Mem. staff book design, prodn. various pubs. N.Y.C., 1947-51; assoc. art editor U. Okla. Press, Norman, 1951-53; art editor U. Okla. Press, 1953-55; asst. mng. editor Charles E. Merrill Books, Middletown, Conn., 1955-57; dir. Wesleyan U. Press, Middletown, 1957-80; editor Cornell Maritime Press, 1980-90; Treas. Assn. Am. Univ. Presses, 1970-72, pres. 1976-77. Contbr. articles to profl. pubs. Mem. Publishers Lunch Club (N.Y.C.), Phi Beta Kappa. Democrat. Club: Rotarian. Home: 101 Idlewild Ave Easton MD 21601-2814

LOCKYER, CHARLES WARREN, JR., corporate executive; b. Phila. Apr. 6, 1944; s. Charles Warren and Mary Alice (Underwood) L.; B.A.,

Fordham U., 1966; M.A., Princeton U., 1968, Ph.D., 1971; m. Karen A. Damiani, Jan. 22, 1966; children: Charles Warren III, Larissa A., Daphne M. Vice pres. Fidelity Bank, Phila., 1970-79; v.p., chief fin. officer Pubco Corp., Glenn Dale, Md., 1980-82; exec. v.p. Perpetual Savs. Bank, F.S.B., Alexandria, VA, 1982-90; pres. Alleco Inc., Cheverly, Md., 1991—; dir. Gulfstream Land & Devel. Corp., Plantation, Fla., 1980-86. Trustee Jeanes Hosp., Phila., 1973-87; dir. Foulkeways at Gwynedd (Pa.), 1975-80; mem. adv. com. classics Princeton U., 1978-83. Woodrow Wilson fellow, 1966. Mem. Phi Beta Kappa. Home: 4409 Glenridge St Kensington MD 20895 Office: Alleco Inc 1 Allegheny Circle Cheverly MD 20781

LODDER, ROBERT ANDREW, chemistry and pharmaceutics educator; b. Cin., May 31, 1959. BS, Xavier U., Cin., 1981, MS, 1983; PhD, Ind. U., 1988. Teaching asst. Xavier U., 1981-83; teaching asst. Ind. U., Bloomington, 1983-85, rsch. asst., 1985-87; asst. prof. chemistry and pharmaceutics U. Ky., Lexington, 1988—. Contbr. articles to profl. jours.; patentee in field. Recipient 100 award R & D mag., 1988, Tomas Hirschveld award Pitts. Conf., 1988; 1st prize IBM Supercomputing Competition, 1990, NSF New Young Investigator award 1992; Technicon near-infrared analysis rsch. fellow, 1987. Mem. AAAS, ASTM, Coun. for Near-Infrared Spectroscopy (del.-at-large to nat. bd. dirs.), Am. Chem. Soc., Am. Pharm. Assn. Pharm. Scientists, Am. Pharm. Assn., Ky. Acad. Sci. Office: U Ky Coll Pharmacy Rose St Lexington KY 40536-0082

LODER, MICHAEL WESCOTT, librarian; b. Easton, Pa., July 11, 1945; s. Theodore Charles Loder Jr. and Mary Sue (Wescott) Ubben; m. Linda Ellen Zuryk, Dec. 21, 1968; Michael Wescott Jr., Laura Ellen, Lisa Sue. BA, Union Coll., 1967; MS in Journalism, U. Oreg., 1974, MLS, 1978. Media technician Olympic Coll., Bremerton, Wash., 1975-77; asst. libr. Coll. Ganado, Ariz., 1978-80; reference libr. Bethany Coll., W.Va., 1980-83; libr. Pa. State U., Schuylkill Haven, 1983—. Leader pipe band. Capt. USAF, 1967-71. Mem. ALA, Ea. U.S. Pipe Band Assn., Pa. Libr. Assn. Office: Pa State U Schuylkill Campus 240 University Dr Schuylkill Haven PA 17972-2210

LODER, VICTORIA KOSIOREK, information broker; b. Batavia, N.Y., May 27, 1945; d. Leon Stanley and Jennie Joann (Amatrano) Kosiorek; m. Ronald Raymond Loder, Nov. 6, 1965. BS in Bus. Mgmt., Roberts-Wesleyan Coll., Rochester, N.Y., 1989; MLS, SUNY, Buffalo, 1992; postgrad. in Religious Study, Liberty U., 1993—. Tech. info. specialist Eastman Kodak Co., Rochester, 1985-92; reference libr. Xerox Corp., Webster, N.Y., 1993-95; mgr. strategy and integration libr. Xerox Corp., Fairport, N.Y., 1995—; v.p., treas. Victron Design Svc. USA, Kent, N.Y., 1988—; pres., owner Alpha Omega Info Source, Kent, N.Y., 1993—. Republican. Avocations: clothing design/construction, horticulture/landscape design, floral design.

LODEWICK, PHILIP HUGHES, equipment leasing company executive; b. Bklyn., Dec. 31, 1944; s. Robert John and Louise Mary (Bockhold) L.; m. Christine Helen Lobeck, July 5, 1969; children: Alyssa Erin, Kendra Blythe. BS, U. Conn., 1966, MBA, 1967. With sales dept. IBM Corp., N.Y.C., 1969-71; officer Boothe Fin. Corp., San Francisco, 1971-80; pres. The Tradewell Corp., equipment leasing co., Ridgefield, Conn., 1980—; gen. ptnr. Sierra Assoc. IV, San Francisco, 1981-88; CFO Wicklo's Maple Hill Farm, Ridgefield, 1983—; bd. dirs. Barberton Ltd., London, Ancora Coffee Roasters Inc.; mem. bd. overseers U. Conn. Bus. Sch. Bd. dirs. St. Andrew's Luth. Ch., Ridgefield, 1979—; mem. Conn. Refugee Resettlement Commn., 1985-88; bd. dirs., treas. Family Y in Ridgefield, 1985-89; founder, dir. Discovery Ctr., 1986—; founder, pres. A Better Chance in Ridgefield, 1987—. With AUS, 1967-69, Korea. Mem. Computer Lessors and Dealers Assn., Golden Bridge Hounds, L.I. Golden Retreiver Club (pres. 1979-80). Republican. Lutheran. Avocations: golf, tennis, basketball, travel, reading. Home: 201 Spring Valley Rd Ridgefield CT 06877-1229 Office: Tradewell Corp Ridgefield CT 06877

LODEWYK, ERIC, chemist, pharmaceutical executive; b. The Hague, The Netherlands, Nov. 15, 1940; came to U.S., 1973; s. Anthony Johannes and Henrietta (Flierboom) L. BS, U. Amsterdam, Holland, 1965, PhD, 1968. Rsch. chemist Syntex Bahamas, Freeport, The Bahamas, 1969-71, group leader, 1971-73; sr. rsch. chemist Syntex Chems. Inc., Boulder, Colo., 1973-77, group leader, 1977-79, mgr. process rsch., 1979-86, dir. rsch. and devel., 1986-91; group dir. process rsch. and devel. Syntex Corp. Tech. Ctr., Boulder, 1991—. Holder 20 pharms. patents. Mem. Am. Chem. Soc., Dutch Chem. Soc., Boulder C. of C., Boulder Country Club. Home: 7324 Island Cir Boulder CO 80301-3716 Office: Syntex Chems Inc 2075 55th St Boulder CO 80301-2880

LODGE, ARTHUR SCOTT, mechanical engineering educator; b. Waterloo, Lancashire, Eng., Nov. 20, 1922; s. Wilfred Claude and Jean Dea (Scott) L.; m. Helen Catherine Bannatyne, July 18, 1945; children: Keith Bannatyne, Alison Mary Shambrook, Timothy Patrick. B.A., U. Oxford, 1945, M.A., 1948, D.Phil., 1948. Jr. sci. officer Admiralty, Eng., 1942-45; theoretical physicist NRC, Montreal, Que., Can., 1945-46, Brit. Rayon Research Assn., Manchester, Eng., 1948-60; sr. lectr. Math Inst. Sci. and Tech., U. Manchester, 1961-68; prof. dept. engring. mechanics U. Wis., Madison, 1968-91, Hougen vis. prof., 1991, prof. emeritus, 1991—; v.p. Bannatek Co., Inc., Madison, 1981—. Author: Elastic Liquids, 1964 (citation classics award 1981), Body Tensor Fields..., 1974; contbr. articles to profl. jours.; patentee stressmeter. Recipient Byron Bird award U. Wis.-Madison, 1980; grantee U.S. govt. agys. Fellow Inst. Physics London; mem. NAE, Soc. Rheology (Bingham medal 1971), Brit. Soc. Rheology (Gold medal 1983). Republican. Episcopalian. Avocation: piano playing.

LODGE, EDWARD JAMES, federal judge; b. 1933. BS cum laude, Coll. Idaho, 1957; LLB, U. Idaho, 1961. Mem. firm Smith & Miller, 1962-63; probate judge Canyon County, Idaho, 1963-65; judge Idaho State Dist. Ct., 1965-88; U.S. bankruptcy judge State of Idaho, 1988; dist. judge, now chief judge U.S. Dist. Ct. Idaho, 1989—. Recipient Kramer award for excellence in jud. adminstrn.; named three time All-Am., Distg. Alumnus Coll. Idaho; named to Charter Mem. Hall of Fame Boise State. Mem. ABA, Idaho Trial Lawyer Assn., Idaho State Bar Assn., Idaho Dist. Judges Assn., U.S. Bankruptcy Judges Assn., Boise State Athletic Assn., Elks Club. Office: US Dist Ct PO Box 040 550 W Fort St Boise ID 83724-0101

LODGE, GEORGE C(ABOT), business administration educator; b. Boston, July 7, 1927; s. Henry Cabot Jr. and Emily (Sears) L.; m. Nancy Kunhardt, Apr. 23, 1949; children: Nancy Lodge Burmester, Emily Lodge Pingeon, Dorothy Lodge Peabody, Henry, George Jr., David. AB cum laude, Harvard U., 1950. Polit. reporter, columnist Boston Herald, 1950-54; dir. info. U.S. Dept. Labor, Washington, 1954-58, asst. sec. labor for internat. affairs, 1958-61; U.S. del. to ILO, chmn. governing body, 1960-61; lectr. Grad. Sch. Bus. Adminstrn., Harvard U., Boston, 1961-68, assoc. prof., 1968-72, prof. bus. adminstrn., 1972-91, Jaime and Josefina Chua Tiampo prof. bus. adminstrn., 1991—. Author: Spearheads of Democracy: Labor in the Developing Countries, 1962, Engines of Change: United States Interests and Revolution in Latin America, 1970, The New American Ideology, 1975, The American Disease, 1984, Perestroika for America, 1990, Comparative Business-Government Relations, 1990, Managing Globalization in the Age of Independence, 1995; co-author: Ideology and National Competitiveness, 1987; editor: U.S. Competitiveness, 1987; editor: U.S. Competitiveness in the World Economy, 1984. Rep. candidate U.S. Senate, Mass., 1962. With USN, 1945-46. Named one of 10 Outstanding Young Men in U.S., U.S. Jr. C of C., 1961, Arthur S. Fleming award, 1961. Mem. Coun. Fgn. Rels., Carnegie Endowment for Internat. Peace (trustee), Robert F. Kennedy Meml. (trustee), Inter-Am. Found. (vice chmn.), Fed. City Club. Office: Harvard U Bus Sch Soldiers Fld Boston MA 02163

LODGE, JAMES ROBERT, dairy science educator; b. Downey, Iowa, July 1, 1925; s. Labon Ferrel Lodge and Margaret Clara (Elliott) Funk; m. Jean Agnes Wessel, June 14, 1947; children—Julie Beth, James Robert. B.S., Iowa State U., 1952, M.S., 1954; Ph.D., Mich. State U., 1957. Research asst. Mich. State U., East Lansing, 1954-57; research asso. U. Ill., Urbana, 1957-60; asst. prof. reproductive physiology U. Ill., 1960-63, assoc. prof., 1963-69, prof., 1969-91, prof. emeritus, 1991—. Co-author: Reproductive Physiology and Artificial Insemination of Cattle; 2d edit. 1978; contbr. articles to profl. jours. Asst. coach girls softball Babe Ruth Little League, Urbana, 1972-74. Served with AUS, 1944-46. Recipient Outstanding Instr. award Dairy Club

U. Ill., 1969, Alpha Zeta Outstanding Instr. award U. Ill. Coll. Agr., 1981, Campus award for excellence in undergrad. teaching U. Ill., 1984, D.E. Becker award, 1987, Outstanding Advisor award Student Affiliated div. Am. Dairy Sci. Assn., 1988; Alpha Zeta Outstanding Instr. award U. Ill. Coll. Agr., 1991, Karl E. Gardner Outstanding Undergrad. Adviser award, 1991; NIH rsch. fellow, 1969. Fellow Am. Soc. Animal Sci.; mem. Am. Physiol. Soc., AAAS, Soc. Study Reproduction, Am. Dairy Sci. Assn. (student affiliate advisor 1986-88), Am. Soc. Animal Sci., Soc. Cryobiology, NY Acad. Sci., Masons, Sigma Xi, Phi Kappa Phi (chmn. scholarship com. 1973, 77), Gamma Sigma Delta. Mem. commn. edn. Methodist Ch., 1975-78. Home: 1701 S Cottage Grove Ave Urbana IL 61801-5925 Office: U Ill Dept Animal Scis 312 Animal Sci Lab 1207 W Gregory Dr Urbana IL 61801-3838

LODISH, HARVEY FRANKLIN, biologist, educator; b. Cleve., Nov. 16, 1941; s. Nathan H. and Sylvia B. (Friedman) L.; AB, Kenyon Coll., 1962, DSc (hon.), 1982; PhD, Rockefeller U., 1966; m. Pamela Chentow, Dec. 29, 1963; children: Heidi, Martin, Stephanie. Postdoctoral fellow Med. Rsch. Coun. Lab. of Molecular Biology, Cambridge, Eng., 1966-68; asst. prof. biology M.I.T., Cambridge, Mass., 1968-71, assoc. prof., 1971-76, prof., 1976—; vis. scientist Imperial Cancer Rsch. Fund, Lincoln's Inn Fields, London, 1977-78; vis. prof. U. Calif., San Francisco Med. Ctr., 1977, Pa. State U. Med. Ctr., 1977; Staples vis. prof. U. Maine, 1989; Wellcome vis. prof. U. Oreg., 1990; Roering vis. lectr. U. Wash. Med. Sch., 1991; Sackler vis. scholar Tel Aviv U., 1994; Berson Meml. lectr. Internat. Endocrinology Congress, 1992; Presdl. lectr. Internat. Hematology Congress, 1992; McGinnis Meml. lectr., 1994; cons. scientist medicine Children's Hosp. Med. Ctr., Boston, 1977—; cons. in pediatric oncology Sidney Farber Cancer Inst., 1977—; cons. Ministry Edn. and Rsch., Denmark, 1991-92; mem. Whitehead Inst. Biomed. Rsch.; sci. adv. bd. Damon Biotech., Inc., Fisher Sci. Group, Genzyme, Inc., Arris Pharm. Co., Millenium Corp., Astra AB, Sweden; pres. Bioinfo. Assocs., Inc.; cons. biotech.; mem. NSF adv. panel in devel. and cellular biology; mem. NIH study sect. of molecular biology and cell biology; adv. bd. Biozentrum, U. Basel, Switzerland, Fred Hutchinson Cancer Ctr., chair, Seattle, Cleve. Clin. Rsch. Found., chair, European Molecular Biology Lab., Heidelberg, Germany; cons. NIH, Am. Cancer Soc. Vice chairperson Gordon Rsch. Conf., 1975, chairperson, 1976, 85, 89. Trustee Kenyon Coll., 1989—. Recipient NIH Career Devel. award, 1971-75, grantee, 1968—, Stadie award and lecture Am. Diabetes Assn., 1989; NSF grantee, 1971—; Am. Cancer Soc. grantee, 1971-76, Guggenheim fellow, 1977-78, Rockefeller fellow, 1962-66. Fellow AAAS, Am. Acad. Microbiology; mem. NAS, Am. Soc. for Microbiology, Am. Soc. of Biol. Chemists (nominating com. 1979, 86), Am. Soc. for Cell Biology (coun. 1983-85), Am. Chem. Soc., Phi Beta Kappa, Sigma Xi. Contbr. numerous articles on biochemistry to profl. jours.; mem. editorial bds. Jour. Biol. Chemistry, 1974-80, 82-87, Jour. Cell Biology, 1974-77, Nucleic Acids Rsch., 1976-88, Jour. Supramolecular Structure, 1978-88, Virology, 1979-84; assoc. editor Molecular and Cellular Biology, 1980-81; editor: Molecular and Cellular Biology, 1982-87; mem. bd. of reviewing editors Science, 1991—. Home: 195 Fisher Ave Brookline MA 02146-5706 Office: Whitehead Inst Biomed Rsch 9 Cambridge Ctr Cambridge MA 02142-1479

LODISH, LEONARD MELVIN, marketing educator, entrepreneur; b. Cleve., Aug. 1, 1943; s. Nathan H. and Sylvia (Friedman) L.; m. Susan Joyce Fischer, July 11, 1965; children: Max, Jacob, Chaim. AB magna cum laude, Kenyon Coll., 1965; PhD, MIT, 1968. Asst. prof. mktg. U. Pa., Phila., 1968-71, assoc. prof., 1971-75, prof. mktg., 1975-87, chmn. mktg. dept., 1991-92., 1984-88, Samuel R. Harrell prof., 1988—; founding dir. Evergreen Health Group, Inc., 1984-91; bd. dirs. Info. Resources, Inc., Chgo., Franklin Electronic Pub. Inc., Mt. Holly, N.J., Geotek Comm., Ramsey, N.J., J&J Snack Foods, Inc., Pennsauken, N.J.; co-founder, prin. Mgmt. Decisions Systems, Inc., Waltham Mass., 1967-85; co-founder, dir. Shadow Broadcast Svcs., Bala Cynwyd, Pa., 1991—. Author: The Advertising and Promotion Challenge: Vaguely Right or Precisely Wrong?, 1986; mem. editorial bd. Mgmt. Sci., Jour. Mktg. Sci., Mktg. Sci., Jour. Personal Selling and Sales Mgmt.; contbr. articles to profl. jours. Pres. Temple Beth Hillel/Beth El, Wynnewood, Pa., 1983-85, bd. dirs. 1975—. Mem. Inst. Mgmt. Scis. (Franz Edelman award 1987), Ops. Research Soc. Am., Am. Mktg. Assn., Phi Beta Kappa. Jewish. Home: 301 Kent Rd Wynnewood PA 19096-1814 Office: U Pa Wharton Sch Mktg Dept Philadelphia PA 19104

LODWICK, GWILYM SAVAGE, radiologist, educator; b. Mystic, Iowa, Aug. 30, 1917; s. Gwylim S. and Lucy A. (Fuller) L.; m. Maria Antonia De Brito Barata; children by previous marriage: Gwilym Savage III, Philip Galligan, Malcolm Kerr, Terry Ann. Student, Drake U., 1934-35; B.S., State U. Iowa, 1942, M.D., 1943. Resident pathology State U. Iowa, 1947-48, resident radiology, 1948-50; fellow, sr. fellow radiologic and orthopedic pathology Armed Forces Inst. Pathology, 1951; asst., then asso. prof. State U. Iowa Med. Sch., 1951-56; prof. radiology, chmn. dept. U. Mo. at Columbia Med. Sch., 1956-78, research prof. radiology, 1978-83, interim chmn. dept. radiology, 1980-81, chmn. dept. radiology, 1981-83, prof. bioengring., 1969-83, acting dean, 1959, assoc. dean, 1959-64; assoc. radiologist Mass. Gen. Hosp., 1983-88, radiologist, 1988-91; hon. radiologist Mass. Gen. Hosp., Boston, 1991—; vis. prof. dept. radiology Harvard Med. Sch., 1983-93; cons. in field; vis. prof. Keio U. Sch. Medicine, Tokyo, 1974; chmn. sci. program com. Internat. Conf. on Med. Info., Amsterdam, 1983; trustee Am. Registry Radiologic Technologists, 1961-69, pres., 1964-65, 68-69; mem. radiology tng. com. Nat. Inst. Gen. Med. Scis., NIH, 1966-70; com. radiology Nat. Acad. Scis.-NRC, 1970-75; chmn. com. computers Am. Coll. Radiology, 1965, Internat. Commn. Radiol. Edn. and Info., 1969-73; cons. to health care tech. div. Nat. Ctr. for Health Services, Research and Devel., 1971-76; dir. Mid-Am. Bone Tumor Diagnostic Ctr. and Registry, 1971-83; adv. com. mem. NIH Biomed. Image Processing Grant Jet Propulsion Lab., 1969-73; nat. chmn. MUMPS Users Group, 1973-75; mem. radiation study sect. div. research grants NIH, 1976-79, mem. study sect. on diagnostic radiology and nuclear medicine div. research grants, 1979-82, chmn. study sect. on diagnostic radiology div. research grants, 1980-82; mem. bd. sci. counselors Nat. Library of Medicine, 1985, chmn. 1987-89; dir. radiology Spaulding Rehab. Hosp., 1986-92. Adv. editorial bd. Radiology, 1965-86, cons. to editor, 1986-91; adv. editorial bd. Current/Clin. Practice, 1972-88; mem. editorial bd. Jour. Med. Systems, 1976—, Radiol. Sci. Update div. Biomedia, Inc., 1975-83, Critical Revs. in Linguistic Imaging, 1990; mem. cons. editorial bd. Skeletal Radiology, 1977-82, Contemporary Diagnostic Radiology, 1978-80; assoc. editor Jour. Med. Imaging, 1989—. Served to maj. AUS, 1943-46, ETO. Decorated Sakari Mustakallio medal Finland; named Most Disting. Alumnus in Radiology, State U. Ia. Centennial, 1970; recipient Sigma Xi Research award U. Mo., Columbia, 1972, Gold medal XIII Internat. Conf. Radiology, Madrid, 1973, Founder's Gold medal Internat. Skeletal Soc., 1990. Fellow AMA (radiology rev. bd. coun. med. edn., coun. rep. on residency rev. bd. for radiology 1969-74), Am. Coll. Radiology (co-chmn. ACR-NEMA standardization com. 1983-90, NEMA Med. Tech. Leadership award 1995); mem. NAS1Inst. Medicine, Am. Coll. Med. Informatics (founding), Nat. Acad. Practice in Medicine, Radiol. Soc. N.Am. (3d v.p. 1974-75, chmn. ad hoc com. representing assoc. scis. 1979-87, chmn. assoc. scis. com. 1981-87), Assn. Univ. Radiologists, Mo. Radiol. Soc. (1st pres. 1961-62), Salutis Univins; hon. mem. Portuguese Soc. Radiology and Nuclear Medicine, Tex. Radiol. Soc., Ind. Roentgen Soc., Phila. Roentgen Ray Soc., Finnish Radio. Soc. (ho.), Rotary, Harvard of Boston Club, Cosmos, Alpha Omega Alpha. Home: 3900 Galt Ocean Dr # 307 Fort Lauderdale FL 33308-6631

LÖE, HARALD, dentist, educator, researcher; b. Steinkjer, Norway, July 19, 1926; s. Haakon and Anna (Bruem) L.; m. Inga Johansen, July 3, 1948; children: Haakon, Marianne. D.D.S., U. Oslo, 1952; Dr.Odont., 1961; hon. degrees, U. Gothenburg, 1973, Royal Dental Coll., 1980, U. Athens, 1980, Catholic U., Leuven, 1980, U. Lund, 1983, Georgetown U., 1983, U. Bergen, 1985, U. Md., 1986, U. N.J., 1987, Royal Dental Coll., Copenhagen, 1988, U. Toronto, 1989, U. Detroit, 1990, U. S.C., 1990, U. Helsinki, Finland, 1992, Pacific U., 1993, U. Milan, Italy, 1994. Instr. Sch. Dentistry, Oslo U., 1952-55; research assoc. Norwegian Inst. Dental Research, 1956-62; Fulbright research fellow, research asso. dept. oral pathology U. Ill., Chgo., 1957-58; Univ. research fellow Oslo U., 1959-62, assoc. prof. dept. periodontology, 1960-61; prof. dentistry, chmn. dept. periodontology Royal Dental Coll., Aarhus, Denmark, 1962-72; asso. dean, dean-elect Royal Dental Coll., 1971-72; prof., dir. Dental Research Inst. U. Mich., Ann Arbor, 1972-74; dean, prof. periodontology Sch. Dental Medicine U. Conn., Farmington, 1974-82; dir. Nat. Inst. Dental Research, Bethesda, Md., 1983-94; prof. Sch. Dental Medicine U. Conn. Health Ctr., Farmington, 1994—;

vis. prof. periodontics Hebrew U., Jerusalem, 1966-67; hon. prof. Med. Scis. U. Beijing, 1987; cons. WHO, NIH. Served with Norwegian Army, 1944-48. Recipient 75th Anniversary award Norwegian Dental Assn., 1958, Aalborg Dental Soc. prize Denmark, 1965, William J. Gies Periodontology award, 1978, Internat. prize Swedish Dental Soc., 1988, U.s. Surgeon Gen.'s medal and Exemplary award, 1988, Internat. award Swedish Dental Assn., 1989; decorated Knight of Danebrog by Queen of Denmark, 1972, Comdr. of the Royal Norwegian Order of Merit by the Kin g of Norway, 1989. Mem. AAAS, ADA (Gold medal 1994), Danish Dental Assn., Am. Acad. Periodontology, Am. Assn. Dental Rsch., Am. Soc. Preventive Dentistry (internat. award), Mass. Dental Soc. (internat. award), Internat. Assn. Dental Rsch. (award for basic rsch. in periodontology 1969, pres. 1980), Internat. Coll. Dentists, Scandinavian Assn. Dental Rsch., Scandinavian Soc. Periodontology. Office: U Conn Health Ctr Sch Dental Medicine Farmington CT 06030-1710

LOEB, BEN FOHL, JR., lawyer, educator; b. Nashville, May 15, 1932; s. Ben Fohl and Frances (Paysinger) L.; m. Anne Nelson, Sept. 23, 1961 (div. 1982); children: Charles Nelson, William Nelson. BA, Vanderbilt U., 1955, JD, 1960. Bar: Tenn. 1960, U.S. Supreme Ct. 1966, N.C. 1975. Assoc. Crownover, Branstetter & Folk, Nashville, 1960-64; asst. dir. Inst. Govt. U. N.C., Chapel Hill, 1964—; prof. pub. law and govt. Inst. Govt., 1972—; counsel to N.C. legis. coms. on motor vehicle law and transp., Raleigh, 1973-83; cons. on alcohol beverage control, 1985-89; cons. on wildlife, natural and scenic areas, 1989-93; mem. U. N.C. Faculty Coun., 1994—. Author: Traffic Law and Highway Safety, 1970, Alcohol Beverage Control Law, 1971, Motor Vehicle Law, 1975, Legal Aspects of Dental Practice, 1977, Eminent Domain Procedure, 1984; assoc. editor Vanderbilt Law Rev., 1959-60. Served to 1st lt. U.S. Army, 1955-57. Mem. ABA, Tenn. Bar Assn., Phi Beta Kappa, Phi Delta Phi, Pi Kappa Alpha (chpt. pres. 1954-55), Carolina Club (Chapel Hill). Democrat. Baptist. Home: 17 Bluff Trl Chapel Hill NC 27516-1603 Office: U NC Inst Govt Cb 3330 Knapp Bldg Chapel Hill NC 27599

LOEB, FRANCES LEHMAN, civic leader; b. N.Y.C., Sept. 25, 1906; d. Arthur and Adele (Lewisohn) Lehman; student Vassar Coll., 1924-26; L.H.D. (hon.), NYU, 1977; m. John L. Loeb, Nov. 18, 1926; children: Judith Loeb Chiara, John L., Ann Loeb Bronfman, Arthur Lehman, Deborah Loeb Brice. N.Y.C. commr. for UN and Consular Corps, 1966-78. Exec. com. Population Action Com., Washington; life mem. bd. Children of Bellevue, Inc., 1974—; bd. dirs. Internat. Presch., Inc., N.Y. Landmarks Conservancy; chmn. bd. East Side Internat. Community Ctr., Inc.; mem. UN Devel. Corp., 1972-94; life trustee Collegiate Sch. for Boys, N.Y.C.; trustee Cornell U., 1979-88, trustee emeritus, 1988—; trustee Vassar Coll., 1988—; bd. overseers Cornell U. Med. Coll., 1983-88 (life mem. 1988—), Inst. Internat. Edn. (life). Mem. UN Assn. (dir.). Clubs: Cosmopolitan, Vassar, Women's City (N.Y.C.). Home: 730 Park Ave New York NY 10021-4945 also: Anderson Hill Rd Purchase NY 10577 also: Lyford Cay, Nassau The Bahamas

LOEB, JANE RUPLEY, university administrator, educator; b. Chgo., Feb. 22, 1938; d. John Edwards and Virginia Pentland (Marthens) Watkins; m. Peter Albert Loeb, June 14, 1958; children: Eric Peter, Gwendolyn Lisl, Aaron John. BA, Rider Coll., 1961; PhD, U. So. Calif., 1969. Clin. psychology intern Univ. Hosp., Seattle, 1966-67; asst. prof. ednl. psychology U. Ill., Urbana, 1968-69, asst. coord. rsch. and testing, 1968-69, coord. rsch. and testing, 1969-72, asst. to vice chancellor acad. affairs, 1971-72, dir. admissions and records, 1972-81, assoc. prof. ednl. psychology, 1973-82, assoc. vice chancellor acad. affairs, 1981-94, prof. edn. psychology, 1982—. Author: College Board Project: the Future of College Admissions, 1989. Chmn. Coll. Bd. Coun. on Entrance Svcs., 1977-82; bd. govs. Alliance for Undergrad. Edn., 1988-93; active charter com. Coll. Bd. Acad. Assembly, 1992-93. HEW grantee, 1975-76. Mem. APA, Am. Ednl. Rsch. Assn., Nat. Coun. Measurement in Edn., Harvard Inst. Ednl. Mgmt. Avocation: the french horn. Home: 1405 N Coler Ave Urbana IL 61801-1625 Office: U Ill 1310 S 6th St Champaign IL 61820-5796

LOEB, JEROME THOMAS, retail executive; b. St. Louis, Sept. 13, 1940; s. Harry W. and Marjorie T. Loeb; m. Carol Bodenheimer, June 15, 1963; children: Daniel W, Kelly E. BS, Tufts U., 1962; MA, Washington U., St. Louis, 1964. Asst. dir. rsch., dir. EDP, div. v.p., dir. mgmt. info. scvs. Famous-Barr div. May Dept. Stores Co. St. Louis, 1964-74, v.p. mgmt. info. svcs./EDP parent co., 1974-77, sr. v.p., CFO Hecht's div., Washington, 1977-79; exec. v.p. devel. May Dept. Stores Co. St. Louis, 1979-81, exec. v.p., CFO, 1981-86, vice chmn., CFO, 1986-93, pres., 1993—; also bd. dirs. Bd. dirs. Jr. Achievement of Mississippi Valley, 1980—, chmn., 1993—; bd. dirs. Jr. Achievement Nat. Bd., 1988—; bd. dirs. Jewish Hosp. St. Louis, 1984—, vice chmn. 1988; bd. commrs. St. Louis Sci. Ctr., 1991—, vice chmn., 1994; bd. dirs. BJC Health Sys., 1992—; mem. pres. cabinet Am. Jewish Com., 1994—. Mem. Westwood Country Club, Boone Valley Golf Club. Office: May Dept Stores Co 611 Olive St Saint Louis MO 63101-1721

LOEB, JOHN LANGELOTH, banker, broker; b. St. Louis, Nov. 11, 1902; s. Carl Morris and Adeline (Moses) L.; m. Frances Lehman, Nov. 18, 1926; children: Judith Loeb Chiara, John Langeloth, Ann Loeb Bronfman, Arthur Lehman, Deborah Loeb Brice. Student, Dartmouth Coll., 1920-21; SB cum laude, Harvard U., 1924, LLD (hon.), 1971. With Am. Metal Co. (Pitts. office), 1924-26, 26-28, Wertheim & Co., 1929-30; ptnr. Loeb, Rhoades & Co. Inc., N.Y.C., 1931-55, sr. ptnr., 1955-77, chmn., 1977-79; chmn. fin. com. Loeb, Rhoades, Hornblower & Co., 1978-79; vice chmn. Loeb Ptnrs. Corp., N.Y.C., 1980—, also bd. dirs.; gov. N.Y. Stock Exchange, 1951-54; adv. com. on internat. bus. problems State Dept., 1967-69, 70—. Hon. trustee Montefiore Hosp.; chmn., CEO Jacob and Valeria Langeloth Found.; bd. overseers Harvard U., 1962-68; hon. gov. N.Y. Hosp.; trustee, hon. chmn. Inst. Fine Arts, NYU. With Treasury Dept., Office War Moblzn. 1942-44, Washington. Mem. Coun. Fgn. Rels., N.Y. C. of C., SAR, City Midday Club, Sky Club, Century Country Club (White Plains, N.Y.), Harvard Club, Lyford Cay Club. Office: Loeb Ptnrs Corp 375 Park Ave New York NY 10152-0002

LOEB, JOHN LANGELOTH, JR., investment counselor; b. N.Y.C., May 2, 1930; s. John Langeloth and Frances (Lehman) L.; children: Nicholas, Alexandra. Grad., Hotchkiss Sch., 1948; A.B. cum laude, Harvard, 1952, M.B.A., 1954; LL.D. (hon.), Georgetown U. With Loeb, Rhoades & Co., N.Y.C., from 1956; gen. ptnr., mem. mgmt. com. Loeb, Rhoades & Co., 1959-73, mng. ptnr., pres., 1971-73, ltd. ptnr., 1973-84; chmn. bd. Holly Sugar Co., Colo., 1969-71; amb. to Denmark Copenhagen, 1981-83; chmn. John L. Loeb, Jr. Assocs., N.Y.C., 1984—; U.S. del. to 38th session Gen. Assembly of UN; spl. advisor environ. matters to Gov. Nelson A. Rockefeller, 1967-73; chmn. Gov. N.Y. Coun. Environ. Advisors, 1970-75; pres. Winston Churchill Found., 1981—; trustee Ednl. Testing Serv., Princeton, N.J., 1986-93. Trustee Montefiore Hosp. and Med. Ctr., Mus. City N.Y., 1966-94, John and Frances L. Loeb Found., Am. U., Washington; mem. vis. com. Sch. Pub. Health Loem Drama Ctr., 1987-93. Lt. USAF, 1954-56. Decorated Grand Cross of the Order of Dannebrog (Denmark); recipient Lee Max Friedman award Am. Jewish Hist. Soc., Disting. Patriot award SAR; Hon. Comdr. of the Most Excellent Order of the Brit. Empire. Mem. Downtown Assn. (N.Y.C.), City Midday Club, Harvard Club, Century Country Club, Sleepy Hollow Club (Westchester, N.Y.), Buck's Club, Brooks's Club, Hurlingham Club (London), Royal Swedish Yacht Club (Stockholm), Royal Danish Yacht Club (Copenhagen), Lyford Cay Club (Nassau, Bahamas). Home: Ridgeleigh 194 Anderson Hill Rd Purchase NY 10577-2101 Office: Loeb Family Office 375 Park Ave Ste 801 New York NY 10152-0001

LOEB, LEONARD L., lawyer. BBA, U. Wis., 1950, JD, 1952, Bar: Wis. 1952, U.S. Supreme Ct. 1960. Sole practice Milw., 1952—; faculty family mediation inst. Harvard Law Sch.; lectr. family law Marquette U., U. Wis., Madison; cons. revisions Wis. Family Code Wis. Legislature; mem. com. for review of initiatives in child support State of Wis. Author: Systems Book for Family Law; contbr. articles to profl. jours. Served to col. JAGC, USAF, 1952-53. Fellow Am. Bar Found., Am. Acad. Matrimonial Lawyers (past charter pres. Wis. chpt., past nat. chpt.); mem. ABA (past chmn. family law sect., del. to ho. of dels.), Wis. Bar Assn. (pres.), Wis. Bar Found. (bd. dirs.), Milw. Bar Assn. (past chmn. family law sect., past pres.), Concordia Coll. (Wis.) Paralegal Adv. Bd. Office: 1125 Bank One Pl Milwaukee WI 53202

LOEB, MARSHALL ROBERT, journalist, magazine editor; b. Chgo., May 30, 1929; s. Monroe Harrison and Henrietta (Benjamin) L.; m. Elizabeth Peggy Loewe, Aug. 14, 1954; children: Michael, Margaret. BJ, U. Mo., 1950; postgrad., U. Goettingen, Germany, 1950-51. Reporter Garfield News and Austinite, Chgo., 1944-45; reporter, columnist Garfieldian and Austin News, Chgo., 1946-47, 49-51; reporter Columbia Missourian, 1948-50; staff corr. UP, Frankfurt, Germany, 1952-54; reporter St. Louis Globe-Democrat, 1955-56; contbg. editor Time mag., 1956-61, assoc. editor, 1961-65, sr. editor, 1965-80, econs. editor and columnist, 1978-80; mng. editor Money Mag., 1980-86; editor Time Inc. Mag. Devel., 1984-86; mng. editor Fortune, 1986-94, editor-at-large, 1994—; daily commentator CBS Radio Network; assoc. fellow Yale U., Berkeley Coll., 1977—. Author (with William Safire) Plunging Into Politics, 1962, Marshall Loeb's Money Guide, 1983, ann. edits. 1985—, Money Minutes, 1987. Recipient INGAA award U. Mo., 1966; Gerald M. Loeb award UCLA Sch. Mgmt., 1974; John Hancock award, 1974; Champion Media award for econ. understanding citation, 1978, first prize, 1981; Dallas Press Club award, 1978; Freedoms Found. award, 1978; N.Y. citation Sigma Delta Chi, 1979; Nat. Assn. Home Builders award, 1984; Great Am. Patriot award Jefferson Barracks Chapel Assn., 1988, Journalism medal U. Mo., 1988, N.Y. award Navy League, 1989, TJFR Bus. Journalism Luminaries award 1990. Fellow World Econ. Forum (Geneva), Nat. Neurofibromatosis Found. (dir.), Econ. Club of N.Y. (dir.), Knight-Bagehot Fellowship (chair bd. adv.), Recording For the Blind (dir.); mem. Council Fgn. Relations, Brit.-Am. C. of C. (v.p. 1979-81, dir. 1979-84), Am. Soc. Mag. Editors (v.p. 1986-88, pres. 1988-90), Overseas Press Club Am. (dir. 1963-65, treas. 1964-65). Jewish. Home: 31 Montrose Rd Scarsdale NY 10583-1129 Office: Fortune Mag Time & Life Bldg 1271 Ave Of The Americas New York NY 10020-1300

LOEB, NACKEY SCRIPPS, publisher; b. Los Angeles, Feb. 24, 1924; d. Robert Paine and Margaret (Culbertson) Scripps; m. William Loeb, July 15, 1952 (dec. 1981); children—Nackey Loeb Scagliotti, Edith Loeb Tomasko. Student, Scripps Coll. Pub. Union-Leader Corp., Manchester, N.H., 1981—, Neighborhood Pubs., Inc., Goffstown, N.H., 1993—. Republican. Baptist. Home: Paige Hill Rd Goffstown NH 03045 Office: Union Leader Corp 100 William Loeb Dr Manchester NH 03103

LOEB, PETER KENNETH, money manager; b. N.Y.C., Apr. 8, 1936; s. Carl M. and Lucille H. (Schamberg) L.; m. Jeanette Winter, Nov. 1, 1980; 1 child, Alexander Winter; children by previous marriage: Peter Kenneth Jr., Karen Elizabeth, James Matthew. BA, Yale U., 1958; MBA, Columbia U., 1961. Security analyst Loeb, Rhoades & Co., N.Y.C., 1961-66, syndicate dept. ptnr., 1966-71, with trading/instl. sales sect., 1971-79; mng. dir. corp. fin. Shearson Corp., N.Y.C., 1979-83; mng. dir., portfolio mgr. PaineWebber Inc., N.Y.C., 1983-92; ptnr. Shufro, Rose & Ehrman, N.Y.C., 1992—; mem. com. on securities Am. Stock Exch., 1978-80; mem. del. to Beijing symposium N.Y. Stock Exch., 1986. Coach, games ofcl. Manhattan Spl. Olympics, 1980—; bd. dirs., co-chmn. devel. com. N.Y. Spl. Olympics, 1985-89; chmn. devel. com. Spl. Olympics Internat., 1986—; bd. dirs., 1989—; mem. com. on univ. investments Columbia U., 1977-85, trustee, 1979-85, vice-chmn. alumni adv. bd., 1986-92; fund chmn. Columbia U. Bus. Sch., 1964-66, mem. alumni counseling bd., 1970—, pres. Columbia Bus. Sch. Assocs., 1971-73, mem. bd. overseers, 1976—; dir. City Ctr. Theatre Found.; trustee Allen Stevenson Sch., 1969—, Langeloth Found., 1972—, N.Y. Infirmary-Beekman Downtown Hosp., 1978-85; mem. adv. bd. Atoms Track Club Bedford-Stuyvesant, 1970—; cert. track ofcl. USA Track and Field, 1985—; mem. marshals com. Westchester Golf Classic, 1970—; contbg. mem. Mus. Modern Art, Met. Mus. Art; mem. Statue of Liberty/Ellis Island Found., Friends of Kennedy Ctr., Friends of the Philharm., Friends of Carnegie Hall; mem. Wall St. com. N.Y. Urban Coalition, 1969-71; mem. exec. bd. new leadership div. Fedn. Jewish Philanthropies, 1963-64; vice-chmn. Pacesetter com. Greater N.Y. coun. Boy Scouts Am., 1966-67. Recipient Alumni medal for conspicuous service Columbia U., 1975, Alumni medal for disting. service Columbia U. Bus. Sch., 1976. Mem. SAR, Securities Traders Assn. N.Y., Investment Assn. N.Y. (exec. bd. 1969), Securities Industry Assn. (governing council 1977-79, minority capital com. 1980-85, trustee Econ. Edn. Found. 1986—, vice chmn. 1992—), Nat. Assn. Security Dealers (chmn. dist. 12 com. 1981, gov. 1982-85, chmn. corp. fin. com. 1983-86, vice-chmn. fin. 1984, mem. arbitration com. 1986-89, NASDAQ qualifications com. 1989—), N.Y.C. Baseball Fedn. (pres. 1968-91, chmn. 1992—, award for disting. service 1976), Univ. Club, Doubles Club, Bond Club, Century Country Club, Beta Gamma Sigma, Alpha Kappa Psi, Phi Gamma Delta. Office: Shufro Rose & Ehrman 745 Fifth Ave New York NY 10151

LOEB, RONALD MARVIN, lawyer; b. Denver, Sept. 24, 1932; s. Ellis and Lillian (Mosko) L.; m. Shirley Ross; children: Joshua Ross, Gabriel Ross, Daniel Seth, Jennifer Miriam, Rachel Sarah.. AB with highest honors, UCLA, 1954; LLB cum laude, Harvard U., 1959. Bar: Calif. 1960. Assoc. Irell & Manella Law Firm, L.A., 1959-64, ptnr., 1964—. Co-editor: Duties and Responsibilities of Outside Directors. Mem. adv. bd. Securities Regulation Inst., U. Calif., San Diego; trustee Crossroads Sch. Arts and Scis., Santa Monica, Calif.; founding trustee World Bus. Acad. Mem. ABA, State Bar Assn. Calif., L.A. County Bar Assn., Beverly Hills Bar Assn., Nat. Assn. Securities Dealers (mem. legal adv. bd.). Office: Irell & Manella 1800 Ave Of The Stars Ste 900 Los Angeles CA 90067

LOEB, STEVEN MICHAEL, lawyer; b. N.Y.C., May 8, 1954; s. Gerald and Gloria (Berman) L.; m. Deborah Hollis Kaye, Nov. 29, 1980. BBA, Washington U., 1975; JD, U. Pa., 1979; LLM in Taxation, NYU, 1983. Bar: N.Y. 1980, U.S. Dist. Ct. (so. dist.) N.Y. 1980, Fla. 1981. Assoc. Cleary, Gottlieb, Steen & Hamilton, N.Y.C., 1979-87, ptnr., 1988—; lectr. presenter seminars to profl. orgns. Mem. ABA, N.Y. Bar Assn. (trusts and estates law sect.), N.Y. Estate Planning Coun., Bar Assn. of the City of N.Y. Avocation: sailing. Office: Cleary Gottlieb Steen & Hamilton 1 Liberty Plz New York NY 10006-1401

LOEB, VERNON FREDERICK, journalist; b. Akron, Ohio, Mar. 10, 1956; s. David Frederick and Betty Jane (Miller) L.; m. Patricia Ford, Jan. 7, 1984; children: Kathryn Magdalen, David Frederick, Julia Miller, Frances Ford. BA, U. N.C. 1978. Del. corr. Phila. Inquirer, Dover, Del., 1978-79; capital corr. Phila. Inquirer, Harrisburg, Pa., 1979-82; edn. writer Phila. Inquirer, Phila., 1982-84, city hall bureau chief, 1984-89, 92—; S.E. Asia corr. Phila. Inquirer, Manila, Philippines, 1989-92; city hall bur. chief Phila. Inquirer, 1992—. Methodist. Avocations: photography, tennis, running. Office: Phila Inquirer 400 N Broad St Philadelphia PA 19130-4099

LOEB, VIRGIL, JR., oncologist, hematologist; b. St. Louis, Sept. 21, 1921; s. Virgil and Therese (Meltzer) L.; m. Lenore Harlow, Sept. 8, 1950 (dec. Nov. 1987); children: Katherine Loeb Doumas, Elizabeth Loeb McCane, David, Mark; m. Elizabeth Moore, Dec., 1990. Student, Swarthmore Coll., 1938-41; MD, Washington U., St. Louis, 1944. Diplomate Am. Bd. Internal Medicine. Intern Barnes and Jewish Hosps., St. Louis, 1944-45; resident in internal medicine, research fellow in hematology Barnes Hosp., St. Louis, 1947-52; med. faculty Washington U., St. Louis, 1951—, prof. clin. medicine, 1978—; practice medicine specializing in oncology and hematology St. Louis, 1956—; cons. clin. researcher; dir. Cen. Diagnostic Labs., Barnes Hosp., 1952-68; staff numerous hosps., 1951—; cons. Nat. Cancer Inst., 1950-68; chmn. cancer clin. investigation rev. com., 1966—; mem. diagnostic research adv. com., 1972-75, bd. sci. counselors, DCPC, 1983-87; mem. oncology merit rev. bd. VA, 1971-75. Contbr. author books, articles to profl. jours. Bd. dirs. Am. Cancer Soc., mem. nat. adv. com., 1969—, pres. Mo. div., 1983-85, nat. pres., 1986-87; bd. dirs. St. Louis Blue Cross and Blue Shield, Bi-State Red Cross; trustee John Burroughs Sch., 1966-69. Served with M.C. AUS, 1945-47. Fellow ACP; mem. Cen. Soc. Clin. Research, Inst. Medicine of Nat. Acad. Sci., Am. Assn. Cancer Research, Internat. Soc. Hematology, Am. Soc. Hematology, St. Louis Soc. Internal Medicine (pres. 1974), Am. Soc. Clin. Oncology, Am. Assn. for Cancer Edn., St. Louis Met. Med. Soc. (hon.), Sigma Xi, Alpha Omega Alpha. Home: 24 Deerfield Rd Saint Louis MO 63124-1412 Office: Barnes Hosp 1 Barnes Hospital Plz Saint Louis MO 63110

LOEBIG, WILFRED F., health care executive; b. Wesley, Iowa, Feb. 3, 1936; s. Wifred Francis and Faye Maxine L.; m. Margaret Ann Schmitz, oct. 6, 1960; children: William, Brian, Mary, Margaret, Maria, Blaise. BS, U. Iowa, 1958, MS, 1960. Admistrv. asst. Mercy Hosp., Council Bluff, Iowa,

1958-60; assoc. adminstr. Ft. Dodge (Iowa) Mercy Hosp., 1960-71; pres. St. Elizabeth Hosp., Appleton, Wis., 1971-77; exec. dir. Timken Mercy Med. Ctr., Canon, Ohio, 1977-83; pres., chief exec. officer Wheaton (Ill.) Franciscan Svcs., Inc., 1983—; pres. Area Hosp. Adminstrs. Coun.; mem. Ohio Adv. Coun. to Bd. Nursing Edn. and Nurse Registration. Served with Med. Service Corps, USAF, 1960-63. Mem. Am. Coll. Hosp. Admistrs., Am. Hosp. Assn., Ohio Hosp. Assn. (trustee), Greater Canton C. of C., Rotary. Roman Catholic. Office: Wheaton Franciscan Svcs Inc PO Box 667 Wheaton IL 60189-0667

LOEBLICH, HELEN NINA TAPPAN, paleontologist, educator; b. Norman, Okla., Oct. 12, 1917; d. Frank Girard and Mary (Jenks) Tappan; m. Alfred Richard Loeblich, Jr., June 18, 1939; children: Alfred Richard III, Karen Elizabeth Loeblich, Judith Anne Loeblich Covey, Daryl Louise Loeblich Valenzuela. BS, U. Okla., 1937, MS, 1939; PhD, U. Chgo., 1942. Instr. geology Tulane U., New Orleans, 1942-43; geologist U.S. Geol. Survey, Washington, 1943-45, 47-59; mem. faculty UCLA, 1958—; prof. geology, 1966-84, prof. emeritus, 1985—, vice chmn. dept. geology, 1973-75; research assoc. Smithsonian Instn., 1954-57; assoc. editor Cushman Found. Foraminiferal Research, 1950-51, incorporator, hon. dir., 1950—. Author: (with A.R. Loeblich Jr.) Treatise on Invertebrate Paleontology, part C, Protista 2, Foraminiferida, 2 vols., 1964, Foraminiferal Genera and Their Classification, 2 vols., 1987, Foraminifera of the Sahul Shelf and Timor Sea, 1994; author: The Paleobiology of Plant Protists, 1980; mem. editl. bd. Palaeoecology, 1972-82, Paleobiology, 1975-81; contbr. articles to profl. jours., govt. publs. and encys. Recipient Joseph A. Cushman award Cushman Found., 1982; named Woman of Yr. in Sci. Palm Springs Desert Mus., 1987; Guggenheim fellow, 1953-54. Fellow Geol. Soc. Am. (sr., councilor 1979-81); mem. Paleontol. Soc. (pres. 1984-85, patron 1987, medal 1982), Soc. Sedimentary Geology (councilor 1975-77, hon. mem. 1978, Raymond C. Moore medal 1984), UCLA Med. Ctr. Aux. (Woman of Yr. medal), AAUP, Internat. Paleontological Assn., Paleontol. Rsch. Inst., Am. Microscopical Soc., Am. Inst. Biol. Scis., Phi Beta Kappa, Sigma Xi. Home: 1556 W Crone Ave Anaheim CA 92802

LOEDDING, PETER ALFRED, trade association executive; b. Sewickly, Pa., July 29, 1934; s. Peter Herbert and Alice Regina (Bourne) L.; m. Mary Ellen Cahalan, June 28, 1958; children—Peter, Joseph, Jeffrey. BSBA, Youngstown U., 1967; Grad. Inst. for Orgn. Mgmt., 1988. Credit mgr. Gen. Foods Corp., Newark, Del., 1962-64; v.p. John Blackson Assn., New Castle, Pa., 1964-70, Modulage Homes Co., Niles, Ohio, 1970-72; exec. dir. Redevel. Auth. Authority, Sharon, Pa., 1972-76, Shenango Valley C. of C., Pa., 1980-85; free-lance cons., Sharon, 1976-80; adminstr. Mercer County Devel. Corp., Sharon, 1980-85; exec. dir. Shenango Valley Indsl. Devel. Corp., 1980-85, Mercer County Indsl. Devel. Authority, 1982-85, Mercer County PTA, 1978-85; pres. Capital Region Econ. Devel. Corp., Camp Hill, Pa., 1993-94. Bd. dirs. Shenango Valley Campus, Pa. State U., 1972-84, Shenango Valley Urban League, 1984—. Mem. Am. Inst. Cert. Planners, Am. Planning Assn. (pres. Pitts. region 1972-73), Pa. Assn. Redevel. Ofcls. (v.p. 1976), Williamsport-Lycoming C. of C. (pres. 1985-94). Home: 2312 Valley Rd Harrisburg PA 17104-1432 also: Capital Region Econ Devel Corp 214 Senate Ave Ste 605 Camp Hill PA 17011

LOEFFEL, BRUCE, software company executive, consultant; b. Bklyn., Aug. 13, 1943; s. Samuel and Loretta (Bleiweiss) L.; children: Alisa, Joshua. BBA, Pace U., 1966; MBA, St. John's U., 1971. Certified data processor. Mgr. fin. systems Gibbs & Hill Inc., N.Y.C., 1971-76; mgr. sales, tech. support Mgmt. Sci. Am. Inc., Fort Lee, N.J., 1976-81; dir. mktg. Info. Scis., Inc., Montvale, N.J., 1981-82; dir. bus. devel. Cullinet Software, Inc., Westwood, Mass., 1982-85; exec. v.p. strategic planning Online Data Base Software Inc., Pearl River, N.Y., 1985-88; pres. Corp. Application Software, Inc., Nyack, N.Y., 1988-94; sr. dir. IMRS, Inc., Stamford, Conn., 1994—. With U.S. Army, 1966-71. Mem. Nat. Inst. Cert. Computer Profls. Democrat. Jewish. Avocations: sports, electronics. Home: 107 High Ave Apt 308 Nyack NY 10960-2500 Office: 777 Long Ridge Rd Stamford CT 06902

LOEFFKE, BERNARD, career officer; b. Colmbia, S.Am., Sept. 17, 1934; s. Hans Loeffke and Magola Arnona; m. Francesca Adler, 1985; children: Marc, Kristin. BS, U.S. Mil. Acad., 1957; MA, Middlebury Coll., 1968; PhD, Miami U., 1979; comml. pilot lic., Aviation Sch., Fla., 1972. Commd. 2d lt. U.S. Army, 1957, advanced through grades to maj. gen.; brigade comdr. Inf. Div., Tacoma, Wash., 1975-77; army attache U.S. Embassy, Moscow, 1977-79; def. attache U.S. Embassy, People's Republic of China, 1981-84; chief strategy The Pentagon, Washington, 1980-81; chief of staff 18th Parachute Corps, Ft. Bragg, N.C., 1984-86; comdg. gen. Army South, Republic of Panama, 1986-89; chmn. InterAm. Def. Bd., Washington, 1989-92; dir. White House Fellows, 1974. Author: Societ Foreign Policy Towards Latin America, 1979. Vol. Alexandria (Va.) Fire Dept., 1992. Decorated Silver Star with one oak leaf cluster, Bronze Star, Purple Heart. Home: Quarters # 3 Washington DC 20441 Office: Inter-American Def Bd 2600 16th St NW Washington DC 20441

LOEFFLER, DAVID E., transportation executive; b. Oswego, Kans., Aug. 25, 1946; s. Edwin H. and Agnes M. (Pinter) L.; m. Cynthia K. Rothove, Feb. 2, 1975; children: Kimberly M., Wesley Todd. BBA, Pittsburg (Kans.) State U., 1969. Audit mgr.in./ Arthur Andersen & Co., Kansas City, Mo., 1969-76; asst. controller Kansas City Power and Light, 1976-78; sr. v.p. fin./ adminstrn. Yellow Freight System, Inc., Overland Park, Kans., 1978—. Dean's adv. council Iowa State U., Ames, 1987; mem. mgmt. adv. bd. U. Mo., Columbia, 1987; bd. advisors Pittsburg State U. Sch. Bus. and Econs., 1987. Served with USAR, 1968-74. Named Outstanding Young Alumni Pittsburg State U., 1979. Mem. Nat. Acctg. and Fin. Coun. (pres.-elect 1988), Am. Trucking Assns. Republican. Presbyterian. Club: Blue Hill Country. Avocations: golf, bridge.

LOEFFLER, FRANK JOSEPH, physicist, educator; b. Ballston Spa, N.Y., Sept. 5, 1928; s. Frank Joseph and Florence (Farrell) L.; m. Eleanor Jane Chisholm, Sept. 8, 1951; children: Peter, James, Margaret, Anne Marie. B.S. in Engring. Physics, Cornell U., 1951, Ph.D. in Physics, 1957. Research asso. Princeton U., 1957-58; mem. faculty Purdue U., Lafayette, Ind., 1958—; prof. physics Purdue U., 1962—; vis. prof. Hamburg U., Germany, 1963-64, Heidelberg U., Germany, CERN, Switzerland, 1971, Stanford U. Linear Acceleration Center, 1980-83; trustee, mem. exec. com., chmn. high energy com. Argonne Univ. Assn., 1972-76, 78-79, mem. com. on fusion programs, 1979-80; vis. prof. U. Hawaii, 1985-86. Contbr. to profl. publs. Recipient Antarctic Svc. medal NSF/USN, 1990, Ruth and Joel Spira award for outstanding tchg., 1992. Fellow Am. Phys. Soc., Sigma Xi, Tau Beta Pi. Exptl. research in astrophysics, high energy gamma ray astronomy, high energy particle interactions using counter-wire chamber techniques, prodn. resonant state from strong and electromagnetic interactions and on-line data acquisition-processing systems, cold fusion research. Established gamma ray astronomy lab. at South Pole, Antarctica, 1989, 91, 92. Home: 437 Maple St West Lafayette IN 47906-3016 Office: Purdue U Dept Physics Lafayette IN 47907

LOEFFLER, JAMES JOSEPH, lawyer; b. Evanston, Ill., Mar. 7, 1931; s. Charles Adolph and Margaret Bowe L.; m. Margo M. Loeffler, May 26, 1962; children—Charlotte Bowe, James J. B.S., Loyola U.; J.D., Northwestern U. Bar: Ill. 1956, Tex. 1956. Assoc. Fulbright & Jaworski, Houston, 1956-69, ptnr., 1969-86, sr. ptnr., 1986; sr. ptnr. Chamberlain, Hrdlicka, White, Johnson & Williams, Houston, 1986-90; pvt. practice law Houston, 1990—. Mem. ABA, Ill. Bar Assn., Tex. Bar Assn., Houston Bar Assn., Houston Country Club. Office: Lyric Ctr Ste 1100 440 Louisiana St Houston TX 77002-1634

LOEFFLER, RICHARD HARLAN, retail and technology company executive; b. Kansas City, Mo., Sept. 15, 1934; s. Sidney A. and Lily (Cowell) L.; m. Sheila Kay Gilligan, July 7, 1984; children: Kimberly Anne, Melissa Anne; stepchildren: Patrick K. Gilligan, Todd M. Gilligan. Student, U. Mo.; M.B.A., Pepperdine U., 1975. Ptnr. Forstall & Co., L.A., 1960-65; pres. Beverly Hills Film Corp., Calif., 1962-65; v.p. Bates Gas and Oil Corp., Oakland, Calif., 1965-66; exec. v.p. TRE Corp., Beverly Hills, Calif. 1966-72; chmn., pres. Simplex Industries, Adrian, Mich., 1972-76; pres., chief oper. officer TRE Corp., L.A., 1976-86; chmn., CEO, MemTech Corp., Beverly Hills, 1987-91; chmn. Am. Builders Hardware Corp., Beverly Hills, Calif., 1988-91; chmn., CEO RHL Mgmt. Group, Inc., Beverly Hills, Calif.,

1992—; pres., COO, bd. dirs. Standard Brands Paint Co., Torrance, Calif., 1992-93; bd. dirs. Alpha Microsystems, Santa Ana, Calif., Future Flow Sys. Inc., Newbury Park, Calif., Lorus Corp., Beverly Hills, Calif. Mem. bus. coun. Nat. Democratic Com., Washington, 1983—; trustee Internat. Assn. for Shipboard Edn.; bd. dirs. U. So. Calif. Cancer Rsch. Assocs. Office: 9903 Santa Monica Blvd Ste 287 Beverly Hills CA 90212

LOEFFLER, ROBERT HUGH, lawyer; b. Chgo., May 27, 1943; s. Julius and Faye (Fink) L.; m. Jane Canter, Sept. 6, 1970; children: James Benjamin, Charles Edward. AB magna cum laude, Harvard Coll., 1965; JD cum laude, Columbia U., 1968. Bar: N.Y. 1969, U.S. Ct. Appeals (2d cir.) 1969, D.C. 1970, U.S. Ct. Appeals (D.C. cir.) 1972, U.S. Supreme Ct. 1976, U.S. Ct. Appeals (9th cir.) 1981, U.S. Ct. Appeals (Fed. cir.) 1992. Law clk. to Hon. Harold R. Medina U.S. Ct. Appeals, 1968-69; assoc. Covington & Burling, Washington, 1969-76; assoc., ptnr. Isham, Lincoln & Beale, Washington, 1976-79; mng. ptnr. Morrison & Foerster, Washington, 1980-89, sr. ptnr., 1990—. Chmn. consumer com. Muskie presdl. campaign, 1972. Mem. ABA (vice chmn. energy law com. adminstrv. law sect. 1980-85), Am. Intellectual Property Law Assn., Fed. Energy Bar Assn. (chmn. oil pipeline regulation), Columbia Law Sch. Assn. Washington (pres. 1993, v.p. 1994—), Univ. Club, Standard Club, Harvard Club (N.Y.C.). Home: 2607 36th Pl NW Washington DC 20007-1414 Office: Morrison & Foerster 2000 Pennsylvania Ave NW Ste 5500 Washington DC 20006-1888

LOEHLE, BETTY BARNES, artist, painter; b. Montgomery, Ala., Mar. 21, 1923; d. Harry McGuinn and Elizabeth (Fowler) B.; m. Richard E. Loehle, Aug. 16, 1947; children—Craig Edward, Alan David, Bruce Barnes, Lynn Elizabeth. Student Auburn U., Harris Sch. Art, Nashville, 1942-46, Evanston Art Ctr., 1964-68. Layout artist Atlanta Art Studios, 1970-75; free lance designer, painter, Atlanta, 1975-80; full time painter, Atlanta, 1980—; dir., publicity chmn., exhibition chmn. Ga. Watercolor Soc., 1981-85; pres. Artists Assocs. Gallery, Atlanta, 1977-79, sec., 1985—. Represented by Abstein Gallery of Art, Atlanta, Little House on Linden Gallery, Birmingham, Ala., Little Art Gallery, Raleigh, N.C. Entries judge Arts Festival of Atlanta, 1974; chmn. Unitarian Ch. Art Com., Atlanta, 1973-76. Recipient Purchase award Decatur Sesquicentennial, Ga., 1974, Hunter Mus. of Art, Chattanooga, 1977, Ga. Council for the Arts, Atlanta, 1977, 1980. Mem. DeKalb Council for the Arts, Ga. Watercolor Soc. (signature mem.; merit awards 1980, 82, 83, 87, 88), So. Watercolor Soc. (signature mem.; silver award 1979, merit award 1980), Ky. Watercolor Soc. (artist mem.), Atlanta Artist Club (exhbn. chmn. 1972-74). Home: 2608 River Oak Dr Decatur GA 30033-2805

LOEHLIN, JOHN CLINTON, psychologist, educator; b. Ferozepore, India, Jan. 13, 1926; s. Clinton Herbert and Eunice (Cleland) L.; m. Marjorie Leafdale, Jan. 2, 1962; children—Jennifer Ann, James Norris. AB, Harvard U., 1947; PhD, U. Calif., Berkeley, 1957. With rsch. dept. McCann-Erickson, Inc., Cleve., 1947-49; instr. to asst. prof. psychology U. Nebr., Lincoln, 1957-64; mem. faculty U. Tex., Austin, 1964—, prof. psychology and computer scis., 1969-92, prof. emeritus, 1992—. Author: Computer Models of Personality, 1968, Latent Variable Models, 1987, Genes and Environment in Personality Development, 1992; co-author: Race Differences in Intelligence, 1975, Heredity, Environment and Personality, 1976, Introduction to Theories of Personality, 1985. With USNR, 1945-47, 51-53. Fellow Ctr. Advanced Study Behavioral Scis., 1971-72. Fellow Am. Psychol. Soc.; mem. Behavior Genetics Assn., Soc. Multivariate Exptl. Psychology. Home: 304 Almarion Dr Austin TX 78746-5644 Office: U Tex Dept Psychology Austin TX 78712

LOEHR, ARTHUR WILLIAM, JR., healthcare executive, nurse; b. Cleve., July 26, 1948; s. Arthur William and Margaret Osborne (Robison) L.; m. Carol Lynn Hiatt; children: Brett Lawrence, Melissa Margaret, Joshua Hiatt. Diploma, Jackson Meml. Hosp., 1971; BS in Health Sci., Fla. Internat. U., 1975, M of Healthcare Adminstrn., 1977. RN, Fla. Psychiat. nurse Jackson Meml. Hosp., Miami, Fla., 1971, nurse cons., 1972, adminstr. pediats., 1973-74, hosp. planner, 1975-77; hosp. planner Duke U. Med. Ctr., Durham, N.C., 1977-80; v.p. planning N.C. Hosp. Assn., Raleigh, 1980-84, Catawba Meml. Hosp., Hickory, N.C., 1984—; preceptor U. N.C. Chapel Hill, N.C., 1988—. V.p., pres. Hospice of Catawba Valley, Hickory, 1985-90, Rape Crisis Ctr., Hickory, 1987-92; mem. Catawba County United Way Bd., 1991—, Family Care Ctr. of Catawba County, bd. dirs., 1992—; Scholar B'nai Brith, Miami, 1971. Fellow Am. Coll. Healthcare Execs.; mem. Rotary Internat. (bd. dirs. 1990-93). Presbyterian. Avocations: golf, fishing, snow skiing. Home: 4322 3d St Pl NW Hickory NC 28601 Office: Catawba Memorial Hospital 810 Fairgrove Church Rd Hickory NC 28602-9643

LOEHR, MARLA, college president; b. Cleve., Oct. 7, 1937; d. Joseph Richard and Eleanore Edith (Rothschuh) L. BS, Notre Dame Coll., South Euclid, Ohio, 1960; MAT, Ind. U., 1969; PhD, Boston Coll., 1988. Joined Sisters of Notre Dame, Roman Cath. Ch., 1956; cert. high sch. tchr., counselor, Ohio. Mem. faculty Notre Dame Acad., Cleve., 1960-64, John F. Kennedy High Sch., Warren, Ohio, 1964-66; adminstrn. asst., dir. residence halls Notre Dame Acad., Chardon, Ohio, 1966-72; dean students Notre Dame Coll., South Euclid, Ohio, 1972-85, acting acad. dean, 1988, pres., 1988—; cons. Nat. Cons. Network, Washington, 1978-85; facilitator Coun. for Ind. Colls., Washington, 1980-84. Author: Mentor Handbook, 1985; co-author: Notre Dame College Model for Student Development, 1980. Hon. mem. Segund Montes Solidarity City Campaign; trustee NCCJ, Notre Dame Coll., Womankind, Ohio Found. of Ind. Colls.; mem. sch. bd. Marotta Montessori Schs. Cleve.; mem. Cleve. Common. on Higher Edn., Leadership Cleve. Class of 1990; vol. Hospice of Western Res. Recipient Career Woman of Achievement award YWCA, 1992; named One of 100 Cleve.'s Most Powerful Women, New Cleve. Woman. Mem. Am. Assn. for Higher Edn., Assn. Ind. Colls. and Univs. Ohio (bd. dirs.), Assn. Governing Bds., Pax Christi, Alpha Sigma Nu, Kappa Gamma Pi. Avocations: photography, hiking, reading, sports. Office: Notre Dame Coll Ohio Office of the President 4545 College Rd South Euclid OH 44121

LOEKS, JAMES, theater chain executive. Co-CHB Sony Theatres, N.Y. Office: Sony Theatres 711 Fifth Ave New York NY 10022*

LOENGARD, JOHN BORG, photographer; editor; b. N.Y.C., Sept. 5, 1934; s. Richard Otto and Margery (Borg) L.; m. Eleanor Sturgis, Aug. 25, 1963 (div. 1987); children: Charles, Jennifer, Anna. B.A., Harvard Coll., 1956. Staff photographer Life mag., N.Y.C., 1961-72, picture editor, 1973-87; freelance photographer, 1987—; columnist Popular Photography mag., N.Y.C., 1987, Am. Photographer, N.Y.C., 1988—. Author: Pictures Under Discussion, 1987, Life Classic Photographs: A Personal Interpretation by John Loengard, 1988, Life Faces: Commentary by John Loengard, 1991, Celebrating the Negative, 1994, Georgia O'Keeffe at Ghost Ranch, 1995; essays in Life mag., The Shakers, 1967, Georgia O'Keeffe, 1968, Vanishing Cowboys, 1970, Photographers Over 80, 1982, Henry Moore, 1983, Interstate 80, 1989. Recipient Ansel Adams award Am. Soc. Mag. Photographers, 1987. Home: 20 W 86th St New York NY 10024-3604 Office: Time & Life Bldg Rm 2841 New York NY 10020

LOENGARD, RICHARD OTTO, JR., lawyer; b. N.Y.C., Jan. 28, 1932; s. Richard Otto and Margery (Borg) L.; m. Janet Sara Senderowitz, Apr. 11, 1964; children: Maranda C., Philippa S.M. AB, Harvard U., 1953, LLB, 1956. Bar: N.Y. 1956, U.S. Dist. Ct. (so. dist.) N.Y. 1958. Assoc. Fried, Frank, Harris, Shriver & Jacobson, predecessor firms, N.Y.C., 1956-64, ptnr., 1967—; dep. tax legis. counsel, spl. asst. internat. tax affairs U.S. Dept. Treasury, Washington, 1964-67; mem. Commerce Clearing House, Riverwoods, Ill., 1982-94. Editorial bd. Tax Transaction Libr.; contbr. articles to profl. publs. Mem. ABA, Assn. Bar City N.Y., N.Y. State Bar Assn. (exec. com. tax sect. 1984—, sec. 1994-95, vice chair 1995-96). Office: Fried Frank Harris Shriver & Jacobson 1 New York Plz New York NY 10004

LOEPER, F. JOSEPH, state senator; b. Dec. 23, 1944; m. Joann M. Loeper; children: F. Joseph III, James H., Joanne M. BS in Edn., West Chester U., 1966; MEd, Temple U., 1970; D of Law (hon.), Widener U., 1993. Tchr. social studies, asst. basketball coach, advisor sch. paper Aldan Sch. Dist., 1966-67; tchr. social studies, football coach Drexel Hill Jr. High Sch. Upper Darby Sch. Dist., 1967-68; dir. leisure svcs. Upper Darby Sch.

Dist. Upper Darby Twp., 1968-78; instr. Pub. Svc. Inst. Millersville, Kutztown and West Chester U., 1972; mem. Rep. State Com. 26th Senatorial Dist., 1972-74; co-adj. instr. Delaware County Community Coll., 1973-74; mem. Upper Darby Gov. Study Commn., 1973-74; treas. Upper Darby Sch. Dist., 1973-78; senator Pa. Senate, 1978—, senate majority caucus sec., 1980-83, senate majority whip, 1984-87, senate majority leader, 1988-92, 94—, minority whip, 1992-93; chmn. Rules and Exec. Nominations com.; mem. Appropriations Com., Banking and Ins. Com., Intergovernment Affairs com.; bd. govs. State Systems of Higher Edn. com.; mem. exec. com. Joint State Gov. Commn. Past chmn. Eastern Delaware County Br. ARC, past bd. dirs. southeastern Pa. chpt.; past bd. dirs. Delaware County Assn. for Retarded Citizens; past pres. Garrettford-Drexel Hill Fire Co., Upper Darby Twp. Fireman's Relief Assn. Recipient Delaware County Citizen of Yr. award, 1990, West Chester Univ. Disting. Alumni award, 1989, Presdl. award Delaware County Fed. Sr. Svcs., 1988, Legis. award Fraternal Order Police, 1985, Legion Honor award Chapel Four Chaplains, 1982, St. Charles Cath. Youth Assn. award, Delaware County Saving League award, YMCA Youth in Gov. award, Citizen of Yr. award Del. C. of C., 1992, Pres. medal West Chester U., 1994. Mem. Pa. Recreation and Park Soc. (Governmental svc. award, 1982), Nat. Edn. Assn. (life), Upper Darby Assn. Suprs. and Administrators, Nat. Rep. Legislators Assn. (Legislator of Yr. 1988), Senate Rep. Campaign Com. (treas.). Office: Rm 362 Main Capital Bldg Harrisburg PA 17120 also: 403 Burmont Rd Drexel Hill PA 19026

LOERKE, WILLIAM CARL, art history educator; b. Toledo, Aug. 13, 1920; s. William Carl and Anna Louisa (Stallbaum) L.; m. Helen Trautmann, 1944; children—Anna Hurd, Timothy, Eric, Alison, Lisa Huff, Ellen, Martha. B.A., Oberlin Coll., 1942; M.F.A., Princeton U., 1948, Ph.D., 1957. Acad. positions history of art Brown U., 1949-59; assoc. prof. Bryn Mawr Coll., 1959-64; prof. art history U. Pitts., 1964-71, chmn. fine arts dept., 1964-69; prof. Byzantine art Harvard U., Dumbarton Oaks Research Library, 1971-88, prof. emeritus, 1988—; dir. studies Ctr. Byzantine Studies, 1971-77; vis. prof. Cath. U. Am., 1978-88; vis. prof. U. Md., 1988-92; mem. adv. bd. Ctr. for Advanced Study in Visual Arts, Nat. Gallery Art, Washington, 1979-82, 89-92; bd. dirs. Internat. Ctr. Medieval Art, 1973-91; mem. mng. com. Am. Sch. Classical Studies, 1973-93. Co-author: The Place of Book Illumination in Byzantine Art, Princeton, 1975, Monasticism and the Arts, 1984, Codex Rossanensis, Commentarium, Rome, 1987, Architecture: Fundamental Issues, N.Y., 1990; contbr. Byzantine East, Latin West: Art Historical Studies in Honor of Kurt Weitzman, 1995; contbr. articles to profl. jours.; contbr. Dictionary of Byzantium, 1991. Served with USNR, 1943-46. Jr. fellow Princeton U., 1946-48, Dumbarton Oaks Harvard U., 1948-49, Danforth Tchr. fellow, 1956-57; Fulbright Rsch. scholar Am. Acad. Rome, 1952-53; recipient A.K. Porter prize Coll. Art Assn., 1961. Mem. Coll. Art Assn., Medieval Acad. Am., Soc. Fellows, Am. Acad. at Rome, Internat. Ctr. Med. Art. Home: 227 Gralan Rd Catonsville MD 21228-4835

LOESCH, HAROLD C., retired marine fisheries biologist, consultant; b. Osage, Tex., Oct. 3, 1926; s. Eldor E. and Martha (Niemeier) L.; m. Mabel Treichler, Oct. 19, 1945; children: Stephen C., Gretchen Drinkard, Jonathan, Frederick. BS in Fisheries, Tex. A&M Univ., 1951; postgrad., Univ. Tex., Port Aransas, 1951, 52; MS in Biol. Oceanography, Tex. A&M Univ., 1954, PhD in Biol. Oceanography, 1962. Prin. marine biologist, acting lab. dir. Dept. Conservation, Bayou la Batre, Ala., 1952-57; teaching asst. Tex. A&M Univ., College Station, 1957-58; assoc. rsch. scientist Tex. A&M Rsch. Found., College Station, 1958-60; shrimp biologist Food & Agrl. Orgn. of UN, Guatamala, 1960-62; fisheries biologist Food & Agrl. Orgn. of UN, Ecuador, 1962-66; fisheries officer Food & Agrl. Orgn. of UN, La Ceiba, Honduras, 1967-68; prof. zoology La. State U., Baton Rouge, 1968-69; prof. marine scis. La. State U., 1970-75; expert marine biologist United Nat. Edn. Social and Cultural Orgn., Guaymas, Sonora, Mex., 1976-79; sr. resource assessment surveyor, project mgr. FAO, UN, Dhaka, Bangladesh, 1981-85; cons. Pensacola, Fla., 1985—; vis. prof. Orgn. Am. States, Guayaquil, Ecuador, 1972, Sch. for Field Study, Beverly, Mass., S. Caicos Isl, BWI, 1990; cons. Univ. Mex. U. N. Ed. Soc. & Cult Orgn., 1979-80. Contbr. articles to profl. jours. With USAF, 1945-46. Mem. AAAS (life), Am. Fisheries Soc., Internat. Acad. Fisheries Sci., Tex. Acad. Sci. (life), World Mariculture Soc., Am. Soc. Ichthyologists and Herpetologists (life), Sigma Xi. Democrat. Lutheran. Avocations: canoeing, wilderness camping, photography, traveling. Home: 2140 E Scott St Pensacola FL 32503-4957

LOESCH, KATHARINE TAYLOR (MRS. JOHN GEORGE LOESCH), communication and theatre educator; b. Berkeley, Calif., Apr. 13, 1922; d. Paul Schuster and Katharine (Whiteside) Taylor; student Swarthmore Coll., 1939-41, U. Wash., 1942; BA, Columbia U., 1944, MA, 1949; grad. Neighborhood Playhouse Sch. of Theatre, 1946; postgrad. Ind. U., 1953; PhD, Northwestern U., 1961; m. John George Loesch, Aug. 28, 1948; 1 child, William Ross. Instr. speech Wellesley (Mass.) Coll., 1949-52, Loyola U., Chgo., 1956; asst. prof. English and speech Roosevelt U., Chgo., 1957, 62-65; assoc. prof. communication and theatre U. Ill. at Chgo., 1968—; assoc. prof. emerita speech in communication and theater, U. Ill., Chgo., 1987—. Contbr. writings to profl. jours.; poetry performances. Active ERA, Ill., 1975-76. Am. Philos. Soc. grantee, 1970; U. Ill., Chgo., grantee, 1970. Mem. MLA, Speech Communication Assn. (Golden Anniversary prize award 1969, chmn. interpretation div. 1979-80), Celtic Studies Assn. N.Am., Pi Beta Phi. Episcopalian. Office: U Ill Dept Performing Arts PO Box 4348 MC/132 Chicago IL 60680

LOESCH, MABEL LORRAINE, social worker; b. Annandale, Minn., July 1, 1925; d. Rudolph and Hedwig (Zeidler) Treichler; m. Harold Carl Loesch, Oct. 19, 1945; children: Stephen, Gretchen, Jonathan, Frederick. BS, La. State U., 1972, MSW, 1974. Cert. Acad. Cert. Social Worker, bd. cert. diplomate. Tchr. Am. schs. Tegucigalpa, Honduras, 1960-61, Guayaquil, Ecuador, 1962-66, La Ceiba, Honduras, 1966-67; supr. clin. svc. Blundon Home, Baton Rouge, 1974-81; social worker, cons. Dhaka, Bangladesh, 1981-85; social worker Manna Food Bank, Pensacola, Fla., 1986—; adj. instr. social work dept. Southern U., Baton Rouge, 1976-81. Editor: Making Do, 1989, Making Do II, 1994. Mem. adv. com. Luth. Ministries of Fla., 1993—. Mem. NASW, Mensa (local sec. 1986-90, chair scholarships com.), Phi Kappa Phi. Democrat. Lutheran. Avocation: genealogy. Home: 2140 E Scott St Pensacola FL 32503-4957

LOESCHER, GILBURT DAMIAN, international relations educator; b. San Francisco, Mar. 7, 1945; s. Burt Garfield and Helen (Aachen) L.; m. Ann Gordon Dull, Sept. 25, 1971; children: Margaret Madeline, Claire Helen. BA, St. Mary's Coll. of Calif., 1967; MA, Monterey Inst. Internat. Study, 1969; PhD, London Sch. Econs./Polit. Sci., 1975. Asst. prof. U. Notre Dame, Ind., 1975-84, assoc. prof., 1984-90, prof., 1990—; asst. dean, 1977-79; vis. fellow London Sch. Econs., 1978-79, Princeton (N.J.) U., 1982-83; rsch. cons. U.S. Select Commn. on Immigration and Refugee Policy, Washington, 1989; sr. rsch. fellow Queen Elizabeth House, Oxford (Eng.) U., 1986-89; rsch. assoc. Internat. Inst. for Strategic Studies, London, 1990-91. Author: Refugee Movements and International Security, 1992, Beyond Charity: International Cooperation and the Global Refugee Problem, 1993; co-author: Calculated Kindness: Refugees and America's Half-Open Door, 1985 (Gustavas Meyers award 1986). Mem. exec. bd. Ind. Consortium for Internat. Programs, 1976-80; bd. dirs. Amnesty Internat., N.Y., 1980-82; mem. adv. com. on internat. experts UN Commn. for Refugees, Geneva, 1992—. Grantee Ford Found., 1988-92, 92-93, Twentieth Century Fund, 1987-89, MacArthur Found., 1990-91. Mem. Internat. Studies Assn., Am. Polit. Sci. Assn., Royal Inst. Internat. Affairs, Internat. Inst. for Strategic Studies. Democrat. Roman Catholic. Avocations: basketball, walking, theater. Office: U Notre Dame Notre Dame IN 46556

LOESCHER, RICHARD ALVIN, gastroenterologist; b. Brockton, Mass., Feb. 6, 1940; s. Vernon Alvin and Anna Marie (Good) L.; m. Linda Rockwell Clifford Loescher, June 5, 1965 (div. Jan. 1982); children: Steven Clifford Loescher, Laura May Loescher. BA, De Pauw U., 1961; MD cum laude, Harvard U., 1965. Diplomate Am. Bd. Internal Medicine, 1972, Am. Bd. Gastroenterology, 1973. Chief Med. Svc. US Pub. Health Svc. Hosp., Lawton, Okla., 1967-69; chief Med. Staff, 1968-69, svc. unit dir., 1969; attending physician Seattle, 1970-71, U. Hosp., Seattle, 1970-71; active staff Sacred Heart Med. Ctr., Eugene, Oreg., 1973—; Eugene (Oreg.) Hosp., 1972-88; courtesy staff McKenzie-Willamette Hosp., Springfield, Oreg., 1982—. Recipient Rector scholarship DePauw U., 1957-61, Maimonides award Harvard Med. Sch., 1965. Mem. AMA, Lane County Med. Soc., Oreg.

Med. Assn., Oreg. Soc. Internal Medicine, Am. Soc. Internal Medicine, Am. Soc. for Gastrointestinal Endoscopy, Am. Acad. Med. Acupuncture, Alpha Omega Alpha, Phi Beta Kappa. Democrat. Unitarian. Avocations: physical fitness, personal growth, magic, outdoor activities. Home: 2345 Patterson St # 34 Eugene OR 97405 Office: 1162 Willamette St Eugene OR 97401

LOESCHER, ROBERT WAYNE, holding company executive; b. Juneau, Alaska, July 5, 1947; s. Al and Esther (Bailey) L.; m. Helen T. Young, June 1, 1968; children: Robert Thomas, Christy Marie; 1 adopted child, Cory MacDonald. BA, Fort Lewis Coll., Durango, Colo., 1969. Field rep. Alaska Legal Services, Juneau, 1969-72; dep. dir. Tlingit Haida Cen. Council Office Devel. Planning, Juneau, 1971-72; exec. dir. Tlingit Haida Housing Devel. Corp., Juneau, 1974-78, Tlingit Haida Regional Elec. Authority, Juneau, 1975-78, Tlingit Haida Regional Housing Authority, Juneau, 1973-78; exec. v.p. Sealaska Corp., Juneau, 1978—; sr. v.p. ops. Sealaska Timber Corp., Ketchikan, Alaska, 1983; lobbyist Sealaska Corp., Juneau, Washington, 1978—; pres., bd. dirs. Klawock (Alaska) Island Dock Corp., 1980—. Mem. Alaska Gov.'s Timber Task Force, Juneau, 1984—; city councilman/assemblyman City and Borough of Juneau, 1970-73. Mem. Alaska Forestry Assn. (bd. dirs. 1986-87), Tlingit Haida Cen. Coun. (del.), Alaska Native Brotherhood. Democrat. Presbyterian. Avocation: commercial fishing. Home: 10645 Misty Ln Juneau AK 99801-7624 Office: Sealaska Corp 1 Sealaska Plz Ste 400 Juneau AK 99801-1276

LOESER, HANS FERDINAND, lawyer; b. Kassel, Germany, Sept. 28, 1920; s. Max and Cecilia H. (Erlanger) L.; m. Herta Lewent, Dec. 14, 1944; children—Helen, Harris M. H. Thomas. Student CCNY, 1940-42, U. Pa., 1942-43; LL.B. magna cum laude, Harvard U., 1950. Bar: Mass. 1950, U.S. Supreme Ct. 1968. Asso. firm Foley, Hoag & Eliot, Boston, 1950-55, ptnr., 1956—; hon. consul-gen. Republic of Senegal; mem. Mass. Bd. Bar Overseers; trustee Vineyard Open Land Found., Martha's Vineyard, Mass.; mem. exec. com. and nat. bd. Lawyers' Com. for Civil Rights Under Law, steering com. and past chmn. Lawyer's Com. for Civil Rights Under Law of Boston Bar Assn.; incorporator Univ. Hosp., Boston, Mt. Auburn Hosp., Cambridge, Mass. Served to capt. U.S. Army, 1942-46. Decorated Bronze Star, Purple Heart; hon. fellow U. Pa. Law Sch., 1978-79, commencement speaker, 1978. Fellow Am. Bar Found., Mass. Bar Found.; mem. ABA, Mass. Bar Assn., Boston Bar Assn. Clubs: Union, Harvard, Cambridge. Office: Foley Hoag & Eliot 1 Post Office Sq Boston MA 02109-2103

LOESER, JOHN DAVID, neurosurgeon, educator; b. Newark, Dec. 14, 1935; s. Lewis Henry and Rhoda Sophie (Levy) L.; m. Susan Winifred Becker, June 11, 1961 (div. 1974); children: Sally Ann, Thomas Eric, Derek William; m. Karen Winslow, Dec. 29, 1977; 1 child, David Winslow. BA, Harvard U., 1957; MD, NYU, 1961. Diplomate Am. Bd. Neurol. Surgery; cert. Nat. Bd. Med. Examiners.; lic. neurosurgeon, Wash. Intern dept. surgery U. Calif. San Francisco, 1961-62; resident neurol. surgery U. Wash., Seattle, 1962-67; asst. prof. neurosurgery U. Calif., Irvine, 1967-68; asst. prof. neurol. surgery U. Wash., Seattle, 1969-75, assoc. prof., 1975-80, prof., 1980—; dir. Multidisciplinary Pain Clinic, 1983—; chief div. of neurosurgery Children's Hosp. & Med. Ctr., 1987-93; Fulbright sr. scholar, Australia, 1989-90. Contbr. articles to profl. jours.; editor profl. books. Served as maj. U.S. Army, 1968-70. Fellow AAAS; mem. Internat. Assn. Study of Pain (sec. 1984-90, pres. 1993—), Am. Pain Soc. (treas. 1980-85, pres. 1986-87), Am. Assn. Neurol. Surgeons, Am. Soc. Functional and Stereotactic Neurosurgery, North Pacific Soc. Neurology and Psychiatry, Wash. Assn. Neurosurgery, Western Neurosurg. Soc., Am. Acad. Pain Medicine, Kings County Med. Soc., Conf. Neurol. Surgeons, Phi Beta Kappa, Alpha Omega Alpha. Avocations: skiing, woodcarving. Office: U Wash Multidisciplinary Pain Ctr RC-95 Seattle WA 98195 also: Univ Wash Med Ctr-Roosevelt Multidisciplinary Pain Ctr 4245 Roosevelt Way NE Bellevue WA 98105

LOESS, HENRY BERNARD, psychology educator; b. Chgo., June 24, 1924; s. Henry William and Alice Cecilia (Mansfield) L.; m. Frances Mary Van Horn, May 26, 1951; children—Kurt, Karin, Andrew, Alan. BS, Northwestern U., 1949, MS, 1950; PhD, U. Iowa, 1952. Prof. psychology, chmn. dept. Lake Forest (Ill.) Coll., 1952-58; Prof. psychology, chmn. dept. Wooster (Ohio) Coll., 1958-88, prof. emeritus, 1988—; vis. lectr. Ohio State U., 1958-63; vis. research scholar U. Calif. at Berkeley, 1963-64, Cambridge (Eng.) U., 1968-69, U. Mich., 1973-74, Yale U., 1980-81; vis. scientist Ohio Acad. Sci., 1962—; regional coord. Am. Inst. Rsch. Project Talent, 1961-69; assoc. North Cent. Assn. Colls. and Secondary Schs., 1970-86; bd. dirs. Habitat for Humanity, Wayne County, 1989—, Hospice of Wayne County, 1990—, Wayne County Bd. Mental Retardation and Devel. Disabilities, 1978-86, 93—. Author articles in field.; cons. editor: Memory And Cognition, 1971—. Served with USAAF, 1943-46. Mem. Am., Midwestern, Eastern psychol. assns., Psychonomic Soc., AAAS, Am. Assn. U. Profs. Sigma Xi. Home: 5410 Lehr Rd Wooster OH 44691-9230

LOEUP, KONG, counselor; b. Battambang, Cambodia, May 26, 1944; s. Kong Niem and Chhit Roeun; m. Ly Keo Thim, Aug. 1968; children: Kong Bandaul, Kong Panlauk. Diploma in edn., U. Phnom Penh, 1965; BA, Antioch U., 1983; MA, U. Colo., Denver, 1987; PhD, Columbia Pacific U., 1987. Tchr. Ministry Edn., Phnom Penh, 1964; counselor, community case worker Internat. Refugee Ctr., Denver, 1983; refugee program coord./counselor Refugee Camps, Thailand; cons. Cambodian Buddhist Soc. of Colo., Denver; counselor Cambodian Community Colo., Denver; pres. Cambodian Cultural Ctr., Denver, 1992—. Pres. Cambodian Fine Arts Preservation Group Colo.; mem. Asian Edn. Adv. Coun., Rep. Presdl. Task Force, 1986. Mem. ASCD. Home and Office: 1804 S Eliot St Denver CO 80219-4904

LOEVI, FRANCIS JOSEPH, JR., consulting company executive; b. N.Y.C., Mar. 29, 1945; s. Francis J. and Ruth E. (DeJongh) L. BA in Labor Mgmt. Rels., Pa. State U., 1967; MS Indsl. Rels., Cornell U., 1971. Instr. labor rels. U. Mo., Columbia, 1969-70; labor rels. advisor HEW, Washington, 1970-74; labor rels. officer Dept. Edn., Washington, 1974-77; pres. Axon Assocs., Inc., Alexandria, Va., 1977—; pres. Potomac Systems, Inc., Alexandria, 1982—; pres. Pub. Adminstrn. Forum, 1985—; mem. AAA Nat. Labor Panel, N.Y.C., 1973—. Author: Arbitration and the Federal Sector Advocate, 1978, Federal Sector Collective Bargaining: A Management Guide, 1980. Contbr. articles to profl. jours. Mem. Soc. Fed. Labor Rels. Profls. (pres. 1973-74, dir. 1974-78), Fed. Labor Rels. Info. Profls. Soc. (dir. 1991-92). Home: 902 Oronoco St Alexandria VA 22314-2235 Office: Axon Group 225 Reinekers Ln Alexandria VA 22314-2875

LOEVINGER, LEE, lawyer; b. St. Paul, Apr. 24, 1913; s. Gustavus and Millie (Strouse) L.; m. Ruth Howe, Mar. 4, 1950; children: Barbara L., Eric H., Peter H. BA summa cum laude, U. Minn., 1933, JD, 1936. Bar: Minn. 1936, Mo. 1937, D.C. 1966, U.S. Supreme Ct., 1941. Assoc. Watson, Ess, Groner, Barnett & Whittaker, Kansas City, Mo., 1936-37; atty., regional atty. NLRB, 1937-41; with antitrust div. Dept. Justice, 1941-46; ptnr. Larson, Loevinger, Lindquist & Fraser, Mpls., 1946-60; assoc. justice Minn. Supreme Ct., 1960-61; asst. U.S. atty. gen. charge antitrust div. Dept. Justice, 1961-63; commr. FCC, 1963-68; ptnr. Hogan & Hartson, Washington, 1968-85; of counsel Hogan & Hartson, 1986—; v.p. dir. Craig-Hallum Corp., Mpls., 1968-73; dir. Petrolite Corp., St. Louis, 1978-83; U.S. rep. com. on restrictive bus. practices Orgn. for Econ. Cooperation and Devel., 1961-64; spl. asst. to U.S. atty. gen., 1963-64; spl. counsel com. sml. bus. U.S. Senate, 1951-52; lectr. U. Minn., 1953-60; vis. prof. jurisprudence U. Minn. (Law Sch.), 1961; professorial lectr. Am. U., 1968-70; chmn. Minn. Atomic Devel. Problems Com., 1957-59; mem. Adminstrv. Conf. U.S., 1972-74; del. White House Conf. on Inflation, 1974; U.S. del. UNESCO Conf. on Mass Media, 1975, Internat. Telecomms. Conf. on Radio Frequencies, 1964, 66. Author: The Law of Free Enterprise, 1949, An Introduction to Legal Logic, 1952, Defending Antitrust Lawsuits, 1977; author first article to use term: Jurimetrics, 1949; contbr. articles to profl. and sci. jours.; editor, contbr.: Basic Data on Atomic Devel. Problems in Minnesota, 1958; adv. bd. Antitrust Bull., Jurimetrics Jour. Served to lt. comdr. USNR, 1942-45. Recipient Outstanding Achievement award U. Minn., 1968; Freedoms Found. award, 1977, 84. Fellow Am. Acad. Appellate Lawyers; mem. ABA (del. of sci. and tech. sect. to Ho. of Dels. 1974-80, del. to joint conf. with AAAS 1974-76, co-chair, 1990-93, liaison 1984-90, 93—, chmn. sci. and tech. sect. 1982-83, coun. 1986-89, standing com. on nat. conf. groups 1984-90), Minn. Bar Assn., Hennepin County Bar Assn., N.Y. Acad. Sci., D.C. Bar Assn., FCC Bar Assn., AAAS, Broadcast Pioneers, Am. Arbitration Assn. (comml. panel), Atlantic Legal Found. (adv. coun.), Cosmos Club (pres.

1990), City Club (Washington), Phi Beta Kappa, Sigma Xi, Delta Sigma Tho, Sigma Delta Chi, Phi Delta Gamma, Tau Kappa Alpha, Alpha Epsilon Rho. Home: 5600 Wisconsin Ave Apt 17D Chevy Chase MD 20815-4414 Office: Hogan & Hartson 555 13th St NW Washington DC 20004-1109 *With age I come increasingly to believe that life is, and should be,a learning experience. This involves a peculiar paradox: Ignorance increases faster than knowledge, as each new fact or principle opens new frontiers for intellectual exploration. Thus, with greater learning comes intellectual humility and skepticism. So, after reaching 75 I am less certain of anything than at 25 I was of everything.*

LOEW, FRANKLIN MARTIN, medical and biological scientist; b. Syracuse, N.Y., Sept. 8, 1939; s. David Franklin and Sarah (Adelaide) L.; m. Mary Moffatt, Sept. 9, 1964; children—Timothy, Andrew. B.S., Cornell U., 1961, D.V.M., 1965; Ph.D., U. Sask., 1971. Lic. veterinarian; diplomate Am. Coll. Lab. Animal Medicine. Research asst. R.J. Reynolds Co., Winston-Salem, N.C., 1965-66; research asst. Tulane U., New Orleans, 1966-67; prof. U. Sask., Saskatoon, Can., 1967-77; dir. comparative medicine Johns Hopkins U., Balt., 1977-82; dean Sch. Vet. Medicine, Tufts U., Boston, 1982—, Henry and Lois Foster prof. comparative medicine, 1985—; v.p. Tufts U. Devel. Corp. Inc., Boston, 1991—; pres. Tufts Biotech. Corp., Boston, 1993—; cons. Can. Coun. Animal Care, Ottawa, Ont., 1969-84; mem. life scis. com. Nat. Acad. Sci., Washington, 1981-88, chmn. inst. lab. animal resources, 1981-87; mem. FDA Commn. on Sr. Biomed. Rsch. Svc. Credentials, 1995—; N.B. lectr. Am. Soc. Microbiology; mem. nat. adv. bd. Ctr. on Bioethics Lit., Kennedy Inst. Georgetown U., 1986—; Schofield lectr. U. Guelph, Can.; Smith lectr. U. Sask.; Schalm lectr. U. Calif.; Univ. lectr. Tex. A&M U.; bd. dirs. Mass. Biotech. Rsch. Inst., Commonwealth BioVentures, Inc.; mem. sci. adv. com. Harvard Primate Rsch. Ctr., 1988—, Mass. Health Resources Inst.; sci. and tech. adv. com. State of Mass., 1988-92; mem. USDA Sec.'s Adv. Com. Nat. Rsch. Initiative, 1992—; pres. Tufts Biotech Corp., 1993—; bd. trustees Marine Biol. Lab., 1990-94, New Eng. Aquarium, 1991—, Guys Drug Rsch. Unit, U.K., 1993-94; mem. panel animal health Nat. Rsch. Coun., 1992—. Author: Vet in the Saddle, 1978; editor: Laboratory Animal Medicine, 1984; contbr. numerous articles to profl. jours. Chmn. bd. trustees Boston Zool. Soc., 1984-88; trustee Worcester Acad., 1984-90; mem. Nat. Ctr. Rsch. Resources adv. coun., NIH, 1988-92, Blue Ribbon adv. coun. USDA, 1987-91; bd. dirs. Ea. States Exhbn., 1988—. Decorated Queen Elizabeth II Jubilee medal Gov.-Gen. Can., 1977; Medal Rsch. Coun. Can. fellow, 1969-71; recipient Charles River prize Am. Vet. Med. Assn., 1988, named Vet. of Yr., 1989; recipient Disting. Svc. award Mass. Vet. Med. Assn., 1992. Mem. NAS/Inst. Medicine, AAAS, Am. Inst. Nutrition, Soc. Toxicology, Assn. Am. Vet. Med. Colls. (pres. 1985-86), Am. Coll. Lab. Medicine (bd. dirs. 1979-82), Nat. Acads. Practice, Fedn. Am. Socs. for Exptl. Biology, Am. Antiquarian Soc., Mass. Agrl. Club. Office: Tufts U Sch Vet Medicine 200 Westboro Rd North Grafton MA 01536-1895

LOEW, RALPH WILLIAM, clergyman, columnist; b. Columbus, Ohio, Dec. 29, 1907; s. William Louis and Wilhelmina (Bauer) L.; m. Genevra Maxine Uhl, June 8, 1939; children—Carolyn Maxine, Janet Elaine. A.B. Capital U., 1928; M.Divinity, Hamma Div. Sch., Springfield, Ohio, 1931; D.D., Wittenberg U., 1947; L.H.D., Susquehanna U., 1972, Wagner Coll., 1974; LL.D., Hartwick Coll., 1979. Ordained to ministry Luth. Ch., 1931. Pastor Millerburg (Ohio) Luth. Parish, 1931-37; asso. pastor Luth. Ch. Reformation, Washington, 1937-44; pastor Holy Trinity Luth. Ch., Buffalo, 1944-75; Del. Luth. World Fedn., Lund, Sweden, 1947, Helsinki, Finland, 1968; Knubel-Miller lectr. United Luth. Ch., 1955; lectr. Retreat for Chaplains, Nat. Luth. Council, Berchtesgaden, Germany, 1956; Brit-Am. exchange preacher, 1966, 72; participant Long Range Planning Conf., India, 1968; pres. bd. fgn. missions United Luth Ch. Am., 1956-60, mem. exec. council, 1962-66, pres. bd. world missions, 1970-72, chmn. div. world missions and ecumenism, 1972-76; dir. dept. religion Chautauqua Instn., 1973-84; pres. ct. adjudication Luth. Ch. Am. Author: The Hinges of Destiny, 1955, The Church and the Amateur Adult, 1955, Confronted by Jesus, 1957, Lutheran Way of Life, 1966, Christmas in the Shadows, 1968, He is Coming Soon, 1972; Contbr.: weekly column From My Window, Buffalo Courier-Express, 1964-70; syndicated column Finding The Way, 1960-67. Pres. Buffalo and Erie County Coun. Chs., 1950-51, Comty. Action Orgn., Buffalo and Erie County; pres. bd. trustees Margaret L. Wendt Found.; trustee Chautauqua Instn., 1988-92; pres. WNY Grantmakers, 1988-90; bd. trustees Habitat for Humanity Internat.; founder Habitat for Humanity, Buffalo, 1974. Recipient Chancellor's medal U. Buffalo, Notable Sermon award Life mag., 1957, numerous others. Home: 342 Depew Ave Buffalo NY 14214-1677

LOEWEN, ERWIN G., precision engineer, educator, consultant; b. Frankfurt, Germany, Apr. 12, 1921; came to U.S., 1937; s. Franz L. and Gladys M. (Marx) L.; m. Joanna M. Wills, Sept. 5, 1952; children: Oliver F., Heidi R. BMechE, NYU, 1941; MS, MIT, 1949, MMechE, 1950, ScD, 1952. Tech. dir. Taft-Pierce Mfg. Co., Woonsocket, R.I., 1952-60; dir. gratings and metrology Bausch & Lomb, Rochester, N.Y., 1960-85; v.p. R&D Milton Roy Co., Rochester, 1985-87, emeritus, 1987—; prof. optics U. Rochester, 1988—; contbr. numerous articles on metal cutting, precision engring., and diffraction grating to profl. jours., chpt. to book. Staff sgt. U.S. Army, 1944-46, PTO. Recipient of Robert M. Burley Prize, 1993, Optical Soc. Am. Fellow ASME (v.p. standardization), Optical Soc. Am. (Robert M. Burley Prize, 1993), Soc. Mfg. Engrs.; mem. Am. Soc. Precision Engrs. (hon.), Soc. Photoinstrumentation Engrs., Internat. Instn. Prodn. Engring. Rsch., Sigma Xi. Avocations: photography, skiing, swimming. Home: 34A Brookhill Ln Rochester NY 14625-2212 Office: Milton Roy Co 820 Linden Ave Rochester NY 14625-2791

LOEWENBAUM, G. WALTER, II, cement, oil and gas company executive; b. 1945. With Howard Well Laboucusse Fredricks Inc., New Orleans, 1967-69, Morgan Keegan & Co. Inc., Memphis, 1979—; chmn. bd. Southdown Inc., 1980—. Office: Southdown Inc 1200 Smith St Ste 2400 Houston TX 77002-4402

LOEWENBERG, GERHARD, political science educator; b. Berlin, Germany, Oct. 2, 1928; came to U.S., 1936, naturalized, 1943; s. Walter and Anne Marie (Cassirer) L.; m. Ina Perlstein, Aug. 22, 1950; children: Deborah, Michael. A.B., Cornell U., 1949, A.M., 1950, Ph.D., 1955. Mem. faculty Mount Holyoke Coll., 1953-69, chmn. dept. sci. 1963, 1963-69, acting academic dean, 1968-69; prof. polit. sci. U. Iowa, Iowa City, 1970—, chmn. dept., 1982-84, dean Coll. Liberal Arts, 1984-92, dir. Comparative Legis. Research Center, 1971-82, 92—; vice chair East-West Parliamentary Practice Project, 1990—; vis. assoc. prof. Columbia, UCLA, 1966, U. Mass. summer session at Bologna, Italy, 1967, Cornell U., 1968; mem. council Inter-Univ. Consortium for Polit. Research, 1971-74, chmn., 1973-74. Author: Parliament in the German Political System, 1967, Parlamentarismus im politischen System der Bundesrepublik Deutschland, 1969, Modern Parliaments: Change or Decline, 1971; co-author: Comparing Legislatures, 1979; co-editor: Handbook of Legislative Research, 1985; co-editor: Legis. Studies Quar.; contbr. articles to profl. jours. Trustee Mt. Holyoke Coll., 1971-84, chmn., 1979-84. Fulbright fellow, 1957-58; Rockefeller fellow, 1961-62; Social Sci. Research Council faculty research fellow, 1964-65; Guggenheim fellow, 1969-70. Mem. Am. Polit. Sci. Assn. (coun. 1971-73, v.p. 1990-91), Midwest Polit. Sci. Assn., Phi Beta Kappa, Pi Kappa Phi, Pi Sigma Alpha. Office: 331 Schaeffer Hall U Iowa Iowa City IA 52242

LOEWENSTEIN, BENJAMIN STEINBERG, lawyer; b. Atlantic City, Aug. 22, 1912; s. Sidney and Cecilia (Steinberg) L.; m. Eleanor Lax Schieren, June 14, 1966; children: Sally L. (Mrs. David S. Well, Jr.), P. Edward: stepchildren: Susan (Mrs. Stanton A. Moss, dec.), Julie (Mrs. Robert Dreidink). A.B., Haverford Coll., 1934; J.D., U. Pa., 1937. Bar: Pa. 1937. Practiced in Phila., 1937—; sr. partner Abrahams & Loewenstein, 1937-87, of counsel, 1988—; Sec., dir. Rojess Corp., Gen. Syndicate Corp., Jonns Inc., Engelside Realty Corp., Sherill Corp., Oak Blvd. Inc., Kahn's Inc., Atlas Rug Cleaners, Inc.; Counsel Diamond Coun. Am., Phila. County Dental Soc.; Del. White House Conf. on Aging; chmn. Task Force on Aging, Pa. Comprehensive Health Plan, Regional Comprehensive Health Planning Delaware Valley, Pa., 1968; mem. Pa. Human Relations Commn., 1974-87. Hon. chmn. bd. Jewish Occupational Coun., 1971—; pres. Jewish Employment and Vocat. Service, 1954-59, hon. pres. 1976—; pres. So. Home for Children, 1968-69, Health and Welfare Coun. Phila., 1969-71; pres. Jewish

Community Rels. Coun. Phila., 1974-77, hon. pres., 1978—; mem. bd. govs. Am. Jewish Com., 1968—, hon. chmn. Phila. chpt.; trustee Community Svcs. Pa., 1968-78; bd. mgrs. Haverford Coll., 1970—; bd. dirs. Vocat. Rsch. Inst., 1960—, United Way of Phila., Fedn. Jewish Agys., Phila., Pa. Law and Justice Inst., 1971-76, Fellowship Commn. Phila., 1972-86, Phila. Anti-Poverty Action Commn., 1976-87, Nat. Inst. on the Holocaust, 1977-82; treas. Interfaith Council on the Holocaust, 1986—; bd. dirs. Quadrangle Retirement Community, 1977—, Martins Run Retirement Community, 1981—. Recipient Community Service award Allied Jewish Appeal Phila., 1956, certificate of appreciation Phila. County Med. Soc., 1961, certificate appreciation Fedn. Jewish Agys., 1972, Phila. Commn. Human Relations award, 1974; certificate Merit Am. Cancer Soc., 1974; Samuel Greenberg Meml. award Nat. Assn. Jewish Vocat. Services, 1980; Human Relations award Am. Jewish Com., 1981; Legion of Honor Chapel of Four Chaplains, 1980. Mem. Am., Pa., Phila. bar assns., Lawyers Club Phila., Socialegal Club Phila., Haverford Coll. Alumni Assn. (pres. 1956-57), Am. Arbitration Assn. (nat. panel arbitrators). Home: 2804 Kennedy House 1901 Kennedy Blvd Philadelphia PA 19103-1578 Home: 198 NW 67th St Apt 306 Boca Raton FL 33487 Office: 1650 Market St Ste 3100 Philadelphia PA 19103-7392

LOEWENSTEIN, JOSEPH F., English literature educator; b. Charleston, W.Va., Oct. 20, 1952; s. Stanley M. and Jean Sinclair (Foster) L.; m. C. Lynne Tatlock, Mar. 12, 1988. BA, Wesleyan U., Middletown, Conn., 1974; MA, Columbia U., 1975; PhD, Yale U., 1982. Vis. lectr. English Wesleyan U., 1980-81; asst. prof. Washington U., St. Louis, 1981-86, assoc. prof., 1986—; chmn. dept., 1992—. Fellow NEH, 1988-89, Exxon Edn. Found., 1985-86; grantee Am. Coun. Learned Socs., 1986. Mem. MLA, Renaissance Soc. Am. Office: Washington U Dept English Box 1122 Saint Louis MO 63130

LOEWENSTEIN, WALTER BERNARD, nuclear power technologist; b. Gensungen, Hesse, Germany, Dec. 23, 1926; came to U.S., 1938; s. Louis and Johanna ((Katz) L.; m. Lenore C. Brauner, June 21, 1959; children: Mark Victor, Marcia Beth. BS, U. Puget Sound, 1949; postgrad., U. Wash., 1949-50; PhD, Ohio State U., 1954. Registered profl. engr., Calif. Rsch. asst., fellow Ohio State U., Columbus, 1951-54; rsch. asst. Los Alamos Nat. Lab., 1952-54; sr. physicist, divsn. dir. Argonne (Ill.) Nat. Lab., 1954-73; dept. dir., dep. divsn. dir. Electric Power Rsch. Inst., Palo Alto, Calif., 1973-89, profl. cons., 1989—, mem. large aerosol containment experiment project bd., 1983-87; mem. Marviksen project bd. Studsvik Rsch. Ctr., Stockholm, 1978-85; mem. LOFT project bd. Nuclear Energy Agy., Paris, 1982-89; mem. tech. adv. nuclear safety Ontario Hydro Corp., 1990—; mem. nuclear engring. dept. adv. com. Brookhaven Nat. Lab., 1992—. With USNR, 1945-46. Recipient Alumnus Cum Laude award U. Puget Sound, 1976. Fellow Am. Phys. Soc., Am. Nuclear Soc. (v.p., pres. 1988-90); mem. Am. Assn. Engring. Socs. (sec., treas. 1990), Nat. Acad. Engring. Jewish. Avocations: history, golf. Home and Office: 515 Jefferson Dr Palo Alto CA 94303

LOEWER, JACKIE, church official; m. Onietta Lower. Conf. treas. N.Am. Bapt. Conf., Oakbrook Terrace, Ill., 1991—; mem. exec. com. N.Am. Bapt. Conf., mem. pension task force, investment task force. Office: N Am Baptist Conference 1 S 210 Summit Ave Villa Park IL 60181

LOEWY, STEVEN A., lawyer; b. N.Y.C., Dec. 21, 1952; s. Samuel Alexander and Irene Dorothy (Aber) L.; m. Dina Rosenberg, Apr. 2, 1978; children: Tamar, David. BA, Washington U., St. Louis, 1974; JD, Yeshiva U., 1979. Bar: Md. 1980, U.S. Supreme Ct. 1983. Assoc. Gordon, Feinblatt, Rothman, Hoffberger & Hollander, Balt., 1980-81, Constable, Alexander, Daneker & Skeen, Balt., 1981-85, Weinberg and Green, Balt., 1985-87; ptnr. Ober, Kaler, Grimes & Shriver, Balt., 1987—; lectr. in law U. Balt., 1981-84; active edn. appeal bd. U.S. Dept. Edn., Washington, 1985-90. Research grantee U.S. Dept. Housing and Devel., 1979. Mem. ABA (chmn. title ins. com., real property sect.), Md. Bar Assn. (real property sect.), Balt. City Bar Assn., Am. Land Title Assn. Republican. Jewish. Home: 6715 Western Run Dr Baltimore MD 21215-2506 Office: Ober Kaler Grimes & Shriver 111 S Calvert St # 2700 Baltimore MD 21202-6174

LOFERSKI, JOSEPH JOHN, electrical engineering educator; b. Hudson, Pa., Aug. 7, 1925; s. Andrew and Mary (Kochuba) L.; m. Sylvia Sweeda, Aug. 27, 1949; children: Marianne Fleury, Patricia Seal, Joseph, Barbara, Michael, Sharon. BS in Physics, U. Scranton, 1948; MS, U. Pa., 1949, PhD, 1953. Research physicist RCA Labs., 1953-60; faculty Brown U., 1961—, prof. engring., 1966—, dean of engring., 1968-74, assoc. dean Grad. Sch., 1980-83; dir. R.I. Ctr. for Thin Film and Interface Rsch., 1987—; res. Solamat, Inc., E. Providence, 1977-83; sci. counsellor U.S. Embassy, Warsaw, 1985-87; mem. U.S./Poland Joint Commn. for Sci. and Tech. Coop., 1988-91; U.S./Poland Nat. Acad. Scis. Exchange fellow Inst. Nuclear Rsch., Swierk, 1974-75; mem. New Eng. Energy Congress, 1978-79; mem. organizing coms. 23 IEEE Photovoltaic Conf., 1956-57, Internat. Photovoltaic Confs., 1984—; gen. chmn. Fifth Internat. Conf. on Solid Films and Surfaces, 1990; cons. in field; lectr. on solar photovoltaic energy, sci. and tech.; vis. chaired prof. Nat. Tsing Hua U., Hasin-chu, Taiwan, 1994—. Mem. editorial bd.: Jour. Solar Energy, 1974-80, 89—, Energy Conversion, 1972—, Jour. Solar Energy Materials, 1978-92, Jour. Solar Energy Materials and Solar Cells, 1992, Progress in Photovoltaics, 1992—; contbr. numerous articles to profl. jours. Served with AUS, 1944-46. Recipient Pioneer award Providence Engring. Soc., 1974; named to Internat. Solar Hall of Fame, 1989. Fellow AAAS, IEEE (William Cherry award 1981); mem. Sigma Xi, Tau Beta Pi. Home: 33 Slater Ave Providence RI 02906-5423 Office: Brown Univ Div Engring Box D Providence RI 02912

LOFGREN, CHARLES AUGUSTIN, legal and constitutional historian; b. Missoula, Mont., Sept. 8, 1939; s. Cornelius Willard and Helen Mary (Augustin) L.; m. Jennifer Jenkins Wood, Aug. 6, 1986. AB with great distinction, Stanford U., 1961, AM, 1962, PhD, 1966. Instr. history San Jose State Coll., 1965-66; asst. prof. Claremont McKenna Coll., 1966-71; assoc. prof., 1971-76, prof., 1976—, Roy P. Crocker prof. Am. history and politics, 1976—. Served with USAR, 1957-63. Mem. Am. Soc. Legal History, Orgn. Am. Historians, Am. Hist. Assn. Republican. Roman Catholic. Author: Government from Reflection and Choice, 1986, The Plessy Case, 1988; contbr. articles to profl. jours. Office: Claremont McKenna Coll Dept History 850 Columbia Ave Claremont CA 91711

LOFGREN, KARL ADOLPH, surgeon; b. Killeberg, Sweden, Apr. 1, 1915; s. Hokan Albin and Teckla Elizabeth (Carlsson) L.; m. Jean Frances Taylor, Sept. 12, 1942; children: Karl Edward, Anne Elizabeth. Student, Northwestern U., 1934-37; M.D., Harvard U., 1941; M.S. in Surgery, U. Minn., 1947. Diplomate Am. Bd. Surgery. Intern U. Minn. Hosps., Mpls., 1941-42; Mayo Found. fellow in surgery, 1942-44, 46-48; asst. surgeon Royal Acad. Hosp., Uppsala, Sweden, 1949; asst. to surg. staff Mayo Clinic, Rochester, Minn., 1949-50; cons. sect. peripheral vein surgery Mayo Clinic, 1950-81; instr. in surgery Mayo Grad. Sch. Medicine, 1951-60, asst. prof. surgery, 1960-74; comdg. officer USNR Med. Co. Mayo Clinic, 1963-67, head sect. peripheral vein surgery, 1966-79; cons. surgery, 1966-79; cons. clinic, 1963-81; assoc. prof. surgery Mayo Med. Sch., 1974-79, prof., 1979-81, emeritus prof., 1982—; cons. surg. staff Rochester Meth. Hosp., St. Mary's Hosp. Contbr. chpts. to textbooks, articles to profl. jours. Mem. adv. bd. Salvation Army, Rochester, 1959-81, 82—, pres., 1962-63. Served to capt. M.C. USNR, 1944-46. Decorated Bronze Star. Fellow ACS; mem. Soc. Vascular Surgery, Midwestern Vascular Surgery Soc., Internat. Cardiovascular Soc., Minn. Surg. Soc., Swedish Surg. Soc. (hon.), Swiss Soc. Phlebology (co-worker), So. Minn. Med. Assn. (pres. 1972-73), Scandinavian Soc. Phlebology (hon.), Am. Venous Forum, Rotary Club, Sigma Xi. Baptist. Home: 1001 7th Ave NE Rochester MN 55906-7074 Office: Mayo Clinic Rochester MN 55905

LOFGREN, ZOE, county government official; b. San Mateo, Calif., Dec. 21, 1947; d. Milton R. and Mary Violet L.; m. John Marshall Collins, Oct. 22, 1978; children: Sheila Zoe Lofgren Collins, John Charles Lofgren Collins. BA in Polit. Sci., Stanford U., 1970; JD cum laude, U. Santa Clara, 1975. Bar: Calif. 1975. D.C. Adminstrv. asst. to Congressman Don Edwards, San Jose, Calif., 1970-79; ptnr. Webber and Lofgren, San Jose, 1979-81; mem. Santa Clara County Bd. Suprs., 1981-94; congresswoman 104th U.S. Congress, Calif. 16th Dist., 1995—; part-time profl. Law U. Santa Clara, 1978-80; jud. com. on crime; house com. on sci., subcommittee on tech., basic rsch. Exec. dir. Community Housing Developers, Inc., 1979-80; trustee San

Jose Community Coll. Dist., 1979-81; bd. dirs. Community Legal Svcs., 1978-81, San Jose Housing Svc. Ctr., 1978-79; mem. steering com. sr. citizens housing referendum, 1978; del. Calif. State Bar Conv., 1979-82, Dem. Nat. Conv., 1976; active Assn. Immigration and Nationality Lawyers, 1976-82, Calif. State Dem. Com., 1975-78, Santa Clara County Dem. Cen. Com., 1974-78, Notre Dame High Sch. Blue Ribbon Com., 1981-84, Victim-Witness Adv. Bd., 1981-94. Recipient Bancroft-Whitney award for Excellence in Criminal Procedure, 1973. Mem. Santa Clara County Bar Assn. (trustee 1979—), Santa Clara County Women Lawyers Com. (exec. bd. 1979-80), Sanata Clara Law Sch. Alumni Assn. (v.p. 1977, pres. 1978), Nat. Women's Polit. Caucus, Assn. of Bay Area Govts. (exec. bd. 1981-86). Office: US House Reps 118 Cannon House Office Bldg Washington DC 20515-0516 also: 635 N First St Ste B San Jose CA 95112

LOFLAND, JOHN FRANKLIN, sociologist, educator; b. Milford, Del., Mar. 4, 1936; s. John Purnell and Juanita (Jobe) L.; m. Lyn Hebert, Jan. 2, 1965. B.A., Swarthmore Coll., 1958; M.A., Columbia U., 1960; Ph.D., U. Calif., Berkeley, 1964. Asst. prof. U. Mich., 1964-68; assoc. prof. sociology Calif. State U., Sonoma, 1968-70; assoc. prof. sociology U. Calif., Davis, 1970-74; prof. U. Calif., 1974-94; prof. emeritus U. Calif., Davis, 1994—. Author: Doomsday Cult, 1966, 77, Analyzing Social Settings, 1971, 3d edit. (with L.H. Lofland), 1995, Protest, 1985, Polite Protesters, 1993, 6 other books; founding editor Jour. Contemporary Ethnography, 1970-74; contbr. articles and revs. to profl. lit. Mem. Am. Sociol. Assn. (chair sect. on collective behavior and social movements 1980-81, chair sect. on sociology of peace and war 1989-90, Outstanding Scholarship award 1987, sect. on collective behavior and social movements), Pacific Sociol. Assn. (pres. 1980-81), Soc. Study Symbolic Interaction (pres. 1986-87). Home: 523 E St Davis CA 95616-3816 Office: U Calif Sociology Dept Davis CA 95616

LOFLAND, LYN HEBERT, sociology educator; b. Everett, Wash., Dec. 2, 1937; d. Lisle Francis and Estelle Mae (Hogan) Hebert; m. Stuart A. Jones, Dec. 28, 1958 (div. 1964); m. John Franklin Lofland, Jan. 2, 1965. BA, Antioch Coll., Yellow Springs, Ohio, 1960; MA, U. Mich., 1966; PhD, U. Calif., San Francisco, 1971. Asst. prof. sociology U. Calif., Davis, 1971-77, assoc. prof., 1977-85, prof., 1985—, vice chair dept., 1986-89, acad. dir. Women's Resource and Rsch. Ctr., 1976-78. Author: A World of Strangers, 1973, The Craft of Dying, 1978; co-author: Analyzing Social Settings, 1984, 95; editor: Toward a Sociology of Death and Dying, 1976; co-editor: The Community of the Streets, 1994. Mem. Am. Sociol. Assn. (chair community and urban sociology sect. 1986-88), Pacific Sociol. Assn. (pres. 1989-90), Soc. for Study Symbolic Interaction (pres. 1980-81), Davis Faculty Assn. (chair 1988-89). Democratic Socialist. Avocations: reading, puzzles, indoor gardening. Home: 523 E Street Davis CA 95616 Office: U Calif Dept Sociology Davis CA 95616

LOFRISCO, ANTHONY F., lawyer; b. Bklyn., 1933. BS, Fordham U., 1955, LLB, 1958. Bar: N.Y. 1958, U.S. Supreme Ct. 1960. Ptnr. Winston & Strawn, N.Y.C. Office: Winston & Strawn 175 Water St New York NY 10038-4918

LÖFSTEDT, BENGT TORKEL MAGNUS, classics educator; b. Lund, Sweden, Nov. 14, 1931; came to U.S., 1967; s. Ernst Martin Hugo and Sigrid (Johanson) L.; m. Maija-Leena Kekomäki, Oct. 15, 1961; children: Ragnar, Torsten, Ritva, Ingvar. M.A., U. Uppsala, Sweden, 1954, Fil. Lic. (Ph.D.), 1957, Fil. doktor, 1961. Asst. prof. Latin U. Uppsala, 1962-67; asso. prof. Mediaeval Latin U. Calif. at Los Angeles, 1967-68, prof., 1968—; contbr. Swedish newspapers Fria Ord, Vägen Framåt. Author: Studien Über die Sprache der langobardischen Gesetze, 1961, Der hibernolateinische Grammatiker Malsachanus, 1965, Zenonis Veronensis Tractatus, 1971, Ars Laureshamensis, 1977, Sedulius Scottus: In Donati artem maiorem, 1977, Sedulius Scottus: In Donati artem minorem, in Priscianum, in Eutychen, 1977, Ars Ambrosiana, 1982, Beatus Liebanensis: Adversus Elipandum, 1984, (with G.J. Gebauer) Bonifatius Ars Grammatica, 1980, (with L. Holtz and A. Kibre) Smaragdus: Liber in Partibus Donati, 1986, Sedulius Scottus: Kommentar zum Evangelium nach Matthäus 1.1-11.1, 1989, (with Leena Löfstedt) Maturin Cordier: De corrupti sermonis emendatione, 1989, Sedulius Scottus, Kommentar zum Evangelium nach Matthäus 11,2 bis Schluss, 1991, (with B. Bischoff) Anonymus ad Cuimnanum, 1992; contbr. articles to profl. jours. Served to lt. Swedish Army, 1959-60. Alexander von Humboldt-Stiftung fellow Munich, 1961-62; Humanities Inst., U. Calif. grantee, 1968, 71; Am. Philos. Soc. grantee, 1971, 74; Am. Council Learned Socs. grantee, 1972, 75. Lutheran. Office: UCLA Dept Classics 405 Hilgard Ave Los Angeles CA 90024-1301

LOFT, KURT, newspaper editor, science writer, music critic; b. Baltimore, Fla., Mar. 5, 1956; s. Ernest E. and Mary (Guilday) L. Student, U. Ctrl. Fla., 1972-79, U. Fla., 1979-81. Music critic Tampa (Fla.) Tribune, 1981—, sci. writer, 1987—. Office: Tampa Tribune 202 S. Parker St Tampa FL 33606*

LOFTFIELD, ROBERT BERNER, biochemistry educator; b. Detroit, Dec. 15, 1919; s. Sigurd and Katherine (Roller) L.; m. Ella Bradford, Aug. 24, 1946 (dec. Dec. 1990); children: Lore Loftfield DeBower, Eric, Linda, Norman, Björn, Curtis, Katherine, Earl, Allison, Ella-Kari. BS, Harvard U., 1941, MA, 1942, PhD, 1946. Research assoc. MIT, Cambridge, 1946-48; research assoc. to sr. research assoc. Mass. Gen. Hosp., Boston, 1948-64; asst. to assoc. prof. biochemistry Harvard U. Sch. Medicine, Boston, 1948-64; prof. biochemistry Sch. Medicine U. N.Mex., Albuquerque, 1964-90, chmn. dept. biochemistry, 1964-71, 78-90, prof. emeritus, 1990—. Contbr. articles on protein biosynthesis and enzymology to profl. jours. Served as corp. U.S. Army, 1945-46. Fellow Damon Runyon Fund, 1952-53, Guggenheim Found., 1961-62; Fulbright fellow, 1977, 83; sr. fellow NIH, 1971-72. Mem. AAAS, Am. Soc. Biol. Chemists, Am. Chem. Soc., Am. Assn. Cancer Research, Biophys. Soc., Marine Biol. Lab. Lutheran. Avocations: sailing, hiking, camping, skiing. Home: 707 Fairway Rd NW Albuquerque NM 87107-5718 Office: Univ NMex Sch of Medicine Dept of Biochemistry Albuquerque NM 87131

LOFTIN, MARION THEO, sociologist, educator; b. Coushatta, La., Sept. 10, 1915; s. John Griffin and Ida Estella (Huckaby) L. B.A., Northwestern La. State Coll., 1936; M.A., La. State U., 1941; Ph.D., Vanderbilt U., 1952. Tchr. pub. high schs. Red River Parish, La., 1935-40; asso. Southeastern La. State Coll., 1946-47; faculty Miss. State U., 1949—, Thomas L. Bailey prof. sociology and anthropology, head dept., 1961-67; assoc. dean Miss. State U. (Grad. Sch.), 1965-77, dean, 1977-79, v.p. grad. studies and research, 1980-85, prof. sociology, v.p. grad. studies and research emeritus, 1986—. Served with AUS, 1941-45. Mem. Am. Sociol. Assn., Rural Sociol. Soc., So. Sociol. Soc., Phi Kappa Phi, Omicron Delta Kappa. Home: Hillcrest Cir Starkville MS 39759

LOFTIN, SISTER MARY FRANCES, health facility administrator; b. Atlanta, Mar. 25, 1928. B, Marquette U., 1955; M, George Washington U., 1970. Various positions, 1955-66; dir. nursing svcs. Seton Med. Ctr., Austin, 1966-68; adminstrv. resident Med. Ctr. East, Birmingham, Ala., 1969-70, asst. adminstr., 1970-71; asst. adminstr. St. Joseph Hosp. & Health Care Ctr., Chgo., 1971-74; adminstr. St. Thomas Hosp., Nashville, 1974-81; pres. Daus. of Charity Health Sys., Evansville, Ind., 1981-87; pres., CEO Daus. of Charity Nat. Health Sys., St. Louis, 1992-94; with Diocese of Birmingham, Ala., 1995—. Home: St Vincent's Residence 2724 Hanover Cir Birmingham AL 35205-1706 Office: Chancellor's Office Diocese of Birmingham PO Box 12047 Birmingham AL 35202-2047

LOFTIN, RAYMOND VICTOR, JR., oil and gas company executive; b. Houston, Dec. 24, 1927; s. Raymond Victor and Helen Viola (Jones) L.; m. Martha McBride, Apr. 4, 1959 (div. May 1986); children: Helen Louise, Stephen McBride. BA, Rice U., 1948; LLB, U. Tex., 1951. Bar: Tex. 1951. U.S. Supreme Ct. Appeals (5th cir.), U.S. Supreme Ct. Briefing atty. Tex. Supreme Ct., Austin, 1957-58; from atty. to sr. v.p., assoc. gen. counsel Transco Energy Co., Houston, 1961—. With U.S. Army, 1952-54, Korea. Fellow Tex. Bar Found. (life); mem. State Bar Assn. Tex. (chmn. corp. counsel sect. 1977-78), Federal Energy Bar, Houston Bar Assn. Republican. Episcopalian. Avocations: running, hunting, gardening, tennis.

LOFTIS, JACK D., newspaper editor, newspaper executive. Exec. v.p., editor Houston Chronicle. Office: Houston Chronicle Pub Co 801 Texas St Houston TX 77002-2907*

LOFTIS, JOHN (CLYDE), JR., English language educator; b. Atlanta, May 16, 1919; s. John Clyde and Marbeth (Brown) L.; m. Anne Nevins, June 29, 1946; children: Mary, Laura, Lucy. BA, Emory U. 1940; MA, Princeton U., 1942, PhD, 1948. Fellow English Princeton, 1946-48; instr., then asst. prof. English UCLA, 1948-52; faculty Stanford U., 1952-81, prof. English, 1958-81, Bailey prof. English, 1977-81, Bailey prof. emeritus, 1981—, chmn. dept., 1973-76. Author: Steele at Drury Lane, 1952, Comedy and Society from Congreve to Fielding, 1959, La Independencia de la Literatura Norteamericana, 1961, The Politics of Drama in Augustan England, 1963, The Spanish Plays of Neoclassical England, 1973, (with others) The Revels History of Drama in English, Vol. V, 1976, Sheridan and the Drama of Georgian England, 1977, Renaissance Drama in England and Spain: Topical Allusion and History Plays, 1987; editor: (Steele) The Theatre, 1962, Restoration Drama: Modern Essays in Criticism, 1966, (with V.A. Dearing) The Works of John Dryden, Vol. IX, 1966, (Sheridan) The School for Scandal, 1966, (Nathaniel Lee) Lucius Junius Brutus, 1967, (Addison) Essays in Criticism and Literary Theory, 1975, The Memoirs of Anne, Lady Halkett and Ann, Lady Fanshawe, 1979, (with D.S. Rodes and V.A. Dearing) The Works of John Dryden, Vol. XI, 1978, (with P.H. Hardacre) Colonel Bampfield's Apology, 1993; co-editor Augustan Reprint Society, 1949-1952, English Literature, 1660-1800: A Current Bibliography, 1951-56; gen. editor: Regents Restoration Drama Series, 35 vols, 1962-81; mem. editorial bd.: Studies in English Literature, 1966-76, Huntington Library Quar., 1968-76, Wesleyan Edit. Works Henry Fielding, 1970-83, Augustan Reprint Soc., 1985-90. Served with USNR, 1942-46, PTO. Fellow Fund Advancement Edn., 1955-56; Fulbright lectr. Am. studies Peru, 1959-60; Guggenheim fellow, 1966-67; fellow Folger Shakespeare Library, 1967; NEH fellow, 1978-79. Mem. MLA, Phi Beta Kappa, Kappa Alpha. Home: 7 Arastradero Rd Portola Valley CA 94028-8012 Office: Stanford Univ Dept English Stanford CA 94305

LOFTON, KENNETH, professional baseball player; b. East Chicago, Ind., May 31, 1967. Student, U. Ariz. Baseball player Houston Astros, 1988-91, Cleveland Indians, 1992—. Ranked 1st in Am. League for stolen bases, 1992; recipient Am. League Gold Glove award, 1993, 94; named to All-Star Team, 1994. Office: Cleveland Indians 2401 Ontario St Cleveland OH 44115*

LOFTON, THOMAS MILTON, lawyer; b. Indpls., May 12, 1929; s. Milton Alexander and Jane (Routzong) L.; m. Betty Louise Blades, June 20, 1954; children: Stephanie Louise, Melissa Jane. BS, Ind. U., 1951, JD, 1954. Bar: Ind. 1954, U.S. Ct. Appeals (7th cir.) 1959, U.S. Supreme Ct. 1958. Law clk. to justice U.S. Supreme Ct., Washington, 1954-55; ptnr. Baker & Daniels, Indpls., 1958—; dir. Ind. U. Found., bloomington, 1978—; chmn. of bd. Lilly Endowment, Indpls., 1991—; dir. Clowes Fund, 198—; mem. bd. visitors Ind. U. Law, Bloomington, 1976—. Editor-in-chief Ind. Law Jour., 1953. 1st lt. U.S. Army, 1955-58. Recipient Peck award Wabash Coll., 1982. Mem. Order of Coif, Masons, Beta Gamma Sigma. Republican. Presbyterian. Home: 9060 Pickwick Dr Indianapolis IN 46260-1714 Office: Baker & Daniels 300 N Meridian St Indianapolis IN 46204-1755

LOFTUS, DONALD GREGORY, hospital administrator; b. St. Louis, Aug. 17, 1943; s. Charles J. and Mary A. Loftus; m. Christie J. Rivers, Aug. 1, 1992; children :Kelly Anne, Kyle Andrew, Meridith, David, Matthew. B.S. Ind. U., 1965; M.S., Trinity U., 1969. Adminstrv. extern Bloomington Hosp. (Ind.), 1964-65; unit mgr. dept. adminstrv. medicine Presbyn.-St. Luke's Hosp., Chgo., 1965-67; grad. asst. health resources planning unit Tex. Hosp. Assn., San Antonio, 1968; adminstrv. resident Ind. U. Med. Ctr., Indpls., 1968; asst. adminstr. Graham Hosp., Canton, Ill., 1969-73; adminstr. Franklin Hosp., Benton, Ill., 1973-74; exec. v.p. Holy Family Hosp., Des Plaines, Ill., 1974-76; pres., chief exec. officer Appleton Meml. Hosp. (Wis.), 1977-80, United Health Services, Appleton, 1980-83, St. Joseph Health Corp., Fort Worth, 1983, St. Joseph Health Corp., 1984-86; exec. v.p., COO Greater Balt. Med. Ctr., 1988—; rep. Outagamie Community Blood Bank, 1977-79; lectr., preceptor U. Wis. St. Louis U., Trinity U., George Washington U., John Hopkins U.; mem. instructional workshop adv. com. Tri-State Hosp. Assembly, 1976-78; dir. Valley Bank; assoc. clin. prof. U. Wis. Med. Sch., Madison. Hosp. rep. Gov.'s Prison Health Care Adv. Com., State of Wis., 1977-79; bd. dirs. Lake Winnebago Health Systems Agy., 1977—; Dallas-Ft. Worth Hosp. Council, 1984—, Tex. Conf. Cath. Health Facilities, 1985—. Fellow Am. Coll. Hosp. Adminstrs.; mem. Wis. Hosp. Assn. (mem. com. on planning 1978-82), Am. Acad. Polit. and Social Sci., Sigma Iota Epsilon. Office: Greater Baltimore Medical Ctr 6701 N Charles St Baltimore MD 21204

LOFTUS, STEPHEN FRANCIS, naval officer; b. Wellesley, Mass., Oct. 27, 1933; s. Bernard Francis and Margaret Louise (Bushey) L.; m. Martha Jane Smith, Nov. 28, 1959; children: Nancy Marie Loftus Huether, Susan Jane Loftus Arthur. B.S. Mass., 1956; MS in Fin. Mgmt., Naval Postgrad. Sch., Monterey, Calif., 1970. Commd. ensign USN, 1956, advanced through grades to vice adm., 1991, div. officer Carrier Airborne Early Warning Squadron 12, 1957-59, div. officer Patrol Squadron 21, 1963-65, div. officer Comdr. Fleet Air Wing 3, 1965-66; aide to Comdr. Naval Air Systems Command USN, Washington, 1966-68; dept. head Heavy Attack Squadron 21 USN, 1968-69, dept. head Patrol Squadron 24, 1971-72; S-3 dep. program mgr. Naval Air Systems Command USN, Washington, 1972-75; exec. officer Patrol Squadron 45 USN, 1975-76, comdg. officer Patrol Squadron 45, 1976-77; exec. asst. to Chief of Naval Pers. USN, Washington, 1977-79, br. head career programs Office of Chief of Naval Ops., 1979-80, exec. asst., naval aide to Asst. Sec. Navy, 1980-81; comdg. officer Naval Air Sta. USN, Bermuda, 1981-83; dep. comdr., comptr. Naval Sea Systems Command USN, Washington, 1984-86; comdr. Fleet Air Mediterranean USN, 1986-87; dir. office of budgets and reports Dept. of Navy USN, Washington, 1987-89, dir. Office of Program Appraisal, Office of Sec. of Navy, 1989-90, dep. Chief Naval Ops., Office of Chief Naval Ops., 1990—. Contbr. articles to jours. in field. Decorated D.S.M., Def. Superior Svc. medal, Legion of Merit with two gold stars, Disting. Flying Cross, Meritorious Svc. medal, Air medal with Numeral 3, Navy Commendation medal with Combat V, Navy Achievement medal, Rep. Vietnam Gallantry cross. Mem. Am. Soc. Mil. Comptrs. (pres. 1988-90), U.S. Navy Hist. Soc. (trustee 1991), U.S. Naval Undersea Mus. (bd. dirs., chmn. 1991), Am. Soc. Naval Engrs. (hon.), N.Y. Yacht Club, Army-Navy Country Club (Arlington, Va.). Roman Catholic. Office: Navy Dept Dep CNO Logistics Navy # Op-04 Washington DC 20350

LOFTUS, THOMAS ADOLPH, ambassador; b. Stoughton, Wis., Apr. 24, 1945; s. Adolph Olean and Margaret Elaine (Nielson) L.; m. Barbara Carolyn Schasse, Aug. 23, 1969; children: Alec Kristian, Karl Edward. B.S. U. Wis.-Whitewater, 1970; M.A., U. Wis.-Madison, 1971. Analyst Wis. Assembly Dem. Caucus, Madison, 1974-75, adminstrv. asst. to Speaker, 1975-76; mem. Wis. State Assembly, 1977-91; majority leader of Assembly, 1981-82, speaker of the Assembly, 1983-91; dir. WisKids Count Wis. Coun. Children and Families, 1991-93; amb. to Norway Oslo, 1993—; adj. prof. polit. sci. U. Wis.-Whitewater; lectr. Edgewood Coll.; vis. prof. Rutgers U., Eagleton Inst. Author: The Art of Legislative Politics, 1994. Del. Dem. Nat. Conf., 1976, 82, 88, 92; mem. Dem. Nat. Com., 1989-91; Dem. nominee for Gov. of Wis., 1990. Served with U.S. Army, 1965-67. Fellow John F. Kennedy Sch. Govt. Harvard U. Democrat. Lutheran. Home: Psc 691000 Psc 691000 APO AE 09707-5000 Office: Am Embassy Oslo PSC 69 Box 1000 APO AE 09707

LOFTUS, WILLIAM FREDERICK, corporate financial executive, lawyer; b. Niagara Falls, Sept. 26, 1938; s. William H. and Mary O. (Kirchner) L.; m. Bonnie Braxton Geiger, Aug. 26, 1961; children: Stephen Geiger, William Kirchner. A.B., Yale U., 1960; J.D., U. Mich., 1963; LL.M. in Taxation, NYU, 1968. Bar: N.Y. 1963. Practice law N.Y.C., 1963-68; various mgmt positions E.I. duPont de Nemours & Co., Wilmington, Del., 1963-79; dir. tax Allied Signal Corp., Morristown, N.J., 1979-82, v.p., treas., 1982-88; sr. v.p., chief fin. officer US Air Group Inc., Arlington, Va., 1989—. Active Legal Advocacy for Handicapped Children; founder, trustee N.J. Assn. for Hearing Impaired, Inc.; bd. dirs. Deafness Research Found. Mem. Nat. Assn. Corp. Treas., N.Y. State Bar Assn. Clubs: Yale of Central N.J. (Summit) (trustee and officer 1979, sec. 1981-83); Beacon Hill Country; Am. Yacht (Rye,

N.Y.). Home: 1 Devonshire Pl Apt 3001 Boston MA 02109-3515 Office: US Air Group Inc 2345 Crystal Dr Arlington VA 22227-0001

LOGA, SANDA, physicist, educator; b. Bucharest, Romania, June 13, 1932; came to U.S., 1968; d. Stelian and Georgeta (Popescu) L.; m. Karl Heinz Werther, Mar. 1968 (div. 1970). MS in Physics, U. Bucharest, 1955; PhD in Biophysics, U. Pitts., 1978. Asst. prof. faculty medicine and pharmacy Bucharest, 1963-67; rsch. asst. Presbyn./St. Luke's Hosp., Chgo., 1968-69; assoc. rsch. scientist Miles Labs., Elkhart, Ind., 1969-70; rsch. asst. U. Pitts., 1971-78; rsch. assoc. Carnegie-Mellon U., Pitts., 1978-80; health physicist VA Med. Ctr., Westside, Chgo., 1980; med. physicist VA Med. Ctr. N. Chgo, 1980—; assoc. prof. Chgo. Med. Sch., N. Chgo., 1985—. Mem. Am. Assn. Physicists in Medicine, Health Physics Soc. Office: Chgo Med Sch U Health Scis 3333 Green Bay Rd North Chicago IL 60064-3037

LOGAN, DAVID BRUCE, health care administrator; b. Grand Rapids, Mich., Jan. 30, 1942; s. Wesley Goldsmith and Ernestine (Sovereen) L.; m. Joann Fern Jordan, Nov. 5, 1961; children: Jennifer, Julie, Jeanine, David II, Douglas, Dean. MusB, U. Mich., 1964; B Zoology with honors, Mich. State U., 1970; MBA, U. Ill., 1978. Tchr. sci. Flint (Mich.) Pub. Schs., 1970-71; health care adminstr. USAF, Mpls., 1971-75; asst. chief, med. adminstrn. svc. trainee VA, Mpls., 1975-76; asst. chief med. adminstrn. svc. VA, Danville, Ill., 1976-78; asst. med. dist. coord. VA Med. Dist. 15, Indpls., 1978-80; med. dist. coord. VA Med. Dist. 8, Durham, N.C., 1980-87; nat. disaster med. system mgr. VA, Salisbury, N.C., 1987—. Dir. choir Kirk of Kildaire Presbyn. Ch., 1981-85; asst. scoutmaster, scoutmaster Boy Scouts Am., 1978—. Capt. USAF, 1964-68, lt. col. Res. ret. Fellow Am. Coll. Healthcare Execs., Soc. Air Force Res. Med. Officers, Air Force Assn., Res. Officers Assn. (bd. dirs. Minn. 1973-74, jr. v.p. for air 1974-75). Office: Dept VA Med Ctr 1601 Brenner Ave Salisbury NC 28144-2515

LOGAN, FRANCIS DUMMER, lawyer; b. Evanston, Ill., May 23, 1931; s. Simon Rae and Frances (Dummer) L.; m. Claude Riviere, Apr. 13, 1957; children: Carolyn Gisele, Francis Dummer. B.A., U. Chgo., 1950; B.A. Juris, Oxford U., 1954; LL.B. Harvard U., 1955. Bar: N.Y. 1956, Calif. 1989. Assoc. Milbank, Tweed, Hadley & McCloy, N.Y.C., 1955-64; ptnr. Milbank, Tweed, Hadley & McCloy, 1965—. Mem. ABA, N.Y. State Bar Assn., Assn. of Bar of City of N.Y., Calif. Bar Assn., Council on Fgn. Relations, Am. Law Inst. Home: 910 Park Ave New York NY 10021 Office: Milbank Tweed Hadley & McCloy 1 Chase Manhattan Plz New York NY 10005

LOGAN, HENRY VINCENT, transportation executive; b. Phila., Nov. 7, 1942; s. Edward Roger and Alberta (Gross) L.; m. Mary Genzano, Sept. 28, 1963; children: Michele Leah, Maureen Laura, Monica Lynn. BS in Commerce, DePaul U., 1975; M in Mgmt., Northwestern U., 1984. Successively supr. corp. acctg., mgr. gen. acctg., mgr. gen. acctg., dir. corp. acctg. and taxes TTX Co., Chgo., 1962-70, controller, 1970-78, dir. fin. planning, 1978-83, mng. dir., fin. adminstr., 1983-85, v.p., chief fin. officer, 1985-88, sr. v.p. fleet mgmt., 1988—; bd. dirs. Calpro Co., Mira Loma, Calif., RailGon Co., Chgo., Railway Supply Assn. Treas. TTX Co. Polit. Action Com., Chgo., 1980; vol Sch. Dist. 87 Task Force, Glen Ellyn, Ill., 1986. Mem. Nat. Freight Transp. Assn., Intermodal Assn. N.Am. (chmn. legis. com. 1992-94), Union League Club (reception com. 1987-92, fin. com. 1993—), Medinah (Ill.) Country Club. Republican. Roman Catholic. Avocations: golf, music, reading, bicycling. Home: 812 Abbey Dr Glen Ellyn IL 60137-6130

LOGAN, J. MURRAY, investment manager; b. Balt., Mar. 15, 1935; s. Lloyd and Helen Mildred (Gilbert) L.; m. Mary Page Cole, June 19, 1987 (dec. Sept. 1993); 1 child by previous marriage, Maria Charlotte. BA, Johns Hopkins U., 1959. Securities analyst Merrill Lynch Pierce Fenner & Smith, N.Y.C., 1959-62; ptnr. Wood Struthers & Winthrop, N.Y.C., 1962-70; v.p. EFC Mgmt. Corp., L.A., 1970-73, Faulkner, Dawkins & Sullivan, Inc., N.Y.C., 1973-75; chmn. investment policy com. Rockefeller & Co., Inc., N.Y.C., 1975—; bd. dirs Mercury Selected Trust, Luxembourg, U.K. Fund, N.Y.C., Europe Fund, N.Y.C., World Trust Fund, Luxembourg, Coll. Constrn. Loan Ins. Assn., Washington. Trustee Johns Hopkins U., Balt., 1984-91. With USCG, 1954-56. Mem. Racquet and Tennis Club, The Leash. Office: Rockefeller & Co Inc 30 Rockefeller Plz # 5425 New York NY 10112-0001

LOGAN, JAMES KENNETH, federal judge; b. Quenemo, Kans., Aug. 21, 1929; s. John Lysle and Esther Maurine (Price) L.; m. Beverly Jo Jennings, June 8, 1952; children: Daniel Jennings, Amy Logan Sliva, Sarah Logan Sherard, Samuel Price. A.B., U. Kans., 1952; LL.B. magna cum laude, Harvard, 1955. Bar: Kans. 1955, Calif. 1956. Law clk. U.S. Cir. Judge Huxman, 1955-56; with firm Gibson, Dunn & Crutcher, L.A., 1956-57; asst. prof. law U. Kans., 1957-61, prof., dean Law Sch., 1961-68; ptnr. Payne and Jones, Olathe, Kans., 1968-77; judge U.S. Ct. Appeals (10th cir.), 1977—; Ezra Ripley Thayer tchg. fellow Harvard Law Sch., 1961-62; vis. prof. U. Tex., 1964, Stanford U., 1969, U. Mich., 1976; sr. lectr. Duke U., 1987, 91, 93; commr. U.S. Dist. Ct., 1964-67. Author: (with W.B. Leach) Future Interests and Estate Planning, 1961, Kansas Estate Administration, 5th edit., 1986, (with A.R. Martin) Kansas Corporate Law and Practice, 2d edit., 1979, The Federal Courts of the Tenth Circuit: A History, 1992; also articles. Candidate for U.S. Senate, 1968. Served with AUS, 1947-48. Rhodes scholar, 1952; recipient Disting. Service citation U. Kans., 1986. Mem. Am., Kans. bar assns., Phi Beta Kappa, Order of Coif, Beta Gamma Sigma, Omicron Delta Kappa, Pi Sigma Alpha, Alpha Kappa Psi, Phi Delta Phi. Democrat. Presbyterian.

LOGAN, JOHN ARTHUR, JR., retired foundation executive; b. Chgo., Dec. 8, 1923; s. John Arthur and Dorothea (Halstead) L.; m. Ann Orr deForest, Aug. 30, 1960. Grad., Taft Sch., Watertown, Conn., 1942; B.A., Yale, 1949, M.A., 1951, Ph.D., 1954; LL.D., Western Md. Coll.; L.H.D., Hollins Coll. Faculty Yale, 1949-61, asst. prof. history, 1958-61; pres. Hollins Coll., 1961-75, Ind. Coll. Funds Am., N.Y.C., 1975-86; vis. lectr. Salzburg Seminar in Am. Studies, 1961. Author: No Transfer: An American Security Principle, 1961. Served to capt. AUS, 1942-46. Fellow Saybrook Coll., Yale, 1950—. Mem. Phi Beta Kappa. Clubs: Elizabethan (New Haven); Century Assn. (N.Y.C.), Yale (N.Y.C.). Home: 88 Notch Hill Rd Apt 353 North Branford CT 06471

LOGAN, JOHN FRANCIS, electronics company executive, management consultant; b. Norristown, Pa., Apr. 10, 1938; s. Francis Michael and Elizabeth V. L. BS in Bus. Adminstrn., Drexel U., 1961. CPA, N.Y. Auditor Hurdman and Cranston CPA's (merger KPMG Peat Warwick), N.Y.C., 1961-69; v.p. fin., chief fin. officer, treas. Aero Flow Dynamics, Inc., N.Y.C., 1969-84; v.p. fin. and adminstrn., chief fin. officer, treas. Codenoll Tech. Corp., Yonkers, N.Y., 1985-90; v.p. fin., chief fin. officer, treas. VTX Electronics Corp., Farmingdale, N.Y., 1991-92; mgmt. cons. Comtex Info. Systems, Inc./KLMB Group Inc., N.Y.C., 1992—. With U.S. Army, 1962-64. Mem. AICPAs, N.Y. State Soc. CPA's, Pa. Soc.

LOGAN, JOSEPH GRANVILLE, JR., physicist; b. Washington, June 8, 1920; s. Joseph Granville and Lula (Briggs) L.; m. Esther Taylor, June 30, 1944; children—Joseph Michael, Eileen Cecile. B.S., D.C. Tchrs. Coll., 1941; Ph.D. in Physics, U. Buffalo, 1955. Physicist Nat. Bur. Standards, 1944-47, Cornell Aero. Lab. 1947-58; head propulsion research dept. Space Tech. Labs., 1958-61; dir. aerodynamics and propulsion research lab. Aerospace Corp., 1961-67; spl. asst. to dir. research and devel. McDonnell Douglas Astronautics Co., Santa Monica, Calif., 1967-69; mgr. vulnerability and hardening, devel. engrng. McDonnell Douglas Astronautics Co., 1969-74; pres. Applied Energy Scis., Inc., Los Angeles, 1974—; v.p. rsch. and devel. Advent Resources, Inc., Torrance, Calif., 1994—; mem. faculty dept. physics Calif. Poly. U., Pomona, 1977-78; bus. devel. specialist Urban U. Center, U. So. Calif., Los Angeles, 1978-79, assoc. dir., 1979-80, dir., 1980-88. Mem. Am. Phys. Soc., AIAA, Soc. Info. Display, N.Y. Acad. Scis. Home: 3652 Olympiad Dr Los Angeles CA 90043-1144 Office: Applied Energy Scis PO Box 36583 Los Angeles CA 90036-0583

LOGAN, JOSEPH PRESCOTT, lawyer; b. Topeka, Jan. 21, 1921; s. Joseph Glenn and Corinne (Ripley) L.; m. Yvonne Marie Westrate, July 17, 1943; children: John Daniel, Kathleen Elisabeth, Laurie Prescott. AB, Dartmouth Coll., 1942; LLB, Harvard U., 1948. Bar: Mo. 1948, U.S. Dist.

Ct. Mo. 1948. Ptnr. Thompson & Mitchell, St. Louis, 1958—. Pres., chmn. bd. Ranken Jordan Home for Covalescent Crippled Children, St. Louis, 1968-93. Lt. USNR, 1942-46. Mem. ACLU (bd. mem. 1988, civil liberties award 1982), Noonday Club. Democrat. Congregationalist. Avocations: hiking, mountain climbing, sailing. Home: 36 S Gore Ave Saint Louis MO 63119-2910 Office: Thompson & Mitchell 1 Mercantile Ctr Ste 3300 Saint Louis MO 63101-1622

LOGAN, JOYCE POLLEY, education educator; b. Providence, Ky., Sept. 18, 1935; d. Vernon and Hattie Alice Polley; m. Jewell Wyatt Logan (dec.), June 4, 1956; 1 child, James Edward. BS, Murray State U. 1956, MA, 1960; EdD, Vanderbilt U., 1988. Cert. bus. tchr., voc. adminstrn. Student sec. Murray (Ky.) State U., 1954-56; bus. tchr. Hopkins County Schs., Madisonville, Ky., 1956-68; regional coord. Vocational Region 2 Ky. Dept. Edn., Madisonville, 1968-83; prin. Health Occupations Sch., Madisonville, 1983-88; voc., tech. administr. Ky. Dept. Edn., Frankfort, 1988-90; asst. prof. dept. adminstrn. and supervision Coll. Edn. U. Ky., Lexington, 1990—; evaluator Nat. Home Study Coun., Washington, 1981—; field coord. military evaluations, Am. Coun. on Edn., Washington, 1984—. Author: (with A.C. Krizan) Basics of Writing, 1993. Mem. alumni bd. Murray (Ky.) State U. Coll. Bus., 1988—; fundraiser Ky. Spl. Olympics, Madisonville, 1983, YMCA, Madisonville, 1984; mem. edn. com. Greater Leadership Program Madisonville, Ky. C. of C., 1987-88. Named FFA Hon. State Farmer, Ky. FFA., 1979, Woman of the Year, Lion's Club, Madisonville, Ky., 1987, Outstanding Teacher Educator, 1992. Mem. Nat. Bus. Edn. Assn., Am. Vocat. Assn., Ky. Vocat. Assn., Southern Assn. of Colls. and Schs. (trustee 1973, 1976-78, chmn. Commn on Occupational Ednl. Insts. 1973), Ky. Assn. for Sch. Adminstrs., Assn. for Supervision and Curriculum Devel., Phi Delta Kappa, Omicron Delta Kappa (hon.). Avocations: jogging, tennis, reading, piano playing. Home: 1352 Gray Hawk Lexington KY 40502 Office: U KY 11 Dickey Hall Coll of Edn Lexington KY 40506

LOGAN, KENNETH RICHARD, lawyer; b. N.Y.C., Dec. 26, 1944; s. John S. and Hazel (Mathias) L.; m. Grace Winter-Durennel, Aug. 12, 1967; children: Finlay, Emily. BA, Princeton U., 1967; JD, U. Pa., 1972. Bar: N.Y., U.S. Dist. Ct. (so. dist.) N.Y., U.S. Ct. Appeals (2nd cir.). Assoc. Simpson Thacher & Bartlett, N.Y.C., 1972-79; ptnr. Simpson, Thacher & Bartlett, N.Y.C., 1979—. Served with U.S. Army, 1969-70. Office: Simpson Thacher & Bartlett 425 Lexington Ave New York NY 10017-3954

LOGAN, LINDA MARY, art education educator; b. Detroit, Dec. 28, 1942; d. Ervin John Moore, Joseph R. Sanson (stepfather) and Helen (Kolczynski) Moore Sanson; divorced; 1 child, Stephen Kelly. BA, Wayne State U., 1965, MA in Tchg., 1971; postgrad., Oakland C.C. 1989—. Cert. tchr., Mich. Instr. art Detroit Bd. Edn., 1967—; instr. gifted art, 1971—; audio-visual asst. Wayne State U., Detroit, 1960-62; clk. Wayne County Treas., Detroit, summers, 1960-63; pvt. decorative painter, Mich., 1962—; pvt. graphic designer logos, Mich., 1971—; tchr. workshops Detroit Schs., 1988—, Children's Mus., Detroit, 1995; advisor Davis Publs., 1990—; developer core curriculum Detroit Art Edn.; judge Free Press Editl. contest. Co-author art appreciation guide; photographer Detroit Zoo Jour., 1991; cons. Art Edn. Text Books, 1988—; exhibited at group shows at Biagus Gallery, Scarab Club, 1995, Oakland C.C., Mich. Coun. of Arts, Mich. Art Edn. Conf., Focus Gallery, 1980—. Vol. Detroit Inst of Arts, 1992. Mem. Am. Fedn. Tchrs., Mich. Art Edn. Assn., Detroit Art Tchrs. Assn. (treas.), Nat. Art Edn. Assn., Founder's Soc., Greenpeace, Earthwatch. Avocations: painting, drawing, photography, ancient history, water sports. Home: 10705 Nadine Huntington Woods MI 48070

LOGAN, LOX ALBERT, JR., museum director; b. Rutherfordton, N.C., Feb. 7, 1954; s. Lox Albert Sr. and Grace (Hawkins) L.; m. Bernadette Wall, May 6, 1978; children: Mark Thomas, Garrett Michael, Sean Timothy. BS, U.S. Mil. Acad. 1976; MA in History Mus. Studies, SUNY, Cooperstown, 1982; postgrad. Am. History, Marquette U. 1988—. Exec. dir. Wyo. Hist. and Geol. Soc., Wilkes-Barre, Pa., 1983-86; dir. Manitowoc (Wis.) Maritime Mus., 1986—; field reviewer Inst. Mus. Svcs., Washington, 1986—; mem. exec. com. Pa. Fedn. Hist. Socs., Harrisburg, 1983-85. Author: (with others) Maritime America, 1988; contbr. to profl. jour. Bd. dirs. Manitowoc-Two Rivers YMCA, 1989—; mem. scholarship selection com., 1991—; Pa. rep. admissions to U.S. Mil. Acad., 1984-85; coord. Northeast Pa. Records Coop., Wilkes-Barre, 1983-86; mem. Com. Econ. Growth, Wilkes-Barre, 1983-85; mem. Gov.'s Commn. on USS Wisconsin, 1988; rec. sec. adv. com. underwater archaeology State Hist. Soc., 1988; cabinet Maintowoc United Way campaign, 1990—; chmn. Mishabago dist. Boy Scouts Am., 1990-92; bd. dirs., pres. Riverwalk Festival, 1989—. Nat. Mus. Act. fellow Smithsonian Instn., 1982; recipient award Hugenot Soc. N.Y., 1982. Mem. Am. Assn. Mus. (cons. mus. assessment program 1988—), Am. Assn. State and Local History, Wis. Fedn. Mus. (adv. com. 1988-89, treas. 1989-92, exec. com. 1989—), Assn. Gt. Lakes Maritime History (bd. dirs. 1986—, sec. 1986-89, pres. 1989—), Coun. Am. Maritime Museums (bd. dirs. 1989, v.p. 1991-93, pres. 1993—), Presbyn. Hist. Assn. (adv. com. 1989—, moderator 1991—). Presbyterian. Avocations: gardening, running, canoeing. Office: Manitowoc Maritime Mus 75 Maritime Dr Manitowoc WI 54220-6823

LOGAN, MATHEW KUYKENDALL, journalist; b. Norman, Okla., Aug. 19, 1933; s. Leonard Marion and Floy-Elise (Duke) L.; m. Linda Dianne Elderkin, Dec. 31, 1964. B.A. in Journalism, U. Okla., 1955. Reporter UPI, 1957-58; city editor Daily Oklahoman, 1958-69; asst. mng. editor Houston Post, 1969-76, mng. editor, 1976-83; mng. editor Sta. KHOU-TV, Houston, 1984-87; asst. dean for community affairs Med. Sch. Tex., Houston, 1987-92; v.p. pub. affairs and mktg. Hermann Hosp., Houston, 1992—. Served with AUS, 1957. Mem. UPI Editors Tex. (pres. 1977), Tex. AP Mng. Editors Assn. (pres. 1983), Sigma Chi. Methodist. Home: 24 Sunlit Forest Dr The Woodlands TX 77381-2986

LOGAN, NANCY ALLEN, library media specialist; b. Rochester, N.Y., Mar. 27, 1933; d. Warren William and Dorothea Amelia (Pund) Allen; m. Joseph Skinner Logan, Dec. 29, 1952; children: Jennifer Amartha, Joseph Skinner Jr., Susan Logan Huber, Annette Logan Miller. Student, Middlebury Coll., 1951-52; BA, Cornell U., 1955; MLS, SUNY, Albany, 1967; cert. legal asst., Marist Coll., 1983. Cert. libr. media specialist, tchr., social studies tchr., N.Y. Libr. media specialist Hyde Park (N.Y.) Sch. Dist., 1971-93. Editor: Dear Friends, 1989; editor newsletter Sch. Libr. Media Specialists, 1984-85; contbr. articles to profl. publs. Arts chmn. Jr. League, Poughkeepsie, N.Y., 1967-69; dir. Jr. Arts Ctr., 1967-69; adm. chmn., 1970-71; sec. bd. dirs. Poughkeepsie (N.Y.) Tennis Club, 1973-79; indexer periodicals Dutchess County Hist. Soc., Poughkeepsie, 1979-93; county rep. Sch. Libr. Media Specialists, S.E N.Y., 1982, exhibits chmn. ann. meeting, 1983, 84; vol. libr., indexer Jamestown (R.I.) Philomenian Libr., 1993—; bd. dirs. Friends of Jamestown Philomenian Libr., 1994—. Mem. Newport Hist. Soc., Beavertail Lighthouse Assn. (bd. dirs. 1994—), New Eng. Hist. Geneal. Soc., Phi Delta Kappa. Avocations: reading, sailing, swimming, travel, bicycling. Home: 149 Seaside Dr Jamestown RI 02835-3117

LOGAN, RODMAN EMMASON, jurist; b. West Saint John, N.B. Can. Sept. 7, 1922; s. Gilbert Earle and Emma Zela (Irwin) L.; m. Evelyn Pearl DeWitt, June 19, 1948; children: John Bruce DeWitt, Ian David Alexander, Mary Jane Irwin, Bruce Rodman Hans. BA, U. N.B., 1949, BCL, 1951, DCL (hon.), 1988; DCL, St. Thomas U., Fredericton, N.B., 1974. Bar: N.B. 1951, created Queen's Counsel 1972. Partner firm Logan, Bell and Church, Saint John, N.B., 1951-70; elected to Legis. Assembly, 1963, 67, 70, 74, 78; minister of labor and provincial sec. Province of N.B., 1970-77; atty.-gen. and minister of justice, 1977-82; justice Ct. of Queen's Bench, 1982—. Served with Can. Armed Forces, 1942-45, U.K., N.W. Europe and Central Mediterranean Forces. Mem. Royal Commonwealth Soc. Anglican. Clubs: Royal Can. Legion, Carleton and York Regtl. Home: RR 2, 273 Nerepis Rd, Westfield, NB Canada E0G 3J0 Office: Provincial Bldg, 110 Charlotte St, Saint John's, NF Canada E2L 2J3

LOGAN, SANDRA JEAN, economics and business educator; b. Dayton, Ohio, Jan. 3, 1940; d. Max B. and Edna E. (Sanderson) Parrish; m. John E. Logan, Apr. 25, 1964. BA, Drew U., 1962; MBA, Columbia U., N.Y.C., 1964; PhD, U. S.C. 1976. Piano tchr. Whippany, N.J., 1957-64; lab. analyst Bear Creek Mining Co., Morristown, N.J., summer 1957, 58; rsch. asst. Drew U., Madison, N.J., summer 1962; staff asst. N.J. Bell Telephone Co., Newark, summer 1963, 64-67; instr. bus. U. Toledo, 1967-69; asst. prof.

econs. and bus. S.C. State Univ., Orangeburg, 1970-76; prof. econs. and bus. Newberry (S.C.) Coll., 1976—, acting v.p. acad. affairs, 1993-95; cons. econs., Ohio and S.C., 1967—; N.J. Bell Telephone Co., Newark, 1968; lectr. bus. Ea. Mich. U., Ypsilanti, spring 1969. Active Coldstream Home Owners Assn., Columbia, S.C., 1972-80; officer St. Andrews Woman's Club, Columbia, 1969-76. Rsch. grantee U. S.C. and S.C. State U., 1974-75. Mem. Am. Econs. Assn., So. Econs. Assn. Republican. Presbyterian. Home: 112 Smiths Market Ct Columbia SC 29212-1923 Office: Newberry Coll College St Newberry SC 29108

LOGAN, TERRY JAMES, soil chemist, educator; b. Georgetown, Guyana, Feb. 6, 1943; s. David A. and Elsa (Gonsalves) L.; m. Marilyn A. Winters, June, 1964 (div. 1972); 1 child, David; m. Cynthia A. Hawk, June 9, 1973; children: Noelle, Jennifer. BS in Soil Sci., Calif. Poly. State U., 1966; MS in soil chemistry, Ohio State U., 1969, PhD in Soil Chemistry, 1971. Prof. natural resources Ohio State U., Columbus, 1971—; cons. to govt. and industry, 1971—; dir. Environ. Sci. Grad. Program, Ohio State AU., 1991—. Contbr. 170 articles to profl. jours. Fellow Am. Soc. Agronomy (Environ. Quality award 1989), Soil Sci. Soc. Am.; mem. AAAS, Soil Conservationists Soc. Am., Am. Chem. Soc., Soc. Environ. Toxicology and Chemistry. Avocation: running. Office: Ohio State U Sch Natural Resources Columbus OH 43210

LOGAN, VICKI, advertising executive; b. Oakland, Calif., Aug. 3, 1954; d. Robert Lee and Freida Elizabeth (Luckett) L. BS in Bus. Adminstrn. magna cum laude, Pepperdine U., 1976; M in Internat. Mgmt. with honors, Am. Grad. Sch. Internat. Mgmt., 1979. Asst. to dep. dir. HUD, Washington, 1978; account exec. Doyle Dane Bernbach Advt., Inc., N.Y.C., 1979-81; sr. v.p., creative dir. Jordan, McGrath, Case, Taylor & McGrath Advt., N.Y.C., 1981—. Office: Jordan McGrath Case & taylor Inc 445 Park Ave New York NY 10022-2606

LOGANBILL, G. BRUCE, logopedic pathologist; b. Newton, Kans., Sept. 6, 1938; s. Oscar and Warrene (Rose) L. B.A., Bethel Coll. Kans., 1956; M.A., U. Kans., 1958; Ph.D., Mich. State U., 1961; postdoctoral fellow, Inst. Logopedics, 1965-66. Mem. faculty Kalamazoo Coll., 1961-63; mem. faculty Fresno (Calif.) State U., 1966-68; mem. faculty Calif. State U., Long Beach, 1968—, prof., 1975—; lectr. on speech communication and pathologies, Argentina, Denmark, France, Japan, Can., India, Scotland, Czechoslovakia, USSR, Germany, People's Republic of China; U.S. rep. 2d Internat. Congress de Melodie-Therapie du Language en accord Nat. Coll. Psychiatry, Paris, 1990. Author: The Bases of Voice, Articulation and Pronunciation, 1974, 5th edit., 1992; contbr. more than 30 articles to profl. jours. Mem. Speech Assn., Western Speech Comm. Assn., Am. Speech and Hearing Assn., Calif. Speech and Hearing Assn., Internat. Assn. Logopedics and Phoniatrics, Internat. Phonetics Assn., Assn. Calif. State U. Profs. (univ. chpt. pres. 1985, Calif. del. NEA/Calif. Tchrs. Assn. 1990), others. Republican. Episcopalian. Office: Calif State U Long Beach 1250 N Bellflower Blvd Long Beach CA 90840-0004

LOGE, FRANK JEAN, II, hospital administrator; b. Redlands, Calif., May 28, 1945; s. J. Phillip Loge and Helen M. (Booker) Loge Power; m. Sharon Lee Entrekin, Feb. 11, 1967; children—Frank III, Christopher, Gregory. BA, Claremont Men's Coll., Long Beach, Calif., 1967; MBA, Calif. State U.-Long Beach, 1969; postgrad., UCLA Sch. Pub. Health, 1972-73. Mgr. mgmt. analysis UCLA, 1972-73, asst. dir. fin., 1973-74; dir. fin. U. Calif. Davis Med. Ctr., Sacramento, 1975-79, dep. dir. hosp. and clinics, 1979-84, dir. hosp. and clinics, 1984—. Office: U Calif Davis Med Ctr 2315 Stockton Blvd Sacramento CA 95817-2201

LOGEMAN, JOHN DONALD, air force officer; b. Cin., July 6, 1939; s. John Donald and Marcella Frances (Gruter) L.; m. Audrey Ann Feudner, Dec. 30, 1961; children: Brian J., Pamela J., Keith M., Scott A., John E. BBA in Mktg., U. Wis., 1961; postgradd., Armed Forces Staff Coll., 1972, Indsl. Coll. Armed Forces, 1981. Commd. 2d lt. USAF, 1961, advanced through grades to maj. gen., 1989; comdr. 561st Tactical Fighter Squadron, George AFB, Calif., 1979-80, 35th Component Repair Squadron, George AFB, 1980, 67th Tactical Reconaissance Wing, Bergstrom AFB, Tex., 1984-86; comdt. 28th Air Div., Tactical Air Command, Tinker AFB, Okla., 1986-89; asst. dep. dir. force devel. Hdqrs. USAF, Washington, 1981-82; comdt. USAF Fighter Weapons Sch., Nellis AFB, Nev., 1982-84; vice comdr. Hdqrs. 12th Air Force, Bergstrom AFB, 1986; dep.chief staff for logistics Hdqrs. Tactical Air Command, Langley AFB, Va., 1989-92; commdr. NATO Airborne Early Warning Force, Mons, Belgium, 1992—. Decorated Silver Star, Legion of Merit, DFC, Air medal. Mem. Air Force Assn., Order of Daedalians. Roman Catholic. Avocations: golf, bowling, hunting, flying. Home: 2 Bobs Ct Hampton VA 23666-2800 Office: NAEWFC PO Box 671 # 450 Mons VA 23665-5541

LOGEMANN, JERILYN ANN, speech pathologist, educator; b. Berwyn, Ill., May 21, 1942; d. Warren F. and Natalie M. (Killmer) L.; BS, Northwestern U., 1963; MA, 1964, PhD, 1968. Grad. asst. dept. communicative disorders Northwestern U., 1963-68; instr. speech and audiology DePaul U., 1964-65; instr. dept. communicative disorders Mundelein Coll., 1967-71; research assoc. depts. neurology and otolaryngology and maxillofacial surgery Northwestern U. Med. Sch., Chgo., 1970-74, asst. prof., 1974-78, dir. clin. and research activities of speech and lang., 1975—, assoc. prof. depts. neurology, otolaryngology and comm. scis. and disorders, 1978-83, prof., 1983, chmn. dept. communicative disorders, 1982—, Jean and Ralph Sundin Prof. of Comm. Scis. and Disorders, 1982—; mem. assoc. staff Northwestern Meml. Hosp., 1976—, N. Chgo. VA Hosp., 1983—, Evanston (Ill.) Hosp., 1988—, Children's Meml. Hosp., Chgo., 1988—; cons. in field; assoc. dir. cancer control. Ill. Comprehensive Cancer Council, Chgo., 1980-82. Mem. rehab. com. Ill. div. Am. Cancer Soc., 1975-79, chmn., 1979—; mem. upper aerodigestive tract organ site com. Nat. Cancer Inst., 1986-89. Postdoctoral fellow Nat. Inst. Neurologic Disease, Communicative Disorders and Stroke, Northwestern U., 1968-70; fellow Inst. Medicine Chgo., 1981—; grantee Nat. Cancer Inst., 1975—, Am. Cancer Soc., 1981-82. Fellow Am. Speech, Lang. and Hearing Assn. (pres.-elect 1993, pres. 1994), Inst. Medicine; mem. Internat. Assn. Logopedics and Phoniatrics, AAUP, Acoustic Soc. Am. (program com. Chgo. regional chpt.), Linguistic Soc. Am., Speech Comm. Assn., Am. Cleft Palate Assn., Ill. Speech and Hearing Assn. (DiCarlo award 1988), Chgo. Heart Assn., Chgo. Speech Therapy and Auditory Soc., Conn. Speech Lang. Hearing Assn. (past pres. 1995). Author: The Fisher-Logemann Test of Articulation Competence, 1971, Evaluation and Treatment of Swallowing Disorders, 1983; Manual for the Videofluorographic Evaluation of Swallowing, 1985, 93, Videofluoroscopic Evaluation of Swallowing, 1986; assoc. editor Jour. Speech and Hearing Disorders, Jour. Head Trauma Rehab., Dysphagia jour., 1978-82. Office: Northwestern U Med Sch 303 E Chicago Ave Chicago IL 60611 also: Dept Comm Sci & Disorder 2299 Sheridan Rd Evanston IL 60208-0837

LOGGIA, ROBERT, actor; b. S.I., N.Y., Jan. 3, 1930; s. Benjamin and Elena (Blandino) L.; m. Audrey O'Brien; children: Tracey, John, Kristina, Cynthia. Student, Wagner Coll., S.I., 1947-49; B. Journalism, U. Mo., Columbia, 1951. Appeared in Broadway prodns. Toys in the Attic, 1961, Three Sisters, 1964, Boom Boom Room, 1973-74; TV series T.H.E. Cat, 1968-69, The Nine Lives of Elfego Baca, 1958-59, Mancuso F.B.I., 1989-90 (Emmy Best Actor award nominee), Sunday Dinner, 1991; films include Somebody Up There Likes Me, 1956, The Garment Jungle, 1957, Cop Hater, The Lost Missile, 1958, Cattle King, 1963, Greatest Story Ever Told, 1965, Che!, 1969, First Love, 1977, Speed Trap, Revenge of the Pink Panther, 1978, The Ninth Configuration (Twinkle Twinkle Little Kane), S.O.B., 1981, An Officer and a Gentleman, 1982, Trail of the Pink Panther, 1982, Scarface, 1983, Psycho II, 1983, Curse of the Pink Panther, 1983, Prizzi's Honor, 1985, Jagged Edge, 1985 (Acad. Best Supporting Actor award nominee 1986), Armed and Dangerous, 1986, Over the Top, 1986, Hot Pursuit, 1986, That's Life, 1986, The Believers, Big, 1988, Oliver & Company (voice), 1988, Triumph of the Spirit, 1989, Gaby, 1989, Marrying Man, 1990, Opportunity Knocks, 1990, Necessary Roughness, 1991, Gladiator, 1992, Innocent Blood, 1992, Bad Girls, 1994, I Love Trouble, 1994; TV miniseries Echoes in the Darkness, Favorite Son, 1989, Wild Palms, 1993; TV appearances include Chicago Conspiracy Trial, 1988 (Ace Best Actor award nominee), Afterburn, 1992, Merry Christmas Baby, 1992, Nurses on the Line, 1993, Mercy Mission, 1993, White Mile, 1994, Lifepod, 1993, Between Love & Honor, 1995,

Jake Lassiter, 1995. With U.S. Army, 1951-53. Office: Creative Artists Agy 9830 Wilshire Blvd Beverly Hills CA 90212-1825 Pursue excellence.

LOGGIE, JENNIFER MARY HILDRETH, medical educator, physician; b. Lusaka, Zambia, Feb. 4, 1936; came to U.S., 1964, naturalized, 1972; d. John and Jenny (Beattie) L. M.B., B.Ch., U. Witwatersrand, Johannesburg, South Africa, 1959. Intern Harare Hosp., Salisbury, Rhodesia, 1960-61; gen. practice medicine Lusaka, 1961-62; sr. pediatric house officer Derby Children's Hosp., also St. John's Hosp., Chelmsford, Eng., 1962-64; resident in pediatrics Children's Hosp., Louisville, 1964, Cin., 1964-65; fellow clin. pharmacology Cin. Coll. Medicine, 1965-67; mem. faculty U. Cin. Med. Sch., 1967—, prof. pediatrics, 1975, asso. prof. pharmacology, 1972-77. Contbr. articles to med. publs.; editor Pediatric and Adolescent Hypertension, 1991. Grantee Am. Heart Assn., 1970-72, 89-90. Mem. Am. Pediatric Soc. (elected), Midwest Soc. Pediatric Research. Episcopalian. Home: 1133 Herschel Ave Cincinnati OH 45208-3112 Office: Children's Hosp Rsch Found Elland And Bethesda Ave Cincinnati OH 45229

LOGGINS, KENNY (KENNETH CLARKE LOGGINS), singer, songwriter; b. Everett, Wash., Jan. 17, 1947; s. Robert George and Lina Clelia (Massie) L.; m. Julia Cooper. Student, Pasadena City Coll. Mem. groups, Second Helping, Loggins & Messina, Electric Prunes, rec. artist, Columbia Records and Sony Wonder Records; songwriter, Milk Money and Gnossos Music Pub. Co.; solo albums include: Celebrate Me Home, 1977, Nightwatch, 1978, Keep the Fire, 1979, Alive, 1980, Footloose, 1984, Vox Humana, 1985, Back to Avalon, 1988, Leap of Faith, 1991, Outside From the Redwoods, 1993, Return to Pooh Corner, 1994; albums with Messina include: Sittin' In, 1971, Loggins & Messina, 1972, Full Sail, 1973, On Stage, 1974, Motherlode, 1975, So Fine, 1975, Native Sons, 1976, Best of Friends, 1977, Finale, 1978, Best of Loggins and Messina, 1980; other albums: stage: Kenny Loggins on Broadway, 1988; composed and performed theme for This Island Earth (The Disney Channel), 1993 (Cable Ace award, Best Original Song, Emmy award). Adv. bd. Earthtrust. Recipient Rock 'n Roll Sports Classic Gold medal, Grammy award for What A Fool Believes, 1980, Grammy award for This is It, 1981, Harry Chapin award We are the World. Mem. ASCAP, Nat. Assn. Rec. Arts and Scis. Office: care William Morris Agy 151 El Camino Dr Beverly Hills CA 90212

LOGIE, DENNIS WAYNE, minister; b. Longmont, Colo., Mar. 18, 1940; s. Wayne Edward and Fern Maxine (Jacobson) L.; m. Burgl Dagmar Kaiser, Jan. 15, 1961; children: Hans Dennis, Heidi Elisabeth. Student, Stanford U., 1958-60, Fuller Sem., 1978. Ordained to ministry Christian Ch., 1977. Systems officer Crocker Nat. Bank, San Francisco, 1964-76, dir. data processing edn., 1976-78; minister 1st Christian Ch., Redwood City, Calif. 1978-81, sr. minister, 1981—; del. Heavenly Hills Christian Camp, Twain-Harte, Calif., 1978—; founder, bd. dirs. No. Calif. Ministers Retreat, San Rafael, Calif., 1983—. Contbr. articles and essays to various publs. Mem. parents adv. group Selby Ln. Sch., Atherton, Calif., 1974-76; treas. Band-Aids, Woodside (Calif.) H.S., 1976-79; co-founder, bd. dirs. Lay Inst. for Tng., Redwood City, 1976-81; bd. dirs. San Jose (Calif.) Christian Coll. 1976-82, 88-94; founding mem. South County Coalition for Prevention of Substance Abuse, 1991—; chaplain Redwood City Police Dept., 1994—. Mem. No. Calif. Evangelistic Assn. (bd. dirs. 1987-), Redwood City Clergy Assn. (pres. 1979-85, 88-), Calif. PTA (life). Republican. Avocations: tennis, softball. Home: 164 Oakfield Ave Redwood City CA 94061-3622 Office: 1st Christian Ch 233 Topaz St Redwood City CA 94062-2817

LOGIE, JOHN HOULT, mayor, lawyer; b. Ann Arbor, Mich., Aug. 11, 1939; s. James Wallace and Elizabeth (Hoult) L.; m. Susan G. Duerr, Aug. 15, 1964; children—John Hoult Jr., Susannah, Margaret Elizabeth. Student Williams Coll., 1957-59; BA, U. Mich., 1961, JD, 1968; MS, George Washington U., 1966. Bar: Mich. 1969, U.S. Dist. Ct. (we. and ea. dists. 1969) Mich., U.S. Ct. Appeals (6th cir. 1987). Assoc. Warner, Norcross & Judd, Grand Rapids, Mich., 1969-74, ptnr., 1974—; mayor City of Grand Rapids, 1992—; program coord. condemnation law sect. Inst. Continuing Legal Edn.; guest lectr. Grand Rapids Community Coll., Grand Valley State U., Western Mich. U.; legal counsel to 15 West Mich. hosps.; instr. U.S. Naval Acad., 1964-66. Pres. Grand Rapids PTA Council, 1971-73, Heritage Hill Assn., 1976, sec., trustee 1971-84; chmn. Grand Rapids Urban Homesteading Commn., 1975-80, Grand Rapids Hist. Commn., 1985-90, Grand Rapids/Kent County Sesquicentennial Com., 1986-88; MEM. Headlee Blue Ribbon Commn., 1993-94; v.p. bd. dirs. Goodwill Industries, Grand Rapids, 1973-79, Am. Cancer Soc., Grand Rapids, 1970-81; pres., trustee Hist. Soc. Mich., 1984-90. Lt. USN, 1961-66. Mem. ABA (forum com. on health law 1980—), Mich. Bar Assn. (chmn. condemnation com. real property sect. 1985-88), Grand Rapids Bar Assn. (dir. young lawyers sect. 1970), Am. Acad. Hosp. Attys., Mich. Soc. Hosp. Attys. (pres. 1976-77), Nat. Health Lawyers Assn., Univ. Club (dir. 1979-82, pres. 1980-82), Peninsular Club, Williams Club (NYC). Avocations: sailing, hunting, fishing. Home: 601 Cherry St SE Grand Rapids MI 49503-4726 Office: Warner Norcross and Judd 900 Old Kent Bldg Grand Rapids MI 49503 also: Office of Mayor 300 Monroe Ave NW Grand Rapids MI 49503-2206

LOGSDON, JOHN, engineering consulting company executive. Exec. v.p. Harris Group Inc., Seattle. Office: Harris Group Inc 2901 3rd Ave 600 Seattle WA 98121*

LOGSDON, RICHARD HENRY, retired librarian and educator; b. Upper Sandusky, Ohio, June 24, 1912; s. Henry John and Odelia Marie (Seifert) L.; m. Lois Irene Kupfer, Sept. 22, 1934 (dec. June 1986); children: Mary Josephine, John Richard, Elizabeth Irene, Rachel Anne. AB, Western Res. U., 1933, BSLS, 1934; Ph.D., U. Chgo. 1942. Librarian State Tchrs. Coll., Alamosa, Colo., 1934-39; Madison Coll., Harrisonburg, Va., 1939-43; prof. library sci., head dept. U. Ky., 1943-45; chief librarian U.S. Office Edn., 1945-47; asst. dir. VA Library Service, 1947; asst. dir. Columbia U. Libraries, 1947-48, asso. dir., 1948-53, dir., 1953-69, prof. library service, 1956-69, adj. prof. library service, 1969-72; univ. dean for libraries City U. N.Y., 1969-71; prof. library sci. City U. N.Y. (Queens Coll.), 1969-79, acting chmn. dept., 1973, chmn. dept., 1976-77; Adviser library architecture and adminstrn. Kabul U., Govt. Afghanistan, 1959; chmn. Coordination Com. for Slavic and East European Library Resources, 1961-62; program cons. Albert Schweitzer Center, Gt. Barrington, Mass., 1981-84. Author: (with others) The Columbia University Libraries, 1958, (with Irene K. Logsdon) Library Careers, 1963, Library Manpower and Education in Indiana, 1973, also articles profl. jours. Mem. Leonia Bd. Edn., 1953-55; mem. N.Y. Regents Adv. Council, 1964-74, Gov.'s Library Com., 1965-70, Commrs. Com. Library Devel., 1967-70; cons. manpower and edn. Ind. State Library, 1971-73; Bd. visitors Tufts U. Libraries; bd. overseers Case- Western Res. U.; v.p., bd. dirs. N.Y. Met. Reference and Research Library Agy., 1964-70, exec. dir., 1970-72; bd. govs. Laymen's Club, Cathedral of St. John the Divine, 1981—; bd. dirs. Omega Liturgical Dance Group, 1981—. Served as lt. Bur. Naval Personnel USNR, 1943-45. Mem. A.L.A. (mem. bd. edn. for librarianship 1946-51, chmn. 1950-51, chmn. commn. nat. plan for library edn. 1963), Assn. Research Libraries (dir. 1962-65, chmn. 1964), Assn. Coll. and Research Libraries (chmn. univ. sect. 1954-55), Middle Atlantic States Assn. Coll. and Secondary Schs. (mem. commn. on higher instrns. 1951-58, exec. com. 1956-58), N.Y. Library Assn. (pres. 1965-66). Club: Grolier (council 1965-69). Home: 601 W 113th St New York NY 10025-7937

LOGUE, DENNIS EMHARDT, financial economics educator, consultant; b. Bklyn., Mar. 28, 1944; s. Joseph Paul and Helen Rose (Emhardt) L.; m. Marcella Julia Watson, June 11, 1966; children: Dennis E. Jr., Patrick G. A.B., Fordham U., 1966; M.B.A., Rutgers U., 1968; Ph.D., Cornell U., 1971. Asst. prof. Ind. U., Bloomington, 1971-73; sr. economist U.S. Treasury, Washington, 1973-74; prof. bus. Tuck Sch., Dartmouth Coll., Hanover, N.H., 1974—; now Steven Roth prof. mgr., former assoc. dean; founding bd. dirs. Ledyard Nat. Bank. Author: Legislative Influence on Corporate Pension Plans, 1979, The Investment Performance of Corporate Pension Plans, 1988, Managing Corporate Pension Plans, 1991; editor: Handbook of Modern Finance, 1993; co-editor Fin. Mgmt., 1978-81. Served to 1st lt. U.S. Army, 1966-68. Mem. Am. Econ. Assn., Am. Fin. Assn. (bd. dirs. 1981-84), Fin. Mgmt. Assn. (bd. dirs., pres. 1995—), Knights of Malta, Order Holy Sepulchre, N.Y. Athletic Club, Rotary, Beta Gamma Sigma. Republican. Roman Catholic. Home: 1 River Ridge Rd Hanover NH 03755-1910 Office: Dartmouth Coll Amos Tuch Sch Bus Admi Hanover NH 03755

LOGUE, EDWARD JOSEPH, development company executive; b. Phila., Feb. 7, 1921; s. Edward J. and Resina (Fay) L.; m. Margaret DeVane, June 7, 1947; children: Katherine, William DeVane. B.A., Yale U., 1942, LL.B., 1947. Bar: Pa. 1948, Conn. 1950. Practiced in Phila., 1948; legal sec. Gov. Chester Bowles, Hartford, Conn., 1949-51; spl. asst. to ambassador Chester Bowles, New Delhi, 1952-53; devel. adminstr. City of New Haven, 1954-60, City of Boston, 1961-67; vis. Maxwell prof. govt. Boston U., 1967-68; pres., chief exec. officer N.Y. State Urban Devel. Corp., 1968-75; pres. Roosevelt Island Devel. Corp., 1969-75, Logue Devel. Co., Inc., 1976—, South Bronx Devel. Orgn., Inc., 1978-85; chief exec. officer Logue Boston, 1987-1994; Thomas Jefferson prof. Sch. Architecture, U. Va., spring 1985; sr. lectr. Sch. Architecture and Planning, MIT, 1985-89; prin. devel. cons. to Ft. Lincoln New Town, Washington, 1968; vis. lectr. Yale Sch. Law, 1957-77; chmn. Task Force on Housing and Neighborhood Improvement, N.Y.C., 1966; mem. Critical Choices Commn., 1973-76; founder Vineyard Open Land Found., 1970; mem. vis. com. Harvard U. Sch. Design, 1969-75; mem. resource team Mayor's Inst. on City Design. Chmn. Dukes County Charter Commn., 1991-92; advisor to Mayor Jackson and Corp. for Olympic Devel., Atlanta, 1993. With USAAF, 1943-45. Decorated Air medal with clusters. Mem. AIA (hon. mem.), Am. Acad. Arts and Scis., Tavern Club (Boston), Century Club (N.Y.C.), Union Boat Club (Boston), Saturday (Boston), Yale Club (N.Y.C.), Phi Beta Kappa (hon.). Democrat. Home: Scotchman's Bridge Ln West Tisbury MA 02575 Office: Logue Devel Co 94 Charles St Boston MA 02114-4643

LOGUE, FRANK, arbitrator, mediator, urban consultant, former mayor New Haven; b. Phila., Aug. 18, 1924; s. Edward J. and Resina (Fay) L.; m. Mary Ann Willson, June 10, 1950; children: Nancy, Jennifer, Jonathan. BA, Yale U., 1948, JD, 1951. Bar: Conn. 1951. Practiced in Bridgeport and Trumbull, Conn., 1951-64; dir. Community Action Inst., OEO Regional Tng. Center, New Haven, 1965-69, Nat. Urban Fellows, New Haven, 1969-75; alderman City of New Haven, 1972-75; mayor, 1976-79; prosecutor Town of Trumbull, 1955-57; town atty., 1957-61; regional cons. U.S. Civil Rights Commn., 1961-63; lectr. New Haven Police Acad., 1965-70; vis. asst. prof. So. Conn. State Coll., 1968-69; assoc. fellow Morse Coll., Yale U., 1968—; mem. adv. bd. Yale U. Sch. Mgmt., 1976-80, mem. faculty, 1980-81; vice chmn. Inst. Pub. Mgmt., 1975-82; chmn. task force on arts Nat. League Cities, 1977-79; mem. adv. bd. U.S. Conf. Mayors, 1977-79; panelist pub. programs div. Nat. Endowment for Humanities, 1974-78; mem. Pres.'s Adv. Commn. on the Holocaust; chmn. bd. dirs. Internat. Inst. Public Mgmt. 1979-82; mem. Conn. Adv. Com. Intergovtl. Relations, 1984-86; pub. interest arbitrator Conn. Dept. Edn., 1985—; pub. mem. alt. panel Conn. Bd. Mediation and Arbitration, 1986-89. Author: Who Administers—Access to Leadership Positions in the Administration of Government, 1972. Served with inf. AUS, 1944-45, ETO. Mem. Am. Arbitration Assn. (labor panel). Home and Office: 173 Livingston St New Haven CT 06511-2209

LOGUE, JOHN JOSEPH, psychologist; b. Phila., Nov. 16, 1929; s. Edwin J. and Ellen V. (Mallon) L.; m. Evelyn Bortnick, Apr. 24, 1954; 1 child, Eileen Logue Handel. BS, Temple U., 1954, MEd, 1958, EdD, 1966. Lic. psychologist Pa., Md., N.J.. Del. Ptnr., cons. RHR Internat., Phila., 1966-88; mgmt. psychologist pvt. practice Phila. 1988—. With U.S. Army, 1954-56. Mem. APA (indsl., orgn., cons., counseling, edn. divsns.), Quaker City Yacht Club. Home: 1942 Greymont St Philadelphia PA 19116 Office: 205 Keith Valley Rd Horsham PA 19044-1408

LOGUE, JOSEPH CARL, electronics engineer, consultant; b. Phila., Dec. 20, 1920; s. Percival J. and Mathilda (Moser) L.; m. Jeanne Martha Neubecker, Mar. 28, 1943; children: Raymond, Marilyn, Paul. BEE, Cornell U., 1944, MEE, 1949. Instr. Cornell U., Ithaca, N.Y., 1944-49, asst. prof., 1949-51; engr. IBM, Poughkeepsie, N.Y., 1951-86; dir. IBM Research Div., Yorktown Heights, N.Y., 1986; cons. Lorex Industries Inc., Poughkeepsie, 1986—. 30 patents in field; contbr. papers to profl. publs. IBM fellow. Fellow IEEE, AAAS; mem. Nat. Acad. Engring., Research Soc. Am. Avocations: flying, scuba diving, photography. Home: 52 Boardman Rd Poughkeepsie NY 12603-4228

LOGUE-KINDER, JOAN, government official; b. Richmond, Va., Oct. 26, 1943; d. John T. and Helen (Harvey) Logue; m. Lowell A. Henry Jr., Oct. 6, 1963 (div. Sept. 1981); children: Lowell A. Henry III, Catherine D. Henry, Christopher Logue Henry; m. Randolph S. Kinder, Dec. 13, 1986. Student, Wheaton Coll., 1959-62; BA in Sociology, Adelphi U., 1964; cert. in edn., Mercy Coll., Dobbs Ferry, N.Y., 1971; postgrad., NYU, 1973; cert. in edn., St. John's U., 1974. Asst. to dist. mgr. U.S. Census Bur., N.Y.C., 1970; tchr. and adminstr. social studies Yonkers (N.Y.) Bd. Edn., 1971-75; dir. pub. rels. Nat. Black Network, N.Y.C., 1976-83; corp. v.p. NBN Broadcasting (formerly Nat. Black Network), N.Y.C., 1984-90; sr. v.p. The Mingo Group/ Plus, N.Y.C., 1990-91; v.p. Edelman Pub. Rels. Worldwide, N.Y.C., 1991-93; dep. asst. sec. pub. affairs U.S. Dept. Treasury, Washington, 1993-94, asst. sec. pub. affairs, 1994—; cons. in field. Mem. alumnae recruitment coun. Wheaton Coll.; mem. Nigerian-Am. Friendship Soc., 1978-81; bd. dirs. Westchester Civil Liberties Union, 1974-77, Greater N.Y. coun. Girl Scouts U.S., 1985—, Operation PUSH, 1985—; del. White House Conf. on Small Bus.; active polit. campaigns, including Morris Udall for U.S. Pres, Howard Samuels for Gov.; sr. black media advisor Dukakis/Bentsen presdl. campaign, 1988; conv. del. N.Y. State Women's Polit. Caucus, 1975, pres. Black caucus, 1976-77. Recipient Excellence in Media award Inst. New Cinema Artists, 1984. Mem. World Inst. Black Commun. (bd. dirs. 1983-91), Women in Comm., Inc., Advt. Women of N.Y., 100 Black Women. Home: Apt 204W 1080 Wisconsin Ave NW Washington DC 20007 Office: Dept of Treasury 1500 Pennsylvania Ave Washington DC 20220

LOH, HORACE H., pharmacology educator; b. Canton, Republic China, May 28, 1936. BS, Nat. Taiwan U., Taipei, Republic China, 1958; PhD, U. Iowa, 1965. Lectr. dept. pharmacology U. Calif. Sch. Medicine, San Francisco, 1967; assoc. dept. biochem. Wayne State U., Detroit, 1968-70; lectr., rsch. assoc. depts. psychiatry, pharmacology Langley Porter Neuropsychiatric Inst. U. Calif. Sch. Medicine, San Francisco, 1970-72, assoc. prof. depts. psychiatry, pharmacology Langley Porter Neuropsychiatric Inst., 1972-75, prof. depts. psychiatry, pharmacology Langley Porter Neuropsychiatric Inst., 1975-88; prof., head dept. pharmacology U. Minn. Med. Sch., Mpls., 1989—; Frederick and Alice Stark prof., head dept. pharmacology, 1990—; chmn. annual meeting theme com. on receptors Fedn. Am. Socs. for Exptl. Biology, 1984; mem. exec. com. Internat. Narcotic Rsch. Conf., 1984-87, chair sci. program annual meeting, 1986; mem. adv. com. Nat. Tsing Hua U. Inst. Life Scis., Taiwan, Republic China, 1985-89; mem. exec. com. Com. on Problems of Drug Dependence, Inc., 1985-88; mem. sci. adv. coun. Nat. Found. for Addictive Diseases, 1987—; cons. U.S. Army R & D Dept. Defense, 1980-84. Mem. editorial adv. bd. Life Scis., 1978—, Substance and Alcohol Abuse, 1980— Neurochemistry Internat., 1980-88, Neuropharmacology, 1982—, Neurosci. Series, 1982-83, Annual Rev. Pharmacology and Toxicology, 1984-89, Jour. Pharmacology and Exptl. Therapeutics, 1987—; assoc. editor Annual Rev. Pharmacology and Toxicology, 1994-95, CRC Critical Rev. in Pharmacological Scis., 1987-88; author 56 book chpts.; editor 1 book; contbr. 300 articles to profl. jours. Recipient Career Devel. award USPHS, 1973-78, 78-83, Rsch. Scientist award, 1983-88, 1989-94, Humboldt award for sr. U.S. scientists (Fed. Republic Germany), 1977. Mem. Am. Coll. Neuropsychopharmacology (honorific awards com. 1988—), Am. Soc. Pharmacology and Exptl. Therapeutics (program com. 1978-86, trustee bd. publs. 1987-93, com. on confs. 1990-93), Chinese Bioscientists in Am. (pres. 1985-86), Western Pharmacology Soc. (councilor 1980-83, pres 1984-85). Office: U Minn Med Sch Dept Pharmacology 3 249 Millard Hall Minneapolis MN 55455

LOH, JOHN M., career military officer. Gen. USAF; comdr. Air Combat Command. Office: ACC/CC Ste 100 205 Dodd Blvd Langley AFB VA 23665-2788

LOH, WALLACE D., university dean. Dean Sch. Law U. Wash. Office: Univ of Wash Sch Law Condon Hall 1100 NE Campus Pky Seattle WA 98105-6617

LOHAN, DIRK, architect; b. Rathenow, Germany, Feb. 14, 1938; came to U.S., 1962; s. Wolfgang and Marianne (Mies Van Der Rohe) L.; m. Heidemarie Schaefer, June 20, 1959 (div. 1971); children: Caroline Beatrice, Lars; m. Pamela H. Stone, Feb. 14, 1991. Diplom Ingenieur, Tech. U.

Munich, 1962. Architect Mies Van Der Rohe, Chgo., 1962-69, ptnr., 1969-74; ptnr. Fujikawa Conterato Lohan & Assocs., Chgo., 1974-82; pres. FCL Assocs., Chgo., 1983-85; pres., chief exec. officer Lohan Assocs., Chgo., 1986—. Prin. archtl. works include, TRW Hdqrs., Cleve., 1983, McDonald's Hdqrs., Chgo., 1983, Ameritech Hdqrs., Chgo., 1991, Oceanarium, Shedd Aquarium, Chgo., 1991. Bd. dirs. Adler Planetarium, Chgo., 1983; pres. Soc. Contemporary Art, 1978-79; trustee Ill. Inst. Tech., Chgo., 1987—; pres. SOS Children's Village of Ill., 1991, SOS Children's Village of U.S.A., 1993—. Fellow AIA (honor awards). Clubs: Chgo. Yacht, Tavern, Chgo. Arts. Office: Lohan Assocs 225 N Michigan Ave Ste 800 Chicago IL 60601-5918 also: Lohan Assocs, GmbH Kochstrasse 16, 10969 Berlin Germany

LOHER, WERNER J., entomology educator; b. Landshut, Bavaria, Germany, June 27, 1929; came to U.S., 1967; s. Josef and Franziska (Fischer) L.; m. Elisabeth Zierl, 1 child, Thomas. Dr. rer. nat., Univ. Munich, Germany, 1955; Dr. phil., U. London, Imperial Coll., England, 1959; Dr. habil., Univ. Tubingen, Germany, 1965. Cert. biology educator. Asst. prof. Univ. Tubingen, Germany, 1960-65, assoc. prof., 1965-67; assoc. prof. Univ. Calif., Berkeley, Calif., 1967-70, prof., 1970—; dir. R.B. Gump South Pacific Biol. Rsch. Sta., Moorea, French Polynesia, 1985—. U.S. Senior Rsch. award Alexander von Humboldt Found., 1989-90. Mem. Fellow Calif. Acad. Sci.; mem. Acad. Sci. and Lit. (Mainz). Office: U Calif Berkeley Dept Environ Sci Policy Giannini Hall # 140 Berkeley CA 94720

LOHF, KENNETH A., librarian, writer; b. Milw., Jan. 14, 1925; s. Herman A. and Louise (Krause) L. AB, Northwestern U., 1949; AM, Columbia U., 1950, MS in Library Sci., 1952. Asst. librarian spl. collections Columbia U., N.Y.C., 1957-67; librarian rare books and manuscripts Columbia U., 1967-92. Author: Thirty Poems, 1966, Joseph Conrad at Mid-Century: Editions and Studies, 1957, The Achievement of Marianne Moore: A Bibliography, 1958, Yvor Winters: A Bibliography, 1959, Frank Norris: A Bibliography, 1959, Sherwood Anderson: A Bibliography, 1960, An Index to The Little Review, 1914-1929, 1961, The Collection fo Books, Manuscripts and Autograph Letters in the Library of Jean and Donald Stralem, 1962, Indices to Little Magazines, 1953-64, The Literary Manuscripts of Hart Crane, 1967, The Jack Harris Samuels Library, 1974, The Centenary of John Masefield's Birth, 1978; (poems) Seasons, 1981, Arrivals, 1987, Fictions, 1990, Passages, 1991, Places, 1992, Endings/Beginnings, 1994; editor: Hart Crane, Seven Lyrics, 1966, Collections and Treasures of the Rare Book and Manuscript Library of Columbia University, 1985, New York Elegies and Other Poems, 1995, Poets in a War, 1995; editor Columbia Library Columns, 1981-92; contbr. prefaces, afterwards, essays and articles to profl. publs. Sec.-treas. Friends of Columbia U. Librs., 1973-92; mem. coun. Am. Mus. Britain. 1st lt. USAAF, 1943-46. Mem. Knickerbocker Club, Century Club, Grolier Club (coun., sec. 1987-90, pres. 1990-94), Coun. Fellows Pierpont Morgan Libr. Episcopalian. Home: 560 Riverside Dr Apt 21B New York NY 10027-3236

LOHMAN, GORDON R., manufacturing executive; b. 1934. BS, MIT, 1955. Rsch. metallurgist, project engr. Amsted Industries, Inc., Chgo., 1958-61; project engr. Amstead Rsch. Labs. Amstead Rsch. Labs., Chgo., 1961-67; dir. rsch. Amstead Industries, Inc., Chgo., 1967-68, pres. rsch., 1968-76, pres. MacWhyte divsn., 1976-78, v.p. 1978-87, exec. v.p., then pres., 1987-88, pres., COO, 1988-90, pres., CEO, 1990—; trustee Ill. Inst. Tech.; bd. dirs. Am. Brands, Inc., CIPSCO. Lt. USAF, 1955-58. Office: Amsted Industries Inc 205 N Michigan Ave Chicago IL 60601-5914*

LOHMAN, JOHN FREDERICK, editor; b. Bismarck, N.D., Oct. 29, 1935; s. William Ernest and Viola (Paulson) L.; m. Dorothy Louise Stolp, July 13, 1962; children—Sheryl, Susan, Timothy, Jeffrey. B.S. in Engring., N.D. State U., 1960. Copy boy The Forum, Fargo, N.D., 1952-56, reporter, 1957-68, night editor, 1969-71, city editor, 1972-76, mng. editor, 1977-86, assoc. editor, 1987—; outdoor editor, 1988—. Mem. AP Mng. Editors Assn. Eagles. Avocations: hunting; fishing. Home: 2029 33rd Ave S Fargo ND 58104-6563

LOHMAN, WALTER REARICK, banker; b. Ashland, Ill., Nov. 14, 1917; s. Harry Joseph and Annette (Rearick) L.; m. Carol L. Coultas, June 26, 1948; children: Marian Carol, Roberta Baxter. B.S., Ill. Wesleyan U., 1939. Accountant U.S. Dept. Agr., 1939-41; with Pleasant Plains State Bank, Ill. 1941-42; dir. Pleasant Plains State Bank, with State Bank of Ashland, Ill., 1946-62, pres., 1957-62; exec. v.p. 1st Nat. Bank of Springfield, Ill., 1962-67; pres. 1st Nat. Bank of Springfield, 1967-81, chmn. bd., 1977-85; pres. First Bank of Ill. Co., Springfield, 1972-83, chmn. bd., 1983-87; bd. dirs. State Bank of Ashland, 1st Nat. Bank Springfield, First Bank of Ill. Co. and subs., MII Inc., Lincoln, Ill. Pres. Meml. Med. Ctr., 1983, 84, 85; chmn. bd. Meml. Med. Ctr. Found., 1989-91; bd. dirs. Ill. Indsl. Devel. Authority; trustee Ill. Wesleyan U. 1st lt. AUS, 1942-46, PTO. Recipient Distinguished Alumni award Ill. Wesleyan U., 1971; Distinguished Eagle Scout award Boy Scouts Am., 1973. Mem. Assn. for Modern Banking in Ill. (chmn. 1981-83), Ill. C. of C. (v.p., dir.), Springfield C. of C. (pres. 1969, 76-82). Clubs: Mason (Springfield) (Shriner), Illini Country (Springfield), Sangamo (Springfield). Home: 38 Oakmont Dr Springfield IL 62704-3116 Office: Firstbank Ill Co 205 S 5th St Apt 900 Springfield IL 62701-1437

LOHMILLER, JOHN M. (CHIP LOHMILLER), professional football player; b. Woodbury, Minn., July 16, 1966. Student, U. Minn. Placekicker Washington Redskins, 1988—. Named kicker The Sporting News NFL All-Pro team, 1991. Played in Pro Bowl, 1991. Office: Washington Redskins Dulles Internat. Airport PO Box 17247 Washington DC 20041*

LOHMULLER, MARTIN NICHOLAS, bishop; b. Phila., Aug. 21, 1919; s. Martin Nicholas and Mary Frances (Doser) L. B.A., St. Charles Borromeo Sem., Phila., 1942; D.Canon Law, Catholic U. Am., 1947. Ordained priest Roman Catholic Ch., 1944; officialis Diocese Harrisburg, Pa., 1948-63; vicar for religious Diocese of Harrisburg, 1958-70; pastor Our Lady of Good Counsel parish, Marysville, Pa., 1954-64, St. Catherine Laboure Parish, Harrisburg, 1964-68; consecrated Bishop of Ramsbury, 1970; vicar gen. Archdiocese Phila., 1970-94; aux. bishop of Phila., 1970-94; pastor Old St. Mary's Parish, Phila., 1976-89, Holy Trinity Parish, Phila., 1976-89.

LOHNES, WALTER F. W., German language and literature educator; b. Frankfurt, Germany, Feb. 8, 1925; came to U.S., 1948, naturalized, 1954; s. Hans and Dina (Koch) L.; m. Claire Shane, 1950; children: Kristen, Peter, Claudia. Student, U. Frankfurt, 1945-48, Ohio Wesleyan U., 1948-49, U. Mo., 1949-50; PhD, Harvard U., 1961. Asst., Inst. German Folklore, U. Frankfurt, 1947-48; instr. German U. Mo., 1949-50; head dept. German, Phillips Acad., Andover, Mass., 1951-61; asst. prof. Stanford (Calif.) U., 1961-65, assoc. prof., 1965-68, prof., 1969—, dir. NDEA Inst. Advanced Study, 1961-68, chmn. dept. German studies, 1973-79, dir. Inst. Basic German, prin. investigator NEH grant, 1978-80; vis. prof. Woehler-Gymnasium, Frankfurt, 1956-57, Middlebury Coll., 1959, U. N.Mex., 1980, 81, 86, U. Vienna, 1990, Coll. de France, Paris, 1992; mem., chmn. various coms. of examiners Ednl. Testing Svc. and Coll. Bd.; chmn. German Grad. Record Exam. Author: (with V. Nollendorfs) German Studies in the United States, 1976, (with F. W. Strothmann) German: A Structural Approach, 1968, 4th rev. edit., 1988; (with E.A. Hopkins) Contrastive Grammar of English and German, 1982, (with Martha Woodmansee) Erkennen und Deuten, 1983, (with J.A. Pfeffer) Grunddeutsch, Texte zur gesprochenen deutschen Gegenwartssprache, 3 vols., 1984, (with D. Benseler and V. Nollendorfs) Teaching German in America: Prolegomena to a History, 1988; contbr. numerous articles to profl. jours.; editor: Unterrichtspraxis, 1971-74. Bd. dirs. Calif. Youth Symphony, 1977-78, Oakland (Calif.) Symphony Youth Orch., 1978-80. Decorated Fed. Order of Merit (Germany); Medal of Honor in Gold (Austria); German Govt. grantee, 1975, 76, 78. Mem. MLA, Am. Assn. Tchrs. of German (v.p. 1961-62, 70-71, Outstanding Educator award 1993), Am. Assn. Applied Linguistics, Am. Coun. on Tchg. Fgn. Langs., German Studies Assn., Internat. Vereinigung Germanische Sprach und Literaturwissenschaft. Home: 733 Covington Rd Los Altos CA 94024-4903 Office: Stanford U Dept German Studies Stanford CA 94305-2030

LOHR, GEORGE E., state supreme court justice; b. 1931. BS, S.D. State U.; JD, U. Mich. Bar: Colo. 1965, Calif. 1969. Former judge Colo. 9th Dist. Ct., Aspen; assoc. justice Colo. Supreme Ct., Denver, 1979—. Office: Supreme Ct Colo State Judicial Bldg 2 E 14th Ave Denver CO 80203

LOHR, HAROLD RUSSELL, bishop; b. Gary, S.D., Aug. 31, 1922; s. Lester ALbert and Nora Helena (Fossum) L.; m. Theola Marie Kottke, June 21, 1947 (div. Dec. 1973); children: Philip Kyle, David Scott, Michael John; m. Edith Mary Morgan, Dec. 31, 1973. BS summa cum laude, S.D. State U., 1947; PhD, U. Calif.-Berkeley, 1950; MDiv summa cum laude, Augustana Theol. Sem., Rock Island, Ill., 1958. Ordained to ministry Augustana Luth. Ch., 1958; installed as bishop, 1980. Research chemist Argonne Nat. lab., Lemont, Ill., 1950-54; pastor Luth. Ch. of Ascension, Northfield, Ill., 1958-70; assoc. exec. Bd. Coll. Edn., N.Y.C., 1970-73; dir. research Div. Profl. Leadership, Phila., 1973-77, assoc. exec., 1977-80; synodical bishop Luth. Ch. in Am., Fargo, N.D., 1980-87; synodical bishop Evang. Luth. Ch. in Am., Moorhead, Minn., 1988-91, ret., 1991; mem. exec. council Luth. Ch. in Am., N.Y.C., 1982-87; mem. commn. of peace and war, 1983-85. Contbg. author: Growth in Ministry, 1980; also articles to sci. jours. Bd. dirs. Gustavus Adolphus Coll., 1980-87, Luther Northwestern Sem., St. Paul, 1980-87, Concordia Coll., Moorhead, Minn., 1988-91; mem. ch. coun. Evang. Luth. Ch. in Am., Chgo., 1990-91, disciplinary hearing officer, 1992—, interim dir. synodical rels., 1993-94; mem. bd. govs. Chgo. Ctr. Religion and Sci., 1987—; mem. Summit on Environ., Joint Appeal in Religion and Sci., Washington, 1992. With U.S. Army Inf., 1943-46, 2d lt., 1944-46, 2d lt., 1946. Recipient Suomi award Suomi Coll., 1983. Mem. Phi Kappa Phi. Democrat. Home: 154 Woodridge Rd Marlborough MA 01752-3327

LOHR, WALTER GEORGE, JR., lawyer; b. Balt., Mar. 3, 1944; s. Walter George and Janet Louise (Cartee) L.; children: Lila Meredith, Walter George III, Frederick Boyce. AB, Princeton U., 1966; LLB, Yale U., 1969. Bar: Md. 1969. Law clk.to Hon. Harrison L. Winter U.S. Cir. Ct., Richmond, Va., 1969-70; assoc. Piper & Marbury, Balt., 1970-74, ptnr., 1977-88; ptnr. Hogan & Hartson, Washington, 1992—; asst. atty. gen. State of Md., Balt., 1974-76; prin. Walter G. Lohr Jr., Balt., 1988-92; bd. dirs. Danaher Corp., Washington, Cartermill, Inc., Balt., Diginet Comm., Inc., Rockville, Md., Sky Alland Rsch., Inc., Laurel, Md.; mem. adv. bd. Prudential Venture Ptnrs., N.Y.C., 1985-93. Trustee Balt. Mus. Art, Gilman Sch. Office: Hogan & Hartson 111 S Calvert St 16th fl Baltimore MD 21202

LOHRER, RICHARD BAKER, investment consultant; b. Boston, Nov. 30, 1932; s. Leo and Elizabeth Louise (Kaiser) L.; m. Ruth Willa Gutekunst, Feb. 15, 1958; children: Richard Baker, William L., Elizabeth G., Andrew M. A.B., Harvard U., 1954; M.B.A., NYU, 1961. Asst. sec. comml. lending Irving Trust Co. (now Bank of N.Y.), N.Y.C., 1957-64; asst. to v.p. fin. and treas. Nat. Dairy Products Corp. (now Kraft Foods Divsn. of Philip Morris, Inc.), N.Y.C., 1964-71; asst. treas. Martin Marietta Corp. (now Lockheed Martin Corp.), N.Y.C., 1971-74; with Northrop Corp. (now Northrop Grumman Corp.), Los Angeles, 1974-90; treas. Northrop Corp. (now Northrop Grumman Corp.), 1977-87, v.p trust investments, 1987-90; prin., pres. R.B. Lohrer Assocs., Inc., Palos Verdes Estates, Calif., 1990—. Bd. dirs., pres. Cmty. Helpline, Inc., 1992—. Mem. L.A. Treas. Club (pres. 1981), L.A. Pension Group, Boston Latin Sch. West Coast Alumni Assn. (bd. dirs., pres. 1982-84), Fin. Exec. Inst. Harvard Club of So. Calif., Palos Verdes Country Club, Masons. Republican. Presbyterian.

LOHSE, AUSTIN WEBB, banker; b. N.Y.C., Jan. 22, 1926; s. Henry Vincent and Gertrude (Schroeder) L.; m. Virginia Meyer Butler, May 14, 1949; children: Constance Butler, John Daniel. B.A., Dartmouth Coll., 1947. Credit analyst Irving Trust Co., N.Y.C., 1947-52; with Am. Express Internat. Banking Corp., N.Y.C., 1952-73; asst. v.p. Am. Express Internat. Banking Corp., 1958-61, v.p., 1961-68, sr. v.p., 1968-73; v.p. Charterhouse Group Internat. Inc., N.Y.C., 1973-78, R.T. Madden & Co. Inc., N.Y.C., 1978-81; pres. A.W. Lohse & Co. Inc., N.Y.C., 1981—; former dir. Am. Express Bank G.M.B.H., Frankfurt, Germany, Am. Express Bank S.P.A., Rome, Am. Express Securities S.A., Paris, LB/Amex Ltd., London, Eng. Mem. Casque and Gauntlet Soc., Beta Theta Pi. Republican. Episcopalian. Clubs: Short Hills (N.J.); Knickerbocker (N.Y.C.). Home: 7 Taylor Rd Short Hills NJ 07078-2225 Office: 630 5th Ave New York NY 10111-0001

LOHSE, DAVID JOHN, physicist; b. N.Y.C., Sept. 14, 1952; s. Edward and Mildred Edna (Hofmeister) L.; m. Maria Isabel Magdalena Garcia, Sept. 2, 1978. BS, Mich. State U., 1974; PhD, U. Ill., 1978. Rsch. assoc. Nat. Bur. of Standards, Gaithersburg, Md., 1978-80; rsch. engr. Exxon Chem. Co., Linden, N.J., 1980-89; staff engr. Exxon Rsch. & Engring. Co., Annandale, N.J., 1989—. Inventor graft polymers; contbr. articles to profl. jours. NRC/NSF fellow, 1978-80. Mem. Am. Chem. Soc. (sec. polymer material sci. engring. divsn. 1995—), Am. Phys. Soc., N.Y. Acad. Scis. (chmn. polymers divsn. N.Y.C. chpt. 1991-95). Home: 556 Stony Brook Dr Bridgewater NJ 08807-1947 Office: Exxon Rsch & Engring Corp Rt 22 E Annandale NJ 08801

LOIELLO, JOHN PETER, public affairs executive, consultant; b. Oceanside, N.Y., Aug. 16, 1943; s. Rosario Paul and Mary Agnes (Butler) L.; m. Elaine Margaret Robinson, June 14, 1944. BA in History, Fordham U., 1965; MA in History, SUNY, Buffalo, 1973; PhD in African History, U. London, 1980. Tchr. history The Gow Sch., South Wales, N.Y., 1967-71; instr. U. Md. (U.K.), London, 1976-78; exec. dir. Dem. Party Com. Abroad, Washington and London, 1978-80; sr. cons. Assn. Am. Chambers of Commerce in Latin Am., Washington, 1980; spl. asst. to chmn. NEH, Washington, 1978-82; assoc. dir. Democracy Prog., Washington, 1982-83; founding exec. dir. Nat. Dem. Inst. for Internat. Affairs, Washington, 1983-85; pres. Gowran Internat., Washington, 1985—; pres. Alcide de Gaspari Found. (USA), Washington, 1987-89. Contbr. articles to profl. jours. Commr. Commn. on Platform Accountability, Dem. Nat. Com., Washington, 1981-85, chmn. fgn. policy subcom., 1980, platform com., 1980; sec. Tax Equity for Ams. Abroad, London, 1977-79; sec. Dems. Abroad, London, 1976-79. African Studies scholar, U. London, 1974-78, grantee, 1975. Mem. Nat. Italian Am. Found., Royal African Soc. Democrat. Roman Catholic. Avocations: travel, racquetball, swimming. Office: Gowran Internat 1215 17th St NW Washington DC 20036-3089

LOIN, E. LINNEA, social services administrator; b. Middletown, Conn., Nov. 20, 1942; d. Alfred William Skinner and Ada Patricia Moore; m. Peter Michael Loin, Sept. 16, 1972. BA, U. Conn., 1965. Social worker State of Conn., Middletown and Hartford, 1964-69; case supr. State of Conn., Hartford, 1969-74; program supr. State of Conn., Hartford, Manchester and Rockville, Hartford, 1984-90, Willimantic, 1990—; state liaison Nat. Ctr. for Child Abuse and Neglect, Washington, 1985-90. Editor: Connecticut's Children, 1985, Common Cause, 1987-89. Town rep. Crown Cable Adv. Bd., Willimantic, 1993-94. Democrat. Avocations: swimming, walking, reading, travel, water sports. Home: 29 Cowles Rd Willington CT 06279 Office: DCYS Region 6 1320 Main St Willimantic CT 06226-1910

LOIS, GEORGE, advertising agency executive; b. N.Y.C., June 26, 1931; s. Harry and Vasilike (Thanasoulis) L.; m. Rosemary Lewandowski, Aug. 27, 1951; children: Harry (dec.), Luke. Student, Pratt Inst., 1949-51, D.F.A. (hon.), 1982. Designer Reba Sochis, 1951; designer CBS-TV, 1954-56; art dir. Sudler & Hennessey, 1956-57, Doyle, Dane, Bernbach, 1958-59; partner, creative dir. Papert, Koenig, Lois, Inc., N.Y.C., 1960-67; chmn. bd., chief exec. officer Lois Holland Callaway Inc., N.Y.C., 1967-78; chmn. bd., creative dir. Lois/USA, N.Y.C., 1978—. Author: George, Be Careful, 1972, The Art of Advertising, George Lois on Mass Communication, 1977, What's the Big Idea?, 1991. Served with AUS, 1952-54, Korea. Elected to Art Dirs. Hall of Fame, 1978, Creative Hall of Fame, 1980. Mem. N.Y. Art Dirs. Club (pres. 1971-73). Office: Lois/USA 40 W 57th St New York NY 10019

LOIUDICE, THOMAS ANTHONY, gastroenterologist, researcher; b. Wilmington, Del., Dec. 3, 1942; s. Dominick and Carmela (Vignola) Loi; m. Jean Anne Lang, June 20, 1970; children: Christopher, Mark. BS, St. Joseph's U., 1966; DO, Chgo. Coll., 1972. Diplomate Am. Bd. Family Practice, Am. Bd. Internal Medicine, Am. Bd. Nutrition; lic. physician Tenn., Pa., Ind., Ohio, N.Y., Fla. Intern U. Health Ctr. Pitts. Hosp., 1972-73, jr. asst. resident in internal medicine, 1973-74, sr. asst. resident in internal medicine, 1974, fellow cardiology, 1975; fellow gastroenterology and clin. nutrition Union U., Albany, N.Y., 1975-77; pres. Akron (Ohio) Gastroenterology Assocs., Inc., 1978—; instr. Northeastern Ohio U., Akron, 1977-83, asst. prof., assoc. prof. gastroenterology, 1983-91, prof., 1991—; head subsect. nutrition, 1986—; sec.-treas. Tri-County Emergency Med. Svc., Inc., 1983—; clin. rsch. assoc. Smith, Kline & French Labs., 1983—; mem.

sr. teaching staff St. Thomas Med. Ctr., Akron, chief nutrition, head nutritional support team, 1989—; mem. courtesy staff Barberton Citizens Hosp., Barberton, Ohio, Cuyahoga Falls (Ohio) Gen. Hosp.; mem. jr. staff Akron Gen. Med. Ctr.; mem. staff Akron City Hosp.; speaker in field. Contbr. numerous articles to So. Med. Jour., Gastroeterology, Ob/Gyn., Am. Jour. Gastroenterology, Am. Jour. Digestive Disease, Am. Jour. Clin. Nutrition, N.Y. Jour. Medicine, and other. Grantee William H. Rorer, Smith Kline and French, Ortho Pharm. Corp., Glaxo Pharm. Fellow ACP, Am. Coll. Angiology, Am. Coll. Gastroenterology, Am. Coll. Nutrition, Royal Soc. Medicine (Eng., affiliate); mem. AMA, AAAS, Am. Coll. Emergency Physicians, Am.Soc. Contemporary Medicine and Surgery, Am. Soc. Internal Medicine, Am. Gastroenterology Assn., Am. Assn. for Study Liver Disease, Am. Soc. Gastrointestinal Endoscopy, Am. Fedn. Clin. Rsch., Ohio Med. Assn., Ohio Soc. Internal Medicine, Northeastern Ohio Soc. Gastrointestinal Endoscopy, Summit County Med. Soc. Roman Catholic. Achievements include research in treatment of radiation enteritis with nutritional support and steroids; in zinc and radiation enterities; in tagamet prophylasic in the prevention of gastric ulcers produced by non-steroidal anti-inflamatory agents. Office: Akron Gastroenterology Assoc 444 N Main St Ste 324 Akron OH 44310-3110

LOKEN, JAMES BURTON, federal judge; b. Madison, Wis., May 21, 1940; s. Burton Dwight and Anita (Nelson) L.; m. Caroline Brevard Hester, July 30, 1966; children: Kathryn Brevard, Kristina Ayres. BS, U. Wis., 1962; LLB magna cum laude, Harvard U., 1965. Law clk. to chief judge Lumbard U.S. Ct. Appeals (2d Cir.), N.Y.C., 1965-66; law clk. to assoc. justice Byron White U.S. Supreme Ct., Washington, 1966-67; assoc. atty. Faegre & Benson, Mpls., 1967-70, ptnr., 1973-90; gen. counsel Pres.'s Com. on Consumer Interests, Office of Pres. of U.S., Washington, 1970; staff asst. Office of Pres. of U.S., Washington, 1970-72; judge U.S. Ct. Appeals (8th cir.), St. Paul, 1991—. Editor Harvard Law Rev., 1964-65. Mem. Minn. State Bar Assn., Phi Beta Kappa, Phi Kappa Phi. Avocations: golf, running. Home: PO Box 75848 Saint Paul MN 55175-0848 also: Cir Courts Appeals 8th Circuit 316 Robert St N Saint Paul MN 55101-1423*

LOKENSGARD, JON A., school system administrator. Supt. Sierra Vista (Ariz.) Unified Sch. Dist. State finalist Nat. Supt. Yr. award, 1993. Office: Sierra Vista Unified Dist 3555 Fry Blvd Sierra Vista AZ 85635

LOKER, ELIZABETH ST. JOHN, newspaper executive; b. Leonardtown, Md., Jan. 1, 1948; d. William Meverell and June Whiting (Farner) L.; m. Donald Scott Rice, Sept. 11, 1980. B.A., George Washington U., 1969. Analyst Met. Washington Council Govt., 1973-74; analyst, programmer Washington Post, 1974-75, mgr. systems research, 1976, dir. data processing, 1976-78, asst. to pub., 1979, v.p. advanced systems, 1979—, v.p. sys. and engring., 1992—. Contbr. chpt. to book. Trustee Greater Washington Research Ctr., also mem. exec. com.; mem. bus. coun. Washington Opera; bd. dirs. Washington Chamber Symphony. Mem. Newspaper Systems Group (past pres.), Assn. for Computing Machinery, Soc. Info. Mgmt., Ops. Research Soc. Am., Inst. Mgmt. Sci. Avocations: antiques; gardening; historic preservation. Office: Washington Post Co 1150 15th St NW Washington DC 20071-0002

LOKEY, FRANK MARION, JR., broadcast executive, consultant; b. Ft. Worth, Oct. 15, 1924; s. Frank Marion Sr. and Corinne (Whaley) L. Student, Smith-Hughes Evening Coll., 1955-59. Asst. gen. mgr., mgr. sales, news anchor Sta. WLW-A TV (now named WXIA-TV), Atlanta, 1955-66; co-owner, gen. mgr. Sta. WAIA, Atlanta, 1960-62; S.E. news corr., talk show host CBS News N.Y., N.Y.C., 1960-66; asst. to owner, gen. mgr. Sta. WBIE-AM-FM, Atlanta, 1962-64; asst. to pres., gen. mgr. Stas. KXAB-TV, KXJB-TV, KXMB-TV, Aberdeen, Fargo, Bismarck, S.D., N.D., 1966-67; exec. v.p., gen. mgr. Sta. WEMT-TV, Bangor, Maine, 1967-70; pres., gen. mgr. Stas. KMOM-TV, KWAB-TV, Odessa-Midland, Big Spring, Tex., 1970-75; exec. v.p., gen. mgr. Sta. KMUV-TV (now named KRBK-TV), Sacramento, Calif., 1975-77; CEO Lokey Enterprises, Inc., Sacramento, L.A., El Centro, Calif., 1977—; also chmn. bd. dirs.; cons., Troubleshooter 16 TV stas. nationwide, 1977—; cons., actor 5 movie prodn. cos., Hollywood, Calif., 1980—; cons., outside dir. Anderson Cons., Manhattan, L.I., N.Y., 1981—; network talk show host/news corr. for 7 news orgns. worldwide, 1984—; bd. dirs. Broadcast Audience Behavior Rsch., Manhattan, 1986—, mem. inner circle, 1986—. Creator, originator approach to real estate mktg. Hon. mem. Imperial County Bd. Suprs., El Centro, 1986—, El Centro City Coun., 1987—. Mem. Am. Legion. Baptist. Avocations: producer big bands parties, movie acting, ancient history, tracing family tree, franchisor of The Party Place (night club/ballroom chain for seniors with big-band music). Home: 592 Wensley Ave El Centro CA 92243-3955 Office: Lokey Enterprises Inc 626 Main St El Centro CA 92243

LOKEY, HAMILTON, retired lawyer; b. Atlanta, Aug. 30, 1910; s. Hugh Montgomery and Rebecca Crawford (Hamilton) L.; m. Muriel Ann Mattson, July 18, 1944; children—Hamilton Jr., William Mattson, Fletcher, Ann Montgomery, Rebecca Hazel. A.B., U. Ga., 1931, LL.B., 1933. Bar: Ga. bar 1933, U.S. Supreme Ct. bar 1938. Asso. firm Harold Hirsch & Marion Smith, Atlanta, 1933-37; individual practice law Atlanta, 1937-39; ptnr. Lokey & Bowden, Atlanta, 1939-95; mem. Ga. Gen. Assembly, 1953-56; practising lawyer in residence U. Ga. Law Sch., 1977; chmn. Ga. State Bd. Bar Examiners, 1974-78. Served with USN, 1942-45, 50-52. Mem. Am., Ga., Atlanta bar assns., Lawyers Club Atlanta, Internat. Assn. Ins. Counsel, Am. Coll. Trial Lawyers, Internat. Acad. Trial Lawyers, Am. Judicature Soc., World Assn. Lawyers, Phi Beta Kappa, Phi Kappa Phi. Democrat. Episcopalian. Club: Piedmont Driving. Home: 737 Woodward Way NW Atlanta GA 30327-1254 Office: 2500 Tower Pl Atlanta GA 30326

LOKKEN, LAWRENCE, law educator; b. 1939. BA, Augsburg Coll., 1960; JD, U. Minn., 1967. Bar: Minn. 1967. Asst. prof. U. Ga., 1968-70; vis. assoc. prof. U. Minn., 1973-74; assoc. prof. U. Fla., 1974-77, prof., 1977-82; vis. prof. NYU, 1980-82, prof., 1982—; vis. prof. Duke U., 1988, Leiden U., Netherlands, 1978, 93. Co-author: (with Boris I. Bittker) Federal Taxation of Income, Estates and Gifts, 5 vols., 1989, 90, 91, 92, 93, Fundamentals of International Taxation, 1991. Mem. Order of the Coif. Office: NYU Sch Law 40 Washington Sq S New York NY 10012-1005

LOLLEY, WILLIAM RANDALL, minister; b. Troy, Ala., June 2, 1931; s. Roscoe Lee and Mary Sara (Nunnelee) L.; m. Clara Lou Sparks, Aug. 28, 1952; children: Charlotte, Pam. AB, Samford U., 1952, DD (hon.), 1980; BD, Southeastern Sem., 1957, ThM, 1958; ThD, Southwestern Sem., 1962; DD (hon.), Wake Forest U., 1971, U. Richmond, 1984; LLD (hon.), Campbell U., 1986; LittD (hon.), Mercer U., 1988. Ordained to ministry So. Bapt. Conv., 1951; pastor First Bapt. Ch., Winston-Salem, N.C., 1962-74; pres. Southeastern Bapt. Theol. Sem., Wake Forest, N.C., 1974-88; pastor First Bapt. Ch., Raleigh, N.C., 1988-90, Greensboro, N.C., 1990—. Author: Crises in Morality, 1963, Bold Preaching of Christ, 1979, Servant Songs, 1994. Democrat. Club: Rotary. Home: 3200 W Market St Greensboro NC 27403-1456 Office: First Bapt Ch Greensboro NC 27403

LOLLI, ANDREW RALPH, industrial engineer, former army officer; b. Seatonville, Ill., Oct. 15, 1907; s. Joseph Fredrick and Adolfa (Fiocchi) L.; m. Mary H. Tatsapaugh, Jan. 14, 1983. Student Armed Forces Staff Coll., 1950, Nat. War Coll., 1957, N.Y. Inst. Fin., 1971; BS, Dickinson Coll., 1922; postgrad. Fordham U., 1952. Enlisted in U.S. Army, 1940, advanced through grades to maj. gen., 1960; chief plans and priorities Allied Forces So. Europe, 1952-56; comdr. Air Def. units, N.Y. and San Francisco, 1957-60; comdr. X.X U.S.A. Corps, 1961-62, XV, 1962-63, comdr. Western NORD Region, Hamilton AFB, Calif., 1963-66; ret., 1966; exec. asst. Hughes Aircraft Co., Fullerton, Calif., 1967; dir. gen. services State of Calif., Sacramento, 1967-70; v.p. Sigmatics, Newport Beach, Calif., 1970-73, Intercoast Investments Co., Sacramento, 1975-76; pres. Andrew R. Lolli Assocs. Inc., San Francisco 1973—; Lolman Inc., San Francisco, 1976—; commr. Small Bus. Adv. Commn., San Francisco, 1989-93; pres. bd. trustees Commonwealth Equity Trust, 1974-80; vice chmn. Calif. Pub. Works bd., 1967-69; mem. adv. panel Nat. Acad. Scis. and Engring. in Research, Washington, 1968-70; mem. fed. state and local govt. adv. panel Fed. Gen. Services, Washington, 1968-69. Bd. dirs. Columbia Boys Park Club, San Francisco, Lab. for Survival, San Francisco; mem. Presido of San Francisco Restoration Adv. Bd., 1994. Decorated D.S.M., Legion of Merit with oak leaf cluster, Bronze Star with oak leaf cluster; named Man of Year, Italian

Sons of Am., 1964. Mem. Nat. Assn. Uniformed Services, Assn. U.S. Army, Ret. Officers Assn. Roman Catholic. Developed short notice inspection system for army air def. missiles, 1960. Home: 1050 N Point St San Francisco CA 94109-8302 Office: 286 Jefferson St San Francisco CA 94133-1126

LOMAN, MARY LAVERNE, retired mathematics educator; b. Stratford, Okla., June 10, 1928; d. Thomas D. and Mary Ellen (Goodwin) Glass; m. Coy E. Loman, Dec. 23, 1944; 1 child, Sandra Leigh Loman Easton. B.S., U. Okla., 1956, MA, 1957, PhD, 1961. Grad. asst., then instr. U. Okla., Norman, 1956-61; asst. prof. math. U. Ctrl. Okla., Edmond, 1961-62; assoc. prof. U. Cen. Okla., Edmond, 1962-66, prof., 1966-93; prof. emeritus U. Ctrl. Okla., Edmond, 1993—; ret., 1993. NSF fellow, 1965-67. Mem. Math. Assn. Am., Nat. Coun. Tchrs. Math., Okla. Coun. Tchrs. Math. (v.p. 1972-76), Higher Edn Alumni Coun. Okla., VFW Aux., Delta Kappa Gamma. Home: 2201 Tall Oaks Trl Edmond OK 73003-2325

LOMAS, BERNARD TAGG, college president emeritus; b. Mackinaw City, Mich., Aug. 14, 1924; s. Percy L. and Eva (Tagg) L.; m. Barbara Jean West, June 21, 1947; children: Paul Neil, David Mark. AB, Albion Coll., 1946, DD, 1965; BD, Oberlin Grad. Sch. Theology, 1948; MDiv., Vanderbilt U., 1967; LLD, Adrian U., 1983. Ordained minister Meth. Ch., 1948. Minister William St. Meth. Ch., Delaware, Ohio, 1950-54; counsellor to students Ohio Wesleyan U., 1950-54; sr. minister Trinity Meth. Ch., Portsmouth, Ohio, 1954-60; sr. minister heading staff of five ministers Epworth-Euclid Ch., Univ. Circle, Cleve., 1960-70; pres. Albion (Mich.) Coll., 1970-83, chancellor, 1983-88, pres. emeritus, 1988—; cons. Am. Enterprise Inst., Washington, 1980-81; pers. and human rels. cons. to U.S. and fgn. bus. Author 5 books; contbr. numerous articles to edn. and religious jours. Organizer, head Citizens Com. for Law Enforcement, Portsmouth, 1957-58; founding mem. pres. Christian Residences Found.; bd. dirs. Goodwill Industries Cleve., 1964-70; trustee St. Lukes Hosp., Cleve., 1965-70; bd. govs. Greater Mich. Found., 1978-83; bd. dirs. Christian Children's Fund, 1978-81; counselor Heritage Found., Washington, 1984—. Bd. Inst. Am. Univs., Aix En Provence-France, 1988—. Mem. Masons, Shriners, Rotary.

LOMAS, LYLE WAYNE, agricultural research administrator, educator; b. Monett, Mo., June 8, 1953; s. John Junior and Helen Irene Lomas; m. Connie Gail Frey, Sept. 4, 1976; children: Amy Lynn, Eric Wayne. BS, U. Mo., 1975, MS, 1976; PhD, Mich. State U., 1979. Asst. prof., animal scientist Kans. State U. S.E. Agrl. Rsch. Ctr., Parsons, 1979-85, assoc. prof., head, 1985-92, prof., head, 1992—. Contbr. articles to refereed sci. jours. Mem. Am. Soc. Animal Sci., Am. Registry Profl. Animal Scientists, Am. Forage and Grassland Coun., Rsch. Ctr. Adminstrs. Soc. (bd. dirs. 1993—), Parsons Rotary Club (bd. dirs. 1992—), Phi Kappa Phi, Gamma Sigma Delta. Presbyterian. Achievements include research in ruminant nutrition, forage utilization by grazing stocker cattle. Home: RR 1 Box 31 Dennis KS 67341-8916 Office: Kans State Univ Southeast Agrl Rsch Ctr PO Box 316 Parsons KS 67357-0316

LOMASON, HARRY AUSTIN, II, automotive company executive; b. Detroit, Oct. 6, 1934; s. William Keithledge and Neva L.; children by previous marriage: Kimri Elizabeth Lomason Massey, Krista Anne Lomason Massell, William Keithledge, Peter Kevin; m. Mary Alice Pushkarsky, June 26, 1971; children: Harry Austin, Heather Alice. Student, Ga. Inst. Tech., 1953-56; B.B.A., Ga. State U., 1959. With Douglas & Lomason, Farmington Hills, Mich., 1960—, asst. sec., 1966-72, v.p., sec., 1972-76, pres., chief operating officer, 1976-82, pres., chief exec. officer, 1982—; chmn. Douglas & Lomason Co., Farmington Hills, 1993—; also bd. dirs. Douglas & Lomason, Farmington Hills, Mich.; v.p. bd. dirs. Douglas y Lomason de Mex. S.A. de C.V., 1987—; chmn., bd. dirs. Bloomington-Normal (Ill.) Seating Co., Mich. Mfrs. Assn.; bd. dirs., mem. exec. com. The Am. Supplier Inst., The Amerisure Cos., Detroit; bd. examiners Malcolm Baldridge Nat. Quality Award com., 1988. Bd. dirs. Detroit Symphony Orch. Hall, 1979—; bd. dirs. Mich. Thanksgiving Parade Found., Harper-Grace Hosp. Mem. Engring. Soc. Detroit, Soc. Automotive Engrs., Detroit Club, Detroit Athletic Club, Detroit Golf Club, Cherokee Town and Country Club (Atlanta), Marianna (Ark.) Country Club, Lake Country Club (Orchard Lake, Mich.). Episcopalian. Home: 2900 Pine Lake Rd West Bloomfield MI 48324-1945 Office: Douglas & Lomason Co 24600 Hallwood Ct Farmington MI 48335-1671

LOMAX, JOHN H., financial service company executive; b. Macon, Ga., Mar. 28, 1924; s. John H. and Regis (Garrity) L.; m. Ann E. Davis, Dec. 30, 1947; children: J. Harvey, Jan (Mrs. Ben Teal). BBA, U. Ga., 1948; student, U. N.C., 1962. Exec. v.p. Am. Credit Corp., Charlotte, N.C., 1958-76; exec. v.p. Assocs. Corp. of N.Am., Dallas, 1976-87; dir. Gulf Coast Consol. Office Resolution Trust Corp., Houston, 1989-91, dir. north ctrl. region, 1991-92; v.p. S.W. region Resolution Trust Corp., Dallas, 1992-94; pres. Am. Money Corp., Dallas, 1994—; chmn., CEO Policy Funding Corp., Dallas, 1995—. Bd. dirs. Dallas Summer Musicals. Capt. USAF, 1942-46. Home: 4215 Glenaire Dr Dallas TX 75229-4140 Office: Resolution Trust Corp 3500 Maple Ave Dallas TX 75219-3901

LOMAX, PEGGY QUARLES, gifted and talented education educator; b. Bradenton, Fla., Dec. 21, 1941; d. Archie Eugene and Katherine Louise (Stowe) Q.; m. David W. Ridge, Dec. 27, 1958 (div. July 1972); m. Robert T. Lomax, Nov. 23, 1978; children: Anita Ann, Michael Wade. BS in Intermediate Edn., Appapachian State U., 1977; MA im Mid. Sch. Edn., Lenoir Rhyne Coll., 1987. Cert. tchr., sch. adminstr., N.C. Media asst. J.B. Little Elem. Sch., Arlington, Tex., 1969-72; pub. info. officer Appalachian State U., Boone, N.C., 1974-77; tchr. academically gifted Gamewell Mid. Sch., Lenoir, N.C., 1977-89; William Lenoir (N.C.) Mid. Sch., 1989-93; tchr., coord. gifted and talented Mayflower (Ark.) Pub. Schs., 1993—. Pres. Lenoir Bus. and Profl. Orgn., 1984-85; spl. registration commr. Caldwell County, 1985-87; bd. dirs. Caldwell County Libr., 1985-87; mem. N.C. Commn. on Youth and Children, 1987-89; mem. youth com. Mt. Grove Bapt. Ch. Recipient Caldwell County Human Rels. award, 1987=88; grantee Caldwell County C. of C., 1992, Z. Smith Reynolds Found., 1993. Mem. NEA, ASCD, N.C. Assn. Educators (v.p. 1985-86, 90-91, pres. 1986-87, 92-93), N.C. League Mid. Schs. (bd. dirs. 1981-84, v.p.), N.C. Assn. Gifted Educators, Caldwell County Assn. Educators (pres. 1984-85), Arkansans for Gifted and Talented Edn., Nat. Mid. Sch. Assn., Arkansas Assn. Gifted Adminstrs., Kappa Delta Pi.

LOMBARD, ARTHUR J., law educator; b. N.Y.C., Nov. 30, 1941; s. Maurice and Martha (Simons) L.; m. Frederica Koller, Aug. 18, 1968; children: David, Lisa. BS in Acctg. magna cum laude, Columbia U., 1961; JD, Harvard U., 1964. Bar: N.Y. 1964, U.S. Ct. Appeals (2d cir.) 1965, U.S. Supreme Ct. 1970, U.S. Ct. Appeals (6th cir.) 1972, Mich. 1976. Law clk. to J. Edward Lumbard chief judge U.S. Ct. Appeals (2d cir.), N.Y.C., 1964-65; teaching fellow law sch. Harvard U., Cambridge, Mass., 1965-66; instr. Orientation Program in Am. Law, Assn. Am. Law Schs., Princeton, N.J., 1966; prof. law Wayne State U., Detroit, 1966-87, assoc. dean law, 1978-85; prof. Detroit Coll. Law, 1987—, dean, chief adminstrv. officer, 1987-93; chmn. revision of Mich. class action rule com. Mich. Supreme Ct., 1980-83; reporter rules com., U.S. Dist. Ct. (ea. dist.) Mich., 1978—. Contbr. articles to profl. jours. Mem. Mich. Civil Rights Commn., 1991—, co-chmn., 1992-93, chmn., 1993—. Home: 10 Rose Terrace St Grosse Pointe MI 48236-3766 Office: 1807 City County Bldg Detroit MI 48226

LOMBARD, DAVID NORMAN, lawyer; b. Seattle, Dec. 6, 1949; s. John Cutler and Dororthy Marie (Brandt) L.; m. Susan Elliott, Oct. 22, 1983; children: Matthew, Jeffrey, Megan. BA, U. Wash., 1973; JD, U. Puget Sound, Tacoma, 1976. Bar: Wash. 1976, U.S. Dist. Ct. (we. dist.) Wash. 1976, U.S. Dist. Ct. (ea. dist.) Wash. 1983, U.S. Ct. Appeals (9th cir.) 1976. Law clk. Wash. State Supreme Ct., Olympia, 1976-77; assoc. Schwabe, Williamson, Ferguson & Burdell, Seattle, 1977-82, ptnr., 1983-93; Jameson Babbitt Stites & Lombard Seattle, 1993—. Mem. Rainier Club, Wash. Athletic Club. Presbyterian. Office: Jameson Babbitt Stites & Lombard 999 Third Ave Ste 1900 Seattle WA 98104

LOMBARD, JOHN JAMES, JR., lawyer; b. Phila., Dec. 27, 1934; s. John James and Mary R. (O'Donnell) L.; m. Barbara Mallon, May 9, 1964; children: John James, William M., James G., Laura K., Barbara E. BA cum laude, LaSalle Coll., Phila., 1956; JD, U. Pa., 1959. Bar: Pa. 1960. Assoc., Obermayer, Rebmann, Maxwell & Hippel, Phila., 1960-65, ptnr., 1966-84, fin. ptnr., 1980-84; ptnr. Morgan, Lewis & Bockius, Phila., 1985—, mgr. personal law sect., 1986-90, vice chair personal law sect., 1990-92, chair, 1992—; sec., dir. Airline Hydraulics Corp., Phila., 1969—. Bd. dirs. Redevel. Authority Montgomery County, Pa., 1980-87, Gwynedd-Mercy Coll., Gwynedd Valley, Pa., 1980-89, LaSalle College High Sch., Wyndmoor, Pa., 1991—. Mem. ABA (chmn. com. simplification security transfers 1972-76, chmn. membership com. 1972-82, mem. council real property, probate and trust law sect. 1979-85, sec. 1985-87, div. dir. probate div. 1987-89, chair elect 1989-90, chair 1990-91, co-chair Nat. Conf. Lawyers & Corp. Fiduciaries), Pa. Bar Assn. (ho. of dels. 1979-81), Phila. Bar Assn. (chmn. probate sect. 1972), Am. Coll. Trust and Estate Counsel (editor Probate Notes 1983, bd. regents 1986-91, mem. exec. com. 1988-91, elder law com. 1993—), Internat. Acad. Estate and Trust Law (exec. com. 1984-88, 90—), Am. Bar Found., Internat. Fish and Game Assn. Clubs: Union League (Phila.); Ocean City (N.J.) Marlin and Tuna, Ocean City Yacht. Co-author: Durable Power of Attorney—A Systems Approach, 1984, 3d edit. 1994; contbr. articles to profl. jours. Office: Morgan Lewis & Bockius 2000 One Logan Sq Philadelphia PA 19103

LOMBARD, JUDITH MARIE, human resource policy specialist; b. Harmony, Maine, June 7, 1944; d. Clayton Selden and Helen Mae (Wentworth) L. BA, U. Maine, 1966; MPA, U. So. Calif., 1982, D of Pub. Adminstrn., 1987. Psychodramatist HEW, Washington, 1966-68; creative arts therapist U.S. Health and Human Svcs., Washington, 1968-87; sr. therapist Mental Health Svcs., Washington, 1987-88; tng. officer USDA, Washington, 1988-92; mem. adj. faculty U. So. Calif., L.A., 1988-92, Shenandoah U., Winchester, Va., 1993—; employee devel. specialist U.S. Office Personnel Mgmt., Washington, 1992—; pvt. cons., Alexandria, Va., 1988—. Author (book chpt.) How Public Organizations Work, 1991, (handbook) Supervisor's Guide, 1993; contbr. articles to profl. jours. Fundraiser, county chair Maine State Soc., Washington, 1980—; mem. fundraising bd. doctorial assn. U. So. Calif., Washington, 1986—; active Del Ray Citizens Assn., Alexandria, 1982—. Recipient Dorothy Dix award St. Elizabeth's Hosp., Washington, 1982. Mem. Am. Soc. Pub. Adminstrn., Nat. Therapeutic Recreation Soc., Am. Therapeutic Recreation Assn. (pres. Washington chpt. 1990), Med. Soc. Washington (pres. 1990), Nat. Recreation and Parks Assn. (elections chair 1990, 91), D.C. Jungian Soc., Chesapeake Bay Orgnl. Devel. Network. Avocations: telecommunications, travel, refinishing antique furniture, hiking, card games. Office: US Office Personnel Mgmt 1900 E St NW Washington DC 20415

LOMBARD, RICHARD SPENCER, lawyer; b. Panama Canal Zone, Jan. 28, 1928; s. Eugene C. and Alice R. (Quinn) L.; m. Arlene Olson, Dec. 27, 1952; children: Anne, James. AB, Harvard U., 1949, JD, 1952. Bar: N.Y. 1953, Tex. 1971. Assoc. Haight, Gardner, Poor & Havens, N.Y.C., 1952-55; mem. law dept. Creole Petroleum Corp., Caracas, Venezuela, 1955-65, mgr., 1963-65; gen. counsel Esso Chem. Co., N.Y.C., 1966-69; assoc. gen. counsel Humble Oil & Refining Co., Houston, 1969-71; asst. gen. counsel Exxon Corp., N.Y.C., 1971-72, assoc. gen. counsel, 1972-73, gen. counsel, 1973-93, v.p., 1980-93; counsel Baker & Botts, Dallas, 1993—; trustee Parker Sch. Fgn. and Comparative Law, Columbia U., 1977—, Southwestern Legal Found., 1978, Practicing Law Inst., 1980. Author: American-Venezuelan Private International Law, 1965. Served with AC AUS, 1946-47. Fellow Am. Bar Found.; mem. ABA, Am. Law Inst., Am. Arbitration Assn. (bd. dirs., chmn. bd. 1983-86), N.Y. State Bar Assn., Assn. Bar City of N.Y., State Bar of Tex., Dallas Bar Assn., Univ. Club (N.Y.C.). Office: Baker & Botts LLP 2001 Ross Ave Dallas TX 75201

LOMBARDI, CELESTE, zoological park administrator; b. Columbus, Ohio, Feb. 16, 1955; d. Adam Dominic and Frances Elizabeth (Varda) L.; m. Terence Lawrence Smith, Mar. 26, 1990; 1 child Matthew Peachey. BS in Zoology, Ohio State U., 1978. Zoo keeper Children's Zoo Columbus Zoo, 1978-83, supr. Children's Zoo, 1983-90, asst. curator mammals, 1990-93, gen. curator, 1993—. TV appearances include David Letterman Show, Good Morning America, PM Magazine, and various local news shows. Mem. Am. Assn. Zool. Parks and Aquariums, Am. Assn. Zoo Keepers. Roman Catholic. Home: 4190 Rutherford Rd Powell OH 43065-9733 Office: Columbus Zoo PO Box 400 9990 Riverside Dr Powell OH 43065-9606

LOMBARDI, CORNELIUS ENNIS, JR., lawyer; b. Portland, Oreg., Feb. 12, 1926; s. Cornelius Ennis and Adele (Volk) L.; m. Ann Vivian Foster, Nov. 24, 1954; children—Cornelius Ennis, Gregg Foster, Matthew Volk. B.A., Yale, 1949; J.D. U. Mich., 1952. Bar: Mo. bar. Since practiced in Kansas City, Mo.; mem. firm Blackwell, Sanders, Matheny, Weary & Lombardi, 1957-92, of counsel. Former pres. Kansas City Mus. Assn., Estate Planning Coun. of Kansas City; trustee Pembroke Country Day Sch.; chmn. soc. of fellows Nelson Gallery Found. Served with USMCR, 1944-46. Mem. Order of Coif, Phi Alpha Delta, Kansas City Country Club. Home: 5049 Wornall Rd Kansas City MO 64112-2423 Office: 2 Pershing Sq 2300 Main St Ste 1100 Kansas City MO 64108-2415

LOMBARDI, EUGENE PATSY, orchestra conductor, violinist, educator, recording artist; b. North Braddock, Pa., July 7, 1923; s. Nunzio C. and Mary (Roberto) L.; m. Jacqueline Sue Davis, Mar. 1955; children: Robert, Genanne. BA, Westminster Coll., 1948; MA, Columbia U., 1948; Edn. Specialist, George Peabody Coll., 1972; MusD, Westminster Coll., 1981. Band dir. Lincoln High Sch., Midland, Pa., 1948-49; orch. dir. Male High Sch., Louisville, 1949-57; Phoenix Union High Sch., 1957-57; orch. dir., prof. Ariz. State U., Tempe, 1957-89. Condr., Phoenix Symphonette, 1954-61, 70-73, Phoenix Symphony Youth Orch., 1956-66, Phoenix Pops Orch., 1971-83, asst. concertmaster, Phoenix Symphony Orch., 1950-62, concertmaster, 1962-69, asst. condr., 1967-69, mem., Newart String Quartet, 1965-89, concertmaster, Flagstaff Festival Symphony, 1967-81, Flagstaff Festival Chamber Orch., 1967-81, Phoenix Chamber Orch., 1970-83, condr., music dir., Sun City (Ariz.) Symphony Orch., 1983-87. Served with USAAF, 1943-46. Decorated Bronze Star; named Outstanding Grad. Westminster Coll., 1948; recipient Alumni Achievement award, 1976, gold medal Nat. Soc. Arts and Letters, 1973, Disting. Tchr. award Ariz. State U. Alumni, 1974, Phoenix Appreciation award, 1983. Mem. Music Educators Nat. Conf., Am. String Tchrs. Assn. (pres. Ariz. unit 1965-67), Am. Fedn. Musicians, Ariz. Music Educators Assn. (pres. higher edn. sect. 1973-75, Excellence in Teaching Music award 1989), Ind. Order Foresters, Phi Delta Kappa, Phi Mu Alpha. Republican. Presbyterian. Home: 920 E Manhatton Dr Tempe AZ 85282-5520

LOMBARDI, FREDERICK MCKEAN, lawyer; b. Akron, Ohio, Apr. 1, 1937; s. Leonard Anthony and Dorothy (McKean) L.; m. Margaret J. Gessler, Mar. 31, 1962; children: Marcus M., David G., John A., Joseph F. BA, U. Akron, 1960; LLB, Case Western Res., 1962. Bar: Ohio 1962, U.S. Dist. Ct. (no. dist.) Ohio 1964, U.S. Ct. Appeals (6th cir.) 1966. Prin., shareholder Buckingham, Doolittle & Burroughs, Akron, 1962—, dept. chmn., comml. litigation dept., 1989—. Bd. editors Western Res. Law Rev., 1961-62. Trustee, mem. exec. com., v.p. Ohio Ballet, 1985-93; trustee Walsh Jesuit H.S., 1987-90, Akron Golf Charities (mem., bd. trustees); chmn. formation com.; 1st pres. St. Hilary Parish Coun., trustee, 1976-78; mem. Soc. of Benchers, Case Western Res. Law Sch., 1989 (mem., bd. govs., 1995-98); past chmn. World Series of Golf, Ohio State Bar Assn. (mem., counsel of dels. 1995-98). Mem. Ohio State Bar Assn., Akron Bar Assn. (trustee 1991-94), Fairlawn Swim and Tennis Club (past pres.), Portage Country Club (fin. com.), Akron City Club, Downtown Rotary Club of Akron (fin. com.), Pi Sigma Alpha. Democrat. Roman Catholic. Office: Buckingham Doolittle & Burroughs 50 S Main St Akron OH 44308-1828

LOMBARDI, JOHN BARBA-LINARDO, broadcasting executive; b. Toronto, Ont., Can., Dec. 4, 1915; s. Léonardo and Teresa L.; m. Antonia Lena Crisologo, July 4, 1949; children: Leonard, Theresa Maria, Donina Antonia. Grad. high sch., Toronto; student, Toronto Cen. Tech. Sch. Trumpet player Benny Palmer's Band, London, Ont., 1930-42; with Lombardi Grocery; later pres. Lombardi Italian Foods Ltd.; producer Italian radio programs Stas. CHUM, CKFH, from 1946; founder, pres., mng. dir. CHIN Radio/TV Internat. (multilingual broadcasting), 1966—; pres. Bravo Records & Music Ltd. Co.; Carpejon Investments Ltd.; Italian Shows Ltd.; chmn., pres. Radio 1540 Ltd. Originator ann. Johnny Lombardi Talent and Song Festival. Originator CHIN Internat. Picnic, free ann. festival ethnocultural music, song, dance; mem. Toronto Gen. Hosp. Found.; founding dir. gov. Villa Colombo; founding officer Italian Immigrant Aid Soc.; trustee Nat. Arts Centre Corp., 1982-85; patron Ont. Mus. Arts Ctre, 1989—; founder, host Italian Spring Festival, 1988; bd. dirs. Can. Coun. Christian and Jews, 1990; supporting mem. numerous civic organs., hosps. univs. and schs. including Easter Seal Soc., Boys/Girls Clubs Can., Kidney Found. Can., Cath. Charities, Hebrew Culture Orgn. Can., Can. Citizenship Found., Can. Opera Co., United Way; supporter elimination of apartheid in South Africa, eliminatin of anti-semitism, 1992; founding mem. Met. Toronto Police Community Projects Found., 1990. Sgt. Can. Army, 1942-46, ETO. Recipient Ethnic Entrepreneur of Yr. award, 1994, Fed. Citation of Citizenship, 1994, Silver medal for Elimination of Racial Discrimination, 1995; named Officer Brother-Order of St. John, 1994. Mem. Broadcast Execs. Soc., Can. Assn. Ethnic (Radio) Broadcasters (pres. 1981), Toronto Musicians Assn. (life), Composers/Authors & Pubs. Assn. Can. (SOCAN), Can. Italian Bus. and Profl. Assn. Toronto, YMCA, Variety Club (award 1985), Soc. for Recognition of Can. Talent Inc., Ont. Multicultural Assn. (patron), Can. Coun., Nat. Coun. Boy Scouts Can. (hon.), Can./Holland 1945 Liberation Soc. Office: CHIN, 622 College St, Toronto, ON Canada M6G 1B6

LOMBARDI, JOHN V., university administrator, historian; b. Los Angeles, Aug. 19, 1942; s. John and Janice P. Lombardi; m. Cathryn Lee; children: John Lee, Mary Ann. B.A., Pomona Coll., 1963; M.A., Columbia U., 1964, Ph.D., 1968. Prof. contratado Escuela de Historia, Universidad Central de Venezuela, Caracas, 1967; lectr. history Ind. U. S.E., Jeffersonville, 1967-68; asst. prof. Ind. U. S.E., 1968-69; vis. asst. prof. Ind. U., Bloomington, 1968-69; asst. prof. history Ind. U., 1969-71, assoc. prof., 1971-77, prof., 1977-87, dir. Latin Am. studies program, 1971-74, dean Internat. Programs, 1978-85, dean Coll. Arts and Scis., 1985-87; prof. history Johns Hopkins U., 1987-89, provost, vp. for acad. affairs, 1987-89; pres. U. Fla., Gainesville, 1989—. Author: (with others) Venezuelan History: A Comprehensive Working Bibliography, 1977, People and Places in Colonial Venezuela, 1976, Venezuela: Search for Order, Dream of Progress, 1982; Mem. editorial bd.: (with others) UCLA Statis. Abstracts Latin Am, 1977—; contbr. (with others) articles to profl. jours. Fulbright-Hayes research fellow, 1965-66. Mem. Am. Hist. Assn., Latin Am. Studies Assn., Pan Am. Inst. Geography and History, Academia Nacional de la Historia (corr. mem .). Office: U Fla Office of Pres Gainesville FL 32611

LOMBARDO, GAETANO (GUY), venture capitalist; b. Salemi, Italy, Feb. 4, 1940; came to U.S., 1947; s. Salvatore and Anna Maria L.; Sc.B. with honors, Brown U., 1962; Ph.D. in Physics, Cornell U., 1971; m. Nancy B. Emerson, Sept. 2, 1967 (div. 1993); children: Nicholas Emerson, Maryanne Chilton. Sr. staff Arthur D. Little Inc., Cambridge, Mass., 1967-77; v.p. logistics Morton Salt Co., Chgo., 1977-78; dir. logistics and distbn. Gould Inc., Chgo., 1978-80; corp. dir. Bendix Corp., Southfield, Mich., 1980-82; group v.p. Bendix Indsl. Group, 1982-84; founder, pres., chief exec. officer Comau Productivity Systems, 1984-86; pres. Nelmar Corp., 1983-90; chmn., chief exec. officer Courtesy Mfg. Co., Elk Grove, Ill., 1988—; pres. Poplar Industries, Inc., 1989—; chmn. I.A. Bedford, Ltd., Des Moines; vis. prof. ops. mgmt. Boston U., 1973. Contbr. articles on physics and bus. mgmt. to profl. jours. Office: Poplar Industries Inc 30 Monument Sq Concord MA 01742-1857

LOMBARDO, PHILIP JOSEPH, broadcasting company executive; b. Chgo., June 13, 1935; s. Joseph Pete and Josephine (Franco) L.; m. Marilyn Ann Tellefsen, June 22, 1963; children: Dean, Jeffrey. Student, U. Ill., 1953-55; BA in Speech, Journalism and Radio/TV, U. Mo., 1958, postgrad. speech, 1958; grad. advanced mgmt. program, Harvard U., 1976. Account exec. Sta. WWCA, Ind., 1959-60; producer-dir. Sta. WBBM-TV, Chgo., 1960-65; program mgr., account exec. Sta. WLWT, Cin., 1965-67; v.p., gen. mgr. Sta. WGHP-TV, N.C., 1968-73; pres., chief exec. officer Corinthian Broadcasting Corp., N.Y.C., 1973-82; chmn., pres., chief exec. officer Champlain Communications Corp., N.Y.C., 1982-84; mng. gen. ptnr. Citadel Communications Co. Ltd., N.Y.C., 1982—; chmn., pres., chief exec. officer Citadel Communications, Co. Ltd., C.C.C. Communications Corp., Lombardo Communications, Inc., P.J.L. Investments, Inc., N.Y.C., 1984—; mng. gen. ptnr., nat. sales rep. U.S. and Can. TV stas. Can. Communications Co., Toronto, 1985—; mng. gen. ptnr. Coronet Communications Co., N.Y.C., 1985—; bd. dirs. The Gabelli Group, The Lynch Corp., N.Y.C. Mem. adv. bd. Salvation Army; com. budget, bd. dirs. United Fund; mem. com. High Point (N.C.) United Schs.; 1st vice chmn. Central Carolina chpt. Nat. Multiple Sclerosis Soc., 1968-73; bd. dirs. High Point Arts Council, 1968-73. Served with AUS, 1959, 62. Recipient Disting. Svc. award Freedom Found., Am. Legion; High Point (N.C.) Youth Coun. Mem. Dirs. Guild Am., Internat. Radio and TV Soc. (bd. govs.). Clubs: Winged Foot Golf, Marco Polo, Board Room, Bronxville Field, Chgo. Press. Lodges: Rotary, Kiwanis. Home: 24 Masterton Rd Bronxville NY 10708-4804 Office: Citadel Comm Co 17 Kraft Ave Bronxville NY 10708-4103

LOMBARDO, TONY, film editor. Editor: (films) A Wedding, 1978, A Perfect Couple, 1979, Cheech & Chong's Nice Dreams, 1981, Blame It on the Night, 1984, Reckless, 1984, P.K. and the Kid, 1987, (with Thomas Stanford) Born to Race, 1988, Man Outside, 1988, Uncle Buck, 1989, (with Frank Morriss) The Hard Way, 1991, (with Barry B. Leirer) The Distinguished Gentleman, 1992, My Cousin Vinny, 1992, Greedy, 1994, (TV movie) By Dawn's early Light, 1989. Office: The Gersh Agency 232 N Canon Dr Beverly Hills CA 90210*

LOMELI, MARTA, elementary education educator; b. Tijuana, Baja Calif, Mex., Oct. 28, 1954; came to U.S. 1954; d. Jesus and Guadalupe (Ascencio) Lomeli; m. Rudolph Benitez, 1978 (div. 1982); children: Pascual Lomeli Benitez; m. David E. Miller, Aug. 16, 1991. BA, San Diego State U., 1977. With M & N Tree Nursery, Vista, Calif., 1957-70; libr. Vista Boys Club, 1969-70; vol. tutor MECHA U. Calif. San Diego, La Jolla, 1971-73; tchr. aide San Diego City Schs., 1976-77; bilingual educator National City (Calif.) Schs., 1978—; mem. restructuring com. Lincoln Acres Sch., 1991. Author numerous poems. Mem. Lincoln Acres Com. to Advise the Prin., National City, 1986-88, Com. to Advise the Supt., National City, 1986-88; art editor Lincoln Jr. H.S., Vista, Calif., 1964-65, Third World U. Calif., San Diego, 1970-73; mem. Lincoln Acres Sch. Site Coun., 1988-89; mem. high tech. com. Nat. Sch. Dist., 1993-94; vol. tchr. St. Vincent de Paul's Ctr. for Homeless, San Diego, 1991-93, Shaolin Kempo; mem. Paradise Hills Citizens Patrol, 1994—. Karate Black belt, 1st degree. Mem. Calif. Tchrs. Assn. (site rep. Nat. City 1985), Calif. Assn. Bilingual Edn. (sec. 1986), Nat. Assn. Bilingual Edn., La Raza Club (pres., co-founder 1970). Democrat. Avocations: drawing cartoons, karate. Home: 6920 Alsacia St San Diego CA 92139-2101

LOMICKA, WILLIAM HENRY, investor; b. Irwin, Pa., Mar. 9, 1937; s. William and Carabel L.; m. Carol L. Williams, Feb. 14, 1979; 1 son, Edward W. B.A., Coll. Wooster, Ohio, 1959; M.B.A., U. Pa., 1962. Sr. securities analyst Guardian Life Ins. Co., N.Y.C., 1962-65; treasury svcs. mgr. L.B. Foster Co., Pitts., 1966-68, Welch Foods Co., Westfield, N.Y., 1969-70; asst. treas. Ashland Oil, Inc., Ky., 1970-75; Sr. v.p. fin. Humana Inc., Louisville, 1975-85; pres., fin. cons. Old South Life Ins. Co., Louisville, 1985-87; sec. econ. devel. Commonwealth of Ky., 1987-88; acting pres. Citizens Security Life Ins. Co., Louisville, 1988-89; pres. Mayfair Capital, Inc., Louisville, 1988—; bd. dirs. Vencor, Inc., Regal Cinemas, Inc., Advocat, Inc. Bd. dirs., vice chmn. Louisville Downtown Devel. Corp.; trustee Bellarmine Coll. Served with USAR, 1962-63. Home: 402 Mockingbird Valley Rd Louisville KY 40207-1322 Office: Capital Holding Ctr Ste 2510 400 W Market Louisville KY 40202

LOMO, LEIF, electrical manufacturing company executive; b. Aalesund, Norway, July 1, 1929; came to U.S., 1951, naturalized, 1962; s. Leif and Ingeborg Rebekka (Helseth) L.; m. Mary Goodbar, Sept. 5, 1959; children—Caroline H., Erik H. B.S. in Aero. Engring., U. Colo., 1954, M.S. in Aero. Engring., 1959. Flight test engr. Cessna, Wichita, Kans., 1954-57; sales engr. Boeing Corp., Renton, Wash., 1959-65; pres. Murray Iron Works, Burlington, Iowa, 1965-73, Trane-Europe, Epinal, France, 1973-78, A. B. Chance, subs. Emerson Electric Co., Centralia, Mo., 1978-88; group v.p. Emerson Electric Co., St. Louis, 1983-88; chmn., pres., CEO A. B. Chance Industries Inc., Centralia, 1988-94; ret., 1994; pres. Malby Pump Co., Mission, Kans., 1994—. Served to chief petty officer Royal Norwegian Navy, 1949-50. Office: 19700 N Hwy 124 Centralia MO 65240-1395

LOMON, EARLE LEONARD, physicist, educator, consultant; b. Montreal, Que., Can., Nov. 15, 1930; came to U.S. 1951, naturalized, 1965; s. Harry and Etta (Rappaport) L.; m. Ruth Margaret Jones, Aug. 4, 1951; children: Martha Glynis, Christopher Dylan, Deirdre Naomi. B.Sc., McGill U., Montreal, 1951; Ph.D., MIT, 1954. NRC Can. overseas research fellow Inst. Theoretical Physics, Copenhagen, 1954-55; fellow Weizmann Inst., Rehovoth, Israel, 1955-56; research assoc. lab. nuclear studies Cornell U. Ithaca, N.Y., 1956-57; assoc. prof. theoretical physics McGill U. Montreal, 1957-60; assoc. prof. physics MIT, Cambridge, 1960-70, prof., 1970—; vis. staff mem. Los Alamos Nat. Lab., 1968—; project dir. Unified Scis. and Math. for Elem. Schs., Cambridge, 1970-77; adj. prof. U. Louvain-la-Neuve, Belgium, 1980; vis. prof. U. Paris, 1979-80, 86-87, UCLA, 1983, U. Wash., 1985; vis. rschr. Kernforschungsanlage Jülich, 1986—, U. Geneva, 1993, CERN, Geneva, 1994, IPN, Orsay, 1994; Lady Davis vis. prof. Hebrew U., Jerusalem, 1993-94. Contbr. articles to profl. jours. Guggenheim Meml. Found. fellow CERN, Geneva, 1965-66; Dupont fellow, 1952-53; Ossabaw Island Project fellow (Ga.), 1978; Sci. Research Council fellow U. London, 1980. Fellow Am. Phys. Soc.; mem. Can. Assn. Physicists. Office: MIT 6-304 77 Massachusetts Ave Cambridge MA 02139-3594

LOMONOSOFF, JAMES MARC, marketing executive; b. Van Nuys, Calif., Apr. 29, 1951; s. Boris Marc and Eileen Fairfax (Thomson) L.; m. Elisabeth Maas, June 12, 1982; children: Marc Frederik, James Forrest. BA in Econs., Colgate U., 1973; MBA in Gen. Mgmt., U. Va., 1975. With Saatchi and Saatchi Advt., N.Y.C., 1975-93, v.p.; account supr., 1975-85, sr. v.p., mgmt. supr., 1986-87, exec. v.p., mgmt. dir., 1987—, pres. Collateral Plus div., 1987-90; pres. chief exec. officer Saatchi & Saatchi Specialized Communications, 1991-92; account dir. VDB/Compton B.V., Amsterdam, The Netherlands, 1980-83; acct. dir. Saatchi and Saatchi Compton S.A., Madrid, 1983-84; regional acct. dir. Saatchi and Saatchi Compton Worldwide, London, 1984-86; mng. dir., CEO BSB/Saatchi and Saatchi, Prague, 1992-93; v.p. internat. mktg. Walt Disney Attractions Inc., Lake Buena Vista, Fla., 1994—. Mem. Beta Theta Pi. Republican. Home: 10905 Bayshore Dr Windermere FL 34786-7801 Office: Walt Disney Attractions Inc PO Box 10000 Lake Buena Vista FL 32830-1000

LONBORG, JAMES REYNOLD, dentist, former professional baseball player; b. Santa Maria, Calif., Apr. 16, 1942; s. Reynold H. and Ada (Rayn) L.; m. Rosemary Irene Feeney, Nov. 21, 1970; children: Phoebe Lea, Claire Elizabeth, Nicholas James, Nora Kathleen, John Bartholomew, Jordon Michael. B.A., Stanford U., 1964; D.M.D., Tufts U. Dental Sch., 1983. Baseball player Boston Red Sox, 1965-71, Milw. Brewers, 1972; pitcher Phila. Phillies, 1973-79; gen. dentist; asst. to adminstr. New Eng. Rehab. Clinic, Woburn, Mass., 1972-74. Recipient Cy Young award, 1967. Recorded 1000th maj. league strikeout, Aug. 19, 1973; career record 157 wins, 137 losses. Home: 498 First Parish Rd Scituate MA 02066-3201 Office: 105 Webster St Hanover MA 02339

LONCOSKY, WALTER BEUGGER, real estate manager; b. Gowanda, N.Y., Nov. 12, 1935; s. Walter Herman and Ida B. (Beugger) L.; m. Anita Lucile Thorp, June 27, 1964; 1 child, Helga B. BA in Journalism and Pub. Adminstrn., Columbia Pacific U., 1984, MA in Journalism and Pub. Adminstrn., 1985; diploma Gen. Bible, Liberty U., 1985. Lic. real estate broker, Pa.; cert. conservationist, Pa.; erosion and sediment control inspector, Pa.; ordained to ministry Bapt. Ch., 1984. Sports editor Danville (Pa.) News, 1956-58; performance specialist U.S. Agr. Stabilization & Cons. Dept., Danville, 1961-68; info. specialist Pa. Dept. Agr., Harrisburg, 1968-70; editor, owner Montour News Svc., Danville, 1971-80; pres., owner Skyco, Inc., Bloomsburg, Pa., 1981—; chmn., dir. Conservation Dist., Montour County, Pa., 1967-80; mem. adv. bd. County Planning Commn., Danville, 1969-80; chmn. Environ. Adv. Coun., Derry Twp., Pa., 1971-78; panel mem. Pa. Rural Studies Program, Danville, 1975. Author: Preservation of Agricultural Land, 1969, Columbia-Pacific Press, 1984. Bd. mem. Area Agy. on Aging, Danville, 1972-80; chmn. Home Rule Task Force, Danville, 1973; constable Derry Twp., Pa., 1976-82; bd. mem. County Dem. Com., Montour County, 1976-80. With U.S. Army, 1958-60. Named Hon. Chpt. Farmer Future Farmers Am., Turbotville, Pa., 1971; W.K. Kellogg Found. fellow, 1973; recipient award of merit World of Poetry, 1987. Mem. Pa. Assn. Environ. Profls., Rainbow Morgan Horse Assn., Masons, Elks. Democrat. Avocations: gardening, hiking, political science, soccer. Office: Skyco Inc 1000 S Market St Bloomsburg PA 17815

LOND, HARLEY WELDON, editor, publisher; b. Chgo., Feb. 5, 1946; s. Henry Sidney and Dorothy (Shaps) L.; m. Marilyn Moss, Aug. 20, 1981. BA in Journalism, Calif. State U., L.A., 1972. Adminstrv. dir. Century City Ednl. Arts Project, L.A., 1972-76, hon. dir., 1982—; founder, editor Intermedia mag., L.A., 1974-80; prodn. mgr. FilmRow Publs., L.A., 1981; assoc. editor Box Office mag., Hollywood, Calif., 1981-84, editor, assoc. pub., 1984-94; dir. publs. Entertainment Data, Inc., 1994-95; pres. CyberPod Prodns., 1995—; syndicated columnist Continental Features, Washington, Tel-Aire Publs., Dallas, 1986—; hon dir. Monterey (Calif.) Film Festival, 1987; mem. media adv. bd. Cinetex Internat. Film Festival, 1988; cons. Take 3 Info. Svc. Editor: Entertainment Media Electronic Info. Svc.; contbr. articles to profl. publs. Calif. Arts Council grantee, 1975, Nat. Endowment for Arts grantee, 1976-77. Mem. MLA, Soc. Profl. Journalists, Assn. for Edn. in Journalism and Mass Communication, Speech Communication Assn., Soc. for Cinema Studies. Office: CyberPod Prodns 1109 Longwood Ave Los Angeles CA 90019

LONDON, ALAN E., lawyer; b. Pitts., Mar. 13, 1945. BA, Yale U., 1967, JD, 1972. Bar: Pa. 1972. Ptnr. Reed Smith Shaw & McClay, Pitts. Mem. Phi Beta Kappa. Office: Reed Smith Shaw & McClay 435 6th Ave Pittsburgh PA 15219-1886

LONDON, ANDREW BARRY, film editor; b. Bronx, N.Y., Jan. 1, 1949; s. Max Edward and Nellie (Steiner) L. BA in Cinema magna cum laude, U. So. Calif., 1970. Represented by Mont. Artists, Santa Monica, Calif. Prin. works include (features) The Meteor Man, 1993, F/X 2, 1991, Rambo III, 1988, Planes, Trains and Automobiles, 1987, Link, 1986, Cloak & Dagger, 1984, Psycho II, 1983, The True Story of Eskimo Nell, 1975, (TV shows) Don't Talk to Strangers, 1994, Day of Reckoning, 1993, Mortal Sins, 1992, Running Delilah, 1992, True Tales, 1992, Sweet Poison, 1991, Tales from the Crypt, 1989-90, (pilot) Beauty and the Beast, 1987, The Christmas Star, 1986; sound editor: Wolfen (MPSE Golden Reel award 1982), Hammett, Roadgames, Psycho II, I'm Dancing As Fast As I Can, Perfect, Protocol, Coal Miner's Daughter, The Long Riders, others. Mem. Acad. Motion Picture Arts and Scis., Motion Picture Sound Editors (Golden Reel award 1982), Phi Beta Kappa. Office: Montana Artists 2d Fl 625 Montana Ave Santa Monica CA 90403

LONDON, BARRY JOSEPH, lawyer; b. Hartford, Conn., Nov. 3, 1946; s. Irving Walter and Lillian (Gottlieb) L.; m. Nancy C. Floyd; children: Michael Floyd, Stephen Floyd. B.S. cum laude, U. Pa., 1968, J.D. summa cum laude, 1971. Bar: D.C. 1971, Fla. 1972, U.S. Tax Ct. 1973, Calif. 1982. Assoc. firm Cohen & Uretz, Washington, 1971-77; ptnr. Cohen & Uretz, 1978-82, Lillick & Charles (formerly Lillick, McHose & Charles), San Francisco, 1982—; lectr. Nat. Law Ctr., George Washington U., 1977-81; adj. prof. law Georgetown U. Law Ctr., 1981; chair U.S. Activities of Foreigners and Tax Treaties com. Co-author: Tax Return Preparer's Liability, 1985. Contbr. articles to legal pubis. Recipient Peter McCall prize 1971, Bernard A. Chertcoff prize, 1971, Oscar Milton Davis prize, 1971; Carrye G. Barenkopf scholar, 1970-71. Mem. ABA (chair taxation sect.), D.C. Bar, Fla. Bar, Calif. Bar, Am. Coll. Tax Counsel, Order of Coif, Beta Gamma Sigma. Democrat. Club: Lillick & Charles 2 Embarcadero Ctr Fl 26 San Francisco CA 94111

LONDON, HERBERT IRA, humanities educator; b. N.Y.C., Mar. 6, 1939; s. Jack and Esta (Epstein) L.; m. Joy Weinman, Oct. 13, 1942 (div. 1974); children: Staci, Nancy; m. Vicki Pops, Nov. 18, 1950; 1 child, Jaclyn. BA, Columbia U., 1960, MA, 1961; PhD, N.Y. U., 1966; DL, U. Aix-Marseille, Aix-en-Provence, France, 1982, Grove City Coll., 1993. Teaching fellow N.Y. U., N.Y.C., 1963-64, instr., 1964-65, asst. prof., 1967-68, univ. ombudsman, 1968-69, assoc. prof., 1969-73, prof., 1973—, dean Gallatin div., 1972-92, John M. Olin U. Prof. Humanities, 1992—; instr. New Sch. for Social Research, N.Y.C., 1964-65; research scholar Australian Nat. U., Canberra, Australia, 1966-67; bd. overseers Ctr. for Naval Analysis, Wash-

ington, 1983—; trustee Hudson Inst., Indpls., 1979—, research fellow 1974—; sr. fellow Nat. Strategy Info. Ctr. Created TV programs: Myths That Rule America, The American Character; contbr. numerous articles to profl. jours. Bd. dirs., chmn. Nat. Assn. Scholars, N.Y.C., 1986; bd. advisors Coalition for Strategic Def. Initiative, Washington, 1986; candidate for mayor of N.Y.C., 1989; conservative candidate for gov., N.Y., 1990, 94; candidate for comptroller of N.Y. State, 1994. Recipient Def. Sci. award Def. Sci. Jouranl, 1985, Fulbright award U.S. Govt., 1966-67, Anderson award NYU, 1965; named Danforth Assoc. Danforth Found., 1971. Mem. Freedom House, Am. Hist. Assn., Edn. Excellence Network, Heritage Found (assoc. scholar 1983—), Ethics and Pub. Policy Ctr. (assoc. scholar 1985—), Nat. Strategy Info. Ctr., N.Y.C., 1984. Republican. Jewish. Avocations: writing, tennis. Home: 2 Washington Square Vlg New York NY 10012-1701 Office: NYU 113 University Pl New York NY 10003-4527

LONDON, J. PHILLIP, information technology company executive; b. Oklahoma City, Apr. 30, 1937; s. Harry Riles and Laura Evalyn (Phillips) L.; children: J. Phillip Jr., Laura McLain. BSc, U.S. Naval Acad., 1959; MSc, U.S. Naval Postgrad. Sch., 1967; D in Bus. Adminstrn., George Washington U., 1971. Commd. ensign USN, 1959, advanced through grades to capt., resigned, 1971; program mgr. Challenger Research Inc., 1971-72; mgr. CACI Internat. Inc., Arlington, Va., 1972-76, v.p., 1976-77, sr. v.p., 1977-79, exec. v.p., 1979-82, pres. operating div., 1982-84, pres., chief exec. officer, 1984-90, chmn. bd., 1990—. Recipient Alumni of Yr. award George Washington U. Sch. Govt. & Bus. Adminstrn., Washington, 1987, High Tech Entrepreneur award KPMG Peat Marwick, 1995. Episcopalian. Club: George Town. Office: CACI Internat Inc 1100 N Glebe Rd Arlington VA 22201-4798

LONDON, MARTIN, lawyer; b. Glen Cove, N.Y., Apr. 4, 1934; s. Abraham and Rebecca (Lasker) L.; m. Mellanie Bell, May, 1958 (div. 1973); children: Jesse, Lizbeth; m. Doris Wilke, July 28, 1983. AB, Cornell U., 1955; LLB, NYU, 1957. Bar: N.Y. 1958, U.S. Dist. Ct. (so. dist.) N.Y. 1962, U.S. Tax Ct. 1968, U.S. Dist. Ct. (ea. dist.) N.Y. 1969, U.S. Ct. Appeals (2d cir.) 1969, U.S. Dist. Ct. D.C. 1970, U.S. Supreme Ct. 1971, U.S. Ct. Appeals (6th and 7th cirs.) 1982, U.S. Ct. Appeals (4th cir.) 1990. Assoc. Gallop, Climenko & Gould, N.Y.C., 1958-61; assoc. Paul, Weiss, Rifkind, Wharton & Garrison, N.Y.C., 1962-68, ptnr., 1969—; spl. counsel judiciary relations com. First Judicial Dept., 1973-74; counsel gov.'s judicial nomination com., 1975-82, chmn. deptl. disciplinary com., 1980-85; spl. trial counsel Ct. on the Judiciary, 1977. Served as sgt. U.S. Army, 1957-58, 61-62. Mem. Am. Coll. Trial Lawyers, Assn. of Bar of City of N.Y., Fed. Bar Council, Am. Arbitration Assn. (nat. panel arbitrators). Avocations: deep sea fishing, skiing. Office: Paul Weiss Rifkind Wharton & Garrison 1285 Ave of Americas New York NY 10019-6028

LONDON, RAY WILLIAM, clinical and forensic psychologist, consultant, researcher; b. Burley, Idaho, May 29, 1943; s. Loo Richard and Maycelle Jerry (Moore) L. AS, Weber State Coll., 1965, BS, 1967; MSW, U. So. Calif., 1973, PhD, 1976, Exec. MBA, 1989, cert. in Dispute Resolution, Pepperdine U., 1993. Diplomate: Am. Bd. Psychol. Hypnosis (dir. 1984—, pres. 1989—); Am. Acad. Behavioral Medicine, Am. Bd. Psychotherapy, Am. Bd. Med. Psychotherapy, Internat. Acad. Medicine and Psychology., Am. Bd. Profl. Neuropsychology, Am. Bd. Adminstrv. Psychology, Am. Bd. Examiners Clin. Soc. Work, Am. Bd. Clin. Hypnosis in Social Work (pres. 1989-91), Am. Bd. Profl. Psychology, Am. Bd. Family Psychology (dir. 1993—), Am. Bd. Child and Adolescent Psychology (dir. 1992—), NASW Clin. Soc. Work; cert. Am. Assn. Sex Therapists, Soc. Med. Analysts; registered internat. cons., cert. mgmt. cons., congl. asst. U.S. Ho. of Reps., 1964-65; rsrch. assoc. Bus. Advrs., Inc., Ogden, Utah, 1965-67; dir. counseling and consultation svcs. Meaning Found., Riverside, Calif., 1966-69; mental health and mental retardation liaison San Bernardino County (Calif.) Social Svcs., 1968-72; clin. trainee VA Outpatient Clinic, L.A., 1971-72, Children's Hosp., 1972-73, clin. fellow, 1973-74; clin. trainee Reiss Davis Child Study Ctr., L.A., 1973-74, L.A. County-U. So. Calif. Med. Ctr., 1973; psychotherapist Benjamin Rush Neuropsychiat. Ctr., Orange, Calif., 1973-75; clin. psychology postdoctoral intern Orange County (Calif.) Mental Health, 1976-77; postdoctoral fellow U. Caif.-Irvine-Calif. Coll. Medicine, 1978; clin. psychologist Orange Police Dept., 1974-80; pvt. practice consultation and assessment, Santa Ana, Calif., 1974—; chief oper. officer London Assocs. Internat., 1974-80; cons. to public schs., agys., hosps., bus., nationally and internationally, 1973—; presenter nat. and internat. lectures, seminars and workshops; pres. bd. govs. Human Factor Programs, Ltd., 1976—; pres. Internat. Bd. Medicine and Psychology, 1980-84; chief exec. officer Human Studies Ctr., 1987—; pres., chief exec. officer London Assocs. Internat.; Organizational Behavior-Crisis-Devel. Cons., 1980—; research affil. Ctr. for Crisis Mgmt. U. So. Calif. Grad. Sch. Bus. Adminstrn., 1988-90; pres., chief exec. officer Am. Bd. Clin. Hypnosis, Inc.; mem. faculty UCLA, U. So. Calif., Calif. State U., U. Calif., Irvine, Calif. Coll. Medicine, Internat. Cong. of Psychosomatic Medicine, Internat. Coll.; research assoc. Nat. Commn. for Protection of Human Subjects of Biomed. and Behavioral Research, 1976; fellow Inst. for Social Scientists on Neurobiology and Mental Illness, 1978. Editor: Internat. Bull. Medicine and Psychology, 1980—, A.B.C.D. Report, 1988— behavioral medicine Australian Jour., 1980, adv. editor Internat. Jour. Clin. and Exptl. Hypnosis, 1981-92, mng. editor, 1991—, assoc. editor, 1992—; cons. editor Internat. Jour. Psychosomatics, 1984—; Experimentelle und Klinische Hypnose, 1987—, cons. Am. Jour. Forensic Psychology, 1986, Jour. Mgmt. Consulting, 1992—; pub: London Behavioral Medicine Assessment, 1982, A Behavior-Cris-Development newsletter, ABCD Newsnote; producer: TV series Being Human, 1980; contbg. author World Book Ency. and books; contbr. articles to profl. jours. Recipient Congl. recognition U.S. Ho. of Reps., 1978, Morton Prince award, 1993; named scholar laureate Erickson Advanced Inst., 1980. Fellow Internat. Acad. Medicine and Psychology (dir. 1981—), Soc. Clin. Social Work (dir. 1979-80), Royal Soc. Health, Am. Coll. Forensic Psychology, Soc. Clin and Experimental Hypnosis (bd. dirs. 1985—, treas. 1987-89); Profl. Acad. Custody Evaluators; mem. Acad. Psychosomatic Medicine, Am. Psychol. Assn., Am. Group Psychotherapy Assn., Am. Orthopsychiat. Assn., N.Y. Acad. Sci., Soc. Behavioral Medicine, Internat. Psychosomatic Inst., Australian Coll. Pvt. Consulting Psychologists, Australian Psychol. Soc., Internat. Coun. Psychologists, Acad. Mgmt., Assn. Profl. Cons., Inst. Mgmt. Cons., Ip. Dirs., Nat. Assn. Corp. Dirs., Profl. and Tech. Cons. Assn., Soc. Indsl. and Orgnl. Psychology, Assn. Profl. Cons., Soc. Calif. Mediation Assn. (mem. law soc.), Acad. Family Mediators, Am. Bd. Forensic Examiners, Am. Soc. Trial Cons., Am. Psychology Law Soc., Nat. Assn. Expert Witnesses, Soc. Profls. in Dispute Resolution, Toastmasters, Phi Delta Kappa, Delta Sigma Rho, Tau Kappa Alpha, Pi RhoPhi, Lambda Iota Tau. Office: London Assocs Internat 18062 Irvine Blvd Ste 200 Tustin CA 92680-3328

LONDONER, DAVID JAY, investment banker, analyst; b. Bklyn., Mar. 23, 1937; s. David Marcus and Amy Blanche Londoner; m. Clara Fleischmann, Feb. 5, 1967; children: David-Marc, John Alexander. AB, Columbia U., 1958, MS, 1959. Chartered fin. analyst, N.Y. Analyst H. Hentz & Co., N.Y.C., 1960-67; v.p. E.F. Hutton & Co., N.Y.C., 1967-70; sr. v.p. Edward A. Viner & Co., N.Y.C., 1970-71; exec. v.p. Black Securities, N.Y.C., 1971-72; with Wertheim Schroder & Co. Inc., N.Y.C., 1972—, assoc. mng. dir., 1986-89, mng. dir., 1989—. Author: The Changing Economics of Entertainment, 1978, Moving Toward Consolidation in the Entertainment Industry, 1989. trustee Am. Mus. Moving Image, N.Y.C., 1985—. With USAR, 1969-75. Fellow Am. Inst. Chartered Fin. Analysts; mem. Fin. Analysts Fedn., N.Y. Soc. Security Analysts, Media and Entertainment Analysts of N.Y., Econ. Club of N.Y., Wyantenuck Country Club (Great Barrington, Mass.). Office: Wertheim Schroder & Co Inc 787 7th Ave New York NY 10019-6018

LONERGAN, JEANETTE NANCY, nurse; b. Chgo., Feb. 19, 1943; d. Morris J. and Nellie (Sofan) Kraitsik; m. Thomas Joseph Lonergan, Apr. 27. 1964; children: Thomas Francis, Alicia Lynn. BSN, Bellarmine Coll., 1991; ADN, Jefferson Community Coll., Louisville, 1983. RN, Ky., Ind. Owner Faze II Needlework, Louisville, 1975-78; co-owner, v.p. Lonergan and Assocs., Louisville, 1978—; staff nurse Clark Meml. Hosp., Louisville, 1983-86; competency evaluator Jefferson State Voc., Louisville, 1989—; nurse asst. instr. ARC, Louisville, 1989—. Contbr. poem (hon. mention 1989). vol. Clarksville Little Theater, Jeffersonville, Ind., 1976—, Robertson House, Louisville, 1988—; instr. AIDS ARC. Recipient Merit award Clarksville Little Theater, 1991. Mem. Nat. Coun. Jewish Women, Women's Am. Orgn. (rehab. through tng.), Hadassah, Jewish Hosp. Women's Guild,

Internat. Soc. for AIDS Edn., Delta Epsilon Sigma, Sigma Theta Tau. Avocations: reading, needlework. Home: 3825 Chatham Rd Louisville KY 40218-4703

LONERGAN, WALLACE GUNN, economics educator, management consultant; b. Potlatch, Idaho, Mar. 18, 1928; s. Willis Gerald and Lois (Gunn) L.; m. Joan Laurie Penoyer, June 1, 1952; children: Steven Mark, Kevin James. BA, Coll. Idaho, 1950; MBA, U. Chgo., 1955, PhD, 1960. Asst. dir., asst. prof. bus. Indsl. Relations Ctr. U. Chgo., 1960-70, assoc. dir., assoc. prof., 1970-74, dir., prof., 1974-84; vis. prof. Rikkyo U., Tokyo, 1985; vis. fellow Merton Coll. Oxford (Eng.) U., 1986; chair, prof. bus., econs. divsn. Albertson Coll. Idaho, Caldwell, 1987—; v.p. Human Resources Research Cons., Chgo., 1980-87. Author: Leadership and Morale, 1960, Group Leadership, 1974, Performance Appriasal, 1978, Leadership and Management, 1979. Chmn. Episcopal Commn. on Higher Edn., Chgo., 1970-80, mgmt. com. United Way Chgo., 1982-85. 1st lt. U.S. Army, 1950-53, Korea. Named Disting. Alumni Coll. Idaho, 1962; vis. scholar Internat. Anglican Exchange, N.Y.C., 1976, Tokyo, 1986. Mem. Internat. House Japan, Internat. Indsl. Relations Research Assn., Acad. Mgmt., Rotary. Avocations: power walking, hiking. Home: 812 E Linden St Caldwell ID 83605-5335 Office: Albertson Coll Idaho Bus Econs Divsn 2112 Cleveland Blvd Caldwell ID 83605-4494

LONEY, GLENN MEREDITH, drama educator; b. Sacramento, Dec. 24, 1928; s. David Merton and Marion Gladys (Busher) L. BA, U. Calif., Berkeley, 1950; MA, U. Wis., 1951; PhD, Stanford U., 1953. Teaching asst. U. Calif., Berkeley, 1949-50, Stanford U., Calif., 1952-53; instr. San Francisco State U., 1955-56, U. Nev., Las Vegas, 1956; prof. U. Md., Europe, N. Africa, Middle East, 1956-59; instr. Hofstra U., Hempstead, N.Y., 1959-61; Adelphi U., Garden City, N.Y., 1959-61; mem. faculty Bklyn. Coll. and City U. Grad. Ctr., 1961—; prof. theater, 1971—. Author: Briefing and Conference Techniques, 1959, Peter Brook Midsummer Night's Dream, 1974, The Shakespeare Complex, 1974, Young Vic Scapino, 1975, Your Future in the Performing Arts, 1980, The House of Mirth-The Play of the Novel, 1981, Twentieth Century Theatre, 1983, California Gold Rush Drama, Musical Theatre in America, 1984, Unsung Genius, 1984, Creating Careers in Music Theatre, 1988, Staging Shakespeare, 1990; editor: The Modernist. Served with AUS, 1953-55. Fellow Am. Scandinavian Found.; mem. AAUP, Am. Theatre Critics Assn., Outer Critics Circle (sec.), Am. Music Critics Assn., Am. Soc. Theatre Research, Internat. Fedn. Theatre Research, Theatre Library Assn., Theatre Hist. Soc., Phi Beta Kappa, Alpha Mu Gamma, Phi Eta Sigma, Phi Delta Phi. Democrat. Office: CUNY Grad Ctr Theater 33 W 42nd St New York NY 10036-8003

LONEY, LINDA CHRISTINE, pediatrician; b. Herington, Kans., Mar. 29, 1949; d. James Monroe and Leonella Marie (Vinduska) L.; m. Thomas Warren Cooper, Sept 28, 1974; children: Rachel, Nathan. BA, U. Kans., 1971; MD, Wash. U., 1976. Diplomate Nat. Bd. Med. Examiners. Chief resident St. Louis Children's Hosp., 1978-79, founder, cons. sexual abuse clinic, 1978-83; instr. pediatrics Washington U. Sch. Medicine, St. Louis, 1980-83; pediatrician Med. Care Group, St. Louis, 1983, Bur. Spl. Med. Services, Concord, N.H., 1984-86; chief clin. pediatrics Mass. Hosp. Sch., Canton, 1986-90; staff pediatrician Mass. Hosp. Sch., 1991—, Watertown Health Ctr., 1994—; med. cons. Cole Harrington Children's Ctr., Canton, 1986—; speaker in field, 1977-85; instr. pediatrics Harvard Med. Sch., 1990-91; mem. staff Children's Hosp., Boston, Mass., 1990-91. Mem. adv. bd. Raphael House, St. Louis, 1980-83, Parents Anonymous, Boston, 1986. Fellow Am. Acad. Pediatrics, Mass. Acad. Pediatrics (com., cons. 1986—); mem. Phi Beta Kappa. Democrat. Jewish. Avocations: reading, piano, writing, yoga. Home: 30 Hamlin Rd Newton MA 02159-1002 Office: Watertown Health Ctr 85 Main St Watertown MA 02172

LONEY, MARY ROSE, airport administrator. Dir. aviation Phila. Internat. Airport. Office: Phila Pa Dept Comm Div Aviation 3751 Island Ave Phila Airport Philadelphia PA 19153

LONG, ALFRED B., former oil company executive, consultant; b. Galveston, Tex., Aug. 4, 1909; s. Jessie A. and Ada (Beckwith) L.; student S. Park Jr. Coll., 1928-29, Lamar State Coll. Tech., 1947-56, U. Tex., 1941; m. Sylvia V. Thomas, Oct. 29, 1932; 1 child, Kathleen Sylvia (Mrs. E.A. Pearson, II). With Sun Oil Co., Beaumont, Tex., 1931-69, driller geophys. dept., surveyor engring. dept., oper. operating dept., engr. prodn. lab., 1931-59, regional supr., 1960-69, cons., 1969—. Sr.'s bd. dirs. Bapt. Hosp., Beaumont, Tex.; chaplain sr.'s vols. bd. dirs., S.E. Tex. Rehab. Hosp., Beaumont, Seniors-Lawmen Coun.; chaplain Jefferson County Program Planning Com., 1964; mem. tech. adv. group Oil Well Drilling Inst., Lamar U., Beaumont. Active Citizens Police Acad. Mem. Soc. Petroleum Engrs., Am. Petroleum Inst., Am. Assn. Petroleum Geologists, IEEE, Houston Geol. Soc., Gulf Coast Engring. and Sci. Soc. (treas. 1962-65), U.S. Power Squadron, Soc. Wireless Pioneers. Recipient Nat. Jefferson award for Outstanding Pub. Svc. Am. Inst. for Pub. Svc., 1992, Community Svc. award Quarter Century Wireless Assn., 1994, Sensational Seniors of the U.S. honor CBS TV, 1994. Inventor various oil well devices. Office: PO Box 7266 Beaumont TX 77726-7266

LONG, ALVIN WILLIAM, title insurance company executive; b. Steubenville, Ohio, Oct. 9, 1923; s. Roger H. and Emma (Reiley) L.; m. Ethelle Sherman, Jan. 1, 1944; children—Roger H., Sherry Long McBain. J.D., John Marshall Law Sch., 1949, LL.D., 1977; M.B.A., U. Chgo., 1955. Bar: Ill. 1950. V.p. Chgo. Title & Trust Co., 1960-63, sr. v.p., 1966-69, exec. adminstrv. officer, 1969-71, pres., chief exec. officer, 1971—, chmn., 1981, hon. chmn. ret., 1982—, also dir.; sr. v.p. Chgo. Title Ins. Co., 1963-66, pres., 1967—, chmn. bd., 1981-82, hon. chmn. ret., 1982—, also dir. Bd. dirs. Bradner Central Co.; pres. Chgo. Central Area Com., 1980-82; trustee John Marshall Law Sch.; bd. dirs. Ill. Childrens Home and Aid Soc., pres., 1975-77; mem. citizens bd. and alumni council U. Chgo. Served to 1st lt. USAAF, 1943-45. Recipient Distinguished Alumni citation John Marshall Law Sch., 1968. Mem. Ill., Bar Assn., Am. Land Title Assn. (pres. 1970-71), Law Club Chgo., Comml. Club Chgo., Chgo. Club, Flossmoor (Ill.) Country Club, Quail Ridge Country Club (Fla.).

LONG, ANTHONY ARTHUR, classics educator; b. Manchester, Eng., Aug. 17, 1937; came to U.S. 1983; s. Tom Arthur and Phyllis Joan (LeGrice) L.; m. Janice Calloway, Dec. 30, 1960 (div. 1969); 1 child, Stephen Arthur; m. Mary Kay Flavell, May 25, 1970 (div. 1990); 1 child, Rebecca Jane. B.A., U. Coll. London, 1960; Ph.D., U. London, 1964. Lectr. classics U. Otago, Dunedin, N.Z., 1961-64; lectr. classics U. Nottingham, Eng., 1964-66; lectr. Greek and Latin U. Coll. London, 1966-71; reader in Greek and Latin U. London, 1971-73; Gladstone prof. Greek U. Liverpool, Eng., 1973-83; prof. classics U. Calif., Berkeley, 1982—; pub. orator U. Liverpool, Eng., 1981-83; Irving Stone prof. lit. U. Calif., Berkeley, 1991—, chmn. dept. classics, 1986-90; mem. Inst. Advanced Study, Princeton, N.J., 1970, 79; vis. prof. U. Munich, 1973, Ecole Normale Supérieure, Parice, 1993; Cardinal Mercier prof. philosophy U. Louvain, Belgium, 1991; mem. Mellon Fellowships Selection Com., 1984-90; mem. selection com. Stanford U. Humanities Coun., 1985-86. Author: Language and Thought in Sophocles, 1968 (Cromer Greek prize 1968), Problems in Stoicism, 1971, Hellenistic Philosophy, 1974, 2d edit., 1986, (with Fortenbaugh and Huby) Theophrastus of Eresus, 1985, (with Sedley) The Hellenistic Philosophers, 1987, (with Dillon) The Question of Eclecticism, 1988, (with Bastianini) Hierocles, 1992, (with others) Images and Ideologies, 1993; editor: Classical Quar., 1975-81, Classical Antiquity, 1987-90; gen. editor: (with Barnes) Clarendon Later Ancient Philosophers, 1987—. Served to lt. Royal Arty., Eng., 1955-57. Named hon. citizen City of Rhodes, Greece; sr. fellow humanities coun. Princeton U., 1978, Bye fellow Robinson Coll., Cambridge, 1982, Guggenheim fellow, 1986-87, sr. fellow Ctr. for Hellenic Studies, 1988-93, fellow NEH, 1990-91, Wissenschaftskolleg fellow, Berlin, 1991-92, William Evans fellow U. Otago, New Zealand, 1995. Fellow Am. Acad. Arts and Scis., Brit. Acad. (corr.); mem. Classical Assn., Aristotelian Soc., Am. Philol. Assn., Phi Beta Kappa (hon.). Avocations: music, walking, travel. Home: 1088 Tevlin St Albany CA 94706-2467 Office: U Calif Dept Classics Berkeley CA 94720

LONG, BEVERLY GLENN, lawyer; b. Omaha, Mar. 1, 1923; d. Max Edgar and Allise Katherine Dorothea (Nielsen) Glenn; m. Jacob Emery Long, May 6, 1950. AB in Econs., U. Chgo., 1944; JD, Columbia U., 1947.

Bar: N.Y. 1948, R.I. 1951, U.S. Dist. Ct. (so. dist.) N.Y. 1949, U.S. Tax Ct. 1949, U.S. Dist. Ct. R.I. 1951, U.S. Ct. Appeals (2d cir.) 1949, U.S. Ct. Appeals (1st cir.) 1958, U.S. Ct. Claims 1960, U.S. Supreme Ct. 1960. Assoc. Edwards & Angell, Providence, 1950-59, ptnr., 1959-86, of counsel, 1986—. Adv. com. child welfare services R.I. Dept. Social Welfare, 1959-66; personnel com. Big Bros. R.I., 1964-67; mem. Gov's Com. Status of Women, 1965; chmn. R.I. Children's Code Commn., 1967-74; fund raiser Columbia U. Sch. Law, 1947-88, R.I. area for U. Chgo., 1951—; bd. dirs. Child Welfare League of Am., Inc., 1975-80, Children's Friend and Service, Inc., 1966-75, 77-79, Providence chpt. ARC, 1967-72; bd. dirs. St. Mary's Home for Children, 1966-80, v.p., 1978-80; bd. dirs. R.I. Conf. Social Work, 1961-66, Council Community Services, Inc., 1957-64; task force evaluation of criminal justice program LEAA, 1974-78; active United Way Southeastern New Eng., Inc., 1951-81, ad hoc adv. com., exec. budget com., 1971-78, bd. dirs., 1973-74, ABA sr. lawyers div. coun., 1986-91, sec. 1991—. Recipient citation for pub. service U. Chgo., 1959. Fellow Am. Bar Found., R.I. Bar Found.; mem. ABA (Outstanding State Membership Chmn. award 1984), R.I. Bar Assn. (ho. dels., exec. com., pres., Merit award 1990), New Eng. Bar Assn. (bd. dirs.), Fed. Bar Assn., Am. Law Inst., Am. Judicature Soc. (bd. dirs. 1988-90), U.S. Supreme Ct. Hist. Soc., Columbia Club N.Y., U. Club R.I. Republican. Home: 200 Elmgrove Ave Providence RI 02906-4233

LONG, BRIAN JOSEPH, newspaper publishing executive; b. Springfield, Mass., Sept. 12, 1946; s. Brian Joseph and Eileen Agnes (Curran) L.; m. Linda Louise McKinnon, May 5, 1973; children: Joan Marilyn, David Patrick. BA in Math., Am. Internat. Coll., 1969, MBA, 1975. Compositor Springfield Newspapers, 1969, 71-72, purchasing agt., 1972-74, purchasing agt./systems mgr., 1974-77, systems mgr., 1977-81, systems dir., 1981-85, systems dir./asst. prodn. mgr., 1985-87, ops. mgr., 1987-91, gen. mgr., 1991—; bd. dirs. Springfield Ctrl. Corporator Am. Internat. Coll., Springfield, 1991—, Mercy Hosp., Springfield, 1989—. Sgt. U.S. Army, 1969-71. Mem. New Eng. Newspaper Assn. (chair fin. and gen. mgmt. com. 1993—). Avocations: sports, reading. Office: Springfield Newspapers 1860 Main St Springfield MA 01103-1073

LONG, CARL FERDINAND, engineering educator; b. N.Y.C., Aug. 6, 1928; s. Carl and Marie Victoria (Wellnitz) L.; m. Joanna Margarida Tavares, July 23, 1955; children: Carl Ferdinand, Barbara Anne. S.B., MIT, 1950, S.M., 1952; D.Eng., Yale U., 1964; A.M. (hon.), Dartmouth Coll., 1971. Registered profl. engr., N.H. Instr. Thayer Sch. Engring., Dartmouth Coll., Hanover, N.H., 1954-57; asst. prof. Thayer Sch. Engring., Dartmouth Coll., 1957-64, assoc. prof., 1964-70, prof., 1970-94, assoc. dean, 1970, dean, 1972-84, dean emeritus, 1984—; prof. emeritus, 1994—; dir. Cook Design Ctr. Thayer Sch. Engring., Dartmouth Coll., 1984-94; engr. Western Electric Co., Alaska, 1956-57; v.p. ops., dir. Controlled Environment, 1975-81; pres., dir. Q-S Oxygen Processes, Inc., 1979-87; N.H. Water Supply and Pollution Control Com., U.S. Army Small Arms Systems Agy.; mem. New Eng. Constrn. Edn. Adv. Council, 1971-74; mem. adv. com. U.S. Patent and Trademark Office, 1975-79; mem. ad hoc vis. com. Engrs. Council for Profl. Devel., 1973-81; pres., dir. Roan of Thayer, Inc., 1986-93; bd. dirs. Micro Tool Co., Inc., Micro Weighing Systems, Inc., 1986-91, Roan Ventures, Inc., 1987-91; pres., dir. Hanover Water Works Co., 1989—. Mem. Hanover Town Planning Bd., 1963-75, chmn., 1966-74; trustee Mt. Washington Obs., 1975-92; bd. dirs. Eastman Community Assn., 1977-80; mem. corp. Mary Hitchcock Meml. Hosp., 1974—. NSF Sci. Faculty fellow, 1961-62; recipient Robert Fletcher award Thayer Sch. of Engring., 1985, Fellow Members awd., Am. Soc. for Engineering Education, 1992. Fellow AAAS, ASCE, Am. Soc. Engring. Edn. (chmn. New Eng. sect. 1977-78, chmn. council of sects. Zone 1, dir. 1981-83); mem. Sigma Xi, Chi Epsilon, Tau Beta Pi. Republican. Baptist. Home: 25 Reservoir Rd Hanover NH 03755-1311

LONG, CHARLES FRANKLIN, corporate communications executive; b. Norman, Okla., Jan. 19, 1938; s. James Franklin and Mary Katherine (Nemecek) L.; m. Joan Harmon, Sept. 16, 1961; children: Charles Franklin, David Hampton, Stephen Andrew. B.A., U. Okla., 1961. Sports writer San Angelo (Tex.) Standard-Times, 1961-62; news reporter Norman Transcript, 1962-63; asso. editor Sooner mag., U. Okla., 1963-66; news editor Quill mag., Chgo., 1967-71; editor Quill mag., 1971-80; sr. editor Cahners Pub. Co., Des Plaines, Ill., 1981-83; mgr. internal communications Beatrice Cos., Inc., Chgo., 1983-86, dir. communications, 1986-88; dir. corp. communications Tellabs Ops., Inc., Lisle, Ill., 1989—. Author: With Optimism for the Morrow, 1965. Bd. dirs. Wheaton (Ill.) Youth Outreach, 1988—, Western DuPage Spl. Recreation Asssn. Found., 1994— (Vol. of Yr. 1994). Named to Okla. Journalism Hall of Fame, 1979. Mem. Pub. Relations Soc. Am., Internat. Assn. Bus. Communicators (Spectra Excellence award Chgo.), Am. Mktg. Assn., Soc. Profl. Journalists-Sigma Delta Chi, Beta Theta Pi. United Methodist. Home: 1106 N Washington St Wheaton IL 60187-3860 Office: Tellabs Ops Inc 4951 Indiana Ave Lisle IL 60532-3818 *My parents, through gentle persuasion and by their own example, taught their sons to be curious and conscientious. I suppose it was those principles which eventually led me into a career in journalism and to come to realize that the supreme test of any good journalism is the measure of its public service—to serve the truth; to subscribe to ethical standards; to enlighten the public as to the nature and meaning of journalistic pursuits, especially in how those efforts support the American people's stake in their First Amendment to the Constitution.*

LONG, CHARLES HOUSTON, history of religion educator; b. Little Rock, Aug. 23, 1926; s. Samuel Preston and Diamond Geneva (Thompson) L.; m. Alice Freeman, June 21, 1953; children—John, Carolyn, Christopher, David. Diploma, Dunbar Jr. Coll., 1946; B.D., U. Chgo., 1953, Ph.D., 1962; L.H.D., Dickinson Coll., 1971. Mem. faculty U. Chgo., 1956-74, prof. history of religions, 1971-74; mem. faculty U. Chgo. Div. Sch., 1956-74, prof., 1971-74, dean students, 1956-60; William Rand Kenan, Jr. prof. history of religions U. N.C., Chapel Hill, 1974-88; also bd. govs. U. N.C. (U. N.C. Press); prof. history of religions Duke U., 1974-88; Jeannette K. Watson prof. history of religions Syracuse U., 1988-91, dir. humanities doctoral program, 1988-91; prof. dept. religious studies, dir. Rsch. Ctr. in Black Studies U. Calif., Santa Barbara, 1991—; dir. seminar Nat. Endowment Humanities, summers 1977, 78, yr. 1979-80; bd. commrs. Assn. Am. Colls. ; bd. govs. U. N.C. Press, 1975-88. Author: Alpha: The Myths of Creation, 1963; founding editor (with others): History of Religions jour, 1961-74; editor (with Joseph Kitagawa and Mircea Eliade) History of Religions: Essays in Understanding, 1959, Myths and Symbols: Essays in Honor of Mircea Eliade, 1969, Significations, 1986; gen. editor series Studies in Religion, 1978—; editorial bd. cons. Ency. Britannica; founding editor, editorial advisor jour. History of Religions, 1990—; mem. editl. bd. jour. Ecumene, 1994—; contbr. articles to hist.-religious jours., Ency. Britannica., Ency. Religion. Mem. N.C. Humanities Council; bd. dirs. Fund for Theol. Edn. Served with USAAF, 1944-46. Recipient Alumnus of Yr. award Div. Sch., U. Chgo., 1987, profl. achievement citation U. Chgo. Alumni Assn., 1991; Guggenheim fellow, 1971-72. Mem. Am. Acad. Religion (pres. 1973-74), Internat. Assn. Historians Religion, Am. Soc. Study Religion (founding mem.), Soc. Study Black Religion (founding mem.). Office: U Calif Rsch Black Studies 4603 S Hall Santa Barbara CA 93106

LONG, CHARLES THOMAS, lawyer; b. Denver, Dec. 19, 1942; s. Charles Joseph and Jessie Elizabeth (Squire) L.; m. Susan Rae Kircheis, Aug. 9, 1967; children: Brian Christopher, Lara Elizabeth, Kevin Charles. BA, Dartmouth Coll., 1965; JD cum laude, Harvard U., 1970. Bar: Calif. 1971, U.S. Dist. Ct. (cen. dist.) Calif. 1971, U.S. Ct. Appeals (9th cir.) 1975, D.C. 1980, U.S. Dist. Ct. D.C. 1981. Assoc. Gibson, Dunn & Crutcher, Los Angeles, 1970-77, ptnr., 1977-79; ptnr. Gibson, Dunn & Crutcher, Washington, 1979-83; dep. gen. counsel Fed. Home Loan Bank Bd., Washington, 1984-85; ptnr. Jones, Day, Reavis & Pogue, Washington, 1985—; ex officio mem. Fed. Savs. and Loan Adv. Coun. 1988-89; speaker on fin. instns. Contbr. articles to profl. jours. Pres. Leigh Mill Meadows Assn., Great Falls, Va., 1980. Served to lt. USNR, 1965-67. Mem. ABA, Calif. Bar Assn., D.C. Bar Assn., Coun. for Excellence in Govt., Women in Housing and Fin., Herrington Harbour Sailing Assn., Westwood Country Club (Vienna, Va.). Republican. Methodist. Avocations: sailing, photography. Office: Jones Day Reavis & Pogue Met Sq 1450 G St NW Ste 600 Washington DC 20005-2088

LONG, CHARLES WILLIAM, child and adolescent psychiatrist; b. Helena, Ark., Sept. 22, 1947; s. Benjamin Asa and Laura Jo (Underwood) L.; m. Heather Barbara Murray, Sept. 19, 1987; children: Charles William 2d, Lindsay Catherine. BS in Biology and Chemistry, Ark. State U., 1969; MD, U. Ark., Little Rock, 1976. Diplomate in gen. psychiatry and child and adolescent psychiatry Am. Bd. Psychiatry and Neurology. Chief resident in psychiatry William S. Hall Psychiat. Inst., Columbia, S.C., 1978-79; from instr. to asst. prof. dept. neuropsychiatry U. S.C. Sch. Medicine, Columbia, 1978-80, asst. clin. prof., 1980-82; chief child and adolescent psychiatry WSHPI, Columbia, 1978-80; pvt. practice Columbia, 1982-88; from vice chief to chief psychiatry Bapt. Med. Ctr., Columbia, 1983-87; med. dir. Psychiat. Health Svcs., Columbia, 1987-88; pvt. practice Charter Hosp. Charleston, S.C., 1988—, assoc. med. dir., 1994—; med. dir. adolescent psychiatry Charter Hosp. Charleston, 1991—, pres. med. staff, 1993—; psychiat. cons. Univ. Devel. Disability, Columbia, 1982-83. Mem. Am. Psychiat. Assn., Am. Acad. Child Psychiatry, Am. Soc. Adolescent Psychiatry, S.C. Med. Assn., Charleston Med. Soc. Avocations: physical fitness, Tae Kwon Do (black belt).

LONG, CLARENCE WILLIAM, accountant; b. Hartford City, Ind., Apr. 17, 1917; s. Adam and Alice (Weschke) L.; m. Mildred Bernhardt, Aug. 8, 1940; children: William Randall, David John, Bruce Allen. B.S., Ind. U., 1939. With Ernst & Young, Indpls., 1939—, ptnr., 1953—; mem. econ. exec. com. Gov. Ind., 1968-73. Mem. nat. budget and consultation com. United Way of Am., 1968-70; bd. dirs. United Fund Greater Indpls., 1966—, treas., 1968—; bd. dirs. Jr. Achievement, Inc., 1966-67; mem. exec. com. Nat. Jr. Achievement, 1966-67; mem. fin. com. Indpls. Hosp. Devel. Assn., 1966-67; trustee Ind. U., 1975-84; trustee Art Assn. Indpls., pres., 1977-86; mem. adv. com. to dir. NIH, 1986-92. Mem. Am. Inst. C.P.A.'s (council 1959-62), Ind. Assn. C.P.A.'s, Nat. Assn. Accountants, Ind. C. of C. (dir.), Delta Chi, Beta Alpha Psi, Alpha Kappa Psi. Republican. Lutheran. Clubs: Woodstock (Indpls.) (dir. 1958-60), Columbia (Indpls.) (dir. 1971-77, pres. 1976), Royal Poinciana Golf Club (Naples, Fla.). Home: 607 Somerset Dr W Indianapolis IN 46260-2924 Office: 1 Indiana Sq Indianapolis IN 46204-2002

LONG, DAVID L., magazine publisher. Publisher Sports Illustrated, N.Y.C. Office: c/o Sports Illustrated Time Inc. 1271 Ave of the Americas New York NY 10020*

LONG, DEE, state legislator; b. 1939; m. Nicholas Long; 2 children. BA, Northwestern U.; postgrad., U. Minn. Legislator State of Minn., St. Paul, 1978—; speaker of House; mem. rules and legis. administrn. com., taxes com., ways and means com. Home: 2409 Humboldt Ave S Minneapolis MN 55405-2540 Office: Minn Ho of Reps State Capitol Saint Paul MN 55155

LONG, DONLIN MARTIN, surgeon, educator; b. Rolla, Mo., Apr. 14, 1934; s. Donlin M. and Davene E. (Johnson) L.; m. Harriett Page, June 13, 1959; children: Kimberley Page, Elisabeth Merchant, David Bradford. Student, Jefferson City Jr. Coll., 1951-52; M.D., U. Mo., 1959; Ph.D., U. Minn., 1964. Diplomate: Am. Bd. Surgery. Intern U. Minn. Hosps., Mpls., 1959-60; resident U. Minn. Hosps., 1960-64; resident in neurosurgery Peter Bent Brigham and Children's Hosp. Med. Center, Boston, 1965; practice medicine specializing in neurosurgery Balt., 1971-; asst. prof. neurosurgery U. Minn. Hosps., 1967-70, neurosurgeon, 1967-73, asso. prof., 1970-73; neurosurgeon-in-chief dept. neurosurgery Johns Hopkins Hosp., 1973—; prof. and chmn. dept. neurosurgery Johns Hopkins U., 1973—; mem. prin. staff Applied Physics Lab., 1976—; cons. neurosurgery Mpls. VA Hosp., 1967-73, John F. Kennedy Inst., 1977, Balt. City Hosp., 1973—. Contbr. numerous articles on neuropathology and surgery to profl. jours.; contbr. to book chpts. in field. Served with USPHS, 1965-67. Mem. Soc. Neurosci., Am. Assn. Neuropathologists, Soc. Neurol. Surgeons, AAAS, AMA, Balt. Neurol. Soc., Internat. Assn. Study of Pain, Internat. Soc. Pediatric Neurosurgery, William T. Peyton Soc., Congress Neurol. Surgeons, Johns Hopkins Med. and Surg. Assn., Electron Microscopy Soc. Am., Md. Neurosurg. Soc., Am. Acad. Neurosurgery, Am. Assn. Neurol. Surgery, Neurol. Soc. Am., Cajal Club, Sigma Xi, Omicron Delta Kappa, Alpha Omega Alpha, Phi Eta Sigma, Pi Mu Epsilon, Mystical 7. Home: 9 Blythewood Rd Baltimore MD 21210-2401 Office: Johns Hopkins Hosp Dept Neurosurgery Meyer 7-109 600 N Wolfe St Baltimore MD 21287-7709

LONG, DOUGLAS CLARK, philosophy educator; b. Ann Arbor, Mich., May 25, 1932; s. Dwight Clark and Marjorie Isabel (Grant) L.; m. Annie Nicole Groven, Aug. 21, 1961; children—Matthew Groven, Jonathan Wilson. B.A., U. Mich., 1954; M.A., Harvard U., 1955, Ph.D., 1963; postgrad., Oxford U., Eng., 1958-59. Instr. UCLA, 1960-62, asst. prof., 1962-67; vis. asst. prof. U. Wash., Seattle, 1965; assoc. prof. U. N.C., Chapel Hill, 1967-79; prof. U. N.C., 1979—, asst. chmn. dept., 1979-82, 91-92; vis. assoc. prof. Brown U., Providence, 1969. Contbr. articles to profl. jours. Woodrow Wilson fellow, 1954; grantee NSF, 1967, NEH, 1976-77. Mem. Am. Philos. Assn., Phi Beta Kappa. Home: 419 Granville Rd Chapel Hill NC 27514-2723 Office: U N C C B # 3125 Dept Philosophy Chapel Hill NC 27599-3125

LONG, EARLINE DAVIS, elementary education educator; b. Chgo., Mar. 31, 1944; d. Augustus (step father) and Eddie Virginia (Long) Grant; children: Tommie A. Grant, Virginia C. Sears. BS in Edn., Chgo. State U., 1971, MA in Adminstrn., 1983. Cert. tchr., adminstr., Ill. Electronic order writer Spiegels, Chgo., 1962-65; sr. elk. Chgo. Police Dept., 1966-72; tchr. Chgo. Bd. Edn., 1972—; consulting tchr. Teachers' Union, Chgo., 1990-92; continuing edn. courses in computer literacy, alcohol and drug edn., improving tchr. effectiveness, immersion week-end in Spanish. Home: 9608 S Eggleston Ave Chicago IL 60628-1106

LONG, EDWARD ARLO, business consultant, retired manufacturing company executive; b. Detroit, May 5, 1927; s. Arlo Russell and Florence Viola (Magown) L.; m. Lorraine Ruth Nordin, May 21, 1947; children: Karin Louise Long Schelke, Marian Elizabeth Long Benton. B.S., Wayne State U., 1956, MBA, 1964. Mfg. mgr. Ex-Cell-O Corp., Detroit, 1950-68; v.p. mktg. Colonial Broach & Machine, Warren, Mich., 1968-70; group v.p. Blue Bird Body Co., Fort Valley, Ga., 1970-75; pres. tool equipment div. Chgo. Pneumatic Tool, Franklin, Pa., 1975-77; group v.p. Joy Mfg. Co., Pine Bluff, Ark., 1977-87; v.p. gen. mgr. Wheeling Machine Products Co./Cooper Industries, Pine Bluff, 1987-94; retired, 1994; dir. Security Nat. Bank, Wheeling, W.Va. Bd. dirs. Franklin Hosp., 1975-76, Oglebay Inst., Wheeling 1981-83, Ohio Valley Hosp. Trust, Wheeling, 1982-83, Ark. Ind. Colls., 1984, Jefferson County Indsl. Found., 1985, Pine Bluff Fifty for the Future, 1985, Pine Bluff Symphony Orch., 1987, Leadership Pine Bluff, 1990. Served with USCG, 1945-46. Scholar Nat. Office Mgmt. Assn., 1952, Beta Gamma, Detroit, 1953. Mem. AIME, Am. Petroleum Inst., Duquesne (Pitts.) Club, Rotary, Alpha Kappa Psi, Psi Chi, Sigma Iota Epsilon. Democrat. Lutheran. Home and Office: 7409 S Laurel St Pine Bluff AR 71603-8121

LONG, EDWIN TUTT, surgeon, data base company executive; b. St. Louis, July 23, 1925; s. Forrest Edwin and Hazel (Tutt) L.; m. Mary M. Hull, Apr. 16, 1955; children: Jennifer Ann, Laura Ann, Peter Edwin. AB, Columbia U., 1944, M.D., 1947. Diplomate Am. Bd. Surgery, Am. Bd. Thoracic Surgery. Rotating intern Meth. Hosp., Bklyn., 1947-78; surg. intern U. Chgo. Clinics, 1948-49, resident in gen. surgery, 1952-55, resident in thoracic surgery, 1955-57; asst. prof. surgery U. Chgo., 1957-59; thoracic and cardiovascular surgeon, chief surgery dept. Watson Clinic, Lakeland, Fla., 1960-69; asso. prof. surgery U. Pa., Phila., 1970-73; thoracic and cardiovascular surgeon Allegheny Cardiovascular Surg. Assocs., Pitts, 1973-88; exec. v.p. Mailings Clearing Ho. and Roxbury Press, Inc., 1988-90, pres., 1990—, chmn., bd. dir., 1991—; dir. Watson Clinic Rsch. Found., 1965-69; bd. dirs. Roxbury Press, Inc., Cardiac Telecom, Inc., Pitts. Pressure Vectorography Rsch. grantee Alfred P. Sloan Found., 1963; patentee gas sterilizer, 1969. Capt. USAF, 1950-52. Mem. Am. Coll. Cardiology, Internat. Cardiovascular Soc., Allegheny Vascular Soc. (pres. 1987), Ea. Vascular Soc. (founding mem.), Soc. Thoracic Surgery (founding mem.), Direct Mktg. Assn., Kansas City Club, Rotary, Sigma Xi, Beta Theta Pi. Home and Office: 1415 Torrey Pines Dr Columbia MO 65203 Office: Roxbury Press Inc 601 E Marshall St Sweet Springs MO 65351-0295

LONG, ELIZABETH VALK, magazine publisher; b. Winston-Salem, N.C., Apr. 29, 1950; d. Henry Lewis and Elizabeth (Fuller) V. BA, Hollins Coll.,

1972; MBA, Harvard Bus. Sch., 1979. Clin. adminstr. Mass. Gen. Hosp., Boston, 1973-77; asst. to circulation dir. Time Mag.-Time Inc., N.Y.C., 1979-80, 81-82; circulation dir. Fortune Mag.-Time Inc., N.Y.C., 1982-84, Sports Illustrated-Time Inc., N.Y.C., 1984-85, Time Mag.-Time Inc., N.Y.C., 1985-86; publisher Life Mag.-Time Inc., N.Y.C., 1987-93; pres. Time Mag., 1993—. Trustee Hollins Coll., 1987—; mem. bus. com. Mus. Modern Art, N.Y.C.; mem. bd. visitors Wake Forest U., Winston-Salem, N.C.; bd. dirs. Hanover Direct, Inc., Weehawken, N.J.; mem. Com. of 200. Recipient Matrix award N.Y. Women in Comms., 1992, Silver Medal award Am. Advt. Fedn., 1993. Mem. Phi Beta Kappa. Avocations: golf, gardening. Office: Time Inc Time & Life Bldg 1271 Ave of Americas New York NY 10020-1393

LONG, EUGENE THOMAS, III, philosophy educator, administrator; b. Richmond, Va., Mar. 16, 1935; s. Eugene Thomas and Emily Joyce (Baker) L.; m. Carolyn Macleod, June 25, 1960; children: Scott, Kathryn. BA, Randolph-Macon Coll., Ashland, Va., 1957; BD, Duke U., 1960; PhD, U. Glasgow (Scotland), 1964. Asst. prof. philosophy Randolph-Macon Coll., 1964-67, assoc. prof., 1967-70; assoc. prof., U. S.C., Columbia, 1970-73, prof., 1973—, chmn. dept., 1972-87. Mem. S.C. Com. for Humanities, 1980-85; mem. adv. bd. The Franklin J. Matchette Found., 1992—. Recipient Research award NEH, 1968, Duke U./U. N.C. Coop. Program in Humanities, 1968-69. Mem. Soc. Philosophy in Religion (pres. 1980-81), Metaphys. Soc. Am. (sec. treas. 1977-81, exec. coun. 1991—), So. Soc. Philosophy and Psychology (exec. council 1976-79), Am. Philos. Assn. (sec. treas. eastern div. 1985-94). Author: Jaspers and Bultmann, 1968; Existence, Being and God, 1985; contbr., editor: God, Secularization & History, 1974, Experience, Reason and God, 1980; contbr., editor Prospects for Natural Theology, 1992; editor in chief Internat. Jourl for Philosophy of religion, 1990—; assoc. editor Internat. Jour. Philosophy of Religion, 1975-90, So. Jour. Philosophy, 1978—; contbr., co-editor: God and Temporality, 1984, Being and Truth, 1986; mem. adv. editorial bd. The Works of William James, 1974-88, The Correspondence of William James, 1988—; contbr. articles to profl. jours. Office: U SC Dept Philosophy Columbia SC 29208

LONG, E(VELYN) CLAUDINE, finance planning executive, educator; b. Laurel, Miss.; d. William Andy and Ada Eunice (Clearman) Parrish; m. Jack M. Long, Sept. 26, 1948; children: John R., Jaime E., Susan E., Mary E. AA in Bus., Mundelein Coll., 1981; grad., Coll. Fin. Planning, 1987. Cert. fin. planner. Mgr. women's div. Manpower, Inc., Oklahoma City, 1964-65; with Liberty Nat. Bank and Trust Co., 1965-87, sr. v.p., 1981; v.p. Banks of Mid-Am., Inc., 1987; v.p., mgr. Liberty Found., Inc., 1987; dir. fin. planning Seidman Fin. Services, Oklahoma City, 1987—; adj. prof. Coll. Fin. Planning, Oklahoma City U., 1987, selection com. Parry scholarship Coll. Nursing; mem. Better Bus. Bur. Mem. exec. com. Last Frontier council Boy Scouts Am., 1988; mem. exec. com. Oklahoma City Beautiful, chmn. Penny Campaign, 1988; pres. Oklahoma City Pub. Sch. Found., Inc., 1988; mem. Heritage Hills Assn., YMCA Fund Drive, 1987, YWCA Fund Drive Rape Crisis Ctr., Okla. Heritage Assn. Hall of Fame Program com., Jour. Record Corp. Woman of Yr. com.; bd. dirs. Downtown Now, Okla. Arts Inst., Okla. Mus. Art, Allied Arts Found., YWCA Assoc., Deskset. Named one of Outstanding Ladies in the News, Okla. Hospitality Club, 1975, 86; recipient Byliners award/Fin. Women in Communication, 1987, Outstanding Vol. award Fund Raiser Execs., 1988. Mem. Inst. Chartered Fin. Planners, Exec. Women Internat. (past pres. Oklahoma City chpt.), Charter 35, Econ. Club for Women, Contbrs. Adv. Group, Oklahoma City C. of C. Republican. Baptist. Club: Toastmasters. Home: 423 NW 21st St Oklahoma City OK 73103-1924 Office: Grant Thornton 2 Leadership Sq Ste 300 Oklahoma City OK 73102

LONG, FRANCIS MARK, electrical engineer, educator; b. Iowa City, Nov. 10, 1929; s. Frank B. and Hilda B. (Rohret) L.; m. Mary Ann Coyne, June 8, 1964 (dec. Apr. 1994); children: Ann Brett, Mary Bronwyn, Thomas Martin Carver, Caitlin Frances. B.S., U. Iowa, 1953, M.S., 1956; Ph.D., Iowa State U., 1961; NIH fellow, Stanford U. and Lawrence Livermore Lab, 1972-73. With Collins Radio Co., Cedar Rapids, Iowa, summers 1952, 55, Douglas Aircraft Co., Santa Monica, Calif., summer 1953, USNAMTC, Point Mugu, Calif., summer 1956, Good All Electric Co., Ogallala, Nebr., summer 1957, Lawrence Radiation Lab., Livermore, Calif., summer 1967, Globe Union Co., Milw., summer 1975, Naval Rsch Lab., Washington, 1988, 89, 91; instr. U. Wyo., Laramie, 1956-58; prof. elec. engring. U. Wyo., 1960—, head elec. engring. dept., 1977-87; instr. Iowa State U., 1958-60; dir. Wyo. Biotelemetry, Inc., Rocky Mountain Bioengring. Symposium; pres. Alliance for Engring. in Medicine and Biology, 1983, 84, mem. exec. com., 1979-89; conf. chmn., procs. editor 1st, 2d, 3d and 5th Internat. Conf. on Wildlife Biotelemetry. Author: (with E.M. Lonsdale) Introductory Electrical Concepts, 1967, rev. edit., 1977; co-author: (with R.G. Jacquot) Introduction to Engineering Systems, 1988. Trustee St. Paul's Newman Center Parish, 1969-72; mem. City of Laramie Planning Commn., 1970-72. Served with C.E. U.S. Army, 1953-55. Decorated citation Republic of Korea Army C.E.; recipient G.D. Humphrey Outstanding Faculty award U. Wyo., 1973, Western Electric Fund award for engring. teaching, 1978. Mem. IEEE (life), Am. Soc. Engring. Edn. (v.p., dir., 1st Outstanding Biomed. Engring. Educator award biomed. engring. divsn. 1981, chmn. Elec. Engring. divsn. 1986-87), Internat. Soc. for Hybrid Microelectronics, Sigma Xi. Democrat. Roman Catholic. Home: 507 S 24th St Laramie WY 82070-4916 Office: PO Box 3295 Laramie WY 82071-3295

LONG, FRANKLIN ASBURY, chemistry educator; b. Great Falls, Mont., July 27, 1910; s. F.A. and Ethel (Beck) L.; m. Marion Thomas, 1937; children: Franklin, Elizabeth. A.B., U. Mont., 1931, M.A., 1932; Ph.D., U. Calif., 1935. Instr. chemistry U. Calif., 1935-36, U. Chgo., 1936-37; instr. chemistry Cornell U., 1937-38, prof., 1939-79, prof. emeritus, 1979—, chmn. dept., 1950-60, v.p. research and advanced studies, 1963-69, Henry Luce prof. sci. and society, 1969-79, dir. program on sci., tech. and society, 1969-73, dir. peace studies program, 1976-79; adj. prof. U. Calif., Irvine, 1988—; dir. United Tech. Corp., Exxon Corp., 1969-81, cons., 1970-82; Mem. President's Sci. Adv. Com. 1961-66; asst. dir. U.S. Arms Control and Disarmament Agy., 1962-63, cons., 1963-73, 77-79 dir. Arms Control Assn. 1971-76; mem. adv. com. for planning and instnl. affairs NSF, chmn., 1973-74, mem. adv. panel for policy research analysis, 1976-80; co-chmn. Am. Pugwash Steering Com., 1974-79; mem. Indo-U.S. subcom. for ednl. and cultural affairs, 1974-82, co-chmn., 1977-82; bd. dirs. Assoc. Univs., Inc., 1947-74, hon. bd. dirs., 1975—; bd. dirs. Albert Einstein Peace Prize Found., 1979—, Fund for Peace, 1981—. Mem. editorial bd.: Am. Scientist, 1974-81, Bulletin of the Atomic Scientists, 1986—; Contbr. articles on chemistry, sci. policy and pub. affairs and arms control and disarmament to books, jours., encys. and reference works. Faculty Trustee Cornell U., 1956-57, Alfred P. Sloan Found., 1970-83, Fund for Peace, 1981—. Recipient U.S. Medal of Merit, 1948, (Korea) Dongbaeg medal, 1975; Guggenheim fellow, 1970. Fellow AAAS (v.p. 1976-80, Abelson prize 1989); mem. NAS, Coun. on Fgn. Rels., Am. Chem. Soc. (Charles Lathrop Parsons award 1985). Home: 446 Cambridge St Claremont CA 91711

LONG, GREGORY ALAN, lawyer; b. San Francisco, Aug. 28, 1948; s. William F. and Ellen L. (Webber) L.; m. Jane H. Barrett, Sept. 30, 1983; children: Matthew, Brian, Michael, Gregory. BA, magna cum laude, Claremont Men's Coll., Calif., 1970; JD cum laude, Harvard U., 1973. Bar: Calif. 1973, U.S. Dist. Ct. (cen. dist.) Calif. 1973, U.S. Ct. Appeals (9th cir.) 1976, U.S. Supreme Ct. 1977, U.S. Ct. Appeals (fed. cir.) 1984. Assoc. Overton, Lyman & Prince, L.A., 1973-78, ptnr., 1978-87; ptnr. Sheppard, Mullin, Richter & Hampton, 1987—; arbitrator L.A. Superior Ct. Fellow Am. Bar Found.; mem. ABA (young lawyers div. exec. coun. 1978-88, chmn. 1984-85, ho. of dels. 1983-89, exec. coun. litigation sect. 1981-83), Calif. Bar Assn. (del. 1976-82, 87-88), L.A. County Bar Assn. (exec. com. 1979-82, trustee 1979-82, barristers sect. exec. coun. 1976-82, pres. 1981-82, exec. council trial lawyers sect. 1984-88, chair amicus briefs com. 1989-92). Office: Sheppard Mullin Richter & Hampton 333 S Hope St Bldg 48 Los Angeles CA 90071-3003

LONG, HARRY (ON-YUEN ENG), chemist, rubber science and technology consultant; b. Passaic, N.J., June 22, 1932; s. Eng Yick and Yue York (Ng) L.; m. Linda Lai-King Yu, Sept. 18, 1960; 1 child, Steven Eng Park-Ning. BS, N.J. Inst. Tech. Newark, 1959. Chief devel. engr., belts and splty. products Uniroyal, Inc., Passaic, 1959-62, devel. engr. hose and expansion joints, 1962-67, sr. process engr., 1967-71; chief devel. engr.

Raybestos-Manhattan, Inc., Passaic, 1971-72; chief chemist Goodall Rubber Co., Trenton, N.J., 1972-76, tech. mgr., 1976-90; v.p. tech. Pelmor Labs. Inc., Newtown, Pa., 1990—. Editor, author: Basic Compounding and Processing of Rubber, 1985. Mem. AAAS, ASTM, Am. Chem. Soc. (area dir. Rubber div. 1990-92, Spl. Svc. award Rubber div. 1985), Phila. Rubber Group (chmn. 1980). Achievements include development of the rubber technology course used by the subdivisions of the rubber division of American Chemical Society throughout the U.S., Canada, Mexico and Colombia; organization of national symposium on rubber compounding. Office: Pelmor Labs Inc 401 Lafayette St Newtown PA 18940-2151

LONG, HELEN HALTER, author, retired educator; b. St. Louis; d. Charles C. and Ida (May) Halter; m. Forrest E. Long, June 22, 1944. A.B., Washington U., St. Louis, 1927, A.M., 1928; Ph.D., N.Y. U., 1937. Grad. fellow Washington U., 1927-28; tchr. social studies Venice, Ill., 1928-30; asst. prof. social sci. N.Y. State Coll. for Tchrs., Albany, 1930-38; tchr. pub. schs. Mamaroneck, N.Y., 1938-42; prin. elem. and jr. high schs., 1942-54, asst. supt. schs., 1954-61; dir. Instl. Instructional Improvement, N.Y.C., 1962-88; pres. Books of World, Sweet Springs, Mo., 1962-73; bd. dirs. Roxbury Press, Sweet Springs, Mo., 1963—; teaching fellow, instr. Sch. Edn. NYU, 1936-43; assoc. editor Clearing House, 1935-55. Author: Society in Action, 1936, National Safety Council Lesson Units, 1944-52, (with Forrest E. Long) Social Studies Skills, 8th edit, 1976 (with Forrest E. Long); assoc. editor Clearing House, 1935-55. Mem. Phi Beta Kappa, Pi Gamma Mu, Kappa Delta Pi, Alpha Xi Delta (Diamond Jubilee Outstanding Women award 1968). Home: The Gatesworth One McKnight Pl # 255 Saint Louis MO 63124

LONG, HERBERT STRAINGE, classics educator; b. Dexter, N.Y., Mar. 23, 1919; s. Herbert A. and Kathleen (Strainge) L.; m. Charlotte Rider, June 7, 1952; children: Alison Long Stambaugh, George. A.B., Hamilton Coll., 1939, Litt.D., 1972; M.A., Princeton, 1941, Ph.D., 1942. Fellow Am. Acad. in Rome, 1941-42; instr. math. Hamilton Coll., 1943-44, Edward North prof. Greek, 1952-68; instr. math. Colgate U., 1944-46; asst. prof. classics Yale U., 1946-51; prof. classics Case Western Res. U., 1968-86, prof. emeritus, 1986—, chmn., 1983-86; lectr., 1986-92; mem. mem. Inst. Advanced Study, Princeton, N.J., 1951-52, 65-66; spl. research fellow Am. Sch. Classical Studies, Athens, Greece, 1958-59. Author: Oxford Classical Text of Diogenes Laertius, 1964. Mem. Am. Philol. Assn. (award merit 1965), Shaker Hist. Soc. (trustee 1969-71), Phi Beta Kappa. Home: 84 Kendal Dr Oberlin OH 44074-1904

LONG, HOWARD CHARLES, physics educator emeritus; b. Seizholtzville, Pa., Dec. 12, 1918; s. Howard William and Isabella Geneva (Reese) L.; m. Frances Monroe Hoke, Apr. 16, 1945; children—Howard Charles, David William, Carol Joyce. B.A. Northwestern U., 1941, postgrad., 1941-42; Ph.D., Ohio State U., 1948. Asst. prof. physics Washington and Jefferson Coll., 1948-51; head Electromagnetism Influence Fields sec., U.S. Naval Ordnance Lab., 1951-52; assoc. prof., dept. chmn. physics Am. U., 1952-53; prof. physics, chmn. dept. Gettysburg Coll., 1953-59; prof. physics Dickinson Coll., 1959-81, chmn. dept., 1963-75, Joseph Priestley Chair of Natural Philosophy, 1973, prof. emeritus, 1981—; cons. physicist Naval Ordnance Lab., White Oak, Md., 1952-73, McCoy Electronics Co., Mt. Holly Springs, Pa., 1958-59. Contbr. articles to ednl. jours. Active Boy Scouts Am. Served with USNR, 1944-45. Active Boy Scouts Am. Served with USN, 1944-45. Mem. Am. Assn. Physics Tchrs. (sec.-treas. Central Pa. sect. 1958-59, v.p. 1959-60, pres. 1960-61), A.A.U.P. (sec.-treas. Dickinson chpt. 1963-64, v.p. 1964-65, pres. 1965-66), A.A.A.S., Am. Phys. Soc., Cumberland Conservancy. Methodist (chmn. adminstrn. bd. 1961-62, chmn. ofcl. bd. 1957-59, mem. conf. bd. edn. 1971-73). Home: 240 Belvedere St Carlisle PA 17013-3501 Office: Dickinson Coll Carlisle PA 17013

LONG, JAMES ALFRED, financial services company executive; b. Oceanside, N.Y., July 4, 1942; s. Clymer Alfred and Gladys (Serbe) L.; m. Susan Miller, Sept. 30, 1972; children: Jennifer, Allison, Andrew. AB, Dartmouth Coll., 1964; MBA, Columbia U., 1966. Dir. mergers and acquisitions Sperry & Hutchinson Co., N.Y.C., 1970-73, asst. to pres. furnishings div., 1974-75; dir. asset mgmt. Am. Can Co., Greenwich Conn., 1976-78, v.p. mergers and acquisitions, 1979-81, sr. v.p mergers and acquisitions, 1982-86, exec. v.p. mergers and acquisitions, 1987—. Contbg. author: Leveraged Buyout, 1985. Served to lt. USN, 1966-69. Mem. Assn. Corp. Growth. Methodist. Clubs: Union League (N.Y.C.); Roton Point (Rowayton, Conn.); Country Club Darien. Office: Primerica Corp American Ln Greenwich CT 06831-2551

LONG, JAMES M., judge; b. Danville, Va., Feb. 16, 1937; s. William Taylor and Mabel (Stephens) L.; m. Catherine Carden, Sept. 1, 1962; children: John David, Mary Catherine. BA in Pol. Sci., U. N.C Chapel Hill, 1959, LLB, 1963. Ptnr. Ramsey & Long, Roxboro, N.C., 1964-70; judge rec.'s ct. Caswell County, Yanceyville, N.C., 1964-70; judge N.C. Superior Ct., Pilot Mountain, 1970—; Pres. N.C. Conf. Superior Ct. Judges, 1987-88; v.p. N.C. Bar Assn., 1990-91. Recipient Disting. Svc. award Caswell County Jaycees, 1970, Gov.'s award, N.C., 1987; named Citizen of Yr., Pilot Mountain (N.C.) Civic Club, 1981. Mem. Nat. Conf. State Trial Judges (exec. com. 1992—). Office: NC Superior Ct PO Box 900 Pilot Mountain NC 27041-0900

LONG, JAN MICHAEL, state legislator; b. Pomeroy, Ohio, May 31, 1952; s. Lewis Franklin and Dorothy (Clatworthy) L.; m. Susan Louise Custer, May 12, 1978; children: John D., Justin M., Jason M. BA, Ohio State U., 1974; JD, Capital U., 1979. Adminstrv. asst. Congressman Doug Applegate, Washington, 1974-77; asst. prosecuting atty. Pickaway County, Circleville, Ohio, 1979-80; Ohio state sen. Columbus, 1987—. Named one of Outstanding Young Men Am. U.S. Jaycees, 1987. Mem. Pickaway County Bar Assn. (treas. 1985-86, sec. 1986-87). Democrat. Home: 522 Glenmont Dr Circleville OH 43113-1523 Office: Ohio Senate Rm 134 Statehouse Columbus OH 43215

LONG, JEANINE HUNDLEY, state legislator; b. Provo, Utah, Sept. 21, 1928; d. Ralph Conrad and Hazel Laurine (Snow) Hundley; m. McKay W. Christensen, Oct. 28, 1949 (div. 1967); children: Cathy Schuyler, Julie Schulleri, Kelly M. Christensen, C Brett Christensen, Harold A. Christensen; m. Kenneth D. Long, Sept. 6, 1968. AA, Shoreline C.C., Seattle, 1975; BA in Psychology, U. Wash., 1977. Mem. Wash. Ho. of Reps., 1983-87, 93-94, mem. bd. joint com. pension policy, Inst. Pub. Policy; mem. Wash. Senate, 1995—. Mayor protem, mem. city coun. City of Brier, Wash., 1977-80. Republican. Office: PO Box 40482 Olympia WA 98504-0482

LONG, JOHN BROADDUS, JR., economist, educator; b. Bklyn., Feb. 28, 1944; s. John Broaddus and Katherine Lumpkin (Wicker) L.; m. Carol Elaine Stephens, Aug. 6, 1966; children—Jennifer Tipton, Owen Rosser, John McCauley. B.A., Rice U., 1966; Ph.D., Carnegie-Mellon U., 1971. Asst. prof. U. Rochester, N.Y., 1969-74, assoc. prof., 1974-84, prof., 1984—. Editor Jour. Fin. Econs., 1982—; contbr. articles to profl. jours. Office: U Rochester William E Simon Grad Sch Bus Adminstrn Wilson Blvd Rochester NY 14627

LONG, JOHN D., retired insurance educator; b. Earlington, Ky., July 21, 1920; s. John Boyd and Effie (Yates) L.; m. Hazel Elinor Schindler; children: Douglas P., Martha S. Caughey, Elinor J. Badanes. BS, U. Ky., 1942; MBA, Harvard U., 1947; D. Bus. Adminstrn., Indiana U., 1954. CLU, CPCU. Instr. De Pauw U., Greencastle, Ind., 1947; instr. Indiana U., Bloomington, 1947—, asst. prof., 1954-56, assoc. prof., 1956-59, prof., 1959-90, acting dean sch. bus., 1983-84, Arthur M. Weimer prof. bus., 1985-90, Arthur M. Weimer prof. bus. emeritus, 1990—; bd. dirs. Meridian Ins. Cos., Indpls., 1975—; property-liability ins. cons. and expert witness. Author: Ethics, Morality, and Insurance, 1971; co-editor: Property and Liability Insurance Handbook, 1965; editor: Issues in Insurance, 1978; author numerous ins. related monographs; contbr. articles to profl. jours. Served to capt. U.S. Army, 1943-46, 51-52. Mem. Soc. CPCUs, Am. Risk and Ins. Assn. (pres. 1966-67, Elizur Wright award 1975), Am. Inst. Propery and Liability Underwriters (trustee 1978-89). Republican. Office: Ind U Sch of Bus 447 Bloomington IN 47405

LONG, JOHN MALOY, university dean; b. Guntersville, Ala., Dec. 28, 1925; s. Sam James and Lilian (Letson) L.; m. Mary Lynn Adams, July 7,

1950; children: John Maloy, Deborra Lynn. B.S., Jacksonville State U., 1949, LL.D., 1971; M.A., U. Ala., 1956. Dir. bands Oneonta (Ala.) High Sch., 1949-50; dir. bands. Ft. Payne (Ala.) High Sch., 1950-55; dir. bands Robert Lee High Sch., Montgomery, Ala., 1955-65; dir. bands. Troy (Ala.) State U., 1965—, chmn. music dept., 1969, dean Sch. Fine Arts, 1971, dean Coll. Arts and Scis., 1972—. Contbr. articles to mags. Pres. Troy City Sch. Bd., 1977; mem. Ala. Hist. Commn., 1976—. Served with AUS, 1944-46. Recipient citation fo excellence Nat. Band Assn., 1972, Disting. Citizens Service award City of Montogomery, 1964, Cert. Appreciation State of Ala., 1964, Algernon Sydney Sullivan award, 1989, Sudler Order of Merit, 1994; named one of top 10 band dirs. in U.S. Sch. Musician Mag., 1969, to Bandmasters Hall of Fame, 1977; named Ala. Outstanding Educator, Ala. Music Educators Assn.; 1984; new music bldg.l named in honor Troy State U., 1975, named Disting. prof., 1989. Mem. Am. Bandmaster Assn. (pres. 1987-88), Am. Sch. Band Dirs. Assn. (state pres. 1968-72), Coll. Band Dirs. Nat. Assn. (state pres.), Nat. Band Assn. (named to Hall of Fame, chmn. Hall of Fame), Omicron Delta Kappa Phi, Mu Alpha, Pi Beta Mu, Phi Delta Kappa, Kappa Kappa Psi (Nat. Disting. Svc. to Music award 1979), Delta Chi. Democrat. Methodist. Lodges: Masons; Shriners; Rotary (past pres.). Office: Troy State U John M Long Hall Troy AL 36082

LONG, JOHN PAUL, pharmacologist, educator; b. Albia, Iowa, Oct. 4, 1926; s. John Edward and Bessie May L.; m. Marilyn Joy Stokesberry, June 11, 1950; children: Jeff, John, Jane. B.S., U. Iowa, 1950, M.S., 1952, Ph.D., 1954. Research scientist Sterling Winthrop Co., Albany, N.Y., 1954-56; asst. prof. U. Iowa, Iowa City, 1956-58, assoc. prof., 1958-63, prof. pharmacology, 1963—, head dept., 1970-83. Author 315 research publs. in field. Served with U.S. Army, 1945-46. Recipient Abel award Am. Pharm. Assn., 1958; Ebert award Pharmacology Soc., 1962. Mem. Am. Soc. Pharm. Exptl. Therapy, Soc. Exptl. Biol. Medicine. Republican. Home: 1817 Kathlin Dr Iowa City IA 52246-4617 Office: U Iowa Coll Medicine Dept Pharmacology Iowa City IA 52242

LONG, KENNETH ROBERT, natural gas company executive, lawyer; b. Camden, N.J., Oct. 21, 1940; s. John McClintock and Eleanor May (Davis) L.; m. Karen Marie Draut, Feb. 3, 1962; children: Kristin Elizabeth, Keith Timothy. BA, Ohio Wesleyan U., 1962; JD, Ohio State U., 1965; MBA in Fin., Miami U., Oxford, Ohio, 1966. Bar: Wash. 1966, Ohio 1967, Pa. 1970. Individual practice law Seattle, 1967-70; counsel, asst. sec. Koppers Co., Inc., Pitts., 1970-75; gen. counsel, sec. Wean United, Pitts., 1975-76; gen. atty., asst. sec. Consol. Natural Gas Co., Pitts., 1976-88; v.p., gen. counsel East Ohio Gas Co., Cleve., 1988—; exec. com., chmn. fin. com. United Distbn. Cos. Mem. ABA, Pa. Bar Assn., Allegheny County Bar Assn., Ohio Bar Assn., Wash. Bar Assn., Fed. Energy Bar, Am. Gas Assn. (mem. legal sect. mng. com.), Am. Soc. Corp. Secs. (pres. Ohio chpt.), Cleve. Housing Partnership (pres.). Presbyterian. Home: 2976 Manchester Rd Cleveland OH 44122-2522 Office: East Ohio Gas Co 1717 E 9th St Cleveland OH 44114-2800

LONG, LELAND TIMOTHY, geophysics educator, seismologist; b. Auburn, N.Y., Sept. 6, 1940; s. Walter K. and Carmalita Rose Long; m. Sarah Alice Blackard, Mar. 1970; children: Sarah Alice, Katherine Rose, Amy Virginia. BS in Geology, U. Rochester, 1962; MS in Geophysics, N.Mex. Inst. Mining and Tech., 1964; PhD in Geophysics, Oreg. State U., 1968. Registered prof. geologist, Ga. From asst. to assoc. prof. sch. geophysical scis. Ga. Inst. Tech., Atlanta, 1968-81, prof., 1981, divsn. chmn. earth scis. divsn., 1982-84; collaborator in seismology USGS; cons. in seismology, seismic road vibrations and gravity data analysis. Contbr. articles to profl. jours. Office: Ga Inst Tech Earth and Atmospheric Sciences Atlanta GA 30332

LONG, MADELEINE J., mathematics and science educator; b. N.Y.C.; d. Harry L. and Irma (Silverman) L. B.A., Queens Coll., 1960; M.Ed., Harvard U., 1963; Ed.D., Columbia U., 1967. Tchr. Westbury (N.Y.) Sch. System, 1960-61; teaching fellow Harvard U., 1962-63; prof. edn. L.I. U., asst. to dean, 1967-69, chmn. dept., 1969-76, dir. div. edn., dir. grad. programs at Westchester br. campus, 1977-83, dir. Inst. Advancement Math. and Sci., 1983-91; program officer (on leave from L.I. U.) NSF, Washington, 1991-93; sr. program officer NSF, Arlington, Va., 1993—; vis. scientist, spl. asst. comprehensive design planning, Nat. Sci. Found., 1992—; sr. program officer Urban Systemic Initiative, 1993—; dir. summer trng. programs N.Y.C. Bd. Edn., 1978, 79, 81; reader NSF, 1973, 77, 79, 85, 88, 90, career access panelist and chair, 1988; reader Fund for Improvement Postsecondary Edn., 1984, 85, 87, N.J. Bd. Higher Edn., Minority Instns. Sci. Improvement Program; cons. to various univs. and sch. systems.; lectr. various orgns.; appointed coun. on excellence and equity in math. and sci. edn. N.Y. State, 1986-91. Mem. editorial bd. Jour. Coll. Sci. Teaching, 1986-89; contbr. articles to profl. jours. Mem. edn. subcom. Mayor's Commn. on Sci. and Tech., 1989-91. Columbia U. fellow, 1963-64; grantee NSF, 1972, 78, 79, 80, 81, 84-87, 87-91, 91—, Carnegie Eden, 1975, Fund for Improvement Postsecondary Edn., 1983-87, title II Edn. for Econ. Security act N.Y. State. Fellow Philosophy of Edn. Soc.; mem. AAAS (chair sect. Q, Sci. Edn., chmn. edn. section) Assn. Supervision and Curriculum Devel., N.Y. Acad. Sci., Nat. Sci. Tchrs. Assn., Nat. Coun. Tchrs. Math., Am. Ednl. Rsch. Assn., Kappa Delta Pi. Office: NSF 4201 Wilson Blvd Arlington VA 22201

LONG, MARIE KATHERINE, public relations consultant, researcher; b. Cleve., Dec. 8, 1925; d. Mike Kurilich and Katherine (Grasso) Kurilich; m. Elgen Marion Long, May 12, 1946; children: Donna Marie Long Weiner, Harry Elgen. Student, Cleve. Coll., 1943-44, Harbor Jr. Coll., L.A., 1954-55. Lic. real estate agt., Calif. Exec. sec. Fawick Airlfex Co., Cleve., 1943-44, Pillsburg and Globe Mills, L.A., 1944-48; ptnr. Elgen Long, gen. contractor, San Mateo, Calif., 1958-77, Woodside (Calif.) Investment Co., 1964-71; logistics mgr. pub. rels. Crossroads Endeavor, Woodside, 1971—; pub. rels. cons. Elgen Long Enterprises, San Mateo, 1971—; research on Amelia Earhart disappearance, San Mateo, 1972—; adminstrv. coord., project mgr. pub. rels. Internat. Human Potential Orgns., San Francisco, 1977-82; cons. to books and mags., 1971—. Troop leader Girl Scouts U.S.A., San Mateo, 1954-61; fundraiser Woodside High Sch. Band, 1966-68; Am. Heart Assn., also other orgns., San Mateo, 1973—; v.p. Western Aerospace Mus., Oakland, Calif., 1982—, also life mem.; mem. People to People, Hunger Project; adv. com. USN Meml. Found. Mem. Internat. Platform Soc., Peninsula Press Club. Democrat. Avocations: reading, bowling, music, dancing, aviation history. Home and Office: 11975 Danvers Circle San Diego CA 92128

LONG, MAURICE WAYNE, physicist, electrical engineer, radar consultant; b. Madisonville, Ky., Apr. 20, 1925; s. Maurice K. and Martha Ann (Nourse) L.; m. Patricia Lee Holmes, Feb. 25, 1950 (dec. Aug. 1961); children: Anne Catherine Long Key, Jane Elizabeth Long Rice; m. Beverly Ann Benson, Jan. 1, 1963; stepchildren: Theodore Douglas Downing, Beverly Patricia Downing. BEE, Ga. Inst. Tech., 1946, MS in Physics, 1957, PhD, 1959; MSEE, U. Ky., 1948. Registered profl. engr., Ga. Rsch. asst. Ga. Inst. Tech., Atlanta, 1946-47, rsch. engr., then spl. rsch. engr., asst. rsch. prof., prin. rsch. physicist, 1950-68, prof. elec. engring., 1968-73, head radar devel. br., 1955-60, chief div. electronics, 1959-68, dir. Engring. Expt. Sta. (now Ga. Tech. Rsch. Inst.), 1968-75; dir. rsch., sec., asst. treas. Ga. Tech. Rsch. Inst., 1968-75; liaison scientist U.S. Office Naval Rsch. London Br., 1966; bd. dirs. Ga. Tech. Rsch. Inst., 1968-82; mem. com. on remote sensing programs for earth resources surveys NAS, 1977, space applications adv. com., subcom. on remote sensing NASA, 1983-86; mem. Acad. Electromagnetics, MIT, 1990; mem. various coms. on radar U.S. Army, Navy, Air Force, NASA, 1967—. Author: Radar Reflectivity of Land and Sea, 1975, 2d edit., 1983; editor, contbg. author: Airborne Early Warning System Concepts, 1992; contbr. numerous articles to profl. jours., chpts. to books; patentee in field. Mem. Ga. Gov.'s Sci. Adv. Coun., 1973-84, chmn. ad hoc com. on tech. growth in Ga., 1974. Fellow IEEE (life); mem. Acad. Electromagnetics, Internat. Union Radio Sci. (commn. F.), Assn. Old Crows, Sigma Xi. Avocations: sailing, traveling. Home: 1036 Somerset Dr NW Atlanta GA 30327-3736

LONG, MAXINE MASTER, lawyer; b. Pensacola, Fla., Oct. 20, 1943; d. Maxwell L. and Claudine E. (Smith) M.; m. Anthony Byrd Long, Aug. 27, 1966; children: Deborah E., David M. AB, Bryn Mawr Coll., 1965; MS, Georgetown U., 1971; JD, U. Miami, 1979. Bar: Fla. 1979, U.S. Ct. Appeals (5th cir.) 1980, U.S. Dist. Ct. (so. dist.) Fla. 1980, U.S. Ct. Appeals (11th cir.) 1981, U.S. Dist. Ct. (mid. and no. dists.) Fla. 1987. Law clk. to U.S.

dist. judge U.S. Dist. Ct. (so. dist.) Fla., Miami, 1979-80; assoc. Shutts & Bowen, Miami, 1980-90, of counsel, 1990-92, ptnr., 1992—. Mem. Fla. Bar Assn. (chair bus. litigation com., assoc. exec. coun. bus. law sect.), Dade County Bar Assn. (mem. fed. cts. com., recipient pro bono award/Vol. Lawyers for the Arts 1989). Office: Shutts & Bowen 201 S Biscayne Blvd Miami FL 33131

LONG, MELVIN DURWARD, university president; b. Daytona Beach, Fla., Nov. 12, 1931; s. Melvin Durward and Ramona Bernice (Robinson) L.; m. Estrella Niña Celorio; children: Melvin Durward III, Carl Patrick, Elena Colleen. BS, Troy (Ala.) State U., 1953; MA, Auburn U., 1956; PhD, U. Fla., 1959. Vice chancellor U. Wis., 1968-70, chancellor cen. system, 1971-73; exec. dir. select com. on Calif. master plan, assoc. dir. Calif. Coordinating Coun. for Higher Edn., 1970-71; v.p. U. Calif., Berkeley, 1973-75; v.p. for acad. affairs U. Hawaii System, Honolulu, 1975-79, v.p. 1981-84; chancellor U. Hawaii Manoa, Honolulu, 1979-81; interim v.p. for fin. U. Wyo., Laramie, 1981-83; scholar in residence Nat. Assn. State Univ. and Land Grant Colls., 1984; pres. Sangamon State U., Springfield, Ill., 1984-91, pres. emeritus, Regency prof. econ. history, 1991—; vice chancellor for strategic planning and devel. Ill. Bd. Regents, 1991-92; v.p. fin. and adminstrn., treas., bd. trustees Fashion Inst. Tech., N.Y.C., 1993—; sr. fellow Edn. Commn. on the State, vis. rsch. profl. U. Fla., 1991-92; v.p. fin. and adminstrn., treas. bd. trustees Fashion Inst. Technology, N.Y.C., 1993—. Author, editor: Student Protest, 1970, The Future of State Public Universities, 1985; contbr. articles on U.S. history and higher edn. to profl. jours. Mem. Am. Assn. State Univs. and Colls. (com. on policies and purposes 1984-88, bd. dirs. 1988-90). Home: 108 E Hazel Dell Springfield IL 62707-9516 Office: Fashion Inst Technology 7th Ave and 27th St New York NY 10010

LONG, MICHAEL THOMAS, lawyer, manufacturing company executive; b. Hartford, Conn., Feb. 22, 1942; s. Michael Joseph and Mary Fagan (Maguire) L.; m. Ann Marie O'Connell, Sept. 9, 1967; children: Michael, Maura, Deirdre. BBA, U. Notre Dame, 1964; JD, U. Conn., 1967, postgrad., 1968. Bar: Conn. 1967. Law clk. U.S. Bankruptcy Ct., U.S. Dist. Ct., Hartford, 1966-68; supr. indsl. rels. Ensign-Bickford Industries, Inc., Simsbury, Conn., 1968-72, contract adminstr., 1972-74, div. controller, 1974-79, mgr. govt. and legal affairs, 1978-81, gen. counsel, sec., 1981-83, v.p., gen. counsel, sec., 1983—; bd. dirs. Ensign-Bickford Co.; pres., chief exec. officer, Ensign-Bickford Haz-Pros Inc., 1989—; U. Notre Dame Alumni Clubs of Greater Hartford scholarship chmn., 1990—. Chmn. Dem. Town Com., Simsbury, 1971-81, Dem. State Ctrl. Com. of Conn., 1992—; Bradley Internat. Airport Com., Windsor Locks, Conn., 1983—; mem. pub. bldg. com. Town of Simsbury, 1981-85, mem. cultural, parks and recreation com., 1986-87, mem. fin. bd., 1987—; mem. Simsbury Jr. Achievement, 1970-74; pres. parish council St. Mary's Ch., Simsbury, 1982-85; chmn. Bradley Internat. Airport Commn., 1983-91. Named Home Town Hero Town of Simsbury, 1987; recipient Man of Yr. award U. Notre Dame Alumni Clubs of Greater Hartford, 1995. Mem. ABA, Conn. Bar Assn., Hartford County Bar Assn., Inst. Makers of Explosives (bd. govs. 1987—, chmn. legal affairs com. 1986-93, 95—), Am. Corp. Counsel Assn. (bd. dirs. Hartford chpt. 1988—), Greater Harford C. of C. (bd. dirs. 1991-94), Internat. Soc. Explosive Engrs., Simsbury Farms Men's Club (founder 1972), Hop Meadow Country Club. Democrat. Roman Catholic. Home: 9 Metacom Dr Simsbury CT 06070 Office: Ensign-Bickford Industries Inc 10 Mill Pond Ln Simsbury CT 06070-2429

LONG, OPHELIA, hospital administrator; b. Birmingham, Ala., Dec. 5, 1940; m. Henry Long; children: Donald, Celeste, Camile. AA, Los Angeles City Coll., 1962; BS, Calif. State U., Los Angeles, 1971; postgrad., U. So. Calif., 1985—. Jr. staff nurse Kaiser Found. Hosp., Los Angeles, 1962-63, gen. duty staff nurse, 1963-65, specialty unit staff nurse, 1965, nursing care coordinator ICU, 1966, supr. ICU, 1966-70, instr., 1970-72, asst. dir. critical care nursing, 1972-81; dir. nursing Kaiser Permanente Med. Ctr., West Los Angeles, 1981-84, hosp. adminstr., 1984—; Instr. leadership skills, Kaiser Permanente Med. Ctr., Los Angeles, 1975; apptd. Dist. XI Med. Quality Assurance com. Bd. Med. Examiners, 1976-81; mem. staff West Los Angeles Community Coll., 1981—. Dir. Operation Learn, 1970-72; active Youth Motivational Task Force, 1974—, Calif. State U. at Los Angeles Adv. Com., 1979—, Los Angeles SW Coll., 1979—, Los Angeles Trade-Tech. Coll., 1979—; Joint Nat. Com. High Blood Pressure of NIH Heart, Blood and Lung Inst., 1982—, Joint Nat. Com. Heart Blood and Lung Inst., 1983—; bd. dirs. U. So. Calif. Community Freedom Sch., 1970-73. Named Outstanding Alumni, Los Angeles Community Coll., 1984, Distng. Alumni, Calif. State U. at Los Angeles, 1985; recipient Outstanding Nurse of Yr. award, 1983. Mem. Nat. Black Nurses' Assn., Inc. (1st v.p 1978-82, bd. dirs. 1982-83, pres. 1983—), Council Black Nurses (chairperson Ways and Means com. 1972-74, pres. 1974-75, award 1973), Critical Care Nurses Assn., Nephrology Nurses Assn., Calif. Nurses Assn., Black Congress on Health and Law, Congl. Black Caucus-Health Brain Trust, Nursing Alumni Assn. Los Angeles City Coll. (pres. 1970-72), Chi Eta Phi. Home: 2431 W 116th St Inglewood CA 90303

LONG, PATRICIA GAVIGAN, elementary education educator, English language educator; b. Bryn Mawr, Pa., Mar. 5, 1942; d. Thomas and Martha Mary Gavigan; m. James Robert III, Nov. 22, 1978; children: Jon Rhys Long, Martha Lucille Long. AA, AssumptionColl., Mendham, N.J., 1964; BS in Elem. Edn., St. Joseph's Coll., Phila., 1970; MEd, Pa. State. U., 1975. Cert. Tchr. grades 1-7, mid. sch., 6-8. Reading Specialist, K-12, Pa., Va. Grade 2 tchr. St. Nicholas Elem. Sch., Jersey City, N.J., 1962-64; grade 1 and 2 tchr. St. Lawrence Elem. Sch., Harrisburg, Pa., 1964-66, Holy Trinity Elem. Sch., Hazelton, Pa., 1966-68; grade 3 tchr. St. Margaret's Elem. Sch., Narberth, Pa., 1968-75; reading resource tchr. K-5 Arrowhead Elem. Sch., Virginia Beach, Va., 1975-84; reading tchr. grade 8-9 Stonewall Jackson Jr. High, Mechanicsville, Va., 1984-89; grade 6 tchr. Stonewall Jackson Middle Sch., Mechanicsville, Va., 1989—. Named Reading Tchr. of Yr. Arrowhead Elem. Sch. Virginia Beach, Va., 1978, Stonewall Jackson/Richmond Area Reading Coun., Richmond, Va., 1992. Mem. PTA Stonewall Jackson Middle Sch., Richmond Area reading Coun., Va. State Reading Coun., Hanover Edn. Assn. Va. Edn. Assn., NEA, Richmond Area English Coun., Va. Area Tchr. of English, Arrowhead PTA Bd. Republican. Roman Catholic. Avocations: reading, walking, wallpapering, painting, helping others. Office: Stonewall Jackson Middle School RR 2 Box 461 Mechanicsville VA 23111-4699

LONG, PHILLIP CLIFFORD, museum director; b. Tucson, Oct. 11, 1942; s. Hugh-Blair Grigsby and Phyllis Margaret (Clay) L.; m. Martha Whitney Rowe, Aug. 26, 1972; children:-Elisha Whitney, Charlotte Clay, Elliot Sherlock. B.A., Tulane U., 1965. Sec. Fifth Third Bancorp, Cin., 1976-94; asst. sec. Fifth Third Bank, Cin., 1975-76, sec., 1976-77, asst. v.p., 1977-79, v.p., sec., 1979-88, sr. v.p., sec., 1988-94; dir. Taft Mus., Cin., 1994—. Trustee Art Acad. Cin., 1980-94, Cin. Symphony Orch., 1981-87, Contemporary Arts Ctr., 1974-84, Cin. Nature Ctr., 1982-88, Taft Mus., 1987—, Cin. Country Day Sch., 1991—; trustee, treas., Cin. Music Hall, 1981-92, Convalescent Hosp. for Children, 1989—; Cin. Assn. for Perfoming Arts, 1992—. Mem. The Camargo Club, Queen City Club. Home: 4795 Burley Hills Dr Cincinnati OH 45243-4007 Office: Taft Mus 316 Pike St Cincinnati OH 45202-4293

LONG, RALPH STEWART, clinical psychologist; b. Pitts., Feb. 23, 1926; s. Ralph S. and Virginia (Hawk) L.; m. Vera Lazorchak, June 16, 1951; children: Karen Virginia, Brian Reed, Lauri Michelle. BS, Lock Haven U., 1950; MEd, Pa. State U., 1951; PhD, Washington U. St. Louis, 1965. Lic. psychologist, Tex. Commd. 2d lt. USAF, 1951, advanced through grades to lt. col., 1968; psychologist various hosps. USAF, U.S. and Europe, 1951-71; ret., 1971; dir. psychol. svcs. Community Ctr. Mental Health, Mental Retardation, Wichita Falls, Tex., 1971-72; psychol. cons. Family Counseling Ctr., Wichita Falls, 1972-74; dir. psychol. svcs. Nueces County Mental Health-Mental Retardation Community Ctr., 1974-77; dir. Corpus Christi Counseling Ctr./Physicians-Surgeons Hosp., Tex., 1977-79, Psychol. Cons. Corpus Christi, 1979-82; exec. dir. Personal Dynamics Inst., Corpus Christi, 1982—; instr. dept. psychology McKendree Coll., Lebanon, Ill., 1962-63; instr. So. Ill. U., 1962-64; adj. prof. human rels. Webster U., Webster Groves, Mo., 1976-79, 88-93; adj. prof. psychology Del Mar Coll., Corpus Christi 1977-83, adj. prof. bus. adminstrn., 1991-93; cons. Tex. Dept. Corrections, 1988-90; bd. dirs. Creative Living, 1986—; cons., trainer Crisis Svcs., 1980—; profl. adv. bd. North Tex. Regional Coun.

Alcoholism, 1971-74, Mental Health Assn. Coastal Bend, 1974-83, Wichita Mental Health Assn., 1965-67, 70-74; adj. prof. Embry-Riddle U., Corpus Christi, 1991-93; consulting psychologist Nueces County Juvenile Justice Ctr., Corpus Christi, 1992—, Warm Springs Rehab. Ctr., Corpus Christi, 1992—, MCC Managed Behavioral Care, Inc., Eden Prairie, Minn., 1992—; bd. dirs. Consumer Credit Counseling Svc. South Tex., 1983—. Contbr. to profl. jours.; presenter in field. With USN, 1944-51. Named Am. Man Sci., 1962. Fellow Soc. Air Force Clinical Psychologists; mem. APA, DAV, Tex. Assn. Mental Health (exec. com. 1980-83), Air Force Assn., Nat. Register Health Svc. Providers in Psychology, Masons, Sigma Xi. Avocations: painting, writing, travel, camping, fishing. Office: Personal Dynamics Inst 1819 S Brownlee Blvd Corpus Christi TX 78404-2901

LONG, RICHARD PAUL, civil engineering educator, geotechnical engineering consultant; b. Allentown, Pa., Nov. 29, 1934; s. Peter Anthony and Matilda (Stier) L.; m. Mary Elizabeth Doyle, Aug. 29, 1964; children: Marybeth, Christopher. BCE, U. Cin., 1957; MCE, Rensselaer Poly. Inst., 1963, PhD, 1966. Registered profl. engr., Conn. NSF postdoctoral fellow Rensselaer Poly. Inst., Troy, N.Y., 1966-67; from asst. to assoc. prof. civil engring. U. Conn., Storrs, 1967-77, prof., head dept., 1977-90; com. mem. Transp. Research Bd., Washington, 1971—. Contbr. articles to profl. jours.; co-inventor, patentee prefabricated subsurface drain, stress laminated timber bridges. Pres. Mansfield Middle Sch. Assn., Storrs, 1977-79; commr. Mansfield Housing Authority, Storrs, 1987—, chmn., 1988-93. 1st lt. U.S. Army, 1958-61. Recipient T.A. Bedford prize Rensselaer Poly. Inst., 1966, AT&T Found. award for Teaching Excellence, 1988, Recognition award Conn. Soc. Profl. Engrs., 1989. Fellow ASCE; mem. Conn. Soc. Civil Engrs. (sec. 1986-88, pres.-elect 1988-89, pres. 1989-90), Am. Soc. Engring. Edn. Roman Catholic. Avocations: jogging, travel. Home: 31 Westgate Ln Storrs Mansfield CT 06268-1506 Office: Univ Conn U-37 Dept Of Civil Engring Storrs CT 06269-3037

LONG, ROBERT DOUGLAS, financial service executive; b. Lawton, Okla.; s. Robert E. and Marilyn (Whitlock) L.; m. Susan Elizabeth Biondo, Oct. 5, 1956. BA in Econs., McGill U., 1977, postgrad., 1978. Assoc. First Boston Corp., N.Y.C., 1978-81, 1981-85, v.p., 1982-85, dir., 1987-92, mng. dir., 1992—; exec. v.p., head investment banking Nomura Securities Internat., N.Y.C., 1992—. Office: Nomura Securities Co 2 World Financial Ctr # B New York NY 10281-1001

LONG, ROBERT EMMET, author; b. Oswego, N.Y., June 7, 1934; s. Robert Emmet and Verda (Lindsley) L. BA, Columbia Coll., 1956; MA, Syracuse U., 1964; PhD, Columbia U., 1968. Instr. SUNY, Cortland, 1962-64; asst. prof. Queens Coll., CUNY, N.Y.C., 1968-71; writer, 1971—. Author: The Great Succession: Henry James and the Legacy of Hawthorne, 1979, The Achieving of the Great Gatsby, 1979, Henry James: The Early Years, 1983, John O'Hara, 1983, Nathanael West, 1985, Barbara Pym, 1986, James Thurber, 1988, James Fenimore Cooper, 1990, The Films of Merchant Ivory, 1991, Ingmar Bergman: Film and Stage, 1994; editor numerous books; contbr. articles to profl. jours. and popular mags. Democrat. Episcopalian. Avocations: films, theater, ballet, jazz, travel. Address: 254 S Third St Fulton NY 13069

LONG, ROBERT EUGENE, banker; b. Yankton, S.D., Dec. 5, 1931; s. George Joseph and Malinda Ann (Hanson) L.; m. Patricia Louise Glass, June 19, 1959; children: Malinda Ann, Robert Eugene, Jennifer Lynn, Michael Joseph. B.S. in Acctg., U. S.D., 1956; M.B.A., U. Mich., 1965; grad., Madison Grad. Sch. Banking, 1973, Nat. Comml. Lending Grad. Sch., Okla., 1977. Cert. comml. lender. Financial analyst Chrysler Corp., 1958-59; supr. finance Ford Motor Co., 1966-67; with First Wis. Bankshares Corp., Milw., 1967—; v.p. fin. First Wis. Bankshares Corp., 1973—; exec. v.p. 1st Wis. Fond du Lac, 1978—; dir. 1st Wis. Nat. Bank of Southgate, Waukesha and Fond du Lac; exec. v.p., dir. West Allis State Bank, 1979-81, pres., dir., 1981—; chief exec. officer, 1983—; sr. v.p. adminstrn. Park Banks, 1987—; speaker/chmn. banking seminars Am. Mgmt. Assn., 1970—. Pres. local br. Aid Assn. Luth., 1970—, corp. bd. dirs., 1982—, vice chmn. bd., 1989—; pres. Mt. Carmel Luth. Ch., Milw., 1972; team capt. Re-elect Nixon campaign, 1972; bd. dirs. Luth. Social Svcs. of Wis. and Upper Mich., 1978—, bd., 1983—; bd. dirs. Luther Manor, 1981, Luther Manor Found., 1984, pres. bd. dirs. United Luth. Program for Aging, 1986—; bd. dirs. Wis. Inst. Family Medicine, 1985, pres., 1992—; vice chmn. adv. coun. West Allis Meml. Hosp., 1993—. With USAF, 1951-52. Recipient Good Citizenship award Am. Legion, 1948. Mem. Wis. Assn. Family Practice (bd. dirs. 1992—), Wauwatosa C. of C. (bd. dirs. 1992—), Alpha Tau Omega. Lutheran. Clubs: Western Racquet (Elm Grove, Wis.) (dir. 1976—); Bluemound Golf and Country; Elmbrook Swim (pres. 1977-78). Lodges: Masons, Shriners, Jesters. Home: N21W24052D Dorchester Dr Pewaukee WI 53072 Office: Park Banks 330 E Kilbourn Ave Milwaukee WI 53202-3121

LONG, ROBERT LIVINGSTON, consultant, photographic equipment executive; b. Abbeville, S.C., Jan. 3, 1937; s. Clarance Blakely and Amy (Wolff) L.; m. Phyllis Jo Crews, May 30, 1959; children: J. Blake, Brynn Diane, Brant Wolff. BSCE, U. S.C., 1959; grad. in Indsl. Mgmt. Program, U. Tenn., 1967. Chem. engr. Tenn. div. Eastman Kodak Co., Kingsport, 1959-66, gen. mgmt. staff tech. Tenn. div., 1966-74, mgr. licensing chemicals div., 1974-80, dir. mfg. staff Tenn. div., 1980-83, v.p., dir. planning div., chemicals div., 1983-86; v.p., dir. corp. planning Eastman Kodak Co., Rochester, N.Y., 1986-92, sr. v.p., 1989; cons., Melbourne Beach, Fla., 1992—; bd. dirs. Sun Microsystems Inc., Mt. View, Calif. Participant Tenn. Exec. Devel. Program, Knoxville, 1974; multiple adv. bd. City of Kingsport, 1978-86; bd. dirs. Boy's Club Greater Kingsport, 1965-81, chmn., 1973-75; bd. dirs. Holston Valley Hosp. and Med. Ctr., Kingsport, 1983-86, Rochester Gen. Hosp., 1988-92. Sgt. U.S. Army N.G., 1955-63. Recipient Medallion, Boys Club Am., 1976, Bronze Keyston award Boys Club Am., 1985. Mem. Am. Inst. Chem. Engrs., Soc. for Info. Mgmt., Acad. Natural Scis. (bd. dirs. environ. assocs. 1982-85), Sigma Alpha Epsilon. Episcopalian. Lodge: Rotary (chmn. cons. Kingsport 1975-86).

LONG, ROBERT LYMAN JOHN, naval officer; b. Kansas City, Mo., May 29, 1920; s. Trigg A. and Margaret (Franklin) L.; m. Sara Helms, Aug. 28, 1944; children: Charles Allen, William Trigg, Robert Helms. BS, U.S. Naval Acad., 1943; grad., Naval War Coll., 1954. Commd. ensign USN, 1943, advanced through grades to adm., 1977; assigned PTO; comdr. two nuclear polaris submarines, 1966-68; comdr. service force for 7th fleet, 1968-69; dep. comdr. Naval Ship Systems Command, 1969-72; comdr. submarine force U.S. Atlantic Fleet, 1972-74; dep. chief naval ops. for submarine warfare Washington, 1974-77; vice chief naval ops., 1977-79; comdr.-in-chief U.S. Forces Pacific, 1979-83; bd. dirs. GTE. trustee Ctr. for Naval Analyses, 1984—; mem. bd. visitors Nat. Def. U., 1985—. Decorated D.S.M. (two), Legion of Merit (three), Bronze Star. Clubs: Cosmos, N.Y. Yacht. Home: 247 Heamans Way Annapolis MD 21401-6303

LONG, ROBERT M., newspaper publishing executive; m. June Long; children: Shannon, Bob. BBA, Dyke Coll. CPA, Ohio. From acct. to treas. and contr. Plain Dealer Pub. Co., Cleve., 1965-92, exec. v.p., 1992—; v.p. Plain Dealer Charities, Inc., Delcom, Inc. Trustee Dyke Coll., Cleve. Ballet, St. Vincent Quadrangle, Inc.; bd. dirs. Jr. Achievement; active Leadership Cleve., 1993. Mem. Internat. Newspaper Fin. Execs. (bd. dirs.), Ohio Soc. CPAs, Cleve. Treas. Club. Office: The Plain Dealer Pub Co 1801 Superior Ave Cleveland OH 44114*

LONG, ROBERT MERRILL, retail drug company executive; b. Oakland, Calif., May 19, 1938; s. Joseph Milton and Vera Mai (Skaggs) L.; m. Eliane Quilloux, Dec. 13, 1969. Student, Brown U., 1956-58; BA, Claremont Men's Coll., 1960. With Longs Drug Stores Inc., Walnut Creek, Calif., 1960—, dist. mgr., 1970-72, exec. v.p., 1972-75, pres., 1975-77, pres., chief exec. officer, 1977-91; chmn., chief exec. officer Longs Drug Stores, Walnut Creek, Calif., 1991—. Mem. Nat. Assn. Chain Drug Stores (dir.). Office: Longs Drug Stores Corp PO Box 5222 141 N Civic Dr Walnut Creek CA 94596-3858

LONG, ROBERT RADCLIFFE, fluid mechanics educator; b. Glen Ridge, N.J., Oct. 24, 1919; s. Clarence D. and Gertrude (Cooper) L.; m. Cristina Nersing, 1962; children: John Radcliffe, Robert W. AB in Econs, Princeton, 1941; MS in Meteorology, U. Chgo., 1949, PhD, 1950. Meteorologist U.S.

Weather Bur., Paris, France, 1946-47; asst. prof. Johns Hopkins U., Balt., 1951-56, assoc. prof., 1956-59, prof. fluid mechanics, 1959-88, prof. emeritus, 1988—, dir. hydrodynamics lab., 1951-88; assoc. dept. aero. and mech. engring. Ariz. State U. Author: Mechanics of Solids and Fluids, Engineering Science Mechanics; also articles in field. Home: PO Box 10381 Sarasota FL 34278

LONG, RONALD ALEX, real estate and financial consultant, educator; b. Scranton, Pa., Dec. 9, 1948; s. Anthony James and Dorothy Agnas (Posgay) L.; m. Geraldine Sinneway, July 17, 1976; 1 child, Elizabeth Dorothy. BA, Bethany Coll., Lindsburg, Kans., 1971; MAT, Trenton (N.J.) State Coll., 1973; BS, Spring Garden Coll., 1980; MBA, St. Joseph's U., Phila., 1985; postgrad., Widener U., 1992—; cert., Grad. Realtor Inst., 1990. Cert. real estate instr. Substitute tchr. Hackettstown and Roxbury (N.J.) Sch. Bds., 1971-72; prof., chmn. bus. adminstrn. dept. Spring Garden Coll., Phila. 1973-92; sales assoc. Red Carpet Real Estate, Doylestown, Pa., 1980—; cons. real estate Doylestown, 1980—; cons. mgmt. Budd Wheel Corp., Phila., 1978-82; pres., prin. Aladdin Fin. Svcs., Inc.; prin. Loan Finders, Inc.; dir. Met. Real Estate Sch., Doylestown, 1991—; cons. The Princeton Group Telecom. Specialist. Co-author: Explorations in Macroeconomics, 1988, Explorations in Microeconomics, 1989; contbr. articles to area newspapers. Site dir. ARC Blood Mobile, 1975-91; bd. dirs Buckingham (Pa.) PTA, 1984-88. Recipient Legion Honor award Chapel of the 4 Chaplains, Phila., 1984. Mem. Nat. Assn. Realtors, Pa. Assn. Realtors, Bucks County Assn. Realtors, Profl. Assn. Diving Instrs. (cert.), Bus. Club (treas. 1969-71, pres. 1970-71), Alpha Chi, Pi Sigma Chi, Eta Beta Phi, Delta Theta Phi. Republican. Avocations: scuba diving, karate, surface and underwater photography, running. Home: 2698 Cranberry Rd Doylestown PA 18901-1770

LONG, SARAH ANN, librarian; b. Atlanta, May 20, 1943; d. Jones Lloyd and Lelia Maria (Mitchell) Sanders; m. James Allen Long, 1961 (div. 1985); children: Andrew C., James Allen IV; m. Donald J. Sager, May 23, 1987. BA, Oglethorpe U., 1966; M in Librarianship, Emory U., 1967. Asst. libr. Coll. of St. Matthias, Bristol, Eng., 1970-74; cons. State Libr. of Ohio, Columbus, 1975-77; coord. Pub. Libr. of Columbus and Franklin County, Columbus, 1977-79, dir. Fairfield County Dist. Libr., Lancaster, Ohio, 1979-82, Dauphin County Libr. System, Harrisburg, Pa., 1982-85, Multnomah County Libr., Portland, Oreg., 1985-89; system dir. North Suburban Libr. System, Wheeling, Ill., 1989—; chmn. Portland State U. Libr. Adv. Coun., 1987-89. Contbr. articles to profl. jours. Bd. dirs. Dauphin County Hist. Soc., Harrisburg, 1983-85, ARC, Harrisburg, 1984-85; pres. Lancaster-Fairfield County YWCA, Lancaster, 1981-82; vice-chmn. govt. and edn. div. Lancaster-Fairfield County United Way, Lancaster, 1981-82; sec. Fairfield County Arts Coun., 1981-82; adv. bd. Portland State U., 1987-89. Recipient Dir.'s award Ohio Program in Humanities, Columbus, 1982; Sarah Long Day established in her honor Fairfield County, Lancaster, Bd. Commrs., 1982. Mem. ALA (elected coun. 1993—), Pub. Libr. Assn. (pres. 1989-90, chair legis. com.), Ill. Libr. Assn. (pub. policy com. 1991—). Office: N Suburban Libr Systems 200 W Dundee Rd Wheeling IL 60090

LONG, SARAH ELIZABETH BRACKNEY, physician; b. Sidney, Ohio, Dec. 5, 1926; d. Robert LeRoy and Caroline Josephine (Shue) Brackney; m. John Frederick Long, June 15, 1948; children: George Lynas, Helen Lucille Corcoran, Harold Roy, Clara Alice Lawrence, Nancy Carol. BA, Ohio State U., 1948, MD, 1952. Intern Grant Hosp., Columbus, Ohio, 1952-53; resident internal medicine Mt. Carmel Med. Ctr., Columbus, 1966-69, chief resident internal medicine, 1968-69; med. cons. Ohio Bur. Disability Determination, Columbus, 1970—; physician student health Ohio State U., Columbus, 1970-73; sch. physician Bexley (Ohio) City Schs., 1973-83; physician advisor to peer rev. Mt. Carmel East Hosp., Columbus, 1979-86, employee health physician, 1981—; physician cons. Fed. Black Lung Program, U.S. Dept. Labor, Columbus, 1979—. Mem. AMA, Ohio State Med. Assn., Franklin County Acad. Medicine, Alpha Epsilon Delta, Phi Beta Kappa. Home: 2765 Bexley Park Rd Columbus OH 43209-2231

LONG, SHARON RUGEL, molecular biologist, plant biology educator; b. San Marcos, Tex., Mar. 2, 1951; d. Harold Eugene and Florence Jean (Rugel) Long; m. Harold James McGee, July 7, 1979; 2 children. BS, Calif. Inst. Tech., 1973; PhD, Yale U., 1979. Rsch. fellow Harvard U., Cambridge, Mass., 1979-81; asst. prof. molecular biology Stanford U., Palo Alto, Calif., 1982-87, assoc. prof., 1987-92, prof., 1992—; investigator Howard Hughes Med. Inst., 1994—. Assoc. editor (jour.) Plant Physiology, 1992—; editor, mem. editl. bd. Jour. Bacteriology; mem. editl. bd. Molecular Plant-Microbe Interactions; editl. com. Ann. Review Cell Biology. Recipient postdoctoral award NSF, 1979, NIH, 1980, Shell Rsch. Found. award 1985, Presdl. Young Investigator award NSF, 1984-89, Faculty awards for women, 1991; rsch. grantee NIH, Dept. Energy, NSF; MacArthur fellow, 1992-97. Fellow AAAS, Am. Acad. Arts and Scis., Am. Acad. Microbiology; mem. NAS, Genetics Soc. Am., Am. Soc. Plant Physiology (Charles Albert Shull award 1989), Am. Soc. Microbiology, Soc. Devel. Biology, Am. Soc. for Microbiologists. Office: Stanford U Dept Biol Scis Stanford CA 94305-5020

LONG, SHELLEY, actress; b. Fort Wayne, Ind., Aug. 23, 1949; m. Bruce Tyson; 1 child, Juliana. Student, Northwestern U. Writer, assoc. prodr., co-host Chgo. TV program Sorting It Out, 1970s (3 local Emmys 1970); mem. Second City, Chgo.; guest TV appearances various shows including M.A.S.H., Love Boat, Family; regular TV series Cheers, 1982-87, Good Advice, 1993-94; motion pictures include A Small Circle of Friends, 1980, Caveman, 1981, Night Shift, 1982, Losin' It, 1983, Irreconcilable Differences, 1984, The Money Pit, 1986, Outrageous Fortune, 1987, Hello Again, 1987, Troop Beverly Hills, 1989, Don't Tell Her It's Me, 1990, Frozen Assets, 1992, The Brady Bunch Movie, 1995; TV films include The Cracker Factory, 1979, The Promise of Love, 1980, The Princess and the Cabbie, 1981, Memory of a Murder, 1992, A Message from Holly, 1992, The Women of Spring Break, 1995; TV mini-series, Voices Within: The Lives of Trudy Chase, 1990. Recipient Emmy award Outstanding Actress in a Comedy Series for Cheers, 1983. Office: Creative Artists Agy Ron Meyer 9830 Wilshire Blvd Beverly Hills CA 90212

LONG, THAD GLADDEN, lawyer; b. Dothan, Ala., Mar. 9, 1938; s. Lindon Alexander and Della Gladys (Pilcher) L.; m. Carolyn Wilson, Aug. 13, 1966; children: Louisa Frances, Wilson Alexander. AB, Columbia U., 1960; JD, U. Va., 1963. Bar: Ala. 1963, U.S. Dist. Ct. (no. dist., so. dist., mid. dist.) Ala., U.S. Ct. Appeals (11th cir., 5th cir.), U.S. Supreme Ct. Assoc. atty. Bradley, Arant, Rose & White, Birmingham, Ala., 1963-70; ptnr. Bradley, Arant, Rose & White, Birmingham, 1970—; adj. prof. U. Ala., Tuscaloosa, 1988—. Co-author: Unfair Competition Under Alabama Law, 1990, Protecting Intellectual Property, 1990; mem. editl. bd. The Trademark Reporter; contbr. articles to profl. jours. Trustee Oscar Wells Trust for Mus. Art, Birmingham, 1983—, Canterbury Meth. Found., 1993—, sec., 1993—; vice chmn., trustee Sons Revolution Found., Ala., 1994—; chmn. Greater Birmingham Arts Alliance, 1977-79, Columbia U. Secondary Schs. Com. Ala. Area, 1975—; trustee, treas. Birmingham Music Club; pres. Birmingham-Jefferson Hist. Soc., 1995—; mem. Birmingham Com. Fgn. Rels.; chmn. Entrepreneurship Inst. Birmingham, 1989. Mem. U.S. Patent Bar, Internat. Trademark Assn., Ala. Law Inst., Birmingham Legal Aid Soc. (bd. dirs.), Am. Assn. (chmn., founder bus. Torts and Antitrust sect.), U. Va. Law Alumni (chmn. Birmingham chpt. 1984-89), S.R. (pres. 1994—), Gen. Soc. S.R. (gen. solicitor 1994—), Am. Arbitration Assn., Omicron Delta Kappa, Order of the Coif. Republican. Methodist. Avocations: travel, writing, table tennis. Home: 2880 Balmoral Rd Birmingham AL 35223-1236 Office: Bradley Arant Rose & White 1400 Park Pl Tower Birmingham AL 35203

LONG, THOMAS LESLIE, lawyer; b. Mansfield, Ohio, May 30, 1951; s. Ralph Waldo and Rose Ann (Cloud) L.; m. Peggy L. Bryant, Apr. 24, 1982. AB in Govt., U. Notre Dame, 1973; JD, Ohio State U., 1976. Bar: Ohio 1976, U.S. Dist. Ct. (so. dist.) Ohio 1976, U.S. Dist. Ct. (no. dist.) Ohio 1977, U.S. Ct. Appeals (6th cir.) 1978. Assoc. Alexander, Ebinger, Fisher, McAlister & Lawrence, Columbus, Ohio, 1976-82, ptnr., 1982-85; ptnr. Baker & Hostetler, Columbus, 1985—. Mem. ABA, Ohio Bar Assn., Columbus Bar Assn., Fed. Bar Assn., Assn. Trial Lawyer Am. Democrat. Roman Catholic. Club: Capitol (Columbus). Home: 2565 Leeds Rd Columbus OH 43221-3613 Office: Baker & Hostetler 65 E State St Columbus OH 43215-4213

LONG, THOMAS MICHAEL, investment banker; b. Tulsa, June 30, 1943; s. Thomas Marvin Long and Marcia Acosta; m. Catherine Howell, Dec. 30, 1964; children: Jane Alexander, Hampton Howell. B.A. in Govt. cum laude, Harvard U., 1965; M.B.A. with distinction, Harvard U., Boston, 1971. Dir. Ohio Plan Ohio U., Athens, 1966-68; with Boston Cons. Group, 1968-69; ptnr. Brown Bros. Harriman & Co., pvt. bankers, N.Y.C., 1971—; co-mgr. 1818 Fund, L.P., 1818 Fund 11, L.P., 1989—; bd. dirs. Alveco Energy Co., Houston, Winrock Enterprises, Inc., Little Rock, Columbia Hosp. Corp., Ft. Worth., The Ekco Group, Nashua, N.H. Contbr. articles on mergers and acquisitions and banking industry consolidation to Am. Banker, Bankers Mag., Investment Dealers Digest. Trustee Greenwich Country Day Sch., 1987-92, The Hosp. Chaplaincy, Inc., N.Y.C., 1992—. Corning Glass traveling fellow Harvard U., 1965-66. Mem. Milbrook Club (Greenwich), Knickerbocker Club (N.Y.C., India House Club (N.Y.C.), Country Club of Little Rock. Democrat. Roman Catholic. Home: 3 Old Mill Rd Greenwich CT 06830-3342 Office: Brown Bros Harriman & Co 59 Wall St New York NY 10005-2818

LONG, TIMOTHY SCOTT, chemist, consultant; b. Racine, Wis., Dec. 20, 1937; s. Leslie Alexander and Esther (Sand) L.; m. Karen M. Koniarski, July 13, 1985; children by previous marriage: Corinne, Christine. BS in Chemistry, Winona State U., 1975. Staff chemist IBM, Rochester, Minn., 1962-77; adv. chemist IBM, Harrison, N.Y., 1977-80, IBM Instruments, Inc., Danbury, Conn., 1980-81; mgr. Midwest Instrument Ctr. IBM Instruments, Inc., Chgo., 1981-85; mgr. corp. environ. engring. IBM, Stamford, Conn., 1985-89; industry cons. IBM, White Plains, N.Y., 1989-92; environ. cons. Geraghty & Miller, Inc., Rochelle Park, N.J., 1992-94, Indpls., 1994—; mem. World Environ. Ctr., N.Y.C., 1985-89; adv. bd. Coop. Ctr. Rsch. in Hazardous and Toxic Substances, Newark, 1985-89. Author: Testing for Prediction of Material Performance, 1972, Methods for Emissions Spectrochemical Analysis, 1977, 2d edit., 1982; contbr. articles to Applied Spectroscopy, Soc. Applied Spectroscopy (chmn. Minn. sect. 1976-77), Assn. Am. Indian Affairs, Soc. Plastics Engrs. (bd. reviewers 1975-76). Achievements include demonstration of world's first application using ion chromatography in the analysis of indsl. waste water. Home: 559 E Lord St Indianapolis IN 46202 Office: Geraghty & Miller Inc 251 East Ohio St Ste 1010 Indianapolis IN 46204

LONG, TOM, insurance company executive. Pres. Blue Cross Blue Shield, Chattanooga, Tenn., 1968—. Office: Blue Cross Blue Shield of Tenn 801 Pine St Chattanooga TN 37402

LONG, TOM, manufacturing company executive; b. Charleston, W.Va., Apr. 19, 1932; s. Mary (Saunders) Nielsen; m. Delores Faye Holt, Aug. 6, 1954; children: Gary, Tom Jr., Debra, Rex. BSEE, U. Dayton, 1965, MBA, 1967; grad. advanced mgmt. program, Harvard U., 1985. Field engr. Tektronix Inc., Chgo., 1960-61, Dayton, Ohio, 1961-67; mktg. mgr. Beaverton, Oreg., 1967-71, engring. mgr.-gen. instruments, 1971-74, div. gen. mgr., 1973-74, v.p., gen. mgr. communications group, 1981-83, v.p., gen. mgr. design automation group, 1984-87, v.p., gen. mgr. tech. group, 1988—; pres. Grass Valley (Calif.) Group, 1974-81; exec. v.p. Analogic, Peabody, Mass., 1983-84; trustee Tektronix Found., Beaverton, 1985—; pres. Tektronix Devel. Co., Beaverton, 1984—; chmn., chief exec. officer TriQuint Semicondr. Inc., Beaverton, 1985-91. Served to staff sgt. USAF, 1950-54. Mem. Soc. Motion Picture and TV Engrs. Republican. Avocations: racquetball, volleyball. Office: Tektronix Inc M/S 50-408 PO Box 500 Beaverton OR 97077-0001

LONG, WALTER EDWARD, international trade company executive, consultant; b. Little Rock, Nov. 11, 1935; s. James Edward and Daisy Mae (Cooper) L. BA summa cum laude, Philander Smith Coll., 1957; MA in Psychology, U. Pa., 1960. Mgr. indsl. and psychol. testing Richton Co. Inc., Newark, 1960-63; pres. Best Resume Co., Inc., N.Y.C., 1963-65; pres., chief exec. officer PHAT Advt. Cons., Inc., N.Y.C., 1965-74; chmn. Nubian Internationale, Ltd. PHAT Advt. Cons., Inc., 1973-78; sr. v.p. internat. trade Daniels & Cartwright, Inc., 1978-80; pres., chief exec. officer Epic Internat. Trade, Ltd., 1980—, Am. Gas & Energy Corp., 1988—; v.p. internat. trade Swiss Bullion Internat. Corp., 1988-91; CEO GlobalArk Internat. Trade Ltd., Little Rock, 1991—; pres. Walter Long Assocs., 1991—; v.p. internat. trade World Trade Ctr., Memphis, 1993-94; spl. trade and fin. devel. cons., Namabia, S. Africa, 1993—; sr. cons./coord. World Econ. Developers Unlimited, N.Y.C., 1995—; dir. Pepsi-Cola, Mali, West Africa, 1995—; bd. dirs. Harlem br. N.Y. Urban Coalition, N.Y.C., 1972-74; condr. internat. trade seminars Queens (N.Y.) Coll., 1968. With U.S. Army, 1958-60. N.Y. Film Inst. grantee, 1973. Mem. Am. Psychol. Assn., Masons. Democrat. African Methodist Episcopalian. Avocations: golf, chess, writing, video-sound buff, travel. Office: GlobalArk Internat Trade 7500 Azalea Dr Little Rock AR 72209-4417

LONG, WILLIAM ALLAN, retired forest products company executive; b. Columbus, Ohio, Aug. 25, 1928; s. Allan C. and Dorothy (Crates) L.; m. Ann Cors, Aug. 27, 1954; children: Leslie, David, Steven, Jeffrey. B.A., Ohio Wesleyan U., 1951. Vice pres. Diamond Internat., N.Y.C., 1951-70; exec. v.p. Overhead Door Corp., Dallas, 1970-75; v.p. St. Regis Paper Co., N.Y.C., 1975-79; group v.p. Inland Container Corp., Indpls., 1979-93; ret., 1993. Sgt. U.S. Army, 1946-47. Republican. Presbyterian. Home: 5010 Plantation Dr Indianapolis IN 46250-1639

LONG, WILLIAM EVERETT, retired utility executive; b. Oklahoma City, Sept. 3, 1919; s. William Everett and Hazel Kathleen (Stafford) L.; m. Frances Jeanne Baum, Aug. 7, 1942; children: Susan Jeanne, Nancy Lee. Student, U. Colo., 1937-39, Northwestern U., 1940. With Houston Natural Gas Corp., 1949-84, sr. v.p., gen. mgr. distbn. div., 1971-78, sr. v.p., chief adminstrv. officer, 1981-84. Served with USAAF, 1941-46; Served with USAF, 1951-53; mem. Res. (ret.). Mem. Christian Ch. (Disciples of Christ). Clubs: Lakeside Country, Masons. Home: 9585 Longmont Dr Houston TX 77063-1026 *I am blessed with parents who, when I was a youth, instilled in me a good sense of social, moral and civic values. They prepared me to seek opportunity, accept responsibility and respect my fellow man.*

LONG, WILLIS FRANKLIN, electrical engineering educator, researcher; b. Lima, Ohio, Jan. 30, 1934; s. Jesse Raymond and Cerelda Elizabeth (Stepleton) L.; m. Ginger Carol Miller; children: Andrew Mark, Kristin Kay, David Franklin. BS in Engring. Physics, U. Toledo, 1957, MSEE, 1962; PhD, U. Wis., 1970. Registered profl. engr., Wis. Project engr. Doehler Jarvis div. Nat. Lead Co., Toledo, Ohio, 1957, 59-60; instr. U. Toledo, 1962-66; mem. tech. staff Hughes Rsch. Labs., Malibu, Calif., 1969-73; asst., then assoc. prof. depts. extension engring. and elec. engring. U. Wis., Madison, 1973-80, prof., chair dept. extension engring., 1980-83, prof. depts. engring., profl devel. and elec. and computer engring., 1985—; dir. ASEA Power System Ctr., New Berlin, Wis., 1983-85; prin. Long Assocs., Madison, 1973—; cons. Dept. Energy, Washington, 1978—, ABB Power Systems, Raleigh, N.C., 1985—. Editor EMTP Rev., 1987-91; contbr. articles to profl. jours.; patentee power switching. Mem. adv. com. energy conservation Wis. Dept. Labor, Industry and Human Rels., Madison, 1977-79; mem. Wis. chpt. Sierra Club, 1977; pres. bd. dirs. Madison Urban Ministries, 1993—. 2d lt. Signal Corps., U.S. Army, 1958. Recipient Disting. Alumnus award U. Toledo, 1983, award of excellence U. Wis.-Extension, 1987; Sci. Faculty fellow NSF, 1966. Fellow IEEE (Meritorious Achievement in Continuing Edn. award 1991); mem. Internat. Conf. on Large High Voltage Electric Systems (expert advisor 1979—). Mem. United Ch. of Christ. Avocation: canoeing. Home: 1444 E Skyline Dr Madison WI 53705-1133 Office: U Wis 432 N Lake St Madison WI 53706-1498

LONGAKER, NANCY, elementary school principal. Prin. Tualatin (Oreg.) Elem. Sch. Recipient Elem. Sch. Recognition award U.S. Dept. Edn., 1989-90. Office: Tualatin Elem Sch 19945 SW Boones Ferry Rd Tualatin OR 97062

LONGAKER, RICHARD PANCOAST, political science educator emeritus; b. Phila., July 1, 1924; s. Edwin P. and Emily (Downs) L.; m. Mollie M. Katz, Jan. 25, 1964; children—Richard Pancoast II, Stephen Edwin, Sarah Ellen, Rachel Elise. B.A. in Polit. Sci., Swarthmore Coll., 1949; M.A. in Am. History, U. Wis., 1950; Ph.D. in Govt, Cornell U., 1953. Teaching asst. Cornell U., 1950-53, vis. asso. prof., 1960-61; asst. prof. Kenyon Coll., 1953-

54, asso. prof., 1955-60; asst. prof. U. Calif., Riverside, 1954-55; faculty U. Calif., Los Angeles, 1961-76, chmn. dept. polit. sci., 1963-67, prof., 1965-76, dean acad. affairs grad. div., 1970-71; prof. Johns Hopkins U., Balt., 1976-87, provost and v.p. for acad. affairs, 1976-87; prof. emeritus, cons. western states office Johns Hopkins U., Santa Monica, Calif., 1987—. Author: The Presidency and Individual Liberties, 1961; co-author: The Supreme Court and the Commander in Chief, 1976, also articles, revs. Served with AUS, 1943-45. Mem. Am. Polit. Sci. Assn. Office: 16550 Chalet Ter Pacific Palisades CA 90272-2344

LONGAN, GEORGE BAKER, III, real estate executive; b. Kansas City, Mo., Apr. 20, 1934; s. Benjamin Hyde and Georgette Longan O'Brien; divorced; 1 child, Nancy Ann Longan LaPoff. BSBA, U. Ariz., 1956; postgrad., U. Kans., 1956-57. Cert. real estate broker. Sr. v.p., gen. mgr. Paul Hamilton Co., Kansas City, 1963-84; pres. Eugene D. Brown Co., Kansas City, 1984-93; v.p. J.C. Nichols Real Estate, 1993-94; bd. dirs. Genesis Relocation Network, N.J. Served to staff sgt. USAF, 1958-62. Mem. Nat. Real Estate Assn. (bd. dirs. 1991-94), Mo. Real Estate Assn. (bd. dirs. 1987-90), Real Estate Bd. Kansas City (bd. dirs. 1987-90), Met. Kansas City Real Estate Bd. (pres. 1992), Beta Sigma Psi, Sigma Chi. Episcopal. Avocations: antique collecting, tennis. Home: 2701 E Camino Pablo Tucson AZ 85718-6625 Office: Roy H Long Realty Co 6424 E Tanque Verde Tucson AZ 85715

LONGANECKER, DAVID A., federal official. BA in Sociology, Wash. State U., 1968; MA in Student Personnel Work, George Washington U., 1971; EdD in Adminstrn. and Policy Analysis in Higher Edn., Stanford U., 1978. With student affairs and residence life dept. George Washington U., Washington; with Congl. Budget Office, Washington, 1977-81; with Minn. Higher Edn. Coordinating Bd., 1981-84, exec. dir., 1984-88; exec. dir., exec. dir. dept. higher edn., officer Gov. Roy Romer's cabinet Colo. Commn. Higher Edn., 1988-93; asst. sec. postsecondary edn. U.S. Dept. Edn., Washington, 1993—; past. pres. State Higher Edn. Exec. Officers orgn.; commr. We. Interstate Commn. Higher Edn.; mem. postsecondary edn. and tng. for workplace com. Nat. Acad. Scis., commn. on ednl. credit and credentials Am. Coun. Edn.; mem. various bds. and coms. including Exec. Com. Minority Edn. Coalition Colo., Gov.'s Commn. Families and Children, Math., Sci. and Tech. Commn. Office: Dept of Education Post Secondary Education Office 7th and D Sts SW Washington DC 20202-9175

LONGANECKER, EDWIN SNYDER, JR., special education services educator; b. Gettysburg, Pa., Sept. 13, 1944; s. Edwin Snyder and Mary E. (Jacobs) L.; m. Mary E., Apr. 24, 1971; children: Lance Poock, Lori Poock, Edwin III. BA, Parson Coll., 1968; MA in Sch. Adminstrn., N.E. Mo. State U., 1973, MA in Spl. Edn., 1977. Tchr. of English Pekin Community Schs., Packwood, Iowa, 1968-70; head English dept. Hedrick Community Schs., Hedrick, Iowa, 1970-71; tchr. lang. arts Mt. Pleasant (Iowa) Community Schs., 1971-74; prin. Great River Area Edn. Agy. # 16, Burlington, Iowa, 1974-79, spl. edn. cons., 1979-88, supr. instructional svcs., 1988—. Co-author: (manual) How to Conduct an Effective Child Find, 1990, Model Policy and Procedure for Students with Behavior Disorders, 1989; author: Parent Guide to Attention Deficit Disorder, 1985, Monitoring of Medicine Intervention for School Related Behavior Problems, 1983, The Use of Medication Intervention for Class Behavior Problems, 1986; contbg. author: Training for Parents, Volunteers and Paraprofessionals Who Work With Young Children, 1992. Recipient numerous grants. Mem. Coun. Exceptional Children, Optimist (bd. dirs.), Phi Delta Kappa (pres. 1985-87, 1994-95). Republican. Lutheran. Avocations: antiques, skiing, boating, golf. Home: RR 4 Box 241 Mount Pleasant IA 52641-9387 Office: Great River Area 16 PO Box 1065 1200 University Pl Burlington IA 52601-5462

LONGBRAKE, WILLIAM ARTHUR, bank executive; b. Hershey, Pa., Mar. 15, 1943; s. William Van Fleet and Margaret Jane (Barr) L.; m. Martha Ann Curtis, Aug. 23, 1970; children: Derek Curtis, Mark William, David Robert, Dorothy Eleanor Lois. BA, Coll. of Wooster, 1965; MA, U. Wis., 1968, MBA, 1969; D. Bus. Adminstrn., U. Md., 1976. Jr. asst. planner Northeastern Ill. Planning Commn., Chgo., 1966; instr. Coll. Bus. and Mgmt., U. Md., 1969-71, lectr., 1976, 79-81; fin. economist FDIC, Washington, 1971-75, sr. planning specialist Office Corp. Planning, 1975-76, spl. asst. to chmn., acting compt., 1977-78; assoc. dir. div. banking rsch. Compt. of Currency, Treasury Dept., Washington, 1976, dep. dir. econ. rsch. and analysis div., 1976-77; dep. compt. for rsch. and econ. programs, 1978-81, acting sr. dep. compt. for policy, 1981-82, sr. dep. compt. for resource mgmt., 1982; exec. v.p., chief fin. officer Wash. Mut. Savs. Bank, Seattle, 1982-85; exec. v.p. finance and ops., 1985-86, sr. exec. v.p., 1986-88, sr. exec. v.p., chief fin. officer, 1988—, dir. Abarim Bus. Computers Inc., 1993—; WM Trust Co., 1989-93, WM Life Co., 1994—; trustee Washington Mutual Savings Bank Found., 1982—; small bus. cons. Mem. College Park (Md.) Citizen's Adv. Com. on Code Enforcement, 1973-74, cons., 1975; lectr. Albers Sch. Bus. Seattle U., 1985, student mentor, 1994—; bd. dirs. Puget Sound Coun. Fin. Insts., Seattle, Dir. 1986-90, v.p., 1988, pres., 1989-90; mem. Seattle Mcpl. League, 1986—; treas., 1988-90, pres. 1990-93, mem. exec. com., 1988—, devel. com., 1992—, bus. planning com., 1992-93, strategic planning com., 1993—; Capitol Hill Housing Improvement Program, Seattle, 1988—, exec. com., 1989—, chmn. outreach and tech. assistance com., 1990-92; bd. visitors Sch. Nursing U. Washington, 1991—; mem. adv. com. Ctr. for the Study of Banking and Fin. Markets U. Wash., Seattle, 1983-92, chmn., 1986-90; mem. of local initiative support corp. Seattle/Tacoma Adv. Bd., 1989-91; bd. dirs. Diabetes Rsch. Coun., Seattle, 1984-89, v.p., 1987-88; bd. dirs. N.W. Symphony Orch., Seattle, 1987-89, treas. 1988-89, adv. bd. 1989—; trustee Kenney Presbyn. Home, West Seattle, 1987—, treas., 1988—, exec. com., chmn. fin. com.; trustee Intiman Theatre Co., Seattle, 1988-92; chmn. tax com. Wash. Savs. League, 1987—, legis. regulatory com. 1991—; mem. Seattle Comprehensive Plan Implementation Task Force, 1993-94; chmn. adv. bd. Wash. State Affordable Housing, 1993—; dir. Nat. Assn. Housing Partnerships, 1993—; mem. King County Growth Mgmt., planning coun. affordable housing task force, 1992-93; co-chair Gov.'s Task Force on Affordable Housing, Washington, 1992-93, chmn. bd. dirs. Threshold Housing, 1992—; mem. Impact Fees commn., 1991-92, Coun. Washington's Future, arrangement's chair, 1988-91; devel. bd. Musicomedy Northwestm 1983-84, trustee 1984; mem. U.S. Soccer Fedn., referee Seattle Youth Soccer Assn., 1982—; dir., sec. Presbyn. Pub. Corp., 1993—. Recipient Kenneth E. Trefftz prize Western Fin. Assn. 1971, cert. of recognition William A. Jump Meml. Found., 1978. Mem. Am. Econs. Assn., Am. Fin. Assn., Fin. Mgmt. Assn. (dir. 1978-80), Fin. Execs. Inst. (Puget Sound chpt., bd. dirs. 1988—, chmn. acad. rels. com. 1988-93, chmn. tech. com. 1989-90, treas. 1990-91, v.p. 1991-93, pres. 1993-94, chmn. nominating com. 1994—), Coll. of Wooster Alumni Assn. (pres. Washington Alumni Assn. 1976, pres. Seattle Alumni Assn. 1983—, trustee 1988—, mem. fin., audit, religious dimension, student rels. com. alumni bd. 1988—), Columbia Tower Club. Presbyn. (trustee 1973-75, chmn. 1975, elder, 1979-82, clk. 1980-82, deacon 1985-88, treas. 1993—). Assoc. editor Fin. Mgmt., 1974-78; mem. editorial adv. bd. Issues in Bank Regulation, 1977-84, Jour. Econs. and Bus., 1980-83; contbr. articles to profl. jours. Mem. Nat. Coun. Savings Instns., (mortgage fin. com. 1989). Avocations: jogging, painting, si39 18th Ave E Seattle WA 98112-3929 Office: Wash Mut Savs Bank PO Box 834 1201 3rd Ave Seattle WA 98101

LONGCHAMPT, MICHEL, steel executive; b. Toulon, France, 1934. Grad., Ecole Superieure des Scis. Econ. and Comml., 1958. Far East rep. Pont A Mousson, France, 1964-73, comml. mgr. steel pipe divsn., 1974-76; with Francosteel Corp., N.Y.C., 1976—, now pres. Office: Francosteel Corp 345 Hudson St New York NY 10014-4502

LONGENECKER, HERBERT EUGENE, biochemist, former university president; b. Lititz, Pa., May 6, 1912; s. Abraham S. and Mary Ellen (Herr) L.; m. Marjorie Jane Segar, June 18, 1936; children: Herbert Eugene, Marjorie Segar Longenecker White, Geoffrey Herr, Stanton Lee. B.S., Pa. State U., 1933, M.S., 1934, Ph.D., 1936; D.Sc., Duquesne U., 1951; LL.D., Loyola U., 1962; Litt.D., U. Miami, 1972; D.Sc., U. Ill., 1976, Loyola U. of South, 1976. Instr. biochemistry Pa. State U., 1935-36; NRC fellow univs. Liverpool (Eng.), Cologne (Germany), Queen's, Kingston, Can., 1936-38; sr. research fellow and lectr. in chemistry U. Pitts., 1938-41, asst. research prof. chemistry, 1941-42; prof. chemistry and dir. Buhl Found. Research Project,

1942-44; dean research in natural scis. U. Pitts., 1944-55; dean U. Pitts. (Grad. Sch.), 1946-55; v.p. U. Ill. Med. Center, 1955-60; pres. Tulane U., 1960-75, pres. emeritus, 1975—; mng. dir. World Trade Ctr., New Orleans, 1976-79; dir. Equitable Life Ins. Soc. U.S., 1968-84, cons. dir., 1984-92; dir. CPC Internat., 1966-85; mem. food and nutrition bd. NRC, 1943-53, chmn. com. on food protection, 1948-53; mem. com. on chem. warfare R & D Bd., 1949-53; mem. rsch. coun. Chem. Corps. Adv. Bd., 1949-65; pres. Nat. Commn. on Accrediting, 1964-66; mem. coun. Nat. Inst. Gen. Med. Scis., 1963-66; mem. site selection panel for high energy accelerators NAS, 1964-66; mem. nat. selection com. Fulbright Student awards, 1953-55; chmn. West Europe sect. Fulbright Student Awards, 1954-55; mem. coun. Nat. Inst. Environ. Health Scis., 1970-71; mem. panel on sci. and tech. Ho. of Reps. Com. on Sci. and Astronautics, 1970-76; mem. adv. panel on ROTC affairs Office Sec. Def., 1961-75, chmn. 1968-75; mem. Commn. on Pvt. Philanthropy and Pub. Needs, 1973-77. Pres. Pitts. Housing Assn., 1948-51; bd. govs. Inst. Medicine Chgo., 1957-60; trustee Council of So. Univs., 1960-75, pres., 1964-65; pres. Univs. Research Assn., 1971-72; trustee Inst. Def. Analyses, 1959-88, vice chmn., 1984-88; chmn. acad. adv. bd. U.S. Naval Acad., 1966-72; trustee Nat. Med. Fellowships, Inc., 1965-72; bd. dirs. Council Fin. Aid to Edn., 1964-71; trustee Inst. Service to Edn., Inc., 1965-71; trustee Am. Univs. Field Staff, 1960-74, pres., 1962-63; sec.-treas. Assn. Am. Univs., 1969-72, pres., 1972-73; trustee S.W. Research Inst., 1960-69; bd. dirs. World Trade Ctr., New Orleans, 1961—, Nat. Merit Scholarship Corp., 1969-75; trustee Sloan Found., 1970-84, Inst. for Future, 1975-76, La. Expo, Inc., 1976-82, United Student Aid Funds, 1971-85, Pacific Tropical Bot. Garden, 1974-77, Council of the Ams., 1976-79; trustee Nutrition Found., 1961-85, chmn., 1965-72; mem. bd. Indian Springs Sch., 1987-88. Recipient Army and Navy Cert. for service during World War II, USN Disting. Pub. Service award; Disting. Alumni award Pa. State U., 1960; Papal award Bene Merenti, 1977. Fellow Am. Public Health Assn., Am. Inst. Nutrition, Am. Inst. Chemists; mem. Am. Chem. Soc. (chmn. Pitts. sect. 1946-47), Am. Soc. Biol. Chemists, Am. Council Edn. (chmn. commn. on fed. relations 1963-65, coordinating com. 1972-74), Am. Oil Chemists Soc. (v.p. 1946-47), Nat. League Nursing, Sigma Xi (exec. com. 1965-70, pres. 1980-81), Phi Delta Kappa, Sigma Pi. Club: Boston (New Orleans). Home: 2717 Highland Ave S Apt 1002 Birmingham AL 35205-1730

LONGENECKER, JOHN BENDER, biochemist, nutritionist, educator; b. Salunga, Pa., July 8, 1930; married, 1954; 2 children. BS, Franklin & Marshall Coll., 1952; MS, U. Tex., 1954, PhD in Biochemistry, 1956. Rsch. biochemist EI du Pont de Nemours & Co., Inc., Del., 1956-61; group leader Mead Johnson & Co., Ind., 1961-64; prof. nutrition, head divsn. U. Tex., Austin, 1964—. Grantee USPHS, 1964-71, Allied Health Fellow grantee, 1969-74. Mem. Am. Chem. Soc., Am. Inst. Nutrition, N.Y. Acad. Sci. Achievements include research on interrelationships among nutrients; in vivo plasma amino acid studies to evaluate protein and amino acid nutrition; nutritional status studies. Address: 2305 Preston Trails Cir Austin TX 78747*

LONGENECKER, MARK HERSHEY, JR., lawyer; b. Akron, Ohio, Feb. 16, 1951; s. Mark Hershey and Katrina (Hetzner) L.; m. Ruth Rounding, June 17, 1978; children: Emily Irene, Mark Hershey III. BA, Denison U., 1973; JD, Harvard U., 1976. Bar: Ill. 1976, Ohio 1979. Atty. Lord, Bissell & Brook, Chgo., 1976-79; ptnr. Frost & Jacobs, Cin., 1979—. Bd. govs. Ohio Fair Plan Underwriting Assn., Columbus, 1989-92; dir. Seven Hills Neighborhood Houses, Cin., 1990—. Mem. Cin. Country Club, Queen City Club, Gyro Club, Harvard Club (Cin. pres. 1993-94). Office: Frost & Jacobs 2500 PNC Ct 201 E 5th St Cincinnati OH 45202-4117

LONGEST, BEAUFORT BROWN, health services administration educator, research director; b. Rose Hill, N.C., Oct. 22, 1942; s. Beaufort Brown and Mary (Faircloth) L.; m. Carolyn Hepler, Jan 23, 1965; children: Brant, Courtland. BS, Davidson Coll., 1965; MHA, Ga. State U., 1969, PhD in Bus. Adminstrn., 1972. Instr. health adminstrn. Coll. Bus. Adminstrn., Ga. State U., 1969-72, asst. prof. health adminstrn., 1972-75; clin. asst. prof. preventive medicine and community health Sch. Medicine, Emory U., 1974-75; asst. prof. hosp. and health svcs. mgmt. J.L. Kellogg Grad. Sch. Mgmt., Northwestern U., 1975-78, faculty assoc. Ctr. Health Svcs. and Policy Rsch., 1978-79, assoc. prof. hosp. and health svcs. mgmt., 1979; prof. health svcs. adminstrn. Grad. Sch. Pub. Health and Joseph M. Katz Grad. Sch. Bus., U. Pitts., 1980—; prof. bus. adminstrn., 1987—; dir. Health Policy Inst., 1980—; dir. Health Adminstrn. Program, 1984-91, faculty assoc. Ctr. Med. Ethics, 1987—; lectr. in field, 1976—; condr. seminars including Am. Assn. Clin. Chemists, Am. Soc. Woman Accts., Am. Soc. Med. Tech., Ga. Hosp. Assn., Hosp. Assn. Pa., Gov.'s Policy Group, Pa., Ohio Hosp. Assn., Ontario Hosp. Assn., VA., many others; mem. cons. U. Pitts.; dir. Midland-Colt Retiree Med. Plan, Media Info. Svc. Adv. Bd., Biomed. Tech. Devel. Corp. Adv. Bd.; cons. Am. Soc. Med. Tech., 1972-74, Fetter Family Health Ctr., Charleston, S.C., 1974-75, Hosp. Fin. Mgmt. Assn., 1974-75, Am. Acad. Pediatrics, 1977, DuPage County Health Systems Agy., 1978, Health Care Fin. Adminstrn., 1989, U.S. Agy. Internat. Devel., Kingston, Jamaica, Gov.'s Policy Group, Pa., 1989, Sec. Health, Pa., 1990-91, Mfrs. Assn. Northwest Pa., 1992, Pan Am. Health Orgn., 1992. Author: Principles of Hospital Business Office Management, 1975, Management Practices for the Health Professional, 1976, 4th edit., 1990, (with others) Hospital Cost Containment Programs, A Policy Analysis, 1978, (with J.S. Rakich and T.R. O'Donovan) Managing Health Care Organizations, 1977, (with J.S. Rakich and K. Darr) Cases in Health Services Management, 1983, 3d edit., 1992, Managing Health Services Organizations, 2d edit., 1985; contbr. numerous articles, book chpts. papers to anthologies, profl. jours.; author rsch. monograph; book reviewer in field; editorial cons. Harper and Row, Inc., Health Professions Press, Little, Brown Pub. Co., Nat. Health Pub., Reston Pub. Co., Inc., W.B. Saunders Co. Dir. The Grove Sch., 1978-80; Hosp. Utilization Project, 1985-87; mem. adv. bd. work-study program minority students Chgo. Hosp. Coun., 1978-79, rsch. adv. com. Hosp. Utilization Project, 1982-83, steering com. Pitts. Program Affordable Health Care, 1984-88, com. health policy and planning Hosp. Coun. Western Pa., 1986—, health care and human svcs. Task Force, Leadership Pitts., 1985, 87, community problem solving com. United Way Allegheny County, 1986-89, chmn. community problem solving com. on frail elderly and disabled, 1989-92, mem. resource panel health and human svcs. Allegheny County 2001 Project, 1992, steering com. HSR&D devel. grant VA Med. Ctr., 1992-93; external examiner U. West Indies, Kingston, Jamaica, 1985-89. W.K. Kellogg Found. fellow, 1977-78. Fellow Am. Coll. Healthcare Execs. (ad hoc com. univ. program faculty 1982, regent's advisor 1985-89, com. book of yr. 1985-88, chmn. com. book of yr. 1988, com. awards and testimonials 1988, membership com. subcom. recruitement 1991-92, chmn. membership com. subcom. recruitement 1991-92); mem. Acad. Mgmt. (1st place rsch proposal award 1976), Am. Hosp. Assn., Am. Pub. Health Assn., Assn. Health Svcs. Rsch., Assn. Pub. Policy Analysis and Mgmt., Assn. Univ. Programs Health Adminstrn. (nom. com. bd. dirs. 1987, 88, adv. panel clin. edn. health adminstrn. 1986), Beta Gamma Sigma. Avocation: gardening. Office: U Pitts Health Pol Inst Grad Sch Pub Health 130 Desoto St Pittsburgh PA 15213-2535

LONGFELLOW, LAYNE ALLEN, psychologist, educator; b. Jackson, Ohio, Oct. 23, 1937; s. Hershel Herman and Opal Edna (Pursley) L. BA in Psychology magna cum laude with honors, Ohio U., 1959; MA, U. Mich. 1961, PhD, 1967. Asst. prof. psychology Reed Coll., Portland, Oreg., 1967-68; postdoctoral fellow Ctr. for Studies of the Person, La Jolla, Calif., 1968-70; asst. prof. psychology Prescott (Ariz.) Coll., 1970-71, chmn. dept., 1971-72, acad. v.p., 1972-74; dir. seminars Menninger Found., Topeka, 1975-78; dir. wilderness exec. seminars Banff Ctr., Alta., Can., 1978-86; pres. Lecture Theatre, Inc., Prescott, Ariz., 1981—; internat. lectr., cons. 1978—; adj. faculty Union Grad. Sch. and Humanistic Psychology Inst., 1974-84. Composer: Ten Songs, 1969, Uncommon Festival of Christmas, 1974; creator Body Talk, 1970, The Feel Wheel, 1972; video prodr., author: The Mountain Waits, 1983 (Gold medal N.Y. Festival of TV), Generations of Excellence, 1992, Beyond Success, 1993, Earth is Alive, 1993, Healthy, Wealthy and Wise, 1994, (with W M Hubbard) Visual Feast, 1995. Active ACLU. Woodrow Wilson fellow, NSF fellow, NIMH fellow. Mem. APA, Nat. Speakers Assn., Nature Conservancy, Phi Beta Kappa. Home: PO Box 809 Yellow Springs OH 45387 Office: Lecture Theatre Inc PO Box 4317 Prescott AZ 86302-4317

LONGFIELD, WILLIAM HERMAN, health care company executive; b. Chgo., Aug. 8, 1938; s. William A. and Elizabeth (Beringer) L.; m. Nancy

Shofstall, June 10, 1961; children: William, Scott. BS, Drake U., 1960; grad. bus. mgmt. program, Northwestern U., 1972. Pres. Convertors div. Am. Hosp. Supply, Evanston, Ill., 1961-82; exec. v.p., dir. Lifemark, Inc., Houston, 1982-83; pres., chief exec. officer Cambridge Group, Inc., Dallas, 1983-89; pres., CEO C.R. Bard, Inc., Murray Hill, N.J., 1989—, also bd. dirs.; bd. dirs. United Dental Care, Dallas, Overlook Mgmt. Corp., Manor Care Inc., Balt., Centenary Coll., Health Industry Mfrs. Assn.; exec. resident U. Colo., 1980, 81, 82; chmn. bd. Internat. Non-Wovens Assn., N.Y.C., 1975-82. Chmn., dir. Deerfield (Ill.) Youth Orgn., 1975-80; trustee Sch. Medicine and Dentistry U. N.J. Recipient Pres.' award Nat. Nurse Cons. Assn., 1980. Mem. Baltrusol Golf Club, Echo Lake Country Club. Republican. Presbyterian. Avocations: golf, tennis. Office: C R Bard Inc 730 Central Ave New Providence NJ 07974

LONGHOFER, RONALD STEPHEN, lawyer; b. Junction City, Kans., Aug. 30, 1946; s. Oscar William and Anna Mathilda (Krause) L.; children: Adam, Nathan, Stefanie. BMus, U. Mich., 1968; JD, 1975. Bar: Mich. 1975, U.S. Dist. Ct. (ea. dist.) Mich., U.S. Ct. Appeals (6th cir.), U.S. Supreme Ct. Law clk. to judge U.S. Dist. Ct. (ea. dist.) Mich., Detroit, 1975-76; ptnr. Honigman, Miller, Schwartz & Cohn, Detroit, 1976—, chmn. litigation dept., 1991—. Editor Mich. Law Rev., 1974-75. Served with U.S. Army, 1968-72. Mem. ABA, Detroit Bar Assn., Fed. Bar Assn., Detroit Club, Detroit Econ. Club, U. Mich. Pres. Club, Order of Coif, Phi Beta Kappa, Pi Kappa Phi, Pi Kappa Lambda. Home: 18062 Blue Heron Dr W Northville MI 48167-9234 Office: Honigman Miller Schwartz & Cohn 2290 1st National Bldg Detroit MI 48226

LONGIN, THOMAS CHARLES, academic administrator; b. Lewistown, Mont., Nov. 17, 1939; s. Charles Otto and Anne Dorothy (Vavrovsky) L.; m. Nancy Tillinghast; children: Kevin C., Teresa L., Karl T., Anne M. BA in History, Carroll Coll., 1962; MA in History, Creighton U., 1965; PhD in Am. History, U. Nebr., 1970. Instr. Carroll Coll., Helena, Mont., 1965-67; asst. prof. Va. Tech., Blacksburg, 1970-73; asst. prof., then assoc. prof. Ithaca (N.Y.) Coll., 1973-82, dean humanities and scis., 1976-82, provost, 1985—; v.p. acad. affairs Seattle U., 1982-85. Office: Ithaca Coll Coll of the Provost 350 Job Hall Ithaca NY 14850-7012

LONGLEY, BERNIQUE, artist, painter, sculptor; b. Moline, Ill., Sept. 27, 1923; d. Eli James and Effie Marie (Coen) Wilderson; 1 child, Bernique Maria Glidden. Grad., Art Inst. Chgo., 1945. One-woman shows at Mus. N.Mex., 1947, 50, 52, Appleman Gallery, Denver, 1950, VanDieman-Lillienfield Galleries, N.Y.C., 1953, Knopp-Hunter Gallery, Santa Fe, 1954, 57, 58, Gallery Five, Santa Fe, 1964, 65, Coll. Santa Fe, 1967, Sanger-Harris, Dallas, 1968, Lars Laine Gallery, Palm Springs, Calif., 1969, Canyon Rd. Gallery, Santa Fe, 1972, Summer Gallery, Santa Fe, 1973, 74, 75, 76, Cushing Galleries, Dallas, 1977, Gov.'s Gallery, N.Mex. State Capitol, 1978, Santa Fe East, Austin, Tex., 1979, Santa Re East Gallery, 1985, 86, 88, Leslie Levy Gallery, 1985-86, Artists of Am. exhbn., Denver, 1993-94; group shows include Denver Art Mus., 1948, N.Mex. Highlands U., 1957, Lars Laine Gallery, 1961, 63, Santa Fe Festival of Arts, 1977, 78, 79, 80, Leslie Levy Gallery, Scottsdale, Ariz., 1985-86, Santa Fe East, 1985-86, 88, Invitational Mask Exhbn., Bank of Santa Fe, 1987, Hickory (N.C.) Mus., 1989, Contemporary S.W. Gallery, Santa Fe, 1989-90, many others; retrospective exhbn. Santa Fe East Gallery, 1982; represented in permanent collection Mus. N.Mex., Fine Arts Ctr., Colorado Springs, Colo., Coll. Santa Fe; collection of Oprah Winfrey, 1987, other pvt. collections; subject of book Bernique Longley-A Retrospective, 1982. Bryan Lathrop Fgn. Travelling fellow, 1945. Mem. Art Inst. Chgo. Alumni Assn., Artists Equity Assn. Home and Home and Studio: 427 Camino Del Monte Sol Santa Fe NM 87501-2825

LONGLEY, GLENN, biology educator, research director; b. Del Rio, Tex., June 2, 1942; s. Glenn L. and Cleo M. (Tipton) L.; m. Francis Van Winkle, Aug. 5, 1961; children: Kelly Francis, Kristy Lee, Katherine Camille, Glenn C. BS in Biology, S.W. Tex. State U., 1964; MS in Zoology and Entomology, U. Utah, 1966, PhD in Environ. Biology, 1969. Prof. aquatic biology, dir. Edwards Aquifer Rsch. Ctr. S.W. Tex. State U., San Marcos, 1979—. Contbr. 138 papers to profl. jours. or meetings. Recipient more than 50 grants or contracts for water related studies; named Eminent Hydrologist, Am. Inst. Hydrology and Am. Water Resource Assn., 1993. Fellow Tex. Acad. Sci. (past. pres.); mem. Am. Water Resource Assn., Tex. Orgn. for Endangered Species (past pres.), Tex. Water Conservation Assn., Tex. Water Pollution Control Assn. (past pres.), Assn. Groundwater Scientists and Engrs., Water Environment Fedn., Sigma Xi (life), Phi Sigma (former chpt. pres.). Achievements include research on redescription and assignment to the new Lirceolus of the Texas troglobitic water slater, Asellus smithii, the larva of a new subterranean water beetle, Haideoporus texanus, watchlist of endangered, threatened and peripheral vertebrates of Texas, the generic status and distribution of Monodella texana Maguire, the only known North American Thermosbaeneacean, the Edwards Aquifer, Hadocerus taylori, a new genus and species of phreatic Hydrobiidae from South-Central Texas, Phreatoceras, a new name for Hadoceras Hershler and Longley, Phreatodrobia coronae, a new species of cavesnail from southwestern Texas, reproductive patterns of the subterranean shrimp Palaemonetes antrorum Benedict from Cental Texas, population size, distribution, and life history of Eurycea nana in the San Marcos River. Home: 814 Palomino Ln San Marcos TX 78666 Office: SW Tex State U Edwards Aquifer Rsch Ctr San Marcos TX 78666

LONGLEY, MARJORIE WATTERS, newspaper executive; b. Lockport, N.Y., Nov. 2, 1925; d. J. Randolph and Florence Lucille (Craine) Watters; m. Ralph R. Longley, Oct. 1, 1949 (dec.). B.A. in English with highest honors cum laude, St. Lawrence U., 1947. Sports editor, feature writer Lockport Union Sun and Jour., 1945; with N.Y. Times, N.Y.C., 1948-88, asst. to v.p. consumer mktg., 1975-78, circulation sales mgr., 1978-79, sales dir., 1979-81, dir. pub. affairs, 1981-88; pres. Gramercy Internat., Inc. (mktg. and pub. rels.), N.Y.C., 1988—; dir. pub. affairs and pub. info., N.Y.C. Off-Track Betting Corp., 1990-94; mem. Nat. Newspapers' Readership Coun., 1979-82; mem. adv. coun. API, 1980-85. Author: America's Taste, 1960. Trustee St. Lawrence U., 1969-75, 77—; mem. bd. dirs. Am. Forum for Global Edn., 1977—; pres. N.Y. State Adult Edn. Coun., 1974-77; mem. N.Y. State Adv. Coun. for Vocat. Edn., 1976-81, postsecondary edn., 1978-81, Mayor's Coun. Environment of N.Y.C., 1983—; bd. dirs. Nat. Charities Info. Bur.; chmn. 42d St. Edn., Theatre, Culture, 1984-88, chmn. emeritus, 1988—. Mem. Nat. Inst. Social Scis., Am. Mgmt. Assn. (nat. mktg. coun. 1972-89, bd. dirs. 1986-88), Nat. Arts Club, Overseas Press Club, Phi Beta Kappa. Democrat. Baptist. Office: Gramercy Internat Inc 34 Gramercy Park E New York NY 10003-1731

LONGMAN, ANNE STRICKLAND, educational consultant; b. Metuchen, N.J., Sept. 17, 1924; d. Charles Hodges and Grace Anna (Moss) Eldridge; m. Henry Richard Strickland, June 22, 1946 (dec. 1960); m. Donald Rufus Longman, Jan. 20, 1979 (dec. 1987); children: James C., Robert H. BA in Bus. Adminstrn., Mich. State U., 1945; teaching credentials, U. Calif., Berkeley, 1959; postgrad., Stanford U., 1959-60; MA in Learning Hand, Santa Clara U., 1974. Lic. educator. Exptl. test engr. Pratt & Whitney Aircraft, East Hartford, Conn., 1944-45; indsl. engr. Marchant Calculators, Emeryville, Calif., 1957-58; with pub. rels. Homesmith, Palo Alto, Calif., 1959-62; cons. Right to Read Program, Calif., 1978-79; monitor, reviewer State of Calif., Sacramento, 1976-79; tchr. diagnosis edn. Cabrillo Coll., Aptos, Calif., 1979-79; lectr. edn. U. Calif., Santa Cruz, 1970-79; cons. Santa Cruz Bd. Edn., 1970-79; reading researcher Gorilla Found., Woodside, Calif., 1982—; bd. mem. Western Inst. Alcoholic Studies, L.A., 1972-73; chmn. Evaluation Com., Tri-County, Calif., 1974; speaker Internat. Congress Learning Disabilities, Seattle, 1974; ednl. cons. rsch. on allergies, 1993—. Author: Word Patterns in English, 1974-92, Cramming 3D Kids, 1975—, 50 books for migrant students, 1970-79; contbr. articles on stress and alcoholism and TV crime prevention for police, 1960-79. Founder Literacy Ctr., Santa Cruz, 1968-092; leader Girl Scouts U.S.A., Santa Cruz, 1947-50; vol. Thursday's Child, Santa Cruz, 1976-79, Golden Gate Kindergarten, San Francisco, 1947-57. Recipient Fellowships Pratt & Whitney Aircraft, 1944, Stanford U., 1959. Mem. Internat. Reading Assn. (San Francisco 1975), Santa Clara Valley Watercolor Soc., Los Altos Art Club (v.p. 1992), Eichler Swim and Tennis Club. Republican. Episcopalian. Avocations: watercolor painting, travel, drama. Home and Office: 153 Del Mesa Carmel Carmel CA 93923

LONGMAN, GARY LEE, accountant; b. Kewanee, Ill., Apr. 25, 1948; s. Howard L. and Dorothy (Wenk) L.; m. Ruth Ann Biesboer; children: Gregory, Rebecca. AA, Joliet (Ill.) Jr. Coll., 1968; BS in Acctg., No. Ill. U., 1970. CPA, Ill. Staff acct. KPMG Peat Marwick, Chgo., 1970-72, sr. acct., 1972-74, mgr., 1974-80, ptnr., 1980-91, ptnr.-in-charge Chgo. office mfg. practice, 1991—, ptnr.-in-charge Chgo. audit dept., 1991-93, midwest ptnr.-in-charge info., comm. & entertainment, 1993—. Bus. adv. coun. Dept. Commerce, DePaul U., 1991—; bd. dirs. Jr. Achievement, Chgo. Mem. AICPAs, Ill. Soc. CPAs, LaGrange Country Club. Office: KPMG Peat Marwick 303 E Wacker Dr Chicago IL 60601-5212

LONGMAN, RICHARD WINSTON, mechanical engineering educator; b. Iowa City, Sept. 2, 1943; s. Lester Duncan and Florence Lydia (Brown) L. B.A. in Physics and Math., U. Calif.-Riverside, 1965; M.S. in Aerospace Engring., U. Calif., San Diego, 1967. M.A. in Math., 1969, P.h.D. in Aerospace Engring., 1969. Mem. tech. staff Bell Telephone Labs., Whippany, N.J., 1969-70; asst. prof. mech. engring. Columbia U., 1970-74, assoc. prof., 1974-79, prof., 1979—; mem. vis. faculty MIT, Nat. Cheng Kung U., Taiwan, U. Bonn, W. Ger., U. Newcastle, Australia, Technische Hochschule, Darmstadt, Federal Republic of Germany, Univ. Augsburg, Federal Republic of Germany, U. Heidelberg, Federal Republic of Germany; cons. in field. Mng. editor: Jour. of the Astron. Scis., 1976-83; contbr. numerous articles in field to profl. jours. Recipient Alan Berman Rsch. Pub. awards Naval Rsch. Lab., 1988, 91; NDEA fellow, 1966-69, NASA-ASEE fellow, 1973-74; Alexander von Humboldt fellow, 1977, 80; NRC sr. fellow NASA Langley Rsch. Ctr., 1990-91. Fellow AIAA, Am. Astron. Soc. (v.p. publications 1978-80, v.p. tech. 1980-82, 1st v.p. 1982-84, bd. dirs. 1985-88, Dirk Brouwer award), Brit. Interplanetary Soc.; mem. ASME (recipient Best Paper award 1982), Sigma Xi, Tau Beta Pi, Pi Mu Epsilon, Pi Tau Sigma. Office: Columbia Univ Dept Mech Engring New York NY 10027

LONGMIRE, WILLIAM POLK, JR., physician, surgeon; b. Sapulpa, Okla., Sept. 14, 1913; s. William Polk and Grace May (Weeks) L.; m. Jane Jarvis Cornelius, Oct. 28, 1939; children—William Polk III (dec.), Gill, Sarah Jane. A.B., U. Okla., 1934; M.D., Johns Hopkins, 1938; M.D. hon. degrees, U. Athens, Greece, 1972, Northwestern U., 1976, U. Lund, Sweden, 1976; M.D. (h.c.), U. Heidelberg, Germany, 1974. Diplomate Am. Bd. Surgery (chmn. 1961-62). Intern surgery Johns Hopkins Hosp., Balt., 1938-39, resident surgery, 1944, surgeon in charge plastic out-patient clinic, 1946-48, surgeon, 1947-48; Harvey Cushing fellow exptl. surgery Johns Hopkins, 1939-40, Halsted fellow surg. pathology, 1940, successively instr., asst. prof. assoc. prof. surgery, 1943-48; prof. surgery UCLA, 1948-81, prof. emeritus, 1981—, chmn. dept., 1948-76; cons. surgery Wadsworth VA Hosp., Los Angeles County Harbor Hosp., 1945-76, VA disting. physician, 1982-87; guest prof. spl. surgery Free U. Berlin, Fed. Republic Germany, 1952-54; vis. prof. surgery Mayo Grad. Sch. Medicine, 1968, Royal Coll. Physicians and Surgeons of Can., 1968; chmn. surgery study sect. NIH, USPHS, 1961-64; mem. Conf. Com. on Grad. Edn. in Surgery, 1959-66, chmn., 1964-66; mem. spl. med. adv. group to med. dir. VA, 1963-68, vice chmn., 1967-68; chmn. surgery tng. com. NIH, 1969-70; mem. pres.' cancer panel Nat. Cancer Inst., 1982-91; Wade vis. prof. Royal Coll. Surgeons Edinburgh, 1972; nat. civilian cons. surgery Air Surgeon USAF; surg. cons. Surgeon Gen. U.S. Army, 1961-88; commr. Joint Commn. on Accreditation of Hosps., 1975-80. Editor: Advances in Surgery, 1975-76; editorial bd.: Annals of Surgery, 1965—. Served as maj. USAF, 1952-54; spl. cons. Air Surgeon Gen.'s Office. Recipient hon. certificate for advancement cardiovascular surgery Free U. of Berlin, 1954, certificate for high profl. achievement USAF, 1954, Gold medal UCLA, 1980, prize Societe Internationale De Chirurgie, 1987; inducted into Okla. Hall of Fame, 1980. Fellow ACS (chmn. forum com. fundamental surg. problems 1961-62, regent 1962-71, chmn. bd. regents 1969-71, pres. 1971-73, Sheen award N.J. chpt. 1987); hon. fellow Assn. Surgeons Great Britain and Ireland, Royal Coll. Surgeons Ireland, Royal Coll. Surgeons Edinburgh, Royal Coll. Surgeons Eng., Italian Surg. Soc., Association Française de Chirurgie, Japan Surg. Soc.; mem. AMA (mem. council on med. edn. 1964-69), Soc. Scholars of Johns Hopkins U., Soc. Clin. Surgeons, Am. Surg. Assn. (pres. 1967-68), Pacific Coast Surg. Assn., Western Surg. Assn., So. Surg. Assn., Soc. U. Surgeons, Internat. Soc. Surgery, Internat. Fedn. Surg. Colls. (pres. 1984-87), Internat. Surgical Group, (pres. 1993), Am. Thoracic Surgery, Pan-Pacific Surg. Assn., Los Angeles Surg. Soc. (pres. 1956), Bay Dist. Surg. Soc., Soc. Surgery Alimentary Tract (pres. 1975-76), Calif. Med. Assn. (sec. surg. sect. 1950-51, chmn. sci. bd. 1966-67, Golden Apple award 1990), James IV Assn. Surgeons (pres. 1981), Soc. Surg. Chairmen (pres. 1970-72), Sociedad Argentina di Cirugia Digestiva (hon.), Italian Surg. Soc. (hon.), Phi Beta Kappa, Alpha Omega Alpha; corr. mem. Deutsche Gesellschaft fur Chirugie. Home: 10102 Empyrean Way Bldg 8 Unit 203 Los Angeles CA 90067 Office: U Calif Med Ctr Los Angeles CA 90024

LONGNAKER, JOHN LEONARD, retired insurance company executive, lawyer; b. Lamartine, Pa., July 17, 1926; s. Homer L. and Esther B. (Hanst) L.; m. Elma J. Mays, June 21, 1952; children: John C., Susan E. B.S., Clarion Coll., 1948; J.D., U. Mo., 1961. Bar: Kans. 1961, Pa. 1972, U.S. Dist. Ct. (ea. dist.) Pa. 1972, U.S. Supreme Ct., 1989. Claim adjuster Pa. Nat. Mut. Casualty Ins. Co., Worthington, Pa., 1950-53; claims mgr. Pa. Nat. Mut. Casualty Ins. Co. (Midwest Office), Kansas City, Mo., 1953-72; co. atty. Pa. Nat. Mut. Casualty Ins. Co., Harrisburg, Pa., 1972-78; sec., gen. counsel Pa. Nat. Mut. Casualty Ins. Co., 1978-83, pres., 1983-90, chmn., chief exec. officer, 1990-92, also dir.; ret. Pa. Nat. Life, 1992. Bd. dirs. Capital area United Way (ret.), Harrisburg Symphony Assn. (ret.). Wi th USN, 1946. Mem. ABA, Pa. Bar Assn., Dauphin County Bar Assn. Republican. Presbyterian. Clubs: Hershey Country.

LONGNECKER, DAVID E., anesthesiologist, educator; b. Kendallville, Ind., 1939. MD, Ind. U., 1964, MA in Anesthesiology, 1968. Diplomate Am. Bd. Anesthesiology. Intern Blodgett Meml. Hosp., Grand Rapids, Mich., 1964-65; resident in anesthesiology U. Ind., 1965-69; asst. prof. dept. anesthesiology U. Mo., 1970-73; assoc. prof. dept. anesthesiology U. Va., Charlottesville, 1974-78, prof., 1978-88; Robert D. Dripps prof., chmn. dept. anesthesia U. Pa., Phila., 1988—. Mem. ACS, Am. Soc. Anesthesiology, Inst. Medicine. Office: U Pa Medical Ctr Dept Anesthesia 3400 Spruce St Philadelphia PA 19104-4283

LONGO, GEORGE P., superintendent. Supt. Sheboygan (Wis.) Area Sch. Dist. Named state finalist Nat. Supt. of Yr. award, 1993. Office: Sheboygan Area Sch Dist 830 Virginia Ave Sheboygan WI 53081-4427

LONGO, LAWRENCE DANIEL, physiologist, gynecologist; b. Los Angeles, Oct. 11, 1926; s. Frank Albert and Florine Azelia (Hall) L.; m. Betty Jeanne Mundall, Sept. 9, 1948; children: April Celeste, Lawrence Anthony, Elizabeth Lynn, Camilla Giselle. BA, Pacific Union Coll., 1949; MD, Coll. Med. Evangelists, Loma Linda, Calif., 1954. Diplomate: Am. Bd. Ob-Gyn. Intern Los Angeles County Gen. Hosp., 1954-55, resident, 1955-58; asst. prof. ob-gyn UCLA, 1962-64; asst. prof. physiology and ob-gyn U. Pa., 1964-68; prof. physiology and ob-gyn Loma Linda U., 1968—; head ctr. for perinatal biology Loma Linda U. Sch. Medicine, 1974—; mem. perinatal biology com. Nat. Inst. Child Health, NIH, 1973-77; chmn. reprodn. scientist devel. program NIH; NATO post. Consiglio Nat. delle Richerche, Italian Govt. Editor: Respiratory Gas Exchange and Blood Flow in the Placenta, 1972, Fetal and Newborn Cardiovascular Physiology, 1978, Charles White and A Treatise on the Management of Pregnant and Lying-in Women, 1987; co-editor: Landmarks in Perinatology, 1975-76, Classics in Obstetrics Gynecology, 1993; editor classic pages in ob-gyn. Am. Jour. Ob-Gyn.; contbr. articles to profl. jours. Served with AUS, 1945-47. Recipient Frank A. and Florine A. Longo lectureship in faith, knowledge, and human values Pacific Union Coll., 1993. Fellow Royal Coll. Ob-Gyns., Am. Coll. Ob-Gyns.; mem. Am. Assn. History Medicine (coun.), Am. Osler Soc. (bd. govs., sec.-treas.), Am. Physiol. Soc., Assn. Profs. Ob-Gyn., Perinatal Rsch. Soc., Soc Gynecologic Investigation (past pres.), Neurosci. Soc., Royal Soc. Medicine. Adventist. Office: Loma Linda U Sch Medicine Ctr Perinatal Biology Loma Linda CA 92350

LONGOBARDI, JOSEPH J., federal judge; m. Maud L.; 2 children: Joseph J. Longobardi III, Cynthia Jean Hermann. BA, Washington Coll., 1952; LLB, Temple U., 1957. Deputy atty. gen. State Del., Wilmington, 1959-61, tax appeal bd., 1973-74; ptnr. Longobardi & Schwartz, Wilmington, 1964-72, Murdoch, Longobardi, Schwartz & Walsh, Wilmington 1972-74;

judge Superior Ct. State of Del., Wilmington, 1974-82; vice chancellor Ct. Chancery, State Del., Wilmington, 1982-84; federal judge U.S. Dist. Ct. Del., Wilmington, 1984—, chief judge, 1989—; assoc. editor Temple Law Rev. Recipient Paul C. Reardon award Nat. Ctr. for State Cts., 1981, S.S. Shull Meml. awrd for excellence in legal rsch. and writing. Office: US Dist Ct 844 N King St # 40 Wilmington DE 19801-3519

LONGOBARDO, ANNA KAZANJIAN, mechanical engineer; b. N.Y.C.; d. Aram Michael and Zarouhy (Yazejian) Kazanjian; m. Guy S. Longobardo, July 12, 1952; children: Guy A., Alicia Longobardo Langston. Student, Barnard Coll., 1947; BSME, Columbia U., 1949, MSME, 1952. Sr. systems engr. Am. Bosch Arma Corp., Garden City, N.Y., 1950-65; rsch. sect. head gyroscope Sperry Rand Corp., Gt. Neck, N.Y., 1965-68; rsch. sect. head systems mgmt., 1968-73; mgr. engring. personnel, utilization dir. hdqrs. Sperry Corp., Gt. Neck, 1973-77, mgr. systems mgmt. program planning, 1977-81, mgr. planning systems mgmt. group, 1981-82; dir. tech. svc. Systems Devel., Unisys Corp., Gt. Neck, 1982-89, dir. field engring., 1989-93, dir. strategic initiatives, 1993-95; bd. dirs. and chmn. exec. compensation com. Woodward-Clyde Group, Denver. Contbr. articles to profl. publs. Trustee Columbia U., N.Y.C., 1990—, chmn. engring. coun., 1987-91, exec. com., 1994—; mem. Bronxville Planning Bd., chmn. Bronxville Design Rev. Com. Recipient hon. citation Wilson Coll. Centennial, 1970, Alumni medal for conspicuous svc. Columbia U., 1980; named One of 100 N.Y. Women of Influence, New York Woman mag., 1986. Fellow Soc. Women Engrs. (founder and pioneer); mem. AIAA (sr.), Columbia U. Engring. Alumni Assn. (pres. 1977-81), Columbia U. Alumni Fedn. (pres. 1981-85), Bronxville Field Club.

LONGONE, DANIEL THOMAS, chemistry educator; b. Worcester, Mass., Sept. 16, 1932; s. Daniel Edward and Anne (Novick) L.; m. Janice B. Bluestein, June 13, 1954. B.S., Worcester Poly. Inst., 1954; Ph.D., Cornell U., 1958. Research fellow chemistry U. Ill., Urbana, 1958-59; mem. faculty dept. chemistry U. Mich., Ann Arbor, 1959—, assoc. prof., 1966-71, prof., 1971—; cons. Gen. Motors Research Co., 1965-77. Am. Chem. Soc.-Petroleum Research Fund internat. fellow, 1967-68; Fulbright scholar, 1970-71. Mem. Am. Chem. Soc., Sigma Xi, Tau Beta Pi, Phi Lambda Upsilon. Home: 1207 W Madison St Ann Arbor MI 48103-4729 Office: U Mich 3537 Chemistry Ann Arbor MI 48109

LONGSTAFF, RONALD E., federal judge; b. 1941. BA, Kans. State Coll., 1962; JD, U. Iowa, 1965. Law clk. to Hon. Roy L. Stephenson U.S. Dist. Ct. (so. dist.) Iowa, 1965-67, clk. of ct., 1968-76, U.S. magistrate judge, 1976-91; fed. judge U.S. Dist. Ct. (so. dist.) Iowa, Des Moines, 1991—; assoc. McWilliams, Gross and Kirtley, Des Moines, 1967-68; adj. prof. law Drake U., 1973-76. Mem. Iowa State Bar Assn. (chmn. spl. commn. to revise Iowa exemption law 1968-70, mem. adv. com. 8th cir. ct. appeals 1988—). Office: US Dist Ct 407 US Courthouse Des Moines IA 50309

LONGSTREET, HARRY STEPHEN, television producer, director, scriptwriter; b. Bklyn., Feb. 24, 1940; s. Stephen and Ethel Muriel (Godoff) L.; m. Diana Gail Bodlander, Nov. 25, 1962 (div. Jan. 1977); children: Stacy Robyn, Gregory Stephen; m. Renee Myrna Schmidt, Jan. 9, 1977. Student, U. So. Calif., 1962-64. Producer Voyagers, 1983, Trauma Center, 1983, Misfits of Science, 1986; supervising producer Hot Pursuit, 1984, Shadow Chasers, 1985; exec. producer TV show Fame, 1986-87, Rags to Riches, 1987—. Scriptwriter: (TV shows) Quincy, Father Murphy, Jack & Mike, Magnum PI, Designing Women, (TV films) The Gathering Part II, 1979, The Promise of Love, 1980, The Sky's No Limit, 1984; exec. producer, scriptwriter: Night Walk, 1989; dir.: Identity Crisis, 1984, The Big Contract, 1987, Alice Doesn't Work Here Anymore, 1987, The Jenifer Graham Story, 1989, Alien Nation, 1989-90; exec. prodr. With A Vengeance, 1992; writer, dir.: Sex, Love and Cold Hard Cash, 1993, A Vow to Kill, 1995. Served with USAR, 1960-67. Mem. Writers Guild Am. (Outstanding Script nominee 1984, 90, Genesis award 1989, Humanitas nominee 1990), Dirs. Guild Am., Acad. TV Arts and Scis.

LONGSTREET, STEPHEN (CHAUNCEY LONGSTREET), author, painter; b. N.Y.C., Apr. 18, 1907; m. Ethel Joan Godoff, Apr. 22, 1932; children: Joan, Harry. Student, Rutgers Coll., Harvard U.; grad., N.Y. Sch. Fine and Applied Art, 1929; student in Rome, Paris. Ind. artist, writer, 1930—; staff lectr. Los Angeles Art Assn., 1954, UCLA, 1955, 58-59, lectr. Los Angeles County Mus., 1958-59; staff mem. arts and humanities dept. UCLA, 1965—; prof. art, dir. dept. Viewpoints Inst. of Gen. Semantics, Los Angeles, 1965; prof. modern writing U. So. Calif., Los Angeles, 1975-80. Began as painter; contbr. to French, Am. and English mags.; also cartoonist; radio writer for NBC, CBS, and other networks, writer shows for Rudy Vallee, Deems Taylor, John Barrymore, Bob Hope, Ellery Queen; writer popular series detective stories for Lippincott and Morrow under pen name Paul Haggrad, film critic Saturday Rev., 1941; mem. editorial staff Time mag., 1942. Screenwriters mag., 1947-48; critic L.A. Daily News, Book Pages, 1948; assoc. producer Civil War series The Blue and Gray, NBC, 1959—; author: All or Nothing, 1983, Delilah's Fortune, 1984, Our Father's House, 1985; painting exhibited: L.A., 1946, 48, N.Y., 1946, London, 1947; one-man shows include Padlia Galleries, L.A., 1970, Memphis Mus., 1979, Erie Mus., 1981, Coll. of Libr. of Congress, 1980, Jazz Age Revisited, 1983, Smithsonian Nat. Portrait Gallery, 1983, Sr. Eye Gallery, Long Beach, Calif. 1990, Columbus (Ohio) Mus. Art, 1992, tour of Japan, 1994; retrospective show Longstreet the Mature Years, L.A., 1983, Jazz-The Chgo. Scene, Regenstein Libr. U. Chgo., 1989, Columbus (Ohio) Mus. Fine Arts; author: The Pedlocks, 1951, The Beach House, 1952, The World Revisited, 1953, A Century of Studebaker on Wheels, 1953, The Lion at Morning, 1954, The Boy in the Model-T, 1956, Real Jazz, 1956, The Promoters, 1957, The Bill Pearson Story, 1957, (in French), Complete Dictionary of Jazz, 1957, Man of Montmatre, 1958, The Burning Man, 1958, The Politician, 1959, The Crime, 1959, Geisha, 1960, Gettysburg, 1960, A Treasury of the World's Great Prints, 1961, Eagles Where I Walk, 1961, The Flesh Peddler, 1962, A Few Painted Feathers, 1963, War In Golden Weather, 1965, Pedlock & Sons, 1965, The Wilder Shore: San Francisco '49 to '06, 1968, A Salute to American Cooking, (with Ethel Longstreet), 1968, War Cries on Horseback, An Indian History, 1970, The Canvas Falcons, 1970, Chicago: 1860-1920; a history, 1973, The General, 1974, (with Ethel Longstreet) World Cookbook, 1973, Win or Lose, 1977, The Queen Bees, 1979, Storm Watch, 1979, Pembroke Colors, 1981, From Storyville to Harlem - 50 years of the Jazz Scene, 1987, Magic Trumpets--The Young Peoples Story of Jazz, 1989, (poems) Jazz Solos, 1990, My Three Nobel Prizes; Life with Faulkner, Hemingway and Sinclair Lewis, 1991; editor, illustrator: The Memoirs of W.W. Windstaff Lower Than Angels, 1993; writer screen plays including Uncle Harry, 1943, Rider on a Dead Horse, The Imposter, First Travelling Saleslady, Stallion Road, 1946, The Jolson Story, 1947, Helen Morgan Story, 1956, plays including High Button Shoes, 1947, Gauguin, 1948, All Star Cast, Los Angeles, A History, 1977, (TV series) Playhouse 90, TV writer for Readers Digest Theatre, 1955; contbr. dialogue for films Greatest Show on Earth, Duel In the Sun. Pres. Los Angeles Art Assn., 1973-90. Recipient Stafford medal London, 1946, Bowman prize, 1948, Photo-Play mag. Gold medal for The Jolson Story, 1948, Billboard-Donaldson Gold medal for High Button Shoes, 1948. Mem. Motion Picture Acad. Arts and Letters, Writers Guild Am. (bd. dirs. 1948), Phi Sigma (charter mem.). Clubs: Sketch, Daguerreotype Society, Winadu Players. *I seem to have stumbled into the most dangerous world history since the fall of Rome. This time little of civilization may survive. The vulgarization of the culture by TV and lack of an American greatness in the White House can bring Orwell's world into being. But mankind will most likely remain in some form in his polluted planet, recalling what was the past. Man will always remain an undomesticated animal; rather kill than think.*

LONGSTREET, VICTOR MENDELL, government official; b. Louisville, Jan. 1, 1907; s. Joseph Emens and Allan Bemus (McKinley) L.; m. Mary Margaret Landry, 1930 (dec.); 1 child, Katherine Allan; m. Dorothy Bennett, 1986. BS magna cum laude, Harvard U., 1930. Economist AT&T, 1930-31; sr. economist Fed. Res. Bd., 1931-43; assoc. chief div. econ. devel. Dept. State, 1945-48; program rev. officer ECA U.S. Spl. Mission to Netherlands, The Hague, 1948-49; dep. U.S. sr. rep. Fin. Comm., NATO, 1950-51; dep. dir. Office Trade and Fin., Econ. Coop. Adminstrn., Paris, 1951-52; v.p., mgr. Louisville br. Fed. Res. Bank, St. Louis, 1953-57; dir. mgmt. rsch. Schering Corp., 1957-62; asst. sec. Dept. Navy, 1962-65; assoc. dir. Internat. Mgmt. Group of Boston, 1966-69; chmn. The Boston Group, Inc., 1970-79; bd. dirs.

N.Am. Fund Mgmt. Corp. Author: Financial Control in Multi-National Companies, 1971. Served from capt. to lt. col. AC, U.S. Army, 1943-45. Mem. Harvard Club (N.Y.C.), Phi Beta Kappa. Address: 3912 Brownlee Rd Louisville KY 40207 Address: Westchester Apts 745B 4000 Cathedral Ave NW Washington DC 20016

LONGSTRETH, BEVIS, lawyer; b. N.Y.C., Jan. 29, 1934; s. Alfred Bevis and Mary Agnes (Shiras) L.; m. Clara St. John, Aug. 10, 1963; children: Katherine Shiras, Thomas Day, Benjamin Hoyt. B.S. cum laude, Princeton U., 1956; LL.M., Harvard U., 1961. Bar: N.Y. 1962. Assoc. Debevoise & Plimpton, N.Y.C., 1962-70, ptnr., 1970-81; commr. SEC, Washington, 1981-84; ptnr. Debevoise & Plimpton, 1984—; lectr. Columbia U. Law Sch., N.Y.C., 1975-81, prof., 1994—; cons. Ford Found., 1971-72; cons. to Comptroller Gen. of U.S.; mem. pension fin. com. World Bank, 1987—; bd. govs. Am. Stock Exch., 1992—; bd. dirs. INVESCO, plc, Capstead Mortgage Co. Author books, numerous articles on investment, securities and law. Bd. dirs. Symphony Space Inc.; trustee Nathan Cummings Found., 1991—, trustee, 1993—; New Sch. for Social Rsch., 1987—; chmn. fin. com. Rockefeller Family Fund, 1972-81, 84—, mem., 1986—. Lt. USMC, 1956-58. Mem. Am. Law Inst., Assn. of Bar of City of N.Y. Democrat. Home: 322 Central Park W New York NY 10025-7629 Office: Debevoise & Plimpton 875 3rd Ave New York NY 10022-6225

LONGSWORTH, CHARLES R., foundation administrator; b. Fort Wayne, Ind., Aug. 21, 1929; s. Maurice A. and Marjorie K. L.; m. Polly Ormsby, June 30, 1956; children: Amy Porter, Elizabeth King, Laura Cramer, Anne Graybill. B.A., Amherst Coll., 1951; M.B.A., Harvard U., 1953. Mktg. trainee Campbell Soup Co., Camden, N.J., 1955-58; account exec. Ogilvy & Mather, Inc., N.Y.C., 1958-60; asst. to pres. Amherst (Mass.) Coll., 1960-65; chmn. edn. trust Hampshire Coll., Amherst, 1966, v.p., sec., 1966-71, pres., 1971-77, pres. emeritus, 1992; pres., chief operating officer Colonial Williamsburg Found., Va., 1977-79, pres., CEO, 1979-92; chmn. Colonial Williamsburg Found., 1991-94, chmn. emeritus, 1994—; dir. Houghton Mifflin Co., Flight Safety Internat., Crestar Fin. Corp., Roadway Svcs. Inc., Saul Ctrs. Inc., Am. Pub. Radio, Va. Ea. Shore Corp. Author: (with others) The Making of a College, 1966, Five Colleges: Five Histories, 1993; contbr. articles to profl. jours. Chmn. bd. trustees Amherst Coll.; trustee Colonial Williamsburg Found., 1977-94, Emeritus Nat. Trust His. Preservation; bd. dirs. Ctr. for Public Resources. Lt. USMC, 1953-55. Mem. Am. Philos. Soc., Am. Antiquarian Soc., Univ. Club (N.Y.C.), Century Assn. Club (N.Y.C.), Commonwealth Club (Richmond, Va.), Phi Beta Kappa. Clubs: University (N.Y.C.), Century Assn. (N.Y.C.); Commonwealth (Richmond, Va.). Home: Davis Hill Farm Davis Hill Rd Royalston MA 01368 Office: Colonial Williamsburg PO Box C Williamsburg VA 23187-3707

LONGSWORTH, EILEEN CATHERINE, library director; b. N.Y.C., Feb. 7, 1950; d. Francis L. and Maurine E. (Romkey) Brannigan; m. Laurence S. Woodworth, June 16, 1970 (div. 1982); 1 child, David; m. Bruce Todd Longsworth, May 28, 1983. Student, Dunbarton Coll., 1966-68; BA, U. Md., 1970; MS in Libr. Sci., Cath. U., Washington, 1973. Dept. head Anne Arundel County Pub. Libr., Annapolis, Md., 1974-75; br. librarian, 1975-79; adult services specialist Enoch Pratt Free Libr., Balt., 1979-84; asst. dir. Salt Lake City Pub. Libr., 1984-87; dir. Salt Lake County Libr. System, 1987—. Mem. ALA, Utah Libr. Assn. Democrat. Home: 860 Terrace Hills Dr Salt Lake City UT 84103-4021 Office: Salt Lake County Libr System 2197 E 7000 S Salt Lake City UT 84121-3139

LONGSWORTH, ROBERT MORROW, college professor; b. Canton, Ohio, Feb. 15, 1937; s. Robert H. and Margaret Elizabeth (Morrow) L.; m. Carol Herndon, Aug. 16, 1958; children—Eric D., Margaret W., Ann E. A.B., Duke U., 1958; M.A., Harvard U., 1960, Ph.D. 1965. Asst. prof. Oberlin Coll., 1964-70, assoc. prof., 1970-75, prof. English, 1975—, dean Coll. Arts and Scis., 1974-84. Author: The Cornish Ordinalia, 1967, The Design of Drama, 1972. Contbr. articles to profl. jours. Danforth Found. fellow. Fellow Am. Council Learned Socs., Nat. Humanities Ctr.; mem. MLA, Medieval Acad. Am., Cornwall Archaeol. Soc., Phi Beta Kappa.

LONGUEMARE, R. NOEL, JR., federal official; b. El Paso, Tex., Mar. 26, 1932; s. Robert Noel Sr. and Lorenza (Escajeda) L.; m. Julianna Josephine Isdebski, June 6, 1959; 1 child, Maria Christine. BSEE, U. Tex., El Paso, 1952; MSE, Johns Hopkins U., 1958. Corp. v.p., gen. mgr. electronic sys. group Westinghouse Electric, Balt., 1952-93; prin. dep. under sec. of def. acquisition and tech. Dept. Def., Washington, 1993—; cons. Def. Sci. Bd., Washington, 1988-91, mem., 1991-93; mem. Air Force Sci. Adv. Bd., Washington, 1990-93. Recipient Greer award Nat. Security Indsl. Assn., 1993. Fellow IEEE; mem. AAAS, AIAA (sr.). Democrat. Roman Catholic. Achievements include 8 patents. Avocation: piano. Home: 12408 Benson Branch Rd Ellicott City MD 21042

LONGWELL, JOHN DORNEY, petroleum engineer; b. Newark, Dec. 24, 1954; s. John Plaeger and Marion Reed (Valleau) L.; m. Mary Ellen Kennedy, Feb. 16, 1980; children: Chris, Kelly, Michael, Jeanne. BS in Mech. Engring., Syracuse U., 1976. Registered engr. in ing., Colo. Prodn. engr. Texaco, Inc., Morgan City, La., 1977-79; The Superior Oil Co., Lafayette, La., 1979-80; drilling engr. II The Superior Oil Co., Lafayette, 1980-81; sr. petroleum engr. Dome Petroleum Corp., Denver, 1981-84; ops. mgr. Golden Buckeye Petroleum Corp., Denver, 1984-88; ops. mgr. Prima Energy Corp., Denver, 1989-90, v.p. ops., 1990—; bd. dirs. Colo. Oil and Gas Assn., Denver, 1985—. Cubmaster Boy Scouts Am. Indian Hills, Colo., 1990-91. Grantee NSF, Syracuse U., 1975. Mem. Soc. Petroleum Engrs. Avocations: hunting, fishing, dirt bikes. Office: Prima Oil & Gas Co 1801 Broadway Ste 500 Denver CO 80202-3833

LONGWELL, JOHN PLOEGER, chemical engineering educator; b. Denver, Apr. 27, 1918; s. John Stalker and Martha Dorothea (Ploeger) L.; m. Marion Reed Valleau, Dec. 11, 1945; children: Martha Reed, Elizabeth Ann, John Dorney. B.S. in Mech. Engring., U. Calif., Berkeley, 1940; Sc.D. in Chem. Engring, M.I.T., 1943. With Exxon Research & Engring. Co., Linden, N.J., 1943-77; dir. Exxon Research & Engring. Co. Central Basic Research Lab., 1960-69; sr. sci. adv. Exxon Research & Engring. Co. (Central Basic Research Lab.), 1969-77; prof. chem. engring. M.I.T., Cambridge, 1977—. Contbr. articles to profl. jours. Recipient Sir Alfred Egerton medal for contbns. to combustion Nat. Acad. Engring., 1976. Mem. Am. Chem. Soc., Combustion Inst. (past pres.), Am. Inst. Chem. Engrs. (award 1979), Sigma Xi, Tau Beta Pi. Republican. Patentee in field. Home: 22 Follen St Cambridge MA 02138-3503 Office: MIT Rm 66-456 Cambridge MA 02139

LONGWORTH, RICHARD COLE, journalist; b. Des Moines, Mar. 13, 1935; s. Wallace Harlan and Helen (Cole) L.; m. Barbara Bem, July 19, 1958; children: Peter, Susan. BJ, Northwestern U., 1957; postgrad., Harvard U., 1968-69. Reporter UPI, Chgo., 1958-60; parliamentary corr. UPI, London, 1960-65; corr. UPI, Moscow, 1965-68, Vienna, 1969-72; diplomatic corr. UPI, Brussels, 1972-76; econ. and internat. affairs reporter Chgo. Tribune, 1976-86, bus. editor, econ. columnist, 1987-88, chief European corr., 1988-91, sr. writer, 1991—; internat. affairs commentator Sta. WBEZ-FM, Chgo., 1984—. Served with U.S. Army, 1957-58. Nieman fellow, 1968-69; recipient award for econ. reporting U. Mo., 1978, 80, John Hancock award for econ. reporting, 1978, 79, 82, Gerald Loeb award for econ. reporting, 1979, Media award for econ. understanding Dartmouth Coll., 1979, award Inter-Am. Press Assn., 1979, Peter Lisagor award Sigma Delta Chi, 1979, Sidney Hillman award, 1985, Lowell Thomas award for travel writing, 1985, Beck award for fgn. corr., 1986, Domestic Reporting award, 1987, Overseas Press Club award, 1994. Mem. Chgo. Com. of Council Fgn. Rels., Assn. Am. Corrs. in London. Office: Chicago Tribune 435 N Michigan Ave Chicago IL 60611

LONGYEAR, RUSSELL HAMMOND, retail executive; b. Flushing, N.Y., Apr. 12, 1935; s. Ralph Vangaasbeck and Catherine Brierly (Bellows) L.; m. Miriam J. Prosswimmer, Sept. 7, 1957; children: Andrew Hammond, Martha Louise. BA, Bowdoin Coll., 1957. Comml. salesman So. New Eng. Telephone, New London, Conn. 1957-58; equipment systems analyst So. New Eng. Telephone, New Haven, 1960-61; sr. rsch. analyst J.C. Penney Co., N.Y.C., 1961-63, systems supr., 1963-65, project mgr., 1965-66, stockroom facility coord., 1966-69, distbn. plan mgr., 1969-73, mgr. ops. studies, 1973-75, mgr. co. communications, 1975-88; v.p., dir. communications J.C. Penney Co., Dallas, 1988-94; bd. dirs. Bus. TV Corp. Ltd.,

London, Trans European Corp. TV, London. Chair bd. trustees Congl. Ch. Manhasset, N.Y., 1975, chair bd. deacons, 1983. 1st lt. U.S. Army, 1958-60. Mem. Internat. Teleconferencing Assn. (bd. dirs. 1984-87), Internat. Assn. Bus. Communicators, Internat. TV Assn. Republican. Office: J C Penney Co PO Box 10001 Dallas TX 75301-4314

LONKART, GEORGIA FAITH, banker; b. Trenton, N.J., Jan. 17, 1947; d. George W. and Laura L. (Tilghman) Balles; m. Robert S. Lonkart, Apr. 8, 1967; children: Kevin. L., Scott C. Student, Rutgers U., Camden, 1972-75; BA in English, U. R.I., 1982. Fin. aid officer Brown U., Providence, 1980-84; ops. mgr. R.I. Hosp. Trust Nat. Bank, Providence, 1984-85, ops. officer, 1985-86, asst. v.p., 1986-87, v.p., 1987-89; mgr. sr. ops. Bank of Boston, 1989-90; 1st v.p. R.I. Hosp. Trust (subs. Bank of Boston), Providence, 1990-91; dir. cons. fin. ops. Bank of Boston, 1991-93; sr. cons. banking and investment svcs. KPMG Peat Marwick, Boston, 1994—. Mem. Am. Inst. Bankers, Consumer Bankers Assn. Avocations: piano, gardening, golf. Home: 62 Carue Dr North Scituate RI 02857-1013 Office: KPMG Peat Marwick One Boston Pl Boston MA 02108

LONNEBOTN, TRYGVE, battery company executive; b. Bergen, Norway, Oct. 4, 1937; came to U.S., 1965; s. Trygve and Nora Gertrude (Hoyland) L.; m. Aud Amalie Engesaeter, Sept. 28, 1963; children: Anne V., Paal T. MChemE, Tech. U. Norway, 1963. With Rayovac Corp., Madison, Wis., 1965—; project engr., then. project mgr., 1965-74, materials mgr., 1974-75, plant mgr., 1975-77, dir. ops., 1977-79, v.p. tech., 1979-82, v.p. ops., 1982-86, sr. v.p. ops., 1986—, also bd. dirs. Served to sgt. Norwegian Army, 1957-58. Mem. Norges Ingenior Furening (Norwegian Engring. Soc.). Lutheran. Club: Torskeklubben, Ygdrasil (Madison). Lodge: Sons of Norway. Avocations: hiking, soccer, music. Office: Rayovac Corp 601 Rayovac Dr Box 4960 Madison WI 53711

LONNEKE, MICHAEL DEAN, radio and television marketing executive; b. Wichita, Kans., Jan. 15, 1943; s. John Henry and Lillian Eleanor (Millspaugh) L.; m. Charlene Bertha Wilson, Apr. 10, 1975; children: Rebecca, Marietta, Alison. Student, Wichita State U., 1962-63, Friends U., 1961-66. Ops. mgr. Sta. KCMO, Kansas City, Mo., 1968-80; program dir. Sta. WCAU/CBS, Phila., 1980-81; v.p., gen. mgr. Sta. WGSO, New Orleans, 1981-83, Sta. KRNT/KRNQ-FM, Des Moines, 1983-85, Sta. KHOW, Denver, 1985-86, Sta. WMAQ/WKQX-FM (NBC Inc.), Chgo., 1986-89; pres. broadcast divsn. TransAm. Mktg. Svcs., Inc., Washington, 1994—, v.p., gen. mgr. Metromedia Internat., Moscow, Russia, 1994—. Bd. dirs. Youth Symphony of DuPage (Ill.); pres. Loudoun Symphony Orch. Mem. Radio-TV News Dirs. Assn. (bd. dirs. 1970-72), Nat. Assn. Broadcasters. Am. Radio Relay League, Quarter Century Wireless Assn., U.S. Yacht Club, Masons. Republican. Episcopalian.

LONNER, THOMAS DUNSTAN, museum director; b. San Francisco, May 27, 1942; s. Ernest B. and Lisa K. Lonner; m. Elizabeth Ward. BA, San Francisco State U., 1966, MA, 1970; PhD, U. Calif., San Francisco, 1976. Projects coordinator Peat, Marwick, Mitchell & Co, Anchorage, 1976-79; dir. subsistence div. Alaska Fish and Game, Juneau, 1979-81; dir. Ctr. for Alcohol Studies, Anchorage, 1981-85, Alaska State Museums, Juneau, 1986—. Contbr. articles to profl. jours. Home: 2318 Columbia St SW Olympia WA 98501-2844 Office: Alaska State Mus 395 Whittier St Juneau AK 99801-1746

LONNGREN, KARL ERIK, electrical and computer engineering educator; b. Milw., Aug. 8, 1938; s. Bruno Leonard and Edith Irene (Osterlund) L.; m. Vicki Anne Mason, Feb. 16, 1963; children: Sondra Lyn, Jon Erik. B.S. in Elec. Engring., U. Wis., 1960, M.S., 1962, Ph.D., 1964. Postdoctoral appointment Royal Inst. Tech., Stockholm, 1964-65; asst. prof. elec. engring. U. Iowa, Iowa City, 1965-67; assoc. prof. U. Iowa, 1967-72, prof., 1972—; vis. scientist Danish Atomic Energy, Riso, 1982, Inst. Space and Astron. Sci., Tokyo, 1981, Los Alamos Sci. Labs. (N.M.), 1979, 80, Math. Research Ctr., Madison, 1976, Inst. Plasma Physics, Nagoya, Japan, 1972, others. Author: Introduction to Physical Electronics, 1988; co-author: Introduction to Wave Phenomena, 1985; co-editor: Solitons in Action, 1978. Recipient Disting. Svc. citation U. Wisc. Madison, 1992. Fellow Am. Phys. Soc., IEEE. Presbyterian. Home: 21 Prospect Pl Iowa City IA 52246-1932 Office: U Iowa Dept Elec & Computer Engring Iowa City IA 52242

LONNQUIST, GEORGE ERIC, lawyer; b. Lincoln, Nebr., Mar. 29, 1946; s. John Hall and Elizabeth Claire (Hanson) L.; m. Sandra Lynn Wise, May 7, 1971; children: Alethea, Courtenay, Barrett. BS, U. Nebr., 1968; JD, U. Nebr., 1971; LLM, NYU, 1974. Bar: Calif. 1983, Oreg. 1972, Nebr. 1971. Law clerk Oreg. Supreme Ct., Salem, 1971-72; dep. legis. counsel Oreg. Legislature, Salem, 1972-73; ptnr. Meysing & Lonnquist, Portland, 1974-78; v.p., assoc. gen. counsel Amfac, Inc., Portland and San Francisco, 1978-84; sr. v.p., gen. counsel Homestead Fin. Corp., Millbrae, Calif., 1984-91, Homestead Savings, Millbrae, 1984-93; pvt. practice law San Francisco, 1993—. Democrat. Roman Catholic. Avocation: woodcarving. Home: 846 E Greenwich Pl Palo Alto CA 94303-3416 Office: Lincoln Center Dr Foster City CA 94404

LOO, BEVERLY JANE, publishing company executive; b. L.A.; d. Richard Y. and Bessie E. Sue Loo. B.A., U. Calif., Berkeley. Dir. subs. rights Prentice-Hall, Inc., N.Y.C., 1957-59; fiction editor McCall's mag., 1959-62; exec. editor and dir. subs. rights, gen. books div. McGraw-Hill Book Co., N.Y.C., 1962-82; pres. Beverly Jane Loo Assocs., Inc., N.Y.C., 1982-85; sr. editor, dir. subs. rights World Almanac Pharos Books, N.Y.C., 1985-88; dir. mktg. and subs. rights Paragon House, N.Y.C., 1988-91; dir. mktg. and sales Thomasson-Grant, Charlottesville, Va., 1991-93; dir. pub. and comm. programs U. Va. Div. Continuing Edn., Charlottesville, 1993—. Clubs: Arts (London); Overseas Press (N.Y.C.); Va. Writers. Home: Lewis & Clark Sq # 701 250 W Main St Charlottesville VA 22902-5079 Office: Zehmer Hall 104 Midmont Ln Charlottesville VA 22903-2449

LOO, THOMAS S., lawyer; b. 1943. BS, U. So. Calif., JD. Bar: Calif. 1969. Ptnr. Bryan Cave, Santa Monica, Calif. Office: Bryan Cave 120 Broadway St Ste 500 Santa Monica CA 90401-2386

LOOKSTEIN, HASKEL, rabbi; b. N.Y.C., Mar. 21, 1932; s. Joseph H. and Gertrude S. (Schlang) L.; m. Audrey Katz, June 21, 1959; children: Mindy Cinnamon, Debbie Senders, Shira Baruch, Joshua. BA, Columbia U., 1953; MA, Yeshiva U., 1963, PhD, 1979. Ordained rabbi, 1958. Rabbi Congregation Kehilath Jeshurun, N.Y.C., 1958—; prin. Ramaz Sch., N.Y.C., 1966—; pres. N.Y. Bd. Rabbis, N.Y.C., 1986-88; chmn. rabbinic cabinet United Jewish Appeal, N.Y.C., 1985-87. Author: Were We Our Brothers' Keepers? The Public Response of American Jews to the Holocaust, 1938-44, 1985. Chmn. N.Y. Coalition for Soviet Jewry, N.Y.C., 1989—; v.p. United Jewish Appeal-Fedn., N.Y.C., 1990—). Mem. Rabbinical Coun. Am. (v.p. 1990—). Office: Synagogue Council of America 327 Lexington Ave New York NY 10016

LOOMAN, JAMES R., lawyer; b. Vallejo, Calif., June 5, 1952; s. Alfred R. and Jane M. (Halter) L.; m. Donna G. Craven, Dec. 18, 1976; children: Alison Marie, Mark Andrew, Zachary Michael. BA, Valparaiso U., 1974; JD, U. Chgo., 1978. Bar: Ill, 1978, U.S. Dist. Ct. (no dist.) Ill. 1978, U.S. Claims Ct. 1979. Assoc. Isham, Lincoln & Beale, Chgo., 1978-83; assoc. Sidley & Austin, Chgo., 1983-86, ptnr., 1986—; bd. dirs. Pace Inst. Inc., Chgo. Mem. ABA, Ill. State Bar Assn., Chgo. Bar Assn., Chgo. Athletic Assn., Skokie Country Club. Lutheran. Office: Sidley & Austin 1 First Nat Plz Chicago IL 60603

LOOMIS, CAROL J., journalist; b. Marshfield, Mo., June 25, 1929; d. Harold and Mildred (Case) Junge; m. John R. Loomis, Mar. 19, 1960; children: Barbara, Mark. Student, Drury Coll., 1947-49; B in Journalism, U. Mo., 1951. Editor Maytag News, Maytag Co., Newton, Iowa, 1951-54; rsch. assoc. Fortune mag., N.Y.C., 1954-58, assoc. editor, 1958-68, mem. bd. editors, 1968—. Office: Fortune Mag 1271 Ave Of The Americas New York NY 10020-1300

LOOMIS, HENRY, former broadcasting company executive, former government official; b. Tuxedo Park, N.Y., Apr. 19, 1919; s. Alfred Lee and Ellen Holman (Farnsworth) L.; m. Mary Paul Macleod, May 18, 1946 (div. Jan. 1974); children—Henry, Mary, Lucy, Gordon; m. Jacqueline C. Williams, Jan. 19, 1974; stepchildren—Charles Judson Williams, John Chalmers Williams, David Finley Williams, Robert Wood Williams. AB, Harvard, 1941; ed., U. Calif., 1946. With radiation lab. U. Calif., 1945-47; asst. to pres. MIT, 1947-50; asst. to chmn. research and devel. bd. Dept. Def., 1950-51; cons. Psychol. Strategy Bd., Washington, 1951-52; staff Pres.'s Com. Internat. Info., 1953; chief Office Research and Intelligence, USIA, 1954-57; staff to Spl. Asst. to Pres. for Sci. and Tech., 1957-58; dir. broadcasting service Voice of Am. USIA, 1958-65; dep. commr. edn. HEW, 1965-66; ptnr. St. Vincents Island Co., N.Y.C., 1966-69; dep. dir. USIA, 1969-72; pres. Corp. for Pub. Broadcasting, Washington, 1972-78; trustee, vice chmn. bd. dirs. Mitre Corp., 1967-69, 78-91. Vice chmn. bd. dirs. Nat. Mus. Natural History, Smithsonian Instn., 1991-92, trustee, 1992-95; trustee Mus. Sci. and History, Jcksonville, 1991—; bd. dirs. Jacksonville Zool. Soc. Recipient Rockefeller Pub. Service award for fgn. affairs, 1963. Home: 4661 Ortega Island Dr Jacksonville FL 32210-7500

LOOMIS, HOWARD KREY, banker; b. Omaha, Apr. 9, 1927; s. Arthur L. and Genevieve (Krey) L.; AB, Cornell U., 1949, MBA, 1950; m. Florence Porter, Apr. 24, 1954; children: Arthur L. II, Frederick S., Howard Krey, John Porter. Mgmt. trainee Hallmark Cards, Inc., Kansas City, Mo., 1953-56; sec., controller, dir. Mine Service Co., Inc., Ft. Smith, Ark., 1956-59; controller, dir. Electra Mfg. Co., Independence, Kans., 1959-63; v.p., dir. The Peoples Bank, Pratt, Kans., 1963-65, pres., 1966—; pres., dir. Gt. Plains Leasing, Inc., Pratt, 1966-80, Central States Inc., Pratt, 1970-76, Krey Co. Ltd., Pratt, 1978—; fin. chmn. Econ. Lifelines, Topeka; bd. dirs. All Ins., Inc., Pratt, Kans. Devel. Credit Corp., Topeka; past pres. Pratt County United Fund. Bd. dirs., past chmn. Cannonball Trail chpt. ARC; bd. dirs., past comdg. gen. Kans. Cavalry; past pres. Investment Com., Kanza coun. Boy Scouts Am. With AUS, 1950-52. Mem. Kans. C. of C. and Industry (past transp. chmn., dir., v.p.), Pratt Area C. of C. (past pres., dir.), Kans. Bankers Assn. (past dir.), Fin. Execs. Inst. (Wichita chpt.), Sigma Delta Chi, Chi Psi. Republican. Presbyterian. Club: Park Hills Country (past pres.). Lodges: Elks, Rotary. Home: 502 Welton St Pratt KS 67124-0928 Office: The Peoples Bank 222 S Main St Pratt KS 67124-1102

LOOMIS, JOHN NORMAN, psychiatrist; b. Dallas, Aug. 9, 1933; s. Glenn LaVerne and Maria Jeanette (Doyle) L.; B.A., Rice U., 1954; M.D., Cornell U., 1958. Intern Meth. Hosp., Bklyn., 1958-59; resident Westchester div. N.Y. Hosp., White Plains, N.Y., 1959-62; practice medicine specializing in psychiatry, N.Y.C., 1962-78; asst. attending psychiatrist N.Y. Hosp., 1972-80; asst. prof. psychiatry Cornell U. Med. Coll., 1972-80; dir. Loomis Internat. Inc., oil field service co., Houston, 1964—, v.p. 1970-75, chmn. bd., 1975—. Bd. dirs. Madison Square Boys' and Girls' Club, N.Y.C., 1965-93, The Hudson Rev., N.Y.C., 1983—. Mem. Am. Psychiat. Assn., N.Y. Acad. Scis., Phi Beta Kappa. Clubs: Knickerbocker (N.Y.C.). Office: PO Box 6408 Pasadena TX 77506-0408

LOOMIS, PHILIP CLARK, investment executive; b. Plainville, Conn., Sept. 24, 1926; s. Winfield Hathaway and Lucy Erma (Clark) L.; m. Jean Ann Slater, 1950 (div. 1970); children: Philip Clark Jr., Leslie Jean, Martha Lynn; m. Greta Elaine Gustafson, 1970. BA in Econs., Yale U., 1949; MBA in Fin. with distinction, Wharton Sch. U. Pa., 1950. Chartered fin. analyst. Trust investment specialist No. Trust Co., Chgo., 1950-54; investment analyst, portfolio mgr. Hartford (Conn.) Ins. Group, 1954-61; ptnr./dir. of rsch. Eastman, Dillon Union, N.Y.C., 1961-66; ptnr.-in-charge, rsch. svcs. div. Francis I. duPont & Co., N.Y.C., 1967-70; v.p. rsch. Dean Witter & Co., N.Y.C., 1971-73; v.p., dir. rsch. Reynolds Securities, Inc., N.Y.C., 1974-78; dir. Office of Securities Markets Policy, Dept. Treasury, Washington, 1978-81; freelance cons. N.Y.C., 1981-86; v.p. Crispi Wagner & Co., N.Y.C., 1987-89; ind. cons. and money mgr., 1989—. Mem. N.Y. Soc. Security Analysts, Assn. for Investment Mgmt. and Rsch. Avocations: music, opera, ballet, do-it-yourself. Home and office: 130 East End Ave New York NY 10028-7553

LOOMIS, ROBERT DUANE, publishing company executive, author; b. Conneaut, Ohio, Aug. 24, 1926; s. Kline C. and Louise C. (Chapman) L.; m. Gloria Colliani, Apr. 12, 1956 (div.); 1 dau., Diana Rachel; m. Hilary Paterson Mills, Sept. 18, 1983; 1 child, Robert Miles. B.A., Duke U., 1950. Assoc. editor Rinehart & Co., N.Y.C., 1956-58; v.p., exec. editor Random House, Inc., N.Y.C., 1958—. Author: Story of the U.S. Air Force, 1959, Great American Fighter Pilots, 1961, All About Aviation, 1964. Served with USAF, 1945. Recipient Roger Klein award for creative editing, 1977. Home: 68 W 11th St New York NY 10011-8673 Office: Random House Inc 201 E 50th St New York NY 10022

LOOMIS, WESLEY HORACE, III, former publishing company executive; b. Kansas City, Mo., July 29, 1913; s. Wesley Horace, Jr. and Mary (Gary) L.; m. Mary Bradford Paine, Apr. 17, 1937; children: Mary Elizabeth (Mrs. R.M. Norton), Jonathan Lee (dec.), Frederick Pierson. Grad., Hackley Sch., Tarrytown, N.Y., 1931; B.S. in Engring. and Bus. Adminstrn, MIT, 1935. Indsl. engr. Automatic Elec. Co., Chgo., 1935-42; pres. Loomis Advt. Co., 1946-55, Gen. Telephone Directory Co., Des Plaines, Ill., 1956-78; v.p. Dominion Directory Co., Vancouver, B.C., 1956-64; pres. Dominion Directory Co., 1964-78, Courtnay Pty., Ltd., Adelaide, Courtnay Pty., Ltd. S.A. Australia, Directories (Australia) Pty., Ltd.; Melbourne, Australia, Gen. Telephone Directory Co. C por A, Santo Domingo, 1971-78, Directorio Telefonico Centroamericano, S.A., 1972-78; dir. Directorio Telefonico de El Salvador (SA). Pres. Episc. Charities 1969-70, dir., 1962-83, now life trustee; trustee emeritus U.S. Naval Acad. Found., Annapolis, Md.; bd. dirs. Traveler Aid Soc. Met. Chgo./Immigrants' Service League, 1957-80, pres., 1960-61; chmn. Travelers Aid Internat., Social Service Am. 1973-77; bd. dirs. Travelers Aid Assn. Am., 1977-82, pres., 1978-80; pres. Ind. Telephone Hist. Found., 1967-81, trustee, 1981—; trustee emeritus Colby-Sawyer Coll., New London, N.H., sec., 1976-81; mem. corp. devel. com. M.I.T., 1979-81; trustee Ill. Bus. Hall of Fame, 1981-83; bd. dirs., trustee, chmn. planning com. Mote Marine Lab., Sarasota, Fla., 1983—. Served to lt. col., Ordnance AUS, 1942-46. Decorated hon. mil. mem. Order Brit. Empire; laureate Am. Nat. Bus. Hall of Fame, 1980; elected to Ind. Telephone Hall of Fame, 1981, Calif. chpt., 1990. Mem. Ind. Telephone Pioneers Assn. (pres. 1964-66), Racquet Club (Chgo.), Field and Bird Key Yacht (Sarasota), Longboat Key Club, Masons (32 deg.), Phi Gamma Delta. Republican. Episcopalian (warden). Home: Apt 305 700 John Ringling Blvd Sarasota FL 34236-1505

LOOMIS, WORTH (ALFRED WORTHINGTON LOOMIS), college president, manufacturer; b. N.Y.C., May 18, 1923; s. Alfred F. and Priscilla (Lockwood) L.; m. Louise Harding Earle, June 17, 1950; children: Lucy Williams, Ruth Lockwood, Susan Fellows, Alfred Fullerton II, Charles Harvey, Charlotte Earle. BS in Indsl. Engring., Yale U., 1947; MBA in Internat. Fin., NYU, 1955. Securities analyst Reynolds & Co., N.Y.C., 1948-50; indsl. engr., part owner Internat. R&D Corp., Istanbul, Turkey, 1950-51; prodn. mgmt. automotive parts div. Clevite Corp., Cleve., 1951-58; with Medusa Portland Cement Co., Cleve., 1958-70, v.p. fin., sec., bd. dirs.; v.p. fin. Dexter Corp., Windsor Locks, Conn., 1970-75, pres., 1975-88, also bd. dirs.; pres. Hartford (Conn.) Grad. ctr., 1989—, also trustee; trustee Mechanics Savs. Bank, Hartford; bd. dirs. Capewell Components Co., Hartford, Chemstone Corp., Strasburg, Va., Cigna Funds, Springfield, Mass., Colt's Mfg. Co., Inc., Hartford, Conn. Natural Gas, Hartford, Covenant Mut. Ins. Co., Hartford, So. New Eng. Telephone Co., New Haven, Spencer Turbine Co., Windsor, Conn.; chmn. bd. dirs. Life Techs., Gaithersburg, Md.; pres. bd. trustees Colt Bequest Inc., Hartford, 1989—. Trustee Alpha Ctr., Washington, Am. Inst. for Mng. Diversity, Morehouse Coll., Atlanta, Hartford Sem., Kazanjian Econs. Found., Oneonta, N.Y., Trinity Coll., Hartford, Yale Berkeley Divinity Sch., New Haven; mem. Goodrich Social Settlement, Cleve., 1960-70, chair, 1964-66; mem. exec. com. Cuyahoga County Reps., 1963-70; mem. Cleveland Heights (Ohio) Bd. Edn., 1964-67, pres., 1967; mem. exec. com. Nat. Com. for Indsl. Mission, Detroit, chair, 1966-72; vice chair Cleve. subcom. U.S. Commn. on Civil Rights, 1966; mem. bd. overseers NYU Stern Sch. of Bus.; bd. dirs. Hartford Hosp., 1979-89, sec. bd., 1982-83; bd. dirs. Bus. Coalition on Health, Hartford, chmn. bd., 1983-89; trustee Hartford Coll. for Women, chmn. bd. trustees, 1986-89; trustee Hartford Courant Found., chmn. bd. trustees, 1982-84. Sgt. USAF, 1943-46, PTO. Mem. NAM (bd. dirs. 1978-81), Conn. Bus. and Industry Assn. (bd. dirs. 1982-86), Soc. of Cin., Century Assn., Cruising Club of Am., Economic Club, Hartford Golf Club, Royal Ocean Racing Club, Tavern Club. Episcopalian. Home: 70 Terry Rd Hartford CT 06105-1109 Office: Hartford Grad Ctr 275 Windsor St Hartford CT 06120-2910

LOOMSTEIN, ARTHUR, real estate company executive; b. St. Louis, July 27, 1939; s. Meyer and Ann (Mariam) L.; m. Kay Diane Oppenheim, Aug. 22, 1975; children: David Jay, Debi, Debra Ann. BSBA, Washington U., St. Louis, 1961, JD, 1964. Pres. Centerco Properties Inc., St. Louis, 1961—. Recipient Disting. Citizen Citation, St. Louis Regional Commerce and Growth Assn., 1973. Mem. Bldg. Owners and Mgrs. Assn. Met. St. Louis (bd. dirs. 1969-75, treas. 1971-72, pres. 1973-74), Soc. Real Property Adminstrs. (founding mem.). Clubs: Meadowbrook Country. Avocations: swimming, golfing, thoroughbred racing. Home: 5 Somerset Downs Saint Louis MO 63124-1031 Office: Centerco Properties Inc 7730 Carondelet Ave Saint Louis MO 63105-3372

LOONEY, GERALD LEE, medical educator, administrator; b. Bradshaw, W.Va., Nov. 22, 1937; s. Noah Webster and Anna Belle (Burris) L.; m. Linda Louise Pluebell, Oct. 19, 1962 (div. Apr. 1975); children: Deborah Lynn, Catherine Ann, Karen Marie, Kelli Rachelle; m. Patricia Marie Terrazas, Dec. 22, 1987. AB, Johns Hopkins U., 1959, MD, 1963; MPH, Harvard U., 1968. Diplomate Am. Bd. Preventive Medicine, Am. Bd. Pediatrics. Resident pediatrics Yale-New Eng. Med. Ctr., Boston, 1965-67; physician-in-chief Kennedy Meml. Hosp., Boston, 1969-71; asst. prof. family and cmty. medicine U. Ariz. Coll. Medicine, Tucson, 1971-72; asst. prof. emergency medicine U. So. Calif. Sch. Medicine, L.A., 1972-77; assoc. clin. prof. medicine U. Calif., Irvine, 1991—; emergency dept. dir. Glendale (Calif.) Adventist Med. Ctr., 1978-84; edn. dir. Orthopaedic Hosp., L.A., 1985-88; urgent care dir. Bay Shore Med. Group, Torrance, Calif., 1988-93; med. dir. Surecare and LAX Clinics Centinela Hosp., Inglewood, Calif., 1993—; bd. dirs. Beach Cities Health Dist., Redondo Beach, Calif., 1992-93. Avocation: history. Home: 230 S Catalina Ave # 413 Redondo Beach CA 90277 Office: Centinela Airport Clinic 9601 S Sepulveda Blvd Los Angeles CA 90045

LOONEY, J. CARSON, architectural firm executive. BS in Engring. Tech./Architecture, Memphis State U., 1979; student, Harvard U., 1993. Lic. architect, Tenn., Ark., Miss., Ohio, Ill., Maine; cert. Nat. Coun. Archtl. Registration Bds. Residential designer Archtl. Arts, Inc., Memphis, 1976-79; project architect Hall and Waller and Assocs., Inc., Memphis, 1980; prtr./designer Looney/Ricks Design Group, Memphis, 1979-83; job capt. Jackson/Bronson/Lemons/Hudspeth Architects, Memphis, 1979-80; project architect Jackson and Bronson Architects, Inc., Memphis, 1980-83; with Looney Ricks Kiss Architects, Inc., Memphis, 1983—; founding architect Nat. Bldg. Mus., 1986; head judge Best Homes Miss. Awards, Miss. Mag., 1990; archtl. judge 12th Ann. Builder's Choice Design and Planning Nat. Awards Competition, Builder Mag., 1992, 1994 So. Home Awards, So. Living Mag.; advisor Old Town Cordova Neotraditional Master Plan, Memphis and Shelby County Office Planning and Devel., 1993. Prin. works include Cook and Love Shoes, Jackson, Miss., Chickasaw Bluff Coop., Memphis, Squash Blossom Food Store renovation, Memphis, Looney Residence, Memphis, Babcock Gifts, Memphis, Ricks Residence, Memphis, Audobon Homes, Memphis, Evergreen Plz., Memphis, Looney Ricks Kiss Architects, Inc. Offices, Memphis, Lodge and Guest Quarter Quailwood Plantations, Red Banks, Miss., Ruth's Chris Steak Ho., Memphis, Albers Fine Art Gallery, Memphis, MidSouth Hosp. Pool and Gymnasium Bldg., Memphis, FirstBank Ark., Brinkley, Archer Malmo Offices, Memphis, Poteet Residence, Memphis, Harbor View Dr. Townhomes, Memphis, 332 Avalon, Memphis, John Austin House, Memphis, Rowhouses on Harbor Crest Dr., Memphis, Reisman Cottages, Memphis, WKNO Auction Ho., Memphis, Dryve Cleaners, Memphis, Uhlhorn Enterprises Home, Kremser Contracting Home, Chambers & Chambers Home, South Bluff Townhomes, Memphis, M.S. Carriers, Inc. Exec. Hdqs., Memphis, Memphis Cancer Ctr., V.A. Cafeteria, Memphis, Brenner Residence, Memphis, Reisman Shotguns, Memphis, others; contbr. articles to profl. jours. Gen. mem. internat. festival poster com. Memphis in May, 1982, unveiling co-chmn., 1983, pub. rels. chmn., 1984; archtl./facilities chmn. Art Today-Arts Pk. Festival, 1984; mem. design rev. bd. Ctr. City Commn. Memphis Bus. Dist., 1985—; active Memphis Brooks Mus. Art; appointee alt. bd. Memphis and Shelby County Land Use Control Bd., 1988—; appointee bd. I-40, Midtown Corridor Redevelopment Com., 1988-91; appointee City of Memphis Task Force Residential Devel., 1993. Recipient Cert. of Recognition, Memphis State U., 1987, numerous archtl. design awards for comml. and residential works. Mem. AIA (mem. spl. projects Memphis chpt. 1983, mem. pub. rels. com. 1984, treas. 1986), Am. Planning Assn. (Tenn. chpt.), Nat. Trust Hist. Preservation, Tenn. Soc. Architects, Urban Land Inst., Memphis Heritage, Inc. (bd. dirs. 1986-89, v.p. 1988-89), Congress New Urbanism (founding), Lambda Alpha Internat. (mid-Am. chpt.). Office: Looney Ricks Kiss Arch Inc 88 Union Ctr Ste 900 Memphis TN 38103

LOONEY, NORMAN EARL, pomologist, plant physiologist; b. Adrian, Oreg., May 31, 1938; came to Can., 1966; s. Gaynor Parks and Lois Delilah (Francis) L.; m. Arlene Mae Willis, Oct. 4, 1957 (div. 1982); children: Pamela June, Patricia Lorene, Steven Paul; m. Norah Christine Keating, July 16, 1983. BSc in Agr. Edn., Washington State U., 1960, PhD in Horticulture, 1966. Rsch. scientist Agr. Can., Summerland, B.C., 1966-71, scientist, sect. head, 1972-81, sr. scientist, 1982-87, sr. scientist, sect. head, 1987-90, prin. scientist, sect. head, 1991—; vis. scientist food rsch. divsn. CSIRO, Sydney, Australia, 1971-72, East Malling Rsch. Sta., Maidstone, Kent, 1981-82, Dept. Horticulture U. Lincoln, Christchurch, New Zealand, 1990-91; sec. Expert Com. on Horticulture, Ottawa, Ont., Can., 1986-90; chmn. working group on growth regulators in fruit prodn. Internat. Soc. for Hort. Sci., Wageningen, The Netherlands, 1987-94, coun. mem. Can., 1992—, chmn. fruit sect., 1994—. Contbr. numerous articles and chpts. to sci. publs. Fellow Am. Soc. Hort. Sci. Achievements include patent for Promotion of Flowering in Fruit Trees (U.S. and foreign). Office: Agr Can Rsch Sta, Summerland, BC Canada V0H 1Z0

LOONEY, RALPH EDWIN, newspaper editor, author, photographer; b. Lexington, Ky., June 22, 1924; s. Arville Zone and Connie Elizabeth (Boyd) L.; m. Clarabel Richards, Dec. 7, 1944. B.A., U. Ky., 1948. Various positions including proof reader, photographer, chief photographer, sports writer, reporter Lexington Leader, 1943-52; reporter Albuquerque Tribune, 1953-54; reporter, copy editor, chief copy editor St. Louis Globe-Democrat, 1955-56; city editor Albuquerque Tribune, 1956-68, asst. mng. editor, 1968-73, editor, 1973-80; editor Rocky Mountain News, Denver, 1980-89; columnist Scripps Howard News Svc., 1989-93, Tribune, Albuquerque, 1989-93. Author: Haunted Highways, the Ghost Towns of New Mexico, 1969, O'Keeffe and Me, 1995; contbr. articles to mags. including Nat. Observer, others; photographs to mags. Founder, mem. N.Mex. Motion Picture Commn., 1967-76; v.p., bd. dirs. Albuquerque C. of C., 1971-75; bd. dirs. Albuquerque Indsl. Devel. Soc., 1971-80; bd. advisors Lovelace Med. Ctr., Albuquerque, 1976-80; bd. advs. UPI, 1983-86; bd. dirs. Newspaper Features Coun., 1984-89; mem. exec. coun. St. Joseph Hosp., 1986—. Recipient N.Mex. medal of Merit, 1968, Robert F. Kennedy Journalism award, 1970, George Washington Honor medal Freedoms Found., 1969, 19 E.H. Shaffer awards N.Mex. Press Assn., 1965-80; named Colo. Newspaper Person of the Yr., 1988, Newspaper Features Coun. Jester award, 1989. Mem. N.Mex. Press Assn. (state pres. 1976), Colo. Press Assn. (bd. dirs. 1982-85), Sigma Delta Chi (N. Mex. pres. 1960). Methodist. Home: 6101 Casa De Vida Dr NE Albuquerque NM 87111-1140

LOONEY, RICHARD CARL, bishop; b. Hillsville, Va., Feb. 14, 1934; s. Carl and Ruth (Bourne) L.; m. Carolyn Adele McKeithen, Sept. 3, 1957; children: Teresa, David, Jonathan. B.A., Emory U., 1955; BD, Emory U., 1957; postgrad., Edinburg (Scotland U.), 1956; BD, Emory U., 1957; postgrad., Union Theol. Sem., Richmond, Va. Ordained to ministry United Meth. Ch. as deacon, 1955, as elder, 1959. Pastor Rising Fawn (Ga.) Cir., 1957-61, Pleasant View-Wyndale Charge, Abington, Va., 1961-65, Pleasant View, Abington, Va., 1965-67, White Oak United Meth. Ch., Chattanooga, 1968-71, Broad St. United Meth. Ch., Cleveland, Tenn., 1972-75; dist. supt. Chattanooga Dist., 1976-78; pastor Munsey Meml. United Meth. Ch., Johnson City, Tenn., 1979-86, Church St. United Meth. Ch., Knoxville, Tenn., 1987-88; elected bishop Southeastern Jurisdiction, United Meth. Ch., Macon, Ga., 1988—. Office: The United Meth Ctr PO Box 13616 Macon GA 31208-3616

LOONEY, WILLIAM FRANCIS, JR., lawyer; b. Boston, Sept. 20, 1931; s. William Francis Sr. and Ursula Mary (Ryan) L.; m. Constance Mary O'Callaghan, Dec. 28, 1957; children: Willam F. III, Thomas M., Karen D., Martha A. AB, Harvard U., JD. Bar: Mass. 1958, D.C. 1972, U.S.

Supreme Ct. 1972, U.S. Dist. Ct. (ea. dist.) Mich. 1986. Law clk. to presiding justice Mass. Supreme Jud. Ct., 1958-59; assoc. Goodwin, Procter & Hoar, Boston, 1959-62; chief civil div. U.S. Attys. Office, 1964-65; ptnr. Looney & Grossman, Boston, 1965-94, sr. counsel, 1995—; asst. U.S. atty. Dist. Ct. Mass., 1962-65; spl. hearing officer U.S. Dept. of Justice, 1965-68; mem. Mass. Bd. Bar Overseers, 1985-91, vice chmn., 1990-91; corp. mem. Greater Boston Legal Svcs., Inc., 1994—. Mem. Zoning Bd. of Appeals, Dedham, Mass., 1971-74; bd. dirs. Boston Latin Sch. Found., 1981-85, pres. 1981-84, chmn. bd. dirs., 1984-86; trustee Social Law Libr., 1994—. Fellow Am. Coll. Trial Lawyers; mem. Mass. Bar Assn. (co-chmn. standing com. lawyers responsibility for pub. svc. 1987-88), Boston Bar Assn. (pres. 1984-85, coun. mem. 1985-90, chmn. sr. lawyers sect. 1992-94, Maguire award for Professionalism 1995), Nat. Assn. Bar Pres.'s, Boston Latin Sch. Assn. (pres. 1980-82), life trustee 1982—, Man of Yr. 1985), USCG Found. (bd. dirs. 1987—), Norfolk Golf Club, Harvard Club, New Seabury Golf Club. Democrat. Roman Catholic. Home: 43 Coronation Dr Dedham MA 02026-6230 Office: 101 Arch St 9th Fl Boston MA 02110-1112

LOOPER, GEORGE KIRK, religious society executive; b. Gould, Okla., Feb. 18, 1943; s. Ishmel Guy and Edna Mae (Burge) L.; m. Vivian Kay Swanson, Dec. 13, 1963; children: Michael Edward, Steven Allen, Jodell Lin. BS in Sci., Northeastern Okla. Tchrs. Coll, 1966; MS in Physics, U. Wyo., 1973; MS in Elem. Edn., Western Carolina U., 1968. Cert. tchr., N.C., Colo., Kans., Okla. Exec. dir. Seventh Day Bapt. Missionary Soc., Westerly, R.I. Republican. Seventh-day Baptist. Home: 7 State St Westerly RI 02891

LOORY, STUART HUGH, journalist; b. Wilson, Pa., May 22, 1932; s. Harry and Eva (Holland) L.; m. Marjorie Helene Dretel, June 19, 1955; children: Joshua Alan, Adam Edward, Miriam Beth. B.A., Cornell U., 1954; M.S. with honors, Columbia U., 1958; postgrad., U. Vienna, Austria, 1958. Reporter Newark News, 1955-58; Reporter N.Y. Herald Tribune, 1959-61, sci. writer, 1961-63, Washington corr., 1963-64; fgn. corr. N.Y. Herald Tribune, Moscow, 1964-66; sci. editor Metromedia Radio Stas., 1962-64, Moscow corr., 1964-66; sci. writer N.Y. Times, 1966; White House corr. Los Angeles Times, 1967-71; fellow Woodrow Wilson Internat. Center for Scholars, Washington, 1971-72; exec. editor WNBC-TV News, 1973; Kiplinger prof. pub. affairs reporting Ohio State U., Columbus, 1973-75; assoc. editor Chgo. Sun-Times, 1975-76, mng. editor, 1976-80; v.p., mng. editor Washington bur. Cable News Network, 1980-82, Moscow bur. chief, 1983-86, sr. correspondent, 1986, exec. producer, 1987-90; exec. dir. internat. rels. Turner Broadcasting System, Inc., Atlanta, 1988—; editor-in-chief CNN World Report, 1990-91; v.p. CNN, 1990—; exec. v.p. Turner Internat. Broadcasting, Russia, 1993—; v.p.; supervising prodr. Turner Original Prodns., 1995—; lectr. in field. Author: (with David Kraslow) The Secret Search for Peace in Vietnam, 1968, Defeated: Inside America's Military Machine, 1973, (with Ann Imse) Seven Days That Shook the World: The Collapse of Soviet Communism, 1991; contbr. articles mags. and encys. Recipient citation Overseas Press Club, 1966; Raymond Clapper award Congl. Press Gallery, 1968; George Polk award L.I.U. 1968; Du Mont award U. Calif. at, Los Angeles, 1968; Distinguished Alumni award Columbia, 1969; 50th Anniversary medal Columbia Sch. Journalism, 1963; Edwin Hood award for diplomatic corr. Nat. Press Club, 1987; Pulitzer traveling scholar, 1958. Jewish. Office: Cable News Network 1 Cnn Center Plz Atlanta GA 30335

LOOSBROCK, CAROL MARIE, information management professional; b. Dubuque, Iowa, Aug. 21, 1936; d. Julius Carl and Elizabeth Cecilia (Kurz) L. BA, Clarke Coll., 1958; postgrad., Art Inst. Chgo., 1959-63; MS, Am. U., 1979. With Dept. Def., Washington, 1968—, analyst, 1979—. Mem. AAAS, Assn. Computing Machinery (mem. Washington D.C. symposium steering coms. 1980-81, mem. exec. coun. 1981-84), N.Y. Acad. Scis. (life), Am. Security Coun. Found. (U.S. congl. adv. bd. 1984—, Coalition for Peace through Strength Leadership award, coalition for Desert Storm, coalition for internat. security), Am. Mus. Natural History. Republican. Home: 4514 Connecticut Ave NW Washington DC 20008 Office: The Pentagon Washington DC 20310

LOOSEN, SISTER SISTER ANN MARITA, nun, health care executive; b. Kansas City, Mo., May 1, 1923; d. Irving R. and Mary Louise (Meaney) L. BS in Nursing, St. Mary Coll., Leavenworth, Kans., 1965; MHA, U. Minn., 1967. Joined Sisters of Charity, Roman Catholic Ch., 1950. Administr. Kennedy Child Study Ctr., Santa Monica, Calif., 1968-75; assoc. adminstr. St. John Hosp. and Health Ctr., Santa Monica, 1971-75; asst. dir. hosps. Sisters of Charity of Leavenworth (Kans.) Health Svcs. Corp., 1975-78; adminstr. St. John Hosp., Leavenworth, 1978-80; pres. St. Francis Hosp. and Med. Ctr., Topeka, 1980-91; pres., CEO Providence Med. Ctr., Kansas City, Kans., 1991-95; ret., 1995; bd. dirs. Cath. Health Affairs Kans., St. John's Hosp. and Health Ctr., Santa Monica, Calif., Providence Med. Ctr., Tri-Source, 1992—; Preferred Health Profls., 1991—. Bd. dirs. ARC, Santa Monica, in 1970s, United Way, 1993-95, Douglas Cmty. Health Ctr., 1994-95. Fellow Am. Coll. Health Care Execs. (regent for Kans.); mem. Kans. Hosp. Assn. (bd. dirs. 1986-93, chmn. bd. 1992), Kansas City Area Hosp. Assn. (bd. dirs.), Topeka C of C. (bd. dirs. 1984-86). Avocations: music, reading, cooking, hiking. Office: Providence Med. Ctr. 8929 Parallel Pky Kansas City KS 66112-3607

LOPACH, JAMES JOSEPH, political science educator; b. Great Falls, Mont., June 23, 1942; s. John Ernest and Alma Marie (Schapman) L.; divorced, Dec. 10, 1991; children: Christine, Paul. AB in Philosophy, Carroll Coll., 1964; MA in Am. Studies, U. Notre Dame, 1967, MAT in English Edn., 1968, PhD in Govt., 1973. Mgr. Pacific Telephone, Palo Alto, Calif., 1968-69; adminstr. City of South Bend, Ind., 1971-73; prof. U. Mont., Missoula, 1973—, chmn. dept. polit. sci., 1977-87, assoc. dean Coll. Arts and Scis., 1987-88, acting dir. Mansfield Ctr., 1984-85, spl. asst. to the univ. pres., 1988-92, assoc. provost, 1992—; cons. local govts., state agys., 1973—. Author, editor: We the People of Montana, 1983, Tribal Government Today, 1990, Planning Small Town America, 1990; contbr. articles to profl. jours. Roman Catholic. Office: U Mont Dept Polit Sci Missoula MT 59812

LOPATA, HELENA ZNANIECKA, sociologist, researcher, educator; b. Poznan, Poland, Oct. 1, 1925; d. Florian Witold and Eileen (Markley) Znaniecki; m. Richard Stefan Lopata, Feb. 8, 1946 (wid. July 1994); children: Theodora Karen Lopata-Menasco. B.A., U. Ill., 1946, M.A., 1947; Ph.D., U. Chgo., 1954; DSc (hon.), Guelph U., Can., 1995. Lectr. U. Va. Extension, Langley AFB, 1951-52, DePaul U., 1956-60; lectr. Roosevelt U., 1960-64, asst. prof. sociology, 1964-67, assoc. prof., 1967-69; prof. sociology Loyola U., Chgo., 1969; chmn. dept. sociology Loyola U., 1970-72, Center for Comparative Study of Social Roles, 1972—; mem. NIMH Rev. Bd., 1977-79; mem. Mayor's Council Manpower and Econ. Devel., 1974-79; mem. adv. com., chair tech. com. White House Conf. on Aging, 1979-81; adv. council Nat. Inst. Aging, 1978-83. Author: Occupation: Housewife, 1971, Widowhood in an American City, 1973, Polish Americans: Status Competition in an Ethnic Community, 1976, City Women: Work, Jobs, Occupations, Careers, Vol. I, America, 1984, Vol. II, Chicago, 1985 (with Debra Barnewolt and Cheryl Miller) City Women in America, 1986; (with Henry Brehm) Widows and Dependent Wives: From Social Problem to Federal Policy, 1986, Polish Americans, 1994, Circles and Settings: Role Changes of American Women, 1994; adv. editor: Sociologist Quar., 1969-72, Jour. Marriage and Family, 1978-82, Symbolic Interaction, 1989—; editor: Marriages and Families, 1973, Research on the Interweave of Social Roles: (with Nona Glazer and Judith Wittner), vol. I, Women and Men, 1980 (with David Maines), vol. 2, Friendship, 1981, (with Joseph Pleck) vol. 3, Families and Jobs, 1983, vol. 4, Current Research on Occupations and Professions, 1987, vol. 4, 1987, Widows: The Middle East, Asia and the Pacific, 1987, Widows: North America, 1987; (with David Maines) Friendship in Context, 1990; adv. bd. Symbolic Interaction, 1977-89; contbr. articles to profl. jours. Bd. dirs. Wellesley Center of Research and Women, 1979-84. Recipient Research award Radcliffe Coll., 1982; grantee Chgo. Tribune, 1956, Midwest Coun: Social Research on Aging, 1964-65, Adminstrn. on Aging, 1967-69, 68-71, Social Security Adminstrn., 1971-75, also 1975-79, Indo-Am. Fellowship Program: Coun. for Internat. Exchange Scholars, 1987-88, Rsch. Stimulation grantee Loyola U. Chgo., 1988, 92; named Faculty Mem. of Yr., Loyola U., 1975. Fellow Midwest Coun. for Social Rsch. on Aging (pres. 1969-70, 91-92, postdoctoral tng. dir. 1971-77), Ill. Sociol. Assn. (pres. 1969-70), Gerontol. Soc. Am. (chmn. social and behavioral sci. sect. 1980-81),

Internat. Gerontol. Assn.: mem. Soc. for Study Social Problems (chmn. spl. problems com. 1971, v.p. 1975, coun. 1978-80, pres. 1983, Disting. Scholar award family div. 1989), Am. Sociol. Assn. (coun. 1978-81, chmn. sect. family 1976, chmn. sect. sex roles 1975, Sorokin awards com. 1970-73, publs. com. 1972-73, nominations com. 1977, chmn. sect. on aging 1982-83 (Disting. Career award, 1992 Section on Aging), Cooley-Blumer awards com., 1984, Jessie Bernard awards com. 1984-86, disting. scholarly publ. awards selection com. 1988-89, awards policy com. 1990-92, co-chair com. on internat. sociology, 1992—), Soc. for the Study of Symbolic Interaction (mem 1977—, Mead award for Life Time Achievement, 1993), Internat. Sociol. Soc. (com. on family rsch. com. on work 1972—, rsch. com. on aging 1990—), Midwest Sociol. Assn. (state dir. 1972-74, pres. 1975-76, chair 1994—, publs. com. 1993—), Nat. Coun. Family Rels. (Burges award 1990, chair internat. sect. 1991-93), Polish Inst. of Arts and Scis. in Am. (dir. 1976-82), Polish Welfare Assn. (bd. dirs. 1988-91), Internat. Inst. Sociology, 1994—, Sociologists for Women in Society (mem. task force alternative work patterns, pres. 1993-94, adv. editor Gender and Society 1993-94), Soc. Study Symbolic Interaction (G.H. Mead award 1993), Hon. Doctor of Sci., Guelph U. Can. Home: 5815 N Sheridan Rd # 917 Chicago IL 60660-3859 Office: Loyola Univ Dept Sociology 6Seridan Rd Chicago IL 60626-5311

LOPATIN, ALAN G., lawyer; b. New Haven, Conn., May 25, 1956; s. Paul and Ruth (Rosen) L.; m. Debra Jo Engler, May 17, 1981; children: Jonah Adam, Asa Louis. BA, Yale U., 1978; JD, Am. U., 1981. Bar: D.C. 1981, U.S. Supreme Ct. 1985. Law clk. Fed. Maritime Commn., Washington, 1980-81; counsel com. on post office and civil service U.S. Ho. of Reps., Washington, 1981-82, counsel com. on budget, 1982-86, dep. chief counsel, 1986-87, counsel Temporary Joint Com. on Deficit Reduction, 1986, dep. gen. counsel Com. on P.O. and Civil Service 1987-90; gen. counsel Com. on Edn. & Labor, Washington, 1991-94; pres. Ledge Counsel, Inc., Washington, 1994—; mem. presdl. task force Health Care Reform, Washington, 1993. Mem. ABA, D.C. Bar Assn., Nat. Dem. Club, Yale Club. Democratic. Jewish. Home: 4958 Butterworth Pl NW Washington DC 20016-4354 Office: Ledge Counsel Inc 4958 Butterworth Pl NW Washington DC 20016

LOPATIN, DENNIS EDWARD, immunologist, educator; b. Chgo., Oct. 26, 1948; s. Leonard Harold and Cynthia (Shifrin) L.; m. Marie S. Ludmer, June 6, 1971 (div. 1983); 1 child, Jeremy; m. Constance Maxine McLeod, July 24, 1983. BS, U. Ill., 1970, MS, 1972, PhD, 1974. Postdoctoral fellow Northwestern U. Med. Sch., Chgo., 1974-75; rsch. scientist U. Mich., Ann Arbor, 1976-90, prof., 1982—. Contbr. articles to sci. jours. Mem. Am. Assn. Immunologists, Am. Soc. Microbiology, Internat. Assn. Dental Rsch., Sigma Xi. Office: U Mich Sch Dentistry Ann Arbor MI 48109-1078

LOPER, CARL RICHARD, JR., metallurgical engineer, educator; b. Wauwatosa, Wis., July 3, 1932; s. Carl Richard Sr. and Valberg (Sundby) L.; m. Jane Louise Loehning, June 30, 1956; children: Cynthia Louise, Anne Elizabeth. BS in Metall. Engring., U. Wis., 1955, MS in Metall. Engring., 1958, PhD in Metall. Engring., 1961; postgrad., U. Mich., 1960. Metall. engr. Pelton Steel Casting Co., Milw., 1955-56; instr., rsch. assoc. U. Wis., Madison, 1956-61, asst. prof., 1961-64, assoc. prof., 1964-68, prof. metall. engring., 1968-88, prof. materials sci. and engring., 1988—; assoc. chmn. dept. metall. and mineral engring. U. Wis., 1979—; rsch. metallurgist Allis Chalmers, Milw., 1961; cons., lectr. in field. Author: Principles of Metal Casting, 1965; contbr. over 250 articles to profl. jours. Chmn. 25th Anniversary of Ductile Iron Symposium, Montreal, 1973; sec. Yedrasil Lit. Soc., 1986-87. Foundry Edni. Found. fellow, 1953-55; Wheelabrator Corp. fellow, 1960; Ford Found. fellow, 1960; recipient Adams Meml. award Am. Welding Soc., 1963, Howard F. Taylor award, 1967, Service citation, 1969, 72, others; recipient Silver medal award of Sci. Merit Portuguese Foundry Assn., 1978, medal Chinese Foundrymen's Assn., 1989. Fellow Am. Soc. Metals (chmn. 1969-70), AIM; mem. Am. Foundrymen's Soc. (bd. dirs. 1967-70, 76-79, best paper award 1966, 67, 85, John A. Penton gold medal 1972, Hoyt Meml. lectr. 1992, Foundry Edni. Found. dirs. award 1994), Am. Welding Soc., Foundry Edni. Found., Torske Klubben (bd. dirs., co-founder 1978—), Blackhawk Country Club, Sigma Xi, Gamma Alpha, Alpha Sigma Mu, Tau Beta Pi. Lutheran. Achievements include significant contributions to understanding the solidification and metallurgy of ferrous and non-ferrous alloys; recognized authority on solidification and cast iron metallurgy, and on education in metallurgy and materials science. Office: U Wis Cast Metals Lab 1509 University Ave Madison WI 53706-1595

LOPER, GEORGE WILSON, JR., physical education educator; b. Phila., Sept. 1, 1927; s. George Wilson Sr. and Emma Margaretta (Davis) L.; m. Eleanor Ruth Shell, mar. 10, 1951 (div. Aug. 1967); children: George Wilson III, Carol Ann Loper Cloud; m. Jeanne Ann Lodeski, Aug. 12, 1967; children: Lynn Jeanne Loper Sakers, Anne Marie Loper Todd, John Vincent. BS, W. Chester State U., 1954; MEd, Temple U., 1957. Cert. tchr. Fla. Tchr., coach Media (Pa.) Pub. Schs., 1954-63, Duval County Sch. System, Jacksonville, Fla., 1963-67; tchr., dept. chmn., coach Bradford County Sch. System, Starke, Fla., 1967—. Dir. March Dimes Walkathon, Starke, 1970; coord. Spl. Olympics, Starke, 1970-89, chmn. Adminstrv. Bd. First Meth. Ch., Starke, 1970; co-chmn. Toys for Tots USMC, Starke, 1976, 78. With USMC Res., 1945-87. Named Coach of Yr. Fla. Times Union, 1966, 67, Coach of Yr. Cross Country Gainesville Sun, 1985, 86. Mem. AAHPERD (life), NEA, Nat. Health Assn. (life), Nat. High Sch. Coaches Assn., Fla. Athletic Coaches Assn. (state vice chmn. 1972—, Meritorious Svc. award 1988, Nat. Boys Track Coach of Yr. 1991, Life Membership award 1992), The Athletic Congress (lead instr. 1987—, internat. level track official 1983—, Track Hall of Fame 1987, Fla. Officials Assn. (high sch. games com. 1964—, state vice chmn. track 1972—), Bradford Edn. Assn. (v.p. 1977-79). Democrat. Methodist. Avocations: reading, music, art, swimming and track officiating. Home: RR 2 Box 1674 Starke FL 32091-9539 Office: Bradford High Sch 581 N Temple Ave Starke FL 32091-2609

LOPER, JAMES LEADERS, broadcasting executive; b. Phoenix, Sept. 4, 1931; s. John D. and Ellen Helen (Leaders) L.; m. Mary Louise Brion, Sept. 1, 1955; children: Elizabeth Margaret Sehran (Mrs. Michael K. Sehran), James Leaders Jr. BA, Ariz. State U., 1953; MA, U. Denver, 1957; PhD, U. So. Calif., 1967; DHL (hon.), Columbia Coll., 1973; LLD (hon.), Pepperdine U., 1978. Asst. dir. bur. broadcasting Ariz. State U., Tempe, 1953-55; news editor, announcer Sta. KTAR, Phoenix, 1955-56; dir. ednl. TV, Calif. State U., Los Angeles, 1960-64; v.p. Community TV So. Calif., Los Angeles, 1962-63; asst. to pres. Sta. KCET-Pub. TV, Los Angeles, 1963-65, sec., 1965-66, dir. ednl. services, 1964-65, asst. gen. mgr., 1965-66, v.p., gen. mgr., 1966-69, exec. v.p., gen. mgr., 1969-71, pres., gen. mgr., 1971-76, pres., CEO, 1976-82; exec. dir. Acad. TV Arts and Scis., 1983—; pres., chmn., audit com. Western Fed. Savs. and Loan Assn., L.A., 1979-83; bd. dirs. Global View, Washington; chmn. bd. dirs. Tennessee Ernie Ford Enterprises, 1994—; chmn. bd. Pub. Broadcasting Service, Washington, 1969-72; dir. Calif. Arts Coun., 1991—; adj. prof. Sch. Cinema and TV U. So. Calif., 1984—; sr. lectr. U. So. Calif., Los Angeles 1969-70; pres. Western Ednl. Network, 1968-70; mem. Gov.'s Ednl. TV and Radio Adv. Com., Calif., 1968-74; U.S. rep. CENTO Conf. Radio and TV, Turkey, 1978, trustee Internat. Council Nat. Acad. TV Arts and Scis., 1988—. Contbr. articles to profl. jours; contbr. to ETV: The Farther Vision, 1967, Broadcasting and Bargaining: Labor Relations in Radio and Television, 1970. Mem. adv. bd. Jr. League of Los Angeles, 1970-76, Jr. League of Pasadena, 1972-75, Los Angeles Jr. Arts Ctr., 1968-72; exec. v.p. Assocs. of Otis Art Inst., 1971-77, pres., 1975-77; chmn., dir. The Performing Tree, Los Angeles; bd. dirs. Los Angeles Civic Light Opera Co., 1974—, v.p., 1975—; bd. dirs. Sears-Roebuck Found., 1976-79; chmn. bd. visitors Annenburg Sch. Communications, U. So. Calif., 1975-80; trustee Poly. Sch., Pasadena; mem. Calif. State Arts Commn., 1991. Recipient Disting. Alumnus award Ariz. State U., 1972; Alumni award of Merit, U. So. Calif., 1975; Gov.'s award Hollywood chpt. Nat. Acad. TV Arts and Scis., 1975; Alumni Achievement award Phi Sigma Kappa, 1975; named Centennial Alumnus Nat. Assn. of State Univs. and Land Grant Colls., 1988. Named to Hall of Fame Walter Cronkite Sch. Comms., Ariz. State U., 1994 Mem. Acad. TV Arts and Scis. (past gov., v.p. Hollywood chpt., trustee nat. acad.), TV Acad. Found., Hollywood Radio and TV Soc. (treas., dir.), Western Ednl. Soc. Telecommunications (past pres.), James Calif. Pub. TV Stas. (past pres.), Young Pres.'s Orgn., Phi Sigma Kappa, Pi Delta Epsilon, Alpha Delta Sigma, Sigma Delta Chi. Presbyterian (chmn. Mass Media Task Force So. Calif. synod 1969-75). Clubs: Valley Hunt (Pasadena), Bel-Air Bay, California, Los Angeles, 100 of Los Angeles, Calif. (Los Angeles). Office: Acad TV Arts and Scis PO Box 7344 North Hollywood CA 91603-7344

LOPER, MERLE WILLIAM, law educator; b. Webster City, Iowa, July 9, 1940; s. Clifford Matthew and Alfrieda Sophia (Hiller) L.; m. Jean Allyn Kelley, Oct. 7, 1967; 1 dau., Kelley. B.A., Northwestern U., 1962; J.D., U. Chgo., 1965. Bar: Ind. 1966, Maine 1974, U.S. Supreme Ct. 1979. Law clk. U.S. Dist. Ct., Ft. Wayne, Ind., 1965-66; atty. div. civil rights Dept. Justice, 1966-69; teaching fellow Harvard U. Law Sch., 1969-71; assoc. prof. law U. Maine, 1971-75, prof., 1975—; vis. prof. Shanghai Maritime U., 1988; chief cons. Maine Probate Law Revision Commn., 1976-81; cons. probate rules com. Maine Supreme Ct., 1980-94; exec. sec., counsel Maine Com. Jud. Responsibility and Disability, 1983—; pvt. practice civil rights litigation law Portland, Maine, 1975-83; cons. on commn. in pub. affairs and law, civil rights litigation; cons. com. on ct. structure Maine Jud. Coun., 1984-85; convocation scholar on constn. U. So. Maine, 1987-88. Bd. dirs. Maine Civil Liberties Union., 1981-82; mem. legal panel Maine Civil Liberties Union, 1982-83. Office: 246 Deering Ave Portland ME 04102-2837 Be open to the world.

LOPER, ROBERT BRUCE, theater director, educator; b. Olathe, Colo., June 30, 1925; s. Roy Major and Charlotte (Matthews) L.; m. Shirley McClurg, Aug. 28, 1948; children—William, Matthew. B.A., U. Colo., 1948, M.A., 1951; Ph.D. in Elizabethan Lit. (Fulbright scholar Stratford-on-Avon 1951-53), Birmingham (Eng.) U., 1957. Actor, also documentary film writer N.Y.C., 1948-49; radio writer and newscaster Tacoma, 1949-50; faculty Stanford, 1953-68; prof., 1962-68, head dept. drama, 1963-68; founder Stanford Repertory Theatre, 1965; prof. drama U. Wash., 1968—; mem. San Franciso Actor's Workshop, 1960-64; dir., actor Oreg. Shakespeare Festival, Ashland, 1955—; vis. dir. Brecht's Caucasian Chalk Circle at Vancouver (Can.) Internat. Festival, 1959, Seattle Repertory Theatre, 1967; actor, dir. Contemporary Theatre, Empty Space Theatre, 1968—; dir. Joe Egg, The Price; guest dir. Talbot Theatre Centre, London, Ont., 1970. Actor, dir. Oedipus Rex, Death of a Salesman, Member of the Wedding, 1987, Seattle Repertory Theatre, 1967, Awake and Sing, Joe Egg, And Miss Reardon Drinks a Little, The Prize, 1987, A Contemporary Theatre, 1968—; dir. Billy Bishop, Old Times, Otherwise Engaged, Duet for One, 1985, Empty Space Theatre, 1975, Wozzeck; actor Fool for Love, 1984, Intiman Theatre, Waterworks, Kennedy Ctr., 1988; featured actor Bergen Internat. Festival, Norway, 1969; premiere Centralia (Pritchard), Stand Still (Arlin); producer (stage works) Am. premiere Dallapiccola's opera Night Flight, 1962, Alchemist, 1960. Mem. Phi Beta Kappa, Tau Kappa Delta. Home: 2641 E Helen St Seattle WA 98112-3619 The theatre has been my obsession and my religion. Directing a play is a kind of communion, the sharing of a fictional struggle which illuminates the more chaotic struggles and obsessions of our day-to-day lives. In making us more civilized, less lonely, the theatre can be teaching at its best.

LOPES, LOLA LYNN, psychologist, educator; b. Jackson Heights, N.Y., Mar. 14, 1941; d. Ivan Correa and Elizabeth (Edgemon) L.; m. Gregg Clifford Oden, Apr. 18, 1980. BA, U. Redlands, 1962; MA, Calif. State U., Long Beach, 1971; PhD, U. Calif. San Diego, La Jolla, 1974. Asst. prof. psychology U. Wis., Madison, 1974-81, assoc. prof., 1981-87, prof., 1987-90, chmn. dept., 1988-90; Pomerantz prof. bus. U. Iowa, Iowa City, 1990—. Contbr. articles to profl. jours. Sloan Found. fellow, U. Chgo., 1981. Mem. Soc. for Judgement and Decision Making (pres. 1989-90), Psychonomic Soc., Cognitive Sci. Soc., Soc. for Math. Psychology, Am. Psychol. Soc., Sigma Xi. Home: 2021 Laurence Ct NE Iowa City IA 52240-9150 Office: U Iowa Dept Mgmt And Orgns Iowa City IA 52242

LOPES, MARIA FERNANDINA, commissioner; b. Ganda, Angola, Portugal, Dec. 12, 1934; came to U.S., 1963; d. Rodrigo do Carmo and Maria Jose Fernandes (Mendes) Marques; m. Fernandes Esteves Lopes, Aug. 11, 1962; children: Lisa Maria Lopes Moss, Mark Esteves. Student, Lisbon (Portugal) Comml. Inst., 1953, Massasoit Community Coll., Brockton, Mass., 1988. With archives dept. Portuguese Govt., Lisbon, 1958-62; congl. aide Congresswoman Margaret M. Heckler, Fall River, Taunton, Mass., 1972-74; mem. Taunton (Mass.) Sch. Com., 1976-93; commr. Bristol County, Mass., 1991—. Founder Day of Portugal, 1974. Avocations: traveling, politics, antiques, music. Home: 28 Worcester St Taunton MA 02780-2041 Office: Office County Commissioners Superior Courthouse Nine Court St PO Box 208 Taunton MA 02780

LOPEZ, ANDY, university athletic coach. Head coach Pepperdine U. Waves, 1989-94, U. Florida, 1994—. NCAA Divsn. IA Champions, 1992. Office: U Florida Athletic Dept Gainesville FL 32611*

LOPEZ, BARRY HOLSTUN, writer; b. Port Chester, N.Y., Jan. 6, 1945; s. Adrian Bernard and Mary Frances (Holstun) L.; m. Sandra Jean Landers, June 10, 1967. BA, U. Notre Dame, 1966, MA in Teaching, 1968; postgrad., U. Oreg., 1968-69; LHD (hon.), Whittier Coll., 1988, U. Portland, 1994. Free-lance writer, 1970—; assoc. The Freedom Forum Media Studies Ctr., N.Y.C., 1985—. Author: Desert Notes, 1976, Giving Birth to Thunder, 1978, Of Wolves and Men, 1978 (John Burroughs Soc. medal 1979, Christophers of N.Y. medal 1979, Pacific Northwest Booksellers award in nonfiction 1979), River Notes, 1979, Winter Count, 1981 (Disting. Recognition award Friends Am. Writers in Chgo. 1982), Arctic Dreams, 1986 (Nat. Book award in nonfiction Nat. Book Found. 1986, Christopher medal 1987, Pacific Northwest Booksellers award 1987, Frances Fuller Victor award in nonfiction Oreg. Inst. Literary Arts 1987), Crossing Open Ground, 1988, Crow and Weasel, 1990 (Parents Choice Found. award), The Rediscovery of North America, 1991, Field Notes, 1994 (Pacific Northwest Bookseller award in fiction 1995); also numerous articles, essays and short stories; contbg. editor Harper's mag., 1981-82, 84—, N.Am. Rev., 1977—; works translated into Japanese, Swedish, German, Dutch, Italian, French, Norwegian, Chinese, Finnish, Spanish. Recipient award in Lit., Am. Acad. of Arts and Letters, 1986, Gov.'s award for Arts, 1990, Lannan Found. award, 1990, Antarctic Svc. medal USN/NSF, 1989; John Simon Guggenheim Found. fellow, 1987, Pacific N.W. Booksellers award in fiction, 1995. Mem. PEN Am. Ctr., Authors Guild, Poets and Writers.

LOPEZ, DELMIRA CASTRO, school system administrator; b. Lubbock, Tex., Apr. 9, 1954; d. Juventino Lopez and Eloisa (Lopez) Castro; m. Joe Alvarado, Dec. 24, 1976; children: Joe Geoffrey, Justin Timothy. BS, Tex. Tech U., 1976, MEd, 1985. Tchr. Lubbock (Tex.) Ind. Sch. Dist. 1976-93, asst. prin., 1993—. Conf. leader Bapt. Gen. Conv. Tex., 1989-92. Mem. ASCD, Tex. Classroom Tchrs. Assn., Lubbock Area Assn. Bilingual Edn. (pres. 1992-93, pres.-elect 1991-92, Outstanding Bilingual Educator 1991), Tex. Elem. Prins. and Suprs. Assn., Tex. Assn. for Bilingual Edn., Lubbock Classroom Tchrs. Assn. (FR rep. 1990), Phi Delta Kappa, Delta Kappa Gamma. Republican. Avocations: reading, soccer, exercising, bicycling. Home: 4214 45th St Lubbock TX 79413

LOPEZ, FRANCISCO, IV, health care administrator; b. San Jose, Costa Rica, Aug. 31, 1956; s. Francisco III and Myriam (Bolanos) L.; m. Marie Jeanne de Lassus; children: Matthew Chase, Kathryn Louise, Elizabeth Myriam Jane, James Austin. BS, La. State U., 1976, MHA, Tulane U., 1980. Adminstrv. asst. Mercy Hosp. of New Orleans, 1980-81, asst. v.p., 1981-82, v.p., 1982-85, exec. v.p., 1985-86, chief operating officer, 1986—; exec. v.p. Mercy Health Sys., 1995—; pres. St. Mary's Hosp., 1995—; bd. cons. St. John's Place, New Orleans, 1986—. V.p. Calhoun/Palmer Neighborhood Assn., New Orleans, 1984-85; bd. dirs. Holy Name of Jesus Sch., New Orleans, 1985, United Cerebral Palsy, New Orleans, 1986, Mount St. Mary High Sch., Okla. Cath. Health Care Assn. Recipient Associated U. Programs in Health Adminstrn. scholarship, 1979, Nat. Hispanic scholarship, 1980. Fellow Am. Coll. Health Care Execs. (Foster G. McGaw scholarship 1979); mem. Am. Hosp. Assn., Fedn. Am. Hosps., New Health Care Mgrs., So. Yacht Club (new Orleans), Greens Country Club (Oklahoma City), Oakwood Country Club. Clubs: So. Yacht (new Orleans); Greens Country (Oklahoma City). Avocations: tennis, travel, swimming. Home: 617 Glenridge Dr Edmond OK 73013 Office: Mercy Health System 4300 W Memorial Rd Oklahoma City OK 73120-8397

LOPEZ, GERALD P., law educator; b. 1948. BA, U. So. Calif., 1970; JD, Harvard U., 1974. Law clk. to presiding justice U.S. Dist. Ct. (so. dist.) Calif., San Diego, 1974-75; pvt. practice law San Diego, 1975-79; asst. prof. Calif. Western Sch. Law, San Diego, 1976-78; vis. prof. UCLA, 1978-79, acting prof., 1979-83, prof., 1983-85; vis. prof. Harvard U., Cambridge,

Mass., 1983-84; vis. prof. Stanford (Calif.) U, 1984-85, prof., 1985—. Office: Stanford U Stanford Law Sch Nathan Abbott Way Stanford CA 94305

LOPEZ, JOE A., school system administrator. Supt. Cuba (N.Mex.) Ind. Schs., 1978—. Recipient Nat. Superintendent of the Yr. award, New Mexico, Am. Assn. of School Administrators, 1993. Office: Cuba Ind Schs PO Box 70 Cuba NM 87013

LOPEZ, JOSEPH JACK, oil company executive, consultant; b. N.Y.C., July 26, 1932; s. Florentino Estrada and Leah (Bodner) L.; m. June Elliott, June 20, 1953; children: Karen Marie Lopez Lynch, Debra Jo Lopez Newton, Laura Jean Lopez Berrell. Student, CCNY, 1955-59. Project estimator Chem. Constrn.-Engrs., N.Y.C., 1960-64, Dorr Oliver-Engrs., Stamford, Conn., 1964-66; chief estimator R.M. Parsons-Engrs., Frankfurt, Germany, 1966-74; mgr. project svcs. A.G. McKee-Engrs., Berkley Heights, N.J., 1974-76; mgr. tech. svcs. Rsch. Cottrell Corp., Sommerville, N.J., 1976-78; cons. Booz Allen & Hamilton, Abu Dhabi, United Arab Emirates, 1978-84; v.p. XL Tech. Corp., N.Y.C., 1984-87; cons. Qatar Gen. Pete Corp., Doha, 1987-90; pres. J. Lopez Cons., Babylon, N.Y., 1990—; estimator Combustion Engrng. Co., N.Y.C., 1955-60. With USAF, 1950-54. Mem. Am. Assn. Cost Engrs., Project Mgmt. Inst. Republican. Roman Catholic. Home and Office: 15 Hinton Ave Babylon NY 11702

LOPEZ, JUDITH CARROLL, lawyer; b. Boulder, Colo., Dec. 22, 1945; d. Robert Warren and Irene Caroll (Young) Adams; m. Richard Manuel Lopez, Mar. 19, 1967 (div. Nov. 1975); children: Heather Linn, Amber Elise. BA, Colo. Coll., 1967; JD, U. Wyo., 1979. Assoc. R. Michael Mullikin, Jackson Hole, Wyo., 1979-81; pvt. practice Jackson Hole, 1981-82; atty. KN Energy, Inc., Lakewood, Colo., 1982-88; assoc. Hawley & Vanderwerf, Denver, 1988-89; corp. counsel ANR Freight System, Inc., Golden, Colo., 1990—; bd. dirs. Edit, Inc. Bd. mgrs. Stonebridge Townhomes Homeowners Assn., Lakewood, 1993—. Mem. Transp. Lawyers Assn., Wyo. Bar Assn. Avocations: skiing, hiking, bridge. Office: ANR Freight System Inc 1819 Denver West Dr Bldg 26 Golden CO 80401

LOPEZ, LOURDES, ballerina; b. Havana, Cuba, 1958; came to U.S., 1959. Studied with, Alexander Nigodoff and Martha Mahr, Miami, Perry Brunson; attended, Sch. of Am. Ballet, N.Y.C. Mem. corps de ballet N.Y.C. Ballet, 1974-80, soloist, 1980-84, prin., 1984—. Created roles in Peter Martins' Sonate di Scarlatti and Rejouissance; other repertory includes: La Sonnambula, Divertimento No. 15, Serenade, Stars and Stripes, Apollo, Kammermusik No. 2, Firebird, The Four Seasons, The Goldberg Variations, Moves, Violin Concerto, Concerto Barocco, Theme and Variations, N.Y.C. Ballet's Balanchine Celebration, 1993, Cortège Hongrois, others; appeared in PBS series Dance in Am. Office: care NYC Ballet Inc NY State Theater Lincoln Ctr Plz New York NY 10023*

LOPEZ, MANUEL, immunology and allergy educator; b. Bucaramanga, Colombia, Sept. 30, 1939; married; 4 children. BS, Colegio San Pedro Claver, Bucaramanga, 1956; MD, Univ. Javeriana, Bogota, Colombia, 1963. Diplomate Am. Bd. Allergy and Immunology, Am. Bd. Diagnostic Lab. Immunology. Intern Hosp. San Juan De Dios, Bucaramanga, 1962-63, resident, 1963-64, med. dir., 1969-71; clin. and rsch. fellow dept. medicine allergy unit Harvard U. and Harvard Med. Sch. at Mass. Gen. Hosp., Boston, 1964-68; dir. med. rsch. Univ. Indsl. De Santander, Bucaramanga, 1968-69; dir. immunology svc. lab. La. State Med. Ctr., New Orleans, 1971-74; asst. prof. medicine med. ctr. La. State U., New Orleans, 1971-74; from clin. asst. prof. to assoc. prof. med. sch. Tulane U., New Orleans, 1974-89, prof., 1989—, dir. immunology diagnostic lab. med. sch., 1974-83, dir. clin. immunology labs., 1983—, program dir. allergy and immunology tng. program, 1990—, acting chief sect. allergy and clin. immunology, 1990-91, chief, 1991—; mem. med.-sci. adv. com. Asthma and Allergy Found. Am., 1986-89; ad hoc mem. immunological sci. study sect. NIH, 1987, allergy and clin. immunology spl. reviewer immunology and transplantation rsch. com., 1988, mem. gen. clin. rsch. ctrs. com., 1993—; reviewer merit rev. grants VA, 1988, 89, 90; grant program reviewer Ctrs. of Excellence, DHH, 1991; mem. allergic products adv. com. FDA, 1993—; mem. spl. rev. com. Nat. Inst. Allergy and Infectious Diseases, 1993; presenter in field. Mem. editl. bd. Jour. Allergy and Clin. Immunology, 1986-94, reviewer, 1987-88; contbr. articles to profl. jours. and chpts. to books. Fellow John Simmon Guggenheim Meml. Found., 1964-66. Fellow Am. Acad. Allergy and Clin. Immunology (mem. internat. com. 1986-89, mem. immunotherapy of asthma com. 1987—, mem. Latin Ctrl. and South Am. com. 1987—, chmn. internat. grant aids 1988-89, mem. continuing med. edn. com. 1992-94), Am. Coll. Chest Physicians; mem. Am. Assn. Immunologists, Am. Fedn. Clin. Rsch., Am. Thoracic Soc., U.S.-Colombian Med. Assn. (pres. IX Congress 1989), La. Allergy Soc., N.Y. Acad. Scis., Southeastern Allergy Assn., Assn. Med. Lab. Immunologists, Internat. Assn. Aerobiology, Cordoba Allergy Soc. (hon.), Sigma Xi. Office: Tulane U Med Sch Clin Immunology Sect 1700 Perdido St 3d Flr New Orleans LA 70112

LOPEZ, MARLENE, chief executive officer, Bronx Psychiatric Center; b. South Amboy, N.J., Aug. 1, 1939; d. Frank and Antoinette (Charoullo) L.; 1 child, Sean. BA, Livingston Coll., 1974; MSW, Rutgers U., 1975, PhD, 1986. Asst. fed. liaison N.J. Dept. Human Services, Trenton, 1975-76; program devel. specialist N.J. div. Mental Health, Princeton, 1976-77; asst. hosp. adminstr. Marlboro Psychiat. Hosp., N.J., 1977-81; chief exec. officer Ancora Psychiat. Hosp., Hammonton, N.J., 1981-86; N.Y.C. regional dir. N.Y.C. Office Mental Health, 1986—, CEO, Bronx Psychiat. Ctr., 1988; faculty mem. Einstein Med. Sch., Bronx, 1988. Sec. League Women Voters, Madisontownship, N.J., 1965. Mem. Nat. Assn. Mental Health Adminstrn., N.Y.C. Faculty Dirs. Assn. (N.Y.C. rep.), Assn. Hispanic Mental Health Profls. Avocations: yoga instr., cyclist, tennis, skiing.

LOPEZ, NANCY, professional golfer; b. Torrance, Calif., Jan. 6, 1957; d. Domingo and Marina (Griego) L.; m. Ray Knight, Oct. 25, 1982; children: Ashley Marie, Erinn Shea, Torri Heather. Student, U. Tulsa, 1976-78. Author: The Education of a Woman Golfer, 1979. First victory at Bent Tree Classic, Sarasota, Fla., 1978; named AP Athlete for 1978; admitted to Ladies Profl. Golf Assn. Hall of Fame, 1987, to PGA World Golf Hall of Fame, 1989. Mem. Ladies Profl. Golf Assn. (Player and Rookie of Yr. 1978). Republican. Baptist. Wiiner 33 LPGA Tour events, 2 maj. championships. Office: care Internat Mgmt Group Ste 1300 1 Erieview Plz Cleveland OH 44114*

LOPEZ, RAMON, recording industry executive. Now chmn. bd. dirs. WEA Internat. Inc., N.Y.C. Office: WEA Internat Inc 75 Rockefeller Plz New York NY 10019-6907*

LOPEZ, THOMAS JOSEPH, naval officer; b. Powellton, W.Va., Jan. 20, 1940; s. Peter. J. and Juanita O. (Holstein) L.; m. Vivian J. Hall, Feb. 27, 1960; children: Thomas J. II, Dominique M. BA in Internat. Rels. cum laude, W.Va. Inst. Tech., 1959; MS in Pers. Mgmt., Naval Postgrad. Sch., 1973; HHD (hon.), W.Va. Tech. Inst., 1989. Commd. ensign USN, 1964, advanced through grades to capt.; 1st lt., combat info. officer, anti-submarine divsn. officer USS E.A. Greene (DD 711), 1965-67; weapons officer USS W.L. Lind (DD 703), 1967-69; comdg. officer River Divsn. 153, 1969-70; flag sec., asst. surface ops. Comcrudesgru Eight, 1974-77; exec. officer USS Truett (FF-1095), 1977-79; cruiser-destroyer Atlantic placement officer Bur. Naval Pers., 1979-80; spl. asst. for navy pers. Office of Sec. of Navy, 1980-82; comdg. officer USS Stump (DD-978), 1982-84. Decorated D.S.M., Navy D.S.M., Legion of Merit (3), Bronze Star with combat V, Navy Commendation medal with combat V (2), Navy Achievement medal with combat V, Vietnam Cross of Gallantry, Nat. Def. Svc. medal with 2 stars; named Disting. West Virginian, Gov. of W.Va., 1984, Outstanding West Virginian, pres. of Salem Coll. and U.S. Senator Randolph, 1984, W.Va. Man of Yr., Italian Heritage Festival, 1989. Office: Dept Navy Naval Operations Box 117 Powellton WV 25161

LOPEZ-COBOS, JESUS, conductor; b. Toro, Spain, Feb. 25, 1940; m. Alicia Ferrer, May 15, 1987; 3 children. PhD in philosophy and music, U. Madrid, 1964; diploma composition, Madrid Conservatory, 1966; diploma conducting, Vienna (Austria) Acad., 1969. Gen. music dir. Deutsche Oper Berlin, 1981-90; prin. guest condr. London Philharm. 1981-86; prin. condr., artistic dir. Spanish Nat. Orch., 1984-89; music dir. Cin. Orch., 1986—;

music dir. Orchestre de Chambre de Lausanne, Switzerland, 1990, condr.; also condr. concerts Edinburgh Festival, London Symphony, Royal Philharm., N.Y. Philharm., L.A. Philharm., Chgo. Symphony, Cleve. Orch., Phila. Orch., Berlin Philharm., Berlin Radio Orch., Amsterdam Concertgebouw, Vienna Philharm., Swiss Romande, Muncih Philarharm., Hamburg NDR, Oslo Philharm., Zurich Tonhalle, Israel Philharm., opera prodns. at Royal Opera House, Covent Garden, London, La Scala, Milan, Italy, Met. Opera, N.Y.C., Paris Opera, others; recs. include Lucia di Lammermoor New Philham. Orch., Otello, recital and operatic disc with José Carrera and London Symphony Orch., Liszt's Dante Symphony with Swiss Romande, Falla's Three-Cornered Hat, R-K Capricio Espangnole, Chiabrier's Espana with L.A. Philharm., others. Recipient 1st prize Besancon Internat. Condr.'s Competition, 1969, Prince of Asturias award Spanish Govt., 1981, 1st Class Disting. Svc. medal Fed. Republic of Germany, 1989. Office: Cin Symphony Orch 1241 Elm St Cincinnati OH 45210-2267 also: Orchestre de Chambre de Lausanne, Chemin de devin 72, CH-1012 Lausanne Switzerland*

LÓPEZ-MORILLAS, JUAN, Spanish and comparative literature educator; b. Jaén, Spain, Aug. 11, 1913; came to U.S., 1935; s. Emilio López-Morillas and Teresa Ortiz; m. Frances Mapes, Aug. 12, 1937; children: Martin, Consuelo, Julian. BLitt, U. Madrid, 1929; PhD, U. Iowa, 1940; LHD (hon.), Brown U., 1979. Asst. prof. romance langs. U. Iowa, Iowa City, 1940-43; asst. prof. Spanish Brown U., Providence, 1943-47, assoc. prof. Spanish, 1947-51, prof. Spanish and comparative lit., 1951-65, Alumni/Alumnae Univ. prof., 1965-73, William R. Kenan prof. humanities, 1973-78, prof. emeritus, 1978—, chmn. dept. Spanish and Italian, 1960-67, chmn. dept. comparative lit., 1967-71; prof. Spanish and comparative lit. U. Tex., Austin, 1978-79, Ashbel Smith prof., 1979-89, prof. emeritus, 1989—; vis. scholar U. Ctr. in Va., 1976-77. Author: El Krausismo español, 1956, Intelectuales y espirituales, 1961, Hacia el 98, 1972, Racionalismo pragmatico, 1988; editor, translator books; contbr. articles to profl. jours. Decorated Order of Isabella the Catholic by King Juan Carlos of Spain, 1985; grantee Am. Coun. Learned Socs., Am. Philos. Soc.; Phi Beta Kappa vis. scholar, 1966-67; Guggenheim fellow, 1950-51, 57-58. Mem. Internat. Assn. Hispanists (pres. 1980-83), Hispanic Soc. Am., MLA (mem. exec. com. 1981-85), Academia Norteamericana de la Lengua Española, Royal Spanish Acad. (corr.). Democrat. Avocations: travel, photography. Home: 2200 Hartford Rd Austin TX 78703-3127 Office: U Tex Dept Spanish Portuguese Austin TX 78712

LOPICCOLO, JOSEPH, psychologist, educator, author; b. L.A., Sept. 13, 1943; s. Joseph E. and Adeline C. (Russo) Lo P.; m. Leslie Joan Matlen, June 20, 1964 (div. 1978); 1 child, Joseph Townsend; m. Cathryn Gail Pridal, Dec. 20, 1980; 1 child, Michael James. BA with highest honors, UCLA, 1965; MS, Yale U., 1968, PhD, 1969. Lic. psychologist, Mo. Asst. prof. U. Oreg., Eugene, 1969-73; assoc. prof. U. Houston, 1973-74; prof. SUNY, Stony Brook, 1974-84, Tex. A&M U., College Station, 1984-87; prof. psychology U. Mo., Columbia, 1987—, chmn. dept., 1987-90. Author: Becoming Orgasmic, 1976, 2d edit., 1988, also book chpts.; editor: Handbook of Sex Therapy, 1978; contbr. numerous articles to profl. jours. Woodrow Wilson Found. fellow; NIH rsch. grantee, 1973-84. Fellow Am. Psychol. Assn.; mem. Internat. Acad. Sex Rsch., Soc. for Sci. Study of Sex (pres. 1983-84, Alfred Kinsey Meml. Rsch. award), Phi Beta Kappa, Sigma Xi. Office: U Mo Dept Psychology 210 McAlester Hall Columbia MO 65211

LOPINA, LAWRENCE THOMAS, manufacturing executive; b. Chgo., Nov. 9, 1930; s. Thomas F. and Augustine A. (Schwantes) L.; PhB, U. Notre Dame, 1952; MBA, DePaul U., 1953; MBA, U. Chgo., 1963; m. Marion T. Toomey, Nov. 5, 1955; children: Douglas D. Lawrence M., Mary E., Celeste N., James P. Jr. CPA, Wis.; cert. mgmt. acct. Acct. Haskins & Sells, CPA's, Chgo., 1952-53; acctg. positions with Motorola, Inc., Chgo., 1953-63; div. contr. then v.p. fin. fluid power group Applied Power, Inc., Milw., 1963-74; sr. v.p. fin. Broan Mfg. Co., Inc., Hartford, Wis., 1974—, former dir. With AUS, 1953-55. Mem. AICPA, Inst. Mgmt. Accts., Fin. Execs. Inst. (past pres. Milw. chpt.), Wis. Inst. CPA's, Catholic League (Wisc. chpt. treas.), Beta Gamma Sigma. Club: KC. Office: 926 W State St Hartford WI 53027-1066

LOPPNOW, MILO ALVIN, clergyman, former church official; b. St. Charles, Minn., Jan. 13, 1914; s. William and Doretta (Penz) L.; m. Gertrude Stoltz, Feb. 6, 1942; children—Donald, Bruce, David. B.A., Moravian Coll., 1937; M.Div., Moravian Theol. Sem., 1940, D.D., 1970. Ordained to ministry Moravian Ch. in Am., 1940; pastor congregations nr. Wisconsin Rapids, Wis., 1940-41, Waconia, Minn., 1941-53; pastor congregations nr. Lakeview Ch., Madison, Wis., 1953-64; dist. pres. Western Dist. Moravian Ch., Madison, 1965-78; elected bishop, 1970. Chmn. Youth Commn., Madison, 1957-63; Trustee Moravian Coll., 1954-78, Moravian Theol. Sem., Bethlehem, Pa.; former chaplain, dir. devel. Marquardt Meml. Manor, Watertown, Wis.

LOPREATO, JOSEPH, sociology educator, author; b. Stefanaconi, Italy, July 13, 1928; came to U.S., 1950; s. Frank and Marianna (Pavone) L.; m. Carolyn H. Prestopino, July 18, 1954; (div. 1971); children: Gregory F., Marisa S. Schmidt; m. Sally A. Cook, Aug. 24, 1972 (div. 1978). BA in Sociology, U. Conn., 1956; MA in Sociology, Yale U., 1957; PhD in Sociology, 1960. Asst. prof. sociology U. Mass., Amherst, 1960-62; vis. lectr. U. Rome, 1962-64; assoc. prof. U. Conn., Storrs, 1964-66; prof. sociology U. Tex., Austin, 1968—; chmn. dept. sociology U. Tex., 1969-72; vis. prof. U. Catania, Italy, 1974, U. Calabria, Italy, 1980; mem. steering com. Council European Studies, Columbia U., 1977-80; chmn. sociology com. Council for Internat. Exchange of Scholars, 1977-79; mem. Internat. Com. Mezzogiorno, 1986—; Calabria Internat. Com., 1988—. Author: Italian Made Simple, 1959, Vilfredo Pareto, 1965, Peasants No More, 1967, Italian Americans, 1970, Class, Conflict and Mobility, 1972, Social Stratification, 1974, The Sociology of Vilfredo Pareto, 1975, La Stratificazione Sociale negli Stati Uniti, 1945-1975, 1977, Human Nature and Biocultural Evolution, 1984, Evoluzione e Natura Umana, 1990, Mai Più Contadini, 1990; contbr. articles to profl. jours. Mem. Nat. Italian-Am. Com. for U.S.A. Bicentennial; mem. exec. com. Congress Italian Politics, 1977-80. Served to cpl. U.S. Army, 1952-54. Fulbright faculty research fellow, 1962-64, 73-74; Social Sci. Research Council faculty research fellow, 1963-64; NSF faculty research fellow, 1965-68; U. Tex. Austin research fellow, spring 1985, spring 1993; Guido Dorso award for U.S.A., Italy, 1992. Mem. AAAS (behavioral sci. rsch. prize com. 1992-94), Internat. Sociol. Assn., Am. Sociol. Assn., European Sociobiolog. Soc., Evolution and Behavior Soc., So. Sociol. Soc. (assoc. editor Am. Sociol. Rev. 1970-72, Social Forces 1987-90, Jour. Polit. and Mil. Sociology 1980—), Internat. Soc. Human Ethology. Catholic-Episcopalian. Office: Univ of Tex Dept Sociology Austin TX 78712

LOPRESTI, MARILYN ANGELA, school system administrator; b. N.Y.C., Oct. 11, 1944; d. Mario Vincent and Theresa (Capalbi) Caccioppoli; m. Anthony C. LoPresti, Feb. 12, 1966; children: Vincent Joseph, Christine Marie. BA, St. Johns U., 1966; MA, SUNY, Stony Brook, 1974; PhD, NYU, 1986. Cert. dist. adminstr., sch. adminstr. and supr., elem. tchr., 7-12 social studies tchr., N.Y. From social studies tchr. to asst. prin. Longwood High Sch., Middle Island, N.Y., 1974-85; asst. prin. Kings Park (N.Y.) High Sch., 1985-87; pers. adminstr. Kings Park Sch. Dist., 1987-88; asst. prin. William T. Rogers Middle Sch., Kings Park, 1988-91; elem. and sec. curriculum and instruction adminstr. Kings Park Ctrl. Sch. Dist., 1991—. Contbr. articles to profl. jours. Impartial hearing officer N.Y. State Edn. Dept., 1992—. Mem. Phi Delta Kappa (v.p. 1983-85, pres. 1985-87). Home: PO Box 715 Miller Place NY 11764 Office: Kings Park Ctrl Sch Dist 101 Church St Kings Park NY 11754

LOPRESTI, PHILIP VINCENT, electrical engineer, researcher, consultant; b. Johnstown, Pa., Sept. 27, 1932; s. Philip and Lucy Marietta (Angelo) L.; m. Patricia Jeanne Litzinger, Jan. 31, 1959; children: Daniel P., David B., Amy P. BSEE, U. Notre Dame, 1954, MSEE, 1958; PhDEE, Purdue U., 1963. Rsch. engr. Westinghouse Rsch. Labs., Pitts., 1963-64; asst. prof. elec. engring. Ill. Inst. Tech., Chgo., 1964-67, Northwestern U., Evanston, Ill. 1967-70; cons. mem. tech. staff AT&T Bell Labs., Princeton, N.J., 1970—; mem. engring. accreditation commn. Accreditation Bd. for Engring. and Tech., 1989-94. Author numerous articles on automatic control theory, computer-aided circuit design, digital signal processing. 1st lt. U.S. Army,

1955-56. Fellow IEEE (mem. publs. bd. 1986-87, mem. tech. activities bd. 1993, cirs. and systems soc., v.p. confs. 1988-90, v.p. adminstrn. 1990-92, pres.-elect 1992, pres. 1993, past pres. 1994). Office: AT&T Engring Rsch Ctr PO Box 900 Princeton NJ 08542-0900

LOPRETE, JAMES HUGH, lawyer; b. Detroit, Sept. 17, 1929; s. James Victor and Effie Hannah (Brown) LoP.; m. Marion Ann Garrison, Sept. 11, 1952; children: James Scott, Kimberly Anne, Kent Garrison, Robert Drew. AB, U. Mich., 1951, JD with Distinction, 1953. Bar: Mich. 1954. Practiced law Detroit, 1953—; atty. Chrysler Corp., Detroit, 1953; assoc. firm Monaghan, LoPrete, McDonald, Yakima & Grenke, P.C. and predecessor firms, Detroit, from 1954; mem. firm Monaghan, LoPrete, McDonald, Yakima & Grenke, P.C. and predecessor firms, 1966—, pres., 1979—; bd. dirs. Drake's Batter Mix Co., Orsco Inc.; instr. legal writing Wayne State U., Detroit, 1955-57. Trustee U. Mich. Club of Detroit Scholarship Fund, 1967, pres., 1982— Samuel Westerman Found., 1971—, pres., 1984, John R. & M. Margrite Davis Found. Fellow Am. Coll. Trust and Estate Counsel, Internat. Acad. Estate and Trust Law; mem. ABA, Oakland County bar assns., State Bar Mich., Detroit Athletic Club (dir. 1983-88, sec. 1986-88), Orchard Lake Country Club, U. Mich. of Greater Detroit (pres. 1966). Home: 2829 Warner Dr Orchard Lake MI 48324-2449 Office: Monaghan LoPrete McDonald et al 1700 N Woodward Ave Ste A Bloomfield Hills MI 48304-2249

LOQUASTO, SANTO, theatrical set designer; b. Wilkes-Barre, Pa.. Grad., King's Coll., Wilkes-Barre; student, Yale U. Drama Sch. Set designer for repertory cos. including Hartford Stage Co., Long Whart Theater, New Haven, Conn., 1967-68, Yale Sch. Drama Repertory Theater. N.Y.C. debut Astor Place, 1970; set designer Broadway and off-Broadway prodns. Sticks and Bones, 1971, That Championship Season; designer other prodns. including The Secret Affairs of Mildred Wild, 1972, Siamese Connections, The Orphan, As You Like It, King Lear, A Public Prosecutor is Sick of It All, Washington, 1973, The Tempest, The Dance of Death, Pericles, The Merry Wives of Windsor, Richard III, Mert and Phil, Cherry Orchard, Hartford Stage Co., That Championship Season, London, 1974, A Midsummer Night's Dream, A Doll's House, Hamlet, The Comedy of Errors, Awake and Sing, Kennedy's Children, 1975, Murder Among Friends, Heartbreak House, Legend, Measure for Measure, The Glass Menagerie, Hartford, 1976, The Lower Depths, The Cherry Orchard, Agamemnon, Cafe Crown (Antoinette Perry award, 1989); scenery and costume design, Jakes's Women, 1992; film prodn. designer, Shadows and Fog, 1992; costumes only Golda, 1977, Curse of the Starving Class, The Play's the Thing, The Mighty Gents, Stop the World - I Want to Get Off, King of Hearts, 1978, Sarava, The Goodbye People, Bent, 1979, Grand Hotel, 1990; prin. designer costumes only, Twyla Tharp Dance Found.; other ballet design includes Don Quixote for Am. Ballet Theater, 1978, Heart of the Matter for Joffrey Ballet, 1986, costumes for La Salle des Pas Perdus for Les Grand Ballets Canadiens, 1988, set and costumes for Pastorale, Nat. Ballet Can., 1990; designer sets and costumes for opera including La Dafne, Spoleto Festival, Italy, 1973; designer sets for opera including San Diego Opera, Opera Soc. Washington, San Francisco Spring Opera. Recipient Drama Desk award and Variety Poll of N.Y., Drama Critics award for Sticks and Bones and That Championship Season 1971, 72;; prodn. designer films Radio Days, 1987, Bright Lights, Big City, 1988, Big, 1988. Recipient Antoinette Perry award (Tony), 1990.

LORAN, ERLE, artist; b. Mpls., Oct. 3, 1905; m. Clyta Sisson, May 8, 1937 (dec. Mar. 1982); m. Ruth Schorer, July 22, 1993. Student, U. Minn., 1922-23; grad., Mpls. Sch. Art, 1926; M.F.A. (hon.), 1968. Travelled and painted in Europe, 1926-30; prof. art U. Calif., Berkeley; now prof. emeritus. U. Calif.; participant Cezanne, the Lateworks Symposium Mus. Modern Art, 1977. Represented in permanent collections of Denver Art Mus., San Francisco Mus. Art, U. Minn., Santa Barbara Mus. Art, San Diego Mus. Art, Krannert Art Mus. of U. Ill., 1965, Art Mus. U. Calif. Berkeley, Oakland (Calif.) Mus., Smithsonian Instn., Washington, also numerous pvt. collections; U.S. Treasury Dept. purchases Great Shipyards and Last Year's Swamplands; works in large exhbns. in U.S. since 1933, numerous one-man shows, 1934—; including Oakland Mus., 1981, San Francisco Gallery, Paula Anglim, Bergruen Gallery, 1989, Univ. Art Mus., Berkeley, Calif., 1990, DeYoung Mus., San Francisco, 1994; invited nat. exhbns. Mus. Modern Art, 1935, Whitney Mus. Am. Art, 1943, 44, 48, Carnegie Inst., 1942, Pa. Acad., 1945, Met. Mus. Art, 1950, 51, 53, also 9 other nat. mus.; author: Cezanne's Composition, 1943, 45, 46, 47, 63, 70, 77, 81, paperback edit., 1985; also author numerous critical essays on art; chpts. on Cezanne in Les Peintres Celebres (Lucien Mazenod), Paris, 1948. Recipient numerous prizes and awards.; Awarded Paris prize ($6,000) by John Armstrong Chaloner Found., N.Y.C., 1926. Club: Arts (Berkeley). Home: 10 Kenilworth Ct Kensington CA 94707-1320

LORAND, LASZLO, biochemist, educator; b. Gyor, Hungary, Mar. 23, 1923; came to U.S., 1952, naturalized, 1957; s. Hugo and Margaret (Klein) L.; m. Joyce A. Bruner, Nov. 28, 1953; 1 dau., Michelle Alexandra. Absolutorium, U. Budapest Med. Sch., 1948; Ph.D. in Biomolecular Structure, U. Leeds, Eng., 1951; D.Sc. hon., U. Ill., 1983. Demonstrator dept. biochemistry U. Budapest, 1946-48; research asst. U. Leeds, 1948-52; research asso., asst. prof. dept. physiology and pharmacology Wayne U. Med. Sch., Detroit, 1952-55; faculty Northwestern U., Evanston, Ill., 1955-93; prof. chemistry Northwestern U., 1961-74, prof. biochemistry and molecular biology, 1974-93; dep. dir. for basic scis. Northwestern U. Cancer Ctr., 1990-91; rsch. prof. dept. cell and molecular biology Northwestern U. Med. Sch., Chgo., 1993—; mem. hematology study sect. NIH, 1973-77; disting. investigator Feinberg Cardiovascular Rsch. Inst., 1993—. Editor: Proteolytic Enzymes (Methods in Enzymology series); editorial bd.: Inflammation; contbr. articles to profl. jours. Trustee marine biol. lab. Woods Hole, Mass., 1983-87, 87-91. Recipient USPHS Rsch. Career award Nat. Heart Inst. 1962-93, James F. Mitchell internat. award for heart and vascular rsch., 1973, Lalor Faculty award, 1957, Disting. Career award for contbns. to hemostasis, 1983, NIH Merit award, 1989; Beit Meml. fellow, 1951, Lady Davis fellow Hebrew U., Jerusalem, 1985, Japan Soc. for Promotion Sci. fellow, 1989-90. Mem. NAS, Am. Soc. Biochem. Molecular Biologists, Am. Chem. Soc., Biochem. Soc. (London), Phys. Soc., Am. Heart Assn., Soc. Cell Biology, Internat. Soc. Hematology, Internat. Soc. Thrombosis and Hemostasis, Am. Physiol. Soc., Assn. Rsch. in Vision and Ophthalmology. Home: 180 Harbor St Glencoe IL 60022-1940 Office: Northwestern U Med Sch Dept CM Biology 303 E Chicago Ave Chicago IL 60611

LORANT, STEFAN, author; b. Budapest, Hungary, Feb. 22, 1901; came to U.S., 1940, naturalized, 1948.; m. Laurie Jean Robertson, 1963 (div. 1978); children: Christopher Stefan, Mark Imre. Ed., Acad. of Econs., Budapest, 1919; LLD, Knox Coll., 1958; MA, Harvard U., 1961; LHD (hon.), Syracuse U., 1985; D (hon.), Bradford U., Eng., 1989. Editor Das Magazin, Leipzig, 1926, Bilder Courier, Berlin, 1926-27, Münchner Illustrierte Presse, Munich, 1928-33, Weekly Illustrated, London, 1934, Lilliput, London, Eng., 1937-40, Picture Post, London, 1938-40. Author: Wir vom Film, 1928, I Was Hitler's Prisoner, 1935, Chamberlain and the Beautiful Llama, 1940, Lincoln: His Life in Photographs, 1941, The New World, 1946 (Carey-Thomas award 1946), F.D.R.: A Pictorial Biography, 1950, The Presidency: The History of Presidental Elections from Washington to Truman, 1951, Lincoln: A Picture Story of His Life, 1952, The Life of Abraham Lincoln, 1954, The Life and Times of Theodore Roosevelt, 1959, The Glorious Burden: The American Presidency, 1968, Sieg Heil!: An Illustrated History of Germany from Bismarck to Hitler, 1974, Pete: The Life of Peter F. Flaherty, 1978, My Years in England: Fragment of an Autobiography, 1982, The Years Before Hitler 1918-1933, 1991; editor: Pittsburgh: The Story of an American City, 1964. Recipient Literary award (Pitts.), 1965. *

LORBER, MORTIMER, physiology educator, researcher; b. N.Y.C., Aug. 30, 1926; s. Albert and Frieda (Levin) L.; m. Eileen Segal, May 20, 1956; children: Kenneth, Stephanie. BS, NYU, 1945; DMD cum laude, Harvard U., 1950, MD cum laude, 1952. Diplomate Nat. Bd. Med. Examiners. Rotating intern A.M. Billings Hosp., 1952-53; resident in hematology Mt. Sinai Hosp. N.Y.C., 1953-54, asst. resident in medicine, 1957; asst. resident medicine Georgetown U. Hosp., Washington, 1958; instr. assoc. prof. dept. physiology and biophysics Georgetown U., Washington, 1959-68, assoc. prof., 1968; lectr. physiology U.S. Naval Dental Sch., Bethesda, Md., 1962-70, Walter Reed Army Inst. Dental Rsch., Washington, 1963-70; guest scientist Naval Med. Rsch. Inst., Bethesda, 1978-83. Contbr.: The Merck

Manual, 14th, 15th and 16th edit., 1982, 87, 92; contbr. articles to profl. jours. Lt. USNR, 1954-56. Recipient Lederle Med. Faculty award Lederle Co., Pearl River, N.Y., 1960-63, USPHS Rsch. Career Devel. award Nat. Inst. Dental Rsch., Bethesda, 1963-70; grantee Am. Cancer Soc., USPHS. Mem. Am. Physiol. Soc., Am. Soc. Hematology, Assn. Rsch. in Vision and Ophthalmology, Internat. Assn. Dental Rsch. Jewish. Achievements include discovery that the ground substance is masked but not lost in calcification, removal of spleen is followed by a reticulocytosis that is permanent in dogs, dogs have many more young reticulocytes in their blood than man, stretching of skin increases mitoses in the rat showing physical factors can modulate DNA and cell division, adult Gaucher cells contain iron secondary to erythrophagocytosis, the spleen protects against insecticide-induced hematoxicity, biological armature provides internal stability to exocrine glands. Home: 5823 Osceola Rd Bethesda MD 20816-2032 Office: Georgetown U Sch Medicine 3900 Reservoir Rd NW Washington DC 20007-2187

LORCH, ERNEST HENRY, lawyer; b. Frankfurt, Germany, Oct. 11, 1932; came to U.S., 1940; s. Alexander and Kate (Freundt) L. AB, Middlebury Coll., 1954; JD, U. Va., 1957; JD (hon.), Fairfield U., 1987. Bar: N.Y. 1958. Assoc. Olwine, Connelly, Chase, O'Donnell & Weyher, N.Y.C., 1957-65, ptnr., 1965-84; pres., chief oper. officer Dyson-Kissner-Moran Corp., N.Y.C., 1984-90, pres., chief exec. officer, 1990-91; chmn., chief exec. officer, 1991-92, ret., 1992; of counsel Whitman, Breed, Abbott & Morgan, N.Y.C., 1992—; chmn. bd. dirs. Varlen Corp., Chgo.; bd. dirs. Tyler Corp. Dir. various inner city athletic assns., N.Y.C., 1959—, The DYSM Found., N.Y.c., 1985-92; trustee, officer, dir. The Riverside Ch., N.Y.C., 1961—. Mem. ABA, N.Y. State Bar Assn. Office: Whitman Breed Abbott & Morgan 200 Park Ave New York NY 10166

LORCH, GEORGE A., manufacturing company executive; b. Glenridge, N.J., 1941. BS, Va. Poly. Inst. & State U., 1963. With Armstrong World Industries, Inc., 1963—, v.p. mktg. E&B div., 1974-76, mktg. mgr., 1976-78, gen. sales mgr., 1978-83, then group v.p. carpet ops., from 1983, past exec. v.p., now chmn. bd., CEO, dir. Office: Armstrong World Industries Inc Liberty & Charlotte Sts Lancaster PA 17604*

LORCH, KENNETH F., lawyer; b. Indpls., July 24, 1951. BSBA, Washington U., 1973; JD, John Marshall Sch. Law, 1976. Bar: Ill. 1976, U.S. Dist. Ct. (no. dist.) Ill. 1977; CPA, Ill. Ptnr. Holleb & Coff, Chgo. Mem. Chgo. Bar Assn. (exec. com., Cook County Probate Ct. rules and forms com., mem. legis. com., mem. probate practice com. 1991, mem. trust law com., chmn. estate planning com., mem. young lawyers sect. 1983-85), Chgo. Estate Planning Coun., Com.-Agy./Ct. Sr. Citizen Issues, Jewish Fedn. Chgo. (vice chair profl. adv. com.). Office: Holleb & Coff 55 E Monroe St Ste 4100 Chicago IL 60603

LORCH, MARISTELLA DE PANIZZA (MRS. INAMA VON BRUN-NENWALD), Romance languages educator, writer, lecturer; b. Bolzano, Italy, Dec. 8, 1919; came to U.S., 1947, naturalized, 1951; d. Gino and Giuseppina (Cristoforetti) de Panizza; m. Claude Bové, Feb. 10, 1944 (div. 1955); 1 dau., Claudia; m. Edgar R. Lorch, Mar. 25, 1956; children: Lavinia Edgarda, Donatella Livia. Ed.; Liceo Classico, Merano, 1929-37; Dott. in Lettere e Filosofia, U. Rome, 1942; DHL (hon.), Lehman Coll., CUNY, 1993. Prof. Latin and Greek Liceo Virgilio, Rome, 1941-44; assoc. prof. Italian and German Coll. St. Elizabeth, Convent Station, N.J., 1947-51; faculty Barnard Coll., 1951-90, prof., 1967—, chmn. dept., 1951—, chmn. medieval and renaissance program, 1972-86; founder, dir. Ctr. for Internat. Scholarly Exch., Barnard Coll., 1980-90; dir. Casa Italiana, Columbia U., 1969-76, chmn. exec. com. Italian studies, 1980-90, dir. Italian Acad. Advanced Studies in Am., 1991—. Author: Critical edit. L. Valla, De vero falsoque bono, Bari, 1970, (with W. Ludwig) critical edit. Michaelida, (with K. Hieatt), 1976, On Pleasure, 1981, A Defense of Life: L. Valla's Theory of Pleasure, 1985, (with E. Grassi) Folly and Insanity in Renaissance Literature, 1986, (with F. Colombo, M. Spaziani, Sinisca) All' America, 1990; editor: Il Teatro Italiano del Renascimento, 1981, Humanism in Rome, 1983, La Scuola, New York, 1987; mem. editorial bd. Italian jour. Romanic Review; also articles on Renaissance lit. and theater. Chmn. Am. Ariosto Centennial Celebration, 1974; chmn. bd. trustees La Scuola N.Y., 1986-91; trustee Lyceé Française de N.Y., 1986—. Decorated Cavaliere della Repubblica Italiana, 1973, Commendatore della Repubblica Italiana, 1988; recipient AMITA award for Woman of Yr. in Italian Lit., 1973, Columbus '92 Countdown prize of excellence in humanities, 1990, Elen Cornaro award Sons of Italy Woman of Yr., 1990, Father Ford award, 1994. Mem. Medieval Acad. Am., Renaissance Soc. Am., Am. Assn. Tchrs. Italian, Am. Assn. Italian Studies (hon. pres. 1990-91), Internat. Assn. for Study of Italian Lit. (Am. rep., assoc. pres. 8th Congress 1973), Acad. Polit. Sci. (life), Pirandello Soc. (pres. 1972-78), Arcadia Acad. (Asteria Aretusa 1976). Home: 445 Riverside Dr New York NY 10027-6842

LORCH, WILLIAM CHARLES, transportation executive; b. Peoria, Ill., Nov. 17, 1945; s. Carl and Marie (Huffman) L.; m. Mary Kay Hull, Aug. 26, 1983; 1 child, William Eric. BS, U.S. Mcht. Marine Acad., Kings Point, N.Y., 1967; postgrad., U. Wash., 1968-70, Alaska Pacific U., 1988—. Ops. mgr. Cascade Shipping Co., Seattle, 1970-77; port mgr. Alaska Maritime Agys., Valdez, 1977-86; gen. mgr. Alaska Maritime Agys., Anchorage, 1986—; pres. No. Marine Ventures, Inc., 1989—; gen. mgr. GSI Enery Group, 1989—; info. mgr. U.S. Mcht. Marine Acad., 1986—. Commr. Alaska Bd. Marine Pilots, 1988—; chmn. Transp. Commn., Alaska, 1982-86; mem. Soviet-Am. com. Alaska Hist. Soc. Mem. U.S. Naval Inst., Propeller Club U.S., Am. Alpine Club (mem. Alaska sect. 1990—), Valdez Alpine Club (v.p. 1978-84), Valdez Yacht Club (pres. 1980-82). Avocations: mountain climbing, sailing. Office: Alaska Maritime Agys 1600 A St Anchorage AK 99501-5145

LORD, ANTHONY, retired architect; b. Asheville, N.C., Feb. 17, 1900; s. William Henry and Helen (Anthony) L. BS in Mech. Engring., Ga. Sch. Tech., 1922; BFA in architecture, Yale U., 1927. Registered profl. engr., N.C.; registered architect, N.C. Ptnr. Lord and Lord, Architects, Asheville, 1929-33; craftsman of decorative wrought iron Asheville Hand-Forged Iron, Asheville, 1930-35; pvt. practice Asheville, 1935-40; v.p. Six Assocs. Architects and Engrs., Asheville, 1940-70; ret., 1970. Prin. works include Asheville Citizen-Times Bldg., 1938, dormitories, librs., svc. bldgs., office bldgs., adminstrn. bldgs. for U. N.C., Greensboro, U. N.C., Asheville, Western Carolina U., Montreat-Anderson Coll., Warren Wilson Coll., Swannanoa, N.C., Asheville Sch. for Boys, 1948-70, Am. Enka Corp. lab. and office bldg., 1960-66, first unit, Meml. Mission Hosp., Asheville, 1950; retrospective exhbn. of architecture, ironwork, painting, Asheville Art Mus., 1984. Trustee (emeritus) Pack Meml. Libr., Asheville-Buncombe Libr. System, Asheville, 1943-88, chmn. bd. trustees, 1959-79; bd. advisors Warren Wilson Coll., 1983—; life mem., 1989; mem. Asheville Tree and Greenway Commn., 1979, hon. mem., 1993—; mem. Downtown Devel. Strategies Task Force, 1988—. Named to Western N.C. Creative Arts Hall of Fame, Asheville, 1988. Fellow AIA; mem. N.C. AIA, Pen and Plate Club (pres. 1958), Downtown Club. Democrat. Avocation: urban environ. improvement. Address: PO Box 2450 Asheville NC 28802-2450

LORD, ESTHER A., corporate executive; b. 1932. Student, Ind. U., Am. Inst. Banking. With Assocs. Corp. N.Am., N.Y.C., 1965—, asst. treas., 1976-80, asst. v.p., 1980-82, v.p., 1982-87, sr. v.p., asst. treas., 1987—. Office: Assocs Corp N Am PO Box 660237 Dallas TX 75266-0237

LORD, EVELYN MARLIN, former mayor; b. Melrose, Mass., Dec. 8, 1926; d. John Joseph and Mary Janette (Nourse) Marlin; m. Samuel Smith Lord Jr., Feb. 28, 1948; children: Steven Arthur, Jonathan Peter, Nathaniel Edward, Victoria Marlin, William Kenneth. BA, Boston U., 1948; MA, U. Del., 1956; JD, U. Louisville, 1969. Bar: Ky. 1969, U.S. Supreme Ct. 1973. Exec. dir. Block Blight Inc., Wilmington, Del., 1956-60; mem. Del. Senate, Dover, 1960-62; administrv. asst. county judge Jefferson County, Louisville, 1968-71; corr. No. Ireland News Jour. Co., Wilmington, 1972-74; legal adminstr. Orgain, Bell & Tucker, Beaumont, Tex., 1978-83; v.p. Tex. Commerce Bank, Beaumont, 1983-84; councilman City of Beaumont, 1980-82, mayor pro tem, 1982-84, mayor, 1990-94; tourism dir. U.S. Conf. Mayors, 1994, mem. adv. bd., chmn. arts, culture and recreation policy com. Tex. Commerce Bank. Bd. dirs. Symphony Soc. S.E. Tex., 1990—, Beaumont Cmty. Found., 1990—, S.E. Tex. Art Mus., 1990—, Lincoln Inst.

Lant. Policy; trustee, pres. Beaumont United Way, 1995; exec. bd. Three Rivers coun. Boy Scouts Am., 1978-84, 89-95; pres. Kentuckian coun. Girl Scouts U.S., Louisville, 1966-70. Recipient Silver Beaver award Boy Scouts Am., Beaumont, 1979, Disting. Alumni award Boston U., 1983, Disting. Leadership award Nat. Assn. Leadership Orgns., Indpls., 1991, Labor-Mgmt. Pub. Sector award, 1991, Disting. Grad. award Leadership Beaumont, 1993, Rotary Svc. Above Self award, 1994; named Citizen of Yr., Sales and Mktg. Assn., 1990, Beaumont "Man of Yr.", 1993. Mem. LWV (Del. state pres. 1960-62, mem. bd. Tex. stae 1978-80), Bus. and Profl. Women Assns. (Woman of Yr. 1983), 100 Club (pres. 1995), Girl Scouts Am. (life), Rotary (hon.), Sigma Kappa (life), Phi Kappa Phi, Delta Kappa Gamma (hon.), Sigma Iota Epsilon (hon.), Beta Sigma Phi (hon.). Avocations: writing, reading, African violets. Home: 1240 Nottingham Ln Beaumont TX 77706-4316

LORD, GEORGE DEFOREST, English educator; b. N.Y.C., Dec. 2, 1919; s. George deForest and Hazen (Symington) L.; m. Ruth Ellen du Pont, Mar. 22, 1947 (div. 1978); children: Pauline, George deForest Jr., Edith (dec.), Henry; m. Louise Robins Hendrix, 1978 (div. 1992); m. Marcia Adkisson Babbidge, 1993. BA, Yale U., 1942, PhD, 1951. Instr. English Yale U., New Haven, 1947-66, prof., 1966—; master Trumbull Coll., 1963-66, dir. directed studies, 1968-70, assoc. chmn. English dept., 1983-86; dir. Fiduciary Trust, N.Y., 1969-91; cons. PBS TV program Transformations of Myth Through Time, 1982-90; lectr. in field. Author: Homeric Renaissance: the "Odyssey" of George Chapman, 1956, Poems on Affairs of State, 1963, Andrew Mavell, Complete Poetry, 1968, rev. edit., 1985, Andrew Marvell: A Collection of Critical Essays, 1968, Anthology of Poems on Affairs of State, 1975, Heroic Mockery: Variations on Epic Themes from Homer to Joyce, 1977, Trials of the Self: Heroic Ordeals in the Epic Tradition, 1983, Classical Presences in Seventeenth-Century English Poetry, 1987 (Outstanding acad. book 1987 Choice mag.); gen. editor Poems on Affairs of State: Augustan Satirical Verse, 1660-1714, 7 vols., 1963-75; contbr. articles, revs. to acad. jours. Trustee Winterthur Mus., 1952-80, Mary Holmes Coll., West Point, Miss., 1971-80, Fair Haven Housing, 1972-78; trustee, advisor Outward Bound USA, 1977—; vestryman Calvary Episcopal Ch., Stonington, Conn., 1986-89. Morse fellow 1954-55, NEH sr. fellow, 1982. Mem. MLA, English Inst., Renaissance Soc. Am., Am. Acad. in Rome, The Century Assn. Home: 3 Diving St Stonington CT 06378 Office: Yale U Dept English New Haven CT 06520

LORD, HAROLD WILBUR, electrical engineer, electronics consultant; b. Eureka, Calif., Aug. 20, 1905; s. Charles Wilbur and Rossina Camilla (Hansen) L.; B.S., Calif. Inst. Tech.; 1926; m. Doris Shirley Huff, July 25, 1928; children—Joann Shirley (Mrs. Carl Cook Disbrow), Alan Wilbur, Nancy Louise (Mrs. Leslie Crandall), Harold Wayne. With Gen. Electric Co., Schenectady, 1926-66, electronics engr., 1960-66; pvt. cons. engr., Mill Valley, Calif., 1966—. Coffin Found. award Gen. Electric Co., 1933, GE Inventors award, 1966. Fellow IEEE (life, tech. v.p. 1962, Centennial medal 1984, IEEE Magnetics Soc. 1984 Achievement award). Contbr. articles to profl. jours. Patentee in field. Home and Office: 1565 Golf Course Dr Rohnert Park CA 94928-5638

LORD, JERE JOHNS, retired physics educator; b. Portland, Oreg., Jan. 3, 1922; s. Percy Samuel and Hazel Marie (Worstel) L.; m. Miriam E. Hart, Dec. 30, 1947; children—David, Roger, Douglas. Physicist U. Calif. Radiation Lab., Berkeley, 1942-46; research assoc. U. Chgo., 1950-52; asst. prof. physics U. Wash., Seattle, 1952-57; assoc. prof. U. Wash., 1957-62, prof., 1962-92, prof. emeritus, 1992—. Fellow AAAS, Am. Phys. Soc.; mem. Am. Assn. Physics Tchrs. Home: 6803 52nd Ave NE Seattle WA 98115-7744 Office: U Wash Dept Physics Physics FM-15 Seattle WA 98195

LORD, JEROME EDMUND, federal education administrator, writer; b. Waterbury, Conn., Dec. 24, 1935; s. James Andrew and Mary Frances (Hayes) L.; m. Eleanor Louise Collins, Apr. 22, 1967; children: Hayes Alexander FitzWarin, Stavely Hampston deHodnet, Savile Collins de Montenay, Dorian Warfield d'Amours, Wallis Jennings dePantulf. BA, Georgetown U., 1957; MA, Boston Coll., 1962, Columbia U., 1963; PhD, Columbia U., 1969; diploma (hon.), U. Madrid, 1962. Tchr. The Taft Sch. Peekskill Mil. Acad., 1957-60; editor, lang. recs. supr. Allyn and Bacon Inc., Boston, 1961-62; administrv. assoc. internat. programs and services Tchrs. Coll. Columbia U., N.Y.C., 1963-65, assoc. in higher edn., 1965-66; asst. prof. edn., exec. asst. to dean acad. devel. CUNY, 1965-67, assoc. prof. edn., exec. asst. to vice chancellor exec. office, 1967-69; dir. rsch. Ford and Carnegie Study of Fed. Politics of Edn. Brookings Instn., Washington, 1969-70; program officer Nat. Ctr. for Ednl. Tech., U.S. Dept. Edn., Washington, 1971-73; sr. assoc. Nat. Inst. Edn., Washington, 1973-86, Office Ednl. Rsch. and Improvement, Dept. Edn., Washington, 1986—; cons. in field; lectr. in field; advisor to vol. edn. policy group Office Dir. Def. Edn., U.S. Dept Def., 1975-76; chmn. Fed. Interagy. Panel for Rsch. on Adulthood; mem. various nat. panels and coms. Playwright: Teresa, 1971, The Election, 1972, Audition!, 1973, Decent Exposure, 1979, Amazing Grace, 1987, Heads You Win, 1991; writer Perfectly Proper, 1993; contbr. articles to profl jours. Trustee St. John's Child Devel. Ctr., Washington, 1978-83; mem. nat. bd. sponsors Protestant and Orthodox Ctr., N.Y. World's Fair, 1964; mem. adv. bd. N.Y.C. Urban Corps, 1965-69, others; mem. coun. of friends Folger Shakespeare Libr.; sponsor Nat. Symphony; mem., donor reception rooms Dept. State. M.T. Runyan scholar, 1967-68; fellow W.T. Kellogg Found, 1968-69, Rinehart Found, 1970-71, others. Mem. Pilgrim Soc., Washington Opera, Soc. Friends St. George's and Desc. Knights of Garter, Friends of Blair House, Pilgrims of the U.S., City Tavern Club, Met. Club, Kappa Delta Pi, Phi Delta Pi, Eta Sigma Phi. Episcopalian. Avocations: writing, historic preservation, music, art history, architecture. Office: 555 New Jersey Ave NW Washington DC 20208-0001

LORD, M. G., writer; b. La Jolla, Calif., Nov. 18, 1955; d. Charles Carroll and Mary (Pfister) L.; m. Glenn Horowitz, May 19, 1985. B.A., Yale U., 1977. Reporter N.Y. Bur. Wall St. Jour., N.Y.C., summer 1976; editorial artist Chgo. Tribune, 1977-78; editorial cartoonist, columnist Newsday, N.Y.C., 1978-94; cartoons syndicated L.A. Times Syndicate, 1984-89; column syndicated Copley News Svc., 1989-94. Author: Mean Sheets, 1982, Prig Tales, 1990, Forever Barbie: The Unauthorized Biography of a Real Doll, 1994. Resident humanities fellow U. Mich., 1986-87. Club: Yale (N.Y.C.). Office: c/o Janis Vallely Literary 320 Riverside Dr New York NY 10025

LORD, MARVIN, apparel company executive; b. N.Y.C., Sept. 22, 1937; s. Harry and Irene (Taub) L.; m. Joan Simon, Aug. 5, 1961; children—Elisa Anne, Michael Harris. B.S., Long Island U., Bklyn., 1959. Mdse. mgr. Oxford Industries, Inc., N.Y.C., 1964-66, gen. mdse. mgr., 1966-70, v.p., gen. mgr., 1970-73; pres. Holbrook Co., Inc. Div Oxford Industries Inc., N.Y.C., 1970-85; pres., chief exec. officer Crystal Brands, Inc.-Youthwear Group, N.Y.C., 1985—; pres. Cluett Shirtmakers, N.Y.C., 1988—, M.L. Enterprises, Roslyn Heights, N.Y., 1990—; pres., chief oper. officer Sanyo Fashion House, N.Y.C., 1991—; pres., CEO MAternity Resources Inc., N.Y.C., 1994—. Chmn. Fathers Day Coun., N.Y.C., 1984—. Recipient Disting. Alumni award L.I. U., 1987. Mem. Mens Fashion Assn., Young Menswear Assn. Jewish. Avocation: tennis. Home: 53 Parkway Dr Roslyn Heights NY 11577-2705 Office: Maternity Resources Inc New York NY 11577

LORD, ROY ALVIN, retired publisher; b. Middletown, Ohio, July 2, 1918; s. Arthur Edwin and Mary Marie (Bell) L.; m. Elizabeth Frances Powell, Nov. 1, 1941; children—Thomas A., Frances A., William F. B.A., Ohio Wesleyan U., 1941; postgrad., Harvard U. Bus. Sch., 1962. With advt. sales Time Inc., N.Y.C. and Chgo., 1946-55; upper midwest mgr. advt. sales Time Inc., Mpls., 1955-62; nat. advt. sales mgr. Time Inc., N.Y.C., 1963-68; pres. ML&A Inc., N.Y.C., 1968-73; v.p. In-Store Pubs., N.Y.C., 1973-74; pres. The Weekend Co., Inc., 1974-76; pub. A.D. Pubs., Inc., N.Y.C., from 1976. Bd. dirs. Minn. Orchestral Assn., 1957-62; Minn. state chmn. Crusade for Freedom, 1960-62. Served with AC U.S. Army, 1942-45. Presbyterian.

LORD, WALTER, author; b. Balt., Oct. 8, 1917; s. John Walter and Henrietta Mactier (Hoffman) L. B.A., Princeton U., 1939; LL.B., Yale U. 1946. Editor bus. information services, 1946-53, engaged in advt., 1953-56, civilian aide to sec. army for So. N.Y. area, 1964-66. Author: A Night to Remember, 1955, Day of Infamy, 1957, The Good Years, 1960, A Time to Stand, 1961, Peary at the Pole, 1963, The Past That Would Not Die, 1965,

Incredible Victory, 1967, The Dawn's Early Light, 1972, Lonely Vigil, 1977, The Miracle of Dunkirk, 1982, The Night Lives On, 1986; editor: The Fremantle Diary, 1954. Bd. dirs. Union Settlement, N.Y.C., 1959—, chmn., 1962-64; bd. dirs. Mcpl. Art Soc., N.Y.C., 1958-67; trustee N.Y. Soc. Library, 1963—, Mus. City N.Y., 1964-72, N.Y. Hist. Soc., 1965—; trustee Soc. Am. Historians, 1972—, pres., 1981-84; trustee Gilman Sch., Balt., 1962-80, Council Authors Guild, Inc., 1966-72, Coun. Authors League, 1972-83, sec., 1975-80; trustee N.Y. State Maritime Mus., 1968-79, South St. Seaport Mus., 1980—, Ocean Liner Mus., 1982—; mem. adv. bd. Protect Historic Am. Mem. Soc. Am. Historians, Authors Guild, ASCAP. Clubs: 14 W. Hamilton St. (Balt.); Century Assn. (N.Y.C.); Metropolitan (Washington).

LORD, WILLIAM GROGAN, financial holding company executive; b. Hearne, Tex., Oct. 21, 1914; s. Otis G. and Erminee G. Lord; m. Dorothy Nell Manning, Dec. 28, 1938 (dec.); children: Roger Griffin, Sharon Lord Caskey; m. Betty Fowler Hendrick, May 24, 1986. L.H.D. (hon.), Southwestern U., Georgetown, Tex., 1967. Sr. chmn. bd. dirs. TeleCom Corp., Houston, 1958—; sr. chmn. First Tex. Bancorp, Inc., Georgetown, 1971—; bd. dirs. Frozen Food Express Industries, Inc., Dallas; sr. chmn. bd. 1st Tex. Bancorp, Inc., Georgetown; mem., chmn. State Securities Bd., 1971-83. Trustee, mem. exec. com., vice chmn. bd. Southwestern U., 1958. Served to 1st lt. F.A. AUS, World War II. Decorated Purple Heart, Air medal with 4 oak leaf clusters; named Most Worthy Citizen Georgetown C. of C., 1971. Mem. Nat. Assn. Small Bus. Investment Cos. (past pres.), Regional Assn. Small Bus. Investment Cos, Tex. Research League, Tex. Philosophical Soc. Republican. Methodist. Clubs: Ramada (Houston), River Oaks Country (Houston); Austin (Austin, Tex.), Headliners (Austin, Tex.); St. Anthony (San Antonio). Office: PO Box 649 Georgetown TX 78627-0649

LORD, WINSTON, diplomat; b. N.Y.C., Aug. 14, 1937; s. Oswald Bates and Mary (Pillsbury) L.; m. Bette Bao, May 4, 1963; children: Elizabeth Pillsbury, Winston Bao. BA, Yale U., 1959; MA, Fletcher Sch. Law and Diplomacy, Tufts U. in cooperation with Harvard U., 1960; LLD (hon.), Williams Coll., 1979, Tufts U., 1987, Dominican Coll., 1990; DS in Bus. (hon.), Bryant Coll., 1990. Mem. staff congl. rels., polit.-mil. and econ. affairs U.S. Dept. State, Washington 1961-64, Geneva, 1965-67; mem. staff internat. security affairs U.S. Dept. Def., Washington, 1967-69; mem. staff NSC, White House, Washington, 1969-73; also spl. asst. to asst. to pres. for nat. security affairs NSC, White House, 1970-73; dir. policy planning staff U.S. Dept. State, Washington, 1973-77; pres. Coun. Fgn. Rels., N.Y.C., 1977-85; U.S. amb. to People's Republic of China Beijing, 1985-89; freelance lectr., writer, N.Y.C., 1989-93; asst. sec. state for East Asian affairs Dept. State, Washington, 1993—; sr. counsellor Pres.'s Nat. Bipartisan Commn. on Ctrl. Am., 1983-84; vice chmn. Internat. Rescue Com., 1991-92. Chmn. Nat. Endowment for Democracy, 1992-93, The Carnegie Endowment Nat. Commn. on Am. and the New World, 1991-92; former bd. dirs. U.S.-Japan Found., Nat. Com. on U.S.-China Rels.; former bd. advisors Fletcher Sch. Law and Diplomacy. Mem. Asia Soc., Coun. Fgn. Rels. (pres. 1977-85).

LORE, MARTIN MAXWELL, lawyer; b. Milw., June 13, 1914; s. Michael and Jean (Dinerstein) L.; m. Doris Silver, Mar. 19, 1944; children: Amy L. Kovner, Dr. Cathy Jo. BA, U. Wis., 1934, LLB, 1936; LLM, Harvard, 1937; BCS, Strayer Coll. Accountancy, 1939. Bar: Wis. 1936, N.Y. 1946, D.C. 1947, Fla. 1977, U.S. Supreme Ct. 1939; CPA, D.C. Assoc. Rubin, Zabel & Ruppa, Milw., 1936-37; with Office Undersec. Treasury, 1937-38; spl. atty. office chief counsel, bur. IRS, 1938-40; trial counsel IRS (New Eng. div. tech. staff), 1940-42, IRS (N.Y. div.), 1945-47; tax counsel S.J. Foosaner, Newark, 1947-48; pvt. law practice N.Y.C., 1948-72; mem. firm Zissu Lore Halper & Robson, N.Y.C., 1972-76; counsel Zissu Lore Halper & Robson, 1976-80; sr. ptnr. Lore & Levy, N.Y.C., 1981—; pres. bd. Fed. Tax Forum, Inc.; lectr. Tax Workshop, 1953-55, law sch. St. John's U., 1954, Fairleigh Dickinson U., 1955-56; specialist fed. tax matters, lectr. taxation NYU, 1946-50, 65, Practising Law Inst., 1947-48, Tax Inst., 1948, Pa. State Coll., 1949-50, U. W.Va., U. San Francisco, 1951, SUNY, Stony Brook, 1978-79; tax cons. Med. Econs.; pres., dir. Estate Planning Coun. N.Y.C.; part-time employee Melnik & Karan, Milw., 1933-36. Author: The Administration of The Federal Income Tax Through the United States Board of Tax Appeals, 1937, How to Win a Tax Case, 1955, Thin Capitalization, 1958; co-editor: Jour. of Taxation; chmn. bd. editors: How To Work with the Internal Revenue Code of 1954; contbr. articles to legal and accounting jours. Lt. comdr. Office Gen. Counsel, U.S.N., 1942-44. Mem. ABA (com. income taxation estates and trusts), N.Y. State Bar Assn., Assn. of Bar of City of N.Y. (taxation com., com. on trusts, estates and surrogate's cts.), Fed. Bar Assn. (chmn. com. fed. taxation), AICPA (sec. fed. tax lawyers com.), D.C. Accts., County Lawyers Assn. (taxation com.), Seawane Club (bd. govs.), Lawyers Club (N.Y.C.), Harvard Club (N.Y.C.), Barristers (Washington). Home: 46 Broome Ave Atlantic Beach NY 11509-1214 Office: Lore & Levy 1 Madison Ave New York NY 10010-3603

LORELL, MONTE, newspaper editor. Managing editor Page One, USA Today, Arlington, Va. Office: USA Today 1000 Wilson Blvd Arlington VA 22209*

LORELLI, CHARLES A., lawyer, chemical company executive; b. N.Y.C., Jan. 30, 1953. BS in Acctg., U. Del., 1975; JD, U. Pa., 1978. Atty. Allied Signal, Inc., Morristown, N.J., 1978-83; sr. v.p., gen. counsel Reichhold Chems., Inc., Research Triangle Park, N.C., 1983—. Office: Reichhold Chems Inc PO Box 13582 Durham NC 27709-3582

LORELLI, MICHAEL KEVIN, personal care products executive; b. N.Y.C., Apr. 17, 1950; s. Domenic and Effie (Stankevich) L.; m. Judith Bryant; children: Karen, Elizabeth. BE, NYU, 1972, MBA in Mktg., 1973. Dir. mktg. Clairol Co., N.Y.C., 1973-81; v.p. gen. mgr. internat. div. Playtex, Stamford, Conn., 1981-84; v.p. mktg. Apple Computer, Cupertino, Calif., 1984-85; exec. v.p. Pepsi-Cola Co., Somers, N.Y., 1985-88; pres. Pepsi-Cola East, Somers, N.Y., 1989-92, Pizza Hut Internat., 1993-94, Latin Am.-Tambrands, Inc., White Plains, N.Y., 1994—. Bd. dirs. Keep Am. Beautiful, United Way, Rosenbluth Travel, Am. Health Found.; trustee Sarah Lawrence Coll.; active Boy Scouts Am., Madison Sq. Boys & Girls Club. Republican. Roman Catholic. Avocations: flying, golf, tennis. Office: Tambrands Inc 777 Westchester Ave White Plains NY 10604

LOREN, SOPHIA, actress; b. Rome, Sept. 20, 1934; d. Riccardo Scicolone and Romilda Villani; m. Carlo Ponti, Apr. 12, 1967; children: Carlo Ponti, Edoardo. Student, Scuole Magistrali Superiori. Films include E Arrivato l'Accordatore, 1951, Africa sotto i Mari, La Favorita, La Tratta Delle Bianche, 1952, Aida, Tempi Nostri, Ci Troviamo in Gellera, La Domenica Della Buona Genti, Il Paese dei Campanelli, Un Giorno in Pretura, Due Notti con Cleopatra, Pelegrini d'Amore, Attila, Carosello Napoletano, 1953, Miseria e Nobilta, Gold of Naples, Woman of the River, Too Bad She's Bad (Best Actress award Buenos Aires Festival), 1954, Lucky To Be A Woman, Sign of Venus, The Millers Wife, Scandal in Sorrento, 1955, Pride and Passion, Boy on a Dolphin, Legend of The Lost, 1957, Desire Under the Elms, Houseboat, The Key (Best Actress award Japan), 1958, That Kind of Woman, Black Orchid, 1959 (Best Actress Venice Festival, David Di Donatello award Italy, Victoire Popularity award France), Heller in Pink Tights (Best Actress Rapallo Festival Italy), It Started in Naples, A Breath of Scandal, The Millionaires, 1960, Two Women, (11 Best Actress awards including Oscar, Hollywood, Di Donatello award, Cannes Film Festival, N.Y. Critics, Golden Globe, Brit. Film Acad., others from Ireland, Japan, Belgium, Spain, France, W. Ger., also other awards), El Cid, Madame, Bocaccio 70, 1961, The Condemned of Altona, Five Miles to Midnight, 1962, Yesterday, Today and Tomorrow, (Best Actress Di Donatello award, Golden Globe award), 1963, The Fall of the Roman Empire, Marriage Italian Style, 1964 (Best Actress Di Donatello award, Golden Globe award, Alexander Korda award Brit. Film Inst., others), Operation Crossbow, Lady I, Judith, 1965. Arabesque, A Countess From Hong Kong, 1966, Happily Ever After, Ghosts, Italian Style (Best Fgn. Actress Diploma USSR), 1967, More Than A Miracle, (Ramo d'Oro award Italy, other awards), 1968, Sunflower (Best Actress Di Donatello award), 1969, The Priest's Wife, 1970, Lady Liberty, White Sister, 1971, Man of La Mancha, 1972, The Voyage (Di Donatello award), 1973, Brief Encounter, The Verdict, 1974, The Cassandra Crossing, A Special Day, 1977, Firepower, 1978, Brass Target, 1979, Blood Feud, 1981; TV film appearances include Sophia Loren: Her Own Story, 1980, Angela, 1982, Aurora, 1985, Mother Courage, 1986, The Fortunate Pilgrim

(Best Actress of Yr. for TV mini-series), 1987, La Ciociara, 1989, Ready to Wear (Prêt-à-Porter), 1994. Recipient numerous awards including Nastro d'Argento, Italy, 14 Bambi and Bravo Popularity awards, Fed. Republic Germany, 3 Prix Uilenspigoel Fiamingo award, Belgium, Popularity awards Am. Legion, Tex. Cinema Exhibitors, 4 Snosiki Popularity awards, Finland, 2 Best Actress awards Bengal Film Journalists Assn., India, Box-Office Favourite Medal, Italy, Helene Curtis award, U.S.A., Simpatia Popularity award, Italy, Rudolph Valentino Screen Svcs. award, Italy, Best Actress award Moscow Film Festival, Hon. Acad. award, 1990; named Most Popular Actress in Italy. Office: Via di Villa Ada 10, Rome I-00199, Italy*

LORENTZ, WILLIAM BEALL, pediatrician; b. Glenville, W.Va., July 8, 1937; s. William Beall and Mary Gay (Garrett) L.; m. Anne Lynne Hickman, June 20, 1960 (div. Aug. 30, 1977); children: Pamela Lynne, Lisa Anne, William Chad; m. Suzy Vernice Gibson, Sept. 5, 1977. BA, W.Va. U., 1959; MD, Jefferson Med. Coll., 1963. Diplomate Am. Bd. Pediatrics, Sub-board of Pediatric Nephrology. Internship Harrisburg (Pa.) Polyclinic Hosp., 1963-64, resident in pediatrics, 1964-65; resident in pediatrics U. Tex. Med. Br., Galveston, Tex., 1965-67; med. corp USN, Quantico (Va.) Naval Hosp., 1967-69; fellow in renal physiology U. N.C. Sch. of Medicine, Chapel Hill, 1969-71; asst. prof. pediatrics U. Tex. Med. Br., Galveston, 1971-74, Bowman Gray Sch. Medicine, Winston-Salem, N.C., 1974-75; assoc. prof. pediatrics Bowman Gray Sch. Medicine, Winston-Salem, 1975-81; prof. pediatrics Bowman Grey Sch. Medicine, Winston-Salem 1981—; assoc. chief staff N.C. Bapt. Hosp., 1991—; med. dir. Medcost, Winston-Salem, 1989—; cons. physician Allegheny Regional Hosp., Low Moor, Va., 1988; pres. Piedmont Med. Found., Winston-Salem, 1983-88. Contbr. articles to profl. jours. Lt. comdr. USN, 1966-69. Mem. Soc. for Pediatric Rsch., Am. Pediatric Soc., Am. Acad. Pediatrics. Am. Soc. Nephrology, Am. Soc. for Pediatric Nephrology. Democrat. Presbyterian. Avocation: running. Office: Bowman Gray Sch Medicine 300 S Hawthorne Rd Winston Salem NC 27157-0001

LORENTZEN, CARL WARREN, chemical company executive; b. N.Y.C., Dec. 23, 1929; s. Carl P. and Elvira C. (Kallies) L.; m. Karen M. Hansen, Apr. 22, 1956; children: Eric Carl, Leif Parker, Kyle David, Kristen Anne, Keira Jean. B.A., Adelphi Coll., 1951; grad., Advanced Mgmt. Program, Harvard Bus. Sch., 1977. Dir. mktg. Charles Pfizer, N.Y., 1962-64; dir. mktg. chem. div. S.C. Johnson & Sons, Inc., N.Y., 1964-66, v.p. mktg. organic div., 1967-69; pres. polymers div. W. R. Grace & Co., N.Y., 1969-71; exec. v.p. Dewey & Almy subs. W.R. Grace, N.Y., 1971-75, pres. organic chem. div., 1975-78, v.p., 1978-85, sr. v.p. specialty chem. div., 1986—; dir. Cambridge Trust Co.; adj. faculty mem. U. Lowell, Mass. Served to 1st lt., inf. U.S. Army, 1951-54. Mem. Soc. Chem. Industry, Comml. Devel. Assn., Drug, Chem. and Allied Trades Assn. (pres.), Chem. Mfrs. Assn. (bd. dirs.). Clubs: Southport (Maine); Yacht. Office: W R Grace & Co 1114 Avenue Of The Americas New York NY 10036-7701

LORENZ, ANNE PARTEE, special education educator, consultant; b. Nashville, Aug. 6, 1943; d. McCullough and Mary Elizabeth (Shemwell) Partee; m. Philip Jack Lorenz, Jr., Nov. 26, 1970; stepchildren: Brenna Ellen, Philip Jack III. Student, Rhodes Coll., 1961-63, 64; BS, George Peabody Coll., 1966; postgrad., Ga. State U., 1967-68; MS, George Peabody Coll., 1969. Clerk Tenn. State Libr. Archives, Nashville, 1963-64; tchr. learning disabilities Howard Sch., Atlanta, 1966-68; prin., tchr. learning disabilities Sewanee (Tenn.) Learning Ctr., 1969-78; tchr. learning disabilities Clark Meml. Sch., Winchester, Tenn., 1978-79; tutor, cons. learning disabilities Anne Partee Lorenz Tutoring Consultation Svc., Sewanee, 1979—; psychol. cons. U. of South, 1974-78; cons. St. Andrew's-Sewanee Sch., Tenn., 1980—. Active mem. Coun. Exceptional Children, 1968-79; treas. Franklin County Dem. Party; sec Sewanee Precinct Dem. Party, 1974-76; del. dist. and state Dem. Conf.; vol. Cordelle-Lorenz Obs., U. of the South, 1970—. Mem. Tenn. LWV (pres., bd. dirs.), Franklin County LWV (pres.), Learning Disabilities Assn. Tenn. (1st Tchr. Yr. 1975), Children and Adults with Attention Deficit Disorders. Avocations: wild flowers, bird and wild animal watching, walking, reading, crocheting. Home and Office: 390 Onteora Ln Sewanee TN 37375

LORENZ, EDWARD NORTON, meteorologist, educator; b. West Hartford, Conn., May 23, 1917; m. Jane Logan, 1948; 3 children; 3 children. AB, Dartmouth Coll., 1938, DSc (hon.), 1992; AM, Harvard U., 1940; SM, MIT, 1943, DSc, 1948; DSc (hon.), McGill U., 1983, U. Ariz., 1989, Rutgers U., 1990. Asst. meteorologist MIT, Cambridge, 1946-48, mem. staff, 1948-54, asst. prof., then assoc. prof., 1955-62, prof. meteorology, 1962-87; head dept. meteorology & physical oceanography MIT, 1977-81, emeritus prof., 1987—; vis. assoc. prof. UCLA, 1954-55. Recipient Craoford prize Swedish Acad. Scis., 1983, Roger Revelle medal Am. Geog. Union, 1993, Carl Gustaf Rossby Rsch. medal, 1969, Elliott Creson medal Franklin Inst., 1989. Fellow NAS, Am. Acad. Arts & Scis., Indian Acad., Norwegian Acad. Sci. & Letters; mem. Am. Meteorological Soc. (hon., Clarence Leroy Meisinger award 1963), Royal Meteorological Soc. (hon., Symons Meml. Gold medal 1973), USSR Acad. Scis. (fgn. mem.). Office: MIT Dept Earth Atmospheric & Planetary Sci Cambridge MA 02139*

LORENZ, HUGO ALBERT, insurance executive; b. Elmhurst, Ill., July 5, 1926; s. Hugo E. and Linda T. (Trampel) L. B.S., Northwestern U., 1949; LL.B., Harvard U., 1952. Bar: Ill. 1954. Mem. patent staff Bell Telephone Labs., Murray Hill, N.J., 1952-53; atty. First Nat. Bank Chgo., 1954-58; gen. counsel N.Am. Life Ins. Co. Chgo., 1958-73; dir., v.p., gen. counsel, sec. Globe Life Ins. Co., Chgo., 1973-95; v.p. Union Fidelity Life Ins. Co., Chgo., 1993—; sec. Gt. Equity Life Ins. Co., Chgo., 1977-80, Pat Ryan & Assos. Inc., Va. Surety Co., Chgo., 1977—. Bd. dirs. Sr. Ctrs. Met. Chgo., 1977-93, pres., 1983-85; trustee Hull House Assn., 1983-88. With USNR, 1944-46. Mem. Am. Bar Assn., Assn. Life Ins. Counsel, Connoisseurs Internat. (pres.), Internat. Wine and Food Soc. Chgo. (gov. and oenologist 1980—). Unitarian. Home: 950 A N Clark St Chicago IL 60610 Office: Aon Corp 123 N Wacker Dr Chicago IL 60606-1700

LORENZ, JOHN DOUGLAS, college official; b. Talmage, Nebr., July 2, 1942; s. Orville George and Twila Lucille (Larson) L.; m. Alice Louise Hentzen, Aug. 26, 1967; 1 child, Christian Douglas. BS, U. Nebr., 1965, MS, 1967, PhD, 1973. Systems analyst U. Nebr., Lincoln, 1967-73; asst. prof. GMI Engring. and Mgmt. Inst., Flint, Mich., 1973-74, assoc. prof., 1974-78, prof., 1978—; dept. head, 1984-87, asst. dean, 1986-88, provost, dean faculty, 1988-92, Richard L. Terrell prof. acad. leadership, 1990—, v.p for acad. affairs, provost, 1992—; cons. GM, Detroit, 1973-82, various orgns. Contbr. articles to profl. jours. Judge Internat. Sci. and Engring. Fair, various locations, 1989—. Mem. NSPE, Soc. Mfg. Engrs. (sr.), So. Automotive Engrs., Engring. Accreditation Commn. of Accreditation Bd. for Engring. and Tech., Am. Soc. Engring. Edn., Antique Auto Racing Assn., Model Engine Collectors Assn., Antique Model Race Car Club. Home: 3122 Beechtree Ln Flushing MI 48433-1945 Office: GMI Engring and Mgmt Inst 1700 W 3rd Ave Flint MI 48504-4898

LORENZ, JOHN GEORGE, librarian, consultant; b. N.Y.C., Sept. 28, 1915; s. John W. and Theresa T. (Wurtz) L.; m. Josephine R. Trumbull, Oct. 1, 1944; children: Laurence T., Janice R. B.S. (Library fellow), CCNY, 1939; B.S. in L.S, Columbia U., 1940; M.S. in Pub. Adminstrn., Mich. State U., 1952. With Queens Borough (N.Y.) Library, then Schenectady Pub. Library, 1940-44; chief reference div. Grand Rapids Pub. Library, 1944-46; asst. librarian Mich. State Library, 1944-56; with U.S. Office Edn., 1957-65, dir. div. library services and relations, 1961-65; dep. librarian of congress Library of Congress, Washington, 1965-76; exec. dir. Assn. Research Libraries, 1976-80; library cons., 1980—; interim dir. libraries Cath. U. Am., 1982-83; liaison mem. com. sci. and tech. info. exec. office, 1966-73; interim dir. CAPCON, 1985; spl. asst. to librarian Georgetown U. Library, 1985-87; interim dir. Washington Research Library Consortium, 1987-88; coord. libr. stats. program Nat. Commn. on Librs. and Inf. Sci., 1988—; exec. com. Nat. Book Com., 1968-74. Author numerous articles in field; contbr. to books. Presdl. appointee Nat. Hist. Publs. and Records Commn., 1979-83. Recipient Superior Svc. award HEW. Mem. ALA (coun. 1960-64, 69-73, chmn. panel UNESCO 1965-70, exec. bd. 1970-75, Lippincott award 1993), D.C. Libr. Assn., Internat. Fedn. Libr. Assn. (mem. program devel. group 1974-78), Am. Nat. Stds. Inst. (treas. libr. stds. com. 1980-88), Cosmos Club, Kenwood Golf and Country Club. Home: 5629 Newington Rd

Bethesda MD 20816-3321 Office: US Nat Commn on Librs Info Sci 1110 Vermont Ave NW Washington DC 20005-3522

LORENZ, KATHERINE MARY, banker; b. Barrington, Ill., May 1, 1946; d. David George and Mary (Hogan) L. BA cum laude, Trinity Coll., 1968; MBA, Northwestern U., 1971; grad., Grad. Sch. for Bank Adminstrn., 1977. Ops. analyst Continental Bank, Chgo., 1968-69, supr. ops. analysis, 1969-71, asst. mgr. customer profitability analysis, 1971-73, acctg. officer, mgr. customer profitability analysis, 1973-77, 2d v.p., 1976, asst. gen. mgr. contr.'s dept., 1977-80, v.p., 1980, contr. ops. and mgmt. svcs dept., 1981-84, v.p., sector contr. retail banking, corp. staff and ops. depts., 1984-88, v.p., sr. sector contr. pvt. banking, centralized ops. and corp. staff, 1988-90, v.p., sr. sector contr. bus. analysis group/mgmt. acctg., 1990-94, mgr. contrs. dept. adminstrn. and tng., 1990-94; v.p., chief of staff to chief adminstrv. officer Bank of Am. Ill., Chgo., 1994—. Mem. Nat. Assn. for Bank Cost and Mgmt. Acctg., Execs. Club Chgo. Office: Bank of Am Ill 231 S La Salle St Rm 1320 Chicago IL 60697

LORENZ, LEE SHARP, cartoonist; b. Hackensack, N.J., Oct. 17, 1932; s. Alfred Lloyd and Martha (Castagnetta) L.; m. Jill Allison Runcie, Sept., 1986; children: Christopher, Matthew, Martha, Ava. Student, Carnegie Inst. Tech., 1950-51; BFA, Pratt Inst., 1954. Staff cartoonist New Yorker mag., 1958—, art editor, 1973—; profl. cornetist, 1955—. Cartoonist: Here it Comes, 1968; author, illustrator: Scornful Simkin, 1980; collection Now Look What You've Done, 1977; Illustrator: Real Men Don't Eat Quiche, 1982, A Bridge Bestiary, 1986, Collection The Golden Age of Trash, 1987; author-illustrator: A Weekend in the Country, 1985. Trustee Swann Coll. of Cartoon and Caricature, 1978—; dir. Mus. for African Art. Mem. Century Club. Home: PO Box 131 Easton CT 06612-0131 Office: 20 W 43rd St New York NY 10036-7400

LORENZ, MICHAEL DUANE, veterinary medicine educator; m. Velda Clark. BS, DVM, Okla. State U., 1969. Formerly with U. Ga. Coll. Vet. Medicine, Athens; dean Kans. State U. Coll. Vet. Medicine, Manhattan, 1988-94. Mem. Nat. Acads. of Practice in Vet. Medicine. Office: Kans St U Coll Vet Medicine Dept Clinical Scis Office of Dean Manhattan KS 66506

LORENZ, RICHARD THEODORE, JR., lawyer; b. Chgo., Nov. 10, 1931; s. Richard Theodore and Catherine Lucille (Blumenthal) L.; m. Jane Benner, Sept. 10, 1955; 1 child, Anne. BSME, U. Notre Dame, 1953; JD, Loyola U., Chgo., 1964. Bar: Ill. 1964, U.S. Dist. Ct. (no. dist.) Ill. 1964, U.S. Supreme Ct. 1971; CPA. Ill. Engr. Underwriters Labs., Chgo., 1953-54; plant mgr. Lorenz Garment Co., Chgo., 1956-59; acct. Murphy, Lanier and Quinn, Chgo., 1959-65; atty. McDermott, Will and Emery, Chgo., 1965—. Served with U.S. Army, 1954-56. Mem. Chgo. Bar Assn., Ill. Bar Assn., Union League. Roman Catholic. Office: McDermott Will & Emery 227 W Monroe St Chicago IL 60606-5016

LORENZ, COBY, emeritus engineering educator; b. Oakland, Calif., Nov. 30, 1905; s. Coby and Catherine (O'Keefe) L.; m. Ina Voss, Aug. 7, 1937; children: Robert, Jacklyn, Donald, Kenneth. BSME, U. Calif., Berkeley, 1929, MSME, 1934. Profl. engr., Calif. Rsch. engr. Nat. Adv. Com. for Aeronautics, 1929-31; rsch. asst. U. Calif., Berkeley, 1931-34; rsch. engr. Calif. Forest and Range Exptl. Sta., 1934-37; prof. engring. U. Calif., Davis, 1937-69. Recipient John Scott medal City of Phila., 1976, Cyrus McCormick Gold medal Am. Soc. Agrl. Engrs., Chgo., 1981. Achievements include design of first commercial mechanical harvester for canning tomatoes. Home: Country Club Dr Carmel Valley CA 93924

LORENZEN, ROBERT FREDERICK, ophthalmologist; b. Toledo, Ohio, Mar. 20, 1924; s. Martin Robert and Pearl Adeline (Bush) L.; m. Lucy Logsdon, Feb. 14, 1970; children: Roberta Jo, Richard Martin, Elizabeth Anne. BS, Duke, 1948, MD, 1948; MS, Tulane U., 1953. Intern, Presbyn. Hosp., Chgo., 1948-49; resident Duke Med. Center, 1949-51, Tulane U. Grad. Sch., 1951-53; practice medicine specializing in ophthalmology, Phoenix, 1953—; mem. staff St. Joseph's Hosp., St. Luke's Hosp., Good Samaritan Hosp., Surg. Eye Ctr. of Ariz. Pres. Ophthalmic Scis. Found., 1970-73; chmn. bd. trustees Rockefeller and Abbe Prentice Eye Inst. of St. Luke's Hosp., 1975—. Recipient Gold Headed Cane award, 1974; named to Honorable Order of Ky. Cols. Fellow ACS, Internat. Coll. Surgeons, Am. Acad. Ophthalmology and Otolaryngology, Pan Am. Assn. Ophthalmology, Soc. Eye Surgeons; mem. Am. Assn. Ophthalmology (sec. of ho. of dels. 1972-73, trustee 1973-76), Ariz. Ophthal. Soc. (pres. 1966-67), Ariz. Med. Assn. (bd. dirs. 1963-66, 69-70), Royal Soc. Medicine, Rotary (pres. Phoenix 1984-85). Republican. Editor in chief Ariz. Medicine, 1963-66, 69-70. Office: 367 E Virginia Ave Phoenix AZ 85004-1275

LORENZETTI, OLE JOHN, pharmaceutical research executive, ophthalmic research and development executive; b. Chgo., Oct. 25, 1936; s. Natale and Quintilia (Bertochinni) L.; m. Lorna Joyce Bailey, June 20, 1961; children: Elizabeth Anne, Maria Anne, Dario. BS, U. Ill., Chgo., 1958; MS, Ohio State U., 1963, PhD, 1965; MBA (hon.), MIT, 1989. Rsch. fellow Ohio State U., Columbus, 1964-65; scientist Miles Labs., Elkhardt, Ind., 1965-67; sr. scientist Dome Labs. div. Miles Labs., Elkhardt, 1967-69; sr. scientist R&D Alcon Labs., Ft. Worth, 1969-72, mgr. R&D div. pre clin. sci., 1972-75, assoc. dir. R&D div. dermatology, 1975-80, dir. ophthal. R&D, 1980-83, sr. dir. surg. R&D, 1983-92, sr. dir. therapeutic rsch./licensing, 1992-94; v.p. therapeutic rsch./licensing, 1994—; asst. prof. pharmacology Health Scis. Ctr. U. Tex., Dallas, 1970-90; clin. prof. dermatology Health Scis. Ctr., U. Tex., Dallas, 1974-80; adj. prof. Tex. Christian U., 1972-82; J.J Able lectr. pharmacology Ohio No. U., 1965, 69; Kaufman-Lattimer lectr. Ohio State U., 1967, 70, 73, 78; vis. lectr. in therapeutic and drug rsch. U. Ill., 1973-80; toxicologist cons. South Bend, Ind. Municipality, 1967-69, Tarrant County, Tex., 1970-73; vis. lectr. U. Tex. Med. Schs., 1990—. Mem. editorial bd. Jour. Pharm. Sci., 1974-84, Cutis, 1977-89, Jour. Sci. Investigative Dermatology, 1978-82; contbr. articles to profl. jours., book chpts., govt. reports. Am. Heart Assn. fellow Ohio State U., 1964. Fellow Acad. Pharm. Scis. (pharmacology-toxicology sect.), Am. Acad. Clin. Toxicology, Soc. Cosmetic Chemists, Soc. for Exptl. Biology and Medicine; mem. AAAS, Am. Pharm. Assn., N.Y. Acad. Sci., Am. Chem. Soc., Soc. Investigative Dermatology, Drug Metabolism Group, Am. Soc. Pharmacology and Exptl. Therapeutics, Western Pharmacology Soc., Am. Coll. Toxicology, Inflammation Rsch. Assn., Am. Soc. Clin. Pharmacology, Am. Acad. Ophthalmology, Assn. for Rsch. and Vision and Ophthalmology, Drug Info. Assn., Rotary (pres. 1990), Sigma Xi, Rho Chi. Avocations: ranching, horses, sailing, marathon running. Office: Vice Pres Ther Rsch & Devel Alcon Labs Inc 6201 South Fwy Fort Worth TX 76134-2001

LORENZINI, PAUL G., manufacturing executive; b. 1939. BS in Edn., S.E. Mo. State, 1962. With Sunshine Biscuit, N.Y.C., 1963-67; plant mgr. Mobil Chem., Rochester, N.Y., 1967-69; with Bunzl Distbn. USA, Inc., Saint Louis, 1969—, now chmn. bd. Office: Bunzl Distribution USA Inc 701 Emerson Rd Ste 410 Saint Louis MO 63141-6743

LORENZ-MEYER, WOLFGANG, aeronautical engineer; b. Wohltorf, Lauenburg, Germany, Mar. 6, 1935; s. Paul Lorenz and Martha Maria Bothilde (Russ) L-M.; m. Erika Baeumler, Oct. 12, 1962; children: Ulrike, Stefan Lorenz, Klaus. Diploma in Mech. Engring., Tech. High, Hannover, Germany, 1962; D in Engring., Tech. U., Braunschweig, Germany, 1968. Scientist Aerodynamische Versuchsanstalt, Göttingen, Germany, 1963-69; dep. head of inst. Deutsche Forschungs-und Versuchsanstalt für Luft-und Raumfahrt, Göttingen, 1969-80, div. chief, 1973-86; cons. engr. pvt. practice, Göttingen, 1986—; lectr. Deutsche Forschungs-und Versuchsanstalt für Luft-und Raumfahrt to Supersonic Tunnel Assn., U.S., 1971-86; German mem. NATO Def. Rsch. Group AC 243 Project Group 7/Working Group 1, Brussels, 1973-76; rep. Deutsche Forschungsanstalt für Luft-und Raumfahrt to European Transonic Windtunnel related working group, Amsterdam, 1976-86. Contbr. articles to Jahrbuch der Wissenschaftlichen Gesellschaft für Luft-und Raumfahrt, Jahrbuch der Deutschen Gesellschaft für Luft-und Raumfahrt, Ing. Arch. and others, 1966-79. Recipient Ernst-Mach-Preis, Deutsche Forschungs-und Versuchsanstalt für Luft-und Raumfahrt, Bonn, Germany, 1968. Mem. AIAA, Deutsche Gesellschaft f. Luft-und Raumfahrt, Verein Deutscher Ingenieure. Lutheran. Achievements include U.S., European patents for active suppression of flow-induced vibration on sting supported wind-tunnel models; contbrs to strain-gauge balance devel. under cryogenic conditions; wind tunnel corrections and measuring accuracy

in transonic flow. Home: Sudetenlandstrasse 4, 37085 Göttingen L Saxony, Germany

LORENZO, ALBERT L., academic administrator. BS, U. Detroit, 1965, MBA, 1966; LLD (hon.), Walsh Coll. Accountancy and Bus. Adminstrn., 1987. Asst. dir. housing U. Detroit, 1964-65; staff acct. McManus, McGraw and Co., Detroit, 1964-66; asst. prof. acctg. Macomb Community Coll., Warren, Mich., 1966-68, bus. mgr. 1968-74, contr., 1974-75, v.p. bus., 1975-79, pres., 1979—; lectr. pub. speaker, presenter in field. Dir. rsch. SBA, 1966; mem. Mayor's Adv. Com. Small Bus., Detroit, 1967-70, base-community coun. Selfridge Air NG, 1978-86, steering com. March of Dimes, 1980-86, adv. coun. Met. Affairs Corp., 1982—, Mich. Competitive Enterprise Task Force, 1988-90, adv. bd. Nat. Inst. Leadership Devel., 1988—; Community Growth Alliance Macomb County, 1982—; selection panel Heart of Gold am. awards Southeastern Mich. United Way, 1990; chair div. II United Found., 1981; apptd. commr. State Mich. High Edn. Faciltes Authority, 1988-90; bd. dirs. N.E. Guidance Community Mental Health Ctr., 1976-79, Mich. Nat. Bank Macomb, 1981-87, Indsl. Tech. Inst., 1982—; trustee Nat. Commn. Coop. Edn., 1985—; trustee St. Joseph Hosp., 1984-87, sec. 1985-87, mem. adv. bd. 1981-83. Recipient Resolution of Tribute Mich. State Senate, 1979, Italian-Am. Citizen Recognition award, 1980, Volkswagen Am. Recognition award, 1982, Excellence in Speech Writing award Internat. Assn. Bus. Communicators, 1988, Nat. Leadership award U. Tex., 1989, Thomas J. Peters Nat. Leadership award, 1989; named Pres. of Yr. Am. Assn. Women in Community and Jr. Colls., 1985. Mem. Am. Assn. Community and Jr. Colls., World Future Soc., Met. Mus. Art, Mich. Community Coll. Assn., Econ. Club Detroit. Office: Macomb Community Coll 14500 E 12 Mile Rd Warren MI 48093-3896

LORENZO, MICHAEL, engineer, government official, real estate broker; b. Newton, N.J., 1920; m. Anastasia Hackett; 5 children. BS in Chemistry and Physics, Pa. State U., 1947; MEA, George Washington U., 1956, postgrad., 1975-78; postgrad., USDA Grad. Sch. Registered profl. engr., D.C., Md.; cert. Internat. Property Specialist (CIPS), FIPC. Field instrumentation engr. Fischer and Porter Co., Harboro, Pa., 1947-52; aerospace engr. Dept. Def., 1952-65; with Westinghouse Electric Corp., Friendship, Md., 1965-81; mgr. Air Resources Westinghouse Mgmt. Services, Inc., 1966-70, dir. environ. quality control, 1970-73; founder, pres. Tech. Protection Engring. Co., 1982—; dep. under-sec. def. Washington, 1981-82; founder, prin. broker First Lady Realty Co., 1986—. Author: (with others) Chemical Equipment Costs, 1950; assoc. editor: Missile and Rockets, 1958-61; contbr. articles to profl. jours.; patentee stall surge sonic sensor. Rear Admiral AC USN, World War II, Korea. Decorated D.S.M., D.F.C. (2), Air medals (7). Mem. Profl. Tennis Registry. Office: First Lady Realty Corp 3126 Shadeland Dr Falls Church VA 22044-1726 Healthy mind requires healthy body and vice versa. Per Winston Churchill "A Democracy is the worst form of Government that was ever invented except for all the others." It's my time in life to give back.

LORENZO, NICHOLAS FRANCIS, JR., lawyer; b. Norfolk, Va., Nov. 22, 1942; s. Nicholas and Jean W. L.; m. Patricia C. Connare, Sept. 7, 1968; children: Nicholas Michael, Matthew Christopher. B.A., St. Francis Coll., 1964; J.D., Duquesne U., 1968. Bar: Pa. 1968, U.S. Dist. Ct. (we. dist.) Pa. 1969, U.S. Supreme Ct. 1976, U.S. Dist. Ct. (mid. dist.) Pa. 1977, U.S. Ct. Appeals (3d cir.) 1983. Assoc. R. Edward Ferrero, Punxsutawney, Pa., 1968-70; pvt. practice law, Punxsutawney, 1970-79; pres. Lorenzo and Lundy, P.C., Punxsutawney, 1979-81, Nicholas F. Lorenzo, Jr. P.C., Punxsutawney, 1981-90, Lorenzo & Kulakowski, P.C., 1990—; instr. Sch. Continuing Edn., Pa. State U., 1969-73. Bd. dirs. Punxsutawney Area Hosp., 1972-74; mem. parish council S.S.C.D. Roman Cath. Ch., 1978-84, pres., 1979-84; bd. dirs. dist. Council Boy Scouts Am., 1982-84. Mem. ABA, Jefferson County Bar Assn. (v.p. 1980-82, pres. 1982-84), Pa. Bar Assn., Pa. Bar Inst. (bd. dirs. 1988-94), Pa. Trial Lawyers Assn. (bd. govs.), West Pa. Trial Lawyers Assn., Assn. Trial Lawyers Am., Nat. Bd. Trial Advocacy (civil cert.). Republican. Club: Punxsutawney Country. Lodges: K.C., Elks, Eagles Pat Rotary (pres. Punxsutawney 1973). Home: 180 Monticello Dr Punxsutawney PA 15767-9638 Office: 410 W Mahoning St Punxsutawney PA 15767-1908

LORGE, WILLIAM DAVID, state legislator, farmer; b. Bear Creek, Wis., Aug. 31, 1960; s. Gerald D. and Christina C. (Ziegler) L. BA in Internat. Relations, U. Wis., 1983. Real estate broker W. Lorge Sales, Bear Creek, Wis., 1988—; mem. Wis. State Assembly, Madison, 1989—; chairperson Assembly state affairs com.; mem. excise and fees com., mem. tourism, hwys. and ins. coms., consumer affairs com., criminal justice com., corrections com. Wis. State Assembly; mem. Wis. Trust for Hist. Preservation. Sponsor Christian Children's Fund, 1979—; mem. criminal justice com., corrections com. Wis. Trust for Hist. Preservation. Named Legislator of Yr., Wis. Conservation Congress, 1992. Mem. NRA, KC, Nat. Conf. of Ins. Legislators, U.S. Jaycees, Lions. Republican. Roman Catholic. Home: PO Box 8343 Madison WI 53708 Office: Wis State Assembly PO Box 8952 302 N State Capitol Madison WI 53708-8952

LORIAUX, MAURICE LUCIEN, artist, ecclesiologist; b. Chanute, Kans., Aug. 27, 1909; s. Amour Joseph and Eva (Goosens) L.; m. Susan Bowman, Oct. 17, 1935; children: Donald Lynn, Michael Maurice. B.A., U. Tulsa, 1931; M.A., Northwestern U., 1933; pvt. student, Berger Sandzen, Laura Requa, George Serraz. Dir. string dept. U. Tulsa, 1933-38; exec. dir. Santa Fe (N.Mex.) Studios of Church Art, 1947-66; pres. Art Horizons, 1961—; founder, pres. Southwest Art League Seminars; dir. Georgia O'Keeffe Country Workshops. Designer over 300 church interiors, Am. and abroad; condr. annual seminars art, Santa Fe; works include mural Healing, Tex. Med. Ctr., Houston, 1967; restoration of Old Mission, Santa Barbara, Calif., 1964, The Cabrini Shrine, Denver, 1956, Las Supper mural (1st distinctive award achievement Am. Assn. Arts), the Junipero Serra monument, Sacramento. Recipient First award of merit Church Property Adminstrn., 1966, Okla. Art and Humanities award of distinction in sculpture and arts, 1978; award of distinction Sierra Clubs Am. Fellow Stained Glass Assn. Am.; mem. Am. Internat. Stained Glass Inst. (founder, pres.), Artes Italia, Community Entertainment Assn. (pres. 1940-44). Home and Office: 812 Camino Acoma Santa Fe NM 87505-4932

LORIE, JAMES HIRSCH, business administration educator; b. Kansas City, Feb. 23, 1922; s. Alvin J. and Adele (Hirsch) L.; m. Sally Rosen, June 16, 1948 (div. 1953); 1 child Susan; m. Nancy A. Wexler, June 19, 1958 (dec. 1966); stepchildren: Katherine Wexler, Jeffrey Wexler; m. Vanna Metzenberg Lautman, Aug. 27, 1967; stepchildren: Erika Lautman, Victoria Lautman, Karl Lautman. A.B., Cornell U., 1942, A.M., 1945; Ph.D., U. Chgo., 1947. Research asst. Cornell U., Ithaca, N.Y., 1944-45; mem. staff seminar Am. civilization Salzburg, Austria, 1947; mem. faculty U. Chgo. Grad. Sch. Bus., 1947—, prof. bus. adminstrn., asso. dean, 1956-61; dir. Center Research in Security Prices, 1960-75, cons. divsn. rsch. and statistics bd. govs. Fed. Res. Sys., 1950-52; cons. U.S. Treas. Dept., 1973-74; bd. dirs. Acorn Fund, N.Y.C., Thornburg Mortgage Asset Co., Inc., Ardco Inc., Chgo.; mem. Nat. Market Adv. Bd., 1975-77. Author: (with Harry V. Roberts) Basic Methods of Marketing Research, 1951, (with Richard A. Brealey) Modern Developments in Investment Management, 1972, (with Mary T. Hamilton) The Stock Market: Theories and Evidence, 1973; contbr. articles to profl. jours. Served with USCGR, 1942-44. Mem. Am. Econ. Assn., Mont Pelerin Soc., Nat. Assn. Securities Dealers (dir. 1972-75), Phi Beta Kappa. Clubs: Arts (Chgo.); Quadrangle (U. Chgo.). Home: 2314 N Lincoln Park W Chicago IL 60614-3454

LORIMER, LINDA KOCH, college official; m. Ernest McFaul Lorimer; children: Katharine Elizabeth, Peter Brailler. AB, Hollins Coll., 1974; JD, Yale U., 1977; DHL, Green Mountain Coll., 1981, Washington Coll., 1992, Randolph-Macon Coll., 1992. Bar: N.Y. 1978, Conn. 1982. Assoc. Davis Polk and Wardwell, N.Y.C., 1977-78; asst. gen. counsel Yale U., New Haven, 1978-79, assoc. gen. counsel, 1979-84, assoc. provost 1983-87, acting assoc. v.p. human resources, 1984-85; prof. law, pres. Randolph-Macon Woman's Coll., Lynchburg, Va., 1987-93; sec. Yale Univ., New Haven, 1993—; lectr. Yale Coll. Undergrad. Seminars, 1980, 83; bd. dirs. Sprint, McGraw Hill; past mem. exec. com. Women's Coll. Coalition; mem. corp. Yale U., 1980-93, chair Virginia Rhodes scholarship com., 1991-93. Chair editorial bd. Jour. Coll. and Univ. Law, 1983-87. Former trustee Hollins Coll., Berkeley Div. Sch.; mem. com. on responsible conduct rsch. Inst. Medicine, NAS, 1988; bd. dirs. Norfolk Acad.; cabinet mem. United

Way of Greater New Haven. Mem. Nat. Assn. Coll. and Univ. Attys. (exec. bd. 1981-84), Nat. Assn. Schs. and Colls. of United Meth. Ch. (1st v.p.), Assn. Am. Colls.(bd. dirs., chmn. bd.), Am. Assn. Theol. Schs. (bd. dirs.), Mory's Assn., Phi Beta Kappa. Episcopalian. Home: 87 Trumbull St New Haven CT 06511 Office: Woodbridge Hall Yale Univ New Haven CT 06520-9999

LORINCZ, ALBERT BELA, physician, educator; b. Budapest, Hungary, Sept. 6, 1922; came to U.S., 1922, naturalized, 1944; s. Frank Coleman and Theresa (Csore) L.; m. Ann Marie Callaghan, Mar. 23, 1946; children: Margaret Alice, Albert Gregory, Paul Francis, Ann Elizabeth, Thomas Andrew, Catherine Bernadette, Peter Henry. B.S. in Biochemistry, U. Chgo., 1944, M.D., 1946. Diplomate: Am. Bd. Obstetrics and Gynecology. Intern Ill. Central Hosp., Chgo., 1946-47; resident obstetrics and gynecology Chgo. Lying-In Hosp., 1949-53; asst. prof. obstetrics and gynecology U. Chgo. Med. Sch., 1958-61, prof., 1966-71; clin. prof. Stanford U. Sch. Medicine, 1971—; prof. obstetrics and gynecology, chmn. dept. Creighton U. Sch. Medicine,1961-66; dir. dept. obstetrics and gynecology Creighton Meml.-St. Joseph's Hosp., Omaha, 1961-66; chmn. dept. obstetrics and gynecology Archbishop Bergan Mercy Hosp., Omaha, 1964-66; chief obstetrics Booth Meml. Hosp., Omaha, 1961-66; cons. VA Hosp., Omaha; also: Douglas County Hosp., Omaha, 1962-66; attending physician Chgo. Lying-In Hosp., Billings Hosp., Chgo., 1966-71; med. dir., chief obstetrics and gynecology Valley West Gen. Hosp., Los Gatos, Calif., 1971-75; chief staff Valley West Gen. Hosp., 1976, 84; mem. staff O'Connor Hosp., San Jose Hosp.; mem. staff, sec. dept. ob-gyn Santa Clara Valley Med. Ctr., bd. dirs., 1982-88; mem. staff Alexian Bros. Hosp., Good Samaritan Hosp., others. Contbr. articles to profl. jours. Mem. med. adv. bd. Nat. Found.-March of Dimes; bd. dirs. Santa Clara Valley PSRO, 1978-84. Served to 1st lt. M.C. AUS, 1944-46; to lt. col. 1948-58; col. Res., 1966-82 (ret.). Fellow ACS, Am. Coll. Obstetricians and Gynecologists; mem. AAAS, Am. Assn. Gynecologic Laparoscopists, Am. Chem. Soc., N.Y. Acad. Scis., Am. Fertility Soc., Am. Inst. Chemists, Assn. Profs. Gynecology and Obstetrics, Gynecol. Soc. for Study Breast Disease, Am. Soc. Reproductive Medicine, Am. Geriatric Soc., Royal Soc. Medicine (affiliate), Omaha-Midwest Clin. Soc., Chgo., San Francisco gynecol. socs., AMA, World Med. Assn., Am. Assn. for Lab. Animal Sci., Central Assn. Obstetricians and Gynecologists, Am. Assn. for Maternal and Infant Health, Am. Mil. Surgeons U.S., Reticuloendothelial Soc., Shufelt Soc. Santa Clara County, Pan Pacific Surg. Assn., Peninsula Gynecologic Soc., AAUP, Internat. Fertility Assn., Pan Am. Med. Assn., Am. Soc. Abdominal Surgeons, Pro-Life Med. Assn. Calif. (pres.), Am. Assn. Pro-Life Obstetricians and Gynecologists, Assn. for Advancement Med. Instrumentation, Santa Clara Valley PSRO (pres., dir.), Calif. Assn. Obstetricians and Gynecologists, Signa Xi. Democrat. Roman Catholic. Club: Central Travel. Home: 18816 Devon Ave Saratoga CA 95070-4606 Office: 15899 Los Gatos Almaden Rd Los Gatos CA 95032-3739

LORINCZ, ALLAN LEVENTE, physician, educator; b. Chgo., Oct. 31, 1924; s. Frank C. and Theresa (Csore) L.; m. Lillian Irene Staffan, Feb. 2, 1952; children—Donald, Linda, Alice. B.S., U. Chgo., 1945, M.D., 1947. Intern U. Chgo. Hosps., 1947-48, resident, 1948-51; mem. faculty U. Chgo. Med. Sch., 1951—, prof. dermatology, 1967—, head dermatology sect., 1960-91; chief dept. dermatology Walter Reed Army Inst. Rsch., Washington, 1954-56; nat. cons. in dermatology Surgeon Gen. of USAF, 1962-65; spl. cons. USPHS, 1961-64; mem. com. on cutaneous system NRC, 1962-68. Mem. Chgo. Dermatol. Soc. (pres. 1963), Phi Beta Kappa, Sigma Xi, Alpha Omega Alpha. Research in physiology and biochemistry of skin, cutaneous fungous diseases, acne, psoriasis. Home: 9905 S Kilbourn Ave Oak Lawn IL 60453-3539 Office: U Chgo 5841 S Maryland Ave Chicago IL 60637-1463

LORING, ARTHUR, lawyer, financial services company executive; b. N.Y.C., Oct. 13, 1947; s. Murray and Mildred (Rogers) L.; m. Vicki Hootstein, June 4, 1978. B.S. in Commerce, Washington and Lee U., 1969; J.D. cum laude, Boston U., 1972. Bar: Mass. 1972. Atty. Fidelity Mgmt. & Research Co., Boston, 1972; sr. legal counsel Fidelity Mgmt. & Research Co., 1980-82, v.p., gen. counsel, 1984-93; sr. v.p., gen. counsel, 1993—; v.p.-legal FMR Corp., Boston, 1982—; sec. Fidelity Group of Funds, Boston, 1982—; dir. Fidelity Capital Pubs. Inc., 1991—; bd. govs. Investment Co. Inst., 1988-90; chmn. ICI SEC Rules Com., 1990—; mem. adv. bd. Fund Directions, 1993—. Mem. ABA (securities regulation com.), Boston Bar Assn., Cavendish Club (dir. 1981-84), Boston Chess Club (pres. Brookline, Mass. 1981-83), Pinebrook Country Club, Polo Club of Boca Raton. Republican. Jewish. Avocations: golf, bridge, exercise. Home: 37 Brimmer St Boston MA 02108-1034 Office: Fidelity Mgmt & Rsch Co 82 Devonshire St Boston MA 02109-3614

LORING, CALEB, JR., investment company executive; b. Boston, Feb. 5, 1921; s. Caleb and Suzanne (Bailey) L.; m. Rosemary Merrill, Feb. 12, 1943; children—Caleb, David, Rosemary, Keith. A.B., Harvard U., 1943, LL.B., 1948. Bar: Mass. 1948, U.S. Dist. Ct. Mass. 1948. Asso., then partner firm Gaston, Snow, Motley & Holt, Boston, 1948-70; dir., trustee Loring, Wolcott and Coolidge Office-Fiduciary Services, Boston, 1948-86; v.p. dir. Puritan Fund, Inc., and all other funds in Fidelity Group of Funds, Boston, 1973-86; treas. Fidelity Mgmt. & Research Co., 1959-86; mng. dir. FMR Corp. (parent co. Fidelity Mgmt. & Rsch. Co.), Boston, 1986—; dir. Fidelity Investments, Boston, 1974—. Served with USNR, 1943-46. Mem. Am. Bar Assn., Mass. Bar Assn., Boston Bar Assn. Office: Fidelity Investments 82 Devonshire St Ste 8sa Boston MA 02109-3614

LORING, GLORIA JEAN, singer, actress; b. N.Y.C., Dec. 10, 1946; d. Gerald Louis and Dorothy Ann (Tobin) Goff; m. Alan Willis Thicke, Aug. 22, 1970 (div. 1986); children: Brennan Todd, Robin Alan; m. Christopher Beaumont, June 18, 1988 (div. 1993); m. René Lagler, Dec. 20, 1994. Grad. high sch. Owner Glitz Records, L.A., 1984—; pres. Only Silk Prodns., L.A., 1985-90; owner Silk Purse Prodns., 1992—. Began profl. singing, Miami Beach, 1965; appeared in numerous TV shows; featured singer: Bob Hope's Ann. Armed Forces Christmas Tour, 1970; featured several record albums; featured actress: Days of Our Lives, 1980-86; composer: TV themes Facts of Life, 1979, Diff'rent Strokes, 1978; author: Days of Our Lives Celebrity Cookbook, 1981, Vol. II, 1983, Living the Days of Our Lives, 1984, Kids Food and Diabetes, 1986, Parenting a Diabetic Child, 1991, The Kids Food and Diabetes Family Cookbook, 1991. Celebrity chmn. Juvenile Diabetes Found. Recipient Humanitarian of Yr. award Juvenile Diabetes Found., 1982, 88, Parents of Yr. award, 1984, Woman of Yr. award Jeweler's Assn. Am., 1986. Mem. Nat. Acad. Songwriters (gold mem.). *I feel the most important element in any life is to continue reaching out, growing, and learning. Don't be afraid to ask. Don't be afraid to challenge. Don't be afraid.*

LORING, JOHN ROBBINS, artist; b. Chgo., Nov. 23, 1939; s. Edward D'Arcy and China Robbins (Logeman) L. B.A., Yale U., 1960; postgrad., Ecole Beaux Arts, Paris, 1960-63. Disting. vis. prof. U. Calif., Davis, 1977; bur. chief Archtl. Digest mag., N.Y.C., 1977-78; assoc. dir. Tiffany and Co., N.Y.C., 1979—; exec. v.p., design dir., 1981-84; sr. v.p. design and merchandising, 1984—; mem. acquisitions com. dept. prints and illustrated books Mus. Modern Art, N.Y.C., 1990—. Contbg. editor: Arts. mag. 1973—; books include: The New Tiffany Tablesettings, 1981, Tiffany Taste, 1986, Tiffany's 150 Years, 1987, The Tiffany Wedding, 1988, Tiffany Parties, 1989, The Tiffany Gourmet, 1992; one-man exhbns. include, Balt. Mus. Art, 1972, Hundred Acres Gallery, N.Y., 1972, Pace Edits., 1973, 77, Long Beach Mus. Art, 1975, A.D.I. Gallery, San Francisco, 1976, group exhbns. include, Phila. Mus. Art, 1971, N.Y. Cultural Center, 1972, Biennale Graphic Art, Ljubljana, Yugoslavia, 1973, 77, Intergrafia 74, Krakow, Poland, 1974, Bklyn. Mus. Nat. Print Exhbn., 1974, Art Inst. Chgo., 1975, R.I. Sch. Design, 1976; represented in permanent collections, Mus. Modern Art, N.Y.C., Whitney Mus. Am. Art, Chgo. Art Inst., Boston Mus. Fine Arts, R.I. Sch. Design, Balt. Mus. Art, Yale U. Art Gallery; commd. by, U.S. Customhouse, N.Y.C., Prudential Ins. Co. Am. Eastern Home Office, Woodbridge, N.J., City of Scranton, Pa., Western Savs., Phila. Recipient Edith Wharton design & Art Soc., 1988. Office: Tiffany & Co 727 Fifth Ave New York NY 10022-2503 also: Doubleday 1540 Broadway New York NY 10036 *I look on whatever talents I may have as natural resources to be given freely wherever needed. A lot has been given out; a lot has come in.*

LORKOVIC, TATJANA, librarian; b. Beograd, Yugoslavia, Jan. 17, 1933; d. Krunoslav and Antonija (Benišek) Bujas; m. Hrvoje Lorkovic, Sept. 8, 1956 (div. 1980); children: Maja, Radoslav, Ivan. Diploma, Music Acad. Zagreb, Yugoslavia, 1953, U. Croatia, Zagreb, 1957; student, U. London, 1963-64; MLS, U. Minn., 1968; MA in Russian Lang. and Lit., U. Iowa, 1972. Instr. in Serbo-Croatian lang. Workers U. of Zagreb, Yugoslavia, 1957-59; staff mem. State Ctr. for Edn. of Mgrs., Zagreb, 1959-63; Slavic libr. U. Iowa Librs., Des Moines, 1968-89, head cataloging dept., 1973-85, 86-89, libr. III, 1974, libr. IV, 1981, adminstr. serials, binding and marking ops., 1984; curator Slavic and East European collections Sterling Meml. Libr., Yale U., New Haven, 1989—; fellow Pierson Coll., Yale U., 1989—; chair East Coast Consortium for Slavic Collections, 1993—; lectr., presenter in field. Editor, transl.: The University of the Future (Miroslav Pecujlic), 1987, (with Tomas J. Whitby) Introduction to Soviet National Bibliography, 1979; contbr. articles to profl. jours. U.S. Inst. of Peace grantee, 1991; Fulbright scholar, 1982. Mem. ALA (mem. nominating com. for cataloging and classification sect. of resources and tech. svcs. divsn. 1983-84, 89-90), Am. Assn. Advancement Slavic Studies. Office: Yale U Libr Slavic & E European Collection 130 Wall St PO Box 208240 New Haven CT 06520

LORNE, SIMON MICHAEL, lawyer; b. Hampton, Eng., Feb. 1, 1946; came to U.S., 1952, naturalized, 1961; s. Henry Thomas and Daphne Mary (Brough) L.; AB cum laude, Occidental Coll., 1967; JD magna cum laude, U. Mich., 1970; children: Christopher, Michele, Allison, Nathan James, Katrina. Admitted to Calif. bar, 1971; assoc. firm Munger, Tolles & Olson, L.A., 1970-72, ptnr., 1972-93; gen. counsel U.S. SEC, 1993—; vis. assoc. prof. law U. Pa., 1977-78, acting dir. Ctr. Study of Fin. Instns., 1977-78; lectr. in law, corp. fin. U. So. Calif., 1986-88. Author: Acquisitions and Mergers: Negotiated and Contested Transactions, 1985. Mem. L.A. Mayor's Com. on Internat. Trade Devel., 1979-81; bd. dirs., sec. L.A. Internat. Trade Devel. Corp., 1982-85; mem. adv. com. to U.S. Senator S.I. Hayakawa on Internat. Trade, 1979-82; bd. govs. Econ. Literacy Coun. Calif., 1981-87; mem. Nat. Legal Adv. Commn., Nat. Assn. Security Dealers, 1989-93. Served with USMCR, 1967-68. Mem. Los Angeles Area C. of C. (exec. com., internat. commerce com., leadership mission to People's Republic of China, 1980), ABA, Los Angeles County Bar Assn. (exec. com. bus. and corps. law sect., chmn. 1984-85), Calif., Jonathan Club. Republican. Roman Catholic. Home: # 1211 2801 New Mexico Ave NW Washington DC 20007 Office: SEC Mail Stop 6-6 450 5th St NW Washington DC 20549

LORSCH, JAY WILLIAM, business educator; b. St. Joseph, Mo., Oct. 8, 1932; s. Hans R. and Serina B. (Levin) L.; m. Patricia Welbourn, July 1, 1978; children by previous marriage: Robin, Jon, David. AB, Antioch Coll., 1955; MS, Columbia U., 1956; DBA, Harvard U., 1964. Rsch. fellow Harvard U. Grad Sch. Bus. Adminstrn., Boston, 1964-65; from asst. prof. to prof. Harvard U. Grad. Sch. Bus Adminstrn., Boston, 1965—; Louis E. Kirstein prof. human relations Harvard U. Grad. Sch. Bus. Adminstrn., Boston, 1977—; sr. assoc. dean, dir. rsch., 1986—; with controller's dept. Hallmark Cards, Inc., 1959; bd. dirs. Brunswick Corp., Sandy Corp. Author: Product Innovation and Organization, 1965, (with Gene Dalton and Paul R. Lawrence) Organizational Structure and Design, 1967, (with Lawrence) Organization and Environment: Managing Differentiation and Integration, 1967, Organizational Development: Diagnosis and Action, 1969, Studies in Organization Design, 1970, (with Louis B. Barnes) Managers and Their Careers: Cases and Readings, 1972, (with Lawrence) Organization Planning: Cases and Concepts, 1972, Managing Groups and Intergroup Relations, 1972, (with Stephen A. Allen) Managing Diversity and Interdepndence: An Organizational Study of Multidivisional Firms, 1973, (with John J. Morse) Organizations and Their Members: A Contingency Approach, 1975, (with Lawrence and Barnes) Organizational Behavior and Adminstration, 1976, Understanding Management, 1978, Decision Making at the Top, 1983, Handbook of Organizational Behavior, 1987; Pawns or Potentates, 1989; contbr. to bus. and mgmt. jours., 1983. Lt. U.S. Army, 1956-59. Recipient Book of Yr. award Acad. of Mgmt., 1978. Avocations: tennis, swimming. Office: Harvard U Grad Sch Bus Adminstrn Soldiers Field Boston MA 02163

LORSUNG, THOMAS NICHOLAS, editor-in-chief, director; b. Milw., June 9, 1938; s. Nicholas A. and Margaret (Senger) L.; m. Mary Jelen, Aug. 27, 1960; children: Kristin Lorsung Shulder, Anne K., Erin M. BJ, Marquette U., 1960. Reporter Journal-Times, Racine, Wis., 1961-63; reporter, photographer, news editor Cath. Rev., Balt., 1963-69; photo, copy editor The Sentinel, Milw., 1969-72; photo editor Nat. Cath. News Svc., Washington, 1972-75, news editor, 1975-76, mng. editor, 1976-89; dir., editor-in-chief Cath. News Svc. (formerly Nat. Cath. News Svc.), Washington, 1989-95; chmn. bd. dirs. Carroll Pub., Washington, 1993—. Mem. Cath. Press Assn. (bd. dirs. 1991—, St. Francis de Sales award 1995), Internat. Cath. Union of the Press, Fed. Cath. News Agencies (v.p. 1992). Avocations: photography, running, biking, choral singing. Home: 5367 Iron Pen Pl Columbia MD 21044-1812 Office: Catholic News Svc 3211 4th St NE Washington DC 20017-1106

LORTEL, LUCILLE, theatrical producer; b. N.Y.C., Dec. 16, 1905; d. Harry and Anna (Moes) Wadler; m. Louis Schweitzer, Mar. 23, 1931 (dec.). Student, Adelphi Coll., 1920, Am. Acad. Dramatic Arts, 1920-21, abroad; DFA (hon.), U. Bridgeport, 1985. Established White Barn Theatre, Westport, Conn., 1947—; owner, producer Lucille Lortel Theatre (originally Lucille Lortel's Theatre de Lys), N.Y.C., 1955—; artistic dir. ANTA Matinee Series, N.Y.C., 1956—; founder Am. Shakespeare Festival Theatre, Stratford, Conn., 1955. Appeared in various stage plays including: Caesar and Cleopatra, 1925; The Dove, 1925; One Man's Woman, 1926; radio appearances, 1935; producer various stage plays, including Three Penny Opera, 1955, I Knock at the Door, 1957, Cock a Doodle Dandy, 1958, The Balcony, 1960, The Blood Knot, 1964, A Streetcar Named Desire, 1973; co-producer plays including Angels Fall, 1983 (Tony nomination), As Is, 1984 (Tony nomination), Blood Knot, 1985 (Tony nomination), numerous others. V.p. exec. com. bd. dirs. Friends of Theatre Collection of Mus. City of N.Y.; mem. adv. bd. Nat. Theatre of Deaf, Chester, Conn.; trustee Goodspeed Opera House, East Haddam, Conn. Recipient 2 awards Greater N.Y. chpt. ANTA, 1958, Off-Broadway award, 1956, 58, 60, 84, Margo Jones award, 1962, award Nat. ANTA, 1962, Villager award, 1979, Cert. Merit City of N.Y., 1980, Arnold Weissberger award Theatre Hall Fame, 1982, Spl. citation N.Y. Drama Critics, 1983, Lee Strasberg Lifetime Achievement in Theatre award, 1985, Spl. Theatre World award, 1985, Exceptional Achievement award Women's Project Am. Pl. Theatre, 1986, George M. Cohan award Cath. Actors Guild Am., 1986, 1st citation Mus. Am. Theatre, New Haven, 1986, numerous others. Office: Lucille Lortel Theatre 121 Christopher St New York NY 10014-4204

LORTON, LEWIS, dentist, researcher, computer scientist; b. N.Y.C., Nov. 3, 1939; s. Frederick S. and Rosell (Engel) L.; divorced; children: Elizabeth, Mark, Michael S.; m. Jacqueline Carol Andor, Aug. 3, 1982; children: Michael E., Erin. BA, Brandeis U., 1960; DDS, U. Pa., 1964; MSD, Ind. U., 1978. Pvt. practice West Medway, Mass., 1964-66; commd. lt. U.S. Army, 1966, advanced through grades to col., 1983, researcher, 1974, 1976—; cons. Armed Forces Inst. Pathology, Washington, 1986—; chief info. mgr. Henry M. Jackson Found., 1989-91; v.p. Klemm Analysis Group, Inc., 1991-92; pres. Lorton Associates, 1992-94; exec. dir. Health Care Open Systems & Trials, Inc., 1994—. Contbr. numerous articles to profl. jours. Recipient Carl Schlack award Assn. Mil. Surgeons U.S., 1988. Fellow Am. Forensic Soc.; mem. Internat. Assn. Dental Rsch., Am. Assn. Dental Rsch., Am. Soc. Forensic Odontology, Soc. for Clin. Trials. Avocations: statistics, computers, fly fishing, squash. Home: 10096 Hatbrim Ter Columbia MD 21046-1318 Office: 414 Hall of the States 444 N Capital Washington DC 20001

LORY, MARC H., hospital administrator; b. Bklyn., June 23, 1948; s. Jerome and Mildred (Platzick) L.; m. Audrey Manheimer, Nov. 2, 1985; 1 child from previous marriage, Rebecca. BEd, U. Miami, 1971; MPA, NYU, 1976. Nuclear medicine technologist Albert Einstein Coll. Medicine, Bronx, N.Y., 1971-74; adminstrv. resident Montefiore Hosp. & Med. Ctr., Bronx, 1974-75, adminstr., dept. neurology, 1975-77, asst. dir., 1977-81; v.p. St. Luke's-Roosevelt Hosp. Ctr., N.Y.C., 1981-86; chief oper. officer Roosevelt Hosp., N.Y.C., 1981-86; v.p., chief exec. officer U. Medicine & Dentistry of N.J.-Univ. Hosp., Newark, 1986—; trustee Ctr. for Preventive Psychiatry, N.Y., Univ. Health Systems, N.J., Essex chpt. ARC, N.J. Contbr. articles to profl. jours. Mem. Am. Hosp. Assn., Transplant Found. N.J., N.J. Hosp. Assn. Jewish. Office: UMDNJ Hosp 150 Bergen St Newark NJ 07103-2406

LOS, MARINUS, agrochemical researcher; b. Ridderkerk, The Netherlands, Sept. 18, 1933; came to U.S., 1960; s. Cornelis and Neeltje (Zoutewelle) L.; m. Lorraine Betty Lowe, May 11, 1957; children: Simon, Sija, Michael, Martin (dec.). BS, Edinburgh U., Scotland, 1955, PhD, 1957. Sr. rsch. chemist Am. Cyanamid Co., Princeton, N.J., 1960-71, group leader, 1971-84, sr. group leader, 1984-86, mgr. crop protection chems., 1986-88, assoc. dir. crop scis., 1988-92, rsch. dir. crop scis., 1992—. Recipient Disting. Inventor of 1990 award Intellectual Property Owners, Inc., Washington, 1990, Thomas Alva Edison Patent award R&D Coun. of N.J., 1991, Nat. Medal of Tech. NSF, 1993, Perkin medal Soc. Chemical Industry, 1994; Achievement award Industrial Rsch. Inst., 1994, Award for Creative Invention Am. Chem. Soc., 1995. Mem. AAAS, Am. Chem. Soc., Plant Growth Regulator Soc. Achievements include 53 patents. Office: Am Cyanamid Co PO Box 400 Princeton NJ 08543-0400

LOSACCO, LESLEY HERDT, supervisor, educator; b. Pitts., Mar. 31, 1936; d. Leslie Weyman and Grace Langhans Henig (Lauterbach) Herdt; m. Raymond B. Losacco, July 31, 1964. BMFA-BMFAME, Carnegie-Mellon U., 1959, MFA-MFAME, 1969; PhD, Duquesne U., 1983. Cert. AGO-FAGO, tchr. music, supr. music. Supr., music tchr. North Hills Sch. Dist., Pitts. Author: The Music Course of Study. Recipient Community Leadership in Music awards, Gift of Time tribute Am. Family Inst., 1990. Mem. ASCD, Music Educators Nat. Conf., Pa. Music Educators Assn., North Hills Edn. Assn., Am. Guild of Organists, Orff-Shlwerk Assn., Phi Kappa Phi, Sigma Alpha Iota. Home: 161 Lakewood Ave Pittsburgh PA 15229-1729 Office: 135 Sixth Ave Pittsburgh PA 15229-1291

LOSADA, MARCIAL FRANCISCO, research scientist, psychologist; b. Rancagua, Chile, July 3, 1939; came to U.S., 1973; s. Marcial and Hortensia (Menendez) L.; m. Giovanna Morchio, Jan. 5, 1964; children: Ximena, Andrea. MA, U. Mich., 1975, PhD, 1977. Prof. Univ. Catolica, Chile, 1969-73; sr. study dir. U. Mich., Ann Arbor, 1977-80; dir. Coherent Forecasting Systems, Ann Arbor, 1981-84; sr. rsch. scientist Electronic Data Systems, Warren, Mich., 1985-86; sr. rsch. scientist EDS Ctr. for Machine Intelligence, Ann Arbor, 1986-88, program dir., 1989-90; dir. EDS Ctr. for Advanced Rsch., Ann Arbor, 1991—. Mem. Am. Psychol. Soc. Achievements include development of group analyzer, a system for dynamic analysis of group interaction. Office: EDS Ctr for Advanced Rsch 2001 Commonwealth Blvd Ann Arbor MI 48105-2947

LOSCALZO, JOSEPH, biochemist, cardiologist; b. Camden, N.J., Oct. 26, 1951; s. Joseph and Dolores Rita (Ventura) L.; m. Anita Beth Sendrow, Mar. 10, 1974; children: Julia, Alexander. AB summa cum laude, U. Pa., 1972, MD and PhD, 1978. Diplomate Am. Bd Internal Medicine; cert. in cardiovascular medicine. Postdoctoral fellow U. Pa., Phila., 1978; resident in internal medicine Brigham and Women's Hosp., Boston, 1978-81, clin. fellow cardiology, 1981-83, chief med. resident, 1983-84, instr. medicine, 1983-85; clin. fellow medicine Harvard Med. Sch., Boston, 1978-81, asst. prof. medicine, 1985-88, assoc. prof., 1989—; chief cardiol. sect. Brockton West Roxbury VA Med. Ctr., Boston, 1989-93; disting. prof. medicine, prof. biochemistry Boston U., 1994—; dir. Whitaker Cardiovasc. Inst., Sch. Medicine, 1994—, vice chmn. dept. medicine, chief cardiovasc. medicine, 1994—; mem. rsch. rev. com. Am. Heart Assn., 1988—; rsch. rev. cons. Nat. Heart, Lung and Blood Inst., Bethesda, Md., 1990—. Author: (with others) books on vascular biology and medicine, thrombosis and hemostasis; assoc. editor New England Journal of Medicine; contbr. mem. editorial bd.: Circulation, Circulation Research, Journal Thrombusis and Thrombolysis, Jouranl Vascular Medicine Biology, American Journal of Cardiology, articles to profl. jours. Recipient Med. Scientist Tng. award NIH, 1972-77, Rsch. Career Devel. award, 1989-94, Clin. Scientist award Am. Heart Assn., 1983-88. Fellow ACP, Am. Coll. Cardiology; mem. Am. Fedn. Clin. Rsch., Am. Soc. Clin. Investigation, Assn. Univ. Cardiologists, Am. Soc. Biol. Chemistry, Phi Beta Kappa. Achievements include five patents related to nitric oxide congeners. Office: Boston U Sch Medicine Whitaker Cardiovasc Inst 700 Albany St Boston MA 02118-2394

LOSCAVIO, ELIZABETH, dancer; b. Jacksonville, Fla.. Student, Contra Costa Ballet Sch., Pacific N.W. Ballet Sch., San Francisco Ballet Sch. Co. apprentice San Francisco Ballet, 1986, mem. corps de ballet, 1986-88, soloist, 1988-90, prin. dancer, 1990—. Performances include Romeo and Juliet, The Sleeping Beauty, Swan Lake, Nanna's Lied, Haffner Symphony, Con Brio, Handel-a Celebration, Menuetto, Contradanses, Ballet D'Isoline, Intimate Voices, La Fille mal gardée, Ballo della Regina, Tchaikovsky Pas de Deux, Theme and Variations, Who Cares?, Symphony in C, Tarantella, Rubies, Stars and Stripes, The Four Temperaments, A Midsummer Night's Dream, Rodeo, Maelstrom, La Pavane Rouge, Dark Elegies, Grand Pas de Deux, Flower Festival at Genzano, Rodin, Connotations, Le Corsaire Pas de Deux, Sunset, In the Night, Interplay, The End, The Comfort Zone, Dreams of Harmony, The Wanderer Fantasy, The Sons of Horus, Nutcracker, Divertissemet d'Auber, Vivaldi Concerto Grosso, New Sleep, La Sylphide. Recipient Isadora Duncan award, 1991. Office: San Francisco Ballet 455 Franklin St San Francisco CA 94102-4471*

LO SCHIAVO, JOHN JOSEPH, university executive; b. San Francisco, Feb. 25, 1925; s. Joseph and Anne (Re) Lo S. A.B., Gonzaga U., 1948, Ph.L. and M.A., 1949; S.T.L., Alma Coll., 1962. Joined S.J., Roman Catholic Ch., 1942; tchr. St. Ignatius High Sch., San Francisco, 1949-50; instr. philosophy and theology U. San Francisco, 1950-52, 56-57, 61-62, v.p. for student affairs, dean of students, 1962-68, pres., 1977-91, chancellor, 1991—; pres. Bellarmine Coll. Prep. Sch., San Jose, 1968-75. Bd. dirs. St. Mary's Hosp. and Med. Ctr., Sch. of Sacred Heart. Mem. Olympic Club, Bohemian Club, Univ. Club. Office: U San Francisco 2130 Fulton St San Francisco CA 94117

LOSCHIAVO, LINDA BOSCO, library director; b. Rockville Ctr., N.Y., Aug. 31, 1950; d. Joseph and Jennie (DelRegno) Bosco; m. Joseph A. LoSchiavo, Sept. 7, 1974. BA, Fordham U., 1972, MA, 1990; MLS, Pratt Inst., 1974. Picture cataloguer Frick Art Reference Libr., N.Y.C., 1972-75; sr. cataloguer Fordham U. Libr., Bronx, N.Y., 1975-87, head of retrospective conversion, 1987-90, systems libr., 1990-91, dir. libr. at Lincoln Ctr., 1991—; libr. cons. Mus. Am. Folk Art Libr., N.Y.C., 1985-90; indexer Arco Books, N.Y.C., 1974. Editor: Macbeth, 1990, Julius Ceasar, 1990, Romeo and Juliet, 1990. Mng. producer Vineyard Opera, N.Y.C., 1981-88. Mem. ALA, N.Y. Tech. Svcs. Librs., Beta Phi Mu, Alpha Sigma Nu. Home: 317 Collins Ave Mount Vernon NY 10552 Office: Fordham Univ Library 113 W 60th St New York NY 10023

LOSCIUTO, LEONARD ANTHONY, psychologist, educator; b. N.Y.C., Mar. 8, 1940. BS, CCNY, 1961; MS, Pudue U., 1963, PhD, 1966; 1980. Cons. Batten, Barton, Durstein and Osborne, Inc., 1962-68, Social Security Adminstrn., Balt., 1971-72; asst. prof. psychology Rutgers U., 1965-68; assoc. prof. psychology Temple U., 1969-81, prof. psychology, 1981-84, prof. mktg., 1984—; adj. prof. psychology Temple U., 1984—; study dir. Inst. for Survey Rsch., Temple U., 1968-71, asst. dir. 1971, acting dir., 1971-72, dir., 1972—; cons. in field; sci. adv. bd. nat. radon survey com. EPA, 1987—; grant reviewer NIH, 1972-76, spl. emphasis panels NIH, 1975. Rsch. Ctr. Contbr. numerous articles to profl. jours. Fellow Am. Psychol. Assn. (mem. consumer and population rsch. divsn.), Am. Assn. for Pub. Opinion Rsch. Home: 335 Oak Terrace Saint Davids PA 19087 Office: Inst for Survey Rsch Temple U 1601 North Broad St Philadelphia PA 19122

LOSEE, THOMAS PENNY, JR., publisher; b. Mineola, N.Y., Dec. 9, 1940; s. Thomas Penny and Jeanne Hubbell (Grandeman) L.; m. Muriel Frances Hahn, Apt. 25, 1964; children: Thomas Penny III, Kendall Louise; m. Clark Edward Graebner Jr., Aug. 28, 1993. A.B., Duke U., 1963. Advt. salesman Look mag., 1964-71; advt. dir. House Beautiful, 1971-72; pub. Harper's Bazaar, N.Y.C., 1972-76, House Beautiful, 1976—; v.p., asst. to gen. mgr. Hearst Mag. div., 1981—; v.p., pub. Sci. Digest mag., 1983—; Archtl. Digest mag., 1989-91; sr. v.p., pub. dir. Knapp Communications, 1991—; pub. Archtl. Digest mag. CondÉ Nast Pubs., 1993—. Mem. editorial bd. Duke Mag. Trustee Taft Sch. With USAR, 1963-69. Mem. Mag. Pubs. Assn. (bd. dirs.), Univ. Club, Creek Club, Cold Spring Harbor Beach Club, Coral Beach Club (Bermuda), Beta Theta Pi. Republican.

Episcopalian. Home: PO Box 471 Cold Spring Harbor NY 11724-0471 Office: 350 Madison Ave New York NY 10017-3704

LOSEFF, LEV LIFSCHUTZ, Russian educator; b. Leningrad, USSR, June 15, 1937; came to U.S., 1976.; s. Vladimir Lifschultz and Assia Genkina; m. Nina P Mokhov, Apr. 20, 1959; children: Dimitry, Marie. MA in Philology, U. Leningrad, USSR, 1959; PhD, U. Mich., 1981. Journalist The Sakhalin Oil-Worker Newspaper, Okha-in-Sakhalin, 1959-60; free-lance writer Leningrad, 1961-62; editor Kostyor Mag., Leningrad, 1962-75; part-time editor Ardis Pub. House, Ann Arbor, Mich., 1976-78; vis. prof. Mich. State U., East Lansing, 1978-79; from instr. to prof. Dartmouth Coll., Hanover, N.H., 1979—; prof. Dartmouth Coll., Hanover. Author: On the Beneficence of Censorship: Aesopian Language in Modern Russian Literature, 1984,(essays) Eats, 1984, (poems) A Miraculous Raid, 1985, A Privy Councillor, 1988; editor: Mikhail Bulgakov, Notes on the Cuffs, 1981, Nikolay Oleynikov, Ironic, 1982, Brodsky's Poetics, 1986, Norwich Symposia on Russian Literature and Culture, (Boris Pasternak), 1991, (with Valentina Polukhina) Brodsky's Poetics and Aesthetics, 1990; contbr. articles to profl. jours. Book review broadcasts, Voice of Am. Russian Svc., 1979—, Radio Liberty, BBC, Radio France. Mem. Am. Assn. Advancement of Slavic Studies, Am. Assn. Tchrs East European and Slavic Lang. Office: Russian Dept Dartmouth College Hanover NH 03755

LOSER, JOSEPH CARLTON, JR., dean, retired judge; b. Nashville, June 16, 1932; s. Joseph Carlton and Pearl Dean (Gupton) L.; m. Mildred Louise Nichols, May 25, 1972; 1 child, Joseph Carlton III. Student, U. Tenn., 1950-51, Vanderbilt U., 1952-55; LLB, Nashville YMCA Night Law Sch., 1959. Bar: Tenn. 1959. Pvt. practice, 1959-66; judge Gen. Sessions Ct., Davidson County, Tenn., 1966-69, Cir. Ct. 20th Jud. Dist. Tenn., 1969-86; dean Nashville Sch. Law, 1986—. Mem. ABA, Internat. Acad. Trial Judges, Tenn. Bar Assn., Nashville Bar Assn., Am. Legion, Masons, Shriners, Sigma Delta Kappa, Kappa Sigma.

LOSH, CLIFFORD WILLIAM, lawyer; b. Cleve., Feb. 8, 1951. BBA, U. Notre Dame, 1973; MA, Cambridge U., Eng., 1975; JD, Yale U., 1978. Bar: D.C. 1979, Ill. 1981. With Skadden, Arps, Slate, Meagher & Flom, N.Y.C. Mem. ABA, Ill. State Bar Assn. Office: Skadden Arps Slate Meagher & Flom 919 3rd Ave New York NY 10022-3903 also: 333 W Wacker Dr Chicago IL 60606-1218

LOSHUERTOS, ROBERT HERMAN, clergyman; b. San Francisco, Apr. 28, 1937; s. Joseph Guillermo and Ruth Margarethe (Erdmann) L.; m. Carolyn Angela Reinartz, Aug. 6, 1960; children: William Frederick, John Martin. AA, San Francisco City Coll., 1957; BA, Wittenberg U., 1959; MDiv, Luth. Theol. So. Sem., Columbia, S.C., 1963. Ordained to ministry Evang. Luth. Ch. in Am., 1963. Asst. pastor Meml. Evang. Luth. Ch., 1963-64, Trinity Luth. Ch., Riverside, Calif., 1964-66; pastor Our Saviours Luth. Ch., Oxnard, Calif., 1966-71; assoc. pastor Luth. Ch. of Good Shepherd, Buena Park, Calif., 1971-73; pastor St. Mark's Luth. Ch., Huntsville, Ala., 1973-80; exec. min. Interfaith Mission Svc., Huntsville, 1980—; chmn. pers./ mut. ministry com. Southeastern Synod Evang. Luth. Ch. in Am., Atlanta, 1988-93. Active Humanitarian Svcs. Com., Huntsville, 1985—, Leadership 2000, Huntsville, 1988-89; chmn. adminstrn. com., bd. dirs. Williams-Henson Luth. Home, Knoxville, Tenn., 1986-92; pres. Target Success task force Dept. Human Resources, City of Huntsville, 1988-91, chmn. Mayor's Homeless Adv. Com., 1989-91; mem. Synod Coun.-S.E. Synod ELCA, 1991—. Recipient Brotherhood award NCCJ, 1989, Martin Luther King Jr. Unity award Alpha Phi Alpha, 1990. Mem. Nat. Assn. Ecumenical Staff. Office: Interfaith Mission Svc 411B Holmes Ave NE Huntsville AL 35801

LOSS, JOHN C., architect, retired educator; b. Muskegon, Mich., Mar. 6, 1931; s. Alton A. and Dorothy Ann (DeMars) Forward; m. LaMyrna Lois Draggoo, June 7, 1958. B.Arch., U. Mich., 1954, M.Arch., 1960. Registered architect, Mich. Architect Eero Saarinen & Assocs., Bloomfield Hills, Mich., 1956-57; owner John Loss & Assocs, Detroit, 1960-75; prof., acting dean Sch. Architecture, U. Detroit, 1960-75; prof., head dept. architecture N.C. State U., Raleigh, 1975-79; assoc. dean Sch. Architecture U. Md., College Park, 1981-83, prof. architecture, 1979-93; ret., 1993; dir. Architecture and Engring. Performance Info. Ctr., 1982-93; pvt. practice, Annapolis, College Park, 1979-93, Whitehall, Mich., 1993—; mem. com. NRC-NAS, 1982-93; mem. bldg. diagnostics com. Adv. Bd. on Build Environ., 1983-93; mem. com. on earthquake engring. NRC, 1983-93; leader survey team for tornado damage in Pa. and Ohio, 1985. Author: Building Design for Natural Hazards in Eastern United States, 1981, Identification of Performance Failures in Large Structures and Buildings, 1987, Analysis of Performance Failures in Civil Structures and Large Buildings, 1990, Performance Failures in Buildings and Civil Works, 1991; works include med. clinic, N.C.; Aldersgate Multi Family Housing, Oscoda, Mich. Advisor Interfaith Housing Inc., Detroit, 1966-74; advisor Detroit Mayor's Office, 1967-69, Interim Housing Com. Mich. State Housing Devel. Authority, Lansing, 1969-71, Takoma Park Citizens for Schs. (Md.), 1981-82; advisor, cons. Hist. Preservation Commn., Prince George's County, Md. With U.S. Army, 1954-56. NSF grantee, 1978-81, 1982-84, 86-87, 88-90; named one of Men of Yr., Engring. News Record, 1984. Fellow AIA. Democrat. Roman Catholic. *To participate, as an architect, in the continuing saga of the creation of the built environment and, as a teacher, in the continuing rebirth of our intellectual and spiritual lives remains a very special honor. I feel a sincere debt of gratitude to my mother who read to me when I was a very small child and who launched me on a life of reading and service.*

LOSS, LOUIS, lawyer, retired educator; b. Lancaster, Pa., June 11, 1914; s. Zelig and Elizabeth (Wenger) L.; m. Bernice Segaloff, June 19, 1938; children: Margaret Ruth, Robert Stanley. B.S., U. Pa., 1934; LL.B., Yale U., 1937; A.M. (hon.), Harvard U., 1953. Bar: D.C. 1937, Mass. 1952, U.S. Supreme Ct. 1953. Atty. SEC, 1937-44, chief counsel div. trading and exchanges, 1944-48, assoc. gen. counsel, 1948-52; later law Cath. U. Am., 1941-42; vis. lectr. law Yale U., 1947-52; professorial lectr. law George Washington U., 1949-52; prof. law Harvard U., 1952-62, William Nelson Cromwell prof. law, 1962-84, prof. emeritus, 1984—, dir. program instrn. for lawyers, 1976-84; prof. Faculté Internationale de Droit Comparé, Luxembourg, summer 1958, U. Witwatersrand, summer 1962, Salzburg (Austria) Seminar in Am. Studies, summers 1968, 77, Australian Nat. U., summer 1973; Ford prof. Inst. Advanced Legal Studies, U. London, 1969; Turner Meml. lectr. U. Tasmania, Australia, 1973; Kimber fellow U. Toronto, 1978; Taylor lectr. U. Lagos, Nigeria, 1981; vis. prof. U. Pa., 1989; scholar-in-residence, U. Ga., 1985; draftsman Uniform Securities Act, 1954-56; cons. Internat. Bank, 1963-65, various fgn. govts. Author: Securities Regulation, 1951, supplememt, 1955, 2d edit., 1961, supplement 1969 (6 vols.), 3d edit. (with Joel Seligman) 11 vols., 1988-93, Commentary on the Uniform Securities Act, 1976, Fundamentals of Securities Regulation, 1983, 2d edit., 1988, supplements, 1989-92, Japanese translation, 1989; co-author: Blue Sky Law, 1958; editor: Multinational Approaches-Corporate Insiders, 1976; sr. co-editor: Japanese Securities Regulation, 1983; reporter: Am. Law Inst.'s Fed. Securities Code, 1969-78. Vice chmn. bd., gen. counsel Harvard Coop. Soc., 1961-89, N.Y. Stock Exch. Legal Adv. Com., chmn., 1987-89. Fellow AAAS, Am. Bar Found. (ann. research award 1979); mem. ABA (coun. bus. law 1966-69, 1974-75), Am. Law Inst., Assn. Bar City N.Y. (assoc.), Soc. Pub. Tchrs. Law (assoc.)(Britain), Cosmos Club (Washington), Phi Beta Kappa (hon. Alpha chpt.-Harvard). Home: 39 Meadow Way Cambridge MA 02138-4635

LOSS, MARGARET RUTH, lawyer; b. Phila., June 17, 1946; d. Louis and Bernice Rose (Segaloff) L.; m. Harry Clark Johnson, 1986; 1 child, Elizabeth Loss Johnson. B.A., Radcliffe Coll., 1967; LL.B., Yale U., 1970. Bar: Conn. 1970, N.Y. 1973. Assoc. Sullivan & Cromwell, N.Y.C., 1971-77; with Equitable Life Assurance Soc. U.S., N.Y.C., 1977-88, asst. gen. counsel, 1979-85, v.p. and counsel, 1985-88; counsel LeBoeuf, Lamb, Greene & MacRae, N.Y.C., 1988—; dir. Yale Law Sch. Fund. Mem. ABA, Am. Law Inst., Conn. Bar Assn., Assn. of Bar of City N.Y. Office: LeBoeuf Lamb Greene & MacRae 125 W 55th St New York NY 10019-5369

LOSS, STUART HAROLD, financial executive; b. Lancaster, Pa., June 15, 1946; s. Nathan and Natalie M. (Koenigsberg) L.; m. Rachelle Smithline; children: Jessica Lauren, David Jonathan, Andrew Jordan. BS in Acctg., Syracuse U.; MBA in Fin., NYU. CPA, N.Y. With KPMG Peat Marwick, N.Y.C., 1971-77; exec. v.p., chief fin. officer, sec. TBWA Advt., N.Y.C.,

1977—. Mem. AICPA, N.Y. State Soc. CPAs, N.Y. Credit and Fin. Mgmt. Assn., Treas. Club. Office: TBWA Advt Inc 292 Madison Ave New York NY 10017-6307

LOSSE, JOHN WILLIAM, JR., mining company executive; b. St. Louis, Mar. 16, 1916; s. John William and Claire (Schmedtje) L.; m. Marjorie West Penney, Mar. 7, 1942; children: John William IV, Georgia Shane, Barbara Stevens, Mary Coulter, Penney Gregersen, Jane Momberger. BS, Washington U., St. Louis, 1937; MBA, Harvard U., 1939. Sec.-treas. J.W. Losse Tailoring Co., St. Louis, 1939-41, 45-55; treas., controller, asst. sec. Uranium Reduction Co., Salt Lake City, 1955-62; v.p. finance Atlas Minerals div. Atlas Corp., Salt Lake City, 1962-64; asst. v.p., asst. treas. Am. Zinc Co., St. Louis, 1965-66; v.p. finance, treas. Am. Zinc Co., 1966-70; v.p. finance Conrad, Inc., St. Louis, 1970-71; v.p. finance, sec., dir. Fed. Resources Corp., Salt Lake City, 1971-82, pres., chief exec. officer, dir., 1982-84, 85-86, chief fin. officer, dir., 1986-88, v.p., treas., 1988—, also bd. dirs., 1988-89; sec.-treas. Madawaska Mines Ltd., Bancroft, Ont., Can., 1976-82, pres., bd. dirs., 1983—; pres. Camp Bird Colo., Inc., Ouray, 1983-92; Pres. Utah Natural Resources Council, 1964; tax com. and fin. adv. com. Am. Mining Congress, 1965-84; bd. dirs. Episcopal Mgmt. Corp., Salt Lake City. Bd. dirs. St. Mark's Hosp., Salt Lake City, 1987-88, Arthritis Found., Salt Lake City, 1988—; vice chmn., bd. dirs. St. Mark's Charities, Salt Lake City, 1987-92; mem. investment com. Corp. of the Bishop, Salt Lake City, 1989—. Lt. comdr. USNR, 1941-45. Mem. Utah Mining Assn. (bd. dirs., legis. and tax coms. 1971-91), Country Club of Salt Lake City, Alta Club of Salt Lake City, Phi Delta Theta. Republican. Episcopalian. Office: Fed Resources Corp PO Box 806 Salt Lake City UT 84110-0806

LOSSING, FREDERICK PETTIT, retired chemist; b. Norwich, Ont., Can., Aug. 4, 1915; s. Frank Edgar and Evelyn (Pettit) L.; m. Frances Isabella Glazier; children—Wilda, Patricia, Catherine. B.A., U. Western Ont., London, 1938, M.A., 1940; Ph.D., McGill U., Montreal, Que., Can., 1942. Research chemist Shawinigan Chems. Ltd., Shawinigan Falls, Que., 1942-46; research officer Nat. Research Council Can., Ottawa, Ont., 1946-80; asso. dir. div. chemistry Nat. Research Council Can., 1969-77, prin. research officer, 1977-80; rsch. scientist dept. chemistry U. Ottawa, 1980-94. Fellow Royal Soc. Can., Chem. Inst. Can.; mem. Am. Soc. Mass. Spectrometry, Royal Astron. Soc. Can. Home: 95 Dorothea Dr, Ottawa, ON Canada K1V 7C6

LOSTEN, BASIL HARRY, bishop; b. Chesapeake City, Md., May 11, 1930; s. John and Julia (Petryshyn) L. BA, St. Basil's Coll., 1953; STL, Cath. U., Washington, 1957. Ordained priest Ukrainian Cath. Ch., 1957. Personal sec. to archbishop, 1962-66; contr. Archdiocese, 1966-75; apptd. monsignor, 1968; apptd. titular bishop of Arcadiopolis and aux. bishop Ukrainian Cath. Archeparchy of Phila., 1971-77; vicar gen., 1971, apostolic adminstr., 1976-77; bishop of Stamford, Conn., 1977—. Pres. Ascension Manor. Club: Union League (Phila.). *

LOSTY, BARBARA PAUL, college official; b. Norwich, N.Y., June 16, 1942; d. Henry Edward and Mary Frances (Crowell) Paul; m. Thomas August Losty, Nov. 27, 1965; children: Ellen Christine, Amanda Elizabeth. BA, Wellesley Coll., 1964; MA, U. Conn., 1969, PhD, 1971. Asst. prof. psychology Westminster Coll., Fulton, Mo., 1971-73; asst. prof. psychology Stephens Coll., Columbia, Mo., 1973-75, assoc. dir. sch. liberal and profl. studies, 1975-79, assoc. dean of faculty, 1979-85; dean U. Wis. Ctr.-Sheboygan County, Sheboygan, 1985-91; coord. human svcs. degrees Thomas Edison State Coll., Trenton, N.J., 1992-94; assoc. dean human svcs. degrees, 1994—. Home: 4 Blue Spruce Ct Hightstown NJ 08520-9621 Office: Thomas Edison State Coll 101 W State St Trenton NJ 08608-1176

LO SURDO, ANTONIO, physical chemist, educator; b. Spadafora, Italy, Jan. 1, 1943; came to U.S., 1955, naturalized, 1961; s. Salvatore Giuseppe and Marianna (La Macchia) Lo S.; m. Claudia Piva, Nov. 26, 1988. B.A., Syracuse U., 1965, Ph.D, 1970. Postdoctoral fellow, instr. chemistry Rutgers U., New Brunswick, N.J., 1969-71; vis. faculty Syracuse U., N.Y., 1971-72; research assoc. U. Conn., Storrs, 1972; vis. research assoc., lectr. Ohio State U., Columbus, 1972-74; research assoc. Clark U., Worcester, Mass., 1974-75; chief chemist Cambridge Instrument Co., Inc., Ossining, N.Y., 1975-76; research asst. prof. Rosenstiel Sch. Marine and Atmospheric Sci., U. Miami, Fla., 1977-79, research assoc. prof., 1979-82; chief chemist O'Brien & Gere Engrs., Syracuse, 1982-87; sect. chief, lab. dir. Roy F. Weston/REAC Project, 1988—. Contbr. articles to profl. jours. NSF fellow, 1965-66, 74-76; NIH fellow, 1969-70; Syracuse U. grantee, 1966-69. Mem. AAAS, Am. Chem. Soc., N.Y. Acad. Scis., Sigma Xi, Phi Lambda Upsilon. Home: 6 Chestnut Hill Rd Howell NJ 07731-1708 Office: GSA Raritan Depot 2890 Woodbridge Ave Bldg 209 Edison NJ 08837-3602

LOTAS, JUDITH PATTON, advertising executive; b. Iowa City, Apr. 23, 1942; d. John Henry and Jane (Vandike) Patton; children: Amanda Bell, Alexandra Vandike. BA, Fla. State U., 1964. Copywriter Liller, Neal, Battle and Lindsey Advt., Atlanta, 1964-67, Grey Advt., N.Y.C., 1967-72; creative group head SSC&B Advt., N.Y.C., 1972-74, asso. creative dir., 1974-79, v.p., 1975-79, sr. v.p., 1979-82, exec. creative dir., 1982-86; founding pres. Lotas Minard Patton McIver, Inc., N.Y.C., 1986—. Active scholarship fund raising; bd. dirs. Samuel Eaxman Cancer Rsch., Found., N.Y.C., 1981-88; fundraiser Nat. Coalition for the Homeless, N.Y.C., 1986—. Recipient Clio award, Venice Film Festival award, Graphics award Am. Inst. Graphic Artists, 1970, Effie award, Grad. of Distinction award Fla. State U., 1993; named Woman of Achievement, YWCA, One of Advt. Agys. 100 Best Women Ad Age, 1989. Mem. Advt. Women N.Y. (1st v-p. 1984-87, bd. dirs. 1981-87, Advt. Woman of Yr. 1993), The Ad Coun. (mem. creative rev. bd. 1994—), Kappa Alpha Theta. Democrat. Home: 45 E 89th St New York NY 10128-1232

LOTHROP, KRISTIN CURTIS, sculptor; b. Tucson, Feb. 8, 1930; d. Thomas and Elizabeth (Longfellow) Curtis; m. Francis B. Lothrop, Jr., Dec. 27, 1951; children—Robin B., Thornton K. and Jonathan C. (twins). B.A., Bennington Coll., 1951. Exhbns. include: Nat. Sculpture Soc., 1967-71, NAD, 1968-71, Hudson Valley Art Assn., 1968, Allied Artists Am., 1969, Concord Art Assn., 1970; represented in permanent collection, Brookgreen Gardens, S.C. Recipient Mrs. Louis Bennett award Nat. Sculpture Soc., 1967; Thomas R. Procter award N.A.D., 1968; Dessie Greer award, 1969; Daniel Chester French medal, 1970; hon. mention Hudson Valley Art Assn., 1968; 1st prize Concord Art Assn., 1970, 83; 1st prize Manchester Arts Assn., 1975; 1st prize Hamilton-Wenham Art Show, 1980; Liskin purchase prize Nat. Sculpture Soc., 1986. Mem. Nat. Sculpture Soc., New Eng. Sculptors Assn. (1st prize 1987), The Copley Soc. of Boston (Copley master). Address: 71 Bridge St Manchester MA 01944

LOTITO, MICHAEL JOSEPH, lawyer; b. Carbondale, Pa., July 22, 1948; s. Dominic Joseph and Margaret Mary (Miller) L.; m. Luanne R. McMaster, Nov. 9, 1985; 1 child, Kelly C. AB, Villanova U., 1970, JD, 1974. Bar: Pa. 1974, Calif. 1983; lic. sr. profl. human resources. Assoc. Barley, Snyder, Cooper & Barber, Lancaster, Pa., 1974-76, Jackson, Lewis, Schnitzler & Krupman, N.Y.C., 1976-81; mng. prtnr. Jackson, Lewis, Schnitzler & Krupman, San Francisco, 1982—; bd. dirs. No. Calif. Human Resource Coun., San Francisco. Co-author: Making the ADA Work for You, 1992, What Managers and Supervisors Need to Know About the ADA, 1992, The Americans With Disabilities Act: A Comprehensive Guide to Title I, 1992; contbr. articles to profl. jours. Mem. ABA, Calif. Bar Assn., Soc. for Human Resource Mgmt. (chmn. legis. affairs com. 1988-90, nat. employment law com. 1981-86, legal adv. bd. 1988—, bd. dirs. 1991—, chair edn. task force 1990-92, edn. com. 1993—, vol. counsel to bd. dirs. 1993—), Calif. C. of C. (bd. dirs. 1986-88). Republican. Roman Catholic. Home: 95 Deer Park Ave San Rafael CA 94901-2310 Office: Jackson Lewis Schnitzler & Krupman 525 Market St Ste 3400 San Francisco CA 94105-2742

LOTMAN, HERBERT, food processing executive; b. Phila., Oct. 9, 1933; s. Samuel Meyer and Gertrude L.; m. Karen Levin, Apr. 6, 1957; children: Shelly Hope, Jeffrey Mark. Pres., chmn. bd. Keystone Foods Corp., Bryn Mawr, Pa., 1951; pres. Keystone Foods Corp., 1960, chm. bd., 1960—. Bd. dirs. Nat. Juvenile Diabetes Found. Served with U.S. Army, 1952-54. Mem. Young Pres. Orgn. Office: Keystone Foods Corp 401 E City Ave # 800 Bala Cynwyd PA 19004-1122

LOTOCKY, INNOCENT HILARIUS, bishop; b. Petlykivci Stari, Buchach, Ukraine, Nov. 3, 1915; came to U.S., 1946; s. Stefan and Maria (Tytyn) L. Student at various religious insts., Ukraine, Czechoslovakia; Ph.D. in Sacred Theology, U. Vienna, Austria, 1994. Ordained priest Ukrainian Catholic Ch., 1944, consecrated bishop, 1981; cert. tchr., Mich. Superior-novice master Order St. Basil, Dawson, Pa., 1946-51; provincial superior U.S. province Order St. Basil, N.Y., 1951-53; novice master Order St. Basil, Glen Cove, N.Y., 1958-60; pastor-superior St. George Ch., N.Y.C., 1953-58; pastor St. Nicholas Ch., Chgo., 1960-62; pastor-superior Immaculate Conception Ch., Hamtramck, Mich., 1962-81, also chr., 1962-81; bishop Diocese St. Nicholas, Chgo., 1981-93, ret., 1993; provincial counselor U.S. province Order St. Basil, 1962-80, del. to gen. chpt. Rome, 1963. Active numerous civic orgns. Mem. Nat. Council Cath. Bishops. Home and Office: Diocese St Nicholas in Chgo 2245 W Rice St Chicago IL 60622-4858

LOTSTEIN, JAMES I., lawyer; b. Steubenville, Ohio, Jan. 27, 1944; s. Jack and Dorothy (Nach) L.; m. Paulette L. Gutcheon, June 25, 1972; children: Melissa A., Amanda J. BSBA, Northwestern U., 1965; JD, U. Conn., 1968. Bar: Conn. 1969, U.S. Ct. Appeals (2d cir.) 1971, U.S. Supreme Ct. 1972. From assoc. to ptnr. Hoppin, Carey & Powell, Hartford, Conn., 1969-86; from ptnr. to ptnr.-in-charge Cummings & Lockwood, Hartford, 1986—. Author: An Introduction to the Connecticut Business Corporation Act, 1994. Trustee Conn. Policy and Econ. Coun., Inc., 1990—; mem. Conn. Sec. of State's Bus. Adv. Com. 1st lt. JAGC, USAR, 1968-74. Mem. ABA (chmn. dirs. and officers task force, corp. laws com. 1992), Conn. Bar Awsn. (chmn. mcpl. law and govtls. svcs. com. 1981-, chmn. bus. law sect. 1990-92, co-chmn. Conn. bus. corp. act task force 1993—), Golf Club of Avon (Conn.). Office: Cummings & Lockwood City Pl I Hartford CT 06103

LOTT, DAVID STUART, lawyer; b. Hartford, Conn., Aug. 26, 1943; s. John Francis Lott and Carolyn (Prann) Steigerwalt; m. Margaret Sturgis, Aug. 28, 1965 (div. June 1993); children: John, Katherine, Sarah, Edward; m. Sally Morris, Aug. 29, 1993. BA, Wesleyan U., Middletown, Conn., 1965; MA in History, U. Mich., 1967; JD, U. Va., 1970. Bar: Wis. 1970, Ill. 1989, U.S. Tax Ct., U.S. Ct. Appeals (7th cir.). Assoc. Foley & Lardner, Milw., 1970-78, ptnr., 1978-89; ptnr. Foley & Lardner, Chgo., 1989—; v.p., bd. dirs. Hyre Electric Co. of Chgo., 1990—; lectr. on real estate & taxation Wis. State Bar Continuing Legal Edn. Editor: Wisconsin Condominium Law Handbook. Mem. Sunset Ridge Country Club, Town Club, Ephraim Yacht Club (bd. dirs.), The Clearing of the Ellison Bay, Wis. (bd. dirs.). Home: 922 Ash St Winnetka IL 60093 Office: Foley & Lardner Ste 3300 1 IBM Plz 330 N Wabash Ave Chicago IL 60611-3608

LOTT, IRA TOTZ, pediatric neurologist; b. Cin., Apr. 15, 1941; s. Maxwell and Jeneda (Totz) L.; m. Ruth J. Weiss, June 21, 1964; children: Lisa, David I. BA cum laude, Brandeis U., 1963; MD cum laude, Ohio State U., 1967. Intern Mass. Gen. Hosp., Boston, 1967, resident in pediatrics, 1967-69, resident in child neurology, 1971-74; clin. assoc. NIH, Bethesda, Md., 1969-71; from clin. rsch. fellow to asst. prof. Harvard Med. Sch., Boston, 1971-82; clin. dir. Eunice Kennedy Shriver Ctr. for Mental Retardation, Waltham, Mass., 1974-82; assoc. prof. U. Calif., Irvine, 1983-91, prof., 1992—; chmn. dept. pediatrics U. Calif., Irvine, 1992—, dir. pediatric neurology, 1983—; pres. Prof. Child Neurology, Mpls., 1992—. Editor: Down Syndrome-Medical Advances, 1991; contbr. articles to profl. jours. Sec., treas. Child Neurology Soc., Mpls., 1987-90. Lt. comdr. USPHS, 1969-71. NIH grantee, 1974—; recipient Career Devel. award Kennedy Found., 1976. Fellow Am. Acad. Neurology; mem. Am. Pediatric Soc., Am. Neurol. Assn., Nat. Down Syndrome Soc. (sci. acad. bd. 1985—), Western Soc. for Pediatric Rsch. (councillor 1989-91). Achievements include research in relationship of Down Syndrome to Alzheimer's disease, neurometabolic disease, extracorporeal membrane oxygenation in infants. Office: U Calif Irvine Med Ctr Dept Pediatrics 101 The City Dr S # 27 Orange CA 92668-3201

LOTT, ROBERT VINCENT, newspaper editor; b. Quantico Marine Base, Va., Dec. 3, 1941; s. Vincent Lamar and Sara Mildred (Lawson) L.; m. Sara Jacquelen Lovelady, Jan. 26, 1963; children: Sam, Tim, Danny. BA in Journalism, U. Ala., 1964. Ward attendant Bryce State Hosp., Tuscaloosa, Ala., 1960-63; reporter Columbus (Ga.) Ledger, 1964-66, city editor, 1966-68; copy editor Atlanta Jour., 1968-69, copy desk chief, 1969-73, asst. mng. editor, 1973-79; editor Waco (Tex.) Tribune-Herald, 1979—. Bd. dirs. Tex. Media, Austin, 1992—, Tex. Freedom of Info. Found., Dallas, 1995—; mem. student publs. bd. U. Tex., 1988-90, 95. Recipient James Madison award Tex. Freedom of Info. Found., 1994, Journalism Grad. of Yr. award U. Ala., 1994. Mem. Am. Soc. Newspaper Editors, Tex. Assn. Press Mng. Editors (Freedom of Info. chair 1995). Presbyterian. Avocations: sailboating, fly fishing. Office: Waco Tribune-Herald 900 Franklin Ave Waco TX 76702

LOTT, RONNIE (RONALD MANDEL LOTT), professional football player; b. Albuquerque, May 8, 1959. BS in Pub. Adminstrn., U. So. Calif., 1981. With San Francisco 49ers, 1981-90, L.A. Raiders, 1991-93, N.Y. Jets, 1993-94, Kansas City Chiefs, 1994—. Named to Sporting News Coll. All-Am. team, 1980, Pro Bowl team, 1981-84, 86-91, Sporting News All-Pro team, 1981, 87, 90. Office: Kansas City Chiefs One Arrowhead Dr Kansas City MO 64129*

LOTT, THADDEUS, principal. Prin. Wesley Elem. Sch. Office: Wesley Elem Sch 800 Dillard St Houston TX 77091-2301

LOTT, TRENT, senator; b. Grenada, Miss., Oct. 9, 1941; s. Chester P. and Iona (Watson) L.; m. Patricia E. Thompson, Dec. 27, 1964; children—Chester T., Jr., Tyler Elizabeth. B.P.A., U. Miss., 1963, J.D., 1967. Bar: Miss. 1967. Assoc. Bryan & Gordon, Pascagoula, Miss., 1967; adminstrv. asst. to Congressman William M. Colmer, 1968-72; mem. 93d-100th Congresses from 5th Miss. dist., 1973-89; Rep. whip 97th-100th Congresses from 5th Miss. dist., mem. Ho. Rules com.; U.S. senator from Miss., 1989—, Senate armed svcs. com., budget com., energy, natural resources com., 102d Congress; sec. Senate Rep. Conf., 103d Congress; field rep. for U. Miss., 1963-65; acting alumni sec. Ole Miss Alumni Assn., 1966-67; named as observer from House to Geneva Arms Control talks; chmn. Commerce, Sci. & Transp. subcom. on surface transp. & merchant marine; mem. Senate Republican Policy Com. Recipient Golden Bulldog award, Guardian of Small Bus. award. Mem. ABA, Jackson County Bar Assn., Sigma Nu, Phi Alpha Delta. Republican. Baptist. Lodge: Mason. Office: 487 Russell Senate Office Bldg Washington DC 20510*

LOTTMAN, EVAN, film editor. Editor: (films) Puzzle of a Downfall Child, 1970, Panic in Needle Park, 1971, Scarecrow, 1973, The Effects of Gamma Rays on Man-in-the-Moon Marigolds, 1973, (with others) The Exorcist, 1973 (Academy award nomination best film editing 1973), (with Richard Fetterman) Sweet Revenge, 1976, The Seduction of Joe Tynan, 1979, (with Aram Avakian, Norman Gay, and Marc Laub) Honeysuckle Rose, 1980, Rollover, 1981, The Pilot, 1981, Sophie's Choice, 1982, The Muppets Take Manhattan, 1984, The Protector, 1985, Maximum Overdrive, 1986, On the Yard, 1987, Orphans, 1987, See You in the Morning, 1989, Presumed Innocent, 1990, Beyond Innocence, 1992, The Public Eye, 1992, Missing Pieces, 1992, Guilty as Sin, 1993, (TV movies) Gotham, 1988. Office: 15 W 72nd St New York NY 10023*

LOTWIN, STANFORD GERALD, lawyer; b. N.Y.C., June 23, 1930; s. Herman and Rita (Saltzman) L.; m. Judy Scott, Oct. 15, 1994 (dec.); children: Lori Hope, David, Sean. BS, Bklyn. Coll., 1951, LLB, 1954, LLM, 1957. Bar: N.Y. 1954, U.S. Supreme Ct. 1961, Pa. 1986. Ptnr. Tenzer, Greenblatt, Fallon and Kaplan, N.Y.C., 1987—; of counsel Frankfurt, Garbus, Klein & Selz, N.Y.C., 1983-87. Served with U.S. Army, 1954-56. Fellow Am. Acad. Matrimonial Lawyers (bd. of mgrs. 1984—); mem. N.Y. State Bar Assn. (family law sect.), N.Y. County Trial Lawyers (lectr. 1980—). Office: 405 Lexington Ave New York NY 10174-0002

LOTZ, ARTHUR WILLIAM, retired engineering and construction company executve; b. Bklyn., Feb. 24, 1927; s. Charles Alfred and Clara Marie (Lohman) L.; m. Ethel Dorothea Kummer, Feb. 7, 1953; children—Kenneth Arthur, Diane Claire. B.M.E., Poly. Inst. Bklyn., 1948, M.M.E., 1949. Cons. engr. Ebasco Services Inc., N.Y.C., 1948-66, mng.-prtnr. 1971-76; regional office v.p. Ebasco Services Inc., Atlanta, 1976-80; sr. v.p. engring. and constrn. Ebasco Services Inc., N.Y.C., 1980-83, group v.p. engring.,

1983-87; dir. far east ops. Ebasco Overseas Corp., Tokyo, 1966-71; Chmn. Envirosphere Co., N.Y.C., Ebasco Bus. Cons., N.Y.C.; dir. Ebasco Humphreys Glasgow, Houston. Contbr. articles to profl. jours. Mem. Planning Bd., Oakland, N.J., 1965-66; pres. St. Paul Luth. Ch., Tokyo, 1968-69; elder Rivercliff Luth. Ch., Atlanta, 1977-79, Bethlehem Luth. Ch., Ridgewood, N.J., 1982-84; treas. N.H. Conf. Evang. Luth. Ch. Am., 1989-93. Mem. Pi Tau Sigma. Republican. Avocations: swimming, golf, fishing, gardening.

LOTZ, DENTON, minister, church official; b. Flushing, N.Y., Jan. 18, 1939; s. John Milton and Adeline Helen (Kettell) L.; m. Janice Robinson, Mar. 15, 1970; children: John-Paul, Alena, Carsten. BA, U. N.C., 1961; STB, Harvard Div. Sch., 1966; ThD, U. Hamburg, Fed. Republic Germany, 1970; DD (hon.), Campbell U., 1982, Ea. Bapt. Sem., 1991, Alderson-Broadus, 1995. Ordained to ministry Bapt. Ch., 1966. Prof. mission Bapt. Sem., Ruschlikon, Switzerland, 1972-80; dir. evangelism Bapt. World Alliance, McLean, Va., 1980-88, gen. sec., 1988—; fraternal rep. Am. Bapt. Internat. Ministries To Ea. Europe, Valley Forge, Pa., 1970-80. Author, editor: Baptists in the USSR, 1987; editor: Spring Has Returned to China, 1987. V.p. CARE, N.Y.C., 1981. 1st lt. USMC, 1961-63. Mem. Internat. Religious Liberty Assn. (pres. 1990-91). Office: Bapt World Alliance 6733 Curran St Mc Lean VA 22101-3804

LOTZBIRE, BRUCE JOHN, air force officer; b. Pitts., Jan. 12, 1941; s. Vernon Edward and Bernice Marie (Kelly) L.; m. Christine Ann Sellers, July 27, 1963; children: Rhonda Kay, Warren Scott. BA in Theoretical Econs., Ohio Wesleyan U., 1962. Commd. 2d lt. USAF, 1962, advanced through grades to maj. gen.; various operational, staff and command positions worldwide; now with Office of Def. Coop. Decorated Silver Star (2), Def. D.S.M. Mem. Air Force Assn., Am.-Hellenic C., Order of Daedalians, Propeller Club U.S. (Athens, Greece). Avocations: skiing, sailing, flying. Home: PSC 108 Box 42 Am Embassy Odc APO AE 09842-5000 Office: USAF Odc Greece Useucom APO AE 09841

LOTZE, BARBARA, physicist; b. Mezokovesd, Hungary, Jan. 4, 1924; d. Matyas and Borbala (Toth) Kalo; came to U.S., 1961, naturalized, 1967; Applied Mathematician Diploma with honors, Eotvos Lorand U. Scis., Budapest, Hungary, 1956; PhD, Innsbruck (Austria) U., 1961; m. Dieter P. Lotze, Oct. 6, 1958. Mathematician, Hungarian Cen. Statis. Bur., Budapest, 1955-56; tchr. math., Iselsberg, Austria, 1959-60; asst. prof. physics Allegheny Coll., 1963-69, assoc. prof., 1969-77, prof., 1977-90, prof. emeritus, 1990—, chmn. dept., 1981-84; lectr. in history of physics; speaker to civic groups. Mem. Am. Phys. Soc. (mem. com. internat. freedom of scientists 1993—), Am. Inst. Physics (mem. adv. com. history of physics 1994—), Am. Assn. Physics Tchrs. (coun., sect. rep. Western Pa., chmn. nat. com. on women in physics 1983-84, com. internat. physics edn. 1991-93, Disting. Svc. award 1986, cert. of appreciation 1988), AAUW, N.Y. Acad. Scis., Am. Hungarian Educators Assn. (pres. 1980-82), Wilhelm Busch Gesellschaft (Hanover). Editor: Making Contributions: An Historical Overview of Women's Role in Physics, 1984; co-editor The First War Between Socialist States: The Hungarian Revolution of 1956 and Its Impact, 1984; contbr. articles to profl. jours. Home: 462 Hartz Ave Meadville PA 16335-1325 Office: Alleghency Coll Dept Physics Meadville PA 16335

LOUARGAND, MARC ANDREW, real estate executive, financial consultant; b. San Francisco, July 3, 1945; s. Andrew and Edna Antoinette (McNeil) L.; m. Elizabeth A. Warner, June 18, 1966 (div. Oct. 1978); m. J. R. McDaniel, Feb. 14, 1986. BA, U. Calif., Santa Barbara, 1967; MBA, U. Calif., L.A., 1974, PhD, 1982. Asst. prof. Calif. State Polytech. U., Pomona, 1975-77; assoc. prof. Calif. State U., Northridge, 1977-83, U. Mass., Boston, 1983-88; sr. lectr. Ctr. for Real Estate Devel. MIT, Cambridge, 1986-93; 2d v.p., sr. officer Mass. Mut. Life Ins. Co., Springfield, Mass., 1993-94; mng. dir. Cornerstone Real Estate Advisors, 1995—; cons. in field. Author: CRE2000: Managing the Fifth Strategic Resource, Study Guide to Financial Management, 1986, (with others) Principles and Techniques of Appraisal Review, 1980, Handbook of Real Estate Portfolio Management; assoc. editor Jour. Real Estate Lit., Jour. Real Estate Portfolio Management; contbr. articles to profl. jours. Bd. dirs. Beverly Glen Assn., Bel Air, Calif., 1973-77, Citronia Homeowners Assn., Northridge, Calif., 1978-83; chmn. Carlisle (Mass.) Bd. Assessors, 1985-93. Mem. Am. Real Estate and Urban Econs. Assn., Am. Real Estate Soc., Internat. Assn. Assessing Officers, Fin. Mgmt. Assn., Nat. Trust for Historic Preservation, Vt. Land Trust. Republican. Avocations: tree farming, skiing, building restoration. Home: 32 Longmeadow St Longmeadow MA 01106-1015

LOUBE, SAMUEL DENNIS, physician; b. Rumania, Aug. 26, 1921; came to U.S., 1922, naturalized, 1927; s. Harry and Rebecca (Pollack) L.; m. Emily Wallace, Apr. 14, 1976; children—Julian M., Jonathan B., Susan C., Karen E., Patricia A., Pamela B., Brian R. A.B., George Washington U., 1941, M.D. cum laude, 1943. Diplomate: Am. Bd. Internal Medicine. Intern, then resident in medicine Gallinger Municipal Hosp., Washington, 1943-46; physician USPHS, 1946-48; postdoctoral fellow NIH, 1948-50; research fellow in endocrinology Michael Reese Hosp., Chgo., 1948-49; research fellow in metabolism and endocrinology May Inst. Jewish Hosp., Cin., 1949-50; mem. faculty George Washington U. Med. Sch., 1950-89, clin. prof. medicine, 1975-89, prof. emeritus, 1989; practice medicine specializing in endocrinology and metabolic diseases, Washington, 1950-88, mem. Washington Internal Medicine Group, 1965-88; former chmn. dept. medicine, chief sect. endocrinology Sibley Meml. Hosp. Contbr. articles to med. jours. Fellow ACP; mem. AMA, Am. Diabetes Assn., Endocrine Soc., Am. Soc. Internal Medicine, Diabetes Assn. D.C. (past pres.), Jacobi Med. Soc. (past pres.). Jewish.

LOUBET, JEFFREY W., lawyer; b. Mt. Vernon, N.Y., May 12, 1943; s. Nathaniel R. and Joan (Fleischer) L.; m. Susan Maria Thom, Aug. 29, 1972; 1 child, Thom Carlyle. BA, Colgate U., 1965; JD, St. John's U., 1968; LLM in Taxation, N.Y. U., 1970. Bar: N.Y. 1968, U.S. Tax Ct 1969, U.S. Dist. Ct. (so. dist.) N.Y. 1969, N.Mex. 1976, U.S. Dist. Ct. N.Mex. 1977. Assoc. Poletti, Freidin, Prashker, Feldman & Gartner, N.Y.C., 1969-76; ptnr. Modrall, Sperling, Roehl, Harris & Sisk, Albuquerque, 1976-94; counsel Rodey, Dickason, Sloan, Akin & Robb, Albuquerque, 1994—; lectr. N.Mex. Estate Roundtable, Albuquerque, 1979—; vis. prof. Estate and Gift Tax U. N.Mex., Albuquerque, 1988-89. Contbr. articles to profl. jours. Masters World Record Holder, high hurdles and decathlon. Fellow Am. Coll. Trust and Estate Counsel; mem. N.Mex. Estate Planning Coun., Greater Albuquerque C. of C. (chair tax task force, 1992, chair state govt. com., 1993), YMCA (mem. bd. dirs.). Avocations: track & field, skiing, fly fishing. Home: 2321 Elizabeth NE Albuquerque NM 87112 Office: Rodey Dickason Sloan Akin & Robb PO Box 1888 Albuquerque NM 87103

LOUBRIEL, TERE, bank executive; b. San Juan, P.R., Nov. 10, 1952; d. Benjamin Loubriel and Carmen (Rosado) Diaz; m. Antonio Ríos, July 23, 1977; children: Jessica, Janice. BBA, U.P.R., 1974. CPA, P.R. Sr. auditor Price Waterhouse, Hato Rey, P.R., 1974-78; asst. compt. Banco Popular de P.R., Hato Rey, 1978-79, compt., 1979-89, gen. auditor, 1990-92; gen. auditor, chief quality officer, 1992—. Mem. AICPA, P.R. Inst. CPA's, Inst. Internal Auditors. Roman Catholic. Office: Banco Popular de PR Ave Ponce De Leon #1500 Santurce PR 00907

LOUCHHEIM, DONALD HARRY, journalist; b. N.Y.C., June 6, 1937; s. Joseph Harry and Aline (Bernstein) L.; m. Valerie Pingree Wright, Sept. 6, 1958; children: Jessica Wright, Joseph Pingree, Jeffrey Depew. B.A., Yale U., 1959; M.B.A., Harvard U., 1971. Reporter, New Haven Jour.-Courier, 1959-61; mem. staff Washington Post, 1961-71, Paris bur. chief, 1967-69; owner, pub. Southampton Press, L.I., N.Y., 1971—. Served with AUS, 1959. Office: Southampton Press 135 Windmill Ln Southampton NY 11968-4825

LOUCHHEIM, FRANK PFEIFER, management consultant; b. Phila., Aug. 6, 1923; s. Stuart Fleisher and Julia Louise (Pfeifer) L.; m. Betty Jane Meinel, Sept. 13, 1947; children: Stuart M., John P., Anna Louchheim West. BE, Yale U., 1945. Salesman Motor Parts Co., 1946-56; sales mgr. Peirce-Phelps, Inc., 1956-65; sales mgr., mktg. mgr. Philco Ford Corp., Phila., 1966-69; pres., chief exec. officer Liquid Dynamics Corp., 1970-74; v.p. Haldane Assocs., Phila., 1974-80; chmn., pres., chief exec. officer Right Mgmt. Cons., Inc., Phila., 1980-87, chmn., chief exec. officer, 1987-91, chmn., 1992-94, founding chmn., 1994—. Bd. dirs. Fleisher Art Meml.,

Greater Phila. First, The Penjerdel Coun., Global Interdependence Ctr.; bd. adv. Ctr. for Leadership and Career Studies, Emory U.; adv. coun. Fund for the Future of Phila. With USNR, 1941-46. Mem. Assn. Outplacement Cons. Firms (bd. dirs., v.p. 1992—), Union League Club, Yale Club (Phila., N.Y.C.), Nat. Assn. of Corp. Dirs. (membership chmn.-Del. Valley). Republican. Mem. Christian Sci. Ch. Home: 1333 Gravel Hill Rd Southampton PA 18966-4512 Office: Right Mgmt Cons Inc 1818 Market St Philadelphia PA 19103-3638

LOUCKS, DANIEL PETER, environmental systems engineer; b. Chambersburg, Pa., June 4, 1932; s. Emerson Hunsberger and Eleanor Wright (Johnson) L.; m. Marjorie Ann Grant, June 24, 1967; children: Jennifer Lee, Susan Louise. B.S., Pa. State U., 1954; M.S., Yale U., 1955; Ph.D., Cornell U., 1965. Asst. prof. environ. engring. Cornell U., Ithaca, N.Y., 1965-70; assoc. prof. Cornell U., 1970-74, prof., 1974—, chmn. dept., 1974-80; assoc. dean research and grad. studies Cornell U. (Coll. Engring.), 1980-81; rsch. fellow Harvard U. Cambridge, Mass., 1968; economist IBRD, Washington, 1972-73; vis. prof. MIT, Cambridge, 1977-78; rsch. scholar Internat. Inst. for Applied Sys. Analysis, 1981-82; vis. disting. prof. U. Colo., 1992, U. Adelaide, 1992, Tech. U., Aachen, Germany, 1993, 95; cons. NATO, UN, WHO, FAO, IRBD on water resources and regional devel. projects in Asia, Western and Ea. Europe, Africa and Latin Am., 1970—, EPA on water quality planning USSR, 1975-77; vis. prof. Internat. Inst. Hydraulic and Environ. Engring., Delft, The Netherlands, 1976-80, 86—; environ. adv. bd. U.S. Army Corps Engrs., 1994—. Contbr. articles to jours. and books on math. models. for mng. water resources systems and environ. quality. Bd. dirs., Wilderness Corp., Plymouth, Vt., 1968-87, treas., 1987—; pres. Community Improvement Assn. Ithaca, 1976-77. Served to capt., aviator USNR, 1956-59; mem. Res. Fulbright-Hayes fellow Yugoslavia, 1975; recipient U.S. Sr. Rsch. award Alexander von Humboldt Found., 1992. Fellow ASCE (Walter Huber rsch. award 1970, Julian Hinds award 1986); mem. AAAS, Nat. Am. Geophys. Union, Inst. Mgmt. Scis., Assn. for Computing Machinery, Water Pollution Control Fedn., Am. Water Resources Assn., Internat. Assn. Hydraulic Rsch., Internat. Assn. Hydrologic Scis., Sigma Xi. Home: 116 Crest Ln Ithaca NY 14850-2704 Office: Cornell U Hollister Hall Ithaca NY 14853

LOUCKS, RALPH BRUCE, JR., investment company executive; b. St. Louis, Dec. 10, 1924; s. Ralph Bruce and Dola (Blake) L.; m. Lois Holloway, June 4, 1949 (dec. Sept. 1983); children: Elizabeth, Mary Jane; m. Mary Sutliffe Stahl, June 2, 1984. BA, Lake Forest Coll., 1949; postgrad. U. Chgo., 1950-52. Registered prin. Nat. Assn. Securities Dealers. Investment fund mgr. No. Trust Co., Chgo., 1950-53, Brown Bros. Harriman & Co., Chgo., 1953-55; investment counsel, pres. Tilden, Loucks & Grannis, Chgo., 1955-80; sr. v.p. Bacon, Whipple & Co., 1981-88; sr. v.p. Roberts, Loucks & Co., 1988—. Served with 11th Armored Div., AUS, 1943-45. Decorated Bronze Star medal, Purple Heart. Mem. Investment Analysts Soc., Investment Counsel Assn. Am., Huguenot Soc. Ill. (pres. 1960-61), Nat. Assn. Security Dealers (registered prin.), Soc. Colonial Wars. Clubs: Economic, Racquet, Chgo. Yacht (Chgo.). Office: 250 S Wacker Dr Chicago IL 60606-5834

LOUCKS, VERNON C., JR., healthcare products and services company executive; b. Evanston, Ill., Oct. 24, 1934; s. Vernon Reece and Sue (Burton) L.; m. Linda Kay Olson, May 12, 1972; 6 children. B.A. in History, Yale U., 1957; M.B.A., Harvard U., 1963. Sr. mgmt. cons. George Fry & Assos., Chgo., 1963-65; with Baxter Travenol Labs., Inc. (now Baxter Internat. Inc.), Deerfield, Ill., 1966—, exec. v.p., 1976, also bd. dirs., chief oper. officer, 1980, chief exec. officer, chmn., 1987—; bd. dirs. Dun & Bradstreet Corp., Emerson Electric Co., Quaker Oats Co., Anheuser-Busch Cos.; bd advisors Nestlé U.S.A. Trustee Rush-Presbyn.-St. Luke's Med. Ctr.; assoc. Northwestern U. 1st lt. USMC, 1957-60. Recipient Citizen Fellowship award Chgo. Inst. Medicine, 1982, Nat. Health Care award B'nai B'rith Youth Svcs., 1986, William McCormick Blair award Yale U., 1989, Semper Fidelis award USMC, 1989, Disting. Humanitarian award St. Barnabas Found., 1992, Alexis de Tocqueville award for community svc. United Way Lake County, 1993; named 1983's Outstanding Exec. Officer in the healthcare industry Fin. World; elected to Chgo.'s Bus. Hall of Fame, Jr. Achievement, 1987. Mem. Health Industry Mfrs. Assn. (chmn. 1983), Bus. Roundtable (conf. bd., mem. policy com.), Bus. Coun. Clubs: Chgo. Commonwealth, Commercial, Mid-America; Links (N.Y.C.). Office: Baxter Healthcare Corp 1450 Waukegan Rd Waukegan IL 60085

LOUD, WARREN SIMMS, mathematician; b. Boston, Sept. 13, 1921; s. Roger Perkins and Esther (Nickerson) L.; m. Mary Louise Strasburg, Dec. 27, 1947; children: Margaret Loud McCamant, Elizabeth Ann Loud Liebman, John Alden. S.B., Mass. Inst. Tech., 1942, Ph.D., 1946. Asst. prof. U. Minn., 1947-56, assoc. prof., 1956-59, prof. math., 1959-92, prof. emeritus, 1992—; vis. prof. Math. Rsch. Ctr., U. Wis., 1959-60, Technische Hochschule Darmstadt, Germany, 1964-65, Kyoto U., Japan, 1974-75, U. Florence, 1981-82, U. Trento, 1982, 83; vis. lectr. Math. Assn. Am., 1965—. Mem. Am. Math. Soc., Math. Assn. Am. (bd. govs. 1960-62, 77-80), Soc. Indsl. and Applied Math. (editor Rev. 1961-66, Jour. Applied Math. 1966-75, mem. editorial bd. 1975-79), AAAS. Congregationalist. Achievements include research, publs. in nonlinear ordinary differential equations. Home: 4253 Sheridan Ave S Minneapolis MN 55410-1618 Office: U Minn Sch of Math 206 Church St SE Minneapolis MN 55455-0488

LOUDON, DONALD HOOVER, lawyer; b. Kansas City, Kans., Nov. 20, 1937; s. Donald Charles and Berenice (Hoover) L.; m. W. Sue Cantrell, Aug. 17, 1958; children: Donald H. Jr., Kurt William. BJ, U. Mo., 1959; LLB, U. Kans., 1962. Bar: Mo. 1962, U.S. Supreme Ct. 1977. Reporter Kansas City Times, 1959; assoc. Blackmar, Swanson & Midgley, Kansas City, Mo., 1962-65; asst. gen. counsel Commerce Bank of Kansas City (Mo.), 1965-68; dir., shareholder Morris, King, Stamper & Bold, Kansas City, Mo., 1968-87, Shughart, Thomson & Kilroy, P.C., Kansas City, Mo., 1988—; sec. Torotel, Inc., Grandview, Mo., 1984—. Mem. ABA, Met. Bar Assn. Kansas City, Lawyers Assn. of Kansas City, Delta Tau Delta (bd. dirs. Columbia, Mo.). Presbyterian (elder). Office: Shughart Thomson & Kilroy 12 Wyandotte Plz 120 W 12th St Kansas City MO 64105-1917

LOUDON, DOROTHY, actress; b. Boston, Sept. 17, 1933; d. James E. and Dorothy Helen (Shaw) L.; m. Norman Paris, Dec. 18, 1971 (dec.). Student, Syracuse U., 1951-52. Honorary Coll. summers 1950, 51, Alviene Sch. Dramatic Art, 1952, 53, The Am. Acad. Dramatic Art. Appeared in nat. repertory cos. of The Effect of Gamma Rays on Man in the Moon Marigolds, 1970, Plaza Suite, 1971, Luv, 1965, Anything Goes, 1967; appeared in Broadway prodns. Nowhere to Go But Up, 1962 (Theatre World award), Sweet Potato, 1968, Fig Leaves Are Falling, 1969 (Tony nominee), Three Men on a Horse, 1969 (Drama Desk award), The Women, 1973, Annie (Tony award, Drama Desk award, Outer Critics Circle award), 1976 (Dance Educators Am. award), Ballroom, 1979 (Tony nominee), Sweeney Todd, 1980, West Side Waltz, 1981 (Sarah Siddons award), Noises Off, 1983 (Tony nomination), Jerry's Girls, 1985 (Tony nomination), Driving Miss Daisy, 1988, Annie 2, 1990, Comedy Tonight, 1994; appeared in film Garbo Talks, 1984; numerous appearances on TV shows and talk shows; latest TV appearances In Performance at the White House, A Salute to Stephen Sondheim at Carnegie Hall, 1992; star TV show Dorothy, 1979; appeared in supper clubs The Blue Angel, Le Ruban Bleu, Persian Room; rec.: (CDs) Saloon, Broadway Baby. Mem. Actors Equity, Screen Actors Guild, AFTRA. Office: Lionel Larner Ltd 130 W 57th St #10A New York NY 10019-3325 *I have no "thoughts on my life" that do not include my late husband, Norman Paris. He loved the theatre, as do I, and was my reason for being and my constant inspiration to persevere. That perserverance brought me the coveted Tony award for Miss Hannigan in "Annie." My husband lived to share that glorious moment with me. The award is small consolation, indeed-but the letters of love and encouragement from people all over the country is wondrous. It is a tribute to my husband as well as to me. I will devote my life to the justification of the faith he had in me-and to the faith of all those everywhere who love the theatre.*

LOUGANIS, GREG E., former Olympic athlete, actor; b. San Diego, Jan. 29, 1960; s. Peter E. and Frances I. (Scott) L. Student, U. Miami, Fla., 1978-80; B.A. in Drama, U. Calif., Irvine, 1983. Mem. U.S. Nat. Diving Team, 1976—. Author: Breaking The Surface, 1995. Recipient Silver medal Olympic Games, 1976, 2 Olympic Gold medals, 1984, 2 Olympic Gold

medals, 1988; James E. Sullivan award, Olympic Games, 1984; inducted into Olympic Hall of Fame, 1985; winner 48 U.S. nat. diving titles; World Diving Champion (platform and springboard) 1986, Jesse Owens award, 1987, Pan Am Gold medal, 1979, 83, 87; Gold medalist (platform and springboard) Seoul Olympics, 1988. Home: PO Box 4130 Malibu CA 90264-4130*

LOUGHEAD, THOMAS A., transportation executive; b. 1935. With MSAS Cargo, Eng., 1953-88; chmn bd. MSAS Cargo Internat., Burlingame, Calif., 1988—. Office: MSAS Cargo International Inc 1350 Old Bayshore Burlingame CA 94010

LOUGHEED, PETER, lawyer, former Canadian official; b. Calgary, Alta., Can., July 26, 1928; s. Edgar Donald and Edna (Bauld) L.; m. Jeanne Estelle Rogers, June 21, 1952; children—Stephen, Andrea, Pamela, Joseph. B.A., U. Alta., 1950, LL.B., 1952; M.B.A., Harvard U., 1954. Bar: Alta 1955. With firm Fenerty, Fenerty, McGillivray & Robertson, Calgary, 1955-56; sec. Mannix Co., Ltd., 1956-58, gen. counsel, 1958-62, v.p., 1959-62, dir., 1960-62; individual practice law, from 1962; formerly mem. Alta. Legislature for Calgary West; formerly leader Progressive Conservative Party of Alta., 1965-85; premier of Alta., 1971-85; ptnr. Bennett Jones Verchere, Calgary, 1986—. Office: Bennett Jones Verchere, 4500 Bankers Hall E 855 2d St SW, Calgary, AB Canada T2P 4K7

LOUGHLIN, MARTIN FRANCIS, federal judge; b. Manchester, N.H., Mar. 11, 1923; m. Margaret M. Gallagher; children: Helen, Margaret, Shane, Mary, Sheila, Martina, Caitlin. AB, St. Anselm's Coll., 1947; LLB, Suffolk U., 1951. Bar: N.H. 1952. Assoc. Conrad Danaid, Esq., Manchester, 1953-58, Broderick & Loughlin, Manchester, 1958-63; judge N.H. Superior Ct., Manchester, 1963-79, chief justice, 1978-79; judge U.S. Dist. Ct. N.H., Concord, 1979—; instr. St. Anselm's Coll., Franklin Pierce Law Sch. Contbr. articles to legal jours. Mem. ABA, N.H. Bar, Manchester Bar Asssn. Office: US Dist Ct PO Box 1454 55 Pleasant St Concord NH 03301-3954

LOUGHLIN, MARY ANNE ELIZABETH, television news anchor; b. Biddeford, Maine, July 30, 1956; d. John Francis and Jacqueline Anne (LaLonde) L.; BS, Fla. State U., 1977. Reporter, Sta. WFSU-FM, Tallahassee, 1976; news anchor/producer Sta. WECA-TV, Tallahassee, 1977-81; producer/show host Sta. WTBS-TV, Atlanta, 1981-84; news anchor, producer Cable News Network, Atlanta, 1983-91; anchor Time Man of the Year specials, 1988-90 (Silver award Houston Film Festival); anchor Dem. and Rep. Nat. Conv., 1988; freelance journalist, 1991—. Recipient Woman at Work Broadcast award Nat. Commn. on Working Women, 1982, Grad. Made Good award, Fla. State U., 1987, Archbishop Fulton J. Sheen Angel award Archdiocese of St. Petersburg, 1988. Mem. Women in Cable, Women in Communications, Am. Women in Radio and TV (Woman of Achievement award 1982, 84). Roman Catholic.

LOUGHLIN, WILLIAM JOSEPH, priest, religious organization administrator; b. Wharton, N.J., Mar. 3, 1927; s. William Joseph and Theresa Catherine (May) L. AB, Seton Hall U., 1954, AM, 1957; MDiv, Pope John XXIII Sem., Weston, Mass., 1969; postgrad., Rutgers U., 1959. Ordained priest Roman Cath. Ch., 1969. Deacon St. Mary's Ch., Greenwich, Conn., summer 1968, parochial vicar, 1980-82, 90-92; parochial vicar St. Rose Ch., Newtown, Conn., 1969-70, Assumption Ch., Westport, Conn., 1970-73; defender of the bond Diocesan Marriage Tribunal, Bridgeport, Conn., 1973-82; parochial vicar St. Philip Ch., Norwalk, Conn., 1973-78, St. Augustine Cathedral, Bridgeport, Conn., 1978-80; pastor St. Joseph Ch., Shelton, Conn., 1982-90; dir. pilgrimages Diocese of Bridgeport, 1982—; parochial vicar St. Luke Ch., Westport, 1992—; chaplain to His Holiness Pope John Paul II, Rome, 1988—. Mem. Am. Pers. and Guidance Assn. (evaluation com. Cath. counselors Phila. 1960, Denver 1961), Nat. Vocat. Guidance Assn., KC (Lafayette coun. Dover, N.J. 1947—, Walter J. Barrett Gen. Assembly 1950—). Avocations: collecting Hummel figurines, travel. Home: 16 Walnut St Wharton NJ 07885-2516

LOUGHNANE, LEE DAVID, trumpeter; b. Chgo., Oct. 21, 1946; s. Philip Louis and Juanita (Wall) L. Student, DePaul U., Chgo., 1964-66, Chgo. Conservatory Music, 1966-67. Mem. musical group The Big Thing, 1967, Chicago, 1967—; v.p. Chgo. Music, Inc. Rec. artist: Columbia Records. Named Entertainer of Yr., People's Choice Awards, 1974, Best Instrumental Band, Playboy mag., 1971-75; recipient 3 Grammy awards, 1977. Mem. AFTRA, Nat. Acad. Recording Arts and Scis., Screen Actors Guild, Psi Mu Alpha Sinfonia. Address: care Howard Rose Agy 8900 Wilshire Blvd # 320 Beverly Hills CA 90211-1906*

LOUGHRAN, JAMES NEWMAN, philosophy educator, former university president; b. Bklyn., Mar. 22, 1940; s. John Farley and Ethel Margaret (Newman) L. A.B., Fordham U., 1964, M.A., 1965, Ph.D. in Philosophy, 1975; Ph.D. (hon.), Loyola Coll., Balt., 1993. Joined S.J., 1958; ordained priest Roman Catholic Ch., 1970. Instr. philosophy St. Peter's Coll., Jersey City, 1965-67; asst. dean Fordham U., Bronx, N.Y., 1970-73; tchr. philosophy Fordham U., Bronx, 1974-79, 82-84, dean, 1979-82; pres. Loyola Marymount U., L.A., 1984-91; acting pres. Bklyn. Coll., 1992; Miller Prof. Philosophy John Carroll U., Cleve., 1992-93; interim pres. Mount St. Mary's Coll., Emmitsburg, Md., 1993-94; interim acad. v.p. Fordham U., Bronx, 1994—. Contbr. numerous articles and revs. to popular and scholarly jours. Trustee St. Peter's Coll., Jersey City, 1972-78, 94—, Xavier U., Cin., 1981-84, Canisius Coll., Buffalo, 1994—. Mem. Am. Philos. Assn. Avocation: tennis.

LOUGHREY, KEVIN, lawyer; b. Paterson, N.J., May 18, 1950; s. Charles Michael and Eleanor (McDonald) L.; m. Jane Frances Berry, Dec. 16, 1972; children: Erin, Shannon. BA, Colo. State U., 1972; JD, U. Houston, 1976. Bar: Tex. 1976, Colo. 1977. Assoc. Berke, Rorinson and Leebron, Houston, 1976-77; pvt. practice Colorado Springs, Colo., 1977-79; atty. Rocky Mountain Energy Co. Denver, 1979-80; atty. Amoco Minerals Co., Denver, 1980-82, sr. atty., 1982-84, assoc. gen. counsel, 1985-86, gen. counsel, corp. sec., 1987—. Vice pres. Cherry Knolls Improvement Assn., Littleton, Colo., 1985—. Mem. ABA, Colo. Bar Assn., Denver Bar Assn., Rocky Mountain Mineral Law Found., Am. Soc. Corp. Counsel. Avocations: golf, skiing, tennis, reading, music. Office: Cyprus Minerals Co PO Box 3299 Englewood CO 80155-3299

LOUGHRIN, JAY RICHARDSON, mass communications educator, consultant; b. Mankato, Minn., Oct. 21, 1943; s. J. Richardson and Jane Aileen (Smith) L.; m. Helen Marie Struyk, Aug. 8, 1964 (div. Sept. 1985); children: Jennifer, Amy; m. Yolanda Christina Ramos, July 17, 1986; children: Tawny, Heather. BA in Drama, Calif. State U., Los Angeles, 1968; postgrad., San Diego State U., 1968-69, UCLA, 1970-71, U. Redlands, Calif., 1983-84, Fla. State U., 1990, MA, Whittier (Calif.) Coll., 1992. Prodn. asst. Andrews-Yagemann Prodns., Hollywood, Calif., 1961-63; with merchandising, sales Sta. KTTV-TV, Hollywood, 1963-64; assoc. producer Born Losers Am. Internat. Pictures, Hollywood, 1964; assoc. producer V.P.I. Prodns., Hollywood, 1964, Ralph Andrews Prodns., North Hollywood, Calif., 1965; producer Stein Erikson Ski Films, North Hollywood, 1965, F.K. Rocket Films, North Hollywood, 1966-68; dir. promotion and publicity Sta. KCST-TV, San Diego, 1968-69; prof. mass communication Rio Hondo Coll., Whittier, 1969—; sales mgr. Warren Miller Films, Hermosa Beach, Calif., 1984-85, cons. 1985-86; exec. producer Echo Prodns., Hollywood, 1985-87; cons. Radio Concepts, Los Angeles, 1978-80, Tom Cole Prodns., Los Angeles, 1985-87, Chuck Richards Whitewater, Lake Isabella, Calif., 1984-86; media relations cons. Police Officers Standards and Training, Sacramento, 1986—; venue mgr. Los Angeles Olympic Organizing Com., Long Beach, Calif., 1984. Contbr. articles to Review Publs., Orange Coast mag., Jet Am. mag., Ted Randall Report. Pres. Rue Le Charlene Homeowners Assn., Palos Verdes, Calif., 1984, Hilltop Homeowners Assn., Walnut, Calif., 1989-90; v.p. West Walnut Homeowners Assn., 1988-90. Recipient Pub. Service Programming award Advt. Council, N.Y.C., 1982; named Adviser of Yr., U. So. Calif.'s 50th Annual Journalism Awards, Los Angeles, 1985. Mem. Acad. TV Arts and Scis., Rio Hondo Coll. Faculty Assn. (pres. 1978), So. Calif. Broadcasters Assn. (Pub. Service award 1978). Republican. Avocations: sailing, skiing, whitewater rafting, motorcycling, bicycling. Office: Rio Hondo Coll 3600 Workman Mill Rd Whittier CA 90601-1699

LOUIS, BARBRA SCHANTZ, dean; b. Dover, N.J., Nov. 26, 1940; d. Henry Albert and Priscilla Ruth (Schantz) L.; m. Roger Donald Coss, Sept. 1957 (div. 1973); children: Candee Lee Coss Spizzirri, Lynn Ellen Coss Brandimarte, Amber Mary Coss Gillespie. AA, County Coll. of Morris, Dover, N.J., 1971; BA, Montclair State Coll., 1973, MA, 1973; DEd, Rutgers U., 1985. Cert. secondary tchr. Counselor, adminstr. Bergen Community Coll., Paramus, N.J., 1974-77; exec. asst. to exec. dir. Bergen County Community Action Program, Hackensack, N.J., 1977-80; cons. Nat. Multiple Sclerosis Soc., Teaneck, N.J., 1984-85; dir. devel. Passaic County Community Coll., Paterson, N.J., 1985-90; dean for Continuing Edn. Santa Barbara (Calif.) City Coll., 1990—. Bd. dirs. Edwin Gould Svcs. for Children, N.Y.C., 1980-90, Planned Parenthood of Passaic County, Paterson, N.J., 1989-90, Santa Barbara, Ventura Counties, Calif.; bd. mem. Passaic County Cultural and Heritage Coun., Paterson, 1987-90, Found. for Santa Barbara City Coll., 1992—. Mem. The Hamilton Club (bd. govs. 1988-90). Democrat. Unitarian. Avocations: travel, antique collecting. Home: 126 San Clemente Santa Barbara CA 93109 Office: Santa Barbara City Coll Wake Ctr Continuing Edn Divsn 300 N Turnpike Rd Santa Barbara CA 93111-1931

LOUIS, JOHN (JEFFRY), JR., former ambassador; b. Evanston, Ill., June 10, 1925; m. Josephine Peters, Oct. 10, 1953; children: Kimberly, Tracy, John III. Grad., Deerfield Acad., Mass., 1943; student, Northwestern U., 1943, 46; B.A., Williams Coll., 1947; M.B.A., Dartmouth Coll., 1949. Account exec. Needham, Louis & Brorby, Inc., Chgo., 1952-58; dir. internat. mktg. Johnson's Wax, Racine, Wis., 1958-61; chmn. bd. KTAR Broadcasting Co., Phoenix, 1961-68, Combined Communications Corp., Chgo., 1968-81; ambassador to U.K., 1981-83. Trustee Evanston Hosp., Northwestern U. Served with AUS, 1943-45. Mem. Old Elm Club (Highland Park, Ill.), Pine Valley Golf Club (Clementon, N.J.), Augusta Nat. Golf Course (Ga.). Office: Ste 510 One Northfield Plaza Northfield IL 60093

LOUIS, KENNETH CLAIR, insurance company executive; b. Pitts., Mar. 31, 1938; s. Kenneth Clair and Elizabeth (Grim) L.; m. Barbara B. Brooks, Dec. 30, 1961; children: Jeffrey, Ken, Stephen. BS, Pa. State U., 1961. CLU. Sales mgr. ARMCO Steel Co., Middletown, Ohio, 1965-69; sr. v.p. ins. sales Bus. Men's Assurance Co., Kansas City, Mo., 1969-89; sr. v.p individual ins. Ameritas Life Ins. Corp., Lincoln, Nebr., 1989—; bd. dirs. Ameritas Variable Life Ins. Co., Lincoln, First Ameritas Life Ins. Corp. N.Y. Bd. dirs. Leadership Lincoln, 1991-92, Lied Ctr. for Performing Arts, 1993—. Mem. Am. Soc. CLUs (chmn. fin. com. 1972-75), Gen. Agts. and Mgrs. Assn., Lincoln Assn. Life Underwriters, Life Ins. Mktg. and Rsch. Assn. (bd. dirs. 1991-94). Republican. Presbyterian. Office: Ameritas Life Ins Corp 5900 O St Lincoln NE 68510

LOUIS, LESTER See BROWN, LES

LOUIS, MURRAY, dancer, choreographer, dance teacher; b. N.Y.C., Nov. 4, 1926; s. Aaron and Rose (Mintzer) Fuchs. B.S., N.Y. U., 1951. Principal dancer Nikolais Dance Theatre, 1950-59; assoc. dir. dance div., Henry St. Playhouse, N.Y.C., 1953-70; artistic dir. Nikolais/Louis Found. Dance, N.Y.C., 1970—, Murray Louis Dance Co., 1953—; co-dir. Choreoarts, 1973—; choreographer numerous works, 1953— including Porcelain Dialogues, 1974, Moments, 1975, Catalogue, 1975, Cleopatra, 1976, Ceremony, 1976, Deja Vu, 1976, Glances, 1976, Schubert, 1977, The Canarsie Venus, 1978, Figura, 1978, A Suite for Erik, 1979, Afternoon, 1979, The City, 1980, November Dances, 1980, Aperitif, 1982, A Stravinsky Montage, 1982, Repertoire, 1982, The After Boat, 1983, Frail Demons, 1984, Four Brubeck Pieces (with Dave Brubeck Quartet), 1984, Pug's Land, 1984, The Station, 1985, Revels, 1986, The Disenchantment of Pierrot, 1986, Black and White, 1987, Return to Go, 1987, Horizons, 1994, Alone, 1994; choreographer: By George (music by George Gershwin for Cleve. Ballet), 1987, Act I (with Dave Brubeck Quartet), 1987, Bach II, 1987, Asides, 1987; TV projects include Repertoire Workshop, CBS, N.Y.C., 1965, Proximities, Calligraph for Matyrs, ZDF-TV, Munich, 1974, Soundstage (with Dave Brubeck) PBS, Chgo., 1977, Studio Two, Polish Nat. TV, Warsaw, 1978, Murray Louis Dance Co., TeleFrance 1, Paris, 1982, video AT&T (with Dave Brubeck Quartet), 1988; 5 part film series Dance as an Art Form, 1974; choreographer for 23d, 27th Annual Coty Am. Fashion Critics awards; author: Inside Dance, Letters to Nik from India; Nik and Murray (film by Christian Blackwood), 1986, Murray Louis on Dance, 1992. Chmn. U.S. chpt. Conseil Internat. de la Danse (UNESCO). Served with USNR, 1945-46. Guggenheim fellow, 1969, 73; grantee Rockefeller Found., 1974; Nat. Endowment Arts, 1968, 70, 72, 74-78, Mellon Found., 1976; recipient Critics award Internat. Festival Weisbaden, Ger., 1972, Dance Mag. award, 1977, Grand Medaille de la Ville de Paris, 1979; decorated knight Order of Arts and Letters, France, 1984. Mem. Am. Guild Mus. Artists, Assn. Am. Dance Cos., Asso. Council Arts, Dance Notation Bur. Jewish. Office: Nikolais/Louis Found 375 W Broadway New York NY 10012-4303 *I think, to discover the intuitive force within oneself, and then know how to utilize and trust its judgment, is essential for the creative artist. My aesthetics were achieved by this intuitive judgment.*

LOUIS, PAUL ADOLPH, lawyer; b. Key West, Fla., Oct. 22, 1922; s. Louis and Rose Leah (Weinstein) L.; m. Nancy Ann Lapof, Dec. 28, 1971; children: Louis Benson, IV, Connor Cristina and Marshall Dore (twins). B.A., Va. Mil. Inst., Lexington, 1947; LL.B., U. Miami, Fla., 1950, J.D., 1967. Bar: Fla. 1950, U.S. Dist. Ct. (so. dist.) Fla. Asst. state atty., 1955-57; atty. Beverage Dept. Fla., 1957-60; spl. asst. atty. gen. State of Fla., 1970-71; partner firm Sinclair, Louis, Heath, Nussbaum & Zavertnik (P.A.), Miami, 1960—; mem. Fed. Jud. Nominating Commn., 1977-80; mem. peer rev. com. U.S. Dist. Ct. for So. Dist. Fla., 1983-85. Author: Defamation, How Far Can You Go, Trial and Tort Trends, 1969; contbr.: chpts. to Fla. Family Law, 1967, 72. Founder mem. Palm Springs Gen. Hosp. Scholarship Com., 1968; mem. Dade County Health Facilities Authority, 1979—; trustee Fla. Supreme Ct. Hist. Soc., 1994—. Served to maj. USAAF, 1943-45, ETO. Decorated Air medal with five oak leaf clusters, Bronze Star (7), Purple Heart. Mem. ABA, Fla. Bar (bd. cert. civil trial lawyer and marital and family law, bd. govs. 1970-74), Dade County Bar Assn. (dir. 1954-55, 66-69), Assn. Trial Lawyers Am., Am. Judicature Soc., Va. Mil. Inst. Alumni Assn. Democrat. Jewish. Club: Miami, Bath. Home: 4411 Palm Ln Miami FL 33137-3346 Office: 1125 A I duPont Bldg 169 E Flagler St Miami FL 33131-1209

LOUIS, WILLIAM ROGER, historian, educator, editor; b. Detroit, May 8, 1936; s. Henry Edward and Bena May (Flood) L.; m. Dagmar Cecilia Friedrich; children: Antony Andrew, Catherine Ann. B.A., U. Okla., 1959; M.A., Harvard U., 1960; D.Phil., Oxford U., 1962, D.Litt., 1979. Asst., then assoc. prof. history Yale U., 1962-70; prof. history, curator hist. collections Humanities Research Center U. Tex., Austin, 1970-85; dir. British Studies, 1975—; Kerr chair English history and culture U. Tex., Austin, 1985—; supernumerary fellow St. Antony's Coll., U. Oxford, Eng., 1986—; corr. fellow Brit. Acad., 1993—; Chichele lectr. All Souls Coll., U. Oxford, 1990; Disting. lectr. London Sch. Econs., 1992; dir. summer seminars NEH, 1985, 88, 90, 91. Author: Ruanda-Urundi, 1963, Germany's Lost Colonies, 1967, (with Jean Stengers)The Congo Reform Movement, 1968, British Strategy in the Far East, 1919-1939, 1971, Imperialism at Bay, 1977 (History Book Club), British Empire in the Middle East, 1984 (George Louis Beer prize Am. Hist. Assn. and Tex. Inst. Letters award), In The Name of the God Go! Leo Amery and the British Empire in the Age of Churchill, 1992; editor-in-chief Oxford History of the British Empire, 1993—; editor: (with P. Gifford) Britain and Germany in Africa, 1967, France and Britain in Africa, 1971, The Origins of the Second World War: A.J.P. Taylor and his Critics, 1972, National Security and International Trusteeship in the Pacific, 1972, Imperialism: The Robinson and Gallagher Controversy, 1976, (with William S. Livingston) Australia, New Zealand and the Pacific Islands since the First World War, 1979, (with P. Gifford) The Transfer of Power in Africa, 1982, (with R. Stookey) End of the Palestine Mandate, 1986, (with H. Bull) The Special Relationship: Anglo-American Relations Since 1945, 1986, (with P. Gifford) Decolonization and African Independence, 1988, (with James Bill) Musaddiq, Iranian Nationalism, and Oil, 1988, (with Roger Owen) Suez 1956: The Crisis and Its Consequences, 1989, (with Robert A. Fernea) The Iraqi Revolution of 1958, 1991, (with Robert Blake) Churchill, 1993. Recipient U. Tex. Disting. Grad. Teaching award, Pres. Teaching Excellence award, Liberal Arts Student Coun. award outstanding undergrad. teaching; Marshall scholar; Woodrow Wilson fellow, NEH fellow, Am. Inst. Indian

Studies fellow, Guggenheim fellow, vis. fellow All Souls Coll., U. Oxford, overseas fellow Churchill Coll., U. Cambridge, Eng.; guest scholar Brookings Instn. Fellow Royal Hist. Soc.; mem. Am. Hist. Assn. (life), Coun. on Fgn. Rels. (N.Y.C.), Tex. Inst. Letters, Reform Club (London), Century (N.Y.C.), Met. Club (Washington). Democrat. Office: U Texas Dept History Austin TX 78712

LOUIS-COTTON D'ENGLESQUEVILLE, FRANCOIS PIERRE, automobile company executive; b. Neuilly Seine, France, Sept. 4, 1929; came to U.S., 1955; s. Georges Auguste and Paule Marie Cotton (d'Englesqueville) L.; m. Martine Combaluzier, Apr. 30, 1965 (div.); 1 child, Veronique; m. Mary Elizabeth Thames, June 14, 1986; children: George, Timothy, Jennifer, Mary Beth. BEE, Ecole Brequet, Paris, 1952. Engr. Demarais Freres, Paris, 1954-55, Cadillac Motor Cars div. GM, Detroit, 1955-58; nat. svc. mgr. Peugeot, S.A., N.Y.C., 1958-60; engr. Michelin Tire Group, Woodside, N.Y., 1960-61, Port Authority N.Y. and N.J., N.Y.C., 1962-68; dir. Renault USA, Inc., Washington, 1968-94; cons. Garden City, N.Y., 1994—. Mem. Conseiller du Commerce Exterieur de la France, Soc. Automotive Engrs., Assn. Internat. Automobile Mfrs. (bd. dirs. 1974-94), Cercle Militaire Paris, Army and Navy Club (Washington), Cherry Valley Club (Garden City). Avocations: photography, travel, cooking. Office: 680 Fifth Ave Ste 1601 New York NY 10019

LOUIS-DREYFUS, JULIA, actress. TV appearances include Saturday Night Live, 1982-85, Day by Day, 1986-89, Seinfeld, 1990— (Emmy nomination Supporting Actress-Comedy, 1993, 94); films include Soul Man, 1986, Troll, 1986, Hannah and Her Sisters, 1986, National Lampoon's Christmas Vacation, 1989, Jack the Bear, 1993, North, 1994. Office: TPEG Mgmt 9150 Wilshire Blvd Ste 205 Beverly Hills CA 90212*

LOUNSBERRY, ROBERT HORACE, former state government administrator; b. Carlisle, Iowa, June 22, 1918; s. Horace Charles and Alice Mae (Elmore) L.; m. Muriel Dirks, Aug. 2, 1942; children: William, Beth, Janet, Paul, Steven. BA, Luther Coll., 1940; postgrad., U. Iowa, 1940-42. Farmer McCallsburg, Iowa, 1946-69; dep. sec. agr. Iowa Dept. Agr., Des Moines, 1969-72, sec. agr., 1972-87. Chmn. Story County Bd. Edn., 1950-69; bd. dirs. Iowa Assn. Sch. Bds., 1961-68, Des Moines Area Community Coll., 1964-70; clk. Richland Twp., 1952-64; chmn. Story County Rep. Party, 1964-68, chmn. 5th Rep. Dist., 1968-70; dir Am. Legion Boys State, 1957-88; active Iowa Arboretum, Iowans Right to Work Com.; active Gov's. Com. for Aging; elected to Older Iowa Legislature (spkr. of house 1989); nat. dir. Comm. for Agriculture (sr. citizens adv. com.); active Iowa Aging Coalition, Retired Sr. Vol. Program. With USAAF, 1942-45. Decorated D.F.C., Air medal with 4 oak leaf clusters. Mem. Nat. Assn. Depts. Agr., Am. Assn. Retired Persons, Midwest Assn. State Depts. Agr., Mid-Am. Internat. Agri-Trade Coun., Greater Des Moines C. of C., Davis County Sheeps Producers, Iowa Cattlemen's Assn., Story County Cattlemen's Assn., Res. Officers Assn., Am. Legion (mem. nat. exec. com. 1965-70, state comdr. 1953-54), Lions, Masons, Shriners. Home: RR Mc Callsburg IA 50154

LOUNSBURY, JOHN FREDERICK, geographer, educator; b. Perham, Minn., Oct. 26, 1918; s. Charles Edwin and Maude (Knight) L.; m. Dorothea Frances Eggers, Oct. 3, 1943; children—John Frederick, Craig Lawrence, James Gordon. B.S., U. Ill., 1942, M.S., 1946; Ph.D., Northwestern U., 1951. Asst. dir. rural land classification program Insular Govt., P.R., 1949-52; cons., research analyst Dayton Met. Studies, Inc., Ohio, 1957-60; chmn. dept. earth scis., prof. geography Antioch Coll., 1951-61; prof. geography, head dept. geography and geology Eastern Mich. U., 1961-69; chmn. dept. geography Ariz. State U., 1969-77; dir. Ctr. for Environ. Studies, 1977-80; prof. emeritus Ariz. State U., 1987—; project dir. Geography in Liberal Edn. Project, Assn. Am. Geographers, NSF, 1963-65, project dir. commn. on coll. geography, 1965-74; dir. environment based edn. project US. Office Edn., 1974-75; dir. spatial analysis of land use project NSF, 1975-85. Author articles, workbooks, textbooks. Mem. Yellow Springs Planning Commn., Ohio, dir. research, 1957-60; mem. Ypsilanti Planning Commn., 1961-66; research com. Washtenaw County Planning Commn., 1961-69; mem. cons. Ypsilanti Indsl. Devel. Corp., 1961-63. Served with AUS, 1942-46, ETO. Named Man of Yr., Yellow Springs C. of C., 1956-57. Fellow Ariz.-Nev. Acad. Sci.; mem. Assn. Am. Geographers (chmn. East Lakes div. 1959-61, mem. nat. exec. council 1961-64, chmn. liberal edn. com. 1961-65), Nat. Council Geog. Edn. (chmn. earth sci. com. 1961-68, regional coord. 1961-63, mem. exec. bd. 1968-71, 77-83, v.p 1977-78, pres. 1979-80, Disting. Svc. award 1988, Disting. Mentor award 1990), Mich. Acad. Sci. Arts and Letters (chmn. pub. relations com. 1964-69, past chmn. geography sect.), Ohio Acad. Sci. (past exec. v.p.), Mich. Acad. Sci., Ariz. Acad. Sci., Am. Geog. Soc., AAAS, Sigma Xi, Delta Kappa Epsilon, Gamma Theta Upsilon. Home: 7850 E Vista Dr Scottsdale AZ 85250-7641 Office: Ariz State U Dept Geography Tempe AZ 85281

LOUREY, BECKY J., state legislator; b. 1943; m. Gene Lourey; 11 children. Student, Asbury Coll., U. Minn. Mem. Minn. Ho. of Reps., 1990—, mem. various coms., vice-chair health and housing fin. divsn., mem. internat. trade, tech. and econ. devel. divsn., mem. Legis. Commn. Health Care Access. Democrat. Home: Box 100 Star Rte Kerrick MN 55756 Office: Minn Ho of Reps State Capitol Saint Paul MN 55155

LOURIE, ALAN DAVID, federal judge; b. Boston, Mass., Jan. 13, 1935. A.B., Harvard U., 1956; M.S., U. Wis., 1958; Ph.D., U. Pa., 1965; J.D., Temple U., 1970. Bar: Pa. 1970. Chemist Monsanto Co., St. Louis, 1957-59; lit. scientist, chemist, patent agt. Wyeth Labs., Radnor, Pa., 1959-64; counsel Smith Kline Beechum Corp., Phila., 1964-90, successively as patent agt., atty., dir. corp. patents, asst. gen. counsel, v.p. corp. patents; cir. judge U.S. Ct. Appeals (fed. cir.), Washington, 1990—; mem. U.S. del. to Diplomatic Conf. on Revision of Paris Conv. for Protection of Indsl. Property, 1982, 84; vice chmn. industry functional adv. com. to U.S. Trade Rep. and Dept. Commerce, 1987-90; chmn. U.S. group of U.S.-Japan Bus. Coun. Task Force on Patents. Mem. ABA, Phila. Patent Law Assn. (pres. 1984-85), Am. Intellectual Property Law Assn. (bd. dirs. 1982-85), Assn. Corp. Patent Counsel (treas. 1987-89), Pharm. Mfrs. Assn. (chmn. patent com. 1981-86), Am. Chem. Soc., Cosmos Club, Harvard Club Washington. Office: US Ct Appeals Fed Cir 717 Madison Pl NW Washington DC 20439-0002

LOURIE, NORMAN VICTOR, government official, social worker; b. N.Y.C., Feb. 1, 1912; s. Inte and Elsie (Horowitz) L.; m. Betty Pokrassa, Dec. 31, 1945 (dec. 1975); children: Richard, Iven, Mary Ann, Susan, Sara; m. Dorothy Maxey, Sept. 1, 1991. Student, Cornell U., 1932-35; BS, NYU, 1936; diploma, N.Y. Sch. Social Work; MSW, Columbia U., 1938; DHL Adelphi U., 1976. Rsch. assoc. Russell Sage Found. Greater N.Y. Fund, N.Y.C. Health and Welfare Coun., 1937-39; asst. dir. Bronx House Settlement, N.Y.C., 1939- 41; dir. Madison Settlement House, 1941-43, Hawthorne Cedar Knoll Sch., 1946-51; DHL Adelphi Coll. Grad. Sch. Social Work, 1948-51; dir. Assn. Jewish Children, Phila., 1951-55; exec. dep. sec., and sec. Pa. Dept. Pub. Welfare, 1955-80; policy adv. Inst. Econ. Devel., Washington, 1979-82; cons. Pa. Dept. Public Welfare, 1980-81; vis. prof. U. Pa. Sch. Social Work; prof. Norman Lourie Archives, U. Pa. Van Pelt and Grad. Sch. Social Work Libraries, 1975, Philippine Women's U., 1982; sr. policy advisor Nat. Immigration, Refugee and Citizenship Forum, 1982-90; sr. policy advisor Schirm Assocs.-Head Injury, 1987-93; chmn. Nat. Task Force on Definition of Developmental Disabilities, 1977; mem. Vietnamese Children's Resettlement Adv. Com., 1976; chmn. Nat. Coalition for Refugee Resettlement, 1978-82; cons. NIMH, Office Econ. Opportunity, Nat. Commn. on Marijuana and Drug Abuse, Social Rehab. Service, Health and Human Services; speaker White House Conf. on Children and Youth, 1950, 60, 70, White House Conf. on Aging, 1960; welfare cons. Fels Inst., Wharton Sch. U. Pa., 1953-55; mem. bd. Joint Commn. Mental Health of Children, 1965-67, chmn. com. on studies, mem. 1965-67; adv. council Pres.'s Com. on Juvenile Delinquency and Youth; chmn. bd. trustees Community Mental Health and Family Services, Refugee Camps, Southeast Asia, 1982-84, emeritus, 1984-94; instr. part-time Grad. Sch. U. Pa., Pitts., Columbia U. Author books in field; chmn. editorial bd.: Jour. Jewish Communal Service, 1952-58, Child Welfare, 1962-64; editorial bd.: Social Casework, 1969-72, Jour. Social Work Edn, 1970-72, Jour. Adminstrn. and Social Work; contbr. to encys., jours. Bd. dirs. Am. Child Guidance Found., Indochinese Community Ctr., Washington, 1986-94, Internat. Child Mental Health, Nat. Accreditation Council for Blind; adv. com. Bryn. Mawr Sch.

Social Work; bd. dirs. Alan Gutmacher Inst., 1976-80, Soc. for Study Traumatic Stress Studies, 1985-87, Indochinese Cultural Ctr., Washington, 1985-89; mem. adv. bd. Indochinese Refugee Action Ctr., 1985-94; life sr. advisor Tri-County Planned Parenthood, Harrisburg, Pa., 1988-94; bd. dirs. Sr. Citizen's Ctr., Harrisburg, 1988-94. 1st lt., inf., Med. Service Corps, AUS, 1943-46; acting chief psychiat. social worker USAR, Pentagon, 1946-51. Recipient Man of Yr. award Am. Soc. Pub. Adminstrn., 1963, Heritage and Social Svcs. award Gov. of Pa., 1991. Fellow Am. Orthopsychiat. Assn. (chmn. legis. com. 1956-60, pres. 1966-67, Ortho Lourie Family award), Am. Psychiat. Assn. (hon.); mem. NASW (pres. 1961-63, chmn. commn. on social policy and action 1958-60, chmn. poverty com. 1964-66, Lifetime Svc. award Pa. chpt. 1990), Am. Pub. Welfare Assn. (dir., 1st v.p. 1965-66, chmn. fed. policy com., W.S. Terry Meml. merit award 1971), Nat. Council State Adminstrs. (exec. com. 1972-79, emeritus 1979-94, chmn. health com. 1974-75, chmn. supplementary security income liaison com. 1976-79), Child Welfare League Am. (dir. 1960-62, chmn. editorial bd.), Nat. Rehab. Assn., Internat. Child Welfare Union, Internat. Council Social Welfare (chmn. U.S. com. 1971-75, exec. com. 1975-79), Nat. Conf. Social Welfare (dir. 1971-75, v.p. 1972-73, pres. 1975-76), Alumni Assn. Columbia Sch. Social Work, Internat. Assn. Workers for Maladjusted Children (Am. br. chmn. 1972-79, permanent rep. to UN 1973-79), Nat. Inst. Pub. Mgmt. (bd. dirs. 1977-79), Soc. Traumatic Stress Studies (bd. dirs. 1968-86), Cosmos Club (Washington). Home: 5740 Union Deposit Rd Harrisburg PA 17111-4708 *Literature is full of solutions to the anger and violence which continue to characterize the current society. My current experience, in retirement, with refugee programs in Southeast Asia and other parts of the world, leads me to conclude that our glorious civilization of knowledge and science is still too much marred with hate and inequality. Our protestations of religion are suspect because of our behavior. Poverty and violence are our greatest sins, as is inequality. Only when we act out that each person is a holy place and we learn to love our children and our species more than we hate and fight, will we have the right to say we are civilized. We are good at rescue, but very poor at prevention. We should respect that every person is a holy place.*

LOUSBERG, SISTER MARY CLARICE, hospital executive; b. Fleming, Colo., Aug. 21, 1929; d. Edward P. and M. Irene (Berg) L. R.N., St. Joseph Hosp., Denver, 1952; B.S. in Nursing Edn., St. Mary Coll., Leavenworth, Kans., 1969; M.P.A. in Health Care Adminstrn., U. So. Calif., 1971. Nursing supr. St. John's Hosp., Helena, Mont., 1954-59, supr. obstetrics, Santa Monica, Calif., 1959-63; operating room supr. Providence Hosp., Kansas City, Kans., 1963-66; dir. nursing service DePaul Hosp., Cheyenne, Wyo., 1966-68, pres., 1979-88; adminstr. St. James Community Hosp., Butte, Mont., 1972-79; patient representative St. Mary's Hosp. & Med. Ctr., 1991—; bd. dirs. St. Joseph Hosp., Denver, 1980-87, 92—, Laramie County Health Planning Com., Cheyenne, 1980-84. Mem. Wyo. State Cert. of Need Rev. Bd., Cheyenne, 1982-83, Cheyenne MX Impact Com., 1982-87. Named Boss of Yr., Am. Bus. Women's Assn., Cheyenne, 1980. Fellow Am. Coll. Hosp. Adminstrs. (Regent Wyo. 1982-88); mem. Wyo. Hosp. Assn. (chmn. bd. dirs. 1986), Catholic Hosp. Assn., Mont. Hosp. Assn. (pres. 1976-77).

LOUTREL, CLAUDE YVES, corporate official; b. Nanterre, France, Oct. 1, 1930; arrived in Belgium, 1957; s. Marcel and Odette (Diguet) L.; m. Anne Beatrice Dumont, July 6, 1957; children: Catherine, Bernard. Degree in engring., Ecole Centrale des Arts et Manufactures, Paris, 1954. Engr., various positions Solvay S.A., Brussels, 1957-72, Milan, 1972-74; mem. exec. com. Solvay S.A., Brussels, 1975—, also bd. dirs.; chmn. Solvay Polymers Corp., Houston, 1974—; vice chmn. Solvay Am., Houston, 1984—. Decorated chevalier de l'Ordre de la Couronne, officier de l'Ordre de Léopold (Belgium), commdr. Most Noble Order of Crown of Thailand. Office: Solvay SA, rue du Prince Albert 33, 1050 Brussels Belgium also: Solvay Am Inc 3333 Richmond Ave Houston TX 77098

LOUTSENHIZER, MARVIN JERRY, manufacturing executive; b. Bryan, Ohio, May 19, 1938; s. Harold Kenneth and Hazel Sarah (Martin) L.; m. Sara Ruth Loutsenhizer; children—Troy Kevin, Bradley Marvin, Natalie Joy. B.S., Manchester Coll., 1960; M.B.A., Ind. U., 1965. Various positions Gen. Telephone Co., Fort Wayne, Ind., 1966-71; acctg. mgr. Hardware Wholesalers, Fort Wayne, 1971-76, controller, 1976-78, dir. fin., 1978-80, v.p. fin., 1980—; v.p., dir. Travel Place, Fort Wayne, 1978-88. Chmn. Manchester Coll. Alumni Northeastern Ind., Fort Wayne, 1983; bd. dirs. Alumni Leadership Fort Wayne, 1988, 89; v.p., bd. dirs. Manchester Coll. Alumni, 1988-89; treas. United Way of Allen County, Fort Wayne, 1985—; chmn. bd. dirs., exec. com. Lincolnshire Ch. of Brethren, Fort Wayne, 1984—. Recipient Outstanding Alumni Services award Manchester Coll., 1984. Mem. Nat. Assn. Accts. (pres. 1979-80, pres. Lincoln Trails Regional Coun. 1983-84), Fin. Execs. Inst., Manchester Coll. Alumni Assn. (nat. v.p., bd. dirs. 1988-89). Republican. Avocations: golf; jogging; reading; travel. Home: 6027 Landover Pl Fort Wayne IN 46815-7616

LOUTTIT, JAMES RUSSELL, publishing company executive; b. Monongahela, Pa., May 15, 1924; s. James S. and Orilla (Hutchinson) L.; m. Eleanor H. Ely, Mar. 19, 1986; children: J. Kipling, Dana M. B.A., U. Pitts., 1950. Reporter Canton (Ohio) Repository, 1950-51; feature writer, asst. city editor L.I. (N.Y.) Daily Press, 1951-56; advt. exec. McCann-Erickson, N.Y.C., 1956-57; speech writer Esso Standard Oil Co., N.Y.C., 1957-63; product mgr. Western Pub. Co., N.Y.C., 1963-69; exec. v.p. David McKay Co. Inc., N.Y.C., 1969-74; pres. David McKay Co. Inc., 1974-86, Fodor's Travel Guides, 1978-86; v.p. Morgan-Grampian, Inc., 1982-86; pres. Editorial Ink Ltd., Durham, N.C., 1986-90. Author: Adobe Walls, 1963, The New Skipper's Bowditch, 1984; co-author: (with Eleanor Louttit) Bantam's Scotland, 1991. Served with USNR, 1942-46, PTO.

LOUTTIT, WILLIAM A., supermarket chain executive; b. 1946; married. Grad., CUNY City Coll. With Grand Union Co., Wayne, N.J., fin. analyst N.Y. region, 1973-75, v.p. L.I. div., 1975-80, sr. v.p. Atlanta div., 1980-81, 1st. sr. v.p. Atlanta, then from 1981, then exec. v.p. Atlanta ops., exec. v.p. merchandising, 1984—, also bd. dirs. Office: Grand Union Co 201 Willowbrook Blvd Wayne NJ 07470

LOUX, GORDON DALE, organization executive; b. Souderton, Pa., June 21, 1938; s. Curtis L. and Ruth (Derstine) L.; m. Elizabeth Ann Nordland, June 18, 1960; children: Mark, Alan, Jonathan. Diploma, Moody Bible Inst., Chgo., 1960; BA, Gordon Coll., Wenham, Mass., 1962; BD, No. Bapt. Sem., Oak Brook, Ill., 1965, MDiv, 1971; MS, Nat. Coll. Edn., Evanston,Ill., 1984; LHD (hon.), Sioux Falls Coll., 1985. Ordained to ministry, Bapt. Ch., 1965. Assoc. pastor Forest Park (Ill.) Bapt. Ch., 1962-65; alumni field dir. Moody Bible Inst., Chgo., 1965-66, dir. pub. rels., 1972-76; dir. devel. Phila. Coll. Bible, 1966-69; pres. Stewardship Svcs., Wheaton, Ill., 1969-72; exec. v.p. Prison Fellowship Ministries, Washington, 1976-84, pres., CEO, 1984-88; pres., CEO Prison Fellowship Internat., Washington, 1979-87, Internat. Students, Inc., Colorado Springs, Colo., 1988-93; pres. Stewardship Svcs. Group, Colorado Springs, 1994—. Author: Uncommon Courage, 1987, You Can Be a Point of Light, 1991; contbg. author: Money for Ministries, 1989, Dictionary of Christianity in America, 1989. Bd. dirs. Evang. Coun. for Fin. Accountability, Washington, 1979-92, vice chmn., 1981-84, 86-87, chmn., 1987-89; vice chmn. Billy Graham Greater Washington Crusade, 1985-85; bd. dirs. Evang. Fellowship of Mission Agys., 1991—. Named Alumnus of Yr., Gordon Coll., 1986. Mem. Broadmoor Golf Club (Colo. Springs). Republican. Home: 740 Bear Paw Ln Colorado Springs CO 80906-3215 Office: The Stewardship Svcs Group PO Box 60037 Colorado Springs CO 80960

LOUX, MICHAEL JOSEPH, philosophy educator; b. St. Paul, Aug. 17, 1942; s. Marvin Ralph and Magdalene (Klug) L.; m. Ann Kimble, June 11, 1966; children: Laurie, Michael, Christopher, Sandy, Julie. B.A., Coll. St. Thomas, 1964; A.M., U. Chgo., 1965, Ph.D., 1968. Asst. prof. philosophy U. Notre Dame, Ind., 1968-74, assoc. prof., 1974-79, prof. 1979—; chmn. dept. philosophy, 1982-83, dean Coll. Arts and Letters, 1983-91; vis. assoc. prof. philosophy U. Va., Charlottesville, 1976-77. Author: Substance and Attribute, 1978, Ockham's Theory of Terms, 1974, Primary Ousia: An Essay on Aristotle's Metaphysics Z and H, 1991; editor: Universals and Particulars, 1972, The Possible and the Actual, 1980. Democrat. Roman Catholic. Home: 3520 Windingwood Dr South Bend IN 46615-3128 Office: U Notre Dame Dept Philosophy Notre Dame IN 46556-0368

LOUX, NORMAN LANDIS, psychiatrist; b. Souderton, Pa., June 27, 1919; s. Abram Clemmer and Martha Wasser (Landis) L.; m. Esther Elizabeth Brunk, June 4, 1941; children—Philip Michael, Elizabeth Ann, Peter David. Student, Eastern Mennonite Coll., 1940-42; B.A., Goshen Coll. 1943; M.D., Hahnemann Med. Coll. 1946; postgrad., Yale, 1950-51. Intern Hahnemann Hosp., Phila., 1947; gen. practice medicine Souderton, 1947-48; psychiat. resident Butler Hosp., Providence, 1949-50; chief service, clin. dir. asst. supt. Butler Hosp., 1951-55; founder Penn Found. Mental Health, Inc., Sellersville, Pa., 1955; med. dir. Penn Found. Mental Health, Inc., 1955-80; chief Psychiat. Svc. Grand View Hosp., Sellersville, 1955-80; pres. med. staff Grand View Hosp., 1963-64; exec. com., joint conf. com. Mem. Gov.'s Adv. Com. for Mental Health and Mental Retardation, 1955-80; mem. Pa. State Bd. Pub. Welfare, 1971-85. Bd. dirs. Dock Woods Retirement Community, 1989—, Adult Communities Total Svcs. Inc., 1990—. Co-recipient Earl D. Bond award, 1964; recipient Achievement award Souderton Lions Cub, 1963, Community Svc. award B'nai B'rith, 1976, citation for achievements Mennonite Med. Assn., 1978; dept. of psychiatry Grand View Hosp. rededicated in his name, 1992. Fellow Am. Psychiat. Assn., A.C.P., Pa. Psychiat. Soc., Am. Coll. Psychiatrists; mem. AMA, Pa., Bucks County med. socs., Group for Advancement Psychiatry, Southeastern Mental Health Assn., Acad. Religion and Mental Health. Mem. Mennonite Ch. Home: 138 Cowpath Rd Souderton PA 18964-2007 Office: Penn Found Mental Health Inc PO Box 32 Sellersville PA 18960-0032

LOVE, BEN F., banker; b. Paris, Tex., Nov. 19, 1924; s. Benton F. and Nell Peyton (Scott) L.; m. Margaret Janelle McKean, Sept. 20, 1947; children: Jeffery Benton, Janelle Margaret, Julie McKean. BBA, U. Tex., 1948. Founded paper mfg. firm which merged with Gibson Greeting Card Co., 1962; pres. River Oaks Bank and Trust Co., Houston, 1965-67; sr. v.p. Tex. Commerce Bank Nat. Assn., 1967-68, exec. v.p., 1968-69, pres., 1969-72, chmn. bd., chief exec. officer, 1972-80; pres. Tex. Commerce Bancshares Inc., 1971-72, ret. chmn. bd., chief exec. officer, 1972-89, dir., cons.; pres. Assn. Res. City Bankers, 1981, hon. mem.; dir. Internat. Monetary Conf., 1986-88, ; bd. dirs. Burlington No. Inc., Cox Enterprises Inc., Enterprises, Inc., Eli Lilly and Co., Proler Internat. Corp., Mitchell Energy and Devel. Corp. Author: People and Profits: A Bank Case Study, 1968. Chmn. council of overseers Jesse H. Jones Grad. Sch. Adminstrn., Rice U. Capt. 8th Air Force, USAAF, 1943-45. Decorated 11 combat decorations including D.F.C.; recipient Disting. Alumnus award U. Tex., 1975; named Houston's Cultural Leader of Yr., 1977, Key Houstonian of Yr., 1982, Tex. Bus. Exec. of Yr., 1983; named to Tex. Bus. Hall of Fame, 1989. Presbyterian. Office: Boy Scouts Am PO Box 152079 1325 W Walnut Hill Ln Irving TX 75015

LOVE, BEN HOWARD, retired organization executive; b. Trenton, Tenn., Sept. 26, 1930; s. Ben Drane and Virginia (Whitehead); m. Ann Claire Hugo, Mar. 4, 1933; children: Ben H. Jr., Phillip H., Leigh Ann, Mark E. BS, Lambuth Coll., 1955, HHD (hon.), 1986; Dr. Philanthropy (hon.), Pepperdine U., 1987; LHD (hon.), Montclair State U. With Boy Scouts Am., 1955—; dist. exec., Jackson, Tenn., 1955-60; scout exec. Delta area council, Clarksdale, Miss., 1960-64; dir. Nat. council, North Brunswick, N.J., 1964-68; scout exec. Longhorn council, Ft. Worth, 1968-71; scout exec. Sam Houston council, Houston, 1971-73; dir. Northeast region, Dayton, N.J., 1973-85; chief scout exec. Nat. council, Irving, Tex., 1985-93; bd. dirs. Emperion Corp., Am. Gen. Series Portfolio Co., Mid-America Waste Systems Inc. Served with U.S. Army, 1951-52. Recipient Gold medal SAR, Bronze Wolf award World Scout Orgn. Republican. Presbyterian. Club: La Cima (bd. dirs. Irving chpt. 1985—). Avocations: tennis, golf, swimming, reading, spectator sports. Office: Boy Scouts Am Nat Coun 4407 Eaton Cir Colleyville TX 76034-4653

LOVE, CLINTON KENNETH, finance company executive; b. Corpus Christi, Tex., Dec. 7, 1952; s. Clinton Howard and Cherre Loucille (Cormany) L.; m. Jeanne Charlotte Waller, June 22, 1973; children: Chloe Marie, Jeanne Claire. BBA with honors, U. Tex., 1976. CPA; cert. mgmt. acct. Various positions Touche Ross & Co. (name changed to Deloitte & Touche 1989), Austin and Houston, Tex., 1976-86; ptnr. Touche Ross & Co. (name changed to Deloitte & Touche 1989), Chgo., 1987; ptnr.-in-charge Touche Ross & Co. (name changed to Deloitte & Touche 1989), Schaumburg, Ill., 1988-92; ptnr.-in-charge of audit Deloitte & Touche, Chgo., 1992—; nat. instr. Touche Ross & Co., 1980—; instr., guest speaker Tex. Soc. CPAs, Ill. CPA Soc., U. Tex., U. Ill., Nat. Assn. Accts. Contbg. editor: Financial Reporting Series, 1986; editorial advisor Jour. of Accountancy, 1984-86. Mem. bus. adv. coun. U. Ill., Champaign, 1988-89, Schaumburg Bus. Devel. Commn., 1988-90; mem. adv. coun. U. Tex. Sch. Bus. Dept. Acctg., Austin, 1991—; mem. steering com. Project Discovery, U. Ill., 1991—. Mem. AICPA (instr., guest speaker), Inst. CPAs, Mid-Am. Club. Office: Deloitte & Touche 2 Prudential Plz 180 N Stetson Ave Chicago IL 60601-6710

LOVE, DANIEL JOSEPH, consulting engineer; b. Fall River, Mass., Sept. 27, 1926; s. Henry Aloysius and Mary Ellen (Harrington) L.; m. Henrietta Maurisse Popper, June 10, 1950 (dec. Mar. 1986); children: Amy, Timothy, Terence, Kevin; m. Adeline Aponte Esquivel, Feb. 11, 1989; stepchildren: Eric, Brian, Jason. BSEE, Ill. Inst. Tech., 1951, MSEE, 1956; MBA, Calif. State U., Long Beach, 1973. registered profl. engr., Calif., Ariz., Ill., La.; cert. fire protection, Calif. Test engr. Internat. Harvester Co., Chgo., 1951-52; designer Pioneer Svc. & Engring. Co., Chgo., 1952-53; project engr., ops. mgr. Panellit Co., Skokie, Ill., 1953-60; mktg. mgr. Control Data Co., Mpls., 1961-62; mktg. mgr., asst. to pres. Emerson Electric Co., Pasadena, Calif., 1963-65; pres., gen. mgr. McKee Automation Co., North Hollywood, Calif., 1965-68; engring. specialist Bechtel Co., Vernon and Norwalk, Calif., 1968-80; chief elec. engr. Bechtel Co., Madrid, 1980-83; engring. specialist Bechtel Co., Norwalk, Calif., 1983-87; cons. engr. Hacienda Heights, Calif., 1987—. Contbr. articles to jours. in field. Pres. Wilson High Sch. Band Boosters, Hacienda Heights, 1971-73. With USN, 1944-46. Named Outstanding Engr., Inst. for Advancement Engring., 1986. Fellow IEEE (disting. lectr., chmn. Met. L.A. sect. 1973-74, chmn. L.A. coun. 1977-78, chmn. protection com. 1990-91, Richard Harold Kaufmann award 1994, Ralph H. Lee prize paper award 1995); mem. NSPE, Instrument Soc. Am. (sr.), Soc. Fire Protection Engrs. Republican. Roman Catholic. Avocations: duplicate bridge, travel, walking, writing. Home: 16300 E Soriano Dr Hacienda Heights CA 91745

LOVE, DAVID, accountant; b. Cambridge, Mass., Jan. 31, 1935. BS in Econs., U. Pa., 1956; JD, Harvard U., 1959. Bar: Mass.; CPA, Mass. Mng. ptnr. Laventhol & Horwath, Boston, 1974—. Office: Laventhol & Horwath 2 Center Plz Boston MA 02108-1906

LOVE, DAVIS, III, professional golfer. Mem. Ryder Cup Team, 1993. Winner The Internat., 1990, MCI Heritage Classic Champion, 1991, 92, Tournament Players Championship, 1992, 93, Greater Greensboro Open, 1992. Address: care PGA Tour 112 TPC Blvd Ponte Vedra Beach FL 32082-3046*

LOVE, EDITH HOLMES, theater producer; b. Boston, Oct. 17, 1950; d. Theodore Rufus and Mary (Holmes) L. Student, Denison U., 1968-72; BFA, U. Colo., 1973. Freelance designer various orgns., Atlanta, 1974-75; costumer Atlanta Children's Theatre, 1975-77; prodn. acct. David Gerber Co., L.A., 1980-81; bus. mgr. Alliance Theatre/Atlanta Children's Theatre, 1977-79, adminstrv. dir. 1981-83, gen. mgr., 1985-87; bd. dirs. Midtown Bus. Assocs., 1988-94; adv. bd. Stage Hands, Inc., Atlanta, 1983-89; exec. com. Prodn. Valves, Inc., Atlanta, 1985-89; adv. com. arts mgmt. program Carnegie Mellon U. Mem. Cultural Olympiad Task Force 1996 Summer Olympic Games, 1992—, Met. Atlanta Arts Fund Bd.; bd. dirs. Atlanta Convention and Visitor's Bur., 1990—. Recipient Deca award for Outstanding Bus. Women in Atlanta, 1992. Mem. League Resident Theatres (treas. 1987—), Atlanta Theatre Coalition (exec. com. 1987-91, pres. 1989), Atlanta C. of C. (bd. dirs. bus. coun. for arts 1988—), Leadership Atlanta. Office: Alliance Theatre Co 1280 Peachtree St NE Atlanta GA 30309-3502

LOVE, FRANKLIN SADLER, retired trade association executive; b. Rock Hill, S.C., Nov. 9, 1915; s. Franklin Sadler and Edna (Hull) L.; m. Jessie Huggins, Apr. 10, 1943; children: Judith (Mrs. J. Lindsay Freeman), Beverly (Mrs. Ronald Sparrow), Franklin Sadler III, Glenn. A.B., Presbyn. Coll., Clinton, S.C., 1937. Sec. Cotton Mfrs. Assn. S.C., Clinton, 1937-42, Am.

Cotton Mfrs. Assn., Charlotte, N.C., 1946-49; sec. treas. Am. Textile Mfrs. Inst., 1949-79, v.p., 1979-80, ret., 1980; speaker numerous civic and bus. groups; Adviser Internat. Cotton Adv. Com., 1958. Former mem. adv. bd. Charlotte Salvation Army; former bd. dirs. Charlotte Council on Alcoholism. Capt. Ordnance dept. AUS, 1942-46. Recipient Alumni citation for outstanding achievement Presbyn. Coll., 1955; certificate of merit Ala. Textile Mfrs. Assn., 1972. Mem. Def. Supply Assn. (pres. Carolinas chpt. 1952), Phi Psi, Rotary (pres. Charlotte chpt., del. internat. conf. 1961), Goodfellows Club (Charlotte), Charlotte Execs. Club (former sec.). Presbyterian. Home: 5100 Sharon Rd Charlotte NC 28210

LOVE, JEFFREY BENTON, lawyer; b. Houston, Oct. 4, 1949; s. Benton Fooshee and Margaret (McKean) L.; m. Katherine Brownlee, Dec. 30, 1972; children: Benton Fooshee III, Elizabeth Houston. BA, Vanderbilt U., 1971; JD, U. Tex., 1976. Bar: Tex. 1976. Assoc. Liddell, Sapp, Zivley Hill & LaBoon, L.L.P., Houston, 1976-81, ptnr., 1982—; adv. dir., 1990—, vice chmn. bd. dirs. nominating com. 1992—, Trust Audit Com. 1992—; dir. Tex. Commerce Bank-Houston, regional adv. bd., Kinark Corp., 1985-88, St. Luke's Episc. Hosp.; hon. consul gen. Sweden in Tex., 1983-89, U. Tex. Devel. Bd., 1991—; mem. com. for Tex. campaign U. Tex., 1992—; assoc. mem. bd. visitors U. Tex. M. D. Anderson Cancer Ctr., 1991—. Pres. Sunrisers Houston Breakfast Assn., Houston, 1979; dir. exec. com. Houston Grand Opera Assn., Houston, 1979-86; dir., chmn. Children's Fund, Inc., Houston, 1981-82; bd. dirs. Tex. Bus. Hall of Fame Found., chmn. bd. dirs., 1987, awards com. 1992—; bd. dirs. March of Dimes, Houston, 1986, chmn. 1989, bd. nominations com. 1992—; adv. dir. Eileen McMillin Blood Ctr., Meth. Hosp.; bd. govs., exec. com., sec. The Forum Club, 1987-92, The Hospice Tex. Med. Ctr. Cap. Campaign, 1991, St. John Divine Episcopal Ch. Cap. Campaign, 1992; bd. dirs., exec. com. Nat. Conf. Christians and Jews, Inc., 1987-90; mem. devel. council Tex. Children's Hosp., 1987—; mem. adv. bd. Covenant House Tex., 1988—; group chmn. frontier divsn. United Way, 1992; mem. fund-raising com. Houston READ Commn.-Campaign for Literacy, 1988—; Houston Internat. Festival: co-chmn., Mayor's Gala, 1993, group chmn. United Way Frontier Divsn., 1992, mem. underwriters com. Huston Ballet Ball, 1992, bd. dirs., co-chmn. fund raising Post Oak Little League, 1992, Post Oak Pony League, 1994; bd. dirs., mem. exec. com. Houston Youth Symphony & Ballet, 1990—, pres., 1992-93, chmn., emcee 1993 Cultural Leader of Yr. Dinner; bd. dirs. Grand Opera Assn., Houston, 1979-86; hon. chair Lupus Disease Benefit, 1992; mem. underwriters com. Houston Ballet Ball, 1992. Recipient Outstanding Young Texas Ex award U. Tex. Ex Students Assn., 1988, 5 Outstanding Young Houstonian awards Houston Jr. C. of C., 1988, 5 Outstanding Young Texan awards Tex. Jaycees, 1988; named one of Outstanding Young Men in Am., U.S. Jaycees, 1988; decorated Knighthood of Royal Order of North Star King Carl XVI Gustaf of Sweden, 1989. Mem. ABA, Houston C. of C., Houston Bar Assn., Tex. Bar Assn., Swedish Am. Trade Assn. (bd. dirs. 1983—), Swedish Am. C. of C., U. Tex. Law Alumni Assn. (bd. dirs. 1981—), nat. pres., chmn. exec. com. 1986-87), Phi Delta Theta Alumni Assn. Episcopalian. Clubs: River Oaks, Allegro, Houston. Home: 3744 Inwood Dr Houston TX 77019-3002 Office: Liddell Sapp Zivley Hill & LaBoon LLP 600 Travis St 3400 Texas Commerce Towers Houston TX 77002-3095

LOVE, JOHN WESLEY, JR., English language and reading educator; b. Springfield, Mo., May 1, 1932; s. John Wesley Sr. and Violet Mae (Bradshaw) L.; m. Virginia N. Kyser, 1960 (div. 1974); m. Edith Mae McNut, June 12, 1987; stepchildren: Karen Goodwin Davis, Dawn M. Goodwin. BS in English, S.W. Mo. State U., 1960; MA in Reading Edn., U. South Fla., 1968; EDS, Fla. State U., 1980, PhD in Edn., 1987. Tchr. Polk County Bd. Pub. Instrn., Bartow, Fla., 1957-69; prof. reading and English Polk C.C. Winter Haven, Fla., 1969—, adminstr., 1971-73, mem. faculty senate, 1978-89. Mem. Phi Delta Kappa. Office: Polk Community Coll 999 Avenue H NE Winter Haven FL 33881-4256

LOVE, JOSEPH L., history educator, cultural studies center administrator; b. Austin, Tex., Feb. 28, 1938; s. Joseph L. Sr. and Virginia (Ellis) L.; m. Laurie Reynolds, Dec. 23, 1978; children: Catherine R., David A.; children from previous marriage: James A., Stephen N. AB in Econs. with honors, Harvard U., 1960; MA in History, Stanford U., 1963; PhD in History with distinction, Columbia U., 1967. From instr. to prof. U. Ill., Urbana-Champaign, 1966—; dir. ctr. Latin Am. and Caribbean studies, 1993—; rsch. assoc. St. Antony's Coll. Oxford U., 1982; vis. prof. Pontifical Cath. U., Rio de Janeiro, 1987; presenter in field. Author: Rio Grande do Sul and Brazilian Regionalism, 1882-1930, 1971, São Paulo in the Brazilian Federation, 1889-1937, 1980; editor: (with Robert S. Byars) Quantitative Social Science Research on Latin America, 1973, (with Nils Jacobsen) Guiding the Invisible Hand: Economic Liberalism and the State in Latin American History, 1988; bd. editors Latin Am. Rsch. Rev., 1974-78, Hispanic Am. Hist. Rev., 1984-89, The Americas, 1995—; contbr. articles to profl. jours. Fulbright-Hays Rsch. grantee; vis. fellow Social Sci. Rsch. Coun., IREX, Guggenhiem, U. São Paulo Inst. Ortega y Gasset; Sr. Rsch. fellow NEH, others; Sr. Univ. Scholar, U. Ill., 1993—. Mem. Am. Hist. Assn., Conf. Latin Am. History (chair Brazilian studies com. 1973, mem. gen. com. 1983, Conf. prize 1971), Latin Am. Studies Assn. Unitarian. Office: U Ill Ctr Latin Am and Caribbean Studies 910 S 5th St Room 201 Champaign IL 61820

LOVE, KENNETH DEL, design company director, consultant; b. Evergreen Park, Ill., Apr. 9, 1940; s. Delbert Bouquet and Anne Dorthy (Pavlik) L.; m. Diane Althoff, June 6, 1961; children: Timothy Del, Damon Todd. BFA in Indsl. and Graphic Design, U. Ill., 1962; postgrad., Northwestern U. Designer Montgomery Ward, Chgo., 1962-63; design dir., exec. v.p. Peter Muller-Munk Assocs., Pitts., 1963-73; asst. dir. planning and design Finley-Green-InterAm. Trade and Culture Ctr., Miami, Fla., 1973-74; assoc. ptnr. Chermayeff & Geismar Assocs., N.Y.C., 1974-78; mng. ptnr., creative dir. Anspach Grossman Portugal, N.Y.C., 1978—; co-owner, ptnr., designer Maury Wills Stolen Base Restaurant, Pitts., 1969-72. Designer, creative dir. logos, symbols and media-wide application for numerous corps. including K-Mart, Texaco, Ameritech, Navistar, Borg Warner, Supervalu, BF Goodrich, Fidelity Investments, Time Warner, 1974—. Recipient Sun Logotype award Time mag., 1983, K-Mart Identity award Identity mag., 1991. Mem. Am. Inst. Graphic Artists (Design System award 1982-83, Unisys Identity award 1985-86), Design Mgmt. Inst., Conf. Bd. Avocations: American popular music, art, gardening, films. Office: Anspach Grossman Portugal 711 3rd Ave New York NY 10017-4014

LOVE, KENNETH EDWARD, real estate, investment and business consultant; b. Bamberg, S.C., Dec. 8, 1941; s. Murray Eugene and Mozelle (Bodiford) L.; widowed; children: Kenneth E. II, Karen C., Kimberly Ann. Student, So. Meth. U., 1960, Columbia Coll., 1961; BS in History, U. S.C., 1963. Magistrate State of S.C., Columbia, 1970-73; real estate broker Crown KEL, Inc., Columbia, 1973-87; exec. v.p. McDaniels So. Chems., Columbia, 1984—; pres. Crown KEL, Inc. Pub. Co., Columbia, 1986—; Owner Antiques Inc., Columbia, 1978—. Trustee Allen U., Columbia, 1973; mem. exec. com. S.C. Dem. Party, Columbia, 1962-74, chmn. 1971—; mem. U.S. Fgn. Affairs Panel, 1986—; chmn. So. East Dem. Regional Dist., 1994; mem. White Ho. Com. Policies. Served to sgt. USA Army, 1957-59. Named Outstanding Young Man Columbia City, 1972, Outstanding Dem. Nat. Dem. Party, 1992. Mem. S.C. Citizens and Merchants Assn. (pres. 1994—), Greater Columbia Assn. Avocations: woodworking, medical research reading, politics. Home: 500 Northwood Rd Lexington SC 29072 Office: Crown KEL Inc PO Box 42231 Columbia SC 29206-0001

LOVE, MARGARET COLGATE, lawyer; b. Balt., June 9, 1942; d. H.A. and Margaret West (Dennis) L.; 1 child, Jenny West. BA, Sarah Lawrence Coll., 1963; MA, U. Pa., 1969; JD, Yale U., 1977. Bar: Washington, 1977. Lawyer Shea & Gardner, Washington, 1977-79; spl. counsel office of legal counsel U.S. Dept. Justice, Washington, 1979-88, dep. assoc. atty. gen., 1988-89, assoc. dep. atty. gen., 1989-90, pardon atty., 1990—. Mem. ABA (standing com. on ethics and profl. responsibility chair 1994—). Office: Dept Justice 500 1st St NW 4th Fl Washington DC 20530

LOVE, MICHAEL KENNETH, lawyer; b. Richmond Height, Mo., Oct. 2, 1951; s. Clarence Kenneth and Helen (Schlapper) L.; m. Gloria Pia Miccioli, Sept. 8, 1979; children: Claire Pia, Patrick Kenneth. BS in Forestry, U. Mo., 1974; JD, George Washington U., 1977. Bar: Va. 1977, D.C. 1978, Md. 1981. Asst. dir. model procurement code project ABA, Washington, 1977-80; assoc. Wickwire, Gavin & Gibbs, P.C., Vienna, Va., 1980-84; ptnr.

Wickwire, Gavin & Gibbs, P.C., Vienna, 1984-86, Smith, Pachter, McWhorter & D'Ambrosio, Vienna, 1986—. Contbr. articles to profl. publs. Mem. ABA (chmn. subcontracting and constrn. com. pub. contract law sect. 1984-92, constrn. com. 1990-91, chair constrn. divsn. 1993-94), Am. Arbitration Assn., Nat. Contract Mgmt. Assn., Nat. Security Indsl. Assn., Va. Bar Assn. Office: Epstein Becker & Green 1227 25th St NW Washington DC 20037

LOVE, MIRON ANDERSON, judge; b. Houston, Oct. 25, 1920; s. Robert William and Josephine (Moody) L.; m. Marjorie Skiles, Dec. 21, 1948; children: Ross, Mark. BA, So. Meth. U., 1948; LLB, So. Tex. Law Sch., 1951. Bar: Tex. 1951, U.S. Dist. Ct. Tex. 1952, U.S. Supreme Ct. 1967. Asst. dist. atty. Harris County (Tex.) Dist. Atty.'s Office, Houston, 1951-53; pvt. practice Houston, 1953-58; adminstrv. judge 177th Dist. Ct., Harris County, Houston, 1958—. Pres. Nat. Conf. Met. Cts. 1st St. USAF, 1944-46, PTO. Mem. Internat. Acad. Trial Judges (mem. bd. regents). Democrat. Unitarian. Office: 177th Dist Ct 301 San Jacinto Rm 100 Houston TX 77002

LOVE, RICHARD EMERSON, equipment manufacturing company executive; b. N.Y.C., Dec. 15, 1926; s. Emerson C. and Ruth A. (Mealley) L.; m. Margaret A. Lloyd, June 24, 1950; children—Mary-Ann, Nancy, Jane, Thomas. Grad., N.Y. State Maritime Coll., 1946; AAS, Hofstra Coll., 1955. Group v.p. Crane Co., N.Y.C., 1967-72, U.S. Filter Co., N.Y.C., 1972-75; group pres. Peabody Internat. Corp., Stamford, Conn., 1975-77; exec. v.p. Peabody Internat. Corp., Stamford, 1978-85; group v.p. Pullman Co. (merged with Peabody Internat. Corp.), Stamford, 1985-87; v.p. ops. Hosokowa Micron Internat. Inc., N.Y.C., 1987-93; dir., cons. Hosokawa Micron Internat., N.Y.C., 1993—. Served with USN, 1948-49. Mem. ASME, Instruments Soc. Am. Office: Hosokowa Micron Internat Inc 780 3d Ave New York NY 10017

LOVE, RICHARD HARVEY, lawyer; b. Washington, Aug. 31, 1915; s. Leo Young and Grace Marie (Jett) L.; m. Betty Zane Schofield, Nov. 14, 1942 (dec. Sept. 1967); children: Richard, Robert, Edward, William, Elizabeth. AB, U. Md., 1936, LLB, 1938. Bar: Md., D.C. 1939. Law clk. U.S. Dist. Ct., Balt., Md., 1938-40; pvt. practice Washington, Md., 1940-41, 46—; counsel Bd. Zoning Appeals, Prince Georges County, Md., 1953-55. Editor Judge Adv. Jour., 1948-81. Served to maj. AUS, 1941-46; col. Judge Adv. Gen.'s Corps Res., 1946-75. Decorated Legion of Merit U.S. Army, 1972. Mem. ABA, Md. Bar Assn., Bar Assn. D.C., Prince Georges County Bar Assn., Judge Advocates Assn. (exec. sec. 1948-81, dir. emeritus 1981—), Res. Officers Assn., Mil. Order Fgn. Wars (past nat. comdr. gen.), Assn. U.S. Army, Army-Navy Club, Order of Coif, Phi Kappa Phi. Republican. Roman Catholic. Home: 6905 Carleton Ter College Park MD 20740-3620 Office: 6419 Baltimore Ave Riverdale MD 20737-1065

LOVE, ROBERT LYMAN, educational consulting company executive; b. Oswego, N.Y., July 28, 1925; s. Robert Barnum and Marion Alberta (Peavy) L.; m. Janet May Fuller, June 26, 1948; children: Robert H., Andrew L., Charles D., Cynthia S. Student, U. Rochester, 1943-44; A.B., Syracuse U., 1945, postgrad. in medicine, 1946-48, M.Ed., 1949; postgrad., Cornell U., 1963-64. Sci. tchr. Middlesex Valley Central Sch., Rushville, N.Y., 1949-53; mem. faculty Agrl. and Tech. Coll., SUNY-Alfred, 1953-81; prof., dean Agrl. and Tech. Coll., SUNY (Sch. Allied Health Techs.), until 1981, dean emeritus, 1981—; pres. Edn. Cons. Services, Alfred Station, N.Y., 1981—; former mem. bd. dirs. Nat. Tech. Inst. Deaf; program evaluation steering com. AMA; allied health reviewer HEW; chmn. health sub-com. 39th Congl. Dist. Author: He and She, An Introduction to Human Sexuality and Birth Control, 1970; editor: Upward Mobility for Lab Personnel, 1970. Fin. sec., mem. adminstrv. bd. Alfred United Meth. Ch.; mem. Roving Vols. in Christ's Svc., 1982-91, bd. dirs. 1984-86, 89-91, chmn. bd. dirs., 1989-90; mem. Selected Vols. in Christ's Svc., 1987-88; litercy vol.; pres., bd. dirs. Genesee Valley Habitat for Humanity, Inc., 1993-95; treas. 1995—; Allegany County Office for Aging Handyman's Svc. Fellow Sci. Tchrs. Assn. N.Y. State, Am. Soc. Allied Health Professions; mem. Gideons Internat. (past pres. Hornell Camp), Literacy Vols. Am. (bd. dirs. Allegany County chpt. 1990-93), Masons, Order Eastern Star. Republican. Home: 5366 Jericho Hill Rd Alfred Station NY 14803-9736 Office: Edn Cons Svc 5366 Jericho Hill Rd Alfred Station NY 14803-9736 *Having had the opportunity to work with young people has kept me young and knowing the Lord has saved me.*

LOVE, ROBERT WILLIAM, JR., retired physician, government administrator; b. Springfield, Mo., June 28, 1929; s. Robert William and Ruby Gladys (Teel) L.; m. Barbara Joyce Few, July 5, 1974; children—Robert William, III, Curry Maria, Rebecca Anne. A.B., Drury Coll., 1950; M.D., St. Louis U., 1954. Intern Kansas City (Mo.) Gen. Hosp., 1954-55, resident in surgery, 1955-59; staff surgeon VA Hosp., Asheville, N.C., 1961-62; chief gen. surgery VA Hosp., 1962-72, asst. chief surg. service, 1962-72; chief of staff VA Hosp., Mountain Home, Tenn., 1972-74; dir. field ops. VA Central Office, Washington, 1974-75; dir. ops. rev. and analysis, 1975-79; med. dir., evaluation and analysis office VA Central Office, 1979-85; dir. VA Outpatient Clinic, Pensacola, Fla., 1985-91; asst. clin. prof. surgery Duke U., 1967-72. Served to capt. M.C. USNR, 1959-61. Recipient dirs. commendation VA Hosp., Mountain Home, 1974, Adminstrs. commendation, VACO, 1985. Mem. A.C.S., Assn. VA Surgeons, Naval Res. Assn., Res. Officers Assn., Assn. Mil. Surgeons U.S., Escambia County Med. Soc., Alpha Omega Alpha. Research in magnification lymphangiographic radiography, Tb and gastric ulcer, med. treatment of spinal Tb. Home: 8774 Thunderbird Dr Pensacola FL 32514-5659

LOVE, RODNEY J., food distribution executive; b. 1938. BS, Okla. State U., 1962. With IGA Co., 1956—, advt. mgr., buyer, tng. and sales mgr., 1962-73; asst. mng. mgr. Assoc. Grocers Colo., Denver, 1974-77, v.p. ops., exec. v.p., gen. mgr., 1977-78, pres., chief exec. officer, 1978—, also bd. dirs.

LOVE, RODNEY MARVIN, retired judge, former congressman; b. Dayton, Ohio, July 18, 1908; s. Robert Marvin and Sallie Ray (Schenck) L.; m. Margaret Louise Sullivan, Dec. 29, 1934; children—Nancy, Robert. B.A., Ohio State U., 1930; LL.B., U. Dayton, 1933. Bar: Ohio bar 1933. Practiced in Dayton, 1933-45; probate judge, 1945-60; mem. 89th Congress from 3d Dist. Ohio; partner law firm of Smith & Schnacke, Dayton, 1960-64, 67-69; judge of Common Pleas Court, 1969-80. Former mem. bd. dirs. Ohio Mental Health Assn., Community Mental Health and Retardation; past pres. bd. trustees Ohio Soldiers and Sailors Orphans Home, Xenia. Mem. Ohio Bar Assn. (exec. com.), Dayton Bar Assn. (past pres.), Fed. Bar Assn., Ohio Common Pleas Judges Assn., Ohio Assn. Probate Ct. Judges (exec. com., past pres.). Democrat. Clubs: Mason (Dayton) (32 deg., Shriner), Sertoma (Dayton) (dist gov., past pres.); World Fixers. Home: 1701 Far Hills Ave Dayton OH 45419

LOVE, WARNER EDWARDS, biophysics educator; b. Phila., Dec. 1, 1922; s. J. Warner E. and Elizabeth (Ford) L.; m. Lois Jane Hosbach, Dec. 26, 1945; children: Rebecca Edwards, Michael Warner. B.A. in Zoology, Swarthmore Coll., 1946; Ph.D. in Physiology, Yale U., 1951. Fellow, then assoc. biophysics U. Pa., 1951-55; research fellow, then research assoc. physics Inst. Cancer Research, Fox Chase, Pa., 1955-57; faculty Johns Hopkins U., 1957—, prof. biophysics 1965—, dept. chmn., 1971-74, 80-83. Served with Am. Field Service, 1943-45, with U.S. Army, 1945-46. Mentioned in dispatches AFS. Research on x-ray crystal structure analysis of biol macro-molecules, particularly hemoglobins. Office: Johns Hopkins U 3400 N Charles St Baltimore MD 21218-2608

LOVE, WILLIAM EDWARD, lawyer; b. Eugene, Oreg., Mar. 13, 1926; s. William Stewart and Ola A. (Kingsbury) L.; m. Sylvia Kathryn Jaureguy, Aug. 6, 1955; children: Kathryn Love Petersen, Jeffrey, Douglas, Gregory. B.S., U. Notre Dame, 1946; M.A. in Journalism, U. Oreg., 1950, J.D., 1952. Bar: Oreg., 1952. Newspaper reporter Eugene Register Guard, 1943-44, 47-52; asst. prof. law, asst. dean Sch. Law U. Wash., Seattle, 1952-56; ptnr. Cake, Jaureguy, Hardy, Buttler & McEwen, Portland, Oreg., 1956-69; pres., chmn., chief exec. officer Equitable Savs. & Loan, Portland, 1969-82; sr. ptnr. Schwabe, Williamson & Wyatt, Portland, 1983—; chmn. Oreg. Savs. League, 1976; dir. Portland Gen. Electric, 1976-83, Fed. Home Loan Bank of Seattle, 1976-79, 85—, adv. council, Washington, 1978-80; exec. dir. Health, Housing, Ednl. & Cultural Facilities Authority, 1990—. Author: (with Jaureguy) Oregon Probate Law and Practice, 2 vols. 1958. Contbr. articles to profl. jours. Commr., past chmn. Oreg. Racing Commn., 1963-79; pres. Nat. Assn. State Racing Commrs., 1977-78; commr. Port of Portland, 1979-86, pres., 1983; referee Pac-10 football, 1960-81, Rose Bowl, 1981; active United Way, Boy Scouts Am., Portland Rose Festival, polit. campaigns; mem. adv. coun. Jockeys' Guild, Inc., 1990—. Served to lt. (j.g.), USN, 1944-47. Mem. Oreg. Bar Assn., Multnomah County Bar Assn. Republican. Clubs: Arlington, Multnomah Athletic, Golf (Portland). Home: 10225 SW Melnore St Portland OR 97225-4356 Office: Schwabe Williamson & Wyatt 1211 SW 5th Ave Portland OR 97204-3713

LOVEALL, CLELLON LEWIS, transportation administrator, civil engineer; b. Carthage, Tenn., June 13, 1938; s. Clellon Reuben and Blanche Mavis (Thompson) L.; m. Jane Ellen Johnson, July 16, 1960; children: Lisa Renee, Sharon Kay, Angela Dawn. B in Engring., Vanderbilt U., 1959. Lic. profl. engr. Bridge design engr. Tenn. Dept. Transp., Nashville, 1959-63, sr. bridge design engr., 1963-66, chief bridge design engr., 1966-69, asst. state bridge engr., 1969-78, state bridge engr., 1978-86, asst. dir. planning and devel., 1986—; keynote speaker U.S.-European Conf. on Bridge Evaluation, Repair, and Rehab., Paris, 1987, Engring. Found. Conf. Mng. Am.'s Aging Bridge Sys., 1989, Pitts. Internat. Bridge Conf., 1989, Western Bridge Engrs. Seminar, 1991, U.S.-European Workshop on Bridge Rehab., Darmstadt, Germany, 1992. Mem. ASCE (chpt. dir. com. redundancy, Govt. Civil Engr. of Yr. 1984), ASTM (sec. C-27.20 precast concrete structure), Am. Concrete Inst., Prestressed Concrete Inst. (bridge com.), Post Tensioning Inst. (charter mem., tech. adv. bd.), Segmental Bridge Inst., Am. Iron and Steel Inst. (steel bridge rsch. task force), Am. Assn. State Hwy. and Transp. Ofcls. (subcom. on design, subcom. bridges and structures 1987-92), Tenn. Soc. Profl. Engrs. (state dir., state sec., Nashville pres. 1986-87, Engr. of Yr. 1990), Transp. Rsch. Bd. Roman Catholic. Avocations: golf, tennis. Office: Tenn Dept Transp Bur Planning & Devel James K Polk Bldg 505 Deaderick St Ste 700 Nashville TN 37219

LOVEDAY, WILLIAM JOHN, hospital administrator; b. Lynn, Mass., Nov. 4, 1943; Married. B, Colby Coll., 1967; MHA, U. Chgo., 1970. Adminstrv. asst. Meml. Med. Ctr., Long Beach, Calif., 1970-71, asst. adminstr., 1971-74, v.p., 1974-82, exec. v.p., 1982-88; pres., chief exec. officer Meth. Hosp. Ind., Inc., Indpls., 1988—. Home: 7828 Traders Cove Ln Indianapolis IN 46254-9614 Office: Meth Hosp Ind PO Box 1367 Indianapolis IN 46206-1367

LOVEJOY, ALLEN FRASER, retired lawyer; b. Janesville, Wis., Oct. 9, 1919; s. Henry Stow and Mary Fraser (Beaton) L.; m. Betty Foote, Dec. 20, 1944; children: Jennifer Lovejoy Craddock, Charles F., Allen F. BA, Yale U., 1941, LLB, 1948. Bar: N.Y. 1949, U.S. Ct. Appeals (2d cir.) 1975. Assoc. Breed, Abbott & Morgan, N.Y.C., 1948-58, ptnr., 1958-87. Served with U.S. Army, 1944-46; ETO. Decorated Purple Heart with oak leaf cluster; recipient Frank M. Patterson award Yale U., 1941. Fellow Am. Numis. Soc. (life, councillor 1988—, 1st v.p. 1990—). Am. Numis. Assn. Republican. Episcopalian. Clubs: Pilgrims (N.Y.C.); Mid Ocean (Bermuda); Stanwich (Greenwich, Conn.); Riverside (Conn.) Yacht. Author: La Follette and the Establishment of the Direct Primary in Wisconsin, 1890-1904, 1941; co-author: Early United States Dimes, 1796-1837, 1984; contbr. articles to numismatic publs. Home: 100 Club Rd Riverside CT 06878-2032

LOVEJOY, BARBARA CAMPBELL, sculptor, architectural designer; b. Detroit, Oct. 31, 1919; d. Robert Bruce and Mona (Goodwin) Campbell; m. William Edward Gibson, Oct. 27, 1941 (dec. Aug. 1969); children: Linda Dean Gibson Stoner, William Kent; m. John Marshall Lovejoy, Jan. 27, 1971 (dec. Nov. 1994). B of Design, Tulane U., 1941; studied sculpture with Lothar Kestenbaum; also studied with Yuri Hollosy, New Orleans. Archtl. designer Aurora Devel. Co., New Orleans, 1950-60; pvt. practice archtl. design New Orleans, 1960-70; chief designer D.H. Holmes Store Planning, New Orleans, 1970-78; dir. store planning and interior design Wray Williams Display Co., New Orleans, 1978-86. One-woman shows include D.H. Homes Canal St. Window Exhbn., New Orleans, 1981, Kaplan'a Art Exhibit, Alexandria, La., 1983, 85, Ea. Art Assoc., Fairhope, Ala., 1985; exhibited in group shows at Salon de Refuses, New Orleans, 1967, Edgewater Mall, 1980, New Orleans Commodity Exchange, 1982, Palm Beach (Fla.) Art Galleries, 1984, (Patron's award in sculpture 1983), Peyton Meml. Arts Festival, Alexandria, 1983-85, 91, 93 (Patron's award 1983, Spl. Purchase award 1984), U. New Orleans Gallery, 1983-84, St. Tammany Art Assn., Covington, La., 1984, 90, New Orleans Women's Caucus for Art, 1985, New Orleans Acad. Art Summer Group Show, 1985, New Orleans Ctr. Contemporary Art, 1984-86, Grand Festival Art at Grand Hotel, Point Clear, La., 1985, 87, La. Women Artists, Baton Rouge, 1987, 5th Juried Exhbn. for La. Artists, 1987-88, Decatur Arts Alliance, 1990, Memphis Arts Festival, 1990 (Patron's award in sculpture), Mystic Conn. Art Gallery, 1991, Artist in Still Zinsel Gallery, New Orleans, 1988-91, Miriam Walmsley Gallery, 1992, Masur Mus. Art, Monroe, La., 1992, 95, La. Competition, Baton Rouge, 1993, 95, Art for Advocacy, La., 1993, 95, Carol Robinson Gallery, 1994-95. Recipient 1st place Painting award Chevron Art Exhibition, 1965, 66, 1st Place Sculpture award Nat. Art Appreciation Soc., 1984, numerous other awards New Orleans Mus. Art, 1985, Art for Advocacy, 1993. Mem. Am. Soc. Interior Designers (prof.), Women's Caucus for Art, Southeastern Women's Caucus for Art. Presbyterian. Home and Studio: 100 Finland Pl New Orleans LA 70131

LOVEJOY, RAY, film editor. Editor: (films) 2001: A Space Odyssey, 1968, The Ruling Class, 1972, A Day in the Death of Joe Egg, 1972, Fear Is the Key, 1973, Little Malcolm and His Struggle Against the Eunuchs, 1974, Ghost in the Noonday Sun, 1974, The Shining, 1980, Krull, 1983, The Dresser, 1983, Sheena, 1984, Eleni, 1985, Aliens, 1986, Suspect, 1987, The House on Carroll Street, 1988, Batman, 1989, Homeboy, 1989, Mr. Frost, 1990, Year of the Comet, 1992, A Far Off Place, 1993. Office: Sandra Marsh Mgt 9150 Wilshire Blvd Ste 220 Beverly Hills CA 90210*

LOVEJOY, THOMAS EUGENE, tropical and conservation biologist, association executive; b. N.Y.C., Aug. 22, 1941; s. Thomas Eugene and Audrey Helen (Paige) L.; m. Charlotte Seymour, 1966 (div. 1978); children: Elizabeth Paige and Katherine Seymour (twins), Anne Williams. BS, Yale U., 1964, PhD in Biology, 1971; DSc (hon.), Colo. State U., 1989, Williams Coll., 1990; LHD (hon.), Lynn U., 1991. Co-chmn. premed. adv. bd. U. Pa., 1971-72; exec. asst. to sci. dir. Acad. Natural Scis., Phila., 1972-73, asst. to v.p. for resources and planning, 1972-73; program dir. World Wildlife Fund-U.S., Washington, 1973-78, v.p. for sci., 1978-85, exec. v.p., 1985-87; asst. sec. environ. & external affairs Smithsonian Instn., Washington, 1987-94, counselor to sec. for biodiversity and environ. affairs, 1995—; sci. advisor to Sec. Interior, 1993; bd. dirs. Manhattan Life Ins. Co., N.Y.C., chmn. exec. com. 1982-87, dir., 1986—; rsch. assoc. in ornithology Acad. Natural Scis., 1971—; bd. dirs. Wildlife Preservation Trust Internat., 1974—; bd. dirs. Henry Fdn. for Botanical Rsch. 1975—; prin. advisor Minimum Critical Size of Ecosys. Project, 1979—; mem. commn. ecology IUCN, 1980—; founder, advisor Nature series Sta. WNET, 1980—; vis. lectr. on tropical ecology Yale U. Sch. Forestry and Environ. Studies, 1982. Co-author: Nearctic Avian Migrants in the Neotropics, 1983; co-editor: Key Environments: Amazonia, 1985, Conservation of Tropical Forest Birds, 1985, Global Warming and Biological Diversity, 1992; contbr. articles, chpts. to profl. publs. Mem. Smithsonian Coun., 1982-87; trustee Millbrook Sch., N.Y., 1971—, Rocky Mountain Biol. Lab., 1983—, Acad. Natural Scis. Phila., 1987—, The Ozone Soc., 1990—, U.S.-Brazil panel White House Office of Sci. and Tech., Washington, 1986-87; past chmn. U.S. Man and Biosphere Com., 1987—; treas., mem. exec. com. Sci. Com. on Problems of the Environ., 1988-91; sec. J. Paul Getty Wildlife Conservation prize, Washington, 1974-87, jury mem. 1988—; mem. adv. & tech. bd. Fundacion Neotropica and de Parques Nacional, Costa Rica, 1987—; mem. White House Sci. Coun., exec. office Pres., 1988-90; mem. Pres.'s Coun. Advisors in Sci. & Tech., 1990-92; dir. Rainforest Alliance, 1988—; sci. coun. FPCN (Conservation Found., Peru), 1988—; mem. adv. bd. Am. Soc. Protection Nature Israel, 1988—; coprin. investigator World Wildlife Fund/INPA, North Manaus, Brazil, 1979—; bd. govs. N.Y. Botanical Garden, N.Y.C., 1986—; dir. Ctr. for Plant Conservation, 1987—; bd. dirs. Fundacion Maquipucuna, Ecuador, 1988—; Resources for the Future, 1989—, World Resources Inst., 1989—, Peruvian Cultural Ctr., 1989—. Grantee Nat. Geog. Soc., NIH, NSF, Mellon Found., Rockefeller Found.; recipient Ibero-Am. award II Ibero Am. Ornithological Congress, 1983, Cert. of Merit, Goeldi Mus., 1985, 50th Anniversary medal Brazilian Nat. Parks, 1987, Carr medal Fla. Mus. Natural History, 1990;

named comdr. Order of Merit of Mato Grosso, 1987, comdr. Order of Rio Branco, Brazil, 1988, UN Environment Programme Global 500 Roll of Honour, 1992. Fellow AAAS (wildlife panel 1981), N.Y. Zool. Soc., Linnean Soc. London, Am. Ornithologists Union; mem. Am. Inst. Biol. Scis. (bd. dirs. 1989—, pres. 1991-92), Ecol. Soc. Am., Brit. Ecol. Soc., Brit. Ornithologists Union, Cooper Ornithol. Soc., Soc. Study of Evolution, Internat. Union for Conservation of Nature (species survival commn.), Soc. for Conservation Biology (gov. 1986-89, pres. 1989-91), Century Club, Cosmos Club, Knickerbocker Club, New Haven Lawn Club. Home: 8526 Georgetown Pike Mc Lean VA 22102-1206 Office: SI 317 Smithsonian Instn Washington DC 20560

LOVEJOY, WILLIAM JOSEPH, automotive company executive; b. Bklyn., Sept. 2, 1940; s. William G. and Catherine J. (Barry) L.; m. Geraldine V. Smith, Feb. 12, 1966; children: William Jerome, Catherine Elizabeth. BS, St. Francis Coll., 1975; MBA, Fairleigh Dickinson U., 1981. Teller First Nat. City Bank, Bklyn., 1959-62; mem. credit staff GMAC, Bklyn., 1962-71; mgr. GMAC, Parsippany, N.J., 1974-75; asst. control mgr. GMAC, Washington, 1975-78; regional mgr. GMAC, Denver, 1981-84; group v.p. mktg. GMAC, Detroit, 1988-89, exec. v.p. ops., 1990, pres., 1990-92; gen. mgr. GM Svc. Parts Operation, Flint, Mich., 1992—. With U.S. Army, 1961-62. Avocations: swimming, bicycling. Office: GM Svc Parts Operation 6060 W Bristol Rd Flint MI 48503

LOVELACE, BYRON KEITH, lawyer, management consultant; b. Vernon, Tex., Feb. 15, 1935; s. Joseph Edward and Hattie Pearl (Brians) L.; m. Sandra Alene Daniel, June 17, 1961; children: Kirk Daniel, Bethany Alene, Amy Kathleen. BS in Chem. Engring., U. Tex., 1958, MS, 1961, PhD, 1973; JD, South Tex. Coll. Law, 1978. Bar: Tex. 1978. R & D engr. Core Labs., Dallas, 1960-61; with Tex. Instruments, Inc., Dallas and Houston, 1961-78, mgr. process control for advanced tech., 1969-70, reliability mgr. metal oxide semicondr. (MOS) div., 1971-75, MOS reliability dir., 1975-78; pres. P-V-T Inc., Houston, 1978-80, Mgmt. Resources Internat., Houston, 1980—; pvt. practice Law Offices of Keith Lovelace, Houston, 1980—. Contbr. articles to profl. jours.; patentee in field. Mem. Houston Clean City Commn., 1991-94. With U.S. Army, 1953. Tex. Instruments fellow, 1965-68; FMC Corp. fellow, 1958-60; Eastern States Petroleum and Chem. scholar, 1957-58; Ethyl Corp. scholar, 1956-57. Mem. ABA, Am. Chem. Soc. (award 1958), Am. Inst. Chem. Engrs., Soc. Petroleum Engrs. (vice chmn. reservoir group 1979-80), State Bar Tex., Trial Lawyers Am., S.W. Houston C. of C. (bd. dirs. 1988-91, pres. 1990-91), Tau Beta Pi (chpt. v.p. 1958-59), Omega Chi Epsilon. Home: 11580 S Kirkwood Rd Stafford TX 77477-1304 Office: Ste 1480 7322 SW Fwy Houston TX 77074

LOVELACE, ELDRIDGE HIRST, retired landscape architect, city planner; b. Kansas City, Kans., Mar. 16, 1913; s. Charles Wilson and Eva (Hirst) L.; m. Marjorie Van Evera, May 15, 1937; children: Jean (Mrs. William C. Stinchcombe), Richard. B.F.A. in Landscape Architecture, U. Ill., 1935. Registered profl. engr., Mo. With Harland Bartholomew & Assocs., Inc., St. Louis, 1935—81; mem. firm Harland Bartholomew & Assocs., Inc., 1943-79, chmn. bd., 1979—81; cons., 1981—; prepared comprehensive city plans numerous cities including Toledo, Baton Rouge, Oklahoma City, Vancouver, Waco, Lincoln, Washington; master plans for naval facilities Hawaiian Islands and P.I.; also plans parks, subdivs., housing projects; Vice pres. Internat. Fedn. Landscape Architects, 1975-77, sec. gen., 1980—81. Author: Harland Bartholomew: His Contributions to American Urban Planning. Mem. bd. commrs. Tower Grove Park, 1971—, pres. 1986-94. Fellow Am. Soc. Landscape Architects (past sec.), ASCE; mem. Am. Inst. Cert. Planners. Clubs: Mo. Athletic (St. Louis). Home: 5 Brookside Ln Saint Louis MO 63124-1814

LOVELACE, JON B., investment management company executive; b. Detroit, Feb. 6, 1927; s. Jonathan Bell and Marie (Andersen) L.; m. Lillian Pierson, Dec. 29, 1950; children: Carey, James, Jeffrey, Robert. A.B. cum laude, Princeton U., 1950. Personnel asst. Pacific Finance Co., 1950-51; with Capital Research & Mgmt. Co., L.A., 1951—, treas., 1955-62, v.p., 1957-62, exec. v.p., 1962-64, pres., 1964-75, 82-83, chmn. bd., 1975-82, 83—, also dir.; chmn. bd. Investment Co. Am., 1982—, Capital Income Builder, 1987—; Am. Mut. Fund Inc., 1971—; bd. dirs. Capital Research Co., 1967—, Am. Pub. Radio; pres., dir. New Perspective Fund. Trustee Claremont McKenna Coll.; mem. bd. fellows Claremont U. Ctr.; mem. adv. bd. Stanford U. N.E. Asia/U.S. Forum on Internat. Policy; trustee Calif. Inst. Arts, chmn., 1983-88; trustee Santa Barbara Med. Found. Clinic, J. Paul Getty Mus., chmn. 1988—. Mem. Council on Fgn. Relations, Sierra Club. Clubs: Princeton (N.Y.C.), University (N.Y.C.); Calif. (Los Angeles). Home: 333 S Hope St Fl 52 Los Angeles CA 90071-1406 also: 780 El Bosque Rd Santa Barbara CA 93108-1310 Office: J Paul Getty Trust 401 Wilshire Blvd Ste 1000 Santa Monica CA 90401

LOVELACE, JULIANNE, library director; b. Jackson, Miss., July 30, 1941; d. Benjamin Travis and Julia Elizabeth (Knight) Robinson; m. William Frank Lovelance, July 6, 1963 (div. Mar. 17, 1972); 1 child, Julie Lynn. BA in History, So. Meth. U., 1963; MLS, U. North Tex., 1970. Clk. Dallas Pub. Libr., 1963-64, children's libr. asst., 1964-66, children's libr., 1966-69; libr. Richardson (Tex.) Pub. Libr., 1971-72, supr. pub. svcs., 1972-87, dir., 1987—. Bd. dirs. Richardson unit Am. Cancer Soc.; mem. exec. bd. Youth Svcs. Coun., Richardson Adult Literacy Ctr.; mem. Altrusa Internat., Inc. Richardson, Leadership Richardson Alumni Assn., Friends of the Richardson Pub. Libr. Mem. ALA, Tex. Libr. Assn., Pub. Libr. Adminstrs. North Tex. Avocations: horse racing, blackjack. Office: Richardson Pub Libr 900 Civic Center Dr Richardson TX 75080-5210

LOVELACE, ROBERT FRANK, health science facility administrator, researcher; b. Elizabethton, Tenn., Oct. 7, 1950; s. Douglas Clayton and Doris Ivalee (Guy) L.; m. Diane Marie Wamsley, June 3, 1972; children: Jason Robert, Geoffrey Mark. BS, Phila. Coll. Bible, 1972; MA, Ea. Sem., Phila., 1974; PhD, Temple U., 1988. Lic. nursing home adminstr. Adminstr. research The Franklin Inst., Phila., 1974-79, adminstr. contracts, 1979-81; dir. research adminstrm. The Grad. Hosp., Phila. 1981-88; adminstr. Elm Terr. Gardens, Lansdale, Pa., 1988—; adj. lectr. Temple U., Phila., 1983-86, Wilkes Coll., 1986-90, Rutgers U., 1989-93, St. Joseph's U., 1993—; exec. dir., sec.-treas. GRadtech, Phila., 1985-88. Contbr. articles to profl. jours. V.p., bd. dirs. Elm Terr. Gardens, Lansdale, 1986-88; dir. bd. Christian edn. 1st Bapt. Ch., Lansdale, 1985-88, 90-96, chmn. program com., 1987-90, chmn. worship svcs. com., 1992. Mem. Am. Coll. Health Care Adminstrs., Nat. Coun. Univ. Rsch. Adminstrs., Soc. Rsch. Adminstrs. (mem. editorial bd. jour. 1986-90), Rsch. and Devel. Mgmt. Assn. Republican. Home: 553 Millers Way Lansdale PA 19446-4059 Office: Elm Terr Gardens 660 N Broad St Lansdale PA 19446-2361

LOVELADY, STEVEN M., newspaper editor; b. Morganfield, Ky., July 2, 1943; s. Talmage C. and Virginia Dell (Fortenberry) L.; m. Linda R. Higgins, June 18, 1965 (div. Apr. 1979); children—Stephanie, Sara; m. Ann Judith Kolson, Apr. 30, 1979. B.J., U. Mo., 1965. Midwest corr. Wall Street Jour., Chgo., 1965-66; west coast corr. Wall Street Jour., Los Angeles, 1966-69; page 1 rewriteman Wall Street Jour., N.Y.C., 1969-72; asst. mng. editor Phila. Inquirer, 1972-75, assoc. mng. editor, 1975-80, assoc. exec. editor, 1980-91, mng. editor, 1991—; directed Pulitzer prize-winning news coverage, 1977, 79, 85, 87, 88, 89; Pulitzer prize juror, 1989, 90; seminar leader Poynter Inst., St. Petersburg, Fla., 1981, 82, 85, 87. Active Center City Phila. Residents Assn. Mem. AP Mng. Editors. Avocation: breeding and racing thoroughbred horses. Office: Phila Inquirer 400 N Broad St Philadelphia PA 19130-4099

LOVELAND, DONALD WILLIAM, computer science educator; b. Rochester, N.Y., Dec. 26, 1934; s. Roger Platt and Dorothy (Dobbin) L.; m. Amy Straw, May 21, 1966; children: Robert Philip, Douglas Roger. AB, Oberlin Coll., 1956; SM, MIT, 1958; PhD, NYU, 1964. Mathematician, programmer IBM, Yorktown Heights, N.Y., 1958-59; asst. prof. math. NYU, 1964-67; asst. prof., then assoc. prof. math. and computer sci. Carnegie-Mellon U., Pitts., 1967-73; prof., chmn. dept. computer sci. Duke U., Durham, N.C., 1973-78, 91-92, prof. computer sci., 1973—; disting. faculty visitor IBM Rsch. Ctr., Yorktown Heights, 1979-80; program chmn., editor procs. 6th Conf. on Automated Deduction, 1982, trustee corp. controls, 1994—. Author: Automated Theorem Proving: A Logical Basis, 1978; co-editor: (with W.W. Bledsoe) Automated Theorem Proving: After 25

Years, 1984; mng. editor book series Artificial Intelligence, 1983-92; editorial bd. Artificial Intelligence, 1983-93, Jour. Automated Reasoning. Grantee NSF, 1970-73, 75-77, 88-92, 92—, Air Force Office Sci. Rsch., 1981-86, Army Rsch. Office, 1984-91. Mem. Assn. for Computing Machinery, Assn. for Symbolic Logic, Am. Assn. for Artificial Intelligence (elected fellow 1993), AAAS. Home: 3417 Cambridge Dr Durham NC 27707-4507 Office: Duke Univ Box 90129 Durham NC 27708-0129

LOVELAND, EUGENE FRANKLIN, petroleum executive; b. Anderson, Ind., Sept. 11, 1920; s. Irving Eugene and Clare (McFarlane) L.; m. Joan King, Aug. 4, 1944; children: Jeffrey, David C. and Peter F. (twins), Mark, Laurie E. B.A., Wesleyan U., Middletown, Conn. With Shell Oil Co., 1946-80, v.p. central mktg. region, 1968-71; v.p. oil products Shell Oil Co., Houston, 1972-80; pres. Transworld Oil USA, Inc. (formerly T.W. Oil Inc.), Houston, 1981—; chmn., chief exec. officer T.W. Oil Inc., 1983-89, ret., 1989; bd. dirs. Transworld Oil Ltd., Bermuda. Bd. dirs. Lyric Theatre, Houston, Am. Dance Cos.; chmn. Houston Ballet Found., Combined Arts Corp., Campaign, Houston, Greater Houston Skating Coun., vice chmn. Better Bus. Bur., Houston; hon. counsul gen. Republic of Malta in Tex.; dir. Cultural Arts Coun. Houston, 1989-93; chmn. Greater Houston Ice Skating Coun., 1989—; mem. exec. com. Houston Internat. Festival, 1992; chmn. devel. commn. Fay Sch., 1992. With USNR, 1943-45. Decorated D.F.C., Air medal (2); recipient Disting. Alumnus award Wesleyan U., 1993. Mem. Mil. and Hospitaller Order St. Lazarus Jerusalem, Petroleum Club of Houston. Office: Transworld Oil USA Inc 654 N Belt Dr E Ste 400 Houston TX 77060-5993

LOVELESS, EDWARD EUGENE, education educator, musician; b. Lafayette, Ind., July 29, 1919; s. Benjamin Moses and Belva Lucille (Bowles) L.; m. Jean Evelyn Skinner, May 18, 1941; children: Linda Louise Loveless Reeder, Kathleen Beal Loveless Bodine, Stephen Edward, Melissa Jane Loveless Campbell, Benjamin Warwick. B.S., Purdue U., 1940, M.S., 1941; Ed.D., Stanford U., 1960. Tchr., prin., supt. public schs. Ind., 1941-57; asst. Stanford U., 1957-60; prin. public schs. Palo Alto, Calif., 1961-65; asst. prof. sch. adminstrn. San Francisco State Coll. and assoc. prof. San Jose State Coll., 1960-65; assoc. prof. U. Nev., Reno, 1965-72; prof. U. Nev., 1972-85, prof. emeritus, 1986—; vis. prof. Purdue U., summers 1965, 68, 75; prof. exec. devel. program USAF, Crete, spring 1973. Author: (with Frank Krajewski) The Teacher and School Law: Cases and Materials in the Legal Foundations of Education, 1974, (with J. Clark Davis) The Administrator and Educational Facilities, 1982; contbr. over 70 articles to profl. jours.; editor: Who's Who in Northern Nevada Education, 1976; spkr. on sch. vandalism; clarinetist, saxaphonist, vocalist Jean and Ed (musical duo), 1984—; musical tours Ms World Discoverer, Singapore, The South Seas, New Guinea, Western Samoa, Tonga, Fiji, Tahiti, others, 1984-85; performance South Pacific Coll., Stanford U. Alumni Assn., 1985; command performance King Tauf-ahau Tupou IV, Tonga, 1985; commd. performance Trident submarine USS Nev., 1986; concert U.S. Embassy, Geneva, Switzerland, 1987; recs. include Songs of the 30's and 40's, The Gershwin Bros., The Best of Irving Berlin, Jerome Kern Favorites, Hoagy & Benny Revisited, An Evening with Cole Porter, We Like Rodgers & Hart, The Genius of Duke Ellington, Easy Listening, Songs of Jule Styne, A Tribute to Jimmy Van Heussen, Rodgers and Hammerstein Music, 1989, cassette tape series for Wickenburg (Ariz.) Hist. Mus., 1989, Golden Anniversary performance Purdue U., 1990, 74th Birthdays Cassette, 1993. Performer, concert artist for retirement homes and hosps., Palo Alto, Calif., 1990—. Recipient Commendations for providing benefit concerts and performances Sierra Health Care Ctr., 1985, Salvation Army Family Emergency, 1986, VA Hosp., 1988, Daus. of Norway, 1988, Westwood Retirement Home, 1989, State of Nev. Employees Assn., 1989; recipient Certs. of Appreciation Riverside Hosp., 1986, Carson Convalescent Ctr., 1987, Reno Lions Club, 1987, Thank-U-Gram Physicians Hosp., 1988, Manor at Lakeside, 1988, award Washoe County Sr. Citizens Ctr., 1989, Sharon Heights Convalescent Hosp., Palo Alto, Calif., 1993. Mem. NEA, Nev. Edn. Assn., Internat. Soc. Gen. Semantics, Nat. Soc. Profs., Navy League, Kappa Sigma, Phi Delta Kappa (cert. for disting. service 1974, placque of appreciation Gamma Psi chpt. 1976). Democrat. Presbyterian (elder). Home: 2895 W Moana Ln Reno NV 89509-7802 also: 2170 Princeton Palo Alto CA 94306

LOVELESS, GEORGE GROUP, lawyer; b. Baldwinsville, N.Y., Sept. 16, 1940; s. Frank Donald and Mayme (Lont) L.; m. Shirley Morrison, Nov. 27, 1965; children: Michael, Peter. BS, Cornell U., 1962, MBA, 1963; JD, U. Md., 1968. Bar: Pa. 1969, U.S. Dist. Ct. (ea. dist.) Pa., U.S. Ct. Appeals (3d cir.). Ptnr. Morgan, Lewis & Bockius, Phila., 1968—. With USAFR, 1963-68. Republican. Presbyterian. Home: 11 Rose Valley Rd Moylan PA 19063-4217 Office: Morgan Lewis & Bockius 2000 One Logan Sq Philadelphia PA 19103

LOVELESS, JAMES KING, art educator; b. Saginaw, Mich., Apr. 24, 1935; s. James Clifton and Edris Maureen (King) L.; m. Ruthann Speer, Oct. 5, 1974; children—Elizabeth, Ellen, Karen, Douglas, David. A.B., DePauw U., 1957; M.F.A., Ind. U., 1960. Asst. prof. art Hope Coll., Holland, Mich., 1960-64; asst. prof. U. Ky., Lexington, 1964-66; prof. Colgate U., Hamilton, N.Y., 1966—. One-man shows include: Everson Mus., Syracuse, N.Y., 1978, Fine Arts Gallery, SUNY, Oneonta, 1984; exhibited in group shows: Munson-Williams-Proctor Inst., Utica, N.Y., 1979, traveling exhbn. sponsored by Mus. Am. Art, Washington; 1981-83; represented in permanent collection: Munson-Williams-Proctor Inst., Utica, Picker Gallery, Colgate U., Hamilton, N.Y., Chase Manhattan Bank, N.Y.C., Gettysburg (Pa.) Coll. Fellow Yaddo Millay Colony. Mem. Hamilton Club. Home: RR 1 Box 124 Hamilton NY 13346-9737 Office: Colgate Univ Dept Fine Arts Hamilton NY 13346

LOVELESS, PATTY (PATTY RAMEY), country music singer; b. Pikeville, Ky., Jan. 4, 1957; m. Terry Lovelace (div.); m. Emory Gordy, Jr., Feb. 1989. Recording artist MCA, 1985-93, Sony Music, 1993—. Albums: Patty Loveless, 1987, If My Heart Had Windows, 1988, Honky Tonk Angel, 1988 (gold), On Down the Line, 1990, Up Against My Heart, 1991, Only What I Feel, 1993, Greatest Hits, 1993, When Fallen Angels Fly, 1994; # 1 hit singles Timber, I'm Falling in Love, Chains. Named Favorite New Country Artist by Am. Music Awards, 1989; recipient TNN Music City News Country Award, Female Artist, 1990; inductee Grand Ole Opry, 1988. Office: PO Box 4450 New York NY 10101-4450*

LOVELL, CARL ERWIN, JR., lawyer; b. Riverside, Calif., Apr. 12, 1945; s. Carl Erwin and Hazel (Brown) L.; m. Danna I. Wale; children: Carl Erwin III, Timothy C., Tishia R., Ashley P., Garrett T. BA, Vanderbilt U., 1966, JD, 1969. Bar: Nev. 1969, D.C. 1971, U.S. Supreme Ct. 1973. Jr. editor Land and Water Law View, 1973-89; instr. bus. law U. Nev., Las Vegas, Clark County C.C.; city atty. City of North Las Vegas, Nev., 1970-73, City of Las Vegas (elected), 1973-77; v.p., sec.-treas., legal counsel Circus Circus Hotels, Inc., Las Vegas, 1977-83; sr. ptnr. Lovell, Bilbray & Potter, Las Vegas, 1984-89; pvt. practice, 1989—; legal counsel Gold Coast Hotel & Casino, 1989—; v.p., dir. Air Nev. Airlines, Inc. Bd. dirs., v.p. Better Bus. Bur., 1983-91; chmn. NCCJ; pres. Clark County Young Dems., 1971-72; chmn. Nat. Inst. Mcpl. Law Officers Consumer Protection Adv. Com., 1973-77, Nev. Crime Commn. Bd., 1974-77; U.S. rep. to China Internat. Trade and Law Talks, 1987; arbitrator, AAA, 1989—; bd. dirs. Nat. Kidney Found.; pres., trustee Nev. Donor Network, Inc., 1992—. Served with USAF, 1966-68. Mem. ABA, Am. Trial Lawyers Assn., Nev. State Bar, Nev. Trial Lawyers Assn., Elks (justice Las Vegas chpt. 1985-88). Office: 2801 S Valley View Blvd Ste 1B Las Vegas NV 89102-0116

LOVELL, CHARLES C., federal judge; b. 1929; m. Arilah Carter. BS, U. Mont., 1952, JD, 1959. Assoc. Church, Harris, Johnson & Williams, Great Falls, Mont., 1959-85; judge U.S. Dist. Ct. Mont., Helena, 1985—; chief counsel Mont. Atty Gen.'s Office, Helena, 1969-72. Served to capt. USAF, 1952-54. Mem. ABA, Am. Judicature Soc., Am. Trial Lawyers Am. Office: US Dist Ct PO Drawer 10112 301 S Park Ave Helena MT 59626

LOVELL, EDWARD GEORGE, engineering mechanics educator; b. Windsor, Ont., Can., May 25, 1939; s. George Andrew and Julia Anne (Kopacz) L.; children: Elise, Ethan. B.S., Wayne State U., 1960, M.S., 1961; Ph.D., U. Mich., 1967. Registered profl. engr., Wis. Project engr. Bur. Naval Weapons, Washington, 1959, Boeing Co., Seattle, 1962; test engr. Ford Motor Co., Troy, Mich., 1960; instr. U. Mich., Ann Arbor, 1963-67;

design engr. United Tech., Hartford, Conn., 1970; prof. engring. U. Wis., Madison, 1968—, chmn. dept. engring. mechanics and astronautics, 1992—; cons. structural engring. to govt. labs., indsl. orgns., maj. textbook pubs., 1968—. Contbr. numerous articles to profl. jours. Postdoctoral research fellow Nat. Acad. Sci., 1967; NATO Sch. fellow, 1973; NSF fellow, 1961. Mem. Wis. Fusion Tech. Inst., Wis. Ctr. for Applied Microelectronics, Sigma Xi, Tau Beta Pi, Phi Kappa Phi. Office: U Wis Dept Engring Mechs and Astronautics 1415 Johnson Dr Madison WI 53706-1691

LOVELL, FRANCIS JOSEPH, III, investment company executive; b. Boston, Mar. 21, 1949; s. Frank J. and Patricia Anna (Donnellan) L. BBA, Nichols Coll., 1971. With Brown Bros. Harriman & Co., Boston, 1971—, deputy mgr., 1990—; alumni dir. St. Columbkille Sch., Brighton, Mass. Mem. New Eng. Hist. Gen. Soc., Union Club of Boston. Republican. Home: 25 Pomfret St West Roxbury MA 02132-1809 also (summer): 48 Hidden Village Rd West Falmouth MA 02574 Office: 40 Water St Boston MA 02109-3661

LOVELL, GLENN MICHAEL, film critic; b. Bishop Stortford, Eng., Sept. 21, 1948; came to U.S., 1952; s. Lester Eugene and Audrey Mary (Caton) L.; divorced; 1 child, Andrew Hurst Lovell. BA cum laude, Lycoming Coll., 1970; MA, Pa. State U., 1972. TV-film-book critic Hollywood Reporter, L.A., 1972; entertainment editor Richmond (Va.) Mercury, 1973, Miami Beach Sun-Reporter, 1974, Fort Lauderdale (Fla.) Sun-Sentinel, 1976-80; theater critic San Jose (Calif.) Mercury News, 1980-82, film critic, 1982—; film critic Sta. KARA-FM, San Jose, 1985-86, Sta. KOMEúFM, San Jose, 1985-86; instr. film San Jose State U. adult ext. program, 1984-87, De Anza Coll., Cupertino, Calif., 1989, 94; film commentary Sta. KGO, San Francisco, 1985—; judge Palo Alto (Calif.) Film Festival, 1983; panel moderator The Screenwriter's Workshop, San Francisco, 1991, Cinequest panel, San Jose, 1994. Revs. published in numerous newspapers including Atlanta Constitution, Boston Globe, Chgo. Tribune, Cin. Enquirer, Des Moines Register, Detroit Free Press, L.A. Daily News, Miami Herald, New York Daily News, Phila. Inquirer, San Francisco Chronicle, Washington Post, others; also freelance work Aquarian Weekly, Calif. Theatre Ann., Cinefantistique Mag., Fla. Monthly, The Hollywood Reporter, L.A. Free Press, Miami Herald, Toronto Star; co-writer (short film) Night Ride, Miami Film Festival, 1977. Union rep. Newspaper Guild, Bay Area, San Jose, 1991, 94. Nominee Nat. Soc. Film Critics, 1995. Democrat. Avocations: running, scuba, skiing. Home: 975 Terra Bella Ave San Jose CA 95125-2656 Office: San Jose Mercury News 750 Ridder Park Dr San Jose CA 95190

LOVELL, JAMES FREDERICK, academic administrator; b. Lovell, Okla., June 9, 1934; s. James Wood and Ruth Louise (Newbold) L.;m. Janis K. Crall, May 30, 1954; children: Ralph, Randall, Rhonda, Diana Ruth. BS, Okla. State U., 1956, MS, 1958; PhD, Kans. State U., 1964. High sch. tchr. Hardesty, Okla., 1956-58; mem. faculty Pa. State Coll., 1963-66; mem. faculty Southwestern State U., Weatherford, Okla., 1966-79, chmn. biol. sci. nursing and allied health, 1967-79; asst. dir. dept. Allied health edn. and accreditation AMA, Chgo., 1979-82; asst. dean for adminstrv. svcs. Sch. Allied Health Tex. Tech. U. Health Scis. Ctr., Lubbock, 1982-85, dir. devel., 1985-86; asst v.p. for grad. studies, rsch. and continuing edn. Emporia State U., Kans., 1986-88; v.p. for acad. affairs Southern Ark. U., Magnolia, 1988-93; v.p. acad. affairs NE Okla. A & M, Miami, 1993—; dir. projects on environ. edn. NSF, 1973, 75, 79; bd. dirs. Regional Health Adminstrs., Inst. Am. Assn. State Colls. and Univs.; mem. State Regents Coms. for Assessment of Gen. Edn. Curricula and Off-Campus Funding for Acad. Courses, 1989—. Author: Flora of Jennings Blazing Star Nature, 1966; publs. on preparation and adminstrn. of accreditation surveys, AMA; 1972-79, Annals of Okla. Acad. Sci., 1972-79, Trans. of Okla. Jr. Acad. Sci., 1973-78, Physicians Current Procedural Terminology, CPT-4, 6th edit., 1982. Mem. state nursing adv. com. State Bd. Regents, 1972; co-chm. Coll. United Fund, 1970-72; pres. Weatherford Sch. System PTA, 1971; chmn. Okla. Pollution Control Bd., 1975-79; vice chmn. dist. V Okla. Health System Agy., 1976-78, chmn. 1978-79. With M.C.U.S Army, 1958-59. Recipient Outstanding Educator of Am. award, 1971-73. Fellow AAAS; mem. Ecol. Soc. Am., Am. Inst. Biol. Scis. (state pub. responsibility dir. 1977-79), Okla. Acad. Sci. (exec. sec.-treas. 1972-79, mng. editor Proc., 1972-78, Annals, 1972-79), Higher Edn. Alumni Assn., Nat. League Nursing, Okla. Med. Rec. Assn. (hon.), Am. Assn. for Higher Edn., Nat. Coun. Instl. Adminstrs., Lions, Heaco, Phi Delta Kappa. Methodist (chmn. adminstrv. bd.). Home: 1212 Sky Ln Miami OK 74354 Office: NE Okla A&M VP Acad Affairs PO Box 3694 Miami OK 74354

LOVELL, MALCOLM READ, JR., public policy institute executive, educator, former government official, former trade association executive; b. Greenwich, Conn., Jan. 1, 1921; s. Malcolm Read and Emily (Monihan) L.; m. Celia Coghlan, 1978; children by previous marriage: Lucie, Sara. Annette, Caroline. Grad., Lawrenceville Sch., 1939; student, Brown U., 1939-42; I.A., Harvard U., 1943; M.B.A, Harvard, 1946. With Ford Motor Co., Dearborn, Mich., 1946-58; mgr. employee services Am. Motors Corp., Detroit, 1958-61; chmn. State Labor Mediation Bd., Detroit, 1963; dir. Mich. Office Econ. Opportunity, 1964, Mich. Employment Security Commn., Detroit, 1965-69; exec. asso. Manpower, Urban Coalition, 1969; dep. asst. sec. of labor and manpower adminstr., 1969-70, asst. sec. of labor for manpower, 1970-73; pres. Rubber Mfrs. Assn., 1973-81; asst. dir. Office Policy Coordination and Econ. Affairs, Office Pres.-Elect, 1980; undersec. Dept. Labor, Washington, 1981-83; vis. scholar Brookings Instn., Washington, 1983-85; disting. vis. prof. govt. and dir. Labor Mgmt. Inst. George Washington U., 1985-92; pres. Nat. Planning Assn., 1992—; sr. fellow Hudson Inst., 1985-88; mem. Nat. Adv. Coun. on Vocat. Edn., 1975-79, Nat. Commn. for Manpower Policy, 1977-79; chmn. sec. labor Task Force on Econ. Adjustment and Worker Dislocation, 1985-86. Vice pres. Birmingham (Mich.) Sch. Bd., 1956-60; bd. dirs. Nat. Alliance Bus., 1984—; bd. dirs. Travelers Aid of Washington, 1983—, pres., 1985-86; Served to lt. USNR, 1943-46. Mem. City Tavern Club (Washington), Clean Plate (Washington), Cosmos Club (Washington), Alpha Delta Phi. Quaker. Office: Nat Planning Assn 1424 16th St NW Washington DC 20036-2211

LOVELL, MICHAEL C., economics educator; b. Cambridge, Mass., Apr. 11, 1930; s. Reginald Ivan and Rose Mary (Chittenden) L.; m. Adrienne Goolkasian, June 21, 1959; children—Leslie Rosemary, Stacie Alice, George Ivan, Martin Benjamin. B.A., Reed Coll., 1952; M.A., Stanford U., 1954; Ph.D., Harvard U., 1959. Instr. Yale, 1958-59, asst. prof., 1959-63; mem. staff Cowles Found., 1958-63; assoc. prof. Grad. Sch. Indsl. Adminstrn., Carnegie-Mellon U., 1963-66, prof., 1966-69; prof. econs. Wesleyan U., Middletown, Conn., 1969—; chmn. dept. Wesleyan U., 1973-75, 94—; vis. prof. sch. Orgn. and Mgmt. Yale U., 1981-82, 86, 88; cons. Pres.'s Coun. Econ. Advisors, 1964, 67; sr. adviser Brookings Panel on Econ. Activity, 1974-90. Author: (with Albert Hirsch) Sales Anticipants and Inventory Behavior, 1969, Macroeconomics: Measurement, Theory and Policy, 1975, (with Attila Chikan) The Economics of Inventory Management, 1988; assoc. editor Econometrica, 1965-68, Jour. Econs. and Bus., 1983-86, Jour. Econ. Behavior and Orgn., 1987—, Rev. Econs. and Stats., 1991-92, Social Sci. Computer Rev., 1993—; fgn. editor Rev. Econ. Studies, 1968-70. With U.S. Army, 1953-55. Recipient 1st prize Joint Council Econ. Edn., Kazanjian Found. awards program for teaching econs., 1973-74; Ford Found. Faculty Research fellow, 1964-65; Social Sci. Research Council Tng. fellow, 1957-58; Earhart Found. fellow, 1956-57; Harvard Grad. Sch. fellowship, 1955-56; W.H. Robinson fellowship, 1952-53; NSF research grantee, 1962-64, 66-68, 70-72. Fellow Econometric Soc.; mem. Am. Econ. Assn. (chmn. publs. com. 1975-78), Am. Statist. Assn. (assoc. editor Jour. 1975-78), Internat. Soc. Inventory Rsch. (exec. com., chmn. inventories and nat. economy sect. 1982—, pres. 1992-94). Home: Carriage Dr Durham CT 06422 Office: Wesleyan U Middletown CT 06457

LOVELL, ROBERT GIBSON, retired physician, educator; b. Ann Arbor, Mich., May 13, 1920; s. Alfred H. and Grace G. L.; m. Betty Sweeney, May 15, 1948; children—Robert Gibson, Christine, John, David, Cynthia. A.B., U. Mich., 1941, M.D., 1944. Intern U. Mich. Hosp., Ann Arbor, 1946-48; resident U. Mich. Hosp., 1948-50; practice medicine, specializing in internal medicine Ann Arbor, 1959—; instr. U. Mich. Med. Sch., 1950-53, asst. prof. internal medicine, 1953-57, assoc. prof., 1957-73, clin. prof., 1973—, asst. dean, Med. Sch., 1957-59; allergy cons. USAF) Pres. Eisenhower's Commn. on Vets. Pensions. Author: (with Sheldon and Mathews) Manual of Clinical Allergy, 1967; Contbr. (with Sheldon and Mathews) articles to med. jours.

Served to maj., M.C. USAF, 1955-56. Fellow Am. Acad. Allergy, Am. Coll. Chest Physicians; mem. Mich. Allergy Soc. (past pres.). Episcopalian.

LOVELL, ROBERT MARLOW, JR., investment company executive; b. Orange, N.J., June 24, 1930; s. Robert Marlow and Agnes Whipple (Keen) L.; m. Barbara Jane Cronin, Jan. 16, 1960; children—Kimberley, Kerry, Anthony, Matthew. B.A. with honors in History, Princeton U., N.J., 1952. Trainee Halsey, Stuart & Co., N.Y.C., 1955-57; assoc. Lehman Bros., N.Y.C., 1957-64, assoc. dir., investment adv. service, 1965-67; v.p. New Court Securities Corp., N.Y.C., 1968-70; fin. v.p. Crum & Forster, Morristown, N.J., 1970-73, sr. v.p. fin., 1973-85; pres. First Quadrant Corp., 1985-88, chmn. bd., 1988—; trustee Coll. Retirement Equities Fund; chmn. investment com. Morristown Meml. Hosp. Contbr. articles to profl. jours. Former chmn. fin. com. Morristown Meml. Hosp. Served to lt. (j.g.) USNR, 1952-55. Mem. Fin. Analysts Fedn., N.Y. Soc. Securities Analysts. Ins. Investment Officers, Am. Fin. Assn. Republican. Club: Princeton Quadrangle. Home: Featherbed Ln PO Box 561 New Vernon NJ 07976-0561 Office: First Quadrant Corp PO Box 939 100 Park Ave Florham Park NJ 07932-1004

LOVELL, THEODORE, electrical engineer, consultant; b. Paterson, N.J., May 10, 1928; s. George Whiting and Ethel Carol (Berner) L.; m. Wilma Syperda, May 8, 1948 (div. Oct. 1961); m. Joyce Smelik, July 15, 1962; children: Laurie, Dorothy Jane, Valerie, Cynthia, Karen, Barbara. BEE, Newark Coll. Engring., 1948; postgrad., Canadian Inst. Tech., 1950. Exec. dir. Lovell Electric Co., Franklin Lakes, N.J., 1955-82; ptnr., exec. dir. Lovell Design Services, Swedesboro, N.J., 1982—. Author engring. computer software, 1982. Bd. dirs., treas. Contact "Help" of Salem County, 1991-93; pres. Bloomingdale Bd. Edn., N.J., 1970-82; mem. Mcpl. Planning Bd., Bloomingdale, 1980-82, Swedesboro/Woolwich Bd. Edn., 1987-94, v.p., 1990-92, pres. 1993-94; mayoral candidate Borough of Bloomingdale, 1982. Recipient Outstanding Service award Lake Iosco Co., Bloomingdale, 1985, 20 Yr. Svc. award N.J. Sch. Bd. Assn., 1994. Mem. Am. Soc. Engring. Technicians, Radio Club Am., Dickinson Theater Organ Soc. Republican. Presbyterian. Avocations: sailing, theater organ music. Home: 502 Liberty Ct Swedesboro NJ 08085-9416 Office: Lovell Design Svcs PO Box 366 Swedesboro NJ 08085-0366

LOVELL, WALTER CARL, engineer, inventor; b. Springfield, Vt., May 7, 1934; s. John Vincent and Sophia Victoria (Klementowicz) L.; m. Patricia Ann Lawrence, May 6, 1951; children: Donna, Linda, Carol, Patricia, Diane, Walter Jr. B of Engring., Hillyer Coll., Hartford, Conn., 1959. Project engr. Hartford Machine Screw Co., Windsor, Conn., 1954-59; design engr. DeBell and Richardson Labs., Enfield, Conn., 1960-62; cons. engr. Longmeadow, Mass., 1962—; freelance inventor Wilbraham, Mass., 1965—. Numerous patents include Egg-Stir mixer, crown closure sealing gasket, circular unleakable bottle cap, sonic wave ram jet engine, solid state heating tapes, card key lock; composer over 50 country-and-Western songs. Achievements include patents for sonic wave ram jet engine, solid state heat and resistor tape, card key lock, security lock system.

LOVELY, THOMAS DIXON, banker; b. N.Y.C., Apr. 2, 1930; s. Thomas John and Margaret Mary (Browne) L.; AB, Adelphi U., 1954, MA, 1956, MBA, 1958; m. Erna Susan Fritz, June 16, 1956; children: Thomas John Hall, Richard Robert. Treas., Pepsi Cola Bottling Co., Garden City, N.Y., 1957-60; assoc. prof. mgmt. and communications CUNY, 1958-77; dist. adminstr. Lido Beach (N.Y.) Pub. Schs., 1971-80; chmn. bd., pres. Fidelity Fed. Savs. and Loan Assn., Floral Park, N.Y., 1980-82, chmn. bd., pres. Fidelity N.Y., 1982—; v.p., dir. N.Y. Enterprise Co. Trustee, SUNY, 1992, chmn. bd. SUNY Old Westbury Coll. Found., 1989—, vice chmn. bd. trustees Adelphi U., 1967-91, chmn. bd. govs. Univ. Sch. Banking and Money Mgmt., 1975—; trustee Nassau County (N.Y.) Med. Center, 1982—; exec. v.p., treas. Nassau County coun. Boy Scouts Am., 1986—, pres., 1989-92; regional chmn. campaign U.S. Treasury Savs. Bonds Sales, Long Island, 1987—; pres., trustee Meadowbrook Med. Edn. Found., Inc., 1987—. Mem. SAR, L.I. Insured Savs. Group (v.p.). Clubs: Pinehurst Country (N.C.), Cherry Valley Country (Garden City). Home: 52 Locust St Garden City NY 11530-6329 Office: Fidelity NY Fed Savs Bank 1000 Franklin Ave Garden City NY 11530-2910

LOVEN, ANDREW WITHERSPOON, environmental engineering company executive; b. Crossnore, N.C., Jan. 31, 1935; s. Andrew Witherspoon Loven and Annie Laura (Crowell) Stewart; m. Elizabeth Joann DeGroot, June 20, 1959; children: Laura Elizabeth, James Edward. BS, Maryville Coll., 1957; PhD, U. N.C., 1962. Registered profl. engr., Va., Ga., Iowa, Md., N.C., S.C., D.C., Ohio, Fla., Mich. Rsch. assoc. U. N.C., Chapel Hill, 1962-63; sr. rsch. chemist Westvaco Corp., Charleston, S.C., 1963-66; mgr. carbon devel. Westvaco Corp., Charleston, 1966-71, mgr. Westvaco Wastewater Cons. Service, 1967-71; mgr. engring. concepts Engring.-Sci. Inc., McLean, Va., 1971-74; v.p., regional mgr. Engring.-Sci. Inc., Atlanta, 1974-80, group v.p., 1980-86; pres., chief exec. officer Engring. Sci. Inc., Pasadena, Calif., 1986-95, also chmn. bd. dirs.; exec. v.p. Parsons Engring. Sci. Inc., Pasadena, Calif., 1995—. Contbr. articles to profl. jours. NSF grantee, 1958-59; recipient Maryville Coll. Alumni Citation award, 1992. Mem. Am. Acad. Environ. Engrs. (membership com. 1985—), Water Pollution Control Fedn., Am. Inst. Chem. Engrs., Am. Water Works Assn., Nat. Soc. Profl. Engrs., Am. Pub. Works Assn., Constrn. Industry Presidents Forum, Willow Springs Club, Sigma Xi, Alpha Gamma Sigma. Avocations: golf, hiking. Home: #202 330 W California Blvd Pasadena CA 91105 Office: Engring-Sci Inc 100 W Walnut St Pasadena CA 91124-0001

LOVENTHAL, MILTON, writer, playwright, lyricist; b. Atlantic City, Jan. 19, 1923; s. Harry and Clara (Feldman) L.; m. Jennifer McDowell, July 2, 1973. BA, U. Calif., Berkeley, 1950, MLS, 1958; MA in Sociology, San Jose State U., 1969. Researcher Hoover Instn., Stanford, Calif., 1952-53; librarian San Diego Pub. Library, 1957-59; librarian, bibliographer San Jose (Calif.) State U., 1959-92; tchr. writing workshops, poetry readings, 1969-73; co-producer lit. and culture radio show Sta. KALX, Berkeley, 1971-72; editor, pub. Merlin Press, San Jose, 1973—. Author: Books on the USSR, 1951-57, 57, Black Politics, 1971 (featured at Smithsonian Inst. Special Event, 1992), A Bibliography of Material Relating to the Chicano, 1971, Autobiographies of Women, 1946-70, 72, Blacks in America, 1972, The Survivors, 1972, Contemporary Women Poets an Anthology, 1977, Ronnie Goose Rhymes for Grown-Ups, 1984; co-author: (Off-Off-Broadway plays) The Estrogen Party to End War, 1986, Mack the Knife, Your Friendly Dentist, 1986, Betsy & Phyllis, 1986, The Oatmeal Party Comes to Order, 1986, (play) Betsy Meets the Wacky Iraqi, 1991, Bella and Phyllis, 1994; co-writer (mus. comedy) Russia's Secret Plot to Take Back Alaska, 1988. Recipient Bill Casey Award in Letters, 1980; grantee San Jose State U., 1962-63, 84. Mem. Assn. Calif. State Profs., Calif. Alumni Assn., Calif. Theatre Coun. Office: PO Box 5602 San Jose CA 95150-5602

LOVERDE, PAUL S., bishop; b. Framingham, Mass., Sept. 3, 1940. Grad., Th Thomas Sem., Bloomfield, Conn., 1960; B.A. summa cum laude, St. Bernard Sem., Rochester, N.Y.; Licentiate in Sacred Theology, Gregorian U., Rome, Italy, 1966; Licentiate in Canon Law, Cath. U., Washington, D.C., 1982. Ordained priest, Dec. 18, 1965. Asst. pastor St. Sebastian Church, Middletown, CT, 1966-69; Catholic chaplain Wesleyan U., Middletown, CT, 1966-68; chaplain, Religion instructor & chmn. of Religious Studies Dept. St. Bernard Girls' Sch., New London, CT, 1969-72; Religion instructor & chmn. Religious Studies Dept. St. Bernard HS, Montville, CT, 1972-73; assoc. defender of the Bond Diocesan Tribunal of Norwich, 1970-81; Catholic chaplain Conn. Coll., New London, CT, 1970-79; dir. of Campus Ministry Diocese of Norwich, 1973-79; campus min. Eastern Conn. State Coll., Willimantic, CT, 1973-76; mem. bd. of dirs. Conn. Catholic Conf., 1973-78; vicar for priests Diocese of Norwich, 1975-79; chmn. bd. of vicars for priests, Diocese of Norwich, 1975-79; vice-officialis Diocesan Tribunal, 1981-88; chmn. bd. of conciliation/arbitration for priests, 1982-85; exec. coord. bd. of conciliation & arbitration, 1983-89; mem. Presbytral Council, 1983-90, chmn., 1985-89; priests' rep. Diocesan Pastoral Council, 1984-88, vice-chmn. 1984-87; Bishop's del. for clergy, 1985-88; mem. Coll. of Consulters, 1985-90; reg. rep. U.S. Catholic Bishop's Nat. Adv. Council, 1986-90; appointed titular bishop of Ottabia, 1988; aux. bishop Diocese of Hartford, 1988-94; bishop Diocese of Ogdensburg, 1994—; mem. Continuing Edn. for the Clergy Comm. for Diocese of Norwich, 1966-71; mem. Clergy Assn. of Middletown, 1966-69; bd. of dirs., Conn. Project Equality, 1968-73;

vocation promoter Middletown area, 1968-69; Diocese of Norwich rep., Task Force on Race & Ministry with Minorities, 1970; mem. Senate of Priests of Norwich Diocese, 1971-75 (v.p. 1971-72; pres. 1972-75); v.p. Church Vocations Task Group, 1973-79; temp. admin., Holy Trinity Church, Pomfret, CT, 1981; temp. admin. St. Catherine of Siena Church, Preston, CT, 1982, 85-86. contributor of articles to The Priest, Pastoral Life, and Today's Parish. 1st Hon. Brother, Altruism House, New London, CT, 1970. Address: Bishops Residence 624 Washington St Ogdensburg NY 13669*

LOVETT, CHARLES M., genetics educator; b. Oceanside, N.Y., Nov. 23, 1951; m. Jennifer Gordon; 4 children. BS, Calif. State Poly. U., 1979, MS, 1980; PhD in Biochemistry, Cornell U., 1985. Asst. prof. Williams Coll. 1985-92, assoc. prof. chemistry, 1992—. Achievements include research on transcriptional regulation of inducible DNA repair in bacillus subtilis; regulation of competence development in bacillus subtilis. Office: Williams Coll Dept Chemistry Bronfman Sci Ctr Williamstown MA 01267*

LOVETT, CLARA MARIA, university administrator, historian; b. Trieste, Italy, Aug. 4, 1939; came to U.S., 1962; m. Benjamin F. Brown. BA equivalent, U. Trieste, 1962; MA, U. Tex.-Austin, 1967, PhD, 1970. Prof. history Baruch Coll., CUNY, N.Y.C. 1971-82, asst. provost, 1980-82; chief European div. Library of Congress, Washington, 1982-84; dean Coll. Arts and Scis., George Washington U., Washington 1984-88; provost, v.p. academic affairs, George Mason U., Fairfax, Va., 1988-93; on leave from George Mason U.; dir. Forum on Faculty Roles and Rewards Am. Assn. for Higher Edn., 1993-94; pres. No Ariz. U., Flagstaff, 1994—; vis. lectr. Fgn. Service Inst., Washington, 1979-85; bd. dirs. Inst. for Research in History, N.Y.C., 1981-82; exec. council Conf. Group on Italian Politics, 1980-83, others; lectr., cons. Fgn. Service Inst. State Dept., 1979—; adv. bd. European program Wilson Ctr., 1986—; bd. dirs. Assn. Am. Colls., 1990—. Author: The Democratic Movement in Italy 1830-1876, 1982 (H.R. Marraro Prize, Soc. Italian Hist. Studies); Giuseppe Ferrari and the Italian Revolution, 1979 (Phi Alpha Theta book award); Carlo Cattaneo and the Politics of Risorgimento, 1972 (Soc. for Italian Hist. Studies Dissertation award), (bibliography) Contemporary Italy, 1985; co-editor: Women, War, and Revolution, 1980, (essays) State of Western European Studies, 1984; contbr. sects. to publs. U.S., Italy. Organizer Dem. clubs Bklyn., 1972-76; exec. com. Palisades Citizens Assn., Washington, 1985-87; vestry mem. St. David's Episc. Ch., Washington, 1986-89. Fellow Guggenheim Found., 1978-79, Woodrow Wilson Internat. Ctr. for Scholars, 1979 (adv. bd. West European program), Am. Council Learned Socs., 1976, Bunting Inst. of Radcliffe Coll., 1975-76, others. Named Educator of Yr., Va. Fedn. of Bus. and Profl. Women, 1992. Mem. Am. Hist. Assn. (officer 1984-87), Am. Assn. Higher Edn. (cons. 1979—), Council for European Studies, Am. Soc. for Italian Hist. Studies, Conf. Group on Italian Politics, others. Avocations: choral singing, swimming. Office: No Ariz U Office of Pres PO Box 4092 Flagstaff AZ 86011

LOVETT, JOHN ROBERT, chemical company executive; b. Norristown, Pa., June 17, 1931; s. James and Margaret (Creighton) L.; m. Sandra Miller, May 26, 1956; children: Judy, Jackie, John Robert Jr. BS, Ursinus Coll., 1953; MS, U. Del., 1955, PhD, 1957. Rsch. chemist Exxon Rsch., Linden, N.J., 1957-64; dir. Exxon Rsch./Exxon Chem., Linden, 1964-70; v.p. Paramins Exxon Chem., Houston, 1970-74; tech. mgr. Exxon Chem., Linden 1974-76; v.p. rsch. Air Products and Chems., Inc., Allentown, Pa., 1976-81; pres. Europe Air Products and Chems., Inc., Hersham, Eng., 1981-88; group v.p. chems. Air Products and Chems., Inc., Allentown, 1988-92, exec. v.p. gases & equipment, 1992-93, exec. v.p. strategic planning and tech., 1993—. Mem. AICE, Chem. Mfrs. Assn. (bd. dirs. 1990-95), Am. Chem. Soc., Soc. Chem. Industry. Office: Air Products & Chems Inc 7201 Hamilton Blvd Allentown PA 18195-9642

LOVETT, LYLE, musician; b. Klein, Tex.; s. William and Bernell; m. Julia Roberts, Jun. 27, 1993. Degree in Journalism, Tex. A&M U., 1980, grad. studies in German. Albums: Lyle Lovett, 1986, Pontiac, 1988, Lyle Lovett and His Large Band (Grammy award), 1989, Joshua Judges Ruth, 1992, I Love Everybody, 1994; contbd. songs to Deadicated, all-star tribute to Grateful Dead; contbd. songs to films: The Switch, 1987, The Crying Game, 1992, The Firm, 1993; appeared in films: The Player, 1992, Short Cuts, 1993, Ready to Wear (Prêt-à-Porter), 1994, TV appearances: Austin City Limits. Office: c/o MCA Records 70 Universal City Plz Universal City CA 91608*

LOVETT, MILLER CURRIER, management educator, clergyman; b. Lynn, Mass., Mar. 18, 1923; s. Charles William and Phoebe Frances (Miller) L.; m. Dorothy Johnsen, Feb. 14, 1946 (div.); children: Anne E., Celeste M., Peter W., Rebecca J.; m. Virginia Lavelli, May 26, 1971. BSBA, Boston U., 1944, STB, 1946, PhD, 1964; postgrad., MIT, 1970-72. Pastor Wesley United Meth. Ch., Medford, Mass., 1946-52; sr. pastor United Meth. Ch., Ellensburg, Wash., 1952-62, Congl. Ch., Laconia, N.H., 1965-70; assoc. prof. bus. adminstrn. Belknap Coll., Center Harbor, N.H., 1970-73; prof. bus. adminstrn. Bunker Hill Community Coll., Charlestown, Mass., 1973-77; assoc. prof. mgmt. Boston State Coll., 1977-82, U. Mass., Boston, 1982—; founder and exec. dir. Social Ventures Trust, Lexington, Mass., 1985—; mem. cmty. econ. devel. projects, Peru, USA, 1985—, Boston, 1990—. Contbr. articles to profl. jours. Lt. col. CAP USAF, 1955—. Recipient Disting. Svc. award Ellensburg Jr. C. of C., 1956. Mem. Am. Mgmt. Assn., Mass. Tchrs. Assn., Alternate Trade Organization Network, Masons. Avocations: stamp and coin collecting. Home: PO Box 1669 25 Spindle Point Rd Meredith NH 03253-1669 Office: U Mass Coll Pub & Community Svc Boston MA 02125-3393

LOVETT, RADFORD DOW, real estate and investment company executive; b. Jacksonville, Fla., Sept. 6, 1933; s. William Radford and Agnes (Dow) L.; AB, Harvard U., 1955; m. Katharine Rutledge Howe, June 25, 1955; children: Katharine, William Radford, Philip, Lauren. With Merrill Lynch, Pierce, Fenner & Smith Inc., N.Y.C., 1958-78; mng. dir. Capital Markets Group, 1975-78; pres. Piggly Wiggly Corp., Jacksonville, 1978-82; chmn. bd. Commodores Point Terminal Corp., Jacksonville, 1978—; dir. First Union Corp., Fla. Rock Industries Inc., FRP Properties, Inc., Am. Heritage Life Investment Corp., Winn-Dixie Stores, Inc. Trustee, Drew U., 1976-79, St. Vincent's Found., Jacksonville Zool. Soc. Lt., F.A., U.S. Army, 1955-57. Episcopalian. Office: 1010 E Adams St PO Box 4069 Jacksonville FL 32201

LOVETT, ROBERT G., lawyer; b. York, Pa., Aug. 17, 1944. BA, U. Pitts., 1966; JD, Duquesne U., 1969. Bar: Pa. 1970. Office: Reed Smith Shaw & McClay 435 6th Ave Pittsburgh PA 15219-1886

LOVETT, WENDELL HARPER, architect; b. Seattle, Apr. 2, 1922; s. Wallace Herman and Pearl (Harper) L.; m. Eileen Wintoure, Sept. 3, 1947; children: Corrie, Clare. Student, Pasadena Jr. Coll., 1943-44; B.Arch., U. Wash., 1947; M.Arch., Mass. Inst. Tech. 1948. Architect, designer Naramore, Bain, Brady & Johanson, Seattle, 1948; architect, assoc. Bassetti & Morse, Seattle, 1948-51; pvt. practice architect Seattle, 1951—; instr. architecture U. Wash., 1948-51, asst. prof., 1951-60, assoc. prof., 1960-65, prof., 1965-83, prof. emeritus, 1983—; lectr. Technische Hochschule, Stuttgart, 1959-60. Prin. works include nuclear reactor bldg. U. Wash., 1960, Villa Simonyi, Medina, Wash., 1989. Pres. Citizen's Planning Council, Seattle, 1968-71. Served with AUS, 1943-46. Recipient 2d prize Progressive Architecture U.S. Jr. C. of C., 1949; Internat. design award Decima Triennale di Milano, 1954; Arch. Record Homes awards, 1969, 72, 74; Interiors award, 1973; Sunset-AIA awards, 1959, 62, 69, 71; Fulbright grantee, 1959; AIA fellow, 1978. Mem. AIA (sec. Wash. chpt. 1953-54, bd. dirs. Found. Seattle chpt. 1991-92, Seattle chpt. medal 1993, pres. sr. coun. 1991-92), Plestcheeff Inst. (bd. dirs. 1992). Patentee in field. Home and Office: 420 34th Ave Seattle WA 98122-6408

LOVETT, WILLIAM ANTHONY, law and economics educator; b. Milw., Sept. 2, 1934. AB, Wabash Coll., 1956; JD, NYU, 1959; PhD in Econs., Mich. State U., 1969. Bar: N.Y. 1960. Atty. U.S. Dept. Justice, Washington, 1962; economist FTC, Washington, 1963-69; prof. Tulane U., New Orleans, 1969—, dir. internat. law, trade and fin. program, 1985—; Joseph Merrick Jones prof. law and econs., 1991—. Author: Inflation and Politics, 1982, Banking and Financial Institutions Law, 1984, 88, 92, World Trade Rivalry, 1987. Root-Tilden scholar, 1956-59. Mem. ABA, Am. Econs. Assn., Am. Soc. Internat. Law, Phi Beta Kappa. Office: Tulane Law Sch New Orleans LA 70118

LOVETTE, BLAKE DUANE, food company executive; b. North Wilkesboro, N.C., Dec. 19, 1942; s. Charlie Odell and Ila Ruth (Bumgarner) L.; m. Julia Lee Wooten, June 30, 1963; children: Sena Maria Lovette Brown, Angela Blake, Amy Camille. BS in Poultry Sci., N.C. State U., 1965. With Holly Farms Poultry Ind., Inc., various locations, 1965-78; exec. v.p. Holly Farms Poultry Ind., Inc., Wilkesboro; pres. Valmac Industries, Tasty Birds Foods, Russellville, Ark., 1978-84; v.p. Tyson Foods, Onc., Russellville, 1984; pres. Shenandoah Products subs. Perdue Foods, Inc., Harrisonburg, Va., 1984; exec. v.p. Perdue Foods, Inc., Salisbury, Md., 1988; pres., COO Holly Farms Foods, Inc., Wilkesboro, 1988-90; pres. Lovettte Co., Inc., North Wilkesboro, N.C., 1990—; pres. NBC, 1984-85. Republican. Methodist. Avocation: skiing. Home: 102 Meadow Brook Ct North Wilkesboro NC 28659-4636 Office: Lovette Co Inc Hwy 115 S North Wilkesboro NC 28659

LOVICK, NORMAN, accountant; b. Wilson, N.C., July 10, 1942; s. Henry J. and Ella (Lovick) Webb; children: Norman Lovick Jr., Michael D. BS, Durham (N.C.) Coll., 1963; AA, N.C. Cen. Coll., Durham, 1961; MS, Am. U., 1964; Adv. Deg., USDA Grad. Sch., Washington, 1971. Acctg. analyst U.S. Dept. Treasury, Washington, 1967-76; fin. analyst Midland Nat. Corp., Wheaton, Md., 1976-78; cpa, cert. fin. planner Lovick's Fin. Assocs., Hyattsville, Md., 1978-88, chief exec. officer, pres., 1985—; gen. agt. Bankers United, Cedar Rapids, Iowa, 1977-79; notary pub. With U.S. Army, 1965-67. Mem. Nat. Assn. Accts., D.C. Life Underwriters., Nat. Assn. Life Underwriters, Nat. Soc. Pub. Accts., Am. Inst. Profl. Bookkeepers, D.C. Soc. Ind. Accts., Am. Mgmt. Assn., Masons (32 deg., chaplain). Democrat. Pentecostal Ch. Avocations: fishing, boating, reading, dancing. Office: Lovick's Fin Assocs 3601 Hamilton St Ste 201 Hyattsville MD 20782-3954

LOVIN, KEITH HAROLD, university administrator, philosophy educator; b. Clayton, N.Mex., Apr. 1, 1943; s. Buddie and Wanda (Smith) L.; m. Marsha Kay Gunn, June 11, 1966; children—Camille Jenay, Lauren Kay. B.A., Baylor U., 1965; postgrad., Yale U., 1965-66; Ph.D., Rice U., 1971. Prof. philosophy Southwest Tex. State U., San Marcos, 1970-77, chmn. dept. philosophy, 1977-78; dean liberal arts Southwest Tex. State U., 1978-81; provost, v.p. acad. affairs Millersville U., Pa., 1981-86; provost, v.p. acad. and student affairs U. So. Colo., Pueblo, 1986-92; pres. Maryville U. St. Louis, 1992—. Contbr. articles on philosophy of law, philosophy of religion to profl. publs.; mem. adv. bd. Southwest Studies in Philosophy, 1981-90. Bd. dirs. Boys Hope, Jr. Achievement Mississippi Valley, Inc., United Way, Nat. Coun. Alcohol and Drug Abuse, St. Louis Intercollegiate Athletic Conf., Ind. Colls. and Univs. of Mo., Higher Edn. Coun., 1992—. Mem. Chesterfield Ch. of C. (leadership club), Univ. Club, Media Club. Avocation: flying. Home: 13664 Conway Rd Saint Louis MO 63141-7234 Office: Maryville U 13550 Conway Rd Saint Louis MO 63141-7232

LOVING, ALVIN DEMAR, JR., artist, educator; b. Detroit, Sept. 19, 1935; s. Alvin Demar and Mary Helen (Green) L.; m. Wyn Cortes Riser, Aug. 28, 1969; children: Alvin III, Laurie, Alicia, Ann. BFA, U. Ill.; MFA, U. Mich. Assoc. prof. Art Dept. CCNY, 1992—; Lectr., numerous residencies in field. One person shows include June Kelly Gallery, N.Y., 1990, 92, Pace U., N.Y., 1992, Sande Webster Gallery, Phila., 1991, Arts in the Acad., Washington, 1991, Franklin & Marshall Coll., Lancaster, Pa., 1990, The Bronx Mus. Arts, N.Y., 1989, The Harlem Sch. Art, N.Y., 1989, Liz Harris Gallery, Boston, 1988, G.R. N'Namdi Gallery, Detroit, 1983, 88, U. Vt., Burlington, 1984, 87, Studio Mus. Harlem, 1977, 86, Onyx Art Gallery, N.Y., 1984, Diane Brewer Gallery, N.Y., 1983, Grippe-Zivian Gallery, N.Y., 1979, Notre Dame U., South Bend, Ind., 1975, Ohio State U., Columbus, 1974, Tyler Sch. Art, Phila., 1973, Gertrude Kasle Gallery, Detroit, 1969; exhibited in group shows at Am. Acad. Inst. Arts and Letters, 1991, Alitash Kebebe L.A., 1991, Manhattanville Coll., N.Y., 1991, Sande Webster Gallery, 1990, Albright Knox Art Gallery, Buffalo, N.Y., 1989, Detroit Inst. Art, 1990, Centro Cultural Ciudad de Buenos Aires, 1989, Mint Mus., Charlotte, N.C., 1987, Montclair (N.J.) Mus., 1987, Cleve. U. Art Gallery, 1985, Bucknell U., Lewisburg, Pa., 1984, Cleve. Mus. Art, 1983, Currier Gallery, Manchester, N.H., 1982, Met. Mus. Art, 1979, Sarah Lawrence Coll., Bronxville, N.Y., 1977, N.Y. Cultural Ctr., 1974, Whitney Mus. Am. Art, N.Y., 1971, 72, Galérie Meaght, Paris, France, 1970; represented in permanent collections including Met. Mus. Art, Whitney Mus. Am. Art, Detroit Inst. Art, Toledo Mus. Art, Currier Gallery, Newark Mus., Renaissance Ctr., Mus. of N.H., Akron Art Mus., Franklin & Marshall Coll., U. Mich., Vassar Coll., Bell Atlantic, Washington; pub. commns. include People Mover, Millender Sta., City of Detroit, Internat. Departure Hall Kennedy Internat. Airport, City Walls, Ave. of the Ams. and 42d St., N.Y.; contbr. articles to profl. jours. Recipient Nat. Endowment for Arts, 1970, 71, 75, 76, 85; CAPS grantee N.Y. State Coun. on the Arts, 1975; Guggenheim fellow for Painting, 1986; Teaching fellow U. Mich., 1965, Rakham Meml. fellow, U. Mich., 1964. Office: 145 W 42nd St New York NY 10036-6509

LOVING, GEORGE GILMER, JR., retired air force officer; b. Roanoke, Va., Aug. 7, 1923; s. George Gilmer and Ora Page (Carr) L.; m. Mary Ambler Thomasson, Jan. 15, 1945; children—Cary Ambler, Betty Page Behler. Student, Lynchburg Coll., 1941; B.A., U. Ala., 1960; M.A. in Internat. Affairs, George Washington U., 1965; grad., Air War Coll., 1965. Commd. 2d lt. U.S. Army Air Force, 1943; advanced through grades to lt. gen. U.S. Air Force, 1975; fighter pilot, test pilot, operations officer, fighter squadron comdr., 1943-55; U.S. adviser (Nat. War Coll.), Republic of China, 1960-62; staff planner Hdqrs. U.S. Air Force, Washington, 1965-69; comdr. Air Command and Staff Coll., 1970-73; dir. plans Hdqrs. U.S. Air Force, Washington, 1973-75; Joint Chiefs Staff rep. for mut. and balanced force reductions Washington, 1975; comdr. 6th Allied Tactical Air Force Izmir, Turkey, 1975-77; comdr. U.S. forces Japan; comdr. 5th Air Force Yokota Air Base, Japan, 1977-79; ret., 1979; cons. RAND Corp., 1979-80; exec. dir. Marie Selby Bot. Gardens, Sarasota, Fla, 1981-88. Decorated D.S.M. with 2 oak leaf clusters, Silver Star medal, Legion of Merit, D.F.C. with oak leaf cluster, Meritorious Service medal, Air Force Commendation medal, Air medal with 25 oak leaf clusters.; N.Y.C. Council on Fgn. Relations fellow, 1969-70. Mem. Am. Fighter Aces Assn. Episcopalian. Club: Sarasota Yacht. Home: 508 Whitfield Ave Sarasota FL 34243

LOVING, SUSAN B., lawyer, former state official; m. Dan Loving; children: Lindsay, Andrew, Kendall. BA with distinction, U. Okla., 1972, JD, 1979. Asst. atty. gen. Office of Atty. Gen., 1983-87, first asst. atty. gen., 1987-91; atty. gen. State of Okla., Oklahoma City, 1991-94; atty. Lester & Bryant, P.C., Oklahoma City, 1995—; adj. prof. U. Tulsa Coll. of Law, 1994; vice chair Okla. Pardon and Parole Bd., 1995—. Bd. dirs. Bd. for Freedom of Info., Okla. Inc., Boy Scouts of Am., Legal Aid of West Okla., Okla. Com. for Prevention Child Abuse; mem. med. steering com. Partnership for Drug Free Okla., 1993—; adv. bd. Law and You Found. Recipient Nat. Red Ribbon Leadership award Nat. Fedn. Parents, Headliner award, By-liner award Okla. City and Tulsa Women in Comm., First Friend of Freedom award, Freedom of Info., Okla., Dir. award Okla. Dist. Attys. Assn. Mem. Okla. Bar Assn. (past chmn. adminstrv. law sect., mem. adminstrn. of justice com., farm crisis task force), Phi Beta Kappa. Office: Lester & Bryant PC 119 N Robinson Oklahoma City OK 73120-4625

LOVING, WILLIAM RUSH, JR., public relations company executive, consultant; b. Norfolk, Va., Sept. 14, 1934; s. William Rush and Margaret Elizabeth (Billups) L.; m. Jane Parker, July 1963 (div. Dec. 1987); children: Katharine G., Margaret Borden, Leslie R.; m. Marsha Thaler, June 30, 1989 (div. June 1994). BA, U. Richmond, 1956. Lt. U.S. Army, 1957-59; reporter Richmond (Va.) Times-Dispatch, 1959-62, bus. editor, 1965-69; reporter The Virginian-Pilot, Norfolk, 1962-63; info. coord. Va. Mus. Fine Arts, Richmond, 1963-65; assoc. editor Fortune mag., N.Y.C., 1969-79; asst. dir. U.S. Office Mgmt. and Budget, Washington, 1979-80; pres. Loving Asssocs. Ltd., New Hope, Pa., 1980—, Loving Assocs. Ltd. Va., Alexandria, 1989—; dir. Railway Svc. Corp.; trustee Loving Assocs. Pension and Profit Sharing Funds, New Hope, Pa. Editor: How To Protect What's Yours, 1983; contbr. numerous articles to Fortune mag. Mem. Old Town Civic Assn., Alexandria, 1986—, The Torpedo Factory, Alexandria, 1986—. Mem. Nat. Press Club, R.R. Pub. Rels. Assn., Bucks County C. of C., Va. Hist. Soc. Avocations: photography, painting. Home: 405 S Lee St Alexandria VA 22314-3815 Office: 519 Oronoco St Alexandria VA 22314-2305

LOVINGER, SOPHIE LEHNER, child psychologist; b. N.Y.C., Jan. 15, 1932; d. Nathaniel Harris and Anne (Rosen) Lehner; m. Robert Jay Lovinger, June 18, 1957; children: David Fredrick, Mark Andrew. BA, Bklyn. Coll., 1954; MS, City Coll., N.Y.C., 1959; PhD, NYU, 1967. Sr. clin. psychologist Bklyn. State Hosp., 1960-61; grad. fellow NYU, N.Y.C., 1961-67; psychotherapy trainee Jamaica (N.Y.) Ctr., 1964-67; asst. prof. Hofstra U., Hempstead, N.Y., 1967-70; prof. Cen. Mich. U., Mt. Pleasant, 1970—; psychotherapist, psychoanalyst N.Y.C. and Mt. Pleasant, Mich., 1964—. Author: Learning Disabilities and Games, 1978, Language-Learning Disabilities, 1991; contbr. articles to profl. jours. Fellow Am. Orthopsychiat. Assn.; mem. Am. Psychol. Assn., Nat. Register Health Svc. Providers. Office: 405 S Main St Mount Pleasant MI 48858-2522

LOVINGER, WARREN CONRAD, emeritus university president; b. Big Sandy, Mont., July 29, 1915; s. Wilbur George and Ruth Katherine (Hokanson) L.; m. Dorothy Blackburn, Aug. 14, 1937; children—Patricia Mae, Jeanie, Warren Conrad. B.A., U. Mont., 1942, M.A., 1944; Ed.D., Columbia U., 1947. Tchr., prin. Pub. Schs. Mont., 1937-43; instr. history U. Mont., Missoula, 1943-44; pres. No. State Coll., Aberdeen, S.D., 1951-56; pres. Central Mo. State U., Warrensburg, 1956-79, pres. emeritus, 1979—; exec. sec. Am. Assn. Colls. for Tchr. Edn., 1947-51, nat. pres., 1963-64; nat. pres. Am. Assn. State Colls. and Univs., 1974-75; mem. del. to study effects of Marshall Plan on Western Europe, 1950; leader study of tchr. edn. in Fed. Republic of Germany, 1964; leader del. People's Republic of China, 1975; mem. comparative study tour of Republic of China, 1976. Author: General Education in Teachers Colleges, 1948; contbr. articles to profl. jours. Served as lt. USNR, 1944-46, ETO. Recipient Silver Beaver award Boys Scouts Am., 1970; Outstanding Civilian Service award Dept. Army, 1979. Mem. Mo. Tchrs. Assn., Am. Assn. Sch. Adminstrs., Mo. Assn. Sch. Adminstrs., Columbia U. Alumni Assn., Stover C. of C., Am. Legion, Gideons Internat., Phi Kappa Phi, Phi Delta Kappa, Kappa Delta Pi,. Baptist. Lodges: Masons, Shriners, Rotary, Lions. Avocations: travelling; writing; fishing; farming.

LOVINS, AMORY BLOCH, physicist, energy consultant; b. Washington, Nov. 13, 1947; s. Gerald Hershel and Miriam (Bloch) L.; m. L. Hunter Sheldon, Sept. 6, 1979. Student, Harvard U., 1964-65, 66-67, Magdalen Coll., Oxford, Eng., 1967-69; MA, Oxford U., Oxford, 1971; DSc (hon.), Bates Coll., 1979, Williams Coll., 1981, Kalamazoo Coll., 1983, U. Maine, 1985; LLD (hon.), Ball State U., 1983; D of Environ. Sci. (hon.), Unity Coll., 1992. Jr. research fellow Merton Coll., Oxford, England, 1969-71; Brit. rep., policy advisor Friends of the Earth, San Francisco, 1971-84; regent's lectr. U. Calif., Berkeley and Riverside, 1978, 81; v.p., dir. research Rocky Mountain Inst., Old Snowmass, Colo., 1982—; govt. and indsl. energy cons., 1971—; vis. prof. Dartmouth Coll., 1982; disting. vis. prof. U. Colo., 1982; prin. tech. cons. E Source, 1989—; prin. The Lovins Group, 1994—. Author: (also layout artist and co-photographer) Eryri, The Mountains of Longing, 1971, The Stockholm Conference: Only One Earth, 1972, Openpit Mining, 1973, World Energy Strategies: Facts, Issues, and Options, 1975, Soft Energy Paths: Toward a Durable Peace, 1977; co-author: (with J. Price) Non-Nuclear Futures: The Case for an Ethical Energy Strategy, 1975, (with L.H. Lovins) Energy/War: Breaking the Nuclear Link, 1980, Brittle Power: Energy Strategy for National Security, 1982, (with L.H. Lovins, F. Krause, and W. Bach) Least-Cost Energy: Solving the CO2 Problem, 1982, 89, (with P. O'Heffernan, sr. author, and L.H. Lovins) The First Nuclear World War, 1983, (with L.H. Lovins, sr. author, and S. Zuckerman) Energy Unbound: A Fable for America's Future, 1986, (hardware reports) The State of the Art: Lighting, 1988, The State of the Art: Drivepower, 1989, The State of the Art: Appliances, 1990, The State of the Art: Water Heating, 1991, The State of the Art: Space Cooling and Air Handling, 1992; co-photographer (book) At Home in the Wild: New England's White Mountains, 1978; author numerous poems; contbr. articles to profl. jours., reports to tech. jours.; patentee in field. Recipient Right Livelihood award Right Livelihood Found., 1983, Sprout award Internat. Studies Assn., 1977, Pub. Edn. award Nat. Energy Resources Orgn., 1978, Pub. Svc. award Nat. Assn. Environ. Edn., 1980; Mitchell prize Mitchell Energy Found., 1982, Delphi prize Onassis Found., 1989, Nissan prize Internat. Symposium Automotive Tech. and Automation, 1993, Award of Distinction, Rocky Mountain chpt. AIA, 1994; MacArthur fellow John D. and Catherine T. MacArthur Found., Chgo., 1993. Fellow AAAS, World Acad. Art and Sci., Lindisfarne Assn.; mem. Fedn. Am. Scientists, Am. Phys. Soc. Avocations: mountaineering, photography, music. Home and Office: 1739 Snowmass Creek Rd Snowmass CO 81654-9199 *Personal philosophy: Devotion to efficient and sustainable use of resources as a path to global security, with emphasis on how advanced technologies, market economics, and Jeffersonian politics can provide new solutions to old problems or better still avoid them altogether.*

LOVINS, L. HUNTER, public policy institute executive; b. Middlebury, Vt., Feb. 26, 1950; d. Paul Millard and Farley (Hunter) Sheldon; m. Amory Bloch Lovins, Sept. 6, 1979; 1 child, Nanuq. BA in Sociology, Pitzer Coll., 1972, BA in Polit. Sci., 1972; JD, Loyola U., L.A., 1975; LHD, U. Maine, 1982. Bar: Calif. 1975. Asst. dir. Calif. Conservation Project, L.A., 1973-79; exec. dir., co-founder Rocky Mountain Inst., Snowmass, Colo., 1982—; vis. prof. U. Colo. Boulder, 1982; Henry R. Luce vis. prof. Dartmouth Coll., Hanover, N.H., 1982; pres. Nighthawk Horse Co., 1993, Lovins Group, 1994. Co-author: Brittle Power, 1982, Energy Unbound, 1986, Least-Cost Energy Solving the CO2 Problem, 2d edit., 1989. Bd. dirs. Renew Am., Basalt and Rural Fire Protection Dist., Telluride Inst., E Source, Roaring Park Polocrosse Assn.; vol. firefighter. Recipient Mitchell prize Woodlands Inst., 1982, Right Livelihood Found. award, 1983, Best of the New Generation award Esquire Mag., 1984. Mem. Am. Quarter Horse Assn. Avocations: rodeo, fire rescue, polocrosse. Office: Rocky Mountain Inst 1739 Snowmass Creek Rd Snowmass CO 81654-9199

LOVITT, GEORGE HAROLD, advertising executive; b. Bridgeport, Conn., June 7, 1922; s. Leon H. and Sarah (Lubetkin) L.; m. Nancy Posner, Nov. 27, 1947; children: Alison Lovitt Reinfeld, Charles, Robert, Patricia. B.A., NYU, 1944. Asst. to publicity dir. Prentice-Hall, Inc., N.Y.C., 1946-48; advt. and publicity dir. John Wiley & Sons, Inc., N.Y.C., 1948-52; successively account exec., v.p., pres., chmn. Franklin Spier Inc., N.Y.C., 1952-82; pres. Keynote Mktg., Inc., N.Y.C., 1982-84; adj. prof. English dept. Hofstra U., 1986. Trustee Baldwin Pub. Library, 1971-76, 77-78. Served with inf. AUS, 1943-46. Decorated Purple Heart. Home: 40 Interlaken Est Lakeville CT 06039-2104

LOVITZ, JON, actor, comedian; b. Tarzana, Calif., July 21, 1957. Attended, U. Calif.-Irvine; studied acting, Film Actors Workshop. Began performing in comedy improvisation with the Groundlings, L.A.; TV work includes (series) Foley Square, 1985, Saturday Night Live, NBC, 1985-90, The Critic, 1994—, (voice); feature films include The Last Resort, 1986, Ratboy, 1986, Jumpin' Jack Flash, 1986, Three Amigos, 1986, Big, 1988, My Stepmother is an Alien, 1988, Brave Little Toaster, 1989 (voice), Mr. Destiny, 1990, An American Tail: Fievel Goes West, 1991 (voice), A League of Their Own, 1992, Mom and Dad Save the World, 1990, Coneheads, 1993, National Lampoon's Loaded Weapon I, 1993, City Slickers II: The Legend of Curley's Gold, 1994, North, 1994, Trapped in Paradise, 1994. Address: care Brillstein/Grey Entertainment 9150 Wilshire Blvd Ste 350 Beverly Hills CA 90212

LOW, ANTHONY, English language educator; b. San Francisco, May 31, 1935; s. Emerson and Clio (Caroli) L.; m. Pauline Iselin Mills, Dec. 28, 1961; children: Louise, Christopher, Georgianna, Elizabeth, Peter, Catherine, Nicholas, Alexandra, Michael, Frances, Jessica, Edward, Charlotte. A.B. Harvard U., 1957, M.A., 1959, Ph.D., 1965. Mem. faculty Seattle U., 1965-68; mem. faculty NYU, N.Y.C., 1968—; prof. English lit., 1978—, chmn. dept. English, 1989-95; vis. scholar Jesus Coll., Cambridge, Eng., 1974-75. Author: Augustine Baker, 1970, The Blaze of Noon, 1974, Love's Architecture, 1978, The Georgic Revolution, 1985, The Reinvention of Love, 1993; editor: Urbane Milton, 1984. Pew Evangelical writing, 1995. Mem. Milton Soc., Donne Soc., MLA, Renaissance Soc., Phi Beta Kappa. Home: 7 Christopher Rd Ridgefield CT 06877-2407 Office: NYU Dept English 19 University Pl New York NY 10003-4501

LOW, BARBARA WHARTON, biochemist, biophysicist; b. Lancaster, Eng., Mar. 23, 1920; came to U.S., 1946, naturalized, 1956; d. Matthew and Mary Jane (Wharton) L. B.A. (Coll. scholar), Somerville Coll., Oxford (Eng.) U., 1942, M.A., 1946, DPhil, 1948. Research fellow Calif. Inst. Tech., 1946-47; research assoc. in phys. chemistry Harvard U. Med. Sch., 1948, assoc. in phys. chemistry, 1948-50; assoc. mem. Univ. Lab. Phys. Chemistry Related to Medicine and Public Health, 1950-54; asst. prof. phys. chemistry Harvard U., 1950-56; assoc. prof. biochemistry Columbia U. Coll. Physicians and Surgeons, 1956-66, prof., 1966-90, prof. emeritus, 1990—; cons. USPHS; mem. biophysics and biophys. chemistry study sect. divsn. rsch. grants NIH, 1961, 66-69, open study sect. 1988, 90; mem. rsch. coun. Pub. Health Rsch. Inst. Coty N.Y., 1973-78, bd. dirs., 1974-78; prof. associe U. Strasbourg, France, 1965; vis. prof. Japan Soc. Promotion Sci., Tohoku U., Sendai, Japan, 1975; invited lectr. Chinese Acad. Scis., 1981, Soviet Acad. Scis., 1988; mem. seminar oon archaeology of Ea. Mediterranean, Ea. Europe and Near East, Columbia U. Contbr. articles to chem., biochem., biophys., and crystallographic jours., also chpts. in books. Recipient Career Devel. award NIH, 1963-68; NIH sr. research fellow, 1959-63. Fellow Am. Acad. Arts and Scis.; mem. AAAS, Am. Crystallographic Assn., Am. Inst. Physics, Am. Soc. Biol. Chemists, Biophys. Soc., Royal Soc. Chemistry, Harvey Soc., Internat. Soc. Toxinology, Protein Soc., Soc. Neurosci. Achievements include determination of three dimensional structure of penicillin; structure determination of protein implicated in neurological block; discovery of pi helix; co-developer use of heavy atoms in protein crystal structure determination; introduction of low temperature studies for protein data collection and of polaroid photography of protein X-ray diffraction patterns; established probable binding site of snake venom neurotoxins to Acetylcholine receptor. Office: Columbia U Dept Biochem & Mo Bio 630 W 168th St New York NY 10032-3702

LOW, BOON CHYE, physicist; b. Singapore, Feb. 13, 1946; came to U.S., 1968; s. Kuei Huat and Ah Tow (Tee) Lau; m. Daphne Nai-Ling Yip, Mar. 31, 1971; 1 child, Yi-Kai. BSc, U. London, Eng., 1968; PhD, U. Chgo., 1972. Scientist High Altitude Observatory Nat. Ctr. for Atmospheric Rsch., Boulder, Colo., 1981-87, head coronal interplanetary physics sect., 1987-90, acting dir., 1989-90, sr. scientist, 1987—; mem. mission operation working group for solar physics NASA, 1992-94. Mem. editorial bd. Solar Physics, 1991—. Named Fellow Japan Soc. for Promotion of Sci., U. Tokyo, 1978, Sr. Rsch. Assoc., NASA Marshall Space Flight Ctr., 1980. Mem. Am. Physical Soc., Am. Astron. Soc., Am. Geophysical Union. Office: Nat Ctr for Atmosph Rsch PO Box 3000 Boulder CO 80307-3000

LOW, DANA EVARTS, consulting engineer; b. Orange, N.J., Dec. 5, 1932; s. George Evarts and Dorothea (Dodge) L.; m. Anne Elizabeth Eshelman, Aug. 10, 1957; children: Virginia, Richard, Christopher. A.B., Dartmouth Coll., 1954; M.S., Thayer Sch. Engring., 1955; postgrad., Columbia U., 1958-60. Registered profl. engr., 8 states. Jr. engr. Howard Needles Tammen, Bergendoff, N.Y.C., 1958-60; engr. Tippetts, Abbett, McCarthy, Stratton, cons. engrs., architects and planners, N.Y.C., 1960-65, assoc., 1965-71, assoc. ptnr., 1972, ptnr., 1973—; chmn. bd. dirs. Internat. Road Fedn., Washington, 1982—. Contbr. articles to tech. engring. mags. and jours. Bd. dirs. Bus. Council for Internat. Understanding, N.Y.C. Served to lt. (j.g.) USN, 1955-58. Fellow ASCE, Inst. Transp. Engrs. Republican. Clubs: Union League (N.Y.C.); Innis Arden Golf (Old Greenwich, Conn.). Home: 203 Shore Rd Old Greenwich CT 06870-2419 Office: TAMS Cons Inc 655 3d Ave New York NY 10017*

LOW, DONALD GOTTLOB, retired veterinary medicine educator; b. Cheyenne Wells, Colo., May 14, 1925; s. John Louis and Marie (Gabriel) L.; m. Jeanette Maxine Reedy, Dec. 4, 1948 (div. Feb. 1972); children: Ronald, Raymond, Richard, Christine, Cheryl; m. Jane M. Herschler, May 12, 1973. D.V.M., Kans. State U., 1947; Ph.D., U. Minn., 1956. Pvt. practice vet. medicine, 1947-49; dist. veterinarian U.S. Dept. Agr., 1949-50; instr. U. Minn., 1950-53, 55-56, assoc. prof., 1956-60, prof., 1960-65, head dept. vet. hosps., 1965-70; prof., head dept. clin. scis. Colo. State U., 1971-74; prof. vet. medicine, dir. teaching hosp. U. Calif.-Davis, 1974-80, assoc. dean instrn., 1982-83, assoc. dean pub. programs, 1983-93; ret., 1993. Author: (with Osborne, Finco) Small Animal Urology, 1972; Contbr. articles to tech. jours. Active Boy Scouts Am., PTA. Served with AUS, 1943-44; as capt. 1953-55. Recipient Disting. Teaching award U. Minn., 1965, Disting. Svc. award, 1990, 91, Robert W. Kirk award for Disting. Svc., Am. Coll. Vet. Internal Medicine, Disting. Alumnus award Kans. State U. and the Vet. Med. Alumni Assn., 1994. Mem. Am. Coll. Vet. Internists (founder), Am., Colo. Vet. Med. Assns., Am. Animal Hosp. Assn. (Veterinarian of Year 1970), Nat. Acad .Practice-Vet. Medicine, Calif. Vet. Med. Assn. (pres. award 1988), Calif. Acad. Vet. Medicine (Excellence in Continuing Edn. award 1989), Phi Zeta. Methodist. Home: 26778 County Road 34 Winters CA 95694-9064

LOW, EMMET FRANCIS, JR., mathematics educator; b. Peoria, Ill., June 10, 1922; s. Charles Walter and Nettie Alys (Baker) Davis; m. Lana Carmen Wiles, Nov. 23, 1974. B.S. cum laude, Stetson U., 1948; M.S., U. Fla., 1950, Ph.D., 1953. Instr. physics U. Fla., 1950-54; aero. research scientist NACA, Langley Field, Va., 1954-55; asst. prof. math. U. Miami, Coral Gables, Fla., 1955-60; assoc. prof. U. Miami, 1960-67, prof., 1967-72, chmn. dept. math., 1961-66; acting dean U. Miami (Coll. Arts and Scis.), 1966-67, assoc. dean, 1967-68, assoc. dean faculties, 1968-72; prof. math. Clinch Valley Coll., U. Va., 1972-89, dean, 1972-86, chmn. dept. math. scis., 1986-89; emeritus prof. math., 1989—; vis. research scientist Courant Inst. Math. Scis., NYU, 1959-60. Contbr. articles to profl. jours. Served with USAAF, 1942-46. Recipient award for excellence in teaching Clinch Valley Coll., 1988. Mem. Am. Math. Soc., Math. Assn. Am., Soc. Indsl. and Applied Math., Nat. Council Tchrs. of Math., Southwest Va. Council Tchrs. of Math., AAUP, AAAS, Sigma Xi, Delta Theta Mu, Phi Delta Kappa, Phi Kappa Phi. Clubs: Univ. Yacht (Miami, Fla.); Kiwanis.

LOW, FRANCIS EUGENE, physics educator; b. N.Y.C., Oct. 27, 1921; s. Bela and Eugenia (Ingerman) L.; m. Natalie Sadigur, June 25, 1948; children—Julie, Peter, Margaret. B.S., Harvard U., 1942; M.A., Columbia U., 1947, Ph.D., 1949. Mem. Inst. Advanced Study, 1950-52; asst. prof. U. Ill., Urbana, 1952-55, asso. prof. 1955-56; prof. physics MIT, Cambridge, 1957-67, Karl Taylor Compton prof., 1968-85, Inst. prof., 1985-92, Inst. prof. emeritus, 1992—; dir. Center for Theoretical Physics, 1973-76, dir. Lab. for Nuclear Scis., 1979-80, provost, 1980-85; cons. in field; mem. high energy physics adv. panel Dept. Energy, 1972-76, chmn., 1987-90. Contbr. articles to profl. jours. Served with USAAF, 1942-43; Served with AUS, 1944-46. Mem. NAS (nat. coun. 1986-89), Am. Phys. Soc. (chmn. divsn. particles and fields 1974, councillor-at-large 1979-82), Fedn. Am. Scientists (nat. coun. 1973-77), Am. Acad. Arts and Scis., Internat. Union of Pure and Applied Physics (commn. on particles and fields 1976-82). Home: 28 Adams St Belmont MA 02178-3525 Office: MIT Rm 6-301 Cambridge MA 02139

LOW, FRANK NORMAN, anatomist, educator; b. Bklyn., Feb. 9, 1911; s. William Wans and Hilda (Nelson) L. BA, Cornell U., 1932, PhD, 1936; DSc (hon.), U. N.D., 1983. Postdoctoral Charlton fellow Sch. Medicine Tufts Coll., Boston, 1936-37; instr. to asst. prof. U. N.C., Chapel Hill, 1937-45; assoc. Sch. Medicine U. Md., Balt., 1945-46; assoc. prof. U. W-Va., Morgantown, 1946; asst. prof. Johns Hopkins Med. Sch., Balt., 1946-49; assoc. prof. to prof. anatomy Sch. Medicine La. State U., New Orleans, 1949-64, vis. prof., 1981—; rsch. prof. anatomy U. N.D., Grand Forks, 1964-81, emeritus, 1981—; Chester Fritz Disting. prof., 1975-77; mem. regional rev. bd. Am. Heart Assn., Grand Forks, 1971-74. Author: (with J.A. Freeman) Electron Microscopic Atlas of Normal and Leukemic Human Blood, 1958; assoc. editor Am. Jour. Anatomy, 1971-91; contbr. over 100 rsch. articles to profl. jours. Participant People's Republic China-U.S. exchange program, People to People; citizen ambr. Soviet Union, 1991; del. Anniversary Caravan '91, People to People Internat., Russia, Uzbekistan. Mem. Am. Assn. Anatomists (exec. com. 1976-80, Henry Gray award 1989), Am. Soc. Cell Biology, La. Soc. Electron Microscopy (chmn. 1962), Am. Assn. History of Medicine, World Trade Ctr. (New Orleans), Sigma Xi (pres. U. N.D. chpt. 1977). Avocation: travel, history of medicine. Office: La State Med Ctr Dental Sch 1100 Florida Ave New Orleans LA 70119-2799

LOW, HARRY WILLIAM, judge; b. Oakdale, Calif., Mar. 12, 1931; s. Tong J. and Ying G. (Gong) L.; m. May Ling, Aug. 24, 1952; children: Larry, Kathy, Allan. AA, Modesto Jr. Coll., 1950; AB Polit. Sci. with honors, U. Calif., Berkeley, 1952, LLB, 1955. Bar: Calif. 1955, U.S. Ct. Appeals (9th cir.) 1955. Commr. Workmen's Compensation Commn., 1966; teaching assoc. Boalt Hall, 1955-56; dep. atty. gen. Calif. Dept. Justice, 1956-66; judge Mcpl. Ct., San Francisco, 1966-74; presiding judge Mcpl. Ct., 1972-73; judge Superior Ct., San Francisco, 1974-82; presiding justice Calif.

Ct. Appeals, 1st dist., 1982-92; pres. San Francisco Police Commn., 1992—; mem. Jud. Arbitration and Mediation Svcs., 1992—, Commn. on Future of Cts., 1991-94, Commn. on Future of Legal Profession, 1993—. Contbr. articles to profl. jours. Chmn. bd. Edn. Ctr. for Chinese, 1969—, Chinese-Am. Bilingual Sch.; bd. visitors U.S. Mil. Acad., 1980-83; bd. dirs. Friends of Recreation and Parks, Salesian Boys Club, World Affairs Coun., 1979-85, NCCJ, San Francisco chpt. St. Vincent's Boys Home, Coro Found., 1970-76, San Francisco Zool. Trust, 1987, Union Bank, 1993—; pres. San Francisco City Coll. Found., 1977-87, Inst. Chinese Western History U. San Francisco, 1987-89. Mem. ABA (chmn. appellate judges conf. 1990-91, commr. on minorities), San Francisco Bar Assn., Chinese Am. Citizens Alliance (pres. San Francisco chpt. 1976-77, nat. pres. 1989-93), Calif. Judges Assn. (pres. 1978-79), Calif. Jud. Coun., State Bar Calif. (rsch. editor publs. 1958-76, pub. affairs com. 1987—, exec. bd. 1992—), Calif. Conf. Judges (editor jour. cts. commentary 1973-76), Calif. Judges Assn. (exec. bd.), Asian Bus. League (dir. 1986—), Nat. Ctr. State Cts. (bd. dirs.), San Francisco Bench Bar Media Commn. (chmn. bd. dirs. 1977-87), Nat. Ctr. State Cts. (bd. dirs. 1987—), Phi Alpha Delta. *Try to enjoy whatever task you are doing and enjoy the good company of those with whom you associate. Be an active part of the community and try to improve it. Keep busy and try to understand and respect others.*

LOW, JAMES A., physician; b. Toronto, Ont., Can., Sept. 22, 1925; s. Donald M. and Doris V. (Van Duzer) L.; m. Margery Una, Oct. 5, 1952; children: Donald E., Margeret P., Norman I. M.D., U. Toronto, 1949. Intern Toronto Gen. Hosp., 1949-50; resident in ob-gyn U. Toronto, 1950-54, clin. instr. dept. ob-gyn, 1955-65; fellow ob/gyn Duke U., 1955; prof. and chmn. dept. ob-gyn Queens U., Kingston, Ont., Can., 1965-85; prof. Queens U., 1985—. Mem. editorial bd. Ob-Gyn., 1986-89, Am. Jour. Ob-Gyn., 1995—. Served with Can. Navy, 1943-45. Fellow Royal Coll. Physicians and Surgeons Can. (chmn. splty. com. 1976-82, chmn. manpower com. 1984-92); mem. Assn. Profs. Ob-Gyn Can. (sec.-treas. 1972-80, pres. 1983-84), Am. Gynecol. and Obstet. Soc., Soc. Gynecol. Investigation, Soc. Obstetricians and Gynecologists of Can., Can. Soc. Clin. Investigation, Am. Acad. Cerebral Palsy, Internat. Incontinence Soc. Home: 185 Fairway Hills, Kingston, ON Canada K7M 2B5 Office: Queens U, Dept Ob-Gyn, Kingston, ON Canada K7L 3N6

LOW, JAMES PATTERSON, professional association executive; b. Hartford, Conn., July 25, 1927; s. Marshall and Margaret (Fleming) L.; m. Patricia Marian Siegman, Oct. 20, 1956; children—Lisa Patricia Low Lawson, Lori Patterson. BA, U. Md., 1953; MBA, Fla. Atlantic U., 1972; LLD, Northwood Inst. Mgr. Assn. dept. U.S.C. of C, Washington, 1958-66; pres. Am. Soc. Assn. Execs., 1966-82; chmn., CEO Dynamics, Inc., Washington; chmn. Dynamics Fin. Inc. Bd. dirs. U. Md. Found., U. Md. Sch. Pub. Affairs and Sch. Bus. Decorated Bronze Star, Combat Inf. badge; recipient Key award and named Assn. Exec. of Yr., Assn. Trends mag., 1980. Mem. Congl. Country Club (Bethesda, Md.), Met. Club (Washington), Sigma Nu.

LOW, JOHN WAYLAND, lawyer; b. Denver, Aug. 7, 1923; s. Oscar Wayland and Rachel E. (Stander) L.; m. Merry C. Mullan, July 8, 1979; children: Lucinda A., Jan W. BA, Nebr. Wesleyan U., 1947; JD cum laude, U. Denver, 1951. Bar: Colo. 1951, U.S. Dist. Ct. (Colo. dist.) 1951, U.S. Ct. Appeals (10th cir.), U.S. Supreme Ct. 1960. Ptnr. Sherman & Howard LLC, Denver, 1951-93, counsel, 1993—. Trustee U. Denver, 1987—; chmn. bd. Denver Symphony Assn., 1989-90; vice chmn. Colo. Symphony Assn., 1990—; chmn. Colo. Alliance of Bus., Denver, 1983-87. 1st lt. U.S. Army, 1942-46, CBI. Recipient Learned Hand award Am. Jewish Com., 1989, Outstanding Alumni award U. Denver, 1994. Mem. ABA, Colo. Bar Assn., Denver Bar Assn., University Club of Denver, Garden of Gods Club (Colorado Springs). Republican. Mem. United Ch. of Christ. Office: Sherman & Howard 633 17th St Ste 3000 Denver CO 80202-3665

LOW, JOSEPH, artist; b. Coraopolis, Pa., Aug. 11, 1911; s. John Routh and Stella (Rent) L.; m. Ruth Hull, Oct. 21, 1940; children: Damaris, Jennifer. Student, U. Ill., 1930-32, Art Students League N.Y., 1935. founder, 1959; since propr. Eden Hill Press. Engaged in printmaking and graphic arts, 1942—; exhbns. include, Princeton, Dartmouth, Williams, U. Ill., Phila. Mus. Art, Brandeis U., Grinnell Coll., Carnegie Inst. Tech., Herron Art Inst., Indpls., U. Ky., others; rep. permanent collections, Princeton, Dartmouth, U. Ky., State Dept., Library of Congress, Chapin Library at Williams Coll., U. Ill., Wesleyan U. Middletown, Conn., U. Mass. Fine Arts, San Francisco Pub. Library, Boston Atheneum, Boston Mus. Fine Arts, Harvard Coll. Library, Pratt Inst., U. Okla., Newberry Library, Chgo., Met. Mus. Art, Ohio State U., Bodleian Library, Oxford U., pvt. collections. Home: RFD 278 Chilmark MA 02535

LOW, MORTON DAVID, physician, educator; b. Lethbridge, Alta., Can., Mar. 25, 1935; s. Solon Earl and Alice Fern (Litchfield) L.; m. Cecilia Margaret Comba, Aug. 22, 1959 (div. 1983); children—Cecilia Alice, Sarah Elizabeth, Peter Jon Eric; m. Barbara Joan McLeod, Aug. 25, 1984; 1 child, Kelsey Alexandra. M.D., C.M., Queen's U., 1960, M.Sc. in Medicine, 1962; Ph.D. with honors, Baylor U., 1966. From instr. to asst. prof. Baylor Coll. Medicine, Houston, 1965-68; assoc. prof. medicine U. B.C., Vancouver, Can., 1968-78, prof. medicine, 1978-89, clin. assoc. dean, 1974-76, assoc. dean rsch. and grad. studies, 1977-78, coord. health scis., 1985-89; creator Health Policy Rsch. Unit U. B.C., Vancouver, 1987; dir. U. Tex. Health Sci. Ctr., Houston, 1989—, prof. neural scis. Grad. Sch. Biomed. Scis., 1989—, dir. Health Policy Inst., 1990—; prof. neurology U. Tex. Med. Sch., Houston, 1989—; prof. health policy and mgmt. Sch. Pub. Health U. Tex., 1989—; cons. in neurology U. Hosp. Shaughnessy site, Vancouver, 1971-89, U. B.C. site, Vancouver, 1970-89; dir. dept. diagnostic neurophysiology Vancouver Gen. Hosp., 1968-87; cons. in EEG, 1987-89; exec. dir. Rsch. Inst., 1981-86; mem. med. sci. adv. com. USIA, 1991-93. Mem. editorial bd. numerous jours.; contbr. articles to profl. jours. Bd. dirs. Greater Houston Ptnrship., 1994—; mem. governing bd. Houston Mus. Natural Sci., 1991—; trustee Kinkaid Sch., Houston, 1991—. Med. Rsch. Coun. Can. grantee, 1968-80. Fellow Am. EEG Soc., Royal Coll. Physicians and Surgeons, Royal Soc. Medicine (London); mem. AMA, Tex. Med. Assn. (coun. on med. edn. 1990—), Can. Soc. Clin. Neurophysiology, Internat. Fedn. Socs. for EEG and Clin. Neurophysiology (rules com. 1977-81, sec. 1981-85), Assn. Acad. Health Ctrs. (task force on access to care and orgn. health services 1988—, assoc.chmn. 1992-92, chmn. 1992, task force on instl. values 1989—), Harris County Med. Assn., Am. Coun. Edn., Forum Club of Houston (governing bd. 1991—). Avocations: sailing instructing; photography; youth soccer coach; vol. ski-patrol; flying. Office: U Tex-Houston Health Sci PO Box 20036 Houston TX 77225-0036

LOW, PAUL M., mortgage banking executive, food service executive; b. Flint, Mich., Oct. 27, 1930; s. Samuel and Helen (Freed) L.; m. Nedda Luisa Alcazar, May 23, 1968; children: Lori Ellen Schwartz, Marcia Nedda Millard, Paul M. Jr. JD, U. Miami, 1956. V.p. The Lomas & Nettleton Co. (now Lomas Mortgage USA), Dallas, 1958-79, sr. v.p., 1979-84, exec. v.p., 1984-87, pres., 1987-90; chmn. Enterdine Inc., Dallas, 1991—, New Am. Financial LP, Dallas, 1992—; chmn. New Am. Fin. L.P.; bd. dirs. Capstead Mortgage Corp., Dallas. Bd. dirs. Mental Health Assn. Dallas County, 1986—; v.p. bd. dirs. Mental Health Assn. Tex.; mem. exec. com. North Tex. chpt. March of Dimes, 1985—; past pres., bd. dirs. Cedars Med. Ctr., Miami, 1976—; chmn. Parent's Fund and Adv. Coun. of Kenyon Coll. Staff sgt. USAF, 1950-53. Mem. Fla. Bar Assn., Tex. Bar Assn., Dallas Bar Assn., Mortgage Bankers Assn. of Am., Tex. Real Estate Com. Democrat. Jewish. Club: Brookhaven Country. Avocations: golf, fishing, reading, travel. Office: New Am Financial LP Ste 500 8115 Preston Rd Dallas TX 75225

LOW, PAUL REVERE, business machine company executive; b. Elizabeth, N.J., Mar. 16, 1933; s. Paul R. and Bertha (Branch) L.; m. Anne Goodrich; children: John, Paul Jr., Lynda, Scott. BSEE, U. Vt., 1955, MS in Physics, 1957; PhD in EE, Stanford U., 1963. Dir. East Fishkill (N.Y.) Lab. IBM Corp., 1969-70; asst. gen. mgr. mfg. IBM Corp., Burlington, Vt., 1970-71; gen. mgr. IBM Corp., Burlington, 1971-74; dir. devel. system Products div. IBM Corp., East Fishkill and Poughkeepsie, N.Y., 1974-75, v.p. devel. and mfg., System Products div., 1975; devel. lab. dir. East Fishkill div. IBM Corp., 1979-80, gen. mgr. East Fishkill div., 1981-83; v.p. Gen. Tech. div. IBM Corp., N.Y., 1983-84; v.p. IBM Corp., White Plains, N.Y., 1984—; bd.

dirs. Dutchess Bank & Trust Co, Poughkeepsie; trustee Rensselaer Poly. Inst. Trustee Marist Coll., Poughkeepsie, 1982—; gen. mgr. United Way Dutchess County, 1983. Fellow IEEE; mem. Am. Electronics Assn., Sigma Xi, Nu Beta Pi. Club: Indian Harbor Yacht (Greenwich, Conn.). Office: IBM Corp Gen Products Divsn RR 1 Somers NY 10589

LOW, PETER W., legal educator; b. Springfield, Mass., May 17, 1937; s. George W. and Doris J. Low; m. Carol Randolph, Sept. 10, 1960; children: Cathryn E., Diana R. AB, Princeton U., 1959; LLB, U. Va., 1963. Bar: Va. 1963, U.S. Supreme Ct. 1970. Law clk. to Chief Justice Earl Warren, U.S. Supreme Ct., Washington, 1963-64; mem. faculty U. Va. Law Sch., Charlottesville, 1964—, asst. dean, 1965-69; assoc. dean, 1969-76, 89-94, Hardy Cross Dillard prof. law, 1975—, v.p., provost, 1994—; vis. prof. Inst. Criminology, Cambridge, Eng., 1970; Salzburg Seminars in Am. Studies, 1972; U. Pa. Law Sch., 1974-75, Stanford Law Sch., 1977; cons. FBI Acad., Quantico, Va., 1972—. Mem. Am. Law Inst., Va. Bar Assn., Order of Coif. Author: (with Jeffries and Bonnie) Criminal Law-Cases and Materials, 2d edit., 1986; (with Jeffries) ALI, Model Penal Code and Commentaries, Part II, 3 vols., 1980, others. Office: U Va Sch Law Madison Hall Charlottesville VA 22901

LOW, PHILIP FUNK, soil chemistry educator, consultant, researcher; b. Carmangay, Alta., Can., Oct. 15, 1921; came to U.S., 1940; s. Philip and Pearl Helena (Funk) L.; m. Mayda Matilda Stewart, June 11, 1942; children—Roseanne, Jeannine, Philip, Lasca, Lorraine, Martin. B.S., Brigham Young U., 1943; M.S., Calif. Inst. Tech., 1944; Ph.D., Iowa State U., 1949. Soil chemistry faculty, agronomy dept. Purdue U., West Lafayette, Ind., 1949—, prof. soil chemistry, 1955-92, prof. emeritus, 1992—; cons. Exxon Prodn. Rsch. Co., Houston, 1960-80, Cold Regions Rsch. Lab., U.S. Army, Hanover, N.H., 1962-67, Battelle, Pacific N.W. Labs., 1980-81, U.S. Salinity Lab., Riverside, Calif., summer 1962; hon. prof. Zhejiang Agrl. U., Hangzhou, Peoples Republic of China, 1987—. Cons. editor Soil Sci., 1957—, Geoderma, 1981-88, Jour. Colloid and Interface Sci., 1993—; assoc. editor Clays and Clay Minerals, 1960-66; contbr. articles to profl. jours.; patentee in field. Pres., Indpls. Stake, Ch. of Jesus Christ of Latter Day Saints, 1959-73; regional rep. Ind. Regions, Ch. of Jesus Christ of Latter Day Saints, 1977-83; bd. dirs. Opera de Lafayette, 1984-85. Served to 1st lt. Air Corps, U.S. Army, 1943-45. Recipient Ann. Research award Purdue chpt. Sigma Xi, 1960, Disting. Visitor award to Australia, Fulbright Ednl. Exchange Program, 1968, Disting. Service award Brigham Young U., 1976, Herbert Newby McCoy Research award Purdue U., 1980; Thurburn Vis. fellow U. Sydney, 1983. Fellow Am. Soc. Agronomy (bd. dirs.), Soil Sci. Soc. Am. (pres.-elect 1971-72, pres. 1972-73, bd. dirs. 1971-74, Soil Sci. Achievement award 1963, Bouyoucus Disting. Career award 1984, Soil Sci. Disting. Svc. award 1993); mem. NAS, Clay Minerals Soc. (Disting. Mem. award 1992), Internat. Soc. Soil Sci., Internat. Assn. for Study Clays. Avocations: collecting art, classical music, hiking, collecting crystal, jade, ceramics. Home: 340 Hollowood Dr West Lafayette IN 47906-2146 Office: Purdue U Agronomy Dept West Lafayette IN 47907

LOW, RICHARD H., broadcasting executive, producer; b. Union City, N.J., Feb. 20, 1927; s. Irving and Regina (Krieger) L.; 1 dau., Jennifer Alix-e. Student, U. Mich., 1947-49; J.D., Columbia U., 1952. With CBS News, 1952-56; with CBS-TV Network, 1956-62, dir. contracts, facilities and program sales, 1959-62; with Young & Rubicam, 1962-84, v.p. TV-radio dept., 1970-72, v.p. programming 1972-73, sr. v.p., 1973-81, responsible for network TV programming and purchasing, 1973-84, includes cable TV, 1984, exec. v.p., dir. broadcast programming and purchasing, 1981-84; pres. Manticore Prodns., Inc. 1985—; pres. Universal Holding Co.; advisor LWV presdl. TV debates, 1980; judge N.Y. World TV Festival, 1979-80, Internat. Emmy awards, 1981-83; panelist Nat. Assn. TV Programming Execs. Conf. 1981; keynote speaker 25th Anniversary seminar, Broadcasters Promotion Assn., 1981; presentor S.I. Newhouse Sch. Pub. Communications, 1981; discussant Ctr. for Communications, 1982. Writer, dir. radio dramas. Mem. media task force Nat. Coun. Arts, 1977, Aspen Inst., 1973; v.p., trustee Am. Mus. Immigration; trustee Town Hall Found.; bd. dirs. U.S Organizing com. 1983 Bicentennial of Air and Space. With U.S. Army, 1945-46. Mem. NATAS (gov. N.Y. 1979-83). Office: 1056 Fifth Ave New York NY 10028-0112 *In the beginner's mind, there are many possibilities.*

LOW, STEPHEN, foundation executive, educator, former diplomat; b. Cin., Dec. 2, 1927; s. Martin and Margaret (Friend) L.; m. Helen Sue Carpenter, Oct. 9, 1954; children: Diego, Rodman, Jesse. B.A., Yale U., 1950; M.A., Fletcher Sch. Law and Diplomacy, Tufts U., 1951, Ph.D., 1956. With Dept. State, various locations, 1956-74; sr. staff mem. NSC, 1974-76; U.S. ambassador to Zambia, 1976-79, U.S. ambassador to Nigeria, 1979-81; dep. Fgn. Service Inst. Dept. State, 1982-87; dir. Bologna (Italy) Ctr. Sch. Advanced Internat. Studies Johns Hopkins U., 1987-92; pres. Assn. Diplomatic Studies and Tng., 1992—. Served with AUS, 1946-47. Address: 2855 Tilden St NW Washington DC 20008

LOWD, JUDSON DEAN, oil and gas processing equipment manufacturing executive; b. Chelsea, Mass., June 8, 1918; s. Dana Joseph and Olive Wanda (Dean) L.; m. Alice Carroll, Sept. 6, 1975; 1 dau., Dana. BS in Mech. Engring. with honors, Worcester Poly. Inst., Mass., 1940. Mgr. oil field equipment div. Parkersburg Rig & Reel Co., W.Va., 1948-56; exec. v.p. internat. mktg. ops. C-E Natco, Tulsa, 1957-73, pres., 1973-82; chmn. C-E Randall, 1980-84; bd. dirs. Ocean Corp., Houston; pres. Nat. Tank France, Paris; vice chmn. Williams TEch., Inc.1985-90. Trustee U. Tulsa, 1977-87, Goodland Children's Home, Hugo, Okla., 1976-82, Lebanese Am. U., Beirut, 1973-87, dir. and overseer acads.; bd. dirs. Jr. Achievement Tulsa, 1978-81, Tulsa United Way, 1975-80; elder Presbyn. Ch., 1954—; pres. Tulsa Execs. Svc. Corps, 1987. Officer AUS, 1941-48, ETO. Decorated Bronze Star; named Marketer of Year, Am. Mktg. Assn., 1974. Mem. ASME (life), Inst. Petroleum (U.K.), Tulsa C. of C. (dir.), Sigma Xi, Tau Beta Pi. Republican. Clubs: So. Hills Country, Tulsa, Tulsa So. Tennis (Tulsa); Lost Hound Hunt (Edmond, Okla.). Office: Philtower Bldg Ste 815 427 S Boston Tulsa OK 74103

LOWDEN, JOHN L., retired corporate executive; b. Yakima, Wash., Oct. 29, 1921; s. Roy Ruben and Hildegarde Annie (Grommesch) L.; m. Janet Katherine Langan, Jan. 21, 1961; children: Susan Elizabeth, Jonathan Roy, Andrew Matthias. B.A., U. Nev., 1949. Account supr. Campbell-Ewald Advt., 1951-57, Erwin, Wasey Advt., 1957-59; advt. dir. Gen. Dynamics Corp., 1959-61; account supr. Foote, Cone & Belding, 1961-63; with ITT Corp., 1963-84, v.p. corp. rels. and advt., 1977-84. Author: Silent Wings at War, 1992. Served with USAAF, 1941-45. Decorated Air Medal with Oak Leaf Cluster and Order of William by the Queen of The Netherlands; seven unit battle stars. Roman Catholic.

LOWDEN, SCOTT RICHARD, lawyer; b. Stamford, Conn., Feb. 28, 1940; s. Elmer W. and Edna L.; m. Nancy Reyna Todd, Sept. 1, 1962; children: Scott, Chris. BA, Wesleyan U., Middletown, Conn., 1962; Fulbright fellow, U. Madrid, 1962-63; LLB, Harvard U., 1966. Bar: Mass. bar 1967, N.C. bar 1977. Atty. United Fruit Co., Boston, 1966-70, Textron Inc., Providence, 1970-75; v.p., gen. counsel Korf Industries, Inc., Charlotte, N.C., 1975-81; solo practice Charlotte, N.C., 1981-85; ptnr. Cannon & Blair, 1985-88; dep. gen. counsel NCNB Tex., Dallas, 1989-92; v.p. law Am. Airlines, Dallas-Ft. Worth, 1992-93; v.p., gen. counsel INDRESCO Inc., Dallas, 1994—. Mem. ABA. Home: 9205 Westwind Ct Dallas TX 75231

LOWDEN, SUZANNE, state legislator; b. Camden, N.J., Feb. 8, 1952; m. Paul W. Lowden; children: Christopher, Jennifer, Paul, William. BA magna cum laude, Am. U.; MA cum laude, Fairleigh Dickinson U. Resort industry exec.; mem. Nev. State Senate, 1993—, majority whip, 1993—. Active Juvenile Diabetes Found., United Way of So. Nev. With USO, 1971, Vietnam. Recipient Woman of Achievement award Women's Leag. Las Vegas C. of C. Republican. Home: 992 Pinehurst Dr Las Vegas NV 89109 Office: Nev State Senate State Capitol Carson City NV 89710

LOWDER, RACHAEL DELLA, company executive, consultant; b. Winston Salem, N.C., July 10, 1942; d. Fred Noah and Evelyn Lucille (Mock) Motsinger; m. Larry L. Lowder, Feb. 8, 1964 (div. 1976); children: Jon Sheldon, Russell Stephen. BA, Wake Forest U., 1964; MS, N.C. State U., 1972. Tchr. various schs., 1964-72; editor, mgr. gen. svcs. Nat. Assn. Coll. Univ. Bus. Officers, Washington, 1973-77; pub. mgr., dir. pub. rels. Am.

Automobile Assn., Falls Church, Va., 1977-80; dir. publicity and info. Resources for the Future, Inc., Washington, 1980-84; dir. comm., v.p. comm. and mktg., exec. v.p. World Pres.' Orgn., Washington, 1985—; editor, publicity cons. Project on the Fed. Social Rose, Washington, 1984-85, Am. Automobile Assn., Falls Church, 1989; editor Integon Corp., Winston-Salem, 1987-88; editor, rsch. asst. Bowman Gray Sch. of Medicine, Winston-Salem, 1989-90. Pub. rels. com. Fairfax (Va.) Symphony, 1979-86; bd. dirs. D.C. Bur. of Rehab., Washington, 1985-87, Young Audiences of D.C., Washington. Mem. Am. Soc. Assn. Exec., Greater Washington Soc. Assn. Execs. Office: World Pres Orgn 601 Pennsylvania Ave NW Ste 520 Washington DC 20004-2660

LOWE, CAROL HILL, social services director; b. Washington, Sept. 12, 1943; d. Lawrence Alexander and Corinne (Thorne) Hill; m. John W. Lowe, Nov., 1968 (div. 1981); 1 child, Paul Alejandro. BA cum laude, Albright Coll., 1965; MSW summa cum laude, Howard U., 1967; cert., John F. Kennedy Sch. of Govt., 1986. Caseworker Child Welfare Dept., City of Washington, 1966-67; caseworker welfare U.S. Dept. Pub. Welfare, Washington, 1967-68, Child Welfare Dept., City of Washington, 1968-70; sr. worker, supr. Social Rehab. Agy., 1970-78; assoc. chief Office of Maternal and Child Health, 1978-82; spl. asst. Office of City Adminstr., 1982-85; exec. dir. DC Commn. for Women, 1986—. Mem. Task Force on Pay Equity, Older Adult Learning Com., Child Devel. Coordinating Coun., Employment and Tng. Coalition, Washington, 1985—, D.C. Child Support Advocacy Coalition and Adv. Com., Instl. Appeals Bd., Domestic Ptnrship. Commn.; bd. dirs. Washington Urban League, 1968—, chairperson, 1983-85; bd. dirs. DC United Way, 1984—, Nat. Assn. Commns. for Women, Women in Mcpl. Govt.; mem. Leadership Washington Bd. Trade/Jr. League Program, 1987. Fellow Nat. Assn. Social Workers (cert.); mem. NOW, Black Women's Agenda, Nat. Coun. Negro Women, Assn. Black Women Attys., D.C. Urban Mgmt. Assn., Nat. Assn. Black Pub. Adminstrs., Bus. Profl. Women U.S.A. Democrat. Episcopalian. Office: DC Commn for Women 2000 14th St NW Washington DC 20009-4473

LOWE, CLAYTON KENT, visual imagery, cinema, and video educator; b. Endicott, N.Y., July 10, 1936; s. Clayton Edwin and Loretta Arlene (Terry) L.; m. Janet E. Snider, 1957 (div. 1977); children: Steven Scott, Kim Ann Parker, David William, Rebecca Michelle Sobel; m. Robin S. McKell, 1980 (div. 1993). BA, Bethany Coll., 1958; MS, Butler U., 1967; PhD, Ohio State U., 1970; BD, Christian Theol. Sem., Indpls., 1962. Pastor Bellaire (Ohio) Christian Ch., 1957-58, Beallsville (Ohio) Christian Ch., 1958, Russellville (Ind.) Christian Ch., 1958-60, Montclair (Ind.) Christian Ch., 1960-61; youth dir. St. Paul United Ch. of Christ, Columbus, 1967-70; asst. prof. journalism U. Ga., 1970-72; asst. prof. communications Ohio State U., Columbus, 1972-73, asst. prof. photography and cinema, 1973-74, assoc. prof., 1974—, chairperson photography and cinema, 1974-78, dir. grad. studies photography and cinema, 1989-92; assoc. prof. emeritus Ohio State U. 1992—; comml. TV prodr., dir. writer Stas. WISH-TV, 1960-66, WLWI-TV, 1966-67, WOSU-TV, 1967-70; moderator World Film Classics, Educable TV-25, 1991—; also bd. dirs.; E.R.I.C. evaluator-film theory, 1973-78; juror Columbus Internat. Film and TV Festival, 1993, 94. Book reviewer The Arts Edn. Rev. of Books; editor: The Movies on Media Catalog, 1995. Eli Lilly Found. grantee, 1961-63, Ohio State U. Devel. of Media on Media Study Collection grantee, 1985; Recipient Casper award for A Thing Called Hope, WISH-TV, 1966, Regional Emmy for A Tribute to Dr. King, WOSU-TV, 1968; nominated for regional Emmys for Lucasville, WOSU-TV, 1970, High Street, WOSU-TV, 1975. Mem. NATAS (bd. govs. Ohio chpt. 1973-74), AAAS, Univ. Film and Video Assn. (pres.), Ohio State U. Dept. Photography and Cinema Alumni Assn. (pres. 1994—, bd. dirs. 1994—), Kiwanis Internat. Home: 68 Walhalla Rd Columbus OH 43202-1441

LOWE, DONALD CAMERON, corporate executive; b. Oshawa, Ont., Can., Jan. 29, 1932; s. Samuel John and Carales Isobel (Cox) L.; m. Susan Margaret Plunkett, July 22, 1955; children: Michelle, Jeffrey, Steven. B.Applied Sci., U. Toronto, 1954; M.S. (Athlone fellow 1957), U. Birmingham, Eng., 1957; grad. internat. sr. mgrs. seminar, Harvard U., 1975. With Gen. Motors Can. Ltd., 1957-71; asst. gen. mgr., then gen. mgr. Gen. Motors Can. Ltd., St. Therese, Que., 1969-71; dir. mfg. Vauxhall Motors Ltd., Luton, Eng., 1971-75; pres., chief exec. officer Pratt & Whitney Aircraft Ltd., Can., 1975-80; also chmn. bd.; pres. comml. products div. Pratt & Whitney Aircraft Group, East Hartford, Conn., 1980-82; chmn., chief exec. officer Allied Can. Inc., 1982-83; pres., chief exec. officer Kidd Creek Mines Ltd., 1983-86, Canadair div. Bombardier Inc., Montreal, 1986-92—; bd. dirs. Bayridge Resources, Trilon Fin., Can. Tire Corp., Alta Natural Gas, Devtek Corp., Scott's Hospitality, Fleet Aerospace, Butler Svc. Group; chmn. Sedgwick Ltd., Bombardier, Inc., Ingersoll-Rand Can., Haley Industries, Exal Aluminum Inc., Strongco. Bd. govs. Université de Montréal; hon. dir. Can. Aviation Hall of Fame. Mem. Aerospace Industries Assn. Can., Conf. Bd. Can., Les Ambassadeurs Club (London), Muskoka Lakes Golf and Country Club (Port Carling), Donalda Club, Granite Club, Cambridge Club (Toronto). Office: Sedgwick Ltd, PO Box 439 Toronto Dominion Ctr, Toronto, ON Canada M5K 1M3

LOWE, FELIX CALEB, publishing executive; b. Mountain City, Tenn., Nov. 12, 1933; s. Ned Tillie and Sarah (Lochery) L.; m. Susan Johnson, Nov. 24, 1961; children: Christopher, Joshua. B.S., East Tenn. State U., 1959, postgrad., 1960; postgrad., Ga. State U., Statesboro, 1961, Fed. Exec. Inst., Charlottesville, Va., 1983. Tchr. Arlington County Bd. Edn., Va., 1959-62; editor, mktg. mgr. Macmillan Co., N.Y.C., 1962-68; mktg. dir. Entelek Inc., Newburyport, Mass., 1968-69; sales mgr. Brookings Instn., Washington, 1969-76; dir. Smithsonian Instn. Press, Washington, 1976-94; with U.Va., 1994; pub. Rivilo Books, Bluffton, S.C., 1994—; lectr. George Washington U., 1978—, Howard U., East Tenn. State U.; mem. adv. bd. Nat. Hist. Pub. and Records Com., Washington, 1978—; mem. U.S. pub. del. to Soviet Union, 1987. Author: John Ross: Cherokee Indian Chief, 1989. Coach, Little River Soccer Club, Annandale Boys Club, Braddock Road Youth Club, 1974—. Named Alumni of Yr., East Tenn. State U. 1981. Mem. Assn. Am. Univ. Presses, Washington Book Pubs. (co-founder, exec. sec. 1981-82). Baptist. Club: Nat. Press (Washington). Home: 113 Gascoigne Bluff Rd Bluffton SC 29910 Office: Rivilo Books 113 Gascoigne Bluff Rd Bluffton SC 29910

LOWE, FLORENCE SEGAL, retired public relations executive; b. N.Y.C.; d. Samuel I. and Rose (Cantor) Segal; BS in Edn., U. Pa., 1930; postgrad. Sch. Social Svc., 1935-36; m. Herman Albert Lowe, June 27, 1935; children: Lesley Ellen Lowe Israel, Roger Bernard. Guidance counsellor Phila. Pub. Schs., 1935-41; Washington corr. Variety and Daily Variety, Phila. Daily News, Manchester Union Leader, TV Guide, 1942-58; spl. pub. rels. Radio Sta. WIP, Phila. and Metromedia, 1958-60; coord. spl. projects Metromedia, 1960-70; spl. asst. to chmn. pub. affairs NEA, Washington, 1970-86; sr. cons. arts and cultural comm. Kamber Group, 1986-93, ret., 1994. Mem. pub. rels. and advt. com. Nat. Symphony, 1952-56; mem. Sec. State's Commn. on Travel, 1970-71; mem. Coordinating Com. for Ellis Island, 1982-87; mem. Com. for Nancy Hanks Endowment for Arts, Duke U. Recipient All-Army Entertainment Contest award, 1958; spl. achievement award Nat. Endowment for Arts Chmn., 1983; Spl. Merit award Fed. Govt., 1981, Spl. Achievement award, 1983, Disting. Svc. award, 1985. Mem. Am. Women in Radio and TV (founder, pres. 1954-55), Am. News Women's Club (Woman of Yr. com.), Coun. Jewish Women, Women in Communications (citation for meritorious reporting 1962), Nat. Press Club, Women's Nat. Press Club (treas. 1954, v.p. 1956), Washington Press Club (bd. dirs. 1968-71, 83-84), Am. News Women's Club (v.p. 1969-70), Washington Press Club Found. Home: 2801 New Mexico Ave NW Washington DC 20007-3921 Office: Kamber Group 1920 L St NW Washington DC 20036-5004

LOWE, FRANK BUDGE, business executive; b. Aug. 23, 1941; s. Stephen and Marion Lowe; 2 children. Student, Westminster Sch. Founder, chmn. The Lowe Group, N.Y.C., 1981—; bd. dirs. Interpub. USA. Avocations: tennis, skiiing, shooting. Office: The Lowe Group 1345 Avenue Of The Americas New York NY 10105-0010

LOWE, HARRY, museum director; b. Opelika, Ala., Apr. 9, 1922; s. Harry Foster and Lois (Fletcher) L. B.F.A., Auburn U., 1943, M.F.A., 1949; student, Cranbrook Acad., 1951, 53. Prof. art, dir. Art Gallery, Auburn U., 1957-59; dir. Tenn. Fine Arts Center, Nashville, 1959-64; curator exhibits Nat. Mus. Am. Art (formerly Nat. Collection Fine Arts), Smithsonian

Instn., 1964-72, dep. commr. U.S. Exhbn. at Venice Biennale, 1966, asst. dir. for ops., 1972-74, asst. dir., 1974-81, acting dir., 1981-82, dep. dir., 1983-84, dep. dir. emeritus, 1985—; 1st pres. Tenn. Assn. Museums, 1960. Served with F.A. AUS, World War II, ETO. Home: 802 A St SE Washington DC 20003-1340 Office: Nat Mus Am Art Smithsonian Instn Washington DC 20560

LOWE, JAMES ALLEN, school superintendent; b. Pocatello, Idaho, Aug. 10, 1936; s. James Merwin and Ruby (Bennett) L.; m. Joanne Stanger, Dec. 28, 1955; children—Jill, Jann, James, Jeffrey A., Julie, Jared G. A. S., Weber Coll., 1956; B.S., U. Utah, 1958; M.S., N.Mex. Highlands Coll., 1963; Ed.D. Utah State U., 1973. Tchr. math., sci. Davis Sch. Dist., Farmington, Utah, 1961-68; grad. asst. Utah State U., Logan, 1968-69; asst. prof. Brigham Young U.-Hawaii campus, Laie Hawaii, 1969-71; tchr. math. Viewmont High Sch., Bountiful, Utah, 1971-74; prin. Star Valley High Sch., Afton, Wyo., 1974-77; supt. Lincoln County Sch. Dist. #2, Afton, 1977—; recipient Nat. Superintendent of the Yr. awd., Wyoming, Am. Assn. of School Administrators, 1992. Co-editor Brigham young U. Hawaii Edn. Dept., 1970-71. Contbr. articles to profl. jours. Bishop Ch. of Jesus Christ of Latter-day Saints, Afton, 1978-83. NSF fellow, 1962, 67. Mem. Wyo. Assn. Sch. Admnstrs., Phi Delta Kappa. Home: 366 E 5th Ave Afton WY 83110 Office: Lincoln County Sch Dist #2 PO Box 219 Afton WY 83110-0219

LOWE, JOHN, III, consulting civil engineer; b. N.Y.C., Mar. 14, 1916; s. John and Rose Marie (Jahoda) L.; m. Jeanne Wright, June 19, 1943; children: Jonathan Alan, Barbara Jean, Heather Ellen. B.S. in Engring., CCNY; M.S.C.E., MIT. Registered profl. engr., N.Y., La., PR., Calif. Instr. U. Md., College Park, 1937-40, MIT, Cambridge, Mass., 1941-44; physicist David Taylor Model Basin, Carderock, Md., 1945; chief soils engr. Tippetts-Abbett-McCarthy-Stratton, N.Y.C., 1945-55, assoc. ptnr., 1956-62, ptnr., 1962-83; pvt. practice cons., 1984—; adj. assoc. prof. NYU, 1949-51; lectr. soil mechanics CCNY, 1953-60; 8th Terzaghi lectr., 1971, 4th Nabor Carrillo lectr., 1978, 2d U.S. Com. on Large Dams lectr., 1982, Marty Kapp lectr., 1986; keynote address Roller Compacted Concrete II, 1988; cons. Corps. Engrs., Washington, 1962-80. Contbr. chpts. to 4 books, 38 articles in field to profl. jours. Decorated comdr. Order of Alouites (Morocco); recipient Townsend Harris medal Alumni CCNY, 1982. Fellow ASCE; mem. NAE, U.S. Com. Large Dam (chmn. 1977-78), Nat. Com. Soil Mechanics and Found. Engring., Moles, Univ. Club, Bronxville Field Club.

LOWE, JOHN BURTON, molecular biology educator, pathologist; b. Sheridan, Wyo., June 13, 1953; s. Burton G. and Eunice D. Lowe. BA, U. Wyo., 1976; MD, U. Utah, 1980. Diplomate Am. Bd. Pathology. Asst. med. dir. Barnes Hosp. Blood Bank, St. Louis, 1985-86; instr. Sch. of Medicine Washington U., St. Louis, 1985, asst. prof. Sch. of Medicine, 1985-86; asst. investigator Howard Hughes Med. Inst., Ann Arbor, Mich., 1986-92, assoc. investigator, 1992—; asst. prof. Med. Sch. U. Mich., Ann Arbor, 1986-91, assoc. prof. Med. Sch., 1991—. Contbr. articles to Jour. Biol. Chemistry, Genes and Devel., Nature, Cell. Office: U Mich Howard Hughes Med 1150 W Medical Center Dr Ann Arbor MI 48109-0726

LOWE, JONATHAN WAYNE, lawyer; b. Miami, Dec. 15, 1947. BS, U. Pa., 1970; JD, Harvard U., 1975. Bar: U.S. Dist. Ct. (no. dist.) Ga. 1975. Assoc. Alston & Bird, Atlanta, 1975-82, ptnr., 1982—. Trustee Paideia Sch., Atlanta, 1986—; mem. Leadership Atlanta, 1989. 1st lt. U.S. Army, 1970-72. Recipient Spl. Vol. award Gov. of State Ga., 1985. Mem. Ansley Golf Club. Office: Alston & Bird 1201 W Peachtree St NW Atlanta GA 30309-3400

LOWE, JUSTUS FREDERICK, JR., software company executive; b. Mpls., Sept. 27, 1927; s. Justus Frederick and Frances (Passmore) L.; m. Mary Cardle, Sept. 7, 1951; children: Meredith Ann, Justus Frederick III, Cynthia Evans, John Passmore. A.B. cum laude, Princeton U., 1950; M.B.A., Harvard U., 1952. Mgr. def. systems mktg. Univac div. Sperry Rand Corp., mgr. Univac mil. systems and product applications, mgr. def. products; gen. mgr. Boston Microwave products div. Control Data Corp., 1972-74, gen. mgr. Boston Systems div., 1968-72, eastern regional mgr. research and devel. and spl. systems, 1964-68; dir., chmn., pres., chief exec. officer SofTech, Inc., Waltham, Mass., 1979-91, chmn., 1991—; bd. dirs Associated Industries of Mass. Office: SofTech Inc 460 Totten Pond Rd Waltham MA 02154

LOWE, KATHLENE WINN, lawyer; b. San Diego, Dec. 1, 1949; d. Ralph and Grace (Rodes) Winn; m. Russell Howells Lowe, Oct. 7, 1977; 1 child, Taylor Rhodes. BA in English magna cum laude, U. Utah, 1971, MA in English, 1973, JD, 1976. Bar: Utah 1976, U.S. Dist. Ct. Utah 1976, U.S. Ct. Appeals (10th cir.) 1980, Calif. 1989, U.S. Dist. Ct. (ctrl. dist.) Calif. 1990. Assoc. Parsons, Behle & Latimer, Salt Lake City, 1976-80, ptnr., 1980-84; v.p. law Skaggs Alpha Beta Inc., Salt Lake City; now ptnr. Brobeck, Phleger & Harrison, Newport Beach, Calif. Contbg. editor Utah Law Rev., 1975-76. Mem. ABA, Utah Bar Assn., Salt Lake City Bar Assn., Phi Kappa Phi. Avocations: fly fishing, reading, skiing, golfing, traveling. Office: Brobeck Phleger & Harrison 4675 MacArthur Ct Ste 1000 Newport Beach CA 92660-1884

LOWE, KENNETH STEPHEN, magazine editor; b. St. Paul, July 18, 1921; s. Malcolm and Erma Alta (Henderson) L.; m. Marie Elizabeth Contway, June 18, 1949; children—Stephen, Scott, Stuart. B.A., U. Mich., 1948. Telegraph editor Daily Mining Jour., Marquette, Mich., 1948-51, assoc. editor, 1951-55, editor, 1955-72; various pub. relations positions Mich., 1972-75; editor Mich. United Conservation Clubs, Lansing, 1975—. Mem. Mich. Conservation Commn., Lansing, 1961-63; pres. Upper Peninsula Child Guidance Clinic, Marquette, 1965-66, Peter White Library Bd., 1965-67. Mem. Outdoor Writers Assn. Am., Mich. Outdoor Writers Assn. (award 1951-52), Mich. United Conservation Clubs (Merit award 1958, Spl. Conservation award 1987). Democrat. Avocations: hunting; fishing; dogs; birding. Home: 1037 Blanchette Dr East Lansing MI 48823-1821

LOWE, MARVIN, artist; b. Bklyn., May 19, 1922; m. Juel Watkins, Apr. 1, 1949; 1 dau., Melissa. Student, Julliard Sch. Music, 1952-54; BA, Bklyn. Coll., 1956; MFA, U. Iowa, 1961. Prof. fine arts Ind. U., Bloomington, 1968-92; vis. artist-lectr. in colls., mus., univs., 1970—. Exhibited in 54 one-man shows; over 200 group and invitational exhbns.; participated in U.S. info. exhbns. in Latin Am., Japan, USSR, and most of European countries; represented in 84 permanent collections including Phila. Mus. Art, Bklyn. Mus., Smithsonian Instn., Brit. Mus., Japan Print Assn., N.Y.C. Pub. Library, Calif. Palace of Legion of Honor, San Francisco, Boston Pub. Library, Columbia U., Libr. of Congress, Indpls. Mus. Art, Ringling Mus., Honolulu Acad. Art, Ft. Wayne Mus. Art, Purdue U., Mus. Fine Art, Springfield, Mass. Served with USNR, 1942-45. Fellow Nat. Endowment for Arts, 1975; fellow Ford Found., 1979, Ind. Arts Commn., 1987; recipient numerous Purchase awards, 1960—. Office: Ind U Sch Fine Arts Bloomington IN 47405 *As a visual artist, I have tried to refrain from making public statements about my work which ultimately must speak for itself. As a teacher of art, I have tried to communicate what I have learned about art throughout my life, hoping to motivate my students as best I can to try to make their own contribution in the future through their lives and their work.*

LOWE, MARY FRANCES, federal government official; b. Ft. Meade, Md., Apr. 15, 1952; d. Benno Powers and Peggy Catherine (Moore) L. B.A. Coll. William and Mary, 1972; M.A., Fletcher Sch. Law and Diplomacy, 1974, M.A. Law and Diplomacy in, 1975; diplome, Grad. Inst. Internat. Studies U. Geneva, Switzerland, 1975; M.P.H. in epidemiology, Johns Hopkins Sch. Hygiene and Pub. Health, 1986. External collaborator ILO, Geneva, 1974; legis. asst. to U.S. Senator Richard S. Schweiker Washington, 1975-76; profl. staff mem. health and sci. rsch. subcom. U.S. Senate Com. Labor and Human Resources, Washington, 1976-81; sci. div. U.S. Dept. HHS, Washington, 1981-85; sr. asst. to commr. program policy FDA, 1985-89; sr. asst. pesticide programs EPA, 1989—; rep. U.S. delegations 34th and 35th World Health Assemblies, Geneva, 1981, 82; alt. trustee Woodrow Wilson Internat. Ctr. Scholars. Mem. Soc. for Epidemiologic Rsch., Am. Assn. World Health, Exec. Women in Govt., Soc. Risk Analysis, Washington World Affairs Coun., Delta Omega. Home: 7920 Spotswood Dr Alexandria VA 22308-1125 Office: EPA 401 M St SW Washington DC 20460-0001

LOWE, MARY JOHNSON, federal judge; b. N.Y.C., June 10, 1924; m. Ivan A. Michael, Nov. 4, 1961; children: Edward H. Lowe, Leslie H. Lowe, Bess J. Michael. BA, Hunter Coll., 1952; LLB, Bklyn. Law Sch., 1954; LLM, Columbia U., 1955; LLD, CUNY, 1990. Bar: N.Y. 1955. Pvt. practice law N.Y.C., 1955-71; judge N.Y.C. Criminal Ct., 1971-72; acting justice N.Y. State Supreme Ct., 1972-74; judge Bronx County Supreme Ct., 1974; justice N.Y. State Supreme Ct., 1977, 1st Jud. Dist., 1978; judge U.S. Dist. Ct. (so. dist.) N.Y., 1978-91, sr. judge, 1991—. Recipient award for outstanding service to criminal justice system Bronx County Criminal Cts. Bar Assn., 1974, award for work on narcotics cases Asst. Dist. Attys., 1974. Mem. Women in Criminal Justice, Harlem Lawyers Assn., Bronx Criminal Lawyers Assn., N.Y. County Lawyers Assn., Bronx County Bar Assn., N.Y. State Bar Assn. (award for outstanding jud. contbn. to criminal justice Sect. Criminal Justice 1978), NAACP, Nat. Urban League, Nat. Council Negro Women, NOW. Office: US Dist Ct US Courthouse Foley Sq New York NY 10007-1501

LOWE, RALPH EDWARD, lawyer; b. Hinsdale, Ill., Nov. 24, 1931; s. Charles Russell and Eva Eleanor (Schroeder) L.; m. Patricia E. Eichhorst, Aug. 23, 1952; children: John Stuart, Michael Kevin, Timothy Edward. BA, Depauw U., 1953; LLB, U. Ill., 1956. Bar: Ill. 1956, U.S. Dist. Ct. (no. dist.) Ill. 1957, Ga. 1974, U.S. Dist. Ct. (no. dist.) Ga. 1980, S.C. 1990. Assoc. Ruddy & Brown, Aurora, Ill., 1956-58; ptnr. Lowe & Richards, Aurora, 1959-62, Vincent, Lowe & Richards, Aurora, 1963-71; pvt. practice Aurora, 1972-74, Aurora and Atlanta, 1974-85; ptnr. Lowe & Steinmetz, Ltd., Aurora and Atlanta, 1985-91; chmn. Inter-Am. Devel. Corp., Ill., 1965-67. Office: 407 W Galena Blvd Aurora IL 60506-3946

LOWE, RANDALL BRIAN, lawyer; b. Englewood, N.J., Nov. 20, 1948. BA, U. R.I., 1970; JD, Washington U., 1973. Bar: Ill. 1973, Conn. 1975, D.C. 1976, U.S. Ct. Appeals (2d and D.C. cirs.) 1976, N.J. 1977, U.S. Dist. Ct. N.J. 1977, U.S. Ct. Appeals (3d cir.) 1977, U.S. Ct. Appeals (9th cir.) 1979, N.Y. 1980, U.S. Dist. Ct. (ea. and so. dists.) N.Y. 1980. Atty. Callis & Filcoff, Granite City, Ill., 1973-75, AT&T, Washington and N.Y.C., 1975-78, ITT Corp, 1978-83; Surrey & Morse, Washington, 1983-86; ptnr. Jones, Day, Reavis & Pogue, Washington, 1986-94, Piper & Marbury, Washington, 1994—. Office: Piper & Marbury 3251 E Imperial Hwy Brea CA 92621-6722

LOWE, ROB, actor; b. Charlottesville, Va., Mar. 17, 1964; m. Sheryl Berkoff, July 22, 1991. Appeared in films including The Outsiders, 1983, Class, 1983, The Hotel New Hampshire, 1984, Oxford Blues, 1984, St. Elmo's Fire, 1985, Youngblood, About Last Night..., 1986, Square Dance, 1987, Illegally Yours, Masquerade, 1988, Bad Influence, 1991, The Dark Backward, 1991, Wayne's World, 1992, Frank and Jesse (also prodr.), 1994, Billy the Third, 1995; TV appearances include (series) A New Kind of Family, (movie) Thursday's Child, (spls.) A Matter of Time, Schoolboy Father, Stephen King's The Stand. Office: UTA 9560 Wilshire Blvd 5th fl Beverly Hills CA 90212*

LOWE, ROBERT CHARLES, lawyer; b. New Orleans, July 3, 1949; s. Carl Randall and Antonia (Morgan) L.; m. Theresa Louise Acree, Feb. 4, 1978. 1 child, Nicholas Stafford. BA, U. New Orleans, 1971; JD, La. State U., 1975. Bar: La. 1975, U.S. Dist. Ct. (ea. dist.) La. 1975, U.S. Ct. Appeals (5th cir.) 1980, U.S. Dist. Ct. (we. dist.) La. 1978, U.S. Supreme Ct. 1982. Assoc. Sessions, Fishman, Rosenson, Boisfontaine, and Nathan, New Orleans, 1975-80, ptnr., 1980-87; ptnr. Lowe, Stein, Hoffman, Allweiss and Hauver, 1987—. Author: Louisiana Divorce, 1984; mem. La. Law Rev., 1974-75; contbr. articles to profl. jours. Mem. ABA, La. State Bar Assn. (chmn. family law sect. 1984-85), La. Assn. Def. Counsel, New Orleans Bar Assn. (chmn. family law sect. 1991-92), La. State Law Inst., La. Trial Lawyers Assn., Order of Coif, Phi Kappa Phi. Republican. Home: 9625 Garden Oak Ln River Ridge LA 70123-2005 Office: Lowe Stein Hoffman Allweiss and Hauver 701 Poydras St Ste 3600 New Orleans LA 70139-3600

LOWE, ROBERT CHARLES, lawyer, banker; b. Seattle, Jan. 15, 1927; s. Martin M. and Helen (Yaster) L.; m. Hope Lucille Sperstad, Mar. 21, 1952; children: Karen, Karlton, Nelson, Inez. B.A., U. Wash., 1953; LL.B., U. Denver, 1959. Bar: Alaska 1961. Accountant Haskins & Sells (C.P.A.s), Los Angeles, 1953-54; agt. Internal Revenue Service, 1954-57; atty. State Alaska, 1960; mem. firm Hughes, Thorsness, Lowe, Gantz & Clark, Anchorage, 1960-75; pres. Safeco Title Agy., Inc., Anchorage, 1975-79; chmn. bd. Peoples Bank & Trust Co., Anchorage. Served with USNR, 1944-46. Mem. Am., Alaska, Anchorage bar assns., Anchorage Estate Planning Council (pres. 1970), Rotary. Home: 1933 Beaver Pl Anchorage AK 99504

LOWE, ROBERT EDWARD, finance company executive; b. Winnipeg, Man., Can., Oct. 31, 1940; s. Mark Currie and Florence Irene L. Lowe; m. Isabella Lowe Hunter Liddell, Oct. 1, 1965; children: Susan Patricia, Donna Jane, Mark William. MBA, York U., Toronto, 1975. Chartered acct. Ptnr. Coopers & Lybrand, Toronto, 1971; pres. Coopers & Lybrand Ltd., Toronto, 1975-80, chmn., 1980—, 1980—; bd. dirs Olympia & York Devels. Ltd., Toronto, Olympia & York U.S.A., N.Y. Lt. Can. Army Res., 1958-61. Mem. Insolvency Inst. Can., Toronto Golf Club, Can. Club, Nat. Club. Mem. Conservative Party. Presbyterian. Avocations: golf, sailing. Office: Coopers & Lybrand, 145 King St W Ste 2300, Toronto, ON Canada M5H 1V8

LOWE, ROBERT STANLEY, lawyer; b. Herman, Nebr., Apr. 23, 1923; s. Stanley Robert and Ann Marguerite (Feese) L.; m. Anne Kirtland Selden, Dec. 19, 1959; children: Robert James, Margaret Anne. AB, U. Nebr., 1947, JD, 1949. Bar: Wyo. 1949. Ptnr. McAvoy & Lowe, Newcastle, 1949-51, Hickey & Lowe, Rawlins, 1951-55; county and pros. atty. Rawlins, 1955-59, pvt. practice, 1959-67; assoc. dir., dir. Am. Judicature Soc., Chgo., 1967-68, 68-74; counsel True Oil and affiliated cos., Casper, Wyo., 1974—; bd. dirs., sec. Hilltop Nat. Bank, Casper; mem. legal adv. div. Nat. Ski Patrol Sys., 1975-88; pres. Snowy Range Ski Corp., 1963-66; city atty. City of Rawlins, 1963-65; atty., asst. sec. Casper Mountain Ski Patrol, 1988—. Co-editor: Selected Readings on the Administration of Justice and its Improvement, 1969, 71, 73, Current Issues on the Judiciary, 1971, Judicial Disability and Removal Commissions, Courts and Procedures, 1969, 70, 72, 73, others; contbr. articles to legal jours. Mem. Wyo. Ho. of Reps., 1952-54; del. Dem. Nat. Conv., 1952, alt. del., 1956; mem. exec. com. Wyo. Dem. Ctrl. Com., 1953-55; bd. dirs. Vols. in Probation, 1969-82; leader legal del. to China, People to People, 1986; mem. Wyo. Vets. Affairs Coun., 1994—; mem. legis. com. United Vets. Coun. Wyo., 1993—; trustee, pres. Trroopers Found., Inc., 1994—; bd. dirs., co-chmn. WW II Commemorative Cmty. Program. Lt. (j.g.) U.S. Maritime Svc., U.S. Mcht. Marine, 1943-46. Recipient Dedicated Community Worker award Rawlins Jr. C. of C., 1967, Yellow merit award Nat. Ski Patrol System, 1982, 85, 87, 88. Fellow Am. Bar Found. (life); mem. VFW (post adv. 1991—, nat. aide-de-camp 1993-94), Am. Judicature Soc. (dir. 1961-67, 85-89, bd. editors 1975-77, Herbert Harley award 1974), ABA (sec. jud. admnstrn. divsn. lawyers conf., exec. com. 1975-76, chmn. 1977-78, chmn. judicial qualification and selection com. 1986-93, coun. jud. admnstrn. div. 1977-78, mem. com. to implement jud. admnstrn. standards 1978-82, Ho. of Dels. state bar del. 1978-80, 86-87, state del. 1987-93, Assembly del. 1980-83), Wyo. State Bar (chmn. com. on cts. 1961-67, 77-87), Nebr. State Bar Assn., Ill. State Bar Assn., D.C. Bar Assn., Colo. Bar Assn., Inter-Am. Bar Assn., Selden Soc., Inst. Jud. Admnstrn., Rocky Mountain Oil and Gas Assn. (legal com. 1976—, chmn. 1979-82, 90-91), Rocky Mountain Mineral Law Found. (trustee 1980—), Am. Law Inst., Newcomen Soc., Order of Coif, Mil. Order of Coatie, Delta Theta Phi (dist. chancellor 1982-83, chief justice 1983-93, assoc. justice 1993—; Percy J. Power Meml. award 1983, Gold Medallion award 1990), Casper Rotary Club. Mem. Ch. of Christ, Scientist. Home: 97 Primrose St Casper WY 82604-4018 Office: 885 River Cross Rd Casper WY 82601-1758

LOWE, WILLIAM C., business products and systems company executive. BS, Lafayette Coll., 1962. With IBM, Armonk, N.Y., 1962-88, dir. devel. mfg. ops. systems div., 1975-77, dir. strategic systems, then admnstrv. asst. to div. pres., 1977-78, system mgr. entry level systems, then lab. dir. gen. systems div., 1978-81; v.p. info. systems div. gen. mgr. IBM Rochester, N.Y., 1981-82, v.p. system devel., system products div., 1982-83, asst. group exec. info. systems and communications group, 1983-85, pres. entry systems div., 1985-86, v.p., pres. entry systems div., 1986-88; exec. v.p. devel. mfg. Xerox Corp., Stamford, Conn., 1988-91; pres., COO Gulfstream

Delaware Corp., Savannah, Ga., 1991—. Office: Gulfstream Del Corp 500 Gulfstream Rd Savannah GA 31407-9643

LOWELL, HOWARD PARSONS, government records administrator; b. Rockland, Maine, May 10, 1945; s. Chauncey Vernon Lowell and Delia Coffin (Parsons) Morey; m. Marcia Barrell, Feb. 15, 1969 (div. 1980); m. Charlesa Ann Gatson, July 27, 1985, 1 stepson, Garrett Timmons. BA, U. Me., Orono, 1967; MS, Simmons Coll., 1974. Admnstrn. svcs. officer Maine state archives, Augusta, 1968-72; ednl. specialist Mass. bur. libr. ext., Boston, 1974-75; dir. Revere (Mass.) Pub. Libr., 1975-76; freelance cons. Salem, Oreg., 1976-81, Denver, 1976-81; admnstr. Okla. resources br. Okla. Dept. Librs., Oklahoma City, 1981-89; archivist and records administrator State of Del., 1990—; acting dir. N.E. Document Conservation Ctr., Andover, Mass., 1978. Mem. Acad. Cert. Archivists, Nat. Assn. Govt. Archives and Records Admnstrs. (bd. dirs. 1985-87, pres. 1992-94), Phi Beta Kappa, Phi Kappa Phi, Phi Alpha Theta, Beta Phi Mu. Democrat. Mem. Unitarian Ch. Office: Bur Archives and Record Mgmt Hall of Records PO Box 1401 Dover DE 19903

LOWELL, JULIET, author; b. N.Y.C., Aug. 7, 1901; d. Max and Helen (Kohut) Loewenthal; m. Leo E. Lowell, Aug. 17, 1922 (dec.); children—Margot, Ross; m. Ben Lowell, 1945. A.M., Vassar Coll., 1922. lectr. Vassar Coll., June 1987. Writer, 1920—, newspaper columnist, lectr.; writer comedy script; appeared on radio programs Underwood Typewriter, Ford Motor Co., Sanka Coffee, also TV shows throughout U.S., Can.; made films for Fox, Warner Bros. motion picture cos., 30 shorts for RKO.; author: Dumb-Belles Lettres, 1933, Dear Sir, 1944, Dear Sir or Madam, 1946, Dear Mr. Congressman, 1948, Dear Hollywood, 1950, Dear Doctor, 1955, 68, Dear Justice, A Book for the Just, the Unjust, and Those Who Just Like to Laugh, 1958, Dear Folks, 1960, Dear Man of Affairs, 1961, Dear VIP, 1963, It Strikes Me Funny, 1964, Boners in the News, 1967, Humor U.S.A, 1968, Dear Candidate, 1968, Racy Tales For Adults and Adultresses, 1969; contbr. article on war humor to Ency. Brit, 1947, articles to nat. mags.; author weekly column Juliet Lowell's Celebrity Letters, Sunday supplement Family Weekly, 1972—. Chmn. book com. N.Y.-Tokyo Sister City Affiliation.; Mem. bd. Hecksher Found. for Children, DD II. Mem. Authors League Am., Internat. Platform Assn., Vassar Alumnae Assn. Clubs: Woman's Press, Overseas Press. Home: Towers of Chestnut Hill 250 Hammond Pond Pky Chestnut Hill MA 02167-3946 *Doing what I like to do has provided me with a living and kept me content, sharing my fun with others. I have been able to find a bright spot in most situations. Naturally there have been problems and sorrows. The only way to entirely circumvent them is to be stillborn. I prefer to have been born alive and lively. Born on a train, lower berth. Date of birth August 7, date of death as yet undetermined.*

LOWELL, WAYNE BRIAN, financial officer; b. Lakeland, Fla., Apr. 20, 1955; s. Robert Earle and Joan (Weber) L.; m. Nan Jean Bjornstad, May 31, 1980; children: Christopher Earle, Jonathan Paul. BS summa cum laude, U. Md., 1977; MBA with honors, U. Calif., Irvine, 1985. Sr. acct. Deloitte, Haskins and Sells, Costa Mesa, Calif., 1977-81; asst. controller Burlington Air Express Irvine, Calif., 1981-86; corp. controller Pacificare Health Systems, Cypress, Calif., 1986, chief fin. officer, 1986-92, exec. v.p., 1992—; bd. dirs. Columbia Gen. Life Ins. Co., Laguna Hills, Calif., Pacific Care Oreg., Portland. Mem. Am. Ins.t CPA's, Fin. Execs. Inst. (cert.) Nat. Assn. Accts., Beta Alpha Psi (pres., sec. 1975-77). Republican. Avocations: running, bike riding, hiking, reading. Office: PacifiCare Health Systems 5995 Plaza Dr Cypress CA 90630-5028

LOWEN, GERARD GUNTHER, mechanical engineering educator; b. Munich, Germany, Oct. 25, 1921; came to U.S., 1939; s. Charles and Stefanie (Frank) L.; m. Doris Julie Wolff, July 2, 1952; children: Deborah Lowen-Klein, Nicole Vianna, Daniel. BSME, CCNY, 1954; M of Mech. Engring., Columbia U., 1958; D of Engring., Tech. U. Munich, 1963. Registered profl. engr., N.Y. Machinist, tool and diemaker Germany and the U.S., 1938-54; lectr. mech. engring. CCNY, 1954-59, asst. prof., 1959-64, assoc. prof., 1964-69, prof., 1969—; Herbert Kayser prof., 1987—, chmn. mech. engring. dept., 1987-90; assoc. dean grad. studies, engring., 1990—; cons. in field. Contbr. articles to profl. jours.; patentee in field. Named Outstanding Tchr., CCNY, 1984; NSF grantee, 1968-89. Fellow ASME (machine design award 1987); mem. Am. Soc. Engring. Edn., Verein Deutscher Ingenieure, Soc. Mfg. Engrs., AAAS, N.Y. Acad. Sci. Jewish. Avocations: reading, history, hiking. Home: 484 Eisenhower Ct Wyckoff NJ 07481-2206 Office: CCNY Grad Engring Office Convent Ave New York NY 10031-2604

LOWEN, WALTER, mechanical engineering educator; b. Cologne, Germany, May 17, 1921; came to U.S., 1936, naturalized, 1945; m. Sylvia Lowen, May 22, 1943; children: Robert Gary, John Gordon. BS in Mech. Engring. N.C. State Coll., 1943, M.S., 1947; student, Oak Ridge Sch. Reactor Tech., 1955; D.Sc., Swiss Fed. Inst. Tech., 1963. Instr. N.C. State Coll., 1943-47; faculty Union Coll., Schenectady, 1947-68; prof. mech. engring. Union Coll., 1956-68, chmn. div. engring., 1956-60, 66-67, acting chmn. mech. engring. dept., 1959-60, chmn. dept., 1966-67; prof., dir. Sch. Advanced Tech. SUNY, Binghamton, 1967-68, dean Sch. Advanced Tech., 1968-77, prof. systems sci., 1968-90, Thomas J. Watson sch. prof. emeritus, 1991—; cons. Oak Ridge Nat. Lab., Knolls Atomic Power Lab., Alco Products, Inst. Applied Tech. of Nat. Bur. Standards.; adj. faculty IBM Systems Research Inst., 1979-89; vice chmn. Niskayuna Sch. Centralization Bldg. Com., 1954; co-founder Vols. for Internat. Tech. Assistance, Inc., 1960—. Author: Dichotomies of the Mind, 1982. NSF fellow to Switzerland, 1961-62. Mem. ASME (sect. vice-chmn. local chpt. 1959-60), Am. Soc. Engring. Edn., Sigma Xi, Tau Beta Pi, Pi Tau Sigma, Phi Kappa Phi. Home: 152 Moore Ave Binghamton NY 13903-3151

LOWENBERG, MICHAEL, lawyer; b. Bklyn., Mar. 6, 1943; s. Leo and Edna (Hanft) L.; m. Julie Goldberg, June 13, 1965; children: Daniel, Frances, Anthony. BA, Bklyn. Coll., 1963; LLB, Harvard U., 1966. Bar: Tex. 1966, U.S. Dist. Ct. (no. dist.) Tex. 1966, U.S. Ct. Appeals (5th cir.) 1967. Assoc. Akin, Gump, Strauss, Hauer & Feld, L.L.P., Dallas, 1966-71; prof. corp. ptnr. Akin, Gump, Strauss, Hauer & Feld, P.C., Dallas, 1972—. Pres. Dallas Legal Services Found., 1972; chmn. Dallas chpt. Am. Jewish Com., 1973-74. Mem. ABA, Tex. Bar Assn., Bar Assn. of 5th Cir. (bd. dirs.), Dallas Bar Assn., Nat. Legal Aid and Defenders Assn., Def. Rsch. Inst. Democrat. Home: 5551 Montrose Dr Dallas TX 75209-5609 Office: Akin Gump Strauss Hauer & Feld 4100 First City Center 1700 Pacific Ave Dallas TX 75201-4618

LOWENFELD, ANDREAS FRANK, legal educator, arbitrator; b. Berlin, May 30, 1930; s. Henry and Yela (Herschkowitsch) L.; m. Elena Machado, Aug. 11, 1962; children: Julian, Marianna. AB magna cum laude, Harvard U., 1951, LLB magna cum laude, 1955. Bar: N.Y. 1955, U.S. Supreme Ct. 1961. Assoc. Hyde and de Vries, N.Y.C., 1957-61; spl. asst. to legal adv. U.S. Dept. State, 1961-63; asst. legal adviser for econ. affairs, 1963-65, dep. legal adviser, 1965-66; fellow John F. Kennedy Inst. Politics, Harvard U., Cambridge, Mass., 1966-67; prof. law Sch. Law, NYU, N.Y.C., 1967—, Charles L. Denison prof. law, 1981-94, Herbert and Rose Rubin prof. internat. law, 1994—; arbitrator internat. comml. panels ICC. Mem. ABA, Assn. of Bar of City of N.Y., Am. Soc. Internat. Law, Am. Arbitration Assn. (arbitrator), Coun. Fgn. Rels., Inst. de Droit Internat. Author: (with Abram Chayes and Thomas Ehrlich) International Legal Process, 1968-69; Aviation Law, Cases and Materials, 1972, 2d edit., 1981; International Economic Law, vol. I, 1975, 3d edit., 1995, vol. II, 1976, 2d edit., 1982, vol. III, 1977, 2d edit., 1983, vol. IV, 1977, 2d edit., 1984, vol. VI, 1979, 2d edit., 1983, Conflict of Laws, Federal, State and International Perspectives, 1986, International Litigation and Arbitration, 1993, International Litigation: The Quest for Reasonableness, 1995; editor, co-author: Expropriation in the Americas: A Comparative Law Study, 1971; assoc. reporter Am. Law Inst. Restatement on Foreign Relations Law; contbr. articles and book revs. on pub. internat. law, internat. econ. law, air law, conflict of laws, arbitration, history and politics to profl. jours. Home: 5776 Palisade Ave Bronx NY 10471-1212 Office: NYU Sch Law 40 Washington Sq S New York NY 10012-1099

LOWENFELS, FRED M., lawyer; b. Richmond, Va., Mar. 22, 1944; s. Fred C. and Joan (Weber) L.; m. Joan Roberta Brafman, June 16, 1968; children: Erica Anne, Helene Beth. AB, Harvard U., 1965, JD, 1968; postgrad., Univ. Libre de Bruxelles, 1968-69. Bar: N.Y. 1969. Assoc. Wolf,

Haldenstein, Adler, Freeman & Herz, N.Y.C., 1970-74; sr. v.p., gen. counsel Transammonia Inc., N.Y.C., 1974—. Trustee Jewish Home and Hosp. for the Aged, N.Y.C., 1974—. Mem. Assn. Bar. City of N.Y., Am. Corp. Counsel Assn., Harvard Club N.Y.C. Office: Transammonia Inc 350 Park Ave New York NY 10022-6022

LOWENFELS, LEWIS DAVID, lawyer; b. N.Y.C., June 9, 1935; s. Seymour and Jane (Phillips) L.; m. Fern Gelford, Aug. 15, 1965; children: Joshua, Jacqueline. BA magna cum laude, Harvard U., 1957, LLB, 1961. Bar: N.Y. 1961. Ptnr. Goldfield, Charak, Tolins & Lowenfels, N.Y.C., 1967-74, Tolins & Lowenfels, N.Y.C., 1974—; adj. prof. law Seton Hall U. Law Sch.; lectr. law Practicing Law Inst., Southwestern Legal Found., U. Minn., Fed. Bar Assn., 1972; pub. gov. Am. Stock Exch. Co-author: Securities Fraud and Commodities Fraud, 6 vols., 1994; contbr. articles to profl. jours. With USAR, 1957-63. Mem. ABA (fed. regulation of securities com. 1978—, lectr.), N.Y. County Lawyers Assn. (securities and exchanges com. 1974—), Phi Beta Kappa, Harvard Club. Avocations: reading, writing, athletics. Office: Tolins & Lowenfels 12 E 49th St New York NY 10017-1028

LOWENKAMP, WILLIAM CHARLES, JR., medical device engineer, researcher, consultant; b. N.Y.C., Oct. 9, 1941; s. William Charles Sr. and Margaret (Poll) L.; m. Martha Marie Engle, Aug. 1964 (div. 1968); 1 child, Kristina Monica; m. Deborah Diane Grimm, July 13, 1991; 1 child, Eric Thomas; 1 stepchild, Cory York. BA, Sussex Coll., Eng., 1977; MSc, City U. L.A., 1987, PhD, 1990. Sr. ops. supr. Johnson & Johnson, Inc., Southington, Conn., 1969-74; sr. mfg. supr. TSI, Inc., New Milford, Conn., 1974-76; sr. mfg.-ops. supr. U.S. Surg. Corp., Stamford, Conn., 1976-78; v.p. Lowenkamp Mfg. Co., Jackson, New Milford, Miss., 1980-87; pres. Lowenkamp Internat. Inc., Hazelhurst, Miss., 1987—; cons. WAH-SHEN, China, 1993—; cons. SAF-T-MED, Dallas, 1993—. Author: On Life and Love, 1982, The Country Poet on the Road Again, 1983, (manual) QA-GMP for Small Medical Device Manufacturers, 1988; contbr. articles to profl. jours. With U.S. Army, 1959-64. Mem. ASTM (voting), AAAS, Am. Soc. for Quality Control (sr.), Am. Chem. Soc., Inst. for Environ. Scis. (sr.), N.Y. Acad. Sci., Internat. Union Pure Analytical Chemists (Europe), Inst. Indsl. Engrs. Achievements include patents for cathether batch processing procedure, for blood collection device; patents pending for retractable needle-syringe, for bio-hazard culture dish, for cord clamp. Home: 13022 Monticello Rd Hazlehurst MS 39083-9108 Office: Lowenkamp Internat Inc 13022 Monticello Rd Hazlehurst MS 39083-9108

LOWENSTEIN, ALAN VICTOR, lawyer; b. Newark, Aug. 30, 1913; s. Isaac and Florence (Cohen) L.; m. Amy Lieberman, Nov. 23, 1938; children: John, Roger, Jane Lowenstein Forsyth. AB, U. Mich., 1933; M.A., U. Chgo., 1935; LL.B., Harvard U., 1936. Bar: N.J. 1936. Practiced in Newark and Roseland, 1936—; sr. partner Lowenstein, Sandler, Kohl, Fisher & Boylan, 1961—; assoc. atty. Temporary Nat. Econ. Com., 1938-39; asst. prof. Rutgers U. Law Sch., 1951-57; chmn. N.J. Corp. Law Revision Commn., 1959-72; spl. hearing officer Dept. Justice, 1961-65; chmn. bd. United Steel & Aluminum Corp., 1976—. Pres. Jewish Community Council Essex County, 1950-53, United Way Essex and West Hudson, 1953-55; chmn. Newark Charter Commn., 1953, Newark Citizens Com. Mcpl. Govt., 1954-58, Newark Community Survey, 1959-60; v.p. Council Jewish Fedns., 1965-68, assoc. treas., 1981; pres. N.J. Symphony Orch., 1971-73, chmn. bd., 1973-76; mem. adv. council Rutgers U. Sch. Social Work, 1955-64; vice chmn. Liberty State Park Devel. Corp., 1984—; bd. overseers Rutgers U. Found., 1994—. Recipient Brotherhood award Nat. Conf. Christians and Jews, 1972, Trustees award for Disting. Community Service, 1980, N.J. Inst. Tech., 1984, Equal Justice award Legal Services N.J./N.J. State Bar Assn., 1988. Mem., N.J., Essex County Bar Assns., Am. Judicature Soc., Order of the Coif, Phi Beta Kappa (v.p. N.J. 1951-52), Phi Kappa Phi, Tau Kappa Alpha. Home: 285 N Ridgewood Rd South Orange NJ 07079-1503 also: PO Box 3892 Rd 3 Vergennes VT 05491 Office: Lowenstein Sandler et al 65 Livingston Ave Roseland NJ 07068-1725

LOWENSTEIN, DANIEL HAYS, lawyer, educator; b. N.Y.C., May 10, 1943; s. Nathan and Elizabeth (Carr) L.; m. Sharon Yagi, Feb. 14, 1970; children—Aaron, Nathan. A.B., Yale U., 1964; LL.B., Harvard U., 1967. Bar: N.Y. 1968, Calif. 1969. Staff atty. Calif. Rural Legal Assistance, 1968-71; dep. sec. State of Calif., 1971-75; 1st chmn. Calif. Fair Polit. Practices Commn., 1975-79; prof. law UCLA, Los Angeles, 1979—; cons. on freedom of info. legislation, Que., Can., 1979. Contbr. articles on campaign fin., legis. districting, bribery and initiative elections to profl. publs.; author leading text on Am. election law. Bd. dirs. Common Cause, 1979-85, Ams. for Nonsmokers' Rights; counsel to House Dem. of Calif., 1981-82; draftsman Calif. Polit. Reform Act, 1974. Office: UCLA Law Sch 405 Hilgard Ave Los Angeles CA 90095-1476

LOWENSTEIN, DEREK IRVING, physicist; b. Hampton Court, Eng., Apr. 26, 1943; came to U.S., 1946; s. Siegfried and Ilse (Mildenberg) L.; m. Elaine Hartmann, July 6, 1968; children: Jessica R., Peter D. BS, CCNY, 1964; MS, U. Pa., 1965, PhD, 1969. Postdoctoral fellow U. Pa., Phila. 1969-70; research assoc. U. Pitts., 1970-73; asst. physicist Brookhaven Nat. Lab., Upton, N.Y., 1973-75; assoc. physicist Brookhaven Nat. Lab., 1975-77, physicist, 1977-83, sr. physicist, 1983—; head Exptl. Planning and Support div., 1977-84, dep. chmn. accelerator dept., 1981-84, chmn. Alternating Gradient Synchrotron dept., 1984—; assoc. mem. U.S.-Russia Joint Coordinating Commn. on Fundamental Properties of Matter, 1983—, U.S.-Japan Commn. on High Energy Physics, 1984—; mem. Dept. of Energy High Energy Physics Adv. Panel, 1993—. Contbr. articles on particle and accelerator physics to profl. jours. Fellow Am. Phys. Soc.; mem. AAAS, N.Y. Acad. Scis., Sigma Xi. Office: Brookhaven Nat Lab Ags Dept Upton NY 11973

LOWENSTEIN, JAMES GORDON, former diplomat, international consultant; b. Long Branch, N.J., Aug. 6, 1927; s. Melvyn Gordon and Katherine Price (Goldsmith) L.; m. Dora Laurinda Richardson, June 11, 1955 (div. 1977); children: Laurinda Vinson, Price Gordon; m. Anne Cornely de la Selle, July 4, 1981. Grad., Loomis Sch., 1945; B.A., Yale U., 1949; postgrad., Harvard Law Sch., 1955-56. With Office Spl. Rep. in Europe, Econ. Cooperation Adminstrn., Paris, 1950-51; mem. U.S. Spl. Mission to Yugoslavia, Sarajevo, 1951; fgn. svc. officer Bur. European Affairs Dept. State, 1957-58; fgn. service officer Am. Embassy, Colombo, Ceylon, 1959-61, Belgrade, Yugoslavia, 1961-64; cons. Fgn. Relations Com., U.S. Senate, Washington, 1965-74; prin. dep. asst. sec. state for European affairs Washington, 1974-77; ambassador to Luxembourg, 1977-81; with Bur. European Affairs, Dept. State, 1981-82; ptnr. IRC Group, Washington, 1982-87; sr. cons. APCO Assocs., Washington, 1988—; mem. internat. observer group Sri Lanka elections, 1993, 94; vice chmn. U.S. Bus. Coun. for Southeastern Europe; past sec. bd. Emerging Eastern European Fund; co-founder, bd. dirs. French-Am. Found.; bd. dirs. Washington Found. for European Studies; bd. Citizens Exch. Coun.; past mem. adv. coun. Sch. Advanced Internat. Studies and Bologna (Italy) Ctr. Johns Hopkins U.; mem. staff Naval War Coll. Past trustee Madeira Sch., Lacoste Sch. of the Arts in France. Lt. (j.g.) USNR, 1952-55. Decorated chevalier Légion d'Honneur (France); Grand Croix de la Couronne de Chene (Luxembourg). Mem. Coun. Fgn. Rels., Internat. Inst. Strategic Studies (London). Clubs: Metropolitan (Washington); Army-Navy Country (Arlington, Va.); Century Assn. Knickerbocker (N.Y.C.); Harbor (Seal Harbor, Maine); Travellers, Racing (Paris). Home: 3139 O St NW Washington DC 20007-3117 also: 32 Rue de Verneuil, 75007 Paris France Office: Ste 900 1615 L St NW Washington DC 20036-3308

LOWENSTEIN, LOUIS, legal educator; b. N.Y.C., June 13, 1925; s. Louis and Rahmina (Steinhardt) L.; m. Helen Libby Small, Feb. 12, 1953; children: Roger Spector, Jane Ruth, Barbara Ann. B.S., Columbia, 1947, LL.B. 1953; M.F.S., U. Md., 1951. Bar: N.Y. 1953. Pvt. practice law N.Y.C. 1954-78; Assoc. Judge Stanley H. Fuld, N.Y. Ct. Appeals, 1953-54; assoc., then partner Hays, Sklar & Herzberg, 1954-68; partner Richard Kramer, Lowenstein, Nessen, Kamin & Soll, 1968-78; Simon H. Rifkind prof. law and fin. Columbia U. Law Sch., 1980—; project dir. Instl. Investor Project, 1988-94; pres. Supermarkets Gen. Corp., Woodbridge, N.J., 1978-79; bd. dirs. Liz Claiborne, Inc. Author: What's Wrong with Wall Street, 1988, Sense and Nonsense in Corporate Finance, 1991; contbr., co-editor: Knights, Raiders and Targets, 1988; editor in chief Columbia Law Rev., 1951-53. Vice pres.,

mem. exec. com. Fedn. Jewish Philanthropies N.Y.; pres. Jewish Bd. Family and Children's Services N.Y., 1974-78; trustee Beth Israel Med. Center, N.Y.C., 1975-81. Served to lt. (j.g.) USNR, 1943-46. Mem. Am. Bar Assn., Assn. of Bar of City of N.Y., Am. Law Inst. Home: 1 Fountain Sq Larchmont NY 10538-4105 Office: Columbia U Law Sch 435 W 116th St New York NY 10027-7201

LOWENSTEIN, PETER DAVID, lawyer; b. N.Y.C., Dec. 31, 1935; s. Melvyn Gordon and Katherine Price (Goldsmith) L.; m. Constance Cohen; children from previous marriage: Anthony, Kate E., Christopher. BA, Trinity Coll., 1958; LLB, Georgetown U., 1961. Bar: Conn. 1962, N.Y. 1963. With SEC, Washington, 1961-63; assoc. Whitman & Ransom, N.Y.C., 1963-70, ptnr., 1970-83; sec., gen. counsel Value Line, Inc., N.Y.C., 1983-87; v.p., sec., gen. counsel Service Am. Corp., Stamford, Conn., 1988-90; ptnr. O'Connor, Morris & Jones, Greenwich, Conn., 1990-92, pvt. practice, 1992—; legal counsel Value Line Mutual Funds. Bd. dirs. Grand St. Settlement, N.Y.C., 1970-92, Greenwich Health Assn., Conn., 1978-85; bd. dirs. Greenwich chpt. ARC, 1989-94, vice chmn., 1991-93. Mem. Nantucket Yacht Club, Greenwich Field Club. Home: 496 Valley Rd Cos Cob CT 06807-1627 Office: Two Greenwich Plz Ste 100 Greenwich CT 06830-5436

LOWENSTEIN, RALPH LYNN, university dean emeritus; b. Danville, Va., Mar. 8, 1930; s. Henry and Rachel (Berman) L.; m. Bronia Grace Levenson, Feb. 6, 1955; children: Joan, Henry. AB, Columbia U., 1951, MS in Journalism, 1952; PhD in Journalism, U. Mo., 1967. Reporter Danville (Va.) Register, 1952, El Paso Times, 1954-57; asst. prof. journalism U. Tex. at El Paso, 1956-62, assoc. prof., 1962-65; publs. editor Freedom of Info. Ctr., Columbia, Mo., 1965-67; vis. prof., head journalistic studies Tel Aviv U., 1967-68; assoc. prof. Sch. Journalism, U. Mo., Columbia, 1968-70; prof. Sch. Journalism, U. Mo., 1970-76, chmn. news-editorial dept., 1975-76; press critic CBS Morning News, 1975-76; dean Coll. Journalism and Communications, U. Fla., Gainesville, 1976-94. Author: Bring My Sons from Far, 1966; (with John C. Merrill) Media, Messages and Men, 2nd edit., 1979, Macromedia, 1990; editor: (with Paul Fisher) Race and the News Media, 1967. Served with Israeli Army, 1948-49; AUS, 1952-54. Recipient Research in Journalism award Sigma Delta Chi, 1971, Disting. Svc. award Columbia Journalism Alumni, 1957, 30th Anniversary award State of Israel, 1978, Freedom Forum Journalism Adminstr. of Yr. award, 1994. Mem. Assn. Edn. in Journalism and Mass Comm. (pres. 1990-91), Kappa Tau Alpha. Home: 1705 NW 22d Dr Gainesville FL 32605

LOWENSTINE, JAMES R., metal products manufacturing company executive; b. 1923; married. With Cen. Steel & Wire Co., Chgo., 1945—, v.p. ops., 1949-56, pres., 1956—, chmn., 1971—, now also chief exec. officer, bd. dirs. Office: Central Steel & Wire 3000 W 51st St Chicago IL 60632-2198

LOWENSTINE, MAURICE RICHARD, JR., retired steel executive; b. Valparaiso, Ind., Feb. 28, 1910; s. Maurice Richard and Etta (Hamburger) L.; m. Miriam Jean Richards, Nov. 9, 1940; children: Martha Jean, Linda Jane, Mark Richards. Student, U. Mich., 1928-29, U. Ariz., 1929-30. With Central Steel & Wire Co., Chgo., 1932-71, exec. v.p., treas., dir., 1942-71; Chmn. exec. com. Steel Service Center Inst., 1962-64. Chmn. bd. Greater Hinsdale Cmty. Chest, 1960; bd. dirs. Chgo. area coun. Boy Scouts Am., 1967-95, Hinsdale Cmty. House, 1961-64; vice commodore Chgo. Sea Explorer Scouts, 1973-95. Episcopalian. Clubs: Chgo. Yacht; Ruth Lake Country. Address: 407 E 3rd St Hinsdale IL 60521-4224

LOWENTHAL, ABRAHAM FREDERIC, international relations educator; b. Hyannis, Mass., Apr. 6, 1941; s. Eric Isaac and Suzanne (Moos) L.; m. Janet Wyzanski, June 24, 1962 (div. 1983); children: Linda Claudina, Michael Francis; m. Jane S. Jaquette, Jan. 20, 1991. A.B., Harvard U., 1961, M.P.A., 1964, M.A., Ph.D., 1971; postgrad., Harvard Law Sch., 1961-62. Tng. assoc. Ford Found., Dominican Republic, 1962-64; asst. rep. Ford Found., Lima, Peru, 1969-72; asst. dir., then dir. of studies Coun. Fgn. Rels., N.Y.C., 1974-76; dir. Latin Am. program Woodrow Wilson Internat. Ctr. for Scholars, Washington, 1977-83; exec. dir. Inter-Am. Dialogue, Washington, 1982-92; prof. Sch. Internat. Rels., U. So. Calif., Los Angeles, 1984—; dir., ctr. internat. studies U. So. Calif., 1992—; pres. Pacific Coun. Internat. Policy, L.A., 1995—; vis. fellow, rsch. assoc. Ctr. Internat. Studies, Princeton U., 1972-74; vis. lectr. polit. sci. Cath. U. Santiago, Dominican Republic, 1966; lectr. Princeton U., 1974; spl. cons. Commn. U.S.-Latin Am. Rels., N.Y.C., 1974-76; mem. internat. adv. bd. Ctr. U.S.-Mex. Rels., U. Calif.-San Diego, 1981—; mem. internat. adv. bd. Helen Kellogg Inst., 1984—; cons. Ford Found., 1974—. Author: The Dominican Intervention, 1972, 2nd edit., 1995, Partners in Conflict: The United States and Latin America in 1990s, 1991; editor, contbg. author: The Peruvian Experiment: Continuity and Change Under Military Rule, 1975, Armies and Politics in Latin America, 1976, Exporting Democracy: The United States and Latin America, 1991; co-editor, contbg. author: The Peruvian Experiment Reconsidered, 1983, The California-Mexico Connection, 1993; editor Latin Am. and Caribbean Record, vol. IV, 1985-86, vol. V, 1986-87, Latin America in a New World, 1994; mem. editorial bd. Jour. Inter-Am. Studies and World Affairs, Hemisphere, Internat. Security, 1977-83, Wilson Quar., 1977-83; contbr. articles to profl. jours. Mem. nat. adv. coun. Amnesty Internat., 1977-83, Ctr. for Nat. Policy, 1986—. Mem. Internat. Inst. Strategic Studies, Am. Polit. Sci. Assn. (coun. 1979-81), Latin Am. Studies Assn. (exec. coun. 1979-81), Coun. Fgn. Rels., Overseas Devel. Coun., Human Rights Watch, Calif. com. Democrat. Jewish. Home: 903 Stanford St Santa Monica CA 90403-2223 Office: Pacific Coun Internat Policy Los Angeles CA 90089-0035

LOWENTHAL, ARLINE MAE, marketing research executive; b. Buffalo, Aug. 8, 1931; d. Harry and Lena (Michaels) Jaffey; m. Richard Irwin Lowenthal, July 6, 1952 (div. 1975); children: Lauren Ileen, Robin Beth, Andrew Jaffey. BS in Psychology, U. Buffalo, 1953. Women's program dir. Sta. WXRA-Radio, Buffalo, 1953-57; v.p., co-founder Survey Svc. of Western N.Y., Buffalo, 1958-74; pres., chief exec. officer Analysis Rsch. Ltd., San Diego, 1975—; owner Austin-McClain Assocs., 1978—; owner, pres. A.P.E.L. Travel Internat., 1985—; co-founder, co-dir. Mercadotecnia Y Publicidad AP, Mex.; elected San Diego del., vice chmn. to 1980 White House Conf. on Small Bus.; elected del. San Diego White House Conf. com., 1986—; co-chmn. Govt. Procurement Sect. for Calif. Conf. on Small Bus., 1986—. Contbr. articles to profl. jours. Trustee Ysidro U. Mem. Market Rsch. Assn. (editor nat. profl. jour. Viewpoint, conf. chairperson, Ednl. Think Tank com., Pres.' award), Am. Mktg. Assn., Am. Assn. Pub. Opinion Researchers, Qualitative Rsch. Cons. Assn., Soc. of the Quill. Avocations: travel, flower arranging, crafts. Office: Analysis/Rsch Ltd 4655 Ruffner St Ste 180 San Diego CA 92111-2226

LOWENTHAL, CONSTANCE, art historian; b. N.Y.C., Aug. 29, 1945; d. Jesse and Helen (Oberstein) L. BA cum laude, Brandeis U., 1967; AM, Inst. Fine Arts, NYU, 1969; PhD, Inst. Fine Arts, NYU, N.Y.C., 1976. Mem. faculty Sarah Lawrence Coll., Bronxville, N.Y., 1975-78; asst. mus. educator Met. Mus. Art, N.Y.C., 1978-85; exec. dir. Internat. Found. Art Research, N.Y.C., 1985—; bd. dirs. Internat. Art and Antiques Loss Register Ltd., Ctr. for Edn. Studies, Inc. Regular contbr. Art Crime Update column Wall Street Jour., 1988—; contbr. articles to Mus. News and other profl. publs. Office: Internat Found for Art Rsch 46 E 70th St New York NY 10021-4928

LOWENTHAL, HENRY, greeting card company executive; b. Frankfurt, Germany, Oct. 26, 1931; came to U.S., 1940, naturalized, 1945; s. Adolf and Kella (Suss) L.; m. Miriam Katzenstein, June 29, 1958; children—Sandra, Jeffry, Joan Chana, Benjamin, Avi. B.B.A. cum laude, City U. N.Y., 1952, M.B.A., 1953; J.D., N.Y. U., 1962. CPA. Lectr. acctg. Baruch Coll., N.Y.C., 1952-53; auditor Price Waterhouse & Co., N.Y.C., 1955-62; v.p., controller Am. Greetings Corp., Cleve., 1962-68, controller, 1966-68, sr. v.p., chief fin. officer, 1977—; v.p. fin., treas. Tremco Inc., Cleve., 1968-77; mem. adv. bd. Case Western Res. U. Dept. Accountancy, 1986—. Chmn. bd. dirs. Rabbinical Coll. Telshe, 1974-77, v.p., 1977-90; v.p. Hebrew Acad. Cleve., 1977—; pres. Agudath Israel of Cleve., 1978-95, treas., 1995—; v.p. Agudath Israel Am., 1989—; bd. dirs. Jewish Cmty. Fedn., Cleve., 1979-88, 90—, chmn. audit com., 1992—; trustee Mt. Sinai Med. Ctr., Cleve., 1992-; chmn. citizens rev. com. Cleveland Heights-Univ. Heights Sch., 1972-73, mem. lay fin. com. 1974-79; mem. Cleveland Heights Citizens Adv. Com. for Cmty. Devel., 1976-79. With AUS, 1953-55. Mem. AICPA, Assn. of Publicly Traded Cos. (budget & fin. com. 1986—, bd. dirs. 1987—, treas.

1990—), Fin. Execs. Inst. (sec. N.E. Ohio chpt. 1979-80), Ohio Soc. CPA's, Greater Cleve. Growth Assn., Beta Gamma Sigma, Beta Alpha Psi. Home: 3394 Blanche Ave Cleveland OH 44118-2128 Office: Am Greetings Corp 1 American Rd Cleveland OH 44144-2301

LOWENTHAL, JACOB, finance executive; b. Frankfurt, Germany, July 27, 1938; came to U.S., 1941; s. Adolf and Kella (Suss) L.; m. Fanny Z. Rothschild, Aug. 27, 1960; children: Joyce Lowenthal Meisner, David, Evelyn Weisz Lowenthal, Leon A. BBA, CCNY, 1959. CPA, N.Y. Jr. acct. Skydell & Shatz CPAs, N.Y.C., 1959-60; mgr. George Funaro & Co. CPAs, N.Y.C., 1960-68; contr., asst. sec. Advanced Computer Tech, N.Y.C., 1968-76; contr. AGS Computers Inc., Mountainside, N.J., 1976-80, Software Design Assocs., N.Y.C., 1980-83; v.p. fin. and adminstrn. Vista Concepts Inc. subs. NYNEX, N.Y.C., 1983-94; computer cons. N.Y.C., 1994—. EMT Hatzalah, N.Y.C., 1980—; treas. Congregation Khal-Adath Jeshurun, N.Y.C., 1977-89. Mem. AICPA, N.Y. State Soc. CPAs, Cheshbonot. Home: 100 Bennett Ave New York NY 10033 Office: 5 Hanover Sq 16th Fl New York NY 10004

LOWER, LOUIS GORDON, II, insurance company executive; b. N.Y.C., July 3, 1945; s. Elmer Wilson and Gilberta Madeleine (Stengel) L.; m. Adrienne Adair Borger, Sept. 26, 1970; children—Brandon Wilson, Samatha June. BA, Yale U., 1967; MBA, Harvard U., 1970. Asst. v.p. Amprop, Inc., Miami, Fla., 1970-73; v.p. Gale Orgn., Miami, 1973-76; dir. real estate Allstate Ins. Co., Northbrook, Ill., 1976-80, v.p. investments, 1980-85, group v.p. investments, 1985-86, sr. v.p., treas., 1986-89; exec. v.p. Allstate Life Ins. Co., Northbrook, 1989, pres., 1990—; bd. dirs. Ill. Life Ins. Coun.; chmn. bd. dirs. Northbrook Life Ins. Co., Lincoln Benefit Life, Surety Life, Allstate Life Ins. Co. of N.Y. Bd. dirs. North Suburban YMCA, Northbrook, 1984—, Evanston (Ill.) Hosp. Corp., Chgo. Bot. Garden. Served with USAR, 1968-73. Clubs: Skokie Country (Glencoe, Ill.); Key Biscayne Yacht (Fla.). Avocations: tennis; waterskiing. Home: 76 Woodley Rd Winnetka IL 60093-3746 Office: Allstate Life Ins Co 3100 Sanders Rd Northbrook IL 60062

LOWER, ROBERT CASSEL, lawyer, educator; b. Oak Park, Ill., Jan. 8, 1947; s. Paul Elton and Doris Thatcher (Heaton) L.; m. Jean Louise Lower, Aug. 24, 1968 (dec. Aug. 1985); children: David Elton, Andrew Bennett, James Philip Thatcher; m. Cheryl Bray, July 26, 1986. A.B. magna cum laude with highest honors, Harvard U., 1969, J.D., 1972. Bar: Ga. 1972. Assoc. Alston & Bird, Atlanta, 1972-78, ptnr., 1978—; adj. prof. Emory U., 1978-85, 92. Contbr. articles to law jours. Co-founder, pres. Ga. Vol. Lawyers for the Arts, Inc., 1975-79; chmn. Fulton County (Ga.) Arts Council, 1979-87; trustee Woodruff Arts Ctr., Piedmont Coll., Ga. Found. Ind. Colls. Mem. Ga. Bar Assn., Atlanta Bar Assn., Midtown Bus. Assn. (bd. dirs. 1988-90), Author's Ct., Harvard Club (Ga.), Ansley Golf Club, Phi Beta Kappa. Presbyterian. Avocations: running, music, bonsai. Home: 935 Plymouth Rd NE Atlanta GA 30306-3009 Office: Alston & Bird One Atlantic Ctr 1201 W Peachtree St NW Atlanta GA 30309-3400

LOWERY, CHARLES DOUGLAS, history educator, academic administrator; b. Greenville, Ala., May 8, 1937; s. Reuben F. and Frances Louise (Jordan) L.; m. Sara Bradford, June 24, 1961; children: Thomas Bradford, Douglas Trenton, Charles Daniel. BA, Huntingdon Coll., 1959; MA, Fla. State U., 1961; PhD, U. Va., 1966. Asst. prof. history Ball State U., Muncie, Ind., 1964-66; from asst. prof. to prof. Miss. State U., Starkville, 1966—, head dept. history, 1985—, asst. dean Coll. Arts and Scis., 1971-74, assoc. dean, 1974-81, dir. Inst. for Humanities, 1981-85. Author: James Barbour: The Biography of A Jeffersonian Republican, 1984, (with others) America: The Middle Period, 1973; Encyclopedia of African-American Civil Rights: From Emancipation to the Present, 1992; contbr. articles to profl. jours. Mem. Citizen's Adv. Coun., Starkville, 1971; mem. Miss. Com. for Humanities, Jackson, 1986-88; vice chmn. Miss. Humanities Coun., Jackson, 1988-89. Grantee NEH, 1980, 81, 84, Miss. Humanities Coun., 1983, 84, 88. Mem. Orgn. Am. Historians, Soc. Historians of Early Am. Rep., So. Hist. Soc., Miss. Hist. Soc. (com. chmn. 1989-90). Democrat. Presbyterian. Avocations: camping, travel, fishing, historical preservation. Home: 609 Sherwood Rd Starkville MS 39759-4009 Office: Miss State U Dept History Drawer H Mississippi State MS 39762

LOWERY, CLINTON HERSHEY, former naval officer; b. Pitts., Apr. 10, 1929; s. Robert John and Alma May (Hershey) L.; m. Elenore Berenda, July 28, 1956; children: Gregg C., Michael J., Keith D., Kim A., Douglas S. B.S., U. Pitts., 1951, M.D., 1955. Diplomate: Am. Bd. Surgery. Intern St. John's Gen. Hosp., Pitts., 1955-56; resident Naval Regional Med. Ctr., Portsmouth, Va., 1958-62; commd. capt. USN, 1956, advanced through grades to rear adm., 1979; staff surgeon Naval Regional Med. Ctr., Camp Lejeune, N.C., 1962-66; asst. chief surgery Portsmouth, 1966-72; comdr. 1st Med. Bn. RVN, 1967-68; chief of surgery Camp Pendleton, Calif., 1972-74; dir. clin. services Charleston, S.C., 1974-77; comdr. Camp Pendleton, 1977-79; asst. chief Bur. Medicine and Surgery for Health Care Programs, Washington, 1979-82; fleet surgeon U.S. Pacific Fleet, U.S. Pacific Command, 1982-83; ret., 1983; v.p. risk mgmt. Pa. Hosp. Ins. Co., Camp Hill, 1983-86. Decorated Legion of Merit. Fellow ACS, ACP; mem. Southeastern Surg. Soc., Assn. Mil. Surgeons, Am. Coll. Physician Execs. Home: 115 Rydal Ln Pittsburgh PA 15237-4009

LOWERY, DOMINIC GERALD (NICK), professional football player; b. Munich, Germany, May 27, 1956. BA, government, Dartmouth U., 1978. Place kicker New England Patriots, 1978, Kansas City Chiefs, 1980-94, N.Y. Jets, 1994—. Played in Pro Bowls 1981, 90, 92; NFL All-Pro team kicker, The Sporting News, 1990. NFL record for most seasons (11) with 100 or more points, 19 team records with the Kansas City Chiefs including ALL-Time Leading Scorer. Most accurate kicker in NFL history. 2nd most field goals in NFL history. Office: New York Jets 1000 Fulton Ave Hempstead NY 11550

LOWERY, JOSEPH E., clergyman; m. Evelyn Gibson; 3 daus. Student, Knoxville Coll., Ala. A&M Coll., Payne Coll., Wayne U., Payne Theol. Sem., Garrett Theol. Sem., Chgo. Ecumenical Inst.; AB, BD, LLD, Clark Coll., 1975; DD (hon.), Morehouse Coll.; DLitt (hon.), Dillard U.; LLD (hon.), Atlanta U. Ordained to ministry United Methodist Ch.; pastor Warren St. United Meth. Ch., Mobile, Ala., 1952-61; adminstrv. asst. to Bishop Golden, Nashville, 1961-64; pastor St. Paul United Meth. Ch., Birmingham, Ala., 1964-68, Central United Meth. Ch., Atlanta, 1968-86, Cascade United Meth. Ch., 1986-92; co-founder SCLC, v.p., until 1967, chmn. bd., 1967-77, pres., 1977—; mem. Commn. on Religion and Race, chmn. merger rev. com. United Meth. Ch., 1968-76; del. World Meth. Council, London, Gen. Confs. United Meth. Ch.; instr. Candler Sch. Theology and Nursing Sch., Emory U., 1970-71. Chmn. coordinating com. on civil rights in Nashville, 1963-64; pres. Ministerial Alliance, Birmingham, Birmingham OEO community Action Agy., Enterprises Now, Inc.; bd. dirs. Meth. Pub. Ho., 1960-72, Met. Atlanta Rapid Transit Authority, 1975—, Martin Luther King, Jr. Ctr. for Social Change; co-chair anniversary March on Washington, 1983, 88, 93; initiated Gun Buy Back Program, Atlanta, now nationally, 1993. Recipient Equal Opportunity award Atlanta Urban League, 1975, awards Nat. Conf. Black Mayors, Martin Luther King Jr. Peace prize, Martin Luther King, Jr. Ctr. for Non-Violent Social Change, 1990, Martin Luther King Jr. Human Rights award George Washington U., 1990, also awards Ebony mag., others; named one of 15 Greatest Black Preachers Ebony mag.; 1st recipient MLK award for freedom Boston U., 1992. Office: So Christian Leadership Conf 334 Auburn Ave NE Atlanta GA 30303-2604

LOWERY, LAWRENCE FRANK, mathematic science and computer educator; b. Oakland, Calif., June 26, 1932. AA, U. Calif., Berkeley, 1952, BA, 1954, MA, 1962, EdD, 1965. Assoc. dean Sch. Edn. U. Calif., Berkeley, 1980-84, prof., 1965—. Contbr. articles to profl. jours.; also books, videos and films; prolific writer. Numerous leadership roles in field. With U.S. Army, 1954-56. Mem. AAAS, ASCD, Am. Edn. Rsch. Assn. (res. rev. bd.), Assn. for the Edn. Tchrs. Sci., Phi Delta Kappa. Home: 650 Diablo Rd Danville CA 94526-2802

LOWERY, LEE LEON, JR., civil engineer; b. Corpus Christi, Tex., Dec. 26, 1938; s. Lee Leon and Blanche (Dietrich) L.; children: Kelli Lane, Christianne Lindsey. B.S. in Civil Engring. Tex. A&M U., 1960, M.E.,

1961, Ph.D., 1965. Prof. dept. civil engring. Tex. A&M U., 1960; rsch. engr. Tex. A&M Rsch. Found., 1962—; pres. Pile Dynamics Found. Engring., Inc., Bryan, Tex., 1962—; pres. Tex. Measurements, Inc., College Station, 1965—; pres. Interface Engring. Assos., Inc., College Station, 1969—; dir. Braver Corp. Bd. dirs. Deep Found. Inst. Recipient Faculty Disting. Achievement Teaching award Tex. A&M U., 1979, Zachary Teaching award, 1989, 91, award of merit Tex. A&M Hon. Soc., 1991; NDEA fellow, 1960-63. Mem. ASCE, NSPE, Tex. Soc. Profl. Engrs., Sigma Xi, Phi Kappa Phi, Tau Beta Pi. Baptist. Achievements include patents in field. Home: 2905 S College Ave Bryan TX 77801-2510 Office: Tex A&M U Dept Civil Engring College Station TX 77843

LOWERY, WILLIAM HERBERT, lawyer; b. Toledo, June 8, 1925; s. Kenneth Alden and Drusilla (Pfanner) L.; m. Carolyn Broadwell, June 27, 1947; children: Kenneth Latham, Marcia Mitchell. PhB, U. Chgo., 1947; JD, U. Mich., 1950. Bar: Pa. 1951, U.S. Supreme Ct. 1955. Assoc. Dechert Price & Rhoads, Phila., 1950-58, ptnr., 1958-89, mng. ptnr., 1970-72; mem. policy com., chmn. litigation dept., 1962-68, 81-84; of counsel Dechert Price & Rhoads, Phila., 1989—; counsel S.S. Huebner Found. Ins. Edn., Phila., 1970-89; faculty Am. Conf. of Legal Execs., Pa. Bar Inst.; permanent mem. com. of visitors U. Mich. Law Sch. Author: Insurance Litigation Problems, 1972, Insurance Litigation Disputes, 1977. Pres. Stafford Civic Assn., 1958; chmn. Tredyffrin Twp. Zoning Bd., Chester County, Pa., 1959-75; bd. dirs. Paoli (Pa.) Meml. Hosp., 1966-89, chmn., 1972-75; bd. dirs. Main Line Health, Radnor, Pa., 1984-89; permanent mem. Jud. Conf. 3d Cir. Ct. Served to 2d lt. USAF, 1943-46. Mem. ABA (chmn. life ins. com. 1984-85, chmn. Nat. Conf. Lawyers and Life Ins. Cos. 1984-88), Order of the Coif, Royal Poinciana Golf Club, Vineyards Country Club, Phi Gamma Delta, Phi Delta Phi. Home: Apt S-4 2777 Gulf Shore Blvd N Naples FL 33940 Office: Dechert Price & Rhoads 4000 Bell Atlantic Tower 1717 Arch St Philadelphia PA 19103-2713

LOWEY, NITA M., congresswoman; b. N.Y., July 5, 1937; m. Stephen Lowey, 1961; children: Dona, Jacqueline, Douglas. BS, Mt. Holyoke Coll., 1959. Community activist, prior to 1975; asst. sec. state State of N.Y., 1975-87; former mem. 101st-102nd Congresses from 20th N.Y. dist., 1989-92; mem. 103rd-104th Congresses from 18th N.Y. dist., 1993—; mem. appropriations com., 1993—. Democrat. Office: US Ho of Reps 2421 Rayburn HOB Washington DC 20515*

LOWI, THEODORE J(AY), political science educator; b. Gadsden, Ala., July 9, 1931; s. Alvin R. and Janice (Haas) L.; m. Angele M. Daniel, May 11, 1963; children: Anna Amelie, Jason Daniel. BA, Mich. State U., 1954; MA, Yale U., 1955, PhD, 1961; HLD (hon.), Oakland U., 1972; LittD (hon.), SUNY, Stony Brook, 1988; Doctour honoris causa, Fondation Nationale des, Sciences Politiques, Paris, 1992. Mem. faculty dept. govt. Cornell U., 1959-65, 72—, asst. prof., 1961-65, John L. Senior prof. Am. instns., 1972—; assoc. prof. U. Chgo., 1965-69, prof., 1969-72; Gannett disting. prof. Rochester Inst. Tech., 1986-87, 90-91; fellow Ctr. Advanced Study in Behavioral Scis., 1977-78; chair Am. civilization U. Paris, 1981-82. Author: At the Pleasure of the Mayor, 1964, (with Robert Kennedy) The Pursuit of Justice, 1964, The End of Liberalism, 2d edit., 1979, Japanese edit., 1981, French edit., 1987, The Politics of Disorder, 1971, (with others) Poliscide, 1976, (with others) Nationalizing Government: Public Policies in America, 1978, Incomplete Conquest: Governing America, 1981, The Personal President: Power Invested, Promise Unfilled, 1985, Spanish edit., 1994, (with B. Ginsberg) American Government: Freedom and Power, 1990, 3d edit., 1994, (with B. Ginsberg) Embattled Democracy, The End of the Republican Era, 1995; Anthologies: Private Life and Public Order, 1968, Legislative Politics U.S.A., 3d edit., 1972. Recipient J. Kimbrough Owen award Am. Polit. Sci. Assn., 1962, French-Am. Found. award, 1981-82, Fulbright award, 1981-82, Harold Lasswell award Policy Studies Orgn., 1986, Richard Neustadt award for Best Book on Presidency, 1986; Social Sci. Rsch. Coun. fellow, 1963-64; Guggenheim Found. fellow, 1967-68; Nat. Endowment for Humanities fellow, 1977-78; Ford Found. fellow, 1977-78; Fulbright 40th Anniversary Disting. fellow, 1987. Mem. Am. Polit. Sci. Assn. (v.p. 1985-86, pres. 1991), Policy Studies Orgn. (pres. 1977), Internat. Polit. Sci. Assn. (1st v.p. 1994—). Home: 101 Delaware Ave Ithaca NY 14850-4707 If there is a how-to of success it is this: a passion for work, an ethic of workmanship, and an idea of what, in the end, is a good product.

LOWITT, RICHARD, history educator; b. N.Y.C., Feb. 25, 1922; s. Eugene and Eleanor (Lebowitz) L.; m. Suzanne Catharine Carson, Sept., 1953; children: Peter Carson, Pamela Carson. B.S.S., CCNY, 1943; M.A., Columbia U., 1945, Ph.D., 1950. Instr. U. Md., College Park, 1948-52; asst. prof. U. R.I., Kingston, 1952-53; faculty mem. Conn. Coll., New London, 1953-66, prof. history, 1966; prof. history Fla. State U., Tallahassee, 1966-68, U. Ky., Lexington, 1968-77; prof., chmn. dept. history Iowa State U., Ames, 1977-87, prof., 1987-89; prof. U. Okla., Norman, 1990—; mem. Iowa Humanities Bd., 1987-89; vis. prof. U. Colo. summer, 1953, Yale U., 1961-62, Brown U., 1965-66, U. Chattanooga, summer 1965, Emory U., Atlanta; Sutton vis. prof. U. Okla., 1989-90. Author: A Merchant Prince of the 19th Century, 1954, George W. Norris, 3 vols., 1963, 71, 78; editor: Nils Olsen and the Bureau of Agricultural Economics, 1980; co-editor: One Third of a Nation-Lorena Hickok Reports on the Great Depression, 1981, The New Deal and the West, 1984, Letters From An American Farmer: The Eastern European and Russian Correspondence by Roswell Garst, 1987, Henry A. Wallace's Irrigation Frontier: On the Trail of the Cornbelt Farmer, 1990, Bronson M. Cutting, Progressive Politician, 1992, Politics in the Postwar American West, 1995. Trustee Pub. Library, Lexington, 1973-77. NEH sr. fellow, 1974, John Simon Guggenheim Found. fellow, 1957; grantee Social Sci. Rsch. Coun., 1958, Am. Coun. Learned Socs., 1962, Am. Philos. Soc., 1964, Huntington Libr., 1986; recipient Gaspar Perez de Villagra award Hist. Soc. N.Mex., 1993. Mem. Am. Hist. Assn., So. Hist. Assn. (membership com. 1973, Ramsdell Prize com. 1975, program com. 1983, nominating com. 1990), Western History Assn. (bd. editors 1986-88, Merit award 1992), Orgn. Am. Historians (nominating com. 1970, Turner Prize com. 1972-76, bd. editors 1985-87), Agrl. History Soc. (exec. com. 1973-75, pres. 1991-92). Democrat. Office: Univ Okla Dept History Norman OK 73019

LOWMAN, GEORGE FREDERICK, lawyer; b. N.Y.C., Oct. 29, 1916; s. William H. and Mary (Canty) L.; m. Mary Farrell, Oct. 4, 1947; children—John F., Peter H., Patricia A. A.B., Harvard U., 1938, J.D., 1942. Bar: Conn. 1946. Since practiced in Stamford; assoc. Cummings & Lockwood, 1946-52, ptnr., 1952—; chmn. bd., chmn. exec. com., dir. Farrell Lines Inc.; v.p., dir. Wee Burn Land Co., 1963-66; Conn. trial referee, 1983—; chmn. bd., dir. Argonaut Lines Inc., Farrell Lines Tankers Inc.; dir. Am. S.S. Owners Mut. Protection & Indemnity Assn., Inc.; bd. govs. Nat. Maritime Council; bd. mgrs. Am. Bur. Shipping. Chmn. Darien YMCA-YWCA fund campaign, 1956; chmn. fund campaign Darien ARC, 1953-54, bd. dirs., 1953-59; mem. exec. com. Alfred W. Dater council Boy Scouts Am., 1956; chmn. Darien Cancer Fund, 1959-60; pres., bd. dirs. Silvermine Guild Artists, 1967-77; bd. dirs., trustee King Sch., Stamford; trustee Low-Heywood Sch.; advisory com. U. Bridgeport Law Sch.; pres. B/G India House, N.Y.C., 1980—. Served to lt. col. AUS, 1942-46. Decorated Legion of Merit, Bronze Star. Fellow Am. Coll. Trial Lawyers, Internat. Acad. Trial Lawyers, Am. Bar Found.; mem. ABA, Conn. Bar Assn. (past pres.), Stamford Bar Assn. (past pres.), Harvard U. Alumni Assn. (v.p.), Marine Soc. N.Y.C. (hon.), St. Andrew's Soc., Conn. Srs. Golf Assn., Delta Upsilon. Home: 40 Allwood Rd Darien CT 06820-2416 Office: 10 Stamford Forum Stamford CT 06901-3240

LOWMAN, ROBERT PAUL, psychology educator, academic administrator; b. Lynwood, Calif., Jan. 23, 1947; s. Hubert Alden and Martha Guynn (Howard) L.; m. Kathleen Marie Drew, June 25, 1972; children: Sarah Guynn, Amy Katherine. AB, U. So. Calif., 1967; MA, Claremont U., 1969, PhD, 1973. Asst. prof. U. Wis., Milw., 1972-76; adminstrv. officer APA, Washington, 1976-81; asst. dean Kans. State U., Manhattan, 1981-86, assoc. dean grad. sch., 1986-90, assoc. vice provost, 1990-91; dir. rsch. svcs. and adj. assoc. prof. psychology U. N.C., Chapel Hill, 1991—; assoc. vice chancellor for rsch. U.N.C., 1994—. Editor: APA's Guide to Rsch. Support, 1981; contbr. over 30 articles to profl. jours. Recipient numerous grants. Mem. APA (sec. bd. sci. affairs 1976-81, sec. com. on internat. rels. in psychology 1978-81), AAAS, Am. Psychol. Soc., Soc. for Psychologists in Mgmt., Nat. Coun. Univ. Rsch. Adminstrs., Soc. Rsch. Adminstrs., Phi Kappa Phi, Phi Beta Kappa, Phi Eta Sigma, Psi Chi. Democrat. Methodist.

Home: 104 Chesley Ln Chapel Hill NC 27514-1459 Office: Univ NC Office Rsch Svcs CB# 4100 Chapel Hill NC 27599-4100

LOWNEY, BRUCE STARK, artist; b. Los Angeles, Oct. 16, 1937; s. Franklin and Thelma (Poirier) L. B.A., North Tex. State U., 1959; M.A., San Francisco State U., 1966. printer-fellow Tamarind Lithography Workshop Inc., Los Angeles, 1967; printmaking supr. Mpls. Coll. Art and Design, 1971; vis. artist Chgo. Art Inst., 1972, 77, Western Ill. State U., 1973. One man shows, Elaine Horwitch Galleries, Santa Fe, 1975, 80, Louise Allrich Gallery, San Francisco, 1975, Martha Jackson Gallery, N.Y.C., 1975, Hill's Gallery, Santa Fe, 1978, Elaine Horwitz Gallery, Santa Fe, 1982, Rettie y Martinez, Santa Fe, 1986; group shows include, Library of Congress, 1975, U. N.D. 1978, Allrich Gallery, 1977, Mus. of Albuquerque, 1980; represented in permanent collections, Chgo. Art Inst., Yale U., Mus. Fine Arts, Santa Fe, Mpls. Mus. Art, No. Ill. U. Vol. Peace Corps, Papua New Guinea, 1992-94. Served with U.S. Army, 1962-64. Nat. Endowment for Arts grantee, 1974; Western States Art Found grantee, 1979; recipient Louis Comport Tiffany award, 1974. Home and Studio: 800 Oso Ridge Rt El Morro Grants NM 87020

LOWREY, E. JAMES, food service company executive; b. Lubbock, Tex., Feb. 21, 1928; s. E. J. and Sarah Ruth (Cooper) L.; m. Stella Jean Oates, Apr. 28, 1950; children—Jane Lynwood Tierney, Ernest James Jr. BBA, U. Tex., 1949. CPA, Tex. With Howard T. Cox & Co., Austin, Tex., 1949-51; ptnr. Frazer & Torbet, Houston, 1951-55, 59-70, Elgin-Butler Brick Co., Austin, 1955-59; sr. v.p. River Oaks Bank and Trust Co., Houston, 1971-73; v.p. fin., treas. SYSCO Corp., Houston, 1973-76, sr. v.p. adminstrn. and fin., 1976-78, exec. v.p. fin. and adminstrn., 1978-93 (ret.); also bd. dirs. SYSCO Corp. Mem. Am. Inst. CPA's, Tex. Soc. CPA's, (pres. Houston chpt. 1970-71). Republican. Presbyterian. Office: Sysco Corp 1390 Enclave Pky Houston TX 77077-2025

LOWRIE, GERALD M., communications executive; b. Elaine, Alaska, July 13, 1935; m. Shirley Ruth Johnston; children: Lynn, Richard. BS, Memphis State U., 1957. With sales and mktg. IBM, 1961-68; exec. dir. Am. Bankers Assn., Washington, 1968-85; sr. v.p. corp. hdqrs. AT&T, Washington, 1985—, also bd. dirs.; mem. adv. bd. Am. Security Bank. Mem. Washington Steering Com.; chmn. com. Bus.-Govt. Rels. Coun.; bd. dirs. Greater Washington Bd. of Trade. Mem. Circle Nat. Gallery Art, Computer and Bus. Equipment Mfrs. Assn. (bd. dirs.), John F. Kennedy Ctr. Performing Arts, U.S. League Women Voters (corp. adv. com.), Nat. Mus. Women in Art (bd. dirs.), Nat. Planning Assn. (com. mem.), Washington Performing Arts Soc. (bd. dirs., exec. com.), Memphis State U. Alumni Assn., Burning Tree Club, Capitol Hill Club, City Washington Club, City Tavern Club, Georgetown Club, One 16 Club. Office: AT&T Corp Hdqrs 1120 20th St NW Ste 1000 Washington DC 20036-3406

LOWRIE, JEAN ELIZABETH, librarian, educator; b. Northville, N.Y., Oct. 11, 1918; d. A. Sydney and Edith (Roos) L. A.B., Keuka Coll., 1940, LLD (hon.), 1973; B.L.S., Western Res. U., 1941, Ph.D., 1959; M.A., Western Mich. U., 1956. Childrens librarian Toledo Pub. Library, 1941-44; librarian Elementary Sch., Oak Ridge, Tenn., 1944-51; exhange tchr., librarian Nottingham, Eng., 1948-49; campus sch. librarian Western Mich. U., Kalamazoo, 1951-56; asso. prof. Western Mich. U. (Sch. Librarianship), 1958-61, prof., 1962-83, dir. sch., 1963-81; mem. faculty U. Ky., summer 1951, U. Calif. at Berkeley, summer 1958; Chmn. Internat. Steering Com. for Devel. Sch. Libraries; also del. World Conf. Orgns. Teaching Profession, meetings, Paris, 1964, Vancouver, 1967, Dublin, 1968, Abidjan, 1969, Sydney, 1970; pres. Internat. Assn. Sch. Librarianship, 1971-77, exec. sec., 1978—; mem. exec. bd. Internat. Fedn. Library Assns. and Instns., 1979-83. Author: Elementary School Libraries, rev. edit., 1970, School Libraries: International Developments, 1972, 2d edit., 1991, also articles; adviser: filmstrip Using the Library, 1962. Recipient Distbn-Macrae award ALA, 1957, Profl. Achievement award Keuka Coll. Alumni, 1963. Mem. ALA (pres. 1973-74), Mich. Library Assn., Assn. Libr. & Info. Sci. Educators, Am. Assn. Sch. Librarians (dir., past pres., 1st President's award 1978), Delta Kappa Gamma, Beta Phi Mu. Club: Altrusa (Kalamazoo). Home: 1006 Westmoreland Ave Kalamazoo MI 49006-5544

LOWRIE, WALTER OLIN, management consultant; b. North Braddock, Pa., Apr. 7, 1924; s. Robert Newell and Laura Rae (Essick) L.; m. Dorothy Ann Williams, Aug. 28, 1948; children: Susan, Allison, James. B.S. in Aero. Engring., MIT, 1948; Dr. Engring. (hon.), U. Central Fla., 1985. With Martin Marietta, 1948-86; v.p., program dir. Viking Program Martin Marietta, Denver, 1972-77; v.p., program dir. Missile X Martin Marietta, 1977-78, v.p. tech. ops. Denver div., 1978-80, v.p., gen. mgr. space and electronics, 1980-82; pres. Martin Marietta Orlando, Fla., 1982-86; pvt. practice mgmt. cons. Maitland, Fla., 1986—. Bd. dirs. U. Ctrl. Fla. Found., Orlando, 1983-91; gen. chmn. 42d Internat. Sci. and Engring. Fair, 1991; mayor City of Bow-Mar, Colo., 1964-68; mem. Colo. Gov.'s Adv. Commn. on Corrs., 1979-80; bd. dirs. Indsl. Devel. Commn. Mid-Fla. Inc. Orlando, 1983; chmn. Met. Transp. Authority of Greater Orlando, 1985-86; trustee Orlando Sci. Ctr., 1986—, chmn. bd. trustees, 1994—. 1st lt. USAAF, 1943-45, ETO. Decorated DFC; decorated Air medal with 6 oak leaf clusters; recipient Disting. Pub. Service award NASA, 1977. Fellow Am. Astronaut. Soc.; assoc. fellow AIAA (Space Systems Engr. of Yr. award 1977). Republican. Presbyterian.

LOWRIE, WILLIAM G., oil company executive; b. Painesville, Ohio, Nov. 17, 1943; s. Kenneth W. and Florence H. (Strickler) L.; m. Ernestine R. Rogers, Feb. 1, 1969; children: Kristen, Kimberly. BChemE, Ohio State U., 1966. Engr. Amoco Prodn. Co. subs. Standard Oil Co. (Ind.), New Orleans, 1966-74, area supt., Lake Charles, La., 1974-75, div. engr., Denver, 1975-78, div. prodn. mgr., Denver, 1978-79, v.p. prodn., Chgo., 1979-83; v.p. supply and marine transp. Standard Oil Co. (Ind.), Chgo., 1983-85; pres., Amoco Can., 1985-86; sr. v.p. prodn., Amoco Prodn. Co., 1986-87, exec. v.p. USA, 1987-88; exec. v.p. Amoco Oil Co., Chgo., 1989-90, pres., 1990-92; pres. Amoco Prodn. Co., 1992-94; exec. v.p. E&P sector Amoco Corp., 1994—. Bd. dirs. Dupage Health Svcs., Inc., Jr. Achievement, Northwestern Meml. Corp.; trustee, bd. dirs. Nat. 4-H Coun. Named Outstanding Engring. Alumnus, Ohio State U., 1979, Disting. Alumnis Ohio State U., 1985. Mem. Am. Petroleum Inst., Soc. Petroleum Engrs., Mid-Am. Club (Chgo.). Republican. Presbyterian. Office: Amoco Corp PO Box 87703 Chicago IL 60680-0703

LOWRY, A. ROBERT, federal government railroad arbitrator; b. Salem, Oreg., Jan. 16, 1919; s. Archie R. and Emaline (Hyland) L.; m. Nancy Jo Srb, May 3, 1975. Student, Albion (Idaho) Normal Coll., 1938. With U.P. R.R., 1937-53; local chmn.. then asst. to pres. Order R.R. Telegraphers, 1949-64; v.p., pres. then Transp.-Communications Employees Union, 1964-68; pres. TC div., internat. v.p. Brotherhood Ry. and Airline Clks., 1969-72; supt. ops. Amtrak, 1972-73, dir., top labor rels. officer, 1973-75, asst. v.p., top labor rels. officer, 1975-79; now neutral arbitrator for fed. govt. and R.R. industry San Antonio. Served to lt. col. AUS, 1941-46, USAR, 1946-65, ret. Lodge: Mason, Shriners. Home and Office: 13919 Bluff Wind San Antonio TX 78216-7923

LOWRY, BATES, art historian, museum director; b. Cin., June 21, 1923; s. Bates and Eleanor (Meyer) L.; m. Isabel Barrett, Dec. 7, 1946; children: Anne, Patricia. PhB, U. Chgo., 1944, MA, 1952, PhD, 1955. Asst. prof. U. Calif., Riverside, 1954-57, Inst. Fin. Arts NYU, 1957-59; prof., chmn. dept. art Pomona Coll., Claremont, 1957-63, Brown U., Providence, 1963-68; dir. Mus. Modern Art, N.Y.C., 1968-69; prof., chmn. dept. art U. Mass., Boston, 1971-80; dir. Nat. Bldg. Mus., Washington, 1980-87; cons. dept. photography Getty Mus., 1992, 93; disting. vis. prof. U. Del. Newark, 1988-89; founder, pres. Com. to Rescue Italian Art, 1966-76; mem. arts coun. MIT, 1974-80. Author: Visual Experience, 1961, Renaissance Architecture, 1962, Building a National Image, 1985, Looking for Leonardo, 1993; editor: College Art Association Monograph Series, 1957-63, 68, Architecture of Washington D.C., 1977-79, Art Bull., 1965-68; mem. editorial bd. Smithsonian Instn. Press, 1981-87. Mem. bd. cons. NEH, 1975-81. Decorated Grand Officer of Order of Star of Solidarity, Italy, 1967; recipient Gov.'s award for contbn. to art R.I., 1967; fellow Radcliffe Inst., 1972, Inst. for Advanced Study, 1971. Mem. Coll. Art Assn. (bd. dirs. 1962-65), Soc. Archtl. Historians (bd. dirs. 1959-61, 63-65), Dunlap Soc. (pres. 1974-92).

Academia del Disegno (hon. mem. Italy). Home: 255 Mass Ave Boston MA 02115

LOWRY, BRUCE ROY, lawyer; b. Lima, Ohio, Mar. 4, 1952; s. Lewis Roy and Gloria May (Rekers) L.; m. Kathleen Ann Sherman, Sept. 1, 1973; children: Bruce Benjamin, Tyler Sherman. BA cum laude, Ohio State U., 1974, JD cum laude, 1977. Bar: Ohio 1977. Tax intern Coopers & Lybrand, CPAs, Columbus, Ohio, 1976-77; assoc. Smith & Schnacke, LPA, Dayton, Ohio, 1977-84; chmn. tax dept. Smith & Schnacke, LPA, 1984-89; tax ptnr. Thompson, Hine and Flory, Dayton, 1989—; discussion leader Ohio Soc. CPAs, Cleve., 1980-95; adj. prof. U. Dayton Coll. Law, 1981-82; mem. faculty Ohio Continuing Legal Edn. Inst., 1987-95, mem. tax curriculum com.; mem. faculty Banff (Alta., Can.) Ctr. for Mgmt.-Internat. Tax, 1991. Contbr. articles to profl. jours. Nat. swimming ofcl. YMCA, S.W. Ohio, 1990-93; chmn. Miami County Planning Commn., Troy, Ohio, 1991-95; bd. dirs. Miami Valley coun. Boy Scouts Am., Dayton, 1988-95. Recipient award of merit Ohio Legal Ctr. Inst., 1987, Golden Rule award, 1991, Up and Comer in Dayton award, 1991. Mem. Internat. Bar Assn., Internat. Fiscal Assn., Tipp City C. of C. (chmn. econ. devel. com. 1989-91), Rotary Club Tipp City (pres.). Avocations: tennis, golf. Office: Thompson Hine & Flory 2000 Courthouse Pla NE PO Box 8801 Dayton OH 45401-8801

LOWRY, CHARLES WESLEY, clergyman, lecturer; b. Checotah, Okla., Mar. 31, 1905; s. Charles Wesley and Sue (Price) L.; m. Edith Clark, June 14, 1930; children: Harriet Richards Lowry King, Charles Wesley, Atherton Clark, James Meredith Price; m. Kate Rowe Holland, Jan. 11, 1960. BA, Washington and Lee U., 1926, DD, 1959; MA, Harvard U., 1927; BD, Episcopal Theol. Sch., 1930; DPhil, Oxford (Eng.) U., 1933. Ordain deacon Episcopal Ch., 1930. Priest Episcopal Ch., 1931; traveling fellow Episc. Theol. Sch., 1930-32; Episc. chaplain U. Calif., 1933-34; prof. systematic theology Va. Theol. Sem., 1934-43; rector All Saints' Ch., Chevy Chase, Md., 1943-53; lectr. theology Seabury Western Theol. Sem., 1947, Phila. Div. Sch. (Bohlen lectr.), 1947, 49-50, Gen. Theol. Sem., 1951-52; chmn. Bd. Examining Chaplains, Diocese of Washington, 1945-53, sec., standing com., 1945-51; ofcl. del. from U.S. Internat. Conv. on Peace and Christian Civilization, Florence, Italy, 1952; chmn., exec. dir. Found. for Religious Action in Social and Civil Order, 1953-59, pres., 1960—, project research dir. on morals revolution, 1973-75; cons. FCDA, 1953-55; cons. Air War Coll. 1953, lectr., 1953-54; lectr. Naval War Coll., 1955, Nat. War Coll., 1957, 59-61, Command and Staff Coll., 1961-62, Indsl. Coll. Armed Forces, 1963, Inst. Lifetime Learning, 1964-66, Campbell Coll. Sch. Law, 1979, 80; also lectr. various seminars; lectr. philosophy and polit. sci. Sandhills Community Coll., 1967-69, 71, 89; spl. lectr. Oxford (Eng.) Poly. Coll., 1974; spl. lectr. Washington and Lee U., 1977, baccalaureate preacher, 1984; dir. Nat. Conf. on Spiritual Founds. Am. Democracy, Washington, 1954-55, 57, 59; minister The Village Chapel, Pinehurst, N.C., 1966-73; mem. faculty Wallace O'Neal Day Sch., Southern Pines, N.C., 1976—; columnist Pinehurst Outlook, 1977-78, Moore County News, 1978-79, The Pilot, 1979—; priest assoc. Emmanuel Epis. Ch., Southern Pines, 1981—. Author: The Trinity and Christian Devotion, 1946, Christianity and Materialism (Hale Sermon), 1948, Communism and Christ, rev. edit, 1962 (Brit. edit. 1954), Conflicting Faiths, 1953, The Ideology of Freedom vs. The Ideology of Communism, 1958, To Pray or Not to Pray, rev. edit, 1968, The Kingdom of Influence, 1969, William Temple: An Archbishop for All Seasons, 1982, The First Theologians, 1986, Constitution Commentary, 1989; (with others) Anglican Evangelicalism, 1943, Encyclopaedia of Religion, 1945, The Anglican Pulpit To-Day, 1953; editor: Blessings of Liberty, 1956-90; contbr. articles to profl. publs. Chmn. Nat. Jefferson Davis Hall of Fame Co., 1960, 64-65; candidate for U.S. Congress 10th Dist. Va., 1962; mem. N.C. Bicentennial Constn. Conv., 1985-89. Recipient George Washington medal Freedoms Found., 1955, 59, 61, 68, other award, 1953, 81. Mem. Am. Peace Soc. (past pres.), Am. Polit. Sci. Assn., Internat. Platform Assn., Am. Theol. Soc. (treas. 1955-70, 72, past v.p.), Cum Laude Soc. (pres. O'Neal chpt.), World Conf. Faith and Order, Phi Beta Kappa, Omicron Delta Kappa, Delta Sigma Rho, Sigma Upsilon. Clubs: Achilles (Oxford and Cambridge); Rotary (dist. gov. 1970-71), Chevy Chase, Pinehurst Country, Nat. Press. Address: 160 Longleaf Rd Southern Pines NC 28387-2832 A religious view of life is not an easy optimism. The serious person knows the force of moral evil or sin. But when in the great religions we meet a Power that transforms, we see with new eyes. We are saved by hope and by faith and love.

LOWRY, EDWARD FRANCIS, JR., lawyer; b. L.A., Aug. 13, 1930; s. Edward Francis and Mary Anita (Woodcock) L.; m. Patricia Ann Palmer, Feb. 16, 1963; children: Edward Palmer, Rachael Louise. Student, Ohio State U., 1948-50; A.B., Stanford, 1952, J.D., 1954. Bar: Ariz. 1955, D.C. 1970, U.S. Supreme Ct. 1969. Camp dir. Quarter Circle V Bar Ranch, 1954; tchr. Orme Sch., Mayer, Ariz., 1954-56; trust rep. Valley Nat. Bank Ariz., 1958-60; pvt. practice, Phoenix, 1960—; assoc. atty. Cunningham, Carson & Messinger, 1960-64; ptnr. Carson, Messinger, Elliott, Laughlin & Ragan, 1964-69, 70-80, Gray, Plant, Mooty, Mooty & Bennett, 1981-84, Eaton, Lazarus, Dodge & Lowry Ltd., 1985-86; exec. v.p., gen. counsel Bus. Realty Ariz., 1986—; pvt. practice, Scottsdale, Ariz., 1986-88; ptnr. Lowry & Froeb, Scottsdale, 1988-89, Lowry, Froeb & Clements, P.C., Scottsdale, 1989-90, Lowry & Clements P.C., Scottsdale, 1990, Lowry, Clements & Powell, P.C., Scottsdale, 1991—; asst. legis. counsel Dept. Interior, Washington, 1969-70; mem. Ariz. Commn. Uniform Laws, 1972—, chmn., 1976-88; judge pro tem Ariz. State Ct. Appeals, 1986, 92-94. Chmn. Council of Stanford Law Socs., 1968; vice chmn. bd. trustees Orme Sch., 1972-74, treas., 1981-83; bd. trustees Heard Mus., 1965-91, life trustee, 1991—, pres., 1974-75; bd. visitors Stanford Sch. Law; magistrate Town of Paradise Valley, Ariz., 1976-83; juvenile ct. referee Maricopa County, 1978-83. Served to capt. USAF, 1956-58. Fellow Ariz. Bar Found. (founder); mem. ABA, Maricopa County Bar Assn., D.C. Bar Assn., State Bar Ariz. (chmn. com. uniform laws 1979-85), Stanford Law Soc. Ariz. (past pres.), Scottsdale Bar Assn. (bd. dirs. 1991—, v.p. 1991, pres. 1992—), Ariz. State U. Law Soc. (bd. dirs.), Nat. Conf. Commrs. Uniform State Laws, Delta Sigma Rho, Alpha Tau Omega, Phi Delta Phi. Home: 7600 N Moonlight Ln Paradise Vly AZ 85253-2938 Office: Lowry Clements & Powell PC Ste 1120 2901 N Central Ave Phoenix AZ 85012 also: 2901 N Central Ave # 1120 Phoenix AZ 85012

LOWRY, EDWIN R., petroleum company executive; b. 1928. BS U. Pa., 1949, LLB, 1952. Land and legal rep. Ecuador Petroleum Co., 1957-58, Bolivia Petroleum Co., 1958-59; legal analyst Chevron Exploration Co., 1956-57, land and legal rep., 1959-64; on spl. assignment Am. Overseas Petroleum Co., 1964-65; v.p. Huntington Beach Co., 1965-66; dir. Chevron Oil Co. of Venezuela, 1966-69; land and govt. relations counsel Chevron Overseas Petroleum Co., 1960-71; with Chevron Corp., San Francisco, 1956—, asst. mgr. fgn. ops., 1971-73, mgr. fgn. ops., 1973-79, v.p. fgn. ops. from 1979, now v.p. fgn. ops., corp. planning and devel. Served to 1st lt. USAF, 1952-54. Office: Chevron Corp 555 Market St San Francisco CA 94105-2801

LOWRY, FREDERICK SHERWOOD, minister, association director; b. Providence, May 12, 1935; s. David Sherwood and Lucy Cecile (Casey) L.; m. Leuntje Alida Schipper, Apr. 25, 1967; children: David Sherwood, Jan Willem Schipper. AB, Dartmouth Coll., 1956; M of Div., Yale U., 1959; cert., Ecumenical Inst., Geneva, 1963. Ordained to ministry, United Ch. of Christ, 1960. Pastor Orient Congrl. Ch., L.I., N.Y., 1960-64; adminstrv. asst. Miss. Delta Ministry Nat. Council Chs., Greenville, 1964-67; dir. Migrant Ministry Washington State Council Chs., Seattle, 1967-69; child care worker Kitsap Youth Homes, Bremerton, Wash., 1969-70; dir. Woburn (Mass.) Council Social Concern, 1970-73; pastor Plymouth Congrl. Ch., Syracuse, N.Y., 1974-80; exec. dir. Community Ministry Fairfax County, Reston, Va., 1980—. Mem. sch. adv. com.-Human Life Curriculum, 1982—, Planned Parenthood Adv. Com., Fairfax, 1982—, Fairfax Com. 100, 1983—, Emergency Shelter Study Com., Fairfax County, 1984, mem. adv. bd. North Va. Youth Service Coalition, Fairfax, 1985—. Mem. Nat. Assn. Ecumenical Staff, Washington Area Community Ministries, Interfaith Conf. Washington. Democrat. Home: 1579 Inlet Ct Reston VA 22090-4425 Office: Community Ministry Fairfax 1920 Association Dr Rm 507 Reston VA 22091

LOWRY, GLENN DAVID, art gallery director; b. N.Y.C.; s. Warren and Laure (Lynn) L.; m. Susan Chambers, Aug. 24, 1974; children: Nicholas, Alexis, William. BA, Williams Coll., 1976; MA, Harvard U., 1978, PhD, 1982. Asst. curator Fogg Art Mus., Harvard U., Cambridge, Mass., 1978-

80; rsch. asst. Archeol. Survey of Mediterranean Town of Amalfi, Italy, 1980; curator Oriental art Mus. Art, R.I. Sch. Design, Providence, 1981-82; dir. Joseph and Margaret Muscarelle Mus. Art, Williamsburg, Va., 1982-84; curator Nr. Ea. art Arthur M. Sackler and the Freer Gallery Art, Smithsonian Instn., Washington, 1984-90, curatorial coord., 1987-89; dir. Art Gallery Ont., Toronto, Can., 1990-95, Mus. Modern Art, N.Y.C., 1995—. Co-author: Fatehpur-Sikri: A Source Book, 1985, From Concept to Context: Approaches to Asian and Islamic Calligraphy, 1986, An Annotated Checklist of the Vever Collection, 1988, A Jeweler's Eye: Art of the Book from the Vever Collection, 1988, Timur and the Princely Vision: Persian Art and Culture in the Fifteenth Century, 1989, Europe and the Arts of Islam: The Politics of Taste, 1991. Trustee Metro Toronto Conv. and Visitors Assn. Recipient Inst. Turkish Studies Travel award Smithsonian Instn., 1980, Spl. Exhbns. award, 1987, Scholarly Studies award, 1990. Mem. Assn. Art Mus. Dirs., Can. Assn. Mus. Dirs., Coll. Art Assn. Home: 27 Parkwood Ave, Toronto, ON Canada M4V 2W9 Office: Mus Modern Art 11 W 53rd St New York NY 10019

LOWRY, JAMES DAVID, author, consultant; b. Wichita, Kans., May 24, 1942; s. Frederick Brennan and Mary (Mullendore) L.; children: Anne Harrison, Blythe Brennan, Terrell Brennan, James Sargent. B.S., Okla. State U., 1965; LL.B., U. Okla., 1968. Bar: Pa. bar 1968. Mem. Liebert, Harvey, Bectle & Short, Phila., 1968-69; counsel Systems Capital Corp., Phila., 1969-71; v.p., counsel Provident Nat. Bank, 1971-73; sr. v.p., sr. ops. Provident Nat. Corp., Phila. 1973-76; exec. v.p., chief adminstrv. officer Provident Nat. Corp., 1976-78; also dir. subs.; v.p.-fin., gen. mgr. Petroleum Heat and Power Co., Phila., 1978-80; chmn., pres., chief exec. Bancshares of N.J., 1981-83, No. Nat. Corp.; chmn., pres. The Bank of N.J.; chmn. The Trustees' Pvt. Bank, 1981-84; pres., chief exec. officer Equibank, Equimark, 1984-85; mng. dir. Lowry Bittel, Perrot & Co., 1985-91; chmn. Hopper Soliday Corp., 1986-91, Blue Hill Conservatory, Blue Hill, Maine, 1991—. Served with U.S. Army, 1960-62. Mem. ABA, Pa. Bar Assn., Phila. Bar Assn., Racquet Club, Corinthian Yacht Club, Rittenhouse Club (Phila.), Mill Dam Club (Wayne, Pa.), Bar Harbor Yacht Club (Maine). Home: Beech Hill Rd Blue Hill ME 04614 Office: Blue Hill Conservatory PO Box 330 Blue Hill ME 04614-0330

LOWRY, JAMES HAMILTON, management consultant; b. Chgo., May 28, 1939; s. William E. and Camille C. L.; 1 child, Aisha. BA, Grinnell Coll., 1961; M in Polit. and Instl. Adminstrn., U. Pitts., 1965; PMD, Harvard U., 1973. Assoc. dir. Peace Corps, Lima, Peru, 1965-67; spl. asst. to pres., project mgr. Bedford-Stuyvesant Restoration Corp., Bklyn., 1967-68; sr. assoc. McKinsey & Co., Chgo., 1968-75; pres. James H. Lowry & Assos., Chgo., 1975—; mem. Small Bus. Adv. Com.; bd. dirs. Johnson Products Co. Burrell Advt. Mem. vis. com. Harvard U., adv. bd. J.L. Kellogg Grad. Sch. Mgmt. Northwestern U.; trustee Grinnell Coll.; bd. dirs. Chgo. United, Northwestern Hosp., Chgo. Pub. Libr., Chgo. Fgn. Affairs, African-Am. Inst. John Hay Whitney fellow, 1963-65; co-chmn. Chgo. United. Mem. Harvard Alumni Assn. (dir., vis. com.), Inst. Mgmt. Cons., Econ. Club, Monroe Club, Univ. Club, Comml. Club of Chgo. Home: 3100 N Sheridan Rd Chicago IL 60657-4954 Office: 218 N Jefferson St Chicago IL 60661-1112

LOWRY, LARRY LORN, management consulting company executive; b. Lima, Ohio, Apr. 12, 1947; s. Frank William and Viola Marie L.; m. Jean Carroll Greenbaum, June 23, 1973; 1 child, Alexandra Kristin. BSEE, MIT, 1969, MSEE, 1970; MBA, Harvard U., 1972. Mgr. Boston Consulting Group, Menlo Park, Calif., 1972-80; sr. v.p., mng. ptnr. Booz, Allen & Hamilton Inc, San Francisco, 1980—. Western Electric fellow, 1969, NASA fellow, 1970. Mem. Sigma Xi, Tau Beta Pi, Eta Kappa Nu. Presbyterian. Home: 137 Stockbridge Ave Atherton CA 94027-3942

LOWRY, LOIS (HAMMERSBERG), author; b. 1937. Author: A Summer to Die, 1977, Find a Stranger, Say Goodbye, 1978, Anastasia Krupnik, 1979, Autumn Street, 1980, Anastasia Again!, 1981, Anastasia at Your Service, 1982, The One Hundredth Thing about Caroline, 1983, Taking Care of Terrific, 1983, Anastasia, Ask Your Analyst, 1984, Us and Uncle Fraud, 1984, Anastasia on Her Own, 1985, Switcharound, 1985, Anastasia Has the Answers, 1986, Anastasia's Chosen Career, 1987, Rabble Starkey, 1987, All About Sam, 1988, Number the Stars, 1989 (John Newbery medal 1990), Your Move, J.P.!, 1990, Anastasia at This Address, 1991, Attaboy, Sam!, 1992, The Giver, 1993 (John Newbery medal 1994), Anastasia Absolutely, 1995. Address: 8 Lexington Ave Cambridge MA 02138-3319 Office: care Houghton Mifflin 222 Berkeley St Boston MA 02116-3748

LOWRY, MIKE, governor, former congressman; b. St. John, Wash., Mar. 8, 1939; s. Robert M. and Helen (White) L.; m. Mary Carlson, Apr. 6, 1968; 1 child, Diane. B.A., Wash. State U., Pullman, 1962. Chief fiscal analyst, staff dir. ways and means com. Wash. State Senate, 1969-73; govtl. affairs dir. Group Health Coop. Puget Sound, 1974-75; mem. council King County Govt., 1975-78, chmn., 1977; mem. 96th-100th congresses from 7th dist. Wash., 1979-1989; governor State of Wash., 1993—. Chmn. King County Housing and Community Devel. Block Grant Program, 1977; pres. Wash. Assn. Counties, 1978. Democrat. Address: Legislative Bldg PO Box 40002 Olympia WA 98504*

LOWRY, WILLIAM KETCHIN, JR., insurance company executive; b. Columbia, S.C., Oct. 4, 1951; s. William Ketchin and Beverly Hubbard (Frazee) L.; m. Elaine Diana Kent, June 22, 1984; children: Jennifer Lyn, Julia Ann, Samuel Ketchin. BS in Bus. Adminstrn., U. S.C., 1972, M in Acctg., 1973. CPA, S.C. Supr. Ernst & Whinney, Columbia, 1973-81; sr. mgr. Price Waterhouse, Hartford, Conn., 1981-83, Phila., 1983-84; dir. corp. systems devel. and analysis Am. Can Co., Greenwich, Conn., 1984-86; v.p., treas., chief fin. officer Phoenix Re Corp. and Reinsurance Co., N.Y.C., 1986-90, sr. v.p., treas., chief fin. officer, 1990; v.p., treas. Transnational Ins. Co., N.Y.C., 1989-90; bd. dirs., v.p., treas. Nat. Bus. Brokers, Inc., Greenlawn, N.Y., 1989-90; sr. v.p., CFO SCOR U.S. Corp., SCOR Reins. Co. Gen. Security Assurance Corp., N.Y.C., 1990-93; sr. v.p., CFO Constn. Reins Corp., 1993—, bd. dirs., treas.; sr. v.p., treas., bd. dirs. Constn. Reins. Corp. Sirius Reins. Corp., 1993—; pres. CRC Corsair, Inc., 1995—. Pres., bd. dirs. Groves Homes Assn., Columbia, 1980-81; diaconate West Side Presbyn. Ch., Ridgewood, N.J., 1989-91. Fellow Life Mgmt. Inst.; mem. AIPCA, Am. Soc. CLUs, Fin. Execs. Inst., Soc. Ins. Rsch., Soc. Fin. Examiners, Inst. Mgmt. Accts., S.C. Assn. CPAs, City Midday Drug and Chem. Club, Downtown Athletic Club, Forest Lake Club, Saddle River Valley Swim & Tennis Club, Beta Gamma Sigma, Omicron Delta Kappa, Beta Alpha Psi, Omicron Delt Epsilon, Sigma Phi Epsilon. Presbyterian. Avocations: horseback riding, golf. Home: 22 Autumn Ct Upper Saddle River NJ 07458 Office: Constn Reins Corp 110 William St New York NY 10038-3901

LOWTHER, GERALD HALBERT, lawyer; b. Slagle, La., Feb. 18, 1924; s. Fred B. and Beatrice (Halbert) L.; m. Sandra Jo Frank; children by previous marriage: Teresa, Craig, Natalie, Lisa. A.B., Pepperdine Coll., 1951; J.D., U. Mo., 1951. Bar: Mo. 1951. Since practiced in Springfield; ptnr. firm Lowther, Johnson, Joyner, Lowther, Cully & Housley; Mem. Savs. and Loan Commn. Mo., 1965-68, Commerce and Indsl. Commn. Mo., 1967-73; lectr. U. Tex., 1955-57, Crested Butte, Colo., 1958-59. Contbr. articles law jours. Past pres. Ozarks Regional Heart Assn.; Del., mem. rules com. Democratic Nat. Conv., 1968; treas. Dem. Party Mo., 1968-72, mem. platform com., 1965, 67, mem. bi-partisan commn. to reapportion Mo. senate, 1966; Bd. dirs. Greene County Guidance Clinic, Ozark Christian Counseling Service, Greene County, Mo.; past pres. Cox Med. Center. Served with AUS, 1946-47; Col. staff of Gov. Hearnes 1964, 68, Mo. Mem. ABA, Mo. Bar Assn., Greene County Bar Assn., Def. Orientation Conf. Assn., Internat. Assn. Ins. Counsel, Def. Rsch. Inst., Springfield C. of C. Clubs: Kiwanian (pres. 1962), Quarterback (pres. 1958), Tip Off (pres. 1960). Home: 2320 Englewood Springfield MO 65806 Office: 300 John A Hammons Pkwy Springfield MO 65806

LOWY, FREDERICK HANS, university president, psychiatrist; b. Grosspetersdorf, Austria, Jan. 1, 1933; arrived in Can., 1951; s. Eugen and Maria (Braun) L.; m. Anne Louise Cloudsley, June 25, 1965 (dec. 1973); children: David, Eric, Adam; m. Mary Kathleen O'Neil, June 17, 1975; 1 dau., Sarah. BA, McGill U., Montreal, Que., Can., 1955, MD, 1959. Intern, resident in internal medicine Royal Victoria Hosp., Montreal, Que., Can.; resident in psychiatry U. Chi., Cin. VA Hosp.; psychoanalytic tng.

Montreal Psychoanalytic Inst.; psychiatrist Allan Meml. Inst.-Royal Victoria Hosp., Montreal-McGill U. Faculty Medicine, 1965-70; psychiatrist-in-chief Ottawa Civic Hosp.; also prof. dept. psychiatry U. Ottawa Faculty Medicine, 1971-74; prof. psychiatry, chmn. dept. U. Toronto Faculty Medicine; also dir. Clarke Inst. Psychiatry U. Toronto, 1974-80, dean Sch. Medicine, 1980-87, dir. Ctr. for Bioethics, 1989-95; rector, vice chancellor Concordia U., Montreal, 1995—. Author numerous papers in field; co-editor: A Method of Psychiatry, 1980, Alzheimer's Disease Research, 1991. Fellow Royal Coll. Physicians and Surgeons, Am. Coll. Psychiatrists; mem. Internat. Psychoanalytic Assn., Can. Psychiat. Assn. (editor jour. 1972-76), Am. Psychiat. Assn., Am. Coll. Psychoanalysts, Am. Coll. Psychiatrists. Office: Concordia U Office Rector, 1455 de Maisonneuve Blvd W, Montreal, PQ Canada H3G 1M8

LOWY, GEORGE THEODORE, lawyer; b. N.Y.C., Oct. 6, 1931; s. Eugene and Elizabeth Lowy; m. Pier M. Foucault, Sept. 7, 1957. BA cum laude, LLB cum laude, NYU. Bar: N.Y. 1955, U.S. Dist. Ct. (so. dist.) N.Y. 1958, U.S. Supreme Ct. 1972, U.S. Ct Appeals (2d cir.) 1975. Assoc. Cravath, Swaine and Moore, N.Y.C., 1957-65, ptnr., 1965—; trustee NYU Law Ctr. Found.; bd. dirs. Equitable Life Assurance Soc. U.S., Eramet, Calif.; adj. prof. NYU Law Sch., 1983—. Fellow ABA; mem. Am. Law Inst., Assn. of Bar of City of N.Y., Internat. Bar Assn., Union Internat. des Avocats, Cercle Interallie Paris. Home: 580 Park Ave New York NY 10021-7313 Office: Cravath Swaine & Moore World Wide Pla 825 8th Ave New York NY 10019-7416

LOWY, JAY STANTON, music industry executive; b. Chgo., Nov. 22, 1935; s. Joseph Alfred and Minnie Lowy; m. Diane Friedland, Oct. 10, 1959 (div.); children—Dana Kim, Jeffrey Mark; m. Brenda Belle Orloff, Mar. 22, 1982; 1 child, Jason Louis. Student, UCLA, 1954-58. Gen. mgr. Robbins Feist & Miller Music Pub. Cos., 1959-67, Famous Music Corp., 1967-69; v.p. Dot and Paramount Records, 1969-71; pres., chief operating officer Capitol-EMI Music Pub. Cos., 1971-73; v.p., gen. mgr. Jobete Music Co., Inc. (Motown Industries), Hollywood, Calif., 1976-86; cons., personal mgr., 1986—. Served with AUS, 1958. Named one of Top 200 Music Execs. Billboard Mag., 1976, Old Master Purdue U., 1979. Mem. Nat. Acad. Recording ARts and Scis. (nat. pres. and chmn. bd. trustees 1979-81), Calif. Copyright Conf. (pres. 1977-78), Tau Epsilon Phi. Democrat. Jewish. Home: 5516 Aura Ave Tarzana CA 91356-3006

LOXLEY, JOHN, economics educator; b. Sheffield, Eng., Nov. 12, 1942; arrived in Can., 1975; s. John and Elizabeth (Antcliff) L.; m. Zeeba Dawood, June 10, 1967 (div.); children: Salim John, Camille Elizabeth; m. Aurelie Mogan, Sept. 15, 1989; children: Raina Ilene, Matthew Reuben. BA in Econs. with honors, U. Leeds, Eng., 1963, PhD in Econs., 1966. Lectr. econs. dept. Makerere U., Kampala, Uganda, 1966-67; rsch. mgr. Nat. Bank Commerce, Tanzania, 1967-69; sr. lectr. dept. econs. U. Dar es Salaam, Tanzania, 1969-72; first dir. Inst. Fin. Mgmt., Dar es Salaam, 1972-73, UN Devel. Program prof. econs. and planning, head dept., 1973-74; sec. (dep. minister) resource and econ. devel. sub-com. of cabinet Govt. of Man., Winnipeg, Can., 1975-77; prof. econs. U. Man., 1977—, head dept., 1984—; chair Cmtys. Econ. Devel. Fund, Winnipeg, 1975-78; chair and pres. Channel Area Loggers, Man. Crown Corp., Winnipeg, 1976-78; vis. prof. U. Leeds, 1987-88; advisor, cons. Govt. Mozambique, 1978, 88, Govt. Tanzania, 1981, 82, 83, 84, Govt. Uganda, 1986, 87, Ctrl. Bank Madagascar, 1985, St. Kitts and Nevis, 1991, 92, ANC/COSATU, South Africa, 1991, 92, 93, Royal Commn. Aboriiginal Pegdes, 1993-95; ptnr., pres. HKL & Assocs. Ltd. Author: The International Monetary Fund and the Poorest Countries, 1984, Debt and Disorder, 1986; co-editor: Towards Socialist Plannings, 1972, Structural Adjustment in Africa, 1989; editorial bd. Studies in Polit. Economy, 1979-92, Can. Jours. Devel. Studies; Rev. African Polit. Economy, 1985—. Bd. dirs., mem. exec. bd. Soc. for Manitobans with Disabilities, Winnipeg, 1983-89, mem. hon. adv. coun., 1989-90; bd. dirs., mem. exec. bd. Can. Rehab. Coun. for Disabled, Winnipeg, 1987-89; pres. Can. Assn. for Study Internat. Devel.; chmn. CHOICES—A Coalition for Social Justice, 1990-92; mem. Can. Commonwealth Scholarship and Fellowship Com., 1991-94. N.-S. Inst. vis. fellow, Ottawa, Ont., Can., 1982-83. Mem. Can. Econs. Assn., Can. Assn. for Study Internat. Devel. (v.p.), Can. African Studies Assn. Avocations: soccer, squash. Office: U Man Dept Econs, 501 Fletcher Argue Bldg, Winnipeg, MB Canada R3T 2N2

LOY, FRANK ERNEST, foundation executive; b. Nuremberg, Germany, Dec. 25, 1928; came to U.S., 1939; s. Alfred Loewi and Elizabeth (Loeffler) L.; m. Dale Haven, 1963; children: Lisel, Eric Anthony. B.A., UCLA, 1950; LL.B., Harvard U., 1953. Bar: D.C. 1953, Calif. 1954. With firm of O'Melveny & Myers, Los Angeles, 1954-65; spl. asst. to adminstr. FAA, 1961-63; spl. cons. to adminstr. AID, 1963-64; dep. asst. sec. state for econ. affairs, 1965-70; sr. v.p. Pan Am. World Airways, Inc., N.Y.C., 1970-73; pres. Pennsylvania Co., Washington, 1974-79, Penn Central Corp., 1978-79; dir. Bur. Refugee Programs, Dept. State, Washington, 1980-81; pres. German Marshall Fund of U.S., 1981—; instr. corp. fin. Grad. Sch. Commerce, U. So. Calif., 1959-61; dir. Applied Bioscience Internat. Inc. Chmn. bd. trustees Goddard Coll., Vt., 1976-78, Environ. Def. Fund, 1983-90, The Washington Ballet, 1991-94, The League of Conservation Voters, 1993—; U.S. mem. Bd. Regional Environ. Ctr. for Cen. and Ea. Europe, Budapest. With U.S. Army, 1953-55. Home: 3230 Reservoir Rd NW Washington DC 20007-2955 Office: Marshall German Fund of US 11 Dupont Cir NW Washington DC 20036-1207

LOYND, RICHARD BIRKETT, consumer products company executive; b. Norristown, Pa., Dec. 1, 1927; s. James B. and Elizabeth (Geigus) L.; m. Jacqueline Ann Seubert, Feb. 3, 1951; children: Constance, John, Cynthia, William, James, Michael. B.S. in Elec. Engring., Cornell U., 1950. Sales engr. Lincoln Electric Co., Cleve., 1950-55; with Emerson Electric Co., St. Louis, 1955-68; pres. Builder Products div. Emerson Electric Co., 1965-68, v.p. Electronics and Space div., 1961-65; v.p. ops. Gould, Inc., Chgo., 1968-71; exec. v.p. Eltra Corp., N.Y.C., 1971-74; pres. Eltra Corp., 1974-81; chmn. Converse, Inc., 1982-84; chmn., chief exec. officer Interco Inc., St. Louis, 1989—. Home: 19 Randall Dr Short Hills NJ 07078-1957 Office: Interco Inc 101 S Hanley Rd Saint Louis MO 63105-3406

LOZANO, JOSE, nephrologist; b. San Vicente, El Salvador, Feb. 11, 1941; came to U.S., 1968; s. Jose E. and Transito Maria (Mendez) L.; m. Hilda Berganza, Jan. 27, 1965; children: Jose E., Claudia Maria. MD, U. El Salvador, 1965. Diplomate Am. Bd. Internal Medicine, Am. Bd. Nephrology. Rotating intern Nat. Med. Ctr., San Salvador, El Salvador, 1963-64; asst. resident in internal medicine Rosales Hosp., San Salvador, 1965-66, resident in internal medicine, 1966-67, chief resident in internal medicine, 1967-68; resident in internal medicine Baylor U. Affiliated Hosps., Houston, 1968-70, fellow in nephrology, 1970-71, 73-74; asst. prof. medicine U. El Salvador, 1971-72; internist and nephrologist Social Security Hosp., San Salvador, 1971-72; instr. in medicine Baylor Coll. Medicine, Houston, 1974-75, asst. prof. medicine in nephrology, 1975-76, clin. asst. prof. medicine, 1976-80; mem. staff internal medicine St. Elizabeth Hosp., Beaumont Med./Surg. Hosp., Bapt. Hosp., Beaumont, Tex., 1976; med. dir. Golden Triangle Dialysis Ctr., Beaumont, 1977—, BMA Jasper, Jasper, Tex., 1986, BMA Orange, Orange, Tex., 1987-90; med. dir. Golden Triangle Dialysis Ctr., Beaumont, 1977; med. dir. BMA Jasper, Tex., 1986, Orange, Tex., 1987-90; mem. Kidney Health Care Adv. Com., 1981-82; pesenter in field. Contbr. articles to profl. publs. Mem. AMA, ACP, Am. Soc. Nephrology, Internat. Soc. Nephrology, Tex. Med. Assn., Harris County Med. Soc., Jefferson County Med. Soc., Am. Coll. Physicians Execs., Physicians for A Nat. Health Plan. Avocations: study of socioeconomic factors in healthcare in U.S., Catholic theologies. Home: 4655 Ashdown St Beaumont TX 77706-7723 Office: Beaumont Nephrology Assocs 3282 College St Beaumont TX 77701-4610

LOZANO, RUDOLPHO, federal judge; b. 1942. BS in Bus., Ind. U., 1963, LLB, 1966. Mem. firm Spangler, Jennings, Spangler & Dougherty. P.C., Merrillville, Ind., 1966-88; judge U.S. Dist. Ct. (no. dist.) Ind., Hammond, 1988—. With USAR, 1966-73. Mem. ABA, Ind. State Bar Assn., Def. Rsch. Inst. Office: US Dist Ct 205 Fed Bldg 507 State St Hammond IN 46320-1529

LOZANSKY, EDWARD DMITRY, physicist, author, consultant; b. Kiev, Ukraine, Feb. 10, 1941; came to U.S., 1977; s. Dmitry R. and Dina M.

(Chizhik) L.; m. Tatiana I. Yershov, Feb. 27, 1971; 1 child, Tania. MS, Moscow Phys. Engring. Inst., 1966; PhD, Inst. Atomic Energy, Moscow, 1969; LHD, Waynesburg Coll. Asst. prof. Moscow State U., 1969-71; assoc. prof. Mil. Tank Acad., Moscow, 1971-75; prof. U. Rochester, N.Y., 1977-80, Am. U., Washington, 1981-83, L.I. U., Bklyn., 1983-87; pres. Independent U., Washington, 1987-91; exec. dir. Andrei Sakharov Inst., Washington, 1981-86; pres. Russia House, Inc., 1991—, Am. U. in Moscow, 1992—, Am. Univs. in Russia, Ukraine and New Independent States, 1994—. Author: Theory of the Spark, 1976, For Tatiana, 1984, Andrei Sakharov, 1986, Mathematical Competitions, 1988, Democracy: USA-Russia, 1994. Mem. Russian Acad. of Soc. Scis. Republican. Jewish. Avocations: skiing, chess, lecturing on Russia. Office: Russia House 1800 Connecticut Ave NW Washington DC 20009-5731

LOZIER, ALLAN G., manufacturing company executive; b. 1933. Student, U. Nebr. With Lozier Corp., Omaha, ltd. ptnr., 1953-57, gen. ptnr., 1957-64, pres., treas., 1964-82, chmn. bd. dirs., 1982—. Office: Lozier Corp 6336 Pershing Dr Omaha NE 68110*

LOZOFF, BO, nonprofit organization administrator; b. Miami, Fla., Jan. 10, 1947; s. Eli Saul and Molly (Rubitzky) L.; m. Sita Linda Shrager, Sept. 25, 1966; 1 child, Joshua Elias Bo. Student, Tulane U., 1963-64, U. Fla., 1967. Rsch. assoc. Psychical Rsch. Found., Durham, N.C., 1972-74; mgr. Sunshine Farms Yoga Ashram, Durham, 1973-77; dir. Prison-Ashram Project, Durham, 1973—, Human Kindness Found., Durham, 1973—, Kindness House, Mebane, N.C., 1994—; cons. in field. Author: We're All Doing Time, 1984, Lineage and Other Stories, 1987, Inner Corrections, 1989, Just Another Spiritual Book, 1990. Recipient Quetlalcotyl award Xat Medicine Soc., 1986, Temple Award for Creative Altruism, Inst. of Noetic Scis., 1994. Office: Human Kindness Foundation Rt 1 Box 201-N Durham NC 27705

LOZYNIAK, ANDREW, manufacturing company executive; b. N.Y.C., July 28, 1931; s. Stephen and Helen (Pupchek) L.; m. Florence Slovitski, Nov. 24, 1955; children: Cynthia, Andrew, Richard, Wendy, Cathy. Grad., U. Conn., 1954. Pres. Fermont div. Dynamics Corp. Am., 1968-70; group v.p. Dynamics Corp. Am., Greenwich, Conn., 1970; exec. v.p. Dynamics Corp. Am., 1970, pres., 1970—, chmn. bd., 1978—, also dir.; bd. dirs. CTS Corp., Elkhart, Ind. Mem. Patterson, Indian Harbor Yacht Club. Office: Dynamics Corp Am 475 Steamboat Rd Greenwich CT 06830-7197

LU, DAVID JOHN, history educator, writer; b. Keelung, Taiwan, Sept. 28, 1928; came to U.S., 1950, naturalized, 1960; s. Ming and Yeh (Lai) L.; m. Annabelle Compton, May 29, 1954; children: David John, Daniel Mark, Cynthia King, Stephen Paul. B.A. in Econs. Nat. Taiwan U., 1950; postgrad., Westminster Theol. Sem., Phila., 1950-52; M. Internat. Affairs, Columbia, 1954; certificate, East Asian Inst., 1954, Ph.D., 1960. Editor Prentice-Hall, Inc., 1956-60; instr. Rutgers U., 1959; asst. prof. history Bucknell U., Lewisburg, Pa., 1960-64; assoc. prof. Bucknell U., 1964-69, prof., 1969-94, prof. emeritus, 1994—, dir. Ctr. for Japanese Studies, 1965-94; cons. on global edn. Pa. Dept. Edn., 1961-62, TR, U.S. Dept. Edn., 1973-85; resident dir. associated Kyoto program Doshisha U., 1987-88. Author: From the Marco Polo Bridge to Pearl Harbor, 1961, (Japanese edit.) Taiheiyo Senso e no Dotei, 1967, Sources of Japanese History, 2 vols, 1974, Bicentennial History of the United States (in Japanese), 1976, The Life and Times of Matsuoka Yosuke, 1880-1946, 1981, Inside Corporate Japan, the Art of Fumble-free Management, 1987; translator: The China Quagmire, 1983, What Is Total Quality Control? The Japanese Way, 1985; Kanban, Just-in-Time at Toyota, 1986, Total Quality Control for Management: Strategies and Techniques from Toyota and Toyoda Gosei, 1987, TQC (Total Quality Control), The Wisdom of Japan, 1988; contbr. Sekai to Nippon, weekly, Tokyo. Fulbright-Hays scholar Japan, 1966-67. Presbyterian. Home: 635 Broadway St Milton PA 17847-2407

LU, HUIZHU, computer scientist, educator; b. 1936; m. Yin Ming Wang, 1961; children: Serkuang, Qiang. BS in Physics, Fudan U., Shanghai, 1961; MS in Computer Science, U. Okla., 1983, PhD in Computer Science, 1988. Lectr. Shanghai U. Technology, Shanghai, China, 1961-80; visiting research associate, scientist U. Okla., Norman, 1981-85; asst. prof. Okla. State U., Stillwater, 1985-92, assoc. prof., 1992—; prin. investigator of projects Okla. Dept. Health, Okla. Dept. Environ. Quality. Co-author: Digital Measurement Techniques, 1980; contbr. numerous rsch. articles to profl. jours. Recipient numerous rsch. grants. Mem. Assn. for Computing Machinery, IEEE Computer Soc., Sigma Xi. Office: Oklahoma State U 213 Mathematical Sci Bldg Stillwater OK 74078

LU, PAUL HAIHSING, mining engineer, geotechnical consultant; b. Hsinchu, Taiwan, Apr. 6, 1921; came to U.S., 1962; m. Sylvia Chin-Pi Liu, May 5, 1951; children: Emily, Flora. BS in Mining Engring., Hokkaido U., Sapporo, Japan, 1945; PhD in Mining Engring., U. Ill., 1967. Sr. mining engr., br. chief Mining Dept. Taiwan Provincial Govt., Taipei, 1946-56; sr. indsl. specialist mining and geology U.S. State Dept./Ag. for Internat. Devel., Taipei, 1956-62; rsch. mining engr. Denver Rsch. Ctr. Bur. of Mines, U.S. Dept. Interior, 1967-90; geotech. cons. Lakewood, Colo., 1991—. Contbr. over 60 articles to profl. jours. Rsch. fellow Hokkaido U., 1945-46, Ill. Mining Inst., 1966-67. Mem. Internat. Soc. for Rock Mechanics, Soc. for Mining, Metallurgy, and Exploration (AIME), Mining and Materials Processing Inst. Japan, Chinese Inst. of Mining and Metall. Engrs. (dir., mining com. chair 1960-62, Tech. Achievement award 1962). Achievements include development of prestressed concrete mine supports; invention of new technologies of rock stress measurement with hydraulic borehole pressure cells and measurement of geomechanical properties of rock masses with borehole pressure cells; invention of integrity factor approach to mine structure design. Home and Office: 1001 S Foothill Dr Lakewood CO 80228-3404

LU, PONZY, molecular biology educator; b. Shanghai, China, Oct. 7, 1942; came to U.S., 1949, naturalized, 1963; s. Abraham and Beth (Chou) L.; m. Heidi Fahl, Jan. 13, 1975; 1 child, Kristina. B.S., Calif. Inst. Tech., 1964; Ph.D., MIT, 1970. Arthritis Found. postdoctoral fellow Max Planck Inst., Goettingen, Fed. Republic Germany, 1970-73; asst. prof. dept. chemistry U. Pa., Phila., 1973-78; assoc. prof. U. Pa., 1978-82, prof., 1982—; mem. study sect. NIH, 1982-86, 92—; mem. Univ. Space Reseach Assn./NASA Biotechnology Discipline Working Group, microgravity sci. and applications div., 1986-91. Recipient Career Devel. award NIH, 1977-82. Mem. Am. Soc. Biochemistry, Molecular Biology, Biophys. Soc., Sigma Xi. Office: Univ Pa Dept Chemistry Philadelphia PA 19104

LU, WUAN-TSUN, microbiologist, immunologist; b. Taichung, Taiwan, July 8, 1939; came to U.S., 1964; s. Yueh and Jinmien Lu; m. Rita Man Rom, July 25, 1970; children: Dorcia, Loretta. BS in Agrl. Econs., Nat. Taiwan U., 1960; MS in Microbiology, Brigham Young U., 1968; PhD, U. Okla., 1978. Microbiologist, chemist Murray Biol. Co., L.A., 1969-71; microbiologist Reference Lab., North Hollywood, Calif., 1971-73; rsch. assoc. U. Okla., Okla. City, 1973-78; lab. supr. Reference Med. Lab., San Jose, Calif., 1980; mng. dir. Anakem Labs., Los Gatos, Calif., 1981-85; toxicologist SmithKline Labs., San Jose, 1981; founder, pres. United Biotech, Inc., Mountain View, Calif., 1983—, dir., chmn., mng. dir., 1987—; bd. dirs. Sino-U.S. Hunan Bioengring., Co., Ltd., Bios Instrment Lab., Inc., Mountain View, Calif.. Mem. Am. Soc. Clin. Pathologists, Am. Soc. Clin. Chemists, Delta Group. Office: United Biotech Inc 110 Pioneer Way # C Mountain View CA 94041-1517

LUBAR, JEFFREY STUART, journalist; b. Rockville Centre, N.Y., Apr. 15, 1947; s. Sidney and Rose (Grupsmith) L.; m. Barbara Ruth Bigelman; children—Debra, Adam, Rachel. B.A., Am. U., 1969. Dir. Washington News Bur., Susquehanna Broadcasting Co., 1969-86; v.p. pub. affairs Nat. Assn. Realtors, 1987—; Mem. exec. com. of corrs. Radio-TV Assn. (U.S. Congress), 1974-75. Served with AUS, 1969-75. Mem. Burke Racquet Club, Swim and Tennis Club at Fairfax Station, Nat. Press Club. Jewish. Home: 6307 Karmich St Fairfax VA 22039-1622 Office: 700 11th St NW Washington DC 20001-4507

LUBAR, SHELDON BERNARD, venture capitalist; b. Milw., May 21, 1929; s. Joseph J. and Lottie (Stern) L.; m. Marianne Segal, Aug. 31, 1952;

children: Kristine, David, Susan, Joan. BBA, U. Wis., 1951, LLB, 1953; DCS, U. Wis., Milw., 1988. V.p. Marine Nat. Exch. Bank, Milw., 1953-61; pres. Marine Capital Corp., Milw., 1961-65; chmn., pres. Mortgage Assocs., Inc., Milw., 1966-73; asst. sec., commr. FHA, Dept. HUD, U.S. Govt., Washington, 1973-74; pres. Midland Nat. Bank, Milw., 1975-76; chmn. Lubar & Co., Inc., Milw., 1977—; Christiana Co., Inc., Milw., 1987—; bd. dirs. Mass. Mut. Life Ins. Co., Springfield, Firstar Bank Corp., Milw., MGIC, Milw., Christiana Cos., Inc., Milw., Amertech, Inc., Chgo. Author: (with others) Financing Economic Development, 1990. Pres. Milw. Art Mus., 1977-80, Wis. Policy Rsch. Inst., Milw., 1987—; trustee Marquette U., Milw., 1985-91; regent U. Wis. System, 1991—. Avocations: mountain climbing, skiing, jogging, swimming. Office: Lubar & Co Inc 777 E Wisconsin Ave Milwaukee WI 53202

LUBATTI, HENRY JOSEPH, physicist, educator; b. Oakland, Calif., Mar. 16, 1937; s. John and Pauline (Massimino) L.; m. Catherine Jeanne Berthe Ledoux, June 29, 1968; children: Karen E., Henry J., Stephen J.C. AA, U. Calif., Berkeley, 1957, AB, 1960; PhD, U. Calif., 1966; MS, U. Ill., 1963. Research assoc. Faculty Scis. U. Paris, Orsay, France, 1966-68; asst. prof. physics MIT, 1968-69; assoc. prof., sci. dir. visual techniques lab. U. Wash., 1969-74, prof., sci. dir. visual Techniques lab., 1974—; vis. lectr. Internat. Sch. Physics, Erice, Sicily, 1968, Herceg-Novi, Yugoslavia Internat. Sch., 1969, XII Cracow Sch. Theoretical Physics, Zapokane, Poland, 1972; vis. scientist CERN, Geneva, 1980-81; vis. staff Los Alamos Nat. Lab., 1983-86; guest scientist SSC Lab., 1991-93; mem. physics editorial adv. com. World Sci. Pub. Co. Ltd., 1982-93. Editor: Physics at Fermilab in the 1990's, 1990; contbr. numerous articles on high energy physics to profl. jours. Alfred P. Sloan research fellow, 1971-75. Fellow AAAS, Am. Phys. Soc.; mem. Sigma Xi, Tau Beta Pi. Office: U Wash Visual Techniques Lab Physics FM 15 Seattle WA 98195

LUBAWSKI, JAMES LAWRENCE, health care administrator; b. Chgo., June 4, 1946; s. Harry James and Stella Agnes (Pokorny) L.; m. Kathleen Felicity Donnellan, June 1, 1974; children: Kathleen N., James Lawrence, Kevin D., Edward H. BA, Northwestern U., 1968, MBA, 1969, MA, 1980. Asst. prof. U. Northern Iowa, Cedar Falls, 1969-72; instr. Loyola U., Chgo., 1974-76; dir., market planning Midwest Stock Exchange, Chgo., 1976-77; dir. mktg. Gambro Inc., Barrington, Ill., 1977-79; mktg. mgr. Travenol Labs., Deerfield, Ill., 1979-82; dir. mktg. Hollister Inc., Libertyville, Ill., 1982-84; pres., chief exec. officer Neomedica Inc., Chgo., 1984-86; v.p. bus. devel. Evangl. Health Svcs., Oak Brook, Ill., 1986-87; pres., chief exec. officer Cath. Health Alliance Met. Chgo., 1987—; bd. dirs. Cath. Health Alliance Met. Chgo., 1987, CHAMC Ventures, Chgo., 1988, Ill. Cath. Health Assn., Chgo., 1990. Author: Food and Man, 1974, Food and People, 1979; co-editor: Consumer Behavior in Theory and in Action, 1970. Am. Assn. Advt. Acys. Faculty fellow, 1973. Mem. Evanston Golf Club, Equestrian Order of Knights of Holy Sepulchre. Avocation: golf, fishing. Office: Cath Health Alliance Met 320 N Michigan Ave Ste 900 Chicago IL 60601-3710

LUBBEN, DAVID J., lawyer; b. Cedar Rapids, Iowa, 1951. BA, Luther Coll., 1974; JD, U. Iowa, 1977. Bar: Minn. 1977. Ptnr. Dorsey & Whitney, Mpls. Office: Dorsey & Whitney PLLP 220 S 6th St Minneapolis MN 55420-1498

LUBBERS, AREND DONSELAAR, university president; b. Milw., July 23, 1931; s. Irwin Jacob and Margaret (Van Donselaar) L.; m. Eunice L. Mayo, June 19, 1953 (div.); children—Arend Donselaar, John Irwin Darrow, Mary Elizabeth; m. Nancy Vanderpol, Dec. 21, 1968; children—Robert Andrew, Caroline Jayne. AB, Hope Coll., 1953; AM, Rutgers U., 1956; LittD, Central Coll., 1977; DSc, U. Sarajevo, Yugoslavia, 1987; LHD, Hope Coll., 1988; DSc, Akademia Ekonomiczna, Krakow, Poland, 1989. Research asst. Rutgers U., 1954-55; research fellow Reformed Ch. in Am., 1955-56; instr. history and polit. sci. Wittenberg U., 1956-58; v.p. devel. Central Coll., Iowa, 1959-60; pres. Central Coll., 1960-69, Grand Valley State U., Allendale, Mich., 1969—; mem. Am. Assn. State Colls. and Univs. seminar in India, 1971, Fed. Commn. Orgn. Govt. for Conduct Fgn. Policy, 1972; USIA insp., Netherlands, 1976; mem. pres.' commn. NCAA, 1984-87, 89—; bd. dirs. Grand Bank, Grand Rapids, Mich. Student community ambassador from Holland, Mich. to Yugoslavia, 1951; bd. dirs. Grand Rapids Symphony, 1976—; bd. dirs. Butterworth Hosp., 1988. Recipient Golden Plate award San Diego Acad. Achievement, 1962, Golden-Emblem Order of Merit Polish Peoples Republic, 1988; named 1 of top 100 young men in U.S. Life mag., 1962. Mem. Mich. Coun. State Univs. Pres. (chmn. 1988), Grand Rapids World Affairs Council (pres. 1971-73), Phi Alpha Theta, Pi Kappa Delta, Pi Kappa Phi. Home: 801 Plymouth Ave SE Grand Rapids MI 49506-6555 Office: Grand Valley State U Coll Landing 1 Campus Dr Allendale MI 49401-9401

LUBECK, MARVIN JAY, ophthalmologist; b. Cleve., Mar. 20, 1929; s. Charles D. and Lillian (Jay) L. A.B., U. Mich., 1951, M.D., 1955, M.S., 1959. Diplomate Am. Bd. Opthamology; m. Arlene Sue Bitman, Dec. 28, 1955; children: David Mark, Daniel Jay, Robert Charles. Intern, U. Mich. Med. Ctr., 1955-56, resident ophthalmology, 1956-58; jr. clin. instr. ophthalmology, 1958-59; pvt. practice medicine, specializing in ophthalmology, Denver, 1961—; mem. staff Rose Hosp., Porter Hosp., Presbyn. Hosp., St. Luke's Hosp.; assoc. clin. prof. U. Colo. Med. Ctr.; cons. ophthalmologist State of Colo. With U.S. Army, 1959-61. Fellow ACS; mem. Am. Acad. Ophthalmology, Denver Med. Soc., Colo. Ophthalmol. Soc., Am. Soc. Cataract & Refractive Surgery. Home: 590 S Harrison Ln Denver CO 80209-3517 Office: 3865 Cherry Crk North Dr Denver CO 80209-3803

LUBELL, HAROLD, economic consultant; b. N.Y.C., Mar. 29, 1925; s. Morris and Fannie (Bell) L.; m. Claudie Marchaut, 1962; children: Martin, Diana. BA, Bard Coll., 1944; MPA, Harvard U., 1947, MA in Econs., 1948, PhD in Econs., 1953. Economist Fed. Res. Bd., Washington, 1944-45; ECA/MSA, Paris, 1949-53; Economist AID, Ankara, Turkey, 1965-68, New Delhi, 1969-71, Washington, 1978-82, Cairo, 1982-85, Dakar, 1985-89; economist Falk Project for Econ. Research, Jerusalem, 1954-57, Rand Corp., Santa Monica, Calif., 1957-62; with Ford Found., Saigon, Vietnam, Kuala Lumpur, Malaysia, 1963-64; economist World Employment Program, ILO, Geneva, 1971-78; econ. cons. 1989—. Author: Middle East Oil Crises and Western Europe's Energy Supplies, 1963, Urban Development and Employment: the Prospects for Calcutta, 1974, The Informal Sector in the 1980s and the 1990s, 1990. Office: 25 Rue de Lille, Paris 75007, France

LUBER, THOMAS J(ULIAN), lawyer; b. Louisville, Feb. 16, 1949; s. John J. and Martha E. (Cotton) L.; m. Dorothy Ann Carter, Dec. 19, 1975; children: Katharine Ann, Allison Julia. BS in Acctg., U. Louisville, 1972, JD with honors, 1976; LLM in Taxation, NYU, 1977. Bar: Ky. 1976. Agt. IRS, Louisville, 1972-73; assoc. Fahey & Gray, Louisville, 1977-79; from assoc. to ptnr. Wyatt, Tarrant & Combs and predecessor firms, Louisville 1979—, chmn. tax sect., 1983—; lectr. U. Louisville, 1978-80; speaker in field; bd. advisors Jour. Multistate Taxation. Contbr. articles to profl. jours. Bd. dirs. Univ. Pediatrics Found., Louisville, Univ. Ob-gyn. Found., Louisville, Assumption High Sch., Louisville. With USAF, 1967-69. Mem. ABA, Ky. Bar Assn. (chmn. tax sect. 1983-84), Louisville Bar Assn., Ky. Inst. Fed. Taxation (mem. planning com. 1981—, chmn. 1984—), Jefferson Club, Big Spring Country Club, Tavern Club. Democrat. Roman Catholic. Avocations: tennis, bicycling. Home: 2324 Saratoga Dr Louisville KY 40205-2021 Office: Wyatt Tarrant & Combs 2800 Citizens Plz Louisville KY 40202-2898

LUBET, STEVEN, law educator; b. 1949. JD, U. Calif., Berkeley, 1973. Staff atty. Legal Asst. Fedn., Chgo., 1973-75; prof. Northwestern U., Evanston, Ill., 1975—; lectr. DePaul U., Chgo., 1974-75. Office: Northwestern U Sch Law 357 E Chicago Ave Chicago IL 60611-3008

LUBETKIN, CHARLES SCHILLER, retail executive; b. Newark, Feb. 1, 1932; s. William and Dorothy (Kimmel) L.; m. Rona Zimmerman; Sept. 6, 1955; children: Jay, David, Beth. BS, N.J. Inst. Tech. (formerly Newark Coll. Engring.), 1953. Sales mgr. Brick Ch. Appliance, Inc., Orange, N.J., 1956-60, ops. mgr., 1960-62, warehouse mgr., 1962-67, v.p., 1967-72, exec. v.p., 1972-81, pres., 1981—. Active Better Bus. Bur., N.J. Econ. Devel. Council; first chmn. Econ. Devel. Com., Orange, 1977. Served to 1st lt. USAF, 1953-56. Mem. N.J. Retail Mchts. Assn., Omicron Delta Kappa, Tau Beta Pi. Office: Brick Ch Appliance Inc PO Box 3060 Edison NJ 08818-3060

LUBETSKI, EDITH ESTHER, librarian; b. Bklyn., July 16, 1940; d. David and Leah (Aronson) Slomowitz; m. Meir Lubetski, Dec. 23, 1968; children: Shaul, Uriel, Leah. BA, Bklyn. Coll., 1962; MS in L.S., Columbia U., 1965; MA in Jewish Studies, Yeshiva U., 1968. Judaica librarian Stern Coll. N.Y.C., 1965-66, acquisitions librarian, 1966-69, head librarian, 1969—; Author: (with Meir Lubetski) Building a Judaica Library Collection, 1983; contbr. articles to profl. jours. Mem. ALA, Assn. Jewish Libraries (corr. sec. 1980-84, pres. N.Y. chpt. 1984-86, nat. v.p. 1984-86, nat. pres. 1986-88, Fanny Goldstein Merit award 1993), N.Y. Library Assn. Home: 1219 E 27th St Brooklyn NY 11210-4622 Office: Yeshiva U Hedi Steinberg Libr 245 Lexington Ave New York NY 10016-4605

LUBETZKY, CAROLE DIANE, elementary education educator, math-science specialist; b. L.A., Oct. 4, 1942; d. Lawrence and Bessie (Gursky) Schneider; m. David H. Lubetzky, Aug. 27, 1967; 1 child, Darren H. BS, San Jose State U., 1965; postgrad., U. Calif., Berkeley, UCLA. Cert. elem. tchr., Md. Tchr. Ascot Elem. Sch., L.A., 1966-67, Greenbelt (Md.) Elem. Sch., 1967—. Recipient 1st Pl Md. State Bicentennial, 1st Pl. Nat. Statistics Contest (grades 4-6), 1992. Mem. NEA, ASCD, Nat. Sci. Tchrs. Assn., Nat. Coun. Social Studies, Nat. Coun. Tchrs. Math., Am. Statis. Soc., Md. Coun. Tchrs. Math. Republican. Office: Greenbelt Elem Sch Greenbelt MD 20770

LUBIC, RUTH WATSON, association executive, nurse-midwife; b. Bucks County, Pa., Jan. 18, 1927; d. John Russell and Lillian (Kraft) Watson; m. William James Lubic, May 28, 1955; 1 son, Douglas Watson. Diploma, Sch. Nursing Hosp. U. Pa., 1955; BS, Columbia U., 1959, MA, 1961, EdD in Applied Anthropology, 1979; Cert. in Nurse Midwifery, SUNY, Bklyn., 1962; LLD (hon.), U. Pa., 1985; DSc (hon.), U. Medicine and Dentistry, N.J., 1986; LHD (hon.), Coll. New Rochelle, 1992; DSc (hon.), SUNY, Bklyn., 1993; LHD (hon.), Pace U., 1994. RN, Pa. Mem. faculty Sch. Nursing, N.Y. Med. Coll.; mem. faculty Maternity Ctr. Assn., SUNY Sch. Nurse-Midwifery, Downstate Med. Ctr.; staff nurse through head nurse Meml. Hosp. for Cancer and Allied Disease, N.Y.C., 1955-58; clin. assoc. Grad. Sch. Nursing N.Y. Med. Coll., N.Y.C., 1962-63; parent educator, cons. Maternity Ctr. Assn., N.Y.C., 1963-67, gen. dir., 1970—; bd. dirs. Am. Assn. for World Health U.S. Com. for WHO, 1975-94, pres., 1980-81; mem. bd. maternal child and family health rsch. NRC, 1974-80; mem. Commn. on Grads Fgn. Nursing Schs., 1979-83, v.p., 1980-91, treas., 1982-83; bd. govs. Frontier Nursing Svc., 1982-92; bd. dirs. Pan Am. Health and Edn. Found., pres., 1987-88; vis. lectr. King Edward Meml. Hosp., Perth, Australia, 1991; Kate Hanna Harvey vis. prof. communl. health nursing Frances Payne Bolton Sch. Nursing, Case Western Res., 1991; Lansdowne lectr. U. Victoria, B.C., Can., 1992. Author: (with Gene Hawes) Childbearing: A Book of Choices, 1987; contbr. articles to profl. jours. Recipient Letitia White award, Florence Nightingale medal, 1955, Rockefeller Pub. Svc. award, 1981, Hattie Hemschemeyer award, 1983, Alumnae award Sch. Nursing U. Pa., 1986, Tchrs. Coll. Columbia U., 1992, Disting. Svc. award Frances Payne Bolton Sch. Nursing, Case Western Res., U. 1993, McArthur Fellowship award, 1993, Hon. Recognition N.Y. State Nurses Assn., 1993, Nurse-Midwifery Faculty award Columbia U., 1993, Spirit of Nursing award Vis. Nurses Svc. of N.Y., 1994, MAES-MacInnes award Divsn. Nursing, NYU, 1994; named Maternal-Child Health Nurse of Yr., ANA, 1985, Hon. Recognition, ANA, 1994. Fellow AAAS, Am. Acad. Nursing, N.Y. Acad. Medicine; mem. APHA (mem. com. on internat. health, sec. maternal and child health coun. 1982, mem. governing coun. 1986-89, mem. nominating com. 1987, mem. action bd. 1988-90), Am. Coll. Nurse-Midwives (v.p. 1964-66, pres.-elect 1969-70), Soc. Applied Anthropology, Inst. Medicine of NAS, Nat. Assn. Childbearing Ctrs. (pres. 1983-91), Herman Biggs Soc. Cosmopolitan Club, Sigma Theta Tau. Office: 48 E 92nd St New York NY 10128-1316 *As a professional nurse-midwife and public health scientist, the guiding principles of my professional life are to listen carefully to the families to be served and to combine their needs with proven scientific knowledge in constructing models for care. It is my belief that the primary purpose of maternal and child health programs is to assist families to achieve a sense of self-confidence about their ability to bring forth and rear offspring in conjunction with, but not dependent upon, professional guidance.*

LUBICK, DONALD CYRIL, lawyer; b. Buffalo, Apr. 29, 1926; s. Louis and Minna D. (Nabith) L.; m. Susan F. Cohen, June 5, 1960; children:Jonathan, Caroline, Lisa. BA summa cum laude, U. Buffalo, 1945; JD magna cum laude, Harvard U., 1949. Bar: N.Y. 1950, Fla. 1974, D.C. 1981; lic. fgn. law cons. Ont., 1989. Teaching fellow Harvard U. Law Sch., 1949-50; lectr. law U. Buffalo, 1950-61; assoc., then ptnr. Hodgson, Russ, Andrews, Woods & Goodyear, Buffalo and Washington, 1950-61, 64-77, 81-94; tax legis. counsel Treasury Dept., Washington, 1961-64; asst. sec. for tax policy Treasury Dept., 1977-81; dir. tax adv. program for countries of Ctrl. and Ea. Europe and former Soviet Union Treasury Dept., Paris, 1994—. Author (with Hussey) Basic World Tax Code and Commentary, 1992. Chmn. Tax Revision Com., City of Buffalo, 1958; mem. adv. com. to select Com. on Election Reform, N.Y. State Legislature, 1974, mem. adv. group to commr. internal revenue, 1976. Served with USAAF, 1945-46. Harvard Internat. Tax Program sr. fellow, 1991—. Mem. ABA, Am. Law Inst., Am. Bar Found., N.Y. State Bar Assn., Fla. Bar Assn., Erie County Bar Assn. Democrat. Jewish. Office: Paris Embassy OECD, PSC 116 TAP, Paris France

LUBIN, BERNARD, psychologist, educator; b. Washington, Oct. 15, 1923; s. Israel Harry and Anne (Cohen) L.; m. Alice Weisbord, Aug. 5, 1957. B.A., George Washington U., 1952, M.A., 1953; Ph.D., Pa. State U. 1958. Diplomate: Am. Bd. Profl. Psychology, Am. Bd. Psychol. Hypnosis; lic. psychologist, Mo., Tex. Intern St. Elizabeths Hosp., 1952-53, Roanoke (Va.) VA Hosp., 1954-55, Wilkes-Barre (Pa.) VA Hosp., 1955; USPHS postdoctoral fellow, postdoctoral residency in psychotherapy U. Wis. Sch. Medicine, 1957-58; staff psychologist, instr. dept. psychiatry Ind. U. Sch. Medicine, Indpls., 1958-59; chief psychologist adult outpatient service Ind. U. Sch. Medicine, 1960-62, assoc. prof., 1964-67; dir. psychol. services Dept. Mental Health, Indpls., 1962-63; dir. div. research and tng. Dept. Mental Health, 1963-67; dir. div. psychology Greater Kansas City (Mo.) Mental Health Center, 1967-74; prof. dept. psychiatry U. Mo. Sch. Medicine, Kansas City, 1967-74, 76—; prof., dir. clin. tng. program dept. psychology U. Houston, 1974-76; prof., chmn. dept. psychology U. Mo. at Kansas City, 1976-83, Curators' prof., 1988; cons. Am. Nurses Assn., Panhandle Eastern Pipeline Co., Eli Lilly Pharm. Co., U.S. Sprint, Inst. Psychiat. Research, Ind. U. Med. Center, Ind. U. Sch. Dentistry, Goodwill Industries, USPHS Bur. Health Services, mental retardation div., (univ.-affiliated facilities br.), U.S. VA, Baylor U. Med. Sch., U. Tex. Health Scis. Center, Houston, 1974-76; Mem. tng. staff Nat. Tng. Labs. Inst.; dean or faculty mem. numerous confs., 1960—; exec. sec. Ind. Assn. for Advancement Mental Health Research and Edn., 1962-67. Author: (with M. Zuckerman) Multiple Affect Adjective Check List: Manual, 1965, 2d edit., 1985, (with E.E. Levitt) The Clinical Psychologist: Background, Roles and Functions, 1967, Depression: Concepts, Controversies, and Some New Facts, 1975, 2d edit., 1983, Depression Adjective Check Lists: Manual, 1967, rev. edit., 1994, (with L.D. Goodstein and A.W. Lubin) Organizational Development Sourcebooks I and II, 1979; (with W.A. O'Connor) Ecological Approaches to Clinical and Community Psychology, 1984, (with D.C. Martin and R.A. Blanc) Study Guide and Readings for Abnormal Psychology, 1984, (with Alice W. Lubin) Comprehensive Index to the Group Psychotherapy Literature: 1906-1980, 1987, (with A.W. Lubin) Family Therapy: A Bibliography, 1937-86, 1988, (with R. Gist) Psychosocial Aspects of Disaster, 1989 (with R.V. Whitlock) Homelessness in America: A Bibliography with Selective Annotations, 1894-1994, also articles; editorial bd. Jour. Community Psychology; mem. editorial bd. Internat. Jour. Group Psychotherapy, Profl. Psychology: Research and Practice; cons. reader, bd. dirs. Jour. Cons. and Clin. Psychology. pres. Midwest Group for Human Resources, Inc., 1965-69, trustee, 1965. Recipient N.T. Veatch award disting. rsch. and creative activity, 1982, UKC Faculty fellowship, 1994. Fellow Am. Psychol. Assn. (chmn. sponsor approval com., exec. bd. div. cons. psychology, council rep.), Mo. Psychol. Assn. (exec. bd. mem.), AAAS, Am. Group Psychotherapy Assn. (editorial com.); mem. Midwestern Psychol. Assn., Ind. Psychol. Assn. (pres. 1967), World Fedn. for Mental Health, Conf. Psychologist Dirs. and Cons. in State, Fed. and Territorial Mental Health Programs (editor Conf. Proc. 1966-68, editor Perspective 1966-68, mem. exec. com. 1964-68), Inter-Am. Congress Psychology, Cert. Consultants Internat. (charter), NTL Inst. (bd. dirs. 1986-92), Sigma Xi, Phi Kappa Phi, Psi Chi (v.p. for midwest, mem. nat. coun. 1986-90, pres.-elect 1991-92, pres. 1992-93, past pres. 1993-94). Office: U

Mo Kansas City Dept Psychology 5307 Holmes St Kansas City MO 64110-2437

LUBIN, DONALD G., lawyer; b. N.Y.C., Jan. 10, 1934; s. Harry and Edith (Tannenbaum) L.; m. Amy Schwartz, Feb. 2, 1956; children: Peter, Richard, Thomas, Alice Lubin Spahr. BS in Econs., U. Pa., 1954; LLB, Harvard U., 1957. Bar: Ill. 1957. Ptnr., chmn. exec. com. Sonnenschein Nath & Rosenthal, Chgo., 1957—; bd. dirs., mem. exec. com. McDonald's Corp.; bd. dirs. Molex, Inc., Daubert Industries Inc., Charles Levy Co., Tennis Corp. Am., Arcade Holdings, Inc.; former v.p., dir. San Diego Nat. League Baseball Club, Inc.; former dir., mem. exec. com. First Nat. Bnak of Highland Park; former mem. Spl. Commn. on Adminstrn. of Justice in Cook County, Chgo. Former mem. Navy Pier Redevel. Corp., Highland Park Cultural Arts Commn.; life trustee, former chmn. bd. Highland Park Hosp., Ravinia Festival Assn.; trustee, mem. exec. com. Rush-Presbyn.-St. Luke's Med. Ctr.; trustee Orchestral Assn. Chgo.; bd. dirs., v.p. and sec. Ronald McDonald Children's Charities, Inc., Chgo. Found. for Edn., Smithsonian Inst., Washington; former bd. dirs., v.p., sec. Ragdale Found.; bd. govs. Art Inst. Chgo., Chgo. Lighthouse for the Blind; mem. citizens bd. U. Chgo.; mem. council Children's Meml. Hosp.; former bd. overseers Coll. Arts and Sci., U. Pa. Woodrow Wilson vis. fellow. Fellow Am. Bar Found., Ill. Bar Found., Chgo. Bar Found.; mem. ABA, Ill. Bar Assn., Chgo. Bar Assn., Law Club Chgo., Chgo. Hort. Soc. (past bd. dirs.), Econ. Club, Comml. Club (sec., civic com.), Chgo. Club, Std. Club, Lakeshore Club, Beta Gamma Sigma. Home: 2269 Egandale Rd Highland Park IL 60035-2501 Office: Sonnenschein Nath & Rosenthal 233 S Wacker Dr Ste 8000 Chicago IL 60606-6404

LUBIN, MARTIN, cell physiologist educator; b. N.Y.C., Mar. 30, 1923; m. Dorothy Alpern, Sept. 5, 1942; children—Peter, Adam, Thomas, John Caleb. B.A., Harvard U., 1942, M.D., 1945; Ph.D. in Biophysics, MIT, 1954. Research assoc. biology MIT, 1953-54; assoc. pharmacology then asst. prof. pharmacology Harvard U. Med. Sch., 1957-68; prof. microbiology Dartmouth Med. Sch., 1968—. Served with AUS, 1946-48. USPHS fellow, 1949-51; Childs Meml. Fund med. research fellow, 1951-53; Guggenheim fellow and Commonwealth Fund research fellow Lab. Molecular Biology, Cambridge, Eng., 1965-67. Home: 21 Lyme Rd Hanover NH 03755-1406

LUBIN, MARY LUELLA, nursing home administrator; b. Glastonbury, Conn., Apr. 24, 1932; d. Robert Harley and Luella (Sampson) Kellogg; m. Michael D. Lubin, Sept. 10, 1955; children: Elizabeth Lubin Hughes, James Kellogg. BS, Simmons Coll., 1954; MA, Calif. State U., 1970. RN, Calif.; cert. gerontol. nurse. Pub. health nurse New Haven VNA and Sacramento Health Depts., 1954-56; lectr. pub. health. nursing Boston Coll., Chestnut Hill, Mass., 1965-67; rehab. nurse specialist Internat. Rehab. Assn., Atlanta, 1975-76; dir. staff devel. Nat. Health Enterprises, San Leandro, Calif., 1980-81; dir. nursing services Hillhaven Corp., Alameda, Calif., 1981-85, adminstr., 1985-87, dist. dir., 1987-89; dir. hosp.-based svcs. Guardian Health Group, Corte Madera, Calif., 1989—; co-owner Yram Applications Software, San Leandro, 1982-91. Vol. leader United Way, Sacramento, 1976-80; nurse vol. USAF and ARC, Sacramento, 1958-64, Japan, 1970-72; bd. dirs. Support Svcs. for Srs. of Alameda County, Hayward, Calif., 1986-91. Fellow Am. Coll. Health Care Adminstrs. (cert.). Avocations: oriental art, antiques. Home: 1235 View Dr San Leandro CA 94577-5334 Office: Guardian Health Group 5725 Paradise Dr Ste 550 Corte Madera CA 94925

LUBIN, MICHAEL FREDERICK, physician, educator; b. Phila., Mar. 20, 1947; s. Leonard and Ethel Sybil (Stern) L. BA, Johns Hopkins U., 1969, MD, 1973. Resident Emory U. Affiliated Hosp., Atlanta, 1973-76; asst. prof. medicine Emory U. Sch. Medicine, Atlanta, 1976-82, assoc. prof. medicine, 1982—; dir. div. gen. medicine, 1989-95; dir. preoperative clinic Grady Hosp., Atlanta, 1995—; chmn. housestaff evaluation com. Dept. medicine Emory U. Sch. Medicine; chmn. pharmacy and therapeutics com. Grady Hosp. Editor: Medical Management of the Surgical Patient, 1982, 3d rev. edit., 1995; editor Medical Rounds, 1988-90; mem. editl. bd. I-M: Internal Medicine, 1992—; contbr. to Med. Knowledge Self Assessment Program X, 1994. Hartford scholar in Geriatrics UCLA, 1984-85. Fellow ACP; mem. Am. Geriatrics Soc., Soc. Gen. Internal Medicine. Office: Emory U Sch Medicine 69 Butler St SE Atlanta GA 30303-3033

LUBIN, STEVEN, concert pianist, musicologist; b. N.Y.C., Feb. 22, 1942; s. Jack and Sophie (Auslander) L.; m. Wendy Lubin, June 2, 1974; children: Benjamin, Nathaniel. AB in Philosophy, Harvard U., 1963; MS in Piano, Juilliard Sch. Music, 1965; PhD in Musicology, NYU, 1974. Mem. faculty Juilliard Sch. Music, N.Y.C., 1964-65, Aspen (Colo.) Music Sch., 1965; Mem. faculty Vassar Coll., Poughkeepsie, N.Y., 1970-71; coordinator grad. music theory program Cornell U., Ithaca, N.Y., 1971-75; adj. prof. Sch. Arts, SUNY, Purchase, 1975—; founding mem. The Mozartean Players, 1978—. Mem., NYU Electronic Composers Workshop, 1967-68; concert pianist tours in U.S. and Europe, 1976—; appeared as fortepiano soloist and condr. in Authentic-Instrument concert series, N.Y.C., 1981—; rec. artist Decca, Arabesque Records, Harmonia Mundi; filmed solo performances for Brit. documentary TV in London and Vienna, 1986; soloist in complete Beethoven piano concertos for London/Decca Records, 1987; performed complete cycle Beethoven concertos, London, 1987; solo recordings (new series) Decca including Beethoven Sonatas, 1991; contbr. articles to N.Y. Times, Keyboard Classics, others. Martha Baird Rockefeller grantee, 1968. Mem. Am. Mus. Soc., Soc. Music Theory.

LUBINSKY, MENACHEM YECHIEL, communications executive; b. Hanover, Germany, Apr. 13, 1949; arrived in country 1950; s. Chaim P. and Pesa (Lubinsky) L.; m. Hindy Deborah Fink, Jan. 14, 1973; children: Tziporah, Meiri, Tzviya. BBA, CUNY, 1975, MBA, 1982. Asst. to pres. Agudath Israel of Am., N.Y.C., 1971-72; dir. Boro Park Sr. Citizens Ctr. Bklyn., 1973-74, Project COPE, N.Y.C., 1975-80; dir. gov., pub. affairs Agudath Israel of Am., N.Y.C., 1981-84; pres. Lubinsky, Schild Assocs., N.Y.C., 1985-86, Lubicom, 1987-90, Integrated Mktg. & Comm. Inc., N.Y.C., 1990—; v.p. Agudath Israel of Am., Inc.; pres. Integrated Mktg. and Comm. Author: Op-Ed-Page, New York Times, 1984, Struggle and Splendor. Bd. dirs. Ohel Children's Home, Jewish Com. Rels. Coun., 1986; pres. Met. N.Y. Coordinating Coun. on Jewish Poverty; v.p. Agudath Israel of Am.; mem. domestic affairs com. United Jewish Appeal, 1992—; mem. Pvt. Industry Coun. City of N.Y. Mem. Pub. Relations Soc. Am., League of Advt. Avocation: tennis.

LUBIN, GLORIA BECKER, physicist; b. Phila., May 16, 1933; d. Samuel Albert and Anne (Gorrin) B.; m. Yale Jay Lubkin, June 14, 1953 (div. Apr. 1968); children: David Craig, Sharon Rebecca. AB, Temple U., 1953; MA, Boston U., 1957; postgrad., Harvard U., 1974-75. Mathematician Fairchild Stratos Co., Hagerstown, Md., 1954, Letterkenny Ordnance Depot, Chambersburg, Pa., 1955-56; physicist TRG Inc., N.Y.C., 1956-58; acting chmn. dept. physics Sarah Lawrence Coll., Bronxville, N.Y., 1961-62; v.p. Lubkin Assocs., electronic cons., Port Washington, N.Y., 1962-68; assoc. editor Physics Today Am. Inst. Physics, N.Y.C., 1963-69; sr. editor Physics Today Am. Inst. Physics, 1970-84, editl. dir., 1994—; cons. in field; mem. Nieman acdn. com. Harvard U., 1978-82; co-chmn. search/adv. com. Theoretical Physics Inst., U. Minn., 1987-89, co-chmn. oversight com. 1989—; mem. mng. com. Westinghouse Sci. Writing Prizes, 1988-91; mem. selection com. Knight Fellowships. 1990. Contbr. articles to profl. publs. Gloria Becker Lubkin Professorship of Theoretical Physics established in her honor U. Minn., 1990; Nieman fellow, 1974-75. Fellow AAAS (mem. nominating com. for sect. B physics 1987-89, chair 1989), Am. Phys. Soc. (exec. com. history of physics divsn. 1983-86, 92—, exec. com. forum on physics and soc. 1977-78); mem. N.Y. Acad. Scis. (chair The Scis. pub. com. 1992-93), Nat. Assn. Sci. Writers, Sigma Pi Sigma. Jewish. Office: Am Inst Physics One Physics Ellipse College Park MD 20740

LUBKIN, VIRGINIA LEILA, ophthalmologist; b. N.Y.C., Oct. 26, 1914; d. Joseph and Anna Fredericka (Stern) L.; m. Arnold Malkan, June 6, 1944 (div. 1949); m. Martin Bernstein, Aug. 28, 1949; children: Ellen Henrietta, James Ernst, Roger Joel, John Conrad. BS, NYU, 1933; MD, Columbia U., 1937. Diplomate Am. Bd. Ophthalmology. Intern Harlem Hosp. N.Y.C., 1938-40; asst. resident neurology Montefiore Hosp., N.Y.C., 1940, asst. resident pathology, 1940-41, fellow in ophthalmology, 1941-42; resident ophthalmology Kings County Hosp., Bklyn., 1942-43, Mt. Sinai Hosp., N.Y.C., 1943-44; attending ophthalmologist, assoc. clin. prof. emeritus Mt.

Sinai Sch. Medicine, 1944—; pvt. practice N.Y.C., 1945-90; rsch. prof. N.Y. Med. Coll., 1986—; co-creator, now chief of rsch. bioengineering lab. N.Y. Eye and Ear Infirmary (name now The Advent), N.Y.C., 1978—, now chief rsch.; creator first grad. course in oculoplastics and bi-yearly symposia in devel. dyslexia Mt. Sinai Sch. Medicine; educator courses in psychosomatic ophthalmology Am. Acad. Ophthalmology, 1950-60, educator course in complications of blepharoplasty, 1980-90; bd. dirs. Jewish Guild for the Blind; lectr. surg. ophthalmology in French Cameroon, Presbyn. Mission, 1951; lectr. in numerous countries including India, 1976, 92, Pakistan, 1976, 84, China, 1978, Sri Lanka, 1979, South Africa, 1982, Singapore, 1984, Thailand, 1984, Argentina, 1986, Peru, 1987. Author: (with others) Ophthalmic Plastic and Reconstructive Surgery, 1989; contbr. articles to profl. jours. Pres. N.Y. Soc. for Clin. Ophthalmology, 1979-80. Grantee Intraocular Lens Implant Mfrs., 1989. Fellow AMA, AAAS, Am. Soc. Ophthalmic Plastic and Reconstructive Surgery (founding), Am. Coll. Surgeons, N.Y. Acad. Medicine, N.Y. Acad. Scis., Am. Acad. Ophthalmology, Am. Soc. Cataract and Refractive Surgery, PanAm. Soc. Ophthalmology, N.Y. Soc. Clin. Ophthalmology, Soc. Light Treatment and Biol. Rhythms, Phi Beta Kappa, Alpha Omega Alpha. Home: 1 Blackstone Pl Bronx NY 10471 Office: NY Eye and Ear Infirmary Rm 232 South Bldg 310 E 14th St New York NY 10003

LUBLINSKI, MICHAEL, lawyer; b. Eskilstuna, Sweden, Sept. 11, 1951; came to U.S., 1956; s. Walter and Dora L. BA magna cum laude, CCNY, 1972; JD, Georgetown U., 1975. Bar: N.Y. 1976, Calif. 1980, Ct. Internat. Trade 1981, U.S. Dist. Ct. (cen. dist.) Calif. 1981, U.S. Dist. Ct. (so. dist.) N.Y. 1981, U.S. Ct. Appeals (D.C. cir.) 1982. Atty. U.S. Customs Service, Washington, 1975-79, U.S. Dept. Commerce, Washington, 1980; assoc. Mori & Ota, Los Angeles, 1980-84; assoc. Kelley Drye & Warren, Los Angeles, 1984-85, ptnr., 1986—. Panel moderator Calif. continuing edn. of bar Competitive Bus. Practices Inst., Los Angeles and San Francisco, 1984. Mem. ABA, Calif. Bar Assn., Los Angeles County Bar Assn. (arbitrator 1981-82, chmn. customs law sect. 1986). Avocations: travel, photography, movies. Home: 2609 Creston Dr Los Angeles CA 90068-2207 Office: Kelley Drye & Warren 515 S Flower St Los Angeles CA 90071-2200

LUBORSKY, FRED EVERETT, research physicist; b. Phila., May 14, 1923; s. Meyer and Cecelia (Miller) L.; m. Florence R. Glass, Aug. 25, 1946; children—Judith, Mark, Rhoda. B.S., U. Pa., 1947; Ph.D., Ill. Inst. Tech. 1952. Teaching-research asst. Ill. Inst. Tech., Chgo., 1947-51; research assoc. Gen. Elec. Co., Schnectady, 1951-52, West Lynn, Mass., 1952-58; research physicist Gen. Elec. Co., Schenectady, 1958-92; gen. chmn. 2d Joint Internat. Magnetism and Magnetic Materials Conf., 1979; chmn. adv. com. Conf. on Magnetism and Magnetic Materials, 1980. Editor: Amorphous Metallic Alloys, 1984; mem. editorial bd. Internat. Jour. Rapid Solidification, 1984—; mem. editorial adv. bd. Internat. Jour. Magnetism, 1972—; contbr. articles to profl. jours.; patentee in field. Served with USN, 1944-46. Recipient citation achievement in indsl. sci. AAAS, 1956; Brit. Sci. Research Council fellow, 1977; Coolidge fellow in research and devel. Gen. Elec. Corp., 1978. Fellow IEEE (editorial bd. Transactions on Magnetics jour. 1968—, editor-in-chief 1972-75, editorial bd. Spectrum jour. 1972-73, Centennial medal 1984, mem. Fellows com. 1993—), Am. Inst. Chemists, N.Y. Acad. Scis.; mem. Nat. Acad. Engring., Magnetics Soc. of IEEE (pres. 1975-77, named disting. lectr. 1979, achievement award 1981), Am. Chem. Soc., Materials Research Soc. Home: 1162 Lowell Rd Schenectady NY 12308-2512

LUBOVITCH, LAR, dancer, choreographer; b. Chgo.. Student, Art Inst. Chgo., U. Iowa, Juilliard Sch. Music, Am. Ballet Theatre Sch., Martha Graham, Anthony Tudor. Debut with Pearl Lang Dance Co., 1962; danced with modern cos. Glen Tetley, John Butler, Sophie Maslow and Donald McKayle; also with Manhattan Festival Ballet, Santa Fe Opera and Harkness Ballet; formed Lar Lubovitch Dance Co., 1968, choreographer, 1968—, guest choreographer, Bat-Dor Dance Co., Gulbenkian Ballet, Dutch Nat. Ballet, Ballet Rambert, Pa. Ballet, Am. Ballet Theatre, Royal Danish Ballet, Bejart Ballet XX Century, Alvin Ailey Am. Dance Theater, John Curry Ice Dancing Co., Les Grandes Ballets Canadiens, Stuttgart Ballet, N.Y.C. Ballet, Pacific N.W. Ballet, Paris Opera Ballet, White Oak Dance Project; ballets choreographed include Blue, 1968, Freddie's Bag, 1968, Journey Back, 1968, Greeting Sampler, 1969, Whirligogs, 1969, Unremembered Time-Forgotten Place, 1969, Variations and Theme, 1970, Ecstasy, 1970, Sam Nearlydeadman, 1970, The Teaching, 1970, Some of the Reactions,1970, The Time Before, 1971, Clear Lake, 1971, Air, 1972, Joy of Man's Desiring, 1972, Chariot Light Night, 1973, Scherzo for Massah Jack, 1973, Three Essays, 1974, Zig Zag, 1974, Avalanche, 1975, Rapid Transit, 1975, Session, 1975, Eight Easy Pieces, 1975, Girl on Fire, 1975, Marimba, 1976, Les Noces, 1976, Scriabin Dances, 1977, Exultate Jubilate, 1977, North Star, 1978, Valley, 1978, Tiltawhirl, 1979, Up Jump, 1979, Mistral, 1980, Cavalcade, 1980, American Gesture, 1981, Beau Danube, 1981, Big Shoulders, 1983, Tabernacle, 1983, Adagio and Rondo, 1984, A Brahms Symphony, 1985, Concerto Six Twenty-Two, 1986, Blood, 1986, Of My Soul, 1987, Musette, 1988, Rhapsody in Blue, 1988, Fandango, 1989, Just Before Jupiter, 1990, Hautbois, 1990, Sinfonia Concertante, 1991, Waiting for the Sunrise, 1991, American Gesture, 1992, So In Love, 1994, others; choreographer Sleeping Beauty (WGBH-TV), 1987, Into the Woods (Broadway), 1987, Salome, (Broadway), 1992, The Red Shoes (Broadway), 1993, The Planets (A&E-TV). Guggenheim fellow; CAPS grantee, NEH grantee; nominee Tony award, 1988, Astaire award, 1993-94. Address: care Lubovitch Dance Co 15 W 18th St New York NY 10011-4604

LUBY, THOMAS STEWART, lawyer; b. Meriden, Conn., Jan. 12, 1952; s. Robert M. and Ruth (McGee) L.; m. Paula F. Falcigno, July 19, 1985; children: Elizabeth, Caroline, Katherine. BA, Yale U., 1974; JD, U. Conn., 1977. Bar: Conn., U.S. Dist. Ct. Conn., U.S. Ct. Appeals (2d cir.). Law clk. to Hon. T. F. Gilroy Daly U.S. Dist. Ct., Bridgeport, Conn., 1977-78; asst. U.S. atty. New Haven, Conn., 1978-81; ptnr. Luby, Olson, Mango & Gaffney, Meriden, 1981—; mem. grievance com. U.S. Dist. Ct. Conn., 1985-90, chmn. 1990-91. Rep. Conn. Gen. Assembly, 1987-92, house majority leader, 1993-94; co-chair Conn. Task Force on Groundwater Strategy, 1987-89, chmn. commerce com., 1991-92. Recipient Spl. Achievement award U.S. Dept. Justice, 1980, Outstanding Pub. Service award United Way, 1986; named Legis. Leader of Yr., Greater Hartford C. of C., 1990, Person of Yr., Gov.'s Tourism Council, 1991. Mem. Conn. Bar Assn. Democrat. Roman Catholic. Home: 32 Westfield Rd Meriden CT 06450-2426

LUCA-MORETTI, MAURIZIO, scientist, nutrition researcher; b. Rome, June 2, 1945; s. Giuseppe and Elena (Moretti) L.; m. Anna Grandi, Jan. 2, 1974; 1 child, Elena. BS, Ministry of Edn., Caracas, Venezuela, 1969; PhD in Allied Health Scis., Pacific Western U., 1990, DSc in Human Nutrition, 1990; MD (hon.), Universidad Santo Tomas, La Paz, Bolivia, 1994. Rschr. Inst. Italiano di Terapia Fisica e Medicina Interna, Rome, 1974-76, sr. rschr., 1976-78, dir. rsch., 1978-80; dir. rsch. Inst. Italiano di Terapia Fisica e Medicina Interna, Caracas, Venezuela, 1980-88; dir. human nutrition rsch. program and AIDS rsch. program InterAm. Med. and Health Assn., Boca Raton, Fla., 1989—, pres., 1989—; gen. sec. World Acad. Medicine, 1992—; prof. emeritus Pacific We. Univ., New Orleans, 1992; hon. prof. Universidad de Granada, Spain, 1994, Universidad Nacional Pedro Enrique Ureña, Santo Domingo, Dominican Rep., 1994; prof. emeritus, Pacific Western Univ., New Orleans, 1992. Recipient medal Univ. Asuncion, Paraguay, 1992, medal Univ. Granada, Spain, 1993. Fellow NAS (Dominican Rep.), Royal Nat. Acad. Medicine Spain, Royal Acad. Scis. Spain, Royal Acad. Medicine Salamanca, Royal Acad. Medicine Granada, Royal Acad. Medicine Valencia, Nat. Acad. Medicine Bolivia, Nat. Acad. Medicine Ecuador, Nat. Acad. Medicine Paraguay, Nat. Acad. Medicine Dominican Rep., Acad. Medicine Maracaibo. Achievements include patents in nutritional amino acids formulations with extremely high human Net Nitrogen Utilization (NNU). Office: InterAm Med and Health Assn 3025 Saint James Dr Boca Raton FL 33434

LUCAS, ALEXANDER RALPH, child psychiatrist, educator; b. Vienna, Austria, July 30, 1931; came to U.S., 1940, naturalized, 1945; s. Eugene Hans and Margaret Ann (Weiss) L.; m. Margaret Alice Thompson, July 6, 1956; children: Thomas Alexander, Nancy Elizabeth Watson, Alexander Eugene, Peter Clayton. B.S., Mich. State U., 1953; M.D., U. Mich., 1957. Diplomate Am. Bd. Psychiatry and Neurology. Intern U. Mich. Hosp., 1957-58; resident in child psychiatry Hawthorn Ctr., Northville, Mich., 1958-59, 61-62, staff psychiatrist, 1963-65, sr. psychiatrist, 1965-67; resident in psychiatry Lafayette Clinic, Detroit, 1959-61, rsch. child psychiatrist, 1967-

71, rsch. coord., 1969-71; asst. prof. psychiatry Wayne State U., 1967-69, assoc. prof., 1969-71; cons. child and adolescent psychiatry Mayo Clinic, 1971—; assoc. prof. Mayo Med Sch., 1973-76, prof., 1976—; head sect. child and adolescent psychiatry Mayo Clinic, Rochester, Minn., 1971-80. Author: (with C. R. Shaw) The Psychiatric Disorders of Childhood, 1970. Fellow Am. Acad. Child and Adolescent Psychiatry (editl. bd. jour. 1976-82), Am. Orthopsychiat. Assn. (life), Am. Psychiat. Assn. (life); mem. Minn. Soc. Child and Adolescent Psychiatry (pres. 1993-95), Soc. Biol. Psychiatry, Soc. Profs. Child and Adolescent Psychiatry, Sigma Xi. Research in biol. aspects of child psychiatry, psychopathology, psychopharmacology, eating disorders, psychiat. treatment of children, adolescents, and young adults. Office: Mayo Clinic 200 1st St SW Rochester MN 55905-0001

LUCAS, AUBREY KEITH, university president; b. State Line, Miss., July 12, 1934; s. Keith Caldwell and Audelle Margaret (Robertson) L.; m. Ella Frances Ginn, Dec. 18, 1955; children: Margaret Frances, Keith Godbold (dec.), Martha Carol, Alan Douglas, Mark Christopher. BS, U. So. Miss., 1955, MA, 1956; PhD, Fla. State U., 1966. Instr. Hinds Jr. Coll., Raymond, Miss., 1956-57; pres. Delta State U., Cleveland, Miss., 1971-75; Asst. dir. reading clinic U. So. Miss., Hattiesburg, 1955-56, dir. admissions, 1957-61, registrar, 1963-69, dean Grad. Sch., 1969-71, pres., 1975—. Author: The Mississippi Legislature and Mississippi Public Higher Education, 1890-1960; contbg. author: A History of Mississippi, 1973. Bd. dirs. Pine Burr Area coun. Boy Scouts Am., Miss. Inst. Tech. Devel., Miss. Power Co., Miss. Assn. Coll., 1979-80, Miss. Arts Commn., 1977-87, Salvation Army, Pine Burr; mem. gen. bd. Global Ministries, United Meth. Ch., mem. gen. bd. higher edn. and ministry, 1992—; chmn. Miss. Arts Commn., 1983-85; campaign chmn. Forest United Way, 1979, So. U. Conf., 1995—; state chmn. Am. Cancer Soc., 1978; mem. Commn. on Nat. Devel. Psychoanalyzed Edn., 97th Congress; pres. Miss. Econ. Coun., 1982-83; lay leader Miss. Meth. Conf., 1980-88, mem. adminstrv. bd., 1989-92; bd. visitors Air U., 1990-94, chmn., 1991-92; mem. exec. bd. Commn. on Colls. of So. Assn. Colls. and Schs., 1990-93. Mem. So. Assn. Colls. and Schs. (mem. exec. bd. commn. on colls. 1990-93, v.p. commn. on colls. 1993, mem. exec. coun.), Hattiesburg C. of C., Miss. Forestry Assn., Newcomen Soc. N.Am., Am. Assn. State Colls. and Univs. (bd. dirs. 1982-86, chmn. 1984-85), Am. Coun. Edn. (bd. dirs. 1984-86), Miss. Inst. Arts and Letters, Red Red Rose Club, Sigma Phi Epsilon, Omicron Delta Kappa, Phi Kappa Phi, Pi Gamma Mu, Pi Tau Chi, Kappa Delta Pi, Phi Delta Kappa, Kappa Pi. Home: 3701 Jamestown Rd Hattiesburg MS 39402-2336 Office: U So Miss Box 5001 Hattiesburg MS 39406-5001

LUCAS, BARBARA B., electrical equipment manufacturing executive; b. 1945. BA, U. Md., 1967; MA, Johns Hopkins U., 1968. V.p. sec. Equitable Bancorp, 1977-85; v.p. pub. affairs, corp. sec. Black & Decker Corp., Balt., 1985—; bd. dirs. Goulds Pumps, Inc. Office: Black & Decker Corp 701 E Joppa Rd Baltimore MD 21286-5559

LUCAS, BILLY JOE, philosophy educator; b. Houston, Jan. 7, 1942; s. Joseph Cuthel and Billie Louise (Smith) L.; m. Diana Stephens, July 13, 1965 (div. 1976); children: Lisa Ann, Deborah Lynn; m. Shelby Hearon, Apr. 19, 1981. BA, U. Houston, 1970; MA, McMaster U., 1972; PhD, U. Tex., 1981. Instr. Houston Community Coll., 1973-77; asst. instr. U. Tex., Austin, 1978-81; asst. prof. Manhattanville Coll., Purchase, N.Y., 1981-86, assoc. prof., 1986-89, prof., 1989—; adj. edn. policy cons. to the pres. Manhattanville Coll., 1990-91, 92-93; invited del. Citizen Amb. Program Philosophy Del., People's Rep. China, 1993. Assoc. editor Internat. Jour. for Philosophy of Religion, 1990—; contbr. articles to profl. jours. Mem. AAAS, Soc. for Philosophy of Religion (exec. coun. 1986-93, v.p. 1989-90, pres. 1990-91), Assn. for Symbolic Logic, Computer Soc. of IEEE (tech. com. on multiple valued logic 1987—), Am. Acad. Religion, Am. Philos. Assn. (logic sect. adv. com. 1990-93), N.Am. Soc. for Social Philosophy (exec. coun. 1986-93, co-chair Eastern div. 1986-90), Am. Math. Soc., N.Y. Acad. Scis., Phi Kappa Phi. Achievements include complete axiomatization of the minimal modal logic in which each formula is provably equivalent to a formula of finite degree, related work on reduction laws in deontic and other modal logics, applications of formal logic to philosophy, and logic curriculum development. Office: Manhattanville Coll 2900 Purchase St Purchase NY 10577-2132

LUCAS, C. PAYNE, development organization executive; b. Spring Hope, N.C., Sept. 14, 1933; s. James Russell and Minnie (Hendricks) L; m. Freddie Emily Myra Hill, Aug. 29, 1964; children: Therese Raymonde, C. Payne Jr., Hillary Hendricks. BA in History, U. Md.; LLD (hon.), U. Md., 1975; MA in Govt., Am. U. Asst. dir. Peace Corps, Togo, 1964; dir. Peace Corps, Niger, 1965-67; dir. Africa region Peace Corps, 1967-71; pres. Africare, Washington, 1971—; lectr. in field. Author: (with Kevin Lowther) Keeping Kennedy's Promise-The Peace Corps: Unmet Promise of the New Frontier, 1978; contbr. articles to profl. publs. Bd. dirs. Coun. of Fgn. Rels., Overseas Devel. Coun., World Resources Inst., InterAction, Population Action Internat., Environ. and Energy Study Inst.; chmn. African Devel. Found. Recipient Disting. Fed. Svc. award Pres. Lyndon B. Johnson, Presdl. Hunger award for Outstanding Achievement, Pres. Ronald Reagan, 1984, Aggrey medal Phelps-Stokes Fund, 1986, Order of Disting. Svc. award Pres. Kenneth Kaunda of Zambia, 1986, Recognition awards Nat. Order of Rep. Niger, 1988, Zambia, Cote D'Iroire, Senegal, Benin, Disting. Bicentennial award Land Grant Coll., 1990, Hubert H. Humphrey Pub. Svc. award APSA, 1991. Mem. Cosmos Club, Omega Psi Phi. Office: Africare 400 R St NW Washington DC 20001-1918

LUCAS, CAROL LEE, biomedical engineer; b. Aberdeen, S.D., Feb. 13, 1940; d. Howard Cleveland and Sarah Ivy (Easterby) Nogle; B.A., Dakota Wesleyan U., 1961; M.S., U. Ariz., 1967; Ph.D., U. N.C., 1973; m. Richard Albert Lucas, Feb. 26, 1961; children—Wendy Lee, Sean Richard. Tchr. Spanish, Mitchell (S.D.) High Sch., 1960-61; tchr. math, English, sci. U.S. Army, Furth, Ger., 1961-62; systems analyst Cargill Inc., Mpls., 1962-65; research assoc. U. N.C., Chapel Hill, 1973-76, lectr., 1976-77, asst. prof. curriculum in biomed. engring. and math, 1977-84, assoc. prof. dept. surgery, 1984-89, prof. dept. surgery, 1989—, acting chmn. curriculum biomed. engring. and math., 1990-92, chmn. biomed. engring., 1992—; NIH trainee, 1968-73. Mem. IEEE, Am. Heart Assn., N.C. Heart Assn., Biomed. Engring. Soc., Cardiovascular System Dynamics Soc., Am. Inst. Biol. and Med. Engrs. Democrat. Methodist. Contbr. articles to profl. jours. Home: 2421 Sedgefield Dr Chapel Hill NC 27514-6810 Office: U NC Sch Medicine Dept Biomed Engring 152 Macnider Hall Chapel Hill NC 27599-7575

LUCAS, CAROL MCCANN, vocational education educator; b. Ferrellsburg, W.Va., Feb. 9, 1945; d. Mason and Essie (Adkins) McCann; m. Lonnie C. Lucas, Feb. 20, 1965; 1 child, Joshua Tad. AB, Marshall U., 1968, MS, 1978, postgrad., 1990. Cert. home economist, W.Va. Tchr., prin. Francis Creek Elem. Sch., Harts, W.Va., 1965-66; tchr. Cammack Jr. High Sch., Huntington, W.Va., 1968-75; tchr. home econs. Barboursville (W.Va.) Mid. Sch., 1979-80, 87—, Barboursville High Sch., 1980-87; adviser Future Homemakers Am., Barboursville, 1980—; adviser Future Homemakers Am., Barboursville, 1980—, Outstanding chpt., 1991. Sec. Otterbein United Meth. Women, Huntington, 1987-89, v.p., 1990-92. Mem. NEA, Am. Home Baking Assn. (Top 40 Home Econs. Tchr. 1994), Am. Vocat. Assn., Am. Home Econs. Assn. (cert. home economist), W.Va. Edn. Assn., W.Va. Vocat. Assn., W.Va. Home Econs. Assn. (Outstanding Consumer and Homemaking Program 1991), Cabell County Edn. Assn. Republican. Avocations: needlecrafts, painting, piano, writing. Office: Barboursville Mid Sch Main St Barboursville WV 25504

LUCAS, CRAIG, playwright, screenwriter; b. Atlanta, Apr. 30, 1951; s. Charles Samuel and Eleanore Ritchard (Alltmont) L. BFA, Boston U., 1973. Playwright (plays) Missing Persons, 1981, Reckless, 1983, Blue Window, 1984 (L.A. Drama Critic's award 1986), Prelude To A Kiss, 1988 (Obie award 1990, Outer Critic Circle award 1990), (mus. play, book) 3 Postcards (Best Mus. 1986/87, Burus Mantle), God's Heart, 1995 (movie) Blue Window, 1987, Longtime Companion, 1989, Prelude To A Kiss, 1991, Reckless, 1995. Guggenheim fellow, N.Y.C., Rockefeller fellow, N.Y.C., Bellaggio fellow. Mem. Dramatists Guild (coun.), South Coast Repertory (assoc. artist), Circle Repertory. Address: Peter Franklin William Morris Agy 1350 6th Ave New York NY 10019

LUCAS, CYNTHIA, ballet mistress, dancer; b. San Rafael, Calif.. Studies with, Leona Norman. Formerly with Royal Winnipeg Ballet, Joffrey II Co.;

mem. corps de ballet Nat. Ballet Can., Toronto, Ont., 1972-76, 2nd soloist, 1976-78, 1st soloist, 1978-89, ballet mistress, 1989—. Created roles including Farmer's Daughter in Apples at the Shaw Festival, The Chic Couple in The Party for CBC-TV, Sweet Young Thing in La Ronde; performances include Isabelle-Marie in Mad Shadows, Catherine Sloper in Washington Square; leading role in Kudelka's The Rape of Lucerne, 1980, The Merry Widow, 1986; dancer in Toronto Internat. Festival premiere Onegin, 1984. Office: National Ballet of Canada, 157 King St East, Toronto, ON Canada M5C 1G9*

LUCAS, DEAN HADDEN, retired educator; b. Avera, Ga., June 2, 1931; d. Thomas Clayton and Lonice Ethyl (Williams) Hadden; m. Ben F. Lucas, June 27, 1953 (dec. Mar. 1992); children: Jon Gregory, Barry Hadden, Angela d'Arcy; m. Ray Ninche Renbarger, Sept. 10, 1994. Student, U. Ga., 1951; BS in Home Econs. Edn., Berry Coll., 1952; MAT in Home Econs. Edn., Winthrop Coll., 1969; postgrad., Clem. U., 1976-77, U. S.C., 1977, 80, 81, 88, S.C. State Coll., 1985, 87. Asst. home demonstration agt. Ga. Extension Svc., Calhoun, 1952; home demonstration agt. Ga. Extension Svc., Alma, 1952-53; 1st grade tchr. Tenn. Edn. Dept., East Ridge, 1953-54; 4th grade tchr. Kershaw County Sch. Dist., Camden, S.C., 1954-55, home econs. tchr., 1955-57; asst. home dem. agt. Clemson Extension Svc., Camden, 1958-61, home dem. agt., 1963-69, assoc. home economist, 1970-74; assoc. county extension leader Clemson Extension Svc., Sumter, S.C., 1974-76; home econs. instr. Kershaw County Sch., Camden, 1976-93, ret., 1993. Writer curriculum guides for home econs. courses. Mem. adv. bd. Dist. Home Econs., Kershaw County, S.C., 1985-92, Supt. Adv. Coun., Camden, 1989-90, Teen Coalition, Camden, 1989-92, Teen Pregnancy Prevention, Kershaw County, 1985-89; mem. Kershaw County Jr. Welfare League, Camden, 1959-92; co-sponsor, organizer SADD Chpt. at North Central, Kershaw, 1988; Clemson U. del. Nat. 4-H Conf., Chgo., 1974, Home Econs. Educators Citizens Amb. Program, Russia, Hungary, 1992; tchr. Sunday sch. Bapt. Ch. Named for Nat. Disting. Svc., Nat. Extension Home Econs. Assn., 1973, S.C. Home Econs. Tchr. of Yr., S.C. Home Econ. Assn., 1990. Mem. NEA, Am. Vocat. Assn. (del. to policy seminar), S.C. Vocat. Assn. (v.p. 1989-90, 92), S.C. Assn. Home Econs. Tchrs. (pres. 1989-90), Am. Home Econs. Assn. (legis. contact 1988-91, Vocat. Home Econs. Tchr. of Yr. 1993, Vocat. Tchr. of Yr. 1993), S.C. Edn. Assn. Cert. Home Economists. Avocations: running, workouts, boating, cooking, traveling. Home: 1136 Brookgreen Ct Camden SC 29020-3716 Office: North Cen High Sch 3000 Lockhart Rd Kershaw SC 29067-9661

LUCAS, DONALD LEO, private investor; b. Upland, Calif., Mar. 18, 1930; s. Leo J. and Mary G. (Schwamm) L.; BA, Stanford U., 1951, MBA, 1953; m. Lygia de Soto Harrison, July 15, 1961; children: Nancy Maria Lucas Thibodeau, Alexandra Maria Lucas Ertola, Donald Alexander. Assoc. corp. fin. dept. Smith, Barney & Co., N.Y.C., 1956-59; gen., ltd. ptnr. Draper, Gaither & Anderson, Palo Alto, Calif., 1959-66; pvt. investor, Menlo Park, Calif., 1966—; bd. dirs. Cadence Design Systems, San Jose, Calif., Delphi Info. Systems, Inc., ICOT Corp., San Jose, Kahler Corp., Rochester, Minn., Oracle Systems, Redwood Shores, Calif., Quantum Health Resources Inc., Racotek, Inc., Mpls., Macromedia, San Francisco, TriCord Systems, Inc., Plymouth, Minn., Tri Care, Inc., Atlanta; Mem. bd. regents Bellarmine Coll. Prep., 1977—; regent emeritus U. Santa Clara, 1980—. 1st lt. AUS, 1953-55. Mem. Am. Coun. for Capital Formation, Stanford U. Alumni Assn., Stanford Grad. Sch. Bus. Alumni Assn., Order of Malta, Stanford Buck Club, Vintage Club (Indian Wells, Calif.), Menlo Country Club (Woodside, Calif.), Menlo Circus Club (Atherton, Calif.), Jackson Hole Golf and Tennis Club, Teton Pines Club, Zeta Psi. Home: 224 Park Ln Atherton CA 94027-5411 Office: 3000 Sand Hill Rd # 3-210 Menlo Park CA 94025-7116

LUCAS, FRANK D., congressman; b. Cheyenne, Okla., Jan. 6, 1960; m. Lynda L. Bradshaw, 1988. BS, Okla. State U., 1982. Mem. Okla. Ho. of Reps., 1989-94, 103d Congress from 6th Okla. Dist., 1994—. Baptist. Office: US Ho of Reps 107 Cannon Washington DC 20515-3606 Home: Rte 2 Box 136A Cheyenne OK 73628

LUCAS, FRANK EDWARD, architect; b. Charleston, S.C., Oct. 31, 1934; m. Edith R. Dority; children: Susan R. Lucas Tezza, Kelly E., Julie C. Lucas Rodenberg. BArch, Clemson U., 1959. Registered architect, S.C., Fla., N.C., W.Va., Ala., Ga., Va., Ky. Founder, architect (now LS3P Architects Ltd.) Lucas and Stubbs Assocs., Charleston, S.C., 1964—; chmn. bd. dirs. LS3P Architects Ltd. Mem. Charleston County Bd. Rev., Bldg. and Elec. Codes, 1972-85; mem. St. Philip's Episcopal Ch., former vestryman, sr. warden, lay reader St. James Episcopal Ch.; trustee Cities in Schs., Charleston, 1974-78; past pres. nine county region Girl Scouts Am., 1988-90; affiliate S.C. Sch. Bds. Assn.; bd. dirs. Charleston World Trade Ctr., S.C. Golf Expo; hon. chmn. March of Dimes Walkathon, 1991; pres. adv. coun. Clemson U.; mem. Am. Cancer Soc., Trident Tech. Coll. Found., Coll. Charleston Found.; mem. S.C. Def. Base Devel.; bd. dirs. S.C. Athletic Hall of Fame. Recipient Elizabeth O'Neill Verner award S.C. Arts Commn., 1990; featured in exhibit at Gibbes Art Gallery titled 20 Yrs. of Design Excellence, 1988. Fellow AIA; mem. S.C. AIA (pres. 1970), S.C. Econ. Developers Assn., Soc. Am. Mil. Engrs., Charleston Trident C. of C. (chmn. red carpet com. 1964-70, bd. dirs. 1974-77, v.p. pub. affairs 1988-89, past pres. 1990-91), Preservation Soc. Charleston, S.C. Hist. Soc., Carolina Art Assn., S.C. Arts Found. (bd. dirs.), Executives Assn. Greater Charleston (pres. 1983), Greater Charleston Real Estate Bd., Clemson Archtl. Found. (bd. dirs. 1967-73, 77-81, 86—, pres. 1975, 81, 89), Hibernian Soc. (mng. com. 1984-94), Hibernian Soc. Found. (v.p. 1990-92, pres. 1992-94), Country Club of Charleston (bd. dirs. 1976-79, exec. com. 1991), S.C. State C. of C. (bd. dirs. 1989-90, com. to reorganize state govt. 1990, exec. com. 1992), S.C. Arts Commn. (bus. and arts awards adv. com.), Assn. of Citadel Men, IPTAY Clemson U., Clemson Alumni Assn., Clemson Low Country Assn., Palmetto State Tchrs. Assn. (affiliate), Carolina Yacht Club, Capital City Club (charter), The Summit Club, Rotary (N. Charleston chpt.), Country Club Charleston (bd. dirs. 1973-76), Hibernian Sch. Found. (bd. dirs.). Home: 1459 Burningtree Rd Charleston SC 29412-2602 Office: 24 N Market St Ste 300 Charleston SC 29401-2640

LUCAS, FRED VANCE, pathology educator, university administrator; b. Grand Junction, Colo., Feb. 7, 1922; s. Lee H. and Katherine W. (Vance) L.; m. Rebecca Ross Dudley, Dec. 21, 1948; children: Fred Vance, Katherine Dudley Lucas Volk. A.B., U. Calif.-Berkeley, 1942; M.D., U. Rochester, 1950. Am. Bd. Pathology. Intern, postgrad. fellow in pathology U. Rochester, 1950-51, asst. in pathology, 1951-53, Lilliy fellow, 1952-53, Gleason fellow, 1953-54, instr., 1953-54, asst. prof., 1954-55; chief resident in pathology Strong Meml. Hosp., 1953-54; practice medicine specializing in pathology; assoc. prof. Coll. Physicians and Surgeons, Columbia U., 1955-60; assoc. attending pathologist Presbyn. Hosp., N.Y.C., 1955-60; prof., chmn. pathology U. Mo.-Columbia Sch. Medicine, 1960-77; research assoc. Space Sci. Research Ctr., 1964-70; prof. pathology Vanderbilt U., 1977-89, dir. program planning, dir. med. services, 1977-79, acting assoc. v.p. med. affairs, 1979, assoc. v.p. med. affairs, 1979-81, acting exec. dir. hosp., assoc. v.p. med. affairs, 1981-82, assoc. vice-chancellor med. affairs, 1982-89; cons. in field. Contbr. numerous articles to med. jours. Del WHO, Geneva, 1971; bd. dirs. Univs. Assoc. Research and Edn. in Pathology; commr. for Mo. and Ark. Coll. Am. Pathologists, 1975-77. Served in U.S. Army, 1942-46. Recipient Lederle Faculty award, 1954-56; recipient Disting. Service award Columbia U., 1967, Edn. and Social Affairs medal U. Mo.-Columbia, 1975, Student exec. com. service award U. Mo.-Columbia, 1975. Fellow Coll. Am. Pathologists, Am. Soc. Clin. Pathologists; mem. Am. Pathologists Assn., Internat. Acad. Pathology, Harvey Soc., Sigma Xi, Alpha Omega Alpha (lectr. 1977). Democrat. Roman Catholic. Home: 333 Lee Dr Apt G12 Baton Rouge LA 70808-4985

LUCAS, GEORGE RAMSDELL, JR., philosophy educator; b. San Angelo, Tex., Sept. 8, 1949; s. George Ramsdell and Clare Elizabeth (Baldwin) L.; m. Patricia Cook; children: Jessica, Kimberly, Theresa. BS summa cum laude, Coll. William and Mary, 1971; PhD, Northwestern U., 1978. Asst. prof., chmn. dept. philosophy Randolph-Macon Coll., Ashland, Va., 1978-83; assoc. prof., chmn. dept. philosophy Santa Clara (Calif.) U., 1982-86; assoc. prof. Emory U., Atlanta, 1986-87; prof. philosophy Clemson (S.C.) U., 1987-91; asst. dir. rsch. div. NEH, Washington, 1991—. Author: The Genesis of Modern Process Thought, 1983, The Rehabilitation of Whitehead, 1989; editor: Lifeboat Ethics: Moral Dilemmas of World Hunger, 1976, Poverty, Justice and the Law, 1986; philosophy editor SUNY Press, Albany, 1989—

also articles. Am. Coun. Learned Socs. fellow, 1982; Fulbright rsch. fellow, 1989. Mem. Am. Philos. Assn., Metaphys. Soc. Am. (exec. coun. 1987-92), Hegel Soc. Am., Omicron Delta Kappa, Phi Beta Kappa. Office: NEH 1100 Pennsylvania Ave NW Rm 31 Washington DC 20506-0001

LUCAS, GEORGE W., JR., film director, producer, screenwriter; b. Modesto, Calif., May 14, 1944. Student, Modesto Jr. Coll.; BA, U. So. Calif., 1966. Chmn. Lucasfilm Ltd., San Rafael, Calif. Creator short film THX-1138 (Grand prize Nat. Student Film Festival, 1967); asst. to Francis Ford Coppola on The Rain People; dir. Filmmaker (documentary on making of The Rain People); dir., co-writer THX-1138, 1970, American Graffiti, 1973; dir., author screenplay Star Wars, 1977; exec. producer More American Graffiti, 1979, The Empire Strikes Back, 1980, Raiders of the Lost Ark, 1981, Indiana Jones and the Temple of Doom, 1984, Labyrinth, 1986, Howard the Duck, 1986, Willow, 1988, Tucker, 1988, Radioland Murders, 1994; exec. producer, co-author screenplay Return of the Jedi, 1983; co-exec. producer Mishima, 1985; co-author, co-exec. producer Indiana Jones and the Last Crusade, 1989; exec. producer (TV series) The Young Indiana Jones Chronicles, 1992-93. Office: Lucasfilm Ltd PO Box 2009 San Rafael CA 94912-2009

LUCAS, HENRY CAMERON, JR., information systems educator, writer, consultant; b. Omaha, Sept. 4, 1944; s. Henry Cameron and Lois (Himes) L.; m. Ellen Kuhbach, June 8, 1968; children: Scott C., Jonathan G. B.S. in Indsl. Adminstrn. magna cum laude, Yale U., 1966; M.S., MIT, 1968, Ph.D., 1970. Cons. Arthur D. Little, Inc., Cambridge, Mass., 1966-70; asst. prof. computer and info. systems Stanford U., Calif., 1970-74; assoc. prof. computer applications and info. systems NYU, 1974-78, prof., chmn. dept. info. systems, 1978-84; on leave IBM European Systems Research Inst., Belgium, 1981; INSEAD Fontainebleau, France, 1985; prof. info. systems NYU, 1985—. Author: Computer-Based Information Systems in Organizations, 1973, The Information Systems Environment, 1980, (with F. Land, T. Lincoln and K. Supper) Casebook for Management Information Systems, 3d edit., 1985, The Analysis, Design and Implementation of Information Systems, 4th edit., 1992, Information Systems Concepts for Management, 5th edit., 1994, Coping with Computers: A Manager's Guide to Controlling Information Processing, 1982, Introduction to Computers and Information Systems, 1986, Managing Information Services, 1989; editor Indsl. Mgmt., 1967-68; mem. editorial bd. Sloan Mgmt. Rev., 1975-91; assoc. editor MIS Quar., 1977-83; editor in chief Systems, Objectives, Solutions, 1980—; contbr. articles to profl. jours. Recipient award for excellence in teaching NYU Sch. Bus., 1982. Mem. Assn. Computing Machinery, Inst. Mgmt. Scis., Phi Beta Kappa, Tau Beta Pi. Home: 18 Portland Rd Summit NJ 07901-3044 Office: NYU 44 W 4th St 9-67 New York NY 10012-1126

LUCAS, J. RICHARD, retired mining engineering educator; b. Scottdale, Pa., May 3, 1929; s. J.W. and Mary (Hirka) L.; m. Joan H. Hathaway, Aug. 30, 1952; children: Eric Scott, Jay Hathaway. Student, Pa. State U., 1947-48; B.S. in Math. and Physics, Waynesburg Coll., 1951; B.S. in Mining Engring, W.Va. U., 1952; M.S. in Mining Engring, U. Pitts., 1954; Ph.D., Columbia, 1965. Registered profl. engr., Va., Ohio, W.Va. Miner Crucible Steel Co., 1947-52; field engr. Joy Mfg. Co., 1952-54; mem. faculty Ohio State U., Columbus, 1954-61; head dept. mining engring. Va. Poly. Inst. and State U., Blacksburg, 1961-71, head div. minerals engring., 1971-76, head dept. mining and minerals engring., 1976-87, Massey prof. mining and minerals engring., 1987-92; dir. mining systems design and ground control Generic Mineral Tech. Ctr.; ret., 1992; chmn. exec. com. Am. Inst. on Coal Mining Health, Safety and Rsch., 1969-87. Mem. Am. Inst. Mining, Metall. and Petroleum Engrs., AAAS, Coal Mining Inst., W.Va. Coal Mining Inst., AAUP, Nat., Va. socs. profl. engrs., Am. Soc. Engring. Edn., Va. Acad. Sci., Soc. Mining Engrs. (bd. dirs., chmn. coal div.). Home: 408 Hemlock Dr Blacksburg VA 24060-5232

LUCAS, JAMES E(VANS), operatic director; b. San Antonio, Mar. 15, 1933; s. Mason Harley and Nora Norton (Evans) L. B.A., Hiram Coll., 1951; postgrad., Stanford U., 1951-52, Juilliard Sch. Music, 1952-53. mem. faculty Temple U., 1965-71, Mannes Coll. Music, 1964-70, Manhattan Sch. Music, 1970-78, Carnegie-Mellon U., 1977-79; prof. music, stage dir. Ind. U., 1987-94. Free-lance operatic stage dir.; worked for numerous opera cos. in U.S., Can., including, Met. Opera, San Francisco Opera, N.Y.C. Opera, Can. Opera Co.; dir. for various summer festivals. Mem. Am. Guild Musical Artists, Am. Fedn. Musicians, Can. Actors Equity. Home and Office: 201 W 85th St New York NY 10024-3957

LUCAS, JAMES WALTER, federal government official; b. Frankfort, Ind., Oct. 20, 1940; s. Walter Kenneth and Hester (Kesterson) L.; m. Sara Sue Stewart, Feb. 17, 1962; 1 dau., Catherine Anne. BS, Ball State U., 1963, MA, 1964; postgrad., Am. U., 1977, Harvard U., 1990; DA, George Mason U., 1995. Asst. dir. intelligence coordination Nat. Security Council, Washington, 1975-76; exec. asst. to dep. dir. CIA, Washington, 1976-77, dep. exec. sec., 1977-79; CIA program budget officer Intelligence Community Staff, 1979-81; dep. asst. sec. U.S. Dept. Air Force, 1981-82, prin. dep. asst. sec., 1982-83; dir. crisis mgmt. planning staff Nat. Security Council, 1983-85; Disting. prof., dean Def. Intelligence Coll., Washington, 1985-93; assoc. dir. liaison Def. Intelligence Agy., 1993—; adj. prof. U. Md.-Far East div., 1970-71, Def. Intelligence Coll., 1974-83; guest lectr. Am. U., Washington, 1971-77; cons. Pres.'s Fgn. Intelligence Adv. Bd. Author: Intelligence and National Security in the Nixon Administration, 1972, Simulation and Strategic Intelligence Analysis, 1973, Information Needs of Presidents, 1989, Organizing the Presidency: The Role of the Director of Central Intelligence, 1995. Pres. Muncie Young Republican's Club, Ind., 1959-64; pres. Muncie Students for Goldwater, 1964; mem. Rep. Nat. Com., Reston Rep. Assn. With USAF, 1965-77, brig. gen. Res., 1977—. Decorated Bronze Star medal, Meritorious Service medal, Republic of Vietnam Gallantry Cross with Palm. Mem. Am. Polit. Sci. Assn., Internat. Studies Assn., Air Force Assn., Nat. Mil. Intelligence Assn., Res. Officers Assn., Pi Sigma Alpha, Phi Gamma Mu, Sigma Chi. Lodge: Masons. Office: Def Intelligence Agy Washington DC 20301

LUCAS, JO DESHA, law educator, editor; b. Richmond, Va., Nov. 7, 1921; s. Robert Desha and Hill Miller (Carter) L.; m. Johanna Westley, June 17, 1950; children: Robin Desha, John Carter. A.B., Syracuse U., 1947, M.P.A., 1951; LL.B., U. Va., 1951; LL.M., Columbia U., 1952. Bar: Va. 1952. Asst. prof. law U. Chgo., 1953-57, assoc. prof., 1957-61, prof., 1961—, Arnold I. Shure prof. law, 1982—; chmn. Ill. Supreme Ct. Rules Com., 1974—; reporter Fed. Adv. Com. on Appellate Rules, 1976-78. Author cases on admiralty; co-author: Moore's Federal Practice, 1970—; contbr. articles to legal revs., 1970—. Served with USAAF, 1943-46. Mem. Va. Bar, Chgo. Bar Assn., Order of Coif, Phi Beta Kappa. Home: 5504 S Harper Ave Chicago IL 60637-1830 Office: U Chgo Law Sch 1111 E 60th St Chicago IL 60637-2702

LUCAS, JOHN ALLEN, lawyer; b. Washington, Aug. 1, 1943; s. George Luther and Opal (McColium) L.; m. Carol Kaine, June 7, 1969; children: John Christian, Helen Elizabeth, David Marshall, Kerri Christine. BS, U.S. Mil. Acad., 1969; JD, U. Tex., 1977. Bar: Tex. 1978, Tenn. 1984, N.Y. 1986. Assoc. Hunton & Williams, Richmond, Va., 1977-83; ptnr. Hunton & Williams, Knoxville, Tenn., 1984—; prof. law U. Richmond, 1979-80; lectr. various legal seminars, 1979—. Contbr. articles to profl. jours. Bd. dirs. Knoxville Boys Club, 1984-88; bd. dirs. Tenn. Juvenile Diabetes Assn., 1989—. Capt. U.S. Army, 1969-74. Mem. ABA, Va. Bar Assn., Tenn. Bar Assn. Roman Catholic. Avocations: mountain climbing, sport parachuting, white-water kayaking, triathlons. Office: Hunton & Williams PO Box 951 Knoxville TN 37901

LUCAS, JOHN HARDING, JR., professional basketball coach; b. Durham, N.C., Oct. 31, 1953; s. John and Blondola L.; m. Debbie Fozard, 1978; children Tarvia, John III, Jai. BA, U. Md., 1976. Profl. basketball player Houston Rockets, 1976-78, 84-86, 89-90, Golden State Warriors, 1978-81, Washington Bullets, 1981-83, San Antonion Spurs, 1983-84, Milw. Bucks, 1986-88, Seattle Supersonics, 1988-89; owner Miami Tropics; head coach San Antonio Spurs, 1993-94; head coach, gen. mgr., v.p. basketball ops. Philadelphia 76ers, 1994—; mem. Jr. Davis Cup Team. Named to NBA All-Rookie team, 1977, NBA All-Star, 1977-78. First pick in NBA draft, 1976; placed # 10 NBA all-time assist leader. Office: Philadelphia 76ers Veterans Stadium Philadelphia PA 19148*

LUCAS, JOHN KENNETH, lawyer; b. Chgo., July 9, 1946; s. John and Catherine (Sykes) L.; m. Mary Ellen McElligott, Oct. 14, 1972; 1 child, John Patrick. BS with distinction, Ill. Inst. Tech., 1968; JD, DePaul U., 1972. Bar: Ill. 1972. Assoc. Horton, Davis, McCaleb & Lucas, Chgo., 1972-74; ptnr. McCaleb, Lucas, & Brugman and predecessor firms, Chgo., 1975-84; shareholder Willian, Brinks, Hofer, Gilson & Lione, Chgo., 1984-85; ptnr. Willian, Brinks, Hofer, Gilson & Lione Ltd., Chgo., 1986—; hearing officer Ill. Pollution Control Bd., 1981-86; adj. prof. De Paul U. Coll. of Law, 1986-93. Mem. ABA, Ill. Bar Assn., Chgo. Bar Assn., Fed. Cir. Bar Assn., Bar Assn. of 7th Fed. Cir., Am. Intellectual Property Law Assn., Patent Law Assn. Chgo., Lic. Execs. Soc., Internat. Assn. Protection Indsl. Property, Legal Club of Chgo., Phi Alpha Delta, Tau Beta Pi, Eta Kappa Nu. Office: Willian Brinks Hofer Gilson & Lione 455 N Cityfront Plaza Dr Chicago IL 60611-5599

LUCAS, JUNE H., state legislator; m. Frank A. Budak; children: Deven Armeni, Adrien. Student, Youngstown State U. Mem. Ohio Ho. of Reps., 1986—, mem. energy and environment, judiciary and criminal justice coms., vice-chairwoman agr. and natural resources com. Contbr. articles to Warren Tribune Chronicle. Active Animal Welfare League. Named Woman of Yr., Coalition Labor Union Women, YWCA, 1988. Mem. NOW (Trumbull County chpt.), LWV, Ohio Bus. and Profl. Women, Ohio Farm Bur., Mosquito Creek Devel. Assn., Farmer's Union, Sierra Club. Democrat. Home: 1435 Locust St Mineral Ridge OH 44440-9721 Office: Ohio House of Reps Office of House Mems Columbus OH 43215

LUCAS, MALCOLM MILLAR, state supreme court chief justice; b. Berkeley, Calif., Apr. 19, 1927; s. Robert and Georgina (Campbell) L.; m. Joan Fisher, June 23, 1956; children: Gregory, Lisa Georgina. B.A., U. So. Calif., 1950, LL.B., 1953. Bar: Calif. 1954. Ptnr. firm Lucas, Deukmejian and Lucas, Long Beach, Calif., 1955-67; judge Superior Ct., L.A. 1967-71, U.S. Dist. Ct. (cen. dist.) Calif., 1971-84; assoc. justice Calif. Supreme Ct., 1984-87, chief justice, 1987—. Republican. Avocation: golf. Office: Calif Supreme Ct South Tower 303 2nd St San Francisco CA 94107-1366

LUCAS, PANOLA, elementary educator; b. Pikeville, Ky., Nov. 18, 1932; d. Robert Lee and Trulie Ann (Pinson) Fields; m. Kenneth R. Lucas, Dec. 7, 1956 (div. Apr. 1984); 1 child, Nathan Wade. BS in Vocat. Home Econs., Marshall U., 1971; elem. teaching cert., W.Va. State Coll., 1976; cert. prin., W.Va. Coll. Grad. Studies, elem., mid., jr. and sr. high sch. prin., supt., supr. gen. instrn., vocat. adminstr., 1986. Tchr. Buffalo (W.Va.) High Sch., 1972; tchr. homebound Putnam County Bd. Edn., Winfield, W.Va., 1972-86; tchr. Poca (W.Va.) Elem. Sch., 1986-91, Scott Teays Elem. Sch., Scott Depot, W.Va., 1991—. Mem. W.Va. Profl. Educators, Kappa Delta Pi. Democrat. Baptist. Avocations: reading, travel, gardening, bowling, dancing. Home: 205 Hillside Dr # B Nitro WV 25143-2327

LUCAS, RHETT ROY, artist, chemical engineer, lawyer; b. Columbia, S.C., Nov. 27, 1941; s. Spurgeon LeRoy and Elizabeth (Wells) L.; m. Uta Henkel, Apr. 12, 1967 (div. 1973). BSChemE, U. S.C., 1963; JD, NYU, 1967; postgrad., U. Glasgow, Scotland, 1965-66. Bar: U.S. Supreme Ct., Calif., D.C. Rsch. assoc. Twentieth Century Fund, N.Y.C., 1968-69; gen. counsel James Madison Inst., N.Y.C., 1969-72, Population Law Ctr., San Francisco, 1972-75; prin. Lucas & Assocs., Washington, 1972-84; artist Beverly Hills (Calif.) Fine Arts, 1984-86, The Rhett Lucas Collection, Santa Fe, and Scottsdale, Ariz., 1988-94. Prin. author U.S. Supreme Ct. briefs in Roe v. Wade, 1972, U.S. vs. Vuitch, 1971, Doe vs. Bolton, 1972 (ACOG amicus); others; contbr. articles to profl jours.; painter approx. 200 nat. and state parks; exhbns. include Oxford U., 1988, Banff Ctr., 1989, Grand Canyon Nat. Park, Ariz., 1991, 92, Capital Reef Nat. Park, Canyonlands Nat. Park, Cumberland Gap Hist. Nat. Park, Death Valley Nat. Pk., John Wesley Powell Meml. Mus., 1992, Powell River History Mus., 1992-93, O'Laurie (Canyonlands) Mus.; also exhbns. in Santa Fe, New Masters Gallery, Taos, N.M., Scottsdale, Fuller Lodge, Los Alamos, N. Mex., Petroglyph Nat. Monument, Casa Grande Art Mus., Hubbell's Trading Post Nat. Hist. Pk. Co-founder NARAL, N.Y.C., 1969. Root-Tilden scholar NYU Law Sch., 1963-67; Rotary Found. fellow U. Glasgow, 1965-66; population rsch. grantee Rockefeller Found., 1972-74. Mem. Am. Soc. Marine Artists, Am. Inst. Conservation, Coll. Art Assn., Scottsdale Artist's League, Rockport (Mass.) Art Assn. (life), Wilderness Soc., Can. Alpine Club, Zero Population Growth, Sierra Club (life), Nat. Geog. Soc. (life), Rotary, Order of Coif, Mensa, Phi Beta Kappa, Tau Beta Pi, Blue Key (pres.). Avocations: travel, photography, art collecting.

LUCAS, ROBERT ELMER, soil scientist; b. Malolos, The Philippines, June 27, 1916; (parents Am. citizens); s. Charles Edmund and Harriet Grace (Deardorff) L.; m. Norma Emma Schultz, Apr. 27, 1941; children: Raymond and Richard (twins), Milton, Keith, Charles. BSA, Purdue U., 1939, MS, 1941; PhD, Mich. State U., 1947. Research asst. Va. Agrl. Research Sta., Norfolk, 1941-43; farmer Culver, Ind., 1943-44; grad. asst. Mich. State U. East Lansing, 1945, assoc. prof. soil sci., 1951-57, prof., 1957-77, prof. emeritus, 1977—; agronomist William Gehring, Inc., Rensselaer, Ind., 1946-50, 77-78; vis. prof. Everglades Research Sta. U. Fla., Belle Glade, 1979-80. Author chpts. in books, research reports. Leader Boy Scouts Am., Lansing, Mich., 1961-72, dist. chmn. Chief Okemos (Mich.) Coun. Boy Scouts Am., 1965-66; pres. Okemos Cmty. Sr. Citizens, 1987-88; pres. Lansing Area Farmers Agrl. Club, 1992, sec.-treas., 1994-95. Named Outstanding Specialist Mich. Coop. Extension Specialist Assn., 1967. Fellow Soil Sci. Soc. Am., Am. Soc. Agronomy (contbr. articles to jour.); mem. Internat. Peat Soc. (del. 1963—), U.S. Peat Soc., Mich. Onion Growers Assn. (sec. 1953-72), Mich. Muck Farmers Assn. (sec. 1953-72, Assoc. Master-Farmers award 1966), Mich. Mint Growers Assn. (sec. 1953-60). Republican. Lutheran. Avocations: traveling, gardening, sports, genealogy. Home: 3827 Dobie Rd Okemos MI 48864-3703 Office: Mich State Univ Dept Of Crop Sci East Lansing MI 48824

LUCAS, ROY EDWARD, JR., minister; b. Shawnee, Okla., Dec. 19, 1955; s. Roy Edward Sr. and Shirley Ann (Padgett) L.; m. Roberta Lee Duncan, Feb. 28, 1975; children: Jonathon Edward, Jerebeth Glenae. BA, Okla. Bapt. U., 1978, BA in Edn., 1979; MDiv, Southwestern Bapt. Theol. Sem., Ft. Worth, 1984, MRE, 1985, PhD, 1993. Ordained to ministry So. Bapt. Conv., 1978; cert. elem. tchr., Okla. Assoc. pastor Temple Bapt. Ch., Shawnee, 1975, Calvary Bapt. Ch., Shawnee, 1975-79; pastor Brandon (Tex.) Bapt. Ch., 1982-85, Fox (Okla.) Bapt. Ch., 1985-90, Union Hill Bapt. Ch., Purcell, Okla., 1990—; instr. Sem. Ext.-Enon Assn., Ardmore, Okla., 1986-89; teaching fellow Southwestern Bapt. Sem., 1989. Home: 612 N 6th Ave Purcell OK 73080-2202 Office: Union Hill Bapt Ch RR 2 Box 80 Purcell OK 73080-9630

LUCAS, SHIRLEY AGNES HOYT, management executive; b. Chicago, Aug. 21, 1921; d. Howard L. and Lucille P. (Von Krippenstapel) Hoyt; m. William H. Lucas, Feb. 2, 1952; 1 child, Lucille Shirley. Student, Northwestern U., 1941-42. V.p. Lucas Co., Chgo., 1980—. Mem. Ill. Hosp. Assn. (Leadership award 1975), Aux. Christ Hosp. and Med. Ctr. (life, past bd. dirs., cotillion chmn., housewalk chmn.). Republican. Lutheran. Avocations: tennis, horseback riding, golf, biking, needle point. Office: Lucas Co 9127 S Kedzie Ave Evergreen Park IL 60642-1606

LUCAS, STANLEY JEROME, radiologist, physician; b. Cin., Mar. 23, 1929; s. Morris and Ruby (Schaen) L.; m. Judith Esther Schulzinger, May 14, 1953; children—Barbara Ellen, Daniel Nathan, Betsy Diane, Marvin Howard, Ronna Sue. B.S., U. Cin., 1948, M.D., 1951. Diplomate Am. Bd. Radiology. Intern Cin. Gen Hosp., 1951-52, resident, 1952-53, 55-57; practice medicine specializing in radiology Cin., 1957—; mem. staff William Booth Meml. Hosp., 1957-61, Speer Meml. Hosp., 1957-61, Jewish Hosp., Cin., 1961—; past chmn. bd. Iona, Inc.; bd. dirs. Physicians Ins. Co., Ohio Profls. Ins. Co. Chmn. med. div. United Appeal, 1978, Jewish Welfare Fund, 1980; bd. dirs., treas. Midwest Found. Med. Care; founder Choicecare, Inc., 1978-86; mem. policy devel. com. Local Health Planning Agy., 1978-82. Capt. USAF, 1953-55. Honoree. Jewish Nat. Fund, 1994. Fellow Am. Coll. Radiology; mem. Radiol. Soc. N.Am., AMA (alt. del. 1982-87, del. 1987—), Ohio State Med. Assn. (del. 1975-85, 1st dist. councilor 1985-90, pres. elect 1991, pres. 1992-93), Cin. Acad. Medicine (pres. 1976-77), Radiol. Soc. Cin. (pres. 1967), Am. Roentgen Ray Soc., Phi Beta Kappa, Phi Eta Sigma. Club: Losantiville Country. Jewish. Home: 6760 E Beechlands Dr

Cincinnati OH 45237-3728 Office: 2905 Burnet Ave Cincinnati OH 45219-2403

LUCAS, WILLIAM MAX, JR., structural engineer, university dean; b. Lamar, Mo., July 23, 1934; s. William Max and Margaret (Jones) L.; children—Jennifer Lynn Lucas Wyatt, Sarah Frances Lucas Whittington, Amy Johanne. B.S., U. Kans., 1956, M.S., 1962; Ph.D., Okla. State U., 1970. Registered profl. engr., Kans., Mo. Structural engr. Finney & Turnipseed, Topeka, 1960-62; prof. structural engring. U. Kans., Lawrence, 1962-74, 78-80, dir. facilities planning, 1974-78, dean Sch. Architecture and Urban Design, 1980-94; prof. arch. and archtl. engring., 1962—; owner W.M. Lucas, Engr., Lawrence, 1964—. Author: Matrix Analysis for Structural Engineers, 1968, Structural Analysis for Engineers, 1978; contbr. articles to profl. jours. Mem. Lawrence Bd. Bldg. Code Appeals, 1967-73, Kans. Bldg. Commn., 1982-84; pres. bd. dirs. United Fund, Lawrence, 1976; chmn. Lawrence/Douglas County Planning Commn., 1977-79. Mem. Am. Soc. for Engring. Edn., Assn. Collegiate Schs. Architecture, Nat. Soc. Archtl. Engrs., Sigma Xi, Tau Beta Pi, Tau Sigma Delta. Club: Lawrence Country. Home: 2629 Bardith Ct Lawrence KS 66046-4536 Office: U Kans Sch Architecture & Urban Design Lawrence KS 66045

LUCAS, WILLIAM RAY, aerospace consultant; b. Newbern, Tenn., Mar. 1, 1922; married 1948; 3 children. B.S., Memphis State U., 1943; M.S., Vanderbilt U., 1950, Ph.D. in Chem. Metallurgy, 1952; L.H.D. (hon.), Mobile Coll., 1977; D.Sc. (hon.), Southeastern Inst. Tech., 1980, U. Ala., Huntsville, 1981. Instr. chemistry Memphis State U., 1946-48; chemist guided missile devel. div. Redstone Arsenal, 1952-54, chief chem. sect., 1954-55; chief engr. material sect. Army Ballistic Missile Agy., 1955-56, chief engr. material br., 1956-60; with Marshall Space Flight Center, NASA, 1960—, material div., 1963-66, dir. propulsion and vehicle engring. lab., 1966-68, dir. program devel., 1968-71, dep. dir., 1971-74, dir., 1974-86; pvt. practice aerospace cons. Hunstville, Ala., 1986—. Served as lt. USNR, 1943-46. Recipient Exceptional Sci. Achievement medal NASA, 1964, 2 Exceptional Service medals, 1969, Disting. Service medal, 1972, Disting. Service award, 1981, 86; Presdl. rank Disting. Exec., 1980; Roger W. Jones award for outstanding exec. leadership Am. U., 1981; Space award for outstanding contbns. in field of space VFW, 1983; Disting. Alumni award Memphis State U., 1984; Aubrey D. Green award Lions Club Ala., 1986; named one of Tenn. Outstanding Scientists and Engrs., Tenn. Tech. Found., 1986; named to Ala. Engring. Hall of Fame, 1990. Fellow Am. Soc. Metals, Am. Astronautical Soc. (Space Flight award 1982), AIAA (Oberth award 1965, Holger N. Toftoy award 1976, Elmer A. Sperry group award 1986); mem. Nat. Acad. Engring., Am. Chem. Soc., Sigma Xi, Tau Beta Pi. Research in materials engring. metallurgy, inorganic chemistry, environ. effects on materials, especially space environ.

LUCASSEN, SIGURD, labor union administrator. Gen. pres. United Brotherhood of Carpenters and Joiners of Am., Washington, D.C. Office: United Brotherhood Carpenters & Joiners Am Carpetners Bldg 101 Constitution Ave NW Washington DC 20001-2133

LUCCA, JOHN JAMES, retired dental educator; b. Bklyn., July 12, 1921; s. Thomas and Marie (Ciancia) L.; m. Mary A. Pascarell, June 22, 1946; children—Diane, Eileen, Denise, Nancy, John, William. A.B., NYU, 1941; D.D.S., Columbia, 1947. Diplomate: Am. Bd. Prosthodontics. Research fellow prosthetics Columbia Dental Sch., 1949-52, instr., 1952-57, assoc. prof., 1957-64, head clin. prosthodontics; and postgrad. instr. 1st, 10th Dist. dental socs., 1954-87, prof. dentistry, 1964-87, dir. div. prosthodontics; prof. emeritus Columbia U., 1987—; cons. Westchester County Med. Ctr.; attending emeritus Presbyn. Hosp.; cons., lectr. U.S. Naval Dental Sch.; mem. examination com. N.E. Regional Bd. Dental Examiners; mem. med. staff Valley Hosp. Contbr. to dental jours., chpts. to various textbooks. Extraordinary minister of the Eucharist, 1974—; mem. parish council Mt. Carmel Ch., 1985—; hon. police surgeon N.Y.C. Police Dept., 1964—. Served with AUS 1944-45. Recipient Ella M. Ewell medal Columbia, 1947. Fellow N.Y. Acad. Dentistry, Internat. Coll. Dentists Am. Coll. Dentists, Greater N.Y. Acad. Prosthodontics (pres. 1968), Internat. Coll. Prosthodontists, Am. Acad. Osseo Integration, Am. Coll. Prosthodontics (charter, pres. N.J. state sect. 1979-81); mem. Am. Equilibration Soc., First Dist. Dental Soc. (chmn. prosthodontia sect. 1971), Am. Prosthodontics Soc., Williiam Jarvie Rsch. Soc., Chgo. Acad. Dental Rsch., Knight of Malta, Omicron Kappa Upsilon (pres. Epsilon Epsilon chpt. 1967). Home: 524 Eastgate Rd Ridgewood NJ 07450-2204

LUCCHESI, BRUNO, sculptor; b. Lucca, Toscana, Italy, July 31, 1926; came to U.S., 1958; s. Giovanni and Natalina (Magnani) L. Maestrodarte, Art Institute, Lucca, 1949. Art instr. U. Florence, Italy, 1950-57, New Sch. for Soc. Res., N.Y.C., 1960-70, Nat. Acad. of Design, N.Y.C. 1970-80; Art seminars: U. Utah, George Washington U., Marshal U., Hartford U. Author: Terracotta, 1976, Modelling Head, 1977, Modelling Figure, 1980. Recipient of Lion of S. Marco award Holion Cultural Soc., N.Y.C., 1981. Home: 30 Fifth Ave New York NY 10011

LUCCHESI, JOHN CHARLES, genetics educator; b. Cairo, Sept. 3, 1934; m., 1995; 2 children. AB, La Grange Coll., 1955; MS, U. Ga., 1958; PhD, U. Calif., Berkeley, 1963. Rsch. assoc., biology NIH, U. Oreg., 1963-65; Cary C. Boshamer prof. biology, genetics U. N.C., Chapel Hill, 1965-90; Asa G. Candler prof., chmn. biology Emory U., Atlanta, 1990—; vis. investigator Max-Planck Inst. Biologie, Türingen, 1969, U. Cambridge dept. genetics, 1984; chmn. genetics study sect. divsn. rsch. grants NIH, 1987-90. Recipient NIH Rsch. Career Devel. award, 1970-75. em. Genetics Soc. Am. (v.p. 1990, pres. 1991). Office: Emory U Dept Biology 1510 Clifton Rd Owr Rsch Ctr Atlanta GA 30322*

LUCCHINO, LAWRENCE, lawyer, sports executive; b. Pitts., Sept. 6, 1945; s. Dominic A. and Rose (Rizzo) L. A.B. cum laude, Princeton U., 1967; J.D., Yale U., 1972. Bar: Calif. and Pa. 1973, D.C. 1975. Counsel Impeachment Inquiry, House Judiciary Commn., Washington, DC, 1974; assoc. Williams & Connolly, Washington, 1975-79, ptnr., 1979—; sec., bd. dirs., gen. counsel Washington Redskins Football Club, 1978-85; bd. dirs., gen. counsel Balt. Orioles Baseball Club from 1979, v.p., 1982-88, pres., CEO, 1988-93; CEO San Diego Padres Baseball Club, 1994—; bd. dirs Army Times, Springfield, Va. Trustee Nat. Found. on Counseling, Princeton, N.J., 1984—; bd. dirs. Nat. Aquarium Natl., Balt. Symphony, Princeton Electronic Bd., Babe Ruth Mus. Mem. ABA. Democrat. Roman Catholic. Office: PO Box 2000 San Diego CA 92112-2000

LUCCI, SUSAN, actress; b. Scarsdale, N.Y., Dec. 23, 1946; d. Victor and Jeanette L.; m. Helmut Huber, 1969; children: Liza Victoria, Andreas Martin. BA, Marymount Coll., 1968. Portrays Erica in TV series All My Children, 1970—; appearances in other series include: Fantasy Island, The Love Boat, The Fall Guy; TV films: Invitation to Hell, 1985, Mafia Princess, 1985, (mini-series) Anastasia: The Mystery of Anna Anderson, 1986, Haunted by Her Past, 1988, Lady Mobster, 1988, The Bride in Black, 1990, The Women Who Sinned, 1991, Double Edge, 1992, Between Love and Hate, 1993, French Silk, 1994; host of spl. with Tony Danza 99 Ways to Attract the Right Man. Recipient 13 Emmy nominations for best actress in daytime drama series, numerous other awards. Office: All My Children 320 W 66th St New York NY 10023 also: ICM 8942 Wilshire Blvd Beverly Hills CA 90211

LUCE, CHARLES FRANKLIN, former utilities executive, lawyer; b. Platteville, Wis., Aug. 29, 1917; s. James Oliver and Wilma Fisher (Grindell) L.; m. Helen G. Oden, Oct. 24, 1942; children: James O., Christine Mary, Barbara Anne, Charles Franklin. B.A., LL.B., U. Wis., 1941; Sterling fellow, Yale U. 1941-42. Bar: Wis. 1941, Wash. 1946, Oreg. 1945, N.Y. 1981. Law clk. Justice Hugo L. Black, U.S. Supreme Ct., 1943-44; gen. practice law Walla Walla, Wash., 1946-61; adminstr. Bonneville Power Adminstrn., Dept. Interior, Portland, Oreg., 1961-66; under sec. interior Washington, 1966-67; chmn. bd. Consol. Edison Co. of N.Y., Inc., 1967-82, chief exec. officer, 1967-81, chmn. emeritus, 1982—; ptnr. Preston, Thorgrimson, Ellis & Holman, Portland, Oreg., 1982-86; spl. counsel Met. Life Ins. Co., 1987-94; dir. emeritus UAL and Met. Life Ins. Co.; trustee Hudson River Found.; trustee emeritus Columbia U., N.Y.C. Mem. N.Y., Wash., Wis. bar assns., Phi Beta Kappa, Order of Coif. Episcopalian. Office: Consol Edison 4 Irving Pl New York NY 10010

LUCE, GLENDA L., health facility administrator; b. Torrance, Calif., Sept. 14, 1958. AS in Nursing, Rio Hondo Coll., 1981; BSN, Pacific Union Coll., 1985; MHA, Calif. State U., L.A., 1990. Nursing dir. critical care unit White Meml. Hosp., L.A.

LUCE, GREGORY M., lawyer. Bar: D.C., Va., Md. With Jones, Day, Reavis & Pogue, Washington. Mem. ABA, Nat. Health Lawyers Assn., Am. Acad. Hosp. Attys., Va. State Bar (past chair, mem. bd. govs. health law sect.). Office: Jones Day Reavis & Pogue 1450 G St NW Washington DC 20005-2088

LUCE, HENRY, III, foundation executive; b. N.Y.C., Apr. 28, 1925; s. Henry Robinson and Lila Hotz (Tyng) L.; m. Patricia Potter, June 27, 1947 (div. 1954); children: Lila Frances, Henry Christopher; m. Claire McGill, Aug. 6, 1960 (dec. June 1971); stepchildren: Kenneth, William, James; m. Nancy Bryan Cassiday, Aug. 15, 1975 (dec. Mar. 1987); stepchildren: Richard, Bryan (dec.); m. Leila Eliott Burton Hadley, Jan. 5, 1990; stepchildren: Arthur T. Hadley III, Victoria Smitter Barlow, Matthew Smitter Eliott, Caroline Smitter Nicholson. B.A., Yale U., 1945; L.H.D., St. Michael's, 1973, L.I. U., 1986, Pratt Inst., 1991; LLD (hon.), Coll. of Wooster, 1994. Commr.'s asst. Hoover Commn. on Orgn. Exec. Br. of Govt., 1948-49; reporter Cleve. Press, 1949-51; Washington corr. Time Inc., 1951-53, Time writer, 1953-55, head new bldg. dept., 1956-60, asst. to pub., 1960-61; circulation dir. Fortune and Archtl. Forum, 1961-64, House & Home, 1962-64; v.p. Time Inc., 1964-80, chief London bur., 1966-68; pub. Fortune, 1968-69; pub. Time, 1969-72, dir. corp. planning, 1972-80; dir. Time, Inc., 1967-89, Time Warner Inc., 1989—; pres., chmn., CEO Henry Luce Found., Inc., 1958-89; pres. The New Mus. Contemporary Art, 1977—; chmn. Am. Security Systems Inc. Trustee Princeton Theol. Sem., Coll. Wooster, Eisenhower Exch. Fellowships, Ctr. Theol. Inquiry, Temple of Understanding, China INst. in Am., Christian Ministry in Nat. Pks., N.Y. Hist. Soc.; mem. Am. Coun. UN Univ.; pres. Assn. Am. Corrs. in London, 1968; dir. Nat. Com. on US China Rels., Fishers Island Devel. Co. Lt. (j.g.) USNR, 1943-46. 2d Am. recipient medal for disting. philanthropy Am. Assn. Museums, 1994. Mem. Univ. Club (coun. mem.), Pilgrims Club (exec. com.), Explorers Club, Fishers Island Club, Hay Harbor Club. Presbyterian (elder). Office: 720 Fifth Ave Ste 1500 New York NY 10019-4107 also: Fishers Island NY 06930 also: Mill Hill Rd Mill Neck NY 11765

LUCE, R(OBERT) DUNCAN, psychology educator; b. Scranton, Pa., May 16, 1925; s. Robert Rennselaer and Ruth Lillian (Downer) L.; m. Gay Gaer, June 6, 1950 (div.); m. Cynthia Newby, Oct. 5, 1968 (div.); m. Carolyn A. Scheer, Feb. 27, 1988; 1 child, Aurora Newby. BS, MIT, 1945, PhD, 1950; MA (hon.), Harvard U., 1976. Mem. staff research lab electronics MIT, 1950-53; asst. prof. Columbia U., 1953-57; lectr. social relations Harvard U., 1957-59; prof. psychology U. Pa., Phila., 1959-69; vis. prof. Inst. Advanced Study, Princeton, 1969-72; prof. Sch. Social Scis., U. Calif., Irvine, 1972-75; Alfred North Whitehead prof. psychology Harvard U., Cambridge, Mass., 1976-81, prof., 1981-83, Victor S. Thomas prof. psychology, 1983-88, Victor S. Thomas prof. emeritus, 1988; chmn. Harvard U., 1988-94; disting. prof. cognitive sci. U. Calif., Irvine, 1988-94, dir. Irvine Rsch. Unit in math. behavioral sci., 1988-92, disting. rsch. prof. cognitive sci. and rsch. prof. econs., 1994—; dir. Inst. for Math. Behavioral Sci., 1992—; chmn. assembly behavioral and social scis. NRC, 1976-79. Author: (with H. Raiffa) Games and Decisions, 1957, Individual Choice Behavior, 1959, (with others) Foundations of Measurement, I, 1971, II, 1989, III, 1990, Response Times, 1986, (with others) Stevens Handbook of Experimental Psychology, I and II, 1988, Sound & Hearing, 1993. Served with USNR, 1943-46. Ctr. Advanced Study in Behavioral Scis. fellow, 1954-55, 66-67, 87-88, NSF Sr. Postdoctoral fellow, 1966-67, Guggenheim fellow, 1980-81; recipient Disting. award for Rsch. U. Calif., Irvine, 1994. Fellow AAAS, Am. Psychol. Assn. (disting. sci. contbn. award 1970, bd. sci. affairs 1993—); mem. Am. Acad. Arts & Scis., Am. Philos. Soc., Nat. Acad. Scis. (chmn. sect. psychology 1980-83, class behavioral and social scis. 1983-86), Am. Math. Soc., Math. Assn. Am., Fedn. Behavioral Psychol. and Cognitive Scis. (pres. 1988-90), Psychometric Soc. (pres. 1976-77), Psychonomic Soc., Soc. Math. Psychology (pres. 1979), Am. Psychol. Soc. (bd. dirs. 1989-91), Sigma Xi, Phi Beta Kappa, Tau Beta Pi. Home: 20 Whitman Ct Irvine CA 92715-4057 Office: U Calif Social Sci Tower Irvine CA 92717

LUCE, SUSAN MARIE, library director; b. Ypsilanti, Mich., Mar. 4, 1948; d. Walter Stanley and Irene Elizabeth (Gallaway) Rybka; m. Paul Trescott Jackson, July 10, 1971 (div. Apr. 1986); m. John Archer Luce, Jr., Nov. 19, 1988. BA in History, U. Mich., 1968, AMLS, 1969. Acquisitions libr. Oakland U., Rochester, Mich., 1969-71; head circulation dept. Lincoln Libr., Springfield, Ill., 1972-73; dir. Alpha Park Pub. Libr. Dist., Bartonville, Ill., 1973-87, Ontario City Library! City Libr., 1988—. Mem. ALA, Calif. Libr. Assn. Office: Ontario City Library 215 East C Ontario CA 91764

LUCERO, GENE A., lawyer; b. San Diego, Dec. 10, 1947. BA cum laude, Stanford U., 1970; JD, U. Calif., 1972. Bar: Colo. 1973, U.S. Dist. Ct. (Colo. dist.) 1973, U.S. Ct. Appeals (10th cir.) 1973, Calif. 1974, D.C. 1990, U.S. Ct. Appeals (D.C. cir.) 1992, U.S. Dist. Ct. (ctrl. dist.) Calif. 1992. Asst. atty. gen. litigation sect. Office Atty. Gen., Colo., 1975-78; dep. dir. Office of Compliance Action/Peace Programs, 1978-80; dep. regional administr. Region VIII, EPA, Denver, 1980-82; dep. dir. Office Emergency and Remedial Response, 1982; ptnr. Latham & Watkins, L.A. Contbr. articles to profl. jours. Office: Latham & Watkins Ste 4000 1900 Avenue Of The Stars Los Angeles CA 90067-4503

LUCEY, JEROLD FRANCIS, pediatrician; b. Holyoke, Mass., Mar. 26, 1926; s. Jeremiah F. and Pauline A. (Lally) L.; m. Ingela Barth, Oct. 7, 1972; 1 child, Patrick; children by previous marriage: Cathy, David. AB, Dartmouth Coll., 1948; MD, NYU, 1952. Intern Bellevue Hosp., N.Y.C., 1952-53; resident in pediatrics Columbia-Presbyn. Med. Ctr., 1953-55; rsch. fellow Harvard-Children's Hosp., 1955-56; rsch. fellow in biochemistry U. Vt., 1956-60, from asst. prof. to prof. pediatrics, 1961-74, prof., 1974—; rsch. fellow in biol. chemistry Harvard Coll. 1960-61; cons. NIH; vis. prof. Royal Soc. Medicine, Eng., 1980; Wallace prof. neonatology, 1995. Editor Pediatrics, 1974—; contbr. articles on neonatology, phototherapy and transcutaneous oxygen to profl. jours. With USNR, 1944-46. Recipient Humboldt Sr. Scientist award, 1978, United Cerebral Palsy Rsch. award, 1984, McDonald prize, 1991, Humanitarian medal Am. Lung Assn., 1991, Apgar award, 1993, 94; Markel scholar, 1960-65, Humbolt scholar, 1978. Fellow Am. Acad. Pediatrics (Grulee award 1988, APGAR award 1993); mem. Royal Soc. Medicine, World Congress on Perinatal Medicine (pres. 1993), Indian Pediatric Soc. (hon., Gold medal 1994). Home: 52 Overlake Park Burlington VT 05401-4012 Office: Mary Fletcher Hosp McClure Rm 718 111 Colchester Ave Burlington VT 05401-1473

LUCEY, JOHN DAVID, JR., lawyer; b. Phila., May 4, 1930; s. John David and Eleanor (Gallagher) L.; m. Carol Ann Henderson, Oct. 29, 1955; children—John David, Michael Dakin, Timothy Gallagher, Carol Anne. A.B., U. Pa., 1953, LL.B., 1956. Bar: Pa. 1957. Mem. firm LaBrum and Doak, Phila., 1957—; instr. estate counselling Temple U. Sch. Law, 1977-86; course planner, author, lectr. Pa. Bar Inst., 1967—. Mem. Phila. Bar Assn. (chmn. sect. probate and trust law 1976), Pa. Bar Assn., ABA, Am. Coll. Probate Counsel. Republican. Roman Catholic. Club: Union League of Phila. Home: 1237 Hagys Ford Rd Narberth PA 19072-1103 Office: LaBrum & Doak 1818 Market St Ste 2900 Philadelphia PA 19103-3629

LUCEY, THOMAS WILLIAM, banker; b. Albany, N.Y., June 20, 1940; s. Cornelius Augustus and Grace Helen (Larkin) L.; m. Patricia Rose Vano, July 9, 1966; children—Timothy, Matthew. B.S. in Acctg., Sienna Coll., 1966. C.P.A., N.Y. Audit mgr. Peat, Marwick, Mitchell & Co. Albany, N.Y., 1966-77; sec., treas Norstar Bancorp., Albany, 1975-78, v.p., sec., 1978-82; chmn., chief exec. officer, dir. Norstar Bank of the Hudson Valley, Newburgh, N.Y., 1982-85; pres., chief exec. officer Norstar Bank N.A. Buffalo, 1985—; also dir. Norstar Bank N.A. Pres. Greater Niagara Frontier council Boy Scouts Am. Served with USMC, 1958-62. Recipient Americanism award Anti-Defamation League of B'nai B'rith, 1984. Mem. Am. Inst. C.P.A.s, N.Y. State Soc. C.P.A.s, Am. Soc. Corp. Secs., Planning Execs. Inst. (chpt. pres.). Republican. Roman Catholic. Club: Powelton (Newburgh). Office: Norstar Bank NA 10 Fountain Plz Buffalo NY 14202-2220

LUCHAK, FRANK ALEXANDER, lawyer; b. Alberta, Can., Feb. 19, 1950; came to U.S., 1956; s. George and Elizabeth (Szilagyi) L. AB in Econs., Princeton U., 1972; JD, SUNY, Buffalo, 1978. Bar: Pa. 1978, N.J. 1979, U.S. Dist. Ct. N.J. 1979, U.S. Dist. Ct. (ea. dist.) Pa. 1980, U.S. Supreme Ct. 1986. Assoc. Harvey, Pennington et al, Phila., 1977-81; assoc. Duane, Morris & Heckscher, Phila., 1981-86, ptnr., 1986—; mng. ptnr. N.J. office, 1994—. Mem. ABA, Pa. Bar Assn., Phila. Bar Assn. (civil and jud. procedures rules com.), Pa. Assn. Def. Counsel, Phila. Assn. Def. Counsel, Def. Research Inst. Home: 27 S Hinchman Ave Haddonfield NJ 08033-3714 Office: Duane Morris & Heckscher 51 Haddonfield Rd Ste 340 Cherry Hill NJ 08002-4810

LUCHE, THOMAS CLIFFORD, foreign service officer; b. Bklyn., Jan. 24, 1934; s. Theodore Paul Albert and Jennie Kristine (Thompsen) L.; m. Winifred Jean Bogardus, May 26, 1959; children: Stephen Edward, Jenna Elizabeth, Sarah Hope. BS in Gen. Forestry, SUNY, Syracuse, 1955; student employment tng. program, Scandinavian Am. Found., Denmark and Finland, 1955-56. Various positions USAID, Saigon, Vietnam, 1957-63; rural devel. officer Jsoeph Z. Taylor Assocs., Chiang Mai, Thailand, 1967-70, USAID, Upper Volta, 1975-79; area coord. USAID, Arusha, Tanzania, 1979-81; grants officer USAID, Washington, 1981-83; gen. devel. officer USAID, Accra, Ghana, 1983-85; spl. projects officer USAID, Washington, 1985-87; rep. USAID, Praia, Cape Verde, 1987-92; rep. USAID, Burkina Faso, 1992-94, ret., 1994. Recipient Vietnam Civilian Service medal, 1968, HRH The Princess Mother's Memorial medal, Thailand, 1969. Mem. Am. Fgn. Svc. Assn., Sr. Fgn. Svc. of the USA, Soc. Am. Foresters. Democrat. Episcopalian. Avocations: fishing, hunting, water sports, opera, ballet.

LUCHETTI, ROBERT JAMES, architect, industrial designer; b. San Francisco, June 1, 1949; s. Lawrence Leo and Petranella Helen (Mortiga) L.; m. Leita Hagemann, May 9, 1987. AB in Environ. Design, U. Calif., Berkeley, 1971; MArch, Harvard Grad. Sch. Design, 1974. Registered architect, Mass., Tex., S.C., Minn., Fla. Asst. prof. dept. visual & environ. studies Harvard U., Cambridge, Mass., 1975-76, 78-84; asst. prof. sch. environ. design King Abdulaziz U., Jeddah, Saudi Arabia, 1976-78; assoc. Cambridge Seven Assocs., Inc., 1975-76, 78-87; prin., pres. Robert Luchetti Assocs., Inc., Cambridge, 1987—. Contbr. articles to profl. jours. Recipient Boston Exports award Boston Soc. Architects, 1986, Julia Amory Appleton Travelling fellowship Harvard U., 1974, Honor award Boston Soc. of Architect, 1991; winner Internat. Competition for a New Office Furniture System, 1983. Mem. AIA, Nat. Coun. Archtl. Registration. Office: Robert Luchetti Assocs Inc 14 Arrow St Cambridge MA 02138-5106

LUCHT, JOHN CHARLES, management consultant, executive recruiter, writer; b. Reedsburg, Wis., June 1, 1933; s. Carl H. and Ruth A. (Shultis) L.; m. Catherine Ann Seyler, Dec. 11, 1965 (div. 1982). BS, U. Wis., 1955, LLB, 1960. News dir. Sta. WISC-AM/FM, Madison, Wis., 1952-55; merchandising dir. The Bartell Group (radio and TV stas.), Milw., 1955-56; instr. U. Wis. Law Sch., 1959-60; TV contracts exec., account exec. J. Walter Thompson Co., N.Y.C., 1960-64; product mgr., new products mgr. dir. new product mktg. Bristol-Myers Co., N.Y.C., 1964-69; dir. mktg. W.A. Sheaffer Pen Co., Ft. Madison, Iowa, 1969-70; gen. mgr. Tetley Tea div. Squibb Beech-Nut Inc., N.Y.C., 1970-71; v.p. Heidrick & Struggles, N.Y.C., 1971-77; pres. The John Lucht Consultancy, Inc., N.Y.C., 1977—, The Viceroy Press Inc., 1987—; Lectr. in field. Author: Rites of Passage at $100,000 Plus, The Insiders's Guide to Executive Job-Changing, Executive Job-Changing Workbook. Mem. Soc. Am. Bus. Editors and Writers, Internat. Assn. Corp. and Profl. Recruiters, State Bar Wis., N.Y. Bd. Trade, Assn. Exec. Search Cons., Nat. Assn. Corp. Profl. Recruiters, N.Y. Acad. Scis., Overseas Press Club, Met. Club, Can. Club, Phi Beta Kappa, Phi Eta Sigma, Phi Kappa Phi, Phi Delta Phi, Sigma Alpha Epsilon. Office: Olympic Tower 641 Fifth Ave New York NY 10022-5908

LUCIA, PHILIP JOHN, insurance company executive; b. Tarrytown, N.Y., Dec. 9, 1928; s. Pasquale Joseph and Winifred Edna (McGuinn) L.; m. Ruth Marie Zong, May 17, 1952; children: Maria, Patrick, Wendy. BS in Acctg., Lasalle U., Phila., 1951. Underwriting mgr. Allstate Ins. Co., White Plains, N.Y., 1954-63, Fireman's Fund, N.Y.C., 1963; v.p. regional mgr. Nationwide Ins. Co., Harrisburg, Pa., 1963—. Bd. trustees Community Gen. Osteo. Hosp., Harrisburg, 1987—, mem. audit com. human resource com., strategic planning com.; vice chmn. Pa. Ins. Polit. Action com., Phila., 1988—. With U.S. Army, 1951-53. Republican. Lutheran. Office: Nationwide Mut Ins Co 1000 Nationwide Dr Harrisburg PA 17110-9775

LUCIANO, ROBERT PETER, pharmaceutical company executive; b. N.Y.C., Oct. 9, 1933; s. Peter and Jennie (Mastro) L.; m. Barbara Ann Schiavone, June 21, 1953; children: Susan Ann, Richard Peter. BBA, CCNY, 1954; JD, U. Mich., 1958. Sr. tax assoc. Royall Koegel & Rogers (now Rogers & Wells), N.Y.C., 1958-66; atty. CIBA Corp., Summit, N.J., 1966-68, asst. sec., 1968-70; asst. gen. counsel, dir. pub. affairs CIBA Pharm. Co., Summit, 1970-71, v.p. mktg., 1973-75; v.p. planning and adminstrn. pharm. div. CIBA-GEIGY Corp., Summit, 1971-73, pres. pharm. div., 1975-77; pres. Lederle Labs. div. Am. Cyanamid Co., Pearl River, N.Y., 1977-78; sr. v.p. adminstrn. Schering-Plough Corp., Kenilworth, N.J., 1978-79, exec. v.p. pharm. ops., 1979-80, pres., chief operating officer, 1980-82, pres., chief exec. officer, 1982-84, chmn. bd., pres., chief exec. officer, 1984-86, chmn. bd., chief exec. officer, 1986—; bd. dirs. C.R. Bard Inc., Murray Hill, N.J., Bank of N.Y. Co. Inc., N.Y.C. Asst. editor: U. Mich. Law Rev., 1957-58. Served with U.S. Army, 1954-56. Mem. ABA, N.Y. Bar Assn., Nat. Assn. Mfrs. (bd. dirs. 1982—), N.J. State C. of C. (bd. dirs. 1986—). Republican. Clubs: Union League, Sky, Econ. (N.Y.C.). Office: Schering-Plough Corp PO Box 1000 1 Giralda Farms Madison NJ 07940-1027*

LUCID, ROBERT FRANCIS, English educator; b. Seattle, June 25, 1930; s. Philip Joseph and Nora May (Gorman) L.; m. Joanne K. Tharalson, Sept. 18, 1954; 1 son, John Michael. B.A., U. Wash., 1954; M.A., U. Chgo., 1955, Ph.D., 1958. Faculty U. Chgo., 1957-59, Wesleyan U., Middletown, Conn., 1959-64; faculty U. Pa., Phila., 1964—; prof. English U. Pa., 1975—, chmn. dept. English, 1980-85, 90-91, chmn. faculty senate, 1976-77, master Hill Coll. House, 1979—. Editor: Journal of Richard Henry Dana, 1968, The Long Patrol, 1971, Norman Mailer, the Man and His Work, 1971. Served with USAF, 1951-53. Recipient Lindback award U. Pa., 1975, Abrams award, 1986; Yaddo fellow, 1970. Mem. MLA, AAUP, PEN (exec. bd. 1987-93), Am. Studies Assn. (exec. sec. 1964-69), Princeton Club (N.Y.C.), Penn Club (N.Y.C.). Office: U Pa Dept English Philadelphia PA 19104

LUCIDO, CHESTER CHARLES, JR., marketing company executive; b. Pitts., Dec. 5, 1939; s. Chester C. and Alma (Dolence) L.; m. Linda G. Firrell, June 16, 1962; children: Chester C. III, Bradley J., Kristen L. BS in Mgmt., Pa. State U., 1961. Sales rep. Prentice-Hall, Englewood Cliffs, N.J., 1962-63, supr. sales, 1963-66, dist. mgr., 1966-69, editor, 1969-71, mgr. regional sales, 1971-72, exec. editor, 1972; pub., v.p. Glencoe Press, Encino, Calif., 1972-77; v.p. Little, Brown & Co., Boston, 1977-86, sr. v.p., 1986-88; pres., chief exec. officer Van Nostrand Reinhold, N.Y.C., 1988-89, Southwestern Pub. Co., Cin., 1990-93; COO Encore Mktg. Internat., Inc., Lanham, Md., 1994—. With U.S. Army, 1961-62. Mem. Assn. Am. Pubs. (mem. exec. coun. higher edn. 1977-87, chmn. 1987, profl. and scholarly exec. coun. 1988-89, sch. exec. coun. 1990-91), Am. Soc. Travel Agts. Republican. Episcopalian. Avocation: reading, running. Home: 5 Deepwater Ct Edgewater MD 21037 Office: Encore Mktg Internat 4501 Forbes Blvd Lanham Seabrook MD 20706

LUCIDO, LOUIS CHARLES, finance company executive; b. Kings County, N.Y., Oct. 15, 1948; s. Gaspare Louis and Beatrice Cecile (Mailloux) L.; student U. Okla., 1966-68, Nassau Community Coll., 1970-71, Hofstra U., 1971-73, profl. insts., 1978; m. Carolyn M. Post, Aug. 19, 1972; children: Suzanne, Dennis, Nicole, Samantha. Portfolio mgr. Citibank, N.Y.C., 1969-73; risk mgr. U.S. govt. securities W.H. Morton, N.Y.C., 1973; risk mgr. U.S. govt. securities, sales mgr., discretionary asset mgr. Merrill Lynch, N.Y.C., 1973-80; exec. v.p. Merrill Lynch Mgmt. Services Inc., 1980-81, also bd. dirs., emm. exec. com.; v.p. Merrill Lynch, Pierce, Fenner & Smith, 1981-87; v.p., sr. portfolio mgr., dir. fixed income mgr., structured investment mgr. MLPF&S, 1981-87; risk mgr. taxable fix income, mgr. structured investment Smith Barney, 1987-88; sr. v.p., mgr. portfolio restructuring group and mem. taxable fixed income risk mgmt. com. Donalson, Lufkin & Jenrette Securities Corp., 1988-90; sr. v.p., dir. Progressive Capital Mgmt.,

Inc., Jersey City, 1991-92; mng. dir. Hyperion Capital Mgmt. Inc., 1992—; pres. HTA, HTB, HTO, HTT, Hyperion Distbrs. Mem. St. James Sch. Bd., Seaford, N.Y., 1979-82. Republican. Roman Catholic. Avocations: tennis, softball, guitar, stamp collecting. Spl. confidential fin. analyses for ofcl. fgn. monetary authorities. Office: Hyperion Capital Mgmt Inc 520 Madison Ave New York NY 10022-4213

LUCIER, JAMES MICHAEL, advertising executive; b. Grand Forks, N.D., Feb. 5, 1920; s. Alfred Joseph and Mildred Perry (Fahar) L.; B.A., U. Minn., 1946; postgrad. U. So. Methodist, 1965; m. Juliann K. Dunlap, July 26, 1991; children: Edward, Kelley, John, Jane, Teddi, James. Sales exec. Times, Ft. Smith, Ark., 1946-47; sales mgr. KRKN, Ft. Smith, 1947-48; dir. advt. Times, Fayetteville, Ark., 1948-51; sales exec. Express, San Antonio, 1952-53; mgr. Sunday mag. Times, Dallas, 1953-65; dir. advt. and advt. and pub. relations Home Furniture Co., Dallas, 1965-81; advt. mgr. Smith Furniture Co., Dallas, 1981-85; staff v.p. Home Furnishings Internat. Assn., 1985—; owner Lucier Assocs. Advt., Dallas, 1965—. Editor, assoc. pub. Home Furnishings Rev., 1986—. Unit chmn. United Way, 1965-81; precinct chmn. Democratic Party, 1974-85; mem. bd. Dem. Forum, 1974-75; pres. bd. dirs. Dallas council USO; mem. orgns. com. Greater Dallas Sesquicentennial Com., 1983-86. Served with inf., AUS, 1942-44, USAAF, 1944-45, USAF, 1951-52. Decorated Air medal with 2 oak leaf clusters. Mem. Retail Furniture Assn. Greater Dallas (pres. 1971-72, pres. 1983-84, dir. 1972-85), Sigma Delta Chi, Theta Chi. Episcopalian. Clubs: Exchange (pres. E.Dallas 1967, pres. Tex. dist. 1969-70, nat. dir. 1970-72, chmn. nat. edn. com 1974-76, fin. com. 1976-80), U. Minn. Alumni (past pres.), Vagabond, Dallas Magic Circle (past pres.). Home: 4345 Meadowdale Ln Dallas TX 75229-5339 Office: Home Furnishings Internat Assn 110 World Trade Ctr Dallas TX 75258

LUCIER, P. JEFFREY, publishing executive; b. Manchester, N.H., June 20, 1941; s. Paul A. and Elaine (Wilson) Fraser L.; m. Judith Margaret Akers, Dec. 21, 1963 (div. 1975); children—Kathryn Elizabeth, Amy Wilson; m. Velma Lee Frye, Nov. 27, 1976 (div. 1981); m. Susan Elizabeth Hess, May 25, 1985; children: Madalyn Antonette, Caitlin Elaine. B.A., Union Coll., N.Y., 1963; M.A., U. Chgo., 1964. Instr. English Northwestern U., Evanston and Chgo., Ill., 1967-69; registered rep. Paine Webber, Akron, Ohio, 1969-71; asst. to pres. Banks-Baldwin Law Pub., Cleve., 1971-74, v.p. editorial, 1974-76, exec. v.p., 1977-78, pres., editor-in-chief, 1978—. Trustee Horizon Montessori Sch. Mem. Graphic Communication Assn., Ohio Regional Assn. Law Libraries. Democrat. Roman Catholic. Club: Cleve. City. Office: Banks Baldwin Law Pub Co 1904 Ansel Rd Cleveland OH 44106-4108

LUCK, DAVID JONATHAN LEWIS, biologist, educator; b. Milw., Jan. 7, 1929; s. Max and Sarah (Plonsker) L. S.B., U. Chgo., 1949; M.D., Harvard, 1953; Ph.D., Rockefeller U., 1962. House officer Mass. Gen. Hosp., Boston, 1953-54; resident physician Mass. Gen. Hosp., 1957-58; research asso. Rockefeller U., 1962—, mem. faculty, 1964—, prof. biology, 1968—; v.p. acad. affairs, 1994. Editor: Jour. Cell Biology, 1968-74. Served to capt. USAF, 1955-57. Decorated Commendation medal with oak leaf cluster. Mem. Am. Soc. Biol. Chemists, Am. Soc. Cell Biologists, Nat. Acad. Sci. Club: University (N.Y.C.). Home: 205 E 78th St New York NY 10021

LUCK, EDWARD CARMICHAEL, association executive; b. Urbana, Ill., Oct. 17, 1948; s. David Johnston and Adele Suzanne (Kanter) L.; m. Dana Dee Zaret, June 19, 1971; 1 dau., Jessica Robin. B.A. cum laude with high distinction in Internat. Relations, Dartmouth Coll., 1970; M.I.A., Columbia U., 1972, M.A., 1973, M.Ph., 1974. Project dir. conventional arms control UN Assn. of U.S.A., N.Y.C., 1974-77, dep. dir., dep. v.p. for policy studies, 1977-82, v.p. policy studies, 1982-83, exec. v.p., 1983-84, pres., 1984-94, pres. emeritus, sr. policy advisor, 1994—; cons. social sci. dept. Rand Corp., Santa Monica, Calif., 1973-76. Co-editor, contbr. On The Endings of War, 1980; editor, contbr. Arms Control: The Multilateral Alternative, 1983; contbr. articles to profl. publs. Herbert H. Lehman fellow and Internat. fellow Columbia U., 1970-73; jr. fellow, cert. Russian Inst., Columbia U, 1973-74. Mem. Coun. Fgn. Rels., Century Assn. Democrat. Home: 136 Elm Rd Briarcliff Manor NY 10510-2225

LUCK, GARY EDWARD, career officer; b. Ft. Scott, Kans., Aug. 5, 1937; s. Elmer E. and Helen (Lambie) L.; m. Deana D., July 1959 (div. Oct. 1989; children: Gary E. Jr., Kim Luck Goble; m. Leah Marie Patrick, July 6, 1991. BS, Kans. State U., 1960; MBA, Fla. State U., 1971; PhD, Gerge Washington U., 1981. Commd. 2d lt. U.S. Army, 1960, advanced through grades to lt. gen.; chief Force Mod. Div. Dept. Chief of Staff for Ops., Washington, 1978-89; comdr. 2d Brigade, 8th Inf. Div. (Mechanized), Europe, 1979-81; chief of staff 8th Inf. Div. (Mechanized), Europe, 1981-82; dir. Force Programs Office of Dep. Chief of Staff for Ops. and Plans, Washington, 1982-84; asst. div. comdr. 101st Airborne Div. (AASLT), Ft. Campbell, Ky., 1984-85; comdg. gen. 2d Inf. Div., 8th U.S. Army, Republic of Korea, 1985-86, Joint Spl. Ops. Command, Ft. Bragg, N.C., 1986-89, U.S. Spl. Ops. Command, Ft. Bragg, 1989-90; comdg. gen. XVIII Airborne Corps, Ft. Bragg, 1990—, Saudi Arabia, 1990—. Decorated Def. D.S.M., D.S.M. with oak leaf cluster, Legion of Merit with oak leaf cluster, D.F.C. with two oak leaf clusters, Bronze Star with oak leaf cluster, Purple Heart, Meritorious Svc. medal, 16 Air medals with V Device, Army Commendation medal, Nat. Def. Svc. medal, Vietnam Svc. medal, S.W. Asia Svc. medal, Army Svc. ribbon, Combat Infantryman badge, others. Mem. Assn. U.S. Army. Avocations: golf, fishing, reading. Office: 18th Airborne Corps Macomb And Armistead St Fort Bragg NC 28307

LUCK, GEORG HANS BHAWANI, classics educator; b. Bern, Switzerland, Feb. 17, 1926; came to U.S., 1951; s. Hans and Hanna (Von Ow) L.; m. Harriet Richards Greenough, June 15, 1957; children: Annina, Hans, Stephanie. Student, U. Bern, 1945-49, 50-51, Ph.D., 1953; student, U. Paris, 1949-50; A.M. (Smith-Mundt fellow), Harvard, 1952. Instr. classics Yale U., 1952-53; instr. classics Brown U., 1953-55, vis. prof., 1969; instr. classics Harvard U., 1955-58; vis. prof. classics Yale, 1968; lectr. classics U. Mainz, 1958-62; prof. classics U. Bonn, 1962-71; vis. prof. Johns Hopkins U., 1970-71, prof. classics, 1971-90; prof. emeritus, 1990—; chmn. dept. classics Johns Hopkins U., 1973-75; vis. prof. classics UCLA, 1974, U. Fribourg, 1989; lectr. Smithsonian Instutions, 1992. Author: Der Akademiker Antiochos, 1953, The Latin Love Elegy, 1959, 2d edit., 1969, Über einige Interjektionen, d. lat. Umgangssprache, 1964, Ovid, Tristia, text, transl. and commentary, 2 vols., 1967-77, Untersuchungen zur Textgeschichte Ovids, 1969, Eine Schweizerreise: Aus dem Tagebuch des Alfred Miell von Salisbury, 1981, Arcana Mundi: Magic and the Occult in the Greek and Roman World, 1985 (Spanish and Italian edits. 1994), Lukan, Der Bürgerkrieg, 1985, Der Dichter in der Kutsche, 1986; editor: Tibullus, Carmina, 1987, Magie und andere Geheimnisschaften der Antike, 1990; editor-in-chief Am. Jour. Philology, 1971-81, 86-89; edito Noctes Romanae, 1975—; contbr. articles to profl. jours. Guggenheim fellow, 1958-59; Swiss Nat. Research Council grantee, 1976-77. Mem. Johns Hopkins Club. Episcopalian. Home: 1108 Bryn Mawr Rd Baltimore MD 21210-1213 Office: Johns Hopkins U Classics Dept Baltimore MD 21218 *I am not sure I know what success really means, but I do know today that the rewards for your work or your dedication or your experience and skill do not come from outside; they must be found within you, as a gift from God.*

LUCK, JAMES I., foundation executive; b. Akron, Ohio, Aug. 28, 1945; s. Milton William and Gertrude (Winer) L.; children: Andrew Brewer, Edward Aldrich, L. BA, Ohio State U., 1967; MA, U. Ga., 1970. Caseworker Franklin County Welfare Dept., Columbus, Ohio, 1967-69; dir. forensics Tex. Christian U., Ft. Worth, 1970-74; assoc. dir. Bicentennial Youth Debates, Washington, 1974-76; exec. dir. Nat. Congress on Volunteerism and Citizenship, Washington, 1976-77; fellow Acad. Contemporary Problems, Columbus, Ohio, 1977-79; exec. dir. Battelle Meml. Inst. Found., Columbus, 1980-82; pres. Columbus Found. 1981—; exec. dir. Columbus Youth Found. and Ingram-White Castle Found., Columbus, 1981—; bd. dirs. Cardinal Group of Founds.; co-chmn. Task Force on Citizen Edn., Washington, 1977; mediator Negotiated Investment Strategy, Columbus, 1979; chmn. Ohio Founds. Conf., 1985; cons. HEW, Peace Corps. Author: Ohio-The Next 25 Years, 1978, Bicentennial Issue Analysis, 1975; editor: Proceedings of the Nat. Conf. on Argumentation, 1973; contbr. articles to profl. jours. Trustee Godman Guild Settlement House, Columbus, 1979-81, Am. Diabetes Assn., Ohio, 1984-88; chmn. spl.

com. on displacement Columbus City Coun., 1978-80; bd. dirs. Commn. on the Future of the Professions in Soc., 1979. Mem. Donors Forum Ohio. Clubs: Capital, University, Columbus Met., Kit-Kat. Lodge: Rotary. Avocations: travel, reading. Home: 1318 Hickory Ridge Ln Columbus OH 43235-1131 Office: The Columbus Found 1234 E Broad St Columbus OH 43205-1463

LUCKE, ROBERT VITO, merger and acquisition executive; b. Kingston, Pa., July 26, 1930; s. Vito Frank and Edith Ann (Adders) L.; m. Jane Ann Rushin, Aug. 16, 1952; children: Thomas, Mark, Carl. BS in Chemistry, Pa. State U., 1952; MS in Mgmt., Rensselaer Polytech Inst., 1960. Polymer chemist Uniroyal Naugatuck (Conn.) Chem. Div., 1954-60; comml. devel. engr. Exxon Enjay Div., Elizabeth, N.J., 1960-66; gen. mgr. Celanese Advanced Composites, Summit, N.J., 1966-70; bus. mgr. polymer div. Hooker Chem., Burlington, N.J., 1970-74; gen. mgr. Oxy Metal Industries Environ. Equipment. Divs., Warren, Mich., 1974-79; v.p., gen. mgr. Hoover Universal Plastic Machinery Divs., Manchester, Mich., 1979-84; pres. Egan Machinery, Somerville, N.J., 1984-87; pres., chief exec. officer Krauss Maffei Corp., Cin., 1987-93; pres. Dubuc, Lucke, Koring Co., Inc., Cin., 1990—; instr., Chem. Market Rsch. Assn., 1974. Author: (with others) Plastics Handbook, 1972; inventor, patentee in field. 1st lt. Corp Engrs., 1952-54, Korea. Senatorial scholar, Pa. State U., 1948-52. Mem. Am. Chem. Soc., Soc. Plastics Engrs. (sect. engr. STDS com. 1969), Tech. Assn. Pulp Paper Industry, Comml. Devel. Assn., Assn. Corp. Growth. Avocations: golf, skiing, travel, gardening. Office: Dubuc Lucke & Co Ste 1005 120 W 5th St Cincinnati OH 45202-2710

LUCKER, JAY K., library administrator, consultant; b. N.Y.C., Feb. 23, 1930; s. Joseph Jerome and Ella (Schwartz) L.; m. Marjorie Stern, Aug. 17, 1952; children—Amy Ellen, Nancy Judith. A.B., Bklyn. Coll., City U. N.Y., 1951; M.S., Columbia, 1952; postgrad., N.Y. U., 1955-57. Head procurement br., acquisition div. New York Pub. Library, 1954-57, first asst., acting chief, sci. and tech. div., 1957-59; asst. univ. librarian for sci. and tech., asso. prof. Princeton U. Library, 1959-68, asso. univ. librarian, prof., 1968-75; dir. libraries Mass. Inst. Tech., Cambridge, 1975—; Chmn. bd. dirs. Captain Library Services Corp., 1972-75; vis. lectr. Drexel U. Grad. Sch. Library Service, 1962-67; lectr. Simmons Coll. Grad. Sch. Library and Info. Sci., 1984—; vice chmn. New Eng. Library Info. Network, 1978-79, chmn., 1980-82. Bd. dirs. Boston Libr. Consortium; mem. adv. coms. Brown U., Tufts U., Washington U., St. Louis, Libr. Congress, Copying Info. Inc. Served with Signal Corps U.S. Army, 1952-54. Council on Library Resources fellow, 1970-71. Mem. ALA (council 1978-82), AAAS, Am. Soc. Info. Sci., N.J. Library Assn. (Distinguished Service award coll. and univ. sect. 1975), Assn. Research Libraries (chmn. interlibrary loan com. 1976-80, dir. 1977-80, pres. 1980-81), Spl. Libraries Assn., Phi Beta Kappa, Alpha Phi Omega, Beta Phi Mu. Office: MIT Librs Rm 14s-216 Cambridge MA 02139

LUCKER, RAYMOND ALPHONSE, bishop; b. St. Paul, Feb. 24, 1927; s. Alphonse and Josephine (Schiltgen) L. B.A., St. Paul Sem., 1948, M.A., 1952; S.T.L., U. St. Thomas, Rome, 1965, S.T.D., 1966; Ph.D., U. Minn., 1969; LHD honoris causa, Coll. St. Catherine, 1993. Ordained priest Roman Cath. Ch., 1952, bishop, 1971. Asst. dir. Confrat. of Christian Doctrine, Archdiocese of St. Paul, 1952-58, dir., 1958-68; prof. catechetics St. Paul Sem., 1957-68; dir. dept. edn. U.S. Cath. Conf., Washington, 1969-71; consecrated bishop, 1971; aux. bishop of St. Paul and Mpls., 1971-76; bishop of New Ulm, Minn., 1976—. Author: Aims of Religious Education, 1966, Some Presuppositions on Released Time, 1969, My Experience: Reflections on Pastoring, 1988; contbg. author: Catholic Social Thought, 1990, The Universal Catechism Reader, 1990, Living the Vision, 1992. Recipient Nat. Catechetical award, 1991. Home: 1400 6th St N New Ulm MN 56073-2057 Office: Catholic Pastoral Ctr 1400 6th St N New Ulm MN 56073-2057

LUCKETT, PAUL HERBERT, III, manufacturing executive; b. El Paso, Tex., Feb. 6, 1935; s. Paul Herbert Jr. and Maxine (Mooney) L.; m. Caroline Foisie, Oct. 6, 1956 (div. Mar. 1991); children: Elizabeth Winkler, Christopher Lloyd; m. Cheryl Elaine Kanoff, June 15, 1991. BSChemE, MIT, 1956. Various positions El Paso Products Co., El Paso Co., 1956-69; exec. v.p. Beaunit Corp., El Paso Co., Raleigh, N.C. and N.Y.C., 1969-77; pres. Penn Athletic Co., Gencorp., Monroesville, Pa., 1977-82; pres. wallcovering divsn. Gencorp., Hanckensack, N.J., 1982-89; COO Insilco, Midland, Tex., 1989-91; dir. bus. devel. Wagner & Brown, Midland, 1991—; pres., CEO Flamecoat Systems, Inc., 1991-94; assoc. Bariston, Inc., West Palm Beach, Fla., 1994—. 2d lt. U.S. Army, 1957. Mem. Union League Club (N.Y.C.), Racquet Club (Midland), Delta Kappa Epsilon. Roman Catholic. Avocations: bicycling, hiking, snorkeling, tennis. Office: Bariston (USA) Inc 400 N Congress Ave West Palm Beach FL 33401-9999

LUCKEY, ROBERT REUEL RAPHAEL, retired academic administrator; b. Houghton, N.Y., Nov. 19, 1917; s. James Seymour and Edith Bedell (Curtis) L.; m. Ruth Ida Brooks, Aug. 25, 1945; children: James, John, Linda, Peter, Daniel (dec.), Thomas. BS, BA, Houghton Coll., 1937; MA, N.Y. U., 1939; PhD, Cornell U., 1942; LittD, Houghton Coll., 1980; LLD, Marion Coll., 1987. Secondary tchr. Wilson (N.Y.) Cen. Sch., 1937-39; math. & physics instr. Houghton Coll., 1942, assoc. prof., prof. math. and physics, alumni dir., 1954, dir. devel., v.p. in devel.; pres. Marion (Ind.) Coll., 1976-84, 1986-87. Pres. Seneca Council Boy Scouts Am., Olean, N.Y., 1964-65; assessor Township of Caneadea, N.Y., 1951-76. Recipient Silver Beaver award Boy Scouts Am., 1965; named Alumnus of Yr. Houghton Coll., 1976, Disting. Alumnus Houghton Coll., 1984, Sagamore of the Wabash by Gov. of Ind., 1980. Mem. Grant County C. of C. (bd. dirs. 1981-84). Republican. Wesleyan. Avocations: golfing, personal computers. Home: RR 1 Box 23A Houghton NY 14744-9718

LUCKING, PETER STEPHEN, marketing consultant, industrial engineer; b. Kalamazoo, Oct. 11, 1945; s. Henry William, Sr., and Mary (Lynn) L.; m. Marilyn Barbara Jensen, Dec. 18, 1971. BA, Western Mich. U., 1968; BS in Indsl. Engring., 1973. Indsl. engr. Motorola, Phoenix, 1974, Revlon, Inc, Phoenix, 1974-75; indsl. engr. Hooker Chem. and Plastics Co., Niagara Falls, N.Y., 1975-76, sr. corp. indsl. engr., 1976-77; indsl. engr. Carborundum Co., Niagara Falls, 1977-78; cons. H.B. Maynard and Co., Pitts., 1978-85; mgr. indsl. engring. Carrier, Tyler, Tex., 1985-88; cons. H.B. Maynard and Co., Pitts., 1988-92; pres., mktg. cons. MARPET Systems, Inc., 1992—; lectr. in field, 1989. Advisor, Jr. Achievement, Niagara Falls, 1977. Author chpts. to books. Served with U.S. Army, 1969-70, Vietnam. Mem. Inst. Indsl. Engrs. (sr. mem., region v.p. 1983-85), Inst. Indsl. Engrs. (pres. Niagara Frontier chpt. 1977-78, paper presented fall conf.). Democrat. Roman Catholic. Home: 12826 Weatherstone Dr Florissant MO 63033-4045 Office: MARPET Systems Inc 11220 W Flossant Ste 141 Saint Louis MO 63033

LUCKING, ROBERT A., English literature educator; b. Beatrice, Nebr., Aug. 27, 1946; s. Alfred and Nora (Peters) L. BS, U. Nebr., 1968, PhD, 1975; EdS, Vanderbilt U., 1970. Prof. Valparaiso (Ind.) U., 1976-84, Old Dominion U., Norfolf, Va., 1984—. Fulbright scholar to Denmark, 1975, Fulbright scholar to India, 1982. Mem. Nat. Coun. Tchrs. of English (chmn. internat. concerns). Home: 4754 River Shore Dr Portsmouth VA 23703 Office: Old Donimion Univ 5215 Hampton Blvd Norfolk VA 23529-0161

LUCKMAN, CHARLES, architect; b. Kansas City, Mo., May 16, 1909; m. Harriet McElroy, 1931; children: Charles, James M., Stephen A. Grad. magna cum laude, U. Ill., 1931; LLD, U. Miami, Fla., 1950; AFD (hon.), Calif. Coll. Arts and Crafts, 1958; DFA (hon.), Adelphi U., 1986; LLD (hon.), Pepperdine U., 1989. Lic. architect, 1931 Registered architect, 48 states and D.C. sr. registration Nat. Archtl. Registration Bds. Employed in architect's office for license qualifications, 2 years; joined Colgate- Palmolive- Peet Co. as retail salesman, 1931, Chgo. sales supr. 1933; mgr. Colgate- Palmolive-Peet Co. as retail salesman (Wis. dist.), 1934; divisional mgr. Colgate- Palmolive-Peet Co. as retail salesman (Cin. hdqrs.), 1935; with Pepsodent Co. (later Pepsodent Div. of Lever Bros. Co.), 1935-50, sales promotion mgr., sales mgr., 1935-36, v.p. in charge sales, 1936, in charge sales and advt., 1937, v.p., gen. mgr., 1938, exec. v.p., 1942-43, pres., 1943-46; exec. v.p. Lever Bros., Jan.-July 1946, pres., 1946-50; pres., partner Pereira & Luckman, Los Angeles, 1950-58; founder, ptnr. The Luckman Partnership, Inc., 1958—; chmn. bd., chief exec. officer Ogden Devel. Corp., 1968-74, Luckman Mgmt. Co., 1973—; dir. Hollywood Bowl. Maj. projects include Madison Sq. Garden, N.Y.C., Conv. and Exhbn. Center, Los Angeles, U.S. World's Fair Pavilion, N.Y.C., Los Angeles World Zoo, U. Calif. at Santa

Barbara, Civic Plaza, Phoenix, Prudential Center, Boston, State Office Bldg. Madison, Wis., Phoenix Civic Plaza, Los Angeles Internat. Airport, First Nat. Bank of Ariz, Phoenix, Broadway Plaza, Los Angeles, United Calif. Bank, Los Angeles, U. Del. Student Living Center, La Jolla VA Hosp, Aloha Stadium, Honolulu, 9200 Sunset Tower, Los Angeles, Manned Space Craft Center, Houston, VA Hosp, West Los Angeles, Calif., Hoover Library and Linear Accelerator Center, Stanford U., 1st Natl Bank of Oreg, Portland, Forum, Inglewood, Calif., Ralph M. Parsons Co. hdqrs, Pasadena, Calif., Nat. Security and Resources Study Center, Los Alamos, Hyatt Regency Hotels, Dearborn, Mich., Phoenix, City Hall and Police Bldg., Inglewood, Xerox Corp. hdqrs., Stamford, Conn., Warner Bros. Office Bldg., Burbank, Calif., Orange County Conv./Civic Ctr., Orlando, Fla.; also numerous other pub. bldgs; author: (autobiography) Twice in a Lifetime, 1988. Pres., chmn. bd. Los Angeles Orchestral Soc., 1962; v.p., dir. So. Calif. Symphony Assn.; mem. bd. assocs., pres. council George Pepperdine Found., Los Angeles; trustee Calif. State Colls.; chmn. bd. trustees, 1963-65; bd. govs. Library Presdl. Papers; trustee Nat. Art Mus. Sport; mem. U. Ill. Found.; Calif. mem. Ednl. Commn. of States; mem. bd. Am. Nat. Red Cross, YMCA; bd. dirs., past pres. AID-United Givers.; Mem. Pres.'s Commn. on Equality of Treatment and Opportunity in Armed Services and Civil Rights, Gov.'s Commn. Met. Area Problems; dir. Advt. Council; trustee Adelphi U.; chmn. Citizens Food Com., 1947; mem. Commerce and Industry Assn. N.Y.C., Los Angeles World Affairs Council, Com. Econ. Devel., Council U.S. Assocs. of Internat. C. of C.; bd. dirs. Nat. Adv. Council Community Chest, Am. Heritage Found.; bd. assocs. Northwestern U., Calif. Inst. Tech.; chmn. Nat. Council Trustees of Freedoms Found. at Valley Forge, 1986. Decorated Star of Solidarity Republic of Italy; chevalier Nat. Order Legion of Honor France; Order of St. John; recipient Horatio Alger award Am. Schs. and Colls. Assn., George Washington Honor medal Freedom's Found., 1964, 67, 68, Make Am. Beautiful award Nat. Assn. Realty Bds.; named Outstanding Mgmt. Exec. N.Y. Mgmt. Club, Man of Year Constrn. Industries, 1974; Disting. Achievement award U. Ill., 1970; Henry Laurence Gantt medal Am. Mgmt. Assn. and ASMF, 1981. Mem. AIA (Fellowship award 1963), Ill. Soc. Architects, U.S. Jr. C. of C. (One of Outstanding Young Men 1945, dir.), Tau Beta Pi, Theta Tau, Gargoyle. Home and Office: The Luckman Management Co 9220 W Sunset Blvd West Hollywood CA 90069-3501

LUCKMAN, SHARON GERSTEN, arts administrator; b. Sioux City, Iowa, Oct. 10, 1945; d. Robert S. and Libbie (Izen) Gersten; m. Peter Luckman, Nov. 22, 1968 (div. 1979); children: Melissa, Gregory; m. Paul Shapiro, Dec. 13, 1981. BS, U. Wis., 1967; cert. Inst. Not-For-Profit Mgmt., Columbia U. 1982. Dir. 92nd St YM/YHA Dance Ctr., N.Y.C., 1978-86; dir. devel. & new ventures Twyla Tharp Dance Found., N.Y.C., 1986-87, exec. dir., 1988; dir. Vol. Lawyers for the Arts, N.Y.C., 1988—; dance tchr. 92nd St. Y, N.Y.C., 1963-78, Nassau Community Coll., Garden City, N.Y., 1963-78, Long Beach (N.Y.) Pub. Schs., 1963-78; dir. Brant Lake (N.Y.) Dance and Sports Ctr., 1980-86. Chairperson Laban/Bartenieff Inst. Movement Studies, N.Y.C., 1984-87. Democrat. Jewish. Avocations: tennis, skiing, rollerblading. Office: Volunteer Lawyers for Arts 1285 Ave of the Ams 3d Fl New York NY 10019

LUCKNER, HERMAN RICHARD, III, interior designer; b. Newark, Ohio, Mar. 14, 1933; s. Herman Richard and Helen (Friednour) L. BS, U. Cin., 1957. Cert. interior designer and appraiser. Interior designer Greiwe Inc., Cin., 1957-64; owner, internat. designer Designers Loft Interiors, Cin., 1964—; owner Designer Accents, Cin., 1991—. Mem. bd. adv. Ohio Valley Organ Procurement Ctr., Cin., 1987—, U. Cin. Fine Arts Collection and Hist. Southwest Ohio. Mem. Am. Soc. Interior Designers, Appraisers Assn. Am., Metropolitan Club. Republican. Avocations: needlepoint, collecting 18th century Chinese porcelain. Home and Office: 555 Compton Rd Cincinnati OH 45231-5005

LUCKOVICH, MIKE, cartoonist; b. Seattle, 1960. BS, U. Wash., 1982. Cartoonist Greenville (S.C.) News; editorial cartoonist New Orleans Times- Picayune, 1984-89, Atlanta Constitution, 1989—. Recipient Pulitzer Prize nomination, 1986, Overseas Press Club award, 1989, Nat. Headliner award Press Club of Atlantic City, 1991, Pulitzer for editorial cartooning, 1995. Office: Atlanta Journal-Constitution 72 Marietta St NW Atlanta GA 30303*

LUCKOW, LYNN D. W., publishing executive; b. Hettinger, N.D. 1949. Grad. U. N.D., 1971, Ind. U., 1974. Pres., pub. Jossey-Bass Inc. Pub., San Francisco. Home: 666 Post St San Francisco CA 94109-8232 Office: Jossey-Bass Inc Pub 350 Sansome St Fl 5 San Francisco CA 94104-1304*

LUCKY, ANNE WEISSMAN, dermatologist; b. N.Y.C., May 11, 1944; d. Jacob and Gertrude (Tetelman) Weissman; m. Paul A. Lucky, May 19, 1972; children: Jennifer, Andrea. BA, Brown U., 1966; MD, Yale U., 1970. Diplomate Nat. Bd. Med. Examiners, Am. Bd. Pediatrics/subspecialty of pediatric endocrinology, Am. Bd. Dermatology. Intern and resident in pediatrics The Children's Hosp. Med. Ctr., Boston, 1970-73; fellow in human genetics and pediatrics Yale U. Sch. Medicine, New Haven, Conn., 1973-74; resident in dermatology Yale U. Sch. Medicine, 1979-81, instr. pediatrics, 1980-81, assoc. prof. dermatology and pediatrics, 1981-83; clin. assoc. Reprodn. Rsch. Br./Nat. Inst. Child Health/NIH, Bethesda, Md., 1974-76; asst. prof. pediatrics Wyler Children's Hosp./Pritzker Sch. Med./U. Chgo. Hosps., 1976-79; assoc. prof. dermatology, pediatrics U. Cin. Coll. Medicine, 1983-88; pvt. practice Dermatology Assocs. of Cin, Inc., 1988—; pres. Dermatology Rsch. Assocs., Inc., Cin., 1988—; dir. Dermatology Clinic Children's Hosp. Med. Ctr., Cin., 1989—; adj. assoc. prof. dermatology and pediatrics, U. Cin. Coll. Medicine, 1988-94. Editorial bd. Pediatric Dermatology, 1982—, Archives of Dermatology, 1983-94; contbr. numerous articles to profl. jours., publs. Recipient the Janet M. Glasgow Meml. Scholarship, Am. Women's Med. Assn., 1970, the Ramsey Meml. Scholarship award Yale U. Sch. Medicine, 1968, others; grantee USPHS, 1964-66, 67, 68-70, NIH, 1977-79, 79-82, 82-87, 84-87, 87-93, others. Mem. The Lawson Wilkins Pediatric Endocrine Soc., Soc. for Pediatric Dermatology (bd. dirs. 1984-87, pres. 1990-91), Am. Acad. Dermatology, Soc. Investigative Dermatology, Soc. for Dermatologic Genetics of the Am. Acad. Dermatology, Endocrine Soc., Acad. of Medicine/Cin., Women's Faculty Assn./The Children's Hosp. Med. Ctr., The Women's Derm. Soc. (bd. dirs. 1993—), Ohio State Med. Assn., Soc. Pediatric Rsch., Cin. Derm. Soc., Sigma Xi, Phi Beta Kappa, Alpha Omega Alpha. Office: Derm Assocs of Cin 7691 Five Mile Rd Cincinnati OH 45230

LUCKY, ROBERT WENDELL, electrical engineer; b. Pitts., Jan. 9, 1936; s. Clyde Arthur and Grace Katherine (Luck) L.; m. Joan Miriam Jackson, Aug. 19, 1961; children: David William, Karen Joan. BSEE, Purdue U., 1957, MS, 1959, PhD, 1961, hon. doctorate, 1988; hon. doctorate, N.J. Inst. Tech., 1991. With Bell Telephone Labs., Holmdel, N.J., 1961—; supr. signal theory Bell Telephone Labs., 1964-65, head dept. advanced data communications, 1965-76, dir. Electronic and Computer Systems Research Lab., 1977-81, exec. dir. research Communications Scis. Div., 1982-92; v.p. applied rsch. Bellcore, 1992—; mem. engring. adv. bd. Purdue U., 1973-75; mem. USAF Sci. Adv. Bd., 1979—, vice chmn., 1983-86, chmn., 1986-89; mem. adv. com. NSF, 1983-85; bd. dirs. Engring. Index, 1984-86; mem. engring. adv. bd. Bradley U., 1979-84, U. Calif.-Santa Barbara, 1980—. Author: Principles of Data Communication, 1968, Silicon Dreams, 1989, Lucky Strike Again, 1993; editor: Proc. of IEEE, 1974-76, Computer Communication, 1975; cons. editor: Plenum Press, 1979—. Bd. dirs. Computer Mus., Boston, 1985—. Named Distinguished Alumnus Purdue U., 1969; Marconi Internat. Fellowship prize, 1987. Fellow IEEE (v.p. 1978-79, exec. v.p. 1980-81, publs. bd. 1970-76, bd. govs. info. theory group 1969-74); mem. NAE (computer tech. bd. 1986-90, printing com. bd., 1991—, commn. on phys. scis. 1991—), Am. Acad. Arts and Scis., European Acad. Arts and Scis., Communications Soc. (pres. 1977-79, Achievement award 1975), Eta Kappa Nu (nat. dir. 1974-76). Patentee in field. Home: 48 Gillespie Ave Fair Haven NJ 07704-3309 Office: Bell Core 331 Newman Springs Rd Red Bank NJ 07701*

LUCOW, MILTON, lawyer; b. Detroit, Oct. 4, 1924; s. Louis and Dora (Schupps) L.; m. Audrey B. Kline, Mar. 30, 1947; children: Celia (Mrs. James Stegman), Michael B. LLD, Wayne State U., 1948. Bar: Mich. bar 1948. Since practiced in Detroit; ptnr., pres. firm Garan, Lucow, Miller, Seward & Cooper (P.C.), Detroit, 1948—; lectr. in field; mediator Wayne

Circuit Ct. Mich., 1973—. Pres. Detroit Svc. Group, 1983-87; bd. dirs. Jewish Welfare Fedn. Detroit; pres. Temple Emanu-El, 1960-62; chmn. Madrasha Coll. Jewish Learning, 1977-80, United Found., atty.'s sec., 1985; pres. United Hebrew Schs. Detroit, 1974-77. Sgt. U.S. Army, 1943-45, ETO. Decorated Purple Heart, Metz medal, Bronze Star. Mem. ABA, Am. Arbitration Assn. (arbitrator), Detroit Bar Assn., Mich. Bar Assn. (mem. del. assembly 1979-80), Def. Rsch. Inst. Tam-O-Shanter Club (pres. 1979-72), Longboat Key Club. Avocations: golf, tennis, squash. Home: 7529 Danbury Dr West Bloomfield MI 48322-3564 Office: Garan Lucow Miller Seward & Cooper 1000 Woodbridge St Detroit MI 48207-3117

LUCY, DENNIS DURWOOD, JR., neurologist; b. Little Rock, July 3, 1934; s. Dennis Durwood and Ann Louise (Besiegel) L.; m. Patricia Wilch, Nov. 26, 1958; children: Stephen H., Vincent A., Denise D., David D. B.S., U. Ark., 1959, M.D., 1959. Diplomate: Am. Bd. Psychiatry and Neurology. Intern U. Ark. Med. Scis., 1959-60, resident in internal medicine, 1960-62, resident in psychiatry, 1962-63; resident in neurology U. Iowa Hosp., 1963-64, 65-66; instr., acting head dept. neurology U. Ark., 1964-65, prof., 1974—, chmn. dept. neurology, 1966-94; mem. exec. com. U. Ark. Coll. Medicine, 1979-83, chmn. council Departmental Chairmen, 1980-81; chief of staff Univ. Hosp., 1973-76. Bd. dirs. Ark. chpt. Multiple Sclerosis Soc., 1965-78; mem. Ark. Council Devel. Disabilities, 1971-74; bd. dirs. Ark. chpt. Epilepsy Soc., 1972-76; bd. dirs. Holy Souls Cath. Sch., 1974-77, pres. bd., 1976-77. Recipient Golden Apple award U. Ark., 1968-69. Mem. AMA, Am. Acad. Neurology, Ark. Med. Soc., Pulaski County Med. Soc., Alpha Omega Alpha. Roman Catholic. Home: 17 Robinwood Little Rock AR 72207-2241 Office: 4301 W Markham St Little Rock AR 72205-7101

LUCY, ROBERT MEREDITH, lawyer; b. Poplar Bluff, Mo., Apr. 16, 1926; s. James Raymond and Lucile Hargrove (Meredith) L.; m. Mary White George, June 10, 1947; children—Meredith Lucy Knight, Celia Lucy Denton, John Rackley, Robert Meredith Jr. BS, U.S. Naval Acad., 1947; JD, George Washington U., 1954, MS in Internat. Affairs, 1968. Bar: Mo. 1954, D.C. 1954. Commd. 2d lt. USMC, 1947; advanced through grades to col., 1974; student Air War Coll. Maxwell AFB, Montgomery, Ala., 1967-68; staff judge adv. 1st Marine Div., Danang, Vietnam, 1969-70; asst. for legal affairs Office Asst. Sec. Navy for Manpower and Res. Affairs, Washington, 1970-71; legal advisor, legis. asst. to chmn. Joint Chiefs of Staff, Washington, 1971-74; ret., 1974; ptnr. Bryan Cave, St. Louis, 1974—; chmn. litigation dept. Bryan, Cave, St. Louis, 1992-94, vice chmn., 1994—. Decorated Bronze Star, Legion of Merit (3). Mem. ABA (litigation sect.), TechLaw Group (pres. 1994—). Presbyterian. Home: 38 Picardy Ln Saint Louis MO 63124-1628 Office: Bryan Cave 1 Metropolitan Sq Saint Louis MO 63102-2750

LUDDEN, DAVID, Asian studies educator. Student, Yale U., 1966-70; BA, MA in South Asia Regional Studies, U. Pa., 1972, PhD in History, 1978. Asst. prof. of history U. Va., 1979-80; asst. prof. history and South Asia regional studies U. Pa., Phila., 1981-87, assoc. prof., 1987—, chmn. grad. group, 1991—, chmn. dept. South Asia regional studies, 1992—; presenter in field. Author monographs; translator: The Kuruntokai: An Anthology of Classical Tamil Love Poetry in Translation, 1976; editor vol.: Agricultural Production Systems, 1994; series edior Critical Histories, 1993—; contbr. articles to profl. jours. Nat. Def. Fgn. Lang. fellow, 1971-74, NEH fellow for univ. faculty, 1990; Social Sci. Rsch. Coun. Rsch. grantee, 1974, 85, 86, NEH Translation grantee, 1978-81, U. Pa. Summer Rsch. grantee, 1982, U. Pa. Rsch. Found. grantee, 1983, 86, Fulbright-Hayes Rsch. grantee, 1984, AIIS Short-Term Rsch. grantee, 1987, NEH Travel grantee, 1988, Pew Meml. Trust grantee, 1992, Am. Inst. Indian Studies grantee, 1992. Mem. Assn. Asian Studies (mem. exec. com. South Asia microfilm project 1992—, mem. South Asia coun. 1994—), Social Sci. Rsch. Coun./ACLS (mem. joint com. on South Asia 1991—, mem. ctrl. selection com. 1992). Office: U Pa History Dept 207 College Hall Philadelphia PA 19104-6379 also: U Pa S Asia Regional Studies 820 Williams Hall Philadelphia PA 19104-6305

LUDDEN, JOHN FRANKLIN, financial economist; b. Michigan City, Ind., May 6, 1930. BS in Econs., U. Wis., 1952, MS in Econs., 1955; postgrad., U. Mich., 1955-59. Wage and hour investigator U.S. Dept. Labor, 1960, mgmt. intern, 1960-61, labor economist, 1963; economist, instr. U.S. Bur. of Labor Statis., 1961-63; economist Office of Internat. Ops. IRS, 1963-68, fin. economist Audit div., 1968-86, fin. economist Office of the Asst. Commr. Internat., 1986—. With U.S. Army, 1952-54. Recipient Spl. Svc. award U.S. Dept. of Treasury, 1967, 68, Spl. Achievement award U.S. 1984, Spl. Svc. award, 1987, Spl. Act award, 1990. Mem. Am. Econ. Assn.

LUDENIA, KRISTA, psychologist, health facility administrator; b. Alexandria, Minn., Dec. 20, 1942; d. Dell John and Ethel Agnes (Balder) L.; children: Peter Jonathan, John Thomas, Kristin Ashley. BA, BS, Quincy Coll., 1967; MS, Ind. U., 1969; PhD, U. Mo., 1972. With VA Med. Ctr., 1972—, asst. chief alcohol and drug unit, Danville, Ill., 1972-74, clin. psychologist, St. Cloud, Minn., 1974-76, coordinator mental hygiene clinic, 1976-78, chief psychology service, Wichita, Kans., 1978-80, chief psychology service, Bay Pines, Fla., 1980-82, health systems adminstr., St. Louis, 1982-84, assoc. med. ctr. dir., Danville, 1984-86, Boston, 1986-88, med. ctr. dir., Ft. Wayne, Ind., 1988-89, Saginaw, Mich., 1989-92, Cleve, 1992—. Recipient Dir.'s Commendation for EEO, 1978, Leadership award VA, 1978, 1979, VA Dir.'s Commendation, 1981, 1982, 84-88, 92. Mem. APA, Am. Coll. Healthcare Exexs., Nat. Register Health Care Providers. Office: VA Med Ctr 10000 Brecksville Rd Brecksville OH 44141

LUDERS, ADAM, ballet dancer; b. Copenhagen, Feb. 16, 1950; came to U.S., 1975; s. Sten Otto and Hanne Marie (Jansen) L. Student, Royal Danish Ballet Sch. Mem., Royal Danish Ballet Co., 1968-72, prin. dancer, London Festival Ballet Co., 1972-75, N.Y.C. Ballet Co., 1975-94; TV appearance in Choreography by Balanchine; guest artist TV appearance in, Paris Opera Ballet Co., Royal Danish Ballet Co., tour of, Japan, 1979, appearance at, White House, 1978. Office: NYC Ballet Co NY State Theater Lincoln Ctr Plz New York NY 10023 Although the road to becoming a successful dancer is hard and never ending, I have been fortunate in many respects: I have the Bournonville tradition in teaching and performing as a sound basis for my technique, and the choreography of George Balanchine.

LUDGIN, CHESTER HALL, baritone, actor; b. N.Y.C., May 20, 1925; s. Michael and Dora Josephine L. Student, Lafayette Coll., 1943, Am. Theatre Wing Profl. Tng. Program, 1948-50. Premiere leading baritone roles in: The Crucible, 1961, The Golem, 1962, Angle of Repose, 1976, A Quiet Place, 1983; appeared in major opera houses throughout the world, including San Francisco Opera Co., N.Y.C. Opera Co., Netherlands Opera, La Scala Opera, Vienna State Opera; singing actor in: musical comedies including Kismet, summer 1972, Most Happy Fella, summer 1977, Shenandoah, summer, 1978, Student Prince, summer 1980, South Pacific, summer 1981, Fanny, summer 1986. Co-chmn. exec. com. Norman Treigle Meml. Fund, 1975—. Served with inf. U.S. Army, 1943-46. Mem. Am. Guild Musical Artists, Actors Equity, AGVA, AFTRA. Home: 205 West End Ave New York NY 10023-4804 Office: care Thea Dispeker Artists Rep 59 E 54th St New York NY 10022-4211 In observing many of my colleagues in the performing arts as well as those in other walks of life, I long ago came to the conclusion that it is wiser and more personally fulfilling to avoid compromising one's principles in the hope of advancing one's career. If there is truly a talent present, the act of quietly going about one's business with maximum efficiency makes the ultimate statement. Awareness by others of that talent inevitably follows.

LUDGUS, NANCY LUCKE, lawyer; b. Palo Alto, Calif., Oct. 28, 1953; d. Winston Slover and Betty Jean (Brilhart) Lucke; m. Lawrence John Ludgus, Apr. 8, 1983. BA in Polit. Sci. with highest honors, U. Calif., Berkeley, 1975; JD, U. Calif., Davis, 1978. Bar: Calif. 1978, U.S. Dist. Ct. (no. dist.) Calif. 1978. Staff atty. Crown Zellerbach Corp. San Francisco, 1978-80, Clorox Co., Oakland, Calif., 1980-82; staff atty. Nat. Semiconductor Corp., Santa Clara, Calif., 1982-85, corp. counsel, 1985-92, sr. corp. counsel, asst. sec., 1992—. Sec. Nat. Semiconductor Employees Polit. Action Com., Santa Clara, 1992—. Mem. ABA, Am. Corp. Counsel Assn., Calif. State Bar Assn., Phi Beta Kappa. Democrat. Avocations: travel, jogging, opera. Office: Nat Semiconductor Corp 1090 Kifer Rd M/S 16-135 Sunnyvale CA 94086

LUDINGTON, CHARLES TOWNSEND, JR., English and American studies educator; b. Bryn Mawr, Pa., Jan. 31, 1936; s. Charles Townsend and Constance (Cameron) L.; m. Jane Ross, Feb. 22, 1958; children: David, Charles, James, Sarah. BA, Yale U., 1957; MA, Duke U., 1964; PhD, Duke U., 1967. Tchr. English Ransom Sch., Miami, Fla., 1960-62; from asst. prof. to prof. English U. N.C., Chapel Hill, 1967-78, Cary C. Boshamer prof. English and Am. Studies, 1982—, chair Am. studies curriculum, 1986—; part-time instr. Duke U., 1963-66; resident scholar U.S. Internat. Communication Agy., 1980-81; vis. prof. U.S. Mil. Acad., West Point, N.Y., 1988-89. Author: John Dos Passos, 1980 (Mayflower award 1981), Marsden Hartley, 1992; editor: The Fourteenth Chronicle, 1973. 1st lt. USMCR, 1957-60. Recipient Outstanding Svc. medal U.S. Army, 1988-89; Fulbright fellow, 1971-72, Nat. Humanities Ctr. fellow, 1985-86. Mem. Am. Studies Assn. South Atlantic MLA, PEN. Democrat. Avocations: tennis, golf, reading. Office: U NC Curriculum in Am Studies Greenlaw Hall CB# 3520 Chapel Hill NC 27599-3520

LUDINGTON, JOHN SAMUEL, manufacturing company executive; b. Detroit, May 7, 1928; s. Samuel and Fredda (Holden) L.; m. Dorothy Lamson, Feb. 14, 1953; children: Thomas, Laura, Ann. BS in Econs, Albion (Mich.) Coll., 1951, D. of Econs. (hon.), 1989; LLD (hon.), Saginaw Valley State Coll.; DBA (hon.), S.D. Sch. Mines and Tech.; HHD (hon.), Northwood Inst.; PhD in Econs. (hon.), Albion Coll. With Dow Corning Corp., Midland, Mich., chmn.; dir. Comerica Bank-Midland. Trustee Albion Coll., former chmn. bd.; trustee Midland Community Ctr., Strosacker Found. Served with AUS. Methodist. Office: Dow Corning Corp PO Box 994 Midland MI 48686

LUDLAM, JAMES EDWARD, lawyer; b. Portland, Oreg., Nov. 26, 1914; s. James Edward and Bernice (Ayers) L.; m. Jane Hyde, Sept. 27, 1941; children—James Edward III, Charles E. B.A., Stanford U., 1936; J.D., Harvard U., 1939. Bar: Calif. 1940. Assoc. Musick & Burrell, 1940-41, 44-53; ptnr. Musick, Peeler & Garrett, Los Angeles, 1954—, now sr. ptnr. Mem. governing bd. Nat. Health Found., Calif. Civic Light Opera Assn., Los Angeles Civic Light Opera. Served as lt. USN, 1941-44. Recipient award of merit Calif. Hosp. Assn., 1970; Trustee award Am. Hosp. Assn., 1976. Fellow Am. Coll. Hosp. Adminstrs. (hon.), Am. Coll. Legal Medicine (hon.), Am. Bar Found.; mem. ABA, State Bar Calif., Am. Soc. Hosp. Attys., Harvard Law Sch. Assn. So. Calif. Republican. Contbr. articles to health care jours. Home: 519 S Orange Grove Blvd Apt 30 Pasadena CA 91105-1708 Office: Musick Peeler & Garrett 1 Wilshire Blvd Ste 2000 Los Angeles CA 90017-3806

LUDLAM, JAMES EDWARD, III, insurance company executive; b. L.A., Jan. 9, 1943; s. James Edward and Jane Bramen (Hyde) L.; m. Mary Patricia McVee, Apr. 12, 1969; children—Jay, Erin. B.A. in Econs., Claremont McKenna Coll., 1965. M.B.A. U. So. Calif. 1967. Vice pres. group pensions Prudential Ins. Co., Florham Park, N.J., 1968-82; sr. v.p. Home Life Ins. Co., N.Y.C., 1982-90; v.p. employer sponsored plans Security Life of Denver, Denver, 1991-93; pres. CEO First ING Life of N.Y., 1993-94; pres., COO Rocky Mountain Life Ins. Co., Denver, 1994—. Mem. corp. United Way, Morris County, N.J., 1980-91; campaign exec. United Way, Denver, 1991—; bd. dirs. Mile High United Way, 1995—. Democrat. Presbyterian. Avocations: reading; investing; golf; rafting.

LUDLUM, DAVID BLODGETT, pharmacologist, educator; b. N.Y.C., Sept. 30, 1929; s. C. Daniel and Elsie B. (Blodgett) L.; B.A., Cornell U., 1951; Ph.D., U. Wis., 1954; M.D., N.Y.U., 1962; m. Carlene L. Dyke, Dec. 23, 1952; children—Valerie Jean Ludlum Wright, Kenneth David. Research scientist Dupont Co., Wilmington, Del., 1954-58; intern Bellevue Hosp., N.Y.C., 1962-63; asst. prof. pharmacology Yale U., 1963-68; assoc. prof. U. Md., 1968-70, prof., 1970-76; prof. pharmacology Albany (N.Y.) Med. Coll., 1976-86 , chmn. dept. pharmacology, 1976-80, prof. medicine, 1980-86, dir. oncology research, 1980-86; prof. pharmacology and medicine U. Mass. Med. Sch., 1986—; adj. prof. chemistry Rensselaer Poly. Inst., Troy, N.Y., 1977-80; vis. prof. oncology Johns Hopkins U., 1973-76; vis. prof. Courtauld Inst., London, 1970. WARF fellow, 1951-52; NSF fellow, 1952-54; Am. Heart Assn. fellow, 1960-62; grantee in field; recipient NIH Research Career Devel. award 1968; Markle scholar in acad. medicine, 1967-72; lic. physician, N.Y., Conn., Md. Mem. Am. Soc. Pharmacology and Exptl. Therapeutics, Am. Soc. Clin. Pharmacology and Therapeutics, Am. Assn. Cancer Research, Am. Soc. Biochem. and Molecular Biology, Am. Chem. Soc., Phi Beta Kappa, Sigma Xi, Phi Kappa Phi, Alpha Omega Alpha. Assoc. editor Cancer Rsch., 1980-87, 89—; contbr. articles to profl. jours.; patentee in field. Home: 24 Linda Ct Delmar NY 12054-3512 Office: U Mass Med Sch Worcester MA 01655

LUDLUM, ROBERT, author; b. N.Y.C., May 25, 1927; s. George Hartford and Margaret (Wadsworth) L.; m. Mary Ryducha, March 31, 1951; children: Michael R., Jonathan C., Glynis J. BA with distinction, Wesleyan U., 1951. Actor Broadway, TV, 1952-60; prodr. No. Jersey Playhouse, Ft. Lee, 1957-60, N.Y.C., 1960-69, Playhouse-on-the-Mall, Paramus, N.J., 1960-70; novelist, 1969—. Author: The Scarlatti Inheritance, 1971, The Osterman Weekend, 1972, The Matlock Paper, 1973, Trevayne, 1973, The Cry of the Halidon, 1974, The Rhinemann Exchange, 1974, The Road to Gandolfo, 1975, The Gemini Contenders, 1976, The Chancellor Manuscript, 1977, The Holcroft Covenant, 1978, The Matarese Circle, 1979, The Bourne Identity, 1980, The Parsifal Mosaic, 1982, The Aquitaine Progression, 1984, The Bourne Supremacy, 1986, The Icarus Agenda, 1988, The Bourne Ultimatum, 1990, The Road to Omaha, 1992, The Scorpio Illusion, 1993, The Apocalypse Watch, 1995. Served with USMC, World War II. Recipient Scroll of Achievement Am. Nat. Theatre and Acad., 1960. Mem. Authors Guild. Office: care Henry Morrison Inc PO Box 235 Bedford Hills NY 10507*

LUDOVICI, ANTHONY, security investment executive; b. Bronxville, N.Y., June 11, 1927; s. Angelo and Mary (Santucci) L.; m. Matilda Margaret Mary McCormick, Apr. 8, 1961; 1 child, Michael Anthony. Student, NYU. Trainee Baker Weeks & Co., 1949-53; analyst A.M. Kidder, 1954-64; dir. rsch. Gude Winmill & Co., N.Y.C., 1964-70, Peter P. McDermott & Co., N.Y.C., 1970-73; mgr. rsch. dept. Wood Walker & Co., N.Y.C., 1973-74; v.p., sr. investment analyst Tucker Anthony Inc., N.Y.C., 1974-84, sr. v.p., sr. investment analyst, 1984—. Sr. editor Market Chronicle. Chmn. Eastchester Narcotics Coun., 1970-74, Office Drug Abuse Eastchester, 1970-76, feasibility com. to purchase country club for Eastchester, 1979, recreation commn., Eastchester, 1982-84; rep. on Westchester County Urban Devel. Adv. Group, Eastchester, 1978-79; mem. blue ribbon panel to study feasibility of Westchester County owned electric utility, 1980; mem. Rep. Com. Westchester County and Town Eastchester. Recipient Town Eastchester Appreciation award Westchester County Proclomation. Mem. Nat. Assn. Petroleum Analysts, Oil Analyst Group N.Y., Diversified Industry Analysts, Elec. Equipment Analyst Group, Auto Analyst Group, Lake Isle Country Club (chmn. bd. 1980-84), Westchester County Med. Ctr. (bd. dirs. 1987), N.Y. Soc. Security Analysts, Fin. Analysts Fedn., Am. Stock Exch. Club (charter, membership com.), VFW, Kiwanis (past pres.). Office: Tucker Anthony Inc One World financial Ctr 200 Liberty St New York NY 10281

LUDTKE, JAMES BUREN, business and finance educator; b. Waterloo, Iowa, Mar. 4, 1924; s. Henry George and Eteska (Buren) L.; m. Jean Seaver Edwards, Sept. 8, 1948; children—Melissa, Leslie, Mark, Betty, Rebecca. Student, Iowa Tchrs. Coll., 1942-43, N.W. Mo. State Tchrs. Coll., 1943-44; B.A., State U. Iowa, 1947, M.A., 1948, Ph.D., 1951. Instr. econs. U. Iowa, 1947-51; mem. faculty U. Mass., Amherst, 1951-86, prof. fin., 1960-86, chmn. dept. gen. bus. and fin., 1958-70. Author: The American Financial System: Markets and Institutions, 2d edit, 1967. Served with USNR, 1943-46. Sloan fellow Mass. Inst. Tech., 1961-62; Ford Found. faculty fellow Harvard U., summers 1961, 66. Mem. Am. Fin. Assn., Fin. Mgmt. Assn., AAUP (pres. Mass. state conf. 1977-80, treas. Assembly of State Confs. 1980-82). Home: 30 Wachusett Hyannis Port MA 02647-9999

LUDWIG, ALLAN IRA, photographer, author; b. N.Y.C., June 9, 1933; s. Daniel and Honey (Fox) L.; m. Janine Lowell, Aug., 1955 (div. 1991); children: Katherine Arabella, Pamela Vanessa, Adam Lowell; m. Gwendolyn Akin, 1992; children: Allan B. Ludwig Jr., Alison Ludwig. BFA, Yale U., 1956, MA, 1962, PhD, 1964. Instr., R.I. Sch. Design, 1956-58; asst. instr. Yale U., 1958-64; asst. prof. Dickinson Coll., 1964-65; assoc. prof., 1965-68; assoc. prof. Syracuse U., 1968-69; pres. Automated Communications, Inc.,

Verona, N.J., 1969-75; dir. Ludwig Portfolios, 1975-90; mem. exec. bd. Alternative Mus. N.Y.C., 1978-88, chmn. bd. dirs., 1982-83; cons. presses U. Mass., U. Ga., Boston Mus. Fine Arts, Smithsonian Instn. Author: Graven Images: New England Stonecarving and its Symbols, 1966; author exhbn. catalogues; one-person shows include: Silvermine (Conn.) Guild of Art, 1955, Davison Art Ctr., Wesleyan U., Middletown, Conn., 1961, Portland Mus. of Art, Portland, 1962, Met. Mus. and Art Ctrs., Miami, Fla., 1976, Jorgenson Art Gallery, U. Conn., Storrs, 1976, Alternative Mus., N.Y.C., 1977, Watson Art Gallery, Norton, Mass., 1978, Alonzo Gallery, N.Y.C., 1978, 79, Cayman Gallery, N.Y.C., 1980, Il Diaframma, Milan, Italy, 1981, Simon Gallery, Montclair, N.J., 1983, art gallery Farleigh Dickinson U., Madison, N.J., 1984, Ctr. for Creative Photography, Tucson, 1986, The Twining Gallery, N.Y.C., 1986, Cepa Gallery, Buffalo, The Shadai Gallery, Tokyo Inst. of Tech, Tokyo, 1987, White Columns, N.Y.C., 1988, O'Kane Gallery, Houston, 1988, Farideh Cadot Gallery, N.Y.C., 1988, XYZ Gallery, Ghent, Belgium, 1989, Northlight Gallery, 1990, Ariz. State U., Tempe, 1990, Galerie Farideh Cadot, Paris, 1990, Pamela Auchincloss Gallery, N.Y.C., 1991, 92, 94, Gallery 954, Chgo., 1994, Gallery at 777, L.A., 1994, Houston Ctr. for Photography, 1995, Hudson River Mus. Westchester, Yonkers, N.Y., 1995—; exhibited in group shows at Bannister Art Gallery, Providence, 1979, Westmoreland County (Pa.) Mus. Art, 1979, Ind. Am. Photography exhbn., Warsaw, Cracow, Katowice, Gdynia, Poland, 1980, Alonzo Gallery, N.Y.C., 1980, Alternative Mus., N.Y.C., 1981, Floating Found. for Photography, N.Y.C., 1981, World Photographic Archive, Parma, Italy, 1984, Diverse Works, Houston, 1985, The State Mus., Trenton, N.J., 1985, San Francisco Mus. Modern Art, 1986, Mus. Photog. Arts, San Diego, 1987, Public Image Gallery, N.Y.C., 1985; Alternative Mus., N.Y.C., 1986, Internat. Ctr. for Photography, N.Y.C., 1987, Farideh Cadot Gallery, N.Y.C., 1987, 88, Farideh Cadot Gallery, Paris, 1988, de Cordova and Dana Mus., Lincoln, Mass., 1988, Musee d'Art Moderne de la Ville de Paris, 1988, Musee d'Art et Histoire, Fribourg, Switzerland, 1988, Nat. Mus. of Am. Art, Washington, 1988, Security Pacific Corp., Gallery At The Plaza, L.A., 1988, Houston Ctr. for Photography, 1988, Catherine Edelman Gallery, Chgo., 1989, Musee fur Minerologie und Geologie, Leiden, Holland, 1989, The Friends of Photography, Ansel Adams Ctr., San Francisco, 1989, Alternative Mus., N.Y.C., 1989, Mus. of Contemporary Art, Chgo., 1989, The Walker Art Ctr., Mpla., 1990, Musee Zool. U. Louis Pasteur, Strasbourg, France, 1990, Akin Gallery, Boston, 1990, Monserrat Gallery, Beverly, Mass., 1990, Hallwalls, Buffalo, 1990, Natur Mus. Seckenberg Forshungsinstitut, Frankfort, Germany, 1990, Art 21-90, Basel, Switzerland, 1990, The Walker Art Ctr., Mpls., 1990, Lights Works, St. Paul, 1990, The Boston Athenaeum, 1990, Arts Festival Braga, Portugal, 1991, Nat. Mus. Am. Art, Washington, 1991, Addison Gallery Am. Art, Andover, Mass., 1991, The New Mus., N.Y.C., 1991, Mus. Fine Arts, Houston, 1992, Ctr. for Photography-Mid-Town, N.Y.C., 1992, Univ. Gallery, Clark U., Worcester, Mass., 1992, Long Beach (Calif.) Mus. Art, 1992, Preservation House, B.C., Can., 1992, Henry Art Gallery, U. Wash., Seattle, 1992, Akin Gallery, Boston, 1992, Internat. Mus. Photography George Eastman House, Rochester, N.Y., 1993, Wadsworth Athenaeum, Hartford, Conn., 1993, Th New Museum, N.Y.C., 1993, Akin Gallery, Boston, 1993, Ctr. for Photography at Woodstock, 1993, Montage, Rochester, N.Y., 1993, Gallery 954 Chgo., 1993, Parko Gallery, Tokyo, 1993, Addison Gallery Am. Art, Andover, Mass., 1994, New Mus., N.Y.C., 1994, Mus. Photographic Arts, San Diego, 1995, Mus. Contemporary Art, Chgo., 1995; represented in permanent collections: Mus. Modern Art, N.Y.C., Library of Congress, Washington, Smithsonian Instn., Washington, Archives Am. Art, Washington, Snite Mus. Art, Notre Dame, Ind., Walker Art Ctr., Mpls., Mus. Photog. Art, San Diego, N.Y.C., Polaroid Found. Collection, Cambridge, Mass., Yale U. Art Gallery, New Haven, Conn., San Francisco Mus. Modern Art, Ctr. for Creative Photography Collection, Tucson, Shadai Gallery, Tokyo, Espace Photographique de Paris, L.A. County Mus. of Art, Mus. Fine Arts, Houston, Metropolitan Mus. Art, N.Y.C., The State Mus., Trenton, N.J. Regional chmn. Campaign for Yale Art Sch. Div., Met. N.Y.C. area, 1975-76. Bollingen Found. fellow, 1961-63; Am. Philos. Soc. fellow, 1964-66; Am. Coun. Learned Socs. fellow, 1967-68; NEH fellow, 1967; recipient USIS Merit award, 1966; Merit award Assn. State and Local History, 1967-68; Harriette Merrifield Forbes award Assn. Gravestone Studies, U. Conn., Storrs, 1981; Polaroid Found. grantee, 1987-88, Arts grantee N.J. State Coun., 1990, Agfa Corp. grantee, 1990, NEA grantee, 1990-91. Democrat.

LUDWIG, CHRISTA, mezzo-soprano; b. Berlin; d. Anton and Eugenie (Besalla) L.; m. Walter Berry, Sept. 29, 1957 (div. 1970); 1 son, Wolfgang; m. Paul-Emile Deiber, Mar. 3, 1972. Ed. German schs. Appeared at, Staedtische Buehnen, Frankfurt, W.Ger., 1946-52, Landestheater, Darmstadt, W. Ger., 1952-54, Hannover, W.Ger., 1954-55, Vienna (Austria) State Opera, 1955—, Avery Fisher Hall, N.Y.C., 1978, appearances in, U.S., 1958—, including Met. Opera, N.Y.C., 1959, 66-71, 73-74, Carnegie Hall, N.Y.C. 1959, 69, 70, 71, 74, Lyric Opera, Chgo., 1959-60, 70-71, 73-74, Philharmonic Hall, N.Y.C., 1968, 69, 72, 74, guest artist, London, Buenos Aires, Munich, Berlin, Tokyo, Salzburg Festival, Athens Festival, Saratoga Festival, Hunter Coll., Met. Mus., Scala Milano, Expo 67, Montreal, and others, rec. artist. Decorated Commdr. des Arts et des Lettres, France, 1988, Goldenes Ehren Zeichen Stadt, Salzburg, 1988, Goldene Ehrennadel Stadt, Wien, Austria, 1988; chevalier Legion d'Honneur, France, 1989; recipient Mozart medal, Mahler medal, Hugo Wolf medal, Silver Rose, Vienna Philharm., Golden Ring, Vienna Staatsoper, Medaille de City of Paris, 1993, Musician of Yr. award Musical Am., 1994; named Kammersaengerin, Govt. of Austria, 1962. Office: Heidrun Artmueller Goethegasse, 1010 Vienna Austria also: care Colbert Artists Mgmt 111 W 57th St New York NY 10019-2211 *I express with my talent one of the many possibilities given to human beings. To get through to the heart of the people is my wish.* *

LUDWIG, EDMUND VINCENT, federal judge; b. Phila., May 20, 1928; s. Henry and Ruth (Viner) L.; children: Edmund Jr., John, Sarah, David. AB, Harvard U., 1949, LLB, 1952. Assoc. Duane, Morris & Heckscher, Phila., 1956-59; ptnr. Barnes, Biester & Ludwig, Doylestown, Pa., 1959-68; judge Common Pleas Ct., Bucks County, Pa., 1968-85, U.S. Dist. Ct. (ea. dist.), Phila., 1985—; mem. faculty Pa. Coll. of the Judiciary, 1974-85; presenter Villanova (Pa.) U. Law Sch., 1975-80, lectr., 1984—; vis. lectr. Temple Law Sch., 1977-80; clin. assoc. prof. Hahnemann U., Phila., 1977-85; mem. Pa. Juvenile Ct. Judge's Commn., 1978-85; chmn. Pa. Chief Justice's Ednl. Com., 1984-85; pres. Pa. Conf. State Trial Judges, 1981-82; mem. 3rd Cir. Ct. of Appeals Task Force on Equal Treatment in the Cts., 1994—. Contbr. articles to profl. jours. Chmn. Children and Youth Adv. Com., Bucks County, 1978-83; mem. Pa. Adv. Com. on Mental Health and Mental Retardation, 1980-85; founder, bd. dirs. Today, Inc., Newtown, Pa., 1971-85, Probation Vols., Bucks County, 1971-81; bd. dirs. New Directions for Women, Del. Valley, 1988—; mem. Pa. Joint Coun. Criminal Justice, Inc., 1979-80; mem. Joint Family Law Council Pa., 1979-85; vice chmn. Human Services Council Bucks County, 1979-81; mem. Com. to Study Unified Jud. System Pa., 1980-82, Pa. Legislative Task Force on Mental Health Laws, 1986-87; chmn. Juvenile Justice Alliance, Phila., 1992—; co-chmn. Doylestown (Pa.) Revitalization Bd., 1993—. Recipient Disting. Svc. award Bucks County Corrections Assn., 1978, Spl. Svc. award Big. Bros., 1989, Humanitarian award United Way Bucks County, 1980, Founder's award Vol. Svcs., 1982, Spl. award Bucks County Juvenile Ct., 1985, Humanitarian award Ctrl. Bucks County C. of C., 1994. Mem. ABA, Pa. Bar Assn. (chmn. com. legal svcs. to disabled 1990-92), Fed. Bar Assn. (hon.), Harvard Club (N.Y.C. and Phila., v.p. 1979-80), Harvard Law Sch. Assn. (mem. exec. com. 1993—). Office: 12614 US Courthouse Independence Mall W 601 Market St Philadelphia PA 19106-1510

LUDWIG, EDWARD LEE, director athletics, educator, coach; b. Lebanon, Pa., Sept. 7, 1948; s. William Franklin and Kathleen Jane (Gerberich) L.; m. Elaine Faye Stine, Mar. 30, 1968; children: Terry Lee, Travis Lew. BS, East Stroudsburg (Pa.) U., 1970. Cert. edn. tchr., Pa. Tchr., coach No. Lebanon Sch. Dist., Fredericksburg, Pa., 1970—; intramural and athletics dir., 1986—. Vice pres. coun. Zion Luth. Ch., Jonestown, Pa., 1986-90. Republican. Lutheran. Avocations: tennis, golf, skiing. Office: No Lebanon High Sch PO Box 100 Fredericksburg PA 17026-0100

LUDWIG, EUGENE ALLAN, U.S. comptroller of the currency, lawyer; b. Bklyn., Apr. 11, 1946; s. Jacob and Louise (Rabiner) L.; m. Carol Lynn Friedman, Mar. 11, 1978; children: Abigail Sarah, Elizabeth Madelaine Cathleen, David Maxwell. BA magna cum laude, Haverford Coll., 1968;

BA, MA, Oxford U., Eng., 1970; LLB, Yale U., 1973. Bar: D.C. 1973. Assoc. Covington & Burling, Washington, 1973-81, ptnr., 1981-93; comptr. of the currency Dept. of the Treasury, Washington, 1993—; pres. Yale Legis. Svcs., 1972-73; guest lectr. Harvard U., Georgetown U., 1974-77, 79, Yale U., 1989. Editor Yale Law Jour., 1972-73; mem. editorial bd., Jour. Internat. Banking Law, 1989; contbr. articles to profl. jours. Office: Comptroller of the Currency Independence Sq 250 E St SW Washington DC 20219*

LUDWIG, GEORGE HARRY, physicist; b. Johnson County, Iowa, Nov. 13, 1927; s. George McKinley and Alice (Heim) L.; m. Rosalie F. Vickers, July 21, 1950; children: Barbara Rose, Sharon Lee, George Vickers, Kathy Ann Ramsay. BA in Physics cum laude, U. Iowa, 1956, MS, 1959, PhD in Elec. Engring., 1960. Head fields and particles instrumentation sect. Goddard Space Flight Center, NASA, 1960-65, chief info. processing div., 1965-71, assoc. dir. for data ops., 1971-72; dir. systems integration Nat. Environ. Satellite Service, NOAA, 1972-75, dir. ops., 1975-80, tech. dir., 1980; sr. scientist Environ. Rsch. Labs. NOAA, Boulder, Colo., 1980-81; dir. Environ. Rsch. Labs. NOAA, 1981-83; asst. to chief scientist NASA, 1983-84 ret., ind. cons. data mgmt. and space sta. design, 1983-92; sr. rsch. assoc. Lab. for Atmospheric and Space Physics U. Colo., 1985-91; vis. sr. scientist NASA hdqrs., Calif. Inst. Tech., 1989-91; prin. designer radiation detection instrumentation for numerous sci. spacecraft including Explorer I, 1956-65; co-discoverer Van Allen radiation belts; expert on NASA sci. and applications research data processing; oversaw devel. and operation U.S. Nat. Environ. Satellite System, 1972-80; oversaw environ. research program Nat. Oceanic and Atmospheric Adminstrn., 1981-83. Served from pvt. to capt. USAF, 1946-52. Van Allen scholar, 1958; research fellow U.S. Steel Found., 1958-60; recipient Exceptional Service medal NASA, 1969, Program Adminstrn. and Mgmt. award NOAA, 1977, Exceptional Sci. Achievement medal NASA, 1984. Mem. IEEE (sr.), Am. Geophys. Union, Am. Meteorol. Soc., Phi Beta Kappa, Sigma Xi, Phi Eta Sigma, Eta Kappa Nu. Home: 215 Aspen Trail Winchester VA 22602

LUDWIG, HARVEY FRED, environmental engineer; b. Saskatoon, Sask., Can., Dec. 4, 1916; s. Rudolf Fred and Emily H. (Sikora) L.; m. Frances Roggero, Mar. 1, 1939 (div. Sept. 1969); children—Larry G., Lynne D. (Mrs. James Roe), Leslie J.; m. Vanida Sivamitre, Dec. 23, 1969; children—Wanee G., Yingtoy G. B.S. in Civil/San. Engring. U. Calif. at Berkeley, 1938, M.S., 1942; D.Engring., Clemson U., 1965. San. engr. San Francisco Bay Area, 1938-43, USPHS, Washington, 1943-46; assoc. prof. U. Calif. at Berkeley, 1949-51; cons. engr., 1946—; chmn. bd., pres. Engring. Sci., Inc., Arcadia, Calif. and Washington, 1956-72; v.p., dir. Zurn Industries, Erie, Pa., 1970-72; pres. SE Asia Tech., Bangkok, Thailand, 1973—. Contbr. numerous articles to profl. jours. Served to col. USPHS, 1943-46, 51-56. Recipient Goodell prize Am. Water Works Assn.; Hering medal ASCE; Eddy medal Water Pollution Control Fedn. Mem. Nat. Acad. Engring., Phi Beta Kappa, Sigma Xi, Tau Beta Pi, Chi Epsilon, Delta Omega. Club: Cosmos (Washington). Home: 43 Alston Pl Santa Barbara CA 93108-1803 Office: PO Box 8-101, Bangkok Thailand 10900

LUDWIG, KARL DAVID, psychiatrist; b. Johnstown, Pa., June 9, 1930; s. Karl Döring and Kathryn Bride (Palmer) L.; m. Darlene Ann Fisher, July 9, 1959; children: John D., Karl David Jr., Elizabeth Ann Craig, Mark D., Michael D. BA in Biology, St. Vincent Coll., 1952; postgrad., Pa. State U., 1952-53, St. Mary's Sem. & Univ., Balt., 1953-54; MD, U. Pitts., 1960. Intern U.S. Naval Hosp., Phila., 1960-61; resident psychiatry Ea. Pa. Psychiat. Inst., Phila., 1961-64; fellow psychiat. rsch. and teaching Jefferson Med. Coll., Phila., 1964-66; rsch. psychiatrist, dir alcoholism program Friends Hosp., Phila., 1966-73; staff psychiatrist Haverford State Hosp., Haverford, Pa., 1964-71; cons. in psychiatry VA Hosp., Coatesville, Pa., 1968-70; chief outpatient svcs. Northeast Community Mental Health Ctr., Phila., 1973; clin. dir. Northeast Community Mental Health Ctr., 1973-80; supt. Dixmont State Hosp., Sewickley, Pa., 1980-81; dir. inpatient psychiatry Sewickley Valley Hosp., Sewickley, 1981—; pres. med. staff Friends Hosp., Phila., 1969-71, Northeast Community Mental Health Ctr., Phila., 1974-75. Pres Phila. Navy chpt. Res. Officers Assn. of U.S., 1976-77, dept. Pa., 1978-79; bd. trustees Valley Care Assn., Sewickley, 1983-93; bd. dirs. Valley Care Nursing Home, Sewickley, 1983-93. Capt. med. corps USNR, ret. Fellow Am. Psychiat. Assn.; Psychiat. Physicians Pa. (pres. 1990-91); mem. AMA, Pitts. Psychiat. Soc. (pres. 1985-86), Pa. Med. Soc., Allegheny County Med. Soc., Am. Legion. Republican. Roman Catholic. Home: 2168A Reis Run Rd Pittsburgh PA 15237-1425

LUDWIG, LEROY FRANK, retail store executive; b. Remsen, Iowa, Apr. 28, 1923; s. Joseph Francis and Lela Marie (Pitz) L.; m. Genevieve Frances Boet, Nov. 22, 1945; children—LaRinda Ludwig Saylor, LeRoy Frank, Geri Ludwig Dempsey. Student, Chgo. Tech. Coll., 1941-42, Drury Coll., Springfield, Mo., 1943, U. Calif.-Berkeley Extension; cert. in real estate, Chabot Coll., Hayward, Calif., 1978. Archtl. drafter Safeway Stores, Inc., Oakland, Calif., 1945-57; design mgr. Safeway Stores, Inc., Oakland, 1957-74, project engr., 1974-77; div. property mgr. Safeway Stores, Inc., Fremont, 1979-82, real estate dir., 1982-84; v.p., real estate div. mgr. Safeway Stores, Inc., Oakland, 1984-86, v.p. real estate, div. mgr. facilities engring., 1986—. Pres., Oakland Zool. Soc., 1972-73. Served with USAAF, 1943-45, ETO. Decorated Air medal with four oak leaf clusters. Mem. Internat. Council of Shopping Ctrs., Nat. Assn. Corp. Real Estate Execs., Am. Legion. Roman Catholic. Home: 3221 Round Hill Dr Hayward CA 94542-2121 Office: Safeway Stores Inc 201 4th St Oakland CA 94607-4311

LUDWIG, PATRIC E., health care group executive; b. Mpls., Jan. 18, 1939; s. Roy and Gertrude (Anderson) L.; m. Carol Elizabeth Grasley, Oct. 29, 1960; children: Jana Kaye, David James, Mark Thomas. BS in Engring., U. Mich., 1962, MBA, 1963. Assoc. dir. Community Systems Found., Md., 1963-67, Hosp. Assn. N.Y. State, 1967-74; formerly pres. Mich. Hosp. Assn., Lansing, from 1974; now pres., chief exec. officer Bronson Healthcare Group, Kalamazoo, Mich.; mem. Mich. Health Planning Adv. Coun., 1975-76, Mich. Statewide Health Coordinating Coun., 1976-83; cons. Nat. Ctr. Health Svcs. R&D, HEW, from 1972; chmn. Co-author: Management Engineering for Hospitals, 1970. Chmn. trustees Community Systems Found., 1969-70, 72; mem. placement commn. Mich. Commn. for Blind Employer, 1980—. Recipient Outstanding Svc. award Community Systems Found., 1972. Mem. Am. Hosp. Assn., Am. Soc. Hosp. Assn. Execs. (cert. assn. exec.), Am. Pub. Health Assn., Hosp. Mgmt. Systems Soc. (Outstanding LIt. award 1971), State Hosp. Assn. Execs. Forum, Lay Adminstrs. Mut. Benefit Soc., Mich. Health Econs. Coalition, Orgn. Execs. Mich., Lansing C. of C., Hosp. Adminstrs. Study Soc., Rotary, Capitol Club. Office: Bronson Healthcare Group 1 Healthcare Plz Kalamazoo MI 49007

LUDWIG, RICHARD JOSEPH, ski resort executive; b. Lakewood, Ohio, July 28, 1937; s. Mathew Joseph and Catherine Elizabeth (Sepich) L.; m. Emily Kathleen Popovich, Dec. 2, 1961 (div. Feb. 1967); 1 dau., Susan Kay; m. Erleen Catherine Halambeck Ramus, July 22, 1977; children: Charleen, Tracey, Charles. Cassandra. Student. Ohio State U., 1955-59; BBA Fenn Coll., Cleve. State U. 1963. C.P.A., Ohio. Sr. acct. Ernst & Whinney, Cleve., 1964-66; supervising acct. Ernst & Young, 1966-70; asst. treas. Midland Ross Corp., 1970-71; treas. Midland Ross Corp., 1971-76; v.p. fin., treas. U.S. Realty Investments, 1976-78, v.p-fin., chief fin. officer, 1978-79; owner Boston Mills Ski Resort, Inc., Peninsula, Ohio, 1979—, Brandywine Ski Resort, Inc., Sagamore Hills, Ohio, 1990—. Mem. Firestone Country Club (Akron, Ohio), Saddlebrook Club (Wesley Chapel, Fla.), Black Diamond Ranch Club (Lecanto, Fla.), Walden Country Club (Aurora, Ohio). Home: 5106 Pinelake Rd Wesley Chapel FL 33543-4459 Office: PO Box 175 7100 Riverview Rd Peninsula OH 44264

LUDWIG, RICHARD MILTON, English literature educator, librarian; b. Reading, Pa., Nov. 24, 1920; s. Ralph O. and Millie (Smeltzer) L. A.B., U. Mich., 1942; A.M., Harvard U., 1943, Ph.D. 1950. Mem. faculty Princeton U., 1950-86, prof. English, 1968-86, dir. spl. program humanities, 1956-64; dir. Am. civilization program, 1969-71, assoc. univ. librarian for rare books and spl. collections, 1974-85; teaching fellow Harvard, 1946-50, mem. faculty summer sch., 1951, 52. Editor Princeton U. Library Chronicle, 1977-85; editor: Aspects of American Poetry, 1963, Letters of Ford Madox Ford, 1965, Dr. Panofsky & Mr. Tarkington, 1974; co-editor: Major American Writers, 1952, Nine Short Novels, 1952, Guide to American Literature and Its Backgrounds, Since 1890, 1972, Literary History of the United States,

1974, Advanced Composition, 1977, Annals of American Literature, 1986, 89. Served with AUS, 1944-46. Dexter traveling fellow Harvard, 1950; Jonathan Edwards preceptor Princeton, 1954-57; McCosh Faculty fellow, 1967-68. Mem. MLA, Am. Studies Assn. Home: 143 Hartley Ave Princeton NJ 08540-5613

LUDWIG, VERNELL PATRICK, gas pipeline company executive; b. Algona, Iowa, Nov. 5, 1944; s. Vernell Peter and Alice Marcella (Joynt) L.; m. Susan Lee, Nov. 30, 1968; children: Maryanne, David. BSME, Iowa State U, Ames, 1966; MBA, Harvard U., 1972. Sr. cons. Resource Planning Assocs., Cambridge, Mass., 1974-77; mgr. Tex. Ea. Gas Pipeline Co., Houston, 1977-80, asst. to pres., 1980-81, gen. mgr., 1981-82, v.p., 1982-83, sr. v.p., 1983-86; v.p. Transwestern Pipeline Co., Houston, 1982-83, sr. v.p., 1983-84; exec. v.p. Algonquin Energy, Inc., Boston, 1986-90, pres., 1991-93; v.p. corp. devel. Panhandle Ea. Corp., Houston, 1993—. Mentor Greater Houston Partnership CEO Roundtable, 1994—; chm. Boston subcom. New Eng. com. for corp. support Joslin Diabetes Found., 1992-93. Lt. USN, 1967-70, Vietnam. Mem. ASME, Interstate Natural Gas Assn., Am. Gas Assn., New England Gas Assn. (bd. dirs. 1989-93), Pi Tau Sigma. Office: Panhandle Ea Corp 5400 Westheimer Ct Houston TX 77056-5310

LUDWIG, WILLIAM FRANK, retired investment banker, lawyer; b. Sanford, Fla., Feb. 2, 1930; s. William Aubin and Helen Ann (Hausser) L.; m. Theresa Fisk, June 30, 1956 (div. 1974); children: William Aubin, Amelia Ann Ludwig Gunn; m. Gaye Glading McIntosh, Dec. 26, 1981; children: John McIntosh Ludwig, Julia McIntosh Ludwig. AB, U. Pa., 1951; JD, Columbia U., 1958. Bar: N.Y. 1959. Credit trainee Irving Trust Co., N.Y.C., 1955; loan officer U.S. AID, Washington, 1965-67; counsel Morgan Guaranty Trust Co., N.Y.C., 1958-64, comml. banker, 1968-85; investment banker Morgan Lewis Githens & Ahn, Greenwich, Conn., 1986-93. Avocations: tennis, reading, bridge, opera. Home: 1817 E Sandpointe Pl Vero Beach FL 32963

LUDWIKOWSKI, RETT RYSZARD, law educator, researcher; b. Skawina, Cracow, Poland, Nov. 6, 1943; came to U.S., 1982; s. Ryszard and Maria L.; children: Mark, Agnes. MA, Jagiellonian U., Poland, 1966, PhD in Law, 1971, D in Legal/Polit. Ideas, 1976. Bar: D.C. 1987; cert. legal counselor, 1973. Chmn. modern polit. movement/ideas Jagiellonian U., Cracow, 1976-82, chmn. div. bus., 1976-81, chmn. div. law, 1980-81; sr. fellow Marguerite Eyer Wilbur Found., Santa Barbara, Calif., 1981-82; vis. prof. politics Elizabethtown (Pa.) Coll., 1983; vis. scholar Hoover Inst., Stanford (Calif.) U., 1983; vis. prof. politics Alfred U., N.Y., 1983; vis. prof. politics Cath. U. Am., Washington, 1984, prof. law, 1985—, dir. comparative and internat. law inst., 1992—; vis. scholar Max Planck Inst., Hamburg, Fed. Republic of Germany, 1990. Author: Conservatism of Kingdom of Poland, 1976 (Ministry of Sci. award 1977), Black Radicalism in USA, 1976 (Pres. of Univ. award), Main Currents of Polish Political Thought, 1982, The Crisis of Communism, 1986 (grants and awards of Wilbur Found., Hoover Inst., Stanford U.), Continuity and Change in Poland, 1991, (with W.F. Fox) The Beginning of the Constitutional Era, 1993, others; contbr. articles to profl. jours. 2d lt. Polish Army. Recipient Vis. Prof. award Earhart Found., 1982—, award of Wilbur Found.; Disting. scholar Heritage Found. grantee, 1981-82; grantee Hoover Inst., Stanford U., Bradley Found., 1992, Earhart Found., 1992-94, Max Planck Inst. grantee, 1990. Mem. ABA, The Smithsonian Assocs., Polish Inst. Arts and Scis., Wilson Ctr. Assocs. (charter mem.). Avocations: tourism.

LUEBKE, NEIL ROBERT, philosophy educator; b. Pierce, Nebr., Sept. 15, 1936; s. Robert Carl and Cinderetta Amelia (Guthmann) L.; m. Phyllis Jean Madsen, June 15, 1957; children: Anne Elizabeth, Karen Marie. B.A., Midland Coll., 1958; M.A., Johns Hopkins U., 1962, Ph.D., 1968. Asst., assoc. then prof. philosophy Okla. State U., Stillwater, 1961-85, head philosophy dept., 1979-85, 89—; dir. Exxon Critical Thinking Project, 1971-74. Contbr. articles to profl. jours. Woodrow Wilson nat. fellow, 1958-59. Mem. Am. Philos. Assn., Soc. Bus. Ethics, Mountain-Plains Philos. Conf. (chmn. 1971-72, 80-81), Southwestern Philos Soc. (pres. 1980-81), Phi Kappa Phi (nat. v.p. 1992-95). Democrat. Lutheran. Home: 616 W Harned Ave Stillwater OK 74075-1303 Office: Okla State U Dept Philosophy 226 Hanner Bldg Stillwater OK 74078-0220

LUECKE, JOSEPH E., insurance company executive; b. 1927; married. BA, La Salle Coll., 1950. With Lumbermen's Mut. Casualty Co., 1951—, chmn., chief exec. officer, dir., 1981—; with Kemper Corp., Long Grove, Ill., 1951—, chmn., CEO, 1979-83, chmn., pres., CEO, 1983-86, chmn. bd. dirs., CEO, 1986-92; chmn., CEO Am. Motorists Ins. Co., Long Grove, also bd dirs; chmn. bd. dirs., CEO Am. Mfrs. Mutual Ins. Co., Long Grove, 1993—; bd. dirs. Kemper Fin. Svcs. Inc., Chgo., Chgo., Kemper Reinsurance Co., Long Grove, Am. Mfrs. Mut. Ins. Co., Am. Motorists Ins. Co., Kemper Ins. Co. Ltd., Kemper Internat. Ins. Co. (Pre.) Ltd.; bd. dirs., chmn. bd. Kemper Corp., Seven Continents Ins. Co. Ltd.; bd. dirs., mem. exec. com. Kemper Internat. Corp., Kemper Mgmt. Co. Ltd., Kemper, S.A.; bd. dirs., pres., mem. fin. com. Lumbermens Mut. Casualty Co. Chmn. James S. Kemper Found. Office: Am Mfrs Mutual Ins Co Kemper Ct 1 Kemper Dr Lake Zurich IL 60049

LUECKE, RICHARD WILLIAM, biochemist; b. St. Paul, July 12, 1917; s. Frederick William and Susan (Trautz) L.; m. Eleanor Virginia Rohrbacher, Nov. 1, 1941; children—Glenn R., Joan E., Ruth A. B.A., Macalester Coll., 1939, M.S., 1941; Ph.D., U. Minn., 1943. Assoc. prof. A&M U., Tex., 1943-45; assoc. prof. biochemistry Mich. State U., East Lansing, 1945-49; prof. Mich. State U., 1949-87, prof. emeritus, 1987—; cons. Merck Sharpe & Dohme Labs., 1963-76; mem. nutrition bd. FAO. Contbr. articles to profl. jours.; mem. editorial bd.: Jour. Nutrition, 1974-78. Mem. Am. Assn. Animal Sci. (Research award 1956), Am. Chem. Soc., AAAS, Am. Inst. Nutrition, Brit. Nutrition Soc., Am. Soc. Biol. Chemists, N.Y. Acad. Sci., Soc. Exptl. Biology and Medicine. Home: 1893 Birchwood Dr Okemos MI 48864-2766 Office: Dept Biochemistry Mich State U East Lansing MI 48824

LUEDDE, CHARLES EDWIN HOWELL, lawyer, corporation executive; b. St. Louis, Apr. 4, 1944; s. Henry William and Jane Elisabeth (Howell) L.; m. Jane Richmond Smallridge, Sept. 21, 1974; children: William Heath, Robert Chalmers. Bar: Mo. 1969. Jr. ptnr. Bryan, Cave, McPheeters & McRoberts, St. Louis, 1969-74, 76-77, sr. ptnr., 1978-83; exec. v.p., gen. counsel, sec. AMEDCO, Inc., St. Louis, 1983-87; ptnr., officer Greensfelder, Hemker & Gale, P.C., St. Louis, 1987—; sec. PMR Holdings, Inc., Washington, 1993—, St. Louis, 1993—; bd. dirs., cons. Huntco Inc., St. Louis, 1986-93; bd. dirs. Community LifeCare Enterprises, Springfield, Ill., 1985-91. Bd. dirs. St. Louis Charitable Found., 1986-91, Circus Arts Found. Mo., 1991—. Mem. ABA, Bar Assn. Metro St. Louis (chmn. bus. law sect. 1980-81), Am. Soc. Corp. Secs., Order of Coif. Home: 750 Cella Rd Saint Louis MO 63124-1612 Office: 1800 Equitable Bldg 10 S Broadway Saint Louis MO 63102

LUEDERS, EDWARD GEORGE, author, poet, educator, editor; b. Chgo., Feb. 14, 1923; s. Carl G. and Vera (Simpson) L.; m. Julia Demaree, June 5, 1946 (div. Apr. 1991); children: Kurt D., Joel E., Julia Anne; m. Deborah Keniston, Aug. 11, 1992. A.B., Hanover Coll., 1947; M.A., Northwestern U., 1948; Ph.D., U. N.Mex., 1952. Instr. U. N.Mex., 1948-52, asst. prof. English and speech, 1952-57; asso. prof. English Long Beach State Coll., 1957-61; prof., chmn. dept. English Hanover Coll., 1961-66; prof. English U. Utah, Salt Lake City, 1966—; chmn. dept. U. Utah, 1969-71, dir. creative writing, 1980-83, univ. prof., 1987-88, prof. emeritus, 1988—; mem. faculty Bread Loaf Sch. English, 1990—; editorial chmn. Coll. and Adult Reading List of Books in Lit. and Fine Arts, 1962; dir. Seminar Am. Poetry, Am. Studies Rsch. Ctr., Hyderabad, India, 1971; writer-in-residence Sch. of Ozarks, 1971, Behrend campus Pa. State U. 1972, sch. arts, U. Wis., Madison, 1987, Deep Springs Coll., 1989. Author: Carl Van Vechten and the Twenties, 1955, Carl Van Vechten, 1965, Images and Impressions: Poems by Brewster Ghiselin, Edward Lueders and Clarice Short, 1969, The Gang from Percy's Hotel and Other Poems, 1971, The Clam Lake Papers, A Winter in the North Woods, 1977, The Wake of The General Bliss, 1989; editor: (with others) Reflections on a Gift of Watermelon Pickle and Other Modern Verse, 1966, 2d edit. 1995, Some Haystacks Don't Even Have Any Needle and Other Complete Modern Poems, 1969, (with Primus St. John) Zero Makes Me Hungry, 1976, Writing Natural History: Dialogues with Authors, 1989; Western Humanities Rev., 1969-72; gen. editor: Peregrine

Smith Literary Naturalists Series, 1989-92, Nature and Environmental Studies, 1993—. Bd. dirs. Ucross Found., 1989—. Served with USAAF, 1943-46, CBI. Recipient Poetry prize Utah Inst. Fine Arts Creative Writing Competition, 1969, Disting. Alumni award Hanover Coll., 1972, Nat. Endowment Arts Creative Writing fellow, 1983, Utah Humanities Coun. Gov.'s award in the Humanities, 1992. Home: 958 S Windsor St Salt Lake City UT 84105

LUEDERS, WAYNE RICHARD, lawyer; b. Milw., Sept. 23, 1947; s. Warren E. and Marjorie L. (Schramek) L.; m. Patricia L. Rasmus, Aug. 1, 1970 (div. Nov. 1990); children: Laurel, Daniel, Kristin. BBA with honors, U. Wis., 1969; JD, Yale U., 1973. Bar: Wis. 1973. Acct. Arthur Andersen & Co., Milw., 1969-70; atty. Foley & Lardner, Milw., 1973-80; ptnr. Foley & Lueders, Milw., 1980—; bd. dirs. numerous cos. Bd. dirs. Riverdge Nature Ctr., Milw., 1983-92, Milw. Pro Soccer, 1986—, Milw. Art Mus., 1992—, Child Abuse Prevention Fund, Milw., 1989—; mem. adv. bd. Florentine Opera Co., 1992—; class agt. Yale Law Sch., 1978—. With U.S. Army, 1969-75. Mem. ABA, AICPA (Wisc.), Wis. Bar Assn., Milw. Bar Assn., Estate Counselors Forum, Univ. Club (Milw.), Phi Kappa Phi. Avocations: theater, racquetball, violin. Office: Foley & Lardner 777 E Wisconsin Ave Milwaukee WI 53202-5367

LUEDTKE, LUTHER S., academic administrator. Pres. Calif. Luth. U., Thousand Oaks. Office: Calif Luth U Office of President 60 Olsen Rd Thousand Oaks CA 91360-2700

LUEDTKE, ROLAND ALFRED, lawyer; b. Lincoln, Nebr., Jan. 4, 1924; s. Alfred C. and Caroline (Senne) L.; m. Helen Snyder, Dec. 1, 1951; children: Larry O., David A. B.S., U. Nebr., 1949, J.D., 1951. Bar: Nebr. 1951. Since practiced in Lincoln, 1951—; mem. Luedtke, Radcliffe & Evans (and predecessor), 1973-79; dep. sec. state State of Nebr., 1953-60; spl. legis. liaison Nebr. Dept. State, 1953-60; corps and elections counsel to sec. of state State of Nebr., 1960-65; senator Nebr. Unicameral Legislature, 1967-78, speaker, 1977-78; lt. gov. State of Nebr., 1979-83; mayor City of Lincoln, 1983-87; of counsel McHenry, Haszard & Flowers, Lincoln, 1987—; exec. sec. Gov. Nebr. Com. Refugee Relief, 1954-58; del., conferee nat. confs. Past pres. Lancaster County Cancer Soc.; crusade chmn. Nebr. div. Am. Cancer Soc., 1981-82; past dist. v.p., fin. chmn. Boy Scouts Am.; treas. Nebr. Young Republicans, 1953-54; jr. pres. Founders Day, Nebr. Rep. Com., 1958-59; chmn. Lancaster County Rep. Com., 1962-64; bd. dirs. Concordia Coll. Assn., Seward, Nebr., 1962-66, pres., 1965-66; bd. dirs. Lincoln Lutheran Sch. Assn., 1961-65, pres., 1964-65; bd. dirs. Immanuel Health Ctr. Omaha; Tabitha Found., Lincoln, 1986—, v.p. chmn. bd., 1979-83; bd. dirs. Nebraskaland Found., Lincoln, 1980—, pres. 1990-93; bd. dirs. Coords. for Adult Literacy, Nebr., 1984—, v.p. 1990-92. Served with AUS, 1943-45, ETO. Decorated Bronze Star, Purple Heart; recipient Disting. Service award Concordia Tchrs. Coll., 1965, Disting. Alumni award Lincoln High Sch., 1983. Mem. Am. Bar Assn., Nat. Conf. State Legislators (chmn. criminal justice task force 1975-77, chmn. consumers affairs com. 1975-77, exec. com. 1977-78), Nat. Conf. Lt. Govs. (exec. com. 1981-83), U.S. Conf. Mayors (chmn. human devel. com.), Nat. Conf. Cities (bd. dirs., bd. advisor human devel. com. NLC), Nat. League Cities (bd. dirs.), Nebr. Bar Assn., Lincoln Bar Assn., Am. Legion, DAV, VFW, Lincoln C. of C., Lincoln Gateway Sertoma Club (pres. 1962-63, chmn. bd. 1963-64), Delta Theta Phi. Lutheran. Office: McHenry Haszard & Flowers Ste 870 NBC Ctr Lincoln NE 68508

LUELLEN, CHARLES J., retired oil company executive; b. Greenville, S.C., Oct. 18, 1929; s. John B. and Dorothy C. (Bell) L.; m. Jo S. Riddle, July 11, 1953; children: Margaret L. Briggs, Nancy L. Bissell. B.S., Ind. U., 1952. Sales rep. Ashland Oil Inc., Ky., 1952-70, v.p. sales, 1970-72, group v.p. sales, 1972-80, pres., chief operating officer, 1986-92; also dir. emeritus Emeriti-Ashland Oil, Inc., Ky.; pres. Ashland Petroleum Co., 1980-86; bd. dirs. Nat. Convenience Stores, Houston, Tosco Corp., Stamford, Conn., Shell Polypropylene Co., Houston; bd. dirs. Kings Daus. Hosp., Ashland, 1981-87, Ashland Area YMCA, 1980-92, Nat. Chamber Found., Washington, 1987-92; trustee Centre Coll., Danville, Ky., 1988, Joint Coun. for Econ. Edn., N.Y.C. Mem. Beta Gamma Sigma. Home: 3409 Monte Vista Dr Austin TX 78731-5722 Office: Ashland Oil Inc PO Box 391 Ashland KY 41105-0391 also: Ashland Oil Inc 1000 Ashland Dr Russell KY 41169

LUENBERGER, DAVID GILBERT, electrical engineer, educator; b. Los Angeles, Sept. 16, 1937; s. Frederick Otto and Marion (Crumly) L.; m. Nancy Ann Iversen, Jan. 7, 1962; children: Susan Ann, Robert Alden, Jill Alison, Jenna Emmy. B.S.E.E., Calif. Inst. Tech., 1959; M.S.E.E., Stanford U., 1961, Ph.D. in Elec. Engring., 1963. Asst. prof. elec. engring Stanford (Calif.) U., 1963-67, assoc. prof. engring.-econ. systems, 1967-71, prof., 1971—, dept. chmn., 1980-91; tech. asst. dir. U.S. Office Sci. and Tech., Exec. Office of Pres., Washington, 1971-72; vis. prof. MIT, Cambridge, 1976; guest prof. Tech. U. of Denmark, Lyngby, 1986. Author: Optimization by Vector Space Methods, 1969, Linear and Nonlinear Programming, 1973, 2d edit., 1984, Introduction to Dynamic Systems, 1979, Microeconomic Theory, 1995; contbr. articles to tech. jours. Recipient Hendrik W. Bode Lecture prize Control Systems Soc., 1990. Fellow IEEE; mem. Econometric Soc., Soc. for Advancement Econ. Theory, Soc. for Promotion of Econ. Theory, Inst. Mgmt. Sci., Soc. Econ. Dynamics and Control (pres. 1987-88), Math Programming Soc., Palo Alto Camera Club, Sigma Xi, Tau Beta Pi. Lutheran. Office: Stanford U Dept Engring-Econ Systems Terman Ctr # 314 Palo Alto CA 94305-4025

LUENING, OTTO, composer, conductor, flutist, educator; b. Milw., June 15, 1900; s. Eugene and Emma (Jacobs) L.; m. Ethel Codd, Apr. 19, 1927 (div.); m. Catherine Brunson, Sept. 5, 1959. Student, State Acad. Music, Munich, 1915-17; diploma, Mcpl. Conservatory Music, Zurich, Switzerland, 1919; student, U. Zurich, 1919-20; D.Mus. (hon.), Wesleyan U., 1963, Wis. Conservatory of Music, 1979; D.Mus (hon.), U. Wis.-Milw., 1985; D.F.A. (hon.), U. Wis.-Madison, 1977; Litt.D. (hon.), Columbia U., 1981. Assoc. prof. U. Ariz., 1932-34; chmn. music dept. Bennington (Vt.) Coll., 1934-44; dir. music Bennington Sch. of Arts, 1940-41; assoc. prof., chmn. music dept. Barnard Coll., 1944-48; prof. music Columbia and Barnard Coll., 1948-68, prof. emeritus of music, 1968—; music chmn. Sch. Arts Columbia U., 1968-70; prof. Joline Found., 1947-64; mus. dir. Brander Matthews Theatre, Columbia U., 1944-59; mem. composition faculty Juilliard Sch., N.Y.C., 1971-73; co-dir. Columbia-Princeton Electronic Music Center, 1959-80; Bennington Coll. Disting. Hadley fellow, 1975; vis. composer U. S.C., 1978, U. Wis., Kenosha-Parkside, 1979, 80, 81, 82, N.Y. U., 1979, Bklyn. Coll., 1981; commd. N.Y. Philharmonic, BMI, NEA, McKim Fund at Library of Congress; Phi Beta Kappa vis. scholar and hon. mem., 1966; spl. cons. Silver Burdett Co.; mem. ednl. advisory com. Guggenheim Found., 1964-69; life mem. Nat. Inst. Arts and Letters, v.p., 1953; mem. music com. Yaddo, 1936, 37, 38, 40, 47; mem. exec. com. New Music Quar. Records; mem. advisory com. Fed. Music Project in Vt.; mem. Vt. Music Library Com.; co-founder Am. Music Ctr. N.Y.C., chmn., 1940-60; bd. dirs. Vt. Symphony Orch., 1939; founder, mem. Am. Composers Alliance, pres., 1945-51; co-founder Composer's Recs., Inc., pres., 1968-70, chmn. bd., 1970-75, co-pres., 1975-77; bd. mem. Am. Composers Orch., 1974—, Composers Forum; mem. exec. bd. League of Composers, 1943; bd. dirs. Internat. Soc. Contemporary Music, 1974-81; nat. chmn. Am. composition Nat. Fedn. Music Clubs, 1943; mem. com. Soc. for Publ. Am. Music, 1945, Com. on Contemporary Music in U.S.A., Music Educators Nat. Conf., 1943; U.S. del. Internat. Composers Conf., Stratford, Ont., 1960; U.S. music advisory com. UNESCO, 1953—; guest lectr. Bourges Internat. Music Festival. Flutist, condr. operetta and symphony orchs., Munich and Zurich, 1915-20; conducted first all-Am. opera performance, Chgo., 1922; coach, exec. dir. opera dept., Eastman Sch. Music, 1925-28, asst. condr., later condr., Rochester Am. Opera Co., guest condr., Am. Opera Co., N.Y.C., 1928; guest condr. N.Y. Philharm. Symphony Chamber Orch., 1936; guest condr. Vt. Symphony Orch., 1978, 85, Res Musica Balt., 1984, Internat. Festival of the Americas, Miami, 1984, vis. composer, trustee Am. Acad. in Rome, composer-in-residence, 1958, 61, 65; vis. composer Peabody Inst. Music, 1977, composer-in-residence, 1977-79; vis. composer, Bennington Coll. summer workshops, 1977-79, composer-in-residence Chamber Music Conf. and Composers' Forum, Bennington, 1988, Skaneateles Festival, 1991, Cin. Conservatory, Canonical Studies and Fanfare for Those We Have Lost for Wind Orch., 1993, Green Lake, Wis., 1993; retrospective concert and exhibn. of composers' collection, N.Y. Pub. Libr. of Performing Arts at Lincoln Ctr. for 90th Birthday ; other 90th Birthday performances include Sage City (Vt.) Symphony, New Paltz, N.Y.,

Conn. Early Music Festival, concert at Merkin Hall by Goodman Chamber Choir, N.Y.C.; commission performance Symphonic Fantasia #10, Woodstock Chamber Orch.; performances at Eastman Sch. Music, New Eng. Conservatory for 90th Birthday; also appeared as composer and flute soloist; appeared (with Ethel Luening) in concerts, U.S., Can. and Europe, 1928-41; author: The Odyssey of an American Composer: Autobiography, 1980; (with others) The Development and Practice of Electronic Music, 1975; contbr.: The Liberation of Sound, 1972, On the Wires of Our Nerves, 1989; also articles; composer over 300 works in varios musical forms, many compositions played by Am., fgn. symphony orchs., chamber music socs. and soloists, recs., Composer Recs. Inc.; also published: (in collaboration with Vladimir Ussachevsky) pioneer works for tape recorder including Rhapsodic Variations, Poem in Cycles & Bells, Concerted Piece for tape recorder and orch., taped electronic music solos and with orch.; recs. include Orchestra Works, 1917-92, 1994. Named hon. alumnus U. Wis., Parkside, 1981; recipient David Bispham medal Am. opera, 1933, award Nat. Inst. of Arts and Letters, 1946, citation for outstanding achievements and contbns. to edn. and music Wis. Senate and Ho. of Reps., 1965, 76, Thorne Music Fund Found. award, 1972, citation Nat. Assn. Composers and Condrs., 1966, Am. Composers Alliance Laurel Leaf award, 1970, Laurel Wreath award, 1985, award NEA, 1974, 77, medallion and citation Wis. Acad. Scis., Arts and Letters, 1977; named hon. alumnus U. Wis., Parkside, 1981, Creative Arts award and medal for music Brandeis U., 1981, Nat. Music Council Am. Eagle award, 1985, BMI citation, 1985, citation for svc. and dedication League Composers and Internat. Soc. for Contemprary Music, 1986, citation by Electro-Acoustic Soc. in U.S., Busoni Award Busoni Found., 1991; Guggenheim fellow, 1930-32, 74-75. Mem. N.Y. Acad. Scis. Clubs: Columbia U., Faculty, Century Assn. (N.Y.C.). Broadcasts and concerts in honor of 75th, 80th, 83d and 85th and 90th birthdays, N.Y.C., Milw., Munich, San Francisco, L.A., Houston, Washington, Boston, Denver, Louisville, Cologne (Fed. Republic Germany), Bourges (France), Moscow, London, Netherlands. Home: 460 Riverside Dr New York NY 10027-6820 *Be patient, healthy and practice.*

LUENING, ROBERT ADAMI, agricultural economics educator emeritus; b. Milw., Apr. 20, 1924; s. Edwin Garfield and Irma Barbara (Adami) L.; m. Dorothy Ellen Hodgskiss, Aug. 27, 1966. B.S., U. Wis., 1961, M.S., 1968. Dairy farmer Hartland, Wis., 1942-58; fieldman Waukesha County Dairy Herd Improvement Assn., Waukesha, Wis., 1958; adult agr. instr. Blair Sch. Dist., Wis., 1961-63; extension farm mgmt. agt. U. Wis.-Racine, 1963-69; extension farm record specialist Dept. Agrl. Econs. U. Wis.-Madison, 1969-88; free-lance work, 1988—. Author: (with others) The Farm Management Handbook, 1972, 7th edit., 1991, Teacher's Manual, 1991, Managing Your Financial Future Farm Record Book Series, 1980, 4th edit., 1987, USDA Yearbook of Agriculture, 1989, Beef, Sheep and Forage Production in Northern Wisconsin, 1992; writer mag. column: Agri-Vision, 1970-88. Founder, exec. pres. Lüning Family Orgns. U.S.A., Inc. Recipient John S. Donald Excellence in Teaching award U. Wis.-Madison, 1980; recipient Wis. State Farmer award Vocat. Agr. Inst. Wis., 1980, Second Mile award Wis. County Agts. Assn., 1980, Outstanding Svc. to Wis. Agr. award Farm and Industry Short Course, 1989. Mem. Am. Soc. Farm Mgrs. and Rural Appraisers (coll. v.p. 1976, chmn. editorial com. 1978-80, sec.-treas. 1968-80, pres. Wis. chpt. 1982, Silver Plow award 1988), Epsilon Sigma Phi (Disting. Service award 1988), Alpha Gamma Rho. Presbyterian. Lodge: Masons. Home: 5313 Fairway Dr Madison WI 53711-1038 Office: U Wis Dept Agrl Econs 427 Lorch St Rm 321 Madison WI 53706-1503

LUEPKE, HENRY FRANCIS, JR., lawyer; b. St. Louis, May 12, 1935; s. Henry Francis and Genevieve (Barthold) L.; m. Judith Claire Schicker, Dec. 27, 1958; children: Caroline, Gretchen, Henry, Mary Claire. BA cum laude, U. Notre Dame, 1957; JD, St. Louis U., 1960. Bar: Mo. 1960, Ill. 1960, U.S. Dist. Ct. (ea. dist.) Mo. 1960, U.S. Dist. Ct. (so. dist.) Ill., 1960, U.S. Supreme Ct. 1973. Assoc. Lewis, Rice, Tucker, Allen & Chubb, St. Louis, 1960-68; mem. Lewis, Rice & Fingersh, L.C., St. Louis, 1968-86, mem. in charge of adminstrn., 1986—; lectr. Sch. Commerce, St. Louis U., 1962-68; gen. counsel Environ. Improvement and Energy Resources Authority, Jefferson City, Mo., 1978—; chmn. lawyers div. Arts and Edn. Fund, St. Louis, 1988. Author: Guide to Probate Practice, 1962; mem. editorial bd. St. Louis U. Law Jour., 1959-60; contbr. articles to profl. jours. Chmn. Civil Svc. Bd., University City, Mo., 1974—; bd. dirs. Ozark Nat. Scenic River's Ways Commn., Van Buren, Mo., 1977-81; legal counsel, treas. Teasdale for Gov. Com., Jefferson City, Mo., 1977-81. Recipient Award of Yr. Notre Dame Club-St. Louis, 1984, Alumni Svc. award St. Louis U., 1987, Cross of Affiliation award Acad. of Visitation, 1988. Mem. ABA, Mo. Bar Assn., Ill. Bar Assn., Bar Assn. Met. St. Louis, Notre Dame U. Law Assn., Mo. Athletic Club (bd. dirs. 1991-94, pres. 1993-94), St. Louis Hinder Club. Democrat. Roman Catholic. Avocations: handball, fly fishing, bird hunting, canoeing. Office: Lewis Rice & Fingersh 500 N Broadway Ste 2000 Saint Louis MO 63101

LUEPKER, RUSSELL VINCENT, epidemiology educator; b. Chgo., Oct. 1, 1942; s. Fred Joeseph and Anita Louise (Thornton) L.; m. Ellen Louise Thompson, Dec. 22, 1966; children: Ian, Carl. BA, Grinnell Coll., 1964; MD with distinction, U. Rochester, 1969; MS, Harvard U., 1976. Intern U. Calif., San Diego, 1969-70; resident Peter Bent Brigham Hosp., Boston, 1973-74; cardiology fellow Peter Bent Brigham Hosp./Med., Boston, 1974-76; asst. prof. divsn. epidemiology med. lab. physiol. hygiene U. Minn., Mpls., 1976-80, assoc. prof., 1980-87, assoc. dir. divsn. epidemiology, 1986-91, prof. divsn. epidemiology and medicine, 1987—, dir. divsn. epidemiology, 1991—; cons. NIH, Bethesda, Md., 1980—, U. So. Calif., L.A., 1985—; vis. prof. U. Goteborg, Sweden, 1986, Ninewells Med. Sch., Dundee, Scotland, 1995. Lt. comdr. USPHS, 1970-73. Harvard U. fellow, 1974-76, Bush Leadership fellow, 1990; recipient Prize for Med. Rsch. Am. Coll. Chest Physicians, 1970, Nat. Rsch. Svc. award Nat. Heart, Lung and Blood Inst., Bethesda, 1975-77, Disting. Alumni award Grinnell Coll., 1989. Fellow ACP, Am. Coll. Cardiology, Am. Heart Assn. Coun. on Epidemiology (chmn. 1992-94), Am. Coll. Epidemiology; mem. Delta Omega Soc. (Nat. Merit award 1988). Office: Univ Minn Sch Pub Health Div Epidemiology 1300 S 2nd St Ste 300 Minneapolis MN 55454-1015

LUERS, WILLIAM HENRY, art museum administrator; b. Springfield, Ill., May 15, 1929; s. Carl U. and Ann L. (Lynd) L.; m. Wendy Woods Turnbull, Oct. 18, 1979; children by previous marriage: Mark B., David L., William F., Amy L. A.B., Hamilton Coll., 1951, LL.D. (hon.), 1984; M.A., Columbia U., 1957; postgrad., Northwestern U., 1951-52. Commd. fgn. service officer Dept. State, 1957; vice consul Naples, Italy, 1957-60; 2d sec. Am. Embassy, Moscow, 1963-65; polit. counselor Am. Embassy, Caracas, Venezuela, 1969-73; dep. exec. sec. Dept. State, 1973-75; dep. asst. sec. for inter Am. affairs, Washington, 1975-77; dep. asst. sec. European affairs (Soviet-Eastern Europe), 1977-78; ambassador to Venezuela, Caracas, 1978-82, Czechoslovakia, Prague, 1983-86; pres. Met. Mus. Art, N.Y.C., 1986—; bd. dirs. Transco Energy Co., Houston, IDEX Corp., Northbrook, Ill., Scudder New Europe Fund, N.Y., Scudder Global/Internat. Funds; dir.'s visitor Inst. Adv. Study, Princeton, N.J., 1982-83; vis. lectr. Woodrow Wilson Sch., Princeton U., 1983; bd. trustees Rockefeller Bros. Found., N.Y.C. Active adv. coun. Trust for Mut. Understanding, N.Y.C.; trustee adv. coun. Appeal of Conscience Found., N.Y.C.; bd. dirs. Inst. for East West Studies, N.Y.C., Am. Acad. Diplomacy, Washington. Fellow Am. Acad. Arts and Scis.; mem. Coun. on Fgn. Rels. Episcopalian. Office: Met Mus Art 1000 Fifth Ave New York NY 10028-0113

LUERSSEN, FRANK WONSON, retired steel company executive; b. Reading, Pa., Aug. 14, 1927; s. George V. and Mary Ann (Swoyer) L.; m. Joan M. Schlosser, June 17, 1950; children: Thomas, Mary Ellen, Catherine, Susan, Ann. BS in Physics, Pa., State U., 1950; MSMetE, Lehigh U., 1951; LLD (hon.), Calumet Coll.; DPS (hon.), Xavier U. Metallurgist research and devel. div. Inland Steel Co., East Chicago, Ind., 1952-54; mgr. various positions Inland Steel Co., 1954-64, mgr. research, 1964-68, v.p. research, 1968-77, v.p. steel mfg., 1977-78, pres., 1978-85, chmn., 1983-92; bd. dirs. Morton Internat., Inc. Contbr. articles on steelmaking tech. to various publs. Trustee Northwestern U., 1980—; trustee, sec., treas. Munster Sch. Bd., 1957-66. With USNR, 1945-47. Named disting. alumnus Pa. State U. Fellow Am. Soc. Metals; mem. AIME (Disting. life mem., B.F. Fairless award, Howe meml. lectr. 1988-91), Am. Iron and Steel Inst. (Gary medal, chmn. 1989-90), Nat. Acad. Eng. Home and Office: 8226 Parkview Ave Munster IN 46321-1419

LUETKEHOELTER, GOTTLIEB WERNER (LEE), retired bishop, clergyman; b. Wheatwyn, Sask., Can., Nov. 16, 1929; s. Henry William and Marie Louise (Schlepper) L.; m. Betty Edwards, July 25, 1959; children—David Lee, Jonathan Richard. B.A., U. Sask., 1952; B.D., Lutheran Coll. and Sem., Saskatoon, Sask., 1955; S.T.M., Vancouver Sch. Theology, 1975; DD, St. John's Coll., 1990. Ordained to ministry United Luth. Ch. in Am., 1955. Pastor Markinch-Wheatwyn-Cupar Parish, 1955-57; pastor St. Mark's Luth. Ch., Regina, Sask., 1957-61, Erloeser Luth. Ch., Phila., 1961-63, Faith Luth. Ch., Burnaby, B.C., Can., 1963-69, Trinity Luth. Ch., Edmonton, Alta., Can., 1969-76; bishop Central Can. Synod, Luth. Ch. in Am., Winnipeg, Man., Can., 1976-85; bishop Man./Northwestern Ont. Synod, Evang. Luth. Ch. in Can., Winnipeg, Man., 1985-94; ret., 1994; mem. exec. coun. Luth. Ch. in Am., N.Y.C., 1978-85; mem. Luth. Merger Commn., Can., 1978-85, Anglican-Luth. Dialogue, Can., 1983—. Bd. govs. Luth. Theol. Sem., Saskatoon, 1976-94. Served with Can. Navy, 1953-55. Avocations: golf; swimming.

LUFFSEY, WALTER STITH, transportation executive; b. Richmond, Va., Mar. 15, 1934; s. Roland Emmit and Bernice Irene (Hall) L.; m. Louise Arlington Hicks, Dec. 19, 1956; children: Dennis Glenn, Melinda Denise. Student, U. Richmond, 1952-55, Agrl. Dept. Grad. Sch., 1963-65. With FAA, 1957—; supervisory air traffic control specialist FAA, Atlantic City, 1960-63; air traffic control specialist research FAA, 1963-65, sr. air traffic control analyst systems research and devel. service, 1965-71; chief program analysis and reports br. FAA, Washington, 1971-72; asst. chief program mgmt. staff FAA, 1972-73, spl. asst., assoc. adminstr. for engring. and devel., 1973-74, chief program mgmt. staff system research and devel. service, 1974-75, tech. asst., assoc. adminstr. policy devel. and rev., 1975-78, tech. asst., assoc. adminstr. policy and internat. aviation affairs, tech. asst. to the assoc. adminstr. for aviation standards, 1978-79, dep. assoc. adminstr. for aviation standards, 1979-80, assoc. adminstr. for aviation standards, 1980-85, assoc. adminstr. for air traffic, 1985-86, dir. advanced aviation system design team, 1986-89; sr. v.p. ops. and planning Tech. and Mgmt. Assistance, Washington, 1989-90, exec. v.p., 1990—; pres. WSL Enterprises, Arlington, 1989—. Author: Air Traffic Control: How to Become an FAA Air Traffic Controller, 1990; contbr. articles to profl. jours. Served with USAF, 1955-58. Recipient Meritorious Achievement award Air Traffic Control Assn., 1965; recipient Spl. Achievement award FAA, 1970, 78, 85, Disting. Service award Aviation Week and Space Tech.-Flight Safety Found., 1982; Sec.'s award for outstanding achievement, 1982; Meritorious Exec. award-Presdl. Rank, 1983; Adminstr.'s Superior Achievement award for excellence in equal employment opportunity, 1985, numerous others. Mem. AIAA (mem. aero. policy com.), Soc. Sr. Aerospace Execs., Nat. Aero. Assn., Exptl. Aircraft Assn., Aircraft Owners and Pilots Assn., Profl. Women Contrs. Assn., Air Traffic Control Assn. (hon. mem. award 1986, chair pubs. com.), John Marshall Cadet Alumni Assn., Soc. Airway Pioneers, Va. Aero. Hist. Soc., Order of Quiet Birdmen, Aero Club, Nat. Aviation Club (past pres., gov emeritus), Kiwanis (past pres. Crystal City club). Home: 1805 Crystal Dr #713-S Crystal Park Arlington VA 22202 Office: Tech & Mgmt Assistance 600 Maryland Ave SW Ste 420 Washington DC 20024-2520 also: WSL Enterprises PO Box 16223 Arlington VA 22215-1223

LUFKIN, LIZ, newspaper editor. Entertainment editor The San Francisco Chronicle, Calif. Office: The San Francisco Chronicle 901 Mission St San Francisco CA 94103-2988*

LUFRANO, MICHAEL RICHARD, federal government official; b. Chgo., July 8, 1965; s. Ned Nathan and Joan Audrey (Gold) L. BA, U. Ill., 1987; JD, Harvard U., 1992. Assoc. city atty. City of Atlanta, 1992-93; spl. asst. to pres., dep. dir. advance White House, Washington, 1993—; issues dir., speechwriter Dukakis for Pres., Boston, 1987-88. Scholar Rotary Internat., 1987. Office: The White House Washington DC 20500

LUFT, HAROLD S., health economist; b. Newark, N.J., Jan. 6, 1947; s. George and Kay (Grossman) L.; m. Lorraine Ellin Levinson, May 24, 1970; children: Shira Levinson, Jana Levinson. A.B., Harvard U., 1968, AM, 1970, Ph.D., 1973. Systems analyst, rsch. asst. Harvard Transport Rsch., Cambridge, Mass., 1965-68; systems analyst Harvard Econ. Rsch. Project, Cambridge, Mass., 1968-72; instr. econs. Tufts U., Medford, Mass., 1972-73; postdoctoral fellow Harvard Ctr. Community Health, Boston, 1972-73; asst. prof. health econs. Stanford U., Calif., 1973-78; prof. health econs., acting dir. Inst. Health Policy Studies, U. Calif., San Francisco, 1978—; cons. Applied Mgmt. Scis., Silver Spring, Md., 1979—, Robert Wood Johnson Found., Princeton, N.J., 1982—; study sect. Nat. Ctr. Health Services, Rockville, Md., 1981-83. Author: Poverty and Health, 1978, Health Maintenance Organizations, 1981, 2d edit., 1988, (with Deborah Garnick, David mark, Stephen McPhee) Hospital Volume, Physician Volume, and Patient Outcomes, 1990, HMOs and the Elderly, 1994; contbr. chpts. to books, articles to profl. jours. Advisor, fin. planning com. Mid-Peninsula Health Service, Palo Alto, Calif., 1984—. NSF fellow, Carnegie Found. fellow, Grad. Prize fellow Harvard U., 1968-72, fellow Ctr. for Advanced Study in Behavioral Scis., 1988-89. Mem. Am. Pub. Health Assn., Am. Econ. Assn., Inst. Medicine (mem. coun.), Western Econ. Assn. Home: 1020 Ramona St Palo Alto CA 94301-2443 Office: U Calif Inst for Health Policy Studies 1388 Sutter St Fl 11 San Francisco CA 94109-5427

LUFT, RENE WILFRED, civil engineer; b. Santiago, Chile, Sept. 21, 1943; came to U.S., 1968; s. David and Malwina (Kelmy) L.; m. Monica Acevedo, Aug. 24, 1970; children: Deborah Elaine, Daniel Eduardo. CE, U. Chile, 1967; MS, MIT, 1969, DSc, 1971. Registered profl. engr., Alaska, Calif., Wash., Mass., N.H., R.I., Republic of Chile; registered structural engr., Vt. Asst. prof. civil engring. U. Chile, 1967-68; research asst. MIT, Cambridge, Mass., 1969-71, vis. lectr., 1983-84; staff engr. Simpson, Gumpertz & Heger Inc., Arlington, Mass., 1971-74, sr. staff engr., 1975-78, assoc., 1978-83, sr. assoc., 1984-90; prin. Simpson, Gumpertz & Heger Inc., San Francisco, 1990-91; head design div. Simpson, Gumpertz & Heger Inc., 1991—; sec. seismic adv. com. Mass. Bldg. Code Commn., 1978-80, chmn., 1981-82; mem. Boston seismic instrumentation com. U.S. Geol. Survey; mem. slabs on ground com. Post-Tensioning Inst., 1994—. Contbr. articles to profl. jours. Mem. design overview com., bldg. seismic safety coun. Earthquake Hazards Reduction Program, 1983-91, chmn. rsch. com. 1987-88. Mem. ASCE, Boston Soc. Civil Engrs. (chmn. seismic design adv. com. 1981-86, Clemens Herschel award for tech. paper 1980, pres.'s award for leadership in earthquake engring. 1984), Am. Concrete Inst., Earthquake Engring. Research Inst., Structural Engrs. Assn. Calif., NSPE (Young Engr. of Yr., 1979), Sigma Xi, Chi Epsilon. Home: 109 Ardith Dr Orinda CA 94563-4201 Office: 221 Main St Ste 1500 San Francisco CA 94105-1934

LUFTGLASS, MURRAY ARNOLD, manufacturing company executive; b. Bklyn., Jan. 2, 1931; s. Harry and Pauline (Yaged) L.; children by previous marriage: Paula Jean, Bryan Keith, Robert Andrew, Richard Eric; m. Christine L. Novick, May 29, 1988; 1 child, Andrew William. BS, Ill. Inst. Tech., 1952; MS, U. So. Calif., 1959; MBA, U. Conn., 1972.With Shell Chem. Co., Torrance, Calif., 1955-60, N.Y.C., 1960-61, Wallingford, Conn., 1961-64, Torrance, 1964-66, N.Y.C., 1966-69; asst. gen. mgr. Westchester Plastics div. Ametek, Inc., Mamaroneck, N.Y., 1969-75; dir. corp. devel. Ametek, Inc., N.Y.C., 1975-76, v.p., 1976-83, sr. v.p. corp. devel., 1984—. Served to lt. (j.g.) USN, 1952-55. Mem. NAM, Soc. Plastics Industry, Assn. Corp. Growth, Soc. Plastics Engrs., Tau Beta Pi, Beta Gamma Sigma, Phi Lambda Upsilon. Club: University (N.Y.C.). Contbr. articles to profl. jours., publs. Patentee in field. Office: Ametek Inc 410 Park Ave New York NY 10022-4407

LUGAR, RICHARD GREEN, senator; b. Indpls., Apr. 4, 1932; s. Marvin L. and Bertha (Green) L.; m. Charlene Smeltzer, Sept. 8, 1956; children: Mark, Robert, John, David. B.A., Denison U., 1954; B.A., M.A. (Rhodes scholar), Oxford (Eng.) U., 1956. Mayor Indpls. 1968-75; vis. prof. polit. sci. U. Indpls., 1976; mem. U.S. Senate, 1977—, chmn. com. fgn. relations, 1985-86, chmn. com. on agr., 1995—; chmn. Nat. Rep. Senatorial Com., 1983-84; Treas. Lugar Stock Farm, Inc.; mem. Indpls. Sch. Bd., 1964-67, v.p., 1965-66; vice chmn. Adv. Commn. on Intergovtl. Relations, 1969-75; pres. Nat. League of Cities, 1970-71; mem. Nat. Commn. Standards and Goals of Criminal Justice System, 1971-73; Del., mem. resolutions com. Republican Nat. Conv., 1968, del., mem. resolutions com., 1992, Keynote speaker, 1972, del., speaker, 1980; mem. internat. adv. council Inst. Internat. Studies. Author: Letters to the Next President, 1988. Trustee Denison U.,

U. Indpls.; bd. dirs. Nat. Endowment for Democracy, Am. Running and Fitness Assn.; bd. dirs. Youth for Understanding. Served to lt. (j.g.) USNR, 1957-60. Pembroke Coll., Oxford U. hon. fellow. Mem. Blue Key, Phi Beta Kappa, Omicron Delta Kappa, Pi Delta Epsilon, Pi Sigma Alpha, Beta Theta Pi. Methodist. Club: Rotary. Office: US Senate 306 Hart Senate Bldg Washington DC 20510

LUGAR, THOMAS R., manufacturing executive. With Allison Div. Gen. Motors Co., Indpls., 1955-57; pres. Thomas L. Green & Co., Indpls., 1957—; chmn. Methodist Hosp. of Ind., Indpls. Office: Thomas L. Green & Co. Inc. 202 N Miley Ave Indianapolis IN 46222

LUGENBEEL, EDWARD ELMER, publisher; b. Balt., June 6, 1932; s. Nimrod Augustus and Victoria Elizabeth (Shilling) L.; m. Alice Marie Smith, June 12, 1953; children: Craig Edward, Susan Elizabeth, Douglas Paul, Leslie Jean. B.S., U. Md., 1954. With Prentice-Hall, Inc., N.J., 1957-76; exec. editor, asst. v.p. Prentice-Hall, Inc., 1972-76; pres. D. Van Nostrand Co., div. Litton Ednl. Pub., Inc. (pubs. coll. textbooks), N.Y.C., 1976-81; v.p. Lynne Palmer Exec. Recruitment, Inc., N.Y.C., 1981-83; v.p., editorial dir. W.B. Saunders Med. Pubs., Phila., 1983-85; exec. editor Columbia U. Press, N.Y.C., 1985—. Served as 1st lt. USAF, 1954-57. Mem. AAAS, Am. Inst. Biol. Scis., Am. Geophys. Union, Soc. Vertebrate Paleontology, Internat. Assn. Landscape Ecology, Soc. Conservation Biology, Delta Sigma Pi. Office: 136 S Broadway Irvington NY 10533

LUGER, DONALD R., engineering company executive; b. Elizabeth, N.J., May 12, 1938; s. George A. and Elizabeth M. Luger; m. Pat Sanders, Feb. 17, 1968 (dec. 1982); m. Sharon L. Luger, May 14, 1983; children: Christopher Daniel, Morgan Kathleen. BCE, Auburn U., 1962, MSCE, Auburn U., 1964, exec. program Stanford U., 1979. Registered profl. engr., N.C., Ga., Mich., Va., N.Y. Structural engr. NASA, Huntsville, Ala., summer 1962; area engr. E.I. DuPont Co. Nashville, 1964; structural engr. Hayes Internat. Corp., Huntsville, 1964-65; resident engr. Fibers Industries, Inc., Shelby, N.C. and Greenville, S.C., 1965-66; project mgr. Lockwood Greene Engrs., Inc., Atlanta, 1967-71, sr. project mgr., 1971-74, v.p., corp. dir., 1974-78, sr. v.p., corp. dir., 1978-82, pres., 1982—, chief exec. officer, 1983—. Mem. ASCE, NSPE, Ga. Soc. Profl. Engrs., So. Ctr. for Internat. Studies, Auburn U. Alumni Assn., Auburn Alumni Engring. Coun., Stanford Alumni Assn., Constrn. Industry Pres. Forum, Commerce Club, Atlanta Athletic Club.*

LUGO, ARIEL E., ecologist, botanist, federal agency administrator; b. Mayagüez, P.R., Apr. 28, 1943; m. Helen Nunci; 2 children. BS in Biology, U. P.R., 1963, MS in Biology, 1965; PhD in Ecology, U. N.C., 1969. Asst. prof. dept. Botany U. Fla., Gainesville, 1969-73, 75-76, assoc. prof., 1976-79, acting dir. ctr. for wetlands, 1977-78; asst. sec. planning and resource analysis P.R. Dept. Natural Resources, Puerta de Tierra, 1973-74, asst. sec. sci. and tech., 1974-75; staff mem. Coun. Environ. Quality Exec. Office Pres., Washington, 1978-79; head divsn. ctr. energy and environ. rsch. U. P.R., 1980-88; project. leader Internat. Inst. Tropical Forestry, USDA Forest Svc., Rio Piedras, P.R., 1980-92, dir., 1986-92, acting dir., supervisory rsch. ecologist, 1992-94; dir. Internat. Inst. Tropical Forestry, USDA Forest Svc., Washington, 1994—; cons. Save Our Bays Assn., 1970, Am. Oil Co., 1972, H.W. Lochner, Inc., 1972, U.S. Postal Svc., 1972, U.S. Forest Svc., 1972, U.S. Dept. Interior, 1972, 73, 76, 77, U.S. EPA, 1974, U.S. Justice Dept., 1974, 78, UNESCO, 1975-76, 78, 83, 85-86, P.R. Dept. Natural Resources, 1975, 76, S.W. Fla. Regional Planning Coun., 1976-77, Environ. Quality Bd., 1976, 77, Fla. Dept. Natural Resources, 1976, Rockefeller Found., 1976, Nat. Audubon Soc. 1977, County of Lee, Fla., 1977, Nat. Wildlife Fedn., 1978, World Bank, 1978, Orgn. Am. States, 1979, 80, Collier County Nature Conservancy, 1980; hon. prof., lectr. U. P.R., 1974-76, 80—, hon. assoc. prof., 1985-88; with dept. Environ. Engring. Scis., Ctr. Latin Am. Studies U. Fla., Gainesville, 1977, dept. Botany, 1980-92; co-chmn. Fed. Com. Ecol. Reserves, 1977-79; mem. Man and Biosphere directorate 7-B Caribbean Islands, 1978-79, chmn. directorate I Tropical Forest Ecosystems, 1980-89, chmn. directorate Tropical Ecosystems, 1990; mem. Endangered Species Scientific Authority, Interagy. Arctic Rsch. Coordinating Com., Interagy. Tropical Deforestation Task Force, 1978-79, Tropical Diversity Interagy. Com., 1985; chmn. rsch. com. Latin Am. Forestry Commn. UNESCO, 1980—; mem. commn. on ecology Internat. Union Conservation Nature and Natural Resources, 1980-86; nat. rsch. coun. ecol. problems associated with devel. humid tropics, 1980-82; exec. com. U.S. Man and Biosphere program, 1981-84, nat. com. 1990; sr. adv. com. to Pres. U. P.R., 1982-88, chmn., 1985-88; scientific advisor Inst. Energy Analysis, Oak Ridge, Tenn., 1982-84; active Decade of Tropics Internat. Union Biol. Scis., 1985-88; adv. com. Yale Tropical Resources Inst., 1985—; advisor coastal zone program tropical countries, R.I. U., 1985-88; review team dept. forestry, Sch. Forest Resources and Conservation U. Fla., 1989; nat. rsch. coun. com. sustainable agriculture and the environment in the humid tropics, 1990-93; mem. grad. faculty dept. Environ., Population and Organismic Biology, U. Colo., Boulder, 1990-91; apptd. Consejo Consultivo del Programa de Patrimonio Nacional, 1990-92; expert witness in field. Mem. editorial bd. Vegetatio, 1981-82, Jour. Litoral, 1982—, Acta Cientifica, 1987—, Jour. Sustainable Forestry, 1991—, Restoration Ecology, 1992—, assoc. editor; mem. editorial bd. Forest Ecology and Mgmt., 1994—; contbr. articles to profl. jours. Trustee Fla. Defenders of Environment, 1980-81; rsch. assoc. Islands Resources Found., U.S. Virgin Islands, 1980—; bd. overseers Harvard Coll., com. to visit dept. Organismic and Evolutionary Biology, 1989—; bd. govs. Soc. Conservation Biology, 1989-91; bd. dirs. P.R. Conservation Found., 1990—. Recipient Disting. Scientist award Interam. U., San Juan, P.R., 1992; grantee U. Fla., 1969, 70, 71-72, U.S. Forest Svc., 1970, U.S. Dept. Interior, 1971, 72-75, Br. Sport Fisheries and Wildlife, 1971-73, 73-76, , Am. Oil Co., 1972, Fla. Dept. Natural Resources, 1972-75, H.W. Lochner, Inc., 1972, State of Fla., 1972-74, Inst. Food and Agrl. Scis., 1973, NSF, 1974, 81-83, 88—, U.S. EPA, 1977-79, Conservation Found., 1977, U.S. Dept. Energy, 1978-82, 83-87, 8 Man and the Biosphere Consortium, 1980-87, 90-91, U.S. AID, 1982-83, FAO, 1983, U.S. Oceanographic Adminstrn., 1984-85, Tech. Wetlands Coun., 1986, World Wildlife Fund, 1989; Fullbright-Hayes fellow U. La Plata, Argentina, 1978. Mem. AAAS (coun. Caribbean divsn. 1990-92), Ecology Soc. Am., Internat. Soc. Tropical Foresters (exec. com. 1990-93), Soc. Ecol. Restoration and Mgmt. (founding 1988, bd. dirs. 1992), Internat. Soc. Tropical Ecology (bd. bearers 1990-93), Internat. Assn. Ecology, Fla. Acad. Scis, Soc. Caribbean Ornithology, P.R. Acad. Arts and Scis., Sigma Xi, Beta Beta Beta (hon. Zeta Zeta chpt.). Achievements include research in assessment of role of tropical forests in the carbon cycle of the world; studies of tropical tree plantations in Puerto Rico; comparisons of plantations and natural forests; relations between forest management and soil and water quality in Caribbean forests; studies of tropical wetlands; study on rate of decomposition in the tropics. Home: 1528 Tamesis El Paraiso San Juan PR 00926 Office: USDA Forest Svc Internat Inst Tropical Forestry PO Box 25000 San Juan PR 00928-5000

LUGT, HANS JOSEF, physicist; b. Bonn, Germany, Sept. 12, 1930; came to U.S., 1960; s. Josef and Elisabeth (Pütz) L.; m. Anneliese W. Scheller, Nov. 22, 1957; children: Christian H., Brigitte M. Prae Diploma, Bonn U. Fed. Republic of Germany, 1953; diploma, Aachen U., Fed. Republic of Germany, 1956; PhD, Stuttgart U., Fed. Republic of Germany, 1960. Asst., physics lab. Ruhrgas Co., Essen, Fed. Republic of Germany, 1954-57, head, physics lab., 1957-60; rsch. physicist U.S. Naval Weapons Lab., Dahlgren, Va., 1960-66; sci. cons. David Taylor Rsch. Ctr., Bethesda, Md., 1967-74, div. head, 1974-78, sr. rsch. physicist, 1978—. Author: Vortex Flow in Nature and Technology, 1983, reprint, 1995, Introduction to Vortex Theory, 1995; also over 110 articles to profl. jours. and govt. reports. Recipient Humboldt award Fed. Republic of Germany, 1981, Disting. Civilian Svc. award USN, 1982. Fellow Am. Physical Soc., Washington Acad. Scis.; mem. Am. Hist. Soc., Am. Goethe Soc. (pres. 1985-87), German Soc. for Applied Math. and Mechanics, Sigma Xi. Achievements include discovery of vortex breakdown in pipes; explanation of autorotating plates, Navier-Stokes computer simulations. Office: Carderock Div Naval Surface Warfare Ctr Bethesda MD 20084-5000

LUHRING, JOHN WILLIAM, former bank executive; b. Los Angeles, Sept. 11, 1912; s. Otto August and Lillian Louise (Fritz) L.; m. Josephine Ferentzy, Nov. 12, 1958; children by previous marriage: Karen Maria, John Dietrich. J.D., Southwestern U., 1934, LL.D. 1974; grad., Pacific Coast Sch. Banking, 1950. Bar: Calif. 1936. With Union Bank, Los Angeles, 1931-

74, trust counsel, gen. atty., 1931-43, asst. cashier, 1943-45, asst. v.p., 1945-53, regional v.p., 1953-63, v.p. charge So. Calif. dept. Bus. Devel. Div., 1960-63, regional v.p. Wilshire Center regional head office, 1963-67, regional v.p., gen. mgr. hdqrs. banking office, 1967-69, exec. dir. pub. affairs, 1969-74; past dir., mem. exec. com. Harbor Ins. Co.; dir. sec., former pres. Third Laguna Hills Mut.; exec. dir. Friends of Cultural Center, Inc., Palm Desert, Calif., 1974-79. Mem. adv. com. YWCA, 1955-60; mem. investment com. YMCA, 1951-74; past pres. bd. commrs. Dept. Water and Power; dir. Met. Water Dist. So. Calif., 1962-67; pres. Community TV So. Calif., 1967-72; mem. Nat. Adv. Com. Oceans and Atmosphere, 1972-76; pres., dir. Golden Rain Found. Laguna Hills; chmn. Airport Adv. Assos., 1964-74; pres. adv. council Liberty Park; pres. William H. Parker Meml. Scholarship Fund, 1966-74; mem.-at-large Los Angeles council Boy Scouts Am., 1950-74; bd. dirs. ARC, 1951-64, 66-68, exec. com., 1956-64; treas.; bd. dirs. Braille Inst., 1960-75, Vets. Service Center, 1950-60; bd. dirs., past pres. U.S.O., 1964-66; trustee Resthaven Sanitarium, 1956-58; trustee, chmn. exec. com. Southwestern U., pres., chmn. bd., 1974—80; bd. dirs Saddleback Community Hosp. Found., 1980-83, also bd. dirs. hosp., 1981—83; chmn. bd. dirs. Aliso Viejo Housing Opportunities Corp., 1982—. Decorated knight Order St. Lazarus Jerusalem. Mem. ABA, Los Angeles Bar Assn., State Bar Calif., Beverly Hills Wine and Food Soc., Chevaliers du Tastevin (grand officer), Commanderie de Bordeaux, Wine and Food Soc. So. Calif. (past chmn. bd. govs.), L.A. C. of C. (past dir., chmn. aerospace com.), Founding Friends Harvey Mudd Coll., Ephebian Soc., Alpha Phi Gamma. Home: 55172H Paseo Del Lago Laguna Hills CA 92653-2601

LUHRS, H. RIC, toy manufacturing company executive; b. Chambersburg, Pa., Mar. 22, 1931; s. Henry E. and Pearl (Beistle) L.; m. Grace B. Walke, June 12, 1973; children by previous marriage: Stephen Frederick, Christine Michelle, Terriann, Patricia Denise. BA, Gettysburg Coll., 1953. With The Beistle Co., Shippensburg, Pa., 1948-53, 1959—; pres., gen. mgr. Beistle Co., 1962-90, chmn. bd., 1978—; bd. dirs. Mellon Bank, Commonwealth region; dir., vice chmn. CompuPix Tech. Inc., 1984-88, pres., 1986-88, gemologist, 1977—; owner Luhrs Gem Testing Lab., 1977—, Luhrs Jewelry, 1976—, Allied Leasing Co., Shippensburg, 1968; pres. South Lac Devel. Co., 1986-92; owner Gun Depot, Shippensburg, 1992; chmn. The Walking Quail, Sports Goods Store, Shippensburg. Pres. Shippensburg Public Library, 1964-66, 1970-72, 76-78, bd. dirs., 1963-82; pres. Community Chest, 1965, bd. dir., 1963-72; pres. Shippensburg Area Devel. Corp., 1966-72; bd. dirs., trustee Carlisle (Pa.) Hosp., 1967-71, Chambersburg Hosp., 1969-75; mem. consumer adv. coun. Capital Blue Cross, 1976-78; bd. dirs. Fla. Atlantic U. Found., 1988-91, Shippensburg U. Found., 1991—. Capt. USAF, 1953-59. Mem. SAR (life), Shippensburg Hist. Soc. (bd. dirs. 1968), Shippensburg C. of C. (pres. 1965, bd. dirs. 1964-65), Toy Mfrs. Assn. (bd. dirs. 1969-71), Nat. Sml. Businessmen's Assn., NRA (life, benefactor), NRA Whittington Ctr. Founder's Club, NRA Golden Eagles, Shippensburg Fish and Game Assn. (life, pres. 1963), Carlisle Fish and Game Assn. (life), Am. Legion (life) VFW (life), Cumberland Valley Instl. Mgmt. Club, York Printing House Craftsmen, Masons (32 deg.), Shriners, Tall Cedars of Lebanon. Lutheran. Office: 1 Beistle Plz Shippensburg PA 17257

LUICK, ROBERT BURNS, lawyer; b. Belmond, Iowa, Aug. 6, 1911; s. Albert Lee and Estella Margaret (Burns) L.; m. Evelyn Pelletier, Nov. 21, 1942 (dec.); children: Elisabeth, Susan, Sarah, Nancy. AB, U. Minn., 1933, LLB, 1936; MBA cum laude, Harvard U., 1939. Bar: Mass. 1941. Atty. New Eng. Mut. Life Ins. Co., Boston, 1939-43; of counsel to Sullivan & Worcester, Boston, 1943-93; bd. dirs. Ionics, Inc., Watertown, Mass., Continental Cablevision, Inc., Boston, Setra Systems, Inc., Acton, Mass. and others; pres. and dir. Boston Investment Co. Mem. ABA, Boston Bar Assn., Knights of Malta, Union Club, Longwood Cricket Club. Avocations: tennis, painting, music. Home: 51 Rutledge Rd Belmont MA 02178-3322

LUIGS, CHARLES RUSSELL, gas and oil drilling industry executive; b. Evansville, Ind., Apr. 4, 1933; s. Charles Anthony and Agnes A. (Russell) L.; m. Mary M. McClaine, Sept. 7, 1957; children: Charles Edwin, James Russell, Carol Lynn, Susan Nadine, Michael Alan. B.S. in Petroleum Engring., U. Tex., 1957; student, St. Edwards U., 1951-52. With U.S. Industries, various locations, 1957-76; v.p. U.S., Industries, 1969-71, exec. v.p., 1971-74, pres., 1974-76; dir. U.S. Industries 1971-76; pres., chief exec. officer, dir. Global Marine, Inc., 1977—, chmn. bd., 1982—. Mem. Internat. Assn. Drilling Contractors (dir.), Nat. Soc. Profl. Engrs., AIME. Clubs: Houstonian, Houston, Westlake (Houston). Home: PO Box 4577 Houston TX 77210-4577 Office: Global Marine Inc 777 N Eldridge Pky Houston TX 77079-4425

LUIKART, FORDYCE WHITNEY, management consultant; b. Cleve., Aug. 17, 1910; s. Louis Edward and Grace (Latham) L.; m. Margaret Clark, Sept. 7, 1935; children—Clark W., James L., John F. A.B. cum laude, Ohio Wesleyan U., 1933, teaching certificate, 1934. Teaching fellow, asst. Maxwell Grad. Sch. Citizenship and Pub. Affairs, Syracuse U., 1934-37; instr. social sci. State Tchrs. Coll., Brockport, N.Y., 1937-39; mgr. br. office U.S. CSC, Cleve., 1942-44; chief investigations div. U.S. CSC, Washington, 1944-45; chief orgn. and methods staff U.S. CSC, 1945-46, chief inspection div., 1947-50, dir. exec. devel. program, 1950-51, exec. vice chmn. fed. personnel council, 1951, chief examining and placement div., 1951-53; dep. dir. adminstrn. HEW, 1953-54, dir. adminstrn., 1954; vis. lectr. pub. personnel adminstrn. Maxwell Grad. Sch., 1946-62; sr. staff mem. Brookings Instn., 1962-76, cons., 1976—; pvt. cons. on govt. orgn. and mgmt., exec. devel. and tng., 1976—; cons. on govt. orgn. with Cresap, McCormick & Paget (mgmt. cons.), 1955-57; cons. staff dir. Pres.'s Com. on Career Exec. Service, Sept. 1957; dir. Fed. Aviation Orgn. Study, White House Staff, 1957-58; asst. adminstr. personnel and tng. FAA, 1958-62; lectr. Eisenhower Exchange Fellowship Inc. Program, 1979—. Author pub. personnel adminstrn. articles profl. jours. Pres. Group Health Assn., Inc.; trustee Community Group Health Found., Washington; Spl. adv. asst. to mem. Commn. Orgn. of Exec. Br. (Hoover Commn.), 1948-49; spl. adv. personnel and civil service to Greek Govt., E.C.A. mission, 1949-50. Mem. Pub. Personnel Assn., Soc. Personnel Adminstrn. (pres. 1952-53), Phi Beta Kappa, Omicron Delta Kappa, Sigma Chi. Methodist. Home: 3257 Beech St NW Washington DC 20015-2207 Office: Brookings Instn Washington DC 20036

LUIKART, JOHN FORD, investment banker; b. Washington, Apr. 9, 1949; s. Fordyce Whitney and Margaret Lucille (Clark) L.; m. Lorry Adele Haycock, June 2, 1973; children: Erin Kristine, James Benjamin, John Thomas. BA, Ohio Weslyan U., 1971. Ptnr. Prescott Ball and Turben, Cleve., 1977, sr. v.p., mgr. fixed income, 1982-86, exec. v.p., also bd. dirs., 1986-88; pres. Sutro & Co., San Francisco, 1989—, also bd. dirs.; pres. Selected Money Mkt. Fund, Chgo., 1986, 1993 Advisors, Cleve., 1986; mgr. Ohio Bond Fund, Cleve., 1983—; chmn. NASD Dist. Bus. Conduct Com. 1994; bd. dirs. John Hancock Clearing Corp., J.H.M. Capital Corp., J.H.M. Mortgage Securities, l.p. Chmn. Ohio Mcpl. Adv. Council, Cleve., 1978-79. Mem. Cleve. Bond Club (pres. 1980). Methodist. Avocations: sports, reading. Office: Sutro & Co 350 Sansome St San Francisco CA 94104-1304

LUING, GARY ALAN, financial management educator; b. Collins, Iowa, Apr. 24, 1937; s. Dwight Orn and Marjorie Mae (Clemons) L.; m. Sherry Lea Gates, Dec. 19, 1954; 1 child, Heather Sherry-Anne. B.S. cum laude, Stetson U., 1960; M.A., U. Ill., 1961; Dr. Adminstrn. (hon.), Canadian Sch. Mgmt. Auditor Arthur Andersen & Co., Chgo., 1963; prof. Fla. Atlantic U., Boca Raton, 1965—; dean Sch. Bus., 1970-87; cons. U.S. Treasury; expert witness on valuing closely held corps., 1972—; lectr., U.S., various fgn. countries; dir. Fla. Liquid Assets, Templeton Trust Co.; mem. faculty Internat. Assn. Fin. Planners. Editor Fla. C.P.A. 1974; assoc. editor Intellect, 1975-79; tax editor Quick Print, 1988—; contbr. articles to profl. jours. Chmn. Palm Beach County Transp. Com., 1972-75. Served to 1st lt. U.S. Army, 1961-63. Recipient Disting. Service Fla. Accountants Assn., 1971. Hon. fellow Internat. Soc. Preventive Medicine, Canadian Sch. Mgmt.; mem. AICPA, Am. Acctg. Assn., Acctg. Rsch. Assn., Beta Gamma Sigma, Beta Alpha Psi, Phi Beta Phi (pres. 1974), Phi Kappa Phi. Baptist. Home: 9550 NW 42d Ct Coral Springs FL 33065 In the professions, as in life, so much is owed to those who have gone before.

LUISO, ANTHONY, international food company executive; b. Bari, Italy, Jan. 6, 1944; s. John and Antonina (Giustino) L.; m. Nancy Louise Bassett, June 26, 1976. B.B.A., Iona Coll., 1967; M.B.A., U. Chgo., 1982. Audit sr. Arthur Andersen & Co., Chgo., 1966-71; supr. auditing Beatrice Foods Co.,

Chgo., 1971-74, adminstr. asst. to exec. v.p., 1974-75, v.p. ops. internat. div., dairy div., 1975-77, exec. v.p. internat. div., 1977-82, prof. internat. div., 1982-83, chief operating officer internat. food group, 1984-86, pres. U.S. Food segment, from 1986; group v.p. Internat. Multifoods Corp., Mpls., until 1988, COO, 1988-89, chmn., CEO, pres., 1989—; bd. dirs. Black & Decker Co. Mem. adv. council U. Chgo. Grad. Sch. of Bus. Served with USAR, 1968-74. Mem. AICPA. Republican. Roman Catholic. Clubs: Univ. (Chgo.), Internat. (Chgo.). Office: Internat Multifoods Corp Multifood Tower PO Box 2942 Minneapolis MN 55402*

LUJAN, HERMAN D., university president; m. Carla Lujan; 3 children. B in Polit. Sci., St. Mary's Coll. Calif.; M in Polit. Sci., U. Calif., Berkeley; PhD in Polit. Sci., U. Idaho. Faculty mem., adminstr. U. Kans., dir. inst. social and environ. studies, 1972-78; dir. divsn. state planning and rsch. Gov. of Kans., 1974-75; prof. polit. sci. dept. U. Wash., lectr. Japanese exec. mgmt. program, sch. bus., v.p. minority affairs, 1978-88, vice provost, 1988-91; pres. U. No. Colo., 1991—; bd. dirs Bank One, Greeley, Colo. Author several books; contbr. articles to profl. jours. Bd. dirs. Boy Scouts Am., Latin Am. Ednl. Found. Mem. Rotary (Greeley). Office: U No Colo Office of Pres Univ Of No Colo CO 80639

LUJAN, MANUEL, JR., former U.S. secretary of the interior, former congressman; b. San Ildefonso, N.Mex., May 12, 1928; s. Manuel and Lorenzita (Romero) L.; m. Jean Kay Couchman, Nov. 18, 1948; children: Terra Kay Everett, James Manuel, Barbara Frae, Robert Jeffrey. BA, Coll. Santa Fe, 1950; postgrad., St. Mary's (Calif.) Coll., 1946-47. Engaged in ins. bus. Santa Fe and Albuquerque, 1948; mem. 91st-100th Congresses 1st N.Mex. Dist., 1969-89; mem. interior and insular affairs com., energy and environ. subcom., sci. and tech. com. Dept. of Interior, 1969, sec., 1989-93. Office: Manuel Lujan Agys PO Box 3727 Albuquerque NM 87190

LUKAC, GEORGE JOSEPH, fundraising executive; b. Garfield, N.J., Mar. 6, 1937; s. Michael and Elizabeth (Gall) L.; m. Alice Louise Osborn, Nov. 8, 1958; children: Mark Robert (dec.), Amy Elizabeth. BA in Polit. Sci., Rutgers U., 1958. Trainee, systems reviewer Prudential Ins. Co., Newark, 1958-59; asst. editor comm. dept. Johnson & Johnson, New Brunswick, N.J., 1959-61; editor Rutgers Alumni Monthly Rutgers U., New Brunswick, 1961-66, asst. dir. alumni rels. and devel., 1966-77; exec. dir. Sangamon State U. Found., Springfield, Ill., 1977-81; dir. devel. and pub. rels. Mo. Hist. Soc., St. Louis, 1981-84; v.p. devel. Rio Grande (Ohio) U., 1984-86; exec. dir. St. Luke's Hosps. Meritcare Found., Fargo, N.D., 1986-90; pres., CEO Venice (Fla.) Hosp. Found., 1990-92; pres. Lehigh Valley Hosp. Trust Fund, Allentown, Pa., 1992—; vol. cons. Presbyn. chs., Fargo, Ballwin, Mo. and Venice, Fla., 1978-92; social welfare groups, Fargo, Ballwin, Venice and Allentown, 1978—; ofcl. cons. Ohio Arts Coun., Columbus, Ohio, 1986; instr., adviser, speaker univs., groups, confs., 1978—; jury mem. 1982 CASE Nat. Awards Contest. Editor: Aloud to Alma Mater, 1966, Copyright-The Librarian and the Law, 1972 (Citation N.J. Writers Conf. 1974); contbr.: Big Gifts, 1990; contbr. articles to mags. and profl. jours. Loaned exec. United Way, Fargo, 1987-88, capt., com. mem., 1988-90; bd. dirs. Red River Dance Co., Fargo, 1989-90; v.p. bd. dirs. Ronald McDonald House, Fargo, 1987-90; mem. Indsl. Devel. Corp. of Lehigh Valley, 1992—; Rep. nat. com. 1994 Chmn.'s Campaign Adv. Panel. Recipient Citation N.J. Writers Conf., 1974, Ashmead award Rutgers Fund, 1968,76, Spl. Recognition award CASE Nat. Alumni Mag. Competition, 1966, award Rutgers Fund, 1961. Mem. Nat. Soc. Fund Raising Execs. (cert., found. bd. dirs.), Inst. on Philanthropy U. Ind. (charter assoc.), Hawk Mt. Sanctuary Pa., Assn. Hosp. Philanthropy, Nat. Conf. Nonprofit Bds., Allentown Rotary Club. Republican. Presbyterian. Avocations: writing, volunteer consulting, nature, music. Home: 2085 Brook Cir Macungie PA 18062 Office: Lehigh Valley Hosp Trust Fund 1243 S Cedar Crest Blvd Allentown PA 18103

LUKACS, JOHN ADALBERT, historian, retired educator; b. Budapest, Hungary, Jan. 31, 1924; came to U.S., 1946, naturalized, 1953; s. Paul and Magdalena Maria L.; m. Helen Schofield, May 29, 1953 (dec. 1970); children: Paul, Annemarie; m. Stephanie Harvey, May 18, 1974. Ph.D., Palatine Joseph U., Budapest, 1946. Prof. history Chestnut Hill Coll., 1947-94, Chmn. dept. history, 1947-74, ret., 1994; vis. prof. history La Salle Coll., 1949-82, Columbia U., 1954-55, U. Toulouse, France, 1964-65, U. Pa., 1964, 67, 68, Johns Hopkins U., 1970-71, Fletcher Sch. Law, Diplomacy, 1971-72, Princeton U., 1988; vis. prof. U. Budapest, 1991, U. Pa., 1995. Author books, including: The Great Powers and Eastern Europe, 1953, A History of the Cold War, 1961, Decline and Rise of Europe, 1965, The Passing of the Modern Age, 1970, Historical Consciousness, 1968, 2d edit., 1985, The Last European War, 1939-41, 1976; 1945, Year Zero, 1978, Philadelphia: Patricians and Philistines, 1900-1950, 1981, Outgrowing Democracy: A historical interpretation of the U.S. in the 20th Century, 1984, Budapest 1900, 1988, Confessions of an Original Sinner, 1990, The Duel (Hitler vs. Churchill 10 May-31 August 1940), 1991, the End of the 20th Century and the End of the Modern Age), 1993, Destinations Past, 1994; contbr. numerous articles, essays, revs. to hist. and lit. jours. Chmn. Schuylkill Twp. (Pa.) Planning Commn. Recipient Ingersoll prize, 1991. Fellow Soc. Am. Historians; mem. Am. Catholic Hist. Assn. (pres. 1977). Home: Valley Park Rd Phoenixville PA 19460

LUKAS, J. ANTHONY, journalist; b. N.Y.C., Apr. 25, 1933; s. Edwin Jay and Elizabeth (Schamberg) L.; m. Linda Healey, Sept. 18, 1982. BA magna cum laude, Harvard U., 1955; postgrad., Free U. Berlin, 1955-56; hon. degree, Northeastern U., 1986, Colby Coll., 1987. Reporter, city hall corr. Balt. Sun, 1958-62; mem. staff N.Y. Times, 1962-72, assigned to the Congo, 1962-65, assigned to India, 1965-67, assigned to N.Y.C., 1967-68; roving nat. corr. N.Y. Times, Chgo., 1969-70; staff writer Sunday mag., N.Y.C., 1970-72; Nieman fellow Harvard U., 1968-69, fellow Inst. Politics, 1976-77; vis. fellow NYU, 1991; fellow Yale U., 1973-78; adj. prof. journalism Sch. Pub. Commn., Boston U., 1977-78; adj. prof. Columbia U. Sch. of the Arts, 1995; vis. lectr. Yale U., 1973; adj. lectr. Kennedy Sch. Govt., Harvard U., 1979-80; cons. Hastings Ctr., 1979-80; mem. steering com. Reporter's Com. on Freedom of Press, 1970-84; mem. exec. com. PEN Am. Ctr., 1977-83; judge gen. non-fiction Am. Book Awards, 1983, 86, Pulitzer Prize, 1988; mem. study group urban sch. desegregation Am. Acad. Arts and Scis., 1977-78; mem. exec. bd. N.Y. Coun. Humanities, 1986-88; mem. faculty Wesleyan Writers Conf., 1986, New Orleans Writers Conf., 1991, N.Y. State Summer Writers Inst., 1987-88. Contbg. editor: New Times mag., 1973-75; sr. editor: More Journalism Rev., 1972-77, assoc. editor, 1977-78; mem. editorial bd. Book-of-the Month Club, 1989-94, The Am. Prospect; contbr. articles to Gentlemen's Quar., Rolling Stone, Atlantic, Harpers, Saturday Rev., The Nation, New Republic, Psychology Today, Esquire, Reader's Digest, New York, others, 1958—; host radio program: In Conversation, Sta. WOR, N.Y.C., 1973-74; author: The Barnyard Epithet and Other Obscenities: Notes On The Chicago Conspiracy Trial, 1970, Don't Shoot—We Are Your Children, 1971, Nightmare: The Underside of the Nixon Years, 1976, Common Ground: A Turbulent Decade in the Lives of Three American Families, 1985. Mem. exec. bd. N.Y. Coun. Humanities, 1986-88; mem. Com. for Pub. Justice, 1972-88. With AUS, 1956-58. Recipient George Polk Meml. award L.I. U., 1967, Pulitzer prize for local spl. reporting, 1968, Page One award N.Y. Newspaper Guild, 1968, Mike Berger award Columbia Sch. Journalism, 1968, Am. Book award, 1985, Pulitzer prize for gen. non-fiction, 1986, Nat. Book Critics Circle award, 1986, Robert F. Kennedy Book award, 1986, Polit. Book of Yr. award The Washington Monthly, 1986; named Literary List N.Y. Pub. Libr., 1986; Guggenheim fellow, 1979-80. Fellow Soc. Am. Historians; mem. Author's Guild (sec. 1989-91), Signet Soc., Phi Beta Kappa, Harvard Club, St. Botolph Club (Boston), The Century Assn.

LUKASH, BARBARA LYNNE, dermatologist; b. New Hyde Park, N.Y., Aug. 27, 1950; d. Gladys Joyce (Horowitz) L.; m. Ben Zane Cohen, June 18, 1978; children: David, Jesse. BS, U. Wis., 1972; MD, Tulane U., 1976. Diplomate Am. Bd. Dermatology. Intern L.I. Jewish Hosp.; resident U. Chgo. Hosps. and Clinics; pvt. practice dermatology Bronxville, N.Y., 1987—. Fellow Am. Acad. Dermatology; me. Westchester County Med. Soc., N.Y. Med. Soc. Avocations: gardening, culinary arts. Office: 824 Bronx River Rd Bronxville NY 10708

LUKASIK, STEPHEN JOSEPH, information technology executive; b. S.I., N.Y., Mar. 19, 1931; s. Stephen Joseph and Mildred Florence (Tynan) L.; m. Marilyn Bertha Trappiel, Jan. 31, 1953 (div. 1982); children: Carol J.,

Gregory C.; Elizabeth A.; Jeffrey P.; m. Virginia Dogan Armstrong, Feb. 11, 1983; stepchildren: Elizabeth L., Alan D. B.S., Rensselaer Poly. Inst., 1951; M.S., MIT, 1953, Ph.D., 1956. Dir. Advanced Research Project Agy., Washington, 1966-74; v.p. Xerox Corp., Rochester, N.Y., 1974-76; chief scientist and sr. v.p. Rand Corp., Santa Monica, Calif., 1977-79; chief scientist FCC, Washington, 1979-82; v.p. and mgr. Northrop Research and Tech. Ctr., Palos Verdes, Calif., 1982-85, corp. v.p. for tech., 1985-90; v.p. for tech. TRW Space and Def. Sector, Redondo Beach, Calif., 1990-92; CEO SAIC, San Diego, Calif., 1992—; dir. Face to Face Game Co.; cons. numerous gov. orgns. Assoc. editor: The Info. Soc. Trustee Stevens Inst. Tech., Hoboken, N.J., 1975-92; trustee Harvey Mudd Coll., Claremont, Calif., 1987—. Served to capt. USAR. Recipient Sec. Def. Disting. Civilian Service medal, 1973, 74. Mem. Am. Phys. Soc., AAAS. Club: Cosmos, D.C., George Town, D.C., Regency, Los Angeles. Home: 1714 Stone Canyon Rd Los Angeles CA 90077-1915

LUKE, DAVID LINCOLN, III, paper company executive; b. Tyrone, Pa., July 25, 1923; s. David Lincoln and Priscilla Warren (Silver) L.; m. Fanny R. Curtis, June 11, 1955. AB, Yale U., 1945; LLD (hon.), Juniata Coll., 1967, Lawrence U., 1976, Salem Coll., 1983, W. Va. U., 1984. V.p., dir. Westvaco Corp., N.Y.C., 1953-57, exec. v.p., dir., 1957-62, pres., bd. dirs. 1962-80, chief exec. officer, 1963-88, chmn. bd. dirs., from 1980; bd. dirs. Clupak, Inc., McGraw Hill Inc., N.Y. Stock Exch. Chmn. bd. trustees Cold Spring Harbor Lab.; bd. dirs. Josiah Macy Jr. Found.; past chmn., trustee emeritus Hotchkiss Sch. Served from aviation cadet to capt. USMCR., 1942-45. Mem. Am. Paper Inst. (past chmn.), Inst. Paper Sci. and Tech. (trustee, past chmn.). Clubs: Links, The River (N.Y.C.); Piping Rock, Megantic Fish and Game Corp. *

LUKE, DENNIS ROBERT, state legislator, home building company executive; b. Salem, Oreg., Dec. 13, 1946; s. LeRoy Willard and Alice Lucille (Magnason) L.; m. Joanne Elaine Copley, Jan. 13, 1968; children: Matthew Mark, Brian Lee. Student, Oreg. State U., 1965-68. Owner, mgr. Luke Builders Inc., Bend, Oreg., 1974—; mem. Oreg. Ho. of Reps., Salem, 1993—. Contbr. articles to various pubs. Bd. dirs., sec. Ctrl. Oreg. People's Utility Dist., Bend, Redmond, 1980-84; scoutmaster troop 25, com. mem., bd. dirs. Boy Scouts Am., 1977—. Recipient 10-yr. award Boy Scouts Am. 1987. Mem. Nat. Assn. Home Builders (nat. bd. dirs., com.), Oreg. Builders Assn. (past pres., bd. dirs., com., State Builder of Yr. 1991, dir. builders ins. agy. 1991—), Ctrl. Oreg. Builders Assn. (past pres., bd. dirs.), Deschutes County Far Bur., Ea. Star Grange, Elks, Eagles. Republican. Lutheran. Avocations: fishing, hiking, bowling, hunting, gardening. Home: PO Box 9069 Bend OR 97708-9069

LUKE, JAMES PHILLIP, manufacturing executive; b. Bklyn., Nov. 11, 1942; s. Edmon George and Gertrude Caroline (Sanial) L.; A.B., Princeton U., 1965 M.B.A., Columbia U., 1968; m. Elizabeth Joanne Hooke, Sept. 21, 1968; children—James Phillip, Karin Margaret, Shelby Elizabeth, Thomas Edmon. Exec. trainee WestPoint Pepperell, Inc., N.Y.C., 1968-69, salesman, Atlanta, 1969-70; venture devel. mgr. Internat. Paper Co., Inc., N.Y.C., 1970-71, dist. mgr. Formed Fabrics div., Atlanta, 1971-72, div. controller, Lewisburg, Pa., 1972-75; dir. planning Blessings Corp., Inc., N.Y.C., 1975-77, v.p. fin., Piscataway, N.J., 1977—; also sec.-treas., 1984-88, exec. v.p., sec.-treas. 1988—. Served to lt. USNR, 1965-67. Roman Catholic. Mem. Am. Soc. Corp. Secs. Clubs: Princeton of N.Y., Two Rivers Country. Home: 3012 Hearthstone Dr Williamsburg VA 23185 Office: Blessings Corp 200 Enterprise Dr Newport News VA 23603

LUKE, JOHN A., JR., paper, packaging and chemical company executive; b. Nov. 24, 1948; s. John Anderson Sr. and Joy (Carter) L.; m. Kathleen Allen, June 30, 1984; children: Lindsay Allen, Elizabeth Carter, John A. III. BA, Lawrence U., 1971; MBA, U. Pa., 1979. Unit sales mgr. Procter & Gamble, 1974-77; corp. assoc. Westvaco Corp., N.Y.C., 1979-81, sr. fin. analyst, 1981-82, asst. treas., 1982-83, treas., 1983-86, v.p. treas., 1986, 1986-87, sr. v.p. mktg., internat. and Brazilian subsidiary, 1987-90, exec. v.p., 1990-92, pres., CEO, 1992—; bd. dirs Arkwright Ins., Boston, The Tinker Found., Americas Soc., Coun. of Ams., ACCION Internat.; bd. trustees Lawrence U.; mem. Coun. on Fgn. Rels. Bd. govs. NCASI; dir. United Negro Coll. Fund. Mem. Am. Forest and Paper Assn. (dir., exec. com.), UN Assn. of U.S.A. (gov.), Univ. Club. Office: Westvaco Corp 299 Park Ave New York NY 10171-0001*

LUKE, JOHN ANDERSON, paper company executive; b. Tyrone, Pa., Nov. 30, 1925; s. David Lincoln and Priscilla Warren (Silver) L.; m. Joy Carter, Dec. 21, 1946; children: John Anderson, Hope S., Jane T., William H. BA, Yale U., 1949. Personnel asst. Westvaco Corp., Charleston, S.C., 1949-51; personnel mgr. Westvaco Corp., 1951-53, asst. mgr. adminstrn., 1953-55; mill mgr. Westvaco Corp., Luke, Md., 1955-60; mgr. fine papers div. Westvaco Corp., 1960-74; v.p. Westvaco Corp., N.Y.C., 1966-74, sr. v.p., 1974-76, exec. v.p. — v.p. 1976-80, pres., 1980-88, pres., chief exec. officer, 1988-92, dir.; ret.; chmn. Internat. Com. Served with USAAF, 1943-45. Mem. New Canaan Country Club. Office: Westvaco Corp 299 Park Ave New York NY 10171-0001

LUKE, RANDALL DAN, retired tire and rubber company executive, lawyer; b. New Castle, Pa., June 4, 1935; s. Randall Beamer and Blanche Wilhelmina (Fisher) L.; m. Patricia Arlene Moody, Aug. 4, 1962 (div. Jan. 1977); children: Lisa Elin, Randall Sargent; m. Saralee Frances Krow, Mar. 1, 1979; 1 stepchild, Stephanie Sogg. BA in Econs. with honors, U. Pa., 1957, JD, 1960. Bar: Ohio 1960, Calif. 1962, Ill. 1989. Assoc., ptnr. Daus, Schwenger & Kottler, Cleve., 1965-70; ptnr. Kottler & Danzig, Cleve., 1970-75, Hahn, Loeser, Freedheim, Dean & Wellman, Cleve., 1975-81; assoc. gen. counsel The Firestone Tire & Rubber Co., Akron, Ohio, 1981-82, v.p., assoc. gen. counsel and sec., 1982-88; v.p., assoc. gen. counsel and sec. Bridgestone/Firestone, Inc., Akron, 1988-91; of counsel Hahn Loeser & Parks, Cleve., 1991—. Trustee Akron Art Mus., 1982-87, Akron Symphony Orch., 1986-87, Cleve. Opera League, 1992—. Served to Capt. USNR, 1960-81; ret. 1981. Mem. ABA, Assn. Corp. Secs., Calif. Bar Assn., Ohio Bar Assn., Ill. Bar Assn. Republican. Clubs: Cleve. Skating (Shaker Heights, Ohio); Union (Cleve.); Univ. Club of Chgo. Avocations: tennis, jogging, skiing, swimming. Home: 13901 Shaker Blvd Cleveland OH 44120-1588 Office: Hahn Loeser & Parks 200 Public Sq Cleveland OH 44114-2303

LUKEHART, CHARLES MARTIN, chemistry educator; b. DuBois, Pa., Dec. 21, 1946; s. David Blair and Grace Dorothy (Lundgren) L.; m. Marilyn Orleana McKinney, Aug. 4, 1973; children: Mark, Brian, Laura. BS in Chemistry, Pa. State U., 1968; PhD in Inorganic Chemistry, MIT, 1972. Postdoctoral assoc. Tex. A&M U., College Sta., 1972-73; asst. prof. chemistry Vanderbilt U., Nashville, 1973-77, assoc. prof. chemistry, 1977-82, prof., 1982—. Author: Fundamental Transition Metal Organometallic Chemistry, 1985. Rsch. fellow Alfred P. Sloan Found., 1979-81. Mem. Am. Chem. Soc. (chmn. Nashville sect. 1979, 92), Materials Rsch. Soc. Office: Vanderbilt U Dept Chemistry Box 1822 Sta B Nashville TN 37235

LUKENBILL, GREGG, sports promoter, real estate developer; b. Sacramento, Aug. 15, 1954; s. Frank and Leona L.; children: Jake, Molly, Ben. BS in Bus. Adminstrn., Calif. State U. Owner, developer/builder Lukenbill Enterprises, Sacramento Valley Region; mng. gen. ptnr. Sacramento Kings Profl. Basketball/NBA, 1983-92, ARCO Arena, 1985-93; pres. Hyatt Regency, Sacramento, 1986-92; owner Sky King Inc.; pilot. Office: Lukenbill Enterprises 3600 Power Inn Rd Sacramento CA 95826-3826

LUKENS, ALAN WOOD, retired ambassador and foreign service officer; b. Phila., Feb. 12, 1924; s. Edward Clark and Frances (Day) L.; m. Susan Atkinson, Dec. 29, 1962; children: Lewis Alan, Susan Lukens Stone, Frances Lukens Bennett, Timothy Eric. AB, Princeton U., 1948; postgrad., U. Sorbonne, Paris, 1948, U. Madrid, 1948, Georgetown U., 1951; LLD (hon.), St. Lawrence U., 1987. Tchr. St. Albans Sch., Washington, 1950-51; joined U.S. Fgn. Svc., 1951; vice consul Ankara, Turkey, 1952; Istanbul, Turkey, 1953; pub. affairs officer Martinique, 1954-56; with news divsn. State Dept. 1956-57; U.S. del. 12th UN Gen. Assembly, 1957; mem. internat. staff NATO, Paris, 1958-60; consul Brazzaville, 1960; U.S. rep. to Independence of Congo, Brazzaville, Chad, Gabon, Central African Republic, 1961; charge d'affaires Am. Embassy, Bangui, Central African Republic, 1961, Paris, 1961-63, Rabat, Morocco, 1963-65; chief personnel Bur. African Affairs, State Dept.; 1965-67; dep. chief mission, counselor embassy Dakar, 1967-70,

Nairobi, 1970-72; chief jr. officer div. personnel State Dept., 1973-75; dir. Office Iberian Affairs, 1974-75; counselor, dep. chief mission Am. Embassy, Copenhagen, 1975-78; with Bur. African Affairs, Dept. State, Washington, 1978-79; consul gen. Cape Town, South Africa, 1979-82; dir. office analysis for Western Europe, Bur. Intelligence and Research, Dept. State, Washington, 1982-84; A.E.& P. People's Republic of Congo, 1984-87; cons. on internat. affairs and crisis mgmt. Dept. of State, 1987-93; lectr. on Africa. Pres. St. Barnabas Soc. Fund; chmn. com. on Africa Washington Nat. Cathedral. With AUS, 1943-46. Recipient Commendable Service award State Dept., 1961. Mem. Washington Inst. Fgn. Affairs (bd. dirs.), Diplomatic and Consular Officers Ret., Rotary, Princeton Club N.Y.C., Washington Club Nairobi (pres. Paris chpt. 1961-63), Princeton U. Alumni Coun. (mem. exec. com.), Explorers Club Washington (bd. dirs.) Chevy Chase Club. Episcopalian. Home: 18 Grafton St Chevy Chase MD 20815-3428

LUKENS, BETTY FAYE, health facility manager; b. Galveston, Tex., Sept. 23, 1944; d. Groby D. and Faye Tyler; m. Jerry Lynn Lukens, Apr. 10, 1970; children: Jon Scott Sanford, Michael Craig Sanford; stepchildren: Theresa Lynn, Jerry Lynn. ADN cum laude, Alvin Community Coll., 1975. RN, Tex.; lic. chemical dependency counselor. Staff nurse U. Tex.-MB, Galveston; charge nurse St. Mary's Hosp., Galveston; exec. dir. Alcohol and Drug Abuse Program of Brazoria County, Lake Jackson, Tex.; supr., nurse mgr. St. Mary's Hosp., Galveston; nurse mgr. U. Tex. Health Sci. Ctr. Harris County Psychiat. Ctr., Houston; staff nurse III pediat. ICU U. Tex. Med. Br.; rehab. cons. Health Benefit Mgmt., Tex. Workers Compensation Ins. Fund; co-founder Health Care Profls. Recovery, 1987. Nurse adv. Tex. Peer Asst. Program for Nurses. Mem. TAADAC, Internat. Case Mgmt. Assn., Nat. Consortium of Chemically Dependent Nurses. Home: 214 W Sherwood Dr Alvin TX 77511-5110

LUKENS, PAUL BOURNE, financial executive; b. Meriden, Conn., Oct. 29, 1934; s. George Price and Elsie (Bourne) L.; m. Gail Perry Todd, July 7, 1956; children: Jennifer C. Lukens Holmes, Julie Lukens Belsky. B.S. in Accounting, U. Conn., 1956. C.P.A. Conn. Sr. accountant Webster Blanchard & Willard (merged with Price Waterhouse & Co. 1962), 1956-62; audit mgr. Price Waterhouse & Co., Hartford, Conn., 1962-69; with Aetna Life & Casualty Co., Hartford, Conn., 1969-77; v.p. treas. Aetna Variable Annuity Life Ins. Co. (subs), 1972-75, v.p. corp. planning dept. parent co., 1975-77; v.p., controller INA Corp., 1977-82, Cigna Corp., 1982-89; pres. CIGNA Holdings, Inc., 1989-90, chmn., 1990—; cons. corp. acctg. and fin. reporting, 1990—. Contbg. author: Property-Liability Insurance Accounting, 1974. Trustee Episcopal Hosp., Phila., 1981-85. Mem. Am. Inst. C.P.A.s (acctg. standards exec. com. 1983-85), Conn. Soc. C.P.A.s (bd. govs. 1973-75), Fin. Execs. Inst. (com. on corp. reporting 1979—, bd. dirs. Phila. chpt. 1982-85), Fin. Acctg. Standards Bd. (emerging issues task force). Home: 638 Glenwood Village West Chester PA 19380-5703 Office: Cigna Holdings Inc 1 Beaver Valley Rd Wilmington DE 19803-1115

LUKER, KRISTIN, sociology educator; b. San Francisco, Aug. 5, 1946; d. James Wester and Bess (Littlefield) L. BA, U. Calif., Berkeley, 1968; PhD, Yale U., 1975. Postdoctoral fellow U. Calif., Berkeley, 1974-75, asst. prof. sociology, San Diego, 1975-81, assoc. prof., 1981-85, prof., 1985-86, co-dir. women's studies program, 1984-85, prof. jurisprudence and social policy, sociology, Berkeley, 1986—. Author: Taking Chances: Abortion and the Decision Not to Contracept, 1976 (hon. mention Jessie Bernard award), Abortion and the Politics of Motherhood, 1984 (Charles Horton Cooley award 1985). Bd. dirs. Ctr. for Women's Studies and Services, San Diego, Ctr. for Population Options, Washington. Recipient Disting. Teaching award U. Calif., San Diego, 1984; Guggenheim Found. grantee, 1985. Mem. Am. Sociol. Assn., Sociologists for Women in Soc. Office: U Calif Berkeley Jurisprudence & Social Policy 2240 Piedmont Ave Berkeley CA 94720-0001

LUKOWSKI, STANLEY J., banker; married. BS, Villanova U., 1983; MBA, Columbia U., 1985. V.p. Ea. Bank, Lynn, Mass., 1976-81, pres., chief operating officer, 1981—. Office: Eastern Bank 270 Union St Lynn MA 01901-1380

LULLA, JACK DAVID, polymer engineer; b. N.Y.C., Jan. 15, 1929; s. Joseph and Fannie L.; m. Rita Vernon, Apr. 2, 1955; children: Bruce, Joel, Stephen, Margot. BS, CCNY, 1950. Rsch. chemist Tech. Tape, N.Y.C., 1951-55, plant mgr., 1955-56; v.p. R & D Tech. Tape, New Rochelle, N.Y., 1956-88, Tesa Tuck Inc., New Rochelle, 1988—; 1988—. Col U.S. Army, 1952-54. Avocations: music, tennis, reading. Home: 40 E 88th St Apt 11D New York NY 10128-1176 Office: Tesa Tuck Inc Le Fevre Ln New Rochelle NY 10801

LUM, GRETCHEN YATES, poet, small business owner; b. Honolulu, June 10, 1945; d. Francis Gordon and Annabelle (Johnson) Yates; m. Philip Wayne Lum, May 30, 1967 (div. Dec. 1984); 1 child, Jadine Alexandra. BFA, Calif. Coll. Arts & Crafts, 1970. Art tchr. Montclair Recreation Ctr., Oakland, Calif., 1975-76; graphic designer East Design, San Francisco, 1976-77, Kaiser Aluminum, Oakland, 1978-83, Blue Cross Calif., Oakland, 1983-86; owner Graphic Design, Oakland, 1986-89; antique and art dealer Conn. and N.Y., 1990—; owner Rare Objects of Art, Ridgefield, Conn., 1992—. Author: Standing on Tiptoes, 1991; rec. The Sound of Poetry, 1993, Visions, 1994, (anthology) Whispers in the Wind, Best Poems of 1995. Mem. coun. for the arts Aldrich Mus. Contemporary Art, Ridgefield, 1992-94. Recipient Merit award Golden Poems of the Western World, Washington, 1989, Editor's Choice award Nat. Libr. Poetry, Owings Mills, Md., 1993, 95. Mem. Ridgefield Artist Guild, Internat. Club, Internat. Soc. of Poets, Art Students League of N.Y., Community Ctr. Ridgefield. Avocation: Siddha yoga.

LUM, JEAN LOUI JIN, nurse educator; b. Honolulu, Sept. 5, 1938; d. Yee Nung and Pui Ki (Young) L. BS, U. Hawaii, Manoa, 1960; MS in Nursing, U. Calif., San Francisco, 1961; MA, U. Wash., 1969, PhD in Sociology, 1972. Registered nurse, Hawaii. From instr. to prof. Sch. Nursing U. Hawaii Manoa, Honolulu, 1961—; acting dean, 1982, dean, 1982-89; project coordinator Analysis and Planning Personnel Svcs., Western Interstate Commn. Higher Edn., 1977; extramural assoc. div. Rsch. Grants NIH, 1978-79; mem. mgmt. adv. com. Honolulu County Hosp., 1982—; mem. exec. bd. Pacific Health Rsch. Inst., 1980-88; mem. health planning com. East Honolulu, 1978-81; mem. rsch. grants adv. coun. Hawaii Med. Svcs. Assn. Found., Nat. Adv. Coun. for Nursing Rsch., 1990-93. Contbr. articles to profl. jours. Trustee Straub Pacific Health Found., Honolulu. Recipient Nurse of Yr. award Hawaii Nurses Assn., 1982; named Disting. Practitioner in Nursing, Nat. Acads. of Practice, 1986; USPHS grantee, 1967-72. Fellow Am. Acad. Nursing; mem. Am. Nurses Assn., Am. Pacific Nursing Leaders Conf. (pres. 1983-87), Council Nurse Researchers, Nat. League for Nursing (bd. rev. 1981-87), Western Council Higher Edn. for Nurses (chmn. 1984-85), Western Soc. for Research in Nursing, Am. Sociol. Assn., Pacific Sociol. Assn., Assn. for Women in Sci., Hawaii Pub. Health Assn., Hawaii Med. Services Assn. (bd. dirs. 1985-92), Western Inst. Nursing, Mortar Bd., Phi Kappa Phi, Sigma Theta Tau, Alpha Kappa Delta, Delta Kappa Gamma. Episcopalian. Office: U Hawaii-Manoa Sch Nursing Webster 409 2528 The Mall Honolulu HI 96822

LUMADUE, DONALD DEAN, hobby and crafts company executive; b. El Reno, Okla., Sept. 30, 1938; s. Harry Basil and Muriel Ellen (Craven) L.; m. Joyce Anne Hayes, June 28, 1958; children: Dawnia, Donald, Robert, Ronald. Student USCG Acad., 1956-57. Lab. technician Charles Pfizer & Co., Groton, Conn., 1957-60; indsl. engr. Sonoco Products, Mystic, Conn., 1960-67; partner Joydon's, New London, Conn., 1958—, House of Leisure, New London, 1965—, Hobby Crafts, New London, 1968—; pres. NEI, Inc., New London, 1968-83; lectr., author in field. Mem. New Eng. Hobby Industry Assn. (pres. 1977-74, 86-88, bd. dirs 1983-90, 92's award 1993-94), Hobby Industry Assn. Am. (chmn. Wholesaler bd. 1976-78, 82—, exec. show bd. 1985-93, Pres.'s award 1986), Nat. Assn. Wholesalers (trustee 1976—), Mgmt. Club S.E. Conn. (pres. 1961-62, 77-78). Office: 78-88 Captains Walk New London CT 06320

LUMBARD, JOSEPH EDWARD, JR., federal judge; b. N.Y.C., Aug. 18, 1901; s. Joseph Edward and Martha Louise (Meier) L.; m. Polly Poindexter, Sept. 4, 1929; children: Abigail, Thomas. A.B. cum laude, Harvard U., 1922, LL.B., 1925, LL.D., 1970; LL.D., William Mitchell Coll. U. Bridgeport, Northwestern U., N.Y. Law Sch.; Columbia U.; S.J.D. (hon.), Suffolk U. Asst. U.S. atty. So. Dist N.Y., 1925-27; spl. asst. atty. gen. N.Y.

State, in Queens Sewer investigation and prosecution of Maurice E. Connelly, 1928-29; mem. firm Fogarty, Lumbard & Quel, 1929-31; asst. to William J. Donovan in bankruptcy inquiry conducted by Assn. Bar City N.Y. and others, 1929; asst. U.S. atty. charge criminal div. So. Dist. N.Y., 1931-33; mem. firm Donovan, Leisure, Newton, Lumbard & Irvine (and predecessor firms), 1934-53; spl. asst. atty. gen. N.Y. State, in Drukman murder prosecutions, 1936; def. counsel U.S. vs. Standard Oil and 23 oil cos., 1937-38; spl. asst. atty. gen. N.Y. State charge Election Frauds Bur., 1943; justice Supreme Ct. N.Y. State, June-Dec. 1947; U.S. atty. So. Dist. N.Y., 1953-55; U.S. circuit judge 2d Circuit, 1955—; chief judge U.S. Court Appeals, 2d Circuit, 1959-71. Contbr. to law jours. Bd. overseers Harvard, 1959-65; trustee William Nelson Cromwell Found. Jud. fellow Am. Coll. Trial Lawyers; mem. ABA (chmn. spl. com. minimum standards for criminal justice 1964-68, Gold medal 1968), N.Y. State Bar Assn. (Gold medal 1969), Assn. Bar City N.Y., S.R. Republican. Unitarian. Clubs: Country (Fairfield); Harvard, Century (N.Y.C.). Home: 490 Hillside Rd Fairfield CT 06430-2145

LUMET, SIDNEY, film director; b. Phila., June 25, 1924; s. Baruch and Eugenia (Wermus) L.; m. Rita Gam (div.); m. Gloria Vanderbilt, Aug. 27, 1956 (div. 1963); m. Gail Jones, Nov. 23, 1963 (div. 1978); m. Mary Gimbel, Oct. 1980; children: Amy, Jenny. Ed., Profl. Children's Sch.; student, Columbia. Tchr. acting High Sch. of Profl. Arts. Author: (with Alfred A. Knopf) Making Movies, 1995; appeared as child actor in several plays including Dead End, 1935, George Washington Slept Here, 1940-41, My Heart's in the Highlands, 1939; dir. summer stock, 1947-49; assoc. dir., CBS, 1950, dir., 1951-57; TV shows include Omnibus; films including Twelve Angry Men, 1957, Stage Struck, 1958, That Kind of Woman, 1959, The Fugitive Kind, 1960, A View from the Bridge, 1961, Long Days Journey into Night, 1962, Fail Safe, 1964, The Pawnbroker, 1965, The Hill, 1965, The Group, 1966, The Deadly Affair, 1967, The Sea Gull, 1968, Bye, Bye Braverman, 1968, The Appointment, 1969, (with Joseph L. Mankiewicz) King: A Filmed Record, 1969, Last of the Mobile Hot Shots, 1970, The Anderson Tapes, 1971, Child's Play, 1972, the Offence, 1973, Serpico, 1974, Lovin' Molly, 1974, Murder on the Orient Express, 1974, Dog Day Afternoon, 1975, Network, 1976, Equus, 1977, The Wiz, 1978, Just Tell Me What You Want, 1979, Prince of the City, 1981, Deathtrap, 1981, The Verdict, 1982, Daniel, 1983, Garbo Talks, 1984, Power, 1985, The Morning After, 1986, Running on Empty, 1988, Family Business, 1989, Q & A, 1990, A Stranger Among Us, 1992, Guilty As Sin, 1993; over 200 plays for TV Playhouse 90, Kraft TV Theatre, Studio One; staged: play Caligula, 1960. Recipient D.W. Griffith Lifetime Achievement award, 1993. Mem. Dirs. Guild Am. (hon. life). Office: Amjen Entertainment Inc 259 W 54 St New York NY 10019

LUMLEY, JOHN LEASK, physicist, educator; b. Detroit, Nov. 4, 1930; s. Charles S. and Jane Anderson Campbell (Leask) L.; m. Jane French, June 20, 1953; children: Katherine Leask, Jennifer French, John Christopher. B.A., Harvard, 1952; M.S. in Engring, Johns Hopkins, 1954, Ph.D., 1957; Haute Distinction Honoris Causa, Ecole Central de Lyon, France, 1987. Postdoctoral fellow Johns Hopkins, 1957-59; mem. faculty Pa. State U., 1959-77, prof. aerospace engring., 1963-74, Evan Pugh prof. aerospace engring., 1974-77; Willis H. Carrier prof. engring. Cornell U. 1977—; prof. d'echange U. d'Aix-Marseille, France, 1966-67; Fulbright sr. lectr. U. Liege; vis. prof. U. Louvain-La-Neuve, Belgium; Guggenheim fellow U. Provence and Ecole Centrale de Lyon, France, 1973-74. Author: (with H.A. Panofsky) Structure of Atmospheric Turbulence, 1964, Stochastic Tools for Turbulence, 1970, (with H. Tennekes) A First Course in Turbulence, 1971; also articles.; tech. editor: Statistical Fluid Mechanics, 1971, 75, Variability of the Oceans, 1977; assoc. editor: Physics of Fluids, 1971-73; assoc. editor Ann. Rev. of Fluid Mechanics, 1976-85, co-editor, 1986—; chmn. tech. editorial bd.: Izvestiya: Atmospheric and Oceanic Physics, 1971—; editorial bd.: Fluid Mechanics: Soviet Research, 1972-94; editor Theoretical and Computational Fluid Dynamics, 1989—; prin.: films Deformation of Continuous Media, 1963, Eulerian and Lagrangian Frames in Fluid Mechanics, 1968. Recipient medallion U. Liege, Belgium, 1971, Timoshenko medal ASME, 1993. Fellow Am. Acad. Arts and Scis., Am. Acad. Mechanics, Am. Phys. Soc. (exec. com. divsn. fluid dynamics 1972-75, 81-84, chmn. exec. com. divsn. fluid dynamics 1982, 87-89, Fluid Dynamics prize 1990), AIAA (assoc., fluid and plasma dynamics award 1982, Hugh L. Dryden rsch. lectureship 1996); mem. NAE, AAAS, N.Y. Acad. Sci., Soc. Natural Philosophy, Am. Geophys. Union, Johns Hopkins Soc. Scholars (charter), Sigma Xi. Home: 743 Snyder Hill Rd Ithaca NY 14850-8708 Office: Cornell U 238 Upson Hall Ithaca NY 14853

LUMPE, SHEILA, state legislator; b. Apr. 17, 1935; m. Gustav H. Lumpe, 1958. AB, Ind. U.; postgrad., Johns Hopkins U.; MA, U. Mo. Mem. Mo. Ho. of Reps. Trustee Mo. Consol. Health Care Plan; active Civil Liberties Union; mem. bd. 604 Victims Svc. Coun.; bd. dirs. People to People. Democrat. Home: 6908 Amherst Ave Saint Louis MO 63130-3124 Office: Mo Ho of Reps State Capitol Jefferson City MO 65101

LUMPKIN, JOHN HENDERSON, retired banker; b. Fairbanks, Alaska, Jan. 28, 1916; s. Hope Henry and Mary Isobel (Henderson) L.; m. Caroline Sparrow Dalton, Apr. 8, 1942; children: John Henderson, Caroline Dalton (Mrs. Sozzi). BA, U. S.C., 1937, doctorate (hon.); LLB, Harvard U., 1940; doctorate (hon.), Columbia Coll., Coker Coll., Benedict Coll. Bar: N.Y. 1940. With firm White & Case, N.Y.C., 1940-41, Boyd, Bruton & Lumpkin, Columbia, S.C., 1946-64; sr. exec. v.p. S.C. Nat. Bank, Columbia, 1964-65, pres., 1965-70, chief exec. officer, 1965-81, chmn. bd., 1970-81; ret., 1981, hon. chmn. bd.; of counsel The McNair Firm, P.A. 1983-92. Chmn. trustee S.C. Found. Ind. Colls.; trustee Brookgreen Gardens (chmn. exec. com.). Lt. comdr. USNR, 1941-46. Decorated Commendation medal. Recipient Algernon Sydney Sullivan award U. S.C., 1963; inductee S.C. Bus. Hall of Fame, 1991. Mem. 4th Circuit Jud. Conv., S.C. C. of C. (pres. 1971-72), Columbia C. of C. (pres. 1953-54), ABA, S.C. Bar Assn., Richland County Bar Assn., S.C. Bankers Assn. (pres. 1974-75). Office: NCNB Tower PO Box 11390 Fl Columbia SC 29211-1390

LUMPKIN, JOHN ROBERT, public health physician, state official; b. Chgo., July 28, 1951; s. Frank and Beatrice (Shapiro) L.; m. Mary S. Blanks, Jan. 28, 1984; children: Alia, John R. Jr. BS, Northwestern U., Evanston, Ill., 1973; MD, Northwestern U., Chgo., 1974; MPH, U. Ill., Chgo., 1985. Diplomate Am. Bd. Emergency Medicine. Intern U. Chgo. Hosps., 1975, resident anesthesiology, 1976-78, vice chmn. emergency medicine, 1981-84; asst. prof. U. Chgo., 1978-84; asst. dir. emergency medicine South Chgo. Hosp., 1984-85; staff physician St. Mary of Nazareth Hosp., Chgo., 1985; assoc. dir. Ill. Dept. Pub. Health, Springfield and Chgo., 1985-90, dir., 1990—; cons. Egyptian Ministry Health, Cairo, 1986-90; mem. sec's adv. com. on injury control Ctrs. for Dis. Control, Atlanta, 1989-93. Fellow Am. Coll. Emergency Physicians (bd. dirs. 1987-93); mem. Soc. Tchrs. Emergency Medicine (pres. 1981-82), Ill. Coll. Emergency Physicians (pres. 1982-83, Bill B. Smiley award 1986), Assn. State and Territorial Health Ofcls. (pres.-elect 1994-95). Avocations: racquetball, model trains, football, computers. Office: Ill Dept Pub Health 100 W Randolph St Ste 6-600 Chicago IL 60601-3218

LUMPKIN, LEE ROY, dermatologist, educator; b. Oklahoma City, Sept. 6, 1925; s. Lee R. and Martha S. (Lockard) L.; m. Mona F. Long, Jan. 28, 1953; children: Lee Roy III, Patricia J., Megan E., Julie A., William S. BA, U. Okla., 1949, MD, 1953. Intern Tripler Gen. Hosp., Honolulu, 1953-54; gen. practice medicine San Francisco, 1955-57; commd. capt. U.S. Air Force, 1957, advanced through grades to col., 1968; resident in dermatology Walter Reed Gen. Hosp., Washington, 1958-61; chief of dermatology Madrid, Spain, 1961-64; fellow in dermatopathology Armed Forces Inst. Pathology, Washington, 1964-65; chief USAF Regional Center, Carswell AFB, Tex., 1964-67; chief dermatology USAF Med Center, Lackland AFB, San Antonio, 1967-72; assoc. clin. prof. dermatology U. Tex. Sch. Medicine, San Antonio, 1969-72; ret. U. Tex. Sch. Medicine, 1972; clin. prof. dermatology Albany (N.Y.) Med. Center, 1972-92; ret. Editor: Bull. Assn. Mil. Dermatologists, 1968-71; mem. editorial bd. Mil. Medicine, 1968-76; contbr. articles to med. jours. Decorated Bronze Star medal, Air Force Commendation medal with oak leaf cluster, Meritorious Service medal; recipient James Clarke White award, 1971. Fellow Am. Acad. Dermatology, ACP, Am. Coll. Cryosurgery; mem. Assn. Profs. Dermatology, Dermatology Found.; Internat. Soc. Pediatric Dermatology, N.Am. Clin. Dermatology Soc., Internat. Soc. Tropical Dermatology, Soc. Air Force Physicians (pres.-elect), New Eng. Dermatol.

Soc., Central N.Y. Dermatol. Soc., N.Y. State Soc. Dermatology (bd. govs. 1980-83, pres. 1981-83). Episcopalian. Home: 223 Lancaster St Albany NY 12210-1131

LUMRY, RUFUS WORTH, II, chemist, educator; b. Bismarck, N.D., Nov. 9, 1920; s. Rufus Worth and Mabel (Will) L.; m. Gayle Kelly, Mar. 27, 1943 (div. Aug. 1973); children—Rufus Worth III, Ann Eliza, Stephen Ellis. A.B., Harvard U., 1942, M.S., 1948, Ph.D., 1948. Research chemist div. 8 Nat. Def. Research Council, 1942-45; NRC fellow Harvard U., 1946-48; Merck fellow nat. scis. U. Utah, 1948-51, asst. prof. chemistry and biochemistry, 1951-53; mem. faculty U. Minn., 1953—, prof. chemistry, 1956-91, prof. emeritus, 1991—, also now dir. Lab. Biophys. Chemistry; vis. prof. Inst. Protein Research, Osaka, Japan, 1961, U. Rome, Italy, 1964, U. Calif., San Diego, 1977, U. Va., 1978, U. Granada, Spain, 1985; cons. in field, 1948—. Author: (with W. Reynolds) Mechanisms of Electron Transfer, 1966, (with R. Gregory) The Fluctuating Enzyme, 1986; also articles. NSF sr. postdoctoral fellow Carlsberg (Denmark) Lab., 1959-60. Mem. Am. Chem. Assn., Am. Inst. Biol. Scis., Am. Biophysics Soc., Am. Soc. Biol. Chemists, Sigma Xi. Democrat. Home: 940 Franklin Ter Minneapolis MN 55406-1153

LUMSDAINE, EDWARD, mechanical engineering educator, university dean; b. Hong Kong, China, Sept. 30, 1937; came to U.S., 1953; s. Clifford Vere and Miao Ying Lumsdaine; m. Monika Amsler, Sept. 8, 1959; children: Andrew, Anne Josephine, Alfred, Arnold. BS in Mech. Engring., N.Mex. State U., Las Cruces, 1963, MS in Mech. Engring., 1964, ScD, 1966. Research engr. Boeing Co., Seattle, 1966-67, asst. prof. to assoc. prof. S.D. State U., Brookings, 1967-72; assoc. prof. to prof. U. Tenn., Knoxville, 1972-77; prof., sr. research engr. phys. sci. lab., dir. N.Mex. solar energy inst. N.Mex. State U., Las Cruces, 1977-81; prof., dir. energy, environ. and resources ctr. U. Tenn., Knoxville, 1981-83; dean engring., prof. U. Mich., Dearborn, 1982-88, U. Toledo, 1988-93; dean of engring. Mich. Technol. U., Houghton, 1993—; vis. prof. Cairo U., Egypt, 1974, Tatung Inst. Tech., Taipei, China, 1978, Qatar U., Doha, 1983; UNESCO expert cons. to Egypt, 1979-80; dir., cons. E&M Lumsdaine Solar Cons., Hancock, Mich., 1979—; cons. Oak Ridge (Tenn.) Nat. Lab., 1979-82, BDM Corp., Albuquerque, 1984, Ford Motor Co., Dearborn, Mich., 1984—, Am. Supplier Inst., Dearborn, 1986—. Author: Industrial Energy Conservation for Developing Countries, 1984, (with Monika Lumsdaine) Creative Problem Solving: An Introductory Course for Engineering Students, 1990, Creative Problem Solving: Thinking Skills for a Changing World, 1995; contbr. software packages, articles to profl. jours. Served with USAF, 1954-58. NASA faculty fellow, 1969, 70; grantee NSF, NASA, U.S. Dept. Energy, Dept. Navy, ASHRAE, AID, Ford Motor Co. Fellow AIAA, ASME; mem. NSPE, ASTM, Am. Soc. Engring. Edn., Internat. Solar Energy Soc., Am. Solar Energy Soc., Am. Assn. Higher Edn. Presbyterian. Office: Mich Tech U Coll Engring Houghton MI 49931

LUMSDEN, IAN GORDON, art gallery director; b. Montreal, Que., Can., June 8, 1945; s. Andrew Mark and Isobel Dallas (Wilson) L.; m. Katherine Elizabeth Carson, July 28, 1979; 1 child, Craig Ian. B.A., McGill U., 1968; postgrad., Mus. Mgmt. Inst., U. Calif., Berkeley, 1991. Curator art dept. N.B. Mus., Saint John, 1969; curator Beaverbrook Art Gallery, Fredericton, N.B., 1969-83, dir., 1983—; bd. dirs. ArtsAtlantic; mem. Cultural Property Export Rev. Bd., 1982-85; mem. program com. 49th Parallel Ctr. for Contemporary Can. Art., 1990-92. Author exhbn. catalogues; contbr. numerous articles to Can. art periodicals. Mem. Can. Museums Assn. (sec.-treas. 1973-75), Can. Art Mus. Dirs. Orgn. (1st v.p. 1977-83, pres. 1983-85), Atlantic Provinces Art Gallery Assn. (chmn. 1970-72), Am. Assn. Museums, Union Club (St. John, N.B.). Mem. Anglican Ch. of Can. Home: Fernholme, 725 George St, Fredericton, NB Canada E3B 1K6

LUMSDEN, LYNNE ANN, publishing company executive; b. Battle Creek, Mich., July 30, 1947; d. Arthur James and Ruth Julia (Pandy) L.; m. Jon B. Harden, May 3, 1986; 1 child, Heather Lynne. Student, U. Paris, 1967-69; BA, Sarah Lawrence Coll., 1969; postgrad., City Grad. Ctr., 1979-81, NYU, 1970-71; cert. of mgmt., Am. Mgmt. Assn., 1982. Copy editor Harcourt, Brace, Jovanovich, N.Y.C., 1970-71; editor Appleton-Century Crofts, N.Y.C., 1971-73, Coll. div. Prentice-Hall, Englewood Cliffs, N.J., 1974-78; sr. editor Coll. div. Prentice-Hall, 1978-81; asst. v.p., editor-in-chief Spectrum Books, 1981-82; v.p. editorial dir., gen. pub. div., 1982-85; exec. v.p., publ., co-owner Dodd, Mead & Co., Inc., N.Y.C., 1985-89; owner, chmn. JBH Communications Inc., Hartford, Conn., 1989—; pub. Hartford News and Southside Media, 1989—. Class agt. for ann. fund Kingswood-Oxford Sch. Mem. Women in Comm., Harford Jr. League, Friends of Mark Twain, Hartford Club, Pubs. Lunch Club, N.Y.C. Sandbar Club, Town and Country Club, Hartford Golf Club. Episcopalian. Home: 16 Oak Ridge Ln West Hartford CT 06107-3505 Office: 191 Franklin Ave Hartford CT 06114-2517

LUND, BERT OSCAR, JR., publisher; b. Stillwater, Minn., Nov. 8, 1920; s. Bert O. and Mary O. (Vordal) L.; m. Katherine Kingsley, July 31, 1943; children—Katherine Lund Cohen, Julie Lund Everett, Bert Oscar. B.B.A., U. Minn., 1942; postgrad., Harvard U., 1943. Advt. salesman Webb Co., St. Paul, 1946-54; advt. mgr. Webb Co., 1954-61; pub. Farmer Mag. 1961—, v.p. pub., 1963—, also dir.; v.p. pub. Pub. Cons., 1985—; dir. Audit Bur. Circulations, Gt. No. Ins. Co.; pres. Midwest unit Farm Papers, Inc., 1971; dir. Gt. No. Ins. Co., 1980—. Vice pres. Indianhead Council, Boy Scouts Am., 1974, Minn. Agrl. Soc., 1981; chmn. ops. com. St. Paul Civic Center Authority, 1972; bd. dirs. Minn. Council on Econ. Edn., 1969, Cath. Digest, 1980; chmn. trustee Dunwoody Inst., 1980, Will Reference Library, 1984; trustee Minn. Med. Found. Served to lt. USNR, 1943-46. Mem. Agrl. Pubs. Assn. (past pres., dir.), State Farm Mag. Bur. (past pres., dir.), Advt. Club Minn (past pres.), U. Minn. Alumni Assn. (treas.), Sigma Alpha Epsilon. Republican. Episcopalian. Clubs: Minnesota, Royal Poinciana Country Club, Hole-in-Wall Golf, Somerset Country. Home: 2151 Upper St Dennis Rd Saint Paul MN 55116-2823

LUND, SISTER CANDIDA, college chancellor; b. Chgo.; d. Fred S. Lund and Katharine (Murray) Lund Heck. BA, Rosary Coll., River Forest, Ill.; MA, Catholic U. Am.; PhD, U. Chgo., 1963; DLitt (hon.), Lincoln Coll., 1968; LLD (hon.), John Marshall Law Sch., 1979; LHD honoris causa, Marymount Coll., 1979; LittD (hon.), St. Mary-of-the Woods Coll., 1994. Pres. Rosary Coll., 1964-81, chancellor, 1981—. Editor: Moments to Remember, 1980, The Days and the Nights: Prayers for Today's Woman, In Joy and in Sorrow, 1984, Coming of Age, 1992, Nunsuch, 1982, God and Me, 1988, Praymates, 1993; author, editor: If I Were Pope, 1987; contbr.: Why Catholic. Mem. women's bd. U. Chgo., 1984—; bd. dirs. The Chgo. Network, 1983-86, The Park Ridge Ctr., 1987—. Recipient Profl. Achievement award U. Chgo. Alumni, 1974, U.S. Catholic award, 1984. Fellow Royal Soc. Arts; mem. Thomas More Assn. (bd. dirs. 1975—), The Arts Club (bd. dirs. 1987—). Home and Office: Rosary Coll 7900 Division St River Forest IL 60305-1099

LUND, DALE A., sociology educator, researcher; b. Salt Lake City, Apr. 18, 1951; Elden A. and Pearl A. Lund; m. Patty Rawlings, June 26, 1975; children—Matthew, Angela. B.S. in Psychology, U. Utah, 1973, M.S. in Sociology, 1976, Ph.D. in Med. Sociology, 1979. Instr. dept. sociology N.D. State U., 1975-76; teaching fellow, assoc. instr. dept. sociology U. Utah, 1976-79; asst. prof. dept. sociology Valdosta State Coll., 1979-80; vis. asst. prof. dept. family and consumer studies U. Utah, 1980-81; project dir., research asst. prof., assoc. dir. Research Gerontology Ctr., Coll. Nursing U. Utah; cons., workshop leader in field. Mem. target 5 com. Utah div., Am. Cancer Soc., 1978-79; chmn. target 5 task force Valdosta, Ga. div., Am. Cancer Soc., 1979-80; chmn. smoking cessation and health promotion com., Utah div. Am. Cancer Soc., 1980—, mem. exec. com., bd. dirs., 1980—; campaign worker Utah Democratic Party. Recipient Outstanding Tchr. award Dept. Sociology, U. Utah, 1978, 79. Mem. Gerontol. Soc. Am., Am. Sociol. Assn., Pacific Sociol. Assn., Am. Arthritis Found. (allied health professions sect.). Author: Human Development, 1981; contbr. articles, reports on health issues to profl. jours.; profl. meetings. Office: U Utah Coll Nursing Gerontol Ctr Salt Lake City UT 84112

LUND, DARYL BERT, college dean; b. San Bernardino, Calif., Nov. 4, 1941; s. Bert Harry and Edna Susan Agnes (McFarlane) L.; m. Dawn Kreft, June 15, 1963; children: Kristine Kay, Eric Scott. BS in Math., U. Wis.,

1963, MS in Food Sci., 1965, PhD in Food Sci. and Chem. Engring., 1968. Rsch. asst. U. Wis., Madison, 1963-67, from instr. to assoc. prof. food sci., 1967-77, prof. food sci., 1977-87, chair dept. food sci., 1984-87; chair dept. food sci., assoc. dir. Agrl. Experiment Sta. Rutgers State U. N.J., New Brunswick, 1988-89, interim exec. dean agriculture and natural resouces, dean Cook Coll., 1989-91, exec. dean agriculture and natural resources, exec. dir. N.J. Agrl. Experiment Sta., dean Cook Coll., 1991-95; dean agrl. and life scis. Cornell U., Ithaca, N.Y., 1995—; mem. tech. advisors coun. Grand Met., Mpls., 1990—. Co-author, co-editor: Handbook of Food Engineering, 1992; author 20 chpts. in books including Advances in Food Engineering, 1992, Aseptic Processing and Packaging, 1993; co-editor numerous books including Wild Rice Processor's Handbook, 1972, Fouling and Cleaning in Food Processing, 1989; contbr. 200 tech. papers to profl. jours. Fellow Inst. Food Technologists (pres. 1991-92, Internat. award 1995); mem. Am. Soc. Agrl. Engring. divsn. chair 1978-79, Food Engring. award 1987), AIChE, Am. Inst. Nutrition. Avocations: golf, travel, wood working. Home: 18 Redcoat Dr East Brunswick NJ 08816-2759

LUND, DAVID NATHAN, artist; b. N.Y.C., Oct. 16, 1925; s. Isidore and Mollie (Hirschfield) Lifshitz; m. Sally Harriet Amster, June 17, 1961 (dec. Feb. 1988); children: Andrew Ethan, Giuliana Elizabeth; m. Judith Manelis. BA, Queens Coll., 1948; postgrad., NYU, 1948-50. Adj. asst. prof. painting, drawing, design Cooper Union Art Sch., 1955-57, 59-66, 67-74; instr. painting Cummington (Mass.) Sch. Arts, 1963; instr. in painting Haystack Sch., Deer Isle, Maine, 1963; instr. in drawing and painting Parsons Sch. Design, 1963-66, 67-69; lectr. in drawing Queens Coll., 1964-66; vis. prof. painting Washington U., St. Louis, 1966-67, 85; asst. prof. painting and drawing Columbia U., 1969-82; vis. prof. painting Boston U., 1975-76; vis. critic; lectr. in field; juror Nat. Selection Com., Fulbright Grants In Art; cons. in painting Creative Artists Public Service, 1979-81; vis. artist Winston-Salem Arts Council and Associated Artists of Winston-Salem, 1975. One-man shows include Grand Central Moderns Gallery, N.Y.C., 1954, Galleria Trastevere, Rome, 1959, Grace Borgenicht Gallery, N.Y.C., 1960, 63, 66, 67, 69, 76, 78, 80, 83, 86, Martin Schweig Gallery, St. Louis, 1966, Kirkland Coll., 1971, Arts Council Winston-Salem, N.C., 1975, Creiger-Seson Gallery, Boston, 1981, Meredith Contemporary Art Gallery, Balt., 1982, U. Alaska, Fairbanks, 1983, Washington U., St. Louis, 1985, Allport Gallery, San Francisco, 1984, A.J. Laderman Fine Arts, Hoboken, N.J., 1990; group shows include Whitney Mus., N.Y.C., 1958, 60, 61, 62, 77, Galleria Schneider, Rome, 1959, Palazzo Venezia, Rome, 1959, Galleria San Marco, Rome, 1959, Washington Gallery Art, 1963, Am. embassy, Athens, Greece, 1966-67, White House, Washington, 1966-67, 67-68, 68-69, Nat. Collection Fine Arts, Washington, 1972-73; represented in permanent collections Whitney Mus., Toronto (Ont., Can.) Gallery Art, Art Gallery Ont., Toronto, Corcoran Gallery Art, Washington, Ft. Worth Art Center, U. Mass., Montclair (N.J.) Mus., Haas Gallery at Bloomsburg State Coll., Kranert Art Gallery, Champagne, Ill., also other public and pvt. collections. Fulbright grantee Rome, 1957-59. Mem. Nat. Acad. Design, Artists Equity. Jewish. Subject of numerous profl. publs.

LUND, DORIS HIBBS, dietitian; b. Des Moines, Nov. 10, 1923; d. Loyal Burchard and Catharine Mae (McClymond) Hibbs; m. Richard Bodholdt Lund, Nov. 9, 1946; children: Laurel Anne, Richard Douglas, Kristi Jane Lund Lozier. Student, Duchesne Coll., Omaha, 1941-42; BS, Iowa State U., 1946; postgrad., Grand View Coll., Des Moines, 1965; MS, Iowa State U., 1968. Registered dietitian, lic. dietitian. Clk. Russell Stover Candies, Omaha, 1940-42; chemist Martin Bomber Plant, Omaha, 1942-43; dietitian Grand Lake (Colo.) Lodge, 1946; tailoring instr. Ottumwa Pub. Schs., 1952-53; cookery instr. Des Moines Pub. Schs., 1958-62; dietitian Calvin Manor, Des Moines, 1963; home economist Am. Wool Coun., Am. Lamb Coun., Denver, 1963-65, The Merchandising Group of N.Y., 1965-68, Thomas Wolff, Pub. Rels., 1968-70; home economist weekly TV program Iowa Power Co., 1968-70; cons. in child nutrition programs Iowa Dept. Edn., Des Moines, 1970-95; Mem. Iowa Home Economists in Bus. (pres. 1962-63), PEO, Pi Beta Phi (Iowa Gamma chpt. pres. 1945-46). Pres. Callanan Jr. H.S. PTA, 1964, Roosevelt H.S. PTA, 1966; pres., mem. Ctrl. Presbyn. Mariners, Des Moines; ruling elder, clk. of session Ctrl. Presbyn. Session, Des Moines, 1972-78; mem. Friendship Force Internat., 1982—. Duchesne Coll. 4 yr. scholar. Mem. Iowa Home Economists in Bus. (pres. 1962-63), PEO, Pi Beta Phi (pres. 1945-46). Republican. Avocations: international travel, writing, sailing, sewing, cooking. Home: 105 34th St Des Moines IA 50312 Office: Iowa Dept Edn Grimes State Office Bldg Des Moines IA 50319

LUND, GEORGE EDWARD, retired electrical engineer; b. Phila., Feb. 17, 1925; s. Harold White and Hannah (Lawford) L.; m. Shirley Bolton Stevens, Sept. 24, 1960; children: Marsha (Mrs. Donald Barnett), Roger, Sharon Stevens (Mrs. David Bailey), Gretchen (Mrs. Kevin J. Collette). BEE, Drexel U., 1952; MEE, U. Pa., 1959; postgrad. in computer sci., Villanova U., 1981-83. Project engr. Burroughs Corp., Paoli, Pa., 1952-86; project engr. UNISYS Corp., Paoli, 1986-90, ret., 1990. Assoc. editor, contbr.: Digital Applications of Magnetic Devices, 1960; patentee in field. With USN, 1943-46, ETO. Mem. IEEE (sr.), Eta Kappa Nu. Republican. Methodist. Avocations: photography, amateur radio. Home: 923 Pinecroft Rd Berwyn PA 19312-2123

LUND, H. ROALD, plant scientist, educator; b. Fargo, N.D., May 15, 1933; s. Haakon and Ruby Margaret (Davidson) L.; m. Janet Olive Thompson, Oct. 5, 1957; children: Jeffrey, Susan, Anders, Adrian. BS, N.D. Agrl. Coll., Fargo, 1955, MS in Agronomy, 1958; PhD in Plant Breeding and Genetics, Purdue U., 1965. Asst prof. agronomy N.D. Agrl. Coll., 1959-62; grad. rsch. asst. dept. agronomy Purdue U., West Lafayette, Ind., 1962-65; assoc. prof. agronomy N.D. State U., Fargo, 1965-69, prof. agronomy, asst. dean Coll. Agr., asst. dir. Agrl. Sta., 1970-74, assoc. dean Coll. Agr., assoc. dir. Agrl. Expt. Sta., 1974-79, dean, dir. Coll. Agr., dir. Agrl. Expt. Sta., 1979-94, dir. Biotech. Inst., 1989—, prof. crop and weed scis., 1994—; officer Nat. Assn. State Univs. and Land Grant Colls.; officer Coun. Adminstrv. Heads in Agr.; mem. North Ctrl. Regional Rsch. Planning Com., Nat. Agrl. Rsch. com.; sec. N.D. State U. Rsch. Found. 1987-94; bd. dirs. Gate city Fed. Savs. Bank, Fargo, N.D. Rural Rehab. Corp., Concord Mfg. Co., Fargo. Mem. Pesticide Control Bd., State of N.D., 1980—, mem. Seed Arbitration Bd., 1990—, mem. Gov.'s Com. to Rev. Cost Saving Suggestions, 1992—. Served to 1st lt. U.S. Army. Mem. Am. Soc. Agronomy, Republican. Lutheran. Avocations: gardening, travel, reading, public speaking. Home: North Dakota State Univ Agricultural Experiment Station Box 126A Rte 4 Pelican Rapids MN 56572 Office: ND State U PO Box 5051 Fargo ND 58105*

LUND, LOIS A., food science and human nutrition educator; b. Thief River Falls, Minn., Aug. 9, 1927; d. Robert J. and E Luella (Tosdal) L. BS, U. Minn., 1949, MS, 1954, PhD, 1966. Instr. foods U. Iowa, 1951-55, U. Minn., 1955-63; assoc. prof., dir. core studies program, asst. dir. Sch. Home Econs., 1966-68; research fellow U.S. Dept. Agrl., 1963-66; assoc. dean, dir. Sch. Home Econs. Ohio State U., 1969-72; dean Coll. Human Ecology Mich. State U., East Lansing, 1973-85, prof. food sci. and human nutrition, 1985—; bd. dirs. Consumers Power Co., Jackson, Mich., CMS Energy, Dearborn, Mich. Contbr. articles to profl. jours. Recipient Betty award for excellence in teaching U. Minn., 1958, 63, 68, Hon. Alumni award Mich. State U., 1977, Outstanding Achievement award U. Minn. Alumni Assn., 1977. Mem. Am. Coun. on Consumer Interest, Am. Assn. Cereal Chemists, Inst. Food Technologists, Am. Dietetic Econs. Assn., Soc. for Nutrition Edn., Pi Lambda Theta, Phi Kappa Phi, Phi Upsilon Omicron, Omicron Nu (nat. treas. 1971-74, 84-86), Sigma Delta Epsilon. Lutheran. Avocation: gardening. Home: 5927 Shadowlawn Dr East Lansing MI 48823-2379 Office: Mich State U Dept Food Sci and Human Nutrition East Lansing MI 48824

LUND, PETER ANTHONY, broadcast executive; b. Mpls., Jan. 12, 1941; s. Arthur Harold and Elizabeth (Rohan) L.; m. Theresa Mary Kessel, Sept. 3, 1960; children: Mark, Timothy. Ed., St. Thomas Coll., 1958-62. Announcer, sales rep. Sta. KCCR, Pierce, S.D., 1961-62; sales rep. Sta. KELO-TV, Sioux Falls, S.D., 1962-64; sales rep., sales mgr. Sta. WTTC, Mpls., 1964-66; sales mgr. Westinghouse Broadcasting Co., 1966-71; v.p., gen. mgr. Sta. KSDO, San Diego, Calif., 1972-75, Sta. WTOP, Washington, 1975-77; v.p. CBS owned AM Stas., N.Y.C., 1977-80; v.p., gen. mgr. WBBM-TV, Chgo., 1980-83, WCBS-TV, N.Y.C., 1983-84; exec. v.p. CBS Sports, N.Y.C., 1984-85, pres., 1985-87; pres. Multimedia Entertainment, N.Y.C., 1987-90;

exec. v.p.; pres. mktg. CBS, 1990-94; exec. v.p., pres. CBS TV Network, N.Y.C., 1994-95; pres. CBS Broadcast Group, N.Y.C., 1995—. Home: 100 Warwick Rd Bronxville NY 10708-5715 Office: CBS 51 W 52nd St New York NY 10019-6101

LUND, STEVE, agronomist, research administrator; b. Exeland, Wis., Dec. 3, 1923; s. Robert Henry and Annie Belle (McHenry) L.; m. Gracemary Henrietta Bernskoetter, Jan. 29, 1946; children: Steve, John R., Thomas A., Cynthia M., Lisa A. BS, Clemson Coll., 1949; MS, U. Wis., 1951, PhD, 1953. Extension agronomist Clemson Coll., 1953-54; asst. research specialist Rutgers U., New Brunswick, N.J., 1954-57, assoc. research specialist, 1957-62, research prof., 1962-75, chmn. dept. soils and crops, 1971-75, prof. emeritus, 1975—; supt. and prof. Oreg. State U., Columbia Basin Agrl. Research Ctr., Pendleton, 1975-85; prof. emeritus Oreg. State U., Pendleton, 1985—. Contbr. articles to profl. jours. Served to 1st sgt. U.S. Army, 1943-46. Mem. Crop Sci. Soc. Am., Am. Soc. Agronomy, Sigma Xi, Alpha Zeta, Phi Kappa Phi, Phi Eta Sigma, Pendleton Country Club. Avocations: golf, skiing, bridge. Home: 1201 SW 23rd St Pendleton OR 97801-4404 Office: Columbia Basin Agrl Rsch 1201 SW 23rd St Pendleton OR 97801-4404

LUND, VICTOR L., retail food company executive; b. Salt Lake City, 1947; married. BA, U. Utah, 1969, MBA, 1972. Audit mgr. Ernst and Whinney, Salt Lake City, 1972-77; sr. v.p. Skaggs Cos. Inc., from 1977; v.p., contr. Am. Stores Co., 1980-83, sr. v.p., contr., from 1983, exec. v.p., co-chief exec. officer, vice-chmn., chief fin. and adminstrv. officer, now pres., CEO, dir., 1992—. Office: Am Stores Co PO Box 27447 Salt Lake City UT 84127-0447 also: Am Stores Co 709 East South Temple Salt Lake City UT 84102*

LUND, WENDELL LUTHER, lawyer; b. Prentice, Wis., Dec. 31, 1905; s. Rev. Carl A. and Bertha Elizabeth L.; m. Anne Catherine Grove, Nov. 8, 1934 (dec.); children: Judith (Mrs. Barton Biggs), Carole (Mrs. John A. Benning), Mary Wendell; m. Marian Alice Hope, 1981. A.B., Augustana Coll., Rock Island, Ill., 1927, D.H.L., 1968; A.M., Columbia U. 1930; J.D., Georgetown U., 1938; Ph.D., Princeton U., 1933. Checker C.&N.W. R.R. (iron ore docks) Escanaba, Mich., 1922-23; worked in tie yard and iron ore docks C.&N.W. R.R. (iron ore docks), summers 1924-27; tchr. Upsala Coll., E. Orange, N.J., 1927-29; asso. prof. English Augustana Coll., 1930-31, exec. sec., 1933-34; exec. sec. Upper Monongahela Valley Com., Washington, 1934; mem. Taylor Act Com., Dept. Interior, 1934; sec. Mich Adminstrv. Bd., Lansing, 1941; exec. dir. Mich. Unemployment Compensation Com. 1941-42; dir. labor prodn. div. WPB, also mem. War Manpower Commn. 1942-43; spl. asst. to chmn. WPB, 1943; practicing atty., mem. firm Lund & O'Brien & predecessor firms, Washington, 1943—; chmn., CEO Schonstedt Instrument Co., 1993—; Del. World Council of Chs., Evanston, 1954, Uppsala, Sweden, 1968; mem. Bd. Pensions, Lutheran Ch. in Am., 1963-67, 70-79, pres., 1967-68, 74-79; Democratic nominee for Congress, 11th Mich. Dist., 1940; presdl. elector, 1944. Contbr. articles to profl. jours. Bd. dirs. Augustana Coll., 1974-88. Mem. ABA, Bar Assn. D.C., Phi Beta Kappa. Clubs: Congressional Country (Washington), Burning Tree (Washington), Metropolitan (Washington); Bird Key Yacht (Sarasota, Fla.); Princeton (N.Y.C.). Home: 1255 N Gulfstream Ave Sarasota FL 34236-8920 Office: 1825 K St NW Ste 1010 Washington DC 20006-1202

LUNDBACK, STAFFAN BENGT GUNNAR, lawyer; b. Stockholm, Sweden, Mar. 23, 1947; came to U.S., 1965; s. B. Holger and Ingrid (Fjellstrom) L.; m. Lee Craig, June 14,1969; children: Hadley Elizabeth, Erik Burchfield. Student, U. Stockholm, 1966-67; BA, U. Rochester, 1970; JD, Boston U., 1974. Bar: N.Y. 1975, Fla. 1983. Assoc. Nixon, Hargrave, Devans & Doyle, Rochester, N.Y., 1974-83; ptnr. Nixon, Hargrave, Devans & Doyle, Rochester, 1983—; bd. dirs. Scandinavian Seminar, Amherst, Mass.; chmn. Scanamerican Properties, Inc., Atlanta, 1989—. Mem. Swedish-Am. C. of C. (sec., bd. dirs. 1994—), Genesee Valley Club, Phi Beta Kappa. Avocations: music, literature, sports, current events, photography. Office: Nixon Hargrave Devans & Doyle PO Box 1051 Clinton First Sq Rochester NY 14603

LUNDBERG, CONSTANCE K., law educator; b. Salt Lake City, July 1, 1947; d. Horace William and Nedra (Hurst) Lundberg; m. Boyd C. Erickson, Jan. 21, 1981. BA with distinction, Ariz. State U., 1968; JD, U. Utah., 1972. Bar: Utah. Ptnr. Parson, Behle & Latimer, Salt Lake City, 1972-74, 77-82; counsel Council on Environ. Quality, Washington, 1975-76; prof., assoc. dean, law libr. Brigham Young U., Provo, Utah, 1982—; of counsel Parson, Behle & Latimer, 1982-86. Co-author: Mineral Acquisition on the Public Domain, 1985; contbr. articles on resource law to profl. jours. Vice chmn. Utah Bd. Oil, Gas and Mining, Salt Lake City, 1983-88; mem. Utah Constnl. Revision Commn., Salt Lake City, 1978-79; trustee Rocky Mt. Mineral Law Found., Boulder, Colo., 1978-89. Mem. Utah State Bar Assn. (chmn. natural resources sect. 1980-81), Utah Coll. Libr. Coun. . Democrat. Mormon. Home: 749 Sunny Ln Orem UT 84058-6006 Office: Brigham Young U J Reuben Clark Law Sch Libr Provo UT 84602

LUNDBERG, FERDINAND EDGAR, author; b. Chicago, Ill., Apr. 30, 1902; s. Otto Ferdinand and Hannah (Svendsen) L.; m. Elizabeth Young, Sept. 19, 1941; children: Randolph Horner, Laurence Young. Student, Chgo. City Jr. Coll., 1921-23; BS, Columbia U., 1948, MA, 1956. Journalist Chgo. Daily Jour., 1924-26, U.P.I., 1926-27; fin. writer N.Y. Herald Tribune, 1927-34; economist WPB and War Shipping Adminstrn., 1941-45; editor Twentieth Century Fund, N.Y.C., 1946-51; adj. prof. social philosophy NYU, 1952-65; vis. prof. Carnegie Inst. Tech., 1956-57; lectr. Finch Coll., Bklyn. Acad. Arts and Scis.; sec. Conf. on Methods in Philosophy and Scis., New Sch. Social Rsch., N.Y.C., 1958-62; sec. Com. for Cultural Freedom, 1939-41. Author: Imperial Hearst, 1936, America's Sixty Families, 1937, Modern Woman: The Lost Sex, 1947, The Treason of the People, 1953, The Coming World Transformation, 1963, The Rich and the Super-Rich, 1968, Scoundrels All, 1968, The Rockefeller Syndrome, 1975, Cracks in the Constitution, 1980, The Myth of Democracy, 1989, The Natural Depravity of Mankind, 1994; editor: Medical Studies in Merchant Seaman, 1943. Fellow Am. Sociol. Assn.; mem. Am. Philos. Assn., Am. Assn. U. Profs. Home: 598 Quaker Rd Chappaqua NY 10514-1509

LUNDBERG, GEORGE DAVID, II, medical editor, pathologist; b. Pensacola, Fla., Mar. 21, 1933; s. George David and Esther Louise (Johnson) L.; m. Nancy Ware Sharp, Aug. 18, 1956 (div.); children: George David III, Charles William, Carol Jean; m. Patricia Blacklidge Lorimer, Mar. 6, 1983; children: Christopher Leif, Melinda Suzanne. AA, North Park Coll., Chgo. 1950; BS, U. Ala., Tuscaloosa, 1952; MS, Baylor U., Waco, Tex., 1963; MD, Med. Coll. Ala., Birmingham, 1957; ScD (hon.), SUNY, Syracuse, 1988, Thomas Jefferson U., 1993, U. Ala., Birmingham, 1994, Med. Coll. Ohio, 1995. Intern Tripler Hosp., Hawaii; resident Brooke Hosp., San Antonio; assoc. prof. pathology U. So. Calif., Los Angeles, 1967-72, prof., 1972-77; assoc. dir. labs. Los Angeles County-U. So. Calif. Med. Ctr., 1968-77 prof., chmn. dept. pathology U. Calif.-Davis, Sacramento, 1977-82; v.p. scientific info., editor Jour. AMA, Chgo., 1982-91, editor in chief scientific publ., 1991—; vis prof. U. London, 1976, Lund U., Sweden, 1976; dir. clin. pathology Northwestern U., Chgo., 1982—; clin. prof. Georgetown U., Washington, 1982-93; adj. prof. health policy Harvard U., Boston, 1993—; vis. prof. pathology, 1994—. Author, editor: Managing the Patient Focused Laboratory in Medical Decision Making, 1983, 51 Landmark Articles in Medicine, 1984, AIDS from the Beginning, 1986, Caring for the Uninsured and Underinsured, 1991, Violence, 1992; contbr. articles to profl. jours. Served to lt. col. M.C., U.S. Army, 1956-67. Fellow Am. Soc. Clin. Pathologists (past pres.), Am. Acad. Forensic Sci.; mem. N.Y. Acad. Scis., Inst. Medicine, Alpha Omega Alpha. Democrat. Episcopalian. Office: JAMA 515 N State St Chicago IL 60610-4320

LUNDBLAD, ROGER LAUREN, research director; b. San Francisco, Oct. 31, 1939; s. Lauren Alfred and Doris Ruth (Peterson) L.; m. Susan Hawly Taylor, Oct. 15, 1966 (div. 1985); children: Christina Susan, Cynthia Karin. BSc, Pacific Luth. U., 1961; PhD, U. Wash., 1965. Rsch. assoc. U. Wash., Seattle, 1965-66, Rockefeller U., N.Y.C., 1966-68; asst. prof. U. N.C., Chapel Hill, 1968-74, assoc. prof., 1971-77, prof. pathology and biochemistry, 1977-91; adj. prof., 1991—; dir. sci. tech. devel. Baxter-Biotech, Duarte, Calif., 1991—; vis. scientist Hyland div. Baxter Healthcare, Glendale, Calif., 1988-89. Author: Chemical Reagents for Protein Modification, 1984, 2d edit., 1990; editor: Chemistry and Biology of Thrombin, 1977, Chemistry and Biology of Heparin, 1980, Techniques in Protein Modifica-

tion, 1994; contbr. articles to profl. jours. Recipient Career Achievement award U. N.C., 1986. Mem. Am. Soc. Biochem. Molecular Biology, Am. Soc. Microbiology, Am. Heart Assn., Sigma Xi. Office: Baxter Biotech Hyland Divsn 1720 Flower Ave Duarte CA 91010

LUNDBY, MARY A., state legislator; b. Carroll County, Feb. 2, 1948; d. Edward A. and Elizabeth Hoehl; m. Michael Lundby, 1971; 1 child, Daniel. BA in History, Upper Iowa U., 1971. Former staff asst. Senator Roger Jepsen; mem. Iowa State Senate. Active Solid Waste Adv. Com. Republican. Home: 1240 14th St Marion IA 52302-2562 Office: Iowa State Senate State Capitol Des Moines IA 50319

LUNDE, HAROLD IRVING, management educator; b. Austin, Minn., Apr. 18, 1929; s. Peter Oliver and Emma (Stoa) L.; m. Sarah Jeanette Lysne, June 25, 1955; children: Paul, James, John, Thomas. B.A., St. Olaf Coll., 1952; M.A., U. Minn., 1954, Ph.D., 1966. Assoc. prof. econs. Macalester Coll., St. Paul, 1957-64; fin. staff economist Gen. Motors Corp., N.Y.C., 1965-67; corp. sec. Dayton Hudson Corp., Mpls., 1967-70; mgr. planning and gen. research May Dept. Stores Co., St. Louis, 1970-72; v.p. planning and research May Dept. Stores Co., 1972-78; exec. v.p. adminstrn. Kobacker Stores, Inc., Columbus, Ohio, 1979; prof. mgmt. Bowling Green (Ohio) State U., 1980—. Mem. Acad. Internat. Bus., Acad. Mgmt., Am. Econ. Assn., Nat. Assn. Bus. Economists, Planning Forum, Case Research Assn., Decision Scis. Inst., Phi Beta Kappa, Phi Kappa Phi, Omicron Delta Kappa, Beta Gamma Sigma. Home: 880 Country Club Dr Bowling Green OH 43402-1602 Office: Bowling Green State U Bowling Green OH 43403

LUNDEBERG, PHILIP KARL, curator; b. Mpls., June 14, 1923; s. Olav Knutson and Vivian Juliet (Boraas) L.; m. Eleanore Lillian Berntson, July 18, 1953; 1 son, Karl Fredrik. B.A. summa cum laude, Duke U., 1944, M.A., 1947; Ph.D. (Austin fellow 1949), Harvard U., 1954. Asst. to historian U.S. Naval Ops. in World War II, Navy Dept., 1950-53; asst. prof. history St. Olaf Coll., 1953-55, U.S. Naval Acad., 1955-59; assoc. curator naval history Nat. Mus. History and Tech., Smithsonian Instn., 1959-61, curator of naval history, 1961-84, curator emeritus, 1984—; chmn. Internat. Congress Maritime Museums, 1972-75; v.p. U.S. Commn. on Mil. History, 1975-79, pres., 1980-83; sec. Internat. Commn. Mus. Security, 1975-79; pres. Council Am. Maritime Museums, 1976-78. Author: The Continental Gunboat Philadelphia, 1966, Samuel Colt's Submarine Batter, 1974; co-author: Sea Power: A Naval History, 1960, 81; contbg. author: Magnificent Voyagers, 1985, Ships, Seafaring and Society, 1987, To Die Gallantly, 1994, Guide to Sources of U.S. Military History, 1975, edit., 1993; editor: Bibliographie de L'Histoire des Grandes Routes Maritimes: États-Unis D'Amérique, 1970; exhibits: Armed Forces of U.S., 1961, By Sea and By Land, 1981. With USNR, 1943-83, 89, comdr. Res. Ret., 1992. With USNR, 1943-83, 89, comdr. Res. ret., 1992. Decorated Bronze Star, Purple Heart; recipient Bronze medal Internat. Commn. Mil. History, 1975. Fellow Am. Mil. Inst. (Moncado prize 1964, v.p. 1968-71, pres. 1971-73); mem. Coun. Am. Maritime Mus. (hon.), N.Am. Soc. for Oceanic History, Naval Hist. Found., Naval Order of U.S., Internat. Congress Maritime Mus. (life mem.), Phi Beta Kappa. Home: 1107 Cotton Dr Alexandria VA 22308-2009

LUNDEBERG, ROGER VICTOR, inventor, scientist, writer; b. Hartford, Conn., Jan. 18, 1934; s. Edgar C. and Olga Maybel (Wadlund) L. Student, Hartford State Tech. Coll., 1977-80, 84-86, Charter Oak Coll., Farmington, Conn., 1988-90; AS, Manchester Community Coll., 1983; student, Hartford Tech. Coll., 1977-80, 84-86, U. Hartford, 1957, 87. Inventor, sec.-treas. Parts Feeders Corp., Hartford, 1958-61; inventor Lundeberg Engring. Co., Hartford, 1954-87; editor AMSCOR, East Hartford, Conn., 1987-92. Inventor rotary engines, transistor feeder, hydro-planing craft, velcro, seethrough envelope, permanent-pressed clothes, zip-loc bags, snowmobile, silencer, scale, energized arrow, helicopter; author: My World, 1985, A Point of View, 1989, I Speak for Myself, 1994. Vol. Friendship Ctr., East Hartford, 1981. Mem. AAAS, N.Y. Acad. Sci. (assoc.), Am. Mensa. Avocaitons: numismatics, composing music, writing poetry, art. Home: 860 Main St East Hartford CT 06108

LUNDELIUS, ERNEST LUTHER, JR., vertebrate paleontologist, educator; b. Austin, Tex., Dec. 2, 1927; s. Ernest Luther and Hazel (Halton) L.; m. Judith Weiser, Sept. 28, 1953; children—Jennifer, Rolf Eric. B.S. in Geology, U. Tex., 1950; Ph.D. in Paleozoology, U. Chgo., 1954. Postdoctoral Fulbright scholar to Western Australia, 1954-55; postdoctoral research fellow Calif. Inst. Tech., 1956-57; mem. faculty U. Tex., Austin, 1957—; prof. vertebrate paleontology U. Tex., 1969; John Andrew Wilson prof. vertebrate paleontology, 1978—. Served with AUS, 1946-47. Fulbright sr. scholar to Australia, 1976. Home: 7310 Running Rope Austin TX 78731-2132 Office: U Tex Dept Geol Scis Austin TX 78712

LUNDEN, JOAN, television personality; b. Fair Oaks, CA, Sept. 19, 1950; d. Erle Murray and Gladyce Lorraine (Somervill) Blunden; children: Jamie Beryl, Lindsay Leigh, Sarah Emily. Student, Universidad de Las Americas, Mexico City, U. Calif., Calif. State U.; Am. River Coll., Sacramento, Calif. Began broadcasting career as co-anchor and prodr. at Sta. KCRA-TV and Radio, Sacramento, 1973-75; with Sta. WABC-TV, N.Y.C., 1975—, co-anchor, 1976-80; co-host Good Morning America, ABC-TV, 1980—; host special report TV for Whittle Comm.; host Everyday with Joan Lunden, 1989; film appearances include: Macho Callahan, 1970, What About Bob?, 1991; co-author: (with Andy Friedburg) Good Morning, I'm Joan Lunden, 1986, (with Michael Krauss) Joan Lunden's Mother's Minutes, 1986, Your Newborn Baby; syndicated columnist: Parent's Notes. Recipient Outstanding Mother of Yr. award, Nat. Mother's Day Com., 1982; Albert Einstein Coll. of Yeshiva U. Spirit of Achievement award; Nat. Women's Polit. Caucus award; NJ Divsn. of Civil Rights award; Baylor U. Outstanding Woman of the Year award. Office: Good Morning Am 147 Columbus Ave New York NY 10023-5900*

LUNDERGAN, BARBARA KEOUGH, lawyer; b. Chgo., Nov. 6, 1938; d. Edward E. and Eleanor A. (Erickson) Keough; m. James A. Lundergan, Dec. 29, 1962; children—Matthew K., Mary Alice. B.A., U. Ill., 1960; J.D., Loyola U., Chgo., 1964. Bar: Ill. 1964, U.S. Dist. Ct. (no. dist.) Ill. 1964, U.S. Tax Ct. 1974. With Seyfarth, Shaw, Fairweather & Geraldson, Chgo., 1964—, ptnr., 1971—. Fellow Am. Coll. Trust and Estate Counsel; mem. ABA (com. on fed. taxation), Ill. Bar Assn. (coun. sect. on fed. taxation 1983-91, chair 1989, coun. sect. on trusts and estates sect. coun. 1992—editl. bd. Ill. Bar Jour. 1993—), Chgo. Bar Assn. (chmn. trust law com. 1982-83, com. on fed. taxation). Office: Seyfarth Shaw Fairweather & Geraldson 55 E Monroe St Chicago IL 60603

LUNDGREN, DAVID ALBERT, product design engineer; b. Englewood, N.J., Nov. 22, 1959; s. Daniel Paul and Janet Norma (Nutt) L. BE, Stevens Inst. Tech., 1981; BSME, MIT, 1983. Design engr. Hewlett-Packard, Greeley, Colo., 1981-86; devel. engr. Pixar Co., San Rafael, Calif., 1986—. Mem. The Solstice Soc., Sigma Xi, Tau Beta Pi. Democrat. Avocations: guitar, motorcycling, bicycling, writing, endurance road rallying. Home: 305 Wickham Dr Mill Valley CA 94941-3443 Office: Apple Computer Inc 20730 Valley Green Dr Cupertino CA 95014

LUNDGREN, LEONARD, III, retired secondary education educator; b. San Francisco, June 22, 1933; s. Leonard II and Betty (Bosold) L.; m. Jane Gates, June 12, 1976. AA, City Coll. San Francisco, 1952; AB, San Francisco State U., 1954, MA, 1958, postgrad., 1958-71. Cert. tchr., Calif. Phys. edn. tchr., athletic coach Pelton Jr. High Sch., San Francisco, 1958-59; social studies tchr., dept. chair, phys. edn. tchr., athletic coach Luther Burbank Jr. High Sch., San Francisco, 1959-78; history, govt. econs., geography tchr. George Washington High Sch., San Francisco, 1978-93; water safety instr. ARC, San Francisco, 1946-61; mem. Calif. Quality Teaching Ctr. Conf. Bd., 1965-67. Author: Guide for Films and Filmstrips, 1966, Teacher's Handbook for Social Studies, 1966, Guide for Minority Studies, 1968. Sch. v.p. PTA, 1980-81; v.p. Lakeside Property Owners Assn., San Francisco, 1986-898, legis. adv., 1988-95; v.p. West of Twin Peaks Coun., San Francisco, 1986-87; pub. affairs polit. econ. cons., Calif., 1993—. With USN, 1954-56. Fulbright scholar, Greece, 1963; recipient Svc. Pin, ARC, 1961. Mem. NEA (life, del. 1970, 72-76), Calif. Tchrs. Assn. (state coun. rep. 1963-74), San Francisco Studies, Calif. Coun. Social Studies (v.p. San Francisco chpt. 1969-70), San Francisco Classroom Tchrs. Assn. (pres. 1972-73, Gavel award 1973), Calif. Ret. Tchrs. Assn. (life, legis. chmn. San

LUNDIN, BRUCE THEODORE, engineering and management consultant; b. Alameda, Calif., Dec. 28, 1919; s. Oscar Linus and Elizabeth Ellen (Erickson) L.; m. Barbara Ann Bliss, July 27, 1946 (wid. Feb. 1981); children: Dianne, Robert, Nancy; m. Jean Ann Oberlin, Mar. 22, 1982. BSME, U. Calif.-Berkeley, 1942; D of Engring. (hon.), U. Toledo, 1975. Chief engine research NASA Lewis Ctr., Cleve., 1952-58, asst. dir. 1958-61, assoc. dir., 1961-68, dir., 1969-77; dep. assoc. adminstrn. NASA, Washington, 1968-69; adv. U.S. Air Force Sci. Adv. Bd., Washington, 1961-77; mem. Aerospace Safety Adv. Bd., Washington, 1961-72; staff dir. Pres.'s Commn. on the Accident at Three Mile Island, 1981; mem. TM1-2 Safety Adv. Bd., 1981-89; chmn. Rockwell Internat. Safety Oversight Panel, 1988-89. Pres. Westshore Unitarian Ch., Rocky River, Ohio, 1967-68; trustee Southwest Gen. Hosp., Berea, Ohio, 1970-75. Recipient Outstanding Leadership medal NASA, 1965, Pub. Service award NASA, 1971, 75, Disting. Service medal NASA, 1971, 77, Engineer of the Year award Nat. Space Club, 1975. Fellow AIAA; mem. Nat. Acad. Engring. Avocations: woodworking; gardening; reading; travel. Home: 5859 Columbia Rd North Olmsted OH 44070-4611

LUNDINE, STANLEY NELSON, state government official, former congressman, lawyer; b. Jamestown, N.Y., Feb. 4, 1939; children: John Ludwig, Mark Andrew. Mayor of Jamestown, 1969-76; mem. 95th-97th Congresses from 39th N.Y. Dist., 98th-99th Congress from 34th N.Y. Dist., 1976-87; lt. gov. State of N.Y., Albany, 1987—; mem. banking, fin. and urban affairs coms., sci. and tech. com., select com. on aging. Office: State Capitol Office Of Lt Gov Rm 326 Albany NY 12224

LUNDING, CHRISTOPHER HANNA, lawyer; b. Evanston, Ill., June 15, 1946; s. Franklin J. and Virginia (Hanna) L.; children: Elizabeth, Nelson, Alexander, Andrew, Kirsten; m. Barbara J. Fontana, Aug. 19, 1989. BA, Harvard U., 1968; JD, Yale U., 1971. Bar: N.Y. 1972, Fla. 1972, U.S. Supreme Ct. 1975. Law clk. to judge 2d Cir. U.S. Ct. Appeals, N.Y.C., 1971-72; assoc. Cleary, Gottlieb, Steen & Hamilton, N.Y.C., 1973-79 ptnr., 1980—; chmn. Legal Sves. N.Y.C. 1987-94. Chmn. Belle Haven Tax Dist., Greenwich, Conn., 1986—. Fellow Am. Bar Found.; mem. N.Y. County Lawyers Assn. (bd. dirs. 1988-94). Episcopalian. Home: 276 Otter Rock Dr Greenwich CT 06830-7045 Office: Cleary Gottlieb Steen & Hamilton 1 Liberty Pla New York NY 10006

LUNDMAN, RICHARD JACK, sociology educator; b. Chgo., Apr. 19, 1944; s. Oscar Yngve and Mabel Josephine (Hansen) L.; m. Jean Elizabeth Planty, June 24, 1967; children: Robert Joel; Julie Marie. BA, Beloit Coll., 1966; MA, U. Ill., 1968; PhD, U. Minn., 1973. Asst. prof. sociology U. Del., Newark, 1972-75; asst. prof. sociology Ohio State U., Columbus, 1975-78, assoc. prof. sociology, 1978-84, prof. sociology, 1984—, chmn. grad. studies dept. of sociology, 1984-89. Author: Corporate and Governmental Deviance: Problems of Organizational Behavior in Contemporary Society, 1978, 5th edit., 1996, Prevention and Control of Juvenile Delinquency, 1994, 2d edit., 1993; (with M. David Ermann) Police Behavior: A Sociological Perspective, 1980, Police and Policing, 1980, Corporate Deviance, 1982; contbr. numerous articles to profl. jours. Mem. Am. Sociol. Assn., Am. Soc. Criminology. Democrat. Avocations: swimming, golfing, reading. Office: Ohio State U Dept Sociology 190 N Oval Mall Columbus OH 43210-1321

LUNDQUIST, CHARLES ARTHUR, university official; b. Webster, S.D., Mar. 26, 1928; s. Arthur Reynald and Olive Esther (Parks) L.; m. Patricia Jean Richardson, Nov. 28, 1951; children: Clara Lee, Dawn Elizabeth, Frances Johanna, Eric Arthur, Gary Lars. BS, S.D. State U., 1949, DSc, 1979; PhD, U. Kans., 1953. Asst. prof. engring. research Pa. State U., 1953-54; sect. chief U.S. Army Ballistic Missile Agy., Huntsville, Ala., 1956-60; br. chief (NASA-Marshall Space Flight Center), Huntsville, 1960-62; dir. Space Scis. Lab., 1973-81; asst. dir. sci. Smithsonian Astrophys. Obs., Cambridge, Mass., 1962-73; assoc. Harvard Coll. Obs., 1962-73; dir. rsch. U. Ala., Huntsville, 1982-90, assoc. v.p. for rsch, 1990—. Editor: (with G. Veis) Smithsonian Institution Standard Earth, 1966, The Physics and Astronomy of Space Science, 1966, Skylab's Astronomy and Space Sciences, 1979. Served with U.S. Army, 1954-56. Recipient Exceptional Sci. Achievement medal NASA, 1971; Hermann Oberth award AIAA, 1978. Mem. AAAS, N.Y. Acad. Scis., Am. Grophys. Union, Am. Astron. Soc., Am. Phys. Soc., Nat. Speleological Soc. Home: 214 Jones Valley Dr SW Huntsville AL 35802-1724 Office: U Ala Office of Assoc VP for Rsch Research Instit Rm M-65 Huntsville AL 35899

LUNDQUIST, DANA R., health facility administrator; b. Mpls., Sept. 12, 1941; s. R. Dana and Mary Jane (Norton) L.; children: Brenda A., Sheila R. BA, Valparaiso U., 1963; postgrad., U. Hawaii, 1963-64, U. Colo., 1963; MBA, U. Chgo., 1966. Adminstrv. asst. U. Chgo. Hosps. and Clinics, 1966-67, asst. supt., 1967-68, asst. dir., 1968-70; officer, bd. dirs. affiliates Hamot Health Systems, Inc., Erie, Pa., 1970-92, pres. parent co., 1981-92, cons. to bd., 1992—; cons. Blue Cross Western Pa., 1992-93, sr. v.p.,1993—; lectr. grad. program in hosp. adminstrn. U. Chgo., 1967-70; mem. Erie County Hosp. Coun., 1978-92, pres., 1982; bd. dirs. Hosp. Coun. Western Pa., 1978-92, vice chmn.; exec. com. Pa. Coun. Teaching Hosps., 1986-90; adv. coun. risk mgmt. Pa. Hosp. Ins. Co., 1982-90, bd. dirs. Vol. Hosps. Am. of Pa., 1985-92, chmn. bd.; bd. visitors The Behrend Coll., Pa. State U., 1990-92; bd. dirs. Pa. Med. Coll., 1991-92, Hardware Hawaii, 1989—. Mem. Erie Conf. on Community Devel., 1981-92, bd. dirs., 1988-92; bd. dirs. N.W. Pa. Buy Right Coun., 1986-92, United Way Erie County, 1983-92; mem. pres.'s coun. Villa Maria Coll., Erie, 1981-90, bd. incorporators Gannon U., Erie, 1981-92; mem. pastoral bd. St. Paul's Luth. Ch., Erie, 1973-78, v.p., 1974-78; mem. Erie Down Town Coalition Steering Com., 1990-92, chmn., 1991-92, numerous other activities. Fellow Am. Coll. Healthcare Execs. (former regents adv. coun. Pa.); mem. Am. Hosp. Assn. (governing coun. sect. met. hosps. 1987, alt. ho. of dels. 1988), Hosp. Assn. Pa. (polit. action com. 1981-92), Pa. C. of C. U. Chgo. Hosp. Alumni Assn. (exec. com. 1967-70, 87-92, sec.-treas. 1988), Rotary, Rivers Club. Office: Blue Cross Western PA 5th Ave Pl Ste 3012 Pittsburgh PA 15222-3099 Home: PO Box 22130 Pittsburgh PA 15222

LUNDQUIST, GENE ALAN, cotton company executive; b. Bakersfield, Calif., Feb. 25, 1943; s. Felix Waldemar and Elsia Geneva (Bartlett) L.; m. Linda Fern Smotherman, June 17, 1966; 1 child, Nels Eric R. S., Colo. State U., 1964. Info. specialist Calcot Ltd., Bakersfield, 1969-71, field rep., 1971-74, asst. v.p., 1974-77, asst. v.p., corp. sec., 1977-80, v.p., corp. sec., 1980—; bd. dirs. Calif. Farm Water Coalition, Water Assn. Kern County; apptd. Calif. Gov.'s Agrl. Summit. Bd. dirs. Kern County Water Agy., Bakersfield, 1975-91, Bakersfield Salvation Army, 1985-88. Served with U.S. Army, 1965-67. Decorated Army Commendation medal; Calif. Agr. Leadership Found. fellow, 1973. Mem. Cotton Bd. (alt. dir. 1981-84), Nat. Cotton Council Am. (del. 1984—), Calif. Cotton Growers Assn. (adv. com. 1976—), Calif. Planting Cotton Seed Distrbrs. (adv. com. 1976—). Republican. Mem. Mennonite Brethren Ch. Avocations: golf; tennis; running; landscaping; reading. Office: Calcot Ltd 1601 E Brundage Ln PO Box 259 Bakersfield CA 93302

LUNDQUIST, JAMES HAROLD, lawyer; s. Harold L. and Beatrice (Anderson) L.; m. Beverly J. Williams, 1955; children: John Redfield, Ann Tecla Walter. AB, Millikin U., 1953; JD, John Marshall Law Sch., 1955. Bar: Ill. 1955, N.Y. 1961, D.C. 1961, U.S. Supreme Ct. 1956. Pvt. practice Chgo., 1954-55; with Barnes, Richardson & Colburn, N.Y.C., Washington, Chgo., 1957—, ptnr., 1966—; adj. prof. Bklyn. Law Sch., 1981-92; bd. dirs. YKK Corp. of Am. Author: Europe and the New U.S. Bloc Politik, 1992. Sec., trustee East Hampton Hist. Soc., 1993—; chmn. Nassau County Mental Health Bd., 1965-70; corp. mem. Community Svc. Soc. N.Y., 1970-78; bd. dirs. NCCJ, N.Y., 1965-79; GATT dispute panelist, 1980-81. Served U.S. Army, 1955-56. Decorated Chevalier de l'ordre National du Merite Francais, 1980, Cavaliere Ordine al Merito della Repubblica Italia, 1994. Mem. ABA (chmn. standing com. on customs law 1968-73), Assn. of Bar of City of N.Y., Customs and Internat. Trade Bar Assn. (pres. 1978-80), Fed. Bar Assn., Italy-Am. C. of C. (pres. 1985-87), Union League (N.Y.C.), Univ. Club (Washington). Democrat. Methodist. Office: Barnes Richardson & Colburn 475 Park Ave S New York NY 10016-6901

LUNDQUIST, JOHN MILTON, librarian, author, lecturer, travel writer; b. Twin Falls, Idaho, Sept. 22, 1938; s. Milton Rocine and Mildred (Toolson) L.; m. Suzanne Evertsen, Sept. 6, 1966 (div. July 1985); children: Jennifer, Lila, Eric, Margaret, John, Jack. BA in History, Portland State U., 1970; MLS, Brigham Young U., 1972; MA in Near Eastern Studies, U. Mich., 1974, PhD in Near Eastern Studies, 1983. Instr. anthropology and religious instrn. Brigham Young U., Provo, Utah, 1979-83, asst. prof. anthropology and religious instrn., 1983-85; mem. faculty New Sch. for Social Rsch., N.Y.C., 1986-88; Susan and Douglas chief libr. Oriental divsn. N.Y. Pub. Libr., N.Y.C., 1985—; rschr. Archive for Rsch. in Archetypal Symposlism, N.Y.C., 1987—; lectr. Inst. for Asian Studies, Inc., N.Y.C., C.G. Jung Found. N.Y., 1993; adj. assoc. prof. art history and archaeology Columbia U., N.Y.C., 1987-89; adj. assoc. prof. Near Eastern langs. and lit. NYU, N.Y.C., 1987; speaker, lectr. in field; dir. excavation Am. Sch. Oriental Rsch., Tell Quarqur, Syria, 1981-85, field archaeologist, Syria, 1979-82; area supr. Am. Expedition to Tell Hadidi, Syria, summers 1974-76; extensive travel, rsch., field work People's Republic of China (including Tibet), Japan, Hong Kong, Taiwan, India, Indonesia, others. Author: The Temple: Meeting Place of Heaven and Earth, 1993, Japanese edit., 1994, Babylon in European Writing and Art Civilizations of the Ancient Near East, 1995; contbr. articles to The N.Y. Times and other publs.; bd. editors Jour. Temple Studies, 1993—; translator lang. and lang. behavior abstracts. Mem. Internat. Assn. Orientalist Librs., Am. Inst. Archaeology (bd. govs. N.Y.C. chpt.), Am. Schs. Oriental Rsch. (corp. instnl. rep. 1985—), Oriental Club N.Y.C. (pres. 1992—), East Side Conservative Club, Phi Kappa Phi. Republican. Mormon. Avocations: marathon running, martial arts. Home: 881 7th Ave # 1001 New York NY 10019-3210 Office: NY Pub Libr Oriental Divsn Fifth Ave and 42d St New York NY 10018

LUNDQUIST, WEYMAN IVAN, lawyer; b. Worcester, Mass., July 27, 1930; s. Hilding Ivan and Florence Cecilia (Westerholm) L.; m. Joan Durrell, Sept. 15, 1956 (div. July 1977); children—Weyman, Erica, Jettora, Kirk; m. Kathryn E. Taylor, Dec. 28, 1978; 1 child, Derek. BA magna cum laude, Dartmouth Coll., 1952; LLB, Harvard U., 1955. Bar: Mass. 1955, Alaska 1961, Calif. 1963, Vt. 1994. Assoc. Thayer, Smith & Gaskill, Worcester, 1957-60; atty. U.S. Attys. Office, Mass. and Alaska, 1960-62; assoc. Heller, Ehrman, White & McAuliffe, San Francisco, 1963-65, ptnr., 1967—; counsel, v.p. State Mut. Life Ins. Co., Worcester, 1965-67; vis. prof. environ. studies Dartmouth Coll., Hanover, N.H., 1980, 84; vis. scholar Dickey Ctr. for Internat. Understanding, 1994—; program chmn. 1990 Moscow Conf. on Law and Bilateral Econs. Rels.; mem. U.S. adv. com. Alaska/Can./Soviet No. Justice Conf., 1993-94, N.Y., San Francisco Cutting Edge Lawyer Liability Programs, 1989. Author: (fiction) The Promised Land, 1987; contbr. articles to profl. jours. Trustee Natural Resources Def. Coun., 1982-91. Recipient CPR Significant Achievement award, 1987. Fellow ABA (founder and chmn. litigation sect. 1978-79, chmn. Soviet Bar Assn. liaison com. 1986, co-chmn. spl. com. for study discovery abuse 1976-83, spl. com. on tort liability system 1981-84, superfund 301e study group advisor to U.S. Congress, 1983), Am. Coll. Trial Lawyers; Dartmouth Lawyer's Assn. (founding mem.), Am. Antiquarian Soc. (councillor), Fgn. Rels. Coun., Assn. Life Ins. Coun., U.S. Supreme Ct. Hist. Soc., No. Dist. Hist. Soc., Sierra Club, Friends of the Earth, Sequoia, Dartmouth Lawyers Assn., Swedish Am. C. of C. (pres., bd. dirs. western area U.S. 1982-89). Avocations: squash, skiing, writing. Home: 8 Occom Ridge Hanover NH 03755 Office: Heller Ehrman White & McAuliffe 333 Bush St San Francisco CA 94104 also: PO Box 200 Norwich VT 05055

LUNDSGAARDE, HENRY PEDER, anthropology educator, researcher; b. Copenhagen, Dec. 22, 1938; came to U.S., 1957; s. Henry Thorvald and Ragnhild (Rasmussen) L.; m. Anette Rothenborg, June 24, 1967 (div. 1986); children—Peter, Thorsten, Allan, Erik. B.A., U. Calif., Santa Barbara, 1961; M.S., U. Wis., 1963, Ph.D., 1966. Research asst. dept. anthropology U. Oreg., 1964-65; asst. prof. anthropology U. Calif., Santa Barbara, 1965-70; fellow in law and anthropology Harvard U. Law Sch., Cambridge, Mass., 1969-70; assoc. prof. anthropology, chmn. dept. U. Houston, 1970-72; research assoc. dept. medicine Coll. Medicine U. Vt., 1976-78; prof. anthropology U. Kans., Lawrence, 1972—, chmn. dept. anthropology, 1972-76; assoc. dir. Salt Lake City Regional Med. Edn. Ctr., VA Med Ctr., Salt Lake City, 1987-89; cons. VA Regional Info. Sys. Ctr., Salt Lake City, 1989; adj. prof. med. informatics U. Utah Sch. Medicine, 1987-95; adj. rsch. asst. dept. anthropology U. Oreg., 1964-65; lectr. in field. Author: Cultural Adaptation in the Southern Gilbert Islands, 1966, Murder in Space City: A Cultural Analysis of Houston Homicide Patterns, 1977; (with others) Human Problems in Computerized Medicine, 1981; editor, author: Land Tenure in Oceania, 1974; contbr. articles to profl. jours. Fellow Woodrow Wilson Found., 1961, 64, Am. Council Learned Socs., 1963, 69, Harvard U. Law Sch., 1969, grantee NSF, NIH, Wenner-Gren Found. Home: 1502 W 25th Street Ct # D6 Lawrence KS 66046-4016 Office: U Kans Dept Anthropology Lawrence KS 66045

LUNDSTEDT, SVEN BERTIL, behavioral and social scientist, educator; b. N.Y.C., May 6, 1926; s. Sven David and Edith Maria L.; m. Jean Elizabeth Sanford, June 16, 1951; children: Margaret, Peter, Janet. AB, U. Chgo., 1952, PhD, 1955; SM, Harvard U., 1960. Lic. in psychology, N.Y., Ohio; cert. Council for Nat. Register of Health Services. Asst. dir. Found. for Research on Human Behavior, 1960-62; asst. prof. Case-Western Res. U., Cleve., 1962-64, assoc. prof., 1964-68; assoc. prof. administrv. sci. Ohio State U., Columbus, 1968-69, prof. pub. policy and mgmt., 1969—, Ameritech Research prof., 1987-89, prof. internat. bus. and pub. policy, 1988—; affiliate scientist Battelle PNL, 1994—; chmn. Battelle endowment program for tech. and human affairs, 1976-80, mem. Univ. Senate; dir. project on edn. of chief exec. officer Aspen Inst., 1978-80; advisor Task Force on Innovation, U.S. Ho. of Reps., 1983-84, Citizens Network for Fgn. Affairs, 1988—; mem. Am. Com. on U.S. Soviet Relations, 1985—, chair trade and negotiation project; cons. E.I. duPont de Nemours & Co., B.F. Goodrich Co., Bell Telephone Labs., Battelle Meml. Inst., Nat. Fulbright Award Com.; invited speaker Royal Swedish Acad. Scis., 1989. Author: Higher Education in Social Psychology, 1968; co-author: Managing Innovation, 1982, Managing Innovation and Change, 1989; author, editor: Telecommunications, Values and the Public Interest, 1990; contbr. articles to profl. jours. Pres., Cleve. Mental Health Assn., 1966-68; mem. Ohio Citizen's Task Force on Corrections, 1971-72. Served with U.S. Army, 1944-46. Harvard U. fellow, 1960; grantee Bell Telephone Labs., 1964-65, NSF, 1965-67, Kettering Found., 1978-80, Atlantic Richfield Found., 1980-82, German Marshall Fund of U.S. to conduct internat. ednl. joint ventures on econ. negotiations, Budapest, Hungary, 1990; recipient Ohio Ho. of Reps. award, 1986. Mem. Am. Psychol. Assn., Internat. Inst. for Applied Systems Analysis (innovation task force, nat. adv. com. project internat. negotiation with Am. Acad. Arts and Scis., founder, chmn. U.S. Midwest Assn. for IIASA 1986—, sr. social sci. advisor 1994—), Am. Acad. Arts and Scis. (chmn. PIN com. on east/west trade negotiation), Am. Soc. for Pub. Adminstrn. (pres. Central Ohio chpt. 1975-77, founder, chmn. com. on bus. govt. relations, 1977-79, editorial bd. Pub. Adminstrn. Rev., 1978-82), Internat. Soc. Panetics (sec. bd. govs., founding mem.). Unitarian. Home: 197 Riverview Park Dr Columbus OH 43214-2023 Office: Ohio State U Sch Pub Policy and Mgmt 1775 S College Rd Columbus OH 43210-1309

LUNDSTROM, MARJIE, newspaper editor. Grad., U. Nebr. Columnist, editor, nat. corr. The Denver Post, 1981-89; with The Sacramento Bee, 1989-90, 91—; nat. corr. Gannett News Svc., Washington, 1990-91. Recipient Pulitzer Prize for nat. reporting, 1991. Office: The Sacramento Bee 2100 Q St PO Box 15779 Sacramento CA 95852

LUNDY, DANIEL FRANCIS, communications company executive; b. N.Y.C., Nov. 29, 1930; s. Daniel M. and Josephine Elizabeth (Corcoran) L.; m. Janet M. Taylor, Dec. 27, 1952; children: Daniel Thomas, Joanne, Mary Elizabeth, Susan Teresa. B.S., Fordham U., 1952; J.D., St. John's U., N.Y.C., 1958. Bar: N.Y. 1959, D.C. 1970, N.J. 1971; C.P.A. Corp. tax dir. Merck & Co., Inc., 1964-70; tax atty. Shanley & Fisher (Esqs.), Newark, 1970-72; partner Coopers & Lybrand (C.P.A.s), N.Y.C., 1973-76; sr. v.p., dir. taxes ITT, N.Y.C., 1976—. Contbr. to profl. jours. Served with AUS, 1952-54. Mem. Am. Inst. C.P.A.s Internat. Fiscal Assn (pres. 1990-91). Home: 121 E Sailboat Ln Beach Haven NJ 08008-3365 Office: ITT Corp 1330 6th Ave New York NY 10019-5422

LUNDY, JOSEPH E., lawyer; b. Phila., Dec. 30, 1942; s. Martin L. and Adele E. (Zion) L.; m. Bonnie Verbit, Aug. 30, 1966; children: Seth Harris, Nancy Elizabeth. BS in Econs., U. Pa., 1965; JD, Temple U., 1968; LLM in Taxation, N.Y. U., 1969. Bar: Fla. 1968, Pa. 1969. Assoc. MacCoy, Evans & Lewis, Phila., 1969-73, ptnr., 1974-76; ptnr. Montgomery, McCracken, Walker & Rhodes, Phila., 1976-88, Ballard, Spahr, Andrews & Ingersoll, Phila., 1988—; adj. prof. law Temple U., 1974—. Editor-in-Chief Jour. Taxation of Exempt Orgns. Trustee Pa. Coll. Podiatric Medicine, Phila.; assoc. trustee U. Pa., Phila.; bd. overseers U. Pa. Univ. Mus., Phila. Fellow Am. Coll. Tax Counsel; mem. ABA (exempt orgn. com., com. govt. subcoms.). Am. Acad. Hosp. Attys., Phila. Bar Assn. (vice chair tax sect. 1988-90, chair 1990-92). Office: Ballard Spahr Andrews & Ingersoll 1735 Market St 51st Fl Philadelphia PA 19103

LUNDY, J(OSEPH) EDWARD, retired automobile company executive; b. Iowa, Jan. 6, 1915; s. Vern E. and Mary L. (Chambers) L. B.A., State U. Iowa, 1936. Fellow Princeton U., 1936-39, mem. econs. faculty, 1940-42, beginning as planning ofcl.; with Ford Motor Co., Dearborn, Mich., 1946-85, successively dir. fin. planning and analysis, gen. asst. contr., 1946-57, treas., 1957-61, v.p., contr., 1961-62, v.p. fin., 1962-67, exec. v.p., 1967-79, dir. and vice-chmn. fin. com., 1979-85; dir. research and analysis Office Statis. Control, Hdqrs. USAAF, 1945. Served from pvt. to maj. USAAF, 1943-45. Decorated Legion of Merit. Mem. Phi Beta Kappa, Delta Upsilon. Roman Catholic. Clubs: Detroit Princeton, Detroit. Home: 7 Brookwood Ln Dearborn MI 48120-1302

LUNDY, JOSEPH R., lawyer; b. Chgo., Jan. 21, 1940; s. Francis Lorain and Alice (Whitcomb) L. BA, Princeton U., 1962; JD, George Washington U., 1970. Bar: D.C. 1970, Ill. 1971, U.S. Supreme Ct. 1978. Legis. asst. to U.S. Congressman Abner J. Mikva, Washington, 1969-70; assoc. atty. Schiff Hardin & Waite, Chgo., 1971-73, 76-79; state rep. Ill. Gen. Assembly, Springfield, 1973-77; ptnr. Schiff Hardin & Waite, 1980—; adj. prof. Sch. of Law Northwestern U., 1994—. Commr. Ill. Commn. Uniform State Laws, 1976-79; dir. Legal Assistance Found. Chgo., 1980-83; mem. Gov.'s Commn. Administrv. Rules, Chgo., 1977-84. Mem. Chgo. Bar Assn. (chmn. antitrust com. 1983-84), Chgo. Coun. Lawyers (v.p. 1977-78, bd. govs. 1975-81), Am. Judicature Soc. Avocations: tennis, opera, piano, travel, reading. Office: Schiff Hardin & Waite 7200 Sears Tower Chicago IL 60606

LUNDY, MARY ANN WEESE, religious organization administrator. Dir. nat. bd. Nat. Student YWCA of USA, N.Y.C., 1982-87; dir. women's ministry unit Presbyn. Ch. (USA), Louisville, 1987-93, assoc. dir. gen. assembly, 1994; vis. scholar Hartford Sem., 1994—. Office: Presbyterian Church 100 Witherspoon St Louisville KY 40202

LUNDY, ROLAND, publishing executive; b. 1950. Grad., Baylor U., 1972. With Word Inc., Irving, Tex., 1972—, now pres.

LUNDY, VICTOR ALFRED, architect, educator; b. N.Y.C., Feb. 1, 1923; s. Alfred Henry and Rachel Lundy; m. Shirley Corwin, 1947 (div. 1959); children: Christopher Mark, Jennifer Alison; m. Anstis Manton Burwell, Sept. 19, 1960; 1 child, Nicholas Burwell. BArch, Harvard U., 1947, MArch, 1948. Registered architect, Tex., N.Y., Calif. Pvt. practice architecture Sarasota, Fla., 1951-59, N.Y.C., 1960-75; prin. Victor A. Lundy & Assocs., Inc., Houston, 1976-84; design. prin., v.p. HKS Inc., Dallas, 1984—; vis. prof. Grad. Sch. Design, Harvard U., Sch. Architecture, Yale U., Columbia U., U. Calif., Berkeley, Calif. Poly. State U. San Luis Obispo, U. Houston, U. Rome, others; U.S. specialist-architect in U.S.I.A. exhibit, USSR, 1965. Responsible for design St. Paul's Luth. Ch., Sarasota, 1959, new sanctuary, 1970, 1st Unitarian Ch. of Fairfield County, Westport, Conn., 1961, 1st Unitarian Congl. Soc., Hartford, Conn., 1964, Ch. of Resurrection, East Harlem Protestant Parish, N.Y.C., 1966, exhbn. bldg. and exhibit for AEC in S.Am. (Buenos Aires, Rio de Janeiro, Bogota, Santiago), 1967 (Silver medal for exhbn. Archtl. League N.Y. 1965), recreation shelters for Nat. Mus. History and tech., Smithsonian Instn., Washington, 1967, U.S. States Tax Ct. bldg. and pla., Washington, 1976, U.S. Embassy, Colombo, Sri Lanka, for Office of Fgn. Bldgs., Dept. State, 1983 (U.S. Presdl. Design Awards Program 1988, Fed. Design Achievement award), Austin Centre-Omni Hotel, Austin, Tex., 1984, One Congress Pla., Austin, Tex., 1984, Walnut Glen Tower, Dallas, 1985, Mack Ctr. II, Tampa, Fla., 1990, Greyhound Corp. Ctr., Phoenix, 1991, GTE Telephone Ops. World Hdqrs., Irving, Tex., 1991, others; archtl. work represented in Berlin Internat. Archtl. Exposition, 1957, Sao Paulo Internat. Biennial Exposition, 1957, 5th Congress Union Internat. Des Architectes, Moscow, 1958, Expo '70 Kansas, Osaka, Japan, 1970, travelling exhbn. of architecture in S.Am. Sgt. inf. U.S. Army, 1943-46, ETO. Decorated Purple Heart; recipient Gold medal award Buenos Aires Sesquicentennial Internat. Exhbn., 1960, Gold medal award Buenos Aires Sesquicentennial Internt.Exhbn., 1960; Silver medal Archtl. League N.Y., 1965; Charles Hayden Meml. Scholastic scholar, 1939-43, Edward H. Kendall scholar Harvard U., 1947-48, Rotch travelling scholar Boston Soc. Architects, 1948-50; travelling fellow Harvard U., 1948-50; Dept. State grantee, 1965. Fellow AIA. Avocations: painting, sculpture. Home: 701 Mulberry Ln Bellaire TX 77401 Office: HKS Inc 1111 Pla of the Americas N Ste LB 307 Dallas TX 75201

LUNDY, WALKER, newspaper editor; b. St. Petersburg, Fla.; m. Saralyn Lundy; 2 children. BSJ, U. Fla. Reporter Atlanta Jour.-Constitution; reporter, city editor Detroit Free Press; mng. editor, exec. editor Tallahassee Democrat; mng. editor Ft. Worth Star-Telegram; editor Arkansas Gazette, Little Rock; gen. editor, sr. v.p. St. Paul Pioneer Press, 1990—, exec. editor, sr. v.p., 1990—. Office: Northwest Publs Inc 345 Cedar St Saint Paul MN 55101-1014*

LUNEV, ALEKSANDR (SASHA), dancer; b. Leningrad, 1965. Grad., Choreographic Inst., 1983. Dancer Kirov, 1983; prin. dancer Boston Ballet; now premiere danseur, artistic advisor Tulsa Ballet Theatre, Tulsa, OK. Performed throughout the USSR, France, Italy, Germany, U.S., Can. and Japan; tour with Kirov to London and Paris; major dance roles include Giselle, Swan Lake, Sleeping Beauty, Chopiniana, La Sylphide, Les Sylphides, Fountain of Bakchisarai, Corsaire; debut in the U.S. with the Boston Ballet. Office: Tulsa Ballet Theatre 4512 S Peoria Ave Tulsa OK 74105*

LUNGER, IRVIN EUGENE, university president emeritus, clergyman; b. Williamsport, Pa., June 28, 1912; s. George Lee and Mabel Clara (Griggs) L.; m. Eleanor Jeanne Zink, Feb. 10, 1939 (dec. Aug. 1955); children: Susan Ann (Mrs. Lee C. Brown) (dec.), Kathryn Elizabeth (Mrs. Bob Willis) (dec.); m. Kay Walsh Ritchey, June 19, 1957; foster son, Owsley Ritchey. A.B. magna cum laude, Bethany Coll., 1934, Litt.D. (hon.), 1959; B.D., U. Chgo., 1935, A.M., 1936, Ph.D., 1938; postgrad., U. Munich, Germany, 1936-37; L.H.D. (hon.), U. Ala., 1965, Transylvania U., 1980; Litt.D. (hon.), Eastern Ky. U., 1974. Ordained to ministry Disciples of Christ Ch., 1932; minister Christian Ch., Morristown, 1930-34, University Ch. Disciples of Christ, Chgo., 1939-55; prof. religion, dean Morrison Chapel, Transylvania U., Lexington, Ky., 1955-56, acad. dean, 1956-57, pres., 1957-76, pres. emeritus, 1976—, interim pres., 1981-82; dir., pres., Bd. Higher Edn., Disciples of Christ, 1963-64; interim minister Christian Ch., Frankfort, Ky., 1980, Christian Ch., Danville, Ky., 1985. Contbr. to: Faith of the Free, 1940. Pres. bd. dirs. Henry Clay Found., Lexington, 1968-87; chmn. exec. com. Ky. Ind. Coll. Found., 1967-68, Ky. chmn. Rhodes Scholarship Selection Com., 1960-67; mem. Gov.'s Commrn. Higher Edn., Ky., 1966-69; chmn. bd. dirs. Living Arts and Sci. Center, Inc., 1968-69; bd. dirs. Ednl. Adv. and Reference Corp., N.Y.C; bd. dirs. United Fund, 1959-65, pres., 1962-64; chmn. bd. dirs. Lexington Pub. Library, 1966-70; bd. dirs. Fund for Advancement of Edn. and Research, U. Ky. Med. Center, 1974-87 . Mem. Washington Ky. acad. coun., 1959. Mem. Council Ind. Ky. Colls. and Univs. (pres. 1966, 68), Conf. Ch.-Related Colls. of South (pres. 1970), Omicron Delta Kappa, Tau Kappa Alpha, Beta Theta Pi. Democrat. Home: 461 Herrington Woods Harrodsburg KY 40330

LUNGREN, DANIEL EDWARD, state attorney general; b. Long Beach, Calif., Sept. 22, 1946; s. John Charles and Lorain Kathleen (Youngberg) L.; m. Barbara Kolls, Aug. 2, 1969; children: Jeffrey Edward, Kelly Christine, Kathleen Marie. AB cum laude, Notre Dame U., 1968; postgrad., U. So. Calif. Law Sch., 1968-69; J.D., Georgetown U., 1971. Bar: Calif. 1972. Staff asst. Sen. George Murphy, Sen. William Brock, 1969-71; spl. asst. to co-

chmn. Rep. Nat. Com., dir. spl. programs, 1971-72; assoc., selected as ptnr. Ball, Hunt, Hart, Brown & Baerwitz, Long Beach, 1973-78; mem. 96th-97th Congresses from 34th, 98th-100th Congresses from 42d Calif. Dist., 1979-1989, Rep. State Cen. Com. Calif., 1974-89; ptnr. Diepenbrock, Wulff, Plant & Hannegan, Sacramento, 1989-90; atty. gen. State of Calif., Sacramento, 1991—. Bd. dirs. Long Beach chpt. ARC, Boy's Club, 1976-88; committeeman Rep. Nat. Com., Calif., 1988—. Recipient Good Samaritan award Los Angeles Council Mormon Chs., 1976. Republican. Roman Catholic. Office: Office of the Atty Gen 1515 K St Sacramento CA 95814-4017

LUNGSTRUM, JOHN W., federal judge; b. Topeka, Kans., Nov. 2, 1945; s. Jack Edward and Helen Alice (Watson) L.; m. Linda Eileen Ewing, June 21, 1969; children: Justin Matthew, Jordan Elizabeth, Alison Paige. BA magna cum laude, Yale Coll., 1967; JD, U. Kans., 1970. Bar: Kans. 1970, Calif. 1970, U.S. Dist. Ct. (ctrl. dist.) Calif., U.S. Ct. Appeals (10th crct.). Assoc. Latham & Watkins, L.A., 1970-71; ptnr. Stevens, Brand, Lungstrum, Golden & Winter, Lawrence, Kans., 1972-91; U.S. Dist. judge Dist. of Kans., Kansas City, Kans., 1991—; lectr. law U. Kans. Law Sch., 1973—; mem. faculty Kans. Bar Assn. Coll. Advocacy, Trial Tactics and Techniques Inst., 1983-86; chmn. Douglas County Rep. Ctrl. Com., 1975-81; mem. Rep. State Com.; del. State Rep. Convention, 1968, 76, 80. Chmn. bd. dirs. Lawrence C. of C., 1990-91; pres. Lawrence United Fund, 1979; pres. Independence Days Lawrence, Inc., 1984, 85, Seem-to-be-Players, Inc., Lawrence Rotary Club, 1978-79; bd. dirs. Lawrence Soc. Chamber Music, Swarthout Soc. (corp. fund-raising chmn.); mem. Lawrence Art Common., Williams Scholarship Fund, Lawrence League Women Voters, Douglas County Hist. Soc.; bd. trustees, stewardship chmn. Plymouth Congl. Ch.; pres. Lawrence Round Ball Club; coach Lawrence Summertime Basketball; Vice chmn. U. Kans. Disciplinary Bd.; bd. govs. Kans Sch. Religion; bd. dirs. Kans. Day Club, 1980, 81. National Merit scholar, Yale Nat. scholar. Fellow Am. Bar Found.; mem. ABA (past mem. litigation and ins. sect.), Douglas County Bar Assn., Johnson County Bar Assn., Wyandotte County Bar Assn., Kans. Bar Assn. (vice chair legislative com., subcom. litigation, mem. continuing legal edn. com.), U Kans. Alumni Assn. (life), Phi Beta Kappa, Phi Gamma Delta, Phi Delta Phi. Avocations: basketball, hiking, skiing. Office: US Courthouse 812 N 7th St Rm 207 Kansas City KS 66101

LUNIN, JOSEPH, lawyer; b. Jersey City, Oct. 30, 1940; s. Benjamin Lunin and Ethel Ranz; m. Diana Sussman, Aug. 13, 1967; children: Jennifer, Benjamin. BA, Rutgers U., 1963, LLB, 1966; LLM, NYU, 1973. Bar: N.J. 1966. Legal sec. to judge appellate div. N.J. Superior Ct., 1966-67; assoc. Pitney, Hardin, Kipp & Szuch, Morristown, N.J., 1970-73, ptnr., 1974—; adj. faculty Rutgers U. Grad. Sch. Bus., Newark, 1972-77, adj. prof. Law Sch., 1988-93; cons. N.J. Corp. Law Revision Commn., 1970-73. Author: Forms for Practice Under the New Jersey Nonprofit Corporation Act, 1983, rev. edit., 1991, Forms for Practice Under the New Jersey Business Corporation Act, 1991; editor: Rutgers Law Rev., 1965-66, Organization and Sale of Small Business, 1968-70. Served to capt. U.S. Army, 1968-70, Vietnam, 1969. Mem. ABA, N.J. Bar Assn. (chmn. nonprofit law revision com. 1975—, chmn. corp. and bus. law sect. 1982-84), Morristown Club. Unitarian. Office: Pitney Hardin Kipp & Szuch PO Box 1945 Park Ave in Morris County Morristown NJ 07962-1945

LUNINGHAM, ROBERT DONALD, radio marketing consultant; b. Russellville, Ark., June 14, 1955; s. Carrel A. and Clara J. (Chenowith) L.; m. Barbara Potts, July 4, 1955; children: Terri Luningham Zolyniak, Randall, Martin. Student, Ark Sch. Broadcasting, 1957; cert. radio mktg. cons., Radio Advt. Bur., 1988. Announcer Sta. KWAK, Stuttgart, Ark., 1957-59, Sta. KYVA, Gallup, N.Mex., 1959-61; program dir. Sta. KRZE, Farmington, N.Mex., 1961-63; sales mgr. Sta. KRZE, Farmington, 1963-65, sta. mgr., 1965-67; gen. mgr. Sta. KRSY, Roswell, N.Mex., 1967-72; account exec. Sta. KCUB-KIIM, Tucson, 1972—, radio mktg. cons., 1988—. Bd. govs. West Tex. Beautify Council, El Paso, 1980-81. With USN, 1953-57. Named Mr. DJ USA, Sta WSM, Nashville, 1960. Mem. Tucson Advt. Club (chmn. media auction 1987, Advt. Person of Yr. award 1984), Optimists (pres. Roswell 1970-71, Tucson 1974-75, It. gov. West Tex. 1971-72, Outstanding Ariz. Pres. award 1975). Libertarian. Home: 5531 N Arroyo Grande Dr Tucson AZ 85718-5444

LUNN, JANET LOUISE SWOBODA, writer; b. Dallas, Dec. 28, 1928; naturalized Can. citizen, 1950; m. Richard Lynn, 1950; children: Eric, Jeffrey, Alexander, Katherine, John. Student, Queen's U., Kingston, Ont., Can., 1947-50; LLD (hon.), Queen's U., 1992; hon. diploma, Loyalist Coll. Applied Arts, 1993. Author: (with Richard Lunn) The County, 1967, Double Spell, 1968, Larger Than Life, 1979, The Twelve Dancing Princesses, 1979 (IODE Children's Book award 1979, one of tenb best children's Can. Libr. Assn.), The Root Cellar, 1981 (Children's Book of Yr., Can. Libr. Assn. 1982, Tchr.'s Choice for 1983, Am. Nat. Coun. Tchrs. English, Young Reader Medal 1988, Reviewers' Choice Booklist), Shadow in Hawthorn Bay, 1986 (Honor list Internat. Bd. Books for Young People 1986, Young Adult Book of Yr. award Sask. Libr. Assn. 1986, Book of Yr. IODE 1986), Amos's Sweater, 1988 (Ruth Schwartz award Can. Booksellers' Assn. 1989), Duck Cake for Sale, 1989, One Hundred Shining Candles: A Christmas Story, 1990, (with Christopher Moore) The Story of Canada, 1992 (Info. Book award Children's Lit. Round Tables of Can. 1993, Mr. Christie Book award 1993); editor: The Unseen, 1994. Recipient Vicki Metcalk award for body of work for children Can. Author's Assn., 1981, Can. Coun. award for children's lit. Mem. Can. Children's Book Ctr. (bd. dirs. 1989, v.p. 1990); IBBY Can. (bd. dirs. 1989), Writer's Union of Can. (2d vice chair 1979-80, 1st vice chair 1983-84, chair 1984-85), Can. Soc. Children's Authors, Illustrators and Performers, PEN Internat. Home: RR 2, Hillier, ON Canada K0K 2J0 Office: RR #2, Hillier, ON Canada K0K 2J0

LUNN, JUDITH SASKA, newspaper editor, journalist; b. Budapest, Hungary, July 4, 1935; came to U.S., 1939; d. Laszlo and Mildred Amalia (Friedman) S.; m. Robert Charles Lunn, June 15, 1957; children: Susan Breedlove, Linda. BFA, RISD, 1956. Designer Jonathan Logan and Jack Horowitz, N.Y.C., 1955-57; copy writer Sanger's, Titche's, Dallas, 1958-66; reporter Fashion Week, Dallas and L.A., 1967-68; fashion and style editor Houston Post, 1972-82, fashion and H editor, 1983—; freelance Houston publs., 1982-83; lectr. Houston C.C., clubs, orgns., Houston, 1972—. Appeared Good Morning Houston TV talk show, 1982-92. Judge Textile and Costume Inst. Houston Mus. Fine Arts, 1991-94. Recipient Fashion Reporter's award, 1973, Lulu award Men's Fashion Assn. 1979, 80 (2), 82 (2), Dallas Market Ctr. 20th Ann. Editorial award/home furnishings, 1980, Penney-Mo. Journalism award U. Mo. Sch. Journalism, 1974, 76, Atrium award U. Ga. Coll. Journalism & Mass. Comm./Atlanta Apparel Mart, 1980, 85, 87, 88, 92, George A. Hough 3d award for Overall Superiority in Reporting on Apparel Industry, 1992. Mem. Fashion Group Internat. of Houston (chmn. bazaar 1978). Avocations: photography, travel writing, cooking, decorating. Home: 711 William # 402 Houston TX 77002*

LUNSFORD, JULIUS R(ODGERS), JR., lawyer; b. Weston, Ga., Jan. 22, 1915; s. Julius Rodgers and Mary (Robinson) L.; m. Mary Eugenia Vann, Aug. 24, 1941; children: J. Rodgers III, Clark V., Alan H. BA, Mercer U., 1935; JD, U. Ga., 1936. Bar: Ga. 1936, U.S. Ct. Customs and Patent Appeals 1953-82, U.S. Ct. Mil. Appeals 1955, U.S. Supreme Ct. 1955, D.C. 1975, U.S. Ct. Appeals for Fed. Cit. 1982. With legal dept. The Coca-Cola Co., 1936-75; asst. v.p., mgr. trademarks and unfair competition dept., 1972-75; ptnr. Beveridge, DeGrandi, Kline & Lunsford, Atlanta, 1975-79; sr. ptnr. Hurt, Richardson, Garner, Todd & Cadenhead, Atlanta, 1980-87; ptnr. Jones, Askew & Lunsford, Atlanta, 1987-92; cons., presenter expert testimony, 1992—; mem. law faculty Mercer U. Law Sch. 1990—; lectr. in field. Contbr. numerous articles to profl. jours.; contbg. author: The Trademark Reporter, 1949—. Trustee, bd. dirs. Mercer U., Macons, Ga., 1988-93. Capt. USNR, 1942-75, ret., 1975. Mem. ABA (chmn. state trademark rights and statues com. 1968-69), U.S. Trademark Assn. (pres. 1971-72, bd. dirs 1959-66, 67-72, 74-77), Lawyers Club of Atlanta, Am. Intellectual Property Law Assn., Corporate Bar Assn., Atlanta Bar Assn., Kiwanis, Kappa Alpha Order. Democrat. Baptist. Avocations: sports fan and spectator. Home: 4187 Conway Valley Rd NW Atlanta GA 30327-3607

LUNT, HORACE GRAY, linguist, educator; b. Colorado Springs, Colo., Sept. 12, 1918; s. Horace Fletcher and Irene (Jewett) L.; m. Sally Herman, June 2, 1963; children: Elizabeth, Catherine. A.B., Harvard U., 1941; M.A., U. Calif., Berkeley, 1942; postgrad., Charles U., Prague, Czechoslovakia,

1946-47; Ph.D. (Rockefeller fellow), Columbia U., 1950. Lectr. in Serbo-Croatian Columbia U., 1948-49; asst. prof. Slavic langs. and lit. Harvard U., 1949-54, asso. prof., 1954-60, prof., 1960—, Samuel H. Cross prof. Slavic langs. and lits., 1965-89, Samuel H. Cross prof. Slavic langs. and lits., emeritus, 1989—, chmn. dept. Slavic langs. and lits. 1959-73, 75-76, 82-83; chmn. Slavic and East European Lang. and Area Ctr., 1983-89; mem. exec. com. Russian Rsch. Ctr., 1970-91, fellow, 1991—; mem. exec. com. Harvard Ukrainian Research Inst., 1974-91, fellow, 1991—. Author: Grammar of the Macedonian Literary Language, 1952, Old Church Slavonic Grammar, 1955, 6th, rev. edit., 1974, Fundamentals of Russian, 1958, 2d rev. edit., 1968, Progressive Palatalization of Common Slavic, 1981; editor: Harvard Slavic Studies, 1953-70. Served with U.S. Army, 1942-45. Guggenheim fellow, 1960-61. Mem. Macedonian Acad. Arts and Scis. (corr.). Home: 75 Bradford Rd Weston MA 02193-2142 Office: Boylston 301 Harvard U Cambridge MA 02138

LUNT, JACK, lawyer; b. Hartford, Conn., Oct. 19, 1944. BS magna cum laude, U. Utah, 1966, JD, 1969. Bar: Utah 1969. Assoc. Jones, Waldo, Holbrook & McDonough, Salt Lake City, 1969-73, ptnr., 1974-89; pres., exec. v.p. law and adminstrn. Am. Stores Properties, Inc., Salt Lake City, 1989-93; sr. v.p., asst. gen. counsel, corp. sec. Am. Stores Co., Salt Lake City, 1993—. Mem. ABA, Salt Lake County Bar Assn., Utah Bar Assn. Office: Am Stores Co 709 E South Temple Salt Lake City UT 84102-1205

LUNT, OWEN RAYNAL, biologist, educator; b. El Paso, Tex., Apr. 8, 1921; s. Owen and Velma (Jackson) L.; m. Helen Hickman, Aug. 8, 1953; children: David, Carol, Janet. BA in Chemistry, 1947, PhD in Agronomy, 1951. Mem. faculty UCLA, 1951-93, prof. plant nutrition, 1964-72, prof. biology, 1972—, acting chmn. dept. biophysics, 1965-70, prof. emeritus, 1993; dir. Lab. Biomed. and Environ. Scis., 1968-93; researcher in soil chemistry, fertility, plant physiology; tech. expert Internat. Atomic Energy Agy to Colombia, 1970, Kenya, 1983, Malaysia, 1985, Uruguauy, 1987. Served with USN, 1944-46. Fellow Am. Soc. Agronomy, Soil Sci. Soc. Am.; internat. Soc. Soil Sci., AAAS, Am. Nuclear Soc. (L.A. chpt.), Sigma Xi. Home: 1200 Roberto Ln Los Angeles CA 90077-2334 Office: UCLA 900 Veteran Ave Los Angeles CA 90024-2703 *I was reared in a cheerful, harmonious family on a farm. During childhood, we were poor. We all had chores and the entire household was willing to work. The family was very generous with others who were less fortunate. Unwavering allegiance to high ethical and moral standards was expected. The whole family was active in the Mormon church. Neither parent had finished high school, but they read extensively. From an early age, I understood the family would support me in securing any educational objectives. In retrospect, I believe I had one of the best of starts.*

LUNTZ, THEODORE MICHAEL, recycling company executive; b. Canton, Ohio, June 4, 1926; s. Abe M. and Fanny (Telpansky) L.; m. Idarose Schock, Aug. 23, 1953; children: W. Jean, Pamela, Brian, Jill. BA, Yale U., 1948. Pres. Marquette Steel Co., Cleve., 1952; v.p., treas. Luntz Corp., Canton, 1952-72, exec. v.p., 1972-84, pres., 1984-90; CEO, chmn. Luntz Corp., 1990—; v.p. 62 Land Inc., Canton, 1972—. Bd. dirs. Baldwin Wallace Coll., Montefiore Home, Hawken Sch., Boy Scouts Am., NCCJ, Cleve. Coll. Jewish Studies; chmn. Schnurmann House, Cathedral Latin Sch., Beachwood Am. Field Svcs. With U.S. Army, 1950-52. Mem. Nat. Inst. Scrap Iron and Steel (pres. No. Ohio chpt. 1970-74, nat. bd. dirs. 1975, co-chmn. fin. com. 1985-87), Oakwood Club, Rotary (bd. dirs.Cleve. club). Republican. Avocations: skiing, tennis, sailing, jogging, music. Home: 29776 Gates Mills Blvd Cleveland OH 44124-4645 Office: Luntz Corp 4250 E 68th St Cleveland OH 44105-5733

LUO, GANGMING, mechanical engineer; b. Ningbo, China, Jan. 2, 1960; came to U.S., 1989; B in Engring., Xi'an Jiao Tong U., 1982; M in Engring., Shanghai Jiao Tong U., 1984; PhD, CUNY, 1994. Lectr. dept. engring. mechanics Shanghai Jiao Tong U., 1984-89; post-doctoral rsch. asst. dept. mechanical engring. City Coll. of CUNY, 1994—. Recipient Devel. award in sci. and tech. China Ship Structure Corp., 1987. Mem. ASME (Best Paper award 1992, Melville medal 1993). Office: CUNY Dept of Mechanical Engring Convent Ave at 137th St New York NY 10031

LUONGO, C. PAUL, public relations executive; b. Winchester, Mass., Dec. 31, 1930; s. Carmine and Carmela (Gilberti) L. Grad., Cambridge Sch. Radio-TV, 1955; diploma, Bentley Coll., 1951; BSBA, Suffolk U., 1955; MBA, Babson Coll., 1956; AAS (hon.), Grahm Jr. Coll., 1970. Jr. exec. Raytheon Co., Lexington, Mass., 1956-59; account exec. Young & Rubicam, Inc., 1959-62; v.p. Copley Advt. Agy., Boston, 1962-64; pres. C. Paul Luongo Co., Boston, 1964—. Guest appearances include: (TV programs) Today Show, NBC-TV, 1984-89, Tomorrow Show, NBC-TV; TV-radio programs, Can.; author: America's Best!, 1980; contbr. syndicated newspaper-mag. features to Pub. Rels. Today; contbg. editor Travel Smart, N.Y., mo. newsletter. Pub. rels. dir. Anthony Spinazzola Meml. Scholarship Found., Boston U., 1986—; vol. U.S.S. Constn. Mus., Boston, Sta. WGBH-TV, Boston, TV Auctions, 1991—; mem. Boston Ctr. for Internat. Visitors, French Libr., Boston, Mus. Fine Arts, Black Ships Festival, Inc., Newport, R.I.; chmn. centennial ba.. Belcourt Castle, Newport, 1994. With AUS, 1952-54. Mem. Bostonian Soc., Boston Stockbrokers Club, Newcomen Soc. N.Am., Internat. Food, Wine and Travel Writers Assn., Am. Inst. Wine and Food, Japan-Am. Soc. R.I., Neighborhood Assn. of Back Bay, Inc., Back Bay Assn., Suffolk U. Gen. Alumni Assn. (bd. dirs. 1994—). Home: Copley Square Boston MA 02116 Office: 441 Stuart St Boston MA 02116-5000 *I believe in the work ethic, integrity and the maximum utilization of time for work and recreational activities. I loathe prejudice in any form, dishonesty and indolent people.*

LUPBERGER, EDWIN ADOLPH, utility executive; b. Atlanta, June 5, 1936; s. Adolph and Esma L.; m. Mary Jane McAlister Redmon, Jan. 6, 1989; children by previous marriage: David Todd, Edward Townsend. A.B. in Econs, Davidson (N.C.) Coll., 1958; M.B.A., Emory U., 1963. Asst. v.p. Southern Co. Services, Inc., Atlanta, 1963-69; v.p., treas. Gulf Power Co., Pensacola, Fla., 1969-77; sr. v.p. fin. Indpls. Power & Light Co., 1977-79; sr. v.p., chief fin. officer Middle South Utilities, Inc., New Orleans, 1979-85; chmn., CEO Entergy Corp., New Orleans, 1985—. Ensign USN, 1960. Mem. Edison Electric Inst., Univ. Club, Met. Club. Presbyterian.

LUPE, JOHN EDWARD, JR., finance executive; b. Columbus, Ohio, Jan. 4, 1939; m. Betty Jo Davis; children: Teresa, John. BS, Ohio U., 1960. CPA, Ohio. Staff acct. Haskins & Sells, Columbus, 1960-65; sr. tax acct. Rockwell Internat., Pitts., 1965-67; tax mgr. Roadway Services, Akron, Ohio, 1967-70, Nat. Standard, Niles, Mich., 1970-76; controller Nat. Standard, Niles, 1976; controller Lennox Internat., Dallas, 1976-79, v.p., controller, 1979-83, exec. v.p. fin. and treas., 1983—. Mem. Fin. Execs. Inst., Tax Execs. Inst., Nat. Assn. Mfrs. Lodge: Masons. Home: 12928 St Andrews Dr Oklahoma City OK 73120-8817 Office: Lennox Internat Inc 2100 Lake Park Blvd Richardson TX 75080-2254

LUPE, RONNIE, chairman of apache tribe; b. Cibecue, Ariz., 1930. Student in Bus. and Acctg., Ariz. State Univ. From councilman to chmn. White Mountain Apache Tribe, Ft. Apache Indian Reservation, Ariz., 1964—. Office: White Mountain Apache Tribe Office of Chmn PO Box 700 Whiteriver AZ 85941-0700

LUPERT, LESLIE ALLAN, lawyer; b. Syracuse, N.Y., May 24, 1946; s. Reuben and Miriam (Kaufman) L.; m. Roberta Gail Fellner, May 19, 1968; children: Jocelyn, Rachel, Susannah. BA, U. Buffalo, 1967; JD, Columbia U., 1971. Bar: N.Y. 1971. Ptnr. Orans Elsen & Lupert, N.Y.C., 1971—. Contbr. articles to profl. jours. Mem. ABA, N.Y. State Bar Assn. (trial lawyers sect.), Assn. of Bar of City of N.Y. (com. fed. legislation 1977-80, profl. and jud. ethics com. 1983-86, com. on fed. cts. 1986-89, 95—), Phi Beta Kappa. Office: Orans Elsen & Lupert 1 Rockefeller Plz New York NY 10020-2001

LUPICA, MICHAEL THOMAS, sports columnist; b. Oneida, N.Y., May 11, 1952; s. Benedict and Lee Lupica. B.A., Boston Coll., 1974. Corr. Boston Globe, 1970-74; columnist Boston Phoenix, 1971-75, Boston mag., 1974-75; feature writer Washington Star, 1974-75; basketball writer, columnist N.Y. Post, 1975-76; columnist N.Y. Daily News, 1980—; writer

syndicated TV spls.; contbg. editor World Tennis, 1974-81. Mem. Newspaper Guild Am. Office: NY Daily News 220 E 42nd St Ste 817 New York NY 10017-5858

LUPIN, ELLIS RALPH, physician, lawyer, coroner; b. New Orleans, Apr. 1, 1931; s. Albert I. and Yetta (Linneck) L.; m. Freda Merlin, Mar. 18, 1951; 1 child, Jay Stephen. BS in Pharmacy, Loyola U., New Orleans, 1952, PharmD, 1983; JD, Loyola U. South, New Orleans, 1988; MD, La. State U., 1956. Diplomate Am. Bd. Ob-Gyn. Bar: La. Practice medicine specializing in ob-gyn. Zoller, Lupin, Levinson, Cohen & Castillo, New Orleans, 1962—; atty. Middleberg, Riddle & Gianna; chief dep. coroner City of New Orleans, 1974-86; pvt. med.-legal practice; cons. Nat. Med. Enterprises, Inc., E.R. Lupin, Ltd., 1984—; med. legal cons. Surgeon Gen., U.S. Army. Bd. dirs. ARC, New Orleans, 1965-90, St. Charles Gen. Hosp., 1972-92, U. New Orleans Found., 1990-92, City of Vieux Carre Commn., 1995—; trustee New Orleans Symphony, 1982-90, Lupin Found., 1980—, Children's Hosp. of New Orleans, 1984—, Jewish Welfare Fedn. of New Orleans, 1972, 80, 84, Jewish Family and Children Svcs., 1972-76, New Orleans Mus. Art, 1993, bd. trustees, 1994—; chmn. bd. dirs. La. State Mus., 1984-88, 92—; chmn. Upper Pontabla Commn., 1982-90; mem. adv. bd. Ladies Luekemia League, 1980—, Sophie Gumbel Guild, 1980—, others. With USAF, 1958-60; col. La. N.G. Fellow Am. Coll. Legal Medicine; mem. Jefferson Parish Med. So., Gyecology Laser So., Royal Soc. Medicine, New Orleans Ob-Gyn Soc., La. State Bar Assn. Jewish. Lodge: Masons. Avocation: collecting antiques. Home: 1021 Chartres St New Orleans LA 70116-3239 Office: Zoller Lupin Levinson Cohen & Castillo 515 Westbank Expy Gretna LA 70053-5644

LUPKE, DUANE EUGENE, insurance company executive; b. Ft. Wayne, Ind., July 17, 1930; s. Walter Herman and Lucy (Bell) L.; married, Sept. 14, 1957; children: Diane Carol, Mark Duane, David Burgess, Andrea Lucy. BS, Ind. U., 1952. CPCU. With Lupke Rice Clancy Assocs., Ft. Wayne, Ind., 1954—, pres., 1969—; underwriting mem. Lloyds of London, 1973—. Dir. Luth. Hosp. of Ind., Ft. Wayne, 1986—; Concordia Ednl. Found., Ft. Wayne, 1980—, Canterbury Sch. Found., Ft. Wayne, 1980—. Lt. U.S. Army, 1952-54. Lutheran. Home: 1407 Hawthorne Rd Fort Wayne IN 46802 Office: Lupke Rice Clancy Assocs PO Box 11309 Fort Wayne IN 46857

LUPKIN, STANLEY NEIL, lawyer; b. Bklyn., Mar. 27, 1941; s. David B. and Sylvia (Strassman) L.; m. Anne Rachel Fischler, June 3, 1962; children: Jonathan Daniel, Deborah Eve. BA, Columbia Coll., 1962; LLB, NYU, 1966. Bar: N.Y. 1966, U.S. Dist. Ct. (so. and ea. dists.) N.Y. 1970, U.S. Ct. Appeals (2d cir.) 1970, U.S. Supreme Ct. 1971. Asst. dist. atty., sr. trial atty., chief indictment bur. N.Y. County Dist. Atty.'s Office, N.Y.C., 1966-71; asst. commr. City of N.Y., 1966-71; 1st dep. commr., commr. Dept. Investigation, N.Y.C., 1978-82; ptnr. Litman, Asche, Lupkin, Gioiella & Bassin, N.Y.C., 1982—; mem. faculty Nat. Coll. Dist. Attys., Houston, 1974-75, FBI Nat. Acad., Quantico, Va., 1980-82; chmn. com. on criminal justice opns. Assn. of Bar of City of N.Y., 1982-85. Co-author book: Anatomy of A Municipal Franchise: N.Y.C. Bus Shelter Program, 1973-79, 4 vols., 1981. Trustee, counsel Solomon Schechter Sch. of Queens, Flushing, N.Y., 1974—; mem. secondary schs. com. admissions office Columbia Coll., N.Y.C., 1987—. With USAR, 1963-69. Mem. N.Y. State Bar Assn. (chmn. com. on def. 1985—, chmn. com. on prosecution 1977-85, exec. com. criminal justice sect. 1977—, Prosecutor of Yr. 1981), N.Y. State Assn. Criminal Def. Lawyers, Nat. Assn. Criminal Def. Lawyers, N.Y. Criminal Bar Assn., Soc. Columbia Grads. (v.p. 1989—). Avocations: classical music, Talmudic law. Office: Litman Asche Lupkin Gioiella & Bassin 45 Broadway Atrium New York NY 10006

LUPO, FRANK MICHAEL, architect; b. Buffalo, July 17, 1950; s. Michael and Raffaela (Giardina) L.; m. Mary Evelyn Stockton, May 4, 1985. BArch, U. Cin., 1974; MArch, Yale U., 1983. Registered architect, N.Y., Calif., N.J. With Studio Works, Los Angeles, 1978-79, Morphosis, Los Angeles, 1979-80, Gwathmey Siegel and Assocs., N.Y.C., 1983-85; ptnr., prin. N.Y. Architects, N.Y.C., 1985-93; prin. Frank Lupo Architect, N.Y.C., 1994—; participant Biennale di Venezia, 1985. Recipient Citation Progressive Architecture mag., 1980,82, N.Y.C. Design awards AIA, 1990, 91; William Wirt Wichester Traveling fellow, 1985. Office: Frank Lupo Architects Loft 12B 448 W 37th St New York NY 10018

LUPONE, PATTI, actress; b. Northport, L.I., N.Y., Apr. 21, 1949; d. Orlando Joseph and Angela Louise (Patti) LuP.; m. Matt Johnston; 1 child, Joshua Luke. BFA, The Juilliard Sch., 1972. Off-Broadway prodns. include: The Woods, School for Scandal, The Lower Depths, Stage Directions; appeared in Broadway prodns.: Next Time I'll Sing to You, The Time of Your Life, The Three Sisters, The Robber Bridegroom (Tony award nominee), The Water Engine, The Beggar's Opera, Edward II, The Baker's Wife, 1976, The Woods, 1977, Working, 1978, Catchpenny Twist, 1978, As You Like It, 1982, The Cradle Will Rock, 1983, Stars of Broadway, 1983, Edmond, 1982, Oliver, 1984; star Broadway musicals Evita, 1979 (Best Actress in Musical Tony award 1980), Anything Goes, 1987, Pal Joey, 1995; London prodns. Les Miserables, 1985, Sunset Boulevard, 1993; films include: King of the Gypsies, 1978, 1941, 1979, Fighting Back, 1982, Witness, 1985, Wise Guys, 1986, Driving Miss Daisy, 1989; TV Appearances include: Kitty, The Time of Your Life, Lady Bird in LBJ, 1987, The Water Engine, 1992, Family Prayers, 1993; TV series, Life Goes On, 1989-93. Office: Duva-Flack Assocs Inc Ste 1407 200 West 57th St New York NY 10019*

LUPTON, ELLEN, curator, graphic designer; b. Phila., Dec. 1, 1963; d. William La Rue and Mary Jane Laura (Hohman) L.; m. Jerry Abbott Miller, Sept. 22, 1990. BFA, Cooper Union, 1985. Curator Herb Lubalin Study Ctr, The Cooper Union, N.Y.C., 1985-92; curator of contemporary design Cooper-Hewitt Nat. Mus. of Design, Smithsonian Institution, N.Y.C., 1992—; ptnr., cons. Design Writing Rsch., N.Y.C., 1985—. Author: Mechanical Brides: Women and Machines from Home to Office, 1993, (with J.A. Miller) The Bathroom, The Kitchen and The Aesthetics of Waste, 1992; editor: (with Miller) The Bauhaus and Design Theory, 1991. Mem. Am. Inst. Graphic Arts (bd. dirs. 1992—). Democrat. Office: Cooper-Hewitt Mus 2 E 91st St New York NY 10003*

LUPU, RADU, pianist; b. Galati, Romania, Nov. 30, 1945; s. Meyer and Ana (Gabor) L. Attended Conservatoire, Moscow, USSR, 1961-69. London debut, 1969, Berlin, 1971, U.S. debut with Cleve. Orch. in N.Y.C., appearances with worldwide maj. orchs., including Berlin Philharmonic, Vienna Philharmonic, Israel Philharmonic, Orch. de Paris, Concertgebouw, N.Y. Philharmonic, Phila. Symphony Orch., Chgo. Symphony Orch., Cleve. Symphony Orch.; recs. include Beethoven cycle with Israel Philharmonic and Zubin Mehta, Schubert Sonatas, Beethoven Sonatas, Mozart Sonatas for Violin and Piano with Szymon Goldberg, Schubert Lieder with Barbara Hendricks, Mozart and Schubert duets and Mozart Concerto for 2 pianos, both with Murray Perahia, Brahms Piano Concerto #1 Mozart and Beethoven Quintets in E Flat. Recipient 1st prize Van Cliburn Internat. Piano Competition, 1966; Enescu Competition, 1967; Leeds Internat. Piano Competition, 1969.

LUPULESCU, AUREL PETER, medical educator, researcher, physician; b. Manastiur, Banat, Romania, Jan. 1, 1923; came to U.S., 1967, naturalized, 1973; s. Peter Vichentie and Maria Ann (Dragan) L. MD magna cum laude, Sch. Medicine, Bucharest, Romania, 1950; MS in Endocrinology, U. Bucharest, 1960; PhD in Biology, Faculty of Scis., U. Windsor, Ont., Can. Diplomate Am. Bd. Internal Medicine. Chief Lab. Investigations, Inst. Endocrinology, Bucharest, 1950-67; research assoc. SUNY Downstate Med. Ctr., 1968-69; asst. prof. medicine Wayne State U., 1969-72; assoc. prof., 1973—; vis. prof. Inst. Med. Pathology, Rome, 1967; cons. VA Hosp., Allen Park, Mich., 1971-73. Author: Steroid Hormones, 1958, Advances in Endocrinology and Metabolism, 1962, Experimental Pathophysiology of Thyroid Gland, 1963, Ultrastructure of Thyroid Gland, 1968, Hormones and Carcinogenesis, 1983, Hormones and Vitamins in Cancer Treatment, 1990; reviewer for various sci. jours.; contbr. chpts., numerous articles to profl. publs.; research on hormones and tumor biology; studies regarding role of hormones and vitamins in carcinogenesis. Fellow Fedn. Am. Socs. for Exptl. Biology; mem. Electron Microscopy Soc. Am., Soc. for Investigative Dermatology, N.Y. Acad. Sci., AMA (physician's recognition award 1983, 86), Am. Soc. Cell Biology, Soc. Exptl. Biology and Medicine, AAAS.

Republican. Home: 21480 Mahon Dr Southfield MI 48075-7525 Office: Wayne State U Sch Medicine 540 E Canfield St Detroit MI 48201-1928

LUREY, ALFRED SAUL, lawyer; b. Greenville, S.C., Oct. 17, 1942; s. Meyer and Pearl Sarah (Zaglin) L.; m. Betsy Ann Bennett, June 13, 1982; children: Mollie K., Allison A.; 1 stepchild, Amy E. Startari. AB, Duke U., 1964; LLB, Harvard U., 1967. Bar: Calif. 1967, U.S. Ct. Appeals (4th cir.) 1968, Ga. 1970, U.S. Dist. Ct. (no. dist.) Ga. 1971, U.S. Ct. Claims 1972, U.S. Ct. Appeals (5th cir.) 1976, U.S. Ct. Appeals (11th cir.) 1982. Law clk. to chief justice U.S. Ct. Appeals (4th cir.), Richmond, Va., 1967-69; assoc. Kilpatrick & Cody, Atlanta, 1969-75, ptnr., 1975—; adj. prof. law Emory U., 1989. With USAR, 1968-74. Am. Coll. of Bankruptcy fellow; Angier B. Duke Meml. scholar Duke U., 1960. Mem. Am. Bankruptcy Inst., Calif. Bar Assn., Ga. Bar Assn., Phi Beta Kappa, Phi Eta Sigma. Jewish. Avocations: physical fitness, tennis, reading. Home: 5115 Jett Forest Trl NW Atlanta GA 30327-4559 Office: Kilpatrick & Cody 1100 Peachtree St Ste 2800 Atlanta GA 30309-4530

LURIA, MARY MERCER, lawyer; b. Boston, Dec. 29, 1942; d. Albert and Mabel (Jacomb) Mercer; m. Nelson J. Luria, June 19, 1967. AB, Radcliffe Coll., 1964; LLB, Yale U., 1967. Bar: N.Y. 1968. Assoc. Simpson, Thacher & Bartlett, N.Y.C., 1967-68, Hale & Dorr, Boston, 1968-69; assoc. Satterlee & Stephens, N.Y.C., 1969-74, ptnr., 1974-86; ptnr. Patterson, Belknap, Webb & Tyler, N.Y.C., 1986—. Mem. ABA, N.Y. State Bar Assn., Assn. of Bar of City of N.Y., Metropolitan Club. Avocations: gardening, photography. Home: 45 E 85th St New York NY 10028-0957 Office: Patterson Belknap et al 1133 Ave of the Americas New York NY 10036-9999

LURIA, ZELLA HURWITZ, psychology educator; b. N.Y.C., Feb. 18, 1924; d. Hyman Hurwitz and Dora (Garbarsky) H.; m. Salvador Edward Luria, Apr. 18, 1945; 1 child, Daniel David. BA, Bklyn., 1944; MA, Ind. U., 1947, PhD, 1951. lic. clin. psychologist, Mass. Ford Found. post-doctoral fellow U. Ill., Urbana, 1951-53, Russell Sage found. fellow, 1953-56, clin. researcher, 1954-58; asst. prof. psychology Tufts U., Medford, Mass., 1958-62, assoc. prof., 1962-70, prof., 1970—; psychiatry lectr. Mass. Gen. Hosp., Boston, 1970-79; vis. scholar Stanford U., 1977, 83; vis. prof. UCLA, 1992, U. Mich., 1993. Sr. author: Psychology of Human Sexuality, 1979, Human Sexuality, 1987. Postdoctoral fellow USPHS, Paris, 1963-64, Bunting fellow Radcliffe Coll., 1989-90; Mellon Found. Faculty grantee Wellesley Coll., 1979-80. Mem. Tufts U. Am. Assn. Univ. Profs. (pres. 1986-87). Home: 221 Mount Auburn Cambridge MA 02138-9999 Office: Tufts Univ Dept Of Psychology Medford MA 02155

LURIE, ALISON, author; b. Chgo., Sept. 3, 1926; children: John, Jeremy, Joshua. AB, Radcliffe Coll., 1947. Lectr. English Cornell U., 1969-73; adj. assoc. prof. English Cornell U., Ithaca, N.Y., 1973-76, assoc. prof., 1976-79, prof., 1979—. Author: V.R. Lang: A Memoir, 1959, Love and Friendship, 1962, The Nowhere City, 1965, Imaginary Friends, 1967, Real People, 1969, The War Between the Tates, 1974, Only Children, 1979, The Language of Clothes, 1981, Foreign Affairs, 1984, The Truth About Lorin Jones, 1988, Don't Tell the Grownups, 1990, Women and Ghosts, 1994. Recipient award in lit. Am. Acad. Arts and Letters, 1978, Pulitzer prize in fiction, 1985; fellow Yaddo Found., 1963-64, 66, Guggenheim Found., 1965, Rockefeller Found., 1967. Office: Cornell U Dept English Ithaca NY 14853

LURIE, ALVIN DAVID, lawyer; b. N.Y.C., Apr. 16, 1923; s. Samuel and Rose L.; m. Marian Weinberg, Aug. 21, 1944; children: James, Jeanne, Margery, Jonathan. AB, Cornell U., 1943, LLB, 1944. Bar: N.Y. 1944, D.C. 1978. Ptnr. various N.Y.C. law firms, 1944-74, including Lurie & Rubin, 1961-68, Aranow, Brodsky, Bohlinger & Einhorn, 1968-74; asst. commr. for employee plans and exempt orgns. IRS, Washington, 1974-78; ptnr. Chadbourne, Parke, Whiteside & Wolff, N.Y.C., 1978-80; counsel Chadbourne, Parke, Whiteside & Wolff, 1980-84; ptnr. Meyers, Tersigni, Lurie, Feldman & Gray, N.Y.C., 1984-91; counsel Meyers, Tersigni, Lurie, Feldman & Gray, 1992-94; pvt. practice N.Y.C., 1994—; mem. adv. bd. NYU Tax Inst., 1978-90, Tax Mgmt. adv. bd., 1978—. Author: Lurie's Commentaries on Pension Design, 1980, Lurie's Guide to VEBAs, 1983, Collected Commentaries on Pensions, 1984, ESOPs Made Easy, 1985. Contbr. articles to law revs., tax jours. Mem. ABA, Fed. Bar Assn., N.Y. State Bar Assn. (chmn. spl. com. pension simplification 1986—), Assn. Bar City N.Y., Am. Coll. Tax Counsel, N.Y. Bar Found. Office: 295 Madison Ave New York NY 10017 *Hard work, in intensive spurts, is my formula. The work must be varied, permitting application of different skills in constantly changing, creative ways. But one thing more is needed: readiness to seize the moment; for only in that way will new opportunities come, with new achievements and recurrent gratification.*

LURIE, HAROLD, engineer, lawyer; b. Durban, South Africa, Mar. 28, 1919; came to U.S., 1946, naturalized, 1952; s. Samuel Isaac and Dora (Mitchell) L.; m. Patricia Elkin, Mar. 26, 1959 (div. 1978); children—Diana Isabel, David Andrew. BS, U. Natal, South Africa, 1940, MS, 1946; PhD, Calif. Inst. Tech., 1950; JD, Northeastern U., 1989. Bar: Mass. 1989, D.C. 1991, U.S. Supreme Ct. 1993. Lectr. aeros. Calif. Inst. Tech., 1948-50, asst. prof. applied mechanics, 1953-56, assoc. prof., 1956-64, prof. engring. sci., 1964-70, assoc. dean grad. studies, 1964-70; dir. research and devel. New Eng. Electric System, 1971-79; dean engring. Poly. Inst. N.Y., Bklyn., 1979-81; dean Coll. Engring. Northeastern U., Boston, 1981-86; acting dir. advanced systems dept. Electric Power Rsch. Inst., 1974-75; cons. Yankee Atomic Electric Co., 1970-71; head weapons effectiveness group RAND Corp., 1950-52; sr. devel. engr. Oak Ridge Nat. Lab., 1956-57; vis. scholar U. Washington Law Sch., 1990-91; acting exec. dir. Calif. Coun. on Sci. and Tech., 1992—. Office: Calif Coun on Sci and Tech 1201 Dove St Ste 680 Newport Beach CA 92660

LURIE, HUGH JAMES, psychiatrist, educator; b. Chgo., May 22, 1935; s. Harold Hiram and Gertrude (Geitner) L.; m. Edythe Bruce Hammond, Oct. 7, 1961; children: Nicholas Hubbard, Jessica Stevens, Hugh Sterling. AB, Harvard U., 1955; MD, Yale U., 1961. Diplomate Am. Bd. Psychiatry and Neurology, Am. Bd. Child Psychiatry, Am. Gd. Geriatric Psychiatry. Resident in pediatrics Johns Hopkins U., Balt., 1961-63; resident in gen. psychiatry McLean Hosp.-Harvard U., Belmont, Mass., 1965-67; resident in child psychiatry Children's Hosp., Judge Baker Clinic, Harvard U., Boston, 1967-69; med. dir. Child Guidance Clinic, Tacoma, 1969-80; chief psychiatrist Good Samaritan Mental Health Ctr., Puyallup, Wash., 1980—; clin. assoc. prof. psychiatry U. Wash. Sch. Medicine, Seattle, 1969-72, clin. assoc. prof., 1972-75, clin. prof., 1975—; coord. behavioral scis. Medex, physician asst. program, 1975—. Author: Clinical Psychiatry for the Primary Physician, 1985; writer, prod. about 85 ednl. videotapes for Am. Psychiat. Assn., U. Wash., Assn. Am. Med. Colls., Acad. Family Practice, 1976—; exec. prodr. ednl. video Time Mirror, 1979 (bronze medal N.Y. Film and Video Festival 1979). Bd. dirs. Sta. KVOW, pub. radio, Seattle, 1988-94. Lt. M.C., USN, 1963-65. Recipient hon. mention Assn. for Acad. Psychiatry, 1990. Fellow Am. Psychiat. Assn. (mem., chmn. video subcom. 1978-95), Am. Acad. Child and Adolescent Psychiatry; mem. Group for Advancement Psychiatry (social issues com. 1994—), Wash. State Psychiat. Assn. (co-chmn. geriatrics com. 1992—), Wash. State Coun. Child and Adolescent Psychiatry. Avocations: playing chamber music (violin, viola), etching. Home: 1417 E Aloha St Seattle WA 98112 Office: Good Samaritan Mental Health Ctr 325 E Pioneer Puyallup WA 98372

LURIE, PAUL MICHAEL, lawyer; b. Chgo., Apr. 9, 1941; s. Haskell and Fay (Weinstein) L.; m. Margaret Berman, Aug. 2, 1966; children: Alexander, Rachel, Daniel, Matthew. BA, U. Mich., 1962, JD, 1965. Bar: Ill. 1965, U.S. Dist. Ct. (no. dist.) Ill., U.S. Ct. Appeals (7th cir.), U.S. Supreme Ct. Assoc. Fischel & Kahn, Chgo., 1967-68; ptnr. Fohrman, Lurie, Sklar & Simon, Ltd. Chgo., 1968-86, Neal, Gerber, Eisenberg & Lurie, Chgo., 1987-89, Schiff, Hardin & Waite, Chgo., 1989—; adj. prof. U. Ill. Coll. Art, Architecture and Urban Scis.; cons. Australian Law Reform Commn.; founder, gen. counsel, bd. dirs. Chgo. Architecture Found., 1976-86; counsel, bd. dirs. Chgo. Archtl. Assistance Ctr., 1979-89. Mem. editorial bd. Fed. Publs., Inc., constrn. adv. bd.; contbr. articles to profl. jours. Fellow Am. Coll. Constrn. Lawyers; mem. ABA (forum com. on constrn. industry, tort and ins. practice sect., design and constrn. com.), ASCE (hon. affiliate mem.), AIA (hon. mem. Chgo. chpt.), Internat. Bar Assn., Ill. Bar Assn., Chgo. Bar Assn. (former chmn. and founder land devel. and constrn. com.), Chgo. Coun. Lawyers, Nat. Inst. Bldg. Sci. (consultive coun.), Am. Consulting Engrs. Counsel (gen. counsel's forum), Am. Arbitration Assn. (former chmn. constrn. adv. coun. Chgo. region, constrn. industry arbitrator), Internat. Constrn. Contracts Com., Chgo. Nat. Swedish Inst. for Bldg. Rsch., Com. on Post-constrn. Liability and Ins., Cliff Dwellers Club, Standard Club. Jewish. Office: Schiff Hardin & Waite 7200 Sears Tower Chicago IL 60606

LURIE, RANAN RAYMOND, political analyst, political cartoonist, artist, lecturer; b. Port Said, Egypt, May 26, 1932; came to U.S., 1968, naturalized, 1974; s. Joseph and Rose (Sam) L. (parents Israeli citizens); m. Tamar Fletcher, Feb. 25, 1958; children: Rod, Barry, Daphne, Danielle. Student, Herzelia High Sch., Tel Aviv, Israel, 1949; student, Jerusalem Art Coll., 1951. Corr. Maariv Daily, 1950-52; features editor Hador Daily, 1953-54; editor-in-chief Tevel mag., 1954-55; staff polit. cartoonist Yedioth Aharonot Daily, 1955-66, Honolulu Advertiser, 1979; lectr. polit. cartooning U. Hawaii; univ. lectr. in fine arts, polit. cartoon and polit. analysis Am. Program Bur., Boston.; polit. cartoonist Time Internat. mag., 1994—; chmn. bd. dirs. Cartoonews Inc. Author: Among the Suns, 1952, Lurie's Best Cartoons, 1961, Nixon Rated Cartoons, 1973, Pardon Me, Mr. President, 1974, Lurie's Worlds, 1980, So sieht es Lurie, 1981, Fed. Republic Germany, Lurie's Almanac (U.K.), 1982, (U.S.A.), 1983, Taro's International Politics, Japan, 1984, Lurie's Middle East, Israel, 1986; creator: The Expandable Painting, 1959; Cartoons used as guidelines in several encys., polit. sci. books.; 22 shows, Israel, Can., U.S., 1960-75, including, Expo 67, Can., Dominion Gallery, Montreal, Que., Can., Lim Gallery, Tel Aviv, 1965, Overseas Press Club, N.Y.C., 1962, 64, 75, U.S. Senate, Washington, Honolulu Acad. Fine Arts, 1979; represented by Circle Gallery, 1988—; exhibited numerous group shows including, Smithsonian Instn., 1972, Circle Gallery, Washington, 1989; creator Japan's nat. cartoon symbol Taro-San, Taiwan's nat. cartoon symbol Cousin Lee; polit. cartoonist, Life Mag., N.Y.C., 1968-73, polit. cartoonist, interviewer, Die Welt, Bonn, W. Ger., 1980-81; contbr.: N.Y. Times, 1970—; contbg. editor, polit. cartoonist, Newsweek Internat., 1974-76, editor, polit. cartoonist, Vision Mag. of South Am., 1974-76, syndicated United Features Syndicate, 1971-73; syndicated nationally by Los Angeles Times, also internationally by, N.Y. Times to over 260 newspapers, 1973-75, internationally by Editors Press Syndicate (345 newspapers), King Features Syndicate, 1975-83; syndicated in U.S. by Universal Press Syndicate, 1982-86, Cartoonews Internat. Syndicat, 1986—; polit. cartoonist, The Times of London, 1981-83, ABC's Nightline, 1991—, World News Show, 1993; sr. polit. analyst, editorial cartoonist Asahi Shimbun, Japan's largest daily newspaper, 1983-84; sr. analyst and polit. cartoonist U.S. News & World Report, 1984-85; chief editorial dir. Editors Press Service, 1985; joined staff MacNeil/Lehrer News Hour (PBS) as daily polit. cartoonist, analyst. Served as maj. Combat Paratroop, Israeli Army Res., 1950-67. Recipient highest Israeli journalism award, 1954; U.S. Headliners award, 1972; named Outstanding Editorial Cartoonist of Nat. Cartoonist Soc., 1971-78; Salon award Montreal Cartoon, 1971; N.Y. Front Page award, 1972, 74, 77; cert. merit U.S. Publ. Designers, 1974; award Overseas Press Club, 1979; John Fischetti polit. cartoon award, 1982, 86; sr. adj. fellow Ctr. Strategic Internat. Studies, Washington; Ranan R. Lurie Internat. Polit. Cartoon ann. award created in his honor by Nat. Fedn. Hispanic Owned Newspapers, 1994, RananR. Lurie Internat. award for Polit. Cartooning created by U.N. Soc. of Writers, 1995. Mem. Soc. Profl. Journalists, Nat. Cartoonists Soc. Am., Assn. Editorial Cartoonists, Mensa, Overseas Press Club, Friars Club. Inventor 1st electronically animated TV news cartoon; creator 1st syndicated bus.-news cartoon Lurie's Business World; 102 million readers of 1,098 newspapers in 102 countries; 1995 Guinness Book of World Records. Office: Cartoonews Inc 9 Mountain Laurel Dr Greenwich CT 06831 *The moment of truth will come when the cartoonist gauges the margin of time from the day he drew the cartoon. Then he can see how clearly or unclearly he has evaluated the situation through his work. Eventually, the simple facts and reality always win. Then it becomes apparent that wishful thinking is meaningless and the capacity to evaluate the project and even predict the events that are happening will eventually cement the professional status and integrity of the cartoonist.*

LURIE, RON, mayor. Former city councilman Las Vegas, Nev.; mayor, 1987—. Office: City Hall Office of Mayor 400 Stewart Ave Las Vegas NV 89101-2942

LURIE, WILLIAM L., lawyer, association executive; b. Latrobe, Pa., Feb. 8, 1931; s. Samuel C. and Josephine M. (Agnes) L.; m. Rita F. Mandel, Aug. 31, 1952; children: Ellen, Lynn, Jay. BS, Northwestern U., 1952, MBA, 1954, J.D., 1955. Bar: Mich. 1955, Ill. 1955, N.Y. 1956. With Gen. Electric Co. (various locations), 1955-69, v.p., gen. mgr. internat. support div., 1969-72, v.p. internat. strategic planning, 1972-74; v.p., gen. counsel Internat. Paper Co., N.Y.C., 1974-76; v.p. external affairs Internat. Paper Co., 1976, exec. v.p. diversified bus., gen. counsel, 1976-84; pres. The Bus. Roundtable, N.Y.C., 1984—. Office: 200 Park Ave Ste 2222 New York NY 10166-0097

LURTON, H. WILLIAM, retired retail executive; b. Greenwich, Conn., Sept. 18, 1929; s. William Pearl and Elizabeth (McDow) L.; m. Susan Harvey, Oct. 26, 1980; children: Scott, Carrie, Nancy, Jennifer, Barbara, Diana, Deborah, Sarah. B.A., Principia Coll., 1951. Sales rep. Jostens Inc., Mpls., 1955-61; yearbook sales and plant mgr. Jostens Inc., Visalia, Calif., 1961-66; gen. sales mgr. yearbook div. Jostens Inc., v.p., gen. mgr. yearbook div., 1969-70, corp. exec. v.p., 1970-71, mem. exec. com., 1970-72, pres., 1971-75, chief operating officer, 1971-72, chief exec. officer, 1972-94, chmn. bd., 1975-94, also dir.; ret., 1994; dir. Deluxe Inc., Pentair, Inc. Bd. dirs. U.S. C. of C., Mpls. YMCA. Served with USMC, 1951-53. Mem. Quail Ridge Country Club (Boynton Beach, Fla.), La Quinta Resort Country Club (Calif.), Tammaron Country Club (Durango, Colo.), Mpls. Clubl. Clubs: Wayzata (Minn.) Country, Minneapolis. Home: 3135 Jamestown Rd Long Lake MN 55356-9648

LURTON, HORACE VANDEVENTER, brokerage house executive; b. Washington, Oct. 16, 1941; s. Horace Harmon III and Eleaner (Pentz) L.; m. Nancy Taylor Mackall, Aug. 30, 1964 (dec. 1992); children: Bowie VanDeventer, Sallie Taylor. Student, Gettysburg U., 1962; BS, Am. U., 1965. Registered prin. SEC. Stockbroker Thomson, McKinnon & Auchincloss, Washington, 1966-76, Dean Witter Reynolds, Chevy Chase, Md., 1977-79; stockbroker, branch mgr., dir. Johnston, Lemon & Co., Inc., Washington, 1989-90; v.p., branch mgr. Janney, Montgomery, Scott, Washington, 1990—. Active various orgns. and charities, Washington, Md. Episcopalian. Avocation: biking. Home: 5004 Scarsdale Rd Bethesda MD 20816-2438 Office: Janney Montgomery Scott 1225 23rd St NW Washington DC 20037-1102

LURVEY, IRA HAROLD, lawyer; b. Chgo., Apr. 6, 1935; s. Louis and Faye (Grey) L.; m. Barbara Ann Sirvint, June 24, 1962; children: Nathana, Lawrence, Jennifer, Jonathan, David, Robert. BS, U. Ill., 1956; MS, Northwestern U., 1961; JD, U. Calif., Berkeley, 1965. Bar: Calif. 1965, Nev. 1966, U.S. Dist. Ct. (cen. dist.) Calif. 1966, U.S. Tax Ct. 1966, U.S. Ct. Appeals (9th cir.) 1966, U.S. Supreme Ct. 1975. Law clk. to hon. justices Nev. Supreme Ct., Carson City, 1965-66; from assoc. to ptnr. Pacht, Ross, Warne, Bernhard & Sears, Inc., 1966-84; predecessor firm Shea & Gould, Los Angeles; founding ptnr. Lurvey & Shapiro, Los Angeles, 1984—; lectr. legal edn. programs; mem. Chief Justice's Commns. on Ct. Reform, Weighted Caseloads; mediator family law L.A. Superior Ct.; primary cons. CFL family law treatise, 1994—. Editor Community Property Jour., 1979-80, Primary Consultant CFL 2d, 1994; columnist Calif. Family Law Monthly; contbr. articles to profl. jours. Former chmn. Los Angeles Jr. Arts Ctr.; past pres. Cheviot Hills Homeowners Assn.; exec. v.p.; counsel gen. studies comn. Hillel Acad. Sch., Beverly Hills, Calif., 1977—. Served with U.S. Army, 1957-58. Fellow Am. Acad. Matrimonial Lawyers (pres. So. Calif. chpt. 1991-92, mem. nat. bd. govs. 1992—), Internat. Acad. Matrimonial Lawyers; mem. ABA (chair-elect family law sect. 1995—, sec. 1993-94, vice chmn. 1994-95, governing coun. 1986—, fin. officer 1991-92, chmn. support com., chmn. continuing legal edn., chmn. policy and issues com., vice chmn. com. arbitration and mediation, bd. of editors Family Adv. mag.), Calif. Bar Assn. (editor jour. 1982-85, chmn. family law sect. 1986-87, exec. com. family law sect. 1982-88, specialization adv. bd. family law 1979-82), L.A. County Bar Assn. (chmn. family law sect. 1981-82), exec. com. family law 1989—), Beverly Hills Bar Assn. (chmn. family law sect. 1976-

77). Home: 2729 Motor Ave Los Angeles CA 90064-3441 Office: Lurvey & Shapiro Ste 2520 2121 Avenue Of The Stars Los Angeles CA 90067

LUSAS, EDMUND WILLIAM, food processing research executive; b. Woodbury, Conn., Nov. 25, 1931; s. Anton Frank and Damicele Nellie (Kasputis) L.; m. Jeannine Marie Muller, Feb. 2, 1957; children—Daniel, Ann, Paul. B.S., U. Conn., 1954; M.S., Iowa State U., 1955; Ph.D. U. Wis., 1958; M.B.A., U. Chgo., 1972. Project leader Quaker Oats Research Labs., Barrington, Ill., 1958-61, mgr. canned pet foods research, 1961-67, mgr. pet foods research, 1967-72, mgr. sci. services, 1972-77; assoc. dir. Food Protein Research and Devel. Ctr., Tex. A&M U., College Station, 1977-78, dir., 1978-93, head fats, oils and extrusion programs, 1993—. Author over 100 publs.; patentee in field. Assoc. editor Jour. Am. Oil Chem. Soc., 1980-88. Fund raiser YMCA, Crystal Lake, Ill., 1970-77, chmn. fin. com., 1977. Recipient F.N. Peters research award Quaker Oats Co., 1968. Mem. Am. Oil Chemists Soc., Inst. Food Technologists (Gen. Foods research fellow 1956, 57), Am. Chem. Soc., Am. Assn. Cereal Chemists, Am. Soc. Agrl. Engrs., Nutrition Today Soc., Guayule Soc. Am., Sigma Xi, Phi Tau Sigma. Avocation: fishing. Home: 3604 Old Oaks Dr Bryan TX 77802-4743 Office: Texas A & M Univ Food Protein Rsch Deve Ctr College Station TX 77843

LUSCINSKI, STEVEN MICHAEL, corporate executive; b. Boston, Nov. 4, 1951; s. Anthony P. and Agnes V. (Nawoichek) L.; m. Cathryn Creveling, Jan. 9, 1982; children: Steven Jr., Keith, Laura. BSCE, Northeastern U., 1974; MSCE, MIT, 1976; MBA, Cornell U., 1980. Registered profl. engr. R.I. Engr. Stone & Webster, Boston, 1971-78; cons., researcher Brookhaven Nat. Labs., L.I., N.Y., 1978-80; mgr. corp. planning UGI, Valley Forge, Pa., 1980-84; chief fin. officer Accu-Sort Systems, Telford, Pa., 1984-85; exec. v.p., gen. mgr. Accu-Sort Systems, Telford, 1985—; bd. dirs. Accu-Sort Systems, Telford, ATS, Ellington, Conn., ScanQuest Corp., San Diego; mem. exec. com. Saga Ins. Home: Windsong Dr Doylestown PA 18901 Office: Accu Sort Systems 511 School House Rd Telford PA 18969-1196

LUSCOMBE, GEORGE A. II, lawyer; b. Jefferson, Iowa, Oct. 22, 1944. BS, U. Ill., 1966, JD, 1969; LLM, George Washington U., 1972. Bar: Ill. 1969, U.S. Supreme Ct. 1972, U.S. Claims Ct. 1972, D.C. 1972. Asst. br. chief legislation and regulations divsn. IRS Office Chief Counsel, 1972-73; ptnr. Mayer, Brown & Platt, Chgo.; adj. prof. law IIT, 1987—; speaker in field. Mem. ABA (chmn. com. depreciation and investment tax credit, sect. taxation 1980-82), Ill. State Bar Assn. (chmn. fed. tax sect. coun. 1991-92), Chgo. Bar Assn. (chmn. gen. income tax divsn., fed. tax sect. 1977-79), D.C. Bar. Office: Mayer Brown & Platt 190 S La Salle St Chicago IL 60603-3410

LUSCOMBE, HERBERT ALFRED, physician, educator; b. Johnstown, Pa., Aug. 9, 1916; s. Herbert O. and Clara C. (Geiselhart) L.; m. Sally T. McHugh; children: Herbert J., Susan M., Jill A. B.S., St. Vincent Coll., 1936; M.D., Jefferson Med. Coll., 1940. Diplomate: Am. Bd. Dermatology. Intern Jefferson Hosp., Phila., 1940-43, resident, 1946-48; resident U. Pa., 1948-49; mem. faculty Jefferson Med. Coll. Thomas Jefferson U., Phila., 1949—, prof., chmn. dept. dermatology, 1959-86; chief attending dermatologist Thomas Jefferson U. Hosp., 1959—, prof. emeritus of dermatology, 1987—, sr. attending dermatologist, 1987—; cons. dermatology Wills Eye Hosp., Lankenau Hosp., Herbert A. Luscombe lectr. in dermatology, 1984—. Contbr. articles to profl. jours. Recipient Clark Finneraud award Dermatology Found., 1981. Fellow AMA, Soc. Investgative Dermatology, Am. Acad. Dermatologists, Sigma Xi; mem. Phila. Dermatologic Soc. (pres. 1963-64), Alpha Omega Alpha. Roman Catholic. Club: Aronimink Golf. Home: 600 Old Gulph Rd Narberth PA 19072-1622 Office: Jefferson Med Coll 111 S 11th St Philadelphia PA 19107-4824

LUSHER, JEANNE MARIE, pediatric hematologist, educator; b. Toledo, June 9, 1935; d. Arnold Christian and Violet Cecilia (French) L. BS summa cum laude, U. Cin., 1956, MD, 1960. Lic. physician, Mich.; cert. pediatrics and hematology/oncology Am. Bd. Pediatrics. Resident in pediatrics Tulane divsn. Charity Hosp. La., New Orleans, 1961-64; fellow in pediatric hematology-oncology Child Rsch. Ctr. Mich., Detroit, 1964-65, St. Louis Children's Hosp./Washington U., 1965-66; instr. pediatrics Sch. Medicine Washington U., St. Louis, 1965-66; from instr. to assoc. prof. pediatrics Sch. Medicine Wayne State U., Detroit, 1966-74, prof. pediatrics, 1974—; dir. divsn. hematology-oncology Children's Hosp. Mich., Detroit, 1976—; Marion I. Barnhart prof. hemostasis rsch. Sch. Medicine Wayne State U., Detroit, 1989—; med. dir. Nat. Hemophilia Found., N.Y.C., 1987-94, chmn. med. and sci. adv. coun., 1994—. Author, editor: Treatment of Bleeding Disorders with Blood Components, 1980, Sickle Cell, 1974, 76, 81, Hemophilia and von Willebrand Disease in the 1990's, 1991, Acquired Bleeding Disorder in Children, 1981, F VIII/von Willebrand Factor and Platelets in Health and Disease, 1987, Inhibitors to Factor VIII, 1994, The Science and Politics of Women's Health in America, 1995. Mem. Citizens Info. Com., Pontiac Township, Mich., 1980-82; apptd. mem. Hazardous Waste Incinerator Commn., Oakland County, Mich., 1981. Recipient Disting. Alumnus award U. Cin. Alumni Assn., 1990. Mem. Am. Bd. Pediatrics (chmn. sub-bd. hematology-oncology 1988-90), Am. Soc. Heatology (chmn. sci. com. pediatrics 1991-92), Am. Pediatric Soc., Mich. Humane Soc., Internat. Soc. Thrombosis-Hemostasis (chmn. factor VII/IX subcom. 1985-90, sec., chmn. elect scientific and standardization com. 1994—), Soc. Pediatric Rsch. Avocations: nature, wildlife, hiking, gardening. Office: Children's Hosp Mich 3901 Beaubien Detroit MI 48201

LUSHT, KENNETH MICHAEL, business administration educator; b. N.Y.C., Dec. 22, 1942; m. Elizabeth Enloe Hall; children: Elizabeth, Alexander. BBA, Emory U., 1964; PhD, Ga. State U., 1973. Prof. bus. adminstrn. Pa. State U., University Park, 1973—, acad. program dir. continuing edn., 1983—, dir. inst. for real estate studies, 1986—, chmn. dept. ins. and real estate, 1989—; pres. Kenneth M. Lusht Cons., State College, 1983—. Author 2 textbooks; editorial bd. Jour. of the Am. Real Estate And Urban Econs. Assn., 1986-92, Jour. of Property Rsch., 1990—, Appraisal Jour., 1991—, Jour. of Real Estate Fin., 1993—; contbr. articles to profl. jours. Vis. fellow RMIT, 1989, 95, Vis. Rsch. fellow U. West Sydney, 1993, U. Hong Kong, 1994, 95; recipient Wagner award Am. Inst. of Real Estate Appraisers, 1986. Mem. Am. Real Estate and Urban Econs. Assn. (pres. 1987, bd. dirs. 1982-84, 88-90), Am. Real Estate Soc. Office: Coll Bus Pa State U 409 Bab University Park PA 16802

LUSIC, RONALD R., retail company executive; b. 1947; married. BA, U. Wis., 1975. Stock clk. Red Owl Foods Stores, 1965-67; from stock clk. to mgr. Sentry Food Stores, 1967-70; with Godfrey Co., Waukesha, Wis., 1970-82, 87—; labor rels. mgr., 1970-80, dist. mgr. labor rels., from 1980, now exec. v.p.; with Hub City Foods, 1982-87, v.p. sales, 1982-83, pres., 1983-87. Office: Godfrey Co 1200 W Sunset Dr Waukesha WI 53186-6597

LUSK, HARLAN GILBERT, national park superintendent; b. Jersey City, June 22, 1943; s. Harlan H. and Mary M. (Kuhl) L.; m. Catherine L. Rutherford, Oct. 11, 1986. BA in History, Gettysburg Coll., 1965. Supervisory historian Cape Hatteras Nat. Seashore, Manteo, N.C., 1968; historian Nat. Pk. Svc., Washington, 1968-69; programs specialist So. Utah Group, Cedar City, 1968-70; pk. supt. Wolf Trap Farm Pk., Vienna, Va., 1970-72; supervisory pk. ranger Blue Ridge Pkwy., Roanoke, Va., 1972-74; pk. supt. Appomattox (Va.) Courthouse, Nat. Hist. Pk., 1974-76, Valley Forge (Pa.). Nat. Hist. Pk., 1976-81, Big Bend (Tex.) Nat. Pk., 1981-86, Glacier Nat. Pk., West Glacier, Mont., 1986-94; pk. supt. Albright Tng. Ctr. Grand Canyon Nat. Pk., Ariz., 1994—; chief, Divsn. Tng. and Employee Nat. Park Svc., Washington, 1995—; organizer 1st regional conf. Rio Grande Border, States on Pks. and Wildlife, Laredo, Tex., 1985. Bd. dirs. Tech. Com. on Pks. & Recreation Cen. Va. Planning Dist., 1972-74, Fed. Exec. Assn. Roanoke Valley, 1972-74, Flathead Basin Commn., 1986—, Flathead Conv. & Visitor Assn., 1986—; prin. founder, 1st pres., Appomattox County Hist. Soc., 1974-76; trustee Sci. Mus. Assn. Roanoke Valley, 1972-74, Nature Conservancy Mont., 1994—; ex-officio Friends of Valley Forge, 1977-81; founder, ex-officio, bd. dirs. Valley Forge Pk. Interpretive Assn., 1977-81; founder Big Bend Area Travel Assn., chmn., 1984-86. Recipient Meritorious Svc. award. Dept. Interior, 1986. Mem. Glacier Natural History Assn. (ex officio 1986-94), Glacier Nat. Pk. Assocs. (founder, ex-officio 1989-94), George Wright Soc., Lions, Rotary. Avocations: golf, antiques, computers, collecting artwork, hiking. Office: Grand Canyon Nat Pk Albright Tng Ctr West Glacier MT 86023

LUSK, WILLIAM EDWARD, real estate, oil company executive; b. Medicine Lodge, Kans., May 16, 1916; s. William Edward and Teresa (Rhoades) L.; m. Anita Ballard, Feb. 1, 1942; children—William Edward, Janet Kathryn and James Raymond (twins). B.S. in Edn., A.B. in Econs, Ft. Hays State Coll., 1939; student, Washburn U., 1936; postgrad., Kans. U., 1940-41. Tchr. Protection (Kans.) High Sch., 1939-41; mgr. real estate dept. Wheeler, Kelly & Hagny Investment Co., Wichita, Kans., 1946-63; cofounder, exec. v.p., treas., dir. Clinton Oil Co., Wichita, 1963-73; pres. Lusk Real Estate Co., 1963—, Lusk Investment Co., 1973—; Pres. Wichita Real Estate Bd., 1961. Founder Lusk Found., 1968, William E. Lusk Scholarship, Ft. Hays State Coll., 1969; bd. dirs. Jr. Achievement Wichita. Served with USNR, 1942-46; comdr. Res. Named Kans. Realtor of Year Kans. Assn. Real Estate Bds., 1962; recipient Alumni Achievement award Ft. Hays Kan. State Coll., 1971. Mem. VFW, Sojourners, Res. Officers Assn., Naval Res. Officers Assn., Navy League, Phi Alpha Delta, Alpha Kappa Psi (hon.). Methodist (bd. dirs. 1969-72, pres. chmn. 1969—.) Clubs: Wichita Country, Wichita (bd. dirs. 1969-72, pres. 1972), McConnell AFB Officers. Lodge: Masons (32 degree). Home: 6 W Parkway N Wichita KS 67206 Office: 1608 E Lewis Wichita KS 67211-1823 *In business and personal relationships I have found strength in times of adversity and self-control in times of success by forming the habit of calling to mind this guideline: Things are never as good as they seem to be on the day they look good-nor are things as bad as they seem to be on the day they appear bad.*

LUSKIN, ROBERT DAVID, lawyer; b. Chgo., Jan. 21, 1950; s. Bert L. and S. Ruth (Katz) L.; m. Fairlea A. Sheehy, Aug. 23, 1975; children: Peter Duncan, Charles Cassimer. BA magna cum laude, Harvard U., 1972, JD magna cum laude, 1979; postgrad., Oxford (Eng.) U., 1972-75. Bar: D.C. 1979, U.S. Ct. Appeals (1st, 4th, 5th, 6th, 8th, 9th, 11th, D.C. cirs.) 1979, U.S. Supreme Ct. 1983. Law clk. to Hon. Louis F. Oberdorfer U.S. Dist. Ct. for D.C., Washington, 1979-80; spl. counsel organized crime racketeering sect. U.S. Dept. Justice, Washington, 1980-82; ptnr. Onek, Klein & Farr, Washington, 1982-89, Powell, Goldstein, Frazer & Murphy, Washington, 1989-93, Comey, Boyd & Luskin, Washington, 1993—; lectr. in law U. Va. Sch. Law, 1992—. Rhodes scholar, 1972-75. Mem. ABA (chmn. RICO com. 1986-94), Harvard Law Sch. Assn. Washington (pres.). Home: 3244 38th St NW Washington DC 20016-3729 Office: Comey Boyd & Luskin 2828 Pennsylvania Ave NW Ste 200 Washington DC 20007

LUSKY, LOUIS, legal educator; b. Columbus, Ohio, May 15, 1915; s. Leonard Morris and Amy (Kleeman) L.; m. Ruth Agnes Anderson, Aug. 31, 1946; children: Mary Hibbard Friedman, John Anderson; 1 child by previous marriage, Peter Joris. BA, U. Louisville, 1935; LLB, Columbia, 1937. Bar: N.Y. 1938, Ky. 1947. Law clk. to Supreme Ct. Justice Harlan F. Stone, 1937-38; assoc. Root, Clark, Buckner & Ballantine, N.Y.C., 1938-42, 44-45; civilian mem. ops. analysis sect. 8th Air Force, 1943-44; with legal div. U.S Mil. Govt., Germany, 1945-46; ptnr. Wyatt & Grafton, Louisville, 1947-51; sole practice Louisville, 1952-63; prof. law Columbia Law Sch., 1963-85, Betts prof. law, 1979-85, prof. emeritus, 1985—. Author: (with others) Southern Justice, 1965, By What Right?, 1975, Our Nine Tribunes, 1993. Mem. ABA, ACLU (nat. com. 1963-67, nat. bd. 1967-70), Am. Law Inst. Home: 623 Eastbrook Rd Ridgewood NJ 07450-2114 Office: 435 W 116th St New York NY 10027-7201 also: 1250 E Ridgewood Ave Ridgewood NJ 07450-3989

LUSS, DAN, chemical engineering educator; b. Tel Aviv, Israel, May 5, 1938; came to U.S., 1963, naturalized, 1973; s. Manfred and Gertrude (Weinstein) L.; m. Amalia Rubin, Sept. 4, 1966; children: Noya, Limor. BS, Technion Inst. Tech., Haifa, Israel, 1960, MSc, 1963; PhD, U. Minn., 1966. Registered profl. engr., Tex. Asst. prof. chem. engring. U. Minn., Mpls., 1966-67; asst. prof. chem. engring. U. Houston, 1967-69, asso. prof., 1969-72, prof., 1972—, chmn. dept., 1975—; assoc. dir. Tex. Ctr. for Superconductivity, 1988-92; cons. to several chem. cos. Editor: Revs. in Chem. Engring.; mem. editorial bd. Sci. and Engring. Catalysis Rev. Fellow Am. Inst. Chem. Engrs. (Allan P. Colburn award 1973, Profl. Progress award 1979, Wilhelm award 1986, chmn. awards com., former mem. editorial bd. jour./former dir.), Am. Chem. Soc. (Honor scroll award of Indsl. Engring. Chemistry div. 1967); mem. NAE, Am. Soc. Engring. Edn. (Curtis McGraw award 1977 3M-Chem. Engring. lectureship award 1985). Home: 6242 Paisley Houston TX 77096-3727 Office: U Houston Dept Chem Engring Houston TX 77204-4792

LUSSEN, JOHN FREDERICK, pharmaceutical laboratory executive; b. N.Y.C., Jan. 5, 1942; s. Frederick Maurice and Kathleen (Herlihy) L.; m. Kathleen Elizabeth Sheppard; children: Tara, Eric, Gregory. BS in Fin., Fordham U., 1963, JD, 1967; LLM in Tax, NYU, 1971. Bar: N.Y. 1967. Tax atty. Pfizer Inc., N.Y.C., 1971-74; mgr. taxes SCM Corp., N.Y.C., 1974-79; v.p. taxes Abbott Labs., Abbott Park, Ill., 1979—. Capt. U.S. Army, 1968-70. Mem. ABA, Tax Execs. Inst., Bus. Roundtable (tax subcom.). Avocations: tennis, golf. Home: 1055 Westleigh Rd Lake Forest IL 60045 Office: Abbott Labs D367 AP6D 100 Abbott Park Rd Abbott Park IL 60004

LUSSIER, GILLES, monsignor. Office: Evêché CP 470, 2 rue St Charles Borromee Nord, Joliette, PQ Canada J6E 6H6

LUSSIER, JEAN-PAUL, dentistry educator; b. Montreal, Que., Can., Sept. 17, 1917; s. Eugene and Parmelia (Gauthier) L.; m. Juliette Laurin, May 4, 1943; children: Louis, Renee Lussier Brecknock, Josee, Anne Lussier Morin, Pierre, Helene Lussier Black, Andre. BA, U. Montreal, 1938, DDS, 1942, MS, 1952; PhD, U. Calif., San Francisco, 1959; DSc (hon.), McGill U., 1972. Mem. U. Montreal faculty medicine, dept. physiology, 1946-52, 54-57, mem. faculty dentistry, 1957-62, 79-83, prof. emeritus, 1983—, dean, 1962-79, chmn. health scis. coordinating com., 1979-83; rsch. fellow U. Calif.-San Francisco, 1952-54; cons. WHO, 1972—; bd. dirs. Sacred Heart Hosp., Montreal. Recipient award Am. Acad. Dental Medicine, 1958, award Alpha Omega, 1962. Fellow Am. Coll. Dentists, Internat. Coll. Dentists, Acad. Dentistry Internat. (hon.), Royal Coll. Dentists, Academie dentaire du Quebec; mem. Fedn. Dentaire Internationale, Can. Dental Assn. (hon.). Home: 3507 Vendome St, Montreal, PQ Canada H4A 3M6

LUST, BARBARA C., psychology and linguistics educator; d. John Benedict and Virginia (Sleth) L. BA in English Lit., Manhattanville Coll., 1963; postgrad., Fairleigh Dickinson, 1965, The New Sch. for Social Rsch., 1965-66, U. Geneva, Switzerland, 1968-69; MA in English Lit., Fordham U., 1971; PhD Devel. Psychology, CUNY, 1975. Post doctoral fellow dept. linguistics and philosophy MIT, Cambridge, 1974-76; from asst. prof. to prof. dept. human development and family studies Cornell U., Ithaca, N.Y., 1976—; field rep. cognitive studies program, 1987—; co-dir., 1992—; prof. modern langs. & linguistics, 1990—; vis. prof. SUNY, Binghamton, 1977; vis. scientist MIT, 1984, 90; vis. scholar Kelaniya U., Sri Lanka, 1984, U.S. Ednl. Found., 1984; cons. in field, lectr. various colls. and univs. Author: Studies in the Acquisition of Anaphora (vol I 1986, II 1987); co-editor, author: Synthetic Theory & First Language Acquisition, 1994 (vol. I and II); co-author: Studies in the Cognitive Basis of Language Development, 1975; contbr. articles to prof. jours., chpts. to books. Grantee NIMH, 1976, NSF, 1979-88, 92-93; fellow Nat. Inst. Health, 1990, NSF, 1989-91; Smithsonian grant Am. Inst. Indian Studies, 1980-81; recipient Travel award Linguisticic Soc. Am. and NSF, 1982, Rsch. award NSF, 1988-89, James McKeen Cattell award, 1992-93, N.Y. State Coll. Human Ecology award, 1976-79, 83. Fellow AAAS (chair linguistics and the lang. scis. 1993-94); mem. APA, Linguistic Soc. Am. (del. to AAAS psychology sect 1988—), Am. Psychological Soc., Internat. Assn. Study Child Language, Soc. Rsch. Child Devel., Internat. Soc. Woman in Cognitive Neuroscience, Internat. Soc. Korean Linguistics, New Eng. Child Lang. Assn., N.Y. Acad. Scis., Soc. Philosophy and Psychology, Linguistic Assn. Great Britian, Piaget Soc. Democrat. Office: Cornell U Human Devel & Family Studies Ng 28 Marth Van Rensse Ithaca NY 14853

LUSTBADER, PHILIP LAWRENCE, lawyer; b. Balt., May 14, 1949; s. I. William and Evelyn (Kandel) L.; m. Randy R. Tatarka, June 28, 1970; children: Michael Howard, Jamie Robyn. BS, Wharton Sch., U. Pa., 1970; JD summa cum laude, Temple U., 1973. Bar: Pa. 1973, N.J. 1974, U.S. Dist. Ct. (ea. dist.) Pa. 1974, U.S. Dist. Ct. N.J. 1974, U.S. Ct. Appeals (3d cir.) 1975. Assoc. Wolf, Block, Schorr & Solis-Cohen, Phila., 1973-78; corporate counsel Subaru of Am., Inc., Cherry Hill, N.J., 1978-80, asst. v.p., corp. counsel,

1980-83, v.p.; gen. counsel, 1983-86, group v.p., gen. counsel and sec., 1987-90, sr. v.p., gen. counsel, sec., 1991-92, Lustbader and Assocs. P.C., Attys. at Law, Phila., 1993-94; v.p. gen. counsel, sec. GeoPhone Corp., Annapolis, Md., 1995—; bd. dirs. Subaru of Am., Inc., 1987-90. Exec. editor Temple Law Quar., 1972-73. Mem. ABA, Phila. Bar Assn. Office: GeoPhone Corp 73 Franklin St Annapolis MD 21401

LUSTENBERGER, LOUIS CHARLES, JR., lawyer; b. Chgo., Mar. 13, 1936; s. Louis Charles and Virginia (Chesrown) L.; m. Anita T. Anderson, June 17, 1961; children: Louis, Gwyn. BA, Williams Coll., 1959; LLB, Harvard U., 1962. Bar: N.Y. 1963, U.S. Dist. Ct. (so. and ea. dist.) N.Y. 1964, U.S. Dist. Ct. (we. dist.) N.Y. 1986, U.S. Ct. Appeals (2d cir.) 1964, U.S. Ct. Appeals (3d cir.) 1989, U.S. Ct. Appeals (5th cir.) 1980, U.S. Supreme Ct. 1978, U.S. Ct. Appeals (10th cir.) 1993. Assoc. Donovan, Leisure, Newton & Irvine, N.Y.C., 1962-71, ptnr., 1971—. Sr. warden St. Barnabas Ch., Irvington, N.Y., 1980-82; chmn. Irvington Zoning Bd., 1989—. Fellow Am. Coll. Trial Lawyers; mem. Assn. of Bar of City of N.Y., N.Y. State Bar Assn., N.Y. County Lawyers Assn., Phi Beta Kappa. Republican. Presbyterian. Home: 86 Fargo Ln Irvington NY 10533-1202 Office: Donovan Leisure Newton & Irvine 30 Rockefeller Plz New York NY 10112

LUSTER, GEORGE ORCHARD, professional society administrator; b. Pitts., Mar. 20, 1921; s. James W. and Gertrude (Orchard) L.; m. Edith A. Townsend, May 3, 1946 (dec. May 1989); children: Thomas, Carolea, Patricia; m. Mary Jane Herbolich, Oct. 1990. B.S. with honors, U. Pitts., 1949. C.P.A., 1951. Acct., Am. Inst. Research, Pitts., 1948-49; mgr. Price Waterhouse (C.P.A.s), Pitts., 1949-59; treas., asst. sec. Mellon Inst., Pitts., 1959-67; treas. Carnegie-Mellon U., 1967-80; asst. sec., asst. treas., supervising com. Bellefield Boiler Plant, Pitts., 1962-71; treas., asst. sec. MPC Corp., Pitts., 1963-80; dir. adminstrn. Fin. Execs. Inst., 1980-86; Instr. Robert Morris Sch., 1955-59, U. Pitts., 1959. Bd. dirs. Central Blood Bank, Pitts., 1973-80. Served with USAAF, 1943-46. Mem. Fin. Execs. Inst., AICPA, Pa. Inst. CPAs, Air and Waste Mgmt. Assn. (treas. 1966—), River Bend Golf Club, Alpha Kappa Psi, Beta Gamma Sigma. Republican. Methodist. Home: 9238 SE Deerberry Pl Tequesta FL 33469-1804 *Individual success is relative to the challenges that one meets through life and how one perceives them as opportunities to learn, to be creative, and to be innovative in defining and planning actions to achieve one's goals.*

LUSTER, MARTIN ARNOLD, state legislator; b. N.Y.C., Apr. 4, 1942; s. Hyman I. and Esta G. (Green) L.; m. Barbara Kirschbaum, Apr. 11, 1964; children: Brian D., Ann D. BS, L.I. U., 1963; LLB, NYU, 1966. Bar: N.Y. 1966. Ptnr. Gaier & Luster, N.Y.C., 1967-76, Luster, Salk, Henry & Tischler and predecessor firm, Ithaca, N.Y., 1980-88; pvt. practice Trumansburg, N.Y., 1976-80; mem. N.Y. State Assembly, Albany 1989—, chair task force on utility rate settlements, 1990, sec. majority conf., 1994, chair subcoms. on rural health and on librs.; bd. dirs. UniPeg, Corning, N.Y.; mem. exec. com. N.Y. State Biodiversity Inst., Albany, 1994. Officer Tompkins County Econ. Opportunity Corp., Ithaca, 1972-83; bd. dirs. Alpha House, Trumansburg, 1979-83, Leadership Tompkins, Ithaca, 1992—; town supr. Town of Ulysses, N.Y., 1984-88. Named Newsmaker of Yr., Am. Community Cable TV, 1989; recipient Cert. of Recognition Atlantic chpt. Sierra Club, 1992, Cert. of Appreciation, Ithaca Neighborhood Housing Svcs, 1993. Democrat. Jewish. Avocations: sailing, hiking. Office: NY State Legislature Rm 639lob Albany NY 12248

LUSTGARTEN, IRA HOWARD, lawyer; b. N.Y.C., July 31, 1929; s. Louis and Florine Josephine (Van Mindeno) L.; m. Rhoda Manne, Oct. 24, 1954; children: Lise Anne, Nancy Ellen. AB, NYu, 1950; LLB, Columbia U., 1958. Bar: N.Y. 1958, Fla. 1978, U.S. Dist. Ct. (so. dist.) N.Y. 1959, U.S. Ct. Claims 1985, U.S. Ct. Appeals (fed. cir.) 1989. Assoc. Proskauer Rose Goetz Mendelsohn, N.Y.C., 1958-68, ptnr., 1968-79; ptnr. Willkie Farr & Gallagher, N.Y.C., 1979—; lectr. law Columbia U. Served to lt. USNR, 1951-55. Mem. ABA, Am. Law Inst., Am. Coll. Probate Counsel Found. (past pres.), Am. Coll. Probate Counsel, N.Y. Bar Assn. (past chmn. trusts and estates law sect.), Assn. of Bar of City of N.Y. (former chmn. trusts, estates, and surrogate cts.), Pub. Adminstrs. N.Y. (adm. bd. oversee), Fla. Bar Assn., Internat. Acad. Estate and Trust Law, N.Y. (legis. adv. com. to rev. law of trusts and estates). Office: Willkie Farr & Gallagher 1 Citicorp Ctr 153 E 53rd St New York NY 10022-4611

LUSZTIG, PETER ALFRED, university dean, educator; b. Budapest, Hungary, May 12, 1930; s. Alfred Peter and Susan (Szabo) L.; m. Penny Bicknell, Aug. 26, 1961; children: Michael, Cameron, Carrie. B in Com., U. B.C., Vancouver, Can., 1954; MBA, U. Western Ont., London, Can., 1955; PhD, Stanford U., 1964. Asst. to comptroller B.C. Electric, Vancouver, 1955-57; instr. fin. U. B.C., 1957-60, asst. prof. fin., 1962-64, assoc. prof., 1964-68, Killam sr. research fellow, 1968-69, prof., 1968—; dean Faculty Commerce, 1977-91; bd. trustees BC Health Benefit Trust; bd. dirs. Canfor Corp., Royal Ins. (Can.) Western Assurance, Roins Holding Co.; fed. commr. BC Treaty Commn.; vis. prof. IMEDE, Switzerland, 1973-74, London Grad. Sch. Bur. Studies, 1968-69, Pacific Coast Banking Sch., 1977—; sr. advisor B.C. Ministry of Econ. Devel., Small Bus. and Trade, 1991. Author: Report of the Royal Commission on Automobile Insurance, 2 vols., 1968, Financial Management in a Canadian Setting, 5th rev. edit., 1993, Report of the Commission on the B.C. Tree Fruit Industry, 1990. Ford Found. faculty dissertation fellow, Stanford U., 1964. Mem. Am. Fin. Assn., Fin. Mgmt. Assn. Lutheran. Office: Dept Commerce & Bus. Adminstrn BC Vancouver, BC Canada V6T 1Z2

LUTALI, A. P., governor of American Samoa; b. Aunu'u, American Samoa, Dec. 24, 1919; married. Gov. Am. Samoa, 1985-89, 93—; spkr. of the House Senate, Am. Samoa, 1956-57, pres., 1965-67, v.p., 1988—; chair Constnl. Conv., 1966. Mem. Am. Samoa Bar Assn. (founder 1972). Office: Governor's Office Pago Pago AS 96799*

LUTER, JOHN, news correspondent, educator; b. Knoxville, Tenn., Jan. 17, 1919; s. John Thomas and Bertha Mae (Carver) L.; m. Mary Hickey, 1948 (dec.); 1 child, Linda; m. Yvonne Spiegelberg, 1966 (div. 1971); m. Nan Hoyt Lawrence, 1974. BA, St. Mary's U., Tex., 1939, postgrad., 1939-42; fellow Time Inc., Sch. Advanced Internat. Studies, Washington, 1945. Reporter San Antonio Light, 1939-42, Washington Star, 1942-44; Wash. corr. Time mag., 1944-45; war corr. Time mag., Pacific, 1945; fgn. corr. Time and Life mags., Southeast Asia, 1945-46, Japan, 1946-47, Israel, 1948-49, Italy, 1949-54; asst. editor internat. edit. Life mag., 1954-56; reporter, writer CBS News, 1957-58; asso. editor Newsweek mag., 1958-61; radio news commentator Stas. WQXR and QXR-FM Network, 1960-61; coord. advanced internat. reporting program Columbia Grad. Sch. Journalism, 1961-72; dir. Maria Moors Cabot Prize Program, 1961-74; mem. profl. staff Bank St. Coll. Edn., 1973-74; prof., dir. journalism U. Hawaii, Honolulu, from 1974, prof. and chmn. journalism dept., 1982-92, prof. journalism, 1992—. Adv. editor: Columbia Journalism Rev., 1961-72. Chmn. internat. rels. com. N.Y.C. Protestant Coun., 1968-71; chmn. adv. screening com. communications Sr. Fulbright Program, 1970-73; trustee Overseas Press Club Found., 1962-72, chmn., 1964-65; bd. dirs. UN Assn. N.Y.C., 1973-74; chmn. Honolulu Community Media Coun., 1982-84. Mem. Assn. Edn. Journalism and Mass Communications, Assn. Schs. Journalism and Mass Communications, Honolulu Com. Fgn. Rels., Pacific and Asian Affairs Coun., Soc. Profl. Journalists (mem. chpt. exec. coun. 1966-69, 89-90), Japan Am. Soc., Overseas Press Club (pres. N.Y.C. 1962-63), Outrigger Canoe Club. Home: 340 Alta Ave San Antonio TX 78209-4513 Office: U Hawaii 208 Crawford Hall 2550 Campus Rd Honolulu HI 96822-2217

LUTER, JOSEPH WILLIAMSON, III, meat packing and processing company executive; b. Smithfield, Va., 1940; married. BBA, Wake Forest Coll., 1962. Pres. Smithfield Packing Co., Arlington, Va., 1964-69, Bryce Mountain Resort Inc., 1969-75; with Smithfield Foods Inc., Arlington 1975—, pres., 1975-86, 89—, chief exec. officer, 1975—, chmn., 1977—, also bd. dirs. Office: Smithfield Foods Inc 561 N Church St Smithfield VA 23430*

LUTES, DONALD HENRY, architect; b. San Diego, Mar. 7, 1926; s. Charles McKinley and Helen (Bjoraker) L.; m. Donnie Wageman, Aug. 14, 1949; children: Laura Jo, Gail Eileen, Dana Charles. B.Arch., U. Oreg., 1950. Pvt. archtl. practice Springfield, Oreg., 1956-58; ptnr. John

Amundson, Springfield, 1958-70; pres. Lutes & Amundson, Springfield, 1970-72; ptnr. Lutes/Sanetel, 1973-86; adj. assoc. prof. architecture U. Oreg., 1964-66, 89—; chmn. Springfield Planning Commn., 1956-64, Urban Design and Devel. Corp., 1968-70, Eugene Non-Profit Housing, Inc., 1970. Architect: Springfield Pub. Library, 1957, Mt. Hood Community Coll, 1965-79, Shoppers Paradise Expt. in Downtown Revitalization, 1957. Chmn. Springfield United Appeal, 1959. Served to 1st lt. AUS, 1943-46, 51-52. Decorate Bronze Star; named Jr. 1st Citizen, Springfield C. of C., 1957, 1st Citizen, 1968, Disting. Citizen, 1994. Fellow AIA (bd. dirs. 1987-90, v.p. 1991); mem. Rotary, Theta Chi. Home and Office: 778 Crest Ln Springfield OR 97477-3601

LUTGEN, ROBERT R., newspaper editor; b. Fairmont, Minn., Oct. 27, 1949; s. William J. and Barbara Estella (Sanger) L.; m. Teresa L. Palm, July 17, 1971; children: Mark, Kyle, Laura. BA, Ctrl. Wash. State Coll., 1971. Reporter, asst. city editor Yakima (Wash.) Herald Republic, 1970-77; city editor Bryan (Tex.) Eagle, 1977-81; city editor Texarkana (Tex.) Gazette, 1981-83, mng. editor, 1983-87; asst. mng. editor Ark. Dem., 1987-91; mng. editor Ark. Dem.-Gazette, 1991—. Recipient Best News Story award, Editorial Writing award, Headline Writing award AP Mng. Editors Assn. 1985. Mem. Ark. AP (pres. 1989-90), Mng. Editors Assn. (bd. dirs. 1986-91). Avocations: travel, golf, reading. Home: 5 Nicole Ct North Little Rock AR 72118 Office: Ark Dem-Gazette 121 E Capitol Little Rock AR 72201*

LUTGENS, HARRY GERARDUS, food company executive; b. Geleen, The Netherlands; s. Hubertus and Antoinetta (Ramakers) L.; m. Denyse Richard; children: Louise, Carolyn. Cert. Administrv. Mgr., U. Toronto, Ont., Can., 1969, Cert. Gen. Acct., 1971. From acct. to mgr. fin. planning analysis Miracle Food Mart div. Steinberg Inc., Rexdale, Ont., 1963-74, regional mgr., 1974-78; various mgmt. positions to pres., gen. mgr. Valdi Foods Inc., Rexdale, 1978-93; ret., 1993. Mem. Cert. Gen. Accts. Assn., Cert. Adminstrv. Mgrs. Assn. Avocations: traveling, golf, home repair. Home: 20 Inverary Cres, Agincourt, ON Canada M1T 2W5 Office: Valdi Foods Inc, 135 Queens Plate Dr Ste 300, Rexdale, ON Canada M9W 6V1

LUTH, WILLIAM CLAIR, research manager; b. Winterset, IA, June 28, 1934; s. William Henry Luth and Ora Anna (Klingaman) Sorenson; m. Betty L. Heubrock, Aug. 23, 1953; children: Linda Diane, Robert William, Sharon Jean. BA in Geology, U. of Iowa, 1958, MS in Geology, 1960; PhD in Geochemistry, Penn State U., 1963. Research assoc. in geochemistry Pa. State U., University Park, Pa., 1963-65; asst. prof. geochemistry MIT, Cambridge, Mass., 1965-68; assoc. prof. geology Stanford U., 1968-77, prof. of geology, 1977-79; supr. geophysics div. Sandia Nat. Labs, Albuquerque, N. Mex., 1979-82; mgr. geosciences dept. Sandia Nat. Labs, Albuquerque, 1982-90; mgr. geoscis. rsch. program U.S. Dept. Energy, Washington, 1990—, acting dir. divsn. engring. & geosci., 1994—; geoscientist US ERDA/DOE Washington, 1976-78; faculty sabbatical Sandia Laboratories, Albuquerque, N. Mex., 1975, visiting staff mem. Los Alamos Nat. Lab, 1978. Contbr. articles to profl. jours. Served with U.S. Army, 1953-56. Grantee NSF, 1964-78. Avocations: photography, shooting. Home: 7516 Miller Fall Rd Rockville MD 20855-1122 Office: US Dept Energy ER-15 Washington DC 20545

LUTHER, DARLENE, state legislator; b. 1947; m. Bill Luther; 2 children. BA, U. St. Thomas. Mem. Minn. Ho. of Reps., 1993—. Home: 6809 Shingle Creek Dr Minneapolis MN 55445-2647 Office: Minn Ho of Reps State Capitol Saint Paul MN 55155

LUTHER, DAVID BYRON, glass company executive; b. Utica, N.Y., May 26, 1936; s. Everett David and Mary (Brown) L.; m. Geraldine Frost; children: Leslie, Gregory, Valorie. B.S., Syracuse U., 1958, M.B.A., 1961. Dir. personnel resources Corning Glass Works, N.Y., 1974-76, asst. corp. controller, 1976-78, dir. corp. planning, 1978-79, dir. info. services, 1979-80, v.p. personnel, 1980-83, v.p. quality, 1983-85, sr. v.p., corp. dir. quality, 1985-94, ret., 1994; founder, prin. Luther Quality Assocs., 1994—; mem. Human Resource Roundtable, N.Y.C., 1981-83; judge Malcolm Baldrige Nat. Quality Award, 1988-91; co-chair exec. com. N.Y. State Excelsior Quality Award; exec. in residence sch. mgmt. Syracuse U., mem. adv. bd.; chmn. Excelsion Inc., 1992-95; mem. steering com. Conf. Bd. Total Quality Mgmt. Ctr.; mem. adv. bd. ABS Quality Evaluations, Inc. Bd. dirs. Southeastern Steuben County United Way, Corning, 1975-77; advisor Donovan Acad., Corning, 1980-82; trustee Corning Community Coll., 1980-83; trustee Coll. Ctr. of Finger Lakes, Corning, 1981—, chmn. bd. trustees, 1988-90; nat. chmn. Koalaty Kid. Served to 1st lt. U.S. Army, 1958-60. Mem. Conf. Bd. Quality Coun. (co-founder 1985), Assn. for Mfg. Excellence, Am. Soc. Quality Control (treas. 1992-93, pres.-elect 1993-94, pres. 1994-95, chmn. 1995—), Internat. Acad. Quality. Roman Catholic. Home: 22 Overbrook Rd Painted Post NY 14870-9339 Office: 85 E Market St Corning NY 14830

LUTHER, DAVID GASTON, JR., lawyer; b. Asheville, N.C., Apr. 23, 1951; s. David Gaston Sr. and Eula Mae (Archer) L.; m. Sally A. Schreiber, April 2, 1977; 1 child, Amanda. AB, Duke U., 1973; JD, Stanford U., 1976. Bar: Tex., Calif. Assoc. Luce, Hennessy, Smith & Castle, Dallas, 1976, Hughes, Luce, Hennessy, Smith & Castle, Dallas, 1976-79; ptnr. Hughes & Hill, Dallas, 1979-85, Hughes & Luce, Dallas, 1985—. Book rev. editor Stanford U. Law Rev., 1975-76. Active Lyric Opera of Dallas, 1982—. Mem. ABA, Calif. Bar Assn., Tex. Bar Assn., Dallas Bar Assn. Office: 2737 Purdue Ave Dallas TX 75225-7910 Office: Hughes & Luce 1717 Main St Ste 2800 Dallas TX 75201-4685

LUTHER, FLORENCE JOAN (MRS. CHARLES W. LUTHER), lawyer; b. N.Y.C. June 28, 1928; d. John Phillip and Catherine Elizabeth (Duffy) Thomas; J.D. magna cum laude, U. Pacific, 1963; m. William J. Rappe (dec.); children—Kevin P., Brian T.; m. 2d, Charles W. Luther, June 11, 1961. Admitted to Calif. bar; mem. firm Luther, Luther, O'Connor & Johnson, Sacramento, 1964—. Mem. faculty McGeorge Sch. Law, U. Pacific, Sacramento, 1966-88, prof., 1968-88, prof. emeritus, 1988—. Judge Bank Am. Achievement awards, 1969-71. Bd. dirs. Sacramento Suicide Prevention League, 1969-70. Mem. ABA, Calif., Sacramento County bar assns., AAUP, Womens Legal Groups, Am. Judicature Soc., Order of Coif, Iota Tau Tau. Mem. bd. advisors Community Property Jour., 1974—; state decision editor, 1974—. Home: 11101 Fair Oaks Blvd Fair Oaks CA 95628-5136 Office: PO Box 1030 Fair Oaks CA 95628-1030

LUTHER, GEORGE AUBREY, orthopedic surgeon; b. Keokuk, Iowa, Dec. 11, 1933; s. George August and Leda (Galbraith) L.; m. Dorothy Gould Luther, Aug. 18, 1956; children: Melinda, George Bradley. AB, Cen Meth. U., 1955; MD, Vanderbilt U., 1959. Diplomate Am. Bd. Orthopaedic Surgery. Intern Vanderbilt U. Hosp., Nashville, 1959-60, resident, 1961-64, instr., 1964; resident St. Louis City Hosp., 1962-71; pres. St. Louis Orthopedic Inst., 1965—; pres. med. staff St. Joseph Hosp., St. Louis, 1982-83; trustee St. Joseph Hosp., 1981-84. Contbr. article profl. jours. Served to maj. U.S. Army, 1967-69. Fellow Am. Acad. Orthopedic Surgery, ACS (admissions com. 1982—); mem. AMA, Mo. Orthopedic Soc. (v.p. 1985-86, pres. 1986-87), St. Louis Metro. Med. Soc. (counselor 1983-85), Vanderbilt Orthopedic Soc. (pres. 1981-82), Tenn. Soc. of St. Louis. Republican. Presbyterian. Club: Bellerive Country. Avocations: music, sports. Home: 177 Ladue Oaks Ct Saint Louis MO 63141-8128

LUTHER, WILLIAM P., congressman; b. Fergus Falls, Minn., June 27, 1945; s. Leonard and Eleanor L.; m. Darlene Luther, Dec. 16, 1967; children: Alexander, Alicia. BS in Elec. Engring. with high distinction, U. Minn., 1967; JD cum laude, U. Minn. Law Sch., 1970. Judicial clerkship 8th cir. U.S. Ct. Appeals, 1970-71; atty. Dorsey & Whitney Law Firm, Mpls., 1971-74, William P. Luther Law Office, Mpls., 1974-83; founder, sr. ptnr. Luther, Ballentin & Carruthers Law Firm, Mpls., 1983-92; state sen. 47th dist. State of Minn. 1977-94, asst. maj. leader, 1983-94; rep. 6th dist. U.S. House of Reps., 1995—. Home: 6375 St. Croix Trail N # 147 Stillwater MN 55082 Office: US House Reps 1419 Longworth HOB Washington DC 20515 also: 1811 Weir Dr Ste 150 Woodbury MN 55125*

LUTHEY, GRAYDON DEAN, JR., lawyer; b. Topeka, Sept. 18, 1955; s. Graydon Dean Sr. and S. Anne (Murphy) L.; m. Deborah Denise McCullough, May 26, 1979; children: Sarah Elizabeth, Katherine Alexandra. BA in Letters with highest honors, U. Okla., 1976, JD, 1979; Fellow in The-

ology, Oxford (Eng.) U., 1976. Bar: Okla. 1979, U.S. Ct. Appeals (10th cir.) 1979, U.S. Dist. Ct. (no. we. and ea. dists.) Okla. 1980, U.S. Supreme Ct. 1982. Assoc. Jones, Givens, Gotcher, Bogan & Hilborne, Tulsa, 1979-84, ptnr., 1984-92, also bd. dirs.; ptnr. Hall, Estill, Hardwick, Gable, Golden & Nelson, Tulsa, 1992—, also bd. dirs.; adj. assoc. prof. U. Tulsa, 1985-87, adj. prof., 1987—; vis. fellow in theology Keble Coll., Oxford (Eng.) U., 1976; presiding judge Okla. Temporary Ct. Appeals, 1992-93; mem. Okla. Supreme Ct. Rules Com., 1992—. bd. dirs. Tulsa Ballet, 1987—; chmn. Tulsa Pub. facilities Authority, 1990-93; trustee Episcopal Theol. Sem. of S.W., 1991—, exec. com., 1992—; vice chmn. Univ. Hosps. Authority, 1993-94, chmn. 1994—. Nat. Merit scholar U. Okla., 1973. Fellow Am. Bar Found.; mem. ABA, Okla. Bar Assn. (chmn. continuing legal edn. com. 1989-91), Tulsa County Bar Assn. (bd. dirs. 1983-89, Disting. Svc. award 1988), Am. Inns of Ct. (barrister), Summit Club, Golf Club Okla., Beta Theta Pi, Phi Beta Kappa, Omicron Delta Kappa. Office: Hall Estill Hardwick Gable Golden & Nelson 320 S Boston Ste 400 Tulsa OK 74103-3708

LUTHI, WILFRIED T., manufacturing executive; b. 1920. With Alltransport, Inc., N.Y.C., 1946-54, R.G. Hobelman & Co., Inc., Balt., 1954-60; with Schenker Internat. Inc., Jersey City, N.J., 1960-90, chmn., sec., 1990—. Office: Schenker International Inc 10 Exchange Pl 1500 Jersey City NJ 07302

LUTHRINGSHAUSER, DANIEL RENE, manufacturing company executive; b. Fontainebleau, France, July 23, 1935; came to U.S., 1937; s. Ernest Henri and Jeanne (Guerville) L.; m. Carol King; children: Mark Ernest, Heidi Elizabeth. BS, NYU, 1956, MBA, 1970. With exec. tng. program, internat. pub. relations Merck & Co. Inc., Rahway, N.J. and N.Y.C., 1962-65; dep. mktg. dir. Merck Sharp & Dohme Internat., Brussels, 1965-66; mktg. service dir. Paris, 1966-69; gen. mgr. Merck Sharp & Dohme/Chibret, Paris, 1970-74; v.p. mktg. Merrell (France), Paris, 1974-78; v.p. gen. mgr. Revlon Devel. Corp., Paris, 1978-82, Medtronic Europe, Paris, Africa, Middle East, 1982-86; v.p. internat. Medtronic Inc., Mpls., 1986—; bd. dirs. Medtronic Found., Mpls., 1986-91; chmn. Internat. Assn. of Prosthesis Mfrs., Paris, 1983-85. Bd. dirs. Am. Hosp. Paris, 1983-86, Minn. Internat. Ctr., 1990—; mem. Am. Club Paris, 1970-80, Medtronic Found., Mpls., 1986-91. Served to capt. USAF, 1956-62. Recipient Gold medal Am. Mktg. Assn., 1956. Club: Ausable (Keene Valley, N.Y.). Avocations: gardening, golf, squash, skiing. Home: 480 Peavey Rd Wayzata MN 55391-1529 Office: Medtronic Inc 7000 Central Ave NE Minneapolis MN 55432-3576

LUTHY, RICHARD GODFREY, environmental engineering educator; b. June 11, 1945; s. Robert Godfrey Luthy and Marian Ruth (Ireland) Haines; m. Mary Frances Sullivan, Nov. 22, 1967; children: Matthew Robert, Mara Catherine, Jessica Bethlin. BSChemE, U. Calif., Berkeley, 1967; MS in Ocean Engring., U. Hawaii, 1969; MSCE, U. Calif., Berkeley, 1974, PhDCE, 1976. Registered profl. engr., Pa.; diplomate Am. Acad. Environ. Engrs. Rsch. asst. dept. civil engring. U. Hawaii, Honolulu, 1968-69; rsch. asst. div. and hydraulic engring. U. Calif., Berkeley, 1973-75; asst. prof. civil engring. Carnegie Mellon U., Pitts., 1975-80, assoc. prof., 1980-83, prof., 1983—; assoc. dean Carnegie Inst. Tech., 1986-89, head dept. civil and environ. engring., 1989—; cons. sci. adv. bd. U.S. EPA, 1983—, Bioremediation Action Com., 1990-92; cons. U.S. Dept. Energy, 1978—, various pvt. industries; del. water sci. and tech. bd. NAE, Washington and Beijing, 1988; mem. tech. adv. bd. Remediation Techs., Inc., Concord, Mass., 1989, Fostin Capital, Pitts., 1991-94, Balt. Gas & Elec., 1992—. Contbr. articles to tech. and sci. jours. Chmn. Conf. on Fundamental Rsch. Directions in Environ. Engring, Washington, 1988. Lt. C.E. Corps, USN, 1969-72. Recipient George Tallman Ladd award Carnegie Inst. Tech., 1977. Mem. ASCE (Pitts. sect. Prof. of Yr. award 1987), Assn. Environ. Engring Profs. (pres. 1987-88, Nalco award 1978, 82, Engring. Sci. award 1988), Water Pollution Control Fedn. (rsch. com. 1982-86, awards com. 1981-84, 89-94, std. methods com. 1977—, groundwater com. 1989-90, editor jour. 1989-92, Eddy medal 1980), Internat. Assn. on Water Quality (Founders award U.S. Nat. Com. 1986, 93, orgnl. com. 16th Biennial Conf. Washington 1992), Am. Chem. Soc. (divsn. environ. chemistry, mem. editorial adv. bd. Environ. Sci. Tech. 1992—, chair Gordon Rsch. Conf. Environ. Scis. 1994—). Presbyterian. Home: 620 S Linden Ave Pittsburgh PA 15208-2813 Office: Carnegie Mellon U Dept Civil & Environ Engrin Pittsburgh PA 15213-3890

LUTJEHARMS, JOSEPH EARL, commissioner; b. Woodruff, Kans., Oct. 30, 1933; m. Gail G. Burton, Nov. 1954 (div. Nov. 1976); children—Gary, Lisa; m. Mary C. Seiboldt, Sept. 1979; stepchildren—Jay Seiboldt, Sarah Seiboldt, Eric Seiboldt. A.B., Nebr. State Coll., 1958; Ed.M., U. Nebr. Lincoln, 1960; Ed.D., U. No. Colo., 1968. Grad. asst. U. No. Colo., Greeley, 1967-68; asst. supt. instrn. West Valley Sch. Dist., Yakima, Wash., 1968-69; asst. supt. for bus. Laramie County Dist. 1, Cheyenne, Wyo., 1969-70; supt. of schs. Laramie County Dist. 1, Cheyenne, 1970-77; dep. commr. edn. Nebr. Dept. Edn., Lincoln, 1977-83, commr. edn., 1983—; vis. prof. U. Wyo. Grad. Sch., Laramie, 1974, U. No. Colo. Grad. Sch., Greeley, 1974-77, U. Nebr. Tchrs. Coll., Lincoln, 1977-82; cons. Am. Internat. Sch., Kabul, Afghanistan, 1971. Author articles, papers in field. Mem. Nebr. Ednl. TV Commn., Lincoln, 1983—; mem. State Coll. Bd. Trustees, 1983—. Served with U.S. Army, 1953-55. Mem. Am. Assn. Sch. Adminstrs., Nebr. Council Sch. Adminstrs., Phi Delta Kappa. Home: 1820 Memorial Dr Lincoln NE 68502-3249 Office: Edn Dept 301 Centennial Mall S Lincoln NE 68509

LUTKEN, DONALD C., utility company executive; b. Jackson, Miss., Mar. 26, 1924; s. Peter Koch and Erma (Curry) L.; m. Melissa Turner, June 11, 1946; children: Melissa (Mrs. Hugo Newcomb, Jr.), Isabel Poteat (Mrs. W.L. Eggart), Donald C., Edwin Poteat. BS, U.S. Naval Acad., 1946. With Miss. Power & Light Co., Jackson, 1949—, exec. v.p. ops., 1969-70, pres., 1970—, chief exec. officer, 1971—, chmn., 1984-89, chmn. emeritus, 1989, also bd. dirs.; v.p. Mid. South Energy, Inc.; bd. dirs. Unifirst Fed. Savs. and Loan Assn., Lamar Life Corp.; Miss. chmn. payroll U.S. Savs. Bond div. Treasury Dept. Mem. exec. bd. Andrew Jackson council Boy Scouts Am., adv. bd. S.E. region Area IV; trustee Belhaven Coll., Mary Baldwin Coll., So. Research Inst., Miss. Found. Ind. Colls.; past deacon Jackson Presbyn. Ch.; bd. dirs. Cen. Miss. Growth Found., Jackson State U. Devel. Found. Served with USNR, 1946-49. Mem. Jackson C. of C., Jackson Symphony League, Newcomen Soc., Miss. State U. Alumni Found., Nat. Assn. Electric Cos., Miss. Soc. Profl. Engrs., ASME, IEEE, Edison Electric Inst., Miss. Mfrs. Assn., Miss. Econ. Assn., Miss. Hist. Soc. Clubs: Jackson Country, Univ., Capital City Petroleum (Jackson). Lodge: Rotary. Home: Rte 2 RR 2 Box 250 Jackson MS 39209-9205 Office: Miss Power & Light Co PO Box 1640 Jackson MS 39215-1640

LUTLEY, JOHN H., precious metals company executive; b. Chefoo, China, Feb. 10, 1935; came to U.S., 1978; s. Albert French and Martha Davis (Bullitt) L.; m. Mary Heather Maingot, July 18, 1959; children: Elizabeth, Jennifer, Richard. B.A. in Metallurgy, Cambridge U., 1958. With Johnson Matthey Group, Malvern, Pa., Eng., Can., 1958-84; owner, pres. Klein & Saks, Inc., Washington, 1984—; pres. Gold Inst.; exec. dir. Silver Inst. Office: Klein & Saks Inc 1026 16th St NW Suite 101 Washington DC 20036

LUTRINGER, RICHARD EMIL, lawyer; b. N.Y.C., Feb. 4, 1943; s. Emil Vincent Lutringer and Alice Rich Danser; m. Dagmar Bonitz, May 1, 1970 (div. 1980); m. Clarinda Higgins, Oct. 11, 1980; children: Emily, Eric. AB, Coll. of William and Mary, 1964; JD, Cornell U., 1967; M.Comparative Law, U. Chgo., 1969. Bar: D.C. 1967, N.Y. 1972, U.S. Tax Ct. (so. dist.) N.Y. 1972. Assoc. Whitman & Ransom, N.Y.C., 1971-80, ptnr., 1980-94; ptnr. Morgan, Lewis & Bockius, N.Y.C., 1994—. Vice pres. N.Y.-N.J. Trail Conf., N.Y.C., 1976-80. Mem. ABA, Internat. Bar Assn., Assn. of Bar of City of N.Y. (chmn. com. fgn. and comparative law 1990-93). Am. Fgn. Law Assn. (pres. 1989-93, treas. 1986-89), European-Am. C. of C. (vice chair trade com. 1992—). Avocations: sailing, hiking, skiing. Home: 2 Owenoke Park Westport CT 06880-6851 Office: Morgan Lewis & Bockius 101 Park Ave New York NY 10178-0060

LUTTER, PAUL ALLEN, lawyer; b. Chgo., Feb. 28, 1946; s. Herbert W. and Lois (Muller) L. BA, Carleton Coll., 1968; JD, Yale U., 1971. Bar: Ill. 1971, U.S. Tax Ct. 1986. Assoc. Ross & Hardies, Chgo., 1971-77, ptnr., 1978—. Co-author: Illinois Estate Administration. 1993. Dir. Howard Brown Health Ctr. Mem. ABA, Chgo. Bar Assn. Home: 2214 N Magnolia Ave Chicago IL 60614-3104 Office: Ross & Hardies 150 N Michigan Ave Ste 2500 Chicago IL 60601-7567

LUTTIG, J. MICHAEL, federal judge; b. 1954. BA, Washington and Lee U., 1976; JD, U. Va., 1981. Asst. counsel The White House, 1981-82; law clk. to Judge Antonin Scalia U.S. Ct. of Appeals D.C. Cir., 1982-83; law clerk to chief justice Warren Burger Supreme Ct. of U.S. 1983-84, spl. asst. to chief justice Warren Burger, 1984-85; assoc. Davis Polk & Wardwell, 1985-89; prin. dep. asst. atty. gen., office of legal counsel U.S. Dept. of Justice, 1989-90, asst. atty. gen., office of legal counsel, counselor to atty. gen., 1990-91; judge U.S. Cir. Ct. (4th cir.), McLean, Va., 1991—. Mem. Nat. Adv. Com. of Lawyers for Bush, 1988, Lawyers for Bush Com., 1988. Mem. ABA, Va. Bar Assn., D.C. Bar Assn. Office: Circuit Ct 8280 Greensboro Dr Ste 780 Mc Lean VA 22102-3807

LUTTINGER, JOAQUIN MAZDAK, retired physics educator, researcher; b. N.Y.C., Dec. 2, 1923; s. Paul and Shirley Luttinger; m. Abigail Thomas, Oct. 13, 1942 (div.); 1 child, Catherine Thomas. SB, MIT, 1944, PhD, 1947. Asst. prof. physics U. Wis., 1950-52; mem. Inst. Advanced Study, 1952-53; assoc. prof. physics U. Mich., Ann Arbor, 1953-57; NRC sr. postdoctoral fellow Ecole Normale Supérieure, Paris, 1957-58; prof. physics U. Pa., 1958-60; prof. physics Columbia U., 1960-93, chmn. dept., 1977-80; ret., 1993; exchange prof., Moscow, 1962. Contbr. over 80 articles to profl. jours. Swiss Am. Exchange fellow, 1947-48, Nat. Research fellow, 1948-49, Sr. Postdoctoral fellow Rockefeller U., 1968, Guggenheim fellow Rockefeller U., 1975-76. Mem. Nat. Acad. Scis., Am. Acad. Arts and Scis. Office: Columbia Univ Dept of Physics 826 Pupin Lab New York NY 10027

LUTTNER, EDWARD F., career management consultant; b. Cleve., Feb. 16, 1942; s. John J. and Angela (Haberbosch) L.; m. Nancy E., July 15, 1977; children: Amy, Mark. BA, Loyola U., 1966, MDiv, 1974; MA, U. Detroit, 1970. Cert. NASD. Dir. standards-devel. Bernard Haldane Assocs., Boston, Internat. Career Consulting Corp., Waltham, Mass.; v.p. career mgmt. svcs. Bernard Haldane Assocs., Cleve.; dir. profl. svcs. Right Assocs., Phila.; pres. Elby Career Group, Inc., Cleve. V.p Rotary, Fairview Park, 1988-89. Mem. AACD, Nat. Career Devel. Assn.

LUTTS, RALPH HERBERT, museum administrator, scholar, educator; b. Quincy, Mass., Jan. 7, 1944; s. Herbert Warren Lutts and Jean May (MacKenzie) Easton. AB in Biology, Trinity U., San Antonio, 1967; EdD, U. Mass., 1978. Curator, educator Mus. Sci., Boston, 1967-73; naturalist Hampshire Coll., Amherst, Mass., 1973-80; natural sci. faculty Hampshire Coll., 1976-84; dir. Blue Hills Trailside Mus., Mass. Audubon Soc., Milton, 1980-90; dir. edn. Va. Mus. Natural History, Martinsville, 1990-92, dir. outreach div., 1992-94, rsch. assoc., 1994—; assoc.faculty Goddard Coll., Plainfield, Vt., 1995—; pres. Alliance for Environ. Edn. 1988-89; founding pres. New Eng. Environ. Edn. Alliance, 1980-84; assoc. Ctr. for Animals and Pub. Policy, Tufts U. Sch. Vet. Medicine, North Grafton, Mass., 1989-90; dept. dir. mid-atlantic region Global Network of Environ. Edn. Ctrs., 1993—, bd. dirs, 1994—. Author: The Nature Fakers: Wildlife, Science and Sentiment, 1990; founding editor New Eng. Jour. Environ. Edn., 1985-88; contbr. articles to profl. jours. Pres. Hitchcock Ctr. for Environ., Amherst, Mass., 1977-79; treas. Mass. Environ. Edn. Soc., 1982-84; mem. Blue Hills citizens' adv. com. Met. Dist. Commn., 1988-89, mgmt. adv. com., 1989-90; mem. sec.'s adv. group on environ. edn. Mass. Exec. Office for Environ. Affairs, 1989-90. Recipient New Eng. Regional awrd for achievement New Eng. Environ. Edn. Alliance, 1989. Mem. AAAS, Am. Soc. Environ. History, Assn. for the Study of Lit. and Environ., Forest History Soc. (Ralph W. Hidy award 1993), N.Am. Assn. Environ. Edn., Am. Nature Study Soc. (bd. dirs. 1990—, pres. 1995—), Authors Guild, Popular Culture Assn. (area chair 1993—), Nat. Writers Union, Martinsville Rotary Club (Paul Harris fellow). Avocations: environ. history, natural history, woodworking, book collecting.

LUTTWAK, EDWARD NICOLAE, policy and business consultant; writer; b. Arad, Transylvania, Nov. 4, 1942; came to U.S., 1972, naturalized, 1981; s. Josif Menashe and Clara (Baruch) L.; m. Dalya Iaari, Dec. 14, 1970; children: Yael Rachel, Joseph Emmanuel. B.Sc. with honors, London Sch. Econs., 1964; Ph.D. (Univ. fellow), Johns Hopkins U., 1975. Vis. prof. polit. sci. Johns Hopkins U., 1973-78; sr. fellow Georgetown U. Center Strategic and Internat. Studies, 1978-87, research prof. internat. security affairs, 1978-82, Burke chair in strategy, 1987—; dir. geo-econs., 1991-94, sr. fellow, 1994—; cons. Office of Sec. of Def., Nat. Security Coun. and Dept. State; cons. Office of Sec. of Def., Nat. Security Coun., Dept. of Def. Army, Navy and U.S. Air Force, Fgn. (allied) Govs. and U.S., overseas bus. entities. Author: Coup d'Etat, 19 edits. including 12 for lang. translations, 1968-79, Dictionary of Modern War, 1971 (also Spanish edit.), The Political Uses of Sea Power, 1975 (also Japanese edit.), The Israeli Army, 1975, 85, (also Chinese edit.), The Grand Strategy of the Roman Empire, 1976 (also Hebrew, Italian and French edits.), Strategy and Politics: Collected Essays, 1980, The Grand Strategy of the Soviet Union, 1983 (also Italian and French edits.),The Pentagon and the Art of War: The Question of Military Reform, 1985 (also Italian, Japanese and Korean edits.), Strategy and History: Collected Essays, On the Meaning of Victory, 1986 (also Italian edit.), Strategy: The Logic of War and Peace, 1987 (also Chinese, French and Italian edits.), (with Stuart Koehl) Dictionary of Modern War, 1991 (also Italian edit.), The Endangered American Dream, 1993 (also French, Italian, German and Japanese edits.). Republican. Jewish. Office: CSIS 1800 K St NW Washington DC 20006-2200

LUTWAK, LEO, physician, educator; b. N.Y.C., Mar. 27, 1928; s. Herman and Charlotte (Safirstein) L.; m. Cecile Kroshinsky, Dec. 23, 1950 (dec. 1976); children: Mark Steven, Diane Ellen, Paul Jonathan, Jean Rachel, Robert Ira; m. Victoria Jones, 1976; children: David Morris, Aviva Ruth. B.S., City Coll. N.Y., 1945; M.S., U. Wis., 1946; Ph.D., U. Mich., 1950; M.D., Yale U., 1956. Biochemist Brookhaven Nat. Lab., 1950-52; dept. surgery Yale, 1952-56; intern medicine Duke Hosp., 1956-57; clin. assoc. NIH, 1957-59, sr. investigator, 1960-63; resident medicine USPHS Hosp., San Francisco, 1959-60; asst. clin. prof. medicine Georgetown U., 1961-63; Jamison prof. clin. nutrition, prof. univ. health services, also dir. clin. nutrition unit Cornell U., 1963-72; prof. medicine U. Calif. at Los Angeles Med. Sch.; also prof. nutrition Sch. Pub. Health, 1972-76; chief sect. endocrinology, nutrition and metabolism VA Hosp., Sepulveda, Calif., 1972-76; chmn. dept. medicine Akron (Ohio) City Hosp., 1976-78; prof. medicine, prof. and program dir. nutritional scis. NE Ohio Univs. Coll. Medicine, 1976-84; med. officer Food and Drug Adminstrn., 1992—; adj. prof. Akron U., 1977-84; NRC sr. research fellow Ames Research Lab., NASA, Calif., 1970-71; vis. prof. medicine Stanford Med. Sch., 1970-71; spl. research endocrinology, bone physiology, obesity; cons. adv. panel NIH, 1964-68, Gerontol. Soc., 1966; cons. NASA, 1964—, Tompkins County Hosp., 1963-72. Author articles in field. Pres. Ithaca Assn. Jewish Studies, 1964. Fellow Am. Inst. Chemists, Am. Coll. Nutrition, A.C.P.; mem. Soc. Exptl. Biology and Medicine, AAAS, Am. Fedn. Clin. Research, Am. Bd. Nutrition (dir., v.p. 1980-81, pres. 1981-82), Am. Inst. Nutrition, Am. Physiol. Soc., Am. Diabetes Assn., Ala. Diabetes Assn. (bd. dirs. 1988-89), Akron Diabetes Assn. (dir. 1976-83), Am. Soc. Clin. Nutrition, Pan Am. Med. Assn., Western Soc. Clin. Research, Endocrine Soc., N.Y. Acad. Scis., Phi Beta Kappa, Sigma Xi, Phi Lambda Upsilon. Office: FDA Office Drug Evaluation Divsn M&End prod 5600 Fishers Ln Rockville MD 20857-0001

LUTZ, CARL FREIHEIT, academic administrator; b. Lansing, Mich., Dec. 8, 1934; s. Paul and Edmunda (Freiheit) L.; m. Vivian Ericson; m. Aug. 18, 1959; children—Timothy Paul, Elizabeth. B.S. in Metallurgy, Mich. State U., 1956; M.S., Carnegie Inst. Tech., 1957, Ph.D., 1959; postgrad. student, Max Planck Inst. Physics, 1959-60. Asst. prof. USAF Acad., 1960-63; sr. engr. Rockwell-Standard Corp., Detroit, 1963-66, Kaiser Aluminum Co., Spokane, 1966-67; v.p., dean engring. S.D. Sch. Mines and Tech., Rapid City, 1967-74; dep. commr. higher edn. State of Ind., Indpls., 1974-79; chancellor Ivy Tech. State Coll., South Bend and others, 1979—. Served with USAF, 1960-63. Mem. Am. Soc. Engring. Edn., Am. Inst. Mining, Metall. and Petroleum Engrs., Am. Soc. Metals, Soc. Research Adminstrs., Sigma Xi, Delta Sigma Phi.

LUTZ, CHRIS P., research physicist. Rsch. scientist IBM Almaden Rsch. Ctr., San Jose, Calif. Recipient Newcomb Cleveland prize AAAS, 1993-94. Office: IBM Almaden Rsch Ctr 650 Harry Dr San Jose CA 95120-6099*

LUTZ, FRANCIS CHARLES, university dean, civil engineering educator; b. Pottsville, Pa., Apr. 5, 1944; s. Charles Henry and Pauline Anna (Weislo) L.; m. Evelyn Florence Zommer, Apr. 29, 1972; 1 child, Stephanie Diane. BSCE, N.J. Inst. Tech., 1966; MSCE, NYU, 1967, PhD, 1971. Assoc. M. Disko Assocs., West Orange, N.J., 1970-72; asst. prof. civil engring. Worcester Poly. Inst., Mass., 1972-76; prof., assoc. dean Worcester Poly. Inst., 1980-90, dean undergrad. studies, 1990—; dir. Washington Project Ctr., 1974-88; cons. Council on Environ. Quality, Washington, 1974-75; reviewer NSF. Co-editor: Studies in Science, Technology and Culture, Worcester Poly. Inst.; contbr. articles to profl. jours. Trustee Worcester Ctr. for Crafts, 1992—; mem. Boston Fed. Exec. Bd., 1972-74, Cen. Mass. Regional Planning Commn., Worcester, 1975-77. Am. Council on Edn. fellow, 1988-89; honors scholar NYU. Mem. ASCE, Am. Soc. Engring. Edn., Boynton Assn. (pres. 1982, 83), Sigma Xi, Chi Epsilon. Office: Worcester Poly Inst 100 Institute Rd Worcester MA 01609-2247

LUTZ, FRANK WENZEL, education administration educator; b. St. Louis, Sept. 24, 1928; s. Vincent J. and Helen M. (Scrivens) L.; m. Susan Virginia Bleikamp, July 12, 1958; children: Paul E., Andrew C., Lynn S. AA, Harris Tchrs. Coll., 1948; BS, Washington U., 1950, MS, 1954, EdD, 1962. Instr. Washington U., St. Louis, 1961-62; from asst. to assoc. prof. NYU, N.Y.C., 1964-68; dir. div. policy studies Pa. State U., State College, 1968-73; prof. edn. adminstrn. Pa. State U., 1974-80; dean Sch. Edn. Eastern Ill. U., 1981-82, asst. to v.p., 1982-83; prof., dir. Ctr. Policy Studies East Tex. State U., Commerce, Tex., 1983-92, prof. edn. adminstrn., 1991-92; lectr. Nova S.W. U., 1991—; mem., pres. Pattonville (Mo.) Sch. Bd., 1960-62; mem. adv. com. Opportunities Acad. Mgmt. Tng., Phila., 1975-90. Author seven books, numerous book chpts. in field; contbr. over 100 articles to profl. jours. Deacon 1st Presbyn. Ch., Commerce, Tex., 1989-91. Doctoral fellow Washington U., 1960-61; grantee U.S. Office Edn., OEO. Mem. Am. Ednl. Rsch. Assn. (sect. Div. LA 1970-72, dir. rsch. pre-session 1969, program com. 1970), Commerce Rotary (pres. 1991-92, chair internat. svc. 1994—), Phi Delta Kappa (life, pres. Washingto U. chpt. 1960, 1st v.p. East Tex. State U. chpt. 1985). Avocations: appaloosa horses, opera, classical music. Home: PO Box 51 Nederland CO 80466-0051 Office: East Tex State U Edn North Building Rm 214 Commerce TX 75428

LUTZ, JAMES GURNEY, lawyer; b. Cin., Sept. 18, 1933; s. Arthur Harold and Frances (Gurney) L.; children: Monica, Susan. JD, U. Cin. 1960. Bar: Ohio 1960, U.S. Dist. Ct. (so. dist.) Ohio 1961, U.S. Ct. Appeals (6th cir.) 1961, U.S. Tax Ct. 1975, U.S. Supreme Ct. 1975. Ptnr. Barbour, Kinpel & Allen, Cin., 1960-68; chief counsel E.C. Industries Inc., Cin., 1968-71; sr. ptnr. Lutz Boster & Cornetet, Cin., 1971—; pres., mem. bd. dirs. Motivation Dynamics Inc., Cin., 1978-85. Advisor, staff Hamilton County Vocat. Schs., Cin., 1968; advisor U. Cin. Coll., 1970-75; mem. adv. counsel Wyoming (Ohio) Bd. Edn., 1972-75; mem. bd. Ohio Pvt. Industry Coun., Columbus, 1975; gen. counsel S.W. Ohio Autistic Assn., Cin., 1970-84. Mem. ABA, Am. Trial Lawyers Assn., Ohio State Bar Assn., Cin. Bar Assn. Avocations: psychology, computer science. Office: Lutz Boster & Cornetet 130 Tri County Pky Cincinnati OH 45246

LUTZ, JOHN SHAFROTH, lawyer; b. San Francisco, Sept. 10, 1943; s. Frederick Henry and Helena Morrison (Shafroth) L.; m. Elizabeth Boschen, Dec. 14, 1968; children: John Shafroth, Victoria. BA, Brown U., 1965; JD, U. Denver, 1971. Bar: Colo. 1971, U.S. Dist. Ct. Colo. 1971, U.S. Ct. Appeals (2d cir.) 1975, D.C. 1976, U.S. Supreme Ct. 1976, U.S. Dist. Ct. (so. dist.) N.Y. 1977, U.S. Tax Ct. 1977, U.S. Ct. Appeals (10th cir.) 1979, N.Y. 1984, U.S. Ct. Appeals (9th cir.) 1990, U.S. Dist. Ct. (no. dist.) Calif. 1993. Trial atty. Denver regional office U.S. SEC, 1971-74; spl. atty. organized crime, racketeering sect. U.S. Dept. Justice, So. Dist. N.Y., 1976-77; atty. Kelly, Stansfield and O'Donnell, Denver, 1977-78; gen. counsel Boettcher & Co., Denver, 1978-87, Kelly, Stansfield and O'Donnel, Denver, 1987; spl. counsel, 1987-88, ptnr., 1988-93; of counsel LeBoeuf, Lamb, Greene and Mac Rae, 1993-94, ptnr. 1995—; allied mem. N.Y. Stock Exch., 1978-87; speaker on broker, dealer, securities law and arbitration issues to various profl. orgns. Contbr. articles to profl. jours. Bd. dirs. Cherry Creek Improvement Assn., 1980-84, Spalding Rehab. Hosp., 1986-89; chmn., vice-chmn. securities sub sect. Bus. Law Sect. of Colo. Bar, 1990, chmn., 1990-91. Lt. (j.g.), USNR, 1965-67. Mem. ABA, Colo. Bar Assn., Denver Bar Assn., Am. Law Inst., Securities Industry Assn. (state regulations com. 1982-86), Nat. Assn. Securities Dealers, Inc. (nat. arbitration com. 1987-91), St. Nicholas Soc. N.Y.C., Denver Law Club, Denver Country Club, Denver Athletic Club (dir. 1990-93), Rocky Mountain Brown Club (founder, past pres.), Racquet and Tennis Club, Roxborough. Episcopalian. Office: LeBoeuf Lamb Greene & MacRae 633 17th St Ste 2800 Denver CO 80202-3628

LUTZ, JULIE HAYNES, astronomy and mathematics educator; b. Mt. Vernon, Ohio, Dec. 17, 1944; d. Willard Damon and Julia Awilda (Way) Haynes; m. Thomas Edward Lutz, July 8, 1967; children: Melissa, Elisa. BS, San Diego State U., 1965; MS, U. Ill., 1968, PhD, 1971. Asst. prof. astronomy Wash. State U., Pullman, 1972-78, asst. dean sci., 1978-79, assoc. prof., 1978-84, assoc. provost, 1981-82, prof., 1984—; chair math. and astronomy dept., 1992—; rsch. fellow Univ. Coll. London, England, 1976-77, 82-83; vis. resident astronomer Cerro Tololo Inter-Am. Obs., 1988-89; dir. div. astron. scis. NSF, 1990-92. Contbr. on astron. research to profl. jours. Fellow AAAS (mem. com. 1982-85, mem. nominating com. 1992—, chair sect. D 1993—), Royal Astron. Soc.; mem. Am. Astron. Soc. (chair publs. bd. 1986-88), Astron. Soc. Pacific (bd. dirs. 1988—, v.p. 1989, pres. 1990-92), Internat. Astron. Union. Avocations: cooking, backpacking, fishing. Home: 1200 NE Mcgee St Pullman WA 99163-3818 Office: Wash State U Program in Astronomy Pullman WA 99164-3113

LUTZ, KARL EVAN, lawyer; b. Dearborn, Mich., Dec. 18, 1949; s. Wallace G. and Marguerite E. (Smith) L.; m. Jeanne Daniel, June 30, 1973; children: Daniel Karl, Charles Littlefield, Kelsey Eldridge. BA, Yale U., 1972; JD, U. Mich., 1975. Bar: Ill. 1975, N.Y. 1990. Assoc. Kirkland & Ellis, Chgo., 1975-81, ptnr., 1981—. Office: Kirkland & Ellis 200 E Randolph Dr Chicago IL 60601-6401

LUTZ, MATTHEW CHARLES, geologist, oil company executive; b. Bunkie, La., Mar. 28, 1934; s. John Matthew and Maxie Mae (Andrus) L.; m. Patricia Dawnn Feazel, Apr. 11, 1953; children: Matt, Jr., Cyndy, Tracey, Clay. BS, U. Southwestern La., 1956. Various geol. profl. positions Tidewater-Getty Oil Co., 1956-71; asst. dist. geologist Getty Oil Co., Houston, 1971-73, dist. geologist, Midland, Tex., 1973-78, central div. geologist, Tulsa, 1978-80, offshore dist. exploration mgr., Houston, 1980, so. div. exploration mgr., Houston, 1980-82, gen. mgr. offshore exploration and prodn., Houston, 1982-83, exploration mgr. so. div., Houston, 1983-84; sr. v.p. exploration Enserch Exploration Inc., Dallas, 1984-92, also dir.; vice chmn. & bus. devel. mgr. Hunter Resources, Inc., Irving, Tex., 1993—, also bd. dirs.; bd. dirs. Enserch Internat. Exploration Inc., Dallas, Enserch Processing Inc., Dallas, 1984-92. Mem. Am. Assn. Petroleum Geologists, Houston Geol. Soc., Dallas Geol. Soc., Mid-Continent Oil Gas Assn., Am. Petroleum Inst., Independent Petroleum Assn. Am. Republican. Baptist. Clubs: Dallas Petroleum, Las Colinas Sports. Avocations: travel, golf, hunting. Office: Hunter Resources Inc Ste 1200 600 East Las Colinas Blvd Irving TX 75039

LUTZ, RAYMOND PRICE, industrial engineer, educator; b. Oak Park, Ill., Feb. 27, 1935; s. Raymond Price and Sibyl Elizabeth (Haralson) L.; m. Nancy Marie Cole, Aug. 23, 1958. BSME, U. N.Mex., 1958, MBA, 1962; PhD, Iowa State U., 1964. Registered profl. engr., N.Mex., Okla. With Sandia Corp., Albuquerque, summers 1958-63; instr. mech. engring. U. N.Mex., 1958-62; asst. to assoc. prof. indsl. engring. N.Mex. State U., 1964-68; prof. head indsl. engring. U. Okla., 1968-73; prof., acting dean U. Tex. Sch. Mgmt., Dallas, 1973-76, dean, 1976-78, exec. dean grad. studies and research, 1979-92, prof. sys. mgmt., 1992—; cons. Bell Telephone Labs., Tex. Instruments, Kennecott Corp., Bath Iron Works, City of Dallas, Oklahoma City; cons. U.S. Army, USAF, U.S. Dept. Transp., Los Angeles and Seattle public schs.; mem. shipbldg. productivity panel NRC. Editor: The Engring. Economist, 1973-77, Indsl. Mgmt., 1983-87. Pres., bd. dirs. United Cerebral Palsy, Dallas, 1978, treas. 1984-85; bd. dirs., treas. Amigos Bibliographic Network, Dallas, 1984-90; chmn., bd. dirs. S.W. Police Inst., Dallas, 1980—; v.p., bd. dirs. Santa Fe Opera, 1988-95; bd. dirs. Dallas Opera, 1989—. Fellow AAAS, Am. Inst. Indsl. Engrs. (v.p. industry & mgmt. divsns., trustee, dir. engring. economy divsn., systems engring. group); mem. Am. Soc. Engring. Edn. (chmn. engring. economy divsn., Eugene L.

LUTZ, ROBERT ANTHONY, automotive company executive; b. Zurich, Switzerland, Feb. 12, 1932; came to U.S., 1939; s. Robert H. and Marguerite (Schmid) L.; m. Betty D. Lutz, Dec. 12, 1956 (div. 1979); children: Jacqueline, Carolyn, Catherine, Alexandra; m. Heide Marie Schmid, Mar. 3, 1980 (div. Dec. 1992); m. Denise Ford, Apr. 17, 1994; 2 stepchildren. BS in Prodn. Mgmt., U. Calif., Berkeley, 1961, MBA in Mktg., 1962; LLD, Boston U., 1985. Research assoc., sr. analyst IMEDE, Lausanne, Switzerland, 1962-63; sr. analyst forward planning Gen. Motors Corp., N.Y.C., 1963-65; mgr. vehicle div. Paris, 1966-69; staff asst., mng. dir. Adam Opel, Russelsheim, Germany, 1965-66; asst. mgr. domestic sales Adam Opel, Russelsheim, Fed. Republic of Germany, 1969, dir. sales Vorstand, 1969-70; v.p. Vorstand BMW, Munich, 1972-74; gen. mgr. Ford of Germany, Cologne, Fed. Republic of Germany, 1974-76; v.p. truck ops Brentwood, Eng., 1976-77; pres. Ford of Europe, Brentwood, Eng, 1977-79, chmn., 1979-82; also bd. dirs. Brentwood, Eng.; exec. v.p. Ford Internat., Dearborn, Mich., 1982-84, Chrysler Motors Corp., Highland Park, Mich., from 1986; pres., COO Chrysler Corp., Highland Park, Mich. Adv. bd. Sch. Bus., U. Calif., Berkeley, 1979—. Served to capt. USMC, 1954-59, Okinawa, Japan, Korea. Named Alumnus of Yr., Sch. Bus., U. Calif., 1983; Kaiser Found. grantee 1962. Mem. UN Assn. (econ. policy coun.), Soc. Automotive Engrs. Republican. Avocations: skiing, motorcycling, bicycling, helicopter flying. Office: Chrysler Corp 12000 Chrysler Dr Detroit MI 48288

LUTZ, THEODORE COMPTON, newspaper publishing executive. V.p. circulation, bus. mgr. The Washington Post, D.C. Office: Washington Post Co 1150 15th St NW Washington DC 20005-2706*

LUTZ, WILLIAM LAN, lawyer; b. Chgo., May 18, 1944; s. Raymond Price and Sibyl (McCright) L.; m. Jeanne M. McAlister, Dec. 27, 1969; children: William Lan, David Price. B.S., U. Tex., 1965, J.D., 1969. Bar: Tex. 1969, N.Mex. 1970. Assoc. Martin, Lutz, Cresswell & Hubert and predecessor firms, Las Cruces, N.Mex., 1969-82; former U.S. atty. dist. N. Mex. U.S. Dept. Justice, Albuquerque, 1982-91; ptnr. Martin, Lutz & Brower, P.C., Las Cruces, N.Mex., 1991—. Mem. ABA, N.Mex. Bar Assn. Methodist. Office: Martin Lutz & Brower PO Drawer W 2100 N Main St Ste 3 Las Cruces NM 88001-1129

LUTZER, DAVID JOHN, college dean, mathematics professor; b. Sioux Falls, S.D., Mar. 27, 1943; s. Alois John and Marcia Estelle (Nelsen) L.; m. Victoria DeFilippo, Feb. 6, 1982; children: Jacob, Carl, Lisa, Joseph. BS, Creighton U., 1964; Diploma in Advanced Mathematics, Oxford U., England, 1966; PhD, U. Wash., 1970. Asst. prof. math. U. of Pitts., 1970-75, assoc. prof., 1975-78; vis. prof. Tex. Tech U., Lubbock, 1976-77, assoc. prof., 1977-78, prof., 1978-82; prof., chmn. dept. Miami U., Oxford, Ohio, 1982-87; dean, prof. Coll. William and Mary, Williamsburg, Va., 1987—. Contbr. articles to profl. jours. NSF fellow, 1964, 66; Rhodes scholar, 1964. Mem. Am. Math. Soc. (editor Proceedings 1976-83), Math. Assn. Am., Soc. Indsl. and Applied Math. Office: Coll William and Mary Sch Arts and Scis Williamsburg VA 23187

LUVISI, LEE, concert pianist; b. Louisville, Dec. 12, 1937; m. Nina Hussey, June 20, 1959; 1 son, Brian. Student, Curtis Inst. Music, 1952-57. Mem. faculty Curtis Inst. Music, 1957-62; artist in residence U. Louisville Sch. Music. Artist-mem., Chamber Music soc. Lincoln Ctr. Office: U Louisville Sch Of Music Louisville KY 40292 also: Michal Schmidt Artists Int 59 E 54th St New York NY 10022

LUX, JOHN H., corporate executive; b. Logansport, Ind., Feb. 3, 1918; s. Carl Harrison and Mary Emma (Dunn) L.; m. Betty F. Passow, Aug. 27, 1940; children: John Ernst, Courtney Rae; m. Bernice Weitzel Brown, 1965; m. Linda Merrill Brown, Mar. 2, 1978; children: Julia Elizabeth, Jenifyr Claire. B.S., Purdue U., 1939; Ph.D., 1942. Asst. dir. research and devel. The Neville Co., 1943-46; v.p., cons. Atomic Basic Chems., 1946-47; dir. research Witco Chem. Co., 1947-50; mgr. new product devel. Gen. Electric Co., 1950-52; v.p. Shea Chem. Co., 1952-55; pres., dir. Haveg Industries, Inc., Wilmington, Del., 1955-66, Haveg Corp., Tourlux Mgmt. Corp. (P.R.); chmn. bd. Hemisphere Products Corp. (P.R.), Reinhold Engring. & Plastics Co., Norwalk, Calif., Alan Super-Temperatures Wires Co.; pres. Ametek, Inc., 1966-69, chmn. bd., chief exec. officer, 1969-90, chmn. bd., 1990-93; ret., 1993. Mem. Am. Inst. Chem. Engrs., Am. Chem. Soc., Phi Lambda Upsilon. Club: Met.

LUX, MICHAEL SCOTT, federal government official; b. Lincoln, Nebr., May 13, 1960; s. John Elton and Ethel Carolyn (Carne) L.; m. Barbara Leigh Laur, Dec. 30, 1983. Exec. dir. Nebr. Project Energy Independence and Nebr. Energy Coalition, 1981-83; polit. dir. Iowa Citizen Action Network, 1983-84, exec. dir., 1984-87; nat. dep. polit. dir. Joe Biden for Pres. campaign, 1987; nat. cons. Paul Simon for Pres. campaign, 1987-88; founding ptnr., advisor Strategy Group, 1988-90, 90—; exec. v.p. Iowa Fedn. Labor, AFL-CIO, 1990-92; nat. constituency dir. Clinton-Gore Campaign, 1992; dir. Office of Constituency Outreach, Presdl. Transition, 1992-93; spl. asst. to Pres. for pub. liaison Washington, 1993—; VISTA vol. Small Farms Action Group, 1980-81; summer organizer Nebraskans for Peace, 1981. Vol. Iowa Dem. Party, Des Moines and Cedar Rapids, 1983-92; co-founder, bd. mem. Green Vote, Boston, 1989-92; bd. mem. Health Policy Corp. Iowa, Des Moines, 1990-92, Iowa Workers' Compensation Adv. Bd., Des Moines, 1990-92; exec. v.p. Iowa Citizen Action Network, Des Moines, 1990-92. Mem. Internat. Assn. Machinists and Aerospace Workers. Democrat. Methodist. Avocations: basketball, reading.

LUXEMBURG, WILHELMUS ANTHONIUS JOSEPHUS, mathematics educator; b. Delft, Netherlands, Apr. 11, 1929; s. Everardus H. and Digna (Van Kranendonk) L.; m. Geetruida Zappeij, Aug. 2, 1955; children—Ronald P., Jacqueline T. B.A., U. Leiden, Netherlands, 1950, M.A., 1953; Ph.D., Delft Inst. Tech., 1955. Postdoctoral fellow NRC Can., 1955-56; mem. faculty U. Toronto, 1956-58; faculty Calif. Inst. Tech., Pasadena, 1958—; prof. math. Calif. Inst. Tech., 1962—, exec. dir. for math., 1970-85; cons. Burroughs Corp., Pasadena, 1963-64. Mem. Am., Dutch math. socs., Math. Assn. Am., Canadian Math. Congress, Soc. for Indsl. and Applied Math., Royal Acad. Scis. Amsterdam (Humboldt award 1980). Research and publs. on theory of integration, spaces of measurable functions, ordinary differential equations, numerical analysis, topological linear spaces, Boolean algebras, axiomatic set theory, theory of Riesz spaces, non-standard analysis. Home: 817 S El Molino Ave Pasadena CA 91106-4411

LUXENBERG, MALCOLM NEUWAHL, ophthalmologist, educator; b. Philipsburg, Pa., July 29, 1935; s. Maurice and Henrietta (Neuwahl) L.; m. Sandra Diane Rosen, June 16, 1957; children: Steven Neuwahl, Cathy Ann. Student, Tulane U., 1953-56; M.D., U. Miami, Fla., 1960. Diplomate: Am. Bd. Ophthalmology. Intern Cin. Gen. Hosp., 1960-61; resident in neurology U. Vt. Affiliated Hosps., Burlington, 1961-63; resident in ophthalmology Bascom Palmer Eye Inst., U. Miami-Jackson Meml. Hosp., Miami, Fla., 1963-66; asst. prof. ophthalmology Coll. Medicine, U. Iowa, Iowa City, 1968-70; chief ophthalmology service VA Hosp., Iowa City, 1968-70; practice medicine specializing in ophthalmology West Palm Beach, Fla., 1970-72; clin. assist. prof. ophthalmology Bascom Palmer Eye Inst., Sch. Medicine, U. Miami, 1971-72; prof., chmn. dept. ophthalmology Med. Coll. Ga., Augusta, 1972—; cons. ophthalmology VA Hosp., Augusta, 1972—; Sr. surgeon USPHS, 1966-68; bd. dirs. Am. Bd. Ophthalmology. Recipient Outstanding Civilian Service Medal Dept. of Army, 1986. Mem. AMA, Am. Acad. Ophthalmology (hon. award 1986), Am. Ophthalmol. Soc., Assn. Univ. Profs. in Ophthalmology (pres. 1982-83), Ga. Soc. Ophthalmology, Med. Assn. Ga., Richmond County Med. Soc. Home: 512 Scotts Way Augusta GA 30909-3238 Office: Med Coll Ga Dept Ophthalmology Augusta GA 30912

LUXMOORE, ROBERT JOHN, soil and plant scientist; b. Adelaide, South Australia, Australia, Nov. 7, 1940; came to U.S.; 1966; s. John Alexander and Mary Elinor (Martin) L.; Annetta Paule Watson, Oct. 18, 1975. B Agrl.

Sci., U. Adelaide, 1962, B. Agrl. Sci. with honours, 1963; PhD, U. Calif., Riverside, 1969. Cert. profl. soil scientist. Agronomist Dept. Agr., Adelaide, 1963-66; rsch. assoc. U. Ill., Champaign-Urbana, 1969-70; soil physicist U. Calif., Riverside, 1970-71; rsch. assoc. U. Wis., Madison, 1971-72; rsch. scientist Oak Ridge (Tenn.) Nat. Lab., 1973-86, sr. rsch. scientist, 1986—; cons. Ctr. for Law and Social Policy, Washington, 1979; com. mem. NRC, Washington, 1989-90. Editor: Coupling of Carbon, Water and Nutrient, 1986; contbr. articles to profl. jours. and chpts. to books. Com. mem. Rural Abandoned Mines Program, Morgan County, Tenn., 1979-81; bd. dirs. Tenn. Citizens for Wilderness Planning, Oak Ridge, 1988-91. Recipient Tech. Achievement award Martin Marietta Energy Systems, 1987; Australian Cattle & Beef Rsch. scholar, 1962. Fellow AAAS, Soil Sci. Soc. Am. (tech. editor 1988-90, editor-in-chief 1991-93); mem. Internat. Union Forestry Rsch. Orgns. (chmn. working party 1983-90, coord. dep. subject group 1991—), Am. Geophys. Union. Home: 295 Solomon Hollow Rd Harriman TN 37748-9803 Office: Oak Ridge Nat Lab PO Box 2008 Oak Ridge TN 37831-6038

LUZA, RADOMIR VACLAV, historian, educator; b. Prague, Czechoslovakia, Oct. 17, 1922; s. Vojtech V. and Milada (Vecera) L.; m. Libuse Ladislava Podhrazska, Feb. 5, 1949; children: Radomir V., Sabrina. JuDr, U. Brno, Czechoslovakia, 1948; M.A., N.Y. U., 1958, Ph.D., 1959. Assoc. prof. modern European history La. State U., New Orleans, 1966-67; prof. history Tulane U., New Orleans, 1967—; scholar-in-residence Rockefeller Found., Bellagio Study Ctr., 1988; prof. gen. history Masaryk U., Brno, Czech Republic. Author: The Transfer of the Sudeten Germans, 1964, History of the International Socialist Youth Movement, 1970, (with V. Mamatey) A History of the Czechoslovak Republic, 1918-1948, 1973, Austro-German Relations in the Anschluss Era, 1975, Österreich und die grossdeutsche Idee in der NS-Zeit, 1977, Geschichte der Tschechoslowakischen Republik 1918-1948, 1980, A History of the Resistance in Austria, 1938-1945, 1984, Der Widerstand in Österreich, 1938-1945, 1985, La République Tchécoslovaque 1918-1948, 1987; editorial bd. East European Quar., Austrian History Yearbook, Contemporary Austrian Studies. With Czechoslovak Resistance, 1939-45. Recipient all Czechoslovak mil. decorations; prize Theodor Körner Found., Vienna, 1965; grantee Social Research Council, Am. Philos. Soc., Council Learned Socs., Fulbright Com., NEH. Mem. Am. Hist. Assn., Conf. on Slavic and East European History, Czechoslovak History Conf., So. Conf. Slavic Studies, Am. Assn. Advancement Slavic Studies, German Studies Assn., Am. Com. to Promote Studies of Habsburg Monarchy, Central European History Conf. Hussite. Home: 18 Golf Club Dr Langhorne PA 19047-2163 Office: Tulane U Dept History New Orleans LA 70118

LUZKOW, JACK LAWRENCE, history educator, writer, consultant; b. Detroit, Dec. 18, 1941; s. Irving and Sally (Eagle) Farber; m. Susan Frankel, Mar. 27, 1964 (div. Dec. 1973); 1 child, Catherine Alexis; m. Virginia Ann Trieglaff, May 15, 1976; 1 child, Frank Jason. BA, Wayne State Univ., 1966; MA, St. Louis Univ., 1975, PhD, 1981. Bibliographic specialist Southern Ill. Univ., Carbondale, 1979-81; history prof. Union Coll., Barbourville, Ky., 1981-84, Marycrest Coll., Davenport, Iowa, 1984-90, Teikyo-Marycrest Univ., Davenport, Iowa, 1990—; pres. Cons. Global Learning, Davenport, 1992—; v.p. Lonetree Enterprises, Davenport, 1991—; v.p. Marycrest Acad. Senate, Davenport, 1990-91; past pres. Inst. Ednl. Seminars, Davenport, 1988; speaker Vis. Artists Series, Davenport, 1985. Contbr. articles to profl. jours. V.p. Latin Am. Human Rights Action Ctr., Iowa City, Iowa, 1988-90. Recipient Mellon-James Still fellowship, Univ. Ky., 1982, 84, rsch. grant Ky. Humanities Coun., Barbourville, 1984, dean's grant Marycrest Coll., 1986, 89, 90, Teikyo Marycrest Univ., 1991. Mem. Nat. Soc. Sci. Assn. (nat. governing & nat. bd. 1990—), European Studies Assn., Radical Historians of Am., Mo. Valley Hist. Assn. Office: Teikyo Marycrest U 1607 W 12th Davenport IA 52804 Home: 1804 Pershing Ave Davenport IA 52803

LYALL, KATHARINE C(ULBERT), academic administrator, economics educator; b. Lancaster, Pa., Apr. 26, 1941; d. John D. and Eleanor G. Lyall. BA in Econs., Cornell U., 1963, PhD in Econs., 1969; MBA, NYU, 1965. Economist Chase Manhattan Bank, N.Y.C., 1963-65; asst. prof. econs. Syracuse U., 1969-72; prof. econs. Johns Hopkins U., Balt., 1972-77; dir. grad. program in public policy Johns Hopkins U., 1979-81; dep. asst. sec. for econs. Office Econ. Affairs, HUD, Washington, 1977-79; v.p. acad. affairs U. Wis. System, 1981-85; prof. of econ. U. Wis., Madison, 1982—; acting pres. U. Wis. System, Madison, 1985-86, 91-92, exec. v.p., 1986-91, pres., 1992—; bd. dirs. Kemper Ins. Cos.; mem. bd. Carnegie Found. for Advancement of Teaching. Author: Reforming Public Welfare, 1976, Microeconomic Issues of the 70s, 1978. Mem. Mcpl. Securities Rulemaking Bd., Washington, 1990-93. Mem. Am. Econ. Assn., Assn. Am. Univs., Phi Beta Kappa. Home: 6021 S Highlands Ave Madison WI 53705 Office: U Wis System Office of Pres 1720 Van Hise Hall 1220 Linden Dr Madison WI 53706

LYBARGER, JEFFREY ALLEN, epidemiology research administrator; b. Granite, Ill., 1951. MD, So. Ill. U., 1976. Diplomate Am. Bd. Gen. Preventive Medicine; Pub. Health. Intern cardiology St. Louis U.Glennon Hosp., 1976-77; dir. Agency for Toxic Substances and Disease Registry, Division of Health Studies, Altanta, Ga.; resident occupational medicine U. Cincinnati, 1979-81; resident pub. health, pub. medicine Ctrs. for Disease Control, Atlanta, 1982-84. Mem. Am. Pub. Health Assn., Soc. for Epidemiol. Rsch. Office: Agy for Toxic Substances & Disease Registry 1600 Clifton Rd NE Mail Stop E31 Atlanta GA 30333*

LYBECKER, MARTIN EARL, lawyer; b. Lincoln, Nebr., Feb. 11, 1945; s. Earl Edward and Jeanette Frances (Kiefer) L.; m. Andrea Kristine Tollefson, Dec. 27, 1969; children: Carl Martin, Neil Anders. BBA, U. Wash., 1967, JD, 1970; LLM in Taxation, NYU, 1971; LLM, U. Pa., 1973. Bar: Wash. 1970, D.C. 1972, Pa. 1982. Atty. investment mgmt. div. SEC, Washington, 1972-75, assoc. dir. div., 1978-81; assoc. prof. SUNY, Buffalo, 1975-78; ptnr. Drinker Biddle & Reath, Washington, 1981-87, Ropes & Gray, Washington, 1987—; adj. prof. Georgetown U., Washington, 1974-75, 80-81; vis. assoc. prof. Duke U., Durham, N.C., 1977-78. Contbr. articles to law revs. Fellow U. Pa. Ctr. for Study of Fin. Instns., 1971-72. Mem. ABA (mem. subcom. on investment cos. and investment advisers, mem. subcom. on securities activities of banks, mem. com. on fed. regulation of securities bus. law sect., chairperson com. on devels. in investment svcs. bus. law sect., chairperson subcom. on bank holding co. activities and subcom. on fiduciary svcs. of com. of banking bus. law sect.), Univ. Club Washington. Home: 2806 Daniel Rd Bethesda MD 20815-3149 Office: Ropes & Gray Ste 1200 S 1001 Pennsylvania Ave NW Washington DC 20004-2505

LYDFORD, CYNTHIA WINSLOE, nurse administrator; b. Prince Edward Island, Can., Sept. 18, 1932; d. Robert John and Roma L. (Wright) L. AAS, Queens Coll., 1957; BS, NYU, 1962, MA, 1963. Staff nurse, hematology, cardiology VA Med. Ctr., Bklyn., 1963-64, head nurse, dermatology svc., 1964-67, relief head nurse, GI svc., '67; staff nurse, med. svc. VA Med. Ctr., Northport, L.I., 1967-68, instr. nursing edn., 1968-69, clin. inservice coord., 1969-71, acting assoc. chief, 1968-71, clin. specialist, medicine and surgery, 1971, asst. chief nursing svc., med./surg., 1971-79, acting chief, nursing svc., 1971-79; appointed chief, nursing svc. VA Med. Ctr., Castle Point, N.Y., 1979—. Recipient Faculty award in Nursing Sci. Mem. ANA, Am. Nurses Assn., NYU Nurses Assn, Nurses House (founder Hudson Valley chpt).

LYDICK, LAWRENCE TUPPER, federal judge; b. San Diego, June 22, 1916; s. Roy Telling and Geneva (Lydick) L.; m. Gretta Grant, Aug. 7, 1938; children: Gretta Grant, Lawrence Tupper; m. Martha Martinez, Oct. 1969; 1 child, Chip. A.B., Stanford U., 1938, LL.B. (Crothers law scholar), 1942; Sigma Nu exchange scholar, U. Freiburg, Germany, 1938-39; postgrad., Harvard U., 1943, Mass. Inst. Tech., 1943-44. Bar: Calif. 1946. Since practiced in L.A.; dir. disputes div. 10th region Nat. War Labor Bd., San Francisco, 1942-43; asst. to pres., gen. counsel U.S. Grant Export-Import, Ltd., L.A., 1946-48; assoc. Adams, Duque & Hazeltine, L.A., 1948-53, ptnr., 1953-71; U.S. dist. ct. judge Central Dist. Calif., 1971—. Bd. vis. Stanford Law Sch. Lt. USNR, 1943-46. Mem. Am. Law Inst. Republican. Office: US Dist Ct 34 Civic Center Plz Santa Ana CA 92701-4025

LYDOLPH, PAUL EDWARD, geography educator; b. Bonaparte, Iowa, Jan. 4, 1924; s. Guy W. and Pauline (Ruschke) L.; m. Mary J. Klahn, Dec.

17, 1966; children by previous marriage—Edward, Donald, Paul, Thomas, Andrew. B.A., U. Iowa, 1948; M.S., U. Wis., 1951, Ph.D., 1955; student, Harvard U., 1944, MIT, 1945, UCLA, 1956, U. Calif. at Berkeley, 1956-57. Tchr. math. Pisgah (Iowa) Pub. Sch., 1946-47, Packwood (Iowa) Pub. Sch., 1947-49; asst. prof., then assoc. prof. Los Angeles State Coll., 1952-59; mem. faculty U. Wis. at Milw., 1959—, prof. geography, 1962-92, emeritus, 1992—, chmn. dept., 1963-69, 71-72; Lectr. U. Hawaii, summer 1965, Oxford U., Stockholm Sch. Econs., 1970; C.I.C. Exchange prof. U. Mich. Ann Arbor, 1977, U. Iowa, Iowa City, 1978; Smithsonian Instn. tour dir. to, USSR, 1976, 77, 78, 79. Author: Geography of the USSR, 5th edit., 1990, Climates of the USSR, vol. 7, World Survey of Climatology, 1977, Weather and Climate, 1985, The Climate of the Earth, 1985, also articles; Festschrift written by colleagues in his honor: Soviet Geography Studies in Our Time, 1987. Served with USAAF, 1943-47. Ford Found. fellow, 1956-57. Home: N8328 Snake Rd Elkhart Lake WI 53020 Office: U Wis Dept Geography Milwaukee WI 53201

LYDON, THOMAS J., federal judge; b. Portland, Maine, June 3, 1927. B.A., U. Maine, 1952; LL.B., Georgetown U., 1955, LL.M., 1957. Bars: Maine, D.C. Trial atty. civil div. Dept. Justice, Washington, 1955-67, chief Ct. Claims sect. civil div., 1967-72; sr. judge U.S. Ct. Clms., Washington, 1972—. Office: US Claims Ct 717 Madison Pl NW Washington DC 20005-1011

LYFORD, CABOT, sculptor; b. Sayre, Pa., May 22, 1925; s. Frederic Eugene and Eleanor (Cabot) L.; m. Joan Ardyth Richmond, June 22, 1953; children: Matthew, Julia, Thaddeus. BFA, Cornell U., 1950. Exec. trainee NBC, N.Y.C., 1952-54; producer and dir. J. Walter Thompson, N.Y.C., 1954-57, Sta. WGBH-TV, Boston, 1957-59; program mgr. Sta. WENH-TV, Durham, N.H., 1959-63; chmn. Dept. Art The Phillips Exeter (N.H.) Acad., 1963-86. Prin. sculptures include pub. monuments in Portland, Maine and Portsmouth, N.H., Berwick, Maine; represented in permanent collections at Portland Mus., Chattanooga Mus., Indpls. Mus., Wichita (Kans.) Mus., Ogunquit (Maine) Mus., Currier Gallery, Manchester, N.H., Addison Gallery, Andover, Mass. With inf. U.S. Army, 1943-46, PTO. Recipient Sculpture prize Nat. Design Acad., 1990. Home and Studio: PO Box 104 HC 62 New Harbor ME 04554-9005

LYKES, JOSEPH T., III, shipping company executive; b. Galveston, Tex., Mar. 6, 1948. BA, Washington and Lee U., 1970. Sr. v.p. Lykes Bros. Steamship Co., New Orleans. Office: Lykes Ctr 300 Poydras St New Orleans LA 70130-3233

LYKINS, MARSHALL HERBERT, insurance company executive; b. Cin., Mar. 5, 1944; s. Herbert Cooper and Hilda Freda (Krall) L.; m. Betty Foushee Sweaney, June 27, 1970; 1 child, Elizabeth Foushee. BS, U. Chgo., 1966; M in Actuarial Sci., U. Mich., 1968. Actuarial student New Eng. Mut. Life Ins. Co., Boston, 1970-72, asst. actuary, 1972-75, assoc. actuary, 1975-78, 2d v.p. and actuary, 1978-85, v.p. and actuary, 1986—. Active Beacon Hill Civic Assn., Boston, 1970—, Byron St. Assn., Boston, 1982—; treas. King's Chapel, 1995—. Served with USPHS, 1968-70. Fellow Soc. Actuaries; mem. Chartered Life Underwriters, Am. Council of Life Ins. (com. on N.Y. expense limitations 1982—), Life Office Mgmt. Assn. (com. on profitability studies 1985—), Actuaries Club of Boston (treas. 1979—), U. Chgo. Alumni of Boston, U. Mich. Alumni of Boston, Phi Kappa Phi, Beta Gamma Sigma. Unitarian. Club: U. Club (Boston). Avocations: skiing, jogging, bridge. Home: 14 Byron St Boston MA 02108-3401 Office: New Eng Mut Life Ins Co 501 Boylston St Boston MA 02116-3706

LYKOS, PETER GEORGE, educator, scientist; b. Chgo., Jan. 22, 1927; s. George Peter and Theodora (Psimoulis) L.; m. Marie Nina Shumicki, July 2, 1950; children—George, Kristina, Andrew. B.S., Northwestern U., 1950; Ph.D., Carnegie Inst. Tech., 1955. Prof. chemistry Ill. Inst. Tech., 1955—, dir. computation center and computer sci. dept., 1963-71, dir. Interactive Instrnl. TV, 1976-78; cons. solid state sci. Argonne Nat. Lab., 1958-66; assoc. dean for acad. planning Armour Coll. Engring. & Sci. Ill. Inst. Tech., 1993—; cons. radiation therapy Michael Reese Hosp., Chgo., 1966-71; head computer impact on soc. NSF, 1971-73; pres. Four Pi, Inc., Oak Park, Ill., 1966-80; chmn. com. on computers in chemistry, chemistry divsn. NAS-NRC; dir. Assn. Media-based Continuing Engring. Edn.; sci. cons. NTU (video satellite), 1988—; dir. Project Chemnet, 1984; Coll. Bd. Advanced Placement com. to create Advanced Placement Exam in Computer Sci., 1982. Author tech. articles. Bd. dirs. Oak Park Pub. Library, 1976-81; trustee Beacon Unitarian Ch. Served with USNR, 1944-46. Mem. Am. Chem. Soc. (chmn. edn. com. Chgo., co-dir. Operation Interface I, chmn. div. computers in chemistry, three term on com. profl. tng. 1980s, organizer materials chemistry secretariat 1988-91, adv. bd. Chemistry and Engring. News), Assn. Computing Machinery (chmn. Chgo., nat. lectr., chmn. spl. interest group on computers and soc., liaison to Am. Fedn. Info. Processing Socs. 1976-78, chmn. com. on computers and public policy), Sigma Xi (chmn. Chgo. chpt., program planning com.), Alpha Chi Sigma, Phi Sigma. Home: 316 N Ridgeland Ave Oak Park IL 60302-2325 Office: Ill Inst Tech Chicago IL 60616

LYLE, CHARLES THOMAS, association executive; b. Duluth, Minn., July 16, 1946; s. Thomas Joseph and Ann (Seglem) L.; m. Maxine Seidel, Aug. 16, 1980. B.A. cum laude, U. Minn., 1968; M.A., U. Del., 1971. Dir. Monmouth County Hist. Assn., Freehold, N.J., 1971-78; dir. mus. properties Nat. Trust for Hist. Preservation, Washington, 1978-80; dir. Hist. Soc. Del., Wilmington, 1980-90, Md. Hist. Soc., Balt., 1990—. Contbr. articles to profl. jours. James Wright Hunt scholar U. Minn.; Hagley fellow U. Del.; Am. Friends of Attingham Summer Sch. scholar, 1977. Mem. Nat. Trust for Hist. Preservation (bd. advisors 1980-89), Am. Assn. for State and Local History (publs. com. 1986-89), Middle Atlantic Assn. Mus., Am. Assn. Mus. (accreditation vis. com. 1976—), Sea Bright Beach Club, Md. Club, Engrs. Club, 14 West Hamilton St. Club. Home: 905 Drohomer Pl Baltimore MD 21210-1342 Office: Md Hist Soc 201 W Monument St Baltimore MD 21201-4674

LYLE, GLENDA SWANSON, state legislator; b. Knoxville, Tenn.; d. Richard and Olivia Swanson; children: Kipp, Elsie, Jennifer, Anthony. BA, U. Denver, 1964; MA, U. Colo., 1973. Former dir. cmty. and personal svcs., instr. early childhood edn., dir. preschool lab C.C. of Denver/Auraria; owner Planners, Inc.; mem. Colo. Ho. of Reps., 1992—, mem. various coms., 1993—. Del. White Ho. Conf. Small Bus., 1980-86; mem. Regional Transp. Dist. Bd., 1986-92. Regulatory Agy. Adv. Bd., Mayor's Planning Bd., Nat. Pub. Lands Adv. Coun., Gov.'s Small Bus. Coun., Colo. Mkt. and Distributive Edn. Adv. Coun., Va Neal Blue Ctr. Mem. Am. Planning Assn., Conf. Minority Transp. Ofcls. (nat. bd. dirs.), Black Women Polit. Action (founding mem.), Black C. of C. (bd. dirs.). Democrat. Office: Colo House of Reps State Capitol Denver CO 80203

LYLE, JOHN TILLMAN, landscape architecture educator; b. Houston, Aug. 10, 1934; s. Leo Tillman and Martha Ellen (Rawlins) L.; m. Harriett Laverna Fancher, Dec. 28, 1967; children: Alexander Tillman, Cybele Katsura. BArch, Tulane U., 1957; postgrad., Royal Acad. of Fine Arts, Copenhagen, 1965-67; M of Landscape Architecture, U. Calif., Berkeley, 1966. Registered architect, Calif. Architect Stanford (Calif.) U., 1959-62; urban designer John Carl Warnecke & Assocs., San Francisco, 1963-65; prof. Calif. State Poly. U., Pomona, 1968—; vis. prof. Liubliana (Yugoslavia) U., 1982, Instituto Universitario Di Architectura, Venice, Italy, 1988, U. Sao Paulo, Brazil, 1989, Kyushu Inst. Design, Fukuoka, Japan, 1990; dir. design bldg. and landscape Inst. for Regenerative Studies, 1984—. Author: Design For Human Ecosystems, 1985 (award Assn. Am. Pubs. 1985, Am. Soc. Landscape Architects 1986); contbr. articles to profl. jours. Mem. bd. govs. Desert Studies Consortium, Mojave Desert, 1984-88. Recipient Honor award Calif. Coun. Landscape Architects, 1988; named Fulbright Disting. prof., U.S. Dept. State, 1982, Disting. Educator, Coun. Educators in Landscape Architecture, 1989; Fulbright scholar U.S. Dept. State, 1966-68. Fellow Am. Soc. Landscape Architects (Design for Sustainable Devel. award 1994). Democrat. Avocations: hiking, skiing. Home: 580 N Hermosa Ave Sierra Madre CA 91024-1117 Office: Calif State Poly U 3801 W Temple Ave Pomona CA 91768-2557

LYLE, JOHN WILLIAM, JR., state senator, lawyer, social sciences educator, secondary school principal; b. Providence, May 19, 1950; s. John

William and Lois (Smith) L.; m. Lori A. Lyle, Feb. 16, 1992. BA, Barrington Coll., 1973; MEd, Providence Coll., 1978; JD, Suffolk U., 1992 Tchr. Lincoln (R.I.) Sch. Dept., 1974—; senator State of R.I., Dist. 34, 1981-86, 91-94, minority whip, 1993-94; tchr. William Davies Vocat. Sch.-Summer Sch., Lincoln, 1975, 77; dir. student affairs Brown U. Summer Acad., Providence, 1987; asst. prin. Lincoln Sr. H.S.; mem. adj. faculty R.I. Coll., Providence, 1990—, Community Coll. R.I., Lincoln, 1991—. Contbr. articles to profl. jour. Bd. dirs. Blackstone Valley Tourism Council; trustee Cumb-Line Boys and Girls Club, Cumberland, R.I., 1982; mem. R.I. Rep. Cen. Com., Providence, 1979—; Rep. candidate for Sec. of State of R.I., 1986; lines person USTA, N.Y.C., 1985—; Robert A. Taft Inst. fellow, 1975, 79; recipient Outstanding Alumnus award Barrington Coll., 1982, Disting. Alumnus award, 1984; Appreciation award No. R.I. Sr. Services, 1983, John E. Fogarty award, 1995, Johns Hopkins U. Close Up fellow. Mem. R.I. Bar Assn., R.I. Assn. Social Studies Tchrs., Nat. Conf. State Legis., R.I. Am. Secondary Sch. Prins., Lincoln Tchrs. Assn. (exec. bd. 1987-90).Avocations: travel, reading, running, tennis. Office: RI Senate State House Providence RI 02903

LYLE, ROBERT EDWARD, chemist; b. Atlanta, Jan. 26, 1926; s. Robert Edward and Adaline (Cason) L.; m. Gloria Gilbert, Aug. 28, 1947. B.A., Emory U., 1945, MS, 1946; Ph.D. U. Wis.-Madison, 1949. Asst. prof. Oberlin Coll., Ohio, 1949-51; asst. prof. U. N.H., Durham, 1951-53; assoc. prof. U. N.H., 1953-57, prof., 1957-76; prof., chmn. dept. chemistry U. North Tex., Denton, 1977-79; v.p. chemistry, chem. engr. S.W Rsch. Inst., San Antonio, 1979-91; v.p. GRL Cons., San Antonio, 1992—; vis. prof. U. Va., Charlottesville, 1973-74, U. Grenoble, France, 1976; adj. prof. Bowdoin Coll., Brunswick, Maine, 1975-79, U. Tex., San Antonio, 1985—. Mem. editorial bd. Index Chemicus, 1976—. USPHS fellow Oxford U., Eng., 1965; recipient honor scroll award Mass. chpt. Am. Inst. Chemistry, 1971; Harry and Carol Mosher awardee, 1986. Fellow AAAS; mem. AACR, Am. Chem. Soc. (councilor 1965-84, 86-92, medicinal chemistry div.), Royal Soc. Chemistry, Alpha Chi Sigma (editor Hexagon 1992—). Methodist. Office: GRL Cons 12814 Kings Forest St San Antonio TX 78230-1511

LYLES, JEAN ELIZABETH CAFFEY, journalist; b. Abilene, Tex., Mar. 2, 1942; d. Wiley Luther and Pauline Linn (Marlin) Caffey; m. James Vernon Lyles, Aug. 23, 1969 (div. Aug. 1987). Student, McMurry Coll., 1960-61; BA with honors, U. Tex., 1964. Copy editor Christian Century mag., Chgo., 1972-74, assoc. editor, 1974-84, editor at large, 1984—; assoc. editor Religious News Svc., N.Y.C., 1984-87; sr. news editor The Lutheran, Chgo., 1987-91; news dir. United Meth. News Svc., Evanston, Ill., 1991-94; freelance photojournalist, 1995—. Author: A Practical Vision of Christian Unity, 1982; contbg. author: The First Amendment in a Free Society, 1979, Fearfully and Wonderfully Weird, 1990; editor: Church Street newsletter, 1995—; contbg. editor Wittenburg Door, 1982-87; columnist Inside the Am. Religion Scene, 1985-87, The Underground Ecumenist, 1989-92; mem. editorial bd. Mid-Stream, Indpls., 1984—; mem. exec. com. Associated Church Press, 1989-91; editor (newsletter) Church Street, 1995. Mem. Religion Newswriters Assn., Am. Guild Organists, Hymn Soc. Am., United Meth. Assn. of Communicators. Democrat. Episcopalian. Home: 922 North Blvd Apt 501 Oak Park IL 60301-1243

LYLES, MARK BRADLEY, high technology company executive, dentist; b. Paducah, Ky., Dec. 3, 1957; s. Kendall Smith Lyles and Charlotte Dean (Ruley) Martell; m. Catherine Lynn Gregg, March 17, 1984 (div. June 1995); children: Austin Bradley, Dahlon Patrick. AS, BS, BA in Biology and Chemistry, Murray (Ky.) State U., 1978, SCT vice EDS in Chemistry/Higher Edn., 1981; DMD, U. Louisville, 1986; postgrad., U. Tex., San Antonio, 1991—. Resident in maxillofacial surgery U. Tex. Health Sci. Ctr., 1991—, doctoral Candidate dept. of Cellular and Structural Biology; founder, chief exec. officer, pres. Talis Techs., Inc., San Antonio, 1992—; founder, pres., chief sci. officer Materials Evolution and Devel. U.S.A., Inc. (M.E.D. USA), San Antonio, 1993—; pres. subs. Venus Dental Materials, Inc., Vulcan Sci. Corp., Inc., J & L Pharms., Inc., Phoenix Filters, Inc., Pegasus, Inc., Genesis Advanced Tissue Engring., Inc., Dynamic Ceramics, Inc.; presenter in field. Contbr. articles to profl. jours.; inventor use of ultra-low density fused fibrous ceramics for indsl. applications, use of fused fibrous ceramics in dental materials, implantable sys. for cell growth control, filters for polynuclear aromatic hydrocarbon containing smoke. Lt. comdr. USNR, 1983—. Recipient dentist-scientist award Nat. Inst. Dental Rsch., 1991—; scholarships dept. chemistry and bd. regents Murray State U., 1975-77; grad. coop. edn. fellow Nat. Ctr. Toxicol. Rsch., EPA, FDA, 1979-80 grad. fellow U. Louisville, 1981-82. Mem. Am. Coll. Oral and Maxillofacial Surgeons (Walter Lorenz residents' rsch. award 1994), Acad. Osseointegration, Acad. Gen. Dentistry, Navy Inst., Assn. Mil. Surgeons U.S., Hon. Order Ky. Cols., Naval Res. Officers Assn., Phi Delta Kappa. Republican. Avocations: rifle and pistol marksmanship, weight training, sailing, travel, convertibles. Home: Apt 222 11020 Huebner Oaks Ave San Antonio TX 78230 Office: Materials Evolution & Devel USA Inc 9030 Wurzbach Rd San Antonio TX 78240

LYMAN, ARTHUR JOSEPH, financial executive; b. Evergreen Park, Ill., May 18, 1953; s. Arthur Edward and Margaret (O'Conner) L.; m. Janet Lee Wenzel, Sept. 9, 1984; children: Christina Lee, Alissa Mary, Arthur Joseph Jr. BA, Knox Coll., 1975; M in Mgmt., Northwestern U., 1977. CPA, Ill.; CFP. Audit supr. Arthur Andersen & Co., Chgo., 1977-83; fin. planning analyst Montgomery Ward & Co., Chgo., 1983-84; dir. fin. and adminstrn. ctrl. region Coopers & Lybrand, Chgo., 1984-88, CFO Midwest region, 1989-93, nat. dir. fin. field ops., 1993—. Mem. AICPA, Fin. Execs. Inst. (bd. dirs. Chgo. chpt. 1992—), Ill. Inst. CPA's, Pi Sigma Alpha, Tau Kappa Epsilon (honor award 1988, chmn. bd. trustees 1988-93). Roman Catholic. Home: 3 Cornell Dr Lincolnshire IL 60069-3222 Office: Coopers & Lybrand 203 N La Salle St Chicago IL 60601-1210

LYMAN, CHARLES PEIRSON, comparative physiologist; b. Brookline, Mass., Sept. 23, 1912; s. Henry and Elizabeth (Cabot) L.; m. Jane Hunnewell Cheever, June 21, 1941; children—Charles Peirson, Jane Sargent, Theodore, David Russell, Elizabeth Anne. A.B., Harvard U., 1936, A.M., 1939, Ph.D., 1942. Asst. curator mammals Mus. Comparative Zoology, Harvard U., Cambridge, Mass., 1945-51; assoc. curator mammals Mus. Comparative Zoology, Harvard U., 1951-56, research assoc., 1956-58, curator in mammalogy, 1968-82; curator Warren Anat. Mus., Harvard Med. Sch., Boston, 1970-82; assoc. Harvard Med. Sch., 1949-60, asst. prof. anatomy, 1960-67, assoc. prof. anatomy, 1967-76, prof. biology, 1976-82; mem. NIH Study Sect., 1965-69; mem. nat. adv. bd. Biotron, 1965-75; mem. standing com. Trustees Public Reservations; trustee Mass. Soc. Promoting Agr. Contbr. articles, mostly on hibernation in mammals and reactions of mammals to environ. extremes, to profl. jours. Served to maj. USAF, 1942-45. NSF grantee, 1960-82; NIH grantee, 1955-76. Fellow AAAS; mem. Am. Zool. Soc., Am. Physiol. Soc., Am. Acad. Arts and Sci., Sigma Xi. Republican. Unitarian. Clubs: Harvard, Tavern, Dedham Country and Polo. Home: 105 Elm St Canton MA 02021-1255

LYMAN, DAVID, lawyer; b. Washington, Sept. 25, 1936; s. Albert Moses and Freda (Ring) L.; m. Yubol Pumsathit, Nov. 10, 1979. BS in Elec. Engring., Duke U., 1958; cert. U.S. Naval Officers Submarine Sch., 1960; JD, U. Calif.-San Francisco, 1965; postgrad. in fgn. and comparative law Columbia U., 1974. Bar: Calif. 1966; registered elec. engr., Thailand. Assoc. Fitzsimmons & Petris, Oakland, Calif., 1965-66; Lempres & Seyranian, Oakland, 1966-67; Tilleke & Gibbins, R.O.P., Advocates and Solicitors, Bangkok, assoc. ptnr. 1967-84, sr. ptnr., 1984—; dir. Goodyear (Thailand) Ltd., Triumph Internat. (Thailand) Ltd.; founding mem. Prime Minister Thailand's Fgn. Investment Adv. Council, 1975, chmn. Fgn. C. of C. in Thailand Law Change Proj for the Prime Minister, 1992; mem. USAID Adv. Com. on U.S.-Thai Trade and Investment, 1988; founder, mem. steering com. tech. cooperation office U.S. Asia Environ. Partnership Program. 1994. Contbr. articles to profl. publs. Chmn. King Bhumiphol Rama IX Park U.S. Geodesic Dome Pavillion Com., 1987; founding mem. Thailand Bus. Coun. Sustainable Devel., 1993—; founder Davos Group World Economic Forum on Anti-Corruption Standards for Global Business, 1995—, co-founder, advisor Cmty. Svcs. Bangkok, 1985; advisor Thailand Soc. Prevention of Cruelty to Animals; co-founder Vietnam-Am. C. of C., 1992—. Served with U.S. Navy, 1958-68; lt. comdr. Res. Recipient U.S. Naval Inst. prize, 1958, Am. Jurisprudence prize, 1965; U.S. Dept. Commerce cert., 1987; Paul Harris fellow, 1987, Thai Prime Minister's Cert. of Achievement 1990, 92,

Am. Cof C. Disting. Svc. Award, 1990. Mem. Am. C. of C. in Thailand (bd. govs. 1973—, v.p. 1974, 83-85, pres. 1975, 86), Asia-Pacific Coun. of Am. C. of C. (vice chmn. 1975-77, 85-89, 92-93, bd. dirs. 1975, 86), AmCham Environ. Coun. (founder, 1992), Environ. Bus. Exchange (creator 1993), Thai Bd. Trade (bd. dirs. 1975, 86), Fgn. Chambers of Commerce Working Group (sec. 1982-87, chmn. 1987-90), Thailand bd. of Investment Environ. Study Adv. Com., 1993, World Econ. Forum (program fellow Europe/East Asia Econ. Forum 1992-94), Lex Mundi (bd. dirs. 1989-91), ABA, Calif. Bar Assn., Intl. Bar Assn., LAWASIA, Thailand Trademark Assn., U.S. Naval Inst. (life), Naval Submarine League, Internat. Oceanographic Found. (life), Thailand Bus. Coalition AIDS Assn. (founder, 1994), 999 Wildlife Trust, Wildlife Fund Thailand, Chaine Des Rotisseurs (charge de mission), Jewish Assn. Thailand, Nat. Trust (U.K.), Capital Club, Tau Epsilon Phi, Phi Alpha Delta, Beta Gamma Sigma (hon.). Republican. Jewish. Clubs: Royal Bangkok Sports, Heritage (founder Gov. 1985—), Fgn. Corrs. of Thailand (life). Lodge: Rotary (1969-89, sec. 1982-83, v.p. Bangkok 1984-85), Community Services of Bangkok (founder, acting pres. 1986, v.p. 1986-87, bd. dirs. 1985-88). Avocations: scuba diving, swimming, outdoor photography. Home: 39/221 Moo 2 Nichada Thani Soi 11, Tambol Bangtalad Amphur Pakkred, Nonthaburi 11120, Thailand Office: Tilleke and Gibbins ROP, 64/ 1 Soi Tonson, Ploenchit Rd, Bangkok 10330, Thailand

LYMAN, FREDERIC A., mechanical and aerospace engineering educator, researcher; b. Syracuse, N.Y., Sept. 4, 1934; s. Frederic A. and Elsie (Samson) L.; m. Marilyn Mawson, Dec. 18, 1954; children—Ruth, Martha, Sarah. B.S. in Mech. Engring., Syracuse U., 1955, M.S. in Mech. Engring., 1957; postgrad., John Hopkins U., 1957-59; Ph.D. in Mechanics, Rensselaer Poly Inst., 1961. Registered profl. engr., N.Y. Test engr. heavy mil. electronics dept. Gen. Electric Co., Syracuse, summer 1954; instr. mech. engring. dept. Syracuse U., 1955-57, assoc. prof. mech. and aerospace engring., 1970-78, prof., 1978—; grad. research and teaching asst. mechanics dept. Rensselaer Poly. Inst., Troy, N.Y., 1960-61; preceptor dept. civil engring. and engring. mechanics Columbia U., N.Y.C., 1961-62; research engr. theoretical analysis sect. NASA-Lewis Research Ctr., Cleve., 1962-66; head plasma flow sect. NASA-Lewis Research Ctr., 1966-67; assoc. prof. engring. Case Western Res. U., Cleve., 1967-70; vis. research engr. dept. aerospace and mech. scis. Princeton U., N.J., 1977-78; prin. research engr. Case/NASA Lewis Inst. for Computational Mechanics in Propulsion, Cleve., 1985-86. Contbr. articles to profl. jours.; mem. translators' panel Prikladnaia Matematika i Mekhanika (Applied Mathematics and Mechanics), 1962-66, Magnitnaya Gidrodinamika (Magnetohydrodynamics), 1971-72; cons. on Russian tech. lit. in applied mechanics and mech. engring. Applied Mechanics Revs., 1982-83. Research grantee NSF, Dept. of Energy, 1973, 78. Mem. ASME, AAUP (pres. Syracuse chpt. 1981-82), Am. Soc. Elec. Engring. (space engring. com. 1968-71, mech. engring. div. rep. to St. Lawrence sect. 1976-77). Democrat. Unitarian. Avocations: language; literature. Home: 323 Scott Ave Syracuse NY 13224-1725 Office: Syracuse Univ 151 Link Hall Syracuse NY 13244

LYMAN, HENRY, retired publisher, marine fisheries consultant; b. Boston, Oct. 30, 1915; s. Henry and Elizabeth (Cabot) L.; m. Marjorie Borum, June 27, 1953. AB cum laude, Harvard Coll., 1937. Reporter Cape Cod Colonial, Hyannis, Mass., 1937-38; reporter Athol Daily News, Mass., 1938-40; editor Open Road Pub. Co., Boston, 1946-48; publisher Salt Water Sportsman, Boston, 1948-85, pub. emeritus, 1985—; advisor Internat. Conv. Conservation of Atlantic Tunas, Washington, 1976-86, New England Fishery Mgmt. Coun., Saugus, Mass., 1980—; bd. dirs. Atlantic Salmon Fedn., N.Y.C., Nat. Coalition for Marine Conservation, Savannah, Ga., Environ. League Mass., Boston; mem. U.S. sect. North Atlantic Salmon Conservation Orgn., Edinburgh, Scotland, 1983-92. Author: Bluefishing, 1953, rev. edit., 1987, Successful Bluefishing, 1974, (with others) The Complete Book of Striped Bass Fishing, 1954, The Complete Book of Weakfishing, 1959, Tackle Talk, 1971, Bottom Fishing, 1984; contbr. articles on marine fisheries matters. Trustee New England Aquarium, Boston, 1973-88, life trustee, 1988—; founding. trustee Coldwater Conservation Fund, Vienna, Va., 1993—; trustee Manomet Bird Obs., Mass., 1978-90, hon. trustee, 1990—; bd. dirs. Samual Cabot, Inc., Boston, 1974-91, Fund for Preservation of Wildlife and Natural Areas, Boston, 1979-89; incorporator Harvard Mag., Cambridge, Mass., 1979—. Comdr. USNR, 1940-46, 52-53. Mem. Nat. Wildlife Fedn. (bd. dirs. 1983-89), New England Outdoor Writers Assn. (life., bd. dirs. 1960-62), Outdoor Writers Assn. Am., Tavern Club (sec. 1980-83, pres. 1983-84), Harvard Club, Phi Beta Kappa. Avocations: angling; hunting. Home: Apt 367 10 Longwood Dr Westwood MA 02090-1144 Office: Salt Water Sportsman 77 Franklin St Boston MA 02110-1510

LYMAN, JOHN, psychology and engineering educator; b. Santa Barbara, Calif., May 29, 1921; s. Oren Lee and Clara Augusta (Young) L. A.B. in Psychology and Math., UCLA, 1943, M.S., 1950, Ph.D. in Psychology, 1951. Research technician Lockheed Aircraft Corp., Burbank, Calif., 1940-43; mathematician Lockheed Aircraft Corp., 1943-44; with dept. psychology UCLA, 1947—, assoc. prof., 1957-63, prof., 1963—, from instr. to assoc. prof. Sch. Engring. and Applied Sci., 1950-63, prof. Sch. Engring. and Applied Sci., 1963—, chmn. engring. systems dept., 1978-84, head Biotech. Lab., 1958-80, head Human-Machine-Environment Engring. Lab., 1981—; prof. materials sci. and engring., 1984-91; prof. emeritus Sch. Engring. and Applied Sci. UCLA, 1991—; research engr. Inst. Traffic and Transp., 1967-73; vis. prof. bioengring. Technol. Inst., Delft, Netherlands, 1965; spl. cons. Nat. Acad. Scis., Washington, 1973; cons. VA, Los Angeles, 1962-66, 67-76, NIH, 1963-66, 68-73, med. devices div. FDA, 1976-78, Perceptronics, Inc., Woodland Hills, Calif., 1978—, other agys. and cos.; bd. dirs. Perceptronics, Inc., Mega Graphics, Inc., also chmn. bd. Author chpts. in books, articles in profl. jours.; editor in field. Served to lt. (j.g.) U.S. Navy, 1944-46. Recipient Japanese Govt. Research award for Fgn. Specialists (Robotics), 1985, also numerous fellowships and grants. Fellow Am. Psychol. Assn., Am. Psychol. soc., Soc. Engring. Psychologists, AAAS, Human Factors Soc. (Paul Fitts award 1971, pres. 1967-68, Pres. Disting. Svc. award 1991); mem. Biomed. Engring. Soc. (pres. 1980-81), IEEE, Am. Soc. Engring. Edn., Am. Assn. Artificial Intelligence, Robotics Internat., Robotics Soc. Japan, Soc. Mfg. Engrs., Sigma Xi, Tau Beta Pi. Office: UCLA 5732 Boelter Hall Los Angeles CA 90024

LYMAN, PEGGY, dancer, choreographer, educator; b. Cin., June 28, 1950; d. James Louis and Anne Earlene (Weeks) Morner; m. David Stanley Lyman, Aug. 29, 1970 (div. 1979); m. Timothy Scott Lynch, June 21, 1982; 1 child, Kevin Kynch. Grad. high sch., Cin. Solo dancer Cin. Ballet Co., 1964-68, Contemporary Dance Theater, 1970-71; chorus dancer N.Y.C. Opera, 1969-70; Radio City Music Hall Ballet Co., 1970; chorus singer and dancer Sugar, Broadway musical, N.Y.C., 1971-73; prin. dancer Martha Graham Dance Co., N.Y.C., 1973-88, rehersal dir., 1989-90; artistic dir. Martha Graham Ensemble, N.Y.C., 1990-91; faculty Martha Graham Sch., 1975—; head dance div. No. Ky. U., 1977-78; artistic dir. Peggy Lyman Dance Co., N.Y.C., 1978-89; asst. profl. dance, guest choreographer Fla. State U., Tallahassee, 1982-89; guest choreographer So. Meth. U., Dallas, 1986; adjudicator Nat. Coll. Dance Festival Assn., 1983—; co-host To Make a Dance, QUBE cable TV, 1979; mem. guest faculty Am. Dance Festival, Durham, N.C., 1984; site adjudicator Nat. Endowment for Arts, 1982-84; tchr. Hartford Ballet Sch., 1992—, East Conn. Concert Ballet, 1992—; guest faculty Wesleyan U., Middletown, Conn., 1992; guest artist Conn. Coll., 1993; chair dance dept. Hartt sch. U. Hartford, Conn., 1994—; freelance master tch. internat. univs. Prin. dancer Dance in America, TV spls., 1976, 79, 84; guest with with Rudolph Nureyev, Invitation to the Dance, CBS-TV, 1980; guest artist Theatre Choregraphique Rennes, Paris, 1981, Rennes, France, 1983, Adelaide U., 1991; site dir. Martha Graham's Diversion of Angels for student concert U. Mich., 1992, Martha Graham's Panorama, U. Ill., Champaign-Urbana, 1993. Founding mem. Cin. Arts Coun., 1976-78. Mem. Am. Guild Mus. Artists. Office: Hartford Ballet 224 Farmington Ave Hartford CT 06105-3597

LYMAN, PRINCETON NATHAN, ambassador; b. San Francisco, Nov. 20, 1935; s. Arthur and Gertrude (Kramer) L.; m. Helen Carolyn Erman, July 7, 1957; children: Cindy, Sheri, Lori. B.A., U. Calif., Berkeley, 1957; M.A., Harvard U., 1959, Ph.D., 1961. Program officer U.S. Aid Mission, Seoul, Korea, 1964-67; research assoc. Harvard U., Cambridge, Mass., 1967-68; dir. civic participation div. AID, Washington, 1968-71, equal employment counselor, 1969-71, dir. devel. resources for Africa, 1971-76; dir. U.S. Aid Mission, Addis Ababa, Ethiopia, 1976-78; dep. asst. sec. Africa Bur. U.S. Dept. State, Washington, 1981-86, U.S. amb. to Nigeria, 1986-89, dir.

Bur. Refugee Programs, 1989-92, U.S. amb. to South Africa, 1992—; professorial lectr. Johns Hopkins U., Washington, 1980-86. Contbr. articles and book chpts. to profl. publs. Recipient AID Meritorious Honor award, 1966, Superior Honor award, 1970, 86, President's Meritorious Svc. award, 1989, 91; President's Disting. Svc. award, 1993. Mem. Am. Fgn. Service Assn. (v.p. 1969-70, bd. dirs.), Coun. Fgn. Rels. Office: Am Embassy Pretoria c/o DOS PO Box 9536 Washington DC 20521

LYMAN, RICHARD R., journalist; b. Gary, Ind., Dec. 30, 1954; s. Richard Walden and Willadean Mary (Volk) L.; m. Barbara Ann Whitaker, Sept. 12. Grad., Ind. U. Bus.; labor writer The Times, Hammond, Ind., 1977; reporter UPI, Chgo., 1977-78; reporter, editor Kansas City Star, Mo., 1978-82; reporter Phila. Inquirer, 1982-83, movie critic, 1983—. Co-recipient Pulitzer Prize award, 1981. Mem. Sigma Delta Chi. Club: Pen and Pencil (Phila.).

LYMAN, RICHARD WALL, foundation and university executive, historian; b. Phila., Oct. 18, 1923; s. Charles M. and Aglae (Wall) L.; m. Elizabeth D. Schauffler, Aug. 20, 1947; children: Jennifer P., Holly Lyman Antolini, Christopher M., Timothy R. BA, Swarthmore Coll., 1947, LLD (hon.) 1974; MA, Harvard U., 1948, PhD, 1954, LLD (hon.), 1980; LLD (hon.), Washington U., St. Louis, 1971, Mills Coll., 1972, Yale U., 1975; LHD (hon.), U. Rochester, 1975, Coll. of Idaho, 1989. Teaching fellow, tutor Harvard U., 1949-51; instr. Swarthmore Coll., 1952-53; instr., then asst. prof. Washington U., St. Louis, 1953-58; mem. faculty Stanford U., 1958-80, 88-91, prof. history, 1962-80, 88-91, Sterling prof., 1980-91, assoc. dean Sch Humanities and Scis., 1964-66, v.p. provost, 1967-70, pres., 1970-80, pres. emeritus, 1980—, dir. Inst. Internat. Studies, 1988-91, prof. dept. history, 1991—; pres. Rockefeller Found., 1980-88; spl. corr. The Economist, London, 1953-66; bd. dirs. Council on Founds., 1982-88, Independent Sector, 1980-88, chair, 1983-86, Nat. Com. on U.S.-China Relations, 1986—; dir. IBM, 1978—, Chase Manhattan Corp., 1981-82. Author: The First Labour Government, 1957; editor: (with Lewis W. Spitz) Major Crises in Western Civilization, 1965, (with Virginia A. Hodgkinson) The Future of the Nonprofit Sector, 1989; editorial bd. Jour. Modern History, 1958-61. Mem. Nat. Council on Humanities, 1976-82, vice chmn., 1980-82; chmn. Commn. on Humanities, 1978-80; trustee Rockefeller Found., 1976-88 , Carnegie Found. Advancement of Teaching, 1976-82; bd. dirs. Nat. Assn. Ind. Colls. and Univs., 1976-77; chmn. Assn. Am. Univs., 1978-79. Served with USAAF, 1943-46. Decorated officier Legion of Honor; Fulbright fellow London Sch. Econs., 1951-52, hon. fellow, 1978—; Guggenheim fellow, 1959-60. Fellow Royal Hist. Soc.; mem. Am. Acad. Arts and Scis., Am. Hist. Assn., Council on Fgn. Relations, Conf. Brit. Studies, Phi Beta Kappa. Office: Stanford U Sch Edn Stanford Ca 94305

LYMAN, ROBERT HOWARD, veterans association executive; b. Long Beach, Calif., Sept. 2, 1949; s. Herbert Stewart and Eleanor Louise (Mcconnell) L.; m. Carol Ann Rybik, Oct. 23, 1981; 1 stepchild, Brian Orman. BA in History, Asbury Coll., 1971; MS in Sys. Mgmt., U. So. Calif., 1984. With USMC, 1971-91, commd. 2d lt., 1973, advanced through grades to maj., 1983, ret., 1991; exec. dir. Naval Enlisted Res. Assn., Falls Church, Va., 1991—. Mem. Ret. Officers Assn., Exch. Club of Capitol Hill. Republican. Roman Catholic. Avocation: golf. Office: NERA 6703 Farragut Ave Falls Church VA 22042

LYMAN, WILLIAM W., JR., retired architect; b. New London, Conn., Aug. 31, 1916; s. William Welles and Gladys Estelle (Latimer) L.; m. Margaret Helen Whittemore, July 12, 1941 (div. Sept. 1970); children: Cheryl, Steven, Philip, Susan, Donna, Patricia; m. Joan Evelyn Dalrymple, Sept. 26, 1970. BArch, U. Mich., 1939; MArch, Harvard U., 1940. Architect various orgns., Boston, 1941-42; pvt. practice Cambridge, Mass., 1947-53; chief designer Smith, Hinchman & Grylls, Detroit, 1953-56; architect Swanson Assocs., Bloomfield Hills, Mich., 1956-59, Smith & Smith Assocs., Royal Oak, Mich., 1959-62; architect Jickling Lyman & Powell Assocs., Inc., Birmingham, Mich., 1962-81, ret., 1981; mem. faculty Harvard U., Cambridge, Mass., 1947-53; lectr. on early Am. furniture, 1975—. Pres. Cambridge Coun. PTAs, 1950-52, Harlan Sch. PTA, 1960-61; treas. Mass. Coun. for Better Schs., 1950-52; chmn. Citizens Elem. Curriculum Study Birmingham Pub. Schs., 1962-63; bd. dirs. South Oakland Symphony Soc., 1960-63, Birmingham Teen. Ctr., 1965-67, Birmingham Community House, 1967-70, Profl. Skills Alliance, Detroit, 1973-75, Birmingham Hist. Bd., 1969-73, chmn., 1972-73; chmn. Birmingham Hist. Dist. Study Com., 1975-77, Community Devel. Svcs., Portsmouth, N.H., 1993—; pres. Birmingham Hist. Soc., 1980-81, bd. dirs. 1967-70; chmn. acquisitions com. John W. Hunter House, 1974-82; bd. govs. Warner House Assn., Portsmouth, N.H., 1983-91, chmn. 1986-88. U.S. Coast Guard, 1942-46. Fellow AIA; mem. Mich. Soc. Architects (pres. 1970). Unitarian. Home: 171 Gates St Portsmouth NH 03801-4607

LYMBERIS, COSTAS TRIANTAFILLOS, environmental engineer; b. Athens, Greece, Mar. 29, 1944; came to U.S. 1962; s. Triantafillos and Stella (Orologa) L.; m. Gwyneth Johnson, Dec. 20, 1967 (div. 1971); m. Dionisia Helen Theofilopoulos, Sept. 24, 1972; children: Stella C., Cleo C. BS in Physics, UCLA, 1967; MS in Physics, Calif. State U., L.A., 1970; postgrad., U. Calif., Berkeley, 1971. Mech. and corrosion specialist Petrola Internat., Athens, 1977-83; mech. engr. AMAX-USMR, Carteret, N.J., 1983-85; engring. mgr. Mimikos Group of Cos., Pireaus, Greece, 1985-86; environ. mgr. Elsco, N.J. div., South Plainfield, 1986-88; engiron. engr. TRC Environ. Cons., Somerset, N.J., 1988-89; mech. engr. Leonard Engring., Cranford, N.J., 1989-90; corrosion engr. Ebasco Svcs., Inc., N.Y.C., 1991-92; environ. engr. Corps of Engrs., U.S. Army, N.Y.C., 1992—; adj. prof. physis Seton Hall U., South Orange, N.J., 1984, 88, 90, 94—; prof. physics, math. Middlesex County Coll., Edison, N.J., 1987—. Mem. ASME, AAAS, Am. Assn. Physics Tchrs., Nat. Assn. Corrosion Engrs. (cert. corrosion specialist), Sigma Pi Sigma. Democrat. Greek Orthodox. Home: 34 Robin Rd Rumson NJ 07760-1829 Office: US Army Corps of Engrs 26 Federal Plz Rm 1811 New York NY 10278-0004

LYNAM, JIM, professional basketball coach; b. Sept. 15, 1941; m. Kay Lynam; 3 children. Student, St. Joseph's U. Coll. basketball coach various univs.; asst. coach Portland Trailblazers (NBA), 1981-82; head coach San Diego Clippers (name now Los Angeles Clippers), 1983-85; asst. coach Phila. 76ers, 1985-88, head coach, 1988-94; head coach Washington Bullets, 1994—. Office: Washington Bullets US Air Arena Landover MD 20785*

LYNAM, TERENCE JOSEPH, lawyer; b. Dublin, Ireland, Mar. 25, 1953; came to U.S., 1958; s. Thomas Joseph and Bridget Anne (O'Carroll) L.; m. Melinda Anne Steagall, Aug. 23, 1980; children: Sean, Laura, Thomas. BA, U. Pa., 1975; JD, Georgetown U., 1978. Bar: D.C. 1978, Va. 1980, U.S. Supreme Ct. 1985. Law clk. D.C. Superior Ct., Washington, 1978-79; appellate atty. U.S. Dept. Justice, Washington, 1979-80, spl. asst. U.S. Atty., 1980, trial atty. fraud sect. criminal div., 1980-84; assoc. Heron, Burchette, Ruckert & Rothwell, Washington, 1984-86, ptnr., 1986-90; ptnr. Akin, Gump, Strauss, Hauer & Feld, Washington, 1990—. Vol. Gore for Pres., Washington, 1988. Roman Catholic. Avocations: sports, music. Office: Akin Gump Strauss Hauer & Feld Ste 400 1333 New Hampshire Ave NW Washington DC 20036-1564

LYNAUGH, JOSEPH T., health care executive; b. 1939. Various positions Health and Hosps. Corp., N.Y.C., 1960-79; project mgr. McAuto Systems Group, Inc., N.Y.C., 1979-83; founder Sanus Corp. Health Systems, Fort Lee, N.J., 1983—. Office: Sanus Corp Health Systems 1 Parker Plz Fort Lee NJ 07024-2937

LYNCH, BENJAMIN LEO, oral surgeon educator; b. Omaha, Dec. 29, 1923; s. William Patrick and Mary (Rauber) L.; m. Colleen D. Cook, Nov. 10, 1956; children: Kathleen Ann, Mary Elizabeth Patrick, George, Martha, Estelle. BSD, Creighton U., 1945, DDS, 1947, MA, 1953; fellow, U. Tex., 1947-48; MSD, Northwestern U., 1954. Diplomate Am. Bd. Oral and Maxillofacial Surgery. Asst. instr. oral surgery Creighton U., 1948-50, instr. 1950-52, asst. prof., 1952-53; dean Creighton U. (Sch. Dentistry), 1954-61, assoc. prof. oral surgery, dir. dept., 1954-55, prof. oral surgery, 1957-86, prof. emeritus, 1986—, dir. oral surgery dept. 1954-67; also coordinator grad. and postgrad. programs; chief oral surgeon Douglas County Hosp., Omaha, 1951-63; pres. dental staff Children's Meml. Hosp., Omaha, 1952, 59; co-founder cleft palate team Children's Meml. Hosp., 1959; chmn. dept.

dentistry Bergan-Mercy Hosp., Omaha, 1963-68; mem. exec. com., head dental staff Luth. Hosp., 1963-66; bd. dirs. Nebr. Dental Service Corp., 1972-78, pres., 1974-78; treas. Children's Meml. Hosp. Med.-dental staff, 1979-81; guest lectr. Walter Reed Grad. Sch. Medicine, 1957-58. Mem. Omaha-Douglas County Health Bd., 1966-68, v.p., 1967, pres., 1968; exec. com. Nebr. div. Am. Cancer Soc., 1963-67; bd. dirs. Nebr. Blue Cross, 1968-89, Creighton U. Alumni Coun., Omaha chpt., 1989—; trustee United Cath. Social Svcs., 1989—; adv. bd. to dean Creighton U. Dental Sch., 1984—, vice chmn., 1992-93, chmn. 1993-94; pres. Creighton U. Graybackers, 1991—. Served at Walter Reed U.S. Army Med. Ctr., 1955-57. Recipient Alumni merit award Creighton U., 1978; named one of Ten Outstanding Young Omahans, 1952, 53, 58; inducted into Nebr. Dental Hall of Fame, 1981. Fellow Am. Coll. Dentists (pres. Nebr. chpt. 1973-74); mem. Am. Soc. Oral Surgeons, Midwest Soc. Oral Surgeons, Nebr. Soc. Oral Surgeons (founder 1957, pres. 1961), Nebr. Dental Soc. (trustee 1964-66), Omaha Dist. Dent Soc. (pres. 1963-64), Am. Coll. Oral-Maxillofacial Surgeons (founding mem.), Nebr. Soc. Dental Anesthesiology (founder, 1st pres.), Alpha Sigma Nu, Omicron Kappa Epsilon, Delta Sigma Delta. Home: 509 S Happy Hollow Blvd Omaha NE 68106-1224

LYNCH, BEVERLY PFEIFER, education and information studies educator; b. Moorhead, Minn., Dec. 27, 1935; d. Joseph B. and Nellie K. (Bailey) Pfeifer; m. John A. Lynch, Aug. 24, 1968. B.S., N.D. State U., 1957, L.H.D. (hon.); M.S., U. Ill., 1959; Ph.D., U. Wis., 1972. Librarian Marquette U., 1959-60, 62-63; exchange librarian Plymouth (Eng.) Pub. Library, 1960-61; asst. head serials div. Yale U. Library, 1963-65, head, 1965-68; vis. lectr. U. Wis., Madison, 1970-71, U. Chgo., 1975; exec. sec. Assn. Coll. and Research Libraries, 1972-76; univ. librarian U. Ill.-Chgo., 1977-89; dean Grad. Sch. Libr. and Info. Sci. UCLA, 1989-94, prof. Grad. Sch. Edn. and Info. Studies, 1989—. Author: (with Thomas J. Galvin) Priorities for Academic Libraries, 1982, Management Strategies for Libraries, 1985, Academic Library in Transition, 1989, Information Technology and the University, 1995. Named Acad. Librarian of Yr., 1981. Mem. ALA (pres. 1985-86), Acad. Mgmt., Am. Sociol. Assn., Bibliog. Soc. Am., Caxton Club, The Chicago Network, Grolier Club, Arts Club Chgo., Phi Kappa Phi. Office: UCLA Grad Sch Edn and Info Mailbox 91521 3026 Moore Hall Los Angeles CA 90025-1521

LYNCH, CHARLES ALLEN, investment executive, corporate director; b. Denver, Sept. 7, 1927; s. Laurence J. and Louanna (Robertson) L.; divorced; children: Charles A., Tara O'Hara, Casey Alexander; m. Justine Bailey, Dec. 27, 1992. BS, Yale U., 1950. With E.I. duPont de Nemours & Co., Inc., Wilmington, Del., 1950-69, dir. mktg., 1965-69; corp. v.p. SCOA Industries, Columbus, Ohio, 1969-72; corp. exec. v.p., also mem. rotating bd. W.R. Grace & Co., N.Y.C., 1972-78; chmn. bd., chief exec. officer Saga Corp., Menlo Park, Calif., 1978-86, also dir.; chmn., chief exec. officer DHL Airways, Inc., Redwood City, Calif., 1986-88; also dir.; pres., chief exec. officer Levolor Corp., 1988-89, also bd. dir., chmn. exec. com. of bd., 1989-90; chmn. Market Value Ptnrs. Co., Menlo Park, Calif., 1990-95; chmn., dir. Fresh Choice, Inc., Santa Clara, Calif., 1995—; chmn., 1995—; also bd. dirs.; bd. dirs. Pacific Mut. Life Inst. Co., Nordstrom, Inc., PST Vans, Inc., SRI Internat., Palo Alto Med. Found., Age Wave, Inc.; chmn. BJ Holdings, Inc., La Salsa Franchise, Inc. Bd. dirs. United Way, 1990-92, past chmn. Bay Area campaign, 1987; chmn., dir. Bay Area Coun.; past chmn. Calif. Bus. Roundtable; mem. adv. bd. U. Calif.-Berkeley Bus. Sch., Governance Bd. Mem. Yale Club (N.Y.C.), Internat. Lawn Tennis Club, Menlo Country Club (Calif.), Pacific Union Club (San Francisco), Coral Beach and Tennis Club (Bermuda), Vintage Club (Indian Wells, Calif.), Menlo Circus Club. Republican. Home: 96 Ridgeview Dr Atherton CA 94027 Office: 2901 Tasman Dr # 109 Santa Clara CA 95054

LYNCH, CHARLES ANDREW, chemical company executive; b. Bklyn., Jan. 6, 1935; s. Charles Andrew and Mary Martina (McEvoy) L.; m. Marilyn Anne Monaco, July 30, 1960; children: Nancy Callan, Cara Martina. BS, Manhattan Coll., 1956; PhD, U. Notre Dame, 1960. Rsch. chemist Esso Rsch. & Engring. Co., Linden, N.J., 1960-65; rsch. supr. FMC Corp., Organic Chem. Div., Balt., 1965-72; rsch. mgr. FMC Corp., Indsl. Chem. Div., Princeton, N.J., 1972-74; exec. v.p. Am. Oil & Supply Co., Newark, 1974-80; tech. dir., dir. sales & mktg., dir. rsch. & bus. devel., v.p. tech. Hatco Corp., Fords, N.J., 1981-95; with Calivera Cons., 1995—. Contbr. articles to profl. jours.; patentee in field (U.S. and foreign). Mem. Am. Chem. Soc., Am. Oil Chemists Soc., Soc. Automotive Engrs., Soc. Tribiologists and Lubrication Engrs. (N.Y. sect. chmn. 1980-81), Ind. Lubricant Mfrs. Assn. (bd. dirs. 1985-88), Commercial Devel. Assn., Chem. Mgmt. and Resources Assn. Office: Hatco Corp 1020 King George Post Rd Fords NJ 08863

LYNCH, CHARLES J., secondary school principal. Prin. St. Isaac Joques Sch., Hinsdale, Ill. Recipient Elem. Sch. Recognition award U.S. Dept. Edn., 1989-90. Office: St Isaac Joques Sch 421 S Clay St Hinsdale IL 60521-4087

LYNCH, CHARLES THEODORE, SR., materials science engineering researcher, administrator, educator; b. Lima, Ohio, May 17, 1932; s. John Richard and Helen (Dunn) L.; m. Betty Ann Korkolis, Feb. 3, 1956; children: Karen Elaine Ostdiek, Charles Theodore Jr., Richard Anthony, Thomas Edward. BS, George Washington U., 1955; MS, U. Ill., 1957, PhD in Analytical Chemistry, 1960. Group leader ceramics div. Air Force Materials Lab., Wright-Patterson AFB, Ohio, 1962-66; lectr. in chemistry Wright State U., Dayton, Ohio, 1964-66; chief advanced metall. studies br. Air Force Materials Lab., Wright-Patterson AFB, Ohio, 1966-74, sr. scientist, 1974-81; head materials div. Office of Naval Rsch., Arlington, Va., 1981-85; pvt. practice cons. Washington, 1985-88; sr. engr. space ops. Vitro Corp., Washington, 1988—; USAF liaison mem. NMAB Panels on Solids Processing, Ion Implantation and Environ. Cracking, Washington, 1955-68, 78, 81; U.S. rep. AGARD structures and materials panel NATO, 1983-85. Co-author: Metal Matrix Composites, 1972; editor, author: Practical Handbook of Materials Science, 1989; editor: (series) Handbook of Materials Science, vol. I, 1974, vol. II, 1975, vol. III, 1975; vice chmn. editorial bd. Vitro Corp. Tech. Jour., 1989-92, chmn., 1993; contbr. articles to profl. jours. including Jour. Am. Ceramics Soc., Analytical Chemistry, Sci., Transactions AIME, Corr. Jour., Jour. Inorganic Chemistry, SAMPE, Jour. Less Common Metals. Mem., soloist George Washington U. Traveling Troubadours, Washington, 1950-55; choir dir. Trinity United Ch. of Christ, Fairborn, Ohio, 1966-81, Univ. Bapt. Ch., Champaign, Ill., 1957-60, Chapel II, Wright-Patterson AFB, Ohio, 1960-64; pres. Pub. Sch. PTO, 1967-69. 1st lt. USAF, 1960-62. Bailey scholar U. Ill., 1958-60; recipient Commendation medal USAF, 1962, Outstanding Achievement cert. NASA, 1992, award Soc. for Tech. Comm. Publ., 1993. Mem. Am. Chem. Soc. (treas. 1966-67, chmn. audit sect. 1967-68), ASM Internat. (sec. oxidation and corrosion com. 1980-81, chmn. 1981-82). Presbyterian. Achievements include patents for new corrosion inhibitors including encapsulated types, and for alkoxides and oxides; co-development of the refractory ceramic Zyttrite, the first high density translucent zirconia made from thermal or hydrolytic decomposition of mixed alkoxides followed by hot pressing; pioneered general approach of organometallic compounds as precursors of high purity, fine particulate, materials. Home: 5629 Kemp Ln Burke VA 22015-2041 Office: Vitro Corp Space Ops 400 Virginia Ave SW Ste 825 Washington DC 20024-2730

LYNCH, DANIEL, newspaper editor, writer; b. Elmira, N.Y., Feb. 27, 1946; s. Joseph Patrick and Betty (Reed) L.; m. Donna L. Rimmer, Aug. 16, 1969; children: Kathleen Ellen, Kevin Rimmer. BS, Temple U., 1969. Polit. reporter Phila. Inquirer, 1970-74; Queens editor Newsday, L.I., N.Y., 1974-79; mng. editor Times Union, Albany, N.Y., 1979—; bd. dirs. N.Y. State AP. Author: (novels) Deadly Ernest, 1986, A Killing Frost, 1987, Deathly Pale, 1988, Brennan's Point, 1988, Bad Fortune, 1989, Yellow, 1992. Sgt. N.J. Air N.G., 1969-75. Named Author of Yr. Albany Pub. Libr., 1989; recipient first prize award for columns N.Y. AP, 1988. Mem. N.Y. State Soc. Newspaper Editors (pres. 1990-91), N.Y. AP Assn. (pres. 1994—). Roman Catholic. Avocations: sailing, fly fishing, painting. Office: Times Union News Pl PO Box 15000 Albany NY 12212-5000

LYNCH, DAVID K., film director, writer; b. Missoula, Mont., Jan. 20, 1946; s. Donald and Sunny L.; m. Peggy Reavey, 1967 (div.); daughter: Jennifer; m. Mary Fisk, 1977 (div.); son: Austin. Ed., Pa. Acad. Fine Arts, Philadelphia. Co-screenwriter, dir.: (films) Eraserhead, 1978, The Elephant Man, 1980 (Acad. award), Dune, 1984; screenwriter, dir.: (films) Blue Velvet,

1986, Wild at Heart, 1990 (Palme d'Or, Cannes Internat. Film Festival), Twin Peaks: Fire Walk With Me, 1992; creator: (TV series) Twin Peaks, 1990, American Chronicles, 1990, On the Air, 1992, Hotel Room, 1993, (performance piece) Industrial Symphony #1, 1989. Am. Film Inst. grantee. Mem. Dirs. Guild Am. Office: CAA 9830 Wilshire Blvd Beverly Hills CA 90212-1804*

LYNCH, DAVID WILLIAM, physicist, educator; b. Rochester, N.Y., July 14, 1932; s. William J. and Eleanor (Fouratt) L.; m. Joan N. Hill, Aug. 29, 1954 (dec. Nov. 1989); children: Jean Louise, Richard William, David Allan; m. Glenys R. Bittick, Nov. 14, 1992. B.S., Rensselaer Poly. Inst., 1954; M.S., U. Ill., 1955, Ph.D., 1958. Asst. prof. physics Iowa State U., 1959-63, assoc. prof., 1963-66, prof., 1966—, chmn. dept., 1985-90, disting. prof. liberal arts and scis., 1985—; on leave at U. Hamburg, Germany; dir. Microelectronics Rsch. Ctr. Iowa State U., 1995—; and U. Rome, Italy, 1968-69; sr. physicist Ames Lab. of Dept. of Energy; acting assoc. dir. Synchrotron Radiation Ctr., Stoughton, Wis., 1984; vis. prof. U. Hamburg, summer 1974. Fulbright scholar U. Pavia, Italy, 1958-59. Fellow Am. Phys. Soc.; mem. Optical Soc. Am., AAAS. Research on solid state physics. Home: 3315 Ross Rd Ames IA 50014-3959

LYNCH, EDWARD STEPHEN, corporate executive; b. Holyoke, Mass., Oct. 5, 1911; s. Edward Joseph and Katherine Veronica (Moriarty) L.; m. Anna Azzariti, Aug. 3, 1946; children—Julia M., Edward G., Robert G., Stephen G. A.B., Amherst Coll., 1931; M.A., Harvard U., 1934, Ph.D., 1936. Instr. econs. Princeton, 1935-38; asst. prof. econs. Iowa State Coll., 1938-41; chief supply ops. Allied Commn., Rome and Unrra Italy, 1945-46; chief economist IBRD, Washington, 1946-48; chief economist, acting exec. v.p. Export-Import Bank Washington, 1948-59; v.p. overseas cos. Westinghouse Internat., 1960-66; v.p., treas. ITT Europe, Inc., Brussels, Belgium, 1966—; v.p. ITT Corp., 1973-76; cons., 1976—; cons. economist Sogen Swiss Internat. Corp., N.Y.C., 1977—; consultore Prefecture of Econ. Affairs of the Holy See, Vatican City, 1979-93. Served with AUS, 1943-45. Inducted into Holyoke High Sch. Hall of Fame, 1988; Amherst Meml. fellow, 1932, Henry Lee fellow, 1934-35; Christopher Weld scholar, 1933. Mem. Am. Econs. Assn., Council on Fgn. Relations, Phi Beta Kappa. Home: Via Salaria 408, 00199 Rome Italy

LYNCH, ELOISE, state legislator; b. Sept. 2, 1927. Student, Kans. Wesleyan; MA, Kans. State U., 1961; PhD, U. Kans., 1981. Former tchr.; mem. Kans. Ho. of Reps. Democrat. Home: 705 S Santa Fe Ave Salina KS 67401-4944 Office: Kans State Senate State Capital Topeka KS 66612

LYNCH, EUGENE F., federal judge; b. 1931. B.S., U. Santa Clara, 1953; LL.B., U. Calif., 1958. Assoc. O'Connor, Moran, Cohn & Lynch, San Francisco 1959-64, ptnr., 1964-71; judge Mcpl. Ct., San Francisco 1971-74; justice Superior Ct. City and County San Francisco, 1974-82; judge U.S. Dist. Ct. (no. dist.) Calif., San Francisco, 1982—. Office: US Dist Ct PO Box 36060 450 Golden Gate Ave San Francisco CA 94102

LYNCH, FRANCIS CHARLES, lawyer; b. Pittsfield, Mass., Nov. 4, 1944; s. Frank Charles and Elizabeth Ellen (Dowd) L.; m. Sally Mapp Walker, June 24, 1972; children: William Mapp, Edward Walker, Katherine Francis. Student, London Sch. Econs., 1964-65; BS summa cum laude, Boston Coll., 1966; LLB, Yale U., 1969. Bar: S.D. 1969, Rosebud Sioux Tribal Ct. 1969, Oglala Sioux Tribal Ct. 1970, U.S. Dist. Ct. S.D. 1970, U.S. Dist. Ct. Mass. 1971, U.S. Ct. Appeals (1st cir.) 1973, U.S. Supreme Ct. 1980. Reginald Haber Smith fellow Rosebud Legal Svcs., Rosebud, S.D., 1969-70; assoc. Featherston, Homans & Klubock, Boston, 1971-73, Goodwin, Procter & Hoar, Boston, 1973-76; ptnr. Lynch & Walker, Boston, 1976; assoc. Newman & Meserve, Boston, 1977-78; assoc. Palmer & Dodge, Boston, 1978-79, ptnr., 1980—; asst. bar counsel Bd. Bar Overseers, Boston, 1976-77; commr. Mass. Com. Against Discrimination, Boston, 1973; lectr. profl. seminars. Contbr. articles to profl. jours. Trustee Bank Five for Savs., Arlington, Mass., 1980-87. Mem. Boston Bar Assn. (chair com. on fed. appointment of counsel/indigents plaintiffs in civil cases 1982-89). Democrat. Avocations: squash, tennis, golf. Home: 44 Woodland Rd Newton MA 02166-2322 Office: Palmer & Dodge 1 Beacon St Boston MA 02108-3106

LYNCH, FRANK JOSEPH, insurance company executive; b. S.I., N.Y., Mar. 19, 1930; s. Frank J. and May (McBreen) L.; m. Patricia Crane, Apr. 27, 1957; children—Frank, Michael, Megan, Carmel. B.A., Wagner Coll., 1951; LL.B., N.Y. Law Sch., 1962. Bar: N.Y. 1962. Underwriter Fireman's Fund Ins. Co., N.Y.C., 1950-53; analyst Ebasco Services, Inc., N.Y.C., 1954-55; with U.S. Aviation Underwriters, Inc., N.Y.C., 1956—; sr. v.p., chief underwriter, 1971-72, pres., 1972-77, chmn. bd., chief exec. officer, 1977—. Chmn. bd. trustees Delbarton Prep Sch., Morristown, N.J., 1982—; Chestnut Hill Coll., Pa., 1984—; Morris Mus., Morristown, 1984—; Tri-County Scholarship Fund, Paterson, N.J., 1984—; Wall St. Club, Spring-brook Golf Club, Baltusrol Golf Club, County Club of the Rockies. With USNR, 1947-51, USAF, 1951. Republican. Roman Catholic. Home: Crestley Van Beuren Rd Morristown NJ 07960 Office: US Aviation Underwriters Inc One Seaport Pla 199 Water St New York NY 10038-3526

LYNCH, GERALD JOHN, management consultant; b. Detroit, Feb. 22, 1906; s. Patrick John and Julia (O'Meara) L.; m. Mary Romaine Livernois, July 20, 1937 (dec. Jan. 1988); children: Terence, Rose Mary Korostoff, Laura Lee Lynch Foley, Gerald John, Julie Anne (Mrs. Steven S. Russell); m. Carmela J. Lombadi, Nov. 4, 1989. AB, Wayne U., 1929, MA, 1935; JD, U. Detroit, 1933; DBA (hon.), U. Dayton. Bar: Mich. bar 1933. Pvt. practice Detroit, 1933-42; dir. war contract adminstrn. dept. Fisher Body divsn. GM, 1942-46; dir. war contract adminstrn. dept., exec. asst. controller, dir. Washington office; exec. asst. to group exec. tractor and internat. group, dir. Office Def. Products and Govtl. Rels., Ford Motor Co., 1946-56; pres. subs. Office Def. Products and Govtl. Rels. Ford Motor Co. (Aerountronic Sys., Inc.), 1956-59, v.p., gen. mgr. aeronutronic divsn., 1959-62, group v.p. def. products, 1960-62; chmn. bd. Menasco Mfg. Co., 1962-81; dir., group v.p., cons. to chmn. Colt Industries Inc., Burbank, Calif., 1981-87; mgmt. cons. Pasadena, Calif., 1988—. Trustee Don Bosco Tech. Inst.; bd. dirs. St. John's Seminary. Mem. Met. Club (Washington), Calif. Club (L.A.), Annandale Club, Ironwood Country Club, Eldorado Club, Univ. Club. Office: 301 E Colorado Blvd Ste 900 Pasadena CA 91101-1911 also: 49-196 Quercus Ln Palm Desert CA 92260

LYNCH, GERALD WELDON, college president, psychologist; b. N.Y.C., Mar. 24, 1937; s. Edward Dewey and Alice Margaret (Weldon) L.; m. Eleanor Gay Sherry, Dec. 5, 1970; children: Timothy, Elizabeth. B.S., Fordham Univ., 1958; Ph.D., N.Y. U., 1968. Tech. employment rep. Bell Telephone Labs., N.Y.C., 1958-63; psychologist VA Hosp., N.Y., Palo Alto, Calif., 1964-68; asst. prof. psychology John Jay Coll. Criminal Justice, N.Y.C., 1967-71; dir. student activities John Jay Coll. Criminal Justice, 1968-70, asso. prof., 1971-74, prof., 1974—, dean students, 1968-71, v.p., 1971-76, pres., 1976—; chmn. Use of Force in Jails, N.Y.C., 1987—. Contbr. articles to profl. jours. Chmn. N.Y.C. Police Found., 1972-96; mem. N.Y. State Casino Gambling Study Panel, 1979, N.Y. State Fire Fighting Pers. Edn. and Stds. Com., 1980—, Westchester County Spl. Task Force on Dept. Pub. Safety Svcs.; mem. N.Y. State Fire Safety Task Force, 1981, N.Y. State Crime Control Planning Bd., 1979-86; chmn. bd. advisors Channel 13, 1984-87; chmn. N.Y.C. Fire Safety Found., 1984—; vice chmn. U.S. Marshals Found., 1987—; pres. Cath. Interracial Coun., 1990—; chmn. Mayoral Search Com. for Police and Fire Commn. Recipient Criminal Justice award N.Y. State Bar Assn., 1977; Disting. Alumni award in edn. Fordham Coll. Alumni Assn., 1978; Brotherhood award NCCJ, 1985; named Person of Yr., N.Y.C. chpt. Indsl. Security Assn., 1987, N.Y.C. Police Dept. Patrolwomen's Endowment Assn., 1987, Man of Yr., Police Self Support Group, 1989. Mem. Acad. Criminal Justice Scis., Am. Soc. Criminology, Am. Assn. State Colls. and Univs., AAAS, Am. Psychol. Assn. Democrat. Roman Catholic. Office: CUNY John Jay Coll Criminal Justice 899 10th Ave New York NY 10019

LYNCH, GERARD E., law educator; b. N.Y.C., Sept. 4, 1951; s. Gerard Norman and Marjorie Ann (Werner) L.; m. Karen Marisak, June 10, 1972; 1 child, Christopher Marisak Lynch. BA, Columbia U., 1972, JD, 1975. Bar: N.Y. 1976, U.S. Supreme Ct., U.S. Ct. Appeals (2d, 4th and D.C. cirs.). Law clk. U.S. Ct. Appeals, N.Y.C., 1975-76, U.S. Supreme Ct., Washington,

1976-77; asst. U.S. atty. So. Dist. N.Y., N.Y.C., 1980-83; chief criminal div. U.S. Dist. Ct. (so. dist.) N.Y., N.Y.C., 1990-92; assoc. independent counsel Iran/Contra, 1988-90; asst. prof. Columbia U., N.Y.C., 1977-80, assoc. prof., 1980-87, prof. law, 1987—, vice dean, 1993—; of counsel Howard, Darby & Levin, N.Y.C., 1992—. Office: Columbia U Sch Law 435 W 116th St New York NY 10027-7201

LYNCH, HARRY JAMES, biologist; b. Glenfield, Pa., Jan. 18, 1929; s. Harry James and Rachel (McComb) L.; m. Pokum Lee Lynch. BS, Geneva Coll., Beaver Falls, Pa., 1957; PhD, U. Pitts., 1971; postgrad. Bio-Space Tech. Tng. Program, NASA and U. Va., 1970. Clin. chemist West Penn Hosp., Pitts., 1955-56; grad. teaching asst. U. Pitts., 1966-71, sr. teaching fellow, 1971; postdoctoral fellow MIT, Cambridge, 1973-75, rsch. assoc. dept. nutrition, lab. neuroendocrine regulation, 1973-75, lectr., 1976-81, rsch. scientist dept. brain and cognitive sci., 1982-92; cons. Ctr. for Brain Scis. and Metabolism Charitable Trust, 1992—. Contbr. more than 60 articles on the pineal gland to profl. jours. and books; patentee on implantable programmed microinfusion apparatus, 1981. With USN, 1950-54. NIH postdoctoral fellow 1971-73. Mem. Soc. Light Treatment and Biol. Rhythms. Democrat. Avocation: study of animal behavior. Office: MIT E25-615 77 Massachusetts Ave Cambridge MA 02139-4307

LYNCH, HOLLIS RALPH, history educator; b. Port de Spain, Trinidad and Tabago, Apr. 21, 1935; came to U.S., 1966; s. Rupert Herman and Violet Evangeline (Gardiner) L.; m. Sharon Ann Fisher, Apr. 7, 1966 (div. Dec. 1978); children: Shola Ayn, Nnenna Jean, Ashale Herman, Oklemeno John. BA, U. B.C., Vancouver, Can., 1960; PhD, U. London, 1964. Lectr. U. Ife (Nigeria), 1964-66; assoc. prof. Roosevelt U., Chgo., 1966-68, SUNY, Buffalo, 1968-69; prof. history Columbia U., N.Y.C., 1969—, dir. Inst. African Studies, 1971-74, 86—. Author: Edward Wilmot Blyden, 1967, Black American Radicals and the Liberation of Africa, 1978; editor: The Black Urban Condition, 1973. Mem. adv. council U.S Archives for N.E., N.Y., 1975-77. Woodrow Wilson Internat. Ctr. for Scholars Research fellow, 1976, Am. Council Learned Socs. Research fellow, 1978-79. Mem. Am. Hist. Assn. (com. of coms. 1973), Assn. African Studies. Avocations: tennis, chess, dancing. Office: Columbia U Dept of History 420 W 118th St New York NY 10027-7213

LYNCH, JAMES ALEXANDER, architect; b. Ames, Iowa, July 24, 1923; s. Verne Marquis and Lorretta (Munson) L.; m. Helen Peterson, Feb. 1, 1958; children: Michael J., Douglas R. BS, Iowa State U., 1949. Reg. profl. architect & engr., Iowa. Intern architect Brooks-Borg, Des Moines, 1949-52, James Allan, Omaha, 1952; architect Noel Wallace, Omaha, 1953-54, Amos Emery, Des Moines, 1955, Normile & Lynch, Des Moines, 1956-59, Russell & Lynch, Des Moines, 1959-65, James Lynch & Assocs., Des Moines, 1966-68, 79—, Lynch Payne Champion Bernabe, Des Moines, 1969-79; pres. Iowa Bd. Architect Examiners, 1973-82; mem. City of Des Moines Archtl. Adv. Com., 1993—. Chmn. Archtl. Adv. Com. to Urban Renewal Bd., Des Moines, 1969-73; mem. Bldg. Code Bd. Appeals, Des Moines, 1958, Gov's. Economy Com., 1979. Mem. AIA (Iowa chpt. 1966, bldg. design awards 1967, 68, 70), Des Moines Club (pres. 1976), Rotary. Republican. Avocations: flying, wine, cooking, photography, sketching. Office: Lynch & Quick Assocs PC 206 6th Ave Ste 700 Des Moines IA 50309

LYNCH, JAMES C., newspaper editor. Exec. editor The Daily News, N.Y.C. Office: The Daily News 220 E 42 St Ste 817 New York NY 10017*

LYNCH, JAMES HENRY, JR., lawyer; b. Union City, N.J., Mar. 15, 1931; s. James Henry and Henrietta May (Sitler) L.; m. Jacqueline Van Hook, Feb. 24, 1962; children—James III, Lisa. Student, Rutgers U.; J.D., Columbia U., 1958. Bar: N.Y. 1959. Asst. gen. counsel assn. Stock Exchange Firms, N.Y.C., 1960-66; adminstrv. v.p. Glore Forgan, N.Y.C., 1966-70; ptnr. Dupont Glore Forgan, N.Y.C., 1970-72; exec. v.p. Dupont Walston, N.Y.C., 1972-74; ptnr. Spear Leeds & Kellogg, N.Y.C., 1974-85, ret.; chmn Sherwood Securities, N.Y.C., Consol. Purchasing Svcs., Inc., Bernardsville, N.J. Trustee Found. for Ednl. Advancement, Newark, 1982—, Edn. for Youth Soc., Scotch Plains, N.J., 1982—, Mayor Tewksbery Zormship, N.J. Served to capt. U.S. Army, 1951-54, W. Ger. Mem. City Midday Club (N.Y.C.), Black River Club. Roman Catholic. Office: Spear Leeds & Kellogg PO Box 18 Pottersville NJ 07979

LYNCH, JOHN A., lawyer, state senator; b. New Brunswick, N.J., Oct. 21, 1938; s. John A. Lynch; m. Deborah A. Lynch; children: Patricia, John P., Matthew J. L. Grad. Holy Cross Coll., 1960; LLB, Georgetown U., 1963. Bar: N.J. 1963; ptnr. Lynch, Martin, Philobosian, Chansky, Fitzgerald & Kane, North Brunswick, Brielle and Somerville; pres. N.J. Senate, 1990-92, minority leader, 1992—; mayor City of New Brunswick, 1979-91. Mem. Gov's Commn. on Sci. and Tech. Mem. Middlesex County Trial Lawyers Assn. (past pres.). Home: 11 Cotter Dr New Brunswick NJ 08901-1506 Office: 100 Bayard St New Brunswick NJ 08901-2102 also: NJ State Senate Trenton NJ 08625

LYNCH, JOHN BROWN, plastic surgeon, educator; b. Akron, Ohio, Feb. 5, 1929; s. John A. and Eloise L.; student Vanderbilt U., 1946-49; M.D., U. Tenn., 1952; children: John Brown, Margaret Frances Lynch Callihan; m. Mary Joyce Burrus, Dec. 1, 1994. Rotating intern John Gaston Hosp., Memphis, Tenn., 1953-54; resident in gen. surgery U. Tex. Med. Br., Galveston, 1956-59, resident in plastic surgery, 1959-62, instr., 1962, asst. prof. surgery, 1962-67, asso. prof., 1967-72, prof., 1972-73; prof. plastic surgery, chmn. dept. plastic surgery Vanderbilt U. Med. Center, 1973—. Served as capt. USAF, 1954-56. Diplomate Am. Bd. Plastic Surgery (chmn.). Fellow ACS; mem. Singleton Surg. Soc. (pres. 1982-83), AMA, Am. Soc. Plastic and Reconstructive Surgeons (pres. 1983-84), Am. Assn. Plastic Surgeons, Plastic Surgery Research Council, Am. Cleft Palate Assn., Am. Burn Assn., Soc. Head and Neck Surgeons, Internat. Burn Assn., Pan Am. Med. Assn., Am. Cancer Soc. (pres. Galveston County, Tex., Chpt. 1968), So. Med. Assn. (pres.-elect 1983-84), Tenn. med. Assn., Nashville Acad. Medicine, Tenn. Soc. Plastic Surgeons, Southeastern Soc. Plastic Surgeons, Southeastern Surg. Soc., H. William Scott, Jr. Soc., Nashville Surg. Soc., Am. Soc. Maxillofacial Surgeons, So. Surg. Assn., Am. Surg. Assn., Sigma Xi. Contbr. numerous articles to med. publs.; editor: (with S.R. Lewis) Symposium on the Treatment of Burns, 1973. Home: 5810 Hillsboro Rd Nashville TN 37215 Office: Vanderbilt Hosp Rm 230mcs Nashville TN 37232

LYNCH, JOHN EDWARD, JR., lawyer; b. Lansing, Mich., May 3, 1952; s. John Edward and Miriam Ann (Hyland) L.; m. Brenda Jayne Clark, Nov. 16, 1984; children: John E. III, Robert C., David B., Patrick D., Jacqueline E. AB, Hamilton Coll., 1974; JD, Case Western Res. U., 1977. Bar: Conn. 1978, Ohio 1980, U.S. Dist. Ct. (no. dist.) Ohio 1980, U.S. Ct. Appeals (6th cir.) 1980. Assoc. Thompson, Weir & Barclay, 1977-78; law clk. U.S. Dist. Judge, Cleve., 1978-80; assoc. Squire, Sanders and Dempsey, Cleve., 1980-86, ptnr., 1986—; master bencher Am. Inns of Ct. Found., 1987—; mem. civil justice reform act adv. group U.S. Dist. Ct. (no. dist.) Ohio. Del. Hamilton Coll. Alumni Coun., 1992—, regional chair alumni admissions, 1993—; mem. Cuyahoga County Rep. exec. com. (Cleve.), 1984—; mem. Seton Soc. St. Vincent Hosp. Fund. Mem. The Club (Cleve.). Roman Catholic. Avocations: golf, jogging. Home: 6075 Deepwood Dr Chagrin Falls OH 44022-2569 Office: Squire Sanders & Dempsey 4900 Society Ctr Cleveland OH 44114

LYNCH, JOHN JOSEPH, electronics company executive; b. Boston, Dec. 23, 1931; s. John James and Margaret Joan (Crowley) L.; m. Christine Mary Sullivan, Feb. 13, 1954; children: John J. II, Christine M. O'Hurley, Michael J., Kevin C., James M. BSBA, Boston Coll., 1953; MBA, Harvard, 1958. Asst. mgr. internat. audit Raytheon, Lexington, Mass., 1958-61; contr. U.S. Sonics Corp., Cambridge, Mass., 1961-62; treas., bus. mgr Adams-Russell Electronics Co., Inc., Waltham, Mass., 1962-70; dir. Adams-Russell Electronics Co., Inc., 1964—, v.p. fin., 1970-80, pres., chief ops. officer, 1980-82, pres., chief exec. officer, 1982-88; chmn., chief exec. officer Adams-Russell Electronics Co., Inc. (name changed to Adams-Russell, Inc.), 1988-89; pres., chief operating officer M/A-Com Inc., Burlington, Mass., 1989—; bd. dirs. SofTech, Inc., Waltham, Mass. High Tech. Coun., Boston. Trustee Associated Cath. Hosps., Brighton, Mass., 1984—, Mass. Eye and Ear Infirmary, Boston, 1986—; bd. dirs. Am. Heart Assn. Mass. Affilitate, Needham, 1984-

88. Lt. USNR, 1953-56, Western Pacific and Newport, R.I. Office: M/A-Com Inc 60 South Ave # 507 Burlington MA 01803-4904

LYNCH, JOHN PATRICK, classics educator, university official; b. Great Barrington, Mass., Aug. 30, 1943; s. John Joseph and Sophia (Pruhenski) L.; m. Sheilah Eileen Fulbright, Sept. 21, 1973; children—Bernadette, Brendan. B.A. with high honors, Harvard U., 1965; M.A., Yale U., 1968, M.Phil., 1969, Ph.D., 1970. Cert. in archaeology, Am. Sch. Classical Studies, Athens, Greece, 1967. Asst. prof. classics U. Calif., Santa Cruz, 1970-73, assoc. prof., 1974-85, prof., 1985—, acting dean humanities, 1993, provost Cowell Coll., 1983-89, assoc. dir. Edn. Abroad Program, U. Calif. Study Ctr. in London, 1979-81; jr. fellow Harvard U. Ctr. Hellenic Studies, Washington, 1976-77; mem. Inst. Advanced Study, Princeton, N.J., 1989-90. Author: Aristotle's School, 1972; contbg. author: The Cambridge Ancient History, Vol. 6, 1994; editor: Second World and Green World, 1989. Fellow NEH, summer 1973, U. Calif. Humanities Inst., summer 1972, NDEA Title IV, 1967-70, Rotary Internat., 1966-67, Woodrow Wilson, 1965-66; Harvard Coll. scholar, 1961-65. Mem. Am. Philol. Assn. (Excellence in Teaching Classics award 1992), Calif. Classical Assn., Hellenic Soc. (U.K.), Petronian Soc., Virgilian Soc. Democrat. Roman Catholic. Home: 204 King St Santa Cruz CA 95060-3408 Office: U Calif Cowell College Santa Cruz CA 95064

LYNCH, JOHN PETER, lawyer; b. Chgo., June 5, 1942; s. Charles Joseph and Anne Mae (Loughlin) L.; m. Judy Godvin, Sept. 21, 1968; children: Julie, Jennifer. AB, Marquette U., 1964; JD, Northwestern U., 1967. Bar: Ill. 1967, U.S. Ct. Appeals (7th cir.) 1979, U.S. Ct. Appeals (5th cir.) 1976, U.S. Supreme Ct. 1979. Ptnr. Kirkland & Ellis, Chgo., 1973-76, Hedlund, Hunter & Lynch, Chgo., 1976-82, Latham, Watkins, Hedlund, Hunter & Lynch, Chgo., 1982-85, Latham & Watkins, Chgo., 1985—. Mem. vis. com. Northwestern U. Law Sch. Served as lt. USN, 1968-71. Mem. ABA, Ill. Bar Assn., Assn. Trial Lawyers Am., Order of Coif, City Club, Exec. Club, Met. Club. Notes and Comments editor Northwestern U. Law Rev., 1967. Home: 439 Sheridan Rd Kenilworth IL 60043-1220 Office: Latham & Watkins Ste 5800 Sears Tower Chicago IL 60606

LYNCH, JOHN T., management consultant; b. 1948. With Towers Perrin, N.Y.C., 1969—, pres., 1990—. Office: Towers Perrin 245 Park Ave New York NY 10167*

LYNCH, JOHN THOMAS, science foundation administrator, physicist; b. Washington, Mar. 21, 1938; s. John Thomas and Mary Ellen (Kaye) L.; m. Leslie Gray, June 22, 1959 (div. June 1972); children: John Thomas III, Michael Gray; m. Carol Richins, July 5, 1980. BS in Physics, Va. Poly. Inst., 1963; MS in Physics, U. Wis., 1965, PhD, 1972. Lab. technician Nat. Bur. Standards, Washington, 1957-60; rsch. scientist U. Wis., Madison, 1965-78; staff mem. Los Alamos (N.Mex.) Nat. Labs., 1978-81; program scientist NASA Hdqs., Washington, 1981-85; program dir. aeronomy and astrophysics Polar programs NSF, Washington, 1985—. Contbr. articles to sci. jours. Recipient Antarctic svc. medal USN, 1986. Mem. AAAS, Am. Geophys. Union, Astron. Soc. Pacific. Avocation: sailing. Office: NSF Polar Programs 4201 Wilson Blvd Arlington VA 22230

LYNCH, KEVIN A., book publishing executive. Pub. Paulist Press, Mahwah, N.J. Office: Paulist Press 997 Macarthur Blvd Mahwah NJ 07430-2045

LYNCH, LILLIAN, retired secondary education educator; b. Cairo, Ga., Aug. 28, 1937; d. Dave Royal Sr. and Georgie Ann (Walker) Cochran; m. William Howard Lynch, Dec. 17, 1960. BS, Ft. Valley State Coll., 1960; MEd, U. Ga., 1972. Cert. tchr. Ga. Tchr. home econs. Carver High Sch., Monroe, Ga., 1960-74, Monroe Area Comprehensive High Sch., 1974-92; ret., 1992; mem. adv. bd. mental health Monroe, Ga., 1980-85. Jury com-mr.City/Walton County Govt., Monroe, 1991—. Mem. Am. Vocat. Assn., Nat. Vocat. Vocat. Home Econs. Tchrs., NAACP, Ga. Vocat. Assn., Ga. Assn. Home Econs. Educators, Alpha Kappa Alpha. Democrat. Baptist. Avocations: recipes, aerobics, wedding cons., interior design. Home: 1620 Peters Cemetery Rd NE Monroe GA 30655

LYNCH, LINDA LOU, reading and language arts specialist/educator; b. L.A., Feb. 9, 1941; d. Alexander Alfred and Gizella Mary (Bajus) Laszloffy; m. John Joseph Lynch, June 13, 1964; children: Valerie Ann, Colinda Lee, Lee Anne Ellen. BS, Calif. State U. Northridge, 1964; MEd, Loyola Marymount U., L.A., 1990; EdD, Pepperdine U., 1995. Cert. tchr., Calif. Computer programmer Union Bank, L.A., 1962-64; substitute tchr. various sch. dists. Calif., 1964-68, 79-80; tchr. Richard H. Dana Mid. Sch., Hawthorne, Calif., 1980-88; reading specialist Wiseburn Sch. Dist., Hawthorne, 1988-91, 94—; elem. sch. tchr. Juan de Anza Elem. Sch., Hawthorne, 1991-93; reading specialist Wiseburn Sch. Dist., 1994—; adj. faculty mem. Loyola Marymount U., L.A., 1991—, dir. reading program Grad. Sch., 1992; tchs. asst. Pepperdine U., L.A., 1992-94, teaching asst., 1993, asst. dir. student tchrs., 1993, adj. prof., 1994—; adj. prof. Chapman U., L.A., 1995—. Mem. NEA, AAUW, ASCD, Am. Edn. Rsch. Assn., Internat. Reading Assn., Calif. Reading Assn., Ventura County Reading Assn., Calif. Tchrs. Assn., Wiseburn Faculty Assn., Phi Delta Kappa. Democrat. Roman Catholic. Home: 5443 W 119th St Inglewood CA 90304

LYNCH, MARTIN ANDREW, retail company executive; b. Chgo., Oct. 5, 1937; s. George Irwin and Cecilia Veronica (Corley) L.; m. Shirley Ann McKee, Oct. 20, 1962; children: Kathleen Marie, Kevin Michael, Karen Ann, Daniel Patrick, Michelle Eileen. BSc, DePaul U., 1962. CPA, Ill., Calif. Audit mgr. Price Waterhouse & Co., Chgo., 1962-69; asst. to pres. Scot Lad Foods, Chgo., 1969-70; v.p. fin. N.Am. Car Corp., Chgo., 1970-76; sr. v.p. fin. Tiger Internat. Inc., L.A., 1976-83; exec. v.p., chief fin. officer Duty Free Shoppers Group Ltd., San Francisco, 1983-89, Casino USA Inc., Santa Barbara, Calif., 1989—, Smart & Final Inc., Santa Barbara, 1989—. Mem. AICPA, Calif. CPA Soc., Fin. Execs. Inst., Nat. Assn. Whole Grogery, Inst. Food Distbn. Assn., Bel Air Country Club (L.A.). Roman Catholic. Avocations: jogging, swimming, skiing, golf. Office: Casino USA 524 Chapala St Santa Barbara CA 93101

LYNCH, MAXINE, newspaper executive b. Cleve.; children: Arana, Arrian. BS in Journalism, Kent State U., MPA, 1978. Publicist, dir. parks project Ohio Conservation Found.; copy desk intern Cleve. Press; reporter Akron Beacon Jour.; reporter Plain Dealer, Cleve., 1980-88, asst. city editor, 1988-89, asst. mng. editor personnel and adminstrn., 1989-90, mng. editor personnel, 1990—. Mem. Plymouth Ch., Shaker Heights. Mem. Am. Soc. Newspaper Editors, Soc. Profl. Journalists, AP Mng. Editors, Alpha Kappa Alpha, Press Club Cleve. Avocations: walking, creative dance. Office: The Plain Dealer 1801 Superior Ave E Cleveland OH 44114-2107*

LYNCH, MILTON TERRENCE, retired advertising agency executive; b. Denver, Feb. 27, 1931; s. Thomas Lillis and Pauline Regina (Yaeger) L.; m. Katherine Marie Stamey, July 19, 1958; children—Carrie Elizabeth, Michael Thomas, Brian Wilson. B.F.A., Washington State U., Pullman, 1953. Promotion mgr. Gen. Mills, Inc., Palo Alto, Calif., 1956-62; v.p. Robert Ebey Co., Palo Alto, Calif., 1962-66; exec. v.p. Steedman, Cooper & Busse, San Francisco, 1966-74; owner, prin. Lynch & Assocs., San Francisco, 1974-78; exec. v.p. Lynch & Rockey Advt., San Francisco, 1978-84; pres., chief exec. officer Evans/Lynch Rockey, Inc., San Francisco, 1984-87; chmn., chief exec. officer Evans/San Francisco, 1987-90; dir. Evans Communications, Salt Lake City. Served to capt. Inf. U.S. Army, 1953-55. Mem. San Francisco Advt. Golf Assn. (pres. 1982-83). Republican. Roman Catholic. Avocations: golf; tennis; gardening. Home: 12779 Homes Dr Saratoga CA 95070-4016

LYNCH, NANCY ANN, computer scientist, educator; b. Bklyn., Jan. 19, 1948; d. Roland David and Marie Catherine (Adinolfi) Evraets; m. Dennis Christopher Lynch, June 14, 1969; children: Patrick, Kathleen. BS, Bklyn. Coll., 1968; PhD, MIT, 1972. Asst. prof. math. Tufts U., Medford, Mass., 1972-73, U. So. Calif., Los Angeles, 1973-76, Fla. Internat. U., Miami, 1976-77; assoc. prof. computer sci. Ga. Tech. U., Atlanta, 1977-82; assoc. prof. computer sci. MIT, Cambridge, 1982-86, prof. computer sci., 1986—; Ellen Swallow Richards chair MIT, 1982-87; cons. Computer Corp. Am., Cambridge, 1984-86, Apollo Computer, Chelmsford, Mass., 1986-89, AT&T Bell Labs, Murray Hill, N.J., 1986-89, Digital Equipment Corp.,

1990. Contbr. numerous articles to profl. jours. Mem. Assn. Computing Machinery. Roman Catholic. Office: MIT NE43-525 Cambridge MA 02139

LYNCH, PATRICIA GATES, broadcasting organization executive consultant, former ambassador; b. Newark, Apr. 20, 1926; d. William Charles and Mary Frances (McNamee) Lawrence; m. Mahlon Eugene Gates, Dec. 19, 1942 (div. 1972); children: Pamela Townley Gates Sprague, Lawrence Alan; m. William Dennis Lynch. Student, Dartmouth Inst., 1975. Broadcaster Sta. WFAX-Radio, Falls Ch., Va., 1958-68; pub. TV host Sta. WETA, Washington, 1967-68; broadcaster NBC-Radio, Europe, Iran, USSR, 1960-61; internat. broadcaster, producer Voice of Am., Washington, 1962-69; staff asst. to First Lady The White House, Washington, 1969-70; host Voice of Am. Breakfast Show, Morning show, 1970-86; U.S. ambassador to Madagascar and the Comoros, 1986-89; dir. corp. affairs Radio Free Europe/Radio Liberty, Washington, 1989-94; worldwide lectr., 1968-86; adv. com. Ind. Fed. Savs. and Loan Assn., Washington, 1970-86. Author stories on Am. for English teaching dept. Radio Sweden, 1967-68, others on internat. broadcasting. Chair internat. svc. com. Washington chpt. ARC, 1979-86; bd. visitors Duke U., Durham, N.C. Grantee USIA, 1983; recipient Pub. Service award U.S. Army, 1960. Mem. Coun. Am. Ambs., (bd. dirs.), Assn. Diplomatic Studies and Tng. Dept. State (bd. dirs.), Am. Women in Radio and TV (pres. 1966-67), Am. News Women's Club, Washington Inst. Fgn. Affairs (bd. dirs.), Internat. Student House, D.C. (bd. dirs.). Republican. Episcopalian. Avocations: travelling, reading, volunteer work, wildlife conservation.

LYNCH, PATRICK, lawyer; b. Pitts., Nov. 11, 1941; s. Thomas Patrick and Helen Mary (Grimes) L.; m. M. Linda Maturo, June 20, 1964; children: Megan, Kevin, Colin, Brendan, Erin, Brian, Liam, Eamonn, Kilian, Caitlin, Ryan, Declan, Cristin, Mairin, Sean. BA in Philosophy, Loyola U., Los Angeles, 1964, LLB, 1966. Bar: Calif. 1967, U.S. Dist. Ct. (cen., so., no. and ea. dists.) Calif., U.S. Ct. Appeals (9th cir.), U.S. Supreme Ct. Ptnr. O'Melveny & Myers, Los Angeles, 1966—; panelist PLI Annual Antitrust Law Inst., 1982-93. Bd. editors Matthew Bender Fed. Litigation Guide Reporter. Fellow Am. Coll. Trial Lawyers; mem. L.A. County Bar Assn. Office: O'Melveny & Myers 400 S Hope St Los Angeles CA 90071

LYNCH, PATRICK, petroleum company executive; b. 1937. BBA, Iona Coll., 1959. Traveling auditor Texaco Inc., White Plains, N.Y., 1961-67, asst. mgr., 1967-74, asst. compt., 1974-79, dep. compt., 1979-80, assoc. compt., 1980-85, sr. asst. treas., gen. mgr. fin. dept., 1986-88, dep. treas., gen. mgr. fin. dept., 1986-88, compt., 1988—. Office: Texaco Inc 2000 Westchester Ave White Plains NY 10650-0002

LYNCH, PAUL VINCENT, safety engineer, consultant; b. Bklyn., Apr. 11, 1932; s. John Andrew and Mary Catherine L.; m. Nancy Gates; children: David, Marianne. BA, St. Anselm's Coll., Manchester, N.H., 1954; postgrad. Fordham U., 1958-59, U. N.H., 1969-71. Registered profl. engr. in safety engring., Calif. Corp. ins. specialist Allied Chem. Corp., 1959-66; asst. to dir. risk mgmt. Am. Metal Climax, Inc., N.Y.C., 1966-68; lectr. risk mgmt., adminstr. safety U. N.H., Durham, 1969-71; assoc. prof. safety N.H. Vocat.-Tech. Coll., 1971-75; pres. Lynch Assocs., Inc., cons., Pittsfield, N.H., 1972-75; regional safety officer GSA, 1976-79; safety mgr. Calif. Bur. Land Mgmt., U.S. Dept. of Interior, Sacramento, 1979-86, bur. def. liaison officer and dep. dept. def. liaison officer Region IX Fed. Emergency Mgmt. Assn., 19979-86, emergency preparedness and disaster planning coord., 1979-86, chief safety mgmt. Bur. Land Mgmt. U.S. Dept. Interior, Washington, 1986-94, ret., 1994; guest lectr. in risk mgmt. Am. Mgmt. Assn., 1959-68; v.p. N.H. Safety Coun., 1972-74; mem. Vt. Roundtable for Fire and Bldg. Safety, 1972-75, Vt. Adv. Coun. on Fire Safety, 1972-75; advisor Vt. Occupl. Safety and Health Rev. Bd., 1972-75; instr. safety mgmt. Am. River Coll., Sacramento, 1975-76; pvt. cons., 1994—. Prodr., host Around Town, Hingham (Mass.) Cmty. TV, 1994—. Active Boy Scouts Am., 1962—, dist. vice chmn. Nat. Capitol Area coun., 1987-92, membership chmn., mem. exec. bd. Golden Empire Coun., 1978-86, dist. chmn., 1984-85. With U.S. Army, 1955-57. Recipient Silver Beaver award Boy Scouts Am., 1977. Mem. Am. Soc. Safety Engrs. (pres. Sacramento chpt. 1981-82; regional v.p., nat. long range planning com., chmn. legis. affairs com., adminstr. pub. sector divsn., named divsn. Safety Profl. of Yr. 1986, named pub. sector divsn. safety profl. of yr. 1986, Sacramento chpt. Safety Profl. Yr. 1986, chmn. sch. safety task force Nat. Safety Coun. 1988-91), Am. Indsl. Hygiene Assn., Vets of Safety (pres. Sacramento chpt. 1984-85), Rotary (sec. Pittsfield club 1970-73). Author, editor govt. publs.

LYNCH, PETER GEORGE, artist; b. Aug. 5, 1932. BFA, Pratt Inst., Bklyn., 1954; postgrad., CCNY. pub. Limited Editions Prints (11 eds.), News-n-viewsletter; Concerns-Art, Art Marketing and the Environment. Exhibitions include: (internat. and nat.) The Art Gallery of La Merced, Maracaibo, Venezuela, Nephente Mundi Internat. Competition, Allied Artist Am., Nat. Arts Club, Chautauqua Instn., Acad. Artist Assn. Nat. Exhibition, Internat. Festival of The Arts, Mexico-Douglas, Wiesner Gallery Intertnat., Global Visions, Fed. Pla., Gallery Cozumel, Yergeau Mus. Internat. d'Art, Montreal, Que. (Named One of Best Am. Painters, One of Best Am. Printmakers, 1991, Deuxieme prix Ann. Ctr. P.R.D. Montreal Exhbn., 1992), and numerous others; (regional and local) Arsenal Gallery, Color Meml., Vega Fine Arts, Casino Gallery, Fulton Gallery, Artifax Galleries, Cabrini Gallery, Ten Talents Gallery, Inroads Multimedia Ctr. among others; author: (dossiers) Collaborative Photolithographic Prints: Publishing Your Own, 1990, Direct Marketing: Survival Factors and the Artist, 1990, Succeeding as a Fine Artist: Professionalism in a Difficult Environment, 1991, Artist's Eye vs. Photographers Eye: Shooting Your Art Right, 1991, Overused and Underexplored: The Paradox of Print Media: Effective Advertising for Creative People, 1991, Direct-Contact Marketing: Art Fairs and Festivals, 1991, The Video Portfolio: A New User-Friendly Marketing Tool, 1991, Survival Factors and The Artist; Keeping Up or Dropping Out, 1994, Creativity-What On Earth Is It? Where Can We Get Some?, 1994. With U.S. Army, 1956-58. Recipient Citation for Superior Competence, U.S. Army Air Def. Command, 1958, Hon. Mention Nat. Exhibition at Bakersfield, 1985, Second Place Assn. Artist Nat. Exhibition, 1985, Cert. of Merit, Academic Artist Assn. Annual Nat. Exhibition, 1986, First Place Nephente Mundi Internat. Art Competition, 1987, Watson-Guptill award Lake Worth Silver Anniversary Exhbn., 1991.

LYNCH, PETER JOHN, dermatologist; b. Mpls., Oct. 22, 1936; s. Francis Watson and Viola Adeline (White) L.; m. Barbara Ann Lanzi, Jan. 18, 1964; children: Deborah, Timothy. Student, St. Thomas Coll., 1954-57; B.S., U. Minn., 1958, M.D., 1961. Intern U. Mich. Med. Center, 1961-62, resident in dermatology, 1962-65; clin. instr. U. Minn., 1965; chief dermatology and venereal disease Martin Army Hosp., Columbus, Ga., 1966-68; asst. prof. to asso. prof. dermatology U. Mich. Med. Center, 1968-73; asso. prof. to prof. dermatology U. Ariz., Tucson, 1973-86; chief sect. dermatology U. Ariz., 1973-86, asso. head dept. internal medicine, 1977-86; prof., head dermatology U. Minn. Med. Sch., Mpls., 1986-95; med. dir. ambulatory care U. Minn. Health System, 1993-95; prof., chmn. dept. dermatology U. Calif., Davis, 1995—. Author: (with S. Epstein) Burckhardt's Atlas and Manual of Dermatology and Venereology, 1977, Dermatology for the House Officer, 1982, 3rd edit., 1994, (with W.M. Sams) Principles and Practice of Dermatology, 1990, (with I.E. Edwards) Genital Dermatology, 1994. Served with AUS, 1966-68. Decorated Army Commendation Medal; recipient Disting. Service award for faculty U. Mich., 1970, Disting. Faculty award U. Ariz., 1981. Mem. Am. Acad. Dematology (bd. dirs. 1974-78, v.p. 1991-92), Assn. Profs. Dematology (bd. dirs. 1976-80, pres. 1994—), Internat. Soc. Study of Vulvar Disease (bd. dirs. 1976-79, pres. 1983), Soc. Investigative Dermatology, Am. Bd. Dermatology (bd. dirs. 1984-89), Gougerot Soc. (Bronze Medal award), Alpha Omega Alpha. Democrat. Roman Catholic. Home: 332 Sandpiper Dr Davis CA 95616 Office: U Calif Dept Dermatology 1605 Alhambra Blvd # 2300 Sacramento CA 95816

LYNCH, PETER S., retired portfolio manager; b. Boston, 1944; m. Carolyn Lynch; children: Mary, Annie, Beth. BA, Boston Coll., 1965; MBA, U. Pa., 1968. With Fidelity Investments, Boston, 1969-90; mgr. Fidelity Magellan Fund, 1977-90; trustee Fidelity Investments, 1990—; bd. dirs. Morrison Knudsen, W.R. Grace; guest lectr. Boston Coll. Author (with John Rothchild): One Up on Wall Street (1989), Beating the Street (1993), (bestselling books). Fin. advisor Lynch Fund, Boston Coll., Boston Pub. Libr., Third Century Found., Order of Malta, Cath. Schools Found., chmn.

Named to Nat. Bus. Hall of Fame. Fellow Am. Acad. Arts & Scis. Office: 27 State St Boston MA 02109-2706

LYNCH, ROBERT EMMETT, mathematics educator; b. Chgo., Feb. 5, 1932; s. Joseph Burke and Mildred Cecilia (Bildhauser) L.; m. Martha Bolling Hacker, Oct. 8, 1955; children: Barbara Ann, William Robert, Pamela Elizabeth. B Engring. Physics, Cornell U., 1954; MS, Harvard, 1959, PhD, 1963. Sr. rsch. mathematician Gen. Motors Rsch. Lab., Warren, Mich. 1961-64; assoc. prof. computer sci. and math. U. Tex., Austin, 1964-67; assoc. prof. computer sci. and math. Purdue U., West Lafayette, Ind., 1967-85, prof., 1985—. Author: (with Garrett Birkhoff) Numerical Solution of Elliptic Problems, 1984; (with John R. Rice) Computers, Their Impact and Use/with Basic, 1975, Computers, Their Impact and Use/With Fortran, 1977, Computers, Their Impact and Use/with PL/1, 1978. Lt. USAF, 1955-57. Office: Purdue Univ Computer Sci Dept West Lafayette IN 47907

LYNCH, ROBERT MARTIN, lawyer, educator; b. St. Louis, Mar. 28, 1950; s. Raymond Burns and Nancy Winn (Roeder) L.; m. Cynthia Kay Allmeyer, June 7, 1974; children: Christopher, Kelly, Stephanie. AB, St. Louis U., 1972, JD, 1975. Bar: Mo. 1975, D.C. 1985, Tex. 1992. Law clk. to presiding justice Mo. Ct. Appeals, St. Louis, 1975-76; atty. Southwestern Bell Telephone Corp., St. Louis, 1976-79, atty. network, 1979-83, gen. atty., 1983-88, v.p., asst. gen. counsel, 1988-91; v.p., gen. counsel Tex. office Southwestern Bell Telephone Co., Dallas, 1991-93; v.p., gen. counsel external affairs Southwestern Bell Telephone Co., San Antonio, 1993—; instr. paralegal studies St. Louis Community Coll., 1977—. Mem. ABA, Tex. Bar, Dallas Bar Assn., Mo. Bar Assn. (adminstrv. law com. coun.), St. Louis Bar Assn. (chmn. adminstrv. law com. 1981-82), Am. Corp. Counsel Assn. (chmn. communications com. St. Louis chpt.). Republican. Avocations: racquetball, writing. Office: Southwestern Bell 175 E Houston San Antonio TX 78205

LYNCH, ROBERT N., clergy member. Gen. sec. Nat. Conf. Cath. Bishops, Washington. Office: US Cath Conf 3211 4th St NE Washington DC 20017-1194

LYNCH, RONALD P., financial manager; b. N.Y.C., Nov. 6, 1935; s. Robert Joseph and Mary Louise (Farraher) L.; m. Susan M. Eckert, Apr. 21, 1963; children: Ronald P. Jr., Charles R., Andrew E. BS in Agrl. Econs., Cornell U., 1958. With The Corp. Texaco Co., 1959-65; regional sales mgr. Lord, Abbett & Co., 1977-80; western mgr. Lord, Abbett & Co., San Francisco, 1975-77; ptnr. Lord, Abbett & Co., 1977-80, sr. ptnr., 1980-83, chief mktg. and operating officer, 1980—, dir. asset mgmt., 1983-84, mng. ptnr., 1983—, also chmn. bd. subs. fund corps. Mem. Cornell U. Council; mem. adv. council S.C. Johnson Grad. Sch. Mgmt., Brunswick Sch.; trustee Greenwich Health Assn.; bd. dirs. Mem. Investment Co. Inst. (exec. com., bd. govs., mem. various coms.), Securities Industry Assn., Inc. (mem. investment cos. com. 1985—, chmn. 1983-85), Nat. Assn. Securities Dealers, Inc. (mem. investment cos. com., 1983—, chmn. bus. conduct com. 1979), Bond Club N.Y. Clubs: Wall Street (N.Y.C.); Field of Greenwich (Conn.), Round Hill; Burlinghame Country (Hillsborough, Calif.); Waynesborough Country (Paoli, Pa.). Home: 162 Round Hill Rd Greenwich CT 06831-3746 Office: Lord Abbett & Co GM Bldg 767 Fifth Ave New York NY 10153

LYNCH, ROSE PEABODY, art gallery executive; b. Dallas, June 6, 1949; d. Russell Vincent and Rose Peabody (Parsons) L.; m. Peter Stuart Milhaupt, Feb. 12, 1972 (div. 1977); m. James Alexander Torrey, Apr. 22, 1989. AAS, Bennett Coll., 1969; BA, Princeton U., 1971; MBA, Harvard U., 1982. Personal asst. Halston, Ltd., N.Y.C., 1975-76; assoc. dir. retail promotion Revlon, Inc., N.Y.C., 1976-80; dir. mktg. devel. Elizabeth Arden, N.Y.C., 1980-85; dir. mktg. Charles of the Ritz, N.Y.C., 1985-87; pres. Danskin, N.Y.C., 1987-89, Trowbridge Gallery, U.S., N.Y.C., 1989-93; cons., acting chief operating officer LeRoi Princeton Inc., 1991-92; v.p. merchandising-fragrance Victoria's Secret, Reynoldsburg, Ohio, 1993—; bd. dirs. Manhattan Theatre Club. Republican. Episcopalian. Avocations: running, skiing, tennis, riding. Office: Victoria's Secret 4 Limited Pky Reynoldsburg OH 43068-5302

LYNCH, SANDRA LEA, lawyer; b. Oak Park, Ill., July 31, 1946; d. Bernard Francis and Eugenia Tyus (Shepherd) L.; 1 child, Stephen Lynch Bowman. AB, Wellesley Coll., 1968; JD, Boston U., 1971. Bar: Mass. 1971, U.S. Dist. Ct. Mass. 1973, U.S. Dist. Ct. R.I., U.S. Ct. Appeals (1st cir.) 1974, U.S. Supreme Ct. 1974. Law clk. U.S. Dist. Ct., Providence, 1971-72; asst. atty. gen. Mass. Atty. Gen.'s Office, Boston, 1972-73; gen. counsel Mass. Dept. Edn., Boston, 1973-78; assoc. Foley, Hoag & Eliot, Boston, 1978-81, ptnr., 1981—; spl. counsel Jud. Conduct Commn., 1990-92; nominated to U.S. Ct. Appeals (1st cir.) by Pres. U.S., 1995. Contbr. articles to legal jours. Recipient Disting. Service award Planned Parenthood League of Mass., 1981. Mem. ABA (com. on partnership, ho. of dels.), Boston Bar Assn. (pres. 1992-93, bd. bar overseers 1982-86, joint bar com. 1986). Office: Foley Hoag & Eliot 1 Post Office Sq Boston MA 02109

LYNCH, SONIA, data processing consultant; b. N.Y.C., Sept. 17, 1938; d. Espriela and Sadie Beatrice (Scales) Sarreals; m. Waldro Lynch, Sept. 18, 1981 (div. Oct. 1983). BA in Langs. summa cum laude, CCNY, 1960; cert. in French, Sorbonne, 1961. Systems engr. IBM, N.Y.C., 1963-69; cons. Babbage Systems, N.Y.C., 1969-70; project leader Touche Ross, N.Y.C., 1970-73; sr. programmer McGraw-Hill, Inc., Hightstown, N.J., 1973-78; staff data processing cons. Cin. Bell Info. Systems, 1978-89; sr. analyst AT&T, N.Y.C., 1982; lead tech. analyst Automated Concepts Inc., Arlington, Va., 1992-94, cons., 1994—; with Johns Hopkins Applied Physics Lab., Laurel, Md., 1994—. Elder St. Andrew Luth. Ch., Silver Spring, 1992—. Downer scholar CUNY, 1960, Dickman Inst. fellow Columbia U., 1960-61. Mem. Assn. for Computing Machinery, Phi Beta Kappa. Democrat. Avocations: needlework, sewing. Home: 13705 Beret Pl Silver Spring MD 20906-3030

LYNCH, TERESA ANN, state legislator; b. Mpls., Jan. 15, 1954; d. Leslie Alvin Steinberg and Joanne (Pouliot) Brand; m. David C. Lynch, May 18, 1974; children: Emily, Erin, Anna, Tessa. Grad. interpreter tng. program, St. Paul Tech. Coll., 1983. Interpreter Anoka-Hennepin Sch. Dist., Mpls., 1983-87; state rep. Minn. Ho. of Reps. Dist. 50B, Anoka-over, Minn., 1988—. Asst. caucus leader Rep. House Caucus, St. Paul, 1992-94; vice chair Rules & Legislative Administration. Named Legislator of Yr., Assn. of Minn. Counties, St. Paul, 1992; recipient Legis. Recognitive award Nat. Assn. of the Deaf, 1992; named Legislator of Yr., Minn. Assn. Deaf Citizens, 1993. Republican. Avocations: reading, tennis. Office: Minn House of Reps 295 State Office Bldg Saint Paul MN 55155

LYNCH, THOMAS C., career military officer; m. Kathleen Quinn; children: Jill, Alison, Thomas Jr. Grad., U.S. Naval Acad., 1964, Armed Forces Staff Coll.; MA, George Washington U. Commd. ensign USN, 1964, advanced through grades to rear adm., 1991; main propulsion asst. USS Stribling; engring. officer USS Dickson; asst. dir. Candidate Guide Office U.S. Naval Acad., Md.; commissioning exec. officer USS Jesse L. Brown; with surface war plans and programs divsn. Office Chief Naval Ops., Washington; comdr. USS Truett, 1977-80, Destroyer Squadron 24, Cruise Destroyer Group Twelve, 1989-91; from adminstrv. asst. to dir. Senate liaison USN Office Legis. Affairs; supt. U.S. Naval Acad., Md., 1991-94; now dir. Navy Rules and Mission Study Group. Office: Dept Navy The Pentagon Rm 4E566 Washington DC 20350

LYNCH, THOMAS FRANCIS, archeologist, educator; b. Mpls., Feb. 25, 1938; s. Francis Watson and Viola Eugenie (Le Blanc) L.; m. Barbara Amy Deutsch, Feb. 4, 1961 (div. 1989); children: Elizabeth Ann, Jean Margaret, Julia Frances; m. Jane Ellen Flaherty, Oct. 7, 1989; children: Clare Viola, William Finn. B.A., Cornell U., 1960; M.A., U. Chgo., 1962, Ph.D., 1967. Archeologist Idaho State U. Mus., Pocatello, 1963-64; instr. to prof. and chmn. anthropology dept. Cornell U., Ithaca, 1964-93; dir. Cornell Intercollege Program in Archeology, 1971-74, 75-82; rsch. prof. Universidad Catolica del Norte, Antofagasta, Chile, 1976-77, rsch. assoc., 1983—, adj. prof., 1994—; dir. Brazos Valley Mus. Natural History, 1995—. Author: Guitarrero Cave: Early Man in the Andes, 1980; assoc. editor Am. Antiquity, 1986-90; mem. editorial bd. Latin Am. Antiquity, Andean Past, Chungara, Estudios Atacameños; contbr. articles to profl. jours. Recipient NSF, Nat. Geographic Soc., and other research grants for archeol. excava-

tions in Peru, Chile and Ecuador, 1964—. Fellow AAAS; mem. Soc. for Am. Archeology, Prehistoric Soc. Gt. Britain, Am. Quaternary Assn., Inst. Andean Rsch. (dir. 1976-79), N.Y. Archaeology. Coun., Am. Assn. Mus., Soc. for History Discoveries, Ctr. for Study First Ams. (scientific coun.), Inst. Andean Studies, Assn. Cornell U. Emeritus Profs., Soc. for Econ. Botany, Centro de Estudios Andinos Cuzco (cons. mem.), Soc. Chilena de Arqueologia, Phi Beta Kappa.

LYNCH, THOMAS JOSEPH, museum manager; b. Omaha, Nebr., Feb. 15, 1960; s. James Humphery and Patricia Mae (Gaughan) L. BA in History, U. Nebr. 1984. Grad. tchng. asst. U. Nebr., 1984-86; mus. asst. Father Flanagan's Boys' Home, Boys Town, Nebr., 1986-88; mus. assoc. Father Flanagan's Boys' Home, Boys Town, 1988-93, mus. mgr., 1993—. Contbr. Boys Town: a Photographic History, 1992, Letters from the Front: Boys Town on the Battlefield from Pearl Harbor to the Persian Gulf, 1995. Vol. Omaha Metro Arts, 1988, Bot. Gardens, 1994; adv. bd. Metro Area History Day, Omaha, 1995. Named Most Valuable Player Father Flanagan's Boys' Home, 1992. Mem. Am. Assn. for State and Local History, Am. Mus. Assn., Nebr. Mus. Assn. Office: Boys Town Hall of History 14057 Flanagan Blvd Boys Town NE 68010

LYNCH, THOMAS PETER, securities executive; b. N.Y.C., May 3, 1924; s. Michael Joseph and Margaret Mary (Fitzgerald) L.; m. Madeleine D'Eufemia, June 3, 1950; children: Francine, Richard. Student, Syracuse U., 1943-44; B.B.A., Baruch Coll., 1947. Acct. Deloitte, Haskins & Sells, N.Y.C., 1947-56; partner Bache & Co., N.Y.C., 1956-61; v.p. E.F. Hutton Group Inc., N.Y.C., 1962-67; sr. v.p. E.F. Hutton Group Inc., 1967-72, exec. v.p., 1972-83, pres., dir., 1983-85; ret., 1985; pres., dir. Cash Res. Mgmt. Inc., 1976-85. Served with U.S. Army, 1943-46. Decorated Bronze Star. Mem. AICPA, Fin. Execs. Inst., India House, Canoe Brook Country Club, Baltusrol Golf Club, Johns Island Club, Morris County Golf Club.

LYNCH, THOMAS WIMP, lawyer; b. Monmouth, Ill., Mar. 5, 1930; s. William Brennan and Mildred Maurine (Wimp) L.; m. Elizabeth J. McDonald, July 30, 1952; children: Deborah, Michael, Maureen, Karen, Kathleen. BS in Geology, U. Ill., 1955, MS in Geology, 1958, JD, 1959. Bar: Ill. 1960, Okla. 1960, U.S. Supreme Ct. 1971, Tex. 1978. Staff atty. Amerada Hess Corp., Tulsa, 1959-72, asst. gen. counsel, 1972-75; mem. Hall, Estill, Hardwick, Gable, Collingsworth & Nelson, Tulsa, 1975; v.p., gen. counsel Tex. Pacific Oil Co., Inc., Dallas, 1975-80, Oryx Energy Co., Dallas, 1980—; adj. prof. law U. Tulsa, 1974; trustee Southwestern Legal Found., chmn., lectr. ann. oil and gas short course, 1976—, v.p. Oil and Gas Edn. Ctr.; mem. legal com. Interstate Oil Compact Commn. Served with USN, 1948-49, U.S. Army, 1951-53. Mem. ABA, Tex. Bar Assn. (coun. oil, gas and mineral law sect.), Dallas County Bar Assn., Dallas Petroleum Club, Roman Catholic. Office: Oryx Energy Co 13155 Noel Rd Dallas TX 75240-5067

LYNCH, TIMOTHY JEREMIAH-MAHONEY, realty holding company executive, author; b. June 10, 1952; s. Joseph David and Margaret Mary (Mahoney) L. MS, JD in Taxation, Golden Gate U., 1981; MA, PhD in Modern European History, U. San Francisco, 1983; Licentiate, Inter-Am. Acad., Rio de Janeiro, 1988; PhD in Classics and Divinity/Theology, Harvard U., 1988; JSD in Constl. Law, Hastings Law Ctr., 1990. Bar: D.C. 1989, Calif. U.S. Ct. Appeals (2d cir.) 1989, U.S. Ct. Appeals (4th cir.) 1990. Legal bus., tax, counsel Lynch Real Estate, San Francisco, 1981-85; researcher, writer Kolb, Roche & Sullivan, San Francisco, 1986-88; chmn. internat. law dept. Timothy J.M. Lynch & Assocs., San Francisco, 1987-88, chmn., mng. dir. law dept., 1988—; chmn., pres., chief exec. officer Lynch Real Estate Investment Corp., San Francisco, 1989—; ptnr. Lynch Investment Corp.; bd. lawyer/arbitrators Pacific Coast Stock Exch., NASD, 1994—; chmn. bd. Lynch Holdings Corp. Group; corp. counsel, sr. ptnr. L.A. Ctr. Internat. Comml. Arbitration, 1991—; rsch. prof. Canon law and Ecumenical Ch. history grad. theological union U. Calif. Berkeley, 1992—; vis. scholar Patristic theology and classical philosophy of Ecumenical doctrines U. Laval, Quebec, Can., 1993—; vis. scholar Medieval ch. history U. Leeds, Eng., 1993—; arbitrator Iran-U.S. Claims Tribunal, The Hague, 1993; mem. internat. corp. adv. bd. J.P. Morgan and Co., N.Y.C.; bd. dirs. Morgan-Stanley Corp., N.Y.C.; chmn. Latin Am., African and Middle East Corp. Groups J.P. Morgan Internat, Corp.; adv. bd. Morgan Stanley Corp., N.Y.C. Author: (10 vol. manuscript) History of Ecumenical Doctrines and Canon Law of Church; editorial bd. Internat. Tax Jour., 1993; author: Publishers National Endowment for Arts and Humanities Classical Translations: Latin, Greek, and Byzantine Literary Texts for Modern Theological-Philosophical Analysis of Social Issues; Essays on Issues of Religious Ethics and Social, Public Policy Issues, others; editorial bd. Internat. Tax Jour., 1993; contbr. articles to profl. jours. Dir., vice chmn. Downtown Assn. San Francisco; councillor, dir. Atlantic Coun. U.S., 1984—; corp. counsel, chmn. spl. arbitrator's tribunal on U.S.-Brazil trade, fin. and banking rels. Inter-Am. Comml. Arbitration Commn., Washington; chmn. nat. adv. com. U.S.-Mid. East rels. U.S. Mid. East Policy Coun., U.S. State Dept., Washington, 1989—; mem. Pres. Bush's Adv. Commn. on Econ. and Public Policy Priorities, Washington, 1989; mem. conf. bd. Mid. East Policy Coun., U.S. State Dept., Washington, 1994—. Recipient Cmty. Svc. honors Mayor Dianne Feinstein, San Francisco, 1987, Leadership awards St. Ignatius Coll. Prep., 1984, Calif.'s Gold State award, 1990, AU-ABA Achievement award, 1990; named Civic Leader of Yr., Nat. Trust for Hist. Preservation, 1988, 89; named to Presdl. Order of Merit, 1991; recipient Internat. Leader of Achievement award Internat. Biog. Ctr., Cambridge, Eng., 1994-95, named Internat. Man of Yr., Internat. Biog. Ctr. and Brit. Fgn. Ministry. Mem. ATLA, Internat. Bar Assn. (various coms., internat. litigation, taxation, labor issue), Am. Soc. Ch. History, Am. Hist. Assn., Am. Philol. Assn., Medieval Acad. Am., U.S. Supreme Ct. Hist. Soc., J Canon Law Soc. U.S., Nat. Assn. Scholars (Eminent Scholar of Yr. 1993), Netherlands Arbitration Inst. (mem. Gen. Panels of Arbitrators, mem. Permanent Ct. Arbitration), Calif. Coun. Internat. Trade (GATT com., tax com., legis. com.), Practicing Law Inst., Am. Fgn. Law Assn. (mem. editl. bd. Working Groups on Rsch. Jour. for Legal systems of Africa, Mid. East, Latin Am., EEC and Soviet Union), U.S.-China Bus. Coun. (export com., GATT com., banking and fin. com., import com.), Bay Area Coun. (corp. mem.), Nat. Acad. Conciliators (Spl. award), Internat. Bar (mem. U.S. Group on Model on Insolvency Corp. Acts), Ctr. Internat. Comml. Arbitration, Comml. Club (various positions), Am. Soc. Internat. Law, Washington Fgn. Asia-Pacific Lawyers Assn., Soc. Profls. in Dispute Resolution, British Inst. Internat. and Comparative Law, Internat. Law Assn. (U.S. br.), Urban Land Inst. Internat., Mid. East Inst. (Am.-Arab Affairs Coun.), Inter-Am. Bar Assn., 1987—, Calif. Trial Lawyers Assn., Ctr. Reformation Rsch. (co-chmn. Calif. State Com. on U.S.-Mid. East Econ. and Polit. Rels.), Am. Com. on U.S.-Japan Rels., Japan Soc. No. Calif., Pan-Am. Assn. San Francisco, Soc. Indsl./Office Realtors, Assn. Entertainment Lawyers London, Royal Chartered Inst. Arbitrators (London), Soc. Indsl. and Office Realtors, Urban Land Inst., San Francisco Realtors Assn., Calif. Realtors Assn., Coun. Fgn. Rels., Chgo. Coun. Fgn. Rels., Conf. Bd., San Francisco Urban and Planning Assn., U.S. Trade Facilitation Coun., Asia Soc., Am. Petroleum Inst., Internat. Platform Assn., San Francisco Ct. of C. (bus. policy com., pub. policy com., co-chmn. congl. issues study group), Am. Inst. Diplomacy, Overseas Devel. Coun. (Mid. East, Russian Republics, Latin Am. studies group), Internat. Vis. Ctr. (adv. bd.), Fin. Execs. Inst., Nat. Assn. Corp. Dirs., Heritage Found. (bd. dirs.), Nat. Assn. Indsl. and Office Properties, Pres. Club, Nat. Assn. Bus. Economists, Villa Taverna Club, Palm Beach Yacht Club, Pebble Beach Tennis Club, Calif. Yacht Club, Commonwealth Club, City Club San Francisco, British Bankers Club, London. Republican. Roman Catholic. Avocations: theater, social entertainment events, opera, ballet, fine arts. Home: 501 Forest Ave Palo Alto CA 94301-2631 Office: 540 Jones St Ste 201 San Francisco CA 94102-2022

LYNCH, WILLIAM DENNIS, JR., broadcast journalist; b. Salina, Kans., Sept. 11, 1945; s. William Dennis and Jean (Donelan) L.; children—Brendan Merrick, Patrick Hoctor. Student, U. Kans., 1963-66. Reporter, anchorman WTOP-AM-TV, Washington, 1968-70; newscaster WNEW-AM, N.Y.C., 1970-71; reporter WCBS Radio, N.Y.C., 1971-73, asst. news dir., 1973-75; corr. NBC News, N.Y.C. and Washington, 1975-81, CBS News, N.Y.C. and Washington, 1981—; anchor CBS World News Roundup, N.Y.C., 1985—; adj. prof. Sch. Journalism, Fordham U., N.Y.C., 1973-75. Served with U.S. Army, 1966-68. Recipient Rube Goldberg award N.Y. Sigma Delta Chi, 1973; N.Y. State AP Broadcasters' award, 1973, Champion-Tuck award,

1985. Mem. AFTRA (N.Y. local bd. 1988-94), Mus. of Broadcasting (mem. creative coun. 1988—). Office: CBS News 524 W 57th St New York NY 10019-2902

LYNCH, WILLIAM REDINGTON, lawyer; b. N.Y.C., Nov. 17, 1928; s. Francis Russell Vincent and Helen Adams (Barrett) L.; m. Mary Pomeroy Grant, Aug. 22, 1958; children: Melissa L. Woolford, Elizabeth Barrett, Cynthia Pomeroy, Kimberly Townsend, Sarah Phillips. Student, Phillips Exeter Acad., 1944-47; BA, Yale U., 1951; JD, Columbia U., 1958. Bar: N.Y. 1959, Conn. 1963. Assoc. Milbank Tweed Hadley & McCloy, N.Y.C., 1958-62; assoc. Cummings & Lockwood, Stamford, Conn., 1962-66, ptnr., 1966—, ptnr. in charge Greenwich office, 1978-88; bd. dirs. Greenwich Plaza Inc., 1970-74, Harrison & Ellis Inc., Cairo, Ga., 1985-87, Greenwich News Inc., 1986-90; chmn. ADM Mgmt. Corp., 1989-91. Chmn. Pub. Works Com., Greenwich, 1974-77, Greenwich United Way Campaign, 1975-76; vice chmn. Greenwich Bd. Edn. 1977-81, Rep. Town Mtg. 1967-77; dir., sec. Forum World Affairs, 1992—. Lt. USNR, 1952-56. Mem. ABA, Conn. Bar Assn., Greenwich Bar Assn. (pres. 1979-80), Greenwich Field Club (pres. 1973-75), Round Hill Club (dir. 1992, sec. 1993—). Congregationalist. Home: 100 Bedford Rd Greenwich CT 06831-2719 Office: Cummings & Lockwood 2 Greenwich Pla Greenwich CT 06830

LYNCH, WILLIAM THOMAS, JR., advertising agency executive; b. Evergreen Park, Ill., Dec. 3, 1942; s. William T. and Loretta J. L.; m. Virginia Louise Venteicher, Aug. 21, 1965; children: Kelly, Maureen, Kim, Meagan, Molly. BA, Loras Coll., 1964; MBA, U. Iowa, 1966. Media trainee Leo Burnett Co. Inc., chgo., 1966-68, asst. account exec., 1968-76, v.p., 1976-79, sr. v.p., 1979-82, exec. v.p., 1981-85; vice chmn. Leo Burnett USA, chgo., 1985-89; chmn., chief exec. officer Leo Burnett USA Chgo., 1987-91; pres. Leo Burnett Co. Inc., Chgo., 1992-93; pres., chief exec. officer Leo Burnett Worldwide, Chgo., 1993; CEO, pres. Leo Burnett Worldwide, Leo Burnett Co. Inc., Chgo., 1993—. Mem. coun. U. Chgo. Grad. Sch. Bus.; bd. dirs. Chgo. United, Northwestern Meml. Hosp., Chgo. Mem. Econ. Club Chgo. Roman Catholic. Avocations: tennis, running, skiing, gardening, antiques. Office: Leo Burnett Co Inc 17 Bougainvillea Ave Key West FL 33040-6226*

LYNCH, WILLIAM WALKER, savings and loan association executive; b. Washington, Sept. 18, 1926; s. Talbott and Gertrude (Farrell) L.; m. Barbara Van Sant, Apr. 21, 1951; children: John S., William Walker, Franklin P., Mark F. BA, George Washington U., 1950. Vice pres., treas., dir. Met. Mortgage Co., Washington, 1950-55; dir., mem. exec. com. Prog. Fed. Savs. & Loan Assn., Washington, 1953-58; v.p., treas., dir. Anderson & Co. Inc., Washington, 1953-59; with 1st Fed. Savs. & Loan Assn. of Palm Beaches, West Palm Beach, Fla., 1959—, exec. v.p. 1966-89, pres., chief exec. officer, 1989-94, chmn. bd., 1994—; chmn. 1st Palm Beach Bancorp., 1994—; mem. tournament com. 53d PGA Championship, 1971; mem. tournament com. 19th World Cup, Internat. Golf Assn., 1971, 69th PGA Championship, 1987; dist. dir. Fla. League Fin. Instns., 1991; bd. dirs. Fla. Bankers Assn. 1994. Treas. Herbert Hoover Dike Dedication com., 1960; asst. treas. Fla. Kennedy-Johnson campaign, 1960; bd. dirs. Am. Cancer Soc., 1967-69, 79—, hon. life dir. local United Way, 1962-64. With USNR, 1944-46. Recipient Free Enterprise Companion medal Palm Beach Atlantic Coll., 1989. Mem. West Palm Beach C. of C. (bd. dirs. 1970), Old Guard Soc. of Palm Beach Golfers, Kiwanis (bd. dirs. West Palm Beach club 1961, v.p. 1970-71, pres. 1971-72), City Club, No. Palm Beach Country Club, Pi Kappa Alpha. Republican. Roman Catholic. Home: 1032 Country Club Dr North Palm Beach FL 33408-3716 Office: First Federal Savings & Loan Assn 215 S Olive Ave West Palm Beach FL 33401-5617

LYNCH, WILLIAM WRIGHT, JR., investment executive, engineer; b. Dallas, Aug. 26, 1936; s. William Wright Sr. and Alma Martha (Hirsch) L.; m. June 11, 1960; children: Mary Margaret, Katherine. BSEE, U. Ariz., 1959; MBA, Stanford U., 1962. Pres. Ins. Bldg. Corp., Dallas, 1965-84; ptnr. Estacado Ptnrs., Dallas, 1985—, Encino Co., Dallas, 1970—, Cimarron Properties Co., Tucson, 1972-83; pres., bd. dirs. Argus Realty Corp., Dallas, 1972—; bd. dirs. Lynch Properties Inc., Dallas, Lynch Investment Co., Dallas, G.P. Bourrous Trucking Co., Inc., Dallas, Tex. Metal Works, Inc., Beaumont, Tex.; adv. dir. Sun Valley Fruit Co., Albuquerque, Patent Smith Tech., LTD, Enersyst Devel. Ctr., Inc., Dallas, 1995—. Bd. dirs. Dallas Symphony Orch., 1966-74, Dallas Civic Music, 1970-77, Ednl. Opportunities Inc., Dallas, 1973-90, Dallas Coun. World Affairs, 1990—; trustee W. W. Lynch Found., Dallas, 1968—. Capt. U.S. Army, 1959-60. Mem. Brook Hollow Club, Verandah Club, M.O. Club (Tuscon). Republican. Episcopalian. Office: Lynch Investment Co Ste 1600 LB-16 1845 Woodall Rodgers Fwy Dallas TX 75201-2233

LYNDEN, FREDERICK CHARLES, librarian; b. San Jose, Calif., Jan. 20, 1939; s. John Ross Jr. and Madeleine Lawton (Speik) L.; m. Deborah Reid Oehler, July 7, 1964; 1 child,Madeleine Scandrett. BA in Internat. Rels., Stanford U., 1960, MA in Am. History, 1961; MA in LS, U. Minn., 1963. Reference libr. Bancroft Libr., U. Calif., Berkeley, 1964-66, Meyer Libr., Stanford U., 1966-67; order libr., asst. chief acquisition dept. Stanford U. Libr., 1968-77; assoc. univ. libr. Brown U. Libr., Providence, 1977—. Assoc. editor Advances in Librarianship, 1991—, Pub. Rsch. Quar., 1985-94. Treas. Friends of Barrington (R.I.) Pub. Libr., 1984-86. Coun. on Libr. Resources fellow, 1977-78; Martinus Nijhoff Internat. travel grantee, The Hague, 1986; Blackwell N.Am. scholar, 1989. Mem. ALA (coun.), Assn. Coll. and Rsch. Librs. (pres. New Eng. chpt. 1990-91), Internat. Fedn. Libr. Assns. (standing com. on stats 1991—), Brown Faculty Club (sec. 1991—). Episcopalian. Avocations: tennis, gardening. Office: Brown U Libr Rockefeller Libr Box A Providence RI 02912

LYNDON, MAYNARD, architect; b. Howell, Mich., Sept. 6, 1907; s. Roy J. and Alethea (Hill) L.; m. Joyce Earley, 1962; children: Donlyn, Maynard, Jo. BS, U. Mich., 1928. Registered architect, U.K. Architect Dept. Interior, Washington, 1933-35, Lyndon & Smith, Detroit, 1935-42; prt. practice architecture L.A., 1942-72; archtl. researcher France, 1972—; prin. Lyndon Design Counsellors, London; critic Coll. Architecture, U. So. Calif.; design cons. U. Md., 1965; mem. archtl. commn. Claremont Coll. Exhibited in Am. Pavillion Internat. Exposition, Paris, 1935, Royal Soc. Brit. Architects, 1937, Am. Fedn. Arts, Washington, 1938, Trois Siecles d'aus Stats-Unis, Musco de Jeu de Paume, Paris, 1938, Fifth Pan-Am. Congress Architecture, Uruguay, 1940, Archtl. League, N.Y.C., 1941, Mus. Modern Art, N.Y.C., 1942, U. Calif. Berkeley, 1993, UCLA, 1993, U. Calif. Berkeley, 1995, U. Calif., L.A., 1995, U. Tex., 1995; retrospective exhbns. include Coll. Environ. Design U. Calif. Berkeley, 1993; architect: Tenth Ch., 28th Ch. of Christ, Scientist, L.A., 1954, 72, Bunche Hall, UCLA, 1964, physics rsch. labs. and lecture hall U. Calif., Riverside, 1965, adminstrv. tower Calif. State U., L.A., 1969, also pub. schs. Ojai, Monrovia, Vista, Malibu, Calif. Mem. L.A. County Bd. Appeals, 1960-64. Recipient 1st prize nat. competition edn. bldgs. Northville Sch., 1937, 2d prize Beecher High Sch., 1940, Silver medal, diploma 5th Pan-Am. Congress Architects, 3d prize nat. competition for store-front design, 1942. Fellow AIA (mem. Calif. chpt. 1959, nat. award of merit 1939, 50, 51, honor awards So. Calif. chpt. 1954, 57, 66); mem. Calif. Coun. Architects (exec. adminstrv. com. 1960). Address: Rheinpromenade 12 Rheinhein, 79790 Küssaberg Germany

LYNDS, BEVERLY TURNER, retired astronomer; b. Shreveport, La., Aug. 19, 1929; d. Homer Emory and Nettie Lee (Robertson) Turner; m. Clarence Roger Lynds, June 19, 1954 (div. Oct. 1986); 1 dau., Susan Elizabeth; m. Leo Goldberg, Jan. 2, 1987 (dec. Nov. 1987). B.S., Centenary Coll., 1949; postgrad., Tulane U., 1949-50; PhD, U. Calif., Berkeley, 1955. Research assoc. U. Calif., 1955-58, Nat. Radio Astronomy Obs., Green Bank, W.Va., 1959-60; asst. prof. astronomy U. Ariz., 1960-65, assoc. prof., 1965-71; assoc. astronomer, asst. to dir. Kitt Peak Nat. Obs., Tucson, 1971-75; astronomer, asst. dir. Kitt Peak Nat. Obs., 1976-77, astronomer, 1977-86; cons. Assn. Univs. for Rsch. in Astronomy, 1986-87; assoc. Ctr. for Astrophysics and Space Astronomy U. Colo., Boulder, 1987—; edn. program coord. Unidata, UCAR, 1991—. Author: (with others) Elementary Astronomy, 1959; editor: (with others) Dark Nebulae, 1971. Mem. AAAS (chmn. sect. D), Internat. Astron. Union, Am. Astron. Soc. (councillor), Am. Meteorol. Soc., Am. Indian Sci. and Engring. Soc. *Knowing that there are many ways of making a contribution to the world we live in and choosing to use the opportunities available can result in a personal satisfaction which is the best form of success.*

LYNE, ADRIAN, director; b. Peterborough, Eng., Mar. 4, 1941. Dir. feature films: Foxes, 1980, Flashdance, 1983, 9 1/2 Weeks, 1986, Fatal Atraction, 1987 (Acad. award nomination), Jacob's Ladder, 1990, Indecent Proposal, 1993. Mem. Dirs. Guild Am. Office: ICM 8899 Beverly Blvd Los Angeles CA 90048*

LYNE, AUSTIN FRANCIS, sporting goods business executive; b. Newton, Mass., Jan. 7, 1927; s. Daniel Joseph and Susan Markham O'Brien L.; m. Ann Blair, Nov. 27, 1954; children: Austin Francis, Jane Markham, Elizabeth Morgan, James Blair, Michael Davitt, Stephen Christopher. B.A., Harvard U., 1948; postgrad., U. Geneva, Switzerland, 1948-49. Store clk. 1st Nat. Stores Inc., Somerville, Mass., 1949-50, mgmt. trainee, 1950, warehouse supr., 1950, buyer, 1950-64, sales promotion mgr., 1964-67, advt. mgr., 1967, v.p. sales devel., 1968-73, sr. v.p. services, 1973-76, mgmt. cons., 1976-77; pres., treas. The Good Sport, Inc., Cohasset, Mass., 1977—. Coach Belmont Youth Hockey Assn., 1963-78; mem. Concord (Mass.) Rep. Town Com., 1964—, treas., 1967-74; dirs. Internat. Friendship League, Elizabeth Peabody Settlement House, 1961-67, Concord-Carlisle Cmty. Chest, 1983-89; trustee Fenn Sch., 1972-78, Belmont Hill Sch., 1972-73, corporator, 1973—, Robert B. Brigham Hosp., 1971—. Served with USNR, 1945-46. Mem. Sorrento Village Improvement Assn. Clubs: Harvard in Concord (pres. 1965-67), Concord Country, Megunticook Rod and Gun, Harvard Varsity. Home: 68 Sudbury Rd Concord MA 01742-2420 Office: 166 Cushing Hwy Cohasset MA 02025

LYNE, SUSAN MARKHAM, magazine editor, publication director; b. Boston, Apr. 30, 1950; d. Eugene and Ruth (Lally) L.; m. George Crile III; children: Susan Markham, Jane Halle. Assoc. editor City Mag., San Francisco, 1975-76; west coast editor New Times, San Francisco, 1976-77; mng. editor New Times, N.Y.C., 1978, The Village Voice, N.Y.C., 1978-82; v.p. creative devel. IPC Films, N.Y.C., 1982-85; ptnr. Lazar/Lyne Films, N.Y.C., 1985-86; founding editor Premiere mag., N.Y.C., 1987—. Bd. mem. babies heart fund Babies and childrens Hosp., 1990-94. Mem. Am. Soc. Mng. Editors (bd. dirs. 1993—). Office: Premiere Mag 2 Park Ave New York NY 10016

LYNES, JAMES WILLIAM, SR., communications company executive; b. Waverly, Iowa, July 26, 1928; s. James Kendall and Lenore Clair (Kuethe) L.; m. Opal Marie Kerdus, Aug. 24, 1954; 1 child, James William Jr. Student, U.S. Mil. Acad., 1946-47; BA in History, Wartburg Coll., 1950. Rural letter carrier U.S. Postal Svc., Plainfield, Iowa, 1951-86; corp. sec. Butler-Bremer Mut. Telephone Co., Plainfield, Iowa, 1962—, asst. bd. dirs. pres. Iowa Rural Letter Carriers Assn., 1981-83, v.p. 1979-81, state bd. dirs. 1976-83. Vice chmn. Bremer County Bd. Health, Waverly, Iowa, 1969-84, Waverly-Shell Rock Hospice, 1989-93, pres., 1992-93; fin. chmn. Bremer County Rep. Ctrl. Com., Waverly, 1987-92; mayor pro-tem City of Plainfield, Iowa, 1985-89, 91-94, mayor, 1994—, coun. mem., 1983-94; pres. Bremer County Hist. Soc., 1966—. With U.S. Army, 1951-53. Named Lion of Yr. Waverly Lions Club, 1988; Melvin Jones fellow, 1994. Mem. Plainfield Lions (sec. Plainfield chpt. 1971-72, pres. Waverly chpt. 1982-83, editor bulletin 1978—), Kopper Klowns (pres. 1980-81), Waterloo German-Am. (v.p., 1979-80), A.F. & A.M., Shriners. Lutheran. Home: 219 Main St # 218 Plainfield IA 50666-9753

LYNETT, GEORGE VINCENT, newspaper publisher; b. Scranton, Pa., Dec. 1, 1943; s. Edward James and Jean Marie (O'Hara) L.; m. Patricia Brady, June 4, 1966; children:—Sheila Ellen, George Vincent, James Brady, Sharon Elizabeth. A.B. in English, Coll. of Holy Cross, 1965; M.B.A., U. Scranton, 1971; J.D., Georgetown U., 1978. Co-pub. Scranton Times and Sunday Times, 1967—; assoc. Haggerty, McDonnell, O'Brien & Wright, Scranton, 1978—; dir. 3d Nat. Bank and Trust Co., Scranton. Co-chmn. United Way of Lackawanna County, 1972; chmn. Lackawanna County Cancer Crusade, 1969; pres. Allied Services for Handicapped, 1973-75; trustee U. Scranton, 1970-76. Served with USNR, 1965-67. Mem. Lackawanna Bar Assn., Pa. Bar Assn., Pa. Newspaper Pubs. Assn., Am. Newspaper Pubs. Assn. Democrat. Roman Catholic. Club: Scranton Country. Office: The Scranton Times 147-149 Penn Ave Scranton PA 18503-2022*

LYNETT, LAWRENCE WILSON, electronics company executive; b. N.Y.C., Sept. 11, 1921; s. James Degge and Lillian (Lonquist) L.; 1 dau. Michele. B.B.A., Manhattan Coll., 1943. With IBM Corp., 1946—, dir. adminstrv. rsch., 1966—; assoc. adminstrv. mgmt. Simmons Coll., 1966—; mem. Nat. Adv. Com. for Bus. Edn. Curriculum Devel., 1973—. Chmn. editorial bd.: Impact, 1977—; mem. editorial bd. Adminstrv. Mgmt. Mag., 1983—. Chmn. bd. trustees AMS Rsch. Found. Lt. comdr. USNR, WWII, PTO. Decorated Navy Commendation ribbon; Presdl. Commendation for devel. adminstrv. mgmt. program for U.S. Govt. Mgrs., 1966. Mem. Adminstrv. Mgmt. Soc. (internat. pres. 1966-67, bd. dirs. 1980-83, Diamond Mgmt. key 1963, Internat. Mgmt. award 1967, Internat. Ambassador award 1985, Silver medal for mgmt. achievements 1988), Office Execs. Assn. N.Y. (pres. 1960-61, Leadership award 1961), Am. Mgmt. Assn. (v.p. gen. svcs. dir., bd. dirs. 1975-87). Home: 11 Purchase Hills Dr Purchase NY 10577-1615 Office: IBM Corp Old Orchard Rd Armonk NY 10504 *The most effective way to cope with change is to help create it.*

LYNETT, WILLIAM RUDDY, publishing, broadcasting company executive; b. Scranton, Pa., Jan. 18, 1947; s. Edward James and Jean O'Hara L.; children: Scott, Jennifer, Christopher P. B.S., U. Scranton, 1972. Pub. Scranton Times, 1966—; pres., chief exec. officer Shamrock Communications, Inc., 1971—; pres. Towanda Daily Rev., 1977-81, Owego Pennysaver Press, Inc., 1977-81; owner, Pres. Mgmt. Program, Harvard U., 1990. Bd. dirs. Community Med. Center, Scranton; chmn. Mayor's Library Fund Drive, 1974; chmn. spl. gifts div. Heart Fund, 1975; bd. govs. Scranton Area Found.; trustee U. Scranton, 1990—. Mem. Nat. Assn. Broadcasters, Pa. Assn. Broadcasters, Am. Newspaper Pubs. Assn., Pa. Newspaper Pubs. Assn., Greater Scranton C. of C. (chmn. membership drive 1980-81). Democrat. Roman Catholic. Clubs: Scranton Country, Elks, K.C. Office: 149 Penn Ave Scranton PA 18503

LYNG, RICHARD EDMUND, former secretary of agriculture; b. San Francisco, June 29, 1918; s. Edmund John and Sarah Cecilia (McGrath) L.; m. Bethyl Ball, June 25, 1944; children: Jeanette (Mrs. Gary Robinson), Marilyn (Mrs. Daniel O'Connell). Ph.B. cum laude, U. Notre Dame, 1940; PhD (hon.), Carroll Coll., 1988. With Ed J. Lyng Co., Modesto, Calif., 1945-66, pres., 1949-66; dir. Calif. Dept. Agr., 1967-69; asst. sec. Dept. Agr., Washington, 1969-73, dep. sec., 1981-85; vice chmn. Commodity Credit Corp., 1981-85; pres. Lyng & Lesher, Inc., Washington, 1985-86; Sec. of Agr. Dept. Agr., Washington, 1986-89; pres. Am. Meat Inst., Washington, 1973-79; pvt. cons., 1980; dir. Commodity Credit Corp., 1969-73, Nat. Livestock and Meat Bd., 1973-76, Tri-Valley Growers, 1975-81; bd. govs. Federal Agriculture Rsch. Found., 1974-77, Chgo. Merc. Exch.; chmn. food industry trade adv. com. Commerce Dept.; chmn. U.S. Child Nutrition Adv. Com., 1971-73; mem. animal health com. NAS; sr. rsch. fellow Harvard U. Sch. Bus. Adminstrn., 1989-91; chmn. export adv. com. Nat. Dairy Bd., 1989—; bd. dirs. Ecosci., Corp, 1991—; trustee Internat. Life Sci. Inst., 1990—. Chmn. Stanislaus County (Calif.) Republican Central Com., 1961-62; dir. agr. div. Pres. Ford Com., 1976; co-dir. farm and food div. Reagan-Bush Campaign, 1980. Served with AUS, 1941-45. Mem. Washington Golf and Country Club, Del Rio Country Club (hon.) Roman Catholic.

LYNHAM, C(HARLES) RICHARD, foundry company executive; b. Easton, Md., Feb. 24, 1942; s. John Cameron and Anna Louise (Lynch) L.; m. Elizabeth Joy Card, Sept. 19, 1964; children: Jennifer Beth, Thomas Richard. BME, Cornell U., 1965; MBA with distinction, Harvard U., 1969. Sales mgr. Nat. Carbide Die Co., McKeesport, Pa., 1969-71; v.p. sales Sinter-Met Corp., North Brunswick, N.J., 1971-72; sr. mgmt. analyst Am. Cyanamid Co., Wayne, N.J., 1972-74; gen. mgr. ceramics and additives div. Foseco Inc., Cleve., 1974-77, dir. mktg. steel mill products group, 1977-79, pres., chief exec. officer Exomet, Inc. subs. Foseco, Inc. Conneaut, Ohio, 1979-81, Fosbel Inc. subs. Foseco, Inc., Cleve., 1981-82; gen. mgr. splty. ceramics group Ferro Corp., Cleve., 1982-84, group v.p. splty. ceramics, 1984-92; owner, pres. Harbor Castings, Inc., North Canton, Ohio, 1992—; bd. dirs. Hi-Temp Inc., Cleve., Chick Master Incubator Inc., Corrpro Com-

panies, Inc. Patentee foundry casting ladle, desulphurization of metals. Mem. adv. bd. East Asia program Cornell U. Capt. C.E., U.S. Army, 1965-67. Decorated Bronze Star with one oak leaf cluster. Mem. Am. Foundrymen's Soc., Cornell U. Alumni Coun., Cornell U. Alumni Class 1963 (past c.p., past pres.), Cornell U. Alumni Fedn. (past pres., bd. dirs., past v.p.), Cornell U. East Asia Program (adv. bd.), Chippewa Yacht Club (commodore 1982), Cornell Club of N.E. Ohio (past pres., bd. dirs.). Republican. Congregationalist. Avocations: sailing, genealogy. Home: 970 Hickory Grove Ave Medina OH 44256-1616 Office: Harbor Castings Inc 4321 Strausser St NW North Canton OH 44720-7197

LYNN, ARTHUR DELLERT, JR., economist, educator; b. Portsmouth, Ohio, Nov. 12, 1921; s. Arthur Dellert and Helen B. (Willis) L.; m. Pauline Judith Wardlow, Dec. 29, 1943; children: Pamela Wardlow, Constance Karen, Deborah Joanne, Patricia Diane. Student, Va. Mil. Inst., 1938-39, U.S. Naval Acad., 1939; BA, Ohio State U., 1941, MA in Econs., 1943, JD, 1948, PhD in Econs., 1951; postgrad. in law, U. Mich., 1968-70. Bar: Ohio 1948, U.S. Supreme Ct. 1966. Upper Ohio Valley corr. Cin. Enquirer, 1937-38; ptnr. Lynn & Lynn, Portsmouth, 1949-50; chief clk. to dir. Ohio Dept. Hwys., 1957; mem. faculty Ohio State U., Columbus, 1941-86, prof. econs., 1961-86, asst. dean, 1959-62, assoc. dean Coll. Commerce and Adminstrn., 1962-65, assoc. dean faculties, assoc. provost, 1965-70, assoc. dean Coll. Adminstrv. Sci., 1984-86, assoc. dean emeritus Coll. Bus., 1986—, lectr. Coll. Law, 1961-67, adj. prof. law, 1967-86, prof. pub. adminstrn., 1969-86, prof. emeritus pub. policy and mgmt., 1986—, lectr. exec. devel. program, 1958-71, acting dir. divsn. pub. adminstrn., summers 1973, 74, acting dir. Sch. Pub. Adminstrn., summer 1975, 84-86; vis. prof. econs. Ohio Wesleyan U., 1958-59, U. Calif., Berkeley, summer 1972; vis. lectr. USAF Inst. Tech. Wright-Patterson AFB, Ohio, 1959-60; mem. Ohio Gov.'s Econ. Rsch. Coun., 1966-70; mem. assoc. faculty Lincoln Inst. Land Policy, Cambridge, Mass., 1989—. Author: Building the House: The Ohio State University School of Public Administration, 1969-89; editor: The Property Tax and Its Administration, 1970, Property Taxation, Land Use and Public Policy, 1976, Land Value Taxation, 1982; editorial adv. bd.: Tax Bramble Bush, 1959-70; assoc. editor: Nat. Tax Jour., 1971-88; bd. editors: Am. Jour. Econs. and Sociology, 1981—. Trustee Griffith Meml. Found. Ins. Edn.; chmn. external econs. adv. com. Marietta Coll., 1975-79; assoc. Nat. Regulatory Rsch. Inst., 1980—; mem. Alcohol, Drug Addiction and Mental Health Svcs. Bd., Franklin County, Ohio, 1990—; bd. dirs. Ohio Alliance for Mentally Ill, 1992-95. 1st lt. F.A. AUS, 1942-46, PTO. Rsch. fellow Ohio Dept. Mental Health, 1991-92. Mem. ABA (chmn. com. state and local taxes sect. taxation 1961-63), Ohio Bar Assn., Columbus Bar Assn., Am. Econ. Assn., Royal Econ. Assn., Nat. Tax Assn. (chmn. com. model property tax assessment and equalization methods and procedures 1961-65, mem. exec. com. 1965-73, v.p., pres. 1969-70), Tax Inst. (adv. coun. 1960-63), Nat. Tax Assn.-Tax Inst. Am. (sec. 1975-84, treas. 1984-88, bd. dirs. 1975-88, counselor 1988—, hon. 1988—), Am. Arbitration Assn. (nat. panel), Ohio Coun. Econ. Edn. (bd. dirs. 1964-74), Com. on Taxation, Resources, and Econ. Devel. (co-chmn. 1979-87), Internat. Fiscal Assn., Inst. Internat. Assn. Assessing Officers (edn. adv. com.), Torch Club, Faculty Club, Rotary, Omicron Delta Epsilon, Beta Theta Pi, Phi Delta Phi, Beta Gamma Sigma, Pi Sigma Alpha, Pi Alpha Alpha. Republican. Episcopalian. Home: 2679 Wexford Rd Columbus OH 43221-3217 Office: 1775 S College Rd Columbus OH 43210-1309

LYNN, C(HARLES) STEPHEN, franchising company executive; b. LaGrange, Ga., July 27, 1947; s. Charles Hubert and Norma Lee (Batey) L.; m. Milah Faith Pass, Sept. 4, 1976. B.S in Indsl. Engring., Tenn. Tech. U., 1970, M.B.A., U. Louisville, 1973. Indsl. engr. Brown & Williamson Corp., Louisville, 1970-73; dir. distbn. div. Ky. Fried Chicken Corp., Louisville, 1973-77; pres., chief exec. officer MarQuest, Inc. subs. Century 21 Real Estate Corp., Irvine, Calif., 1978-80; v.p. Century 21 Real Estate Corp., Irvine, 1978-80; exec. v.p., dir., chief operating officer Burtson Corp., Marina Del Rey, Calif., 1980-83; chmn., pres., CEO Sonic Corp., Oklahoma City, 1983—; also bd. dirs. Sonic Industries, Inc., Oklahoma City; bd. dirs. Okla. Healthcare Corp., City Bank. Bd. dirs. Salvation Army, Oklahoma City, U. Okla. Sch. of Bus., Okla. Art Mus., Allied Arts, Oklahoma City U., Young Pres.'s Orgn., Bapt. Hosp. Found., Scope Ministry Internat., Tenn. Tech. Sch. Engring.; bd. trustees U. Louisville. Mem. Inst. Indsl. Engrs. (pres. 1973), Nat. Restaurant Assn., Internat. Franchise Assn. (bd. dirs. past chmn.), Okla. C. of C. (bd. dirs., past chmn.), Oklahoma City C. of C. (bd. dirs.), Nat. Cowboy Hall of Fame (bd. dirs.), Acad. State Goals, Fellowship Christian Athletes. Republican. Presbyterian. Avocations: tennis; basketball; reading; movies; travel. Home: 6907 Avondale Oklahoma City OK 73116 Office: Sonic Corp 101 Park Ave Ste 1400 Oklahoma City OK 73102-7202

LYNN, D. JOANNE, physician, ethicist, health services researcher; b. Oakland, Md., July 2, 1951; d. John B. and Mary Dorcas (Clark) Harley; m. Barry W. Lynn; children: Christina, Nicholas. BS summa cum laude, Dickinson Coll., 1970; MD cum laude, Boston U., 1974; MA in Philosophy and Social Policy, George Washington U., 1981; MS Clin. Evaluative Scis., Dartmouth Coll., 1995. Diplomate Am. Bd. Internal Medicine. Resident internal Medicine The George Washington U. Med. Ctr., 1974-77, Robert Wood Johnson Clin. Scholar, 1977-78; emergency rm. physician, triage physician Washington VA Hosp., 1977-78; faculty assoc. for medicine and humanities divsn. experimental programs George Washington U., Washington, 1978-81, co-dir. ICU rsch. unit, 1986-92, dir. divsn. aging studies, 1988-92, prof. health care scis. and medicine, 1991-92, assoc. chairperson dept. health care scis., 1990-92; dir of the Ctr. to Improve the Care of the Dying George Washington U., 1995—; prof. medicine, cmty. and family medicine, sr. assoc. Ctr. Evaluative Clin. Scis. Dartmouth-Hitchcock Med. Ctr., Hanover, N.H., 1992-95, assoc. dir. Ctr. for Aging, 1992-95; Robert Wood Johnson clin. scholar George Washington U., 1977-78, sr. fellow Ctr. Health Policy Rsch. 1991-92; asst. dir. med. studies The Pres. Commn. for Study of Ethical Problems in Medicine and Biomed. and Behavioral Rsch., 1981-83; med. dir. The Washington Home, 1983-89, Hospice of Washington, 1979-91, George Washington Cancer Home Care Program and Home Health Svcs. of The Washington Home, 1990-92, staff physician, 1979-92; fellow Hastings Ctr., 1984—; mem. working group on guidelines for care of terminally ill, 1985-87, rsch. project on ethical issues in care and treatment of chronically ill, 1985-87, working group on new physician-patient relationship, 1991-94, v.p., 1987, chair fellows nominating com., 1991; mem. coordinating coun. on life-sustaining med. treatment decision making by cts. Nat. Ctr. State Cts., 1989-93; fellow Kennedy Inst., 1991; mem. geriat. and gerontology adv. com. Dept. Vet. Affairs, 1991—; mem. bioethics com. Vets. Health Adminstrn., 1991-93; active Washington Area Seminar on Sci., Tech., and Ethics, 1982-92, Nat. Clin. Panel on High-Cost Hospice Care, Washington, 1991; presenter in field. Author chpts. to books; mem. editl. bd. The Ency. of Bioethics, 1994-95; mem. adv. editl. bd. Biolaw, 1983, The Hospice Jour., 1984—, Med. Ethics for the Physician, 1985-92, Med. Humanities Rev., 1986—, Cambridge Quar., 1991-95; contbr. articles, revs. to profl. jours. Peter Jeffries and Jeanne Arnold scholar, 1973; recipient Wellington Parlin Sci. Scholarship award, 1979, Dr. Bertha Curtis prize Boston U. Med. Sch., 1974, Nat. Bd. award Med. Coll. Pa., 1992. Fellow ACP (mem. subcom. on aging 1986-91), Am. Geriatrics Soc. (mem. com. public policy 1983—, mem. ethics com. 1988, chair subcom. on ethics and policy 1986, chair ethics com. 1991—, bd. dirs. 1991—); mem. AAAS, APHA, Am. Fedn. Clin. Rsch., Am. Health Care Assn. (mem. task force on AIDS 1987-89), Am. Hosp. Assn. (mem. spl. com. on biomedical ethics 1983-85, 89-94), Am. Med. Dirs. Assn., Am. Soc. Law and Medicine, Am. Task Force Care Adminstrs. (mem. nat. adv. com. wandering patients 1987-88), Nat. Inst. on Aging (mem. senile dementia of Alzheimer's type, mem. rsch. ethics task force 1981-82, Am. Geriatrics Soc. rep. 1984-86), Soc. Health and Human Values (mem. gov. coun. 1981-84), Inst. Medicine (mem. com. on future issues in med. tech. devel. 1992-94), N.H. Med. Soc., Soc. Health and Human Values (mem. gov. coun. 1981-84), Internat. Hospice Inst. (mem. physician's adv. com. 1984-86), Med. Soc. D.C. (mem. legis. affairs com. 1985-92, vice chairperson 1991-92), Soc. Gen. Internal Medicine (mem. editl. adv. bd. Jour. 1988-91). Office: Ctr Improve Care Dying/Pol Outcomes/ Human Val Rm2B 408 2150 Pennsylvania Ave NW Washington DC 20037

LYNN, EUGENE MATTHEW, insurance company executive; b. Kansas City, Mo., Nov. 6, 1918; s. Eugene M. and Marthield (Ellis) L.; m. Mary E. Spoors, Mar. 12, 1947 (dec.); 1 dau., Diane E.; m. Christine E. Koppl, Jan. 19, 1980. Student John B. Stetson U., 1937-39. Pilot Trans World Airlines, 1944-47; v.p. U.S. Epperson Underwriting Co., Boca Raton, Fla., 1949-55, pres., 1955—; pres. LIG Ins. Agy., Inc., Boca Raton, 1978—; v.p. Universal Underwriters Ins. Co., Kansas City, 1949-55, pres., 1955-82. Hon. chmn. bd., trustee Boca Raton Community Hosp.; trustee Lynn U. Boca Raton. Clubs: Boca Raton Hotel and Club, Royal Palm Yacht and Country (Boca Raton, Fla.), Delray Beach (Fla.), Ocean Reef (Key Largo, Fla.), Indian Creek Country, (Miami Beach), Fisher Island Surf (Miami Beach). Home: 565 Alexander Palm Rd Boca Raton FL 33432-7986 Office: Lumbermens Undwrt Aliance 2501 N Military Trl Boca Raton FL 33431-6356

LYNN, EVADNA SAYWELL, investment analyst; b. Oakland, Calif., June 1935; d. Lawrence G. Saywell; m. Richard Keppie Lynn, Dec. 28, 1962; children: Douglas, Lisa. BA, U. Calif., Berkeley, MA in Econs. With Dean Witter, San Francisco, 1958-61, 70-71, Dodge & Cox, San Francisco, 1961-69; v.p. Clark, Dodge & Co., San Francisco, 1971-73; chartered fin. analyst. V.p. Paine Webber, N.Y.C., 1974-77, Wainwright Securities, N.Y.C., 1977-78; 1st v.p. Merrill Lynch Capital Markets, N.Y.C., 1978-90; sr. v.p. Dean Witter Reynolds, N.Y.C., 1990—. Mem. N.Y. Soc. Security Analysts, San Francisco Security Analysts (treas. 1973-74). Mem. Fin. Women's Club of San Francisco (pres. 1967). Office: Dean Witter Reynolds 2 World Trade Ctr New York NY 10048

LYNN, FREDRIC MICHAEL, sportscaster, former professional baseball player; b. Chgo., Feb. 3, 1952; s. Fredric Elwood and Marie Elizabeth (Marshall) L.; m. Natalie Brenda Cole, Oct. 7, 1986; children from previous marriage: Jason Andrew, Jennifer Andrea. Student, U. So. Calif., 1971-73. Center fielder Boston Red Sox, 1973-81, Calif. Angels, 1981-84, Balt. Orioles, 1985-88, Detroit Tigers, 1988-89, San Diego Padres, 1990; sportscaster ESPN, 1992—. Am. League batting champion, 1979; mem. Am. League All-Star Team, 1975-79, All-Star Team, 1975-83; named Most Valuable Player and Rookie of Yr., Am. League, 1975, Most Valuable Player in Play-Offs, Am. League, 1982, Most Valuable Player All Star Game, 1983, Center Fielder of 70's; recipient Rawlings Gold Glove award, 1975, 78, 79, 80, Seagrams Seven Crowns of Sports award, 1979. Mem. Major League Baseball Players Assn. Republican. Lutheran. Home: 7336 El Fuerte St Carlsbad CA 92009*

LYNN, JAMES DOUGAL, newspaper editor, journalist; b. Houlton, Maine, June 14, 1934; s. Charles Edward and Ethel Florence (Cripe) L.; m. Nancy Deborah Solomon, Jan. 30, 1965 (div. July 1979); children: Nina Vanessa, Nora Melissa. AB, Princeton U., 1955. Reporter L.I. Star-Jour., 1955-61; writer Newsweek, N.Y.C., 1961-63; copy editor, city hall reporter, state capital bur. chief N.Y. Herald Tribune, 1963-66; info. officer Temp. State Commn., N.Y.C., 1966-67; editorial dir. Sta. WABC-TV and Radio, N.Y.C., 1967-69; pub. affairs dir. Sta. WMCA-Radio, N.Y.C., 1969-72; editorial writer, dep. editorial page editor, opinion pages editor Newsday, L.I., 1972—. Jefferson fellow East-West Ctr., Honolulu, 1983. Office: Newsday Inc 235 Pinelawn Rd Melville NY 11747-4250

LYNN, JAMES THOMAS, investment banker, insurance company executive, government executive, lawyer; b. Cleve., Feb. 27, 1927. BA, Western Res. U., 1948; LLB, Harvard U., 1951. Bar: Ohio 1951, D.C. 1977. Gen. counsel U.S. Dept. Commerce, 1969-71, under sec., 1971-73; sec. HUD, 1973-75; dir. Office Mgmt. and Budget, 1975-77; asst. Pres. U.S., 1975-77; with Jones Day Reavis & Pogue, Cleve., 1951-69; with Jones Day Reavis & Pogue, Washington, 1977-84, ptnr., 1960-69, mng. ptnr., 1977-84; with Aetna Life & Casualty Co., Hartford, Conn., 1984, vice chmn., 1984, chmn., CEO, 1984-92, also bd. dirs.; sr. advisor Lazard Frères & Co., N.Y.C., 1992—; bd. dirs. Pfizer, Inc., TRW Inc. Case editor Harvard Law Rev.; 1950-51. Served with USNR, 1945-46. Mem. Phi Beta Kappa. Office: Lazard Frères & Co 5335 Wisconsin Ave NW Ste 440 Washington DC 20015-2030

LYNN, JANET (JANET LYNN NOWICKI SALOMON), professional figure skater; b. Chgo., Apr. 6, 1953; m. Richard Marc Salomon, 1975; 5 children. Figure skater, 1955—, profl. skater, 1973—; mem. Ice Follies, 1972—; Performed ice show to raise money for Shriners Hosps. Crippled Children and Burn Research Insts., 1973; mem. speakers bur. Fellowship Christian Athletes, 1970—. Inducted to Skating Hall of Fame, 1994. U.S. Nat. Ladies Figure Skating champion, 1969-73; Olympic and World Bronze medallist, 1972; World Ladies Figure Skating Silver medalist, 1973. Home: 4215 Marsh Ave Rockford IL 61114-6143 I have found that I want to do what is right for the Glory of God in Christ. As in anything, skating has been a challenge. I have tried to meet each challenge in my skating only with love for what I was doing instead of a selfish desire only to win.

LYNN, LARRY, engineering executive; b. Seattle, Sept. 5, 1930; s. Eldin Verne and Irma (Tuell) Lynn; m. Emily Jean Badger, Oct. 4, 1952 (div. 1988); m. Shirley Marie Pieczynski, Sept. 27, 1988. BS in Physics, Tufts U., 1951. Assoc. divsn. head, mem. steering com. Lincoln Lab. M.I.T., Lexington, Mass., 1953-79; dir. defensive systems Office of the Undersecretary of Defense, Washington, 1979-81; dep. dir. Adv. Rsch. Project Agy., Washington, 1981-85; v.p., COO Atlantic Aerospace Electronics, Greenbelt, Md., 1985-93; dep. under sec. defense Office Sec. Defense, Washington, 1993-95, dir. adv. rsch. project agy., 1995—. contbr. numerous articles to profl. jours. Lt. JG USNR, 1951-53. Mem. AIAA (sr. mem.), IEEE (sr. mem.). Home: 6324 Manchester Way Alexandria VA 22304 Office: Office Sec Defense The Pentagon 3E1045 Washington DC 20301

LYNN, LAURENCE EDWIN, JR., university administrator, educator; b. Long Beach, Calif., June 10, 1937; s. Laurence Edwin and Marjorie Louise (Hart) L.; m. Patricia Ramsey Lynn; 1 dau., Katherine Bell; children from previous marriage—Stephen Louis, Daniel Laurence, Diana Jane, Julia Suzanne. A.B., U. Calif., 1959; Ph.D. (Ford Found. fellow), Yale, 1966. Dir., dep. asst. sec. def. (OASD/SA) Dept. Def., Washington, 1965-69; asst. for program analysis NSC, Washington, 1969-70; assoc. prof. bus. Grad. Sch. Bus., Stanford (Calif.) U., 1970-71, vis. prof. pub. policy, 1982-83; asst. sec. planning and evaluation HEW, 1971-73; asst. sec. program devel. and budget U.S. Dept. Interior, Washington, 1973-74; sr. fellow Brookings Instn., 1974-75; prof. pub. policy John Fitzgerald Kennedy Sch. Govt. Harvard U., Cambridge, Mass., 1975-83; dean Sch. Social Service Adminstrn. U. Chgo., 1983-88, prof., sch. of social svc. adminstrn. and Harris grad. sch. pub. policy studies, 1983—; dir. Ctr. for Urban Rsch. and Policy Studies, 1986—; dir. Mgmt. Inst., 1992—. Author: Designing Public Policy, 1980, The State and Human Services, 1980, Managing the Public's Business, 1981, Managing Public Policy, 1987, Public Management as Art, Science, and Profession, 1995; co-author: The President as Policymaker, 1981; contbr. articles to profl. jours. Bd. dirs. Chgo. Met. Planning Coun., 1984-89, Leadership Greater Chgo., 1989-92; mem. coun. of scholars Libr. of Congress, 1989-93. 1st lt. AUS, 1963-65. Recipient Sec. Def. Meritorious Civilian Svc. medal, Presdl. Cert. of Disting. Achievement, Vernon prize. Fellow Nat. Acad. Public Adminstrn.; mem. U. Calif. Alumni Assn., Council on Fgn. Relations, Assn. Pub. Policy Analysis and Mgmt. (past pres.), Phi Beta Kappa. Home: 5000 S Cornell Ave Chicago IL 60615-3041 Office: Univ Chgo 969 E 60th St Chicago IL 60637-2640

LYNN, LORETTA WEBB (MRS. OLIVER LYNN, JR.), singer; b. Butcher Hollow, Ky., Apr. 14, 1935; d. Ted and Clara (Butcher) Webb; m. Oliver V. Lynn, Jr., Jan. 10, 1948; children—Betty Sue Lynn Markworth, Jack Benny (dec.), Clara Lynn Lyell, Ernest Ray, Peggy, Patsy. Student pub. schs. Sec.-treas. Loretta Lynn Enterprises; v.p. United Talent, Inc.; hon. chmn. bd. Loretta Lynn Western Stores. Country vocalist with MCA records, 1961—(numerous gold albums); most recent album Just a Woman, 1985, (with Conway Twitty) Making Believe, 1988, Greatest Hits Live, 1992, 1993. Author: Coal Miner's Daughter, 1976. Hon. rep. United Giver's Fund, 1971. Named Country Music Assn. Female Vocalist of Year 1967, 72, 73, Entertainer of Year, 1972, named Top Duet of 1972, 73, 74, 75; recipient Grammy award 1971, Am. Music award 1978, named Entertainer of Decade, Acad. Country Music 1980; inducted into Country Music Hall of Fame, 1988; first country female vocalist to record certified Gold album. Office: care MCA Records Inc 70 Universal City Plz Universal City CA 91608*

LYNN, MITCHELL GORDON, retail company executive; b. Los Angeles, Nov. 22, 1948. BA in Econs., UCLA, 1970, MSBA, 1971. CPA, Calif. Acct. Kenneth Leventhal & Co., Los Angeles, 1971-76; controller Sunset

Pools, San Diego, 1977-78; controller The Price Co., San Diego, 1979-83, v.p. fin., treas., 1984-87; exec. v.p. Price Club Industries (subs. Price Co.), 1987-89, pres., 1989-90; exec. v.p. The Price Co., 1989-90, pres., 1990—, also bd. dirs. Bd. dirs. Kensington Social and Athletic Club, San Diego. Mem. Am. Inst. CPA's, Calif. Soc. CPA's. Office: Price Co PO Box 85466 San Diego CA 92186-5466

LYNN, NAOMI B., university president, public administration educator; b. N.Y.C., Apr. 16, 1933; d. Carmelo Burgos and Maria (Lebron) Berly; m. Robert A. Lynn, Aug. 28, 1954; children: Mary Louise, Nancy, Judy Lynn Chance, Jo-An. BA, Maryville (Tenn.) Coll., 1954; MA, U. Ill., 1958; PhD, U. Kans., 1970. Instr. polit. sci. Cen. Mo. State Coll., Warrensburg, Mo., 1966-68; asst. prof. Kans. State U., Manhattan, 1970-75, assoc. prof., 1975-80, acting dept. head, prof., 1980-81, head polit. sci. dept., prof., 1982-84; dean Coll. Pub. and Urban Affairs, prof. Ga. State U., Atlanta, 1984-91; pres. Sangamon State U., Springfield, Ill., 1991—; cons. fed., state and local govts., Manhattan, Topeka, Atlanta, 1981-91; bd. dirs. Bank One, Springfield. Author: The Fulbright Premise, 1973; editor: Public Adminstration, The State of Discipline, 1990, Women, Politics and the Constitution, 1990; contbr. articles and textbook chpts. to profl. pubs. Bd. dirs. United Way of Sangamon County, Springfield Symphony Assn., 1992—. Recipient Disting. Alumni award Maryville Coll., 1986; fellow Nat. Acad. Pub. Adminstrn. Mem. Nat. Assn. Schs. Pub. Affairs and Adminstrn. (nat. pres.), Am. Soc. Pub. Adminstrn. (nat. pres. 1985-86), Am. Polit. Sci. Assn. (mem. exec. coun. 1981-83, trustee 1993—), Am. Assn. State Colls. and Univs. (bd. dirs.), Midwest Polit. Sci. Assn. (mem. exec. coun. 1976-79), Women's Caucus Polit. Sci. (pres. 1975-76), Greater Springfield C. of C. (bd. dirs., accreditation task force 1992); Springfield Urban League (bd. dirs. 1993—), Pi Sigma Alpha (nat. pres.). Presbyterian. Office: Sangamon State U Office of the President Springfield IL 62794-9243

LYNN, OTIS CLYDE, former army officer; b. nr. Flynn's Lick, Tenn., Feb. 14, 1927; s. Dillard A. and Jennie Sue (Pruett) L.; m. Jacque Gilbert, Mar. 17, 1946; children: Clyde Gilbert, Gary Jackson. Student, Vanderbilt U., 1944-45; B.G.E., U. Omaha, 1963; M.S., George Washington U., 1968. Commd. 2d lt. U.S. Army, 1946, advanced through grades to maj. gen., 1972; chief of staff 2d Div., Korea, 1970; comdr. 1st Brigade 2d div., Korea, 1971; asst. div. comdr. 101st Div., Fort Campbell, Ky., 1974; chief of staff XVIII Airborne Corps, Fort Bragg, N.C., 1975, U.S. Forces, Japan, 1975-78; comdg. gen. 25th Inf. Div., Schofield Barracks, Hawaii, 1978-80; chief staff U.S. Army in Europe, Heidelberg, Fed. Republic Germany, 1980-82; ret., 1982, ret. real estate broker. Decorated Silver Star with two oak leaf clusters, Def. Superior Service medal, Legion of Merit (with two oak leaf clusters), Bronze Star, Air Medal, D.S.M., Purple Heart. Mem. Assn. of U.S. Army. Mem. Ch. of Christ. Home: 140 Arborvitae Dr Pks NC 28512-6200

LYNN, ROBERT WOOD, theologian, educator, dean; b. Wheatland, Wyo., Apr. 3, 1925; s. William McGregor and Janet (Reid) L.; m. Katharine Mitchell Wuerth, Mar. 8, 1952; children—Thomas Taylor, Janet MacGregor, Elizabeth Mitchell, Sarah McKee. A.B., Princeton U., 1948; B.D., Yale U., 1952; Th.D., Union Theol. Sem., N.Y.C., 1962. Ordained to ministry Presbyn. Ch., 1952; asst. minister Montview Presbyn. Ch., Denver, 1952-59; mem. faculty Union Theol. Sem., N.Y.C., 1959-75, dean Auburn program, 1960—, prof., 1965-75; v.p. Lilly Endowment, Inc., 1976-84, sr. v.p., 1985-89; vis. prof. Drew U., Andover Newton Theol. Sch., Fordham U., Tchrs. Coll., Columbia U.; scholar in residence Bangor Theol. Sem., 1989—. Author: Protestant Strategies in Education; co-author: The Big Little School; also articles. Trustee Louisville Sem., 1990—, Yale U., 1991—. Served with AUS, 1943-44. Woodrow Wilson fellow, 1948-49; Presbyn. Grad. fellow, 1959-60. Home: PO Box 3290 Leeds ME 04263

LYNN, THEODORE STANLEY, lawyer; b. N.Y.C., Aug. 2, 1937; s. Irving and Sydell (Gorlie) L.; m. Linda Isabel Freeman, July 21, 1968; children: Jessica, Douglas. AB, Columbia U., 1958; LLB, Harvard U., 1961; LLM, NYU, 1962; SJD, George Washington U., 1972. Law clerk U.S. Tax Ct., Washington, 1962-64; teaching fellow in law George Washington U., Washington, 1963-64; ptnr. Webster & Sheffield, N.Y.C., 1964-90; ptnr. Stroock & Stroock & Lavan, N.Y.C., 1991—; cons. Adminstrv. Conf. U.S., Washington, 1974-75; founding counsel Pension Real Estate Assn., Washington, 1981-84 . Author: Real Estate Limited Partnerships, 3d edit., 1991, Real Estate Investment Trusts, 2d edit., 1994; contbr. articles to profl. jours.; Spl. asst. Mayor John V. Lindsay, N.Y.C. 1966-69; sec. Manhattan Sch. of Dance, 1974-93; trustee Birch Wathen Lenox Sch., N.Y.C., 1975-93; bd. dirs. Manhattan Community Bd. #6, N.Y.C., 1977—, chair nominating com., 1992-94; bd. dirs. Citizens Union, 1991—. Mem. ABA, Fed. Bar Council, Assn. of Bar of City of N.Y., Univ. Club. Presbyterian. Office: Stroock & Stroock & Lavan 7 Hanover Sq New York NY 10004-2616

LYNN, THOMAS NEIL, JR., medical center administrator, physician; b. Ft. Worth, Feb. 14, 1930; s. Thomas Neil and Florence Van Zandt (Jennings) L.; m. Virginia Carolyn Harsh, July 26, 1952; children: Thomas Neil, Leslie Elizabeth, Kathryn Barry. B.S., U. Okla., 1951, M.D., 1955. Diplomate: Am. Bd. Internal Medicine, Am. Bd. Preventive Medicine. Intern Barnes Hosp., St. Louis, 1955-56; resident Barnes Hosp., 1956-57; clin. asso Nat. Heart Inst. NIH, Bethesda, Md., 1957-59; chief resident medicine U. Okla. Hosps., 1959-61; med. staff U. Hosps. and Clinics, 1970-72; staff Okla. Children's Meml. Hosp., Presbyn. Hosp., Va Hosp., Oklahoma City; instr. asst. prof. community health Okla. Med. Center, 1961-63, asso. prof., 1963-67, prof., chmn. dept., 1970-76; acting dean U. Okla. Coll. Medicine, 1974-76, dean, 1976-80; v.p. for med. staff affairs Bapt. Med. Center, Oklahoma City, 1980—; Mem. governing bd. Okla. Physician Manpower Tng. Commn., 1974-80, Ambulatory Health Care Consortium, Inc., 1977-78; mem. Okla. Bd. Medicolegal Examiners. Contbr. articles to profl. jours. Bd. dirs. Okla. Arthritis Found., 1978-82, v.p., 1981-82; bd. dirs. North Care Mental Health Ctr. 1981-87, pres., 1986-87, Oklahoma City Community Coun., 1982-90; med. dir. Okla. Organ Sharing Network, 1989-90; mem. Bd. Health Oklahoma City-County Health Dept., 1983-85; bd. dirs. Okla. chpt. Am. Heart Assn., 1984-86; mem. Nat. Commn. on Cert. Physician Assts., 1987-90. Fellow Am. Coll. Preventive Medicine; mem. AMA, Okla. Med. Assn. (trustee 1981-87, chmn. bd. trustees 1986-87), Oklahoma County Med. Soc. (trustee), Am. Acad. Family Physicians, Okla. Acad. Family Physicians, Sigma Xi, Alpha Omega Alpha, Phi Sigma, Alpha Tau Omega. Presbyn. Home: 3136 Pine Ridge Rd Oklahoma City OK 73120-5918 Individuals should live their life and conduct their affairs such that all succeeding generations will be benefitted and be glad that these people lived.

LYNN, TONY LEE, import company executive; b. Burke City, N.C., Oct. 13, 1939; s. Craig and Marie (Lowman) L.; m. Cindy Robson; 1 child, Gretchen. Student, Lenoir Rhyne Coll., 1958-62, N.C. Sch. Banking, 1972, Sch. Banking of South, Baton Rouge, 1972-75, Am. Inst. Banking, 1976. Dist. mgr. Am. Credit Co., Atlanta, 1961-66; v.p. First Nat. Bank Catawba County, Hickory, N.C., 1966-76; exec. v.p. Dixie Boat Works, Newton, N.C., 1976-82; founder, pres. Friitala Am., Hickory, 1982—. Named one of Outstanding Young Men of Am., 1975. Mem. Am. Inst. Banking (past. bd. dirs., pres. Hickory unit), Catawba County C. of C. (lifetime hon. mem.), Nat. Ski Patrol (tng. officer, sr. profl.). Home: RR 2 Box 586F Hickory NC 28601-9703 Office: Friitala Am 231 10th St NW Hickory NC 28601

LYNN, WALTER ROYAL, civil engineering educator, university administrator; b. N.Y.C., Oct. 1, 1928; s. Norman and Gussie (Gdalin) L.; m. Barbara Lee Campbell, June 3, 1960; children: Michael Drew. B.S., U. Miami, 1950; M.S., U. N.C., 1955; Ph.D., Northwestern U., 1963. Registered profl. engr., N.Y. State registered land surveyor, Fla. Land surveyor Ehly Constrn. Co., Miami, Fla., 1950-51; chief party Rader Engring. Co., Miami, 1951; supt. sewage treatment, lectr. civil engring. U. Miami, 1951-53, asst. prof. mech. engring., 1954-55, asst. prof. civil engring., 1955-57, research asst. prof. marine lab., 1957-58, assoc. prof. civil and indsl. engring., 1959-61; dir. research Ralph B. Carter Co., 1957-58; assoc. prof. san. engring. Cornell U., Ithaca, N.Y., 1961-64; prof. civil and environ. engring. Cornell U., 1964—, dir. Center Environ. Quality Mgmt., 1966-76, dir. Sch. Civil and Environ. Engring., 1970-78, dir. Program on Sci., Tech. and Society, 1980, dean univ. faculty, 1988-93, actg. prof. pub. health Med. Coll. 1971-80; mem. spl. adv. commn. on solid wastes NRC, 1968-76, mem. com. to rev. Washington met. water supply, 1976-84, chmn., 1980-84, mem. bd. water sci. and tech., 1982-86, chmn., 1982-85, mem. com. on water resources rsch., 1987-90, chmn., 1988-90; mem. U.S. Nat. Com. for the Decade on

Nat. Disaster Reduction, 1991—, chmn., 1991—; cons. WHO, 1969—, Rockefeller Found., 1976-81, SEARO, 1978; chmn. N.Y. State Water Resources Planning Coun., 1986—, NRC Bd. on Nat. Disasters, 1992— (chmn. 1992—). Editor: (with A. Charnes) Mathematical Analysis of Decision Problems in Ecology, 1975; assoc. editor: Jour. Ops. Research, 1968-76, Jour. Environ. Econs. and Mgmt, 1972-88; contbr.: chpt. to Human Ecology and Public Health, 1969; author articles. Chmn. Ithaca Mayor's Citizens Adv. Com., 1964-65, Ithaca Urban Renewal Agy., 1965-68; trustee Cornell U., 1980-85; bd. dirs. Cornell Research Found., 1978—. Served with AUS, 1946-48. Recipient Disting. Alumnus award U. Miami, 1985, Pub. Svc. award Universities Coun. on Water Resources, 1991, Conservation Svc. award U.S. Dept. Interior, 1994. Fellow ASCE (life), AAAS; mem. Nat. Acad. Engrs. Mex. (corr.), Sigma Xi, Phi Kappa Phi., Chi Epsilon. Home: 102 Iroquois Pl Ithaca NY 14850-2221

LYNN, WILLIAM J., III, federal agency administrator. BA, Dartmouth Coll., 1976; MA in Public Affairs, Princeton U., 1982; JD, Cornell Law Sch., 1980. Exec. dir. defense orgn. project Ctr. for Strategic and Internat. Studies, 1982-85; sr. fellow Strategic Devel. Ctr. Nat. Defense U.; mem. staff Sen. Edward M. Kennedy, 1987-93; asst. for budget Office of Sec. Defense, dir. for program analysis and evaluation. Author: (book) Toward A More Effective Defense, 1985; contbr. articles to profl. jours. Office: Office Sec Defense Rm 3E 836 The Pentagon Washington DC 20301*

LYNNE, GILLIAN BARBARA, choreographer, dancer, actress, director; b. Bromley, Eng., Feb. 20, 1926; d. Leslie and Barbara (Hart) Pyrke; m. Peter Land, May 17, 1980. Ed., Baston Sch., Bromley; Arts Ednl. Sch. Leading soloist Sadler's Wells Ballet, 1944-51; star dancer London Palladium, 1951-53. Dancing debut with Royal Ballet; soloist roles included: The Black Queen (Checkmate), The Lilac Fairy (Sleeping Beauty), The Queen of the Wilis (Giselle) and The Black Ballerina (Ballet Imperial, Symphonic Variations); role in film, Master of Ballantrae, 1952; lead in Can-Can, Coliseum, 1954-55; Becky Sharp in Vanity Fair, Windsor Theatre, 1956; guest principal dancer: Samson and Delilah, Sadler's Wells Ballet, 1957, Aida, and Tannhauser, Covent Garden, 1957, Puck in A Midsummer Night's Dream, BBC TV, 1958; star dancer in Chelsea at Nine (featured dance segments), Granada TV, 1958; lead in New Cranks, Lyric and Hammersmith Theatres, 1959; roles in Wanda, Rose Marie, Cinderella, Out of My Mind, and lead in revue, 1960-61; leading lady, 5 Past Eight Show, Edinburgh, 1962, Queen of Cats, London, 1962-63; conceived, directed, choreographed, and starred in Collages, Edinburgh Festival, 1963, Royal Variety Performance Simple Man Extract, 1989; staged: England Our England, Revue, Princes Theatre, 1961; choreographer: The Owl and the Pussycat (1st ballet), Western Theatre Ballet, 1962, Queen of the Cats, London Palladium, 1962-63, Wonderful Life (1st film), 1963-64, Every Day's a Holiday, and Three Hats for Lisa (musical films), 1964, The Roar of the Greasepaint, and Pickwick, Broadway, 1965, The Flying Dutchman, Covent Garden, 1966, Half a Sixpence (film), 1966-67, How Now Dow Jones, Broadway, 1967, Midsummer Marriage, Covent Garden, 1968, The Trojans, Covent Garden, 1969, 1977, Breakaway (ballet), Scottish Theatre Ballet, 1969, Phil the Fluter, Palace Theatre, 1969, Ambassador Theatre, Her Majesty's Theatre, 1971, Man of La Mancha (film), 1972, The Card, Queen's, 1973, Hans Andersen, London Palladium, 1975, The Way of The World, Aldwych, 1978; My Fair Lady, nat. tour and Adelphi, 1979, Parsifal, Covent Garden, 1979, (also assoc. dir.) Cats, New London Theatre, 1981 (Olivier award 1981), Broadway 1982, nat. tour, 1983, dir. and choreographer prodn. in Vienna, 1983 (Silver Order of Merit, Austria, 1984), L.A., Sydney, 1985, East Berlin, 1987, also Can., Japan, Australia, Moscow, 1989, Paris, 1989 (Molière award Best Musical), Amsterdam, 1990, Café Soir (ballet), Houston Ballet Co., 1985, Cabaret, Strand, 1986, The Phantom of the Opera, Her Majesty's Theatre, 1986, Broadway, Japan, Vienna, 1989, Stockholm, Chgo., Hamburg, Australia, 1990, Canada, 1991, Amsterdam, 1993, Manchester, Eng., 1993, A Simple Man (ballet), Sadler's Wells, 1988, Aspects of Love, Prince of Wales Theatre, 1989, Broadway, 1990, The Brontës (ballet), Northern Ballet Theatre, 1995; choreographer, dir.: The Match Girls, Globe Theatre, 1966; Bluebeard, Sadlers Wells Opera, 1966, new prodn., Coliseum, 1969), Love on the Dole (musical), Nottingham Playhouse, 1970; Liberty Ranch, Greenwich, 1972, Once Upon a Time, Duke of York's, 1972, Jasperina, Amsterdam, 1978, Valentine's Day, Chichester, 1991, Globe, 1992, A Simple Man (BBC-TV) (Brit. Acad. award for conception, direction and choreography 1988); dir. Round Leicester Square, Prince Charles Theatre, 1963, Tonight at Eight, Hampstead, 1970, Fortune, 1971, Lillywhite Lies, Nottingham, 1971, A Midsummer Night's Dream, Stratford, 1977, Tomfoolery, Criterion, 1980, Jeeves Takes Charge, Fortune, 1980, off-Broadway, 1983, L.A., 1985, To Those Born Late, New End Theatre, 1981, La Ronde, RSC, Aldwych, 1982, (also appeared in) Alone Plus One, Newcastle, 1982, The Rehearsal, Yvonne Arnaud, Guildford and tour, 1983, Cabaret, Strand, 1986; staged: England Our England (revue), Princes, 1961, 200 Motels (pop-opera film), 1971, musical nos. in Quilp (film), 1974, A Comedy of Errors, Stratford, 1976 (Olivier award 1977), TV musical, 1977, As You Like It (musical), Stratford, 1977, Songbook, Globe Theatre, 1979, Once in a Lifetime, Aldwych Theatre, 1979 (Olivier award for best play 1978), new stage act for Tommy Steele, 1979, wedding sequence in Yentl (film), 1982, European Vacation II (film), Pirelli Calendar, 1988, Pickwick, Chichester and Sadler's Wells, 1993; conceived, directed dance for Life Gala, Her Majesty's Theatre, 1991; choreographer and staging: (films) Mr. Love, Under Milkwood, Quilp; choreographer for TV: Peter and the Wolf (narrated and mimed all 9 parts), 1958, At the Hawk's Well (ballet), 1975, There Was a Girl, 1975, The Fool on the Hill (1st Colour Spl. for ABC; Best Musical, Best Prodn. awards in Australia 1977), with Australian Ballet and Sydney Symphony Orch., staged Sydney Opera House, 1975, Muppet Show series, 1976-80 (Golden Rose Montreux award 1977); (also musical staging) Alice in Wonderland, 1985, shows and specials for Val Doonican, Perry Como, Petula Clark, Nana Mouskouri, John Curry, Harry Secombe, Ray Charles, and Mike Burstein, also produced and devised Noel Coward and Cleo Laine spls.; directed for TV: Mrs. F's Friends, 1981, Easy Money, 1982, Le Morte d'Arthur, 1983; for internat. TV in various capacities as producer, deviser, stager, choreographer and dir.: 1989 Royal Variety Performance (Andrew Lloyd Webber segment), The Look of Love, BBC North West, (BBC) A Simple Man, The Morte D'Arthur, Easy Money, The Various Ends of Mrs. F.'s Friends, The Look of Love, Pickwick, It's Topol, Val Doonican, Nana Mouskouri, Soccer Dance, Tiptoes, There Was a Girl, A World of Music, The Great American Songbook; (ABC) The Fool on the Hill; (LTW) Marvellous Party, Tickertape Children's Series, Cleo Laine Sings; (CBS/USA) Alice in Wonderland; (ATV) The Muppet Show, Marty Feldman Show; (VARA/Holland) The Mike Burstyn Show; (Thames) Comedy Tonight, The Royal Variety Show, 1991, 93, Sadlers Wells Theatre, 1993, Pickwick Chichester Festival Theatre, 1993; pub. contbr. to Cats, The Book of the Musical; articles in Dancing Times. Mem. Pickwick Club. Address: care Lean Two Prodns Ltd, 18 Rutland St Knightsbridge, London SW7 IEF, England*

LYNNE, JEFF, rock musician, composer; b. Birmingham, Eng., Dec. 30, 1942. Musician with The Nightriders, Eng., The Move, also The Electric Light Orch.; albums include No Answer, 1971, ELO, II, 1973, On the Third Day, 1973, Eldorado, 1974, Face the Music, 1975, Ole ELO, 1976, A New World Record, 1976, The Light Shines On, 1977, 3 Light Years, 1978, ELO, 1978, Out of the Blue, 1978, Discovery, 1979, The Light Shines On, Vol. 2, 1979, Greatest Hits, 1979, Xanadu, 1980, Box of Their Best, 1980, Secret Messages, 1984, Balance of Power, 1986, Afterglow, 1990, ELO Part II, 1991, (with Traveling Willburys)Traveling Wilburys, 1988, Traveling Wilburys Vol. 3, 1990, (solo) Armchair Theatre, 1990; producer various artists including Dave Edmunds, George Harrison, Daryl Hall. Recipient Grammy award (with Traveling Wilburys), 1990. *

LYNTON, ERNEST ALBERT, physicist, educator, former university official; b. Berlin, Germany, July 17, 1926; came to U.S., 1941, naturalized, 1945; s. Arthur J. and Lizzie (Kiefe) Lowenstein; m. Carla Ellen Kaufmann, Aug. 4, 1953; children—David Michael, Eric Daniel. B.S., Carnegie Inst. Tech., 1947; M.S., 1948; PhD, Yale, 1951. AEC postdoctoral fellow U. Leiden, Holland, 1951-52; faculty Rutgers U., 1952-74, prof. physics, 1962-74; dean Rutgers U. (Livingston Coll.), 1965-73; Commonwealth prof. U. Mass., Boston, 1974-95, sr. v.p. acad. affairs, 1974-80, sr. research assoc. N.E. Resource Ctr. for Higher Edn.; vis. prof. Fulbright fellow U. Grenoble, France, 1959-60; cons. NSF, 1965-70, Ford Found., 1973, 80-82, Spelman Coll., 1980— Cambridge Coll., 1982-83, OECD, 1981-93, Coun. of Europe, 1982-83, Carnegie Found., 1992—; Am. Assn. Higher Edn., 1992—; mem. Commn. on Higher Edn. Mid. States Assn., 1972-74; adv. bd. Princeton Sch.

Architecture, 1971-80; chmn. Mass. Commn. Telecoms., 1981-83. Author: Superconductivity, 3d edit., 1968 (translated into French, Russian, German); Missing Connection Between Business and the Universities, 1984, (with Sandra Elman) New Priorities for the University, 1987, Making the Case for Professional Service, 1995; exec. editor Met. Univs., 1988—; contbr. articles to profl. jours. Pres. Princeton (N.J.) Jewish Ctr., 1964-66; bd. dirs. Princeton Assn. Human Rights, 1962-65; Mercer County chpt. ACLU, 1966-70; trustee Marlboro Music, 1982—. With AUS, 1944-46. Fellow Am. Phys. Soc. Home: 14 Allerton St Brookline MA 02146-7727

LYNTON, HAROLD STEPHEN, lawyer; b. N.Y.C., Nov. 2, 1909; widowed, Mar. 12, 1990; children: Stephen Jonathan, Richard David, Andrew Edward; m. Hattie Gruenstein Kalish, Jan. 27, 1991. AB magna cum laude, Yale U., 1929; JD cum laude, Harvard U., 1932. Bar: N.Y. 1933, U.S. Supreme Ct. 1947. Ptnr. Kaufman, Gallop, Gould, Climenko & Lynton, N.Y.C., 1934-51, Lynton & Klein and predecessors, N.Y.C., 1951-80; ptnr. Shea & Gould, N.Y.C., 1980-91, counsel, 1992-94; counsel Dornbush Mensch Mandelstam & Schaeffer, N.Y.C., 1994—; gen. counsel, trustee, mem. adv. bd. Barron Collier Cos., Naples, Fla., 1945—; also bd. dirs. Barron Collier Cos. and predecessors, Naples, Fla. Capt. AUS, 1943-45. Mem. ABA, N.Y. State Bar Assn., Assn. of Bar of City of N.Y., N.Y. County Lawyers Assn., Yale Club N.Y., Sunningdale Country Club, Phi Beta Kappa. Avocations: travel, theatre, tennis, swimming. Home: 971 Fenimore Rd Larchmont NY 10538-1025 Office: Dornbush Mensch et al 747 3rd Ave New York NY 10017-2803

LYON, ANDREW BENNET, economics educator; b. Elmhurst, Ill., June 6, 1958; s. Richard M. and Rhee Lyon; m. Jennifer A. Sour, May 31, 1987; 1 child, Sarah. AB, Stanford U., 1980; PhD, Princeton U., 1986. Economist Jt. Com. on Taxation, U.S. Congress, Washington D.C., 1985-87; asst. prof., dept. econ. U. Md., College Park, 1987-93, assoc. prof., dept. econ., 1993—; vis. fellow Brookings Inst., 1994—; cons. and expert witness, 1987—; dir. Unisys Credit Corp., Detroit, 1991-92; sr. econ. Coun. Econ. Advisers, 1992-93. Contbr. numerous articles to profl. jours. Nat. Bur. Econc. fellow, 1987-94. Mem. Am. Econ. Assn., Nat. Tax Assn. (Outstanding Doctoral Dissertation award 1986, Fed. Tax Com. 1991), Phi Beta Kappa. Office: U Md Dept Econs College Park MD 20742

LYON, BRYCE DALE, historian, educator; b. Bellevue, Ohio, Apr. 22, 1920; s. E. Paul and Florence (Gundrum) L.; m. Mary Elizabeth Lewis, June 3, 1944; children—Geoffrey P., Jacqueline M. AB, Baldwin-Wallace Coll., 1942; PhD, Cornell U., 1949; PdD (hon.), 1972; LittD (hon.), U. Ghent, 1988. Asst. prof. history U. Colo., 1949-51, Harvard U., 1951-56; assoc. prof. U. Ill. at Urbana, 1956-59; prof. U. Calif. at Berkeley, 1959-65; Barnaby and Mary Critchfield Keeney prof. history emeritus Brown U., 1965-86, chmn. history dept., 1968-75. Author: Medieval Institutions, 1954, From Fief to Indenture, 1957, A History of the World, 1960, Constitutional and Legal History of Medieval England, 1960, Medieval History, 4th rev. edit., 1962, The High Middle Ages, 1964, The Middle Ages in Recent Historical Thought, 2d edit., 1965, Medieval Finance, 1967, The Origins of the Middle Ages, 1971, Henri Pirenne: A Biographical and Intellectual Study, 1974, The Journal de Querre of Henri Pirenne, 1976, Studies of West European Medieval Institutions, 1978, The Wardrobe Book of William de Norwell (1338-1340), 1983, The Birth of Annales History: The Letters of Lucien Febvre and Marc Bloch to Henri Pirenne (1921-1935), 1991, Réflexions d'un solitaire by Henri Pirenne, 1994. Served with AUS and USAAF, 1942-46. Fellow Royal Hist. Soc., Am. Acad. Arts and Scis., Medieval Acad., Belgian Royal Acad.; mem. Econ. History Assn., Am. Hist. Assn., Conf. Brit. Studies. Home: HC 63 Box 108 Alstead NH 03602-7720

LYON, CARL FRANCIS, JR., lawyer; b. Sumter, S.C., May 9, 1943; s. Carl Francis and Sophie (Goldstrum) L.; m. Maryann Mercier; children—Barbara Ruth, Sarah Frances, Carl Francis, III. A.B., Duke U., 1965, J.D. with honors, 1968. Bar: N.Y. 1969, D.C. 1977. Assoc., then ptnr. Mudge Rose Guthrie Alexander & Ferdon, N.Y.C., 1968—, mem. exec. com., 1986-87, 94—. Contbr. articles to profl. publs. Mem. ABA (vice-chmn. spl. com. on energy fin. 1988-91), N.Y. State Bar Assn., D.C. Bar Assns., Am. Pub. Power Assn., Duke U. Law Alumni Coun., Order of Coif, Phi Alpha Delta. Office: Mudge Rose Guthrie Alexander & Ferdon 180 Maiden Ln New York NY 10038-4925

LYON, DAVID WILLIAM, research executive; b. Lansing, Mich., Mar. 26, 1941; s. Herbert Reid and Mary Kathleen (Slack) L.; m. Catherine McHugh Dillon, July 8, 1967. BS, Mich. State U., 1963; M in City and Regional Planning, U. Calif., Berkeley, 1966, PhD, 1972. Regional economist Fed. Res. Bank Phila., 1969-71; research dir. human and econ. resources The N.Y.C.-Rand Inst., 1972-75, v.p., 1975; sr. economist The Rand Corp., Santa Monica, Calif., 1975-77, dep. v.p., 1977-79, v.p. domestic research div., 1979-93, v.p. external affairs, 1993-94; pres., CEO Pub. Policy Inst. Calif., 1994—; adj. prof. U. Pa., 1975; mem. adv. bd. Inst. for Civil Justice, 1987-93, Rand-Urban Inst. Program for Rsch. on Immigration Policy, 1988-91, Drug Policy Rsch. Ctr., 1989-93, So. Calif. Health Policy Rsch. Consortium, 1989-94, Rand Ctr. for U.S.-Japan Rels., 1989-93, Rand Ctr. for Asia-Pacific Policy, 1993—; dir. Coll. Environ. Design Coun., U. Calif., Berkeley, 1979-90. Contbr. articles to profl. jours.; publs. com. Rand Jour. Econs., 1984-94. Bd. dirs. Sr. Health and Peer Counseling Ctr., Santa Monica, Calif., 1985-94, pres., 1989-91. Mellon fellow in city planning, 1966-68; Econ. Devel. Adminstrn. grad. fellow, 1966. Mem. Coun. on Fgn. Rels., Japan Am. Soc. So. Calif. (bd. dirs. 1990—), Asia Soc. (so. Calif. adv. bd.), Riviera Tennis Club (Pacific Palisades, Calif.), Delta Phi Epsilon. Office: Pub Policy Inst Calif 500 Washington Ste 800 San Francisco CA 94111

LYON, JAMES BURROUGHS, lawyer; b. N.Y.C., May 11, 1930; s. Francis Murray and Edith May (Strong) L. BA, Amherst Coll., 1952; LLB, Yale U., 1955. Bar: Conn. 1955, U.S. Tax Ct. 1970. Asst. football coach Yale U., 1953-55; assoc. Murtha, Cullina, Richter and Pinney (and predecessor), Hartford, Conn., 1956-61, ptnr., 1961—; mem. adv. com., lectr. and session leader NYU Inst. on Fed. Taxation, 1973-86; mem. IRS Bklyn. Key Dist.'s Exempt Orgns. Liaison Group, 1993—. Chmn. 13th Conf. Charitable Orgns. NYU on Fed. Taxation, 1982; trustee Kingswood-Oxford Sch., West Hartford, Conn., 1961-91, hon. trustee, 1991—, chmn. bd. trustees, 1975-78; trustee Old Sturbridge Village, Mass., 1974—, chmn. bd. trustees, 1991-93; trustee Ella Burr McManus Trust, Hartford, 1980—, Ellen Battell Stoeckel Trust, Norfolk, Conn., 1994—, Hartford YMCA, 1985—, St. Francis Found., 1991—, Watkinson Libr., 1990—; trustee Wadsworth Atheneum, Hartford, 1968—, pres., 1981-84, hon. trustee, 1993—; sec. bd., trustee Horace Bushnell Meml. Hall, Hartford, 1993—, trustee, 1994—; corporator Inst. Living, 1981—; Hartford Hosp., 1975—, St. Francis Hosp., Hartford, 1976, Hartford Pub. Libr., 1979—, Hartford Sem., 1991; bd. dirs. Conn. Policy and Econ. Coun., Inc., 1991—; mem. Conn. adv. com. New Eng. Legal Found., 1991—; bd. vis. Hartford Art Sch., 1995—. Recipient Eminent Svc. medal Amherst Coll., 1967, Nathan Hale award Yale Club Hartford, 1982, Disting. Am. award No. Conn. chpt. Nat. Football Found. Hall of Fame, 1983, Community Svc. award United Way of the Capital Area, 1986. Fellow ABA (mem. exempt orgn. com., co-chairperson subcom. on mus. and other cultural orgns. sect. of taxation 1988—), Am. Coll. Tax Counsel; mem. Am. Law Inst., Hartford Golf Club, Yale Club, Union Club N.Y.C., Dauntless Club (Essex, Conn.), Wianno Club (Osterville, Mass.), Mory's Assn. (New Haven), Phi Beta Kappa. Office: 185 Asylum St Hartford CT 06103-3401

LYON, JAMES CYRIL, chemical society executive; b. Eldorado, Ill., May 14, 1937; s. James S. and Helen D. (Podrasky) L.; m. Sandra K. Lasseter, June 14, 1958; children: Lori Anne, Lisa J. BS, So. Ill. U., Carbondale, 1959; MS, No. Ill. U., DeKalb, 1967. Tchr. English, coach Bremen High Sch., Midlothian, Ill., 1959-61, Maine Twp. High Sch. East, Park Ridge, Ill., 1961-64; bus. mgr., treas. Nat. Coun. Tchrs. of English, Urbana, Ill., 1964-71; exec. dir. Am. Oil Chemists' Soc., Champaign, Ill., 1971—; Internat. Soc. for Fat Rsch., 1992—. Bd. dirs. Champaign-Urbana Conv. and Visitors Bur., 1987-95, chmn., 1988-92; bd. dirs. Champaign County Hist. Mus., 1975-81, pres. 1980, Champaign County Econ Devel. Partnership, 1995—. Mem. Am. Soc. Assn. Execs., Ill. Soc. Assn. Execs., Found. for Internat. Meetings (bd. dirs. 1982), Champaign Country Club, Rotary, Phi Delta Kappa, Kappa Delta Pi. Republican. Avocations: travel, reading, golf. Home: 24 Field East Champaign IL 61821-6535 Office: Am Oil Chemists Soc PO Box 3489 Champaign IL 61826-3489

LYON, JAMES KARL, German language educator; b. Rotterdam, Holland, Feb. 17, 1934; came to U.S., 1937; s. T. Edgar and Hermana (Forsberg) L.; m. Dorothy Ann Burton, Dec. 22, 1959; children: James, John, Elizabeth, Sarah, Christina, Rebecca, Matthew, Melissa. BA, U. Utah, 1958, MA, 1959; PhD, Harvard U., 1963. Instr. German Harvard U., Cambridge, Mass., 1962-63, asst. prof., 1966-71; assoc. prof. U. Fla., Gainesville, 1971-74; prof. U. Calif. San Diego, La Jolla, 1974-94, provost Fifth Coll., 1987-94; prof. dept. Germanic and Slavic langs. Brigham Young U., Provo, Utah, 1994—; vis. prof. U. Augsburg, Germany, 1993. Author: Konkordanz zur Lyrik Gottfried Benns, 1971, Bertolt Brecht and Rudyard Kipling, 1975, Brecht's American Cicerone, 1978, Bertolt Brecht in America, 1980, Brecht in den USA, 1994. Capt. M.I., U.S. Army, 1963-66. NEH fellow, 1970, Guggenheim Found. fellow, 1974; Ford Found. grantee, 1988, 91. Mem. MLA, Am. Assn. Tchrs. German, Internat. Brecht. Soc., Phi Beta Kappa. Democrat. Mormon. Avocations: back-packing, fishing. Office: BYU Dept Germanic & Slavic Langs 4094 Jesse Knight Human Bld Provo UT 84602-6120

LYON, JAMES ROBERT, utilities executive; b. Otterville, Mo., Nov. 30, 1927; s. William H. and Laura Virginia (Eubank) L.; m. Janet Drescher, Sept. 1, 1951; children: Sally Beth, Suzanne. Student, Mo. Valley Coll., 1945-46; B.S.E.E., U. Mo., 1951. Engr., Bonneville Power Adminstrn., Portland, Oreg., 1951-53; with Iowa Power & Light Co., 1953—, v.p. ops., 1966-71, sr. v.p., 1971-73, exec. v.p., 1973-79, pres., 1979-91; ret. Pres. United Way, 1978-79; dir. Share Care, Ltd., Des Moines, Des Moines Area Community Coll. Found. Served with U.S. Army, 1945-47. Mem. Midwest Gas Assn. (dir.), Nat. Soc. Profl. Engrs., Iowa Engring. Soc., Iowa Mfg. Assn. Office: Iowa Power & Light Co PO Box 657 Des Moines IA 50303-0657

LYON, JEFFREY, journalist, author; b. Chgo., Nov. 28, 1943; s. Herbert Theodore and Lyle (Hoffenberg) L.; m. Bonita S. Brodt, June, 20, 1981; children: Lindsay, Derek. BS in Journalism, Northwestern U., 1965. Reporter Miami (Fla.) Herald, 1966-74; reporter Chgo. Today, 1966-74; reporter Chgo. Tribune, 1974-76, columnist, 1976-80, 94—, feature writer specializing in sci., 1980—; creative writing adj. prof.; coord. joint sci. and journalism programs Columbia Coll., Chgo., 1987—, dir., 1988—. Author: Playing God in the Nursery, 1985, Altered Fates: Gene Therapy and the Retooling of Human Life, 1995; also newspaper series Altered Fates, 1986 (Pulitzer Prize 1987). Mem. State of Ill. Perinatal Adv. Com., Springfield, 1986-90; mem. pediatric ethics com. U. Chgo. Hosps., 1985-90; bd. dirs. Shore Community Svcs. to Retarded Citizens, Evanston, Ill., 1985-90; mem. Action Com. for Little City, Palatine, Ill., 1979—. Recipient Nat. Headliner award Atlantic City Press Club, 1984, Citizen Fellow award Inst. Medicine of Chgo., 1987, Peter Lisagor award, 1990. Office: The Chgo Tribune Chgo Tribune Co 435 N Michigan Ave Chicago IL 60611-4001

LYON, PHILIP K(IRKLAND), lawyer; b. Warren, Ark., Jan. 19, 1944; s. Leroy and Maxine (Campbell) L.; children by previous marriage: Bradford F., Lucinda H., Bruce P., Suzette P., John P., Martin K., Meredith J.; m. Jayne Carol Jack, Aug. 12, 1982. JD with honors, U. Ark., 1967. Bar: Ark. 1967, U.S. Supreme Ct. 1970, Tenn. 1989. Sr. ptnr., dir. ops. House, Wallace, Nelson & Jewell, P.A., Little Rock, 1967-86; pres. Jack, Lyon & Jones, P.A, Little Rock & Nashville, 1986—. Instr. bus. law, labor law, govt. bus. and collective bargaining U. Ark., Little Rock, 1969-72, lectr. practice skills and labor law, U. Ark. Law Sch., 1979-80. Co-author: Schei and Grossman Employment Discrimination Law, 2d edit., 1982; editor-in-chief Ark. Law Rev., 1966-67. Bd. dirs. Ark. Law Rev., 1978-93, v.p. 1990-92; bd. dirs. Southwestern Legal Found., 1978—; mem. editorial bd. Entertainment Law & Fin., 1993—. Mem. ABA (select com. liason office fed. contract compliance programs 1982—, select com. liason EEOC 1984—, select com. immigration law, forum com. entertainment and sports industries), Ark. State C. of C. (bd. dirs. 1984-88), Greater Little Rock C. of C. (chmn. community affairs com. 1982-84, minority bus. affairs 1985-89), Assn. Trial Lawyers Am., Ark. Bar Assn. (chmn. labor law com. 1977-78, chmn. labor law sect. 1978-79, chmn. lawyers helping lawyers com. 1988-94), Tenn. Bar Assn. (labor sect., lawyers helping lawyers com. 1989—, lawyers concerned for lawyers com.), Nashville Bar Assn. (entertainment law com., lawyers concerned for lawyers com.), Pulaski County Bar Assn., Ark. Trial Lawyers Assn., Country Music Assn., Acad. of Country Music, Nashville Entertainment Assn., Nashville Songwriters Assn. Internat., Copyright Soc. of South, Capitol Club. Recipient Golden Gavel award Ark. Bar Assn., 1978, Writing Excellence award Ark. Bar Found., 1980. Home: 350 Ardsley Pl Nashville TN 37215 also: 17 Heritage Park Cir North Little Rock AR 72116-8528 Office: Jack Lyon & Jones PA 11 Music Cir S Nashville TN 37215 also: Jack Lyon & Jones PA 425 W Capitol 3400 TCBY Tower Little Rock AR 72201 One of the true secrets of success is to concentrate your efforts—for if you apply these efforts everywhere at once then you will accomplish very little anywhere.

LYON, RICHARD, mayor, retired naval officer; b. Pasadena, Calif., July 14, 1923; s. Norman Morais and Ruth (Hollis) L.; m. Cynthia Gisslin, Aug. 8, 1975; children—Patricia, Michael, Sean; children by previous marriage—Mary, Edward, Sally, Kathryn, Patrick (dec.), Susan. B.E., Yale U., 1944; M.B.A., Stanford U., 1953. Command. ensign USN, 1944; advanced through grades to rear adm. SEAL, 1974; served in Pacific and China, World War II, 1944; with Underwater Demolition Team Korea; recalled to active duty as dep. chief Naval Res. New Orleans, 1978-81; mayor City of Oceanside, Calif., 1992; mem. Chief Naval Ops. Res. Affairs Adv. Bd., 1978-81; exec. v.p. Nat. Assn. Employee Benefits, Newport Beach, Calif., 1981-90; mem. Bd. Control, U.S. Naval Inst., 1978-81; pres. Civil Svc. Commn., San Diego County, 1990, Oceanside Unified Sch. Bd., 1991. Pres. bd. trustees Children's Hosp. Orange County, 1965, 72. Decorated Legion of Merit. Mem. Nat. Assn. Securities Dealers (registered prin.), Newport Harbor Yacht Club, Rotary Club (Anaheim, Calif. pres. 1966). Republican. Episcopalian. Home: 4464 Inverness Dr Oceanside CA 92057-5052

LYON, RICHARD HAROLD, educator, physicist; b. Evansville, Ind., Aug. 24, 1929; s. Chester Clyde and Gertrude (Schucker) L.; m. Jean Wheaton; children—Katherine Ruth, Geoffrey Cleveland, Suzanne Marie. A.B., Evansville Coll., 1952; Ph.D. in Physics (Owens-Corning fellow), Mass. Inst. Tech., 1955; D.Eng., U. Evansville, 1976. Asst. prof. elec. engring. U. Minn., Mpls., 1956-59; Mem. research staff Mass. Inst. Tech., 1955-56, lectr. mech. engring., 1963-69, prof. mech. engring., 1970-95, prof. emeritus, 1995—, head mechanics and materials div., 1981-86; NSF postdoctoral fellow U. Manchester, Eng., 1959-60; sr. scientist Bolt Beranek & Newman, Cambridge, 1960-66, v.p., 1966-70; chmn. Cambridge Collaborative, Inc., 1972-90; v.p. Grozier Pub., Inc., 1972; pres. Grozier Tech. Systems, 1976-82, RH Lyon Corp., 1976—. Author: Transportation Noise, 1974, Theory and Applications of Statistical Energy Analysis, 1975, 2d edit., 1994, Machinery Noise and Diagnostics, 1987. Bd. dirs. Boston Light Opera, Ltd., 1975; mem. alumni bd. U. Evansville, 1988—. Fellow Acoustical Soc. Am. (assoc. editor Jour. 1967-74, exec. coun. 1976-70, v.p. 1989-90, pres. 1993-94); mem. NAE, Sigma Xi, Sigma Pi Sigma. Research, publs. in fields of nonlinear random oscillations, energy transfer in complex structures, sound transmission in marine and aerospace vehicles, building acoustics, environmental noise, machinery diagnostics, home theater audio systems. Home: 60 Prentiss Ln Belmont MA 02178-2021 Office: MIT Dept Mechanical Engrin Cambridge MA 02139 also: RH Lyon Corp 691 Concord Ave Cambridge MA 02138-1002

LYON, RONALD EDWARD, management consultant, computer consultant; b. Kansas City, Kans., Apr. 13, 1936; s. William Edward and Lillian (Gee) L.; m. Josette Paula Larré, July 24, 1959; children: Michael Alan, Mark Alexander, Matthew Adam, Collette Allison. Owner Hansler Outboard & Austin Aqua Sports, Austin, Tex., 1959-63; gen. mgr. Wayne Green Ent.-73 Mag., Peterboro, N.H., 1965; with Computer Control Corp., Peterboro, N.H., 1965-71; sales person Radio Shack (Tandy) & Sterling Elec. Co., Maine, N.H., Vt. areas, 1971-82; sales engr. Pall Corp./Russell Assocs. Inc., Watertown, Mass., 1982-87; mgr. eastern region Fansteel/Wellman Dynamics, 1984-87; CEO, COO Laryon Assocs., Inc., Keene, N.H., 1987—. With USAF, 1955-59. Mem. U.S. Power Squadron, Soc. for Preservation and Encouragement of Barber Shop Quartet Singing in Am. Avocations: sailing, ham radio, computers, skiing, square dancing. Home: Mcintire Rd Munsonville NH 03457 Office: Laryon Assocs Inc 178D Main St Keene NH 03431-3739

LYON, SHERMAN ORWIG, rubber and chemical company executive; b. Greenwich, Conn., Sept. 4, 1939; s. James R. and June K. (Orwig) L.; m. Nell Collar, June 15, 1968 (div. 1990); children: Jeffrey, Michelle; m. Sharon Feldman, Jan. 25, 1992. BSChemE, Purdue U., 1961; grad. exec. program, Stanford U., Palo Alto, Calif., 1978. Process engr., prodn. supt. Monsanto Co., St. Louis, 1961-69, mktg. mgr., 1969-72; gen. mgr. chem. div. Mallinckrodt, Inc., St. Louis, 1972-78, v.p. specialty chems., 1978-80; group v.p. Celanese Corp., Chatham, N.J., 1980-82; pres. Copolymer Rubber & Chem. Corp., Baton Rouge, 1982-89; sr. v.p. Armstrong Rubber Co., New Haven, 1983-89; exec. v.p. Armtek Corp., 1987; pres., chief exec. officer Lyon Investment Corp., 1986-92. Mem. exec. bd. Istrouma area council Boy Scouts Am., Baton Rouge, 1984; bd. dirs. Gulf South Research Inst., Baton Rouge, 1984, Woman's Hosp. (dir. 1985-86), United Way Baton Rouge Area (dir. 1985-87), Baton Rouge C. of C. (dir. 1985-87). Recipient Iron Key, Purdue U., 1961. Mem. Internat. Inst. Synthetic Rubber Producers (bd. dirs. 1983-89, pres. N.Am. sect. 1985-86), Synthetic Organic Chem. Mfg. Assn. (bd. govs. 1981-82), Am. Inst. Chem. Engrs., Nat. Futures Assn., Managed Futures Assn., Baton Rouge C. of C. (bd. dirs. 1983-86), Tau Beta Pi, Omicron Delta Kappa (founding mem. Purdue chpt. 1961), Sigma Phi Epsilon, City Club, Baton Rouge Country Club. Republican. Office: Lyon Investment Corp Ste 140 10161 Centurion Pkwy N Jacksonville FL 32256

LYON, STERLING RUFUS, justice; b. Windsor, Ont., Can., Jan. 30, 1927; s. David Rufus and Ella Mae (Cuthbert) L.; m. Barbara Jean Mayers, Sept. 26, 1953; children: Nancy, Andrea, Peter, Jennifer, Jonathan. B.A., U. Winnipeg, 1948; LL.B., U. Man., 1953. Bar: Man. 1953, created Queen's Counsel 1960. Crown atty., atty. gen. Man., 1953-57; mem. Man. Legis. Assembly, 1958-69, 76-86; atty. gen. Man., 1958-63, 66-69; minister of mcpl. affairs, 1960-61, of pub. utilities, 1961-63, of mines and natural resources, 1963-66, of tourism and recreation, 1966-68, commr. No. affairs, 1966-68; leader Progressive Conservative Party, 1975-83; premier of Man., 1977-81; leader of the opposition, 1976-77, 81-83; mem. Her Majesty's Privy Council for Can., 1982; apptd. justice Man. Ct. of Appeal, Winnipeg, 1986—; chmn. 1st Can. Conf. on Pollution, Montreal, 1966, Can. Premier's Conf., 1980-81; pres. Can. Coun. Resource Ministers, 1965-66. Former trustee Ducks Unltd.; trustee Delta Waterfowl Found.; bd. regents U. Winnipeg, 1972-76. With RCAF Res., 1950-53. Recipient U. Winnipeg Alumni Assn. Jubilee award, 1973. Office: Law Cts, Winnipeg, MB Canada R3C 0V8

LYON, WALDO KAMPMEIER, physicist; b. Los Angeles, May 19, 1914; s. Charles R. and Anna (Kampmeier) L.; m. Virginia Louise Backus, Aug. 28, 1937; children: Lorraine Mae, Russell Roy. A.B., UCLA, 1936, M.A., 1937, Ph.D., 1941. Research physicist, head submarine and Arctic research br. U.S. Naval Electronics Lab., 1941-66; sr. scientist wave measurement group Bikini Atom Bomb Test, 1946; submarine physicist USN-Byrd Antarctic Expdn., 1946; chief sci. Joint U.S.-Canadian Beaufort Sea Sci. Expdns., 1950-54, chief scientist Arctic submarine research, 1964—; dir. Arctic Submarine Lab., 1966-85; lectr., physicist U. Calif. at Los Angeles, 1948-49. Recipient Disting. Civilian Svc. award U.S. Navy, 1955, 58, Disting. Civilian Service award Dept. Def., 1956, President's Distinguished Fed. Civilian Svc. award, 1962, Edward Dickson UCLA Alumnus award, 1963, Gold medal award Am. Soc. Naval Engrs., 1959, Silver medal Societe de Geographie, Paris, 1983, Bronze medal Royal Inst. Navigation, 1985, Silver Bushnell award Am. Def. Preparedness Assn., 1993. Sr. scientist 1st submarine polar transit Arctic Ocean, U.S.S. Nautilus, 1958 1st winter North Pole transit U.S.S. Skate, 1959, 1st transpolar N.W. passage, U.S.S. Sea Dragon, 1960, sr. scientist 1st dual submarine North Pole expdn., 1962; chief scientist North Pole Submarine Expdns. by Queenfish, 1967, Whale, 1969, Hammerhead, 1970, Hawkbill, 1973, Bluefish, 1975, Gurnard, 1976, Flying Fish, 1977, Pintado, 1978, Archerfish, 1979, Silversides, 1981. Home: 1330 Alexandria Dr San Diego CA 92107-3937 Office: Arctic Submarine Lab Naval Ocean Systems Ctr 49250 Fleming Rd San Diego CA 92152-7202

LYON, WAYNE BARTON, manufacturing company executive; b. Dayton, Oct. 26, 1932; m. Maryann L., 1961; children: Karyn, Craig, Blair. B-SChemE, U. Cin., 1955; MBA in Mktg., U. Chgo., 1969. Registered profl. engr., Mich. Tech. rep. Union Carbide, Chgo., 1955-62; product devel. mgr., v.p. bus. devel. Ill. Tool Works, Chgo., 1962-72; group v.p., exec. v.p. Masco Corp., Taylor, Mich., 1972-85, pres., coo, 1985—, also bd. dirs.; bd. dirs. Emco Ltd., London, Ont., Can., 1973, Masco Corp., Taylor, Mich., Payless Cashways Inc., Formica Corp.; lectr. AMA, Comerica Inc., 1993. Patentee in field. Bd. govs., trustees Cranbrook Kingswood Schs., Bloomfield Hills, Mich., 1984—, Orchard Lake Country Club, Mich., 1985-90. Capt. U.S. Army, 1955-63. Mem. Fairlane Club (Dearborn, Mich.), TPC of Mich. Club, Orchard Lake Country Club, Bloomfield Hills Country Club. Office: Masco Corp 21001 Van Born Rd Taylor MI 48180-1340

LYON, WILFORD CHARLES, JR., insurance executive; b. Blackfoot, Idaho, June 1, 1935; s. Wilford Charles and Nellie Anna (Estenson) L.; m. Eleanor Perkins, Aug. 23, 1957; children: Katherine Ann, Wilford Charles III. BS, Ga. Inst. Tech., 1958; MA in Actuarial Sci., Ga. State Coll., 1962. Asst. v.p. Ind. Life and Accident Ins. Co., Jacksonville, Fla., 1963-69, asst. v.p., dir. methods and planning dept., 1969-70, v.p., home office coordinator, 1970-79, pres., chief adminstrv. officer, 1979-84, chmn. bd., chief exec. officer, 1984—, also bd. dirs.; bd. dirs. Ind. Ins. Group, Jacksonville; trustee, mem. exec. com. Edward Waters Coll., Jacksonville, 1983—, chmn., bd. visitors, 1993—. Trustee Gator Bowl Assn., Jacksonville, 1981—, pres., 1981; pres. Jacksonville C. of C., 1984; trustee community TV, Inc., Jacksonville, 1980-93, chmn., 1991-92; trustee Univ. Hosp., Jacksonville, Inc., 1985-86; bd. dirs. YMCA Fla.'s First Coast, 1985—, sec., 1986, vice chmn., 1987, chmn., 1988 (Svc. to Youth award 1991); mem. 1991 Nat. Vol. Week, Vol. Jacksonville, Inc. Recipient Disting. Svc. award Jacksonville Jaycees, 1972, Jack Donnell award Outstanding Businessman of the Year, 1983, Dick Hutchinson award Sertoma Club South Jacksonville, 1972, Svc. to Mankind award, 1972, Boss of Yr. award Profl. Secs. Internat., 1972-73, Victory Crusade award Fla. Cancer Soc., 1969, Ins. Industry Community Svc. award Jacksonville Assn. Life Underwriters, 1986, C.G. Snead Meml. award Jacksonville Assn. of Life Underwriters, 1991, Top Mgmt. award Sales and Mktg. Execs. of Jacksonville, 1990, Clanzel T. Brown award Jacksonville Urban League, 1991, Svc. to Youth award YMCA of Fla.'s First Coast, 1991, Humanitarian award NCCJ, 1994. Mem. Life Insurers Conf. (exec. com. 1981-91, chmn. 1981-86, sec. 1984-85, vice chmn. 1985-86, chmn. 1986-87), Am. Coun. Life Ins. (Fla. state v.p. 1981—, bd. dirs. 1987-88, bd. dirs. Polit. Action Com. 1988-94), Southeastern Actua ries Club, Rotary Club of Jacksonville (pres. Mandarin club 1977-78, Paul Harris fellow, dist. gov. 697 1985-86), Masons, York Rite, Scottish Rite Bodies, Shriners (potentate Morocco Temple 1973). Republican. Presbyterian. Home: 1129 Mapleton Rd Jacksonville FL 32207 Office: Ind Life & Accident Ins Co 1 Independent Dr Jacksonville FL 32276

LYON, WILLIAM, builder; b. 1923. Student, U. So. Calif. With Lyon & son, Phoenix, 1945-50; with William Lyon Devel. Co., Newport Beach, Calif., 1954-72, pres.; with William Lyon Co., Newport Beach, 1972—, now chmn. bd. Office: William Lyon Co 4490 Von Karman Ave Newport Beach CA 92660-2008

LYON, WILLIAM CARL, sports columnist; b. Carmi, Ill., Feb. 10, 1938; s. Clyde William and Harriet Kathryn (Murphy) L.; m. Ethel Gay Slade, Nov. 6, 1964; children—James Charles, John William. Student, Western Mil. Acad., Alton, Ill., 1956; B.S. in Liberal Arts, U. Ill., Champaign, 1961. Feature writer, sports writer, police reporter Champaign-Urbana News-Gazette, 1956-66; sports writer, gen. columnist Evansville (Ind.) Courier & Press, 1966-69; mng. editor East St. Louis (Ill.) Metro-East Jour., 1969-71, Champaign-Urbana News-Gazette, 1971-72; bus. editor Phila. Inquirer, 1972-73, sports writer, syndicated columnist, 1973—; Author: It's All in the Game, We Owed You One; contbr. numerous articles to mags. in U.S. and Can.; TV commentary twice weekly. Author: It's All in the Game, We Owed You One; contbr. numerous articles to mags. in U.S. and Can. Served with inf. U.S. Army, 1961. Named Sportswriter of the Yr., State of Pa., 1977, 79-85; recipient 69 state and nat. awards for writing, Best Newspaper Writing award , Am. Newspaper Editors, 1980, Nat. Headliner award, 1988; inducted into Pa. Sports Hall of Fame, 1989. Mem. Baseball Writers Am., Profl. Hockey Writers Assn., Am. Football Writers Assn. Am., Sigma Delta Chi. Methodist. Home: 89 Cherry Hill Ln Broomall PA 19008-1508 Office: Phila Inquirer 400 N Broad St Philadelphia PA 19130-4099

LYONS, CHAMP, JR., lawyer; b. Boston, Dec. 6, 1940; m. Emily Lee Oswalt, 1967; children—Emily Olive, Champ III. A.B., Harvard U., 1962; LL.B., U. Ala., 1965. Bar: Ala. 1965, U.S. Supreme Ct. 1973. Law clk. U.S. Dist. Ct., Mobile, Ala., 1965-67; assoc. Capell, Howard, Knabe & Cobbs, Montgomery, Ala., 1967-70; ptnr. Capell, Howard, Knabe & Cobbs, 1970-76, Helmsing, Lyons, Sims & Leach, Mobile, 1976—; mem. adv. commn. on civil procedure Ala. Supreme Ct., 1971—, chmn., 1985—. Author: Alabama Practice, 1973, 2d edit., 1986; contbr. articles to law jours. Mem. ABA, Ala. Bar Assn., Mobile Bar Assn. (pres. 1991), Am. Law Inst., Ala. Law Inst., Farrah Law Soc., Harvard U. Alumni Assn. (S.E. regional dir. 1988-91, v.p.-at-large 1992-94, 1st v.p. 1994-95, pres. 1995—). Office: Helmsing Lyons Sims & Leach 200 LaClede Bldg PO Box 2767 Mobile AL 36652-2767

LYONS, CHARLES R., drama educator; b. Glendale, Calif., Apr. 27, 1933; s. James Grey and Daphne Mae (Burlingham) L.; m. Leila B. Phee, Dec. 22, 1956; children: John Christopher, James Charles. AB, Stanford U., 1955, AM, 1956, PhD, 1964. Asst. prof. Principia Coll., Elsah, Ill., 1964-68; assoc. prof. U. Calif., Berkeley, 1968-72, prof., assoc. dean, 1972-73; prof., chmn. Stanford (Calif.) U., 1973-85, Margery Bailey prof. english and dramatic lit., 1985—, chmn. grad. studies in drama, 1985—; vis. prof. Washington U., St. Louis, 1966. Author: Brecht: Despair and Polemic, 1968, Shakespeare and the Ambiguity of Love's Triumph, 1971, Ibsen: the Divided Consciousness, 1972, Samuel Beckett, 1983; editor: Critical Essays on Henrik Ibsen, 1987, Hedda Gabler: Gender, Role, and World, 1990; editorial bd. Comparative Drama, Kalamazoo, Mich., 1977—; Jour. Dramatic, Lit. and Theory, Lawrence, Kans, 1986—. Bd. dirs. San Francisco Archives for Performing Arts, 1985—. Served to lt. USNR, 1956-60. Recipient Younger Scholar award NEH, 1968; Guggenheim Found. fellow, 1977. Mem. Modern Language Assn., Samuel Beckett Soc. Democrat. Home: 728 Tolman Dr Palo Alto CA 94305-1045 Office: Stanford U Dept Drama Stanford CA 94305

LYONS, DAVID BARRY, philosophy and law educator; b. N.Y.C., Feb. 6, 1935; s. Joseph and Betty (Janower) L.; m. Sandra Yetta Nemiroff, Dec. 18, 1955; children—Matthew, Emily, Jeremy. Student, Cooper Union, 1952-54, 56-57; B.A., Bklyn. Coll., 1960; M.A. (Gen. Electric Found. fellow), Harvard U., 1963, Ph.D. (Woodrow Wilson dissertation fellow), 1963; postgrad., Oxford (Eng.) U., 1963-64. Asst. prof. philosophy Cornell U., Ithaca, N.Y., 1964-67; asso. prof. Cornell U., 1967-71, prof. philosophy, 1971-90, Susan Linn Sage prof. philosophy, 1990-95; chmn. dept. philosophy, 1978-84; prof. law, 1979-95, Boston U., 1995—. Author: Forms and Limits of Utilitarianism, 1965, In the Interest of the Governed, 1973, Ethics and the Rule of Law, 1984, Moral Aspects of Legal Theory, 1993, Rights, Welfare, and Mill's Moral Theory, 1994; editor: Philos Rev., 1968-70, 73-75. Recipient Clark award Cornell U., 1976; Woodrow Wilson hon. fellow, 1960-61, Knox travelling fellow, 1963-64; Guggenheim fellow, 1970-71, Soc. for Humanities fellow, 1972-73, Nat. Endowment for Humanities fellow, 1977-78, 84-85, 93-94. Mem. Am. Philos. Assn., Am. Soc. Polit. and Legal Philosophy, Soc. Philosophy and Public Affairs, Aristotelian Soc. Office: Boston U Law Sch 765 Commonwealth Ave Boston MA 02215

LYONS, DENNIS GERALD, lawyer; b. Passaic, N.J., Nov. 20, 1931; s. Denis A.G. and Agnes C. (Dyt) L.; m. Anna Maria Nuñez, 1983; 1 child, Alexandra; children by previous marriage: Andrew, Sarah, Tessa. A.B., Holy Cross Coll., 1952; J.D., Harvard U., 1955. Bar: D.C. 1955, N.Y. 1956, U.S. Supreme Ct 1960. Law clk. U.S. Supreme Ct., Washington, 1958-60; assoc. firm Arnold & Porter, Washington, 1960-62; ptnr. Arnold & Porter, 1963—; v.p., gen. counsel, dir. Gulf United Corp., Jacksonville, Fla., 1968-80; asst. sec. Braniff Airways, Dallas, 1966-77; trustee GMR Properties, Boston, 1971-81; dir. Gulf Broadcast Co, Dallas, 1983-86; vis. prof. law U. Va., Charlottesville, 1982-83; Pres. Harvard Law Rev., 1954-55. Served with USAF, 1955-58. Mem. ABA, Am. Law Inst. Home: 4710 Jamestown Rd Bethesda MD 20816-2923 Office: 1200 New Hampshire Ave NW Washington DC 20036-6801

LYONS, ELLIS, lawyer; b. Scranton, Pa., Mar. 24, 1915; s. Charles and Anna (Abrams) L.; m. Anita Chester, June 12, 1952; children: Charles, Cathy. Student, U. Scranton, 1933-34; A.B. (Coll. scholar), Oberlin Coll. 1936; J.D. (Univ. fellow), Northwestern U., 1939; LL.D. hon., Pa. Coll. Optometry, 1983. Bar: D.C. 1939, U.S. Supreme Ct 1946. Atty. Dept. Justice, 1940-43; spl. asst. to U.S. Atty. Gen., 1945-50; chief legal cons. U.S. Dept. Justice, 1950-53; acting asst. atty. gen. U.S., 1952-53; partner firm Perlman, Lyons and Emmerglick (and predecessors), Washington, 1953-65, Volpe, Boskey and Lyons, Washington, 1965-94; of counsel, 1995—; instr. bus. law Am. U., 1963-66; gen. counsel Am. Optometric Assn., 1968-94; gen. counsel, sec. Am. Automotive Leasing Assn., 1960-93, Equipment Leasing Assn. Am., 1961-94. Served to lt. USCG, 1943-45. Mem. D.C. Bar, Bar Assn. D.C., Fed. Bar Assn., Am. Bar Assn., Am. Law Inst., Phi Beta Kappa, Tau Epsilon Rho. Home: 4101 Blackthorn St Chevy Chase MD 20815-5053 Office: 918 16th St NW Ste 602 Washington DC 20006-2902

LYONS, FREDERICK WILLIAM, JR., pharmaceutical company executive; b. Youngstown, Ohio, Nov. 7, 1935; s. Frederick William and Edith (Barnes) L.; m. Carol Lee deBruin, Aug. 30, 1957; children: Linda Kay, Stephen Frederick. B.S., U. Mich., 1957; M.B.A., Harvard U., 1959. Div. mgr. cost acctg. and purchasing Alcon Labs., Inc., Fort Worth, 1959-61; salesman Alcon Labs., Inc., 1961-62; dir. mktg. Conal Pharms., Inc., Chgo., 1962-64, gen. mgr., 1964-65, v.p., gen. mgr., 1965-70; v.p., gen. mgr. Marion Labs., Inc., Kansas City, Mo., 1970-72, sr. v.p., dir., pres. Pharm div., 1972-74, exec. v.p., dir., 1974-77, pres., dir., 1977—, chief operating officer, from 1977, now also chief exec. officer; dir. Commerce Bank of Kansas City (N.A.). Mem. nat. adv. council Ariz. Heart Inst. Mem. Pharm. Mfrs. Assn. (dir.), ACT Found., Rho Chi, Phi Kappa Phi, Phi Gamma Delta. Office: Marion Labs Inc PO Box 8480 10236 Marion Park Dr Kansas City MO 64137

LYONS, GENE MARTIN, political scientist, educator; b. Revere, Mass., Feb. 29, 1924; s. Abraham M. and Mary (Karger) L.; m. Micheline Pohl, Sept. 5, 1951; children—Catherine Anne, Daniel Eugene, Mark Lucien. B.A., Tufts Coll., 1947; license en Scis. Politiques, Grad. Inst. Internat. Studies, Geneva, Switzerland, 1949; Ph.D., Columbia, 1958. Mgmt. officer Internat. Refugee Orgn., Geneva, 1948-52; budget and adminstrv. officer UN Korean Reconstrn. Agy., 1952-56; mem. faculty Dartmouth Coll., 1957-94, prof. govt., 1965-94, vis. prof. Affairs Center, 1961-66, 73-75, asso. dean faculty social scis., 1974-78; rsch. fellow Dickey Ctr. Dartmouth Coll., Hanover, N.H., 1994—; vis. lectr. Nat. Mgmt. MIT, 1966-71; asst exec. sec. adv. com. govt. program behavioral scis. Nat. Acad. Scis., 1966-68; dir. dept. social scis. UNESCO, 1970-72; mem. U.S. Nat. Commn. for UNESCO, 1975-80, vice chmn., 1977-78; adv. U.S. del. UNESCO 19th Gen. Conf. 1976, 20th Gen. Conf., 1978; U.S. rep. to UNESCO European Conf., 1977; prof. associé U. Paris I, 1986; exec. dir. acad. council on the UN system, 1987-92. Author: Military Policy and Economic Aid: The Korean Case, 1961; co-author: (with J.W. Masland) Education and Military Leadership, 1959, (with L. Morton) Schools for Strategy, 1965, The Uneasy Partnership, 1969; Editor: Social Research and Public Policies, 1975; editor, contbr. America: Purpose and Power, 1965, Social Science and the Federal Government, 1971; co-editor, contbr. Beyond Westphalia?, 1995, The United Nations System: The Policies of Member States, 1995. Served with AUS, 1943-46. Mem. Acad. Coun. on UN System, Internat. Studies Assn., Coun. on Fgn. Rels. Home: Main St Norwich VT 05055 Office: Dartmouth Coll Dickey Ctr Hanover NH 03755

LYONS, GEORGE SAGE, lawyer, oil industry executive, former state legislator; b. Mobile, Ala., Oct. 1, 1936; s. Mark, Jr. and Ruth (Kelly) L.; m. Elsie Crain, Feb. 5, 1960; children-George Sage, Amelia C. B.A. in Econs, Washington and Lee U., Lexington, Va., 1958; LL.B., U. Ala., 1960. Bar: Ala. 1960. Practice in Mobile, 1962—; sr. ptnr. Lyons, Pipes & Cook, 1962—; mem. Ala. Ho. of Reps., 1969-75, speaker ho., 1971-75; pres. LPC Oil Co., Inc., Amelia Land Co., Inc.; chmn., dir. Crain Oil Co., Inc., Guntersville, Ala.; dir. Jordan Industries, Inc. State Docks; mem. exec. com. Ala. Petroleum Coun.; mem. Tenn.-Tombigbee Waterway Devel. Authority, 1966-70, 91-95; chmn. Ala. Commn. on Higher Edn., 1971-78. Trustee 11th cir. Hist. Soc. Served to capt., JAGC U.S. Army, 1960-62. Decorated Army Commendation medal. Fellow Am. Bar Found., Nat. Assn. Bond Lawyers, Coun. Ala. Law Inst., Farrah Law Soc. (trustee); mem. Am. Ala., Mobile County bar assns., Mid-Continent Oil and Gas Assn. (dir. Ala.-Miss. div.),

Maritime Law Assn. U.S., Omicron Delta Kappa, Phi Delta Phi. Episcopalian. Home: 107 Carmel Dr E Mobile AL 36608-2479 Office: 2 N Royal St Mobile AL 36602-3896

LYONS, J. ROLLAND, civil engineer; b. Cedar Rapids, Iowa, Apr. 27, 1909; s. Neen T. and Goldie N. (Hill) L.; BS, U. Iowa, 1933; m. Mary Jane Doht, June 10, 1924; children: Marlene R. Sparks, Sharon K. Hutson, Mary Lynn Lyons. Jr. hwy. engr. Works Projects Adminstrn. field engr. Dept. Transp., State Ill., Peoria, 1930-31, civil engr. I-IV Cen. Office, Springfield, 1934-53, civil engr. V, 1953-66, municipal sect. chief, civil engr. VI, 1966-72. Civil Def. radio officer Springfield and Sangamon County (Ill.) Civil Def. Agy., 1952—. Recipient Meritorious Service award Am. Assn. State Hwy. Ofcls., 1968, 25 Yr. Career Service award State Ill., 1966, Cert. Appreciation Ill. Mcpl. League, 1971. Registered profl. engr., Ill.; registered land surveyor, Ill. Mem. NSPE, Ill. Assn. State Hwy. Engrs., State Ill. Employees Assn., Am. Pub. Works Assn., Am. Assn. State Hwy. Ofcls., Ill. Soc. Profl. Engrs., Amateur Trapshooters Assn., Sangamon Valley Radio Club, Lakewood Golf and Country Club, KC, Abe Lincoln Gun Club, South Fork Conservation Club, Ill. and Nat. Soc. Profl. Engrs. Address: 3642 Lancaster Rd Springfield IL 62703-5022

LYONS, JAMES ELLIOTT, lawyer; b. Lexington, Mo., Mar. 10, 1951; s. james Elliott and Elouise (Blackman) L.; m. Mary Jane McCarthy, June 30, 1979; children: Sean Austin, Caitlan Maureen. BA with honors, U. Mo., 1973; JD, NYU, 1976. Bar: Mo. 1976, N.Y. 1977, Calif. 1984. Assoc. Stinson Mag Thompson McEvers & Fizzell, Kansas City, Mo., 1976-77; assoc. Skadden, Arps, Slate et al., N.Y.C., L.A., 1977-84; law clk. U.S. Dept. Justice, N.Y.C., 1978; ptnr. Skadden, Arps, Slate et al., L.A., 1984—. Mem. ABA (chmn. securities trials & takeover litigation subcom. 1986—), Mo. Bar Assn., Univ. Club (L.A.), Wilshire Country Club. Democrat. Home: 332 S Arden Blvd Los Angeles CA 90020-4734 Office: Skadden Arps Slate et al 300 S Grand Ave Bldg 3400 Los Angeles CA 90071-3144

LYONS, JAMES ROBERT, federal official. BS in Forest and Wildlife Mgmt. with high honors, Rutgers U., 1977; M in Forestry, Yale U., 1979. Program analyst U.S. Fish and Wildlife Svc. Dept. Interior, 1979-82; dir. resource policy Soc. Am. Foresters, Bethesda, Md., 1982-86; staff dir. subcom. forests, family farms, engergy Com. Agriculture, 1986, staff asst. com. agr., 1987-93; asst. sec. agr. natural resources and environ. USDA, Washington, 1993—, under sec. natural resources and environment; agrl. advisor Cong. Leon Panetta, 1989-91. Office: USDA Natural Resources & Environment 14th & Independence Ave SW Washington DC 20250-0002

LYONS, JEFFREY, film critic. Co-host Sneak Previews, Chgo. Office: Sneak Previews Sta WTTW-TV 5400 N Saint Louis Ave Chicago IL 60625-4623 also: Sta WCBS-AM 51 W 52nd St New York NY 10019-6119

LYONS, JERRY LEE, mechanical engineer; b. St. Louis, Apr. 2, 1939; s. Ferd H. and Edna T. Lyons. Diploma in Mech. Engring., Okla. Inst. Tech., 1964; M.S.M.E., Southwest U., 1983, Ph.D. in Engring. Mgmt., 1984. Registered profl. engr., Calif.; cert. mfg. engr. in product design. Project engr. Harris Mfg. Co., St. Louis, 1965-70, Essex Cryogenics Industries, St. Louis, 1970-73; mgr. engring. rsch. Chemetron Corp., St. Louis, 1973-77; cons. fluid controls Wis. U., 1977—; pres., chief exec. Yankee Ingenuity, Inc., St. Louis, 1974—; v.p., gen. mgr. engring. rsch. and devel. Essex Fluid Controls div. Essex Industries, Inc., St. Louis, 1977-90; pres. Lyons Pubs. Co., St. Louis, 1983—; pres., chief exec. officer Innovative Controls div. Yankee Ingenuity, Inc., Ft. Wayne, Ind., 1991—; chmn. exec. bd. continuing engring. edn. in St. Louis for U. Mo., Columbia, 1980-81; bd. dirs. Intertech., Inc., Houston; cons. fluid power dept. Bradley U., Peoria, 1977-84. Author: Home Study Series Course on Actuators and Accessories, 1977, The Valve Designers Handbook, 1983, The Lyons' Encyclopedia of Valves, 1975, 93, The Designers Handbook of Pressure Sensing Devices, 1980, Special Process Applications, 1980; co-author: Handbook of Product Liability, 1991; contbr. articles to profl. jours. Served with USAF, 1957-62. Recipient Winston Churchill medal, 1988, Dwight D. Eisenhower Achievement award of honor, 1990; named Businessman of Week (KEZK radio), Eminent Churchill fellow Winston Churchill Wisdom Soc. Fellow ASME; Mem. Soc. Mfg. Engrs. (chmn. Mo. registration com. 1975-90, chmn. St. Louis chpt. 1979-80, internat. dir. 1982-84, 85-87, Engr. of Yr. 1984, internat. award of merit 1985), Nat. Soc. Profl. Engrs., Mo. Soc. Profl. Engrs., St. Louis Soc. Mfg. Engrs. (chmn. profl. devel., registration and cert. com. 1975-79), Instrument Soc. Am. (mem. control valve stability com. 1978-84), Computer and Automated Systems Assn. (1st chmn. St. Louis chpt. 1986-91), St. Louis Engrs. Club (award of merit 1977, Wisdom award of Honor 1987, mem. Wisdom Hall of Fame 1987), Am. Security Council (committeeman 1976—), Nat. Fluid Power Assn. (com. on pressure ratings 1975-77), Am. Legion. Lutheran. Home and Office: 2607 Northgate Blvd Fort Wayne IN 46835-2986

LYONS, JOHN DAVID, French, Italian and comparative literature educator; b. Springfield, Mass., Oct. 14, 1946; s. John Joseph and Loretta Francis (Feighery) L.; m. Patricia Stuart, July 31, 1971; 1 dau., Jennifer Catherine. A.B., Brown U., 1967; M.A., Yale U., 1968, Ph.D., 1972. Asst. prof. French, Italian and comparative lit. Dartmouth Coll., Hanover, N.H., 1972-78, assoc. prof., 1978-82, prof., 1982-87, chmn. comparative lit. program, 1981-84, chmn., prof. dept. French and Italian, 1987.; dir. Am. Univ. Ctr. for Film and Cultural Studies, Paris, 1984-85; prof. French U. Va., Charlottesville, 1987-92, Commonwealth prof. French, 1993—, chmn. dept., 1989-92. Author: A Theatre of Disguise, 1978, The Listening Voice, 1982, Exemplum, 1989; co-editor: Mimesis: Mirror to Method, 1982, Dialectic of Discovery, 1983, Critical Tales, 1993; editor: Art, Architecture, Text: The Late Renaissance, 1989; assoc. editor Continuum, 1987-93; editor Academe, 1994—; mem. editl. adv. bd. Philosophy and Literature. Recipient Robert Fish award Dartmouth Coll., 1978; Woodrow Wilson fellow, 1967; Am. Coun. Learned Socs. study fellow, 1979; NEH fellow, 1985-89, 92-93, Ctr. for Advanced Studies U. Va. fellow, 1987-89. Office: U Va Dept French Lang and Lit Charlottesville VA 22903

LYONS, JOHN WINSHIP, government agency administrator, chemist; b. Reading, Mass., Nov. 5, 1930. A.B. in Chemistry, Harvard U., 1952; A.M. in Phys. Chemistry, Washington U., St. Louis, 1963, Ph.D. in Phys. Chemistry, 1964. With Monsanto Co., 1955-73, group leader, sect. mgr. research dept., inorganic chems. div., 1962-69, mgr. comml. devel., head fire safety center, 1969-73; mem. ad hoc panel on fire research Nat. Bur. Standards, Washington, 1971-73; dir. Center for Fire Research, 1973-77, Inst. Applied Tech., 1977-78, Nat. Engring. Lab., 1978-89; acting dep. dir. Nat. Bur. Standards, 1983; dir. Nat. Inst. Standards and Tech., Gaithersburg, Md., 1990-93, Army Rsch. Lab., Adelphi, Md., 1993—; chmn. Products Rsch. Com. (trust which adminstrs. fire rsch. fund), 1974-79; vis. lectr. various univs.; co-chmn. U.S.-Japan Natural Resources Panel on Fire Rsch., 1975-78; mem. adv. com. on engring NSF, 1981-90; mem. bd. visitors U. Md. Coll. Engring., 1980-90; mem. adv. com. Naval Rsch. Lab., 1985; mem. com. on fed. labs. Office Sci. and Tech. Policy. Author: Viscosity and Flow Measurement, 1963, The Chemistry and Uses of Fire Retardants, 1970; Fire, 1985; contbr. numerous articles to profl. pubis. Chmn. blue ribbon com. on rsch. and pub. svc. U. Md., 1993. Recipient Gold medal Dept. Commerce, 1977, Pres.'s Mgmt. Improvement award White House, 1977, Pres.'s Disting. Exec. Rank award, 1981, E.U. Condon award, 1986. Fellow AAAS, Washington Acad. Sci.; mem. Am. Chem. Soc. (chmn. St. Louis sect. 1971-72), Nat. Fire Protection Assn. (bd. dirs. 1978-84), ASTM (bd. dirs. 1985-87), Nat. Acad. Engring., Sigma Xi. Office: Army Rsch Lab 2800 Powder Mill Rd Adelphi MD 20783-1197

LYONS, JOSEPH CHISHOLM, lawyer; b. Halifax, N.S., Can., Oct. 17, 1927; s. James Norbert and Frances (Chisholm) L.; m. Julianne Roach, Oct. 5, 1957; children: Juli, Catherine, Patricia, Chisholm, Elizabeth, John-Mark, Mathew. B.A., St. Francis-Xavier U., 1948; LL.B., Dalhousie Law Sch., 1951; M.B.A., Harvard U., 1953. Bar: created Queen's counsel 1966. Partner firm Smith, Lyons, Torrance, Stevenson & Mayer (barristers & solicitors), Toronto, Ont., Can.; vice chmn. Allen Group Inc., Zirex; pres. Allen Group Can. Inc.; Rothmans of Can. Ltd.; Toronto Air King Ltd.; bd. dirs. Chas. T. Main Can. Ltd., Browning-Ferris Industries Can. Ltd., Can. Kawasaki Motors Ltd., Falk Can. Inc., Prestonia Products Inc. Mem. Can. Bar Assn. Mem. Progressive-Conservative Party. Roman Catholic. Clubs: National (Toronto), Toronto Golf (Toronto). Office: Scotia Pla Ste 6200, 40 King St W, Toronto, ON Canada M5H 3Z7

LYONS, LAURENCE, securities executive; b. Jersey City, Aug. 11, 1911; s. Louis and Teresa (Serge) L.; m. Gertrude Starr, Sept. 1, 1945; 1 son, Jonathan. BS, NYU, 1934, postgrad., 1935. Securities analyst Allen & Co., N.Y.C., 1935-52; with Allen Co., Inc., N.Y.C., 1952—; v.p., 1989—. Mem. Soc. Security Analysts. Home: 1 Kensington Gate Apt 221 Great Neck NY 11021-1229 Office: Allen & Co Inc 711 Fifth Ave New York NY 10022-3109

LYONS, OREN, Native American chieftain, conservationist. Chief Onondaga Nation. Recipient Audubon medal Nat. Audubon Soc., 1993. Office: The Onondaga Nation PO Box 200 Nedrow NY 13120*

LYONS, PAUL MICHAEL, producer, film; b. Washington, Aug. 21, 1932; s. Thomas William and Nora (Bagley) L.; m. Bernadette Marie O'Rourke, Oct. 24, 1953; children—Stephen W., Loretta N., Sharon D. Student, Georgetown U., 1950-52. V.p. Charlie Papa Prodns., Rockville, Md., 1972-79; v.p., gen. mgr. Capital Film Labs., Washington, 1979-81; pres., chief exec. officer Am. Bus. Media Council, Inc., Washington, 1982-83; v.p., owner Images and Ideas, Vienna, Va., 1967—; exec. dir. Occupational Safety and Health Rev. Commn., Washington, 1984-90; dir. mktg. Nat. Empowerment TV, Washington, 1993—. Film editor Treasures of King Tut, 1977 (nominated Academy award); prodn. mgr. (film) Carry the Fire, Olympic Torch Relay, 1984. Mem. Vienna Town Council, 1968-76; chmn. Bicentennial Commn., Vienna, 1971-76; mem. Fairfax County Rep. Com., Va., 1978-84. Recipient Disting. Service award Jaycees of Vienna, 1965; named Citizen of the Yr. Vienna C. of C., 1976. Mem. Council on Internat. Nontheatrical Events (mem. adv. bd. 1979-92), Council on Nat. Policy (bd. govs. 1982—), Soc. Motion Picture & TV Engrs. (bd. mgrs.), White House News Photographers Assn. (pres. 1990-92), Washington Film Council (pres. 1982-83). Roman Catholic. Home: 603 Upham Pl NW Vienna VA 22180-4128

LYONS, PAUL VINCENT, lawyer; b. Boston, July 19, 1939; s. Joseph Vincent and Doris Irene (Griffin) L.; m. Elaine Marie Hurley, July 13, 1968; children: Judith Marie, Maureen Patricia, Paula Anne, Joseph Hurley. BS cum laude, Boston Coll., 1960; MBA, NYU, 1962; JD, Suffolk U., Boston, 1968. Bar: Mass. 1968, U.S. Cir. Ct. (1st cir.) 1969, U.S. Supreme Ct. 1991. Div. adminstrn. mgr. Pepsi-Cola Co., N.Y.C., 1962-64; mem. bus. faculty Burdett Coll., Boston, 1964-68; atty. NLRB, Boston, 1968-73; assoc. Foley, Hoag & Eliot, Boston, 1973-77, ptnr., 1978—; mem. faculty Boston U. 1972-74. Mem. Town Meeting, Milton, Mass., 1986—, mem. pers. bd., 1994—. Lt. U.S. Army, 1960-62. Mem. ABA, Mass. Bar Assn., Boston Bar Assn. Office: Foley Hoag & Eliot 1 Post Office Sq Boston MA 02109-2103

LYONS, RICHARD CHAPMAN, former urologist; b. Corry, Pa., Nov. 23, 1919; s. Arch C. and Araline (Drought) L.; m. Norma Lydia Wright, Dec. 25, 1945; children: Dorothy A., John C., Sanford D., Timothy R., Valerie A. Grad. U. Pa., 1941; MD, U. Pitts., 1944. Diplomate Am. Bd. Urology. Intern, St. Elizabeth Hosp., Washington, 1945; resident, Mayo Clinic, Rochester, Minn., 1945-46, 48-50; civilian physician U.S. Army, 1946-47; chmn. dept. urology, Hamot Med. Ctr., Erie, Pa., 1955-68, practitioner, surgeon, 1950-86, founder, head urology residency program, 1958-68; hon. mem. med. staffs St. Vincent Health Ctr., Erie, 1951-86; mem. Pa. State Bd. Med. Edn. and Licensure, 1971-83, chmn., 1976-78, 81-85; dir. NW Pa. Corp., Oil City, Mellon-North, Erie; mng. ptnr. Lyons Properties Ltd. Partnership. Trustee Gannon U. Named Disting. Pennsylvanian, Gannon U., 1981. Recipient Integrity award Soc. for Advancement Intergrity in Pub. Life. Fellow ACS (gov. 1975-81); mem. AMA, Pa. Med. Soc., Erie County Med. Soc., Pa. Urologic Assn. (pres. 1974), Mayo Clinic Alumni Assn., Mayo Urol. Alumni Assn. (pres. 1976), Erie Club, Kahkwa Club, Erie Yacht Club, Univ. Club (Pitts.), Elks. Republican. Roman Catholic. Home: 52 Royal Palm Dr Fort Lauderdale FL 33301-1409

LYONS, THOMAS PATRICK, economics educator; b. Groton, Conn., Sept. 8, 1953. BA in Asian Studies, Cornell U., 1979, MA in Econs., 1982, PhD in Econs., 1983. Asst. prof. econs. Dartmouth Coll., Hanover, N.H., 1983-87; vis. asst. prof. Cornell U., Ithaca, N.Y., 1986-88, asst. prof., 1988-91; assoc. prof., 1991—; dir. East Asia program Cornell U., Ithaca, N.Y., 1991-94. Author: Economic Integration and Planning in Maoist China, 1987, China's War on Poverty, 1992; contbr. numerous articles to profl. jours. With USN, 1972-76. Rsch. grantee Ford Found., 1987. Mem. Am. Econ. Assn., Assn. for Asian Studies. Office: Cornell U Dept Econs 110 Uris Hall Ithaca NY 14853

LYONS, WILLIAM CLAYPOOL, engineering educator and consultant; b. Bronxville, N.Y., Nov. 26, 1937; s. Thomas Edward and Lucile (Marks) L.; m. Alahna Carter Weller, Feb. 25, 1961 (div. July 1980); children: Andrew W., Terrence W., Dale W. BS in Geol. Engring., U. Kans., Lawrence, 1961, MS in Engring. Mechanics, 1962, PhD, 1965. Registered profl. engr., N.Mex. Jr. engr. Phillips Petroleum Co., Bartlesville, Okla., 1961-62; instr. U. Kans., Lawrence, 1962-64; postdoctoral fellow Northwestern U., Evanston, Ill., 1964-65; staff mem. Sandia Nat. Lab., Albuquerque, 1965-69; asst. group leader Los Alamos (N.Mex.) Nat. Lab., 1969-76; tech. asst. to dir. U.S. ERDA/Fuel Cycle, Germantown, Md., 1976-77; pres. Rift Pneumatics Inc., Farmington, N.Mex., 1977-80; prof. N.Mex. Inst. Mining Tech., Socorro, 1977—; adj. prof. U. N.Mex., Albuquerque, 1966-68; rsch. fellow Polish Acad. Sci., Warsaw, 1963-64; Disting. vis. prof. U.S. Air Force Acad., Colorado Springs, 1993-94. Author: Air and Gas Drilling Manual, 1984; author, editor: Standard Petroleum & Natural Gas Engineers Handbook, 1995. Soccer referee NCAA, 1975-85. With USMCR, 1955-61. Recipient Energy Innovation award U.S. Dept. Energy, 1988. Mem. ASCE, NSPE, Soc. Petroleum Engrs., Am. Soc. Engring. Edn. Achievements include patents for drilling devices. Avocations: fishing, skiing, writing. Home: 1008 Rocky Rd Socorro NM 87801 Office: NMex Inst Mining Tech Dept Petroleum Engring MSEC Bldg Rm 300 Socorro NM 87801

LYSAUGHT, PATRICK, lawyer; b. Kansas City, Kans., Sept. 12, 1949; s. Mathew Aloysius and Loretta Rose (Storen) L.; m. Patricia Caspar, June 27, 1970; children: Geoffrey James, Kevin Michael. BA, Creighton U., 1971, postgrad. Law Sch., 1971; JD with distinction, U. Mo., 1974. Bar: Mo. 1975, U.S. Dist. Ct. (we. dist.) Mo. 1975, U.S. Ct. Appeals (8th cir.) 1975. Law clk. to chief judge U.S. Dist. Ct. (we. dist.) Mo., Kansas City, 1975-76; assoc., then shareholder firm Jackson & Sherman, P.C., Kansas City, Mo., 1976-83; v.p., bd. dirs. Sherman, Wickens, Lysaught & Speck, P.C., Kansas City, Mo., 1983-91; ptnr., shareholder Shook, Hardy & Bacon, Kansas City, Mo., 1991—; bd. dirs. Western Mo. Def. Lawyers, 1985—; faculty mem. Trial Acad., 1990. Author: Techniques in the Use and Management of Demonstrative Evidence, 1984, Cross Examination of the Lay Witness, 1988, Federal Preemption As A Bar To State Tort Claims, 1988, Premises Liability Major Disasters-Structural Failures, Fires and Environmental. Mem. ABA (antitrust-civil practice com.), Kansas City Bar Assn. (fed. practice com., civil procedure com.), Mo. Orgn. Def. Lawyers (charter), Internat. Assn. Def. Counsel (pharm. med. device and biotech com., toxic and hazardous substance com., products liability com., excess and reins. com.), Am. Bd. Trial Advocates, Def. Research Inst. (products liability and profl. liability coms., lectr. drug and med. device), Leawood Country Manor Homes Assn. (bd. dirs., v.p., pres.), Phi Kappa Psi. Roman Catholic. Office: Shook Hardy & Bacon 1 Kansas City Pl 1200 Main St Kansas City MO 64105

LYSAUGHT, THOMAS FRANCIS, publishing company executive; b. Chgo., July 5, 1936; s. Thomas Francis and Eleanor Annette (O'Brien) L.; children: Thomas, Mary Therese, Eileen, Ruth, Judy. B.S. in Elec. Engring., Ill. Inst. Tech., 1959, postgrad., 1959-61; J.D., Chgo.-Kent Coll. Law, 1966; M.B.A., U. Chgo., 1969. Bar: Ill. 1966, U.S. Ct. Custom and Patent Appeals 1972, U.S. Supreme Ct. 1973. Engr. Motorola Co., Chgo., 1959-61; patent counsel GTE Automative Elec. Corp., Northlake, Ill., 1961-73; v.p. law GTE Directories Corp., Des Plaines, Ill., 1973-78, v.p. law and planning, 1978-81, v.p. info. service, law and planning, from 1981, dir., 1973-89; now pres., also bd. dirs. GTE Directories Corp., DFW Airport, Tex. Mem. ABA, Tex. Bar Assn., Dallas Bar Assn., Assn. for Corporate Growth, Planning Forum. Roman Catholic. Office: GTE Directories Corp PO Box 619810 W Airfield Dr Dallas TX 75261-9810

LYSINGER, REX JACKSON, energy company executive; b. Pitts., Aug. 14, 1937; s. Mark and Clare Ann (Long) L.; m. Jodene Elizabeth Scott, Sept. 19, 1958; children: Teri Jo, Beth Ann, Rex Jay, Holly Sue. B.S. in Indsl. Engring., U. Pitts., 1959. V.p., engr., cons., mgr. Stone & Webster,

N.Y.C., 1965-74; v.p. Stone & Webster, Houston, 1974-75; v.p. corp. planning Ala. Gas Corp., Birmingham, 1975-77, pres., 1977-84; chmn., pres., chief exec. officer Energen Corp., Birmingham, 1984-91; chmn., chief exec. officer Ala. Gas Corp., Birmingham, 1991—, Taurus Exploration Co.; bd. dirs. SouthTrust Bank Ala. Bd. dirs. Leadership Birmingham, Leadership Ala., Salvation Army, Bus. Coun. of Ala.; bd. dirs., past pres. Jefferson/Shelby County div. Am. Heart Assn.; bd. dirs. United Way, Birmingham, pres., 1990; bd. dirs. Pub. Affairs Rsch. Coun. of Ala.; trustee So. Rsch. Inst.; state campaign chmn. U.S. Savs. Bonds, 1988-89; chmn. Gas Rsch. Inst., 1990-91; bd. dirs. Brookwood Hosp. With USAR, 1960-61. Mem. Am. Gas Assn. (bd. dirs.), So. Gas Assn. (chmn. 1987-88, bd. dirs.), Birmingham Area C. of C. (past pres., chmn. 1984-85, bd. dirs.), The Club, Summit Club, Downtown Club, Country Club of Birmingham, Rotary (past dir. Birmingham club). Home: 3408 Brookwood Trce Birmingham AL 35223-2879 Office: Energen Corp 2101 6th Ave N Birmingham AL 35203-2748

LYST, JOHN HENRY, newspaper editor; b. Princeton, Ind., Mar. 28, 1933; s. John Henry and Marguerite (McQuinn) L.; m. Sharon Long, Dec. 29, 1956; children: Shannon M., Barbara A., Audrey K., Ellen K. AB, Ind. U., 1955. Reporter Indpls. Star, 1956-67, bus. columnist, from 1967, editor editl. page; corr. N.Y. Times, from 1964. Served with AUS, 1956-59. Mem. Indpls. Press Club (pres. 1968, bd. dirs. 1969), Sigma Delta Chi. Office: Ctrl Newspapers Inc PO Box 145 Indianapolis IN 46206-0145*

LYSTAD, MARY HANEMANN (MRS. ROBERT LYSTAD), sociologist, author, consultant; b. New Orleans, Apr. 11, 1928; d. James and Mary (Douglass) Hanemann; m. Robert Lystad, June 20, 1953; children: Lisa Douglass, Anne Hanemann, Mary Lunde, Robert Douglass, James Hanemann. A.B. cum laude, Newcomb Coll., 1949; M.A., Columbia U., 1951; Ph.D., Tulane U., 1955. Postdoctoral fellow social psychology S.E. La. Hosp., Mandeville, 1955-57; field rsch. social psychology Ghana, 1957-58, South Africa and Swaziland, 1968, Peoples Republic of China, 1986; chief sociologist Collaborative Child Devel. Project, Charity Hosp. La., New Orleans, 1958-61; feature writer African div. Voice Am., Washington, 1964-73; program analyst NIMH, Washington, 1968-78; asso. dir. for planning and coordination div. spl. mental health programs NIMH, 1978-80; chief Nat. Ctr. for Prevention and Control of Rape, 1980-83, Ctr. Mental Health Studies of Emergencies, 1983-89; pvt. cons. specializing on mental health implications social and econ. problems Bethesda, Md., 1990—; cons. on youth Nat. Goals Research Staff, White House, Washington, 1969-70. Author: Millicent the Monster, 1968, Social Aspects of Alienation, 1969, Jennifer Takes Over P.S. 94, 1972, James the Jaguar, 1972, As They See It: Changing Values of College Youth, 1972, That New Boy, 1973, Halloween Parade, 1973, Violence at Home, 1974, A Child's World As Seen in His Stories and Drawings, 1974, From Dr. Mather to Dr. Seuss: 200 Years of American Books for Children, 1980, At Home in America, 1983; editor: Innovations in Mental Health Services to Disaster Victims, 1985, Violence in the Home: Interdisciplinary Perspectives, 1986, Mental Health Response to Mass Emergencies: Theory and Practice, 1988. Recipient Spl. Recognition award USPHS, 1983, Alumna Centennial award Newcomb Coll., 1986. Home and Office: 4900 Scarsdale Rd Bethesda MD 20816-2440

LYSTAD, ROBERT ARTHUR LUNDE, retired university dean, educator; b. Milw., Aug. 10, 1920; s. Arthur Frederick and Lulu Marion (Lunde) L.; m. Anita E. Firing, June 11, 1945 (dec. 1952); m. Mary Agnes Hanemann, June 20, 1953; children: Lisa Douglass, Anne Hanemann, Mary Lunde, Robert Douglass, James Hanemann. B.A., U. Wis., 1941; B.D., Drew Theol. Sem., 1944; Ph.D. in Anthropology, Northwestern U., 1951. Prof. anthropology Tulane U., 1951-61, head dept. sociology and anthropology Newcomb Coll., 1959-61; asso. prof. African studies Sch. Advanced Internat. Studies, Johns Hopkins U., 1961-64, prof., 1964-91, assoc. dean for acad. affairs, 1980-91; acting assoc. dean, 1992; cons. Voice of Am., various depts. U.S. govt., 1961-86, various ednl. and rsch. instns. in Japan, Korea, People's Republic of China, Taiwan, 1981. Author: The Ashanti: A Proud People, 1958; also articles in field.; editor: The African World: A Survey of Social Research, 1965. Mem. Ohio Conf. Methodist Ch., 1944-73. Recipient Founder's award Sch. Advanced Internat. Studies, 1991; fellow Social Sci. Research Council Gold Coast and Ivory Coast, 1949-50; grantee Carnegie Corp., Ghana, 1957-58. Home: 4900 Scarsdale Rd Bethesda MD 20816-2440

LYSYK, KENNETH MARTIN, judge; b. Weyburn, Sask., Can., July 1, 1934; s. Michael and Anna (Maradyn) L.; m. Patricia Kinnon, Oct. 2, 1959; children: Joanne, Karen (dec.), Stephanie. B.A., McGill U., 1954; LL.B., U. Sask., 1957; B.C.L., Oxford U., 1960. Bar: Sask., B.C., Yukon, apptd. Queen's counsel 1973. Lectr. U. B.C., 1960-62, asst. prof., 1962-65, assoc. prof., 1965-68, prof., 1968-69; adviser Constl. Rev. sect. Privy Council Office, Govt. of Can., Ottawa, 1969-70; prof. Faculty of Law U. Toronto, 1970-72; dep. atty. gen. Govt. of Sask., Regina, 1972-76; dean Law Sch., U. B.C., Vancouver, 1976-82; judge Supreme Ct. of B.C., Vancouver, 1983—; chmn. Alaska Hwy. Pipeline Inquiry, 1977; sole commr. Yukon Electoral Boundaries Commn., 1991. Mem. Can. Bar Assn., Internat. Commn. Jurists (Can. sect.; v.p. for B.C. 1992—), Can. Inst. for Adminstrn. of Justice (pres. 1989-91). Office: Law Ct, 800 Smithe St, Vancouver, BC Canada V6Z 2E1

LYTHCOTT, MARCIA A., newspaper editor. Op-ed editor Chicago Tribune, Ill. Office: Chicago Tribune 435 N Michigan Ave Chicago IL 60611

LYTLE, ANDREW NELSON, author, editor; b. Murfreesboro, Tenn., Dec. 26, 1902; s. Robert Logan and Lillie Belle (Nelson) L.; m. Edna Langdon Barker, June 20, 1938; children—Pamela, Katharine Anne, Lillie Langdon. A.B., Vanderbilt U., 1925; student, Baker's 47 Workshop, Yale Sch. of Drama, 1927-28; Litt.D. (hon.), Kenyon Coll., 1965, U. Fla., 1970, U. South, 1973; L.H.D., Hillsdale Coll., 1985. Prof. history U. South, also mng. editor Sewanee Rev., 1942-43, prof. English, editor, 1961-73, ret., 1973; Lectr. U. Iowa Sch. Writing, 1946, lectr., acting head, 1947; lectr. creative writing U. Fla., 1948-61; leader humanities div. internat. seminar Harvard, summer 1954; tchr. Vanderbilt U., Nashville, spring 1974, U. Ky., Lexington, 1976. Author several books, 1930—; latest titles The Velvet Horn, 1957, A Novel, Novella and Four Stories, 1958, the Hero With the Private Parts, 1966, A Wake for the Living, a family chronicle, 1975, Southerners and Europeans, essays in a time of disorder, 1989, From Eden to Babylon, essays, 1990, Kristin: A Reading by Andrew Lytle, 1992; editor: latest titles Craft and Vision: The Best Fiction from the Sewanee Review, 1971; contbr. articles, verse, fiction to various publs. Guggenheim fellow for creative work in fiction, 1940-41, 41-42, 60-61; Kenyon Rev. fellow for fiction, 1956; recipient Nat. Found. Arts and Humanities award, 1966-67, prize Lyndhurst Found., 1985; Brown fellow U. of South, fall 1978, 81-82; prize Ingersoll Found., 1986. Mem. Assn. Little Mags. Am. (officer), So. Acad. Letters, Arts and Scis., Council Lit. Mags.,The Fellowship of Southern Writers (founding fellow), Phi Beta Kappa, Kappa Alpha (Southern). Episcopalian. Home: Monteagle SS Assembly Monteagle TN 37356

LYTLE, ELLEN JUANITA WILSON, special education educator; b. Port Arthur, Tex., Jan. 26, 1941; d. Walter Dean and Velma Juanita (Henry) Wilson; m. Donald L. Lytle, Jr., Apr. 12, 1963 (div. Mar. 1979); children: David Anthony, Shannon Wilson. BA in Elem. Edn., U. Southwestern La., 1963, MEd, 1972; spl. edn. cert., McNeese State U., 1992, postgrad., 1992-94; D of Psychology, Kennedy-Western U., 1994. Cert. tchr., spl. edn. assessor, computer lit., La. Tchr. Duson (La.) Elem. Sch. Lafayette Parish, 1963-65, N.P. Moss Elem. Sch. Lafayette Parish, Lafayette, 1965-70, St. Antoine Elem. Sch. Lafayette Parish, Lafayette, 1970-72; substitute tchr. French and band Merryville (La.) High Sch. Beauregard Parish, 1987; tchr. spl. edn. Pickering Elem. Sch. Vernon Parish, Leesville, La., 1989-92; alt. spl. edn. H.S. classes Pickering H.S. Vernon Parish, Leesville, 1992-94; ednl. diagnostician Vernon Parish Spl. Edn. Ctr., Leesville, 1994—; spkr. spl. edn. super conf., 1992, 94. Author: (juvenile) Tales of the Circus, 1990, Histories of Louisiana Fairs, Festivals, and Historic Places, Book 1, 1993, Book 2, 1994, Louisiana: Festival of Color Coloring Book, 1994; illustrator: Chad and the Mighty Dragon, 1992 and illustrator: Tales; creator classroom games. Officer Homemakers Club, Beauregard Parish, 1975-88; sec. La. Assn. Fairs and Festivals 1985-89; sec-treas. Beauregard Parish Fair Assn., DeRidder,

1980—. Mem. Coun. for Exceptional Children (sec. La. fedn. coun. 1995), Assn. Profl. La. Educators, La. Ednl. Diagnosticians Assn., Kappa Kappa Iota (pres. 1993-94). Methodist. Avocations: arts and crafts, sewing, travel, writing. Home: 3570 Neale Oilfield Rd Deridder LA 70634-9540 Office: Pickering HS 497 Le Bleu Rd Leesville LA 71446 also: Vernon Parish Spl Edn Ctr 201 Belview Rd Leesville LA 71446

LYTLE, L(ARRY) BEN, insurance company executive, lawyer; b. Greenville, Tex., Sept. 30, 1946; children: Hugh, Larry. BS in Mgmt. Sci. and Indsl. Psychology, East Tex. State U., 1970; JD, Ind. U., 1980. Computer operator/programmer U.S. Govt., Ft. Smith, Ark., 1962-63; customer engr. Olivetti Corp., San Antonio, 1963-64; mgr. computer ops. and computer software LTV Electrosystems, Greenville, 1964-69; project mgr. electronic fin. system, dir. systems planning Assocs. Corp. N.Am., South Bend, Ind., 1969-74; asst. v.p. systems Am. Fletcher Nat. Bank, Indpls., 1974-76; with Assoc. Ins. Cos., Inc., Indpls., 1976—, pres., 1987—, COO, 1987-89, CEO, 1989—, now also chmn.; bd. dirs.; CEO, chmn. bd. dirs. Anthem Cos., Inc., Acordia, Inc.; chmn. bd. dirs. AdminaStar, Inc., Health Networks Am., Inc., Novalis, Inc., Robinson-Conner Nev., Inc.; bd. dirs. The Shelby Ins. Group, Raffensperger, Hughes & Co., Inc., Acordia Benefits, Inc., Indpls. Power and Light Co., Indpls. Power and Light Co. Enterprises; mem. adv. bd. CID Venture Ptnrs., Ltd. Partnership; rschr., cons. state and fed. govt. orgns., including, Adv. Coun. on Social Security, Pepper Commn. of U.S. Congress, others. Chmn. health policy commn. State of Ind., Indpls., 1990-92; bd. dirs., mem. exec. com. Community Leaders Allied for Superior Schs.; bd. dirs. Indpls. Convention and Visitors Bur., Indpls. Symphony Orch.; mem. Corp. Community Coun.; active various civic orgns., including United Negro Coll. Fund, Indpls. Mus. Art. Mem. ABA, Ind. Bar Assn., Indpls. Bar Assn., Ind. State C. of C. (bd. dirs.), Indpls. C. of C. (bd. dirs.). Home: 410 N Park Ave Indianapolis IN 46202-3642 Office: Assoc Ins Cos Inc 120 Monument Cir Indianapolis IN 46204-4906

LYTLE, ROBERT FRANK, lawyer; b. Oberlin, Kans., Nov. 27, 1931; s. Howard Ivan and Sylvia Gladys (Godfrey) L.; m. Shirley June Kurz, Aug. 14, 1954; children: Susan Elizabeth Stewart, Robert F. Jr. Student, U. Kansas City, 1949-52; BA, U. Kans., 1953, LLB, 1955. Bar: Kans., Mo., U.S. Dist. Ct. Mo., U.S. Dist. Ct. Kans., U.S. Ct. Mil. Appeals, U.S. Supreme Ct. Assoc. Mudge, Stern, Baldwin & Todd, N.Y.C., 1955-56; ptnr. Bennett Lytle Wetzler Martin & Pishny and its predecessors, Prairie Village, Kans., 1958—; coll. atty. Johnson County C.C., Overland Park, 1967—. Editor in chief Kans. Law Rev., 1954-55; contbr. articles to profl. jours. Lt. USAF, 1956-58. Mem. Order of Coif. Presbyterian. Office: Bennett Lytle Wetzler Martin & Pishny 5000 W 95th St Ste 300 Prairie Village KS 66208

LYTTLE, DOUGLAS ALFRED, photographer, educator; b. Three Rivers,, Mich., July 7, 1919; s. Stephen Henry and Ruth (Marshall) L.; m. Vivian M. Quell, October 12, 1991; children: Judith Ann Lyttle Nelson, Janet Ruth Lyttle Chobanian, Marsha Jane Lyttle Pidek. B.S. cum laude, U. Mich. 1941. Organic research chemist Merck and Co., Rahway, N.J., 1941-45, Upjohn Co., Kalamazoo, Mich., 1945-60; prin. Douglas Lyttle Photographer, Kalamazoo, 1961-69; mem. faculty Sch. Photog. Arts and Scis., Rochester (N.Y.) Inst. Tech., 1969-83, prof. emeritus, 1983—; freelance photographer. Exhibitor photographs; presenter audio-visual programs based on travels; contbr. photographs to mags. Mem. Profl. Photographers Am., Am. Soc. Photographers, Phi Beta Kappa. Office: 10 Downing Dr Pittsford NY 14534-3612 *The Christian faith, its morality, spirit and theology as active fellowship with God in Christ, is the basis for a life in which people are most important. Honesty with self and others, caring, commitment and a continuing reach for excellence and growth have been keystones for every endeavour. If there has been 'success' it has been a gift and a result.*

LYTTON, ROBERT LEONARD, civil engineer, educator; b. Port Arthur, Tex., Oct. 23, 1937; m. Robert Odell and Nora Mae (Verrett) L.; m. Eleanor Marilyn Anderson, Sept. 9, 1961; children: Lynn Elizabeth, Robert Douglas, John Kirby. BSCE, U. Tex., 1960, MSCE, 1961, PhD, 1967. Registered profl. engr., Tex., La.; registered land surveyor, La. Assoc. Dannebaum and Assocs., Cons. Engrs., Houston, 1963-65; U.S. NSF fellow U. Tex., Austin, 1965-67, asst. prof., 1967-68; NSF postdoctoral fellow Australian Commonwealth Sci. & Indsl. Rsch. Orgn., Melbourne, Australia, 1969-70; assoc. prof. Tex. A&M U., College Station, 1971-76, prof., 1976-90, Wiley chair prof., 1990—, dir. ctr. for infrastructure engring., 1991—; divsn. head Tex. Transp. Inst. 1982-91, head infrastructure and transp. divsn. civil engring. dept., 1993—; bd. dirs. MLA Labs., Inc., Austin, 1980—; v.p. bd. dirs. MLAW Cons., Inc., 1980—, Austin, ERES Cons., Inc., 1981—, Champaign, Ill.; prin. investigator strategic hwy. rsch. program A005 rsch. project, 1990-93. Patentee for system identification and analysis of subsurface radar signals. Mem. St. Vincent de Paul Soc., Houston, 1963-65, Redemptorist Lay Mission Soc., Melbourne, Australia, 1969-70. Capt. U.S. Army, 1961-63. Recipient SAR medal of honor St. Mary's U., 1957, Soc. Am. Mil. Engrs. Outstanding Sr. cadet U. Tex., 1979, Disting. Mil. grad award, 1960, Hamilton Watch award Coll. Engring., 1960. Fellow ASCE; mem. NSPE, Transp. Rsch. Bd. (chmn. com. AWL06 1987-93), Internat. Soc. for Soil Mechanics & Found. Engring. (U.S. rep. tech. com. TC-6 1987—, keynote address 7th internat. conf. on expansive soils 1992, mem. organizing com. 1st internat. conf. on unsaturated soils in Paris 1995), Assn. Asphalt Paving Technologists, Post-Tensioning Inst. (adv. bd.), Tex. Soc. Profl. Engrs., Internat. Union of Testing and Rsch. Labs for Materials and Structures (mem. com. reflection cracking of pavements 1988—), Internat. Soc. Asphalt Pavements, Pi Kappa Delta, Chi Epsilon, Tau Beta Pi, Phi Kappa Phi, Sigma Xi. Roman Catholic. Office: Tex A&M U 508G CE/TTI Bldg College Station TX 77843

MA, FENGCHOW CLARENCE, agricultural engineering consultant; b. Kaifeng, Honan, China, Sept. 4, 1919; came to U.S., 1972; s. Chao-Hsiang and Wen-Chieh (Yang) Ma; m. Fanny Luisa Corvera-Achá, Jan. 20, 1963; 1 child, Fernando. BS in Agr., Nat. Chekiang U., Maytan, Kweichow, China, 1942; postgrad., Iowa State U., 1945-46. Cert. profl. agronomist, Republic of China, 1944; registered profl. agrl. engr., Calif. Chief dept. ops. Agrl. Machinery Operation and Mgmt. Office, Shanghai, China, 1946-49; sr. farm machinery specialist Sino-Am. Joint Commn. on Rural Reconstrn., Taipei, Taiwan, Republic of China, 1950-62; agrl. engring. adviser in Bolivia, Peru, Chile, Ecuador, Liberia, Honduras, Grenada, Bangladesh FAO, Rome, 1962-80; consulting agrl. engr. to USAID projects in Guyana & Peru IRI Rsch. Inst., Inc. Stamford, Conn., 1981-82, 83, 85; chief adviser Com. Internat. Tech. Coop. Taipei, 1984-85; pres. FCM Assocs., Inc., 1962—; short consulting missions to Paraguay, Saudi Arabia, Indonesia, Malawi, Swaziland, Barbados, Dominica, Ivory Coast, Vietnam, Philippines and others. Author papers, studies; contbr. articles to profl. publs. Mem. Am. Soc. Agrl. Engrs. Avocations: reading, stamp and coin collecting. Home: 1004 Azalea Dr Sunnyvale CA 94086-6747 Office: PO Box 70096 Sunnyvale CA 94086-0096

MA, JING-HENG SHENG, East Asian languages educator; b. Beijing, Mar. 15, 1932; came to U.S., 1963; d. Xue Shu and Guo Ying (Yin) Sheng; m. Wei-Yi Ma, Sept. 28, 1958; children: Lyou-fu, Syau-fu. BEd, Taiwan Normal U., 1958; MA, Philippine Women's U., 1963; MA in Applied Linguistics, U. Mich., 1971, PhD in Linguistics, 1983. Instr. Chinese Cornell U. Extension Program, Taipei, Taiwan, 1959-62; lectr. Chinese U. Mich., Ann Arbor, 1963-84; assoc. prof., chairperson dept. East Asian langs. Williams Coll., Williamstown, Mass., 1984-88; vis. prof. Chinese Dept., Wellesley Coll., 1988-89, prof., chairperson dept., 1989—. Author: Chinese Language Patterns, 1985, A Study of the Mandaring Chinese Verb Suffix Zhe, 1986, At Middle Age: A Learning Guide for Students of Chinese, 1988, 2nd edit. 1991, Strange Friends: A Learning Guide for Students of Chinese, 1989, 2nd edit. 1991, Great Wall: A Learning Guide for Students of Chinese, 1990, The True Story of Ah Q: A Learning Guide for Students of Chinese, 1992, Difficult Points in Chinese Grammar, 1992. Mem. Chinese Lang. Tchr.'s Assn. (exec. bd. 1990-93), Assn. for Asian Studies. Home: 10 Nonesuch Dr Natick MA 01760-1041 Office: Wellesley Coll Chinese Dept Pendleton E Wellesley MA 02181

MA, TAI-LOI, library curator, Chinese studies specialist; b. Canton, China, Oct. 14, 1945; came to U.S., 1970; s. James Chun-Woon and Mary (Wong) M. BA, U. Hong Kong, 1969; MA, U. Chgo., 1972, PhD, 1987. Cataloger East Asian Libr., U. Chgo., 1972-78, head cataloger, 1978-87, curator, 1987—; cons. Chinese collection Kinsey Inst. Rsch., Bloomington, Ind., 1983; fellowship panelist NEH, Washington, 1988—; mem. internat. adv.

com. Chinese rare books project Rsch. Librs. Group, Mountain View, Calif., 1988—; mem. adv. bd. East Asian Libr. Jour., Princeton, N.J., 1990—; cons. Chinese collection Libr. Congress, 1995. Translator: Traditional Chinese Stories, 1978; contbr. articles to profl. publs. Fellow, scholar U. Chgo., 1970-73; Mellon Found. fellow Princeton U., summer 1980; conf. travel grantee Am. Coun. Learned Socs., Canton, 1983, Com. on Scholarly Comm. with China, Beijing, 1993. Mem. ALA, Assn. for Asian Studies (com. on East Asian librs. exec. group 1989-92, subcom. chmn. 1993—). Office: U Chgo East Asian Collection Regenstein Libr 1100 E 57th St Fl 5 Chicago IL 60637-1502

MA, TSO-PING, electrical engineering educator, researcher, consultant; b. Lan-Tsou, Gan-Su, China, Nov. 13, 1945; came to U.S., 1969; s. Liang-Kway and Zwey-Yueen (Liu) Ma; m. Pin-fang Lin, June 10, 1972; children: Mahau, Jasmine. B.S., Nat. Taiwan U., 1968; M.S., Yale U., 1972, Ph.D. 1974. Teaching asst. Yale U., New Haven, 1971-74, asst. prof. elec. engring., 1977-80, assoc. prof., 1980-85, prof., 1985—, chmn. dept. elec. engring., 1991—, acting chmn. dept. elec. engring., 1988, vis. lectr., 1976-77, advisor Yale Chinese Student Svc., 1977—; Yale Mainland-Taiwan Soc.; staff engr. IBM, Hopewell Junction, N.Y., 1974-77; cons. in field. Contbr. articles to profl. jours. Patentee in field. Bd. dirs. New Haven Chinese Sch., 1982—; Grantee Rsch. Corp., 1978, Mobil Found., 1981-84, G.E. Found., 1984; recipient Conn. Yankee Ingenuity award, 1991. Fellow IEEE (chmn. various coms. 1986—, officer semiconductor interface specialists conf. 1986-88); mem. Materials Rsch. Soc., Am. Phys. Soc., Orgn. of Chinese Ams. (pres. New Haven chpt. 1988-90, bd. dirs. 1990—), Electrochem. Soc., Conn. Acad. Sci. and Engring., Yale Figure Skating Club (v.p. 1991-93), Yale Sci. and Engring. Assn., Sigma Xi (v.p. Yale chpt. 1986, pres. 1987-88). Avocations: music, violin, skating. Home: 169 Northford Rd Branford CT 06405-2823 Office: Yale Univ Dept Elec Engring 15 Prospect St New Haven CT 06520-8284

MA, YO YO, cellist; b. Paris. Studied with Leonard Rose, Juilliard Sch. Music, N.Y.C.; AB, Harvard U., 1976. Appeared with Pablo Casals, Isaac Stern, Leonard Bernstein, performed throughout world with maj. orchs.; rec. artist SONY Classical; debut at age 9, Carnegie Hall, N.Y.C.; recordings include Portrait of Yo-Yo Ma, China and Japan: Japanese Melodies, Anything Goes (with Stephanie Grapelli), Hush (with Bobby McFerrin), Yo-Yo Ma at Tanglewood. Recipient Avery Fisher prize, 1978; Grammy awards, 1984, 85, 86 (2); Edison award, 1984. Office: CBS Records c/o Sony Music Entertainment Inc 550 Madison Ave New York NY 10022-3200 also: HaroldHott Ltd, 31 Sinclair Rd, London WI4 0NS, England*

MAAG, URS RICHARD, statistics educator; b. Winterthur, Switzerland, Jan. 20, 1938; m. Tannis Yvonne Arbuckle, July 31, 1965; children: Liane, Karin, Eric. Diploma in Math, Swiss Fed. Inst. Tech., Zurich, 1961; M.Sc., U. Toronto, Can., 1962, Ph.D. 1965. Asst. prof. U. Montreal, Que., Can., 1965-72; assoc. prof. U. Montreal, Can., 1972-78, prof., 1978—. Contbr. articles to profl. jours. Mem. Statis. Soc. Can. (sec. 1973-77, pres. 1980), Am. Statis. Assn. (pres. Montreal chpt. 1975-77), Internat. Statis. Inst., Can. Assn. Rd. Safety Profls. Home: 3484 Marlowe Ave, Montreal, PQ Canada H4A 3L7 Office: U Montreal Dept Math and Stats, CP 6128 Succ Centreville, Montreal, PQ Canada H3C 3J7

MAAHS, KENNETH HENRY, SR., religion educator; b. Peoria, Ill., June 19, 1940; s. Silas Henry Maahs and Lydia Nettie (Heinold) Blessman; m. Vivian Louise Dawn Englert, Sept. 1, 1962; children: Kirsten Allison Dawn, Kenneth Henry Jr. BA in Philosophy/Theology magna cum laude, Simpson Coll., 1962; MDiv, Fuller Theol. Sem., Pasadena, Calif., 1965; ThM in N.T. Studies, Princeton Theol. Sem., 1966; PhD in Old Testament Studies, So. Bapt. Theol. Sem., Louisville, 1972. Ordained to ministry Missionary Ch./Am. Bapt. Conv., 1968. Instr. N.Sask (N.Y.) Coll., 1966-67, Bethel Coll., Mishawaka, Ind., 1968; prof. Bibl. studies Ea. Coll., St. Davids, Pa., 1972—, Abram Clemens chair, 1986—, chmn. dept. religion-philosophy, 1985-88, chmn. humanities div., 1988-92, 95; faculty mem. The Jerusalem Ctr. for Biblical Studies, 1994—; interim pastor Columbus (N.J.) Bapt. Ch., 1975-76, Roxborough Bapt. Ch., Phila., 1980-81, Bapt. Temple, Blue Bell, Pa., 1981-83, Willowgrove (Pa.) Bapt. Ch., 1988, Belmont Bapt. Ch., Broomall, Pa., 1989, Lower Merion Bapt. Ch., Bryn Mawr, Pa., 1989-90, 2d Bapt. Ch. Germantown, Pa., 1990-92, Roxborough Bapt. Ch., Phila., 1992-93, No. Wales (Pa.) Bapt. Ch., 1994—; adj. prof. Ea. Bapt. Theol. Sem., 85, 89, Lay Acad. of Phila. Bapt. Assn., 1984-86, 88, 90, 94, Fuller Theol. Sem./Young Life's Inst. Youth Ministries, 1986-87, 89.; keynote speaker Am. Bapt. Women's Regional Conf., 1983; feature lectr. Am. Bapt. Commn. on Continuing Edn., 1985. Recipient Legion of Honor award Chapel of Four Chaplains, 1983, Lindback award Ea. Coll., 1984; named Prof. of Yr. Ea. Coll., 1983-84. Mem. Soc. Bibl. Lit., Delta Epsilon Chi. Republican. Home: 346 E Valley Forge Rd Kng Of Prussa PA 19406-2035 Office: Ea Coll Saint Davids PA 19087

MAARBJERG, MARY PENZOLD, office equipment company executive; b. Norfolk, Va., Oct. 2, 1943; d. Edmund Theodore and Lucy Adelaide (Singleton) Penzold; m. John Peder Maarbjerg, Oct. 20, 1966; 1 son, Martin Peder. A.B., Hollins Coll., 1965; M.B.A., Wharton Sch., Pa., 1969. Cons. bus. and fin., Stamford, Conn., 1977-78; corp. staff analyst Pitney Bowes, Inc., Stamford, Conn., 1978-80, mgr. pension and benefit fin. 1980-81, dir. investor relations, 1981-85; v.p. planning and devel. Pitney Bowes Credit Corp., Norwalk, Conn., 1985-86; treas., v.p. planning Pitney Bowes Credit Corp., 1986-94; v.p. mkt. devel. and mng. dir. Asia Pacific Bowes Fin. Svcs., 1994-95, v.p. ops. and mng. dir., 1995—. Mem. adv. com. City of Stamford Mcpl. Employees Retirement Fund, 1980-85; mem. fin. adv. com. YWCA, Stamford, 1982-86; bd. dirs. Stamford Symphony, 1985—, Vis. Nurses Assn., 1984-86, Am. Recorder Soc., 1986—. Fellow Royal Statis. Soc.; mem. Fin. Execs. Inst., Phi Beta Kappa. Congregationalist. Office: Pitney Bowes Credit Corp 201 Merritt Seven Norwalk CT 06856

MAAS, DUANE HARRIS, distilling company executive; b. Tilleda, Wis., Aug. 26, 1927; s. John William and Adela (Giessel) M.; m. Sonja Johnson, Mar. 11, 1950; children: Jon Kermit, Duane Arthur, Thomas Ervin. B.S., U. Wis., 1951. With Shell Chem. Corp., 1951-59; plant mgr. Fleischmann Distilling Corp., Owensboro, Ky., 1959-63, Plainfield, Ill., 1963-65; asst. to v.p. Barton Distilling Co., Chgo., 1965-68; exec. asst. to pres. Barton Distilling Co., 1968; v.p. adminstrn., 1968; v.p., gen. mgr. Barton Brands, Inc., Chgo., 1968—72; pres. Leaf Confectionery div. W.R. Grace, Chgo., 1972-74; v.p., gen. mgr. Romano Bros., Chgo., 1974-79; v.p., sec.-treas. Marketing Directions Inc., Chgo., 1974-77; pres. Associated Wine Producers, Inc., 1979—; exec. v.p., chief exec. officer Mohawk Liqueur, Detroit, 1980-86; v.p. McKesson Wine & Spirits Group of N.Y., Detroit, 1982-86; pres. Mgmt. Cons. Services Co., Chgo., 1986—; past pres. Barton Distilling (Can.), Ltd.; past mng. dir. Barton Distilling (Scotland), Ltd.; past dir. Barton Distillers Europe, Barton Internat., Ltd. Sec.-treas. Plainfield Twp. Park Dist., 1967-70; chmn. Plainfield Planning and Zoning Commn., 1965-70. Served with USAAF, 1945-47. Mem. Wis. Alumni Assn. Lutheran. Home: 13264 W Highway 29 Bowler WI 54416 Office: 3135 Centennial Ct Highland Park IL 60035-1015

MAAS, JAMES BERYL, psychology educator, lecturer, filmmaker; b. Detroit, Aug. 9, 1938; s. Royal Sheldon and Mary Ann (Weiner) M.; m. Nancy Christine Neaher, July 28, 1979; children: Daniel, Justin. BA, Williams Coll., 1960; MA, Cornell U., 1963, PhD, 1966. Asst. prof. psychology Cornell U., Ithaca, N.Y., 1964-70, assoc. prof., 1970-79, prof., 1979—, chmn. dept., 1985-90, Stephen H. Weiss Presdl. fellow, 1993—; Fulbright prof. Uppsala (Sweden) U., 1979; mgmt. cons. IBM, Armonk, N.Y., 1983—; observer BBC-TV, London, 1974; vis. prof. Stanford (Calif.) U., 1979. Producer: (films) Until I Get Caught, 1980 (Am. FilmFest award 1980), Learning to See, 1983 (Am. FilmFest award 1983); producer, dir. Let's Build it Together, 1985 (Am. FilmFest award 1985), Where Have All the Teachers Gone, 1987; producer Bravo Gloria, 1988, Sleep Alert!, 1990, To Light a Fire, 1992, Asleep in the Fast Lane, 1995; producer 9 nat. PBS TV spls. Winner 42 film festivals for documentary films; recipient Clark Disting. Teaching award Cornell U., 1972, Rush Silver medal Psychiat. Assn., 1978, 79, 80. Mem. Am. Psychol. Assn. (pres. div. on teaching 1974-75, disting. teaching award 1973). Avocations: tennis, photography, sailing. Office: Cornell U 210 Uris Hall Ithaca NY 14853-7601

MAAS, JAMES WELDON, psychiatrist; b. St. Louis, Oct. 26, 1929; s. James Werner and Agnes Pohlman (Weldon) M.; m. Joanne Henderson, Dec. 23, 1953 (div. 1972); 1 child, Elizabeth; m. Marilyn S. Loren, Oct. 18, 1972; children: James W., Jonathan W. AB, Wash. U., 1950, MD, 1954. Diplomate Am. Bd. Psychiatry. Sect. head NIMH, Bethesda, Md., 1960-65; prof. psychiatry U. Ill. Med. Sch., Chgo., 1966-72; prof. psychiatry Yale U., New Haven, 1972-82; Hugo A Auler prof., 1976; Hugo A. Auler prof. psychiatry and pharmacology U. Tex. Health Sci. Ctr., San Antonio, 1987—; vis. scientist Cambridge, Eng. Contbr. articles to profl. jours. and books. Maj. USAF, 1956-58. Grantee NIMH, 1968—; 1994 award for excellence in psychiatry, Tex. Assn. Psychiat. Physicians. Fellow Am. Psychiat. Assn. (life), Am. Coll. Neuropsychopharmacology, Davenport Coll., Yale U.; mem. Cosmos Club. Avocations: fishing, fiction writing. Office: Univ Tex Health Sci Med Sch 7703 Floyd Curl Dr San Antonio TX 78284-7700

MAAS, JANE BROWN, advertising executive; b. Jersey City; d. Charles E. and Margaret (Beck) Brown; m. Michael Maas, Aug. 30, 1957; children: Katherine, Jennifer. BA, Bucknell U., 1953; postgrad., U. Dijon, France, 1954; MA, Cornell U., 1955; LittD, Ramapo Coll., 1986, St. John's U., 1988. Assoc. producer Name That Tune TV Program, N.Y.C., 1957-64; v.p. Ogilvy and Mather Inc., N.Y.C., 1964-76; sr. v.p. Wells, Rich, Greene, Inc., N.Y.C., 1976-82; pres. Muller Jordan Weiss Inc., N.Y.C., 1982-89; pres. Earle Palmer Brown Cos., N.Y.C., 1989-92, chmn., 1992-94, chmn. emeritus, 1994—. Co-author: How to Advertise, 1975, Better Brochures, 1981, Adventures of a Advertising Woman, 1986, The New How to Advertise, 1992, Christmas in Wales: a Homecoming, 1994. Trustee Bucknell U., Lewisburg, 1976-86, Fordham U., N.Y., 1983-91; mem. bd. govs. com. Scholastic Achievement, 1985-92; active Girls Scouts U.S. Greater N.Y., 1970-76; mem. adv. bd. William E. Simon Grad. Sch. Bus., U. Rochester, 1989—; pub. dir. AIA, 1993—. Recipient Matrix award Women in Communications, 1980, N.Y. Advt. Woman of Yr., 1986. Mem. Am. Archtl. Found. (regent 1993—), Am. Assn. Advt. Agys. (bd. govs.). Avocations: creative writing, jogging. Home: PO Box 1109 Westhampton Beach NY 11978-7109

MAAS, JOE (MELVIN JOSEPH MAAS), federal agency administrator; b. Washington; s. Melvin Joseph and Katherine (Endress) M.; m. Constance Mary Haile, June 13, 1965; children: Christine, Michael, Kevin. BS, U. Md., 1965; postgrad., Stanford U., 1972-73. Dir. career edn. U.S. Dept. Labor, Washington, 1969-73; dep. dir. pers. SBA, Washington, 1973-76, dir. pers., 1976-82, asst. adminstr., 1982—; mem. Internat. Pers. Assn., 1981-83, chairperson, 1982. Bd. dirs., treas. Snowden Mill Assn., Silver Spring, Md. 1991. Cpl. USMC, 1957-58. Mem. Fed. Exec. Adminstrs. Assn., Sr. Exec. Assn., Volkswagen Club (pres. Washington club 1988—). Roman Catholic. Home: 2213 Aventurine Way Silver Spring MD 20904-5253 Office: SBA 409 3rd St SW Washington DC 20416-0005

MAAS, PETER, writer; b. N.Y.C., June 27, 1929; s. Carl and Madeleine (Fellheimer) M.; m. Audrey Gellen, Apr. 4, 1962 (dec. July 1975); 1 child, John Michael; m. Suzanne Jones, Feb. 1, 1986; 1 child, Terrence. B.A., Duke U., 1949; postgrad., The Sorbonne, Paris, 1950. Reporter N.Y. Herald Tribune, Paris, 1950-54; assoc. editor Collier's mag., 1954-56; sr. editor Look mag., 1959-61; contbg. writer Sat. Evening Post, 1961-66; cons. Curtis Pub. Co., 1966-67; contbg. editor New York mag., 1968-71. Free lance contbr. to nat. mags., newspapers, 1954—; author: The Rescuer, 1967, The Valachi Papers, 1969, Serpico, 1973, King of the Gypsies, 1975, Made in America, 1979, Marie: A True Story, 1983, Manhunt, 1986, Father and Son, 1989, In A Child's Name, 1990, China White, 1994, Killer Spy, 1995; works included in anthology. Served with USNR, 1952-54. Mem. PEN Am. Center, Author's Guild. Roman Catholic. Office: care Internat Creative Mgmt 40 W 57th St New York NY 10019-4001

MAAS, SALLY ANN, newspaper editor, journalist; b. Portage, Wis., Apr. 10, 1947; d. Franklin Arthur and Mabel Gladys (Engen) Maas; m. Robert A. Marshall, Aug. 3, 1973. BJ, U. Wis., 1969. Reporter, The Paper, Oshkosh, Wis., 1969-70; feature writer The Press, Binghamton, N.Y., 1970-71; feature writer The Press-Enterprise, Riverside, Calif., 1971-76, lifestyle editor, 1976-83, feature editor 1983-85, asst. mng. editor features and art, 1985—. Recipient Outstanding Woman of Achievement award Bus. and Profl. Women's Club, 1981. Mem. Soc. Newspaper Design, Women in Communications, LWV, Sigma Delta Chi. Club: Twin Cities Press (past pres.). Home: 30001 Live Oak Canyon Rd Redlands CA 92373-7940 Office: The Press-Enterprise Co 3512 14th St Riverside CA 92501-3814

MAAS, TERRY LEO, investment banker; b. St. Louis, Dec. 6, 1946; s. Clifford Joseph and Dorothy Marie (Mayernick) M.; m. Sharon Eileen Schick, Aug. 26, 1972; children: Brett Charles, Bryan Clifford. BS with honors, UCLA, 1968; MBA, Calif. State U., Dominguez Hills, 1975, M of Pub. Adminstrn., 1978. Adminstrv. mgr. KMS Tech. Ctr., Los Angeles, 1972-75; investment broker Merrill-Lynch, Los Angeles, 1975-78; mgr. West Coast Rauscher Pierce Refsnes, Inc., Los Angeles, 1978-81; asst. regional mgr. Rauscher Pierce Refsnes, Inc., Phoenix, 1981-86; SW regional mgr. Security Pacific Mcht. Bank, Phoenix, 1986-88; sr. v.p. Citibank, Phoenix, 1988—; faculty Nat. Real Estate Devel. Conf., San Francisco, 1984-85; group leader Valley Leadership Conf., Phoenix, 1985; speaker forum in push fin. UCLA, 1984. Bd. dirs. East Scottsdale Little League, 1982-88. Served to 1st lt. USAF, 1969-72. Mem. UCLA Alumni Assn., Lambda Chi Alpha. Republican. Lutheran. Club: Phoenix Stock and Bond. Avocations: softball, rose gardening. Home: 9300 N 58th St Paradise Vly AZ 85253-1765 Office: Citibank 3300 N Central Ave Phoenix AZ 85012-2501

MAAS, WERNER KARL, microbiology educator; b. Kaiserslautern, Germany, Apr. 27, 1921; came to U.S., 1936, naturalized, 1945; s. Albert and Esther (Meyer) M.; m. Renata Diringer, Oct. 15, 1960; children—Peter, Andrew, Helen. AB, Harvard U., 1943; PhD, Columbia U., 1948. Postdoctoral fellow Calif. Inst. Tech., Pasadena, 1946-48; commd. officer USPHS, Tb Research Lab., Cornell U. Sch., N.Y.C., 1948-54; asst. prof. pharmacology NYU, 1954-57, assoc. prof. microbiology, 1957-63, prof., 1963-94, prof. emeritus, 1994—, chmn. dept. basic med. scis., 1974-81. Career grantee USPHS, 1962-94. Mem. Am. Soc. Biol. Chemists, Genetics Soc. Am., Am. Soc. Microbiology. Home: 86 Villard Ave Hastings on Hudson NY 10706-1821 Office: 550 1st Ave New York NY 10016-6481

MAASBERG, BILL ARTHUR, publisher; b. Mokelumne Hill, Calif., Apr. 1, 1917; s. Arthur Otto and Sophie (Loible) M.; m. Freddie Ann Leavens, Oct. 15, 1938; children: Bill Jr., James E. Stationary steam engr. Pacific Gas and Elec. Co., San Francisco, 1939-41, Avon, 1941-49; with Walnut Growers Assn., Stockton, Calif., 1950-70, Calif. Conservations Ctr., Jamestown, 1972-83; ret.; pub. Pilots. Inventor Step-N-Chek; author: Pilots International Bed and Breakfast Fly-Inn Club, 1989. Pres. The Golden Chain Coun., 1991-92; mem. Tuolumne Hist. Soc. With USN, 1932-36. Mem. Tuolumne County Aero. Assn., U.S. Pilot's Assn., Calif. Pilot's Assn. Home: PO Box 1847 11257 John Wallace Dr Columbia CA 95310

MAASS, ARTHUR, political science and environmental studies educator; b. Balt., July 24, 1917; s. Arthur Leopold and Selma (Rosenheim) M. A.B., Johns Hopkins, 1939; M.P.A., Harvard, 1941, Ph.D., 1949. Adminstrv. asst. Bur. Budget, 1939-40; intern Nat. Inst. Pub. Affairs, 1939-40; research technician Nat. Resources Planning Bd., 1941-42; budget analyst Dept. Navy, 1946; water resources analyst Natural Resources Task Force, Hoover Commn., 1948; faculty Harvard, 1949—, prof. govt., 1959-67, Frank G. Thomson prof. govt., 1967-84, prof. emeritus, 1984—, chmn. dept., 1963-67; cons. Office Dir. Budget, 1949, Office Sec. Interior, 1950-52, Pres.'s Materials Policy Commn., 1951-52, TVA, 1952, C.E., 1961—, Bur. Reclamation, 1971, Ministry Water Conservancy, People's Republic China, 1980—; vis. prof. polit. sci. U. Calif. at Berkeley, 1951, U. P.R., 1955, El Colegio de México, 1986, U. Internat. Menendez y Pelayo, Valencia, Spain, 1990. Author: Muddy Waters, The Army Engineers and the Nation's Rivers, 1951, Congress and the Common Good, 1983, Water Law and Institutions in the Western U.S.: Comparisons with Early Developments in California and Australia, Contemporary Developments in Australia and Recent Legislation Worldwide, 1990; co-author: Area and Power, 1959, Design of Water-Resource Systems: New Techniques for Relating Economic Objectives, Engineering Analysis and Governmental Planning, 1962, A Simulation of Irrigation Systems, 1971, rev., 1974, 78, 87, Chinese edit., 1980, . . . and the Desert Shall Rejoice: Conflict, Growth and Justice in Arid Environments,

1978, rev. edit., 1986, Un Modelo de Simulacion Para Sistemas de Regadio, 1985; contbr. articles to profl. jours. Served to lt. comdr. USNR, 1942-46. Guggenheim fellow, 1955; Fulbright research fellow Spain, 1960-61; Faculty research fellow Social Sci. Research Council, 1961. Club: Harvard (N.Y.C.). Home: 63 Atlantic Ave Boston MA 02110-3716 Office: Harvard U Littauer Ctr Cambridge MA 02138

MAASS, R. ANDREW, museum director; b. N.Y.C., Apr. 11, 1946; m. Ruth Borenstein, June 30, 1968; children: Annie, Kern Daniel. BA, U. Wis., 1968; MA, New Sch. for Social Research, N.Y.C., 1972; postgrad., SUNY, Oneonta, 1973. Asst. dir. Neighborhood Conservation Bur., N.Y.C., 1970; coordinator, supr. of ecology Mus. of City of N.Y., 1970-71; asst. program dir. South St. Seaport Mus., N.Y.C., 1971-72; dir. Fresno (Calif.) Arts Ctr., 1973-80, Tucson Mus. of Art, 1980-84, Tampa (Fla.) Mus. of Art, 1985—. Mem. Am. Assn. Mus., Assn. Art Mus. Dirs., Fla. Art Mus. Dirs. Assn. (pres.), S.E. Mus. Conf., Fla. Assn. Mus. (sec.). Office: Tampa Mus Art 600 N Ashley Dr Tampa FL 33602-4307

MAATMAN, GERALD LEONARD, insurance company executive; b. Chgo., Mar. 11, 1930; s. Leonard Raymond and Cora Mae (Van Der Laag) M.; children: Gerald L. Jr., Mary Ellen; m. Bernice Catherine Brummer, June 3, 1971. BS, Ill. Inst. Tech., 1951. Asst. chief engineer Ill. Inspection & Rating Bureau, Chgo., 1951-58; prof., dept. chmn. Ill. Inst. Tech., Chgo., 1959-65; v.p. engring. Kemper Group, Chgo., 1966-68, pres. Nat. Loss Control Service Corp., 1969-74; v.p. corp. planning Kemper Group, Long Grove, Ill., 1974-79, sr. v.p. info. services group, 1979-85, exec. v.p. ins. ops., 1985-87; pres. Kamper Nat. Ins. Co., Long Grove, Ill., 1987-90; pres., chief exec. officer Kemper Nat. Ins. Cos., Long Grove, Ill., 1989-92; chmn. bd., chief exec. officer Kamper Nat. Ins. Co., Long Grove, Ill., 1992-95, dir., 1987—. Bd. dirs. Advs. for Auto and Hwy. Safety, 1992—, Nat. Down Syndrome Soc., Underwriters Labs. Lt. (j.g.) USCGR, 1952-54. Mem. Am. Inst. Assn. (bd. dirs. 1992-95), Ins. Inst. for Hwy. Safety (bd. dirs. 1991—), Wynstone Golf Club, Tau Beta Pi. Republican. Roman Catholic. Office: Kemper Nat Ins Co Kemper Ctr Long Grove IL 60049

MAAZEL, LORIN, conductor, musician; b. Neuilly, France, Mar. 6, 1930; s. Lincoln and Marie (Varencove) M.; m. Dietlinde Turban, 1986; 3 children; 4 children from previous marriages. Studies with, Vladimir Bakaleinikoff, student, U. Pitts., Mus. D. (hon.), 1968; H.H.D., Beaver Coll., 1973. Debut as condr., 1938; condr. Am. symphony orchs., 1939—; violin recitalist; European debut, 1953; festivals include Bayreuth, Salzburg, Edinburgh; tours include S.Am., Australia, USSR, Japan, Korea, People's Republic China; artistic dir. Deutsche Opera Berlin, 1965-71; assoc. prin. condr. New Philharm. Orch., London, 1970-72; dir. Cleve. Orch., 1972-82, condr. emeritus, 1982-86; dir. Vienna State Opera, 1982-84; music dir. Pitts. Symphony Orch., 1988—, Orchestre Nat. de France, 1988-90, Bavarian Radio Symphony Orch., Munich, 1993—. Decorated officer Legion d'Honneur 1981; Finnish Commdr. of the Lion; Portuguese Commdr.; Bundesverdienstkreuz, Germany. Office: Pitts Symphony Orch 600 Penn Ave Pittsburgh PA 15222-3209*

MABBS, EDWARD CARL, management consultant; b. St. Louis, Sept. 8, 1921; s. Ralph I. and Anna (Renner) M.; m. Margaret E. von Paulsen, Oct. 16, 1943; children: Susan, Carl, Kenneth, Meg. BS in Mech. Engring., Cornell U., 1943. Registered profl. engr. With Linde div. Union Carbide Corp., Newark, Essington, Pa., Tonawanda, N.Y., 1946-55; plant mgr. Wright Hoist div., York, Pa., 1955-62; group v.p. Am. Chain & Cable Co., Bridgeport, Conn., 1962-68, exec. v.p., 1968-71; pres., CEO, dir. Esterline Corp., N.Y.C., 1971-72; pres. Indsl. Components group Rockwell Internat. Corp., Pitts., 1972-75; pres., CEO, dir. Incom Internat. Inc., Pitts., 1975-81; mgmt. cons. Tavernier, Fla., 1981-84; chmn., CEO, dir. L.B. Foster Co., Pitts., 1984-86; dir. Cross & Trecker Corp., Signode Industries, Arnold Corp., SPD Techs., Inc. Trustee emeritus Point Park Coll.; v.p. Pomperaug coun. Boy Scouts Am.; dir. Friends of Islamorada Area State Parks. Served to capt. U.S. Army, 1943-46, ETO. Mem. Internat. Materials Mgmt. Soc. (past dir.), Am. Prodn. and Inventory Control Soc. (past dir.), Bridgeport (Conn., York, Pa.) C. of C. (past dir.), Material Handling Inst. (past pres.). Home: PO Box 679 Tavernier FL 33070-0679

MABEE, CARLETON, historian, educator; b. Shanghai, China, Dec. 25, 1914; s. Fred Carleton and Miriam (Bentley) M.; m. Norma Dierking, Dec. 20, 1945; children: Timothy I., Susan (Mrs. Paul Newhouse). A.B., Bates Coll., 1936; M.A. (Perkins scholar), Columbia U., 1938, Ph.D., 1942. With Civilian Pub. Svc., 1941-45; Instr. history Swarthmore (Pa.) Coll., 1944; tutor Olivet (Mich.) Coll., 1947-49; asst. prof. liberal studies Clarkson Coll. Tech., Potsdam, N.Y., 1949-51; asso. prof. Clarkson Coll. Tech., 1951-55; prof., 1955-61; dir. social studies div. Delta Coll., University Center, Mich., 1961-64; prof., chmn. dept. humanities and social scis. Rose Poly. Inst., Terre Haute, Ind., 1964-65; prof. history State U. Coll. at New Paltz, N.Y., 1965-80; prof. emeritus State U. Coll. at New Paltz, 1980—; participant in projects for Am. Friends Service Com., 1941-47, 53, 63; Fulbright prof. Keio U., Tokyo, 1953-54. Author: The American Leonardo, A Life of Samuel F.B. Morse, 1943, The Seaway Story, 1961, Black Freedom: The Nonviolent Abolitionists from 1830 through the Civil War, 1970, Black Education in New York State: From Colonial to Modern Times, 1979; author: (with Susan Mabee Newhouse) Sojourner Truth: Slave, Prophet, Legend, 1993; also articles; editor: (with James A. Fletcher) A Quaker Speaks from the Black Experience: The Life and Selected Writings of Barrington Dunbar, 1979. Trustee Young-Morse Hist. Site, Poughkeepsie, N.Y.; bd. dirs. Wallkill Valley Land Trust, New Paltz, N.Y. Recipient Pulitzer prize in biography, 1944, Bergstein award for excellence in teaching Delta Coll., 1963, Anisfield-Wolf award race rels., 1971, Gustavus Myers award for outstanding book on human rights, 1994; rsch. grantee Rsch. Found. SUNY, 1965, 67, 68, 80, Am. Philos. Soc., 1970, Nat. Inst. Edn., 1973-76, NSF, 1982-83. Mem. N.Y. State Hist. Assn., Phi Beta Kappa, Delta Sigma Rho. Methodist. Home: 2121 Rte 44-55 Gardiner NY 12525-9636

MABEY, RALPH R., lawyer; b. Salt Lake City, May 20, 1944; s. Rendell Noel and Rachel (Wilson) M.; m. Sylvia States, June 5, 1968; children: Rachel, Elizabeth, Emily, Sara. BA, U. Utah, 1968; JD, Columbia U., 1972. Bar: Utah 1972, U.S. Dist. Ct. Utah 1972, U.S. Ct. Appeals (10th cir.) 1976, N.Y. 1985, U.S. Supreme Ct. 1988, U.S. Ct. Appeals (4th cir.) 1988, U.S. Ct. Appeals (3d cir.) 1993. Law clk. Atty. Gen., Salt Lake City, 1970, U.S. Dist. Ct., Salt Lake City, 1972-73; ptnr. Irvine, Smith & Mabey, Salt Lake City, 1973-79; U.S. bankruptcy judge U.S. Ct., Salt Lake City, 1979-83; ptnr. LeBoeuf, Lamb, Greene & MacRae, Salt Lake City and N.Y.C., 1983—; adj. prof. Brigham Young U. Sch. Law, Provo, Utah, 1983—, U. Utah Coll. Law, Salt Lake City, 1983-85. Mng. editor Norton Bankruptcy Law Adviser, 1983-85; contbg. author: Collier Bankruptcy Manual, 1986—, Collier on Bankruptcy, 15th Edition. With USAR, 1968-74. Mem. ABA (bus. bankruptcy com., joint task force bankruptcy court structure and insolvency processes), Nat. Bankruptcy Conf., Am. Bankruptcy Inst., Am. Coll. Bankruptcy (bd. regents). Republican. Mormon. Avocation: running. Home: 253 S 1550 E Bountiful UT 84010-1350 Office: LeBoeuf Lamb Greene & MacRae 1000 Kearns Bldg 136 S Main Salt Lake City UT 84101-1685 also: 125 W 55th St New York NY 10019-5369

MABLEY, JACK, newspaper columnist, communications consultant; b. Binghamton, N.Y., Oct. 26, 1915; s. Clarence Ware and Mabelle (Howe) M.; m. Frances Habeck, Aug. 29, 1940; children: Mike, Jill, Ann, Pat, Robert. B.S., U. Ill., 1938. With Chgo. Daily News, 1938-61, reporter, writer, columnist, 1957-61; columnist Chgo.'s Am., 1961-69, asst. mng. editor, 1966-69; editor Chgo. Today, 1969-73; columnist Chgo. Today, Chgo. Tribune, 1973-74, Chgo. Tribune, 1974-87; pres. Mabley & Assocs., Corp. Communications, Glenview, Ill., 1982; columnist Daily Herald, Arlington Heights, Ill., 1987—; Lectr. journalism Northwestern U., 1949-50. Pres. Village of Glenview, Ill., 1957-61, Skokie Valley Community Hosp. Skokie, Ill., 1977-79. Served from ensign to lt. USNR, 1941-45. Recipient Media award Nat. Assn. for Retarded Citizens, 1977. Home and Office: 2275 Winnetka Rd Glenview IL 60025-1825

MABRY, DONALD JOSEPH, university administrator, history educator; b. Atlanta, Apr. 21, 1941; s. Jerry Leon and Eunice Leigh (Harris) M.; m. Susan Strong Johnston, July 28, 1962 (div. Oct. 1986); children: Scott, Mark; m. Paula Ann Crockett, Dec. 18, 1992. BA, Kenyon Coll., Gambier, Ohio, 1963; MEd, Bowling Green State U., 1964; PhD, Syracuse U., 1970. Instr.

St. Johns River Community Coll., Palatka, Fla., 1964-67; rsch. asst. fin. aid Syracuse (N.Y.) U., 1967-68, teaching fellow in history, 1968-69, Maxwell fellow, 1969-70, vis. lectr. dept. history, 1969, 70; asst. to chancellor U. Kans., Lawrence, 1978-79; from. asst. prof. to prof. dept. history Miss. State U., Mississippi State, 1970—, asst. to pres., 1979-81, assoc. dean for budget and rsch., 1991—; sr. fellow Ctr. for Internat. Security and Strategic Studies, Miss. State U., 1981—. Author: Mexico's Accion Nacional, 1973, The Mexican University and the State, 1982, (with others) Neighbors–Mexico and the United States, 1981; editor: The Latin American Narcotics Trade and U.S. National Security, 1989; contbr. articles to profl. jours. Mem. Am. Coun. on Edn. (exec. com. Coun. of Fellows 1980-83), South Ea. Coun. on Latin Am. Studies. Avocation: computer telecommunications. Home: 206 Hiwassee Dr Starkville MS 39759-2117 Office: Coll Arts and Scis Miss State U Mississippi State MS 39762

MABRY, GUY O., manufacturing company executive; b. 1926. BS, U. Kans., 1950. V.p. Owens Corning Fiberglass Corp., 1964-80, sr. v.p., 1980-86, exec. v.p., 1986-90, ret.; bd. dirs. BMC West, Boise, Idaho, ABC Corp., Virginia Beach, Va.

MABUS, RAYMOND EDWIN, JR., ambassador, former governor; b. Starkville, Miss., Oct. 11, 1948; s. Raymond Edwin and Lucille M. (Curtis) M.; m. Julia Hines, Jan. 3, 1987. BA summa cum laude, U. Miss., 1969; MA, Johns Hopkins U., 1970; JD magna cum laude, Harvard U., 1976. Bar: Tex. 1976, D.C. 1978, Miss. 1982. Law clk. U.S. Cir. Ct. Appeals, Montgomery, Ala., 1976-77; legal counsel Ho. of Reps., Washington, 1977-78; assoc. Fried, Frank et al., Washington, 1979-80; gov's. legis. aide State of Miss., Jackson, 1980-83, state auditor, 1984-88, gov., 1988-92; U.S. amb. to Saudi Arabia Jackson, 1994—; chmn. So. Regional Edn. Bd., 1988-89. Lt. (j.g.) USN, 1970-72. Woodrow Wilson scholar Johns Hopkins U., 1969; named among Top 40 under 40 Esquire mag., 1987; recipient Martin Luther King Jr. Social Responsibility award, 1990, Miss. Assn. of Educators Friends of Edn. award, 1990. Mem. So. Govs. Assn. (chm. 1989-90). Democrat. Methodist. Avocations: spectator sports, walking, reading. Office: Am Embassy Unit 61307 APO AE 09803-1307

MACADAM, WALTER KAVANAGH, consulting engineering executive; b. N.Y.C., Nov. 16, 1913; s. John Moore and Mary (Kavanagh) MacA.; m. Rilla Reed, Jan. 30, 1941; children: Ann (Mrs. Dennis P. Delorier), Marie (Mrs. Paul Hoffman), Clair (Mrs. Bruno Aimi), Daniel, David, Barbara. B.S. and M.S. in Elec. Engring., Mass. Inst. Tech., 1937. With AT&T, 1937-68, with long lines dept., 1951-53, 54-56; supt. engring Distant Early Warning radar installation in Arctic for Western Electric Co., 1953-54; transmission engr. AT&T, 1956-59, bldg. and equipment engr., 1959, asst. chief engr., 1959-60, v.p. def., 1960-68; v.p. engring. N.Y. Telephone Co., 1968-73; cons. engr., 1973—. Bd. dirs. United Engring. Trustees, 1965-73, pres., 1971; mem. N.H. Legis. Acad. Sci. and Tech., 1980-82, N.H. Adv. Panel on Pub. Utility Legis., 1985-86. Recipient Vail medal AT&T, 1937. Fellow IEEE (dir. 1963-68, pres. 1967 Centennial medal); mem. ASME, Nat. Soc. Profl. Engrs., Sigma Xi, Tau Beta Pi, Eta Kappa Nu. Club: K.C. (4 deg.). Home: 9 Pinewood Vlg West Lebanon NH 03784-3120

MACAL, ZDENEK, conductor; b. Jan. 8, 1936. Ed., Janacek Music Acad. Music dir. Milw. Symphony Orch., 1986—; chief condr. Cologne Radio Orch., 1970-74; former chief condr. Prague Symphony, Hannover Radio Orch., Sydney Symphony Orch. Office: Milw Symphony Orch 330 E Kibourn Ave Ste 900 Milwaukee WI 53202*

MACAN, WILLIAM ALEXANDER, IV, lawyer; b. Boston, Nov. 21, 1942; s. William A. and Carol (Whitten) M.; m. Jane Mitchell Ahern, Sept. 3, 1965; children—Sandra Jane, William Andrew. BS, Haverford Coll., 1964; LLB, U. Pa., 1967. Bar: Pa. 1968, U.S. Tax Ct. 1970. Law clk. to judge U.S. Tax Ct., Washington, 1967-69; assoc. firm Morgan, Lewis & Bockius, Phila., 1969-76; ptnr. Morgan, Lewis & Bockius, 1976—; lectr. legal instns., seminars. Author publs. on tax-oriented equipment leasing, other tax subjects. Mem. ABA, Pa. Bar Assn., Phila. Bar Assn. Republican. Presbyterian. Office: Morgan Lewis & Bockius 101 Park Ave New York NY 10178-0060 also: 2000 One Logan Sq Philadelphia PA 19103

MACARIO, ALBERTO JUAN LORENZO, physician; b. Naschel, Argentina, Dec. 1, 1935; came to U.S., 1974, naturalized, 1980; s. Alberto Carlos and Maria Elena (Giraudi) M.; MD, Nat. U. Buenos Aires, 1961; m. Everly Conway, Mar. 16, 1963; children: Alex, Everly. Intern, Ramos Mejia Hosp., Buenos Aires, 1958-60, resident 1960; resident Rivadavia Hosp., Buenos Aires, 1961-62, physician-hematologist, 1962-64; fellow NRC Argentina, Buenos Aires, 1964-69; head dept. radioactive isotopes Inst. Hematological Investigations, Nat. Acad. Medicine Argentina, Buenos Aires, 1967-69; Eleanor Roosevelt fellow Internat. Union Against Cancer, Dept. Technology, Karolinska Inst., Stockholm, 1969-71; mem. sci. staff Lab. Cell Biology, NRC Italy, Rome, 1971-73; head Lab. Immunology, Internat. Agy. Rsch. on Cancer, WHO, Lyons, France, 1973-74; research scientist Brown U., Providence, 1974-76, Div. Labs. and Rsch. N.Y. State Dept. Health, Albany, 1976-79; chief hematology Clin. Lab. Center, N.Y. State Dept. Health, Albany, 1979-81, dir. clin. and exptl. immunology sect. Lab. Medicine Inst., 1981-83; rsch. physician, 1981—, Wadsworth Ctr. for Labs. and Rsch. N.Y. State Dept. of Health; prof. Dept. Biomed. Scis. Sch. Pub. Health U. at Albany, 1985—, mem. senate at SUNY Albany, N.Y., 1989-94; adj. prof. pathology and lab. medicine Albany Med. Coll., 1991—; grant reviewer for nat. and internat. agys.; manuscript reviewer for sci. jours. Recipient Diploma de Honor prize Nat. U. Buenos Aires, 1961, Bernardino Rivadavia prize Nat. Acad. Medicine Argentina, 1967, Ciencia e Investigation prize Argentinian Soc. Advancement Sci., 1967; Ford Found.-NAS travel fellow, 1968, Eleanor Roosevelt fellow, 1969. Mem. Scandinavian Soc. Immunology, Italian Assn. Immunologists, French Soc. Immunology, Am. Assn. Immunologists, Am. Soc. Microbiology (sect. editor Manual of Clin. Lab. Immunology 5th edit. 1994—), Am. Soc. Investigative Pathology. Achievements include patents in field; discovered primary myeloperoxidase deficiency in leucocytes; developed method for immunologic identification of bacteria that produce methane gas; discovered antigenic diversity of these bacteria in natural and manufactured ecosystems; described structural topography of methanogenic bacteria and population dynamics in granular microbial consortia; found novel multicellular forms of archaebacteria; isolated for the first time the genes in the dnaK locus from an archaebacterium. Editor multivol. treatise Monoclonal Antibodies Against Bacteria and treatise Gene Probes for Bacteria; contbr. articles to profl. jours., chpts. to books. Office: Empire State Pla/Dept Health Wadsworth Ctr Labs Rsch PO Box 509 Albany NY 12201

MACARTHUR, CAROL JEANNE, pediatric otolaryngology educator; b. Glendale, Calif., Aug. 23, 1957; d. Seth Gerald and Barbara Jeanne (Shaw) MacA.; m. Geoffrey Buncke, Dec. 14, 1990; 1 child, Keith Davis. BS, Occidental Coll., 1979; MD, UCLA, 1984. Diplomate Am. Bd. Otolaryngology. Instr. dept. otolaryngology U. Calif.-Davis, Sacrememto, 1989-90; clin. fellow in otology and laryngology Harvard U. Med. Sch., Boston, 1990-91; asst. prof., dir. pediatric otolaryngology U. Calif., Irvine, 1991—, asst. prof. dept. pediatrics, 1993-95, program dir. dept. otolaryngology-head and neck surgery, 1992-95. Recipient investigator devel. award Am. Acad. Facial Plastic and Reconstructive Surgery, 1993. Fellow ACS, Am. Acad. Pediat.; mem. Assn. Women Surgeons, Soc. for Ear, Nose and Throat Advances in Children, Am. Cleft Palate Craniofacial Assn., Am. Acad. Otorlaryngology-Head and Neck Surgery, Alpha Omega Alpha. Office: U Calif Med Ctr 101 City Dr S Bldg 25 Orange CA 92668

MACARTHUR, JOHN RODERICK C. G. (RICK MACARTHUR), magazine publisher, journalist; b. N.Y.C., June 4, 1956; s. J. Roderick and Christiane (L'Etendart) MacA. BA, Columbia Coll., 1978. Reporter Wall Street Jour., Chgo., summer 1977, Washington Star, 1978, Bergen Record, Hackensack, N.J., 1978-79; Chgo. Sun Times, 1979-82; asst. fgn. editor UPI, N.Y.C., 1982; pres., pub. Harper's Mag., N.Y.C., 1983—. Author: Second Front: Censorship and Propaganda in the Gulf War, 1992. Bd. dirs. Com. to Protect Journalists, Overseas Press Club, Death Penalty Info. Ctr. Fellow N.Y. Inst. Humanities; mem. Econ. Club of N.Y. Office: Harper's Mag 666 Broadway Fl 11 New York NY 10012-2317

MACAT, JULIO, cinematographer. Cinematographer: (films) Home Alone, 1990, Only the Lonely, 1991, Home Alone 2: Lost in New York, 1992, So I

Married an Axe Murderer, 1993, Ace Ventura, Pet Detective, 1994. Office: care Spyros Skouras Sanford Skouras Gross & Assocs 1015 Gayley Ave 3rd Fl Los Angeles CA 90024*

MACAULAY, COLIN ALEXANDER, mining engineer; b. Montreal, Que., Can., Dec. 26, 1931; s. Kenneth Douglas and Eunice S. (Guild) M.; m. Elizabeth Ann Rowsell, Aug. 27, 1955; children: Douglas C., James. R. Robert C. B.Engring. in Mining, McGill U., Montreal, 1954, M.Engring., 1955. Registered profl. engr., Ont. Gen. mgr., dir. Palabora Mining Co., Transvaal, Republic South Africa, 1972-82; dep. chmn., mng. dir., chief exec. Rössing Uranium Ltd., Namibia, 1982-88; pres., chief operating officer Rio Algom Ltd., Toronto, Ont., Can., 1988-91, pres., ceo, 1991—; chmn. bd. dirs. Highland Valley Copper, B.C. Mem. Ont. Mining Assn. (bd. dirs. 1990-91), Mining Assn. Can. (dir.), Can. Inst. Mining and Metallurgy, Assn. Profl. Engrs. Ont. Home: 70 Roxborough Dr, Toronto, ON Canada M4W 1X1 Office: Rio Algom Ltd, 120 Adelaide St W Ste 2600, Toronto, ON Canada M5H 1W5

MACAULAY, DAVID (ALEXANDER), author, illustrator; b. Burton-on-Trent, Eng., Dec. 2, 1946; s. James and Joan (Lowe) M.; m. Janice Elizabeth Michel, 1970 (div.); 1 child, Elizabeth Alexandra; m. Ruth Marris, 1978 (div.); m. Charlotte Valerie. BArch, R.I. Sch. Design, 1969. Instr. interior design R.I. Sch. Design, Providence, 1969-73, instr. two-dimensional design, 1974-76, adj. faculty dept. illustration, 1977-79; tchr. art Central Falls (R.I.) Pub. Schs., 1969-70, Newton, Mass., 1972-74; designer Morris Nathanson Design, 1969-72. Author, illustrator: Cathedral: The Story of Its Construction, 1973 (Caldecott Honor book 1973), City: A Story of Roman Planning and Construction, 1974, Pyramid, 1975 (Christopher medal 1975), Underground, 1976, Castle, 1977 (Caldecott Honor book 1977), Great Moments in Architecture, 1978, Motel of the Mysteries, 1979, Unbuilding, 1980, Electricity, 1983, Mill, 1983, BAAA, 1985, Why the Chicken Crossed the Road, 1987, The Way Things Work, 1988, Black and White, 1990 (Caldecott medal 1991), Ship, 1993, Shortcut, 1995; illustrator: Help! Let Me Out!, 1982, The Amazing Brain, 1984. Recipient Wash. Children's Book Guild award, 1977, AIA medal, 1978. *

MACAULAY, HUGH L., retail company executive; b. Toronto; s. Leopold and Hazel Charlton (Haight) M.; m. Dorothy Jean Taylor, Sept. 11, 1946; children—Barbara, Robert James, Andrew Taylor. B.A. in Journalism, U. Western Ont., 1948. With Pub. & Indsl. Relations Ltd., 1948-52; with Ford Motor Co., 1952-54, Lawrence Motors Ltd., 1954-55; owner York Mills Pontiac Ltd. and York Mills Leasing Ltd., 1955-70; vice chmn. Ont. Hydro, Toronto, 1979, chmn., 1979-83; chmn. Can. Tire Corp. Ltd., Toronto, 1984-94, CEO, 1985-87, also dir. Mem., chmn. bd. Ryerson Poly. Inst., 1964-71; bd. govs. York U.; mem. Commn. on Post-Secondary Edn., 1969-71; chmn. Commn. on Orgn. of Progressive Conservative Party, 1971-76. Served with Royal Can. Naval Vol. Res., 1943-45. Mem. Rosedale Golf Club, John's Island Club (Vero Beach, Fla.), Albany Club. Avocations: boating; golf. Office: Can Tire Corp Ltd/Sta K, 2180 Yonge St Box 770, Toronto, ON Canada M4P 2V8

MACAULAY, LAWRENCE A., Canadian government official; b. St. Peters Bay, Sept. 9, 1946; s. Archibald and Bernadette MacAulay; m. Frances Elaine O'Connell, Aug. 16, 1972; children: Carolyn, Rita, Lynn. Mem. House of Commons, 1988—, apptd. assoc. critic for fisheries and oceans, 1989, apptd. critic for srs. and assoc. critic for fisheries, 1990; sec. of state for vets. Govt. of Can., 1993—; mem. standing com. on forestry and fisheries, caucus com. on health and social devel.; acclaimed chair Atlantic Caucus, 1992. Roman Catholic. Office: Veterans Affairs Can, 161 Grafton St PO Box 7700, Charlottetown, PE Canada C1A 8M9*

MACAULAY, RONALD KERR STEVEN, linguistics educator, former college dean; b. West Kilbride, Ayrshire, Scotland, Nov. 3, 1927; came to U.S., 1965; s. Robert Wilson and Mary Robb (McDermid) M.; m. Janet Grey, July 25, 1956; children: Harvey, Anna. M.A., U. St. Andrews, 1955; Ph.D., UCLA, 1971. Lectr. Brit. Inst., Lisbon, Portugal, 1955-60, Brit Council, Buenos Aires, Argentina, 1960-64; asst. prof. linguistics Pitzer Coll., Claremont, Calif., 1965-67; assoc. prof. Pitzer Coll., 1967-73, prof., 1973—, dean faculty 1980-86. Author: Language, Social Class and Education, 1977, Generally Speaking: How Children Learn Language, 1980, Locating Dialect in Disourse: The Language of Honest Men and Bonnie Lasses in Ayr, 1991, The Social Art: Language and its Uses, 1994; editor: (with R.P. Stockwell) Linguistic Change and Generative Theory, 1972. Home: 317 W 7th St Claremont CA 91711-4312 Office: Pitzer Coll 1050 N Mills Ave Claremont CA 91711-6101

MACAULEY, ROBIE MAYHEW, retired editor; b. Grand Rapids, Mich., May 31, 1919; s. George William and Emma (Hobart) M.; m. Anne Draper, June 19, 1948; m. Pamela Painter, Aug. 9, 1979; 1 child, Cameron. A.B. Kenyon Coll., 1941; M.F.A., U. Iowa, 1950; postgrad. U. London, 1964-65; D.Litt., Kenyon Coll., 1986. Instr. English Bard Coll., 1946-47, U. Iowa, 1947-50; asst. prof. U. N.C., 1950-53; editor Kenyon Rev., 1959-66; sr. editor Playboy mag., Chgo., 1966-77; exec. editor Houghton Mifflin Co., Boston, 1977-88; lectr. State Dept., Australia, 1962; adj. prof. Harvard U. Extension, 1988—; co-dir. Ploughshares Internat. Writing Seminar, Emerson Coll. European Ctr., Kasteel Well Netherlands, 1990—. Author: (novel) The Disguises of Love, 1952, A Secret History of Time to Come, 1979; (short stories) The End of Pity, 1957; co-author: Criticism Technique in Fiction, 1964, rev. edit., 1987, The Seven Basic Quarrels of Marriage, 1991. With AUS, 1942-46. Guggenheim fellow, 1964; Fulbright research fellow, 1964-65; O'Henry Short Story winner, 1967. Mem. PEN. Avocation: Home: PO Box 792 South Wellfleet MA 02663-0792 also: 65 Marlborough St Boston MA 02116

MACAVOY, PAUL WEBSTER, economics educator, university dean; b. Haverhill, Mass., Apr. 21, 1934; s. Paul Everett and Louise Madeline (Webster) MacA.; m. Katherine Ann Manning, June 13, 1955; children: Libby, Matthew. A.B., Bates Coll., 1955, LL.D., 1976; M.A., Yale, 1956, Ph.D. 1960. Asst. to full prof. MIT, Cambridge, Mass., 1963-74, Henry R. Luce prof. pub. policy, 1974-75; mem. Pres.'s Coun. Econ. Advisers, 1975-76; prof. econs. and mgmt. Yale U., 1976-81, Beinecke prof. econs., 1981-83; dean W.E. Simon Grad. Sch. Bus. Admin. U. Rochester, 1983-91; Williams Bros. prof. Yale Sch. Mgmt. Yale U., 1991—, dean Yale Sch. Mgmt., 1992—; bd. dirs. Chase Manhattan Bank Corp., Alumax Inc, Open Environment Corp., Lafarge Corp. Author: Price Formation in Natural Gas Fields, 1962, Economic Strategy for Developing Nuclear Breeder Reactors, 1969, (with Stephen Breyer) Energy Regulation by the Federal Power Commission, 1974, (with R. Pindyck) The Economics of the Natural Gas Shortage, 1975, The Economics and Politics of International Commodity Agreements, 1977, The Regulated Industries and the Economy, 1979, World Crude Oil Prices, 1981, Energy Policy, 1983, Explaining Metals Prices, 1988, Industry Regulation and the Performance of the American Economy, 1992; editor: Ford Administration Papers on Regulatory Reform, 8 vols, 1977-78, Privatization and State-Owned Enterprise: Assessment for the United Kingdom, Canada and the United States, 1988. Home: 420 Humphrey St New Haven CT 06511-3711 Office: Yale Sch Mgmt Box 208200 New Haven CT 06520-8200

MACAVOY, THOMAS COLEMAN, glass manufacturing executive, educator; b. Jamaica, N.Y., Apr. 24, 1928; s. Joseph V. and Edna M. Mac A.; m. Margaret M. Walsh, Dec. 27, 1952; children: Moira Mac Avoy Brown, Ellen Mac Avoy Jennings, Christopher, Neil. B.S. in Chemistry, Queens Coll., 1950; M.S. in Chemistry, St. John's U., 1952, D.Sc. (hon.), 1973; Ph.D. in Chemistry, U. Cin., 1952. Chemist, Charles Pfizer & Co., Bklyn., 1957-60; mgr. electronics research Corning Glass Works, N.Y., 1960-64; dir. phys. research Corning Glass Works, 1964-66, v.p. electronic products div., 1966-69, v.p tech. products div., 1969-71, pres., 1971-83, vice-chmn., 1983-87; prof. mgmt. grad. sch. U. Va., 1988—; bd. dirs. Quaker Oats Co., Chubb Corp., Lubrizol Corp. Patentee in field; contbr. articles to tech. jours. Trustee Corning Mus. Glass; past pres. Boy Scouts Am. With USN, 1946; with USAF, 1952-53. Recipient Silver Antelope award Boy Scouts Am., 1976, Silver Beaver award, 1975, Silver Buffalo award, 1982, Bronze Wolf award, 1988. Roman Catholic. Office: U Va Darden Grad Sch Bus Adminstrn Charlottesville VA 22096

MACBAIN, WILLIAM HALLEY, minister, theology educator, seminary chancellor; b. Cambridge, Ont., Can., Aug. 12, 1916; s. George Alexander and Grace Ann (Wilkins) MacB.; m. Mary Ann Munday, Aug. 20, 1941; children: Grace Elizabeth MacBain Silvester, Constance Marilyn MacBain Parker. Licentiate in Theology, Toronto Baptist Sem., Ont., 1939; DD (hon.), Cen. Bapt. Sem., Toronto, 1962. Ordained to ministry Bapt. Ch., 1940. Pastor, founder Temple Bapt. Ch., Sarnia, Ont., 1937-64; pastor Forward Bapt. Ch., Toronto, 1964-73; dir., gen. sec. Fellowship Fgn. Missions, Toronto, 1973-81; chancellor Cen. Bapt. Sem., 1981-93, Heritage Bapt. Bible Coll. and Theol. Sem., London, Ont., 1993—; pastor emeritus Forward Bapt. Ch., Toronto, 1994—; chmn. Can. Bd. Greater Europe Mission, 1963-73. Mem. Fellowship Evang. Bapt. Chs. in Can. (pres. 1953-54, 83-84). Conservative. Home: 35 Wynford Heights Crescent, Apt 2603, Don Mills, ON Canada M3C 1L1 Office: Heritage Bapt Bible Coll and Theol Sem, 30 Grand Ave, London, ON Canada N6C 1K8

MACBETH, ANGUS, lawyer; b. L.A., May 9, 1942. BA, Yale U., 1964, LLB, 1969. Bar: N.Y. 1970, D.C. 1981. Law clk. to Hon. Harold R. Tyler, Jr. U.S. Dist. Ct. (so. dist.) N.Y., 1969-70, asst. U.S. atty. criminal divsn., 1975-77; chief pollution control sect. Land and Natural Resources Divsn., U.S. Dept. Justice, 1977-79, dep. asst. atty. gen., 1979-81; ptnr. Sidley & Austin, Washington; adj. prof. law N.Y. Law Sch., 1985—; spl. counsel Wartime Relocation and Internment Civilians Commn., 1981-83. Mem. D.C. Bar (steering com. energy and natural resources divsn. 1982-84), N.Y. State Bar Assn. (exec. com. sect. environ. law 1981—)., Phi Beta Kappa. Office: Sidley & Austin 1722 I St NW Washington DC 20006-3705

MACBRIDE, THOMAS JAMISON, federal judge; b. Sacramento, Mar. 25, 1914; s. Frank and Lotta Kirtley (Little) MacB.; m. Martha Harrold, Nov. 7, 1947; children—Peter, Thomas Jamison, David, Laurie. A.B., U. Calif. at Berkeley, 1936, J.D., 1940. Bar: Calif. 1940. Dep. atty. gen. Calif., 1941-42; pvt. practice Sacramento, 1946-61; U.S. dist. judge Eastern Dist. Calif., Sacramento, 1961-67; chief judge Eastern Dist. Calif., 1967-79, sr. judge, 1979—. Mem. U.S. Temporary Emergency Ct. Appeals, 1982-87; mem. Criminal Justice Act Com., U.S. Jud. Conf., 1969-88; mem. U.S. Jud. Conf., 1975-78; chmn. Criminal Justice Act Com. of U.S. Jud. Conf., 1979-88; mem. U.S. Fgn. Intelligence Surveillance Ct., 1979-80. Pres. Town Hall, Sacramento, 1952, N.E. area YMCA, 1960; mem. Calif. Legislature from Sacramento County, 1955-60 mem. Nat. Commn. on Reform Fed. Criminal Laws, 1967-71; bd. dirs. Sacramento YMCA; trustee U. Calif., San Francisco Found., 1982—; bd. dirs. Sacramento Regional Found., 1988—; founding dir. League to Save Lake Tahoe, 1965. Lt. USNR., 1942-46. Mem. ABA, U. Calif. Alumni Assn. (v.p. 1955, 60), Mason (33 deg., Shriner, Jester), Rotarian (pres. 1966-67), Sutter Club, Univ. (pres. 1951-52), Comstock (pres. 1975-76), Senator Outing (sec.-treas.), Kappa Sigma, Phi Delta Phi. Democrat. Office: US Dist Ct US Courthouse 650 Capitol Mall Sacramento CA 95814-4708

MACBURNEY, EDWARD HARDING, bishop; b. Albany, N.Y., Oct. 30, 1927; s. Alfred Cadwell and F. Marion (McDowell) MacB.; m. Anne Farnsworth, Feb. 20, 1965; W. Norton Grubb, Page F. Grubb, James S. Grubb. AB, Darmouth Coll., 1949; STB, Berkeley Divinity Sch., 1952; HHD (hon.), St. Ambrose U., 1987; DD (hon.), Nashotah House, 1988. Ordained to ministry Episcopal Ch. as deacon, 1952, as priest, 1952, as bishop, 1988. Asst. St. Thomas' Ch., Hanover, N.H. 1953-63, rector, 1963-73; dean Trinity Cathedral, Davenport, Iowa, 1973-87; bishop Diocese of Quincy, Peoria, Ill., 1988—. Trustee Berkeley Divinity Sch., New Haven, 1964-70, St. Luke's Hosp., Davenport, 1973-87, Nat. Orgn. Episcopalians for Life, Fairfax, 1991—, Nashotah House, 1991—; v.p Episcopal Synod Am., Ft. Worth, 1988—; mem. panel White House Fellowships, St. Louis, 1976-84; bd. dirs. Noel, 1991—. Democrat. Office: Diocese of Quincy 3601 N North St Peoria IL 61604

MACCALLUM, ROBERT KENNETH, lawyer; b. Saint John, Can., Feb. 11, 1955; came to U.S., 1986; s. John Duncan and Shirley Constance (Wills) MacC.; m. Theresa A. Boyle, Oct. 22, 1982' 1 child, Lauren C. BBA, U. New Brunswick, Can., 1977, LLB, 1979; LLM, Columbia U., 1986. Bar: New Brunswick 1979, N.Y. 1987. Assoc. Gilbert, McGloan, Gillis, Saint John, 1979-86, Cadwalader, Wickersham & Taft, N.Y.C., 1987-88, Milbank, Tweed, Hadley & McCloy, N.Y.C., 1988—. Contbr. articles to profl jours. Lord Beaverbrook scholar U. New Brunswick, 1976, 77, 78. Mem. ABA, Can. Bar. Assn., N.Y. State Bar Assn. Office: Milbank Tweed Hadley McCloy 1 Chase Manhattan Plz New York NY 10005-1401

MACCARTHY, JOHN PETERS, banker; b. St. Louis, Apr. 6, 1933; s. John D. and Ruth (Peters) MacC.; m. Talbot Leland June 21, 1958; children: John Leland, Talbot Peters. B.A., Princeton U., 1954; LL.B., Harvard U., 1959. Bar: Mo. 1959. Ptnr. Bryan, Cave, McPheeters & McRoberts, St. Louis, 1959-68; sec. Centerre Trust Co., St. Louis, 1969-72, exec. v.p., dir., 1972-75, pres., chief operating officer, 1975-79; chief exec. officer Centerre Trust Co., St. Louis, 1979-84; dir. Centerre Trust Co., St. Louis, 1979-88; pres., chief exec. officer Centerre Bank Nat. Assn., St. Louis, 1984-88; chmn., chief exec. officer Boatmen's Trust Co., St. Louis, 1988—; vice chmn., sec. Centerre Bancorp, 1983-88; vice chmn. Boatmen's Bancshares, Inc., 1988—; dir. Union Electric Co., St. Louis. Pres. bd. trustees St. Louis Country Day Sch., 1977-79; trustee Washington U.; pres. emeritus, trustee St. Louis Art Mus., 1981—. Lt. USN, 1954-56. Mem. St. Louis Country Club (pres. 1982-84), Bogey Club (pres. 1986-87), Noonday Club (pres. 1977). Republican. Episcopalian. Office: Boatmen's Trust Co PO Box 14737 Saint Louis MO 63178-4737

MACCARTHY, TALBOT LELAND, civic volunteer; b. St. Louis, Jan. 28, 1936; d. Austin Porter Leland and Dorothy (Lund) Follansbee; m. John Peters MacCarthy, June 21, 1958; children: John Leland MacCarthy, Talbot MacCarthy Payne. BA, Vassar Coll., 1958. Sec., treas. Station List Pub. Co., St. Louis, 1975-85, pres., 1985-90. Trustee Robert E. Lee Meml. Assn. Arts and Edn. Coun. Greater St. Louis, pres., 1978-80, emerita; trustee St. Louis Art Mus.; past trustee St. Louis Mercantile Libr. Assn., Family & Children's Svc. Greater St. Louis, Health and Welfare Coun. Greater St. Louis, Jr. Kindergarten St. Louis Page Park YMCA, Scholarship Found. St. Louis, Friends St. Louis Art Mus. Bd., St. Louis St. Michael and St. George Sch. Bd.; chmn. Mo. Arts Coun., 1980-85; past chmn. Vol. Action Ctr. Greater St. Louis, ; past vice chmn. bd. dirs. Mary Inst.; past pres. Jr. League St. Louis; mem. Nat. Coun. Arts, 1985-91. Recipient Woman of Achievement citation St. Louis Globe Democrat, 1979, Mo. Citizens for Arts/Arts Advocacy award, 1987, Mo. Arts Award, 1993. Mem. Vassar Club St. Louis (past pres.), Mary Inst. Alumnae Assn. (past pres.), Colonial Dames Am., Garden Club St. Louis. Republican. Episcopalian. Avocations: tennis, visual arts, performing arts.

MACCARTHY, TERENCE FRANCIS, lawyer; b. Chgo., Feb. 5, 1934; s. Frank E. and Catherine (McIntyre) MacC.; m. Marian Fulton, Nov. 25, 1961; children—Daniel Fulton, Sean Patrick, Terence Fulton, Megan Catherine. B.A. in Philosophy, St. Jospeh's Coll., 1955; J.D., DePaul U., 1960. Bar: Ill. 1960, U.S. Dist. Ct. (no. dist.) Ill. 1960, U.S. Ct. Appeals (7th cir.) 1961, U.S. Supreme Ct. 1966. Assoc. prof. law Chase Coll. Law, Cin., 1960-61; law clk. to chief judge U.S. Dist. Ct., 1961-66; spl. asst. atty. gen. Ill., 1965-67; exec. dir. Fed. Defender Program, U.S. Dist. Ct. (no. dist.) Ill., Chgo., 1966—; mem. nat. adv. com. on criminal rules; 7th cir. criminal jury instrn. com.; chmn. Nat. Defender Com.; chmn. bd. regents Nat. Coll. Criminal Def.; faculty Fed. Jud. Ctr., Nat. Coll. Criminal Def., Nat. Trial Advocacy, U. Va. Trial Advocacy Inst., Harvard Law Sch. Trial Advocacy Program, Western Trial Advocacy Inst., Northwestern U. U. Ill. Defender Trial Advocacy course, Loyola U. Trial Advocacy Program; lectr. in field. Contbr. articles on criminal law to profl. jours. Bd. dirs. U.S.O. Served as 1st lt. USMC, 1955-57. Recipient Nat. Legal Aid and Defender Assn./ABA Reginald Heber Smith award, 1986, Alumni Merit award St. Joseph Coll., 1970, Cert. of Distinction USO, 1977, Harrison Tweed Spl. Merit award Am. Law Inst./ABA, 1987, Bill of Rights award Ga. chpt. ACLU, 1986, William J. Brennan award U. Va., 1989, Alumni Svc. award DePaul U. Coll. Law, 1994, Am. Significant Contbns. award Calif. Attys. for Criminal Justice; named to Outstanding Young Men of Am., 1970. Mem. ABA (past chmn. criminal justice sect., ho. of dels.), Ill. Bar Assn., Chgo. Bar Assn., 7th Cir. Bar Assn., Nat. Assn. Criminal Def. Lawyers (Disting. Svc. award 1993), Nat. Legal Aid and Defender Assn., Nat. coll. Criminal Def. (chair), Union League of Chgo. (pres.). Democrat. Roman Catholic. Office: US Dist Ct No Dist Ill 219 S Dearborn St Ste 1142 Chicago IL 60604-1705

MACCARTY, COLLIN S., neurosurgeon; b. Rochester, Minn., Sept. 20, 1915; s. W.C. MacCarty; married; 3 children. AB, Dartmouth Coll., 1937; MD, Johns Hopkins U., Balt., 1940; MS in Neurosurgery, U. Minn., 1944. Diplomate Am. Bd. Neurol. Surgery. Surg. house officer Johns Hopkins Hosp., Balt., 1940-41; fellow in neurosurgery Mayo Found., Rochester, 1944; instr. neurol. surgery on grad. faculty U. Minn., Rochester, 1947-53, asst. prof., 1953-57, assoc. prof., 1957-61, prof., 1961-73; prof. Mayo Med. Sch./U. Minn., Rochester, 1973-80, assoc. prof. and emeritus, 1975-77, dir., 1977-80, prof. emeritus, 1980—; mem. neurosurg. staff Mayo Clinic, Rochester, 1946-75, sr. cons., 1975, chmn. med. staff, 1965-66; sec. for congress affairs World Fedn. Neurosurg. Socs., 1965-69, chmn. program com., mem. liaison com., mem. adminstrv. coun.; adv. com. to dean Dartmouth Med. Sch., 1968-72, bd. overseers, 1973—; chmn. bd., 1977-79; adv. bd. Bur. of Medicine and Surgery, Dept. of Navy, 1970; nat. cons. in neurosurgery Air Force, Wilford Hall Hosp., Lackland AFB, Tex., 1971; cons. in neursurgery to Surgeon Gen., USN, 1977-80; vis. prof. neurosurgery Western Res. U., Cleve., 1966, Johns Hopkins U., 1969, U. Okla., 1971, Ohio State U., 1977, U. Tex., 1979; Caldwell lectr. Am. Roentgen Ray Soc., 1974; Elsberg lectr. N.Y. Soc. Neurol. Surgery, 1981. Author: (monograph) The Surgical Treatment of Intracranial Meningiomas, 1961; co-author: Primary Intramedullary Tumors of the Spinal Cord and Filum Terminale, 1964; contbr. over 158 articles to various med. jours. With USN, 1944-46. Mem. AMA (residency rev. com., sect. on med. edn. 1967-72), ACS, Am. Assn. Neurol. Surgeons (v.p. 1965, pres. 1970, bd. dirs. 1965-73, del. to World Fedn. 1973-77), Neurosurg. Soc. of Am. (v.p. 1954, pres. 1959, rep. to AANS bd. dirs. 1965-69), Minn. Med. Assn., Zumbro Valley Med. Soc., Minn. Soc. Neurol. Scis., Soc. Neurol. Surgeons, So. Minn. Med. Assn., Minn. Neurosurg. Soc., Found. for Internat. Edn. in Neurol. Surgery, Inc., Societa Italiana de Neurochirurgia (corr. mem.), Egyptian Soc. Neurol. Surgeons (hon.), Japan Soc. Neurol. Surgeons (hon.), Internat. Travellers Club, Neurosurg. Travel Club, Sigma Xi (chpt. pres. 1979-80). Home: Hc 60 Box 71a Cable WI 54821-9510

MACCAULEY, HUGH BOURNONVILLE, banker; b. Mt. Vernon, N.Y., Mar. 12, 1922; s. Morris Baker and Alma (Gardiner) MacC.; m. Rachael Gleaton, Aug. 30, 1943 (div. May 1980); m. Felice Cooper, Dec. 2, 1980. Student, Rutgers U., 1939-41, Tex. Christian U., 1948-50, U. Omaha, 1957-59. With 102nd Cavalry, Essex Troop N.J. Nat. Guard, 1940-42; commd. 2d lt. U.S. Army, 1943; advanced through grades to col. U.S. Army, USAF, Washington, 1943-73; v.p. Great Am. Securities, San Bernardino, Calif., 1979-94; chmn. bd. Desert Community Bank, Victorville, Calif., 1980—; account exec. Gorian Thornes, Inc., San Bernardino, Calif., 1995—. bd. dirs. Air Force Village West, 1986-88; chmn. bd. and CEO Gen. and Mrs. Curtis E. Lemay Found., 1987—. Decorated Air medal, Legion of Merit. Mem. Daedalian Soc., Rotary. Republican. Presbyterian. Avocation: golf. Home: 1630 Monroe St Riverside CA 92504-5539 Office: Gorian Thornes Inc Ste 103 350 W 5th St San Bernardino CA 92402 *Personal philosophy: Whatever the game play by the rules.*

MACCHIAROLA, FRANK JOSEPH, political science, business and law educator; b. N.Y.C., Apr. 7, 1941; s. Joseph John and Lucy (Bernardo) M.; m. Mary Teresa Collins, June 13, 1970; children: Joseph John, Michael Collins, Frank Joseph. B.A. St. Francis Coll., 1962, L.H.D. (hon.), 1981; LL.B., Columbia U., 1965, Ph.D., 1970; L.H.D. (hon.), Coll. S.I., 1983; LL.D. (hon.), Dominican Coll., 1983, Manhattan Coll., 1983. From fellow to prof. polit. sci. CUNY, 1964-83, v.p., 1977-78; asst. v.p. Columbia U., N.Y.C., 1973-74; dep. dir. N.Y. State Emergency Fin. Control Bd. for N.Y.C., 1976-77; chancellor of schs. N.Y.C. Public Sch. System, 1978-83; pres., chief exec. officer N.Y.C. Partnership, Inc., 1983-87; pres. Acad. of Polit. Sci., 1987-91; prof. bus. Columbia U., N.Y.C., 1987-91; dean Benjamin N. Cardozo Sch. of Law, Yeshiva U., N.Y.C., 1991—; of counsel Newman, Tannenbaum, Helpern, Syracuse and Hirschtritt, N.Y.C.; bd. dirs. Jeffries Group Inc.; trustee Manville Personal Injury Settlement Trust. Mem., pres. Community Sch. Bd. 22, N.Y.C., 1973-78; mem., vice chmn. bd. trustees St. Joseph's Coll., 1977—. Decorated cavalieri Order of Merit Italy; recipient cert. of merit Dirigible Soc. Am., 1976. Democrat. Roman Catholic. Office: 900 3rd Ave New York NY 10022-4728 also: 55 Fifth Ave New York NY 10003

MACCINI, LOUIS JOHN, economic educator; b. Cambridge, Mass., Aug. 3, 1942; s. Joseph and Jennie (Leccacorvi) M.; m. Carol Monterisi, June 25, 1965; children: Michael S., Sharon L. BS in Economics, Boston Coll., 1965; PhD in Economics, Northwestern U., 1970. From asst. prof. to assoc. prof. economics The Johns Hopkins U., Balt., 1969-86, prof., 1986—, chair, 1992—; ad hoc com. mem. graduate fin. aid, Johns Hopkins U., editorial bd., public interest investment adv. com., law sch. com., med. sch. com., and other coms.; mem. recruiting chair dept. grad. student advisor dept., and other depts. Referee Am. Econ. Review, Jour. Econ. Dynamics and Control, Oxford Econ. Papers, and others; contbr. articles to profl. jours. Grantee NSF. Mem. Am. Econ. Assn., The Econometric Soc., Internat Soc. Inventory Rsch. Office: Johns Hopkins U 3400 N Charles St Baltimore MD 21218-2685

MACCLUGGAGE, REID, newspaper editor, publisher; b. Norwich, Conn., Oct. 18, 1938; s. Everett Reid and Edith Kathryn (Bowen) MacC.; m. Joellen Thompson, Mar. 29, 1965 (div. 1980); children: Stewart Reid, Scot Thompson; m. Linda Howell, May 30, 1981; 1 dau., Katherine Elizabeth. B.A., U. Hartford, 1962. Asst. state editor Hartford (Conn.) Courant, 1965-69, state editor, 1969-74, asst. mng. editor, 1974-82, mng. editor, 1982-84; editor, pub. New London (Conn.) Day, 1984—; bd. dirs. Day Pub. Co.; juror Pulitzer Prize. Trustee Day Trust, Dr. Martin Luther King Meml. Scholarship Trust Fund, Pine Point Sch.; commr. New London Pier Dist.; founder Bodenwein Fellowship for Minorities; incorporator Lawrence and Meml. Hosp. Recipient Disting. Alumnus award U. Hartford, 1983. Mem. AP Mng. Editors Assn. (bd. dirs.). Office: The Day Pub Co 47 Eugene O'Neil Dr PO Box 1231 New London CT 06320

MACCOBY, ELEANOR EMMONS, psychology educator; b. Tacoma, May 15, 1917; d. Harry Eugene and Viva May (Johnson) Emmons; m. Nathan Maccoby, Sept. 16, 1938 (dec. Apr. 1992); children: Janice Maccoby Carmichael, Sarah Maccoby Bellina, Mark. BS, U Wash., 1939; MA, U. Mich., 1949, PhD, 1950. Study dir. div. program surveys USDA, Washington, 1942-46; study dir. Survey Rsch. Ctr. U. Mich., Ann Arbor, 1946-48; lectr., rsch. assoc. dept. social rels. Harvard U., Cambridge, Mass., 1950-58; from assoc. to full prof. Stanford (Calif.) U., 1958-87, chmn. dept. psychology, 1973-76, prof. emeritus, 1987—; elected Nat. Acad. of Sci., 1993. Author: (with R. Sears and H. Levin) Patterns of Child-Rearing, 1957, (with Carol Jacklin) Psychology of Sex Differences, 1974, Social Development, 1980, (with R.H. Mnookin) Dividing the Child: Social and Legal Dilemmas of Custody, 1992; editor: (with Newcomb and Hartley) Readings in Social Psychology, 1957, The Development of Sex Differences, 1966. Co-chair Carnegie Task Force on Meeting Needs of Children. Recipient Gores award for Excellence in Teaching Stanford U., 1981, Disting. Contbn. to Edn1. Research award Am. Ednl. Research Assn., 1984, Disting. Sci. Contbn. to Child Devel. award Soc. for Research in Child Devel., 1987, Disting. Sci. Contbns. award Am. Psychol. Assn., 1988; named to Barbara Kimball Browning professorship Stanford U., 1979—. Fellow Soc. for Rsch. in Child Devel. (pres. 1981-83, mem. governing coun. 1963-66), Am. Psychol. Assn. (divsn. 7 pres. 1971-72, G. Stanley Hall award 1982), Am. Psychol. Soc.; mem. NAS, Western Psychol. Assn. (pres. 1974-75), Inst. for Rsch. on Women and Gender, Social Sci. Rsch. Coun. (chmn. 1984-85), Carnegie Coun. on Adolescence, Inst. Medicine, Am. Acad. Arts and Scis. Democrat. Avocations: tennis, vocal music. Home: 729 Mayfield Ave Palo Alto CA 94305-1016 Office: Stanford U Dept Psychology Stanford CA 94305-2130

MACCOMBIE, BRUCE FRANKLIN, composer, college administrator; b. Providence, Dec. 5, 1943; s. Franklin S. and Florence (Corbishley) MacC.; m. Frances Holliday, Sept. 4, 1965 (div. 1970); m. Turi Gundersen, Mar. 10, 1979; 1 child, Juliana. BA, U. Mass., 1967, M of Music, 1968, DFA (hon.), 1986; PhD, U. Iowa, 1971. Assoc. prof. Yale U., New Haven, 1975-80; v.p. G. Schirmer Mus. Publs., N.Y.C., 1980-85; dean, provost The Juilliard Sch., N.Y.C., 1986-92; dean Sch. for Arts Boston U., 1992—. Composer numerous musical works. Recipient Goddard Lieberson award Am. Acad. Inst. Arts and Letters, N.Y.C., 1979. Mem. Coll. Music Soc., Charles Ives Soc. (bd. dirs.). Office: Boston U Sch for Arts 855 Commonwealth Ave Boston MA 02215

MACCONKEY, DOROTHY I., academic administrator; b. New Brunswick, N.J.; d. Donald Thurston and Dorothy Bennett (Hill) Ingling; m. Joseph W. MacConkey, June 19, 1949 (dec. Aug. 1975); children: Donald Franklin, Diane Margaret, Dorothy Frances; m. Karl Schmeidler, May 26, 1994. BA, Beaver Coll., 1947; MA, Wichita State U., 1953; PhD, U. Md., 1974; LLD (hon.), Beaver Coll., 1988. Lectr. Wichita (Kans.) State U., 1950-51; rsch.-campaign assoc. United Fund and Council, Wichita, 1951-62; rsch.- com coordination Health and Welfare Council of Nat. Capital Area, Washington, 1963-65; exec. dir. multi-program agy. Prince Georges County Assn. for Retarded Children, Hyattsville, Md., 1965-66; prof. George Mason U., Fairfax, Va., 1966-76, asst. vice pres., acting dean, 1976-82; v.p., dean of coll. Hiram (Ohio) Coll., 1982-85; pres. Davis & Elkins (W.Va.) Coll., 1985—; bd. dirs. Davis Trust Co., Elkins, 1987—; adv. bd. George Mason U. Found., Fairfax, 1976—; trustee Beaver Coll., Glenside, Pa., 1971-87; cons., evaluator North Cen. Assn., Chgo., 1985—, commr., 1993—; mem. exec. com., pres. Assn. Presbyn. Colls. and Univs.; mem. bd. Svc. Opportunity Colls., Presbyn. Found., trustee, 1993—. Pres. County Chasers of Am., 1985—. Recipient Citizen award for service to handicapped, Fairfax County, 1981, Goddin Women Alumni award, 1985, Woman of Yr. in Edn. award W.Va. Fedn. Women's Clubs, 1986. Mem. Coun. of Pres.', Nat. Assn. Intercollegiate Athletics, Coun. Ind. Colls. (bd. dirs.). Office: Davis and Elkins Coll Office of Pres 100 Campus Dr Elkins WV 26241-3996

MACCORMACK, CHARLES FREDERICK, academic administrator; b. Oct. 27, 1941; married; two children. AB, Middlebury Coll., 1963, EdD (hon.), 1982; MIA, Columbia U., 1965, PhD, 1974. Staff assoc. internat. div. First Nat. City Bank, Caracas, Venezuela, 1964; instr. latin-Am. politics U. N.H., Durham, 1967; asst. to dean Internat. Fellows Program Columbia U., N.Y.C., 1967-68; rsch. fellow fgn. policy studies Brookings Instn., Washington, 1969-70; dir. internat. career tng. program Experiment Internat. Living, Brattleboro, Vt., 1970-74; v.p. programs Save the Children Fedn./ Community Devel. Found., Westport, Conn., 1974-77; pres. The Experiment Internat. Living/Sch. for Internat. Tng., Brattleboro, 1977—; bd. dirs. Arthur D. Little Mgmt. Edn. Inst., Ptnrs. Internat. Edn. and Tng., Am. Forum for Global Edn., Landmark Coll. Mng. editor Jour. Internat. Affairs. Mem. founding com. U., 1971-72, Vt. Commn. Edn. and the Econ. Future, 1982, coun. advisors Peace Corps Future Team, 1987, Coun. Fgn. Rels., N.Y.C., global awareness adv. bd. Wheaton Coll., Norton, Mass.; mem. exec. com., chair devel. assistance com., co-chair com. refugee svcs. Am. Coun. Voluntary Internat. Action. Universidad Cen. de Venezuela Fulbright fellow, Caracas, Venezuela, 1965-66, Universidad Nacional Autonoma de Mexico NSF fellow, Mexico City, 1968-69, Edward John Noble Leadership fellow, 1963-65; Gould scholar, Middlebury scholar, Travelli scholar, 1959-63. Home: 95 North St Easton CT 06612-1039 Office: The Experiment Internat Living Kipling Rd Brattleboro VT 05301

MACCRACKEN, MARY JO, physical education educator; b. Akron, Ohio, Oct. 6, 1943; d. Joel Milton and Mary Ellen (Frame) Weaver; m. Alan Lemuel MacCracken Jr., Aug. 23, 1969; 1 child, Alan Lemuel III. BA, Coll. of Wooster, 1965; MA, U. Akron, 1969; PhD, Kent State U., 1980. Tchr., coach Hudson (Ohio) Pub. Schs., 1965-68; instr. U. Akron, 1968-78, asst. prof., then assoc. prof., 1978-88, prof., 1988—; dir. Motor Behavior Lab., 1986—; collaboration tchr. Ritzman Sch., Akron, 1978-93, Mason Sch., Akron, 1978-93, St. Martha's Sch., Akron, 1993-94, Our Lady of Elms, 1994—; presenter at profl. confs. Contbr. articles to refereed jours. Sunday sch. tchr. Christ Ch. Episcopal, Hudson, 1979-92; vol. Liltin' Leaguers, Jt. League Cleve., 1979-93; faculty mentor Akron High Sch. Drop-Out program, 1989. Grantee Ohio Bd. Regents, 1987-92. Mem. AAHPERD (v.p. health Midwest dist. 1990-92; meritorious honor award Ohio assn. 1988), Am. Psychol. Assn., N.Am. Soc. for Psychology of Sport and Phys. Activity, Nat. Assn. Phys. Edn. in Higher Edn. (sec.), Delta Kappa Gamma (Annie Webb Blanton award 1980). Republican. Avocations: antiques, genealogy, tennis, golf, sailing. Home: Box 631 431 N Main St Hudson OH 44236-2247 Office: U Akron Motor Behavior Lab MH 81 Akron OH 44325-5103

MACCRACKEN, PETER JAMES, marketing executive, communications executive; b. Trieste, Italy, Dec. 27, 1952; came to U.S., 1956; s. James and Kirsten (Koch) MacC. BA summa cum laude, Albion Coll., 1975; MA, U. Calif., Santa Barbara, 1978. Asst. mgr. GranTree Furniture Rental, San Leandro, Calif., 1979-81; freelance writer San Diego, 1981-82; corp. editor Scripps Meml. Hosps., La Jolla, Calif., 1982-84; sr. v.p. Berkman & Daniels Mktg., San Diego, 1984-89; v.p. Stoorza, Zeigaus & Metzger, Inc., San Diego, 1989-90; pres. MacCracken & McGaugh, San Diego, 1990—. Contbr. over 500 articles, photographs to numerous pubs. Recipient 30 bus. comm. awards. Mem. Pub. Rels. Soc. Am. (bd. dirs. 1992—, pres. elect San Diego chpt. 1995), Internat. Assn. Bus. Communicators (pres. San Diego chpt. 1985), Am. Inst. Wine & Food (bd. dirs. 1990—, sec. San Diego chpt. 1995), Phi Beta Kappa. Democrat. Avocations: wines, science fiction, fiction, music. Office: 701 B St Ste 2200 San Diego CA 92101-8111

MACCRATE, ROBERT, lawyer; b. Bklyn., July 18, 1921; s. John and Flora (MacNicholl) MacC.; m. Constance Trapp, May 4, 1946; children: Christopher Robert, Barbara Constance MacCrate Gatti, Thomas John. BA, Haverford Coll., 1943, LLD (hon.), 1987; LLB, Harvard U., 1948; LLD (hon.), Union U., 1986, Dickinson Sch. of Law, 1987, William Mitchell Coll. Law, 1994. Bar: N.Y. 1949, U.S. Supreme Ct. 1955, D.C. 1965. Assoc. Sullivan & Cromwell, N.Y.C., 1948-51, 51-55, ptnr., 1956-59, 62-91, ret. 1991; law sec. N.Y.Appelate Div. Presiding Justice David W. Peck, 1951; counsel N.Y. Gov. Nelson A. Rockefeller, 1959-62; spl. counsel U.S. Army for Investigation Mylai incident, 1969-70; counsel N.Y. State Ct. on Judiciary, 1971; mem. jud. selection com. for fed. judgeships Senator Jacob K. Javits, 1972-80; mem. jud. nominating com. N.Y. 2d Jud. Dept., 1975-82; trustee Lawyers Com. for Civil Rights Under Law, 1976—; chmn. emeritus Fund for Modern Cts., 1978—; cons. N.Y. Profl. Edn. Project, 1994—. Co-author: Appellate Justice in New York, 1982, Legal Education and Professional Development—an Educational Continuum, 1992; contbr. articles to profl. jours. Bd. mgrs. Haverford Coll., 1971-85, emeritus 1986—. Lt. USNR, 1943-46. Recipient Justice System Improvement award Coun. for Ct. Excellence, 1988, Gold medal Nat. Inst. Social Scis., 1989. Fellow Am. Bar Found. (chmn. N.Y. state 1973-80, bd. dirs. 1989—, sec. 1992-94, v.p. 1994—); mem. ABA (pres. 1987-88, del. 1972-78, 89—, N.Y. State del. 1979-81, bd. govs. 1981-84, 86-89, chair task force law schs. and the profession 1989-92, chair spl. adv. com. internat. activities 1988-89, 2d cir. mem. standing com. on fed. judiciary 1984-86, mem. commn. on opportunities in profession 1993—), N.Y. State Bar Assn. (pres. 1972-73, del. 1972—), Assn. of Bar of City of N.Y. (v.p. 1969-71, chmn. exec. com 1968-69, chmn. libr. com 1977-80, chmn. 2d century com. 1989-92), Bar Assn. Nassau County, D.C. Bar Assn., N.Y. County Lawyers Assn. (Disting. Svc. award 1991), Nat. Bar Assn., Am. Coll. Trial Lawyers, Am. Soc. Internat. Law (exec. coun. 1975-80), Union Internationale des Avocats, Acad. Polit. Sci. (bd. dirs. 1975-94), Am. Judicature Soc. (pres. 1979-81, bd. dirs. and mem. exec. com. 1974-83, Justice award 1989), Practising Law Inst. (trustee and mem. exec. com. 1972-95, Seligson award 1995), Am. Law Inst. (exec. com. coun. 1975—, ABA com. on continuing profl. edn. 1994—, chair subcom. on future 1994—), N.Y. Bar Found. (pres. 1976-91), Phi Beta Kappa. Home: 40 The Terrace Plandome NY 11030-1349 Office: Sullivan & Cromwell 250 Park Ave Rm 1610 New York NY 10177-0021

MAC CRAWFORD, EDWIN, health facility administrator. Pres., ceo, coo Charter Medical Corp., Macon, Ga. Office: Charter Medical Corporation 577 Mulberry St Macon GA 31298

MAC CREADY, PAUL BEATTIE, aeronautical engineer; b. New Haven, Sept. 29, 1925. BS in Physics, Yale U., 1947; MS, Calif. Inst. Tech., 1948, PhD in Aeros. cum laude, 1952. Founder, pres. Meteorology Research Inc., 1951-70, Atmospheric Research Group, 1958-70; founder, 1971, chief exec. officer, chmn. AeroVironment Inc., Pasadena, Calif.; leader team that developed Gossamer Albatross for human-powered flight across English Channel, 1979, Solar Challenger, ultralight aircraft powered by solar cells, 1981, GM-Sunrayocr, 1987, GM-Impact, 1990; cons. in field, 1951—; mem. numerous govt. tech. adv. coms. Author research papers in field. Recipient Collier trophy Nat. Aero. Assn., 1979, Edward Longsreth medal Franklin Inst., 1979, Gold Air medal Fedn. Aero. Internat., 1981; Inventor of Yr. award Assn. Advancement Innovation and Invention, 1981; named Engr. of Century ASME, 1980. Mem. AIAA (Reed Aero. award 1979), Nat. Acad. Engring., Am. Acad. Arts and Scis., Am. Meteorol. Soc. (chmn. com.

atmospheric measurements 1968-69, councillor 1971-74). Office: AerOvironment Inc 222 E Huntington Dr Ste 200 Monrovia CA 91016-3500*

MACCRIMMON, KENNETH ROBERT, management educator; b. Hamilton, Ont., Can., Dec. 28, 1937; s. Archibald Robert and Dorothy Anna (Williams) MacC.; m. Marilyn L. Turner, Feb. 3, 1962; children: Karyn, Keith, Brian. B.S., UCLA, 1959, M.B.A., 1960, Ph.D., 1965. Asst. prof. bus. adminstrn. Carnegie-Mellon U., 1964-68, asso. prof., 1968-70; prof. bus. adminstrn. U. B.C. (Can.), Vancouver, 1970-81; E.D. MacPhee prof. mgmt., 1981—; asst. dean grad. studies, 1978-79; J.L. Kellogg Disting. Prof. strategy and decision Northwestern U., Chgo., 1980-82; cons. to industry and govt.; vis. prof. econs. and psychology U. Calif., Santa Barbara, 1985; vis. prof. mgmt. Shanghai Jiao Tong U., China, 1985; Social Scis. and Humanities Research Council sabbatical leave fellow, 1975-76, 83-84; mem. adv. panel NSF, 1988-91. Co-author: Taking Risks, 1986. Contbr. articles on mgmt., econs, and psychology to acad. and profl. publs.; mem. editorial bd. Jour. Behavioral Decision Making, 1991—, Jour. Risk and Uncertainty, 1987-92. Social Scis. and Humanities research grantee, 1972-85, 88—. Mem. Econometric Soc., Am. Econ. Assn., Ops. Research Soc., Instl. Mgmt. Scis., Can. Assn. Univ. Tchrs. Office: U BC, Faculty of Commerce, Vancouver, BC Canada V6T 1Z2

MACCRINDLE, ROBERT ALEXANDER, lawyer; b. Glasgow, Scotland, Jan. 27, 1928; s. Fergus Robertson and Jean (Hill) MacC.; m. Pauline Dilys, Aug. 18, 1959; children: Guy Stephen, Claire. LLB, U. London, 1948; LLM, U. Cambridge, 1952. Called to Bar Eng. and Wales, 1952; created Queen's Counsel, 1963; bar: Hong Kong 1965; conseil juridique France, 1978-91. Barrister Temple, London, 1952-76; Bencher Gray's Inn, London, 1969—; ptnr. Shearman & Sterling, N.Y.C., 1976-94, of counsel, 1995—; avocat au Barreau de Paris, 1991—. Flight lt. RAF, 1948-50. Fellow Am. Coll. Trial Lawyers. Club: University (N.Y.C.). Avocation: golf. Home: 88 Ave de Breteuil, Paris 75015, France also: Shearman & Sterling 599 Lexington Ave & 53d St New York NY 10022

MACCUBBIN, ROBERT PURKS, literature and culture educator; b. Balt., Oct. 30, 1939; s. Walter Aubrey and Mary Anna (Purks) M.; 1 child, Gwyneth Marie Gang; m. Martha J. Hamilton-Phillips, Sept., 1986; children: Charles Aubrey Phillips, Glencora Alison. BA in Biology, Johns Hopkins U., 1961; MA in English, U. Ill., 1962, PhD in English, 1968. From asst. prof. to prof. Coll. William and Mary, Williamsburg, Va., 1964-95; fellow Thomas Reid Inst. for Rsch. in Cultural Studies and the Humanities, Aberdeen (Scotland) U., 1995. Author: The Age of William III & Mary II: Power, Politics & Patronage, 1688-1702, 1989; editor: (jour.) Eighteenth-Century Life, 1983— (Best Spl. Issue award Conf. Editors Learned Jours. 1984); editor: "Tis Nature's Fault": Unauthorized Sexuality During the Enlightment, 1987, Science & Technology & Their Cultural Contexts, 1982, British Literature & Culture, 1986, English Culture at the End of the 17th Century, 1988, Manners of Reading, 1992, The Art & Architecture of Versailles, 1993, Europe and the South Pacific, 1994; contbr. articles to profl. jours. NEH grantee, 1988-89. Mem. MLA, FHC Soc., Am. Soc. 18th-Century Studies (exec. bd. east ctrl. chpt. 1983—, Clifford prize 1986, 87, Best Article award southeast chpt. 1987, 92), Soc. for Theatre Rsch., Pvt. Libr. Assn., Grolier Club. Avocations: gardening, acting, baseball. Office: Coll William & Mary English Dept Williamsburg VA 23185

MACCURDY, RAYMOND RALPH, JR., modern language educator; b. Oklahoma City, May 12, 1916; s. Raymond R. and Ada May (Eastl) MacC.; m. Blanche Hermine Wolf, June 2, 1939; children—George Grant II, William Douglas. B.A., La. State U., 1939; M.A., 1941; Ph.D., U. N.C. 1948. Assoc. prof. modern langs. U. Ga., 1948-49; Assoc. prof. modern langs. U. N.Mex., Albuquerque, 1949-53, prof., 1953—, chmn. dept. modern and classical langs., 1963-68; Nat. Def. Edn. Act. coordinator lang. Programs Am. Assn. Tchrs. Spanish and Portuguese, 1958-59. Author: The Spanish Dialect in St. Bernard Parish, Louisiana, 1950, Francisco de Rojas Zorrilla and the Tragedy, 1958, Francisco de Rojas Zorrilla, 1969; Editor: La Vida en el Ataud, 1961, Lucrecia y Tarquino, 1963, Numancia Cercada y Numancia destruida, 1977, Tirso de Molina, El Burlador de Sevilla, 1965, Del rey abajo, ninguno, 1970, Spanish Drama of the Golden Age-Twelve Plays, 1971, The Tragic Fall: Don Alvaro de Luna and Other Favorites in Spanish Golden Age Drama, 1978, Caesar of Sante Fe, 1990. Served to maj. AUS, World War II, CBI. Julius Rosenwald fellow, 1941, 46; Fund for Advancement Edn. fellow, 1954-55; Fulbright research scholar Spain, 1960-61. Mem. Rocky Mountain Modern Lang. Assn. (pres. 1957), Hispanic Soc. Am. Home: 1804 Newton Pl NE Albuquerque NM 87106-2527

MAC DIARMID, WILLIAM DONALD, physician; b. Arcola, Sask., Can., June 22, 1926; s. John Angus and Evaline (Reed) MacD.; m. Bette Nell Brown, May 16, 1953; children—John A., Margaret A., Donald G., Andrew L. B.A., U. Sask., 1947; M.D., U. Toronto, 1949. Intern Pasqua Hosp., Regina, Sask., 1949-50; family physician, mem. med. staff Pasqua Hosp. and Regina Gen. Hosp., 1950-53; mem. staff Shaunavon (Sask.) Union Hosp., 1953-58; resident in internal medicine, fellow in endocrinology and metabolism U. Utah Affiliated Hosps., Salt Lake City, 1958-62; research asst. in human genetics Univ. Coll. Hosp. Med. Sch., London, 1962-64; mem. faculty U. Utah Med. Sch., 1964-69; prof. medicine U. Man. Med. Sch., Winnipeg, 1969-75, 79-91, chmn. dept., 1979-85; physician-in-chief St. Boniface Gen. Hosp., 1969-75, St. John's Gen. Hosp. and Health Sci. Ctr., 1975-79, Health Sci. Ctr. of Winnipeg, 1979-85; health svcs. cons., 1986—; prof., chmn. dept. medicine Meml. U. Nfld. Med. Sch., 1975-79; pres. Swift Current and Dist. Med. Soc., 1956-57; mem. bd. Com. for Accreditation of Can. Med. Schs., 1985-91, chmn., 1988-91; cons. Health Care Systems, 1967—. Bd. dirs. Man. Med. Services Found., 1986-91, Winnipeg Mcpl. Hosps., 1986-89; chmn. bd. Man. Cancer Treatment and Research Found., 1987-88; v.p. Man. Med. Coll. Found., 1988-91. Fellow ACP, Royal Coll. Physicians and Surgeons Can., Can. Coll. Med. Geneticists; mem. Am. Soc. Human Genetics, Can. Med. Assn. (com. on ethics 1987-91, coun. on med. edn. 1988-91), Man. Med. Assn.) dir. 1981-83, 87—, chmn. bd. 1982-83, hon. sec. 1988-91, hon. treas. 1989-90, chmn. com. on ethics 1987-91), Can. CancerSoc., chmn. CanSurmount and bd. dirs. Vancouver Island Dist. 1993—). Home and Office: 4142 Cortez Pl, Victoria, BC Canada V8N 4R8

MACDONALD, A. EWAN, food products executive. MA, U. Edinburgh, Scotland, 1964. With Leo Burnett, 1966-81, McCann-Erickson, 1981-85; pres., COO, past CEO Del Monte Corp., 1985—. Office: Del Monte Corp 1 Market Plz San Francisco CA 94105-1019

MACDONALD, ALAN G., trade association administrator; b. Cambridge, Mass., June 16, 1944; s. Michael John and Dorothy (Cummings) M.; m. Jane Hess, July 22, 1967; children: Alan John, Daniel Brennan. AB, Dartmouth Coll., 1966; JD, Boston Coll., 1969. Bar:. Asst. atty. gen. Commonwealth of Mass., Boston, 1969-75; dir., govt. rels., New Eng. and Washington Gulf Oil Corp., Boston/Pitts./Washington, 1975-79; mgr., state govt. rels., New Eng. Gen. Electric Co., Boston, 1979-89; exec. dir. Mass. Bus. Roundtable, Boston, 1989—; bd. dirs., corp. sec. Mass. Product Devel. Corp., Boston; corporator Winchester (Mass.) Savs. Bank, 1988—. Chmn. Bd. Selectmen, Winchester, 1982-83, 85-86. Mem. Dartmouth Alumni Club of Eastern Mass. (bd. dirs. 1980—, v.p. 1986-89, pres. 1989—), Winchester Country Club. Avocations: golf, curling. Office: Mass Business Roundtable 250 Boylston St Boston MA 02116-3954

MACDONALD, ALAN HUGH, librarian, university administrator; b. Ottawa, Ont., Can., Mar. 3, 1943; s. Vincent C. and Hilda C. (Durney) MacD.; m. Elizabeth Whalen; children—Eric Paul Henry, Nigel Alan Christopher. B.A., Dalhousie U., 1966; M.A., 1969; B.L.S., U. Toronto, Ont. 1964. With Dalhousie U., 1964-78, law librarian, 1965-67, 69-71, asst. univ. librarian, 1970-72, health sci. librarian, 1972-78; lectr. Sch. Library Services, 1969-78; dir. info. svcs. U. Calgary, Alta., 1988—; dir. libraries U. Calgary, Alta., Can., 1979-92, univ. orator, 1989—; dir. U. Calgary Press, 1984-90; chmn. Alta. Library Network, 1981-89; librarian N.S. Barristers Soc., 1969-74; mem. adv. bd. Nat. Libr. Can., 1972-76, Health Scis. Resource Centre, Can. Inst. Sci. and Tech. Info., 1977-79; mem. Coun. of Prairie Univ. Librs., 1979-92, chair, 1984-85, 89, 91; Bassam lectr. U. Toronto Faculty Info. Studies, 1994. Mem. editorial bd. America: History and Life (ABC-CLIO), 1985-93. Pres. TELED Community Media Access Orgn., Halifax, N.S., 1972-74; mem. Minister's Com. on Univ. Affairs, Alta., 1979-83; bd. dirs. Alta. Found. for Can. Music Ctr., 1985-92; v.p. Can. Inst. for Hist.

Microreprodn., 1990-94, treas., 1994—. Council Library Resources fellow, 1975; exec. fellow Univ. Microfilms Internat., 1986; recipient Disting. Acad. Librarian award Can. Assn. of Coll. and Univ. Libraries, 1988. Mem. Can. Libr. Assn. (treas. 1977-79, pres. 1980-81), Atlantic Provinces Libr. Assn. (pres. 1977-78), Libr. Assn. Alta. (v.p. 1988-89, Pres.'s award 1992), Can. Health Libr. Assn. (treas. 1977-79, Can. Assn. Law Librs., Australian Libr. and Info. Assn. (assoc. 1977), N.Z. Libr. Assn., Bibliog. Soc. Can., Foothills Libr. Assn., Can. Assn. Info. Sci. Pres. 1979-80), Can. Assn. Rsch. Librs. (bd. dirs. 1981-86, v.p. 1985-86), Calgary Free-Net Soc. (mem. steering com. 1994—, v.p. 1995—). Office: U Calgary, 2500 University Dr NW A164, Calgary, AB Canada T2N 1N4

MACDONALD, ANDREW STEPHEN, management consulting firm executive; b. Fairbanks, Alaska, July 15, 1953; s. Bernard L. and Rosemary (Unger) MacD.; m. Josephine A. Joanne, Aug. 4, 1972; children: Peter, Stephen, Charles. BA in Acctg., Seattle U., 1974. CPA, cert. mgmt. cons. Acct. Boeing Aerospace, Seattle, 1976-79; owner, pres. Triak Corp., Seattle, 1977—; pres. Exec. Cons. Group, Inc., Seattle, 1979—. Mem. AICPA, Inst. Mgmt. Cons., Wash. Soc. CPAs, Columbia Tower Club. Home: 10300 Lakeshore Blvd NE Seattle WA 98125 Office: Exec Cons Group Inc Ste 2700 1111 3d Ave Seattle WA 98101

MACDONALD, BRIAN SCOTT, educational administrator; b. Sudbury, Ont., Can., June 6, 1939; s. David William and Katherine Lillian (McKinnon) MacD.; m. Margaret Louise Young, Aug. 11, 1962 (dec. Apr. 1985); children—Heather Anne, David Colin, Michael Alexander. B.A. with honors, Royal Mil. Coll., Kingston, Ont., 1961; M.B.A. cum laude, York U., Toronto, Ont., 1980; postgrad., U. Toronto, 1980—. Tchr., cons. Bd. Edn., Ont., Can., 1966-80; exec. dir. Can. Inst. Strategic Studies, Toronto, Ont., Can., 1982-89; pres. Strategic Insight Planning and Communications, 1989—. Editor: Parliament and Defence Policy, 1982, War in the 80's: Men Against High Tech, 1983, Canada's Strategies for Space, 1984, The Grand Strategy of the Soviet Union, 1984, Defence and the Canadian Economy, 1984, Canada's Strategies for the Pacific Rim, 1985, High Tech and the High Seas, 1985, Canada, the Caribbean, and Central Am., 1986, Terror, 1986, Tactics and Technology, 1987, A Grand Strategy for the United States?, 1988, Airwar 2000, 1989, Canadian Strategic Forecast 1989, 1989, Space Strategy: Three Dimensions, 1989; contbg. editor Def. Policy Rev., 1994—. Pres. Royal Can. Arty. Assn., Toronto, 1976; vice chmn. Conf. Def. Assns., Ottawa, Ont., 1975; gov. Can. Corps of Commissionaires, Toronto, 1984-86; hon. aide de camp to Gov. Gen. Can., Ottawa, 1984-86; comdr. Toronto Militia Dist., 1984-86; bd. dirs. Atlantic Coun. Can., 1986—, v.p., 1991; bd dirs. Royal Can. Mil. Inst., 1986-87. Served to col. Can. Army, 1957-86. Marsh-McLennan scholar, 1977, Dept. Nat. Def. scholar, 1981-82. Mem. Assn. Polit. Risk Analysts, Toronto Bd. Trade, Can. Ops. Rsch. Soc.. Home: 169 Newton Dr, Willowdale, ON Canada M2M 2N6

MACDONALD, CAROLYN HELMS, gifted education educator; b. Leesburg, Va., Oct. 15, 1941; d. Edmund Davis and Mary Irene (Peters) Helms; m. John Mount MacDonald, July 27, 1963 (div. Dec. 1984); children: Christina Hope, Heather Laurel, Katherine Anne. BS, East Tenn. State U., 1964; MS, Nova U., 1979. Cert. elem. tchr., jr. coll. tchr., gifted tchr., Fla. Elem. tchr. Shoemaker Elem. Sch., Gate City, Va., 1964-65, Bakersfield Elem. Sch., Aberdeen, Md., 1965-66, Brookview Elem. Sch. Jacksonville, Fla., 1966-68, Holiday Hill Elem. Sch., Jacksonville, Fla., 1968-69, Arlington Annex 5th Grade Ctr., Jacksonville, 1972-73; elem. tchr., social studies, lang. arts specialist Loretto Elem. Sch., Jacksonville, 1973-81, tchr. gifted, 1981—; mem. steering com. for gifted edn. Duval County Sch. Bd., 1982-85, del. to Murmansk, USSR, 1991; ESOL trainer, 1991—. Pres. Mandarin Cmty. Club, Jacksonville, 1980; mem. Panel on Sewage Treatment Problems, 1979, Neighborhood Cancer Drive Com., 1979-84, Com. to Assess Cmty. Recreation Needs, Jacksonville, 1981-82; sponsor ARC. Recipient placque Mandarin Community Club, Jacksonville, 1974-77; named Outstanding Safety Patrol Sponsor North Fla., 1993. Mem. Fla. Jr. Coll. Woman's Club (v.p. 1969-71, pres. 1971-72, Outstanding Young Woman Am. 1971), Southjr. Woman's Club (v.p. 1970-73), Phi Mu Alumnae (v.p. 1989-90), Delta Kappa Gamma. Democrat. Methodist. Avocations: reading, traveling, decorating, walking, the arts. Home: 2905 Isser Ct Jacksonville FL 32257-5626 Office: Loretto Elem Sch # 30 3900 Loretto Rd Jacksonville FL 32223-2098

MACDONALD, CLIFFORD PALMER, editor, writer; b. Winchester, Mass., Apr. 30, 1919; s. Frederick Cameron and Helen Maud (Palmer) M. Student, Bryant & Stratton Bus. Sch., 1937-38. Chief of publs. Office of Mil. Govt. for Germany, U.S. Army, 1945-46; mgr. Midwest br. Whittemore Assocs., Cleve., 1947-50; asst. dir. fund-raising Am. Bapt. Conv., N.Y.C. 1950-63; writer Marts and Lundy, N.Y.C., 1963-66; editor Am. Bible Soc., N.Y.C., 1966—; active various bds. and coms. Nat. Council Chs., Religion in Am. Life, Lord's Day Alliance, other religious orgns. Served to capt. U.S. Army, 1941-46, ETO. Current editor, writer one of oldest continuous publs. in U.S., first issue appearing in 1818. Office: Am Bible Soc 1865 Broadway New York NY 10023-7503

MACDONALD, DAVID ROBERT, lawyer; b. Chgo., Nov. 1, 1930; s. James Wear and Frances Esther (Wine) M.; m. Verna Joy Odell, Feb. 17, 1962; children: Martha, Emily, David, Rachel, Rebecca. B.S., Cornell U., 1952; J.D., U. Mich. 1955. Bar: Ill. 1955, Mich. 1955, D.C. 1983. Practiced in Chgo., 1957-74; mem. firm Kirkland, Ellis, Hodson, Chaffetz & Masters, Chgo., 1957-62, partner, 1962; partner Baker & McKenzie, Chgo., 1962-74, 77-81, 83—; asst. sec. of Treasury for enforcement, ops. and tariff affairs Dept. Treasury, Washington, 1974-76; undersec. of Navy, 1976-77; dep. U.S. Trade Rep., 1981-83; bd. dirs. Chgo. City Bank and Trust Co., Mestek, Inc. (N.Y. Stock Exch.). Bd. dirs. Chgo. Crime Commn., 1977-81; nat. chmn. U. Mich. Law Sch. Fund, 1977-79; mem. com. visitors U. Mich. Law Sch., 1962—. Served with AUS, 1955-57. Mem. ABA, Chgo. Bar Assn., D.C. Bar Assn., Chgo. Assn. Commerce and Industry (bd. dirs. 1977-81), Order of Coif, Econ. Club (Chgo.), Cosmos Club (Washington). Home: 6605 Radnor Rd Bethesda MD 20817-6324 Office: Baker & McKenzie 815 Connecticut Ave NW Washington DC 20006-4004

MACDONALD, DIGBY DONALD, scientist, science administrator; b. Thames, New Zealand, Dec. 7, 1943; came to U.S., 1977; s. Leslie Graham and Francis Helena (Verry) M.; m. Cynthia Lynch, 1969; m. Mirna Urquidi, July 6, 1985; children: Leigh Vanessa, Matthew Digby, Duncan Paul, Nahline. BS in Chemistry, U. Auckland, New Zealand, 1965; MS in Chemistry with honors, U. Auckland, 1966; PhD, U. Calgary, Alta., Can., 1969. Asst. research officer Atomic Energy of Can., Pinawa, Man., Can., 1969-72; lectr. Victoria U., Wellington, New Zealand, 1972-75; sr. research assoc., assoc prof. Alta. Sulfur Research U. Calgary, 1975-77; sr. metallurgist SRI Internat., Menlo Park, Calif., 1977-79; prof. metall. engring. Ohio State U., Columbus, Ohio, 1979-84; lab dir., dep. dir. phys. scis. divsn. SRI Internat., Menlo Park, 1984-91; prof. material sci. engring., dir. Ctr. Advanced Materials Pa. State U., 1991—; adj. prof. Ohio State U., 1984; W.B. Lewis Meml. lectr. Atomic Energy Can., 1993cons. in field. Author: Transient Techniques in Electrochemistry, 1977; contbr. numerous articles to profl. jours.; patentee in field. Nat. Research Council scholar, Ottawa, Can., 1967-69; recipient Research award Ohio State U., 1983. Fellow Nat. Assn. Corrosion Engrs. (pub. com. 1982-85, Whitney award 1992); mem. Electrochem. Soc. (divsn. editor 1982-84, C. Wagner Meml. award 1991). Avocations: sailing, flying. Home: 1010 Greenbriar Dr State College PA 16801-6935 Office: Pa State U Ctr Advanced Materials 517 Deike Bldg University Park PA 16802

MACDONALD, DONALD ARTHUR, publishing executive; b. Union City, N.J., Nov. 30, 1919; s. Richard A. and Marie (McDonald) M.; m. Ruth Moran, Dec. 21, 1942; children: Ronald A., Martha J., Marie C., Donald A., Charles A. BS cum laude, NYU, 1948, MBA, 1950. Advt. sales rep. Wall St. Jour., Dow Jones & Co., Inc., N.Y.C., 1953-55; mgr. New Eng. and Can. ter., 1955-58, ea. advt. mgr., 1958-61, exec. advt. mgr., 1961-63, advt. dir. sales promotion and prodn. depts., 1963-67, v.p. advt. sales, 1970-74, sr. v.p., 1974—, also dir.; vice chmn. Dow Jones & Co. Inc., N.Y.C., 1979—; also dir. Dow Jones & Co. Inc.; dir. Far Ea. Econ. Rev., Hong Kong; chmn. coun. judges Advt. Hall of Fame, 1972-78. Author: An Arrow for Your Quiver, 1994. Capt. AUS, 1942-46, World War II. Named to Advt. Hall of Fame, 1985. Mem. Am. Advt. Fedn. (dir. 1962—, past chmn., Barton A. Cummings Gold Medal award, 1995), Advt. Fedn. Am. (past gov. 2d dist., past chmn. joint commn., past chmn.), Advt. Council (dir.), N.Y. Advt.

Club (past dir., Silver medal award 1965), Beta Gamma Sigma. Clubs: Downtown Athletic (N.Y.C.), Yale (N.Y.C.); Rumson Country (N.J.). Home: 15 Buttonwood LnE Rumson NJ 07760-1045

MACDONALD, DONALD IAN, health care administrator; b. N.Y.C., Apr. 15, 1931; s. Donald and Laura (Holmes) M.; m. Roberta W., June 27, 1959; children—Sally, Jane, Andrew, Ian. B.A., Williams Coll., 1952; M.D., Temple U., 1958. Diplomate Am. Bd. Pediatrics. Intern Duval Med. Ctr., Jacksonville, Fla., 1958-59; resident in pediatrics St. Christopher's Hosp. for Children, Phila., 1959-62, chief resident, 1961-62; pvt. practice Clearwater, Fla., 1962-84; clin. assoc. prof. Coll. Medicine U. South Fla., Tampa, 1980-84; clin. prof. Coll. Medicine U. South Fla., 1987-92; dep. asst. to the pres. and dir. Drug Abuse Policy Office, The White House, Washington, 1987-89; adminstr. Alcohol, Drug Abuse and Mental Health Adminstrn., Rockville, Md., 1984-88; acting asst. sec. for health HHS, 1985-86; chmn., CEO Employee Health Programs, Inc., Bethesda, Md., 1993—; interim dir. White House Conf. for a Drug Free Am., 1987, Office Substance Abuse Prevention; chmn. drug abuse com. Fla. Med. Assn., 1980-84; pres. sci. adv. com. Am. Council for Drug Edn., N.Y.C., 1981. Author: Drugs, Drinking and Adolescents, 1984. Bd. dirs. ARC, Washington, 1984-89, Nat. Fedn. of Parents for Drug Free Youth, Silver Spring, Md., 1981-83, Childrens Hospice Internat., Alexandria, Va., 1990—. Served with U.S. Army, 1952-54. Recipient Disting. Alumni award sch. medicine Temple U., 1986, Alumni Achievement award Stony Brook Sch., 1987, Disting. Service medal USPHS Commd. Corps, 1987, Nelson J. Bradley Outstanding Service award Nat. Assn. Addiction Treatment Providers, 1987. Fellow Am. Acad. Pediatrics (pres. Fla. chpt. 1982-84); mem. AMA, Am. Soc. Addiction Medicine (cert.), Nat. Assn. Children. Alcoholics, Nat. Assn. Children Alcoholics, Fla. Pediatric Soc. (pres. 1982-84). Republican. Presbyterian. Avocations: reading, sailing.

MACDONALD, DONALD STOVEL, lawyer; b. Ottawa, Ont., Can., Mar. 1, 1932; s. Donald Angus and Marjorie (Stovel) M.; m. Ruth Hutchison, Mar. 4, 1961 (dec. Mar. 1987); children: Leigh, Nikki, Althea, Sonja; m. Adrian M. Lang, Sept. 10, 1988; step-children: Maria (dec.), Timothy, Gregory, Andrew, Elisabeth, Amanda, Adrian. Student, Ashbury Coll., Ottawa; BA, U. Toronto, 1951; LLB, Osgoode Hall Law Sch., 1955; LLM, Harvard, 1956; diploma internat. law, Cambridge U., 1957; LLD, St. Lawrence U., U N.B. Saint John, 1990; D.Eng., Colo. Sch. Mines. Bar: Called to Ont. bar 1955. Assoc. McCarthy & McCarthy, Toronto, 1957-62; M.P. for Toronto-Rosedale, 1962; reelected, 1963, 65, 68, 72, 74; parliamentary sec. to Minister of Justice, 1963-65, to Minister of Finance, 1965, to Sec. of State for External Affairs, 1966-68, to Minister of Industry, 1968; pres. Privy Council and Govt. House Leader, 1968; minister of nat. def., 1970-72, minister energy, mines and resources, 1972-75, minister of finance, 1975-77; ptnr. firm McCarthy & McCarthy, Toronto, 1977-88; high commr. for Canada to U.K., 1988-91; counsel McCarthy Tétrault, Toronto, 1991—; spl. lectr. U. Toronto Law Sch.; chmn. Royal Commn. on Econ. Union and Devel. Prospects for Can., 1982-85; chmn. Inst. for Rsch. on Pub. Policy, Montreal, 1991—, Siemens Electric Ltd., 1991—, Design Exchange, Toronto, 1993—; bd. dirs. Alta Energy Co. Ltd., Banister, Inc., Celanese Can. Inc., Hambros Can. Inc., Banister Found. Inc., Rainy River Forest Products Inc., Slough Estates Can., Sun Life Assurance Co. Can., TransCan. Pipelines Ltd.; trustee The Clan Donald Lands Trust, Skye, Scotland, 1991—. Named Freeman of the City of London, 1990, hon. fellow Trinity Hall, Cambridge U., 1994, Companion of the Order of Can., 1994. Mem. Queen's Privy Coun. Can., Delta Kappa Epsilon. Liberal. Baptist. Office: McCarthy Tétrault PO Box 48, Toronto-Dominion Twr Ste 4700, Toronto, ON Canada M5K 1E6

MACDONALD, DONALD WILLIAM, architect; b. Calgary, Alta., Can., May 7, 1935; came to U.S. 1957; s. Wallace Harold and Dorothy Louise (DeFaye) M.; m. Kerstin Maria Lindberg, July 22, 1965 (div. 1979); children: Pia, Ian, Denise. BArch, U. Okla., 1962; MS, Columbia U., 1963. Registered architect, Calif., Nev., N.Mex., Colo. Archtl. draftsman Bell and McCulloch Architects, Edmonton, Alta., 1955-57; archtl. designer Anshen and Allen Architects, San Francisco, 1965-67; prin. Donald MacDonald Architects, San Francisco, 1967—; assoc. prof. U. Calif.-Berkeley, 1965-66; prof. advisor Cogswell Coll., San Francisco, 1979-81, U. Okla., Norman, 1982—; lectr. archtl. sch. Idaho State U., Pocatello, 1974, Posnan (Poland) Inst. Art and Architecture, 1974, Portsmouth Inst. Tech., Eng., 1974, U. Okla., Norman, 1982, Tex. Tech U., Lubbock, 1984, Auburn (Ala.) U., 1986, Tulane U., New Orleans, 1987, Moscow Inst. Architecture, 1987, U. Calif. Berkeley, 1987, Mich. State U., Lansing, 1988, Ga. Inst. Tech., 1993, San Francisco Inst. Architecture, 1992—, U. Okla. Coll. Architecture, 1992, Archtl. Inst. B.C. Vancouver, 1991, McGill U., 1991, U. Cin., 1991, Woodbury U., Burbank, 1993, Boston Archtl. Sch., 1993, San Jose State U., 1994; lectr. in field; jury mem. Nat. Competition of Plywood Structures, Seattle, 1972, La. AIA Archtl. Design Competition, 1988, Miss. AIA Archtl. Competition, 1988, McGill U., 1991, Northern Calif. Home and Garden, 1991, City Boston Pub. Facilities Dept., 1992, San Diego Housing Commn., 1992; mem. juror panel in field; mem. San Francisco Civil Service Archtl. Selection Com., 1974; examiner Calif. Archtl. Registration Bd., 1979; prof. Calif. Coll. Arts and Crafts, San Francisco, 1988; faculty design studio San Francisco Inst. Architecture, fall 1990; jury chmn. N.C. AIA Archtl. Design Competition, 1988, Alta. Assn. Archs. U. Calgary, 1994, panel mem. 1994; East-West advisor energy conservation in housing Greenpeace, U.S.A.; presenter 9th Ann. Monterey Design Conf., 1989. Author: (with others) Bruce Goff: Toward Absolute Architecture, 1988; guest editor: Architecture and Urbanism, 1978; contbr. articles to profl. and consumer jours., U.S., Eng., Germany, Can., Poland, Russia, China, Italy, Japan. Received recognition through the media ABC, CNN, NBC, Time, People, Internat. Herald Tribune, Der Spiegel, London Observer, etc. for the invention of the City Sleeper, an exptl. environment for the homeless, studio house, and earthquake bed, 1991; exhbns. of architectural designs include Royal Inst. British Architects, London, 1985, 92, Contract Design Ctr., San Francisco, 1989, Contemporary Coll. Arts and Crafts, San Francisco, 1989, Contemporary Realist Gallery, San Francisco, 1989, San Francisco chpt. AIA, 1989, Calif. Sch. Bd. Assn., San Jose, Calif., 1989, Philippe Bonnafont Archtl. Drawings, San Francisco, 1990, Columbia U., N.Y.C., 1991, Mill Valley (Calif.) City Hall, 1991, San Mateo (Calif.) County Fair, 1991, Randolph Street Gallery, Chgo., 1991, Portland (Oreg.) chpt. AIA, 1991, San Francisco Examiner Home Buyers and Sellers Fair, 1993, San Francisco Embarcadero Waterfront Competition Exhibit, 1993. Recipient Regolo d'Or award Domas Milan, Italy, 1966, Okla. U. Regent's Disting. Alumni award, 1988, Honor award Calif. Coun. AIA, 1987, Commendation award for Golden Gate Toll Plaza in San Francisco Calif. Counc. AIA, 1987, also for toll booth award of excellence in archtl. conservation Found. for San Francisco Archtl. Heritage, 1989, Community Assistance award for innovative housing Calif. Coun. AIA, 1989, selected projects award Rolex Awards for Excellence, 1990, Fed. Design Achievement award, Presdl. Design awards, Nat. Endowment for Arts, 1991, World Habitat awards, grand prize Bldg. and Social Housing Foundation World Habitat awards, 1990, Gold Nugget awards, Grand award, Merit award Pacific Coast Builders and Sun/Coast ArchitectBuilder mag., 1991, SF mag. and Showplace Sq. Group Designers on Parade award, 1991, Maxwell award of excelence Fannie Mae, 1992, Oakland Orchids award AIA and Oakland Design Advocates, 1992, WorldDesign 92 award City and County of San Francisco, 1992; winner Hon. Mention Am. Plywood Assn., 1986, first place Housing Cost Reduction Co., Mich. State Housing Authority, 1987, No. Calif. Home and Garden mag. DIFFA Design Competition, 1990. Fellow AIA (honor awards San Francisco chpt. 1983, jury mem. San Mateo (Calif.) design awards program 1990); mem. Constrn. Specification Inst., McIntosh Archtl. Soc. Scotland, Columbia Archtl. League N.Y., Archtl. Assn. London. Clubs: St. Andrews Soc. (San Francisco); Chelsea Art (London); Columbia N.Y. Home: 743 Northpoint St San Francisco CA 94109 Office: Donald MacDonald Architects 1620 Montgomery St # 140 San Francisco CA 94111-1016

MACDONALD, FLORA ISABEL, Canadian government official; b. North Sydney, N.S., Can., June 3, 1926; d. George Frederick and Mary Isabel (Royle) MacD. Attended Empire Bus. Coll.; grad., Nat. Def. Coll., 1972; D.H.L. (hon.), Mt. St. Vincent U., 1979. Formerly in various secretarial positions; with Progressive Conservative Party Hdqrs., Ottawa, Ont., Can., 1956-65, exec. dir., 1957-66; adminstrv. officer, tutor dept. polit. studies Queen's U., 1966-72; also adv. Student Vocat. Bur.; mem. Can. Parliament for Kingston and the Islands, Ont., 1972-88; Progressive Conservative spokesman for Indian affairs and no. devel. Can. Parliament, 1972; for housing and urban devel., 1974; chmn. Progressive Conservative Caucus Com. on Fed.-Provincial Relations, 1976; sec. of state for external affairs, 1979-80, for external affairs and nat. def., 1980, minister employment and immigration, 1984-86, min. comms., 1986-89; chairperson Internat. Developmental Rsch. Ctr., 1992—; spl. adv. Commonwealth of Learning, 1990-91; bd. dirs. Can. Trust Co.; v.p. Kingston and Islands Progressive Conservative Assn., 1962-72; nat. sec. Progressive Conservative Assn. of Can., 1966-69; exec. dir. Com. for Ind. Can., 1971; pres. Elizabeth Fry Soc. of Kingston, 1968-70; vis. fellow Ctr. for Canadian Studies U. Edinburgh, 1989; host T.V. series North South Vision T.V., 1990-94. Bd. dirs. Can. Crafts Coun., CARE, Carnegie Commn. Re Preventing Deadly Conflict, Ctr. for Refugee Studies York U., Friends of the Nat. Lib., Queen's U. Coun., Refugee Policy Group, Washington, Shashtri Indo-Can. Inst.; chairperson Capital Fundraising Campaign Mount St. Vincent U., Halifax, 1990-94. Decorated Officer Order of Canada, 1995, Order of Ontario. Fellow Royal Soc. Arts (London); mem. Can. Inst. Fgn. Affairs (dir. 1969-73), Can. Polit. Sci. Assn. (dir. 1972-75), Can. Inst. Internat. Affairs, Can. Civil Liberties Assn. (bd. dirs.), Commonwealth Human Rights Initiative, Nat. Mus. of Scotland (hon. patron Can);U.N. (Eminent Persons to study Trans-Nat. Corps. in South Africa). Mem. United Ch. of Canada. Office: Internat Devel Rsch Ctr, 250 Albert St PO Box 8500, Ottawa, ON Canada K1G 3H9

MACDONALD, GEORGE FREDERICK, anthropologist, Canadian museum director; b. Cambridge, Ont., Can., July 4, 1938; s. George and Jane (Gorton) MacD.; m. Joanne Elizabeth Rice, Sept. 9, 1961; children: Christine, Grant. BA, U. Toronto, 1961; PhD, Yale U., 1966. Joined archaeol. divsn. Nat. Mus. Can., 1964-66, with west coast archaeol., 1966-68, head west Can. sect., 1968-69, chief archaeol. divsn., 1969-72, chief archaeol. survey Can., 1972-78; rsch. fellow Mus. Fur Volkerkunde, Basel, Switzerland, 1977-78; sr. archaeologist Nat. Mus. Can., 1978-82; rsch. fellow Fla. State Mus., Gainesville, 1980-81; head new accomodation task force Nat. Mus. Can., 1982; exec. dir. Mus. Civilization, 1982—; vis. fellow Mus. Anthropology U. B.C., 1981; lectr. Trent U., U. Ottawa, Carleton U., Simon Fraser U.; bd. dirs. Nat. Hist. Sites & Monuments, Can., Can. Mus. Construction Corp. Author: Ninstints: Haida World Heritage Site, 1983, Haida Monumental Art, 1983, Museum for the Global Village, 1989; contbr. articles to profl. jours. Mem. Can. del. drafting com. UNESCO Conv. on World Heritage, Paris, 1972; Can. del. Commn. Experts, Mohenjo, Daro, Pakistan, 1973; mem. hon. com. Nat. Mus. Am. Indian Nat. campaign, Washington, 1991—. Recipient James award Victoria Coll. U. Toronto, 1961; Wenner Oren fellow, Yale, 1964-65; mem. Can. Coun. Govt. Can., Yale, 1962-63. Mem. Can. Archeol. Assn. (pres. 1968). Home: 29 Lynott St, Cantley, PQ Canada J0X 1L0 Office: Can Mus Civilization Sta B, 100 Laurier St PO Box 3100, Hull, PQ Canada J8X 4H2

MACDONALD, GORDON CHALMERS, management consultant; b. Boston, Sept. 27, 1928; s. Frank C. and Anna E. (MacLean) MacD.; m. Eileen T. Harkins, May 25, 1952; children: Brian P., Peter G., Keith A., Audrey A. AA, Boston U., 1950, BBA, 1952; grad. advanced mgmt. program, Harvard U., 1979. Grad. tng. program Westinghouse Electric Corp., Pitts., 1952-64, regional/zone mgr., 1953-60; nat. mdse. mgr. Westinghouse Electric Corp., Metuchen, N.J., 1960-64; asst. to v.p. sales mgr. Magnavox Co., N.Y.C., 1964-68; v.p. mktg. GTE Corp., Batavia, N.Y., 1968-69; dir. mktg. Mitsubishi Internat. Corp., Lincolnwood, Ill., 1969-75; v.p. Mitsubishi Internat. Corp., N.Y.C., 1975-88, sec., 1984-88; advisor Mitsubishi Internat. Corp., 1989-91; bd. dirs. Mitsubishi Internat. Corp., N.Y.C., 1976-88; prin., mgmt. cons. G.C. MacDonald & Assocs., Greenwich, Conn., 1988—; exec. con. IBC Am., Plano, Tex. Chmn. Sea Explorers com. Boy Scouts Am., Greenwich, 1976-81. With U.S. Army, 1946-48. Club: U.S. Power Squadron (comdr. 1981-82, exec. com. 1987—) (Greenwich). Avocations: sailing, skiing, bridge. Home: 42 Birchwood Dr Greenwich CT 06831-3354

MACDONALD, GORDON JAMES FRASER, geophysicist; b. Mexico City, July 30, 1929; s. Gordon and Josephine (Bennett) MacD.; m. Marcelline Kuglen (dec.); children: Gordon James, Maureen, Michael; m. Betty Ann Kipniss; 1 son, Bruce; m. Margaret Stone Jennings. A.B. summa cum laude, Harvard U., 1950, A.M., 1952, Ph.D., 1954. Asst. prof. geology, geophysics Mass. Inst. Tech., 1954-55, assoc. prof. geology, geophysics, 1955-58; staff assoc. geophysics lab. Carnegie Inst. Washington, 1955-58; cons. U.S. Geol. Survey, 1955-60; prof. geophysics UCLA, 1958-68; dir. atmospheric rsch. lab., 1960-66, assoc. dir. UCLA (Inst. Geophysics and Planetary Physics), 1960-68; v.p. rsch. Inst. for Def. Analyses, 1966-67, exec. v.p., 1967-68, trustee, 1966-70; vice chancellor for rsch. and grad. affairs U. Calif. at Santa Barbara, 1968-70, prof. physics and geophysics, 1968-70; mem. coun. on Environ. Quality Washington, 1970-72; Henry R. Luce prof. environ. studies and policy, dir. environ. studies program Dartmouth Coll., 1972-79; trustee The MITRE Corp., McLean, Va., 1968-70, 72-77, exec. com., 1972-77; disting. vis. scholar The MITRE Corp., 1977-79, chief scientist, 1979-83, v.p., chief scientist, 1983-90; prof. internat. rels., rsch. dir. U. Calif., San Diego, 1990—; cons. NASA, 1960-70, mem. lunar and planetary missions bd., 1967; mem. Def. Sci. Bd., Dept. Def., 1966-70; cons. Dept. State, 1967-70; mem. Pres.'s Sci. Adv. Com., 1965-69; adv. panel on nuclear effects Office Tech. Assessment, 1975-77. Author: The Rotation of the Earth, 1960; co-author: Sound and Light Phenomena: A Study of Historical and Modern Occurrences, 1978, The Long-Term Impacts of Increasing Atmospheric Carbon Dioxide Levels, 1982, Global Climate and Ecosystem Change, 1990; contbr. articles to sci., tech. jours. Fellow AAAS, Am. Mineral. Soc., Am. Meteorol. Soc., Geol. Soc. Am., Am. Geophys. Union, Am. Acad. Arts and Scis., Am. Philos. Soc.; mem. Am. Math. Soc., Nat. Acad. Scis. (chmn. environ. studies bd. 1970, 72-73, chmn. commn. on natural resources 1973-77), Royal Astron. Soc. (fgn. assoc.), Geochem. Soc. Am., Seismol. Soc. Am., Soc. Indsl. and Applied Math., Coun. Fgn. Rels., Cosmos Club, Sigma Xi. Office: U Calif San Diego Inst Global Conflict Coop 9500 Gilman Dr La Jolla CA 92093-5003

MACDONALD, HUGH IAN, university president emeritus, economist, educator; b. Toronto, Ont., Can., June 27, 1929; s. Hugh and Winnifred (Mitchell) M.; m. Dorothy Marion Vernon, June 4, 1960; 5 children. B.Com., U. Toronto, 1952; M.A. (Rhodes scholar) Oxford (Eng.) U., 1954, B.Phil., 1955; LLD (hon.), U. Toronto, 1974. Lectr. U. Toronto, 1955-62, asst. prof., 1962-65; dean of men U. Toronto (Univ. Coll.), 1956-65; chief economist Govt. Ont., Toronto, 1965-67; dep. treas. Govt. Ont., 1967, dep. treas., dep. minister comms., 1968, dep. treas., dep. minister econs. and intergovtl. affairs, 1972; pres. York U., North York, Ont., 1974-84; prof., dir. York Internat., 1984-94, prof., pres. emeritus, 1994—; past pres. World U., Univ. Svc. Can.; chmn. Hockey Can., The Commonwealth of Learning. Recipient Can. Centennial medal, 1967, Queen's Silver Jubilee medal, 1977, Officer, Order Can., 1977, Commemorative medal 125th Anniv. Can. Confederation, 1992. Office: York U, 4700 Keele St, North York, ON Canada M3J 1P3

MACDONALD, IAN DUNCAN, commercial credit information executive; b. Sudbury, Ont., Can., Aug. 27, 1944; s. Charles Max and Ruth Gloria (Lyons) MacD.; m. Carmen Medora Payne, Aug. 16, 1969; children: Conrad Max, Scott Alexander, Tracy Anne. BA, McMaster U., Hamilton, Ont., 1967. Credit reporter Dun & Bradstreet Can. Ltd., Toronto, Ont., 1967-68, reporting supr., 1968-69, sales rep., 1969-71, gen. mgr. div. mktg. svcs., 1971-73, gen. sales mgr., 1973-76; gen. mgr. Screening Systems Internat. Ltd., Toronto, 1976-77; regional mgr. Creditel of Can. Ltd., Toronto, 1977-83, v.p. div. credit reporting, 1983-91, sr. v.p., 1991—; mem. Can. Credit and Fin. Exec. Inst., Toronto, 1967-91. Mem. Can. Credit Granters Assn., World Trade Centre-Toronto, Toronto Bd. Trade. Achievement: landscape painting, classical guitar playing. Home: 2 Vista Humber Dr, Weston, ON Canada M9P 3R7 Office: Creditel of Can Ltd, 110 Sheppard Ave East, North York, ON Canada M2N 6S1

MACDONALD, JAMES ROSS, physicist, educator; b. Savannah, Ga., Feb. 27, 1923; s. John Elwood and Antonina Jones (Hansell) M.; m. Margaret Milward Taylor, Aug. 3, 1946; children: Antonina Hansell, James Ross IV, William Taylor. B.A., Williams Coll., 1944; S.B., Mass. Inst. Tech, 1944, S.M., 1947; D.Phil. (Rhodes scholar) Oxford (Eng.) U., 1950, D.Sc., 1967. Mem. staff Digital Computer Lab., Mass. Inst. Tech., 1946-47; physicist Armour Research Found., Chgo., 1950-52; assoc. physicist Argonne Nat. Lab., 1952-53; with Tex. Instruments Inc., Dallas, 1953-74; v.p. corporate research and engring. Tex. Instruments Inc., 1968-73, v.p. corporate research and devel., 1973-74; cons., 1974—; dir. Simmons Precision Products Inc., 1979-83; William Rand Kenan Jr. prof. physics U. N.C., Chapel Hill, 1974-91, prof. emeritus, 1991—; mem. editorial bd. Jour. Applied Physics, 1984-86; adj. prof. biophysics U. Tex. Med. Sch., Dallas, 1954-74; mem. solid state scis. panel NRC, 1965-73; mem. adv. com. for sci. edn. NSF, 1971-73; mem. vis. com. physics Mass. Inst. Tech., 1971-74; mem. external adv. com. Engring. Expt. Sta., Ga. Inst. Tech., 1976-79. Editor, contbr.: Impedance Spectroscopy-Emphasizing Solid Materials and Systems, 1987; contbr. more than 200 articles to profl. jours. Mem. Dallas Radio Commn., 1967-71; mem. sci. adv. coun. Callier Hearing and Speech Ctr., Dallas, 1974-78; bd. dirs. League for Ednl. Advancement in Dallas, 1965-70; mem. adv. com. Weber Rsch. Inst., 1985-90. Fellow Am. Phys. Soc. (com. on applications of physics 1975-78, George E. Pake prize 1985), IEEE (awards 1962, 74, assoc. editor Transactions of Profl. Group on Audio 1961-66, Transactions on Audio and Electroacoustics 1966-73, recipient Edison Gold medal 1988), AAAS; mem. Nat. Acad. Engring. (exec. com. assembly of engring. 1975-78, council 1971-74), Nat. Acad. Scis. (chmn. numerical data adv. bd. 1970-74, mem. com. on motor vehicle emissions 1971-74, chmn. com. on motor vehicle emissions 1973-74, mem. com. on satellite power systems 1979-81, mem. com. on sci., engring., and pub. policy 1981-83, mem. commn. on phys. scis., math. and resources 1985-88, mem. report review com., 1990—), Am. Inst. Physics. (governing bd. 1975-78, chmn. com. on profl. concerns 1976-78), Electrochem. Soc., Audio Engring. Soc., Phi Beta Kappa, Sigma Xi, Tau Beta Pi. Achievements include 10 patents in field. Office: Univ NC Dept Physics and Astronomy Chapel Hill NC 27599-3255

MACDONALD, JOHN BARFOOT, research foundation executive; b. Toronto, Ont., Can., Feb. 23, 1918; s. Arthur Albert and Gladys Lillian (Barfoot) M.; m. Liba Bockova, July 10, 1967; children—Kaaren, Grant, Scott, Vivian, Linda. D.D.S. with honors, U. Toronto, 1942; M.S. in Bacteriology, U. Ill., 1948; Ph.D in Bacteriology, Columbia U., 1953; A.M. (hon.), Harvard U., 1956; LL.D. (hon.), U. Man., 1962, Simon Fraser U., 1965, Wilfrid Laurier U., 1976, Brock U., 1976, U. Western Ont., 1977; D.Sc. (hon.), U. B.C., 1967, U. Windsor, 1977. Chmn. div. dental research U. Toronto, 1953-56, prof. bacteriology, 1956; dir. Forsyth Dental Infirmary, Boston, 1956-62; prof. microbiology Harvard U. Sch. Dental Medicine, 1956-62; pres. U. B.C., 1962-67; exec. dir. Council Ont. Univs., 1968-76; pres. Addiction Research Found., Toronto, 1976-81; chmn. Addiction Research Found., 1981-87; chmn. commn. pharm. services Can. Pharm. Assn., 1967; rev. officer unicameral expt. U. Toronto, 1977; bd. dirs. Donwood Found., 1966-79, chmn., 1972-75; bd. dirs. Banff Sch. Advanced Mgmt., 1962-67, chmn., 1966-67; vice chmn. Ont. Council Health, 1981-84; cons. in field. Served with Dental Corps Can. Army, 1944-46. Home: 30 Metropolitan Cres, Keswick, ON Canada L4P 1L5

MACDONALD, JOHN THOMAS, educational administrator; b. Utica, N.Y., Nov. 21, 1932; s. Gerald Clement and Mildred (Hayes) MacD.; m. Marcia Sprague Gallup; children: Terrence, Anthony, Elizabeth, Michele, Elise, Denise. BS, Northeastern U., 1958, MEd, 1960; PhD, U. Conn., 1970. Cert. elem. and secondary sch. tchr., prin., supt., Mass., Conn. Supervising prin. Noank, Ft. Hill. and Poquonnock Elem. Schs., Groton, Conn., 1962-66, Robert E. Fitch Jr. High Sch., Groton, 1966-70; rsch. asst. Ednl. Resources and Devel. Ctr. U. Conn., Storrs, 1969-70; supt. schs. Wallingford (Conn.) Pub. Schs., 1970-73, Walpole (Mass.) Pub. Schs., 1973-78, Dartmouth (Mass.) Pub. Schs., 1978-86; commr. edn. State Dept. Edn., Concord, N.H., 1986-90; asst. sec. for elem. and secondary edn. U.S. Dept. Edn., Washington, 1990-93; dir. state leadership ctr. Coun. of Chief State Sch. Officers, Washington, 1993—; mem. Postsecondary Edn. Commn., Concord, 1986-90, Assoc. for Tchr. Edn., Concord, 1986-90, Profl. Standards Bd., Concord, 1986-90; trustee Univ. System of N.H., Durham, 1986-90; mem. Surgeon Gen's Task Force, 1990-93; mem. White House Coun. on Indian Edn., 1990-93; mem. Interagy. Com. on Sch. Health, 1990-93, others. Contbr. articles to profl. jours. Co-chmn. Emergency Sch.-Aide Proposals, U.S. Office Edn., 1973-75; mem. Mass. Adv. Commn. for Ednl. TV, 1983-86; mem. N.H. Task Force on Child Abuse, 1987-90; mem. nat. adv. coun. Northeastern U., 1990—; mem. Galaxy Classroom Nat. Adv. Coun. Galaxy Inst. for Edn., 1992—; mem. sch. health policy initiative Ctr. for Population & Family Health Columbia U., 1992—; mem. Packard roundtable to children Ctr. for Health Policy George Washington U., 1992—; mem. adv. com. external program rev. CDC, 1992—. Recipient Sears B. Condit award, 1958, Alumni award Northwestern U., 1973, Recognition award Coun. of Chief State Sch. Officers, 1990. Fellow Phi Delta Kappa, Phi Alpha Theta; mem. N.H. Sch. Bldg. Authority, Mass. Assn. Sch. Supts. (pres. 1985-86). Office: Coun. Chief State Sch Officers Ste 700 1 Massachusetts Ave NW Washington DC 20001-1431

MACDONALD, JOSEPH ALBERT FRIEL, lawyer; b. Halifax, N.S., Canada, Dec. 10, 1942; s. Charles F.H. and Mary E. (Friel) M.; m. Linda Lee Bergstrom, Sept. 15, 1967; children: Charles Lloyd, Mary Georgette. B.A., Dalhousie U., Halifax, 1963, LL.B., 1966; LL.M., NYU, 1967. Bar: N.S. 1967, Queen's Counsel 1983. Assoc. McInnes, Cooper & Robertson, Halifax, 1967-74, ptnr., 1975—; chmn. bd. N.S. Power, Inc., 1980—; gov. Mt. St. Vincent U., 1987-94. Bd. dirs. Izaak Walton Killam Hosp. for Children, 1989—. Mem. Internat. Bar Assn., Can. Bar Assn., N.S. Barristers Soc., Can. Tax Found., Halifax Club. Conservative. Roman Catholic. Home: 2915 Somerset Ave, Halifax, NS Canada B3L 3Z4 Office: NS Power Inc, PO Box 910 1894 Barrington St, Halifax, NS Canada B3J 2W5

MACDONALD, JOSEPH FABER, bishop; b. Little Pond, P.E.I., Can., Jan. 20, 1932. Ordained priest Roman Cath. Ch., 1963; ordained bishop Diocese of Grand Falls, Nfld., Can., 1980—. Office: Chancery Office 311 W 17th St PO Box 996 Grand Island NE 68802

MACDONALD, KAREN HOPE COWART, educator, reading specialist; b. Denver, Dec. 10, 1942; d. John Roscoe Cowart and Wanda Lorraine (Johnson) Cook; m. Charles Monte Dennis, Aug. 26, 1961 (div. 1979); children: Van Loren, Jon Charles, Kit Emery, Wanda Renee Dennis McGuire. BS in Edn., N.Mex. State U., 1975; MA in Edn., Ea. N.Mex. U., 1983. Cert. tchr., Tex., N.Mex. Tchr. 1st grade Carlsbad (N.Mex.) Mcpl. Schs., 1975-76; tchr. reading, 1st grade Hobbs (N.Mex.) Mcpl. Schs., 1976-87; reading tchr., dept. chair Bel Air High Sch., El Paso, 1987-94; instr. reading workshops Ea. N.Mex. U., Portales, 1982-86; reading instr. El Paso C.C., 1990—. Mem. ASCD, MADD, Internat. Reading Assn. (pres. Hobbs coun. 1985-86, bd. dirs. El Paso coun. 1989-92), Civitan, Women in Politics, Phi Delta Kappa. Democrat. Methodist. Avocations: reading, physical fitness. Home: 4651 Oakwood Dr Apt 40 Odessa TX 79761-2022

MACDONALD, KEN CRAIG, geophysicist; b. San Francisco, Oct. 14, 1947; m. Rachel Haymon, 1984. BS in Engring. Physics, U. Calif. Berkeley, 1970; PhD in Marine Geophysics, MIT/Woods Hole, 1975. Cecil H. and Ida Green postdoctoral scholar Scripps Instn. of Oceanography, 1975-76, asst. rsch. geophysicist, lectr., 1976-80; assoc. prof. U. Calif., Santa Barbara, 1980-83; prof. marine geophysics Dept. Geol. Scis. U. Calif., 1983—; co-chief scientist Legs I and II, chief scientist Leg III GORDA Expedition, 1976, ALVIN Mid-Atlantic Ridge, 1978; prin. ALVIN diver, 1978; ALVIN diver Tamayo Expedition, 1979; co-chief scientist RISE Expedition, 1979; chief scientist R/V Gyre, 1981, CERES Expedition, 1982, Protea Expedition R/V Melville, 1983; co-chief scientist R/V Thomas Washington, 1983; prin. ALVIN diver R/V Atlantis II, 1985; chief scientist R/V Moana Wave, SeaMARC II studies of the East Pacific Rise, 1990. Assoc. editor Jour. of Geophys. Rsch, 1979-82, Earth and Planetary Sci. Letters, 1978-88; mem. editorial bd. Marine Sci. Revs., 1986—; editor Marine Geophys. Rsch's, 1986-90; contbr. numerous articles to profl. jours. Mem. ALVIN Rev. Com., 1979-82; mem. Ocean Sci. Bd. of NAS, 1980-83, Lithosphere Panel Advanced Ocean Drilling Project, 1983-85, Ocean Scis. Panel, NSF, 1984-86, COSOD II planning com.; mem. various RIDGE coms., RIDGE steering com., 1987-90; mem. NSF Ocean Scis. Strategic Plan for Rsch. and Edn. Com., 1993-94. Regents scholar at Berkeley, 1966-70, NSF Grad. fellow, 1970-73, Cecil H. and Ida Green scholar at Inst. Geophysics and Planetary Physics, U. Calif., San Diego, 1975-76; recipient Mineral Tech. scholarship U. Calif., Berkeley, 1967-70, AAAS Newcomb-Cleveland prize, 1980, Robert L. and Bettie P. Cody prize and medal Scripps Instn. of Oceanography, 1994; named U. Utah Disting. lectr., 1984, U. Hawaii SOEST Disting. lectr., 1990. Mem. Am. Geophys. Union, Geol. Soc. Am. Avocations: windsurfing, fly fishing. Office: U Calif Santa Barbara Dept Geol Sci Santa Barbara CA 93106

MACDONALD, KENNETH, journalist, former editor; b. Jefferson, Iowa, Sept. 3, 1905; s. William Arthur and Mabel (Swearingen) McD.; m. Helen Inman, June 17, 1929; 1 child, Stephen. A.B., U. Iowa, 1926. With Des Moines Register and Tribune, 1926-86, successively reporter, copyreader, telegraph editor, city editor, mng. editor, exec. editor, v.p., 1946-76, editor, 1953-76, editorial chmn., 1976-77, pub., 1960-70, dir., 1940-86; Bd. dirs. A.P., 1956-65, 1st v.p., 1963-65; adv. bd. Pulitzer prizes, 1958-70. Co-author: Drink Thy Wine with a Merry Heart, 1983. Trustee Simpson Coll., chmn. bd., 1957-59. Served as air combat intelligence officer USNR, World War II, PTO. Mem. Am. Soc. Newspaper Editors (dir. 1950-56, pres. 1955), Sigma Delta Chi. Mem. Episcopal Ch. Club: Des Moines. Home: 3412 Southern Hills Dr Des Moines IA 50321-1319

MAC DONALD, MALCOLM MURDOCH, editor, publisher; b. Uniontown, Pa., June 15, 1935; s. Morgan Bowman and Ruth (Newcomb) Greene Mac D.; m. Constance Emily Marsh, June 13, 1959; children—Randall Malcolm, Alison Margaret, Ellen Marsh. B.A., Trinity Coll., Conn., 1957. Coll. rep. Midwest D. Van Nostrand Co. Inc., Princeton, N.J., 1958-62, assoc. sci. editor, 1962, sci. editor, 1963-68; sci. editor Van Nostrand Reinhold Co., N.Y.C., 1968-70; editor Pa. State U. Press, State College, 1970-72; chief editor U. N.C. Press, Chapel Hill, 1972-76, asst. dir., 1975-76; asst. dir., editor U. Ga. Press, Athens, 1976-78; dir. U. Ala. Press, 1978—; acting dir. U. Ala. Library, 1980-81; cons. in field. Author: (With Cecil E. Johnson) Society and the Environment, 1971, (with Robert E. Davis) Chemistry and Society, 1972. Mem. Assn. Am. Univ. Presses (bd. dirs. 1982-84), Omicron Delta Kappa. Office: U Ala Press Box 870380 Tuscaloosa AL 35487

MACDONALD, MARY ELIZABETH, nursing administrator, educator; b. Westboro, Mass., July 17, 1918; d. Hugh D. and Sarah (Campbell) MacD. Diploma, Mass. Gen. Hosp. Sch. Nursing, Boston, 1942; AB magna cum laude, Emmanuel Coll., Boston, 1939; MA, Columbia U., 1950, Suffolk U., Boston, 1987. Asst. prof., dir. basic nursing edn. program Boston Coll. Sch. Nursing, Chestnut Hill, Mass., 1950-53; assoc. dean, prof. nursing edn. U. Mass. Sch. Nursing, Amherst, 1953-67; dir. dept. analytical studies Mass. Gen. Hosp., Boston, 1967-68, dir. dept. nursing, 1968-83; cons. nursing adminstr. Surgeon Gen. U.S. Army; mem. HHS Coun. on Teaching Grants, Policy Adv. Bd., Joint Commn. on Accreditation of Hosps.; cons. in nursing edn. to numerous schs. and profl. publs. Recipient Alumni Career Achievement award Emmanuel Coll., Boston, 1992. Fellow Am. Acad. Nursing; mem. AAUP, Internat. Coun. Nurses, Am. Nurses Assn., Nat. League Nursing, Mass. Nurses Assn., Mass. League Nursing, Sigma Theta Tau, Phi Lambda Theta, Kappa Delta Pi, Kappa Gamma Pi. Home: 8 Whittier Pl Apt 20 Boston MA 02114-1402

MACDONALD, MICHAEL R., retail executive. Exec. v.p., cfo asst. sec. P.A. Bergner & Co., Milw., Wis. Office: P A Bergner & Co 331 W Wisconsin Ave Milwaukee WI 53203-2201

MACDONALD, R. FULTON, venture developer, business educator; b. Monmouth County, N.J., Dec. 24, 1940; s. James Fleming Smith Macdonald and Jane Macfarlane Barnes Abbott; m. Carol Jean Archer (div.); 1 child, Paige Brubaker Smith; m. Laura Boswell; children: George Dewey Boswell, James Fleming Smith Macdonald II. AB, U. Pa., 1963, MBA, 1969; post-grad. sr. mktg. mgmt., Stanford U., 1979. Systems mgr., mcht. John Wanamaker, Inc., Phila., 1969-74; prin. Booz, Allen & Hamilton, N.Y.C., 1974-79; pres. Irwill Industries, N.Y.C., 1979-82, Internat. Bus. Devel. Corp., N.Y.C., 1982—; chmn. IBEX Mktg. Corp., N.Y.C., 1988—; pres. Simfer Operational Internat., Inc., N.Y.C., 1984; vice chmn. Neusteter Co., Denver, 1984-85; dir. Fragrances Selective, Inc., 1985-87; mng. dir. Stuyvesant Group Internat., Dutch Am. Bus. Advisors, N.Y.C. and Amsterdam, 1987-88; chmn. Am. Bus. Media, Inc., 1989-90, One Ams., Inc., Washington, 1990—; mng. dir. Synoptics Devel. Corp., N.Y.C., 1992—; adj. prof. Grad. Bus. Sch., Columbia U., N.Y.C., 1984-85, Mgmt. Inst. NYU, 1992—, chmn. Globalization Adv. Bd., 1993—; strategic advisor Singapore, 1994—. Designer Manpower Mgmt. Concepts computer system, 1972—; contbr. articles to bus. publs. Capt. inf. U.S. Army, 1963-67, Vietnam. Decorated Bronze Star. Mem. Inst. Mgmt. Consultants (cert. mgmt. cons. 1989), Global Econ. Action Inst., Soc. Mayflower Descendants, Soc. Coll. Alumni U. Pa. (pres. 1973-74, bd. mgrs. 1975—), Ripon Soc. (Washington), Penn Club (N.Y.) Republican. Christian Scientist. Avocation: squash. Home: 721 5th Ave New York NY 10022-2523 Office: Internat Bus Devel Corp 730 5th Ave Ste 900 New York NY 10019-4105

MACDONALD, RICHARD, production designer. Prodn. designer: (films) Eva, 1962, The Servant, 1964, King and Country, 1965, Modesty Blaise, 1966, Far from the Madding Crowd, 1967, Secret Ceremony, 1968, Boom!, 1968, A Severed Head, 1971, The Assassination of Trotsky, 1972, Jesus Christ Superstar, 1973, Galileo, 1975, The Romantic Englishwoman, 1975, The Day of the Locust, 1975, Marathon Man, 1976, Exorcist II: The Heretic, 1977, F.I.S.T., 1978, The Rose, 1979, ...And Justice for All, 1979, Altered States, 1980, Cannery Row, 1982, Something Wicked This Way Comes, 1983, Supergirl, 1984, Electric Dreams, 1984, Plenty, 1985, Spacecamp, 1986, Coming to America, 1988, The Russia House, 1990, The Addams Family, 1991, The Firm, 1993. Office: Smith/Gosnell/Nicholson & Assoc PO Box 1166 1515 Palisades Dr Pacific Palisades CA 90272*

MACDONALD, RICHARD ANNIS, pathologist, physician, educator; b. Manistee, Mich., July 23, 1928; s. Robert R. and Julia (Graczyk) MacD. A.B., Albion Coll., 1951; M.D., Boston U., 1954. Intern Boston City Hosp., 1954-55, resident in pathology, 1955-59; mem. faculty Harvard Med. Sch., 1958-65, instr., 1959-60, asst. prof., 1962-65; prof. pathology Sch. Medicine U. Colo., 1966-69, Boston U. Med. Sch., 1969-70; prof. pathology, chmn. dept. pathology U. Mass. Med. Sch., Worcester, 1970-73; prof. pathology Boston U. Sch. Medicine, 1973-85, U. South Fla., 1985-89; chief pathology service Norwood (Mass.) Hosp., 1973-83; assoc. chief staff research and edn. Denver VA Hosp., 1968-69; chief lab. service, 1968-69, Boston VA Hosp., 1969-70, VA Hosp., Bay Pines, Fla., 1985-89; Mem. study sec. NIH, 1967-69; mem. evaluation com. on research and edn. VA, 1966-68. Author: Hemochromatosis and Hemosiderosis, 1964, Computers in Pathology; also articles. Served with USPHS, 1943-45. Mem. AMA, Am. Soc. Exptl. Pathology, Internat. Acad. Pathology, Mass. Med. Soc., New Eng. Soc. Pathology, Soc. Computers in Medicine, Mass. Soc. Pathology (treas. 1979-81, exec. com. 1977-85, pres. 1981-83), Phi Beta Kappa. Address: 931 Village Blvd Ste 905 West Palm Beach FL 33409-1944

MACDONALD, ROBERT ALAN, language educator; b. Salamanca, N.Y., Mar. 25, 1927; s. Guy E. and Hildur V. (Helene) MacD. B.A., U. Buffalo, 1948; M.A., U. Wis., 1949, Ph.D., 1958. Asst. prof. U. Richmond, Va., 1955-61, assoc. prof., 1961-67, prof. Spanish, 1967-95; ofcl. project reviewer NEH, Washington, 1977-95, Social Sci. and Humanities Research Council, Ottawa, Ont., Can., 1985-93. Author: Espéculo, texto jurídico atribuido a Alfonso X, 1990, Alfonso X, Libro de las Tahurerías, 1995; editor Bull. of Fgn. Lang. Assn. Va., 1962-67, 72-86; contbr. articles to profl. jours. Served with U.S. Army, 1946-47, 51-53. A.L. Markham traveling fellow U. Wis., 1958-59; Am. Council Learned Socs. fellow, 1976; fellow and grantee U. Richmond, 1958-94; named Cultural Laureate of Va., 1977; recipient Disting. Service award Fgn. Lang. Assn. Va., 1981. Mem. Acad. Am. Rsch. Historians on Medieval Spain, Am. Assn. Tchrs. of Spanish and Portuguese (past pres. state chpt.), AAUP (past pres. local chpt.), Am. Council on Teaching Fgn. Langs., Medieval Acad. Am., MLA. Club: Torch (Richmond).

MACDONALD, ROBERT BRUCE, county official; b. Delhi, N.Y., Dec. 28, 1930; s. Ernest Jamison and Daisy (Beers) MacD.; m. Ferne Huffman, Aug. 17, 1965; 1 child, Robert Bruce II. BS Govt., Pub. Adminstrn., Am. Univ., 1961; postgrad., U. Okla., 1981-83. Enlisted USAF, 1950-59; adminstrv. officer U.S. Govt., Washington, 1961-68; asst. to assoc. adminstr. rsch. and devel. Nat. Hwy. Traffic Safety Adminstrn., Washington, 1968-78; exec. dir. Delaware County Indsl. Devel. Agy., Delhi, N.Y., 1978—. Mem. SUNY Bus. & Industry Counsel, So. Tier East Planning and Devel. Bd., Econ. Devel. Com., Kiwanis (pres. Delhi chpt. 1984-85). Home: 41 Delview Ter Delhi NY 13753-1055 Office: Delaware County Indsl Devel Agy PO Box 506 Delhi NY 13753-0506

MACDONALD, ROBERT RIGG, JR., museum director; b. Pitts., May 11, 1942; s. Robert Rigg and Ruth (Johnson) M.; m. Catherine Ronan, Nov. 27, 1965; children: Matthew, Robert, Catherine. B.A., U. Notre Dame, 1964, M.A., 1965; M.U. Pa., 1970. Asst. curator Smithsonian Instn., Washington, 1965; curator Mercer Mus., Doylestown, Pa., 1966-70; dir. New Haven Colony Hist. Soc., 1970-74, La. State Mus., New Orleans, 1974-85, Mus. of City of N.Y., 1985—; adj. prof. mus. studies NYU, 1989—; mem. Commn. on Mus. for a New Century. Editor: New Haven Colony Furniture, 1973, Louisiana Images 1880-1920, 1975, Louisiana Black Heritage, 1977 Louisiana Portraitures, 1979, Louisiana Legal Heritage, 1981, The Sun King: Louis XIV and the New World, On Being Homeless in New York, 1987, Broadway! 125 Years of Musical Theater, Hives of Sickness: Public Health and Epidemics in New York City, 1995. Active Nat. Endowment for Humanities. Decorated chevalier de l'Ordre des Arts et des Lettres (France), cruz de Caballero de la Order de Isabel La Catolica (Spain); assoc. fellow Berkeley Coll., Yale U., 1978; Hagley fellow U. Del., 1970-71; Univ. scholar U. Notre Dame, 1964-65. Mem. Am. Assn. State and Local History (coun.), Am. Assn. Mus. (pres. 1985-88, chmn. ethics task force 1988-91), Century Assn. Roman Catholic. Home: 35 Edgewood Ln Bronxville NY 10708-1946 Office: Mus NYC 1220 Fifth Ave New York NY 10029

MACDONALD, ROBERT TAYLOR, newspaper executive; b. Mt. Vernon, N.Y., Oct. 25, 1930; s. Joseph Taylor and Mary Gertrude (Broderick) MacD.; m. Christiana Barbara Besch, June 25, 1960 (div. 1977); children: Gregory, Michael, Jennifer; m. Gillian S. Tripier, 1978. B.S., Yale, 1952; M.B.A., Wharton Sch. of U. Pa., 1958. Pub. Mariner (monthly trade mag.), 1956; bus. mgmt. cons., 1958-61; v.p., adminstrn., dir. N.Y. Herald Tribune, Inc., 1961-63, exec. v.p., 1963-66; pub. N.Y. Herald Tribune-Washington Post Internat., 1966-67, Internat. Herald Tribune, 1967-77; chmn. Hudson Research Europe, Ltd., 1977-87; mng. dir. MacDonald & Co., 1980—; v.p. internat. ops. Washington Post Co., 1966-70, asst. to chmn., 1968-70. Bd. govs. Am. Hosp. of Paris. Served as lt. USNR, 1953-56. Mem. Fgn. Policy Assn., Am. C. of C. in Paris (dir.), Phi Gamma Delta. Clubs: Yale (N.Y.C.), Wharton MBA (N.Y.C.) (dir., past pres.); Apawamis (Rye, N.Y.); Travelers (Paris). Office: Ste 701 9393 Midnight Pass Rd Sarasota FL 34242-2963

MACDONALD, RODERICK, library director; b. Mpls., Mar. 13, 1931; s. Roderick and Frances Ruth (Lawrence) Mac D.; m. Joanne Gaffney, Jan. 4, 1958; children: Maria Halliday, Roderick III, David, Louise. B.A., Macalester Coll., 1953; M.A., U. Minn., 1959. City librarian Free Pub. Library, Kaukauna, Wis., 1959-61; reference librarian, asst. prof. Macalester Coll., 1961-66; dir. Anoka County Library, Mpls., 1966-69, Pub. Library, Des Moines, 1969-78, Dakota County Library System, Eagan, Minn., 1978—. Served with AUS, 1953-55. Mem. ALA, Iowa Library Assn. (legis. chmn. 1971), Minn. Library Assn. (pres. 1968). Democrat. Home: 4928 5th Ave S Minneapolis MN 55409-2645 Office: 1340 Wescott Rd Saint Paul MN 55123-1029

MACDONALD, R(ONALD ANGUS) NEIL, physician, educator; b. Calgary, Alta., Can., Jan. 6, 1935; s. Angus Neil and Florence Mary (Macdonald) MacD.; m. Mary Jane Whiting, June 30, 1962; children: Cynthia, David, James, Gavin. BA, U. Toronto, 1955; MD, CM, McGill U., Montreal, 1959. Demonstrator, lectr. McGill U., 1965-67, assoc. dean, faculty of medicine, 1967-70; assoc. dir., dir. Oncology Day Ctr., Royal Victoria Hosp., Montreal, 1967-71; exec. dir. Provincial Cancer Hosps. Bd., Edmonton, Alta., Can., 1971-75; prof. medicine U. Alta., Edmonton, 1971-94; dir. Cross Cancer Inst., Edmonton, 1975-80, 1981-87; assoc. dir., prof. palliative care Royal Victoria Hosp., Montreal, 1980-81; prof. palliative medicine Alta. Cancer Found., Edmonton, 1987-94; dir. cancer ethics program Inst. Recherches Cliniques Montreal, 1994—; prof. oncology McGill U., 1994—; mem. cancer expert adv. panel WHO, Geneva, 1986—; Can. rep. Cancer Pain project, 1983—. Co-editor: Oxford Textbook of Palliative Medicine, 1993; contbr. articles on treatment of cancer pain and other topics to profl. jours. Recipient Queen's Jubilee medal, 1977, Alta. Achievement award, 1980, Blair award Nat. Cancer Inst., 1980, Edmonton Achievement award, 1994. Fellow Coll. Physicians and Surgeons Can., Royal Coll. Physicians Edinburgh (hon.); mem. Can. Cancer soc. (nat. bd. dirs. 1981-87), Can. Oncology Soc. (pres. 1977-87), Am. Soc. Clin. Oncology (sec.-treas. 1980-82), Can. Soc. Palliative Care Physicians (pres. 1993-94). Roman Catholic. Avocations: squash, history. Office: Inst. Recherches Cliniques Montreal, 110 Pine Ave W, Montreal, PQ Canada H2W IR7

MACDONALD, THOMAS COOK, JR., lawyer; b. Atlanta, Oct. 11, 1929; s. Thomas Cook and Mary (Morgan) MacD.; m. Gay Anne Everiss, June 30, 1956; children: Margaret Anne, Thomas William. B.S. with high honors, U. Fla., 1951, LL.B. with high honors, 1953. Bar: Fla. 1953. Practice law Tampa, 1953—; mem. firm Shackleford, Farrior, Stallings & Evans, 1953—; mem. adv. com. U.S. Ct. Appeals (5th cir.), 1975-78, (11th cir.), 1988-93; spl. coun. Gov. of Fla., 1963; spl. counsel U. Fla., 1972—; del. 5th cir. Jud. Conf. 1970-81. Mem. Fla. Student Scholarship and Loan Commn., 1963-67, Fla. Jud. Qualifications Commn., 1983-88, vice chmn. 1987, chmn., 1988; bd. dirs. Univ. Community Hosp., Tampa, 1968-78, Fla. West Coast Sports Assn., 1965-80, Hall of Fame Bowl Assn., 1989-93, Jim Walter Corp., 1979-87; mem. Hillsborough County Pub. Edn. Study Commn., 1965; lic. lay eucharistic min. Episcopal Ch., 1961—; chancellor Episcopal Diocese of S.W. Fla., 1990-93; bd. dirs. U. Fla. Found., 1978-86, Shands Teaching Hosp., U. Fla., 1981—; counsel Tampa Sports Authority, 1983—. Recipient Disting. Alumnus award U. Fla., 1976, George C. Carr award Fed. Bar Assn., 1991. Fellow Am. Coll. Trial Lawyers (chmn. state com. 1990-91), Am. Bar Found., Fla. Bar Assn. (chmn. com. profl. ethics 1966-70, bd. govs. 1970-74, bar mem. Supreme Ct. com. on stds. conduct governing judges 1976, Fla. bd. cert. appellate lawyer); mem. ABA (com. on ethics and profl. responsibility 1970-76), Am. Law Inst. (life), 11th Cir. Hist. Soc. (trustee 1982—, pres. 1989-94), U. Fla. Nat. Alumni Assn. (pres. 1973), Phi Kappa Phi, Phi Beta Phi, Fla. Blue Key, Kappa Alpha. Episcopalian. Home: 1904 S Holly Ln Tampa FL 33629-7004 Office: PO Box 3324 Tampa FL 33601-3324

MACDONALD, WAYNE DOUGLAS, publisher; b. Port Elgin, Ont., Can., Sept. 20, 1940; s. John Murdock and Irene Juliana (Lunow) MacD.; m. Marjorie Anne Farwell, Apr. 28, 1968; children: Scott, Ryan. Journalist Kitchener (Ont.)-Waterloo Record, 1964-75, mgn. editor, 1975-79, dir. resource and devel., 1985-88, editor, 1988-90, pub., 1990—; assignment editor Toronto Star, 1979-82; comm. dir. Ministry of Consumer Affairs, Toronto, Canada, 1982-84, Ministry of Health, Toronto, Canada, 1984-85; bd. dirs. Can. Press, Toronto, 1992-93; mem. adv. coun. U. Western Ont. Sch. Journalism, London, Ont., 1993. Mem. Rotary of Kitchener-Waterloo (com. for ednl. excellence), Westmount Golf and Country Club, Univ. Club. Office: Kitchener-Waterloo Record, 225 Fairway Rd S, Kitchener, ON Canada N2G 4E5

MACDONALD, WILLIAM LLOYD, architectural historian; b. Putnam, Conn., July 12, 1921; s. William Lloyd and Susan Elisabeth (Elrod) MacD.; children: Noel, Nicholas. AB, Harvard U., 1949, AM, 1953, PhD, 1956. Instr. Boston Archtl. Ctr., Mass., 1950-54; from asst. prof. to assoc. prof. Yale U., 1956-65; A.P. Brown prof. Smith Coll., Northampton, Mass., 1965-80; archtl. historian, Washington, 1980—; exec. sec. Byzantine Inst., Boston, 1950-54. Author: Early Christian and Byzantine Architecture, 1962, Northampton Massachusetts Architecture and Buildings, 1976, Piranesi's Carceri: Sources of Invention, 1976, Architecture of the Roman Empire I 1982, II, 1986 (Alice Davis Hitchcock prize); The Pantheon, 1976, (with J.A. Pinto) Hadrian's Villa and its Legacy, 1995. Lt. USAAF, 1942-45. Recipient Kevin Lynch award Dept. of Urban Studies MIT; Emerton, Shaw fellow Harvard U., Cambridge, Mass., 1949, 50, Vets. Nat. scholar, 1948; J. Paul Getty Ctr. scholar, Santa Monica, 1985-86. Fellow Am. Acad. Arts and Scis., Am. Acad. Rome (Prize fellow 1954-56); mem. AIA (life), Soc. Archtl. Historians (bd. dirs.), Soc. for Promotion of Roman Studies (life), Soc. for Libyan Studies. Home: 3811 39th St NW Washington DC 20016-2835

MACDONOUGH, JOHN N., beverage company executive. Past pres., COO Miller Brewing Co., Milw., chmn. bd., CEO, 1994—. Office: Miller Brewing Co 3939 W Highland Blvd Milwaukee WI 53208

MACDOUGAL, GARY EDWARD, corporate director, foundation trustee; b. Chgo., July 3, 1936; s. Thomas William and Lorna Lee (McDougall) MacD.; children: Gary Edward, Michael Scott; m. Charlene Gehm, June 15, 1992. BS in Engring., UCLA, 1958; MBA with distinction, Harvard U., 1962. Cons. McKinsey & Co., L.A., 1963-68, ptnr., 1968-69; chmn. bd., chief exec. officer Mark Controls Corp. (formerly Clayton Mark & Co.), Evanston, Ill., 1969-87; gen. dir. N.Y.C. Ballet, 1993-94; chmn. Gov. Task Force on Human Svcs. Reform State of Ill., 1993—; sr. advisor and asst. campaign mgr. George Bush for Pres., Washington, 1988; apptd. chmn. Bulgarian-Am. Enterprise Fund, Chgo. and Sophia, Bulgaria, 1991-93; bd. dirs., 1991—; apptd. to U.S. Commn. on Effectiveness of UN, 1992-93; bd. dirs., chmn. fin. com. United Parcel Svc. Am., Inc., Atlanta; bd. dirs. Union Camp Corp., Wayne, N.J., CBI Industries, Oak Brook, Ill.; adv. dir. Saratoga Ptnrs., N.Y.; instr. UCLA, 1969. Contbr. articles to profl. jours., chpts. to books. Trustee Annie E. Casey Found., UCLA Found., 1973-79, W.T. Grant Found., 1992-94, Russell Sage Found., 1981-91, chair, 1987-90; apptd. by Pres. Bush as pub. del., alt. rep., U.S. Del. UN 44th Gen. Assembly, 1989-90; commr. Sec. Labor's Commn. on Workforce Quality and Productivity, Washington, 1988-89. Lt. USNR, 1958-61. Mem. Harvard Club (N.Y.C.), Econ. Club (Chgo.), Harvard Bus. Sch. Club (Chgo.), Kappa Sigma. Episcopalian. Home: 505 N Lake Shore Dr Apt 2711 Chicago IL 60611-3406

MACDOUGALL, HARTLAND MOLSON, trust company director, retired bank executive; b. Montreal, Que., Can., Jan. 28, 1931; s. Hartland Campbell and Dorothy (Molson) MacD.; m. Eve Gordon, Oct. 29, 1954; children: Cynthia, Wendy, Keith, Willa, Tania. Ed., LeRosey, Switzerland, 1947-48, McGill U., 1949-53, Advanced Mgmt. Program, Harvard U., 1976. With Bank Montreal, various locations, 1953-84; vice chmn. Bank Montreal, 1981-84; chmn., dir. Royal Trustco Ltd., Toronto, 1984-93; dep. chmn. London Ins. Group, Inc.; dir. The Bermudiana Found. of Can. Founding chmn. Heritage Can., St. Michael's Hosp. Found., The Japan Soc., chmn., adv. com. Can.-Japan Bus. Com.; gov., past chmn. Coun. Can. Unity; dir. Friends of the Youth Awards Inc., U.S.; pres. Royal Agrl. Winter Fair; mem. Internat. Coun. Music Ctr. L.A., Adv. Coun. U. B.C.; gov. Olympic Trust; bd. dirs. Can. Soc. for Weismann Inst., Empire Club Found.; sen. Stratford Shakespearean Found.; former chmn. The Duke of Edinburgh Awards Internat. Coun. Decorated Order of Can., 1981, Comdr. Royal Victorian Order; recipient Order of the Rising Sun, Gold and Silver Star, Govt. of Japan, 1995. Avocations: skiing, tennis, farming. Office: Ste 1110, 70 York St, Toronto, ON Canada M5J 1S9

MACDOUGALL, JOHN DOUGLAS, earth science educator; b. Toronto, Ont., Can., Mar. 9, 1944; s. Lorn Graham and Grace A. (Virtue) MacD.; m. Shiela Dawn Ward, June 8, 1968; children: Christopher David, Katherine Heather. BS, U. Toronto, 1967; MS, McMaster U., 1968; PhD, U. Calif.-San Diego, 1972. Asst. research geologist U Calif., Berkeley, 1972-74; prof. earth scis. Scripps Inst. Oceanography U Calif.-San Diego, La Jolla, 1974—, chmn. geol. research div., 1985-89. Contbr. articles to profl. jours. Fellow Meteoritical Soc. :mem. AAAS, Geochem. Soc., Am. Geophys. Union. Home: 534 Bonair St La Jolla CA 92037-6112 Office: Scripps Inst Oceanography # 0220 La Jolla CA 92093

MACDOUGALL, PETER, lawyer; b. Boston, Sept. 22, 1937; s. Duncan Peck and Hildegard (Moebius) MacD. AB, Harvard U., 1958, LLB, 1963. Assoc. Ropes & Gray, Boston, 1964-73, ptnr., 1973—. Sheldon fellow Harvard U., 1963-64. Club: Harvard (Boston). Avocations: concert and opera going, gardening, reading, travel. Office: Ropes & Gray 1 International Pl Boston MA 02110-2600

MACDOUGALL, WILLIAM LOWELL, magazine editor; b. Des Moines, July 24, 1931; s. David Gregory and Elizabeth Jeanette (Dugan) MacD. A.B., Willamette U., Salem, Oreg., 1952; M.J. in Journalism (Pulitzer scholar 1953-54), Columbia U. 1953. Reporter Washington Star, 1958-62; corr. Los Angeles Times, 1962-63; assoc. editor, then London corr. U.S. News & World Report, 1964-68; asst. mng. editor U.S. News & World Report, Washington, 1978-86; mng. editor Artsreview mag. NEA, 1987-83; pres. Atlantic Media Co., Arlington, Va., 1989. Author: American Revolutionary: A Biography of General Alexander McDougall, 1977. Served with USAF, 1954-57. Recipient George Washington medal Freedoms Found., 1978, citation U.S. Bicentennial Commn., 1976. Methodist. Office: Atlantic Media Co 5000 37th St N Arlington VA 22207-1823

MAC DOWELL, ANDIE (ROSE ANDERSON MACDOWELL), actress; b. Gaffney, S.C., Apr. 21, 1958. Films include: Greystoke, 1984, St. Elmo's Fire, 1985, sex, lies and videotape, 1989, Green Card, 1990, Hudson Hawk, 1991, The Object of Beauty, 1991, The Player, 1992, Ruby, 1992, Groundhog Day, 1993, Short Cuts, 1993, Four Weddings and a Funeral, 1994, Bad Girls, 1994, Unstrung Heroes, 1995; TV includes Women and Men 2: In Love There Are No Rules, 1991, Sahara's Secret. Office: ICM 321 Westminster Ave Los Angeles CA 90020-4652*

MAC DOWELL, SAMUEL WALLACE, physics educator; b. Camaragibe, Brazil, Mar. 24, 1929; came to U.S., 1963; s. Samuel Wallace and Maria Anita (Amazonas) Mac D.; m. Myriam Ramos Da Silva, Feb. 2, 1953; children: Ana Myriam, Samuel Wallace, Maria Dolores. BSc in Engring., U. Pernambuco, Brazil, 1951; PhD in Math. Physics, Birmingham (Eng.) U., 1958. Rsch. assoc. Princeton (N.J.) U., 1959-60; assoc. prof. Centro Brasileiro De Fisicas Pesquisas, Rio de Janeiro, 1960-63; fellow Inst. for Advanced Study, Princeton, 1963-65; assoc. prof. Yale U., New Haven, 1965-67, prof., 1968—. Fellow Am. Phys. Soc.; mem. Brazilian Acad. Scis. Roman Catholic. Office: Yale U Sloane Physics Lab PO Box 6666 New Haven CT 06511

MACE, JOHN WELDON, pediatrician; b. Buena Vista, Va., July 9, 1938; s. John Henry and Gladys Elizabeth (Edwards) M.; m. Janice Mace, Jan. 28, 1962; children—Karin E., John E., James E. B.A., Columbia Union Coll., 1960; M.D., Loma Linda U., 1964. Diplomate: Am. Bd. Pediatrics, Sub-bd. Pediatric Endocrinology. Intern U.S. Naval Hosp., San Diego, 1964-65, resident in pediatrics, 1966-68; fellow in endocrinology and metabolism U. Colo., 1970-72; asst. prof. pediatrics Loma Linda (Calif.) U. Med. Center, 1972-75, prof. pediatrics, 1975—; med. dir. Loma Linda U. Children's Hosp., 1990-92, physician-in-chief, 1992—. Contbr. articles to profl. jours. Treas. Found. for Med. Care, San Bernardino County, 1979-80, pres., 1980-82; mem. Congl. Adv. Bd., 1984-87; pres. So. Calif. affiliate Am. Diabetes Assn., 1985-86, 1987-89; chmn. adv. bd. State Calif. Children's Svcs., 1986—; bd. dirs. So. Calif. Children's Cancer Svcs., 1993-94, Loma Linda Ronald McDonald House, 1991—, Aetna Health Plans of Calif., 1993-95, Loma Linda U. Health Care. With USN, 1962-70. Named Loma Linda U. Sch. Medicine Alumnus of Yr., 1994. Mem. AAAS, Am. Acad. of Pediatrics, N.Y. Acad. Sci., Calif. Med. Soc. (adv. panel genetic diseases State Calif., 1975—), Western Soc. Pediatric Rsch., Lawson Wilkens Pediatric Endocrine Soc., Assn. Med. Pediatric Dept. Chairmen, Sigma Xi, Alpha Omega Alpha. Office: Loma Linda U Sch Medicine Barton & Anderson Sts Loma Linda CA 92350

MACER, DAN JOHNSTONE, retired hospital administrator; b. Evansville, Ind., May 25, 1917; s. Clarence Guy and Ann (Johnstone) M.; m. Eugenia Loretta Andrews, June 1, 1943; children: Eugenia Ann, Dan James. B.S., Northwestern U., 1939, M.S. in Hosp. Adminstrn. with distinction, 1959. Chief hosp. ops. VA br. office, St. Paul, 1947-50; asst. mgr. VA hosps., Ft. Wayne, Ind., 1951, Kerrville, Tex., 1952, Augusta, Ga., 1952-56; mgr. VA Hosp., Sunmount, N.Y., 1956-58; dir. VA Research Hosp., Chgo., 1958-62; mem. hosp. adminstrn. faculty Northwestern U., 1959-61; dir. VA Hosps., Pitts., 1962-67; asst. vice chancellor health professions U. Pitts., 1968-71; prof. med. and hosp. adminstrn. U. Pitts. Grad. Sch. Pub. Health, 1962-71; prof. Coll. Health and Coll. Medicine, U. Okla., 1971-89, retired, 1989; dir. VA Hosps. and Clinics, Oklahoma City, 1971-76, VA Med. Dist. 20 (Okla.-Ark.), 1971-76; lectr. George Washington U., 1961-71; v.p. Hosp. Casualty Co., Oklahoma City, 1978-89; pres. Dan J. Macer & Assos., Inc.; cons. to health field; cons. nat. health profl. assns., indsl. corps., archtl. corps, health planners; cons. Health Services and Mental Health Administrn., HEW, 1968. Mem. editorial bd.: Nursing and Health Care, 1980-88; author articles in field. Coordinator civil def. and disaster planning all hosps., Chgo. no. North Side, 1961; chmn. welfare and planning council Savannah River Community Chest, Augusta, 1954-56; chmn. group 12 Fed. sect., govt. div. United Fund Allegheny County, 1964-65; mem. Fed. Interagy. Bd. Dirs., 1964-68; sec. U. Pitts. Health Center, 1969-71; chmn. health com. Health and Welfare Assn. Alleghany County, 1970-71; chmn. devel. com. Northwestern U. Alumni Program in Hosp. Adminstrn., 1962-63; chmn. adv. com. Regional Med. Program Western Pa., 1966-71; mem. steering com. Comprehensive Health Planning Western Pa.; dir. Am. States Regional Conf., 1971; vice chmn. procedures com., mem.-at-large exec. com. Okla. Regional Med. Program, 1971-78; mem. Gov's Adv. Com. Comprehensive Health Planning, 1971-80, Gov's Com. Employment of Handicapped, 1972, Pres.'s Com. Employment of Handicapped, 1962; chmn. VA chief med. dir.'s com. for evaluation and reorgn. VA health care delivery services, 1974-76; chmn. planning com. for constrn. New Children's Meml. Hosp., 1974-78; chmn. Gov's Ad Hoc Com on Fed.-State Planning, 1973-78; mem. Gov's Health Scis. Center planning and adv. com., 1973-78, State Health Planning Council, 1973-78; chmn. Okla. Health Goals and Planning Priorities Com., 1973-80; bd. dirs. Comprehensive Health Planning Agy., Western Pa.; bd. dirs. Health Services Corp., 1969-71, Okla. affiliate Am. Heart Assn., 1980-89; trustee Okla. Council Health Careers and Manpower, 1976-80; examiner Am. Coll. Hosp. Adminstrs. Lt. col. Med. Adminstrv. Corps, AUS, 1941-46. Decorated Bronze Star, Purple Heart; recipient citations VFW, 1959, citations Am. Legion, 1956, 58, citations DAV, 1964, citations Okla. Regional Med. Program, 1976, citations Okla. Gov's Office Health Planning, 1976, Laura G. Jackson award in recognition exceptional service in field of hosp. adminstrn., 1971, Disting. Service award Coll. Pub. Health U. Okla., 1987, Disting. Dedicated Service award Okla. Hosp. Assn., 1987; Leadership programs established in his honor Coll. Pub. Health, U. Okla. Fellow Am. Pub. Health Assn., Am. Coll. Health Care Execs. (life); mem. Am. Hosp. Assn. (life, mem. council med. edn. 1976-79), Hosp. Assn. Pa. (vice chmn. med. relations 1965-66, chmn. rehab. com. 1965-66, vice chmn. council on profl. practices, dir.), Hosp. Council Western Pa., Assn. Am. Med. Colls. (exec. com. council teaching hosps.), Oklahoma City C. of C. (vice chmn. research and edn. div. 1975-80), Northwestern U. Alumni Assn. (pres. Acacia chpt. 1961, hosp. adminstrn. chpt. 1962). Clubs: Kiwanian. (Chgo.); University (Pitts.); Petroleum; Twin Hills Golf and Country (Oklahoma City), University (Oklahoma City). Home: 2925 Pelham Dr Oklahoma City OK 73120-4348

MACERA, SALVATORE, industrial executive; b. Cambridge, Mass., May 3, 1931; s. Benedetto and Anna (DeVellis) M.; m. Josephine Guarnaccia (div.); children: Michael, Richard, Michelle; m. Daphne Lee. B.B.A. Northeastern U., 1960; grad., MIT Sloan Sr. Exec. Program, 1967. Financial analyst Ford Motor Co., 1955-58; v.p. finance and adminstrn. LFE Electronics div. Lab. for Electronics, Boston, 1958-63; v.p., chief financial officer Itek Corp., 1963-73, exec. v.p., 1973-82, also dir.; pres. Itek Electronics and Optical Industries, 1980-82; chmn., chief exec. officer Camelot Ind., 1981-82; chmn. Bristol Med. Elec., Boston; pres. R.V. Whitehall; chmn. The Fin. Adv. Ctre., Ltd.; bd. dirs. Harbor Nat. Bank, Boston, Fossella Assocs., Patriot Bancorp., Infinite Corp., Saxby Computer Corp., Baker & Lander, Internat. Ins. Corp., Whitman Group Inc., Conifer Group, David Banash and Co., Steinroe Variable Annuity Trust, Steinroe Variable Annuity Fund. Mem. budget com. Fin. Inst.; trustee Bentley Coll.; bd. dirs. Assoc. Industries Mass. With AUS. Home: 507-509 Rowes Wharf Boston MA 02109

MACERO, TEO, composer, conductor; b. Glens Falls, N.Y., Oct. 30, 1925; s. Daniel and Angeline (De Fabio) M.; m. Jeanne Marie Crawley; 1 child, Suzanne E. BS, Juilliard Sch. Music, 1951, MS, 1953. Condr., composer, performer with N.Y. Philharm., Kansas City (Mo.) Symphony Orch., Buffalo Symphony, Santa Clara (Calif.) Symphony Orch.; composer with Pa. Ballet Co., Robert Joffrey Ballet Co., Anna Sokolow Ballet Co., Winnipeg (Can.) Ballet Co.; producer with various artists including Miles Davis, Dave Brubeck, Duke Ellington, Count Basie, Leonard Bernstein, Mahalia Jackson; lectr. Contemporary Am. music and jazz. Producer 18 Gold Records including Chorus Line (original cast album), Bitches Brew (Miles Davis), Sun Goddess (Ramsey Lewis), The Graduate (Simon & Garfunkel), Time Out (Dave Brubeck), Robert Palmer; composer, condr.: (TV films) Sgt Matlovich vs. U.S. Army Air Corp, Top Secret, Teddy Kennedy Jr. Story, 1986, Special Friendships, 1987; (films) Cassius Clay, Skill, Brains & Guts, Jack Johnson; (documentary) The Body Human; (TV series) Lifeline, Omni; composer: Time Plus Seven, Acoustic Suspension, Christmas Tree; (ballet) Everything Goes, 1982; (opera) Once A Slave. Served with USN, 1943-47, PTO. Club: Metropolitan (N.Y.C.). Home: PO Box 932 Quogue NY 11959-0932

MACESICH, GEORGE, econnomics professor; b. Cleve., May 27, 1927; m. Susana Sonja Svorkovich, Feb. 16, 1955; children: Maja, Milena, George M.P. AA, George Washington U., 1951, BA, 1953, MA, 1954; PhD, U. Chgo., 1958. Tchg. and rsch. positions while completing graduate study, 1953-58; rsch. economist U.S. C. of C., Washington, 1958-59; asst. prof. Econs. Fla. State U., Tallahassee, Fla., 1959-61; assoc. prof. Econs. Fla. State U., Tallahassee, 1961-63; prof. Econs. Fla. State U., Tallahassee, 1963—, U. Belgrade, Yugoslavia, 1972—; mem. Editorial Bd. So. Econ. Jour., 1961-63; cons. U.S. Dept. Commerce, 1961-65; vis. economist Nat. Bank of Yugoslavia, 1965; founding dir. Ctr. for Yugoslav-Am. Studies, Rsch. and Exchanges, Fla. State U., 1961—; Inst. Comparative Policy Studies Rsch. and Exchanges, 1992—; cons. Jour. of Political Economy, U. Chgo., 1968-81, The Coun. of Grad. Schs. in U.S., Washington, 1971-82, Jour. of Money, Credit and Banking, 1977-89; editorial bd. Foreign Trade and Cycles, 1970-76, So. Economic Jour., 1972-76; and numerous other roles related to economics. Author, co-author or editor of 30 published books and over 100 articles including The International Monetary Economy and the Third World, 1981, Politics of Monetarism: Its Historical and Institutional Development, 1984, Monetary Reform and Cooperation Theory, 1989, Money and Democracy, 1990, (with D. Dimitrijevic) The Money Supply Process: A Comparative Analysis, 1990, World Debt and Stability, 1990, Reform and Market Democracy, 1991, Yugoslavia in the Age of Democracy: Essays on Economic and Political Reform, 1992, Monetary Policy and Politics: RulesVersus Discretion, 1992; contbr. numerous articles to profl. jours. Bd. dirs. Coun. Econ. Devel., Tallahassee, Fla., 1961-63, Nikola Tesla Meml. Soc., 1980-81; mem. U.S. - Yugoslav Economic Coun., 1987—, Inst. for Internat. Edn. Screening Com. 1984-87. With U.S. Navy 1944-53. Recipient Ford Found. fellowship, 1959-60, Fulbright fellowship, 1965, Order of Yugoslav Star with Gold Wreath, Yugoslav Govt., 1983, award of Merit, U. Zagreb, 1989. Mem. Am. Acad. Polit. and Social Sci., Am. Econ. Assn., Am. Foreign Policy Assn., Am. Statis. Assn., So. Economic Assn., U.S. Naval Inst., Pi Gamma Mu. Home: 2401 Delgado Dr Tallahassee FL 32304-1303 Office: Inst Comparative Policy and Dept Economics Fla State U Tallahassee FL 32306

MACEWAN, BARBARA ANN, middle school educator; b. Adams, Mass., Apr. 22, 1938; d. Thomas Lawrence and Vera (Ziemba) Gaskalka; m. George Louie MacEwan, Feb. 16, 1963; children: Rebecca, Debra. BS in Edn. cum laude, North Adams State Coll., 1959; MEd with honors, Plymouth State Coll., 1994. Cert. K-8, secondary social studies tchr., sch. libr., Mass. Tchr. Town of Valatie, N.Y., 1959-61, 62-63, Dept. Def., Aschefensburg, Germany, 1961-62, Town of East Longmeadow, Mass., 1964; asst. children's libr. Springfield (Mass.) Libr., 1964; tchr. history Southwick (Mass.)-Tolland Regional Schs., 1971—; state coord. Nat. History Day, 1989-92. Author: The Old Cemetery: Southwick, 1977, Shays Rebellion, 1987. Sec. Southwick Hist. Soc., 1976-79, treas., 1979-86, pres., 1986-94; trustee Moore House, Southwick, 1989—; chair Southwick Hist. Commn., 1994—; active Mass. Curriculum Framework Focus Group, 1994—. Recipient recognition New Eng. League Mid. Schs., 1991; Horace Mann grantee Southwick Sch. Com., 1982. Mem. ASCD, NEA, Mass. Tchrs. Assn., Hampden County Tchrs. Assn., Southwick Edn. Assn., New Eng. History Tchrs. Assn., New Eng. Oral History Assn., Nat. Coun. for Social Studies, Mass. Coun. for Social Studies (recognition 1992), Western Mass. Coun. for Social Studies (bd. dirs. 1987—), Mass. Assn. Indian Media, Nat. Mus. Am. Indian, New Eng. Native Am. Inst., Pioneer Valley Reading Coun., Phi Delta Kappa. Roman Catholic. Avocations: gardening, walking, reading, travel. Office: Powder Mill Mid Sch 94 Powder Mill Rd Southwick MA 01077-9324

MACEWAN, NIGEL SAVAGE, merchant banker; b. Balt., Mar. 21, 1933; s. Nigel Savage and Ellen (Wharton) MacE.; children: Alison, Nigel, Pamela, Elizabeth. BA, Yale U., 1955; MBA, Harvard U., 1959. Assoc. Morgan Stanley & Co., N.Y.C., 1959-62, White, Weld & Co., N.Y.C., 1962-63; v.p. R.S. Dickson & Co., Charlotte, N.C., 1963-68; chmn. Fin. Cons. Internat. Ltd., Brussels, 1965-68; successively gen. ptnr., exec. v.p., pres., dir. White, Weld & Co., N.Y.C., 1968-78; sr. v.p., dir. Merrill Lynch, Pierce, Fenner & Smith, N.Y.C., 1978-87; chmn. Merrill Lynch Capital Ptnrs., N.Y.C., 1985-87; pres., CEO Kleinwort Benson, N.Am. Inc., N.Y.C., 1987-93, also bd.

dirs.; chmn. Kleinwort Benson North Am., Inc., Kleinwort Benson Holdings, Inc., Alex Brown Kleinwort Benson Realty Advs.; bd. dirs. Kleinwort Benson Group plc, Kleinwort Benson Ltd., Kleinwort Benson Australian Income Fund, 1992—; adj. prof. bus. adminstrn. NYU, 1973-75. Pres. Tokeneke Tax Dist., Darien, 1978-80, later treas. Served with USN, 1955-57. Mem. Securities Industry Assn. (chmn. N.Y. group 1975-76), Links Club, N.Y. Yacht Club, Yale Club N.Y., Wee Burn Country Club, Tokeneke Club, Tarrantine Club (Dark Harbor, Maine). Republican. Episcopalian. Home: 69 Hale Ln Darien CT 06820-6225 Office: Kleinwort Benson NAm Inc 200 Park Ave New York NY 10166-0005

MACEWEN, EDWARD CARTER, communications executive; b. Cleve., Feb. 12, 1938; s. Kenneth Donald and Helen (von Den Steinen) MacE.; m. Janet Ellen Sandrock; children: Michael, Bonnie. BFA, Carnegie Mellon U., 1960; MA, Fairfield U., 1984. Art dir. Andrews, Bartlett & Assocs., Cleve., 1960-63; producer Wilding, Inc., Cleve., 1963-66; dir. corp. advt. PPG Industries, Inc., Pitts., 1966-79; v.p. corp. communications, pres. GTE Found. GTE Corp., Stamford, Conn., 1979—. Mem. Assn. of Nat. Advertisers (bd. dirs.), Ad Coun., The Wisemen. Home: 208 Chestnut Hill Wilton CT 06897 Office: GTE Corp One Stamford Forum Stamford CT 06904

MAC EWEN, GEORGE DEAN, physician, medical institute executive; b. Metcalfe, Ont., Can., Nov. 10, 1927; s. George W. and Catherine (Grant) MacE.; m. Marilyn Ruth Heidelberger, May 29, 1954; children: Kathryn, Jane, Nancy, David, John. M.D., C.M., Queen's U., Kingston, Ont., Can., 1953. Diplomate: Am. Bd. Orthopaedic Surgery (examiner 1971—). Intern D.C. Gen. Hosp., Washington, 1953-54; resident in gen. surgery Emergency Hosp., Washington, 1954-55; fellow in orthopaedic surgery Campbell Clinic, Memphis, 1955-58; asst. med. dir. Alfred I. duPont Inst., Wilmington, Del., 1958-68; surgeon-in-chief Alfred I. duPont Inst., 1961-79, med. dir., 1969-87; chmn. pediatric orthopaedic surgery Children's Hosp., New Orleans, 1987-93; chief orthopaedic sci. VA Hosp., Wilmington, 1960-66, cons. in orthopaedics, The Med. Ctr. Del., 1961—; cons. in orthopaedics Wilmington Med. Center, 1961—; St. Francis Hosp., Wilmington, 1961-86; cons. in orthopaedic surgery Surgeon Gen. U.S. Navy, 1964-72 , USAF Hosp., Dover, Del.; med. cons. John G. Leach Sch., Wilmington; cons. USAF Base, Dover, Del., 1961-86, Evan G. Shortlidge Sch., Wilmington, 1961-70, Pocono Med. Svcs., 1973-74, Walter Reed Army Hosp., Washington, 1978-86; med. adv. com. Del. Systems for Exceptional Children, 1973-86; cons. Surgeon Gen. U.S., 1982-86; emeritus in orthopaedic surgery St. Francis Hosp., Med. Ctr. Del., 1987—; assoc. prof. orthopaedic surgery Jefferson Med. Coll., Thomas Jefferson U., Phila., 1970-76, prof., 1976-86; clin. prof. U. Del., Newark, 1977-80; lectr. U.S. Naval Hosp., Phila., 1964-80; exec. com. Del. sch. health adv. com., 1966-86; med. adv. com. VA Hosp., 1965-79; mem. U. Del. Research Found., 1976-79; mem. subcom. Ctr. for Disease Control, 1990-93. Editor Orthopedic Resident, 1990—; mem. editorial bd. Del. Med. Jour., 1966-69; contbr. articles to books, jours. Bd. trustees Wilmington Coll., 1980—; bd. dirs. Arthritis Found., 1974-77; bd. dirs. Blood Bank of Del., 1969-78, exec. com., 1976-78, hon. mem., 1979—; editorial bd. of Evaluation and Health Professions, 1985—. Fellow Am. Acad. Cerebral Palsy; mem. Acad. of Medicine (Wilmington), Academia Mexicana de Cirugia (hon.), Am. Acad. Orthopaedic Surgeons (chmn., mem. various coms.), Am. Acad. Pediatrics (orthopaedic surg. fellow 1977—), ACS, AMA (ho. of dels. 1982-86), Am. Orthopaedic Assn. (traveling fellow 1967, pres. 1980-81, various coms.), Brit. Orthopaedic Assn. (corr.), Brazilian Orthopaedic Soc. (hon.), Campbell Club (pres. 1979), Can. Orthopaedic Assn. (trustee 1969-75), Coll. of Physicians (Phila.), Cosmos Club, Del. State Med. Soc., Eastern Orthopedic Assn., Fla. Orthopaedic Assn. (hon.), New Castle County Med. Soc. (del. 1970-72), Nat. Assn. Children's Hosps. and Related Instns. (bd. trustees 1980—), N.J. Orthopaedic Soc. (hon.), Del. Soc. Orthopedic Surgeons (charter), Orthopaedic Forum Club, Orthopaedic Rsch. Soc., Pan Am. Orthopedic Orgn., Pediatric Orthopaedic Soc. N.Am. (pres. 1972-73), Pa. Orthopaedic Soc. (hon.), Phila. Orthopaedic Soc. (pres. 1968-69), Scoliosis Rsch. Soc. (founding, exec. com. 1969-74, pres. 1971-73), Societe de Scoliose du Quebec (hon.), Societe Internationale de Chirurgie Orthopedique et de Traumatologie (exec com. 1979-86, SICOT Found. bd. dirs. 1990—), S. African Orthopaedic Assn. (hon.), Tex. Orthopaedic Assn. (hon.), Nat. Neurofibromatosis Found. (med. adv. bd. 1981—), German Orthopaedic Assn. (hon.), Costa Rican Orthopaedic Soc. (hon.), Mexican Orthopedic Soc. (hon.), Japanese Orthopaedic Assn. (hon.), Twentieth Century Orthopaedic Assn., Houston Orthopaedic Soc., La. Orthopaedic Assn., La. State Med. Soc., Mid-Am. Orthopaedic Assn. (hon.), Orleans Parish Med. Soc., So. Med. Assn., So Orthopaedic Assn. (hon.), Sociedad Mexicana de Ortopedia (hon.). Office: PO Box 270 New Castle DE 19720-5040

MACEY, JONATHAN R., law educator; b. 1955. BA, Harvard U., 1977; JD, Yale U., 1982. Bar: Ga. 1986. Law clk. to Hon. Henry J. Friendly U.S. Ct. Appeals (2nd cir.), N.Y.C., 1982-83; asst. prof. Emory U., 1983-86, assoc. prof., 1986-87; vis. assoc. prof. U. Va., 1986-87; prof. Cornell U., 1987-90; vis. prof. U. Chgo., fall 1989, winter 1990—. Mem. ABA (com. on corp. laws), Nat. Assn. Security Dealers (bd. arbitrators). Office: U Chgo Law Sch 1111 E 60th St Chicago IL 60637-2702

MACEY, MORRIS WILLIAM, lawyer; b. Camilla, Ga., Dec. 25, 1922; s. Isadore and Freda (Berman) M.; m. Dora Rosenfield, Dec. 28, 1950; children: Morris William, Jonathan Rosenfield, Rex Philip. A.B., U. Ga., 1946, LL.B., 1943; LL.M., Harvard, 1947. Bar: Ga. 1943, D.C. 1980. Practiced in Atlanta, 1947—; ptnr. Macey, Wilensky, Cohen, Wittner & Kessler; formerly adj. prof. Emory U. Law Sch., U. Ga. Law Sch.; Pres. Comml. Law League Am., 1966-67. Vice chmn., asso. editor: Comml. Law Jour. Chmn. bd. Associated Credit Union; former chmn. Southeastern Bankruptcy Law Inst.; former pres. Consumer Credit Counseling Svc.; former trustee Fisk U. Served with AUS, 1943-46. Mem. ABA (chmn. ad hoc com. on partnerships in bankruptcy, bus. law sect.), Internat. Bar Assn., Ga. Bar Assn., Atlanta Bar Assn., Nat. Bankruptcy Conf., Nat. Conf. Commrs. on Uniform State Laws, Nat. Assn. Comml. Fin. Attys., Am. Law Inst., Am. Coll. Bankruptcy, Am. Bankruptcy Inst., Phi Beta Kappa, Omicron Delta Kappa. Jewish (trustee Temple Sinai 1969-70). Clubs: Lawyers (Atlanta), Harvard (Atlanta), Standard (Atlanta), Commerce (Atlanta). Lodges: Masons; Shriners. Home: 4175 Conway Valley Rd NW Atlanta GA 30327-3607 Office: 133 Carnegie Way NW Ste 700 Atlanta GA 30303-1024

MACEY, WILLIAM BLACKMORE, oil company executive; b. Buffalo, Aug. 1, 1920; s. Richard Charles and Doris (Bourne) M.; m. Jean Olive Mullins, Oct. 6, 1945; 1 dau., Barbara Jean. B.S. in Petroleum Engring, N.Mex. Sch. Mines, 1942; D.Engring. (hon.), N.Mex. Inst. Mining and Tech., 1984. Dist. engr. N.Mex. Oil Conservation Commn., 1946-48; dist. supt. Am. Republics Corp., 1948-52; chief engr. N.Mex. Oil Conservation Commn., 1952-54, state geologist, dir., 1954-56; v.p. Internat. Oil & Gas Corp. (and predecessor co., developers mineral properties), Denver, 1956-60; then pres. Internat. Oil & Gas Corp. (and predecessor co., developers mineral properties), 1960-67; pres. Nielson Enterprises Inc., oil and gas prodn. and pipelines, livestock ranching, 1967-74; v.p., dir. Y-Tex Corp. (mfr. livestock identification tags), 1972-73; pres. GEN Oil Inc. (oil and gas prodn.), 1972-75, Col. Cody Inn (real estate and golf course devel.), 1970-73; pres., dir. Macey & Mershon Oil, Inc., 1974-93; dir. Juniper Oil and Gas Corp., Denver, 1981-83, Ruidoso (N.Mex.) State Bank Holding Co., 1987—; pres. The Macey Corp., Denver, 1985—. Served from 2d lt. to capt. USAAF, 1942-45. Mem. N.Mex. Oil and Gas Assn. (exec. com. 1949-52, 60-61). Episcopalian. Clubs: Garden of the Gods, Skyline Country (Tucson) (dir., treas. 1980-82, pres. 1982-83), Pres.'s N.Mex. Inst. Mines and Tech. (chmn. 1980-82), Pres.'s U. Ariz. Found., AltoLakes Golf and Country, Tucson Country, Ruidoso, N.Mex. Jockey Club (bd. dirs. 1985-88, 91-93, pres. 1993). Home: 7010 N Javelina Dr Tucson AZ 85718-1850 also: PO Box 360 Alto NM 88312 Office: 1801 Broadway Ste 1600 PO Box 2210 Denver CO 80201

MACFADYEN, DAVID JERRY, building research executive; b. Stuttgart, Ark., Jan. 9, 1940; s. Donald James and Mildred (Baker) MacF.; m. Bonnie Jean Page, Sept. 24, 1961 (div. Sept. 1981); children: Megan Page MacFadyen Coursey, Donald James, Jason Lawrence; m. 2d, Allison R. Porter; 1 child, Andrew Dorfman. BSCE, MIT, 1967, MS in Structural Engring., 1969; MBA in Fin., Northwestern U., 1971. Constrn. supt. various cos., 1960-67; rsch. engr. U.S. Gypsum, Des Plaines, Ill., 1967-69; mgr. Dialog Computing Inc., Milford, Conn., 1969-71; div. mgr. Abt Assocs., Inc., Cambridge, Mass., 1971-74; pres. Tech. & Econs., Inc., Cam-

bridge, 1974-82; exec. v.p. Nat. Assn. Home Builders Rsch. Found., Inc., Rockville, Md., 1983-86; pres. Nat. Assn. Home Builders Rsch. Found., Inc., Upper Marlboro, Md., 1986—; chmn., chief exec. officer Smart House Venture, Upper Marlboro, 1985—; also bd. dirs. Smart House Venture; bd. dirs. NAHB Rsch. Found., Inc. Author: In the Bank... Or up the Chimney?, 1975. Mem. Sigma Xi. Home: 15800 Perkins Ln Bowie MD 20716-1641 Office: NAHB Nat Rsch Ctr 400 Prince Georges Blvd Upper Marlboro MD 20772-8731

MACFARLAND, CRAIG GEORGE, natural resource management professional; b. Great Falls, Mont., July 17, 1943; s. Paul Stanley and Jean Elizabeth (Graham) MacF.; m. Janice Lee Bennett, Dec. 23, 1963 (div. 1987); children: Bennett, Francisco; m. Marilyn Ann Swanson, Mar. 19, 1988; stepchildren: Alyssa, Krista, Sara. BA magna cum laude, Austin Coll., 1965; MA, U. Wis., Madison, 1969, PhD in Zoology, 1993; DSc (hon.), Austin Coll., 1978. Dir. Charles Darwin Rsch. Sta., Galapagos Islands, Ecuador, 1974-78; head Wildlands and watershed mgmt. program Cen. Am. Centro Agronomico Tropical de Investigacion Enseñanza, Turrialba, Costa Rica, 1978-85; pres. Charles Darwin Found. for Galapagos Islands, Ecuador, 1985—; cons. natural resources and sustainable devel. in Latin Am. Moscow, Idaho, 1985—; affiliate faculty dept. Resource, Recreation and Tourism, U. Idaho, Moscow, 1988—; affiliate faculty dept. natural resource recreation and tourism Colo. State U., Ft. Collins, 1992. Contbr. to numerous profl. publs. Recipient Internat. Conservation medal Zool. Soc. San Diego, 1978, Order of Golden Ark for internat. conservation, Prince Bernhard of Netherlands, 1984. Mem. Ecol. Soc. Am., Internat. Soc. Tropical Foresters, Assn. Tropical Biology, Soc. Conservation Biology, Nature Conservancy, World Wildlife Fund, Greenpeace. Avocations: cross-country skiing, hiking, camping, skiing. Office: Charles Darwin Found 836 Mabelle Moscow ID 83843-3553

MACFARLAND, ROBERT FREDERICK, bank executive; b. Newburgh, N.Y., Dec. 10, 1931; s. Frederick R. and Martha (Neubert) M.; m. Nancy L. Henderson, Dec. 4, 1950; 1 child, Sharon MacFarland Dillon. BA, Trinity Coll., Hartford, Conn., 1950; cert. banking, Stonier Grad. Sch. Rutgers U., 1968. From br. mgr. to pres. Highland Nat. Bank, Newburgh, N.Y., 1951-81; chmn., chief exec. officer Norstar Mid-Hudson Bank Group, 1981-82, Norstar Long Island Bank Group, 1982-84; exec. v.p. Norstar Bancorp Inc., Albany, N.Y., 1984-86; pres. Norstar Bank of Upstate N.Y., Albany, 1986-87, chmn. chief exec. officer, 1987—. Dir. Capital Region Tech. Devel. Council, 1987—, Albany Area Econ. Devel. Commn., 1987—, Ctr. for Econ. Growth, Saratoga Performing Arts Ctr., Gov's. World Trade Coun.; pres. SUNY at Albany Found. Mem. Hudson Mohawk Assn. Colls. & Univs., 50 Group, Fort Orange Club, Schuyler Meadows Country Club (Loudonville, N.Y.). Office: Norstar Bank Upstate NY 69 State St Albany NY 12207-2504

MACFARLANE, ALASTAIR IAIN ROBERT, business executive; b. Sydney, Australia, Mar. 7, 1940; came to U.S., 1978; s. Alexander Dunlop and Margaret Elizabeth (Swan) M.; m. Madge McCleary, Sept. 24, 1966; children: Douglas, Dennis, Robert, Jeffrey. B in Econs. with honours, U. Sydney, 1961; MBA, U. Hawaii, 1964; postgrad., Columbia U., 1964; AMP, Harvard U., 1977. Comml. cadet B.H.P. Ltd., Australia, 1958-62; product mgr. H.J. Heinz Co., Pitts., 1965-66; gen. mgr. new products div. H.J. Heinz Co., Melbourne, Australia, 1967-72; ptnr., dir., gen. mgr. Singleton, Palmer & Strauss McAllan Pty. Ltd., Sydney, 1972-73; dir., gen. mgr. successor co. Doyle Dane Bernbach Internat. Inc., Sydney, 1973-77; group sr. v.p. Doyle Dane Bernbach Internat. Inc., N.Y.C., 1978-84; pres., chief exec. officer PowerBase Systems, Inc., 1984-85, Productivity Software Internat. L.P., N.Y.C., 1985-86; div. pres., pub. Whittle Comm. L.P., Knoxville, Tenn., 1987-88; chmn., CEO Phyton Techs. Inc., Knoxville, 1988-94; pres., CEO Knox Internat. Corp., Knoxville, 1988-94; chmn., CEO Mich. Bulb Co., Grand Rapids, 1988-94; chmn., CEO Lansinoh Labs., Inc., Oak Ridge, Tenn., 1994—; lectr. Monash U., Melbourne, 1970-71; ind. mgmt. cons., Melbourne, 1970-72; dir. Univ. of Sydney USA Found., 1994—. Author papers in field. V.p. Waverley Dist. Cricket Club, 1975-77. East-West Ctr. fellow, 1962-64; Australian Commonwealth scholar, Australian Steel Industry scholar, 1961. Fellow Australian Inst. Mgmt. (assoc.); mem. Australian Soc. Accts. (assoc.), Harvard Club N.Y.C., Cherokee Country Club. Home: 5210 Rio Vista Ln Knoxville TN 37919-8938 Office: 1670 Oak Ridge Tpke Oak Ridge TN 37830-4933

MACFARLANE, ANDREW WALKER, media specialist, educator; b. Toronto, Ont., Can., Feb. 18, 1928; s. Joseph Arthur and Marguerite (Walker) MacF.; m. Betty Doris Wright Seldon; 1 stepchild, Elizabeth Seldon; children by previous marriage: Jeanie Andreas, Catriona Flora. Student, U. Sask., Can., 1945-46; B.A., U. Toronto, 1949; M.L.S., U. Western Ont., 1977. With Canadian Press, Toronto, 1949; reporter Halifax (N.S., Can.) Chronicle Herald, 1949-51, Scottish Daily Express, Glasgow, 1951-53; subeditor London Evening Standard, 1953-55; copy editor, night editor, feature editor, gen. reporter, daily columnist, asst. to pub. Telegram, Toronto, 1955-64; mng. editor, corporate dir. Telegram, 1964-69, dir. research and devel., 1969-71, exec. editor, 1971—; dir. Citizen's Inquiry br. Ministry Govt. Services, Province of Ont., 1971-72; chmn. dept., dean Grad. Sch. Journalism, U. Western Ont., 1973-80, prof., 1981-93; prof. emeritus U. Western Ont., 1993—; chair mass media studies, dir. Ctr. in Mass Media Studies Grad. Sch. Journalism, U. Western Ont., 1990-93; co-chmn. Ont.-Que. Journalist Exchange. Author: The Neverland of the Neglected Child, 1957, It Seemed Like a Good Idea at the Time, 1983, Local Flavor, 1990; editor: Byline, 1983, Byline Canada, 1984. Bd. dirs. Canadian Medic-Alert, 1959; past bd. dirs. Met. Toronto Children's Aid Soc.; chmn. advisory council Province of Ont. Medal Good Citizenship. Recipient Bowater award, 1960, Nat. Newspaper award, 1958, 59, Nat. Teaching award Poynter Inst. for Media Studies, 1987, Province Ont. Bicentennial medal; Southam fellow, 1961. Mem. Assn. for Edn. in Journalism and Mass Comm., Can. Comm. Assn., Commonwealth Assn. for Edn. in Journalism and Comm. (founding pres.), Toronto Press Club.

MACFARLANE, JOHN ALEXANDER, former federal housing agency administrator; b. Winnipeg, Man., Can., Sept. 6, 1916; s. John MacKay and Annie Catherine (Smith) MacF.; m. Gladys Valda Church, Dec. 20, 1941; children: John Lane, Elizabeth Ann, Janet Christine. BA with honours, U. Man., Winnipeg, 1939. With stats. br. Wartime Prices and Trade Bd., Ottawa, Ont., Can., 1940-46; supr. stats. dept. Cn. Mortgage and Housing Corp., Ottawa, 1946-65, asst. dir. econs. and stats. div., 1965-69, asst. dir. secretariat div., 1969-78; ret., 1978; treas. Caribbean and N.Am. area coun. World Alliance Ref. Chs., Ottawa, 1984—. Treas. Ottawa Valley Cricket Coun., 1946-70, 73-80, pres., 1970-73, 83-88; moderator presbytery Ottawa, Presbyn. Ch. Can., 1994-95. Recipient Long Svc. medal Boy Scouts Assn., 1945, Centennial medal Govt. of Can., 1967, sgl. achievement award for amateur sport Govt. of Ont., 1991; mem. choir St. Andrew's Presbyn. Ch. Mem. Def. Cricket Club (sec.-treas. 1944-46, pres. 1951-76, 78-92). Avocation: stamp collecting. Address: 99 Acacia Ave, Ottawa, ON Canada K1M 0P8 *I have touched many people as the years have passed; if I have helped one for the better I shall rest content.*

MACFARLANE, JOHN CHARLES, utility company executive; b. Hallock, Minn., Nov. 8, 1939; s. Ernest Edward and Mary Bell (Yates) MacF.; m. Eunice Darlene Axvig, Apr. 13, 1963; children: Charles, James, William. BSEE, U. N.D., 1961. Staff engr. Otter Tail Power Co., Fergus Falls, Mn., 1961-64; div. engr. Otter Tail Power Co., Jamestown, N.D., 1964-71; div. mgr. Otter Tail Power Co., Langdon, N.D., 1972-78; v.p. planning and control Otter Tail Power Co., Fergus Falls, 1978-80, exec. v.p., 1981-82, pres. and chief exec. officer, 1982—, also bd. dirs., now chmn.; bd. dirs. Northwest Bank, Fergus Falls, Pioneer Mut. Ins. Co. Pres. Langdon City Commn., 1974-78; chmn. Fergus Falls Port Authority, 1985-86; bd. dirs. Minn. Assn. Commerce and Industry, Minn. Safety Council; chmn. bd. dirs. U. N.D. Energy Research Adv. Council. Served with U.S. Army, 1962-64. Mem. Am. Mgmt. Assn., IEEE (chmn. Red River chpt.), U. N.D. Alumni Assn., Fergus Falls C. of C. Republican. Presbyterian. Lodges: Rotary, Masons. Office: Otter Tail Power Co 215 S Cascade St Fergus Falls MN 56537*

MACFARLANE, MALCOLM HARRIS, physics educator; b. Brechin, Scotland, May 22, 1933; came to U.S., 1956; s. Malcolm P. and Mary (Harris) M.; m. Eleanor Carman, May 30, 1957; children: Douglas, Kenneth,

Sheila, Christine. M.A., U. Edinburgh, Scotland, 1955; Ph.D., U. Rochester, 1960. Research asso. Argonne (Ill.) Nat. Lab., 1959-60; asst. prof. physics U. Rochester, 1960-61; asso. physicist Argonne Nat. Lab., 1961-68, sr. physicist, 1968-80; prof. physics U. Chgo., 1968-80, Ind. U. Bloomington, 1980—; vis. fellow All Souls Coll., Oxford (Eng.) U., 1966-67; mem. nuclear scis. adv. com. Dept. Energy-NSF, 1983—; cons. Ency. Brit. Contbr. articles of theoretical nuclear physics to profl. jours. Guggenheim fellow physics, 1966-67; Alexander von Humboldt Found. sr. scientist award, 1985. Fellow Am. Phys. Soc.; mem. Nuclear Physics sect. Am. Phys. Soc. (mem. exec. com. 1969-71). Home: 3510 E Homestead Dr Bloomington IN 47401-4217 Office: Dept Physics Indiana U Bloomington IN 47405

MACGILLIVRAY, LOIS ANN, academic administrator; b. Phila., July 8, 1937; d. Alexander and Mary Ethel (Crosby) MacG. BA in History, Holy Names Coll., 1966; MA in Sociology, U. N.C., 1971, PhD in Sociology, 1973. Joined Sisters of Holy Names of Jesus and Mary, 1955. Research asst. U. N.C., Chapel Hill, 1969-70, 71-72, instr. sociology, 1970-71; sociologist Rsch. Triangle Inst., Durham, N.C., 1973-75, sr. sociologist, 1975-81; dir. Ctr. for Population and Urban-Rural Studies, Research Triangle Inst., Durham, N.C., 1976-81; pres. Holy Names Coll., Oakland, Calif., 1982-92; mem. steering com. Symposium for Bus. Leaders Holy Names Coll., 1982-92; vis. scholar dept. sociology U. N.C., Chapel Hill, 1992-94; pvt. cons. 1992—; mem. policy bd. Univ. Oakland Met. Forum, co-convenor panel on edn. and youth. Bd. dirs. Oakland Coun. Econ. Devel., 1984-86; bd. dirs. Bay Area Biosci. Ctr., 1990-92, mem. adv. com., 1992-94. Mem. Am. Sociol. Assn., Assn. Ind. Calif. Colls. and Univs. (exec. com. 1985-92, vice chmn. 1989-92), Regional Assn. East Bay Colls. and Univs. (past pres., bd. dirs. 1982-92). Avocation: birding. Home and Office: 101 Hamilton Rd Chapel Hill NC 27514

MACGINITIE, WALTER HAROLD, psychologist; b. Carmel, Calif., Aug. 14, 1928; s. George Eber and Nettie Lorene (Murray) MacG.; m. Ruth Olive Kilpatrick, Sept. 2, 1950; children: Mary Catherine, Laura Anne. B.A., UCLA, 1949; A.M., Stanford U., 1950; Ph.D., Columbia U., 1960. Tchr. Long Beach (Calif.) Unified Sch. Dist., 1950, 1955-56; mem. faculty Columbia U. Tchrs. Coll., 1959-80, prof. psychology and edn., 1970-80; Lansdowne scholar, prof. edn. U. Victoria, B.C., Can., 1980-84; research assoc. Lexington Sch. Deaf, N.Y.C., 1963-69; mem. sci. adv. bd. Ctr. for Study of Reading, 1977-80, chmn. 1979-80. Co-author: Gates-MacGinitie Reading Tests, 1965, 78, 89, Psychological Foundations of Education, 1968; Editor: Assessment Problems in Reading, 1972; co-editor: Verbal Behavior of the Deaf Child, 1969. Life mem. Calif. PTA. Served with USAF, 1950-54. Fellow APA, AAAS, Am. Psychol. Soc., Nat. Conf. Research English, N.Y. Acad. Scis.; mem. Internat. Reading Assn. (pres. 1976-77, Spl. Svc. award 1981), Reading Hall of Fame (pres. 1989-90). Home and Office: PO Box 1789 Friday Harbor WA 98250-1789

MACGOWAN, CHARLES FREDERIC, retired chemical company executive; b. Rock Island, Ill., Nov. 24, 1918; s. Charles John and Clara (Ohge) MacG.; m. Shirley Esther Sutherland, Feb. 22, 1941; children: Lynn Merle, Charles John II. Student, Wright Jr. Coll., Chgo., 1936-37, North Park Coll., Chgo., 1938-39, Harvard, 1955-56. Partner C.B. Isett Co., Chgo., 1946-49; indsl. engr. Graver Tank & Mfg. Co., East Chicago, Ind., 1949-50; asst. bus. mgr. Boilermakers Local 374 State Ind., 1950-54; internat. rep. Internat. Brotherhood Boilermakers, 1954-60; dir. Office Saline Water, U.S. Dept Interior, Washington, 1961-65; spl. asst. to sec. Office Saline Water, U.S. Dept Interior, 1965-66; coordinator intergovtl. relations Fed. Water Pollution Control Adminstrn., 1966-67; govt. relations mgr. Dow Chem. Co., Washington, from 1967; cons. nuclear desalting Internat. Atomic Energy Agy., Vienna, Austria; tech. cons. AFL-CIO.; Chmn. Ind. Boiler and Pressure Vessel Bd., 1960-61. Contbr. articles to profl. jours. Mem. Am. Water Works Assn., Aircraft Owners and Pilots Assn., Md. Acad. Sci. Democrat. Methodist. Club: Mason. Home: 10113 Nedra Dr Great Falls VA 22066

MAC GOWAN, MARY EUGENIA, lawyer; b. Turlock, Calif., Aug. 4, 1928; d. William Ray and Mary Bolling (Gilbert) Kern; m. Gordon Scott Millar, Jan. 2, 1970; 1 dau., Heather Mary. A.B., U. Calif., Berkeley, 1950; J.D., U. Calif. San Francisco, 1953. Bar: Calif. 1953; cert. family law specialist Calif. State Bar Bd. Legal Specialization. Research atty. Supreme Ct. Calif., 1954, Calif. Ct. Appeals, 1955; partner firm MacGowan & MacGowan, Calif., 1956-68; pvt. practice San Francisco, 1968—. Bd. dirs. San Francisco Speech and Hearing Center, San Francisco Legal Aid Soc., J.A.C.K.I.E. Mem. Am., Calif., San Francisco bar assns., Queen's Bench. Clubs: San Francisco Lawyers, Forest Hill Garden. Office: 1 Sansome St Ste 1900 San Francisco CA 94104

MACGRATH, C. RICHARD, retired business executive; b. East Orange, N.J., June 20, 1921; s. Charles Halsey and Elizabeth Eugenia (Fowler) MacGrath; m. Nancy Elizabeth Greenwall, Feb. 11, 1955 (dec. Aug. 1980); children: Andrew Alexander, Frances Fowler, Susan Abigail Talcott. AB, Princeton U., 1943. V.p. Lazard Frères & Co., N.Y.C., 1965-85, ret., 1985—. Dir. Hosp. for Spl. Surgery, N.Y.C., 1980—, Met. Opera Assn., N.Y.C., 1982—; dir., treas. Greenwall Found., N.Y.C., 1957—; bd. dir., Skowhegan Sch. Painting and Sculpture, N.Y.C., 1965—. Capt. AAF, 1943-46. Mem. SAR, Soc. Colonial Wars, St. Nicholas Soc., Soc. of the Cin., Hugenot Soc., Order of the Magna Carta, River Club, Princeton Club, Mid-Ocean Club, Dublin Lake Club, Kane Lodge. Home: 435 E 52nd St New York NY 10022-6445 Home (summer): Beaglesmere Dublin NH 03444

MACGREGOR, DAVID BRUCE, lawyer; b. Miami Beach, Fla., Feb. 21, 1953; s. Bruce Herbert and Mary Don (Doty) MacG.; m. Carol Louise Edler, Aug. 21, 1976; children: Meredith Elder, Christine Elder, Scott Elder. BA magna cum laude, Bucknell U., 1975; JD magna cum laude Georgetown U., 1978. Bar: Pa. 1978, U.S. Dist. Ct. (ea. dist.) Pa., U.S. Ct. Appeals (4th cir.). Law clk. to presiding justice U.S. Ct. Appeals (4th cir.), Richmond, Va., 1978-79; assoc. Morgan, Lewis & Bockius, Phila., 1979-85, ptnr., 1985—. Mem. ABA, Pa. Bar Assn., Phila. Bar Assn. Presbyterian. Avocation: golf. Home: 620 Pembroke Rd Bryn Mawr PA 19010-3614 Office: Morgan Lewis & Bockius 2000 One Logan Sq Philadelphia PA 19103

MACGREGOR, DAVID LEE, lawyer; b. Cedar Rapids, Iowa, Sept. 17, 1932; s. John H. and Beulah A. (Morris) MacG.; m. Helen Jean Kolberg, Aug. 7, 1954; children—Scott J., William M., Brian K., Thomas D. B.B.A., U. Wis., 1954, LL.B., 1956. Assoc. Quarles & Brady and predecessor firms, Milw., 1959-64, ptnr., 1964—; pres. Milw. Estate Planning Council, 1972-73; mem. adv. bd. CCH Fin. and Estate Planning, N.Y.C., 1982-87. Fellow Am. Coll. Trust and Estate Counsel; mem. ABA, Milw. Bar Assn., State Bar Wis. (chmn. taxation sect. 1977-78), Nat. Assn. Estate Planning Councils (pres. 1979-80). Home: Apt 1608 929 N Astor St Milwaukee WI 53202 Office: Quarles & Brady 411 E Wisconsin Ave Milwaukee WI 53202-4409

MACGREGOR, DONALD LANE, JR., retired banker; b. Duluth, Minn., June 21, 1930; s. Donald Lane and Julia (Waldo) MacG.; m. Mary Jo Rouse, Sept. 27, 1959; children—Jeffrey Lane, Steven Scott, John Rouse. Student, Carleton Coll., 1948-51; B.A. in Econs., Macalester Coll., 1956. Asst. cashier 1st Nat. Bank of Mpls., 1956-61; v.p. United Calif. Bank, San Francisco, 1961-69; pres. Ormand Industries, Dallas, 1969-70; v.p. United Calif. Bank, Los Angeles, 1970-71; pres., COO Am. Security Bank (name now First Interstate Bank of Hawaii), Honolulu, 1972-83, pres., CEO, 1983-91. Hon. trustee Hawaii Army Mus. Soc., Honolulu, 1977-91; vice chmn., bd. regents Chaminade U., Honolulu; trustee Hawaii Conf. Found., 1985-91. Capt. USAF, 1951-55. Mem. Am. Bankers Assn. (leadership del. 1984-92), Hawaii Bankers Assn., Hawaii C. of C. (bd. dirs. 1985-91). Republican. Clubs: Outrigger Canoe, Pacific, Waialae Country (Honolulu).

MACGREGOR, GEDDES, author, philosophy educator; b. Glasgow, Scotland, Nov. 13, 1909; came to U.S., 1949, naturalized, 1957; s. Thomas and Blanche (Geddes) MacG.; m. Elizabeth Sutherland McAllister, Aug. 14, 1941 (dec. Sept. 1994); children: Marie, Martin. B.D., U. Edinburgh, 1939, LL.B., 1943; D.Phil., U. Oxford (Queen's Coll.), 1945, D.D., 1959; Dr. ès L. summa cum laude, U. Paris, 1951; L.H.D. (hon.), Western Internat. Coll., 1978. Ordained priest Episcopal Ch., 1968. Sr. asst. chaplain to dean of Chapel Royal, St. Giles' Cathedral, Edinburgh, 1939-41; minister Trinity Ch., Pollokshields, Glasgow, 1941-49; asst. to prof. logic U. Edinburgh, 1947-49; Rufus Jones assoc. prof. philosophy and religion Bryn Mawr Coll., 1949-55,

prof., 1955-60; examiner Swarthmore Coll., Hebrew Union Coll.; dean grad. sch. religion, prof. philos. religion U. So. Calif., 1960-66, Disting. prof. philosophy, 1966-75, Disting. prof. philosophy emeritus, 1975—; vis. prof. U. B.C., 1963, 66, 73, Hebrew Union Coll., 1964-65, World Campus Afloat, Orient, 1974, Mediterranean, 1975, McGill U., 1976, Inst. Shipboard Edn. Round-the-World Voyage, 1977, U. Iowa, 1979, U. Sask., 1979; vis. fellow Ezra Stiles Coll., dept. religious studies Yale, 1967-68, Coll. Preachers, Washington Nat. Cathedral, 1991, also life fellow; canon theologian St. Paul's Cathedral, Los Angeles, 1968-74; honorary canon St. Paul's Cathedral, San Diego, 1987—; spl. preacher St. Paul's Cathedral, London, 1969; spl. preacher Westminster Abbey, 1970; Birks lectr. McGill U., 1976; Warren lectr. U. Dubuque, 1979; guest lectr. Am. Scottish Found., 1981, Rikkyo U., Tokyo, 1981; lectured widely on four continents, since 1981. Author: Aesthetic Experience in Religion, 1947, Christian Doubt, 1951, Les Frontiéres de la morale et de la religion, 1952, From a Christian Ghetto, 1954, The Vatican Revolution, 1957, The Thundering Scot, 1957, The Tichborne, Impostor, 1957, Corpus Christi, 1959, Introduction to Religious Philosophy, 1959, The Bible in the Making, 1959, The Coming Reformation, 1960, The Hemlock and the Cross, 1963 (Gold medal, Calif. Lit. award 1964), God Beyond Doubt, 1966, The Sense of Absence, 1968, A Literary History of the Bible, 1968, So Help Me God, 1970, Philosophical Issues in Religious Thought, 1973, The Rythm of God, 1974, He Who Lets Us Be, 1975, 87, Reincarnation in Christianity, 1978, German transl., 1985, Gnosis, 1979, Scotland Forever Home, 1980, 84, 88, reissued as Scotland: An Intimate Portrait, 1990, The Nicene Creed Illuminated by Modern Thought, 1980, Reincarnation as a Christian Hope, 1981, The Gospels as a Mandala of Wisdom, 1982, The Christening of Karma, 1984 (German transl. 1986), Apostles Extraordinary, 1986, Angels, 1988, Dictionary of Religion and Philosophy, 1989, Images of Afterlife: Beliefs from Antiquity to Modern Times, 1992, French transl. 1995, Angels: Minister of Grace; editor: Immortality and Human Destiny: a Variety of Views, 1986; contbr. to encys. and periodicals. Regent Am-Scottish Found., N.Y.C., 1968—. Served with Brit. civil def.; Chaplain Red Cross World War II. Recipient medal nat. soc. SAR, 1989, Disting. Emeritus award U. So. Calif., 1993. Fellow Royal Soc. Lit. (life); mem. Am. Philos. Assn., Am. Acad. Religion, Speculative Soc. (extraordinary life mem.), Edinburgh U. Dialectic Soc. Internat. Soc. for Philos. Enquiry (The Thousand, diplomate 1986, highest hon. award 1991), Am. Mensa, English-Speaking Union, St. Andrew's Soc. L.A. (hon. chaplain, historian, pres. 1987-88), The Athenaeum, Commonwealth Trust (London), Union Soc. (Oxford), Phi Kappa Phi (Disting. award 1982). Home: 876 S Victoria Ave Los Angeles CA 90005-3751 *Ever since I was old enough to handle money I abhorred debt as slavery and I have since grown to account political forms of debt an even more unendurable yoke.*

MACGREGOR, GEORGE LESCHER, JR., freelance writer; b. Dallas, Sept. 15, 1936; s. George Lescher and Jean (Edge) MacG.; divorced; children: George Lescher III, Michael Fordtran. B.B.A., U. Tex., 1958. Asst. cashier First Nat. Bank in Dallas, 1960-64, asst. v.p., 1964-68; v.p. Nat. Bank of Commerce of Dallas, 1968-70, sr. v.p., 1970-73, exec. v.p., 1973-74; pres., chief exec. officer Mountain Banks Ltd., Colorado Springs, 1974-77; chief exec. officer Highfield Fin. (U.S.A.) Ltd., 1978-83; chmn. bd., chief exec. officer, dir. Dominion Nat. Bank, Denver, 1981-84; chmn. bd., chief exec. officer Royal Dominion Ltd., Denver; chmn. bd., chief exec. officer, dir. Market Bank of Denver, 1983-84; vice chmn., dir. Bank of Aurora, Denver, 1983-84; chmn., pres., chief exec. officer Alamosa Bancorp. of Colo., Denver, 1983-84; pres., chief exec. officer Am. Interstate Bancorp., 1984-88; pres. Banco, Inc., 1984-89; sr. mng. ptnr. Scotland Co., Denver, London, 1988-91; free-lance writer, 1992—. Served with M.C. AUS, 1958-60. Mem. Am. Inst. Banking (hon.), Young Pres.'s Orgn., Koon Kreek Club, Broadmoore Golf Club, Oxford Club, Phi Gamma Delta. Anglican Catholic. Home and Office: 1736 Blake St Denver CO 80202-1226

MACGREGOR, JAMES THOMAS, toxicologist; b. N.Y.C., Jan. 14, 1944; s. James and Phyllis (Bowman) MacG.; m. Judith Anne Anello, July 12, 1969; 1 child, Jennifer Lee. BS in Chemistry, Union Coll., Schenectady, N.Y., 1965; PhD in Toxicology, U. Rochester, 1970. Diplomate Am. Bd. Toxicology. Postdoctoral fellow U. Calif., San Francisco, 1970-72; dir. food safety rsch. USDA, Berkeley, Calif., 1972-88; assoc. prof. U. Calif., Berkeley, 1978-88; pres. Toxicology Consulting Svcs., Danville, Calif., 1988-90; dir. toxicology lab. SRI Internat., Menlo Park, Calif., 1990—; Mem. nat. and internat. sci. working groups and adv. panels, including EPA, Office Tech. Assessment, USDA, ASTM, San Jose State U., U. Calif., Berkeley, Food Safety and Inspection Svc. Mem. editorial bd.: Environ. Molecular Mutagenesis, N.Y.C., 1986-88, Mutation Res., Amsterdam, 1989-91, Mutagenesis, Oxford, 1989-93. Recipient A. Hollaender award, 1995; fellow NIH, 1965-72. Mem. Am. Assn. Cancer Rsch., Soc. Toxicology, Environ. Mutagen Soc. (treas. 1986-89, pres. 1992-93), Genetic Environ. Toxicology Assn. No. Calif. (pres. 1982). Office: SRI Internat 333 Ravenswood Ave Menlo Park CA 94025

MACGREGOR, KENNETH ROBERT, former insurance company executive; b. Ottawa, Ont., Can., July 21, 1906; s. Robert and Margaret (Goundrey) MacG.; m. Charlotte Jessie Donnelly, June 29, 1935; children: Jayne Ennis, Kenneth Robert. B.Sc. in Mech. Engring (hon.), Queens U., 1929. Lectr. Queens U., 1929-30; joined Fed. Dept. Ins., Ottawa, 1930; served in actuarial and exam. brs., later in adminstrn. br., supt. ins. with rank of dep. minister Fed. Dept. Ins., 1953-64; pres. Mut. Life Assurance Co. of Can., 1964-73, chmn., 1973-82; chmn. exec. com. Mut. Life Assurance of Can., 1982-83; hon. chmn. Mut. Life Assurance Co. of Can., 1983-89; hon. dir. Econ. Mut. Ins. Co., Missisquoi Ins. Co., Speech Found. of Ont.; former dir. mem. exec. com. Can. Trust Co., Can. Trust Mortgage Co. Past trustee and hon. life mem. Queens U. Council; former chmn. fin. com. Nat. Cancer Inst. Can. Served as maj. Gov. Gen.'s Foot Guards, 1923-45; mem. Canadian Bisley Rifle Team, 1926-28; comdt. 1957. Fellow Soc. Actuaries (former gov., v.p.); mem. Dominion of Can. Rifle Assn. (life gov.), Canadian Life Ins. Assn. (pres. 1968-69), Can. Cancer Soc. (hon. life), Nat. Cancer Inst. of Can. (hon. life), Rideau Club, Westmount Golf and Country Club, York Club. Presbyterian. Home: 125 John Blvd, Waterloo, ON Canada N2L 1C4

MAC GUIDWIN, MARK J., manufacturing executive. V.p. of finance, cfo Libbey-Owens-Ford Co., Toledo. Office: Libbey Owens Ford Co 811 Madison Ave Toledo OH 43627

MACGUIGAN, MARK R., Canadian federal judge; b. Charlottetown, P.E.I., Can., Feb. 17, 1931; s. Mark R. MacG.; m. Maryellen MacGuigan, June 17, 1961 (div.); children: Ellen, Mark, Thomas; m. Patricia D. Robinson, Dec. 26, 1987. BA, St. Dunstan's U., 1951; MA, U. Toronto, 1953, PhD, 1957; LLB, York U., Toronto, 1958; LLM, Columbia U., 1959, JSD, 1961; LLD, U. P.E.I., 1971, St. Thomas U., 1981, U. Windsor, 1983, Law Soc. Upper Can., 1983. Called to Ont. bar, 1958. Read law with Hon. Mr. Justice Arthur Kelly, 1956-58; asst. prof. law U. Toronto, 1960-63, assoc. prof., 1963-66; vis. assoc. prof. criminal law NYU, 1966; prof. law Osgoode Hall Law Sch., 1966-67; dean Faculty of Law U. Windsor, 1967-68; mem. Fed. Govt. Spl. Com. on Hate Propaganda, 1965-66; advisor to Fed. Govt. Spl. Counsel on Constn., 1967-68; constl. advisor to Gov. P.E.I., 1968; mem. Ho. of Commons for Windsor-Walkerville, 1968-84, chmn. spl. com. on statutory instruments, 1968-69, chmn. spl. joint com. on constn. Can., 1970-72; parliamentary sec. to Minister of Labour, 1974-75, chmn. standing com. on justice and legal affairs, 1975-79; chmn. subcom. on penitentiary system in Can., 1976-77, chmn. spl. joint com. on constn. Can., 1978, opposition critic for solicitor-gen., 1979, Sec. of State for External Affairs, 1980-82, minister of justice, 1982-84; judge Fed. Ct. Appeal, Ottawa, 1984—; pres. Can. sect., Internat. Commn. of Jurists, 1988-90. Author: (monograph) Abortion, Conscience and Democracy, 1994. Office: Fed Ct Can, Kent & Wellington Sts, Ottawa, ON Canada K1A 0H9

MACGUINNESS, ROSEMARY ANNE, lawyer, real estate broker; b. Newry, County Down, No. Ireland, June 26, 1957; came to U.S. 1981.; d. Michael Gerard and Maureen Rosemary (Leavy) MacG.; m. Philip Martin Bellber, Dec. 5, 1987; children: Sam Martin Bellber, Rhys Patrick Bellber, Mason Philip Bellber. B in Civil Law, U. Coll. Dublin, 1978, diploma in European Law, 1979; MS in Criminal Justice, Northeastern U., 1982. Bar: Ireland 1981, Calif. 1994. Legal asst. Bronson, Bronson & McKinnon, San Francisco, 1983; atty. McInerney & Dillon, Oakland, Calif., 1984-87; sr. counsel Pacific Stock Exch., San Francisco, 1987-90, sr. counsel, dir. arbitra-

tion, 1990—. Mem. Queen's Bench. Office: Pacific Stock Exch 301 Pine St San Francisco CA 94104

MACH, DAVID, artist; b. Methil, Fife, Scotland, Mar. 18, 1956. Grad., Duncan of Jordanstone Coll. Art, Dundee, Scotland, 1974-79, Royal Coll. Art, 1979-82; postgrad., Royal Coll. Art, 1985—. One man shows include Richard Booth Bookshop, Hay-on-Wye, Wales, 1981, Lisson Gallery, London, 1982, New 57 Gallery, Edinburgh, Scotland, 1982, Galerie t'Venster, Rotterdam, The Netherlands, 1982, Kingston Poly., Knights Park, 1983, Galerie Andata/Ritorno, Geneva, 1983, 88, Atelier Contemporains d'Arts Plastiques, St. Brieuc, 1983, Mus. of Modern Art, Oxford, 1985, Galerie Foksal, Warsaw, 1985, Stoke City Mus., Stoke-on-Trent, Eng., 1985, Cleve. Art Gallery, 1986, Barbara Toll Fine Arts, N.Y.C., 1986, Mercer Union Gallery, Toronto, 1986, Herning (Denmark) Kunstmuseum, 1986, Seagate Gallery, Dundee, 1986, Nat. Mus. of Photography, Bradford, Eng., 1986, Musee des Arts Decoratifs, Centre du Verre, Paris, 1987, Mentrom Gallery, Barcelona, 1987, Wiener Secession, Vienna, 1987, Nicola Jacobs Gallery, London, 1987, Dunlop Art Gallery, Regina, Sask., Can., 1988, Provincial Mus., Hasselt, Belgium, 1988, BBC TV Ctr., London, 1988, Parvis 2, Tarbes, France, 1988, numerous others; exhibited in group shows at Hildebrandstrasse, Dusseldorf, Fed. Republic Germany, 1982, Lisson Gallery, London, 1982, Riverside Studios, London, 1983, Lijnbaancentrum, Rotterdam, 1983, Air Gallery, London, 1983, 84, Galerie Eric Fabre, Paris, 1984, Internat. Garden Festival, Liverpool, Eng., 1984, Air Gallery, London, 1984, Bluecoat Gallery, Liverpool, 1984, Ave de N.Y., Paris, 1984, Coracle Press and Rees Martin Art Svcs., London, 1984, Barbara Toll Fine Arts, 1985, Middleheim Mus., Antwerp, Belgium, 1985, London Bus. Sch., 1985, Richard Demarco Gallery, Edinburgh, 1985, Canterbury (Eng.) Fringe Festival, 1985, Germans van Eck Gallery, N.Y.C., 1986, Indpls. Mus. Art, 1986, Glyn Vivan Art Gallery, 1986, Laing Art Gallery, 1987, City Artists Gallery, London, 1987, Inst. Contemporary Arts, Boston, 1987, Scottish Nat. Gallery of Modern Art, Edinburgh, Serpentine Gallery, London, 1987, Musee d'art Contemporain, Montreal, 1988, numerous others; represented in permanent collections Fond Regional D'Art Contemporain de Rhone Alps, Paris, Fond Regional D'Art Contemprain, Rennes, France, Brit. Coun. London, Contemporary Art Soc., London, Moderne Museet, Stockholm, Hasbro Corp. Office: San Francisco Artspace 123 S Park St San Francisco CA 94107-1808

MACHADO, EDUARDO OSCAR, playwright; b. Guanabacoa, Cuba, June 11, 1953; came to U.S., 1961; s. Othon Eduardo and Gilda Luz (Hernandez) M.; m. Harriett Marilyn Bradlin, June 19, 1972. Ind. playwright N.Y.C., 1981—. Playwright Rosario and the Gypsies, 1981, The Modern Ladies of Guanabacoa, 1983, Broken Eggs, 1984, Fabiola, 1985, When It's Over, 1987, Why to Refuse, 1987, Once Removed, 1988, Wishing You Well, 1988, Revotillo, 1988, A Burning Beach, 1988, A Burning Beach, 1988, Don Juan in N.Y.C., 1988. Playwriting fellow Nat. Endowment for the Arts, 1981, 83, 85, Rockefeller Found., 1984. Mem. New Dramatists. Roman Catholic.

MACHALE, JOSEPH P., financial executive; b. Aug. 17, 1951. BA with hons., Oxford U., 1973. With Price Waterhouse, London, 1973-78; mng. dir. J.P. Morgan Co., N.Y.C., 1979—. Office: J P Morgan & Co Inc 60 Wall St New York NY 10005-2807

MACHAMER, SYLVIA GERALDINE, special education educator; b. Visalia, Calif., Oct. 3, 1939; d. Henry Ross and Lucille Marian (Alvarez) Mata; m. Milton Lynn Machamer, June 17, 1962; children: Jonathan (dec.), Leah, Anne Marie, Jill, Ryan, Daniel. AA, Coll. of Sequoia, Visalia, Calif., 1959; BA, San Jose State U., 1961, spl. edn. cert., 1977. Cert. elem. tchr., spl. edn. elem. and secondary, Calif. Tchr. 2nd and 3rd grade Noble Sch. Berryessa Dist., San Jose, Calif., 1961-62; 3rd grade tchr. L.A. Sch. Dist., 1962-63; 2nd and head start tchr. Toyon Sch. Berryessa Dist., San Jose, 1963-67; supplemental educator grade 1, 4, 6. Garden Gate Sch., Cupertino, Calif., 1969—; educator learninc handicapped students Garden Gate Sch., Cupertino, 1969—; educator severely handicapped students, 1969—; cons. and workshop presenter to sch. dists. state and nation wide, 1988—; video mentor tchr., Cupertino Union Sch. Dist., 1991-93. Developer Gift of Reading Program, Computerized I.E.P. Program. Chmn. Indian Edn. Parent Com. Fremont High Sch. Dist., 1991-93. Recipient Continuing Svc. award Garden Gate PTA, Cupertino, 1989, Eagle Feather award Title U Coalition, 1993. Mem. De Anza Coll. Cable TV, Computer Using Educators, Parents Helping Parents (Outstanding Educator 1991), Coastal Band of Chumash Nation. Avocations: video, computers, walking, reading, Native Am. affairs. Home: 21753 Castleton St Cupertino CA 95014-4704 Office: Garden Gate Sch 10500 Ann Arbor Ave Cupertino CA 95014-1697

MACHARE, PETER ALLEN, law librarian; b. Queens, N.Y., Mar. 7, 1954; s. Stanley H. and Marion G. (MacDougall) Symolon; m. Sean Patalinjug, June 21, 1991; 1 child, Erica Merifi. BA, Washington & Lee U., 1976; JD, Cath. U. Am., 1981; MLS, U. Md., 1988. Libr. Cath. U. Am., Washington, 1976-83, Nat. Gallery Art, Washington, 1983-89; law libr. U.S. Dept. Agr., Washington, 1989—. Office: US Dept Agr Law Libr Rm M-1406 S Bldg Washington DC 20250-1400

MACHASKEE, ALEX, newspaper publishing company executive; b. Warren, Ohio; m. Carol Machaskee. Degree, Cleve. State U. Sports reporter The Warren (Ohio) Tribune; dir. labor rels. and personnel The Plain Dealer, Cleve., asst. to pub., promotion dir., v.p., gen. mgr., 1985-90, pres., pub., 1990—. Bd. dirs. Cleve. Orch., The New Cleve. Campaign, The Conv. and Visitors Bur. Greater Cleve., The City Club Forum Found., Playhouse Sq. Found., Univ. Hosps. Health System, Inc., Univ. Circle, Inc., Greater Cleve. Growth Assn., Cleve. Tomorrow, North Coast Harbor, Inc., NCCJ, Great Lakes Mus., Greater Cleve. Roundtable, Cleve. Coun. on World Affairs, United Way Svcs.; mem. visiting com. Case Western Res. U. Weatherhead Sch. Mgmt. Mem. Am. Soc. Newspaper Editors (mem. labor rels. subcom.), Newspaper Assn. (mem. labor rels. subcom.). Office: Plain Dealer Pub Co 1801 Superior Ave E Cleveland OH 44114-2107*

MACHATZKE, HEINZ WILHELM, dean, chemistry educator; b. Freiburg, West Germany, Oct. 26, 1932; came to U.S., 1968; s. Friedrich W. and Helene W. (Maluschke) M.; m. Gertraud Zimmermann, Apr. 22, 1962; children: Jorg, Jens. BS, U. Freiburg (West Germany), 1955, MS, 1958, PhD, 1960. Rsch. chemist Bayer AG, Germany, 1962-68; chief chemist Mobay Chem. Corp., Union, N.J., 1968-70, asst. to pres., 1971-72, v.p., 1972-74, gen. mgr. dyes and pigment divsn., 1974-86, group v.p. human resources and quality programs, 1986-89; industry advisor, adj. prof. Duquesne U., Pitts., 1989—; dean Sch. Natural and Environ. Scis., 1994—; rsch. fellow U. Mich., 1960-62. Contbr. articles to profl. jours.; patentee in field. Mem. Am. Chem. Soc. Home: Scaife Rd Sewickley PA 15143 Office: Duquesne U Pittsburgh PA 15282

MACHEN, ARTHUR WEBSTER, JR., lawyer; b. Balt., Dec. 16, 1920; s. Arthur W. and Helen Chase (Woods) M.; m. Rose Bradley Purves, Jan. 24, 1948; children: Arthur W. (dec.), John P., Henry Lewis. AB, Princeton U., 1942; LLB, Harvard U., 1948. Bar: Md. 1948, U.S. Dist. Ct. Md. 1949, U.S. Ct. Appeals (4th cir.) 1949, U.S. Supreme Ct. 1954. Assoc. Armstrong, Machen & Eney, Balt., 1948-51; assoc. Venable, Baetjer & Howard, Balt., 1951-57, ptnr., 1957-89, sr. counsel, 1989—; sec. Schenuit Investments, Inc., Balt., 1980—. Author: A Venerable Assembly: The History of Venable, Baetjer and Howard, 1900-90, 1991; contbr. articles to profl. jours. Trustee Samuel Ready Scholarships, Inc., 1977-89, trustee emeritus 1989—; bd. mgrs. Family and Children's Svc., 1955-69, pres., 1967-69; reporter Charter Bd. Balt. County, 1956; dep. Gen. Conv. Episcopal Ch., 1973, 76, 79, 82; chancellor Episcopal Diocese Md., Balt., 1972-85. Lt. USNR, 1942-46, PTO. Fellow Am. Bar Found., Md. Bar Found.; mem. ABA, Md. State Bar Assn., Balt. City Bar Assn., Am. Law Inst., Am. Judicature Soc., Hamilton Street Club, Phi Beta Kappa. Democrat. Home: 1055 W Joppa Rd Apt 612 Towson MD 21204 Office: Venable Baetjer & Howard 1800 Merc Bank & Trust Bldg 2 Hopkins Plz Baltimore MD 21201-2930

MACHIDA, NAOSHI, airline company executive. Exec. v.p. Japan Air Line Co. Ltd., N.Y.C. Office: Japan Air Lines Co Ltd 655 5th Ave New York NY 10022-5303

MACHIZ, LEON, electronic equipment manufacturing executive; b. Bklyn., June 23, 1924; s. Isadore and Fanny (Klonsky) M.; m. Lorraine Block, Mar. 31, 1951; children: Marc, Linda, Gary. Grad., Cooper Union. Salesman Sun Radio Co., 1942-52; founder Time Electro Sales Co. (merged with Avnet, Inc. 1952-68), Electro Air of Ga. (merged with Avnet, Inc. 1968), 1957-68, Electro Air of Fla., 1960-68; sr. v.p., dir. Avnet Inc., N.Y.C., 1968-80, pres., dir., 1980—, vice chmn., chief exec. officer, from 1986, dir., chmn., chief exec. officer, 1986—. Trustee North Shore Univ. Hosp., Boys' Brotherhood Republic. Office: Avnet Inc 80 Cutter Mill Rd Great Neck NY 11021-3108*

MACHLIN, EUGENE SOLOMON, metallurgy educator, consultant; b. N.Y.C., Dec. 29, 1920; s. Gershon and Rose (Kaplan) M.; m. Edda Servi, May 21, 1960; children: Rona Susan, Argia Debora; m. Gertrude Green, Oct. 15, 1943 (dec. May 1959); 1 child, Chester Elia. BME, CCNY, 1942; MS, Case Inst. Tech., 1948; ScD, MIT, 1950. Aero. rsch. scientist Nat. Adv. Commn. Aeronautics, Cleve., 1942-48; rsch. assoc., asst. prof. MIT, Cambridge, 1948-50, 50-51; asst. prof. Columbia U., N.Y.C., 1951-54, assoc. prof., 1954-58, prof. metallurgy, 1958-89, Howe prof., 1989-91, Howe prof. emeritus, 1991—; cons. Spl. Metals Corp., Utica, N.Y., 1951-76; cons., dir. UV Industries, N.Y.C., 1966-79; summer faculty fellow IBM T.J. Watson Res. Lab., 1984-90. Author: An Introduction to Aspects of Thermodynamics and Kinetics Relevant to Materials Science, 1990, Materials Science in Microelectronics—The Relationships Between Thin Film Processing and Structure, 1995; editor: Synthesis of Metastable Phases, 1980; inventor Udimet 700, 1960. Chmn. solid state scis. adv. com. Office Sci. Rsch. USAF, Washington, 1954-59. Recipient C.H. Mathewson Gold medal AIME, 1954; Guggenheim fellow, 1965. Fellow AIME; mem. Am. Soc. Metals (Achievement award 1961, Edn. award 1974). Democrat. Jewish. Office: Columbia U 500 W 120th St New York NY 10027-6623

MACHLIN, LAWRENCE J., nutritionist, biochemist, educator; b. N.Y.C., June 24, 1927; s. Morris Louis and Lilly (Manevitz) M.; m. Ruth Beerman, May 30, 1953; children: Marc, Steven, Paul. BS, Cornell U., 1948, M in Nutritional Sci., 1949; PhD, Georgetown U., 1953. Nutritional biochemist USDA, AEC, Beltsville, Md., 1949-56; group chief Monsanto Co., St. Louis, 1956-73; sr. group chief Hoffman-La Roche Inc., Nutley, N.J., 1973-85, dir., 1985-92; pres. Nutrition Rsch. and Info. Inc., Livingston, N.J., 1993—; lectr. in nutrition Washington U., St. Louis, 1969-72; adj. prof. nutrition NYU, 1977-82; adj. assoc. prof. nutrition in medicine Cornell U., 1979—; Samuel Brody lectr. U. Mo., Columbia, 1988; Gladys Emerson Vis. prof. UCLA, 1990. Editor: Vitamin E, 1980, Handbook of Vitamins, 1984, rev. edit. 1991; co-editor: Vitamin Intake & Health, 1991; contbr. over 120 articles to profl. jours. Mem. Am. Inst. Nutrition, Am. Soc. Clin. Nutrition, N.Y. Acad. Scis., N.Y. Lipid Club, Soc. for Exptl. Biology and Medicine. Achievements include 4 patents in field; first to demonstrate that growth hormone stimulates milk production in the dairy cow and lean meat production in the pig; demonstrated that vitamin E functioned as in vivo antioxidant and popularized the concept that antioxidant vitamins are important to human health. Home: 18 Locust Pl Livingston NJ 07039-1213 Office: Hoffmann-LaRoche Inc 45 Eisenhower Dr Paramus NJ 07652-1429

MACHLIN, MILTON ROBERT, magazine editor, writer; b. N.Y.C., June 26, 1924; s. Morris Lewis and Lillie (Manevetz) M.; 1 foster son, Jason Sheckley; m. Margaret Ryan, 1988. AB, Brown U., 1948; Degre Avance, U. Paris-Sorbonne, 1949. Reporter, columnist Clifton (N.J.) Morning Leader, 1950-52; editor Service Americain AFP (news wire service), 1952, Magazine House, 1953-55, Hillman Periodicals, 1955-57; mng. editor Argosy mag., 1960—, editor, 1969—, dir. film div.; creative dir. Pelican Prodns., 1974; regional v.p. Council Writers Orgns., 1986. Author: Ninth Life, 1961, Private Hell of Hemingway, 1962, MacArthur—A Fighting Man, 1965, The Search for Michael Rockefeller, 1972, The Family Man, 1974, French Connection II, 1975, The Setup, 1975, Pipeline, 1976, Atlanta, 1979, The Complete UFO Book, 1979, Libby, 1980, Complete UFO Catalogue, 1980, The Gossip Wars, 1980, The Worldshakers, 1984, Strangers in the Land, 1985, Minsky's Burlesque, 1985, Joshua's Altar, 1990. With AUS, 1942-45. Recipient Mystery Writers spl. award, 1976, Porgie award, 1977. Mem. Mystery Writers Am. Club: Explorers. Home: 27 Washington Sq N New York NY 10011-9166

MACHOVEC, FRANK J., psychologist; b. Balt., May 16, 1930; s. James Joseph and Theresa Anna MacH.; m. Evelyn Mary Stultz, May 5, 1951; 1 child, Frank. B.A., U. Md., 1964; M.A., Loyola U., Balt., 1965; Ph.D., Fielding Inst., 1979. Diplomate Am. Bd. Psychol. Hypnosis, Am. Bd. Adminstrv. Phychology, Am. Bd. Med. Psychol.; lic. clin. psychologist. Asst. dir. New Sch. Psychotherapy, Washington, 1970-71; chief psychologist Victoria Hosp., Winnipeg, Man., 1973-75, Alta. Mental Health, Lethbridge, Can., 1975-77; psychologist Alaska Psychiat. Inst., Anchorage, 1977-79, State Hosp. South, Blackfoot, Idaho, 1979-81; dir. psychol. services S. Va. Mental Health Inst., Danville, 1981-86; dir. quality assurance Va. Dept. Mental Health, 1986-90; clin. supr. Va. Youth and Family Svcs., 1980; supr. Am. Assn. Marriage and Family Therapy, 1973—. Author: Hypnosis Complications, 1986, Expert Witness Survival Manual, 1987, Humor Theories, History, 1988, Interview and Interrog, 1989, Cults and Personality, 1989, pvt. investigation, 1991, security svcs., 1992; contbr. numerous articles to profl. jours. Served with USMC, 1950-52. Mem. Soc. Personality Assess, Soc. Clin. and Exptl. Hypnosis, Am. Bd. Medic Psychotherapy, Va. Marriage Family Assn. (pres.), Assn. Marriage Family Therapy, Masons. Avocations: writing, teaching, travel, ham radio.

MACHOVER, CARL, computer graphics consultant; b. Bklyn., Mar. 26, 1927; s. John Herman and Rose (Alter) M.; m. Wilma Doris Simon, June 18, 1950; children: Tod, Julie, Linda. BEE, Rensselaer Poly. Inst., 1951; postgrad., NYU, 1953-56. Mgr. applied engring. Norden div. United A/C Corp., 1951-59; mgr. sales Skiatron Electronics & TV, N.Y.C., 1959-60; v.p. mktg., dir. Info. Displays, Inc. Info. Displays, Inc., Mount Kisco, N.Y., 1960-73; v.p., gen. mgr., Info. Displays, Inc., Mount Kisco, 1973-76; pres. Machover Assocs. Corp., White Plains, N.Y., 1976—; adj. prof. Rensselaer Poly. Inst. Author: Gyro Primer, 1957, Basics of Gyroscopes, 1958; mem. editorial bd. IEEE Computer Graphics and Applications, Computers and Graphics, Spectrum; editor C4 Handbook, 1989; co-editor CAD/CAM Handbook, 1980, Computer Graphics Rev.; contbr. articles to profl. jours. Mem. adv. bd. Pratt Ctr. for Computer Graphics in Design. With USNR, 1945-46. Recipient Frank Oppenheimer award Am. Soc. for Engring. Edn., 1971, Orthagonal award N.C. State U., 1988, Vanguard award Nat. Comp. Graphics Assn., 1993; named to Computer Graphics Hall of Fame Fine Arts Mus. of L.I., Hempstead, N.Y., 1988. Fellow Soc. for Info. Display (pres. 1968-70); mem. IEEE, Assn. for Computing Machinery, Am. Inst. Design and Drafting, Nat. Soc. Profl. Engrs., Nat. Computer Graphics Assn. (bd. dir., pres. 1989-90), Computer Graphics Pioneer, Sigma Xi, Tau Beta Pi, Eta Kappa Nu. Home: 152 Longview Ave White Plains NY 10605-2314 Office: Machover Assocs Corp PO Box 308 152A Longview Ave White Plains NY 10605-2314

MACHULAK, EDWARD LEON, real estate, mining and financial corporation executive; b. Milw., July 14, 1926; s. Frank and Mary (Sokolowski) M.; BS in Accounting, U., Wis., 1949; student spl. courses various univs.; m. Sylvia Mary Jablonski, Sept. 2, 1950; children: Edward A., John E., Lauren A., Christine M., Paul E. Chmn. bd., pres., Commerce Group Corp., Milw., 1962—, San Luis Estates, Inc., 1973—, Homespan Realty Co., Inc., 1974—, Universal Developers Inc., 1972—, Picadilly Advt. Agy., Inc., 1974—; chmn. bd., chief exec. officer, Gen. Lumber & Supply Co., Inc., 1949—; bd. dirs. v.p. San Sebastian Gold Mines, Inc., 1969-73, chmn. bd., pres., 1973—; bd. dirs sec., LandPak, Inc., 1985—; bd. dirs. Edjo Ltd., 1974—, sec., 1976—; ptnr., Weem Assocs., 1974—; bd. dirs. designee Comseb Joint Venture Woodcreek Devel. Corp., 1987. Mem. nat. adv. coun. SBA, 1972-74, co-chmn. 1973, 74. Recipient Recognition award U.S. SBA, 1975, N.W. Festival Corp. 25 Yr. Recognition award San Sebastian Community, Santa Rosa de Lima, El Salvador, 1991, San Sebastian Community El Salvador award, 1992, El Salvador Ministry Edn. award, 1992. Edward L. Machulak Day proclaimed by students of Canton San Sebastian, El Salvador, May 9, 1992; recipient recognition award for valuable consideration of support and svc. to San Sebastian Community, 1992, Cmty. Recognition award Santa Rosa de Lima, 1994. Mem. Nat. Assn. Small Bus. Investment Co's (nat. chmn. legis. com. 1968-73, bd. govs. 1970-74, exec. com. 1971-74, sec. 1972-74, Disting. Service award to Am. Small Bus. 1970),

Midwest Regional Assn. Small Bus. Investment Cos. (bd. dirs. 1968-74, v.p. 1970-71, pres. 1971-72, Outstanding Services award 1972), State of Wis. Council on Small Bus. Investment (chmn. 1973-74), Wis. Bd. Realtors (various coms. 1955-88), Milw. Bd. Realtors (various coms. 1955-88). Pres.' Council Marmion Mil. Acad., Aurora, Ill., 1966-79, lay life trustee, 1972, fin. advisor 1967-71, chmn. spl. fund raising com. 1966-67, planning com. 1972-79; chmn. adv. bd. Jesuit Retreat House, Oshkosh, Wis., 1966-68; chmn., bd. dirs. Spencarian Coll. of Bus., 1973-74; chmn. St. John Cathedral Symphony Concert Com., Milw., 1978; sustaining mem. Met. Mus. Art, 1974—. Served with AUS, 1945-46. Recognized bus. leader in Congl. Record, 1976; named Hon. Life Mem., Mid-Continental Railway, 1963. Clubs: Tripoli Golf (Milw.); Lodge: KC (4th degree 1971—, recognition award 1989). Home: 903 W Green Tree Rd Milwaukee WI 53217-3716 Office: 6001 N 91st St Milwaukee WI 53225-1721

MACIAS, EDWARD S., chemistry educator, university official; b. Milw., Feb. 21, 1944; s. Arturo C. Macias and Minette (Schwenger) Wiederhold; m. Paula Wiederhold, June 17, 1967; children: Matthew Edward, Julia Katherine. AB, Colgate U., 1966; PhD, MIT, 1970. Asst. prof. Washington U., St. Louis, 1970-76, assoc. prof., 1976-84, prof. chemistry, 1984—, chmn. dept., 1984-88, provost, 1988—, interim dean Faculty Arts and Scis., 1994—; cons. Meteorology Rsch., Inc., Altadina, Calif., 1978-81, Salt River Project, Phoenix, 1980-83, Santa Fe Rsch., Bloomington, Minn., 1985-88, AeroVironment, Inc., Monrovia, Calif., 1986-88. Author: Nuclear and Radiochemistry, 1981; editor: Atmospheric Aerosol, 1981; contbr. numerous articles to profl. jours. Bd. dirs Mark Twain Summer Inst., St. Louis, 1984-87, 88-90, The Coll. Sch., St. Louis, 1984-88. Grantee NSF, EPA, Electric Power Rsch. Inst., So. Calif. Edison Co., Dept. Energy, AEC. Mem. Am. Chem. Soc., Am. Assn. Aerosol Rsch. (editorial bd.), Am. Phys. Soc., AAAS. Home: 6907 Waterman Ave Saint Louis MO 63130-4333 Office: Washington U Campus Box 1080 One Brookings Dr Saint Louis MO 63130

MACILVAINE, CHALMERS ACHESON, retired financial executive, former investment executive; b. Bklyn., Oct. 25, 1921; s. James Andrew and Helen Marie (Acheson) MacI.; m. Elizabeth Jean Babcock, Mar. 26, 1943; children: Judith Anne, Joseph Chad, Martha Elizabeth. A.B., Stanford U., 1943. With Kaiser Steel Corp., 1946-73, asst. controller, 1953-62, treas., 1962-70, v.p., 1967-70, v.p. finance and planning, 1970-73; also v.p., dir. subsidiaries; v.p. project financing group Bank of Am., San Francisco, 1973-74; sr. v.p., dep. head Asia div. Bank of Am., 1974-77; sr. v.p.-fin. Peabody Coal Co., St. Louis, 1978-80; sr. v.p., dir. Stifel, Nicolaus & Co., St. Louis, 1980-83; exec. dir. Japan Am. Soc. of St. Louis, 1983-85; pres. Bamerical Internat. Fin. Corp., 1973-74. Served to lt. (j.g.) USNR, 1943-46. Mem. Phi Beta Kappa, Sigma Chi. Club: Tokyo Lawn Tennis, Burns Club of St. Louis. Home: Martin Point Rd PO Box 332 Friendship ME 04547-0332

MACINNIS, FRANK T., construction company executive, holding company executive; b. Camrose, Alta., Can., Nov. 10, 1946; came to U.S., 1978; s. H. Frank and Adele M. (Irving) MacI.; m. Beverley J. McAndrews, Nov. 3, 1977; children: Christopher, Katrina, Lauren, Robbie. BA, U. Alta., Edmonton, Can., 1968, LLB, 1971. Assoc. Liden, Ackroyd & Co. Edmonton, 1971-75; gen. counsel Banister-Price Internat., Tehran, Iran, 1975-77; dir. Banister-Price Overseas, London, 1977-78; exec. v.p. H.C. Price Co., Bartlesville, Okla., 1978-80; chmn., chief exec. officer H.C. Price Constrn. Co., Dallas, 1980-84; pres. Spie Group, Inc., Dallas, 1984—; exec. v.p. Comstock Group, Inc., Danbury, Conn., 1986—; mem. exec. com. Spie Batignolles, Paris, 1985—. Served to lt. Royal Can. Navy, 1964-68. Roman Catholic. Avocations: sports, coin collecting, music. Office: JWP Inc 2975 Westchester Ave Purchase NY 10577-2518

MACINTYRE, ALASDAIR, philosophy educator; b. Glasgow, Scotland, Jan. 12, 1929; came to U.S., 1969; s. Eneas John and Margaret Emily (Chalmers) MacI. B.A., Queen Mary Coll., U. London, 1949; M.A., Manchester U., 1951, Oxford U., 1961; D.H.L. (hon.), Swarthmore Coll., 1983; DLitt (hon.), Queen's U., Belfast, Ireland, 1988; D.O.E. (hon.), Essex (Eng.) U. Lectr. Manchester (Eng.) U., 1951-57, Leeds (Eng.) U., 1957-61; research fellow Nuffield Coll. Oxford (Eng.) U., 1961-62; sr. fellow Council Humanities, Princeton, 1962-63; fellow Univ. Coll., Oxford U., 1963-66; D.U.E. (hon.) U. Essex, Eng., 1966-69; prof. history of ideas Brandeis U., Waltham, Mass., 1969-72; dean Coll. Liberal Arts, Boston U., 1972-73, prof. philosophy and polit. sci., 1972-80; Henry Luce prof. Wellesley (Mass.) Coll., 1980-82; W. Alton Jones prof. Vanderbilt U., Nashville, 1982-88; Henry Luce scholar Whitney Humanities Ctr. Yale U., 1988-89; McMahon/Hank prof. U. Notre Dame, Ind., Ind., 1988-94; prof. arts & scis. Duke U., Durham, N.C., 1995—; Riddell lectr. U. Newcastle on Tyne, Eng., 1964, Bampton lectr. Columbia U., 1966, Gifford lectr. U. Edinburgh, 1988. Author: Marxism and Christianity, 1953, Th Unconscious, 1957, A Short History of Ethics, 1966, Against the Self-Images of the Age, 1971, After Virtue, 1981, Whose Justice? Which Rationality?, 1988, Three Rival Versions of Moral Enquiry, 1990. Queen Mary Coll. fellow, 1984. Fellow Am. Acad. Arts and Scis., Brit. Acad. (corr.); mem. Phi Beta Kappa (hon.). Office: Duke U Dept Philosophy Durham NC 27708

MACINTYRE, A(LFONSO) EVERETTE, lawyer; b. nr. Burlington, N.C., Feb. 3, 1901; s. William Seymour and Ella Mary (Clark) MacI.; m. Reita Jane Lyons, Aug. 20, 1929; 1 son, Miles Everette. A.B., U.N.C., 1926; J.D., George Washington U., 1929. Bar: N.C. 1929, D.C. 1930, U.S. Supreme Ct. 1933, Va. 1938. Practiced in Washington, 1929-96; atty. examiner, rev., sr. and prin. atty., chief div. antitrust trials Bur. Litigation, FTC, Washington, 1930-54; adviser on anti-monopoly cases Bur. Litigation, FTC, 1954-55, commr., 1961-73; staff dir. select com. on small bus US Ho. Reps., Washington, 1955-57; gen. counsel U.S. Ho. Reps., 1957-61; counsel to firm McKean and MacIntyre (formerly McKean, MacIntyre, Wilson & Richardson), Washington, 1973-96. Mem. FBA, ABA, Am. Acad. Polit. and Social Scis., Acad. Polit. Scis. (life), Congl. Country Club. Home: 23371 Blue Water Cir Boca Raton FL 33433-7048 *During my tenure in office, I considered it my duty and obligation to have as my policy, the policy of my government based on the policy of the law, and to serve that policy with unswerving loyalty to my country. It was my idea that the proper course to follow in my work would be to understand the problems presented to me by other officials and other citizens, and I felt that I could do that better by objectively seeking and appraising all relevant factual information concerning such problems.*

MAC INTYRE, DONALD JOHN, college president; b. Detroit, Aug. 19, 1939; s. Donald MacLellan and Ellen (McGrath) MacI.; m. Antoinette Shen, June 2, 1979; children by previous marriage: Honey, Michele, James, John. A.B., U. Detroit, 1961; M.A., U. Iowa, 1963, Ph.D., 1966. Prof. U. Pacific, Stockton, Calif., 1966-73; acad. dean/pres. St. Francis Coll., Biddeford, Maine, 1973-75; acad. v.p. U. San Francisco, 1975-79; pres. Metro. State Coll., Denver, 1979-81, Canada Coll., Redwood City, Calif., 1981-83, Skyline Coll., San Bruno, Calif., 1983-85, John F. Kennedy U., Orinda, Calif., 1985-89, Patricia Montandon & Assocs., San Francisco, 1989-91, Tie Tone, Inc., Mill Valley, Calif., 1991-92, The Fielding Inst., Santa Barbara, Calif., 1993—; cons. Indsl. Rels. Workshops Seminars, Inc., 1978-81, State Bd. Agr. Colo., 1979; assoc. John A. Scalone & Assocs., Orinda, Calif., 1977-85; chmn. adv. com. office adult learning svcs. Coll. Entrance and Exam. Bd., 1980-81; evaluator Women's Equity in Edn. Act Program, 1981. Contbr. articles to profl. jours. Chmn. edn. div. Mile High United Way, Denver, 1980-81; bd. dirs. Nat. Hispanic Center for Advanced Studies and Policy Analysis, 1981-86, Nat. Hispanic U., 1982-86, Chinese Culture Found., 1983-89; chmn. Children As the Peacemakers Found. Recipient award for Commendable Service U. San Francisco, 1979, Henry Clay Hall award, 1976; Disting. Teaching award U. Pacific, 1971; U. Pacific grantee, 1969-71; Don Quixote award Nat. Hispanic U., 1983; hon. mem. World Trade Ctr. Club, Nanjing, Republic of China, 1985—. Mem. Assn. Public Coll. and Univ. Pres.'s (co-chmn. Colo. 1980-81), Internat. Cultural Soc. Korea,. Democrat. Roman Catholic. Club: World Trade Ctr. (hon.) (Nanjing, China). Office: 2112 Santa Barbara St Santa Barbara CA 93105-3544

MACINTYRE, R. DOUGLAS, information technology executive; b. Bennettsville, S.C., Aug. 6, 1951; s. Wade Hampton and Lucy Allen (Tison) M.; m. Elizabeth Wallace, June 30, 1973; children—Robert, Carter, Stewart. BA, U.S. Mil. Acad., 1973; MSBA with honors, Boston U., 1976;

postgrad., Harvard U., Boston, 1985, U. Pa., 1987; exec. program, Stanford U., 1989. Mktg. rep. McDonnell Douglas, Atlanta, 1978-79; mktg. rep. Mgmt. Sci. Am. Inc., Atlanta, 1980-81, dist. mgr., 1982, regional mgr., 1983, v.p., 1984, sr. v.p. mktg., 1985-87, div. pres., 1987-88, exec. vp. U.S. ops., 1988-89; pres. Software 2000, Inc., Hyannis, Mass., 1990-93; pres., CEO Dun & Bradstreet Software, Atlanta, 1994—. Bd. dirs. Sci. and Tech. Mus. Atlanta, 1986-90, United Way Cape Cod, 1991-94, U.S. Mil. Acad. Assn., 1988-89. Capt. U.S. Army, 1973-78. Mem. Am. Software Assn. (dir. 1993—, pres. 1995—). Methodist. Office: Dun & Bradstreet Software 3445 Peachtree Rd Atlanta GA 30326

MACIOCE, FRANK MICHAEL, JR., lawyer, financial services company executive; b. N.Y.C., Oct. 3, 1945; s. Frank Michael and Sylvia Maria (Morea) M.; children: Michael Peter, Lauren Decker, Theodore Kenneth; m. Helen Latourette Duffin, July 9, 1988. BS, Purdue U., 1967; JD, Vanderbilt U., 1972. Bar: N.Y. 1973, U.S. Dist. Ct. (so. dist.) N.Y. 1973, U.S. Ct. Appeals (2d cir.) 1975, U.S. Supreme Ct. 1976. Mem. law dept. Merrill Lynch, Pierce, Fenner & Smith Inc., N.Y.C., 1972-80, v.p., 1978-88, 1st v.p., 1988—; mgr. corp. law dept. Merrill Lynch & Co., Inc., N.Y.C., 1980-93, asst. gen. counsel, 1982; gen. counsel investment banking group, 1993-95, ops., sys. and telecomm. counsel, 1995—, sec. of audit, compensation and nominating coms. bd. dirs., 1978-83, sec. exec. com., 1981-83; mng. dir. Merrill Lynch Overseas Capital, N.V., Netherlands Antilles, 1980-85; sec., dir. Merrill Lynch Employees Fed. Credit Union, N.Y.C., 1978-82; dir. Merrill Lynch Pvt. Capital Inc., N.Y.C., 1981-87, Enhance Fin. Services Inc, N.Y.C., 1988-92. Served with U.S. Army, 1969-70. Mem. ABA, Assn. of Bar of City of N.Y. (com. on corp. law depts.). Home: 22 Essex Rd Summit NJ 07901-2802 Office: Merrill Lynch & Co Inc N Tower World Fin Ctr New York NY 10281-1323

MACIUSZKO, KATHLEEN LYNN, librarian, educator; b. Nogales, Ariz., Apr. 8, 1947; d. Thomas and Stephanie (Horowski) Mart; m. Jerzy Janusz Maciuszko, Dec. 11, 1976; 1 child, Christina Alexsandra. BA, Ea. Mich. U., 1969; MLS, Kent State U., 1974; PhD, Case Western Res. U., 1987. Reference libr. Baldwin-Wallace Coll. Libr., Berea, Ohio, 1974-77, dir. Conservatory of Music Libr., 1977-85; dir. bus. info. svcs. Harcourt Brace Jovanovich, Inc., Cleve., 1985-89; staff asst. to exec. dir. Cuyahoga County Pub. Libr., Cleve., 1989-90; dir. Cleve. Area Met. Library System, Beachwood, Ohio, 1990; media specialist Cleve. Pub. Schs., 1991-93, Berea (Ohio) City Sch. Dist., 1993—. Author: OCLC: A Decade of Development, 1967-77, 1984; contbr. articles to profl. jours. Named Plenum Pub. scholar, 1986. Mem. Spl. Librs. Assn. (pres. Cleve. chpt. 1989-90, v.p. 1988-89, editor newsletter 1988-89), Baldwin-Wallace Coll. Faculty Women's Club (pres. 1975),. Avocation: piano. Office: Midpark HS 7000 Paula Dr Middleburg Heights OH 44130

MACIVER, JOHN KENNETH, lawyer; b. Milw., Mar. 22, 1931; s. Wallace and Elizabeth (MacRae) MacI.; m. Margaret J. Vail, Sept. 4, 1954; children: Douglas B., Carolyn V., Kenneth D., Laura E. BS, U. Wisc., 1953, LLB, 1955. Bar: Wisc. 1955. Sr. ptnr. Michael, Best & Friedrich, Milw., 1955—; mem. various bds. dirs. Chmn. Thompson for Gov. steering coms., 1986, 90, 94; state chmn. Wisc. Bush for Pres. coms., 1980, 88, 92; chmn. Wisc. Nixon for Pres. com., 1968, 72, Olson for Gov. com., 1970; vice chmn. Knowles for Gov. com., 1964, 66; bd. dirs. Milw. Symphony Orch., 1968—, pres. 1981-82; trustee Milw. Symphony Endowment Trust, 1988—; chmn. exec. com., bd. govs. East-West Ctr., 1970-76 (Disting. svc. award Honolulu 1976); pres., chmn. bd. dirs. Nat. Coun. Alcoholism, 1974-77, bd. dirs. 1968-78 (Silver Key award N.Y. 1975); pres., campaign co-chmn. United Performing Arts Fund Greater Milw., 1974-76 (Stiemke award Arts 1988); bd. dirs., exec. com. Greater Milw. Edn. Trust, 1988—, Project New Hope, 1991—; sec., gen. counsel Wisc. Mfrs. and Commerce, 1980—; regent, sec., gen. counsel Milw. Sch. Engring., 1987—; bd. dirs., sec. Pettit Nat. Ice Tng. Ctr., 1992—; bd. dirs. Milw. Nat. Heart Project; bd. dirs., exec. com., founding mem., sec. Competitive Wisc. Inc., 1982—; bd. dirs, vice-chair Met. Milw. Assn. Commerce, 1987—; mem. Greater Milw. Com., 1985—; trustee Milw. County Pub. Mus., 1989-92. Recipient Wisc. Gov's awards in Support of Arts, 1989. Mem. Wisc. Bar Assn. (chmn. commn. litigation costs and delay, past chmn. labor law sect.), Milw. Bar Assn. (chmn. jud. selection and qualifications com.), Milw. Club, Town Club. Republican. Avocations: Am. history, tennis, charities, politics. Home: 959 E Circle Dr Milwaukee WI 53217-5362 Office: Michael Best & Friedich 100 E Wisconsin Ave Milwaukee WI 53202-4107

MACIVER, LOREN, artist; b. N.Y.C., Feb. 2, 1909; d. Charles Augustus Paul and Julia (MacIver) Newman; m. Lloyd Frankenberg. Student, Art Students League, 1919. One-man shows East River Gallery, N.Y.C., 1938, Pierre Matisse Gallery, N.Y.C., 1940-44, 49, 56, 61, 66, 70, Mus. Modern Art Traveling Exhbn., 1941, Vassar Art Gallery, 1950, Wellesley Coll., 1951, Whitney Mus., 1953, Dallas Mus. Fine Arts, 1953, Venice Biennale, 1967, Musée des Beaux Arts, Lyons, France, 1968, Musée de l'Art Moderne de la Ville de Paris, 1968, Pierre Matisse Gallery, N.Y.C., 1981, Rutgers Art Gallery, 1982, U. Art Gallery, 1982, Musée des Ponchettes, Nice, France, 1968, 50-yr. retrospective Newport Harbor Art Mus., Newport Beach, Calif., 1985, Pierre Matisse Gallery, 1987, Mus. Modern Art, 1991, Terry Dintenfass Gallery, 1993; works exhibited Mus. of Modern Art include Federal Art, 1937, Fantastic Art, Dada, Surrealism, 1938, Art In Our Time, 1939, Fourteen Americans, 1946; work in exhbns. Am. art, Jeu de Paume, Paris, 1938, St. Louis Mus., Whitney Mus., Bklyn. Mus., Corcoran Art Gallery, State Dept. exhbn. sent to Europe, 1946, Tolouse Mus. Fine Arts, 1967, Met. Mus. Art, N.Y.C., 1991; represented in permanent collections Mus. Modern Art, Met. Mus., Detroit Inst., Los Angeles, San Francisco, Newark museums, Addison Gallery, Whitney Mus., Wadsworth Atheneum, Smith Coll. Mus., Phillips Collection, Washington, Joseph Hirshhorn Collection, Washington, Williams Coll., Elliott Collection, others. Guggenheim fellow, 1976; recipient 1st prize Corcoran Art Gallery, 1957, 1st prize Art Inst. Chgo., 1961, purchase prize Kranner Art Mus. of U. Ill., 1963, Mark Rothko Found. award, 1972, Lee Krasner award, 1991; Ford Found. grantee, 1960. Mem. Nat. Inst. Arts and Letters. Office: Terry Dintenfass Gallery 50 W 57th St New York NY 10019

MACK, CHARLES DAVID, magazine educator; b. Middletown, Conn., Feb. 1, 1956; s. George Herbert and Irene Louise (Palmer) M. Student, Ctrl. Conn. Coll., 1974-76. Machinist Chapman Mfg. Co., Durham, Conn., 1977-89, Lyman Gun Sites, Middlefield, Conn., 1990-91; editor Matchbox U.S.A., Durham, 1977—; founder, curator Matchbox and Lesney Toy Mus., Durham, 1992—. Author: Matchbox Toys—Regular Wheel Years, 1992, Matchbox Toys—Superfast Years, 1992, Matchbox Toys—Universal Years, 1993. Mem. Matchbox Internat. Collectors Assn., Matchbox Collectors Club. Democrat. Avocations: collecting matchbox toys and 45 rpm records. Home and Office: 62 Saw Mill Rd Durham CT 06422

MACK, CLIFFORD GLENN, investment banker, management consultant; b. Pitts., Feb. 23, 1927; s. Jay Ord and Willa June (Shupe) M.; m. Judith McClain; children: Jeffrey, Cynthia, Marcia. B.B.A., U. Pitts., 1952; M.B.A., Temple U., 1955. Asst. treas. Air Products & Chems., Inc., Allentown, Pa., 1957-69; dir. internat. fin., asst. treas. Harris Corp., Cleve., 1969-75; treas. A.B. Dick Co., Chgo., 1975-83; pres. A.B. Dick Realty Corp., 1978-80, C.G. Mack Assocs. Ltd., Cons., 1983—; ptnr. AVM Fin. Group, Chgo., 1985—. Contbg. author: Credit Management Handbook, 1955; also articles. Served with AUS, 1945-48. Home: 5100 Trent Woods Dr New Bern NC 28562

MACK, CONNIE, III (CORNELIUS MACK), senator; b. Philadelphia, PA, Oct. 29, 1940; s. Cornelius Mack and Susan (Sheppard) McGillicuddy; children: Debra Lynn, Cornelius Harvey. Degree in bus., U. Fla., 1966. Mgmt. tng. Sun Bank, Cape Coral, Fla., 1966-68; v.p. bus. devel. First Nat. Bank, Ft. Myers, 1968-71; sr. v.p., dir. Sun Bank, Cape Coral, Fla., 1971-75; pres., dir. Fla. Nat. Bank, Cape Coral, 1975-82; mem. U.S. Ho. of Reps. from 13th Dist. Fla., Washington, 1983-89; U.S. Senator from Fla., 1989—. Bd. dirs., chmn. Palmer Drug Abuse Program, Cape Coral; bd. dirs. Cape Coral Hosp. Mem. Met. Ft. Myers C. of C., Cape Coral C. of C. Republican. Roman Catholic. Office: US Senate 517 Senate Hart Bldg Washington DC 20510

MACK, CONSUELO COTTER, news anchor and editor; d. J. Holland and Consuelo Cotter; m. Walter Mack; 1 child. BA in English Lit., History,

Polit. Sci., Sarah Lawrence Coll. With various Wall St. investment firms; asst. press sec. Whitney North Seymour Campaign, 1982; founding news editor, co-anchor Bus. Times, ESPN, 1982-86; contbg. reporter The Today Show, NBC, 1986; achnor, exec. editor Today's Business, N.Y.C., 1986; anchor, editor The Wall St. Jour. Report, N.Y.C., 1987—, The Asian Wall St. Jour. Report, N.Y.C., 1993—; guest panelist The Editors, The World in Rev. on PBS and Can. Broadcasting; speaker in field. Supr., vol. Helpline, N.Y. met. area; bd. dirs. Women's Econ. Round Table. Office: Wall St Jour Report 200 Liberty St Fl 10 New York NY 10281-1099

MACK, DANIEL RICHARD, furniture designer; b. Rochester, N.Y., Dec. 23, 1947; s. Richard Cornelius and Virginia Anne (Brayer) M.; m. Theresa Marie Husted, May 31, 1969; children: Kendra, Jessica, Eliza. BA, U. Toronto, Ont., Can., 1969; MA, New Sch. for Social Rsch., 1975. Journalist Sta. WRVR-FM, N.Y.C., 1971-73; spl. journalist NBC Radio, N.Y.C., 1973-75; journalist NBC TV, N.Y.C., 1981-83; asst. prof. Fordham U., Bronx, N.Y., 1975-81; pres. Daniel Mack Rustic Furnishings, Inc., Warwick, N.Y., 1983—; treework cons. Centerbrook Architects, Essex, Conn., 1990-91. Author: Making Rustic Furniture, 1992; represented in permanent collections at Cooper Hewitt Mus., Mus. of Fine Arts, Houston, Mus. of Fine Arts, Boston, Am. Craft Mus. Fellow N.Y. Found. for Arts, 1985-86, 90-91, Mid-Atlantic Arts Found., 1989-90. Home: 14 Welling Ave Warwick NY 10990-1514 Office: 111 W 19th St New York NY 10011-4115

MACK, DENNIS WAYNE, lawyer; b. Chgo., Sept. 11, 1943; s. Walter Andrew and Betty Jane (Klimek) M. B.A., Yale U., 1965; J.D., Harvard U., 1969. Bar: N.Y. 1970. Assoc. firm Curtis Mallet-Prevost Colt & Mosle, N.Y.C. and Paris, 1969-78; sec., gen. counsel Dominion Textile (USA) Inc., N.Y.C., 1978-91; v.p., 1986-91; pvt. practice N.Y.C., 1991—; alt. rep. Internat. Lesbian and Gay Assn. at ECOSOC of UN, 1994. Mem. ABA, N.Y. State Bar Assn., Bar Assn. City N.Y. Home: 180 Riverside Dr New York NY 10024-1049

MACK, EARLE IRVING, real estate company executive; b. N.Y.C., July 11, 1939; s. H. Bertram and Ruth (Kaufman) M.; m. Carol L. Dickey, July 26, 1990; children: Andrew Mack, Beatrice. BBA, Drexel U., 1960; postgrad., Fordham Law Sch., 1961-62; LHD (hon.), Yeshiva U., 1992. Owner, breeder thoroughbred horses Fla., Ky., N.J., N.Y., Md., Can., 1964—; sr. ptnr., CFO The Mack Co., Rochelle Park, N.J., since 1964; mem. adv. bd. N.Y. State Bus. Venture Partnership, 1988—; mem. transition team for Gov. George Pataki, 1994-95. Producer-dir. film The Children of Theater Street, 1977 (Acad. Award nomination). Bd. dirs. Benjamin N. Cardozo Sch. of Law, N.Y.C., 1980—, chmn. exec. com., 1990, vice chmn. bd. dirs., 1991, chmn. bd. dirs., 1992; bd. dirs. N.Y.C. Ballet, 1988—, chmn. N.Y. State Racing Commn., 1983-90; mem. bldg. devel. com. N.Y.C. Holocaust Commn., 1985—, N.Y. State Thoroughbred Racing Capital Investment Fund, 1987—, The New 42d St., Inc., 1990-92; bd. dirs. Dance Thatre of Harlem, N.Y.C., 1987, elected ch-chmn. bd., 1988-89; trustee N.Y. Racing Assn., Inc. 1990—; trustee, exec. com. Yeshiva U., 1992—; 1st lt. USAR, 1960-68. Recipient Can. Sovereign award Horse of Yr., 1993, Can. Sovereign award for best 3 yr. old horse, 1994; named One of Drexel 100, Drexel U., 1992. Mem. Nat. Realty Com. (bd. dirs., exec. com. 1986-88), Urban Land Inst., Union League Club, Univ. Club, Reading Room Club, Turf & Field Club. Avocations: skiing, swimming, jogging, nutrition. Office: The Mack Co 370 W Passaic St Rochelle Park NJ 07662-3009

MACK, EDWARD GIBSON, retired business executive; b. Toronto, Ont., Can., Dec. 4, 1917; s. Edward Gibson and Marion Margaret (Ward) M.; m. Ruth Harriet Davies, Aug. 3, 1940 (dec.); children: Edward Davies, Carol Mack Fuller, Susan Mack Vassel; m. Isolde Maderson, Sept. 30, 1978. Grad., Pickering Coll., 1938; student, Syracuse U., 1938-40, U. Pa., 1945-46. Investment analyst trust dept. Syracuse (N.Y.) Trust Co., 1939-43; acct. Hurdman & Cranstoun, Syracuse, 1943-44; from dist. sales mgr. to dir. mktg. and product research Easy Washing Machine Corp., Syracuse, 1948-55; dir. research Avco Corp., Connersville, Ind., 1955-58; exec. sec. planning and policy bd. Aeronca Mfg. Corp., Middletown, Ohio, 1958-60; pres. E.D.I., State College, Pa., 1960-62; pres., dir. Sherman Indsl. Electronics Inc., Eutectics Inc.; exec. Richards Musical Instruments, Inc., Elkhart, Ind., 1962-65; mgr. supply and distbn. plastic products Union Carbide Ltd., Lindsay, Ont., 1965-68; corp. sec. Dominion Dairies Ltd., Toronto, 1968-73; v.p., sec. Dominion Dairies Ltd., 1973-81; sec., dir. Sealtest (Can.) Ltd. 1968-81. Bd. mgmt. Pickering Coll. Served with U.S. Army, World War II. Mem. Inst. Chartered Secs. and Adminstrs. (assoc.), Am. Legion, Elks, Sigma Chi. Republican. Home: 217-5 Selby Ranch Rd American River Dr Sacramento CA 95864

MACK, J. CURTIS, II, civic organization administrator; b. Los Angeles, Dec. 22, 1944; s. James Curtis and Ahli Christina (Youngren) M.; m. Tamara Jo Kriner, Jan. 23, 1988; children: James Curtis III, Robert Lee. BA cum laude, U. So. Calif., 1967, M in Pub. Adminstrn., 1969, MA, 1976. Asst. to regional dir. VA, Los Angeles, 1973-79; exec. dir. Citizens for the Republic, Santa Monica, Calif., 1979-85; asst. sec. oceans and atmosphere U.S. Dept. Commerce, Washington, 1985-88; pres. Los Angeles World Affairs Coun., 1988—; bd. dirs. Brentwood Bank of Calif. Col. USAFR, 1969—. Mem. Nat. Space Club (bd. dirs. 1987-88). Republican. Episcopalian. Avocation: philatelist. Office: Los Angeles World Affairs Coun Ste 1730 911 Wilshire Blvd Los Angeles CA 90017

MACK, JANE LOUISE, early childhood educator, administrator; b. Drexel Hill, Pa., Nov. 23, 1924; d. George Schober and Estelle Marie (Heyland) Cridland; m. Charles Lawrence Mack, June 10, 1950; children: Jacqueline Judith, Nancy David. BS in Nursing, U. Pa., 1949. Instr. nursing arts U. Pa. Hosp., Phila., 1949-53; nurse Mass. Gen. Hosp., Boston, 1953-55; instr. in nursing Emerson Hosp., Concord, Mass., 1954-55; tchr. kindergarten Reading Clinic, Concord, 1959-62; tchr. 3d grade Bartlett Pvt. Elem. Sch., Arlington, Mass., 1962-63; asst. tchr. Lexington (Mass.) Montessori Sch. 1963-64, tchr., administr., 1964-80, prin., 1980-91, tchr., 1991—, headmistress emerita, 1991—; advisor to elem. newspaper, 1991—. Contbr. articles to profl. jours. Tchr. mother and baby care ARC, Lexington, 1970-72; pres. Lexington Family Counseling Bd., 1976-81; bd. dirs., admissions chair Dana Home of Lexington, 1992—. Jane Mack Bldg. named in her honor Lexington Montessori Sch., 1990. Mem. Am. Montessori Soc. (chairperson Montessori tchrs. 1972-76), N.Am. Montessori Tchrs. Assn., Montessori Schs. Mass. (pres. 1987-91). Republican. Avocations: research, running, cooking, volunteer work, parent education. Home: 7 Parker St Lexington MA 02173-4906

MACK, JEROME D., banker; b. Albion, Mich., Nov. 6, 1920; s. Nate and Jennie (Solomon) M.; m. Joyce Jean Rosenberg, Mar. 30, 1947; children: Barbara Joan, Karen Diane, Marilynn Susan. BA, AA, UCLA, 1943; D.Law (hon.), U. Nev., Las Vegas, 1983. Vice chmn. Valley Capital Corp. (formerly Valley Bank of Nev.), Las Vegas, 1965—; chmn., commr. Nev. State Tax Commn., 1970-89. Mem. Dem. Nat. Fin. Com., Washington; nat. coordinator Humphrey for Pres., Las Vegas, 1968; fin. chmn. Nev. State Dem. Party, 1968; state coordinator, treas. Cannon for Senate Com., 1958; trustee Boy Scouts Am., 1965-87, U. Nev. Las Vegas Land Found., 1965-87; trustee, bd. overseers UCLA. Recipient Israel's Peace award, 1981; named Outstanding Nev. Citizen U. Nev. Las Vegas Alumni, 1981. Democrat. Jewish. Club: Boys (founder, dir.). Avocations: boating, tennis. Office: Valley Capital Corp PO Box 98600 Las Vegas NV 89193-8600

MACK, JOHN EDWARD, III, utility company executive; b. Poughkeepsie, N.Y., Feb. 20, 1934; s. John Edward Jr. and Agnes D. (Albrecht) M.; m. Maureen Whitworth, Sept. 12, 1970; children: John, Todd, Ellen, David. BS, Siena Coll., 1956, LHD (hon.), 1966, MBA, 1966; LHD, Mt. St. Mary Coll., 1994. With Central Hudson Gas & Electric Corp., Poughkeepsie, 1958—; v.p. corp. services, 1974-76, v.p. customer services, 1976-79, exec. v.p., 1979-82, pres., 1982—, CEO, 1986—, chmn. bd., 1989—; also bd. dirs.; pres. Empire State Electric Energy Rsch. Corp.; bd. dirs. Mid Hudson Med. Ctr.; chmn. exec. com. N.Y. Power Pool. Mem. exec. com. Dutchess County (N.Y.) Boy Scouts Am.; bd. dirs. Astor Home for Children, Rhinebeck, N.Y., Marist Coll., N.Y. Bus. Devel. Corp.. Capt. U.S. 1956-58. Recipient Alexis de Tocqueville Volunteerism award United Way, Poughkeepsie, 1988, Americanism award Anti Defamation League, 1988, Citizenship award Hudson-Del. Boy Scouts, 1987, Disting. Citizen award Dutchess County Boy Scouts Am. Mem. Am. Gas Assn., Edison Electric

Inst. (bd. dirs.), Energy Assn. N.Y. State (chmn.). Roman Catholic. Office: Cen Hudson Gas & Electric 284 South Ave Poughkeepsie NY 12601-4879

MACK, JOSEPH P., advertising agency executive; b. Pitts, 1939. BA, Duquesne U., 1961. Formerly vice-chmn., co-chief ops. officer for N.Y. office Saatchi & Saatchi DFS Inc., pres., chief operating officer for N.Y. office, 1988-89, chmn., chief exec. officer for N.Y. office, 1989—. Office: Saatchi & Saatchi DFS Inc 375 Hudson St New York NY 10014-3658

MACK, JULIA COOPER, judge; b. Fayetteville, N.C., July 17, 1920; d. Dallas L. and Emily (McKay) Perry; m. Jerry S. Cooper, July 30, 1943; 1 dau., Cheryl; m. Clifford S. Mack, Nov. 21, 1957. B.S., Hampton Inst., 1940; LL.B., Howard U., 1951. Bar: D.C. 1952. Legal com. OPS, Washington, 1952-53; atty.-advisor office gen. counsel Gen. Svcs. Adminstrn., Washington, 1953-54; trial appellate atty. criminal div. Dept. Justice, Washington, 1954-68; civil rights atty. Office Gen. Counsel, Equal Employment Opportunity Commn., Washington, 1968-75; assoc. judge Ct. Appeals, Washington, 1975-89; sr. judge, 1989—. Mem. Am., Fed., Washington, Nat. Bar Assns., Nat. Assn. Women Judges. Home: 1610 Varnum St NW Washington DC 20011-4206 Office: DC Ct Appeals 500 Indiana Ave NW 6th Fl Washington DC 20001

MACK, PATRICIA, secondary school principal. Prin. Walker Mid. Sch., Salem, Oreg. Recipient Elem. Sch. Recognition award U.S. Dept. Edn., 1989-90. Office: Walker Middle Sch 1075 8th St NW Salem OR 97304-3799

MACK, PATRICIA JOHNSON, newspaper editor; b. New Brunswick, N.J., Oct. 4, 1942; d. Henry Francis and Ann May (Monahan) Johnson; m. Parker Horton Moore, July 22, 1961 (div. 1971); m. Lonnie Burnell Mack, May 23, 1973; children: Tevis Ann, Kelaine Dorothy, Aidan Ruth. Student, Alderson-Broaddus Coll., 1960-61, U. W.Va., 1961, Harvard U., 1961-62, U. Ky., 1962-64. Reporter The Sentinel Greater Media Newspapers, East Brunswick, N.J., 1971-77; reporter, food editor, restaurant critic News Tribune, Woodbridge, N.J., 1977-92; food editor News Tribune/Record, Woodbridge and Hackensack, N.J., 1992—. Bd. dirs. Parents for Deaf Awareness, 1985-87; active Ctrl. Jersey Health Planning Commn., Woodbridge, 1987, Middlesex County Commn. for Handicapped, New Brunswick, 1987-89. Recipient 7 awards N.J. Press Assn., 1987-92, Cardiac Reporting award N.J. divsn. Am. Heart Assn., 1987, Nutrition Writing award Nestle, 1992, Disting. Svc. award N.J. Dietetic Assn., 1993. Mem. Assn. Food Journalists (Best Food Sect. awards 1987, 92, 93). Avocations: swimming, reading, cooking, film. Office: The Record 150 River St Hackensack NJ 07601-7110

MACK, RAYMOND FRANCIS, newspaper executive; b. Aitkin, Minn., Sept. 5, 1912; s. Raymond Frederick and Bertha (Tuller) M.; m. Betty Habes, Oct. 17, 1941; children—Patricia, Douglas. Student pub. schs., Va., Minn. Country circulation mgr. Duluth (Minn.) Herald News Tribune, 1930-40, St. Paul Dispatch Pioneer Press, 1940-42; circulation mgr. Washington Daily News, 1942-58, advt. dir., 1958-59, bus. mgr., 1959-72, pres., 1960-72; asst. gen. bus. mgr. Scripps-Howard Newspapers, 1972-79, exec. cons., 1979—; spl. adviser to pres. Washington Star-News, 1972-75. Past mem. exec. bd. Nat. Capitol council Boy Scouts Am.; past bd. dirs. Nat. Capital Com., YMCA Davis Meml. Goodwill Industries; bd. dirs. Washington area chpt. Nat. Multiple Sclerosis Soc. Mem. Inter-State Circulation Mgrs. Assn. (past pres.), Internat. Circulation Mgrs. Assn. (past dir.), Washington Bd. Trade (past dir.), Washington Conv. and Visitor's Bur. (past dir.). Clubs: Washington (Washington), Advertising (Washington), Nat. Press (Washington), Columbia Country (Washington), Kiwanis (Washington). Home: 3706 Leland St Chevy Chase MD 20815-4904 Office: Scripps Howard 1090 Vermont Ave NW Washington DC 20005-4905

MACK, RAYMOND WRIGHT, university provost; b. Ashtabula, Ohio, July 15, 1927; s. Wright R. and Hazel E. (Card) M.; m. Barbara Leonard, Mar. 1948 (div. 1953); 1 child, Donald Gene; m. Elizabeth Ann Hunter, Oct. 16, 1953; children: Meredith Lou, Julia Glen, Margaret Kingsley. AB with honors, Baldwin-Wallace Coll., 1949; MA, U. N.C., 1951, PhD, 1953; LHD (hon.), DePaul U., 1990. Asst. prof. sociology, anthropology U. Miss., Oxford, 1953; faculty Northwestern U., Evanston, Ill., 1953-95, assoc. prof. sociology, 1957-62, prof. sociology, 1962-95, prof. emeritus, 1995—, chmn. dept. sociology, 1959-67; dir. Ctr. for Urban Affairs, 1968-71, v.p., dean of faculties, 1971-74, provost, 1974-87; dir. program for Bell System execs., 1958-59. Author: (with Freeman and Yellin) Social Mobility, 1957, (with Kimball Young) Sociology and Social Life, 1959, Transforming America, 1967; editor: Principles of Sociology: A Reader in Theory and Research, 1960, Race, Class and Power, 1963, Our Children's Burden, 1967, The American Sociologist, 1968-70, The Changing South, 1970, Prejudice and Race Relations, 1970. Fellow Am. Sociol. Assn. (mem. council 1966-69); mem. Soc. Study Social Problems (pres. 1969-70), Midwest Sociol. Soc. (pres. 1967), Alpha Kappa Delta (pres. 1969-70). Office: Northwestern U Dept Sociology 1810 Chicago Ave Evanston IL 60208

MACK, ROBERT EMMET, hospital administrator; b. Morris, Ill. 1924. M.D., St. Louis U., 1948. Diplomate: Am. Bd. Internal Medicine. Intern St. Marys Hosp. Group, 1948-49; asst. physician; asst. resident, then resident internal medicine St. Louis U., 1949-52; asst. chief radioisope clinic Walter Reed Army Med. Center, 1954-56; chief med. service, chief radioisotope service St. Louis VA Hosp., 1956-61; vis. physician St. Louis City Hosp., 1957-61; chmn. dept. medicine Womans Hosp., Detroit, 1961-66; dir. Hutzel Hosp., Detroit, 1966-71; pres. Hutzel Hosp., 1971-80; v.p. for academic affairs Detroit Med. Center Corp., 1980—; asst. prof. medicine St. Louis U., 1957-61; assoc. prof. medicine Wayne State U., 1961-66, prof., 1966—, dir. admissions, 1978-81, assoc. dean Med. Center Relations, 1981—. Fellow ACP, Am. Coll. Hosp. Adminstrs., Soc. Med. Adminstrs. (pres. 1987-89); mem. AMA, Am. Fedn. Clin. Rsch., Cen. Soc. Clin. Rsch., Am. Endocrine Soc., Am. Physiol. Soc. Home: 3020 S Westview Ct Bloomfield Hills MI 48304-2472 Office: Detroit Medical Ctr 4201 Saint Antoine St Detroit MI 48201-2194

MACK, ROBERT WHITING, lawyer; b. Cambridge, Mass., June 7, 1949; s. Robert Anthony and Caroline Marshall (Shelly) M. BA, Harvard U., 1971, JD, 1974. Bar: Mass. 1974. Assoc. Hale and Dorr, Boston, 1974-79, jr. ptnr., 1979-83, sr. ptnr., 1983-88, of counsel, 1988-89. Mem. Conservation Commn., Lincoln, Mass., 1981-91. Mem. Lincoln Homes Corp. (bd. dirs. 1991-95), Greater Boston Coun. Am. Youth Hostels (bd. dirs. 1990-92, pres. 1991-92), Chiltern Mountain Club (bd. dirs. 1992—, co-chair 1993—), Harvard Gay & Lesbian Caucus (bd. dirs. 1994—, co-chair 1994—). Home: 10 Magazine St 805 Cambridge MA 02139

MACK, RONALD J., park superintendent; b. Ithaca, N.Y., Aug. 13, 1952; s. Voyce Joron and Margaret (Rogers) M.; m. Virlean Hill, Jan. 4, 1955; children: Terrence, Marquisha. BA, Syracuse U., 1973; postgrad., Law Enforcement Tng. Ctr., Glynco, Ga., 1981. Recreation specialist D.C. Parks and Recreation, Washington, 1973-74; park ranger Nat. Park Svc., Washington, 1974-77, Bklyn., 1977-79, S.I., N.Y., 1979-80; supr. park ranger Nat. Park Svc., Sandy Hook, N.J., 1980-87; chief ranger activities Nat. Park Svc., Bklyn., 1987-88; supt. Nat. Park Svc., Hardy, Va., 1988-90, Independence, Mo., 1990-95; chief Nat. Park Svc., Washington, 1995—. Contbr. articles to profl. jours. Mem. City of Independence Heritage, 1990-95, Spl. Events Com., Independence, 1990-95. Mem. Dept. Interior Fed. Credit Union, Community of Concerned Citizens, Roundtable, Employee and Alumni Assn. Nat. Park Svc., Syracuse U. Alumni Assn. Avocations: swimming, historic preservation, recreation activities. Office: Nat Park Svc Nat Capital Region 1100 Ohio Dr SW Washington DC 20242

MACK, THEODORE, lawyer; b. Ft. Worth, Mar. 5, 1936; s. Henry and Norma (Harris) M.; m. Ellen Feinknopf, June 19, 1960; children: Katherine Norma, Elizabeth Ellen, Alexandra. AB cum laude, Harvard U., 1958, JD, 1961. Bar: Tex. 1961, U.S. Sup. Ct. 1971, U.S. Ct. Apls. (5th cir.) 1967, U.S. Ct. Apls. (11th cir.) 1981, U.S. Dist. Ct. (no. dist.) Tex. 1961, U.S. Dist. Ct. (we. dist.) Tex. 1968, U.S. Dist. Ct. (so. dist.) Tex. 1968. Assoc., Mack & Mack, Ft. Worth, 1961-62, ptnr., 1963-70; ptnr., pres., v.p., treas., ptnr. Renfro, Mack, Hudman, P.C., and principals Ft. Worth, 1970-93; spl. counsel McLean & Sanders A Profl. Corp., Ft. Worth, 1993—. Trustee Ft. Worth Country Day Sch., 1976-82; bd. dirs. Beth-El Congregation, 1964-73,

75-78, pres., 1975-77; bd. dirs. Jewish Fedn. Ft. Worth, 1965-72; mem. Leadership Ft. Worth, 1973-74; bd. dirs. Sr. Citizens Ctrs., Inc., 1969-81, Family and Individual Svcs., 1981-84, Presbyn. Night Shelter Tarrant County, Inc., 1992—; pres. Harvard Law Sch. Assn. Tex., 1976-77. Fellow Tex. Bar Found. (life); mem. Tex. Bar Assn., ABA, Tarrant County Bar Assn., Bar Assn. 5th Cir. Ct., Colonial Country Club, Ft. Worth Club, City Club, Harvard Club (N.Y.C., Boston). Democrat. Jewish. Home: 2817 Harlanwood Dr Fort Worth TX 76109-1226 Office: 100 Main Pl Fort Worth TX 76102-3090

MACKALL, LAIDLER BOWIE, lawyer; b. Washington, Aug. 8, 1916; s. Laidler and Evelyn (Bowie) M.; m. Nancy M. Taylor, Aug. 28, 1942; children: Nancy Taylor Mackall Lurton (dec.), Christie Beall Mackall Conrard, Susan Somervell Mackall Smythe, Bruce Bowie Mackall Sloan; m. Prudence Robertson Colbert, July 26, 1978. A.B., Princeton U., 1938; postgrad., Georgetown U., 1938-40, J.D., 1946. Bar: D.C. bar 1947, ICC bar 1951, U.S. Supreme Ct. bar 1958. Law clk. to chief judge of predecessor to D.C. Ct. Appeals, 1946-47; assoc. Minor, Gatley & Drury, Washington, 1947-49, Steptoe & Johnson, Washington, 1949-51; ptnr. Steptoe & Johnson, 1952-86, of counsel, 1986—; mem. D.C. Ct. Appeals Com. on Admissions, 1974-78, D.C. Circuit Jud. Conf., 1983, 85, 86; bd. mgrs. Nat. Conf. Bar Examiners, 1974-77. Served with USAAF, 1940-46, 51. Decorated Silver Star, D.F.C. with oak leaf cluster, Air medal with 5 oak leaf clusters. Fellow Am. Coll. Trial Lawyers (emeritus); mem. ABA (past vice chmn. standing com. aviation ins. law), D.C. Bar, Bar Assn. D.C. (past chmn. com. on negligence, motor vehicle and compensation law), Barristers Club (v.p. 1964), Chevy Chase Country Club, Met. Club, Mid Ocean Club of Bermuda, Wilderness Country Club of Fla., Hawk's Nest Golf Club of Fla. Episcopalian. Home: 6400 Brookville Rd Bethesda MD 20815-3339 Office: 1330 Connecticut Ave NW Washington DC 20036-1795

MACKANESS, GEORGE BELLAMY, retired pharmaceutical company executive; b. Sydney, Australia, Aug. 20, 1922; came to U.S., 1965, naturalized, 1978; s. James Vincent and Eleanor Frances (Bellamy) M.; m. Gwynneth Patterson, May 5, 1945; 1 son, Miles Philip. M.B. B.S. with honors, U. Sydney, 1945; D.C.P., London U., 1949; M.A. with honors, U. Oxford, 1949, D.Phil., 1953. Demonstrator, tutor in pathology Sir William Dunn Sch. Pathology, Oxford, 1949-53; sr. fellow Australian Nat. U., 1954-58, asso. prof., 1958-60, professorial fellow, 1960-63; prof. microbiology U. Adelaide, 1963-65; dir. Trudeau Inst., 1965-76; pres. The Squibb Inst. for Med. Research, Princeton, N.J., 1976-88; clin. prof. dept. medicine Coll. of Medicine and Dentistry of N.J.; adj. prof. pathology N.Y. U. Author articles in field. Recipient Paul Ehrlich-Ludwig Darmstaedter prize, 1975. Fellow Royal Soc. London; mem. Am. Assn. Immunologists, AAAS, Am. Soc. Microbiologists, Internat. Soc. Immunopharmacology. Home: 2783 Little Creek Rd Johns Island SC 29455-6022

MACKAY, ALFRED F., dean, philosophy educator; b. Ocala, Fla., Oct. 1, 1938; s. Kenneth Hood and Julia Horsey (Farhum) MacK.; m. Ann Nadine Wilson, Feb. 4, 1962; children: Douglas Kevin, Robert Wilson. AB, Davidson Coll., 1960; PhD, U. N.C., 1967. Prof. philosophy Oberlin (Ohio) Coll., 1967—, dean Coll. Arts and Scis., 1984-95, acting pres., 1991; vis. asst. prof. philosophy dept. U. Ill., Urbana/Champaign, 1970-71; vis. prof. philosophy dept. Wayne State U., Detroit, 1983. Author: Arrow's Theories: The Paradox of Social Choice, 1980; editor: Society: Revolution and Reform, 1971, Issues in the Philosophy of Language, 1976. Campaign cons. Buddy MacKay for U.S. Senate, Fla., 1988. 1st lt. U.S. Army, Airborne, 1961-63. Fellow Woodrow Wilson Found., 1963-66, Am. Coun. of Learned Socs., 1973, Humanities fellow Rockefeller Found., 1981. Democrat. Avocations: choral singing, automobiles. Office: Oberlin Coll Office of Dean Coll Arts and Scis Oberlin OH 44074

MACKAY, EDWARD, engineer; b. Kilmarnock, Ayrshire, Scotland, Feb. 29, 1936; s. Edward and Gertrude (Black) M.; widowed. Higher Nat. Cert., Glasgow Tech. Coll., Scotland, 1957. Layout engr. Stanley Works, New Britain, Conn., 1957-58; project engr. Grumman Olson, Athens, N.Y., 1961-69, asst. chief engr., 1969-74; chief engr. Grumman Olson, Sturgis, Mich., 1974-78, v.p. engring., 1978—. With U.S. Army, 1959-61. Presbyterian. Avocation: sheep farming. Office: Grumman Olson 1801 S Nottawa St Sturgis MI 49091

MACKAY, HAROLD HUGH, lawyer; b. Regina, Sask., Can., Aug. 1, 1940; s. John Royden and Grace Madeliene (Irwin) MacK.; m. Jean Elizabeth Hutchison, Dec. 27, 1963; children: Carol, Donald. B.A., U. Sask., 1960; LL.B., Dalhousie U., Halifax, N.S., 1963. Bar: Sask. 1964, Queen's Counsel 1981. Assoc. MacPherson Leslie & Tyerman, Regina, 1963-69, ptnr., 1969-75, 76—, mng. ptnr., 1989—; dir. Ipsco Inc., Uranerz Exploration and Mining Ltd., Weyerhauser Can. Ltd., Vigoro Corp., Merfin Hygienic Products, Inc. Trustee Found. for Legal Rsch. Mem. Internat. Bar Assn., Can. Bar Assn., Law Soc. Sask. Mem. United Ch. Office: 1500-1874 Scarth St, Regina, SK Canada S4P 4E9

MACKAY, JOHN ROBERT, II, lawyer; b. Passaic, N.J., Aug. 17, 1934; s. John R. and Janice Faith (Miller) M.; m. Susan Kellett, July 4, 1959 (div. 1985); children: J. Scott, Lauren A., Amanda F.; m. Patricia Margitan, Feb. 14, 1987; 1 child, Paige Elizabeth. AB, Bowdoin Coll., 1956; LLB, Rutgers U., 1965. Bar: N.J. 1965, U.S. Dist. Ct. N.J. 1965. Tech. writer, editor ITT Communication System, Paramus, N.J., 1960-62; law sec. to Chief Justice Weintraub N.J. Supreme Ct., Newark, N.J., 1965-66; atty. Lowenstein Sandler, Roseland, N.J., 1966-70, ptnr., 1970—; chmn. N.J. Corp. Law Revision Com., 1977-88, sec., 1970-73; adj. faculty Seton Hall sch. Law, 1973-75, Rutgers Sch. Law, 1978-81, 95—. Author: New Jersey Business Corporations: Law and Practice, 1992; editor in chief Rutgers Law Review, 1964-65; contbr. articles to profl. jours. Trustee Newark Day Ctr., 1972-82, pres. 1975-77; exec. com., pres. Rutgers Law Alumni Assn., Newark, 1980-81; chmn. fin. com. ARC (Nutley chpt.), 1978-86; exec. com., sec. Williams Ctr. Performing Arts, Rutherford, N.J., 1986-92; trustee United Way Essex, West Hudson, 1979-86. Lt. USN 1956-60 PTO. Mem. ABA (commn. corp. laws 1979-87, com. negotiated acquisitions 1986—), N.J. Bar Assn., Essex County Bar Assn. Office: Lowenstein Sandler 65 Livingston Ave Roseland NJ 07068-1725

MACKAY, KENNETH DONALD, environmental services company executive; b. Detroit, July 18, 1942; s. John and Ina (Finlayson) M.; m. Bonnie Young, Aug. 15, 1964; children: Heather, Laurel. BS, U. Mich., 1964; PhD, U. Minn., 1968. Sr. rsch. chemist Gen. Mills., Mpls., 1968-73, group leader, 1973-77; tech. mgr. Henkel Corp., Mpls., 1977-80, assoc. dir. R&D, 1980-82, v.p., dir. rsch., 1982-86; pres. Henkel Rsch. Corp., Santa Rosa, Calif., 1986-91, Cognis, Inc., Santa Rosa, 1991—. Contbr. articles to profl. jours.; patentee in field. Mayor City of Circle Pines, Minn., 1971-77; mem. Santa Rosa Econ. Devel. Commn., 1987-88; mem. indsl. adv. bd. U. Calif. Berkeley, 1987—, L.A.; bd. dirs. Santa Rosa Symphony, 1987-88. Mem. Am. Chem. Soc., Indsl. Rsch. Inst. Avocations: fishing, tennis, golf. Office: Cognis Inc 2330 Circadian Way Santa Rosa CA 95407-5415

MACKAY, KENNETH HOOD (BUDDY MACKAY), state official, former congressman; b. Ocala, Fl, Mar. 22, 1933; m. Anne Selph; children: Ken, John, Ben, Andy. B.S., B.A., U. Fla., 1954, LL.B. with honors, 1961. Bar: Fla. 1961. Pvt. practice Raymond, Wilson & Karl, Daytona Beach, Fla., 1963; sole practice 98th-100th Congresses from 6th Dist. Fla., Ocala, Fla., 1963—; mem. Fla. Ho. of Reps. 5th dist. Fla., 1968-74; mem. Fla. State Senate, 1974-80, mem. U.S. Ho. Reps. from 6th dist. Fla., 1985-89; lt. gov. State of Fla. Elder Ft. King Presbyn. Ch. With USAF 1955-58. Recipient Nat. Legis. Leadership award, 1976; named Most Valuable Freshman Ho. Mem., 1968, Most Valuable Legislator St. Petersburg Times, 7 times; recipient Allen Morris award. Mem. ABA, Kiwanis. Democrat. Office: Office of Lt Gov The Capitol PL05 Tallahassee FL 32399-0001

MACKAY, MALCOLM, executive search consultant; b. Bklyn., Nov. 6, 1940; s. John F. and Helen (Pflug) MacK.; m. Cynthia Johnson, Aug. 29, 1964; children: Robert Livingston, Hope Winthrop. A.B. Cum laude, Princeton U., 1963; J.D., Harvard U., 1966. Bar: N.Y. 1967. Assoc. Milbank, Tweed, Hadley and McCloy, N.Y.C., 1966-69; dep. supt. N.Y. State Ins. Dept., N.Y.C., 1969-71; 1st dep. supt. N.Y. State Ins. Dept., 1971-73; vice chancellor L.I. U., Greenvale, N.Y., 1973-75; sr. v.p. Blue Cross & Blue Shield of Greater New York, 1975-77, N.Y. Life Ins. Co., N.Y.C., 1977-

89; mng. dir. Russell Reynolds Assocs., N.Y.C., 1989—; bd. dirs. Independence Savs. Bank, Bklyn., Empire Fidelity Investments Life Ins. Co., Hyperion Capital Mgmt., Short Duration Govt. Fund. Trustee Hayden Found., Pratt Inst. Mem. Century Assn., Piping Rock Club. Home: 2 Montague Ter Brooklyn NY 11201-7102 Office: Russell Reynolds Assocs 200 Park Ave New York NY 10166-0002

MACKAY, NEIL DUNCAN, plastic company executive; b. Chelsea, Mass., Nov. 5, 1931; s. Allan Foster and Helen May (Smith) MacK.; m. Marcia Ann McCarthy, Aug. 22, 1953 (dec. 1979); children: Duncan, Jerry, Alan, Neil, Bonnie; m. Beverly J. Burke, May 31, 1991. BS, BA, Northeastern U., Boston, 1954. Gen. mgr. Plastic Molding Corp., Newtown, Conn., 1954-67; market specialist Chem. div. Uniroyal, N.Y.C., 1967-70; project mgr. Colt Ind. Korean Project, N.Y.C., 1970-76; pres. Automatic Injection Molding Corp., Berkeley Heights, N.J., 1976-87, Diamond Mgmt. Cons., Inc., Winchester, N.H., 1988—; bd. dirs. Frazier & Son, Inc., Clifton, N.J., 1987—, Lor-Tech Plastics, Inc., Berkeley Heights, N.J. Author: Korean Plastics, 1973. Mem. Rep. Nat. Com., Washington, 1986-92. Recipient Outstanding Performance award Ministry Nat. Def. Republic of Korea, 1974. Mem. Am. Profl. Capt.'s Assn., Soc. Plastics Engrs. (sec. 1963-70, treas. 1983-86), Scottish-Am. Cultural Soc., St. Andrews Soc. N.Y., Plastic Pioneers Assn., Stuyvesant Yacht Club, Am. Yacht Club. Republican. Presbyterian. Avocation: sailing. Home: 19 Lovely Ln Winchester NH 03470-2916 Office: Diamond Mgmt Cons Inc PO Box 40 Winchester NH 03470-0040

MACKAY, RAYMOND ARTHUR, chemist; b. N.Y.C., Oct. 30, 1939; s. Theodore Henry and Helen Marie (Cusack) M.; m. Mary Dilberian, Aug. 13, 1966; 1 child, Chelsea Christine; children by previous marriage—Brett, Edward. B.S. in Chemistry, Rensselaer Poly. Inst., 1961; Ph.D. in Chemistry, SUNY-Stony Brook, 1966. Research assoc. Brookhaven Nat. Lab., Upton, N.Y., 1966-67; prof. Drexel U., Phila., 1969-83; chief chem. div. Chem. Research and Devel. Ctr., Aberdeen Proving Ground, Md., 1983-91; prof. chemistry, dir. ctr. advanced materials processing Clarkson U., Potsdam, N.Y., 1991—. Contbr. articles to profl. jours. Served to capt. U.S. Army, 1967-69. Grantee, U.S. Army, Dept. Energy, Army Research Office, NSF, Acad. Applied Scis., 1972-83, NATO, 1982-86. Mem. Am. Chem. Soc., Am. Oil Chemists Soc. (assoc. editor), Sigma Xi. Office: Clarkson U PO Box 5665 Potsdam NY 13699-5665

MACKAY, ROBERT BATTIN, museum director; b. Bklyn., Jan. 24, 1945; s. John French and Helen (Pflug) MacKay. B.S., Boston U., 1968, Ph.D. in Am. Studies, 1980; M.Ed., Harvard U., 1972. With Archtl. Heritage, Inc., Boston, 1967-71; dir. So. Preservation of L.I. Antiquities, Setauket, N.Y., 1974—; mem. curatorial com. Mystic Seaport Mus., Conn.; mem. Culture Com. L.I. Assn., Commack, N.Y. Editor: Between Ocean and Empire: An Illustrated History of Long Island, 1985. Mem. hist. dist. adv. commn. Town of Brookhaven, N.Y., 1983—; trustee Theodore Roosevelt Assn., St. Giles Found. For Crippled Children. With U.S. Army, 1969-70, Vietnam. Club: N.Y. Yacht (chmn. hist. com.). Home: PO Box 292 East Setauket NY 11733-0292 Office: Soc Preservation of LI Antiquities 93 N Country Rd Setauket NY 11733

MACKAY, WILLIAM ANDREW, judge; b. Halifax, N.S., Can., Mar. 20, 1929; s. Robert Alexander and Mary Kathleen (Junkin) MacK.; m. Alexa Eaton Wright, July 7, 1954; 1 dau., Margaret Kathleen. B.A., Dalhousie U., 1950, LL.B., 1953, LL.M., 1954; LL.M., Harvard U., 1970; LL.D. (hon.), Meml. U. Nfld., St. F.X. Univ., N.S. Bar: N.S.; Named queen's counsel. Fgn. service officer Dept. External Affairs, Ottawa, Ont., Can., 1954-57; asst. sec. Royal Com., Ottawa, 1955-57; sucessively asst. prof., assoc. prof., prof. law, dean Faculty of law Dalhousie U. (Halifax), N.S., Can., 1957-69, v.p., 1969-80, pres., vice-chancellor, 1980-86; ombudsman N.S., 1986-88; judge Fed. Ct. Can., trial div., Ottawa, Ont., Can., 1988—; chmn. Assn. Atlantic Univs., Halifax, 1981-83; v.p. Assn. Univs. and Colls. Can., 1982-83, pres., 1983-85; pres. Conf. Gov. Bodies Legal Profession Can., 1968-69, Assn. Can. Law Tchrs., 1964-65. Chmn. N.S. Human Rights Com., Halifax, 1967-86; chmn. N.S. Commns. on Salary and Allowances of Elected Provincial Ofcls., 1974, 78, 81, 83, 84, 85; chmn. N.S. Task Force on AIDS, 1987-88. Mem. Can. Bar Assn. Home: 140 Rideau Terr, Apt 11, Ottawa, ON Canada K1M 0Z2 Office: Fed Ct Canada, Ottawa, ON Canada K1A 0H9

MACKAY-LYONS, BRIAN GERALD, architect, urban designer, architecture educator; b. Arcadia, Nova Scotia, Can., Aug. 26, 1954; s. Gerald John and Jeannette Marie (d'Entremont) Lyons; m. Marilyn Joan MacKay, June 21, 1980; children: Renee, Alison, Matthew. Science, Dalhousie U., Nova Scotia, 1972-74; BA in Environ. Design, T.U.N.S., Nova Scotia, 1976, BA in Architecture, 1978; MA in Architecture, Urban Design, UCLA, Calif., 1982. With Design Workshop, N.B., Ltd., Moncton, New Brunswick, Can., 1975, W. Brian Edwards Architect, Ltd., Edmonton, Alberta, Can., 1977; pres. Networks Ltd., Halifax, Nova Scotia, Can., 1978-80; with The Urban Innovations Group, L.A., Calif., 1980-81; teaching assistantship UCLA, Calif., 1980-82; with Moore, Ruble and Yudell, Santa Monica, Calif., 1982, Emodi and MacKay-Lyons Architects, Halifax, Nova Scotia, Can., 1983-85; asst. prof. Tech. U. Nova Scotia, Halifax, Nova Scotia, Can., 1983-89, assoc. prof., 1989—; with Brian MacKay-Lyons Architecture, Urban Design, Halifax, Nova Scotia, Can., 1985—; lectr. in the field. Recipient Royal Archtl. Inst. Can. medal Nova Scotia Tech. Coll., 1978, Nova Scotia Assn. Architects Design Competition Merit award, 1983, 89, award of Excellence, 1986, citation, 1986, 87, 89, medal of Excellence, 1987; Nova Scotia Home award, 1984, 85, 86, The Gov. Gen. medal, 1986, 92, The Can. Architect award of Excellence, 1988, 93, Olympic Arts medal, 1988, The Lt. Gov. medal of Excellence, 1990, 91, 93, The Lt. Gov. award of Merit, 1990, 92, 94, The Lt. Gov. award, 1991, 92; Welton Beckett fellow UCLA, 1980-81, 81-82, GSAUP Entry fellow UCLA, 1980, ILAUD fellow Italy, 1982; Ernest Auerbach scholar UCLA, 1981-82. Avocations: racquet sports, farming, music. Home: 5658 Falkland St, Halifax, NS Canada B3K 5X4 Office: Brian MacKay-Lyons Arch and Urban Design, 2042 Maynard St, Halifax, NS Canada B3K 3Y2

MACKE, KENNETH A., retail executive; b. Templeton, Iowa, Dec. 16, 1938; m. Kathleen O'Farrell; children: Michael, Jeffrey, Melissa. BS, Drake U., 1961. With Dayton Hudson Corp. and affiliates, 1961—, merchandising positions, 1961-73, sr. v.p., gen. merchandising mgr., 1973-76, pres., chief exec. officer, 1976-78, chmn., chief exec. officer, 1978-81, corp. sr. v.p., 1977-81, pres., 1981-82, pres., chief oper. officer, 1982-83, chief exec. officer, 1983-84, chmn., chief exec. officer, 1984—, also bd. dirs.; bd. dirs. 1st Bank Systems, Inc., Gen. Mills, Inc., Unisys Corp. Bd. dirs. United Way Mpls., J.L. Kellogg Grad. Sch. Mgmt., Northwestern U., Nat. Retail Fedn. Office: Dayton Hudson Corp 777 Nicollet Mall Minneapolis MN 55402-2004

MACKE, RICHARD CHESTER, naval officer; b. Freeport, Ill., Jan. 4, 1938; s. Chester O'Dell and Eileen Joan (Schoenhard) M.; m. Janet McKenzie, Aug. 15, 1960 (div. 1976); children: Susan Marie, Cheryl Lynn; m. Barbara Eileen Gabbe, Feb. 22, 1969; children: Belinda Lee, Melissa Rae. BS, U.S. Naval Acad., 1960; MS, Naval Postgrad. Sch., 1972. Commd. ensign USN, 1960, advanced through grades to adm., 1994; exec. officer USS Nimitz USN, Norfolk, Va., 1979-81, comdr. USS Dwight D. Eisenhower, 1984-86, comdr. Carrier Group Two, 1988-90; dir. J6 joint staff, 1991-92, dir. joint chiefs of staff, 1992-94; comdr. Carrier Group Four USN, Norfolk, Va., 1990-91; comdr. USS Camden USN, Bremerton, Wash., 1981-83; exec. asst. naval ops. staff USN, Washington, 1983-84; comdr. naval space command USN, Dahlgren, Va., 1986-88; 16th comdr. in chief U.S. Pacific Command, Camp H.M. Smith, Hawaii, 1994—. Contbr. articles to profl. jours. Decorated Disting. Svc. medal, Def. Superior Svc. medal, Legion of Merit with gold stars, Air medal (14), Meritorious Svc. medal. Mem. Soc. Exptl. Test Pilots, Armed Forces Comm and Elect Assn., Profl. Golfers Am. Avocations: golf, woodworking. Office: Comdr in Chief US Pacific Command Camp H M Smith HI 96861-4028

MACKENDRICK, PAUL LACHLAN, classics educator; b. Taunton, Mass., Feb. 11, 1914; s. Ralph Fulton and Sarah (Harvey) MacK.; m. Dorothy Grace Lau, Mar. 17, 1945; children: Andrew Lachlan, Sarah Ann. A.B. summa cum laude, Harvard U., 1934, A.M., 1937, Ph.D., 1938; postgrad., Balliol Coll., Oxford, 1934-36. Instr. Phillips Acad., 1938-41, Harvard U., 1946; asst. prof. U. Wis., 1946-48, assoc. prof., 1948-52, prof., 1952-75, Lily Ross Taylor prof., 1975-84, prof. emeritus, 1984—; prof.

charge Sch. Classical Studies, Am. Acad. Rome, summers 1956-59; vis. prof. U. Colo., summer 1964; mem. Inst. for Advanced Study, Princeton, 1964-65; vis. prof. U. Ibadan, Nigeria, 1965-66, cons.; vis. prof. charge Intercoll. Ctr. for Classical Studies, Rome, 1973-74; Rockefeller scholar-in-residence Bellagio Center, Italy, 1977; vis. fellow Churchill Coll., Cambridge U., 1977-78; scholar-in-residence Fondation Hardt, Geneva, 1983; Phi Beta Kappa nat. lectr., 1970-71; Sec., dir. Am. Council Learned Socs., 1956-57, dir., 1960-63; vis. lectr. U. Canterbury; N.Z., 1985, Macquarie U., Australia, 1985, Universidade Fed. de Rio de Janeiro, 1987, Universidade de Coimbra, 1989; external examiner U. Tasmania, 1990. Author: (with Herbert M. Howe) Classics in Translation, 1952, (with V.M. Scramuzza) The Ancient World, 1958, The Roman Mind at Work, 1958, The Mute Stones Speak, 1960, 2d edit., 1983, The Greek Stones Speak, 1962, 2d edit., 1981, Western Civilization, 1968, The Athenian Aristocracy, 399-31 B.C, 1969, The Iberian Stones Speak, 1969, Romans on the Rhine, 1970, Roman France, 1972, Dacian Stones Speak, 1975, North African Stones Speak, 1980, The Philosophical Books of Cicero, 1989, Cicero's Speeches: Context, Law, Rhetoric, 1995. Trustee Am. Acad. in Rome, 1966-72; bd. dirs. Nat. Humanities Faculty, 1968-71, chmn., 1969-70. Served to lt. USNR, 1941-45. Fulbright fellow, 1950; Guggenheim fellow, 1957-58; Am. Philos. Soc. grantee, 1981. Mem. Classical Assn. Middle West and South (pres. 1969-70), Am. Philol. Assn. (sec.-treas. 1954-56), Archeol. Inst. Am. Madison Soc. (pres. 1963), Phi Beta Kappa (pres. U. Wis. 1965-66). Home: 208 Bordner Dr Madison WI 53705-2513

MACKENZIE, CHARLES SHERRARD, college president; b. Quincy, Mass., Aug. 21, 1924; s. Charles Sherrard and Dorothy (Eaton) MacK.; m. Florence Evelyn Phelps Meyer, Aug. 28, 1964 (dec. 1981); 1 child, Robert Walter Meyer; m. Lavonne Rudolph Gaiser, Mar. 30, 1985. B.A., Gordon Coll., 1946; M.Div., Princeton Theol. Sem., 1949, Ph.D., 1955; student, Boston U., 1942-43, U. Paris, 1953. Ordained to ministry Congl. Christian Ch., 1949. Pastor Carversville (Pa.) Christian Ch., 1948-51; fellow faculty Princeton Theol. Sem., 1949-51, 53-54; pastor First Presbyn. Ch., Avenel, N.J., 1954-64, Broadway Presbyn. Ch., N.Y.C., 1964-67, First Presbyn. Ch., San Mateo, Calif., 1967-71; pres. Grove City (Pa.) Coll., 1971-91, chancellor, 1991-92; advisor to pres., chief philosphy Reformed Seminary, Orlando, Fla., 1992—; sr. min. Eastminster Presbyn. Ch., Wichita, Kans., 1993; bd. dirs. Covenant Life Ins. Co.; cons. Oxford Project, 1992—; lectr. Oxford U., 1965, U. Hamburg, 1968, Columbia U., 1964-67, Stanford U., 1967-71. Author: The Anguish and Joy of Pascal, 1973, Freedom, Equality, Justice, 1980, The Trinity and Culture, 1985. Mem. Human Relations Commn., San Mateo, 1968-70; mem. Indsl. Devel. Council, Grove City, 1972-75. Served with USAF, 1951-53. Mem. Presbyn. Coll. Union, Am. Assn. Pres.'s Ind. Colls. and Univs. (dir. pres.), Nat. Assn. Ind. Colls. and Univs. (mem. secretariat 1985-91), Freedoms Found. (nat. jury), Duquesne Club (Pitts.), Univ. Club Boston, Citrus Club (Orlando), Evangelical initiative Notre Dame U., Rockford Inst. Main St. com. Republican. Address: Box 945120 Maitland FL 32794

MACKENZIE, DONALD MURRAY, hospital administrator; b. Toronto, Ont., Can., June 5, 1947; s. Donald Alexander and June Cameron MacKenzie; m. Marilyn Adele McNaughton, Jan. 3, 1970; children: Jennifer, Katherine, Kenneth. BA in Econs., U. Toronto, 1968, MA in Polit. Sci., 1970, D Health Adminstr., 1974. Exec. asst. Mt. Sinai Hosp., Toronto, 1974-76, successively asst. exec. dir., exec. dir., v.p., 1974-89; pres. North York Gen. Hosp., Toronto, 1989—; asst. prof. U. Toronto, 1989—. Editor: History of Canadian Hospitals, 1972; contbr. articles to profl. jours. Bd. dirs. Ont. Cancer Treatment & Rsch. Found. Mem. Can. Coll. Health Svc. Execs. (cert., various coms.), Can. Cancer Soc. (hon. life, pres. Ont. div. 1989-91, award of merit 1988), Ont. Hosp. Assn. (bd. dirs.), Toronto Bd. Trade, Parkview Golf Club (bd. dirs.). Anglican. Avocations: golf, tennis, canoe tripping. Office: North York Gen Hosp, 4001 Leslie St, North York, ON Canada M2K 1E1

MACKENZIE, GEORGE, controller, manufacturing executive; b. Drexel Hill, Pa., Mar. 6, 1949; s. George and Dorothy (Weber) MacK.; m. Carol P. MacKenzie, Aug. 19, 1972; children: George C., Bruce D. BS, U. Del., 1971; MBA, U. Chgo., 1973. CPA, Pa. Staff auditor Coopers & Lybrand, Phila., 1971-74, sr. auditor, 1974-76, audit supr., 1976-78, audit mgr., 1978-79; mgr. corp. reporting Hercules, Inc., Wilmington, Del., 1979-83; contr. Hercules, Inc., Wilmington, 1983-88, v.p., contr., 1988-91, v.p. treas., 1991—. Vice chmn. U. Del. Acctg. Adv. Bd., Newark, 1983—. Mem. AICPA, Pa. Inst. CPAs, Nat. Accts. Assn., Fin. Execs. Inst. (sec. Del. chpt. 1985-86, v.p. 1986-87, pres. 1987-88), Beta Alpha Psi. Office: Hercules Inc 1313 N Market St Wilmington DE 19894-0001

MACKENZIE, GEORGE ALLAN, diversified company executive; b. Kingston, Jamaica, Dec. 15, 1931; s. George Adam and Annette Louise (Maduro) MacK.; m. Valerie Ann Marchand, June 30, 1971; children from previous marriage: Richard Michael, Barbara Wynne. Student, Jamaica Coll., Kingston, 1944-48. Commd. flying officer Canadian Air Force, 1951, advanced through grades to lt. gen., 1978; comdr. Canadian Forces Air Command, Winnipeg, Man., 1978-80; resigned Canadian Forces Air Command, 1980; exec. v.p., COO Gendis, Inc., 1980-89, pres., COO, 1989—, also bd. dirs.; pres., COO, chmn. exec. com. Sony of Can., Ltd., Willowdale, Ont., Can., 1993-95, also bd. dirs.; pres., COO Met. Stores of Can., Ltd.; pres. Cobros Import Ltd., Gendis Bus. Svcs.; chmn. exec. com. MMG Mgmt. Group, Saan Stores Ltd.; bd. dirs. Tundra Oil and Gas Ltd., Chauvco Resources Ltd., Gendis Inc. Bd. dirs. St. Boniface Gen. Hosp. Rsch. Found.; coun. mem. Duke of Edinburgh's Award in Can.; mem. regional adv. bd. Carleton U.; mem. jud. coun. Province of Manitoba. Decorated comdr. Order of Mil. Merit, Order St. Johns, Can. Decoration, Knight of St. Lazarus of Jerusalem. Mem. United Services Inst. Can. (hon. v.p.), Canadian Corps Commissaries (gov.), Police Chiefs Research Found. (co-chmn.). Clubs: Rotary (Winnipeg); Lakewood Country (Delta); Manitoba; St. Charles Golf and Country. Home: 383 Christie Rd, St Germain, MB Canada Office: Gendis Inc, 1370 Sony Pl, Winnipeg, MB Canada R3T 1N5

MACKENZIE, JOHN A., federal judge; b. 1917. J.D., Washington and Lee U., 1939. Bar: Va. Assoc. judge Mcpl. Ct. Portsmouth, Va., 1952-62; sole practice, 1939-67; judge U.S. Dist. Ct. for Eastern Dist. Va., Norfolk, from 1967, now sr. judge; mem. Va. Gen. Assembly, 1954-58. Mem. ABA, Va. Bar Assn. Office: US Dist Ct 600 Granby St Rm 340 Norfolk VA 23510-1915

MACKENZIE, JOHN DOUGLAS, engineering educator; b. Hong Kong, Feb. 18, 1926; came to U.S., 1954, naturalized, 1965; s. John and Hannah (Wong) MacK.; m. Jennifer Russell, Oct. 2, 1954; children—Timothy John, Andrea Louise, Peter Neil. BS, U. London, 1952, PhD, 1954. Research asst., lectr. Princeton U., 1954-56; ICI fellow Cambridge (Eng.) U., 1956-57; research scientist Gen. Electric Research Ctr. N.Y.C., 1957-63; prof. materials sci. Rensselaer Poly. Inst., 1963-69; prof. engring. U. Calif., Los Angeles, 1969—; U.S. rep. Internat. Glass Commn., 1964-71. Author books in field (6); editor: Jour. Non-Crystalline Solids, 1968—; contbr. articles to profl. jours. Fellow Am. Ceramic Soc., Royal Inst. Chemistry; mem. Nat. Acad. Engring., Am. Phys. Soc., Electrochem. Soc., ASTM, Am. Chem. Soc., Soc. Glass Tech. Patentee in field. Office: 5732 Boelter Hall Univ of Calif Los Angeles CA 90024

MACKENZIE, JOHN PETTIBONE, journalist; b. Glen Ellyn, Ill., July 19, 1930; s. John W. P. and Elizabeth (Andersen) MacK.; m. Amanda Fisk, Oct. 24, 1959 (div. 1977); children—Bradley John, Alice Fisk, Douglas Bain. B.A. in Am. Studies cum laude, Amherst Coll., 1952; postgrad., Harvard U. Law Sch., 1964-65. Staff writer Washington Post, 1956-77, Supreme Ct. reporter, 1965-77; Walter E. Meyer vis. research prof. law N.Y. U., 1977-78; lectr. law SUNY Buffalo Law Sch., 1979; spl. contbr. to editorial page N.Y. Times, 1977-79; editorial bd. N.Y. Times, 1980—. Author: The Appearance of Justice, 1974; contbr. articles to mags., law books, law revs. Served to lt. (j.g.) USN, 1952-55. Home: 250 W 89th St New York NY 10024-1700 Office: 229 W 43rd St New York NY 10036

MACKENZIE, KENNETH DONALD, management consultant, educator; b. Salem, Oreg., Dec. 20, 1937; s. Kenneth Victor and Dorothy Vernon (Minaker) M.; m. Sally Jane McHenry, June 16, 1957; children: Dorothy Jane Rivette, Carolyn M. McFarland, Susan M. Treber, Nancy M.

Kalb. AB in Math, U. Calif., Berkeley, 1960, PhD in Bus. Adminstrn, 1964. Cert. mgmt. cons. Asst. prof. indsl. adminstrn. Carnegie Mellon U., 1964-67; assoc. prof. industry Wharton Sch. U. Pa., 1967-71; prof. mgmt. scis. U. Waterloo, Ont., 1969-72; Edmund P. Learned disting. prof. Sch. Bus. U. Kans., Lawrence, 1971—; pres. Organizational Systems, Inc., Lawrence, 1976-84; founder, pres. Mackenzie and Co. Inc., Lawrence, 1983—. Author: An Introduction to Continuous Probability, 1969, A Theory of Group Structures, 2 vols., 1976, Basic Theory, 1976, A Theory of Group Structures, vol. II: Empirical Tests, 1976, Organizational Structures, 1978, Organizational Design: The Organizational Audit and Analysis Technology, 1986, The Organizational Hologram: The Effective Management of Organizational Change, 1991, Practitioner's Guide for Improving an Organization, 1995; editor: Organizations Behavior series; mem. editorial bd. of profl. jours. Served with USMCR, 1957-60, with Army N.G., 1960-64. Fellow AAAS; mem. Am. Mgmt. Assn., Acad. Mgmt., Am. Psychol. Assn., Ops. Research Soc., Inst. Mgmt. Scis. (chmn. coll. on orgns. 1983-93), Inst. Mgmt. Cons. Republican. Home: 502 Millstone Rd Lawrence KS 66049-2350 Office: Mackenzie & Co Inc 700 Massachusetts St Ste 301 Lawrence KS 66044-6604 also: U Kans Sch Bus Lawrence KS 66045 *While the pursuit of a better theory of organizations has led me from the classroom to the laboratory and then into the boardrooms of corporations, the thrust of all these many activities has been to develop the science of organizational behavior.*

MACKENZIE, LEWIS WHARTON, military officer; b. Truro, N.S., Can., Apr. 30, 1940; s. Eugene Murdock and Shirley Helena (Wharton) MacK.; m. Dora Rosalie McKinnon; 1 child, Kimm Katheryn. Student, NATO Def. Coll., Rome, 1977; BA in Polit. Sci., U. Manitoba, Winnipeg, Can., 1988; Phd (hon.), St. Francis Xavier U., 1993; LLB (hon.), St. Mary's U., 1993, Acadia U., 1993. Commd. 2d lt. Can. Armed Forces, 1972, advanced through grades to major gen., 1987; teamsite comdr. Internat. Commn. Control and Supervision, Vietnam, 1972; co. comdr. UN Emergency Peace Keeping Force, Cairo, 1973; exec. asst. to comdr. Can. Forces Europe, Lahr, Fed. Republic Germany, 1974-77; comdr. Nicosia dist. UN Peacekeeping Force, Cyprus, 1978; commdg. officer 1st bn. Princess Patricia's Can. Light Infantry, Calgary, 1977-79; faculty mem. Can. Forces Staff Coll., Toronto, 1979-82; dep. chief staff for tng. Can. Army, Montreal, 1983-85; dir. pers. careers officers Can. Armed Forces, Ottawa, 1985-87; dir. Combar Related Employment of Women, Ottawa, 1987-88; comdr. combat tng. ctr. Can. Armed Forces, Gagetown Can. Forces Base, N.B., 1988—; comdr. UN Peacekeeping Force, Ctrl. Am., 1990-91, chief staff Unprotection force, Yugoslavia, 1992, comdr. UN forces to open Sarajevo airport for humanitarian relief, 1992; internat. affairs commentator BATON Broadcasting; host TV documentary "A Soldier's Peace." Author: Peacekeeper, Road to Sarajevo, 1993. Bd. adv. Can. Fedn. for AIDS Rsch.; bd. dirs. Pacific Body Armour. Decorated Meritorious Svc. Cross (2) (only Can.); recipient Birks golf medal Xavier Jr. Coll., Sydney, N.S., Can., 1960, Vimy award, 1993; Internat. fellow U.S. Army Wat Coll., 1982-83, Nat. Sports Car champion, 1981; named to McLean's Hnoro Roll, 1993. Avocation: motor racing. Home and Office: 1 Rowntree Rd Apt 1603, Etobicoke, ON Canada M9V 5G7

MACKENZIE, MALCOLM LEWIS, museum executive; b. El Paso, Tex., Jan. 19, 1926; s. William Forbes and Grace Meldon (Lewis) M.; m. Barbara Lee Webb, Apr. 4, 1952; children: David, Ellen; m. Marianne Eckerstrom, Nov. 22, 1980; stepchildren: Ann-Marie, Vicki, Adam, Lars. Graduate Maine Maritime Acad., 1946; student R.I. Sch. Design, 1948-51; B.A., Brown U., 1951. 3d mate Am. Export Lines, Jersey City, Pacific Tankers, San Francisco, 1946-48; 2d mate Sun Oil Co., Marcus Hook, Pa., 1948; plans dir., account exec. N. W. Ayer & Son, Phila., 1951-63; plans dir., head mktg. dept. Grey & Rogers Advt., Phila., 1963-64; v.p. Daily Svc., Phila., 1964-65; owner, pres. mktg. svcs. Malcolm L. Mackenzie & Assocs., Wilmington, Del., 1966—; pres. Kalmar Nyckel Mus. Inst., 1990—; pres. Christina Marina, Inc., 1992—; dir., sec., treas. Fort Christina Marina, Inc., 1994—; sec. Digital Design Group, Ltd., 1994—; dir., v.p. Wilmington Shipbuilding Co., Inc., 1993—; adminstrv. mgr. Kalmar Nyckel Found., 1986-91; sec.-treas. North Star Charters Inc., Wilmington, 1984—, Kalmar Marine Supplies Ltd., 1992—, Lenape Corp., 1992—; pres. Delmarva Safe Sailing Assocs., Inc., Wilmington, 1977—, pres., bd. dirs. Beta Centaur Holding Co., 1992—; dir. devel., pres. Am. Prestige Arts, Inc., Wilmington, 1970-72; dir. Composite Structures, Inc., Wilmington, 1974-76; dir. Cutter Mohawk Corp., Wilmington, 1981—; mgr., dir. Market Penetration, Wilmington, 1970—; cons. Del. Waterfront 2020; v.p. Landmark Properties, Inc., 1986—; incorporator, registered agt. Peace Please, Inc., Del. Fin. Accts., Inc., 1993—; pres. Active Young Reps., Brandywine Hundred, 1966, Windybush Civic Assn., Wilmington, Del., 1962-66; pres., dir. Coun. of Civic Orgns. of Brandywine Hundred, 1965; bd. dirs. Del. Safety Coun., 1965-73, 74-75, Wilmington Sister Cities, 1980—, Del. Maritime Ctr., 1989—; mem. New Castle County Rev. Bd., 1976-78; mem. CPAC Hwy. Dept. Adv. Bd., Dover, Del., 1979-82; vice chmn. No. New Castle County Land Use Study Group, 1990—. With U.S. Mcht. Svc., 1944-48. Recipient Order of Merit. Boy Scouts Am., 1977, Order of the Arrow, 1974, Woodbadge, 1974; Commodore, Ships on the Shoreline, Inc., Del. Tall Ships Salute, 1982. Mem. Advt. Club Del., Colonial Period Ship Assn. (founding 1987), Del. Media Assn., Swedish Colonial Soc. (councilor), Wilmington Sailboat Show (mgr., owner 1981-89), Nat. Mariner Awards (mgr. 1982—), Cutter Mohawk (capt., 1982-85). Republican. Lutheran. Clubs: Kiwanis (Wilmington) (chmn. internat. com.); Brown U. of Phila. (pres. 1958-61), Brown U. of Del. (pres. 1974-84). Lodge: Masons. Office: 500 Concord Ave Wilmington DE 19802

MAC KENZIE, NORMAN HUGH, retired English educator, writer; b. Salisbury, Rhodesia, Mar. 8, 1915; s. Thomas Hugh and Ruth Blanche (Huskisson) MacK.; m. Rita Mavis Hofmann, Aug. 14, 1948; children: Catherine, Ronald. B.A., Rhodes U., South Africa, 1934, M.A., 1935; Diploma in Edn., 1936; Ph.D. (Union scholar), U. London, 1940; DLitt (hon.), St. Joseph's U., Phila., 1989. Lectr. in English Rhodes U., South Africa, 1937, U. Hong Kong, 1940-41, U. Melbourne, Australia, 1946-48; sr. lectr.-in-charge U. Natal, Durban, 1949-55; prof., head English dept. U. Coll., Rhodesia, 1955-65; dean Faculty Arts and Edn. U. Coll., 1957-60, 63-64; prof., head English dept. Laurentian U., Ont., Can., 1965-66; prof. English Queen's U., Kingston, Ont., 1966-80; emeritus prof. Queen's U., 1980—, dir. grad. studies in English, 1967-73, chmn. council grad. studies, 1971-73, chmn. editorial bd. Yeats Studies, 1972-74; Exec. Central Africa Drama League, 1959-65; mem. exec. com. Can. Assn. Irish Studies, 1968-73. Author: South African Travel Literature in the 17th Century, 1955, The Outlook for English in Central Africa, 1960, Hopkins, 1968, A Reader's Guide to G.M. Hopkins, 1981; editor: (with W.H. Gardner) The Poems of Gerard Manley Hopkins, 1967, rev. edit., 1970; Poems by Hopkins, 1974, U. Natal Gazette, 1954-55, The Early Poetic Manuscripts and Notebooks of Gerard Manley Hopkins in Facsimile, 1989, The Poetical Works of Gerard Manley Hopkins, 1990, rev. 1992, The Later Poetic Manuscripts of G.M. Hopkins in Facsimile, 1991; contbr.: chpts. to Testing the English Proficiency of Foreign Students, 1961, English Studies Today-Third Series, 1963, Sphere History of English Literature, Vol. VI, 1970, rev. edit., 1987, Readings of the Wreck of the Deutschland, 1976, Festschrift for E.R. Seary, 1975, British and American Literature 1880-1920, 1976, Myth and Reality in Irish Literature, 1977; articles to Internat. Rev. Edn., Bull. Inst. Hist. Research, Times Lit. Supplement, Modern Lang. Quar., Queen's Quar., others. Served with Hong Kong Vol. Def. Corps, 1940-45; prisoner of war, China and Japan 1941-45. Brit. Council scholar, 1954; Killam sr. fellow, 1979-81; Martin D'Arcy lectr. Oxford U., 1988-89. Fellow Royal Soc. Can.; mem. English Assn. Rhodesia (pres. 1957-65), So. Rhodesia Drama Assn. (vice chmn. 1957-65), Hopkins Soc. (pres. 1972-75), Yeats Soc. (life), MLA (life), Internat. Hopkins Assn. (bd. scholars 1979—). Home: 416 Windward Pl, Kingston, ON Canada K7M 4E4

MACKENZIE, PETER SEAN, writer, publications designer; b. L.A., Aug. 25, 1954; s. William Duncan and Patricia Ann (Kronschnabel) Mack; m. Carin Willette, Dec. 28, 1983; 1 child, Liam Reynolds. BA, Western Wash. U., 1976. Bus. editor Skagit Valley Herald, Mount Vernon, Wash., 1976-79; mng. editor Stanwood (Wash.)-Camano News, 1979-84; graphic artist Pacific Media Group, Seattle, 1985-90, editor, 1990-93; prin. MacKenzie Creative Systems, Seattle, 1994—; instr. U. Wash. Exptl. Coll., Seattle, 1990-91. Author: Jumper, 1989; rec. artist LP KEZX Album Project, 1987, Victory Music Vol. # 2, 1988; speaker Viacom Cable Pub. Access TV, Seattle, 1990. V.p. Stanwood, Wash. C. of C., 1983. Recipient 1st place newswriting award Wash. Newspaper Pubs. Assn., 1981, 82, 2d place award for comprehensive coverage, 1982, 3d place awards in newswriting, features and spot news, 1983. Mem. Soc. Profl. Journalists (2d place award for investigative reporting 1982, 3d place award for editls. 1983), Greenpeace, Internat. Assn. Scientologists. Avocations: photography, music, political research, philosophy. Home: 316 NW 86th St Seattle WA 98117-3125 Office: MacKenzie Creative Sys PO Box 9627 Seattle WA 98109

MACKENZIE, ROSS, newspaper editor; b. Evanston, Ill., Aug. 25, 1941; s. Henry Wallace Dundas and Marion Elizabeth (Gillies) M.; m. Virginia de Bruyn Kops; children: Alexander Ross, Ross Hale. Diploma, Phillips Exeter Acad., 1959; BA in History, Yale U., 1963; MA in Polit. Philosophy, U. Chgo., 1969. Editor editl. pages Richmond (Va.) News Leader, 1969-92, Richmond Times-Dispatch, 1992—; mem. adv. bd. Lincoln Rev., 1972—, Inst. for Polit. Journalism, 1993—. Contbg. author: Brief Points: An Almanac for Parents and Friends of the U.S. Naval Academy, 1993; editor: Eyewitness: Writings from the Ordeal of Communism, 1993. Mem. adv. bd. Massey Cancer Ctr., 1992—; trustee So. Va. Coll. for Women, 1994—. Recipient Eugene Pulliam fellow Sigma Delta Chi, 1978; runner-up Pulitzer Prize for Commentary, 1982. Mem Am. Soc. Newspaper Editors (mem. writing awards com.), Phila. Soc. (charter mem.), Nat. Press Club, Commonwealth Club (pres. 1985-87), Country Club of Va., Deep Run Hunt Club. Avocations: one-wall handball, tennis, amateur radio, nature. Office: Richmond Times-Dispatch 333 E Grace St Richmond VA 23293

MACKENZIE, WARD D., computer company executive; b. 1939. BS, Worcester Polytechnic Inst.; MBA, Dartmouth Coll. With Digital Equipment Corp.; chmn., CEO Lisp Machine, Inc.; v.p. corp. mktg. Data Gen. Corp.; exec. v.p. strategy and bus. mgmt. HN Bull Info. Systems, Billerica, Mass., 1989—, now exec. v.p. bus. ops. Office: H N Bull Information Sysytems Technology Park Billerica MA 01821

MACKERODT, FRED, public relations specialist; b. Bklyn., Sept. 17, 1938; s. Leroy and Margaret (Murphy) M.; m. Christy Woods, June 7, 1987. Student, NYU, 1958-59. Freelance writer, photographer N.Y.C. and Barcelona, Spain, 1968-73; editor Cars Mag., Popular Publs. Inc., N.Y.C., 1973-76; pres. Fred Mackerodt, Inc. (pub. relations and publicity), N.Y.C., 1976—. Contbr. articles to popular mags.; aviation editor: Popular Mechanics, 1981—. Spl. Dep. Sheriff, Indian River County, Fla., 1994—. Mem. Aviation and Space Writers Am., Internat. Motor Press Assn. (dir.), Alcoholism Coun. of N.Y. (dir.), Publicity Club N.Y., Wings Club, N.Y. Zool. Soc. (aquarium field assoc. 1971—). Home: 209 W 86th St Suite 901 New York NY 10024 Office: 460 W 34th St 20th Fl New York NY 10001

MACKERRAS, SIR (ALAN) CHARLES (MACLAURIN), conductor; b. Schenectady, N.Y. (parents Australian citizens), Nov. 17, 1925; s. Alan Patrick and Catherine M.; m. Helena Judith Wilkins, 1947; 2 children. Student with Vaclav Talich, Prague Acad. Music, 1947-48; DMus (hon.) Hull U., 1990, Nottingham U., 1991, U. Brno, Czech Republic, 1994, York (Eng.) U., 1994, Griffith U., Brisbane, 1994. Prin. oboist Sydney Symphony Orch., Australia, 1943-46; staff condr. English Nat. Opera (formerly Sadler's Wells Opera), London, 1949-53, musical dir., 1970-77; prin. condr. BBC Concert Orch., 1954-56; freelance condr. with most Brit. and many continental orchs., concert tours USSR, S. Africa, N. Am., Australia, 1957-66, U.S. coast-to-coast, 1983; first condr. Hamburg State Opera, 1966-69; chief guest condr. BBC Symphony Orch., 1976-79; chief condr. Sydney Symphony Orch.; Australian Broadcasting Commn., 1982-85; prin. guest condr. Royal Liverpool Philharmonic Orch., 1986-88, Scottish Chamber Orch., 1992, San Francisco Opera, 1993, Royal Philharmonic Orch., 1993; mus. dir. Welsh Nat.Opera, 1987-92; appearances many internat. festivals and opera houses; frequent radio and TV broadcasts; many comml. recordings, notably Handel series for DGG and Janacek operas for Decca, Mozart series for Telarc. Published ballet arrangements Pineapple Poll (Sullivan), Lady and the Fool (Verdi), reconstrn. Sullivan's lost Cello Concerto. Contbr. appendices (book) A Musicians' Musician, articles to Opera Mag., Music and Musicians, other jours. Recipient Evening Standard award for opera 1977, Janacek medal, 1978, Gramophone Record of Yr. award, 1977, 80, Grammy award for best opera recording, 1981; prix Fondation Jacques Ibert, 1983, Record of Yr. award Stereo Rev., 1983, Gramophone Operatic Record of Yr. award, 1983-84, Gramophone Choral Recording of Yr., 1986, Gramophone Best Opera Recording award, 1994; decorated comdr. Order Brit. Empire, 1974; created Knight, 1979; Brit. Council scholar, 1947-48. Fellow Royal Coll. of Music (hon.), L.R.A.M. (hon.). Office: care Marks Mgmt Ltd, 14 New Burlington St, London W1X 1FF, England

MACKEY, DALLAS L., financial consultant, development officer; b. Upper Strasburg, Pa., June 7, 1920; s. Bard Dallas Mackey and Hattie (Kessinger) Mackey Rosenberry; widowed; 1 child, Pamela Dallas. Student, Coll. Charleston. V.p., dir. Seaboard Chem. Corp., Sanford, N.C., 1959-65, First Provident Corp., Florence, S.C., 1961-65; pres., dir. Lee Broadcasting Corp., Sanford, 1956-64; chmn., dir. The MuMac Corp., Charlotte, N.C., 1960—; regional dir. Ketchum, Inc., Charlotte, 1964-78; dir. emeritus office devel. Bowman Gray-Bapt. Hosp. Med. Ctr., Winston-Salem, N.C.; bd. dirs. First Citizens Bank and Trust, Winston-Salem; cons. U. Ill. Found., Champaign, 1980—; chmn. Charlotte Group, Inc.; chmn. bd. dirs. First Counsel, Inc., Charlotte, 1993—; bd. dirs., former chmn. Winston-Salem State U. Found., 1979—; bd. dirs. Blumenthal Home, Winston-Salem, 1985—, Triad United Meth. Home, Winston-Salem, 1984—, N.C. Community Found.; life trustee Brevard Coll. With U.S. Army, 1940-45, ETO. Mem. Assn. Am. Med. Colls. (vice chmn. 1983-84), Assn. for Healthcare Philanthropy, Council Advancement and Support Edn., Newcomen Soc., Rotary Internat. Democrat. Methodist. Clubs: Twin City; Piedmont (Winston-Salem). Avocations: growing roses, public speaking. Home: 3606 Winding Creek Way Winston Salem NC 27106-4325 Office: Bowman Gray Bapt Hosp Med Ctr Medical Center Blvd Winston Salem NC 27157

MACKEY, GEORGE WHITELAW, mathematician, educator; b. St. Louis, Feb. 1, 1916; s. William Sturges and Dorothy Frances (Allison) M.; m. Alice Willard, Dec. 9, 1960; 1 child, Ann Sturges Mackey. B.A., Rice Inst., 1938; A.M., Harvard U., 1939, Ph.D., 1942; M.A., Oxford, 1966. Instr. math. Ill. Inst. Tech., 1942-43; faculty instr. math. Harvard U., 1943-46, asst. prof., 1946-48, assoc. prof., 1948-56, prof. math., 1956-69, Landon T. Clay prof. math. and theoretical sci., 1969-85, prof. emeritus, 1985—; vis. prof. U. Chgo., summer 1955, UCLA, summer 1959, Tata Inst. Fundamental Rsch., Bombay, 1970-71; Walker Ames vis. prof. U. Wash., summer 1961; Eastman vis. prof. Oxford U., 1966-67; assoc. prof. U. Paris, 1978; vis. rschr. Math. Sci. Inst., Berkeley, 1983; vis. prof. U. Calif., Berkeley, 1984; lectr. U. Heidelberg, Germany, 1988, CUNY, 1987, U. Iowa, 1988, Kings Coll. of U. London, 1991; invited lectr. U. Munich, Germany, 1994. Author: Mathematical Foundations of Quantum Mechanics, 1963, Lectures on the Theory of Functions of a Complex Variable, 1967, Induced Representations and Quantum Mechanics, 1968, The Theory of Unitary Group Representations, 1976, Unitary Group Representations in Physics, Probability and Number Theory, 1978, The Scope and History of Commutative and Noncommutative Harmonic Analysis, 1992; contbr. articles math. jours. Served as civilian, operational research sect. 8th Air Force, 1944; applied math. panel NDRC, 1945. Guggenheim fellow, 1949-50, 61-62, 70-71; recipient Humboldt prize Max Planck Inst., Bonn, Fed. Republic of Germany, 1985-86. Mem. Am. Math. Soc. (v.p. 1964-65, Steele prize 1974), Nat. Acad. Scis., Am. Philos. Soc., Am. Acad. Arts and Scis., Phi Beta Kappa, Sigma Xi. Office: Harvard U Dept Math 1 Oxford St Cambridge MA 02138

MACKEY, LEONARD BRUCE, lawyer, former diversified manufacturing corporation executive; b. Washington, Aug. 31, 1925; s. Stuart J. and Margaret B. (Browne) M.; m. Britta Beckhaus, Mar. 2, 1974; children—Leonard B., Cathleen C., Wendy F. B.E.E., Rensselaer Poly. Inst., 1945; J.D., George Washington U., 1950. Bar: D.C. 1951, N.Y. 1954. Instr. elec. engring. Rensselaer Poly. Inst., Troy, N.Y., 1946-47; patent examiner U.S. Patent Office, Washington, 1947-50; atty. Gen. Electric Co., Schenectady and N.Y.C., 1953-60; dir. licensing, assoc. ITT, N.Y.C., 1960-73; v.p., gen. patent counsel, dir. licensing ITT, 1973-90; of counsel Davis Hoxie Faithfull & Hapgood, N.Y.C., 1990-93; cons. licensing and tech. transfer Sarasota, Fla., 1994—. Mem. Recreation Commn., Rye, N.Y., 1966-67; mem. Planning Commn., 1967-70, 72-75, city councilman, 1970-71. Served with USNR, 1943-45; to lt. 1951-53. Mem. ABA (coun. mem., intellectual property law

sect. 1989-93), Am. Intellectual Property Law Assn. (bd. mgrs. 1968-70, pres. 1982-83), Licensing Execs. Soc. U.S.A. (pres. 1978), Licensing Execs. Soc. Internat. (pres. 1986), Eta Kappa Nu, Am. Yacht Club (sec. 1968-70), N.Y. Yacht Club, Masons, Apawamis. Republican. Presbyterian. Office: 219 S Orange Ave Sarasota FL 34236

MACKEY, LOUIS HENRY, philosophy educator; b. Sidney, Ohio, Sept. 24, 1926; s. Louis Henry and Clara Emma (Maurer) M.; children: Stephen Louis, Thomas Adam, Jacob Louis, Eva Maria. B.A., Capital U., 1948; student, Duke, 1948-50; M.A., Yale, 1953, Ph.D., 1954. Instr. philosophy Yale U., 1953-55, asst. prof., Morse fellow, 1955-59; assoc. prof. philosophy Rice U., Houston, 1955-65, prof.; 1965-67; prof. U. Tex., Austin, 1967—. Author: Kierkegaard: A Kind of Poet, 1971, Points of View: Readings of Kierkegaard, 1986; contbr. articles to profl. jours. Recipient Harry Ransom award for Tchng. Excellence, 1987, Pres.'s Assocs. award for Tchng. Excellence, 1991, Grad. Tchng. award 1994; NEH fellow, 1976-77. Episcopalian. Home: 4105 Victory DrA108 Austin TX 78704 Office: 316 WAG U Tex Austin TX 78712

MACKEY, MAURICE CECIL, university president, economist, lawyer; b. Montgomery, Ala., Jan. 23, 1929; s. M. Cecil and Annie Laurie (Kimrey) M.; m. Clare Siewert, Aug. 29, 1953; children: Carol, John, Ann. B.A., U. Ala., 1949, M.A., 1953, LL.B., 1958; Ph.D., U. Ill., 1955; postgrad., Harvard U., 1958-59. Bar: Ala. 1958. Asst. prof. econs. U. Ill., 1955-56; assoc. prof. econs. U.S. Air Force Acad., 1956-57; asst. prof. law U. Ala., 1959-62; with FAA, 1963-65, U.S. Dept. Commerce, 1965-67; asst. sec. U.S. Dept. Transp., 1967-69; exec. v.p., prof. law Fla. State U., Tallahassee, 1969-71; pres. U. South Fla., Tampa, 1971-76; pres., prof. law Tex. Tech U., Lubbock, 1976-79; pres., prof. econs. Mich. State U., East Lansing, 1979-85, prof. econs., 1985—; asst. counsel Subcom. on Antitrust and Monopoly, U.S. Senate, 1962-63; bd. dirs. Community First Bank, Lansing, Mich.; mem. adv. com. U.S. Coast Guard Acad., 1969-71; chmn. Fla. Gov.'s Adv. Com. on Transp., 1975, Nat. Boating Safety Adv. Council, 1975—; mem. adv. council NSF, 1978-81; assoc. China Council, 1979—; Disting. vis. prof. United Arab Emirates U., 1990, 91, 92, 93; bd. dirs. Summit Holding Corp., Lansing. Bd. dirs. Gulf Ridge council Boy Scouts Am.; pres. Chief Okemos council, 1981-82; bd. dirs. Tampa United Fund, Lubbock United Way; chmn., bd. dirs. Debt for Devel. Coalition, 1989—. Served with USAF, 1956-57. Recipient Arthur S. Flemming award Washington Jaycees, 1967. Mem. Fla. Council 100, Tampa Co. of C. (bd. govs.), Am. Assn. State Colls. and Univs. (pres., dir.), Artus, Phi Kappa Phi, Chi Alpha Phi. Office: Mich State U Marshall Hall East Lansing MI 48824

MACKEY, PATRICIA ELAINE, librarian; b. Balt., July 29, 1941; d. Timothy and Hazel Mozelle (Davis) M. BA in Anthropology, CUNY, 1978; MLS, Columbia U., 1981. Asst. libr. I, European Exch. Sys., Mainz-Kastel, Germany, 1966-68; interlibr. loan asst. Poly. U., Bklyn., 1968-72; interlibr. loan asst. Rockefeller U., N.Y.C., 1972-73, sr. libr. asst., 1974-80, libr., 1981-91, head libr., 1991—; mem. various libr. coms., N.Y.C., 1991—. Mentor pub. svc. scholars program for srs. Hunter Coll., CUNY, 1992—. Mem. ALA; N.Y. State Libr. Assn., Assn. Coll. and Rsch. Librs. Democrat. Roman Catholic. Avocations: reading, chess, gardening. Office: Rockefeller U Libr RU Box 263 1230 York Ave New York NY 10021-6399

MACKEY, SALLY SCHEAR, retired religious organization administrator; b. Seattle, Feb. 17, 1930; d. Rillmond Weible and Helen Annajane (Bovee) Schear; m. Hallie Willis Mackey, May 22, 1953; children: Melinda Kay, John Mark, Heather Lynn. BA, U. Wash., 1951; postgrad., San Francisco Theol. Sem., 1951-53. Teenage program dir., camp dir. YWCA, Seattle, 1953-55; sponsor, devel. Wash. Assn. Chs. Immigration and Refugee Program (affiliate Ch. World Svc.), Seattle, 1979-85, dir., 1985-90; bd. dirs., v.p. Ch. Coun. Greater Seattle, 1974-84; bd. dirs. Wash. Assn. Chs., 1976-79; mem. Gen. Assembly Mission Coun. Presbyn. Ch., N.Y.C., 1979-83, adv. com. on ecumenical rels. Presbyn. Ch. (U.S.A.), Louisville, 1989-92; Presbyn. Ch. (U.S.A.); del. to Caribbean Area Coun. World Alliance Reformed Chs., 1987-92. Home: 2127 SW 162nd St Seattle WA 98166-2654

MACKEY, SHELDON ELIAS, minister; b. Bethlehem, Pa., Nov. 20, 1913; s. Elias and Pearl Elizabeth (Cunningham) M.; m. Marie Louise Dillinger, Sept. 20, 1939; children—Peter David, John Harry, Mary Susan, Timothy Andrew, Philip James. AB, Moravian Coll., 1936; BD, Lancaster Theol. Sem., 1939; DD, Franklin and Marshall Coll., 1954; LLD, Ursinus Coll., 1958. Ordained to ministry Evang. and Reformed Ch., 1939; pastor Pa. congregations, 1939-54; administr. coun. to pres. Evang. and Reformed Ch., 1954-57, sec., 1957-78; also editor Yearbook, dir. correlation and sec. gen. council Gen. Synod; ret.; co-sec. United Ch. of Christ, also sec. exec. coun., adminstrv. com., 1957-61, mem. fin. and budget com., exec. sec. stewardship coun., 1961-79, bd. dirs. Pa. S.E. Conf. United Ch. of Christ. Contbr. articles to religious publs. Bd. dirs. Ursinus Coll.; trustee emeritus Lancaster Theol. Sem. Mem. Nat. Council Chs. in U.S.A. Club: Phi Alpha Clergy. Home: 30 Schuylkill Dr Wernersville PA 19565-2011 *Life has a dimension which lies beyond the visible or physical. I believe that this dimension which lies at the heart of my faith is also revealed in art, music and literature. We need to reach out into this dimension which makes life most real.*

MACKEY, WILLIAM ARTHUR GODFREY, computer software company executive; b. Glasgow, Scotland, Mar. 23, 1946; came to U.S., 1970; s. William Arthur and Joan Margaret (Sykes) M.; m. Bianca Ann Dell'Isola, June 9, 1973 (dec. Nov. 1993). BSc in Engring., U. London, 1968, MSc in Engring., 1970; MBA, Harvard U., 1972. Prodn. engr. Rolls-Royce PLC, Glasgow, 1969-70; securities analyst Tucker, Anthony & R.L. Day, Inc., Boston, 1972-74; sr. ops. analyst Textron Inc., Fafnir Bearing div., New Britain, Conn., 1974-76; mfg. controller Loctite Corp., Newington, Conn., 1976-78, mgr. ops. and mktg. additional, 1978-80, mgr. corp. productivity improvement, 1980-83; worldwide product mgr. Otis Elevator Co., Farmington, Conn., 1985-87; pres., chief exec. officer Signum Microsystems, Inc., Bloomfield, Conn., 1982—; bd. dirs. Signum Microsystems, Inc., Bloomfield. Vice chmn. Conn. Com. Newcomen Soc. in U.S., Exton, Pa., 1980—; mem. World Affairs Coun., Hartford, Conn., 1984—, bd. dirs., 1992—; chief staff City of New Haven Blue Ribbon Commn., 1990. Rolls Royce scholar, 1964-69, 70-72. Fellow Royal Commonwealth Soc.; mem. ASME, Soc. Mfg. Engrs. (chmn. elect Hartford chpt., Pres.'s award 1991-92), Conn. Bus. and Industry Assn., Greater Hartford C. of C., Harvard Bus. Sch. Club No. Conn. (bd. dirs.), Royal Automobile Club (London), Royal Scottish Automobile Club (Glasgow), Mason (Wyllys-St. John's Lodge No. 4), Ancient Accepted Scottish Rite (No. Masonic Jurisdiction), Sphinx Temple (Ancient Arabic Nobles of Mystic Shrine). Republican. Congregationalist. Avocations: economics and current affairs, special interest automobiles, 20th century music, sailing, skiing, riding, gardening. Home: 244 Steele Rd West Hartford CT 06117-2742 Office: Signum Microsystems Inc 11 Mountain Ave Bloomfield CT 06002-2343

MACKEY, WILLIAM STURGES, JR., investor, consultant; b. St. Louis, May 27, 1921; s. William Sturges and Dorothy Francis (Allison) M.; m. Margaret Powell, Dec. 10, 1943; children: Dorothy Mackey Lurie, John Powell, James Wescott; m. Barbara Bode, May 26, 1988. B.A., Rice U., 1943; M.B.A., U. Tex., 1950. Assoc. prof. acctg. Rice U., 1946-62; v.p., treas. Mandrel Industries, 1962-66; v.p. fin. Tex. Internat. Airlines, 1966-69; chmn., chief exec. officer Lifemark Corp., 1969-84; bd. dirs. Whole Foods Market, Inc. Served to 1st lt. USAAF, 1943-46. Mem. AICPA, Tex. Soc. CPAs, Houston Philos. Soc., Forum Club of Houston (bd. dirs.), Rice U. Assocs., Lakeside Country Club, Houston City Club. Unitarian. Home: 6333 Buffalo Speedway Houston TX 77005-3309 Office: PO Box 273202 Houston TX 77277-3202

MACKIE, BERT H., postal service administrator. BBA, U. Enid. Lic. securities deal, real estate broker. Gov. U.S. Postal Svc., 1988—; bd. dirs. ONEOK, Inc, Tulsa; pres., bd. dirs. Security Nat. Bank, Enid. Chmn. Okla. State Regent for Higher Edn.; bd. dirs. Okla. Found. Excellence, Joint Indsl. Found.; chmn. bd. dirs. United Way, Enid. Mem. Okla. Banking Assn. (mem. sr. mgmt. com.). Office: Bd of Gov 475 L'Enfant Plz SW Washington DC 20260-1000

MACKIE, DAVID F., gas company executive; b. 1937. LLB, Yale Univ., 1964. Sr. v.p., gen. counsel El Paso, 1974-84; sr. v.p. gas supply and mktg., Transcontinental Gas Pipe Line Corp., 1984—, now pres., chief oper. officer;

pres., chief oper. officer Transco Gas Co., Houston, Transco Gas Supply, Houston, Transco-New England Pipeline Co., Houston, Transco Niagara Pipeline Co., Houston, Transeastern Gas Pipeline Co., Inc., Houston, Transylvania Gas Pipeline Co., Houston. Lt. (j.g.) USNR, 1959-61. Office: Transcontinental Gas Pipeline Corp 2800 Post Oak Blvd Houston TX 77056-6106

MACKIE, FREDERICK DAVID, retired utility executive; b. Ashland, Wis., Aug. 3, 1910; s. David and Johanna (Zilisch) M.; m. Ruth Elizabeth Babcock, Aug. 27, 1937; children—Marilyn Ruth, Frederick D. B.S. in Elec. Engring. U. Wis., 1933. With Madison Gas & Electric Co., Wis., 1934—; exec. v.p. Madison Gas & Electric Co., 1964-66, pres., gen. mgr., 1966-78, chmn. bd., 1976-78, also dir. Recipient Disting. Service citation Coll. Engring., U. Wis., 1969. Mem. IEEE (life), Nat. Soc. Profl. Engrs., Wis. Soc. Profl. Engrs., Wis. Utilities Assn., Madison Tech. Club., Kiwanis, Madison Club. Lutheran. Home: 58 Golf Course Rd Madison WI 53704-1423

MACKIE, ROBERT GORDON, costume and fashion designer; b. Monterey Park, Calif., Mar. 24, 1940; s. Charles Robert and Mildred Agnes (Smith) M.; m. Marianne Wolford, Mar. 14, 1960 (div.); 1 son, Robin Gordon. Student, Chouinard Art Inst., 1958-61. Sketch for Jean Louis, 1962-63; mem. staff Edith Head, 1962-63; pres. prior. Bob Mackie Originals, N.Y.C.; costume designer: (films) Brigadoon, 1954, Divorce, American Style, 1967, ...All the Marbles, 1981, Pennies from Heaven, 1981 (Academy award nomination best costume design 1981), Max Dugan Returns, 1983, (TV movies) Fresno, 1986, (TV series) The Carol Burnett Show, 1967-78, The Sonny and Cher Comedy Hour, 1971-74, Cher, 1975-76, The Diahann Carroll Show, 1976, The Sonny and Cher Show, 1976-77, Donny and Marie, 1976-79, Mama's Family, 1983-85, (TV spls.) Alice Through the Looking Glass, 1967, Carousel, 1967, Kismet, 1967, Fred Astaire Show, 1968, Diana Ross and the Supremes, 1969, Of Thee I Sing, 1972, Once Upon a Mattress, 1973, (theatrical prodns.) The Best Little Whorehouse Goes Public, 1994; costume designer: (films) Lady Sings the Blues, 1972 (Academy award nomination best costume design 1972), Funny Lady, 1975 (Academy award nomination best costume design 1975), Staying Alive, 1983, Brenda Starr, 1987, (theatrical prodns.) On the Town, 1971, Lorelei, 1972; author: Dressing for Glamour, 1969; appeared on Broadway and in TV prodn. Night of 100 Stars II, 1985. Recipient Emmy awards for outstanding costume design, 1966, 67, 69, 70, 76, 78, 84, 88, Emmy award nominations for outstanding costume design, 1972, 74, 75, 76, 77, 79, 80, 83, 86, 87, Costume Designers Guild award, 1984, Fashion Achievement award Otis/Parsons Sch. Design, 1987; named most creative fashion designer in Am. US mag., 1982, 83; honored by Costume Inst. Fine Arts, Houston, 1987, AIDS Project L.A., 1989. Democrat. Address: Bob Mackie Originals 225 W 39th St New York NY 10018-3103*

MACKIEWICZ, EDWARD ROBERT, lawyer; b. Jersey City, July 2, 1951; s. Edward John and Irene Helen (Rakowicz) H. BA, Yale U., 1973; JD, Columbia U., 1976. Bar: NJ 1976, U.S. Dist. Ct. NJ 1976, N.Y. 1977, U.S. Dist. Ct. (so. and ea. dist.) N.Y. 1977, D.C. 1978, U.S. Dist. Ct. D.C. 1978, U.S. Ct. Appeals (D.C. cir.) 1978, U.S. Ct. Appeals (3d cir.) 1980, U.S. Supreme Ct. 1980, Md. 1984, U.S. Ct. Claims 1984, U.S. Ct. Appeals (4th cir.) 1986, U.S. Dist. Ct. Md. 1990. Assoc. Carter, Ledyard & Milburn, N.Y.C., 1976-77; Covington & Burling, Washington, 1977-82; counsel for civil rights litigation solicitor's office U.S. Dept. Labor, Washington, 1982-83; sr. assoc. Jones, Day, Reavis & Pogue, Washington, 1983-85; gen. counsel Pension Benefit Guaranty Corp., Washington, 1985-87; of counsel Pierson, Ball & Dowd, Washington, 1987-89; ptnr. Reed Smith Shaw & McClay, Washington, 1989; gen. counsel Masters, Mates & Pilots Benefit Plans, Linthicum Heights, Md., 1989-92; of counsel Steptoe & Johnson, Washington, 1992—; mem. adv. coun. Sec. of Labor's ERISA, 1991-93; profl. lectr. in law Nat. Law Ctr., George Washington U., 1993—. Mem. Am. Coun. Young Polit. Leaders (del. to Australia 1985), Univ. Club, Yale Club. Home: 3001 Veazey Ter NW Apt 1032 Washington DC 20008-5406 Office: Steptoe & Johnson 1330 Connecticut Ave NW Washington DC 20036

MACKIN, COOPER RICHERSON, university chancellor; b. Selma, Ala., Apr. 26, 1933; s. Thomas R. and Muriel (Green) M.; m. Catherine Barragy, Feb. 15, 1958 (dec.); children: Michele, Patrick, Daniel; m. Mary Kathryn Ruetten, Dec. 14, 1985. B.A., Troy State Coll., 1956; M.A., Tulane U., 1958; Ph.D., Rice U., 1962. Instr. Tex. So. U., 1958-59; asst. prof. N. Tex. State U., Denton, 1962-63; asst. prof. U. New Orleans, 1963-66, assoc. prof., 1966-70, prof. English, 1970—, chmn. dept., 1966-69, dean Coll. Liberal Arts, 1969-80, vice chancellor for acad. affairs, 1980-83, acting chancellor, 1983-84, chancellor, 1984-87, chancellor emeritus, 1987—. Author: William Styron, 1969; Contbr. articles on 17th century English lit. to profl. jours. Bd. dirs. New Orleans chpt. NCCJ, 1969-79, Air U., 1986-88. Served with AUS, 1953-55. Mem. Milton Soc. Am., South Central MLA. Home: 18 Charlotte Dr New Orleans LA 70122-2532 Office: U New Orleans English Dept New Orleans LA 70148

MACKIN, J. STANLEY, banker; b. Birmingham, Ala., 1932. Grad., Auburn Univ., 1954. Chmn., pres., CEO and COO First Ala. Bancshares, Inc., Birmingham. Office: First Ala Bank PO Box 10247 Birmingham AL 35202-0247

MAC KINNEY, ARCHIE ALLEN, JR., physician; b. St. Paul, Aug. 16, 1929; s. Archie Allen and Doris (Hoops) MacK.; m. Shirley Schaefer, Apr. 9, 1955; children—Julianne, Theodore, John. B.A., Wheaton (Ill.) Coll., 1951; M.D., U. Rochester, 1955. Intern, resident in medicine U. Wis. Hosp., 1955-59; clin. assoc. NIH, 1959-61; clin. investigator VA, 1961-64; asst. prof. medicine U. Wis., Madison, 1964-68; assoc. prof. U. Wis., 1968-74, prof., 1974—; med. alumni prof., 1987; chief hematology VA Hosp., Madison, 1964—, chief nuclear medicine, 1964-73, 78-79. Author: Pathophysiology of Blood, 1984. Contbr. articles to med. jours. Trustee Intervarsity Christian Fellowship, 1985-88. Served with USPHS, 1959-61. Danforth asso., 1962. Mem. Am. Soc. Hematology, Am. Fedn. Clin. Research, Central Soc. Clin. Research. Republican. Baptist. Home: 190 N Prospect Ave Madison WI 53705-4071 Office: 2500 Overlook Ter Madison WI 53705-2286

MACKINNEY, ARTHUR CLINTON, JR., retired university official, psychologist; b. Kansas City, Mo., Oct. 16, 1928; s. Arthur Clinton and Doris (Long) MacK.; m. Lois Elizabeth Lineberry, Sept. 5, 1953; children: Arthur Clinton III, Gordon L., Nada L. B.A., William Jewell Coll., 1951; M.A., U. Minn., 1953, Ph.D., 1955. Instr. U. Minn., 1953-55, Macalester Coll., 1955; cons. psychologist R.N. McMurry & Co., Chgo., 1953; research psychologist Gen. Motors Corp., 1955-57; asst. prof. to prof., head dept. psychology Iowa State U., 1957-70; dean grad. studies and Research Wright State U., Dayton, Ohio, 1971-76; vice chancellor for acad. affairs U. Mo.-St. Louis, 1976-86, interim chancellor, 1986; pres. and chief exec. officer U. Ctr. Tulsa, 1986-91, pres. emeritus, 1992-93; vis. disting. prof. U. Tulsa, 1992-94; vis. prof. U. Minn., 1960, U. Calif., 1962-63, 66; mem. Commn. on Instns. Higher Edn., North Cen. Assn., 1980-84; cons. to industry. Contbr. articles to profl. jours. Bd. dirs. Tulsa Edn. Fund. Served with AUS, 1946-47, 51. Fellow Am. Psychol. Assn. (Cattell research design award 1968, pres. div. indsl. and orgnl. psychology 1981-82); mem. Midwestern Psychol. Assn., Mo. Psychol. Assn. (pres. 1981, pres. 1983-84), Iowa Psychol. Assn. (pres. 1966), Sigma Xi, Psi Chi (nat. historian 1983—, nat. council 1983—, Midwestern regional v.p. 1984-85, pres. 1987-88), Kappa Alpha, Phi Kappa Phi. Unitarian. Research on long-term devel. complex human performance. Home: PO Box 236 Ellison Bay WI 54210

MACKINNON, CATHARINE A., lawyer, law educator, legal scholar, writer; d. George E. and Elizabeth V. (Davis) MacKinnon. BA in Govt. magna cum laude with distinction, Smith Coll., 1969; JD, Yale U., 1977, PhD in Polit. Sci., 1987. Vis. prof. U Chgo., Harvard U., Stanford U, Yale U., others, Osgoode Hall, York U., Canada; prof. of law U. Mich., 1990—. Author: Sexual Harassment of Working Women, 1979, Feminism Unmodified, 1987, Toward a Feminist Theory of the State, 1989, Only Words, 1993. Office: U Michigan Law School Ann Arbor MI 48109-1215

MACKINNON, CYRUS LELAND, retired newspaper executive; b. Eldorado, Kans., Aug. 16, 1916; s. Frederick Benjamin and Cecil Prescott (Lel) MacK.; m. Helen Wigglesworth, Feb. 25, 1939; children: Stephen, Peter, Cecil, Anne. B.A., Dartmouth Coll., 1938. Gen. trainee Automatic

Electric Co., Chgo., 1938-41; personnel dir. Sherwin-Williams Co., Chgo., 1941-46; gen. mgr. Franklin Assn., Chgo., 1946-55; mng. dir. Inst. Newspaper Operations (name later changed to Am. Newspaper Pubs. Assn. Research Inst.), Chgo., 1955-59; sales mgr., adminstr. R.R. Donnelley & Sons, Chgo., 1959-65; exec. v.p. chief exec. officer Courier-Jour., 1965-75, Standard Gravure Corp., WHAS, Inc., 1965-81; pres. Courier-Jour. & Louisville Times, 1975-81; bd. dirs. Columbia Books, Inc. Dir. Nat. Pub. Radio, 1976-87. Vice chmn. bd. dirs. Broadway Project, Ky. Show; chmn. bd. Action Now, Inc.; past bd. dirs. Falls Region Health Coun., Housing Now, Inc., Better Govt. Assn. Ill.; trustee Nat. Found./March of Dimes, 1977-87. Mem. Indsl. Rels. Assn. Chgo. (pres. 1946), So. Newspaper Pubs. Assn., Casque and Gauntlet Soc., Helium Club (Louisville), River Valley (Louisville), Psi Upsilon. Home: 6205 Glenhill Rd Louisville KY 40222

MACKINNON, DAVID CAMERON, research and development company executive; b. Ottawa, Ontario, Canada, Sept. 1, 1945; s. Frank and Daphne MacKinnon; m. Betsy MacKinnon, Dec. 29, 1973; children: Katy, Darcy. BA with honors, Dalhousie U., 1967; MBA, York U., 1969; postgrad., U. Western Ontario, 1990. Dir. policy devel., small bus. secretarian Fed. Dept. Indsl. Trade and Commerce, Canada; dir. planning & econs. Dept. Devel., Nova Scotia, Canada; dir. econ. devel. br. Ministry of Treasury and Econs., Nova Scotia, Canada; sr. mgr. info. and govt. affairs Bank of Montreal, Toronto, Ontario, Canada; pres., CEO Ontario Devel. Corp., Toronto, 1986-93; pres. ORTECH Corp., Mississauga, Ontario, 1993—; dir. Canadian Comprehensive Auditing Found., Ottawa. Mem. Canadian Rsch. Mgmt. Assn., Met. Toronto Bd. Trade, Toronto Sailing and Canoe Club. Avocation: sailing. Office: ORTECH Corp, 2395 Speakman Dr, Mississauga, ON Canada L5K 1B3

MACKINNON, GEORGE E., federal judge; b. St. Paul, Apr. 22, 1906; s. James Alexander Wiley and Cora Blanche (Asselstine) MacK.; m. Elizabeth Valentine Davis, August 20, 1938; children: Catharine Alice, James Davis, Leonard Davis. Student, U. Colo., 1923-24; LL.B., U. Minn., 1929. Bar: Minn. 1929, U.S. Supreme Ct. 1947. Asst. gen. counsel Investors Syndicate, Mpls., 1929-42; engaged pvt. practice law, 1949-53, 58-61; elected mem. Minn. Ho. of Reps. from 29th dist., 1934, 36, 38, 40; mem. 80th Congress, 1947-49, 3d Minn. Dist.; U.S. Atty. for Minn., 1953-58; spl. asst. to U.S. Atty. Gen., 1960; gen. counsel, v.p. Investors Mut. Funds, Mpls., 1961-69; judge U.S. Ct. Appeals for D.C. Cir., 1969—; pres. judge U.S. Fgn. Intelligence Surveillance Ct. of Rev., 1979-82; U.S. del. UN Congress Prevention of Crime and Treatment of Offenders, 1985; presiding judge div. U.S. Ct. Appeals for Appointment of Ind. Counsels, 1985-92; mem. U.S. Sentencing Commn., 1985-91. Author: Minn. State Reorganization Act, 1939, State Civil Service Law, 1939, Old Age Assistance Act, 1936. Republican nominee for Gov. of Minn., 1958. Served to comdr. U.S. Navy Air Force, 1942-46. Cited for meritorious service by comdr. Air Force U.S. Atlantic Fleet. Mem. ABA, Minn. Bar Assn., Hennepin County Bar Assn., Delta Tau Delta, Phi Delta Phi. Republican. Episcopalian. Clubs: Minneapolis; Lawyers (Washington); Masons (32 deg.). Home: 11333 Willowbrook Dr Potomac MD 20854-2568 Office: US Ct Appeals 3rd Constitution Ave NW Washington DC 20001

MACKINNON, JOHN ALEXANDER, lawyer; b. Glen Ridge, N.J., Feb. 5, 1949; s. John and Carol McNeir (Cox) M.; m. Anne Rider Patterson, Aug. 19, 1972; children: Lindsay Rider, John William. BA, Williams Coll., 1971; JD, U. Va., Charlottesville, 1974. Assoc. Brown & Wood, N.Y.C., 1974-82, ptnr., 1983—. Trustee, Tuxedo Park Libr., N.Y., 1982-89; mem. chmn., bd. zoning appeals, Tuxedo Park, 1987-89. Mem. The Tuxedo Club. Home: Mtn Farm Rd Tuxedo Park NY 10987 Office: Brown & Wood 1 World Trade Ctr New York NY 10048-0001

MACKINNON, MALCOLM D(AVID), retired insurance company executive, information systems executive; b. Guelph, Ont., Can., Mar. 9, 1931; came to U.S., 1955; s. A.L. and Jean (Butchart) Mack.; m. Betty Campbell, June 18, 1955; children: Sandra, Katherine, Donald. BA, U. Toronto, 1953. CLU; chartered fin. analyst. With Prudential Ins. Co., 1954-94, v.p. Newark, 1979-81, sr. v.p., 1981-82, sr. v.p. Roseland, N.J., 1982-94; retired 1994. Trustee Kean Coll., Union, N.J., 1990-93; chmn. Milburn Short Hills Chpt. Am. Red Cross, 1992-94. Fellow Soc. Actuaries. Club: Canoe Brook Country (Summit, N.J.). Home: 72 Garnet Hill Rd Sunapee NH 03782-2711

MACKINNON, ROBERT, medical products executive. With Westinghouse, Pitts., 1962-69; pres. Siemens Medical Systems Inc., Iselin, N.J., 1983—. Office: Siemens Medical Systems Inc 186 Wood Ave S Iselin NJ 08830-2704

MACKINNON, RODRICK KEITH, corporate administration executive, lawyer; b. Berwick, N.S., Can., Mar. 25, 1943; s. Albert Forbes and Lilian Ruth (Grimm) MacK.; m. Mary Eleanor McAlpine, Aug. 23, 1968; children: Robert, Daniel. BA, Royal Mil. Coll., Kingston, Ont., Can., 1965; LLB, Dalhousie U., Halifax, N.S., 1971. Called to B.C. bar as barrister and solicitor, 1972. Barrister, solicitor various law firms, Vancouver, B.C., Can., 1972-79; legal counsel Genstar Corp., Vancouver, 1980-84, assoc. gen. counsel, sec., 1985-86; legal counsel Imasco Ltd., Montreal, Que., Can., 1987-88; sr. legal counsel Imasco Ltd., Montreal, Que., 1988-89, corp. sec., counsel, 1989—; coach minor league baseball and soccer, Vancouver, 1977-85. Lt. Royal Can. Navy, 1965-68, mem. Res. ret. Mem. Can. Bar Assn., Inst. Corp. Secs. and Adminstrs., Law Soc. B.C., Can. Maritime Law Assn. (exec. com. Vancouver 1981-84), Naval Officers Assn. Can. (exec. com. Vancouver 1978-85), Royal Mil. Coll. Club (exec. com. coll. alumni Vancouver 1978-84), Vancouver Club, Beaconsfield Golf Club (Pointe Claire, Que.), Montreal Badminton and Squash Club. Office: Imasco Ltd, 600 de Maisonneuve Blvd W 20th Fl, Montreal, PQ Canada H3A 3K7

MACKINNON, ROGER ALAN, psychiatrist; b. Attleboro, Mass., Feb. 13, 1927; s. Irville Herbert and Helen (Junk) MacK.; m. Florence Lundgren, Apr. 8, 1949 (div. 1970); children: Carol Louise, Stuart Alan; m. Nadine Trassenster, May 28, 1971. Student, Princeton U., 1944-46; MD, Columbia U., 1950, Cert. Psychoanalytic Med., 1957. Diplomate Am. Bd. Psychiatry and Neurology. Intern E.W. Sparrow Hosp., Lansing, Mich., 1950-51; resident in psychiatry N.Y. State Psychiatric Inst., N.Y.C., 1951-52, 52-54; chief psychiatry Vanderbilt Clinic, Presbyn. Hosp., N.Y.C., 1959-77; prof. clin. psychiatry Coll. Physicians & Surgeons, Columbia U., N.Y.C., 1986—; tng., supervising analyst Columbia U. Psychoanalytic Ctr., 1970—, asst. dir. for selection, 1981-91, dir., 1991—; attending psychiatrist Presbyn. Hosp., N.Y.C., 1972—, N.Y. State Psychiatric Inst., N.Y.C., 1972—; asst. examiner Am. Bd. Psychiatry and Neurology, 1960-70; lectr. in field. Co-author textbook: The Psychiatric Interview, 1971, The Psychiatric Evaluation, 1986; contbr. articles to profl. jours., chpts. to books. Lt. USNR, 1952-54. Recipient George Goldman award Columbia U. Psychoanalytic Ctr., 1989, George E. Daniels award Assn. for Psychoanalytic Medicine, 1995. Fellow Am. Psychiatric Assn. (life), N.Y. Acad. Medicine; mem. Am. Psychoanalytic Assn., N.Y. Psychiatric Soc. (pres. 1987-88). Avocations: woodworking, boating, hiking. Home: 11 Edgewood St Tenafly NJ 07670-2909 Office: 11 E 87th St New York NY 10128-0527 also: Columbia U Ctr Psychoanalytic Tng Rsch 722 W 168th St New York NY 10032-2603

MACKINNON, SALLY ANNE, retired fast food company executive; b. Chgo., Apr. 20, 1938; d. Eugene and Anne Elizabeth (Jones) MacK. B.A., Smith Coll., 1960; postgrad., U. Ark., 1961-62. Brand mgr. Speidel div. of Textron, Providence, 1967-70; mktg. mgr. Candy Corp. Am., Bklyn., 1970-72; v.p. account service William Esty Advt., N.Y.C., 1972-76; mktg. mgr. R.J. Reynolds Tobacco, Winston-Salem, N.C., 1976-84, v.p. new brands, 1984-86; v.p. new products mktg. Ky. Fried Chicken, Louisville, 1986-88; ret., 1988. Democrat. Episcopalian. Avocation: travel. Home: 321 Lamplighter Cir Winston Salem NC 27104-3420

MACKINNON, STEPHEN R., Asian studies administrator, educator; b. Columbus, Nebr., Dec. 2, 1940; s. Cyrus Leland and Helen (Wigglesworth) MacK.; m. Janice Carolyn Rachie, July 15, 1967; children: Rebecca, Cyrus R. BA, Yale U., 1963, MA, 1964; PhD, U. Calif., Davis, 1971. Acting instr. Chinese U., Hong Kong, 1968-69; dir. Asian Studies, prof. History Ariz. State U., Tempe, 1971—; vis. assoc. Chinese Acad. Social Sci., Beijing, 1979-81, 85; mem. U.S. State Dept. Selection Bd., Washington, 1991, Nat. Com. on U.S.-China Rels., N.Y.C., 1991—; cons. PBS film documentary "Dragon and Eagle" on U.S.-China rels., San Francisco, 1986—. Author:

(book) Power/Politics China, 1980; co-author: (books) Agnes Smedley, 1988, China Reporting, 1987; co-editor: (book) Chinese Women Revolution, 1976 (ALA notable book 1976); lectr. on China to local orgns. and TV, 1991—. Commr. Phoenix Sister Cities, 1986-91; treas. Com. on Fgn. Rels., Phoenix, 1988—. Rsch. fellow Am. Coun. Learned Socs., Hong Kong, 1978, Fulbright Found., India, 1977-78; rsch. sr. Com. on Scholarly Com. People's Republic China, Washington-Beijing, 1992. Mem. Assn. Asian Studies (bd. dirs. 1990-91), Am. Hist. Assn. (program com. 1990-91). Avocations: tennis, hiking, jazz. Office: Ariz State U Ctr for Asian Studies 109 W Hall Tempe AZ 85287-1702

MACKINNON, WILLIAM HOWARD, airline executive; b. Sumatra, Indonesia, May 21, 1938; came to U.S., 1941; s. William and Marion Howard (Baker) MacK.; m. Ramona Reames, Dec. 17, 1960; children: Heather, Kevin, Kyle, Adam. BBA, Emory U., 1960; MBA, Ga. State U., 1967. cert. mgmt. acctg. Bus. rep. internat. dept. Trust Co. Bank, Atlanta, 1964-68; v.p. Conway Research, Atlanta, 1968-71; asst. treas. Southern Airways, Atlanta, 1971-79; v.p., treas. Republic Airlines, Mpls., 1979-83, Piedmont Aviation, Inc., Winston-Salem, N.C., 1983-84; sr. v.p., treas. Piedmont Aviation, Inc., Winston-Salem, 1984-86, sr. v.p. fin., 1986-88; exec. v.p. fin. and adminstrn. Braniff Airlines, Dallas, 1988—. Contbr. articles to Travel Investment Mag., 1968-71. Bd. dirs., chmn. loaned execs. Forsyth County (N.C.) United Way, 1986-87. Served as lt. (j.g.) USN, 1961-64. Recipient Excellence Studies in Internat. Fin. award, World Trade Council, Atlanta, 1968. Mem. Nat. Assn. Corp. Treas., Nat. Assn. Accts., Fin. Execs. Inst., Air Transport Assn. (exec. and fin. council 1984-87), U.S.C. of C. (econ. policy com. 1985-87). Republican. Episcopalian. Club: Piedmont (Winston-Salem). Avocations: tennis, fishing, travel. Home: 207 W Jones St Savannah GA 31401-4509 Office: Piedmont Aviation Inc 1 Piedmont Plz Winston Salem NC 27156 Office: Braniff Inc 255 S Orange Ave Ste 875 Orlando FL 32801-3452

MACKINTOSH, CAMERON, musical theater producer; b. Enfield, Middlesex, Eng., Oct. 17, 1946; s. Ian Robert and Diana Gladys (Tonna) M. Student, Prior Pk. Coll., Somerset, Eng., Cen. Sch. for Speech and Drama. Asst. stage mgr. Oliver! tour, British cities, 1965; N.Y. debut as producer, deviser Tomfoolery, Top of the Gate, 1981; London debut producer Little Women, Jeanetta Cochrane, 1967; producer, deviser musicals Anything Goes, Saville, London, 1969, Trelawney, Sadler Wells, Prince of Wales, 1972, The Card, Queens, 1973, Winnie the Pooh, Phoenix, 1974, 75, Owl and the Pussycat Went To See, Westminster, 1975, Side By Side By Sondheim, Wyndhams and Garrick, 1976, Oliver!, Albery, 1977-80, Aldwych, 1983, Godspell, Phoenix, 1975, Her Majesty's P.O.W., Shaftsbury, 1977, Duke of York, 1978, Diary of a Madman, Phoenix, 1977, After Shave, Apollo, 1977, Out On a Limb, Vaudeville, 1977, Gingerbread Man, Old Vic, 1978, 79, Royalty, 1980, Westminster, 1981, My Fair Lady, Adelphi, 1979, Tomfoolery, Criterion, 1980, Jeeves Takes Charge, Fortune, 1981, Cats, New London, 1981, Song and Dance, Palace, 1982, Blondel, Old Vic, Aldwych, 1983, Little Shop of Horrors, Comedy, 1983, Abbacadabra, Lyric Hammersmith, 1983, The Boyfriend, Old Vic. and Albery, 1985, Les Misérables, 1985, The Phantom of the Opera, 1987, Follies, 1989, Miss Saigon, 1989, Five Guys Named Moe, 1990, Moby Dick: Putting It Together, 1992, Carousel, 1993 (Tony award, 1994), Oliver!, 1994; major tours in Britian include Little Women, 1967, Murder at the Vicarage, 1969, Rebecca, 1969, At Home with the Dales, 1970, Salad Days, 1972, Butley, 1973, Winnie the Pooh, 1973-74, Time and Time Again, 1974, Godspell, 1974-80, The Owl and The Pussycat Went To See, 1974, 75, 76, Relativeley Speaking, 1974-75, An Inspector Calls, 1974, Private Lives, 1974, Bell, Book and Candle, 1974, A Merry Whirl of Windsor, 1975, So Who Needs Marriage. 1975, John, Paul, George and Ringo, 1975-76, Rock Nativity, 1975-76, Touch of Spring, 1976, Virginia Woolf, 1976, Lauder, 1976, Oliver!, 1977, 83, Side By Side By Sondheim, 1978-79, My Fair Lady, 1978, 81-82, Rocky Horror Show, 1979-80, Gingerbread Man, 1979, Oklahoma, 1980; also tours various shows to Can., Republic S. Africa, Ireland, Scandinavia, Australia, U.S.A. Mem. Soc. West End Theatres (exec. officer), Dramatists League, League Am. Theaters, Am. Dramatists Guild. Address: Number One, Bedford Sq, London England WC1B 3RA also: 226 W 47th St New York NY 10036-1413

MACKIW, VLADIMIR NICHOLAUS, metallurgical consultant; b. Stanislawiw, Western Ukraine, Sept. 4, 1923; came to Can., 1948, naturalized, 1953; s. Timothy and Irene (Iwanyckyj) M.; m. Bohdanna Irene Kebuz, Nov. 24, 1951. Dipl. Chemist, Univs. Breslau and Erlangen, Germany, 1946; postgrad., U. Louvain, Belgium, 1948; DSc (hon.), U. Alta., Edmonton, 1976. Chemist Lingman Lake Gold Mines, Winnipeg, Man., Can., 1948; with Man. Provincial Bur. Mines, 1949; research chemist Sherritt Gordon Mines Ltd., Toronto, Ont., Can., 1949, dir. research, 1952, dir. research and devel. div., 1955-68, dir., 1964, v.p., 1967, v.p. tech. and corp. devel., 1968-72, exec. v.p., 1972-88; cons. Toronto, 1988—; chmn. Nickel Devel. Inst., Toronto, 1984-86; mem. Nat. Research Council Can., 1971-77; former mem. Nat. Adv. Com. on Mining and Metall. Research; mem. adv. com. to minister energy, mines and resources, 1972-79, co-chmn., 1975-79; presented tech. papers and lectures Federal Republic of Germany, Belgium, Japan, Peoples Republic of China, Australia, Canada; participated in fed. gov. tech. missions to USSR, Belgium, Peoples Republic of China. Contbr. articles to profl. jours.; patentee in field. Recipient Jules Garnier prize Metall. Soc. France, 1966, Gold medal Instn. Mining and Metallurty, London, 1977, fellow award TMS, 1994. Fellow Can. Acad. Engring. (life), Can. Inst. Mining and Metallurgy (Inco Platinum medal 1966, Airey award 1972), Chem. Inst. Can. (R.S. Jane Meml. award 1967); mem. AIME (James Douglas Gold medal 1991), Can. Rsch. Mgmt. Assn. (R&D Mgmt. award 1990, Shevchenko Gold medal Ukrainian Can. Congress), Am. Powder Metallurgy Inst., Am. Soc. Metallurgy Internat. (lectr. Can. chpts. 1990-91), Assn. Profl. Engrs. Alta., Soc. Chem. Industry (Can. sect.), Shevchenco Sci. Soc. (past pres.), Ont. Club. Ukrainian Catholic. Home: 9 Blair Athol Crescent, Toronto, ON Canada M9A 1X6 Office: Sherritt Inc, 5 Hazelton Ave, Toronto, ON Canada M5R 2E1

MACKLEM, MICHAEL KIRKPATRICK, publisher; b. Toronto, Ont., Can., July 12, 1928; s. Hedley Clark and Mary Eileen (Kirkpatrick) M.; m. Anne Woodburne Hardy, Dec. 30, 1950; children—Timothy Street, Nicholas Hardy. B.A., U. Toronto, 1950; A.M. (Charles Scribner fellow), Princeton U., 1952, Ph.D. (Porter Ogden Jacobus fellow, Royal Soc. Can. fellow), 1954. Instr., English Yale U., New Haven, 1954-55; staff editor Ency. Canadiana, 1955-58; asst. to dir. Humanities Research Council of Can., 1958-60; gen. mgr. Oberon Press, Ottawa, Ont., 1966-85; pres. Michael, Hardy, Ltd., Ottawa, 1972—. Author: The Anatomy of the World: Relations Between Natural and Moral Law from Donne to Pope, 1958, God Have Mercy: The Life of John Fisher of Rochester, 1967, Cinderella, 1969, Voyages to New France 1615-1618, 1970, Voyages to New France 1599-1603, 1971, The Sleeping Beauty, 1973, Jacques the Woodcutter, 1977, Liberty and the Holy City, 1978. Can. Council fellow, 1964-65. Home: 555 Maple Ln, Ottawa, ON Canada K1M 0N7 Office: Oberon Press, 400-350 Sparks St, Ottawa, ON Canada K1R 7S8

MACKLER, TINA, artist; b. London; d. Leon and Ethel Mackler; divorced; 1 child, Leonore Bloom. Student, Arts Students League, N.Y.C., Indsl. Sch. Design, N.Y.C., New Sch., N.Y.C. Tchr. art Nat. Acad. Ballet, N.Y.C., 1966-69; tchr. adults West Side YMCA, N.Y.C.; asst. studio instr. Met. Mus. Art, N.Y.C., vol. program, 1990—. Illustrator: Informal Dictionary of Ballet, co-author, illustrator: To Dance, To Live; pub. Dance Horizons, 1977; one-person exhbns. Alfred Valente Gallery, N.Y.C., 1967, Mus. Performing Arts, Lincoln Ctr., N.Y.C., 1973, Adelphi U., L.I., N.Y., 1975, Phila. Art Alliance, 1976, Jackson (Miss.) Mus. Art, 1978, Northeastern U., Boston, 1980; exhibited in group shows Alfredo Gallery, N.Y.C., 1964, 1966, Dutchess Hall Gallery, Poughkeepsie, N.Y., 1969, Wright/Hepburn/Webster Gallery, N.Y.C., 1960, 70, N.Y. Pub. Library, 1973, O'Keefe Centre, Ont., Can., 1974, Ball State U., 1974, N.A.D. annual, 1974, Audubon Artists Annual, 1975, Nat. Pastel Show, 1975, Commedia Dell Art Adelphi U., 1974, Guild Gallery, N.Y.C., 1978, Met. Mus. of Art, 1987-88, Dance Collections, Lincoln Ctr., N.Y.C., 1991, Jackson Gallery, 1994; works represented in permanent collections Nat. Collection Fine Prints, Smithsonian Instn., Washington, Israel Mus., Jerusalem, La Jolla (Calif.) Mus., U. Wis. Mus., Circus World Mus., Baraboo, Wis., Fairleigh Dickinson U., Circus Hall of Fame Mus., Sarasota, Fla., Adelphi U., Creative Dance Found. For Negro Arts, Tuskegee, Ala., Mus. Performing Arts Lincoln Center, N.Y.C., Jackson (Miss.) Mus. Art, Original Print Collectors Group Ltd., Northeastern U., also notable pvt. collections, Am. and abroad; com-

pleted series of studies on Spanish dance and impressions of Spain for Spanish Ministry Info. and Tourism, 1976, 88; represented in original stone lithographs of Rudolf Nureyev, Marcel Marceau, Margot Fonteyn and numerous dance soloists, N.Y. Times Mag., also nat. mags., 1975-78; History of International Art, Accademia Italia; works profiled Joe Franklin TV Show, 1979; represented in Works shown on TV NBC-TV preview, Mus. Performing Arts, Lincoln Center, 1973, Channel 13 TV Art Auction, 1978, 79, 80, 81, 82, 83; Meml. for Dame Margot Fonteyn oil painting; portrait of Margot Fonteyn & Rudolf Nureyev exhibited Lincoln Ctr. for Performing Arts, 1991; exhbn. ballet art with USA Internat. Ballet Competition, Jackson, Miss., 1994. Prints selected for promotional use Texaco, 1979. Home: 25 Central Park W New York NY 10023-7253 I have long felt the influence which the arts exert on the minds and hearts of mankind. Believing, as I do, that the world today stands in need of spiritual truths, ideals and moral standards, it is my desire to reach out and set before the public some of the beauty and grandeur which reside in the human soul and expresses itself through that most primal art - the dance.

MACKLIN, CROFFORD JOHNSON, JR., lawyer; b. Columbus, Ohio, Sept. 10, 1947; s. Crofford Johnson, Sr. and Dorothy Ann (Stevens) M.; m. Mary Carole Ward, July 5, 1969; children—Carrie E., David J. B.A., Ohio State U., 1969; B.A. summa cum laude, U. West Fla., 1974; J.D. cum laude, Ohio State U., 1976. Bar: Ohio 1977, U.S. Tax Ct. 1978. Acct., Touche Ross, Columbus, 1976-77; assoc. Smith & Schnacke, Dayton, 1977-81; ptnr. Porter, Wright, Morris & Arthur, Dayton, 1983-88; shareholder Smith & Schnacke, 1988-89; ptnr. Thompson, Hine & Flory, 1989—; sole practice, Dayton, 1981-82; adj. faculty Franklin U., 1977; adj. prof. U. Dayton Law Sch. 1981. Contbr. articles to profl. jours. Bd. dirs. Easter Seals, 1984-86. Served to capt. USMCR, 1969-74. Fellow Am. Coll. Trust and Estate Counsel; Emem. Dayton Bar Assn. (chmn. probate com. 1981-83), Dayton Trust & Estate Planning (pres. 1983-84), Ohio Bar Assn., ABA. Presbyterian. Home: 3 Forest Pl Glendale OH 45246-4407 Office: Thompson Hine & Flory 2000 Courthouse Pla NE PO Box 8801 Dayton OH 45401-8801

MACKLIN, F. DOUGLAS, bishop. Bishop Ch. of God in Christ, Memphis. Office: Ch of God in Christ 1230 Tipton Memphis TN 38101-9999

MACKLIN, PHILIP ALAN, physics educator; b. Richmond Hill, N.Y., Apr. 13, 1925; s. Egbert Chalmer and Margaret Griswold (Collins) M.; m. Cora Baldwin Galindo, Sept. 5, 1953; children: Susan, Steven, Peter. B.S. cum laude, Yale U., 1944; M.A., Columbia U., 1949, Ph.D., 1956. Physicist Carbide & Carbon Chems. Corp., Oak Ridge, 1946-47; research scientist AEC, Columbia U., 1949-51; instr. physics Middlebury Coll., Vt., 1951-54; acting chmn. dept. Middlebury Coll., 1953-54; mem. faculty Miami U., Oxford, Ohio, 1954—; prof. physics Miami U., 1961-93, chmn. dept., 1972-85, prof. emeritus, 1993—; research scientist Armco Steel Co., summers 1955-56; vis. prof. U. N.Mex., summers 1957-68, Boston U., fall 1985-86; physicist Los Alamos Sci. Labs., summers 1960-62; participant NSF summer insts., 1970-71; vis. scientist MIT, 1985-86. Author publs. in field. Vestryman Holy Trinity Episcopal Ch., Oxford , 1959-61, 67, 71-73, 75-77, mem. fin. com., chmn. blood assurance program, 1980—; lector, 1989—. With USN, 1944-46. Mem. AAAS, AAUP, LWV of Oxford (treas. 1986-88), Am. Phys. Soc., Forum Physics and Soc., Am. Assn. Physics Tchrs., Kiwanis (bd. dirs. 1994—), Torch Club of Butler County (pres. 1982-83), 1809 Club (pres. 1964-65), Campus Ministry Ctr., Union of Concerned Scientists, Phi Beta Kappa, Sigma Xi, Sigma Pi Sigma, Omicron Delta Kappa. Democrat. Achievements include patents in field. Home: 211 Oakhill Dr Oxford OH 45056-2710 Office: 117 Culler Hall Miami Univ Oxford OH 45056

MACKLIN, RUTH, bioethics educator; b. Newark, Mar. 27, 1938; d . Hyman and Frieda (Yaruss) Chimacoff; m. Martin Macklin, Sept. 1, 1957 (div. June 1969); children: Meryl, Shelley Macklin Taylor. BA with distinction, Cornell U., 1958; MA in Philosophy, Case Western Res. U., 1966, PhD in Philosophy, 1968. Instr. in philosophy Case Western Res. U., Cleve., 1967-68, asst. prof., 1968-71, assoc. prof., 1971-76; assoc. for behavioral studies The Hastings Ctr., Hastings-on-Hudson, N.Y., 1976-80; vis. assoc. prof. Albert Einstein Coll. Medicine, Bronx, N.Y., 1977-78, assoc. prof., 1978-84, prof. dept. epidemiology and social medicine, 1984—; cons. NIH, 1986—; advisor WHO, Geneva, 1989; apptd. mem. White House Adv. Com. on Human Radiation Experiments, Washington, 1994—. Author: Man, Mind and Morality, 1982, Mortal Choices, 1987, Enemies of Patients, 1993, Surrogates and Other Mothers, 1994; contbr. articles to ethics, law and med. jours. Fellow The Hastings Ctr., Inst. Medicine of NAS, Am. Philos. Assn. (life), Am. Pub. Health Assn., Am. Soc. Law, Medicine and Ethics, Phi Beta Kappa. Democrat. Office: A Einstein Coll Medicine Dept Epidemiology & Social Medicine 1300 Morris Park Ave Bronx NY 10461-1926

MACKNIGHT, WILLIAM JOHN, chemist, educator; b. N.Y.C., May 5, 1936; s. William John and Margaret Ann (Stuart) M.; m. Carol Marie Bernier, Aug. 19, 1967. B.S., Rochester U., N.Y., 1958; M.A., Princeton U., N.J., 1963, Ph.D., 1964. Research assoc. Princeton U., N.J., 1964-65; asst. prof. chemistry U. Mass., Amherst, 1965-69, assoc. prof. chemistry, 1969-74, prof. chemistry, 1974-76, dept. head polymer sci., 1976-85, prof. polymer sci. and engring., 1985-88, head dept. polymer sci. & engring., 1988—; mem. sci. and tech. adv. bd. Alcoa, Pitts., 1984-86, Diversitech Gen., Akron, Ohio, 1985—; mem. panel for materials sci. Nat. Bur. Standards, Washington, 1983-89. Author: Polymeric Sulfur and Related Polymers, 1965; Introduction to Polymer Viscoelasticity, 2d edit., 1983. Served to lt. USN, 1958-61. Recipient Ford prize in high polymer physics Am. Phys. Soc., 1984; Guggenheim fellow, 1985. Fellow AAAS, Am. Phys. Soc. (exec. com. 1975-76); mem. Am. Chem. Soc., Am. Soc. Rheology. Club: Cosmos. Avocations: Music; sports. Home: 127 Sunset Ave Amherst MA 01002-2019 Office: U Mass Polymer Sci & Engring Dept Graduate Rsch Ctr Amherst MA 01003

MACKOVIC, JOHN, college football coach, athletic director; b. Barberton, Ohio, Oct. 1, 1943; m. Arlene Francis; children: Aimee, John. BA in Spanish, Wake Forest U., 1965; MEd in Secondary Sch. Adminstrn., Miami U., Oxford, Ohio, 1966. Various coaching positions, 1965-72; offensive backfield coach U. Ariz., Tucson, 1973-74; offensive coord. U. Ariz., 1974-75, asst. head coach, 1976; asst. head coach, offensive coord. Purdue U., West Lafayette, Ind., 1976-78; head football coach Wake Forest U., Winston-Salem, N.C., 1978-81; asst. football coach Dallas Cowboys, 1981-83; head football coach Kansas City (Mo.) Chiefs, 1983-87; head football coach U. Ill., 1988-92, dir. of athletics, 1988-92; head coach football U. Tex., Austin, 1992—. Address: PO Box 7399 Austin TX 78713

MACKOWSKI, JOHN JOSEPH, retired insurance company executive; b. Westport, Mass., Feb. 1, 1926; s. John J. and Victoria K. (Skript) Mieczkowski; m. Ruth Williams, Feb. 3, 1951; children: Martha, John Matthew, Daniel, Joan. AB, Duke U., 1948; student, Harvard Advanced Mgmt. Program, 1970, 71. With Ins. Co. of N.Am., Boston, Phila., Chgo., 1948-51; with Atlantic Mut. Ins. Co., N.Y.C., 1951-88, chmn., CEO, to 1988; bd. dirs. F.W. Woolworth Co., RCB Trust Co., Stamford, Conn., Transatlantic Holdings, Inc. Bd. dirs. Seamen's Ch. Inst. N.Y. and N.J. Served to 1st lt. USMCR, 1943-46. Mem. Sawgrass Club (Ponte Vedra Beach, Fla.), Acoaxet Country Club (Westport Harbor, Mass.), Spindle Rock Yacht Club, Sigma Chi, Beta Lambda. Episcopalian. Home: 33 Widgeon Ln Little Compton RI 02837-1960 Other Home: 1506 Birkdale Ln Ponte Vedra Beach FL 32082

MACLACHLAN, ALEXANDER, chemical company executive, retired; b. Boston, Jan. 22, 1933; s. Hugh and Catherine (Sullivan) MacL.; m. Elizabeth Pegues, Jan. 25, 1958; children: Katherine Ellen, Amy Elizabeth, Mary Emily, Alexander Hugh. BS in Chemistry, Tufts U., 1954; PhD in Organic Chemistry, MIT, 1957. With E.I. du Pont de Nemours & Co. Wilmington, Del., 1957—, mktg. dir., printing product dir., 1976-78, dir. plastics dept., 1978-80, dir. research and devel. div. chemical and pigments div., 1980-82, asst. dir. ctrl. R&D dept., 1982-83, dir. ctrl. R&D dept., 1983-86, sr. v.p. tech., 1986-90, sr. v.p. R&D, 1990-93; dep. undersec. tech. partnerships U.S. Dept. of Energy, Washington, 1994—. Trustee Mt. Cuba Astron. Obs., Wilmington, 1986—, Bartol Rsch. inst.; dir. Indsl. Rsch. Inst., 1991-94; bd. overseers Fermilab; mem. Nat. Acad. Engring. Mem. Am. Chem. Soc.

MACLACHLAN, DOUGLAS LEE, marketing educator; b. Hollywood, Calif., Aug. 27, 1940; s. Alexander D. and Patricia E. (Culver) MacL.; m. Natalie Bowditch Knauth, July 23, 1966; children: Heather Bowditch, Trevor Douglas. A.B. in Physics, U. Calif., Berkeley, 1962, M.B.A., 1965, M.A. in Stats., 1970, Ph.D. in Bus. Adminstrn, 1971; student, Hastings Sch. Law, 1965-66. Instr. bus. adminstrn. U. Calif., Berkeley, 1969-70; v.p. Hartec Corp., Newport Beach, Calif., 1965-70; acting asst. prof. U. Wash., Seattle, 1970-71, asst. prof., 1971-74, assoc. prof., 1974-78, prof., chmn. dept. mktg. and internat. bus., 1978-86, prof., acting chair dept. mktg. and internat. bus., 1993-94, Affiliate Program Disting. prof. mktg. and internat. bus., 1986-88, Nordstrom prof. retail mktg., 1988-89, Ford Motor Co. prof. mktg., 1989-90; vis. prof. bus. adminstrn. U. Calif., Berkeley, summer 1974; vis. prof. Institu Européen des Affaires, Fontainebleau, France, 1982-83, Cath. U. Leuven, Belgium, 1991-92; dir. Univ. Book Store, 1985—. Contbr. articles profl. jours.; editorial bd.: Jour. Mktg. Research, 1975-81. Mem. Am. Mktg. Assn. (dir. Puget Sound chpt. 1975-77, 90-91, pres. 1978-79), Inst. Mgmt. Scis., Am. Statis. Assn., Am. Inst. Decision Scis., Assn. Consumer Research, Alpha Kappa Psi, Kappa Delta Rho. Home: 16305 Inglewood Rd NE Bothell WA 98011-3908 Office: University of Washington DJ 10 Seattle WA 98195

MACLACHLAN, GORDON ALISTAIR, biology educator, researcher; b. Saskatoon, Sask., Can., June 30, 1930; s. Hector Ross and Nellie (Glass) M.; m. Sarah Dangerfield, June 26, 1959; children: Mary, Anna. B.A., U. Sask., 1952, M.A., 1954; Ph.D., U. Man., 1956. NRC postdoctoral fellow Imperial Coll., London, 1956-59; asst. prof. U. Alta., Edmonton, 1960-62; assoc. prof. biology McGill U., Montreal, 1962-69, prof., 1970—, chmn. dept., 1970-75, dean. grad. studies, vice prin. rsch., 1980-90. Assoc. editor Can. Jour. Botany, 1980-86; editor Jour. Plant Molecular Biology, 1988-90. Commonwealth prof. Australia, 1975. Mem. Can. Soc. Plant Physiologists (pres. 1973). Home: 561 Argyle Ave, Westmount, PQ Canada H3Y 3B8 Office: McGill U Biology Dept, 1205 Penfield Ave, Montreal, PQ Canada H3A 1B1

MACLACHLAN, KYLE, actor; b. 1960. Actor: film Dune, 1984, Blue Velvet, 1986, The Hidden, 1987, Don't Tell Her It's Me, 1990, The Doors, 1991, Twin Peaks: Fire Walk with Me, 1992, Where the Day Takes You, 1992, Rich in Love, 1993, The Trial, 1993, The Flintstones, 1994; TV series Twin Peaks, 1990-91; TV movies: Against the Wall, 1994, Roswell, 1994. Office: UTA 9560 Wilshire Blvd Beverly Hills CA 90212*

MACLACHLAN, PATRICIA, author; b. Cheyenne, Wyo., Mar. 3, 1938; d. Philo and Madonna (Moss) Pritzkau; m. Robert MacLachlan, Apr. 14, 1962; children: John, Jamie, Emily. BA, U. Conn., 1962. Tchr. English Bennett Jr. High Sch., Manchester, Conn., 1963-79; vis. lectr. Smith Coll., Northampton, Mass., 1986—. Author: The Sick Day, 1979, Arthur, for the Very First Time, 1980 (Golden Kite award Soc. Children's Book Writers 1980), Moon, Stars, Frogs, and Friends, 1980, Through Grandpa's Eyes, 1980, Cassie Binegar, 1982, Mama One, Mama Two, 1982, Tomorrow's Wizard, 1982, Seven Kisses in a Row, 1983, Unclaimed Treasures, 1984 (Boston Globe/Horn Book award 1984), Sarah, Plain and Tall, 1985 (Golden Kite award 1985, Scott O'Dell Historical Fiction award 1985, John Newbery medal 1986, Jefferson Cup award Va. Libr. Assn. 1986, Christopher award 1986, Garden State Children's Book award N.J. Libr. Assn. 1988), The Facts and Fictions of Minna Pratt, 1988 (Parent's Choice award Parent's Choice Found. 1988), Three Names, 1991, Journey, 1991, All the Places to Love, 1993, Baby, 1993, Skylark, 1994. Bd. dirs. Children's Aid Family Svc. Agency, 1970-80. recipient numerous awards for children's fiction. Office: Dept of Edn Smith Coll Northampton MA 01063*

MACLAGAN, JOHN LYALL, retired petroleum company executive; b. Lethbridge, Alta., Can., Oct. 26, 1929; s. Frederick Alexander Lyall and Dora Ellen (Dean) M.; m. Joan Lily Prince, July 15, 1965; 1 dau., Susan. B.Commerce, U. Alta., 1952. Chartered accountant, Alta. Staff auditor Price Waterhouse & Co., Calgary, 1952-56; accountant Union Oil Co. of Calif., Alta., 1956-61; mgr. accounting Union Oil Co. of Can., Ltd., Calgary, 1961-72; treas., comptroller Union Oil Co. of Can., Ltd., 1972-75, v.p. fin., treas., 1975-82; v.p. fin. Omega Hydrocarbons Ltd., Calgary, 1982-94; ret., 1994. Mem. Can. Inst. Chartered Accts. Club: Calgary Petroleum. Home: 308 Roxborough Rd SW, Calgary, AB Canada T2S 0R4

MACLAINE, ALLAN HUGH, English language educator; b. Montreal, Can., Oct. 24, 1924. B.A., McGill U., 1945; Ph.D. in English, Brown U., 1951. Instr. English McGill U., 1946-47, Brown U., 1947-50, U. Mass., 1951-54; from asst. prof. to prof. Tex. Christian U., 1954-62; prof. English U. R.I., 1962—, also dean div. univ. extension, 1967-71. Author: Student's Comprehensive Guide to the Canterbury Tales, 1964, Robert Fergusson, 1965, Allan Ramsay, 1985, also articles. Mem. Coll. English Assn. (pres. 1965, dir. 1961-66), Assn. for Scottish Literary Studies. Office: U Rhode Island Dept English Kingston RI 02881

MACLAINE, SHIRLEY, actress; b. Richmond, Va., Apr. 24, 1934; d. Ira O. and Kathlyn (MacLean) Beatty; m. Steve Parker, Sept. 17, 1954 (div.); 1 child, Stephanie Sachiko. Ed. high sch. Appearances include (Broadway plays) Me and Juliet, 1953, Pajama Game, 1954, (films) The Trouble With Harry, 1954, Artists and Models, 1954, Around the World in 80 Days, 1955-56, Hot Spell, 1957, The Matchmaker, 1957, The Sheepman, 1957, Some Came Running, 1958 (Fgn. Press award 1959), Ask Any Girl, 1959 (Silver Bear award as best actress Internat. Berlin Film Festival), Career, 1959, Can-Can, 1959, The Apartment, 1959 (Best Actress prize Venice Film Festival), Children's Hour, 1960, The Apartment, 1960, Two for the Seesaw, 1962, Irma La Douce, 1963, What A Way to Go, The Yellow Rolls Royce, 1964, John Goldfarb Please Come Home, 1965, Gambit and Woman Times Seven, 1967, The Bliss of Mrs. Blossom, Sweet Charity, 1969, Two Mules for Sister Sara, 1969, Desperate Characters, 1971, The Possession of Joel Delaney, 1972, The Other Half of the Sky: A China Memoir, 1975, The Turning Point, 1977, Being There, 1979, A Change of Seasons, 1980, Loving Couples, 1980, Terms of Endearment, 1983 (Acad. award 1984, Golden Globe-Best Actress), Cannonball Run II, 1984, Madame Sousatzka, 1988 (Best Actress Venice Film Festival, Golden Globe-Best Actress), Steel Magnolias, 1989, Waiting For the Light, 1990, Postcards From the Edge, 1990, Defending Your Life, 1991, Used People, 1992, Wrestling Ernest Hemingway, 1993, Guarding Tess, 1994, Evening Star, 1995; (TV shows) Shirley's World, 1971-72, Shirley MacLaine: If They Could See Me Now, 1974-75, Gypsy in My Soul, 1975-76, Where Do We Go From Here?, 1976-77, Shirley MacLaine at the Lido, 1979, Shirley MacLaine...Every Little Movement, 1980 (Emmy award 1980), (TV movie) Out On A Limb, 1987; prodr., co-dir. documentary: China The Other Half of the Sky; star U.S. tour stage musical Out There Tonight, 1990; author: Don't Fall Off the Mountain, 1970, The New Celebrity Cookbook, 1973, You Can Get There From Here, 1975, Out on a Limb, 1983, Dancing in the Light, 1985, It's All in the Playing, 1987, Going Within: A Guide for Inner Transformation, 1989, Dance While You Can, 1991; editor: McGovern: The Man and His Beliefs, 1972. Office: MacLaine Enterprises Inc 201 Santa Monica Blvd Ste 410 Santa Monica CA 90401-2214*

MAC LAM, HELEN, editor, periodical; b. N.Y.C., Aug. 17, 1933; d. Forrest Mearl and Bertha Margaret (Herzberger) Keen; m. David Carlyle MacLam, Feb. 7, 1953; children: Timothy David, David Andrew. AB Sociology, Heidelberg Coll., 1961; AMLS, U. Mich., 1967; MA African Am. Studies, Boston U., 1978. Dep. clerk Mcpl. Ct., Tiffin, Ohio, 1962-64; subprofessional asst. Heidelberg Coll. Libr., Tiffin, Ohio, 1964-66; collection devel. libr. social scis. Dartmouth Coll. Libr., Hanover, N.H., 1967-83; social scis. editor Choice Mag., Middletown, Conn., 1983—; cons. in field; spkr. in field. Editorial bd. Multicultural Review, 1992-95; contbr. articles to profl. jours. Bd. dirs. Headrest, 1976-80, Hanover Consumer Coop. Soc., 1969-72. Recipient Grant award Rsch. Program for Ethnic Studies Librarianship Fisk U., 1975. Mem. Nat. Assn. Ethnic Studies (pres. 1985-87, assoc. editor publs. 1980-83), African Studies Assn., Africana Libs. Coun. (exec. bd. 1989-91), Am. Soc. Indexers, Freelance Editorial Assn., Women in Scholarly Publishing, Assn. Coll. and Rsch. Librs. (New England chpt.). Home: Rt 2 Box 92 Norwich VT 05055 Office: Choice Mag 100 Riverview Ctr Middletown CO 06457

MACLANE, SAUNDERS, mathematician, educator; b. Taftville, Conn., Aug. 4, 1909; s. Donald Bradford and Winifred (Saunders) MacL.; m. Dorothy M. Jones, July 21, 1933 (dec. Feb. 1985); children: Margaret

Ferguson, Cynthia M. Hay; m. Osa Skotting Segal, Aug. 16, 1986. PhB, Yale U., 1930; AM, U. Chgo., 1931; DPhil, Goettingen, Fed. Republic Germany, 1934; DSc (hon.), Purdue U., 1965, Yale U., 1969, Coe Coll., 1973, U. Pa., 1977, Union Coll., 1990; LLD (hon.), Glasgow U., Scotland, 1971. Sterling Research fellow Yale U., 1933-34; Benjamin Peirce instr. Harvard U., 1934-36; instr. Cornell U., 1936-37, U. Chgo., 1937-38; asst. prof. Harvard U., 1938-41, assoc. prof., 1941-46, prof., 1946-47; prof. math. U. Chgo., 1947-63, chmn. dept., 1952-58, Max Mason Disting. Service prof. of math., 1963-82, prof. emeritus, 1982—; exec. com. mem. Internat. Math. Union, 1954-58; research mathematician Applied Math. Group, Columbia, 1943-44, dir., 1944-45; Mem. Nat. Sci. Bd., 1974-80. Author: (with Garrett Birkhoff) Survey of Modern Algebra, 1942, Homology, 1963, Algebra, 1967, Categories for the Working Mathematician, 1971, Mathematics: Form and Function, 1985, (with I. Moerdijk) Sheaves in Geometry and Logic, A First Introduction to Topos Theory, 1992; editor: Bull. Am. Math. Soc., 1943-46, mng. editor, 1946-47; editor: Trans. Am. Math. Soc., 1949-54; chmn. editorial com., editor Carus Math. Monographs, 1940-45; contbr. articles to Annals Math., other jours. Recipient Nat. Medal of Sci. Nat. Sci. Found., 1989; John Simon Guggenheim fellow, 1947-48, 72-73. Mem. Am. Math. Soc. (coun. mem. 1939-41, v.p. 1946-47, pres. 1973-74, Leroy P. Steele prize 1986), Math. Assn. Am. (v.p. 1948-49, pres. 1950-52, Chauvenet prize for math. expn. 1941, Disting. Svc. award 1975, Proctor prize 1979), Nat. Acad. Sci. (coun. mem. 1958-61, 69-72, v.p. 1973-81, chmn. editorial bd. procs. 1960-68), Royal Danish Acad. Scis. (fgn. mem.), Am. Philos. Soc. (mem. council 1960-63, v.p. 1968-71), Akademie der Wissenschaften (Heidelberg), Royal Soc. Edinburgh, Assn. for Symbolic Logic (exec. com. 1945-47), Am. Acad. Arts and Sci. (coun. mem. 1981-85), Phi Beta Kappa, Sigma Xi. Congregationalist. Home: 5712 S Dorchester Ave Chicago IL 60637-1727

MAC LAREN, DAVID SERGEANT, manufacturing corporation executive, inventor; b. Cleve., Jan. 4, 1941; s. Albert Sergeant and Theadora Beidler (Potter) MacL.; children: Alison, Catherine, Carolyn. AB in Econs., Miami U., Oxford, Ohio, 1955. Chmn. bd., pres., Jet Inc., Cleve., 1961—; founder, chmn. bd., pres. Air Injector Corp., Cleve., 1958-78; founder, pres., chmn. bd. Fluid Equipment, Inc., Cleve., 1962-72; founder, chmn. bd., pres. T&M Co., Cleve., 1963-71, Alison Realty Co., Cleve., 1965—; chmn. bd., pres. Sergeant Realty, Inc., 1979-86; bd. dirs. Gilmore Industries, Cleve., 1975-77, MWL Systems, L.A., 1979-85; mem. tech. com. Nat. Sanitation Found., Ann Arbor, Mich., 1967-90. Patentee in field. Mem. Rep. State Cen. Com., 1968-72; bd. dirs. Cleve. State U. Found., 1986-90. Served with arty. AUS, 1959-58. Fellow Royal Soc. Health (London); mem. Nat. Environ. Health Assn., Am. Pub. Health Assn., Nat. Water Pollution Control Fedn., Cen. Taekwondo Assn. (2d Dan), Jiu-Jitsu/Karati Black Belt Fedn. (black belt instr.), Mercedes Benz Club N.Am. (pres. 1968), H.B. Leadership Soc. (sch. headmaster soc., devel. com. 1976-78), SAR, Soc. Mayflower Descendants, Delta Kappa Epsilon (nat. bd. dirs. 1974-86, dir. Kappa chpt. 1969—), Mentor Harbor Yachting Club, The Country Club, Cotillion Soc., Union League Club (N.Y.C.), Yale Club (N.Y.C.), Deke Club (N.Y.C.). Home: West Hill Dr Gates Mills OH 44040 Office: Jet Inc 750 Alpha Dr Cleveland OH 44143-2125

MACLAREN, NEIL MOORLEY, JR., musician, music educator; b. Cambridge, Mass., July 12, 1932; s. Neil Moorley and Elsie Violet (Elmes) MacL.; m. Mary Peloquin, Oct. 5, 1989. MusB, Westminster Choir Coll., 1957, MusM, 1959; MusD (hon.), Geneva-St. Albans Theol. Coll., 1976. Organist, choir dir. First Presbyn. Ch., Bordentown, N.J., 1957-59; choir dir., accompanist N.J. State Reformatory, Bordentown, 1957-59; pvt. tchr. piano, voice, organ and electronic keyboard, 1959—; organist, choir dir. Deerfield (N.J.) 1st Presbyn. Ch., 1959; min. music, organist, soloist First Bapt. Ch., Fall River, Mass., 1959-64; organist., ch. and sch. mus. dir. St. Mark's Episc. Ch. and Sch., Ft. Lauderdale, Fla., 1964-72; organist, choirmaster St. Peter's Am. Episc. Ch., Deerfield Beach, Fla., 1973-86; faculty piano tchr. Sch. Arts Second Presbyn. Ch., Ft. Lauderdale, 1976-77; organist Temple Kol Ami, Plantation, Fla., 1979-82; tchr. piano, organ, electronic keyboard Suniland Music Shoppe, Plantation, 1981-91; mus. dir. Hawaiian Gardens Choral Group, 1986-93; organist First Ch. Christ Scientist, Pompano Beach, Fla., 1986—; faculty tchr. piano Sch. Arts Coral Ridge Presbyn. Ch., Ft. Lauderdale, 1991—; tenor soloist Phila. area chs., 1957-59; mus. dir. lenten choir and summer daily vacation Bible studies and camp Greater Fall River Coun. Chs., 1959-64; part time tchr. music Henry Lord Jr. H.S., James Morton Jr. H.S., 1959-64; tchr., piano, organ, voice First Bapt. Ch., 1959-64; organist high holy days Temple Beth-El, Fall River, 1959-64; charter mem. Gold Coast Symphony Chorus, 1973-74; part time tchr., chorus dir., accompanist Fla. Oaks Sch., Ft. Lauderdale, 1980-82; village chorus accompanist John Knox Village, Pompano Beach, 1992—; judge Gwen Bari Talent Show, 1980-82. Mem., tenor soloist R.I. Civic Chorale, 1959-64; mem. U. Miami Civic Chorale, 1969-74. With U.S. Army, 1953-55. Mem. Am. Guild Organists (dean Ft. Lauderdale chpt. 1967-69, Svc. Playing cert. 1989), Fla. State Music Tchrs. Assn. (corr. sec. 1993—), Broward County Music Tchrs. Assn. (parliamentarian 1987-89, pres. 1991-93, yearbook editor, newsletter editor 1991—; 2d v.p. 1993—), Toastmasters Internat. (area IV gov. 1978, Outstanding Gov. of Dist. 47, Dist. Toastmaster 1981), Kiwanis. Republican. Episcopalian. Avocations: computers, gardening, photography, physical fitness, swimming. Home: 1861 SW 6th Ave Pompano Beach FL 33060-9019

MACLAREN, ROY, publisher, Canadian federal legislator; b. Vancouver, B.C., Can., Oct. 26, 1934; s. Wilbur and Anne (Graham) MacL.; m. Alethea Mitchell, June 25, 1959; children: Ian, Vanessa, Malcolm. BA, U. B.C., 1955; MA, U. Cambridge, Eng., 1957; postgrad., Harvard U., 1974; MDiv, U. Toronto, 1991. Fgn. service officer Can. Diplomatic Service, Vietnam, Czechoslovakia, Switzerland, UN, 1957-69; dir. corporate pub. affairs Massey-Ferguson Ltd., Toronto, Ont., 1969-74; chmn., chief exec. officer Ogilvy & Mather, Can., Toronto, 1974-76; chmn. C.B. Media Ltd., 1976-83; mem. Toronto Planning Bd., 1974-76; mem. Parliament of Can., 1979-84, 88—, parliamentary sec. to minister energy, mines and resources, 1980-82, minister of state (fin.), 1983-84, minister of nat. revenue, 1984—, minister of internat. trade, 1993—; spl. lectr. U. Toronto, 1970-76; chmn. Can. Govt. Task Force on Rels. Between Govt. and Bus., 1976; former bd. dirs. Royal LePage Ltd., London Ins. Group, Inc., Deutsche Bank (Can) Ltd., Royal LePage Mortgage Corp., Broadview Press. Author: Canadians in Russia, 1918-19, 1976, Canadians on the Nile, 1882-1898, 1978, Canadians Behind Enemy Lines, 1939-1945, 1981, Honourable Mentions, 1986; contbr. articles to jours. Former bd. dirs. Can. Journalism Found., Cambridge U. Can. Trust Fund, Etobicoke Gen. Hosp., Toronto Sch. Theology. Fellow Royal Soc. Arts. Clubs: Royal Can. Yacht, Rideau. Office: House of Commons, Ottawa, ON Canada K1A 0A6

MACLAREN, WALTER ROGERS, allergist, educator; b. Yokohama, Japan, Dec. 7, 1910; s. Walter Wallace and Zaidee (Rogers) McL.; m. Dorothy Agnes Goodwin, June 1942 (div. 1970); children: Walter Jr., Jean, Anne, Elizabeth, Catherine; m. Dorothy Hamblen, July 7, 1971. BA, Queens U., 1933; MD, Harvard U., 1938. Diplomate Am. Bd. Allergy and Immunology (bd. dirs., sec. 1978-83). Practice medicine specializing in asthma, allergy and immunology Pasadena, Calif., 1947—; clin. prof. medicine U. So. Calif. Sch. Med., L.A., 1948—; dir. Allergy and Immunology Cons. Labs., Inc., Pasadena, 1978-88. Contbr. over 30 articles to profl. jours. Bd. dirs. Pasadena Symphony Orch., 1976-82, Pasadena Chamber Orch., 1984-86. Fellow Am. Acad. Allergy and Immunology, Am. Coll. Allergists, Am. Thoracic Soc., Asthma and Allergy Found. Am., Assn. Clin. Immunology and Allergy (pres.), Pasadena C. of C. (health svcs. com. 1990—), Sigma Xi. Republican. Club: Valley Hunt (Pasadena). Office: 94 N Madison Ave Pasadena CA 91101-1740

MACLAUGHLIN, FRANCIS JOSEPH, lawyer; b. Davenport, Iowa, Oct. 5, 1933; s. Francis Joseph and Sylvia (Boone) MacL.; m. Joan Elizabeth Pfeiffer, Oct. 17, 1959; children: Lisa Ann, Christine Ann, Francis Joseph. B.A., Yale U., 1955; J.D., U. Mich., 1958. Bar: Ill. 1958, Calif. 1963. Assoc. Graham, Califf, Harper & Benson, Moline, Ill., 1958-59, Lillick, McHose & Charles, Los Angeles, 1963-70; ptnr. Lillick, McHose & Charles, L.A., 1970-90, White and Case, 1990—. Lt. USN, 1959-63. Mem. ABA, Calif. Bar Assn., Los Angeles County Bar Assn., Maritime Law Assn. U.S. Republican. Office: White & Case 633 W 5th St Ste 1900 Los Angeles CA 90071-2038

MACLAUGHLIN, HARRY HUNTER, federal judge; b. Breckenridge, Minn., Aug. 9, 1927; s. Harry Hunter and Grace (Swank) MacL.; m. Mary Jean Shaffer, June 25, 1958; children: David, Douglas. BBA with distinction, U. Minn., 1949, JD, 1956. Bar: Minn. 1956. Law clk. to justice Minn. Supreme Ct.; ptnr. MacLaughlin & Mondale, MacLaughlin & Harstad, Mpls., 1956-72; assoc. justice Minn. Supreme Ct., 1972-77; U.S. sr. dist. judge Dist. of Minn., Mpls., 1977—; part-time instr. William Mitchell Coll. Law, St. Paul, 1958-63; lectr. U. Minn. Law Sch., 1973-86; mem. 8th Cir. Jud. Council, 1981-83. Bd. editors: Minn. Law Rev, 1954-55. Mem. Mpls. Charter Commn., 1967-72, Minn. State Coll. Bd., 1971-72, Minn. Jud. Council, 1972; mem. nat. adv. council Small Bus. Adminstrn., 1967-69. Served with USNR, 1945-46. Mem. ABA, Minn. Bar Assn., Hennepin County Bar Assn., Beta Gamma Sigma, Phi Delta Phi. Congregational. Office: US Dist Ct 684 US Courthouse 110 S 4th St Minneapolis MN 55401-2216

MACLAURY, BRUCE KING, research institution executive; b. Mount Kisco, N.Y., May 7, 1931; s. Bruce King and Edith Mae (Wills) MacL.; m. Virginia Doris Naef, Jan. 8, 1955; children—John, David. B.A., Princeton, 1953; M.A., Harvard, 1958, Ph.D., 1961. Successively mgr., v.p. fgn. dept. Fed. Res. Bank N.Y., N.Y.C., 1958-69; dep. under sec. for monetary affairs U.S. Treasury Dept., Washington, 1969-71; pres. Fed. Res. Bank of Mpls., 1971-77, Brookings Instn., Washington, 1977—; bd. dirs. Am. Express Bank Ltd., St. Paul Cos., The Vanguard Group. Trustee Nat. Com. on Econ. Edn., 1978—, Com. for Econ. Devel., 1978—; mem. Coun. on Fgn. Rels., N.Y.C., 1962. Lt. AUS, 1954-56. Recipient Exceptional Service award U.S. Treasury Dept., 1971. Mem. Phi Beta Kappa, Cosmos. Home: 5109 Yuma Pl NW Washington DC 20016-4309 Office: Brookings Instn 1775 Massachusetts Ave NW Washington DC 20036-2188

MACLAY, DONALD MERLE, lawyer; b. Belleville, Pa., Feb. 16, 1934; s. Robert Barr and Grace Virginia (Royer) M.; m. Nancy Margaret Hixenbaugh, Sept. 13, 1958; children: Susan Jo (dec.), Timothy Dean. A.B. magna cum laude, Grove City Coll., 1956; LL.B., U. Pa., 1961. Bar: D.C. 1968, Pa. 1970. Commd. fgn. svc. officer U.S. Dept. State, 1961; assigned Am. embassy, Cotonou, Dahomey (Benin), 1962-64, Am. Consulate Gen., Frankfurt, Fed. Republic Germany, 1964-66, U.S. Dept. State, Washington, 1966-69; dir. courses of study Am. Law Inst.-ABA Com. on Continuing Profl. Edn., Phila., 1969-87, dep. exec. dir., 1987—. Served with U.S. Army, 1956-58. Mem. ABA, Pa. Bar Assn., Am. Law Inst. Democrat. Presbyterian. Home: 936 Church Rd Springfield PA 19064-3539 Office: 4025 Chestnut St Philadelphia PA 19104-3099

MACLAY, WILLIAM NEVIN, retired manufacturing and construction company executive; b. Belleville, Pa., Dec. 30, 1924; s. Robert Barr and Grace Virginia (Royer) M.; m. Betty Jane Boucher, June 4, 1949; children: Gary, Dennis, Rebekah, Bonnie, Beth. B.S. magna cum laude, Juniata Coll., 1947; Ph.D. in Phys. Chemistry, Yale U., 1950. Assoc. prof. chemistry Davis and Elkins Coll., Elkins, W.Va., 1950-51; research scientist B.F. Goodrich Co., Brecksville, Ohio, 1951-59; group mgr. Koppers Co., Inc., Monroeville, Pa., 1959-63, asst. sect. mgr., 1963-67; mgr. comml. devel. Koppers Co., Inc., Pitts. 1967-68; v.p. research Koppers Co., Inc., Monroeville, 1968-85; ret., 1985; dir. Indsl. Health Found., Pitts., 1974-77, Genex Corp., Rockville, Md., 1979-81, Kopvenco, Pitts., Ceramatec, Inc., Salt Lake City, 1981-85, Advanced Refractory Techs., Buffalo, 1984-85. Patentee in field. Deacon, ruling elder Presbyn. Ch., Pitts. Mem. Am. Chem. Soc. Republican. Presbyterian. Home: 539 Greenleaf Dr Monroeville PA 15146-1201

MACLEAMY, PATRICK, architectural firm executive. Student, Ecole des Beaux Arts Americaine, Fontainebleau, 1964; BArch, U. Ill., 1966, MArch in Urban Design, 1967; postgrad., Ecole des Beaux Arts Superieure, Paris, 1966. Registered architect, Calif., Mo., Ariz. Prin. Hellmuth, Obata & Kassabaum, Inc., San Francisco, 1966—, also bd. dirs.; guest lectr. Stanford U. Prin. works include George R. Moscone Conv. Ctr., San Francisco, KingKhaled Internat. Airport, Riyadh, Saudi Arabia, Lake Merritt Plz., Oakland, Calif., Hewlett Packard Bldg. # 10, Palo Alto, Calif., Wells Fargo Ctr., Sacramento, Fairmont Hotel, San Jose, Calif., 1201 K Office Bldg., Sacramento, Levi Strauss Hdqs., San Francisco, Apple Computer Rsch. & Devel. Campus, Cupertino, Calif., AT&T Ctr. Pleasanton, Calif., Ten Almaden, San Jose, Std. Alaska Prodn. Co. Hdqs., Anchorage, Visa Corp. Hdqs. Campus Phases I & II, Foster City, Calif., Metro Ctr., Foster City, Calif. Dept. Corrections Reception Ctrs., Wasco and Delano, Calif., Fukuoka (Japan) Internat. Airport Terminal, Chek Lap Kok Internat. Airport, Hong Kong, Saks 5th Ave., San Francisco. Mem. AIA. Office: Hellmuth Obata & Kassabaum Inc 71 Stevenson St Ste 2200 San Francisco CA 94105-2940

MACLEAN, BARRY L., plastic and metal products company executive; b. Evanston, Ill., Apr. 18, 1938; s. John A. Jr. and Dorothy Jean (Barker) MacL; m. Maude Callender, Aug. 29, 1959 (div. Aug. 1966); children: Elizabeth, Margaret; m. Mary Ann Shirley, Sept. 13, 1967; children: Duncan, Gillian, Adrian. BS, Dartmouth Coll., 1960, MS in Engring., 1961. Sec. MacLean-Fogg Co., Mundelein, Ill., 1961-72, pres., chief exec. officer, 1972—, also bd. dirs.; bd. dirs. Western Industries, Inc., Specialty Equipment, L.R. Nelson. Trustee Village of Mettawa, 1971—, Condell Meml. Hosp., Libertyville, Ill., 1973-82, Darmouth Coll.; bd. dirs., past pres. N.E. Ill. coun. Boy Scouts Am., 1973—; bd. overseers, former chmn. Thayer Sch. Engring., Dartmouth Coll., 1974—; chmn., former campaign mgr. Lake County Citizens for Jim Thompson Campaign, 1976; bd. dirs., officer Lake County Rep. Fedn., 1982—; com. chmn. Ill. Job Tng. Coun., 1989—; mem. Young Pres.'s Orgn., 1974-88, chmn. Chgo. chpt., 1987-88. Recipient Good Scout award Boy Scouts Am., 1986, Robert Fletcher award Thayer Sch., Dartmouth Coll., 1989. Mem. Indsl. Fasteners Inst. (bd. dirs. 1982—, chmn. 1988-89), Chief Execs. Orgn., Ill. Mfrs. Assn. (bd. dirs. 1977—, vice chmn. 1988-89, chmn. 1990—, chmn. mfrs. polit. action com. 1985-88, vice chmn. 1989—), Shoreacres Club (Lake Bluff, Ill.), Economic Club, Chicago Club, Onwentsia Club (Lake Forest, Ill.), Loblolly Pines Club (Hobe Sound, Fla.). Avocations: skiing, golf, construction, rare book and map collecting. Home: 15330 W Old School Rd Libertyville IL 60048-9661 Office: MacLean-Fogg Co 1000 Allanson Rd Mundelein IL 60060-3804

MACLEAN, CHARLES (BERNARD), transition, performance recognition and workplace violence prevention consultant; b. Ann Arbor, Mich., Oct. 12, 1945. BS, Wis. State U., Oshkosh, 1967; MA, Mich. State U., 1969, PhD, 1973. Lic. profl. counselor, Tex. Dir. med. edn. Am. Coll. Emergency Physicians, Lansing, Mich. and Dallas, 1974-81; exec. dir. Soc. Tchrs. of Emergency Medicine, Lansing and Dallas, 1976-81; pres. Applied Foresight, Dallas, Tex., 1979—; ptnr. Inman, Maclean & Gaddy, Dallas, 1983-86; sr. v.p. Club Communities Retirement Ctrs., 1983-86; ptnr., exec. v.p. Metropolition Retirement Ctrs., 1986-88; pres. Tri-East Ventures, Inc., 1988-90. Author: (exec. briefing tapes) M.B.A.-Management by Acknowledgement, Acknowledgment--The Missing Piece in the Total Quality Puzzle, (videotape tng. package) Can't Happen...Here!, 1994; dir. (video documentary) Accelerated Career Transition for Ex-Military; contbr. numerous articles to profl. jours. Chmn. community adv. bd. Youth at Risk, 1988-90; mem. Dallas Mayor's Adv. Com. on Crime, 1989-90. Mem. ASTD (v.p. profl. devel. 1982), Assn. for Quality Participation, Nat. Eagle Scout Assn., Oreg. Ethics Commons, Delta Kappa, Psi Chi, Delta Tau Kappa, Delta Sigma Phi. Office: PO Box 14914 Portland OR 97214

MACLEAN, DAVID BAILEY, chemistry educator, researcher; b. Summerside, P.E.I., Can., July 15, 1923; s. William and Lulu Adelaide (Stewart) McL.; m. Helen Shirley Canning, Dec. 28, 1945 (dec. 1950); 1 child, Susan; m. Regina Lane, Sept. 21, 1951; children—David, Richard, Robert, Gillian, stepchildren—Gary Hutton, Dariel Hutton. B.Sc., Acadia U., 1942; Ph.D., McGill U., 1946. Research chemist Dominion Rubber Co., Guelph, Ont., Can., 1946-49; assoc. prof. chemistry N.S. Tech. Coll., Halifax, Can., 1949-54; assoc. prof. chemistry McMaster U., Hamilton, Ont., 1954-60, prof., 1960-89, prof. emeritus, 1989—; mem. Council of Ont. Univs., Toronto, 1982-84. Fellow Royal Soc. Can., Chem. Inst. Can.; mem. Am. Chem. Soc., Am. Soc. Mass Spectroscopy. Home: 394 Queen St S, Hamilton, ON Canada L8P 3T9 Office: McMaster Univ, Dept Chemistry, Main St W, Hamilton, ON Canada L8S 4M1

MACLEAN, GUY ROBERTSON, retired university president; b. Sydney, N.S., Can., Dec. 21, 1929; s. Charles Whitmore and Mary Malinda (Nicholson) MacL.; m. Mary Judith Hunter, June 29, 1963; children—Colin Hunter, Mary Jocelyn. B.A., Dalhousie U., 1951, M.A., 1953; B.A. (Rhodes scholar), Oxford U., 1955, M.A., 1959; Ph.D., Duke, 1958. Asst. prof. Dalhousie U., Halifax, N.S., 1957-61, asso. prof., 1961-65, prof., 1965-80, dean of residence, 1961-63, acting chmn. dept. history, 1963-64, asst. dean faculty grad. studies, 1965-66, dean, 1966-69, dean faculty arts and scis., 1969-75, v.p. academic, 1974-80; pres. Mount Allison U., Sackville, N.S., 1980-86, pres. emeritus, 1986—; ombudsman of N.S., 1989-94; dean of men Kings Coll., 1957-61; lectr. U. Alta., 1963, N.S. Tech. Coll., 1965-66. Editor: introduction The Life and Times of A.T. Galt, 1966; Contbr. articles to profl. jours. Mem. Rhodes Scholarship Com., N.S.; mem. Maritime Provinces Higher Edn. Commn., Social Scis. and Humanities Research Council Can., 1978—; bd. dirs Donner Canadian Found., Toronto; bd. govs. Coll. of Cape Breton; chmn. bd. dirs. Opera East. Served as 2d lt. Canadian Army, 1949-51. Recipient Centennial medal, 1967, Jubilee medal, 1978; Can. Council fellow, 1968-69. Mem. Canadian Hist. Assn. (exec. council 1967-68), Canadian Inst. Internat. Affairs (pres. Halifax 1965), Canadian Rhodes Scholars Assn., Nova Scotia Soccer Assn. (pres. 1976-78). Mem. United Ch. of Can. Club: Waegwoltic. Home: Marlborough Woods, Halifax, NS Canada B3H 1H9

MACLEAN, HECTOR, banker, lawyer; b. Balt., Sept. 15, 1920; s. Angus W. and Margaret (French) MacL.; m. Lyl Francis Warwick, Dec. 18, 1944; 1 dau., Lyl M. Clinard. BS, Davidson Coll., 1941; JD, U. N.C., 1948; LLD (hon.), St. Andrews Presbyn. Coll., 1986; LHD (hon.), Pembroke State U., 1988. Bar: N.C. bar 1948. Pvt. practice, 1948—; chmn. bd., chief exec. officer So. Nat. Bank N.C., So. Nat. Corp.; dir. N.C. Natural Gas Corp. Mayor of Lumberton, 1949-53; mem. N.C. Senate, 1961-71; Pres. Med. Found. N.C.; chmn. N.C. Bicentennial Com. Served from lt. to capt. AUS, 1942-46. Decorated Bronze Star medal. Mem. Robeson County Hist. Soc. (past pres.), Lumberton C. of C., Am., N.C. bar assns., Sigma Alpha Epsilon, Omicron Delta Kappa, Phi Delta Phi. Clubs: Pinecrest Country (Lumberton); Country of N.C. (Pinehurst); Litchfield Country (Pawleys Island, S.C.). Home: 2101 N Elm St Lumberton NC 28358-3637 Office: 500 N Chestnut St Lumberton NC 28358-5551

MACLEAN, JOHN ANGUS, former premier of Prince Edward Island; b. Lewes, P.E.I., Can., May 15, 1914; s. George Allen and Sarah MacL.; m. Gwendolyn Esther Burwash, Oct. 29, 1952; children—Sarah Jean, Allan Duart, Mary Esther, Robert Angus. Student, U. B.C., Can.), Vancouver; B.Sc., Mt. Allison U., 1939, LL.D. (hon.), 1958. Farmer Lewes; mem. Can. House of Commons, Ottawa, Ont., 1951-76, Privy Council Can., 1957—; minister of fisheries Govt. Can., 1957-63; mem. P.E.I. Legislature, 1976-82; premier P.E.I., 1979-81. Leader Progressive Conservative Party of P.E.I., 1976-81; del. NATO Parliamentary Conf., Paris, 1956, Commonwealth Parliametary Conf., Wellington, N.Z., 1965, 18th Parliamentary Course, Westminster, Eng., 1969; del. Inter-Parliamentary Conf. on European Cooperation and Security, Helsinki, 1973, Belgrade, 1975; leader Can. del. Colombo Plan Conf., Tokyo, 1960, FAO Conf., Rome, 1961; mem. Can-Japanese Ministerial Del., Tokyo, 1963; bd. regents Mt. Alison U.; bd. dirs. RCAF Meml. Fund. Served with RCAF, 1939-47; officer Most Venerable Order St. John of Jerusalem at Investiture Ceremony, Rideau Hall, Order of Can. Investiture, Rideau Hall, 1992; former mem. P.E.I. Energy Corp.; sr. adv. bd. Maritime Provinces Edn. Found.; P.E.I.'s Commr. to EXPO' 86; appointed officer of the Order of Can., 1992. Decorated D.F.C.; mentioned in Despatches. Mem. RAF Escaping Soc. (past pres. Can. br.), Commonwealth Parliamentary Assn. (past vice chmn. fed. br.), Mus. Nat. Scis., Nat. Mus. Can. Progressive Conservative. Presbyterian.

MACLEAN, JOHN RONALD, lawyer; b. Pueblo, Colo., Jan. 19, 1938; s. John Ronald and Mary Victoria (Curlin) MacL.; m. Carol Jean Turner, Aug. 18, 1962; children—Leslie Carol, John Ronald. Student, U. Okla., 1956; B.S., U.S. Mil. Acad., 1961; J.D., Vanderbilt U., 1967. Bar: Tex. 1967; cert. in personal injury trial law and criminal law Tex. Bd. Legal Splzn. Practicing atty. Turner & MacLean, Cleburne, Tex., 1967-68; county atty. Johnson County, Tex., 1968-76; dist. atty. 18th Jud. Dist. Tex., 1976-84; dist. judge 249th Jud. Dist. Tex., 1984-91; pvt. practice MacLean & Boulware, 1992—. Pres. Johnson County United Fund, 1976. Served with AUS, 1961-64. Fellow Tex. Bar Found.; mem. Tex. Bar Assn., Johnson County Bar Assn. (pres. 1969), Am. Bd. Trial Advocates (nat. dir.), Tex. Trial Lawyers Assn., Vanderbilt U. Law Sch. Bar Assn. (past pres.), Elks. Democrat. Methodist. Home: 1216 W Westhill Dr Cleburne TX 76031-6021 Office: 11 Main St Cleburne TX 76031

MAC LEAN, LLOYD DOUGLAS, surgeon; b. Calgary, Alta., Can., June 24, 1924; s. Fred Hugh and Azilda (Trudel) MacL.; m. Eleanor Colle, June 30, 1954; children—Hugh, Charles, Ian, James, Martha. B.Sc. (Viscount Bennett scholar), U. Alta., 1946, M.D. (Viscount Bennett scholar), 1949; Ph.D., U. Minn., 1957. Resident U. Minn. Hosp., Mpls., 1950-56; instr. dept. surgery U. Minn., Mpls., 1956-58, asst. prof. surgery, 1958-59, asso. prof., 1959-62; prof. McGill U., Montreal, Que., Can., 1962—; chmn. dept. surgery, 1968-73, 77-82, 87-88; surgeon-in-chief Ancker Hosp., St. Paul, 1957-62, Royal Victoria Hosp., Montreal, 1962-88; Edward Archibald prof. surgery McGill U., 1988-93, prof. surgery 1993—. Contbr. numerous articles on surgery, shock, host resistance and transplantation to profl. jours. Decorated officer Order Can. Fellow Royal Soc. Can.; mem. Am. Surg. Assn. (pres. 1992-93), A.C.S. (pres. 1993-94), Central Surg. Assn. (pres. 1985), Am. Physiol. Soc., Am. Assn. Thoracic and Cardiovascular Surgery, Soc. Surgery of Alimentary Tract. Home: # 1402-80 Berlioz, Montreal, PQ Canada H3E 1N9 Office: McGill Univ, 687 Pine Ave W, Montreal, PQ Canada H3A 1A1

MACLEAN, PAUL DONALD, government institute medical research official; b. Phelps, N.Y., May 1, 1913; s. Charles Chalmers and Elizabeth (Dreyfus) MacL.; m. Alison Stokes, July 16, 1942; children—Paul, David, Alexander, James, Alison. BA, Yale U., 1935; postgrad., U. Edinburgh, Scotland, 1935-36; MD cum laude, Yale U., 1940; DSci (hon.), SUNY, Binghamton, 1986. Intern in medicine Johns Hopkins U., 1940-41; asst. resident medicine New Haven Hosp., Yale Sch. Medicine, 1941-42, research asst. pathology, 1942, asst. prof. physiology, 1949-51, asst. prof. psychiatry, physiology and neurology, 1951-53, assoc. prof. physiology, 1956-57; clin. instr. medicine U. Wash. Med. Sch., Seattle, 1946-47; USPHS research fellow Harvard U. Med. Sch., also Mass. Gen. Hosp., 1947-49; dir. EEG lab. New Haven Hosp., 1951-52; assoc. prof. psychiatry, physiology and neurology, attending physician Grace-New Haven Hosp., 1953-56; sr. postdoctoral fellow NSF dept. physiology U. Zurich, 1956-57; chief sect. limbic integration and behavior Lab. Neurophysiology Intramural Research, NIMH, USPHS, Dept. Health and Human Services, Bethesda, Md., 1957-71; chief lab. brain evolution and behavior Intramural Research, Bethesda, Md., 1971-85; sr. research scientist Intramural Research Program, NIMH, 1985—. Author: The Triune Brain in Evolution, 1990; mem. editorial bd.: Jour. Nervous and Mental Disease. Emeritus trustee L.S.B. Leakey Found. Served to maj. M.C. AUS, 1942-46, PTO. Recipient award for disting. research Assn. for Research in Nervous and Mental Disease, 1964; Salmon medal and Lectureship award, 1966; Superior Service award HEW, 1967; Hincks Meml. lectr. Ont.; Spl. award Am. Psychopathol. Assn., 1971; G. Burroughs Mider NIH Lectureship award, 1972; Karl Spencer Lashley award Am. Philos. Soc., 1972; Adolph Meyer Lectureship award Am. Psychiat. Assn., 1982, Anokhin medal P.K. Anokhin Inst. Normal Physiology USSR Acad. Med. Scis., 1986. Mem. Am. Neurol. Assn., Am. Assn. History of Medicine, Am. Physiol. Soc., Am. Assn. Electroencephalographers, Eastern Assn. Electroencephalographers, Am. Neurol. Surgeons, Soc. Neurosci., Am. Assn. Anatomists, Sigma Xi, Alpha Omega Alpha. Home: 10450 Lottsford Rd # 1218 Mitchellville MD 20721 Office: NIMH Neuroscience Ctr 2700 MLK Jr Ave SE Washington DC 20032

MACLEAN, VICTORIA GRAHAM, journalist, editor; b. Brockville, Ont., Can., June 2, 1948; d. Findlay Barnes and Helen Lois (Graham) MacL.; m. Robert E. Knight, Sept. 29, 1973 (div. Jan. 1985). Student, Trent U. Proofreader, adv. salesman, photo engraver, reporter, editor Brockville Recorder and Times, 1964-72; reporter, columnist, mng. editor St. Albert (Alta., Can.) Gazette, 1976-85; editor Edmonton (Alta.) Sun, 1988—. Columnist Can. Comty. Newspapers, 1980. Avocations: gardening, cooking,

reading. Home: 8547 80th Ave, Edmonton, AB Canada T6C 0T2 Office: Edmonton Sun, Ste 250, 4990 92d Ave, Edmonton, AB Canada T6B 3A1

MACLEISH, ARCHIBALD BRUCE, museum director; b. White Plains, N.Y., May 6, 1947; s. Kenneth and Carolyn Elizabeth (de Chadenedes) MacL.; m. Patricia Ann McCue, Aug. 10, 1974; children: Kenneth Thomas, Padraic Andrew. BA, Johns Hopkins U., 1969; MA, SUNY, Oneonta, 1972. Asst. curator N.Y. State Hist. Assn., The Farmers' Mus., Cooperstown, 1972-73; assoc. curator N.Y. State Hist. Assn., Cooperstown, 1980-83, curator of collections, 1984-93, dir. collections, 1993—; curator of collections The Farmers' Mus., 1984-93, dir. collections, 1993—; curator N.Y. Ky. Mus., Bowling Green, 1973-80; mem. adj. tchg. faculty Cooperstown Grad. Program, 1980—. Author: Care of Antiques and Historical Collections, 1985; editor K.A.M. News, 1975-80. Sec. bd. dirs. Gallery 53, Cooperstown; mem. Ad Hoc Citizen's Com., Cooperstown, 1987—. Mem. Am. Assn. Mus., Am. Assn. for State and Local History, Mid-Atlantic Assn. Mus., Cooperstown Grad. Assn. Democrat. Methodist. Avocations: road running, gardening, guitar, fishing, cross-country skiing. Office: NY State Hist Assn PO Box 800 Lake Rd Cooperstown NY 13326

MACLENNAN, BERYCE WINIFRED, psychologist; b. Aberdeen, Scotland, Mar. 14, 1920; came to U.S., 1949, naturalized, 1965; d. William and Beatrice (MaCrae) Mellis; m. John Duncan MacLennan, Nov. 29, 1944. BSc with honors, London Sch. Econs., 1947; PhD, London U., 1960. Group psychotherapist, youth specialist cons. N.Y.C. and Washington, 1949-63; dir. Ctr. for Prevention Juvenile Delinquency and New Careers, Washington, 1963-66; sect. chief NIMH, Mental Health Study Ctr., Adelphi, Md., 1967-70, chief, 1971-74; regional adminstr. Mass. Dept. Mental Health, Springfield, 1974-75; sr. mental health adv. GAO, Washington, 1976-90; pvt. practice, specialist psychotherapy Bethesda, Md., 1990—; clin. prof. George Washington U., 1970—; group therapy cons. D.C. Mental Health Svcs., 1993—; lectr. Montgomery C.C., 1988-91; mem. tech. adv. com. Prince George's County Mental Health Assn., 1968-84; cons. Washington Bus. Group on Health, 1990-91, KOBA, 1991. Mem. NIMH Prevention Intervention Rsch. Task Force, 1990-91, Montgomery County Victims Assistance Programs, 1990-95; v.p. Compliance, Federally Employed Women, 1979-81; pres. Glenecho chpt. Older Women's League, 1993-94. Fellow APA, Am. Orthopsychiat. Assn.; disting. fellow Am. Group Psychotherapy Assn.; mem. Bethesda Garden Club, Washington Mushroom Club. Democrat.

MACLENNAN, DAVID HERMAN, research scientist, educator; b. Swan River, Man., Can., July 3, 1937; s. Douglas Henry and Sigridur (Sigurdson) MacL.; m. Linda Carol Vass, Aug. 18, 1965; children: Jessica Lynn (dec.), Jeremy Douglas, Jonathan David. B.S.A., U. Man., 1959; M.S., Purdue U., 1961, Ph.D., 1963. Postdoctoral fellow Inst. Enzyme Research, U. Wis., Madison, 1963-64; asst. prof. Inst. Enzyme Research, U. Wis., 1964-68; assoc. prof. Banting and Best Dept. Med. Rsch. U. Toronto, Toronto, Ont., Can., 1969-74; prof. Banting and Best Dept. Med. Rsch. U. Toronto, Ont., 1974-93; John W. Billes prof. med. research U. Toronto, 1987—; univ. prof. Banting and Best Dept. Med. Rsch. U. Toronto, Ont., 1993—; acting chmn. U. Toronto, 1978-80, chmn., 1980-90; prin. investigator Can. Genetic Diseases Network, 1991—; mem. med. adv. bd. Muscular Dystrophy Assn. Can., 1976-87; scientists rev. panel MRC, 1988-90; rsch. rev. panel U. Ottawa Heart Inst., 1991—; chmn. molecular biol. pathol. rev. com. Heart and Stroke Found., Can.; cons. Merck, Sharp and Dohme, West Point, Pa., 1992—. Assoc. editor Can. Jour. Biochemistry, 1972-76; mem. editorial bd. Jour. Biol. Chemistry, 1975-80, 82-87; contbr. articles on muscle membrane biochemistry to profl. jours. Recipient Gairdner Found. Internat. award, 1991; Can. Med. Rsch. Coun. scholar, 1969-71, I.W. Killam Meml. scholar, 1977-78. Fellow Royal Soc. Can., Royal Soc. London; mem. Can. Biochem. Soc. (Ayerst award 1974), Am. Soc. Biol. Chemists, Biophys. Soc. (Internat. Lectr. award 1990). Home: 293 Lytton Blvd, Toronto, ON Canada M5N 1R7 Office: U Toronto-Banting & Best Med Rsch, 112 College St, Toronto, ON Canada M5G 1L6

MACLEOD, DONALD, clergyman, educator; b. Broughton, N.S., Can., Dec. 31, 1914; s. Donald Archibald and Anne (MacKenzie) M.; m. Norma Eliner Harper, Jan. 5, 1948 (dec. Mar. 1972); children: John Fraser, David Ainslie, Anne, Leslie. A.B., Dalhousie U., Halifax, N.S., 1934, M.A., 1935, LL.D., 1978; B.D. (E.F. Grant scholar), Pine Hill Div. Hall, Halifax, 1938, D.D., 1970; Th.D., U. Toronto, 1947. Teaching fellow dept. English Dalhousie U., 1935-38; ordained to ministry Presbyn. Ch., 1938; minister First Ch., Louisburg, N.S., 1938-41; assoc. minister Bloor St. Ch., Toronto, 1941-45; sr. tutor Men's Residences Victoria Coll., Toronto, 1943-45; teaching fellow dept. homiletics Princeton Theol. Sem., 1946-47; asst. prof., 1947-53, assoc. prof., 1953-61, prof., 1961—, Francis L. Patton prof., 1982—; lectr. Princeton Summer Inst. Theology, 1948—; vis. lectr. Westminster Choir Coll., 1952, 55-58; lectr. Gettysburg Sem., 1952, Jr. Pastors Sch., Reading, Pa., 1954, Conf. on Evangelism, Whitby, Ont., 1957, Hampton (Va.) Inst., 1957, Union Sem., Richmond, Va., 1958, Crozier Sem., Chester, Pa., 1961, Ann. Pastors Conf. Am. Luth. Ch., Green Lake, Wis., 1966, Coll. Preachers, Nat. Cathedral Washington, 1967; lectr. continuing edn. Presbyn. Coll., Montreal, 1972-75; Mullins lectr. So. Baptist Theol. Sem., 1970; Kyes' lectr. Kirk in the Hills, Detroit, 1973; Oliver lectr. Nazarene Theol. Sem., 1985; Jameson Jones lectr. Duke U. Sch. Div., 1987; chmn. Synod Com. on Capital Ch., Trenton, N.J.; mem. coms. Christian edn., candidates and credentials, social edn. and action Presbytery New Brunswick; commr. Gen. Assembly United Presbyn. Ch., Oklahoma City, 1965; spl. preacher Princeton, Lehigh, Muhlenberg, Mt. Allison U., Duke U. and Rutgers U. Chapels, Chgo. Sunday Evening Club, Am. Preacher Series Eaton Meml. Ch., Toronto, Chatauqua Evangelist, Riverside Ch., N.Y.C., Fifth Ave. Presbyn. Ch., N.Y.C., Nat. Presbyn. Ch., Washington, Preaching Mission McGuire AFB, Chaplains Seminars, USAF, 1967-68; adv. bd. Chapel of Princeton U. Author: Word and Sacrament, 1960, Presbyterian Worship, 1965, 2d edit., 1981, Higher Reaches, 1971, Proclamation, 1975; editor: Here Is My Method, 1952, Princeton Pulpit Prayers, 1987, Know the Way, Keep the Truth, Win the Life, 1987, The Problem of Preaching, 1987, Palms and Thorns, 1990; editor: Princeton Sem. Bull., 1956-82, Translator Dynamics of Worship, 1967; mem. editorial bd. Theology Today, 1948-61, Pulpit Preaching, 1970—, Pulpit Digest, 1980—; Am. corr.: The United Church Observer, 1947-56; N.J. corr.: The Christian Century, 1957-65; ecumenical editor Good News, Sunday Publs. Inc., 1983—; author bimonthly book column. The Preachers Bookshelf, Monday Morning, 1985—; contbr. Vols. I, IV and VI of Great Sermons and articles profl. publs. Established biennial series: Donald Macleod Lectureship on Preaching, Congl. Ch., Short Hills, N.J., 1989. Fellow Am. Assn. Theol. Schs.; mem. Am. Assn. Theol. Profs. in Practical Fields (exec. com.), Ch. Service Soc. (past v.p.), Clan Macleod Soc. Am. (chaplain), Am. Acad. Homiletics (founder, pres.). Address: Minister in Residence Charlestown Retirement Com 719 Maiden Choice Ln # 238 Baltimore MD 21228-6118 *Too often we interpret the Boy Scouts' slogan "Be Prepared" as a caution against danger or disaster, but its thrust is largely positive. It implies being prepared for every opportunity. Never did I have any particular position in mind, but every door which has opened to me found me ready and equipped for it.*

MACLEOD, GORDON ALBERT, lawyer; b. Buffalo, Mar. 29, 1926; s. Alexander D. and Loraine (Shea) MacL.; m. Lorraine King, July 7, 1951; children: Bruce King, Heather Lea. AB, Hamilton Coll., 1948; LLB, Harvard U., 1951. Bar: N.Y. 1951. Ptnr. Hodgson, Russ Andrews, Woods & Goodyear, Buffalo, 1960-93; lectr. N.Y. State Bankers Assn., Am. Soc. CLUs. Contbr. articles to profl. jours., other publs.; inventor several marketed games. Trustee Creative Edn. Found., Buffalo. Fellow Am. Coll. Trust and Estate Counsel; mem. ABA, N.Y. State Bar Assn. (lectr. trust and estates sect.), Erie County Bar Assn., Phi Beta Kappa. Avocations: playing drums, backgammon, inventing toys and games, writing. Office: Hodgson Russ Andrews Woods 1800 One M & T Pla Buffalo NY 14203

MACLEOD, GORDON KENNETH, physician, educator; b. Boston, Jan. 30, 1929; s. Gordon Kenneth and Margaret J. MacL.; m. Janet B., Aug. 17, 1957; children—Gordon K. III, Alexander B. A.B., Blackburn Coll., 1954; M.D., U. Cin., 1960. Indsl. engr. Procter & Gamble Co., Cin., 1954-56; intern Boston City Hosp., 1960-61; resident, clin. fellow Mass. Gen. Hosp., Boston, 1961-64; research fellow Harvard U., 1962-64; sr. resident, dir. physician Boston VA hosp., 1964-66; asst. clin. prof. medicine Yale U., Jan. 1966-69, assoc. clin. prof. medicine and public health, 1969-71; dir. Health

Maintenance Orgn. Service, HEW, 1971-73; prof. dept. health services adminstrn. Grad. Sch. Public Health, U. Pitts., 1974—, chmn. dept., 1974-83; assoc. clin. prof. medicine Grad. Sch. Public Health, U. Pitts. (Sch. Medicine), 1976-86, clin. prof. medicine, 1986—; sec. health, State of Pa., 1979; mem. affiliate staff W. Penn Hosp.; mem. nat. adv. council div. research resources NIH, 1983-87; cons. Shadyside Hosp.; cons. in field. Editor: (with Mark Perlman) Health Care Capital: Competition and Control, 1978; contbr. articles to profl. jours. Served with U.S. Army, 1948-49. Ford Found. travel grantee, 1973. Fellow ACP, Phila. Coll. Physicians; mem. Allegheny County Med. Soc., AMA (editorial bd. jour.), Am. Public Health Assn., Med. Adminstrs. Conf., Group Health Assn. Am., Pa. Public Health Assn., Pa. State Med. Soc. (pres.), Pitts. Acad. Medicine. Club: Cuttyhunk (Mass.) Yacht. Office: 130 Desoto St Pittsburgh PA 15261 *My first job as an industrial engineer with later training in internal medicine uniquely prepared me for an academic career in health management with intervals as a government executive at federal and state levels. My most challenging assignments were in initiating Health Maintenance Organizations nationally, in managing the health aspects of the nuclear accident at Three Mile Island, and in training young persons for careers in internal medicine and health management.*

MACLEOD, JOHN, college basketball coach; b. New Albany, Ind., Oct. 3, 1937; s. Dan J. and Ann Elizabeth (Welch) MacL.; m. Carol Ann McGroder, Jan. 18, 1974; children: Kathleen, Matthew. BA in History, Bellarmine Coll.; MA in History and Phys. Edn., Ind. State U., 1965. Coach high schs. Ky. Ind.; former coach U. Okla., Norman; head coach Phoenix Suns, NBA, 1973-87, Dallas Mavericks, NBA, 1987-89; former head coach New York Knicks, 1990; now head coach basketball program Notre Dame Univ., South Bend, Ind.; active hon. coach Ariz. Spl. Olympics. Active Soc. for Blind. Served with USAR, 1959-60. Named Coach of Yr. NBA, 1980. Mem. NBA Coaches Assn. (treas.). Office: care U Notre Dame Athletics Dept South Bend IN 46556*

MACLEOD, JOHN AMEND, lawyer; b. Manila, June 5, 1942; s. Anthony Macaulay and Dorothy Lillian (Amend) M.; m. Ann Klee; children: Kerry, Jack. BBA, U. Notre Dame, 1963, JD, 1969. Bar: D.C. 1969, U.S. Supreme Ct. 1980. Assoc. Jones, Day, Reavis & Pogue, D.C., 1969-73; ptnr., 1974-79; ptnr. Crowell & Moring, Washington, 1979—, mem. mgmt. com., 1979-82, 83-86, 91-94, chmn., 1984-85, 93-94. Contbr. articles to profl. jours. Trustee, mem. exec. com. Eastern Mineral Law Found.; bd. dirs. St. Francis Ctr., 1982-91, C&M Internat. 1991-94. Served to lt. U.S. Army, 1963-65. Mem. ABA, D.C. Bar Assn., Notre Dame Law Assn. (dir., exec. bd.), Ptnrs. Leadership Forum, Metropolitan Club (Washington). Home: 4040 Swartz Rd Maurertown VA 22644-9759

MACLEOD, JOHN DANIEL, JR., religious organization administrator; b. Robbins, N.C., Mar. 16, 1922; s. John Daniel Sr. and Sarah Cranor (McKay) MacL.; m. Helen Frances Boggs, Sept. 18, 1945 (dec. Aug. 1990); children: Sarah MacLeod Owens, Mary Marget MacLeod Silberstein, John Daniel III, William Boggs. AB, Davidson (N.C.) Coll., 1942; MDiv, Union Theol. Sem., Richmond, Va., 1945, ThM, 1949, ThD, 1952; DD (hon.), St. Andrews Presbyn. Coll., Laurinburg, N.C., 1992. Ordained to ministry Presbyn. Ch., 1945. Pastor Carolina Beach (N.C.) Presbyn. Ch., 1945-48, Brett-Reed Presbyn. Ch., Sweet Hall, Va., 1949-53, Keyser (W.Va.) Presbyn. Ch., 1953-63; exec. Appomattox Presbytery, Lynchburg, Va., 1963-67, Norfolk (Va.) Presbytery, 1967-76, Westminster Presbytery, St. Petersburg, Fla., 1976-81; exec. Synod of N.C., Raleigh, 1981-88, ret., 1988; interim exec. Coastal Carolina Presbytery, Fayetteville, 1991-93, Holston Presbytery, Kingsport, Tenn., 1993; interim parish assoc. White Meml. Presbyn. Ch., Raleigh, N.C., 1994; interim exec. Western North Carolina Presbyn., Morganton, N.C., 1995; mem., chmn. various local and nat. Presbyn. Ch. coms. Trustee Warren Wilson Coll., 1985-89, N.C. Presbyn. Hist. Soc., 1981—, Mary Baldwin Coll., 1960-68, Davis and Elkins Coll., 1955-61, Massanetta Springs Conf. Ctr., 1956-62; active Mineral County Redevel. Commn., Keyser, 1960-63; mem. N.C. Gov's. Adv. com. on Citizen Affairs, Raleigh, 1983-84; bd. advisors Wake Forest U. Div. Sch., 1991—. Nominee Moderator Presbyn. Ch. USA Gen. Assembly, 1987. Fellow Soc. Antiquaries (Scotland); mem. St. Andrews Soc. (Southern Pines, N.C. chpt., bd. dirs. Tampa, Fla. chpt. 1976-81), N.C. Scottish Heritage Soc. (pres. 1992—), Clan MacLeod Soc. (chaplain, bd. dirs. 1994). Democrat. Avocations: genealogy, history, travel. Home: 114 Silver Creek Rd Morganton NC 29655

MACLEOD, JOHN MUNROE, radio astronomer, academic administrator; b. Vermilion, Alta., Can., Sept. 3, 1937; s. Munroe and Ruth Alberta (Williams) MacL.; m. Patricia Irene Nichols, Dec. 30, 1959; children: Carolyn, Audrey, Darryl. BSc, U. Alta., Edmonton, 1959; PhD, U. Ill., 1964. Radio astronomer NRC Can., Ottawa, 1964-86, head James Clerk Maxwell telescope group Herzberg Inst., 1986—. Union Carbide scholar, 1955-59, McKinley Found. scholar, 1963-64. Mem. Am. Astron. Soc., Can. Astron. Soc. (councillor 1977-80, v.p. 1980-84, pres. 1984-86). Mem. United Ch. of Can. Achievements include co-discovery of the radio variability of BL Lacertae, of long-chain interstellar molecules HC5N, HC7N, HC9N. Office: NRC Herzberg Inst Astrophysics, 100 Sussex Dr, Ottawa, ON Canada K1A 0R6*

MACLEOD, ROBERT ANGUS, microbiology educator, researcher; b. Athabasca, Alta., Can., July 13, 1921; s. Norman John and Eleonora Pauline Bertha (Westerhoff) MacL.; m. Patricia Rosemarie Robertson, Sept. 1, 1948; children—Douglas John, Alexander Robert, Kathleen Mary, David Gordon, Michael Norman, Susan Joan. B.A. with honors in Chemistry, U. B.C., Vancouver, Can., 1943, M.A. in Chemistry and Biology, 1945; Ph.D. in Biochemistry, U. Wis., Madison, 1949. Asst. prof. Queen's U., Kingston, Ont., Can., 1949-52; sr. biochemist Fisheries Research Bd. Can., Vancouver, B.C., 1952-60; assoc. prof. to prof., chmn. dept. microbiology Macdonald Coll., McGill U., Ste. Anne de Bellevue, Que., Can., 1960-86, prof. emeritus, 1986—; Cons. Def. Research Bd., Ottawa, Ont., 1965-75; assoc. editor Can. Jour. Microbiology, Ottawa, 1965-70. Author tech. papers. Recipient Harrison prize Royal Soc. Can., 1960; Can. Soc. Microbiologists award, 1973. Fellow Royal Soc. Can.; mem. Can. Soc. Microbiologists (pres. 1976-77, hon. 1993), Am. Soc. Microbiology (hon. mem. 1992). Avocations: jogging, swimming, fishing. Home: 448 Greenwood Dr, Beaconsfield, PQ Canada H9W 4Z9 Office: MacDonald Coll, Dept Natural Resource Scis, 21111 Lakeshore Rd, Sainte Anne de Bellevue, PQ Canada H9X 3V9

MACLEOD, ROBERT FREDRIC, editor, publisher; b. Chgo., Oct. 15, 1917; s. Ernest F. and Martha W. (Ruzicka) MacL.; children—Merrill, Robert Fredric, E. Jay, Ian. B.A., Dartmouth Coll., 1939. Advt. mgr. Town & Country mag., N.Y.C., 1949; v.p., pub. Harper's Bazaar, N.Y.C., 1950-55, 55-60; v.p., advt. dir. Hearst Mags., N.Y.C., 1960-62; pub. Seventeen mag., N.Y.C., 1962-63; v.p., dir. mktg. Subscription TV Inc., Santa Monica, Calif., 1963-64; editor, pub. 'Teen Mag., Los Angeles, 1965—; now editorial dir., exec. pub.; v.p. Petersen Pub. Co., L.A., 1976—. Served to maj. USMC, 1941-46. Named to Football Hall of Fame, 1977. Club: Bel Air Country. Home: 110 Colony Dr Malibu CA 90265 Office: Teen Mag 6420 Wilshire Blvd Los Angeles CA 90048-5502

MACLEOD, THOMAS D., feed company executive. V.p Sara Lee Corp.; pres., chief exec. officer Kitchens of Sara Lee, 1990; pres., chief oper. officer Iams Co., Dayton, Ohio, 1990—. Office: Iams Co 7250 Poe Ave Dayton OH 45414

MACLEOD, WILLIAM BRIAN, hospital executive; b. Victoria, B.C., Can., June 12, 1951; s. Jacob Eugene and Winnifred Joan (Beecher) M.; m. Lucy Scarbo; children: Magenta Trishan, Collin Wilson, Andrew James. BS, U. Victoria, 1973; DHA, U. Toronto, 1979. Comptr. Kootenay Lake Dist. Hosp., Nelson, B.C., Can., 1973-76, 79-80; asst. exec. dir. St. Joseph's Hosp., London, Ont., Can., 1980-85; pres. Peel Meml. Hosp., Brampton, Ont., Can., 1985-90; pres., CEO Women's Coll. Hosp., Toronto, Ont., Can., 1990—; pres. Women's Coll. Hosp., Toronto, Ont., 1991—; asst. prof. health adminstrn. program U. Toronto. Mem. YMCA, Toronto. Recipient Robert Wood Johnson award, 1978. Mem. Can. Coll. Health Execs., Can. Coll. Health Svcs. Execs. Home: 740 Hurondale Dr, Mississauga, ON Canada M5S 1B2 Office: Womens Coll Hosp, 76 Grenville St, Toronto, ON Canada M5S 1B2

MACLEOD, WILLIAM CYRUS, lawyer, economist; b. Chgo., Apr. 7, 1952; s. Charles William MacLeod and Sarah Ann (Updyke) MacLeod Simitz; m. Michele Benoit, May 5, 1956; 1 child, Christine Michele. BA, Ripon Coll., 1973; PhD, U. Va., 1975; JD, U. Miami, Coral Gables, Fla., 1979. Bar: Ill. 1979, U.S. Dist. Ct. (no. dist.) Ill. 1979, U.S. Ct. Appeals (7th cir.) 1985. Instr. U. Va., Charlottesville, 1976; cons. Law and Econs. Ctr., Coral Gables, 1976-79; assoc. McDermott Will & Emery, Chgo., 1979-82; atty. advisor FTC, Washington, 1982-83, dir. Chgo. region, 1983—. Contbr. articles to profl. publs. Mem. ABA, Ill. Bar Assn. (mem. antitrust council 1983—), Chgo. Bar Assn. Office: Fed Trade Commission Consumer Protection Bur 6th & Pennsylvania Ave NW Washington DC 20580-0002

MACLIN, ALAN HALL, lawyer; b. DuQuoin, Ill., Dec. 22, 1949; s. John E. and Nora (Hall) M.; m. Joan Davidson (div. Dec. 1981); children: Molly, Tess, Anne; m. Jeanne Sittlow, Nov. 17, 1984. B.A. magna cum laude, Vanderbilt U., 1971; J.D., U. Chgo., 1974. Bar: Minn. 1974, U.S. Dist. Ct. Minn. 1974, U.S. Ct. Appeals (8th cir.) 1974, U.S. Ct. Appeals (5th cir.) 1975, U.S. Supreme Ct. 1978. Asst. atty. gen. Minn. Atty. Gen., St. Paul, 1974-80; chief anti-trust div. Briggs & Morgan, St. Paul, 1980—, mem. bd. dirs. 1993—. Mem. Minn. State Bar Assn. (treas. anti-trust sect. 1978-80), Ramsey County Bar Assn. (sec. jud. com. 1980-82), Phi Beta Kappa. Unitarian. Office: Briggs & Morgan 2200 First National Bank Bldg Saint Paul MN 55101

MACLIN, ERNEST, biomedical diagnostics company executive; b. N.Y.C., Jan. 25, 1931; s. Samuel and Dora (Sonsky) M.; m. Edith Samuel, Feb. 18, 1956; children—Alan David, Deborah Ellen, Julie Ann. B.M.E., CCNY, 1952, M.Engring., 1969. Registered profl. engr., N.Y., N.J. Engr. Reeves Instrument Corp., N.Y.C., 1952-54, Adrian Wilson Assocs., Nagoya, Japan, 1956-57; engr. Ford Instrument Co., L.I., N.Y., 1957-58; engr., unit head Kearfott div. Singer Corp., Little Falls, N.J., 1958-68; engr. Ford Instrument Co., L.I., N.Y., 1957-58, Technicon, Tarrytown, N.Y., 1968-69; v.p. research and devel. Electro-Nucleonics Inc., Fairfield, N.J., 1969-90; pres. The Product Devel. Group, 1990—; bd. dirs. Nat. Com. for Clin. Lab. Standards, Villanova, Pa., 1981-87. Contbr. articles to profl. jours.; patentee various instruments. Served to capt. USAF, 1954-57; mem. USAFR ret. Fellow ASME; mem. Am. Assn. Clin. Chemistry. Jewish. Home and Office: 659 Rutgers Pl Paramus NJ 07652-4207

MACMAHON, CHARLES HUTCHINS, JR., architect; b. Fort Seward, Alaska, June 6, 1918; s. Charles H. and Charlotte (Currie) MacM.; m. Ethel Hayward Pearce, Nov. 14, 1942; children—Charles H. III, Charlotte (Mrs. Douglas E. Neumann). Student, Bowdoin Coll., 1936-37, U. Pa., 1937-38; B.Arch., U. Mich., 1942. Dist. mgr. U.S. Gypsum Co., Chgo., 1947-52; gen. sales mgr. Spickelmeier Co., Indpls., 1952-55; with Smith, Tarapata, MacMahon, Inc., Birmingham, Mich., 1956-59; pres. Tarapata-MacMahon-Paulsen, Bloomfield Hills, Mich., 1959-73; cons. Tarapata-MacMahon-Paulsen, 1973—; pres. MacMahon-Cajacob Assos., DeLand, Fla., 1978-92; owner Charles MacMahon Architect, DeLand, Fla., 1992—; mem. Mich. Bd. Registration of Architects, Engrs. and Surveyors, 1964-68; mem. planning bd. City of DeLand, 1978-84. Works include Central Plaza, Canton, O., Gen. Motors Inst, Flint, Mich., Cloisters of DeLand, Fla., Washtenaw Community Coll, Ann Arbor, Mich. Chmn. bd. trustees Bloomfield Twp. Zoning Bd. Appeals, 1968-69; bd. dirs. Brookside Sch., Cranbrook, 1964-68; trustee Inst. for Advanced Pastoral Studies; mem. historic preservation bd. City of DeLand, 1993—. Lt. USNR, 1942-45. Fellow AIA; mem. Sch. Facilities Council (v.p. dir.), Mich. Soc. Architects (pres. 1962-64), Psi Upsilon. Episcopalian. Clubs: Deland Country, Lake Beresford Yacht (Fla.). Address: 115 S Boundary Ave Deland FL 32720

MACMAHON, PAUL, advertising executive; b. Orange, N.J., May 23, 1945; s. Paul J. and Joan (Schoenleber) MacM.; m. Mary Lee O'Neill, May 2, 1966 (div. May 1970); 1 child, Sandra; m. Barbara Jo Wernick, Mar. 8, 1972 (dec. Aug. 1988); children: Matthew, Timothy, Paul, Kathleen, Thomas, Julia; m. Ann Louise Dye, Aug. 7, 1993. A.A., Indian River Jr. Coll, 1966; B.S., Fla. State U., 1968; M.B.A., U. Mich., 1970. Acct. exec. Ted Bates & Co., N.Y.C., 1970-71; account dir. Ted Bates & Co., Ger. and Italy, 1972-74, v.p., 1975-79; sr. v.p. Ted Bates & Co., N.Y.C., 1979-80; sr. v.p. The Bloom Agy., Dallas, 1980-82, exec. v.p., 1982, gen. mgr., 1983-84, pres., 1984, chmn., 1985-88, chief exec. officer, 1988. Republican. Roman Catholic. Home: 126 Red Oak Ln Lewisville TX 75028-3501 Office: The Bloom Agy-Dallas 3500 Maple Ave Dallas TX 75219-3901

MACMANUS, SUSAN ANN, political science educator, researcher; b. Tampa, Fla., Aug. 22, 1947; d. Harold Cameron and Elizabeth (Riegler) MacM. BA cum laude, Fla. State U., 1968, PhD, 1975; MA, U. Mich., 1969. Instr. Valencia Community Coll., Orlando, Fla., 1969-73; rsch. asst. Fla. State U., 1973-75; asst. prof. U. Houston, 1975-79, assoc. prof., 1979-85, dir. M of Pub. Adminstrn. program, 1983-85, rsch. assoc. Ctr Pub. Policy 1982-85; prof., dir. PhD program Cleve. State U., 1985-87; prof. pub. adminstrn. and polit. sci., U. South Fla., Tampa, 1987—, chairperson deptt. govt. and internat. affairs, 1987-93; vis. prof. U. Okla., Norman, 1981—; field rsch. assoc. Brookings Instn., Washington, 1977-82, Columbia U., summer 1979, Princeton (N.J.) U., 1979—, Nat. Acad. Pub. Adminstrn., Washington, summer 1980, Cleve. State U., 1982-83, Westat, Inc., Washington, 1983—. Author: Revenue Patterns in U.S. Cities and Suburbs: A Comparative Analysis, 1978, Federal Aid to Houston, 1983, (with others) Governing A Changing America, 1984, (with Francis T. Borkowski) Visions for The Future: Creating New Institutional Relationships Among Academia, Business, Government, and Community, 1989, Reapportionment and Representation in Florida: A Historical Collection, 1991, Doing Business with Government: Federal, State, Local and Foreign Government Purchasing Practices for Every Business and Public Institution, 1992; writer manuals in field; mem. editorial bds. various jours.; contbr. articles to jours. and chpts. to books. Bd. dirs. Houston Area Women's Ctr., 1977, past pres., v.p. fin., treas.; mem. LWV, Gov.'s Coun. Econ. Advisers, 1988-90, Harris County (Tex.) Women's Polit. Caucus, Houston; bd. dirs. USF Rsch. Found., Inc. Recipient U. Houston Coll. Social Scis. Teaching Excellence award, 1977, Herbert J. Simon Award for best article in 3d vol. Internat. Jour. Pub. Adminstrn., 1981, Theodore & Venette Askounes-Ashford Disting. Scholar award U. South Fla., 1991, Disting. Rsch. Scholar award, 1991; Ford Found. fellow, 1967-68; grantee Valencia Community Coll. Faculty, 1972, U. Houston, 1976-77, 79, 83; Fulbright Rsch. scholar, Korea, 1989. Mem. Am. Polit. Sci. Assn. (program com. 1983-84, chair sect. intergovtl. rels., award 1989, mem. exec. coun. 1994—, pres.-elect urban politics 1994—), So. Polit. Sci. Assn. (v.p. 1990-91, pres.-elect 1992-93, pres. 1993-94, V.O. key award com. 1983-84, best paper on women and politics 1988), Midwest Polit. Sci. Assn., Western Polit. Sci. Assn., Southwestern Polit. Sci. Assn. (local arrangements com. 1982-83, profession com. 1977-80), ASPA (nominating com. Houston chpt. 1983, bd. mem. Suncoast chpt., pres.-elect 1991, Lilly award 1992), Policy Studies Orgn. (mem. editorial bd. jour. 1981—, exec. coun. 1983-85), Women's Caucus Polit. Sci. (portfolio pre-decision rev. com. 1982-83, projects and programs com. 1981, fin.-budget com. 1980-81), Acad. Polit. Sci., Mcpl. Fin. Officers Assn., Phi Beta Kappa, Pi Kappa Phi, Pi Sigma Alpha (mem. exec. coun. 1994—), Pi Alpha Alpha. Republican. Methodist. Home: 2506 Collier Pky Land O'Lakes FL 34639-5228 Office: U South Fla Dept Govt & Internat Affairs Soc 107 Tampa FL 33620

MACMANUS, YVONNE CRISTINA, editor, videoscripter, writer, consultant; b. L.A., Mar. 18, 1931; d. Daniel S. and Josefina Lydia (Pina) MacM. Student, UCLA, NYU, U. So. Calif., U. London. Assoc. editor Bobbs-Merrill, N.Y.C., 1960-63; TV producer Leo Burnett Ltd., London, 1965-66; founding editor, editor-in-chief Leisure Books, L.A., 1970-72; tchr. pub. course UCLA Extension, 1972; sr. editor Major Books, 1974-77; co-pub., editor in chief Timely Books, Chattanooga, 1977; co-owner Write On...!, Chattanooga, 1977—; corp. video PR & video tng., 1983—. Author: Better Luck Elsewhere, Inez, With Fate Conspire, 1974, Bequeath Them No Tumbled House, 1977, Deadly Legacy, 1981, The Presence, 1982, You Can Write a Romance, 1983, (play) Hugo, 1990; contbr. articles to profl. publs. Home and Office: 4040 Mountain Creek Rd Ste 1304 Chattanooga TN 37415-6025

MACMASTER, DANIEL MILLER, retired museum official; b. Chgo., Feb. 11, 1913; s. Daniel Howard and Charlotte Louise (Miller) MacM.; m. Sylvia Jane Hill, Feb. 22, 1935; children—Daniel Miller, Jane Irene (Mrs. Robert W. Lightell). Student, Lakeside Press Tng. Sch., 1930-31, U. Chgo., 1931-34; L.H.D., Lincoln Coll. 1970; D.H.L., DePaul U., 1978. Mem. staff Mus. Sci. and Industry, Chgo., 1933—; acting dir. Mus. Sci. and Industry, 1950, dir., 1951-72, pres., 1968-78, pres. emeritus, 1978—, life trustee, 1968—; gen. mgr. Chgo. R.R. Fair, 1948-49. Author: (with others) Exploring the Mysteries of Physics and Chemistry, 1938; book reviewer; contbr. to newspapers, mags., encys. Mem. Homewood (Ill.) Bd. Edn., 1945-49, pres., 1948-49; mem. U. Ill. Citizens Adv. Com., 1945—; sec. Higher Edn. Commn. Ill., 1955-59; dir. Hyde Park Bank and Trust Co., 1965-86; U.S. State Dept. specialist to Ireland, Germany, Sweden, 1963; dir. Floating Seminar to Greece, 1960, guest mus. cons., Fed. Republic Germany, 1961, Iran, 1973, 74, 76, Hong Kong, 1978, 89, 90, 91, Singapore, Chile and Peru, 1978, Poland, Czechoslovakia, Hungary, 1979, Mexico, 1980, 81, Saudi Arabia, 1981, 82, 84, Colombia, Ecuador and Bolivia, 1983, Taiwan, 1986, 87, 88, 89, 90, 92, 94; mem. Nat. 4-H Svc. Com.; hon. dir. Chgo. Chamber Orch. Soc., pres., 1969-70; bd. dirs. Sears-Roebuck Found., 1970-73, Internat. Coll. Surgeons Hall of Fame; mem. Lincoln Acad. Ill.; hon. trustee U. Chgo. Cancer Rsch. Found.; life trustee Adler Planetarium; dir. emeritus Monmouth Coll.; bd. govs. Chgo. Heart Assn., vice chmn., 1972-73; bd. commrs. Ill. Sesquicentennial, 1968. Decorated Golden Cross Royal Order Phoenix Greece; Officer's Cross Polonia Restituta Poland; Grand Badge of Honor Austria; Grand Badge of Honor of Burgenland Austria; Golden Badge of Honor Vienna; Officer's Cross 1st class Order of Merit Germany; Officer Order of Merit Luxembourg; Order Cultural Merit Poland; Royal Swedish Order North Star; recipient Patriotic Civilian Service award U.S. Army, St. Andrews Soc. Citizen of Yr. award, 1978. Fellow Assn. Sci. and Tech. Centers; mem. Kappa Sigma. Clubs: Tavern, Quadrangle, Commercial. Home: 2311 W 183rd St Apt 209B Homewood IL 60430

MACMASTER, ROBERT ELLSWORTH, historian, educator; b. Winthrop, Mass., Oct. 10, 1919; s. Joseph Oscar and Ruby (Slocomb) MacM.; m. Ann Elizabeth Lynch, Apr. 28, 1942; children—Angus Michael, Martha Ann, David Joseph. A.B., Harvard, 1941, A.M., 1948, Ph.D., 1952. Mem. faculty MIT, 1952-90, prof. history and lit., 1967-90, prof. emeritus, 1990—, chmn. history sect., 1970-72. Author: Danilevsky: A Russian Totalitarian Philosopher, 1967. Served with AUS, 1941-44. Mem. Am. Assn. Advancement Slavic Studies. Home: 461 Main St Hingham MA 02043-4701 Office: MIT Cambridge MA 02139

MACMEEKEN, JOHN PEEBLES, foundation executive, educator; b. Glen Ridge, N.J., Aug. 15, 1924; s. John West and Esther (Strong) M.; m. Mary Swanberg, Nov. 26, 1949; children: Carol B. Macmeeken Luther, John W., Susan G. Student U. Calif., Berkeley, 1941-43, Ind. U., 1943-44; J.D., Harvard U., 1948. Bar: Calif. 1948. Assoc. Chickering & Gregory, San Francisco, 1948-60, ptnr., 1960-82; ptnr. Pettit & Martin, San Francisco, 1982-93; pres. Found. for Books to China, 1993; bd. dirs. Lanark West Corp.; pres. Clinton U., San Francisco, 1995—. Mem. adv. com. Sch. Bus., San Francisco State U.; lectr. law Fudan U., Shanghai, China, East China Normal U., Shanghai, Nanking U., China. Sgt. U.S. Army, 1943-45. Mem. ABA, Calif. Bar Assn., San Francisco Bar Assn., Outlook Club Calif., World Trade Club, Commonwealth Club (Calif.). Republican. Congregationalist. Home: 5708 Glenbrook Dr Oakland CA 94618-1724

MACMILLAN, DOUGLAS CLARK, naval architect; b. Dedham, Mass., July 15, 1912; s. James Duncan and Mary Grace (MacNeill) MacM.; m. Elizabeth Jane Smith, Sept. 9, 1939; children: Douglas Stuart, John Richard; m. Dorothy Hayford, Jan. 1, 1985. B.S., Mass. Inst. Tech., 1934. Registered profl. engr., N.Y., N.J. Engrs. Fed. Shipbldg. & Dry Dock Co., Kearny, N.J., 1934-41; from chief marine engr. to tech. mgr. George G. Sharp (N.A.), N.Y.C., 1941-51; pres. George G. Sharp, Inc., N.Y.C., 1951-69; chmn. bd. George G. Sharp, Inc., 1969-70; cons. naval architect, 1970-83; asst. to gen. mgr., cons. Quincy Shipbldg. div. Gen. Dynamics Corp., 1972-77; bd. dirs. Atomic Indsl. Forum, 1965-67; mem. coms. Nat. Acad. Scis.-NRC; mem. adv. coms. U.S. Navy, USCG. Author papers in field. Past trustee St. Johns Guild, N.Y.C. Recipient Elmer A. Sperry medal ASME-Soc. Naval Architects and Marine Engrs.-Soc. Automotive Engrs.-IEEE-Am. Inst. Aeros. and Astronautics, 1969. Fellow Soc. Naval Architects and Marine Engrs. (hon. v.p., David W. Taylor Gold medal 1969); mem. Nat. Acad. Engring., Am. Soc. Naval Engrs. Mem. United Ch. of Christ. Home: Box 834 Colony Dr East Orleans MA 02643

MACMILLAN, KENNETH, cinematographer. Cinematographer: (TV movies) Smiley's People, 1982, The Aerodrome, 1983, The Ghost Writer, 1984, Past Caring, 1985, Bleak House, 1985, Hotel du Lac, 1986, Pack of Lies, 1987, Day After the Fair, 1987, The Little Match Girl, 1987, (films) A Month in the Country, 1987, A Summer Story, 1988, The Tree of Hands, 1989, Henry V, 1989, King Ralph, 1991, Of Mice and Men, 1992, Rush, 1992, Lassie, 1994. Office: Sandra Marsh Mgt 9150 Wilshire Blvd Ste 220 Beverly Hills CA 90210*

MACMILLAN, KIP VAN METRE, foundation executive; b. Evanston, Ill., Dec. 18, 1937; s. Charles Daniel and Janet Marvia (Van Metre) M.; m. Linda Jean Griesbach, Dec. 22, 1962; children: Christopher, Julia. Sgt., lt., div. comdr. Evanston Police Dept., 1961-88; supr. Polio Plus campaign Rotary Found., Evanston, 1988-90, ret., 1990. Bd. dirs. Youth Orgn. Umbrella, Evanston, 1974, McGaw YMCA, Evanston, 1976-89, Shore, Community Svcs. for Retarded Citizens, Evanston, 1986-90; v.p. Teton Youth & Family Svcs.; chmn. Evanston March of Dimes, 1987; mem. adv. com. Cook County Dept. Children and Family Svcs., Chgo., 1987-90; mem. Ill. Coord. System Response Project-Mass Abuse of Children, Springfield, 1987-89; chmn. Wildcat Dist. Com. Boy Scouts Am.; dir., treas. Evanston Sister City Found., 1989-90; vol. Grand Teton Music Festival. Recipient Top Vol. of Yr. award North Shore mag., 1987, Jay Moore award Youth Orgn. Umbrella, 1988, William Harper award McGaw YMCA, 1975. Mem. Nat. Soc. Fundraising Execs., Internat. Assn. Chiefs of Police, Rotary (bd. dirs. Evanston club 1986-89, bd. dirs. Jackson Hole club, pres. Jackson Hole club 1994-95, Outstanding Rotarian Evanston club 1988), Am. Soc. Indsl. Security, Teton County Peace Officers Assn. (chair congressional awards com.). Republican. Episcopalian.

MACMILLAN, ROBERT SMITH, electronics engineer; b. L.A., Aug. 28, 1924; s. Andrew James and Moneta (Smith) M.; BS in Physics, Calif. Inst. Tech., 1948, MS in Elec. Engring., 1949, PhD in Elec. Engring. and Physics cum laude, 1954; m. Barbara Macmillan, Aug. 18, 1962; 1 son, Robert G. Rsch. engr. Jet Propulsion lab. Calif. Inst. Tech., Pasadena, 1951-55, asst. prof. elec. engring., 1955-58; assoc. prof. elec. engring. U. So. Calif., L.A., 1958-70; mem. sr. tech. staff Litton Systems, Inc., Van Nuys, Calif., 1969-79; dir. systems engring. Litton Data Command Systems, Agoura Hills, Calif., 1979-89; pres. The Macmillan Group, Tarzana, Calif., 1989—; treas., v.p. Video Color Corp., Inglewood, 1965-66. Cons. fgn. tech. div. USAF, Wright-Patterson AFB, Ohio, 1957-74, Space Tech. Labs., Inglewood, Calif., 1956-60, Space Gen. Corp., El Monte, Calif., 1960-63. With USAAF, 1943-46. Mem. IEEE, Am. Inst. Physics, Am. Phys. Soc., Sigma Xi, Tau Beta Pi, Eta Kappa Nu. Research in ionospheric, radio-wave, propagation; very low frequency radio-transmitting antennas; optical coherence and statist. optics. Home: 350 Starlight Crest Dr La Canada Flintridge CA 91011-2839 Office: The Macmillan Group 5700 Etiwanda Ave Unit 260 Tarzana CA 91356-2546

MACMILLAN, WHITNEY, food products and import/export company executive. Chmn., CEO Cargill, Wayzata, Minn. Office: Cargill PO Box 5696 Minneapolis MN 55440-5696

MACMILLAN, WILLIAM HOOPER, university dean, educator; b. Boston, Oct. 21, 1923; s. Alexander Stewart and Leslie (Hooper) M.; m. Anne Stearns, May 29, 1948; children: Leslie Jean, Robert Bruce, William Ian. B.A., McGill U., 1948; Ph.D., Yale U., 1954. Instr. pharmacology U. Vt. Coll. Medicine, 1954-55, asst. prof., 1955-59, asso. prof. 1959-64, chmn. dept. pharmacology, 1962-63; prof. pharmacology, 1964-76, dean Grad. Coll., 1963-69, 71-76; rsch. fellow USPHS, U. Oxford, Eng., 1958-59; cons. New Eng. Assn. Sch. and Colls., 1967-76; Ford Found. project specialist, sci. adv. to Haile Sellassie I U., Addis Ababa,, Ethiopia, 1969-71; prof. biology, dean Grad. Sch. U. Ala., 1976-91, prof. biology, dean emeritus, 1991—; cons. So. Assn. Colls. and Schs., 1976—; exec. com. African grad. Fellowship Program, African-Am. Inst. N.Y.C., 1971-92; chmn. com. biomed. scis. Coun. of Grad. Schs., Washington, 1973-77, bd. dirs., 1985-88; exec. com. N.E. Assn. Grad. Schs., 1975-76; v.p. Conf. So. Grad. Schs.,

1981, pres., 1982; pres. New Eng. Assn. Grad. Schs., 1971; bd. dirs. Oak Ridge Associated Univs., 1987-93. Officer USNR, 1943-46. Mem. Am. Soc. Pharmacology and Exptl. Therapeutics, AAAS, N.Y. Acad. Sci., AAUP, Sigma Xi.

MACMILLEN, RICHARD EDWARD, biological sciences educator, researcher; b. Upland, Calif., Apr. 19, 1932; s. Hesper Nichols and Ruth Henrietta (Golder) MacM.; m. Ann Gray, June 12, 1953 (div. 1975); children: Jennifer Kathleen, Douglas Michael; m. Barbara Jean Morgan, Oct. 23, 1980; 1 child, Ian Richard. BA, Pomona Coll., 1954; MS, U. Mich., 1956; PhD, UCLA, 1961. From instr. to assoc. prof. Pomona Coll., Claremont, Calif., 1960-68, Wig Disting. prof., 1965; assoc. prof., then prof. U. Calif., Irvine, 1968—, chair dept. population and environ. biology, 1972-74, chair dept. ecology and evolutionary biology, 1984-90; prof. emeritus, 1993—; mem. award panel NSF, Washington, 1976-80. Contbr. numerous articles to profl. jours. Chair sci. adv. bd. Endangered Habitats League, 1991-93. Recipient rsch. awards NSF, 1961-83; Fulbright-Hays advanced rsch. fellow Monash U., Australia, 1966-67. Fellow AAAS; mem. Am. Soc. Mammalogists (life), Ecol. Soc. Am. (cert. sr. ecologist), Am. Ornithologists Union, Cooper Ornithol. Soc. (life, bd. dirs. 1982-84). Democrat. Avocations: fly fishing, camping, hiking, nature photography. Home: Rt 1 RK 35 Bishop CA 93514-3030 Office: U Calif White Mtn Rsch Sta Bishop CA 93514 *As world human populations continue to increase, our natural world continues to degrade. It is incumbent upon all of us to accept the responsibility of stewarding our land and its biota as precious and renewable resources.*

MACMINN, ALEENE MERLE B(ARNES), newspaper editor, columnist, educator; b. Salt Lake City, Sept. 19, 1930; d. Harold Sansom and Allie (Rasmussen) Barnes; m. Fraser K. MacMinn, July 28, 1961; children: Margaret A., Gregor Geordie. AA, Glendale Coll., 1950; BA, U. So. Calif., L.A., 1952. Women's page reporter Glendale (Calif.) News-Press, 1948-52; women's page reporter L.A. Times, 1953-57, asst. family editor, 1957-60, asst. TV editor 1960-65, exec. TV editor, 1965-69, asst. entertainment editor, 1969-72, TV Times editor, 1972-91, asst. Calendar editor, entertainment columnist, 1989-93; sr. lectr. U. So. Calif. Sch. Journalism, 1979-92. Mem. Women in Communications, Alpha Gamma Delta. Mem. LDS Ch.

MACMULLEN, RAMSAY, retired history educator; b. N.Y.C., Mar. 3, 1928; s. Charles William and Margaret (Richmond) MacM.; m. Edith Merriman Nye, Aug. 7, 1954 (div. 1991); children: John A., Priscilla N., William R., Lucinda S.; m. Margaret McNeill, Aug. 1, 1992. A.B., Harvard, 1950, A.M., 1953, Ph.D., 1957. Instr., asst. prof. U. Oreg., 1956-61; assoc. prof., prof. Brandeis U., 1961-67, chmn. dept. classics, 1965-66; prof. Yale U., 1967-93, Dunham prof. history and classics, 1979-93, chmn. dept. history, 1970-72, master Calhoun Coll., 1984-90. Author: Soldier and Civilian in the Later Roman Empire, 1963, Enemies of the Roman Order, 1966, Constantine, 1969, Roman Social Relations, 1974, Roman Government's Response to Crisis, 1976, Paganism in the Roman Empire, 1981, Christianizing the Roman Empire, 1984, Corruption and the Decline of Rome, 1988, Changes in the Roman Empire, 1990, (with E.N. Lane) Paganism and Christianity, 1992, Sisters of the Brush, 1995. Recipient Porter prize Coll. Art Assn., 1964; Fulbright fellow, 1960-61; Guggenheim fellow, 1964; Princeton Inst. for Advanced Study fellow, 1964-65; Nat. Endowment for Humanities sr. fellow, 1974-75. Mem. Soc. for Promotion Roman Studies, Assn. Ancient Historians (pres. 1978-81). Home: 25 Temple Ct New Haven CT 06511-6820 Office: Yale U Dept History New Haven CT 06520

MACMURREN, HAROLD HENRY, JR., psychologist, lawyer; b. Jersey City, Sept. 18, 1942; s. Harold Sr. and Evelyn (Almone) MacM.; m. Margaret Bartro, Nov. 21, 1970. BA, William Paterson Coll., Wayne, N.J., 1965; MA, Jersey City Coll., 1973; EdD, St. John's U., N.Y.C., 1985; JD, Rutgers U., 1989. Cert. secondary tchr., N.J.; Bar: N.J. 1989. Instr. Wanaque (N.J.) Bd. Edn., 1965-66, cons. psychologist, 1983-84; instr. Elmwood Park (N.J.) Bd. Edn., 1967-70; coll. faculty mem., psychologist Assoc. Clinic, Jersey City, 1971-72; cons. psychologist Rockaway (N.J.) Bd. Edn., 1972-83; intern lawyer Environ. Law Clinic, Newark, N.J., 1988-89; cons. psychologist Pequannock (N.J.) Bd. Edn., 1984—; coord. of child study team Sandyston Walpack Sch. System; adj. prof. William Paterson Coll.; spkr. and writer in field. Mem. ABA, NEA, N.J. Edn. Assn., N.J. Psychologist Assn., N.J. Bar Assn., Sierra Club, Phi Delta Kappa. Avocations: reading, travel, skiing, hiking. Home: 4 Sytsema Pl Sussex NJ 07461 Office: Pequannock Bd Edn Pequannock NJ 07440

MACNAIR, RACHEL MARY, editor; b. Rockford, Ill., Nov. 4, 1958; d. Wilmer Everett and Dorothy Lois (Kelso) MacN.; 1 child, Matthew Daniel. BA with honors, Earlham Coll., 1978. Pres. Bendix Conversion Project, Kansas City, Mo., 1979-83, Feminists for Life of Am., Kansas City, Mo., 1984-94; v.p. Seamless Garment Network, 1990—; founder Susan B. Anthony List, Kansas City, 1992; editor-in-chief Feminism & Nonviolence Studies Assn., Kansas City, 1994—; owner MacNair Svcs., Kansas City, 1985—; cons. in field. Editor: Prolife Feminism: Yesterday & Today, 1995. Mem. Soc. of Friends. Home and Office: 811 E 47th St Kansas City MO 64110

MAC NAMARA, DONAL EOIN JOSEPH, criminologist; b. N.Y.C., Aug. 13, 1916; s. Daniel Patrick and Rita F.V. (Chambers) Mac N.; m. Margaret Elizabeth Scott, July 30, 1953 (dec. 1990); 1 child, Brian Scott. BS, Columbia U., 1939, M of Phil., 1948; M of Pub. Adminstrn., NYU, 1946; LLD (hon.), August Vollmer U., 1990. Instr. polit. sci. Rutgers U., New Brunswick, N.J., 1948-49; asst. dir. Delinquency Control Inst. L.A., 1949-50; dir. law enforcement program U. So. Calif., 1949-50; vis. prof. U. Louisville, 1950-71, Fla. State U., Tallahassee, 1958, St. Lawrence U., Canton, N.Y., 1954, 56; chmn. Law Enforcement Insts., NYU, 1950-57; coordinator police sci. programs Bklyn. Coll., 1954-57; with N.Y. Inst. Criminology, N.Y.C., 1950-63; assoc. dean N.Y. Inst. Criminology, 1955-56, dean, 1956-63; prof. criminology Center Corrections Tng. CUNY, 1966-67; in charge corrections programs John Jay Coll. Criminal Justice, 1965-85, emeritus disting. prof., 1985; dean doctoral programs August Vollmer U., Orange, Calif., 1987—; dir. summer session CUNY, Ireland, 1970; Disting. vis. prof. U. Melbourne, Australia, 1981; vis. prof. criminology Bar Ilan U., Ramat Gan, Israel, 1982-83; vis. prof. Calif. State U., Spring 1984, U. N.Mex., 1985, U. Tenn., 1986, Calif. State U., 1987-88, Bar Ilan U., Israel, Spring 1989; mng. ptnr. Flath-MacNamara Assocs., N.Y.C., 1958-64; dir. Crime Show Cons., N.Y.C., Traffic Mgmt. Survey Fund, Inc., N.Y.C.; Eastern regional dir. Character Underwriters, Inc., L.A.; vis. mem. faculty Hunter, Queens, Bklyn. colls., 1952-58; vis. lectr. criminology Brandeis U., Waltham, Mass., 1962; lectr. police adminstrn. SUNY, 1966-67; lectr. penology (CCNY), 1965-67; specialist police, correctional adminstrn. grad. program tng. pub. adminstrn., State of N.Y., Albany, 1951-56; criminol. cons. Am. Express Co., 1962-68; cons., Bergen County, N.J., 1967, N.J. Commn. Civil Disorders, 1967-68; vis. prof. criminology U. Utah, Salt Lake City, 1962; pres. League to Abolish Capital Punishment, 1958-70, chmn. bd., 1959-91; col. a.d.c. to commr. Ky. State Police, 1963; external assessor in police and pub. adminstrn. Republic of Ireland, 1975; vis. prof. Inst. Pub. Adminstrn., Dublin, 1974-75. Author: Problems of Sex Behavior, 1968, Perspectives on Correction, 1971, Corrections: Problems of Punishment and Rehabilitation, 1973, Police: Problems and Prospects, 1974, Criminal Justice, 1976, Sex, Crime and the Law, 1977, Incarceration: The Sociology of Imprisonment, 1978, Crime, Criminals and Corrections, 1981, Deviants: Victims or Victimizers, 1984, Deviance, Denigration and Dominance, 1990, also articles.; Am. editor: Excerpta Criminologica, 1965-85; editor-in-chief: Criminology: An Interdisciplinary Jour., 1975-78; asso. editor: Jour. Corrective Psychiatry; editor: UN Crime Conference: Keynote Document Edit., 1981. Exec. v.p. Real Estate Bd., Bronx, N.Y., 1964-65. Served to maj. AUS, 1942-48. Recipient award of honor Internat. Assn. Women Police, 1960, Herbert A. Bloch award Am. Soc. Criminology, 1967, Bruce Smith award Am. Acad. of Criminal Justice Scis., 1990, Lifetime Achievement in Criminal Justice award Am. Soc. for Pub. Adminstrn., 1991. Fellow AAAS (chmn. sci. criminology sect., mem. council 1957-82), Am. Acad. Criminalistics (presiding; mem. Internat. Police Officers Assn. (life), Am. Soc. Criminology (pres. 1960-64), Assn. Psychiat. Treatment Offenders (program coordinator 1954-58), M.P. Assn., Internat. Criminol. Soc., Am. Assn. Criminologists (hon. life), Edn. Research Assn. (exec. dir. 1965-69), Nat. Police Officers Assn. Am. (research dir. 1963-67), Pi Sigma Alpha. Home: 76 Four Corners Rd Warwick NY 10990-3020 Office: 899 10th Ave New York NY 10019-1029

MACNAMARA, THOMAS EDWARD, physician, educator; b. Airdrie, Scotland, May 23, 1929; came to U.S., 1956, naturalized, 1962; s. Edward Francis and Bridget Monica (Fawcett) M.; m. Julia B. Caulfield, Sept. 22, 1956; children: Edward, Brian, Mary, Bridget, Anne. Student, Paisley Tech. Coll., Glasgow U., 1947, MBChB, 1952. Diplomate: Am. Bd. Anesthesiology. Intern Victoria Infirmary, Glasgow, 1953, Leith Hosp., Edinburgh, Bellsdyke Hosp., Larbert, 1954, St. Martins Hosp., Bath, 1954, Birmingham (Eng.) Accident Hosp., 1955; resident in anesthesiology Mass. Gen. Hosp., Boston, 1956; practice medicine specializing in anesthesia Washington, 1957-59, 62—, Boston, 1960-62; mem. staff Georgetown U. Hosp., Mass. Gen. Hosp., Boston; instr. anesthesia Georgetown U., 1957-60, prof., chmn. dept. anesthesia Med. Center, 1962-90; dir. anethesia and surg. svcs. Walter Grant Magnuson Clin. Ctr., NIH, Bethesda, Md., 1990-92; mem. faculty senate Georgetown U., 1967-75, v.p. senate, 1967-70, pres. senate, 1973-75; chief anesthesiology NIH Clin. Center, Bethesda, Md., 1975-83, 92-93; asst. in anesthesia Mass. Gen. Hosp., Harvard U. Med. Sch., 1960-62; cons. VA Hosp., Washington, 1962-92. Editor: Surgical Digest, 1966-70, Clinical Therapeutics, 1976-82. Bd. dirs. Georgetown U. Fed. Credit Union. Fellow Am. Coll. Anesthesiologists (chmn. bd. govs. 1986-87); mem. D.C. Med. Soc., Am. Soc. Anesthesiologists, Md.-D.C. Soc. Anesthesiology (pres. sect. II 1966-67). Home: 2736 N Nelson St Arlington VA 22207-5033 Office: NIH Walter Grant Magnuson Clin Ctr Bldg 10 Bethesda MD 20892

MACNAUGHTON, ANGUS ATHOLE, finance company executive; b. Montreal, Que., Can., July 15, 1931; s. Athole Austin and Emily Kidder (MacLean) MacN.; children: Gillian Heather, Angus Andrew. Student, Lakefield Coll. Sch., 1941-47, McGill U., 1949-54. Auditor Coopers & Lybrand, Montreal, 1949-55; acct. Genstar Ltd., Montreal, 1955; asst. treas. Genstar Ltd., 1956-61, treas., 1961-64, v.p., 1964-70, exec. v.p., 1970-73, pres., 1973-76, vice chmn., chief exec. officer, 1976-81, chmn. or pres., chief exec. officer, 1981-86; pres. Genstar Investment Corp., 1986; bd. dirs. Can. PAcific Ltd., Sun Life Assurance Co. Can. Ltd., Barricj Gold Corp., Varian Assocs. Inc., Wolverine Tube Inc.; past pres. Montreal chpt. Tax Execs. Inst. Bd. govs. Lakefield Coll. Sch.; past chmn. San Francisco Bay Area coun. Boy Scouts Am. Mem. Pacific Union Club, World Trade Club, Villa Taverna (San Francisco), Mt. Royal Club (Montreal), Toronto Club. Office: Genstar Investment Corp 950 Tower Ln Ste 1170 Foster City CA 94404-2127 also: Am Barrick Resources Corp, 24 Hazelton Ave, Toronto, ON Canada M5R 2E2

MACNAUGHTON, DONALD SINCLAIR, health care company executive; b. Schenectady, N.Y., July 14, 1917; s. William and Marion (Colquhoun) MacN.; m. Winifred Thomas, Apr. 10, 1941; children: Donald, David. AB, Syracuse U., 1939, LLB, 1948. Bar: N.Y. 1948. Tchr. history Pulaski (N.Y.) Acad. and Central Sch., 1939-42; pvt. practice Pulaski, 1948-54; dep. supt. ins. N.Y. State, 1954-55; with Prudential Ins. Co. Am., 1955-78, pres., CEO, 1969-70, CEO, chmn. bd. dirs., 1970-78, also bd. dirs.; chmn. bd. dirs. Hosp. Corp. Am., Nashville, 1978-82; chmn. bd. Hosp. Corp. Am., 1982-85; chmn. exec. com. Healthtrust Inc., 1987—. Mem. capital campaign com. Harvard U., 1985—, mem. adv. bd. Bus. and Govt. Ctr., 1983—; trustee Vanderbilt U., Nashville, 1979-95. 1st lt. USAAF, 1942-46, PTO. Named Man of Yr. B'nai B'rith Youth Service, N.Y., 1985, The Ins. Field, 1969; recipient Gold Medal Founders award Internat. Ins. Seminars, N.Y., 1978, Exceptional Achievement citation Dept. Treasury, 1972. Mem. Hosp. Corp. Found. (chmn. 1985—), Bus. Coun. (hon.), Augusta Nat. Golf Club. Avocations: boating, skiing, golf, reading. Office: Health Trust Inc 4525 Harding Rd Nashville TN 37205-2119

MACNAUGHTON, JOHN DAVID FRANCIS, aerospace company executive; b. Moose Jaw, Saskatchewan, Can., Apr. 10, 1932; s. Francis Maurice and Grace Elizabeth Ellen (Moore) MacN.; m. Joy Barbara Spencer; children: Paul, Neil, Jane. Diploma, deHavilland Aero. Tech. Sch., 1954; BSc, Hatfield Coll., U.K., 1954. Engring. supr. deHavilland's Guided Missile Div., 1954-57; chief engr. Garrett Mfg. Ltd., 1958-61; chief mech. engr. deHavilland's Spl. Projects and Applied Research, 1962-68; dir. mech. products dept. Spar Aerospace Ltd., Toronto, Ont., Can., 1968-69, v.p. mktg. and planning, 1969-74, v.p., gen. mgr. remote manipulator systems div., 1974-80, v.p., group exec. space & electronics group, 1981-82, sr. v.p. systems sector, from 1982, exec. v.p., 1988-89, pres., CEO, 1989—; also bd. dirs., 1989—; bd. dirs. Telesat Can., Ottawa, Nat. Quality Inst.; invited spkr. various profl. confs. Contbr. papers to profl. publs. and profl. confs. Dir.-at-large Jr. Achievement Can. Recipient Engring. medal Profl. Engrs. Ont., 1965, Pub. Service medal NASA, 1982, McGregor award Royal Can. Air Force Assn., 1983, Thomas W. Eadie medal Royal Soc. Can., 1984, 125th Can. Anniversary medal, 1993. Fellow Can. Aeronautics and Space Inst. (Casey Baldwin award 1963, McCurdy award 1983); mem. Assn. Profl. Engrs. of Province Ont., Info. Tech. Assn. Can. Rideau (Ottawa) Club, Mississauga Golf and Country Club, Bd. of Trade (Toronto), Founders Club (Toronto), Toronto Club. Home: 1054 Indian Rd, Mississauga, ON Canada L5H 1R7

MACNEE, ALAN BRECK, electrical engineer, educator; b. N.Y.C., Sept. 19, 1920; s. Forrest Frew and Ellen (Breck) M.; m. Lois Fuller Livermore, Feb. 16, 1946; children—Carol, Bruce Forrest, David Breck, Timothy Jay. S.B., S.M., M.I.T., 1943, Sc.D. (George Eastman fellow), 1948. Research asso. Chalmers Tech. U., Gothenburg, Sweden, 1949-50; vis. assoc. prof. Chalmers Tech. U., 1961-62; mem. faculty U. Mich., Ann Arbor, 1950—; prof. elec. engring. U. Mich., 1959-89, prof. emeritus, 1989—; sr. research asso. Goddard Space Flight Center, NASA, 1971-72; mem. vis. tech. staff Sandia Labs., 1980-81. Co-author Modern Circuit Analysis, 1973; contbr. articles to profl. publs.; patentee in field. Recipient B.J. Thompson Meml. prize IRE, 1951, Western Electric Fund award Am. Soc. Engring. Edn., 1968-69. Fellow IEEE, AAAS; mem. Royal Soc. Sci. and Lit. (Gothenbery) (fgn. mem.), Sigma Xi, Eta Kappa Nu, Phi Kappa Phi. Congregationalist. Office: Univ Mich 1215 Eecs Bldg Ann Arbor MI 48109

MACNEE, (DANIEL) PATRICK, actor; b. London, Feb. 6, 1922; s. Daniel and Doratisea Mary (Henry) M.; m. Kate Woodwille, 1965 (div. 1969); children: Rupert, Jenny; m. Baba Majos de Nagyzsebyem Feb. 25, 1988. Student, Webber Douglas Academy Dramatic Art, 1940. Appearences include (theatre) in Eng., 1939-42, 46-52, in Can. and U.S., 1952-60, (films) The Life and Death Colonel Blimp, 1945, Dead of Night, 1946, Hamlet, 1948, The Fatal Night, 1948, All Over The Town, 1949, Hour of Glory, 1949, The Fighting Pimpernel, 1950, The Girl Is Mine, 1950, Dick Barton At Bay, 1950, A Christmas Carol, 1951, Flesh and Blood, 1951, Three Cases of Murder, 1955, Until They Sail, 1957, Les Girls, 1957, Pursuit of the Graf Spee, 1957, Mission of Danger, 1959, Incense for the Damned, 1970, King Solomon's Treasure, 1980, Dick Turpin, 1980, The Hot Touch, 1981, The Creature Wasn't Nice, 1981, The Howling, 1981, The Sea Wolves, 1981, Young Doctors in Love, 1982, Sweet Sixteen, 1983, This Is Spinal Tap, 1984, Shadey, 1985, A View to a Kill, 1985, For the Term of His Natural Life, 1985, Transformations, 1987, Waxwork, 1988, The Chill Factor, 1988, Lobster Man From Mars, 1989, A Stroke of Luck, (TV series) The Avengers, 1960-69, The New Avengers, 1978-80, Gavilan, 1982-83, Empire. 1984, Lime Street, 1985, Tales from the Darkside, 1985, (miniseries) Around the World in 80 Days, 1989, (TV movies) Mister Jerico, 1970, Sherlock Holmes in New York, 1976, Evening in Byzantium, 1978, Rehearsal for Murder, 1982, The Return of the Man From U.N.C.L.E., 1983, Club Med, 1986; author: (with Maggie Cameron) Blind in One Ear, 1988. 1st lt. Brit. Navy, 1942-46. Recipient Variety Artist award of Gt. Britain, 1963. Mem. Actors Equity, AFTRA, Screen Actors Guild, Assn. Can. TV and Radio Artists. Office: Irv Sechter Co 9300 Wilshire Blvd Ste 410 Beverly Hills CA 90212*

MACNEIL, IAN RODERICK, lawyer, educator; b. N.Y.C., June 20, 1929; s. Robert Lister and Katherine Gertrude (Metcalf) Macneil; m. Nancy Carol Wilson, Mar. 29, 1952; children: Roderick, Jennifer, Duncan (dec.), Andrew. BA magna cum laude, U.Vt., 1950; LLB magna cum laude, Harvard U., 1955. Bar: N.H. 1956. Law clk. Hon. Peter Woodbury, 1955-56; asso. Sulloway Hollis Godfrey & Soden, Concord, N.H., 1956-59; mem. faculty Cornell U. Law Sch., Ithaca, N.Y., 1959-72, 74-80, Ingersoll prof. law, 1976-80; Wigmore prof. law Northwestern U. Sch. Law, Chgo., 1980—; vis. prof. U. East Africa, 1965-67, Duke U., 1971-72; profl. law, vis. prof. Advanced Studies, U. Va., 1972-74; vis. fellow Centre for Socio-legal Studies and Wolfson Coll., Oxford U., 1979; hon. vis. fellow faculty law U. Edinburgh, 1979, 87; Rosenthal lectr. Northwestern U. Sch. Law, 1979; Braucher vis. prof. Harvard U., 1988-89. Author: Bankruptcy Law in East Africa, 1966,

Contracts: Exchange Transactions and Relations, 2d edit., 1978, The New Social Contract, 1980, American Arbitration Law: Reformation Nationalization Internationalization, 1992. Served with U.S. Army, 1951-53. Guggenheim fellow, 1978-79. Fellow Royal Soc. Antiquaries (Scotland); mem. Am. Law Inst., ABA, N.H. Bar Assn., Can. Assn. Law Tchrs., Am. Soc. Legal History, Soc. Public Tchrs. Law, Standing Council Scottish Chiefs. Club: New (Edinburgh). Office: Northwestern U Sch Law 357 E Chicago Ave Chicago IL 60611-3069 also: 5/8 Fountainhill Rd, Edinburgh EH9 2NL, Scotland

MAC NEIL, JOSEPH NEIL, archbishop; b. Sydney, N.S., Can., Apr. 15, 1924; s. John Martin and Kate (Mac Lean) Mac N. BA, St. Francis Xavier U., Antigonish, N.S., 1944; postgrad., Holy Heart Sem., Halifax, N.S., 1944-48, U. Perugia, 1956, U. Chgo., 1960; JCD, U. St. Thomas, Rome, 1958. Ordained priest Roman Cath. Ch., 1948. Pastor parishes in N.S., 1948-55; officialis Chancery Office, Antigonish, 1958-59; adminstrn. Diocese of Antigonish, 1959-60; rector Cathedral Antigonish, 1961; dir. extension dept. St. Francis Xavier U., Antigonish, 1961-69, v.p., 1962-69; bishop St. John, N.B., Can., 1969-73; chancellor U. St. Thomas, Fredericton, N.B., 1969-73; archbishop of Edmonton, Alta., 1973—; chmn. Alta Bishops' Conf., 1973—; chmn. bd. Newman Theol. Coll., Edmonton, 1973—, St. Joseph's Coll. U. Alta., Edmonton, 1973—. Vice chmn. N.S. Voluntary Econ. Planning Bd., 1965-69; bd. dirs. Program and Planning Agy., Govt. of N.S., 1969; exec. Atlantic Provinces Econ. Coun., 1968-73, Can. Coun. Rural Devel., 1965-75; bd. dirs. Futures Secretariat, 1981, Ctr. for Human Devel., Toronto, Ont., Can., 1985—; mem. bd. mgmt. Edmonton Gen. Hosp., 1983-92; Edmonton Caritas Health Group, 1992—; mem. Nat. Com. for Can. Participation in Habitat, 1976. Mem. Canadian Assn. Adult Edn. (past pres. N.S.), Canadian Assn. Dirs. Univ. Extension and Summer Schs. (past pres.), Inst. Research on Public Policy (founding mem.), Can. Conf. Cath. Bishops (pres. 1979-81, mem. com. on ecumenism 1985-91, com. on missions 1991—, mem. permanent coun. 1993—). Address: Archbishop of Edmonton, 8421 101st Ave, Edmonton, AB Canada T6A 0L1

MACNEIL, ROBERT BRECKENRIDGE WARE, broadcast journalist; b. Montreal, Que., Can., Jan. 19, 1931; came to U.S., 1963; s. Robert A.S. and Margaret Virginia (Oxner) MacN.; m. Rosemarie Anne Copland, 1956 (div. 1964); children: Catherine Anne, Ian B.; m. Jane J. Doherty, May 29, 1965 (div. 1983); children: Alison N., William H.; m. Donna P. Richards, Oct. 20, 1984. Student, Dalhousie U., 1949-51; BA, Carleton U., 1955; LHD (hon.), William Patterson Coll., 1977, Beaver Coll., Bates Coll., 1979, Lawrence U., 1980, Bucknell U., 1982, George Washington U., Kings Coll., Trinity Coll., U. Maine, 1983, Brown U., 1984, Colby Coll., Carleton Coll., U. S.C., 1985, Franklin and Marshall Coll., 1987, Nazareth Coll., Washington Coll., 1988, Kenyon Coll., 1990, U. Western Ont., 1992, U. Miami, Clark U., 1994, Clark U., 1994. Radio actor CBC, Halifax, N.S., Can., 1950-52; radio/TV announcer CBC, 1954-55; announcer Sta.-CJCH, Halifax, 1951-52; announcer, news writer Sta. CFRA, Ottawa, Ont., Can., 1952-54; sub-editor to filing editor Reuters News Agy., London, 1955-60; news corr. NBC, London, 1960-63; Washington, 1963-65, U.K./U.S., 1965-67; corr. Panorama program BBC, London, 1967-71, 73-75; sr. corr. Nat. Public Affairs Center for TV, Washington, 1971-73; exec. editor, co-anchor MacNeil/Lehrer Report, Sta. -WNET-TV, N.Y.C., 1975—, MacNeil/Lehrer News Hour, PBS, 1983—. Author: The People Machine, The Influence of Television on American Politics, 1968, The Right Place at the Right Time, 1982, Wordstruck, 1989, Burden of Desire, 1992; co-author: The Story of English, 1986; editor The Way We Were 1963, 1988. Recipient Broadcaster of Yr. Internat. Radio and TV Soc., 1991, Paul White award Radio TV News Dirs. Assn., 1990, Medal of Honor U. Mo. Sch. Journalism, 1980. Fellow AAAS, The MacDowell Colony (chmn. 1993); mem. AFTRA, Assn. Radio and TV News Analysts, Writers Guild Am., Century Club (N.Y.C.). Office: WNET/13 356 W 58th St New York NY 10019-1804

MACNEILL, ARTHUR EDSON, physician, science consultant; b. Waltham, Mass., July 14, 1912; s. Charles Alfred and Florence (Wright) MacN.; m. Lydia Mae Rhoades, June 25, 1941; children: Marjorie Ann, Arthur Edson, Jr. AB, Harvard U., 1933, MD, 1937; grad., Army Sch. Aviation Medicine, 1942. Intern Mary Hitchcock Meml. Hosp., Hanover, N.H., 1937-38; physician Health Svc. Dartmouth Coll., 1938-41; acting med. dir. Dartmouth U., 1945-46, instr. anatomy, 1944-46, rsch. assoc. physiol. scis., 1946-50; univ. physician U. Fla., Gainesville, 1946-47; cons. med. and biol. rsch. Fgn. Svc. U.S. Dept. State, 1950; dir. lab. Chronic Disease Rsch. Inst. Buffalo Sch. of Medicine, 1950-56; lectr. medicine U. Buffalo, 1951-57, asst. prof. surgery, Buswell Rsch. fellow, 1957-61; assoc. rsch. prof. surgery SUNY, Buffalo, 1961-64; dir. Inst. Therapeutic Engring., Sunapee, N.H., 1964-65, Dialysis Rsch. Inst., Sunapee, 1964-84; mem. rsch. staff, med. bd. Buffalo Gen. Hosp., 1951-64, cons. surg. rsch. staff, 1957-64, dir. dept. therapeutic engring., 1958-64; rsch. advisor dept. surgery Buffalo Children's Hosp., 1957-66; chief clin. investigative cons. Respiratory Ctr., Buffalo, 1954-55; med. assoc. Crotched Mt. Rehab. Ctr., Greenfield, N.H., 1967-68; med. staff New London (N.H.) Hosp., 1980—, chmn. investigational review com., 1983—; pvt. cons. in field. Developer blood dialyzer, blood pumps, blood flowmeters, blood rheometer, other devices for profl. treatment vital organs; contbr. articles to profl. jours. Served from 1st lt. to maj. M.C. USAAF, 1941-44, surgeon 72d Fighter Wing, 1943-44, staff surgeon, 1944; maj. hon. res., USAF, 1951—. Recipient Maj. Louis Livingston Seaman award Assn. Mil. Surgeons U.S., 1949, 1st award sci. rsch. Med. Soc. State N.Y., 1953, Redway award, 1963. Mem. AAAS, AMA, Instrument Soc. AM. (dir. med. and biol. divsn. 1956-57), N.H. Med. Assn., Grafton County Med. Assn., Assn. Mil. Surgeons, N.Y. Acad. Scis., N.H. Orthopedic Assn., Nat. Kidney Found., Sigma Xi. Methodist. Home: 37 Fairway Dr Grantham NH 03753 Office: PO Box 577 Grantham NH 03753

MACNEILL, JAMES WILLIAM, international government consultant; b. Sask., Can., Apr. 22, 1928; s. Leslie William and Helga Ingeborg (Nohlgren) MacN.; m. Phyllis Beryl Ferguson, Nov. 30, 1953; children: Catherine Anne, Robin Lynne. BA, U. Sask., 1949, BE Mech., 1958, LLD (hon.), 1988; Diplome, U. Stockholm, 1951; DSc (hon.), McGill U., 1992; D of Environ. Studies (hon.), U. Waterloo, 1993; LHD (hon.), Lakehead U., 1994. Spl. adv. on constl. rev. Privy Council Office, Govt. Can., Ottawa, 1967-70; asst. sec. Can. Ministry of State for Urban Affairs, Ottawa, 1970-73; permanent sec. Can. Ministry of State for Urban Affairs, 1973-76; Can. AEP, Can. commr.-gen. UN Human Settlements Conf., Vancouver, B.C., 1975-78; dir. environ. directorate OECD, Paris, 1978-85; sec. gen. World Commn. Environment and Devel., Geneva, 1985-87, Inst. Research Pub. Policy, Ottawa, 1988-93; pres. J.W. MacNeill and Assocs., 1993—; chmn. Internat. Inst. for Sustainable Devel., 1994—; spl. advisor to adminstrn. UN Devel. Program, 1994—. Author: Environmental Management, 1971, Beyond Interdependence, 1991. Recipient Saskatchewan Achievement award, 1985, Silver medal City of Paris, 1984, Climate Inst. award, 1991, Swedish WASA award, 1991, Lifetime Achievement award Govt. of Can. Mem. Assn. Profl. Engrs. Ont., Assn. Profl. Engrs. Sask. Office: 13th Fl, 250 Albert St, Ottawa, ON Canada K2P 1L5

MAC NEISH, RICHARD STOCKTON, archaeologist, educator; b. N.Y.C., Apr. 29, 1918; s. Harris Franklin and Elizabeth (Stockton) MacN.; m. Phyllis Diana Walter, Sept. 26, 1963; children: Richard Roderick, Alexander Stockton. B.A., U. Chgo., 1940, M.A., 1944, Ph.D., 1949; LL.D. (hon.), Simon Frazer U., 1980; LL.D. Guggenheim fellow, Harvard U., 1956; LL.D. Aboriginal fellow, U. Mich., 1946. Supr., dir. U. Chgo. (W.P.A.) 1941-46; head dept. archaeology U. Calgary, 1964-68; anthropologist Nat. Mus. Can., 1949-62; dir. R.S. Peabody Found. for Archaeology, Andover, Mass., 1968-83; prof. dept. archeology Boston U., 1982-86; dir. Andover Found. for Archaeol. Research, 1986—. Contbr. numerous articles and revs. to profl. jours. Apptd. to U.S. Pres. Adv. Com. on Cultural Properties, 1992—. With AUS, 1942-43. Recipient Spinden medal for archaeology, 1964, Lucy Wharton Drexel medal for archaeol. research U. Pa. Mus., 1965, Addison Emery Verrill medal Peabody Mus., Yale U., 1966, hon. Disting. Prof. award Universidad Nacional de San Cristobal de Huamanga, Ayacucho, Peru, 1970, Cornplanter medal for Iroquois research Auburn N.Y., 1977. Mem. AAAS, Soc. Am. Archaeology (exec. council), Nat. Acad. Scis., Brit. Acad., Soc. Am. Archaeology (pres. 1971-72), Am. Anthrop. Assn. (Alfred Vincent Kidder award 1971), Sigma Psi, Alpha Tau Omega. Office: Andover Found Archaeol Research PO Box 83 Andover MA 01810-0002

MAC NELLY, JEFFREY KENNETH, cartoonist; b. N.Y.C., Sept. 17, 1947; s. Clarence Lamont and Ruth Ellen (Fox) Mac N.; m. Marguerite Dewey Daniels, July 19, 1969; children: Jeffrey Kenneth, Frank Daniels; m. Martha Scott Perry, July 13, 1985; 1 child, Matthew Perry; m. Susan Spekin, July 22, 1990. Grad., Phillips Acad., 1965; student, U. N.C., Chapel Hill, 1965-69. Cartoonist, staff artist Chapel Hill Weekly, 1969-70; cartoonist Richmond (Va.) News Leader, 1970-81, Chgo. Tribune, 1981—; creator syndicated comic strip Shoe. Recipient Pulitzer prize for editorial cartoons 1972, 78, 85.

MACNICHOL, EDWARD FORD, JR., biophysicist, educator; b. Toledo, Oct. 24, 1918; s. Edward Ford and Adelaide (Foster) MacN.; m. Anne Proctor Ayer, Sept. 7, 1940; children—Edward Ford III, Anne (Mrs. David A. Brownell). A.B., Princeton, 1941; student, U. Pa., 1946-48; Ph.D., Johns Hopkins, 1952. Staff mem. radiation lab. Mass. Inst. Tech., 1941-46; from instr. to prof. biophysics Johns Hopkins, 1952-68; research biophysicist, asst. dir. Marine Biol. Lab., Woods Hole, Mass., 1972-76; dir. Lab. Sensory Physiology, 1973-84; prof. physiology Boston U. Med. Sch., 1973—; dir. Nat. Inst. Neurol. Diseases and Stroke, 1968-72; acting dir. Nat. Eye Inst., NIH, 1968-69; Mem. visual scis. study sect. NIH, 1963-66; mem. bd. sci. counsellors Nat. Inst. Neurol. Disease, and Blindness, 1965-68, chmn., 1968—; mem. U.S. Nat. Com. Photobiology, 1966-68, U.S. Nat. Com. Pure and Applied Biophysics, 1966. Co-editor: Sensory Processes, 1978-82. Bd. dirs. Deafness Research Found., 1973-83, sec., 1976-78. Recipient certificate of appreciation War Dept.-Navy Dept., 1947. Fellow IEEE (Engring. in Biology and Medicine prize award 1965, Centennial medal 1984, editor trans. biomed. engring. 1963-65); mem. AAAS, Am. Phys. Soc., Am. Physiol. Soc., Biophys. Soc., Soc. for Neurosci. Research in neurophysiology of vision; design instrumentation biol. research. Home: 120 Racing Beach Ave Falmouth MA 02540-1709 Office: Dept Physiology Boston Univ Sch Med 80 E Concord St Roxbury MA 02118-2394 *I have found a career, which has involved research, administration, engineering and teaching, to be both rewarding and challenging. I would regret not having had all these experiences; particularly the contact with different kinds of people having different ways of thinking. I would urge young people, above all, to understand thoroughly the basic principles involved in what they are doing, then work out the details, instead of just learning by rote the details of a narrow specialty.*

MACNIDER, JACK, retired cement company executive; b. Washington, Feb. 21, 1927; s. Hanford and Margaret Elizabeth (McAuley) MacN.; m. Margaret Hansen, Sept. 9, 1950; 1 son, Charles Hanford. Grad., Milton (Mass.) Acad., 1946; BA, Harvard U., 1950, MBA with distinction, 1952. With U.S. Steel Corp., 1952-54; with Northwestern States Portland Cement Co., Mason City, Iowa, 1954-90; v.p., asst. gen. mgr. Northwestern States Portland Cement Co., 1959-60, pres., gen. mgr., 1960-90, chmn. bd., 1979-90, ret., 1990; dir. Portland Cement Assn., 1962-90, chmn., 1974-76; dir. Norwest Bank Mason City; sec.-treas., pres., dir. Mason City Hotel Corp.; pres., dir. Indian Farms, Inc., 1976—; trustee Equitable Life Ins. Co., Iowa, 1964-93. Chmn. North Iowa Med. Ctr., 1974-91; trustee Beloit Coll., Midwest Rsch. Inst., Kansas City, Mo., Iowa Natural Heritage Found., 1979-90, Herbert Hoover Presdl. Libr., 1985—; hon. trustee Upper Iowa U., Fayette; pres. Iowa Coll. Found., 1962. With USMCR, 1944-45. Mem. NAM (dir. 1978-85), Young Pres. Orgn., Portland Cement Assn. (chmn. bd. 1974-75, dir.), Iowa Mfrs. Assn. (chmn. 1971-72, dir.), Mason City C. of C. (pres. 1962), Am. Legion (past post comdr.), Masons, Euchre and Cycle Club (Mason City, Mason City Country Club, Mpls. Club, Univ. Club (Chgo.), Des Moines Club, Los Tree Club (Fla.). Republican. Congregationalist. Address: PO Box 623 Mason City IA 50402-0623

MACOMBER, JOHN D., industrialist; b. Rochester, N.Y., Jan. 13, 1928; s. William Butts and Elizabeth Currie (Ranlet) M.; m. Caroline Morgan, Oct. 21, 1955; children: Janet Morgan, Elizabeth Currie, William Butts II. B.A., Yale U., 1950; M.B.A., Harvard U. 1952. With McKinsey & Co., N.Y.C., France and Switzerland, 1954-73; mng. dir. McKinsey & Co., Geneva, 1961-64; continental coordinator Europe McKinsey & Co., Paris, 1964-68; dir. McKinsey & Co.; pres. Celanese Corp., N.Y.C., 1973-87, chief exec. officer, 1977, chmn., 1980-87; children: J.D. Macomber & Co., N.Y.C., 1987-89; pres., chmn. Export-Import Bank of U.S., Washington, 1989-92; prin. JDM Investment Group, Washington, 1992—. 1st lt. USAF, 1952-53. Clubs: Metropolitan; Links (N.Y.C.), River (N.Y.C.), Union (N.Y.C.), N.Y. Yacht, Metropolitan (Washington). Office: John D. Macomber Investment Group 2806 N St NW Washington DC 20007-0002

MACOMBER, JOHN D., construction executive; b. Boston, Oct. 8, 1955; s. George and Ann L. Macomber; m. Kristin Hodgkins, June 11, 1983; children: Ian D., Eric C. BA, Dartmouth Coll., 1978; MBA, Harvard U., 1983. Project mgr. George B.H. Macomber Co., Boston, 1987-90, v.p., 1983-87, pres., chief exec. officer, 1990—; lectr. MIT. Mem. exec. com. Appalachian Mountain Club, Boston, 1989-93. Mem. U.S. Alpine Ski Team, 1974-76; NCAA All-America in skiing, 1974, 78. Mem. Harvard Bus. Sch. Assn. (pres. 1994-95), Young Pres. Orgn. Avocations: skiing, bicycling, tennis. Office: George BH Macomber Co 530 Atlantic Ave Boston MA 02210

MACOMBER, TRICIA, airport executive. Mgr. ops. Charlotte/Douglas Internat. Airport, Charlotte, N.C. Office: Charlotte/Douglas Internat Airpt Box 19066 Charlotte NC 28219

MACON, JANE HAUN, lawyer; b. Corpus Christi, Tex., Sept. 26, 1946; d. E.H. and Johnnie Mae (De Mauri) Haun; m. R. Laurence Macon, Sept. 6, 1969. B in Internat. Studies, U. Tex., 1967, JD, 1970. Bar: Tex. 1971, Ga. 1971, U.S. Dist. Ct. (we. dist.) Tex. 1973, U.S. Ct. Appeals (5th and 11th cirs.) 1973. Legal staff Office Econ. Opportunity, Atlanta, 1970-71; trial atty. City of San Antonio, 1972-77, city atty., 1977-83; ptnr. Fulbright & Jaworski, LLP, San Antonio, 1983—; pres. Internat. Women's Forum, Washington, 1987-89; bd. dirs. Thousand Oaks Nat. Bank, San Antonio. Legal counsel Nat. Women's Polit. Caucus, 1981—; bd. dirs. Alamo council Boy Scouts Am., San Antonio, 1977—. Named to San Antonio Hall of Fame, 1984; named one of Rising Stars, 1984. Fellow Tex. Bar Found.; Tex. Bar Assn. (chmn. women and the law 1984-85, client security fund com.), Southwest Research Found.; mem. San Antonio Bar Assn., San Antonio Young Lawyers Assn., Women Lawyers Tex. (pres. 1984-85), Tex. Banking Bd., Bexar County Women's Bar Assn. Democrat. Baptist. Home: 230 W Elsmere Pl San Antonio TX 78212-2349 Office: Fulbright & Jaworski LLP 300 Convent St Ste 2200 San Antonio TX 78205-3792

MACON, JERRY LYN, software company owner, software publisher; b. Okla., Jan. 10, 1941; s. James Westwood and Mary Isabelle (Hankins) M.; m. Carol Ann Gloeckler, Aug. 28, 1981; children: Heather, Scott, Karla. BS in Physics magna cum laude, Colo. Coll., 1963; MS in Physics, MIT, 1966; MBA in Fin., U. Colo., 1980. Physics instr. U.S. Naval Acad., Annapolis, Md., 1966-69; stockbroker Merrill Lynch, Colorado Springs, 1969-71; dir. systems analysis and programming Colorado Springs Pub. Schs., 1971-80; co-founder, pres. Alpine Software, Inc., Colorado Springs, 1980-82, Macon Systems Inc., Colorado Springs, 1981—. Author software: DB Master, 1980, Advanced CB Master, 1981, Advanced DB Master for Windows Version 6.0, 1995. Mem. Colorado Springs Fine Arts Ctr., 1982—, Colorado Springs Symphony Coun., 1985—, Colorado Springs Better Bus. Bur., 1990—, Cmdr. USN, 1966-69, USNR, 1959-63, 69-82. Boettcher Found. scholar, 1959; Woodrow Wilson fellow, 1963; MIT rsch. assistantship, 1964. Mem. Nat. Fedn. Ind. Bus., Software Pubs. Assn., Colo. Springs Rose Soc., Colo. Mountain Club, Phi Beta Kappa. Avocations: mountain climbing, hiking, travel, reading history, growing roses. Office: Macon Systems Inc 724 S Tejon St Colorado Springs CO 80903-4042

MACON, MYRA FAYE, library director; b. Slate Springs, Miss., Sept. 29, 1937; d. Thomas Howard and Reba Elizabeth (Edwards) M. BS in Edn., Delta State U., 1959; MLS, La. State U., 1965; postgrad., U. Akron, Ohio; EdD, Miss. State U., 1977. Librarian Greenwood (Miss.) Jr. High Sch., 1959-62, Greenwood High Sch., 1962-63, Grenada (Miss.) High Sch., 1963-64; library supr. Cuyahoga Falls (Ohio) City Schs., 1964-71; assoc. prof. U. Miss., Oxford, 1971-83; dir. libraries Delta State U., Cleve., 1983—. Editor: School Library Media Services for Handicapped; editor: ANRT Newsletter, Miss. Libraries; contbr. articles to profl. jours. Mem. ALA, Southeastern Library Assn., Miss. Library Assn., Exch. Club, Phi Delta Kappa, Beta Phi

Mu, Delta Kappa Gamma, Omicron Delta Kappa. Home: 307 S Fifth Ave Cleveland MS 38732-3153 Office: WB Robers Library Delta State U Cleveland MS 38733

MACON, RICHARD LAURENCE, lawyer; b. Dallas, Dec. 31, 1944; s. Joseph Weldon and Dorothy Marie (Sikes) M.; m. Jane Arian Haun, Sept. 6, 1969. B of Arts in Am. Studies, Yale U., 1967; JD with honors, U. Tex. 1970. Bar: Ga. 1970, Tex. 1972, U.S. Dist. Ct. (we., ea., so. and no. dists.) Tex., U.S. Dist. Ct. (no. dist.) Ga., U.S. Ct. Appeals (5th and 11th cirs.). U.S. Supreme Ct. Assoc. Powell, Goldstein, Frazer & Murphy, Atlanta, 1970-72; ptnr. Cox & Smith, Inc., San Antonio, 1972-92, Akin, Gump, Strauss, Hauer & Feld, San Antonio, 1992—. Bd. dirs. Women Employment Network, Soc. Performing Arts, Monte Vista Hist. Soc., Target 90, Tex. Bank North, United Way Allocations Bd., San Antonio Free Clinic, San Antonio Edn. Employment, Inc., Com. for Alamodome, Com. for Supercollider, State Com. on Mental Retardation, Bexar County Women's Ctr., Bexar County Dem. Exec. Com.; chmn. 19th Senatorial Dist. Dem. Conv., Mayor's Commn. Energy; pres. Atlanta Tex. Execs.. Named as Man of Yr. San Antonio AFL-CIO, Rising Star Tex. Bus. Mag.; recipient Award of Appreciation YWCA, Award by Mexican Am. Legal Def. Fund, Award by Bexar County Edn. Found., Award by Bexar County Women's Polit. Caucus. Mem. Yale Club (pres. South Tex. chpt.), Order of Coif, Phil Delta Phi. Home: 230 W Elsmere Pl San Antonio TX 78212-2349 Office: Akin Gump Strauss Hauer & Feld 300 Convent Ste 1500 San Antonio TX 78205

MACON, SETH CRAVEN, retired insurance company executive; b. Climax, N.C., Mar. 22, 1919; s. Oran T. and Kate (Craven) M.; m. Hazel Lee Monsees, June 27, 1942; children—Carol Susan, Randall Seth. A.B., Guilford Coll., 1940; grad., Am. Coll. Life Underwriters, 1949; postgrad., Inst. Ins. Marketing, So. Methodist U., 1947; exec. program, U. N.C., 1958. With Jefferson Standard Life Ins. Co., 1940-86, v.p., assoc. agy. mgr., 1964-67, v.p., agy. mgr., 1967-70, sr. v.p., dir., mem. finance com., 1970-84; v.p. Jefferson-Pilot Corp., 1974-86, also bd. dirs.; mem. adv. bd. Branch Bank & Trust Co. Author: Action in Recruiting, 1970, Recruiting—Today's Number One Priority in Agency Management, 1979. Trustee Life Underwriters Tng. Coun., 1974-76, So. Theol. Sem. Found., Louisville, 1983-93; trustee Guilford Coll., 1969—, chmn., 1980-88; bd. dirs. N.C. Bapt. Homes, 1983-92; mem. coordinating coun. Coop. Bapt. Fellowship, 1991—. Recipient Disting. Alumnus award Guilford Coll., 1978. Mem. Life Ins. Marketing and Research Assn. Club (1974-78, chmn. 1976-77). Baptist (deacon 1960—, mem. fin. com. 1960-63). Lodge: Rotary. Home: 3803 Madison Ave Greensboro NC 27403-1035

MACOSKA, JILL ANNE, urology and cancer biology educator, researcher; b. Cleve., Mar. 31, 1956; d. Raymond Patrick and Ruth Jeanne (Ormiston) M.; m. David H. Sigmon, July 8, 1989. BA magna cum laude, Kent State U., 1978; MPhil, CUNY, 1986, PhD, 1988. Postdoctoral fellow Harvard U., Cambridge, Mass., 1988-89, Mich. Cancer Found., Detroit, 1989-91; rsch. assoc. Wayne State U., Detroit, 1991-92, asst. prof. urology and cancer biology, 1992—; health sci. specialist VA, Allen Park, Mich., 1993—. Recipient PhD Scholar award Am. Fedn. Urologic Disease, 1991-93; Konheim grad. scholar CUNY, 1985. Mem. Am. Assn. for Cancer Rsch., Women in Cancer Rsch., Soc. for Basic Urologic Rsch., Phi Beta Kappa. Office: Wayne State U Dept Urology 1017 Harper Profl Bldg 4160 John R Detroit MI 48201-1928

MACOVSKI, ALBERT, electrical engineering educator; b. N.Y.C., May 2, 1929; s. Philip and Rose (Winogr) M.; m. Adelaide Paris, Aug. 5, 1950; children—Michael, Nancy. B.E.E., City Coll. N.Y., 1950; M.E.E., Poly. Inst. Bklyn., 1953; Ph.D., Stanford U., 1968. Mem. tech. staff RCA Labs., Princeton, N.J., 1950-57; asst. prof., then assoc. prof. Poly. Inst. Bklyn. 1957-60; staff scientist Stanford Research Inst., Menlo Park, Calif., 1960-71; fellow U. Calif. Med. Center San Francisco, 1971-72; prof. elec. engring. and radiology Stanford U., 1972—, endowed chair, Canon USA prof. engring., 1991—; dir. Magnetic Resonance Systems Research Lab.; cons. to industry. Author. Recipient Achievement award RCA Labs., 1952, 54; award for color TV circuits Inst. Radio Engrs., 1958; NIH spl. fellow, 1971. Fellow IEEE (Zworykin award 1973), Am. Inst. Med. Biol. Engring., Optical Soc. Am.; mem. NAE, Inst. of Medicine, Am. Assn. Physicists in Medicine, Soc. Magnetic Resonance in Medicine (former trustee), Sigma Xi, Eta Kappa Nu. Jewish. Achievements include patents in field. Home: 2505 Alpine Rd Menlo Park CA 94025-6314 Office: Stanford U Dept Elec Engring Stanford CA 94305

MACPHAIL, MORAY ST. JOHN, mathematics educator emeritus; b. Kingston, Ont., Can., May 27, 1912; s. James Alexander and Agnes Mary (Macmorine) M.; m. Frances Marian Patterson, Aug. 17, 1939; 1 child, James Alexander. B.A., Queen's U., 1933; M.A., McGill U., 1934; D.Phil., Oxford U., 1936; D.Sc. (hon.), Carleton U., 1978. Instr. Acadia U. Wolfville, N.S., Can., 1937-39, asst. prof., 1939-41, assoc. prof., 1942-44, prof., 1944-47; instr. Princeton U., N.J., 1941-42; vis. lectr. Queen's U., Kingston, Ont., Can., 1947-48; assoc. prof. Carleton U., Ottawa, Ont., Can., 1948-53, prof., 1953-67, 68-77, prof. emeritus, 1977—; vis. prof. U. Toronto, Ont., Can., 1967-68; assoc. dean Carleton U. Ottawa, Ont., Can., 1956-60, dir. grad. studies, 1960-63, dean grad. studies, 1963-69. Contbr. articles to profl. jours. Fellow Royal Soc. Can.; mem. Am. Math. Soc., Math. Assn. Am., Can. Math. Soc. Avocation: Music. Home: 165 Powell Ave, Ottawa, ON Canada K1S 2A2 Office: Carleton Univ, Dept Math and Stats, Ottawa, ON Canada K1S 5B6

MACPHEE, CRAIG ROBERT, economist, educator; b. Annapolis Royal, N.S., Can., July 10, 1944; came to U.S., 1950; s. Craig and Dorothy (Seney) MacP.; m. Kathleen Gray McCown, Feb. 6, 1966 (div. 1981); children: Paul, Heather, Rob; m. Andrea Joy Sime, June 26, 1983. BS, U. Idaho, 1966; MA, Mich. State U., 1968, PhD, 1970. Asst. prof., then assoc. prof. econs. U. Nebr., Lincoln, 1969-89, prof., 1989—, chmn. econs. dept., 1980-83, 89—; econ. affairs officer UN, Geneva, 1975-77; internat. economist U.S. Dept. Labor, Washington, 1983-84; cons. in field. Author: Economics of Medical Equipment and Supply, 1973, Restrictions on International Trade in Steel, 1974. Mem. Am. Econ. Assn., Midwest Econ. Assn., Nebr. Econ. and Bus. Assn., Delta Sigma Pi (faculty adviser 1982-95), Phi Eta Sigma, Omicron Delta Epsilon. Avocations: running, skiing, sailing, reading. Home: 631 Hazelwood Dr Lincoln NE 68510 Office: U Nebr Coll Bus Dept Econ Lincoln NE 68588-0489

MACPHEE, DONALD ALBERT, academic administrator; b. Portland, Oreg., Jan. 3, 1928; s. Donald Lyman and Helen Adelaide (Randall) MacP.; m. Betty Jo Mincher, Sept. 9, 1950; children: Martha, William, Rebecca. BA, Seattle Pacific Coll., 1950; MA, U. Calif., Berkeley, 1952, PhD, 1959. Instr., asst., assoc. prof. history, acting dean ednl. svcs. and summer session San Francisco State Coll., 1956-64; assoc. prof. to prof. history Calif. State U., Dominquez Hills, 1964-85, mem. acad. planning staff, dean Sch. Social and Behavioral Scis., provost and v.p. acad. affairs, 1964-85; pres. SUNY Coll., Fredonia, 1985—. Contbr. scholarly articles on Am. politics, labor history, historiography, higher education to profl. jours. Bd. dirs. Fredonia (N.Y.) Coll. Found., Brooks Meml. Hosp., Dunkirk, N.Y., No. Chautauqua Community Found., Dunkirk, Chautauqua County Indsl. Devel. Agy., Mayville, N.Y. Mem. Am. Assn. State Colls. and Univs. Com. on policies and priorities), No. Chautauqua C. of C. Office: SUNY Coll at Fredonia Office of Pres Fredonia NY 14063

MACPHERSON, COLIN R(OBERTSON), pathologist, educator; b. Aberdeen, Scotland, Sept. 2, 1924; came to U.S., 1956; s. Donald J.R. and Nora (Tait) M.; m. Margaret E. Mitchell, Dec. 21, 1949; children: Shelagh, Catherine, Janet, Mary. MBChB, U. Cape Town, Union South Africa, 1946, M.Med., MD in Pathology, 1954. Diplomate Anatomic and Clinical Pathology, Blood Banking. Resident, instr. U. Cape Town, 1948-54; fellow Postgrad. Med. Sch., London, 1955-56; asst., assoc. then prof. pathology Ohio State U., Columbus, 1956-75, vice chmn. lab. med., 1961-75; dir. lab. medicine U. Cin., 1975-87, dep. dir. Hoxworth Blood Ctr., 1988-90, prof. dept. pathology and lab. medicine, 1991—. Contbr. articles to profl. jours. Chmn. bd. schs., rev. bd. Nat. Accrediting Agy. for Clin. Lab. Scis., 1968-74. Mem. Am. Soc. Clin. Pathologists. Presbyterian. Avocations: music, color photography. Office: U Cin Med Ctr Goodman St Cincinnati OH 45267-0714

MACPHERSON, ELLE, model; b. Sydney, Australia, Mar. 29, 1964; m. Gilles Bensimon, May 24, 1986 (div.). Appeared on covers of Sports Illustrated swimsuit edit., 1986, 87, 88, 94, Elle, Cosmopolitan, Self; film appearances include Sirens, 1992, Sirens, 1994. Office: Women Model Mgmt 107 Greene St 2nd Fl New York NY 10012

MACQUARRIE, HEATH NELSON, Canadian government official; b. Victoria, P.E.I., Can., Sept. 18, 1919; s. Wilfred and Mary (Mallard) M.; m. Jean Isabel Stewart, Dec. 27, 1949; children: Heather Jean, Flora Mary, Iain Heath. BA, U. Man., 1947; MA, U. N.B., 1949; postgrad., McGill U., 1951-53; LLD, U. P.E.I., 1977. Tchr. pub. and high schs. P.E.I., 1936-43; asst. boys work sec. YMCA, Winnipeg, 1943-47; asst. prof. econs. and polit. sci. U. N.B., 1947-49; lectr. polit. sci. McGill U., 1949-51, prof. polit. sci. and internat. relations, 1952; faculty Brandon Coll., 1951-55; lectr. Carleton U., 1963-64; vis. lectr. Mt. Allison U., summer, 1948, 56, assoc. prof. dept. polit. sci., 1978-79; vis. lectr. Acadia U., summer) 1949, 52, U. Man., summer) 1954; Rockefeller research assoc. U. Toronto, 1955-56; instr. internat. relations Carleton U., 1963-64; Weekly news analyst sta. CKX (radio), 1952-55; analyst and commentator pub. affairs programs CBC. Author: The Conservative Party, Canada and the Third World, Red Tory Blues, 1992; editor (Carleton Libr. edit.) Memoirs of Sir Robert L. Borden; contbr. numerous articles to various publs. 3d v.p. Progressive Conservative Party Can., 1953-55; elected constituency of Queens, 1957, 58, 62, 63, 65; parliamentary sec. for external affairs, 1962-63; elected constituency of Hillsborough, P.E.I. Ho. of Commons, 1968-78; summoned to Senate of Can., 1979; del. UN Gen. Assembly, 1957-59, 63, 71; chmn. com. on internat. affairs Presbyn. Ch. in Can., 1979-84. Decorated Grand Cordon of Order of AL 1stiqlal (Independence) (King Hussein of Jordan); recipient various research awards from Canadian Social Sci. Research Council John S. Ewart Found. and Research Associateship U. Toronto. Mem. P.E.I. Hist. Soc., Inter-Parliamentary Union, Can. Commonwealth Parliamentary Assn. (chmn.), Commonwealth Parliamentary Assn. (del. gen. assembly Bahamas 1969), Can. Inst. Internat. Affairs, Can. Polit. Sci. Assn., Assn. Can. Studies, Charlottetown C. of C., Confedn. Art Gallery and Mus., Can. Bur. Internat. Edn. (bd. dirs.), Masons. Conservative. Office: The Senate, Ottawa, ON Canada K1A 0A4 *While profoundly convinced that we must and should take our work seriously, we are in grave danger if we ever take our poor mortal selves too seriously. As has been said in the long ago, humor is a "saving" grace.*

MACQUEEN, ROBERT MOFFAT, solar physicist; b. Memphis, Mar. 28, 1938; s. Marion Leigh and Grace (Gilfillan) MacQ.; m. Caroline Gibbs, June 25, 1960; children: Andrew, Marjorie. BS, Rhodes Coll., 1960; PhD, Johns Hopkins U., 1968. Asst. prof. physics Rhodes Coll., 1961-63; instr. physics and astronomy Grouber Coll., Towson, Md., 1964-66; sr. research scientist Nat. Ctr. for Atmospheric Research, Boulder, Colo., 1967-90, dir. High Altitude Obs., 1979-86, asst. dir., 1986-87, assoc. dir., 1987-89; prof. physics Rhodes Coll., Memphis, 1990—; prin. investigator NASA Apollo program, 1971-75, NASA Skylab program, 1970-76, NASA Solar Maximum Mission, 1976-79, NASA/ESA Internat. Solar Polar Mission, 1978-83; lectr. U. Colo., 1968-79, adj. prof., 1979-90; mem. com. on space astronomy Nat. Acad. Scis., 1973-76, mem. com. on space physics, 1977-79; mem. Space Sci. Bd., 1983-86. Recipient Exceptional Sci. Achievement medal NASA, 1974. Fellow Optical Soc. Am.; mem. Am. Astron. Soc. (chmn. solar physics div 1976-78), Assn. Univ. Research Astronomy (dir.-at-large 1984-93, chmn. bd. 1989-92), Am. Assn. Physics Tchrs., Sigma Xi.

MAC RAE, ALFRED URQUHART, physicist, electrical engineer; b. N.Y.C., Apr. 14, 1932; s. Farquhar and Eliza J. (Urquhary) Mac R.; m. Peggy M. Hazard, May 13, 1967; children: Susan, Pamela. BS in Physics, Syracuse U., 1954, Ph.D. in Physics, 1960. Dir. integrated circuit devel. Bell Labs., Murray Hill, N.J., 1979-83; dir. satellite communications systems Bell Labs., Homdel, N.J., 1983—; adv. com. to bd. trustees N.J. Inst. Tech., 1981-85. Bd. editor: Vacuum Sci. and Tech, 1965-67, Rev. Sci. Instruments, 1969-71; contbr. articles to jours.; patentee in field. Fellow IEEE (chmn. field awards 1991-93), Am. Phys. Soc.; mem. Bohmische Phys. Soc., IEEE Electron Devices Soc. (pres. 1986-87, chmn. field awards 1989-93, Ebers award 1994). Office: Bell Labs Crawford Cor Rd Holmdel NJ 07733

MACRAE, CAMERON FARQUHAR, III, lawyer; b. N.Y.C., Mar. 21, 1942; s. Cameron F. and Jane B. (Miller) MacR.; m. Ann Wooster Bedell, Nov. 30, 1974; children: Catherine Fairfax, Ann Cameron. A.B., Princeton U., 1963; LL.B., Yale U., 1966. Bar: N.Y. 1966, D.C. 1967, U.S. Dist. Ct. (so. dist.) N.Y. 1975. Atty.-advisor Office of Gen. Counsel to Sec. Air Force, Washington, 1966-69; assoc. Davis, Polk & Wardwell, N.Y.C., 1970-72; dep. supt. and counsel N.Y. State Banking Dept., N.Y.C., 1972-74; sr. ptnr. LeBoeuf, Lamb, Greene & MacRae, N.Y.C., 1975—. Trustee, sec. St. Andrew's Dune Ch., 1982—; hon. chmn. Clear Pool Inc., 1990—. Capt. USAF, 1966-69. Mem. Assn. of Bar of City of N.Y. (past mem. securities regulation com., banking law com.), D.C. Bar Assn. Republican. Episcopalian. Clubs: Links, Racquet and Tennis (N.Y.C.), Meadow (v.p., bd. govs.), Bathing Corp., Shinnecock Hills Golf (Southampton), Cottage (Princeton, N.J.). Note and comment editor Yale Law Jour., 1965-66. Office: LeBoeuf Lamb Greene & MacRae 125 W 55th St New York NY 10019-5369

MACRAE, DONALD ALEXANDER, astronomy educator; b. Halifax, Nova Scotia, Can., Feb. 19, 1916; s. Donald Alexander and Laura Geddes (Barnstead) M.; m. Margaret Elizabeth Malcolm, Aug. 25, 1939; children—David Malcolm, Charles Donald, Andrew Richard. B.A., U. Toronto, Ont., Can., 1937; A.M., Harvard U., Cambridge, Mass., 1940, Ph.D., 1943. Research asst. U. Pa., Phila., 1941-42; lectr. Cornell U., Ithaca, N.Y., 1942-44; scientist Carbide & Carbon Chem. Corp., Oak Ridge, Tenn., 1944-46; asst. prof. Case Inst. Tech., Cleve., 1946-53; assoc. prof. to prof. astronomy, dir. David Dunlap Observatory, U. Toronto, 1953-78, prof. and dir. emeritus, 1978—; trustee Univs. Space Research Assn., Lunar and Planetary Inst., Houston, 1969-76, Can.-France-Hawaii Telescope Corp., Kamuela, Hawaii, 1973-79, Cascatrust, 1991-94. Fellow Royal Soc. Can., Royal Astron. Soc. (London); mem. Can. Astron. Soc., Royal Astron. Soc. Can., Am. Astron. Soc. Home: 427 Glencairn Ave, Toronto, ON Canada M5N 1V4 Office: David Dunlap Observatory, Box 360, Richmond Hill, ON Canada L4C 4Y6

MACRAE, DUNCAN, JR., social scientist, educator; b. Glen Ridge, N.J., Sept. 30, 1921; s. Duncan and Rebecca Kyle (MacRae) m. Edith Judith Krugelis, June 24, 1950; 1 child, Amy Frances. A.B., Johns Hopkins U., 1942; A.M., Harvard U., 1943, Ph.D., 1950. Mem. staff Radiation Lab. Mass. Inst. Tech., 1943-46; instr., then lectr. sociology Princeton, 1949-51; rsch. assoc. Lab. Social Rels., Harvard U., 1951-53; asst. prof. sociology U. Calif., Berkeley, 1953-57; mem. faculty U. Chgo., 1957-72, prof. polit. sci. and sociology, 1964-72; William Rand Kenan, Jr. prof. polit. sci. and sociology U. N.C., Chapel Hill, 1972—; chmn. curriculum in public policy analysis U. N.C., 1980-85; Pres. Policy Studies Assn., 1974-75. Author: Dimensions of Congressional Voting, 1958, Parliament, Parties and Society in France, 1946-58, 1967, Issues and Parties in Legislative Voting, 1970, The Social Function of Social Science, 1976, (with James A. Wilde) Policy Analysis for Public Decisions, 1979, Policy Indicators, 1985; Editor: (with others) Electronic Instruments, 1948, Policies for America's Public Schools, 1988. Fulbright rsch. scholar France, 1956-57. Fellow AAAS, Am. Acad. Arts and Scis.; mem. Am. Polit. Sci. Assn., Am. Sociol. Assn., Am. Econ. Assn., Assn. Pub. Policy and Mgmt., Phi Beta Kappa. Home: 737 Gimghoul Rd Chapel Hill NC 27514-3815

MAC RAE, HERBERT FARQUHAR, retired college president; b. Middle River, N.S., Can., Mar. 30, 1926; s. Murdoch John and Jessie (Matheson) Mac R.; m. Mary Ruth Finlayson, Sept. 24, 1955; children—Roderick John, Elizabeth Anne, Christy Margaret, Mary Jean. Diploma NS, Agrl. Coll., 1952; BSc, McGill U., 1954, MSc, 1956, PhD, 1960, DSc (hon.), 1987. Chemist, food and drug directorate Dept. Nat. Health and Welfare, Ottawa, Ont., 1960-61; mem. faulty Macdonald Coll. McGill U., 1961-72, assoc. prof. animal sci. Macdonald Coll., 1967-70, prof. chmn. dept. Macdonald Coll., 1970-72; prin. N.S. Agrl. Coll., Truro, 1972-89, ret., 1989. Named to Can. Agrl. Hall of Fame, 1994. Fellow Agrl. Inst. Can.; mem. Can. Soc. Animal Sci., Mem. Order of Can., Rotary, Sigma Xi. Home: 7 Hickman Dr, Truro, NS Canada B2N 2Z2

MACRAKIS, KRISTIE IRENE, history of science educator; b. Boston, Mar. 11, 1958; d. Michael S. and Lily Macrakis. BA, Oberlin (Ohio) Coll. 1980; MA, Harvard U., 1983, PhD, 1989. Rsch. asst. Harvard U., Cambridge, Mass., 1980-82, lectr., 1989-91; postdoctoral fellow Humbolt Found., Bonn, Germany, 1990-91; asst. prof. Mich. State U., East Lansing, 1991—. Author: Surviving the Swastika, 1993; contbr. articles to profl. jours. AAUW fellow, WAshington, 1987-88; Social Sci. Rsch. Coun. fellow, N.Y.C., 1984-86; Inst. for Advanced Study fellow, 1993-94. Mem. Am. Hist. Assn., German Studies Assn., N.Y. Acad. Sci., History of Sci. Soc., Sigma Xi. Avocations: music, sports. Office: Mich State U Dept History Morrill Hall 301 East Lansing MI 48824

MACRI, THEODORE WILLIAM, book publisher; b. N.Y.C.; s. Francis Carl and Emma Julia (Fantini) M.; m. Joan Michele Damato; children: Alicia, Theodore William. AB, Villanova U; MA, NYU. With Doubleday & Co. Inc., N.Y.C.; dir. domestic rights, editorial group dir., 1982-83, asst. to pres., 1983; v.p., pub. R.R. Bowker Co., 1983-85; v.p. dir. subs. rights Contemporary Books, Inc., 1985-90; v.p. Carol Pub. Group, Inc., N.Y.C., 1990-94; pres. Ted Macri Assocs., 1994—; Bd. dirs. CUNY Ctr. for Pub., 1983—, Nat. Book Awards. Mem. N.Y. County Republican Com., 1980-81; mem. men's com. Mus. Natural History, N.Y.C., 1978. Served to It. (j.g.) USNR. Named Disting. Alumnus Villanova U., 1983. Mem. Assn. Am. Pubs. (edn. com.), Am. Bookseller's Assn. Republican. Roman Catholic. Club: N.Y. Athletic (N.Y.C.). Office: 10 E End Ave Ste 4E New York NY 10021-1106

MACRO, LUCIA ANN, editor; b. Rhinebeck, N.Y., May 15, 1959; d. Virgil Jordan and Jeannette Anastasia (Jakelski) M.; m. Richard Marchione, 1992. BA, Fordham U., Bronx, 1981. Asst. editor, editor Silhouette Books, N.Y.C., 1985—, sr. editor, 1989—; speaker in field nat. convs. Romance Writers Am., 1985—; interviewed Bus. Week, 1987, CNN, 1991, Sta. WNBC, various newspapers including N.Y. Daily News, Washington Post. Author articles Romantic Times, 1988-89, 93, Romance Writers Report, 1988-89. Recipient Rita award Romance Writers Am., 1990, 92, 94. Democrat. Office: Silhouette Books 300 E 42nd St New York NY 10017-5947

MACRORY, PATRICK FRANCIS JOHN, lawyer; b. Teignmouth, Devon, Eng., Mar. 21, 1941; came to U.S., 1968; s. Patrick Arthur and Marjorie Elizabeth (Lewis) M; m. Ann Kernan, Dec. 17, 1966 (div. Sept. 1987); children: Benedict, Lucinda, Maud, Cecily. BA, Oxford U., Eng., 1962, MA, 1964; LLM, George Washington U., 1971. Barrister-at-law English Supreme Ct. 1964; bar: D.C. 1971. Barrister London, 1965-68; assoc. Arnold and Porter, Washington, 1968-75, ptnr., 1975-1990; ptnr. Akin, Gump, Strauss, Hauer & Feld, Washington, 1990—, head internat. sect., 1993—; vis. assoc. prof. Internat. Christian U., Tokyo, 1977-78; adj. prof. Washington Sch. Law Am. U., 1980—. Editor: Current Legal Aspects of International Trade Law; contbr. numerous articles to profl. jours. Bd. dirs. Internat. Human Rights Law Group, No. Ireland Partnership-U.S.A. Mem. ABA (co-chmn. internat. trade com. 1982-84). Democrat. Episcopalian. Avocations: music, photography. Home: 2427 Tunlaw Rd NW Washington DC 20007-1819 Office: Akin Gump Strauss Hauer & Feld 1333 New Hampshire Ave NW Washington DC 20036-1500

MACSAI, JOHN, architect; b. Budapest, Hungary, May 20, 1926; came to U.S., 1947, naturalized, 1954; s. Ferenc and Margit (Rosenfeld) Lusztig; m. Geraldine Marcus, May 7, 1950; children: Pamela, Aaron, Marian, Gwen. Baccalaureate summa cum laude, Kolcsey Gimnasium, Budapest, 1944; student, Atelier Art Sch., Budapest, 1941-43, Poly. U., Budapest, 1945-47; BArch magna cum laude, Miami U., Oxford, Ohio, 1949. Archtl. designer Skidmore, Owings & Merrill, Chgo., Pace Assos., Chgo., Raymond Loewy Assos., Chgo., 1949-55; ptnr. Hausner & Macsai, Chgo., 1955-71, Campbell & Macsai, Chgo., 1971-74; prin. John Macsai & Assocs. Architects, Inc., Chgo., 1975-90, O'Donnell Wicklund Pigozzi & Peterson, Chgo., 1991—; prof. architecture U. Ill., Chgo., 1970—. Author: High Rise Apartment Buildings: A Design Primer, 1972, Housing, 1976, 2d edit., 1982, Russian edit., 1980, Mexican edit., 1984; co-author: Designing Environments for the Aged, 1977, Housing for a Maturing Population, 1983, (ency.) Highrise Apartment Buildings, 1988; prin. works include Nat. Opinion Rsch. Ctr., U. Chgo., 1967, High Energy Physics Bldg., 1968, Social Svcs. Ctr., 1970; apt. bldgs. Harbor House, 1965, Malibu East, 1972, Waterford apt. bldg., 1976, U. Chgo. faculty townhouses, 1986, Fairfield Ct. housing for the elderly, 1988, Evanston Pl. apt. bldg. and city garage, 1991, 2960 N. Lake Shore Dr. Housing for the Elderly, 1991. Fellow AIA (13 design award citations Chgo. chpt.). Jewish. Home: 1207 Judson Ave Evanston IL 60202-1316 Office: O Donnell Wicklund Pigozzi & Peterson 1 N Franklin St Chicago IL 60606-3401

MACTAGGART, BARRY, retired corporate executive; b. Kandos, Australia, Dec. 29, 1931; came to U.S., 1972; s. Malcolm Ian and Dorothy (Schroder) MacT.; m. Robin Margaret Wilson, Nov. 24, 1962; children: Susan, Ian, Cameron. Cert. acct., Inst. Chartered Accts., Australia, 1954. Audit mgr. Peat, Marwick, Mitchell, Sydney, Australia, 1950-58; auditor, controller eastern area Pfizer Internat., Hong Kong, 1959-64; controller Pfizer Asia, Tokyo, 1964-65, dir. adminstrn., 1966-67; mgr. country Pfizer Australia, 1967-68; pres. Pfizer Asia, Hong Kong, 1968-72; exec. v.p. Pfizer Internat., N.Y.C., 1972-80, pres., 1980-81, pres., chmn. bd. dirs., 1981-91. Mem. Indian Harbor Yacht Club, Hong Kong Club, The Pilgrims Club, John's Island Club, Riomar Day Yacht Club, Univ. and Schs. Club. Home: 180 North Shore Point Vero Beach FL 32963

MACTAGGART, TERRENCE JOSEPH, academic administrator; b. Buffalo, Sept. 20, 1946; s. Joseph Carol and Genieve Mary (Quinn) MacT. BA in English and Philosophy, Canisius Coll., Buffalo, 1967; MA in Lit., St. Louis U., 1971, PhD in Lit., 1976; MBA, St. Cloud (Minn.) State U., 1986. Prof. Blackburn Coll., Carlinville, Ill., 1973-74; dir. Webster U., St. Louis, 1974-77; acting dean U. Alaska, Fairbanks, 1977-79; dean St. Cloud (Minn.) State U., 1979-83; v.p. Met. State U., St. Paul, 1983-86; vice chancellor Minn. State U. System, St. Paul, 1986-87; chancellor U. Wis., Superior, 1987-91, Minn. State U. System, 1991—. Editor: Cost Effective Assessment of Prior Learning, 1983; contbr. articles on higher edn. to profl. jours. Sgt. U.S. Army, 1969-71, Viet Nam. NDEA fellow, 1968-72. Mem. Phi Beta Kappa. Avocations: cross country skiing, sailing. Office: State U System of Minn System Office 555 Park St Ste 230 Saint Paul MN 55103-2111

MACURDY, JOHN EDWARD, basso; b. Detroit, Mar. 18, 1929; s. Blanchard Archibald and Dorathea Rosalie (Radtke) Mc Curdy; m. Justine May Votypka, Apr. 12, 1958; children—Allison Anne, John Blanchard. Student, Wayne State U., 1947; student of Avery Crew, Detroit, 1946. Mem. N.Y.C. Opera, 1959-62, Met. Opera, 1962—. Appeared in U.S., Europe, including San Francisco Opera, La Scala; performances include world premieres Mourning Becomes Electra, Met. Opera, 1967, opening night Anthony and Cleopatra, Met. Opera, 1966, Wuthering Heights, Santa Fe Opera, 1958, Six Characters in Search of an Author, N.Y.C. Opera, 1959, Griffalkin, Tanglewood Festival, 1957; Am. premieres Capriccio, Santa Fe Opera, 1958, Murder in the Cathedral, Empire State Music Festival, Bear Mountain Park, N.Y., 1959, Inspector General, N.Y.C. Opera, 1960; appeared with numerous orchs.; film Don Giovanni, 1979; participant 40th Anniversary Sud-Deutsche Rundfunk, 100th Anniversary Gala Met. Opera, 1983. Served with USAF, 1950-54. Recipient medal for artistic merit during Mich. Week City of Detroit, 1969; inducted into Vocal Hall of Fame, 1985. Mem. Bohemians. Presbyterian. Clubs: Bohemian (San Francisco); Greenwich Country (Conn.). Office: Met Opera Lincoln Ctr New York NY 10023

MACVEY, ALAN MOKLER, program director; b. L.A., Sept. 11, 1946; s. Alfred O. and Ann (Downey) Mokler; m. Carol MacVey, Aug. 6, 1985; 1 child, Joy. BA in English, Stanford U., 1968, MEd, 1970; MFA, Yale U., 1977. English tchr. Palo Alto (Calif.) Sch. Dist., 1969-70, Arlington (Mass.) Sch. Dist., 1970-72; assoc. artistic dir. Theatre Works, Calif., 1972-74; spl. asst. to vice provost Stanford (Calif.) U., 1973-74; prof. theatre Bread Loaf Sch. English, Middlebury, Vt., 1977—, dir. theatre program, 1979—; dir. program in theatre/dance Princeton (N.J.) U., 1980-89, lectr., 1977-91; artistic dir. acting ensemble Princeton, 1977-80, Bread Loaf, 1986—; chair theatre arts dept. U. Iowa, assoc. prof., 1991—. Author 6 original plays; composer, lyricist more than a dozen works for the theatre; dir. more than 70 prodns. Dir. Nat. Endowment for Humanities Insts. for High Sch. Tchrs., 1989, 92, 94. Avocations: music, sports. Office: U Iowa Theatre Arts Dept Theater Bldg Iowa City IA 52242

MAC VICAR, ROBERT WILLIAM, retired university administrator; b. Princeton, Minn., Sept. 28, 1918; s. George William and Elizabeth (Brennan) MacV.; m. Clarice Chambers, Dec. 23, 1948; children—Miriam J., John R. B.A., U. Wyo., 1939, LL.D., 1977; M.S., Okla. State U., 1940; Ph.D., U. Wis., 1946; D.Sci. (hon.), Dankook U., Korea, 1980. Assoc. prof., prof. biochemistry Okla. State U., 1946-64, dean grad. sch., 1953-64, v.p. acad. affairs, 1957-64; v.p. acad. affairs So. Ill. U., Carbondale, 1964-68; chancellor So. Ill. U., 1968-70; pres. Oreg. State U., Corvallis, 1970-84; pres. emeritus Oreg. State U., 1984—; acting pres. Coll. of Ganado, Ariz., 1985; founding mem., bd. dirs. Central Ednl. Midwest Research Lab., chmn. exec. com., 1969-70. Exec. dir. regents task force Ariz. Bd. of Regents, 1987-88; chmn. N.W. Acad. Computing Consortium, 1987-90. Served with U.S. Army, 1939-45. Rhodes scholar, 1939. Mem. Am. Soc. Biol. Chemists, Am. Chem. Soc., Am. Inst. Nutrition, Okla. Acad. Sci., Phi Beta Kappa, Sigma Xi, Phi Kappa Phi. Presbyterian. Home: 1440 NW 14th St Corvallis OR 97330-4660 Office: Oreg State U Corvallis OR 97331

MACVITTIE, PAULA RAE, advertising executive; b. Rhinelander, Wis., Dec. 13, 1950; d. Paul R. and Geraldine Mae (Plant) Alfonsi; m. Ronald B. MacVittie, June 23, 1984. BS in Communication, U. Wis., 1973. Media sales rep. Sta. WAOW-Radio, Tomahawk, Wis., 1973-74; mgr. local sales Sta. WLFI-TV, Lafayette, Ind., 1975-78; pres. Concept Mktg., Inc., Lafayette, 1978-85; account supr. Caldwell VanRiper, Inc., Indpls., 1985-86, v.p., 1986-87, pres., chief exec. officer, 1987—. Mem. pres.'s circle Hudson Inst., Indpls., 1989, 94; Corp. Cmty. Coun., 1989—; exec. com. mem. Cmty. Leaders Allied for Superior Schs., 1989—; bd. dirs Indpls. C. of C., Greater Indpls. Progress Com., United Way Ctrl. Ind. Mem. Am. Mktg. Assn., Ind. Fedn. Advt. Agys. (bd. dirs.), Japan-Am. Soc., Ad Club. Avocations: movies, aerobics, reading. Office: Caldwell VanRiper Inc PO Box 7046 Indianapolis IN 46207-7046

MAC VITTIE, ROBERT WILLIAM, retired college administrator; b. Middletown, N.Y., Dec. 29, 1920; s. Mortimer, Jr. and Mary (Thompson) MacV.; m. Margaret L. Cooper, July 15, 1944; children—Robert William II, Beth Ann, Geralyn Amy. B.Ed., State U. N.Y., Oneonta, 1944; M.A., N.Y. U., 1946; Ed.D., 1954. Elementary tchr. Pine Plains (N.Y.) Central Sch., 1944; social sci. tchr. Meml. Jr. High Sch., Middletown, N.Y., 1944-48; supervising prin. Montowese Sch., North Haven, Conn., 1948-52; Ridge Rd. Sch., North Haven, 1952-53; prof. sch. adminstrn., prin. lab. sch. N.Y. State Coll. Tchrs., Buffalo, 1954-56; dir. div. elementary and secondary edn. State U. N.Y. Coll., Buffalo, 1956-58; dean coll. State U. N.Y. Coll., 1958-63; pres. State U. Coll., Geneseo, 1963-79; emeritus State U. Coll., 1979—; interim pres. SUNY-Fredonia, N.Y., 1985, SUNY-Geneseo, 1988-89; Mem. regional adv. bd. Key Bank, N.A., Oneonta, N.Y., 1978-86; mem. SUNY Commn. Univ. Purposes and Priorities; exec. com. Rochester Area Colls., Inc., 1972-79, SUNY Council Pres.'s, 1970-72, 76-78; bd. dirs. Adams Art Gallery. Author: Handbook for Substitute Teachers, 3d edit, 1959, also numerous articles. Mem. citizens salary adv. com. Kenmore, N.Y., 1957; cons. sch. program evaluation team Tchrs. Coll., Temple U., 1956-57; mem. Livingston County Planning Bd., 1967-73, chmn., 1972-73; bd. dirs. Chautauqua Co. Automobile Club, Inc., Am. Automobile Assn., 1986-93, No. Chautauqua Community Foundation, 1985—, Chautauqua Adult Day Care Ctrs., 1991-92, D.R. Barker Libr., 1992—; mem. adv. bd. Auto Club Western N.Y., 1993—. Paul Harris fellow Rotary Internat. Mem. Am. Assn. Higher Edn., Am. Assn. Sch. Administrs., Am. Assn. Univ. Adminstrs. (pres. 1971-73, dir. 1977-79, gen. sec. 1979-81, Disting. Svc. award 1994), Am. Assn. State Colls. and Univs. (bd. dirs. 1970-79), Phi Delta Kappa, Kappa Delta Pi, Rotary Internat., SUNY of N.Y. and Conferations of SUNY Alumni Assns. (spl. citation Disting. Alumni Svc. award 1994). Lodge: Rotary Internat. Robert W. MacVittie Coll. Union named in his honor SUNY-Geneseo, 1989. Home and Office: 187 Chestnut St Fredonia NY 14063-1601

MAC WATTERS, VIRGINIA ELIZABETH, singer, music educator, actress; b. Phila.; d. Frederick-Kennedy and Idoleein (Hallowell) Mac W.; m. Paul Abée, June 10, 1960. Grad., Phila. Normal Sch. for Tchrs., 1933; student, Curtis Inst. Music, Phila., 1936. With New Opera Co., N.Y.C., 1941-42; artist-in-residence Ind. U. Sch. Music, 1957-58; assoc. prof. U. Ind. Sch. Music, 1958-68, prof. voice, 1968-82, prof. emeritus, 1982—. Singer: leading roles Broadway mus. Rosalinda, 1942-44, Mr. Strauss Goes to Boston, 1945, leading opera roles New Opera Co., N.Y.C., 1941-42, San Francisco, 1944, N.Y.C. Ctr., 1946-51; leading soprano for reopening of Royal Opera House, Covent Garden, London, 1947-48, Guatemala, El Salvador, Cen. Am., 1948-49; debut at Met. Opera, N.Y.C., 1952; TV spls. on NBC include Menotti's Old Maid and the Thief, 1949, Would-be Gentleman (R. Strauss), 1955; leading singer with Met. Opera Co. on coast to coast tour of Die Fledermaus, 1951-52., Met. Opera debut, N.Y.C., 1952, leading soprano Cen. City Opera Festival, Colo., 1952-56; performed with symphony orchs. in U.S., Can., S.Am.; concert recitalist U.S., Can., 1950-62; opened N.Y. Empire State Music Festival in Ariadne auf Naxos (Strauss), 1959; soloist Mozart Festival, Ann Arbor, Mich. Recipient Mile award Album Familiar Music, 1949, Ind. U. Disting. Teaching award, 1979; named One of 10 Outstanding Women of the Yr.; Zeckwer Hahn Phila. Mus. Acad. scholar, 1941-42. Mem. Nat. Fedn. of Music Clubs, Nat. Soc. Arts and Letters, Nat. Soc. Lit. and Arts, Soc. Am. Musicians, Nat. Assn. Tchrs. of Singing, Internat. Platform Assn., Sigma Alpha Iota. Club: Matinee Musical (hon. mem. Phila., Indpls. chpts.). Only original recorded version of Zerbinetta aria from Ariadne auf Naxos (Strauss). Home: 3800 Arlington Rd Bloomington IN 47404-1347 Office: Ind U Sch Music Bloomington IN 47401

MAC WHINNIE, JOHN VINCENT, artist; b. Rockville Centre, N.Y., Apr. 22, 1945; s. Milton Joseph and Inez Genevieve (LaFlamme) Mac W.; m. Virginia Gail Gettling, June, 1985; children: Milton John, Emma Katherine. B.A. magna cum laude, Southampton Coll., 1972. Artist, painter Water Mill, N.Y. Exhibited in group shows: Met. Mus. Art, 1979, Guggenheim Mus., 1979, Lehigh U., 1979, Bklyn. Mus., 1981, Am. Acad. and Inst. Arts and Letters, 1981, New Orleans Mus. Contemporary Art, Guild Hall, Easthampton, N.Y.; one-man shows include: Marlborough Gallery, N.Y., Andre Emmerich Gallery, N.Y.; represented in permanent collections: Guggenheim Mus., Bklyn. Mus., Phillips Collection, Walker Art Ctr., Parrish Art Mus., Guild Hall, numerous others. Recipient First prize in painting Parrish Art Mus., 1971, Excellence in Painting award Heckscher Mus., 1974. Avocations: metaphysics, gardening, antique collecting. Home and Studio: Deerfield Rd Water Mill NY 11976

MACWHORTER, ROBERT BRUCE, retired lawyer; b. Phila., July 12, 1930; s. George Merritt and Marion (Ritchie) MacW.; m. Althea Lucille Davis, June 23, 1956; children: Susan Elizabeth (Mrs. Steven Young), Nancy Jeanne (Mrs. Matthew Oja), Marjorie Anne (Mrs. Carl Friedrichs). A.B., Oberlin Coll., 1953; LL.B., U. Va., 1956. Bar: Va. 1957. Assoc. Shearman & Sterling, N.Y.C., 1956-65, ptnr., 1965-91. Mem. ABA, N.Y. Bar Assn., Order of Coif. Home: 85 Jefferson Ave Maplewood NJ 07040-1228

MACY, JOHN PATRICK, lawyer; b. Menomonee Falls, Wis., June 26, 1955; s. Leland Francis and Joan Marie (LaValle) M. BA, Carroll Coll., 1977; JD, Marquette U., 1980. Bar: Wis. 1980, U.S. Dist. Ct. (we. and ea. dists.) Wis. 1980, U.S. Ct. Appeals (7th cir.) 1980. Assoc. Hippenmeyer Reilly Arenz Molter Bode & Gross, Waukesha, Wis., 1980-83; ptnr. Arenz Molter Macy & Riffle, S.C., Waukesha, 1983—; lectr. in field. Mem ABA, Waukesha County Bar Assn. (pres. 1987-88), Wis. Bar Assn. (chair 1995—), Silver Lake Environ. Assn. (officer 1988-89), Silver Lake Yacht Club (officer 1986-88). Republican. Roman Catholic. Home: 4839 Hewitt's Point Rd Oconomowoc WI 53066 Office: Arenz Molter Macy & Riffle SC 720 N East Ave Waukesha WI 53186-4800

MACY, RICHARD J., state judge; b. Saranac Lake, N.Y., June 2, 1930; m. Emily Ann Macy; children: Anne, Patty, Mark. BS in Bus., U. Wyo., 1955, JD, 1958. Pvt. practice Sundance, Wyo., 1958-85; justice Wyo. Supreme Ct., Cheyenne, 1985—; former chief justice; Crook County atty., 1970-85; mem.

Nat. Conf. Commrs. on Uniform State Laws, 1982—. Mem. Sigma Chi (Nat. Outstanding Sig award 1986). Office: Wyo Supreme Ct Supreme Ct Bldg Cheyenne WY 82002

MADAIO, MICHAEL PETER, medical educator. BS in Biology cum laude, Fairfield U., 1974; MD, Albany Med. Coll., 1974. Diplomate Am. Bd. Internal Medicine, Am. Bd. Nephrology. Intern Med. Coll. Va., Richmond, 1974-75, resident, 1975-77, chief resident, 1977-78; clin. fellow in nephrology Boston U., 1978-79, rsch. fellow in nephrology, 1979-81; rsch. fellow in immunology Tufts U., Boston, 1981-82, instr. in medicine, 1981-82, asst. to assoc. prof., 1982-90; assoc. prof. medicine U. Pa., 1990—, assoc. chief renal electrolye div., 1992—; asst. physician New Eng. Med. Ctr., Boston, 1981-87, physician, 1988-90; reviewer manuscripts and grants in field; lectr. Pathology A Study Sect., NIH, 1992-96. Contbr. articles to profl. jours., publs. Vice-pres. Nat. Kidney Found. Mass., 1987-89, pres. 1989-90; active Lupus Found. Am., Phila., 1991—. Mem. AAAS, Internat. Soc. Nephorology, Am. Soc. Nephrology, Am. Fedn. Clin. Rsch., Am. Heart Assn., Fedn. Am. Socs. for Exptl. Biology, Am. Assn. Immunologists, Nat. Kidney Found., Am. Soc. Clin. Investigation, Alpha Epsilon Delta. Office: Univ Pa 422 Curie Blvd Philadelphia PA 19104-6140

MADANSKY, ALBERT, statistics educator; b. Chgo., May 16, 1934; s. Harry and Anna (Meidenberg) M.; m. Paula Barkan, June 10, 1990; children from previous marriage: Susan, Cynthia, Noreen, Michele. AB, U. Chgo., 1952, MS, 1955, PhD, 1958. Mathematician Rand Corp., Santa Monica, Calif., 1957-65; sr. v.p. Interpub. Group of Companies, N.Y.C., 1965-68; pres. Dataplan Inc, N.Y.C., 1968-70; prof. computer scis. CCNY, 1970-76; prof. bus. adminstrn. grad. sch. U. Chgo., 1976—, assoc. dean, 1985-90, dep. dean, 1990-93; bd. dirs. Analytic Services, Washington, 1975—. Author: Foundations of Econometrics, 1975, Prescriptions for Working Statisticians, 1988. Fellow: Ctr. for Advanced Study in Behavioral Scis., Am. Statis. Assn., Inst. Math. Stats., Econometric Soc. Home: 200 E Delaware Pl Apt 23F Chicago IL 60611-1736 Office: U of Chicago Grad Sch Business Chicago IL 60637

MADANSKY, LEON, particle physicist, educator; b. Bklyn., Jan. 11, 1923. B.S., U. Mich., 1942, M.S., 1944, Ph.D. in Physics, 1948. From asst. prof. to assoc. prof. Johns Hopkins U., Balt., 1948-58, chmn. dept., 1965-68, prof. physics, 1958-77, Decker prof., 1978—; research physicist Brookhaven Nat. Lab., 1952-53. Fellow NSF, 1961, 69, John S. Guggenheim Meml. Found., 1974-75. Fellow Am. Phys. Soc. Home 602 Edenvale Rd Baltimore MD 21209-2702 Office: Johns Hopkins U Dept Physics And Astro Baltimore MD 21218

MADARA, JAMES L., epitheliologist, pathologist, educator; b. Altoona, Pa., Sept. 16, 1950; s. Daniel Rodman and Margaret Jane (Hauser) M.; m. Victoria M. Madara, May 14, 1975; children: J. Maxwell, Alexis Lindsy. BA, Juniata Coll., 1971; MD, Hahnemann Med., 1975. Cert. anatomic and clin. pathology. Instr. pathology Harvard Med. Sch., Boston, 1980-81, asst. prof. pathology, 1981-85, assoc. prof. pathology, 1985-91; assoc. prof. of health scis. and tech. Harvard-M.I.T., Boston, 1986-91. Assoc. editor: Gastroenterology, 1986-91; editorial bd.: Jour. Clin. Investigation, 1987—; contbr. over 80 articles to profl. jours. Grantee NIH, 1980-91. Mem. Am. Soc. for Clin. Investigation (elected), Am. Soc. for Cell Biology, Am. Gastroenterological Assn. (rsch. coun. 1988-90, Ross Rsch. scholar award 1982), Am. Physiol. Soc., Am. Assn. Pathology (Parke/Davis award 1990). Achievements include description of functional sequallea of neutrophil-epithelial cell interactions; recognition that tight junctions between epithelial cells are regulated under physiological conditions. Office: Brigham and Womens Hosp 75 Francis St Boston MA 02115-6195

MADDALA, GANGADHARRAO SOUNDARYARAO, economics educator; b. Hyderabad, Andhra, India, May 21, 1933; came to U.S., 1960; s. Soundarya Rao and Veera Lakshmi (Gollakota) M.; m. Kameswari Modali, May 21, 1967; children: Tara, Vivek. BA, Andhra U., Waltair, India, 1955; MA, Bombay U., 1957; PhD, U. Chgo., 1963. Asst. prof. Stanford (Calif.) U., 1963-67; assoc. prof. U. Rochester (N.Y.), 1967-70, prof. econs., 1970-75; grad. rsch. prof. U. Fla., Gainesville, 1975-93; univ. eminent scholar dept. econs. Ohio State U., Columbus, 1992—; dir. Ctr. for Econometrics and Decision Scis., Gainesville, 1979-93. Author: Econometrics, 1977, Limdep Variables in Econometrics, 1983, Introduction to Econometrics, 1988, Microeconomics, 1989, Econometric Methods and Applications, 1994. Fellow Econometric Soc.; mem. Am. Econ. Assn., Am. Statis. Assn. Office: Ohio State U Arps Hall 1945 N High St Columbus OH 43210-1172

MADDALENA, FRANK JOSEPH, health care executive; b. N.Y.C., Dec. 20, 1941; s. Frank Frederick and Natalie Elizabeth (Mirenda) M.; m. Barbara Louise Kohart, Jan. 6, 1985; children from previous marriage: Nicole Marie, Frank Anthony. BS in Pharmacy, Fordham U., 1965; MS, L.I. U., 1974; MBA, Fordham U., 1977. Assoc. v.p. The Roosevelt Hosp., N.Y.C., 1968-79; assoc. exec. dir. John F. Kennedy Med. Ctr., Edison, N.J., 1979-80; adminstr. Nassau County Med. Ctr., East Meadow, N.Y., 1980-84; exec. v.p. Interfaith Med. Ctr., N.Y.C., 1984-87; exec. dir. Bronx Mcpl. Hosp. Ctr., N.Y.C., 1987-89; v.p. adminstrn. The Presbyn. Hosp. in the City of New York, 1989—; adj. prof. L.I. U./CW Post, Greenvale, N.Y., 1982—. Mem. Hosp. Assn. (del.-at-large regional policy bd., Chgo., 1988-91), Pi Alpha Alpha (hon.). Office: Brookdale Hosp Med Ctr Linden Blvd at Brookdale Plz Brooklyn NY 11212

MADDALENA, LUCILLE ANN, management executive; b. Plainfield, N.J., Nov. 8, 1948; d. Mario Anthony and Josephine Dorothy (Longo) M.; m. James Samonte Hohn, Sept. 7, 1975; children: Vincent, Nicholas, Mitchell. AA, Rider Coll., 1968; BS, Monmouth Coll., 1971; EdD, Rutgers U., 1978. Newscaster, dir. pub. relations Sta. WBRW, Bridgewater, N.J., 1971-73; editor-in-chief Commerce mag., New Brunswick, N.J., 1973-74; dir. pub. relations Raritan Valley Regional C. of C., New Brunswick, N.J., 1973-74; aide pub. relations to mayor City of New Brunswick, 1974; dir. communications United Way Cen. Jersey, New Brunswick, 1974-77; mgmt. cons. United Way Am., Alexandria, Va., 1977-78; pres., owner Maddalena Assocs., Chester, N.J., 1978—; sr. cons. United Research Co., Morristown, N.J., 1980-81; sr. ptnr., dir. OCD Group, Parsippany, N.J., 1984-87; chmn. bd. dirs. OCD Group (subs. Xicom Inc.), Morristown, N.J., 1988; pres. Morris Bus. Group, Chester, 1989—; adj. faculty Somerset County Coll., Bridgewater, N.J., 1970, Fairleigh Dickinson U., 1980; guest lectr. Rutgers U., New Brunswick, N.J., 1975-80; designer publicly offered seminars for Bell Atlantic, 1992—; cons. change Howmet, Alloy, Dover, N.J., 1993; consortium trainer Johnson & Johnson, 1988—. Author: A Communications Manual for Non-Profit Organizations, 1980; editor New Directions for Instl. Advancement, 1980-81. Chmn. pers. com., police com. Chester Borough Coun., 1984-87; pres. Chester Consolidation Study Commn., 1990. Recipient Mayor's Commendation City of New Brunswick, 1973, Chester Borough, N.J., 1988. Mem. AAUW, LWV, Nat. Assn. Press Women, N.J. Elected Women Officials, Kappa Delta Pi. Republican. Roman Catholic. Club: N.J. Sled Dog Assn. Avocation: sled dog racing. Home: 75 Melrose Dr Chester NJ 07930-2304 Office: Morris Bus Group 415 Rt 24 Chester NJ 07930-2626

MADDEN, DAVID, author; b. Knoxville, Tenn., July 25, 1933; s. James Helvy and Emile (Merritt) M.; m. Roberta Margaret Young, Sept. 6, 1956; 1 son, Blake Dana. B.S., U. Tenn., 1957; M.A., San Francisco State Coll., 1958; postgrad., Yale Drama Sch., 1959-60. Faculty Appalachian State Tchrs. Coll., Boone, N.C., 1957-58, Centre Coll., Danville, Ky., 1960-62, U. Louisville, 1962-64, Kenyon Coll., Gambier, O., 1964-66, Ohio U., Athens, 1966-68; writer-in-residence La. State U., Baton Rouge, 1968-92, dir. creative writing program, 1992-94, dir. U.S. Civil War Ctr., 1992—; alumni prof. La. State U., 1994. Author: (novels) Cassandra Singing, 1969, Bijou, 1974, The Suicide's Wife, 1978, Pleasure Dome, 1979, On the Big Wind, 1980, (stories) The Shadow Knows (Nat. Council on Arts selection), 1970, The New Orleans of Possibilities, (lit. criticism) Wright Morris, 1964, Poetic Image in Six Genres, 1969, James M. Cain, 1970, A Primer of the Novel, 1980, Writers' Revisions, 1981, Cain's Craft, 1985, Revising Fiction, 1988, Revel-coveries II, 1988; asst. editor: The Kenyon Rev, 1964-66; editor: Remembering James Agee, 1974; co-editor: (with P. Bach) Classics of Civil War Fiction, 1991. Served with AUS 1953-55. Recipient Rockefeller grant in fiction, 1969; John Golden fellow in playwriting, 1959. Mem. Authors

League, Associated Writing Programs (bd). Democrat. Office: US Civil War Ctr La State U Raphael Semmes Dr Baton Rouge LA 70803

MADDEN, DONALD PAUL, lawyer; b. Winthrop, Mass., Dec. 26, 1933; s. Francis Patrick and Mary Josephine (Doherty) M.; m. Sarah Anne Donovan, Aug. 12, 1966; children—Matthew James, Andrew Peter, Thomas. A.B., Princeton U., 1955; J.D., Harvard U., 1961. Bar: N.Y. 1962, U.S. Dist. Ct. (so. dist.) N.Y. 1962. Assoc. White & Case, N.Y.C., 1961-69, ptnr., 1969—; resident ptnr. Paris office, 1971-76. dir., sec. Am. Hosp. of Paris Found. Served to lt. USMC, 1955-58. Mem. ABA, Assn. Bar City N.Y. Club: Links (N.Y.C.). Office: White & Case 1155 Ave Of The Americas New York NY 10036-2711

MADDEN, EDWARD HARRY, philosopher, educator; b. Gary, Ind., May 18, 1925; s. Harry Albert and Amelia Dorothy (Schepper) M.; m. Marian Sue Canaday, Sept. 15, 1946; children: Kerry Arthur, Dennis William. A.B., Oberlin Coll., 1946, A.M., 1947; Ph.D., U. Iowa, 1950. Prof. philosophy U. Conn., 1950-59, San Jose State Coll., 1959-64, SUNY, Buffalo, 1964-82, U. Ky., 1982—; vis. prof. Brown U., 1954-55, Amherst Coll., 1962, U. Toronto, 1967, Am. U. Beirut, Lebanon, 1969-70; sr. research fellow Linacre Coll., Oxford U., 1978, Inst. Advanced Study, Princeton, 1980-81. Author: Philosophical Problems of Psychology, 1962, Chauncey Wright And The Foundations Of Pragmatism, 1963, Evil And The Concept Of God, 1968, Civil Disobedience And Moral Law, 1968, The Structure Of Scientific Thought, 1960, Causal Powers, 1975, Causing, Perceiving and Believing, 1975, Freedom and Grace, 1982; co-author, editor: Theories of Scientific Method, 1960, Philosophical Perspectives on Punishment, 1968, The Idea of God, 1968; gen. editor: Harvard U. Press, Source Books in History Sci; mem. editorial bd.: The Works of William James, Thoreau Quar., History of Philosophy Quar; mem. adv. bd.: A Critical Edition of the Correspondence of William James (Am. Coun. Learned Socs.). Served with USNR, 1943-45. Recipient Am. Philos. Soc. research grant, 1961, Fulbright-Hays award, 1969-70, Herbert W. Schneider award Soc. for Advancement Am. Philosophy, 1991. Fellow Asa Mahan Soc.; mem. C.S. Peirce Soc. (pres. 1962-63, sec.-treas., editorial bd. Transactions of Soc.), Am. Council Learned Socs. (selection com.), Am. Philos. Assn. (co-chmn. com. publs. 1960-71), Phi Kappa Phi. Home: 106 Pickett Dr Wilmore KY 40390-1223 Office: Univ Ky Dept Philosophy Lexington KY 40506

MADDEN, JAMES DESMOND, forensic engineer; b. Jersey City, Mar. 1, 1940; s. Louis A. and Ann (Desmond) M. BSChemE, U. S.C., 1963, ME, 1966. Registered profl. engr., Ohio; cert. diplomate forensic engr. Process engr. Monsanto Co., Alvin, Tex., 1966-67; process and project engr. Union Carbide Corp., Houston, 1967-70; systems engr. M.W. Kellogg Co., Houston, 1970-73, prin. systems engr., 1974-77; sr. process engr. Litwin Co., Houston, 1973-74; sr. project engr. Davy Powergas, Houston, 1977-78, supervising project engr., 1978-79; mgr. equipment engring. DM Internat., Houston, 1979-80, project engring. mgr., 1980-83; owner, forensic engr. Madden Forensic Engring., Parma, Parma Heights and Brecksville, Ohio, 1983—. Pres. Houston Young Adult Rep. Club, 1970-73; chmn. Tex. Young Adult Rep. Clubs, 1973. NSF rsch. grantee, 1963; NASA fellow, 1963. Mem. ASTM, ASME, NSPE, Soc. Automotive Engrs., Nat. Fire Protection Assn., Am. Chem. Soc., Am. Inst. Chem. Engrs., Inst. Transp. Engrs., Transp. Rsch. Bd. (individual assoc.), Nat. Acad. Forensic Engrs., Sigma Xi, Sigma Pi Sigma, Tau Beta Pi, Omicron Delta Kappa. Office: 10175 Brecksville Rd Cleveland OH 44141

MADDEN, JOHN, television sports commentator, former professional football coach; b. Austin, Minn., Apr. 10, 1936; s. Earl and Mary O'Flaherty M.; m. Virginia Madden; children: Mike, Joe. B.s., Calif. Poly. U., 1959, M.A., 1961. Player Phila. Eagles (NFL team), 1959; asst. coach Hancock Jr. Coll., Santa Maria, Calif., 1960-62; head coach Hancock Jr. Coll., 1962-64; defensive coordinator Calif. State U., San Diego, 1964-66; with Oakland Raiders, Am. Football League (now Am. Football Conf., Nat. Football League), 1967-79, linebacker coach, 1967-69, head coach, 1969-79; head coach NFL Pro Bowl team Am. Football Conf., 1971, 73, 74, 75; head coach 6 Western div. Am. Football Conf. championship teams, Super Bowl champions, 1976; sports commentator, football analyst CBS Sports, 1979-93; appears in TV and radio comls.; sports commentator, football analyst Fox Network, 1994—. Author: Hey, Wait a Minute, I Wrote a Book!, 1984; One Knee Equals Two Feet, 1986; developer (software) John Madden Football, 1988, John Madden Football II, 1993. Named Coach of Year Am. Football League, 1969, Sports Personality of the Yr., Am. Sportscasters Assn., 1985; recipient Emmy awards for sports broadcasting, 1982, 83, 85, 86, 87, 88. Office: care Fox Network PO Box 900 Beverly Hills CA 90213-0900*

MADDEN, JOHN KEVIN, publishing executive; b. Winthrop, Mass., Aug. 18, 1938; s. Francis Patrick and Mary Josephine (Doherty) M.; m. Christine Casson, Dec. 6, 1974; children: Patrick, Nicholas. BA, Princeton U., 1960. Salesman Time Mag., N.Y.C., 1966-70; salesman New York Mag., N.Y.C., 1970-73, advt. mgr., 1973-76, assoc. pub., 1976-78; advt. dir. Self Mag., N.Y.C., 1978-83, pub., 1983-87; pub. HG Mag., N.Y.C., 1987-93, Bon Appetit Mag., N.Y.C., 1993—. Democrat. Roman Catholic. Club: Manursing Island (Rye, N.Y.). Avocations: jogging, tennis. Home: Holly Ln Rye NY 10580 Office: Conde Nast Publs Inc 360 Madison Ave Fl 12 New York NY 10017-3136

MADDEN, JOSEPH DANIEL, trade association executive; b. N.Y.C., Dec. 25, 1921; s. Thomas A. and Margaret (McFadden) M.; m. Eileen M. MacDonnell, Sept. 8, 1951; children: Joseph Daniel, Jr., Maureen A. BS, Fordham U., 1951; MBA, N.Y. U., 1956. Credit investigator Dun & Bradstreet, N.Y.C., 1947-48; credit mgr. Devoe & Raynolds Co., N.Y.C., 1948-50; accounts supr. credit dept. Admiral Corp., N.Y.C., 1950-51; nat. credit mgr. Standard Toch Chems., Inc., S.I., N.Y., 1951-52; with chems. and plastics div. Union Carbide Corp., Danbury, Conn., 1952-62; mgr. Detroit sales office, 1958-60; sr. staff adminstr. Soc. Plastics Industry, Washington, 1962-69; exec. v.p. Drug. Chem. and Allied Trades Assn., Syosset, N.Y., 1969-88, cons. assn. mgmt., 1988—. With U.S. Army, 1942-43. Mem. Am. Soc. Assn. Execs. (cert.), N.Y. Soc. Assn. Execs. (past bd. dirs., Exec. of Yr. award 1988), Soc. Friendly Sons of St. Patrick, Kiwanis (past pres. Bayside, sec.), Am. Assn. Ret. Persons (pres. local chpt.), Toastmasters Internat. (past pres. local club). Home: 201-26 38th Ave Flushing NY 11361-1849

MADDEN, JOSEPH MICHAEL, microbiologist; b. Yokohama, Japan, July 19, 1949; s. John Joseph and Anne Louise (Johnson) M.; m. Rennie K. Robb, Aug. 4, 1973; children: Loren, Mary Kate, Julie. BA, U. Calif., 1971; MS, Ariz. State U., 1974, PhD, 1976. Chief microbiology Brook Army Med. Ctr., Ft. Sam Houston, Tex., 1976-78; rsch. microbiologist FDA Ctr. Food Safety and Applied Nutrition, Washington, 1978-88, dep. dir. microbiology divsn., 1988-91, dir., 1991-93, strategic mgr. microbiology, 1992—. Capt. U.S. Army, 1976-78, USPHS, 1978—. Mem. Am. Soc. Microbiology, Sigma Xi. Roman Catholic. Avocation: refereeing soccer. Office: FDA Ctr Food Safety and Applied Nutrition 200 C St SW Washington DC 20204*

MADDEN, MARTIN GERARD, state legislator, insurance agent; b. Washington, May 24, 1949; s. Anthony M. and Catherine W. (Tracey) M.; m. Julia Gatewood Spangler, July 29, 1988; children: Donald Gerard, Thomas Martin, Christina Lynn. BA in Econs., Iona Coll., 1971. Owner Marty Madden Ins. Ctr., Lanham, Md., 1971—; state del. State of Md. Gen. Assembly, Annapolis, 1991-95; state senator, 1995—; mem. Am. Legis. Exch. Coun. Real Estate & Banking Task Force, Washington, 1991—. Bd. dirs. St. Vincent Pallotti H.S.; mem. Citizens Against Spousal Abuse, MADD, Clark Ridge Citizens Assn. Mem. Nationwide Pres. Club, Chems. Life Coun., Prince Georges Life Underwriters, Nat. Assn. Life Underwriters, Sierra Club, Kiwanis, KC, Elk Ridge Heritage Soc. Republican. Roman Catholic. Avocation: folk art collector. Office: James Senate Office Bldg 402-B Annapolis MD 21401-1991

MADDEN, MICHAEL DANIEL, finance company executive; b. Buffalo, Feb. 16, 1949; s. Daniel Francis and Miriam (Catron) M.; m. Mary Madden, May 1, 1976; children: Daniel, Kristina, Meagan, Michael. BA in Econs. magna cum laude, Le Moyne Coll., 1971; MBA with distinction, N.Y.U., 1973. Assoc. Kidder, Peabody & Co., N.Y.C., 1973-77, v.p., 1977-80, mng. dir., 1980-85, dir. investment banking, 1985-88; head investment banking Lehman Bros., N.Y.C., 1989-93; exec. mng. dir. Global Capital Markets Kidder, Peabody Co., N.Y.C., 1993-94; vice chmn., chief origination officer

Paine Webber Inc., N.Y.C., 1995—. Bd. dirs. Freeport Properties, Inc., Cath. TV Ctr., N.Y.C., 1981-85, LeMoyne Coll., Syracuse, N.Y., 1987—, Canisius Preparatory Sch., Buffalo, N.Y., 1992—. Mem. Am. Petroleum Inst., MBA Assn., Univ. Club, The Creek, Longboat Key Club. Republican. Roman Catholic. Avocations: boxing, hunting, tennis, coin collecting. Office: Paine Webber Inc 1285 Ave of the Americas New York NY 10019

MADDEN, MURDAUGH STUART, lawyer; b. Morgantown, W.Va., Feb. 26, 1922; s. Joseph Warren and Margaret (Liddell) M.; m. Eileen Dillon, June 17, 1978; children by previous marriage: Liddell Louise, Murdaugh Stuart Jr., Michael Mann. Student, Oberlin Coll., 1939-40; BA, George Washington U., 1942; JD, Harvard U., 1948. Bar: D.C. 1948, Va. 1948, U.S. Supreme Ct. 1953. Asst. counsel Bur. Aero., Washington, 1948-50; sole practice Washington, 1950-61, 71—; sr. ptnr. Shaw, Pittman, Potts, Trowbridge & Madden, Washington, 1961-71; gen. counsel Humane Soc. U.S. Atlantic Devel. Co. and related corps. Author: (with Sherman L. Cohn) The Legal Status and Problems of the American Abroad, 1966. Trustee Inst. for Study Nat. Behavior, Princeton, N.J., Friends of India Com., Washington; pres. World Fedn. for Protection Animals, Zurich; v.p. World Soc. forProtection Animals, London. With USAAF, 1942-45, ETO. Mem. ABA (past chmn. internat. and comparative law com. internat. transp., chmn. subcom. on charitable orgns. internat. law sect. 1985—), D.C. Bar Assn., (past dir., past chmn. com. bar ethics), Va. Bar Assn., The Barristers, Am. Soc. Internat. Law, Harvard Law Sch. Assn., Oberlin Alumni Assn., Metropolitan Club, Harvard Club N.Y., Internat. Lawn Tennis Club U.S., Chevy Chase Club, Phi Sigma Kappa. Episcopalian. Home: 2530 Queen Annes Ln NW Washington DC 20037-2148 Office: 2100 L St NW Washington DC 20037-1525

MADDEN, PALMER BROWN, lawyer; b. Milw., Sept. 19, 1945; m. Susan L. Paulus, Mar. 31, 1984. BA, Stanford U., 1968; JD, U. Calif., Berkeley, 1973. Bar: Calif. 1973, U.S. Dist. Ct. (no. dist.) Calif. 1973, U.S. Supreme Ct. 1982. Office mng. ptnr. McCutchen, Doyle Brown & Enersen, Walnut Creek, 1985—. Mem. bd. govs. Continuing Edn. of the Bar; judge pro tem Contra Costa Superior Ct., 1991—; pres. Contra Costa Coun., 1993-94. Mem. Contra Costa County Bar Assn. (dir. 1987—). Democrat. Episcopalian. Office: McCutchen Doyle Brown & Enersen 1331 N California St Walnut Creek CA 94596-5028

MADDEN, PAUL HERMAN, education educator; b. Adairsville, Ga., Sept. 18, 1924; s. William Herbert and Bessie Rosanna (Green) M.; m. Marion Ghiz, July 31, 1954; children: Michael Peter, Kenneth Robert. BS in Edn., W. Ga. Coll., 1967; MEd in Adminstrn/Supervision, Univ. Ga., 1969, EdD in Adminstrn/Supervision, 1976. Enlisted USN, 1941-45; advanced through grades to maj. U.S. Army, 1949-65, ret., 1965; employment interviewer Ga. State Employment Svc., Cedartown, 1947-48; prin. Fish Creek Elem. Sch./ Polk County Schs., Cedartown, 1966-67; asst. prin. jr. high Clark County Schs., Athens, Ga., 1970-72; dir. child care Ga. Mountains Plan Commn., Gainesville, 1972-74; assoc. prof. ednl. adminstrn. Tenn. State U., Nashville, 1976—; cons. elem. and mid. sch. coms., Tenn., 1977-93; pres. Nat. Adult Literary Coun., 1983-84. Pres. Gaines Sch. Civitan Club, Athens, 1976. Decorated combat ribbons USN. Mem. NAESP, NEA, Nat. Mid. Sch. Assn., Nat. Elem. Prin. Assn., Tenn. Elem. Prin. Assn., Tenn. Edn. Assn., Phi Delta Kappa (pres. local chpt. 1972-73, 83-85, Leadership award 1986, 88, 92). Democrat. Avocations: reading, sports. Office: Dept Ednl Adminstrn 3500 John A Merritt Blvd Nashville TN 37209-1561

MADDEN, PAUL ROBERT, lawyer; b. St. Paul, Nov. 13, 1926; s. Ray Joseph and Margaret (Meyer) M.; m. Rosemary R. Sorel, Aug. 7, 1974; children: Margaret Jane, William, James Patrick, Derek R. Sorel, Lisa T. Sorel. Student, St. Thomas Coll., 1944; AB, U. Minn., 1948; JD, Georgetown U., 1951. Bar: Ariz. 1957, Minn. 1951, D.C. 1951. Assoc. Hamilton & Hamilton, Washington, 1951-55; legal asst. to commr. SEC, Washington, 1955-56; assoc. Lewis and Roca, Phoenix, Ariz., 1957-59, ptnr., 1959-90; ptnr. Beus, Gilbert & Morrill, Phoenix, 1991-94; ptnr. Chapman & Cutler, Phoenix, 1994—. Sec. Minn. Fedn. Coll. Rep. Clubs, 1947-48; chmn. 4th dist. Minn. Young Rep. Club, 1948; nat. co-chmn. Youth for Eisenhower, 1951-52; mem. Ariz. Rep. Com., 1960-62; past chmn., bd. dirs. Camelback Behavioral Health Svcs., Scottsdale, Ariz.; bd. dirs. Found. Jr. Achievement Ctrl. Ariz., Cath. Community Found., Phoenix, Heritage Hills Homeowners Assn.; past bd. dirs. Camelback Charitable Trust, The Samaritan Found., Phoenix; past bd. dirs., past chmn. Camelback Hosps., Inc., Scottsdale; past bd. dirs., past pres. Ariz. Club, Phoenix, 1990-93; bd. dirs., past chmn. Found. for Sr. Living, Phoenix; bd. dirs., vice chmn., Cen. Ariz. chpt. ARC; past bd. dirs., past pres. Jr. Achievement Cen. Ariz., Inc. With USNR, 1946-48. Mem. ABA, Ariz. Bar Assn., Maricopa County Bar Assn., Fed. Bar Assn., Fedn. Ins. Counsel, Nat. Health Lawyers Assn., Am. Soc. Hosp. Attys., Nat. Assn. Bond Lawyers, Ariz. Assn. for Indsl. Devel., East Valley Partnership, Phi Delta Phi. Clubs: The Barristers (Washington), Arizona. Home: 5847 N 46th St Phoenix AZ 85018-1234 Office: Chapman & Cutler Two N Central Ave Ste 1100 Phoenix AZ 85004

MADDEN, RICHARD BLAINE, forest products executive; b. Short Hills, N.J., Apr. 27, 1929; s. James L. and Irma (Twining) M.; m. Joan Fairbairn, May 24, 1958; children: John Richard, Lynn Marie, Kathryn Ann, Andrew Twining. B.S., Princeton U., 1951; J.D., U. Mich., 1956; M.B.A., NYU, 1959; PhD (hon.), St. Scholastica Coll., 1994. Bar: Mich. 1956, N.Y. 1958. Gen. asst. treas.'s dept. Socony Mobil Oil Corp., N.Y.C., 1956-57; spl. asst. Socony Mobil Oil Corp. 1958-59, fin. rep., 1960; asst. to pres. Mobil Chem. Co.; also dir. Mobil Chems. Ltd. of Eng., 1960-63; exec. v.p., gen. mgr. Kordite Corp.; also v.p. Mobil Plastics, 1963-66; v.p. Mobil Chem. Co. N.Y.C., 1966-68; group v.p. Mobil Chem. Co., 1968-70; asst. treas. Mobil Oil Corp., 1970-71; chmn. Mobil Oil Estates Ltd., 1970-71; pres., chief exec. to chmn., chief exec. officer Potlatch Corp., San Francisco, 1971-94; ret., 1994; bd. dirs. Potlatch Corp., Pacific Gas and Electric Co., Consolidated Freightways, Inc., Pacific Gas Transmission Co., URS Corp.; former bd. dirs. Del Monte Corp., AMFAC Inc., Bank Calif. N.A. and BankCal Tri-State Corp.; from lectr. to adj. assoc. prof. fin. NYU, 1960-63. Bd. dirs. Smith-Kettlewell Eye Rsch. Inst., Nat. Park Found., mem. exec. com.; com.; trustee emeritus Am. Enterprise Inst.; bd. govs., mem. exec. com. San Francisco Symphony; mem. Bus.-Higher Edn. Forum, Com. for Econ. Devel. Lt. (j.g.) USNR, 1951-54. Mem. N.Y. Bar Assn., Mich. Bar Assn. Roman Catholic. Clubs: Bohemian (San Francisco); Lagunitas (Ross, Calif.); Metropolitan (Washington).

MADDEN, THOMAS J., III, management consultant; b. Ft. Worth, July 6, 1947; s. Thomas J. and Edna Earle (Parker) M., Jr.; B.S. in Nuclear Engring., U. Tenn., 1970; M.S. in Computer Sci., Stevens Inst. Tech., 1972; M.B.A., Fairleigh Dickinson U., 1977; m. Jacquelyn Carol Butler, Aug. 28, 1971; 1 dau., Jacquelyn Lindsey. Mem. tech. staff Bell Telephone Labs., Whippany and Madison, N.J., 1970-74; various staff positions to head nuclear safety and licensing group Jersey Central Power & Light Co., Morristown, 1974-78; mem. staff Theodore Barry & Assocs., N.Y.C., 1978-81, partner, 1982—, v.p., 1982-83, sr. v.p., 1983—. Mem. Am. Nuclear Soc., Inst. Mgmt. Cons. (assoc.). Baptist. Home: 12 Manette Rd Morristown NJ 07960-6344 Office: 50 Rockefeller Plz New York NY 10020-1605 Office: Scott Madden & Assocs 2626 Glenwood Ave Ste 480 Raleigh NC 27608

MADDEN, WALES HENDRIX, JR., lawyer; b. Amarillo, Tex., Sept. 1, 1927; s. Wales Hendrix and Kathryn (Nash) M.; m. Alma Faye Cowden, Nov. 8, 1952; children: Wales Hendrix III, Straughn. B.A., U. Tex., 1950, LL.B., 1952. Bar: Tex. 1952. Practiced in Amarillo; bd. dirs. First Nat. Bank of Amarillo, Mesa Inc.; mem. Tex. Constnl. Revision Commn., 1973. Bd. regents Amarillo Coll., 1958-59, U. Tex., 1959-65; mem. Tex. Coll. and Univ. System Coord. Bd., 1964-69, Amarillo Area Found., Cal Farley's Boys Ranch, Pres.'s Export Coun., 1981; trustee Trinity U. San Antonio; mem. Select Com. Higher Edn., 1985, 87; chmn. SWST Regional Panel, Pres.'s Commn. on White House Fellowships, 1989-90; chmn. bd. Internat. Food and Agrl. Devel., 1990-94. Served with USNR. Named Outstanding Man of Amarillo, 1972; Disting. Alumnus U. Tex., 1979, U. Tex. Law Sch., 1986. Mem. ABA, Amarillo Bar Assn. (pres. 1956), Tex. Philos. Soc., Amarillo C. of C. (pres. 1968), State Bar Tex., State Jr. Bar Tex. (pres. 1956), Friar Soc., Phi Alpha Delta, Phi Delta Theta, Phi Eta Sigma, Pi Sigma Alpha. Presbyterian (elder). Home: 2701 Teckla Blvd Amarillo TX 79106-6048 Office: P O Box 15288 Amarillo TX 79105

MADDEN, WILLIAM J., JR., lawyer; b. Washington, Jan. 9, 1939; s. William John and Anne Hayes M.; m. Imelda Moore, May 23, 1964 (div. 1982); children: Maureen, Edward. AB, Holy Cross Coll., 1961; JD, U. Mich., 1964. Trial atty. Fed. Power Commn., Washington, 1964-68; atty. Debevoise & Liberman, Washington, 1968-83; ptnr. Bishop, Cook, Purcell & Reynolds, Washington, 1983-90, Winston & Strawn, Washington, 1990—; bd. dirs. Fed. Energy Bar Assn., Washington. Bd. dirs. Fairfax County Water Authority, Falls Church, Va., 1977-87. Republican. Roman Catholic. Home: 1465 Hampton Ridge Dr Mc Lean VA 22101-6023 Office: Winston & Strawn 1400 L St NW Washington DC 20005-3509

MADDEX, MYRON BROWN, broadcasting executive; b. Champaign County, Ohio, May 20, 1924; s. Walter Omer and Eva Mae (Brown) M.; m. Wilma Jean Anderson, Mar. 29, 1943; children: James Michael, John Eugene, Martha Jean. Student, Coyne Elec. Sch., Chgo., Moody Bible Inst., Chgo., eves., 1956-58. With R.W. Schetter Jewelry & Radio, Mechanicsburg, Ohio, 1946-51; owner Maddex Radio & TV, Mechanicsburg, 1952-53; chief engr. sta. WJEL-AM&FM, Springfield, Ohio, 1953-54; engr. staf. WMBI-AM&FM, Chgo., 1954-55; traffic supr., asst. to mgr., then asst. mgr. staf. WMBI-AM&FM, 1956-65; gen. mgr., then exec. v.p. sta. WEEC, Springfield, 1965-72; pres. sta. WEEC, 1972—; dir. World Evangelistic Enterprise Corp., 1965—; past bd. dirs. Springfield Youth for Christ. Served with AUS, 1943-45. Mem. Nat. Religious Broadcasters (dir. 1968-89, 1st Midwest chpt. pres. 1969-71, nat. sec. 1982-85), Nat. Assn Evangelicals, Ohio Assn. Evangelicals (bd. dirs. 1984-92, sec. 1985-87, 1st v.p. 1987-89, pres. 1989-91), Springfield C. of C. Home: Box 127 1300 Shrine Rd Springfield OH 45504 Office: 2265 Troy Rd Springfield OH 45504-4299 *During high school, I felt radio was my field. That's about all that interested me. Pearl Harbor occurred 6 months prior to graduation, and the U.S. Army Signal Corps provided training and experience. Returning to civilian life in radio servicing came next. Then . . . I became a Christian. God directed me to Chicago and the pioneer Christian radio station, WMBI. From that day to this, radio, as a ministry, has been my calling.*

MADDIN, ROBERT, metallurgist educator; b. Hartford, Conn., Oct. 20, 1918; s. Isadore I. and Mae (Jacobs) Levine; married, July 8, 1945; children: Leslie, Jill. BS in Metall. Engring., Purdue U., 1942; DEng., Yale U., 1948. Registered profl. engr., Pa. Asst., assoc. prof. Johns Hopkins U., Balt., 1949-55; prof. U. Pa., phila., 1955-73, univ. prof., 1973-83; vis. prof. Harvard U., Cambridge, Mass., 1983-87, curator, 1987—; vis. prof. Oxford (Eng.) U., 1970, fellow Wolfson Coll., 1987; vis. prof. U. Birmingham, Eng., 1953-54; vis. scholar Hebrew U., Jerusalem, 1976; hon. prof. Beijing Sci. and Engring. U., 1986; hon. mem. Japan Metals. Contbr. more than 150 publs. to profl. jours. 1st Lt. USAF, 1942-45. Disting. Sr. Sci. fellow A. von Humboldt Found., Germany, 1989-90; recipient Pomerance award Archaeological Lust Am., 1994. Fellow Am. Soc. Metallurgists, TMS; mem. Mus. Fine Arts-Boston. Avocations: history early metallurgy.

MADDOCK, JEROME TORRENCE, information services specialist; b. Darby, Pa., Feb. 7, 1940; s. Richard Cotton and Isobel Louise (Mezger) M.; m. Karen Rhueama Weygand, Oct. 2, 1965. BS in Biology, Muhlenberg Coll., 1961; MS in Info. Sci., Drexel U., 1968. Editorial assoc. Biol. Abstracts, Phila., 1962-63; mgr. rsch. info. Merck & Co., West Point, Pa., 1963-72; sr. cons. Auerbach Assocs., Inc., Phila., 1972-79; mgr. libr. and info. svcs. Solar Energy Rsch. Inst., Golden, Colo., 1979-88; mgr. info. svcs. Transp. Rsch. Bd., Washington, 1988—; del. Gov.;s Conf. on Libr. and Info. Svc., Pa., 1978; mem. blue ribbon panel to select archivist of U.S., Washington, 1979; U.S. del. to ops. com. on transp. rsch. info. Orgn. for Econ. Cooperation and Devel., 1988—. Bd. dirs. Paoli (Pa.) Pub. Libr., 1976-77. With USAFR, 1962-68. Mem. AAAS, Am. Soc. Info. Sci. (chmn. 1974-75), Elks, Beta Phi Mu, Pi Delta Epsilon. Republican. Episcopalian. Achievements include projection of information science operations 10 years into the future. Home: 20517 Aspenwood Ln Gaithersburg MD 20879-1230 Office: Transp Rsch Bd 2101 Constitution Ave NW Washington DC 20879

MADDOCK, THOMAS SMOTHERS, engineering company executive, civil engineer; b. Norfolk, Va., Mar. 23, 1928; s. John Francis and Mary Eileen (Smothers) M.; m. Caroline Diane Street, Nov. 5, 1977; children: Kimberly Anne, Victoria Anne. BCE with honors, Va. Poly. Inst., 1950; MCE, MIT, 1951; MBA, Stanford U., 1957. Registered profl. engr. in 8 states including Va., Calif., Nev., Ariz., Fla., D.C. V.p., project mgr. Boyle Engring. Corp., Newport Beach, Calif., 1957-72, pres., 1972—; presentations in field; project mgr. AID-financed Master Plan of Water Resources, Santo Domingo, Dominican Republic; project dir. for design and constrn. supervision mcpl. waterworks and irrigation facilities, Libya; supervisor preliminary designs for seawater delivery system ARAMCO, Saudi Arabia; dir. preparation of water wastewater facilities master plans (HUD 701 planning studies for cities), San Luis Obispo County, Calif. Contbr. articles to profl. jours. Pres. Seabee Meml. Fund Scholarship Fund, Washington, 1981-83. Lt. (j.g.) CE, USN, 1952-55; rear adm. CE, USNR. Decorated Navy Commendation medal, Meritorious Svc. medal, Legion of Merit. Fellow Los Angeles Inst. Advancement Engring., ASCE (v.p. Los Angeles sect. 1979); mem. Cons. Engrs. Assn. Calif., Nat. Soc. Profl. Engrs., Soc. Am. Mil. Engrs. Office: Boyle Engring Corp PO Box 7350 Newport Beach CA 92658-7350

MADDOCKS, ROBERT ALLEN, lawyer, manufacturing company executive; b. Missouri Valley, Ia., Dec. 25, 1933; s. Clarence A. and Helen Louise (Unger) M.; m. JoAnn Skaggs, June 2, 1956; children—Todd Duncan, Susan Colette, Amy Annette. B.S., Drake U., 1956; J.D., 1958. Bar: Iowa 1958, U.S. Supreme Ct. 1969, Ohio 1970, Mo. 1972, Colo. 1992. Pvt. practice law Clarion, Ia., 1958-67; atty. Massey Ferguson, Inc., Des Moines, 1967-68; div. gen. counsel Akron, Ohio, 1968-69; asst. sec., gen. counsel, dir. corp. relations Kellwood Co., St. Louis, 1970-73, sec., gen. counsel, 1973-90, v.p., 1978-90, also bd. dirs. subs. cos.; pvt. practice, cons., 1970-90; pvt. practice, cons.; dep. chmn., dir. Smart Shirts Ltd., Hong Kong, 1980-90; sec. Midwest Credit Corp.; Wright County atty., Clarion, 1961-65. Trustee Maryville Coll., St. Louis, 1975-78, Drake U., 1987-94; bd. dirs. Kellwood Found., 1975-90. Mem. Am. Bar Assn., Inter-Am., Ia., Ohio, Mo., Colo. bar assns., Am. Trial Lawyers Assn., Nat. Corporate Secs. Assn., Comml. Law League, Licensing Execs. Soc. Republican. Methodist (lay reader). Clubs: Nat. Apparel Mfrs. Assn. (legal com. 1972-90). Home: 266 Lookout Point Dr Osprey FL 34229-9738

MADDOX, DAVID M., career military officer. Gen. AUS. Office: Department of the Army Chief of Public Affairs Washington DC 20310

MADDOX, (ALVA) HUGH, state supreme court justice, author; b. Andalusia, Ala., Apr. 17, 1930; s. Christopher Columbus and Audie Lodella (Freeman) M.; m. Virginia Ann Roberts, June 14, 1958; children: Robert Hugh, Jane Maddox Vittetoe. A.B. in Journalism, U. Ala., 1952, LL.B., 1957. Bar: Ala. 1957. Law clk. to Hon. Aubrey Cates U.S. Ct. Appeals, Montgomery, 1957; field examiner Chief Atty.'s Office VA, Montgomery, 1958-59; law clk. to Hon. Frank M. Johnson, Jr. U.S. Dist. Ct., Montgomery, 1959-61; practiced law Montgomery, 1961-65; cir. judge, spl. cir. judge Montgomery Cir. Ct. (15th Jud. Cir.), 1963, asst. dist. atty., 1964; legal adviser Gov. George C. Wallace, Montgomery, Ala., 1965-67, Gov. Lurleen B. Wallace, Montgomery, Ala., 1967-68, Gov. Albert P. Brewer, Montgomery, Ala., 1968-69; assoc. justice Supreme Ct. Ala., Montgomery, 1969—; adj. prof. Troy State U., 1976-82, 87—; Auburn U., Montgomery, 1981-82; prof. law Jones Law Inst., Montgomery, 1961-62, 76; mem. adv. bd. JUSTEC Rsch. Author: Billy Boll Weevil: A Pest Becomes a Hero, 1976, Alabama Rules of Criminal Procedure, 1990. Mem. Permanent Study Commn. Ala. Judiciary; past mem. Jud. Conf.; youth legislature YMCA (bd. dirs. YMCA Metro Bd.; Disting. Program Svc. YMCA, 1989), Am. Heart Assn., Montgomery, Ala.; past trustee U. Mobile; past bd. dirs. Tukabatchee Area coun. Boy Scouts Am.; mem. coun. Ala. Law Inst. 2d lt. USAF, 1952-54; col. Res. (ret.). Named Montgomery YMCA Man of the Yr., 1988. Mem. ABA, Ala. Bar Assn. (bar leadership com., bar/bench rels. com., ct. restructuring com.), Am. Judicature Soc., Farrah Law Soc., Inst. Jud. Adminstrn., Ala. Law Inst., Federalist Soc. (bd. dirs.), Montgomery County Am. Inns of Ct. (pres. 1991-92, charter, founder), Jud. Study Commn., Christian Legal Soc., Maxwell AFB Officers Club (Montgomery), Kiwanis (bd. dirs. 1987-89), Omicron Delta Kappa, Phi Alpha Delta, Sigma Delta Chi. Democrat. Baptist. Avocations: handball, tennis, creative writing, photography, woodworking. Home: 3137 Hathaway Pl Montgomery AL 36111-1707 Office: Supreme Ct Ala 300 Dexter Ave Montgomery AL 36104-3741

MADDOX, IRIS CAROLYN CLARK, secondary education educator; b. Wardell, Mo., Apr. 20, 1936; d. Newman Walter and Mary Elizabeth (Edney) Clark; m. James P. Maddox, June 4, 1954; children: James Steven, Sandra Jean. BS cum laude, Prairie View A&M U., 1983, MEd in Indsl. Edn., 1984, MEd in Counseling., 1990. Cert. counselor and tchr., Tex. Tchr. Spring Branch Ind. Sch. Dist., Houston, 1982—; sec. Bus. Office Svcs. Adv. Com., Houston, 1991-92. Mem. Am. Vocat. Assn., Tex. Assn. Continuing Adult Edn., Nat. Assn. Classroom Educators in Bus. Edn., Chi Sigma Iota. Avocations: gardening, collecting antiques and coins. Home: PO Box 430791 Houston TX 77243

MADDOX, JESSE CORDELL, academic administrator; b. La Grange, Ga., Dec. 30, 1931; s. Jesse Garland and Esther Ann (Parmer) M.; m. Brona Faye Moorefield, Mar. 30, 1957; children: Cordell Jr., Michael, Brian, Gayle. BA, Furman U., 1954, LLD (hon.), 1976; M in Div., So. Bapt. Theol. Sem., 1957; DD (hon.), Bapt. Coll. at Charleston, S.C., 1972. Assoc. brotherhood dept. S.C. Bapt. Convention, Columbia, 1957-61; asst. to pres. Furman U., Greenville, S.C., 1961-71; pres. Anderson (S.C.) Coll., 1971-77, Carson Newman Coll., Jefferson City, Tenn., 1977—. Named Man. of Yr., Anderson Realtors, 1979; named to Athletic Hall of Fame Furman U., 1986. Mem. Nat. Jr. Coll. Council (pres. 1974-76), So. Assn. Colls. (commn. on colls. 1979-85), So. Assn., Ch. Related Colls. (pres. 1979), Assn. So. Bapt. Colls. and Schs. (pres. 1989-90). Lodge: Rotary (local pres. 1979). Avocations: tennis, jogging. Home: Laurel Hills RR 3 Jefferson Cy TN 37760-9803 Office: Carson-Newman Coll Office Pres Russell Ave Jefferson City TN 37760

MADDOX, ROBERT ALAN, atmospheric scientist; b. Granite City, Ill., July 12, 1944; s. Robert Alvin and Maxine Madeline (Elledge) M.; m. Rebecca Ann Speer, Dec. 27, 1967; children—Timothy Alan, Jason Robert. Student Purdue U., 1962-63; B.S., Tex. A&M U., 1967; M.S. in Atmospheric Sci., Colo. State U., 1973, Ph.D. in Atmospheric Sci., 1981. Meteorologist, Nat. Weather Service, Hazelwood, Mo., 1967; research meteorologist Geophys. Research & Devel. Center, Ft. Collins, Colo., 1975-76; research meteorologist Atmospheric Physics and Chemistry Lab., NOAA-Environ. Research Labs., Boulder, Colo., 1976-79, meteorologist Office Weather Research and Modification, 1979-82, program mgr. weather analysis and storm prediction, 1982-83, dir. weather research program, 1983-84, program mgr. mesoscale studies, 1984-86; dir. Nat. Severe Storms Lab., Norman, Okla., 1986—; participant numerous sci. workshops; tchr. weather analysis, forecasting, mesoscale phenomena; presenter workshops on mesoscale analysis and heavy precipitation forecasting Nat. Weather Service Forecast Offices; cons. in field. Served to capt. USAF, 1967-75. Decorated Air Force Commendation medal with oak leaf cluster; recipient Superior Performance award NOAA, 1981, Outstanding Sci. Paper award, 1984. Fellow Am. Meteorol. Soc. (councilor 1989-92, chmn. severe elect. storms com. 1991-92, Clarence Leroy Meisinger award 1983, co-editor, assoc. editor Monthly Weather Rev., assoc. editor Weather & Forecasting); mem. Nat. Weather Assn. (award for outstanding contbns. to operational meteorology 1981, co-editor Nat. Weather Digest, Mem. of Yr. award 1992), Sigma Xi, Phi Kappa Phi, Chi Epsilon Pi. Contbr. articles to profl. publs. Office: NOAA/ERL Nat Severe Storms 1313 Halley Cir Norman OK 73069-8480

MADDOX, ROBERT LYTTON, lawyer; b. Middlesboro, Ky., May 18, 1924; s. Robert Lytton and Sybil (Sipher) M.; m. Inez Bentley Pryor, Nov. 23, 1955; children: William Granville, Julie Thornton, Robert Lytton III. AB, Harvard U., 1947, LLB, 1950. Bar: Ky. 1950, U.S. Dist. Ct. (ea. dist.) Ky. 1972, U.S. Dist. Ct. (we. dist.) 1979, U.S. Ct. Appeals (6th cir.) 1974. Assoc. Wyatt, Grafton & Sloss, Louisville, 1950-58; ptnr. Wyatt, Grafton & Sloss, 1958-80, Wyatt, Tarrant & Combs, 1980—; bd. dirs. Whip-Mix Corp., Louisville, Nugent Sand Corp., Louisville, Ky. Tax-Free Income Fund, Lexington, Orr Safety Corp., Louisville. Trustee/treas. Louisville Collegiate Sch., 1976-83, Lees Coll., Jackson, Ky., 1974-86; trustee/pres. Estate Planning Coun., Louisville, 1984-88. With U.S. Army, 1943-45. Decorated Bronze Star medal. Mem. Louisville Country Club, Harmony Landing Country Club, Jefferson Club, Wynn-Stay Club, Rotary. Democrat. Presbyterian. Avocations: golf, bicycling, investing. Home: 1412 Northwind Rd Louisville KY 40207-1665 Office: Wyatt Tarrant & Combs 2800 Citizens Plz Louisville KY 40202

MADDOX, ROBERT NOTT, chemical engineer, educator; b. Winslow, Ark., Sept. 29, 1925; s. R.L. and Mabel (Nott) M.; m. Paula Robinson, Oct. 6, 1951 (dec. Apr. 1984); children—Deirdre O'Neil, Robert Dozier; m. Pauline Razook, Nov. 30, 1987. Student, Iowa State Coll., 1944-45; B.S., U. Ark., 1948; M.S., U. Okla., 1950; Ph.D., Okla. State U., 1955; Sc.D. (hon.), U. Ark., 1991. Registered profl. engr., Okla. Mem. faculty Sch. Chem. Engring., Okla. State U., 1950-51, 52-58, prof., head dept., 1958-77, Leonard F. Sheerar prof., 1976-86, dir. phys. properties lab., 1976-86; design engr. process div. Black, Sivalls & Bryson, Inc., Oklahoma City, 1951-52; adminstrv. v.p., tech. dir. Fluid Properties Research, Inc., 1972-85; chem. engring. cons. Author: Gas and Liquid Sweetening, 1971, rev. ed. 1978, 83, (with J. Erbar) Gas Conditioning and Processing Vol. 3 - Computer Techniques and Applications, 1981, rev. ed. (with L. Lilly), 1988, (with A. Hines) Mass Transfer - Fundamentals and Applications, 1985; also numerous tech. papers. Served with USNR, 1944-45. Recipient award for personal achievement Chem. Engring. mag., 1988; Phillips lectr. in chem. engring. edn., Oklahoma State U., 1989; inducted into Engring. Hall of Fame, U. Ark., 1989; Dr. Robert N. Maddox Professorship in Chem. Engring. established in his honor by Gas Processors Suppliers Assn. at Okla. State U., 1989. Fellow Am. Inst. Chem. Engrs. (chpt. pres. 1956-57, André Wilkins Meml. award 1981, Founder's award 1994); mem. Nat., Okla. (chpt. pres. 1961-62, dir. 1966-68, Engr. of Year 1972); socs. profl. engrs. Am. Soc. Engring. Edn., Am. Inst. Mining Engrs., Soc. Petroleum Engrs., Am. Chem. Soc. (treas. indsl. and engring. chemistry div. 1966-68, chmn. div. 1970, Stewart award 1971), Gas Processors Suppliers Assn. (editorial adv. bd. engring. data book 1972—, Hanlon award 1985, Svc. citation 1987), Sigma Xi, Omega Chi Epsilon (nat. pres. 1968-70), Tau Beta Pi, Alpha Chi Sigma, Omicron Delta Kappa, Sigma Nu (high council 1966-70, regent 1972-74, Hall of Honor 1988). Episcopalian (lay reader, vestryman). Clubs: Elks, Masons. Home: 1710 Davinbrook Ln Stillwater OK 74074-2339

MADDOX, UTRICIA ANTOINETTE, English educator, communications educator; d. Curtis Anthony and Penolope Rotha (Sabusan) M. BA, New Rochelle Coll.; MA, Herbert H. Lehman U.; cert. advanced study, NYU. Cert. sch. dist. adminstr., sch. adminstr., supr., English tchr. Spl. asst. to deputy supt. N.Y.C. Bd. Edn.; prof. English SUNY, Westchester, 1985—; trainer communication skills GM, Westchester, 1987—; mem. Mid. States Rev. Fin. Com., Westchester, Fgn. Born Program Com., Westchester, policy making com. Learning Disabled Students, Westchester, freshman study skills Coll. Success Com., Westchester; speaker in field. Producer, host (radio broadcast mag.) Platinum Plus, 1986—. Mgr. advt. SSACIA, Westchester; co-host tv program Parenting, N.Y.C.; mem. Senate Homelessness Fact Finding Com., Westchester. Mem. ASCD, Nat. Pub. Radio, Nat. Coun. of Tchrs. of English, Lit. Soc. (past v.p.). Avocation: equestrian arts, field hockey, badminton, cryptograms, oil painting. Office: PO Box 95 Bronx NY 10467-0095

MADDREY, E. E., II, textile company executive. Pres., chief exec. officer Delta Woodside Industries, Greenville, S.C. Office: Delta Woodside Industries Inc 233 N Main St Greenville SC 29601-2142*

MADDREY, WILLIS CROCKER, medical educator, internist, academic administrator, consultant, researcher; b. Roanoke Rapids, N.C., Mar. 29, 1939; s. Milner Crocker and Sara Jean (Willis) M.; m. Ann Marie Matt, Apr. 18, 1981; children: Jeffrey, Gregory, Thomas. B.S., Wake Forest U., 1960; M.D., Johns Hopkins U., 1964. Diplomate: Am. Bd. Internal Medicine. Intern Osler Med. Service Johns Hopkins Hosp., Balt., 1964-65, asst. resident, 1965-66, 68-69, chief resident, 1969-70; fellow in liver disease Yale U., 1970-71; asst. prof. medicine Johns Hopkins U., Balt., 1971-75, assoc. prof., 1975-79, prof., 1980-81, asst. dean Sch. Medicine, 1975-79; assoc. dept. medicine Johns Hopkins U., Baltimore, 1979-82; prof., chmn. dept. medicine Jefferson Med. Coll., Phila., 1982-90; v.p. clin. affairs U. Tex. Southwestern Med. Ctr., Dallas, 1990-93, exec. v.p. clin. affairs, 1994—. Assoc. editor: Medicine, 1972-82, Hepatology, 1988—, mem. editorial bd., 1981-84, 86-87, Gastroenterology, 1982-87; bd. editorial cons. Am. Jour. Medicine, 1978-87; contbr. numerous articles, chpts. on liver disease to profl. publs. Bd. dirs.

Am. Liver Found., 1976-80; trustee Magee Rehab. Hosp., Phila., 1982-87. Served with USPHS, 1966-68. Mem. ACP (bd. regents 1984-94, pres. 92-93), Am. Soc. Clin. Investigation, Am. Gastroenterol. Assn., Am. Assn. Study Liver Disease (pres. 1982). Republican. Office: U Tex Southwestern Med Ctr 5323 Harry Hines Blvd Dallas TX 75235-8570

MADDUX, GREG (GREGORY ALAN MADDUX), professional baseball player; b. San Angelo, Tex., Apr. 14, 1966. Grad. high sch., Las Vegas. Baseball player Chicago Cubs, 1984-92, Atlanta Braves, 1992—. Recipient Cy Young award Baseball Writers' Assn. Am., 1992, 93, 94; named to All-Star team, 1988, 92, 94; recipient Gold Glove Award, 1990-94; Sporting News All-Star Team, 1992-94; named Nat. League Pitcher of Yr., Sporting News, 1993; Nat. League Innings Pitched Leader, 1991-92. Office: Atlanta Braves PO Box 4064 Atlanta GA 30302-4064*

MADDUX, PARKER AHRENS, lawyer; b. San Francisco, May 23, 1939; s. Jackson Walker and Jeanette Ahrens M.; m. Mathilde G.M. Landman, Mar. 20, 1966; 1 child, Jackson Wilhelmus Quentin. AB, U. Calif., 1961; JD, Harvard U., 1964. Bar: Calif. 1965, U.S. Dist. Ct. (no. so. and ea. dist.) Calif. 1965, U.S. Ct. Appeals (9th cir.) 1972, U.S. Ct. Claims, 1974, N.Y. 1981, U.S. Supreme Ct. 1982. Assoc., Pillsbury, Madison & Sutro, San Francisco, 1965-72, ptnr., 1973—; lectr. in field. Bd. dirs. Friends of Recreation and Parks, San Francisco; mem. San Francisco Open Space Citizens Adv. Com., Fulbright fellow, 1964-65. Mem. ABA, Calif. Bar Assn., San Francisco Bar Assn., St. Francis Yacht (San Francisco) Club, Harvard Club (N.Y.C., San Francisco), Pacific Union Club. Republican. Unitarian. Contbr. articles to profl. jours. Office: Pillsbury Madison & Sutro 225 Bush St San Francisco CA 94104-4207

MADDY, PENELOPE JO, philosopher; b. Tulsa, July 4, 1950; d. Richard and Suzanne (Lorimer) Parsons. BA in Math., U. Calif., Berkeley, 1972; PhD in Philosophy, Princeton U., 1979. Asst. prof. U. Notre Dame (Ind.), 1978-83; assoc. prof. U. Ill., Chgo., 1983-87; assoc. prof. U. Calif., Irvine, 1987-89, prof., 1989—, dept. chair, 1991-95; mem. editorial bd. Jour. Philos. Logic, 1985—. Author: Realism in Mathematics, 1990; editor Notre Dame Jour. Formal Logic, 1979-84, editl. bd., 1984—; editl. bd. Jour. Symbolic Logic, 1995—. Fellow AAUW, 1982-83, U. Calif., 1988-89; NSF grantee, 1986, 88-89, 90-91, 94-95, Marshall scholar, 1982-83, Westinghouse Sci. scholar, 1968-72. Mem. Assn. Symbolic Logic (mem. exec. com. 1993—), Am. Philos. Assn. (mem. exec. com. 1993—), Philosophy of Sci. Assn. (mem. governing bd. 1993—). Office: U Calif Dept Philosophy Irvine CA 92717

MADEIRA, EDWARD W(ALTER), JR., lawyer; b. Phila., Feb. 10, 1928; s. Edward W. and Alice T. (Thompson) M.; m. Grace Luquer, Oct. 13, 1956; children: Martha L., Melissa P., Amanda T. A.B., U. Pa., 1949, LL.B. 1952. Bar: Pa. 1953. Law clk. Justice John C. Bell, Jr., 1952-53; assoc. atty. Pepper, Hamilton & Scheetz, Phila., 1953-61; ptnr. Pepper, Hamilton & Scheetz, 1961—, vice chmn., 1989-92, co-chmn., 1992-94, chmn. emeritus, 1994—; adj. prof. law Villanova Law Sch., 1992—. Pres. bd. dirs. Defender Assn. Phila. (pub. defender); assoc. trustee U. Pa. 1989—. Fellow Am. Coll. Trial Lawyers; mem. ABA (mem. Ho. of Dels. 1989-92, chmn. com. on fed. jud. improvements), Jud. Conf. of Third Cir., Phila. Bar Assn., Pa. Bar Assn., Internat. Assn. Ins. Counsel. Republican. Episcopalian. Home: 227 Atlee Rd Wayne PA 19087-3835 Office: Pepper Hamilton & Scheetz 3000 Two Logan Sq 18th Arch St Philadelphia PA 19103

MADEIRA, FRANCIS KING CAREY, conductor, educator; b. Jenkintown, Pa., Feb. 21, 1917; s. Percy Childs and Margaret (Carey) M.; m. Jean E. Browning, June 17, 1947. Grad., Avon Old Farms, 1934; student, Julliard Grad. Sch., 1937-43; D.F.A. (hon.), Providence Coll., 1966; D.H.L., R.I. Coll., 1969; Mus.D. (hon.), Brown U., 1976. Instr. music Brown U., 1943-46, asst. prof. music, 1946-56, assoc. prof. music, 1956-66; founder, condr. R.I. Philharm. Orch., 1945-78; concert pianist recitals and condr. concerts, U.S. and Europe; also guest condr. U.S. and fgn. orchs. World premiere Trilogy (JFK-MLK-RFK) (by Ron Nelson), R.I. Philharmonic Orch., 1969. Mem. music panel Maine State Arts Commn., 1987-90; bd. trustees Saco River Festival Assn., 1988-94. Recipient Gov.'s award for excellence in arts, 1972; John F. Kennedy award for service to community, 1978.

MADEIRA, ROBERT LEHMAN, association executive; b. Elizabethtown, Pa., Aug. 30, 1915; s. Isaac Titus and Elsie Hernley (Lehman) M.; m. Mary Elizabeth Evans, Feb. 5, 1938; children: Terry Madeira Harsney, Chase Landre. Student, Juniata Coll., 1933-34; B.S. in Econs, Elizabethtown Coll., 1937; postgrad., Mpls. Honeywell Sch. Aero. Engring., U. Minn., 1945. Pianist, tchr. Elizabethtown, 1935-41; automobile salesman Packard Lancaster Co., Lancaster, Pa., 1937; owner, mgr. Conewago Foods, Elizabethtown, 1938-39; aircraft technician U.S. Air Force Middletown, Pa. and Columbia, S.C., 1941-42; project engr. Mpls. Honeywell, Chgo. and Mpls., 1942-45; mgr. Iceland, Inc., Elizabethtown, 1945-51; exec. sec. Nat. Frozen Food Locker Inst., Elizabethtown, 1951-55; exec. dir. Nat. Inst. Locker and Freezer Provisioners, Elizabethtown, 1955-73, Am. Assn. Meat Processors, Elizabethtown, 1973-80; exec. dir. emeritus Am. Assn. Meat Processors, 1980—; condr. internat. meat processing seminars, Europe, S.Am., Australia, New Zealand, The Orient, Africa, 1962-85. Chmn. Elizabethtown ARC, 1948-49, Elizabethtown Community Chest, 1952-53, Elizabethtown Park Dr., 1950; bd. dirs. Lancaster Com. of 100, 1953-57, Elizabethtown Music Found., 1951-57; bd. dirs. Norlanco Med. Center, Elizabethtown, 1972-75, chmn. fund dr., 1972-73. Recipient Man of Yr. award Nat. Inst. Locker and Freezer Provisioners, 1955; honor cert. Freedoms Found. at Valley Forge, 1976. Mem. Am. Soc. Assn. Execs. (Key award 1971, chartered assn. exec.), C. of C. U.S., Nat. Assn. Exhbn. Mgrs., Nat. Fedn. Ind. Bus., Gideons Internat., Nat. Right-to-Work Com. Republican. Presbyterian. Home: Apt M102 660 Willow Valley Sq Lancaster PA 17602 Office: Am Assn Meat Processors PO Box 269 Elizabethtown PA 17022-0269

MADER, CHARLES LAVERN, chemist; b. Dewey, Okla., Aug. 8, 1930; s. George Edgar and Naomia Jane (Harer) M.; m. Emma Jean Sinclair, June 12, 1960; 1 child, Charles L. II. BS, Okla. State U., 1952, MS, 1954; PhD, Pacific Western U., 1980. Fellow Los Alamos (N.Mex.) Nat. Lab., 1955—; sr. fellow JIMAR, U. Hawaii, Honolulu, 1985-94; pres. Mader Consulting Co., Honolulu, 1985—. Author: Numerical Modeling of Detonation, 1979, Numerical Modeling of Water Waves, 1988, LASL Data Volumes, 1980-82; contbr. numerous articles to profl. jours.; author 70 reports. Scoutmaster Boy Scouts Am., Los Alamos, 1971-85. Fellow Am. Inst. Chemists; mem. Am. Chem. Soc., Am. Phys. Soc., Combustion Inst., Tsunanmi Soc. (editor 1985—), Marine Tech. Soc., Sigma Xi, Pi Mu Epsilon, Phi Lambda Upsilon. Methodist. Achievements include development and definition of field of numerical modeling of explosives and water waves. Home: 1049 Kamehame Dr Honolulu HI 96825-2860 Office: Mader Cons Co 1049 Kamehame Dr Honolulu HI 96825

MADER, DAVID A., federal agency executive; b. Jersey City, July 9, 1948; s. Arthur C. and Margaret F. (Martin) M.; m. Bette J. Sterling, June 20, 1970; 1 child, Eric D. BS in Polit. Sci., Mt. St. Mary's Coll., Emmetsburg, Md., 1970. Asst. computing ctr. dir. IRS, Detroit, 1987-88; asst. dist. dir. IRS, Newark, 1988-90; dep. asst. commr. planning and rsch. IRS, Washington, 1990-92, asst. commr. human resources, 1992-94, chief mgmt. and adminstrn., 1994—. Office: Dept of Treasury Chief Mgmt and Adminstrn 1111 Constitution Ave NW Washington DC 20224-0001

MADERA, CORNELIUS J. J., JR., supermarket chain executive, lawyer, mayor; b. July 24, 1949; s. Cornelius J. Sr. and Adele (Dobrowolski) M.; m. Marjorie Jones, Aug. 24, 1974; children: Meghan, Caitlin, Morgan. AB, MIT, 1970, Brown U., 1971; JD, Boston U., 1974. Bar: N.J. 1974, Mass. 1974, N.Y. 1981. Assoc. Riker, Danzig, Scherer & Debevoise, Morristown, N.J., 1974-78; real estate atty. Gt. Atlantic and Pacific Tea Co., Montvale, N.J., 1978-79; gen. counsel Village Supermarket, Inc., Springfield, N.J., 1979-82; sr. v.p., gen. counsel Big V Supermarkets, Inc., Florida, N.Y., 1982—; instr. U. Shopping Ctrs., Atlanta, 1987; sec. N.J. Atty.'s Ethics Com., Morristown, 1976-78. Trustee Village Tuxedo park, N.Y., 1984—; dep. mayor Tuxedo Park, 1986-89, mayor, 1989—; v.p. Tuxedo Park Sch. Mem. ABA, Fed. Bar Assn., N.Y. Bar Assn., N.J. Bar Assn., Mass. Bar Assn. Club: Tuxedo (Tuxedo Park). Home: Lorillard Rd Tuxedo Park NY 10987 Office: Big V Supermarkets Inc 176 N Main St Florida NY 10921

MADERA, JOSEPH J., bishop; b. San Francisco, Nov. 27, 1927. Ed.: Domus Studiorum of the Missionaries of the Holy Spirit, Coyoacan, D.F., Mexico. Ordained priest Roman Cath. Ch., 1957. Coadjutor to bishop of Fresno, 1980; bishop of Fresno, 1980-91; aux. bishop Archdiocese for Mil. Svcs., Silver Springs, Md., 1991—. *

MADGETT, NAOMI LONG, poet, editor, educator; b. Norfolk, Va., July 5, 1923; d. Clarence Marcellus and Maude Selena (Hilton) Long; m. Julian F. Witherspoon, Mar. 31, 1946 (div. Apr. 1949); 1 child, Jill Witherspoon Stovall; m. William H. Madgett, July 29, 1954 (div. Dec. 1960); m. Leonard P. Andrews, Mar. 31, 1972. BA, Va. State Coll., 1945; MEd, Wayne State U., 1956; PhD, Internat. Inst. for Advanced Studies, 1980; LHD (hon.), Siena Heights Coll., 1991, Loyola U., 1993; DFA (hon.), Mich. State U., 1994. Reporter, copyreader Mich. Chronicle, Detroit, 1945-46; svc. rep. Mich. Bell Telephone Co., Detroit, 1948-54; tchr. English pub. high schs. Detroit, 1955-65, 66-68; rsch. assoc. Oakland U., Rochester, Mich., 1965-66; mem. staff Detroit Women Writers Conf. Ann. Writers Conf., 1968—; lectr. English U. Mich., 1970-71; assoc. prof. English Eastern Mich. U., Ypsilanti, 1968-73, prof., 1973-84, prof. emeritus, 1984—; editor-pub. Lotus Press, 1974-93, dir., 1993—; sr. editor Lotus Poetry Series, Mich. State U. Press, 1993—. Author: (poetry) Songs to a Phantom Nightingale (under name Naomi Cornelia Long), 1941, One and the Many, 1956, Star by Star, 1965, 70, Pink Ladies in the Afternoon, 1972, 90, Exits and Entrances, 1978, Phantom Nightingale: Juvenilia, 1981, Octavia and other Poems (Creative Achievement award Coll. Lang. Assn.), 1988, Remembrances of Spring: Collected Early Poems, 1993; (textbook) (with Ethel Tincher and Henry B. Maloney) Success in Language and Literature B, 1967, A Student's Guide to Creative Writing, 1980; editor: (anthology) A Milestone Sampler: 15th Anniversary Anthology, 1988, Adam of Ife: Black Women in Praise of Black Men, 1992; Tribute In Her Lifetime Afrikan Poets Theatre, 1989. Participant Creative Writers in Schs. program. Recipient Esther R. Beer Poetry award Nat. Writers Club, 1957, Disting. English Tch. of Yr. award, 1967; Josephine Nevins Keal award, 1979; Mott fellow in English, 1965, Robert Hayden Rungate award, 1985, Creative Artist award Mich. Coun. for the Arts, 1987, award Nat. Coalition 100 Black Women, 1984, award Nat. Coun. Tchrs. English Black Caucus, 1984, award Chespeake/Virginia Beach chpt. Links, Inc., 1981, Arts Found. Mich. award, 1990, Creative Achievement award Coll. Lang. Assn., 1988; Arts Achievement award Wayne State U., 1985, The Black Scholar Award of Excellence, 1992; Am. Book Award, 1993; 1st annual Naomi Long Madgett Poetry award offered by Hilton-Long Poetry Found., 1993; Mich. Artist award, 1993; Creative Contbrs. award Gwendolyn Brook Ctr. Black Lit. and Creative Writing Chgo. State U., 1993. Mem. NAACP, Coll. Lang. Assn., So. Poetry Law Ctr., Langston Hughes Soc., Nora Neale Hurston Soc., Am. Acad. Poets, Poetry Resource Ctr. Mich., Detroit Women Writers, Alpha Kappa Alpha. Congregationalist. Home: 18080 Santa Barbara Dr Detroit MI 48221-2531 Office: PO Box 21607 Detroit MI 48221-0607 *I have wanted my life to make a difference. I hope that, through my years of service, I have been an inspiration to the young, especially those who are African American. Through my writing, teaching, and publishing/editing, I have striven for excellence and have demanded that others live up to their potential. I have tried to be honest and to tell the truth.*

MADHAVAN, MURUGAPPA CHETTIAR, economics educator, international consultant; b. Kandramanickam, Tamilnadu, India, Dec. 17, 1932; came to U.S. 1960; s. L. Murugappa Chettiar and Adaikkammai Achi (Meyyappan) M.; m. Nachammai Manickam, May 3, 1953; children: Nachiappa, Nataraj. BA with honors, Annamalai U., India, 1955, MA, 1958; MS, U. Wis., 1963, PhD, 1966. Lectr. in econs. Annamalai U., 1955-60; economist Europe and Mid. East World Bank, Washington, 1963-66, asst. sec. econ. com., 1966-68; dir. Ctr. for Rsch. in Econ. Devel. San Diego State U., 1969-85, prof. econs., 1974—; dir. Asian Studies, 1991—; prof. econs. Nat. Inst. Bank Mgmt., Bombay, 1971-72; vis. prof. econs. Indian Inst. Tech., Madras, 1979-80; Father Carty Meml. lectr. U. Madras, 1980; vis. Fulbright prof. U. of the Philippines, 1987-88; cons. UN Devel. Program, N.Y.C., 1987-88, Gen. Atomics, San Diego, 1993—; advisor Gov. Sim Grinio, The Philippines, 1988. Co-author: The Transfer of Knowledge Through Expatriate Nationals, 1988. Chmn. World Affairs Coun. San Diego, 1991-93; pres. Tamil Nadu Found., Inc., Chgo., 1985-87, life mem.; advisor Mingei Internat. Mus., San Diego, 1985—; pres. San Diego Indian Am. Soc., 1984—. Fulbright fellow, 1960; recipient Hon. Am. award Ams. by Choice, 1987, Leadership and Contbn. award Tamil Nadu Found., 1994. Mem. Am. Econ. Assn., Indian Econ. Assn. (life), Assn. Indian Econ. Studies (life). Democrat. Avocations: reading, walking, organizational activities. Home: 8727 Verlane Dr San Diego CA 92119 Office: San Diego State U Coll Arts and Scis 5300 Campanile Dr San Diego CA 92182

MADIA, GIORGIO, dancer, choreographer; b. Milan, Italy, July 29, 1965; came to U.S. 1988; s. Luigi and Adriana (Bora) M.; m. Nancy Green, Oct. 23, 1989. Grad., Teatro Alla Scala Ballet Sch., Milan, 1984. With Teatro Alla Scala Ballet Co., Milan, 1984-85, Ballet Du XXeme Siecle, Brussels, 1985-87, Milw. Ballet., 1988-89, Pa. Ballet, Phila., 1988-89; soloist Bejart Ballet, Lausanne, Switzerland, 1987-88, Pa. Ballet, Phila., 1989-90, San Francisco Ballet, 1990—. Choreographer Elements, 1989, La Civetta, 1989, A Vous Dire-je Maman, 1991; guest appearances include Nureyev and Friends, 1988-91. Home: 1080 Eddy St Apt 205 San Francisco CA 94109-7602 Office: Pa Ballet 1101 South Broad St Philadelphia PA 19147

MADIGAN, JOHN WILLIAM, publishing executive; b. Chgo., June 7, 1937; s. Edward P. and Olive D. Madigan; m. Holly Williams, Nov. 24, 1962; children: Mark W., Griffith E., Melanie L. BBA, U. Mich., 1958, MBA, 1959. Fin. analyst Duff & Phelps, Chgo., 1960-62; audit mgr. Arthur Andersen & Co., Chgo., 1962-67; v.p. investment banking Paine, Webber, Jackson & Curtis, Chgo., 1967-69; v.p. corp. fin. Salomon Bros., Chgo., 1969-74; v.p., chief fin. officer, dir. Tribune Co., Chgo., 1975-81, exec. v.p., 1981-88; pres., COO Tribune Co., 1994—; pres., chief exec. officer, pub. Chgo. Tribune Co., 1988-94. Trustee Rush-Presbyn.-St. Luke's Med. Ctr., McCormick Tribune Found., Ill. Inst. Tech.; vis. com. Sch. Bus. Adminstrn. U. Mich. With USMC, 1959. Home: 1160 Laurel Ave Winnetka IL 60093 Office: Tribune Co 435 N Michigan Ave Chicago IL 60611

MADIGAN, JOSEPH EDWARD, financial executive, consultant, director; b. Bklyn., June 26, 1932; s. James Peter and Mary (Goldman) M.; m. Catherine Cashman, July 26, 1980; children: Kerri Ann, Kimberly Ann, Elizabeth Ann. BBA cum laude, Baruch Coll., CUNY, 1958; GBA, NYU, 1963. Adminstrv. asst. Assoc. Metals & Minerals Corp., 1961-63; fin. analyst, fgn. exch. trader, corp. portfolio trader AMAX, Inc., 1963-65; mgr. corp. portfolio, dir. cash mgmt., asst. treas. TWA, Inc., 1965-68; treas. Borden, Inc., 1968-76, v.p., treas., 1976-80; exec. v.p., chief fin. officer Wendy's Internat., Inc., Dublin, Ohio, 1980-87; bd. dirs. Cooker Resaturant Corp., Skyline Chili, Inc., Voca Corp., Columbia Parts Supply, Inc., Cardinal Realty Svcs., Inc., Frank Gates Svc. Co., Glick Furniture Co., RWS Enterprises. With USN, 1951-55. Mem. Fin. Execs. Inst., Nat. Investor Rels. Inst., Investor Rels. Assn., Exec. Forum NYU, Baruch Coll.-CUNY Alumni Assn., NYU Alumni Assn., Treas. Club N.Y., Econ. Club Columbus, Country Club At Muirfield Village, Capital Club (Columbus), Imperial Golf Club (Naples, Fla.), Beta Gamma Sigma. Republican. Roman Catholic. Home: 9457 Avemore Ct Dublin OH 43017-9674

MADIGAN, KIMBERLY A., mediator, lawyer; b. Lincoln, Ill., Mar. 21, 1956; d. Edward R. and Evelyn M. (George) M. BA, U. Ill., 1978; JD, Am. U., 1982. Bar: Ill. 1982, D.C. 1984. Atty. Highsaw & Mahoney, Washington, D.C., 1982-86, Weiner, McCaffrey, Brodsky, Kaplan & Levin, Washington, D.C., 1986-90; bd. mem. Nat. Mediation Bd., Washington, D.C., 1990-92, chmn., 1992-93; prin. RBC Assocs., Inc., 1993—; adj. prof. Washington Coll. of Law, Am. U., 1992-93. Mem. ABA, Ill. Bar Assn., D.C. Bar Assn., Women's Bar Assn. Republican. Office: Nat Mediation Bd 122 C St NW Washington DC 20001

MADIGAN, MARTHA, photographer, artist, photography educator; b. Milw.; d. Daniel Francis and Margaret Mary (Breen) M.; m. Jeffrey P. Fuller, Oct. 13, 1979; children: Daniel Fuller, Claire Fuller, Grace Fuller. BS in Art Edn., U. Wis., 1972; postgrad., Ariz. State U., 1972-73; MFA, Sch. Art Inst. Chgo., 1978. Photography, printmaking, art instr. North Shore Country Day Sch., Winnetka, Ill., 1973-78; asst. prof.photography, dept. art, art history Wayne State U., Detroit, 1978-79;

prof., chairperson dept. photography Tyler Sch. Art Temple U., Phila., 1979—. Solo exhbns. include Hayes Gallery, Milw., 1977, Phila. Coll. Art, 1979, Cranbrook Acad. Art, 1981, Univ. of Arts, Phila., 1990, RISD, 1993, Michael Rosenfeld Gallery, N.Y.C., 1994, others; group exhbns. include Union Gallery, U. Wis., 1971-72, Camerawork Gallery, San Francisco, 1977, Hyde Park Art Ctr., Chgo., 1977Artists Market, Detroit, 1978, Chgo. Ctr. Contemporary Photography, 1978, Nat. Coll. Edn., Chgo., 1978, Ill. State Mus., 1978, New Mus., N.Y.C., 1979, So. Ill. Univ., 1979, Jeffrey Fuller Fine Art, Phila., 1980, 81, 82, 83, 84, Beaver Coll., Pa., 1980, Phila. Mus. Art, 1981, Print Club, 1982, U. Colo., Boulder, 1982, Va. Commonwealth Mus., 1982, Bard Coll., N.Y., 1982, L.A. Ctr. Photographic Studies, 1982, Phila. Coll. Art, 1983, Art Inst. Phila., 1983, Franklin Inst., Phila., 1983, Denver Art Mus., 1983, Painted Bride Art Ctr., Phila., 1984, 85, Md. Inst. Coll. Art, Balt., 1984, IBM Gallery, N.Y.C., 1984, Hong Kong Arts Ctr., 1984, Allentown (Pa.) Art Mus., 1985, 93, James Madison U., Harrisonburg, Va., 1985, Ohio State U., 1985, Santa Barbara Mus. Art, 1986, Md. Art Place, Balt., 1986, Rockwell Mus., Corning, N.Y., 1986, Coll. Notre Dame, Balt., 1987, Fine Arts Mus. L.I., 1988, Bucks County (Pa.) C.C., 1988, The Athenaeum No. Va. Fine Art Assn., 1988, Ctr. Contemporary Arts of Sante Fe, 1989, Carnegie Mellon Art Gallery, Pitts., 1989, Moravian Coll., 1989, Moore Coll. Art, Phila., 1990, Pyramid Art Ctr., Rochester, N.Y., 1990, James Danziger Gallery, N.Y.C., 1991, Midtown Payson Gallery, N.Y.C., 1992, Univ. of Arts, Phila., 1992, Acad. Fine Arts, Bratislava, Czechoslovakia, 1992, numerous others; represented in permanent collections Met. Mus. Art, N.Y.C., Phila. Mus. Art, Art Inst. Chgo., Detroit Inst. Arts, Calif. Mus. Photography, Milw. Art Ctr., Madison (Wis.) Art Ctr., Ill. State Mus., Colo. Mountain Coll., K-Mart Collections, Bloomfield Hills, Mich., McDonald's Corp., Oak Brook, Ill., Goldman/Sachs Collections, N.Y.C., Isabel Munoz, Madrid, Spain, David C. Ruttenberg, others; invited lectr., panelist, jurist; workshops in field. Office: Tyler Sch Art Beech and Penrose Aves Elkins Park PA 19027

MADIGAN, MICHAEL J., lawyer; b. Washington, Apr. 18, 1943; s. Helen B. (McGuire) M.; children: Mollie, Shana. BA, U. Conn., 1965; JD, Cath. U., 1968. Law clk. to Hon. Edward A. Tamm U.S. Ct. Appeals (D.C. circ.), 1968-69; asst. U.S. atty. Washington, 1969-73; asst. minority counsel Senate Watergate Com., Washington, 1973-74; counsel to Sen. Howard Baker, Jr. Washington, 1975-76; minority counsel Senate Intelligence Com., Washington, 1976-77; ptnr. Akin, Gump, Strauss, Hauer & Feld, Washington, 1977—, chmn. pro bono com., 1989—; spl. counsel Senate Fgn. Rels. Com. for confirmation hearings in nomination of Sec. of State Alexander Haig, 1981; mem. adv. com. law firm pro bono project ABA, 1991—; pres. Asst. U.S. Attys. Assn., Washington, 1987-88; chmn. Fed. Jud. Appointments Com., Washington, 1991-93; mem. D.C. Fed. Jud. Nominating Commn., Washington, 1993. Mem. Bar Assn. of D.C. (nominating com. 1992-93, budget com. 1992), D.C. Bar Bd. Govs., Women's Bar Assn. D.C. Republican. Roman Catholic. Home: 3909 Ivy Terrace Ct NW Washington DC 20007-2138 Office: Akin Gump Strauss Hauer & Feld 1333 New Hampshire Ave NW Washington DC 20036-1500

MADIGAN, MICHAEL JOSEPH, state legislator; b. Chgo., Apr. 19, 1942; m. Shirley Roumagoux; children: Lisa, Tiffany, Nicole, Andrew. Ed., U. Notre Dame, Loyola U., Chgo. Mem. Ill. Ho. of Reps., 1971—, majority leader, 1977-80, minority leader, 1981-82, house speaker, 1983—; lawyer. Sec. to Alderman David W. Healey; hearing officer Ill. Commerce Commn.; del. 6th Ill. Constnl. Conv.; trustee Holy Cross Hosp.; ex officio mem. adv. com. to pres. Richard J. Daley Coll.; adv. com. Fernley Harris Sch. for Handicapped; committeeman 13th Ward Democratic Orgn. Mem. Council Fgn. Relations, City Club Chgo. Office: House Reps State Capital Bldg Springfield IL 62706

MADIGAN, MICHAEL SCOTT, financial executive, treasurer; b. Rochester, N.Y., Oct. 2, 1946; s. Harold Vincent and Leah Ann (Clark) M.; m. Kathleen Loretta Hirsch, Mar. 23, 1968; children: Amy Leah, Tracey Sarah. BS in Fin., Lehigh U., 1968, MBA, 1969. Fin. analyst RCA Communications, N.Y.C. and Anchorage, 1972-76; mgr. fin. adminstrn. RCA Communications, N.Y.C., 1976-78; dir. fin. planning, analysis Kennecott Corp., Stamford, Conn., 1978-80; v.p. fin. Kennecott Engineered Systems Group, Cleve., 1981; v.p. fin., treas. Dorr Oliver, Inc., Stamford, Conn., 1982—. Served to capt. U.S. Army, 1969-72, Vietnam. Mem. Fin. Execs. Inst. Unitarian. Club: Lake (Wilton, Conn.). Avocations: skiing, running. Office: Dorr-Oliver Inc 612 Wheelers Farms Rd Milford CT 06460-1643

MADIGAN, RICHARD ALLEN, museum director; b. Corning, N.Y., Oct. 29, 1937; s. Myles L. and Rebekah M. (Bacon) M.; AB, Drew U., 1959; m. Mary Jean Smith, June 11, 1960 (div. 1975); children: Richard Allen, Dana Smith, Reese Jennings; m. 2d, Alice Sturrock, Sept. 6, 1975 (div. May 1978); m. 3d, Cara Montgomery, Aug. 5, 1978 (div. July 1987); 1 son, James Myles. Pub. contact rep. Corning Glass Center, 1959, supr. visitor rels., 1959-60; dir. Andrew Dickson White Mus. Art, Cornell U., 1960-63; asst. dir., asst. sec. Corcoran Gallery Art, Washington, 1963-67; dir. N. Tex. Museums Resources Council, 1967-68, Bklyn. Children's Mus., 1968-69; exec. dir. Wave Hill Center Environ. Studies, 1969-74; instr. anthropology dept Lehman Coll., 1968-74; dir. Norton Gallery and Sch. Art, West Palm Beach Fla., 1974-89; sec. Norton Gallery and Sch. of Art, Inc., 1974-80; pvt. art cons., 1989-91; columnist Palm Beach Daily News, 1990-91; contbr. Calif. mag.; exec. dir., CEO Atlantic Ctr. for Arts, New Smyrna Beach, Fla., 1990-91; dir. Decorative Arts Study Ctr., San Juan Capistrano, 1992-94; dir., N.Y. Transit Mus. 1994—; past instr. art dept. George Washington U.; bd. dirs. Palm Beach Festival; lectr. Fgn. Svc. Inst., Dept. State. Mem. Am. Assn. Museums (chmn. coll. and univ. museums sect. 1962-63), Museums Council N.Y.C. (chmn. 1970-71), Fla. Art Mus. Dirs. Assn. (pres. 1978-79, 83-84), S.E. Museums Conf., Assn. Art Mus. Dirs., Palm Beach C. of C. (dir. 1979-91), West Palm Beach C. of C. (dir. 1981-82). Author: The Sculpture of Michael Schreck, 1983. Office: New York Transit Mus 130 Livingston St 9th Fl Box E Brooklyn NY 11201-5106

MADISON, BERNARD L., academic dean, mathematics educator; b. Rocky Hill, Ky., Aug. 1, 1941; s. George G. and Neva (Crump) M.; m. Lyda Sue Madison Wood, June 1, 1969; children: Eva Camille, Blair Bernard. B.S., Western Ky. U., 1958-62; M.S., U. Ky., 1964, Ph.D., 1966. Asst. prof. La. State U., Baton Rouge, 1966-71, assoc. prof., 1971-79, dir. basic and applied math., 1976-79; prof. dept. math., 1979-80; prof., chmn., dept. math. U. Ark., Fayetteville, 1979-89, dean Fulbright Coll. Arts and Scis., 1989—; cons. NRC, 1986-87, project dir., 1987-88. Contbr. articles to profl. jours. Recipient Ogden medal Western Ky. U., 1962. Mem. Am. Math. Soc., Math. Assn. Am., AAUP, Sigma Xi, Sigma Pi Sigma, Pi Mu Epsilon, Lambda Chi Alpha. Democrat. Presbyterian. Home: 573 Rockcliff Rd Fayetteville AR 72701-3809 Office: U Ark Fulbright Coll Old Main # 525 Fayetteville AR 72701

MADISON, JAMES RAYMOND, lawyer; b. White Plains, N.Y., Apr. 27, 1931; s. Raymond S. and Katherine (Sherwin) M.; m. Mary Massey, Sept. 19, 1953; children: Michael, Matthew, Molly. BS, Stanford U., 1953, LLB, 1959. Bar: Calif. 1960, U.S. Dist. Ct. (no. dist.) Calif. 1960, U.S. Dist. Ct. (cen. dist.) Calif. 1970, U.S. Dist. Ct. (ea. dist.) Calif. 1981, U.S. Dist. Ct (so. dist.) Calif. 1988, U.S. Ct. Appeals (9th cir.) 1960, U.S. Supreme Ct, 1973. Assoc. Orrick, Herrington & Sutcliffe, San Francisco, 1959-67, ptnr., 1968—. Trustee Antioch U., Yellow Springs, Ohio, 1980-87; dir. Planned Parenthood of Alameda and San Francisco, 1984-89. Lt. (j.g.) USN, 1953-56. Mem. ABA, ASCE, State Bar Calif., Bar Assn. San Francisco, San Mateo County Bar Assn., Am. Arbitration Assn. (large complex case panel arbitrators and mediators, No. Calif. regional adv. coun.), Lawyers Club San Francisco. Democrat. Episcopalian. Avocation: soccer. Office: Orrick Herrington & Sutcliffe The Old Federal Res Bank Bldg 400 Sansome St San Francisco CA 94111

MADISON, ROBERT PRINCE, architect; b. Cleve., July 28, 1923; s. Robert J. and Nettie (Brown) M.; m. Leatrice L. Branch, Apr. 16, 1949; children: Jeanne Marie, Juliette Branch. Student, Howard U., 1940-43, HHD, 1987; B.Arch., Western Res. U., 1946-48; M.Arch., Harvard, 1952. Mem. various archtl. firms, 1948-52; instr. Howard U., Washington, 1952-54; pres. Robert P. Madison Internat., architects, engrs. and planners, Cleve., 1954—; trustee Am. Automobile Assn.; vis. prof. Howard U., 1961-62; lectr. Western Res. U., 1964-65; mem. U.S. architects del. Peoples Repub. China, 1974. Prin. works include U.S. Embassy Dakar, Senegal, West Africa, 1966,

State of Ohio Computer Ctr., 1988, Cuyahoga County Jail, 1990, Continental Airlines Hub Concourse, Cleve. Internat. Airport, 1991. Mem. tech. adv. com. Cleve. Bd. Edn., 1960—; mem. adv. com. Cleve. Urban Renewal, 1963—; mem. fine arts adv. com. to mayor, Cleve.; mem. archtl. adv. coun. Cornell U.; trustee Case Western Res. U., Cleve. Opera, 1990, NCCJ, 1990, Commn. on Higher Edn., 1990; bd. dirs. Jr. Achievement Greater Cleve.; trustee Cuyahoga County Hosp. Found, 1983—, Univ. Circle Inc., Midtown Corridor Inc.; mem. Ohio Bd. Bldg. Standards, 1986, Cleveland Heights City Planning Commn., 1987. 1st lt., inf. AUS, 1943-46. Decorated Purple Heart; Fulbright fellow, 1952-53; recipient Disting. Svc. award Case Western Res. U., 1989, Disting. Archtl. Firm award Howard U., 1989, Entrepreneur of Yt. award Ernst Young, Inc., Merrill Lynch, 1991; named to Corp. Hall of Fame, Ohio Assembly of Couns., 1991. Fellow AIA (chpt. pres., nat. task force for creative econs. 1976, mem. jury of fellows 1983-85, mem. nat. judicial coun. 1993, Gold Medal Firm award Ohio 1994); mem. Architects Soc. Ohio, Epsilon Delta Rho, Alpha Phi Alpha, Sigma Pi Phi. Home: 2339 N Park Blvd Cleveland OH 44106-3139 Office: Robert P Madison Internat Inc 2930 Euclid Ave Cleveland OH 44115-2463

MADISON, ROBERTA ELEANOR, epidemiologist, educator, consultant; b. Bklyn., Feb. 10, 1932; d. A.I. and Grace (Weinstein) M.; children: Jerry Solomon, Sue Vann. AB in History, UCLA, 1966, MA, 1969, MSPH in Environ. Health, 1972, DrPH, 1974. Chief epidemiological analyst Los Angeles County, L.A., 1972-75; from asst. prof. to assoc. prof. Calif. State U., Northridge, 1975-83, prof. epidemiology and biostatistics, 1983-89; part-time epidemiologist City of Hope, Duarte, Calif., 1977-85; instr. biostatistics UCLA Sch. Pub. Health, 1978-84; v.p. Enrich; cons., biostatistician Northridge Hosp., 1983-91; cons. epidemiology and biostats. Thrasher & Assocs., Northridge, 1988-91, Cytosystems, Cupertino, Calif., 1988-90; cons. epidemiology Warner Day Care Ctr., Woodland Hills, Calif., 1988-90; cons. to phys. therapy masters program Coll. Osteo Medicine of Pacific, 1992-93. Mem. editorial rev. bd. Alzheimers Disease and Assoc. Disorders, 1985—; contbr. articles to profl. jours.; cons. editor: Informed Consent mag., 1994—. Bd. dirs. Basehart Theatre, Woodland Hills, 1986-94. Grantee Am. Lung Assn., Health and Human Svcs., 1995, others. Fellow Am. Coll. Epidemiology, Cancer Rsch. Ctr.; mem. Am. Statis. Assn. (sec. state edn. sect. 1982, workshop organizing com. State Calif. chpt. 1986—), Golden Key Honor Soc. (hon.), Sigma Xi (sec. chpt. 1982). Avocations: walking, camping, reading, concerts. Office: Calif State U 18111 Nordhoff St Northridge CA 91330-0001

MADIX, ROBERT JAMES, chemical engineer, educator; b. Beach Grove, Ind., June 22, 1938; s. James L. and Marjorie A. (Strohl) M.; children: Bradley Alan, David Eric, Michella, Evan Scott. BS, U. Ill., 1961; PhD, U. Calif., 1964. NSF post doctoral fellow Max Planck Inst., Gottingen, Fed. Republic of Germany, 1964-65; asst. prof. chem. engr. Stanford (Calif.) U., 1965-72, assoc. prof., chem. engr., 1972-77; prof. chem. engring. Stanford U., 1977—, chmn., chem. engr., 1983-87, prof. chemistry, 1981—; cons. Monsanto Chem., St. Louis, 1975-84, Shell Oil Co., Houston, 1985-86; Peter Debye lectorship Cornell U., 1985; Eyring lectr. chemistry Ariz. State U., 1990. Contbr. articles to profl. jours. Recipient Alpha Chi Sigma award Am. Inst. Chem. Engrs., 1990, Paul Emmett award Catalysis Soc. N.Am., 1984, Humboldt U.S. Sr. Scientist prize, 1978; For Found. fellow, 1969-72. Mem. Am. Chem. Soc., Am. Vacuum Soc., Calif. Catalysis Soc. (assoc. editor catalysis revs. 1986—). Office: Stanford Univ Dept Chemical Engring Stanford CA 94305

MADOFF, BERNARD LAWRENCE, investment dealer; b. N.Y.C., Apr. 29, 1938; s. Ralph Z. and Sylvia R. (Muntner) M.; m. Ruth Alpern, Nov. 29, 1959; children—Mark, Andrew. B.S., Hofstra U., 1960. Prin. Bernard L. Madoff Investment Securities, N.Y.C., 1960—; bd. dirs. Nat. Securities Clearing Corp., 1984—. Founder North Shore Hosp., Manhasset, N.Y., L.I. Jewish-Hillside Med. Ctr., New Hyde Park, N.Y.; nat. treas. Am. Jewish Congress, N.Y.C. Served to 2d lt., inf. U.S. Army, 1960-62. Mem. Nat. Assn. Securities Dealers (chmn. dist. 12, 1982-83; nat. gov. 1983—; bd. dirs. Market Services Inc. 1981—), Securities Industry Assn., Nat. Securities Traders Assn., Securities Traders Assn. N.Y. Clubs: City Athletic (N.Y.C.). Chub Cay (Bahamas). Office: 18th Fl 885 3rd Ave New York NY 10022

MADONIA, VALERIE, dancer; b. Buffalo. Dancer Nat. Ballet of Can., 1979-81, Am. Ballet Theater, 1981-86, The Joffrey Ballet, N.Y.C., 1987—; mem. Baryshnikov and Co. Tour 1985; guest artist with The Armitage Ballet, 1987, Lines Contemporary Ballet, 1994; dir. Telluride (Colo.) Dance Gallery, 1995—. Office: Telluride Dance Gallery PO Box 1303 Telluride CO 81435

MADONNA (MADONNA LOUISE VERONICA CICCONE), singer, actress; b. Bay City, Mich., Aug. 16, 1958; d. Sylvio and Madonna Ciccone; m. Sean Penn, Aug. 16, 1985 (div. 1989). Student, U. Mich., 1976-78. Dancer Alvin Ailey Dance Co., N.Y.C., 1979. Albums include Madonna, 1983, Like a Virgin, 1985, True Blue, 1986, (soundtrack)Who's That Girl, 1987, (with others) Vision Quest Soundtrack, 1983, You Can Dance, 1987, Like a Prayer, 1989, I'm Breathless: Music From and Inspired by the Film Dick Tracy, 1990, The Immaculate Collection, 1990, Erotica, 1992, Bedtime Stories, 1994; film appearances include A Certain Sacrifice, 1980, Vision Quest, 1985, Desperately Seeking Susan, 1985, Shanghai Surprise, 1986, Who's That Girl, 1987, Bloodhounds of Broadway, 1989, Dick Tracy, 1990, Truth or Dare, 1991, Madonna, 1992, Body of Evidence, 1992, Dangerous Game, 1993; Broadway theater debut in Speed-the-Plow, 1987; author: Sex, 1992. Roman Catholic. Office: Sire Records 75 Rockefeller Plz New York NY 10019*

MADONNA, JON C., accounting firm executive. Chmn., CEO KPMG Peat Marwick, N.Y.C. Office: KPMG Peat Marwick 767 Fifth Ave 47th Fl New York NY 10153*

MADORE, JOYCE LOUISE, gerontology nurse; b. Madison, Kans., Dec. 15, 1936; d. Lionel Wiedmer and Mary Elizabeth (Piley) Murphy; m. Robert Madore, Aug. 15, 1969; children: Carl, Clay. BS, Emporia State U., 1980; diploma, Newman Hosp., 1981. RN, Kans., Mo.; cert. gerontol. nurse, non profit adminstr. Med. charge nurse St. Mary's Hosp., Emporia, Kans., 1971-72; dir. nursing Madison (Kans.) Manor, 1974-81, 82-83; staff nurse Newman Meml. Hosp., Emporia, 1981-82; dir. Daybreak Adult Day Svcs. Springfield (Mo.) Area Coun. of Chs., 1983—; mem. Gov.'s Com. to Establish Rules and Regulations on Adult Day Care Patients State of Mo.; cons. U. Mo. Coop. Extension Svc. Program Guides on Adult Day Care. Contbr. video Understanding Aging Program. Named one of Outstanding Nurses in Mo. St. Louis U., 1989. Mem. NAFE, Adult Day Care Assn. (past sec., exec. past v.p 1989-91), Mo. Nurses Assn., Mo. Adult Day Care Assn. (pres. 1991—). Home: 171 Hilltop Oaks Ln Sparta MO 65753-9801

MADORY, JAMES RICHARD, hospital administrator, former air force officer; b. Staten Island, N.Y., June 11, 1940; s. Eugene and Agnes (Gerner) M.; m. Karen James Clifford, Sept. 26, 1964; children: James E., Lynn Anne, Scott J., Elizabeth Anne, Joseph M. BS, Syracuse U., 1964; MHA, Med. Coll. Va., 1971. Enlisted USAF, 1958, commd. 2d lt., 1964, advanced through grades to maj., 1978; x-ray technician Leesler Area Med. Ctr., Biloxi, Miss., 1959-62; administr. Charleston (S.C.) Clinic, 1971-74, Beale Hosp., Calif., 1974-77; assoc. administr. Shaw Regional Hosp., S.C., 1977-79; ret. USAF, 1979; asst. administr. Raleigh Gen. Hosp., Beckley, W.Va., 1979-81; administr., dir., sec. bd. Chesterfield Gen. Hosp., Cheraw, S.C., 1981-87; pres., CEO Grand Strand Hosp., Myrtle Beach, S.C., 1987-95, trustee, 1987-95; commr. Horry County Planning Commn., 1995—; cons. Healthcare Adminstrn., 1995—; mem. adv. bd. Cheraw Regional Disease Assn. Contbr. articles to profl. publs. Chmn. bd. W.Va. Kidney Found., Charleston, 1980-81; chmn. youth bd. S.C. TB and Respiratory Disease Assn., Charleston, 1972-73; county chmn. Easter Seal Soc., Chesterfield County, S.C., 1984-85; campaign crusade chmn. Am. Cancer Soc., Chesterfield County, 1985-86; chmn. dist. advancement com. Boy Scouts Am. 1987-90; bd. dirs. Horry County United Way, 1989-95, Horry County Access Care, 1989-91; trustee Cheraw Acad., 1982-85, Grand Strand Gen. Hosp., 1987-95, Coastal Acad., 1988-90. Decorated Bronze Star, Vietnamese Cross of Gallantry, Vietnamese Medal of Honor. Fellow Am. Coll. Hosp. Adminstrs., Am. Coll. Health Care Execs.; mem. Am. Acad. Med. Adminstrs., S.C. Hosp. Assn. (com. on legislation 1984-86, trustee 1989-95), Cheraw C. of C. (bd. dirs. 1982-83), Rotary (pres. 1984-85). Republican. Roman Catholic.

MADOW, LEO, psychiatrist, educator; b. Cleve., Oct. 18, 1915; s. Solomon Martin and Anna (Meyers) M.; m. Jean Antoinette Weisman, Apr. 16, 1942; children: Michael, Robert. AB, Western Res. U., 1937, MD, 1942; MA, Ohio State U., 1938. Diplomate Am. Bd. Psychiatry and Neurology. Intern Phila. Gen. Hosp., 1942-43; resident Phila. Gen. Hosp., Jefferson Hosp., Inst. Pa. Hosp., 1943-46; practice medicine specializing in psychiatry Phila., 1948—; prof., chmn. dept. neurology Med. Coll. Pa., Phila., 1958-65; prof., chmn. dept. psychiatry and neurology Med. Coll. Pa., 1965-70, prof., chmn. dept. psychiatry, 1970-81, clin. prof. psychiatry Hershey Med. Ctr., 1982—; sr. cons. psychiatry Inst. Pa. Hosp., Phila., 1975—; tng. analyst, past pres. Phila. Psychoanalytic Inst.; past pres., mem. med. staff Inst. Pa. Hosp. Author: Anger, 1972, Love, 1983, Guilt, 1989; editor: Dreams, 1970, Sensory Deprivation, 1970, Psychomimetic Drugs, 1971, Integration of Child Psychiatry with Basic Resident Program, 1975. Served to capt. AUS, 1944-46. Named Outstanding Educator of Am. Med. Coll. Pa., 1972. Fellow ACP, Am. Psychiatric Assn. (life), Phila. Psychiatric Soc. (Lifetime Achievement award 1991) (past pres.), Am. Coll. Psychiatrists, Am. Coll. Psychoanalysts (pres. 1989-90, Laughlin award 1990); mem. Am. Psychoanalytic Assn., Am. Neurol. Assn., Phila. Psychoanalytic Soc. (past pres.), Alpha Omega Alpha, Phi Soc. Home: 135 Sibley Ave Narberth PA 19072-1318 Office: Inst of Pa Hosp 111 N 49th St Philadelphia PA 19139-2718

MADRID, JAY JOSEPH, lawyer; b. Waterbury, Conn., Nov. 11, 1942; s. Alexander Alfred and Lois (Middlemist) M.; m. Trudy Turner, Nov. 30, 1968; children: Jody Susanne, Mandy Christine. BA, U. Tex., El Paso, 1963; LLB, U. Tex., 1966, JD, 1977; postgrad., Boston Coll., 1970-71; MLA, So. Meth. U., 1977. Bar: Tex.; cert. mediator, Tex. Ptnr. Matthews, Matthews, Sechrist & Marold, Dallas, 1972-78; dir. Winstead, McGuire, Sechrest & Minick, Dallas, 1978—; adj. prof. So. Meth. U. Sch. Law, Dallas, 1980—; faculty Nat. Inst. Trial Advocacy, St. Paul, 1982—; lectr. in field. Contbr. articles to profl. jours. Capt. JAGC, U.S. Army, Vietnam. Fellow Tex. Bar Found.; mem. ABA, Dallas Bar Assn. (chair com. 1985—), Royal Oaks Country Club, City Club. Episcopalian. Avocations: golf, book collecting. Office: Winstead McGuire Sechrest et al 1201 Elm St Ste Dallas TX 75270-2144

MADSEN, BRIGHAM DWAINE, history educator; b. Magna, Utah, Oct. 21, 1914; s. Brigham and Lydia (Cushing) M.; m. Betty McAllister, Aug. 11, 1939; children—Karen Madsen Loos, David B., Linda Madsen Dunning, Steven M. B.A., U. Utah, 1938; M.A., U. Calif., Berkeley, 1940, Ph.D., 1948. Prin. Grade Sch. and Jr. High Sch., Pingree, Idaho, 1938-39; assoc. prof. history Brigham Young U., Provo, Utah, 1948-54; pres., mgr. Madsen Bros. Constrn. Co., Salt Lake City, 1954-61; prof. history Utah State U., Logan, 1961-64; asst. dir. tng. Peace Corps, Washington, 1964-65; first dir. tng. Vols. in Service to Am., Washington, 1965; dean div. continuing edn. U. Utah, Salt Lake City, 1965-66; dep. acad. v.p. U. Utah, 1966-67, adminstrv. v.p., 1967-71, dir. libraries, 1971-73, prof. history, 1973-84, chmn. dept. history, 1974-75. Author: Bannock of Idaho, 1958, The Lemhi: Sacajawea's People, 1980, Corinne: Gentile Capital of Utah, 1980, The Northern Shoshoni, 1980, (with Betty M. Madsen) North to Montana: Jehus, Bullwhackers and Muleskinners on the Montana Trail, 1980; Gold Rush Sojourners in Great Salt Lake City, 1849 and 1850, 1983, The Shoshoni Frontier and the Bear River Massacre, 1985, Chief Pocatello: The "White Plume", 1986, Glory Hunter: A Biography of Patrick Edward Connor, 1990; editor: The Now Generation, 1971, Letters of Long Ago, 1973, A Fortyniner in Utah: Letters and Journal of John Hudson, 1982, B.H. Roberts: Studies of the Book of Mormon, 1985, Exploring the Great Salt Lake: The Stansbury Expedition of 1849-50, 1989. Served to 1st lt., inf. AUS, 1943-46. Mem. Phi Beta Kappa, Phi Kappa Phi., Phi Alpha Theta. Mem. Ch. of Jesus Christ of Latter-day Saints. Home: 2181 Lincoln Ln Salt Lake City UT 84124-2759

MADSEN, DONALD HOWARD, engineering educator, consultant; b. Council Bluffs, Iowa, Oct. 7, 1922; s. Aaron H. and Nomie L. (Petersen) M.; m. Jeanette Eunice Wieman, July 24, 1949; children: Nels Howard, Erik Chris. B.S., Iowa State U., 1944; M.S., Purdue U., 1948, Ph.D, 1953. Registered profl. engr., Iowa, Ill. Asst. eng. Eastman Kodak Co., Rochester, N.Y., 1944-45; instr. U. Kans.-Lawrence, 1949-51; asst. prof. S.D. State U., Brookings, 1953-54; asst. prof. engring. U. Iowa, Iowa City, 1954-57, assoc. prof., 1957-60, prof., 1960-90, prof. emeritus, 1990—; assoc. dean engring., 1967-74; cons. in field, 1970—. Mem. Iowa City Planning and Zoning Commn., 1967-76, chmn., 1972-76. Recipient Naval Ordnance Devel. award USN, Rochester, 1945. Mem. ASME, Am. Soc. Engring. Edn. (pres. Region VI 1959-60), Pi Tau Sigma, Tau Beta Pi, Sigma Pi Sigma. Republican. Home: 1315 Whiting Avenue Ct Iowa City IA 52245-5646 Office: U Iowa Engring Bldg Iowa City IA 52242

MADSEN, GEORGE FRANK, lawyer; b. Sioux City, Iowa, Mar. 24, 1933; s. Frank O. and Agnes (Cuhel) M.; m. Magnhild Norstog, June 28, 1959; 1 child, Michelle Marie. BA, St. Olaf Coll., 1954; LLB, Harvard U., 1959. Bar: Ohio 1960, Iowa 1961, U.S. Dist. Ct. (no. and so. dists.) Iowa, U.S. Ct. Appeals (8th cir.), U.S. Supreme Ct. 1991. Trainee Cargill, Inc., Mpls., 1954; assoc. Durfey, Martin, Browne & Hull, Springfield, Ohio, 1959-61; assoc., then ptnr. Shull, Marshall & Marks, Sioux City, 1961-85; ptnr. Marks & Madsen, Sioux City, 1985—. Author, editor: Iowa Title Opinions and Standards, 1978; contbg. author: The American Law of Real Property, 1991. Sec., bd.dirs. Sioux City Boys Club, 1969-76; mem. Sioux City Zoning Bd. Adjustment, 1963-65; past pres. Morningside Luth Ch., Sioux City; active Iowa Mo. River Preservation and Land Use Authority, 1992—. Lt. USAF, 1954-56. Fellow Iowa State Bar Found.; mem. ABA, Iowa Bar Assn., Woodbury County Bar Assn., St. Olaf Coll. Alumni Assn. (past pres. Siouxland chpt.), Nat. Wildlife Assn., Mont. Wildlife Assn., Rocky Mountain Elk Found., Pheasants Forever, Phi Beta Kappa (past pres. Siouxland chpt.), Rotary Internat. Avocations: skiing, hunting, swimming, riding, reading. Office: 700 4th St Ste 303 PO Box 3226 Sioux City IA 51102

MADSEN, H(ENRY) STEPHEN, retired lawyer; b. Momence, Ill., Feb. 5, 1924; s. Frederick and Christine (Landgren) M.; m. Carol Ruth Olmstead, Dec. 30, 1967; children: Stephen Stewart, Christie Morgan, Kelly Ann. M.B.A., U. Chgo., 1948; LL.B., Yale U., 1951. Bar: Wash. 1951, Ohio 1953, U.S. Supreme Ct. 1975. Research asst. Wash. Water Power Co., Spokane, 1951; assoc. Baker, Hostetler & Paterson, Cleve., 1952-59, ptnr., 1960-88, sr. ptnr., 1989-92; ret., 1992; chmn. bd. trustees Blue Cross Northeastern, Ohio, 1972-81; Danish consul for Ohio, 1973— Served with AC U.S. Army, 1944-46. Decorated Knight Queen of Denmark, 1982. Fellow ABA; mem. Am. Coll. Trial Lawyers (life), Am. Law Inst., Am. Judicature Soc., Ohio Bar Assn., Cleve. Bar Assn., The Country Club of Cleve., The Club at Soc. Ctr. Office: Baker & Hostetler 3200 National City Ctr 1900 E 9th St Cleveland OH 44114-3303

MADSEN, LOREN WAKEFIELD, sculptor; b. Oakland, Calif., Mar. 29, 1943; s. Roy Sondergaard and Kathryn O. (Finerty) M.; m. Libbe Hurvitz, June 30, 1968; children: Anne Lea, Nora Karin. Student, Reed Coll., Portland, 1961-63; B.A., UCLA, 1966, M.A., 1970. One-man shows include Riko Mizuno Gallery, Los Angeles, 1973, 74, Mus. Modern Art, N.Y.C. 1975, David McKee Gallery, N.Y.C., 1976, 77, 82, 84, 86, 90, 92, L.A. Louver Gallery, Venice, Calif., 1976, 78, Hansen Fuller Goldeen Gallery, San Francisco, 1980, Wright State U., Dayton, 1980, U. Mass., 1981, Cheryl Haines Gallery, San Francisco, 1991; group shows include Los Angeles County Mus. Art, 1974, 76, 83, Hayward Gallery, London, 1975, Walker Art Center, Mpls., 1976, Biennale of Sculpture, Sydney, Australia, 1976, Ft. Worth Mus. Art, 1977, Joslyn Art Mus., Omaha, 1979, Hirshhorn Mus., Washington, 1979, Newport Harbor Art Mus., 1982, Freedman Gallery, Albright Coll., 1987, others. Nat. Endowment for Arts grantee, 1975-76, 80-81. Office: 426 Broome St New York NY 10013-3251

MADSEN, PETER ERIC, architecture and real estate development firms executive; b. Boston, May 4, 1945; s. George Peter and May Isabelle (Alger) M.; m. Betsy Ridge, Oct. 12, 1969; children: Sarah Hall, Deane Alger, Joanna Morse, Samuel Alger (dec.). AB, Harvard U., 1967, MArch, 1972. Architect Perry, Dean & Stewart, Boston, 1967, Earl R. Flansburgh & Assoc., Boston, 1968; researcher Harvard U. Grad. Sch. Design, Cambridge, Mass., 1970; writer J. Scribner's, N.Y.C., 1972; architect John Andrews Architects, Toronto, Ont., Can., 1972—; architect ptnr. Graham Gund Architects, Inc., Cambridge, 1972—; pres. The Gunwyn Co., Cambridge,

1984—. Author: A Traveler's Guide to India, 1973, Essex, The Shipbuilding Town, 1976; editor: Dubbing, Hooping and Lofting, 1979. Pres. Castle Hill Found., Ipswich, Mass., 1984-87; v.p. Trustees of Reservations, Beverly, Mass., 1987—; trustee Soc. Preservation of New Eng. Antiques, 1992—, Boston Found. for Arch., 1992—; overseer New Eng. Conservatory of Music, 1994—; mem. alumni coun. Grad. Sch. of Design Harvard U., 1980-86, 92—. Fellow AIA; mem. Urban Land Inst., Boston Soc. Architects (bd. dirs. 1986-89, Honor award 1978, 85), Myopia Hunt Club, Hasty Pudding Club, Manchester Yacht Club, Somerset Club. Episcopalian. Avocations: sailing, music, golf. Office: Graham Gund Architects Inc 47 Thorndike St Cambridge MA 02141-1714

MADSEN, RICHARD WELLINGTON, lawyer; b. Portland, Oreg., Oct. 20, 1938; s. Richard W. Madsen and Adaline A. (Jeffries) Sarver; m. Priscilla A (Judy); children: Richard, Angela, Kristina. BA in Journalism, U. Nev., 1960; LLB, Georgetown U., 1963. Bar: Nev. 1963, D.C. 1967, Idaho 1971, Calif. 1974, D.C. Dep. atty. gen. Nev. Atty. Gen., Carson City, 1963-64; assoc. Jacobs & Speiler, Washington, 1966-69; asst. gen. counsel Boise Cascade Corp., Boise, Idaho, 1969-74; corp. counsel Rohr Industries Inc., Chula Vista, Calif., 1974-79, v.p., gen. counsel, sec., 1979—. Vice pres., sec., gen. counsel Nat. Kidney Found., 1983—; bd. dirs. Bowery Theater, San Diego, 1985—, pres., 1989-90. Capt. U.S. Army, 1963-64. Mem. Calif. Bar Assn., Nev. Bar Assn., Idaho Bar Assn., D.C. Bar Assn., Am. Soc. Corp. Secs. (pres. San Diego chpt. 1983), Am. Corp. Counsel Assn. (sec. San Diego chpt. 1987). Republican. Office: Rohr Industries Inc Foot of H St PO Box 878 Chula Vista CA 91912-0878

MADSEN, STEPHEN STEWART, lawyer; b. Spokane, Wash., Oct. 13, 1951; s. H. Stephen Madsen and Sarah Pope (Stewart) Ruth; m. Rebecca Wetherill Howard, July 28, 1984; children: Stephen Stewart Jr., Lawrence Wetherill, Christina Wetherill. BA, Harvard U., 1973; JD, Columbia U. 1980. Bar: N.Y. 1981, U.S. Dist. Ct. (so. dist.) N.Y. 1981, U.S. Ct. Appeals (6th cir.) 1983, U.S. Ct. Appeals (8th cir.) 1985, U.S. Ct. Appeals (2d, 7th and D.C. cirs.) 1994. Law clk. to presiding judge U.S. Ct. Appeals (2d cir.), N.Y.C., 1980-81; assoc. Cravath, Swaine & Moore, N.Y.C., 1981-88, ptnr., 1988—. Mem. bd. of visitors Columbia U. Sch. of Law, 1991—. Mem. ABA, N.Y. State Bar Assn., New York County Lawyers Assn. Office: Cravath Swaine & Moore Worldwide Pla 825 8th Ave New York NY 10019-7416

MADSON, JOHN ANDREW, architect; b. Mankato, Minn., Nov. 12, 1920; m. Joyce Helen Madson, Sept. 4, 1949; children: Brian A., David G., Paul J., Thomas R., John E., Tracy Ann. BA, U. Minn., 1949, BArch, 1950. Archtl. draftsman, designer Perry E. Crosier & Son, Mpls., 1950-53; architect-in-tng. Magney Tusler & Setter, Mpls., 1953-55; ptnr., prin. Patch Erickson Madson Watten, Inc., Mpls., 1955-89; chief exec. officer Madson & Assocs., Mpls., 1989—. Capt. USAF, 1944-45, ETO. Corp. mem. AIA. Republican. Lutheran. Avocations: playing and collecting jazz, classical music, golf, directing church choir. Home: 17419 N 130th Ave Sun City West AZ 85375-5061

MADVA, STEPHEN ALAN, lawyer; b. Pitts., July 27, 1948; s. Joseph Edward and Mary (Zulick) M.; m. Bernadette A. McKeon; children: Alexander, Elizabeth. BA cum laude, Yale U., 1970; JD, U. Pa., 1973. Bar: Pa. 1973, U.S. Dist. Ct. (ea. dist.) Pa. 1975, U.S. Ct. Appeals (3d cir.) 1976, U.S. Ct. Appeals (11th cir.) 1987, U.S. Supreme Ct. 1985, N.Y. 1990. Asst. defender Defender Assn. Phila., 1973-75 fed. defender, 1975-77, also bd. dirs., 1985—; assoc. Montgomery, McCracken, Walker & Rhoads, Phila., 1977-81, ptnr., 1981—; mem. mgmt. com., 1993—; mem. Fed. Criminal Justice Act Panel; panelist Am. Arbitration Assn. Mem. ABA, Am. Judicature Soc., Internat. Assn. Def. Counsel, Pa. Bar Assn., Phila. Bar Assn. (fed. cts. com.), Def. Rsch. Inst., Hist. Soc. Pa., Yale Alumni Assn. (schs. com.), Yale Rowing Assn. Democrat. Avocations: tennis, distance running, downhill skiing. Home: 2053 Lombard St Philadelphia PA 19146-1314 Office: Montgomery McCracken Et Al 3 Parkway 20th Fl Philadelphia PA 19102

MAECHLING, CHARLES, JR., lawyer, educator, writer; b. N.Y.C., Apr. 18, 1920; s. Charles and Eugenie H. M.; m. Janet Leighton, Sept. 2, 1944; children: Philip Leighton and Eugenie Elizabeth (Mrs. David Buchan). Attended, Birch Wathen Sch., N.Y.C., 1924-37; BA, Yale U., 1941; LLB, U. Va., 1949. Bar: N.Y. 1949, D.C. 1957. Assoc. Sullivan & Cromwell, N.Y.C., 1949-51; atty. Office Sec. Air Force, 1951-52; counsel Electronics Industries Assn., Washington, 1953-56; ptnr. Shaw, Pittman, Potts & Maechling, 1956-61; dir. for internal def. Dept. State, Washington, 1961-63; spl. asst. to undersec. for polit. affairs and amb.-at-large Averell Harriman, 1963-66; dep. gen. counsel NSF, 1966-71, spl. asst. to dir., 1972-74; prof. law U. Va., 1974-76; spl. counsel Kirlin, Campbell & Keating, Washington, 1976-81; sr. fellow Carnegie Endowment for Internat. Peace, 1981-85; vis. fellow, mem. law faculty Cambridge U. (Wolfson Coll.), Eng. 1985-88; guest scholar internat. law Brookings Inst., Washington, 1989-93; internat. cons., 1993—; legal adviser internat. matters NAS, 1972-74, mem. ocean policy com.; mem. law-of-sea and other adv. coms. Dept. State; gen. counsel Fairways Corp., 1959-61; adj. prof. Sch. Internat. Svc., Am. U.; mem. adv. bd. Internat. Peace Acad.; lectr. Acad. Internat. Law, Hague, The Netherlands, Knight Ctr. U. Md.; arbitrator complex, internat. cases Am. Arbitration Assn., Soc. Maritime Arbitrators. Editor-in-chief Va. Law Rev., 1948-49; contbr. articles to N.Y. Times, Washington Post, L.A. Times, profl. and lit. jours.; columnist Newsday, Miami Herald. Bd. dirs. Coun. for Ocean Law, Washington Inst. Fgn. Affairs, U.S. Com. for IIASA; mem. secretariat Joint Chiefs Staff, 1943-44, del., 1943, Cairo Conf.; outside counsel to CIA, 1957-60. Lt. comdr. USNR, 1941-46. Recipient Ross Essay award Am. Bar Assn., 1969. Mem. ABA (past com. chair), Am. Soc. Internat. Law, City Tavern Club (Washington), Cosmos Club (Washington), Yale Club (Washington). Avocation: languages. Home: 3403 Lowell St NW Washington DC 20016-5024 also (summer): Bar Rd, Saint Andrews, NB Canada E0G 2X0

MAEDA, J. A., data processing executive; b. Mansfield, Ohio, Aug. 24, 1940; d. James Shunso and Doris Lucille Maeda; m. Robert Lee Hayes (div. May 1970); 1 child, Brian Sentaro Hayes. BS in Math., Purdue U., 1962, postgrad., 1962-63; postgrad., Calif. State U., Northridge, 1968-75; cert. profl. designation in tech. of computer operating systems and tech. of info. processing, UCLA, 1971. Cons., rsch. asst. computer ctr. Purdue U., West Lafayette, Ind., 1962-63; computer operator, sr. tab operator, mem. faculty Calif. State U., Northridge, 1969, programmer cons., tech. asst. II, 1969-70, supr. acad. applicators, EDP supr. II, 1970-72, project tech. support coord. programmer II, office of the chancellor, 1972-73, tech. support coord. statewide timesharing tech. support, programmer II, 1973-74, acad. coord., tech. support coord. instrn., computer cons. III, 1974-83; coord. user svcs. info. ctr., mem. tech. staff IV CADAM INC subs. Lockheed Corp., Burbank, Calif., 1983-86, coord. end user svcs., tech. specialist computing dept., 1986-87; v.p. bd. dirs. Rainbow Computing, Inc., Northridge, 1976-85; mktg. mgr. Thaumaturge Taro Quipu Cons., Northridge, 1987—; tech. writer applications engring. div. Sterling Software, Woodland Hills, Calif., 1992—; v.p. bd. dirs. Rainbow Computing, Inc., Northridge, 1976-85; dir. Aki Tech./Design Cons., Northridge; tech. cons. Digital Computer Cons., Chatsworth, Calif., 1988; cons. computer tech., fin. and bus. mgmt., sys. integration, 1988-90; tech. customer s/w support Collection Data Sys., Westlake, Calif., 1991; tech. writer Sterling Software Applications Engring. Divsn., 1992—. Author, editor more than 250 user publs., BASIC programming lang. tutorials, ref. manuals, user guides; contbr. articles, papers, and photos to profl. jours. Mem. IEEE, SHARE, Digital Equipment Computer Users Soc. (DECUS, author papers and presentations 1977-81, ednl. spl. interest group 1977-83, steering com. RSTS/E 1979-82, Sterling Software Silver Achievement award 1993). Avocations: photojournalism, vintage automobiles. Office: Sterling Software Applic Engring Divsn 5900 Canoga Ave Woodland Hills CA 91367-5036

MAEDA, TOSHIHIDE MUNENOBU, spacecraft system engineer; b. Sagamihara, Kanagawa, Japan, Apr. 11, 1962; s. Mamoru and Yasuko Hiromi (Yamagishi) M. BS, U. Tokyo, 1986; postgrad., Internat. Space U., Cambridge, Mass., 1988. Engr. space systems div. Hitachi, Ltd., Yokohama, Japan, 1986-89, 92—; engr. Nat. Space Devel. Agy. Japan, Tsukuba, 1990-92. Supr. Newton jour., 1991. Mem. AIAA, Nat. Space Soc., Planetary Soc., Remote Sensing Soc. Japan, Japan Soc. Aero. and Space Sci.

Achievements include patents on thermal control technology for spacecraft components, structural test equipment. Home: 2349 Kamitsuruma, Sagamihara Kanagawa 228, Japan

MAEHL, WILLIAM HARVEY, historian, educator; b. Bklyn., May 28, 1915; s. William Henry and Antoinette Rose (Salamone) M.; m. Josephine Scholl McAllister, Dec. 29, 1941; children: Madeleine, Kathleen. BSc, Northwestern U., 1937, MA, 1939; PhD, U. Chgo., 1946. Asst. prof. history St. Louis U., 1941-42, Tex. A&M U., College Sta., 1943, De Paul U., Chgo., 1944-49; historian Dept. of Def., Karlsruhe, Stuttgart, Fed. Rep. Germany, 1950-52; chief briefing office U.S. hdqrs. EUCOM, Frankfurt, Fed. Rep. Germany, 1952-53; chief historian Artillery Sch. Ft. Sill, Okla., 1954, war plans office Hdqrs. NAMAE, USAF, Burtonwood, Eng., 1954-55; assoc. prof. European history Nebr. Wesleyan U., Lincoln, 1955-57, prof., 1958-62, 65-68; prof. German history Auburn (Ala.) U., 1968-81, prof. emeritus, 1981—; vis. prof. U. Nebr., 1962, U. Auckland, New Zealand, 1963-64, Midwestern U., Wichita Falls, Tex., 1965. Author: German Militarism and Socialism, 1968, History of Germany in Western Civilization, 1979, A World History Syllabus, 3 vols., 1980, August Bebel, Shadow Emperor of the German Workers, 1980, The German Socialist Party: Champion of the First Republic, 1918-33, 1986, monographs, chpts. to books, atomic, biol. and emergency war plans for NAMAE, USAF, classified studies for hist. divsn. USAREUR; contbr. articles to profl. jours.; contbr. poems to A Question of Balance, Tears of Fire, Distinguished Poets of Am., Best Poems of 1995, Journey of the Mind. Grantee Nebr. Wesleyan U., 1959, Auburn U., 1969-73, 79-80, Am. Philosophical Soc., 1973-74, Deutscher Akademischer Austauschdienst, 1978. Mem. Am. Hist. Assn., Phi Kappa Phi, Phi Alpha Theta.

MAEHL, WILLIAM HENRY, historian, university administrator, educational consultant; b. Chicago Heights, Ill., June 13, 1930; s. William Henry and Marvel Lillian (Carlson) M.; m. Audrey Mae Ellsworth, Aug. 25, 1962; 1 child, Christine Amanda. B.A., U. Minn., 1950, M.A., 1951; postgrad (Fulbright fellow), King's Coll., U. Durham, Eng., 1955-56; Ph.D., U. Chgo., 1957; LHD (hon.), Fielding Inst., 1993. Asst. prof. Montclair (N.J.) State Coll., 1957-58; asst. prof. Washington Coll., Chestertown, Md., 1958-59, U. Okla., Norman, 1959-64; assoc. prof. U. Okla., 1964-70, prof. English history, 1970-86; dean Coll. Liberal Studies, 1976-86, vice provost for continuing edn. and public service, 1979-86; pres. The Fielding Inst., Santa Barbara, Calif., 1987-93, pres. emeritus, 1993—; prin. investigator Adult Learning Project, Regents Coll., Albany, N.Y., 1994-97; vis. prof. U. Nebr., summer 1965; vis. fellow Wolfson Coll. Oxford (Eng.) U., spring, 1975; fellow Salzburg Seminar in Am. Studies, 1976. Author: The Reform Bill of 1832, 1967; editor: R.G. Gammage, Chartist Reminiscences, 1981, Continuum: Jour. of the Nat. Continuing Edn. Assn., 1980-83, also articles. Bd. dirs. Alliance for Alternative Degree Programs, 1988-90; trustee Coun. for Adult and Exptl. Learning, 1990-94. With AUS, 1953-55. Leverhulme Research fellow, 1961-62; grantee Am. Philos. Soc., 1961-62, 67-68, 71, 76. Fellow Royal Hist. Soc., Assn. of Grad. Liberal Studies Programs; mem. Am. Hist. Assn., Conf. on Brit. Studies, Soc. for Study Labour History.

MAEHR, MARTIN LOUIS, psychology educator; b. Guthrie, Okla., June 25, 1932; s. Martin J. and Regina (Meier) M.; m. Jane M. Pfeil, Aug. 9, 1959; children—Martin, Michael, Katherine. B.A., Concordia Coll., 1953, M.A., 1959; Ph.D., U. Nebr., 1960. Counselor U. Nebr., Lincoln, 1959-60; asst. prof. to assoc. prof. Concordia Sr. Coll., Fort Wayne, Ind., 1960-67; assoc. prof. ednl. psychology U. Ill., Urbana, 1967-70, prof., 1970—, chmn. dept. ednl. psychology, 1970-75, assoc. dean grad. and internat. programs prof., 1975-77, research prof., dir. Inst. Research on Human Devel., prof. ednl. psychology, 1977-88, assoc. dir. Office Gerontology and Aging Studies, 1980-82; prof. edn. and psychology U. Mich., Ann Arbor, 1988—, chair combined program edn. and psychology, 1988-92; vis. prof. U. Queensland, Australia, 1981; vis. prof., cons. to dean Faculty Edn. U. Tehran, Iran, 1973-74. Author: Sociocultural Origins of Achievement, 1974, (with others) Being a Parent in Today's World, 1980, (with L.A. Braskamp) The Motivation Factor, 1986; editor: Advancement in Motivation and Achievement series; contbr. articles to profl. jours. Lutheran.

MAEROFF, GENE I., educational association administrator, journalist; b. Cleve., Jan. 8, 1939; s. Harry B. and Charlotte (Szabo) M.; children: Janine Amanda, Adam Jonathan, Rachel Judith. B.S., Ohio U., 1961; M.S., Boston U., 1962. Teaching fellow Boston U., 1961-62; news bur. dir. R.I. Coll., 1962-64; religion editor Akron (Ohio) Beacon Jour., 1964-65; with Cleve. Plain Dealer, 1965-71, assoc. editor, 1969-71; edn. writer N.Y. Times, N.Y.C., 1971-86; sr. fellow Carnegie Found. for the Advancement of Teaching, Princeton, N.J., 1986—; contbr. mags. Author: Don't Blame the Kids, 1981, School and College, 1983, The Empowerment of Teachers, 1988, The School-Smart Parent, 1989, Sources of Inspiration, 1992, Team Building for School Change, 1993; (with others) The New York Times Guide to Suburban Public Schools, 1976; contbr. The Human Encounter: Readings in Education, 1976, Human Dynamics in Psychology and Education, 1977, Social Problems, 1978, Education Reform in the '90s, 1992. Trustee Guild-Times Scholarship Fund, Ed Bang Journalism Scholarship Found.; mem. adv. bd. Inst. Ednl. Mgmt., Harvard U., Ednl. Resources Info. Ctr., U.S. Dept. Edn., Nat. Ctr. for Postsecondary Governance. Recipient writing awards Press Club Cleve., A.P. Soc. Ohio, Edn. Writers Assn., AAUP, Internat. Reading Assn. Mem. Blue Key, Omicron Delta Kappa, Kappa Tau Alpha, Phi Sigma Delta. Office: 23 Carriage Pl Edison NJ 08820-4023

MAESTRONE, FRANK EUSEBIO, diplomat; b. Springfield, Mass., Dec. 20, 1922; s. John Battista and Margaret Carlotta (Villanova) M.; m. Jo Colwell, Jan. 20, 1951; children: Mark, Anne. BA, Yale U., 1943; grad. Naval War Coll., 1963. Assignments in Vienna and Salzburg, Austria, 1948, 54, Hamburg, Fed. Republic Germany, 1949, Khorramshahr, Iran, 1960; with NATO, Paris, 1963, Brussels, 1968; dep. asst. sec. gen. NATO, Brussels, 1968-71; counselor of embassy for polit. affairs, Manila, 1971-73; Dept. State adviser to pres. Naval War Coll., 1973; min.-counselor, Cairo, 1974; amb. State of Kuwait, 1976-79; diplomat-in-residence U. Calif., San Diego, 1979; spl. rep. of pres., dir. U.S. Sinai Support Mission, 1980; exec. dir. World Affairs Coun. San Diego, 1984-86; adj. prof. internat. rels., amb.-in-residence U.S. Internat. U., San Diego, 1986-90; bd. dirs. World Affairs Coun., San Diego; mem. adv. bd. Hansen Inst. for World Peace, San Diego State U. Found. With AUS, 1943-46, U.S. Fgn. Svc., 1948-84. Decorated chevalier du Merite Agricole (France). Mem. Internat. Inst. Strategic Studies.

MAFFEI, DOROTHY JEAN, theatre manager; b. Syracuse, N.Y., Dec. 25, 1951; d. Neil Carmine and Leona (Howland) M. BA, Carleton Coll., Northfield, Minn., 1974. Prodn. mgr. Playwrights Horizons, N.Y.C., 1977-81, Hartford (Conn.) Stage Co., 1981-83, Pepsico Summerfare, Purchase, N.Y., 1981, 85; project coord. Amnesty Internat. "A Conspiracy of Hope" Tour, 1986; adminstrv. dir. NYU-Tisch Sch. of the Arts, 1987; mng. dir. Second Stage Theatre, N.Y.C., 1987-91; gen. mgr. PACT Tng. Inc., N.Y.C., 1991, 1991-92; dir. Regional Arts Partnership, 1992—; faculty Fordham U., 1990; adj. faculty NYU/Tisch Sch. Arts, Grad. Acting Prog., 1989-91; bd. dirs. Erpf Ctr.; mem., treas. The New Kingston Valley Assn. Mem. Assn. Non-Profit Theatre in N.Y. (treas. 1989-91). Home: PO Box 235 New Kingston NY 12459-0235

MAFFEI, GREGORY B., investment banker; b. N.Y.C., May 24, 1960; s. Ralph J. and Sheila (Quinn) M. AB, Dartmouth Coll., 1982; MBA, Harvard U., 1986. Analyst Dillon, Read & Co., Inc., N.Y.C., 1982-84, assoc., 1986—; pres. Beacon Hill Cons. Co., Boston, 1984. George F. Baker scholar Harvard U., 1986. Roman Catholic. Home: 1072 2nd Ave New York NY 10022-2860 Office: Dillon Read & Co Inc 535 Madison Ave New York NY 10022-4212

MAFFETT, JOE BAXTER, carpet manufacturing company executive; b. Dec. 18, 1939; m. Patricia Watson, June 19, 1965; children: Theresa Lynn, Laurel Elizabeth. BS in Textile Mgmt., Clemson U., 1962; MS in Textiles, Ga. Inst. Tech., 1965; MBA in Mgmt. Devel., Harvard U., 1973. Dir. design Callaway Mills Inc., LaGrange, Ga., 1962-63; engr. product devel. fiber div. Allied Corp., Hopewell, Va., 1963-64; asst. prof. advanced textile design Ga. Inst. Tech., Atlanta, 1964-65; co-ordinator style/design Allied Corp., Brussels, 1965-68; dir. styling E.T. Barwick Inc. Inc., Chamblee, Ga., 1965-71; v.p. product planning carpet and rug div. WestPoint Pepperell, Dalton, Ga., 1971-73, v.p. ops. carpets and rug div., 1973-74, pres. carpets and rug div.,

1974-79, exec. v.p., chief operating officer, 1977-79; pres., chief operating officer World Carpets Inc., Dalton, 1979-86, also bd. dirs.; chmn. bd. dirs., chief exec. officer Coronet Industries Inc., Dalton, 1986—; cons. in field. Mem. adv. bd. Chattanooga Juvenile Delinquent Ctr., 1977-85; bd. dirs. Symphony and Opera Assn., Chattanooga, 1975-86. Named Outstanding Man of Yr., City Hope Found., 1976, Man of Industry, Floor Covering Ind. Found., 1983. Mem. Carpet and Rug Inst. (vice chmn. and chmn. 1978-79, bd. dirs.), Atlanta Mcht. Mart Internat. Carpet and Rug Market (founding bd.). Clubs: Walden, Mountain City (Chattanooga); Lookout Mountain (Tenn.) Fairyland. Office: Coronet Industries Inc Coronet Dr Dalton GA 30720-2637

MAFFIE, MICHAEL OTIS, utility executive; b. L.A., Jan. 26, 1948; s. Cornelius Michael and Elaine Minie (Wack) M.; m. Nickie Neville, Apr. 10, 1971; children—Wendy, Zachary. B.S. in Acctg, U. So. Calif., 1969, M.B.A in Fin, 1970. Audit mgr. Arthur Andersen & Co., C.P.A.s, Los Angeles, 1970-78; with S.W. Gas Corp., Las Vegas, 1978—, v.p., treas., 1982-84, sr. v.p., treas., 1984-87, exec. v.p fin., 1987-88, pres., chief. oper. officer, 1988—, also bd. dirs.

MAFFITT, JAMES STRAWBRIDGE, lawyer; b. Raleigh, N.C., Oct. 29, 1942; s. James Strawbridge III and Lois (Handy) M.; children: Amy Maffitt Barkley, Margaret Maffitt Kramer); m. Frances Holton, Aug. 15, 1981. BA, Washington and Lee U., 1964, LLB, 1966. Bar: Va. 1966, Md. 1969. Assoc. Apostolou, Place & Thomas, Roanoke, Va., 1966-67; trust officer Mercantile-Safe Deposit & Trust Co., Balt., 1967-71; from assoc. to ptnr. Cable, McDaniel, Bowie & Bond, Balt., 1971-82; ptnr. Maffit & Rothschild, Balt., 1982-85, Anderson, Coe & King, Balt., 1986-90, Miles, Stockbridge & Easton, Balt., 1990—. Chmn. Acad. of the Arts, 1994—; mem. steering com. Upper Shore Regional Tech. Coun., 1992—; mem. exec. com. United Fund of Talbot County, 1994—. Fellow Md. Bar Found.; mem. ABA (ho. dels. 1986-88), Md. Bar Assn. (bd. govs. 1987-), Va. Bar Assn., Balt. City Bar Assn. (pres. 1985-86), Wednesday Law Club, Talbot Country Club, Harbortown Country Club. Republican. Club: Ctr. (Balt.). Avocations: boating, waterfowl hunting, golf. Home: 9498 Martingham Cir Saint Michaels MD 21663 Office: Miles & Stockbridge 101 E Bay St Easton MD 21601 also: Miles & Stockbridge 10 Light St Baltimore MD 21202

MAFFLY, ROY HERRICK, medical educator; b. Berkeley, Calif., Nov. 26, 1927; s. Alfred Emil and Frances Elizabeth (Henderson) M.; m. Marilyn Miles, Feb. 2, 1952; children: Robert, Nancy, Laurie. A.B., U. Calif.-Berkeley, 1949; M.D., U. Calif.-San Francisco, 1952. Intern U. Calif.-San Francisco, 1952-53, resident in medicine, 1953-54, research fellow in medicine, 1959-61; resident in medicine Herrick Meml. Hosp., Berkeley, 1954-55; research fellow in medicine Mass. Gen. Hosp., Boston, 1957-59; asst. prof. medicine Stanford U., Palo Alto, Calif., 1961-65, assoc. prof., 1965-70, prof., 1970-92, assoc. dean students Sch. Medicine, 1983-92, chmn. dept. physiology, 1986-88; ret., 1992; chief renal service VA Med. Ctr., Palo Alto, Calif., 1968-83; mem. adv. com. on renal dialysis ctrs. State of Calif., 1966-70; mem. gen. med. B study sect. NIH, 1967-71; dir. Health Edn. Network, 1980-83; mem. medicine test com. Nat. Bd. Med. Examiners, 1981-88, chmn. medicine test com., 1983-88, mem. com. for comprehensive part II exam., 1987-89; established investigator Am. Heart Assn., 1961-66, mem. rsch. study com., 1972-82, rsch. com., 1976-82. Served to lt. USNR, 1955-57, PTO. Recipient Kaiser award for teaching Stanford U. Sch. Medicine, 1970, 72, 77, 79, 86, 87; recipient Bloomfield award for teaching Stanford U. Sch. Medicine, 1977, Gores award for teaching Stanford U., 1982; Disting. Achievement award Am. Heart Assn. Sci. Council, 1984; Gift of Life award Nat. Kidney Found. No. Calif., 1985. Mem. Am. Heart Assn., Am. Physiol. Soc., Am. Soc. Clin. Investigation (editorial com. 1970-75), Nat. Kidney Found. (sci. adv. bd. 1970-77), Assn. Am. Med. Colls. Home: 1401 Webster St Palo Alto CA 94301-3649 Office: Stanford Univ M-105 Sch Medicine Stanford CA 94305

MAFFRE, MURIEL, ballet dancer; b. Enghien, Val D'Oise, France, Mar. 19, 1966; came to U.S., 1990; d. Bernard and Monique (Berteaux) M. Diploma, Paris Opera Ballet Sch., 1981; Baccalauréat (hon.), France, 1984. Dancer Hamburg Ballet, Fed. Republic Germany, 1983-84; soloist Sarragoza Ballet, Spain; premiere danseuse Monte Carlo Ballet, Monaco, 1985-90; prin. dancer San Francisco Ballet, 1990—; guest artist with Berlinor Staatsoper. Recipient 1st prize Nat. Conservatory, Paris, 1983, Grand prize and Gold medal Paris Internat. Ballet Competition, 1984, Isadora Duncan award, 1990. Office: San Francisco Ballet 455 Franklin St San Francisco CA 94102-4471

MAFI, MOHAMMAD, civil engineer, educator; b. Tehran, Iran, Jan. 12, 1954; s. Javad and Mansoureh Mafi; m. Simin K. Mafi, July 2, 1975; children: Iman, Mona, Ehsan. BS, Sharif U. Tech., Tehran, Iran, 1977; MS, Pa. State U., 1980, PhD, 1985. Registered profl. engr. N.Y., Pa. Asst. prof. dept. civil engring. Union Coll., Schenectady, N.Y., 1985-90, assoc. prof., chmn. dept., 1990-94; pres. SAFE Cons. Bridge Inspection, Design and Rehab., Schenectady, 1985—. Contbr. articles to sci. and engring. publs. Mem. ASCE, Am. Soc. Engring. Edn. (Dow Outstanding Young Faculty award 1989), Am. Concrete Inst., Concrete Reinforcing Steel Inst., Chi Epsilon, Tau Beta Pi. Office: Union Coll Dept Civil Engring Schenectady NY 12308

MAFICO, TEMBA LEVI JACKSON, Old Testament and Semitic languages educator, clergy; b. Chipinge, Zimbabwe, Jan. 28, 1943; came to U.S., 1987; s. Mafico Ntondoyo Jackson and Lucy (Siqalaba Mpofu) Mhlanga Mafico; m. Thecla Chiza, Aug. 31, 1963; 1 child, David. AB, U. London, Salisbury, Rhodesia, 1970; ThM, Harvard U., 1973, MA, 1977, PhD, 1979. Ordained minister United Ch. of Christ, 1964. Ch. minister United Ch. of Christ, Harare, Zimbabwe, 1963-70; sch. chaplain Chikore High Sch., Chipinge, 1971; sr. lectr. U. Zimbabwe, Harare, 1979-86, univ. chaplain, 1979-86; prof. O.T. and Semitic langs. Interdenominational Theol. Ctr., Atlanta, 1988—; cons. globalizaion of theol. schs. Assn. Theol. Schs., 1988—; trustee U. Zimbabwe Evening Sch., 1988—. Contbr. articles to profl. jours. Sec.-treas. Student Christian Movement, Zimbabwe, 1965-70; Manicaland Devel. Assns., Zimbabwe, 1980-86; founder, dir. Univ. Evening Sch., Zimbabwe, 1980-86. Recipient Scholarship award Harvard U., 1971-78; grantee U. Zimbabwe, 1982, 86, Interdenominational Theol. Ctr., Atlanta, 1989, 90, Gammon Theol. Sch., Atlanta, 1990. Mem. Soc. Bibl. Lit., Internat. Assn. Mission Studies, Atlanta O.T. Colloquium (chmn.). Office: Interdenominational Theol Ctr 671 Beckwith St SW Atlanta GA 30314

MAGA, JOSEPH ANDREW, food science educator; b. New Kensington, Pa., Dec. 25, 1940; s. John and Rose Maga; m. Andrea H. Vorperian, June 13, 1964; children: Elizabeth, John. BS, Pa. State U., 1962, MS, 1964; PhD, Kans. State U., 1970. Project leader Borden Foods Co. Syracuse, N.Y., 1964-66; group leader Gen. Soya Co., Chgo., 1966-68; asst. prof. Colo. State U., Ft. Collins, Colo., 1970-72, assoc. prof., 1972-74, prof. food sci., 1974—. Contbr. numerous articles to profl. jours. Mem. Inst. Food Technologists, Am. Chem. Soc., Am. Assn. Cereal Scientists. Office: Colo State U Dept Food Sci Nutritio Fort Collins CO 80523

MAGAD, SAMUEL, orchestra concertmaster, conductor; b. Chgo., May 14, 1932; s. Herman and Doris (Walder) M.; m. Miriam Seefor, Feb. 13, 1955; children: Debra, Carlen. Mus.B., De Paul U., 1955; student, Paul Stassevitch. Orch. violin soloist, beginning 1944; with Chgo. Symphony Orch., 1958—, asst. concertmaster, 1966-72, co-concertmaster, 1972—; concertmaster Grant Park Symphony Orch., 1970-71; dir., 1st violinist Chgo. Symphony Chamber Players; founder Chgo. Symphony Trio; music dir., condr. Kankakee Symphony Orch. (Ill.), from 1984; prof. violin Northwestern U., Evanston, Ill.; also 1st violinist Eckstein Quartet, Chgo. Symphony String Quartet; dir. music, condr. Northbrook Symphony Orch., 1980—; concertmaster Aspen Festival Orch., 1987—. Served with orch. AUS, 1955-58. Office: Northbrook Symphony Orch 801 Skokie Blvd Ste 213 Northbrook IL 60062-4027

MAGALNICK, ELLIOTT BEN, retail medical supply company executive; b. Cleve., Aug. 19, 1945; s. Joseph Hyman and Ann (Resnick) M.; m. Diane Kerner, May 26, 1968 (div. Feb. 1988); children: Joel A., David A.; m. Judy Banjavic, June 9, 1991; stepchildren: Daniel Banjavic, David Banjavic. BS in Bus. Mgmt., Temple U., 1968. Cert. orthopedic fitter Health Industries

Dealer Assn. Retail mgr. Milner Surg. Supply Co., Phila., 1970-72, Colo. Surg. Supply Co., Denver, 1972-73; mgr. non wheelchair retail Wheelchairs, Inc., Englewood, Colo., 1973-77; asst. mgr. ops. Denver Surg. Supply Co. 1977-78; owner, founder The Get Well Shop, Inc., Aurora, Colo., 1978—. Mem. chorus Shir Ami Singers, Denver, 1978-95, Colo. Symphony Orch., Denver, 1986-95; vol. Allied Fedn. Denver, 1984-87; mem. Legion of Merit, Rep. Party, Denver, 1992; donor Belle Bonfils Blood Ctr., 1976—; active Cantor Temple Micah, Denver. Named Disting. Pres., Optimist Internat., 1987. Mem. Colo. Assn. Med. Equipment Suppliers (dealer mem.), Health Industries Dealer Assn. (cert. orthopedic fitter), Luncheon Optimist Club Windsor Gardens (prs. 1986), Masons (master mason Columbine lodge), Colo. Consistory, El Jebel Temple, Rocky Mountain Cantors Assn., 1995—. Jewish. Avocations: bicycling, cross-country skiing, singing, tennis, reading. Office: The Get Well Shop Inc 12028 E Mississippi Aurora CO 80012

MAGARGEE, W(ILLIAM) SCOTT, III, lawyer; b. Abington, Pa., Sept. 3, 1940; m. Annette Bruno, July 6, 1963; children: Scott, Todd, Ashley. AB, Princeton U., 1962; LLB, Yale U., 1966. Bar: Pa. 1966, U.S. Dist. Ct. (ea. dist.) Pa. 1966, U.S. Tax Ct. 1973. Admission officer Princeton (N.J.) U., 1962-63; assoc. Dechert Price & Rhoads, Phila., 1966-75, ptnr., 1975—. Supr. Tredyffrin Twp., Chester County, Berwyn, Pa., 1973-87; bd. trustees Paoli Meml. Hosp., 1988—; mem. citizens adv. com. Southeastern Pa. Transp. Authority, 1988—; bd. dirs. United Way Southeastern Pa., 1994—, chair human resources com., 1993—. Mem. ABA (sect. taxation), Phila. Bar Assn. (pension com. 1981—, chair employee benefits com. sect. taxation 1993—), Princeton Club Phila., Princeton Univ. Alumni Coun. (chmn. 1985-87). Office: Dechert Price & Rhoads 4000 Bell Atlantic Tower 1717 Arch St Philadelphia PA 19103-2713

MAGARIAN, ROBERT ARMEN, medicinal chemist, researcher, educator; b. East St. Louis, Ill., July 27, 1930; s. Leon and Pauline Mary (Struel) M.; m. Charmaine Virginia Kugler, June 24, 1950; children: Paula, Cindy, Leslie, Robert. Student, Washington U., St. Louis, 1951-52; B.A., U. Miss., 1956, B.S. in Pharmacy with highest honors, 1960, Ph.D., 1966. Registered pharmacist, Miss., Ill. Am. Found. for Pharm. Edn. fellow, 1961-66; NIH postdoctoral research fellow U. Kans., Lawrence, 1966-67; asst. prof. St. Louis Coll. Pharmacy, 1966-70; assoc. prof. U. Okla. Coll. Pharmacy, Norman, 1970-76; prof. Oklahoma City, 1978—; exec. dir. Kappa Psi, pharm. frat., 1980—. Assoc. editor Current Medicinal Chemistry. Served with U.S. Army, 1952-54, Korea. Recipient teaching awards Coll. Pharmacy, U. Okla., 1974, 76, 89, Excellence in Rsch. and Svc. award, 1985, Baldwin study-travel award, 1978, Assocs. Disting. Lecturship award, 1988; named Outstanding Prof. Okla. Soc. Hosp. Pharmacists, 1987, Alumni Teaching Excellence award, 1989, Outstanding Teaching award Gamma Omicron, 1990, 91, 92; Mead-Johnson grantee Am. Assn. Colls. Pharmacy, 1968, NSF grantee, 1968-70, Nat. Cancer Inst. grantee, 1987—. Mem. Am. Assn. Colls. Pharmacy, Am. Chem. Soc., Sigma Xi, Phi Kappa Phi, Kappa Psi (exec. dir.), Tchr. Excellence award 1990, 92), Rho Chi (chpt. Rsch. award 1981). Episcopalian. Patentee in field. Office: U Okla Health Sci Ctr Coll of Pharmacy 1110 N Stonewall Ave Oklahoma City OK 73117-1223

MAGARITY, RUSSELL LYNN, banker; b. Corpus Christi, Tex., July 29, 1946; s. Roy Lee and Ira Oleuia (Patterson) M.; m. Susan Ann Byers, June 3, 1967; children: Jennifer Lynn, Jeffrey Alan, Allison Lee. BA in Internat. Rels., U. Okla., 1967; MBA in Fin., Thunderbird Sch. Internat. Mgmt., Ariz., 1973. Credit and mktg. officer Banco Lar Brasileiro, S.A., Rio de Janeiro, 1974-78; v.p., team leader Chase Manhattan Bank, N.A., N.Y.C., 1978; dir. adjutant, country corp. mgr. Banco Lar Brasileiro, S.A., Rio de Janeiro, 1979-80; country corp. mgr., country mgr. Chase Manhattan Bank, N.A., Mexico City, 1981-86; sr. v.p., credit supervising officer Asia Pacific Chase Manhattan Bank, N.A., Hong Kong, 1986-88; sr. v.p. Chase Manhattan Bank, N.A., N.Y.C., 1987—; chief exec. Chase Manhattan Asia Ltd., Hong Kong, 1989—; also bd. dirs. Chase Manhattan Asia Ltd., Hong Kong. Lt. USN, 1967-72, Vietnam. Mem. Young Reps., Am. C. of C. Avocations: sailing, flying, cycling, magic. Office: Chase Manhattan Asia Ltd, 39/F 1 Exchange Sq Central, Hong Kong Hong Kong

MAGAW, JOHN W., federal law enforcement official; b. Columbus, Ohio; m. Helen Mahley; 5 children. BA in Edn., Otterbein Coll., 1957. Patrolman State of Ohio, Columbus, 1958-66; joined U.S. Secret Svc., Columbus, 1967, spl. agt., 1967—; former head protection for U.S. President and First Lady U.S. Secret Svc., Washington, until 1992, 17th dir., 1992-93; dir. Bur. Alcohol, Tobacco & Firearms, Washington, 1993—. Bd. trustees Otterbein Coll., Westerville, Ohio. Recipient Presdl. Rank Meritorious award, 1991. Mem. Fed. Investigators Assn., Internat. Assn. Chiefs of Police (exec. com. adv. com. for internat. policy). Office: Dept Treasury Bur Alcohol Tobacco Firearm 650 Massachusetts Ave NW Washington DC 20223

MAGAW, ROGER WAYNE, construction company executive; b. Beaver, Ohio, Feb. 8, 1933; s. Cecil Elsworth and Thelma Mae (Howerton) M.; m. Virginia May Burdette, July 2, 1955; children: Wayne Robert, Rex Roger. BS, W.Va. State Coll., 1960. Exec. v.p., treas. Union Boiler Co., Nitro, W.Va., 1959—; bd. dirs. mgmt. chmn. Nat. Maintenance Agreements Policy Com., Washington, 1983—. Chmn. Putnam County Vocat. Adv. Com., W.Va., 1968-90. Served with U.S. Army, 1953-55. Mem. Am. Welding Soc., Nat. Assn. Constrn. Boilermaker Employers (pres., bd. dirs. 1983-87), Putnam County C. of C. (chmn., bd. dirs. 1985-87). Republican. Methodist. Lodges: Masons, Shriners. Avocations: motor home camping, farming. Home: RR 2 Box 112 Hurricane WV 25526-9683 Office: Union Boiler Co PO Box 425 Nitro WV 25143-0425

MAGAZINE, ALAN HARRISON, association executive, consultant; b. Cambridge, Mass., May 16, 1944; s. Arnold Lloyd and Ruth Magazine; m. June Ann O'Donohue, June 20, 1971 (div. Feb. 1984); children: Sarah Elizabeth, David Michael; m. Cynthia Louise Cordiner, Aug. 30, 1984. BA, Monmouth Coll., 1966; MPA, Kent State U., 1968; PhD, U.Md., 1976. Sr. cons. Real Estate Research Corp., Washington, 1969-72; exec. dir. Nat. Ctr. for Pub. Service Internships, Washington, 1972-75; nat. policy coordinator Internat. City Mgmt. Assn., Washington, 1973-76; dep. asst. dir. U.S. Commn. on Fed. Paperwork, Washington, 1976-78; dir. office of intergovernmental relations EPA, Washington, 1978-81; dir. Business-Higher Edn. Forum, Washington, 1981-86, pres. coun. on competitivenessadv. com. Congl. Tech. Policy Task Force, 1986-89; adv. bd. George Mason U. Ctr. Conflict Resolution, 1986-89; pres. Health Industry Mfgs. Assn., 1990—; adv. bd. George Mason U. Ctr. Conflict Resolution, 1986-89, Brookings Inst. Ctr. Econ. Progress and Employment, 1986-89; mem. U.S. China Joint Commn. on Commerce & Trade; bd. dirs. Congl. Econ. Leadership Inst., 1986-89—, Shingo Prize, 1990—, adv. com. 1990-94, Healthcare Tech., 1992-95, Calif. Biomedical Found., 1994—. Author: Environmental Management in Local Government, 1977. Bd. dirs. Met. Washington Coun. of Govts., 1972-79; mem. Fairfax County Bd. Suprs., Va., 1972-79; chmn. No. Va. Transp. Commn., 1974-75; mem. No. Va. Planning Dist. Commn., Fairfax, 1976-79; mem. Dickinson Coll. Parents Coun., 1994—. Served with USAFR, 1968-71. Ford Found. fellow, 1970-71. Mem. Econ. Club of Washington D.C. Democrat. Jewish. Avocations: jogging, reading. Home: 1302 Chancel Pl Alexandria VA 22314-4707 Office: Health Industry Mfgs Assn 1200 G St NW Washington DC 20005-3814

MAGAZINER, ELLIOT ALBERT, musician, conductor, educator; b. Springfield, Mass., Dec. 25, 1921; m. Sari Fromkin; 2 children. Student, Nat. Orch. Assn., 1937-40, Princeton U., 1943, Juilliard School of Music, 1946-50. Music dir., prof. music Manhattanville Coll., Purchase, N.Y., 1970—; faculty Westchester Conservatory Music. Debut: Town Hall, N.Y.C., 1952; staff artist, concertmaster CBS-TV and Radio; Networks: condrs. Reiner, Ansermet, Beecham, Stokowski; condr. and sr. violin instr. Westchester Conservatory of Music; vis. condr. Dubuque Symphony; soloist N.Y. Philharm. Symphony, Symphony of the Air, Kol Visrael, symphonies in Chgo., Ft. Myers, Dubuque, York, St. Petersburg; recitals in N.Y.C., Washington, Detroit, Amsterdam, Paris, Jerusalem; star of CBS-TV, The Violin. Recs.: Charles Ives Sonata #2, Charles Ives Trio (with Frank Glazer and David Weber); Vivaldi Concerto in C and Concerto in B (with orchestra Symphonique de Paris); conductor Westchester All County Festival Orch. Mem. AAUP, N.Y. TV Musicians (pres.), CBS Musicians Fund (sec.). Avocations: collecting unique and ancient instruments. Home: 250 Garth Rd Apt 2b3 Scarsdale NY 10583-3922 Office: Westchester Conservatory Symphony Orch 20 Soundview Ave White Plains NY 10606-3399

MAGAZINER, FRED THOMAS, lawyer; b. Phila., July 4, 1947; s. Henry Jonas and Reba (Henken) M.; m. Phyllis Heller, June 28, 1970; children: Daniel, Andrew. BA, Columbia U., 1969, JD, 1976. Bar: Pa., U.S. Dist. Ct. (ea. dist.) Pa., U.S. Ct. Appeals (3rd cir.), U.S. Claims Ct. Law clk. to judge Max Rosenn U.S. Ct. Appeals (3rd cir.), Phila., 1976-77; assoc. Dechert, Price & Rhoads, Phila., 1977-84, ptnr., 1984—. Vice chair citizens adv. com. S.E. Pa. Transp. Authority, 1986—. Mem. ABA, Pa. Bar Assn., Phila. Bar Assn. Democrat. Home: 1021 W Cliveden St Philadelphia PA 19119-3702 Office: Dechert Price & Rhoads 4000 Bell Atlantic Tower 1717 Arch St Philadelphia PA 19103-2713

MAGAZINER, HENRY JONAS, architect; b. Phila., Sept. 13, 1911; s. Louis and Selma (Jonas) M.; m. Reba Henken, June 19, 1938; children: Ellen Louise (Mrs. Alan I. Widiss), Fred Thomas. B.Arch., U. Pa., 1936. Draftsman Phila. City Planning Project, 1936-37; draftsman Louis Magaziner (Architect), Phila., 1937-39; architect Louis Magaziner (Architect), 1946-48; chief Architects' Squad, Day & Zimmermann, Inc., Burlington, Iowa, 1940-41; architect Albert Kahn (Architect), Detroit, 1942; designer Wright Aero. Corp., Wood Ridge, N.J., 1943-45; partner Louis & Henry Magaziner, Phila., 1948-56; architect, planner pvt. practice, 1956-72; regional hist. architect Mid-Atlantic Region, Nat. Park Service, Phila., 1972-87; pvt. practice architecture, 1987—; archtl. adviser Phila. Hist. Commn., 1970-75, mem. archtl. com., 1979-85, chmn. archtl. com., 1972-75; mem. adv. bd. Preservation Coalition Greater Phila. V.p. Phila. Health and Welfare Coun., 1957-61, Phila. chpt. Victorian Soc. in Am., 1975; v.p. for city planning Germantown Cmty. Coun., 1957-62; bd. dirs. Downtown Children's (day care) Ctr., 1956-73, v.p., 1960-61; bd. dirs. Allens Lane Art Ctr., 1945-67, Neighborood Ctr. Phila., 1956-74, Hist. Soc. Pa., 1970-74, Chestnut Hill Hist. Soc., 1970-80, Phila. chpt. Assn. for Preservation Tech., Clean Air Coun., 1980-92, Center City Residents Assn., 1995—; bd. dirs. Maxwell Mansion Mus., pres., 1964-67; trustee Stewardson Meml. Fellowship in Architecture, 1958-90. Recipient Presdl. award for Excellence in Design for the Govt., 1988; named to Germantown Hall of Fame, 1994. Fellow AIA (com. historic resources); mem. Am. Inst. Conservation, Assn. for Preservation Tech., Eastern Nat. Park and Monument Assn., Fellows in Am. Studies (pres. 1983-84), Nat. Trust for Historic Preservation (mem. preservation forum), Pa. Soc. Architects, ASTM (com. on historic preservation standards 1981-90), Phila. Soc. for Preservation of Landmarks, Soc. Archtl. Historians (dir. 1977-80, mem. editorial bd. 55 vol. Buildings of the United States), Building Conservation Internat., T-Square Atelier (pres. 1963-65), Pa. Acad. Fine Arts, Victorian Soc. in Am., Am. Arbitration Assn. (arbitrator), Libr. Co. Phila., Sierra Club, Athenaeum of Phila., Preservation Action, Germantown Hist. Soc. (bd. dirs. 1960-93). Home: 1901 Walnut St Ste 15-B Philadelphia PA 19103-4664 *I do hope that we can pass on to future generations a prejudice-free America having a natural environment without pollution and a man-made environment with its best elements both preserved and appreciated. Achieving these objectives is an unending struggle but one certainly worth winning. God willing, I expect to continue to fight for these ends.*

MAGAZINER, IRA, federal official; b. N.Y.C.; s. Louis and Sylvia M.; m. Suzanne Magaziner, 1981; children: Seth, Jonathan, Sarah. Grad., Brown U. With Boston Consulting Group; co-founder Telesis, 1979-88; issues advisor Clinton campaign, 1992; sr. advisor policy devel. The White House, 1993—, chief architect Health Security Act, 1993. Rhodes scholar Oxford U. Office: Domestic Policy Coun 1600 Pennsylvania Ave NW Washington DC 20500-0001

MAGDOL, MICHAEL ORIN, bank executive; b. N.Y.C., May 18, 1937; s. David Aaron and Ruth (Wein) M.; m. Alice Jane Gates, Aug. 29, 1940 (div. Sept. 1974); 1 child, David; m. Patricia Elizabeth Marshall, Feb. 1, 1943; 1 child, Jennifer. BSE, U. Pa., 1959. Internat. officer Mfrs. Hanover Trust Co., N.Y.C., 1959-65; exec. v.p. J. Henry Schroder Bank, N.Y.C., 1965-87; vice chmn., chief fin. officer, dir. Fiduciary Trust Co. Internat., N.Y.C., 1987—. Bd. dirs. Boy Scouts Am., N.Y.C., 1975—, Children Oncology Soc. N.Y., Lingnan Found. Mem. Am. Bankers Assn. (internat. bd. dirs. 1980-83), N.Y. State Bankers Assn. (chmn. internat. com. 1982—), Univ. Econs. Club, Onteora Club (Tannersville, N.Y.). Office: Fiduciary Trust Co Internat 2 World Trade Ctr New York NY 10048-0002

MAGEDANZ, DOROTHY C., health facility administrator, educator; b. Watertown, S.D., Feb. 4, 1930; d. Nels Chris and Christine Mary (Nelsen) Christensen; m. Robert K. Magedanz, Jan. 5, 1952; children: David, Douglas. BSN, S.D. State U., 1966; MS, U. Minn., 1967. RN. Nurse Community hosps., Minn., S.D., 1951-66; asst. prof. Dept. Nursing Augustana Coll., Sioux Falls, S.D., 1968-73; assoc. chief, nursing educator VA, Portland, Oreg., 1973-74, Kansas City, Mo., 1974-79; chief nursing svc. VA, Madison, Wis., 1979-81, Portland, 1981—. Vets. rep. VA Cen. Office, 1973—. Mem. Rotary Internat. Avocations: music, gardening, antique collecting. Office: VA Adminstrn Med Ctr 3710 SW US Vets Hosp Rd Portland OR 97207

MAGEE, A. ALAN, artist; b. Newtown, Pa., May 26, 1947; s. Richard Forrest and Rena (Cook) M.; m. Monika Gabriele Ruth Siekmann, Jan. 4, 1969. Student, Tyler Sch. of Art, 1965-66, Phila. Coll. Art, 1967-69. Contbr. articles to profl. jours.; one-person shows include Allport Assocs. Gallery, Larkspur, Calif., 1978, 81, Clark Gallery, Lincoln, Mass., 1979, Staempfli Gallery, N.Y.C., 1980, 82, FIAC Grand Palais, Paris, 1983, Norton Gallery and Sch. of Art, West Palm Beach, Fla., 1983, San Jose Mus. of Art, 1983, Newport Art Mus., 1984, Farnsworth Art Mus., Rockland, Maine, 1984, U. Maine, 1985, Fresno Art Ctr., 1985, Los Angeles, 1986, Schmidt-Bingham Gallery, N.Y.C., 1986, 88, 89, Allport Assocs. Gallery, San Francisco, 1986, Joan Whitney Payson Gallery at Westbrook Coll., Portland, Maine, 1990, Farnsworth Art Mus., 1991, James A. Michener Art Mus., Doylestown, Pa., 1991, Ringling Sch. Art & Design, Sarasota, Fla., 1992, Fine Arts Ctr. at Cheekwood, Nashville, 1992, Edith Caldwell Gallery, San Francisco, 1992-93, 95, Edity Lambert Gallery, Santa Fe, 1995; group shows include Farnsworth Art Mus., Rockland, Maine, 1985, Akron (Ohio) Mus. of Art, 1985, Maine Coast Artists, Rockport, 1985, Ark. Art Ctr, Little Rock, 1985, Smithsonian Instn., Nat. Air and Space Mus., Washington, 1985, Wunderlich & Co., N.Y.C., 1986, Light Gallery, N.Y.C., 1986, Schmidt-Bingham Gallery, N.Y.C., 1986, 88, Mus. Fine Arts, Springfield, 1986, Butler Inst. Am. Art, Youngstown, Ohio, 1987, Am. Acad. and Inst. of Arts and Letters, N.Y.C., 1987, Nat. Invitational Drawing Exhbn., 1989, Staempfli Gallery, N.Y.C., 1990, Albrecht Art Mus., St. Joseph, 1990, Nat. Acad. of Design, N.Y.C., 1990; and others; pub. collections include Farnsworth Art Mus., Rockland, Arco Collection, Los Angeles, Achenbach Collection, Palace of the Legion of Honour, San Francisco; Portland (Maine) Mus. of Art, Rutgers U. Art Mus., and others; author: Stones and Other Works, 1987, Alan Magee 1981-91; TV: Visions of Darkness and Light, 1988. Recipient Richard and Hinda Rosenthal Found. award N.Y.C., Am. Book award, Nevelson award, 1982; The Leo Meissner Prize, Nat. Acad. of Design, 1990. Home: Pleasant Point Rd RR 68 Box 132 Cushing ME 04563

MAGEE, DONALD EDWARD, national park service administrator; b. Trenton, N.J., Sept. 24, 1937; s. Donald A. and Anna C. (Bocskowics) M.; m. Linda Kimball, June 27, 1964; children: Kevin, Bonnie Magee Burch, Gale. BS in Forestry Mgmt., U. Mass., 1964. Pk. ranger Bryce Canyon (Utah) Nat. Pk., 1966-68; area mgr. Sunset Crater Nat. Monument, Flagstaff, Ariz., 1968-73; mgmt. analyst Nat. Capital Region, Washington, 1973-80; supt. Stones River Nat. Battlefield, Murfreesboro, Tenn., 1980-89, USS Ariz. Meml., Pearl Harbor, Hawaii, 1989—. With USN, 1956-58. Recipient Excellence of Svc. award Dept. of Interior, 1991. Office: USS Ariz Meml 1 Arizona Memorial Pl Honolulu HI 96818

MAGEE, JOHN FRANCIS, research company executive; b. Bangor, Maine, Dec. 3, 1926; s. John Henry and Marie (Frawley) M.; m. Dorothy Elma Hundley, Nov. 19, 1949; children: Catherine Anne, John Hundley, Andrew Stephen. AB, Bowdoin Coll., 1947; MS, U. Maine, 1952; MBA, Harvard U., 1948. With Arthur D. Little, Inc., Cambridge, Mass., 1950—, v.p., 1961-72, pres., 1972-86, chief exec. officer, 1974-88, chmn., 1986—, also dir.; dir. John Hancock Mut. Life Ins. Co., Boston, Houghton-Mifflin Co., Boston. Author: Physical Distribution Systems, 1967, Industrial Logistics: Analysis and Management of Physical Supply and Distribution Systems, 1968, (with D. M. Boodman) Production Planning and Inventory Management, 1968, (with W. Capacino and W. Rosenfeld) Modern Logistics Manage-

ment, 1985. Trustee New Eng. Aquarium, Boston U. Med. Ctr., Bowdoin Coll., Emerson Hosp., Thompson Island Outward Bound Edn. Ctr. Mem. Ops. Research Soc. Am. (pres. 1966-67), Inst. Mgmt. Scis. (pres. 1971-72), Phi Beta Kappa, Phi Kappa Psi. Clubs: Concord (Mass.) Country (gov. 1971-74); The Country (Brookline, Mass.); Somerset (Boston). Office: Arthur D Little Inc 25 Acorn Park Cambridge MA 02140-2301

MAGEE, PAUL TERRY, geneticist and molecular biologist, college dean; b. Los Angeles, Oct. 26, 1937; s. John Paul and Lois Lorene (Cowgill) M.; m. Beatrice Buten, Aug. 6, 1964; children: Alexander John, Amos Hart. B.S., Yale U., 1959; Ph.D., U. Calif., Berkeley, 1964. Am. Cancer Soc. postdoctoral fellow Lab. Enzymologie, Gif-sur-Yvette, France, 1964-66; mem. faculty Yale U., 1966-77, asst. prof. microbiology, 1966-72, assoc. prof. microbiology and human genetics, 1972-75, assoc. prof. human genetics, 1975-77; dean Trumbull Coll., 1969-72; prof. microbiology, chmn. dept. microbiology and pub. health Mich. State U., East Lansing, 1977-87, dir. Biotech. Research Ctr., 1985-87; dean Coll. Biol. Scis. U. Minn., 1987—; mem. genetics adv. panel NSF, 1978-83, mem. adv. com. biology directorate, 1992—, chair, 1995—; chmn. BBS task force looking to 21st century, 1991; cons. Corning Glass Works, 1978-80, Pillsbury Rsch., 1990—; mem. pers. com. Am. Cancer Soc., 1983-87; mem. microbial genetics and physiology study sect. NIH, 1984-88; co-chmn. com. grad. record exam. biochemistry cell and molecular biology Ednl. Testing Svc., 1988—; mem. microbiology infectious disease rsch. adv. group NIH, 1994—; traveling fellow Japanese Soc. for the Promotion of Sci., 1995. Mem. editorial bd. Jour. Bacteriology, 1975-80, Molecular and Cell Biology, 1981-92. Named Mich. champion masters swimming, 1978-84, 86, Minn. champion masters swimming, 1988, 89, 91-94, nat. YMCA swimming champion, 1990. Mem. AAAS, Am. Soc. Biochemistry and Molecular Biology (ednl. com. 1991—), Am. Soc. Microbiologists, Genetics Soc. Am. Jewish. Office: U Minn Coll Biol Scis Saint Paul MN 55105-1095

MAGEE, ROBERT PAUL, accounting and information systems educator; b. Rochester, N.Y., Apr. 17, 1947; s. Charles Robert and Rosemond (Jones) M.; m. Margaret Ann Chandler, Dec. 28, 1968; children: Paul R., Michael D. AB, Cornell U., 1969, MS, 1972, PhD, 1974. Asst. prof. acctg. Grad. Sch. Bus. U. Chgo., 1973-76; assoc. prof. acctg. and info. systems Kellogg Grad. Sch. Mgmt. Northwestern U., Evanston, Ill., 1976-79, prof. acctg. and info. systems, 1979—, Eric L. Kohler prof., 1986-89, Keith I. DeLashmutt prof., 1989—. Author: Advanced Managerial Accounting, 1986; co-author: Efficient Capital Markets and Accounting, 1975; editor: The Acctg. Rev., 1993—; contbr. articles to Jour. of Acctg. Rsch., The Acctg. Rev., Jour. of Acctg. and Econs., others. Treas. Youth Orgns. Umbrella, Evanston, 1984-89, pres., 1989—. Recipient Notable Contbn. award AICPA, 1978. Mem. Am. Acctg. Assn., Phi Kappa Phi, Beta Gamma Sigma. Home: 2626 Lincolnwood Dr Evanston IL 60201-1227 Office: Northwestern Univ Kellogg Grad Sch of Mgmt Dept Acct 5-2009 Leverone Hall Evanston IL 60201-2962

MAGEE, STEPHEN PAT, economics and finance educator; b. Wichita, Kans., Mar. 17, 1943; s. Lawrence Patrick and Edna Willard (Brock) M.; m. Naneska Nall, Aug. 20, 1965 (div. Dec. 1987); children: Christopher Sean Patrick, Theodore Parker; m. Frances Jean Toepperwein, July 28, 1988. BA in Econs., Tex. Tech. U., 1965, MA in Econs., 1966; PhD in Econs., MIT, 1969. Asst. prof. U. Calif., Berkeley, 1969-71; assoc. prof. U. Chgo., 1971-76; economist The White House, Washington, 1972-73; rsch. fellow Brookings Insts., Washington, 1973-74; prof. fin. and econs. U. Tex., Austin, 1976—, chmn. fin., 1980-84, McDermott prof., 1980-84, Fred H. Moore prof., 1984-92, Charles and Sarah Seay prof., 1992-94; Bayless/Enstar Corp. chairholder, 1994—; mem. econ. adv. bd. U.S. Sec. Commerce, Washington, 1978-79, NSF, 1979; expert witness Mesa Petroleum, Avis Rent-a-Car, El Paso Natural Gas, Kodak, Proctor & Gamble, AB Dick, Exxon; acad. lectr. in 11 fgn. countries for U.S. govt., 1977-88; vis. prof. bus. U. Chgo., 1990-91; expert effects of lawyers on U.S. economy. Author: International Trade (transl. to Japanese, Chinese, Korean), 1980, Black Hole Tariffs and Endogenous Policy Theory, 1989; mem. editorial bd. Rev. Econs. and Stats., 1972-79, Jour. Internat. Econs., 1977-79, Econs. and Politics, 1988-94, Rev. Internat. Econs., 1992-94; contbr. articles to scholarly publs., fin. publs. including Fortune Mag., Wall St. Jour. Capt., Tex. State Soccer Champions, 1984. Grantee NSF, 1972-77; recipient Joe Beasley Teaching award U. Tex. Grad. Sch. Bus., 1979, Outstanding Career Rsch. Contbn. award, 1990, named TopCore MBA prof., 1986. Avocations: soccer, drag racing, photography. Home: 1219 Castle Hill St Austin TX 78703-4125 Office: U Tex Dept Fin Austin TX 78712-1157

MAGEE, WAYNE EDWARD, biochemistry educator, researcher; b. Big Rapids, Mich., Apr. 11, 1929; s. William Fredrick and Elsie E. (Gifford) M.; m. Nannette A. Pierce, June 11, 1951; children: Lawrence, William, John. BA magna cum laude in Chemistry, Kalamazoo Coll., 1951; MS in Biochemistry, U. Wis., 1953, PhD in Biochemistry, 1955. Sci., then sr. sci. Upjohn Co., Kalamazoo, 1955-71; prof. life sci. Ind. State U., 1971-74; prof. biology, head divsn. allied health and life sci. U. Tex., San Antonio, 1975-80, prof., 1980-81; prof. biochemistry, head dept. bacteriology and biochemistry U. Idaho, 1981-85; dir. divsn. Life Scis., prof., head dept. biosci. and biotech. Drexel U., Phila., 1985-92, prof. biosci., 1985—; adj. prof. biology Western Mich. U., 1970-71. Wis. Alumni Found. Grad. fellow, 1951-52; Predoctoral fellow NSF, 1952-55. Fellow AAAS, Am. Chem. Soc., Am. Inst. Biol. Sci., Am. Soc. Biochemistry and Molecular Biology, Am. Soc. Microbiology. Contbr. articles and abstracts to profl. jours., chpts. in books. Research on phospholipid membranes, liposomes as drug carriers, immune modulation, monoclonal antibodies. Home: One Independence Pl 241 S 6th St Philadelphia PA 19106-3726 Office: Drexel U Divsn Life Scis Philadelphia PA 19104

MAGEE, WILLIAM H., chemical company executive; b. Bayonne, N.J., Feb. 5, 1938; s. William Henry and Vera (Cavanaugh) M.; m. Helmtrud Maria Fellermayer, Jan. 21, 1961 (div. Dec. 1980); children: Christina, Thomas, Robert; m. Linda Louise Warren, Feb. 14, 1981. BS, St. Peter's Coll., Jersey City, 1967. Adminstrv. mgr. ARCO Chem. Co., Chgo., 1968-70; mgr. performance reporting and capital ARCO Petroleum Products, N.Y.C., 1970-72; mgr. ops. analysis ARCO Petroleum Products, Los Angeles, 1973, controller, 1973-76, mgr. planning and analysis, 1976-77, v.p. planning and control, 1977-81; v.p., controller Atlantic Richfield Co., Los Angeles, 1981-87; sr. v.p., chief fin. officer Arco Chem. Co., Newtown Sq., Pa., 1987—; also bd. dirs. Arco Chem. Co. Mem. Pres.'s adv. bd. Calif. State U., Los Angeles, 1982-87; pres., chmn. bd. dirs. Los Angeles Internat. Film Exposition, 1983—; chmn. Child Care Study program United Way, Los Angeles, 1982-83. Served with U.S. Army, 1958-60. Mem. Am. Petroleum Inst., Fin. Execs. Inst. Club: University (Los Angeles). Avocations: hiking, snorkeling, biking. Office: ARCO Chem Co 3801 W Chester Pike Newtown Square PA 19073-2387

MAGER, ARTUR, retired aerospace company executive, consultant; b. Nieglowice, Poland, Sept. 21, 1919; came to U.S., 1939, naturalized, 1944; s. Herman and Ella (Kornbluh) M.; m. Phyllis R. Weisman, Aug. 19, 1942; 1 child, Ilana Gail. B.S., U. Mich., 1943; M.S., Case Inst. Tech., 1951; Ph.D. in Aeros., Calif. Inst. Tech., 1953. Registered profl. engr., Ohio. Aero. research scientist NASA Lewis Labs., Cleve., 1946-51; research scientist Marquardt Corp., Van Nuys, Calif., 1954-60; dir. Nat. Engring. Sci. Co., Pasadena, Calif., 1960-61; dir. spacecraft scis. Aerospace Corp., El Segundo, Calif., 1961-64, gen. mgr. applied mechanics div., 1964-68, v.p., gen. mgr. engring. sci. ops., 1968-78, v.p. engring. group, 1978-82, cons., 1982—; mem. BSD Re-entry Panel, 1961-63, NASA com. missile and space vehicle aerodynamics, 1963-65; mem. adv. com. AFML, 1971-72; mem. NASA Adv. Council, 1982-86 ; chmn. NASA Space Applications Adv. Com., 1982-86 ; mem. Aeros. and Space Engring. Bd., NRC, 1982-87; mem. Space Sta. Task Force, NRC, 1983-87, Shuttle Criticality and Hazard Analysis Rev. Bd., 1986-88, DSB NASP Task Force, 1987-88, AFSB Hypersonic Task Force, 1987-88. Contbr. articles to profl. jours. Mem. alumni fund council Calif. Inst. Tech., 1972-74; trustee West Coast U., 1980-92; bd. councilors U. So. Calif. Sch. Engring., 1976-86; mem. devel. disabilities bd. Area X, 1976-80, chmn., 1976-78; 1st v.p. Calif. Assn. Retarded, 1983-85 ; pres. Exceptional Children's Found., 1970-72. Recipient Disting. Alumni award U. Mich., 1969, Golden Rule award Calif. Assn. Retarded, 1977, 89. Fellow Inst. Advanced Engring., AIAA (chmn. Los Angeles sect. 1967-68, bd. dirs. 1975-77, pres. 1980-81), AAAS; mem. Technion Soc., Nat. Acad. Engring.,

Sigma Xi. Home and Office: 1353 Woodruff Ave Los Angeles CA 90024-5129

MAGER, EZRA PASCAL, automobile dealership group executive; b. N.Y.C., Nov. 1, 1941; s. Harold and Naomi (Levinson) M.; m. Sarah Johnson, Mar. 25, 1964 (div.); 1 child, Emma Rachel; m. Reeva Starkman, May 14, 1972; children: Camilla Elizabeth, Michael Johnson. B.A., Cornell U., 1963; M.B.A., Harvard, 1966. Successively v.p., sr. v.p., exec. v.p. and dir. Seiden & DeCuevas, Inc. N.Y.C., 1966-73; exec. v.p., dir. Furman Selz Mager Dietz & Birney, Inc., N.Y.C., 1973-90; vice chmn. United Auto Group, Inc., N.Y.C., 1990—. Pres. Baron de Hirsch Fund. Mem. N.Y. Soc. Security Analysts, Alpha Delta Phi. Democrat. Club: Harvard (N.Y.C.). Home: 141 E 72nd St New York NY 10021 Office: United Auto Group Inc 375 Park Ave New York NY 10152

MAGGIN, BRUCE, communications executive; b. N.Y.C., Apr. 25, 1943; s. Sherwood and Bernice (Lush) M.; m. Jacqueline M. Montagne, Sept. 2, 1973; children: Benjamin M., Daniel M. BA, Lafayette Coll., 1965; JD, Cornell U., 1968, MBA, 1969. Bar: N.Y. 1969. Fin. analyst ABC, N.Y.C., 1970-71, dir. corp. planning, 1974-79, v.p. cost mgmt., 1982-83; sr. v.p. ABC Video Enterprises, Inc. div. Capital Cities/ABC, Inc., N.Y.C., 1983-88; exec. v.p. CC/ABC Video Enterprises, Inc., N.Y.C., 1988-93, CC/ABC Multimedia Group, 1993—; cons. Irving Trust Co., N.Y.C., 1972-73; v.p. planning, devel. Ziff Corp., N.Y.C., 1979-82; bd. dirs. ESPN, Inc., N.Y.C., Lifetime Cablevision, N.Y.C., Phillips Van Heusen, N.Y.C. Home: 8 Lawrence Farms Crsway Chappaqua NY 10514-1210 Office: CC/ABC Inc 77 W 66th St New York NY 10023-6201

MAGGIO, MICHAEL JOHN, artistic director; b. Chgo., July 3, 1951; s. Carlo and Genevieve (Sparacino) M.; m. Janice St. John, Sept. 7, 1974 (div. June 1977); m. Julie Carol Jackson, Mar. 29, 1980 (div. Dec. 1994); 1 child, Ben. BA, U. Ariz., 1973, MA, 1974. Artistic dir. Woodstock (Ill.) Music Theatre Festival, 1980-82, Northlight Theatre, Evanston, Ill., 1983-87; assoc. artistic dir. Goodman Theatre, Chgo., 1987—; artistic advisor Columbia Coll., Chgo., 1987—. Directed Another Midsummer Night, Brutality of Fact, Black Snow, Wings, Shakespeare's A Midsummer Night's Dream, Romeo and Juliet, Uncle Vanya, 1989-90, A Flea In Her Ear, A Christmas Carol, Sunday In The Park With George, Cyrano De Bergerac, The Front Page, The Dining Room; artistic dir. Northlight Theatre premieres of Dealing, City On The Make, Heart of A Dog, (Am. premiere) Ballerina, (world premiere) Sondheim Suite; dir. The Real Thing, West Memphis Mojo, Highest Standard of Living, Endgame, The Winter's Tale, Travesties, Tartuffe, Spokesong, Ladies In Waiting; dir. prodn. of Titus Andronicus for N.Y. Shakespeare Festival; prodns. include McCarter Theatre, Guthrie Theater in Mpls., The Cleve. Playhouse, Ariz. Theatre Co., Actors Theatre of Louisville, Seattle Repertory Co. chmn. Michael Merritt Award and Endowment Fund, Columbia Coll, Chgo. Recipient Joseph Jefferson "Jeff" Citation 1975-76, 78, 93-94, Father of Yr. award, Chgo. Father's Day Com., 1986, Excellence in Arts award De Paul U. Theatre Sch., 1993, Obie award, 1993,. Office: Goodman Theatre 200 S Columbus Dr Chicago IL 60603-6402

MAGGIPINTO, V. ANTHONY, lawyer; b. Tucson, Apr. 15, 1943; s. William Vito and Elizabeth Maria (Rice) M.; m. Maria Teresa Zequeira, Aug. 31, 1976; children: Marshall Albert Nicholas, Spencer William Jonathan. AB cum laude, Southampton Coll., 1970; JD, Fordham U., 1976. Bar: Fla. 1977, N.Y. 1978, U.S. Dist. Ct. (ea. and so. dists.) N.Y. 1979, U.S. Ct. Appeals (2d cir.) 1980. Asst. to pres. Interpub. Group of Cos., N.Y.C., 1965-66; asst. dean of admission Southampton (N.Y.) Coll., 1971-73; investigative aide N.Y. State Com. on Jud. Conduct, N.Y.C., 1974-76; asst. state atty. Dade County State Atty., Miami, Fla., 1977-78; asst. dist. atty. Suffolk Dist. Atty., Hauppage, N.Y., 1978-80; asst. county atty. Suffolk County Atty., Hauppage, 1980-84; sole practice Riverhead and St. James, N.Y. 1982—; mem. spl. coms. on discovery, civil litigation U.S. Dist. Ct. (ea. dist.) N.Y., Bklyn., 1983-90, arbitrator, 1986—, ea. dist. N.Y. adv. group, 1990—, chair jury task force, 1993—. Mem. appeals bd. SSS, 1982—, vice chmn., 1986—. Served with submarine svc. USN, 1961-65. Recipient Disting. Alumni award L.I. U., 1990. Mem. N.Y. State Bar Assn., Suffolk County Bar Assn., Fla. Bar, U.S. Naval Inst., Navy League (judge advocate L.I. coun. 1992—), Submarine League, Alexander Hamilton Inn, Am. Inns of Ct. Republican. Roman Catholic. Club: Nissequogue (N.Y.) Golf (counsel 1980—, bd. govs.). Avocations: hiking, horseback riding. Office: 1212 Roanoke Ave Riverhead NY 11901-2740

MAGGS, PETER BLOUNT, lawyer, educator; b. Durham, N.C., July 24, 1936; s. Douglas Blount and Dorothy (Mackay) M.; m. Barbara Ann Widenor, Feb. 27, 1960; children: Bruce MacDowell, Gregory Eaton, Stephanie Ann, Katherine Ellen. AB, Harvard U., 1957, JD, 1961; postgrad. (exchange student), Leningrad (USSR) State U., 1961-62. Bar: D.C. 1962. Research assoc. Law Sch. Harvard U., 1963-64; assoc. prof. law U. Ill., 1964-67, assoc. prof., 1967-69, prof., 1969-88, William and Marie Corman prof., 1988—, acting dean, 1990; dir. rule of law program Washington, 1994; (with O.S. Ioffe) Soviet Law in Theory and Practice, 1983, (with others) Unfair Trade Practice and Consumer Protection, 1992; (with J. Sprowl) Computer Applications in the Law, 1987, (with others) Computer Law, 1992; designer talking computers for the blind. Fulbright rsch. scholar, Yugoslavia, 1967; East-West Ctr. fellow, 1972, Guggenheim fellow, 1979. Mem. ABA (chmn. com. on Soviet law sect. internat. law 1976-80), Bar Assn. of the Dist. of Columbia, Am. Assn. Advancement Slavic Studies, Assn. Am. Law Schs. (chmn. sect. comparative law 1977), Am. Law Inst. (consultative group, Restatement Law Unfair Competition), Am. Acad. Fgn. Law, Internat. Acad. Comparative Law. Office: U Ill Coll Law 504 E Pennsylvania Ave Champaign IL 61820-6909

MAGID, GAIL AVRUM, neurosurgery educator; b. Chgo., Oct. 15, 1934; s. Harry M. and Henrietta (Busch) M.; m. Janet Louise Reinhardt, June 15, 1962 (div.); children: Allison Drew, Jonathan Alward; m. Roseanne Cipra Muirhead, Sept. 4, 1982. BS, U. Ill., 1954; MD, Chgo. Med. Sch., 1958. Diplomate Am. Bd. Neurol. Surgery. Intern Cook County Hosp., Chgo., 1958-59; resident, then fellow neurol. surgery Mayo Clinic, Rochester, Minn., 1959-61, 63-65; clin. instr. neurosurgery U. Calif., San Francisco, 1965-70, asst. clin. prof., 1970-79, assoc. prof., 1979—; chmn. Dominican Neurol. Inst., Santa Cruz, 1975—; bd. dirs. Dominican Found.; cons. neurosurgery U.S. Army, San Francisco Gen. Hosp. Assoc. editor: Clinical Neurosurgery, 1974. Bd. dirs. Santa Cruz Symphony Assn., 1983-85, U. Calif. Friends of Arts, Santa Cruz, 1985-86. Served to lt. comdr. USN, 1961-63. Fellow ACS, Internat. Coll. Surgeons; mem. AMA, Calif. Med. Assn., Internat. Soc. Pediatric Neurosurgeons, Am. Assn. Neurol. Surgeons, Western Neurosurg. Soc., Cong. Neurol. Surgeons, San Francisco Neurol. Soc. (pres.-elect 1991, pres. 1992), St. Francis Yacht Club (San Francisco). Republican. Home: 241 4th Ave Santa Cruz CA 95062-3815 Office: 1661 Soquel Dr Santa Cruz CA 95065-1709

MAGIDA, ARTHUR JAY, newspaper editor, writer; b. N.Y.C., Aug. 24, 1945; s. Paul and Florence (Krell) M.; m. Helen Margaret Zeidler; children: Sarah, amy, Molly. BA, Marlboro Coll., 1967; MA, Georgetown U., 1972, Calif. Sch. Profl. Psychology, 1979. Gen. reporter Harrisburg (Pa.) Patriot, 1967-68, York (Pa.) Gazette and Daily, 1968-69; writer, editor Ralph Nader's Congress Project, Washington, 1972-74; environ. reporter Nat. Jour., Washington, 1974-76; dir. publs. energy conservation project Nat. Assn. Pks. and Recreation, Washington, 1979-83; freelance writer, editor Washington, 1979-83; asst. editor Balt. Jewish Times, 1983-89, sr. writer, 1990-93, sr. editor, 1994—. Author: The Environment Committees, 1975; contbr. articles to Conde Nast Traveler, Washington Post, Balt. Sun, Christian Sci. Monitor, Travel & Leisure, Jerusalem Report, Boston Globe mag. and op-ed page, numerous others, also widely reprinted; editor books on foster care, spirituality, death and dying. Recipient 15 Simon Rockower awards for excellence in Jewish Journalism, 1984-94, Smolar award for excellence in N.Am. Jewish Journalism Coun. Jewish Fedns., 1988, 90, 5 A.D. Emmart awards A.D. Emmart Fedn., Balt., 1988-93, Nat. Mass Media award NCCJ, 1989-90, Excellence in Journalism award Soc. Profl. Journalists Md. chpt. 1990. Democrat. Office: Baltimore Jewish Times 2104 N Charles St Baltimore MD 21218-5795

MAGIDSON, MICHAEL D., metals products executive; b. 1942. Grad., Miami U., Ohio, 1964, Bklyn. Law Sch. Acct. S.D. Leidesdorf & Co., Inc., N.Y.C., 1964-69; now exec. v.p., CEO Gerald Metals Inc., Stamford, Conn., 1969—. Office: Gerald Metals Inc High Risk Park Stamford CT 06904

MAGIELNICKI, ROBERT L., lawyer; b. Perth Amboy, N.J., Mar. 28, 1947; s. Leon C. and Dorothy M. (Hudanish) M.; m. Kathleen J. Urban, June 14, 1969; children: Robert Jr., Kimberly, Peter, Matthew. AB with honors, Rutgers U., 1967; JD with distinction, Cornell U., 1970. Bar: N.Y. 1971, U.S. Supreme Ct. 1974, D.C. 1990. Commd. lt. USN, 1968; assoc. Donovan Leisure Newton & Irvine, N.Y.C., 1970-71, 74-80; asst. staff judge advocate U.S. Naval Base Subic Bay, Republic of Philippines, 1971-73; asst. prof. law U.S. Naval Acad., Annapolis, Md., 1973-74; assoc. litigation and antitrust counsel Gen. Elec. Corp. Hdqs., Fairfield, Conn., 1980-83, counsel, 1989-90; divsn. gen. counsel Gen. Elec. Factory Automation Products, Charlottesville, Va., 1983-88; ptnr. Kutak Rock, Washington, 1990—. Avocations: tennis, golf, swimming, reading. Office: Kutak Rock 1101 Connecticut Ave NW Washington DC 20036

MAGIERA, FRANK EDWARD, journalist, critic; b. Webster, Mass., Nov. 28, 1945; s. Charles Frank and Marion Margaret (Kralik) M.; m. Janice Lee Rayner, Aug. 20, 1977. BS, Worcester Poly. Inst., 1967. Reporter Worcester (Mass.) Telegram & Gazette, 1970—, drama critic, 1978-89, art critic, 1989—. Lt. (j.g.) USN, 1968-70. Democrat. Avocations: farming, painting, woodworking. Home: Lawrence Rd Dudley MA 01571 Office: Worcester Telegram & Gazette 20 Franklin St Worcester MA 01608-1904

MAGILL, DODIE BURNS, early childhood education educator; b. Greenwood, S.C., July 10, 1952; d. Byron Bernard and Dora Curry B.; m. Charles Towner Magill, May 4, 1974; children: Charles Towner II, Emily Curry. BA, Furman U., 1974; MEd, U. S.C., 1978. Cert. tchr., early childhood, elementary, elementary principal, supv., S.C. Kindergarten tchr. Sch. Dist. Greenville County, 1974-83; early childhood edn. instr. Valdosta (Ga.) State Univ., 1983-84; dir. lower sch. Valwood Sch., Valdosta, 1984-86; kindergarten tchr. Sch. Dist. Greenville County, 1986—; tchr.-in-residence S.C. Ctr. for Tchr. Recruitment, Rock Hill, 1993, mem. policy bd.; workshop presenter and lectr. in various schs. and sch. dists. throughout U.S., 1974—; chmn. S.C. Pub. Kindergarten Celebration, 1994; giv. S.C. State Readiness Policy Group; mem. Southeastern Region Vision for Edn. Adv. Bd., S.C. Coun. Ednl. Collaboration. Demonstration tchr. S.C. ETV (TV show) Sch. Begins with Kindergarten. Mem. Gov. of S.C.'s State Readiness Policy Group, Southeastern Regional Vision for Edn. Adv. Bd., South Carolina Ctr. Tchr. Recruitment Policy Bd. Recipient Ralph Witherspoon award S.C. Assn. for Children Under Six; named Tchr. of Yr., Greenville County, 1992, 93, State of S.C., 1993, S.C. Tchr. of Yr. Coun. of Chief State Sch. Officers, 1993, 94. Mem. Assn. for Childhood Edn. Internat., S.C. Tchr. Forum (chmn. 1993-94), S.C. Early Childhood Assn., Alpha Delta Kappa. Presbyterian. Office: Mountain Park Elem Sch 1500 Pounds Rd SW Lilburn GA 30247

MAGILL, FRANK JOHN, federal judge; b. Verona, N.D., June 3, 1927; s. Thomas Charles and Viola Magill; m. Mary Louise Timlin, Nov. 22, 1955; children: Frank Jr., Marguerite Connolly, R. Daniel, Mary Elizabeth, Robert, John. BS in Fgn. Service, Georgetown U., 1951, LLB, 1955; MA, Columbia U., 1952. Ptnr. Nilles, Hansen, Magill & Davies, Ltd., Fargo, N.D., 1955-86; judge U.S. Ct. Appeals (8th cir.), Fargo, 1986—. Chmn. fin. disclosure com. U.S. Jud. Conf., 1993—. Fellow Am. Coll. Trial Lawyers; mem. ABA (governing coun. pub. utilities sect. 1982-85, chmn. labor law com. 1981), N.D. Bar Assn. (chmn. legis com. 1975), Cass County Bar Assn. (pres. 1970). Republican. Avocations: tennis, sailing, skiing. Home: 1711 7th St S Fargo ND 58103-4945 Office: US Ct Appeals 8th Circuit 248 US PO & Fed Bldg 657 2nd Ave N Fargo ND 58102-4727

MAGILL, ROSALIND MAY, psychotherapist; b. Albany, N.Y., Apr. 27, 1944; d. Fenton Elliot Sr. and Rosalind Pearl (Gross) M.; m. Theodore T. Solomon, May 18, 1970 (div. 1980). Student, N.Y. Inst. Tech., 1963-64, Pace Coll., 1970-71; cert. in process piping design, Voorheese Tech. Inst., 1968; MEd in Counseling and Psychology, Cambridge Coll., 1994. Lic. master pipefitter, Mass.; EIT. Piping designer Badger Am., Inc., Cambridge, Mass., 1976-77; tchr. advanced math. Vision-in-Action, Natick, Mass., 1977-80; plumbing designer R. G. Vanderweil Assocs., Boston, 1980-81; vol. counselor alcohol/substance abuse social detox program Bergen County Hosp., Paramus, N.J., 1981-83; field engr. United Engrs. and Constructors, Phila., 1983-84; tchr. spl. edn. math. and sci. Amesbury (Mass.) High Sch., 1984-85; resident engr. Hoyle, Tanner Assocs., Londonderry, N.H., 1985-86; resident engr., constrn. mgr. dept. environ. mgmt. Commonwealth of Mass., Boston, 1986-89; clin. supr., counselor substance abuse Positive Lifestyles, Mattapan, Mass., 1990-93; dir. Respond Program, substance abuse therapist Ctr. for Family Devel., Lowell, Mass., 1993-94; dir. Respond Program, 1994—; counselor alcoholism and substance abuse Serenity House/Gift of Serenity, 1977-80; counselor substance abuse Baldpate Hosp., Georgetown, Mass., 1984.85. With USMC, 1962. N.Y. State Regent's scholar, 1962. Mem. ACA, Internat. Assn. Addictions and Offender Counselors, Women's Ordination Conf., Daus. Bilitis (pres. N.Y. chpt. 1968-70), Matachine Soc. (bd. dirs. 1968-70).

MAGILL, SAMUEL HAYS, retired college administrator, higher education consultant; b. Decatur, Ga., July 19, 1928; s. Orrin Rankin and Ellen Howe (Bell) M.; m. Martha H. Carmichael, 1988; children: Samuel Hays Jr., Katherine Magill Walters, Suzanne Magill Weintraub. A.B., U. N.C. 1950; B.D., Yale U., 1953; Ph.D., Duke U., 1962; LHD (hon.), Stockton State Coll., 1990. Ordained to ministry Congl. Christian Ch., 1953; gen. sec. Davidson Coll. YMCA, 1953-55; dir. student activities U. N.C., Chapel Hill, 1955-58, asst. dean student affairs, 1958-59; chaplain Dickinson Coll., 1962-63, asst. prof. religion, 1962-66, assoc. prof. religion, 1966-68, dean coll., 1963-68; pres. Council Protestant Colls. and Univs., Washington, 1968-70; exec. asso., chief officer acad. affairs Assn. Am. Colls., 1971-76; pres. Simon's Rock Early Coll., Great Barrington, Mass., 1976-79; pres. Monmouth Coll., West Long Branch, N.J., 1980-93, pres. emeritus, 1993—; higher edn. cons., 1993—. Trustee Jersey Shore Med. Ctr., 1985-93; bd. overseers N.J. Gov.'s Schs., 1986-93. Guerney Harris Kearns fellow in religion, 1960-61; Danforth Found. spl. grad. fellow, 1959-61. Fellow Soc. Values in Higher Edn. (dir. 1969-81); mem. Am. Assembly Collegiate Sch. Bus. (accreditation task force 1989-90), NCAA (pres.'s commn. 1990-93), Am. Coun. Edn. (commn. leadership devel. 1982-85, commn. on minority affairs 1986-89), Harvard Inst. Ednl. Mgmt., Assn. Ind. Colls. and Univs. N.J. (dir. 1980-93, exec. com. 1983—, chair 1987-89), U.S. Assn. for Club of Rome, Order of Golden Fleece U. N.C., Delta Psi, Omicron Delta Kappa. Home: 1058 Fearrington Post Fearington Village NC 27312

MAGINN, JOHN LEO, insurance company executive; b. Omaha, Feb. 17, 1940; s. Walter J. and Ruth C. (Sawtelle) M.; m. Carol Varnes, Aug. 3, 1963; children: Mary Kay, Karen, Colleen, Matthew. BSBA, Creighton U., 1961; MS, U. Minn., 1962. Chartered fin. analyst. Investment analyst Continental Casualty, Chgo., 1962-64; investment analyst Mut. Omaha Ins. Co., 1964-68, asst. v.p., 1968-69, 2d v.p., 1969-76, v.p., asst. treas., 1976-82, exec. v.p., 1982-87, treas., 1987—; sr. exec. v.p., chief ins. officer, 1987—; pres. Mut. Asset Mgmt. Co.; bd. dirs. Companion Life Ins. Co., Rye, N.Y., Kirkpatrick, Pettis, Smith, Polian, Omaha, Mid-Am. Realty Investments. Editor, author: Managing Investment Portfolios, 1983, 2d edit., 1990. Trustee Am. Red Cross Retirement System, 1992—; bd. dirs. Children's Hosp. Found., Omaha, 1991—. Sgt. U.S. Army, 1957-65. Mem. Assn. for Investment Mgmt. and Rsch. (bd. dirs. 1991, chmn. bd. govs.), Inst. Chartered Fin. Analysts (C. Steward Sheppard award 1990). Republican. Roman Catholic. Office: Mut of Omaha Ins Co Mut Omaha Pla Omaha NE 68175

MAGINNIS, MOLLY, costume designer. Costume designer: (films) The New Kids, 1985, Whatever It Takes, 1986, Lucas, 1986, Broadcast News, 1987, Morgan Stewart's Coming Home, 1987, In a Shallow Grave, 1988, Dad, 1989, Look Who's Talking, 1989, Hitchhiker, 1989, Come See the Paradise, 1990, Look Who's Talking Too, 1990, Money Men, 1992, Once Upon a Crime, 1992, Sister Act, 1992, Son-in-Law, 1993, Look Who's Talking Now, 1994, The War, 1994, (TV movies) Combat High, 1986, Perfect People, 1988. Office: 933 17th St #14 Santa Monica CA 90403*

MAGLICH, BOGDAN CVETA, physicist; b. Yugoslavia, Aug. 5, 1938; came to U.S., 1956, naturalized, 1972; s. Cveta and Ivanka (Bingulac) M.; m. Victoria Vesna Bulajic; children: Angelica Dara, Aleksandra Mara Nadine; children by previous marriages: Marko Castle, Ivanka Taylor, Roberta Cveta. Diploma physics, U. Belgrade, 1951; MS, U. Liverpool, Eng., 1955; PhD, MIT, 1959. Staff mem. Lawrence Berkeley Lab., 1959-62; dep. group leader Brit. group, 1962-63; leader Swiss group CERN European Orgn. Nuclear Rsch., 1964-67; vis. prof., joint faculty mem. Princeton U.-U. Pa. accelerator U. Pa., 1967-69; prof. physics, prin. investigator high energy physics Rutgers U., 1969-74; pres., chmn. Fusion Energy Corp., Princeton, N.J., 1972-81, Aneutronix, Inc., 1982-83, Sci. Transfer Assocs., Inc., 1981-84, United Scis., Inc., 1984-87, AE Labs Aneutronic Energy Lab., Inc., 1986-88; pres. Advanced Physics Corp., 1988-94; chmn. Advanced Projects Group, Inc., 1994—; chmn. The Tesla Found., 1985—; resident scientist UN-ILO Seminar Econ. Devel. East Africa, Kenya, 1967; lectr. Postdoctoral Sch. Physics, Yerevan, USSR, 1965, Internat. Sch. Majorana, Italy, 1969; mem. U.S. delegation Internat. Conf. High Energy Physics, Vienna, 1968, Kiev, 1970; spl. rep. of U.S. Pres. to Yugoslavia, 1976; sci. project dir. Univ. Research Ctr., King Abdulaziz U., Saudi Arabia, 1981-82; prin. investigator for aneutronic energy USAF Weapons Lab., 1985-87, USAF Space Tech. Ctr., 1988-89. Editor: Adventures in Exptl. Physics, 1972-80, Living Physics Video Jour. Chmn. Yugoslav-Am. Bicentennial Com., 1975-76; co-chmn. Serbian-Am. Com. for a Dem. Yugoslavia, 1989—; pres. World Serbian Union, Geneva, 1990-92. Recipient White House citation, 1961; Bourgeois d'honneur de Lens Switzerland, 1973; UNESCO fellow, 1957-58. Fellow Am. Phys. Soc.; mem. Serbian Acad. Scis. and Arts (Yugoslavia), Ripon Soc. (bd. govs.), Nassau Club, MIT Club, Sigma Xi. Mem. Serbian Orthodox Ch. Discoverer omega-meson, sonic spark chamber, missing-mass spectrometer, delta-meson, g-meson, S, T and U-mesons, precetron, self collider migma, aneutronic energy process; patentee in field.

MAGLIERY, FRANK THOMAS, hospital administrator; b. New Castle, Pa., June 19, 1943; s. Thomas John and Mary Elizabeth (Panella) M.; m. Carol Phyllis Dulski, Oct. 2, 1972; children: Thomas, John. BS, Duquesne U., 1966; MHA, Xavier U., 1973; MBA, Loyola U., Chgo., 1978. Registered pharmacist. Retail pharmacist Thrift Drug Stores, Sharon, New Castle Pa. and Pitts., 1966-68; hosp. pharmacist West Penn Hosp., Pitts., 1968-71; dir. profl. svcs. Holy Family Hosp., Des Plaines, Ill., 1973-76; sr. v.p. ops. Victory Meml. Hosp., Waukegan, Ill., 1976-83; administr. St. Vincent Carmel (Ind.) Hosp., Carmel, 1983—. Mem. Allocations Com. United Way, Indpls., 1983—; bd. dirs. Am. Heart Assn., Hamilton County, 1988, Circle Seven Tng. Coun., Indpls., 1985—. With USAF, 1967-73. Mem. Carmel Clay C. of C. (pres. elect 1988), Am. Coll. Healthcare Execs., Rotary (v.p. Carmel Club 1988). Roman Catholic. Avocation: tennis. Home: 598 Smokey Row Ct Carmel IN 46033-1947

MAGNANO, SALVATORE PAUL, financial executive, treasurer; b. Portland, Conn., Jan. 10, 1934; s. Salvatore and Lucy (Dimodica) M.; m. Lois Jewel Johnson, July 16, 1955; children: Paul C., Mark J., Peter E. B.Metall. Engring., Rensselaer Poly. Inst., Troy, N.Y., 1955; MBA, Northwestern U., Chgo., 1959. Div. controller Sanders Assocs., Inc., Nashua, N.H., 1962-73; v.p. controller Teledyne Mec, Palo Alto, Calif., 1973-75; div. controller Sanders Assocs., Inc., Nashua, 1975-79; grp. controller Sanders Assocs., Inc., 1979-81, grp. v.p., controller, 1981-86, v.p. fin. and treas., 1986—. Pres. Boys Club of Nashua, 1988-89, bd. dirs., 1981—; bd. dirs. Boys Club of Nashua Charitable Found.; trustee Daniel Webster Coll., Nashua. Lt. USN, 1955-57. Mem. Am. Mgmt. Assn., Fin. Execs. Inst., Beta Gamma Sigma (award for excellence 1959). Office: Lockheed Sanders 65 Spit Brook Rd Nashua NH 03060-5639

MAGNANTI, THOMAS L., management and engineering educator; b. Omaha, Oct. 7, 1945; s. Leo A. and Florence L. Magnanti; m. Beverly A. McVinney, June 10, 1967; 1 child, R. Randall. BS in Chem. Engring., Syracuse U., 1967; MS in Stats., Stanford U., 1969, MS in Math., 1971, PhD in Ops. Rsch., 1972. Asst. prof. Alfred P. Sloan Sch. Mgmt. MIT, Cambridge, Mass., 1971-75; rsch. fellow, vis. prof. Ctr. for Ops. Rsch. and Econometrics Univ. Catholique de Louvain, 1976-77, 89; assoc. prof. Alfred P. Sloan Sch. Mgmt. MIT, 1975-79, prof., 1979-85, George Eastman prof. of mgmt. sci., 1985—, head mgmt. sci. area, 1982-88, co-dir. Ops. Rsch. Ctr., 1986—, founding co-dir. Leaders for Mfg. Program, 1988-94; vis. scientist Bell Labs., 1977, GTE Labs., 1989; vis. scholar Grad. Sch. Bus. Adminstrn., Harvard U., 1980-81; mem. corp. mfg. staff Digital Equipment Corp., 1990; mem. editorial bd. Wadsworth Publishing Co. Series on Ops. Rsch., Jour. Computational Optimization and Applications; mem. adv. bd. North Holland Handbooks in Ops. Rsch. and Mgmt. Sci. Author: Applied Mathematical Programming, 1977, Network Flows, 1993; editor: Jour. Ops. Rsch., 1983-87; co-editor: Math. Programming, 1981-83; assoc. editor SIAM Jour. Algebraic and Discrete Methods, 1981-83, Mgmt. Sci., 1978-81, Ops. Rsch., 1978-81, SIAM Jour. Applied Math., 1976-81, Math. Programming, 1988—; adv. editor Transp. Sci., 1985—, Mktg. Sci., Math. of Artificial Intelligence, 1987-91; contbr. numerous articles to profl. jours. Mem. NSF Sci. and Tech. Exchange Delegation to Soviet Union, 1977, NSF Rsch. Initiation Grant panels, 1985, 90; advisor NSF program on decision, risk and mgmt. sci., 1988, 89; mem. mfg. studies bd. Nat. Rsch. Coun., 1993—. Recipient Gordon Billard award MIT, 1992, Mgmt. Program Exchange grant IREX, Curriculum Devel. grant Sloan Found., 1990-94. Mem. IEEE (com. on large scale systems 1979-83), TIMS (mem. and chmn. various coms.), Nat. Acad. Engring, Ops. Rsch. Soc. Am. (pres. 1988-89, mem. and chmn. various coms., coun. mem. computer sci. tech. sect. 1983-87, co-organizer 1st doctoral consortium 1983, plenary speaker conf. on telecom. 1990), Tau Beta Phi, Pi Mu Epsilon, Phi Kappa Phi. Achievements include research in network analysis and optimization, network design and combinatorial optimization, and applications in manufacturing, telecommunications, and transportation; development of new engineering/management programs. Home: 33 School St Hopkinton MA 01748-2003 Office: MIT Ops Rsch Ctr 77 Massachusetts Ave Cambridge MA 02139-4307

MAGNER, FREDRIC MICHAEL, financial services executive; b. June 27, 1950; m. Rachel Harris, May 14, 1972. BA in Internat. Studies, U. S.C., 1971, MBA, 1972; M of Accountancy, U. So. Calif., 1976. Cert. in mgmt. acctg. Mktg. rep. IBM, L.A., 1976-79; v.p. First Interstate Services Co., El Segundo, Calif., 1979-82, First Interstate Bancorp, Los Angeles, 1982-83; sr. v.p. First Interstate System, L.A., 1983-86, First Interstate Bancorp, L.A., 1986—. Capt. USAF, 1973-76. Mem. Carolina Club of So. Calif. (pres. 1990-95). Home: 2200 Pine Ave Manhattan Beach CA 90266 Office: First Interstate Bancorp 633 W 5th St T71-1 Los Angeles CA 90071

MAGNER, JEROME ALLEN, entertainment company executive; b. Bklyn., Mar. 14, 1929; s. Herman and Evelyn I. (Wolfe) M.; BBA cum laude, CCNY, 1951; m. Frances Ogens, Mar. 22, 1953; children: Merrill, Steven. Asst. to treas., chief acct. Grayson-Robinson Stores, Inc., S. Klein Dept. Stores, Inc., N.Y.C., 1951-59; controller Food Fair Properties, N.Y.C., 1959-61; v.p., controller Am. Leisure Products Corp., N.Y.C. and Providence, 1961-69; sr. v.p. fin., treas. Nat. Amusements, Inc., NE Theatre Corp., Dedham, 1969—. Mem. Met. Controllers Congress, Nat. Assn. Accts., Am. Mgmt. Assn., Nat. Assn. Theatre Owners (bd. dirs.), CCNY Alumni Assn. Office: Nat Amusements Inc 200 Elm St Dedham MA 02026

MAGNER, MARTIN, theatrical producer and director; b. Stettin, Ger., Mar. 5, 1900; came to U.S., 1939, naturalized, 1945; s. Max. and Zerlina (Silberstein) M.; m. Marion Palfi, June 6, 1951. Actor Hamburger kammerspiele, Germany, 1918-20; producer, dir. Nuremberg, Germany, 1921-27, Breslau, Germany, 1928-33, Berlin, 1928-33, Vienna, Austria, 1919-38, Prague, Czechoslovakia, 1933-39; stage dir. Chgo. Opera Co., 1940-41, San Francisco Opera, 1972; producer, dir. NBC, Chgo. and N.Y.C., 1942-49, CBS, N.Y.C., 1950-63; instr., artist-in-residence drama and music U. Chgo., 1941, Northwestern U., 1942-43, Adelphi Coll., 1948, Canisius Coll., 1958; artistic dir. New Theatre Inc., Los Angeles, 1977—. Recipient several documentary awards AMA, Spl. award for maintaining consistently high standards L.A. Drama Critics Circle, 1975, Disting. Lifetime Achievement award L.A. Drama Critics Circle, 1988, Life Time Achievement award Gov. of Calif., 1991; recepient The Cross of merit First Class from the Bundes Repulik of Germany, 1992. Mem. Dirs Guild Am. Home: 1282 S Burnside Ave Los Angeles CA 90019-2677

MAGNESS, BOB JOHN, telecommunications executive; b. Clinton, Okla., 1924; married. Grad., South Western State Coll., 1949. Chmn. Tele-Communications, Inc., Denver; chmn. Community Tele-Communications, Inc.; bd. dirs. Republic Pictures Corp., WestMarc Communications, United Artists Communications, Inc. Office: Tele-Comm Inc PO Box 5630 Denver CO 80217-9523*

MAGNOLI, MICHAEL A., academic official. Pres. Mobile (Ala.) Coll. Office: Univ Mobile PO Box 13220 Mobile AL 36663-0220

MAGNUS, FREDERICK SAMUEL, investment banker; b. Montclair, N.J., Aug. 26, 1932; s. Robert Frederick and Cora (Argue) M. BA, Rutgers U., 1954. Rep., T.L. Watson Co., 1956-57, Goodbody & Co., 1957-58; pres., dir. Godfrey Hamilton & Magnus Co., 1958-61; pres., dir. Magnus & Co., Inc., Passaic, 1961—. With U.S. Army, 1954-56. Office: Magnus & Co Inc 575 Grove St E9 Clifton NJ 07013

MAGNUSON, HAROLD JOSEPH, physician; b. Halstead, Kans., Mar. 31, 1913; s. Joseph Simeon and Margaret Ethel (Matson) M.; m. Ruth Prusia, Feb. 16, 1935 (dec. 1941); children: Karen Margaret Magnuson Mauro), Ruth Ellen; m. Kathryne I. Bause, Dec. 20, 1941 (dec. 1993). AB, U. So. Calif., 1934, MD, 1938; MPH, Johns Hopkins U., 1942. Diplomate: Am. Bd. Preventive Medicine (mem. bd. 1964-75, vice chmn. occupational medicine 1968-75). Intern Los Angeles County Gen. Hosp., 1937-39; research fellow A.C.P., 1939-40; instr. medicine U. So. Calif., 1939-41; commd. asst. surgeon USPHS, 1941, med. dir., 1952; instr. medicine Johns Hopkins, 1943-46; research prof. exptl. medicine U. N.C., 1946-55; chief div. occupational health USPHS, 1956-62; ret., 1962; prof. internal medicine U. Mich. Sch. Medicine, prof. indsl. health, 1962-76, prof. emeritus, 1976—; chmn. dept. U. Mich. Sch. Pub. Health; also dir. U. Mich. Sch. Pub. Health (Inst. Indsl. Health), 1962-69; asso. dean U. Mich. Sch. Pub. Health (Sch. Pub. Health), 1969-76; mem. U.S. delegation ILO Conf., 1958, 59; Chmn. U.S. indsl. toxicology delegation to, USSR, 1963. Fellow A.C.P., A.A.A.S., A.M.A. (chmn. sect. preventive medicine 1966, Hektoen bronze medal 1956), Am. Acad. Occupational Medicine, Am. Pub. Health Assn. (chmn. sect. occupational health 1966, Indsl. Med. Assn., Knudsen award 1970); mem. Soc. Clin. Investigation, Soc. Exptl. Biology and Medicine, Soc. Exptl. Pathology, Mich. Indsl. Med. Assn. (pres. 1965-66), Internat. Congress Indsl. Medicine (v.p. 1969), Rammazzini Soc., Phi Beta Kappa, Sigma Xi, Alpha Omega Alpha, Delta Omega. Home: 18755 W Bernardo Dr Apt 1125 San Diego CA 92127-3012

MAGNUSON, NANCY, librarian; b. Seattle, Aug. 15, 1944; d. James Leslie and Jeanette (Thomas) M.; 2 sons, Daniel Johnson, Erik Johnson. BA in History, 1977; MLS, U. Wash., 1978. With King County Libr. System, Seattle, 1973-80; rsch. asst. Free Libr. Phila., 1980-81; asst. libr. Haverford (Pa.) Coll., 1981-87; libr. dir. Goucher Coll., Balt., Md., 1987—. Contbr. to profl. publs. Mem. ALA (com. on status of women in librarianship, various others), Online Computer Libr. Ctr. Users Coun., Md. Libr. Assn., Congress Acad. Libr. Dirs., NOW, Women's Internat. League for Peace and Freedom, Balt. Bibliophiles, Jane Austen Soc. N.Am. Democrat. Office: Goucher Coll Julia Rogers Libr 1021 Dulaney Valley Rd Baltimore MD 21204

MAGNUSON, NORRIS ALDEN, librarian, history educator; b. Midale, Saskatchewan, Can., June 15, 1932; s. George August and Esther Lydia (Eliason) M.; m. Beverly Sue Carlson, Aug. 17, 1956; children: Douglas, Timothy, Kenneth, Daniel. BA, Bethel Coll., 1954; BD, Bethel Sem., 1958; MA, U. Minn., 1961, PhD, 1968. Instr., asst. libr. Bethel Theol. Sem., St. Paul, Minn., 1959-65, asst. prof., asst. libr., 1965-68, assoc. prof., assoc. libr., 1968-72, prof., head libr., 1972—; chair hist. com. Bapt. Gen. Conf., Arlington Heights, Ill., 1974—; mem. Conf. on Faith and History. Author: Salvation in the Slums, 1977, 2nd edit., 1990, Missionsskolan: The history, 1982; editor Proclaim the Good News, 1986; author (with others) American Evangelicalism, 1990. Mem. Salem Bapt. Ch., chairperson, 1972-73. U. Minn. scholar, 1961-63; Inst. for Advanced Christian Studies fellow, 1968-69. Mem. Am. Theol. Libr. Assn., Minn. Theol. Libr. Assn. (pres. 1974-75, 79-80, 84-85, 88-89). Avocations: tennis, handball, racquetball, travelling. Office: Bethel Coll & Sem 3900 Bethel Dr Saint Paul MN 55112-6979

MAGNUSON, PAUL ARTHUR, federal judge; b. Carthage, S.D., Feb. 9, 1937; s. Arthur and Emma Elleda (Paulson) M.; m. Sharon Schultz, Dec. 21, 1959; children—Marlene, Margaret, Kevin, Kara. B.A., Gustavus Adolphus Coll, 1959; J.D., William Mitchell Coll., 1963. Bar: Minn. 1963, U.S. Dist. Ct. Minn. 1968. Claim adjuster Agrl. Ins. Co., 1960-62; clk. Bertie & Bettenberg Law Firm, 1962-63; ptnr. LeVander, Gillen, Miller & Magnuson, South St. Paul, Minn., 1963-81; judge U.S. Dist. Ct. Minn., St. Paul, 1981—; jurist-in-residence Hamline U. Law Sch., lectr., 1985; lectr. Augustine Coll., 1986, Bethel Coll., 1986, Concordia Coll.-St. Paul, 1987, U. Minn.-Morris, 1987; instr. William Mitchell Coll. Law, 1984—. Mem. Met. Health Bd., St. Paul, 1970-72; legal counsel Ind. Republican Party Minn., St. Paul, 1979-81. Recipient Disting. Alumnus award Gustavus Adolphus Coll., 1982. Mem. ABA, 1st Dist. Bar Assn. (pres. 1974-75), Dakota County Bar Assn., Am. Judicature Soc. Presbyterian. Home: 3047 Klondike Ave N Lake Elmo MN 55042-9717 Office: US Dist Ct 754 Fed Bldg 316 Robert St N Saint Paul MN 55101-1423

MAGNUSON, ROBERT MARTIN, retired hospital administrator; b. Chgo., June 28, 1927; s. Martin David and Adena Marie (Hallberg) M.; m. Patricia Ann McNaughton, Dec. 30, 1960; children: Thomas Martin, Dana Caroline. B.S. cum laude, Lake Forest (Ill.) Coll., 1951; M.B.A., Harvard U., 1955. Factory budget mgr. asst. budget dir. Zenith Radio Corp., Chgo., 1955-57; asst. administr., controller Elmhurst Meml. Hosp., (Ill.), 1957-64; asso. administr. Elmhurst Meml. Hosp., 1964-66, pres., 1966-92; officer, dir. Chgo. Hosp. Council, 1972-79, chmn. bd. dirs., 1983; mem. hosp. adv. council Ill. Dept. Pub. Health, 1972-76; faculty preceptor U. Chgo. Program in Hosp. Adminstrn., 1971-92, Northwestern U. Program in Hosp. and Health Sci. Adminstrn., 1972-92; dir. DuPage County Community Nursing Service, 1964-67, Health Chgo. HMO, 1984-92, Elmhurst Fed. Savs. & Loan Assn., 1971-92; pres. Meml. Health Services, Inc., 1980-92. Pres. Elmhurst Meml. Hosp. Found., 1980-92. Served with USN, 1945-48, 51-52. Mem. Am. Coll. Health Care Execs., Ill. Hosp. Assn. (dist. pres. 1967-69, bd. dirs. 1985-90), Inter-Hosp. Planning Assn. of Western Suburbs (pres., dir.). Republican. Club: Medinah (Ill.) Country.

MAGNUSON, ROGER JAMES, lawyer; b. St. Paul, Jan. 25, 1945; s. Roy Gustaf and Ruth Lily (Edlund) M.; m. Elizabeth Cunningham Shaw, Sept. 11, 1982; children: James Roger, Peter Cunningham, Mary Kerstin, Sarah Ruth, Elizabeth Camilla, Anna Clara. Ba, Stanford U., 1967; JD, Harvard U., 1971; BCL, Oxford U., 1972. Bar: Minn. 1973, U.S. Dist. Ct. Minn. 1973, U.S. Ct. Appeals (8th, 9th, 10th cirs.) 1974, U.S. Supreme Ct. 1978. Chief pub. defender Hennepin County Pub. Defender's Office, Mpls., 1973; ptnr. Dorsey & Whitney, Mpls., 1972—. Author: Shareholder Litigation, 1981, Are Gay Rights Right, The White-Collar Crime Explosion, 1992, Informed Answers To Gay Rights Questions, 1994; contbr. articles to profl. jours. Elder, Straitgate Ch., Mpls., 1980—. Mem. Christian Legal Soc., White Bear Yacht Club. Republican. Home: 625 Park Ave Saint Paul MN 55115-1663 Office: Dorsey & Whitney 220 S 6th St Minneapolis MN 55402

MAGOR, LOUIS ROLAND, conductor; b. Auburn, Nebr., May 16, 1945; s. John William and Eleanor Lucille (Niemann) M. B.Mus. Edn., Northwestern U., 1967, Mus.M., 1974. Choral dir. Avoca Jr. High Sch., Wilmette, Ill., 1968-70; choral dir. Niles North High Sch., Skokie, Ill., 1970-73; dir. San Francisco Symphony Chorus, 1974-82, Schola Cantorum, 1982-85, San Francisco Boys Chorus, 1985-88; artistic dir. Seattle Bach Choir, 1990—; founder The Louis Magor Singers; mem. faculty San Francisco Conservatory of Music, 1976-78, San Francisco State U., 1979-80. Founder West Seattle Children's Chorus, 1990—; condr. Sing-It-Yourself Messiah, 1979-91, Calif. Symphony Chorus, 1990-92. Mem. Pi Kappa Lambda.

MAGOWAN, PETER ALDEN, professional baseball team executive, grocery chain executive; b. N.Y.C., Apr. 5, 1942; s. Robert Anderson and Doris (Merrill) M.; m. Jill Tarlau (div. July 1982; children—Kimberley, Margot, Hilary; m. Deborah Johnston, Aug. 14, 1982. BA, Stanford U.; MA, Oxford U., Eng.; postgrad., Johns Hopkins U. Store mgr. Safeway Stores Inc., Washington, 1968-70; dist. mgr. Safeway Stores Inc., Houston,

1970-71; retail ops. mgr. Safeway Stores Inc., Phoenix, 1971-72; div. mgr. Safeway Stores Inc., Tulsa, 1973-76; mgr. internat. div. Safeway Stores Inc. Toronto, Ont., Can., 1976-78; mgr. western region Safeway Stores Inc., San Francisco, 1978-79; chmn. bd., CEO Safeway Stores Inc., Oakland, Calif. 1980-93, chmn. bd., 1980—; pres., mng. gen. ptnr. San Francisco Giants, 1993—; bd. dirs. Chrysler Corp., Vons Cos. Inc., Caterpillar. Office: San Francisco Giants Candlestick Park San Francisco CA 94124

MAGRATH, C. PETER, educational association executive; b. N.Y.C., Apr. 23, 1933; s. Laurence Wilfrid and Guilia Maria (Dentice) M.; m. Deborah C. Howell, 1988; children: Valerie Ruth, Monette Fay. BA summa cum laude, U. N.H., 1955; PhD, Cornell U., 1962. Mem. faculty Brown U., Providence, 1961-68, prof. polit. sci., 1967-68, assoc. dean grad. sch., 1965-66; dean Coll. Arts and Scis. U. Nebr., Lincoln, 1968-69, dean faculties Coll. Arts and Scis., 1969-72, interim chancellor univ., 1971-72, prof. polit. sci., 1968-72, vice chancellor for acad. affairs, 1972; pres. SUNY, Binghamton, 1972-74, prof. polit. sci., 1972-74; pres. U. Minn., Mpls., 1974-84, U. Mo. System, 1985-91, Nat. Assn. State Univs. and Land Grant Colls., Washington, 1991—. Author: The Triumph of Character, 1963, Yazoo: Law and Politics in the New Republic, The Case of Fletcher v. Peck, 1966, Constitutionalism and Politics: Conflict and Consensus, 1968, Issues and Perspectives in American Government, 1971, (with others) The American Democracy, 2d edit., 1973, (with Robert L. Egbert) Strengthening Teacher Education, 1987; contbr. articles to profl. jours. Served with AUS, 1955-57. Mem. Assn. Am. Univs. (chmn. 1985-86), Phi Beta Kappa, Phi Kappa Phi, Pi Gamma Mu, Pi Sigma Alpha, Kappa Tau Alpha. Office: Nat Assn State U and Land Grant Colls 1 Dupont Cir NW Ste 710 Washington DC 20036-1191 *True personal success cannot be measured by public acclaim, recognition, or status. It grows out of an ability to recognize right from wrong, and to maintain principles of fairness and understanding in all human relationships - regardless of one's role in life. In my case I have tried to fulfill this ideal; I have been willing to exercise leadership by asserting my judgements and views openly and directly on the educational and human issues that came my way.*

MAGRILL, JOE RICHARD, JR., religious organization administrator, minister; b. Marshall, Tex., Aug. 7, 1946; s. Joe Richard and Mary Belle (Chadwick) M. BA summa cum laude, East Tex. State U., 1967; MDiv, Princeton Theol. Sem., 1970, MTh, 1972; MLS, Rutgers U., 1971. Ordained to ministry Cumberland Presbyn. Ch., 1970. Stated supply min. Newsome (Tex.) Cumberland Presbyn. Ch., 1966-67; Christian edn. asst. United Presbyn. Ch., Carlstadt, N.J., 1967-70; order libr. Princeton (N.J.) Theol. Sem., 1969-72; head libr., prof. Memphis Theol. Sem., 1972-79; pastor Brookhaven Cumberland Presbyn. Ch., Nashville, 1987-89; asst. to stated clk. Gen. Assembly Office, Cumberland Presbyn. Ch., Memphis, 1979-83, supr. ctrl. acctg. div., 1980-87, editor The Cumberland Presbyn., 1983-87, chief exec. bd. fin., 1989—, mem. coun. Gen. Assembly, 1993—; mem. Trinity Presbytery of Cumberland Presbyn. Ch., 1970—; sec.-treas. Hist. Found. Cumberland Presbyn. Ch., Memphis, 1974—; bd. dirs. Hist. Found. Presbyn. Ch. U.S., Montreat, N.C., 1980-83. Editor: In the Valley of the Cauca, 1981, One Family Under God, 1982. Recipient achievement award Hist. Found. Cumberland Presbyn. Ch., 1980; scholar Phi Alpha Theta, 1967, Am. Theol. Libr. Assn., 1970. Democrat. Avocations: computers, historical research. Office: Bd Fin Cumberland Presbyn Ch 1978 Union Ave Memphis TN 38104-4134

MAGRILL, ROSE MARY, library director; b. Marshall, Tex., June 8, 1939; d. Joe Richard and Mary Belle (Chadwick) M. BS, E. Tex. State U., 1960, MA, 1961; MS, U. Ill., 1964, PhD, 1969. Asst. to dean women E. Tex. State U., Commerce, 1960-61, librarian II, 1961-63; teaching asst. U. Ill., Urbana, 1963-64; instr. to asst. prof. E. Tex. State U., Commerce, 1964-67; asst. prof. Ball State U., Muncie, 1969-70; asst. prof. to prof. U. Mich., Ann Arbor, 1970-81; prof. U. N. Tex., Denton, 1981—; dir. libr. E. Tex. Bapt. U., Marshall, 1987—; accreditation site visitor ALA, Chgo., 1975—; cons. in field. Co-author: Building Library Collections, 4th edit. 1974, Library Technical Services, 1977, Building Library Collections, 5th edit. 1979, Acquisition Management and Collection Development in Libraries, 2d edit. 1989. Trustee Memphis Theol. Sem., 1988—; treas. Mission Synod of Cumberland Presbyn. Ch., 1989—; bd. fin. Trinity Presbytery, 1989—; mem. Harrison County Hist. Commn., 1995—. Mem. ALA (RTSD Resources Sect. pub. award 1978), Tex. Libr. Assn. Home: 804 Caddo St Marshall TX 75670-2414 Office: E Tex Bapt Univ 1209 N Grove St Marshall TX 75670-1498

MAGRUDER, LAWSON WILLIAM, III, military officer; b. Bryan, Tex., Nov. 5, 1947; s. Lawson William Jr. and Maryanne (Windrow) M.; m. Gloria Ann Banton, July 26, 1969; children: Shannon, Loren, Matthew. BBA in Internat. Mktg., U. Tex., 1969; MA in Pers. Mgmt., Ctrl. Mich. U., 1979; student, U.S. Army Command Gen. Staff Coll., 1979, Army War Coll., 1986. Commd. 2d lt. U.S. Army, 1969, advanced through grades to maj. gen., 1995; rifle platoon leader 82d Airborne Divsn., Ft. Bragg, N.C., 1969-71, 23d Inf. Divsn., Vietnam; asst. brigade ops. officer, co. comdr. 82d Airborne Divsn., 1971-74; ranger co. comdr., bn. adj. 2d Ranger Bn., 1975-77; bn. ops. officer 9th Inf. Divsn., 1977-78; inf. assignment officer U.S. Total Army Pers. Command, 1979-82; brigade ops. officer 172d Light Inf. Brigade, Alaska; comdr. 5th bn. 327th Inf., Alaska, 1982-85; chief tactics, dep. dir. combined arms and tactics dept. U.S. Army Inf. Sch., Ft. Benning, Ga., 1986-88; comdr. 2d brigade 25th Inf. Divsn., Schofield Barracks, Hawaii, 1988-90; exec. asst. to dep. comdr.-in-chief, dep. dir. strategic policy and plans U.S. Pacific Command, 1990-92; asst. divsn. comdr. 10th Mountain Divsn.; comdr. Combined Task Force Kismayo, Somalia, 1992-93; comdg. gen. Joint Readiness Tng. Ctr. U.S. Army, Ft. Polk, La., 1993-95; comdg. gen. U.S. Army South, Ft. Clayton, Panama, 1995—. Pres. Ft. Benning Parish Coun., 1986-88; mem. Ft. Benning Sch. Bd., 1987-88. Decorated Bronze star medal with oak leaf cluster, Legion of Merit with two oak leaf clusters, Air medal, Army Commedation medal with one oak leaf cluster, Def. Superior Svc. medal, Meritorious Svc. medal with three oak leaf clusters. Roman Catholic. Avocations: golfing, running. Home: Quarters 1, Fort Amador Panama Office: Hqs US Army S Ft Clayton Panama APO AA 34004

MAGSIG, JUDITH ANNE, early childhood educator; b. Saginaw, Mich., Nov. 9, 1939; d. Harold Howard and Catherine Louise (Barstow) Gay; m. George Arthur Magsig, June 22, 1963; children: Amy Catherine, Karl Joseph. BA, Alma Coll., 1961. Cert. tchr., early childhood tchr., Mich. 1st grade tchr. Gaylord (Mich.) Schs., 1961-64, spl. edn. tchr., 1965-67, kindergarten tchr., 1968—. instr. Suzuki violin method; second violinist Traverse (Mich.) Symphony Orch., 1985-92. Mem. ASCD, NEA, Mich. Edn. Assn., Gaylord Edn. Assn., Assn. for the Edn. of Young Children, Assn. for Childhood Edn. Internat., Suzuki Assn. Am., Am. String Tchrs. Assn., Order Eastern Star, Voyageurs and Friends of Hartwick Pines, Alpha Delta Kappa (pres. Beta Rho chpt. 1980-82, 84-86). Methodist. Avocations: cross-stitch, camping, canoeing, sewing. Home: S Maple Multi Age Program 590 W 5th St Gaylord MI 49735 Office: S Maple Multi Age Program W 5th St Gaylord MI 49735

MAGUIRE, CARY MCILWAINE, oil company executive; b. Ardmore, Pa., May 30, 1928; s. John Russell and Luna Neal (Ambler) M.; m. Ann Thompson, Feb. 27, 1960; children: Cary McIlwaine, Melinda Ambler, Ann Blaine. BS, U. Pa., 1950. Mgr. Russell Maguire Oil Ops., Dallas and Wichita Falls, Tex., 1955-67; v.p. Alco Controls, St. Louis, 1956-69, Weber Dental Mfg. Co., Canton, Ohio, 1956-69; pres. Columbia Producing Co., N.Y.C., 1967-70, Camm Realty Co., St. Louis, 1967-71; chmn. bd. Staco, Inc., Costa Mesa, Calif. 1977-86, Staco Energy, Dayton, Ohio, 1977—, Stacoswitch, Costa Mesa, 1977—, Components Corp. Am., Dallas, 1976—; chmn., pres. Maguire Oil Co., Dallas, 1969—, Maguire Energy Co., Dallas, 1986—, Maguire Resources Co., Las Vegas, Nev., 1990—; dir. InterFirst Bank, Dallas, 1976-86. Trustee St. Mark's Sch., Dallas, 1974-80, So. Meth. U., Dallas, 1976—, chmn. audit com. 1985-90, chmn. investment com. 1990-91, chmn. exec. bd. bus. sch., 1982—; trustee, vice-chmn. Hockaday Sch., Dallas, 1976-84; founder Maguire Learning Ctr. at Hockaday, Maguire Oil and Gas Inst. at SMU, 1975, Maguire Chair in Oil and Gas Mgmt. at SMU, 1985, Maguire Chair in Ethics at SMU, 1985; mem. vestry St. Michael's and All Angels Ch., Dallas, 1982-84; trustee So. Meth. U., Dallas, 1976—, chmn. audit com., 1985-90, chmn. investment com., 1990-91, chmn. exec. bd. bus. sch., 1982—; foreman Dallas County Grand Jury, 1990. Mem. Nat. Petroleum Coun., Ind. Petroleum Assn. Am. (dir. 1956—, sec.-treas. Dallas

Wildcat com. 1982-84), Mid-Continent Oil and Gas Assn. (exec. com. 1956—), All-Am. Wildcatters, Brook Hollow Golf Club, Dallas Petroleum Club, Idlewild Club, Terpsichorian Club, Calyx Club. Republican. Episcopalian. Avocations: tennis, golf, music. Home: 4606 Park Ln Dallas TX 75220-2025 Office: Maguire Oil Co 4000 Renaissance Tower Dallas TX 75270

MAGUIRE, CHARLOTTE EDWARDS, retired physician; b. Richmond, Ind., Sept. 1, 1918; d. Joel Blaine and Lydia (Betscher) Edwards; m. Raymer Francis Maguire, Sept. 1, 1948 (dec.); children: Barbara, Thomas Clair II. Student, Stetson U., 1936-38, U. Wichita, 1938-39; B.S., Memphis Tchrs. Coll., 1940; M.D., U. Ark., 1944. Intern, resident Orange Meml. Hosp., Orlando, Fla., 1944-46; resident Bellevue Hosp. and Med. Ctr., NYU, N.Y.C., 1954, 55; instr. nurses Orange Meml. Hosp., 1947-57, staff mem., 1946-68; staff mem. Fla. Santarium and Hosp., Orlando, 1946-56, Holiday House and Hosp., Orlando, 1950-62; mem. courtesy and cons. staff West Orange Meml. Hosp., Winter Garden, Fla., 1952-67; active staff, chief dept. pediatrics Mercy Hosp., Orlando, 1965-68; med. dir. med. services and basic care Fla. Dept. Health and Rehab. Services, 1975-84; med. exec. dir., med. services div. worker's compensation Fla. Dept. Labor, Tallahassee, 1984-87; chief of staff physicians and dentists Central Fla. div. Children's Home Soc. of Fla., 1947-56; dir. Orlando Child Health Clinic 1949-58; pvt. practice medicine Orlando, 1946-68; asst. regional dir. HEW, 1970-72; pediatric cons. Fla. Crippled Children's Commn., 1952-70, dir., 1968-70; med. dir. Office Med. Services and Basic Care, sr. physician Office of Asst. Sec. Ops., Fla. Dept. Health and Rehab. Services; clin. prof. dept. pediatrics U. Fla. Coll. Medicine, Gainesville, 1980-87; mem. Fla. Drug Utilization Rev. 1983-87; real estate salesperson, Investors Realty, 1982—; bd. dirs. Stavros Econ. Ctr. Fla. State U., Tallahassee; mem. pres.'s coun. Fla. State U., U. Fla., Gainesville. Mem. profl. adv. com. Fla. Center for Clin. Services at U. Fla., 1952-60; del. to mid-century White House Conf. on Children and Youth, 1950; U.S. del from Nat. Soc. for Crippled Children to World Congress for Welfare of Cripples, London, 1957; pres of corp. Eccleston-Callahan Hosp. for Colored Crippled Children, 1956-58; sec. Fla. chpt. Nat. Doctor's Com. for Improved Med. Services, 1951-52; med. adv. com. Gateway Sch. for Mentally Retarded, 1959-62; bd. dirs. Forest Park Sch. for Spl. Edn. Crippled Children, 1949-54, mem. med. adv. com., 1955-68, chmn., 1957-68; mem. Fla. Adv. Council for Mentally Retarded, 1965-70; dir. central Fla. poison control Orange Meml. Hosp.; mem. orgn. com., chmn. com. for admissions and selection policies Camp Challenge; participant 12th session Fed. Exec. Inst., 1971; del. White House Conf. on Aging, 1980. Mem. Nat. Rehab. Assn., Am. Congress Phys. Medicine and Rehab., Fla. Soc. Crippled Children and Adults, Central Fla. Soc. Crippled Children and Adults (dir. 1949-58, pres. 1956-57), Am. Assn. Cleft Palate, Fla. Soc. Crippled Children (trustee 1951-57, v.p. 1956-57, profl. adv. com. 1957-68), Mental Health Assn. Orange County (charter mem.; pres. 1949-50, dir. 1947-52, chmn. exec. com. 1950-52, dir. 1963-65), Fla. Orange County Heart Assn., AMA, Am. Med. Women's Assn., Am. Acad. Med. Dirs., Fla. Med. Assn. (chmn. com. on mental retardation), Orange County Med. Assn., Fla. Pediatric Soc. (pres. 1952-53), Fla. Cleft Palate Assn. (counselor-at-large, sec.), Nat. Inst. Geneal. Rsch., Nat. Geneal. Soc., Assn. Profl. Genealogists, Tallahassee Geneal. Soc. Club: Governors. Home: 4158 Covenant Ln Tallahassee FL 32308-5765

MAGUIRE, HENRY CLINTON, JR., dermatologist; b. N.Y.C., May 4, 1928; s. Henry Clinton Sr. and Elsie (Smith) M.; m. Elise Avallon; children: Jean Emily, Henry Clinton III, Albert Mahler. BA in Philosophy, Princeton U., 1947; MD, U. Chgo., 1954. Diplomate Am. Bd. Dermatology. Resident in dermatology U. Pa. Hosp., Phila., 1958-61, assoc., 1961-64, asst. prof. dermatology, 1964-66; guest investigator Rockefeller U., N.Y.C., 1966-67; assoc. prof. dermatology Hahnemann Med. Coll., Phila., 1967-77; vis. scientist Inst. Cancer Research, Phila., 1972-75; prof. dermatology, microbiology and immunology Hahnemann Med. Coll., Phila., 1975-87, chmn. dermatology, 1979-87, adj. prof. microbiology and immunology, 1987—; with pigmented lesion clinic Fox Chase Cancer Ctr., Phila., 1979-84; sr. research investigator dept. pathology U. Pa., Phila., 1986-90; adj. clin. rsch. prof. oncology Thomas Jefferson U. Med. Sch., Phila., 1984-90, rsch. prof. oncology and dermatology, 1990—; adj. prof. U. Pa. Sch. Vet. Medicine, Phila., 1978—; mem. study sect. Exptl. Therapeutics 2 Nat. Cancer NIH, 1984-88; mem. editorial bd. Seminars in Oncology, 1983—; mem. biol. response modifier com. Eastern Coop. Oncology Group, 1983-86. Contbr. articles to profl. jours. Served to capt. U.S. Army, 1956-58. Fellow Am. Acad. Dermatology, Phila. Coll. Physicians, Phila. Dermatol. Soc. (past pres.); mem. Am. Assn. Cancer Rsch., Am. Assn. Immunology, Soc. Investigative Dermatology, Am. Soc. Microbiology (past chmn. program com. ea. br.), Sigma Xi. Avocations: baroque music, tennis. Home: 409 N Latches Ln Merion Station PA 19066-1730 Office: Thomas Jefferson U Med Sch Div Med Oncology Ste 1005 Curtis Bldg Philadelphia PA 19107

MAGUIRE, JOHN DAVID, university administrator, educator, writer; b. Montgomery, Ala., Aug. 7, 1932; s. John Henry and Clyde (Merrill) M.; m. Lillian Louise Parrish, Aug. 29, 1953; children: Catherine Merrill, Mary Elizabeth, Anne King. A.B. magna cum laude, Washington and Lee U., 1953, Litt.D. (hon.), 1979; Fulbright scholar, Edinburgh (Scotland) U., 1953-54; B.D. summa cum laude, Yale, 1956, Ph.D, 1960; postdoctoral research, Yale U. and U. Tübingen, Germany, 1964-65, U. Calif., Berkeley, 1968-69, Silliman U., Philippines, 1976-77; HLD (hon.), Transylvania U., 1990. Dir. Internat. Student Ctr., New Haven, 1956-58; mem. faculty Wesleyan U., Middletown, Conn., 1960-70; asso. provost Wesleyan U., 1967-68; vis. lectr. Pacific Sch. Religion and Grad. Theol. Union, Berkeley, 1968-69; pres. SUNY Coll. at Old Westbury, 1970-81, Claremont (Calif.) U. Ctr. and Grad. Sch., 1981—. Author: The Dance of the Pilgrim: A Christian Style of Life for Today, 1967; also numerous articles. Mem. Conn. adv. com. U.S. Commn. Civil Rights, 1961-70; participant White House Conf. on Civil Rights, 1966; advisor, permanent trustee and 1st chmn. bd. dirs. Martin Luther King Ctr. for Social Change, Ar'anta, 1968—; bd. dirs. Nassau County Health and Welfare Coun., 1975—; pres., 1974-76; trustee United Bd. Christian Higher Edn. in Asia, 1975-81, Inst. Internat. Edn., 1980-86, The Tomás Rivera Ctr., Claremont, Calif., 1984—, vice chmn., 1987—; Assn. Ind. Calif. Colls. and Univs., 1985—, chmn. 1990-92, mem. exec. com., 1992—, The Calif. Achievement Coun., 1985-94, chmn. 1990-94, Transylvania U. Bingham Trust, 1987—, Lincoln Found. and Lincoln Inst. of Land Policy, Inc., 1987-94, The JL Found., 1988—, The Bus. Enterprise Trust, 1989—, Ednl. Found. for African Ams., 1991—; founder, chair Calif. Red-Ox Consortium of Higher Edn., 1981—; bd. dirs. Assn. Am. Colls. and Univs., 1981-86, chmn., 1984-85; bd. dirs. Legal Def. and Edn. Fund. NAACP, 1991—, west coast div., 1981—, Thacher Sch., Ojai, Calif., 1982-94, vice chmn., 1986—, Salzburg Seminar, 1992—; mem. Am. Com. on U.S.-Soviet Rels., 1981-92, Blue Ribbon Calif. Commn. on Teaching Profession, 1984-86; mem. governing coun. Aspen Inst. Wye Faculty Seminar, 1984-94; mem. Coun. on Fgn. Rels., 1983—; adv. bd. RAND Ctr. Rsch. Immigration Policy, 1994—; mem. Pres.'s Adv. Coun. to Commn. on Calif. Master Plan for Higher Edn., 1986-87, L.A. Ednl. Alliance for Restructuring Now, 1992—, Calif. Bus. Higher Edn. Forum, 1992—. Recipient Julia A. Archibald High Scholarship award Yale Div. Sch., 1956; Day fellow Yale Grad. Sch., 1956-57; Kent fellow, 1957-60; Howard Found. postdoctoral fellow Brown U. Grad. Sch., 1964-65; Fenn lectr., 7 Asian countries, 1976-77; recipient Lincoln Prince Hall Masons' award outstanding contbns. human rights in Conn., 1965; E. Harris Harbison Gt. Tchr. prize Danforth Found., 1968. Fellow Soc. Values Higher Edn. (pres. 1974-81, bd. dirs. 1972-88); mem. Phi Beta Kappa, Omicron Delta Kappa. Democrat. Office: Claremont U Ctr & Grad Sch Office of Pres 160 E 10th St Claremont CA 91711-6165

MAGUIRE, JOHN PATRICK, investment company executive; b. New Britain, Conn., Apr. 1, 1917; s. John Patrick and Edna Frances (Cashen) M.; m. Mary-Emily Jones, Sept. 8, 1945; children: Peter Dunbar (dec.), Joan Guilford. Student, Holy Cross Coll., 1933-34; degree in bus. adminstrn. with distinction, Babson Inst., 1936; A.B. cum laude, Princeton U., 1941; J.D., Yale U., 1943; PhD (hon.), St. Bonaventure U., 1965. Bar: Conn. 1943, N.Y. 1944. Asso. Cravath, Swaine & Moore (and predecessor), N.Y.C., 1943-50, 52-54, ptnr. or dir. Forbes, Inc.; also mng. editor Investors Adv. Inst. 1951-52; asst. counsel Gen. Dynamics Corp., 1954-60, sec., 1962-87, v.p., 1981-87; sec., gen. counsel Tex. Butadiene and Chem. Corp., 1960-62; pres. J.P. Maguire Investment Advisors, 1987-95; mem. Fiduciary Asset Mgmt. Group. Mem. bd. govs. N.Y. Young Rep. Club, 1951-52; chmn. fin. and investment coms. St. Louis Art Mus., 1984-94; trustee St. Bonaventure U., 1965-71, Webster U., 1983-85, John Burroughs Sch. (chmn. investment com.)

1976-85. Mem. ABA. Clubs: Piping Rock (Locust Valley, L.I.); University (St. Louis); St. Louis Country; Princeton (St. Louis); Tiger Inn (Princeton). Home: 8 Chatfield Place Rd Saint Louis MO 63141-7850

MAGUIRE, MAUREEN K., health facility administrator; b. Boston, Aug. 19, 1940; d. Thomas A. and Katherine (DeMerritt) M. Diploma in nursing, Catherine Laboure, Dorchester, Mass., 1961; BSN, St. Joseph's Coll., Emmitsburg, Md., 1967; MS, Boston U., 1974; postgrad., Tulane U. RN, S.C. Nurse clinician Mass. Gen. Hosp., Boston; assoc. hosp. dir. Tulane U. Hosp., New Orleans; v.p. nursing Morristown (N.J.) Meml. Hosp.; dir. patient care svcs. Med. U. S.C., Charleston; health care mgmt. cons. PCS Group. Contbr. articles to med. jours. Mem. ANA (cert. nursing adminstr.), Nat. League for Nursing (bd. dirs.), Am. Orgn. Nurse Execs., S.C. League for Nursing, Charleston Orgn. Nurse Execs. (pres.), Am. Coll. Health Care Execs. (cert.), Group Mgmt. Orgn., Charleston C. of C.

MAGUIRE, PATRICIA, healthcare administrator; b. Boston, Aug. 15, 1949; d. Justin and Anne (Colby) M. RN, Lawrence Meml. Hosp., Medford, Mass., 1970; BS magna cum laude, Boston Coll., 1979; MSN, U. Wash., 1983. Lic. nurse, Mass., Wash. Staff nurse coronary care unit Lawrence Meml. Hosp., Medford, Mass., 1970-71; staff nurse Beth Israel Hosp., Boston, 1971-72; nursing supr. Beth Israel Hosp., 1972-73, 76-78, head nurse med. nursing svcs., 1973-76, staff nurse emergency unit, 1977-78; head nurse Phillips House Mass. Gen. Hosp., Boston, 1979-80; primary nurse oncology unit, nursing clin. coord. Virginia Mason Med. Ctr., Seattle, 1980-83, nursing fin. dir., 1983-84, asst. dir. nursing svcs., 1985-87, assoc. adminstr., 1987—; conductor seminars in field; lectr. in field; cons. in field. Contbr. articles to profl. jours. Mem. Am. Nurses Assn., Am. Orgn. Nurse Execs., King County Nurses Assn., Lawrence Meml. Hosp. Sch. Nursing Alumni Assn., U. Wash. Sch. Nursing Alumni Assn., Wash. Orgn. Nurse Execs. (mem. fin. com.), Wash. Nurses Assn., Sigma Theta Tau.

MAGUIRE, ROBERT ALAN, Slavic languages and literatures educator; b. Canton, Mass., June 21, 1930; s. Frederick William and Ruth Spalding (Plunkett) M. A.B., Dartmouth Coll., 1951; M.A., cert., Russian Inst., Columbia U., 1953, Ph.D., 1961. Instr. Russian Duke U., 1958-60; asst. prof. Russian Dartmouth Coll., 1960-62, dir. NDEA Russian Lang. Inst., 1962; faculty Sch. Internat. Affairs and Harriman Inst. Columbia U., N.Y.C., 1962—, asst. prof. Russian lang. and lit., 1962-66; assoc. prof. Columbia U., 1966-70, prof., 1970—; Bakhmeteff prof. Russian studies Columbia U., N.Y.C., 1992—; chmn. dept. Slavic langs. Columbia U., 1977-83, 85-88; vis. lectr. Ind. U., 1961, 66, 69; vis. prof. U. Ill., 1976, Yale U., New Haven, 1984, Princeton (N.J.) U., 1991-92; vis. fellow St. Antony's Coll., Oxford (Eng.) U., 1971-72; mem. adv. bd. (Sr. Fulbright-Hays Program), 1971-74, NEH; mem. selection bd. Internat. Research and Exchanges Bd., 1971-74, 77, Council on Internat. Ednl. Exchange, 1973, 78, 80; mem. planning and adv. bd. Am. Council Learned Socs.-USSR Acad. of Sci. Commn. on the Humanities and Social Scis., 1982; editor Soviet-Am. Lit. Project, Duke U./Leningrad U. Press; adv. com. on preservation of Russian periodicals N.Y. Pub. Library; mem. vis. com. dept. Slavic langs., Harvard U., 1988—, chmn., 1990—; selection com. Nat. Humanities Ctr. Author: Red Virgin Soil: Soviet Literature in the 1920's, 1968, 2d edit. 1987, Gogol from the Twentieth Century; Eleven Essays, 1974, 2d edit. 1976, and others; translator: Gogol (V.V. Gippius), 1981 2d edit., 1989; co-translator: Russian Short Stories, II, 1965, The Survivor and Other Poems (Tadeusz Rozewicz), 1976, Petersburg (Andrei Bely), 1978, 80, 83, Building the Barricade (Anna Swirszczynska), 1979, Sounds, Feelings, Thoughts: Seventy Poems (Wislawa Szymborska), 1981, 89, Exploring Gogol, 1994; mem. editorial bd.: Teaching Lang. through Lit, 1965-77; mng. editor, 1978-88; mem. editorial bd.: Slavic Rev., 1966-69, 82-89, Polish Rev., 1980-88; mem. editorial adv. bd.: Princeton Essays in Literature, 1972-77; contbr. articles to profl. jours. Sponsoring com. Leo Tolstoy Mus. and Research Library, 1979—; bd. dirs. Chamber Music Conf. and Composers' Forum of the East, 1983-93. Served with U.S. Army, 1953-55. Ford Found. fellow, 1957-58; Am. Council Learned Socs. fellow, 1967; Guggenheim fellow, 1969-70; named laureate Assn. Authors and Theatrical Composers, Warsaw, Poland, 1981. Mem. Am. Assn. Advancement of Slavic Studies (dir. 1977-79), Am. Assn. Tchrs. Slavic and East European Langs., Nat. Assn. Scholars, MLA (exec. com. div. on Slavic and East European langs. 1986-92), Polish Inst. Arts and Scis., PEN, Kosciuszko Found., Irish-Am. Cultural Inst., Gogol Soc. Am. (pres. 1986). Roman Catholic (parish coun. 1979-89). Home: PO Box 69 Davenport Center NY 13751 Office: Dept Slavic Langs Columbia U New York NY 10027

MAGUIRE, ROBERT EDWARD, retired public utility executive; b. Somerville, Mass., Jan. 25, 1928; s. Hugh Edward and Alice Theresa (Garrity) M.; m. Leona Rosemarie Beaulieu, June 21, 1952; children—Lynne Marie, Steven Francis, Judith Anne, David Robert. B.S. in Chem. Engring. Northeastern U., 1950, B.B.A. in Engring. and Mgmt., 1953. Vice pres., mgr. Lawrence Gas Co., Mass., 1960-68; vice pres., mgr. Mystic Valley Gas Co., Malden, Mass., 1968-70; v.p., regional exec. Mass. Electric Co., North Andover, 1970-71; v.p. New Eng. Power Service Co., Westboro, Mass., 1971-72, New Eng. Electric System, Westboro, Mass., 1972-75; exec. v.p., trustee Eastern Utilities Assocs., Boston, 1975-91. Contbr. to Gas mag. 1959. Vice chmn. Greater Lawrence United Fund Budget Com., 1967; treas., dir. ARC, Lawrence, 1966; trustee Essex-Broadway Savs. Bank, Lawrence, 1966-78; pres., dir. Greater Lawrence C. of C., 1962-64. Recipient Paul Revere Leadership medal Boston C. of C., 1963. Roman Catholic. Club: Lanam (Andover, Mass.). Home: 22 Ivy Ln Andover MA 01810-5018

MAGUIRE, ROBERT FRANCIS, III, real estate investor; b. Portland, Oreg., Apr. 18, 1935; s. Robert Francis Jr. and Jean (Shepard) M.; m. Susan Reddan. B.A., UCLA, 1960. Vice pres. Security Pacific Nat. Bank, L.A., 1960-64; chmn. Maguire Thomas Ptnrs., L.A., 1964—. Chmn. bd. dirs. Los Angeles County Mus. Art; trustee UCLA Found., Bard Coll.; bd. dirs. St. John's Hosp., Music Ctr. Bd. Govs., Calif. Clubs: California (Los Angeles); Valley (Montecito, Calif.), L.A. Country.

MAGURNO, RICHARD PETER, lawyer; b. Suffern, N.Y., June 29, 1943; s. Eugene and Rose (Foresta) M. BS, Georgetown U., 1964; MS, U. Wis., 1965; JD, Fordham U., 1968. Bar: N.Y. 1970, Fla. 1982, U.S. Supreme Ct. 1974, U.S. Ct. Appeals (2d, 5th, 11th cirs.) 1976, U.S. Dist. Ct. (so. and ea. dists.) N.Y. 1979. Atty. Eastern Air Lines, N.Y.C., 1970-73, sr. atty., 1973-76, gen. atty., 1976-79; dir. legal Eastern Air Lines, Miami, Fla., 1980, v.p. legal, asst. sec., 1980-84; gen. counsel, sr. v.p. legal, sec. Eastern Air Lines, 1984-88; ptnr. Lord Day & Lord, Barrett Smith, 1989-94; gen. counsel, sr. v.p. legal Trans World Airlines, St. Louis, 1994—. Author: Romantic Suffern, 1773-1973, 1973. Served in Peace Corps, 1968-69. Mem. ABA, Bar Assn. City of N.Y., Fla. Bar Assn. Democrat. Roman Catholic.

MAH, FENG-HWA, economics educator; b. Kaifeng, Honan, China, Mar. 25, 1922; s. Chiao-Hsiang and Wen-Chieh (Yang) M.; m. Judy Jiann Ting, Sept. 14, 1975. B.L. in Econs., Nat. Peking U., 1947; M.A. in Econs., U. Mich., 1956, Ph.D., 1959. Research asst. U. Mich., Ann Arbor, 1955-58; research fellow U. Calif.-Berkeley, 1959-60; asst. prof. Calif. State U.-Los Angeles, 1960-61; asst. prof. U. Wash., Seattle, 1961-64, assoc. prof., 1964-76, co-chmn. China Program, 1975-83, prof. econs., 1976-87, prof. emeritus, 1987—. Author: Communist China's Foreign Trade: Price Structure and Behavior 1955-1959, 1963, The Foreign Trade of Mainland China, 1971, Literary Essays of Mah Feng-hwa (in Chinese), 1993; contbr. numerous articles on Chinese economy to profl. jours. Orla B. Taylor fellow U. Mich., 1958-59; Fulbright faculty research fellow, 1967-68; Social Sci. Research Council grantee, 1962-65, 71. Mem. Am. Econs. Assn., Assn. Comparative Econ. Studies, Assn. Asian Studies, Phi Kappa Phi. Address: PO Box 15311 Seattle WA 98115-0311

MAH, RICHARD SZE HAO, chemical engineering educator; b. Shanghai, China, Dec. 16, 1934; came to U.S., 1961, naturalized, 1972; s. Fabian Soh Pai and E. Shang (Chang) M.; m. Shopin Stella Lee, Aug. 31, 1962; 1 child, Christopher. B.Sc., U. Birmingham, 1957; D.I.C., Ph.D.; Leverhulme student, Imperial Coll. Sci. and Tech., U. London, 1961; DSc in Engring., U. London, 1992. Jr. chem. engr. A.P.V. Co., Ltd., Crawley, Sussex, Eng., 1957-58; research fellow U. Minn., 1961-63; research engr. Union Carbide Corp. Tech. Center, South Charleston, W.Va., 1963-67; group head/sr. project analyst Esso Maths. & Systems, Inc., Florham Park, N.J., 1967-72; assoc. prof. chem. engring. Northwestern U., Evanston, Ill., 1972-77; prof.

Northwestern U., 1977—; trustee CACHE Corp., Cambridge, Mass., 1974—, sec., 1978-80, v.p., 1982-84, pres., 1984-86; cons. Argonne Nat. Lab., 1975-78, DuPont de Nemours & Co., 1981-89. Contbr. articles to profl. jours. Fellow Am. Inst. Chem. Engrs. (chmn. systems and process design com. 1978-80, chmn. cast div. programming bd. 1979-81, Computing in Chem. Engring. award 1981, E.W. Thiele award 1990); mem. Am. Chem. Soc., Am. Soc. Engring. Edn., Am. Soc. Quality Control (Youden prize 1986), Tau Beta Pi. Mem. United Ch. of Christ. Office: Northwestern U Dept Chem Engring Evanston IL 60208 *Live every day as if it is our last. Each day of life is a marvelous gift of God. Let us count all our blessings and put to use every minute of our day and every resource of our life. Every morning let us marvel at the miraculous world which He has created for us. Every night let us thank God for giving us another day of fulfillment and go to sleep with the expectation of another great day of miracles for tomorrow.*

MAHA, GEORGE EDWARD, research facility administrator, consultant; b. Elgin, Ill., Feb. 15, 1924; s. George William and Agnes (Lux) M.; m. Mary Andrea Rasmussen, June 6, 1953; children: George, Richard, Mary, Andrea, Sarah. BS, U. Notre Dame, 1950; MD, St. Louis U., 1953. Diplomate Am. Bd. Internal Medicine. Intern Mt. Carmel Mercy Hosp., Detroit, 1953-54; resident in internal medicine VA Hosp., St. Louis, 1954-55; fellow St. Louis U. Hosp., 1955-56; NIH fellow in cardiology Duke U., Durham, N.C., 1956-58; chief outpatient svc. VA Hosp., Pitts., 1962-64; staff physician FDA, Washington, 1964-66; exec. dir. clin. rsch. Merck, Sharp & Dohme Rsch. Labs., West Point, Pa., 1966-88; asst. to pres. Clin. Rsch. Internat., Research Triangle Park, N.C., 1988-89; med. dir. Burroughs Wellcome, Research Triangle Park, 1989-91; cons., 1991—; chmn. med. sect. Pharm. Mfr.'s Assn., Washington, 1982-83, mem. steering com., 1975-84. Contbr. 17 articles to profl. jours. Tech. sgt. USAF, 1943-46, PTO. Recipient Mosby award St. Louis U., 1953. Mem. AMA, AAAS, Am. Coll. Cardiology, N.Y. Acad. Sci., Am. Heart Assn., Am. Soc. Clin. Pharmacology and Therapeutics, Alpha Omega Alpha. Roman Catholic. Avocations: reading, fishing, tennis. Home: 313 Marina Bay 2550 Harbourside Dr Longboat Key FL 34228-4170

MAHADEVAN, KUMAR, marine laboratory director, researcher; b. Madras, Tamilnadu, India, Sept. 29, 1948; came to U.S., 1971; s. Sockalingam Ponnusamy and Pankajam (Nadar) M.; m. Linda Claire Goggin, Sept. 27, 1980; children: Andrew, Alexander, Chad, Vijayan. BS, Madras U., 1967; MS, Annamalai U., Chidambaram, India, 1971; PhD, Fla. State U., 1977. Instr. Chingleput (India) Med. Coll., 1967-68, Lakshman's Coll., Madras, 1968-69; rsch. asst. Fla. State U., Tallahassee, 1971-75; staff scientist Conservation Cons., Inc., Palmetto, Fla., 1975-78; sr. scientist Mote Marine Lab., Sarasota, Fla., 1978-79, dir. dir., 1979-86, interim co-dir., 1984, exec. dir., 1986—; mem. Coun. on Ocean Affairs, Washington, 1989-91, steering com. Gulf of Mex. Program, Atlanta, 1988—; mem. South Atlantic and Gulf States Coastal Protection Commn., 1990—; vice chmn. NOAA Marine Rsch. Bd., Gulf of Mex., 1992—. Contbr. articles to profl. publs. Mem. sch. adv. bd., Sarasota, 1988-89; mem. tech. adv. bd. Myakka River, Sarasota, 1987-90; legis. liason Parents Assn. of Sarasota Schs., 1988-89; bd. dirs. Jason Found. for Edn., 1991—. Nat. Merit scholar Univ. Grants Commn., India, 1969-71. Mem. N.Am. Benthological Soc., Oceanography Soc., World Aquaculture Soc., Deep Sea Biol. Soc. (hon.), Fla. Acad. Scis. (councillor 1975), So. Assn. Marine Labs. (pres. 1990, exec. bd. 1986-91), Assn. Marine Labs. of Caribbean (pres. 1987-88, exec. bd. 1984—), Nat. Assn. Marine Labs. (pres. 1994—), Sigma Xi. Republican. Avocations: racquetball, fishing, gardening. Office: Mote Marine Lab 1600 Ken Thompson Pky Sarasota FL 34236-1096

MAHAFFEY, GARY JOHN, architect; b. Waseca, Minn., Apr. 2, 1940; s. Jerome Charles and Margaret Minnie (Kopischke) M.; m. Marlene M. Mahaffey, Sept. 28, 1974 (div. 1987); 1 child, Shannon Lee. BArch, U. Minn., 1963; M in Environ. Design, Yale U., 1970. Registered architect, Minn. Sr. v.p. Leonard Parker Assocs., Architects, Mpls., 1964-69, 70—; staff architect Roche-Dinkeloo Assocs., Architects, New Haven, Conn., 1969-70. Served with USNG, 1964-70. Mem. Minn. Soc. AIA (sec. 1985-87). Avocations: sailing, carpentry. Home: 3844 Thomas Ave S Minneapolis MN 55410-1232 Office: The Leonard Parker Assocs 430 Oak Grove St Minneapolis MN 55403-3234

MAHAFFEY, REDGE ALLAN, movie producer, director, writer; b. Bethesda, Md., Dec. 15, 1949; s. George Newton and Lila Katherine (Drum) M.; m. Ellen Cecilia Cranston, May 30, 1973 (div. Dec. 1980); m. Patricia Jane Guy, Apr. 29, 1984 (div. Sept. 1994); children: Travis Guy, Morgan Nicole; m. Veronica Bird, Sept. 1994; children: Ryan Alexander, Ramsey Blake. BS, U. Md., 1971, MS, 1973, PhD, 1976. NRC postdoctoral fellow Nat. Acad. of Scis., Washington, 1976-77; research physicist Naval Research Lab., Washington, 1977-78; sr. research physicist Sachs/Freeman Assocs., Bladensburg, Md., 1978-79; dir. research Sachs/Freeman Assocs., Bowie, Md., 1979-81; sr. v.p., sec., treas. Sachs/Freeman Assocs., Landover, Md., 1981-91, also bd. dirs., 1985—; mng. ptnr. Ramsway Films, Ltd., 1991—; instr. George Washington U., Washington, 1979-80, Prince George's Coll., 1987; pres. Capitol Contracts, Bowie, 1981-83. Author: A Higher Education, 1989, Me, Myself and I, 1992, Deadly Rivals, 1992; exec. prodr., writer Deadly Rivals, Quest for the Delta Knight, 1993; prodr., writer, dir. Life 101, 1995; contbr. articles on lasers and particle beams to sci. jours., also short stories, essays and poems to mags.; patentee laser, x-rays and particle beams. Recipient Research Publ. award Naval Research Lab., 1978, 1st Place Novel Internat. Lit. Awards, 1988. Mem. IEEE, Am. Phys. Soc., MENSA, Intertel, Nat. Writer's Club, Internat. Platform Assn., Internat. Soc. Phil. Enquiry, Writer's Assn. Anne Arundel County, Bethesda Writer's Ctr., Inst. Noetic Scis. Republican. Club: Sea Dragons Martial Arts(Washington) (treas. 1984-85, instr. 1987-91). Avocations: martial arts, softball. Office: Ramsway Ltd 738 Intrepid Way Davidsonville MD 21035

MAHAL, TAJ (HENRY ST. CLAIR FREDERICKS), composer, musician; b. Mass., May 17, 1942; s. Henry St. Clair and Mildred (Shields) Fredericks; m. Inshirah Geter, Jan. 23, 1976; children: Aya, Taj, Gahmelah, Ahmen, Deva, Nani. BA, U. Mass., Amherst, 1964. Ind. musician, composer, rec. artist, 1964—. Early appearances at Club 47, Boston; rec. artist with Columbia, Warner Brothers, Gramavision labels; tours throughout U.S., Europe, Australia, including State Dept.-sponsored tour of Africa; composer: (album) Taj, Like Never Before, Dancin' the Blues-Private Music (Grammy nomination traditional blues 1993), (film soundtracks) Sounder, Sounder II, Brothers (Best Ethnic Music award, Bay Area Musics Awards 1979), (TV shows) Ewoks, The Man Who Broke a Thousand Chains, Brer Rabbit, The Hot Spot (Grammy nomination as Best Contemporary Blues Album 1990); actor: (films) King of Ragtime, Sounder, Sounder II., (theater) Mule Bone: assoc. artist, Mark Taper Forum, L.A., 1992—. Office: care Folklore Inc 1671 Appian Way Santa Monica CA 90401-3258*

MAHAN, CLARENCE, retired govenment official, writer; b. Dayton, Ohio, Jan. 1, 1939; s. Clarence Mahan and Elsie (Crouch) Diltz; m. Suky Mahan, May 27, 1962; children: Sean, Christiane Elizabeth. BA, U. Md., 1963; MA, Am. U., 1968; MBA, Syracuse U., 1969. Dep. comptroller U.S. Army, Japan, 1974-76; dep. chief program and budget Defense Commn. Agy., Arlington, Va., 1976; aide Asst. Sec. Army, Washington, 1976-77; chief operating appropriations Dept. AF, Washington, 1979-80; dir. fin. and acctg. Dept. Energy, Washington, 1980-81, dep. comptroller, 1981-82; dir. fiscal and contracts mgmt. EPA, Washington, 1982-83, dep. comptroller, 1983-85, dir. Rsch. Mgmt. Mgmt. Office, 1985-95; instr., lectr. in field. Contbr. articles to profl. jours. and hort. mags. With U.S. Army, 1959-62, Korea. Mem. Am. Iris Soc. (bd. dirs., 2d v.p. 1991—), Hist. Iris Preservation Soc. (pres. 1991-93), Soc. Japanese Irises (pres. 1989-92), Reblooming Iris Soc. (bd. dirs. 1986-94). Democrat. Home: 7311 Churchill Rd Mc Lean VA 22101-2001

MAHAN, GERALD DENNIS, physics educator, researcher; b. Portland, Oreg., Nov. 24, 1937; s. Thomas Finley and Julia Kay (Swails) M.; m. Sally Ann Spaugh, Feb. 20, 1965; children—Christopher Parker, Susan Thayer, Roy Finley. A.B., Harvard U., 1959; Ph.D. in Physics, U. Calif.-Berkeley, 1964. Research physicist Gen. Electric Co., Schenectady, 1963-67; part-time Gen. Electric Co., 1967-84; assoc. prof. physics U. Oreg., Eugene, 1967-73; prof. physics Ind. U., Bloomington, 1973-82; disting. prof. Ind. U., 1982-84; disting. prof. physics U. Tenn., Knoxville; disting. scientist Oak Ridge Nat. Lab.; guest prof. Niels Bohr Inst., Copenhagen, 1977-78. Author: Many-Particle Physics, 1981; contbr. numerous articles on physics to profl. jours.

Alfred Sloan fellow, 1968-70. Fellow Am. Phys. Soc. Office: U Tenn Dept Physics Knoxville TN 37996

MAHAN, JAMES CAMERON, lawyer; b. El Paso, Tex., Dec. 16, 1943; m. Eileen Agnes Casale, Jan. 13, 1968; 1 child, James Cameron Jr. BA, U. Charleston, 1965; JD, Vanderbilt U., 1973. Bar: Nev. 1974, U.S. Dist. Ct. Nev. 1974, U.S. Ct. Appeals (9th cir.) 1975, U.S. Tax Ct. 1980, U.S. Supreme Ct. 1980. Assoc. Lee & Beasey, Las Vegas, Nev., 1974-75; mem. firm John Peter Lee Ltd., Las Vegas, 1975-82; sr. ptnr. Mahan & Ellis, Chartered, Las Vegas, 1982—. With USN, 1966-69. Office: Mahan & Ellis Chartered 510 S 9th St Las Vegas NV 89101-7011

MAHAN, JOHN K., dean; b. Youngstown, Ohio, July 22, 1936; s. Kenneth A. and Isabell (Lavery) M.; m. Nancy Moran, Aug. 4, 1967; children: Kevin, Sean, O'Dea. BA in Philosophy, Duquesne U., 1958; MA in English, Kent State U., 1968, PhD in Higher Edn. Adminstrn., 1985. Parole officer Ohio Youth Commn., Toledo, 1962-64; sales mgr. C.W. Tennant, Chgo., Ill., 1964-66; english tchr. Boardman High Sch., Youngstown, Ohio, 1967-69; asst. dir. Kent State U., Ashtabula, Ohio, 1969-71, asst. dean, 1971-85, dean, 1985—; author dir. English Festival Kent State U. Funded Projects, 1986, 87, 88, A Jefferson Meeting, 1988; author co-dir. Human Values In A Changing Soc., Kent State U. Funded Projects, 1980. Pres. Leadership Ashtabula County, Jefferson, Ohio, 1990; charter pres. Literacy Vols. of Am., Ashtabula, 1986; campaign dir. Ashtabula County Children's Svcs. Levy, 1985; mem. Astabula County ITV Coun., Jefferson, 1990—, CDC Task Force on Unemployment, 1992-93, Astabula Found. Task Force on Edn., 1992-93, Private Industry Coun., 1993—. With USAF, 1960-62. Recipient Outstanding Adult and Continuing Edn. Contbr. award N.E. Ohio Assn. for Adult Continuing Edn., 1991. Avocations: swimming, gardening, bridge. Home: 1707 Walnut Blvd Ashtabula OH 44004-2816 Office: Kent State U Office of Dean 3325 W 13th St Ashtabula OH 44004-2205

MAHANES, DAVID JAMES, JR., retired distillery executive; b. Lexington, Ky., June 19, 1923; s. David James and Ethel (Brock) M.; m. Dorothy Jean Richardson, Oct. 28, 1950; 1 child, David James III. BS, U. Ky., 1947; MBA, Harvard U., 1950. Regional mgr. Jack Daniel Distillery, Nashville, 1960-65, v.p., 1965-70; sr. v.p., 1970-71, exec. v.p., 1971-85, pres., 1985-88, chmn. bd. dirs.; chmn. bd. dirs. Early Times Distillery Co., Can. Mist Distilling Co., Thoroughbred Plastics Co. Lt. inf. AUS, 1943-45, ETO; lt. col. AG ret. Runnerup as outstanding sales exec. Gallagher Report, 1982. Mem. SAR (pres. Andrew Jackson chpt.), Soc. Colonial Wars in Tenn. (gov., dep. gov. gen.), English Speaking Union, Res. Officers Assn., So. Srs. Golf Assn., Belle Meade Country Club, Beaver Creek Club, Exch. Club, Tenn. Profl. Golfers Assn. (hon.), Kappa Alpha, Beta Gamma Sigma. Republican. Presbyterian. Home: 104 Adams Park Nashville TN 37205-4702

MAHANTHAPPA, KALYANA THIPPERUDRAIAH, physicist, educator; b. Hirehalli, Mysore, India, Oct. 29, 1934; s. Kalyana and Thippamma (Maddanappa) T.; m. Prameela Talkerappa, Oct. 30, 1961; children: Nagesh, Rudresh, Mahesh. BSc, Central Coll. Bangalore, India, 1954; MSc, Delhi U., 1956; PhD (Faculty Arts and Scis. fellow), Harvard, 1961. Research assoc. U. Cal. at Los Angeles, 1961-63; asst. prof. U. Pa., Phila., 1963-66; mem. Inst. Advanced Study, Princeton, N.J., 1964-65; assoc. prof. physics U. Colo., Boulder, 1966-69; prof. U. Colo., 1969—, faculty research fellow, 1970-71, 76-77, 83-84, 93-94; vis. prof./scientist U. Rome, 1970, Internat. Ctr. for Theoretical Physics, 1971, Cambridge U., 1976-77; cons. Aerojet-Gen., L.A., 1962-63; dir. Summer Inst. Theoretical Physics, Boulder, 1968-69, NATO Advanced Study Inst. in Elem. Particles, 1979, NATO Advanced Rsch. Workshop on Superstrings, 1987; gen. dir. Theoretical Advanced Study Inst. in Particle Physics, 1989—; sr. vis. rsch. fellow Imperial Coll., London, 1983-84. Contbr. articles to profl. jours. Fellow Am. Phys. Soc.; mem. AAAS, Sigma Xi. Research theoretical high energy and elementary particle physics. Home: 2865 Darley Ave Boulder CO 80303-6307

MAHARIDGE, DALE DIMITRO, journalist, educator; b. Cleve., Oct. 24, 1956; s. Steve and Joan (Kopfstein) M. Student, Cleve. State U., 1974-75. Free-lance reporter various publs., Cleve., 1976; reporter The Gazette, Medina, Ohio, 1977-78; free-lance reporter Cleve. Plain Dealer, 1978-80; reporter The Sacramento Bee, 1980-91; lectr. Stanford U., Palo Alto, Calif., 1992—. Author: Journey to Nowhere: The Saga of the New Underclass, 1985, And Their Children After Them, 1989 (Pulitzer Prize for gen. nonfiction 1990), The Last Great American Hobo, 1993; contbr. articles to profl. jours. Nieman fellow Harvard U., 1988; grantee Pope Found., 1994, Freedom Forum, 1995. Democrat. Office: Stanford U Dept Comms Bldg 120 Stanford CA 94305

MAHER, BILL, talk show host, comedian, producer; b. N.Y.C., Jan. 20, 1956; s. Bill and Julie (Berman) M. BA, Cornell U., 1978. Creator, host Politically Incorrect, HBO, N.Y.C. Performances include (theatre) Seymour Glick is Alive But Sick (Steve Allen); (stand-up) The Bob Monkhouse Show, Late Night with David Letterman, The Tonight Show Anniversary Show, The Tonight Show, HBO Spl., 1989, 92; (TV shows) Steve Allen's Music Room, Alice, Sara, Max Headroom, Hard Knocks, Newhart, Murder, She Wrote, The Midnight Hour, Say What?; (TV movies) Out of Time, Rags to Riches, Club Med; (films) D.C. Cab, Rat Boy, House II, Cannibal Women in the Avocado Jungle of Death, Pizza Man; author: (novel) True Story, 1994. Recipient Cableace award Nat. Acad. Cable Programming, 1990, Cableace award for best talk show series, 1995, Cableace award for best talk show host, 1995. Office: HBO, Politically Incorrect 514 W 57th St New York NY 10019

MAHER, BRENDAN ARNOLD, psychology educator, editor; b. Widnes, Eng., Oct. 31, 1924; came to U.S., 1955; s. Thomas F. and Agnes (Power) M.; m. Winifred Barbara Brown, Aug. 27, 1952; children: Rebecca, Thomas, Nicholas, Liam, Niall. B.A. with honours, U. Manchester, Eng., 1950; M.A., Ohio State U., 1951, Ph.D., 1954; student, U. Ill. Med. Sch., 1952-53; A.M. (hon.), Harvard, 1972. Diplomate: Am. Bd. Examiners in Profl. Psychology. Psychologist Her Majesty's Prison, Wakefield, Eng., 1954-55; instr. Ohio State U., 1955-56; asst. prof. Northwestern U., 1956-58; asso. prof. La. State U., 1958-60; lectr. Harvard, 1960-64; chmn. Center Research Personality, 1962-64; prof. U. Wis., 1964-67, 71-72; vis. fellow U. Copenhagen, 1966-67, vis. fellow and research scientist, 1979; prof. psychology Brandeis U., 1967-72; dean Brandeis U. (Grad. Sch.), 1969-71, dean faculty, 1971-72; prof. Harvard U., 1972—, chmn. dept. psychology and social relations, 1973-78, chmn. dept. psychology, 1987-89, dean Grad. Sch. Arts and Scis., 1989-92; assoc. psychologist McLean Hosp., Belmont, Mass., 1968-77; psychologist McLean Hosp., 1977-84; cons. in medicine Peter Bent Brigham Hosp., Boston, 1977-85; cons. in psychology Mass. Gen. Hosp., 1977—. Author: Principles of Psychopathology, 1966, Introduction to Research in Psychopathology, 1970; editor: Progress in Experimental Personality Research, 1964-87, Jour. Cons. and Clin. Psychology, 1972-78; cons. editor: Rev. of Personality and Social Psychology, Clin. Psychology Rev. Served with Brit. Royal Navy, 1943-47. Fellow AAAS, Am. Psychol. Soc.; mem. Brit. Psychol. Assn. (chartered psychologist U.K.), Soc. Rsch. in Psychopathology (pres. 1985-87). Office: Harvard U William James Hall Cambridge MA 02138 also: Giffords Island, Mahone Bay, NS Canada

MAHER, DANIEL CARL, accountant; b. Detroit, Jan. 10, 1954; s. James Michael and Margaret Caroline (Grogan) M.; m. Marilyn Ann Capo, June 27, 1984. BBA, U. Mich., 1976, MBA, 1992. CPA, Mich. Ptnr. Deloitte & Touche, Detroit, 1976—. Treas. Delta Chi Alumni, Ann Arbor, Mich., 1980—; bd. dir. United Way, Detroit, 1987—. Mem. AICPA, Mich. Assn. CPA's, Detroit Athletic Club. Office: Deloitte & Touche 100 Renaissance Ctr Ste 31 Detroit MI 48243-1006

MAHER, DAVID L., drug store company executive; b. Iowa City, 1939. Grad., U. Iowa, 1964. Chmn., pres, chief exec. officer Am. Drug Stores, Inc.; chmn. Osco Drug, Inc. (subs. Am. Drug Stores, Inc.). Office: American Drug Stores Inc 1818 Swift Dr Oak Brook IL 60521-1576

MAHER, DAVID WILLARD, lawyer; b. Aug. 14, 1934, Chgo.; s. Chauncey Carter and Martha (Peppers) M.; BA Harvard 1955, LLB, 1959; m. Jill Waid Armagnac, Dec. 20, 1954; children: Philip Armagnac, Julia Armagnac. Bar: N.Y. 1960, Ill. 1961; pvt. practice Boston, N.Y.C., 1958-60;

assoc. Kirkland & Ellis, and predecessor firm, 1960-65, ptnr. 1966-78; ptnr. Reuben & Proctor, 1978-86, Isham, Lincoln and Beale, 1986-88, Sonnenschein, Nath & Rosenthal, 1988—; gen. counsel BBB Chgo. and No. Ill.; lectr. DePaul U. Sch. Law, 1973-79, Law Sch. of Loyola U., Chgo., 1980-84. Mem. vis. com. to the Div. Sch., U. Chgo., 1986—. Served to 2d lt. USAF, 1955-56. Fellow Am. Bar Found. (lifetime); mem. ABA, Ill. Bar Assn., Chgo. Bar Assn., Bull Valley Hunt Club, Chgo. Lit. Club, Union League Club, Tavern, Club. Roman Catholic. Home: 311 W Belden Ave Chicago IL 60614-3817 Office: Sonnenschein Nath Rosenthal 233 S Wacker Dr Ste 8000 Chicago IL 60606-6404

MAHER, FRANCESCA MARCINIAK, lawyer; b. Chgo., Oct. 27, 1957; d. Edward Allen and Virginia Cecilia (Volini) Marciniak; m. Gary John Maher, July 19, 1986. BA in Econs. cum. laude, Loyola U., Chgo., 1978, JD cum laude, 1981. Bar: Ill. 1981; U.S. Dist. Ct. (no. dist.) Ill. 1981. Assoc. Mayer, Brown & Platt, Chgo., 1981-84, ptnr., 1989—; dir. Ill. Securities Dept., Chgo., 1984-87; mem. N.Am. Adminstrn. Com., Ill. Sec. State's Securities Law Adv. Com., 1991—. Bd. dirs. Ill. Humane Soc., 1990—. Mem. ABA, Chgo. Bar Assn. (securities law com. 1991-92), Ill. Bar Assn., Nat. Assn. Securities Dealers (adv. com. state regulation 1988—). Roman Catholic. Office: Mayer Brown & Platt 190 S LaSalle St Chicago IL 60603-3441

MAHER, JAMES R., laboratory administrator. Pres., ceo Nat. Health Lab. Inc., La Jolla, Calif. Office: National Health Labs Inc 4225 Executive Sq Ste 800 La Jolla CA 92037-1485

MAHER, JOHN FRANCIS, personnel executive; b. Sea Cliff, N.Y., Jan. 23, 1932; s. John Francis and Anna Elizabeth (Flannery) M.; B.S. in Indsl. Relations, Syracuse U., 1958, M.A. in Communications, 1968; m. Jane Esther LesVeaux, Feb. 7, 1957; children—Kathleen, Lynn, Tracy, Joann, John. Accredited Am. Soc. Personnel Adminstrs. Employee relations sepcialist Gen. Electric Co., Syracuse, N.Y., 1960-65; dir. job devel. employment Urban League Syracuse, 1965-67; indsl. relations specialist Singer Co., Auburn, N.Y., 1967-68; dir. human resources and govtl. affairs, corp. staff Garlock Inc., Rochester, N.Y., mgr. orgnl. devel., corp. staff, 1968-72, v.p. personnel, mech. rubber div., Palmyra, N.Y., 1972-75, dir. organizational devel. corp. staff, Rochester, 1975-78; mgr. indsl. relations Graham Mfg. Co., Batavia, N.Y., 1978—; v.p. indsl. relations Graham Corp., 1986—; adj. prof. bus. and mgmt. Rochester Inst. Tech., 1969—; adj. prof. mgmt. Genesee Community Coll., 1977—; clin. lectr. SUNY, Buffalo, 1975—; instr. Cornell U., 1982—; pres. J.F.M. Assocs., mgmt. cons.; arbitrator, mediator ctr. for dispute resolution Am. Arbitration Assn., Rochester, 1987—; dir. R.W. Nelson Inc. Mem. planning bd. Town of Perinton (N.Y.), 1973-74, chmn., pres. Perinton Residents Orgn., 1971-75; bd. dirs. Genesee County United Way. Served with USAF, 1950-54. Mem. Am. Soc. Tng. Dirs., Center Orgnl. Devel., Genesee County C. of C. (dir., pres.), Genesee County Personnel Assn. (v.p.), Bus. Council N.Y., Rochester Indsl. Mgmt. Council. Author: Self Appraisals, 1974; contbr. articles to profl. publs. Home: 14 Crow Hill Dr Fairport NY 14450-3714 Office: Graham Corp 20 Florence Ave Batavia NY 14020-3387

MAHER, KIM LEVERTON, museum administrator; b. Washington, Feb. 25, 1946; d. Joseph Wilson and Helen Elizabeth (Bell) Leverton; m. William Fredrick Maher, June 12, 1965 (div. 1980); 1 child, Lauren Robinson. Student Duke U., 1963-65, George Washington U., 1966; B.A. in English, U. Fla., 1969. Social worker Fla. Health and Rehab. Service, Gainesville, 1969-71, Delray Beach, 1972-74, fraud unit supr., West Palm Beach, 1974-76, direct service supr., 1977-78; ctr. dir. Palm Beach County Employment and Tng. Adminstrn., West Palm Beach, 1979-81; exec. dir. Discovery Ctr., Inc., Ft. Lauderdale, Fla., 1981-92; exec. dir. Mus. Discovery & Sci., Ft. Lauderdale, 1992—. Bd. dirs. Singing Pines Mus., Boca Raton, Fla., 1984—, Broward Art Guild, Ft. Lauderdale, 1985-91; mem. Leadership Broward II, Ft. Lauderdale, 1983-84; mem. faculty Inst. New Sci. Ctrs., 1992. Recipient Cultural Arts award Broward Cultural Arts Found., 1985, Woman of Yr. award Women in Comm., 1990, Woman of Distinction award So. Fla. Mag., 1993. Mem. Am. Assn. Museums, Assn. Sci. and Tech. Ctrs., Southeastern Museums Conf., Fla. Sci. Tchrs. Assn. (bd. dirs.), Fla. Assn. Mus. (bd. dirs. 1989—, pres. 1993-), Leadership Broward Alumnae (curriculum com. 1984—), Fort Lauderdale Downtown Council (bd. dirs. 1992—),13), Women's Exec. Club, Phi Kappa Phi. Republican. Methodist. Avocations: scuba diving; piano; creative writing; collecting art and antiques; painting. Office: Mus Discovery and Sci 401 SW 2nd St Fort Lauderdale FL 33312-1707

MAHER, L. JAMES, III, molecular biologist; b. Mpls., Nov. 28, 1960; s. Louis James and Elizabeth Jane (Crawford) M.; m. Laura Lee Moseng, July 2, 1983; children: Elizabeth Lillian, Christina Ailene. BS in Molecular Biology, U. Wis., 1983, PhD in Molecular Biology, 1988. Fellow U. Wis., Madison, 1983-84, rsch. asst., 1984-88; postdoctoral fellow Calif. Inst. Tech., Pasadena, 1988-91; asst. prof. molecular biology Eppley Inst., U. Nebr., Omaha, 1991—, Eppley Inst., U. Nebr. Med. Ctr. Editorial bd. Antisense Rsch. & Devel. Jour., 1991—; contbr. articles to profl. jours. Musician, Madison Symphony Orch., 1983-88, Calif. Inst. Tech. Symphony Orch., L.A., 1988-91. Gosney fellow, 1988; Am. Cancer Soc. postdoctoral fellow, 1988. Mem. AAAS, Phi Beta Kappa. Evangelical Christian Ch. Achievements include research in chemical and biochemical agents designed to artificially regulate the flow of genetic information in biological systems. Office: Eppley Inst Cancer Rsch 600 S 42d St Omaha NE 68198-6805

MAHER, LOUIS JAMES, JR., geologist, educator; b. Iowa City, Iowa, Dec. 18, 1933; s. Louis James and Edith Marie (Ham) M.; m. Elizabeth Jane Crawford, June 7, 1956; children: Louis James, Robert Crawford, Barbara Ruth. B.A., U. Iowa, 1955, M.S., 1959; Ph.D., U. Minn., 1961. Mem. faculty dept. geology and geophysics U. Wis.-Madison, 1962—, prof., 1970—, chmn. dept., 1980-84. Contbr. articles to profl. jours. Served with U.S. Army, 1956-58. Danforth fellow, 1955-61; NSF fellow, 1959-61; NATO fellow, 1961-62. Fellow AAAS, Geol. Soc. Am.; mem. Am. Quaternary Assn., Ecol. Soc. Am., Wis. Acad. Sci., Arts and Letters, Sigma Xi. Episcopalian. Office: U Wis Dept Geology And Geoph Madison WI 53706

MAHER, PATRICK JOSEPH, utility company executive; b. Dublin, Ireland, Apr. 20, 1936; came to U.S., 1946, naturalized, 1955; s. Pierce Albeus and Mary (Brady) M.; m. Catherine M. Sullivan, Oct. 13, 1962; children: Kathy, Kevin, Erin, Megan. BBA, Iona Coll., 1959; MBA, N.Y. U., 1965. With spl. devel. program Chase Manhattan Bank, N.Y.C., 1961-64, 2d v.p. fiduciary dept., 1964-68; asst. v.p. Nat. Comml. Bank, Albany, N.Y., 1968-70; chief sect. utility fin. N.Y. State Pub. Svc. Commn., Albany, 1970-74; v.p., chief fin. officer Washington Gas Light Co., 1974-80, exec. v.p. fin. and adminstrn., 1980-87, pres., 1987-92, 1992—, chmn. bd. dirs., CEO, 1993—. Served with USAR, 1960-61. Mem. Am. Gas Assn., Nat. Soc. Rate of Return Analysts, Natural Gas Men's Roundtable, Greater Washington Bd. Trade, Nat. Protection Coun., U.S. C. of C., Rotary, N.Y. Athletic Club, Washington City Club. Roman Catholic. Home: RR 2 Box 166H Leesburg VA 22075-9107 Office: Washington Gas 1100 H St NW Washington DC 20080-0001

MAHER, PETER MICHAEL, university dean; b. North Battleford, Sask., Can., Mar. 4, 1940; s. Hugh James and Florence Andrea (Showell) M.; m. Illa Horning, Sept. 5, 1964; children: Andrea, Allison, Jennifer. BE, U. Sask., 1962; MBA, U. Western Ont., 1965; PhD, Northwestern U., 1970. Registered profl. engr., Sask., Alta. Devel. engr. DuPont of Can., 1962-64, new venture analyst, 1965-67; teaching asst. Sir George Williams U., 1966-70; rsch. engr. dept. indsl. engring. and mgmt. sci. Northwestern U., 1968-76; prof., rsch. coord. Faculty of Bus. Adminstrn. and Commerce, U. Alta., 1970-76; dean, prof. adminstrn. Coll. of Commerce, U. Sask., 1976-81; dean, prof. faculty of mgmt. U. Calgary, Alta., 1981—; mem. univ. senate, 1989-92; bd. dirs. Calgary Airport Authority, Computalog Ltd., Can. Inst. for Petroleum Industry Devel., Pratt & Whitney Can., Inc.; witness House of Commons Spl. Commn. Employment Opportunities, 1981; mem. exec. com. Nu-West Ltd., 1982-88; audit com. Contbr. articles to profl. jours. Chmn. edn. div., mem. cabinet United Way, Calgary, 1989-90; creditor Northland Bank, 1985; trustee CNIB White Cane Found., 1989—; bd. dirs. Calgary Econ. Devel. Authority, 1983-90, Banff Mountain Acad., 1990—, Banff Sch. Advanced Mgmt., 1990—, chmn. acad. coun., 1992—; Theatre Calgary, 1992—; mem. corp. St. Thomas More Coll., Saskatoon, 1983—. Mem. Nat.

Rsch. Coun. Can., Can. C. of C. (bd. dirs. 1984-86), Calgary C. of C. (bd. dirs. 1982-86), Am. Assembly Collegiate Schs. Bus. (faculty supply com. 1986—, initial/continuing accreditation com. 1989-92), Can. Fedn. Deans Mgmt. and Adminstrn. Studies (vice chmn. 1981-82, chmn. 1982-84, sec.-treas. 1990—), Internat. Labour Orgn. (UN rep. 1985—), Can. Consortium Mgmt. Schs. (chmn. 1990—), Premier's Coun. on Sci. and Tech. (interman bd. dirs. 1984—). Home: 12 Varbrook Pl NW, Calgary, AB Canada T3A OA2 Office: U Calgary Faculty Mgmt, 2500 University Dr NW, Calgary, AB Canada T2N 1N4

MAHER, PETER SUTTON, banker; b. Boston, Apr. 8, 1944; s. Frank Barry and Josephine Virginia (Loveday) M.; divorced; children: Melissa Wells, Meredith Loveday, Martha Carroll; m. Jean Viner, Nov. 1987. BA, Yale U., 1966; MBA, Harvard U., 1969. Fin. analyst Scovill Mfg. Co., Westbury, Conn., 1969-70; various positions State Street Boston Corp., 1970-85; vice-chmn. State Street Bank & Trust (formerly State Street Boston Corp.), 1985; pres. Maher & Co. Inc., Boston, N.Y.C., 1985—; chief exec. officer Atlantic Holdings L.P., Boston, 1987; chmn. bd. dirs. Atlantic Bank & Trust Co., Boston, 1987; bd. dirs. BMR Bancorp, Atlanta, Bardes Corp., Cin., 1988. Served with U.S.C.G.R. Clubs: Harvard, Somerset (Boston); Yale (N.Y.C.). Office: Atlantic and Trust Co 200 State St Boston MA 02109-2694

MAHER, SHEILA, secondary school principal. Prin. R. L. Turner High Sch., Carrollton, Tex. Recipient Blue Ribbon Sch. award U.S. Dept. Edn., 1990-91. Office: R.L. Turner High Sch 1600 Josey Ln Carrollton TX 75006

MAHER, STEPHEN ALBERT, investment banker; b. Oceanside, N.Y., Nov. 23, 1944; s. Michael John and Anita Marie (Seifert) M.; m. Susan Della Groen, June 9, 1984; 1 child, Franklin Groner. B.S. Fordham U., 1966. Asst. v.p. Bankers Trust Co., N.Y.C., 1967-71; v.p. Discount Corp. N.Y., N.Y.C., 1971-76; v.p., head trader John Nuveen & Co., N.Y.C., 1976-78; sr. v.p., mgr. govt. bond dept. Smith Barney Harris Upham and Co. Inc., N.Y.C., 1978-81, exec. v.p., 1984—; pres. Smith Barney Govt. Securities, Inc., N.Y.C., 1981—; exec. v.p. Nikko Securities, N.Y.C. Author studies on government securities markets. Mem. Pub. Securities Assn., U.S. Fed. Agy. Traders Assn. (chmn. 1973-77). Clubs: Treasury Securities Luncheon, Bond (N.Y.C.). Stanwich (Greenwich, Conn.). Home: 36 Binney Ln Old Greenwich CT 06870-2305 Office: Nikko Securities Co Internat Inc 200 Liberty St New York NY 10281

MAHER, SYLVIA ARLENE, nurse administrator; b. Kansas City, Mo., Nov. 12, 1946; d. Elmer Newton and Enid Louise (Olson) McKinley; m. A.C. Amborn Jr., 1969 (div. 1971); m. Mark Edward Maher, Oct. 14, 1977. Diploma in Nursing, Trinity Luth. Hosp., Kansas City, Mo., 1967; BSN, U. Kans. Med. Ctr., 1971, MA in Nursing, 1975. Nurse Trinity Luth. Hosp., Kansas City, Mo., 1967-71; head nurse emergency svcs. Baptist Meml. Hosp., Kansas City, Mo., 1971-77; clinical nurse specialist Bethany Med. Ctr., Kansas City, Mo., 1977-78, critical care div. dir., 1978-80, v.p. for nursing svcs., 1980—; adj. faculty William Jewell Coll., Liberty, Mo., 1975-77, U. Kans. Med. Ctr., Kansas City, 1979—, Avila Coll., Kansas City, 1981-82. Editorial bd. Jour. of AACN, 1978-84. Mem. Kansas City Nursing Adminstrs. (pres. and pres. elect 1987, 88, Nursing Adminstr. of Yr. 1988), Kans. Forum Women Execs., ANA, Sigma Theta Tau. Avocations: seamstress, rose gardener. Home: 262 Lakeshore Dr W Kansas City KS 66106-9521 Office: Bethany Med Ctr 51 N 12th St Kansas City KS 66102-5177

MAHESH, VIRENDRA BHUSHAN, endocrinologist; b. India, Apr. 25, 1932; came to U.S., 1958, naturalized, 1968; s. Narinjan Prasad and Sobhagyawati; m. Sushila Kumari Aggarwal, June 29, 1955; children: Anita Rani, Vinit Kumar. BSc with honors, Patna U., India, 1951; MSc in Chemistry, Delhi U., India, 1953, PhD, 1955; DPhil in Biol. Sci, Oxford U., 1958. James Hudson Brown Meml. fellow Yale U., 1958-59; asst. research prof. endocrinology Med. Coll. Ga., Augusta, 1959-63; assoc. research prof. endocrinology Med. Coll. Ga., 1963-66, prof., 1966-70, Regents prof. endocrinology, 1970-86, Robert B. Greenblatt prof., 1979—, chmn. endocrinology, 1972-86, chmn., Regents prof. physiology and endocrinology, 1986—, chmn. physiology and endocrinology, 1986—; dir. Ctr. for Population Studies, 1971—; mem. reproductive biology study sect. NIH, 1977-81, mem. human embryology and devel. study sect. NIH, 1988-92, chmn., 1991-93. Contbr. articles to profl. jours., chpts. to books; editor: The Pituitary, a Current Review, Functional Correlates of Hormone Receptors in Reproduction, Recent Advances in Fertility Research, Hirsutism and Virilism, Regulation of Ovarian and Testicular Function; mem. editorial bd. Steroids, 1963—, Jour. of Clin. Endocrinology and Metabolism, 1976-81, Jour. Steroid Biochemistry and Molecular Biology, 1991—, Assisted Reproductive Tech./Andrology, 1993—; mem. adv. bd. Maturitas, 1977-81. Recipient Rubin award Am. Soc. Study Sterility, 1962, Billings Silver medal, 1965; Best Tchr. award freshman class Sch. Medicine, Med. Coll. Ga., 1969, Outstanding Faculty award Sch. Medicine, 1992, Outstanding Faculty award Sch. Grad Studies, 1981, 94, Disting. Teaching award, 1988, Excellence in Rsch. award Grad. Faculty Assembly, 1987-91, 93; Disting. Scientist award Assn. Scientists Indian Origin in Am., 1989, rsch. grantee NIH, 1960—. Mem. Chem. Soc. (Eng.), Soc. Biochem. & Molecular Biol., Soc. Neurosci., Endocrine Soc., Soc. for Gynecologic Investigation, Internat. Soc. Neuroendocrinology, Soc. for Study Reproduction, Am. Physiol. Soc., Internat. Soc. Reproductive Medicine (pres. 1980-82), Soc. Exptl. Biology and Medicine, Am. Fertility Soc., Am. Assn. Lab. Animal Sci., N.Y. Acad. Scis., AAUP, Sigma Xi. Office: Med Coll of Ga Dept Physiology & Endocrinology Augusta GA 30912-3000

MAHEU, SHIRLEY, Canadian legislator; b. Montreal, Que., Can., Oct. 7, 1931; d. George William Johnson and Bertha Hunt; m. René Albert Maheu, Sept. 5, 1953; children: Ronald, Richard, Daniel, Marc. Ed., O'Sullivan Bus. Coll., Vanier Coll. Ins. broker; mcpl. councillor City of Saint-Laurent, Que., 1982-88; mem. from Saint-Laurent Ho. of Commons, 1988—. Pres. Saint-Laurent br. Red Cross Soc. Mem. Ins. Brokers Assn. Que., Saint-Laurent C. of C. Roman Catholic. Office: Ho of Commons, 111 Wellington St PO Box 1103, Ottawa, ON Canada K1A 0A6

MAHEY, JOHN ANDREW, museum director; b. DuBois, Pa., Mar. 30, 1932; s. Manasseh A. and Bernyce (Holdar) M. Student, Columbia U., 1950-52; B.A., Pa. State U., 1959, M.A., 1962. Asst. dir. Peale Mus., Balt., 1964-69; dir. E.B. Crocker Art Gallery, 1969-72, Cummer Gallery of Art, 1972-75, Meml. Art Gallery of U. Rochester, 1975-79; chief curator Philbrook Art Center, Tulsa, 1979-84; dir. San Antonio Mus. Art, 1984-89, Flint (Mich.) Inst. of Arts, 1989—. Contbr. articles on artists to art his. jours.; author exhbn. catalogs. Served with USAF, 1952-57, 62-64. Fulbright scholar, 1962. Mem. Am. Assn. Museums, Assn. Art Mus. Dirs., Phi Beta Kappa, Phi Alpha Theta. Office: Flint Inst of Arts 1120 E Kearsley St Flint MI 48503-1991

MAHL, GEORGE FRANKLIN, psychoanalyst, psychologist, educator; b. Akron, Ohio, Nov. 27, 1917; s. Floyd Alexander and Margaret (Strecker) M.; m. Martha Jane Fenn, Jan. 10, 1944; 1 dau., Barbara Jessica. A.B., Oberlin Coll., 1939, M.A., 1941; Ph.D., Yale, 1948; certificate, Western New Eng. Inst. Psychoanalysis, 1962. Asst. psychology Oberlin Coll., 1939-41; research asst. psychology Yale, 1941-42; mem. faculty Yale U., 1947—, prof. psychiatry and psychology, 1964-88, prof. emeritus, 1988—; tchr. Western New Eng. Inst. Psychoanalysis, 1961-85, pres., 1972-74. Served to 1st lt. AUS, 1942-46. Fellow AAAS, Am. Psychol. Assn.; mem. Ea. Psychol. Assn., Western New Eng. Inst. Psychoanalysis, Western New Eng. Psychoanalytic Soc., Internat. Psychoanalytical Assn., Inst. Psychoanalytic Tng. and Rsch. (N.Y.), Sigmund Freud Soc. Home: 106 Bayard Ave North Haven CT 06473-4303

MAHLE, CHRISTOPH ERHARD, electrical engineer; b. Stuttgart, Germany, Mar. 7, 1938; came to U.S., 1968; s. Ernst Johannes and Else (Wurth) M.; m. Mary Heavenrich, Mar. 23, 1975; children: Lisa, Charles. Diploma engring., Swiss Fed. Inst. Polytech., Zurich, 1961, D of Sci. Tech., 1966. Rsch. asst. Swiss Fed. Inst. Tech., Zurich, Switzerland, 1961-67; with tech. staff Comsat Labs., Clarksburg, Md., 1968-71, sect. head, 1971-73, dept. mgr., 1973-81, dir., 1981-83, exec. dir., 1983-94, v.p., 1995—. Patentee in field; contbr. articles to profl. jours. Fellow IEEE. Avocations:

music, mountain climbing. Office: Comsat Labs 22300 Comsat Dr Clarksburg MD 20871-9475

MAHLER, HARRY BEZ, architect, planner; b. Montclair, N.J., Aug. 8, 1928; s. Harry A. and Pauline Marie (Bez) M.; m. Elizabeth Willett, Oct. 2, 1954; children: Debra, Steven, Suzanne. B.Arch., Columbia U., 1954, William K. Fellows fellow, 1954-55. Successively draftsman, designer, chief designer, assoc., ptnr., sr. ptnr. for design, mem. mgmt. com. The Grad Partnership, Newark, 1949-90; chmn., chief exec. officer Grad. Assocs., P.A., Newark, 1990-94, chmn. emeritus, 1994—; prin. GLS Internat., 1994—; adj. prof. emeritus, curriculum coord. design and drawing Pratt Inst.; past mem. archtl. adv. bd. McGraw-Edison Corp.; chmn. adv. com., past chmn. fee com. N.J. Sch. Architecture; chmn. archtl. div. capital campaign, adv. com. Sch. Architecture N.J. Inst. Tech., mem. bd. overseers; design adv. com. State of N.J. Contbr. articles to profl. jours. Former commr., chmn. Montclair Redevel. Agy.; past chmn. barrier-free architecture com. Easter Seal Soc. N.J.; exec. v.p. Essex coun. Boy Scouts Am., chmn. camp study No. N.J. councils, mem. N.E. Regional Bd.; vice pres. area 2 NE region Boy Scouts Am., mem. Nat. Properties Com. Boy Scouts of Am., mem. nat. coun.; past chmn., mem. real estate and corp. devel. luncheon, past mem. exec. bd., bd. govs. N.J. com. NCCJ; past trustee Montclair YMCA; mem. baseball boosters and kickoff classic coms. N.J. Sports Authority; mem., chmn., pres. Montclair State U. Found. Bd., others. Recipient awards AIA, Illuminating Engrs. Soc., N.J. Soc. Architects, Bell System, Am. Concrete Inst., N.J. Bus. Mag., Am. Cons. Engrs. Coun., Archtl. Record Mag., Am. Planning Assn.; Humanitarian Brotherhood award NCCJ, 1987; Sch. of Architecture award N.J. Inst. Tech., 1987; Silver Beaver award Boy Scouts of Am., 1987, Silver Antelope award, 1991, Northeast Region award, 1987. Fellow AIA (mem. nat. design com.); mem. N.J. Soc. Architects, Execs. Assn. N.J. (past chmn.), Regional Bus. Partnership (bd. dirs.), N.J. State C. of C. (bd. dirs.), N.J. Zool. Soc. (exec. v.p.), Beta Theta Pi. Methodist. Home: 214 Highland Ave Montclair NJ 07043-1010 Office: Grad Assocs PA 2 Gateway Ctr Newark NJ 07102-5003

MAHLER, RICHARD T., finance executive; b. Galt, Ont., Can., May 15, 1943; s. Lawrence Herman and Therese (Trepanier) M.; m. Susan Jane Campbell, May 25, 1968; children: Stephen, Katherine. BSc, U. Waterloo, 1966; MBA, McMaster U., Hamilton, 1975. Asst. contr. Ford Motor Can. Oakville, Ont., 1967-81; v.p. fin., chief fin. officer Amdahl Can. Ltd., Toronto, Ont., 1981-90; v.p., CFO Finning Ltd., Vancouver, B.C., 1990—. Chmn. Oakville Galleries, Ont., 1971-79; pres. U. Waterloo Adv. Coun. 1984-90; bd. dirs. Nat. Ballet Sch., Toronto, 1989—; chmn. coop. coun. Simon Fraser U., 1993—; mem. bus. coun. B.C. Econ. Policy Adv. Group, 1994—. Mem. Fin. Execs. Inst., Coun. Fin. Execs. Conf. Bd. Can., Hollyburn Country Club, Seymour Golf Club, Canadian Club Vancouver. Office: Finning Ltd, 555 Great Northern Way, Vancouver, BC Canada V5T 1E2

MAHLMAN, JERRY DAVID, research meteorologist; b. Crawford, Nebr., Feb. 21, 1940; s. Earl Lewis and Ruth Margaret (Callendar) M.; m. Janet Kay Hilgenberg, June 10, 1962; children—Gary Martin, Julie Kay. A.B., Chadron State Coll., Nebr., 1962; M.S., Colo. State U., 1964, Ph.D., 1967. Instr. Colo. State U., Fort Collins, 1964-67; from asst. prof. to assoc. prof. Naval Postgrad. Sch., Monterey, Calif., 1967-70; rsch. meteorologist NOAA Geophys. Fluid Dynamics Lab., Princeton, N.J., 1970-84, lab. dir., 1984—; lectr. with rank of prof. Princeton U., 1980—; chmn. panel on mid-atmosphere program NAS-NRC, 1982-84, mem. climate rsch. com., 1986-89, mem. panel on dynamic extended range forecasting, 1987-90; mem. U.S.-USSR Commn. on Global Ecology, 1989-92; mem. Bd. on Global Change, 1991—; U.S. rep. world climate rsch. program Joint Sci. Commn., 1991—. Contbr. over 70 articles to profl. jours. Elder Monterey Presbyterian Ch., 1968-70, Lawrence Road Presbyn. Ch., Lawrenceville, N.J., 1972-75; bd. dirs. Lawrence Non-Profit Housing Inc., 1978-88. Recipient Honor Alumnus award Colo. State U., 1995. Fellow Am. Geophys. Union (Jule Charney lectr. 1993), Am. Meteorol. Soc. (awards com. 1984, chmn. upper atmosphere com. 1979, assoc. editor Jour. Atmospheric Sci. 1979-86, councilor 1991-94, Editors award 1978, Carl-Gustaf Rossby rsch. medal 1994). Democrat. Home: 9 Camelia Ct Lawrenceville NJ 08648-3201 Office: Princeton U Geophys Fluid Dynamics Lab PO Box 308/NOAA Princeton NJ 08542-0308

MAHLMANN, JOHN JAMES, educational association administrator; b. Washington, Jan. 21, 1942; s. Charles Victor and Mary Elizabeth (Deye) M.; m. Ning Ning Chang, Feb. 5, 1972; 1 son, Justin Geeng Ming. BFA, Boston U., 1962, MFA, 1963; postgrad., U. Notre Dame, summer 1962; EdD, Pa. State U., 1970. Grad. asst. Boston U., 1962-63, instr., supr. student tchrs., dir. masters degree candidates, 1964-66; grad. asst., research asst. Pa. State U., 1963-64, instr., 1966-67, dir. gallery, art edn. dept., 1966-67; asst. prof. Tex. Tech Coll., 1967-69; chmn. tenure and promotions com.; dir. publs., asst. exec. sec. Nat. Art Edn. Assn., Washington, 1969-71; exec. sec. Nat. Art Edn. Assn., 1971-82; also tour dir. to Japan and Orient; exec. dir. Music Educators Nat. Conf., 1983—; instr. drawing Lubbock Art Assn.; asst. debate coach, asst. coordinator forensics Boston U.; vis. instr., mem. staff George Washington U., No. Va. Community Coll., Tchrs. Coll. N.Y. Exhibited at, Boston U., Pa. State U., Harvard U., Tex. Tech. U., Salem (Mass.) State Coll., Botolph Gallery, Boston, Inst. Contemporary Art, Boston, Barncellar Gallery, Orleans, Mass., State Gallery, State College, Pa., Halls Gallery, Lubbock, Lubbock Art Assn., Loft Gallery, San Antonio, Llano Estacado Art Assn., Hobbs, N.Mex., Purdue U., Cushing Gallery, Dallas, Religious Art Exhbn., Cranbrook Acad. Art, Bloomfield Hills, Mich., Upstairs Gallery, Arlington, Tex., S.W. Tex. State Coll., San Marcos.; Editor: Art Edn., 1970-81, Art Tchr., 1971-80; contbr. articles to mags. Mem. Music Educators Nat. Conf., Nat. Art Edn. Assn., Am. Soc. Assn. Execs., Washington Soc. Assn. Execs., Phi Delta Kappa. Home: 10703 Cross School Rd Reston VA 22091-5105 Office: Music Ed Nat Conf 1806 Robert Fulton Dr Reston VA 22091-1502

MAHMOUD, ADEL A. F., physician, educator, investigator; b. Cairo, Aug. 24, 1941; s. Abdel Fattah and Fathia (Osman) M.; m. Sally L. Hodder. MD, U. Cairo, 1963; PhD, U. London, 1971. House officer U. Cairo Hosps., 1963-65; asst. lectr. U. Ain Shams Med. Faculty and Hosps., Cairo, 1965-68; clin. rsch. assist., WHO fellow Sch. Hygiene And Tropical Medicine U. London, 1969-72; rsch. assoc. to assoc. prof. medicine Dept. Medicine, Med. Sch. Case Western Res. U., Cleve., 1977-87, prof. medicine 1980—; prof. molecular biology and microbiology, 1982—; John H. Hord prof., chmn. dept. medicine Case Western Reserve U., 1987—; physician-in-chief Univ Hosps., 1987—; mem. com. on rsch. grants NAS, 1983-86; mem. nat. adv. allergy and infectious diseases coun. NIH, 1988-92. Editor: (with K. Frank Austen) The Eosinophil in Health and Disease, 1979, (with K.S. Warren) Textbook on Tropical and Geographical Medicine, 1984, (with K.S. Warren) Geographic Medicine for the Practitioner, 1987, (with K.S. Warren) Tropical and Geographical Medicine, 2nd edit., 1990, Tropical and Geographical Medicine Companion Handbook, 2d edit., 1993; guest editor: Bailliere's Clinical Tropical Medicine and Communicable Diseases, 1987; contbr. articles to profl. jours., chpts. to books. Trustee Cleve. Mus. Natural History. Recipient Baily K. Ashford medal, 1983; WHO fellow, 1969-71; Squibb award 1984; Josiah Macy Found. scholar 1980. Mem. Inst. Medicine of NAS, Am. Soc. Clin. Investigation, Am. Soc. Hematology, Assn. Am. Physicians, Am. Assn. Immunology, Infectious Diseases Soc. Am., Am. Soc. Tropical Medicine and Hygiene, Internat. Soc. Infectious Diseases (pres. 1990-92), Cen. soc. Clin. Rsch. (pres. 1992), Sigma Xi, Alpha Omega Alpha. Home: 18900 S Park Blvd Shaker Heights OH 44122-1851 Office: Univ Hosps Cleveland Dept Medicine 11100 Euclid Ave Cleveland OH 44106-1736

MAHMOUD, ALY AHMED, electrical engineering educator; b. Cairo, Jan. 25, 1935; came to U.S., 1960, naturalized, 1970; s. Ahmed Aly and Amina Mohammed (Rashwan) M.; m. Lucinda Lou Keller, Dec. 20, 1962; children: Ramy, Samy. BSc. with distinction and honors (Nat. Honor student), Ain Shams U., Cairo, 1958; M.S., Purdue U., 1961, Ph.D., 1964. Diplomate: Registered profl. engr., Iowa. La. Instr. elec. engring. Ain Shams U., 1958-60; asst. prof. elec. engring. U. N.B., Fredericton, 1964; research engr. No. Electric Research and Devel. Lab., Ottawa, Ont., Can., summer 1964; assist. prof. elec. engring. U. Asyut, Egypt, 1964-66; sr. research elec. engr. Naval Civil Engring. Lab., Port Hueneme, Calif., 1968-69, summer 1970; asst. prof.

elec. engring. U. Mo., Columbia, 1966-71; assoc. prof. U. Mo., 1971-73, prof., 1973-76; prof. elec. engring., dir. Iowa test and evaluation facility, program mgr. Power Affiliates Research Program; supr. Power System Computer Service, Iowa State U., Ames, 1976-85; dean Coll. Engring. U. New Orleans, 1985-88; dean Sch. Engring. and Tech. Ind. U.-Purdue U.-at Ft. Wayne, 1988—; with FPC, summer 1974; program mgr. NSF, 1975-76; cons. in field. Contbr. articles to profl. jours. Vice chmn. Water and Light Adv. Bd. City of Columbia, 1973-76. Am. Friends of Middle East fellow, 1960-68. Sr. mem. IEEE; Mem. Power Engring. Soc., Am. Phys. Soc., Egyptian Profl. Engring. Soc., Am. Soc. Engring. Edn., Sigma Xi, Tau Beta Pi, Eta Kappa Nu. Patentee in field. Home: 5640 Foxcross Ct Fort Wayne IN 46835-2802 Office: Ind U-Purdue U-Ft Wayne Dean Sch Engring and Tech 2101 E Coliseum Blvd Fort Wayne IN 46805-1445 *In this country there are outstanding opportunities for those who are willing to work hard to serve the society and their profession. I am thankful to be in the U.S. and to have found this type of opportunity.*

MAHON, ARTHUR J., lawyer; b. N.Y.C., Jan. 13, 1934; s. Arthur Logan and Mary Agnes (Craine) M.; m. Myra E. Murphy, Aug. 10, 1957; children: Maura, Madonna, Arthur, Nancy. B.A., Manhattan Coll., 1955; JD, NYU, 1958. Bar: N.Y., Fla., D.C. Adj. prof. law NYU Sch. of Law, N.Y.C., 1964-78; ptnr. Mudge, Rose, Guthrie, Alexander & Ferdon, N.Y.C., 1970-94; counsel Donovan Leisure Newton & Irvine, N.Y.C., 1994—. Trustee Manhattan Coll., N.Y., 1988—, Adrian and Jesse Archbold Charitable Trust, N.Y.C., 1976; mem. joint bd. N.Y. Hosp.-Cornell Med. Ctr., N.Y.C., 1990—; com. on trust and estate gift plans Rockefeller U., N.Y.C., 1984—; bd. dirs. United Way Internat., 1988-94, Alexandria, Va.; chmn. planned giving and endowments com. lawyers, bankers, and accts. Archdiocese N.Y., N.Y.C., 1985—; bd. overseers Cornell Med. Coll., N.Y.C., 1986-92, chmn., 1992—; dir. Am. Skin Assn., N.Y.C., 1989—, Noel Found., San Francisco, 1990—; gov. N.Y. Hosp., N.Y.C., 1994—. Served to capt. USAF, 1958-60. Root-Tilden scholar NYU. Mem. N.Y. State Bar Assn., Bar Assn. City of N.Y., Fla. Bar Assn., D.C. Bar Assn., Royal Soc. Medicine Found. (dir. 1977-94, pres. 1979-94). Home: 16 Cambridge Dr Madison CT 06443 Office: Donovan Leisure 30 Rockefeller Plz New York NY 10112

MAHON, ELDON BROOKS, federal judge; b. Loraine, Tex., Apr. 9, 1918; s. John Bryan and Nola May (Muns) M.; m. Nova Lee Groom, June 1, 1941; children: Jana, Martha, Brad. B.A., McMurry Coll., 1939; LL.B., U. Tex., 1942. Bar: Tex. 1942. Law clk. Tex. Supreme Ct., 1945-46; county atty. Mitchell County, Tex., 1947; dist. atty. 32d Jud. Dist. Tex., 1948-60, dist. judge, 1960-63; v.p. Tex. Electric Service Co., Ft. Worth, 1963-64; mem. firm Mahon Pope & Gladden, Abilene, Tex., 1964-68; U.S. atty. U.S. Dist. Ct. (no. dist.) Tex., Ft. Worth, 1968-72, judge, 1972—, now sr. judge. Pres. W. Tex. council Girl Scouts U.S.A., 1966-68; Trustee McMurry Coll. Served with USAAF, 1942-45. Named an outstanding Tex. prosecutor Tex. Law Enforcement Found., 1957. Mem. ABA, Fed. Bar Assn., Ft.-Worth-Tarrant County Bar Assn., Am. Judicature Soc., State Bar Tex. Methodist (past del. confs.). Office: US Courthouse 403 US Courthouse Fort Worth TX 76102

MAHON, JOHN JOSEPH, federal agency adminstrator; b. N.Y.C., Nov. 18, 1938; s. James and Noreen (Hannon) M.; m. Helen Elizabeth Heim, Oct. 22, 1966 (dec. 1975); children: Elizabeth Ann, John Carl; m. Constance Ann Link, Sept. 10, 1977. BS, Fordham U., 1960; MBA, Columbia U., 1963; diploma, U.S. Army Command Staff Coll., 1975, Nat. Def. U., 1977, U.S. Army War Coll., 1982. Commd. 2d lt. U.S. Army, 1960, advanced through grades to col., 1984, ret., 1990; dep. state dir. Corp. for Nat. and Community Svc., N.Y.C., 1985—; vis. lectr. Columbia U., 1964-70. Active LaCrosse Found., Balt.; coach Port Youth Activities, Port Washington, N.Y., 1978-88. Decorated Legion of Merit. Mem. Am. Mktg. Assn. (life, Profl. Cert. of Achievement 1970), Res. Officers Assn. (life, Longtimer award 1985), Columbia U. Club N.Y., Mil. Order World Wars, DAV (hon., Comdr.'s award 1993, 94), N.Y. Soc. Mil. and Naval Officers (life, Soc. medal 1988), U.S. Army Res. Command Assn. (life, Cert. of Appreciation 1990), Am. Legion, VFW, Battle of Normandy Found., Vietnam Vets. Meml., Foster Grandparents Am. Avocations: coaching Little League, church volunteering, Civil War research, travel, working with underprivileged and disadvantaged people. Home: 48 Shadyside Ave Port Washington NY 11050 Office: Corp for Nat & Community Svc 6 World Trade Ctr Ste 758 New York NY 10048-0206

MAHON, MALACHY THOMAS, lawyer, educator; b. N.Y.C., Jan. 4, 1934; s. James and Alice (Rooney) M.; m. Margaret Phyllis Kirwan, Jan. 25, 1958; children: Veronica Mahon Grover, Laura Mahon Chandonnet, Malachy. B.A., Manhattan Coll., 1954; J.D., Fordham U. 1960. Bar: N.Y. 1960. Law clk. to Chief Magistrate John M. Murtaugh, N.Y.C., 1959-60, U.S. Supreme Ct. Justice Tom C. Clark, 1960-61; assoc. Hale Russell & Stentzel, N.Y.C., 1961-62, Mudge Rose Guthrie & Alexander, N.Y.C., 1979-80; of counsel Farrell, Fritz, Caemmerer, Cleary, Burnosky & Armentano, Mineola, NY, 1982-83, Havens & Lombard, Flushing, N.Y., 1994—; prof. Fordham U. Law Sch., 1962-68; prof. law Hofstra U. Law Sch., 1968—, founding dean, 1968-73, S.B. Wilzig disting. prof. banking, 1985—; vis. prof. U. Tex. Law Sch., 1973-74; exec. dir., spl. N.Y. State asst. atty. gen. Meyer Investigation Spl. Attica Prosecutor's Office, 1975; Chief counsel N.Y. Gov.'s Spl. Com. on Criminal Offenders, 1966; mem. Nassau County Bd. Ethics, 1983—, chmn., 1989—. Staff author: Mental Illness, Due Process and the Criminal Defendant, 1968; monthly comml. law continuist: N.Y. Law Jour, 1976-78. Served with U.S. Army, 1954-56. Mem. ABA, N.Y. State Bar Assn., Assn. Bar City N.Y., Am. Law Inst. Home: 45 Thornwood Ln East Hills NY 11577-1616 Office: Hofstra U Law Sch Hempstead NY 11550

MAHON, ROBERT, photographer; b. Wilmington, Del., Dec. 28, 1949; s. Clifton and Mary Veronica (Figash) M.; m. Carol Joyce, Apr. 24, 1983. BA in Am. Studies, U. Del., 1971. One-man show Twining Gallery, N.Y.C., 1985, Mercer Coll., Trenton, N.J., 1993; exhibited in group shows Whitney Mus. Am. Art, 1982, Phila. Mus. Art, 1982, 95, Am. Ctr., Paris, 1982, Mus. Modern Art, N.Y.C., 1983, 84-85, 93, Kolnischer Kunstverein, 1983, Art Inst. Chgo., 1985, Twining Gallery, 1985-86, 88, 89, N.J. State Mus., 1990, Guggenheim Soho, 1994, also others;; represented in permanent collections Phila. Mus. Art, Mus. Modern Art, Met. Mus. Art, N.Y. Pub. Libr., Humanities Rsch. Ctr., U. Tex., Austin, Princeton U. Libr., also pvt. collections. Guggenheim grantee, 1985. Home and Studio: PO Box Q Stockton NJ 08559-0390

MAHONE, BARBARA JEAN, automotive company executive; b. Notasulga, Ala., Apr. 19, 1946; d. Freddie Douglas M. and Sarah Lou (Simpson). B.S. Ohio State U. 1968; M.B.A., U. Mich., 1972; P.M.D. Harvard U. Bus. Sch., 1981. Systems analyst GM, Detroit, 1968-71; sr. staff asst., 1972-74, mgr. career planning, 1975-78; dir. personnel adminstrn. GM, Rochester, N.Y., 1979-81; mgr. indsl. relations GM, Warren, Ohio, 1982-83; dir. human resources mgmt. Chevrolet-Pontiac-Can. group GM, 1984-86; dir. gen. pers. and pub. affairs Inland div. GM, Dayton, Ohio, 1986-88; gen. dir. pers. Inland Fisher Guide div. GM, Detroit, 1989-91, gen. dir. employee benefits, 1991-93; group dir. human resources GM Truck Group, 1994—; chmn. Fed. Labor Rels. Authority, Washington, 1983-84, Spl. Panel on Appeals; dir. Metro Youth; mem. bd. govs. U. Mich. Alumni. Bd. dirs. ARC, Rochester, 1979-82; bd. dirs. Urban League of Rochester, 1979-82; mem. human resroces com YMCA, Rochester, 1980-82; mem. exec. bd. Nat. Council Negro Women; mem. allocations com. United Way of Greater Rochester; bd. dirs. Rochester Area Multiple Sclerosis. Recipient public relations award Nat. Assn. Bus. and Profl. Women, 1976; recipient award for excellence Gen. Motors. Corp., 1978, Mary McLeod Bethune award Nat. Council Negro Women, 1977, Senate Resolution Mich. State Legislature, 1980; named Outstanding Woman Mich. Chronicle, 1975, Woman of Yr. Nat. Assn. Bus. and Profl. Women, 1978, Disting. Bus. Person U. Mich., 1978, 1 of 11 Mich. Women Redbook Mag., 1978. Mem. Nat. Black M.B.A. Assn. (bd. dirs., nat. pres. Disting. Service award, bd. dirs., nat. pres. Outstanding M.B.A.), Women Econ. Club. (bd. dirs.), Indsl. Relations Research Assn., Internat. Assn. for Personnel Women, Kontrup. Soc. Detroit. Republican. Home: 175 Kirkwood Ct Bloomfield Hills MI 48304-2927 Office: GM Truck Group Mail Code 3108-16 31 E Judson St Pontiac MI 48342-2206

MAHONEY, GERALD FRANCIS, manufacturing company executive; b. Bklyn., July 31, 1943; s. Francis B. and Leona (Gray) M.; m. JoAnne A. Maselli, May 2, 1971; children: G. Scott, Ryan J. BA, Adelphi U., 1965; MBA, Northeastern U., 1966. CPA, N.Y. Mgr. Arthur Andersen & Co.,

N.Y.C., 1966-73; asst. contr. Bairnco Corp., N.Y.C., 1973-78, v.p. fin., 1980-81; gen. mgr. Bairnco Corp., Pensauken, N.J., 1979-80; v.p., div. pres. Bairnco Corp., Union, N.J., 1981-83; sr. v.p. fin. and adminstrn. Polychrome Corp., Yonkers, N.Y., 1984-87; pres. Transcript Corp., Brewster, N.Y., 1987-90, Pavey Envelope & Tag Corp., Jersey City, 1991-94; chmn. Mail-Well Envelope, Englewood, Colo., 1994—. Mem. AICPA, N.Y. State Soc. CPA's, Noyac Country Club (Sag Harbor, N.Y., bd. dirs. 1980-83), Glenmoor Country Club (Englewood, Colo.), Ridgewood Country Club (N.J.). Republican. Roman Catholic. Avocations: golf, tennis. Home: 21 Cherry Hills Farm Dr Englewood CO 80110-7170 Office: Am Mail-Well Envelope 23 Inverness Way E Englewood CO 80112

MAHONEY, J. DANIEL, federal judge; b. Orange, N.J., Sept. 7, 1931; s. Daniel Vincent and Louisa (Dunbar) M.; m. Kathleen Mary O'Doherty, Oct. 22, 1955; children: J. Daniel, Kieran Vincent, Francis Kirk, Mary Louisa, Eileen Ann, Elizabeth Anne. B.A. magna cum laude, St. Bonaventure U., 1952; LL.B. (Kent scholar), Columbia U., 1955. Bar: N.Y. 1960. Asso. firm Simpson Thacher & Bartlett, N.Y.C., 1958-62; partner firm Wormser, Keily, Alessandroni, Mahoney & McCann, N.Y.C., 1965-74, Windels, Marx, Davies & Ives, N.Y.C., 1974-86; state chmn. N.Y. Conservative Party, 1962-86; judge U.S. Ct. Appeals (2d cir.), Milford, Conn., 1986—; elected to Electoral Coll., 1980; dir. Nat. Rev., Inc., N.Y.C., 1972-86. Author: Actions Speak Louder, The Story of the New York Conservative Party, 1967. Mem. adv. coun. Pace U., 1985-87; dean's adv. coun. Hofstra U. Sch. Law, 1982-90; bd. fellows Poly. Inst. N.Y., 1981-91. Lt. (j.g.) USCGR, 1955-58. Roman Catholic. Office: 2 Corporate Dr Ste 338 Shelton CT 06484

MAHONEY, JAMES P., bishop; b. Saskatoon, Sask., Can., Dec. 7, 1927. Ordained priest Roman Cath. Ch., 1952; bishop Saskatoon, 1967—. Office: Chancery Office, 106 5th Ave N, Saskatoon, SK Canada S7K 2N7

MAHONEY, JERRY C. D., lawyer; b. Mpls., 1931. BSL, U. Minn., 1953, LLB, 1955. Bar: Minn. 1955. Ptnr. Dorsey & Whitney, Mpls. Office: Dorsey & Whitney 220 S 6th St Minneapolis MN 55402-4500

MAHONEY, JOHN, actor; b. Manchester, Eng., June 20, 1940. MA in English, Western Ill. U.; student, Quincy Coll.; trained for the theater at St. Nicholas Theatre, Chgo. Stage performances include The Water Engine, 1977, The Hothouse, Taking Steps, Death of a Salesman, Orphans, 1985 (Theater World award), The House of Blue Leaves, 1986 (Tony award, Clarence Derwent award), The Subject Was Roses, 1991; films include Mission Hill, 1982, Voyeur, 1984, Code of Silence, 1985, The Manhattan Project, 1986, Streets of Gold, 1987, Tin Men, 1987, Suspect, 1987, Moonstruck, 1987, Frantic, 1988, Betrayed, 1988, Eight Men Out, 1988, Say Anything, 1989, Love Hurts, 1990, The Russia House, 1990, Barton Fink, 1991, Article 99, 1992, In the Line of Fire, 1993, Striking Distance, 1993, Reality Bites, 1994, The Hudsucker Proxy, 1994; TV series: Lady Blue, 1985-86, H.E.L.P., The Human Factor, 1991, Frasier, 1993—; TV movies Chicago Story, 1981, Listen to your Heart, 1983, Dance of the Phoenix, , 1984, The Killing Floor, 1984, First Steps, 1985, Trapped in Silence, 1986, Favorite Son, 1988, (TNT) Dinner at Eight, 1989, (HBO) The Image, 1990, The 10 Million Dollar Getaway, 1991, The Secret Passion of Robert Clayton, 1992; TV special The House of Blue Leaves, 1987. Served AUS. Office: care ICM 40 W 50th St New York NY 10019*

MAHONEY, JOHN L., English literature educator; b. Somerville, Mass., Feb. 4, 1928. AB, Boston Coll., 1950, AM, 1952; PhD, Harvard U., 1957. Instr. of English Boston Coll., 1955-59, asst. prof. of English, 1959-62, assoc. prof., 1962-65, prof., 1965—, chmn. dept., 1962-67, 69-70, dir. PhD program in English, 1970-75, 82-85, mem. edal. policy com. Grad. Sch. Arts and Scis., 1985-87, Rattigan prof. English, 1994—; vis. prof. of English Harvard U. summer sch., 1963, 65, 67, 71, 80, 83, 86; cons. for self-study Weston Coll. Schs. of Philosophy and Theology, Boston Coll., 1965; sem. leader programs for women, Boston Coll., Newton Coll., 1976, 78, 79; mem. numerous acad. coms. and couns.; cons., mem. English adv. com. Commonwealth of Mass., 1968-70; mem. acad. coun. Evening Coll. Arts and Scis. and Bus. Adminstrn., Boston Coll., 1969—, univ. core curriculum devel. com., 1991—; bd. trustees St. John's Sem., Brighton, Mass., com. on acad. affairs, 1980-86; sec. bd. trustees Katharine Gibbs Sch., Boston, 1982-90; mem. adv. bd. Jesuit Inst., Boston Coll., 1987—. Author: The Whole Internal Universe: Imitation and the New Defense of Literature in British Criticism, 1660-1830, 1985, The Persistence of Tragedy: Episodes in the History of Drama, 1985, The Logic of Passion: The Literary Criticism of William Hazlitt, rev. edition, 1981; editor, author intro. and notes: The Enlightenment and English Literature, 1980, The English Romantics: Major Poetry and Critical Theory, 1978, An Essay of Dramatic Poesy and Other Critical Writings by John Dryden, 1965, William Duff's Essay on Original Genius, 1964; contbr. Imagination and the Ways of Genius (in Approaches to Hazlitt), 1986, Teaching the Immortality Ode with Coleridge's Dejection: An Ode (in Approaches to Teaching Wordsworth's Poetry), 1986, and others; editor: (with J. Robert Barth, S.J.) Coleridge, Keats, and the Imagination: Romanticism and Adam's Dream, 1990, Teaching Shelley's Skylark and the Defence of Poetry, (in Approaches to Teaching Shelley's Poetry) 1990; mem. editorial bd. Boston Coll. Mag., 1981-90; author articles, papers delivered at profl. confs.; reviewer for Studies in Romanticism, The Wordsworth Circle, Nineteenth Century Contexts. Active Sacred Heart Parish, Lexington, Mass., del. to Lexington Coun. Chs., 1968, chmn. parish coun., 1969-72, religious edn. commn., 1974-79, 90—, sem. leader Christian Youth Edn., 1969-73, lector, 1972—; mem. Archdiocese of Boston Commn. for Promotion of Parish Couns., 1969-74, Patron Book Selection Com., Cary Meml. Libr., Lexington. Boston Coll. Grad. Sch. fellow, 1950-52, Lehman fellow Harvard U., 1953-55; Boston Coll. Faculty rsch. grantee, 1964, 68, 86, 92, Mellon Found. grantee for rsch. and faculty devel., 1981-82; grantee rsch. Am. Philos. Soc., 1987; recipient Boston Coll. Campus Coun. Tchr. of Yr. award, 1966, Boston Coll. alumni award for excellence in edn., 1978, Boston Coll. Faculty fellowship, spring 1986, 94, André Favat award Mass. Coun. Tchrs. of English, 1988, Prof. of the Yr. award Coun. for the Advancement and Support of Edn. Mass., 1989. Mem. AAUP (pres. Boston Coll. chpt. 1962), MLA, N.E. MLA, Am. Soc. Eighteenth Century Studies, N.E. Soc. Eighteenth Century Studies, Wordsworth-Coleridge Assn. Am., Keats-Shelley Assn. Am., The Johnsonians, Alpha Sigma Nu, Phi Beta Kappa. Office: Boston Coll Dept English Chestnut Hill MA 02167

MAHONEY, MARGARET ANN, lawyer; b. Alliance, Nebr., Apr. 22, 1949; d. John Charles and Grace Margaret (Hoban) M.; m. Peter B. Ogren, June 28, 1980. BA, Coll. of St. Catherine, 1971; JD cum laude, U. Minn., 1974. Bar: Minn. 1974, Fla. 1975, Tex. 1988. Ptnr. Stringer, Courtney & Rohleder, Ltd., St. Paul, 1974-84; U.S bankruptcy judge Dist. Minn., Mpls., 1984-87, So. Dist. Tex., Houston, 1987-89; ptnr. Weil, Gotshal & Manges, Houston, 1989—. Nat. Merit scholar Coll. of St. Catherine. Mem. Dallas Bar Tex., Dallas Bar Assn., Nat. Conf. Bankruptcy Judges (bd. dirs. 1989, adv. com. to adminstrv. office of cts. bankruptcy div. 1988-89), Minn. Bar Assn., Fla. Bar Assn., Sigma Delta Phi, Phi Beta Kappa. Office: Weil Gotshal & Manges 901 Main St Ste 4100 Dallas TX 75202

MAHONEY, MARGARET ELLERBE, foundation executive; b. Nashville, Oct. 24, 1924; d. Charles Hallam and Leslie Nelson (Savage) M. BA magna cum laude, Vanderbilt U., 1946; LHD (hon.), Meharry Med. Coll., 1977, U. Fla., 1980, Med. Coll. Pa., 1982, Williams Coll., 1983, Smith Coll., 1985, Beaver Coll., 1985, Brandeis U., 1989, Marymount Coll., 1990, Rush U., 1993. Fgn. affairs officer State Dept., Washington, 1946-53; exec. assoc. assoc. sec. Carnegie Corp., N.Y.C., 1953-72; v.p. Robert Wood Johnson Found., Princeton, N.J., 1972-80; pres. Commonwealth Fund, N.Y.C., 1980-94; pres. MEM Assocs., Inc., N.Y.C., 1995—. Contbr. articles to profl. jours. Trustee John D. and Catherine T. Mac Arthur Found., 1985—, Dole Found., 1984—, Smith Coll., 1988-93, Columbia U., 1991—; vis. fellow Sch. Architecture and Urban Planning, Princeton U., 1973-80; bd. dirs. Commonwealth on Found., 1982-88; mem. N.Y.C. Commn. on the Yr. 2000, 1985-87, MIT Corp., 1989-89; bd. govs. Am. Stock Exchange, 1987-92; adv. bd. Office of the Chief Med. Examiner, N.Y.C., 1987—; Barnard Coll, Inst. Med. Research, 1986-92; vice chmn. N.Y.C. Mayor's Com. for Pub./Pvt. Partnerships, 1990-93; bd. dirs. Alliance for Aging Rsch., 1987—, Overseas Devel. Coun., 1988—, Nat. Found. Center for Disease Control and Prevention, Inc. 1994—; mem. vestry Parish of Trinity Ch., 1982-89, 91-95; chmn. Atlantic Fellowships Selection Com., 1994—. Recipient Frank H. Lahey Meml. award, 1984, Women's Forum award, 1989, Walsh McDermott award, 1992,

Disting. Grantmaker award Coun. Founds., 1993, Edward R. Loveland award Am. Coll. Physicians, 1994, Special Recognition award AAMC, 1994, Merit medal Lotos Club, 1994, Terrance Keenan Leadership award in Health Philunthrophy, Grantmakers in Health, 1995. Mem. AAAS, Inst. Medicine of NAS, Am. Acad. Arts and Scis., Am. Philos. Soc., Coun. Fgn. Rels., Fin. Women's Assn., N.Y. Acad. Medicine (vice chmn. bd. govs.), N.Y. Acad. Scis., Alpha Omega Alpha. Office: MEM Assocs Inc 521 Fifth Ave Ste 2010 New York NY 10175

MAHONEY, MICHAEL NICHOLAS, newspaper owner; b. Hyannis, Mass., Aug. 24, 1938; s. Nicholas J. and Laurie M. (McMahon) M.; m. Nancy H. Mahoney, Sept. 25, 1980; children: Charles J. Hathaway, Jean M. Waytkus, Nicholas J. Hathaway. Degree, St. Anselm's Coll., Manchester, N.H., 1960. V.p., gen. mgr. Horicon Newspapers, Hoosick Falls, N.Y., 1962-80; ptnr. A&M Printers, Cambridge, N.Y., 1980-83; owner The Express, Mechanicville, N.Y., 1983—. Sgt. USMC, 1960-62. Mem. Greater Hoosick Boxing Club (founder, pres.). Roman Catholic. Avocation: railroad buff. Office: The Express 25 N Main St Mechanicville NY 12118-1936

MAHONEY, MICHAEL ROBERT TAYLOR, art historian, educator; b. Worcester, Mass., Jan. 24, 1935; s. Michael J. and Mary (Taylor) M. Grad., Phillips Acad., 1953; B.A., Yale U., 1959; Ph.D., Courtauld Inst., U. London, 1965. Finley fellow Nat. Gallery Art, 1962-64; fellow Harvard Center Italian Studies, Villa I Tatti, 1963; museum curator Nat. Gallery Art, 1964-69; prof. fine arts, chmn. dept. Trinity Coll., Hartford, Conn., 1969-86; Genevieve Harlow Goodwin prof. fine arts Trinity Coll., 1974—; Incorporator Hartford Pub. Library, 1970—; elector Wadsworth Atheneum, Hartford, 1974-85. Author: The Drawings of Salvator Rosa, 1977, (with Jean Cadogan) Wadsworth Atheneum Paintings II: Italy and Spain; editor: National Gallery of Art Report and Studies in the History of Art, 1968-69. Trustee Cesare Barbieri Found., Trinity Coll., 1977—, Watkinson Library, Trinity Coll., 1985—, Somerset House Art History Found., N.Y.C., 1985—; bd. govs. Hill-Stead Mus., Farmington, Conn., 1992—. Office: Trinity Coll Hartford CT 06106

MAHONEY, MICHAEL SEAN, history educator; b. N.Y.C., June 30, 1939; s. Thomas Michael and Dorothy (Hopkins) M.; m. Jean Carmel Angelilli, Aug. 20, 1960; children: Colin Sean, Bridget Elizabeth. AB, Harvard U., 1960; postgrad., U. Munich., 1960-62; PhD, Princeton U., 1967. Instr. history Princeton (N.J.) U., 1965-67, asst. prof., 1967-72, assoc. prof., 1972-80, prof., 1980—. Author: The Mathematical Career of Pierre de Fermat, 1973, 94, (in Japanese) Mathematics in History, 1982. Bd. edn. regional schs., Princeton, 1983-86; trustee Nat. Found. of Humanities, Arts and Sci., 1986—, chair, 1994—. Deutscher Akademischer Anstauschdienst fellow, 1960; NSF fellow, 1964-69. Mem. History Sci. Soc. (council mem. 1980-82), Soc. for History of Tech. Home: 85 Harrison St Princeton NJ 08540-5355 Office: Princeton U Princeton NJ 08544

MAHONEY, PATRICK MORGAN, retired judge; b. Winnipeg, Man., Can., Jan. 20, 1929; s. Paul Morgan and Joan Ethel Tracy (Patrick) M.; m. Mary Alma Sneath, June 28, 1958; children: Michael G., Patrick M., Sheila M., D'Arcy C. B.A., U. Alta., 1950, LL.B., 1951. Bar: Alta. 1952, apptd. Queen's counsel 1972, U.S. Ct. Mil. Appeals (hon.) 1983. Justice trial div. Fed. Ct. Can., Ottawa, Ont., 1973-83; judge Ct. Martial Appeal Ct. Can., Ottawa, 1973-82; chief justice Ct. Martial Appeal Ct. Can., 1982-94; ret.; judge Fed. Ct. Appeal, 1983-94; ret.; Mem. Parliament for Calgary South, 1968-72, sec. to minister of fin., 1970-71, minister of state, 1972. Mem. Can. Judges Conf. (dir. 1981), Calgary Golf and Country Club. Home: 3 Coltrin Pl, Ottawa, ON Canada K1M 0A5

MAHONEY, RICHARD, state official; b. Phoenix, Ariz. AB magna cum laude, Princeton Univ., 1973; MA, Johns Hopkins Univ., 1975, Ph.D., 1980; JD, Ariz. State Univ., 1980. Sec. of state, Ariz., 1991—. Author: JFK: Ordeal in Africa, 1983. Office: Office of the Sec of State State Capital W Wing 1700 W Washington St Ste 700 Phoenix AZ 85007-2808

MAHONEY, SHEILA IRENE, middle school educator; b. Dallas, Apr. 6, 1945; d. Raymond Francis and June Mary (Hoffman) M. BS in Edn., Ohio State U., 1970; MS in Adminstrn. Supervision, Nova U., Ft. Lauderdale, Fla., 1974-78. Tchr. 4th, 5th grades Avalon Elem. Sch. Collier County Schs., Naples, Fla., 1974-78; tchr. lang. arts, 11th grade Lely High Sch. Collier County Schs., Naples, 1978-80; tchr. lang. arts Gulfview Middle Sch. Collier County Schs., Naples, 1980—; mem. adv. bd. Collier County Reading Coun., Naples, 1975-78. Mem. ASCD, Collier County Reading Coun., Ohio State Alumni Assn., Phi Delta Kappa (adv. bd., historian Naples, 1988-91). Republican. Roman Catholic. Avocations: reading, travel, politics. Home: 255 2nd Ave S Naples FL 33940-5957

MAHONEY, THOMAS HENRY DONALD, historian, educator, government official; b. Cambridge, Mass., Nov. 4, 1913; s. Thomas Henry, Jr. and Frances (Lucy) M.; m. Phyllis Norton, July 14, 1951; children: Thomas Henry IV, Linda, David, Peter, Philip. A.B., Boston Coll., 1936, A.M., 1937; Ph.D., George Washington U., 1944; M.P.A., Harvard U., 1967, D.P.A., 1989. Instr. Gonzaga Sch., Washington 1937-39, Dunbarton Coll., Washington, 1938-39; instr., then asst. prof. history Boston Coll., 1939-44; asst. prof. history Holy Cross Coll., 1944-46; vis. lectr. history and govt. Smith Coll., 1944-45, Wellesley Coll., 1947-48; mem. faculty MIT, 1945-84, prof. history, 1961—, chmn. sect. history, 1963-65, 73-79; vis. prof. U. So. Calif., 1950; Lowell lectr. Boston, 1957; Carnegie fellow Harvard Law Sch., 1965-66; sec. elder affairs Commonwealth of Mass., 1979-83; head Mass. del. White House Conf. on Aging, 1981, mem. policy com., 1995; mem. ethnic com. U.S. Dept. Edn., 1979-83; mem. UN NGO Com. on Aging, N.Y.C., 1985—, chmn., 1987-91; corporator, trustee Cambridgeport Savs. Bank; adv. bd. Mildred & Claude Pepper Found., Washington, Tallahassee, 1989—; panelist, cons. numerous internat. confs. on gerontology; keynote speaker Interparliamentary Union meetings on aging, Bangkok, Guatemala City, Sofia, Budapest, London, 1986-89, New Delhi, 1993, Canberra, 1993, Paris, 1994, Copenhagen, 1994, Madrid, 1995; rep. of Internat. Fedn. Ageing, Montreal to UN, 1994—. Author: Edmund Burke and Ireland, 1960; co-author: Readings in International Order, 1951, China, Japan and the Powers, 3d edit., 1960, The U.S. in World History, 3d edit., 1963, Edmund Burke: The Enlightenment and the Modern World, 1977, 1776, 1977, Aging in Urbanization, 1990; editor: Burke's Reflections, 1955, Selected Writings and Speeches of Edmund Burke on America, 1964. Mem. Mass. Fulbright Com., 1953-74, chmn., 1966-74; observer Vatican City Consistories, 1956, 73, 85, World Assembly on Aging, Vienna, 1982; bd. dirs. Mass. Civic League, 1967—; state rep. Mass. Gen. Ct., 1971-78, chmn. energy and ethics coms., 1977-78; mem. community adv. coun. Jr. League Boston, 1982-86; UN rep. InterParliamentary Conf., Ottawa, 1985, Congress Latin Am. Socs. Gerontology and Geriatrics, Lima, 1984; N.Y. and Washington rep. Centre Internat. de Gérontologie, Paris, 1985-93; mem. Cambridge Sch. Com., 1948-54; chmn. trustees Cambridge Libr., 1948-54, Mass. State Libr., 1952-61; bd. dirs. Internat. Student Fedn.; mem. Cambridge City Coun., 1944-72; sr. advisor internat. issues and questions of aging Congressman Claude Pepper, 1985-88. Recipient Humanitarian of Yr. award Mass. Psychol. Soc., 1983; Am. Council of Learned Socs. fellow, 1938, Guggenheim fellow, 1961-62, Carnegie fellow, 1954, Ford Internat. Rsch. fellow, 1975. Fellow Royal Hist. Soc.; mem. Am. Hist. Assn., Am. Cath. Hist. Assn. (pres. 1957), Mass. Hist. Soc., Cath. Commn. Cultural and Intellectual Affairs, Conf. Brit. Studies, Nat. Conf. State Legislators (sci. and tech. com., intergovtl. rels. com. 1973-78, mem. del. People's Republic of China 1976 and Republic of China, Taiwan 1978, keynoter Singapore Internat. Conf. on Elders 1993). Home: 130 Mt Auburn St Apt 410 Cambridge MA 02138-5779

MAHONEY, WILLIAM FRANCIS, editor; b. Joliet, Ill., Jan. 24, 1935; s. Cletus George and Mildred Marie (Ochs) M.; m. Carroll Frances Johnson, June 28, 1958; children: Erin Michele Alderfer, Kevin William, Megan Ann, Sheila Marie, Nora Aileen. BS in Journalism, Marquette U., 1957. Reporter Ft. Wayne (Ind.) News Sentinel, 1958-59; pub. rels. mgr. Motorola, Inc., Franklin Park, Ill., 1959-66; sr. account exec. Young & Rubicam, Inc. Chgo., 1966-68; pub. info. dir. ABA, Chgo., 1969-71; investor rels. mgr. Chemetron Corp., Chgo., 1971-76; corp. commn. dir. Scott Paper Co. Phila., 1976-80; pub. rels. dir. Esmark Inc., Chgo., 1980-81; prin. Mahoney & Mitchell Incorp., Phila., 1981-89, Investor Rels. Ptnrs., Livingston, N.J., 1993—. Author: Investor Relations: The Professional's Guide to Financial

and Marketing Communications, 1991, The Active Shareholder, 1993; editor Investor Rels. Update. Mem. Nat. Investor Rels. Inst. (pres. Phila. chpt. 1982-84, v.p. 1988—), Pub. Rels. Soc. Am. Vesper Club. Republican. Roman Catholic. Home and Office: 716 S Brandywine St West Chester PA 19382-3511

MAHONY, ROGER M. CARDINAL, archbishop; b. Hollywood, Calif., Feb. 27, 1936; s. Victor James and Loretta Marie (Baron) M. A.A., Our Lady Queen of Angels Sem., 1956; B.A., St. John's Sem. Coll., 1958, B.S.T., 1962; M.S.W., Catholic U. Am., 1964. Ordained priest Roman Cath. Ch., 1962, ordained bishop, 1975, created cardinal priest, 1991. Asst. pastor St. John's Cathedral, Fresno, Calif., 1962, 68-73, rector, 1973-80; residence St. Genevieve's Parish, Fresno, Calif., 1964—; adminstr., 1964-67, pastor, 1967-68; titular bishop of Tamascani, aux. bishop of Fresno, 1975-80; chancellor Diocese of Fresno, 1970-77, vicar gen., 1975-80; bishop Diocese of Stockton (Calif.), 1980-85; archbishop Archdiocese of L.A., 1985-91, cardinal priest, 1991—; diocesan dir. Cath. Charities and Social Svc. Fresno, 1964-70, exec. dir. Cath. Welfare Bur., 1964-70; exec. dir. Cath. Welfare Bur. Infant of Prague Adoption Service, 1964-70; chaplain St. Vincent de Paul Soc., Fresno, 1964-70; named chaplain to Pope Paul VI, 1967; mem. faculty extension div. Fresno State U., 1965-67; sec. U.S. Cath. bishops ad hoc com. on farm labor Nat. Conf. Bishops, 1970-75; chmn. com. on pub. welfare and income maintenance Nat. Conf. Cath. Charities, 1969-70; bd. dirs. West Coast Regional Office Bishops Com. for Spanish-Speaking, 1967-70; chmn. Calif. Assn. Cath. Charities Dirs., 1965-69; trustee St. Patrick's Sem., Archdiocese of San Francisco, 1974-75; mem. adminstrv. com. Nat. conf. Cath. Bishops, 1976-79, 82-85, 87-90, com. migration and refugees, 1976—, chmn. com. farm labor, 1981—, com. moral evaluation of deterrence, 1986-88; cons. com., chmn. for ProLife Activities, 1990—; mem. com. social devel. and world peace U.S. Cath. Conf., 1985, chmn. internat. policy sect., 1987-90; com. justice and peace, Pontifical Couns., 1984-89, 90—, pastoral care of migrants and itinerant people, 1986—, social communications, 1989—. Mem. Urban Coalition of Fresno, 1968-72, Fresno County Econ. Opportunities Commn., 1964-65, Fresno County Alcoholic Rehab. Com., 1966-67, Fresno City Charter Rev. Com., 1968-70, Mexican-Am. Council for Better Housing, 1968-72, Fresno Redevel. Agy., 1970-75, L.A. 2000 Com., 1985-88, Fed. Commn. Agrl. Workers, 1987—, Blue Ribbon Com. Affordable Housing City of L.A., 1988; mem. commn. to Draft an Ethics Code for L.A. City Govt., 1989-90; bd. dirs. Fresno Community Workshop, 1965-67; trustee St. Agnes Hosp., Fresno. Named Young Man of Yr. Fresno Jr. C. of C., 1967. Mem. Canon Law Soc. Am., Nat. Assn. Social Workers. Home: 114 E 2nd St Los Angeles CA 90012 Office: Archdiocese of LA 1531 W 9th St Los Angeles CA 90015-1194*

MAHOWALD, ANTHONY PETER, geneticist, cell biologist, educator; b. Albany, Minn., Nov. 24, 1932; s. Aloys and Cecilia (Maus) Mahowald; m. Mary Lou Briody, Apr. 11, 1971; children: Maureen, Lisa, Michael. BS, Spring Hill Coll., 1958; PhD, Johns Hopkins U., 1962. Asst. prof. Marquette U., Milw., 1966-70; asst. staff mem. Inst. Cancer Rsch., Phila., 1970-72; assoc. prof. Ind. U., Bloomington, 1972-76, prof., 1976-82; Henry Willson Payne prof. Case Western Res. U., Cleve., 1982-90, chmn. dept. anatomy, 1982-88, chmn. dept. genetics, 1988-90; Louis Block prof., chmn. dept molecular genetics and cell biology U. Chgo., 1990—; chmn. Com. Devel. Biology U. Chgo., 1991—. Woodrow Wilson Found. fellow, 1958, NSF fellow, 1958-62. Fellow AAAS, Am. Acad. Arts and Scis., Soc. Scholars Johns Hopkins U.; mem. Nat. Acad. Scis., Genetics Soc. Am. (sec. 1986-88), Soc. Devel. Biology (pres. 1989, editor-in-chief jour. 1980-85), Am. Soc. Cell Biology. Office: U Chgo Dept Molecular Genetics/Cell Biology Chicago IL 60637

MAHR, GEORGE JOSEPH, financial service executive, real estate developer; b. Bklyn., Mar. 9, 1947; s. George Joseph and Mary Ann (Hanrahan) M.; m. Joan Valeroso, Mar. 21, 1970; children: Christopher, Courtney, Kelly. BS in Acctg., N.Y. Inst. Tech., 1970. Auditor Price Waterhouse & Co., Huntington Station, N.Y., 1973-77; mgr. internal audit United Techs. Corp., Hartford, Conn., 1977-83, contr., 1983-84, v.p. fin., chief fin. officer, 1985-86; v.p. fin., chief fin. officer Mostek Corp. div. United Techs. Corp., Carrollton, Tex., 1986, 1987; v.p. bus. devel. SGS-Thomson Microelectronics, Inc., Carrollton; mng. ptnr. Mahr Leonard Mgmt. Co., Dallas, 1988—; chmn. Semicondr. Insights, Inc., Kanata, Ont., Can., Mahr Devel. Corp., Dallas, Lenmar Devel. Corp., Dallas, Mahr Devel. Corp. Fla., Dallas, Sailfish Enterprises, Inc., Dallas; ptnr. DJ Enterprises, Dallas. Dir. Fairhill Sch., Dallas. Home: 2616 Rothland Ln Plano TX 75023-1421 Office: Mahr Leonard Mgmt Co Ste 626 5420 Lyndon B Johnson Fwy Dallas TX 75240-2643

MAHRE, PHIL, alpine ski racer, race car driver; b. Yakima, Wash., May 10, 1957; s. David Robert and Mary Ellen (Chotl) M.; m. Holly Mahre; 3 children. Student, pub. schs. Mem. U.S. Men's Pro Tour, 1989. Olympic Silver medalist in slalom Lake Placid, N.Y., 1980, Olympic Gold medalist, Sarajevo, Yugoslavia, 1984, winner World Cup, 1981, 82, 83, First Interstate Bank Cup slalom, 1989. Office: US Ski Team PO Box 100 Park City UT 84060-0100*

MAHSMAN, DAVID LAWRENCE, religious publications editor; b. Quincy, Ill., Aug. 16, 1950; s. Alvin Henry and Dorothy Marie (Schnack) M.; m. Lois Jean Mohn, July 27, 1975. BS in Journalism, So. Ill. U., 1972; MDiv, Concordia Theol. Seminary, Fort Wayne, Ind., 1983; STM, Concordia Sem., St. Louis, 1995. Staff writer Paddock Publs., Arlington Heights, Ill., 1972-73, Decatur (Ill.) Herald & Rev., 1973-76; press asst. Hon. Tom Railsback U.S. Ho. Reps., Washington, 1976-79; campaign press sec. Hon. Dan Coats U.S. Ho. Reps., Ft. Wayne, Ind., 1979-80, 82; pastor Trinity Luth. Ch., Glen Cove, N.Y., 1983-85; dir. news and info. Luth. Ch.-Mo. Synod, St. Louis, 1985—; exec. editor, contbr. Luth. Witness, St. Louis, 1985—; exec. editor Reporter, St. Louis, 1985—; mem. Inter-Luth. task force on pornography Luth. Coun. U.S.A., 1986; mem. Washington adv. coun. Mo. Synod, Washington, 1987—. Recipient Jacob Scher Investigative Reporting award Women in Comm., 1974, Commendation award Concordia Hist. Inst., 1988. Mem. Concordia Hist. Inst. (life). Republican. Avocations: travel, photography, flying. Office: Luth Ch-Mo Synod 1333 S Kirkwood Rd Saint Louis MO 63122-7295

MAI, CHAO CHEN, engineer; b. Kwangchow, Canton, China, Feb. 26, 1936; came to U.S. 1962, naturalized 1973; m. Shao Shen Yam; children: Glenn, Kenneth. M.S.E.E., Oreg. State U., 1964; Ph.D. in E.E. Utah State U., 1967. Project engr. Sylvania Electric Co., Woburn, Mass., 1967-70; mgr. research and devel. Mostek Corp., Carrollton, Tex., 1970-76, v.p. research and devel., 1976-84; founder, sr. v.p. Dallas Semiconductor Corp., 1984—. Patentee Silicon gate combined with depletion load process, 1974; method for making a semicondr. device, 1985. MOSFET Fabrication Process, 1984. Mem. IEEE, Electrochem. Soc. Current work: Advanced processing technology in integrated circuits. Subspecialties: Integrated circuits; Microchip technology (engineering).

MAI, ELIZABETH HARDY, lawyer; b. Ithaca, N.Y., Nov. 7, 1948; d. William Frederick and Barbara Lee (Morrell) M.; m. Edward John Gobrecht III, May 19, 1990. BA in Am. Studies, Cornell U., 1970; JD, Dickinson Sch. Law, 1975. Bar: Pa. 1975, U.S. Dist. Ct. (mid. dist.) Pa. 1976. Atty. Keystone Legal Svcs., Inc., State Coll., Pa., 1975-76; asst. atty. gen. Pa. Dept. Commerce, Harrisburg, Pa., 1976-77; chief counsel Pa. Dept. Commerce, Harrisburg, 1978; assoc. Wolf, Block, Schorr and Solis-Cohen, Phila., 1979-83, ptnr., 1986—; v.p., gen. counsel EQK Ptnrs., Bala Cynwyd, Pa., 1983-86; chair environ. dept. Wolf, Block, Schorr and Solis-Cohen; mem. long range planning and mktg. com. Loan Workout Group; co-chair Pa. state govt. affairs Internat. Coun. Shopping Ctrs.; founding dir., mem. Comml. Real Estate Women, Phila.; bd. dirs. Nat. Network Comml. Real Estate Women; adj. prof. Villanova (Pa.) U. Sch. Law, 1986—. Active Cornell U. Real Estate Coun., 1990—. Mem. ABA, Am. Coll. Real Estate Lawyers, Pa. Bar Assn., Phila. Bar Assn. Office: Wolf Block Schorr and Solis-Cohen 15th & Chestnut Sts 12th fl Philadelphia PA 19102

MAI, HAROLD LEVERNE, retired federal judge; b. Casper, Wyo., Apr. 5, 1928. BA, U. Wyo., 1950, JD, 1952. Bar: Wyo. 1952, U.S. Supreme Ct. 1963. Sole practice, Cheyenne, Wyo. 1953-62, 67-71; judge Juvenile Ct., Cheyenne, 1962-67; U.S. bankruptcy judge, Cheyenne, 1971-93, ret. 1993. Mem. adv.

bd. Salvation Army. Wyo. Mem. ABA, Wyo. Bar Assn., Laramie County Bar Assn., Nat. Conf. Bankruptcy Judges.

MAI, KLAUS L., oil research company executive; b. Changsha, China, Mar. 7, 1930; s. Ludwig H. and Ilse (Behrend) M.; m. Helen M. Martinchek, July 14, 1957; children: Martin, Michael, Mark, Matthew. BS in Chem. Engring., Gonzaga U., Spokane, Wash., 1951; MS, U. Wash. Seattle, 1952, PhD, 1954. Registered profl. engr., Wash. With Shell Chem. Co., Houston, 1957-74, 77-81; various overseas assignments Shell Chem. Co., 1974-75; v.p. Shell Chem. Co., Houston, 1979-82; v.p. transp. and supplies Shell Oil Co., 1976-82; pres. Shell Devel. Co., Houston, 1982-87; chmn., pres. World Petroleum Congresses, London and Houston, 1987—. Contbr. articles to profl. publs.; patentee. Chmn. bd. dirs. S.W. Rsch. Inst., San Antonio; mem. Gov.'s Sci. and Tech. Coun.; pres., bd. dirs. Keystone Ctr., René DuBos Ctr. Recipient Disting. Alumnus award Gonzaga U., 1982, U. Wash., 1988. Fellow Am. Inst. Chem. Engrs.; mem. Soc. Chem. Industry, Am. Petroleum Inst., Coun. Chem. Rsch. (chmn., bd. dirs.), Keystone Found., Am. Ind. Health Coun. (bd. dirs.), Chem. Indsl. Inst. Toxicology (bd. dirs.), Lakeside Country Club (Houston), Petroleum Club of Houston, Sigma Xi, Tau Beta Pi. Office: World Petroleum Congresses PO Box 79331 Houston TX 77279-9331

MAIBACH, BEN C., JR., service executive; b. Bay City, Mich., 1920. With Barton-Malow Co., Detroit, 1938—, v.p., dir.-in-charge field ops., 1949-53, exec. v.p., 1953-60, pres., 1960-76, chmn. bd., 1976; chmn. and dir. Barton-Malow Ent.; chmn. bd. Cloverdale Equipment Co. Trustee Barton-Malow Found, Maibach Found., 1967—; Greater Del Safety Coun.; chmn. Apostolic Christian Woodhaven, Detroit; bishop Apostolic Christian Ch., Mich., Ont., Fla.; nat. chmn. Apostolic Ch. European Relief Bd., 1991—; bd. dirs. S.E. Mich. chpt. ARC, United Found., Rural Gospel and Med. Missions of India. Home: 34050 Ramble Hills Dr Farmington MI 48331-4224 also: 5525 Azure Way Siesta Isle Sarasota FL 34242 Office: Barton-Malow Co Ste 800 27777 Franklin Rd Southfield MI 48034

MAIBACH, BEN C., III, construction company executive; b. 1946. BS, Mich. State U., 1969. With Barton-Malow Corp., Oak Park, Mich., 1964—, v.p. field ops., 1964-68, systems analyst, programmer, 1968-70, project adminstr., 1970-72, officer mgr., purchasing agt., 1972-73, v.p., 1973-76, exec. v.p., 1976-81, pres., 1981—. Office: Barton-Malow Co PO Box 5200 Detroit MI 48235

MAIBACH, HOWARD I., dermatologist; b. N.Y.C., July 18, 1929; s. Jack Louis and Sidonia (Fink) M.; m. Siesel Wile, July 8, 1953; children—Lisa, Ed, Todd. A.B., Tulane U., 1950, M.D., 1955. Diplomate: Am. Bd. Dermatology. Intern William Beaumont Army Hosp., El Paso, Tex., 1955-56; resident, fellow in dermatology USPHS, Hosp. of U. Pa., 1959-61; asst. instr. U. Pa., 1958-61, lectr., 1960-61; practice medicine specializing in dermatology U. Calif. Hosps., San Francisco, 1961—; asst. prof. dermatology U. Calif. Sch. Medicine, San Francisco, 1961-63; asso. prof. U. Calif. Sch. Medicine, 1967-73; research asso. Cancer Research Inst., 1967—; mem. staff U. Calif.-H.C. Moffitt Hosps., 1961—; cons. Laguna Honda Hosp., 1962-66, chief dermatology service, 1963-67; cons. Letterman Gen. Hosp., Calif. Med. Facility, Vacaville, San Francisco Gen. Hosp., Sonoma State Hosp., Eldridge, Calif., Stanford Research Inst., Menlo Park, Calif., Calif. Dept. Public Health, Berkeley, VA Hosp., Research Inst. Fragrance Materials, Inc., David Grant USAF Hosp. of Travis AFB, Naval Hosp., San Diego, Wilford Hall AFB, Tex., Army Environ. Health Agy., Md.; mem. Internat. Contact Dermatitis Research Com. Editor: Animal Models in Dermatology, 1965; co-editor: Dermatotoxicology and Pharmacology, 1977, Skin Microbiology, 1981; bd. editors: Internat. Jour. Dermatology, 1974—; editorial bd.: Contact Dermatitis: Environ. Dermatology, 1974—, Clin. Toxicology, 1976—; internat. editorial bd.: Excerpta Media, 1976—; author, coauthor, editor of over 30 books and 750 publs. Served to capt. M.C. U.S. Army, 1955-58. Recipient awards Soc. Cosmetic Chemists, 1970, 71, 73. Fellow A.C.P.; mem. Am. Acad. Dermatology (award for essay 1961), San Francisco Dermatol. Soc. (pres. 1970-71), Pacific Dermatol. Assn., Soc. Investigative Dermatology, N.Y. Acad. Scis., Calif. Med. Assn., Am. Fedn. Clin. Research, AMA, San Francisco Med. Soc., Am. Dermatol. Assn., Internat. Soc. Tropical Dermatology, Am. Soc. Clin. Pharmacology and Therapeutics, Am. Coll. Toxicology; hon. mem. Swedish Dermatol. Soc., Am. Vet. Dermatol. Assn., Am. Acad. Vet. Dermatology, Danish Dermatol. Soc., German Dermatol. Soc. Office: Univ of Calif Hosp San Francisco CA 94143

MAIBENCO, HELEN CRAIG, anatomist, educator; b. New Deer, Aberdeenshire, Scotland, June 9, 1917; came to U.S., 1917; d. Benjamin C. and Mary (Brown) Craig; children: Thomas Allen, Douglas Craig. BS, Wheaton (Ill.) Coll., 1948; MS, DePaul U., 1950; PhD, U. Ill., Chgo., 1956. Asst. prof., assoc. prof., then prof. U. Ill., Chgo., 1956-73; prof. Rush U. Chgo., 1973-86, prof. emeritus, 1993—; anatomist dept. rehab. medicine Rush-Presbyn.-St. Luke's Med. Ctr., Chgo., 1986—, rsch. cons., 1973—; prof. emeritus Rush-U. Chgo., 1986—; cons. on grant application NIH, Bethesda, Md. Contbr. articles to profl. jours. Mem. AAAS, Endocrine Soc., Am. Assn. Anatomists, Sigma Xi. Republican. Presbyterian. Home: 1324 S Main St Wheaton IL 60187-6480

MAICHEL, JOSEPH RAYMOND, lawyer, business executive; b. Stanton, N.D., Nov. 24, 1934; s. John and Sarfina (Hoffman) M.; m. Hilda Deichert, Jan. 7, 1961; children: Mary, Mark, Scott. BS in Acctg., U. N.D., 1957, JD with distinction, 1959. Bar: N.D. 1959. Spl. asst. atty. gen. State of N.D., 1959-71; atty. Mont.-Dakota Utilities Co., Bismarck, N.D., 1971-76, gen. counsel, sec., 1976-82, v.p., gen. counsel, sec., 1979-82, group v.p. distbn., 1982-85, pres., 1985-90, pres., chief exec. officer, 1990-94, also bd. dirs., 1982-90; gen. counsel Knife River Coal Mining Co., Bismarck, 1979-82; also bd. dir., pres., dirs. Grassland, Inc., Bismarck, 1978-84; sec., dir. Fidelity Coal Co., 1980-83, Welch Coal Co., 1980-83, Wibaux Gas Co., 1980-83; tchr. bus. law, 1968—; mem. adv. group Dist. N.D. Civil Justice Reform Act; chmn. N.D. Pub. Employees Retirement System. Contbr. articles to legal jours. Mem. adv. coun. U. N.D. Sch. Engring. Mem. N.D. Bar Assn., Burleigh County Bar Assn., North Ctrl. Electric Assn., Midwest Gas Assn., Edison Electric Inst. (bd. dirs.), Delta Sigma Pi, Phi Alpha Delta. Roman Catholic. Office: Montana-Dakota Utilities Co 400 N 4th St Bismarck ND 58501-4022

MAICKEL, ROGER PHILIP, pharmacologist, educator; b. Floral Park, N.Y., Sept. 8, 1933; s. Philip Vincent and Margaret Mary (Rose) M.; m. Lois Louise Pivonka, Sept. 8, 1956; children: Nancy Ellen Maickel Ward, Carolyn Sue Maickel Anderson. BS, Manhattan (N.Y.) Coll., 1954; postgrad., Poly. Inst. Bklyn., 1954-55; M.S., Georgetown U., 1957, Ph.D., 1960. Biochemist Nat. Heart Inst., Bethesda, Md., 1955-65; asso. prof. pharmacology Ind. U., 1965-69, prof., 1969—, head sect. pharmacology med. scis. program, 1971-77; prof. pharmacology and toxicology, head dept. Sch. Pharmacy and Pharmacal Scis. Purdue U., West Lafayette, Ind., 1977-83; dir. lab. animal program Purdue U., West Lafayette, 1988—; acting v.p. product acquisition and devel. BetaMED Pharma., Inc., Indpls., 1983-84. Adv. editor: Pergamon Press, 1970-88; adv. editorial bd.: Neuropharmacology, 1974-88. Bd. dirs. TEAMS, Inc., 1981-87, Am. Coun. on Sci. and Health, 1993—; trustee AAALAC, 1992—. Recipient Alumni award in medicine Manhattan Coll. 1972. Fellow AAAS, Am. Coll. Neuropsychopharmacology, Am. Inst. Chemists (bd. dirs. 1989-92, pres.-elect 1992-94, pres. 1994-96), Royal Soc. Chemistry, Collegium Internat. de Neuro-Psychopharmacologicum; mem. Am. Chem. Soc., Am. Soc. Pharmacology and Exptl. Therapeutics, Am. Soc. Clin. Pharmacology and Therapeutics, ASTM, Soc. Forensic Toxicologists, Internat. Assn. Chiefs Police, Internat. Soc. Psychoneuroendocrinology, N.Y. Acad. Scis., Soc. Neurosci., Soc. Toxicology, Sigma Xi, Rho Chi. Home: 3567 Canterbury Dr Lafayette IN 47905-3714 Office: R E Heine Pharmacy Bldg Purdue Univ Lafayette IN 47907-1334 *As a human being, I hope to be able to do my best in the roles of scientist, teacher, and citizen by fulfilling the academic criteria of teaching, research, and service to the utmost degree humanly possible.*

MAIDA, ADAM JOSEPH, archbishop; b. East Vandergrift, Pa., Mar. 18, 1930. Student, St. Vincent Coll., Latrobe, Pa., St. Mary's U., Balt., Lateran U., Rome, Duquesne U. Ordained priest Roman Cath. Ch., 1956, consecrated bishop, 1984. Bishop Green Bay, Wis., 1984-89; archbishop Detroit, 1990—. Home: 75 E Boston Blvd Detroit MI 48202-1318 Office: Archdiocese of Detroit 1234 Washington Blvd Detroit MI 48226-1800*

MAIDIQUE, MODESTO ALEX, academic administrator; b. Havana, Cuba, Mar. 20, 1940; s. Modesto Maidique and Hilda Rodriguez; m. Ana Hernandez, July 18, 1981; children: Ana Teresa, Mark Alex. BS, MIT, 1962, MS, 1964, PhD, 1970. Instr. MIT, Boston, 1976-79; v.p., gen. mgr. Analog Devices Semiconductor, Boston, 1970-76; asst. prof. Harvard U., Boston, 1976-81; assoc. prof. Stanford U., Palo Alto, Calif., 1981-84; sr. ptnr. Hambrecht and Quist Venture Ptnrs., Palo Alto, Calif., 1981-86; co-founder, dir. U. Miami (Fla.) Innovation and Entepreneurship Inst., 1984-86; pres. Fla. Internat. U., Miami, 1986—. Mem. Pres.'s Edn. Policy Adv. Com.; chmn. Beacon Coun., 1992-93. Recipient Citizenship award HEW, 1973, Teaching award Stanford U., 1983. Mem. IEEE, Assn. Cuban Engrs. Republican. Roman Catholic. Home: 6821 SW 104th St Miami FL 33156-3253 Office: Fla Internat U Office of President Miami FL 33199

MAIDMAN, RICHARD HARVEY MORTIMER, lawyer; b. N.Y.C., Nov. 17, 1933; s. William and Ada (Seegle) M.; m. Lynne Rochelle Lateiner, Apr. 3, 1960 (div. Sept. 1987); children: Patrick, Mitchel, Dagny. BA, Williams Coll., 1955; JD, Yale U., 1959; postgrad. N.Y. U. Grad. Sch. Bus., 1957, Grad. Sch. Law, 1960, 77. Bar: N.Y. 1961, Fla., 1961, U.S. Dist. Ct. 1962, 79, U.S. Ct. Appeals 1966, U.S. Supreme Ct., 1978. Assoc. Saxe, Bacon & O'Shea, N.Y.C., 1962-64; ptnr. Weiner, Maidman & Goldman, N.Y.C., 1964-67; pvt. practice, N.Y.C., and Fla., 1968—; bd. dirs. Microbiol. Scis., Inc.; pres. MBS Equities, Inc., 1970-88, Fashion Wear Realty Co., Inc., N.Y.C., 1975—; mng. gen. ptnr. Richard and David Maidman, N.Y.C., 1972—, Barcelona Hotel Ltd., Miami Beach, Fla., 1975-84, New Haven Projects Co., 1987—; dir. The Farr Companies, Washington, 1990-92; legis. counsel Theodore R. Kupferman, 17th Congl. Dist. N.Y., 1966-68; of counsel Shwal, Thompson & Bloch, N.Y.C. and Geneva, 1976-87; receiver Halloran House Hotel, N.Y.C., 1981. Contbr. articles to profl. jours. Mem. ABA, N.Y. State Bar Assn., Fla. Bar Assn., Assn. Bar City N.Y., Bankruptcy Lawyers Assn. N.Y.C., Real Estate Bd. of N.Y. Home: Steamboat Lndg Sands Point NY 11050 Office: 432 E 87th St New York NY 10128-6502

MAIDON, CAROLYN HOWSER, academic program administrator; b. Chgo., May 13, 1946; d. Lloyd Earl and Esther Lillian (Beck) Howser; m. Charles Randall Maidon, Nov. 21, 1970; children: Randall Scott, April Janel. BS in Edn., Okla. State U., 1968; MS in Edn., N.C. State U., 1984, postgrad., 1987—. Tchr. biology and English Cary (N.C.) High Sch., 1968-71; grad. instr. N.C. State U., Raleigh, 1984-85, asst. affirmative action officer, 1985-89, asst. dir. univ. undesignated program, 1989—. Home: 311 Hemlock St Cary NC 27513 Office: NC State U Box 7105 Raleigh NC 27695-7105

MAIDON, GILLES, dancer; b. Paris. Studied with Raymond Franchetti, studied with Diane Carter. Soloist Ballet de Marseille, Paris, 1976-83; dancer Santiago (Chile) Ballet, 1983-90, Cin. Ballet, 1990-92; prin. artist Ballet West, Salt Lake City, 1992—; guest artist various ballet cos., galas and festivals. Dance performances include Notre Dame de Paris, Peer Gynt, Anna Karenina, Sergeant Early's Dream, Taming of the Shrew, The Great Gatsby, Swan Lake. Office: Ballet West 50 West 200 South Salt Lake City UT 84101*

MAIENSCHEIN, FRED C., physicist; b. Belleville, Ill., Oct. 28, 1925; s. Fred and Ethel (Forsythe) M.; m. Joyce Kylander, Aug. 14, 1948; children: Jane, Jon. B.S. in Chem. Engring, Rose Hulman Inst. Tech., 1945; M.S. in Physics, Ind. U., 1948, Ph.D. in Physics, 1949. Physicist Oak Ridge Nat. Lab., 1951-60, assoc. dir. engring. physics div., 1960-66; co-dir. Oak Ridge Electron Linear Accelerator, 1965-74, dir. engring. physics div., 1966-90, ret., 1990; current neurosci. scholar; mem. com. reactor physics Nuclear Energy Agy., 1962-89; mem. adv. com. radiation aspects of SST, FAA, 1969-74; mem. subcoms. Nat. Com. Radiation Protection, 1959-71. Contbr. articles profl. jours., chpts. in books. Fellow Am. Nuclear Soc.; mem. Am. Phys. Soc., AAAS, Soc. Neurosci., Tau Beta Pi. Home: 838 W Outer Dr Oak Ridge TN 37830-8402

MAIER, ALFRED, neuroscientist; b. Bamberg, Bavaria, Fed. Republic of Germany, Sept. 16, 1929; came to U.S., 1958; s. Johan and Barbara (Rauh) M. BS in Zooology, Calif State U., Long Beach, 1967; PhD in Anatomy, UCLA, 1972. Postdoctoral fellow Dept. Kinesiology, UCLA, 1972-74; instr. Dept. Cell Biology U. Ala., Birmingham, 1974-76, asst. prof. 1976-80, assoc. prof., 1980-89, prof., 1989—; rsch. sabbatical Faculty Biology U. Konstanz, Fed. Republic of Germany, 1984, Dept. Physiology U. Otago, Dunedin, New Zealand, 1990; vis. prof. Faculty of Biology, U. Konstanz, 1985, '86. Contbr. articles and sci. papers to profl. jours and seminars. Recipient Pres.'s award for Excellence in Tchg., U. Ala., 1994, Didactic Instr. of Yr. Sch. Dentistry, 1993, 94, Best Basic Sci. Instr. Sch. Dentistry, 1978, 79, 83, 84. Mem. Soc. for Neurosci., Am. Assn. Anatomists. Avocations: photography, gardening, travel, camping.

MAIER, CHARLES STEVEN, history educator; b. N.Y.C., N.Y., Feb. 23, 1939; s. Louis and Muriel (Krailsheimer) M.; m. Pauline Alice Rubbelke, June 17, 1961; children—Andrea Nicole, Nicholas Winterer, Jessica Elizabeth Heine. A.B., Harvard U., 1960; postgrad., St. Anthony's Coll., Oxford, Eng., 1960-61; Ph.D., Harvard U., 1967. Instr. history Harvard U., Cambridge, Mass., 1967-69, asst. prof., 1969-73, lectr., 1973-75; vis. prof. U. Bielefeld, Fed. Republic Germany, 1976; assoc. prof. history Duke U. Durham, N.C., 1976-79, prof., 1979-81; prof. history Harvard U., Cambridge, Mass., 1981-91, Krupp Found. prof. European studies, 1991—; dir. Ctr. for European Studies, 1994—; rsch. fellow Lehrman Inst., N.Y.C., 1975-76; mem. assoc. staff Brookings Instn., Washington, 1978-84; mem. coun. Fondation Jean Monnet pour l'Europe, Lausanne, Switzerland; mem. joint comm. on We. Europe Social Sci. Rsch. Coun. and Am. Coun. Learned Socs., 1978-84, chmn., 1979-81. Author: Recasting Bourgeois Europe, 1975 (Am. Hist. Assn. George Louis Beer award 1976, Herbert Baxter Adams award 1977), In Search of Stability, 1987, The Unmasterable Past, 1988; editor: The Origins of the Cold War and Contemporary Europe, 1978, rev. edit., 1990, (with Dan S. White) The Thirteenth of May and the Advent of de Gaulle's Republic, 1967, (with Leon Lindberg) The Politics of Inflation and Economic Stagnation, 1985, Changing Boundaries of the Political, 1987, The Marshall Plan and Germany, 1991. Fellow NEH, 1977-78, German Marshall Fund, 1980-81, Guggenheim Found., 1988-89; rsch. grantee MacArthur Found., 1988-89. Fellow Woodrow Wilson Ctr. for Scholars (Washington); mem. Council on Fgn. Relations, Am. Hist. Assn., Soc. Italian Hist. Studies, Soc. Historians of Am. Fgn. Rels., Am. Acad. Arts and Scis., Phi Beta Kappa. Home: 60 Larchwood Dr Cambridge MA 02138-4639 Office: Harvard U Ctr for European Studies Cambridge MA 02138

MAIER, CRAIG FRISCH, restaurant executive; b. Cin., Sept. 20, 1949; s. Jack Craig and Blanche June (Frisch) M. BA, Trinity Coll., Hartford, Conn., 1971; MBA, Columbia U., 1975. With Frisch's Restaurant, Cin., 1975—, exec. v.p., 1987-89, pres., chief exec. officer, 1989—. Bd. dirs. Cin. Mus. Natural History, 1990—, Cin. Playhouse in the Pk., 1992—, Dan Beard coun. Boy Scouts Am., 1992—, Cin. Bus. Com., 1994—, Greater Cin. Cov. and Visitors Bur., 1995—. Mem. Greater Cin. Restaurant Assn. (bd. dirs. 1991—). Republican. Avocations: jogging, gardening, golf. Office: Frisch's Restaurants Inc 2800 Gilbert Ave Cincinnati OH 45206-1206

MAIER, DONNA JANE-ELLEN, history educator; b. St. Louis, Feb. 20, 1948; d. A. Russell and Mary Virginia Maier; m. Stephen J. Rapp, Jan. 3, 1981; children: Alexander John, Stephanie Jane-Ellen. BA, Coll. of Wooster, 1969; MA, Northwestern U., 1972, PhD, 1975. Assoc. prof. U. Tex. at Dallas, Richardson, 1975-78; asst. prof. history U. No. Iowa, Cedar Falls, 1978-81, assoc. prof., 1981-86, prof., 1986—; cons. Scott, Foresman Pub., Glenview, Ill., 1975-94; editl. cons. Children's Press, 1975-76, Macmillan Pubs., 1989-90, Haper-Collins Pubs., 1994. Co-author: History and Life, 1976, 4th edit., 1990; author: Priests and Power, 1983; co-editor African Economic History, 1992—; contbr. articles to profl. jours., essays to books. Mem. Iowa Dem. Com. Cen. Com., 1982-90, chmn. budget com., 1986-90; chmn. 3d Congl. Dist. Cen. Com., 1986-88. Fulbright-Hays fellow, Ghana, 1972, Arab Republic Egypt, 1987; fellow Am. Philos. Soc., London, 1978. Mem. Am. Hist. Assn., African Studies Assn., AAUW (fellow Ghana 1973), Quota Club. Home: 219 Highland Blvd Waterloo IA 50703-4229 Office: U No Iowa Dept History Cedar Falls IA 50614

MAIER, GERALD JAMES, natural gas transmission and marketing company executive; b. Regina, Sask., Can., Sept. 22, 1928; s. John Joseph and Mary (Passler) M. Student, Notre Dame Coll. (Wilcox), U. Man., U. Alta., U. Western Ont. With petroleum and mining industries Can., U.S., Australia, U.K.; responsible for petroleum ops. Africa, United Arab Emirates, S.E. Asia; chmn. TransCan. PipeLines, Calgary, 1984—, also bd. dirs.; 1985-95; bd. dirs. BCE Inc., Bank of N.S., TransAlta Utilities Corp., Du Pont Can. Inc., Alberta Nat. Gas Co., Ltd.; immediate past chmn. Can. Nat. com. for World Petroleum Congresses, Van Horne Inst. for Internat. Transp.; bd. govs. Bus. Coun. on Nat. Issues. Named Hon. Col. King's Own Calgary Rgt., Resource Man of Yr. Alta. Chamber of Resources, 1990; recipient Can. Engr.'s Gold medal Can. Coun. Profl. Engrs., 1990, Disting. Alumni award U. Alta., 1992, Mgmt. award McGill U., 1993, Centennial award Alta Assn. Engrs., Geologists and Geophysicists. Fellow Can. Acad. Engring.; mem. Assn. Profl. Engrs., Geologists and Geophysicists Alta. (past pres.), Can. Inst. Mining and Metallurgy (Past Pres.'s Meml. medal 1971). Avocations: golf, downhill skiing, shooting, fishing. Office: TransCan PipeLines Ltd, 530 8th Ave SW, Calgary, AB Canada T2P 3V6

MAIER, HAROLD GEISTWEIT, legal educator, lawyer; b. Cin., Mar. 25, 1937; s. Alfred F. and Alberta (Wilmes) M.; divorced; children: Marc L., Kurt S. BA in English Lit., U. Cin., 1959, JD, 1963; postgrad. Free U. Berlin, 1959-60; LLM, U. Mich., 1964; postgrad. U. Munich, 1964-65. Bar: Ohio 1963. Mem. faculty of law Vanderbilt U., Nashville, 1965—, prof., 1970—, dir. Transnat. Legal Studies Program, 1973—; David Daniels Allen prof. law, 1988—; faculty San Diego Internat. and Comparative Law Inst. King's Coll. U. London, 1986,87, Regent's Coll., 1989, 91; vis. prof. law U. Pa., 1985, U. N.C., Chapel Hill, 1987; vis. Lyle T. Alverson prof. law George Washington U., Washington, 1987-88; vis. Woodruff prof. internat. law U. Ga., Atlanta, 1995; cons. Office of Sec. Army, Panama Canal Treaty Negotiations, 1976; guest scholar Brookings Instn., Washington, 1976-77; dir. PDS Patrons, Inc. (Univ. Sch. of Nashville), 1975-87, pres., 1978-79; counselor on internat. law office of Legal Adviser, U.S. Dept. State, 1983-84. Recipient Luftbrucke Dankstipendium, Free U. Berlin, 1959-60; Ford internat. studies fellow U. Mich., 1964-65; Vanderbilt U. faculty fellow, 1976-77. Mem. Am. Soc. Internat. Law (exec. coun. 1974-78, 84-87), Am. Soc. for Comparative Study of Law (bd. dirs. 1984-), Am. Law Inst., Order of Coif, Omicron Delta Kappa, Phi Alpha Delta, Tau Kappa Alpha, Pi Delta Epsilon. Bd. editors Am. Jour. Internat. Law, 1984-88; author: (with T. Buergenthal) Public International Law in A Nutshell, 1985, 2d edit., 1989, (with T. Buergenthal, K. Doehring, J. Kokott) Grundzüge des Völkerrechts, 1987, Manual de Derecho Internacional Publico, 1994; contbr. numerous articles in field to profl. jours. Office: Vanderbilt U Sch Law 21st Ave S Nashville TN 37240

MAIER, HENRY B., environmental engineer; b. Yonkers, N.Y., July 11, 1925; s. Henry and Adelaide (Boyce) M.; m. Elizabeth A. Maier, May 4, 1968. BA, Columbia U., 1947; postgrad. Adelphi U., Hofstra U. Prin. Maier Solar Developments, Hempstead, N.Y. Author: Techniques for Seascape Painting. Mem. AIAA, Am. Chem. Soc., N.Y. Acad. Scis. Achievements include patents for elapsed time indicator, multiple reflecting solar collecting system, electroresponsive coatings, fusion power pellets, and fusion power; design of initial stage of work for aerospace vehicle, comet flyby study; development of rapid method for perspective visualizations, for views of engineering and design concepts; definition of geometrics for placement of measuring points by approximation; research on inorganic sulfur and chlorine pollutants from combustion of fossil fuels and from incinerator processes, and their interactive roles in the progressive deterioration of the stratospheric ozone shield previously blocking frequencies in the infrared, far infrared and microwave frequencies, with particular regard to the prediction and pattern formation of major North Atlantic storm systems; study for a comet detecting telescope. Home: 6 Sealey Ave Apt 3K Hempstead NY 11550-1232

MAIER, PAUL LUTHER, history educator, author, chaplain; b. St. Louis, May 31, 1930; s. Walter A. and Hulda (Eickhoff) M.; m. Joan M. Ludtke, 1967; children: Laura Ann, Julie Joan, Krista Lynn, Katherine Marie. MA, Harvard U., 1954; BD, Concordia Sem., St. Louis, 1955; postgrad., U. Heidelberg, Fed. Republic Germany; PhD summa cum laude, U. Basel, Switzerland, 1957; LittD (hon.), Concordia Sem., St. Louis, 1995. Campus chaplain, 1958—; prof. ancient history Western Mich. U., Kalamazoo, 1961—; lectr. in field. Author: A Man Spoke, A World Listened, 1963, Pontius Pilate, 1968, First Christmas, 1971, First Easter, 1973, First Christians, 1976, The Flames of Rome, 1981, In the Fullness of Time, 1991, A Skeleton in God's Closet, 1994; editor: The Best of Walter A. Maier, 1980; editor: Josephus—The Jewish War, 1982; editor, transl.: Josephus—The Essential Writings, 1988, Josephus—The Essential Works, 1995; contbr. over 200 articles and revs. to profl. jours. Recipient Gold Medallion Book award ECPA, 1989, Disting. Faculty Scholar Western Mich. U., 1981, Alumni award tchg. excellence, 1974; named Outstanding Educator in Am., 1974-75, Prof. of Yr. Coun. for Advancement and Support of Edn., 1984, citation Mich. Acad. of Sci., Arts and Letters, 1985. Home: 8383 W Main St Kalamazoo MI 49009 Office: Western Mich U Dept of History Kalamazoo MI 49008

MAIER, PAUL VICTOR, pharmaceutical executive; b. Seattle, Nov. 6, 1947; s. Norman Alvin and Rosalie (Godek) M.; m. Shirley Diehl, Aug. 11, 1979. BS, Pa. State U., 1969; MBA, Harvard U., 1975. Fin. analyst Greyhound Corp, Phoenix, 1975-76; asst. mgr. Wells Service Wells Fargo Bank, San Francisco, 1976-78; v.p. Fin. Cummins Service and Sales, Los Angeles, 1978-84; v.p. treas. ICN Pharms, Inc., Costa Mesa, Calif., 1984-90; v.p. fin. DFS West, 1990-92; v.p., CFO Ligand Pharmaceuticals, Inc., San Diego, 1992—. Chmn. hosp. div. United Way Region V, L.A., 1983-84; bd. dirs. The Wellness Community, San Diego, 1993—. Served with USNR, 1969—. Mem. Fin. Execs. Inst., The Athletic Congress, Pa. State Club of L.A., Harvard Bus. Sch. Assn. So. Calif., Ctr. for Non-Profit Mgmt., Vis. Nurse Assn. L.A. (bd. dirs. 1979-92, chmn.), Protection Mut. Inst. (West Coast adv. bd. 1985-90), L.A. Athletic Club, Point Fermin Flyers. Republican. Roman Catholic. Office: Ligand Pharmaceuticals 9393 Towne Centre Dr Ste 100 San Diego CA 92121-3016

MAIER, PAULINE, history educator; b. St. Paul, Apr. 27, 1938; d. Irvin Louis and Charlotte (Winterer) Rubbelke; A.B., Radcliffe Coll., 1960; postgrad. London Sch. Econs., 1960-61; Ph.D. in History, Harvard U., 1968, L.L.D. (hon.), Regis Coll., 1987; m. Charles Steven Maier, June 17, 1961; children—Andrea Nicole, Nicholas Winterer, Jessica Elizabeth Heine. Asst. prof., then assoc. prof. history U. Mass., Boston, 1968-77; Robinson-Edwards prof. history U. Wis., Madison, 1977-78; prof. history MIT, Cambridge, 1978—, William R. Kenan Jr. prof. history, 1990—, dept. head, 1979-88; mem. coun. Inst. Early Am. History, 1982-84; trustee Regis Coll., 1988—. Recipient Douglass Adair award Claremont Grad. Sch.-Inst. Early Am. History, 1976, Kidger award New Eng. History Tchrs. Assn., 1981; fellow Nat. Endowment Humanities, 1974-75, 88-89; Charles Warren fellow, 1974-75; Guggenheim fellow, 1990. Mem. Orgn. Am. Historians (exec. bd. 1978-82), Am. Hist. Assn. (nominations com. 1983-85, chmn. 1985), Soc. Am. Historians, Am. Antiquarian Soc. (exec. council 1984-89), Colonial Soc. Mass. (exec. coun. 1990-93), Mass. Hist. Soc. Author: From Resistance to Revolution: Colonial Radicals and the Development of American Opposition to Britain, 1765-1766, 1972; The Old Revolutionaries: Political Lives in the Age of Samuel Adams, 1980; The American People: A History, 1986. Home: 60 Larchwood Dr Cambridge MA 02138-4639 Office: MIT E51-216 Cambridge MA 02139

MAIER, ROBERT HAWTHORNE, biology educator; b. N.Y.C., Oct. 26, 1927; s. Ernest Henry and Clara Louise M.; m. Jane Hiob, Aug. 31, 1952; children: Pamela, David, Daniel. B.S., U. Miami, 1951; M.S., U. Ariz., 1952, Ph.D., 1954. Asst. dean Grad. Coll., U. Ariz., 1966-67; asst. chancellor for instrn. and research U. Wis., Green Bay, 1967-69, vice chancellor and dep. chancellor, prof., 1969-75, prof. sci. and environ. change, public and environ. adminstrn., 1975-79; vice chancellor acad. affairs East Carolina U., Greenville, N.C., 1979-83; prof. exptl. surgery, biology, polit. sci. East Carolina U., 1983—; dir. Trace Element Ctr., Sch. Medicine, 1984—; pres., chmn. Nat. Investment Advisors, Inc., 1984—, M 4, Inc., 1988—; bd. dirs. Agronomic Sci. Found.; mem. coun. biotech. U. N.C.; reviewer NC Tech. Devel. Authority, 1989—, NRC, 1990—. Contbr. articles to profl. jours. Bd. dirs. Lakeland chpt. ARC, 1978-79, Children's Svcs. Ea. N.C., 1987-94; mem.

Edn. Task Force, City of Green Bay, 1977-78, N.C. State Panel Advancement of Women in Adminstrn., 1981-84, Gov.'s Commn. on Future of N.C., 1981-84; treas. Ronald McDonald House, 1987-94. Served with U.S. Army, 1954-56. Fellow AAAS, Am. Inst. Chemists, Am. Soc. Agronomy, Soil Sci. Soc. Am.; mem. Am. Chem. Soc., Am. Inst. Biol. Scis. Presbyterian. Office: East Carolina U Greenville NC 27858-4354

MAIER, WALTER ARTHUR, church official; b. Ft. Wayne, Ind., June 14, 1925; s. Walter Arthur and Hulda (Eikhoff) M.; m. Leah Martha Gach, Aug. 27, 1951; children: Walter Arthur III, David Peter Edmund. Student, Harvard U., 1942-43, Concordia Coll., 1943-44; BA, Concordia Sem., 1948; postgrad., Marquette U., 1961-62; STM, Concordia Seminary, 1967, ThD, 1970. Prof. exegital theology Concordia Theol. Sem., Springfield and Ft. Wayne, 1965—; v.p. Luth. Ch.-Mo. Synod, St. Louis, 1973—. Parish pastor Elma, N.Y., Leavittown, Pa. and Milw. Office: Concordia Theol Sem Fort Wayne IN 46825

MAIERHAUSER, JOSEPH GEORGE, entrepreneur; b. Yankton, S.D., Mar. 23, 1927; s. Joseph and Angela M. (Jung) M.; m. Reta Mae Brockelsby, Nov. 25, 1948 (div. 1965); 1 child, Joe; m. Martha Helen Kuehn, Dec. 10, 1965. Student, U.S.D., Vermillion, 1946, S.D. Sch. Mines and Tech., Rapid City, 1947. Sales mgr. Black Hills Reptile Gardens, Rapid City, S.D., 1949-54; operator Colossal Cave Park, Vail, Ariz., 1956—; ptnr. Sta. KRNR, Roseburg, Oreg., 1961—. Mem. adv. bd. Salvation Army, Tucson, 1979-86; govs. appointee San Pedro Rparian Nat. Cons. Area Adv. Com., 1989—; past pres. So. Ariz. Internat. Livestock Assn., 1987-88; bd. dirs. Friends of Western Art., Tucson; co-founder Pima County Parklands Found.. With U.S. Navy Air Corps., 1944-45. Mem. Mountain Oyster Club (pres. 1989-91, bd. dirs. 1980-83). Republican. Avocation: conservation. Home: Bear Paw Vail AZ 85641 Office: Colossal Cave Mountain Park PO Box D70 Vail AZ 85641-0070

MAIER-KATKIN, DANIEL, criminology educator, administrator; b. N.Y.C., Feb. 25, 1945; s. Nathan and Rosalind (Davis) K.; m. Birgit Maier-Katkin, Sept. 20, 1987; children: Andrew Katkin, Rebecca Katkin, Rosalia. B.A., CCNY, 1965; J.D., Columbia U., 1968; diploma in Criminology, Cambridge U., Eng., 1969. Asst. prof. SUNY-Buffalo, 1969-72; asst. prof. Pa. State U., University Park, 1972-74, assoc. prof., 1974-82, prof., head Adminstrn. of Justice dept., 1982-94; prof., dean Sch. Criminology and Criminal Justice Fla. State U., Tallahassee, 1994—. Author: (with others) Delinquency and the Juvenile Justice System, 1976; The Nature of Criminal Law, 1982; contbr. articles on criminology and criminal justice to profl. jours. Sec. Jewish Community Ctr. of State College, Pa., 1985-86. Lydia Rappaport Disting. fellow Smith Coll., 1977; Fulbright fellow, vis. prof. Inst. Psychiatry, U. London Sch. Medicine, 1990-91. Mem. Am. Soc. Criminology. Democrat. Jewish. Office: Fla State U Sch Crimonology & Justice Tallahassee FL 32306-2025

MAIHAFER, HARRY JAMES, retired banker, former army officer; b. Watertown, N.Y., Aug. 8, 1924; s. George A. and Loretta Agnes (Daggett) M.; m. Jeanne Louise Mietzelfeld, June 9, 1949; children: Veronica Maihafer Barnes, Mary Maihafer Thompson, Margaret M., Douglas P. BS, U.S. Mil. Acad., 1949; MA, U. Mo., 1966. Commd. 2d lt. U.S. Army, 1949, col., 1968, ret., 1969; tng. dir. C&S Nat. Bank, Atlanta, 1970-73; sr. v.p., dir. pers. Union Planters Bank, Memphis, 1973-76; sr. v.p., dir. human resources Commerce Union Corp., Nashville, 1977-87, ret., 1987; pres. Middle Tenn. Human Resources Planners, Nashville, 1982-83. Author: From the Hudson to the Yalu--West Point '49 in the Korean War, 1993, Brave Decisions-Moral Courage from the American Revolution to Desert Storm, 1995; contbr. articles on mgmt. and mil. history to profl. jours. Pres. West Point Soc. Mid. Tenn., 1985-86; bd. dirs. St. Mary Villa, nashville, 1982-95, Cath. Charities Tenn., 1990-95. Mem. Assn. Grads. U.S. Mil. Acad., Ret. Officers Assn. Roman Catholic. Avocations: tennis, writing, gardening. Home: 6601 Fox Hollow Rd Nashville TN 37205-3956

MAIKOWSKI, THOMAS ROBERT, priest, educational director; b. Milwaukee, Wis., Oct. 20, 1947; s. Thomas Robert and Eugenia A. (Rogowski) M. BA, St. Francis Coll., Milw., 1970, MS in Edn., 1972; MA, Cardinal Stritch Coll., 1974; MDiv, Kenrick Sem., St. Louis, 1976; BA, Notre Dame Coll., St. Louis, 1976; MEd, Marquette U., 1977; PhD, St. Louis U., 1980; EdD, U. San Francisco, 1992. Ordained priest Roman Cath. Ch., 1976; cert. secondary sch. tchr. and adminstr., Ariz., N.Mex.; cert. elem. tchr., N.Mex. Tchr., adminstr. Cathedral High Sch., Gallup, N.Mex., 1976-78; supt. of schs. Diocese of Gallup, 1978-90; prin. tchr. The Cath. Acad., Farmington, N.Mex., 1980-90; dir. edn. Diocese of Gallup, 1990—. Contbr. articles to religious jours. Maj. USAFR. Mem. Nat. Cath. Ednl. Assn. (exec. com. 1978-81, 87-90), Religious Edn. Assn., Am. Assn. on Mental Retardation, Assn. for Supervision and Curriculum Devel., N.Mex. Assn. Non-pub. Schs. (bd. dirs. 1981-84), Phi Delta Kappa. Address: PO Box 1028 Gallup NM 87305-1028

MAILER, NORMAN, author; b. Long Branch, N.J., Jan. 31, 1923; s. Issac Barnett and Fanny (Schneider) M.; m. Beatrice Silverman, 1944 (div. 1952); 1 dau., Susan; m. Adele Morales, 1954 (div. 1962); children: Danielle, Elizabeth; m. Jeanne Campbell, 1962 (div. 1963); 1 dau., Kate; m. Beverly Bentley, 1963 (div. 1980); children: Michael, Steven; m. Carol Stevens, 1980 (div. 1980); 1 dau., Maggie; m. Norris Church, 1980; 1 son, John Buffalo. SB cum laude, Harvard U., 1943; postgrad., Sorbonne, Paris, France, 1947-48. columnist Village Voice, 1946, Commentary, 1962-63, Esquire, 1962-63; contbg. editor Dissent, 1953-69; co-founding editor Village Voice, 1955. Author: No Percentage, 1941, The Naked and the Dead, 1948, Barbary Shore, 1951, The Deer Park, 1955, The White Negro: Superficial Reflections on the Hipster, 1957, Advertisements for Myself, 1959, Deaths for the Ladies and Other Disasters, 1962, The Presidential Papers, 1963, An American Dream, 1965, Cannibals and Christians, 1966, Why Are We in Vietnam?, 1967 (Nat. Book award nomination 1967), The Short Fiction of Norman Mailer, 1967, The Bullfight, 1967, The Armies of the Night, 1968 (Pulitzer prize for non-fiction 1969, George Polk award 1969), Miami and the Siege of Chicago, 1968 (Nat. Book award for non-fiction 1968), The Idol and the Octopus, 1968, Of a Fire On The Moon, 1970, King of the Hill, 1971, The Prisoner of Sex, 1971, The Long Patrol, 1971, Existential Errands, 1972, St. George and the Godfather, 1972, Marilyn, 1973, The Faith of Graffiti, 1974, The Fight, 1975, Some Honorable Men, 1975, Genius and Lust, 1976, A Transit to Narcissus, 1978, The Executioner's Song, 1979 (Pulitzer Prize for fiction 1980, Nat. Book Critics Circle award nomination 1979, Am. Book award nomination 1980), Of a Small and Modest Malignancy, Wicked and Bristling with Dots, 1980, Of Women and Their Elegance, 1980, Pieces and Pontifications, 1982, Ancient Evenings, 1983, Tough Guys Don't Dance, 1984, The Last Night, 1984, Harlot's Ghost, 1991, How the Wimp Won the War, 1991, Oswald's Tale, 1995; (plays) The Deer Park: A Play, 1967, Strawhead, 1985; editor: Genius and Lust: A Journey Through the Major Writings of Henry Miller, 1976; screenwriter: (films) The Executioner's Song, 1982 (Emmy award nomination outstanding adapted screenplay 1983); screenwriter, prodr., dir., actor: (films) Wild 90, 1967, Maidstone: A Mystery, 1971; screenwriter, prodr.: (films) Beyond the Law, 1968; screenwriter, dir.: (films) Tough Guys Don't Dance, 1987; actor: (films) Ragtime, 1981. Served with AUS, 1944-46. Recipient Edward MacDowell Medal MacDowell Colony, 1973, Nat. Arts Club Gold medal, 1976, Rose award Lord & Taylor, 1985, Emerson-Thoreau Medal for lifetime of literary achievement, 1989; Nat. Inst. and Am. Acad. grantee, 1960; Pappas fellow U. Pa., 1983. Mem. PEN Am. Ctr. (pres. 1984-86), Nat. Inst. Arts and Letters. Office: care Random House Author's Mail 201 E 50th St New York NY 10022-7703*

MAILHOT, LOUISE, judge; b. Montreal, Que., Can., July 23, 1940; d.Gerard and Jeanne (Bousquet) M.; m. Michael Oliver Lloyd, 1974; 2 children. BA, U. Montreal, LLL. Atty. pvt. practice, 1966-80, Justice Superior Ct., 1980-87, Justice Ct. Appeals, 1987—. Office: Ct Appeals, 1 rue Notre Dame Est # 1786, Montreal, PQ Canada H2Y 1B6

MAILLARD, ALBERT ACHILLES JOSEPH, head and neck surgeon, educator; b. Santiago, Chile, Aug. 8, 1943; s. Albert Joseph and Amanda (Holtheuer) M.; 1 child, John David. BS, U. Houston, 1968; MD, U. Tex., Galveston, 1972. Cert. Tex. State Bd. Med. Examiners, Nat. Bd. Med. Examiners, Am. Bd. Otolaryngology. Resident gen. surgery U. Tex. Med. Sch., Houston (Tex.) Affiliated Hosps., 1972-73, U. Tex. Southwestern Med.

Sch., Affiliated Hosp., 1973-74; resident gen. surgery U. Tex. Med. Sch. Houston Affiliated Hosp., 1974-75, resident otolaryngology head and neck surgery, 1975-77; resident U. Tex. Med. Sch. Houston, M.D. Anderson Hosp. & Tumor Inst., 1977-78; instr. otolaryngology U. Tex. Med. Sch., Houston, 1978-82, clin. asst. prof. otolaryngology, head and neck surgery, 1982-84, clin. assoc. prof. otolaryngology, head and neck surgery, 1984—, clin. prof. dept. family practice, 1993—, cons. dept. oncology, 1989—; mem. St. Joseph Hosp. Quality Assurance Rev. Com.-Gen. Surgery, 1989-93, Quality Assurance Rev. Com.-Otolaryngology-Head and Neck Surgery, 1989-93, Bylaws Rev. Com., 1990, Hermann Hosp. Credentials Com., 1990, Hermann Hosp. Tissue Com., 1993, Sci. and Tech. Com., 1993—; pvt. practice, 1979-94; lectr. and presenter in field. Contbr. articles to profl. jours. Charter mem. The Statue of Liberty Found., N.Y., 1983-86, Ellis Island Found., N.Y., 1985-92, Market Sq. Restoration, Houston, 1991. Fellow ACS, Am. Acad. Otolaryngology-Head and Neck Surgery, Am. Soc. for Head & Neck Surgery; mem. AAAS, AMA, Tex. Med. Assn., Harris County Med. Soc., M.D. Anderson Surg. Alumni Assn., The Deafness Rsch. Found., Nature Conservancy, Phi Beta Pi. Roman Catholic. Avocations: anthropology, marine biology, flying, winter sports. Home: 2038 Suffolk Houston TX 77027 Office: AAJ Maillard MD Ste 1508 6410 Fannin Houston TX 77030

MAILLET, ANTONINE, author, educator; b. Bouctouche, N.B., Can., May 10, 1929; d. Leonine Maillet and Virginie Cormier. BA, Coll. Notre-Dame D'Acadie, 1950; MA, Moncton U., N.B., 1959, D es L (hon.), 1972; LLD, Montreal U., Que., Can., 1962; PhD, Laval U., Que., 1970, DLitt (hon.), 1988; D es L (hon.), Acadia U., 1980, St. Mary's U., 1980, Laurentian U., 1981, McGill U., 1982; DLitt (hon.), Carleton U., 1978, Mount Allison U., 1979, St. Thomas U., 1986, Mt. St-Vincent U., 1987, U. Ste-Anne, 1987, Bowling Green U., 1988, Simon Fraser U., 1989, U. Maine, 1990, Concordia U., 1990; LLD (hon.), U. Alta., 1979, Dalhousie U., 1981, U. Toronto, 1982, Queen's U., 1982, St. Francis Xavier U., 1984, Lyon U., 1989, B.C. U., 1991, Royal Mil. Coll. Can., 1992; LittD (hon.), U. New Eng., 1994. Prof. Coll. Notre-Dame D'Acadie, Moncton, 1954-60, Moncton U., 1965-67, Coll. des Jesuites, Que., 1968-69, Laval U., Que., 1971-74, Montreal U., 1974-75, Nat. Drama Sch., Montreal, 1989-91; writer N.B. Hist. Resources Adminstrn., Central Registry, Fredericton, N.B.; assoc. prof. French studies Moncton U., chancelor, 1989; guest Michener Found., Queen's U., 1991. Author: (novels) Pointe-aux-coques, 1958 (Prix Champlain, 1960), On a mangé la dune, 1962, Don l'orignal, 1972 (Prix du Gouverneur General du Can. 1972), Par derrière chez mon père, 1972, Mariàggélas, 1973 (Prix des Volcans (France) 1975, Grand Prix Litteraire de la ville de Montreal, 1973, Prix France Can. 1975, Prix litteraire La Presse 1976), Emmanuel a Joseph a Davit, 1975, Les Cordes-de-Bois, 1977 (Prix des 4 jures 1978), Pélagie-la-charrette, 1979 (Prix Goncourt 1979); Cent ans dans les bois, 1981, La Gribouille, 1982, Crache-à-Pic, 1984; Le Huitième Jour, 1986, L'Oursiade, 1990, Les Confessions de Jeanne de Valois, 1992; (plays): Poire-Acre, 1960 (Best Can. Play Vancouver Theatre Festival, 1960), Les Jeux d'Enfants sont faits, 1960 (Prix du Conseil des Arts 1960), Les Crasseux, 1968, Gapi et Sullivan, 1973, Evangéline Deusse, 1975, Gapi, 1976, La Veuve Enragée, 1977, Le Bourgeois Gentleman, 1978, La Contrebandière, 1981, Les drolatiques, horrifiques et épouvantables aventures de Panurge, ami de Pantagruel, 1983, Garrochés en Paradis, 1986, Margot la Folle, 1987, William S, 1991; (translations) Richard III (Shakespeare), 1989, La Nuit des Rois (Shakespeare), 1993 (Prix de la traduction l'Association québécoise de critiques de théâtre saison 1992-93), La Foire de la Saint-Barthélemy), 1994; (Ben Johnson) La Fontaine ou la Comédie des Animaux, 1995: (other) L'Acadie pour quasiment rien, 1973; author short stories, and children's literature. V.p. Conseil d'administration du Théâtre du Rideau Vert; mem. Conseil Littéraire Fondation Prince Pierre de Monaco, Haut Conseil Francophonie, 1987, Queen's Privy Coun. Can.; chancellor Noncton U., 1989; Conseil des gouverneurs associés de l'Université de Montréal. Decorated officer, comdr. Order of Can., officier des Palmes académiques françaises, chevalier l'Ordre de la Pléiade (Fredericton), officier l'Ordre Nat. du Québec, officier des Arts et des Lettres (France), comdr. l'Ordre du mérite culturel (Monaco); recipient Prix de la meilleure piece canadienne presented at Festival de Theatre, 1958, Prix Litéraire de la Presse, 1976. Mem. Assn. des Ecrivains de Langue Francaise, l'Ordre des francophones d'Amérique, l'Académie des Grandes Montréalais, Des Auteurs Et Compositeurs Dramatiques de France (sec.), Soc. Des Gens de Lettres de France, Soc. Royale du Canada, Academie Canadienne-Francaise, Pen Club.

MAILLOUX, ROBERT JOSEPH, physicist; b. Lynn, Mass., June 20, 1938; s. Joseph H. and Nora S. M.; m. Marlene Schirf, Jan. 14, 1967; children: Patrice, Julie, Denise. BS, Northeastern U., 1961; SM, Harvard U., 1962, PhD, 1965. Physicist NASA Electronics Rsch. Ctr., Cambridge, Mass., 1965-70, Air Force Cambridge Rsch. Labs., Bedford, Mass., 1970-77, Rome Air Devel. Ctr., Bedford, 1977-80; chief antennas and components div., electromagnetic directorate Rome Air Devel. Ctr., 1980-91; sr. scientist Antennas Rome Lab., 1992—; lectr. on antennas, arrays and systems sponsored by Microwave Jour.; lectr. Tufts U., 1985—. Author: Phased Array Antenna Handbook; contbr. chpts. to 8 textbooks, articles to sci. jours. Served with C.E. U.S. Army, 1966-68. Recipient Air Force Marcus O'Day paper award, 1971, Engineer of Yr. award RADC, 1988; RADC fellow, 1988. Fellow IEEE (spl. achievement award 1969, 76, nat. lectr., assoc. editor Transactions on Antennas and Propagation 1984-92, Harry Diamond award 1991); mem. Antenna and Propagation Soc. (chmn. Boston chpt. 1968, nat. meetings chmn. 1977-80, adcom mem. 1977-80, v.p. 1982, pres. 1983), Internat. Sci. Radio Union (Commn. B. tech. activities chmn. 1980—), Sigma Xi (pres. Hanscom chpt. 1980-81), Eta Kappa Nu, Tau Beta Pi. Patentee. Office: RL/ER 31 Grenier St Hanscom AFB MA 01731-3010

MAILMAN, CYNTHIA MARCIA, artist, educator; b. N.Y.C., Dec. 31, 1942; d. Julius and Claire (Russler) M.; m. Silver Sullivan. BS in Art Edn., Pratt Inst., 1964; MFA in Painting, Rutgers U., 1978. Cert. tchr., N.Y. Art instr. Livingston Coll., Rutgers U., New Brunswick, N.J., 1978-80; adj. lectr. art Queensborough Community Coll., Bayside, N.Y., 1981-85; adj. asst. prof. Queensborough Community Coll., CUNY, 1985—; bd. dirs. Coun. on Arts and Humanities for S.I., 1993-95; mem. adv. bd. the Jacques Marchais Mus. of Tibetian Art, S.I., 1995—. One-person shows include The Everson Mus., Syracuse, N.Y., 1981, SOHO 20 Gallery, N.Y.C, 1980, 83, 86, Newhouse Gallery, S.I., N.Y., 1987; group shows include Am. Acad. and Inst. Arts and Letters, N.Y.C., 1978, N.Y. State Mus., Albany, 1981, N.J. State Mus., Trenton, 1985, Columbus (Ohio) Mus., 1985, Minn. Mus. Art, St. Paul, 1987, Sunrise Art Mus., Charlotteville, W.Va., 1987, SOHO 20 Gallery, N.Y.C., 1989-90, 93, 94, 95. Organizer, mem. Stapleton Civic Assn., 1978; bd. dirs., No-Coal, S.I., 1983; asst. chair, Com. for Ralph Lamberti for Borough Pres., S.I., 1985. CAPS grantee N.Y. State Coun. on Arts, 1976, 87, grantee S.I. Coun. on Arts, 1987. Mem. Women's Caucus for Art, SOHO 20 Artists, Coll. Art Assn., Mud Lane Soc. for the Renaissance of Stapleton (pres. 1995). Democrat. Jewish. Avocations: bird watching, guitar, singing, collecting antique purses and jewelry, reading mystery novels. Home and Studio: 52 Broad St Staten Island NY 10304

MAIMAN, THEODORE HAROLD, physicist; b. Los Angeles, July 11, 1927. B.S. in Engring. Physics, U. Colo., 1949; M.S. in Elec. Engring., Stanford U., 1951, Ph.D. in Physics, 1955; PhD (hon.), U. Cordoba, Argentina, 1993. Sect. head Hughes Research Labs., 1955-61; pres., founder Korad Corp., Santa Barbara, Calif., 1961-68, Maiman Assocs., Santa Barbara, Calif., 1968—; v.p., founder Laser Video Corp., Los Angeles, 1972-75; v.p. advanced tech. and new ventures TRW Inc. Electronics and Def. Sector, Los Angeles, 1975-83; vis. prof. Nat. U. Asuncion, Paraguay, 1993. Author papers in field. Served with USNR, 1945-46. Recipient award Fannie and John Hertz Found., 1966; Ballantine award Franklin Inst., 1962; award for devel. laser Aerospace Elec. Soc.-Am. Astron. Soc., 1965, Light award Braille Inst., 1982, Wolf prize in physics, 1984; named Alumni of Century U. Colo., 1976; inducted into U.S. Nat. Inventors Hall of Fame, 1984; named Laureate Japan Prize (electro-optics), 1987. Fellow Soc. Motion Picture and TV Engrs., Am. Phys. Soc. (Oliver E. Buckley prize 1966), Optical Soc. Am. (R.W. Wood prize 1976), Soc. Photog. and Instrumentation Engrs., Royal Coll. Surgeons (hon.), 1994; mem. Nat. Acad. Engring., Nat. Acad. Scis., IEEE, Soc. Info. Display, Sigma Xi, Sigma Pi Sigma, Sigma Tau, Pi Mu Epsilon. Devel. 1st laser.

MAIN, A. DONALD, bishop. Bishop Upper Susquehanna region Evang. Luth. Ch. in Am., Lewisburg, Pa. Office: Evang Luth Ch in Am PO Box 36 192 Reitz Blvd Lewisburg PA 17837

MAIN, DOUGLAS CAMERON, provincial cabinet minister; b. Willow Bunch, Sask., Can., July 18, 1946; s. Claude Bruce and Lillian Marie (Bellefleur) M.; m. Judith Marie Sumner, Apr. 25, 1970; children: Joshua David, Jeremy Scott. Student, U. Winnipeg (Man., Can.), 1967, Athabasca (Alta., Can.), 1986. Mutual fund sales exec. Investors Group, Winnipeg, 1969-70; photo sales and prodn. exec. Martin Photo, Winnipeg, 1970; radio newscaster CTOB Radio, Winnipeg, 1970-72; radio and TV newscaster CFTR-CHFI FM, Toronto, Ont., Can., 1972-73, CKY AM-FM TV, Winnipeg, 1973-75; TV newscaster, producer CITV, Edmonton, Alta., 1975-88; minister of culture and multiculturalism Govt. of Alta., Edmonton, 1989—; freelance TV producer, 1980-89; instr. in journalism Grant MacElwan Community Coll., Edmonton, 1980-89; v.p. CJIL Broadcasting Ltd., Edmonton, 1980-82. Candidate Reform Party of Can., Edmonton, 1988, MLA, Progressive Conservative Assn. Alta., Edmonton, 1989. Mem. Royal Glenora Club (chmn. squash com. 1987-88). Avocations: squash, tennis, golf. Home: 1511 Bearspaw Dr E, Edmonton, AB Canada T6J 5E2 Office: Minister of Culture, Legislature Bldg Rm 418, Edmonton, AB Canada T5K 2B6

MAIN, JACKSON TURNER, history educator; b. Chgo., Aug. 6, 1917; s. John Smith and Dorothy Kinsey (Turner) M.; m. Gloria Jean Lund, June 16, 1956; children: Jackson Turner, Eifiona Llewelyn, Judson Kempton. B.A., U. Wis., 1939, M.A., 1940, Ph.D., 1949; LL.D. (hon.), Washington and Jefferson Coll., 1980. Asst. prof. Washington and Jefferson Coll., Washington, Pa., 1948-50; prof. San Jose State U. (Calif.), 1953-65, U. Md., College Park, 1965-66; prof. history State U. N.Y. at Stony Brook, 1966-83. Author: The Antifederalists 1781-1788, 1961, The Social Structure of Revolutionary America, 1965, The Upper House in Revolutionary America, 1967, Political Parties Before the Constitution, 1973, The Sovereign States, 1775-1783, 1973, Connecticut Society in the Era of the American Revolution, 1977, Society and Economy in Colonial Connecticut, 1985. Served to sgt. USAF, 1941-45. Am. Council Learned Socs. fellow, 1962-63; Nat. Endowment Humanities fellow Center Advanced Studies in Behavioral Scis., Stanford, Calif., 1980-81. Mem. Am. Wis. hist. assns., Orgn. Am. Historians, others. Office: Univ of Colo Dept History Boulder CO 80309

MAIN, ROBERT PEEBLES, hospital administrator; b. Buffalo, Nov. 13, 1943; s. Andrew and Jane (Neary) M.; m. Cleta Miller, June 13, 1964; children—Kelly Ann, Thomas. B.S. in Edn., SUNY-Buffalo, 1965; M.A. in Hosp. and Health Adminstrn., U. Iowa, 1973. Coordinator rehab. medicine services for psychiat. service and drug treatment unit VA Hosp., Iowa City, 1971-72, staff asst. to hosp. dir., 1972-74, asst. to chief staff, Oklahoma City, 1974-76; adj. asst. prof. health care adminstrn. U. Okla. Coll. Health, Oklahoma City, 1975-76; asst. hosp. dir. trainee VA Hosp., Memphis, 1976-77; assoc. hosp. dir. VA Lakeside, Chgo., 1977-79; exec. v.p., chief operating officer Marianjoy Rehab. Ctr., Wheaton, Ill., 1979-88; pres., chief exec. officer Siskin Hosp. for Phys. Rehab., Chattanooga, 1988—. Chmn. fund raising activity Ch. of Holy Spirit, Schaumburg, Ill., 1979-85; bd. dirs Ancilla Home Health, Mended Hearts of DuPage County. Fellow Am. Coll. Healthcare Execs.; mem. Am. Hosp. Assn., Ill Hosp. Assn.(Long Term Care Panel), Chgo. Health Execs. Forum (sec., treas. 1981-82), Ill. Regents Adv. Council, DuPage Subarea Adv. Council, Health Systems Agy., Oklahoma City Met. Hosp. Council.

MAINE, MICHAEL ROLAND, lawyer; b. Anderson, Ind., Feb. 22, 1940; s. Roland Dwight and Vivian Louise (Browning) M.; m. Suzanne Bauman, Aug. 25, 1962; children: Christopher Michael (dec.), Melinda Louise. AB with high distinction, DePauw U.; JD with distinction, U. Mich. Bar: Ind., U.S. Dist. Ct. (so. dist.) Ind., U.S. Ct. Appeals (7th cir.), U.S. Supreme Ct. Assoc. Baker & Daniels, Indpls., 1964-71, ptnr., 1972—. Contbr. articles to profl. jours. Pres. Mental Health Assn. Ind. Indpls., 1985; bd. dirs. Ind. Repertory Theatre, Indpls., 1986—, Community Hosp. N., 1988—, Japan-Am. Soc. of Ind. Inc., 1988—; bd. visitors Sch. Law Ind. U. Indpls.; trustee De Pauw U., Greencastle, Ind., 1990—. Capt. USAF, 1965-68. Named Sagamore of Wabash, Gov. Ind., 1986. Fellow Ind. Bar Found., Indpls. Bar Found.; mem. Ind. Bar Assn. (chmn. fed. judiciary com. 1986—), Indpls. Bar Assn. (sec. 1983, pres. 1985, extraordinary service award 1985), Order of Coif, Phi Beta Kappa. Lodges: Kiwanis (lt. gov. Ind. club 1972, pres. Indpls. club 1969), Masons. Avocations: tennis, sailing. Home: 11021 Fall Creek Rd Indianapolis IN 46256-9403 Office: Baker & Daniels 300 N Meridian St Indianapolis IN 46204-1755

MAINOUS, BRUCE HALE, foreign language educator; b. Appalachia, Va., Aug. 2, 1914; s. William Lazarus and Sibyl (Hale) M.; m. Ruth Marie Daugherty, June 7, 1941; children: Mary Michele (Mrs. Robert F. Chinn), Martha Hale (Mrs. Gary Dougherty). A.B., Coll. William and Mary, 1935; M.A., U. Ill., 1939, Ph.D., 1948; certificates, Sorbonne, Paris, 1958, U. Besançon, France, 1975. Asst. d'anglais Lycée de Nîmes, France, 1935-36; prin. Derby Grade Sch., Va., 1936-37; mem. faculty U. Ill., Urbana, 1937—; prof. French U. Ill., 1964-84, prof. emeritus, 1984—, head dept., 1965-73; dir. Unit for Fgn. Lang. Study and Research, 1972-76, Lang. Learning Lab., 1976-84. Author: (with H.C. Woodbridge) A Sainte-Beuve Bibliography, 1954, Basic French, 2d edit, 1968, (with Donald J. Nolan) Basic French, Workbook and laboratory Manual, 1968; co-author: Spanish for Agricultural Purposes, 1984, (with Maria T. Rund) A Glossary of Spanish-American Agricultural Terms, 1987. Served to lt. USNR, 1942-46; comdr. Res. ret. Decorated officier Ordre des Palmes Académiques; Camargo Found. fellow, 1975. Mem. MLA, Am. Assn. Tchrs. French, Ill. Fgn. Lang. Tchrs. Assn. (pres. 1966-68), Am. Council Teaching Fgn. Langs., Inst. d'Etudes Occitanes, N.Am. Catalan Soc., Corda Fratres Assn. Cosmopolitan Clubs, Phi Kappa Phi, Sigma Delta Pi, Pi Delta Phi. Methodist. Clubs: Dial, Exchange. Home: 502 W Washington St Urbana IL 61801-4052

MAINOUS, THERESA LEI, nursing administrator; b. Ft. Wayne, Ind., Jan. 24, 1957; d. Daniel Keith and Shirley Carolene (Taylor) Votaw; m. Paul David Mainous, Oct. 6, 1979. Diploma in nursing, Parkview Meth. Sch. Nursing, Ft. Wayne, Ind., 1978; BSN, Ind. U., Indpls., 1982, MS in Nursing Adminstrn., 1986. RN, Fla. Supr., clin. charge nurse, staff nurse St. Vincent Hosp., Indpls.; assoc. dir. trauma critical care nursing Cleve. Met. Gen. Hosp.; dir. critical care nursing S.W. Fla. Regional Med. Ctr. Mem. AACN, Sigma Theta Tau (Alpha chpt.). Home: 14585 Aeries Way Dr Fort Myers FL 33912-1702

MAINWARING, THOMAS LLOYD, motor freight company executive; b. Cleve., Aug. 25, 1928; s. Hugh Trevor and Mary Beatrice (Ottman) M.; m. Gladys Fraser Mehr, June 10, 1983; children by previous marriage—Kevin, James, Eileen, Scott, Bruce. B.A., Albion Coll., 1950; M.B.A., Western Res. U., 1958. C.P.A., Ohio. Controller Cleve. Cartage Co., 1959-61, v.p., treas., 1961-64; controller Associated Truck Lines, Inc., Vandenberg Ctr., Grand Rapids, Mich., 1964-69; v.p. fin. Associated Transport, Inc., N.Y.C., 1969-70, exec. v.p. fin. and adminstrn., 1970-72; pres. Ryder Truck Lines Inc. Jacksonville, Fla., 1972-78, exec. v.p., chief operating officer, 1978-81, chief exec. officer, 1981-84; pres. Freight System div. Ryder System Inc., Miami, Fla., 1984-86; cons. trucking industry affairs Arlington, Va., 1986-88; pres., chief oper. officer H & M Internat. Transp., Inc., 1989-91, vice chmn., 1991-92; transp. cons., 1992-93; pres., gen. mgr. E.I. Kane Intermodal Transport, Inc., Balt., 1993—; bd. dirs. Trucking Mgmt., Inc. Contbr. articles to profl. jours. Mem. exec. com. United Way Jacksonville, 1981-84; trustee Albion Coll., 1977; bd. dirs. Goodwill Industries North Fla. Served with AUS, 1950-53. Mem. Am. Trucking Assn. (nat. acctg. and fin. council 1964, pres. 1971, chmn. ATA Found. 1986-88, exec. com. 1985-88), Fla. Trucking Assn. (bd. dirs. 1973, pres. 1979), Am. Mgmt. Assn. (lectr. seminars), Jacksonville Area C. of C. (bd. govs., com. of 100, v.p. internat. 1984), Cen. and So. Motor Freight Tariff Assn. (bd. dirs. 1981-84, pres. 1983, exec. com. transp. rsch. bd. 1987-89), Sigma Nu. Home: 248 Springs Ave Gettysburg PA 17325-1728

MAINWARING, WILLIAM LEWIS, publishing company executive, author; b. Portland, Oreg. Jan. 17, 1935; s. Bernard and Jennie (Lewis) M.; m. Mary E. Bell, Aug. 18, 1962; children: Anne Marie, Julia Kathleen, Douglas Bernard. B.S., U. Oreg. 1957; postgrad., Stanford U. 1957-58. With Salem (Oreg.) Capital Jour., 1958-76, editor, pub., 1962-76; pub. Oreg. Statesman, 1974-76; pres. Statesman-Jour. Co., Inc., Salem, 1974-76, Westridge Press, Ltd. 1977—; pres. MediAmerica, Inc., Portland, 1981—, CEO, 1988—. Author: Exploring the Oregon Coast, 1977, Exploring Oregon's Central and Southern Cascades, 1979, Exploring the Mount Hood Loop, 1992. Pres. Salem Beautification Coun., 1968, Marion-Polk County United

Good Neighbors, 1970, Salem Social Svcs. Commn., 1978-79, Salem Hosp. Found., 1977-81. 2d lt. AUS, 1958; capt. Res. Ret. Mem. Salem Area C. of C. (pres. 1972-73), Oreg. Symphony Soc. Salem (pres. 1973-75), Salem City Club (pres. 1977-78), Sigma Chi. Republican. Presbyterian (ruling elder). Home: 1090 Southridge Pl S Salem OR 97302-5947 Office: Oreg Bus Mag 921 SW Morrison St Ste 407 Portland OR 97205-2722

MAINWARING, WILLIAM ROBERT, bank executive; b. Wilkes-Barre, Pa., Apr. 1, 1943; s. William R. and Dorothy (Edwards) M.; m. Judith Ann Davis; children: Jonnell, William R. Jr. BS, Wilkes Coll., 1965, MBA, 1972; postgrad., Rutgers U., 1974. With credit dept. 1st Ea. Bank N.A., Wilkes-Barre, 1963-67, asst. cashier, 1967-70, asst. v.p., 1970-72, v.p., 1972-75, v.p., sr. credit loan officer, 1975, sr. v.p., 1975-80, exec. v.p., 1980-84, pres., 1984-88, pres., chief exec. officer, 1988—. Served to capt. USAFR, 1966-73. Mem. Pa. Bankers Assn. (mem. fin. com.). Lodge: Masons. Avocations: skiing, tennis. Office: 1st Ea Bank 1st Eastern Pla Public Sq Wilkes Barre PA 18768

MAIO, F. ANTHONY, lawyer; b. Passaic, N.J., Mar. 30, 1937; s. Anthony J. and Santina (Sciarra) M.; m. Maureen Margaret McKeown, Dec. 30, 1960; children: Christopher, Duncan, Todd. BS in Mech. Engring., Stevens Inst. Tech., 1959; LLB cum laude, Boston Coll., 1968. Bar: Wis. 1968, D.C. 1971. Engr., project mgr. Hazeltine Corp., Greenlawn, N.Y. and Avon, Mass., 1959-64; project mgr. Raytheon Corp., Portsmouth, R.I., 1964-65; atty. Foley & Lardner, Milw., 1968-70; ptnr. Foley & Lardner, Washington, 1971-86, Milw., 1986—. Editor Boston Coll. Law Rev., 1967-68. Dir. Arthritis Found., Milw., 1986-88, ARC, Milw., 1986-94. Mem. Order of Coif, Milw. Yacht Club (bd. dirs. 1993-95). Avocations: boating, fishing. Home: 3060 E Newport Ct Milwaukee WI 53211-2910 Office: Foley & Lardner Firstar Ctr 777 E Wisconsin Ave Milwaukee WI 53202-5302

MAIOCCHI, CHRISTINE, lawyer; b. N.Y.C., Dec. 24, 1949; d. George and Andreina (Toneatto) M.; m. John Charles Kerecz, Aug. 16, 1980; children: Charles George, Joan Christine. BA in Polit. Sci., Fordham U., 1971, MA in Polit. Sci., 1971, JD, 1974; postgrad., NYU, 1977—. Bar: N.Y. 1975, U.S. Dist. Ct. (so. and ea. dists.), N.Y. 1975, U.S. Ct. Appeals (2nd cir) 1975. Law clk. to magistrate U.S. Dist. Ct. (so. dist.) N.Y., N.Y.C., 1973-74; atty. corp. legal dept. The Home Ins. Co., N.Y.C., 1974-76; asst. house counsel corp. legal dept. Allied Maintenance Corp., N.Y.C., 1976; atty. corp. legal dept. Getty Oil Co., N.Y.C., 1976-77; v.p., mgr. real estate Paine, Webber, Jackson & Curtis, Inc., N.Y.C., 1977-81; real estate mgr. GK Techs., Inc., Greenwich, Conn., 1981-85; real estate mgr., sr. atty. MCI Telecom. Corp., Rye Brook, N.Y., 1985-93; real estate and legal cons. Wallace Law Registry, 1993—. Bd. dirs. League Women Voters, Dobbs Ferry, N.Y., 1988; co-pres. The Home/Sch. Assn., Immaculate Conception Sch., Irvington, N.Y. Mem. ABA, Nat. Assn. Corp. Real Estate Execs. (pres. 1983-84, treas. 1985-86, bd. dirs. 1986), Indsl. Devel. Rsch. Coun. (program v.p. 1985, Profl. award 1987), N.Y. Bar Assn., Women's Bar Assn. Manhattan, The Corp. Bar (sec. real estate divsn. 1987-89, chmn 1990-92), Home Sch. Assn. Immaculate Conception Sch. (co-pres.), Jr. League Club, Dobbs Ferry Women's Club (program dir. 1981-92, 94—, publicity dir. 1992-94). Avocations: sports, theatre, gardening. Home and Office: 84 Clinton Ave Dobbs Ferry NY 10522-3004

MAIRS, DAVID, symphony conductor; b. Morristown, N.J., Jan. 30, 1943; s. G. Donald and Frances P. (Johnson) M.; children from previous marriage: Stephen, Gregory; m. Elizabeth Ann Powell, Mar. 24, 1975; children: Ellen, Sarah. BM, U. Mich., 1965, MM, 1966; MDiv, Pitts. Theol. Sem., 1983. Cert. tchr. K-12, Mich. 3d horn San Antonio Symphony, 1969-70; assoc. prin. horn Pitts. Symphony, 1970-80; condr. wind ensemble Duquesne U., Pitts., 1981-83; asst. pastor 1st Presbyn. Ch., Flint, Mich., 1983-86, 87-88; asst. condr., music adminstr. Flint Symphony, 1984-88; artistic advisor Adrian (Mich.) Symphony, 1987-88; resident condr. San Antonio Symphony, 1988—; pops condr. Charlotte (N.C.) Symphony, 1993—; music dir. Flint Youth Symphony, 1986-88; chmn. vision 2000 com. N.E. Ind. Sch. Dist., San Antonio, 1990—. Hon. life mem. Tex. PTA, Austin, 1994. With U.S. Army, 1966-69. Mem. Am. Symphony Orch. League, Condr.'s Guild. Avocation: tennis. Office: San Antonio Symphony 222 E Houston Ste 200 San Antonio TX 78205

MAISANO, PHILLIP NICHOLAS, investment company executive; b. Newark, May 15, 1947; s. Salvatore and Mary (Vella) M.; m. Mary-Alice Yanch, Aug. 10, 1968; children: Phillip, Matthew. BA, Belmont (N.C.) Abbey Coll., 1969; MBA, Iona Coll., 1976; postgrad., NYU Law Sch., 1972-73, Columbia U., summer 1987. CLU. Asst. v.p. The Equitable, N.Y.C., 1969-79; v.p. Manhattan Life Ins. Co., N.Y.C., 1979-81; v.p. MONY Fin. Svcs., Purchase, N.Y., 1981-88, sr. v.p., 1989—; pres. Evaluation Assocs. Inc., Norwalk, Conn., 1988—; chief exec. officer Evaluation Assocs. Inc., 1989—; incorporator New Dartmouth Bank, Hanover, N.H., 1991—; bd. dirs. AIG Asset Mgmt., N.Y.C., Restaurant Ins. Assocs., Wilbraham, Mass.; trustee Belmont Abbey Coll., 1992—. Contbr. articles to profl. publs. V.p. No. Bergen Jr. Football League; bd. dirs. Montvale (N.J.) Athletic League; trustee Belmont Abbey Coll., 1992—. 1st lt. USAR. Roman Catholic. Avocations: football coaching, softball, running, golf, skiing. Home: 33 Highland Rd Montvale NJ 07645-2013 Office: 200 Connecticut Ave Norwalk CT 06854-1940

MAISEL, HERBERT, computer science educator; b. N.Y.C., Sept. 22, 1930; s. Hyman and Dora (Goldstein) M.; m. Millicent Sherry Kuhmer, Apr. 13, 1957; children—Scott Alan, Raymond Bruce. B.S., CCNY, 1951; M.S., NYU, 1952; Ph.D., Catholic U. Am., 1964. Mathematician, statistician Dept. Army, Aberdeen, Md., Washington, 1954-63; dir. acad. computer ctr. Georgetown U., Washington, 1963-76, prof. computer sci., 1963—; systems advisor Social Security Adminstrn., Balt., 1976-84; cons. Nat. Bur. Standards, Gaithersburg, Md., 1968-72, Balt. Housing Authority, 1972-73, Social Security Adminstrn., Balt., 1966-73; mem. study group HHS, Washington, 1975-76. Author: An Introduction to Electronic Digital Computers, 1969; Simulation of Discrete Stochastic Systems, 1972; Computers for Social and Economic Development, 1974; Computers: Programming and Applications, 1975; also others. Contbr. articles to profl. jours. Mem. Community Housing Resources Bd., Montgomery County, Md., 1975. Recipient spl. service award Internat. Assn. Parents of Deaf, 1982. Fellow Assn. Computing Machinery (chmn. external activities bd. 1981-86, chmn. mems. and chpts. bd. 1978-80, chmn. nominating com. 1983-84, mem. council, chmn. Washington chpt. 1971-73, Outstanding Contribution award 1986); mem. Am. Statis. Assn., AAAS, Fedn. Am. Scientists, Com. Concerned Scientists, Phi Beta Kappa (chmn. Georgetown chpt. 1974-76), Sigma Xi. Jewish. Office: Georgetown Univ Computer Sci Dept 37th & O Sts NW Washington DC 20057

MAISEL, MICHAEL, shoe designer and manufacturer; b. Newark, Oct. 19, 1947; s. Irving and Betty (Markin) M.; m. Arlette Bernstein, Oct. 18, 1980; children: Ian Albert, Alicia Beth, Noah Shawn, Bette Gabrielle. B.S in Mktg., B.A. in Gen. Bus. Adminstrn., Ariz. State U., 1969. Asst. sales mgr. Mid-Atlantic Shoe Co. div. Beck Industries, N.Y.C., 1969-71; dir. imports Felsway Corp., Totowa, N.J., 1972-73; exec. v.p. Carber Enterprises, N.Y.C., 1973-80; v.p. S.R.O. div. Caressa, N.Y.C., 1980-84; pres. Sandler of Boston, N.Y.C., 1984-85, chmn. bd., 1986—; v.p. Lowell Shoe, Inc., Hudson, N.H., 1992-93; v.p. Selby, U.S Shoe, Cin., 1993—; cons. in field. Mem. 210 Shoe Industry (life), Nat. Shoe Retailers Assn. (bd. dirs.), Nat. Shoe Mfrs. Assn. Republican. Jewish. Designer Carber's shoe, displayed in Met. Mus. Art; nominated for Coty design award, 1974-78; recipient Friendship award City of Cin. Human Rels. Commn., 1994. Office: US Shoe 1 Eastwood Dr Cincinnati OH 45227-1197

MAISEL, SHERMAN JOSEPH, economist, educator; b. Buffalo, July 8, 1918; s. Louis and Sophia (Beck) M.; m. Lucy Cowdin, Sept. 26, 1942; children: Lawrence C., Margaret L. A.B., Harvard U., 1939, M.P.A., 1947, Ph.D., 1949. Mem. bd. govs. FRS, 1965-72; economist, fin. service res. officer Dept. State, 1946-54; teaching fellow Harvard U., 1947-48; asst. prof., assoc. prof., prof. bus. adminstrn. U. Calif. at Berkeley, 1948-65, 72-86; sr. economist Nat. Bur. Econ. Research-West, 1973-78; chmn., bd. dirs. Farmers Savings & Loan, 1986-88; pres. Sherman J. Maisel & Asscs. Inc., 1986—; fellow Fund For Advancement Edn., 1972-53, Inst. Basic Math. with Application to Bus., 1959-60, Center for Advanced Study in Behavioral Scis., 1972; mem. adv. coms. to Bur. Census, FHA, State of Calif., Ford Found.,

Social Sci. Research Council; mem. bldg. research adv. bd. NRC. Author: Housebuilding in Transition, 1953, Fluctuations, Growth, and Forecasting, 1957, Managing the Dollar, 1973, Real Estate Investment and Finance, 1976, Risk and Capital Adequacy in Commercial Banks, 1981, Macroeconomics: Theories and Policies, 1982, Real Estate Finance, 1987, 2d edit., 1992. Bd. dirs. Berkeley Unified Sch. Dist., 1962-65. Served to capt. AUS, 1941-45. Mem. Am. Fin. Assn. (pres. 1973), Am. Econ. Assn., Am. Statis. Assn. Home: 2164 Hyde St San Francisco CA 94109-1701 Office: U Calif Haas Bus Sch Berkeley CA 94720

MAISLIN, ISIDORE, hospital administrator; b. N.Y.C., Aug. 4, 1919; s. Solomon and Rose (Baruch) M.; m. Frances Mussman, Jan. 18, 1948; children—Wendy Sue (Mrs. Neil Robbins), Steven William. B.S., Columbia, 1950, M.S., 1951. Asso. dir. Albert Einstein Med. Center, Phila., 1950-59; asso. dir. Mt. Sinai Hosp. Greater Miami, Mimai Beach, Fla., 1959-63; adminstr. Scranton (Pa.) Gen. Hosp., 1963-64; exec. dir. Jewish Home of Eastern Pa., Scranton, 1964-67; adminstr. South Mountain (Pa.) Restoration Center, 1967—. Served with AUS, 1943-46. Fellow Am. Coll. Hosp. Adminstrs., Am. Pub. Health Assn., Royal Soc. Health. Home and Office: 535 Colfax Ave Scranton PA 18510-2364

MAISSEL, LEON ISRAEL, physicist, engineer; b. Cape Town, South Africa, May 31, 1930; came to U.S., 1956; s. Charles and Emily (Cohen) M.; m. Raina Eve Corren, Jan. 26, 1956; children: Simon, Gerda, Joseph. B.Sc., U. Cape Town, 1949, M.Sc., 1951; Ph.D., U. London, 1955. Staff scientist Philco Corp., Phila., 1956-60; adv. physicist IBM Corp., Poughkeepsie, N.Y., 1960-63, sr. engr., 1963-81, sr. tech. staff mem., 1981-93. Author, editor: Handbook of Thin Film Technology, 1969, An Introduction to Thin Films, 1970; contbr. articles profl. jours.; patentee in field. Recipient Outstanding Invention award IBM Corp., 1968; recipient Outstanding Contbn. award IBM Corp., 1969. Fellow IEEE; mem. Am. Vacuum Soc. (Dir. 1966-68). Democrat. Jewish. Lodge: B'nai B'rith. Home: 16 Smoke Rise Ln Wappingers Falls NY 12590-1220 *Most people, properly trained, can solve well-defined problems. The ability to deal with poorly-defined problems is much rarer and is the key to success in science.*

MAISTO, JOHN F., ambassador; b. Braddock, Pa., Aug. 28, 1938; married; 3 children. BSFS, Georgetown U., 1961; MA, San Carlos Coll., Guatemala, 1962. With BiNational Ctr., Cordoba, Argentina, 1963-66; asst. cultural affairs officer USIA, Cochabamba, Bolivia, 1966-68; with Fgn. Svc., 1968—; adminstrv. asst. Fgn. Svc. Inst. Dept. State, 1968-69; econ. and comml. officer U.S. Embassy, La Paz, Bolivia, 1969-71; internat. rels. officer Ops. Ctr., 1971-72; spl. asst. Office of Counselor, 1972-73; internat. rels. officer office Andean affairs, bur. inter-Am. affairs Dept. State, 1973-75; polit. officer U.S. Embassy, San Jose, Costa Rica, 1975-78, Manila, 1978-82; dep. dir. office Philippine affairs, bur. East Asian and Pacific affairs Dept. State, 1982-84, dir., 1984-86; dep. chief of mission and charge d'affaires Am. Embassy, Panama, 1986-89; dep. permanent U.S. rep. to OAS, 1989-92; dep. asst. sec. state for Ctrl. Am. and Panama Dept. State, 1992-93; U.S. amb. to Nicaragua, 1993—. Office: US Dept State Washington DC 20521-3240 also: US Embassy, Managua Nicaragua

MAITIN, SAM(UEL CALMAN) (SAM MAITIN), artist; b. Phila., Oct. 26, 1928; s. Isaac Boris and Ruth (Pollack) M.; m. Lilyan Miller, Aug. 29, 1964; children—Izak Joshua, Ana Raquel. Grad., Phila. Coll. Art, 1949; B.A., U Pa., 1951. instr. art Phila. Coll. Art, 1949-59, Moore Coll. Art, 1950-52, Phila. Mus. Art, 1961-73, 80-81, Annenberg Sch. Comm. U. Pa., 1964-70; vis. lectr. Kent (Eng.) Inst. Art & Design, Canterbury, 1990, Camberwell Coll. Art, London, 1990. Creator 50 posters for YM/YWHA Arts Council.; one-man shows include: Yoseido Gallery, Tokyo, 1967, 69, 70, Curwen Gallery, London, 1969, Fleisher Gallery, Phila. Mus. Art, 1971, Associated Am. Artists Gallery, Phila., 1979, Joanne Lyon Gallery, Aspen, Colo., 1981, 82, 84, Dolan/Maxwell Gallery, Phila., 1985, 87, Noyes Mus., N.J., 1985, Woodmere Art Mus., Phila., 1994, Art Inst. Phila., 1994; group shows include Phila. Mus. Art Bicentennial Exhbns., 1976, Tate Gallery, 1977, Phila. Artists, Tel Aviv, 1978; represented in permanent collections Library of Congress, Mus. Modern Art, N.Y.C., Nat. Gallery Art, Oakland Mus., Calif., Phila. Mus. Art, Currier Gallery Art, Manchester, N.H., Tate Gallery, London, Pa. Acad Fine Arts, Smithsonian Instn., U. Pa., Picker Mus., Colgate U.; commissions include: (tapestry) Ark Covering, Adath Jeshurun Synagogue, Elkins Park, Pa., 1976, (mural painting) Phila. Dept. Recreation swimming pool, 1978, (mural) Academy House, Phila., 1984, (mural) Christian Assn., U. Pa., 1985, (tapestry) Abington Hosp., Pa., 1985, (dimensional mural) Annenberg Sch. Communications lobby, U. Pa., 1975, expanded, 1985, (3 story dimensional mural) law offices of Morgan, Lewis & Bockius, Miami, Fla., 1987, (ceiling and wall mural banners) Wharton Sch., U. Pa., 1988, (dimensional mural) Children's Hosp., Phila., 1992, (mural-sized dimensional diptych) Kaiserman YM/YWHA, Haverford, Pa., 1992, (50 dimensional paintings) Brady Cancer Treatment Ctr., Voorhees, N.J., 1993. Guggenheim fellow, 1968; recipient award of excellence Art Matters, 1988. Home and Studio: 704 Pine St Philadelphia PA 19106

MAITRA, SUBIR RANJAN, medical educator; b. Calcutta, India, Oct. 2, 1943; came to U.S., 1983; s. Sudhir R. and Nilima (Sanyal) M.; m. Sakti Sanyal, July 6, 1975; 1 child, Soma. BS, Calcutta U., 1964, MS, 1966, PhD, 1971, DSc, 1990. Lectr. in Physiology Banaras U., Varanasi, India, 1973-78, 81-83; sr. Fulbright rsch. scholar Henry Ford Hosp., Detroit, 1979-80, rsch. assoc. in hypertension, 1983-85; rsch. assoc. in physiology Loyola U., Chgo., 1985-86, asst. prof. physiology, 1987-88; dir. trauma rsch. surgery SUNY, Stony Brook, 1988-90, asst. prof., dir. trauma rsch. emergency medicine surgery, 1990-93, assoc. prof., dir. rsch. emergency medicine, 1993—. Recipient Gold medal Calcutta U., 1966; prin. investigator Indian Coun. Med. Rsch., 1981, Univ. Grants Commn., 1983. Mem. AAAS, Am. Physiol. Soc., Shock Soc. Avocations: travel, community activities, sports.

MAIWURM, JAMES JOHN, lawyer; b. Wooster, Ohio, Dec. 5, 1948; s. James Frederick and Virginia Anne (Jones) M.; m. Wendy S. Leeper, July 31, 1974; children: James G., Michelle K. BA, Coll. Wooster, 1971; JD, U. Mich., 1974. Bar: Ohio 1974, D.C. 1986, Md. 1987, N.Y., 1987. Ptnr. Squire, Sanders & Dempsey, Cleve. and Washington, 1974-90; ptnr., group head Crowell & Moring, Washington, 1990—. Contbr. articles to profl. jours. Mem. ABA, D.C. Bar Assn., Leadership Washington, Fed. City Coun., Econ. Club Washington, George Mason U. Century Club (bd. dirs. 1994—). Home: 9419 Brian Jac Ln Great Falls VA 22066-2002 Office: Crowell & Moring 1001 Pennsylvania Ave NW Washington DC 20004-2505

MAIZE, JOHN CHRISTOPHER, dermatology educator; b. Elizabeth, N.J., July 23, 1943; s. Donald Adam and Caroline Marie (Costanzo) M.; m. Janice Lee Bentley, May. 21, 1966; children: Sandra Kristine Tolly, John C. Jr., Jennifer Lee. MD, U. Mich., 1968. Diplomate Am. Bd. Dermatology. Intern U. Mich., Ann Arbor, 1968-69, residency in dermatology, 1969-72; asst. prof. dermatology SUNY, Buffalo, 1972-77, assoc. prof., 1977-80; assoc. prof. Med. U. of S.C., Charleston, 1980-83, prof., 1983-89, prof., chmn. dept. dermatology, 1989—; editor-in-chief Am. Jour. Dermatology, 1986-90; dir. Am. Bd. Dermatology. Author: Pigmented Lesions of the Skin, 1987. Fellow Am. Acad. Dermatology, Am. Soc. Dermapathology (pres. 1995); mem. Am. Dermatol. Assn., Internat. Soc. Dermatopathology (sec. 1987-89, pres. 1989-91), S.C. Med. Assn., S.C. Dermatol. Assn. Roman Catholic. Avocations: fishing, golfing, travelling. Office: Med U SC 171 Ashley Ave Charleston SC 29425-0001

MAJD, MASSOUD, radiology and nuclear medicine educator; b. Yazd, Iran, July 23, 1935; came to U.S., 1961; s. Jalil and Khadijeh M.; m. Fereshten H.S. Javadi, June 23, 1968; children: Kurosh, Katayoon. MD, Tehran U., 1960. Diplomate Am. Bd. Radiology, Am. Bd. Nuclear Medicine. Intern Deaconess Hosp., Buffalo, 1961-62; resident Georgetown U., Washington, 1962-66, instr. radiology, 1965-66, 68-70; asst. prof. Pahlavi U., Shiraz, Iran, 1966-68; asst. prof. George Washington U., 1970-72, assoc. prof., 1972-79, prof. radiology and pediatrics, 1979—; radiologist, dir. pediatric nuclear medicine Children's Nat. Med. Ctr., Washington, 1968—; adj. prof. radiology Georgetown U., 1981—; staff radiologist Georgetown U. Hosp., 1965-66; radiologist Pahlavi U. Hosps, Shiraz, 1966-68; assoc. staff radiology Children's Med. Ctr., 1968-72; sr. attending staff radiology, 1972—; founder dir. sect. nuclear medicine, 1969—; presenter in field. Contbr. chpts. to books and articles to profl. jours. Fellow Am. Acad. Pediatrics; mem. Am. Coll. Radiology (fellow), Am. Coll. Nuclear Physicians

(fellow), Am. Roetgen Ray Soc., Radiologic Soc. N.Am., European Soc. Pediatric Radiology (affiliate), Soc. Pediatric Radiology, Soc. Nuclear Medicine, Assn. Univ. Radiologists, Pediatric Imaging Coun., Frederick N. Silverman Soc., John Caffey Soc., Soc. Uroradiology. Home: 8605 Stirrup Ct Potomac MD 20854-4843 Office: Childrens Nat Med Ctr 111 Michigan Ave NW Washington DC 20010-2970

MAJDA, ANDREW J., mathematician, educator; b. East Chicago, Ind., Jan. 30, 1949; m. Gerta Keller. BS, Purdue U., 1970; MS, Stanford U., 1971, PhD, 1973. Instr. Courant Inst. NYU, 1973-76; from asst. prof. to assoc. prof. U. Calif., L.A., 1976-78, prof., 1978; prof. U. Calif., Berkeley, 1979-84; vis. prof. Princeton (N.J.) U., 1984-85, prof., 1985—. Alfred P. Sloan Found. fellow, 1977-79; recipient medal of college de France, 1982, John von Neumann award Soc. for Indsl. and Applied Math., 1990. Mem. NAS (Applied Math. and Numerical Analysis award 1992). Office: Princeton U Dept Math Fine Hall Princeton NJ 08544

MAJERLE, DANIEL LEWIS, professional basketball player, olympic athlete; b. Traverse City, Mich., Sept. 9, 1965. Student, Ctrl. Mich. Forward Phoenix Suns, 1988—. Mem. Bronze Medal Winning Olympic Team, Seoul, Korea, 1988; mem. NBA All-Defensive second team, 1991, 93; mem. NBA All-Star team, 1992, 93; named to Dream Team II, 1994. Mem. All NBA second team, 1991; NBA All-Star, 1992; Shares NBA Finals single-game playoff record for most three point field goals made-8, 1993. Office: Phoenix Suns 201 E Jefferson Phoenix AZ 85004*

MAJERUS, PHILIP WARREN, physician; b. Chgo., July 10, 1936; s. Clarence Nicholas and Helen Louise (Mathis) M.; m. Janet Sue Brakensiek, Dec. 28, 1957; children: Suzanne, David, Juliet, Karen. BS, Notre Dame U., 1958; MD, Washington U., 1961. Resident in Medicine Mass. Gen. Hosp., Boston, 1961-63; research assoc. NIH, Bethesda, Md., 1963-66; asst. prof. biochemistry Washington U., St. Louis, 1966-75, asst. prof. medicine, 1966-69, assoc. prof. medicine, 1969-71, prof. medicine, 1971—, dir. div. hematology, 1973—, prof. biochemistry, 1976—. Mem. editorial bd. numerous jours. and profl. mags.; contbr. numerous articles to profl. jours. Recipient numerous awards including: Am. Cancer Soc. Faculty Research Assoc. award, 1966-75, Disting. Career award for Contbns. to Hemostasis Internat. Soc. for Thrombosis and Hemostasis, 1985, Alumni/Faculty award Washington U. Sch. Medicine, 1986. Fellow ACP; mem. NAS, Inst. Medicine of NAS, Am. Acad. Arts and Scis., Assn. Am. Physicians, Am. Soc. Hematology (pres. 1991), Am. Fedn. Clin. Rsch., Am. Soc. Biol. Chemists, Am. Soc. Clin. Investigation (pres. 1981-82), Sigma Xi, Alpha Omega Alpha. Home: 7291 Westmoreland Dr Saint Louis MO 63130-4252 Office: Wash Univ Sch of Med Internal Med Saint Louis MO 63110

MAJESTY, MELVIN SIDNEY, psychologist, consultant; b. New Orleans, June 6, 1928; s. Sidney Joseph and Marcella Cecilia (Kieffer) M.; m. Bettye Newanda Gordon, Dec. 18, 1955; 1 child, Diana Sue. BA, La. State U., 1949; MS, Western Res. U., 1951; PhD (USAF Inst. Tech. fellow), Case-Western Res. U., 1967. Commd. 2d lt. USAF, 1951, advanced through grades to lt. col., 1968; program mgr., asst. dir. tng. rsch. Air Force Human Resources Lab., 1967-69; dir. faculty and profl. ednl. rsch. USAF Acad., 1969-72; dir. pilot tng. candidate selection program Officer Tng. Sch., Air Tng.Command, 1972-76; ret. USAF, 1976; personnel selection cons. to Calif. State Pers. Bd., Sacramento, 1976—. Patentee listening center; founded pers. testing for ballistic missile and space systems; directed largest study of fighter pilot selection since World War II; pioneered use of phys. testing as replacement for the maximum age requirement in law enforcement jobs; developed phys. fitness tests and established psychol. screening standards for state highway patrol officer and police officers; contbr. numerous articles to profl. publs. Decorated Commendation medal (2), Meritorious Svc. medal (2). Mem. Am Psychol. Assn., Internat. Pers. Mgmt. Assn., Calif. Psychol. Assn., Western Psychol. Assn., Soc. Indsl. and Orgnl. Psychology, Personnel Testing Coun., VFW, DAV, Am. Legion, Amvets. Home: 216 Gifford Way Sacramento CA 95864-6910 Office: 801 Capitol Mall Sacramento CA 95814

MAJEV, HOWARD RUDOLPH, lawyer; b. N.Y.C., Dec. 10, 1952; s. Benny and Hela (Wolnowicz) M.; m. Janet Brandt; children: Brendan Joshua, Collin Campbell. BA, Johns Hopkins U., 1973; JD, U. Md., 1976. Bar: Md. 1978. Exec. asst. to city coun. pres. City of Balt., Balt., 1985-94; assoc. Weinberg and Green, Balt., 1979-84; ptnr. Weinberg & Green, Balt., 1985-94, Rudnick & Wolfe, Washington, 1994—. Author: (with K.S. Koenig) How to be a Legal Eagle: A Checklist for Remodelers, 1988; dir. Lex Mundi, 1992-94. Dir. Citizens Planning and Housing Assn., Balt., 1985—, pres., 1990-92; bd. dirs. Md. Food Bank, Inc., 1988-92, Florence Crittenton Svcs. of Balt., 1986-87, Sinai Hosp. Balt., 1990-92, Levindale Hebrew Geriatric Home and Hosp., 1991; mem. devel. coun. The Kennedy Krieger Inst., 1988-92; participant Leadership-Greater Balt. Com., 1986. Mem. ABA, Md. State Bar Assn., Balt. City Bar Assn. Avocations: running, rotisserie league baseball, reading, stamp collecting. Office: Rudnick & Wolfe 1300 Eye St NW Ste 280E Washington DC 20005-9999

MAJOR, ANDRÉ, radio producer, writer, educator; b. Montréal, Que., Can., Apr. 22, 1942; s. Arthur and Anna (Sharp) M.; m. Ginette Lepage, June 30, 1970; children—Eric, Julie. Student, Coll. de Montréal, 1955-60. Lit. critic La Presse, Montreal, 1965-79, Le Devoir, Montreal, 1967-70; lecteur Editions du Jour, Montreal, 1964-67, Lemeac, Montreal, 1972-75; radio producer CBC, Radio Canada, Montreal, 1973—; prof. lit. and creative writing Ottawa U., 1977-78, U. Que., 1977, McGill U., 1990. Works include La Chair de poule, 1965, L'Epouvantail, 1974, L'Epidemie, 1975, Les Rescapés, 1978 (Gov. Gen. Can. award), Histoires de Deserteurs, 1991, La Vie provisoire, 1995; poetry collections include Poémes pour durer, 1969; dramas include Une Soirée en octobre, 1975; short stories include La Folle d'Elvis, 1981, L'Hiver au coeur, 1987 (Can.-Belgium award 1991, Prix Athanase-David 1992). Mem. Union des Ecrivains québécois (sec. 1976-79). Office: CBC Radio Can, 1400 E BlvdRene-Levesque, Montreal, PQ Canada H2L 2M2

MAJOR, CLARENCE LEE, novelist, poet, educator; b. Atlanta, Dec. 31, 1936; s. Clarence and Inez (Huff) M.; m. Pamela Ritter, May 8, 1980. BS, SUNY, Albany; PhD, Union Inst. Prof. U. Colo., Boulder, 1977-89, U. Calif., Davis, 1989—. Author: All-Night Visitors, 1969, Dictionary of Afro-American Slang, 1970, No, 1973, Reflex and Bone Structure, 1975, Emergency Exit, 1979, Swallow the Lake, Some Observations of a Stranger at Zune in the Latter Part of the Century, 1989, My Amputations, 1986, Such Was the Season, 1987, Painted Turtle, 1988, Fun and Games, 1990, Parking Lots, 1992, Calling the Wind, 1993, Juba to Jive: A Dictionary of African-American Slang, 1994; poetry: Symptoms & Madness, 1971, Private Line, 1971, The Cotton Club, 1972, Inside Diameter: The France Poems, 1974, Surfaces and Masks, 1988; contbr. articles to Washington Post Book World, L.A. Times Book Rev., N.Y. Times Book Rev. Am. Rev. Recipient Nat. Council on Arts award, Washington, 1970; Western States Book award, Western States Found., Santa Fe, 1986; Fulbright grantee, 1981-83. Office: U Calif Dept of English Sproul Hall Davis CA 95616

MAJOR, COLEMAN JOSEPH, chemical engineer; b. Detroit, Sept. 7, 1915; s. Coleman I. and Anna (Galik) M.; m. Marjorie Lois Shenk, Nov. 21, 1941; children: Roy Coleman, Marilyn M. Phillips Bever. B.S., U. Ill., 1937; Ph.D., Cornell U., 1941. Chief prodn. engr., supt. services Sharples Chems., Inc., Wyandotte, Mich., 1941-50; assoc. prof. chem. engring. U. Iowa, 1950-56; head high energy chems. Am. Potash & Chem. Corp., Whittier, Calif. and Henderson, Nev., 1956-59; prof. chem. engring. U. Iowa, 1959-64; prof., head dept. chem. engring. U. Akron, 1964-70; dean Coll. Engring., also dir. Inst. Technol. Assistance, 1970-80; dir. Inst. Biomed. Engring. Rsch., 1979-80; cons. computers. Contbr. articles to tech. jours. Named Chem. Engr. of Yr., 1979; C.J. Major Scholarship award established in his honor, 1990; recipient Disting. Svc. award U. Akron, 1993. Fellow Am. Inst. Chem. Engrs.; mem. Am. Chem. Soc., Sigma Xi, Tau Beta Pi. Patentee in field. Home: 7838 Jaymes St Dublin OH 43017-8812 *A few guidelines that I have used: 1. Work very hard but find time to relax. 2. Push yourself ahead, but don't hold anyone else back. 3. When gathering facts, be rigorous and unrelenting but when making decisions involving people, use the art of compromise.*

MAJOR, JAMES RUSSELL RICHARDS, historian, educator; b. Riverton, Va., Jan. 7, 1921; s. Julian Neville and Jean (Richards) M.; m.

Blair Louise Rogers, June 9, 1945; children: Blair Louise, Randon Leigh, Clara Jean, James Russell Richards. AB, Va. Mil. Inst., 1942; MA, Princeton U., 1948, PhD, 1949. Mem. faculty Emory U., 1949-90, Charles Howard Candler prof. history, 1980-90, chmn. dept., 1966-70, 76-79, 87-89; vis. prof. Harvard, 1965-66; mem. Inst. Advanced Study Princeton, 1967-68, 79-80; Vice pres. H.W. Dick Co., 1975—. Author: The Estates General of 1560, 1951, Representative Instns. in Renaissance France, 1421-1559, 1960, The Deputies to the Estates General of Renaissance France, 1960, The Western World: Renaissance to the Present, 2d edit, 1971, The Age of the Renaissance and Reformation, 1970, Bellièvre, Sully and The Assembly of Notables of 1596, 1974, Representative Government in Early Modern France, 1980, The Monarchy, The Estates and The Aristocracy in Renaissance France, 1988, From Renaissance Monarchy to Absolute Monarchy: French Kings, Nobles, and Estates, 1994; also articles; bd. editors: Jour. Modern History, 1966-69, French History, 1986-90. Served to capt. AUS, 1942-46. Decorated Silver Star, Bronze Star, Purple Heart with 2 clusters; Fulbright fellow France, 1952-53; Guggenheim fellow, 1953-54, 67-68; Faculty Research fellow Soc. Sci. Research Council, 1955-58; fellow, 1961-62; sr. fellow Nat. Endowment for Humanities, 1973-74. Mem. AAUP (pres. S.E. regional conf. 1965-67, mem. nat. council 1966-69), Am. Hist. Assn. (com. on PhD programs in history, 1969-71, program com. 1976, mem. research div. 1978-81, Leo Gershoy prize com. 1990-92), Internat. Comm. History Representative and Parliamentary Instn. (pres. N.Am. sect. 1975-81), Renaissance Soc. Am. (mem. Council 1971-73), Soc. French Hist. Studies, So. Hist. Assn. (vice chmn. program com., 1967, chmn. European Sect. 1970-71), Société d'histoire de France, Academiè Europeenne d'Histoire, Phi Beta Kappa (senator United chapts. 1970-76). Home: 2223 Hill Park Ct Decatur GA 30033-2716

MAJOR, JEAN-LOUIS, author, French literature educator; b. Cornwall, Ont., Can., July 16, 1937; s. Joseph and Noella (Daoust) M.; m. Bibiane Landry, June 4, 1960; 1 dau., Marie-France. B.A. with honors, U. Ottawa, Ont., 1959, B.Phil., 1959, Licenciate of Philosophy, 1960, M.A., 1961, Ph.D., 1965; research fellow, Ecole Pratique des Hautes Etudes, Paris, 1968-69. Lectr. philosophy College Bruyere, Ottawa, 1960-61; lectr. dept. philosophy U. Ottawa, 1961-65, asst. prof. departement lettres Francaises, 1965-67, assoc. prof. lettres Francaises, 1967-71, prof. lettres Francaises, 1971—, assoc. dean rsch., Faculty of Arts, 1991—; lit. critic, dir. lit. sect. Le Droit (newspaper), 1963-65; vis. prof. U. Toronoto, Ont., 1970-71; editor Corpus d'editions critiques, 1981—, Bibliothèque du Nouveau Monde; chmn. acad. adv. com. Ont. Coun. on Univ. Affairs, 1991-93. Author books including Saint-Exupéry, l'écriture et la pensée, 1968, Léone de Jean Cocteau, 1975, Anne Hébert et le miracle de la parole, 1976, Radiquet, Cocteau "Les joues en feu, ", 1977, Le jeu en étoile, 1978, Paul-Marie Lapointe: la nuit incendiée, 1978, Entre l'ecriture et la parole, 1984, Journal d'Henriette Dessaulles, 1989, Ringuet, Trente arpents, 1991; also numerous articles. Fellow Can. Coun., 1968, 69, 71; grantee Humanities Rsch. Coun. Can., 1975, 85, 90. Fellow Royal Soc. Can., Academie des Lettres et des Sciences humaines. Home: PO Box 357, St-Isidore, ON Canada K0C 2B0 Office: Faculty Arts, U Ottawa, Ottawa, ON Canada K1N 6N5

MAJOR, JOHN CHARLES, judge; b. Mattawa, Ont., Can., Feb. 20, 1931; s. William and Elsie (Thompson) M.; m. Hélène Provencher, 1959; children: Suzan, Peter, Paul, Steven. BComm, Loyola Coll., Montreal, 1953; LLB, U. Toronto, 1957. Bar: Alberta 1958, Queen's Counsel, 1972, Alberta Ct. of Appeal, 1991. With Bennett, Jones & Verchere, Calgary, 1957-91, sr. ptnr., 1967; sr. counsel City of Calgary Police Svc., 1975-85; counsel McDonald Commn., 1978-82; sr. counsel Province of Alta., 1987; mem. Supreme Ct. of Can., 1992—. Fellow Am. Coll. Trial Lawyers; mem. Can. Bar Assn., Can. Inst. of the Adminstrn. of Justice, Can. Judges Conf., The Glencoe Club (Calgary), Calgary Golf and Country Club, Ottawa Hunt and Golf Club. Avocation: golf. Office: Supreme Court of Can, Wellington St, Ottawa, ON Canada K1A 0J1

MAJOR, JOHN KEENE, radio broadcasting executive; b. Kansas City, Mo., Aug. 3, 1924; s. Ralph Hermon and Margaret Norman (Jackson) M.; m. Gracemary Somers Westing, Apr. 9, 1950 (div.); children: John Westing, Ann Somers, Richard Jackson; m. Lee Adair Jordan, June 25, 1970. Student, U. Kansas City, 1940-41; BS, Yale U., 1943; MS, 1947; DSc, U. Paris, 1951. Lab. asst. physics Yale U., 1943-44, instr., research asst. physics, 1952-55; sci. staff spl. studies group, div. war research Columbia U., 1944; instr. physics and chemistry Am. Community Sch., Paris, 1948-49; research fellow Centre National de la Recherche Scientifique, Laboratoire de Chimie Nucleaire, Coll. de France, Paris, 1951; Carnegie Found. fellow Laboratoire Curie, Institut du Radium, Paris, 1951; assoc. prof. physics Western Res. U., 1955-57, chmn. dept., 1955-60, 61-64, Perkins prof. physics, 1957-66; staff assoc. univ. sci. devel. sect. div. instl. programs NSF, 1964-68; prof. physics, dean Grad. Sch. Arts and Scis., U. Cin., 1968-71; prof. physics NYU, 1971-74, dean Grad. Sch. Arts and Scis., 1971-73; vis. scholar Alfred P. Sloan Sch. Mgmt., MIT, 1973-74; prof. physics Northeastern Ill. U., Chgo., 1974-77; v.p. acad. affairs Northeastern Ill. U., 1974-75; cons. NSF, 1968-69; sci. cons. Sonar Analysis Group, 1946-47; gen. mgr. Sta. WONO, Syracuse, N.Y., 1977; dir. research and mktg. Sta. WFMT, Chgo., 1978-81; chmn. bd., pres. KCMA, Inc., 1980—; gen. mgr. Sta. KCMA, 1981-88; mem. exec. com. radio project Ctr. for Pub. Resources, 1980-81; bd. dirs. T. Rowe Price Equity Funds. Contbr. articles to profl. jours. Bd. dirs. Concertime, pres., 1993-95; bd. dirs. Tulsa Opera, Tulsa Philharm. Soc. Lt. (j.g.) USNR, 1944-46. Fellow at Lab. für Technische Physik, Technische Hochschule Munich, 1960-61; Fulbright fellow U. Paris, 1949-50. Mem. Classical Music Broadcasters Assn. (exec. v.p., 1979-80, bd. dir. 1979-82, 85-87, 89-93, pres. 1980-81, 90-91), Cosmos Club (Washington), Sigma Xi. Home: 126 E 26th Pl Tulsa OK 74114-2422 Office: 2021 S Lewis Ave Tulsa OK 74104-5715

MAJOR, KEVIN GERALD, writer; b. Stephenville, Nfld., Can., Sept. 12, 1949; s. Edward and Jessie (Headge) M. B.Sc., Meml. U. Nfld., 1973. Tchr. Roberts Arm, Nfld., 1971-72, Carbonear, Nfld., 1973, Eastport, Nfld., 1974-76; writer, 1976—. Books include Hold Fast (Can. Council award for children's lit. 1979), 1978 (Book of Year award Can. Assn. Children's Librarians 1979, Ruth Schwartz award 1979, Hans Christian Andersen Honour List 1980), Far from Shore, 1981 (Can. Young Adult Book award 1981), Thirty-Six Exposures, 1984, Dear Bruce Springsteen, 1989, Blood Red Ochre, 1989, Eating Between the Lines, 1991 (Book of Year award Can. Assn. Children's Librarians 1992, Ann Connor-Brimer award 1992), Diana: My Autobiography, 1993, No Man's Land, 1995; editor: books include Doryloads, 1974 (Vicky Metcalf award 1992). Mem. Writers Union Can. Anglican. Address: 27 Poplar Ave, Saint John's, NF Canada A1B 1C7

MAJOR, RICHARD DEMAREST, manufacturing company executive; b. Pitts., Apr. 10, 1935; s. Alfred Job and Marjorie Eleanor (Demarest) M.; m. JoAnn Detwiler, June 25, 1977; children: Keith Richard, Barbara Lynn, Jeffrey Briggs. BS in Math., Carnegie-Mellon U., 1956; MBA, U. Pitts., 1961, PhD in Bus. Adminstrn., 1973. Prodn. engr. E.I. duPont de Nemours & co., Niagara Falls, N.Y., 1956-60; mgr. Touche ross & Co., N.Y.C., 1963-69; dept. mgr., fin. staff Ford Motor Co., Dearborn, Mich., 1969-70; pres. Energy Conversion Devices, Inc., Troy, Mich., 1970-73; Hauserman, Inc., Cleve., 1973-84, Hiebert, Inc., Carson, Calif., 1984-87, GF Corp., Youngstown, OH, 1987—. Trustee Leukemia Soc. Am., Cleve., 1979-81, St. Vincents Charity Hosp., 1979-81, Cleve. Ballet, 1981-84, Joffrey Ballet, Los Angeles, 1986; bd. dirs. Youngstown Symphony Soc., 1988—; mem. Leadership Cleve., 1977-78, Leadership Youngstown, 1987-88, bd. dirs. Predoctoral fellow Ford Found., Pitts., 1962-63. Mem. Youngstown C. of C. (bd. dirs. 1988), Youngstown Country Club, Pi Mu Epsilon, Beta Gamma Sigma, Beta Alpha Psi. Home: 151 Newport Dr Youngstown OH 44512-1408 Office: GF Corp PO Box 1108 Youngstown OH 44501-1108

MAJOR, THOMAS D., academic program director; b. South Rim Grand Canyon, Ariz., Aug. 21, 1954; s. Thomas LeGrand and Delna (Farnsworth) M.; m. Vikki Vincent, Aug. 30, 1975; children: Vincent, Madison. BS in Chemistry, So. Utah State U., 1976; MSChemE, Brigham Young U., 1978; MBA, So. Ill. U., 1981. Registered profl. engr. Design engr. Monsanto Co. Corp. Engrs., St. Louis, 1978-81; prodn. engr. Monsanto Oil Co., Denver, 1981-83; asst. v.p. E.F. Hutton, Denver, 1983-85; engring. mgr. MAZE Exploration, Denver, 1985-87; dir. U. Utah Tech. Transfer Office, Salt Lake City, 1987—; bd. dirs. Western Inst. Biomed. Rsch., Salt Lake City. Disting. scholar So. Utah U., 1976. Mem. Assn. Univ. Tech. Mgrs., Lic. Exec. Soc.

Office: U Utah Tech Transfer 421 Wakara Way Ste 170 Salt Lake City UT 84108-1210

MAJORS, JOHNNY (JOHN TERRILL MAJORS), university athletic coach; b. Lynchburg, Tenn., May 21, 1935; m. Mary Lynn Barnwell, June 27, 1959; children—John Ireland, Mary Elizabeth. B.S., U. Tenn., 1957. Head football coach Iowa State U., 1968-72, U. Pitts., 1973-76, U. Tenn. Volunteers, 1977-92, U. Pitts., 1993—. Chmn. E. Tenn. Easter Seals Com., 1977, March of Dimes, 1977. Named Nat. Coll. Coach of Yr., 1973, 76; Head Football Coach NCAA Divsn. 1A Foodball won nat. Championship, 1976; inducted into Nat. Football Hall of Fame, 1987, Tenn. State Hall of Fame. Mem. Am. Football Coaches Assn. (bd. dirs., past pres.), Pitts. Athletic Assn., Univ. Club, Pitts. Field Club, Honors Club in Ooltewah (Tenn.), Sigma Chi, Omicron Delta Kappa. Home: 4215 Bigelow Blvd Pittsburgh PA 15213-2649 Office: U Pitts PO Box 7436 Pittsburgh PA 15213-0436

MAJORS, LEE, actor; b. Wyandotte, Mich., Apr. 23, 1940; m. Farrah Fawcett, July 28, 1973 (div. 1982). Student, U. Ind.; grad., Eastern Ky. State Coll.; student acting with, Estelle Harmon, MGM Studio Acting Sch. Actor: (films) including Will Penny, 1967, The Liberation of L.B. Jones, 1970, Killer Fish, 1979, Agency, Steel, Scrooge, 1988, Keaton's Cop, 1988; (TV movies) including The Six Million Dollar Man, 1973, Just a Little Convenience, 1977, The Ballad of Andy Crocker, 1969, Weekend of Terror, 1970, The Gary Francis Powers Story: The U-2 Incident, 1977, High Noon Part II: The Return of Will Kane, 1980, Starflight: The Plane That Couldn't Land, 1983, The Cowboy and the Ballerina, 1984, Danger Down Under, 1988, Fire! Trapped on the 37th Floor, 1991, (TV series) The Big Valley, 1965-68, The Men from Shiloh, 1970-71, Owen Marshall, Counselor at Law, 1971-73, The Six Million Dollar Man, 1973-78, The Fall Guy, 1981-85, Tour of Duty, 1990, Raven, 1992-93; other TV appearances include: Gunsmoke, The Bionic Woman, Alias Smith and Jones, Bracken's World. Mem. AFTRA, Acad. Motion Picture Arts and Scis. Office: David Shapira & Assocs 15301 Ventura Blvd Ste 345 Sherman Oaks CA 91403*

MAJORS, NELDA FAYE, physical therapist; b. Houston, Aug. 3, 1938; d. Columbus Edward and Mary (Mills) M. Cert. in Phys. Therapy, Hermann Sch. Phys. Therapy, Houston, 1960; BS, U. Houston, 1963. Lic. phys. therapist, Tex. Staff therapist Tex. Med. Ctr. Hermann Hosp., Houston, 1960-61; phys. therapist Chelsea Orthopedic Clinic, Houston, 1961-63; dir. phys. therapy Meml. Hosp. Southwest, Houston, 1963-75; owner, pres. Nelda Majors, Inc., Houston, 1975—; mem. profl. adv. bd. Logos Home Health Agy., Houston, 1985-86; adv. dir. 1st Northwestern Bank, Houston. Active with Meml. Dr. Meth. Ch., Houston, 1963—; ptnr. Houston Proud Ptnr., 1986—; founder, pres. Instnl. Safety Advs. Inc., 1994—; bd. dirs. Texans for the Improvement of Long Term Care Facilities, 1995—. Named All Am. Softball Pitcher, Amateur Softball Assn., 1964, All-Regional and All-State Pitcher, Tex. Amateur Softball Assn., 1954-70; named to Houston Amateur Softball Assn. Softball Hall of Fame, 1994. Mem. Am. Phys. Therapy Assn. (pvt. practice sect.), Tex. Phys. Therapy Assn., U. Houston Alumni Assn., E. Cullen Soc. (U. Houston), N.W. Crossing Optimist Club (Houston, charter mem., bd. dirs.), River Oaks Rotary (Houston), Phi Kappa Phi. Republican. Club: U. Houston Cougar. Avocations: softball, bicycling, traveling, golf, reading.

MAJORS, RICHARD GEORGE, psychology educator; b. Ithaca, N.Y.; s. Richard G. II and Fannie Sue Majors; legal guardian: Lillian A. McGill. AA, Auburn (N.Y.) Community Coll., 1974; BA in History, Plattsburgh State Coll., 1977; PhD in Ednl. Psychology, U. Ill. 1987. Various social svc. positions, 1976-79; probation officer, ct. investigator Plattsburgh, 1979; clin. intern McKinley Health Ctr., Urbana, Ill., 1981; rsch. asst. U. Minn., Mpls., 1981, U. Ill. Urbana, 1981-84; instr. Parkland Community Coll., Champaign, Ill., 1985; rsch. asst. U. Ill., Champaign, 1985-86; postdoctoral fellow U. Kans., Lawrence, 1987-89; postdoctoral fellow, clin. fellow Harvard Med. Sch., Boston, 1989-90; asst. prof. psychology U. Wis., Eau Claire, 1990-93; sr. rsch. assoc. The Urban Inst., Washington, 1993—; presenter in field. Co-author: Coolpose: The Dilemmas of Black Manhood in America, 1992, The American Black Male: His Present Status and Future, 1994; founder Jour. of African Am. Men. Named one of Outstanding Young Men of Am., 1987; APA predoctoral minority fellow, 1984. Fellow APA; mem. Nat. Coun. African Am. Men (chmn., co-founder), Soc. for the Psychol. Study of Ethnic Minority Issues, Am. Orthopsychiat. Assn., Greenpeace, Kappa Delta Pi, Phi Delta Kappa. Avocations: reading, traveling, cycling. Office: The Urban Inst 2100 M St Washington DC 20037

MAJORS, STEVEN WILLIAM, director art museum, artist, art consultant; b. Trenton, N.J., Apr. 16, 1955; s. Steven Andrew and Alvina Henrietta Margaret (Marion) M. AA in Visual Arts, Mercer County C.C., 1978; BFA in Painting and Printmaking, Va. Commonwealth U., 1980; MA in Painting and Studio Arts, C.W. Post Ctr. L.I. U., 1983. Installation design/lighting dir. Hillwood Art Gallery, C.W. Post Ctr. of L.I. U., Greenvale, N.Y., 1981-83; interpreter of exhibits Whaling Mus. Soc., Inc., Cold Spring Harbor, N.Y., 1983; curator Washington County Mus. of Fine Arts, Hagerstown, Md., 1984-88; dir. Torpedo Factory Art Ctr., Alexandria, Va., 1988—; adj. faculty in visual arts, Mercer County C.C., 1983-84; adj. faculty in art and art edn., Frostburg (Md.) State U.,1986-87; adj. faculty in art history, Frederick (Md.) C.C., 1993—; bd. mem. Alexandria (Va.) Commn. for the Arts, 1988-89, Gov.'s Task Force on the Arts, Annapolis, Md., 1987. One-man shows include C.W. Post Ctr. L.I.U., Greenvale, N.Y., 1983, Shepherd Coll., Shepherdstown, W.Va., 1987, Wilson Coll, Chambersburg, Pa., 1988; group exhibitions include Wunsch Arts Ctr., Glen Cove, N.Y., 1983, Mercer County C.C., Trenton, N.J., 1984, Md. Art Place, Baltimore, 1985-86, Harford C.C., Bel Air, Md., 1989, Target Gallery Torpedo Factory Art Ctr., Alexandria, Va., 1992; speaker in field; contbr. layout, photography, and design, to numerous catalogs and brochures. Outstanding Young Men of Am., U.S. Jaycees, 1984. Mem. Coll. Art Assn., Am. Assn. Mus. Avocations: shotokan karate, softball, skiing, biking, hiking. Home: 1226 Martha Custis Dr Alexandria VA 22302 Office: Torpedo Factory Art Ctr City Hall 105 N Union St Alexandria VA 22314

MAJUMDAR, SHARMILA, research scientist, educator; b. Calcutta, W. Bengal, India, Nov. 23, 1961; d. Anil Kumar and Sipra (Roy) M. BSc., U. Delhi, India, 1979-82; MS, Yale U., 1984, MPhil, 1985, PhD, 1987. Assoc. rsch. scientist Yale U., New Haven, Conn., 1987-88, asst. prof., 1988-89; asst. prof. U. Calif., San Francisco, 1989—; mem. alumni sch. com. Yale U., 1988—. Contbg. author; contbr. papers in field. Recipient Engring. award Whittaker Found., 1990—; NIH Career Devel. award, 1993; NIH-RO1 rsch. grantee, 1992. Mem. AAPM, Am. Phys. Soc., Soc. Magnetic Resonance in Medicine, Sigma Xi. Avocations: cooking, reading. Home: 244 Diapian Bay Alameda CA 94502-7911 Office: U Calif Dept Radiology 523 Parnassus Ave San Francisco CA 94143-6533

MAJZOUB, MONA KATHRYNE, lawyer; b. Memphis, June 19, 1949; d. A. Joseph and Mary Majzoub. BA, U. Mich., 1970, MA, 1972, JD, U. Detroit, 1976. Bar: Mich. 1977, U.S. Dist. Ct. (ea. dist.) Mich. 1977. Sr. prin. Kitch, Drutchas, Wagner & Kenney, P.C., Detroit, 1977—. Bd. dirs. Saratoga Community Hosp., Detroit, 1986—, Family Svcs. Detroit and Wayne County, 1988—. Mem. ABA, State Bar Mich. (tort law review com.), Detroit Bar Assn., Women Lawyers Assn. of Mich., Am. Arab Bar Assn. (treas. 1982-86, pres. 1986-94), Am. Hosp. Assn., Mich. Soc. of Hosp. Attys., Nat. Assn. of Women Lawyers, Assn. of Def. Trial Counsel, Inc., Assn. Trial Lawyers of Am., Mich. Def. Trial Counsel, Leadership Detroit XVI. Office: Kitch Drutchas Wagner et al One Woodward Ave 10th Flr Detroit MI 48226-3422

MAK, TAK WAH, biochemist; b. Canton, Republic of China, Oct. 4, 1946; s. Kent and Linda (Chan) M.; m. Shirley Lau, June 7, 1969; children: Julie Shi-Lan, Jennifer Shi-yan. BSc, U. Wis., 1967, MSc, 1969; PhD, U. Alta., Edmonton, Can., 1972; ScD (hon.), Carlton U., Ottawa, 1989, Laurentian U., 1992. Research asst. U. Wis., Madison, 1967-69, U. Alta., Edmonton, 1969-72; postdoctoral fellow U. Toronto, Ont., Can., 1972-74, asst. prof. 1974-78, assoc. prof., 1978-84, prof., 1984—; sr. staff scientist Ontario Cancer Inst., Toronto; dir. and research v.p. Amgen Inst.; vis. prof. U. Wis., Madison, 1980; hon. prof. Beijing Union Med. U., 1986—. Editor: Molecular and Cellular Biology of Hemopolitic Stem Cell Differentiation,

1981, Molecular and Cellular Biology of Neiplasia, 1983, Cancer: Perspective for Control, 1986, The T Receptor, 1987, AIDS: Ten Years Later, 1991; contbr. over 250 sci. articles. Recipient E.W.R. Steacie prize, 1986, Ayerst award Can. Biochem. Soc., 1985, Emil Von Behring prize Marburg (Germany) U., 1986, Gairdner Internat. award Gairdner Found., 1989, King Faisal Internat. prize for medicine King Faisal Found., 1995; hon. mem. Beijing Union Med. U., 1986, rsch. award Can. Found. for AIDS Rsch., 1992; E.W.R. Steacie fellow Nat. Sci. and Engring. Rsch. Coun. Can., 1984. Fellow Royal Soc. London; mem. Royal Soc. Can. (McLaughlin medal 1990), Chinese Acad. Med. Sci. (hon.), Royal Soc. London. Avocations: classical music, tennis. Home: 130 Glen Rd, Toronto, ON Canada M4W 2W3 Office: Ont Cancer Inst, 500 Sherbourne St, Toronto, ON Canada M4X 1K9

MAKAPELA, ALVEN, history educator; b. Mafiking, South Africa, Aug. 28, 1934; came to U.S., 1963; s. Mthunzi Leonard and Fuduka Rose (Mashwa) M.; m. Omega Nomvula Long, June 24, 1964; children: Themba, Dedanizizwe, Andile. BA in History, SUNY, 1965; MA in Econs., New Sch. for Social Rsch., 1967; PhD in History, SUNY, Stonybrook, 1980. Officer UN, N.Y.C., 1967-69; instr. Essex C.C., Newark, 1969-70; prof. Adelphi U., Garden City, N.Y., 1970—; spl. asst. to pres. Adelphi U., 1970—. Democrat. Mem. Seventh Day Adventist Ch. Avocation: farming. Home: RR 1 Box 377C Wyoming DE 19934-9766 Office: Adelphi U Hist Dept Garden City NY 11530

MAKARA, CAROL PATTIE, education educator, consultant; b. Norwich, Conn., Feb. 27, 1943; d. Howard G. and Ruth R. Robinson; m. Benjamin Makara, Feb. 19, 1966; children: Cheryl A., John J. AS, Three Rivers Community-Tech. Coll., 1988; BS, Cen. Conn. State U., 1965; MA, U. Conn., 1967. Cert. tchr., Conn. Tchr. Ledyard (Conn.) Bd. of Edn., 1965-66, Preston (Conn.) Bd. of Edn., 1974—; computer analyst Stanley Bostitch Clinton (Conn.) Plant, summers, 1987-92; evening instr. Three Rivers Cmty. Tech. Coll., 1989—; evening mgr. AutoCad Tng. Ctr., 1990—; coop. mentor tchr. Dept. Edn., Conn., 1988—; advisor Conn. Educators' Computer Assn., 1992—. Author: (with others) Pedagogical Guide: Strategies for Improving Instruction, 1992. Active Fellowship Program for Disting. Tchrs., 1987—. Fellow Conn. Bus. and Industry Assn.; mem. NEA, Conn. Edn. Assn. Home: 89 Mathewson Mill Rd Ledyard CT 06339-1114 Office: Preston Plains Sch 1 Route 164 Preston CT 06365-8818

MAKAREWICZ, JOSEPH THOMAS, research center director, historian; b. Phila., Mar. 6, 1937; s. Joseph Stanley and Mary Sophie (Wozny) M.; m. Bonnie Lee, Aug. 7, 1965. BA, LaSalle U., 1959; MA, Marquette U., 1961; PhD, U. Pitts., 1972. Instr. U. Pitts., 1964-65, sr. rsch. assoc., 1979—; asst. prof. East Stroudsburg (Pa.) State Coll., 1965-68, Pa. State U., Monaca, 1968-79. Editor: Toward a Better Balance, 1989; editor (newsletter) Pa. Ethnic Heritage. Pres. Anthony Wayne Hist. Soc., Beaver County, Pa., 1975-79; v.p. Beaver County Hist. Found., 1988-92; com. mem. Pa. Mus. and Hist. Commn. Quicentennial Com., Harrisburg, 1989-92, mem. cultural adv. com. Newberry Libr. post-doctoral fellow, 1973, NEH fellow, 1983. Mem. Immigration Hist. Soc. (newsletter editor 1991—), Hist. Soc. Western Pa. (collections com. 1988—), Nat. Coun. Social Studies, Pa. Coun. Social Studies, Polish Hist. Soc. Roman Catholic. Avocations: golf, stamp collecting, reading, gardening, travel. Home: 2864 Ridge Road Ext Baden PA 15005-2224 Office: Univ of Pittsburgh 405 Bellefield Hall 315 S Bellefield Ave Pittsburgh PA 15213-3504

MAKELA, BENJAMIN R., editor, research director; b. Hancock, Mich., Mar. 23, 1922; s. Charles Robert and Engel (Kruka) M.; m. Betty Virginia Shade, June 26, 1954; 1 son, Gregory Strickler. B.A., George Washington U., 1943; M.A., Stanford, 1954. Statistician Dept. Commerce, 1946, Nat. Fertilizer Assn. 1947-48; research economist U.S. C. of C, 1948-53; asso. dir. Financial Execs. Inst., N.Y.C., 1953-63; editor Financial Exec., 1963-72; research dir. Financial Execs. Research Found., 1966-83; cons., 1983—; Editor: How to Use and Invest in Letter Stock, 1970, (with William Chatlos) Strategy of Corporate Tender Offers, 1971, (with D.R. Carmichael) Corporate Financial Reporting: The Benefits and Problems of Disclosure, 1976, (with Richard F. Vancil) The CFO's Handbook, 1985: mem. editorial adv. bd. also author objt. Financial Exec.'s Handbook. Served with AUS, 1943-46, 51-53. Mem. Am. Acctg. Assn., Stanford Alumni Club, Squadron A Club, Halifax Club, Smyrna Yacht Club, Men's Garden Club of New Smyrna Beach, Phi Beta Kappa, Pi Gamma Mu, Omicron Delta Gamma, Sigma Nu. Republican. Baptist. Home: 686 Rochester Ct New Smyrna Beach FL 32168-2105

MAKEPEACE, DARRYL LEE, consulting company executive; b. Pitts., Oct. 24, 1941; s. Thomas Henry Makepeace and Nevada Ruth (Wagener) Desin. BS in Indsl. Engring., Pa. State U., 1969; MBA, Pepperdine U., 1982. Dept. mgr. Procter & Gamble, Cin., 1969-72; plant mgr. CBS Mus. Instruments, Fullerton, Calif., 1972-76; dir. mfg. Frigid Coil/Wolf Range, Whittier, Calif., 1977-79; mgr. materials mgmt. Nat. Supply, Los Nietos, Calif., 1979-85; assoc. prof. mgmt. Calif. State U., Fullerton, 1982-86; mgr. mfg. Nat. Supply, Los Nietos, Calif., 1985-86; program mgr. Armco Cumberland Group, Middletown, Ohio, 1986; ptnr., cons. Armco Cumberland Group, Mason, Ohio, 1986-87; prin., owner Cumberland Group, Cin., 1988—; owner Phoenix Cons., Inc., Cin., 1991—; owner, pres. D.L. Makepeace & Assocs., Mason, Ohio, 1991—; assoc. prof. mgmt. Wright State U., Dayton, Ohio, 1987-88, Miami U., Oxford, Ohio, 1988-89. Author: The System, American Iron and Steel Institute, Steel Body Panel Performance Characteristics, 1991; contbr. articles to profl. jours. Served with U.S. Army, 1960-61. Named to Honorable Order of Ky. Cols. Mem. Am. Prodn. and Inventory Control Soc., Inst. Indsl. Engrs., Alpha Pi Mu, Tau Beta Pi, Sigma Tau. Avocations: reading, chess.

MAKHANI, MADAN PAL SINGH, foundry executive; b. Amritsar, India, Oct. 23, 1937; s. Gulzar Singh and Mohinder (Kaur) M.; A.T.S. (Ednl. scholar), Machine Tool Prototype Factory, Bombay, 1957; A.M.I.B.F., City and Guilds London Inst., 1958; m. Betty Jean Lowder, June 10, 1972; children: Madana Marie, Indra, Jogi Patrick. In charge pattern shop and quality control New Haven Foundry (Mich.), 1964; gen. mgr. Old South Forge, Inc., Waycross, Ga., 1965-66; pres. Am. Casting Co., Inc., Tulsa, 1966—, also Am. Investment Casting Co., Inc., Am. Alloy Casting Co. Inc., Am. Foundry Group Inc.; pres. Okla. Steel Castings Co., 1982-85, Am. Alloy plant #2, 1985—; prof. Artisan Tng. Sch., India, 1957. Mem. Am. (dir. Tri-state 1973-75, vice chmn. Tri-state 1976-77, chmn. Tri-state 1977-78), Brit. foundryman socs., Patternmakers League N.Am. (treas. 1968-72), Soc. Mfg. Engrs., Tulsa Mfrs. Club (dir. 1980-81), Purchasing Mgmt. Assn. Tulsa, Investment Casting Inst. Club: Elks. Home: 3514 E 109th St Tulsa OK 74137-6607 Office: 14602 S Grant St Bixby OK 74008-3799

MAKHIJA, MOHAN, nuclear medicine physician; b. Bombay, Oct. 1, 1941; came to U.S., 1969; m. Arlene Zambito, Nov. 11, 1978. MD, Bombay U., 1965. Diplomate Am. Bd. Nuclear Medicine, Am. Bd. Radiology; cert. spl. competence in nuclear radiology. Resident in radiology Morristown (N.J.) Meml. Hosp., 1972-75; resident in nuclear medicine Yale-New Haven Hosp., 1975-76; post-doctoral fellow Yale U. Sch. Medicine, New Haven, 1976-77; jr. attending physician Helene Fuld Med. Ctr., Trenton, N.J., 1977-78; acting dir. dept. nuclear medicine Monmouth Med. Ctr., Long Branch, N.J., 1978, dir. nuclear medicine sect., 1979—, asst. attending radiology, 1978-80, assoc. attending radiology, 1980-83, attending radiologist, 1983—; sr. instr. Hahneman U., Phila., 1978-80, clin. asst. prof., 1980-83, clin. assoc. prof., 1983-91, clin. prof., 1991-94, clin. prof. of Radiologic Scis., Med. Coll. of Pa. and Hahnemann U., 1994—; radiol. cons. to N.J. State Bd. Med. Examiners., 1994. Contbr. articles to profl. jours. Fellow ACP, Am. Coll. Nuclear Physicians (speaker ho. of dels. 1992-93), Am. Coll. Radiology; mem. Monmouth County Med. Soc. (pres. 1991-92), Radiol. Soc. N.J. (chmn. nuclear medicine 1988-94, treas 1994-95, treas. 1995—), Indo-Am. Soc. Nuclear Medicine (pres. 1992-93), Soc. Nuclear Medicine (bd. govs. Greater N.Y. chpt. 1992—). Home: 5 High Ridge Rd Ocean NJ 07712-3460 Office: Monmouth Med Ctr 300 2nd Ave Long Branch NJ 07740-6300

MAKHOLM, MARK HENRY, lawyer, former insurance company executive; b. Maple Valley, Wis., Jan. 10, 1915; s. Henry and Emma Dorothy Agnet (Johnson) M.; m. Phylis Shoger, Nov. 11, 1950; children: Linda Marie, Mark Henry, Martha Marie. B.A. magna cum laude, Northland Coll., Ashland, Wis., 1937; JD, U. Wis., 1950. Bar: Wis. 1950, U.S. Supreme

Ct 1950. Asst. prof. Northland Coll., 1937-38; high sch. tchr. Washburn, Wis., 1939-41; operational supr. E.I. duPont de Neumours & Co. Inc., also U.S. Rubber Co., Kankakee, Ill., 1941-45; high sch. tchr. West Bend, Wis., 1945-47; engaged in retail clothing bus. West Bend, 1947-48; practice in Ashland, 1950-52; mem. firm Anderson, Fisher, Shannon, O'Brien and Rice, Stevens Point, Wis., 1980-86; with Sentry Ins. a Mut. Co.-Sentry Life Ins. Co., Stevens Point, Wis., 1952-80; v.p., gen. counsel Sentry Ins. a Mut. Co.-Sentry Life Ins. Co., 1962-78, exec. v.p., 1978-80, also dir., until 1980; former dir. Middlesex Ins. Co., Gt. S.W. Fire Ins. Co., The Sentry Corp.; Dairyland Ins. Co., Sentry Indemnity Co. Dir. Delta Dental Plan Wis., 1980—. Mem. Am., Wis. bar assns., Internat. Assn. Ins. Counsel, Order of Coif, Phi Delta Phi. Home: 3717 Combs Creek Ln Stevens Point WI 54481

MAKHOUL, JOHN IBRAHIM, electrical engineer, researcher; b. Deirmimas, Lebanon, Sept. 19, 1942; came to U.S., 1964; s. Ibrahim Hanna and Badia (Masoud) M. BEE, Am. U. Beirut, 1964; MEE, Ohio State U., 1965; PhDEE, MIT, 1970. Successively scientist, sr. scientist, supervisory scientist, prin. scientist to chief scientist Bolt Beranek & Newman Inc., Cambridge, Mass., 1970—; rsch. affiliate MIT, Cambridge, 1970—; adj. prof. Northeastern U., Boston, 1982—. Contbr. over 100 articles on speech processing by computer and spectral estimation to profl. jours. Recipient Citation Classic award for paper on linear prediction Inst. Scientific Info., 1982. Fellow IEEE, Acoustical Soc. Am.; mem. Acoustics, Speech and Signal Processing Soc. of IEEE (Sr. award 1978, Tech. Achievement award 1982, Soc. award 1988), Computer Soc. of IEEE, Communications Soc. of IEEE, Info. Theory Soc. of IEEE. Avocation: music. Home: 18 Amberwood Dr Winchester MA 01890-2202 Office: Bolt Beranek & Newman 10 Moulton St Cambridge MA 02138-1191

MAKI, DENNIS G., medical educator, researcher, clinician; b. River Falls, Wis., May 8, 1940; m. Gail Dawson, 1962; children: Kimberly, Sarah, Daniel. BS with high honors in Physics, U. Wis., 1962, MS in Physics, 1964, MD, 1967. Diplomate Am. Bd. Internal Medicine, Am. Bd. Infectious Diseases, Am. Bd. Critical Care Medicine. Physicist, computer programmer Lawrence Radiation Lab., AEC, Livermore, Calif., 1962; intern, asst. resident Harvard Med. unit Boston City Hosp., 1967-69, chief resident, 1972-73; with Hosp. Infections sect. Ctrs. for Disease Control, USPHS, Atlanta, 1969-71; acting chief nat. nosocomial infections study Ctr. for Disease Control, USPHS, Atlanta, 1970-71; sr. resident dept. medicine Mass. Gen. Hosp., 1971-72, clin. and research fellow infectious disease unit, 1973-74; asst. prof. medicine U. Wis., Madison, 1974-78, assoc. prof., 1978-82, prof., 1982—; hosp. epidemiologist, U. Wis. Hosp. and Clinic, Madison, 1974—; Ovid O. Meyer chair in medicine U. Wis., Madison, 1975—, head sec. infectious diseases, 1979—; attending physician Ctr. for Trauma and Life Support U. Wis., 1976—; clinician, rschr., educator in field; mem. program com. Intersci. Conf. on Antimicrobial Agts. and Chemotherapy, 1987-94; mem. program com. Ann. SHEA Mktg., 1992-95. Sr. assoc. editor Infection Control and Hosp. Epidemiology, 1979-93; mem. editl. bd. Jour. Lab. and Clin. Investigation, 1980-86, Jour. Critical Care, 1985—, Jour. Infectious Diseases, 1988-90, Critical Care Medicine, 1989-94; contbr. articles to med. jours. Recipient 1st award for disting. rsch. in Antibiotic Rev., 1980, Internat. CIPI award, 1994, numerous teaching awards and hon. lectrs. Fellow ACP, Am. Coll. Chest Physicians, Infectious Diseases Soc. Am. (coun. 1993-96), Soc. for Critical Care Medicine, Surg. Infection Soc.; mem. Soc. Hosp. Epidemiologists Am. (pres. 1990), Ctrl. Soc. for Clin. Rsch., Am. Soc. Microbiology, Am. Fedn. for Clin. Rsch., Am. Bd. Critical Care Medicine, Alpha Omega Alpha (nat. bd. dirs. 1983-89). Office: U Wis Hosp and Clinics H4/574 Madison WI 53792

MAKI, JERROLD ALAN, medical center administrator; b. Duluth, Minn., Sept. 4, 1947; s. Willio John and Eleanor Edla (Savela) M.; m. Carolyn Helen Dack, Aug. 2, 1969; children: Eric Edward, Emily Miriam, David Dack. BA cum laude, U. Min., Duluth, 1969; MHA, U. Min., Mpls., 1973. Lic. nursing home adminstr., Ohio. Asst. to supr. Investors Diversified Svcs., Inc., Mpls., 1969-7l; assoc. adminstr. North Ottawa Community Hosp., Grand Haven, Mich., 1973-77; v.p. St. Mary's Hosp., Grand Rapids, Mich., 1977-80, Bapt. Med. Ctr., Oklahoma City, 1980-85; exec. v.p., chief operating officer Svc. Frontiers, Inc., Lafayette, Ind., 1985-86; exec. v.p., chief operating officer Mercy Med. Ctr., Springfield, Ohio, 1986-90, pres., chief exec. officer, 1990-95, bd. dirs., 1987-95; sr. v.p. Mercy Health System-We. Ohio, Springfield, 1995—; chairperson accreditation and quality com. Ohio Hosp. Assn., 1993—; mem. bd. dirs. Mercy Managed Care, Ltd., 1995—. Bd. dirs. Mental Health Svcs. Clark County, Springfield, 1987—, Friends of Mercy, Springfield, 1988-95, Springfield Physician-Hosp. Orgn., 1991—; v.p. Springfield Acad. for Community Leadership, 1988-89; bd. deacons for ch., 1990-92, bd. trustees 1993—. Fellow Am. Coll. Healthcare Execs.; mem. Springfield C. of C., Springfield CountryClub, Rotary. Presbyterian. Avocations: stamp and coin collecting, sailing, golf. Home: 2006 W Mile Rd Springfield OH 45503-2732 Office: Mercy Health Sys-Western Ohio 1 S Limestone St Ste # 600 Springfield OH 45501

MAKI, KAZUMI, physicist, educator; b. Takamatsu, Japan, Jan. 27, 1936; s. Toshio and Hideko M.; m. Masako Tanaka, Sept. 21, 1969. B.S., Kyoto U., 1959, Ph.D., 1964. Research asso. Inst. for Math. Scis., Kyoto U., 1964; research asso. Fermi Inst., U. Chgo., 1964-65; asst. prof. physics U. Calif., San Diego, 1965-67; prof. Tohoku U., Sendai, Japan, 1967-74; vis. prof. Universite Paris-Sud, Orsay, France, 1969-70; prof. physics U. So. Calif., Los Angeles, 1974—; vis. prof. Inst. Lau-Langevin, U. Paris-Sud, France, 1979-80, Max-Plank Inst fur Festkorper Forschung, Stuttgart, Germany, 1986-87, U. Paris-7, 1990, Hokkaido U., Sapporo, Japan, 1993, Centre de Recherche sur Tres Basses Temperatures, Grenoble, France, 1993-94, Instituto de Ciencia de Materiales, Madrid, Spain, 1994. Assoc. editor Jour. Low Temperature Physics, 1969-91; contbr. articles to profl. jours. Recipient Nishina prize, 1972, Alexander von Humboldt award, 1986-87; Fulbright scholar, 1964-65; Guggenheim fellow, 1979-80. Fellow Japan Soc. Promotion of Sci., Am. Phys. Soc.; mem. AAAS, Phys. Soc. Japan. Office: U So Calif Dept Physics Los Angeles CA 90089-0484

MAKIGAMI, YASUJI, transportation engineering educator; b. Shenyan, Liaoning, China, June 3, 1936; arrived in Japan, 1946; s. Shikajiro and Masano (Kaneko) M.; m. Fumiko Nishina, June 9, 1964; children: Takeshi, Hiroshi, Satoshi. B.S. of Engring., Kyoto (Japan) U., 1960, D. of Engring., 1975; MS, U. Calif., Berkeley, 1970. Asst. engr. Fushimi Constrn. Office Japan Hwy. Pub. Corp., Kyoto, 1960-62; engr. spl. design sect. Keihin Constrn. Bur. Japan Hwy. Pub. Corp., Kawasaki, Japan, 1962-65; rsch. engr. tech. devel. sect., head office Japan Hwy. Pub. Corp., Tokyo, 1965-69; asst. sect. chief Nagoya Operation Bur. Japan Hwy. Pub. Corp., 1971-73; sect. chief Japan Hwy. Pub. Corp., Shimonoseki, 1973-75; sect. chief Tokyo 1st Operation Bur. Japan Hwy. Pub. Corp., Kawasaki, 1975-77; sect. chief Tokyo 1st Constrn. Bur. Japan Hwy. Pub. Corp., 1978; prof. of transp. engring., councillor Ritsumeukan U., Kyoto, 1978—; bd. dirs. System Sci. Rsch. Inst., Kyoto, 1979—; mem. com. Expressway Tech. Ctr., Tokyo, 1990—; council specialist Ministry of Edn., Tokyo, 1991—. Author: Traffic Engineering, 1984, Civil Engineering Practice, 1988; author, editor: Highway Engineering, 1988, Traffic Engineering, 1990. Fulbright travel grantee, 1968-70. Mem. Japan Rd. Assn., Expressway Rsch. Found., Traffic Engring. Assn., Japan Soc. Civil Engrs. (councillor 1986-87), World Conf. of Transp. Rsch. Avocations: golf, hiking, detective stories. Home: Bamba 2-1-15, Otsu Shiga 520, Japan Office: 1916 Nojicho Kusatsu-shi, Shiga 525, Japan

MAKIHARA, MINORU, diversified corporation executive; b. London, Jan. 12, 1930. BA, Harvard U., 1954. With Mitsubishi Corp., Tokyo, 1956-59, London, 1959-67; with Marine Products dept. Mitsubishi Corp., Tokyo, 1967-70, dep. gen. mgr., 1976-80, v.p., gen. mgr. Marine Products divsn., 1980-83, gen. mgr. mktg. and coordination dept., 1983-85, bd. dirs., 1986-88, mng. dir., 1988-90, sr. mng. dir., 1990-92, pres., 1992—; with then gen. mgr. Mitsubishi Internat. Corp., Seattle, 1970-71, v.p., gen. mgr., 1980-83; gen. mgr. Mitsubishi Internat. Corp., Washington, 1971-76, exec. v.p., gen. mgr., 1985-86; pres. Mitsubishi Internat. Corp., N.Y.C., 1987-90, chmn., 1990-92. Office: Mitsubishi Corp, CPO Box 22, Tokyo 100-91, Japan*

MAKIN, EDWARD, food products executive; b. 1951. Grad. Concordia U., 1972. With Redpath Sugars, Toronto, Ont., Can., 1972-91; with Domino Sugar Corp., 1991-92, pres., CEO, 1992—. Office: Domino Sugar Corp 1114 Ave of the Americas New York NY 10036-7701*

MAKINEN, MARVIN WILLIAM, biophysicist, educator; b. Chassell, Mich., Aug. 19, 1939; s. William John and Milga Katarina (Myllyla) M.; m. Michele de Groot, July 30, 1966; children: Eric William, Stephen Matthew. AB, U. Pa., 1961; postgrad., Free U. Berlin, 1960-61; MD, U. Pa., 1968; DPhil, U. Oxford, Eng., 1976. Diplomate Am. Bd. Med. Examiners. Intern Columbia-Presbyn. Med. Ctr., N.Y.C., 1968-69; rsch. assoc. NIH, Bethesda, Md., 1969-71; vis. fellow U. Oxford, Eng., 1971-74; asst. prof. biophysics U. Chgo., 1974-80, assoc. prof., 1980-86, prof. biochemistry and molecular biology, 1986—, chmn. dept., 1988-93; established investigator Am. Heart Assn., 1971-80; lectr. in field. Contbr. numerous articles to profl. jours. Mem., advisor The Raoul Wallenberg Com. of U.S., 1991—. Sr. surgeon USPHS, 1969-71. John E. Fogarty Sr. Internat. fellow, 1984-85, European Molecular Biology Orgn. sr. fellow, 1984-85, NIH spl. fellow, 1971-74, Berquist fellow Am. Scandinavian Found., 1970. Fellow Am. Inst. Chemists; mem. Am. Chem. Soc., Biophys. Soc., Am. Soc. Biochemistry and Molecular Biology, The Protein Soc., AAAS. Office: U Chgo Dept Biochemistry/Mol Biol 920 E 58th St Chicago IL 60637

MAKINO, SHOJIRO (MIKE MAKINO), chemicals executive; b. Roppongi, Tokyo, Japan, June 5, 1929; s. Taro and Tomiko M.; m. Sachi Hirose, Apr. 24, 1965; 1 child, Genta. BA, Keio U., Tokyo, 1951; MBA, U. Oreg., 1961. Salesman Getz Bros. Shokai, Tokyo, 1951-55; mgr. indsl. sales Getz Bros. and Co., Okinawa, Japan, 1955-59; mgmt. trainee Getz Bros. and Co., San Francisco, 1959-61; sales rep., mgr. Far East Omark Industries, Inc., Portland, Oreg., 1962-67; v.p., gen. mgr. Omark Japan, Inc., Tokyo, 1967-69; v.p. W.R. Grace K.K., Tokyo, 1969-70; pres. W.R. Grace K.K. changed to Grace Japan K.K. (1985), Tokyo, 1970—; corp. v.p. W.R. Grace and Co., N.Y.C., 1988—; v.p. W.R. Grace & Co. Asia Pacific, 1992—, also sr. advisor, bd. dirs., 1995; vice chmn. Polyfibron Techs., Inc., 1995. Past mem. Prime Min.'s Deregulation Com., 1994. Mem. Am. C. of C. (bd. govs. Tokyo chpt. 1988—), Tokyo Golf Club, Hakone Country Club, Hodogaya Country Club, Tokyo East Rotary Club. Office: Grace Japan K K, 6-14-1 Nishi Shinjuku, Tokyo 160, Japan

MAKOUS, WALTER LEON, visual scientist, educator; s. Lawrence and Ruth Lorraine (Luehring) M.; m. Marilyn Ann Carlson, Feb. 2, 1958 (div. 1974); children: Ann, James, Matthew; m. Joyce Brown Menconi, 1974 (div. 1981); m. Barbara Anne Duggins, Apr. 29, 1982. B.S., U. Wis., 1958; M.Sc., Brown U., 1961, Ph.D., 1964. Mem. staff IBM, Yorktown Heights, N.Y., 1963-66; asst. prof. psychology U. Wash., 1966-69, lectr. in physiology and biophysics, 1966-69, assoc. prof. psychology, 1969-74, prof. psychology, 1974-79; prof. psychology, ophthalmology and visual sci. U. Rochester, 1979—, dir. Ctr. for Visual Sci., 1979-90; northwest rep., charter mem. steering com. West Coast Regional Consortium Univs. in Neuroscics., 1976-79; mem. coun. on energy saving through more efficient lighting, NAS-NRC, 1978-79, night vision coun., 1985-86; chmn. ctr. symposium U. Rochester, 1981-82; sensory processes panelist NSF, Washington, 1977-82, mem. adv. com. applied sci. and rsch. applications policy, 1978-81, rev. com. Presdl. Young Investigator award program, 1984; vis. scientist IBM Rsch., 1970-71. Cons. editor Sensory Processes, 1977-79, Jour. of the Optical Soc. Am., 1982-86; Contbr. numerous articles to profl. jours. Served with USNR, 1953-55. Grantee Nat. Eye Inst., 1969—; NSF grantee, 1959-62, 81-82. Fellow AAAS, Am. Psychological Soc., Optical Soc. Am. (mem. coord. vision and physiol. optics com. 1983-89, coord. vision and med. optics com. 1983-89, publs. com. 1985-89, chmn. fellows and hon. mems. com. 1986, editor vision and color 1982-86, feature editor applied vision 1989-90); mem. Assn. Research in Vision and Ophthalmology (chmn. sect. psycho-physics 1977), Soc. Neurosci., Psychonomic Soc., Human Factors Soc. Office: U Rochester Ctr for Visual Sci Rochester NY 14627

MAKOWSKI, EDGAR LEONARD, obstetrician and gynecologist; b. Milw., Oct. 27, 1927; s. Adam and Ernestine (Horn) M.; m. Patricia M. Nock, Nov. 1, 1952; children: Peter, James, Ann, Mary, Thomas, Paul. B.S., Marquette U., 1951, M.D., 1954. Intern Deaconess Hosp., Milw., 1954-55; resident in Ob/Gyn U. Minn., Mpls., 1955-59; asst. prof. U. Minn., 1959-66, asso. prof., 1966; asso. prof. Ob/Gyn U. Colo., Denver, 1966-69; prof. U. Colo., 1969-93, chmn. dept., 1976-88, prof. emeritus, 1993—. Contbr. articles to sci. jours., chpts. to books. Served with AUS, 1946-47. NIH spl. fellow in physiology Yale U., 1963. Mem. Am. Gynecol. and Obstet. Soc. (pres.), Am. Coll. Obstetricians and Gynecologists, Soc. Gynecol. Investigators, Central Assn. Obstetricians and Gynecologists, Colo. Soc. Ob/Gyn., Perinatal Research Soc. (pres.) Roman Catholic. Achievements include radioactive microsphere technique for determination of organ blood flow. Office: U Colo Sch Medicine 4200 E 9th Ave Denver CO 80220-3706

MAKOWSKI, LEE, science administrator, biology and chemistry educator; b. Providence, Nov. 4, 1949; s. Chester Stanley and Frances Margaret (Brown) M.; m. Diane June Rodi, Mar. 25, 1983; children: James Aziz, Nicholas Prakash, Bryan Siva. BS in Physics, Brown U., 1971; MSEE, MIT, 1973, PhD in Elec. Engring., 1976. Postdoctoral fellow Brandeis U., Waltham, Mass., 1976-78, rsch. assoc., 1978-80; asst. prof. biochemistry Columbia U., N.Y.C., 1980-87; assoc. prof. physics Boston U., 1988-91, prof. physics, 1991-92; dir. Inst. Molecular Biophysics Fla. State U., Tallahassee, 1993—, prof. biology and chemistry, 1993—. Contbr. articles to profl. jours.; patentee in field. Rsch. grantee NIH, 1980-93, Tng. grantee, 1988-92, Rsch. grantee NSF, 1982-94. Mem. AAAS. Office: Fla State U Inst Molecular Biophysics Tallahassee FL 32306-3015

MAKOWSKI, M. PAUL, electronics research executive; b. Warsaw, Poland, Jan. 15, 1922; Arrived in U.S. July 1949.; s. Antoni and Stanislawa (Leszowska) M.; m. Eugenia Sawczyn, Dec. 1, 1945; children: Paul, Teresa. BA in chem., Case Western Reserve U., 1957, MS in Physical Chem., 1961, PhD in Electrochem., 1964. Mgr. Smith Phoenix Co., Cleve., 1950-55; chemist Clevite Research Ctr., Clevite Corp., Cleve., 1955-64; mgr. chemistry Materials Research Lab., Gould Inc., Cleve., 1964-73; assoc. dir. Materials Research Gould Inc., Cleve.; dir. Materials Research Lab., Gould Inc., Cleve., 1976-80; v.p. tech. adminstrn. Gould Inc., Rolling Meadows, Ill., 1980-81, v.p. scientific affairs, 1981-87; pres. TECTRA Cons. Inc., Rolling Meadows, Ill., 1988-93; cons. Rolling Meadows, 1994—; mem. Frontiers in Chem. Com. Cleve. 1976-80; bd. dirs. Microelectronics and Computer Corp. Austin, Tex. 1986-87. Inventor several patents in electrodeposition and catalysis. Mem. Ill. Gov.'s Commn. on Sci. and Tech. Chgo., 1986-87, Tech. Commercialization Coun. Ill. Dept. Commerce and Community Affairs. Mem. Am. Chem Soc., Electrochem. Soc. Chgo., Materials Rsch. Soc., Chgo. High Tech. Assn. Avocation: stamp collecting. Home: 305 Shady Dr Palatine IL 60067-7551

MAKOWSKI, PETER EDGAR, hospital executive.; b. Milw., Nov. 21, 1953; s. Edgar Leonard and Patricia Mae (Nock) M.; m. Cynthia Renee Edgerly, Apr. 7, 1979. B.A. in Polit. Sci., Whittier Coll., 1976; M.P.H., UCLA, 1980. Adminstrv. intern Calif. Hosp. Med. Center, Los Angeles, 1977, unit mgr. emergency dept., 1977-78; adminstrv. resident Presbyn. Intercommunity Hosp., Whittier, Calif., 1979-80, adminstrv. dir. support services, 1980-82, v.p. ambulatory/spl. services, 1982-84, v.p. diagnostic/therapeutic services, 1984-85; sr. v.p. Calif. Med. Ctr., Los Angeles, 1985-86; exec. v.p. Queen of the Valley Hosp., West Covina, Calif., 1986—. Mem. adv. council San Gabriel Valley Area Health Edn. Ctr., 1983-84; vice-chmn. adv. com. Trauma Hosp., Los Angeles County, 1987—. Mem. Am. Cancer Soc. (Long Beach SE unit, bd. dirs. 1984-85), Am. Hosp. Assn., Am. Coll. Hosp. Adminstrs. (student assoc.), Health Care Execs. So. Calif., UCLA Hosp. Adminstrn. Alumni Assn., Nat. Honor Soc, Whittier Alumni Assn. (bd. dirs. 1984—). Republican. Roman Catholic. Club: Whittier Host Lions. Home: 18520 Flora Dr Yorba Linda CA 92686-4937 Office: 1115 S Sunset Ave West Covina CA 91790-3999

MAKRI, NANCY, chemistry educator; b. Athens, Greece, Sept. 5, 1962; came to the U.S., 1985; d. John and Vallie (Tsakona) M.; m. Martin Gruebele, July 9, 1992; 1 child, Alexander Makris Gruebele. BS, U. Athens, 1985; PhD, U. Calif., Berkeley, 1989. Teaching asst. U. Calif., Berkeley, 1985-87; rsch. asst. U. Calif., 1986-89; jr. fellow Harvard U., Cambridge, Mass., 1989-91; asst. prof. U. Ill., Urbana, 1991—. Recipient Beckman Young Investigator award Arnold & Mabel Beckman Found., 1993; named NSF Young Investigator, 1993; Packard fellow for Sci. and Engring., David and Lucille Packard Found., 1993, Sloan Rsch. fellow Alfred Sloan Found., 1994, Cottrell scholar Rsch. Corp., 1994. Home: 2208 Wyld Dr Urbana IL

61801-6753 Office: U Ill at Urbana Dept Chem 505 S Mathews Ave Urbana IL 61801-3617

MAKRIANES, JAMES KONSTANTIN, JR., management consultant; b. Springfield, Mass., Jan. 15, 1925; s. James K. and Clara (Allen) M.; m. Judith Alden Erdmann, Sept. 30, 1960; children—Mary, James, Susan, Jane, Mahady. B.A., Amherst Coll., 1944. V.p., gen. mgr. Nat. Paper Box Co. and Nat. Games, Inc., Springfield, 1949-59; merchandising and acct. exec. Young & Rubicam, Inc., N.Y.C., 1959-63; v.p., acct. supr. Young & Rubicam, Inc., 1963-67, sr. v.p., mgmt. supr., 1963-73, exec. v.p., dir., 1973-78; sr. v.p., dir. Haley Assocs., Inc., N.Y.C., 1978-80, pres., 1980—, chief exec. officer, 1985-89; ptnr., dir. Ward & Howell Internat., Inc., N.Y.C., 1989-95; dir. Webb Johnson Assocs., N.Y.C., 1995—. Trustee Boys' Club N.Y., 1976—. With USNR, 1943-46. Mem. Maidstone Club, Racquet and Tennis Club, Links. Home: 415 E 52nd St New York NY 10022 Office: Webb Johnson Assocs 280 Park Ave New York NY 10017

MAKRIS, ANDREAS, composer; b. Salonica, Greece, Mar. 7, 1930; came to U.S., 1950, naturalized, 1962; s. Christos and Kallitza (Andreou) M.; m. Margaret Lubbe, June 12, 1959; children: Christos, Myron. Grad. with highest honors, Nat. Conservatory, Salonica, 1950; postgrad., Kansas City (Mo.) Conservatory, 1953, Mannes Coll. Music, 1956, Aspen Music Festival, 1956-57, Fontainbleau (France) Sch., 1958; pupil of Nadia Boulanger. adv. to Maestro Rostropovich for new music, 1979-90. Compositions premiered and performed in U.S., Europe, Can., S.Am., Japan, USSR; composer-in-residence Nat. Symphony Orch., 1979-90; prin. works include Scherzo for Violins, 1966, Aegean Festival, 1967, Efthymia, 1972, Sirens, 1976, Chromatokinesis, 1978, Anamnesis, 1970, Viola Concerto, 1970, Concerto for Strings, 1966, In Memory, 1979, Fanfare Alexander, 1980, Variations and Song for orch., 1979, Mediterranean Holiday, 1974, Five Miniatures, 1972, Concertino for Trombone, 1970, Fantasy and Dance for saxaphone, 1974, Fourth of July March, 1982, Violin Concerto, 1983, Nature-Life Symphonic Poem, 1983, Caprice "Tonatonal", 1986, Intrigues for solo clarinet and wind ensemble, 1987, Concertante for violin, cello, clarinet, French horn, percussion and orch., 1988, Sonata for cello and piano, 1989, Symphony to Youth for full orch., 1989, Trilogy for orch., 1990, Polychronion chorus and orch., 1990, Procession chorus and brass quintet, 1990, Intrigues for solo clarinet, strings, brass and percussion, 1991, "Concertino" for organ, flute and strings, 1992, "A SYmphony for Soprano and Strings", 1992, Woodwind Quintet, 1993; also works for violin, string quartets, voice quintets, duets and arrangements of Paganini, Bach, Corelli and Fiorillo. Recipient citation Greek Govt., 1980; Student Program grantee Phillips U., Enid, Okla., 1950, grantee Nat. Endowment Arts, 1967, grantee Martha Baird Rockefeller Fund, 1970, grantee Damrosh Found., 1958. Mem. ASCAP (am. awards 1980-92), Internat. Platform Assn. Greek Orthodox. Home: 11204 Oak Leaf Dr Silver Spring MD 20901-1313 Office: Nat Symphony Orch Kennedy Ctr Washington DC 20566 *Two important elements have contributed tremendously to my composing: As a child I was in the midst of war in Greece, and while all wars are terrible, it taught me both self-discipline and an appreciation for simplicity. Just being alive and able to compose makes me very happy. As a student I was not able to have a piano, the most valuable instrument for a composer. I learned to write with only a pencil and paper for full orchestra, and this liberated me both musically and practically.*

MAKUPSON, AMYRE PORTER, television station executive; b. River Rouge, Mich., Sept. 30, 1947; d. Rudolph Hannibal and Amyre Ann (Porche) Porter; m. Walter H. Makupson, Nov. 1, 1975; children: Rudolph Porter, Amyre Nisi. BA, Fisk U., 1970; MA, Am. U., Washington, 1972. Asst. dir. news Sta. WGPR-TV, Detroit, 1975-76; dir. pub. rels. Mich. Health Maintenance Orgn., Detroit, 1974-76, Kirwood Gen. Hosp., Detroit, 1976-77; mgr. pub. affairs, news anchor Sta. WKBD-TV, Southfield, Mich., 1977—, Children's Miracle Network Telethon, 1989—. Mem. adv. com. Mich. Arthritis Found., Co-Ette Club, Inc., Met. Detroit Teen Conf. Coalition, Cystic Fibrosis Soc.; mem. adv. com., bd. dirs. Alzheimers Assn.; mem. exec. com. March of Dimes; pres. bd. dirs. Detroit Wheelchair Athletic Assn.; bd. dirs. Providence Hosp. Found., Sickle Cell Assn., Kids In Need of Direction, Drop-out Prevention Collaborative, Merrill Palmer Inst. Recipient Emmy award for best commentary NATAS, 1993, 10 Emmy nominations NATAS, Editorial Best Feature award AP, Media award UPI, Oakland County Bar Assn., TV Documentary award, Detroit Press Club, numerous svc. awards including Arthritis Found. Mich., Mich. Mchts. Assn., DAV, Jr. Achievement, City of Detroit, Salvation Army, Spirit award City of Detroit, Spirit award City of Pontiac, Golden Heritage award Little Rock Bapt. Ch., 1993; named Media Person of the Yr. Southern Christian Leadership Conf., 1994. Mem. Pub. Rels. Soc. Am., Am. Women in Radio and TV (Outstanding Achievement award 1981, Outstanding Woman in TV Top Mgmt. 1993, Mentor award 1993), Women in Communications, Nat. Acad. TV Arts and Scis., Detroit Press Club, Ad-Craft. Roman Catholic. Office: 26955 W 11 Mile Rd Southfield MI 48034-2292

MALA, THEODORE ANTHONY, physician, consultant; b. Santa Monica, Calif., Feb. 3, 1946; s. Ray and Galina (Liss) M.; children: Theodore S., Galina T. BA in Philosophy, DePaul U., 1972; MD, Autonomous U., Guadalajara, Mex., 1976; MPH, Harvard U., 1980. Spl. asst. for health affairs Alaska Fedn. Natives, Anchorage, 1977-78; chief health svcs. Alaska State Div. of Corrections, Anchorage, 1978-79; assoc. prof., founder, dir. Inst. for Circumpolar Health Studies, U. Alaska, Anchorage, 1982-90; founder Siberian med. rsch. program U. Alaska, Anchorage, 1982, founder Magadan (USSR) med. rsch. program, 1988; commr. Health and Social Svcs. State of Alaska, Juneau, 1990-93; pres. chief exec. officer Ted Mala, Inc., Anchorage, 1993—; pres., ptnr. Mexican-Siberian Trading Co. Monterrey, Mex., 1994—; mem. Alaska rsch. and publs. com. Indian Health Svc., USPHS, 1987-90; advisor Nordic Coun. Meeting, WHO, Greenland, 1985; mem. Internat. Organizing Com., Circumpolar Health Congress, Iceland, 1992-93; chmn. bd. govs. Alaska Psychiat. Inst., Anchorage, 1990-93; cabinet mem. Gov. Walter J. Hickel, Juneau, 1990-93; advisor humanitarian aid to Russian Far East U.S. Dept. State, 1992—; cons. USAID on U.S.-Russian Health Programs, 1994. Former columnist Tundra Times; contbr. articles to profl. jours. Trustee United Way Anchorage, 1978-79; chmn. bd. trustees Alaska Native Coll., 1993—. Recipient Gov.'s award, 1988, Outstanding Svc. award Alaska Commr. Health, 1979, Ministry of Health citation USSR Govt., 1989, Citation award Alaska State Legislature, 1989, 90, 94, Commendation award State of Alaska, 1990, Alaska State Legislature, 1994, Honor Kempton Svc. to Humanity award, 1989, citation Med. Comty. of Magadan region, USSR, 1989; Nat. Indian fellow U.S. Dept. Edn., 1979. Mem. AAUP, Assn. Am. Indian Physicians, N.Y. Acad. Scis., Internat. Union for Circumpolar Health (permanent sec.-gen. 1987-90, mem. organizing com. 8th Internat. Congress on Circumpolar Health 1987-90). Avocations: cross-country skiing, hiking, photography, travel. Home: PO Box 232228 Anchorage AK 99523-2228 Office: 205 E Dimond Blvd Ste 544 Anchorage AK 99515 *Personal philosophy: Progress in the North will come only when circumpolar countries put aside their geopolitical thinking and work together as one northern family.*

MALABRE, ALFRED LEOPOLD, JR., journalist, author; b. N.Y.C., Apr. 23, 1931; s. Alfred Leopold and Marie (Leonard) M.; m. Mary Patricia Wardropper, July 28, 1956; children: Richard C., E. Ann, John A. B.A., Yale U., 1952. Copy editor Hartford (Conn.) Courant, 1957-58; successively reporter, Bonn bur. chief, econs. editor, news editor and Outlook columnist Wall St. Jour., 1958-94, news editor, 1969-94; contbg. editor Harvard Bus. Review, 1995—. Author: Understanding the Economy: For People Who Can't Stand Economics, 1976, America's Dilemma: Jobs vs. Prices, 1978, Investing for Profit in the Eighties, 1982, Beyond Our Means, 1987, Understanding the New Economy, 1988, Within Our Means, 1991, Lost Prophets, 1993. Served with USNR, 1953-56, Korea. Poynter fellow, 1976, Hoover Instn. fellow, 1991; recipient Eccles prize Columbia U., 1988. Mem. Authors Guild, Pilgrim Soc., Union Club, Nat. Golf Links Am. Address: 150 E 73rd St New York NY 10021

MALACARNE, C. JOHN, insurance company executive, lawyer; b. St. Louis, Dec. 26, 1941; s. Claude John and Virginia E. (Miller) M.; m. Kathleen M. Morris, Aug. 27, 1966; children: Tracy, Kristen, Lisa. AA, Harris-Stowe State Coll., 1962; BS in Pub. Adminstrn., U. Mo., 1964, JD, 1967. Bar: Mo. 1967. Asst. counsel Kansas City (Mo.) Life, 1967-71, assoc. counsel, 1971-74, asst. gen. counsel, 1974-76, assoc. gen. counsel, 1976-80, gen. counsel, 1980-81, v.p., gen. counsel, sec., 1981—; bd. dirs. Kansas City

Life Ins. Co., Sunset Life Ins. Co. Am., Calif. Life Ins. Guaranty Assn.; sec., bd. dirs. Old Am. Ins. Co. Sec., bd. dirs. Mid-Continent coun. Girl Scouts U.S.A., Kansas City, 1986-88; v.p., bd. dirs. Kansas City Eye Bank, 1986-91; pres., bd. dirs. Shepherd's Ctr., Kansas City, 1982-84; bd. dirs. Shepherd's Ctr. Internat., 1986-92, Community Mental Health Svcs. Found.; sec. rsch., 1992-94, v.p., 1995—; mem. Bd. Edn. Consolidated Sch. Dist. #4, Jackson County, Mo., 1989-91. Mem. ABA, Kansas City Met. Bar Assn. (vice chmn. corp. counsel com. 1986-87, vice chmn. corp. law 1993-94, chmn. corp. law com. 1994-95), Lawyers Assn. Kansas City (bd. dirs. 1976), Internat. Assn. Def. Counsel (chmn. accident health and life sect. 1982-84, ins. exec. com. 1986, v.p., mem. exec. com. 1988-90), Jr. C. of C. (bd. dirs. 1972), Kiwanis (pres. Kansas City 1975-76). Home: 604 Tam-O-Shanter Dr Kansas City MO 64145-1240 Office: Kansas City Life Ins Co PO Box 419139 Kansas City MO 64141-6139

MALACH, HERBERT JOHN, lawyer; b. N.Y.C., Aug. 3, 1922; s. James J. and Therese (Lederer) M.; m. Patricia Sweeny, Sept. 12, 1953 (dec. 1972); children: Therese, Herbert John, Helen. A.B., Iona Coll., 1951; J.D., Columbia U., 1955. Bar: N.Y. 1957, D.C. 1958, U.S. Dist. Ct. D.C. 1958, U.S. Dist. Ct. (ea. and so. dists.) N.Y. 1958, U.S. Ct. Mil. Appeals 1958, U.S. Ct. Appeals 2d cir.) 1960, U.S. Supreme Ct. 1961, U.S. Dist. Ct. (no. and we. dists. N.Y.) 1988, U.S. Ct. Appeals (fed. cir.) 1988, U.S. Tax Ct. 1988. Pvt. practice N.Y.C., 1957-72, New Rochelle, N.Y., 1960—; lectr. bus. law Iona Coll., New Rochelle, 1957-59, asst. to pres. for community svcs., 1959-62. Vice chmn., exec. dir. Iona Coll. Westchester County Law Enforcement Inst.; spl. counsel N.Y. State Temporary Commn. on Child Welfare; mem. Westchester County Youth Adv. Coun., 1969-73; mem. Law Enforcement Planning. Agy., New Rochelle, 1968-69; adv. counsel Westchester Police Youth Officers Assn.; mem. Westchester County Child Abuse Task Force; mem. New Rochelle Narcotics Guidance Coun., 1972-75; adv. coun. New Rochelle Salvation Army, 1976-79; legal adviser East-End Civic Assn.; law guardian Westchester County Family Ct.; referee New Rochelle City Ct.; arbitrator Civil Ct., Bronx; arbitrator Supreme and County Ct., Westchester. Bd. dirs. Art Inst., Iona Coll., mem. adv. bd. radio activities, adv. bd. criminal justice Iona Coll., bd. dirs. Westchester County Youth Shelter; hon. dep. sheriff Westchester County. Served with AUS, 1942-46. Recipient Patrick B. Doyle award for outstanding service, 1969, William B. Cornelia Founders award, 1976 (both Iona Coll.). Mem. Am. (family law sect.) N.Y. State (com. child welfare, com. family ct.), Bronx County (com. family ct.), Westchester County, New Rochelle Bar Assns., Am. Judicature Soc., N.Y. County Lawyers Assn. (family ct. com.), Criminal Cts. Bar Assn. Westchester County, Am. Fedn. Police, Internat. Narcotic Enforcement Officers Assn., Internat. Acad. Criminology, Am. Acad. Polit. and Social Sci., Am. Profl. Soc. on Abuse of Children, Law Guardians Assn. Westchester County (pres. 1987-89, dir. 1989-90), Am. Psychology-Law Soc., Internat., N.Y. State, Bergen County chiefs of police, Nat. Assn. Coun. for Children, Nat. Sheriffs Assn., Am. Soc. Internat. Law, Iona Coll. Alumni Assn., Inc. (pres., chmn. bd. dirs. 1958-60, 62-64, 72-74, 74-76, dir. 1954-58, 68-72, 76-86, v.p. 1966-68). Office: 105 Harding Dr New Rochelle NY 10801-4641

MALACH, MONTE, physician; b. Jersey City, Aug. 15, 1926; s. Charles and Yetta (Pascher) M.; m. Ann Elaine Glazer, June 15, 1952 (dec. June 1989); children: Barbara Sandra, Cathie Tara, Matthew David; m. Barbara M. Lipstein, Dec. 24, 1994. BA, U. Mich., 1949, MD, 1949. Diplomate Am. Bd. Internal Medicine, Nat. Bd. Med. Examiners. Intern Beth Israel Hosp., Boston, 1949-50; resident Beth Israel Hosp., 1950-51, chief resident, 1951-52; chief resident Kings County Hosp., Bklyn., 1954-55; practice medicine specializing in internal medicine and cardiology Bklyn., 1955—; dir. CCU Bklyn. Hosp., 1955-91, dir. emeritus CCU, 1991—; med. dir. Medicare IPRO Downstate N.Y., 1990—; pres. profl. staff Bklyn. Hosp., 1966-69, chmn. med. bd., 1971-72; attending staff Caledonian Hosp., pres. profl. staff, 1984-85; pres. profl. staff Bklyn. Hosp.-Caledonian Hosp., 1987-89, chmn. med. bd., 1988-89; cons. Kings County Hosp.; tchg. fellow Tufts U. Med. Sch., 1951-52; instr. medicine Downstate Med. Ctr., Bklyn., 1955-59, clin. asst. prof. medicine, 1959-68, clin. assoc. prof.; 1969-76, clin. prof., 1976—; clin. prof. medicine NYU Med. Ctr., 1994—; bd. dirs. Bay St. Landing One Owners Corp., 1985-87; v.p. Ocean View Condos, 1989-90, pres., 1990—. Kings County committeeman Democratic Party, 1964, 65. Served with USNR, 1944-46, to 1st lt. M.C. U.S. Army, 1952-54. Recipient 1st Prize for Crisis Mgmt. Habitat Mag., 1987. Fellow Am. Coll. Chest Physicians, ACP, Am. Coll. Cardiology; mem. AMA (chmn. sect. coun. ofr internal medicine 1980), N.Y. Heart Assn., Am. Soc. Internal Medicine (trustee 1975-79, sec.-treas. 1979—, pres. elect 1981, pres. 1982-83, chmn. investment com. 1985-93), N.Y. State Soc. Internal Medicine (pres. 1973-74, dir. 1974-77, chmn. Bklyn. chpt., v.p. 1971, award of merit 1978), Bklyn. Soc. Internal Medicine (mem. council 1965, pres. 1969-72), Med. Soc. State of N.Y. (chmn. sect. internal medicine 1976, chmn. med. care ins. com. 1988-93), Federated Council for Internal Medicine (chmn. 1979-80), Med. Soc. County Kings (censor 1985-91). Address: 55 Rugby Rd Brooklyn NY 11226-2607 *There is a place for hard work, scrupulous ethics and pride of accomplishment. A great marriage and a fine close family are buffers against adversity.*

MALAFRONTE, DONALD, health executive; b. Bklyn., Dec. 16, 1931; s. Pasquale and Amalia (Castaldo) M.; m. Diane Freedenberg, Jan. 7, 1960 (dec. Nov. 14, 1970); children: Philip, Victor.; m. Hillary Demby, Oct. 30, 1982. B.S., NYU, 1954. Reporter L.I. Daily Press, 1956-58; reporter, editor Newark Star-Ledger, 1958-65, art columnist, 1963-70; adminstrv. asst. to mayor of Newark, 1965-70; dir. Newark Model Cities Program, 1967-70, Newark Community Devel. Adminstrn., 1968-70; chief urban field operations N.J. Regional Med. Program, 1970-73; pres. Urban Health Inst., Roseland, N.J., 1973—; cons. to hosps., local govts., 1970—. Author articles in field. Served with AUS, 1954-56. Recipient Joyce Kilmer fiction prize NYU, 1953. Home: 78 Crestview Rd Mountain Lakes NJ 07046-1223 Office: Urban Health Inst 101 Eisenhower Pky Roseland NJ 07068-1097

MALAGUE, MARIANNE TYNDALL, nursing educator; b. N.Y.C.; d. Henry Francis and Mary (Callan) Tyndall; m. Paul Joseph Malague, June 15, 1963; children: Paul, Marilu. BS, Coll. Mount St. Vincent, 1959; MA, NYU, 1962; postgrad., Tex. Women's U., U. Houston, 1981-85. Staff nurse VA Hosp., Fort Hamilton, N.Y., 1959-60; head nurse St. Vincent's Psychiat. Hosp., Harrison, N.Y., 1960-61; instr. ADN Bronx Community Coll., N.Y.C., 1962-65; instr. Baccalaureate Nursing Adelphi U., Garden City, N.Y., 1967-70; instr. ADN Howard C.C., Columbia, Md., 1973-76; instr. ADN North Harris County Coll., Houston, 1978-88, dist. curriculum coord., 1988-89, divsn. head health occupations, 1989-92; dean sci. and tech., 1992—; test item writer Nat. League Nursing, 1984-85. Mem. Am. Women in Community/Jr. Colls., Nat. Orgn. for ADN, Tex. Nurses Assn., Tex. Jr. Colls. Tchrs. Assn., Houston Orgn. Nursing Execs., Coll. Mt. St. Vincent Alumnae Assn., Sigma Theta Tau. Office: North Harris Coll 2700 W W Thorne Blvd Houston TX 77073-3410

MALAKHOV, VLADIMIR, dancer; b. Krivoy Rog, Ukraine, USSR, Jan. 7, 1968; arrived in Can., 1994; s. Anatoly and Elena Malakhov. Grad., Bolshoi Ballet Acad., Moscow, 1986. Prin. dancer Vienna State Opera, 1992—, Nat. Ballet Can., 1994—, Am. Ballet Theatre, N.Y.C., 1995—; guest artist Am. Ballet Theatre, 1994. Appeared in Giselle, Swan Lake, Nutcracker, Manon, Romeo and Juliette, others; performed in major opera houses worldwide. Recipient Gold medal Varna Ballet Competition, 1986, Gold medal Moscow Ballet Competition, 1986, Serge Lifar prize, 1991.

MALAKOFF, JAMES LEONARD, management information executive; b. Phila., June 20, 1933; s. John and Ida Vera (Partman) M.; m. Anne Bronstein Frisch, June 26, 1955; children: Randi Ellen, John Seymour. B in Aerospace Engring., Rensselaer Poly. Inst., 1954, MS, 1955. Structural methods specialist Grumman Aircraft, Bethpage, N.Y., 1955-62; mem. tech. staff Northrop Corp., Hawthorne, Calif., 1962-65; chief, math. analyst Beckman Instruments, Inc., Fullerton, Calif., 1965-68; dir. data processing Beckman Instruments, Inc., Fullerton, 1968-82; v.p. data processing, 1982-85, v.p., mgmt. info., 1985—; bd. dirs. Little Co. Mary Health Svcs., Little Co. Mary Hosp., San Pedro (Calif.) Peninsula Hosp.; vis. prof. computer sci. Calif. State U., Fullerton, 1981-82, mem. indsl. adv. coun. Sch. Engring. and Computer Sci. Fellow AIAA (assoc.); mem. IEEE (computer group), U.S. Council Internat. Bus. (bus. and industry adv. com., West Coast com. Internat. Info. and Telecommunications Policy), Assn. Computing Machinery, Data Processing Mgmt. Assn. Office: Beckman Instruments Inc 2500 N Harbor Blvd Fullerton CA 92635-2600

MALAMED, SEYMOUR H., motion picture company executive; b. N.Y.C., June 17, 1921; s. Abraham and Bess (Kaisin) M.; m. Doris Raphael, May 19, 1946; children—Margery, Susan, Nancy. B.B.A., City Coll. N.Y., 1942. Engaged in entertainment field, 1954—; asst. to v.p., treas. Screen Gems Co., 1956-62; treas. parent co. Columbia Pictures Corp., 1962—, v.p., 1963-73, exec. v.p., 1973—. Served with AUS, World War II. Mem. Motion Picture Acad. Arts and Scis. Clubs: Friars (N.Y.C.); Metropolis Country (Westchester County); High Ridge Country (Palm Beach, Fla.), Metropolis Country Club. Home: 135 Central Park W Apt 9nc New York NY 10023-2465 Office: 301 W 57th St Ste 336 New York NY 10019

MALAMUD, DANIEL, biochemistry educator; b. Detroit, June 5, 1939; s. Jack and Jennie (Ashe) M.; m. Judith Disner, Mar. 7, 1961; children: Randy, Lisa. BS, U. Mich., 1961; MA, Western Mich. U., 1962; PhD, U. Cin., 1965; MA, U. Pa., 1983. Post-doctoral fellow Temple U., Phila., 1966-68, asst. prof. pathology, 1968-69; asst. biologist Mass. Gen. Hosp., Boston, 1969-72, assoc. biologist, 1972-77; assoc. prof. biochemistry Sch. Dental Medicine, U. Pa., Phila., 1977-84, prof. biochemistry, 1984—, chmn. biochemistry, 1985—; asst. prof. pathology Harvard U., Boston, 1970-77; vis. assoc. prof., Fulbright lectr. U. Philippines, Manila, 1975; vis. scientist Wistar Inst., Phila., 1985; affiliated scientist Monell Chem. Senses Ctr., Phila., 1985—; exchange scientist Hebrew U., Jerusalem, 1982. Author: Autoradiography, 1969; contbr. over 80 articles to profl. jours. and chpts. to books. Recipient Career Devel. award NIH, 1972-77. Mem. Am. Soc. Biol. Chemists, N.Y. Acad. Scis., Am. Soc. Cell Biologists, Am. Soc. Microbiologists. Office: Univ of Pa Sch of Dental Medicine 4001 Spruce St Philadelphia PA 19104-6003

MALAMUD, PHYLLIS CAROLE, journalist, magazine editor; b. Bklyn., Sept. 15, 1938; d. Louis and Hannah (Unterman) Malamud; m. Matthew A. Clark, Jr., Nov. 9, 1986. BA, CCNY, 1960; postgrad. (Russell Sage Found. fellow), Washington U., St. Louis, 1968-69. Publicity asst. Newsweek mag., N.Y.C., 1960-62, researcher, 1962-64, feature reporter, 1964-74, N.Y. polit. reporter, 1975-77; chief New Eng. bur. Newsweek mag., Boston, 1977-83; editor My Turn column Newsweek mag., N.Y.C., 1983-88; freelance writer N.Y.C., 1989—. Contbr. articles to various publs. Trustee Actor's Temple, N.Y.C., 1985—. Recipient Gavel award ABA, 1968, award for article Am. Psychol. Assn., 1975, Page One award N.Y. Newspaper Guild, 1977. Mem. Coffee House Club. Jewish. Home: 210 5th Ave Bldg 1102 New York NY 10010-2102

MALAMY, MICHAEL HOWARD, molecular biology and microbiology educator; b. Bklyn., Apr. 20, 1938; s. Henry R. and Rhoda A. (Resnick) M.; m. Frances E. Siegel, June 15, 1958; children: Adam C., Jocelyn E. B.A., NYU, 1958, Ph.D., 1963. Postdoctoral fellow Pasteur Inst., Paris, 1963-65, Princeton U., N.J., 1965-66; asst. prof. microbiology Tufts U., Boston, 1966-71, assoc. prof. molecular biology, microbiology, 1971-76, prof., 1976—. Mem. editorial bd.: Jour. Bacteriology, Washington, 1971-80. Mem. Am. Soc. Biochemistry and Molecular Biology, Am. Soc. Microbiology. Home: 39 Wildwood St Winchester MA 01890-1748 Office: Tufts U/Molecular Biology 136 Harrison Ave Boston MA 02111-1800

MALAND, TIM, hospitality company executive; b. Mineola, N.Y., May 25, 1953; s. Einar Reidar and Grace Sarah (McDonough) M.; m. Carol Ann Jones, June 21, 1977 (div. May 1979); m. Donna Eliakis, June 27, 1987. BS in Quantitative Systems, Ariz. State U., 1975; internat. exec. program, Insead, 1985; cert., Goethe Inst., 1983. CPA, Nev. Acct. Deloitte, Haskins & Sells, Las Vegas, 1977-79; systems analyst Del E. Webb Corp., Las Vegas, 1979-80; controller Tropicana Hotel, Las Vegas, 1980-81; internat. auditor Ramada Inc., Phoenix, 1981-82, internat. controller, 1982-85; v.p. devel. Asia, Pacific Ramada Inc., Hong Kong, 1985-86; sr. v.p., hotel group controller Ramada Inc., Phoenix, 1987-89; exec. v.p. Trump Pla. Hotel & Casino, Atlantic City, N.J., 1989—. Bd. dirs. Big Brother Valley Big Brother Assn., Phoenix, 1983-85. Mem. Internat. Assn. Hospitality Accts., AICPA, Am. Hotel and Motel Assn., Western Res. Club, Beta Gamma Sigma, Alpha Iota Delta, Beta Alpha Psi. Republican. Roman Catholic. Avocations: tennis, golf, snow skiing. Office: Trump Pla Hotel & Casino Mississippi & The Boardwalk Atlantic City NJ 08401

MALARKEY, MARTIN FRANCIS, JR., cable television executive; b. Pottsville, Pa., May 1, 1918; s. Martin Francis and Gertrude (Cress) M.; m. Catherine Clare McCarthy, May 30, 1935; 1 child, Clare Ann (Mrs. John E. Hampford); m. Elizabeth Koehn Onesto, May 29, 1961. BS in Acctg., LaSalle U., Phila., 1939. V.p. Malarkey's, Inc., Pottsville, 1939-42; pres. Malarkey's, Inc., 1946-50; pres., dir. Trans Video Corps., Washington, 1950-59; chmn. Malarkey, Taylor Assocs., Inc., Washington, 1959—; pres., dir. radio Sta. WRTA, Altoona, Pa., 1956-84; owner Eastern Shore Microwave Relay Co., Washington, 1961-75; pres. radio sta. WMBT, Shenandoah, Pa., 1970-86. Pres. Washington Internat. Horse Show Assn., 1976-77; trustee emeritus Am. U., Washington; trustee Washington Hosp. Ctr.; chmn. Washington Hosp. Ctr. Found. Served with USNR, World War II. Mem. Nat. Cable TV Assn. (founder, 1st pres.), Washington Club, City Tavern Assn., F St. Club, Univ. Club. Pioneer in devel. cable television. Home: 1817 Kalorama Sq NW Washington DC 20008-4021

MALASHEVICH, BRUCE PETER, consulting executive; b. Ridgewood, N.J., Feb. 21, 1952; s. Peter Gabriel and Olga Julia (Pelenko) M.; m. Linda Christine Kauskay, May 11, 1985; children: Jason Kauskay, Jessica Alexandra Kauskay. B.A. cum laude, Woodrow Wilson Sch. Pub. and Internat. Affairs, Princeton U., 1974; M.A., Johns Hopkins U., 1976. Internat. economist U.S. Treasury Dept., Washington, 1975-76; asst. to dir. Econ. Cons. Services div. Wolf and Co., C.P.A.s, Washington, 1976-78; v.p. Econ. Cons. Services Inc., Washington, 1978-88, pres., chief exec. officer, 1988—; also dir. Contbr. articles to internat. studies jours. and nat. bus. newspapers. Crown-Zellerbach scholar Johns-Hopkins U., 1975. Clubs: Princeton of N.Y.; Princeton of Washington; Kenwood Golf and Country. Avocations: tennis; squash; travel; reading history. Office: Econ Cons Svcs Inc 1225 19th St NW Ste 210 Washington DC 20036-2410

MALASPINA, ALEX, soft drink company executive; b. Athens, Greece, Jan. 4, 1931; came to U.S., 1948; s. Spiros and Mary (Souyiouljoglou) M.; m. Doris Woodruff Gould, Sept. 25, 1954; children: Spiros, Ann, Paul, Mark. SB, MIT, 1952, Ph.D., 1955. Coord. new products Pfizer, Inc., N.Y.C., 1955-61; mgr. quality control Coca-Cola Export Corp., N.Y.C., 1961-69, v.p., 1969-78; v.p. Coca-Cola Co., Atlanta, 1978-86, sr. v.p., 1986—; pres. Internat. Life Scis., Washington, 1978—, Internat. Tech. Caramel Assn., Washington, 1977—; v.p. Toxicology Forum, Washington, 1979—, Brit. Indsl. Biol. Rsch. Assn., London, 1991—. Bd. overseers Tufts U. Sch. Medicine, 1995—. Mem. AAAS, N.Y. Acad. Scis., Am. Inst. Chemists, Inst. Food Technologists, Am. Chem. Soc. Greek Orthodox. Home: 425 Kenbrook Dr NW Atlanta GA 30327-4937 Office: Coca-Cola Co 1 Coca-Cola Plz NW Atlanta GA 30313

MALATO, STEPHEN H., lawyer; b. Chgo., Sept. 25, 1953. BA, Western Ill. U., 1975; JD with high honors, Chgo. Kent Coll. Law (now Ill. Inst. Tech.), 1978. Bar: Ill. 1978, U.S. Dist. Ct. (no. dist.) Ill. 1981, U.S. Dist. Ct. (no. dist. trial bar) Ill. 1981. Ptnr. Hinshaw & Culbertson, Chgo. Mem. Chgo. Bar Assn., Legal Club Chgo., Moot Ct. Address: Hinshaw & Culbertson 222 N La Salle St Ste 300 Chicago IL 60601-1081

MALCHOW, DENNIS, food products executive; b. 1945. BS, Long Beach State, Calif. With Oscar Mayer, Chgo., 1967-78; now sr. v.p. Martin-Broer Co., Des Plaines, Ill., 1978—. Office: Martin-Broer Company 1111 E Touhy Ave Des Plaines IL 60018-5803

MALCOLM, ANDREW HOGARTH, journalist, writer; b. Cleve., June 22, 1943; s. Ralph Monteith and Beatrice Florence (Bowles) M.; m. Connie D'Amelio, Nov. 28, 1981; children: Christopher, Spencer, Emily, Keddy. BJ, Northwestern U., 1966, MJ, 1967. Clk. The N.Y. Times, N.Y.C., 1967-68, met. reporter, 1969-70; nat. corr. The N.Y. Times, Chgo., 1971-73, San Francisco, 1973-75; fgn. corr. The N.Y. Times, Vietnam, Thailand, Guam, 1975, Tokyo, 1975-78, Republic of Korea, 1975-78; bur. chief The N.Y. Times, Toronto, Ont., Can. 1978-82, Chgo. 1982-87; asst. nat. editor The N.Y. Times, N.Y.C., 1987-88, nat. affairs corr., columnist, 1988-93; exec. asst. policy and communications Govs. Office, Helena, Mont., 1993—.

Author: Unknown America, 1975, The Canadians, 1985, Final Harvest, 1986, This Far and No More, 1987, Someday, 1991, U.S. 1: America's Original Main Street, 1991, The Land and People of Canada, 1991, Huddle: Fathers, Sons, and Football, 1992. Recipient George Polk award L.I. U., 1975, Page One award N.Y. Newspaper Guild, 1975, 83. Office: Governor's Office State Capitol Helena MT 59620-0801

MALCOLM, ELLEN REIGHLEY, small business owner; b. Hackensack, N.J., Feb. 2, 1947; d. William Ford Reighley and Barbara (Hamilton) Malcolm. BA, Hollins Coll., 1969; MBA, George Washington U., 1984. Regional mgr. Common Cause, Washington, 1971-74, nat. issues coord., 1974-75, so. states coord., 1975-76; pub. info. coord. Nat. Women's Polit. Caucus, Washington, 1978-79, project dir., 1979; media coord. Cambodia Crisis Ctr., Washington, 1980; press sec. to spl. asst. to pres. for consumer affairs White House, Washington, 1980-81; pres. Windom Fund, Washington, 1980—, EMILY's List, Washington, 1985—. Bd. dirs. Ctr. for Policy Alternatives, Washington, 1989—; chair Women's Legal Def. Fund, Washington, 1984—. Democrat. Office: EMILYs List 805 15th St NW Ste 400 Washington DC 20005

MALCOLM, GAROLD DEAN, architect; b. Belle Fouche, S.D., Apr. 25, 1940; s. Gifford Garold Malcolm and Ellen Eve Liming; m. Breta Lois Bailey, 1966 (div. 1982); children: Heather Marie, Allison Claire; m. Lucia Eagon Stenson, 1991. BArch, U. Oreg., 1966. Ptnr. McAdoo, Malcolm & Youel, Architects, 1981—. Prin. works include Creston-Nelson Elec. Substation, Seattle (Honor award Wash. Aggregates and Concrete Assn.), Arboretum Visitor's Ctr., Seattle (Honor award Builders Community Awards Program, People's Choice award Seattle chpt. AIA), Des Moines (Wash.) Libr., Queen Anne Swimming Pool, Seattle. Mem. AIA, Matsumura Kenpo Karate Assn. (black belt). Office: McAdoo Malcolm & Youel Architects 1718 E Olive Way Seattle WA 98102

MALDE, HAROLD EDWIN, retired federal government geologist; b. Reedsport, Oreg., July 9, 1923; s. Emil and Bessie May (Alspaugh) M.; m. Caroline Elizabeth Rose, Dec. 21, 1954; children: Margaret Jean, Melissa Ruth. AB, Willamette U., 1947; postgrad. Harvard U., 1947-48, U. Colo., 1948-51. Geologist, U.S. Geol. Survey, Denver, 1951-87, emeritus, 1987—; mem. Colo. com. for Nat. Register Hist. Places, 1972-80; vol. photographer Nature Conservancy, 1987—; mem. paleoanthropology del. to Peoples Republic China, Nat. Acad. Scis., 1975, mem. various coms. for study surface mining; mem. oil shale environ. adv. panel U.S. Dept. Interior, 1976-80. Contbr. numerous sci. papers to profl. lit. Served to ensign USNR, 1942-44. Recipient Meritorious Service award U.S. Dept. Interior, 1979, Oak Leaf award Nature Conservancy, 1993. Fellow Geol. Soc. Am. (Kirk Bryan award 1970, assoc. editor 1982-88), AAAS, Ariz-Nev. Acad. Sci.; mem. Am. Quaternary Assn., Explorers Club. Democrat. Unitarian. Home: 842 Grant Pl Boulder CO 80302-7415

MALDEN, KARL (MALDEN SEKULOVICH), actor; b. Chgo., Mar. 22, 1914; s. Peter and Minnie (Sebera) Sekulovich; m. Mona Graham, Dec. 18, 1938; children—Mila, Carla. Student, Goodman Theatre, Chgo., 1935-38. pres. Acad. of Motion Arts and Scis.; mem. Citizens Stamp Com., U.S. Govt., Washington. Actor, 1935—; stage plays include Golden Boy, 1938, Gentle People, 1939, Key Largo, 1940, Flight to the West, 1942, Uncle Harry, 1940, All My Sons, 1949, A Streetcar Named Desire, 1950, Desire Under the Elms, 1952, Desperate Hours, 1954; in motion pictures, 1940—, films include: Boomerang, Gunfighter, 1945, Halls of Montezuma, 1950, A Streetcar Named Desire (Acad. award for best supporting actor), 1951, Ruby Gentry, 1952, I Confess, 1953, On the Waterfront, 1954, Baby Doll, 1956, Desperate Hours, 1957, Fear Strikes Out, 1957, The Hanging Tree, 1959, Pollyanna, 1960, One Eyed Jacks, 1961, Parrish, The Adventures of Bullwhip Griffin, 1967, Patton, 1970, Beyond the Poseidon Affair, 1978, Meteor, 1979, Sting II, 1982, Twilight Time, 1982, Billy Galvin, 1987, Nuts, 1987; TV films include: Word of Honor, 1981, Miracle on Ice, 1981, Intent to Kill, 1983, Fatal Vision, 1984 (Emmy award), My Father My Son, 1988, The Hijacking of the Achille Lauro, 1989, Call Me Anna, 1990, Absolute Strangers, 1991, Back to the Streets of San Francisco, 1992; dir.: Time Limit, 1957, Billion Dollar Brain, 1967, Hot Millions, 1968, Hotel, Cat O'Nine Tails, 1971, Wild Rovers, 1971, Summertime Killer, 1973, Nuts, 1987; star TV series Streets of San Francisco, 1972-77, Skag, 1980. Recipient Donaldson award, 1950, Critic's award, 1950. Mem. Acad. Motion Picture Arts and Scis. (pres. 1989-92). Address: 1845 Mandeville Canyon Rd Los Angeles CA 90049-2222

MALDON, ALPHONSO, JR., federal official, retired military officer; b. Bonifey, Fla.; Oct. 6, 1950; m. Carolyn Madden; 1 child, Kiamesha Racha'el. BS, Fla. A&M U., 1972; M in Human Rels., U. Okla., 1975; grad., Armed Forces Staff Coll. 1985. Commd. U.S. Army, 1972, advanced through grades to lt. col.; chief orptl. effectiveness mgmt. U.S. Army, Stuttgart, Germany, 1981-83; pers. officer, comdr. 259th Pers. Svc. Co. U.S. Army, Bamberg, Ger., 1983-84; exec. officer Armed Forces Staff U. U.S. Army, Norfolk, Va., 1985-89; congl. liaison officer U.S. Army Legis. Liaison, U.S. Ho. of Reps. U.S. Army, 1989-93, ret., 1993; spl. asst. to Pres., legis. affairs The White House, Washington, 1993-94, dep. asst. to Pres., milit. affairs, 1994—, dep. asst. to Pres., legis. affairs; admissions, pub. affairs officer West Point. Contbr. features Army pubs. Decorated Def. Meritorious Svc. medal with 2 oak leaf clusters, Army Meritorious Svc. medal with 2 oak leaf clusters, Army Commendation medal with 2 oak leaf clusters, Legion of Merit; Congl. scholar. Office: Legis Affairs 1600 Pennsylvania Ave NW Washington DC 20500

MALDONADO-BEAR, RITA MARINITA, economist, educator; b. Vega Alta, P.R., June 14, 1938; d. Victor and Marina (Davila) Maldonado; m. Larry Alan Bear, Mar. 29, 1975. BA, Auburn U., 1960; PhD, NYU, 1969. With Min. Wage Bd. & Econ. Devel. Adminstrn., Govt. of P.R., 1960-64; assoc. prof. fin. U. P.R., 1969-70; asst. prof. econs. Manhattan Coll., 1970-72; assoc. prof. econs. Bklyn. Coll., 1972-75; vis. assoc. prof. fin. Stanford (Calif.) Grad. Bus. Sch., 1973-74; assoc. prof. fin. and econs. Grad. div. Stern Sch. Bus. NYU, 1975-81, prof., 1981—, acting dir. markets, ethics and law, 1993-94; cons. Morgan Guaranty Trust Co., N.Y.C., 1972-77, Bank of Am., N.Y.C., 1982-84, Res. City Bankers, N.Y.C., 1978-87, Swedish Inst. Mgmt., Stockholm, 1982-91, Empresas Master of P.R., 1985-90; bd. dirs. Medallion Funding Corp., 1985-87; apptd. adv. bd. dirs. equity and diversity in ednl. environs. Mid. States Commn. on Higher Edn., 1991—; trustee Securities Industry Assn., N.Y. Dist. Econ. Edn. Found., 1994—. Author: Role of the Financial Sector in the Economic Development of Puerto Rico, 1970; Co-Author: Free Markets, Finance, Ethics, And Law, 1994; contbr. articles to profl. jours. Trustee Bd. Edn., Twp. of Mahwah, N.J., 1991-92. P.R. Econ. Devel. Adminstrn. fellow, 1960-65; Marcus Nadler fellow, NYU, 1966-67, Phillip Lods Dissertation fellow, 1967-68. Mem. Am. Econs. Assn., Am. Fin. Assn., Metro. Econ. Assn. N.Y., Assn. for Social Econs. (trustee exec. coun. 1994—). Home: 95 Tam O Shanter Dr Mahwah NJ 07430-1526 Office: Mgmt Edn Ctr 44 W 4th St Ste 9-190 New York NY 10012-1126

MALE, ROY RAYMOND, English language educator; b. Bklyn., Mar. 15, 1919; s. Roy Raymond and Mary Edwards (Brooks) M.; m. Carolyn Kate Conlisk, Aug. 19, 1944; children: Marilyn, Frank. B.S., Hamilton Coll., 1939; M.A., Columbia U., 1940; Ph.D., U. Tex., 1950. Instr. English U. Tex., 1946-50; asst. prof. Tex. Tech. Coll., 1950-55; mem. faculty U. Okla., 1955-84, Boyd prof. English emeritus; vis. prof. Bowling Green U., 1962, U. Wash., 1968, U. Tex. at Arlington, 1971. Author: Hawthorne's Tragic Vision, 1957, Enter, Mysterious Stranger, 1979; editor: Types of Short Fiction, 2d edit, 1970, Money Talks, 1981; co-editor: Am. Literary Masters, 1974. Served with AUS, 1940-45. Ford Found. fellow, 1954-55; Recipient Regents award excellence teaching U. Okla., 1968. Mem. Modern Lang. Assn., South Central Modern Lang. Assn. (pres. 1968). Home: Hilton Head Plantation 40 Field Sparrow Rd Hilton Head Island SC 29926-1813

MALEC, RUTH ELLEN, special services director; b. Auburn, N.Y., Aug. 1, 1944; d. Robert James and Edna Louise (Lawrence) Stebbins; m. Edward L. Malec, Sept. 2, 1967 (div. Oct. 1977); children: Edward I., Amy Beth. B. Houghton (N.Y.) Coll., 1966; student, Ohio U., 1966-67; M, Montclair State Coll., 1970. Tchr. Newark Pub. Schs., N.J., 1967-69; social worker Passaic County Bd. Soc. Svcs., Paterson, N.J., 1970-72; Boonton Pub. Schs., N.J., 1979-88; dir. spl. edn. Sch. Union 44, Sabattus, Maine, 1988-90; dir. spl. svcs. Kinnelon Pub. Schs., N.J., 1990-93, Linden (N.J.) Pub. Schs., N.J.,

1993—. Women's ministry Jacksonville Chapel, Lincoln Park, N.J. Mem. ASCD, N.J. Dept. Edn. Prof. Svcs. Coun., N.J. Assn. Sch. Social Workers (v.p. 1985-87, pres. 1987-88), N.J. Assn. for Pupil Svcs. Adminstrs., N.J. Prins. and Suprs. Assn., N.E. Coalition of Ednl. Leaders, Union County Assn. of Dirs. of Spl. Svcs., Morris County Assn. Dirs. Spl. Edn., Knnelon Women's Svc. Orgn. Avocations: reading, music. Home: 35 Cliff Trl Kinnelon NJ 07405-3107 Office: Linden Pub Schs 19 E Morris Ave Linden NJ 07036

MALEC, WILLIAM FRANK, utilities company executive; b. Broadalbin, N.Y., June 22, 1940; s. Henry and Anna Frances M.; m. Sarah Powell, Sept. 11, 1965; children: Charles A., Mariah E. BS cum laude, Niagara U., 1962; MBA, Ind. U., 1967; AMP, Harvard U., 1987. Mgmt. trainee Marine Midland Bank, Buffalo, 1962-63; project budget analyst Cleve. Electric Illuminating Co., 1967-68; asst. treas. Mid-Continent Telephone Co., Hudson, Ohio, 1968-75; v.p. treas. Gulf States Utilities, Beaumont, Tex., 1975-78; treas. Cen. and S.W. Corp., C&W Leasing Inc., CSW Energy Inc., CSW Fin., Inc., Dallas; v.p. treas. Cen. and S.W. Services, Inc., Dallas, 1978-89; pres. C&W Credit, Inc., 1985-89; exec. v.p., CFO TVA, Knoxville, 1989—. Served with U.S. Army, 1963-65. Mem. Nat. Mgmt. Assn., Leading Chief Fin. Officers, Knoxville Racquet Club. Republican. Roman Catholic. Office: TVA 400 W Summit Hill Dr Knoxville TN 37902-1415

MALECHA, MARVIN JOHN, architect, academic administrator; b. Lonsdale, Minn., June 26, 1949; s. George and Barbara Malecha; m. Cynthia Marie Miller, Aug. 8, 1970; children: Peter, Michelle. Student, St. Thomas Coll.; BArch, U. Minn.; M in Design, Harvard U. Registered architect, Calif. Designer Wallace and Mundt Architects, Edina, Minn., 1969-73, Hugh Stubbins and Assocs., Cambridge, Mass., 1973-76; instr. Cambridge Urban Awareness Program, 1973-76, Boston Archtl. Ctr., 1974-76; asst. chmn., asst. prof. dept. architecture Sch. Environ. Design, Calif. State Poly. U., Pomona, 1976-77, chmn., assoc. prof., 1979-82, prof., dean Coll. Environ. Design, 1982-94; dean sch. design N.C. State U., 1994—; chmn. Univ. Fall Conf. com. Calif. State Poly. U., 1984; mem. steering com. Architects for Social Responsibility; mem. bd. advisors Tchrs. cert. program City Bldg. Edn. Program, planning com. So. Calif. Assn. Govts.; vis. critic UCLA, 1985, U., Minn., 1981-83, 87, U. So. Calif., 1980-87, Calif. Poly. State U., San Luis Obispo, 1979-87, Clemson U., 1988; lectr. to schs. and archtl. assns.; cons. in architecture and research, Claremont, Calif., 1976—; master juror Nat. Council Archtl. Registration Bds.; mem. edn. equity com. Calif. State U. System, 1985-86; pres. Calif. Coun. Archtl. Edn., 1986-88; mem. accreditation vis. team for collegiate programs in landscape architecture, 1988—; bd. dirs. Nat. Archtl. Accreditation Bd.; campus architect cons. U. Calif., Riverside, 1990-94. Contbr. aticles to profl. jours. Mem. Art and Liturgy com. Our Lady Assumption Ch., Claremont, Calif. Recipient Ellerbe Archtl. award, 1972, Hon. Mention Mass. Housing Dept., 1976; Rotch scholar, 1980. Fellow AIA (bd. dirs. L.A. chpt. 1982-83, chmn. state and nat. awards coms. 1983-85, chmn. Monterey design conf. com., 1987, Henry Adams award 1973, mem. steering com. architects in edn. com. 1991—, presdl. citation L.A. chpt. 1987, mem. calif. coun. 1994, Excellence in Arch. Edn. award), Soc. Am. Registered Architects, Assn. Collegiate Schs. Architecture (v.p. 1988-89, chair ann. meeting, pres. 1988-89, adminstrs. conf. Washington 1985), Calif. Coun. Archtl. Edn. (pres. 1988-89). Office: NC State U Sch Design Raleigh NC 27695

MALECKI, EDWARD STANLEY, JR., political science educator; b. Chgo., Nov. 16, 1938; s. Edward Stanley and Lucille Clara (May) M.; m. Judith Evelyn Sobczak, Aug. 24, 1962; children: Stephen, Robert. B.A., U. Ill., 1961, LL.B., 1963, M.A., 1965, Ph.D. (Charles Merriam fellow), 1969. Bar: Ill. 1963. Asst. prof. polit. sci. Calif. State U., Los Angeles, 1967-71; assoc. prof. Calif. State U., 1971-76, prof., 1976—, chair dept. Polit. Sci., 1993—. Author: (with H.R. Mahood) Group Politics: A New Emphasis, 1972; contbr. articles to profl. jours. Chmn. Caucus for a New Polit. Sci. 1970-71; ednl. cons. Foothill Urban League, 1969-70; bd. dirs. Pasadena Area Democratic Council, 1974. Calif. State U. Los Angeles Found. grantee, 1971-72, 84-85; HEW-Urban League grantee, 1969-70; NEH fellow, 1987. Mem. Ill. Bar Assn., Am. Polit. Sci. Assn., Am. Sociol. Assn., United Profs. Calif. (chpt. sec. 1974), ACLU (chpt. pres. 1974, 85-86, bd. dirs. So. Calif. 1981), Phi Kappa Phi. Home: 2225 Midwick Dr Altadena CA 91001-2828 Office: 5151 State University Dr Los Angeles CA 90032-4221

MALEFAKIS, EDWARD E., history educator; b. Springfield, Mass., Jan. 2, 1932; s. Emmanuel A. and Despina (Sophoulakis) M.; m. Cali Doxiadis, 1988; children from previous marriage: Michael, Laura. A.B., Bates Coll., 1953; M.A., Johns Hopkins U., 1955; Ph.D., Columbia U., 1965. Instr. Northwestern U., 1962-63, assoc. prof., 1968-71; asst. prof. Wayne State U. Detroit, 1963-64; asst. prof. modern European history Columbia U., 1964-67, prof., 1975—; prof. U. Mich., Ann Arbor, 1971-74. Author: Agrarian Reform and Peasant Revolution in Spain, 1970, Southern Europe in the 19th and 20th Centuries, 1992; editor: Indalecio Prieto, 1975, La guerra civil en España, 1986. Recipient Herbert Baxter Adams award Am. Hist. Assn., 1971, Faculty Teaching award Northwestern U., 1971, medal of honor U. Internacional Menendez Pelayo, 1982, Orden de Mérito Civico (Spain), 1988; Social Scis. Rsch. Coun. grantee, 1967, NEH grantee, 1977; Guggenheim fellow, 1974, Inst. Juan March fellow, 1991. Mem. Modern Greek Studies Assn. (exec. com. 1981-87), Soc. for Spanish and Portuguese Hist. Studies (exec. council 1969-72), Spanish Inst. N.Y.C. (bd. dirs. 1982—). Democrat. Greek Orthodox. Home: 380 Riverside Dr New York NY 10025 Office: Columbia Univ 524 Fayerweather Hall New York NY 10027

MALEK, FREDERIC VINCENT, finance company executive; b. Oak Park, Ill., Dec. 22, 1936; s. Fred W. and Martha (Smickilas) M.; m. Marlene A. McArthur, Aug. 5, 1961; children: Fred W., Michelle A. BS, U.S. Mil. Acad., 1959; MBA, Harvard U., 1964; D of Humanities (hon.), St. Leo Coll., St. Petersburg, Fla., 1970. Assoc. McKinsey & Co., Inc., L.A., 1964-67; chmn. exec. com. Triangle Corp., Columbia, S.C., 1967-69; dep. under sec. HEW, Washington, 1969-70; spl. asst. to Pres. U.S., Washi.gton, 1970-73; dep. dir. U.S. Office of Mgmt. and Budget, Washington, 1973-75; with Marriott Corp., Washington, 1975-88, sr. v.p., 1975-77, exec. v.p. 1978-88; pres. Marriott Hotels and Resorts, 1981-88; pres. Northwest Airlines, Mpls., 1989-90, vice chmn., 1990-91, also bd. dirs.; campaign mgr. Bush-Quayle '92, 1991-92; co-chmn. CB Comml. Real Estate Group, 1989—; chmn. Lodging Opportunities Fund, 1991—, Thayer Capital Ptnrs., 1992—, Thayer Hotel Investors, 1994—; bd. dirs. Automated Data Processing Corp., Am. Mgmt. Sys. Inc., Avis Inc., ICF Kaiser Inc., Nat. Edn. Corp., N.W. Airlines, FPL Group Inc., Paine Webber Funds, Manor Care Inc., Caterair, Internat.; dir. with rank of amb., 1990 Econ. Summit, 1989—; adj. prof. U. S.C., 1986-89; lectr. Kennedy Sch. Govt., Harvard U., 1976. Mem. Pres.'s Commn. on White House Fellows, 1971-75, White House Domestic Coun., 1974-75, Pres.'s Commn. on Pers. Interchange, 1974-76; dep. dir. com. for Re-election of Pres., 1972; Pres.'s Commn. on Pvt. Sector Initiatives, 1982-85, dir. conv. Bush for Pres., 1988; mem. Nat. Coun. on Surface Transp. Rsch., 1993—; nat. adv. bd. Nat. Ctr. Econ. Edn. of Children, 1987—; mem. Pres. Coun. on Phys. Fitness and Sports, 1986-91. Mem. Harvard Club of So. Calif. (bd. dirs., 1st v.p. 1965-67), University Club (com. chmn. 1966-68). Episcopalian. Avocations: biking, skiing. Office: 901 15th St NW Washington DC 20005-2327

MALENICK, DONALD H., metals manufacturing company executive; b. 1939. Steel bander, slitting machine operator, later prodn. mgr. Worthington Industries Inc., Columbus, Ohio, 1958-67, v.p. mfg., 1967-72, exec. v.p., 1972-76, pres., 1976—, chief operating officer, from 1976, also bd. dirs. Office: Worthington Industries Inc 1345 Hall Spencer Rd Catawba SC 29704•

MALENKA, BERTRAM JULIAN, physicist, educator; b. N.Y.C., June 8, 1923; s. Morris and Mollie (Wichel) M.; m. Ruth D. Stolper, Mar. 28, 1948; children—David Jonathan, Robert Charles. A.B., Columbia, 1947; M.A., Harvard, 1949, Ph.D., 1951. Research fellow Harvard, 1951-54; asst. prof. physics Washington U., St. Louis, 1954-56; assoc. prof. Tufts U., Medford, Mass., 1956-60; faculty Northeastern U., Boston, 1960—; prof. physics Northeastern U., 1962-93, prof. emeritus, 1993—. Mem. sci. adv. group Harvard-Mass. Inst. Tech. Cambridge Electron Accelerator, 1956—. Mem. Am., Italian phys. socs., N.Y. Acad. Scis., Phi Beta Kappa, Sigma Xi. Research and publs. on theory of nuclear forces and structure of nucleus, explanation polarization phenomena in high-energy scattering, gamma radia-

tion, electric polarization deuteron, accelerator design. Home: 16 Rutledge Rd Belmont MA 02178-3323 Office: Northeastern Univ Dept Of Physics Boston MA 02115

MALES, WILLIAM JAMES, film producer, make-up artist; b. Mesa, Ariz.; s. James W. and Oveta (Bradshaw) M. Student, Pepperdine U., 1982-86; studies with Vincent J. R. Kehoe, 1980-82, studies with Dick Smith, 1981-83. Make-up artist William J. Males and Assocs., Hollywood, Calif., 1976—; exec. v.p. Bonaire Films, 1984-88; producer AZRAK Films, Inc., Hollywood, Calif., 1986—; co-producer with Bruce Boxleitner Diplomatic Immunity Distbr. Fries Entertainment, Hollywood, Calif., 1991; mgr. market rsch. Universal Pictures, Universal City, Calif., 1993—; CFO Calif. Pension Adminstrs., 1993-95. Studio make-up artist for numerous projects including (films) Aftershock, Family Reunion, Winds of War, Necromancer, Conan the Barbarian, Return of the Living Dead, Scanners, Ragedy Anne, (TV shows) The Blue and the Gray, Crisis at Central High, Skyward, Printer to the Territory, Golden Girls, Hollywood Squares, 21 Jump Street, 9 to 5, (theatrical prodns.) Mama Bear Papa Bear, I'm Not Rappaport, Man of La Mancha, The Gospel Truth, Camelot, Chorus Line (nat. tour), Grease, Godspell, Crucible; line producer (films) Aftershock, (distbr. Paramount Pictures) Dead Time, Lock Down, Necromancer, Ms. Frankenstein, Family Reunion, Rocky I; assoc. producer (films) Castle of Revenge, Alien Warrior, Californio, (TV commls.) Coppertone, Pepsi, Beechcraft, Levi Strauss, Chanel; prodn. dir. Danza/Floricanto USA; prodr. Lord Chamberlain's Players. Mem. NATAS, Acad. TV Arts and Scis. (Emmy nomination 1982), Brit. Acad. Film and TV Arts, Am. Soc. Makeup Artists, Soc. Motion Picture and TV Engrs., Assn. Film Craftsmen (local 531), Nat. Assn. Broadcast Employees and Technicians, Prodrs. Guild Am. Republican. Office: Universal Pictures 8871 Cynthia West Hollywood CA 90069

MALESKA, MARTIN EDMUND, publishing executive; b. Yonkers, N.Y., Apr. 3, 1944; s. Edmund Joseph and Marian (Kolton) M.; m. Elissa Mary Delfini, Apr. 27, 1968; children: Christine, Matthew, Danielle. BS in Chemistry, Fordham U., 1966; MBA in Fin., NYU, 1968. Dir. fin. Celanese do Brasil, São Paulo, Brazil, 1972-77; mng. dir. internat. ops. Pfizer Med. Systems, N.Y.C., 1977-80; dir. planning Macmillan Inc., N.Y.C., 1980-82, now bd. dirs., bd. dirs., v.p. group exec., 1984-88; pres. Nat. Register Pub. Co., N.Y.C., 1982-83; sr. v.p. corp. devel. Maxwell Communication Corp., N.Y.C., 1989-91; bd. dirs. Macmillan Inc., N.Y.C.; mng. dir. Verons, Suhler & Assocs., N.Y.C., 1991-95; pres. Simon and Schuster Inc., 1995—. Capt. USAF, 1968-72. Republican. Roman Catholic. Avocation: racquet sports. Home: 3 Deborah Ln Chappaqua NY 10514 Office: Verons Suhler and Assocs 350 Park Ave New York NY 10022

MALETZ, HERBERT NAAMAN, federal judge; b. Boston, Oct. 30, 1913; s. Reuben and Frances (Sawyer) M.; m. Catherine B. Loebach, May 8, 1947; 1 son, David M. A.B., Harvard, 1935, LL.B., 1939. Bar: Mass. bar 1939, D.C. bar 1952. Mem. staff Truman com. U.S. Senate, 1941-42; atty. antitrust div. Dept. Justice, 1946-50; with OPS, 1950-53, chief counsel, 1952-53; chief counsel anti-trust subcom. U.S. Ho. of Reps., 1955-61; commr. U.S. Ct. Claims, 1961-67; judge U.S. Ct. Internat. Trade, N.Y.C., 1967-87; sr. judge U.S. Dist. Ct. Md., Balt., 1987—. Served with AUS, 1942-46; lt. col. Res. Office: US Dist Ct Md 101 W Lombard St Baltimore MD 21201

MALEY, SAMUEL WAYNE, electrical engineering educator; b. Sidney, Neb., Mar. 1, 1928; s. Samuel Raymond and Inez (Moore) M.; m. Elizabeth Anne Green, June 11, 1963; children—Karen Margaret, Laura Elaine. B.S., U. Colo., 1952, M.S., 1957, Ph.D., 1959; student, U. N.M., 1957-58. Geophysicist Stanolind Oil Co., Lubbock, Tex., 1952; design engr. Beach Aircraft Corp., Wichita, Kan., 1952-53, Dynalectron Corp., Cheyenne, Wyo., 1953-56; research scientist U. Colo., Boulder, 1959-60, vis. lectr., 1960-61, asst. prof., 1961-62, assoc. prof. elec. engring., 1962-67, prof., 1967-91, prof. emeritus, 1991—; mem. Nat. Ctr. Computer Aided Design, Millimeter and Microwave Systems U. Colo., 1988—; cons. Nat. Center Atmospheric Research, 1964, Automation Industries Research Div., Boulder, Colo., 1960-71, Midwec Corp., Ogallala, Neb., 1969-70, IBM, Boulder, 1969—. Author: Combinational Logic Circuits, 1969; contbg. author to 5 survey books on sci. and engring. Served with AUS, 1946-47; Served with USAF, 1947-48. Mem. I.E.E.E., A.A.A.S., Soc. Indsl. and Applied Math. Research electromagnetic theory; communication theory; computer design. Home: 3760 57th St Boulder CO 80301-3016

MALEY, WAYNE ALLEN, engineering consultant; b. Stanley, Iowa, Mar. 9, 1927; s. Neil Gordon and Flossie Amelia (Wharram) M.; m. Marianne Nelson, Aug. 2, 1959; children: James G., Mary G., Mark A. BS in Agrl. Engring., Iowa State U., 1949; postgrad., Purdue U., Ga. Tech., IIT. Power use advisor Southwestern Electric, Greenville, Ill., 1949-53; field agt. Am. Zinc Inst., Lafayette, Ind., 1953-59; mktg. devel. specialist U.S. Steel, Des Moines, Iowa, 1959-65; mktg. rep. U.S. Steel, Pitts., 1965-71, bar products rep., 1972-76; assoc. Taylor Equipment, Pitts., 1977-81; mgr. pub. rels. Am. Soc. Agrl. Engrs., St. Joseph, Mich., 1981-84, dir. mem. svcs., 1984-92; cons. Tech. Tours, St. Joseph, 1992—. Author: Iowa Really Isn't Boring, 1992, (textbook) Farm Structures, 1957, (computer program/workbook) Rim Lift Material Handling, 1970 (Blue Ribbon award 1971); editor: Agriculture's Contract with Society, 1991. Pres. Ednl. Concerns for Hunger Orgn., Ft. Myers, Fla., 1979-81; dist. activity dir. Boy Scouts Am., Moon Twp., 1969-70. With USN, 1945-46. Named Hon. Star Farmer, FFA Ill., 1958, Fellow Am. Soc. Agrl. Engrs. (dir. mem. svcs. 1984-85). Mem. Agrl. Editors Assn., Coun. Engring. Soc. Execs. (bd. dirs. 1984-85), Sigma Xi (pres./del. Whirlpool chpt. 1993-94). Presbyterian. Achievements include patent for fence building machine, for material landing system; design of cable fences; design and installation of steel beverage can recycling center. Home and Office: Tech Tours 2592 Stratford Dr Saint Joseph MI 49085-2714

MALFELD, DIANE D., lawyer; b. Marshalltown, Iowa, 1953. BA, U. Iowa, 1975, JD, 1978. Bar: Minn. 1978. Ptnr. Dorsey & Whitney, Mpls. Mem. Phi Beta Kappa. Office: Dorsey & Whitney 220 S 6th St Minneapolis MN 55402

MALGIERI, NICK, chef, author, educator; b. Newark, Sept. 30, 1947; s. Nufre and Antoinette (LoConte) M. BA in French, Seton Hall U., 1970; AOS in Culinary Arts, Culinary Inst., Hyde Park, N.Y., 1973. Pastrycook Seehotel Meierhof, Zurich, 1973-74, Hotel de Paris, Monte Carlo, 1974, Sporting Club, Monte Carlo, 1974-76, Hotel la Reserve, Beaulieu, France, 1974; pastry chef Windows on the World, N.Y.C., 1976-79; asst. pastry chef Hotel Waldorf Astoria, N.Y.C., 1979; chmn. baking dept. N.Y. Restaurant Sch., N.Y.C., 1979-83; v.p., dir. baking program Peter Kump Cooking Sch., N.Y.C., 1984—; founder, owner Total Heaven Baking Co.; exec. chef Paine Webber; pastry chef Board Room; cons. Inhilco, Inc. Author: Nick Malgieri's Perfect Pastry, 1989, Great Italian Desserts, 1990, How to Bake, 1995; contbr. articles, recipes to newspapers, profl. jours. Mem. Internat. Assn. Culinary Profls. (cert. culinary profl., chmn. certification 1989-91), Amicale Culinaire de Monaco, Societe Culinaire Philanthropique N.Y., Federazione Italiana dei Cuochi, James Beard Found. (coord. competitions 1991—), N.Y. Assn. Cooking Tchrs. (former bd. dirs.), Cooking Advancement, Rsch. and Edn. Found. (former trustee). Home: 277 W 10th St New York NY 10014 Office: Peter Kump Cooking Sch 307 E 92nd St New York NY 10128-5401

MALHERBE, ABRAHAM JOHANNES, VI, religion educator, writer; b. Pretoria, South Africa, May 15, 1930; came to U.S., 1951; s. Abraham Johannes V and Cornelia Aletta (Meyer) M.; m. Phyllis Melton, May 28, 1953; children: Selina, Cornelia, Abraham Johannes VII. BA, Abilene Christian U., 1954; STB, Harvard U., 1957; student, U. Utrecht, The Netherlands, 1960-61; ThD, Harvard U., 1963; LLD (hon.), Pepperdine U., 1981; LHD (hon.), Centre Coll., 1990; STD (hon.), Providence Coll., 1994. Minister Ch. of Christ, Lexington, Mass., 1956-63; asst. and assoc. prof. Abilene (Tex.) Christian U., 1963-67; vis. scholar Harvard Divinity Sch., Cambridge, Mass., 1967-68; assoc. prof. Abilene Christian U., 1968-69, Dartmouth Coll., Hanover, N.H., 1969-70; assoc. prof. Yale Divinity Sch., New Haven, Conn., 1970-77, prof., 1977-81, Buckingham prof., 1981-94, assoc. dean acad. affairs, 1981-94; prof. eremitus, 1994—. Author: Social Aspects of Early Christianity, 1983, Moral Exhortation, 1986, Paul and the Thessalonians, 1987, Ancient Epistolary Theorists, 1988, Paul and the Popular Philosophers, 1989; contbr. articles to profl. jours.; inspiration for

book: Greeks, Romans and Christians: Essays in Honor of Abraham J. Malherbe, 1990. Recipient tchg. award Abilene Christian U., 1965, 67, Outstanding Alumni citation, 1993; NEH fellow 1973. Mem. Soc. Biblical Lit., North Am. Patristic Soc., Studiorum Novi Testamenti Societas, South African New Testament Soc. (hon.), Religious Studies Rev. (editoral bd. 1980—), The Second Century, Novum Testamentum (editorial bd. 1991—). Mem. Ch. of Christ. Home: 71 Spring Garden St Hamden CT 06517-1913 Office: Yale Divinity Sch 409 Prospect St New Haven CT 06511

MALHOTRA, SURIN M., aerospace manufacturing executive; b. New Delhi, Dec. 27, 1948; came to U.S., 1970; s. Shiv D. and Gur D. (Kaushalya) M.; m. Rita Kashyap, Mar. 11, 1977; children: Tina, Amie. BSME, Delhi U., 1970; MSME, Wichita State U., 1971, MS in Adminstrn., 1973; JD cum laude, U. Bridgeport, 1992. Grad. asst. Wichita State U., Wichita, Kans., 1971-73; proj. engr. Norco Inc., Ridgefield, Conn., 1973-75; data processing mgr. Norco Inc., 1975-78, program mgr., 1978-81, dir. materials, 1981-84, dir. contracts, 1984-86, v.p. sales, 1986-88, v.p. mfg. and sales, 1988-89; v.p. ops., 1989—. Inventor, patentee reversing mechanism. Bridgeport scholar, 1989. Mem. Phi Delta Phi. Republican. Hindu. Home: 1 Chipmunk Ter Bethel CT 06801-1429 Office: Norco Inc 139 Ethan Allen Hwy Ridgefield CT 06877-6207

MALICKY, NEAL, college president; b. Sour Lake, Tex., Sept. 14, 1934; s. George and Ethel L. (Reed) M.; m. Margaret A. Wilson, Sept. 2, 1956; children: Michael Neal, Eric Scott, David Matthew. A.B., Baker U., 1956; B.D., So. Meth. U., 1959; Ph.D., Columbia U., 1968; postgrad., Harvard U., 1978. Ordained to ministry Meth. Ch., 1959; pastor Meth. Ch., Moran, Kans., 1959-62, Van Cortlandtville, N.Y., 1962-66; asst. prof., dir. semester on UN Drew U., 1966-69; prof. polit. sci., dean Coll., Baker U., Baldwin City, Kans., 1969-75; acting pres. Coll., Baker U., 1973-75; v.p. acad. affairs, also dean Baldwin-Wallace Coll., Berea, Ohio, 1975-81; pres. Baldwin-Wallace Coll., 1981—. Author: To Keep the Peace, 1965, Non-Governmental Organizations at the United Nations, 1968; contbr. articles to profl. jours. Mem. Leadership Cleve., Nat. Conf. Christian and Jews, Cleve. Commn. Higher Edn., Cleve. Coun. World Affairs, Greater Cleve. Roundtable (chmn. edn. com.), Cleve. Initiative Edn. (vice chmn.), Summit on Edn. (co-convenor), Assn. Independent Colls. Ohio (chmn.). Mem. UN Assn. Clubs: Union of Cleve., Fifty of Cleve. Office: Baldwin-Wallace Coll Office of Pres 275 Eastland Rd Berea OH 44017-2088

MALIGAS, MANUEL NICK, metallurgical engineer; b. Thimena, Greece, May 9, 1943; came to U.S., 1950; s. Nick and Jane M.; children: James Paul, John Michael. BE, Youngstown U., 1966; MS, Youngstown State U., 1974. Sr. material engr. Goodyear Aerospace, Akron, Ohio, 1966-76; plant metallurgist Tex. Bolt, Houston, 1976-81; sr. material engr. N.L. Shaffer, Houston, 1981-83; ind. cons. M&M Metall., Houston, 1983; group leader materials FMC Corp., Houston, 1983—; instr. materials U. Houston; presenter symposia. Contbr. articles to profl. pubs. on weld overlays for severe corrosive svc. and life predication of elastomers. Mem. Am. Soc. Metals (past officer), Am. Petroleum Inst. (chmn. material and welding coms.), Nat. Assn. Corrosion Engrs. (chmn.). Achievements include early design of carbon composite brake for commercial aircraft, use of laser and HVOF process for hard facing. Home: 5907 Winged Foot Dr Houston TX 77069-1322 Office: FMC Corp PO Box 3091 Houston TX 77253-3091

MALIK, HAFEEZ, political scientist, educator; b. Lahore, Pakistan, Mar. 17, 1930; m. Lynda P. Malik; children: Cyrus, Dean. BA, Government Coll., Lahore, Pakistan, 1949; grad. diploma in Journalism, U. Punjab, Lahore, 1952; MS in Journalism, Syracuse U., 1955, MA in Polit. Sci., 1957, PhD in Polit. Sci., 1961. Asst. prof. Polit. Sci. Villanova (Pa.) U., 1961-63, assoc. prof., 1963-67, prof., 1967—; pub. rels. officer City of Lahore, 1950-53; White House correspondent The Nawa-i-Waqt, 1958-61, The Shabaz, 1958-61; mem. grad. com. dept. Polit. Sci. Villanova U., 1961-67, chmn., 1967-78; vis. prof. Fgn. Svc. Inst., Washington, 1961-63, 66-68, 70-85, Syracuse U. 1964, 65, Drexel U., Phila., 1968-69; mem. grad. coun. com. rsch. and publs., 1969-70, grad. adv. com. liberal arts and social studies, 1964-67, faculty libr. com., 1964-67, undergrad. com. polit. sci., 1980—; rank and tenure com., 1991-92; pres. Am. Inst. Pakistan Studies, 1972-88, Pakistan Am. Found., 1972—; exec. dir. Am. Coun. Study of Islamic Socs., 1983—; cons. Soviet Acad. Scis., 1979, Dept. Defense, 1980, Pakistan-U.S. subcommn. edn. and culture, 1985, 88, USIA, 1986; presenter in field. News editor The Daily Magharabi Pakistan, 1948-50; tech. editor: Meteorological and Geoastrophysical Abstracts, Am. Meteorological Soc. 1960-63; author: Muslim Nationalism in India and Pakistan, 1963, rev. edit. 1980, Sir Sayyid Ahmed Khan's History of the Bijnore Rebellion, 1972, rev. edit. 1980, Political Profile of Sir Sayyid Ahmed Khan: A Documentary Record, 1982, Domestic Determinants of Soviet Foreign Policy Towards South Asia and the Middle Ease, 1990, Dilemmas of National Security and Cooperation in India and Pakistan, 1993, Soviet-Pakistan Relations and Current Dynamics, 1993; editor: Iqbal: Poet-Philosopher of Pakistan, 1971, rev. edit., 1974, Sir Sayyid Ahmed Khan's History of the Bijnore Rebellion, 1972, rev. edit., 1982, Soviet-American Relations with Pakistan, Iran, and Afghanistan, 1986; mem. editorial adv. bd. Islam and the Modern Age, Islam Awr Aser-i Jadid, 1969-79; editor Jour. South Asian and Middle Eastern Studies, 1977—; contbr. articles to profl. jours., encyclopedias, chpts. to books. Grantee Office Health, Edn. Welfare, 1974, 1978, Assn. Pakistan and Indic-Islamic Studies/Pakistan Am. Found. 1982. Office: Villanova U Lancaster Pike Villanova PA 19085

MALIK, OM PARKASH, electrical engineering educator, researcher; b. Sargodha, Punjab, India, Apr. 20, 1932; arrived in Can., 1966; s. Arjan Dass and Kesar Bai (Ahuja) M.; m. Margareta Fagerstrom, Dec. 22, 1968; children: Ola Parkash, Mira, Maya. Nat. Diploma in Elec. Engring., Delhi (India) Poly., 1952; M in Engring., Roorkee (India) U., 1962; PhD, London U., 1965; D.I.C., Imperial Coll., London, 1966. Registered profl. engr., Ont., Alta. Asst. engr. Punjab State Elec. Bd., 1953-61, asst. to chief engr., 1957-59; rsch. engr. English Elec. Co., Eng. 1965-66; asst. prof. U. Windsor, Ont., Can., 1966-68; assoc. prof. U. Calgary, Alta., Can., 1968-74, prof., 1974—; assoc. acad. dean faculty engring., 1979-90, acting dean, 1981; cons. prof. Huazhong U. Sci. and Tech., Wuhan, People's Republic China, 1986—. Assoc. editor Can. Elec. and Computer Engring. Jour., 1988—; contbr. more than 300 articles to profl. jours. Indsl. tng. scholar Govt. India, 1952-53, sr. indsl. tng. scholar Confedn. Brit. Industries, 1959-60. Fellow IEEE (Centennial medal 1984, chmn. Western Can. coun. 1983-84, Merit award 1986, chmn. student activities Can. region 1979-82), Inst. Elec. Engrs.; mem. IEEE Power Engring. Soc. (machine theory subcom. 1979—, excitation sys. subcom. 1988—, sys. dynamic performance subcom. 1988—, energy devel. and power generation com. 1990—), Assn. Profl. Engrs., Geologists and Geophysicists Alta. (Vol. Svc. award 1990), Assn. Profl. Engrs. Ont., Am. Soc. Engring. Edn., Can. Elec. Assn. (assoc., controls com.1977-92, chmn. digital control com. 1977-85, chmn. edn. com. 1983-85, mem. expert sys. com. 1989-94), Confederacion Panamericana de Ingenieria Mecanica, Electica y Ramas Afines (v.p. 1987—, bd. dirs. region I, 1991-93). Hindu. Home: 1917-10A Street SW, Calgary, AB Canada T2T 3K2 Office: U Calgary Dept Elec & Computer Engring, 2500 University Dr NW, Calgary, AB Canada T2N 1N4

MALIK, RAYMOND HOWARD, economist, scientist, corporate executive, multi-lingual, inventor, educator; b. Lebanon, Feb. 4, 1933; came to U.S., 1948, naturalized, 1963; s. John Z. and Clarice R. (Malik) M. BA, Valparaiso U., 1950; BSBA and Econs., Simpson Coll., 1951; MSBA. So. Ill. U., 1956, PhD in Electronics and Econs., 1959. Supr. Arabian Am. Oil Co., Beirut, 1952-54; mem. grad. faculty, advisor Ill. State U., 1954-59; prof., head world trade programs Central YMCA Community Coll., Chgo., 1966-74; pres. Malik Internat. Enterprises Ltd., Chgo., 1959—; advisor U.S. Congl. Adv. Bd. Author: The Guide to Youth, Health and Longevity, 1980, Do You Really Need Glasses, 1988; inventor selectric typing elements and mechanism, 1959, heater-humidifier-dehumidifier, 1963, ednl. math toy, 1965, circle of sound concept of sound propogation, 1967, introduced modular concept in color TV (system-three and others), 1973, gamma ray breast cancer detector, 1976, auto-ignition instant hot water heater, 1981, water filter, purifier and softener, 1984, no doze warner, 1985, indoor-outdoor barbeque grill, 1985, infra-red heat massager, 1986; designed and introduced telephone shoulder rest with adjustable mechanism, 1962, electronic telephone (Trimline, others), 1964, modular telephone, 1975, video phone, 1991; pioneer developer interplanetary communications system, 1961.

Deacon, mem. pastor-congl. com., youth and young adult ednl. com. St. George Orthodox Ch., Cicero, Ill.; fundraiser March of Dimes, St. Jude Hosp., Am. Cancer Soc., Am. Heart Fund, numerous others; mem. Am. Task Force for Lebanon, 1992—. Named to Wisdom Hall of Fame, 1987; Fulbright scholar, 1948-50, Methodist Ch. scholar, 1950-51; So. Ill. U. fellow, 1954-59. Mem. IEEE, AAAS, Am. Mgmt. Assn., Am. Econ. Assn., Am. Mktg. Assn., Import Clubs U.S., Internat. Bus. Coun., Internat. Platform Assn., Pres.'s Assn., Nat. Assn. Self-Employed, Imperial Austrian Legion of Honor, Internat. Students Assn., Soc. Mfg. Engrs., Am. Legion, Highlander Club, Phi Beta Kappa, Sigma Xi, Delta Rho, Beta Gamma Sigma, Alpha Phi Omega. Address: PO Box 3194 Chicago IL 60654-0194 *My duties and responsibilities are: to be of service to my community, working and aiding my countrymen and women in the development of leaders, for the betterment of America's future and the world.*

MALIN, HAROLD MARTIN, JR., sexologist, educator; b. Colorado Springs, Aug. 26, 1945; s. Harold M. and Harriett Anne (Heyer) M.; m. Janice Karen Atkins. BA in Chemistry and Biology, Cornell Coll., 1967; postgrad., U. Iowa Med. Sch., 1968, Nat. Found. Study and Treatment of Pathological Gambling, 1985-86; PhD in Human Sexuality, Inst. for Advanced Study of Human Sexuality, 1986; postgrad., Johns Hopkins U., 1986-87. Diplomate Am. Coll. Sexologists. Clin. sexologist Sexology Assocs., Inc., 1985—; cons. clin. sexologist Johns Hopkins Hosp. Sexual Disorders Clinic Johns Hopkins U. Med. Sch., 1987-89, mgr. Johns Hopkins Hosp. Sexual Disorders Clinic, 1989-91, cons. clin. sexologist Johns Hopkins Hosp. Sexual Disorders Clinic, 1991-92, instr. clin. sexology dept. psychiatry and behavioral scis., 1992-95; assoc. prof. clin. sexology, chair clin. studies dept. Inst. for Advanced Study of Human Sexuality, 1992—; cons. clin. sexologist, corp. sec. Nat. Ctr. for Study and Treatment of Pathol. Gambling, Balt., 1986—; cons. clin. sexologist Nat. Inst. for Study, Prevention and Treatment of Sexual Trauma, Balt., 1991—; Drug and Alcohol Prevention Program, Inc., Ocean City, Md., 1991-95; cons. clin. sexologist for program devel. Nat. Ctr. on Instns. and Alternatives, Alexandria, Va. and Balt., 1991-94; sr. case mgmt. supr. Planned Parenthood Shasta-Diablo, Fairfield, Calif., 1994—. Cons. editor Jour. of Sex and Marital Therapy; peer reviewer Jour. Sex Rsch.; contbr. articles to profl. jours. Mem. Am. Profl. Soc. on Abuse of Children, Am. Assn. Sex Educators, Counselors and Therapists, Am. Bd. Sexology (bd. clin. examiners, diplomate, cert. sex therapist, cert. clin. supr., cert. sex rschr.), Assn. Sexologists, Am. Acad. Clin. Sexologists (founding life clin. fellow), Soc. for Sci. Study of Sex, Harry Benjamin Internat. Gender Dysphoria Assn., Ctrl. Md. Sexual Abuse and Treatment Task Force, Sex Edn. Coalition Washington, Inst. Advanced Study of Human Sexuality Alumni Assn. Inc. (pres., bd. dirs.), Intersex Soc. of N.Am. (bd. dirs.). Office: Clinical Sexology Assocs 1525 Franklin St San Francisco CA 94109-9592

MALIN, HOWARD GERALD, podiatrist; b. Providence, Dec. 2, 1941; s. Leon Nathan and Rena Rose (Shapiro) M. A.B., U. R.I., 1964; M.A., Brigham Young U., 1969; B.Sc., Calif. Coll. Podiatric Medicine, 1969, D.P.M., 1972; M.Sc., Pepperdine U., 1978; postgrad. in classic, U. So. Calif., 1983—. Diplomate Am. Bd. Podiatric Pub. Health, Am. Bd. Podiatric Orthopedics. Extern in podiatry VA Med. Ctr., Wadsworth, Kans., 1971-72, Marine Corps Res. Dept., San Diego, 1972; resident in podiatric medicine and surgery N.Y. Coll. Podiatric-Medicine, N.Y.C., 1972-73; resident in podiatric surgery, instr. in podiatric surgery N.Y. Coll. Podiatric Medicine, N.Y.C., 1973-74; pvt. practitioner in podiatric medicine and surgery Bklyn., 1974-77; mem. staff Prospect Hosp., Bronx, N.Y., 1974-77; chief podiatry service, mem. staff, cons. sports medicine David Grant U.S. Air Force Med. Ctr., Travis AFB, Calif., 1977-80; chief podiatric sect., mem. staff VA Med. Ctr., Martinsburg, W.Va., 1980—; instr. ednl. devel. program VA Med. Ctr., Martinsburg, W.Va., 1980—; clin. prof. med. sci. Alderson-Broaddus Coll., U. Osteopathic Medicine and Health Scis.; adj. prof. Barry U. Sch. Podiatric Medicine; dir. extern program Pa. Coll. Podiatric Medicine. Editorial rev. bd. Jour. Contemporary Podiatric Physician, 1991—. Maj. USAF, 1977-80, with Res., 1980—. Fellow Am. Coll. Foot Orthopedics, Am. Coll. Podiatric Physicians, Am. Soc. Podiatric Medicine (pres., archivist), Am. Soc. Podiatric Dermatology, Am. Assn. Hosp. Podiatrists, Am. Coll. Podiatric Radiologists, Royal Soc. Health; mem. Am. Acad. Podiatric Sports Medicine (assoc.), Assn. Mil. Surgeons U.S. (life), Am. Coll. Podiatric Surgery (assoc.), Phi Kappa Theta, Phi Kappa Psi. Home: 210 Shenandoah Rd Apt 2D Martinsburg WV 25401-3723 Office: VA Med Ctr Dept Podiatry Martinsburg WV 25401

MALIN, IRVING, English educator, literary critic; b. N.Y.C., Mar. 18, 1934; s. Morris and Bertha (Silverman) M.; m. Ruth Lief, Dec. 18, 1955; 1 child, Mark. BA, Queens Coll., 1955; PhD, Stanford U., 1958. Acting instr. English Stanford U., 1955-58; instr. Ind. U., 1958-60; from instr. to prof. CCNY, 1960-72, prof., 1972—; cons. Jewish Publ. Soc., 1964, Am. Quar., 1964, NEH, 1972, 79, 80, 81, 82, Bnai B'rith, 1974-75, Yaddo, 1975-77, Jewish Book Coun., 1976, 79, PEN, 1978-82, Princeton U. Press, 1979, Fairleigh Dickinson Press, 1980, Wayne State U. Press, 1980, Internat. Coun. Exch. of Scholars, 1980-81, Duke U. Press, 1981, Jewish Daily Forward, 1981, U. Pitts. Press, 1981, Papers on Lang. and Lit., 1981, U. Ga. Press, 1983, UMI Rsch., 1989, Gordian Press, 1990, Ctr. for Study of Higher Edn. 1990, Mosiac, 1991. Author: William Faulkner: An Interpretation, 1957, New American Gothic, 1962, Jews and Americans, 1965, Saul Bellow's Fiction, 1969, Nathanael West's Novels, 1972, Isaac Bashevis Singer, 1972; co-editor: Breakthrough: A Treasury of Contemporary American Jewish Literature, 1964, William Styron's The Confessions of Nat Turner: A Critical Handbook, 1970, The Achievement of William Styron, 1975; editor: Psychoanalysis and American Fiction, 1965, Saul Bellow and the Critics, 1967, Truman Capote's In Cold Blood: A Critical Handbook, 1968, Critical Views of Isaac Bashevis Singer, 1969, Contemporary American-Jewish Literature: Critical Essays, 1973, Conrad Aiken's Prose, 1982; adv. editor: Studies in American Jewish Literature, Jour. Modern Literature, Review of Contemporary Fiction, Saul Bellow Jour., 20th Century Literature; reviewer: Newsday, Rev. Contemporary Fiction, rev. Commonweal, Hollins Critic, So. Quarterly; co-editor Paul Bowles, 1986, Spl. Issue of 20th Century Lit., James Dickey spl. issue of S.C. Rev., 1994, So. Quarterly, 1995, Tex. Review, 1995. Fellow Yaddo, 1963, Nat. Found. for Jewish Culture, 1963-64, Huntington Libr., 1978. Mem. MLA, AAUP, Am. Studies Assn., Am. Jewish Hist. Soc., Melville Soc., Authors League Am., Soc. Study of So. Lit., Poe Studies Assn., English Inst., Nathaniel Hawthorne Soc., N.Y. Acad. Scis., Poetry Soc. Am., Popular Culture Assn., Nat. Book Critics Circle, Sherwood Anderson Soc., Internat. Assn. Univ. Profs. English, Kafka Soc., English-Speaking Union, Multi-Ethnic Lit. U.S. Soc., Hastings Ctr., Am. Jewish Congress, Assoc. Writing Programs, Nat. Coun. Tchrs. of English, Phi Beta Kappa. Jewish. Home: 96-13 68th Ave Forest Hills NY 11375 Office: CCNY New York NY 10031

MALIN, MICHAEL CHARLES, space scientist, former geology educator; b. Burbank, Calif., May 10, 1950; s. Jack and Beatryce (Solomon) M. AB, U. Calif., Berkeley, 1971; PhD, Calif. Inst. Tech., 1976. Sr. scientist Jet Propulsion Lab., Pasadena, Calif., 1975-78, mem. tech. staff, 1978-79; asst. prof. geology Ariz. State U., Tempe, 1979-82, assoc. prof., 1982-87, prof., 1987-91; pres. Malin Space Sci. Systems, San Diego, 1991—. Co-author: Earthlike Planets, 1981; contbr. articles to profl. jours. MacArthur fellow, 1987-92. Mem. Am. Geophys. Union, Am. Astron. Soc. (div. Planetary Scis.). Office: Malin Space Sci Systems PO Box 910148 San Diego CA 92191-0148

MALIN, ROBERT ABERNETHY, investment management executive; b. Mt. Vernon, N.Y., Dec. 13, 1931; s. Patrick Murphy and Caroline Cooper (Biddle) M.; m. Gail Lassiter, Nov. 5, 1960; children: Alison Campbell, Robert Lassiter. A.B., Dartmouth Coll., 1953, M.B.A., 1954. Asst. to comptroller Biddle Purchasing Co., N.Y.C., 1958-59; with Blyth & Co., Inc., N.Y.C., 1960-71; v.p. Blyth & Co., Inc., 1965-71, dir., 1968-71, sr. v.p. mem. exec. com. 1971-72; sr. v.p. corp. fin. Reynolds Securities Inc., N.Y.C., 1972-74; dir. Reynolds Securities Inc., 1973-74; mng. dir. First Boston Corp., N.Y.C., 1974-90; gen. ptnr. Tiedemann Investment Group, N.Y.C., 1991—. Mem. adv. council Fin. Acctg. Standards Bd., 1973-78. Served as lt. (j.g.) USNR, 1954-57. Mem. Investment Bankers Assn. Am. (v.p. exec. com. 1970-71), Securities Industry Assn. (acctg. com.), Links Club, Bond Club, Beacon Hill Club (Summit, N.J.), Morris County (N.J.) Club, Harbour Ridge Club (Stuart, Fla.). Republican. Home: 105 Whittredge Rd Summit NJ 07901-3709 Office: Tiedemann Investment Group 535 Madison Ave New York NY 10022-4212

MALIN, RONALD H., lawyer, real estate associate, consultant; b. Los Angeles, Aug. 9, 1934; s. William S. and Barbara (Perkins) M.; m. Roni Sue Friedman, Aug. 23, 1960; children: Andrea Kathleen, Allison Lee, Gregory Ryan. BS in Acctg., U. So. Calif., 1956; JD, U. Denver, 1959. Bar: Calif. 1960, Colo. 1960, D.C. 1960. Ptnr. Troy, Malin & Pottinger, Los Angeles, 1970-83; chmn. World Trade Bank, Beverly Hills, Calif., 1983-86; ptnr. Morrison & Foerster, Los Angeles, 1986-87, Fulbright Jaworski & Reavis McGrath, Los Angeles, 1987—; cons., ptnr. Royal Madera Farms, Los Angeles, 1986—; cons. Mitsui & Co. (USA), Inc., Los Angeles, 1987—. Mem. adv. bd. Los Angeles Regional Planning Commn., 1987-88; v.p., sec., bd. dirs. Brit.-Am. C. of C., Los Angeles, 1983-88. Mem. Calif. Bar Assn., Colo. Bar Assn., Regency Club, Calif. Yacht Club. Office: Fulbright Jaworski & Reavis McGrath 700 S Flower St Ste 1500 Los Angeles CA 90017-4202

MALINA, JUDITH, actress, director, producer, writer; b. Kiel, Germany, June 4, 1926; came to U.S., 1945; d. Max and Rosel (Zamora) M.; m. Julian Beck, Oct. 30, 1948 (dec.); m. Hanon Reznikov, May 6, 1988; children—Garrick Maxwell, Isha Manna. Graduate, Dramatic Workshop, New Sch. Social Research, 1945-47. adj. prof. Columbia U. Founder, producer, actress, dir. The Living Theatre, 1947—; dir., actress: The Thirteenth God, Childish Jokes, Ladies Voices, He Who Says Yes and He Who Says No, The Dialogue of the Mannequin and the Young Man, 1951, Man Is Man, 1962, Mysteries and Smaller Pieces, 1964, Antigone, 1965, Paradise Now, 1968, The Legacy of Cain (including Seven Meditations on Political Sadomasochism), 1970-77, Strike Support Oratorium, 1974, Six Public Acts, The Money Tower, 1975, Prometheus, 1978, Masse Mensch, 1980, The Living Theatre Retrospectacle, 1986, The Zero Method, 1991; dir.: Doctor Faustus Lights the Lights, 1951, Desire Trapped by the Tail, Faustina, Sweeney Agonistes, The Heroes, Ubu the King, 1952, The Age of Anxiety, The Spook Sonata, Orpheus, 1954, The Connection, 1959, In the Jungle of Cities, 1960, The Apple, 1961, The Mountain Giants 1962, The Brig, 1963, The Maids, Frankenstein, 1965, The Archeology of Sleep, 1983, Kassandra, 1987, Us, 1987, VKTMS, 1988, I and I, 1989, German Requiem, 1990, Not in My Name, 1994; actress: The Idiot King, 1954, Tonight We Improvise, Phedre, The Young Disciple, 1955, Many Loves, The Cave at Machpelah, 1959, Women of Trachis, 1960, The Yellow Methuselah, 1982, Poland/1931, 1988, Anarchia, 1993; appeared in films: Flaming Creatures, 1962, Amore, Amore, 1966, Wheel of Ashes, 1967, Le Compromise, 1968, Etre Libre, 1968, Paradise Now, 1969, Dog Day Afternoon, 1974, Signals Through the Flames, 1983, Radio Days, 1986, China Girl, 1987, Lost Paradise, 1988, Enemies, A Love Story, 1989, Awakenings, 1990, The Addams Family, 1991, Household Saints, 1993; author: Paradise Now, 1971, The Enormous Despair, 1972, The Legacy of Cain (3 pilot projects), 1973, Seven Meditations on Political Sadomasochism, 1977, Living Means Theater, 1978, Theatre Diaries: Brazil and Bologna, 1978, Poems of a Wandering Jewess, 1983, The Diaries of Judith Malina 1947-57, 1984; translator: Antigone (B. Brecht), 1990. Vice chmn. U.S. Com. for Justice to Latin Am. Polit. Prisoners, 1973-74; sponsor Am. Friends of Brazil, 1973; mem. exec. coun. War Resisters League. Recipient Lola D'Annunzio award, 1959, Page One award Newspaper Guild, 1960, Obie awards, 1960, 1964, 1969, 1975, 87, 89, Grand Prix de Theatre des Nations, 1961, Paris Critics Circle medallion, 1961, Prix de l'Universite Paris, 1961, New Eng. Theatre Conf. award, 1962, Olympio prize Italy, 1967, 9th Centennial medal U. Bologna, Italy, 1988; named Humanist of the Yr., 1984; Guggenheim fellow, 1985. Address: 800 West End Ave New York NY 10025

MALINA, MICHAEL, lawyer; b. Bklyn., Mar. 20, 1936; s. William and Jean (Kutlowitz) M.; m. Anita May Oppenheim, June 22, 1958; children: Rachel Lynn, Stuart Charles, Joel Martin. AB, Harvard U., 1957, LLB, 1960. Bar: N.Y. 1961, U.S. Dist. Ct. (so. and ea. dists.) N.Y. 1962, U.S. Ct. Appeals (2d, 3d, 4th, 9th, and D.C. cirs.) 1965, U.S. Supreme Ct. 1965, U.S. Tax Ct. 1991. Assoc. Kaye, Scholer, Fierman, Hays & Handler, N.Y.C., 1960-69, ptnr., 1969—. Contbr. articles to profl. jours. Mem. ABA (antitrust sect.), N.Y. State Bar Assn. (exec. com. antitrust sect. 1994—, chmn. 1975-82, Robinson-Patman Act com.), Assn. of Bar of City of N.Y. (profl. ethics com. 1985-88), Phi Beta Kappa. Democrat. Jewish. Home: 12 Innes Rd Scarsdale NY 10583-7110 Office: Kaye Scholer Fierman Hays & Handler 425 Park Ave New York NY 10022-3506

MALINA, ROBERT S., investment company executive; b. 1935. BA, Cornell U., 1960; JD, Harvard, 1963. Law clk. to Hon. Jay E Lombard U.S. Ct. Appeals, 1963-70; v.p. E.M. Wardburg, Pincus & Co., N.Y.C., 1970-80; pres. Robert S. Malina, Inc., N.Y.C., 1980—; chmn., CEO Supermarket Devel. Corp., Albuquerque. Office: Supermarket Development Corp 1920 Columbia Dr SE Albuquerque NM 87106-3347

MALINA, ROGER F., astronomer; b. Paris, July 6, 1950; married; children: Xavier, Juri. BS in Physics, MIT, 1972; PhD in Astronomy, U. Calif., Berkeley, 1979. Rsch. aide MIT Ctr. for Space Rsch., Cambridge, 1969-72; summer rsch. aide Cambridge (Mass.) Electron Accelerator, 1971; teaching asst. U. Calif., Berkeley, 1972-73, rsch. asst. space scis. lab., 1973-79, assoc. rsch. astronomer space scis. lab., 1980—; project mgr. for NASA sounding rockets, 1974; organizer Sierra Astrophysics Conf., 1974-76; project scientist for NASA sounding rockets, 1976-78, Berkeley-London-Utrecht extreme ultraviolet spectrometer, 1979-82, FAUST Spacelab 1 Instrument, 1977-84, Extreme Ultraviolet Explorer, 1978-86; co-investigator IUE observations of HZ43, 1981, NGC4242, 1983; co-dir. grant from the Nat. Endowment for the Arts to the Jour. Leonardo, 1984; dir. grant from the Nat. Endowment for the Arts to the Jour. Leonardo, 1985-87; prin. investigator Extreme Ultraviolet Explorer Sci. Instruments, 1985—; exec. dir. EON Astrophysics. Exec. editor Jour. Leonardo, 1982—; co-author and contbr. various articles to profl. jours., 1974—; author numerous papers delivered to sci. meetings, 1974—; speaker on profl. confs., 1977—. Bd. dirs. Bay Area Energy Action, San Francisco, 1977-80, Sun Found. Fellow Brit. Interplanetary Soc. (assoc. 1976), Royal Astron. Soc.; mem. Am. Astron. Soc., Optical Soc. of Am., Internat. Soc. for the Arts, Scis. and Tech. (chmn. bd.), Internat. Acad. of Astronautics (corr. mem. 1987), Sigma-Xi. Office: U Calif Ctr for EUV Astrophysics 2150 Kittredge St Berkeley CA 94720-0001

MALING, GEORGE CROSWELL, JR., physicist; b. Boston, Mass., Feb. 24, 1931; s. George Croswell and Marjory (Bell) M.; m. Norah J. Horsfield, Dec. 29, 1960; children: Ellen P., Barbara J., Jeffrey C. A.B., Bowdoin Coll., 1954; S.B., S.M., MIT, 1954, Elec. Engr., 1958, Ph.D., 1963. Rsch. asst., postdoctoral fellow MIT, 1957-65; adv. physicist IBM Corp., 1965-71; sr. physicist IBM Corp., Poughkeepsie, N.Y., 1971-92; pres. Empire State Software Systems, Ltd., 1992—; dir. Noise Control Found., Inc., Poughkeepsie, 1975—; chmn. com. Sl-acoustics Am. Nat. Standards Com., 1976-79; dir. Inst. Noise Control Engring. Found., Inc., 1993—; mng. dir. Inst. of Noise Control Engring., 1994—. Editor: Noise/News, 1972-92; mng. editor: Noise/News, 1972-92; mng. editor Noise/News Internat., 1993—; assoc. editor Jour. Acoustical Soc. Am., 1976-83; editor tech. proc.; contbr. numerous articles to profl. jours. Served with U.S. Army, 1955-57. Fellow IEEE, AAAS, Acoustical Soc. Am. (exec. coun. 1980-83, Silver medal in noise 1992), Audio Engring. Soc.; mem. Inst. Noise Control Engring. (bd. dirs. 1972-77, pres. 1975), Internat. Inst. Noise Control Engring. (bd. dirs. 1980-86, 90—). Office: ESSS PO Box 2880 Poughkeepsie NY 12603

MALINO, JEROME R., rabbi; b. N.Y.C., June 7, 1911; s. Wolf and Henrietta (Rosenbaum) M.; m. Rhoda Simon, June 9, 1936; children: Frances, Jonathan. B.A., CCNY, 1931; M.H.L., Jewish Inst. Religion, 1935; L.H.D. (hon.), Alfred (N.Y.) U., 1958; D.D. (hon.), Hebrew Union Coll., 1960. Rabbi Baldwin (N.Y.) Jewish Center, 1934-35, United Jewish Center, Danbury, Conn., 1935-81; rabbi emeritus United Jewish Center, 1981—; chaplain Fed. Correctional Inst., Danbury, 1940-83; lectr. Western Conn. State U., 1983-84; adj. lectr. Hebrew Union Coll.-Jewish Inst. Religion, 1983—. Mem. Danbury Bd. Edn., 1949-69; bd. dirs. Danbury Community Action Com.; mem. Danbury Charter Revision Com., 1976, Mayor of Danbury Ad Hoc Com. Racism, 1976. Mem. Central Conf. Am. Rabbis (pres. 1979-81), Am. Religious Communities (pres. 1982-84), Jewish Peace Fellowship, Inst. Religion in Age of Sci., Danbury Music Center, Danbury Concert Assn. Home: 77 Garfield Ave Danbury CT 06810-7906 Office: 141 Deer Hill Ave Danbury CT 06810-7726 *The best way to enhance the meaning of one's own life is to place human values everywhere before all other considerations.*

MALINO, JOHN GRAY, real estate executive; b. N.Y.C., Oct. 15, 1939; s. Joseph and Dorothy (Gray) M.; m. Geraldine Seibel, Mar. 24, 1963 (div.); m. Phyllis Susan Alter, Mar. 29, 1987; children: Joanne, Linda. BA, NYU, 1961. Lic. real estate broker, N.Y. Real estate broker Robert Joseph, N.Y.C., 1961-64; asst. v.p. Loews Corp., N.Y.C., 1964-83, v.p., 1983—. Chmn. Young Men's and Women's Real Estate Assn., N.Y., 1974, N.Y.C. Real Estate Bd., 1982. Lodge: B'nai B'rith (pres. real estate div.). Home: 553 Barnard Ave Woodmere NY 11598-2707 Office: Loews Corp 667 Madison Ave New York NY 10021-8029

MALIS, LEONARD IRVING, neurosurgeon; b. Phila., Nov. 23, 1919; s. Morris Melvin and Dorothy (Brodsky) M.; m. Ruth Gornstein, June 24, 1942; children: Larry Alan, Lynne Paula. MD, U. Va., 1943. Intern Phila. Gen. Hosp., 1943-44; resident in neurology Mt. Sinai Hosp., N.Y.C., 1947, resident in neurosurgery, 1948-50, neurosurgeon in chief, dir. dept. neurol. surgery, 1970—; prof., chmn. dept. neurosurgery Mt. Sinai Sch. Medicine, CUNY, 1970-92, prof. emeritus dept. nursing, 1993—; fellow in neurophysiology Med. Sch., Yale U., 1951; practice medicine specializing in neurosurgery N.Y.C., 1951—; cons. in field. Contbr. numerous articles to profl. jours.; developer various surg. and electronic instruments. Capt. M.C., U.S. Army, World War II. Mem. ACS, Am. Assn. Neurol. Surgery, Congress Neurol. Surgeons, Am. Physiol. Soc., Soc. Neuroscis., Am. Acad. Neurol. Surgery, Harvey Cushing Soc., Alpha Omega Alpha. Office: 1148 5th Ave New York NY 10128-0807

MALITZ, SIDNEY, psychiatrist, educator, researcher; b. N.Y.C., Apr. 20, 1923; s. Benjamin and Etta (Cohen) M. Student, NYU, 1940-42, Tulane U., 1942-43; BM, Chgo. Med. Coll., 1946, MD, 1947. Diplomate Am. Bd. Psychiatry and Neurology. Intern St. Mary's Hosp., Huntington, W.Va., 1946-47; sr. intern Bethesda, Hosp., Cin., 1947-48; resident N.Y. State Psychiat. Inst., N.Y.C., 1948-51; sr. research psychiatrist N.Y. State Psychiat. Inst., 1954-56, acting prin. research psychiatrist, 1956-58, acting chief psychiat. research, chief dept. exptl. psychiatry, 1958-64, chief psychiat. research dept. exptl. psychiatry, 1964-72, dep. dir., 1972-75, acting dir., 1975-76, 81-84, dep. dir., 1976-78, dir. dept. biol. psychiatry, 1984-91; in charge psychiat. drug clinic Vanderbilt Clinic, Presbyn. Hosp., N.Y.C., 1956-75, asst. attending psychiatrist, 1960-66, assoc. attending psychiatrist, 1966-71, attending psychiatrist, 1971-93, acting dir. psychiatry service, 1975-76, 81-84, 93—, consulting psychiatrist; asst. dept. psychiatry Coll. Physicians and Surgeons, Columbia U., N.Y.C., 1955-57, assoc., 1957-59, asst. clin. prof., 1959-65, assoc. prof., 1965-69, prof., 1969-93, vice chmn. dept. psychiatry, 1972-75, acting chmn., 1975-76, 81-84, vice chmn., 1976-78, prof. emeritus, 1993—; mem. panel impartial psychiat. experts N.Y. State Supreme Ct., 1960—; mem. adv. com. subcom.; cons. U.S. Pharmacopeia; mem. adv. com. subcom. health N.Y. State Constl. Conv.; cons. div. med. scis. NRC, Washington, 1967-70; cons. Rush Found., Los Angeles, 1968-75; mem. ad hoc rev. com. to select Nat. Drug Abuse Research Ctrs., Ctr. Studies Narcotic and Drug Abuse, NIMH, 1972-73. Contbr. numerous articles to profl. jours. Recipient Leonard Caemmer award N.Y. State Psychiatric Inst., 1984. Fellow Royal Soc. Medicine (life), Am. Psychiat. Assn. (life, chmn. com. biol. psychiatry 1961-62, program com. 1961-62, sec-treas. chpt. 1962-63, com. rsch. 1966-68, pres. chpt. 1969-70, chmn. Coun. Rsch. and Devel. 1971-73, History and Libr. com. 1989-91), Am. Coll. Neuropsychopharmacology (life); mem. AAAS (coun. 1969-72), N.Y. Acad. Medicine (life), Collegium Internationale Neuropsychopharmacologicum (life), Am. Coll. Psychiatrists (archivist-historian 1978—, liaison to Royal Coll. Psychiatrists 1985—, Bowis award 1989), Royal Coll. Psychiatrists, Am. Coll. Psychoanalysts, N.Y. Soc. Clin. Psychiatry, Assn. Research Nervous and Mental Disease, N.Y. State, N.Y. County med. socs., AMA (cons. coun.l drugs 1960-70), Group Advancement of Psychiatry (rsch. com. 1986-91), N.Y. Acad. Scis. N.Y. Psychiat. Soc. (v.p. 1989-91, pres. 1991-92), Am. Psychopath. Assn., Soc. Biol. Psychiatry, Benjamin Rush Soc. (pres.-elect 1989, pres. 1990-91), Vidonian Soc. (pres. 1989-93), Alpha Omega Alpha. Office: Columbia U Dept Psychiatry 161 Fort Washington Ave New York NY 10032-3713

MALKASIAN, GEORGE DURAND, JR., physician, educator; b. Springfield, Mass., Oct. 26, 1927; s. George Dur and Gladys Mildred (Trombley) M.; m. Mary Ellen Koch, Oct. 16, 1954; children: Linda Jeanne, Karen Diane, Martha Ellen. AB, Yale U., 1950; MD, Boston U., 1954; MS, U. Minn., 1963. Diplomate Am. Bd. Ob-Gyn. Intern Worcester (Mass.) City Hosp., 1954-55; resident in ob-gyn Mayo Grad. Sch. Hosp., Rochester, Minn., 1955-58, 60-61; mem. faculty Mayo Med. Sch., 1962—, prof. ob-gyn, 1976—, chmn. dept. ob-gyn, 1976-86. Author articles in field. Served to lt. comdr. M.C., USNR, 1958-60. Named Tchr. of Yr., Mayo Grad. Sch. Medicine, 1973, 77, Alumnus of Yr., Boston U. Sch. Med., 1990. Mem. Am. Coll. Obstetricians and Gynecologists, Am. Gynecol. and Obstetrical Soc., Am. Radium Soc., ACS, Soc. Gynecologic Oncologists, Assn. Profs. Ob-Gyn., N.Am. Ob-Gyn. Soc., Cen. Assn. Obstetricians and Gynecologists, Minn. Soc. Obstetricians and Gynecologists, Am. Coll. Obstetricians and Gynecologists (pres. 1989-90). Home: 1750 11th Ave NE Rochester MN 55906-4215 Office: Mayo Clinic 200 1st St SW Rochester MN 55905-0001

MALKIEL, BURTON GORDON, economics educator; b. Boston, Aug. 28, 1932; s. Sol and Celia (Gordon) M.; m. Judith Ann Atherton, July 16, 1954 (dec. 1987); 1 child, Jonathan; m. Nancy Weiss, July 31, 1988. BA, Harvard, 1953, MBA, 1955; PhD, Princeton, 1964. Assoc. Smith Barney & Co., N.Y.C., 1958-60; asst. prof. dept. econs. Princeton U., 1964-66, assoc. prof., 1966-68, prof., 1968-81, Rentschler prof. econs., 1969-81, chmn. dept. econs., 1974-75, 77-81; dean Sch. Orgn. and Mgmt., Yale U., 1981-87; Chem. Bank chmn.'s prof. econs. Princeton U., 1988—; mem. Pres.'s Council Econ. Advisors, 1975-77; bd. govs. Am. Stock Exchange; dir. Amdahl Corp., Jeffrey Co., So. New Eng. Telephone Co., Prudential Life Ins. Co. Am., Baker, Fentress & Co., Vanguard Group. Author: The Term Structure of Interest Rates, 1966, (with others) Strategies and Rational Decisions in the Securities Options Market, 1969, A Random Walk Down Wall Street, 1973, 6th edit., 1995, The Inflation-Beater's Investment Guide, 1980. Served to 1st lt. AUS, 1955-58. Mem. Am. Fin. Assn. (dir., pres. 1978). Home: 76 North Rd Princeton NJ 08540-2430 Office: Princeton U Dept Econs Princeton NJ 08544

MALKIEL, NANCY WEISS, college dean, history educator; b. Newark, Feb. 14, 1944; d. William and Ruth Sylvia (Puder) W.; m. Burton G. Malkiel, July 31, 1988. BA summa cum laude, Smith Coll., 1965; MA, Harvard U., 1966, PhD, 1970. Asst. prof. history Princeton (N.J.) U., 1969-75, assoc. prof., 1975-82, prof., 1982—; master Dean Mathey Coll., 1982-86, dean of coll., 1987—. Author (as Nancy J. Weiss): Charles Francis Murphy, 1858-1924: Respectability and Responsibility in Tammany Politics, 1968, (with others) Blacks in America: Bibliographical Essays, 1971, The National Urban League, 1910-1940, 1974, Farewell to the Party of Lincoln: Black Politics in the Age of FDR, 1983 (Berkshire Conf. of Women Historians prize 1984), Whitney M. Young Jr., and the Struggle for Civil Rights, 1989. Trustee Smith Coll., Northampton, Mass., 1984-94, Woodrow Wilson Nat. Fellowship Found., 1975—. Fellow Woodrow Wilson Found., 1965, Charles Warren Ctr. for Studies in Am. History, 1976-77, Radcliffe Inst., 1976-77, Ctr. for Advanced Study in Behavioral Scis., 1986-87. Mem. Am. Hist. Assn., Orgn. Am. Historians (chmn. status women hist. profession 1972-75), So. Hist. Assn., Phi Beta Kappa. Democrat. Jewish. Office: Princeton U Office Dean Of College Princeton NJ 08544

MALKIEL, YAKOV, linguistics educator; b. Kiev, Russia, July 22, 1914; came to U.S., 1940, naturalized, 1946; s. Léon and Claire (Saitzew) M.; m. María Rosa Lida, Mar. 2, 1948 (dec. Sept. 1962). Matura, Werner-Siemens Realgymnasium, Berlin-Schöneberg, 1933; PhD magna cum laude, Friedrich-Wilhelms Universität, Berlin, 1938; LHD (hon.), U. Chgo., 1969; LLD (hon.), U. Ill., 1976; Dr honoris causa, U. Paris, 1983, Free U., W. Berlin, 1983, Georgetown U., 1987, Oxford U., 1989, Salamanca U., 1992. Instr. U. Wyo., 1942; lectr. U. Calif.-Berkeley, 1942-45, instr., 1945-46, asst. prof., 1946-48, assoc. prof., 1948-52, prof. Romance philology 1952-66, mem. grad. council, 1953-57, assoc. dean grad. div., 1963-66, prof. linguistics and Romance philology, 1966-85, 86, 88, research fellow in the humanities, 1968-69, research prof. humanities, 1981; research assoc. Mills Coll., summers 1942-43; vis. assoc. prof. U. So. Calif., summer 1949; vis. lectr. Ind. U., summer 1953; vis. lectr. U. Colo., summer 1958, U. Tex. Linguistic Inst., summer 1960, Linguistic Inst., Ind. U., summer 1964, Linguistic Inst., UCLA, 1966; Collitz prof. Linguistics Inst., 1980; vis. lectr. cursos superiores Melsaga U., 1989-92; lectr. Jennifer summer inst., Soria, Spain; cons. various panels NEH, 1978—; participant symposium Inst. Italian Ency., Rome. Editor in chief Romance Philology Quar., 1947-82, cons. editor, 1982—; assoc. editor Hispanic Rev., Jour. Hispanic Rsch. (London), Romance Quar. (Ky.), Revista de Filologia Española, Voz y Letra (Málaga); author: Essays on Linguistic Themes, 1968, Etymological Dictionaries: A Typological Survey, 1976, Theory and Practice of Romance Etymology, 1989, Etymology; also monographs, articles U.S. and fgn. countries; contbr. to Dictionary of the Middle Ages, Ency. of Romance Linguistics, Ency. of Lexicography. Recipient Guggenheim Meml. Found. 3d award, 1967; Berkeley citation U. Calif., 1985; Faculty Rsch. lectr. U. Calif. Berkeley, 1988-89; Guggenheim fellow, 1948-49, 59; NSF sr. postdoctoral fellow, 1966; Princeton U. fellow, 1977. Mem. Am. Acad. Arts and Scis., Linguistic Soc. Am. (pres. 1965), MLA (founder Romance linguistics group 1946), Linguistic Soc. Paris, Am. Oriental Soc., Philol. Assn. Pacific Coast (v.p. 1963, pres. 1965), Société de Linguistique Romane (exec. com. 1977, 79, 89), Royal Spanish Acad. (corr. mem. 1987—), Società di linguistica italiana (hon.), Ctr. Romance Studies, U. London. Home: 1 Arlington Ln Kensington CA 94707-1108

MALKIN, BARRY, film editor, consultant; b. N.Y.C., Oct. 26, 1938; s. Richard and Helen (Kandix) M.; m. Stephanie Byer, Apr. 5, 1971; 1 child, Sacha Janine. BA, Adelphi U., 1960. Freelance film editor Sacha Prodns., Inc., N.Y.C., 1964—. Editor: (films) The Rain People, 1969, They Might Be Giants, 1971, Who Is Harry Kellerman and Why Is He Saying All Those Terrible Things About Me?, 1971, Cops and Robbers, 1973, One Summer Love, 1976, Somebody Killed Her Husband, 1978, Last Embrace, 1979, (with Edward Beyer and David Ray) One Trick Pony, 1980, Windows, 1980, (with Mark Laub) Four Friends, 1981, (with Laub, Robert Q. Lovett, and Randy Roberts) Hammett, 1982, Rumble Fish, 1983, (with Lovett) The Cotton Club, 1984 (Academy award nomination best film editing 1984), Peggy Sue Got Married, 1986, Gardens of Stone, 1987, Big, 1988, New York Stories ("Life without Zoe"), 1989, The Freshman, 1990, (with Lisa Fruchtman and Walter Murch) The Godfather Part III, 1990 (Academy award nomination best film editing 1990), Honeymoon in Vegas, 1992, It Could Happen to You, 1994. Mem. Acad. Motion Picture Arts and Scis., Motion Picture Editors. Home and Office: 275 Central Park W New York NY 10024

MALKIN, CARY JAY, lawyer; b. Chgo., Oct. 6, 1949; s. Arthur D. and Perle (Slavin) M.; m. Lisa Klimley, Oct. 27, 1976; children: Dorothy R., Victoria S., Lydia R. B.A., George Washington U., 1971; J.D., Northwestern U., 1974. Bar: Ill. 1974, U.S. Dist. Ct. (no. dist.) Ill. 1974. Assoc. Mayer, Brown & Platt, Chgo., 1974-80, ptnr., 1981—. Chmn. spl. events com. Mental Health Assn. 1984-85; mem. steering com. Endowment Campaign of the Latin Sch. Chgo. 1988-92; chmn. annual fund The Latin Sch. of Chgo., 1990-91, trustee, 1991—, v.p., 1992—; mem. exec. com. Friends of Prentice Women's Hosp., 1991-92; bd. dirs. SOS Children's Village Ill., 1992—; mem. M.S. Weiss fund bd. Children's Meml. Hosp., 1989-93; mem. Graziano Fund bd. Children's Meml. Hosp., 1993—. Mem. Order of the Coif, Phi Beta Kappa. Clubs: Saddle and Cycle, Standard, Chicago. Home: 233 E Walton St Chicago IL 60611-1526 Office: Mayer Brown & Platt 190 S La Salle St Chicago IL 60603-3410

MALKIN, JUDD D., diversified corporation executive; b. 1937; married. BS, U. Ill., 1959. CPA, Ill. Pres. Amco Industries, until 1969, Mid-Southern Toyota Distbrs. Inc.; chmn. bd. JMB Realty Corp., Chgo., 1969—; also exec. v.p. Amfac Inc. subs. JMB Realty Corp. Office: JMB Realty Corp 900 N Michigan Ave Chicago IL 60611-1542

MALKIN, MOSES MONTEFIORE, employee benefits administration company executive; b. Revere, Mass., Sept. 18, 1919; s. Irving and Annie (Helfant) M.; m. Hannah Lacob, Oct. 11, 1941. AB, U. N.Y., 1940; BSME, Columbia U., 1948. Enrolled actuary and chartered life underwriter. Engr. GE, Schenectady, N.Y., 1948-50; engr. Gen. Bronze, Inc., Garden City, 1950-51; v.p. Malkin Warehouse, Inc., New Haven, 1951-57; pvt. practice actuary New Haven, 1957-72; pres. actuary Profl. Pensions, Inc., East Haven, Conn., 1972—; presenter pension issues at numerous confs., 1970-80. Pres., founder Milford (Conn.), 1962, Milford Child Guidance Clinic, 1966; pres. Clifford Beers Child Guidance, New Haven, 1971, Jewish Family Svc., New Haven, 1973. Mem. Am. Acad. Actuaries, Am. Soc. Pension Actuaries (instr. 1984), Am. Soc. Chartered Life Underwriters, Grads. Club (New Haven), Phi Beta Kappa, Tau Beta Pi. Jewish. Avocation: instrument rated multi-engine pvt. piloting. Home: Four Tumblebrook Rd Woodbridge CT 06525 Office: Profl Pensions Inc 444 Foxon Rd New Haven CT 06513-2098

MALKIN, PETER LAURENCE, lawyer; b. N.Y.C., Jan. 14, 1934; s. Samuel and Gertrude (Greenberger) M.; m. Isabel L. Wien, July 10, 1955; children: Scott David, Cynthia Allison, Anthony Edward. Grad. cum laude, Poly. Prep. Country Day Sch., 1951; AB summa cum laude, Harvard U., 1955, LLB magna cum laude, 1958. Bar: N.Y. 1958, Conn. 1976, Fla. 1977. Sr. ptnr., chmn. Wien, Malkin & Bettex, N.Y.C. and Palm Beach, Fla., 1960—; gen. ptnr. Empire State Bldg. Assocs., 1961—, 1185 Ave. of Ams. Assocs., N.Y.C., 1978—; bd. dirs. U.S. Trust Corp., N.Y. C. of Commerce and Industry; mem. N.Y.C. Partnership; chmn. W&M Properties Inc., Grand Ctrl. Partnership Inc., 34th St. Partnership, Inc.; dir. Fashion Ctr. Bus. Improvement Dist.; mem. adv. com. Greenwich (Conn.) Japanese Sch., 1992—; gov. Real Estate Bd. N.Y., 1993—. Nat. vice chmn. Harvard Law Sch. Fund, 1967-71, chmn. nat. scholarship com., 1972-75, chmn. maj. gifts com., 1975-76, chmn. N.Y.C. com., 1981-83; founder, bd. dirs. Urban League Southwestern Fairfield County, 1969-73, treas., 1969-71; bd. dirs., mem. exec. com. Lincoln Ctr. for Performing Arts, 1979—; bd. dirs. Inst. Internat. Edn., 1983-89, hon., 1994—; mem. devel. com. N.Y. Pub. Libr., 1979—; trustee Nat. Trust for Hist. Preservation, 1988-91; founding chmn. Greenwich (Conn.) Green & Clean, Inc., 1992—; mem. exec. com. Greenwich chpt. NAACP, 1967-69; trustee Citizens Budget Commn., N.Y.C., 1971-91, Jewish Communal Fund N.Y., 1976-81; hon. trustee Assoc. YM and YWHA Greater N.Y.; dean's coun. Harvard U., 1987—; mem. overseers com. to visit Kennedy Sch. Govt., 1976-82, 83-89, 90—, to visit Harvard Law Sch., 1977-83, mem. exec. com. Program for Ctr. for Jewish Studies, 1974-80; bd. overseers Harvard Coll., 1989-95, mem. overseers com. univ. resources, 1972-75, exec. com., 1985—; dean's adv. com. Harvard Law Sch., 1988-91; mem. steering com. N.Y. Major Gifts, Harvard Coll. Fund, 1993-93; elected dir. Harvard Alumni Assn., 1981-83; chmn. schs. and scholarship com. Harvard U., Greenwich, 1973-79; exec. com. Assn. Better N.Y., 1972—. Recipient Nat. Honor award Nat. Trust Hist. Preservation, 1987, Crain's All-Star award, 1994, Nacore Disting. Man of Yr. award, 1995; fellow Brandeis U., 1970—. Mem. Harvard Law Sch. Assn. N.Y.C. (trustee 1968-70, v.p 1973-74, mem. coun.), Assn. Bar City N.Y. (mem. com. admissions 1965-68, com. assn. bldgs. 1968-72, chmn. com. ins. assn. bldgs. 1967-68), Am. Arbitration Assn. (nat. panel arbitrators), Century Assn., The Links N.Y., The Hasty Pudding Inst. 1770, AD Hon., Harvard Varsity Club (Cambridge), Harvard Club N.Y.C. (bd. mgrs. 1979-81), Harvard Club (Fairfield County, Conn., v.p. 1974-75, bd. dirs. 1976-80), Bailwick Club (founding pres.), Phi Beta Kappa. Office: 60 E 42nd St New York NY 10165-0015 also: 306 Royal Poinciana Plz Palm Beach FL 33480-4020

MALKIN, ROGER D., agricultural products executive; b. 1931. With Federal Compress & Warehouse Co., Memphis, 1968-69, Southwide Inc., Scott, Miss., 1968-69; now chmn. bd. dirs., CEO Delta & Pine Land Co., Scott, Miss., 1972—. Office: Delta & Pine Land Co 1 Cotton Row Scott MS 38772

MALKIN, STANLEY LEE, neurologist; b. Pitts., Nov. 11, 1942; s. Maurice and Bessie Beatrice (Serbin) M.; children: Justin Ross, Keith Richard. BA with honors, U. Pa., 1964; MD, U. Pitts., 1968; Intern, Montefiore Hosp., Pitts., 1968-69; resident in neurology Columbia-Presbyn. Med. Center, N.Y.C., 1969-72; chief neurology service Wright-Patterson AFB, Dayton, Ohio, 1972-74; practice medicine specializing in neurology, N.Y.C.; attending staff Mt. Sinai Hosp.; former dir. Neuro-Diagnostic Lab, Englewood; asst. clin. prof. neurology Mt. Sinai Sch. of Medicine; founder Bergen-Passaic Tomography Center, Fairlawn, N.J.; neurology cons. Regent Hosp.; med. dir. Pain Suppression Labs., Inc.; med. dir. Efficient Health Systems, Inc.-N.Y.C. Healthline; founder, prin. Hosp. Diagnostic Equipment Corp., 1987—; dir., pres. Cancer Treatment Holdings, Inc. 1993—; founder Montvale Med. Imaging Assocs. (N.J.), N.Y. Med. Imaging, N.Y.C., Hosp. Diagnostic Equipment Corp. Co-mcpl. coord. Ft. Lee Citizens for

McGovern, 1972; mem. Edgewater Rent Control Bd., 1978, Nat. Headache Found. Maj. M.C., USAF, 1972-74. Diplomate Am. Bd. Psychiatry and Neurology, Nat. Bd. Med. Examiners. Mem. Am. Acad. Neurology, Am. Assn. Electrodiagnostic Medicine, Am. Soc. Neuro-Imaging (charter), Am. Med. EEG Soc., Am. Assn. for Study of Headache, Nat. Headache Found., Internat. Headache Soc., N.Y. Acad. Scis. Office: 15 Penn Pla 401 7th Ave Ste 189 New York NY 10001-2003 Office: 120 W 44th St Ste 701 New York NY 10036

MALKINSON, FREDERICK DAVID, dermatologist; b. Hartford, Conn., Feb. 26, 1924; s. John Walter and Rose (Volkenheim) M.; m. Una Zwick, June 15, 1979; children by previous marriage: Philip, Carol, John. Student, Loomis Inst., 1937-41; 3 yr. cert. cum laude, Harvard U., 1943, D.M.D., 1947, M.D., 1949. Intern Harvard-Beth Israel Hosp., Boston, 1949-50; resident in dermatology U. Chgo., 1950-54, from instr. to assoc. prof. dept. dermatology, 1954-68; prof. medicine and dermatology U. Ill., Chgo., 1968-71; chmn. dept. dermatology Rush Med. Coll. and Rush-Presbyn.-St. Luke's Med. Ctr., Chgo., 1971-92, Clark W. Finnerud, M.D. prof. dept. dermatology, 1971—; trustee Sulzberger Inst. Dermatol. Communication and Edn., 1976—, pres., 1993—. Editor: Year Book of Dermatology, 1971-78; chief editor: AMA Archives of Dermatology, 1979-83; bd. editors, 1976-84, Jour. AMA, 1979-83; editorial cons. World Book Medical Encyclopedia, 1991—; contbr. articles and abstracts to profl. jours., chpts. to books. Active Evanston (Ill.) Libr. Bd., 1988-94, pres., 1993-94. With M.C. USN, 1950-52. Grantee U.S. Army, 1955-61, USPHS, 1962-73. Mem. AAAS, Am. Acad. Dermatology (v.p. 1987-89, dir. 1964-67), Am. Dermatol. Assn., Soc. Investigative Dermatology (v.p. 1978-79, dir. 1963-68), Am. Fedn. Clin. Rsch., Cen. Soc. Clin. Rsch., Radiation Rsch. Soc., Assn. Profs. of Dermatology (dir. 1982-85), Dermatology Found. (trustee 1980-93, pres. 1983-85), Nat. Coun. on Radiation Protection and Measurements (mem. com. on cutaneous radiobiology 1986-92), Chgo. Dermatol. Soc. (pres. 1964-65, Gold Medal award 1992), Chgo. Lit. Club.

MALKKI, OLLI, paper company executive. Wtih Oy Warstila AB, Helsinki, Finland, 1974-85; pres. Ahlstrom Industrial Holdings, Glens Falls, N.Y., 1991—. Office: Ahlstrom Industrial Holdings Pruyns Is Glens Falls NY 12801

MALKOVICH, JOHN, actor; b. Christopher, Ill., Dec. 9, 1953; m. Glenne Headley, 1982 (div.); children: Amandine and Loewy, with Nicoletta Peyran. Student, Eastern Ill. U., Ill. State U. Co-founder Steppenwolf Theatre, Chgo., 1976. Made N.Y.C. theatrical debut in True West, 1982 (Obie award, Clarence Derwent award); other theatrical appearances include: Death of a Salesman, 1984, Burn This, 1987, States of Shock; dir. Balm in Gilead, 1984-85, Arms and the Man, 1985, The Caretaker, 1986, Coyote Ugly, (Chgo., Kennedy Ctr. for Performing Arts, Washington) 1985, Libra, 1994, Steppenwolf, 1994; appeared in films Places in the Heart, 1984, The Killing Fields, 1984, Eleni, 1985, Making Mr. Right, 1987, Glass Menagerie, 1987, Empire of the Sun, 1987, Miles From Home, 1988, Dangerous Liaisons, 1988, The Sheltering Sky, 1990, Queen's Logic, 1991, The Object of Beauty, 1991, Shadows and Fog, 1992, Jennifer 8, 1992, Of Mice and Men, 1992, In The Line Of Fire, 1993 (Academy award nomination best supporting actor 1993), Alive, 1993, Touchstone, 1994, Para De La Nuages, 1994, Mary Reilly, 1994; co-exec. prodr. The Accidental Tourist, 1988; appeared in TV films Word of Honor, 1981, American Dream, 1981, Death of a Salesman, 1985 (Emmy award 1986), Heart of Darkness, 1994. Office: Smith Malkovich 335 N Maple Dr #135 Beverly Hills CA 90210

MALKUS, DAVID STARR, mechanics educator, applied mathematician; b. Chgo., June 30, 1945; s. Willem V.R. Malkus and Joanne (Gerould) Simpson; children: Christopher, Annelise, Byron, Renata. AB, Yale U., 1968; PhD, Boston U., 1976. Mathematician U.S. Nat. Bur. Standards, Gaithersburg, Md., 1975-77; asst. prof. math. Ill. Inst. Tech., Chgo., 1977-83, assoc. prof., 1983-84; assoc. prof. mechanics U. Wis., Madison, 1984-87, prof., 1987—, chmn. Rheology Rsch. Ctr., 1991-94; chair prof. Nanjing (People's Republic China) Aero. Inst., 1986. Co-author: Concepts and Applications of Finite Element Analysis, 1989; contbr. articles to Computer Methods Applied Mech. Engring., Jour. Computational Physics. Mem. Soc. Rheology. Achievements include research on finite element methods—reduced and selective integration techniques, a unification of concepts. Home: 5595 Mary Lake Rd Waunakee WI 53597 Office: U Wis Dept Engring Mech/Astronaut 1415 Johnson Dr Madison WI 53706-1691

MALKUS, WILLEM VAN RENSSELAER, mathematics educator; b. Bklyn., Nov. 19, 1923; s. Hubert Paul and Alida Fitzhugh (Wright) M.; m. Joanne Starr Simpson, 1948; m. Ulla Charlotte, Dec. 28, 1964; children: David S., Steven W., Karen E., per N. Ph.D. in Physics, U. Chgo., 1950. Asst. prof. natural sci. U. Chgo., 1950-51; phys. oceanographer Woods Hole (Mass.) Oceanographic Instn., 1951-60; prof. geophysics UCLA, 1960-67, prof. geophysics and math., 1967-69; prof. applied math. MIT, Cambridge, 1969—. Contbr. articles to sci. jours. Served to lt. (j.g.) USNR, 1942-46. Guggenheim fellow U. Cambridge, (Eng.) and Stockholm, 1971-72, U. Cambridge, 1979-80; NSF fellow, 1964-65. Fellow Am. Phys. Soc., Am. Acad. Arts and Scis., Am. Geophys. Union; mem. Nat. Acad. Sci. Home: 72 Shade St Lexington MA 02173-7721 Office: MIT RM 2-369 Cambridge MA 02139

MALL, IDA, church administrator. Pres. Intl. Lutheran Women's Missionary League of the Lutheran Church MO Synod International Ctr., St. Louis. Office: Internat Luth Women's Missionary League 3558 S Jefferson Ave Saint Louis MO 63118-3910

MALL, WILLIAM JOHN, JR., aerospace executive, retired air force officer; b. Pitts., Jan. 13, 1933; s. William John and Margaret (Henry) M.; m. Vivian Lea Fenton; children—Michele, William, Catherine. B.B.A., U. Pitts., 1954; M.B.A., George Washington U., 1966; sr. mgrs. in govt. program, Harvard U., 1980. Commd. officer USAF, 1954, advanced through grades to maj. gen., 1981; insp. gen. Mil. Airlift Command., Scott AFB, Ill., 1978; comdr. 436 wing Mil. Airlift Command., Dover AFB, Del., 1979; DCS personnel Mil. Airlift Command, Scott AFB, Ill., 1979-81; comdr. Air Rescue Service, Scott AFB, Ill., 1981-83, 23d AF/MAC, Scott AFB, Ill., 1983-85; assigned to Hdqrs USAF, Bolling AFB, D.C., 1985-86; ret.; dir. integrated logistics support div. Douglas Aircraft Co., Long Beach, Calif., 1987-89, gen. mgr. human resources, 1989-91; exec. dir. LAX Two Corp., L.A., 1991—. Decorated Legion of Merit, Bronze Star, Air medal. Mem. Airlift Assn., Daedalians, Jolly Green Pilots Assn. Avocations: tennis, sailing. Office: LAX Two Corp 200 World Way Los Angeles CA 90045-5859

MALLARD, STEPHEN ANTHONY, retired utility company executive; b. Jersey City, Sept. 15, 1924; s. Stephen F. and Gertrude V. (Donahue) M.; m. Winifred Anne Carey, June 7, 1947; children: Stephen Kevin, Catherine Anne, Eileen Rosemary Mallard McClenehan. M.E., Stevens Inst. Tech, Hoboken, N.J., 1948, M.S.E.E., 1951. With elec. distbn., system planning and devel. Pub. Service Electric and Gas Co., Newark, 1951-77, v.p. system planning, 1977-80, sr. v.p. planning and research, 1980-88, sr. v.p. transmission systems, 1989; pvt. practice engring. Nutley, N.J., 1990—; advisor Brookhave Nat. Lab.; cons. Manhattan Coll. Bd. dirs. Essex chpt. ARC, East Orange, N.J., 1985—, bd. dirs. No. N.J. chpt., 1988—; bd. dirs. Essex County Grand Jury Assn., 1978-87. With USN, 1944-46, PTO. Fellow IEEE; mem. Nat. Soc. Profl. Engrs., Conf. Internationale des Grands Reseaux Electriques a Haute Tension, Eta Kappa Nu, Tau Beta Pi. Roman Catholic. Home and Office: 68 High St Nutley NJ 07110-1134

MALLARDI, JOSEPH L., manufacturing company executive. BS, NYU. With Howmet Turbine Components Corp., Greenwich, Conn., 1954—, v.p., 1977-81, sr. v.p., 1981-85, chief operating officer, exec. v.p., 1985-87, pres., chief exec. officer, 1987—. Office: Howmet Turbine Components 475 Steamboat Rd Greenwich CT 06830-7144

MALLARDI, MICHAEL PATRICK, broadcasting company executive; b. N.Y.C., Mar. 17, 1934; s. Michael Cosmo and Gaetana M.; m. Sylvia J. Mandaliso, Aug. 19, 1961; children: Karen, Stephanie. B.Phil magna cum laude, U. Notre Dame, 1956. With ABC, Inc., 1956-61, 71—; v.p. corp. planning ABC, Inc., N.Y.C., 1971-74; pres. ABC Records and Sales Corp.,

Seattle, 1974-75, Fairfield, N.J., 1974-75; v.p.; chief fin. officer ABC, N.Y.C., 1975-83, exec. v.p., 1983-86, pres. broadcast group, 1986—, also dir.; sr. v.p. Capital Cities/ABC Inc., 1986—; location auditor Metro-Goldwyn-Mayer, Inc., L.A., 1961; bus. mgr. Radio-Press Internat., Inc., N.Y.C., 1961-65; treas. Straus Broadcasting Group, Inc., N.Y.C., 1965-69, v.p., gen. mgr., 1969-71; mem. adv. bd. Chem. Bank; trustee Pierpont Fund, Pierpont Tax Exempt Fund; bd. dirs. MS-TV, Inc. Mem. Good Samaritan Planning Bd., Suffern, N.Y.; bd. dirs. Good Samaritan Hosp., Vets. Bedside Network, Am. Women Econ. Devel., Jr. Achievement. Mem. Internat. Radio and TV Soc. Roman Catholic. Office: Capital Cities/ABC Inc 77 W 66th St # 21 New York NY 10023-6298

MALLARDI, VINCENT, organization executive; b. N.Y.C., Sept. 5, 1942; s. Dominic and Wanda Ruth (Ballard) M.; m. Susan Snyder; m. Avril Y. Stone, Dec. 27, 1986; children: Douglas M., Karen R., Kevan Stone. BBA in Mgmt., St. John's U., N.Y.C., 1971; MBA in Fin., Lehigh U., 1979. Cert. mgmt. cons. Announcer Sta. WLIR-FM, N.Y.C. 1961-67; sound-recording prodr. Audio Rec. & Mfg. Co., N.Y.C., 1961-67; pub. G. Riccordi, music, N.Y.C., 1965-67, Synectics Network Inc., news weekly, Bethlehem, Pa., 1967-72, SNI/Re:Print, Phila., 1973-84; cons. SNI/Caribbean, Miami, Fla., 1985-91; chmn. Printing Brokerage/Buyers Assn., Palm Beach, Fla., 1990—. Author over 12 books; contbg. editor Am. Printer mag., 1979—; editor-in-chief Who's Printing What Monthly, 1989—. Recipient Disting. Saicsman award Sales and Mktg. Execs. Internat. Fellow Soderstrom Soc. of Nat. Assn. Printers and Lithographers; mem. Chaine des Rotisseurs (chevalier). Republican. Episcopalian. Office: Printing Brokerage/Buyers Assn 277 Royal Poinciana Way Palm Beach FL 33480

MALLARY, ROBERT, sculptor; b. Toledo, Dec. 2, 1917; s. Benjamin E. and Laura (Grossman) M.; m. Margot Handrahan, Oct. 29, 1942; children: Michelle, Michael, Martine, Dion. Certificate, La Escuela de las Artes del Libro, Mexico D.F., 1939. mem. faculty U. N.M., 1955-59, Pratt Inst., 1959-67; prof. art U. Mass., Amherst, 1967—. Exhbt. One-man shows, San Francisco Mus. Art., 1944, one-man shows, Crocker Art Gallery, Sacramento, 1944; Calif. Exhibitors Gallery, Los Angeles, 1951, Santa Barbara Mus. Art, 1952, Gumps, San Francisco, 1953, Fine Arts Gallery San Diego, 1953, Urban Gallery, N.Y.C., 1954, Coll. Fine Arts, U. N.M., 1956, Jonson Gallery, Albuquerque, 1957-59, Santa Fe, 1958, Allan Stone Gallery, N.Y.C., 1961, 62, 66, Los Angeles Mus. Art, 1951, 53, 54, Colorado Springs Fine Art Center, 1953, Denver Art Mus., 1955, exhibited in group shows, Denver Art Mus., Sao Paulo, Brazil, 1955, 63, Mus. Modern Art, 1959, 61, 65, Gt. Jones Gallery, N.Y.C., 1959, Guggenheim Mus., 1960, Whitney Mus. Am. Art, 1960, 62, 64, 66, 68, Pace Gallery, Boston, 1960, Stable Gallery, N.Y.C., 1960, Martha Jackson Gallery, N.Y.C., 1961, Inst. Contemporary Art, Houston, 1961, 62, Am. Fedn. Art, Riverside Mus., N.Y.C., 1961, Paris, 1962, Exhbt., Seattle Worlds Fair, 1962, Carnegie Inst., 1962, Denver Mus. Fine Arts, 1962, Art Inst. Chgo., 1962, Allan Stone Gallery, 1961, 62, 66, N.Y. State Coll., Potsdam, 1969; represented in permanent collections, Mus. Modern Art, rep., Whitney Mus. Am. Art, Maremont Found., Smith Coll., Brandeis U., Womens Coll. of U. N.C., U. Tex., Kalamazoo Art Center, U. Cal. at Berkeley, Roswell (N.M.) Mus., Los Angeles Mus. Art, U. N.M., Santa Fe, Drew Coll., N.J.; commd. by, N.Y. Worlds Fair, 1963-64, collaborator (with Dale Owne), mural, Beverly Hilton Hotel, Beverly Hills, Cal., 1955; Dir.: Arstecnica: Interdisciplinary Center for Art and Tech. Guggenheim grantee, 1964-65; fellow Tamarind Workshop, 1962. Mem. Computer Arts Soc., Siggraph/ACM. Research in computer art and computer-supported studies in aesthetics; projects in art and tech.; aesthetics of surface mine reclamation; application of computer-aided design techniques to large-scale environ. sculpture and landscape design; devel. of library of art-oriented computer-graphic programs, subroutines and tutorial exercises for dedicated and time-sharing systems; creative work with computer-graphic paint and image-processing systems and research-and-development projects in computer and video stereographic projection; assemblage relief sculpture; and in stereoscopic projection, in assemblage relief sculpture, and in self-referential and self-documenting installations. Home: PO Box 605 Conway MA 01341-0605

MALLE, LOUIS, film director; b. Thumeries, France, Oct. 30, 1932; s. Pierre and Francoise (Beghin) M.; m. Anne-Marie Deschodt (div.); 2 children from previous relationships; m. Candice Bergen, Sept. 27, 1980; 1 child, Chloe. Student, Inst. d'Etudes Politiques, Paris, 1951-53, Inst. des Hautes Etudes Cinematographiques, Paris, 1953-54. Asst. to Jacques Cousteau, 1953-55; co-prodr. The Silent World, 1955 (Palme d'Or, Cannes Internat. Film Festival); tech. collaborator with Robert Bresson for Un condamne a mort s'est echappe; dir. films Ascenseur pour l'echafaud, 1957 (Prix Louis-Delluc 1958), Les Amants, 1958 (Spl. Jury prize Venice Film Festival 1968), Zazie dans le metro, 1960, Vie Privee, 1962, Le Feu Follet (Spl. Jury prize Venice Film Festival 1963), Viva Maria, 1965, La Voleur, 1966, William Wilson, 1967, Le Souffle au Coeur, 1971, Lacomb Lucien, 1973, Black Moon, 1975, Pretty Baby, 1978, Atlantic City, 1980, My Dinner with Andre, 1980, Crackers, 1984, Alamo Bay, 1985, Au Revoir Les Enfants (Directing honors Brit. Acad. Film and TV Arts), 1987, Milov En Mai, 1990, Damage, 1992, Vanya on 42nd Street, 1994; also TV short subjects India, 1970. Office: ICM Sam Cohn 40 W 57th St New York NY 10019-4001

MALLENBAUM, ALLAN ELIYAHU, marketing executive; b. Bklyn., Nov. 26, 1931; s. Arthur I. and Sophie Mallenbaum; m. Irene Bright, Nov. 16, 1953; children: Stephan J., David N., Sandra L., Cheryl D., Lisa G. B in Psychology, 1952; postgrad., Università Di Padova, Padua, Italy, 1956-60; MBA in Mktg./Internat. Commerce, Baruch Grad. Sch., 1968. Mktg. rsch. Lennon & Newell Advt., N.Y.C.; mktg. dir. Steifel Labs., Oak Hill, N.Y., Belvac Internat., L.I. City, N.Y.; adminstrv. v.p. Alliance Communication Group, N.Y.C., 1984-86; exec. v.p. Resource Network Internat., N.Y.C., 1986-88; mng. dir./founder Kensington High St. Assocs., Plainview, N.Y., 1988—; arbitrator Better Bus. Bur., N.Y.C. Founder United Zionists of the Americas, N.Y.C., Rosa Robota Found., Plainview, N.Y.; co-founder Jewish Survival Legion, N.Y.C.; pres. L.I. Genealogy Computer Soc.; v.p. L.I. Jewish Genealogy Soc. With U.S. Army, 1954-56. Mem. Jewish War Vets., Mensa. Avocations: computer science, new technologies, photography, genealogy.

MALLENDER, WILLIAM HARRY, lawyer; b. Detroit, May 21, 1935; s. Milton F. and Eleanor M. (Rainey) M.; m. Carole Miller, Aug. 8, 1964; children: W. Drew, Gregory. B.A., Yale U., 1957; L.L.B., U. Mich., 1960. Bar: Mich. 1960, N.Y. 1962, Fla. 1970. Assoc. Donovan Leisure, Newton, Irvine, N.Y.C., 1960-69; atty. Ritter & Co., Gibralter Mgmt. Co., GAC Corp., Fort Lauderdale, Fla., 1969-71; v.p., gen. counsel Talley Industries, Inc., Mesa, Ariz., 1971-78, exec. v.p., gen. counsel, sec., 1978-81, dir., 1975—; pres., chief exec. officer Talley Industries, Inc., Phoenix, 1981-83, chmn. bd., chief exec. officer, 1983—; bd. dirs. MicroAge, Inc. Bd. regents Brophy Coll. Preparatory; v.p. Internat. Heart Inst. Found., Phoenix, 1983; bd. dirs. Ariz. Zool. Soc., Phoenix Econ. Growth. Corp., Combined Phoenix Arts and Scis., Phoenix Art Mus.; bd. dirs., pres. Ariz. Mus. for Youth Friends. Mem. ABA, Mich. State Bar, Fla. State Bar, N.Y. State Bar. Office: Talley Industries Inc 2800 N 44th St Phoenix AZ 85008-1500

MALLER, ROBERT RUSSELL, certified management consultant, banker; b. N.Y.C., July 4, 1928; s. Louis and Lucille (Haberman) M.; m. Lois Fischel, June 12, 1951; children: Caryn J., Jay S. BS, U. Coll., NYU, 1950; MBA, NYU, 1957. Cert. mgmt. cons. With U.S. Trust Co. of N.Y., 1956-72, municipal analyst, asst. sec., 1958-61, asst. v.p., 1961-65, v.p., 1965-69, sr. municipal officer, 1959-69, sr. v.p. computer adminstrn., 1969-72; sr. v.p. consumer banking services and ops. Central Savs. Bank, N.Y.C., 1972-74; exec. v.p. Central Savs. Bank, 1974-77; pres. CenBan Mgmt. Services, 1976-77, Mgmt. by Design, Assocs., Inc., 1977-93; sr. v.p., chief oper. officer Washington Fed. Savs. & Loan Assn., 1979-82; mng. dir. Bank Profit Cons. Group, 1986-89; cons. Mgmt. Asset Rev. Corp., 1991—; mem. con. consumer credit, com. bank ops. Savs. Bank Assn. N.Y. State, 1972-77; lectr. banking and finance Hofstra U., 1957-59, asst. prof. fin. 1987-90. Author: Financing Public Education, 1959, A System for a Certificateless Society, 1971, Improving Efficiency Via Policy and Procedures Manuals, 1987. Bd. govs. Municipal Forum of N.Y. 1964-70, v.p. 1967-68, pres. 1968-69; alt. instl. investor adv. com. SEC, 1969-70; pres. Huntington (N.Y.) Union Free Sch. Dist. Bd. Edn., 1966-70, trustee, 1965-70; mem. exec. com. Nassau-Suffolk Sch. Bds. Assn., 1967-69. Served with AUS, 1950-52. Mem. Soc.

Mcpl. Analysts, Mcpl. Analysts Group, Nat. Assn. Mut. Savs. Banks (internal ops. com. 1972-77), Inst. Mgmt. Cons., Zeta Beta Tau. Home and Office: 3 Whitman Ridge Dr Melville NY 11747-1048

MALLERY, ANNE LOUISE, elementary educator, consultant; b. Myersdale, Pa., June 14, 1934; d. Samuel Addison and Ruth Elizabeth (Meehan) M.; m. Richard Gwen Jones, Mar. 9, 1953 (div. 1974); children: Valerie Anne, Joseph Samuel, Richard Alan (dec.). BS in Edn., Calif. U., Pa., 1970, MEd, 1972; EdD, Pa. State U., 1980. From proficiency coord. to prof. elem. edn. Millersville (Pa.) U., 1980—; asst. to pres. for planning MobileVision Tech., Inc., Key Biscayne, Fla., 1990—; assoc. editor Innovative Learning Strategy, Nat. Publ., 1989—; cons. Pequea Valley High Sch., Lancaster, Pa., 1985, Cambridge Adult Edn. Co., 1987, Conawago Elem. Sch., York, Pa., 1991, East Brunswick Pub. Schs., 1995; co-dir. NEH grant, 1993-94. Co-author The Secret Cave Multimodal Reading Program; contbr. numerous articles to profl. jours. Judge Intelligencer Reg. Spelling Bee, Lancaster, 1990,91. Mem. Assn. Pa. State Coll. and U. Faculty, Internat. Reading Assn., Lancaster Lebanon Reading Assn., Assn. Tchr. Educators, Am. Assn. Colls. Tchr. Edn., Am. Reading Forum. Republican. Presbyterian. Avocations: swimming, walking, reading, films. Home: 24 Strawberry Ln Lancaster PA 17602-1639 Office: Millersville Univ Stayer Education Ctr Millersville PA 17551

MALLERY, RICHARD K., lawyer; b. Akron, Ohio, June 7, 1937; s. William Harrison and Elizabeth Mae (Whitmer) M.; m. Frances Ann Kohfeldt, June 7, 1964; children: Kathleen Ann, Craig Taylor, David Whitmer, Patricia Lynn. B.A., DePauw U., 1959; M.A. (Woodrow Wilson fellow), Cornell U., 1960; J.D., Stanford U., 1963. Bar: Ariz. 1964. Law clk. to chief justice Ariz. Supreme Ct., 1963-64; with Snell & Wilmer, Phoenix, 1964-69, ptnr., 1969—, mem. exec. com., 1981—; spl. counsel to appropriations com. Ariz. Ho. of Reps., 1967-68; lectr. law U. Ariz., 1969-71; gen. counsel, dir., mem. exec. com. Southwest Savs. & Loan Assn., 1972-76; lectr. real estate trans. Ariz. State U., 1976-79. Chmn. exec. com. bd. visitors Law Sch., Stanford U., 1987-89; internat. v.p., chmn. U.S. com. Pacific Basin Econ. Council, 1988-91; founding v.p. Combined Met. Phoenix Arts Assn., 1966-77, chmn. adv. bd., 1977-79; pres., bd. dirs. men's arts council Phoenix Art Mus., 1969-70; chmn. charter govt. com. City of Phoenix, 1973, chmn. environ. quality commn., 1971-73; mem. Ariz. Council on Humanities and Pub. Policy, 1977-78; bd. dirs., chmn. exec. com. Ariz. Tomorrow, Inc., 1977-82; founding pres. Herberger Theater Ctr. of City of Phoenix 1984-90; trusteeships Heard Mus. Indian Art and Anthropology, 1971-78, Phoenix Country Day Sch., 1972-76, DePauw U., 1977-85, Hudson Inst., 1979-83, Nat. Symphony Orch., 1979-83, Ariz. Parklands Found., 1985-89; founding sec., treas., dir. Valley Leadership, 1980-83. Am. Field Service Internat. scholar Germany, 1954; Fulbright scholar Eng., 1960. Mem. ABA, Ariz. Bar Assn., Maricopa County Bar Assn., Ariz. Acad., Coun. Fgn. Rels.; Paradise Valley Country Club, Sigma Chi. Democrat. Methodist. Home: 2201 E Georgia Ave Phoenix AZ 85016-3512 Office: Snell & Wilmer 1 Arizona Ctr Phoenix AZ 85004

MALLETT, CONRAD LEROY, JR., state supreme court justice; b. Detroit, Oct. 12, 1953; s. Conrad LeRoy and Claudia Gwendolyn (Jones) M.; m. Barbara Straughn, Dec. 22, 1984; children: Alex Conrad, Mio Thomas, Kristan Claudia. BA, UCLA, 1975; MPA, U. So. Calif., 1979, JD, 1979. Bar: Mich. 1979. Legal asst. to congressman Detroit, 1979-80; dep. pol. div. Dem. Nat. Com., Washington, 1980-81; assoc. Miller, Canfield, Paddock & Stone, Detroit, 1981-82; legal counsel, dir. to gov. State of Mich., Lansing, 1983-84; sr. exec. asst. to Mayor City of Detroit, 1985-86; ptnr. Jaffe, Raitt, Heuer & Weiss, Detroit, 1987-90; justice Mich. Supreme Ct., Lansing, 1990—. Mem. NAACP, Kappa Alpha Psi. Democrat. Roman Catholic. Avocations: writing, fiction. Office: Supreme Ct Office 500 Woodward Ave 20th Fl Detroit MI 48226

MALLETT, HELENE GETTLER, elementary education educator; b. Goshen, N.Y., Aug. 20, 1937; d. John and Anna Gettler; m. Richard David Mallett, July 29, 1967; 1 child, Anna Alma. BS in Fgn. Svc., Georgetown U., 1959; MA, SUNY, Stonybrook, 1989. Supr. Fulbright Program/Europe Inst. Internat. Edn., N.Y.C., 1961-65; editor Am. Assn. Fund Raising Coun., N.Y.C., 1965-67; coord. adult GED/ESL programs BOCES 3, Deer Park, N.Y., 1973-85; tchr. UFSD #3 and UFSD #4, Huntington, N.Y., 1967—; trustee Eastwood Sch., Oyster Bay, N.Y., 1977-83; alumni interviewer, Georgetown U., Washington, 1989—. Mem. AACD, Nat. Coun. for the Social Studies, N.Y. State United Tchrs. (com. 100). Avocations: travel, Angora rabbits, diplomatic history, robots, geography. Home: 79 Little Neck Rd Centerport NY 11721-1615

MALLETTE, MALCOLM FRANCIS, newspaper editor, educator; b. Syracuse, N.Y., Jan. 30, 1922; s. Ralph Joseph and Hermia Ruth (Barry) M.; m. Eleanor Christine Ingram, Sept. 21, 1946; children: Gary, Bruce, David. BS magna cum laude, Syracuse U., 1947. Profl. baseball pitcher Norfolk, Va., Newark, Kansas City, Memphis, Sacramento, Bklyn., Montreal, 1946-52; sports reporter Asheville (N.C.) Times, 1951-54; sports editor Asheville Citizen, 1954-56; sports dir. Winston-Salem (N.C.) Jour. & Sentinel, 1956-59; mng. editor Winston-Salem Jour., 1959-66; assoc. dir. Am. Press Inst., Reston, Va., 1966-69; mng. dir. Am. Press Inst., 1969-75, sec., dir., 1975-79, dir. devel., 1979-87; dir. projects World Press Freedom Com., 1987—; guest lectr. Grad. Sch. Journalism, Columbia, 1969-71, Am. Press Inst., Columbia, 1961-66, U. N.C. Sch. Journalism, 1964; Def. Info. Sch. Ft. Benjamin Harrison, Ind., 1987. Author (with others), editor: Handbook for Journalists of Central and Eastern Europe, 1990, transl. to Polish, Czechoslovakian, Hungarian, Romanian, Bulgarian, Albanian, Russian; author (Seminar) The Story of the American Press Institute, 1992; contbr. articles to various mags. Served to capt. Signal Corps, AC AUS, 1943-46. Mem. AP Mng. Editors Assn. (dir. 1961-66, regent 1976—), AP News Coun. (pres. N.C. 1964), Assn. Profl. Baseball Players (life). Baptist. Club: Rotarian. Home: 2419 Silver Fox Ln Reston VA 22091-2628

MALLETTE, PHYLLIS COOPER SPENCER, medical/surgical nurse; b. Chestertown, Md., Nov. 18, 1944; d. Charles P. and Elma (Brown) Spencer; children: Winsor A. Cooper, III and Elma Cooper Henderson; m. Arthur E. Mallette, June 5, 1982. ASN, Rutgers U., 1965; BSN cum laude, Trenton State Coll., 1978. Cert. critical care, IV therapy, acute respiratory care, OSHA regulations, advanced coronary care, med. office mgmt., case mgmt., utilization rev.; RN, Md., N.J., Pa. Nurse delivery room St. Francis Med. Ctr., Trenton, N.J., 1971-73; nurse ICU Delaware Valley Med. Ctr., Langhorne, Pa., 1973-74; coord. nights Robert Wood Johnson U. Hosp., New Brunswick, N.J., 1974-75; occupational health RN Warner-Lambert/Parke-Davis Co., Morris Plains, N.J., 1977-79; sr. profl. rep. hosp., coord. sales tng. Merck Human Health Svcs. Divsn., Phila., 1979-89; co-coord. 400 trainee field force expansion Merck Sharp & Dohme, Denver, 1989; clin. nurse Johns Hopkins Hosp., Balt., 1989-90; office mgr. Arthur E. Mallette, M.D., Pikesville, Md., 1990-94; quality mgmt. specialist Healthwise of Am., Chesapeake Health Plan, Balt., 1994—; med. cons. N.J. Pub. TV, Trenton, 1974. Mem. Sigma Theta Tau. Democrat. Methodist. Avocations: computer, career coaching youth, mystery and adventure novels. Home: 1 Pomona E Apt 102 Pikesville MD 21208-2853 Office: Chesapeake Health Plan 814 Light St Baltimore MD 21230

MALLEY, JAMES HENRY MICHAEL, industrial engineer; b. Providence, Oct. 15, 1940; s. Leo Henry and Gladys Elizabeth (Canning) M.; children: James Michael, Julie Michele; m. Joyce Sue Marie Greenwell, Aug. 28, 1993. BS in Engring., U.S. Mil. Acad., 1962; MS in Indsl. Engring., U. R.I., 1977. Commd. U.S. Army, 1962-84, advanced through grades to lt. col., ret., 1984; milt. advisor U.S. Army, Rep. of Vietnam, 1964-65; co. comdr. Army Tng. Ctr., Ft. Benning, Ga., 1965-67; ops. and exec. officer First Air Cavalry Div., Vietnam, 1968-69; asst. prof. U. R.I., Kingston, 1969-73; asst. inspector gen. U.S. Army Criminal Investigation Command, Washington, 1973-76; ops. rsch. analyst and study dir. U.S. Army Concepts Analysis Agy., Bethesda, Md., 1977-80; dir. tng. U.S. 7th Army Combined Arms Tng. Ctr., Vilseck, Ger., 1980-81; chief of ops. rsch. and sys. analysis U.S. Army Europe, Heidelberg, Ger., 1981-84; mgr. engring. svcs. Orion Internat. Tech., Inc., Albuquerque, 1985-90; temp. recall, Ops. Desert Shield/Desert Storm U.S. Army, 1991; army after action report integrator ODCSOPS-HQDA, Washington, 1991; prin. analyst Gen. Rsch. Corp., Washington, 1992—; ops. rsch. and analysis exec. Lockheed-Sanders, Merrimack, N.H., 1992—; mgmt. advisor to pres. PC Support, Inc., Albu-

querque, 1986—; presenter numerous symposia, U.S. and Europe. Decorated Silver Stars (2), Legion of Merit, Bronze Stars (3), Air medals (4), Purple Heart, Vietnamese Cross of Gallantry with Gold Star (1) with Palm (2). Mem. Ops. Rsch. Soc. Am., Assn. of U.S. Army, U.S. Naval Inst., Am. Def. Preparedness Assn., Internat. Test & Evaluation Assn. Avocations: volksmarching, kayaking, skiing, rafting, mathematics. Home: PO Box 746 Merrimack NH 03054-0746

MALLEY, KENNETH CORNELIUS, military officer; b. Newark, Dec. 12, 1934; s. Raymond Cornelius and Catherine Mary (Pisarcik) M.; m. Catherine Margaret Potter, June 8, 1958; children: William B., Paul K. BS in Naval Sci., U.S. Naval Acad., 1957; MSEE, Naval Postgrad. Sch., 1963. Commd. ensign USN, 1957, advanced through grades to vice adm., 1991; gunnery officer USS Borden USN, Norfolk, Va., 1957-59, staff ops. officer Destroyer Div. 322, 1959-60; weapons officer USS Farragut USN, Mayport, Fla., 1963-64; proj. officer Bur. Naval Ordnance USN, Washington, D.C., 1964-67; head engring. sect. strategic systems program USN, Washington, 1970-75, head missile br., 1971-80, tech. dir., 1980-85, dir., 1985-91, comdr. naval sea system command, 1991-94; pres. Malley Assocs., 1994-95; v.p. ARINC Inc., Annapolis, Md., 1995—; support dir. naval ordnance sta. USN, Indian Head, Md., 1975-76; head missile br. naval plan rep. office USN, Sunnyvale, Calif., head. engring div., 1969-70. Vol. speaker Chesapeake Bay Found., Annapolis, 1987, 89, 90, 91. Decorated DSM, Legion of Merit with oak leaf cluster, Meritorious Svc. medal, Navy Achievement medal. Mem. Am. Soc. Naval Engrs. (Gold medal 1986), U.S. Naval Inst., Naval Submarine League. Republican. Roman Catholic. Avocations: duck carving, boating. Home: 136 Riverside Rd Edgewater MD 21037-1405

MALLEY, ROBERT JOSEPH, manufacturing company executive; b. Nashwauk, Minn., July 17, 1923; s. Joseph Cyril and Eva May (Troumbly) M.; m. Betty Josephine Gregg, Aug. 10, 1957; children: Robert, Gregg Philip, Elizabeth Lee, Kelly Lynn, Kenneth John. B.S. in Mil. Engring., U.S. Mil. Acad., 1946; M.S. in Civil Engring. U. Minn., 1953. Commd. U.S. Army, 1946, advanced through grades to maj. gen., 1975; assignments in airborne and engring. units, 1946-56; instr. physics U.S. Mil. Acad., West Point, N.Y., 1956-59; with program div. SHAPE Paris, 1960-63; bn. comdr. engring. bn. 1st cav. div. Ft. Benning, Ga. and Vietnam, 1963-66; dist. engr. Los Angeles, 1969-71; with Americal div., 1971-72; project mgr. production base modernization Picatinny Arsenal, N.J., 1973-76; dir. combat support systems Dept. Army, Washington, 1976-78; ret., 1978; v.p. internat. ops. Chamberlain Mfg. Corp., Arlington, Va., 1978-91; v.p. mktg. Nuclear Metals Inc., Concord, Mass., 1991—. Decorated D.S.M., Legion of Merit with 3 oak leaf clusters, Bronze Star, Air Medal with 5 oak leaf clusters. Fellow Soc. Am. Mil. Engrs. (Wheeler award 1965); mem. Am. Def. Preparedness Assn. Roman Catholic. Clubs: Army-Navy Country, K.C. Home: 1122 Ormond Ct Mc Lean VA 22101-2960 Office: 1200 N Nash St Apt 218 Arlington VA 22209-3613

MALLEY, WILLIAM, production designer. Prodn. designer: (films) Prime Cut, 1972, The Exorcist, 1973 (Academy award nomination best art direction 1973), Huckleberry Finn, 1973, Alex & Gypsy, 1976, Citizen's Band, Handle with Care, 1977, The Fury, 1978, (with Dennis Washington) The Ninth Configuration, 1980, Defiance, 1980, Mommie Dearest, 1981, The Star Chamber, 1983, Deal of the Century, 1983, The House of God, 1984, Protocol, 1984, Uforia, 1985, Vision Quest, 1985, Walk Like a Man, 1987, Big Shots, 1987, (with Alan Locke) Dr. Giggles, 1992, (TV movies) The Great Ice Rip-Off, 1974, Pray for the Wildcats, 1974, The Red Badge of Courage, 1974, Griffin and Phoenix, 1976, World War III, 1982, Something About Amelia, 1984, Margaret Bourke-White, 1989, Common Ground, 1990, Dark Avenger, 1990, The Whereabouts of Jenny, 1991, (TV episodes) Alfred Hitchcock Presents, 1986. Office: Smith/Gosnell/Nicholson & Assoc PO Box 1166 1515 Palisades Dr Pacific Palisades CA 90272*

MALLIK, ARJUN, biomedical chemist; b. Karnataka, India, Apr. 6, 1932; came to U.S., 1968; s. Ramaswami P. and Kamala (Iyer) Ayyar; m. Saroja Natarajan, Apr. 10, 1968; 1 child, Kamala. MS in Chemistry, Bombay U., 1955; MS, Indian Inst. of Sci., Bangalore, 1956. Scientist Rubber Rsch. Inst., Kuala Lumpur, Malaya, 1955-57; dir. Ramaswami Ayyar Rsch. Labs., Bangalore, 1958-68; dir., biochemist Reprod. Lab. Ob.-Gyn. Dept. Meth. Hosp., Bklyn., 1968-74; tech. dir. Ashwini Basic Chems. and Drugs (Pvt.) Ltd., Peenya, India, 1975-79; rsch. and devel. dir. Ingeborg Labs., Merrick, N.Y., 1979-80; project mgr. rsch. and devel. Fisher Sci. Co., Fairlawn, N.J., 1980-87; administr. Mallik Med. Practice, Wayne, N.J., 1987—; pres. Arjun Consultancy & Publishing, Inc., Wayne, N.J., 1993—; bd. dirs., chmn. Ashwini Basic Chems. and Drug Pvt. Ltd., Peenya, Bangalore, 1975-79. Contbr. over 30 articles to profl. jours. Pres. Bharathi Soc. of N.Am., N.Y.C., 1972-73; chmn. Hindu Temple Pooja Com., N.Y.C., 1972-75; trustee Carnatic Music Assn. N.Am., N.Y.C., 1989—. Recipient Best Rsch. gold medal Indian Inst. Sci., Bangalore, 1955, Inventor Bronze medal Allied Corp., Morristown, N.J., 1985. Mem. Am. Chem. Soc., Am. Assn. for N.Y. Acad. Scis., Biol. Stain Commn. Hindu. Achievements include patents for new liquid scintillation cocktails for biological and HPLC samples and new biological stains solutions. Office: Mallik Med Practice 2025 Hamburg Tpke Ste K Wayne NJ 07470-6250 also: Arjun Consultancy & Pub PO Box 4314 Wayne NJ 07474-4314

MALLINCKRODT, GEORGE W., bank executive; b. Eichholz, Germany, Aug. 19, 1930; s. Arnold Wilhelm and Valentine (von Joest) von M.; m. Charmaine Brenda Schroder, July 31, 1958; children: Claire, Philip, Edward, Sophie. Student, various bus. schs.; DCL (hon.), Bishops U., Lennoxville, Can., 1994. With AGFA A.G., Munich, 1948-51, Munchmeyer and Co., Hamburg, 1951-53, Kleinwort Sons and Co., London, 1953-54, J. Henry Schroder Banking Corp., N.Y.C., 1954-55, 57-60, Union Bank Switzerland, 1956; with J. Henry Schroder & Co. Ltd., London, 1960—, also bd. dirs.; chmn. Schroders PLC, London, 1984-95, pres., 1995—; chmn. bd. dirs. J. Henry Schroder Bank A.G., Zurich; chmn. Schroders Inc., N.Y.C.; bd. dirs. Schroders Australia Ltd., Sydney, 1984—, Schroder Wertheim and Co. Inc., N.Y.C., 1986—; chmn. Schroders Ltd., Bermuda, 1991-95; bd. dirs. Euris S.A., Paris, Siemens plc., London, Schroder Internat. Mcht. Bankers Ltd., Singapore, Fgn. and Colonial German Investment Trust plc.; mem. Brit. N.Am. com., 1988—; trustee Kurt Hahn Trust, 1991—. Pres. German Brit. C. of C., London, 1992-95; trustee Prague Heritage Found., London, 1992—; mem. CBI City Adv. Group, London; mem. Brit. Mus. Devel. Trust, 1995—; Nat. Art Collection Devel. Coun., 1995—. Recipient Verdienstkreuz Am. Bande Des Verdienstordens Der Bundesrepublik Deutschland, 1986, Verdienstkreuz 1 Klasse Verdienstordens, 1990. Fellow Royal Soc. Arts; mem. Inst. Mgmt. (companion 1986—). Office: Schroders PLC, 120 Cheapside, London EC2V 6DS, England also: Schroders Inc 787 7th Ave New York NY 10019

MALLO-GARRIDO, JOSEPHINE ANN, advertising agency owner; b. Agana, Guam, Mar. 20, 1955; d. Benjamin Corneja and Salvacion (Lacuesta) Mallo; m. John Marco Haniu Garrido, Feb. 16, 1980; children: Josiah Michael, Jordan Thaddeus. Student, U. Guam, Agana, 1972-74; BA in Journalism, Seattle U., 1976; MBA, Pepperdine U., 1982. Reporter Pacific Daily News, Agana, 1976, features editor, 1977-78, asst. city editor, 1978-79; copy editor features Honolulu Star-Bull., 1979-81; advt. copywriter Advt. Factors, Honolulu, 1981-83; communications specialist Liberty House, Honolulu, 1983-84; editor, advt. copywriter Safeway Stores Inc., Oakland, Calif., 1984-88; features writer Tracy (Calif.) Press, 1988-91; mktg. mgr. ComputerLand of Guam, Maite, 1992-93; mktg. officer Citibank, Agana, 1993-94; owner JMG Advt., 1994—; newspaper graphics cons. Pacific Daily News, 1984. Editor/writer Foods Unltd., 1984-88, Tracy Community Hosp. Health Beat and Update, 1988-91; editor Pacific Voice, 1977-78; contbr. articles to profl. jours. Vol. Engaged Encounter, Honolulu, 19890, Trans-Pacific Yacht Race, Honolulu, 1983, United Way, Oakland, 1986; organist St. Patrick's Ch., Honolulu, 1980-84; advt. coord. Easter Seals, Oakland, 1987; advt. bd. mem. Cath. Social Svcs., Agana, Guam, 1993—. Recipient Cert. Achievement award Advt. Age Mag., 1985, Cert Appreciation award Am. Heart Food Festival, 1985, Best in the West award Am. Advt. Fedn., 1986, Retail Nutrition award Nat. Potato Promotion Bd., 1986, Spl. Achievement award Newspaper Spl. Sect. Mother's Day/Father's Day Coun., 1989, 90, Best Feature Story 2d place Calif. Newspaper Pubs. Assn., 1989, 1st place Classified Advt. Assn., 1989, 1st place appetizer Spam Food Festival, 1991. Mem. Guam C. of C. (chair 1993—, media coord. 1993—), Citiclub (exec. sec. 1994-95). Roman Catholic. Avocations: piano, travel.

MALLON, DAVID JOSEPH, JR., lawyer; b. Newark, N.J., Sept. 1, 1946; s. David J. and Elinor (Atkinson) M.; m. Nancy Sue McKee, Apr. 26, 1969; children: David III, Andrew, Michael, Daniel. BA, Cornell U., 1968; JD, Ind. U., 1975. Bar: Ind. 1975, U.S. Dist. Ct. (so. dist.) Ind. 1975, U.S. Dist. Ct. (no. dist.) Ind. 1990, U.S. Dist. Ct. (we. dist.) Mich. 1991, U.S. Cir. Ct. (7th cir.) 1993. Ptnr. Ice Miller Donadio & Ryan, Indpls., 1975—. Lt. USN, 1968-72. Office: Ice Miller Donadio & Ryan 1 Am Square Box 82001 Indianapolis IN 46282

MALLON, MEG, professional golfer. Winner Women's U.S. Open, 1991; 4th ranked woman LPGA Tour, 1992; 2nd major LPGA championship 1991; winner 6 LPGA titles. Office: care LPGA 2570 Volusia Ave Ste B Daytona Beach FL 32114-7103

MALLON, PETER, bishop; b. Prince Rupert, B.C., Dec. 5, 1929; s. Joseph P. and Sheila M. (Keenan) D. Grad., Seminary Christ the King, Burnaby and Mission, B.C. Asst. Holy Rosary Cath., Vancouver, B.C., 1956-64, rector, 1966-82; chancellor Archdiocese Vancouver, 1964-65, dir. religious edn., 1971-73; administr. Guardian Angels Parish, Vancouver, 1965-66; pastor St. Anthony's, West Vancouver, 1982-89; bishop Nelson, B.C., 1989—. Address: 813 Ward St, Nelson, BC Canada V1L 1T4

MALLORY, ARTHUR LEE, university dean, retired state official; b. Springfield, Mo., Dec. 26, 1932; s. Dillard A. and Ferrell (Claxton) M.; m. Joann Peters, June 6, 1954; children: Dennis Arthur (dec.), Christopher Lee, Stephanie Ann, Jennifer Lyn. B.S., S.W. Mo. State Coll., 1954; M.Ed., U. Mo., 1957, Ed.D., 1959; H.H.D., S.W. Bapt. Coll., Mo., 1972. History supr. U. Mo. Lab. Sch., Columbia, 1956-57; asst. to supt. schs. Columbia, 1957-59; asst. supt. schs. Parkway Sch. Dist., St. Louis County, Mo., 1959-64; dean evening div. U. Mo., St. Louis, 1964; pres. S.W. Mo. State U., Springfield, 1964-70, dean Coll. Edn., 1991-94; commr. edn. Mo. Dept. Edn., Jefferson City, 1971-87; dir. Internat. House, U. Mo., Columbia, 1956-59. V.p. Ozarks council Boy Scouts Am., 1967, pres. Gt. Rivers council, 1972-73, Greene County Assn. for Retarded Citizens, 1989—, pres., 1991—; mem. north central region exec. bd., 1984—; bd. dirs. Meml. Community Hosp.; Bd. dirs. Mid-Continent Regional Ednl. Lab., Ozark Pub. Telecoms. Inc., 1989—; chmn. bd. Mo. Council on Econ. Edn.; bd. regents Mo. State Univs.; trustee Pub. Sch. Retirement, William Jewell Coll., 1974-74; chmn. com. bds. So. Bapt. Conv., 1972-73, mem. com. or bds., 1981—; mem. exec. bd. Mo. Bapt. Conv., 1972-75, 77-80; Young Audiences, Inc. adv. com., 1986, ARC Bd., Greene County, 1986, Children's Services Commn., Chmn., 1986—, Edn. Commn. of U.S.; bd. dir. Ozark Pub. TV. Served with U.S. Army, 1954-56. Recipient Disting. Service award Mo. Jr. C. of C., 1966; Distinguished Service award U. Mo., 1976; Faculty/Alumni award U. Mo., 1976; Silver Beaver award Boy Scouts Am., 1983, Good Shepherd and Cross, 1986, Disting. Citizen award, 1986; hon. life mem. Mo. Congress Parents and Tchrs.; named Springfield's Outstanding Young Man of Yr., 1965; Champion of Excellence PUSH, 1978. Mem. Am. Assn. State Colls. and Univs., N. Central Assn. Colls. and Secondary Schs., Council Chief State Sch. Officers, Mo. Assn. Sch. Adminstrs., NEA, Mo. Tchrs. Assn. So. Baptist (deacon). Clubs: Masons (33 deg.), Rotary.

MALLORY, CHARLES KING, III, lawyer; b. Norfolk, Va., Nov. 16, 1936; s. Charles King Mallory Jr. and Dorothy Pratt (Williams) Swanke; m. Florence Beale Marshall; children: King, Raburn, Anne, Richard. BA, Yale U., 1958; JD, Tulane U., 1961. Bar: La. 1961, Calif. 1965, D.C. 1972. Ptnr. Monroe & Lemann, New Orleans, 1965-72; acting exec. dir. SEC, Washington, 1972; dep. asst. sec. U.S. Dept. Interior, Washington, 1973, acting asst. sec., 1974; v.p., gen. counsel Middle South Svcs., Inc., New Orleans, 1975-79; ptnr. Hunton & Williams, Washington, 1979—. Mem. Reagan-Bush Transition Team, Washington, 1980-81, Grace Commn. on Pvt. Sector Survey Cost in the Fed. Govt., Washington, 1983-84. Served to lt. USNR, 1961-65. Mem. ABA, La. Bar Assn., Calif. Bar Assn., D.C. Bar Assn., Fed. Energy Bar Assn., Nat. Assn. Bond Lawyers. Republican. Episcopalian. Office: Hunton & Williams 2000 Pennsylvania Ave NW PO Box 19230 Washington DC 20036

MALLORY, FRANK BRYANT, chemistry educator; b. Omaha, Mar. 17, 1933; s. Deane Havercroft and Helen (Bryant) M.; m. Patricia Ann Livingston, June 30, 1951; children—Mary Susan, Paul Deane, Philip Howard (dec.), Michele; m. Clelia Sara Wood, Nov. 26, 1965. B.S., Yale U., 1954; Ph.D., Calif. Inst. Tech., 1958. Asst. prof. Bryn Mawr (Pa.) Coll., 1957-63, assoc. prof., 1963-69; prof. chemistry Bryn Mawr Coll. (Pa.), 1969—, W. Alton Jones prof. chemistry, 1985—, chmn. dept., 1982-92; acad. dep. to pres. Bryn Mawr (Pa.) Coll., 1978-81; vis. assoc. Calif. Inst. Tech., 1963-64; vis. prof. Yale, 1968, 78-79, lectr., 1977-78; vis. prof. SUNY-Albany, summer 1967; vis. fellow Cornell U., 1970-71; vis. prof. U. Pa., 1988-89. Mem. adv. bd. Jour. Organic Chemistry, 1988-93; contbr. articles to profl. jours. Mem. sci. and arts com. Franklin Inst., Phila. Recipient Bond award Am. Oil Chemists Soc., 1970, Lindback award for disting. tchg., 1992; John Simon Guggenheim fellow, 1963-64, Alfred P. Sloan rsch. fellow, 1964-68, NSF sr. postdoctoral fellow, 1970-71. Mem. Am. Chem. Soc. (exec. com. of organic divsn. 1986-95, symposium officer 1989-95, award Phila. sect. 1989), Phila. Organic Chemists Club (past sec., chmn.). Home: 321 Caversham Rd Bryn Mawr PA 19010-2927 Office: Bryn Mawr Coll Dept Chemistry Bryn Mawr PA 19010

MALLORY, FRANK LINUS, lawyer; b. Calgary, Alta., Can., May 5, 1920; s. Frank Louis and Anna Amy (Allstrum) M.; m. Jean Ellen Lindsey, Jan. 29, 1944; children: Susan Mallory Remund, Ann, Bruce R. AB with distinction, Stanford U., 1941, LLB, 1947. Bar: Calif. 1948. Assoc. Gibson, Dunn & Crutcher, L.A., 1947-54; ptnr. L.A. and Orange County, Calif., 1955-88; cert. specialist taxation law Calif. Bd. Legal Specialization, 1973-89. Pres. Town Hall of Calif., L.A., 1970, Boys Republic, Chino, Calif., 1962-64; pres. Braille Inst. Am., L.A., 1988-92. Lt. (j.g.) USNR, 1942-46. Mem. ABA, Calif. Bar Assn., Los Angeles County Bar Assn., Orange County Bar Assn., Newport Harbor Yacht Club, Big Canyon Country Club, Transpacific Yacht Club (staff commodore). Republican. Home: 633 Bayside Dr Newport Beach CA 92660-7213

MALLORY, KENNETH W., religious organization administrator. Sec. Am. Indian Council of the Reformed Ch. in Am., N.Y.C. Office: Reformed Church in Am 475 Riverside Dr Rm 1811 New York NY 10115-0001

MALLORY, ROBERT MARK, controller, finance executive; b. Mattoon, Ill., Apr. 15, 1950; s. Robert Monroe and Betty Ann (Mudd) M.; m. Diana Marie Burde, Aug. 19, 1972; 1 child, Laura Elizabeth. BS in Accountancy, U. Ill., 1972; M Mgmt., Northwestern U., 1986. CPA, Ill. Staff acct. Price Waterhouse, Chgo., 1972-74; sr. acct., 1974-77, mgr., 1977-79; dir. internal audit Mark Controls Corp., Skokie, Ill., 1979-81; corp. contr. Mark Controls Corp., Skokie, 1981-86, v.p., contr., 1986-88; contr., dir. planning Tribune Co., Chgo., 1988-91, v.p., contr., 1991—. Mem. Am. Inst. CPA's (Elijah Watts Sells award 1972), Ill. CPA Soc., Fin. Execs. Inst., Beta Gamma Sigma. Methodist. Home: 3312 Lakewood Ct Glenview IL 60025-2505 Office: Tribune Co 435 N Michigan Ave Chicago IL 60611-4001

MALLORY, V(IRGIL) STANDISH, geologist, educator; b. Englewood, N.J., July 14, 1919; s. Virgil Sampson and Sarah Lauris (Baum) M.; m. Miriam Elizabeth Rowan, Feb. 3, 1946; children—Charles Standish, Stefan Douglas, Peter Sommers, Ingrid Lauris. A.B., Oberlin Coll., 1943; M.A., U. Calif. at Berkeley, 1948, Ph.D. (Standard Oil of Calif. fellow in paleontology), 1952. Preparator U. Calif. Museum Paleontology, Berkeley, 1946-48; curator foraminifera U. Calif. Museum Paleontology, 1948-50, cons., 1951; lectr. paleontology U. Calif. at Berkeley, 1951; asst. prof. geology U. Wash., 1952-59, asso. prof., 1959-62; prof., chmn. div. geology and paleontology, curator of paleontology Burke Meml. Wash. State Mus., 1962-84, prof. emeritus, mus. curator, 1984—; cons. in petroleum geology and mus. curation, in wines to restaurants; lectr. geology of wine; mem. Gov. of Wash. Commn. on Petroleum Regulations, 1956-57; mem. NSF Paris Basin Field Inst., Paris, Belgium and Luxembourg, 1964; co-dir. NSF Inst. Secondary Sch. Tchrs., Western Wash. State Coll., summers 1963, 65. Author: Lower Tertiary Biostratigraphy of California Coast Ranges, 1959, Lower Tertiary Foraminifera From Media Agua Creek Drainage Area, Kern County, California, 1970, Biostratigraphy—A Major Basis of Paleontologic Correlation, 1970; contbg. author: Lincoln Library Essential Knowledge, 1965, Ency. Brit., 15th edit, 1974; Editor paleontology: Quaternary Research Jour,

1970-77; Contbr. articles to profl. jours. Served with AUS, 1944-46, PTO. Am. Assn. Petroleum Geologists Revolving Fund grantee, 1957; U. Wash. Agnes Anderson Fund grantee, 1963. Fellow AAAS (council 1964—), Geologic Soc. Am.; mem. Am. Assn. Petroleum Geologists (sect. council 1964-84, com. on stratigraphic correlations 1979-85), Paleontologic Soc. (chmn. sect. 1956-58), Geol. Soc. Am., Soc. Econ. Paleontology and Mineralogy, Paleontol. Research Soc., Paleontologische Gesellschaft, Geologische Gesellschaft, Internat. Paleontological Union, N.W. Sci. Soc., Am. Assn. Museums, Mineral Mus. (adv. council 1974-87), Sigma Xi, Theta Tau. Home: 5209 Pullman Ave NE Seattle WA 98105-2139 Office: Burke Meml Wash State Mus DB10 U Wash Seattle WA 98195

MALLORY, WILLIAM BARTON, III, lawyer; b. New River, N.C., June 8, 1944; s. William B. and Marion (Lucas) M.; m. Margaret Mary Milnor; children: Barton, Bennett, Brian, Allison. BA, U. Va., 1966; JD, U. Tenn., 1969. Bar: Tenn. 1969. Assoc. Heiskell, Donelson, Adams, Williams & Wall, Memphis, 1969; gen. counsel Guardsmark Inc., N.Y.C., 1969-73; v.p., gen. counsel The Crump Cos. Inc., Memphis, 1973-86; vice chmn., gen. counsel Guardsmark Inc., Memphis, 1986-93; v.p., gen. counsel Terminix Internat., Memphis, 1994—. Mem. ABA. Club: Memphis Country.

MALLOY, EDWARD ALOYSIUS, priest, university administrator, educator; b. Washington, May 3, 1941; s. Edward Aloysius and Elizabeth (Clark) M. BA, U. Notre Dame, 1963, MA, 1967, ThM, 1969; PhD, Vanderbilt U., 1975. Joine Congregation Holy Cross, 1963, ordained priest Roman Cath. Ch., 1970. Instr. U. Notre Dame, Ind., 1974-75, asst. prof., 1975-81, assoc. prof., 1981-88, prof. theology, 1988—, assoc. provost, 1982-86, pres. elect, 1986, pres., 1987—; bd. regents U. Portland, Oreg., 1985—. Author: Homosexuality and the Christian Way of Life, 1981, The Ethics of Law Enforcement and Criminal Punishment, 1982, Culture and Commitment: The Challenge of Today's University, 1992; contbr. articles to profl. jours. Chmn. Am. Coun. on Edn.; bd. dirs. NCAA Found., 1989—; mem. Bishops and Pres.' com. Assn. Cath. Colls. and Univs., 1988—; bd. dirs. Internat. Fedn. Cath. Univs., 1988—; mem. Pres.'s Adv. Coun. on Drugs, 1989—; mem. adv. bd. AmeriCorps and Nat. Civilian Community Corps, 1994—; interim chmn. Ind. Commn. on Community Svc., 1994—; bd. dirs. Points of Light, Campus Compact. Mem. Cath. Theol. Soc., Am. Soc. Christian Ethics, Bus. Higher Edn. Forum, The Conf. Bd. Office: U Notre Dame Office Pres Notre Dame IN 46556

MALLOY, JAMES MATTHEW, managed care executive, health care consultant; b. N.Y.C., Aug. 26, 1939; s. Peter Joseph and Catherine (Cunningham) M.; m. Joan Elizabeth Wagner, Sept. 9, 1967; children—Stephen, Christopher. B.S., Manhattan Coll., 1961; M.P.H., Yale U. 1967. Asst. to dir. Yale New Haven Hosp., New Haven, Conn., 1967; assoc. administr. Waterbury Hosp., Conn., 1969-75; exec. dir., CEO Jersey City Med. Ctr., N.J., 1975-77; dir., CEO U. Conn. Hosp., Farmington, 1977-82, U. Ill. Hosp. and Clinics, Chgo., 1982-87; exec. v.p. Our Lady of the Resurrection Med. Ctr., Chgo., 1988-89; pres., CEO St. Dominic Jackson Meml. Hosp., Jackson, Miss., 1989-91; sr. v.p. health affairs Miss. and La. Blue Cross/Blue Shield, Jackson, Miss., 1991-92; health care cons. Jackson, 1992-93; pres., CEO, South East Managed Care Orgn., Jackson, 1993—; cons. NIH, Bethesda, Md., 1976-84; dir. Univ. Health Consortium; chmn. Compass Health Plan, Chgo., 1983-87; dir. Hosp. Fund Inc., New Haven, Comprends Inc., Chgo.; lectr. Yale U. Sch. Medicine; adj. prof. U. Ill. Coll. Medicine, Chgo.; assoc. prof. U. Ill. Sch. Pub. Health. Contbr. articles to profl. jours. Chmn. Miss. chpt. Nat. Multiple Sclerosis Assn. Dr. Stuart Hamilton fellow Capital Area Health Consortium, 1982. Fellow Inst. Medicine Chgo., Am. Coll. Healthcare Execs.; mem. Ill. Hosp. Assn. (bd. dirs. 1984-86), Met. Chgo. Healthcare Coun., Yale Alumni Fund, Yale Club (pres. Miss. chpt.), Miss. Bus. Coalition on Health Care (bd. dirs.). Avocations: golf, jogging. Home: 177 St Andrews Dr Jackson MS 39211-2532 Office: P O Box 13844 715 S Pear Jackson MS 39236-3844

MALLOY, JOHN RICHARD, lawyer, chemical company executive; b. Boston, Nov. 26, 1932; s. Thomas Francis and Mary (Field) M.; m. Maraleta Ellerson, May 24, 1960; children: Maureen, John, Megan, Elizabeth. BA, St. John's Sem., Brighton, Mass., 1954; LLB, Boston Coll., 1957. Bar: Mass. 1957. V.p., dir. fin. Remington Arms Co., Inc., Bridgeport, Conn., 1975-78; chief counsel, energy and raw materials E. I. du Pont de Nemours and Co., Wilmington, Del., 1978-79, asst. gen. counsel legal, 1979-83, dir. pub. affairs, 1983-85, v.p. pub. affairs, 1983-85, sr. v.p external affairs, 1985-92, v.p., spl. counsel to chmn. bd., 1992-93; ret. Chmn. Jobs for Del. Grads, Wilmington, 1985—, Del. Compensation Commn., 1988—; trustee Del. Multiple Sclerosis Soc., 1980—, Med. Ctr. of Del., Christiana, 1985—, Del. Pension Fund, 1993—; bd. dirs. Del. Cmty. Found., 1989—, Children's Beach House, 1993—; mem. Minner Commn. (Del.), 1993—; chmn. Del. Coun. on Transp., 1994—. Mem. ABA, Fed. Bar Assn. Democrat. Roman Catholic. Avocations: tennis, golf, skiing. Office: Du Pont Co 1007 N Market St Wilmington DE 19898-0001

MALLOY, MICHAEL TERRENCE, retired journalist and newspaper editor; b. Chgo., Feb. 26, 1936; s. Medard Valentine and Lucille (Zehrol)M.; m. Ruth Gwendolyn Lor, June 5, 1965; children: Linda Jo, Terrence. Student, Reed Coll., 1953-54, Columbia U., 1966-67. Police reporter City News Bur. Chgo., 1956-58; reporter, then bur. chief and chief corr. S.E. Asia UPI, Japan, Laos, India, Vietnam and Thailand, 1960-66; reporter Nat. Observer, Washington, 1968-76, mng. editor, 1976-77; reporter Asian Wall St. Jour., Manila, 1977-80, mng. editor, Hong Kong, 1980-84; mng. editor Dow Jones Can., Toronto, Ont., 1984-94; ret., 1994. Author: Racing Today, 1967, The Art of Retirement, 1967. With U.S. Army, 1958-60.

MALLOY, WILLIAM MICHAEL, book editor, reviewer, writer; b. Cleve., Oct. 29, 1960; s. Leroy Joseph Francis and Betty Jayne (Kubicek) M.; m. Claire Zion, Feb. 14, 1989; 1 child, Rose Zion. BA in Lit., Yale U., 1982. Copyright mgr. G. Schirmer, Inc., N.Y.C., 1982-84; creative dir. Cloverdale Press, N.Y.C., 1985; mng. editor The Mysterious Press, N.Y.C., 1985-88; editor-in-chief The Mysterious Press/Warner Books, N.Y.C., 1988—; cons. 20th Century Crime and Mystery Writers, London, 1989—. Author: The Mystery Book of Days, 1990; contbg. editor The Armchair Detective, 1989—; contbr. critical essays to reference work. Democrat. Avocations: flute, reading, cooking. Office: The Mysterious Press/Warner 1271 Ave of the Americas New York NY 10020

MALLOZZI, COS M., public relations executive; b. Utica, N.Y., Aug. 16, 1951. BA, Syracuse U., 1973. Pub. rels. coun. and intern Congressman D. Mitchell, Washington, 1973-74; assr. pub. rels. dir., sports info. dir. Siena Coll., 1974-75; pub. rels. dir. SUNY, 1975-78; acct. supv. group mgr. Gibbs & Soell, Inc., N.Y.C., 1978-80, gen. mgr., 1980-81, exec. v.p., gen. mgr., 1981-88, pres., 1988—, CEO 1993—. Office: Gibbs & Soell Inc 600 3rd Ave New York NY 10016-2692

MALM, JAMES ROYAL, surgeon; b. Cleve., Sept. 7, 1925; s. Royal Dinsmore and Theodora (Drumont) M.; m. Constance Brooks, July 8, 1950; children—Martha, Melissa, Karen, Sarah. A.B., Princeton, 1947; M.D., Columbia, 1949. Diplomate: Am. Bd. Thoracic Surgery, Am. Bd. Surgery. Intern Pa. Hosp., Phila., 1949-51; surg. resident Presbyn. Hosp., N.Y.C., 1953-57; thoracic surg. resident Presbyn. Hosp., 1957-59, attending surgeon, 1967-90; instr. surgery Columbia, 1959-60, asst. prof., 1960-63, assoc. prof. 1963-67, prof. clin. surgery, 1967-88, prof. surgery, 1988-90, prof. surgery emeritus, 1991—. Served to lt. M.C. USNR, 1951-53. Mem. ACS, N.Y. Heart Assn. (dir.), AMA, Internat. Cardiovascular Soc., Am. Assn. Thoracic Surgery (past pres.), N.Y. Soc. Cardiovascular Surgery, N.Y. Soc. Thoracic Surgery (past pres.), Asian Thoracic and Cardiovascular Soc. (hon.), Soc. Thoracic Surgeons, Soc. U. Surgeons, Soc. Vascular Surgeons, Am. Surg. Assn. Pioneer in use of tissue valves for heart valve replacement and surgery for congenital heart disease; leader in improving the quality of thoracic training in the U.S. Home: Pilot Hill Farm PO Box 4695 Vineyard Haven MA 02568-4695 Office: Milstein Bldg 7GN-435 177 Fort Washington Ave New York NY 10032-3713

MALMAN, LAURIE L., law educator; b. 1946. BA, Vassar Coll., 1968; JD, NYU, 1971. Bar: N.Y. 1972. Assoc. Sullivan & Cromwell, N.Y.C., 1971-79; instr. NYU, 1979-80, asst. prof. 1980-83, assoc. prof. 1983-86, prof., 1986—. Office: NYU Sch Law 40 Washington Sq S New York NY 10012-1005

MALMGREN, HARALD BERNARD, economist; b. Boston, July 13, 1935; s. Berndt Birger and Magda Helena (Nilsson) M.; m Patricia A. Malmgren, 1959 (div. 1975); children: Karen Philippa, Britt Patricia, Erika Nina; m. Linda V. Einberg, Oct. 3, 1987; 1 child, Markus Harald. BA summa cum laude, Yale U., 1957; postgrad., Harvard U., 1959; doctorate in Philosophy, Oxford U., 1961. Asst. prof. dept. engring and economics Cornell U., Ithaca, N.Y., 1961-62; head, econ. group Inst. for Def. Analyses, Washington, 1962-64; asst. U.S. trade rep. Exec. Office Pres. The White House, Washington, 1964-69; sr. fellow Overseas Devel. Coun., 1969-71; ambassador, dep. U.S. trade rep., 1972-75; sr. fellow Woodrow Wilson Internat. Ctr. for Scholars, Washington, 1975-76; prof. George Washington U., Washington, 1976-77; pres. Malmgren, Inc., Washington, 1977—; mng. dir. Malmgren, Golt, Kingston, Ltd., London, 1979—, MG Comml., Budapest, 1991—; mem. adv. coun. CSIS, Washington, 1987—; adv. Senate Fin. Com., Washington, 1970-71, 75-76, Interaction Coun., 1985—. Author: International Economic Peace Keeping, 1972; co-author: Assisting Developing Countries, 1972; editor: Pacific Basin Development, 1972, The World Economy, 1980-90; bd. editors: The International Economy, 1987—, The Washington Quarterly, 1987—; contbr. articles to profl. jours. Mem. Am. Econ. Assn. Met. Club, Reform Club. Home: 7620 Cannonball Gate Rd Warrenton VA 22186 Office: Malmgren Group Ste 901 1133 Connecticut Ave NW Washington DC 20036-4305

MALMSTAD, JOHN EARL, Slavic languages and literatures, educator; b. Bismarck, N.D., June 25, 1941; s. Manley Ellsworth and Joyce Evelyn (David) M. BA summa cum laude with distinction and departmental honors in Russian Lang. and Lit., Northwestern U., 1963; MA in Slavic Langs. and Lits., Princeton U., 1965, PhD in Slavic Langs. and Lits., 1969; AM (hon.), Harvard U., 1985. Instr. Columbia U., N.Y.C., 1968-69, asst. prof. Russian Lit., 1969-73, assoc. prof., 1973-79, prof. dept. slavic langs. and lits., 1979-85; Samuel Hazzard Cross prof. Slavic langs. and lits. Harvard U., Cambridge, Mass., 1985—, assoc. dean, 1993-94; vis. assoc. prof. Stanford U., 1971-72, U. Calif. Berkeley, 1977-78; vis. prof. Harvard U., fall 1982; cons., referee NEH translation awards; lectr. in field; attendee internat. symposia. Editor (with others): The Poetry of Mikhail Kuzmin (3 vols.), 1977, The Poetry of Andrei Bely (3 vols.), 1982-85, Gibel' Senatora, 1986, Vladislav Khodasevich Sobranie sochinenii, 1983, Andrev Bely, Spirit of Symbolism, 1987, Readings in Russian Modernism to Honor Vladimir Markov, 1993; Russian book rev. editor Slavic Rev., 1975-86; assoc. editor Russian Rev., 1986-88; mem. edit. bd. Minuvshee, Feniks, Opyty, Novoe Literaturnoe obozrenie, Modern Russian Lit. and Culture; manuscript rev. profl. jours., univ. presses; contbr. articles to profl. jours. Woodrow Wilson fellow, 1963, NDFL fellow Columbia U., 1963-66, Princeton U., 1967-68, Fulbright-Hays fellow, 1966-67, spring 1981, spring 1987, Woodrow Wilson Dissertation fellow, 1966, ACLS rsch. fellow, 1972, Rsch. fellow Russian Inst. Columbia U., summer 1977, 79, 83, 84, IREX fellow, 1975, John Simon Guggenheim fellow, 1980-81; ACLS grant-in-aid, summer, 1980, IREX/ACLS grantee exch. Acad. Scis. USSR, fall 1981, spring 1987, 91, IREX travel grantee Moscow, 1992. Mem. Am. Assn. Advancement of Slavic Studies, Modern Lang. Assn., Assn. Tchrs. of Slavic and East European Langs., Institut d'Etudes Slaves (Paris), Phi Beta Kappa. Avocations: fine arts, ballet, reading. Home: 8A Cogswell Ave Cambridge MA 02140 Office: Harvard U Dept Slavic Langs/Lit 301 Bolyston Hall Cambridge MA 02138

MALMSTROM, VINCENT HERSCHEL, geography educator; b. Evanston, Ill., Mar. 6, 1926; s. Vincent O.S. and Elsa (Lofstrom) M.; m. Ruth Marie Midtskog, Dec. 22, 1951; children: Ingrid, Karin. A.B. in Geography with distinction, U. Mich., 1947, M.A. in Geography, 1948, Ph.D. in Geography, 1954; postgrad., U. Tex., 1949-50, U. Oslo, Norway, 1950-52. Geographer Army Map Service, Washington, 1948; instr. Mich. Technol. U., 1953-54; asst. prof. Bucknell U., Lewisburg, Pa., 1955-56; instr. Middlebury Coll., Vt., 1956-57, asst. prof., 1958-64, acting. chmn. dept. geography and geology, 1958-60, assoc. prof., 1965-70, prof., 1971-75; prof. geography Dartmouth Coll., Hanover, N.H., 1975—, chmn. dept., 1982-85; guest lectr. Internat. Summer Sch., U. Oslo, 1955; dir. Scandinavian area studies program U. Minn.-Duluth, summer 1958; assoc. prof. U. Vt., summer 1961, vis. asst. prof., 1959-61, vis. prof., fall 1974; asst. dir. NSF Summer Inst. in Geography, Mich. State U., summer 1965; vis. assoc. prof. Mich. State U. summer 1966; vis. critic in cartography Grad. Sch. Design, Harvard U., summer 1970; vis. prof. U. Victoria, B.C., Can., 1972; cons. in field. Mem. adv. bd.: Polar Geography, 1976-82; contbr. articles to profl. jours. Recipient numerous research grants. Mem. Assn. Am. Geographers. Office: Dept Geography Dartmouth Coll Hanover NH 03755

MALMUTH, NORMAN DAVID, program manager; b. Brooklyn, N.Y., Jan. 22, 1931; s. Jacob and Selma Malmuth; m. Constance Nelson, 1970; children: Kenneth, Jill. AE, U. Cin., 1953; MA in Aero. Engring., Polytech. Inst. of N.Y., 1956; PhD in Aeronautics, Calif. Inst. Tech., 1962. Rsch. engr. Grumman Aircraft Engring. Corp., 1953-56; preliminary design engr. N.A. Aviation Div., L.A., 1956-68; teaching asst. Calif. Inst. Tech., L.A., 1961; mem. maths. sci. group Rockwell Internat. Sci. Ctr., 1968-75, project mgr. fluid dynamics rsch., 1975-80, mgr. fluid dynamics group, 1980-82, program mgr. spl. projects, 1982—; cons. Aerojet Gen., 1986-89; lectr. UCLA, 1971-72. Referee AIAA Jour.; bd. editors Jour. Aircraft; contbr. articles to Jour. of Heat Transfer, Internat. Jour. Heat Mass Transfer, and others. Named Calif. Inst. Tech. fellow; recipient Outstanding Alumnus award Univ. Cin., 1990. Fellow AIAA (Aerodynamics award 1991); mem. Am. Acad. Mechanics, Am. Inst. Physics (fluid dynamics divsn.), Soc. Indsl. and Applied Math. Achievements include patent in Methods and Apparatus for Controlling Laser Welding; pioneering development of high aerodynamic efficiency of hypersonic delta wing body combinations, hypersonic boundary layer stability, transonic wind tunnel interference web dynamics, combined asymptotic and numerical methods in fluid dynamics and aerodynamics. Home: 182 Maple Rd Newbury Park CA 91320-4718 Office: Rockwell Sci Ctr PO Box 1085 1049 Camino Dos Rios Thousand Oaks CA 91358

MALONE, DAN F., journalist; b. Dallas, Jan. 22, 1955; s. Charles Ted and Ela Grace (Darden) M.; m. Kathryn Jones, June 27, 1981. BJ, U. Tex., 1978. Editor-in-chief The Daily Texan, Austin, Tex., 1977-78; intern Harte-Hanks Austin Bur., 1978-79; staff writer Corpus Christi (Tex.) Caller-Times, 1979-81, Ft. Worth Star-Telegram, 1981-85; staff writer Dallas Morning News, 1985—, Ft. Worth bureau chief, 1992—; Fox fellow Nat. News Coun., N.Y.C., summer 1978. Recipient Pulitzer prize for investigative reporting, 1992, 1st Place Freedom of Info. Category award Tex. AP Mng. Editor's Assn., 1992, 1st Place Investigative Reporting Inst. Southern Studies, 1992. Office: Dallas Morning News 500 Main St Ste 220 Fort Worth TX 76102-3939

MALONE, DAVID ROY, university administrator, state senator; b. Beebe, Ark., Nov. 4, 1943; s. James Roy and Ila Mae (Griffin) M.; m. Judith Kaye Huff, June 20, 1965 (div. Feb. 1990); 1 child, Michael David. BSBA, U. Ark., 1965, JD, 1969, MBA, 1982. Bar: Ark. 1969, U.S. Dist. Ct. (we. dist.) Ark. 1969, U.S. Tax Ct. 1972, U.S. Ct. Appeals (8th cir.) 1972, U.S. Supreme Ct. 1972. Pvt. practice Fayetteville, Ark., 1969-72; atty. City of Fayetteville, 1969-72; asst. prof. bus. U. Ark., Fayetteville, 1972-76, asst. dean law, 1976-91; mem. Ark. Ho. of Reps., 1980-84; Ark. State Senator, 1984—; exec. dir. U. Ark. Found., 1991—; bd. dirs. Bank of Elkins, S.W. Edn. Devel. Lab., Austin, Tex.; legal adv. coun. So. Regional Edn. Bd., Atlanta, 1991—. Contbr. articles to profl. jours.; bd. dirs. Ark. Law Rev., 1978-92; contbg. author U Ark Press, 1989. Mayor City of Fayetteville, 1979-80; mem. Jud. Article Task Force, Little Rock, 1989-91; chair Motor Voter task force, 1994-95; bd. dirs. Music Festival Ark., 1989-91, Washington County Hist. Soc., 1990—; Walton Arts Ctr. Found., 1994—; chmn. bd. dirs. Washington County Law Libr., 1974-83. Recipient Svc. award Ark. Mcpl. League, 1980, Disting. Service award U. Ark., 1988. Mem. Ark. Bar Assn. (ho. of dels. 1977-81, award of merit 1980, exec. 1981-82, Outstanding Lawyer-Citizen award 1990), Washington County Bar Assn., Ark. Inst. Continuing Legal Edn. (bd. dirs. 1979-88), Fayetteville C. of C. (bd. dirs. 1984—), Ark. Genealogy Soc. (bd. dirs. 1990—). Democrat. Methodist. Avocations: genealogy, stamp collecting. Home: 1928 Austin Dr Fayetteville AR 72703-2713 Office: PO Box 1048 Fayetteville AR 72702-1048

MALONE, DEBRA BEATRICE, elementary education educator; b. Tulsa, July 15, 1945; d. Gene Joseph Dennehy Jr. and Maureen E. (Keaton) Hagin; m. Richard Malone, Nov. 20, 1971 (div. 1976); 1 child, Richard Jr. BS in Edn., U. Tex., El Paso, 1967, postgrad., 1968-88; postgrad., Ea. N.Mex.

U., 1988-89; MEd in computers, Lesley Coll., 1995. Cert. tchr., Tex., N.Mex. Tchr. art and music El Paso Ind. Sch. Dist., 1967-72, 82-88; tchr. grades 4 & 5 Ysleta Ind. Sch. Dist., El Paso, 1976-82; tchr. 1st grade Tularosa (N.Mex.) Pub. Schs., 1988-90, Clint Ind. Sch. Dist., El Paso, 1990-91, Sorocco Ind. Sch. Dist., El Paso, 1991-93; Houghton Mifflin pilot tchr. Sorocco Ind. Sch. Dist., 1991-92, intersession coord., 1991-93, GT coordr., 1994-95, mem. textbook and lang. arts coms. 1992-93; chair whole lang. Tularosa Pub. Schs., mem cirriculum com., 1989; mem. El Paso Collaborative Tchr. Ctr. Bd., Tchr. Edn. Curriculum Coun. Mem. Internat. Reading Assn., Tex. Reading Assn., Tchrs. Applying Whole Lang., Delta Kappa Gamma (scholarship chair 1992), Kappa Kappa Iota (v.p. 1993, Nat. Scholarship award 1994, Tex. Scholarship award 1994). Methodist. Avocations: art, golf, sewing, painting. Home: 15000 Ashford St Apt 67 El Paso TX 79927-6417 Office: Sorocco Ind Sch Dist 2640 Robert Wynn St El Paso TX 79936-3380

MALONE, EDWARD H., financial executive; b. Forest Hills, N.Y., Nov. 11, 1924; s. Edward H. and Gertrude (Gibson) M.; m. Margaret A. Rakers, Sept. 8, 1951; children: Mary Malone Tilney, Edward, Patricia J. Malone Palmer, Jo-Ann Malone Huber. B.S., Columbia U., 1949; M.B.A., N.Y. U., 1950. Bank examiner Fed. Res. Bank of N.Y., N.Y.C., 1949-52; trust officer Lincoln Rochester (N.Y.) Trust Co., 1952-55; with Gen. Electric Co., 1955-86; mgr. private placement investments Gen. Electric Co., N.Y.C., 1959-61, mgr. trust portfolios, 1961-67, mgr. trust investment ops., 1967-70; v.p. Gen. Electric Co., Stamford, Conn., 1970-86; trustee Prudential Savs. Bank, 1966-77; bd. dirs. Allegheny Power System Inc., Butler Capital Corp., Corp. Property Investors, GenRe Corp., Mattel Inc., Warburg Pincus Capital, Fidelity Mutual Funds; chmn. CT Ret. Systems Investment Adv., 1985-87; mem. Pres.'s Commn. for Fin. Structure and Regulation, 1970-71; dir. Darien chpt. ARC, 1982-88. Trustee Rensselaer Poly. Inst.; bd. dirs. Naples Philharm. Ctr. for Arts. Served with USAAF, 1943-45.

MALONE, EDWIN SCOTT, III, radio and television producer, public relations consultant; b. Vernon, Tex., Mar. 25, 1938; s. Edwin Scott and Pauline (King) M.; m. Sandra Sue Ballard, Aug. 19, 1960; children: Melissa, Michael Scott, Paula Sue. BA, So. Meth. U., 1960; MA, Burton Coll.; PhD, Burton Coll. Seminary; HumD (hon.), Golden State U. Pres. Ed Malone Enterprises, Arlington, Tex., 1960—; account exec. David Wade & Assocs., Dallas, 1963-66; ptnr. COMAL Pub. Rels. Cons., Arlington 1970-75; v.p. radio So. Baptist Radio-TV Commn., Ft. Worth, 1965—; cons. Tyndale House Pubs., Inc., Wheaton, Ill. Performer Gourmet TV series, Dallas and Ft. Worth, 1955-60; author: Douglas Genealogy, 1959, Malone Genealogy, 1960, Religious Landmarks of America, 1973; prodr. (series) Accent on Youth, Assignment Travel. Tex. del. White House Conf. on Children and Youth, 1960, 70; mem. exec. com. Longhorn coun. Boy Scouts Am.; active, past pres. Ft. Worth Religious Pub. Rels. Coun. Mem. SAR, NATAS, Am. Soc. Travel Writers, Ft. Worth C. of C., Religious Heritage Am., Nat. Press Club, Soc. War of 1812, Sertoma (past pres.), Acacia, Order of Pythagoras (hon.), Order of St. Dennis of Zante (grand cross, charge d'affair Tex.), Order of Crown of Thorns (grand master), Masons, Shriners (past presiding officer York Rite), DeMolay, Legion of Honor. Home: 1608 Hawthorne Dr Arlington TX 76012-2229

MALONE, JAMES L., lawyer, diplomat; b. Los Angeles, Calif.. BA magna cum laude, Pomona Coll., 1953; JD, Stanford U., 1959. Bar: Calif. 1961, U.S. Supreme Ct. 1970, D.C. 1977. Lectr. law, asst. dean Law Sch. UCLA, 1961-67; prof., dean-elect Coll. Law Willamette U., Salem, Oreg., 1967-68; vis. prof. Law Sch. U. Tex., 1969; atty. Fed. Maritime Commn., 1970-71; asst. gen. counsel, then gen. counsel Arms Control and Disarmament Agy., 1971-76, acting dir., 1981; atty. Doub and Muntzing, Washington, 1978-81; asst. sec. oceans and internat. environ. and sci. affairs Dept. State, Washington, 1981-85; Navy Chair Prof. of Internat. Law Naval Postgrad. Sch., Monterey, Calif., 1987-90; pvt. practice, 1990—; U.S. rep. with personal rank of amb. Conf. of Com. on Disarmament, 1976-77; spl. rep. of Pres. for Law of Sea, 1981-85; chmn. U.S. del. and amb. for Law of Sea Conf., 1981-82; adv. bd. Ctr. for Oceans Law and Policy U. Va. Sch. Law. Contbr. articles to profl. jours. Trustee World Affairs Coun. of Monterey Bay Area. 1st lt. U.S. Army, 1954-56. Mem. ABA, State Bar Calif., D.C. Adv. Coun. (chmn.), S.W. Ctr. for Environ. Rsch. and Policy, Coun. Am. Ambs., Met. Club (Washington), Capitol Hill Club (Washington), Order of Coif, Phi Beta Kappa. Office: PO Box 9024 Monterey CA 93942-9024

MALONE, JAMES LAURENCE, III, lawyer; b. Brighton, Mass., Aug. 5, 1947; s. James Laurence and Mary (Roberts) M.; m. Alice Reno, Nov. 30, 1974; children: Virginia, Kathleen. AB cum laude, Boston Coll., 1969; JD, U. Va., 1972; LLM in Taxation, Georgetown U., 1978. Bar: Va. 1972, Ill. 1982, U.S. Ct. Appeals (fed., 4th, 6th and 7th cirs.), U.S. Ct. Claims, U.S. Dist. Ct. (no. dist.) Ill. Law. clk. to presiding judge U.S. Ct. Claims, Washington, 1972-73; law clk. to Judge Marion T. Bennett U.S. Ct. Claims, 1973-74; trial atty. U.S. Justice Dept., Washington, 1974-79, sr. trial atty., 1979-82; assoc. McDermott, Will & Emery, Chgo. 1982; income ptnr. McDermott, Will & Emerson, Chgo., 1983-85, sr. ptnr., 1986—. Gen. counsel, bd. dirs. Northeast Ill. council Boy Scouts Am., Highland Park; pres., bd. dirs. Country Club of Reston, Va., 1978-80. Mem. ABA (subcom. tax sect.), Fed. Ctr. Bar Assn. (tax appeals com.), Union League (Chgo.), Exmoor Country Club (Highland Park, Ill.), Sankaty Head Golf Club (Nantucket, Mass.), Farmington Country Club (Charlottesville, Va.). Home: 114 De Windt Rd Winnetka IL 60093-3709 Office: McDermott Will & Emery 227 W Monroe St 3100 Chicago IL 60606-5096

MALONE, JAMES WILLIAM, bishop; b. Youngstown, Ohio, Mar. 8, 1920; s. James Patrick and Katherine V. (McGuire) M. A.B., St. Mary Sem., Cleve., 1945; M.A., Cath. U. Am., 1952, Ph.D., 1957. Ordained priest Roman Catholic Ch., 1945; asst. pastor Youngstown, 1945-50; supt. schs. Diocese of Youngstown, 1952-65; instr. admin. administr. St. John's Coll., Cleve., 1953, aux. bishop of Youngstown, 1960-68; bishop, 1968—; apostolic administr. Diocese Youngstown, 1966-68; v.p. Nat. Conf. cath. Bishops, 1980-83; pres. Nat. Conf. Cath. Bishops, 1983-86, mem. Bishops' Com. Ecumenical and Interreligious Affairs; mem. adminstrv. com. co-chmn. Cath./United Meth. Internat. Dialogue; consultor bishops' com. liturgy; bd. dirs. Cath. Conf. Ohio; mem. gen. bd. Ohio Coun. Chs.; mem. Commn. on Social Devel. and World Peace; chmn. Cath. TV Network of Am.; mem. Nat. Coalition on Cath. Health Ministry. Trustee Cath. U. Am.

MALONE, JOHN C., telecommunications executive; b. 1941; m. Leslie. Attended Yale U., Johns Hopkins U. Formerly pres. Jerrold Electronics Corp.; pres., chief exec. officer Tele-Communications, Inc., Denver; chmn., dir. Liberty Media Corp., Denver. Office: Tele-Comm Inc 5619 DTC Pky Englewood CO 80111*

MALONE, JOSEPH D., state treasurer; b. Newton, Mass., Nov. 18, 1954; m. Linda Ploen; children: Joe Jr., Sam, Carolyn Adele. Educated at Harvard Univ., 1978. Treas. state of Mass., 1991—. Office: State House Rm 227 Office Of Treasurer Boston MA 02133

MALONE, JOSEPH JAMES, mathematics educator, researcher; b. St. Louis, Sept. 9, 1932; s. Joseph James and Aurelia Theresa (Shoemaker) M.; m. Dorothy Sue Cleary, Nov. 24, 1960; children: Michael, Barbara, Philip, Patrick. BS, St. Louis U., 1954, MS, 1958, PhD, 1962. Instr. math. Rockhurst Coll., Kansas City, Mo., 1960-62; asst. prof. U. Houston, 1962-67; assoc. prof. Tex. A&M U., College Station, 1967-70, prof. 1970-71; prof. Worcester (Mass.) Poly. Inst., 1971—, chmn. dept. math., 1971-78. Contbr. articles to profl. jours. Mem. Town of Westborough (Mass.) Pub. Schs. Bd., 1974-83, 84-87, Fin. Com., 1992—. With U.S. Army, 1954-56. Mem. AAUP, Am. Math. Soc., Math. Assn. Am. Democrat. Roman Catholic. Achievements include research in near-ring theory and group theory. Home: 45 Adams St Westborough MA 01581-3610 Office: Worcester Poly Inst 100 Institute Rd Worcester MA 01609-2280

MALONE, JOSEPH LAWRENCE, linguistics educator; b. N.Y.C., July 2, 1937; s. Joseph Timothy and Katherine Veronica (O'Connor) M.; m. Pamela Joan Altfeld, Jan. 31, 1964; children—Joseph Timothy II, Otis Taig. B.A., U. Calif.-Berkeley, 1963, Ph.D., 1967. Mem. faculty Barnard Coll., N.Y.C., 1967—, prof. linguistics, 1975—, chmn. dept. 1967—; vis. lectr. U. Pa., 1970; linguistics advisor Grolier Pub. Co. Author: The Science of Linguistics in the Art of Translation, 1988, Tiberian Hebrew Phonology, 1992; editor, contbr. Acad. Am. Ency.; mem. editorial bd. Hellas; contbr. articles to profl. jours. Served with U.S. Army, 1957-60. Grad. fellow U. Calif.-Berkeley, 1965-66, Am. Council Learned Socs., 1966-67. Mem. Linguistics Soc. Am., Am. Oriental Soc., AAUP, N.Am. Conf. Afro-Asiatic Linguistics, Phi Beta Kappa. Democrat. Home: 169 Prospect St Leonia NJ 07605-1929 Office: Barnard Coll New York NY 10027-6598

MALONE, JULIA LOUISE, news reporter, White House correspondent; b. Memphis, Sept. 16, 1947; d. William Battle and Alice Avery (Allen) M. BA, Vanderbilt U., 1969. Copy aide Christian Sci. Monitor, Boston, 1969-71, editorial asst., 1971-72, local reporter, 1972-73, editor Living Page, 1978-80, Congl. reporter, 1980-86; TV corr. Christian Sci. Monitor, Washington, 1987-88; bull. editor Harvard Div. Sch., Cambridge, Mass., 1971; reporter The Fauquier Democrat, Warrenton, Va., 1975-77; nat. reporter Cox Newspapers, Washington, 1986-87, 89—; elected mem. standing com. corrs. House and Senate press galleries, Washington, 1983-85. Recipient award for excellence in bus. and econ. reporting John Hancock Fin. Services, Boston, 1986. Mem. White House Corr. Assn.; Gridiron Club. Home: # G4 4570 MacArthur Blve NW Washington DC 20007-4251 Office: Cox Newspapers 2000 Pennsylvania Ave NW Washington DC 20006-1812

MALONE, KARL (THE MAILMAN), professional basketball player; b. Summerfield, La., July 24, 1963. Student, La. Tech. U., 1981-85. Basketball player Utah Jazz, 1985—; mem. U.S. Olympic Basketball Team (received Gold medal), 1992. Mem. NBA All-Star team, 1988-94; recipient NBA All-Star Game MVP award, 1989, 1993; mem. All-NBA first team, 1989-94; mem. All-NBA second team, 1988; mem. NBA All-Defensive second team, 1988; mem. NBA All-Rookie Team, 1986. Office: Utah Jazz Delta Ctr Salt Lake City UT 84180-1105*

MALONE, MICHAEL GLEN, lawyer; b. L.A., Apr. 12, 1943; s. Thomas Daniel and Virginia (Shupe) M.; m. Susan Cornelia Pierson, May 9, 1970 (div. Nov. 1987); m. Linda Kay Thomson, Dec. 26, 1987. Student, U. So. Calif., 1960-61; BS, U.S. Naval Acad., 1965; JD, U. Calif., San Francisco, 1974. Bar: Calif. 1974, U.S. Dist. Ct. (no. dist.) Calif. 1974, U.S. Ct. Mil. Appeals 1979, U.S. Supreme Ct. 1979. Commd. 2d lt. U.S. Marine Corps, 1965, advanced through grades to lt. col., 1980, served in Republic of Vietnam, USS Coral Sea; appellate mil. judge U.S. Navy-Marine Corps Ct. of Mil. Rev., Washington, 1981-83; ret. U.S. Marine Corps, 1986; assoc. Littler, Mendelson, Fastiff & Tichy, San Francisco, 1986-88; atty. Law Offices of James D. Biernat, Foster City, Calif., 1988—. Mem. ABA, Assn. Trial Lawyers Am., Bar Assn. San Francisco, Marin County Bar Assn., Sonoma County Bar Assn. Republican. Avocation: rugby (referee, mgr. U.S. Combined Svcs. Team). Office: Law Offices James D Biernat 393 Vintage Park Dr Ste 250 Foster City CA 94404

MALONE, MICHAEL PETER, academic administrator, historian; b. Pomeroy, Wash., Apr. 18, 1940; s. John Albert and Dolores Frances (Cheyne) M.; m. Kathleen Malone, Apr. 17, 1983; children: John Thomas, Molly Christine. BA in History, Gonzaga U., 1962; PhD in Am. Studies, Wash. State U., Pullman, 1966. Asst. prof. history Tex. A&M U., College Station, 1966-67; asst. prof., then prof. history Mont. State U., Bozeman, 1967—, dean grad. studies, 1979-89, v.p. acad. affairs, 1989-90; pres. Mont. State U., 1991—; bd. dirs. Buttrey Food & Drug. Author: The Battle for Butte, 1981 (Sick award 1981), Historians and The American West, 1983, (with others) Montana: A History of Two Centuries, 1976, 2d edit., 1991, The American West: A 20th Century History, 1989, James J. Hill, Empire Builder of the Northwest, 1995. Mem. Western History Assn. Home: 2310 Spring Creek Dr Bozeman MT 59715-6191 Office: Mont State U Bozeman MT 59717

MALONE, NANCY, actor, director, producer; b. N.Y.C.; d. James and Bridget (Sheilds) M. Freelance actress, dir., producer, writer. Performer (TV series) The First Hundred Years, Naked City, The Long, Hot Summer (Best Performance by an Actress award); Broadway debut in Time Out For Ginger, other stage performances include Major Barbara, The Makropoulis Secret, A Touch of the Poet, The Trial of the Catonsville Nine; touring performances include The Chalk Garden, The Seven Yr. Itch, A Place For Dolly; actress (films) The Violators, I Cast No Shadow, An Affair of the Skin, Intimacy, The Trial of the Cantonville Nine, The Man Who Loved Cat Dancing, Capricorn One; producer (TV series) including Bionic Woman, 1978, Husbands, Wives and Lovers, 1978, The Great Pretender, 1984, (special) Bob Hope: The First 90 Years, 1993 (Emmy award, Outstanding Variety, Musical or Comedy Special, 1993), Womanspeak, 1983; dir. (TV series) Dynasty, 1984-87, Hotel, 1984-87, Colbys, 1985, Cagney and Lacey, 1987, Rosie O'Niel (Emmy nomination), Sisters (Emmy nomination), Melrose Place, Beverly Hills, Picket Fences; producer, dir. (film) There Were Times Dear, 1986 (John Muir Trustees award, Cine Golden Eagle, Blue Ribbon); founder Nancy Malone Prodns., 1975, Lilac Prodns., 1979. Fellow Leaky Found.; mem. Am. Film Inst. (mem. founder), Women in Film (Chrystal award). Home: 9911 W Pico Blvd Los Angeles CA 90035 Office: care Guild Mgmt 9911 W Pico Los Angeles CA 90035

MALONE, PERRILLAH ATKINSON (PAT MALONE), retired state official; b. Montgomery, Ala., Mar. 17, 1922; d. Odolph Edgar and Myrtle (Fondren) Atkinson. BS, Oglethorpe U., 1956; MAT, Emory U., 1962. Asst. editor, then acting editor Emory U., 1958-64; asst. project officer Ga. Dept. Pub. Health, Atlanta, 1965-68; asst. project dir. Ga. Ednl. Improvement Coun., 1968-69, assoc. dir., 1970-71; dir. career svcs. State Scholarship Commn., Atlanta, 1971-74; rev. coord. Div. Phys. Health, Ga. Dept Human Resources, Atlanta, 1974-79; project dir. So. Regional Edn. Bd., 1979-81; specialist Div. Family and Children Svcs., Atlanta, 1982-91, ret., 1991; mem. Gov.'s Commn. on Nursing Edn. and Nursing Practice, 1972-75, Aging Svcs. Task Force, Atlanta Regional Commn., 1985—; book reviewer Atlanta Jour.-Constn., 1962-79. Recipient Recognition award Ga. Nursing Assn., 1976, Korsell award Ga. Ga. League for Nursing, 1974, Alumni Honor award Emory U., 1964. Mem. Am. Pub. Welfare Assn., Ga. Gerontology Soc. (editor GGS Newsletter 1988-92, Lewis Newmark award 1991). Methodist. Home: 1146 Oxford Rd NE Atlanta GA 30306-2608

MALONE, ROBERT JOSEPH, bank executive; b. Sept. 3, 1944. With Bank of Am., 1969-81; chmn., pres., CEO First Interstate Bank Boise, Idaho, 1981-84; pres., CEO First Interstate Bank Denver, 1984-90; chmn., pres., CEO Western Capital Investment Corp. (now First Bank System, Inc.), Denver, 1990-92; chmn., CEO Bank Western/Central Banks (now First Bank System, Inc.), Denver, 1992-93, Colo. Nat. Bank, Denver, 1993—. Office: Colorado Nat Bank 950 17th St Denver CO 80202-2827

MALONE, ROBERT ROY, artist, art educator; b. McColl, S.C., Aug. 8, 1933; s. Robert Roy and Anne (Matthews) M.; m. Cynthia Enid Taylor, Feb. 26, 1956; 1 child, Brendan Trevor. B.A., U. N.C., 1955; M.F.A., U. Chgo., 1958; postgrad., U. Iowa, 1959. Instr. art Union U., Jackson, Tenn., 1959-60, Lambuth Coll., 1959-61; asst. prof. art Wesleyan Coll., Macon, Ga., 1961-67; assoc. prof. Wesleyan Coll., 1967-68, W.Va. U., 1968-70, So. Ill. U., Edwardsville, 1970-75; prof. So. Ill. U., 1975—. One-man shows at Gallery Illien, Atlanta, 1969, De Cruise Gallery, Miami, 1968, 71, Ill. State Mus., Springfield, 1974, U. Del., Newark, 1978, Elliot Smith Gallery, St. Louis, 1985, Merida Galleries, Louisville, 1985, Yvonne Rapp Gallery, Louisville, 1990, 92, 93, St. John's Coll., Santa Fe, 1991, others; group shows include Bklyn. Mus., 1966, Assoc. Am. Artists Gallery, N.Y.C., 1968, Musée d'Art Modern, Paris, 1970, DeCordova Mus., 1973, 74, St. Louis Art Mus., 1985, Wake Forest U., 1985, New Orleans Mus. Art, 1990, Dakota Internat. Vermillion, 1994; represented in numerous permanent collections including Smithsonian Instn., Washington, USIA, Washington, Library of Congress, Calif. Palace of Legion of Honor, San Francisco, N.Y. Pub. Library, N.Y.C., Victoria and Albert Mus., London, Chgo. Art Inst., Indpls. Mus. Art, Humana Inc., Louisville, State of Ill. Ctr., Chgo., Speed Mus., Louisville, N. Ill. Univ., Capital Devel. Bd., Ill. Recipient numerous regional, nat. awards in competitive exhbns.; Ford fellow, 1977; So. Ill. U. at Edwardsville Art research scholar, 1976, 84. Home: 600 Chapman St Edwardsville IL 62025-1260 Office: Dept Art and Design So Ill U Edwardsville IL 62025

MALONE, THOMAS FRANCIS, university administrator, meteorologist; b. Sioux City, Iowa, May 3, 1917; s. John and Mary (Hourigan) M.; m. Rosalie Doran, Dec. 30, 1942; children—John H., Thomas Francis, Mary E., James K., Richard K., Dennis P. B.S., S.D. Sch. Mines, 1940, D.Eng., 1962; Sc.D., MIT, 1946; L.H.D., St. Joseph Coll., West Hartford, Conn., 1965;

Sc.D. (hon.), Bates Coll., 1988. Instr. MIT, 1942-43, asst. prof., 1943-51, assoc. prof., 1951-56; dir. Travelers Research Ctr., Travelers Ins. Co., Hartford, Conn., 1955-56; dir. research Travelers Research Ctr., Travelers Ins. Co., 1956-69, s.v.p., 1968-70; chmn. bd. Travelers Research Ctr., Inc., 1961-70; dean Grad. Sch., U. Conn., Storrs, 1970-73; chmn. bd. Center for Environment and Men, 1970-71; dir. emeritus Holcomb Research Inst. Butler U., Indpls., 1983—; scholar in residence St. Joseph Coll., 1983-91; Nat. Scis. fellow Resources for Future, 1983-84; chmn. bd. Univ. Corp. for Atmospheric Research.; mem. Conn. Weather Control Bd., 1959-73; mem. panel on sci. and educ., on sci. and astronautics U.S. Ho. of Reps., 1960-1970; nat. adv. com. community air pollution HEW, 1962-66; mem. sci. info. council NSF, 1962-66; rep. Am. Geophys. Union to U.S. Nat. Commn. for UNESCO, 1963-73 chmn. U.S. Nat. Commn., 1965-67; mem. nat. adv. com. on oceans and atmosphere, 1972-75, mem. Conn. Research Commn., 1965-71; mem. com. application sci. and tech. New Eng. Council; chmn. Nat. Motor Vehicle Safety Adv. Council, 1967-70; mem. sci. adv. com. climate impact assessment and response program UN Environ. Program, 1992—. Editor: Compendium of Meteorology, 1951; contbg. editor: Environment, 1992—. Bd. dirs. Engrs. Joint Coun., 1968-70; bd. govs. Ins. Inst. Hwy. Safety, 1968-70; mem. oversight rev. bd. Nat. Acid Precipitation Assessment Program, 1990—. Recipient Robert M. Losey award Inst. Aero. Sci., 1960, Charter Oak Leadership medal Greater Hartford C. of C., 1962, Charles Franklin Brooks award, 1964, Cleveland Abbe award Am. Meteorol. Soc., 1968, Conn. Conservationist of Yr. award, 1966, Guy E. March Silver medal S.D. Sch. Mines, 1976, Internat. Meteorol. Orgn. prize, 1984, Internat. St. Francis Assisi prize for environment, 1991, AAAS Internat. prize, 1994; N.C. State U. disting. scholar, 1990—. Fellow AAAS (internat. sci. coop., 1994), N.Y. Acad. Scis., Am. Meteorol. Soc. (pres. 1960-62), Am. Geophys. Union (past pres., sec. internat. participation 1964, Waldo E. Smith award 1986); mem. Nat. Acad. Scis. (chmn. geophysics research bd. 1969-76, chmn. bd. on internat. orgns. and programs, dep. fgn. sec. 1969-73, fgn. sec. 1978-82), Am. Acad. Arts and Scis., Internat. Council Sci. Unions (v.p., sec.-gen. sci. com. problems environ. 1970-76, treas. 1978-82 Nat. Acad. Engring. (space applications bd. 1973-77), Am. Geog. Soc. (council 1971-77), Royal Irish Acad. (hon.), Conn. Acad. Sci. and Engring. (exec. scientist 1987-91), Sigma Xi (bd. dirs. 1983—, pres. 1988-89, dir. Sigma Xi Ctr. 1992—). Home: 5 Bishop Rd Apt 203 West Hartford CT 06119-1536 Office: NC State U Dept Marine and Atmospheric Scis Box 8208 Raleigh NC 27695

MALONE, TOM, bible college president. Pres. Free Will Baptist Bible College of the Nat. Assn. of the Free Will Baptists, Antioch, Tenn. Office: Natl Assn of Free Will Baptists PO Box 5002 Antioch TN 37011-5002 also: Free Will Baptists Bible College 3606 West End Ave Nashville TN 37205

MALONE, WALLACE D., JR., bank executive; b. Dothan, Ala., 1936; married. BS, U. Ala., 1957; MBA, U. Pa., 1960. With First Nat. Bank, 1959-71; with SouthTrust Corp., Birmingham, Ala., 1972—, now chmn., chief exec. officer, dir. Office: Southtrust Corp 420 N 20th St PO Box 2554 Birmingham AL 35203

MALONE, WILLIAM GRADY, lawyer; b. Minden, La., Feb. 19, 1915; s. William Gordon and Minnie Lucie (Hortman) M.; m. Marion Rowe Whitfield, Sept. 26, 1943; children: William Grady, Gordon Whitfield, Marion Elizabeth, Helen Ann, Margaret Catherine. BS, La. State U., 1941; JD, George Washington U., 1952. Bar: Va. 1952, U.S. Supreme Ct 1971. Statis. analyst Dept. Agr., Baton Rouge, 1941; investigator VA, Washington, 1946-59; legal officer, dep., gen. counsel, asst. gen. counsel VA, 1959-79; pvt. practice law Arlington, Va., 1979—. Editor: Fed. Bar News, 1972-73. Pres. Aurora Hills Civic Assn., 1948-49; spl. asst. to treas. Com. of 100, 1979-81, chmn., 1982-83; pres. Children's Theater, 1968-69; trustee St. George's Episc. Ch., 1979—; chmn. Arlington County Fair Assn., 1979-83. Lt. col. AUS, 1941-46, ETO. Decorated Legion of Merit; recipient Disting. Svc. award, 1979, 3 Superior Performance awards, 1952-72, Outstanding Alumni award George Washington U., 1978. Mem. Fed. Bar Assn. (pres. D.C. chpt. 1970-71, nat. pres. 1978-79), Va. Bar Assn., Arlington County Bar Assn., Nat. Lawyers Club (dir.), Arlington Host Lions, Ft. Myer Officers Club. Home: 224 N Jackson St Arlington VA 22201-1253 Office: 2060 14th St N Ste 310 Arlington VA 22201-2519

MALONE, WINFRED FRANCIS, health scientist; b. Revere, Mass., Feb. 10, 1935; s. Winfred and Margurite (Meehan) M.; m. Eleanor Malone, Aug. 1974. BS, U. Mass., 1957, MS, 1961; MS, Rutgers U., 1963; PhD, U. Mich., 1970. Scientist Nat. Cancer Inst., Bethesda, Md., 1970-81, chief chemoprevention br., 1991-95, acting assoc. dir., 1991-95; chief ACRES Nat. Cancer Inst., 1995—. Contbr. articles to profl. jours. Mem. AAAS, Am. Coll. Toxicology, N.Y. Acad. Scis. Home: 3209 Wake Dr Kensington MD 20895-3216 Office: Nat Cancer Inst EPN 218 Bethesda MD 20892-7329

MALONEY, FRANCIS PATRICK, physiatrist; b. Pitts., Mar. 4, 1936; s. Francis Barrington and Esther Elizabeth (Kuhn) M.; m. Kathryn Brassell Anderson, June 25, 1960 (dec. June 6, 1987); children: Timothy J., Kevin P., J. Christopher; m. Billie Barbara Galloway, Feb. 14, 1990. BA, St. Vincent Coll., 1958; MD, U. Pitts., 1962; MPH, Johns Hopkins U., 1966. Diplomate Am. Bd. Phys. Medicine and Rehab., Am. Bd. Preventive Medicine, Am. Bd. Med. Mgmt. Intern St. Francis Hosp., Pitts., 1962-63; resident gen. preventive medicine Johns Hopkins U. Sch. of Hygiene & Pub. Health, Balt., 1965-67; fellow medicine, med. genetics Johns Hopkins U. Sch. of Medicine, Balt. 1966-68; resident phys. medicine and rehab. U. Minn., Mpls., 1968-70; staff physician Sister Kenny Inst. Mpls., 1970-72; asst. clin. prof. U. Minn., Mpls., 1970-72; asst. prof. phys. medicine and rehab., assoc. prof. U. Colo., Denver, 1972-78, 78-84; prof. head div. of rehab. medicine U. Ark., Little Rock, 1984-91, prof., chmn. dept. phys. medicine and rehab., 1991—; med. dir. Bapt. Rehab. Inst., Little Rock, 1985—; chief rehab. medicine svc. VA Med. Ctr., Little Rock, 1984—. Editor: Interdisciplinary Rehabilitation of Multiple Sclerosis and Neuromuscular Disease, 1984; editor, author: Physical Medicine & Rehabilitation State of the Art Reviews, 1987, Primer on Management, 1987, Rehabilitation of Aging, 1989, Management for Rehabilitation Medicine II, 1993; alt. editor: Archives of Physical Medicine and Rehabilitation, 1989-93. Mem. exec. bd. Greater No. Colo. Chpt. of Muscular Dystrophy Assn. of Am., 1972-82; spl. edn. adv. com. Cherry Creek Sch. Dist., Denver, 1975, vice chmn., 1976, chmn., 1977; med. advisor Denver Commn. on Disabled and Coun. on Aging, Denver, 1980-82, Denver Commn. on Human Svcs., 1982-84; external examiner King Saud U. Med. Sch., Saudi Arabia, 1983; med. adv. bd. Ark. Multiple Sclerosis Soc., Little Rock, 1985-88; chmn. chmn's. coun. Assn. Acad. Physiatrists, Indpls., 1992—. Fellow Am. Acad. Phys. and Rehab.; mem. AMA, Am. Congress of Rehab. Medicine, Am. Acad. Cerebral Palsy, Am. Pub. Health Assn., Am. Bd. Physical Medicine and Rehhilitation (dir. 1988—), Soc. for Exptl. Biology and Medicine, Assn. Acad. Physiatrists, Ark. Med. Soc., Pulaski County Med. Soc., Soc. for Neuroscis. Office: U Ark Med Scis 4301 W Markham Slot #602 Little Rock AR 72205

MALONEY, FRANK, judge, lawyer; b. Worcester, Mass., Nov. 20, 1927; s. Francis James and Dora Marie (Berthiaume) M.; children: Catharine Frances, Edward James. BA, U. Tex., Austin, 1953, LLB, 1956. Bar: Tex. 1956, U.S. Supreme Ct. 1962, Mass. 1969. Asst. dist. atty. Travis Co., Austin, Tex., 1956-60; chief Law Enforcement div. Atty. Gen. State of Tex., Austin, 1960-61; ptnr. Stayton, Maloney, Hearne & Babb, Austin, 1961-79; owner Frank Maloney & Assocs., P.C., Austin, 1979-90; judge Tex. Ct. Criminal Appeals, Austin, 1991—; adj. prof. law U. Tex. Sch. of Law, 1962-85. Co-author: (with Stumberg) Criminal Law and Administration, 1964. Capt. U.S. Army, 1946-51. Fellow Tex. Bar Found.; mem. ABA, Nat. Assn. Criminal Def. Lawyers (pres. 1987-88), Mass. Bar Assn., Tex. Bar Assn., Tex. Criminal Def. Lawyers Assn. (pres. 1971-82), Am. Bd. Trial Advocates, Am. Bd. Criminal Lawyers, Travis County Bar Assn. Home: 1414 Wathen Ave Austin TX 78703-2528 Office: Ct Criminal Appeals Capitol Sta PO Box 12308 Austin TX 78711-2308

MALONEY, GEORGE THOMAS, health industry executive; b. Phila., Aug. 28, 1932; s. John J. and Clara (Becker) M.; m. Sara Marie Carroll, Apr. 26, 1969. B.S., Siena Coll., 1954. Labor relations rep. Gen. Motors, Linden, N.J., 1957-58; salesman C.R. Bard, Inc., Murray Hill, N.J., 1959-63; div. mgr. C.R. Bard, Inc., 1963-64, mdse. mgr., 1965-66, v.p. mdse., 1967-68, corp. v.p. purchasing, 1969-70, group v.p., 1976-77, exec. v.p., 1977-78, pres., chief oper. officer, 1978-88, pres., chief exec. officer, 1989—, chrm., ceo, dir., also bd. dirs., v.p. mktg. svcs. Bard Mktg. div., 1974; v.p. mktg. services

(U.S. Catheter & Instrument Co.), 1970-73; v.p., gen. mgr. Inspiron div. C.R. Bard, Inc., 1974-75, pres., 1975-76; pres., chief exec. officer, 1989, chmn., chief exec. officer, 1991; bd. dirs. Summit Bancorp. Patentee in field med. edn. Trustee Siena Coll., 1990—, Overlook Hosp. Found., 1990—, The Matheny Sch. and Hosp., 1991—, Liberty Sci. Ctr., 1993—, N.J. Symphony Orch., 1993—; bd. dirs. Healthcare Leadership Coun., 1992—. Mem. Health Industry Mfrs. Assn. (bd. dirs. 1991), Healthcare Leadership Coun. (bd. dirs. 1992). Office: C R Bard Inc 730 Central Ave New Providence NJ 07974

MALONEY, GERALD P., utility executive; b. Lawrence, Mass., Mar. 9, 1933; s. Thomas P. and Concetta M.; m. Dorothea Ames. BSEE, MIT, 1955, BSBA, 1955; MBA, Rutgers U., 1962. With Am. Electric Power Co., Inc., Columbus, Ohio, 1955—; controller Am. Electric Power Co., Inc., 1965-70, v.p. fin., 1970-75, sr. v.p. fin., 1975-90, exec. v.p., CFO, 1990—; dir., v.p. fin. Appalachian Power Co., Ind., Mich. Power Co., Ohio Power Co., Ky. Power Co., Wheeling Power Co., Kingsport Power Co., Columbus & So. Power Co.; bd. dirs. Energy Ins. Mut., Ltd., chmn., 1990-92; bd. dirs. Nuclear Electric Ins., Ltd. Mem. Edison Electric Inst. (fin. com.), Beta Gamma Sigma. Home: 128 S Ardmore Rd Columbus OH 43209-1705 Office: Am Electric Power Co 1 Riverside Plz Columbus OH 43215-2355

MALONEY, JAMES EDWARD, lawyer; b. Hackensack, N.J., Apr. 28, 1951; s. Edward James Maloney and Kathleen Elizabeth (Lamont) Leaf. BA, Yale U., 1972; JD, Harvard U., 1975. Bar: Tex. 1975, U.S. Dist. Ct. (no., so., ea. and we. dists.) Tex., U.S. Ct. Appeals (2d, 3d, 5th, 9th and D.C. cirs.), U.S. Supreme Ct. Assoc. Baker & Botts, Houston, 1975-82, ptnr., 1982—; bd. dirs. Fotofest, Inc., Houston Ctr. for Photography, Da Camera. Trustee Woodberry Forest (Va.) Sch., 1991—. Mem. Tex. Bar Assn., Tex. Bar Found., Houston Bar Assn., Houston Bar Found., Tex. Club, Yale Club (Houston, Assn. Yale Alumni rep. 1984-86). Republican. Episcopalian. Home: 2129 Tangley St Houston TX 77005-1640 Office: Baker & Botts 3000 One Shell Plz 910 Louisiana St Houston TX 77002

MALONEY, JAMES HENRY, state senator, lawyer; b. Quincy, Mass., Sept. 17, 1948; s. James Henry Jr. and Katherine Smith (Murphy) M.; m. Mary Angela Draper, Aug. 16, 1980; children: Adele, Anna, Ellen. BA cum laude, Harvard U., 1972; JD, Boston U., 1980. Vol. VISTA, Gary, Ind., 1987-95; exec. dir. Community Action Com. Danbury, Conn., 1974-78; atty. Pinney, Payne, VanLenten, Burrell, Wolfe & Dillman, P.C., Danbury, 1980-86; ptnr. Dice, Maloney & Lenz, P.C., Danbury, 1986-93; mem. Conn. Senate, Hartford, 1987—; asst. majority leader and senate chair fin., revenue and bonding com., 1993-95. Chmn. Danbury Cmty. Endowment 1984-94, dem. candidate for U.S. Congress, 1994. Recipient Disting. Svc. award Jaycees North Fairfield County, 1984, Community Svc. award Midwestern Conn. Coun. on Alcoholism, 1990, Spl. Recognition award Jewish Home for the Elderly, Fairfield County, 1993; named Legislator of Yr., Caucus Conn. Dems., 1990, Conn. Assn. Ind. Ins. Agts., 1992. Roman Catholic. Avocation: sailing. Office: Conn State Senate Legis Office Bldg State Capitol Hartford CT 06106 Office: 240 Main St Danbury CT 06810

MALONEY, JOHN ALEXANDER, retired hospital administrator; b. Knoxville, Tenn., Mar. 1, 1927; s. Harry Lotspeich and Gertrude (Blaetz) M.; m. Doris Ann Akes, Oct. 21, 1964; children: John Patrick, Christopher Michael; stepchildren: Thomas Kent Gaskins, Shelley Arlene Gaskins, William Glenn Gaskins. Student, U. Tenn., 1947-50; certificate in hosp. adminstrn., Ga. State Coll., 1958. Adminstr. Lawrence County Gen. Hosp., Lawrenceburg, Tenn., 1958-60, Morristown-Hamblen (Tenn.) Hosp., 1960-64, Central State Psychiat. Hosp., Nashville, 1964-67, Eastern State Psychiat. Hosp., Knoxville, 1967-72; cons. Project Devel. Corp., Knoxville, 1971-72; adminstr. R.J. Taylor Meml. Hosp., Hawkinsville, Ga., 1972-73; health services cons., 1973-77; unit adminstr. dept. psychiatry and neurology Walter Reed Army Med. Center, Washington, 1977-79; assoc. adminstr. Walter Reed Army Med. Center, 1979-94, chief hosp. support div., 1991-94; ret., 1994; pres. Knoxville Hosp. Coun., 1971-72. Served with USNR, 1944-46; to 2d lt. AUS, 1952-53. Mem. Am. Coll. Hosp. Adminstrs., Tenn. Hosp. Assn., Knoxville Hosp. Council (pres. 1969-70), Am. Pub. Health Assn., Pi Epsilon Rho. Episcopalian. Lodges: Kiwanis; Rotary. Address: 790 N Cedarbluff Rd Apt 605 Knoxville TN 37923

MALONEY, JOHN FREDERICK, retired marketing and opinion research specialist; b. Watertown, N.Y., Apr. 28, 1913; s. John Francis and Grace (Gott) M.; m. Lucia Howard McKellar, Apr. 27, 1940; children—John Frederick, Robert McKellar, Bonnie Patton, Lucia Howard. Grad., Mt. Hermon Sch., 1931; A.B., Princeton, 1935. With Gallup Poll, 1935-38; v.p. Peoples Research Corp., 1939-40; research analyst Young & Rubicam, 1940; Eastern mgr. Nat. Opinion Research Center, 1941; devel. analyst Curtis Pub. Co., 1946; research dir. internat. and U.S. Reader's Digest, 1946-66, corp. research dir., 1966-70; exec. v.p. Reader's Digest Found., 1970-71; cons. Advt. Research Found., N.Y.C., 1972-87; exec. dir. Council of Am. Survey Research Orgns., 1976-79; ret.; Pres. World Assn. Pub. Opinion Research, 1952-53, Market Research Council, 1958-59; chmn. research com. Mag. Pubs. Assn., 1961-65; vice chmn. tech. com. Advt. Research Found., 1956-70. Chmn. Westchester County Social Agys., 1953-57; v.p. Nat. Social Welfare Assembly, 1964-68; nat. chmn. Princeton Ann. Giving, 1968-69; vice-chmn. Princeton U. Fund, 1968-69; pres. United Way Westchester, 1968-71, Princeton Class 1935, 1970-75; chmn. Westchester County adv. com. N.Y. State Urban Devel. Corp., 1970-80; chmn. com. Westchester Community Found., 1981-86. Lt. comdr. USNR, 1941-45; comdg. officer destroyer escort. Decorated Commendation medal. Mem. Am. Mktg. Assn. (pres. N.Y. chpt. 1960, v.p. internat. div. 1972-73). Conglist. (chmn. bd. deacons 1962-63). Clubs: Princeton (N.Y.C.), Coffee House (N.Y.C.). Home: 48 Hamilton Rd Chappaqua NY 10514-3222

MALONEY, MICHAEL JAMES, research scientist; b. Madison, Wis., Aug. 29, 1942; s. James Edward and Wanda Marie (Berry) M; m. Diane Lois Best, Apr. 20, 1962; children—Lane, Robin Maloney Judd, Tracy, Scott. Staff scientist Bjorksten Research Labs., Inc., Madison, Wis., 1962-79 v.p., 1979-84, pres., 1984—. Inventor in field. Contbr. articles to profl. jours. Chmn., Fitchburg Parks Commn. Wis., 1972—; mem. Fitchburg Planning Commn., 1972—. Mem. ASTM, ASM, Soc. Plastics Engrs. Roman Catholic. Office: Bjorksten Rsch Labs Inc 2998 Syene Rd PO Box 9444 Madison WI 53715

MALONEY, MICHAEL PATRICK, lawyer, corporate executive; b. Syracuse, N.Y., June 1, 1944; s. Randolph Bartholomew and Alice Mary (Loban) M.; m. Jane McBurney, May 21, 1977; children: Christopher, Kara. A.B., Georgetown U., 1966; M.B.A., Cornell U., 1968, J.D., 1971. Bar: N.Y. 1972. Assoc. Donovan Leisure Newton and Irvine, N.Y.C., 1971-78; asst. dir. div. market regulation SEC, Washington, 1978-79; gen. counsel, sec. Orion Capital Corp., N.Y.C., 1979—; bd. dirs. Am. Arbitration Assn.; mem. Corp. Severance Com. Mem. N.Y. Bar Assn., Am. Soc. Corp. Secs. (v.p., program chair N.Y. chpt.), Am. Corp. Counsel Assn., Scarsdale Golf Club (Hartsdale, N.Y.), Rockefeller Ctr. Club. Home: 5 Kings Grant Way Briarcliff Manor NY 10510-2521 Office: Orion Capital Corp 600 Fifth Ave New York NY 10020-2302

MALONEY, MILFORD CHARLES, retired internal medicine educator; b. Buffalo, Mar. 15, 1927; s. John Angelus Maloney and Winifred Hill; m. Dione Ethyl Sheppard. BS, Canisius Coll., 1947, postgrad., 1947-49; MD, U. Buffalo, 1953. Diplomate Am. Bd. Internal Medicine. Rsch. chemist Buffalo Electrochem. Co., 1947-49; internship Mercy Hosp./Georgetown U., 1953-54; med. residency Buffalo VA Hosp., 1954-56; cardiology fellow Buffalo Gen. Hosp., 1956-57; chmn. dept. medicine Mercy Hosp., 1969-94; program dir., internal medicine residency Mercy Hosp., Buffalo, 1972-89; with steering com. Assn. Program Dirs. in Internal Medicine, 1976, coun. mem., 1977-80; clin. prof. medicine SUNY, Buffalo, 1981-94; trustee Am. Soc. Internal Medicine, 1984-90; edn. leader med. seminar Am. Soc. Internal Medicine, Austria, Switzerland, France, 1987, Argentina, Brazil, Paraguay, 1988; bd. dirs. Internal Medicine Ctr. for Advancement and Rsch. Edn.; pres. Heart Assn. Western N.Y., Buffalo, 1969; sr. cancer rsch. physician Roswell Park Meml. Cancer Inst., 1959-62; mem. internal medicine liaison com. N.Y. State Soc. 1980-90. Editor (newsletter) N.Y. State Soc. Internal Medicine, 1972-78. bd. dirs. Health Systems Agy. Western N.Y., Buffalo, 1981; exec. com. bd. dirs. Blue Cross Western N.Y., Buffalo, 1987; bd. regents Canisius Coll., Buffalo, 1987—; mem. pres. assocs. SUNY, Buffalo. Capt. M.C., U.S. Army, 1957-59. Recipient Merit award N.Y. State Soc.

Internal Medicine, 1980, Man of Yr. award Heart Assn. Western N.Y., 1982, Ann. Honoree award Trocai Coll., 1986, Disting. Alumni award Canisius Coll., 1991, Berkson Excellence award in Tchg. and Art of Medicine, SUNY at Buffalo, 1992, Outstanding Med. Tchg. Attending award Mercy Hosp./SUNY Med. Residents, 1994; named to Sports Hall of Fame, Canisius Coll., 1978. Fellow ACP (Upstate Physician Recognition award 1989), Am .Coll. Cardiology; mem. AMA (SUNY rep. 1986-94, rep. to sect. med. schs. at annual meetings 1984-94, chmn. sect. on internal medicine 1990-91), Am. Soc. Internal Medicine (trustee 1984-90, pres. 1990-91, chmn. long range planning com.), Va. Soc. Internat. Home: 116 Cove Point Ln Williamstown VA 23185-8613

MALONEY, ROBERT B., federal judge; b. 1933. BBA, So. Meth. U., 1956, Postgrad., 1960. Asst. dist. atty. County of Dallas, 1961-62; ptnr. Watts, Stallings & Maloney, 1962-65, Maloney, Miller & McDowell, 1966-75, Maloney & McDowell, 1976-78, Maloney & Hardcastle, 1979-80, Maloney & Maloney, 1981-84; assoc. judge Tex. Ct. Appeals (5th cir.), Tex., 1983-85; judge U.S. Dist. Ct. (no. dist.) Tex., Dallas 1985—. State rep., Austin, Tex., 1973-82. Mem. Tex. Bar Assn. Office: US Courthouse Earl Cabell Bldg Rm 15E26 1100 Commerce St Dallas TX 75242-1001

MALONEY, ROBERT E., JR., lawyer; b. San Francisco, Sept. 17, 1942; s. Robert E. and Mara A. (Murphy) M.; children: Michael, Sarah. BA magna cum laude, U. Portland, 1964; JD summa cum laude, Willamette U., Salem, Oreg., 1967. Bar: Oreg., Wash., U.S. Dist. Ct. Oreg., U.S. Dist. Ct. (we. dist.) Wash., U.S. Dist. Ct. (ea. dist.) Wash., U.S. Ct. Appeals (9th cir.). Ptnr. Lane Powell Spears Lubersky, Portland, 1967—; bd. dirs., sec. Norm Thompson Outfitters, Inc., Portland, 1981—; chmn. bd. visitors Willamette U. Law Sch., 1993-95; chair, mem. exec. com. Portland Trial Dept.; lawyer's del. 9th Cir. Judicial Conf., 1995—. Judge Pro Tem Multnomah County Cir. Ct., 1994—. Mem. ABA (co-chair products liabilitiy com., trial practice com. 1990-94), Nat. Assn. R.R. Trial Counsel, Fedn. Ins. Corp. Counsel, Oreg. Assn. Def. Counsel (bd. dirs. 1987-94, sec. 1991-92, v.p 1993-94, pres. 1994), Fed. Bar Assn. (exec. com. Oreg. divsn. 1988—, pres. 1994-95), Multnomah Athletic Club. Republican. Roman Catholic. Office: Lane Powell Spears Lubersky 520 SW Yamhill St Portland OR 97204

MALONEY, THERESE ADELE, insurance company executive; b. Quincy, Mass., Sept. 15, 1929; d. James Henry and F. Adele (Powers) M. BA in Econs., Coll. St. Elizabeth, Convent Station, N.J., 1951; AMP, Harvard U. Bus. Sch., 1981. CPCU. With Liberty Mut. Ins. Co., Boston, 1951-94, asst. v.p., asst. mgr. nat. risks, 1974-77, v.p., asst. mgr. nat. risks, 1977-79, v.p., mgr. nat. risks, 1979-86, sr. v.p. underwriting mktg. and adminstrn. 1986-87, exec. v.p underwriting, policy decision, 1987-94, also bd. dirs.; pres. and bd. dirs. subs. Liberty Mut. (Bermuda) Ltd., 1981-94, LEXCO Ltd.; bd. dirs., dep. chmn. Liberty Mut. (U.K.) Ltd., London; bd. dirs. Liberty Mut. Ins. Co., Liberty Mut. Fire Ins. Co., Liberty Mut. Life Assurance Co., Liberty Fin. Co.; mem. faculty Inst. Inst., Northeastern U., Boston, 1969-74; mem. adv. bd., risk mgmt. studies Ins. Inst. Am., 1977-83; mem. adv. coun. Suffolk U. Sch. Mgmt., 1984—; mem. adv. coun. to program in internat. bus. rels. Fletcher Sch. Law and Diplomacy, 1985-94. Mem. Soc. CPCUs (past pres. Boston chpt.), Univ. Club, Algonquin Club (Boston), Boston Club, Mass. Women's Forum.

MALONEY, TIMOTHY FRANCIS, state legislator, lawyer; b. La Rochelle, France, June 12, 1956. JD, U. Balt., 1986; hon. degree, Villa Julie Coll., 1993. Bar: Md. 1986, D.C. 1986. Lawyer Camus & Maloney, Riverdale, Md., 1986—; mem. Md. Gen. Assembly, Annapolis, 1979—. Democrat. Roman Catholic. Office: State House 424 Lowe House Off Bldg 6 Gov Bladen Blvd Annapolis MD 21401

MALONEY, WILLIAM GERARD, retired investment company executive; b. Dansville, N.Y., Apr. 8, 1917; s. William J. and Fannie K. (Kirschner) M.; m. Katherine R. Kenney, Oct. 21, 1940; children: William J., Elizabeth Ann, Stephen G. B.S., U. Pa., 1939. Trainee Hemphill, Noyes & Co., N.Y.C., 1939; mem. research dept. Hemphill, Noyes & Co., 1940-42, 44-45, mgr. corporate fin. dept., 1949, partner, 1951-63, co-mng. partner, 1963-64; coordinating partner Hornblower & Weeks-Hemphill, Noyes, N.Y.C., 1965-71; mgr. br. office adminstrn. Hornblower & Weeks-Hemphill, Noyes, 1969-71, vice chmn. exec. com., dir., 1972-80; sr. mng. dir. Loeb Rhoades, Hornblower & Co., N.Y.C., 1978-80, Shearson, Am. Express Inc., 1979-84; mng. dir. Shearson Lehman Bros. Inc., 1985-87, adv. dir., 1988-89; bd. dirs. N.Am. Royalties Inc.; St. Camillus Health Ctr.; mem. adv. bd. Advanced Tech. Ventures; dir., vice chmn. Hanover Petroleum Corp., 1969-76. Bd. dirs. Med. Biology Inst., 1980-83; trustee Coll. of New Rochelle, 1986-92. Served with U.S. Army, 1942-43. Mem. N.Y. Soc. Security Analysts. Republican. Roman Catholic. Clubs: Met, Nantucket Yacht, Knight Commander of Equestrian Order of Holy Sepulchre of Jerusalem, Knight of Malta, Knight Commander of St. Gregory. Home: 155 Oenoke Ln New Canaan CT 06840-4518 Office: Am Express Tower World Fin Ctr New York NY 10005

MALOOF, GILES WILSON, academic administrator, educator, author; b. San Bernardino, Calif., Jan. 4, 1932; s. Joseph Peters and Georgia (Wilson) M.; m. Mary Anne Ziniker, Sept. 5, 1958 (div. Oct. 1976); children: Mary Jane, Margery Jo. BA, U. Calif. at Berkeley, 1953; MA, U. Oreg. 1958; PhD, Oreg. State U., 1962. Petroleum reservoir engr. Creole Petroleum Corp., Venezuela, 1953-54; mathematician electronics div. research dept. U.S. Naval Ordnance Rsch. Lab., Corona, Calif., 1958-59; asst. prof. math. Oreg. State U., Corvallis, 1958-62, assoc. dept. oceanography, 1963-68, vis. prof. math., 1977-78; prof. math. Boise (Idaho) State U., 1968—, head dept., 1968-75, dean grad. sch., 1970-75; project dir. Dept. Energy Citizens' Workshop Energy Environment Simulator for Eastern Oreg., No. Nev. and Idaho, 1976—. Served with Ordnance Corps, AUS, 1950, 54-56. Author, reviewer of coll. textbooks; contbr. to profi. jours. Recipient Carter award, 1963, Mosser prize, 1966, Oreg. State U. Mem. Math. Assn. Am., Am. Math. Soc., Soc. Indsl. and Applied Math., Northwest Coll. and Univ. Assn. for Sci. (dir. 1973—, pres. 1990-92), Northwest Sci. Assn. (trustee 1977-80), Assoc. Western Univs. (mem. edin. and rsch. com. 1993—), Sigma Xi, Pi Mu Epsilon, Phi Kappa Phi. Home: 1400 Longmont Ave Boise ID 83706-3730

MALOOF, JAMES A(LOYSIUS), mayor, real estate company executive; b. Peoria, Ill., Oct. 18, 1919; s. Nimer and Sarah (Hamady) M.; m. Gertrude Mae Burson, June 28, 1941; children—James Michael, Mark (dec.), Nicholas, Janice. Grad. high sch., Peoria. Pres., owner Jim Maloof Realtor, Peoria, 1969—; mayor City of Peoria, 1985—. Mem. adv. bd. Peoria Civic Ctr. Commn., Jr. League Peoria, Boy's Club Peoria, Lebanon Task Force, local Peoria County Emergency Planning Com., Bradley Community Action Advisory Council; mem. exec. mgmt. bd. St. Jude Children's Research Hosp., Memphis, chmn. bd. dirs. and co-founder midwest affiliate at Meth. Med. Ctr., chmn. first telethon, 1978, past nat. exec. v.p.; chmn. Christian edn. fund drive St. Philomena Parish, Bradley U. Athletic Fund Dr.; chmn. adv. com. Peoria Big Bros. and Big Sisters; mem. Gov.'s Build Ill. Com., Ill. Job Tng. Coordinating Council, Gov.'s Statewide Taskforce on the Homeless; mem. fundraising com. Lakeview Ctr.; bd. dirs. Econ. Devel. Council Peoria Area, Peoria Conv. and Visitors Bur., Peoria Symphony, Peoria YMCA, Meth. Med. Ctr. Found. Served with USAAF, 1943-45. Recipient Pope John award, Jefferson award, Midwest Health, Am-Syrian Lebanese Clubs award, Gov.'s Citation award, Cited Congl. Record, Silver Good Citizenship medal SAR, Internat. Communication and Leadership award Toastmasters Internat., County Old Settler's Assn. award, Appreciation award Zeller Clinic, Patriotism award U.S. Marine Corps, Boss of Yr. award Am. Bus. Womens Assn., Achievement award Phoenician Club, Enterprise award Observer newspaper; named Man of Yr. B'nai Brith, Tri-County Kiwanis. Mem. Peoria Area C. of C. (bd. dirs., exec. com.), Orpheus Club, Italian Am. Soc. (hon.), Peoria Fedn. Musicians (hon.), Epsilon Sigma Alpha (hon.). Republican. Roman Catholic. Club: Creve Coeur (bd. dirs.). Lodge: Kiwanis (past pres. Southwest Peoria chpt.). Leadership Found. Realtor scholarship, Bradley Univ. Office: City of Peoria City Hall Bldg 419 Fulton St Rm 200 Peoria IL 61602-1269

MALOOF, RICHARD C., engineering executive; b. Portsmouth, N.H., Apr. 20, 1945; s. Charles and Julia (Laffey) M.; m. Cecilia Murphy, Sept. 16, 1973; children: Richard Jr., Robert. ASEE, Franklin Inst. 1965; BSEE,

Southeastern Mass. U., 1968; MSEE, Tufts U., 1970. With Bird, Inc., Norwood, Mass., 1971—, pres. roofing div., 1990—; now v.p., CEO Bird Corp., Dedham, Mass. Office: Bird Corp 980 Washington St Ste 120 Dedham MA 02026-6714*

MALOON, JAMES HAROLD, business executive, economist; b. Union City, Ohio, June 22, 1926; s. Charles E. and Bertha (Creviston) M.; children: Sharon Maloon Olson, Craig J., Elizabeth M. Maloon TerHaar, Douglas C.T. AB, Miami U., Oxford, Ohio, 1949; MA, Ind. U., 1951, PhD, 1960. Dir. fin. State of Ohio, 1958-62; exec. v.p. Reston Va. Inc., 1962-63; spl. cons. White House, Washington, 1964; sr. v.p., chief fin. officer, dir. Columbia Gas System Svc. Corp., 1965-72; exec. v.p. Pan-Am. World Airways Inc., 1972-80, dir., 1973-81; chmn., chief exec. officer, pres. Itel Corp., 1980-84; pres., prin. Rock Creek Corp., Naples, Fla., 1982—. Pres. Ohio Bd. Pub. Welfare, 1959-63; mem. Ohio Commn. Higher Edn., 1960-63; bd. dirs. Ohio Community Colls. 1960-63. With USNR, 1944-46. Mem. Sky Club, Univ. Club, Wings Club, Fairfield County (Conn.) Hunt Club, Bankers Club (San Francisco), World Trade Club (N.Y.C.), Pelican Bay Country Club (Naples, Fla.). Research in pub. and bus. adminstrn., econ. devel. underdeveloped nations, higher edn., corp. fin. and mgmt. Office: Rock Creek Corp PO Box 8539 Naples FL 33941-8539

MALOON, JERRY L., lawyer, physician, medicolegal consultant; b. Union City, Ind., Columbus, Ohio; s. James and Bertha Lucille (Creviston) M.; children: Jeffrey Lee, Jerry Lee II. BS, Ohio State U., 1960, MD, 1964; JD, Capital U. Law Sch., 1974. Intern Santa Monica (Calif.) Hosp., 1964-65; tng. psychiatry Cen. Ohio Psychiat. Hosp., 1969, Menninger Clinic, Topeka, 1970; clin. dir. Orient (Ohio) Devel. Ctr., 1967-69, med. dir., 1971-83; assoc. med. dir. Western Electric, Inc., Columbus, 1969-71; pvt. practice law, Columbus, 1978—; pres. Jerry L. Maloon Co., L.P.A., 1981—; medicolegal cons., 1972—; pres. Maloon, Maloon & Barclay Co., L.P.A., 1990-95; guest lectr. law and medicine Orient Devel. Ctr. and Columbus Devel. Ctr., 1969-71; dep. coroner Franklin County (Ohio), 1978-84. Served to capt. M.C., AUS, 1965-67. Fellow Am. Coll. Legal Medicine; mem. AMA, ABA, Ohio Bar Assn., Columbus Bar Assn., Am. Trial Lawyers Assn., Ohio Trial Lawyers Assn., Columbus Trial Lawyers Assn., Ohio State U. Alumni Assn., U.S. Trotting Assn., Am. Profl. Practice Assn. Clubs: Ohio State U. Pres.'s, Buckeye. Home: 2140 Cambridge Blvd Upper Arlngtn OH 43221-4104 Office: 475 E Town St Columbus OH 43215-4706

MALOTT, ADELE RENEE, editor; b. St. Paul, July 19, 1935; d. Clarence R. and Julia Anne (Christensen) Lindgren; m. Gene E. Malott, Oct. 24, 1957. B.S., Northwestern U., 1957. Coordinator news KGB Radio, San Diego, 1958-60; asst. pub. relations dir. St. Paul C. of C., 1961-63; night editor Daily Local News, West Chester, Pa., 1963-65; editor, co-pub. Boutique and Villager, Burlingame, Calif., 1966-76; sr. editor mag. The Webb Co., St. Paul, 1978-84; editor GEM Pub. Group, Reno, 1985—; co-pub. The Mature Traveler, 1987—; mem. faculty Reader's Digest Writers' Workshops. Co-author: Get Up and Go: A Guide for the Mature Traveler, 1989. Recipient numerous awards Nat. Fedn. Press Women, Calif. Newspaper Pubs. Assn., San Francisco Press Club, Calif. Taxpayers Assn., White House Citations. Mem. Internat. Assn. Bus. Communicators (Merit award 1984), Press Women Minn. (numerous awards), Press Women Nev. Avocations: historical research; golf; travel; photography; reading.

MALOTT, FRANK STEPHEN, foreign service officer; b. Pasadena, Tex., Nov. 29, 1949; s. Frank Barhum and Mary Margaret (Williams) M.; m. Leslie Irene Hale, Jan. 14, 1984; B.S. in Bus. Adminstrn., Georgetown U., 1971; M.P.A., U. So. Calif., 1979. Asst. dean Georgetown U., Washington, 1971-73, 78-79; bus. mgr. Coll. and Univ. Personnel, Washington, 1974-77; prin. Hay Assocs., Phila., 1977-78; dir. compensation U. Alaska, Fairbanks, 1980-82; fgn. service officer Dept. State, Washington 1982—, consul, Curaçao, 1984—. Treas., Coll. Young Democratic Clubs Am., 1969-70; v.p. U.S. Youth Council, 1970-71. Mem. Georgetown U. Alumni Assn. (bd. dirs. 1978-84), Am. Fgn. Service Assn., Am. Assn. Higher Edn. Presbyterian. Home: Choncorogaiweg 2 Willemstad, Curaçao Netherlands Antilles Office: Am Consul Curaçao Dept State Washington DC 20520

MALOTT, JAMES RAYMOND, JR., lawyer; b. Globe, Ariz., Feb. 23, 1917; s. James Raymond and Edith (Spencer) M.; m. Carol Hover, Sept. 9, 1939 (div. Sept. 1948); children—James Spencer, Lucinda; m. Barbara Farr, Feb. 20, 1949 (div. Jan. 1974); m. Ruth Austin, Jan. 10, 1975 (dec. Jan. 1986). Student, U. Ariz., 1934-36; A.B., Stanford U., 1938, LL.B., 1941. Bar: Ariz. 1940. Dep. county atty. Gila County, 1943; practice in Globe, 1945—; mem. firm Morris & Malott, 1948-94; ret., 1994. Served to 2d lt. USAAF, 1944-45. Mem. State Bar Ariz. (bd. govs. 1955-60, v.p. 1959-60). Home: 1220 Skyline Dr Globe AZ 85501-2062 Office: 1450 South St Globe AZ 85501-1438

MALOTT, JOHN RAYMOND, foreign service officer; b. Kankakee, Ill., Nov. 5, 1946; s. Raymond Roderick and Ruth Pearl (Jacobs) M.; m. Hiroko Iwami, Nov. 23, 1971; children: David Iwami, Rumi Justine. BA, Northwestern U., 1967; grad., Nat. War Coll., 1983. Civilian advisor U.S. Dept. State, Vietnam, 1969-70; China desk officer U.S. Dept. State, Washington, 1970-71; Am. consul U.S. Dept. State, Kobe, Japan, 1971-73; 1st sec. Am. Embassy U.S. Dept. State, Tokyo, Japan, 1974-77; Sri Lanka desk officer U.S. Dept. State, Washington, 1977-78, India desk officer, 1978-80; Am. consul &, Bombay, India, 1980-82; with Nat. War Coll. &, Washington, 1982-83, dep. dir. Japan Affairs, 1983-85, spl. asst. to Under Sec. State Econ. Affairs, 1985-86; Am. consul gen. &, Osaka, Japan, 1986-89; dir. Japan Affairs &, Washington, 1989-91, sr. seminar, 1991-92, dep. asst. sec. state South Asian Affairs, 1992-93; sr. advisor to Undersec. State for Econ. Affairs, Washington, 1993—. Author: Partners, 1992. Recipient Vietnam Svc. award, 1970, Meritorious Honor award Dept. State, 1982, Superior honor award, 1991. Mem. Am. Fgn. Svc. Assn. Presbyterian. Office: Dept State 2201 C St NW Washington DC 20520

MALOTT, ROBERT HARVEY, manufacturing company executive; b. Boston, Oct. 6, 1926; s. Deane W. and Eleanor (Thrum) M.; m. Elizabeth Harwood Hubert, June 4, 1960; children: Elizabeth Malott Pohle, Barbara Holden, Robert Deane. A.B., U. Kans., 1948; M.B.A., Harvard U., 1950; postgrad., N.Y. U. Law Sch., 1953-55. Asst. to dean Harvard Grad. Sch. Bus. Adminstrn., 1950-52; with FMC Corp., 1952—; asst. to exec. v.p. chems. div. FMC Corp., N.Y.C., 1952-55; controller Niagara Chem. div. FMC Corp., Middleport, N.Y., 1955-59; controller organic chems. div. FMC Corp., N.Y.C., 1959-62; asst. div. mgr. FMC Corp., 1962-63, div. mgr., 1963-65, v.p., mgr. film ops. Am. Viscose div., 1966-67, exec. v.p., mem. president's office, 1967-70; mgr. machinery divs. FMC Corp., Chgo., 1970-72; pres. FMC Corp., from 1972, chief exec. officer, 1972-91, chmn., 1973-91, chmn., exec. com., 1991—; dir. FMC Corp., Amoco Corp., United Techs. Corp. Trustee U. Chgo.; bd. govs. Argonne Labs.; bd. overseers Hoover Instn.; mem. Nat. Bd. of Nat. Mus. of Nat. Hist. Smithsonian Inst.; bd. dirs. Nat. Park Found. Served with USNR, 1944-46. Mem. Bus. Coun., U.S. C. of C., Econ. Club, Chgo. Club, Mid-Am. Club, Explorers Club, Indian Hill Club, Bohemian Club, Phi Beta Kappa, Beta Theta Pi, Alpha Chi Sigma. Office: FMC Corp 200 E Randolph Dr Chicago IL 60601-6401

MALOUFF, FRANK JOSEPH, health care association executive; b. La Junta, Colo., Aug. 21, 1947; s. Phillip Francis and Lillian Aileen (Sayklay) M.; m. Virginia Lynn Frye, Aug. 24, 1968; children: Lynnea, Joseph, J. Daniel, David. BS in Journalism, U. Colo., Boulder, 1969; MS in Health Adminstrn., U. Colo., Denver, 1974; LLD (hon.), Ohio Coll. Podiatric Medicine, 1988. Program adminstr. U. Colo. Health Scis. Ctr., Denver, 1974-83; exec. dir. Ohio Podiatric Med. Assn., Columbus, 1983-89, Am. Podiatric Med. Assn., Bethesda, Md., 1989—; dir. Fund for Podiatric Med. Edn., Bethesda, 1986—, Foothealth Found. Am., Bethesda, 1991—. Contbg. author: Handbook of Healthcare Human Resources Management, 1981; co-author: Pursuing Mastery: Professional Development Tools and Techniques, 1991; columnist in field. Leader Boy Scouts Am., various locations. 1st lt. U.S. Army, 1969-72, Korea. Mem. Am. Soc. Healthcare Edn. and Tng. (officer 1977-81, Disting. Svc. award 1982, past dir.), Am. Soc. Assn. Execs., Am. Inst. Parliamentarians. Roman Catholic. Avocation: lay church ministry. Office: Am Podiatric Med Assn 9312 Old Georgetown Rd Bethesda MD 20814-1646

MALOUIN, JEAN-LOUIS, university dean, educator; b. Three-Rivers, Que., Can., Oct. 5, 1943; m. Hélène Pépin; children: Pascale, Philippe. B in Commerce, Université Laval, Que., 1965, MSc, 1966; PhD, UCLA, 1970. Prof. Bus. Sch., U. Laval, 1966-89, dir. OSD dept., 1971-75, 78-79, assoc. dean acad. affairs, 1979-84, dean, 1984-89; dean faculty of bus. U. Alta., Edmonton, Alta., Can., 1989-92; dean faculty of adminstrn. U. Ottawa, Ottawa, Ont., Can., 1992—; coord. Can. Consortium for the Suuport of the Sea. Editor: The Generation of Scientific Administrative Knowledge, 1986; co-author: L'Innovation Technologique dans les PME Manufacturières: études de cas enquête, 1992. Bd. dirs. Centre québécois de Productivité, du Vêtement, Montréal, 1983-86, Nat. Rsch. Ctr., London, 1986-87, Banff Sch. Advancement Mgmt., 1989-92. Mem. Can. Fedn. Deans (v.p. 1987), Edmonton C. of C. (bd. dirs. 1989-92). Home: 1410 Clay Ct, Gloucester, ON Canada K1C 4T2 Office: U Ottawa Faculty Adminstrn, 136 Jean-Jacques Lussier St, Ottawa, ON Canada K1N 6N5

MALOVANCE, GREGORY J., lawyer; b. Munster, Ind., June 29, 1954. BA in Economics magna cum laude, Emory U., 1975; JD, U. Chgo., 1978. Bar: Ill. 1978, U.S. Dist. Ct. (no. dist.) Ill. 1978, U.S. Ct. Appeals (7th cir.) 1978. Ptnr. Winston & Strawn, Chgo. Mem. ABA (litigation sect., labor and employment rels. sect.), Ill. State Bar Assn., Phi Beta Kappa. Office: Winston & Strawn 35 W Wacker Dr Chicago IL 60601-1614

MALOZEMOFF, PLATO, mining executive; b. Russia, 1909. BS, U. Calif., Berkeley, 1931; MS, Mont. Sch. Mines, 1932. Metall. engr. Pan-Am. Engring., Berkeley, 1933-39; mgr. of mines of pvt. co.'s Argentina and Costa Rica, 1939-42; mining analyst OPA, Washington, 1942-45; with Newmont Mining Corp., N.Y.C., 1945-87, chief exec. officer, 1954-85, chmn. emeritus, 1985—. Bd. dirs. Boys' and Girls' Clubs Am., Tolstoy Found., Inc.; dir. trustee Am. Mus. Natural History; mem. James Madison coun. Libr. of Congress. Office: 230 Park Ave Rm 1154 New York NY 10169-0004

MALPAS, ROBERT, company executive; b. Birkenhead, Eng., Aug. 9, 1927; s. Cheshyre and Louise M.; m. Effie Josephine Dickenson, June 30, 1956. BSc with honors, Durham (Eng.) U., 1948. With ICI, Ltd., Millbank, London, 1948-78, main bd. dir., 1975-78; pres. Halcon Internat., Inc., N.Y.C., 1978-82; mng. dir., main bd. Brit. Petroleum PLC, London, 1983-89; chmn. PowerGen. London, 1988-90, Cookson Group, PLC, 1991—; bd. dirs. BOC Group PLC, Eurotunnel PLC, Repsol SA (Spain). Decorated comdr. Order Brit. Empire; recipient Order of Civil Merit, Spain, 1967. Fellow Engring. Inst. Chem Engrs., Inst. Mech. Engrs., Inst. Energy, Royal Soc. Chemistry (hon.); mem. Royal Swedish Acad. Engring. Scis. (fgn.), Am. Acad. Engring. (fgn. assoc.), River Club (N.Y.C.), RAC Club (London), Mill Reef Club (Antigua).

MALPASS, LESLIE FREDERICK, retired university president; b. Hartford, Conn., May 16, 1922; s. Fred J. and Lilly (Elmslie) M.; m. Winona Helen Cassin, May 17, 1946; children: Susan Heather (Mrs. J. Poulton), Peter Gordon, Jennifer Joy (Mrs. T. Droege), Michael Andrew. BA, Syracuse U., 1947, MA, 1949, PhD, 1952. Diplomate Am. Bd. Profi. Psychology. Psychologist Onondaga County (N.Y.) Child Guidance Center Syracuse, 1947-52; lectr. Syracuse U., also U. Buffalo, 1949-52; asst. prof. then assoc. prof. So. Ill. U., 1952-60; vis. prof. U. Fla., 1959-60; prof. psychology, chmn. div. behavioral scis. U. So. Fla., 1960-63; dean Coll. Arts and Scis., Va. Poly Inst., Blacksburg, 1965-68; v.p. acad. affairs Va. Poly Inst., 1968-74; pres. Western Ill. U., Macomb, 1974-87, pres. emeritus, 1987—; cons. in field; lectr. Duke U., 1988-93. Author books and articles in field. With M.C., AUS, 1944-46. Fellow APA; mem. AAAS, AAUP, Assn. for Higher Edn., Sigma Xi, Psi Chi, Theta Chi Beta, Omicron Delta Kappa, Beta Gamma Sigma, Phi Mu Alpha. Home: 3927 Swarthmore Dr Durham NC 27707-5313 Office: Western Ill U Adams St Macomb IL 61455

MALPHURS, ROGER EDWARD, insurance company executive, chiropractor, biomedical technologist, private commodity trader; b. Lake Worth, Fla., Dec. 15, 1933; s. Cecil Edward and Muriel Thelma (Ward) M.; m. Carolyn Sue Calapp, Feb. 2, 1963(div. 1993); children: Steven, Brian, Darren, Regina, Victoria. BS, U. Utah, 1961; D of Chiropractic, Palmer Coll. Chiropractic West, 1990. Cert. med. technologist; lic. chiropractor, Calif., Ariz. Supr. spl. chemistry Cen. Pathology Lab., Santa Rosa, Calif., 1968-73; mgr. lab. Community Hosp., Santa Rosa, 1973-76; supr. chem., staff asst. Meml. Hosp., Santa Rosa, 1976-85; pres., chief exec. officer R.E. Malphurs Co., Sunnyvale, Calif., 1972—; owner, developer REMCO Mktg. Assocs., Santa Rosa, 1970-71; owner Better Bus. Forms and Typeset, Santa Rosa, 1977-81, commodity pool operator, 1979-80; dept. mgr. immunochemistry Spectra Labs., Fremont, Calif., 1990-95; pvt. commodity trader; clin. trials cons. hematology Abbott Diagnostics, Santa Clara, Calif., 1995—. Author: A New, Simple Way to Win at Blackjack, 1972. Served as squadron commdr. CAP USAF Aux., 1982-84. Mem. Am. Chiropractic Assn., Calif. Chiropractic Assn., Optimists Internat. (youth awards chmn. 1969-74), Am. Pub. Health Assn., Toastmasters (sec./treas. 1988-89), Rep. Senatorial Inner Circle. Republican. Avocations: flying, computers, pistol shooting, oil painting, writing.

MALSACK, JAMES THOMAS, retired manufacturing company executive; b. Milw., Apr. 4, 1921; s. Leonard Henry and Florence Alice (Webb) M.; m. Joyce Irene Niemi, Aug. 1, 1963; children: Thomas James, Claudia Irene, Robert Richard, Thomas John, Pamela Joyce. BSBA, Marquette U., 1946; D Pub. Svc. (hon.), No. Mich. U., 1990. Acct. Price Waterhouse & Co., Milw., 1946-51; with Lake Shore, Inc., Iron Mountain, Mich., 1951-88; exec. v.p. Lake Shore, Inc., 1959-72, pres., chief exec. officer, 1972-84, chmn., 1984-88; dir. First Nat. Bank, Iron Mountain. Trustee No. Mich. U., 1977-89, now trustee emeritus. Mem. VFW. Mem. Masons, Shriners. Republican. Episcopalian. Home (winter): 8326 E LaSenda Scottsdale AZ 85255

MALSON, REX RICHARD, drug and health care corporation executive; b. Stanberry, Mo., Nov. 26, 1931; s. Albert J. Curtis and Nellie E. Coburn (Bussey) M.; m. Jimmie S., May 25, 1956 (dec. 1980); children: Richard Gary, Gregory Neil; m. Vicki L., Feb. 10, 1983 (div. Aug. 1984). B.B.A., Ga. State U., 1961; postgrad. grad. exec. program, U. Chgo., 1967; postgrad. exec. program hon., Stanford U., 1983; LHD (hon.), L.I. U., 1989. Gen. transp. mgr. John Sexton & Co., Chgo., 1964-68; dir. distbn. system Keebler Co., Chgo., 1968-73; with drug and health care group McKesson Corp., San Francisco, 1973-92, vice pres., 1984-86, exec. v.p. ops., 1986-89, pres. & chief operating officer, 1989-92, also vice chmn.,bd. dirs.; ret., 1992; bd. dirs. Sunbelt Beverage Co., Balt., Stationers Distbg. Co., Ft. Worth; chmn. bd. dirs. Armor All Products Corp. Served with U.S. Navy, 1951-55, Korea. Mem. Am. Soc. Traffic and Transp. Republican. Office: McKesson Corp 1 Post St San Francisco CA 94104-5201

MALSTROM, ROBERT A., lawyer; b. Ancon, Panama, May 28, 1946. BS with highest honors, U. Ill., 1969; JD cum laude, U. Mich., 1973. Bar: Ill. 1974. Ptnr. Sidley & Austin, Chgo. With U.S. Army, 1969-71. Mem. Law Club Chgo., Chgo. Estate Planning Coun. Office: Sidley & Austin 1 First Nat Plz Chicago IL 60603

MALTBY, RICHARD ELDRIDGE, JR., theater director, lyricist; b. Ripon, Wis., Oct. 6, 1937; s. Richard Eldridge and Virginia (Hosegood) D.; m. Janet Brenner, 1987; children: Nicholas Avery, David Stevenson, Jordan Brenner, Emily Celia, Charlotte Perry. B.A., Yale U., 1959. Dir. lyricist: Starting Here, Starting Now, 1977; dir. Ain't Misbehavin', 1978 (Tony award, N.Y. Drama Critics Circle award, Drama Desk award, Obie award Best Musical, Tony award Best Dir.); dir., lyricist Baby, 1983 (3 Tony award nominations); dir., co-lyricist Song and Dance, 1985 (Tony award nomination); co-lyricist Miss Saigon, 1989 (London Evening Standard Best Musical, London Drama Critics award, 3 Tony awards); dir., lyricist Closer Than Ever, 1989 (2 Outer Critics Circle awards, Best Off-Broadway Musical, Best Score); ptnr. FWM Producing Group. Mem. ASCAP, Dramatists Guild, Soc. Stage Dirs. and Choreographers. Office: care Flora Roberts Inc 157 W 57th St New York NY 10019-2210

MALTESE, GEORGE JOHN, mathematics educator; b. Middletown, Conn., June 24, 1931; s. Giorgio and Sebastiana (Morello) M.; m. Marlene Erika Kunz, Apr. 14, 1956; children: Christopher, Michelle. BA, Wesleyan U., Middletown, Conn., 1953; postgrad., U. Frankfurt, Germany, 1953-54; PhD, Yale U., 1960. Instr. MIT, 1961-63; asst. prof. U. Md., College Park,

1963-66, assoc. prof., 1966-69; prof. U. Md., 1969-73, U. Münster, Fed. Republic Germany, 1973—; vis. prof. U. Frankfurt, 1966-67, 70-71, U. Palermo, Italy, 1967, 71, 76. U. Pisa, Italy, 1972, U. Kuwait, 1977, U. Bahrain, 1988, U. Oman, 1991. Contbr. articles to profl. jours. Served with AUS, 1954-56. Fulbright fellow, 1953-54; NATO postdoctoral fellow, 1960-61. Mem. Am. Math. Soc., Math. Assn. Am., Unione Matematica Italiana, Deutsche Mathematiker Verein, Austrian Math. Soc. Home: Kampstrasse 9, 48147 Münster Germany Office: Math Inst, Einstein Strasse 62, 48149 Münster Germany

MALTESE, SERPHIN RALPH, state senator, lawyer; b. N.Y.C., Dec. 7, 1932; s. Paul and Frances (Scafidi) M.; m. Constance Mary Del Vecchio, Aug. 27, 1955; children—Andrea Constance, Leslie Serphine, Serphin Ralph (dec.). B.A., Manhattan Coll., 1958; LL.B., J.D. (War Service scholar 1958-62), Fordham U., 1962. Bar: N.Y. bar 1963. Trial atty. for ins. cos., 1963-66; asst. dist. atty., dep. chief homicide bur. Queens County, N.Y., 1966-69; asso. counsel N.Y. State Com. Campaign Disorders, 1969-70; counsel N.Y. State Com. Deaf and Multiple Impaired, 1970; chmn. law com. Buckley for U.S. Senator, 1970; counsel N.Y. State Assembly, 1972-76; counsel N.Y. State Senate, Albany, 1976-88, state senator, 1988—, chmn. senate standing com. on elections, mem. com. on aging, alcoholism and drug abuse, mem. codes and investigations and govt. ops. com.; exec. dir. N.Y. State Conservative Party, 1971-86, exec. vice chmn., 1978-86, state chmn., 1986-88. Chmn. trustees Christ the King Regional H.S., 1976—; pres. We Care Civic Assn., 1968-76, chmn. exec. bd., 1978-88; past cmty. chmn. local Boy Scouts Am.; N.Y. State chmn. Conservatives for Ronald Reagan, 1980. With AUS, 1952-54, Korea. Recipient Charles Edison Meml. award N.Y. State Conservative Party, 1977, St. John's U. Pres.'s medal, 1994. Mem. N.Y. State Bar Assn., Queens Assn. Dist. Attys. Assn., Christopher Columbus Assn. (chmn. 1970—), Young Americans for Freedom (nat. sr. adv. bd.), Am. Conservative Union (nat. bd. dirs.), Internat. Assn. Space Philatelists, Am. Mgmt. Assn., Queens C. of C., Alexander Hamilton Conservative Club (chmn. exec. com. 1971-88), Harold Gray Collectors Soc. (pres.), Met. Post Card Collectors Club, Am. Legion, VFW, Alpha Phi Delta. Roman Catholic. Home: 60-16 74th St Middle Village NY 11373 Office: 71-04 Myrtle Ave Glendale NY 11385 Office: 803 Legislative Office Bldg Albany NY 12247

MALTIN, LEONARD, television commentator, writer; b. N.Y.C., Dec. 18, 1950; s. Aaron Isaac and Jacqueline (Gould) M.; m. Alice Tlusty, Mar. 15, 1975; 1 child, Jessica Bennett. BA, NYU, 1972. Mem. faculty New Sch. for Social Rsch., N.Y.C., 1973-81; curator Am. Acad. Humor, N.Y.C., 1975-76; guest curator dept. film Mus. Modern Art, N.Y.C., 1976; film critic and corr. Entertainment Tonight, Hollywood, Calif., 1982—; author: Movie Comedy Teams, 1970, rev. edit., 1985, Behind the Camera (reprinted as The Art of the Cinematographer), 1971, The Great Movie Shorts (reprinted as Selected Short Subjects), 1971, The Disney Films, 1973, rev. edit., 1984, 95, The Great Movie Comedians, 1978, Of Mice and Magic: A History of American Animated Cartoons, 1980, rev. edit., 1987; co-author: Our Gang: The Life and Times of the Little Rascals, 1977, reprinted as The Little Rascals: The Life and Times of Our Gang, 1992; editor: Leonard Maltin's Movie & Video Guide, 1969, rev. annually Leonard Maltin's Movie Encyclopedia, 1994; prodr., writer, host (video) Cartoons for Big Kids, 1989; writer (TV spl.) Fantasia: The Making of a Disney Classic, 1990; writer, host (video) The Making of the Quiet Man, 1992, The Making of High Noon, 1992, Cartoon Madness: The Fantastic Max Fleischer Cartoons, 1993, Cliffhanger!, 1993. Author: Movie Comedy Teams, 1970, rev. edit., 1985, Behind the Camera (reprinted as The Art of the Cinematographer), 1971, The Great Movie Shorts (reprinted as Selected Short Subjects), 1971, The Disney Films, 1973, rev. edit., 1995, The Great Movie Comedians, 1978, Of Mice and Magic: A History of American Animated Cartoons, 1980, rev. edit., 1987; co-author: Our Gang: The Life and Times of the Little Rascals, 1977, reprinted as The Little Rascals: The Life and Times of Our Gang, 1992; editor: Leonard Maltin's Movie & Video Guide, 1969, rev. annually, Leonard Maltin's Movie Encyclopedia, 1994; producer, writer, host (video) Cartoons for Big Kids, 1989; writer (TV spl.) Fantasia: The Making of a Disney Classic, 1990; writer, host (video) The Making of The Quiet Man, 1992, The Making of High Noon, 1992, Cartoon Madness: The Fantastic Max Fleischer Cartoons, 1993, Cliffhanger!, 1993. Mem. steering com. Hollywood Entertainment Mus., 1989—. Mem. Authors Guild, Soc. for Cinephiles (pres. 1990-91, Man of Yr. 1973), L.A. Film Critics Assn. (pres. 1995-96). Office: care Entertainment Tonight Paramount TV 5555 Melrose Ave Los Angeles CA 90038-3149

MALTZ, J. HERBERT, physician, hospital director; b. Passaic, N.J., Jan. 8, 1920; s. Michael and Esther (Rinzler) M.; m. Sybil Zun, Sept. 27, 1947; 1 child, Roger A. Student, U. Wis., 1938-41; B.A., U. Miami, 1942; M.D., Chgo. Med. Sch., 1947. Diplomate: Am. Bd. Psychiatry and Neurology. Intern Wilmington (Del.) Gen. Hosp., 1947-48; psychiat. resident Ill. Dept. Pub. Welfare, 1948-51; clin. instr. psychiatry Chgo. Med. Sch., 1951-55; practice medicine specializing in psychiatry Chgo., 1951—; asst. to supt. Chgo. State Hosp., 1956-58, supt., 1958-66; med. dir. Ridgeway Hosp., 1966-69, Chgo. Lake Shore Hosp., 1970-85; mem. staff St. Joseph's Hosp., Chgo., Barclay Hosp., Chgo., Ill. Masonic Hosp.; former mem. faculty Northwestern U. Med. Sch., Chgo. Med. Sch. Fellow Am. Psychiat. Assn. Jewish. Home: 3260 N Lake Shore Dr Chicago IL 60657-3955 Office: 4840 N Marine Dr Chicago IL 60640

MALTZ, JEROME PAUL, broadcasting executive; b. Chgo., June 3, 1935; s. Benjamin Nathan and Bess (Packer) M.; m. Margaret Magda Hoffmann, Mar. 27, 1959 (div. Jan. 1978); children: Jason Bess; m. Margi Orly Kaufman, Apr. 20, 1986. BA, UCLA, 1956; MBA, NYU, 1967. Pvt. practice oil lease broker Los Angeles, 1969-73, pvt. practice real estate broker, developer, 1973—; broadcasting exec. Gen. Broadcasting Corp., Los Angeles, 1984—; chmn. Gen. Broadcasting Corp., Los Angeles, 1984—. Served with USAR, 1957-63. Named Man of Yr., Gendel chpt. City of Hope, Los Angeles, 1987. Mem. Calif. Broadcasters Assn. (bd. dirs. 1986—). Democrat. Jewish. Club: Friars (Beverly Hills, Calif.). Avocation: travel. Office: Gen Broadcasting Corp 11685 Magnolia Blvd # A North Hollywood CA 91601-3065

MALTZAN, MICHAEL THOMAS, architect; b. Roslyn Heights, N.Y., Oct. 10, 1959; s. William George and Jaqualine (Cain) M.; m. Amy Louise Murphy, Sept. 25, 1988. Student, Wentworth Inst. Tech., 1977-79; BFA, RISD, 1984, BArch, 1985; MArch, Harvard U., 1988. Lic. architect, Calif. Architect The Architects, Glastonbury, Conn., 1978-80, William D. Warner Assocs., Exeter, R.I., 1980-83, Steven Lerner Assocs., Providence, 1983-84, Schwartz/Silver Assocs., Boston, 1984-86, Machado-Silvetti Assocs., Boston, 1986-88, Frank O. Gehry Assocs., L.A., 1988—; instr. RISD, Providence, 1987, Harvard U., Cambridge, Mass., 1988; co-instr. UCLA, 1989; invited jury critic Harvard U., RISD, So. Calif. Inst. Architecture, L.A., Ariz. State U., tempe, Calif. Coll. Arts and Crafts, San Francisco, U. SO. Calif., L.A., UCLA, Iowa State U., Ames, Miami (Ohio) U. Prin. works include Sweat Equity Housing, Hartford, Conn., 1978-80, Unitarian-Universalist Ch., Vernon, Conn., 1979, Providence Riverfront Study, 1982, Harvard Law Sch. Alumni Bldg. Addition, Cambridge, 1984, 330 Congress St. Renovation, Boston, 1985, 280 Summer St. Renovation, Boston, 1986, City of Leonforte, Italy Master Plan, 1987 (Progressive Architecture award), North Park Apt. Complex Renovation, Chevy Chase, Md., 1988, Walt Disney Concert Hall, 1988— (Progressive Architecture award), Culver City (Calif.) Retail Complex Master Plan, 1990, Villa Olympica Retail and Entertainment Complex, Barcelona, Spain, 1992., U. Toledo Art Sch., 1992 (AIA award), Inner-City Arts Sch., L.A., 1994, various pvt. resdl. bldgs.

MALTZMAN, IRVING MYRON, psychology educator; b. Bklyn., May 9, 1924; s. Israel and Lillian (Mass) M.; m. Diane Seiden, Aug. 21, 1949; children—Sara, Kenneth, Ilaine. B.A., N.Y.U., 1946; Ph.D., State U. Iowa, 1949. Mem. faculty UCLA, 1949—, assoc. prof., 1957-60, prof. psychology, 1961—, chmn. dept., 1970-77. Co-author: Handbook of Contemporary Soviet Psychology, 1969. Fellow APA, AAAS; mem. Phi Beta Kappa, Sigma Xi. Home: 11260-22B Overland Ave Culver City CA 90230-5559

MALVERN, DONALD, retired aircraft manufacturing company executive; b. Sterling, Okla., Apr. 22, 1921; s. George Michael and Anna Francesca (Elsass) M.; m. Ruth Marie Vogler, June 4, 1949; 1 son, Michael John. BSME, U. Okla., 1946. Engr. Victory Architects and Engrs., Clinton,

Okla., 1943, Douglas Aircraft Co., Santa Monica, Calif., 1943; with McDonnell Aircraft Co., St. Louis, 1946-88; exec. v.p. McDonnell Aircraft Co., 1973-82, pres., 1982-86; v.p. McDonnell Douglas Corp., 1973-88; aerospace cons. St. Louis, 1988—; pres. McDonnell Douglas Services, Inc., 1978-82. Trustee Falcon Found., 1983—; bd. visitors Def. Sys. Mgmt. Coll., 1983-86, U. Okla. Coll. Engring., 1988-91; pres. Wings of Hope, 1989-92, chmn., 1992—. 1st lt. USAAF, 1943-46; capt. Mo. Air NG, 1946-51. Inducted into Okla. Aviation and Space Mus.'s Hall of Fame, 1987. Fellow AIAA (Tech. Mgmt. award 1968, Reed Aeros. medal 1980); mem. Am. Def. Preparedness Assn. (pres. St. Louis chpt. 1979-80), Navy League U.S. (life), Nat. Aeros. Assn., Air Force Assn., Armed Forces Mgmt. Assn., Pi Tau Sigma, Tau Beta Pi, Tau Omega, Sigma Tau Beta. Clubs: Bellerive Country, St. Louis. Home: 213 Grand Banks Ct Chesterfield MO 63017-9507

MALVERN, LAWRENCE EARL, engineering educator, researcher; b. Sterling, Okla., Sept. 14, 1916; s. George Michael and Anna Francesca (Elsass) M.; m. Marjorie Malene McCarther, Aug. 8, 1939 (dec. Jan. 1985); 1 dau., Maureen; m. Myra Louise Engelhardt, Sept. 18, 1987. Sc.B., Southwestern Okla. State Coll., 1937; M.A., U. Okla., 1939; Ph.D., Brown U., 1949. High sch. tchr. Marlow, Clinton, El Reno, Okla., 1937-38, 39-40, 40-42; asst. prof. math and mechanics Carnegie-Mellon U., Pitts., 1949-53; assoc. prof. applied mechanics Mich. State U., East Lansing, 1953-58, prof., 1958-69; prof. engring. scis. U. Fla., Gainesville, 1969-93; prof. emeritus. Assoc. editor: Jour. Applied Mechanics, 1978-85; author: Introduction to the Mechanics of a Continuous Medium, 1969, Engineering Mechanics-Statics and Dynamics, 2 vols., 1976. Served to lt. (j.g.) USNR, 1944-46. Guggenheim fellow, 1959. Fellow ASME (Worcester Reed Warner medal 1989), Am. Acad. Mechanics, Assn. Soc. Engring. Sci. (dir. 1967-70), Sigma Xi. Home: 3901 NW 21st Ln Gainesville FL 32605-3566 Office: U Fla 231 Aerospace Bldg Gainesville FL 32611

MALY, KURT JOHN, computer science educator; b. Modling, Austria, Aug. 20, 1944; came to U.S. 1969; s. Anton and Editha (Gneist) M.; m. Christiana Peterlik, Mar. 18, 1972; 1 child, Angela Claudia. Diplom Ingenieur summa cum laude, U. Tech., Austria, 1968; MS, Courant Inst. NYU, 1970, PhD, 1973. Asst. prof. U. Minn., Mpls., 1972-78, assoc. prof., 1978-85, acting head, 1980-82, head, 1982-85; eminent prof., chmn. computer sci. Old Dominion U., Norfolk, Va., 1985—, Kaufman prof., 1991—; hon. prof. Chengdu U. of Sci. and Tech., People's Republic of China, 1986—, Hefei U., People's Republic of China, 1991—, Guangxi Computer Inst., People's Republic of China, 1993—; bd. dirs. Inst. of Info. Tech., Ctr. for Innovative Tech., Blacksburg, Va., 1988-92; bd. dirs., exec. co-dir. Microelectronic and Info. Scis. Ctr., Mpls., 1980-85. Author: Fundamentals of the Computing Sciences, 1978; assoc. editor: Jour. for Microcomputer Application Tech., PRC; contbr. articles to profl. jours. Served with Austrian Air Force, 1963-64. Fellow Sorbonne U., Paris, 1966, Courant Inst., N.Y.C., 1968-72. Mem. Assn. Computing Machinery, IEEE, Sigma Xi. Roman Catholic. Office: Old Dominion U Norfolk VA 23508

MALZAHN, RAY ANDREW, chemistry educator, university dean; b. Fort Madison, Iowa, July 8, 1929; s. Arnold Frederick and Inez (Russel) M.; m. Elizabeth Mae Barrett, Aug. 23, 1953; children—Karen Louise, Janet Elizabeth. B.A., Gustavus Adolphus Coll., 1951; M.S., U. N.D., 1953; Ph.D., U. Md., 1962. Research assoc. U. Ariz., Tucson, 1961-63; asst. prof. chemistry West Tex. State U., Canyon, 1963-65, assoc. prof., 1965-67, prof. chemistry, 1967-80, dean Coll. Arts and Scis., 1967-71, v.p. acad. affairs, 1971-77; prof., dean Sch. Arts and Scis. Mo. So. State Coll., Joplin, 1980—, interim v.p. for acad. affairs, 1993-94. Served with AUS, 1954-56. Mem. Am. Chem. Soc. Home: 1215 Goetz Blvd Joplin MO 64801-1433

MAMANA, JOSEPH, editor; b. Easton, Pa., Sept. 3, 1909; s. Domenico Louis and Maria Filippe (Sacchetti) M.; m. Julia Cericola, Sept. 20, 1935; children: Joseph Jr., James, John, Julianne, June. BS, U. Notre Dame, MA, 1932; postgrad., Muhlenberg Coll., 1932. Cert. tchr., guidance counselor, prin., supt. Tchr. Pocono Sch. for Girls, Pocono Manor, Pa., 1929-30; tchr. U. Notre Dame, Notre Dame, Ind., 1931-32, Easton Sch. Dist., Easton, Pa., 1933-46; guidance counselor Easton Sch. Dist., 1947-50, prin., 1951-72; editor PASSP Schoolmaster Publs., Harrisburg, Pa., 1970-92, editor emeritus, 1992—; investment mgr. Boyd Investment Svcs., Easton, 1974—; pres. Easton Edn. Assn., 1957-59; dist. XI commr. Pa. Interscholastic Athletic Assn., Easton High Sch. Assn., 1955-72; pres. Investment Svcs. Cons., 1974—. Contbr. edn. articles to PASSP Jour., 1970— . Edn. chmn. N.C. Am. Cancer Soc., Bethlehem, Pa., 1947-57, N.C. Am. Heart Assn., Bethlehem, 1957-67; mem. bd. 112U.S. SSS, Easton, 1967-73; police commn. mem. to study police brutality, Easton. Recipient Medal of Honor (educator) Freedoms Found., Valley Forge, Pa., 1965, Notre Dame U. Alumni award, 1992; named Nat. Prin. of Yr., A.C. Croft Pubs., Vision Inc., N.J., 1963; named to Dist. XI Wrestling Hall of Fame, Pa. Interscholastic Athletic Assn., 1981; established Joseph Mamana Award of Merit, Pa. Prins. Assn., 1990. Mem. NEA (life, del. 1957-59), Pa. Assn. Secondary Sch. Prins. (life, chmn. real estate com. 1980-90), Easton Area Schoolmen's Assn. (life, pres. 1948-72, Schoolman of Yr. 1955, 89), Prins. Assn., Notre Dame Univ. Club (Alumni Svc. award 1992), Investments Club (mgr. 1974-95). Avocations: stone masonry, swimming, track, wrestling, collecting rare books. Home: 200 Burke St Easton PA 18042

MAMANGAKIS, JOHN PAUL, health facility administrator. BA in Bus. Adminstrn. and Acctg., Rutgers U., 1978; MBA in Health Adminstrn. and fin., Temple U., 1980. DRG coord. St. Barnabas Med. Ctr., Livingston, N.J., 1980, asst. v.p., 1980-83, v.p. support svcs., 1983-84, v.p. ops. rev., 1984; mgr. Ernst & Whinney, Newark, 1984-85; asst. adminstr. NYU Med. Ctr., N.Y.C., 1986-89, assoc. adminstr., 1989-92; adminstr. Morristown (N.J.) Cardiology Assocs., 1993—; v.p. New Rochelle (N.Y.) Hosp. Med. Ctr., 1993-95. Author: DRG Reference Manual, 1982. Fellow Am. Coll. Healthcare Execs.; mem. Met. Health Adminstrs. Assn., Asst. Hosp. Dirs. Assn. (treas. 1983, v.p. 1984). Home: 50 Fulton Ave Rye NY 10580 Office: New Rochelle Hosp Med Ctr 16 Guion Pl New Rochelle NY 10802

MAMANTOV, GLEB, chemistry educator, consultant; b. Karsava, Latvia, Apr. 10, 1931; s. Alexander V. and Elena (Pribitkov) M.; m. Charmaine Bienvenu, Aug. 11, 1956; children: Tatiana, Mark, Elena. BS, La. State U., 1953, MS, 1954; PhD, 1957. Research chemist, electrochemis. dept. Du Pont, Niagara Falls, N.Y., 1957-58; instr., postdoctoral research assoc. U. Wis., Madison, 1960-61; asst. prof. chemistry U. Tenn., Knoxville, 1961-66, assoc. prof., 1966-71, prof., 1971—, head dept., 1979—, disting. prof. chemistry, 1986—; rsch. participant Oak Ridge Nat. Lab., summers 1962-63, cons., 1962—; exch. scientist to USSR, NAS, 1989; vis. prof. U. Paris, 1991. Served to 1st lt. USAF, 1958-60. NSF travel grantee, 1964, 74, study grantee, 1963, 69; NATO sr. postdoctoral fellow, U. Heidelberg, 1972; Chancellor's research scholar, 1977; U. Tenn. Macebearer, 1980-81. Fellow AAAS, Am. Inst. Chemists; mem. Am. Chem. Soc. (Charles H. Stone award Carolina-Piedmont sect. 1989), Electrochem. Soc. (editor jour. 1980-90, Max Bredig award 1994), Soc. Applied Spectroscopy (Meggers award 1983), Soc. Electroanalytical Chemistry, Phi Beta Kappa, Sigma Xi, Phi Lambda Upsilon, Phi Kappa Phi (faculty scholar award 1990), Omicron Delta Kappa. Office: U Tenn Dept Chemistry Knoxville TN 37996-1600

MAMAT, FRANK TRUSTICK, lawyer; b. Syracuse, N.Y., Sept. 4, 1949; s. Harvey Sanford and Annette (Trustick) M.; m. Kathy Lou Winters, June 23, 1975; children: Jonathan Adam, Steven Kenneth. BA, U. Rochester, 1971; JD, Syracuse U., 1974. Bar: D.C. 1976, U.S. Ct. Appeals (D.C. cir.) 1976, Fla. 1977, U.S. Supreme Ct. 1979, U.S. Dist. Ct. (ea. dist.) 1983, U.S. Ct. Appeals (6th cir.) 1983, Mich. 1984, U.S. Dist. Ct. (no. dist.) Ind. 1984. Atty. NLRB, Washington, 1975-79; assoc. Proskauer, Rose, Goetz & Mendelsohn, Washington, N.Y.C. and L.A., 1979-83; assoc. Fishman Group, Bloomfield Hills, Mich., 1983-85, ptnr., 1985-87; sr. ptnr. Honigman, Miller, Schwartz and Cohn, 1987-94; ptnr. Clark, Klein & BeaumontP.L.C., Detroit, 1995—; pres. Morgan Daniels Co. Inc., 1995—; ptnr. Clark Klein & Beaumont, P.C., Detroit, 1995—; bd. dirs. Mich. Food and Beverage Assn., Air Conditioning Contractors of Am., Mich., Associated Builders and Contractors, Am. Subcontractors Assn. Gen. counsel Rep. Com. of Oakland County, 1986-89, 94—, Constrn. Code Commn. Mich., 1993; bd. dirs. 300 Club, Mich., 1984-90; pres. 400 Club, 1990-93, chmn., 1993—; mem. Associated Gen. Contractors Labor Lawyers Coun.; mem. Repb. Nat. Com., Nat. Rep. Senatorial Com., Presdl. Task Force, Rep. Labor Coun., Washington; city dir. West Bloomfield 1985-87; pres. West Bloomfield Rep. Club,

1985-87; fin. com. Rep. Com. of Oakland County, 1984—; pres. Oakland County Lincoln Rep. Club, 1989-90; bd. dirs. camping svcs. and human resources com. YMCA, 1989-93, Anti-Defamation League, 1989-93; vice chmn. Lawyers for Reagan-Bush, 1984; v.p. Fruehauf Farms, West Bloomfield, Mich., 1985-88; mem. staff Exec. Office of Pres. of U.S. Inquieies/ Comments, Washington, 1981-83. Mem. ABA, Fed. Bar Assn., Mich. Bar Assn., Fla. Bar Assn. (labor com. 1977—), Mich. Bus. and Profl. Assn., Am. Subcontractors Assn. (Southeastern Mich., bd. dirs.), Founders Soc. (Detroit Inst. of Art), D.C. Bar Assn., Detroit Bar Assn., Oakland County Bar Assn., B'nai B'rith (v.p. 1982-83, trustee Detroit coun. 1987-88, bd. dirs. Detroit Barristers unit 1983-91, pres. 1985-87), Detroit Club. Office: Clark Klein & Beaumont PLC 1600 First Fed Bldg Detroit MI 48226 also: Morgan Daniels Co Inc 5484 Crispin Way Rd West Bloomfield MI 48323

MAMATEY, VICTOR SAMUEL, history educator; b. North Braddock, Pa., Feb. 19, 1917; s. Albert Paul and Olga (Darmek) M.; m. Denise M. Perrone, Nov. 20, 1945; children: Albert R., Peter V. Student, Wittenberg Coll., 1938-39, U. Chgo., 1939-40; AM, Harvard U., 1941; PhD, U. Paris, 1949. Asst. prof. history Fla. State U., Tallahassee, 1949-55, assoc. prof., 1955-58, prof., 1958-67, chmn. dept. history, 1964-67; rsch. assoc. hist. U. Ga., Athens, 1967-82, acting dean Coll. Arts and Scis., 1972-73; vis. prof. Columbia U., 1961, Tulane U., 1963. Author: The United States and East Central Europe, 1914-18, 1957, Soviet RussianImperialism, 1964, (with Geoffrey Brunn) The World in the Twentieth Century, 1967, The Rise of the Hapsburg Empire, 1526-1815, 1971, (with Radomir Luza) History of the Czechoslovak Republic, 1918-1948, 1973. With U.S. Army, 1942-46. Guggenheim fellow, 1959. Mem. Am. Hist. Assn. (George Louis Beer prize for best book on internat. history 1958), Am. Assn. For Advancement Slavic Studies. Home: 142 Spruce Valley Rd Athens GA 30605-3332

MAMER, STUART MIES, lawyer; b. East Hardin, Ill., Feb. 23, 1921; s. Louis H. and Anna (Mies) M.; m. Donna E. Jordan, Sept. 10, 1944; children: Richard A., John S., Bruce J. A.B., U. Ill., 1942, J.D., 1947. Bar: Ill. bar 1947. Assoc. Thomas & Mulliken, Champaign, 1947-55; partner firm Thomas, Mamer & Haughey, Champaign, 1955—; lectr. U. Ill. Coll. Law, Urbana, 1965-85; Mem. Atty. Registration and Disciplinary Commn. Ill., 1976-82. Chmn. fund drive Champaign County Community Chest, 1955; 1st pres. Champaign County United Fund, 1957; Pres., dir. U. Ill. McKinley Found., Champaign, 1957-69; trustee Children's Home and Aid Soc. of Ill., v.p., 1977—. Served as pilot USAAF, 1943-45. Mem. Am. Coll. Trust and Estate Counsel (bd. regents 1984-90), Phi Beta Kappa, Phi Gamma Delta. Republican. Presbyterian. Home: 6 Montclair Rd Urbana IL 61801-5824 Office: Thomas Mamer & Haughey 30 E Main St Fl 5 Champaign IL 61820-3629

MAMET, DAVID ALAN, playwright, director, essayist; b. Chgo., Nov. 30, 1947; s. Bernard Morris and Lenore June (Silver) M.; m. Lindsay Crouse, Dec. 1977 (div.); m. Rebecca Pidgeon, Sept. 22, 1991. B.A., Goddard Coll., Plainfield, Vt., 1969. Artist-in-residence Goddard Coll., 1971-73; artistic dir. St. Nicholas Theatre Co., Chgo., 1973-75; guest lectr. U. Chgo., 1975, 79, NYU, 1981; assoc. artistic dir. Goodman Theater, Chgo., 1978; assoc. prof. film Columbia U., 1988; chmn. bd. Atlantic Theater Co. Author (plays): The Duck Variations, 1971, Sexual Perversity in Chicago, 1973 (Village Voice Obie award 1976), Reunion, 1973, Squirrels, 1974, American Buffalo, 1976 (Village Voice Obie award, N.Y. Drama Critics Circle award), A Life in the Theatre, 1976, The Water Engine, 1976, The Woods, 1977, Lone Canoe, 1978, Prairie du Chien, 1978, Lakeboat, 1980, Donny March, 1981, Edmond, 1982 (Village Voice Obie award) Mr. Happiness, 1982, The Disappearance of the Jews, 1983, The Shawl, 1985, Glengarry Glen Ross, 1984 (Pulitzer prize for drama, N.Y. Drama Critics Circle award), Speed-The-Plow, 1987, Bobby Gould in Hell, 1989, The Old Neighborhood, 1991, Oleanna, 1992, The Cryptogram, 1994, (dir. only) Ricky Jay and His 52 Assistants, 1994, (one act) Death Defying Acts, 1995; screenplays: The Postman Always Rings Twice, 1979, The Verdict, 1980, The Untouchables, 1986, House of Games, 1986, (with Shel Silverstein) Things Change, 1987, We're No Angels, 1987, Homicide, 1991 (also dir.), Hoffa, 1991, Oleanna, 1994; (children's books) Warm and Cold with drawings by Donald Sultan, 1985; (essays) Writing In Restaurants, 1986, Some Freaks, 1989, On Directing Film, 1990, The Cabin, 1992; (novel) The Village, 1994, (book) Passover, (poetry) The Hero Pony, 1990; dir. (films) House of Games, 1986, Things Change, 1987, Homicide, 1991, Oleanna, 1994. Recipient Outer Critics Circle award for contbn. to Am. theater, 1978; Joseph Jefferson award nominee for best screen play adaptation, 1983; Rockefeller grantee, 1977; CBS Creative Writing fellow Yale U. Drama Sch., 1976-77.

MAMLOK, URSULA, composer, educator; b. Berlin, Feb. 1, 1928; d. John and Dorothy Lewis; m. Dwight G. Mamlok, Nov. 27, 1947. Student, Mannes Coll. Music, 1942-45; MusB, Manhattan Sch. Music, 1955, MusM, 1958. Mem. faculty dept. music NYU, 1967-74, CUNY, 1971-74; prof. composition Manhattan Sch. Music, N.Y.C., 1974—. Composer: numerous works including Variations and Interludes for 4 percussionists, 1973, Sextet, 1977, Festive Sounds, 1978, When Summer Sang, 1980, piano trio Panta rhei, 1981, 5 recital pieces for young pianists, 1983, From My Garden for solo viola or solo violin, 1983, Concertino for wind quintet, Strings and percussion, 1984, Der Andreas Garten for voice, flute and harp, 1986, Alariana for recorder, clarinet, bassoon, violin and cello, 1986, 3 Bagatelles for harpsichord, 1987, 5 Bagatelles for clarinet, violin, cello, 1988, Rhapsody for clarinet, viola, piano Inward Journey for Piano, 1989, Sonata for violin and piano, 1989, Music for flute, violin, cello, 1990, Girasol, a sextet for flute, violin, viola, cello and piano, 1991, Constellations for orch., 1993. Recipient Serge Koussevitzky Found. commn., 1988, Walter Hinrichsen award Acad. Inst. Arts and Letters, 1989, commn. San Francisco Symphony, 1990; Nat. Endowment Arts grantee, 1974, Am. Inst. Acad. Arts and Letters grantee, 1981, 89, Martha Baird Rockefeller grantee, 1982; John Simon Guggenheim fellow, 1995. Mem. Am. Composers Alliance (dir., Opus One Rec. award 1987), Am. Soc. Univ. Composers, Am. Women Composers, N.Y. Women Composers, Internat. League Women Composers, Music Theory Soc. N.Y., Am. Music Ctr., Internat. Soc Contemporary Music (bd. dirs.), Fromm Found. Commn., Am. Guild Organists Assn. Address: 315 E 86th St New York NY 10028-4714 In my music, I have never striven for novelty nor originality for its own sake. Rather, my primary concern as a composer has been the consolidation of older and newer techniques, as they best serve the work at hand.

MAMMEL, RUSSELL NORMAN, retired food distribution company executive; b. Hutchinson, Kans., Apr. 28, 1926; s. Vyvian E. and Mabel Edwina (Hursh) M.; m. Betty Crawford, Oct. 29, 1949; children: Mark, Christopher, Elizabeth, Nancy. BS, U. Kans., 1949. With Mammel's Inc., Hutchinson, 1949-57, pres., 1957-59; retail gen. mgr. Kans. divsn. Nash Finch Co., Hutchinson, 1959-61; retail gen. mgr. Iowa divsn. Nash Finch Co., Cedar Rapids, 1961-66; dir. store devel. Nash Finch Co., Mpls., 1966-75, v.p., 1975-83, exec. v.p., 1983-85, pres., COO, 1985-91; also bd. dirs. Nash Finch Co., Mpls., Mpls., 1991; pvt. investments, 1991—. With AUS, 1944-46. Home: 6808 Cornelia Dr Minneapolis MN 55435-1608 Office: Nash Finch Co 7600 France Ave S Minneapolis MN 55440-0534

MAMORSKY, JEFFREY DEAN, lawyer; b. New Haven, Conn., Feb. 26, 1946; s. Paul and Mildred Rosaline (Krevolin) M. BA, NYU, 1967, JD, 1972, LLM, 1975. Bar: N.Y. 1972, U.S. Tax Ct. 1974, U.S. Ct. Appeals 1974, D.C., 1978, U.S. Supreme Ct. 1978. Legal editor Prentice Hall Pension & Profit Sharing Library, Englewood Cliffs, N.J., 1968-72; corp. counsel Titan Actuarial Services, N.Y.C., 1972-73; benefits atty. Mobil Oil Corp., N.Y.C., 1973-75; compensation and benefits counsel W.R. Grace & Co., N.Y.C., 1975-77; ptnr. Vedder, Price, Kaufman, Kammholz & Day, N.Y.C., 1977-81; ptnr. Shea & Gould, N.Y.C., 1981-84, Wender, Murase & White, N.Y.C., 1984-86, Rubin Baum, Levin, Constant & Friedman, N.Y.C., 1986-87; Curtis, Mallet-Prevost, Colt & Mosle, 1987—. Served with AUS. Mem. ABA (com. on employee benefits tax sect.), N.Y. State Bar Assn. (com. on employee benefits tax sect.), U.S. C. of C. (employee benefits com.), Assn. Bar City N.Y. Author: Pension and Profit Sharing Plans: A Basic Guide, 1977, Employee Benefits Law, ERISA and Beyond, 1980, updated 1994; editor: Employee Benefits Handbook, Health Care Handbook, Health Care Benefits Guide; editor-in-chief Jour. Compensation and Benefits, Jour. Health Care Benefits; contbr. articles to profl. jours. Office: Curtis Mallet-Prevost Colt 101 Park Ave New York NY 10178-0061

MAMPRE, VIRGINIA ELIZABETH, communications executive; b. Chgo., Sept. 12, 1949; d. Albert Leon and Virginia S. (Joboul) M. BA with honors, U. Iowa, 1971; Masters degree, Ind. U., 1972; spl. cert., Harvard U., 1981. Cert. tchr. Harris Intern WTTW-TV Sta., Chgo., 1972, asst. dir., 1972-73; prod. and dir. WSIU/WUSI-TV Sta., Carbondale, Ill., 1973-74; instr. So. Ill. U., Carbondale, 1972-77; prog. and prod. mgr. WSIU/WUSI-TV, Carbondale, 1974-77; prog. dir. KUHT-TV Sta., Houston, 1977-83; pres. Victory Media, Inc., Houston, 1984-89, Mampre Media Internat., Houston, 1984—; pres. A.I.C.B.; cons. Corp. for Pub. Broadcasting, Washington, 1981-83; chmn. AWRT/YCOC Houston Metro area, 1983-85, pres., 1983—, nat. v.p., 1985-90; adv. coun. PBS, Washington, 1981-83; bd. and programming chmn. So. Edn. Comms., Columbia, S.C., 1978-83; bd. dirs. TVPC; program bd. EEN. Contbg. author/editor to mags. including Focus, 1989, News & Views, 1987-88, In the Black, 1984-93; creator: (report card campaign) Multi-media, U.S., 1985—; exec. prodr. TV spls., pub. affairs and info., 1977-83 (awards 1978-91). Pres. bd. dirs. Houston Fin. Coun., 1983—; pres. Child Abuse Prevention Coun., Houston, 1984—; bd. dirs. Child Abuse Prevention Network, 1990—; officer bd. dirs. Crime Stoppers Houston, 1984—; chmn. exhbns. Mayor's 1st Hearing, Children and Youth, Houston, 1985-88; founder, bd. dirs. Friends of WSIU-TV, 1974-77; chmn. Evening Guild St. John the Divine, St. Kevork/ACYO Nat. sports fair, 1990; rep. for Houston 2d World Conf. on Mayors, Japan, 1989; exec. bd. nat. com. to prevent child abuse, 1990—; bd. dirs. Houston Read Coun., 1995—; mem. nat. faculty Ctr. for Children's Issues, 1995—. Fellow W.K. Kellogg Found., Battle Creek, Mich., 1987-90; recipient award for Excellence Pres. Pvt. Sector, White House, Washington, 1987, Ohio State U., Columbus, 1983, Feddersen award for excellence in Pub. TV Ind. U., Bloomington, 1981, Heritage award Child Abuse Prevention Coun., 1990, Dona J. Stone Founders award Nat. Assn. for Prevention of Child Abuse, 1990; named among Outstanding Women Vols. for community, civic and profl. contbns., Fedn. Houston Profl. Women, 1989; finalist Woman on the Move, 1987, Rising Star, 1987. Mem. Am. Women in Radio and TV (nat. v.p. 1986-90, award 1987, pres. Houston chpt. 1990, bd. dirs. 1988—), Houston Fed. Profl. Women (pres., del. 1986-93, chmn. 1994), Nat. Assn. Ednl. Broadcasters (presenter nat. conv. 1975-76), Tex. Lyceum (v.p. bd. dirs. 1990—), Dephians, Nat. Assn. for Programming TV Execs., Fedn. Houston Profl. Women Ednl. Found. (bd. dirs. 1994—), Ctr. for Bus. Women's Dvce. (bd. dirs. 1993-94). Republican. Episcopalian. Avocations: photography, swimming, sailing, languages, travel. Office: Mampre Media Internat 5123 Del Monte Dr Houston TX 77056-4302

MAN, CAMERON ROBERT JAMES, landscape architect, educator; b. Russell, Man., Can., Feb. 25, 1935; s. Robert John and Helen (Middleton) M.; m. Sharron Jewel Jackson, Apr. 21, 1962 (div. 1972); children—Caius Alexander, Calrossie Robert; m. 2d, Agnes Marie Bourdon, May 26, 1978; children: Alexandre Cameron, Cassandre Helen. B.Arch., U. Man., Ft. Garry, 1959; M. Landscape Architecture, U. Calif.-Berkeley, 1964. Registered landscape architect, B.C. Sr. ptnr. Man, Taylor, Muret & Lantzius, Winnipeg, Man., 1966-72; chmn. dept. landscape architecture Sch. Environ. Design, Calif. State Poly. U., Pomona, 1972-75; pres. Landplan Collaborative, Guelph, Can., 1977-85; prof., head Sch. Landscape Architecture, U. Guelph, 1975-86. Bd. dirs. Landscape Architecture Found., Miss. State U., 1976-83, pres., 1982. Mem. Am. Soc. Landscape Architects (v.p. 1981-83, pres. elect 1991, pres. 1992), Council Educators in Landscape Architecture (v.p. 1974-75, pres. 1975-76). Prog. Conservative. Presbyterian. Office: Miss State U Sch Landscape Architecture Rm 100 Montgomery Hall Mississippi State MS 39762 Home: 108 Tanglewood Dr Starkville MS 39759-2356

MAN, EUGENE HERBERT, chemist, educator, business executive; b. Scranton, Pa., Dec. 14, 1923; s. E. Lester and Celia (Cohen) M.; m. Priscilla R. Perry, Sept. 15, 1976; children—Elizabeth Sue Man Eichenberger, Barbara Ruth, Linda Jeanne Man Manley, Bruce Jonathan, Pamela Irene Perry, Aaron Benjamin Perry. A.B., Oberlin Coll., 1948; Ph.D. (Office Naval Research fellow, E.I. duPont fellow), Duke, 1952. Rsch. chemist E.I. duPont de Nemours & Co., Inc., Wilmington, Del., 1952-60; supr. tech. sect. E.I. duPont de Nemours & Co., Inc., Chattanooga, 1960-61; sr. supr. E.I. duPont de Nemours & Co., Inc., 1961-62; coordinator research U. Miami, Coral Gables, Fla., 1962-66; dean rsch. coordination U. Miami, 1966-77, dean research and sponsored programs, 1977-79, prof. chemistry, 1967-93, prof. marine and atmospheric chemistry, 1971-93, prof. emeritus, 1994—; pres., chief exec. officer Ctr. for Health Techs. Inc., Miami, 1990—; vis. investigator Scripps Instn. Oceanography, 1971-72; Lady Davis faculty fellow Technion, Israel, 1990; bd. dirs. Health Planning Coun., Dade County, Fla., 1970-71; dr. Gulf Univs. Rsch. Consortium, Galveston, Tex., chmn., 1969-71, cons., 1979-81. Contbr. articles profl. jours. Trustee, v.p. Community Mental Health Svc., Dade County, 1967-71; trustee United Fund Dade County, 1967-69; mem., chmn. exec. com. Mental Health Consortium, Dade County, 1966-71; mem. Met. Dade County Cultural Affairs Coun., 1984-89, chmn. sci. com., 1986-90, 1st vice chmn., 1988-89; mem. exec. com. Nat. Coun. Univ. Rsch. Adminstrs., 1967-72; trustee Hospice Found., 1992—; mem. coun. Oak Ridge Assoc. Univs., 1973-79; trustee Miami Mus. Sci., 1990-94, adv. bd., 1995—. 1st lt. AUS, 1943-46. Recipient Harry N. Holmes award in chemistry Oberlin Coll., 1948; NIH grantee, 1983-91. Fellow Am. Inst. Chemists; mem. Am. Chem. Soc., AAAS, Phi Beta Kappa, Sigma Xi (pres. U. Miami chpt. 1981-82), Phi Lambda Upsilon. Patentee in field. Home: 1627 Brickell Ave Apt 1107 Miami FL 33129-1249

MAN, LAWRENCE KONG, architect; b. Kowloon, Hong Kong, July 4, 1953; s. Hon-Kwong Man and Sau-Ching Luk. Student, U. Redlands, 1971-72; BArch, U. Oreg., 1977; MArch, Harvard U., 1978. Registered architect, Mass. Designer, project architect Shepley Bulfinch Richardson & Abbott, Boston, 1978-86; project designer, project architect E. Verner Johnson & Assoc., Boston, 1987-91; owner Lawrence Man Architect, Cambridge, Mass., 1992-95, L.A., 1994-95. Prin. works include Tai Pan Restaurant, Cambridge, Mass. (Honor award AIA 1993, New Eng. award Excellence in Architecture 1993, Design Excellence award Nat. Orgn. Minority Architects 1993), Ti-Sales Office, Sudbury, Mass. (Design Excellence award Nat. Orgn. Minority Architects 1993), Dental Clinic, Reading, Mass. (AIA Interior Architecture award 1992, Interior Design Project award Am. Soc. Interior Designers 1991, Boston Exports citation AIA 1990), Mus. Ctr. Union Terminal, Cin. (Reconstrn. award 1991), Ramesses Pavilion Boston Mus. Sci. (Double Vision award/Double Silver Soc. Environ. Graphics 1990), Smithsonian South Quadrangle Mus., Washington (Boston Exports award/citation AIA 1990, Honor award AIA 1989), Pub. Mus. Grand Rapids (Mich.) River Front Devel., U. Vt. Student Ctr., Burlington, Campus Ctr. Study and Libr. addition Franklin & Marshall Coll., Andover (Mass.) Co. Corp. Hdqs., Emerson Hosp., Concord, Mass., pvt. residences, others. Mem. AIA, Am. Assn. Mus., Boston Soc. Architects, Nat. Orgn. Minority Architects. Avocations: dancing, traveling, music. Home: 2158 Valentine Pl San Marino CA 91108

MANABE, SYUKURO, climatologist; b. Shingu-Mura, Uma-Gun, Ehime-ken, Japan, Sept. 21, 1931; came to U.S., 1958; s. Seiichi and Sueko (Akashi) M.; m. Nobuko Nakamura, Jan. 21, 1962; children: Nagisa M. Bianchini, Yukari C. BS, Tokyo U., 1953, MS, 1955, DS, 1958. Rsch. meteorologist U.S. Weather Bur., Washington, 1958-63; sr. rsch. meteorologist Geophys. Fluid Dynamics Lab. NOAA, Washington, 1963-68; sr. rsch. meteorologist, geophysicist Fluid Dynamics Lab. NOAA, Princeton, N.J., 1968—, mem. sr. exec. svc. of U.S., 1979—; lectr. with rank of prof. Princeton U., 1968—; mem. joint sci. com. World Climate Rsch. Program, 1981-87; mem. bd. on atmospheric sci. and climate NRC, 1988-91; mem. Commn. on Geoscis., Environment and Resources NRC, 1990-93; mem. panel on climate and global change NOAA, 1988—. Recipient Fujiwara award Japan Meteorol. Soc., 1967, gold medal U.S. Dept. Commerce, 1970, Presdl. Rank Meritorious Exec. award Pres. of U.S., 1989, Acad. award of Blue Planet Prize, Asahi Glass Found., Japan, 1992. Fellow Am. Geophys. Union (Revelle medal), Am. Meteorol. Soc. (Meisinger award 1967, 2d Half Century award 1977, Rossby medal 1992); mem. NAS, AAAS, Acad. Europaea (fgn.). Avocations: swimming, running. Home: 8 Princeton Ave Princeton NJ 08540-5236 Office: NOAA Geophys Fluid Dynamics Lab Princeton U PO Box 308 Princeton NJ 08542

MANARA, JAMES ANTHONY, software executive, consultant; b. Westfield, Mass., Sept. 17, 1945; s. James Anthony and Genevieve Sophia (Chlastawa) M.; m. Sheila Aileen Barry, Sept. 6, 1970; children: Gregory James, Beth Ann. BA, Rutgers U., 1973; MBA, Fairleigh Dickenson U.,

1977. Cert. data processing; project mgmt. profl. Programmer AT&T, Bedminster, N.J., 1973-80; v.p. Security Pacific Nat. Bank, Glendale, Calif. 1980-86; mgr. Candle Corp., L.A., 1985-94; dir. 4th Dimension Software, 1994—; sr. instr. UCLA, 1980-93; cons. Sigma Delta Group, Thousand Oaks, Calif., 1986—; speaker in field. Bd. dirs. Hart Pony League Baseball, 1986-89. Sgt. USMC, 1966-70, Vietnam. Republican. Roman Catholic. Avocations: model railroads, youth sports. Office: 4th Dimension Software 11th Fl One Park Plz Irvine CA 92714

MANASSERO, HENRI J. P., hotel executive; b. Carcassonne, France, July 2, 1932; s. Jean and Paule (Guiraud) M.; m. Moya Corrigan, June 7, 1962. Degree in Hotel Adminstrn., French Hotel Sch., 1950. Mgr., Carlton Hotel, Cannes, France, Park Hotel, Bremen, Ger., Midland Hotel, Manchester, Eng.; gen. mgr. Royal Hibernian Hotel, Dublin, 1963-69; dir. food and beverage Trust Houses Forte Internat., 1970-72; asst. mng. dir. Trust Houses Forte Internat., London, 1973-79 v.p., gen. mgr. Pierre Hotel, N.Y.C., 1979-85; pres. Exclusive Hotels div. Trust Houses Forte Hotels Inc., 1986—; pres. Ashling Hotel Cons.; guest lectr. confs., India, Ireland, U.S., France, Mali, Russia. Contbr. articles on food and beverage to European trade mags. Bd. dirs. Am. French Found., Inc. Decorated Chevalier French Order of Merit, 1985. Mem. Irish Hotels and Restaurants Mgrs. Assn. (pres. 1969), Inst. Mgmt. Cons., Hotel and Catering Inst. Brit., Wine and Food Soc., Rotary, Westchester Country Club, Paris-Am. Club, Doubles Club. Address: PO Box 660 Lakeville CT 06039-0660

MANATOS, ANDREW EMANUEL, policy consultant, former government official; b. Washington, July 7, 1944; s. Mike N. and Dorothy V. (Varanakis) M.; m. Tina G. Weber, June 25, 1967; children: Mike A., Nick A., Tom A., George A. B.A., Am. U., 1968, M.A., 1969. Staff post office and civil service com. U.S. Senate, Washington, 1969-73; senate staff dir. post office com., legis. asst. Senator Thomas Eagleton, 1973-77; asst. sec. congl. affairs Dept. Commerce, Washington, 1977-81; owner Manatos & Manatos Inc., Washington, 1981—; creator White House Conf. on Productivity, U.S. Senate Productivity Award, U.S. Congress and You videotape; bd. dirs. Washington Coordinating Coun. of Productivity, 1981-88, Com. for Citizen Awareness, 1985—. Contbr. articles to N.Y. Times, Washington Post, Indianapolis Star. Pres. Brookmont Civic Assn., Bethesda, Md., 1974-76, Tulip Hill Civic Assn, Bethesda, 1978-80, PTA, 1981; Dem. precinct chmn., 1974-81; chmn. Montgomery County Dollars for Dems., 1975; bd. dirs., mem. nat. fin. com., co-chmn. Washington fin. com. Dukakis for Pres., 1987-88, Inst. Confidence in Cong.; mng. trustee Dem. Nat. Com. Victory Fund, 1988. Recipient Cross of Holy Sepulcher, Medal of St. Andrew; named Archon, Greek Orthodox Ch. Office: Manatos & Manatos 601 13th St NW Ste 1150 S Washington DC 20005

MANATT, CHARLES T., lawyer; b. Chgo., June 9, 1936. BS, Iowa State U., 1958; JD, George WAshington U., 1962. Bar: Calif. 1962, U.S. Supreme Ct. 1967, D.C. 1985. Ptnr. Manatt, Phelps & Phillips, Washington. Bd. editors George WAshington Law Rev., 1960-62. Mem. ABA, Calif. State Bar, L.A. County Bar Assn., San Fernando Valley Bar Assn. (pres. 1971-72), Century City Bar Assn., Phi Delta Phi, Delta Sigma Rho. Office: Manatt Phelps & Phillips 1200 New Hampshire NW Ste 200 Washington DC 20036 also: Manatt Phelps & Phillips Trident Ctr E Tower 11355 W Olympic Blvd Los Angeles CA 90064

MANATT, RICHARD, education educator; b. Odebolt, Iowa, Dec. 13, 1931; s. William Price and Lucille (Taylor) M.; m. Sally Jo Johnson, Aug. 20, 1952; children—Tamra Jo, Ann Lea, Joel Price; m. Jacquelyn M. Nesset, Feb. 25, 1970; 1 child, Megan Sue. B.Sc., Iowa State U., 1953, M.S., 1956; Ph.D., U. Iowa, 1964. Prin. Oskloosa (Iowa) Schs., 1959-62; research asso. U. Iowa, Iowa City, 1962-64; mem. faculty Iowa State U., Ames, 1964—; prof. Iowa State U., 1972—, chmn. dept. ednl. adminstrn., 1970-80, 93—, dir. Sch. Improvement Model Projects, 1980—; cons. performance evaluation for public and independent schs.; disting. vis. prof. Calif. State U., L.A. Author: Educator's Guide to the New Design, When Right is Wrong, The Fundamentalists and the Public Schools, The Clinical Manual for Teacher Performance Evaluation Compendics of Professional Growth Plans, (computer software program) Computer Assisted Teacher Evaluation/Supervision, When Right is Wrong: The Fundamentalists and The Public Schools; editor Coll. Scene, Internat. Jour. Ednl. Reform. Served with AUS, 1953-55. Named Disting. Prof., Nat. Acad. Sch. Execs., 1979, Regents' Prof. Edn., 1994. Mem. NEA, Nat. Assn. Secondary Sch. Prins., Am. Assn. Sch. Adminstrs., Assn. Supervision and Curriculum Devel. (named Outstanding Cons. 1981), Phi Kappa Phi, Phi Delta Kappa, Delta Chi. Democrat. Methodist. Home: 2926 Monroe Dr Ames IA 50010-4362

MANBECK, HARRY FREDERICK, JR., lawyer; b. Honesdale, Pa., June 26, 1926; s. Harry Frederick Sr. and Pauline (Holley) M.; m. Lois Marie Lange, May 30, 1953 (dec. July 1973); children: Holley Manbeck Dey, Peter Charles; m. Julia Pauline McCarthy, June 30, 1989; 1 child, Emily Elisabeth. BEE, Lehigh U., 1949; LLB, U. Louisville, 1955. Bar: Ky. 1955, Ind. 1962, Mass. 1965, U.S. Ct. Appeals (fed. cir.) 1982, Conn. 1988, D.C. 1992. From trainee to patent atty. GE, various locations, 1950-57; counsel patent div. GE, Ft. Wayne, Ind., 1957-64; counsel patent air. div. GE, Lynn, Mass., 1964-67; patent counsel major appliance group Louisville, 1967-69; former gen. patent counsel Fairfield, Conn., 1970-90; asst. sec. commerce, commr. patents and trademarks U.S. Patent and Trademark Office, Washington, 1990-92; ptnr. Morgan & Finnegan, Washington, 1992—. Mem. ABA (patent, trademark and copyright sect. 1989-90), Bar Assn. of Ct. Appeals Fed. Cir. (bd. dirs. 1984-87), Assn. Corp. Patent Counsel (pres. 1978-79), Am. Arbitration Assn. (Whitney North Seymour Sr. award 1984), Patterson Club, Belleair Club, Westwood Club. Avocations: golf, boating. Home: 1604 Aerie Ln Mc Lean VA 22101-4657 Office: Morgan & Finnegan 555 13th St NW Ste 480 W Washington DC 20004-1109

MANBECK, HARVEY B., agricultural engineer, wood engineer, educator; b. Reading, Pa., Jan. 11, 1942; m. Glenda Manbeck; children: Eric, Christina. BS, Pa. State U., 1963, MS in Agrl. Engring., 1965; PhD in Engring., Okla. State U., 1970. Rsch. assoc. agrl. engring. dept. Pa. State U., 1965, instr. agrl. engring. dept., 1966, prof. agrl. engring., 1980—; asst. prof. agrl engring. dept. U. Ga., 1970-75, assoc. prof. agrl. engring. dept., 1977-80; assoc. prof., extension agrl. engr. Ohio State U., 1975-77; adminstrv. intern rsch. office Pa. Agrl. Experiment Sta., 1991-92; vis. prof. agrl. engring. U. Manitoba, 1986-87, Shenyang Agrl. U., 1988. Contbr. chpts. to 7 books, over 60 articles to profl. jours. and one textbook. Coach Little League Baseball, 1981-84, leader YMCA Indian Princess Longhouse, 1983-85, Webelo's Cub Scouts 1984, com. mem. Troop 31 Boy Scouts of Am. 1985—. Recipient Outstanding and Premier Tchg. award Coll. Engring. Pa. State U., Outstanding Rsch. award Coll. Engring. Pa. State U., Atherton Excellence in Tchg. award Pa. State U. Mem. ASCE, Am. Soc. Agrl. Engrs. (mem. structures group, vice chair 1978-79, chair 79-81, Pa. state sect., sec.-treas. 1983-84, chair 1985-86, tech. dir. SE divsn. 1993-95, Henry Giese S & E award, 1990), Nat. Soc. Profl. Engrs., Nat. Frame Builders Assn. (mem. editorial review com. for the post-frame profl., chair 1988—), Ga. Soc. Profl. Engrs. (state dir. at large 1974-75, named Outstanding Young Engr. of the Yr. 1972, recipient Outstanding Chpt. pres. award, 1974, various other coms.), Ohio Soc. Profl. Engrs., Am. Soc. for Engring. Edn., Forest Products Rsch. Soc., Jaycees, Pa. State Coaly Soc., Gamma Sigma Delta, Alpha Epsilon, Sigma Xi, numerous other mems. Achievements include development of standard designs and specs for hardwood glulam highway bridges, authorship of national engineering practice for post-frame structural diaphragm design, development of FEM for predicting thermal pressures in grain bins, development of FEM for predicting structural performance of wood-framed, metal-clad diaphagm and development of quality control schemes for poultry housing systems. Home: 912 Anna St Boalsburg PA 16827-1214 Office: Penn St U 210 Agr Engring Bldg University Park PA 16802

MANCALL, ELLIOTT LEE, neurologist, educator; b. Hartford, Conn., July 31, 1927; s. Nicholas and Bess Tuch M.; m. Jacqueline Sue Cooper, Dec. 27, 1953; children: Andrew Cooper, Peter Cooper. B.S., Trinity Coll., Hartford, 1948; M.D., U. Pa., 1952. Diplomate: Am. Bd. Psychiatry and Neurology (dir. 1983—). Intern Hartford Hosp., 1952-54; clk. in neurology Nat. Hosp. Nervous Disease, London, 1954-55; asst. resident neurology Neurol. Inst. N.Y.C., 1955-56; resident neuropathology Mass. Gen. Hosp.,

1956-57, also clin. and research fellow, 1957-58; teaching fellow neuropathology Harvard Med. Sch., 1956-57; asst. prof. neurology Jefferson Med. Coll., 1958-64, assoc. prof., 1964-65; prof. medicine Hahnemann Med. Coll. and Hosp., 1965-76, prof. neurology, chmn. dept., 1976—; dir. Huntington's Disease Diagnostic and Referral Ctr. Hahnemann U.; dir. Hahnemann U. ALS Clinic; chmn. bd. dirs. Phila. Profl. Standards Rev. Orgn., 1981-84; del. Am. Bd. Med. Specialties, 1984—. Author: (with others) The Human Cerebellum: A Topographical Atlas, 1961, (with B.J. Alpers) Clinical Neurology, 1971, Essentials of the Neurological Examination, 1971, 81; contbr. numerous articles to profl. jours. Served with USN, 1945-47. Recipient Christian R. and Mary F. Lindback award, 1969; Oliver Meml. prize ophthalmology U. Pa., 1952. Fellow Am. Acad. Neurology (alt. del. to AMA 1982-86, gen. editor CONTINUUM 1991—); mem. Am. Neurol. Assn., Am. Assn. Neuropathology, Assn. Research in Nervous and Mental Diseases, Soc. Neuroscience, AAUP, Pa. Med. Peer Rev. Orgn. (dir. 1979-84), Phila. Neurol. Soc., Alpers Soc. Clin. Neurology, Coll. Physicians Phila., Neurology, Sydenham Coterie, Phila. County Med. Soc., Pa. State Med. Soc., AMA (sec.-treas. sect. council neurology 1983-86), Am. Med. Soc. on Alcoholism, Neurology Intersoc. Liaison Group, Intersoc. Com. Neurol. Resources, Assn. Univ. Profs. Neurology (pres. 1988-90), Soc. for Exptl. Neuropathology, Am. Bd. Med. Specialties (exec. bd., chair COSEP, 1992—), Am. Bd. Psychiatry and Neurology (v.p. 1990, del. to Am. Bd. Med. Specialities, emeritus dir. 1991—). Home: 2088 Harts Ln Miquon PA 19452 Office: Broad And Vine St Philadelphia PA 19104

MANCEL, CLAUDE PAUL, household product company executive; b. Paris, Oct. 27, 1942; s. Pierre Mancel and Marcelle E. (Grimaud) Mirowicz; m. Annie Simon, Sept., 1967; children: Pacome, Elodie, Sebastien. Diploma in engring., E.N.S.C., Bordeaux, France, 1966, ENSIC, Nancy, France, 1967; MS in Chem. Engring., Worcester (Mass.) Poly. Inst., 1971, PhD in Chem. Engring., 1974; hon. doctorate, Worcester Poly Inst., 1990. Mem. R & D staff Procter & Gamble European Tech. Ctr., Brussels, 1973-80; dir. R & D Procter & Gamble European Tech. Ctr., 1981-85, Procter & Gamble U.S., Cin., 1986-87; mgr. R & D Procter & Gamble European Tech. Ctr., Brussels, 1987-88; v.p. R & D Procter & Gamble Europe and Middle East, 1989-92, v.p. R & D Europe and Middle East L&CP products and worldwide (dish, hard surface cleaner and bleach products), 1993—; chmn. adv. com. dept. chem. engring. Worcester Poly. Inst., 1988—, bd. trustees, 1992—; vice chmn., treas. bd. dirs. Assn. Internat. Savonnerie, 1990; bd. dirs., vice chmn., treas. European Ctr. Ecotoxicology and Toxicology of Chems. Fulbright Found. grantee, 1969. Mem. Sigma Xi. Home: 115 Ave Bellevue, 1410 Waterloo Belgium Office: Procter & Gamble, Temselaan 100, 1853 Strombeek Bever Belgium

MANCHER, RHODA ROSS, federal agency administrator, strategic planner; b. N.Y.C., Sept. 28, 1935; d. Joseph and Hannah (Karpf) Ross; m. Melvin Mancher, May 27, 1962 (dec.); children: Amy Meg, James Marc. B.S. in Physics, Columbia U., 1960; M.S. in Ops. Research, George Washington U., 1978. Cons. pvt. practice, Bethesda, Md., 1994—; staff FEA, Washington, 1974-77; dir. info. systems devel. div. The White House, Washington, 1977-79; dir. office systems devel. Social Security Adminstrn., Balt., 1979-80; dep. asst. atty. gen. Office Info. Tech., Dept. Justice, Washington, 1980-84; assoc. dir. info. resources mgmt. Dept. Navy, Washington, 1985-87; dir. Office Info. Tech. VA, Washington, 1987-94; mem. ad hoc com. on recommendations to merge chem. and biol. info. systems Nat. Cancer Inst., Washington; chmn. permanent com. on info. tech. Iternat. Criminal Police Orgn. (INTERPOL); mem. curriculum com. USDA, adv. bd. computer system security and privacy U.S. Govt.; internat. tech. com. AFCEA. Contbr. articles to profl. publs. Recipient Assoc. Commr.'s citation Social Security Adminstrn., 1980, managerial excellence award Interagy. Com. on ADP, 1983; Meritorious award Sr. Exec. Svc., 1982, 83, 85, 87, 88, 91-93, Presdl. Rank of Meritorious Exec., 1990. Mem. Am. Fedn. Info. Processing Socs. (nat. info. issues panel).

MANCHESKI, FREDERICK JOHN, automotive company executive; b. Stevens Point, Wis., July 21, 1926; s. John Stanley and Luella (Zwaska) M.; m. Judith Knox; children: Mary Lou, Laura, Marcia, Bruce, Amy Frederick-a. BS in Mech. Engring., U. Wis., 1948; LLD (hon.), U. New Haven, 1986; LHD (hon.), Quinnipiac Coll., 1992. With Timken Roller Bearing Co., Canton, Ohio, 1948-57, McKinsey & Co. (mgmt. cons.), N.Y.C., 1957-63, Echlin Inc., Branford, Conn., 1963—; chmn. bd., chief exec. officer Echlin Inc., 1969—; dir. RB&W Corp., Portec, Inc., Automotive Hall of Fame. Contbg. author: Turnaround Management, 1974. Co-chmn. Conn. Hospice, Inc.; chmn. bd. Quinnipiac Coll., Hamden, Conn.; bd. dirs. Jr. Achievement; former trustee Conn. Pub. Expenditure Coun.; mem. New Haven Regional Leadership Coun. Recipient Gold award Wall Street Transcript, 1985; named Automotive Man of Yr., Automotive Warehouse Distbrs. Assn., 1973, Chief Exec. of Decade (Bronze award), Fin. World, 1989, Automotive Industry Leader of Yr. award Automotive Hall of Fame, 1992, Aftermarket Exec. of Yr. award Automotive Parts and Accessories Assn., 1993; named to Automotive Hall of Fame, 1985. Mem. Nat. Acad. Engring., World Bus. Council, Young Pres.'s Orgn., Nat. Soc. Profl. Engrs., NAM (former dir.), Conn. Bus. Industry Assn. (former dir.), Greater New Haven Co. of C. (former dir.), Sigma Alpha Epsilon. Clubs: Pine Orchard Country (New Haven), Quinnipiack (New Haven), New Haven Country (New Haven). Home: 10 Old Farm Rd North Haven CT 06473-4416 Office: Echlin Inc PO Box 451 100 Double Beach Rd Branford CT 06405-4909 Also: Ristance Corp 14155 Esther Ave Mishawaka IN 46545-7395*

MANCHESTER, KENNETH EDWARD, electronics executive, consultant; b. Winona, Minn., Mar. 22, 1925; s. Laurence Edwin and Daisy Idel (Finley) M.; m. Bonnie Lee Hardgrave, June 24, 1946; children: Cynthia Lee, David Scott. AB, San Jose State Coll., 1949; MS, Stanford U., 1950, PhD, 1955. Sr. chemist Shell Devel. Co., Emeryville, Calif., 1955-62; head chemistry sect. Sprague Electric Co., North Adams, Mass., 1962-63, head chemistry dept., 1963-69, dir. semiconductor rsch., devel. and engring., 1969-79; dir. quality assurance and reliability Sprague Electric Co., Worcester, Mass., 1979-85; v.p. corp. R & D Sprague Electric Co., North Adams, 1985-89, Sprague fellow, 1985; cons. semiconductor industry, 1989—; lectr. Rensselaer Poly. Inst., Troy, N.Y., 1967. Contbr. articles to profl. jours.; patentee in field. Chmn. com. Troop 70 Boy Scouts Am. Sgt. U.S. Army Ground Forces, 1943-46, ETO. Mem. Am. Chem. Soc., AIME, Optimist Club, Sigma Xi. Republican. Avocations: woodworking, golf.

MANCHESTER, ROBERT D., venture capitalist; b. Windsor, Ont., Can., Dec. 16, 1942; came to U.S., 1956; s. Lewis R. and Mary I. (Suave) M.; m. Shirley A. Manchester, Sept. 24, 1971; children: Sara A., Robert D., Geoffrey A. B.S., Boston U., 1974; M.B.A., Amos Tuck Sch., Dartmouth U., 1976. Shipping mgr. N. Am. Pharmacal, Dearborn, Mich., 1961-64, plant mgr., 1968-72; investment analyst Narragansett Capital Corp., Providence, 1976-78, v.p., 1978-80, pres., chief operating officer, 1980-86; mng. dir. Narragansett Capital, Inc., Providence, 1986-88; pres., chief exec. officer Manchester & Co., Inc., 1989-91; pres. Manchester Humphreys Inc., 1992—; also bd. dirs. Data Indsl. Corp. Served to capt. U.S. Army, 1964-68. Home: 2 Harbour Rd Barrington RI 02806-4411 Office: Manchester Humphreys Inc 101 Dyer St Providence RI 02903

MANCHESTER, WILLIAM, writer; b. Attleboro, Mass., Apr. 1, 1922; s. William Raymond and Sallie Elizabeth (Thompson) M.; m. Julia Brown Marshall, Mar. 27, 1948; children: John Kennerly, Julie Thompson, Laurie. BA, U. Mass., 1946; AM, U. Mo., 1947; LHD (hon.), U. Mass., 1965, U. New Haven, 1979, Russell Sage Coll., 1990; LittD (hon.), Skidmore Coll., 1987, U. Richmond, 1988. Reporter Daily Oklahoman, 1945-46; reporter, fgn. corr., war corr. Balt. Sun, 1947-55; mng. editor Wesleyan U. Publs., 1955-64; fellow Ctr. for Advanced Studies Wesleyan U., Middletown, Conn., 1959-60; writer-in-residence Wesleyan U., Middletown, 1975—; adj. prof. history, 1979-92; fellow Pierson Coll. Yale U., 1991—; prof. of history emeritus Wesleyan U., 1992—. Author: Disturber of the Peace, 1951, The City of Anger, 1953, Shadow of the Monsoon, 1956, Beard the Lion, 1958, A Rockefeller Family Portrait, 1959, The Long Gainer, 1961, Portrait of a President, 1962, The Death of a President, 1967 (Book-of-the-Month Club selection), The Arms of Krupp, 1968 (Lit. Guild selection), The Glory and the Dream, 1974 (Lit. Guild selection), Controversy and Other Essays in Journalism, 1976, American Caesar: Douglas MacArthur, 1880-1964, 1978 (Book-of-Month Club selection), Goodbye, Darkness, 1980 (Book-of-the-Month Club selection), The Last Lion: Winston Spencer Churchill Visions of

Glory 1874-1932, 1983 (Book-of-the-Month Club selection), One Brief Shining Moment: Remembering Kennedy, 1983 (Book-of-the-Month Club selection), The Last Lion: Winston Spencer Churchill Alone 1932-1940, 1988 (Book-of-the-Month Club selection), In Our Time, 1989, A World Lit Only by Fire: The Medieval Mind and the Renaissance, Portrait of an Age, 1992; contbr. to Ency. Brit., various publs. Pres. bd. trustees Friends of U. Mass. Libr., 1970-71, trustee, 1970-74; bd. dirs. Winston Churchill Travelling Fellowships, 1990—. Sgt. USMC, 1942-45, PTO. Decorated Purple Heart; recipient Dag Hammarskjöld prize Assn. Internationale Correspondents Diplomatiques, Rome, 1967, citation for best book on fgn. affairs Overseas Press Club, 1968, U. Mo. Honor award for disting. svc. in journalism, 1969, Conn. Book award, 1975, Pres.'s Cabinet award U. Detroit, 1981, Frederick S. Troy medal U. Mass., 1981, McConnaughy award Wesleyan U., 1981, N.Y. Pub. Libr. Lit. Lion award, 1983, Disting. Pub. Svc. award Conn. Bar Assn., 1985, Lincoln Lit. award Union League Club N.Y., 1983, Blenheim award Internat. Churchill Soc., 1986, Washington Irving award, 1988, Sarah Josepha Hale award, 1993, Guggenheim fellow, 1959-60. Mem. PEN, Soc. Am. Historians, Am. Hist. Assn., Authors Guild, Century Club. Democrat. Avocation: photography. Office: Wesleyan U Middletown CT 06459

MANCINI, ERNEST ANTHONY, geologist, educator, researcher; b. Reading, Pa., Feb. 27, 1947; s. Ernest and Marian K. (Filbert) M.; m. Marilyn E. Lee, Dec. 27, 1969; children—Lisa L., Lauren N. B.S., Albright Coll., 1969; M.S., So. Ill. U., 1972; Ph.D., Tex. A&M U., 1974. Petroleum exploration geologist Cities Service Oil Co., Denver, 1974-76; asst. prof. geology U. Ala., Tuscaloosa, 1976-79, assoc. prof., 1979-84, prof., 1984—; state geologist, oil and gas supr. State Ala., Tuscaloosa, 1982—. Recipient Nat. Council Citation, Albright Coll., 1983, Pratt-Haas Disting. Lectr. award, 1987-88. Fellow Cushman Found.; mem. Am. Assn. Petroleum Geologists (A.I. Levorsen petroleum geology Meml. award Gulf Coast assn., geol. socs. sect. 1980), Assn. Am. State Geologists (past pres.), Geol. Soc. Am., Soc. Econ. Paleontologists and Mineralogists Gulf Coast sect. (hon., past pres.), Paleontol. Soc. (past pres. southeast sect.), N.Am. Micropaleontology Soc., Internat. Micropaleontology Soc., Ala. Geol. Soc. (past pres.), Sigma Xi, Phi Kappa Phi (past chpt. pres.), Phi Sigma. Presbyterian. Contbr. articles to profl. jours. Home: 15271 Four Winds Loop Northport AL 35476-9120 Office: Geological Survey of Ala PO Box O 420 Hackberry Ln Tuscaloosa AL 35486

MANCINI, NICHOLAS ANGELO, psychologist; b. Newark, May 30, 1944; s. Joseph Michael and Anne Marie (Caputo) M.; m. Gail Helene Reichman, Mar. 20, 1976; children: Michael, Daniel, Brant. BBA in Bus. Adminstrn., Upsala Coll., 1967; MA in Gen. Exper. Psychology, Fairleigh Dickinson, 1975; PhD, Profl. Sch. Psychology, 1985. Diplomate Psychotherapy and Behavioral Medicine, Family Counseling; cert. biofeedback therapist; cert. clin. psychology, N.J.; lic. psychologist Pa.; Calif. County clin. psychologist Cape May County and Mental Health Svc., Inc., Crest Haven, N.J., 1977-85; clin. psychologist N.J. Div. Devel. Disabilities Vineland Devel. Ctr./Hosp., 1985-86. N.J. Div. Youth/Family Svcs., Vineland Childrens Residential, 1986-87; clin. dir., community re-integration Progressive Living, Inc., for traumatic brain injured, Bensalem, Pa., 1987-89; dir. psychology and behavioral medicine Rising Sun, Mirman and St. Vincent med. ctrs., Phila., Springfield, 1987—; dir. psychology Pa. Pain Rehab. Ctr., 1989-90, 95; dir. biofeedback rehab. and behavioral medicine Univ. Med. Ctr./Cooper Hosp.-U. Medicine and Surgery N.J., Camden, 1990-95; founder, dir. Adaptive Behavior Ctrs., Inc.; assoc. prof. Phila. Coll. of Osteopathic Medicine, 1995—. Mem. Phila. Neuropsychology Group (charter), Soc. Behavioral Medicine, Am. Psychol. Soc. (charter), Assn. of Applied Psychophysiology and Biofeedback, Lions. Avocations: tennis, swimming, boating, classical music, wood working. Home: 4 Chapel Hill RD Huntingdon Valley PA 19006 Office: Robert Woods Johnson Med Sch Edn & Rsch Bldg-Dept Psychiatry 401 Haddon Ave Camden NJ 08103

MANCINI, ROCCO ANTHONY, civil engineer; b. Prezza, Abruzzi, Italy, Aug. 16, 1931; came to U.S., 1940; s. Salvatore and Bambina (Tulliani) M.; m. Eileen Clifford, Apr. 11, 1959; children: Charles V., Ann Marie, Linda E., Donna. BSCE, MIT, 1953; cert. in transp. engring., Yale U., 1958. Registered profl. engr., Mass. Supr. devel. planning Mass. Bay Transp. Authority, Quincy, 1966-68, project mgr. traffic engring., devel., 1976-79, mgr. transp. systems mgmt. projects, 1979-80, acting dir. program devel., 1982-87, sr. dir. to Met. Planning Orgn., 1982-87, project mgr. constrn. office, 1987-89, asst. dir. constrn., 1989-92, asst. dir. design and constrn., 1992—; cons. spl. transp. projects, City of Honolulu, 1968-69, Sao Paulo, Brazil, 1968-69; prin. transp. engr. Wilbur Smith and Assocs., 1969-70; New Eng. regional mgr. Tippetts-Abbett-McCarthy-Stratton, 1970-76. Contbr. articles to profl. publs. Mem. Milton (Mass.) Town Meeting, active various town coms. With U.S. Army, 1954-55. Automotive Safety Found. fellow Yale U., 1957-58. Fellow Inst. Transp. Engrs. (pres. New Eng. sect. 1965-66); mem. ASCE (transp. com. 1953—). Achievements include development, design and supervision of transportation construction projects. Home: 49 Columbine Rd Milton MA 02186 Office: Mass Bay Transp Authority 1515 Hancock St Quincy MA 02169

MANCINI, VALERIE, health facility administrator; b. Apr. 23, 1947; came to U.S., 1955; d. John Battista and Theresa (Franco) Mingolla; m. Anthony Michael, May 10, 1969; children: Lisa, Beth. Cert., St. Vincent Hosp. Sch. Nursing, 1968; BSN, Worcester State U., 1981; MBA, Anna Maria Coll., 1984; EdD, U. Mass., 1990. RN, Mass.; cert. childbirth educator. Supr. nursing St. Vincent Hosp., Worcester, Mass., 1978-87, acting dir. patient care svcs., 1987-88, dir. patient care svcs., 1988-89, asst. v.p., 1989, v.p. nursing, 1989—; assoc. prof. grad. sch. nursing U. Mass., 1989—; prof. Anna Maris Coll., 1995—; part-time childbirth educator Childbirth Edn. Assn. of Cen. Mass., 1972-88, dir. ednl. svcs., 1984-88; instr. nursing Quinsigamond Community Coll., Worcester, 1981-87; adj. instr. Worcester State Coll. Mem. Am. Orgn. Nurse Execs., Am. Nurses Assn., Mass. Orgn. Nurse Execs., Cen. Mass. Nurse Execs., Nat. League for Nursing, Northeast Orgn. for Nursing, Sigma Theta Tau. Office: St Vincent Hosp 25 Winthrop St Worcester MA 01604-4593

MANCINO, DOUGLAS MICHAEL, lawyer; b. Cleve., May 8, 1949; s. Paul and Adele (Brazaitis) M.; m. Carol Keith, June 16, 1973. BA, Kent State U., 1971; JD, Ohio State U., 1974. Bar: Ohio 1974, U.S. Tax Ct. 1977, Calif. 1981, D.C. 1981. Assoc. Baker & Hostetler, Cleve., 1974-1980; ptnr. Memel & Ellsworth, Los Angeles, 1980-87, McDermott, Will & Emery, Los Angeles, 1987—; bd. dirs., mem. exec com., mem. corp. com. Health Systems Internat., Inc. Author: Federal Taxation of Hospitals and Health Care Organizations, 1995, (with others) Hospital Survival Guide, 1984, Navigating the Federal Physician Self-Referral Law, 1995; co-author quar. tax column Am. Hosp. Assn. publ. Health Law Vigil, (with L. Burns) Joint Ventures Between Hosps. and Physicians, 1987; contbr. articles to profl. jours. Dir. Music Ctr. Opera League, Cen. L.A. Mem. ABA (tax, bus., real property, probate and trust sects., chair exempt organizing com. 1995—), Calif. State Bar Assn. (tax, bus. law sects.), Ohio Bar Assn., Greater Cleve. Bar Assn., D.C. Bar Assn., Beverly Hills Bar Assn. (chmn. health law com. 1982-84), Nat. Health Lawyers Assn., Am. Acad. Hosp. Attys. (bd. dirs., pres. 1993-94), Calif. Soc. for Healthcare Attys., Bel Air Country Club, The Regency Club. Home: 2727 Patricia Ave Los Angeles CA 90064-4422

MANCKE, RICHARD BELL, university dean, economics educator; b. Bethlehem, Pa., Jan. 11, 1943; s. Donald Bell and Elizabeth (Schlottman) M.; m. Barbara Hobbie, Sept. 4, 1970; 1 child, Max. BA, Colgate U., 1965; PhD, MIT, 1969. Instr. MIT, Cambridge, Mass., 1968-69; staff economist U.S. President's Oil Imports Task Force, Washington, 1969-70; asst. prof. Grad. Sch. Bus., U. Chgo., 1969-71; asst. prof. econs. and law U. Mich. Law Sch., Ann Arbor, 1971-74; assoc. prof. Fletcher Sch. Tufts U., Medford, Mass., 1974-81, prof., 1981-86; mng. ptnr. Wolfeboro (N.H.) Ventures, 1985-92; vis. prof. Fgn. Affairs Coll., Beijing, 1987, Colgate U., Hamilton, N.Y., 1990; prof. Fletcher Sch. Tufts U., 1990—; acad. dean Fletcher Sch., Tufts U., 1991-94; interim dean Fletcher Sch. Tufts U., Medford, Mass., 1994-95; expert witness Cravath, Swaine & Moore, N.Y.C., 1974-82; dir. Intellitech Corp., Key Largo, Fla., 1985-90; rsch. dir. Twentieth Century Fund Energy Policy Task Force, N.Y.C., 1976-77. Author: The Failure of U.S. Energy Policy, 1974, Squeaking By, 1976, Mexican Oil and Natural Gas, 1979; co-author: IBM and the U.S. Data Processing Industry, 1983 (outstanding acad. book award Choice) 1984. Testified before various coms. U.S. Senate, 1972-76; mem. various town bds., Wolfeboro, N.H., 1981-94. Recipient Teaching

Excellence award U. Mich., 1974, Fgn. Affairs Coll., 1987; fellow NSF, 1967, Earhart Found., 1981. Mem. Am. Econs. Assn., Appalachian Mountain Club. Avocations: reading, cycling, hiking. Home: PO Box 432 Wolfeboro NH 03894-0432 Office: Tufts U Fletcher Sch Law and Diplomacy Medford MA 02155

MANCOFF, NEAL ALAN, lawyer; b. Chgo., May 7, 1939; s. Isadore and Sarah (Leviton) M.; m. Alys Belofsky, June 26, 1966; children: Wesley, Frederick, Daniel. BBA, U. Wis., 1961; JD, Northwestern U., 1965. Bar: Ill. 1965, U.S. Dist. Ct. (no. dist.) Ill. 1965. Assoc. Aaron Schimberg & Hess, Chgo., 1965-72, ptnr., 1972-80; ptnr. Schiff Hardin & Waite, Chgo., 1980—. Author: Qualified Deferred Compensation Plans, 1983, Nonqualified Deferred Compensation Agreements, 1987. 1st lt. U.S. Army, 1961-62. Mem. Chgo. Bar Assn. (chmn. employee benefits com. 1984). Office: Schiff Hardin & Waite 7500 Sears Towers Chicago IL 60606

MANCUSO, FRANK G., entertainment company executive; b. Buffalo, July 25, 1933; married. Ed., SUNY. Film buyer, ops. supr. Basil Enterprises, 1958-62; joined Paramount Pictures Corp., 1962, booker Buffalo br., 1962-64, sales rep. Buffalo br., 1964-67, br. mgr., 1967-70; v.p., gen. sales mgr. Paramount Pictures Can. Ltd., 1970-72, pres., 1972-76; U.S. Western div. mgr. Paramount Pictures Can. Ltd., Los Angeles, 1976-77; gen. sales mgr. Paramount Pictures Can. Ltd., N.Y.C., 1977; v.p. domestic distbn. Paramount Pictures Can. Ltd., 1977-79, exec. v.p. distbn. and mktg., 1979-83, pres. Paramount Motion Picture div., 1983-84; chmn., chief exec. officer Paramount Pictures Corp., N.Y.C., 1984-91; chmn, CEO Metro-Goldwyn-Mayer, 1993—. Bd. dirs. Will Rogers Meml. Fund, N.Y.-Cornell Med. Ctr., Burke Rehab. Ctr., UCLA Med. Ctr., Mus. of Broadcasting. Mem. Acad. Motion Picture Arts and Scis. (bd. dirs.), Motion Picture Assn. (bd. dirs.), Am. Film Inst. (bd. dirs.), Motion Picture Pioneers (bd. dirs.), Variety Clubs Internat. (bd. dirs.). Office: MGM/UA 10000 Washington Blvd Los Angeles CA 90066 also: Metro-Goldwyn-Mayer Inc 2500 Broadway St Santa Monica CA 90404-3061 also: Metro-Goldwyn-Mayer Inc 1350 Ave of the Americas New York NY 10019*

MANCUSO, JAMES VINCENT, automobile columnist; b. Batavia, N.Y., June 18, 1916; s. Benjamin J. and Laura (LaRussa) M.; student Gen. Motors Inst., Flint, Mich., 1949, Army War Coll., 1988; m. Clarissa R. Pope, Sept. 8, 1945; children: Richard J., Robert P., Linda M., Laura Lee. Auto salesman C. Mancuso & Son, Inc., 1934-39, gen. mgr., 1939-42; gen. mgr. Batavia Motors (N.Y.), 1945-49; sales rep. Cadillac Motor Car div. Gen. Motors Corp., 1950-53; pres., gen. mgr. Mancuso Chevrolet, Inc., Skokie, Ill., 1953-74, chmn. bd., 1974-84; pres. Mancuso Cadillac/Honda, Inc., Barrington, Ill., 1974-76, chmn. bd., 1975; pres. Mancuso Co., 1984—; pres., Service Survey Systems, 1985—; adv. council Consol. Am. Life Ins. Co.; dir. Lake States Life Ins. Co.; mem. faculty Chevrolet Acad., Wayne State U., 1964; dir. Auto Industries Hwy. Safety Com. Svc. columnist Ward's Auto Dealer mag., 1987-90, Auto Age Mag., 1989—, Dealer Bus. Mag. Chmn. Niles Twp. Jud. Reform Com.; gen. mgr. Niles Twp. Community Fund, 1955; chmn. Skokie's All Am. City Com., 1961. Served from pvt. to maj. USAAF, 1942-46. Mem. Am. Legion, Nat. Auto Dealers Assn. (dir. chmn. pub. relations com.), Chgo. Better Bus. Bur. (dir.), Asso. Employers Ill. (dir.), Skokie C. of C. (pres. 1956), Chgo. Auto Dealers Assn. (dir. 1959-68), Chgo. Auto Trade Assn. (v.p. 1959-60), Chgo. Met. Chevrolet Dealers Assn. (pres. 1957-59), Chgo. Chevrolet Dealers Advt. Assn. (pres. 1969-70). Roman Catholic. Clubs: Rotary (pres. 1960-61), Evanston Golf (pres. 1969-70), Boca (Boca Raton, Fla.). Office: The Mancuso Co 560 Green Bay Rd Winnetka IL 60093-2238

MAND, MARTIN G., financial executive; b. Norfolk, Va., Sept. 26, 1936; s. Meyer J. and Lena (Sutton) M.; m. Shelly Cohen, Aug. 29, 1965; children: Gregory S., Michael E., Brian C. BS in Commerce, U. Va., 1958; MBA, U. Del., 1964. Various fin. staff and mgmt. positions E.I. du Pont de Nemours & Co., Wilmington, Del., 1961-83, v.p. taxes and fin. services, 1983-84; v.p., comptroller, 1984-88, v.p., treas. 1989-90; sr. v.p., CFO No. Telecon Ltd., Mississauga, Ont., Can., 1990-93, exec. v.p.; chmn. pres., CEO Mand Assocs., Ltd., 1995—; dir. First Fed. Savs. and Loan, Wilmington, 1977-83; pres. Fin. Execs. Research Found., 1988-90. Lt. USN, 1958-61. Mem. Fin. Execs. Inst., Am. Mgmt. Assn (chmn. fin. coun.).

MANDARICH, DAVID D., real estate corporation executive; b. 1948. With Majestic Savs. and Loan, 1966-67; formerly chief operating officer, exec. v.p. MDC Holdings Inc.; pres., co-chief operating officer MDC Holdings Inc., Denver, from 1986, now pres., chief operating officer. Office: Richmond Homes Inc II 4600 S Ulster St Ste 400 Denver CO 80237-1808

MANDEL, BABALOO, scriptwriter; b. N.Y.C. Screenwriter: (with Lowell Ganz) Night Shift, 1982, (and with Bruce Jay Friedman) Splash, 1984 (Academy award nomination best original screenplay 1984), (and with Dan Aykroyd) Spies Like Us, 1985, Gung Ho, 1986, Vibes, 1988, Parenthood, 1989, City Slickers, 1991, A League of Their Own, 1992, (and with Billy Crystal) Mr. Saturday Night, 1992, Greedy, 1994, City Slickers II: The Legend of Curley's Gold, 1994, (and with Crystal) Forget Paris, 1995; writer: (TV series) Laverne and Shirley, 1976-83, Busting Loose, 1977, (TV pilots) Herndon and Me, 1983; writer, exec. prodr.: (TV pilots) Gung Ho, 1986, Channel 99, 1988, Knight and Daye, 1989, Parenthood, 1990, A League of their Own, 1993; creator, writer, creative cons.: (with Ganz) Take Five, 1987; appearances include (film) Splash, 1984, (TV) Naked Hollywood, 1991. Office: CAA 9830 Wilshire Blvd Beverly Hills CA 90212*

MANDEL, CAROLA PANERAI (MRS. LEON MANDEL), foundation trustee; b. Havana, Cuba; d. Camilo and Elvira (Bertini) Panerai; ed. pvt. schs., Havana and Europe; m. Leon Mandel, Apr. 9, 1938. Mem. women's bd. Northwestern Meml. Hosp., Chgo. Trustee Carola and Leon Mandel Fund Loyola U., Chgo. Life mem. Chgo. Hist. Soc., Guild of Chgo. Hist. Soc., Smithsonian Assos., Nat. Skeet Shooting Assn. Frequently named among Ten Best Dressed Women in U.S.; chevalier Confrerie des Chevaliers du Tastevin. Capt. All-Am. Women's Skeet Team, 1952, 53, 54, 55, 56; only woman to win a men's nat. championship, 20 gauge, 1954, also high average in world over men, 1956, in 12 gauge with 99.4 per cent; European women's live bird shooting championship, Venice, Italy, 1957, Porto, Portugal, 1961; European woman's target championship, Torino, Italy, 1958; woman's world champion live-bird shooting, Sevilla, Spain, 1959, Am. Contract Bridge League Life Master, 1987. Named to Nat. Skeet Shooting Assn. Hall of Fame, 1970; inducted in U.S. Pigeon shooting Fedn. Hall of Fame, 1992. Mem. Soc. Four Arts. Club: Everglades (Palm Beach, Fla.), The Beach. Home: 324 Barton Ave Palm Beach FL 33480-6116

MANDEL, H(AROLD) GEORGE, pharmacologist; b. Berlin, June 6, 1924; came to U.S., 1937, naturalized, 1944; s. Ernest A. and Else (Crail) M.; m. Marianne Klein, July 25, 1953; children: Marcia Mandel Halgren, Audrey Lynn Mandel Todd. BS, Yale U., 1944, PhD, 1949. Lab. instr. in chemistry Yale U., 1942-44, 47-49; research asso. dept. pharmacology George Washington U., 1949-50, asst. research prof., 1950-52, assoc. prof. pharmacology, 1952-58, prof., 1958—, chmn. dept. pharmacology, 1960—; Advanced Commonwealth Fund fellow Molteno Inst. Cambridge (Eng.) U., 1956; Commonwealth Fund fellow U. Auckland (N.Z.) and U. Med. Scis., Bangkok, Thailand, 1964; Am. Cancer Soc. Eleanor Roosevelt Internat. fellow Chester Beatty Research Inst. London, 1970-71; Am. Cancer Soc. scholar U. Calif., San Francisco, 1978-79; fellow Med. Research Council toxicology unit, Carshalton, Eng., 1986; Burroughs Wellcome Rsch. travel grant, Carshalton, 1988; hon. rsch. fellow dept. biochemistry and molecular biology U. Coll., London, 1993; mem. cancer chemotherapy com. Internat. Union Against Cancer, 1966-73, fellow, Lyon, France, 1989; mem. external rev. com. Howard U. Cancer Research Center, 1972-74; cons. Bur. Drugs, 1975-79, EPA, 1978-82; mem. toxicology adv. com. FDA, 1975-78; mem. med. research service merit rev. bd. in alcoholism and drug dependence VA, 1975-78; mem. cancer spl. program adv. com. Nat. Cancer Inst., 1974-78, chmn., 1976-78; mem. Nat. Large Bowel Cancer Project Working Cadre, 1980-84; mem. com. on toxicology NRC-Nat. Acad. Sci., 1978-82; mem. Kettering award selection com. Gen. Motors Cancer Research Found., 1979-81. Editorial bd.: Jour. Pharmacology and Exptl. Therapeutics, 1960-65, field editor, 1978-94; editorial bd.: Molecular Pharmacology, 1965-69, Rsch. Comm. in Chem. Pathology, Pharmacology, 1972—, Cancer Drug Delivery, Selective Cancer Therapeutics, 1983-92, Cancer Research, 1974-76 assoc. editor, 1977-81. Served with AUS, 1944-46. Recipient John J. Abel award

in pharmacology Eli Lilly and Co., 1958, Disting. Achievement award Washington Acad. Scis., 1958, Golden Apple Teaching award AMA, 1969, 85. Mem. AAAS, Am. Chem. Soc., Am. Soc. Biochemistry and Molecular Biology, Am. Soc. Pharmacology and Exptl. Therapeutics (pres. 1973-74), Am. Assn. Cancer rsch., Assn. Med. Sch. Pharmacology (pres. 1976-78), Nat. Caucus of Basic Biomed. Sci. Chairs (chmn. 1991—), Cosmos Club (Washington), Sigma Xi, Alpha Omega Alpha. Democrat. Research, numerous publs. on cancer chemotherapy, mechanism of growth inhibition, antimetabolites, drug disposition, chemical carcinogenesis. Home: 4956 Sentinel Dr Bethesda MD 20816-3562 Office: George Washington U Dept Pharmacology 2300 I St NW Washington DC 20037-2337

MANDEL, HERBERT MAURICE, civil engineer; b. Port Chester, N.Y., May 11, 1924; s. Arthur William and Rose (Schmeiser) M.; m. Charlotte Feldman, Aug. 22, 1954; children: Rosanne Mandel Levine, Elliott D., Arthur M. BSCE, Va. Poly. Inst., 1948, M Engring., Yale U., 1949. Registered profl. engr., N.Y., Conn., Fla., Md., Mich., Minn., Ohio, Pa., Va., W.Va. Structural engr. Madigan Hyland Co., Long Island City, N.Y., 1949-50; with firm Parsons, Brinckerhoff, Quade & Douglas, Inc., 1950-86; v.p. GAI Cons. Inc., 1986—, prin. staff cons., 1993—; project mgr. Atlanta, 1962, N.Y.C., 1963-70, Honolulu, 1970-74, v.p., 1974, sr. v.p., Pitts., 1977-86; faculty Yale U., 1948-49; adj. faculty Bklyn. Poly. Inst., 1956-64, U. Pitts., 1986; gen. chmn. 6th Internat. Bridge Conf., Pitts., 1989. Author tech. papers; prin. works include (prin.-in-charge) Williamstown-Marietta Bridge, W.Va.-Ohio, Dunbar Bridge, W.Va., I-64 Bridge over Big Sandy River, W.Va.-Kentucky, Davis Creek Bridge, Charleston, W.Va., Tygart R. Bridge, W.Va., Easley Bridge, Bluefield, W.Va., (project mgr.) Newport Bridge, Narragansett Bay, R.I., (designer/project engr.) Hackensack River Bridge, N.J., Housatonic River Bridge, Conn., Arthur Kill Vertical Lift R.R. Bridge, S.I., N.Y., 62nd St. Bridge, Pitts., Savannah River Cantilever Bridge, Ga., I-84 Bridges, Danbury, Conn., (structural rehab designer) Avondale Bridge, N.J., Lincoln Bridge, N.J., B&O R.R. Bridge, Vincennes, Ind., Hawk St. Viaduct, Albany, N.Y., Congress Ave. Bridge, Austin, Tex., Ohio St. Bridge, Buffalo, Panhandle Bridge, Pitts.; project mgr. Interstate Rt. H-3, Honolulu, 1970-74; project dir. design and constrn. Pitts. Light Rail Transit System, 1977-84; designer Elizabeth R. Tunnel, Norfolk, Va., 1950. Served to 1st lt. U.S. Army, 1943-46, 50-52; ETO. Fellow ASCE, Soc. Am. Mil. Engrs. (pres. Pitts. post 1987-88); mem. Am. Ry. Engring. Assn. (steel structures specifications com., 1974—), Nat. Soc. Profl. Engrs., Profl. Engrs. in Pvt. Practice (bd. govs.), Pa. Profl. Engrs. in Pvt. Practice (state vice-chmn. 1992-94, chmn. 1994—), Internat. Assn. Bridge and Structural Engring., Assn. for Bridge Constrn. and Design, Tau Beta Pi, Chi Epsilon, Omicron Delta Kappa, Phi Kappa Phi, Pi Delta Epsilon, Scabbard and Blade. Jewish. Club: Engineers (Pitts.). Home: 920 Parkview Dr Pittsburgh PA 15243-1116 Office: GAI Cons Inc 570 Beatty Rd Monroeville PA 15146-1334

MANDEL, IRWIN DANIEL, dentist; b. Bklyn., Apr. 9, 1922; s. Samuel A. and Shirley (Blankstein) M.; m. Charlotte Lifschutz, Apr. 1, 1944; children: Carol, Nora, Richard. BS, CCNY, 1942; DDS, Columbia U., 1945; DSc (hon.), U. Medicine and Dentistry of N.J., 1981; DOdont (hon.), U. Göteborg, 1984. Rsch. asst. Dental Sch. Columbia U., 1946-48, mem. faculty Dental Sch., 1946—, prof. dentistry, dir. div. preventive dentistry Dental Sch., 1969-84, dir. Ctr. Clin. Rsch. in Dentistry Dental Sch., 1984-91, assoc. dean rsch., 1991-92; prof. emeritus Dental Sch., 1992—; pvt. practice dentistry, 1946-68; vis. prof. various dental schs.; chmn. oral biology and medicine study sect. Nat. Inst. Dental Rsch., 1974-76. Co-author: The Plaque Diseases, 1972; contbr. over 220 articles and chpts. in books. Active local chpt. ACLU, SANE/FREEZE, Physicians for Social Responsibility. Lt. Dental Corps USNR, 1945-46, 52-54. Recipient Career Scientist award N.Y.C. Health Rsch. Council, 1969-72, Leadership award in periodontology Tufts U. Dental Sch., 1971, Internat. award U. Conn. Sch. Dental Medicine, 1979, ann. Seymour J. Kreshover NIDR lecture award, 1986. Fellow AAAS, Am. Coll. Dentists; mem. ADA (chmn. coun. dental rsch. 1978-80, Gold medal for excellence in rsch. 1985), Dental Soc. (Henry Spenadel award 1973, Jarvie-Burkhart Internat. award 1990), Am. Assn. Dental Rsch. (pres. 1980), Am. Assn. Pub. Health Dentists (Disting. Svc. award 1991), Fed. Dentair Internat. (W. D. Miller prize 1992), Internat. Assn. Dental Rsch. (Salivary Rsch. award 1994), N.Y. Acad. Scis., Sigma Xi, Omicron Kappa Upsilon. Home: 60 Pine Dr Cedar Grove NJ 07009-1036 Office: 630 W 168th St New York NY 10032-3702

MANDEL, JACK N., manufacturing company executive; b. Austria, July 16, 1911; s. Sam and Rose M.; m. Lilyan, Aug. 14, 1938. Student, Fenn Coll., 1930-33. Founder, now chmn. fin. com. Premier Indsl. Corp., Cleve. Mem. exec. com. NCCJ; trustee Mood Hosp., 1969—, Fla. Soc. for Blind; life trustee South Broward Jewish Fedn., Cleve. Jewish Welfare Fedn.; pres. Montefiore Home for aged; pres. adv. bd. Barry U.; hon. trustee Hebrew U.; trustee Tel Aviv U. Mus. of the Diaspora; life trustee The Temple, Woodruff Found.; trustee Cleve. Play House. Mem. Emerald Hills Country Club, Beachmont Country Club, Commede Club. Office: Premier Indsl Corp 4500 Euclid Ave Cleveland OH 44103-3736

MANDEL, JOSEPH DAVID, university official, lawyer; b. N.Y.C., Mar. 26, 1940; s. Max and Charlotte Lee (Goodman) M.; m. Jean Carol Westerman, Aug. 18, 1963; children: Jonathan Scott, Eric David. AB, Dartmouth Coll., 1960, MBA, 1961; JD, Yale U., 1964. Bar: Calif. 1965. Law clk. U.S. Ct. Appeals, 9th crct., L.A., 1964-65; lectr. law U. So. Calif. Law Ctr., L.A., 1965-68; assoc. atty. Tuttle & Taylor, L.A., 1965-69, mem., 1970-82, 90-91, of counsel, 1984-90; vice chancellor UCLA, 1991—; lectr. UCLA Law Sch., 1993; v.p., gen. counsel, sec. Natomas Co., San Francisco, 1983; mem. Calif. Legal Corps, 1993—; bd. dirs. Legal Rsch. Network, Inc., 1993—. Pres. Legal Aid Found., L.A., 1978-79; trustee Southwestern U. Sch. Law, 1982, UCLA Pub. Interest Law Found., 1981-82, L.A. County Bar Found., 1974-79, 82, Coro Found., 1989-92, Coro So. Calif. Ctr., 1985-92, pub. coun., 1989-94, community v.p., 1992-94; mem. City of L.A. Bd. Zoning Appeals, 1984-90, vice chmn., 1985-86, 89-90, chmn., 1986-87; mem. exec. com. Yale U. Law Sch. Assn., 1983-89, v.p., 1986-88, chmn. planning com., 1990-92, pres. 1992-94, chmn. exec. com., 1994—; mem. State Bar Calif. Legal Svcs. Trust Fund Commn., 1985-87, chmn., 1985-86; bd. dirs. Western Justice Ctr. Found., 1989—, v.p., 1992—, Harvard Water Polo Found., 1990—; bd. advisors The Pub. Svc. Challenge, Nat. Assn. for Pub. Interest Law, 1990—; bd. govs. Inner City Law Ctr., 1991—; mem. alumni coun. Dartmouth Coll., 1992-95. Recipient Maynard award Legal Aid Found. of L.A., 1991, Shattuck-Price award L.A. County Bar Assn., 1993, West Coast Liberty award Lambda Legal Defense and Edn. Fund, 1994. Mem. Los Angeles County Bar Assn. (pres. 1980-81). Democrat. Jewish. Home: 15478 Longbow Dr Sherman Oaks CA 91403-4910 Office: UCLA Office of the Chancellor 2135 Murphy Hall Los Angeles CA 90095

MANDEL, LEON, III, author; b. Chgo., July 31, 1928; s. Leon Jr. Mandel and Edna (Horn) Seligmann; m. Olivia Eskridge, June 12, 1953; children: Leon, Olivia. Student, Columbia U., 1949, Cornell U. 1950-54, U. Calif., Hastings, 1960. Editor Belmont (Calif.) Courier Bull., 1963, Competition Press, San Francisco, 1964-67; mng. editor Car and Driver Mag., N.Y.C., 1967-68, editor, 1968-71; sr. editor Motor Trend, L.A., 1971-74; editor in chief Crain Communications/Auto Week, Detroit, 1983-87, v.p., pub., 1987—; auto editor Sta. KTVN-TV, Reno, Nev., 1976-82; instr. mag. journalism Truckee Meadows Community Coll., 1980; cons. SRI Internat. Author: Speed with Style: The Autobiography of Peter Revson, 1974, Driven: The American Four-Wheeled Love Affair, 1977, Murder So Real (pseudonym Al Bird), 1978, Fast Lane Summer, 1981, William Fisk Harrah: The Life and Times of a Gambling Magnate, 1982, American Cars, 1982. Mem. Detroit Athletic Club. Home: 166 Country Club Dr Grosse Pointe MI 48236-2902 Office: Auto Week 1400 Woodbridge St Detroit MI 48207-3110

MANDEL, LEONARD, physics and optics educator; m. Jeanne Elizabeth Kear, Aug. 20, 1953; children: Karen Roe, Barry Paul. B.Sc., U. London, Eng., 1947, U. London, Eng., 1948; Ph.D., U. London, Eng., 1951. Tech. officer Imperial Chem. Industries, 1951-54; lectr., sr. lectr. Imperial Coll., U. London, 1954-64; prof. physics U. Rochester, N.Y., 1964—, prof. optics, 1977-80, Lee Du Bridge prof. physics and optics, 1994—; joint sec. Rochester Confs. on Coherence and Quantum Optics, 1966, 72, 77, 83, 89; vis. prof. U. Tex., Austin, 1984; vis. scientist Am. Inst. Physics; Internat. Commn. Optics traveling lectr., 1992. Editor books; contbr. more than 280 articles to profl. jours. Recipient Marconi medal Italian Nat. Rsch. Coun., 1987, Thomas Young medal Inst. Physics Gt. Britain, 1989, 1st recipient Max Born medal, 1982, Ives medal, 1993. Fellow Am. Phys. Soc., Optical Soc. Am. (bd. dirs. 1985-87, assoc. editor jour. 1970-76, 82-84, Optics Letters 1977-79, bd. editors Phys. Rev. 1987-89, Jour. Quantum Optics 1989-93, chmn. com. for society objectives and policy 1977, Wood prize com. 1988, Max Bohr medal com. 1994), N.Y. Acad. Scis. Office: U Rochester Dept Physics Astronomy Rochester NY 14627

MANDEL, MORTON, molecular biologist; b. Bklyn., July 6, 1924; s. Barnet and Rose (Kliner) M.; m. Florence H. Goodman, Apr. 1, 1952; children: Robert, Leslie. BCE, CUNY, 1944; MS, Columbia U., 1949, PhD in Physics, 1957. Scientist Bell Telephone Labs., Murray Hill, N.J., 1956-57; asst. prof. physics dept. Stanford (Calif.) U., 1957-61; scientist Gen. Telephone & Telegraph, Mountain View, Calif., 1961-63; rsch. assoc. dept. genetics Stanford U., 1963-64; rsch. fellow Karolinska Inst., Stockholm, Sweden, 1964-66; assoc. prof. sch. of medicine U. Hawaii, Honolulu, 1966-68, prof., 1968—; cons. Fairchild Semiconductor, Hewlett Packard, Lockheed, Rheem, Palo Alto, Calif., 1957-61. Contbr. articles to profl. jours. Lt. (j.g.) USN, 1944-46. Recipient Am. Cancer Soc. Scholar award Am. Cancer Soc., 1979-80, Eleanor Roosevelt Internat. Cancer fellowship, 1979; named NIH Spl. fellow Karolinska Inst., 1964-66. Fellow Am. Phys. Soc.; mem. Sigma Xi. Achievements include citation classics, optional conditions for mutagenesis by N-methyl-N1-nitro-N-nitrosoquauidine in E. coli K12; calcium dependent bacteriophage DNA infection. Office: Dept of Biochemistry 1960 East-West Rd Honolulu HI 96844

MANDEL, MORTON LEON, industrial corporation executive; b. Cleve., Sept. 19, 1921; s. Simon and Rose (Nusbaum) M.; m. Barbara Abrams, Feb. 27, 1949; children: Amy, Thomas, Stacy. Student, Case Western Res. U., 1939-40, Pomona Coll., 1943; LDH (hon.), Gratz Coll., 1984; LHD (hon.), Hebrew Union Coll., 1986; LDH (hon.), Brandeis U., 1989; LHD (hon.), Yeshiva U., 1993, Hebrew U., 1993, Hebrew Coll. Jewish Studies, 1993. With Premier Indsl. Corp., Cleve., 1940—; sec.-treas. Premier Indus Corp., Cleve., 1946-58, pres., 1958-70, chmn., 1970—; also bd. dirs. Premier Indsl. Corp., Cleve. Pres. Jewish Community Ctrs. of Cleve., 1952-57, now life trustee, Jewish Community Fedn., 1974-77, now life trustee, 1970-74, now hon. pres.; pres. Jewish Comty. Ctrs. Assn.; pres. Coun. Initiatives in Jewish Edn., 1991—; pres. United Way Cleve., 1977-79, chmn., 1979-81, now life trustee; mem. Commn. on Health and Social Services, City of Cleve., 1970-71; trustee Case Western Res. U., 1977-92, now hon. trustee, Mt. Sinai Med. Ctr., Cleve., 1970-79, now trustee emeritus, Cleve. Zool. Soc., 1970-73, Greater Cleve. Roundtable, 1981-83; founding pres. World Confedn. Jewish Community Centers, 1977-81, now hon. pres.; founding chair Nat. Jewish Dem. Coun., 1990-93; bd. govs. Jewish Agy., 1979-88; trustee United Israel Appeal, 1977-88, United Jewish Appeal, 1978-82, Am. Jewish Joint Distbn. Com., 1975-88; founder Cleve. Project MOVE, 1981; founder Clean-Land Ohio, 1981, trustee, 1981—; vice chmn. Cleve. Tomorrow, 1982-88, trustee, 1982—; founder, chmn. Mid-Town Corridor, 1982-85, trustee, 1982—; trustee United Way of Am., 1985-91; trustee Cleve. Social Policy Studies, 1983—, Cleve. Mus. Art, 1990-93, Mus. Arts Assn., 1990—; co-chmn. Operation Independence, 1985-88. Recipient Outstanding Young Man of Yr. award Cleve. Jr. C. of C., 1956, Businessman of Yr. award Urban League of Cleve., 1973, Frank L. Weil award JCC Assn., 1974, Citizen of Yr. award Cleve. Area Bd. Realtors, 1974, Charles Eisenman award Cleve. Jewish Community Fedn., 1977, Mgmt. Performance award Case Western Res. U., 1982, Business Statesman of Yr. award Harvard Bus. Sch. Club of Cleve., 1985, Dively award Corp. Leadership in Urban Devel., 1986, Ben-Gurion Centennial medal State of Israel Bonds, 1986, Presdl. award for Pvt. Sector Initiatives, 1988, Newton D. Baker Disting. Svc. award Case Western Res. U., 1992; named Man of Yr., B'nai Brith, 1980, Leader of Yr., Clean-Land Ohio, 1983, Cleve. Bus. Exec. of Yr., Sales & Mktg. Execs. of Cleve., 1990. Home: 17250 Parkland Dr Cleveland OH 44120-2553 Office: Premier Indsl Corp 4500 Euclid Ave Cleveland OH 44103-3736

MANDEL, OSCAR, literature educator, writer; b. Antwerp, Belgium, Aug. 24, 1926; came to U.S., 1940; m. Adrienne Schizzano. BA, NYU, 1947; MA, Columbia U., 1948; PhD, Ohio State U., 1951. Asst. prof. English U. Nebr., 1955-60; Fulbright lectr. U. Amsterdam, 1960-61; vis. assoc. prof. English Calif. Inst. Tech., 1961-62, assoc. prof. English, 1962-68, prof. 1. 1968—. Author: Collected Lyrics and Epigrams, 1981, Three Classic Don Juan Plays, 1981, Philoctetes and the Fall of Troy, 1981, Annotations to Vanity Fair, 1981, Ariadne, 1982, The Book of Elaborations, 1985, The Kukkurrik Fables, 1987, Sigismund, Prince of Poland, 1989, August Von Kotzebue: The Comedy, The Man, 1990, The Virgin and the Unicorn: Four Plays, 1993, The Art of Alessandro Magnasco: an Essay in the Recovery of Meaning, 1994, numerous others; contbr. articles to profl. jours. Office: Calif Inst Tech Humanities Divsn Pasadena CA 91125

MANDEL, RUTH B., political science educator, educational association administrator, researcher; b. Vienna, Austria; came to U.S., 1947; d. Michael and Lea (Schmelzer) Blumenstock; m. Barrett John Mandel, June 18, 1961 (div. 1976); 1 child, Maud S.; m. Jeffrey Lucker, Feb. 24, 1991. BA, Bklyn. Coll., 1960; MA, U. Conn., 1962, PhD, 1969. Part-time instr. dept. English U. Conn., 1960-66; lectr. dept. English U. Pitts., 1968-70; asst. prof. dept. English Rider Coll., 1970-71; asst. prof. Eagleton Inst. Politics Rutgers U., 1973-78, assoc. prof., 1978-85, prof., 1985—, ednl. coord. Ctr. Am. Woman and Politics, Eagleton Inst. Politics, 1971, dir. ednl. programs and adminstrn., 1971-73, dir., 1973—; organizer Conf. Women in Legis. Leadership, 1985, Conf. Newly Elected Women Legis., 1989; founder Pub. Leadership Edn. Network; designer Nat. Edn. Women's Leadership; TV appearances include CBS Evening News, Nightline, Good Morning Am., Today, Charlie Rose, Nightly Bus. Report; lectr. in field. Author: In the Running: The New Woman Candidate, 1983, The Impact of Women in Public Office: An Overview, 1991; co-editor: The Douglas Series on Women's Lives and the Meaning of Gender; mem. editorial bd. Signs: Jour. Women in Culture and Soc., Women & Politics: Jour. Rsch. and Policy Studies; exec. prodr. (documentary) Not One of the Boys, 1984; contbr. articles to newspapers and mags. including USA Today, Working Woman, Ms. Cons. women in power com. Nat. Commn. on Observance Internat. Women's Yr., 1975; mem. state coordinating com. N.J. Internat. Women's Yr. Conf., 1976, co-chairperson nominating com., 1977; N.J. del. U.S. Nat. Women's Conf., Houston, 1977; mem. Mercer County Commn. Status of Women, 1977-84; appointed by gov. of N.J. Commn. to Study Need and Necessary Fiscal Commitments for Creating Chair Women's Studies at Douglass Coll., 1982, chair com. acad. needs; participant The Women's Dialogue—U.S./U.S.S.R., 1984; mem. program com. Women and Constitution, 1988; organizer Nat. Hispana Leadership Initiative, Ctr. Am. Women and Politics segment, 1988; bd. dirs. Nat. Coun. Rsch. Women, 1985-92, vice-chair, 1989-91, chairperson bd. com. on future, 1988-89; mem. Nat. Commn. Renewal Am. Democracy, 1992-93;appointed by Pres. of U.S. to Holocaust Meml. Coun.; mem. search com. for dir. U.S. Holocaust Meml. Mus., 1992-93, com. collections and acquisitions; appointed by Pres. Clinton vice chairperson U.S. Holocaust Meml. Coun. Named one of N.J.'s Most Powerful Women, N.J. Monthly, 1983; recipient Douglas medal Associate Alumnae Douglass Coll., 1989, Barbara Boggs Sigmund award Women's Political Caucus N.J., 1992, Jerseyan of Week award Sunday Star-Ledger, 1992, Woodrow Wilson Pub. Svc. award Gov. N.J. Award Program, 1992. Office: Rutgers U Ctr Am Women & Politics Eagleton Inst Politics New Brunswick NJ 08901

MANDELBAUM, BARRY RICHARD, lawyer; b. Newark, N.J., Dec. 30, 1936; s. Irving and Henrietta (Brown) M.; children: Kenneth, Lisa; m. Leslie Alexander, Oct. 30, 1983. BA, Colgate U., 1958; LLB, Columbia U., 1961. Bar: N.J. 1961, U.S. Dist. Ct. N.J. 1961. Assoc. Irving Mandelbaum, Newark, 1961-63; ptnr. Mandelbaum, Mandelbaum & Gold, Newark, 1963-79; mng. prin. Mandelbaum, Salsburg, Gold, Lazris, Discenza & Steinberg, P.A., West Orange, N.J., 1979—; bd. dirs. Warwick Ins. Co., Castle Group Inc., Commander Realty Corp., pres. bd. dirs. Growth Bank, Growth Fin. Corp., Castle Group, Inc. Atty., v.p. Mental Health Assn. of East Orange, N.J., 1966—. Mem. ABA, Essex County Bar Assn., N.J. Bar Assn., Phi Beta Kappa. Home: 8 Byron Rd Caldwell NJ 07006-4204 Office: Mandelbaum Salsburg Gold Lazris Discenza & Steinberg 155 Prospect Ave West Orange NJ 07052-4204

MANDELBAUM, HOWARD ARNOLD, marketing/management consultant; b. Newark, May 17, 1941; s. Morris and Minna (Eisenberg) M.; m.

Susan Ganz, June 9, 1963; children: Joel Barry, Sari Beth, Matthew Gary. BS in Indsl. Engring., Lafayette Coll., 1963; MS in Mgmt., MIT, 1965. Advt. rsch. mgr. Hoffmann-La Roche Inc., Nutley, N.J., 1965-68; mgr. mktg. rsch. USV Pharms., N.Y.C., 1968-69; product mgr. Warner-Chilcott, Morris Plains, N.J., 1969-71; v.p. Mabico Automotive Warehouse, Maplewood, N.J., 1972; exec. v.p. William Douglas McAdams Inc., N.Y.C., 1972-93; pres. Mng. Dynamics, Inc., Livingston, N.J., 1994—. Trustee Temple Beth Shalom, Livingston, N.J., 1984-91. Mem. Pharm. Advt. Coun. Office: Mng Dynamics Inc 50 Tremont Ter Livingston NJ 07039-3340

MANDELBROT, BENOIT B., mathematician, scientist, educator; b. Warsaw, Poland, Nov. 20, 1924; came to U.S., 1958; s. Charles and Belle (Lurie) M.; m. Aliette Kagan, Nov. 5, 1955; children: Laurent, Didier. Diploma, Ecole Polytechnique, Paris, 1947; MS in Aeronautics, Calif. Inst. Tech., 1948; PhD in Math., U. Paris, 1952; DSc (hon.), Syracuse U., 1986, Laurentian U., 1986, Boston U., 1987, SUNY, 1988, U. Dallas, 1992, U. Bremen, 1988, Union Coll., 1993, U. Buenos Aires, 1993; DHL (hon.), Pace U., 1989. Jr. mem. and Rockefeller scholar Inst. for Advanced Study, Princeton, N.J., 1953-54; jr. prof. math. U. Geneva, Switzerland, 1955-57, U. Lille and Ecole Polytechnique, Paris, 1957-58; rsch. staff mem. IBM Watson Rsch. Ctr., Yorktown Heights, N.Y., 1958-74, IBM fellow, 1974-93; prof. math. scis. Yale U., New Haven, 1987—; prof. l'Acad. des Scis., Paris, 1995—; vis. prof. econs. Harvard U., 1962-63, vis. prof. applied math., 1963-64, vis. prof. math., 1979-80, prof. practice math., 1984-87; vis. prof. engring. Yale U., 1970; vis. prof. physiology Einstein Coll. Medicine, 1970; Hitchcock prof. U. Calif., Berkeley, 1992; visitor MIT, 1953, also Inst. lectr.; visitor U. Paris, 1966, Coll. de France, Paris, 1973—; Institut des Hautes Etudes Scientifiques, Bures, 1980, Mittag-Leffler Inst., Sweden, 1984, Max Planck Inst. Math., Bonn, 1988; lectr. Yale U., 1970, Cambridge U., 1990, Oxford U., 1990, Imperial Coll., London, 1991, Accademia dei Lincei, Rome; speaker and organizer profl. confs. Author: Logique, Langage et Théorie de l'Information, 1957, Les Objets Fractals: Forme, Hasard et Dimension, 1975, 4th edit., 1995, Fractals: Form, Chance and Dimension, 1977, The Fractal Geometry of Nature, 1982, La Geometria della Natura, 1987; contbr. articles to profl. jours. Recipient Franklin medal Franklin Inst., 1986, Alexander von Humboldt Preis, 1987, Caltech disting. svc. award, 1988, Moet-Hennessy prize, 1988, Harvey prize, 1989, Nev. prize U. Nev. Sys., 1991, Wolf prize for physics, 1993, Honda prize, 1994; nat. lectr. Sigma Xi, 1980-82; Guggenheim fellow, 1968. Fellow AAAS, IEEE (Charles Proteus Steinmetz medal 1988), Am. Acad. Arts and Scis., European Acad. Arts, Scis. and Humanities, Am. Phys. Soc., Inst. Math. Stats., Econometric Soc., Am. Geophys. Union, Am. Statistic Assn.; mem. NAS U.S.A. (fgn. assoc., Barnard medal 1985), Internat. Statis. Inst. (elected), Am. Math. Soc., French Math. Soc. Achievements include orgination of theory of fractals, an interdisciplinary enterprise concerned with financial data and all other shapes and phenomena that are equally rough, irregular or broken up at all scales. Office: IBM PO Box 218 Yorktown Heights NY 10598-0218 also: Yale U Dept Math New Haven CT 06520-8283 *Science would be ruined if (like sports) it were to put competition above everything else, and if it were to clarify the rules of competition by withdrawing entirely into narrowly defined specialties. The rare scholars who are wanderers-by-choice are essential to the intellectual welfare of the settled disciplines.*

MANDELKER, DANIEL ROBERT, law educator; b. Milw., July 18, 1926; s. Adolph Irwin and Marie (Manner) M.; divorced; children: Amy Jo, John David. BA, U. Wis., 1947, LLB, 1949; JD, Yale U., 1956. Bar: Wis. 1949. Asst. prof. law Drake U., 1949-51; atty. HHFA, Washington, 1952-53; asst. prof., then assoc. prof. law Ind. U., 1953-62; mem. faculty Washington U., St. Louis, 1962—; prof. law Washington U., 1963-74, Howard A. Stamper prof. law, 1974—; Walter E. Meyer rsch. prof. law Columbia U., 1971-72; Ford Found. law faculty fellow, London, 1959-60; cons. State of Hawaii Dept. Planning and Econ. Devel., 1972-78, State of Hawaii Office of State Planning, 1993-94; legal resources adv. group Transp. Rsch. Bd., 1991-94; mem. local govt. adv. bd. intergovtl. rels. U.S. Adv. Commn., 1985-88; mem. devel. regulations coun. Urban Land Inst., 1980—; cons. housing subcom., banking and currency com. U.S. Ho. of Reps., 1970-71, cons. policy studies, ins. subcom., banking, fin., urban affairs coms., 1989-91; cons. state and local govts. on land use regulation; Nat. Disting. lectr. Fla. State Jour. Land Use and Environ. Law, 1992; 15th Denman lectr. U. Cambridge, Eng., 1992. Author: Green Belts and Urban Growth: English Town and Country Planning in Action, 1962, Controlling Planned Residential Developments, 1966, Managing Our Urban Environment-Cases, Text and Problems, 1966, 2d edit., 1971, Case Studies in Land Planning and Development, 1968, The Zoning Dilemma, 1971, (with W.R. Ewald) Street Graphics and the Law, 1971, 2d edit., 1988, (with R. Montgomery) Housing in America: Problems and Perspectives, 1973, 2d edit., 1979, Housing Subsidies in the United States and England, 1973, New Developments in Land and Environmental Controls, 1974, Environmental and Land Controls Legislation, 1976, supplement, 1982, (with D. Netsch) State and Local Government in a Federal System, 1977, supplement, 1981, (with D. Netsch and P. Salsich) 2d. edit., 1983, supplement, 1987, (with Netsch, Salsich and Wegner) 3rd edit., 1990, supp. 1992, (with R. Cunningham) Planning and Control of Land Development, 1979, 3d. edit., 1990, (with R. Cunningham and J. Payne) supplement, 1994, Environment and Equity, 1981, (with others) Cases and Materials on Housing and Urban Development, 1981, 2d edit., 1989, Land Use Law, 1982, 3d edit., 1993, supplement, 1994, (with F. Anderson and D. Tarlock) Environmental Protection Law and Policy, 2d edit., 1990, NEPA Law and Litigation, 2d edit., 1992, supplement, 1995, (with J. Gerard and T. Sullivan) Federal Land Use Law, 1986, supplement, 1995; mem. editorial adv. bd. various land use jours. Mem. nat. adv. com. on outdoor advt. and motorist info. Dept. Transp., 1980-81; mem. adv. com. on housing Dem. Caucus, U.S. Ho. of Reps., 1981-82; pres. Nat. Coalition for Scenic Beauty, 1987-88; sr. fellow Urban Land Inst., 1989—; mem. law sch. editorial bd., Michie Co., 1989—. Mem. NAS (com. social and behavioral urban rsch. 1967-68), Am. Planning Assn. (bd. dirs. 1981-84, Housing Policy Task Force 1990-93, property rights task force 1994-95), Order of Coif, Phi Beta Kappa, Phi Kappa Phi. Office: Washington U Sch Law Campus Box 1120 Saint Louis MO 63130

MANDELKERN, LEO, biophysics and chemistry educator; b. N.Y.C., Feb. 23, 1922; s. Israel and Gussie (Krostich) M.; m. Berdie Medvedoff, May, 1946; children: I. Paul, Marshal, David. BA, Cornell U., 1942, PhD, 1949. Postdoctoral rsch. assoc. Cornell U., Ithaca, N.Y., 1949-52; phys. chemist Nat. Bur. Standards, Washington, 1952-62; prof. chemistry and biophysics Fla. State U., Tallahassee, 1962—, R.O. Lawton Disting. prof., 1984—; vis. prof. U. Miami (Fla.) Med. Sch., 1963, U. Calif. Med. Sch., San Francisco, 1964, Cornell U., 1967; mem. biophysics fellowship com. NIH, 1967-70; mem. study panel crystal growth and morphology NRC, 1960; cons. in field. Author: Crystallization of Polymers, 1964, An Introduction to Macromolecules, 1972, 1983; contbr. numerous articles to profl. jours. 1st l. USAAF, 1942-46, PTO. Recipient Meritorious Svc. award U.S. Dept. Commerce, 1957, Arthur S. Fleming award Washington Jaycees, 1958, Mettler award N.Am. Thermal Analysis Soc., Phila., 1984, Disting. Svc. in Advancement of Polymer Sci. award Soc. Polymer Sci., Japan, 1993. Mem. AAAS, N.Y. Acad. Scis., Am. Inst. Chemists, Am. Chem. Soc.)Polymer Chemistry award 1975, Fla. award 1984, Rubber divsn. Whitby award 1989, Charles Goodyear medal 1993, Applied Polymer Sci. award 1989, Disting. Svc. in Advancement of Polymer Sci., 1993, Polymer Divsn. P.H. Flory award 1994, Polymer Materials Sci. & Engring. Divsn. Coop. Rsch. award 1995), Polymer Soc. Japan, Biophys. Soc., Am. Phus. Soc. (Outstanding Educator of Am. 1973, 75), Cosmos Club Washington, Alpha Epsilon Pi. Home: 1503 Old Ft Dr Tallahassee FL 32301-5637 Office: Fla State U Dept Chemistry Tallahassee FL 32306

MANDELL, FLOYD A., lawyer; b. Chgo., June 17, 1948; s. Marvin M. and Estelle (Witt) M.; m. Pamela Sue Cohen, Aug. 31, 1975; children: Chad, Craig. BA magna cum laude, No. Ill. U., 1970; JD, U. Ill., Champaign, 1973. Bar: Ill. 1973, Fla. 1973. Assoc. Dettishell, McAuliffe & Hifestiter, Chgo., 1973-76; sr. ptnr. Katten, Muchin & Zavis, Chgo., 1976—; dir. Chgo. Bar Assn., 1978-80; planning chmn. Ill. Continuing Legal Edn., Intellectual Property Litigation, Chgo., 1995—. Cpl. USAR, 1969-73. Office: Katten Muchin & Zavis 525 W Monroe St Ste 1600 Chicago IL 60661-3693

MANDELL, GERALD LEE, physician, medicine educator; b. N.Y.C., Aug. 20, 1936; s. Herman and Sylvia (Keller) M.; m. Judith Rensin Mandell, Dec. 22, 1960; children: James, Pamela, Scott. BA, Cornell U., 1958; MD, Cornell U., N.Y.C., 1962. Diplomate Am. Bd. Internal Medicine. Intern,

resident N.Y. Hosp. Cornell Med. Ctr., N.Y.C., 1965-67; instr. Med. Coll., Cornell U., N.Y.C., 1968-69; asst. prof. U. Va., Charlottesville, 1969-71, assoc. prof., 1972-75, prof., 1976—, Owen R. Cheatham prof. sci., 1981—, head infectious diseases, 1970—. Editor: Principles and Practice of Infectious Diseases, 1979, 4th edit., 1995. Lt. comdr. USPHS, 1963-65. Recipient Merit award NIH, 1986. Master ACP; mem. Assn. Am. Physicians, Am. Soc. Clin. Investigation, Phi Beta Kappa, Alpha Omega Alpha. Jewish. Avocations: photography, tropical fish, sculling. Office: U Va Med Ctr Box 385 Charlottesville VA 22908-0001

MANDELL, MARK STEVEN, lawyer; b. Providence, R.I., June 27, 1949; s. Leonard Charles and Frances (Friedman) M.; m. Faye Irene Shapiro, July 11, 1982 (div.); children: Rachel, Zachary, Benjamin. BA, U. Ala., 1971; JD, Georgetown U., 1974. Bar: R.I. 1974, Ala. 1975, U.S. Dist. Ct. R.I. 1975, U.S. Ct. Appeals (1st cir.) 1979, U.S. Supreme Ct. 1979. Law clk. to presiding justice U.S. Dist. Ct. R.I., Providence, 1974-75; assoc. Decof, Weinstein & Mandell, Providence, 1975-80; sr. ptnr. Mandell, Diluca & Schwartz, Providence, 1980—; lectr. in field; chmn. Bd. Bar Examiners U.S. Dist. Ct. R.I., 1984—, bar examiner. Author: Value of a Chance, 1986; contbg. author: Ambulatory Gynecology, 1985. Pres. Jewish Community Ctr., Providence, 1982-87; bd. dirs. Miriam Hosp., 1983-86, Urban League R.I., 1987-89, Opportunities Industrialization Ctr., Providence, 1989—; exec. com. Nat. Jewish Welfare Bd., 1987-89, bd. dirs., 1984-89; mem. United Jewish Appeal Leadership Cabinet, 1986—. Mem. ABA, Fed. Bar Assn., R.I. Bar Assn. (pres. 1993—, active continuing legal edn., medico-legal com., ins. com., fed. ct. bench/bar com., young lawyers clerkship com., treas. 1989), R.I. Trial Lawyers Assn. (pres. elect 1986-88, pres. 1988-90), Ala. Bar Assn., Assn. Trial Lawyers Am. (chmn. pres.'s coun. 1989), N.Y. Trial Lawyers Assn., Fla. Trial Lawyers Accad., Calif. Trial Lawyers Assn., Am. Judicature Soc., Am. Soc. Law and Medicine, Tex. Trial Lawyers Assn., Pa. Trial Lawyers Assn. Home: 414 Love Ln East Greenwich RI 02818-4218 Office: Mandell Diluca & Schwartz 1 Park Row Providence RI 02903-1235

MANDELL, SAMUEL W. W., corporate lawyer; b. 1943. AB, Harvard U., 1965; JD, U. Mich., 1969. Assoc. various law firms, 1969-74; dir. corp. law dept. Stop & Shop Cos. Inc., Boston, 1974-78, v.p., gen. counsel, 1978-86, sr. v.p., gen. counsel, 1986—. Office: Stop & Shop Cos Inc PO Box 369 Boston MA 02101-0369

MANDELSON, RICHARD S., lawyer; b. N.Y.C., Dec. 14, 1947. BA with honors, U. Denver, 1970, MBA, 1974; JD cum laude, Washington & Lee U., 1973. Bar: Colo. 1974, U.S. Dist. Ct. (Colo. dist.) 1974, U.S. Ct. Appeals (10th cir.) 1975. Ptnr. Baker & Hostetler, Denver; assoc. prof. bus. and adminstrv. law U. Denver, 1973—. Mem. ABA, Colo. Bar Assn., Denver Bar Assn., Phi Alpha Delta, Omicron Delta Epsilon. Office: Baker & Hostetler 303 E 17th Ave Ste 1100 Denver CO 80203-1264

MANDELSTAM, CHARLES LAWRENCE, lawyer; b. Brookline, Mass., July 6, 1927; s. Felix and Sarah (Odence) M.; m. Gloria Messinger, June 2, 1957; children: Emily F., Peter D. BA, Harvard Coll., 1949; LLB, Yale U., 1952. Bar: Conn. 1952, N.Y. 1953, D.C. 1953. Mem. staff office of gen. counsel Internat. Ladies' Garment Workers Union, N.Y.C., 1952-56; assoc. Kaye, Scholer, Fierman, Hays & Handler, N.Y.C., 1956-60; ptnr. Dornbush Mensch Mandelstam & Schaeffer, N.Y.C., 1968—; bd. dirs. Société d' Exploitation Agricole Rhodanienne, Ampuis, France; counsel North Salem (N.Y.) Open Land Found., 1975—. Comment editor Yale Law Jour., 1951-52; contbr. articles to Yale Law Jour., 1951, 52;. Bd. dirs. Samuel Rubin Found., 1975—, N.Y.C. Sch. Vol. Program, 1991—. With U.S. Army, 1945-46. Mem. Assn. of the Bar City of N.Y., Phi Beta Kappa. Home: 27 W 86th St New York NY 10024-3615 Office: 747 3d Ave New York NY 10017

MANDELSTAM, STANLEY, physicist; b. Johannesburg, South Africa, Dec. 12, 1928; came to U.S., 1963; s. Boris and Beatrice (Liknaitzky) M. BSc, U. Witwatersrand, Johannesburg, 1952; BA, Cambridge U., Eng., 1954; PhD, Birmingham U., Eng., 1956. Boese postdoctoral fellow Columbia U., N.Y.C., 1957-58; asst. rsch. physicist U. Calif., Berkeley, 1958-60, prof. physics, 1963—; prof. of math. physics U. Birmingham, 1960-63; vis. prof. physics Harvard U., Cambridge, Mass., 1965-66, Univ. de Paris, Paris Sud, 1979-80, 84-85. Editorial bd. The Phys. Rev. jour., 1978-81, 85-88; contbr. articles to profl. jours. Recipient Dirac medal and prize Internat. Ctr. for Theoretical Physics, 1991. Fellow AAAS, Royal Soc. London, Am. Phys. Soc. (Dannie N. Heineman Math. Physics prize 1992). Jewish. Office: Univ of Calif Dept Of Physics Berkeley CA 94720

MANDELSTAMM, JEROME ROBERT, lawyer; b. St. Louis, Apr. 3, 1932; s. Henry and Estelle (London) M.; stepchildren: Amy E., Maria A., John M. Gagliardi. A.B., U. Pa., 1954; LL.B., Harvard U., 1957. Bar: Mo. 1957. Since practiced in St. Louis; partner Greenfield, Davidson, Mandelstamm & Voorhees, 1969-81, Schmitz, Mandelstamm, Hawker & Fischer, 1981-82; sole practice, 1982—; bd. dirs. Legal Aid Soc. City and County St. Louis, 1967-75, pres., 1969-70; bd. dirs. Lawyers Reference Service Met. St. Louis, 1976-83, chmn., 1978-83; bd. dirs. Mo. Legal Aid Soc., 1977-82; mem. 22d Jud. Cir. Bar Com., 1983-85, gen. chmn., 1984-85. Mem. St. Louis County Bd. Election Commrs., 1973-77. Served with AUS, 1957. Mem. ABA, Mo. Bar Assn., Am. Arbitration Assn. (panel of arbitrators 1984—), Bar Assn. Met. St. Louis (v.p. 1974-75, treas. 1975-76). Home: 4525 Laclede Ave # 3 Saint Louis MO 63108-2117 Office: 1010 Market St Ste 1600 Saint Louis MO 63101-2082

MANDERS, KARL LEE, neurosurgeon; b. Rochester, N.Y., Jan. 21, 1927; s. David Bert and Frances Edna (Cohan) Mendelson; m. Ann Laprell, July 28, 1969; children: Karlanna, Maidena; children by previous marriage: Karl, Kerry, Kristine. Student, Cornell U., 1946; MD, U. Buffalo, 1950. Diplomate Am. Bd. Neurol. Surgery, Am. Bd. Clin. Biofeedback, Am. Bd. Hyperbaric Medicine, Nat. Bd. Med. Examiners. Intern U. Va. Hosp., Charlottesville, 1950-51, resident in neurol. surgery, 1951-52; resident in neurol. surgery Henry Ford Hosp., Detroit, 1954-56; pvt. practice Indpls., 1956—; med. dir. Community Hosp. Rehab. Ctr. for Pain, 1973—; chief hosp. med. and surg. neurology Community Hosp., 1983, 93; coroner Marion County, Ind., 1977-85, 92—. Served with USN, 1952-54, Korea. Recipient cert. achievement Dept. Army, 1969. Fellow ACS, Internat. Coll Surgeons, Am. Acad. Neurology; mem. Am. Assn. Neurol. Surgery, Congress Neurol. Surgery, Internat. Assn. Study of Pain, Am. Assn. Study of Headache, N.Y. Acad. Sci., Am. Coll. Angiology, Am. Soc. Contemporary Medicine and Surgery, Am. Holistic Med. Assn. (co-founder), Undersea Med. Soc., Am. Acad. Forensic Sci., Am. Assn. Biofeedback Clinicians, Soc. Cryosurgery, Pan Pacific Surg. Assn., Biofeedback Soc. Am., Acad. Psychosomatic Medicine, Pan Am. Med. Assn., Internat. Back Pain Soc., North Am. Spine Soc., Am. Soc. Stereotaxic and Functional Neurosurgery, Soc. for Computerized Tomography and Neuroimaging, Ind. Coroners Assn. (pres. 1979), Royal Soc. Medicine, Nat. Assn. Med. Examiners, Am. Pain Soc., Midwest Pain Soc. (pres. 1988), Am. Acad. Pain Medicine, Cen. Neurol. Soc., Interurban Neurosurg. Soc., Internat. Soc. Aquatic Medicine, James A. Gibson Anat. Soc., Am. Bd. Med. Psychotherapists (mem. profl. adv. council), James McClure Surg. Soc., Brendonwood Country Club, Highland Country Club. Home: 5845 High Fall Rd Indianapolis IN 46226-1017 Office: 7209 N Shadeland Ave Indianapolis IN 46250-2021

MANDERSCHEID, LESTER VINCENT, agricultural economics educator; b. Andrew, Iowa, Oct. 9, 1930; s. Vincent John and Alma (Sprank) M.; m. Dorothy Helen Varnum, Aug. 29, 1953; children: David, Paul, Laura, Jane. BS, Iowa State U., 1951, MS, 1952; PhD, Stanford U., 1961. Grad. asst. Iowa State U., Ames, 1951-52, Stanford (Calif.) U., 1952-56; asst. prof. Mich. State U., East Lansing, 1956-65, assoc. prof., 1965-70, prof., 1970-73, prof., assoc. chmn., 1973-87, prof. chmn., 1987-92, prof., 1992—; reviewer Tex. A&M Agrl. Econ. Program, College Station, 1989; con. Consortium Internat. Earth Sci. Info. Network, Ann Arbor, 1990. Co-author: Improving Undergraduate Education, 1967; contbr. articles to jours. in field. Pres. parish coun. St. Thomas, East Lansing, 1984-87; coll. coord. United Way, East Lansing, 1983-84. Recipient Disting. Faculty award Mich. State U., 1977. Mem. Am. Agrl. Econ. Assn. (pres. 1988-89, bd. dirs. 1982-85, excellence in teaching award 1974), Am. Statist. Assn., Am. Evaluation Assn., Am. Econ. Assn., University Club, Sigma Xi (pres. 1986-87), Phi Kappa Phi (pres. 1979-80). Roman Catholic. Home: 2372 Burcham Dr East Lansing MI 48823-3885 Office: Mich State U Dept of Agrl Econs Circle Dr East Lansing MI 48824-1039

MANDERY, MATHEW M., principal. BS, Bklyn. Coll., 1965, MA, 1971; EdD, Fordham U., 1990. Asst. prin. supr. math. Midwood H.S., Bklyn.; prin. Newtown H.S., Bklyn. Tech. H.S., Jericho (N.Y.) High Sch., 1987—. Author: Achieving Competence in Mathematics, 1987, Achieving Proficiency in Mathematics, 1994. Recipient Blue Ribbon Sch. award U. S. Dept. Edn., 1990-91; named N.Y. State Prin. of Yr., 1992-93, Educator of Yr. Assn. Tchrs. N.Y.C., 1985; Danforth fellow; recipient Disting. Svc. award for Contbns. to Math. Edn., 1984, Cert. of Honor Westinghouse Sci. Talent Search, Disting. Alumnus award Bklyn. Tech. H.S. Alumni Assn., 1993. Mem. Nassau County Secondary Sch. Adminstrs. Assn. (pres.), Headmaster's Assn., Phi Delta Kappa (past pres. St. John's U. chpt.). Office: Jericho High Sch Cedar Swamp Rd Jericho NY 11753

MANDEVILLE, GILBERT HARRISON, consulting engineering executive; b. Bklyn., July 6, 1910; s. Gilbert Spier and Minnie (Ross) M.; m. Mildred Schwagerman, June 20, 1936; 1 child, Terry Melinda. B.S., Seattle U., 1953. Registered profl. engr., Wash. Exec. dir., v.p. Leo O. Daly Co., Seattle, 1952-57; ptnr., cons. engr. Mandeville & Berge, Architects and Engrs., Seattle, 1957-83; dir., sec.-treas. Riverfront Assocs.; dir. U.S. Devel. Co. Chmn. Seattle City Planning Commn., 1960-62, Puget Sound Regional Planning Coun., 1960-62. Lt. comdr. USNR, 1947-52. Fellow ASCE (life); mem. IEEE (life), Am. Arbitration Assn. Presbyterian. Clubs: Seattle Engring. Home: 1132 2d Ave S PO Box 895 Edmonds WA 98020 Office: Mandeville & Berge Archs & Engrs 500 Union St Seattle WA 98101-2332

MANDEVILLE, ROBERT CLARK, JR., former naval officer, business executive; b. Princeton, W.Va., July 18, 1927; s. Robert Clark and Grace (Oney) M.; m. Elizabeth Anne Perry, Oct. 10, 1953; children: Cathy, Karen, Christy, Scott. B.S., U.S. Naval Acad., 1950; M.S., Princeton U., 1959. Commd. ensign U.S. Navy, 1950, advanced through grades to rear adm., 1976; assigned carrier-based fighter and attack squadrons; project mgr. A-6/EA-6 Weapons Systems, Washington, 1970-73; comdg. officer Naval Air Sta. Oceana, Virginia Beach, Va., 1973-74; dir. aviation plans and requirements Navy Dept., Washington, 1974-78; comdr. Light Attack Wing, Pacific, Lemoore, Calif., 1978-80; dep. chief Naval Material for Logistics, Washington, 1980-81; ret., 1981; v.p. Science Applications, Inc., 1981-83; sr. v.p. ManTech Internat., Fairfax, Va., 1983-94; ind. cons., 1994—. Decorated D.F.C. (6), Air medal (13), Bronze Star, Meritorious Service medal, Legion of Merit (2). Mem. Assn. Naval Aviation, Tailhook Assn., Soc. Old Crows, Sigma Xi. Home: 5016 Althea Dr Annandale VA 22003-4144

MANDIL, I. HARRY, nuclear engineer; b. Istanbul, Turkey, Dec. 11, 1919; s. Harry Robert and Bertha (Presente) M. (parents Am. citizens); m. Beverly Ericson, June 22, 1946; children: Jean Dale, Eric Robert. B.S., U. London, Eng., 1939; M.S., MIT, 1941; grad., Oak Ridge Sch. Reactor Tech., 1950; D.Sc. (hon.), Thiel Coll., Greenville, Pa., 1960. Devel., design process controls for textile mills and chem. plants Norcross Corp., 1941-42, asst. to pres. charge field engring., 1946-49; asst. to tech. dir. naval reactors br. reactor devel. div. AEC, 1950-54; dir. reactor engring. div Bur. Ships, also chief reactor engring. br. naval reactors reactor devel. div., 1954-64; prin. officer, dir. MPR Assos., Inc. (engrs.), Washington, 1964-85; cons., dir. MPR Assos., Inc. (engrs.), Alexandria, Va., 1985—; developer nuclear power for propulsion naval vessels, also for Shippingport Atomic Power Ctrl. Sta.; mem., sec. Energy Adv. Bd., Washington, 1990—; mem. corp. vis. com. for nuclear engring. dept. MIT, 1984-93. Author numerous papers in field. Served with USNR, 1942-46. Recipient Meritorius Civilian Service award Navy Dept., 1952, Disting. Civilian Service award, 1959. Home: 701 Heathery Ln Pelican Bay Naples FL 33963 Office: 320 King St Alexandria VA 22314-3238

MANDINE, SALVADOR G., insurance executive; b. N.Y.C., Dec. 31, 1921; s. Salvador Garcia and Asuncion Mandine; m. Carmen Alonso, Nov. 1, 1958; 1 child, Rosalind. Cert. pre-law, CUNY, 1950; LLB, Bklyn. Law Sch., 1953; postgrad., Adelphi U., 1973-74, U. Conn., 1974. Acct. various cos. in internat. trade, N.Y.C., 1945-57; reinsurance acct. Godoy-Sayan Ins. & Banking Orgn., Havana, 1957-60; controller Barnett Internat. Forwarders, Inc., N.Y.C., 1960-63; asst. treas. Gen. Reinsurance Corp., N.Y.C., 1963-74, Greenwich, Conn., 1974-84, Stamford, Conn., 1984-91. Active Rep. Town Meeting, Darien, Conn., 1979-84. With USN, NATOUSA, 1942-45. Decorated African-European Area of Ops. medal, Am. Area of Ops. medal, Asia-Pacific Area of Ops. medal, Victory medal, Good Conduct medal, USN. Mem. AARP, Am. Legion. Republican. Roman Catholic. Avocations: reading, travel, theatre. Home: 13260 SW 99th St Miami FL 33186-2271

MANDINO, OG, author; b. Boston, Dec. 12, 1923; s. Silvio and Margaret T. (Lee) M.; m. Bette L. Lang, Dec. 9, 1957; children: Dana, Matthew. Student, Bucknell U. Coll. 1941. Sales mgr. Combined Ins. Co., Chgo., 1960-65; sales rep. Met. Life Ins. Co., Boston, 1948-60; exec. editor Success Unlimited mag., Chgo., 1965-72; pres. Success Unltd., Inc., Chgo., 1972-76; pres. Matt-Dana Ltd., 1974—, also dir. Author: A Treasury of Success Unlimited, 1967, The Greatest Salesman in the World, 1968, (with Edward R. Dewey) Cycles, The Mysterious Forces That Trigger Events, 1970, U.S. in a Nutshell, 1971, The Greatest Secret in the World, 1972, The Greatest Miracle in the World, 1975, (with Buddy Kaye) The Gift of Acabar, 1978, The Christ Commission, 1980, The Greatest Success in the World, 1981, Og Mandino's University of Success, 1982, The Choice, 1984, Mission: Success!, 1986, The Greatest Salesman in the World, Part II, End of the Story, 1988, A Better Way to Live, 1990, The Return of the Ragpicker, 1992, The Twelfth Angel, 1993, The Spellbinder's Gift, 1994, Secrets For Success and Happiness, 1995. Served to 1st lt. USAAF, 1942-45. Decorated D.F.C., Air medal with 5 oak leaf clusters. Mem. Authors Guild, Authors League, Nat. Speakers Assn., Internat. Speakers Hall of Fame.

MANDL, ALEX J(OHANN), telecommunications company executive; b. Vienna, Austria, Dec. 14, 1943; came to U.S., 1958, naturalized, 1968; s. Otto William and Charlotte J. (Peshek) M.; m. Nancy J. Scott, June 10, 1967; 1 dau., Melanie. BA, Willamette U., 1967; MBA, U. Calif., Berkeley, 1969. With Boise Cascade Corp., 1969-80; dir. internat. fin., asst. treas., then fin. chmn. Boise Cascade Corp., Boise, Idaho, 1973-80; sr. v.p. fin. and corp. planning Seaboard System R.R. Co., Jacksonville, Fla., 1980-85; sr. v.p. corp. devel. and adminstrn. CSX Corp., Richmond, Va., 1985-86; chmn., CEO CSX Tech., 1986-88, Sea-Land Corp. subs. CSX Corp., Iselin, N.J., 1988-91; exec. v.p. comm. svc. group AT&T, N.Y.C., 1991—; bd. dirs. CSX Comm., CSX Transp., Inc., Richmond Renaissance, Cybernetics and Systems Inc. Trustee Jacksonville Art Mus. Mem. Fin. Execs. Inst., Soc. Internat. Treasurers, Young Pres. Orgn., Bus. Week Corp. Planning 100, Mgmt. Policy Council, Council Planning Execs. (conf. bd.), Fin. Execs. Inst. (com. on corp. fin.). Clubs: River, University, The Bull and Bear. Office: AT&T 32 Ave of Americas New York NY 10013

MANDLE, EARL ROGER, university president, former museum administrator; b. Hackensack, N.J., May 13, 1941; s. Earl and Phyllis (Key) M.; m. Gayle Wells Jenkins, July 11, 1964; children: Luke Harrison, Julia Barnes. BA cum laude, Williams Coll., 1963; MA, NYU, 1967, cert. in Museum Training, 1967, postgrad.; DFA (hon.), U. Toledo, 1983, Kenyon Coll., 1986. Intern in drawings Met. Mus. Art, N.Y.C.; intern in sculpture and architecture Victoria and Albert Mus., London, 1966-67; assoc. dir. Mpls. Inst. Arts, 1967-74; assoc. dir. Toledo Mus. Art, 1974-76, dir., 1977-88; dep. dir. Nat. Gallery of Art, Washington, 1988-93; pres. Rhode Island Sch. Design, Providence, R.I., 1993—; chmn. exec. com. Am. Fedn. of Arts, 1987-93; mem. adv. panel New Zealand-U.S. Arts Found.; trustee Internat. Exhbns. Found., Sterling & Francine Clark Art Inst.; adv. panel, Mgmt. Inst.; mem. NEA, Nat. Coun. on Arts; mem. adv. council Nat. Mus. Act, Smithsonian Instn.; mem. adv. com. on mus. mgmt. J. Paul Getty Trust; adv. bd. Charles Hosmer Morse Found., Inc.; trustee Spanish Found. for Restoration of Toledo (Spain); chmn. U.S. Com. on Restoration of Toledo; cons. Nat. Mus. Western Art, Tokyo, Kerr Found., Oklahoma City; chair cultural adv. council Netherlands-Am. Amity Trust, Inc.; mem. exec. Ohio Arts Council; mem. exec. com. Williams Coll. Mus. Art; mem. arts adv. com. Barnes Found., 1991—; com. for the preservation of the Treasury Bldg., hist. advisor, 1989—; vis. prof. Robert Sterling Clark Prof. of Art Williams Coll., Williamstown, Mass., 1993. Contbr. to profl. mags. and jours. Decorated by the His Majesty Juan Carlos Knight of the Order of Isabel the Cath., Spain, 1985; Andover teaching fellow, 1963-64; Ford Found. fellow, 1966; Nat. Endowment Arts fellow, 1974; recipient Am.

Hellenic Educational Progressive award, 1983, Distinguished Citizen for Art award Ohio Art Edn. Assn., 1983, Resolution for Leadership award Ohio Senate, 1983, Governor's award State of Ohio, 1983, Marketer of the Year award Am. Marketing Assn., 1983. Mem. Am. Assn. Mus. (trustee, v.p.), Art Mus. Assn. (pres.), Assn. Art Mus. Dirs., Am. Arts Alliance (trustee, policy com.), Coll. Art Assn., Internat. Council Mus., Intermus. Conservation Assn. (exec. com.), Ohio Found. for Arts, Ohio Art Council, Am. Assn. 18th Century Studies (treas.), Young Pres. Orgn., R.I. Ind. Higher Edn. Assn., Providence C. of C., R.I. Commodores, Confrerie des Chevaliers du Tastevin, Phi Kappa Phi. (hon. mem.), Providence Art Club, Hope Club, Univ. Club, Brown Faculty Club, Tile Club, Century Club (N.Y.C.), The Answer Club, Williams Club (N.Y.C.). Office: Rhode Island Sch Design Office of the President 2 College St Providence RI 02903-2717

MANDLER, GEORGE, psychologist; b. Vienna, Austria, June 11, 1924; came to U.S., 1940, naturalized, 1943; s. Richard and Hede (Goldschmied) M.; m. Jean Matter, Jan. 19, 1957; children: Peter Clark, Michael Allen. B.A., NYU, 1949; M.S., Yale U., 1950, Ph.D., 1953; postgrad., U. Basel, Switzerland, 1947-48. Asst. prof. Harvard U., 1953-57, lectr., 1957-60; prof. U. Toronto, Ont., Can., 1960-65; prof. psychology U. Calif., San Diego, 1965-94, chmn. dept. psychology, 1965-70, prof. emeritus, 1994—; dir. Ctr. Human Info. Processing, U. Calif., San Diego, 1965-90; hon. rsch. fellow Univ. Coll. London., 1977-78, 82-90, vis. prof., 1990—. Author: Mind and Emotion, 1975, (German edit.), 1980, Mind and Body, 1984, (Japanese edit.), 1987, Cognitive Psychology, 1985, Japanese edit., 1991; contbr. articles and revs. to profl. jours.; editor: Psychol. Rev., 1970-76. Served with U.S. Army, 1943-46. Fellow Ctr. for Advanced Study in Behavioral Scis., 1959-60; vis. fellow Oxford U., Eng., 1971-72, 78; Guggenheim fellow, 1971-72. Fellow AAAS, Am. Acad. Arts and Scis.; mem. AAUP, Am. Assn. Advancement Psychology (1974-82); Psychonomic Soc. (governing bd., chmn. 1983), Am. Psychol. Soc., Am. Psychol. Assn. (pres. div. exptl. psychology 1978-79, pres. div. gen psychology 1982-83, mem. coun. reps. 1978-82, William James prize 1986), Internat. Union Psychol. Scis. (U.S. com. 1985-90), Soc. Exptl. Psychologists, Fedn. Behavioral Psychol. and Cognitive Scis. (pres. 1981). Home: 1406 La Jolla Knoll La Jolla CA 92037 Office: U Calif San Diego Dept Psychology La Jolla CA 92093-0109 also: 3 Perrins Ln, London NW3 1QY, England

MANDLER, JEAN MATTER, psychologist, educator; b. Oak Park, Ill., Nov. 6, 1929; d. Joseph Allen and May Roberts (Finch) Matter; m. George Mandler, Jan. 19, 1957; children: Peter Clark, Michael Allen. Student, Carleton Coll., 1947-49; B.A. with highest honors, Swarthmore Coll., 1951; Ph.D., Harvard U., 1956. Research asso. lab. social relations Harvard U., 1957-60; research asso. dept. psychology U. Toronto, Ont., Can., 1961-65; asso. research psychologist, lectr. U. Calif. at San Diego, La Jolla, 1965-73, asso. prof., 1973-77, prof. psychology, 1977-88, prof. cognitive sci., 1988—; mem. adv. com. on memory and cognitive processes NSF, 1978-81; hon. rsch. fellow U. Coll., London, 1978-89, vis. prof., 1990—; hon. mem. Med. Rsch. Coun. Cognitive Devel. Unit, 1982—. Author: (G. Mandler) Thinking: From Association to Gestalt, 1964, Stories, Scripts and Scenes, 1984; assoc. editor Psychol. rev., 1970-76; mem. editl. bd. Child Devel., 1976-89, Discourse Processes, 1977-94, Jour. Exptl. Psychology, 1977-85, Text, 1979—, Jour. Verbal Learning and Verbal Behavior, 1980-88, Lang. and Cognitive Processes, 1985—, Cognitive Devel., 1990—; contbr. articles to profl. jours. Pres. San Diego Assn. Gifted Children, 1968-71; v.p. Calif. Parents for Gifted, 1970-71; mem. alumni council Swarthmore Coll., 1975-78. NIMH research grantee, 1968-81; NSF research grantee, 1981—. Fellow Am. Psychol. Assn. (exec. com. div. 3 1983-85); mem. Psychonomic Soc. (governing bd. 1982-87, chmn. 1985-86), Soc. Research in Child Devel., Cognitive Sci. Soc., Soc. Exptl. Psychologists, Phi Beta Kappa. Office: Dept Cognitive Sci U Calif San Diego La Jolla CA 92093-0515

MANDLER, SUSAN RUTH, dance company administrator; b. Kew Gardens, N.Y., Feb. 11, 1949; d. Ernest and Clea (Reisner) M.; m. Robert Morgan Barnett, July 30, 1982. B.S., Boston U., 1971. Mgr. Pilobolus, Inc., Washington, Conn., mgr., 1977—. Address: PO Box 388 Washington Depot CT 06794*

MANDOR, LEONARD STEWART, real estate company executive; b. Bklyn., Oct. 2, 1946; s. Harris and Helen (Roth) M.; m. Yolande Rosario, June, 1973; children: Samantha, Melissa; m. Sandra Doolittle, Apr. 9, 1983 (div. 1990); 1 child, Gregory. BBA, Kent State U., 1968. Tchr. Pub. Sch. 3, Jersey City, 1969-70; exec. and sales mgr. Paragon Securities, N.Y.C., 1971-72; acct. exec. Merrill Lynch, N.Y.C., 1972-74; exec., mgr. E.N.I. Corp., Seattle, 1974-75; chmn. bd. Stonhenge Capital Corp., N.Y.C., 1975-81; chmn. bd. Concord Assets Group, Boca Raton, Fla., 1981—, also CEO. With U.S. Army, 1970-71. Mem. United Jewish Appeal. Avocations: tennis, reading, golf, travel, skiing. Office: Concord Assets Group 5200 Town Center Circle Boca Raton FL 33486

MANDRA, YORK T., geology educator; b. N.Y.C., Nov. 24, 1922; s. Raymond and Irene (Farruggio) M.; m. Highoohi Kechijian, Jan. 26, 1946. BA, U. Calif., Berkeley, 1947, MA in Paleontology, 1949; PhD in Geology, Stanford U., 1958. From instr. to assoc. prof. geology San Francisco State U., 1950-63, prof., 1964—, head geology sect., chmn. dept., 1960-67; vis. prof. U. Aix-Marseille, France, 1959, Syracuse U., summer 1963, U. Maine, summer 1969, U. Calif., Santa Barbara, summers 1972—; research assoc. U. Glasgow, 1959, Calif. Acad. Scis., 1966-88; vis. scientist New Zealand Geol. Survey, fall 1970. Contbr. numerous articles to profl. jours. Pres. David S. Sohigian Found., 1975—. Served with USAAF, 1942-46. Recipient Neil A. Miner Disting. Coll. Teaching award, 1984; Danforth Found. teaching fellow, 1958, NSF fellow, 1959; NSF rsch. grantee, 1967-77. Fellow Geol. Soc. Am. (Sr.), Calif. Acad. Scis., AAAS; mem. Nat. Assn. Geology Tchrs. (pres. Far Western sect. 1953-54, 73-74, Robert Wallace Webb award 1977), Paleontol. Soc., Soc. Econ. Mineralogists and Paleontologists, Soc. for Environ. Geochemistry and Health. Avocations: walking, reading, music. Office: San Francisco State U Dept Geoscis 1600 Holloway Ave San Francisco CA 94132-1722

MANDRELL, BARBARA ANN, singer, entertainer; b. Houston, Dec. 25, 1948; d. Irby Matthew and Mary Ellen (McGill) M.; m. Kenneth Lee Dudney, May 28, 1967; children: Kenneth Matthew, Jaime Nicole, Nathaniel. Grad. high sch. Country music singer and entertainer, 1959—; performed throughout U.S. and in various fgn. countries; mem., Grand Ole Opry, Nashville, 1972—; star TV series Barbara Mandrell and the Mandrell Sisters, 1980-82, Barbara Mandrell: Get to the Heart, 1987; albums include Midnight Oil, Treat Him Right, He Set My Life To Music, This Time I Almost Made It, This is Barbara Mandrell, Midnight Angel, Barbara Mandrell's Greatest Hits, Christmas at Our House, 1987, Morning Sun, 1990, Greatest Country Hits, 1990, Standing Room Only, 1993. Author (with George Vecsey): Get To the Heart: My Story, 1990. Named Miss Oceanside, Calif., 1965; Named Most Promising Female Singer, Acad. Country and Western Music, 1971; Female Vocalist of Yr., 1978; Female Vocalist of Yr., Music City News Cover Awards, 1979; Female Vocalist of Yr., Country Music Assn., 1979; Entertainer of Yr., 1980, 81; People's Choice awards (6), 1982-84. Mem. Musicians Union, Screen Actors Guild, AFTRA, Country Music Assn. (v.p.). Mem. Order Eastern Star. Home: PO Box 620 Hendersonville TN 37077-0332 Office: Creative Artists Agy 3310 West End Ave 5th Fl Nashville TN 37203*

MANDRI-BELLOT, JOSE ANTONIO, architect; b. Cuernavaca, Morelos, Mexico, June 25, 1943; s. Ramon and Maria A. (Bellot) M.; m. Helen Jones-Perrott, July 20, 1968; children: Alexander, Xavier Cledan, Ramon Nicholas. BSc, King's Coll., 1967; student, U. Newcastle. Asst. naval architect Appledore Shipbuilders, Devon, England, 1967-68; naval architect Secretaria De Marina, Mexico, 1968-71, Rolls-Royce Moto Equipos, Mexico, 1971-74, Ingenieros Navales Asesores, Mexico, 1974-88; dir. Fipesco, Mexico, 1977-78; fleet mgr. Propemex Fishing Fleet, Mexico, 1977-78; ship surveyor Det Norske Veritas, Mexico, 1988-89; dir. Det Norske Veritas Mexico, Mexico, 1989-94. mem., head officer Local Neighbourhood, El Contadero, 1979-94; mem. Solidaridad, Ayotla-State of Puebla, 1988-94; mem., past pres. Anglo Mexican Cultural Inst., Mexico, 1973-94. Recipient scholarship Presidency, 1962-67, Nat. Design award, 1973. Mem. Academia Mexicana De Ingenieria, Assn. Mexicana Ing. Navales (founder, sec. 1987-90), Soc. Naval Architects & Marine Engineers, Royal Instn. of Naval Architects. Avoca-

tions: diving, sailing, hang gliding. Home: Canada 135 El Contadero, Cuajimalpa 05500, Mexico

MANDT, JOHN F., religious organization executive. Pres. Am Baptist Historical Soc., Rochester, N.Y. Office: Am Baptist Historical Soc 1106 S Goodman St Rochester NY 14620

MANDULA, JEFFREY ELLIS, physicist; b. N.Y.C., July 23, 1941; s. Andrew and Gertrude Phyllis (Entenberg) M.; m. Barbara Blumenstein, June 2, 1963. BA, Columbia U., 1962; MA, Harvard U., 1964, PhD, 1966. Postdoctoral fellow Harvard U., Cambridge, Mass., 1966-67; research fellow Calif. Inst. Tech., Pasadena, 1967-69, asst. prof. theoretical physics, 1970-73; mem. Inst. for Advanced Study, Princeton, N.J., 1969-70; assoc. prof. applied math. MIT, Cambridge, 1973-79; prof. physics Washington U., St. Louis, 1979-87; sr. scientist theoretical physics Dept. Energy, Washington, 1987—; program dir. for theoretical physics NSF, Washington, 1980-81; sec. Signition Corp., Los Alamos, N.Mex., 1986—; vis. prof. U. Minn., Mpls., 1979, U. Southampton, Eng., 1979; invited prof. U. Louvain, Belgium, 1980; adj. prof. physics Washington U., St. Louis, 1987—. Contbr. over 80 articles to profl. jours. NSF fellow, 1966, Alfred P. Sloan Found. fellow 1973; recipient Cottrel Research award Research Corp., 1984. Mem. AAAS, Am. Phys. Soc., Fedn. Am. Scientists. Home: 500 23rd St NW Washington DC 20037-2828 Office: US Dept Energy Div High Energy Physic Washington DC 20545

MANDULEY, JOSE CARLOS, government official; b. Havana, Cuba, Sept. 28, 1944; came to U.S., 1961; s. Carlos M. and Esther (Carreras) M.; m. Regina (Siberio) Manduley, Oct. 24, 1987. BA, Bloomfield (N.J.) Coll., 1967; MA, Georgetown U., 1971; PhD, U. Pitts., 1975. Sr. research assoc. The World Bank, Washington, 1967-70; internat. devel. advisor AID U.S. Dept. State, Washington, 1970-77; dep. chief social communication and mktg. UNICEF, N.Y.C., 1977-83; dir. info., tng., and communication Internat. Planned Parenthood Found., N.Y.C., 1983-84; dir. inst. for internat. tng. NYU, 1985-87; dir. Montgomery County Office Minortiy and Cultural Affairs, Office of the County Exec., Rockville, Md., 1987—; cons. to UN, U.S. Dept. State, OAS, WHO, Asian Devel. Bank, 1979-83; project dir., advisor Hispanic Info. and Telecommunica, N.Y.C., 1987. Recipient Cert. of Appreciaton UNICEF, Korea office, Seoul, 1980. Mem. UN Assn. U.S.A (bd. dirs. N.J. chpt.), Am. Soc. Tng. and Devel., Soc. for Intercultural Edn. and Research, U.S. Jaycees (Bloomfield, N.J.) (named one of Outstanding Young Men of Am. 1971). Roman Catholic. Home: 17213 Pinebrook Dr Silver Spring MD 20905-3788

MANEA, NORMAN, writer, educator; b. Suceava, Bukovina, Romania, July 19, 1936; came to U.S., 1988; s. Marcu and Janeta (Braunstein) M.; m. Josette-Cella Boiangiu, June 28, 1969. MS in Engring., Inst. Constrn., Bucharest, Romania, 1959. Engr. Romania, 1954-74, writer, 1969-86; fellow Deutscher Akademischer Austauschdienst, West Berlin, Germany, 1987; fellow Internat. Acad. Scholarship and the Arts Bard Coll., Annandale On Hudson, N.Y., 1989-92, writer in residence, 1992—. Author: October, eight o'clock, 1992, On Clowns: The Dictator & the Artist, 1992, Compulsory Happiness, 1993, The Black Envelope, 1995; contbr. articles, stories to profl. jours. Recipient MacArthur Found. award, 1992, Nat. Jewish Book award Jewish Book Coun., 1993, Literary Lion award Nat. Pub. Libr., 1993; Guggenheim grantee, 1992; Fulbright fellow, 1988. Mem. Am. Pen. Home: 201 W 70th St Apt 10-i New York NY 10023-4333 Office: Bard Coll Dept Lang And Literatu Annandale On Hudson NY 12504

MANEATIS, GEORGE A., retired utility company executive; b. 1926. BSEE, Stanford U., 1949, MSEE, 1950. With GE, 1950-53; with Pacific Gas & Elec. Co., San Francisco, 1953-91, v.p., 1979-81, sr. v.p., 1981-82, exec. v.p., 1982-86, pres., 1986-91, also bd. dirs. Office: Pacific Gas & Electric Co PO Box 770000 123 Mission St H17F San Francisco CA 94177

MANEKER, MORTON M., lawyer; b. N.Y.C., Nov. 14, 1932; s. Arthur and Estelle (Hochberg) M.; m. Roberta S. Wexler, 1985; children: Meryl Colle, Amy Jill, Marion Kenneth. A.B., Harvard U., 1954, LL.B., 1957. Bar: N.Y. State 1957. Pvt. practice N.Y.C., 1957-62; trial atty. antitrust div. Dept. Justice, 1962-63; partner firm Proskauer, Rose, Goetz & Mendelsohn, N.Y.C., 1963—. Trustee, exec. com. Beth Israel Hosp., N.Y.C., 1977—. Mem. ABA Assn., Am. Law Inst., N.Y. State Bar Assn. Jewish. Home: 30 E 65th St Apt 4A New York NY 10021-7048 Office: Proskauer Rose Goetz 1585 Broadway New York NY 10036-8200

MANELLI, DONALD DEAN, screenwriter, film producer; b. Burlington, Iowa, Oct. 20, 1936; s. Daniel Anthony and Mignon Marie (Dean) M.; m. Susan Linda Allen, June 16, 1964 (div. Aug. 1973); children: Daniel, Lisa. BA, U. Notre Dame, 1959. Communications specialist Jewel Cos., Melrose Park, Ill., 1959; script writer Coronet Films, 1960-62; freelance writer Chgo., 1962-63; creative dir. Fred A. Niles Communications Ctrs., Chgo., 1963-67; sr. writer Wild Kingdom NBC-TV, Chgo., 1967-70; freelance film writer, producer Chgo., 1970-76; pres. Donald Manelli & Assocs., Inc., Chgo. and Paris, 1976—. Screenwriter over 150 documentary films, 1970—, numerous episodes Wild Kingdom, 1967-70 (Emmy awards 1969, 70). Recipient numerous awards various orgns. including N.Y. Internat. Film Festival, Houston Internat. Film Festival, Berlin, Paris, Venice Internat. Film Festivals, CINE, 1976—. Mem. Writers Guild Am. Roman Catholic. Avocations: photography, traveling, tennis. Office: 400 W Erie St Chicago IL 60610-4041 also: 1 Rue Goethe, 75116 Paris France *A simple truth is played out in most lives: what we believe ourselves to be, we are. We may be tested with adversity, our own failed efforts, and plain bad luck, but our personal vision gives us strength and persistence. Success brings the satisfaction of fulfilled dreams, and the responsibility to help others form and follow their own visions.*

MANERA, ANTHONY S., retired broadcasting and education executive; b. Ficarra, Sicily, Italy, May 11, 1940; arrived in Can., 1951; s. Sebastiano and Francesca (Radici) M.; m. Raffaella Marchesini, Nov. 4, 1958; children: Deborah, Andrew. BS, Northrop U., 1963; MS, U. So. Calif., 1965. Electronic technician Hughes Aircraft Co., Newport Beach, Calif., 1962-63; electronic engr. Teledyne Systems, Mar Vista, Calif., 1963-64; asst. prof. Northrop U., Inglewood, Calif., 1964-65; instr. Ryerson Poly. U., Toronto, Ont., Can., 1965-67; coord. engring. tech. Sir Sandford Fleming Coll., Peterborough, Ont., Can., 1967-68; dean tech. Confederation Coll., Thunder Bay, Ont., Can., 1968-71; pres. Niagara Coll., Welland, Ont., Can., 1972-78, Vancouver (Can.) C.C., 1978-85; v.p. human resources Can. Broadcasting Corp., Ottawa, 1985-86, sr. v.p., 1986-93, pres., CEO, 1993-95, chmn. bd., pres., CEO, 1994-95. Author: Solid State Electronic Circuits, 1973. Pres. Red Cross, Welland, 1975; bd. dirs. Assn. Can. C.C., Toronto, 1984, Ont. Coun. Regents for Colls., Toronto, 1990-91, Algonquin Coll., Ottawa, 1993—, Nat. Arts Ctr., Ottawa, 1993-95, N.A. TV Inc. Mem. Assn. Profl. Engrs. (Can.). Avocations: gardening, swimming. Home: 55 Thare Crescent, Nepean, ON Canada K2J 2J1 Office: CBC/SRC, 1500 Bronson Ave, Ottawa, ON Canada K1G 3J5

MANERI, REMO R., management consultant; b. Cleve., Aug. 16, 1928; s. Quinto Peter and Lucia (Massenzi) M.; m. Camille Ann Caranna, Aug. 26, 1950; children: Peter, Alisa, Leonard, Celia. B.S. in Chem. Engring., Case Inst. Tech., 1950; grad., Advanced Mgmt. Program, Harvard U., 1969. Devel. engr. Dow Corning, 1950-53, market researcher, 1956, comml. devel. mgr., 1957-63, chief engr., 1964-66, unit mfg. mgr., 1967-69, dir. tech. service and devel., 1970-72, bus. mgr., v.p., 1973-74, mgr. bus., group v.p., 1975-76; pres. Dow Corning U.S.A., 1977-80; exec. v.p. Dow Corning Corp., 1981-82, also bd. dirs.; chmn. bd. Quantum Composites, 1982-85, pres., chmn. bd., 1985-87, chmn. bd., 1987-89, also bd. dirs.; mgmt. cons., 1989—; bd. dirs. Comerica Bank-Midland, Duro-Last Roofing, Inc., Quantum Composites, Inc.; cons. in field. Contbr. articles to profl. jours. Bd. dirs. Midland Hosp. Assn. Served with Signal Corps, U.S. Army, 1954-56. Named Man of Year Adhesives and Sealants Coun., 1988. Mem. Chem. Spltys. Mfg. Assn. (dir.), Am. Chem. Soc., AAAS, Sigma Xi, Tau Beta Pi, Alpha Chi Sigma. Roman Catholic. Club: Midland Country. Patentee in field. Home and Office: 5808 Siebert St Midland MI 48640-2753

MANES, JOHN DALTON, retired hospital administrator, anaesthesiologist; b. Winnipeg, Man., Can., Oct. 29, 1920; s. John Harold and Elizabeth

(Dalton) M.; m. Jean Julia Diggins, Aug. 28, 1946 (dec. 1970); children: Maureen Jean, John William; m. Wilda Ann Suffel, Nov. 7, 1975. B.Sc., McGill U., 1948, M.D., C.M., 1951. Anaesthesiologist Holy Cross Hosp., Calgary, Alta., Can., 1954-86, med. dir., 1967-76, exec. dir., 1976-86; exec. dir. Can. Assn. Med. Clinics, 1967-73. Contbr. articles to profl. jours. Capt. Can. Army, 1940-45. Recipient Queen's Silver Jubilee medal Queen Elizabeth II, 1977. Mem. Can. Med. Assn., Can. Anaesthesia Assn. Progressive Conservative. Roman Catholic. Clubs: Calgary Golf and Country, Glencoe. Avocations: photography; welding; computers. Home: PO Box 369, Sylvan Lake, AB Canada T0M 1Z0 Office: Bentley Gen Hosp, PO Box 30, Bentley, AB Canada T0C 0J0

MANES, STEPHEN GABRIEL, concert pianist, educator; b. Bennington, Vt., Apr. 11, 1940; s. Julius H. and Edna E. (Silberstein) M.; m. Frieda Green, July 7, 1963; children: Sonya Ruth, Daniel Ira. B.S., Juilliard Sch. Music, 1961, M.S., 1963; postgrad. (Fulbright fellow), Acad. Music, Vienna, 1963-64. Vis. instr. music Oberlin Coll. Conservatory, Ohio, 1966-67; asst. prof. Ball State U., Muncie, Ind., 1967-68; prof. music SUNY-Buffalo, 1968—, chair, 1989-93; co-music dir. Sebago-Long Lake Region Chamber Music Festival, North Bridgton, Maine, 1982-85. Concert piano soloist maj. orchs. U.S. and abroad; debuts in Washington, 1962, N.Y.C., 1963, Vienna, Austria, 1964, Berlin, 1975, Amsterdam, 1975, London, 1975, chamber music concerts, radio, TV appearances, four-hand piano recitals with Frieda Manes in U.S., Australia, Can. and P.R.; rec. artist Orion Master Records, 1974—, Spectrum Records, 1986—; mem. Baird Piano Trio, 1986-90. Recipient Kosciuszko Chopin prize, 1960, Town Hall award Concert Artists Guild, 1962; finalist Leventritt Internat. Competition, 1962; Harriet Cohen Internat. Beethoven prize, 1964. Mem. Music Tchrs. Nat. Assn., Coll. Music Soc., Am. Fedn. Musicians. Home: 384 Voorhees Ave Buffalo NY 14216-2116 Office: SUNY-Buffalo Dept of Music 414 Baird Hall Buffalo NY 14260

MANESS, ANTHONY RAY, retired naval officer; b. Long Beach, Calif., Apr. 13, 1940; s. Jim Caldwell and Mildred Bernice (Losier) M.; m. Karen Charles, June 10, 1984; children: Amy, Tracy, Sonia, Jessica. BA, U.S. Naval Acad., 1962; MA in Internat. Law and Diplomacy, Tufts U., 1971. Commd. ensign USN, 1962, advanced through grades to rear adm., 1990; flag lt. DCNO for Plans Policy and Ops., Washington, 1976-77; comdg. officer Patrol Squadron 6, Barbers Point, Hawaii, 1977-79; ops. officer Patrol Wing 2, Barbers Point, 1979-81; exec. asst. to chief naval pers. Washington, 1981-84; comdr. Patrol Wing 1, Kami Seya, Japan, 1984-86; spl. asst. to chief of naval ops. Washington, 1986-88; exec. asst. to chmn. Joint Chiefs of Staff, Washington, 1988-89; dir. Navy Tng. and Edn. Policy, Washington, 1989-90; comdr. Patrol Wings, U.S. Pacific Fleet, Mountain View, Calif., 1990—. Decorated Defense Disting. Svc. medal, Legion of Merit (3). Presbyterian.

MANEY, MICHAEL MASON, lawyer; b. Taihoku, Japan, Aug. 13, 1936; s. Edward Strait and Helen M. M.; m. Suzanne Cochran, Oct. 22, 1960; 1 child, Michele. B.A., Yale U., 1956; M.A., Fletcher Sch. Law and Diplomacy, Tufts U., 1957; LL.B., U. Pa., 1964. Bar: N.Y. 1966, D.C. 1977. Case officer CIA, 1957-61; law clk. Justice John Harlan, Supreme Ct. U.S., Washington, 1964-65; asso. Sullivan & Cromwell, N.Y.C., 1965-70; partner Sullivan & Cromwell, 1971-77, 81—; mng. partner Sullivan & Cromwell, Washington, 1977-81; law fellow Salzburg Seminar in Am. Studies, 1967. Trustee, chmn. bd. Am. Found. for the Blind, Inc. Served to lt. USAF, 1958-60. Mem. ABA, Am. Law Inst., Am. Coll. Trial Lawyers, N.Y. State Bar Assn., Union Club, Yale Club, Down Town Assn., Madison Beach Club, Madison Country Club, Met. Opera Club. Home: 1220 Park Ave New York NY 10128-1733 also: 48 Neptune Ave Madison CT 06443-3210 Office: Sullivan & Cromwell 125 Broad St New York NY 10004

MANFREDI, DAVID PETER, architect; b. Hartford, Conn., Aug. 9, 1951; s. Domenic George and Elizabeth Frances (Ferrando) M. BA, U. Notre Dame, 1973; MA, U. Chgo., 1976; BArch, U. Notre Dame, 1979. Registered architect. V.p. The Architects Collaborative, San Francisco & Cambridge, Mass., 1979-88, Elkus/Manfredi Architects, Boston, 1988—. Prin. works include SONY Gallery, 1992 (Chgo. Interiors Grand Prize 1993), West Roxbury Dist. Courthouse, 1992, Franklin Pierce Law Ctr., 1992. Mem. AIA, Boston Soc. Architects, Phi Beta Kappa. Office: Elkus/Manfredi Architects 530 Atlantic Ave Boston MA 02210-2218

MANFREDI, JOHN FREDERICK, food products executive; b. N.Y.C., Dec. 1, 1940; s. John Frederick and Angela (Morano) M.; m. Doreen Honore Molloy, July 19, 19180; children: Nicole, Kendre, Hadley. Student, Yale U., 1958-61; BA, Columbia U., 1967. Asst. trader Singer & Mackie, N.Y.C., 1964; editor New Haven Jour. Carrier, Fairchild Publs., 1965-68; dir. pub. rels. Gen. Foods, White Plains, N.Y., 1968-74, dir. corp. communications, 1975-80, dir. internat. pub. affairs, 1981-86, dir. pub. affairs worldwide, 1986-87; v.p. pub. affairs Nabisco Foods Group, Parsippany, N.J., 1988, sr. v.p. external and govt. affairs, 1988—; chmn. Internat. Food Info. Coun., Washington, 1990—; chmn. Commn. on Mktg. and Advt., U.S. Coun. for Internat. Bus., N.Y.C., 1990—, Internat. C. of C., Paris, 1990—. Mem. Internat. Advt. Assn. (bd. dirs. 1990—), U.S. Olympic Com. N.J. (chmn.), Internat. Pub. Rels. Assn., Pub. Rels. Soc. Am., Arthur Page Soc., The Wisemen, Nat. Press Club. Office: Nabisco Foods Group 7 Campus Dr Parsippany NJ 07054-4407

MANGAN, CHARLES VINCENT, utility company executive; b. N.Y.C., July 12, 1939; s. James Francis and Anne Frances (Farrell) M.; m. Edna Joyce Plaza, July 23, 1966; children: Christopher, Michele, Suzanne, Theresa, Linda. BSME, Manhattan Coll., 1961; cert. in nuclear tech., Oak Ridge (Tenn.) Sch. Reactor Tech., 1964. Steam turbine engr. Allis-Chalmers Mfg. Co., Milw., 1961-63; nuclear engr. Niagara Mohawk Power Corp., Buffalo, 1963-69; supr. thermal generation planning Niagara Mohawk Power Corp., Syracuse, N.Y., 1969-73, mgr. system engring., 1973-75, mgr. prodn. plant engring., 1975-78, mgr. staff engring., 1978-81, mgr. design engring., 1981-82, v.p nuclear engring. and licensing, 1982-85, sr. v.p., 1985—. Scoutmaster Boy Scouts Am., Liverpool, N.Y., 1978-83; cubmaster Cub Scouts Am., Liverpool, 1976-78; mem. Sch. Dist. Adv. Com., Liverpool, 1973. Mem. Am. Nuclear Soc., ASME (vice chmn. local chpt.), Atomic Indsl. Forum. Republican. Roman Catholic. Avocations: tennis, jogging, electronics. Office: Niagara Mohawk Power Corp 301 Plainfield Rd Syracuse NY 13212-4502

MANGAN, FRANK THOMAS, advertising executive; b. Bklyn., Nov. 14, 1944; s. Francis T. and Margaret M. Mangan; m. Kerry Kilmartin, Nov. 16, 1945; children: Michael T., Jeffrey D. BS, Mt. St. Mary's Coll., Emmitsburg, Md., 1966; postgrad., Fordham U., 1970-72. With Joseph E. Seagram & Sons, N.Y.C., 1967-74; sr. v.p. The Marschalk Co., Inc., N.Y.C., 1974-85, Wells, Rich, Greene, Inc., N.Y.C., 1985-86; v.p. Lord, Geller Federico, Einstein, Inc., N.Y.C., 1986-88; sr.v.p. LINTAS, N.Y.C., 1988-91, Y & R Cos., N.Y.C., 1991—. Republican. Roman Catholic. Club: Tokeneke (Darien, Conn.).

MANGAN, JOHN LEO, retired electrical manufacturing company executive, international trade and trade policy specialist; b. Lakewood, Ohio, May 24, 1920; s. Mark A. and Celia M. (Motley) M.; m. Mildred J. Livingston, June 21, 1946; children: John, Scott. BSME, Carnegie Inst. Tech., 1942. Registered profl. engr., Mass., N.Y. Turbine design engr. Gen. Electric Co., Lynn, Mass., 1946-48; turbine application and sales engr. Gen. Electric Co., Fitchburg and Lynn, Mass, Schenectady, St. Louis, 1948-55; mgr. gas turbine indsl. sales Gen. Electric Co., Schenectady, 1955-60, mgr. gas turbine product planning, 1960-64, mgr. turbine strategy devel., 1966-86; mgr. turbine indsl. customer requirements Boeing Co., Seattle, 1964-66. Contbr. articles profl. jours., chpts. in books; inventor in field. Mem. com. Boy Scouts Am., 1955-59, 64-66; bd. dirs. United Way Schenectady County, Inc., 1991—, chmn., 1992-93. 1st lt. U.S. Army, 1942-46. Recipient Profl. and Social Activities award Gen. Electric Co., 1977. Fellow ASME (v.p. 1975-79, bd. govs. 1983-87, Gas Turbine citation, Centennial medal 1980, Dedicated Svc. award 1988); mem. Internat. Combustion Engine Council (permanent com., v.p. 1977-81). Club: Mohawk Golf (Schenectady). Home: 1345 Ruffner Rd Niskayuna NY 12309-2505

MANGAN, MONA, association executive, lawyer; b. Pittston, Pa., Dec. 29, 1945; d. Joseph H. and Mona C. Mangan; m. Roy N. Watanabe, Oct. 24, 1987; 1 child, Julia. BA, Lock Haven U., 1966; AM, Duke U., 1969; JD, Columbia U., 1975. Bar: N.Y. 1976, U.S. Dist. Ct. (ea. and so. dists.) N.Y.

1979. Congl. staff Senator Wayne Morse of Oreg., 1967-68; staff atty. U.S. Dept. Labor, N.Y.C., 1975-79; trial atty. EEOC, N.Y.C., 1979; asst. exec. dir. Writers Guild Am. East, Inc., N.Y.C., 1979-84, assoc. exec. dir., 1984, exec. dir., 1984—. Recipient Gross award for contbn. to journalism Lock Haven U., 1984. Mem. Assn. Bar City N.Y., ABA, Coalition Motion Picture and TV Unions (v.p.), Pan Am. Fedn. Arts, Mass Media and Entertainment Unions (regional v.p. 1993—), Unions for Performing Arts (treas.), Internat. Affiliation Writers Guilds (treas.), Columbia U. Law Sch. Alumni Assn. Office: Writers Guild Am East Inc 555 W 57th St New York NY 10019-2925

MANGANARO, FRANCIS FERDINAND, naval officer; b. Providence, Feb. 27, 1925; s. Ralph and Ada Susanna (Hobden) M.; m. Carol Anne Slater, Sept. 8, 1948; children: Carol Sue, William Francis, John Thomas, Linda Anne, Mary Kathryn. Student, U. R.I., 1943-44; B.S. in Elec. Engring, U.S. Naval Acad., 1944-47; Naval Engr., MIT, 1956; cert., Advanced Mgmt. Program, Harvard U. Sch. Bus., 1971; cert. pub. utilities exec. program, U. Mich., 1984. Registered profl. engr., Conn. Commd. ensign U.S. Navy, 1947, advanced through grades to rear adm., 1975; served in destroyers Atlantic Fleet, 1947-49, served in submarines Pacific Fleet, 1949-53, repair officer, submarines Pearl Harbor Naval Shipyard, 1956-59, design project officer, submarines Bur Ships, 1959-63; inspection and planning officer Office Supr. of Shipbldg. Groton, Conn., 1963-68; prodn. officer Portsmouth Naval Shipyard, 1968-72, comdg. officer Puget Sound Naval Shipyard, 1972-76, chmn. navy claims settlement bd. Naval Material Command, 1976-78; vice comdr. Naval Sea Systems Command Washington, 1978-80; ret. (Naval Sea Systems Command), 1980; v.p. dir. GPU Nuclear Corp., 1980-90; cons. Burns & Roe Utility Mgmt. Cons., 1990—. Decorated Legion of Merit, DSM. Mem. Soc. Naval Architects and Marine Engrs., Am. Soc. Naval Engrs., Sigma Xi, Tau Beta Pi, Beta Psi Alpha.

MANGANELLO, JAMES ANGELO, psychologist; b. Cambridge, Mass., Nov. 30, 1944; s. Almando and Carmella (Spera) M.; m. Rosemarie Bombara, Dec. 26, 1965; children: Jason, Jennifer. BA, Eastern Nazarene Coll., 1966; MA, Boston U., 1970; EdM, Suffolk U., 1969; EdD, Boston U., 1977; M in Pub. Health, Harvard U., 1980. Instr. biology N.Y. Christian Acad., Bklyn., 1966-67; minister youth, edn. St. Paul Ch., Somerville, Mass., 1967-69; dir., founder Community Nursery Sch., Somerville, 1967-69; resident dir., instr. Malone Coll., Canton, Ohio, 1969-70; clin., research fellow dept. psychiatry Mass. Gen. Hosp., Boston, 1973-75; psychologist North Shore Counseling Ctr., Beverly, Mass., 1975-79; instr. North Shore Community Coll., Beverly, 1975-78; pres. Health Integration Services, Peabody, Mass., 1978-83; clin. fellow dept. psychiatry Harvard U. Med. Sch., Boston, 1983-84; pres. Dr. Manganello & Assocs., Danvers, Mass., 1983—; cons. psychologist Erich Lindemann Mental Health Ctr., Boston, 1971-75, Westwood Lodge, 1973-74. Contbr. articles to profl. jours. Chpt. mem. Rep. Presdl. Task Force, Washington, 1983—; mem. guidance adv. bd. Lexington Christian Acad., Mass., 1977—; mem. pres.'s council Gordon-Conwell Theol. Sem., Hamilton, Mass., 1983—. Mem. AAAS, Am. Orthopsychiat. Assn., Am. Pub. Health Assn., Am. Coll. Health Care Execs., Am. Sci. Affiliation, Soc. for Sci. Study of Religion, MIT Enterprise Forum, Pi Lambda Theta. Avocations: tennis, basketball, music. Home: 2920 NW 26th Ct Boca Raton FL 33434-3656 Office: Liberty Tree Med Ctr Danvers MA 01923

MANGER, WILLIAM MUIR, internist; b. Greenwich, Conn., Aug. 13, 1920; s. Julius and Lilian (Weissinger) M.; m. Lynn Seymour Sheppard, May 30, 1964; children: William Muir, Jr., Lilian Wade (Mrs. Porter Fleming), Stewart Sheppard, Charles Seymour. BS, Yale U., 1944; MD, Columbia U., 1946; PhD, Mayo Found., U. Minn., 1958. Intern, Presbyn. Hosp., N.Y.C., 1946-47, resident, 1949-50; fellow internal medicine Mayo Found., 1950-57; asst. physician Presbyn. Hosp., 1957—; dir. Manger Rsch. Found., 1961-77; clin. asst. vis. physician Columbia div. Bellevue Hosp., 1964-68; asst. attending physician NYU Bellevue Hosp. 1969-77; assoc. attending physician, 1977-83, attending physician, 1983—; instr. medicine Columbia U. Coll. Phys. and Surg., 1957-66, assoc. medicine, 1966-70, lectr., 1981—; asst. attending physician Presbyn. Hosp., 1966—; asst. clin. prof. medicine N.Y.U. Med. Ctr., 1968-75, assoc. clin. prof. medicine, 1975-83, prof. clin. medicine, 1983—; mem. Internat. Med. Council on Drug Use, 1977—; mem. devel. com. Mayo Clinic, 1981-87; vice chmn. bd. Manger Hotels, Inc., 1957-73. Mem. bd. govs. St. Albans Sch., Washington, 1958-64, 67-73, 83-89, chmn., 1967-69; trustee Found. Rsch. in Medicine and Biology, 1971-77, Buckley Sch., 1975-85, Found. for Advancement Internat. Rsch. in Microbiology, 1977-82, Thyroid Found., 1980-85; mem. bd. visitors Boston U. Med. Sch., 1992—; trustee Found. for Depression and Manic Depression, 1978-89, pres., 1980-89; elder Presbyn. Ch., 1968-70, 92-93, trustee, 1962-67, 80-84, deacon, 1959-61. Lt. (j.g.) M.C., USNR, 1947-49. Recipient Meritorious Rsch. award Mayo Found., 1955, Disting. Alumnus award, 1992. Diplomate Nat. Bd. Med. Examiners, Am. Bd. Internal Medicine. Fellow ACP, Acad. Psychosomatic Medicine, Am. Geriatric Soc., Coun. on Geriatric Cardiology, N.Y. Acad. Medicine (admission com. 1976-78, edn. com. 1979-92), Am. Coll. Cardiology, Am. Coll. Clin. Pharmacology, Royal Soc. Health, Am. Inst. Chemists; trustee Nat. Hypertension Assn. (chmn. 1977—), AMA, Am. Soc. Internal Medicine, N.Y. State Med. Soc., N.Y. County Med. Soc., Am. Heart Assn. (fellow council on circulation and council for high blood pressure rsch.), Nat. High Blood Pressure Edn. Program (mem. Coord. Com.), Inter-Am. Soc. Hypertension, Internat. Soc. Hypertension, Am. Thoracic Soc., N.Y. Acad. Sci., AAAS, Am. Physiol. Soc., Am. Chem. Soc., Am. Soc. Pharmacology and Exptl. Therapeutics, Am. Soc. for Clin. Pharmacology and Therapeutics, Clin. Autonomic Rsch. Soc., Am. Autonomic Soc., Med. Strollers, N.Y.C., Endocrine Soc., Pan Am. Med. Assn., Harvey Soc., Rsch. Soc. Exptl. Biology and Medicine, Rsch. Discussion Group (founding mem., sec.-treas. 1958-80), Am. Fedn. Clin. Rsch., Am. Soc. Nephrology, Royal Soc. Medicine (affiliate), Fellows Assn. Mayo Found. (v.p., pres. 1953), Mayo Alumni Assn. (v.p. 1981-82, exec. com. 1981-89, pres. elect 1982-85, pres. 1985-87), Catecholamine Club (founder, sec.-treas. 1967-80, pres. 1981-82), Doctors Mayo Soc., Albert Gallatin Assos., New Eng Soc., S.R. (admin. admissions com. 1959-67, bd. mgrs. 1959-67, 69-70), Soc. Colonial Wars, Sigma Xi, Nu Sigma Nu, Phi Delta Theta, Explorers, Meadow (L.I., N.Y.); Univ.; Yale; N.Y. Athletic (N.Y.C.); Southampton Bathing Corp.; Jupiter Island. Co-author: Chemical Quantitation of Epinephrine and Norepinephrine in Plasma, 1959, Pheochromocytoma, 1977; author: Catecholamines in Normal and Abnormal Cardiac Function; editor, contbr. Hormones and Hypertension, 1966; editor: Am. Lecture Series in Endocrinology, 1962-75; guest editor First Irvine H. Page Internat. Hypertension Rsch. Symposium; contbr. articles to profl. and lay jours. Achievements include research on the mechanism of salt-induced hypertension, and on pheochromocytoma. Home: 8 E 81st St New York NY 10028-0201

MANGES, JAMES HORACE, investment banker; b. N.Y.C., Oct. 8, 1927; s. Horace S. and Natalie (Bloch) M.; m. Joan Brownell, Oct., 1969 (div.); m. Mary Seymour, Mar. 28, 1974; children: Alison, James H. Jr. Grad., Phillips Exeter Acad., 1945; BA, Yale U., 1950; MBA, Harvard U., 1953. With Kuhn, Loeb & Co., N.Y.C., 1954-77, ptnr., 1967-77; mng. dir. Lehman Bros., Kuhn Loeb Inc., N.Y.C., 1977-84, Shearson Lehman Hutton, Inc., N.Y.C., 1984-90; adv. dir. Lehman Bros. N.Y.C., 1990—; dir. Baker Industries, Inc., 1967-77; dir., exec. com. Metromedia, Inc. 1970-86. Trustee The Episcopal Sch., 1978-92, St. Bernard's Sch., 1985—, Phillips Exeter Acad., 1985-89; mem. trustee coun., 1989—. Mem. Bond Club, Yale Club (N.Y.C.), City Midday, Century Country Club (Purchase, N.Y.). Home: 875 Park Ave New York NY 10021-0341 Office: Lehman Bros World Fin Ctr Am Express Tower New York NY 10285

MANGHAM, R. H., church administrator. Sec. Christian and Missionary Alliance. Office: Christian & Missionary Alliance PO Box 35000 Colorado Springs CO 80935

MANGIERI, JOHN NICHOLAS, university administrator; b. New Castle, Pa., Nov. 1, 1946; s. John and Rose Marie (Audino) M.; m. Deborah Ann Hoerner, Aug. 23, 1969; children: Jeffrey Michael, Deanna Ashley. B.S. in Edn., Slippery Rock State Coll., 1968; M.Ed., Westminster Coll., 1969; Ph.D., U. Pitts., 1972. Grad. asst. U. Pitts., 1970-72; asst. prof. edn. Ohio U., Athens, 1972-74; dir. tchr. corps., 1974-78; prof. edn. U. S.C., Columbia, 1978-82; dean Sch. Edn. Tex. Christian U., Fort Worth, 1982-87, dean grad. studies and rsch., 1987-89; provost, vice chancellor acad. affairs U. New Orleans, 1989-92; pres AR St Univ, State Univ, AR, 1992—. Author: (with

Scott Baldwin) Effective Reading Techniques, 1978, (with Bader and Walker) Elementary Reading: A Comprehensive Approach, 1982, (with Staley and Wilhide) Teaching Language Arts: Classroom Application, 1984; contbr. numerous articles to profl. jours. Pres. Appalachian Reading Council, Ohio, 1973-74; pres. Columbia Area Reading Council, 1981-82; bd. dirs. Midwestern Tchr. Corps Network, 1976-80. Mem. Internat. Reading Assn. Office: Ark State U PO Box 10 State University AR 72467-0010

MANGINO, KRISTIN MIKALSON, secondary education educator; b. Spokane, Wash., July 7, 1939; d. Norman Lillard and Mabel Mae (Lewis) Mikalson; m. Paul Angelo Mangino, Aug. 15, 1965; children: Kyle Aaron, Lisan Kristin. Student, Cottey Coll., 1957-58, Ea. Wash. Coll. Edn. (now Ea. Wash. U.), 1958-61; BS in Psychology, Wash. State U., 1961; student, Calif. State U., Fullerton, 1961-66; postgrad., U. Calif., Irvine, 1966; MS in Spl. Edn., Portland State U., 1983. Cert. elem. and secondary tchr., Calif., Wash., Oreg. Tchr. English and reading Jr. High Sch., Anaheim and Monterey, Calif., 1961-68; substitute tchr. Elma (Wash.) Sch. Dist., 1970-71, Evergreen Sch. Dist., Vancouver, Wash., 1974-75; tutor Evergreen Sch. Dist., Vancouver, 1975-84; tutor, substitute tchr. Vancouver and Evergreen Sch. Dists., 1984-88, tutor, 1988—; bd. dirs. Arden Tree Farms; hostess with svc. sales City Welcome Svc., 1986-87; co-pres. Spl. Edn. Adv. Coun., Vancouver, 1986-87; mem. direction svc. bd. Ednl. Svc. Dists. 112, 1980. Officer Philanthropic Ednl. Orgn. (G.X. chpt.), Vancouver, 1984-86, mem., 1984—; sec. Spl. Olympics, Evergreen Sch. Dist., 1989-90; bd. dirs. The Arc, Clark County, 1992-93; D.D. Parent Coalition of Clark County, 1993—; mem. Internat. Rett Syndrome Found. Mem. Berg Freunde Ski Club. Presbyterian. Avocations: travel, reading, gardening, vol. work. Home and Office: PO Box 5542 Vancouver WA 98668-5542

MANGINO, ROBERT, insurance company executive; b. 1936. Grad., Rutgers U., 1954-58, post grad., 1958-60. With Mutual Benefit Co., N.Y.C., 1960-70; sr. v.p. N. Am. Reassurance Co. subs. Swissre Holding N. Am., N.Y.C., 1970—. Office: Swissre Holding N Amer Inc 100 E 46th St # 13 New York NY 10017-2601

MANGION, RICHARD MICHAEL, health care executive; b. Haverhill, Mass., Apr. 26, 1941; s. Michael Anthony and Evelyn (Cote) M.; m. Gail Elizabeth Donne, Apr. 27, 1968; children: Catherine Jean, James Richard, Ian Kyle. BBA, Suffolk U., 1963; MBA, Syracuse U., 1965; MPH, U. Calif., Berkeley, 1972. Asst. adminstr. Nashua (N.H.) Meml. Hosp., 1972-75, assoc. adminstr., 1975-77; pres. and chief exec. officer Harrington Meml. Hosp., Southbridge, Mass., 1977—; lectr. U. N.H., Durham, 1972-74. Pres. Tri-Community Devel. Corp., Southbridge, 1983-88. Capt. USAF, 1966-70. Fellow Am. Coll. Health Care Execs.; mem. Am. Hosp. Assn., Mass. Hosp. Assn., Cen. Mass. Hosp. Council (pres. 1982-84), Cen. Mass. Health Care Found., Tri-Community C. of C. (pres. 1983-84). Democrat. Roman Catholic. Club: Hosp. Supts. Lodge: Rotary. Avocations: tennis, swimming, hiking. Home: 50 Old Village Rd Sturbridge MA 01566-1069 Office: Harrington Meml Hosp 100 South St Southbridge MA 01550-4047

MANGIONE, CHUCK (CHARLES FRANK MANGIONE), jazz musician, composer; b. Rochester, N.Y., Nov. 29, 1940; children: Nancy, Diana. MusB in Music Edn., Eastman Sch. Music, U. Rochester, 1963, MusD (hon.), 1985. Formed quintet with brother Gap, Jazz Bros., 1958-64; tchr. elem. sch. music Rochester, 1963-64; dir. Eastman Jazz Ensemble; mem. faculty Eastman Sch. Music, 1968-72. Freelance musician with bands of Maynard Ferguson and Kai Winding, 1965, trumpet player with, Art Blakey's Jazz Messengers, 1965-67; formed Chuck Mangione Quartet, 1968; guest condr. Rochester Philharm. Orch., 1970, appeared at Montreux Internat. Jazz Festival, 1972; starred on PBS-TV spl. Live from Wolftrap; performed on PBS-TV spl. Grammy Awards show, 1981; ann. tours to Europe, Japan, Australia and S. Am.; performed benefit concerts for Spl. Olympics; also 8-hour marathon to aid Italy's earthquake victims; compositions include Hill Where the Lord Hides (Grammy nomination 1971), Land of Make Believe, 1973 (Grammy nomination for Best Big Band Performance and Best Instrumental Arrangement Accompanying a Vocalist), Bellavia, 1976 (Grammy award), Give It All You Got; theme for 1980 Winter Olympics (Emmy award Music Composition/Direction), 1980 (Grammy nomination for Best Instrumental Composition); albums include Chuck Mangione Quartet, 1972, Chase the Clouds Away, 1975 (gold album, 2 Grammy nominations), Main Squeeze, 1976, Feels So Good, 1977 (gold, platinum and double-platinum album), Children of Sanchez, Save Tonight For Me, 1986 Eyes of the Veiled Temptress, 1988; movie soundtrack, 1978 (Grammy award Best Pop Instrumental Performance), Live at the Hollywood Bowl, 1979, Fun and Games, 1980 (Grammy nomination), Tarentella, 1981. Commd. by Sesquicentennial Com. of City of Rochester to compose and premier spl. work in honor of city's 150th birthday. Made acting debut in film Paradise Blues, 1984; guest star Magnum PI; 1st music video Diana D, completed 1984 (directed by Zbigniew Rybczynski). Named Most Promising Male Jazz Artist, Record World 1975, Jazz Artist of Yr., Instrumentalist of Yr., Most Promising Instrumentalist, Top Fusion Artist, Top Producer, Top Instrumentalist, Outstanding Jazz Artist, Internat. Jazz award winner 1978-79, Georgie award for Instrumental Act of Yr., AGVA 1980, winner Playboy mag. ann. music poll, several times, also 1980 winner for Best Brass, Best Composer and Best Group.; recipient Entertainment award Big Bros. 4th Ann. Sidewalks of N.Y. Awards Dinner, 1983, Regents medal of excellence N.Y. State Bd. Regents, 1984, Jazz Music Campus Entertainment award Nat. Assn. Campus Activities, 1987. His performance at Montreal Internat. Jazz Festival, July 1986, drew largest crowd in history of the event. *

MANGIONE, JERRE GERLANDO, author, educator; b. Rochester, N.Y., Mar. 20, 1909; s. Gaspare and Giuseppina (Polizzi) M.; m. Patricia Anthony, Feb. 18, 1957. B.A., Syracuse U., 1931; M.A. (hon.), U. Pa., 1971, Litt.D. (hon.), 1980; LHD (hon.), SUNY, Brockport, 1987. Writer, Time mag., 1931; book editor Robert M. McBride & Co., N.Y.C., 1934-37; nat. coordinating editor Fed. Writers' Project, 1937-39; spl. asst. to U.S. commr. immigration and naturalization, 1942-48; advt. writer, pub. relations dir., 1948-61; mem. faculty U. Pa., 1961—, dir. writing program, 1965-77, prof. English, 1968-77, emeritus, 1977—, founding dir. Italian Studies Center, 1978-80, coord. cultural events, 1980-82; vis. lectr. Bryn Mawr Coll., 1966-67; vis. prof. Trinity Coll., Rome, summer 1973, Queens Coll., 1980; acting dir. Yaddo, 1977-78; editor WFLM Phila. Guide, 1960-61; book reviewer, 1931—; adv. editor The Humanist, 1979-88; judge Nat. Book Award in Fiction, 1968; adv. editor Italian Americana, 1974-84, 90—; mem. lit. panel NEA, 1980-81; speaker main address Symposium on Italian and Italian-Am. Women in 90s, SUNY, Stony Brook, 1993. Author: Mount Allegro: A Memoir of Italian Life, 1943, 6th edit., 1989 (hist. marker commemorating area erected in Rochester, 1986, stage adaptation premiere, Rochester), 1992, Spanish edit., 1944, Italian edit., 1947, rev., 1983, (novel) Ship and the Flame, 1948, Swedish edit., 1949, Reunion in Sicily, 1950, 2d edit., 1984, Italian edit., 1992, Night Search, 1965, To Walk the Night, Brit. edit., 1966, Italian edit., 1987, Life Sentences for Everybody, 1966, (fables) A Passion for Sicilians: The World around Danilo Dolci, 1968, 3d edit., 1985, America is Also Italian, 1969, The Dream and the Deal: Federal Writers Project (1935-43), 1972, 3d edit., 1983 (nominated for Nat. Book award 1972) Mussolini's March on Rome, 1975, An Ethnic At Large: A Memoir of America in the Thirties and Forties, 1978, 2d edit., 1983, (with Ben Morreale) La Storia: Five Centuries of the Italian American Experience, 1992; (pamphlet on Phila. lit. history) By Reason of Birth or Residence, 1988; contbr. to newspapers and mags. Chmn. lit. arts com. Phila. Art Alliance, 1958-61; mem. adv. bd. U. Pa. Press, 1983-84; founding mem. exec. bd. Am.-Italy Soc., 1959-94, Inst. Contemporary Art U. Pa., 1964-77, Am. Italian Hist. Assn., 1969—, Am. Inst. Italian Studies, 1975-82, Amici, 1981—; pres. Friends Danilo Dolci, Inc., 1969-71. Guggenheim fellow, 1945; Fulbright research fellow, 1965; MacDowell Colony fellow; Yaddo fellow; Va. Ctr. Arts fellow; Rockefeller grantee, 1968; Am. Philos. Soc. grantee, 1971; Earhart Found. grantee, 1975; NEH grantee, 1980-83; decorated knight comdr. Order Star Solidarity Italy, 1971; recipient Key to City Rochester, 1963, 10th ann. Lit. award Friends Rochester Pub. Library, 1966, Justinian Soc. award, 1966, Phila. Athenaeum Lit. award, 1973, Presdl. award Am. Inst. for Italian Culture, 1979, Outstanding Achievement award Am.-Italian Hist. Assn., 1982, Key to City, New Orleans, 1988, Pa. Gov.'s award for Excellence in Humanities, 1989, Leonardo Da Vinci award Italian Heritage and Culture Month Com., 1989; named Person of Yr., Italian Ams. Delaware County, 1978, 1986; Premio Nazionale Empedocle, 1984; Legion of Honor medal Chapel of Four Chaplains, 1984; Mangione papers housed at U. Rochester;

recipient Internat. Arts award Columbus: Countdown 1992, 1990; honored by Libr. of Congress, 1992 for his literary career with an exhibit from his archive titled: Jerre Mangione, An Ethnic at Larger, and the Federal Writers' Project, Christopher Columbus Quincentenary award, 1992, Mariano DiVito Human Achievement award, 1993, Distinction in Lit. Achievement award Columbus Citizens Found., 1993. Fellow Soc. Am. Historians; mem Author's Guild, Franklin Inn, Assn. Writers of Agrigento in Sicily (pres. 1994), Sons of Italy. Home: 3300 Darby Rd Apt 7315 Haverford PA 19041-1075 Office: U Pa Dept English Philadelphia PA 19104

MANGLER, ROBERT JAMES, lawyer; b. Chgo., Aug. 15, 1930; s. Robert H. and Agnes E. (Sugrue) M.; m. Geraldine M. Delich, May 2, 1959; children: Robert Jr., Paul, John, Barbara. BS, Loyola U., Chgo., 1952, MA, 1983; JD, Northwestern U., 1955. Bar: Ill. 1958, U.S. Dist. Ct. (no. dist.) Ill. 1959, U.S. Supreme Ct. 1976, U.S. Ct. Appeals (7th cir.) 1980. Author: (with others) Illinois Land Use Law, Illinois Municipal Law. Village atty., prosecutor Village of Wilmette, 1965-93; mcpl. prosecutor City of Evanston, 1963-65; chmn. Ill. Traffic Ct. Conf., 1977—; pres. Ill. Inst. Local Govt. Law; mem. home rule attys. com. Ill. Mcpl. League. Mem. ABA (chmn. adv. com. traffic ct. program), Nat. Inst. Mcpl. Law Officers (pres.), Ill. Bar Assn. (former chmn. traffic laws and ct. com.), Chgo. Bar Assn. (chmn. traffic ct. seminar, chmn. traffic laws com.), Caxton Club, Phi Alpha Delta. Office: Klein Thorpe & Jenkins Ltd 180 N La Salle St Chicago IL 60601-2501

MANGLONA, BENJAMIN T., commonwealth official; b. Rota, Mariana Islands; s. Prudencio M. and Maria T. M.; m. Magdalena Manglona Manglona, 1959; children: Lillian Manglona Matsumoto, Rebecca Manglona Taisague, Theodore, Marie Manglona Apatng, Joann Manglona San Nicolas, Benjamin M., Jr., Harold M., Debra M. Diaz, Selina Manglona Mesa. Grad., Surveyor's Sch., Palau, 1957; student Internat. Correspondence Sch., Scranton, Pa., 1964-65, Honolulu Community Coll., 1966-67; AS Civil Engring. Tech., U. Guam, 1973; constrn. insp. tng, OICC, Guam, 1971-73. Registered profl. land surveyor. Jr. engring. aide Rota Dist. Adminstrn., 1957, sr. engring. aide, 1958, supr. engring., 1958-59, asst. surveyor and cartographic engr., 1959-68, asst. clk. ct., Rota, part-time 1962-66, sta. mgr. Continental/Air Micronesia, Rota, 1968-69; pub. works officer, Rota, 1970-75; pres. Rota Petroleum Co., B & M Constrn. Co., Rota Community Project Assn.; mem. Mariana Islands Dist. Legislature, 1962-65; mem. Ho. of Reps. Congress of Micronesia, 1965-70, resigned; chmn. Ho. resources and devel. com. 1969-70; appointed Mariana Islands Dist. Legislature, 1975; mem. No. Marianas Legislature, 1976-78; mem. No. Mariana Islands Commonwealth Legislature (Senate), 1978-90, Senate floor leader, chmn. exec. appointments and govt. investigation com., chmn. fiscal affairs com. 1978-80, v.p., chmn. senate fiscal affairs com., 1980-82, v.p., legis. sec., chmn. 1984-85, chmn. fiscal affairs com., 1986-88; elected Senate pres., 1988-90; lt. gov., 1990—; trust terr. rep. S. Pacific Commn. Conf., New Caledonia, 1968; mem. Congress of Micronesia Joint Commn. on Polit. Status, Washington, 1969-70; No. Marianas rep. to numerous USA, UN confs.; 1st v.p. No. Mariana Constl. Conv., 1976; numerous other govtl. appointments and coms.; mem. Trust Terr. Bd. of Land Surveying Examiners, 1972-75; mem. Rota Mcpl. Scholarship Bd. 1969-75; mem. 902 Cons., 1988-90, chmn., 1990—, chmn. 702 multi-yr. covenant funding negotiation, 1991. Mem. Am. Soc. Bldg. and Constrn. Inspectors. Roman Catholic. Home: Songsong Village Rota MP 96951 Office: Office of Gov Capitol Hill Saipan MP 96950

MANGO, WILFRED GILBERT, JR., construction company executive; b. Weehawkin, N.J., July 11, 1940; s. Wilfred Gilbert and Mildred B.M.; children from previous marriage; Christian P., Peter H.; m. Charlene Holt, Feb. 14, 1985; children: Alison L., David H. B.S., Lehigh U., 1963; M.B.A., NYU, 1969. Auditor Hurdman & Cranstown, N.Y.C., 1963-69; dir. fin. Thomas Crimmins Contracting Co., N.Y.C., 1969-77; v.p. fin., mgr. fin. controls ITT Teleplant, Inc., N.Y.C., 1977-78; v.p. fin. George A. Fuller Co. div. Northrop Corp., N.Y.C., 1978-81, now pres., chief exec. officer, dir., 1981—. Past chmn. bd. trustees Marymount Manhattan Coll.; adv. bd. N.Y. Real Estate Inst.; bus. adv. coun. Lehigh U.; bus. coun. Lighthouse for the Blind; mem. Urban Land Inst. Mem. Am. Soc. C.P.A.s, N.Y. State Soc. C.P.A.s. Clubs: Lehigh U. of N.Y., Univ. (N.Y.C.). Home: 12 Dwight Ln Greenwich CT 06831 Office: Fuller Group Inc 451 Park Ave S New York NY 10016

MANGOLD, GLENN E., securities industry executive; b. Newark, June 22, 1942; s. Wilbur Ernest and Beverly Ruth (Martinson) M.; m. Diane Eleanor Fredricks, Dec. 7, 1963; children: Kimberly, Scott, Russell, Jill. BA, Rutgers U., 1963; MBA, NYU, 1969. Corp. trust adminstr. Chase Manhattan Bank, NA, N.Y.C., 1963-66, corp. trust officer, 1966-68, 2d v.p., 1968-73, v.p., 1973-80; sr. v.p. European Am. Bank, N.Y.C., 1980-84, Depository Trust Co., N.Y.C., 1985-88, 1988—. Home: 113 Sutton Dr Berkeley Heights NJ 07922 Office: Depository Trust Co Inc 55 Water St New York NY 10041

MANGOLD, JOHN FREDERIC, manufacturing company executive, former naval officer; b. La Grange, Ill., Jan. 24, 1927; s. John Frederic and Helvig Victoria (Anderson) M.; m. Margaret Ellen Gore, Oct. 25, 1947; children: John, Andrew, Jennifer. BS, U.S. Naval Acad., 1947; MSEE, U.S. Naval Postgrad. Sch., Monterey, Calif., 1958. Registered profl. engr., Conn. Commd. ensign USN, 1947, advanced through grades to comdr., 1962, comdg. officer nuclear submarine U.S.S. Halibut, 1962-63, comdg. officer nuclear tng. unit, 1963-67, ret., 1967; v.p. mfg. Combustion Engring., Inc., Windsor, Conn., 1972-78, group pres., 1982-86, v.p. utilty boilers, 1990-91; pres. Vetco, Inc., Ventura, Calif., 1978-82; cons., 1992; pres. Detrex Corp., Southfield, Mich., 1992-93, bd. dirs., 1993—; bd. dirs. Detrex Corp. Mem. IEEE, U.S.C. of C. (energy com. 1984-87). Republican. Office: 1000 Prospect Hill Rd Windsor CT 06095-1574

MANGOLD, ROBERT PETER, artist; b. North Tonawanda, N.Y., Oct. 12, 1937. Student, Cleve. Inst. Art, 1956-59; B.F.A. Yale U., 1961, M.F.A. 1964. Instr. art Sch. Visual Arts, N.Y.C., 1963—, Hunter Coll., 1964-65, Cornell U., Skowhegan Summer Art Sch., 1968. Exhbns. include, Whitney Mus. Am. Art, N.Y.C., 1968, 73, 79, 83, Albright-Knox Art Gallery, Buffalo, 1970, 78, Solomon R. Guggenheim Mus., N.Y.C., 1971, Documenta, Kassel, W. Ger., 1972, VI, 1977, VII, 1982, La Jolla Mus. Contemporary Art, 1974, Mus. Contemporary Art, Chgo., 1974, N.Y. Cultural Center, 1974, Mus. Modern Art, N.Y.C., 1975, 76, Sidney Janis Gallery, N.Y.C., 1977, Ink, Zurich, 1978, Kunsthalle Bielefeld, W. Ger., 1979, Paula Cooper Gallery, N.Y.C., 1982, 84, 91, Protetch-McIntosh, Washington, 1978, Berkeley & Newberger Mus., Purchase, N.Y., 1985-86, Bard Coll., 1985, Ritter Klagenfurt, Austria, 1992-93; one-person exhbn. Daniel Weinberg Gallery, Los Angeles, 1984, 92, Akron Art Mus., 1984, Lisson Gallery, London, 1990, Pace Gallery, 1992, Le Consortium Dijon, France, 1992, Acad. Inst. Arts & Letters, 1992; retrospective exhbn., Stedelijk Mus., Amsterdam, 1982; represented in permanent collections, Solomon R. Guggenheim Mus., Mus. Modern Art, Whitney Mus. Am. Art, N.Y.C., Mus. Fine Arts, Houston, La Jolla Mus. Contemporary Art, Tate Gallery, London, Stedelijk Mus., Contemp. Art Amsterdam, Stedelijk van Abbemuseum, Eindhoven, Kunsthaus, Zurich, Art Inst. Chgo., Rhona Hoffman Gallery, Chgo., Donald Young Gallery, Chgo., Tex. Gallery. Recipient award Nat. Council on Arts, 1966; Guggenheim grantee, 1969. also: care Shea & Beker Gallery 7th Fl 20 W 57th New York NY 10019

MANGOLD, SYLVIA PLIMACK, artist; b. N.Y.C., Sept. 18, 1938; d. Maurice and Ethel (Rein) Plimack; m. Robert Mangold. Student, Cooper Union, 1956-59; BFA, Yale U., 1961. Exhibited one-person shows Daniel Weinberg Gallery, San Francisco, 1974, Fischbach Gallery, N.Y.C.1974, 75, Annemarie Verna Gallery, Zurich, 1978, 91, Droll-Kolbert Gallery, N.Y.C., 1978, Young Hoffman Gallery, Chgo., 1980, Ohio State U., Columbus, 1980, Droll-Kolbert Gallery, N.Y.C., 1980, Pa. Acad., 1981, Contemporary Arts Mus., Houston, 1981, Madison Art Ctr. (Wis.), 1982, Brooke Alexander, Inc., 1982, 86, Duke Art Mus., N.C., 1982, Rhona Hoffman Gallery, Chgo., 1985, Tex. Gallery, 1986, Fuller Goldeen Gallery, San Francisco, 1987, Brooke Alexander, N.Y., 1989, U. Mich, Ann Arbor, 1992, Minn. inst. Arts, 1992, Grunwald Ctr. for Graphic Arts, UCLA, 1992, Neuberger Mus. Art, SUNY, Purchase, 1993, Davison Art Ctr., Wesleyan U., Middletown, Conn. 1993; group shows at Young Hoffman Gallery, Chgo., 1979, Walker Art Ctr., Mpls., 1979, Droll-Kolbert Gallery, 1979, Denver Art Mus., 1979, U. So. Calif., 1979, Honolulu Acad. Art, 1979, Oakland Mus., (Calif.), 1979,

Univ. Art Mus. of U. Tex.-Austin, 1979, Internat. Biennial Ljibljana, Yugoslavia, Phoenix Art Mus., 1979, Art Latitute Gallery, N.Y.C., 1980, Thorpe Intermedia Gallery, Sparkhill, N.Y., 1980, U. Colo. Art Galleries, Boulder, 1980, Nina Freudenheim Gallery, Buffalo, 1980, U.S. Pavillion of Venice Biennial, 1980-81, Inst. Contemporary Art of U. Pa., Phila, 1980-81, Yale U. Art Gallery, 1981, San Antonio Mus. Art, 1981, Indpls. Mus. Art, 1981, Tucson Mus. Art, 1981, Pa. Acad., 1981, Mus. Art of Carnegie Inst., Pitts., 1981, Brooke Alexander, Inc., N.Y.C., 1982, Ben Shahn Ctr. Visual Arts, 1982, Castle Gallery, Coll. of New Rochelle, N.Y., 1983, Thomas Segal Gallery, Boston, 1982-83, Siegel Contemporary Art, N.Y., 1983, Freedman Gallery, Albright Coll., Reading, Pa., 1983, Fuller Goldeen, San Francisco 1983, Yale U. Art Gallery, New Haven, 1983-84, 86, Wilcox Gallery, Swarthmore, Pa., 1984, The Hudson River Mus., Yonkers, N.Y., 1984, Sardonia Art Gallery, Wilkes Coll., Wilkes-Barre, Pa., 1985, Kent State U. Gallery, Ohio, 1985, Brooke Alexander, N.Y., 1985, John C. Stoller Co., Minn., 1985, Knight Gallery, Spirit Sq. Arts Ctr., Charlotte, N.C., 1986, Mus. Art, R.I. Sch. Design, Providence, 1986, Yale U. Gallery, 1986, CUNY, 1986-87, Lorence Monk Gallery, N.Y.C., Vanguard Gallery, Phila., 1986-087, Aldrich Mus., Ridgefield, 1986-87. Flander's Contemporary Art, Mpls., 1987, Annemarie Verna Galerie, Zurich, 1988, U. N.C., 1988, R.I Sch. Design, 1988, Grace Borgeniont Gallery, N.Y.C., 1988, Fay Gold Gallery, Atlanta, 1988, U. N.C., Greensboro, Three Rivers Arts Festival, Pitts., 1989, Cin. Art Mus., New Orleans Mus. Art, Denver Art Mus., Pa. Acad. Fine Arts, 1989, U. Mich., 1992, Mpls. Inst. Arts, 1992, Grunwald Ctr. Graphic Arts, UCLA, L.A., Neuberger Mus. Art, SUNY Purchase, 1993, Davisob Art Ctr., 1993; exhibited in permanent collections, Albright-Knox Art Gallery, Buffalo, Allen Meml. Art Mus., Oberlin, Ohio, Bklyn. Mus., Dallas Mus. Fine Arts, Detroit Inst. Art, Mus. Fine Arts, Houston, Indpls. Mus. Art, Madison (Wis.) Art Ctr., Milw. Art Mus., Yale U. Art Gallery, Mus. Modern Art, N.Y.C., Mus. Fine Arts, U. Utah, Tampa (Fla.) Mus., Walker Art Mus., Mpls., Whitney Mus. Am. Art, N.Y., Weatherspoon Art Gallery, Greensboro, N.C., Wadsworth Athenaeum, Hartford, U. Mich., Utah Mus. Fine Art. Work reviewed in newspapers and mags.

MANGONE, GERARD J., international and maritime law educator; b. N.Y.C., Oct. 10, 1918; s. Gerard Francis and Viola (Schumm) M.; m. Emma Haddad, Apr. 13, 1958; children—Cleopatra, Regina, Flaminia. A.B. CCNY, 1938; M.A., Harvard, 1947, Ph.D. (Charles Summer prize), 1949. Asst. prof. polit. sci. Wesleyan U., Middletown, Conn., 1948-51; assoc. prof. Swarthmore Coll., 1951-56; prof. polit. sci. and internat. relations Syracuse U., 1956-67; dir. grad. overseas tng. program, exec. asst. to dean Maxwell Grad. Sch., 1961-64, assoc. dean dir. internat. relations program, 1961-67; dean Coll. Liberal Arts, v.p.; provost Temple U., Phila., 1967-69; sr. fellow Woodrow Wilson Internat. Ctr., 1970-72; prof. internat. law U. Del., Newark, 1972-74, dir. Ctr. for Study of Marine Policy, 1973-89, H. Rodney Sharp prof. internat. law and orgn., 1975-89, univ. rsch. prof. internat. and maritime law, 1989—, coord. grad. studies, 1976-79; adj. prof. Maine Maritime Acad., 1992—; vis. prof. Trinity Coll., Mt. Holyoke Coll., Yale, Princeton, Johns Hopkins; Tagore law prof. U. Calcutta, 1979; disting. lectr. U. Ind., 1980; vis. scholar U. Western Australia, 1983, 87, Peking U., 1984, Capetown U., 1986, 89, U. Natal, 1989; mem. Presdl. Commn. Trust Territory Pacific, 1963; cons. AID, 1965-67, Nat. Commn. Marine Resources and Engring. and State Dept., 1967-73, UN, 1965, U.S. Corps Engrs., 1975; vice chmn. exec. com. Commn. Study Orgn. Peace; exec. dir. Pres.' Commn. on UN, 1970-71. Author: The Idea and Practice of World Government, 1951, A Short History of International Organization, 1954, The Elements of International Law, 2d edit, 1967, Marine Policy for America, 1977, 2d edit., 1989, Law for the World Ocean, 1981, Mangone's Concise Marine Almanac, 2d edit., 1991; co-author, editor: The Art of Overseasmanship, 1958, The Overseas Americans, 1960, European Political Systems, 1960, UN Administration of Economic and Social Programs, 1966, Energy Policies of the World, 3 vols, 1976-79, Internat. Straits of the World, 11 vols., 1978-89; editor: Future of Gas and Oil from Sea, American Strategic Minerals, 1984; editor in chief: Marine Policy Reports, 1981-91, Internat. Jour. Marine and Coastal Law, 1991— . Capt. AUS, 1942-46. Mem. Am. Soc. Internat. Law, Internat. Law Assn., Maritime Law Assn., Port of Wilmington Maritime Soc. (bd. dirs. 1980—, chmn. 1989), Francis Alison Soc. (sec. 1990—, award 1983), Del. Acad. Sci. (pres. 1993), Cosmos Club (Washington), Harvard Club (N.Y.C.). Home: 201 Unami Trl Newark DE 19711-7508 Office: Univ Del Grad Coll Marine Studi Newark DE 19716

MANGOUNI, NORMAN, publisher; b. Detroit, Oct. 19, 1932; s. Nazareth Lazarus and Isabelle (Garabedian) M.; m. Anahid Apelian, May 10, 1964; 1 child, Marie-Isabelle. A.B. U. Mich., 1954; M.S., Columbia U. 1955; postgrad., U. Mich. Law Sch., 1957-58. Reporter Ann Arbor (Mich.) News, 1957-59; editor Mich. Alumnus, U. Mich., Ann Arbor, 1959-62; sr. editor Coll. Entrance Exam. Bd., N.Y.C., 1962-64; dir. fin. aid U. Miami, Coral Gables, Fla., 1965-66; dir. State U. N.Y. Press, Albany, 1966-78; pres., gen. editor Scholars' Facsimiles & Reprints, Delmar, N.Y., 1972—; pres. Caravan Books, Delmar, 1972—; Acad. Resources Corp., Las Vegas, Nev., 1988—; corr. DuPont-Columbia Survey and Awards, 1976-78; rep. to com. on standards in field of library work, documentation and related pub. practices Am. Nat. Standards Inst., 1974-78; Exec. asst. to majority caucus Mich. State Senate, 1964. Co-translator: The Gaucho Martin Fierro, 1974; contbr. articles to profl. jours.; mem. editorial bd.: Ararat mag, 1962-66, 77-78. Served to lt. USAF, 1955-57. Mem. Modern Lang. Assn. Am., Middle East Studies Assn. N.Am., Mensa, Phi Sigma Kappa, Sigma Delta Chi, Phi Alpha Delta. Club: Rotary Internat. Home: 410 Lenawee Dr Ann Arbor MI 48104-1866 Office: PO Box 344 Delmar NY 12054-0344

MANGUM, JOHN K., lawyer; b. Phoenix, Mar. 7, 1942; s. Otto K. and Catherine F. Mangum; m. Deidre Jansen, Jan. 10, 1969; children: John Jansen, Jeffery Jansen. Student, Phoenix Coll. 1960-62; BS, U. Ariz., 1965, JD, 1969. Bar: Ariz. 1969. Sr. trial atty. criminal div. Maricopa County Atty.'s Office, Phoenix, 1969-71; ptnr. Carmichael, McClue and Stephens, P.C., Phoenix, 1972-74; sr. ptnr. O'Connor, Cavanagh, 1992-94, Phoenix; pvt. practice, Phoenix, 1994—; ct. commr., judge pro tem Maricopa County super. ct., Phoenix, 1974-78, spl. commr., 1979-82; legal csl. to speaker of Ariz. Ho. of Reps., Phoenix, 1975-86; mem. John K. Mangum and Assocs., P.C., Phoenix, 1974-92; sr. mem. O'Connor & Cavanaugh, 1992-94; pvt. practice, 1994—. Mem. Maricopa County Bd. Health, 1974-79, Ariz. State Commn. on Elected Ofcls. Salaries, 1987-93; chmn. curriculum com., mem. legal asst. adv. com. Phoenix Coll., 1973-75; legal counsel Maricopa County Rep. Com., 1986-90; mem. task force com. on career edn. Phoenix Mayor's Youth Commn., 1972-73; v.p. The Samaritans, 1984-87. Mem. State Bar Ariz. (exec. bd. young lawyers sect. 1974-76), Maricopa County Bar Assn. (pres. young lawyers sect. 1974-75, dir. 1973-75), Ariz. C. of C. (dir. 1974-79), Phoenix Country Club, Ariz. Club, Rotary. Republican. Office: 340 E Palm Ln # 100 Phoenix AZ 85004

MANGUS, RICHARD W., farmer; b. Lakeville, Ind., July 23, 1930; m. Mary E. Annis; children: Marsha S., Russell G., Richard D., Ronald L., Ryan D. Grad., Lakeville High Sch., 1948; student, Purdue U., 1949-51. Dairy farm mgr., operator Lakeville, 1946-87; truck driver Wyatt Trading Co., 1987—. Mem. Ind. Ho. of Reps., 1972—, mem. elections and apportionment com., environ. affairs com., nat. resources com., 1980-95, human affairs com., 1985-87, pub. policy com., 1975-78; chair office natural resources, 1995—. Named Legislator of Yr., Fraternal Order of Police, 1988, Legislator of Yr., Profl. Firefighters Assn., 1988, Sagamore of the Wabash, 1978, 88; recipient Dist. Soil and Water Conservation award, 1986, Environ. Achievement award Izaak Walton League, 1984, Outstanding Citizen of Yr. award Jaycees, 1978, Leadership 20-Yr. Svc. award 4-H, 1985, Friend of 4-H award. Mem. Lions, Masons, Scottish Rite, Order Ea. Star, Lakeville Commerce Assn., Toastmasters. Republican. Brethren Ch. Avocations: reading, speech making, sports. Home: 68735 Us Highway 31 Lakeville IN 46536-9726

MANHART, MARCIA Y(OCKEY), art museum director; b. Wichita, Kans., Jan. 14, 1943; d. Everett W. and Ruth C. (Correll) Yockey; children: Caroline Manhart Sanderson, Emily Alexandrea Morrison. BA in Art, U. Tulsa, 1965, MA in Ceramics, 1971. Dir. edn. Philbrook Art Ctr., Tulsa, 1972-77, exec. v.p., asst. dir., 1977-83, acting dir., 1983-84; exec. dir. Philbrook Mus. Art (formerly Philbrook Art Ctr.), Tulsa, 1984—; instr. Philbrook Art Ctr. Mus. Sch., Tulsa, 1963-72; gallery dir. Alexandre Hogue Gallery, Tulsa U., 1967-69; NEH Challenge Grant panelist, 1991, presenter to AAM Conv., 1991; MAAA Craft Fellowship panelist, 1988, 93, NEA

Craft Fellowship panelist, 1990; curator nat. touring exhibit Nature's Forms/Nature's Forces: The Art of Alexandre Hogue, 1984-85; co-curator internat. exhbn.: The Eloquent Object, 1987-90; curator Sanford and Diane Besser Collection exhbn., 1992. Vis. com. Smithsonian Instn./Renwick Gallery, Washington, 1986; cultural negotiator Gov. George Nigh's World Trade Mission (Okla.), China., 1985; com. mem. State Art Coll. of Okla., 1985—; mem. Assocs. of Hillcrest Med. Ctr., 1983-88, exec. com., 1985-88; com. mem. Neighborhood Housing Services, 1985-87; mem. Mapleridge Hist. Dist. Assn., 1982—; steering com. Harwelden Isnt. for Aesthetic Edn., 1983; com. mem. River Parks Authority, 1976; mem. Jr. League of Tulsa Inc., 1974-78; adv. panel mem. Nat. Craft Planning Project, NEA, Washington, 1978-81; craft adv. panel mem. Okla. Arts and Humanities Council, 1974-76; juror numerous art festivals, competitions, programs; reviewer Inst. Mus. Services, Washington, 1985, 88, 92; auditor Symposium on Language & Scholarship of Modern Crafts, NEA and NEH, Washington, 1981; nominator MacArthur Fellows Program, 1988. Recipient Harwelden award for Individual Contbrn. in the Arts, 1989, Gov.'s award State of Okla., 1992. Mem. Assn. Am. Mus., Assn. Art Mus. Dirs., Art Mus. Assn. Am., Mountain Plains Assn. Mus., Am. Craft Coun., Okla. Mus. Assn., Rotary. Office: Philbrook Mus Art PO Box 52510 Tulsa OK 74152-0510

MANHEIM, MARVIN LEE, business management educator, consultant; b. Elizabeth, N.J., May 14, 1937; s. Isadore and Jean (Litin) M.; m. Margaret Donovan, July 20, 1974; children: Susannah Leigh, Marisa Kara. BS, M.I.T., 1959, PhD in Transp. and Urban Planning, 1964. Rsch. asst. Joint Ctr. for Urban Studies, M.I.T.-Harvard U., 1959-64; asst. prof. civil engring. M.I.T., Cambridge, 1964-69, assoc. prof., 1969-73, prof., 1973-83, head transp. systems div., dept. civil engring., 1966-69, 78-81, dir. tech. and community values project, 1968-83; founding prin. Cambridge Systematics Inc., 1972—; William A. Patterson disting. prof. transp. Kellogg Grad. Sch. Mgmt. Northwestern U., Evanston, Ill., 1983—, prof. dept. civil engring., Transp. Ctr., 1983—; founding prin., dir. Cambridge Info. Internat., 1983-87; founding, prin., bd dirs. Cambridge Systematics Inc., chmn., 1987—; bd. dirs. Harper Group Inc.; steering com. Internat. Conf. Transp. Rsch., 1973, 1st, 2d, 3d, 4th, 5th, 6th World Confs. on Transp. Rsch.; mem. exec. com. Transp. Rsch. Bd., 1978-84; first pres. World Conf. on Transport Rsch. Soc., 1986—; cons. to industry, U.S. and fgn. govt. agys. and internat. orgns. Author: Hierarchical Structure: A Model of Planning and Design Processes, 1964; Fundamentals of Transportation Systems Analysis, 1979; editor: M.I.T. Press Series in Transportation; Proceedings of Internat. Transportation Research Forum, 1966; Proceedings of Internat. Conf. on Transportation Research, 1973; co-editor (with Daniel Brand) Travel Demand Forecasting, 1973. Capt. U.S. Army, 1964-66. Decorated Army Commendation medal; Samuel A. Stouffer fellow, MIT, Harvard U., 1962-64. Mem. Transp. Rsch. Forum (1st pres. New Eng. chpt.), Transp. Rsch. Bd., World Conf. on Transp. Rsch. Soc. (1st pres. 1986—), Inst. Mgmt. Sci., Coun. Logistics Mgmt., Strategic Mgmt. Soc. Jewish. Office: Kellogg Grad Sch Mgmt Northwestern Univ Evanston IL 60208

MANIATIS, THOMAS PETER, molecular biology educator; b. Denver, May 8, 1943; s. Peter T. and Jane V. (Swearingen) M.; m. Jessie Marion Klyce, Aug. 27, 1968; children: Ethan David, Silas Dana. BA, U. Colo., 1965, MA, 1967, PhD in Molecular Biology, Vanderbilt U., 1971. European molecular biology rsch. fellow Med. Rsch. Coun. Molecular Biology, Cambridge, England, 1973-74; NIH fellow Harvard U., 1971-73, rsch. assoc. in biology, 1974-75; asst. prof. Harvard U., Cambridge, Mass., 1975-77, prof. molecular biology, 1981—; sr. staff investigator Cold Spring Harbor Lab., N.Y., 1975-77; assoc. prof. Calif. Inst. Tech., Pasadena, 1977-79, prof., 1979-81; co-founder, advisor Genetics Inst., Boston, 1981—; chmn. dept. biochemistry and molecular biology Harvard U., 1985-88, prof. biochemistry and molecular biology, 1981—. Author: Molecular Cloning, 1982; assoc. editor: Cell. jour., 1978—. Recipient award Rita Allen Found., 1978; recipient Eli Lilly research award Am. Soc. Microbiology, 1981; Richard Lounsbery award for biology and medicine U.S. and French Acads. Sci., 1985. Fellow Am. Acad. Scis.; mem. Nat. Acad. Scis. Office: Harvard U Dept Molecular/Cellular Biology 7 Divinity Ave Cambridge MA 02138-2092*

MANIER, AUGUST EDWARD, philosophy of biology educator; b. Versailles, Ohio, Apr. 7, 1931; s. Francis Vitalis and Whilma Anna (Grillot) M.; m. Dorothy Frances Hickey, June 18, 1955 (div. June 1983); children: Michael, David, Maureen, August Edward Jr., John, Daniel, Jeremy; m. Jenny Ann Pitts, Oct. 18, 1985. BS with high honors, U. Notre Dame, 1953; PhD, St. Louis U., 1961. Lectr. Webster Coll., Webster Groves, Mo., 1956-59; instr. philosophy of biology U. Notre Dame, Ind., 1959-61, asst. prof., 1961-67, assoc. prof., 1967-88, prof., 1988—; NEH vis. fellow Cambridge (Eng.) U., 1971-72. Author: The Young Darwin and His Cultural Circle, 1978; author, editor: Academic Freedom and The Catholic University, 1968, Abortion: New Directions for Policy Studies, 1977. Precinct committeeman South Bend (Ind.) Dem. Com., 1970-80; pres. Woods and Wedge Neighborhood Assn., South Bend, 1975-77, East Side Little League Baseball, 1981-83. Fellow Nat. Humanities Inst., U. Chgo., 1977-78; grantee NSF, 1981-82, 87-88. Mem. AAAS (sec. history and philosophy of sci. 1989—), Am. Philos. Assn., Philosophy of Sci. Assn., History of Sci. Soc., Soc. for Social Studies of Sci. Home: 1444 Sunnymede Ave South Bend IN 46615-1020 Office: U Notre Dame 314 Decio Hall Notre Dame IN 46556-5644

MANIGAULT, PETER, media executive; b. Charleston, S.C., Jan. 13, 1927; s. Edward and Mary (Hamilton) M.; m. Landine Sanford Legendre, Aug. 8, 1959 (div.); children: Gabrielle, Pierre; m. Patricia Lucas Bennett, Dec. 14, 1986. A.B. Princeton U., 1950. With Eve. Post Pub. Co. and subs., Charleston, 1959—; pres., pub. Eve. Post Pub. Co. and subs., 1960-85, chmn., 1985—. Trustee Nat. Trust Historic Preservation, 1963, vice chmn., 1965-74. Served with USNR, 1945-46, 52-53; capt. Res. Decorated Legion of Merit with combat V; Order Mil. Merit (Republic of Korea). Mem. Nat. Audubon Soc. (dir. 1968-74). Office: The Post and Courier 134 Columbus St Charleston SC 29403-4809

MANILOFF, JACK, biophysicist, educator; b. Balt., Nov. 6, 1938; s. Boris and Edith (Cohen) M.; m. Sandra Sue Steele, Dec. 22, 1960; children: Beth Susan, Eric Steele. BA in Biology, Johns Hopkins U., 1960; MS in Biophysics, Yale U., 1964, PhD in Biophysics, 1965. Research assoc. in chemistry Brown U., Providence, 1964-66; asst. prof. microbiology Sch. Medicine and Dentistry, U. Rochester, N.Y., 1966-71; assoc. prof. Sch. Medicine and Dentistry, U. Rochester, 1971-79, prof., 1979—; lectr. Am. Soc. Microbiology Found., 1989-90; mem. Internat. Com. on Taxonomy of Viruses, 1975—, mem. exec. com., 1990—, chair bacterial virus subcom., 1993—; cons. subcom. on taxonomy of mycoplasmatales Internat. Com. Systematic Bacteriology, 1978—. Adv. bd. Archives of Virology, 1995—; contbr. articles to profl. jours. Recipient Research Career Devel. award USPHS, 1970-75; Fogarty Sr. Internat. fellow, 1987-88; Disting. vis. fellow Christ's Coll., Cambridge, Eng., 1987-88; Lady Margaret lectr. Christ's Coll., 1988. Mem. Am. Soc. Microbiology (chmn. mycoplasma divsn. 1993-94), Internat. Orgn. Mycoplasmology, Am. Soc. Virology, Sigma Xi. Office: Univ Rochester Med Ctr Dept Microbiology Box 672 Rochester NY 14642

MANILOW, BARRY, singer, composer, arranger; b. N.Y.C., June 17, 1946; s. Harold Pincus and Edna M. Student, N.Y. Coll. Music. Former positions include mailroom CBS; film editor WCBS-TV. Dir. music Callback series, Ed. Sullivan's Pilots; dir. music, condr., arranger, producer for Bette Midler, singer and composer; recorded hit songs: Can't Smile Without You, I Write the Songs, At the Copa (Grammy award, best male pop performance, 1979), Mandy, Looks Like We Made It; albums include Even Now, 1977, Manilow, 1985, 2 A.M. Paradise Cafe, 1985, Swing Street, 1987, Barry Manilow, 1989, Because It's Christmas, 1990, Showstoppers, 1991, The Complete Collection, Then Some, 1992, Manilow Box Set, 1992; star TV movie Copacabana, 1985; appeared TV specials The Barry Manilow Special (Emmy award, 1977), The Second Barry Manilow Special, also Big Fun on Swing Street, 1988, Barry Manilow: SRO on Broadway, 1989; TV appearances Murphy Brown, 1992; Broadway prodn.: Barry Manilow at the Gershwin, 1989; author Sweet Life: Adventures on the Way to Paradise; recipient Spl. Tony award, 1977, Ruby award After Dark mag. 1976, Photoplay Gold medal award 1976. Office: care Stiletto Ltd 11340 W Olympic Blvd Ste 210 Los Angeles CA 90064-1612*

MANINGER, R(ALPH) CARROLL, engineering executive, consultant; b. Harper, Kans., Dec. 24, 1918; s. Earl Dotterer and Mabel Velma (Haskin) M.; m. Jean Graves Kidder, July 1, 1942; children: Margaret Elisabeth, Mary Carroll, Emily Catherine. BS, Calif. Inst. Tech., 1941. Br. mgr. Gen. Precision Inc., Sunnyvale, Calif., 1953-62; head electronic engring. rsch. Lawrence Livermore Nat. Lab., Livermore, Calif., 1962-72, sr. scientist, 1972-85; owner Holidyne, Danville, Calif., 1985—. Contbr. articles to profl. jours.; patentee in field. Pres. Contra Costa (Calif.) Concert Guild, 1972-76. Fellow IEEE (life); mem. Nuclear and Plasma Scis. Soc. of IEEE (pres. 1980-82). Home and Office: Holidyne 146 Roan Dr Danville CA 94526-1915

MANION, DANIEL ANTHONY, federal judge; b. South Bend, Ind., Feb. 1, 1942; s. Clarence E. and Virginia (O'Brien) M.; m. Ann Murphy, June 29, 1984. BA, U. Notre Dame, 1964; JD, Ind. U., 1973. Bar: Ind., U.S. Dist. Ct. (no. dist.) Ind., U.S. Dist. Ct. (so. dist.) Ind. Dep. atty. gen. State of Ind., 1973-74; from assoc. to ptnr. Doran, Manion, Boynton, Kamm & Esmont, South Bend, 1974-86; judge U.S. Ct. Appeals (7th cir.), South Bend, 1986—. Mem. Ind. State Senate, Indpls., 1978-82. Home: 20725 Riverlan Rd South Bend IN 46637-1029 Office: US Ct Appeals 301 Federal Bldg 204 S Main St South Bend IN 46601-2122*

MANION, JERRY ROBERT, hotel chain executive; b. Mt. Vernon, Ill., Feb. 27, 1938; s. Frances Manion; m. Salley Trinkle, Dec. 30, 1964; children: Courtney Elizabeth, Patrick Robert. BBA, U. Ill., 1960; MS in Bus. Mgmt., So. Ill.U., 1962. Sr. v.p., franchise dir. Quality Inns Internat., Inc., Md., 1977-80; sr. v.p., dir. ops. Metro Hotels, Inc., Tex., 1980-83; pres. Economy Motor Inns, Inc., Tex., 1983-85; pres. hotel group Ramada Inc., Phoenix, 1985-89; exec. v.p. Motel 6 Ops., Dallas, 1989-93; exec. v.p. devel. Richfield Hotel Mgmt. Inc., Englewood, Colo., 1993-94; bd. trustees Ednl. Inst. Adv. Coun., Hotel Sch. No. Ariz. U. Mem. Am. Hotel & Motel Assn. Avocation: tennis. Office: Manion Investments 2701 E Camelback Ste 450 Phoenix AZ 85016

MANION, THOMAS A., college president; b. Aug. 10, 1934; m. Maureen O'Mara; children: Gregory, Marcy, Andrew, Margaret, Vicki, Tina, Thomas. B.B.A., St. Bonaventure U., 1959; M.B.A., Boston Coll., 1962; Ph.D., Clark U., 1968; D.Pedagogy, Bryant Coll., 1973. Chmn. econs. dept., dean grad. sch., acad. provost v.p. Bryant Coll., Smithfield, R.I.; pres. Coll. Saint Rose, Albany, N.Y., 1973-83; St. Norbert Coll., De Pere, Wis., 1983—; bd. dirs. Associated Kellogg Bank, Green Bay, Wis. Bd. dirs. Higher Edn. Aids Bd., State of Wis. Mem. NCAA, Nat. Assn. Ind. Colls. and Univs. (mem. common. on campus concerns), Am. Assn. Higher Edn., Am. Coun. Edn., Nat. Cath. Edn. Assn., Assn. Cath. Colls. and Univs., Coun. Ind. Colls. (bd. dirs.), Wis. Assn. Ind. Colls. and Univs. (pres.), Wis. Found. Ind. Colls., Delta Epsilon, Delta Mu Delta. Office: St Norbert Coll De Pere WI 54115

MANIRE, GEORGE PHILIP, bacteriologist, educator; b. Roanoke, Tex., Mar. 25, 1919; s. Ernest L. and Zera (Ballew) M.; m. Ruth Jacobs, Apr. 10, 1943; children—Sarah, Philip. B.S., N. Tex. State Coll., 1940, M.S., 1941; Ph.D., U. Calif. at Berkeley, 1949. Instr. Southwestern Med. Sch., U. Tex., Dallas, 1949-50; mem. faculty U. N.C. Med. Sch., Chapel Hill, 1950—; prof. bacteriology and immunology U. N.C. Med. Sch., 1959-89, asst. vice chancellor health affairs, 1965-66, chmn. dept., 1966-79, Kenan prof., 1971—, vice chancellor, dean grad. sch., 1979-87; vis. scientist Lister Inst., London, Eng., 1971-72; Fulbright Research scholar Statens Seruminstut, Copenhagen, Denmark, 1956; Alan Gregg Travel Fellow in med. edn. China Med. Bd., 1963-64; vis. prof. Inst. for Virus Research, Kyoto (Japan) U., 1963-64, Inst. for Virus Research, Kyoto (Japan) U. (Japan Soc. Promotion Sci.), 1979. Club: Cosmos (Washington). Research, publs. on chem. biol. and structural characteristics of chlamydiae, microbial pathogenesis. Home: 708 Coker Ln Chapel Hill NC 27514

MANIRE, JAMES MCDONNELL, lawyer; b. Memphis, Feb. 22, 1918; s. Clarence Herbert and Elizabeth (McDonnell) M.; m. Nathalie Davant Latham, Nov. 21, 1951 (div. 1979); children: James McDonnell, Michael Latham, Nathalie Manire Willard. LL.B., U. Va., 1948. Bar: Tenn. 1948, U.S. Supreme Ct. 1957. Pvt. practice Memphis, 1948—, city atty., 1968-71; of counsel Waring Cox, Memphis, 1986—. Editor in chief Va. Law Rev., 1947-48. Served to lt. comdr. USNR, 1941-46. Fellow Am. Coll. Trial Lawyers, Am. Bar Found. (life); mem. ABA, Tenn. Bar Assn. (pres. 1966-67), Memphis and Shelby County Bar Assn. (pres. 1963-64), Tenn. Bar Found. (charter), 6th Circuit Jud. Conf. (life), Raven Soc. Clubs: Memphis Country, Memphis Hunt and Polo. Home: 2927 Frances Pl Memphis TN 38111-2401 Office: Waring Cox Morgan Keegan 50 N Front St Memphis TN 38103-2126

MANIS, MELVIN, psychologist, educator; b. N.Y.C., Feb. 18, 1931; s. Alex and Hanna (Oyle) M.; m. Jean Denby, May 28, 1954; children: Peter Eugene, David Denby. AB in Psychology, Franklin and Marshall Coll., 1951; PhD, U. Ill., 1954. Instr. psychology U. Pitts., 1956-58; rsch. psychologist Ann Arbor VA Med. Ctr., Mich., 1958-89; prof. psychology U. Mich., Ann Arbor, 1966—, assoc. chair dept. psychology, 1990-91. Author: Cognitive Processes, 1966, An Introduction to Cognitive Psychology, 1971; editor Jour. Personality and Social Psychology, 1980-84. Served with USPHS, 1954-56. Mem. APA, Am. Psychol. Soc., Midwestern Psychol. Assn., Soc. Exptl. Social Psychology, AAUP, Phi Beta Kappa, Sigma Xi. Democrat. Jewish. Club: Racquet (Ann Arbor). Home: 20 Harvard Pl Ann Arbor MI 48104-1726 Office: U Mich Dept Psychology Ann Arbor MI 48109

MANISCHEWITZ, BERNARD, food products company executive; b. Cin., Dec. 24, 1913; s. Jacob U. and Pearl (Quitman) M.; m. Esther Manischewitz, July 19, 1932 (div.); children: Elaine (Mrs. Yehiel Sorki), Ruby (Mrs. Yitzchok Gass), Edith E. (Mrs. Howard Best); m. Beatrice Hoffman, Apr. 11, 1976. Certificate in factory mgmt, U. Cin., 1940; B.C.S., N.Y.U., 1944. Asst. supt. B. Manischewitz Co., 1934-42, dir., sec., 1942-49, pres., 1949-76, chmn. bd., 1976-78, chmn. exec. com. and chief exec. officer, 1978-80, chmn. bd., chmn. exec. com., cons., 1980—; Ofcl. del. 7th-11th Internat. Mgmt. Congresses. Chmn. Manhattan div. State of Israel Bonds, 1960-61. Mem. Chief Execs. Forum, Inc. Home: 17 Northwoods Ln Boynton Beach FL 33435 Home: 27 Moran Rd West Orange NJ 07052-2251 Office: One Manischewitz Plaza Jersey City NJ 07302

MANKA, RONALD EUGENE, lawyer; b. Wichita, Kans., Dec. 12, 1944; s. James Ashford and Jane Bunn (Meeks) M.; children: Kimberly Ann, Lora Christine; m. Linda I. Bailey, Mar. 11, 1995. BBA cum laude, U. Kans., 1967; JD cum laude, U. Mich., 1970. Bar: Conn. 1970, Mo. 1974, Kans. 1985. Assoc. Day, Barry & Howard, Hartford, Conn., 1970-73, Lathrop & Norquist, Kansas City, Mo., 1973-78; ptnr. Lathrop & Nordquist, Kansas City, Mo., 1979-82, 85—; group counsel Butler Mfg. Co., Kansas City, 1982-83, div. gen. mgr., 1983-84. Trustee, clk., elder Village Presbyn. Ch., Prairie Village, Kans.; pres. Genesis Sch., Kansas City, 1987-89; devel. chmn. Kansas City Friends of Alvin Ailey, 1987-89; chmn. Kansas City Mus., 1988-92; gen. counsel Spirit Festival, Kansas City, 1985-87, Kansas City C. of C., 1989—; pres. Ctr. for Mgmt. Assistance, Kansas City, 1991-93. Mem. ABA, Mo. Bar Assn. (alt. dispute resolution com. 1986—), Lawyers Assn. Kansas City, Silicon Prairie Tech. Assn. (bd. dirs. 1990-92), Homestead Country Club (pres. 1984-85). Republican. Avocations: bicycling, swimming. Office: Lathrop & Norquist 2345 Grand Ave Ste 2600 Kansas City MO 64108-2684

MANKEL, FRANCIS XAVIER, priest; b. Knoxville, Tenn., Nov. 8, 1935; s. George Whitehead Sr. and Willia Frances (Duncan) M. BA, St. Ambrose U., 1957; STB, St. Mary's Coll., Balt., 1959, STL, 1961; Med. Loyola Coll. Balt., 1965. Ordained priest, Roman Cath. Ch., 1961. Assoc. pastor Holy Ghost Ch., Knoxville, 1962-67; prin. Knoxville Cath. High Sch., 1967-79; pastor Sacred Heart Ch., Lawrenceburg, Tenn., 1979-84, St. John Neumann Ch., Knoxville, 1984-87, Sacred Heart Cathedral, Knoxville, 1987—; vicar gen., chancellor Cath. Diocese Knoxville, 1988—; supt. Cath. Schs., Diocese of Knoxville, 1989-92. Bd. dirs. Knoxville area chpt. ARC, 1986—. Mem. Am. Guild Organists, Knoxville Ministerial Assn. Home: 711 Northshore Dr SW Knoxville TN 37919-7549 Office: 417 Erin Dr Knoxville TN 37919

MANKIEWICZ, FRANK F., journalist; b. N.Y.C., May 16, 1924; s. Herman J. and Sara (Aaronson) M.; m. Holly Jolley, 1952 (div.); children: Joshua, Benjamin; m. Patricia O'Brien, 1988. A.B., UCLA, 1947; M.S., Columbia U., 1948; LL.B., U. Calif.-Berkeley, 1955. Bar: Calif. 1955, D.C. 1985. Engaged in journalism Washington and Los Angeles, 1948-52; practice law Beverly Hills, 1955-61; dir. Peace Corps, Lima, Peru, 1962-64; Latin Am. regional dir. Peace Corps, Washington, 1964-66; press sec. Senator Robert F. Kennedy, 1966-68; syndicated columnist and TV news commentator, 1968-71; nat. polit. dir. Presdl. campaign of Senator George McGovern, 1971-72; columnist Washington Post, 1976-77; pres. Nat. Pub. Radio, 1977-83; vice-chmn. Hill and Knowlton (formerly Gray and Co.), 1983—. Author: Perfectly Clear: Nixon from Whittier to Watergate, 1973, U.S. v. Richard M. Nixon: The Final Crisis, 1974, With Fidel: A Portrait of Castro and Cuba, 1975, Remote Control: Television and the Manipulation of American Life, 1977; contbr. articles to newspapers and mags. Served with inf. AUS, 1943-46. Office: Hill and Knowlton 1341 G St NW # 1100 Washington DC 20005-3105

MANKILLER, WILMA PEARL, tribal leader; b. Stilwell, Okla., Nov. 18, 1945; d. Charley and Clara Irene (Sitton) M.; m. Hector N. Olaya, Nov. 13, 1963 (div. 1975); children: Felicia Marie Olaya, Gina Irene Olaya; m. Charlie Soap, Oct. 13, 1986. Student Skyline Coll., San Bruno College, Calif., 1973, San Francisco State Coll., 1973-75; B.A. in Social Sci., Flaming Rainbow Coll., Okla., 1977; postgrad. U. Ark., 1979. Community devel. dir. Cherokee Nation, Tahlequah, Okla., 1977-83; dep chief, 1983-85, prin. chief, 1985-87; pres. Inter-Tribal Council Okla.; mem. exec. bd. Council Energy Resource Tribes; bd. dirs. Okla. Indsl. Devel. Commn. Bd. dirs. Okla. Acad. for State Goals, 1985—. Author: Mankiller: A Chief and Her People, 1993. Recipient Donna Nigh First Lady award Okla. Commn. for Status of Women, 1985, Am. Leadership award, Harvard U., 1986; inducted Okla. Women's Hall of Fame, 1986. Mem. Cherokee County Democratic Women's Club, Nat. Tribal Chairmen's Assn., Nat. Congress Am. Indians. Avocations: reading; writing. Office: Cherokee Prin Chief PO Box 948 Tahlequah OK 74465-0948*

MANKIN, CHARLES JOHN, geology educator; b. Dallas, Jan. 15, 1932; s. Green and Myla Carolyn (Bohmert) M.; m. Mildred Helen Hahn, Sept. 6, 1953; children: Sally Carol, Helen Francis, Laura Kay. Student, U. N.Mex., 1949-50; B.S., U. Tex. at Austin, 1954, M.A., 1955, Ph.D., 1958. Asst. prof. geology Calif. Inst. Tech., 1958-59; asst. prof. geology U. Okla., 1959-63, asso. prof., 1963-64, prof., 1964—; dir. Sch. Geology and Geophysics, 1963-77, Energy Resources Inst., 1978-87; mem. U.S. Nat. Commn. on Geology, 1977-80; dir. Okla. Geol. Survey, 1967—; former chmn. bd. mineral and energy resources, former mem. commn. on phys. sci., math. and resources Nat. Acad. Scis.; former commr. Fiscal Accountability of Nation's Energy Resources; former chmn. Royalty Mgmt. Adv. Com. Dept. Interior; bd. dirs. Environ. Inst. for Waste Mgmt. Studies, U. Ala. Contbr. articles profl. jours. Recipient Conservation Service award Dept. Interior, 1983. Fellow Geol. Soc. Am. (co-project leader Decade N.Am. Geology, former councillor, chmn. found.), Mineral. Soc. Am.; mem. Am. Assn. Petroleum Geologists (Pub. Service award 1988), Am. Inst. Profl. Geologists (v.p., past pres., Martin Van Couvering Meml. award 1988, mem. found.), Clay Minerals Soc., Geochem. Soc., AAAS, Assn. Am. State Geologists (past pres.), Am. Geol. Inst. (past pres., Ian Campbell medal 1987), Soc. Econ. Paleontologists and Mineralogists (past pres. Mid-Continent sect.), Sigma Gamma Epsilon (nat. sec.-treas.). Home: 2220 Forister Ct Norman OK 73069-5120 Office: Okla Geol Survey Energy Ctr 100 E Boyd St Rm 131N Norman OK 73019-0628

MANKIN, HART TILLER, federal judge; b. Cleve., Dec. 26, 1933; s. Howard Edmonn and Fantine (Tiller) M.; m. Ruth A. Larson, Aug. 14, 1954; children: Margaret, Theodore, Susan. Student, Northwestern U., 1950-52; BA, U. South, 1954, cert. edn. for ministry, 1982; JD, U. Houston, 1960. Bar: Tex. 1960, D.C. 1971, U.S. Supreme Ct. 1968. Pvt. practice Houston, 1960-67; counsel, asst. to pres. Triumph Industries, Houston, 1967-69; gen. counsel GSA, Washington, 1969-71, Dept. Navy, Washington, 1971-73; adminstrv. conf. of U.S. U.S., 1970-71; v.p., gen. counsel Columbia Gas System, Wilmington, Del., 1973-89; assoc. judge U.S. Ct. Vets. Appeals, 1990—; bd. dirs. Del. Trust Co., 1978-89; adj. prof. Sch. Law Widener U., 1989-90. Bd. dirs. Widener U. Law Sch., Del. Humanities Coun., chmn., 1980-82, Am. Ctr. for Enterprise Edn., Inc., chmn. 1985-89. With USAF, 1954-57. Recipient spl. achievement award GSA, 1970, Disting. Pub. Svc. award Dept. Navy, 1973. Mem. ABA, State Bar Tex., D.C. Bar Assn., Fed. Bar Assn., Maritime Law Assn., U.S., Del. State C. of C. (chmn. 1981-83), Fed. Am. Inn of Ct. (master), Army and Navy Club, U.S. Croquet Assn. Episcopalian. Home: 3935 Ivy Terrace Ct NW Washington DC 20007-2139 Office: US Court of Veterans Appeals 625 Indiana Ave NW Washington DC 20004

MANKIN, HENRY JAY, physician, educator; b. Pitts., Oct. 9, 1928; s. Hyman Isaac and Mary (Simons) M.; m. Carole Jane Pinkney, Aug. 20, 1952; children: Allison Joan, David Philip, Keith Pinkney. B.S magna cum laude, U. Pitts., 1952, M.D., 1953; M.A. (hon.), Harvard U., 1973. Diplomate Am. Bd. Orthopaedic Surgery. Intern U. Chgo. Clinics, 1953-54; resident orthopaedics Hosp. for Joint Diseases, N.Y.C., 1957-60; instr. orthopaedics U. Pitts. Sch. Medicine, 1960-62, asst. prof., 1962-64, assoc. prof., 1964-66; dir., prof. orthopaedics Hosp. for Joint Diseases and Mt. Sinai Sch. Medicine, 1966-72; chief orthopaedics Mass. Gen. Hosp., Boston, 1972—; Edith M. Ashley prof. orthopaedics Harvard Med. Sch., 1972—; mem. surgery B study sect. NIH, 1969-73; mem. adv. com. on surg. treatment FDA, 1973-75; corporator Boston Five Cent Savs. Bank, 1982-83; mem. exec. com. Med. Bd. Med. Spltys., 1982-85; adv. council on grad. med. edn., 1986—; mem. Nat. Arthritis Avd. Bd., 1986-89; mem. human resources and research rev. group A Nat. Inst. Arthritis, Metabolism and Digestive Diseases, 1981-85, chmn., 1983-85. Assoc. editor Arthritis and Rheumatism, 1967-77, Jour. Bone and Joint Surgery, 1967-82; mem. editorial bd. Jour. Orthopedic Research, 1982-85; trustee Jour. Bone and Joint Surgery, 1985-91, chmn. bd., 1988-91; contbr. numerous articles to profl., med. jours. Served to lt. comdr. USNR, 1955-57. Fellow ACS, Royal Coll. Surgeons (hon.); mem. Am. Acad. Orthopaedic Surgeons, Acad. Orthopaedic Soc. (pres. 1991-92), Am. Orthopaedic Assn. (pres. 1982-83), Orthopaedic Research Soc. (pres. 1969-70), Musculoskeletal Tumor Soc. (pres. 1991-92), Brit. Orthopaedic Research Soc., Argentine Orthopedic Assn. (hon.), N.Y. Acad. Medicine (chmn. orthopaedic sect. 1971-72), Am. Rheumatism Assn., Soc. Internat. Chirurgerie Orthopaedice et Traumatologia, Hip Soc., Interurban, Forum Orthopaedic clubs, Brit. Orthopaedic Assn. (hon.), Can. Orthopaedic Assn. (hon.), Australian Orthopaedic Assn. (hon.), N.Z. Orthopaedic Assn. (hon.), Japanese Orthopaedic Assn. (hon.), Israel Orthopaedic Assn. (hon.), Thai Orthopaedic Assn (hon.). Home: 185 Dean Rd Brookline MA 02146-4201 Office: Mass Gen Hosp 32 Fruit St Boston MA 02114-2620

MANKIN, ROBERT STEPHEN, financial executive; b. N.Y.C., Mar. 26, 1939; s. Samuel Harry Mankin and Dorothy (Rosenblum) Goldstein; m. Joyce Marie Cabel, June 13, 1971; children: Seth Howard, Laura Nicole, Gina Danielle. BA cum laude, Bklyn. Coll., 1961; MBA, Bernard Baruch Coll., 1970; Dr. Profl. Studies with distinction, Pace U., 1982. Mgr. ABC, N.Y.C., 1969-71, Babcock and Wilcox, N.Y.C., 1971-74; v.p. Chase Manhattan Bank, N.Y.C., 1974-84; sr. v.p. 1st Interstate Bank, N.Y.C., 1984-87; mng. dir., sr. v.p., co-head fixed income mem. mgmt com. Nomura Securities Internat., N.Y.C., 1987-94; mng. dir. Paine Webber, N.Y.C., 1994—; bd. dirs. sec. Nomura Mortgage Capital Corp. N.Y.C.; bd. dirs. pres., CEO Nomura Asset Capital Corp. N.Y.C. Contbr. articles to profl. jours. Mem. Planning Forum, Assn. for Computing Machinery, Assn. Computer Programmers and Analysts (chmn. bd. 1971). Home: 21 Shield Dr Woodcliff Lake NJ 07675-8127 Office: Paine Webber 1285 Ave of Americas New York NY 10019

MANKO, JOSEPH MARTIN, SR., lawyer; b. Phila., Oct. 7, 1939; s. Horace David and Vivian (Greenberg) M.; m. Lynn Kimmelman, June 17, 1962; children: Joseph Jr., Glenn, Wendy. BA magna cum laude, Yale U., 1961; JD cum laude, Harvard U., 1964. Bar: Pa. 1964. Regional counsel EPA, Phila., 1973-75; assoc. Wolf, Block, Schorr & Solis-Cohen, Phila., 1964-72, ptnr., 1972-73, 75-89, chmn. environ. law, 1978-89; founding ptnr. Manko, Gold & Katcher, Phila., 1989—; adj. prof. U. Pa. Law Sch., 1988—. Grant Irey lectr., 1989-90; dir. Pa. Environ. Council, Phila., 1978-85, treas., 1986-87, pres., 1987-89, chmn. 1989—; chair or co-chair numerous environ.

bar assn. coms. Commr. Lower Merion Twp., Ardmore, Pa., 1979-91, 1994—, v.p., 1992, pres. 1993; mem. Com. of 70, Phila., 1978-88; pres. Beth David Reform Congregation, Gladwyne, Pa., 1983-86, trustee, 1978-83, 1986—; trustee Fedn. Jewish Agys., Phila., 1982-86; bd. dirs. Golden Slipper Camp, 1981-84, 88—, Jewish Community Rels. Coun., 1983-88, Lower Merion-Narberth Watershed, 1978—, Delaware River Basin Water Resources Assn., 1993—; mem. Dem. State Com., 1986-90. Mem. ABA, Pa. Bar Assn., Phila. Bar Assn., Phi Beta Kappa. Clubs: Germantown Cricket, Bala Golf (Phila.), Hamilton Bridge, Vesper. Avocations: tennis, golf, walking, classical music. Home: 96 E Levering Mill Rd Bala Cynwyd PA 19004-2611 Office: Manko Gold & Katcher 401 E City Ave Ste 500 Bala Cynwyd PA 19004-1167

MANKOFF, ALBERT WILLIAM, cultural organization administrator, consultant; b. Newark, Aug. 24, 1926; s. Albert and Dorothy M.; m. Audrey Emery, Mar. 18, 1972; 1 child, Robert Morgan. BLS, U. Okla., 1967. With Am. Airlines, Inc., 1947-69; mgr. mgmt. tng. and devel. Am. Airlines Inc., 1957-67; mgr. orgn. devel. Am. Airlines, Inc., Tulsa, 1968-69; dir. personnel Peat, Marwick, Mitchell & Co., Chgo., 1969-72; ptnr. Lexicon, Inc. Cons., Raleigh, N.C., 1972-77; Pacific area mgr. safety and tng. Trailways, Inc. L.A., 1978-80; tng. cons. State of Sacramento, Sacramento, 1980-91; pres. Inst. Am. Hist. Tech., Ojai, Calif., 1987—. Author: Trolley Treasures, 4 vols., 1986-87, The Glory Days, 1989, Tracks of Triumph, 1993, Tarnished Triumph, The Edison Paradigm, 1994, Sacramento's Shining Rails; contbr. articles to profl. jours. Bd. dirs., v.p. OASIS; Midwest Centre for Human Potential, Chgo., 1970-72, Tulsa Urban League, 1962-69; v.p. bd. dirs. Meditation Groups Inc., Ojai, Calif., Psychosynthesis Internat., Ojai Internat. Assn. Managerial and Orgnl. Psychosynthesis, Thousand Oaks, Calif. Avocations: street car and light rail technology, historical trolley photographs, cat humor. Home and Office: PO Box 494 Ojai CA 93024-0494 *Personal philosophy: I believe that the love principle is the most powerful force in the universe, and fear is the most destructive; that we create our own heaven or hell as a consequence of our thought; that we die and are reborn countless times until we master life in the human framework.*

MANKOFF, RONALD MORTON, lawyer; b. Gettysburg, S.D., Oct. 13, 1931; s. Harry B. and Sarah (Frank) M.; m. Joy Faith Shechtman, Nov. 3, 1959; children: Jeffrey Walker, Douglas Frank. BSL, U. Minn., 1952; LLM in Taxation, NYU, 1959. Bar: Minn. 1954, Tex. 1959. With Leonard, Street & Deinard, Mpls., 1957-58; research analyst Inst. Jud. Adminstrn., N.Y.C. 1958-59; assoc. Lyne, Blanchette, Smith & Shelton, Dallas, 1959-60; ptnr. Durant and Mankoff, Dallas, 1960-85; pres. Brice & Mankoff P.C., Dallas, 1985-89, Mankoff, Hill, Held & Metzger, L.L.P., Dallas, 1989—; chmn./gen. counsel Remodeler's Acceptance Corp., 1994—; lectr. law So. Meth. U., 1974-77; speaker in field. Contbr. articles to profl. jours. Chmn. bd. Dallas chpt. Am. Cancer Soc., 1976-77; chmn. Dallas crusade, 1974-75, bd. dirs., mem. exec. com., 1963-88; bd. dirs. Tex. div. Am. Cancer Soc., 1981-94; mem. bd. Dallas Mcpl. Library, 1973-75; exec. com. Dallas Citizens Charter Assn., 1971-75; pres. Dallas Arts Found., Inc., 1973-75; mem. exec. com. Nat. Pooled Income Fund, Council Jewish Welfare Fedns. and Funds, 1975-77; adv. dir. Dallas Community Chest Trust Fund, 1976-78; chmn. Found. Dallas Jewish Fedn., 1976-77; pres. Temple Emanu-el, Dallas, 1977-79; bd. dirs. Jewish Fedn. Greater Dallas, 1977-79, Dallas Civic Opera, 1981-83, World Union Progressive Judaism, 1981-90; mem. S.W. regional liaison com. IRS, 1980-83; exec. com. Union Am. Hebrew Congregations, 1979-89, trustee, 1979—, chmn. nat. coll. com., 1983-87, vice chmn. bd. dirs., 1984-88; sec. Dallas Assembly, 1979-84; exec. com. Jewish Community Relations Council 1982-83, Com. for Qualified Judiciary, 1982— sec. Child Care Partnership, 1984-86, bd. dirs. 1986-88; bd. dirs., Dallas Women's Found., 1985-89, adv. coun. 1989—; bd. dirs. Am. Jewish Com., 1982-88, pres. adv. coun. Dallas chpt. 1986-90; bd. dirs. Girl Scouts U.S., Tex. council 1982-85, Goodwill Industries of Greater Dallas, 1979-83; mem. Mayor's Task Force on Child Care, 1988; bd. govs. Dallas Symphony Assn., 1988—; chmn. Temple Emanu El Found., 1988—. Lt. (j.g.) USN, 1954-57. Mem. ABA, State Bar Tex., Dalls Bar Assn., North Dallas C. of C. (adv. bd. 1986-88), Columbian Country Club (bd. dirs. 1967-73), Zeta Beta Tau, Delta Sigma Rho. Democrat. Jewish. Home: 22 Lakeside Park Dallas TX 75225-8109 Office: One Tutle Creek Village 3878 Oak Lawn Ave Fl 4 Dallas TX 75219-4460

MANLEY, AUDREY FORBES, physician; b. Jackson, Miss., Mar. 25, 1934; d. Jesse Lee and Ora Lee (Buckhalter) Forbes; m. Albert Edward Manley, Apr. 3, 1970. A.B. with honors (tuition scholar), Spelman Coll., Atlanta, 1955; M.D. (Jesse Smith Noyes Found. scholar), Meharry Med. Coll., 1959; MPH, Johns Hopkins U.-USPHS traineeship, 1987; LHD (hon.), Tougaloo (Miss.) Coll., 1990, Meharry Med. Coll., Nashville, 1991; LLD (hon.), Spelman Coll., 1991. Diplomate: Am. Bd. Pediatrics. Intern St. Mary Mercy Hosp., Gary, Ind., 1960; from jr. to chief resident in pediatrics Cook County Children's Hosp., Chgo., 1960-62; NIH fellow neonatology U. Ill. Rsch. and Ednl. Hosp. Chgo., 1963-65; staff pediatrician Chgo. Bd. Health, 1963-66; practice medicine specializing in pediatrics Chgo., 1963-66; assoc. Lawndale Neighborhood Health Ctr. North, 1966-67; asst. med. dir., 1967-69; asst. prof. Chgo. Med. Coll., 1966-67; instr. Pritzker Sch. Medicine, U. Chgo., 1967-69; asst. dir. ambulatory pediatrics, asst. dir. pediatrics Mt. Zion Hosp. and Med. Center, San Francisco, 1969-70; med. cons. Spelman Coll., 1970-71, med. dir. family planning program, chmn. health careers adv. com., 1972-76; med. dir. Grady Meml. Hosp. Family Planning Clinic, 1972-76; with Health Services Adminstrs., Dept. Health and Human Services, 1976—; command. officer USPHS, 1976—; chief genetic diseases services br. Office Maternal and Child Health, Bur. Community Health Services, Rockville, Md., 1976-81; acting assoc. adminstr. clin. affairs Office of Adminstr. Health Resources and Services Adminstrn., 1981-83, chief med. officer, dep. assoc. adminstr. planning, evaluation and legis., 1983-85; sabbatical leave USPHS Johns Hopkins Sch. Hygiene and Pub. Health, 1986-87; dir. Nat. Health Service Corps.; asst. surgeon gen., 1988; dep. asst. Sec. for Health USPHS/HHS, 1989-93, acting asst. Sec. Health, 1993, dep. asst. Sec. Health/intergovtl. affairs, 1993-94; dep. surgeon gen., acting dep. asst. sec. for minority health USPHS, 1994-95; acting surgeon gen., 1995—; mem. U.S. del. UNICEF, 1990-94. Author numerous articles, reports in field. Trustee Spelman Coll., 1966-70. Recipient Meritorious Svc. award USPHS, 1981, Mary McLeod Bethune award Nat Coun. Negro Women, 1979, Dr. John P. McGovern Ann. Lectureship award Am. Sch. Health Assn., Disting. Alumni award Meharry Med. Coll., 1989, Spelman Coll. 108 Founder's Day Convocation, 1989, Disting. Svc. medal USPHS, 1992, Hildrus A. Poindexter award OSG/PHS, 1993, numerous other svc. and achievement awards. Fellow Am. Acad. Pediatrics; mem. Nat. Inst. Medicine of Nat. Acad. Sci., Nat. Med. Assn., APHA, AAUW, AAAS, Spelman Coll. Alumnae Assn., Meharry Alumni Assn., Operation Crossroads Africa Alumni Assn., Delta Sigma Theta (hon.). Home: 2807 18th St NW Washington DC 20009-2205 Office: 200 Independence Ave SW Washington DC 20201-0004

MANLEY, FRANK, English language educator; b. Scranton, Pa., Nov. 13, 1930; s. Aloysius F. and Kathryn L. (Needham) M.; m. Carolyn Mary Holliday, Mar. 14, 1952; children: Evelyn, Mary. B.A., Emory U., 1952, M.A., 1953; Ph.D., Johns Hopkins U., 1959. Instr., then asst. prof. Yale U. New Haven, 1959-64; assoc. prof., then prof. dept. English Emory U., Atlanta, 1964—; chmn. dept. Emory U., 1968-70, Candler prof. English, 1982—, dir. creative writing program, 1990—. Editor: The Anniversaries (John Donne), 1963, A Dialogue of Comfort (St. Thomas More), vol. 12, 1977 and Epistola ad Pomeranum, vol. 7, 1990, Yale edit. More's complete works; author: Resultances, 1980 (Devins award for poetry 1980), Two Masters (co-winner Gt. Am. New Play Contest 9th Ann. Humana Festival New Am. Plays 1985), (with F. Watkins) Some Poems and Some Talk About Poetry, 1985, Within the Ribbons: 9 Stories, 1989, (play) The Trap, 1993. With U.S. Army, 1952-55. Guggenheim Found. fellow, 1966-67, 78-79. Mem. MLA, AAUP. Roman Catholic. Home: 401 Adams St Decatur GA 30030-5207 also: RR5 Box 228 Ellijay GA 30540 Office: Emory U Dept English Atlanta GA 30322

MANLEY, GERTRUDE ELLA, librarian, media specialist; b. Phila., Dec. 29, 1930; d. William Eugene and Anna G. (Price) Lomas; m. Harley E. Manley, Jr., July 20, 1957; children: Marc Alan, Karen Sue Manley Thornton, Gail Ann Manley Rivera. BRE, Shelton Coll., 1955; MSEd, Queens Coll., 1958, MS in Libr. Edn., 1958; postgrad. various. Libr. tchr. Plainedge (N.Y.) Sch. Dist., 1955-60; libr. dir. Huntington (N.Y.) Christian Sch., 1968-70; libr./media specialist Connetquot Ctrl. Sch. Dist. of Islip, Bohemia, N.Y., 1970—. Editor: Manley Family Newsletter, 1983—; contbr.

articles to profl. jours. Mem. nursery sch. bd. New Life Community Ch. Nursery Sch., Sayville, N.Y., 1985-89; administr. pre-sch. story time program, E.J. Bosti Sch., Bohemia, 1972—; sign lang. instr., 1988—, Huffine award chairperson, 1985—; spell bee judge, 1984—; arranger speakers program, 1988—; kindergarten screening participant, 1988—, numerous in-house site-base planning and mgmt. coms., 1990-93. Mem. N.Y. State Ret. Tchrs. Assn. (life), Western Suffolk Ret. Tchrs. Assn. (life), Connetquot Tchrs. Assn. (life). Women scholarship coin. 1978-93), Connetquot Ret. Tchrs. Assn. (sec. 1993—). Baptist/Reformed Ch. of Am. Avocations: family history rsch., genealogy, authoring history articles, reading. Home: 171 Nathan Dr Bohemia NY 11716-1319 Office: Connetquot Ctrl Sch Dist Islip 780 Ocean Ave Bohemia NY 11716-3631

MANLEY, JOAN A(DELE) DANIELS, retired publisher; b. San Luis Obispo, Calif., Sept. 23, 1932; d. Carl and Della (Weinmann) Daniels; m. Jeremy C. Lanning, Mar. 17, 1956 (div. Sept. 1963); m. Donald H. Manley, Sept. 12, 1964 (div. 1985); m. William G. Houlton, May 31, 1991. BA, U. Calif., Berkeley, 1954; DBA (hon.), U. New Haven, 1974; LLD (hon.), Babson Coll., 1978. Sec. Doubleday & Co., Inc., N.Y.C., 1954-60; sales exec. Time Inc., 1960-66, v.p.; 1971-75, group v.p., 1975-84, also bd. dir.; circulation dir. Time-Life Books, 1966-68, dir. sales, 1968-70, pub., 1970-76; chmn. bd. Time-Life Books Inc., 1976-80; vice chmn. bd. Book-of-the-Month Club, Inc., N.Y.C., until 1984; supervising dir. Time-Life Internat. (Nederland) B.V., Amsterdam, until 1984; bd. dirs. Scholastic Inc., Viking Office Products Inc., AON Corp., Sara Lee Corp., BFP Holdings, Inc. Past trustee Mayo Found., Rochester, Minn., Nat. Repertory Orch., William Benton Found.; former mem. adv. coun. Stanford U. Bus. Sch., Haas Sch. Bus. U. Calif.; trustee Vail Valley Inst., Keystone Ctr. Named to Direct Mktg. Hall of Fame, 1993; U. Calif.-Berkeley fellow, 1989. Mem. Assn. Am. Pubs. (past chmn.).

MANLEY, JOHN, Canadian government official; b. Ottawa, Ontario, Canada, Jan. 5, 1950; s. John Joseph Manley and Mildred Charlotte (Scharf) M.; m. Judith Mary Rae, April 21, 1973; children: Rebecca Jane, David John, Sarah Kathleen. Attended, Carleton U., U. Ottawa. Law clerk for Rt. Hon. Bora Laskin Chief Justice Can., 1976-77; chair Ottawa-Carleton Bd. Trade, 1985-86; min. industry Canada, 1993—. elected to H. of C. g.e., 1988. Office: Industry Canada, CD Howe Bldg 235 Queen St, Ottawa, ON Canada K1A 0H5 also: 211-1800 Bank St, Ottawa, ON Canada KIV 0W3*

MANLEY, JOHN FREDERICK, political scientist, educator; b. Utica, N.Y., Feb. 20, 1939; s. John A. and Gertrude Manley; children from previous marriage: John, Laura; m. Kathy Lynn Sharp, 1991; 1 child, Cole Sharp Manley. B.S., Le Moyne Coll., 1961; Ph.D., Syracuse U., 1966. Asst. prof. polit. sci. U. Wis., 1966, assoc. prof., 1969-71; prof., chmn. dept. polit. sci. Stanford U., 1977-80; fellow Center for Advanced Study in Behavioral Scis., 1976-77. Author: The Politics of Finance, 1970, American Government and Public Policy, 1976; author, co-editor: The Case Against the Constitution, 1987. Congressional fellow, 1963-64; Brookings Instn. fellow, 1965-66; Guggenheim fellow, 1974-75; Fulbright fellow U. Bologna, 1992. Office: Stanford U Dept Polit Sci Stanford CA 94305

MANLEY, JOHN HUGO, computing technology executive, educator; b. Highland Park, Mich., July 9, 1932; s. Hugo Edward and Linda Amelia (Kuure) M.; m. Josephine Theresa Catanzaro, Sept. 3, 1958; children: Lisa Linn, Michele Ann, John David, Marc Darrin. B. Metall. Engring., Cornell U., 1955; MS Indsl. Engring., U. Pitts., 1965, PhD, 1971. Metall. engr. GE, Schenectady, N.Y., 1955-56; commd. 2d lt. USAF, 1956, advanced through grades to 1t. col., 1973, ret., 1976; asst. to dir. Johns Hopkins Applied Physics Lab., Laurel, Md., 1976-80; exec. ITT Corp., Stratford, Conn., 1980-83; v.p. Nastec Corp., Southfield, Mich., 1983-85; dir. Software Engring. Inst. Software Engring. Inst. Carnegie Mellon U., Pitts., 1985-87; pres., chmn. Computing Tech. Transition, Inc., Wilmington, Del., 1983—; prof. manufacturing and info. tech. systems engring., dir. mfg. sys. engring. prog. U. Pitts., 1987—; mem. tech. adv. bd. Tartan Labs., Inc., Pitts., Concurrent Techs. Corp., Johnstown, Pa.; mem. com. on nat. weather svc. modernization NRC, 1991-94. Editor-in-chief Jour. Systems and Software, 1978-82; contbr. articles to profl. jours. Pres. Point Field Community Assn., Millersville, Md., 1979-80; v.p. Greater Severna Park Coun., Severna Park, Md., 1980. Lt. col. USAF, 1955-76, Vietnam. Decorated Legion of Merit, Bronze Star. Mem. IEEE Computer Soc. (TC exec. bd.), Soc. Mfg. Engrs., Assn. Computing Machinery, Am. Soc. Engring. Edn., Pitts. Athletic Assn. Republican. Episcopalian.

MANLEY, RICHARD WALTER, insurance executive; b. Malone, N.Y., Dec. 26, 1934; s. Walter E. and Ruth (St. Mary) M.; m. Linda Kimberlin, Dec. 18, 1965; children: Stephanie, Christopher. BS in Bus., U. So. Miss., 1960. Cert. real estate broker. Account exec. Colonial Life and Accident, Hattiesburg, Miss., 1960-63; dist. mgr. Colonial Life and Accident, Oklahoma City, 1963-66; regional dir. Colonial Life and Accident, Denver, 1966-76, zone dir., 1976-82; pres. Commonwealth Gen. Group, Denver, 1982-92, Manley Properties Inc., Denver, 1982-90, Richard W. Manley Commonwealth Gen. Grps., Inc., Denver, 1982—; cons. Capitol Am. Life Ins. Co., Cleve., 1987-92; bd. dirs. (merco) Mercy Hosp., Denver, 1982-87. With USAF, 1956-59. Mem. Nat. Life Underwriters, Sertoma, Cherry Hills C. of C., Rotary, Elks, Alpha Tau Omega. Roman Catholic. Avocations: golfing, racquetball, running. Home: 6510 E Lake Pl Englewood CO 80111-4411

MANLEY, ROBERT EDWARD, lawyer, economist; b. Cin., Nov. 24, 1935; s. John M. and Helen Catherine (McCarthy) M.; m. Roberta L. Anzinger, Oct. 21, 1971 (div. 1980); 1 child, Robert Edward. ScB in Econs, Xavier U., 1956; AM in Econ. Theory, U. Cin., 1957; JD, Harvard U., 1960; postgrad., London Sch. Econs. and Polit. Sci., 1960, MIT, 1972. Bar: Ohio 1960, U.S. Supreme Ct. 1970. Pvt. practice law Cin., 1960—; pres. Manley, Burke, Fischer, Lipton & Cook, 1977; Taft teaching fellow econs. U. Cin., 1956-57, vis. lectr. community planning law Coll. Design, Architecture and Art, 1967-73, adj. assoc. prof. urban planning Coll. Design, Architecture, Art and Planning, 1972-81, adj. prof., 1981—, adj. prof. law, 1980—. Author: Metropolitan School Desegregation, 1978, (with Robert N. Cook) Management of Land and Environment, 1981, others; chmn. editorial adv. bd. Urban Lawyer, 1986—. Mem. Hamilton County Pub. Defender Commn., 1976-79; trustee HOPE, Cin., Albert J. Ryan Found.; counsel, co-founder Action Housing for Greater Cin.; mem. Spl. Commn. on Formation U. Cin. Health Maintenance Orgn., Mayor Cin. Spl. Com. on Housing; chmn. Cin. Environ. Adv. Coun., 1975-76; trustee The Americas Fund for Ind. Univs., 1987—; trustee Ohio Planning Conf., 1982-91, pres., 1987-89, trustee, 1987-90; sec. Cin. Mounted Patrol Com., 1993—; active Bd. Cin. Downtown Coun., 1991—. Mem. ABA (coun. sect. local govt. law 1976-80, 81-85, 88-92), Ohio Bar Assn., Cin. Bar Assn., Am. Judicature Soc., Law and Soc. Assn., Nat. Coun. Crime and Delinquency, Harvard U. Law Sch. Assn. Cin. (pres. 1970-71), Am. Econ. Assn., Am. Acad. Polit. and Social Sci., Queen City Club, Explorers Club (N.Y.C.) (trustee, sec. Clark chpt. 1992—), Athenaeum Club (Phila.), S.Am. Explorers Club (Lima, Peru). Republican. Roman Catholic. Office: Manley Burke Fischer Lipton & Cook 225 W Court St Cincinnati OH 45202-1098

MANLEY, WILLIAM TANNER, economist; b. Bath County, Ky., Aug. 18, 1929; s. Nathan and Flora (Whaley) M.; m. Vertna Jane Alexander, Oct. 30, 1951; 1 son, William Conway. B.S., U. Ky., 1951, M.S., 1955; Ph.D., U. Fla., 1958. Asst. prof. U. Fla., 1958-60, asso. prof., 1960-66; economist Dept. Agr., Washington, 1960-66; dep. dir. mktg. econs. div. Dept. Agr., 1966-68, dir., 1968-73, dir. nat. econ. analysis div., 1973-76; dep. administr. Agr. Mktg. Service, 1976-88; govt. relations advisor Heron, Bruchette, Ruckert and Rothwell Law Firm, Washington, 1988-90; econ. cons. Heron Law Co., Washington, 1990-91, Tuttle and Taylor Law Firm, 1991—; chmn. U.S. Dept. Agr. Yearbook, 1983; economist Tuttle and Taylor Law Firm, 1991—. Contbr. articles on econs. of mktg. to profl. jours. Served with USAF, 1951-53. Recipient cert. of merit Dept. Agr., 1963, 69, Superior Service award, 1979, Disting. Service award Nat. Market News Assn., 1979, Meritorious Service medal U.S. Dept. Air Force, 1979, Presdl. Meritorious Exec. Rank award Sr. Exec. Service, 1983, Disting. Out-of-State Alumnus award U. Ky. Agrl. Alumni Assn., 1987, Presdl. Disting. Exec. Rank award Sr. Exec. Service, 1987, Disting. Service award Dept. Agr., 1988. Mem. Internat., So. assns. agrl. economists, Am. Agrl. Econs. Assn., Fed. Exec. Inst. Alumni Assn. (dir. 1976-78), Res. Officers Assn. Methodist. Home:

4217 Captains Way Amelia Island FL 32034-4351 Office: 1025 Thomas Jefferson St NW Washington DC 20007-5201

MANLY, MARC EDWARD, lawyer; b. Knoxville, Tenn., Mar. 11, 1952; s. William Donald and Jane (Wilden) M.; m. Colby A. Chapman, July 20, 1974; children: Justin C., Allison C. BA summa cum laude, Amherst Coll., 1974; MA in Econs., JD magna cum laude, U. Mich., 1977. Bar: Ill. 1978, D.C. 1988, U.S. Dist. Ct. (no. dist.) Ill. 1978. Assoc. Sidley & Austin, Chgo., 1978-84, ptnr., 1985—. Mem. ABA, Order of Coif, Phi Beta Kappa. Office: Sidley & Austin 1722 I St NW Washington DC 20006-3705

MANLY, SARAH LETITIA, state legislator, ophthalmic photographer, angiographer; b. Greenville, S.C., Feb. 1, 1927; d. Victor Harris and Elsie Clippard (Burnett) Gillespie; m. Basil Manly IV, Sept. 11, 1947; children: Sarah Manly Cornish, Basil V, Jean Manly McDowell, Mary Manly Grant. BS cum laude, Furman U., 1947; postgrad., MIT, 1972, MEd, Clemson U., 1974; postgrad., Cambridge (Eng.) U., 1981. Cert. physics tchr., cert. retinal angiographer. Ward sec. Roper Hosp., Charleston, S.C., 1947; analytical chemist Parker Labs., Charleston, 1948; tchr. sci. Upper Darby (Pa.) Sch. Dist., 1961-63; tchr. physics Sch. Dist. Greenville (S.C) County, 1963-64, 70-76; ophthalmic photographer Basil Manly IV, MD, Greenville, 1976—; lectr. physics Clemson (S.C.) U., 1979-81; state rep. S.C. Ho. of Reps., Columbia, 1989—; cons. MIT, Cambridge, 1972-75, Georgetown U., Washington, 1974-76, NASA, Houston, 1974-76. Editor, cons. physics study guides MIT, 1972-75; editor lab. materials NASA, 1974-76; contbr. articles to profl. jours. Trustee Sch. Dist. Greenville County, 1976-88. Named S.C. Legislator of Yr., S.C. Sch. Bds. Assn., 1991. Mem. Greenville County Med. Aux. (sec. 1953-54), Delta Kappa Gamma. Democrat. Baptist. Avocations: travel, reading, gardening. Home: 2 Chanticleer Dr Greenville SC 29605-3106 Office: 335B Blatt Bldg SC House of Reps Columbia SC 29211

MANLY, WILLIAM DONALD, metallurgist; b. Malta, Ohio, Jan. 13, 1923; s. Edward James and Thelma (Campbell) M.; m. Jane Wilden, Feb. 9, 1949; children—Hugh, Ann, Marc, David. Student, Antioch Coll., 1941-42; B.S., U. Notre Dame, 1947, M.S., 1949; postgrad., U. Tenn., 1950-55. Metallurgist Oak Ridge Nat. Lab., 1949-60, mgr. gas cooled reactor program, 1960-64; mgr. materials research Union Carbide Corp., N.Y.C., 1964-65; gen. mgr. Union Carbide Corp. (Stellite div.), N.Y.C., 1967-69; v.p. Union Carbide Corp. (Stellite div.), Kokomo, Ind., 1969-70; sr. v.p. Cabot Corp., Boston, 1970-83; exec. v.p. Cabot Corp., 1983-86; ret., 1986; also dir. chmn. adv. com. for reactor safety AEC, 1964-65. Served with USMC, 1943-46. Recipient Honor award U. Notre Dame, 1974, Nat. Medal of Tech., Nat. Sci. Found., 1993. Fellow Am. Soc. Metals (pres. 1972-73), AIME, Am. Nuclear Soc. (Merit award 1966); mem. Nat. Acad. Engring., Nat. Assn. Corrosion Engrs., Metall. Soc. Presbyterian. Clubs: Cosmos, Masons. Home: 300 Chamberlain Cove Rd Kingston TN 37763

MANN, ALFRED, musicology educator, choral conductor; b. Hamburg, Germany, Apr. 28, 1917; came to U.S. May 2, 1939, naturalized, 1943; s. Wilhelm and Edith (Weiss) M.; m. Carolyn Owens, Aug. 23, 1948; children: Adrian, John, Timothy. Cert., State Acad. Music, Berlin, Germany, 1937, Royal Conservatory, Milan, Italy, 1938; diploma, Curtis Inst. Music, Phila., 1942; M.A., Columbia U., 1950, Ph.D., 1955; MusD (hon.), Whitworth Coll., 1947, Baldwin-Wallace Coll., 1984, Muhlenberg Coll., Allentown, Pa., 1985. Instr. State Acad. Music, Berlin, 1937-38; instr. Scuola Musicale, Milan, Italy, 1938-39; research asst. Curtis Inst. Music, Phila., 1939-42; chmn. to prof. emeritus Rutgers U., New Brunswick, N.J., 1947—; prof. emeritus musicology Eastman Sch. Music/U. Rochester, N.Y., 1980—; condr. Cantata Singers, N.Y., 1952-59, Bach Choir, Bethlehem, Pa., 1970-80, recs. G.F. Handel, Chandos Anthems, 3 vols., 1964, 65, 66; dir. publs. Am. Choral Found., Phila., 1962—. Author: Study of Fugue, 1958, Theory and Practice, 1987, Bach and Handel: Choral Performance Practice, 1992; editor vols. for Complete Works of Handel, Mozart, Schubert, 1965—, J.J. Fux, Gradus ad Parnassum, 1938, 43, 85, Messiah critical edit. of Handel's conducting score, 1959, 65, 89, Am. Choral Rev., 1962—. Bd. dirs. G.F. Handel Gesellschaft, Halle, Germany. Served with CIC, U.S. Army, 1943-45. Guggenheim fellow, 1958. Fellow Am. Coun. Learned Soc., Am. Philos. Soc., Nat. Found. Humanities; mem. Am. Musicological Soc., Internat. Musicological Soc., Am. Bach Soc. (sec. 1977—), Am. Handel Soc. (hon., bd. dirs. 1965—), Internat. Bach Soc. (hon.), Internat. Schuetz Soc. (bd. dirs. Am. chpt. 1981-82), Bach Riemenschneider Inst. (hon.). Home: 1536 Scribner Rd Penfield NY 14526-9723 Office: Eastman Sch Music 26 Gibbs St Rochester NY 14604-2599

MANN, BERNARD (BERNIE MANN), professional basketball team executive. Former pres. N.J. Nets, East Rutherford, now bd. dirs. Office: NJ Nets Meadowlands Arena East Rutherford NJ 07073*

MANN, BRUCE ALAN, lawyer; b. Chgo., Nov. 28, 1934; s. David I. and Lillian (Segal) M.; m. Naomi Cooks, Aug. 31, 1980; children: Sally Mann Stull, Jonathan Hugh, Andrew Ross. BBA, U. Wis., 1955, SJD, 1957. Bar: Wis. 1957, N.Y. 1958, Calif. 1961. Assoc. Davis, Polk & Wardwell, N.Y.C., 1957-60; assoc. Pillsbury, Madison & Sutro, San Francisco, 1960-66, ptnr., 1967-83; adminstrv. mng. dir. L.F. Rothschild Unterberg Towbin, San Francisco, 1983-87; ptnr. Morrison & Foerster, San Francisco, 1987—; cons. SEC, 1978; vis. prof. law Georgetown U., 1978; lectr. in field; mem. adv. bd. U. Calif. Securities Regulation Inst., 1973—. Contbr. articles to profl. jours. Served with USAR, 1957. Mem. Am. Law Inst., Am. Bar Assn. (chmn. fed. regulation of securities com. 1981-83), State Bar Calif., Bar Assn. San Francisco (bd. dirs. 1974-75), Nat. Assn. Securities Dealers (gov. at large 1981-83). Club: The Family. Office: Morrison & Foerster 345 California St San Francisco CA 94104-2606

MANN, BRUCE H., law educator; b. 1950. AB, AM, Brown U., 1972, JD, 1975, M in Philosophy, 1975; PhD, Yale U., 1977. Bar: Conn. 1975, Tex. 1984. Asst. prof. U. Conn., 1977-79, assoc. prof., 1979-81; vis. assoc. prof. U. Tex., 1981-83; assoc. prof. Washington U., St. Louis, 1983-84, prof., 1984-87; prof. U. Pa., Phila., 1987-88, prof. law and history, 1988—. Editor Law & History Rev., 1987—. Constl. fellow NEH, 1987-88. Mem. Am. Soc. for Legal History (bd. dirs. 1987-89), Law and Soc. Assn., Phi Beta Kappa. Office: U Pa Law Sch 3400 Chestnut St Philadelphia PA 19104-6204

MANN, CEDRIC ROBERT, retired institute administrator, oceanographer; b. Auckland, N.Z., Feb. 14, 1926; came to Can., 1949; s. Duncan and Winifred Mary (Hood) M.; m. Muriel Frances May, Dec. 19, 1950; 1 child, Robin Carl. B.Sc., U. N.Z., 1948, M.Sc., 1950; Ph.D., U. B.C., Vancouver, Can., 1953; D.Eng., N.S. Tech. Coll., Halifax, Can., 1972. Physicist Naval Research Establishment, Halifax, N.S., Can., 1953-61; oceanographer Atlantic Oceanographic Lab., Halifax, N.S., Can., 1961-75, dir., 1975-78; dir. gen. Bedford Inst. Oceanography, Halifax, N.S., Can., 1978-79, Inst. Ocean Scis., Sidney, B.C., Can., 1979-87; Assoc. prof. Dalhousie U., Halifax, 1961-75; chmn. sci. adv. bd. Intergovtl. Oceanographic Commn., Paris, 1978-81; mem. Can. Climate Planning Bd., Ottawa, 1983-86; chmn. Sea Use Council, Seattle, 1981-86. Contbr. articles to profl. jours. Fellow Royal Soc. Can.; mem. Can. Meteorol. and Oceanographic Soc. (life, recipient J.P. Tully medal in oceanography 1994). Anglican. Avocations: golf; gardening. Home: 9751 Ardmore Dr, Sidney, BC Canada V8L 5H5

MANN, CLARENCE CHARLES, real estate company official; b. Oradell, N.J., Oct. 15, 1929; s. Clarence Theodore and Martha Barbara (Koster) M.; m. Joan Elizabeth Schnoor, Nov. 25, 1951 (div. Jan. 1985); 1 child, Gary John. BA, NYU, 1951; MA, U. Pa., 1958, Am. U., Beirut, Lebanon, 1963. Commd. 2d. lt. U.S. Army, 1951, advanced through grades to col., ret., 1977; def. attache to Jordan, 1959-64; mktg. mgr. Litton Industries, Jordan, Saudi Arabia, 1977-81; mktg. mgr. Mid-East Hughes Aircraft Co., Fullerton, Calif., 1981-91; dir. relocation ERA Gem Realty, Tucson, 1992—. Author: Abu Dhabi: Birth of an Oil Shaikhdom, 1964. Decorated Legion of Merit. Mem. Met. Tucson Conv. and Visitors Bureau, Chamber Mil. Affairs Com., Tucson C. of C. Avocations: music, gardening.

MANN, DAVID SCOTT, lawyer; b. Cin., Ohio, Sept. 25, 1939; s. Henry M. and Helen Faye (Bale) M.; m. Elizabeth Taliaferro, Oct. 5, 1963; children: Michael, Deborah, Marshall. AB cum laude, Harvard Coll., 1961, LLB magna cum laude, 1968. Bar: Ohio 1968. Assoc. Dinsmore & Shohl, Cin.,

1968-74, ptnr., 1974-83; mem. Taliaferro and Mann, Cin., 1983-92; councilman City of Cin., 1974-92, mayor, 1980-82, 91; mem. 103d Congress 1st Ohio dist., Washington, 1993-94; mem. armed svcs. com., mem. jud. com. Washington; of counsel Thompson, Hine and Flury, Cin., 1995—. Editor Harvard Law Rev., 1966-68, notes editor, 1967-68; contbr. articles to profl. jours. Mem., chmn. Cin. Bd. Health, 1972-74. With USN, 1961-65. Mem. Cin. Bar Assn. Democrat. Methodist. Home: 568 Evanswood Pl Cincinnati OH 45220-1527

MANN, DAVID WILLIAM, minister; b. Elkhart, Ind., Apr. 17, 1947; s. Herbert Richard and Kathryn (Bontrager) M.; m. Brenda Marie Frantz, June 7, 1969; children: Troy, Todd, Erika. BA, Bethel Coll., 1969; MS, Nat. Louis U., 1986. Ordained to ministry Missionary Ch., 1978. Campus life dir. Youth for Christ, Elkhart, 1969-77; denominational youth dir. Missionary Ch., Ft. Wayne, Ind., 1977-81, Christian edn. dir., 1981-88, U.S. dir. missions, 1990—; assoc. dir. World Ptnrs., Ft. Wayne, 1988-90; dir. Missionary Ch. Vol. Svc., Ft. Wayne, 1983—. Author: (with others) Youth Leaders Source Book, 1985; contbr. articles to profl. jour. Mgr. Little League, Ft. Wayne, 1981-89, bd. dirs. 1986. Mem. Nat. Assn. Evangelicals, Evangelical Fgn. Mission Assn., Denominational Execs. in Christian Edn. (chmn. 1988), Aldersgate Pub. Assn. (bd. dirs. 1985, 87), Nat. Christian Edn. Assn. (exec. com. 1987-89). Avocations: baseball, skiing, fishing, woodworking. Home: 10025 Crown Point Dr Fort Wayne IN 46804-4391 Office: Missionary Ch 3811 Vanguard Dr Fort Wayne IN 46899-9127

MANN, DELBERT, film, theater, television director and producer; b. Lawrence, Kans., Jan. 30, 1920; s. Delbert Martin and Ora (Patton) M.; m. Ann Caroline Gillespie, Jan. 13, 1942; children: David Martin, Frederick G., Barbara Susan, Steven P. B.A., Vanderbilt U., 1941; M.F.A., Yale U.; LL.D. (hon.), Northland Coll. Dir. Town Theatre, Columbia, S.C., 1947-49; stage mgr. Wellesley Summer Theater, 1947-48; floor mgr., asst. dir. NBC-TV, N.Y.C., 1949, dir., 1949-55; freelance film and TV dir., 1954—; former bd. govs. Acad. TV Arts and Scis.; former co-chmn. Tenn. Film, Tape and Music Commn., former pres. Dirs. Guild, Ednl. and Benevolent Found., Cinema Circulus; former lectr. Claremont (Calif.) McKenna Coll. Dir., Philco-Goodyear TV Playhouse, 1949-55, also Omnibus, Ford Star Jubilee, Playwrights 56, Producers Showcase, DuPont Show of the Month, Playhouse 90; films Marty, 1954 (Palme d'Or, Cannes Internat. Film Festival, Acad. Award), The Bachelor Party, 1956, Desire Under the Elms, 1957, Separate Tables, 1958, Middle of the Night, 1959, The Dark at the Top of the Stairs, 1960, The Outsider, 1960, Lover Come Back, 1961, That Touch of Mink, 1962, A Gathering of Eagles, 1962, Dear Heart, 1963, Mister Buddwing, 1965, Fitzwilly, 1967, Kidnapped, 1972, Birch Interval, 1976, Night Crossing, 1982; TV spl. Heidi, 1968, David Copperfield, 1970, Jane Eyre, 1971, The Man Without a Country, 1973, A Girl Named Sooner, 1975, Breaking Up, 1977, Tell Me My Name, 1977, Home To Stay, 1978, All Quiet on the Western Front, 1979, To Find My Son, 1980, All the Way Home, 1981, Bronte, 1982, The Member of the Wedding, 1982, The Gift of Love, 1983, Love Leads the Way, 1984, A Death in California, 1985, The Last Days of Patton, 1986, The Ted Kennedy Jr. Story, 1986, April Morning, 1987, Ironclads, 1991, Against Her Will: An Incident in Baltimore, 1992, Incident in a Small Town, 1993, Lily in Winter, 1994; plays include A Quiet Place, 1956, Speaking of Murder, 1957, Zelda, 1969; opera Wuthering Heights, N.Y.C. Ctr., 1959. Bd. trustees Vanderbilt U., 1962—. 1st lt. USAAF, WWII; B-24 pilot and squadron intelligence officer, 1944-45. Recipient Acad. Award for dir. Marty, 1955. Mem. Dirs. Guild Am. (past pres. 1967-71) (Dirs. Guild award, 1955), Kappa Alpha. Democrat. Presbyterian. Avocation: reading history. Home and Office: Caroline Prodns Inc 401 S Burnside Ave # 11D Los Angeles CA 90036-5372

MANN, DONEGAN, lawyer; b. Birmingham, Ala., Mar. 6, 1922; s. Ephriam DeValse and Edna Atkins (Donegan) M.; m. Frances Virginia Hindman, Apr. 6, 1957 (dec. May 1993); m. Frances M. Jenkins, Jan. 7, 1995. Student, Birmingham-So., 1940-41; AB, George Washington U., 1947, JD, 1950. Bar: U.S. Dist. Ct. D.C. 1950, U.S. Ct. Appeals (D.C. cir.) 1950, U.S. Ct. Claims 1957, U.S. Supreme Ct. 1961, U.S. Ct. Appeals (fed. cir.) 1982. Acting bur. counsel Civil Aeronautics Bd., Washington, 1953-55; gen. rates atty. GAO, Washington, 1955-57; spl. rate counsel Gen. Svcs. Administrn., Washington, 1957-60; assoc. Wolf & Case, Washington, 1960-66; sr. atty., office gen. counsel U.S. Dept. Treasury, Washington, 1966-79; of counsel Shands & Stupar, Washington, 1979-82; pvt. practice Washington, 1984—. Pres. Friends of Great Falls Tavern, Inc., Potomac, Md., 1977-80, bd. dirs., 1981-82. With USN, 1943-46, PTO. Mem. ABA (treas. pub. contracts sect. 1965-66, Svc. award sr. lawyers' divsn. 1991, chair guardianship and conservatorship com. 1989—, sr. lawyers' divsn. task force to reform guardianship laws 1992-94, chair award com. 1975-76), Bar Assn. D.C., Montgomery County Hist. Soc. (exec. v.p. 1980-83, bd. dirs. 1984-86), Fed. Energy Bar Assn., Fed. Bar Assn., D.C. Bar. Democrat. Episcopalian. Avocations: fishing, hunting, golf, tennis, gardening. Office: Ste 204 1000 Connecticut Ave Washington DC 20036

MANN, EMILY BETSY, writer, artistic director, theater and film director; b. Boston, Apr. 12, 1952; d. Arthur and Sylvia (Blut) M.; 1 child, Nicholas Isaac Bamman. BA, Harvard U., 1974; MFA, U. Minn., 1976. Resident dir. Guthrie Theater, Mpls., 1976-79; dir. BAM Theater Co., Bklyn., 1980-81; freelance writer, dir. N.Y.C., 1981-90; artistic dir. McCarter Theater Ctr. for the Performing Arts, Princeton, N.J., 1990—; cons. N.Y. Theatre Workshop, 1987. Author: (plays) Annulla, an Autobiography, Still Life (6 Obie awards 1981, Fringe First award, 1985), Execution of Justice (Helen Hayes award, Bay Area Theatre Critics Circle award, HBO/USA award, Playwriting award Women's Com. Dramatists Guild for Dramatizing Issues of Conscience 1986), To Know a Monster: The Story of the Greensboro Massacre (stage adaptation); co-author: (with Ntozake Shange) (musical) Betsey Brown; (screenplays) Naked, Fanny Kelly, The Winnie Mandela Story, The Greensboro Massacre; dir. Hedda Gabbler, A Doll House, Annulla, Still Life (Obie award), Execution of Justice (Guthrie and Broadway), Betsey Brown, The Glass Menagerie, Three Sisters, Cat On A Hot Tin Roof, Twilight: L.A., 1992 (L.A. NAACP award for best dir.), The Perfectionist, The Matchmaker; adaptor, dir. Miss Julie, Having Our Say (Tony nomination - Direction of a Play, 1995); translator: Nights and Days (Pierre Laville), 1985; pub. in New Plays USA 1, New Plays, 3, American Plays and the Vietnam War, The Ten Best Plays of 1986, Out Front. Recipient BUSH fellowship, 1975-76, Rosamond Gilder award New Drama Forum Assn., 1983, NEA Assocs. grant, 1984, Guggenheim fellowship, 1985, McKnight fellowship, 1985, CAPS award, 1985, NEA Playwrights fellowship, 1986. Mem. Soc. Stage Dirs. and Choreographers (bd. dirs.), Theatre Communications Group (v.p.), New Dramatists, PEN, Writers' Guild, Dramatists' Guild, Phi Betta Kappa.

MANN, GARY T., engineering company executive. Pres. Marietta Martin Tech. Svcs., Bethesda, 1993—. Office: Marietta Martin Tech Svcs 6801 Rockledge Dr Bethesda MD 20817-1836

MANN, GEORGE STANLEY, real estate and financial services corporation executive; b. Toronto, Ont., Can., Dec. 23, 1932; s. David Philip and Elizabeth (Green) M.; m. Saundra Sair, Jan. 2, 1955; children: Michael, Tracy. Attended, North Toronto Collegiate Sch.; LLD (hon.), U. Windsor. Ptnr. Mann & Martel Co. Ltd., 1959-68, chief exec. officer, 1968-70; chief exec. officer United Trust Co., 1970-76; pres. Unicorp Canada Corp., Toronto, 1972-76, chmn. 1976-90; dir. Nat. Bank Canada, 1978-91; chmn. bd. Union Gas Ltd., 1986-93; pres. chmn. bd., Lincorp Holdings, Inc., NYC; chmn. bd. Timbuktu Natural Foods, Toronto; bd. dirs. Lincoln Savs. Bank, N.Y.C., Unicorp Energy Corp., Toronto. Bd. govs. Mt. Sinai Hosp., Toronto. Clubs: Oakdale Golf & Country (Toronto); High Ridge Country (Palm Beach, Fla.). Avocation: golf. Home: Ste 1102, 2 St Clair Ave W, Toronto, ON Canada M4V 1L5 Home: 18 Old Forest Hill Rd, Toronto, ON Canada M5P 2P7 also: 930 S Ocean Blvd Palm Beach FL 33480

MANN, H. GEORGE, lawyer; b. Chgo., Apr. 10, 1937. AB, Harvard U., 1958; JD, Columbia U., 1961. Bar: Ill. 1961. Ptnr. McDermott, Will & Emery, Chgo. Mem. ABA, Ill. State Bar Assn., Chgo. Bar Assn. Office: McDermott Will & Emery 227 W Monroe St Chicago IL 60606

MANN, HERBIE, flutist; b. N.Y.C., Apr. 16, 1930; s. Harry C. and Ruth (Brecher) Solomon; m. Ruth Shore, Sept. 8, 1956 (div. 1971); children: Paul

J., Claudia; m. Jan Clonts, July 11, 1971 (div. 1990); 2 children: Laura, Geoffrey; m. Susan Janeal Arison, 1991. Student, Manhattan Sch. Music, 1952-54. Founder, pres. Herbie Mann Music Corp., N.Y.C., 1959—; founder Kokopelli Music, Santa Fe, 1992—; toured Africa for Dept. State, 1960, Brazil, 1961-62, Japan, 1964, Scandanavia, Cyprus and Turkey, 1971; pres. Herbie Mann Orch., Inc., 5 Face of Music Prodns., Inc., Rupadia Music, Inc. Recorded over 100 albums under own name, 1954—; Memphis Underground, 1969, Push, Push, 1971, Missippi Gambler, 1974, Bird in a Silver Cage, 1977, Caminho De Casa, 1990. Deep Pocket, 1992, The Evolution of Mann: The Herbie Mann Anthology, 1994. Served with AUS, 1948-52. Recipient Downbeat award for flute, 1958-70. Mem. ASCAP, Nat. Acad. Rec. Arts and Scis. Office: Kokopelli Music PO Box 8200 Santa Fe NM 87504*

MANN, J. KEITH, arbitrator, law educator, lawyer; b. May 28, 1924; s. William Young and Lillian Myrle (Bailey) M.; m. Virginia McKinnon, July 7, 1950; children: William Christopher, Marilyn Keith, John Kevin, Susan Bailey, Andrew Curry. BS, Ind. U., 1948, LLB, 1949; LLD, Monmouth Coll., 1989. Bar: Ind. 1949, D.C. 1951. Law clk. Justice Wiley Rutledge and Justice Sherman Minton, 1949-50; practice, Washington, 1950; with Wage Stblzn. Bd., 1951; asst. prof. U. Wis., 1952; asst. prof. Stanford U. Law Sch., 1952-54, assoc. prof., 1954-58, prof., 1958-88, prof. emeritus 1988—, assoc. dean, 1961-85, acting dean, 1976, 81-82, cons. to provost, 1986-87; vis. prof. U. Chgo., 1953; mem. Sec. of Labor's Adv. Com., 1955-57; mem. Pres.'s Commn. Airlines Controversy, 1961; mem. COLC Aerospace Spl. Panel, 1973-74; chmn. and mem. Presdl. Emergency Bds. or Bds. of Inquiry, 1962-63, 67, 71-72; spl. master U.S. vs. Alaska, U.S. Supreme Ct., 1980—. Ensign USN, 1944-46. Sunderland fellow U. Mich., 1959-60; scholar in residence Duke U., 1972. Mem. ABA, AAUP, Nat. Acad. Arbitrators, Indsl. Rels. Rsch. Assn., Acad. Law Alumni Fellows Ind. U., Order of Coif. Editor: book rev. and articles Ind. U. Law Jour. Democrat. Presbyterian. Home: 872 Lathrop Dr Stanford CA 94305-1053 Office: Stanford U Law Sch Stanford CA 94305-8610

MANN, JACINTA, academic administrator, mathematician, educator; b. Pinckneyville, Ill., May 13, 1925; d. Bernard Albert and Magdalen Elizabeth (Ruppert) M. BS, So. Ill. U., 1946; MS, U. Wis., 1947, PhD, 1958. Statistician U. Wis., Madison, 1948-50; novitiate Sisters of Charity, Greensburg, Pa., 1950-53; tchr. secondary math. Altoona (Pa.) Cath. High Sch., 1953-56; with Seton Hill Coll., 1958—, dir. admissions, 1960-67, acad. dean, 1968-71, prof., 1971—; adminstrv. intern Scripps Coll., Claremont, Calif., 1967-68. Contbr. articles to profl. jours. Mem. Pa. Gov.'s Commn. on Women, 1979-89. Recipient faculty award Seton Hill Coll., 1971, Prof. of Yr. award, 1988; Medal of Honor, Inst. for Women Today, 1977, teaching award Freedoms Found., 1987, State Continuing Educator of Yr. award Continuing Edn. Assn. Pa., 1991; Kemper K. Knapp fellow U. Wis., 1957-58, fellow Am. Coun. on Edns., 1967-68. Democrat. Roman Catholic. Avocations: potter, tailor. Home: 10 Meadowbrook Ave Greensburg PA 15601-1759 Office: Seton Hill Coll Greensburg PA 15601

MANN, JAMES BROOKS, lawyer; b. Houston, July 31, 1957; s. George Solomon and Brooksine (Thompson) M. BA, Cornell U., 1979; JD, Harvard U., 1982. Bar: D.C. 1982, U.S. Supreme Ct. 1987, U.S. Ct. Appeals (D.C. cir.) 1982, U.S. Ct. Appeals (fed. cir.) 1983, U.S. Ct. Appeals (5th cir., 6th cir., 10th cir.) 1987, U.S. Ct. Appeals (3rd, 4th cir., 9th cir., 11th cir.) 1988. Assoc. Ivins, Phillips & Barker, Washington, 1982-84, Lane & Edson, Washington, 1984-85; gen. counsel and acting dep. staff dir. U.S. Commn. Civil Rights, Washington, 1985-87; dep. asst. atty. gen. tax div. Dept. of Justice, Washington, 1987—. Mem. Telluride Soc. (trustee 1977—). Republican. Home: 100 W 80th St # 36 New York NY 10024 Office: Dept Justice 10th Constitution Ave NE Washington DC 20530-0001

MANN, JAMES ROBERT, congressman; b. Greenville, S.C., Apr. 27, 1920; s. Alfred Cleo and Nina (Griffin) M.; m. Virginia Thomason Brunson, Jan. 15, 1945; children—James Robert, David Brunson, William Walker, Virginia Brunson. B.A., The Citadel, 1941, LL.D. (hon.), 1978; JD, U. S.C., 1947. Bar: S.C. 1947, U.S. Ct. Appeals (4th cir.) 1948, U.S. Supreme Ct. 1970. Practice in Greenville, 1947—; del. S.C. Ho. of Reps. from, Greenville County, 1949-52; solicitor 13th Jud. Circuit, 1953-63; mem. 91st-95th Congresses 4th Dist., S.C. Sec. Greenville County Planning Commn., 1963-67; Trustee Greenville Hosp. System, 1965-68; bd. govs. Greenville Shriners Hosp., 1983-90. Served to lt. col. AUS, 1941-46; col. USAR ret. Mem. Am., S.C., Greenville County bar assns., Am. Judicature Soc., Greater Greenville C. of C. (pres. 1986), V.F.W. (dep. comdr. 1951-52), Am. Legion. Democrat. Baptist. Lodges: Mason; Shriners; Kiwanis; Elks; Woodmen of World. Office: 812 E North St Greenville SC 29601-3102

MANN, JEFF, special effects expert, executive. With Indsl. Light & Magic, San Rafael, Calif., 1981—, mgr. model and creature shops, 1986—. Creator model and creature projects various films including Star Trek IV: The Voyage Home, 1986, Empire of the Sun, 1987, Star Tours, 1987, Witches of Eastwick, 1987, Batteries Not Included, 1987, Innerspace, 1987, Star Trek: The Next Generation, 1987, Who Framed Roger Rabbit, 2988, Willow, 1988, Indiana Jones and the Last Crusade, 1989, Ghostbusters II, 1989, The Abyss, 1989, Back to the Future II, 1989, Always, 1989, Dreams, 1989, Joe Versus the Volcano, 1990, The Hunt for Red October, 1990, Ghost, 1990, Back to the Future III, 1990, Die Hard II, 1990. Office: Indsl Light & Magic PO Box 2459 San Rafael CA 94912-2459

MANN, JIM (JAMES WILLIAM MANOUSOS), editor, publisher; b. Cambridge, Mass., Dec. 9, 1919; s. Demetrios Peter and Germaine (Lambertz) Manousos; m. Mary Dimitrakis, July 21, 1962. MFA, Fordham U., 1954. Assoc. editor View mag., Yonkers, N.Y., 1951-58; various editorial jobs N.Y.C., 1959-71; pres., editor The Gallagher Report, N.Y.C., 1971-74; pres., treas. Jim Mann & Assocs., Gales Ferry, Conn., 1974—; editor, pub. Media Mgmt. Monographs, 1978-90; editor in chief Pub. Trends & Trendsetters, 1991—; adj. prof. mktg. U. New Haven, Orange, Conn., 1976-82. Author: Solving Publishing's Toughest Problems, 1982, Magazine Editing, 1985, Ad Sales, 1987. Pres. Community Action Network, 1990—.

MANN, JONATHAN MAX, international agency administrator, public health director; b. Boston, July 30, 1947; s. James and Ida (Laskow) M.; m. Marie-Paule Bondat, Jan. 30, 1970; children: Naomi, Lydia, Aaron. BA, Harvard U., 1969, MPH, 1980; MD, Washington U., St. Louis, 1974. Epidemic intelligence service officer USPHS, Ctrs. Disease Control, Atlanta and Santa Fe, 1975-77; med. epidemiologist, dir. AIDS research program, Kinshasa, Zaire, 1984-86; dir. global program AIDS, WHO, Geneva, 1986-90; state epidemiologist, chief med. officer N.Mex. Health Dept., Santa Fe, 1977-84. Mem. editorial bd. Control of Communicable Diseases in Man, Western Jour. Medicine, 1984—. Contbr. articles to profl. jours. Recipient Spl. Commendation N.Mex. Med. Soc., 1980, Friend of N.Mex. Journalism award Sigma Delta Chi, 1979, Disting. Service award School Nursing Com., 1979. Fellow Am. Coll. Preventive Medicine (Recognition award 1982), Am. Coll. Epidemiology; mem. Santa Fe County Med. Soc. (treas. 1981-82, pres. 1983-84), U.S.-Mex. Border Health Assn., Am. Pub. Health Assn.

MANN, KENNETH HENRY, marine ecologist; b. Dovercourt, Essex, Eng., Aug. 15, 1923; emigrated to arrived Canada, 1967, naturalized, 1973; s. Harry and Mabel (Ashby) M.; m. Isabella Gilmour Ness, Apr. 18, 1946; children: Ian Malcolm, Sheila Helen, Colin Gilmour. B.Sc., U. London, 1949; Ph.D., U. Reading, 1953; D.Sc., U. London, 1965. Lectr. zoology, then reader U. Reading, Eng., 1949-64; 64-67; sr. biologist marine ecology lab. Bedford Inst. Oceanography, Dartmouth, Can., 1967-72, dir. marine ecology lab., 1980-86, sr. rsch. scientist, 1986-93, emeritus rsch. scientist, 1993—; prof., chmn. biology Dalhousie U., Halifax, N.S., Can., 1972-80, adj. prof. biology, 1980—. Author: Leeches: Their Structure, Physiology, Ecology and Embryology, 1961, Ecology of Coastal Waters: A Systems Approach, 1982; co-author: (with J. Lazier) Dynamics of Marine Ecosystems: Biological-Physical Interactions in the Sea, 1991, (with R.S. Barnes) Fundamentals of Aquatic Ecology, 1991; editor, contbr.: Network Analysis in Marine Ecology, 1989; editor Jour. Animal Ecology, 1966-67. Served with Royal Air Force, 1942-46. Fellow Royal Soc. Can.; mem. Brit. Ecol. Soc., Am. Assn. Limnology and Oceanography. Home: 23 Woodward Cres, Halifax, NS Canada B3M 1J6 Office: Bedford Inst Oceanography, Box 1006, Dartmouth, NS Canada B2Y 4A2

MANN, KENNETH WALKER, retired minister, psychologist; b. Nyack, N.Y., Aug. 22, 1914; s. Arthur Hungerford and Ethel Livingston (Walker) M. AB, Princeton U., 1937; STB, Gen. Theol. Sem., N.Y.C., 1942; MS, U. Mich., 1950, PhD, 1956. Ordained priest Episcopal Ch., 1942; diplomate Am. Assn. Pastoral Counselors; lic. clin. psychologist, Calif., Conn.; lic. marriage, family and child counselor, Calif. Vicar in Valley Cottage, Pearl River, N.Y., 1941-43; priest in charge Yonkers, N.Y., 1943-45; dir. youth work and Christian edn. Diocese L.A., 1945-47; curate in Beverly Hills, Calif., 1947-49; counselor Bur. Psychol. Svcs., U. Mich., 1951-52; chaplain, clin. psychologist dept. psychiatry St. Luke's Hosp., N.Y.C., also priest-psychotherapist Cathedral St. John Divine, N.Y.C., psychol. examiner ministerial candidates Diocese N.Y., 1952-58; assoc. chaplain Hosp. Good Samaritan, L.A., 1958-65; exec. pastoral svcs., exec. coun. Episc. Ch. N.Y.C., 1965-70; program officer Acad. Religion and Mental Health, N.Y.C., 1970-72; sr. adviser profl. affairs Inst. Religion and Health, 1972-74; sr. psychol. staff Silver Hill Found., New Canaan, Conn., 1974-84; pres. Rockland County (N.Y.) Mins. Assn., 1942-43; exec. sec. social svc. commn. Diocese N.Y., 1943-45; chmn. div. pastoral svcs. Diocese L.A. 1958-65; field dir. Western region Acad. Religion and Mental Health, 1958-61; assoc. nat. chaplain U.S. Power Squadrons, 1956-57. Author: On Pills and Needles, 1969, Deadline for Survival—A Survey of Moral Issues in Science and Medicine, 1970; contbr. articles to profl. jours. Pres. Adoption Inst. L.A., 1964; mem. edn. com. Calif. Heart Assn., 1962-64; trustee, treas. Acad. Religion and Mental Health, 1954-59, mem. profl. bd., 1960-70; trustee Vis. Nurse Assn. L.A., 1963-65, Children's Home Soc. Calif. in L.A., 1964-65, North Conway Inst., 1966-80. USPHS grantee, 1950-51. Fellow AAAS; mem. APA (chmn. com. rels. between psychology and religion 1956-58), Western Psychol. Assn., Calif. Psychol. Assn., L.A. County Psychol. Assn., N.Y. Acad. Scis., Planetary Soc., Assembly Episc. Hosps. and Chaplains, Upper Nyack Tennis Club, The Club (Diocese N.Y.), Princeton Club N.Y. Republican. Home: 32 Tallman Ave Nyack NY 10960-1606 *I have strongly held to the principle that the total "health" of mankind cannot be considered apart from the values and aspirations by which people live, and by which they may even be prepared to die. Amidst the confusions that exist today over loyalties, traditions, and ideals, many are asking: What is the right way to behave? How should I think? What kind of person am I supposed to be? To help such people in quandary to live responsibly, and still be true to their individuality, is a large task, but it is one that is central to a religious ministry. It has always been my chief concern.*

MANN, LESTER PERRY, mathematics educator; b. Milford, Mass., May 30, 1921; s. Lester P. and Viola E. (Tracy) M.; m. Dorothy M. Davis, Oct. 11, 1947; children: Kelly P., Leslie P. BS with high honors, U. Md., 1964, MEd, U. Alaska, Anchorage, 1974; EdD, Boston U., 1983. Cert. elem. tchr., reading specialist and supr., Mass.; cert. elem. tchr., reading specialist, Alaska. Commd. 2nd lt. USAAF, 1941; advanced through grades to maj. USAF, 1954, navigator, weather officer, 1941-64; ret., 1964; resident counselor OEO-Job Corps, 1965-66; flight navigator Südflug, Braniff, Capitol and Japan Air Lines, 1966-73; instr. math., adminstr., curriculum developer U. Alaska, 1974-86, adj. instr., 1987—; instrml. assoc. Mann Assocs., Applied Lifelong Learning, Anchorage, 1983—; instr. Anchorage Community Coll., 1974-86; asst. prof. Embry-Riddle Aero. U., Anchorage, 1987—, acad. advisor, 1987-90; mem. for remedial reading Alaska Talent Bank; vis. adult educator German Adult Edn. Assn., 1984. Mem. Math. Assn. Am., Nat. Coun. Tchrs. Math., Internat. Reading Assn., Am. Assn. Adult and Continuing Edn. (profl., past mem. nomination and election com.), Am. Meteorol. Soc., Phi Alpha Theta, Phi Kappa Phi. Avocations: fishing, sport flying, classical guitar. Home and Office: 2304 Turnagain Pky Anchorage AK 99517-1124

MANN, LOWELL D., religious organization executive. Chmn. Bd. for World Missions. Office: Bd World Mission Brethren in Christ Ch 8 W Bainbridge St Elizabethtown PA 17022-2405

MANN, LOWELL KIMSEY, retired manufacturing executive; b. LaGrange, Ga., June 28, 1917; s. Otis A. and Georgia B. (Mundy) M.; m. Helen Margaret Dukes, Feb. 11, 1944; children: Margaret Ellen, Lowell Kimsey. Grad., Advanced Mgmt. Program, Harvard, 1962. Foreman Callaway Mills, LaGrange, 1935-39, indsl. engr., 1939-42; indsl. engr. Blue Bell, Inc., Greensboro, N.C., 1946-52, chief engr., 1952-61, v.p. engring., 1961-62, v.p. mfg., 1962-68, exec. v.p., 1968-73, pres., 1973-82, chief exec. officer, 1974-83, chmn. bd., 1982-84, ret., 1984; dir. Shadowline Inc., Morganton, N.C., Wachovia Bank & Trust Co., Greensboro, Quality Mills, Mt. Airy, N.C.; mem. So. adv. bd. Arkwright-Boston Ins. Co., 1975-84. Bd. dirs. Learning Inst., N.C., 1969-76; trustee Southeastern Legal Found., 1977-84; deacon Bapt. Ch., 1984-88, chmn., 1986-87. Served to capt. AUS, 1942-46. Recipient Disting. Citizen award Greensboro C. of C., 1983; named Clothing Mfg. Industry CEO of Yr. Fin. World, 1978. Mem. Piedmont Assoc. Industries (bd. dirs., pres. 1966-68), Am. Apparel Mfrs. Assn. (bd. dirs. 1972-78), Nat. MS Soc., NAM (bd. dirs. 1977-84), Beta Gamma Sigma (hon.). Democrat. Club: Sedgefield Country (bd. dirs. 1970-73, 85-88, pres. 1986-88) (Greensboro). Home: Sedgefield 5503 Currituck Pl Greensboro NC 27407-7217 *I believe that honesty, integrity, and fairness are essential in our relationships with others. These shared values will encourage understanding, and, in turn, will create pride in us, opportunities for us, and accomplishments by us.*

MANN, MARCIA L., state agency administrator; b. Pitts., May 20, 1944; d. Walter W. and Helen Mann. BA, Thiel Coll., 1965; MEd, U. Pitts., 1966; PhD, U. Nebr., 1970. Elem. tchr. Montgomery County Schs., Rockville, Md., 1966, Lincoln (Nebr.) City Schs., 1966-69; grad. asst. U. Nebr., Lincoln, 1969-70; asst. prof. edn. U. South Fla., Tampa, 1970-75, assoc. prof. edn., 1976-85, prof. edn., 1986—, assoc. dean clin. edn. and spl. projects, 1984-91; sec. Fla. Lottery, Tallahassee, 1991—; evaluator dept. edn. Pinellas County Inservice Evaluation, 1978, Fla. Tech. U., 1978; vice chairperson Nat. Forum of Field Dirs., 1977, chairperson, 1978; del. dept. edn. State Conv., 1979; mem. Fla. State program Am. Coun. on Edn., 1978; coord. Hillsborough County for Gov. Graham, 1979-83; chair State Adv. Com. on Tchr. Edn., 1987; vis. scholar N.C. Disting. Vis. Scholars Program, Chapel Hill, 1989; mem. edn. stds. commn. State of Fla., 1990-93; active Nat. Coun. for Accreditation Tchr. Edn. Rev. Team Banks, 1977—, Thirteenth Cir. Jud. Nominating Commn., 1979-83, Gov. Commn. on Status of Women, 1981-85, Gov. Adv. Com. on Edn. Block Grants, 1981-85, Joint Exec. and Legis. Task Force for Tchr. Edn. Quality Improvement, 1982-84, Human Resource Devel. Adv. Com., 1987, Gov.-Elect Lawton Chiles' Edn. Core Task Force, 1990-91; cons., presenter in field. Contbr. articles to profl. jours. Vol. dir. comm. network for Graham Campaign, Tampa, 1976-78; vol. coord. rsch. and adminstrv. transition staff Gov. Graham, Tallahassee, 1978-79; vol. mgr. Hillsborough Campaign for Graham, 1978, Hillsborough County Campaign for Commr. Ed. Ralph Turlington, Tampa, 1982, Hillsborough Campaign for U.S. Senate Bob Graham, Tampa, 1986; bd. dirs. March of Dimes, 1986; active Pres. Adv. Com. for Women, 1980, Mil. Acad. Nominating Bd., 1987—. Recipient Gov. award for outstanding Fla. woman, 1981, Profl. Accomplishment award Thiel Coll., 1989. Mem. ASCD, Am. Assn. Colls. for Tchr. Edn. (Showcase of Excellence award for outstanding accomplishments with talented students 1985), Am. Ednl. Rsch. Assn., Assn. Tchr. Educators (del. 1978-82, mem. exec. bd. 1978-82, chairperson nat. ad hoc com. to establish coun. state pres. 1979-80, mem. '90 com. 1984-86), Fla. Assn. Tchr. Educators (chairperson pub. rels. and publicity com. 1975-76, v.p. 1977, chairperson com. for pub. rels. 1977, program chmn. 1977-78, pres. 1978-79, legis. liaison 1979-80), Greater Tampa C. of C. (mem. edn. coun. 1982—, chair state task force on govt. 1984-85), Phi Delta Kappa (chair scholarship fund 1988-89, 90-91). Democrat. Lutheran. Avocations: reading, gardening, flower arranging. Office: Fla Lottery Capitol Complex Tallahassee FL 32399-4002

MANN, MARION, physician, educator; b. Atlanta, Mar. 29, 1920; s. Levi James and Cora (Casey) M.; m. Ruth Maurine Reagin, Jan. 16, 1943; children: Marion Jr., Judith (Mrs. Kenneth Walk). B.S. in Edn, Tuskegee Inst., Ala., 1940; M.D., Howard U., 1954; Ph.D., Georgetown U., 1961, D.Sc. (hon.), 1979; D.Sc. (hon.), U. Mass., 1984; grad. U.S. Army Command and Gen. Staff Coll., 1965, U.S. Army War Coll., 1970. Diplomate: Nat. Bd. Med. Examiners, Am. Bd. Pathology. Intern USPHS Hosp., Staten Island, N.Y., 1954-55; resident Georgetown U. Hosp., 1956-60; practice medicine, specializing in pathology Washington, 1961—; instr. pathology Georgetown U., 1960-61; professorial lectr. Georgetown U. (Sch. Medicine), 1970-73; asst. prof. pathology Howard U. Coll. Medicine, 1961-67, assoc. prof., 1967-70,

prof., 1970, dean, 1970-79; v.p. rsch. Howard U., 1988-91. Capt. AUS, 1942-50; brig. gen. Res. Mem. Inst. Medicine, Nat. Acad. Scis., Alpha Omega Alpha. Mem. United Ch. of Christ. Home: 1453 Whittier Pl NW Washington DC 20012-2845 Office: 520 W St NW Washington DC 20059-0001

MANN, MARVIN L., electronics executive; b. Birmingham, Ala., Apr. 22, 1933; s. Jesse Marvin and Nannie Leola (Thomason) M.; m. Frances Nell Marlin, Dec. 24, 1953; children: Tara Jane, Jeffery Loy. BS, Samford U., 1954; MBA, U. Ala., 1958. Chmn., pres., chief exec. officer Lexmark Internat., Inc., Greenwich, Conn. Office: Lexmark Internat Inc 55 Railroad Ave Greenwich CT 06830-6302*

MANN, MICHAEL K., producer, director, writer; b. Chgo. Ed.: U. Wis. Dir.: (documentary) 18 Days Down the Line; scriptwriter, dir.: (TV movie) The Jericho Mile, 1979 (Dir. Guild Am. Best Dir. award), (film) The Keep, 1983; screenwriter, exec. prodr., dir.: Thief, 1981; screenwriter, dir., prodr.: Manhunter, 1986, Last of the Mohicans, 1992; exec. prodr. (TV show) Miami Vice, Crime Story, (TV miniseries) Drug Wars: Camarena Story (Emmy award), Drug Wars: Cocaine Cartel; scriptwriter: (TV episodes) Starsky and Hutch, Police Story. Mem. Writers Guild. Office: 1658 10th St Santa Monica CA 90404 care: CAA 9830 Wilshire Blvd Beverly Hills CA 90212*

MANN, MICHAEL MARTIN, electronics company executive; b. N.Y.C., Nov. 28, 1939; s. Herbert and Rosalind (Kaplan) M.; m. Mariel Joy Steinberg, Apr. 25, 1965. BSEE, Calif. Inst. Tech., 1960, MSEE, 1961; PhD in Elec. Engring. and Physics, U. So. Calif., 1969; MBA, UCLA, 1984. Cert. bus. appraiser, profl. cons., mgmt. cons., lic. real estate broker, Calif. Mgr. high power laser programs office Northrop Corp., Hawthorne, Calif., 1969-76; mgr. high energy laser systems lab. Hughes Aircraft Co., El Segundo, Calif., 1976-78; mgr. E-0 control systems labs. Hughes Aircraft Co., El Segundo, 1978-83, asst. to v.p., space & strategic, 1983-84; exec. v.p. Helionetics Inc., Irvine, Calif., 1984-85, pres., chief exec. officer, 1985-86, also bd. dirs.; ptnr. Mann Kavanaugh Chernove, 1986-87; sr. cons. Arthur D. Little, Inc., 1987-88; chmn. bd., pres., CEO, Blue Marble Devel. Group, Inc., 1988—; exec. assoc. Ctr. Internat. Cooperation and Trade, 1989—; sr. assoc. Corp. Fin. Assocs., 1990—; exec. assoc. Reece and Assocs., 1991—; dir. Reece & Assocs., 1991—; mng. dir. Blue Marble Ptnrs. Ltd, 1991—; chmn. bd. dirs., CEO Blue Marble Ptnrs., 1992—; chmn., CEO, En Compass Techs., Inc., Torrance, Calif., 1994—; mem. Army Sci. Bd., Dept. Army, Washington, 1986-91; chmn. Ballistic Missile Def. Panel, Directed Energy Weapon Panel, Rsch. and New Initiatives Panel; coms. Office of Sec. of Army, Washington, 1986—, Inst. of Def. Analysis, Washington, 1978—, Dept. Energy, 1988—, Nat. Riverside Rsch. Inst., 1990—; bd. dirs. Datum, Inc.,1988—, Fail-Safe Tech., Corp., 1989-90, Safeguard Health Enterprises, Inc., 1988—, Am. Video Communications, Inc., Meck Industries, Inc., 1987-88, Decade Optical Systems, Inc., 1990—, Forum Mil. Application Directed Energy, 1992—, Am. Bus. Consultants, Inc., 1993—; chmn. bd. Mgmt. Tech., Inc. 1991—, Encompass Tech., Inc., 1994—; bd. dirs., mem. adv. bd. Micro-Frame, Inc. 1988-91; chmn. bd. HLX Laser, Inc., 1984-86; bd. dirs. Cons's. Roundtable, 1992—, Am. Bus. Cons., Inc., 1993—; rsch. assoc., mem. extension teaching staff U. So. Calif., L.A., 1964-70; chmn. Ballistic Missile Def. Subgroup, 1989-90, Tactical Directed Energy Weapons Subgroup, 1988-90; chmn., chief exec. officer Mgmt. Tech., Inc., 1991—; dir. Am. Bus. Cons., Inc., 1993—. Contbg. editor, mem. adv. bd. Calif. High-Tech Funding Jour., 1989-90; contbr. over 50 tech. articles to profl. jours.; patentee in field. Adv. com. to Engring. Sch., Calif. State U., Long Beach, 1985—; chmn. polit. affairs Am. Electronics Assn., Orange County Coun., 1986-87, mem. exec. com., 1986-88; adv. com. several Calif. congressmen, 1985—; mem. dean's coun. UCLA Grad. Sch. Mgmt., 1984-85; bd. dirs. Archimedes Circle U. Soc. Calif., 1983-85, Ctr. for Innovation and Entrepreneurship, 1986-90, Caltech/MIT Venture Forum, 1987-91. Hicks fellow in Indsl. Rels. Calif. Inst. Tech., 1961, Hewlett Packard fellow. Mem. So. Calif. Tech. Execs. Network, IEEE (sr.), Orange County CEO's Roundtable, Pres.' Roundtable, Nat. Assoc. Corp. Dirs., Aerospace/Def. CEO's Roundtable, Am. Def. Preparedness Assn., Security Affairs Support Assn., Acad. Profl. Cons. and Advisors, Internat. Platform Assn., Inst. of Mgmt. Cons's., Pres. Assn., Nat. Assn. Corp. Dirs., Cons's. Roundtable, Pres. Assn., King Harbor Yacht Club. Republican. Avocations: sailing, photography, writing. Home: 4248 Via Alondra Palos Verdes Peninsula CA 90274-1545 Office: Blue Marble Partners 406 Amapola Ave Ste 200 Torrance CA 90501-6229

MANN, NANCY LOUISE (NANCY LOUISE ROBBINS), entrepreneur; b. Chillicothe, Ohio, May 6, 1925; d. Everett Chaney and Pauline Elizabeth R.; m. Kenneth Douglas Mann, June 19, 1949 (div. June 1979); children: Bryan Wilkinson, Laura Elizabeth. BA in Math., UCLA, 1948, MA in Math., 1949, PhD in Biostatistics, 1965. Sr. scientist Rocketdyne Div. of Rockwell Internat., Canoga Park, Calif., 1962-75; mem. tech. staff Rockwell Sci. Ctr., Thousand Oaks, Calif., 1975-78; rsch. prof. UCLA Biomath., L.A., 1978-87; pres., CEO, owner Quality Enhancement Seminars, Inc., L.A., 1982—; pres., CEO Quality and Productivity, Inc., L.A., 1987—; curriculum adv. UCLA Ext. Dept. of Bus. and Mgmt., L.A., 1991—; mem. com. on Nat. Statistics, Nat. Acad. Scis., Washington, 1978-82; mem adv. bd. to supt. U.S. Naval Posgrad. Sch., Monterey, Calif., 1979-82. Co-author: Methods for Analysis of Reliability and Life Data, 1974; author: Keys to Excellence, 1985, The Story of the Deming Philosophy, 2d edit., 1987, 3d edit., 1989; contbr. articles to profl. jours. Recipient award IEEE Reliability Soc., 1982, ASQC Reliability Divsn., 1986. Fellow Am. Statis. Assn. (v.p. 1982-84); mem. Internat. Statis. Inst. Office: Quality and Productivity Inc 1081 Westwood Blvd # 217 Los Angeles CA 90024-2911

MANN, OSCAR, physician, internist, educator; b. Paris, Oct. 13, 1934; came to U.S., 1953; s. Aron and Helen (Biegun) M.; m. Amy S. Mann, July 19, 1964; children: Adriana, Karen. AA with distinction, George Washington U., 1958; MD cum laude, Georgetown U., 1962. Diplomate Am. Bd. Med. Examiners, Am. Bd. Internal Medicine, Am. Bd. Internal Medicine subspecialty Cardiovascular Disease; cert. advanced achievement in internal medicine; re-cert. in internal medicine. Intern Georgetown U. Med. Ctr., Washington, 1962-63, jr. asst. med. resident, 1963-64, clin. fellow in cardiology with Proctor Harvey program, 1965-66; sr. asst. resident in medicine Georgetown svc. D.C. Gen. Hosp., Washington, 1964-65; clin. prof. medicine Georgetown U. Sch. Medicine, 1985—, also chair med. alumni bd.; pvt. practice internal medicine and cardiology, Washington, 1966—; mem. Med.-Nursing Audit Com., CME adv. com., teaching. adv. com., Opthamology dept. rev. com., surgery dept. rev. com., faculty com., search com. for a new dean for acad. affairs Georgetown U. Med. Ctr.; appointed coun. to the dean Georgetown U. Sch. Medicine, 1977—; mem. Instnl. Self Study Task Force. Contbr. articles to profl. jours. Served with the U.S. Army, 1953-55. Recipient Mead Johnson Postgrad. Scholar ACP, 1964-65, Physicians Recognition award AMA, 1987—, Advanced Achievement in Internal Medicine, 1987. Fellow ACP, Am. Coll. Cardiology, Am. Coll. Chest Physicians; mem. AMA, Am. Soc. Internal Med., Am. Heart Assn. (coun. clin. cardiology), Med. Soc. D.C., Cosmos Club, Georgetown U. Alumni Assn. (bd. govs., nat. chmn. of med. alumni fund 1993), Alpha Omega Alpha, Phi Delta Epsilon. Avocations: reading, swimming, biking, fitness, racquetball. Home: 4925 Weaver Ter NW Washington DC 20016-2660 Office: Foxhall Internists PC 3301 New Mexico Ave NW Washington DC 20016-3600

MANN, ROBERT ALLEN, banker; b. Beaumont, Tex., Jan. 31, 1931; s. David Perry and Hattie Lucille (Barclay) M.; m. Mary Louise Myers, Oct. 12, 1952 (div. July 1981); children—Mary Hyden Mann Hunter, David Wake, Allen Barclay; m. Carole Darlene Humphrey, July 10, 1982. BBA in Banking and Fin., So. Methodist U., 1950. Chmn. bd. Citizens State Bank, Woodville, Tex., 1950—; bd. First Fin. Corp., Waco, Tex., 1969—, also bd. dirs.; chmn. bd. First Nat. Bank, Waco, 1971-73, Omnibus Corp., Waco, 1975—, United Bankers Ins. Waco, 1977—; chmn. bd. Sabine Bank, Port Arthur, Tex., 1961-83, First Bank & Trust, Bryan, Tex., 1973-83; pres. Fidelity Services, Waco, 1970-71; mng. ptnr. Cen. Tex. Broadcasting Co., Waco, 1977—; bd. dirs. United Bank of Waco. Bd. dirs. Waco Christian Sch. Served with USAF, 1950-51. Mem. Assn. Bank Holding Cos. World Bus. Council, 49ers (Young Pres. Orgn.) Rep., Rep. Inner Circle, Waco Bus. League (bd. dirs.). Methodist. Clubs: Masons, Shriners, Rotary. Home:

4424 Village Oak Dr Waco TX 76710-1432 Office: United Bankers Inc 510 N Valley Mills Dr Ste 600 Waco TX 76710-6078

MANN, ROBERT NATHANIEL, violinist; b. Portland, Oreg., July 19, 1920; s. Charles Emanuel and Anna (Schnitzer) M.; m. Lucy Rowan, July 27, 1951; children: Lisa, Nicholas. Grad., Inst. Musical Art; diploma, Juilliard Sch. Music; hon. doctorate, Earlham Coll., Mich. State U., Jacksonville U. Mem. faculty Juilliard Sch., 1946—; resident mem. quartet Library of Congress, 1963-88; artistic dir. Revenia Stearns Inst., 1988—; panelist Nat. Endowment for Arts; pres. Walter Naumburg Found. First violinist, Juilliard Quartet, 1946—; composer numerous works for violin, piano, orch., chamber music. Bd. dirs. N.Y. Philharmonic. Served with AUS, 1943-46. Recipient Chamber Music Svc. award, 1991, String Tchrs. award, 1991, Peabody medal of honor, 1991. Mem. Am. Composers Alliance, Juilliard Sch. Music Alumni Assn. Clubs: Century, Bohemian. *

MANN, ROBERT WELLESLEY, biomedical engineer, educator; b. Bklyn., Oct. 6, 1924; s. Arthur Wellesley and Helen (Rieger) M.; m. Margaret Ida Florencourt, Sept. 4, 1950; children: Robert Wellesley, Catherine Louise. SB, MIT, 1950, SM, 1951, ScD, 1957. With Bell Telephone Labs., N.Y.C., 1942-43, 46-47; research engr. MIT, 1951-52, rsch. supr., 1952, mem. faculty, 1953—, prof. mech. engring., 1963-70, Germeshausen prof., 1970-72, prof. engring., 1972-74, Whitaker prof. biomed. engring., 1974-92, Whitaker prof. emeritus, sr. lectr., 1992—; head systems and design div., mech. engring. dept., 1957-68, 82-83, founder, dir. engring. projects lab., 1959-62; founder, chmn. steering com. Center Sensory Aids Evaluation and Devel., 1964-86, chmn. div. health scis., tech., planning and mgmt., 1972-74, founder, dir. Newman biomechanics and human rehab. lab., 1975-92; dir. bioengring. programs Whitaker Coll. MIT, 1986-89; dir. Harvard-MIT Rehab. Engring. Ctr., 1988-93; exec. com. Div. Health Scis. and Tech. Harvard U. MIT joint program, 1972-85; prof., 1979—, mem. Com. on Use of Humans as Exptl. Subjects MIT, 1984-93, co-chair Pub. Svc. Ctr., 1988-92; lectr. engring. Faculty of Medicine, Harvard U., 1973-79; research assoc. in orthopedic surgery Children's Hosp. Med. Center, 1973—; cons. in engring. sci. Mass. Gen. Hosp., 1969—; cons. in field, 1953—; mem. Nat. Commn. Engring. Edn., 1962-69; com. prosthetics research and devel. NRC, 1963-69, chmn. sensory aids subcom., 1965-68, com. skeletal system, 1969-71; mem. com. interplay engring. with biology and medicine Nat. Acad. Engring., 1969-73; mem. bd. health scis. policy Inst. Medicine, 1973-74, 82-86; mem. com. on nat. needs for rehab. physically handicapped Nat. Acad. Scis., 1975-76; mem.-at-large confs. com. Engring. Found., 1975-81; Mem. Commn. on Life Scis., NRC, 1984-88, Commn. on Strategic Tech. for U.S. Army, 1989-93; NRC, commn. on Space Biology and Medicine, 1992-95. Cons. editor: Ency. Sci. and Tech.; assoc. editor: IEEE Trans. in Biomed. Engring., 1969-78, ASME Jour. Biomech. Engring., 1976-82; mem. editorial bd. Jour. Visual Impairment and Blindness, 1976-80, SOMA, 1986-92; mem. editorial adv. bd. new liberal arts program Alfred P. Sloan Found., 1986-92; contbr. numerous articles to profl. jours. Pres., trustee Amanda Caroline Payson Scholarship Fund, 1965-86; bd. dirs. Carroll Ctr. for Blind, 1967-74, pres., 1968-74; mem. corp. Perkins Sch. for Blind, 1970—, Mt. Auburn Hosp., 1972—; trustee Nat. Braille Press, 1991—, pres., 1990-94; mem. Cardinal's adv. com. on social justice Archdiocese of Boston, 1993—; bd. overseers St. Marguerite D'Youville Found., Youville Hosp. and Rehab. Ctr., 1994—. With U.S. Army Signal Corps, 1943-46. Recipient Sloan award for outstanding performance, 1957, Talbert Abrams photogrammetry award, 1962, award Assn. Blind of Mass., 1969, IR-100 award for Braillembos, 1972, Bronze Beaver award MIT, 1975, UCP Goldenson Rsch. for Handicapped award, 1976, H.R. Lissner award, 1977, New Eng. award, 1979, J.R. Killian Faculty Achievement award MIT, 1983, M.L. King Jr. Leadership award MIT, 1995. Fellow Am. Acad. Arts and Scis., Am. Inst. Med. and Biol. Engring., IEEE (mem. editl. bd. Spectrum 1984-86), AAAS, ASME (Gold medal 1977); mem. NAS, Inst. Medicine NAS, NAE, Biomed. Engring. Soc. (bd. dirs. 1981-84), Orthopedic Rsch. Soc., Rehab. Soc. N.Am., MIT Alumni/ae Assn. (pres. 1983-84, Alumni Fund Bd. 1978-80, bd. dirs. 1980-86, 93—, corp. joint adv. com. 1983-84, chair nat. selector com. 1985-88, awards com. 1992-94, chmn. 1994, bd. Tech. Rev. 1986—, chmn., 1993—), Sigma Xi (nat. lectr. 1979-81), Tau Beta Pi, Pi Tau Sigma, Sigma Xi. Roman Catholic. Achievements include patents in field. Home: 5 Pelham Rd Lexington MA 02173-5707 Office: MIT 77 Massachusetts Ave Rm 3-137 Cambridge MA 02139-3594

MANN, SAM HENRY, JR., lawyer; b. St. Petersburg, Fla., Aug. 2, 1925; s. Sam Henry and Vivian (Moore) M.; m. Mary Joan Bishop, Sept. 7, 1948; children: Vivian Louise, Sam Henry III, Wallace Bishop. BA, Yale U., 1948; LLB, Fla. U., 1951. Bar: Fla. 1951, U.S. Dist. Ct. (so. dist.) Fla. 1951, U.S. Ct. Appeals 1955, U.S. Supreme Ct. 1971. Ptnr. Greene, Mann, Rowe, Stanton, Mastry & Burton, St. Petersburg, 1951-84, Harris, Barrett, Mann & Dew, St. Petersburg, 1984—. Trustee, v.p. Mus. Fine Arts, St. Petersburg, 1980-94, Eckerd Coll., St. Petersburg, 1976-79, Webb Sch., Bell Buckle, Tenn., 1966-75; bd. dirs. Regional Community Blood Ctr., St. Petersburg, 1966—, Fla. Blood Svcs., 1993-94; mem., chmn. H. Milton Rogers Heart Found.; bd. dirs., pres. Family and Children's Svc., Inc., 1956-61. With USNR, 1943-46. Fellow Am. Coll. Trial Lawyers, Am. Bar Found., Fla. Bar Found.; mem. ABA, Fla. Bar Assn., Am. Counsel Assn., Def. Rsch. Inst., Internat. Assn. Def. Counsel, Phi Alpha Delta. Republican. Presbyterian. Avocations: RV travel, boating, gardening, workshop. Home: 531 Brightwaters Blvd NE Saint Petersburg FL 33704-3713 Office: Harris Barrett Mann & Dew Ste 1500 Southtrust Bank Bldg Saint Petersburg FL 33731-1441

MANN, SEYMOUR ZALMON, political science and public administration educator emeritus, union official; b. Chgo., Mar. 29, 1921; s. Morris and Sarah (Julius) M.; m. Irene Eincig, Aug. 30, 1942; children: Martin R., Sheldon H., Jeanette P. Student, Wright Coll., 1938-40; BE, No. Ill. U. (formerly No. Ill. State Tchr.'s Coll.), 1942; MA, U. Chgo., 1948, PhD, 1951. Instr. polit. sci. Triple Cities Coll., Syracuse U., 1948-51; asst. prof. Harpur Coll., State U. N.Y., 1951-55, assoc. prof. polit. sci., 1955-60, chmn. dept., 1953-58; dir. pub. adminstrn. and met. affairs program, prof. govt. So. Ill. U., Edwardsville, 1960-67; chmn., prof. urban affairs dept. urban affairs Hunter Coll./CUNY, 1967-77; dir. Urban Research Center, 1967-68, chmn. dept. urban affairs, 1968-73; dep. to execs. dist. council 37, Am. Fedn. State, County and Mcpl. Employees, AFL-CIO, 1977-79; prof. govt. and public adminstrn., assoc. dir. Nat. Center Public Productivity, John Jay Coll. Criminal Justice, CUNY, 1980-86; mem. profl. staff Congress; vis. expert rsch. staff Office Pub. Affairs, High Commr.'s Office, Germany, 1954; cons. Southwestern Ill. Govtl. Study Commn., 1961-62; vis. prof. U. So. Calif. Sch. Pub. Adminstrn., 1967; co-chmn. Ill. U-State Agy. Coun., 1965-67; chmn. nat. commn. on urban affairs Am. Jewish Congress, 1977-81, mem. nat. governing coun., 1991—; cons., coord. spl. projects dist. coun. 37 Am. Fedn. State, County and Mcpl. Employees, N.Y.C., 1972-77. Author: (with others) From the Wagner Act to the Taft-Hartley Act, 1950, (with Charlotte B. Smart) Land Use and Planning in the Cleveland Metropolitan Area, 1959, (with R.R. Boyce) Urbanism in Illinois: Its Nature Importance and Problems, 1965, Chicago's War on poverty, 1966; contbr. to: Cases in State and Local Government, 1961, Cases in American National Government and Politics, 1978, The Politics of Productivity: State and Local Focus, 1980, Labor Management Cooperation and Worker Participation: A Public Sector Focus, 1989, play Summing Up in Public Voices, 1993; mem. editl. bd. Public Productivity and Management Rev., Pub. Voices. Served with AUS, 1943-45, ETO. Fellow Social Sci. Research Council, 1949-50; Fulbright prof. W. Germany, 1953-54; Fulbright prof. Tel Aviv (Israel) U., 1974-75. Mem. Am. Polit. Scis. Assn., Am. Soc. for Pub. Adminstrn. (pres. St. Louis met. chpt. 1964-65), Am. Arbitration Assn. (nat. labor panel), Soc. of Children's Book Writers and Illustrators, Poetry Soc. Va. Home and Office: 203 Yoakum Pkwy # 1111 Alexandria VA 22304 *It will have to be left to others to judge what success I may have obtained. There have, however, been some guiding principles which seemed to have given direction to my life's course and undoubtedly impacted on whatever professional recognition has come my way. These include: a profound respect for democratic ideology—particularly the notion that each person should have the opportunity to achieve his/her fullest potential; a clear recognition that wisdom and knowledge are not the same; and that listening is harder than talking, though it is the most important element in human communication.*

MANN, SUSAN, university educator; b. Ottawa, Ont., Can. Feb. 10, 1941; d. Walter and Marjorie Mann; m. Nicholas Trofimenkoff; 1 child, Britt. BA in Modern History, U. Toronto, 1963; MA in History, U. Western Ont.,

1965; PhD, U. Laval, Que., Can., 1970; LLD (hon.), Concordia U., Montreal, Que, Can., 1989, U. Ottawa, 1994. Lectr. English Toyo Eiwa Jogakuin, Tokyo, 1963-64; lectr. in history U. Montreal, 1966-70; asst. prof. history U. Calgary, Alta., Can., 1970-72; from asst. to assoc. prof. U. Ottawa, Ont., Can., 1972-83, prof. history, 1983—, chmn. dept. history, 1977-80, vice rector acad., 1984-90; pres. York U., Toronto, Ont., 1992—; mem. stamp adv. com. Can. Post Corp., Ottawa, 1988-92; chmn. adv. bd. Nat. Archives Can., 1989-91. Author: (as Susan Mann Trofimenkoff) Action Française: French Canadian Nationalism in the 1920s, 1975, Stanley Knowles: The Man From Winnipeg North Centre, 1982, Dream of Nation: A Social and Intellectual History of Quebec, 1983 (Sec. of State Canadian Studies prize 1984), Visions nationales: Une histoire du Québec, 1986; editor: The Twenties in Western Canada, 1972, Abbé Groulx: Variations on a Nationalist Theme, 1973, (with Alison Prentice) The Neglected Majority: Essays in Canadian Women's History, vol. I, 1977, vol II, 1985; acad. editor Social Scis. in Can., 1974-76; assoc. editor Social History, 1982-84; contbr. articles to profl. jours. Assessor of projects SSHRCC, 1972—; chmn., aid to scholarly publs. com. Social Sci. Fedn. Can., 1976-79; mem. appraisals com. Ont. Coun. Grad. Studies, 1983-84; pres. Can. Hist. Assn., 1984-85; chair status of women com. Coun. Ont. Univs., 1985-88; mem. Summer Inst. Women in Higher Edn. Adminstrn. Bryn Mawr (Pa.) Coll., 1986; co-founder Sr. Women Acad. Adminstrs. Can. Publ. Publ. grantee SSHRCC, 1975, Leave fellow, 1980-81, Doctoral fellow Can. Coun., 1968-70; U. Toronto scholar, 1959-61, U. Western Ont. scholar, 1964. Fellow Royal Soc. Can., Canadian Rsch. Inst. Advancement Women (hon., life, founder, bd. dirs. 1976-78). Office: York Univ Office of Pres, 4700 Keele St, North York, ON Canada M3J 1P3

MANN, THEODORE, theatrical producer and artistic director; b. N.Y.C., May 13, 1924; s. Martin M. and Gwen (Artson) Goldman; m. Patricia A. Brooks, Oct. 5, 1953; children: Andrew, Jonathan. Asso. B.A., Salinas (Calif.) Jr. Coll., 1945; LL.B., Bklyn. Law Sch., 1949. Co-founder, co-producer, artistic dir. Circle in the Square Theatre, N.Y.C., 1951—; co-founder Circle in the Sq. Theatre Sch., 1961. Co-producer: Long Day's Journey into Night (Antoinette Perry award as best prodn. of year 1956-57), 1956 (Pulitzer prize, N.Y. Drama Critics award); producer: Carnegie Hall Concert Series, 1955-69; co-founder: Washington Sq. Park Concert Series, 1955; dir.: A Moon for the Misbegotten, Ah Wilderness!, Morning Becomes Electra, Trumpets of the Lord, Morning, Noon and Night, Arsenic and Old Lace,John and Abigail, The Iceman Cometh, Where's Charley?, The Glass Menagerie, Pal Joey, Romeo and Juliet, Awake and Sing, and many others; producer-dir.: Ford's Theatre, Washington, 1971—; host: radio show Conversations with Circle in the Square Sta, WNYC, 1978; Author: Producers on Producing, 1975. Served with USAAF, 1943-45. Recipient Vernon Rice award, 1956, Page One award Newspaper Guild, 1960, Tony spl. award, 1976. Office: Circle in the Sq Theatre 1633 Broadway New York NY 10019-6708

MANN, THEODORE R., lawyer; b. Kosica, Czechoslovakia, Jan. 31, 1928; came to U.S., 1929, naturalized, 1930; s. Aaron and Bertha (Schreiber) M.; m. Rowena Joan Weiss, 1954; children: Julie Ellen, Rachel Beth, Marcus Eliyahu. Pvt. practice Phila., 1953—; ptnr. Mann, Ungar & Spector; advocate in civil liberties, anti-trust and securities fraud cases. Chmn., pres. Nat. Jewish Community Rels. Adv. Coun., 1976-80; Conf. Pres. Major Am. Jewish Orgns., 1978-80; Nat. Conf. Soviet Jewry, 1981-83; Am. Jewish Congress, 1984-88; Mazon-A Jewish Response to Hunger, 1985-90; co-chair Project Nishma, 1988—; trustee New Israel Fund, Jewish Fund for Christian Rescuers. Fellow Temple U. Alumni. Office: 1709 Spruce St Philadelphia PA 19103-6103

MANN, THOMAS EDWARD, political scientist; b. Milw., Sept. 10, 1944; s. Edward Emil and Eleanor (Hoffman) M.; m. Sheilah Rosenhack, June 4, 1976; children: Edward Matthew, Stephanie Rachael. B.A., U. Fla., 1966; M.A., U. Mich., 1968, Ph.D., 1977. Staff assoc. Am. Polit. Sci. Assn., Washington, 1970-76, asst. dir., 1977-81, exec. dir., 1981-87; co-dir. congress project Am. Enterprise Inst., Washington, 1979-81; dir. govtl. studies Brookings Instn., 1987—, W. Averell Harrimann sr. fellow in Am. governance, 1991—; mem. bd. overseers Nat. Election Study, 1987-94, chmn., 1990-94. Author: Unsafe At Any Margin, 1978; co-author: Vital Statistics on Congress, 1980, 82, 84-85, 87-88, 89-90, 91-92, 93-94, Renewing Congress, 1992, 93; co-editor: The New Congress, 1981, The American Elections of 1982, 1983, Media Polls in American Politics, 1992, Values and Public Policy, 1994, Elections at Home and Abroad, 1994, Congress, the Press, and the Public, 1994; editor: A Question of Balance: The President, The Congress and Foreign Policy, 1990. Mem. Democratic Nat. Com.'s Commn. on Presdl. Nomination and Party Structure, 1975-78; mem. tech. com. Dem. Nat. Com. Commn. on Presdl. Nominations, 1981-82, The Fairness Commn., 1985. U. Mich. NDEA grad. fellow, 1966-69; Am. Polit. Sci. Assn. Congl. fellow, 1969-70. Fellow Am. Acad. Arts and Scis., Nat. Acad. Pub. Adminstrn.; mem. Coun. on Fgn. Rels., Phi Beta Kappa. Home: 6508 Goldleaf Dr Bethesda MD 20817-5837 Office: Brookings Instn 1775 Massachusetts Ave NW Washington DC 20036-2188

MANN, TIMOTHY, corporate executive; b. Hackensack, N.J., July 24, 1942; s. Conklin and Hermione (Hatch) M.; m. Rosemary Teresa Connell, Feb. 26, 1965 (div. July 1993); children: Timothy, Sean Douglas, Patrick Devlin; m. Margaret Ann Tyrie, Nov. 20, 1993. Student U. Colo., 1960-61, Monmouth Coll., 1961-65, BS, 1965; postgrad. U. North Fla., 1980. Product mgr. Am. Brands, Inc., N.Y.C., 1965-70; account supr. Cargill Wilson & Acree, Inc., Richmond, Va., 1970-74; sr. mktg. mgr. Liggett & Myers Tobacco Co., Durham, N.C., 1974-78; sr. v.p. mktg. and sales Swisher Internat., Inc., Jacksonville, Fla., 1978-86, pres., 1986—, mem. mgmt. com., 1978—; pres., CEO export divsn. Swisher Internat., Inc., 1990—. Bd. dirs. Jr. Achievement of Jacksonville, Jacksonville Pvt. Industry Coun.; active Jacksonville Community Coun., Inc., 1980-87, N.E. Fla. Coun. Boy Scouts Am. Recipient N.J. Mortgage Bankers award, 1965. Mem. Cigar Assn. Am. (dir., v.p.), Am. Wholesale Marketers Assn., Tobacco Mchts. Assn. (bd. dirs.), Am. Mgmt. Assn., River Club. Office: Swisher Internat Inc PO Box 2230 Jacksonville FL 32203-2230

MANNE, HENRY GIRARD, lawyer, educator; b. New Orleans, May 10, 1928; s. Geoffrey and Eva (Shainberg) M.; m. Bobbette Lee Taxer, Aug. 19, 1958; children: Emily Kay, Geoffrey Adam. B.A., Vanderbilt U., 1950; J.D., U. Chgo., 1952; LL.M., Yale U., 1953, J.S.D., 1966; LLD, U. Puget Sound, 1987, U. Francisco Marroquin, Guatemala, 1987. Bar: Ill. 1952, N.Y. 1969. Practice in Chgo., 1953-54; asso. prof. Law Sch., St. Louis U., 1956-57, 59-62; prof. Law Sch., George Washington U., 1962-68; Kenan prof. law and polit. sci. U. Rochester, 1968-74; Disting. prof. law, dir. Law and Econs. Center, U. Miami Law Sch., 1974-80; prof. law Law and Econs. Center, Emory U., Atlanta, 1980-86; dean, univ. prof. chmn. Law and Econs. Ctr. George Mason U. Sch. Law, 1986—; vis. prof. law U. Wis., Madison, 1957-59, Stanford (Calif.) Law Sch., 1971-72; dir. Econs. Insts. Fed. Judges, 1976-89. Author: Insider Trading and the Stock Market, 1966, (with H. Wallich) The Modern Corporation and Social Responsibility, 1973, (with E. Solomon) Wall Street in Transition, 1974, Med. Malpractice Guidebook: Law and Economics, 1985; editor: (with Roger LeRoy Miller) Gold, Money and the Law, 1975; editor: (with Roger LeRoy Miller) Auto Safety Regulation: The Cure or the Problem, 1976, Economic Policy and the Regulation of Corporate Securities, 1968, The Economics of Legal Relationships, 1975; editor: (with James Dorn) Econ. Liberties and the Judiciary, 1987. Served to 1st lt. USAAF, 1954-56. Recipient Salvatori award Excellence in Acad. Leadership, 1994; named Cultural Laureate of Va., 1992. Fellow Am. Bar Found.; mem. Am. Law Inst., Am. Econs. Assn., Am. Law and Econs. Assn. (hon. life, Salvatori award for excellence in acad. leadership 1994), Mont Pelerin Soc., Order of Coif, Phi Beta Kappa.

MANNERING, JERRY VINCENT, agronomist, educator; b. Custer, Okla., June 14, 1929; s. James Bryan and Verta (Bates) M.; m. Marjorie McVicker, June 20, 1953; children: Debra Lynn Mannering Zerman, Stephen Scott, Lisa Gaye Mannering Schwingendorf. B.S., Okla. State U., 1951; M.S., Purdue U., 1956, Ph.D., 1967. Cert. profl. soil scientist, profl. soil erosion and sediment control specialist. Grad. asst. Purdue U., West Lafayette, Ind., 1954-56, extension agronomist, prof. agronomy, 1967-89; prof. emeritus, 1990—; research agronomist U. Idaho, Aberdeen, 1956-58; research soil scientist Agrl. Research Sta., USDA, West Lafayette, 1958-67; cons. FAO, Bulgaria, 1972, Govt. of Brazil, 1975. Contbr. numerous articles on agro-

nomy to profl. jours. Served to 1st lt. U.S. Army, 1951-54. Decorated Purple Heart; recipient Hovde award Purdue U. and Ind. Farm Bur., 1982. Fellow Soil Conservation Soc. Am., Soil Sci. Soc. Am., Am. Soc. Agronomy; mem. Internat. Soil Sci. Soc., Internat. Soil Tillage Research Orgn., Lions Club. Office: Purdue Univ Dept Agronomy West Lafayette IN 47907

MANNERS, GEORGE EMANUEL, business educator, emeritus dean; b. N.Y.C., Nov. 26, 1910; s. John Emanuel and Demetra (Kremida) M.; m. Claire Gibson, Oct. 14, 1939; children—George Emanuel, Susan Demetra. B.S. in Commerce, Ga. State U., 1935; M.B.A. in Econs, U. Ga., 1946; Ph.D. in History, Emory U., 1959. Bookkeeper and acct. Ga., 1927-37; pub. acct., 1937; high sch. tchr. Atlanta, 1937-39, 41-42, 46-47; test technician merit system Ga. Labor Dept., 1939-41; mem. faculty Ga. State U. (and predecessor), 1947—; dean Sch. Bus. Adminstrn. Ga. State U., 1950-69, asst. v.p., 1969-70, assoc. v.p., 1970—, Regents' prof., 1971—, dean emeritus, 1977—; dean Sch. Mgmt., Rensselaer Poly. Inst., Troy, N.Y., 1979-80; dir. Univ. Ctr. in Ga., Inc., 1980-83; dean protem, Sch. Bus. and Econs. Mercer U. Atlanta, 1986-87; Mem. Met. Planning Commn., Atlanta, 1949-59, Atlanta Regional Export Expansion Council. Author: History of Life Insurance Company in Georgia, 1891-1955, 1959, also articles. Served to maj. AUS, 1942-46. Mem. So. Econ. Assn., So. Hist. Assn., Atlanta C. of C., Hellenic Study Group, Delta Sigma Pi, Beta Gamma Sigma. Methodist (Sunday sch. tchr.). Club: Kiwanian. Home: 338 Nelson Ferry Rd Decatur GA 30030-2320 Office: 33 Gilmer St SE Atlanta GA 30303-3044 *I have noted that a life devoted to a sound ideal, pursued steadily with character and tolerance, brings the keenest and most lasting happiness. Others feel the fire and assist on the way; impediments become adventures. Challenge and zest accompany one each day; horizons widen. This spirit can be applied by all, in every walk of life, in every field of endeavor, in every land, at all times in history.*

MANNERS, ROBERT ALAN, anthropologist; b. N.Y.C., Aug. 21, 1913; m. Margaret D. Hall, July 6, 1943 (div. July 1955); children: Karen Elizabeth, John Hall; m. Jean I. Hall, Sept. 12, 1955; children: Stephen David, Katherine Dora. B.S., Columbia U., 1935, M.A., 1939, Ph.D., 1950. Instr. U. Rochester, 1950-52; lectr., asst. prof., assoc. prof. Brandeis U., Waltham, Mass., 1952—; Ralph Levitz prof. anthropology Brandeis U., 1973-80, Ralph Levitz prof. emeritus, 1980—, chmn. dept. anthropology, 1963-68, 78-79; vis. prof. Columbia U., summer 1956, Harvard U., summer 1967, Ibero-Am. U., Mexico, 1969-70; mem. social sci. subcom. NIH, 1965-69; Bd. dirs. Research Inst. For Study Man. Co-author: People of Puerto Rico, 1956; editor: (with James Duffy) Africa Speaks, 1961, Process and Pattern in Culture, 1964, The Kipsigis of Kenya, 1967, (with David Kaplan) Theory in Anthropology: A Sourcebook, 1968 and Culture Theory, 1972, Southern Paiute and Chemehuevi: An Ethnohistorical Report, 1974, An Ethnological Report on the Hualapai Indians of Arizona, 1975, Havasupai Indians: An Ethnohistorical Report, 1975; editor-in-chief Am. Anthropologist, 1974-76; contbr. articles to jours. Served to capt. AUS, 1942-46. Fellow Am. Anthrop. Assn.; mem. N.E. Anthrop. Assn. (pres. 1978-79). Home: 134 Sumner St Newton MA 02159-1957

MANNES, ELENA SABIN, film and television producer, director; b. N.Y.C., Dec. 3, 1943; d. Leopold Damrosch and Evelyn (Sabin) M. BA, Smith Coll., 1965; MA, Johns Hopkins U., 1967. Researcher Pub. Broadcast Lab. Nat. Ednl. TV, N.Y.C., 1968-70; writer Sta. WPIX-TV, N.Y.C., 1970-73; assignment editor Sta. ABC-TV, N.Y.C., 1973-76; producer, writer Sta. WCBS-TV, N.Y.C., 1976-80; producer CBS News, N.Y.C., 1980-87, Pub. Affairs TV/Bill Moyers PBS Documentaries, N.Y.C., 1987—; ind. documentary dir. and producer, 1987—. Recipient Emmy awards NATAS, 1984, 85, 87, 90, Peabody award, 1985, Cine Golden Eagle award, 1988, 90, 93, 94, Robert F. Kennedy Journalism award, 1989, DGA awards, 1987, 90. Mem. Writers Guild Am., Dirs. Guild Am., Am. Film Inst. (dir. Workshop for Women). Avocations: tennis, still photography.

MANNES, PAUL, judge; b. Washington, Dec. 25, 1933; A.B., Dartmouth Coll., 1955; LL.B., Georgetown U., 1958, LL.M., 1962. Bar: D.C. 1958, Md. 1965. Judge U.S. Bankruptcy Ct. Dist. Md., 1981—; mem. Jud. Conf. adv. com. on Bankruptcy Rules, 1987—; pres. Nat. Conf. Bankruptcy Judges, 1991-92; bd. dirs. Am. Bankruptcy Inst., 1992—. Mem. Am. Coll. Bankruptcy, Md. State Bar Assn. (mem. lawyer conseling com. 1984-92), Bar Assn. Montgomery County (pres. 1979-80). Office: US Courthouse 6500 Cherrywood Rd Greenbelt MD 20770-1249

MANNICK, JOHN ANTHONY, surgeon; b. Deadwood, S.D., Mar. 24, 1928; s. Alfred and Catherine Elizabeth (Schuster) M.; m. Alice Virginia Gossard, June 9, 1952; children—Catherine Virginia, Elizabeth Eleanor, Joan Barbara. B.A., Harvard U., 1949, M.D., 1953. Diplomate: Am. Bd. Surgery (dir. 1971-77). Intern Mass. Gen. Hosp., 1953-54, resident in surgery, 1956-60; instr. in surgery to asst. prof. Med. Coll. Va., 1960-64; asso. prof. to prof. surgery Boston U., 1964-76, chmn. div. surgery, 1973-76; Moseley prof. surgery Harvard U., 1976-94, Moseley disting. prof. surgery, 1994—; chmn. dept. surgery Peter Bent Brigham Hosp. and Brigham and Women's Hosp., Boston, 1976-94; dir. ednl. programs Harvard Med. Internat., 1994—; mem. medicine study sect., 1967-70; research com. Med. Found., Inc., 1970-76. Author: (with others) Modern Surgery, 1970, Core Textbook of Surgery, 1972, Surgery of Ischemic Limbs, 1972, The Cause and Management of Aneurysms, 1990; mem. editorial bd. AMA Archives of Surgery, 1973-84, Clin. Immunology and Immunopathology, 1972-84, Surgery, 1982—, Brit. Jour. Surgery, 1982-92, European Jour. Vascular Surgery, 1988—; mem. editorial bd. Jour. Vascular Surgery, 1984—, assoc. editor, 1990—; also articles. Served to capt. M.C. USAF, 1954-56. Markle scholar in acad. medicine, 1961-66. Fellow ACS (gov.), Royal Coll. Surgeons (hon., Eng.), Royal Coll. Surgeons (hon., Edinburgh), Royal Australian Coll. Surgeons (hon.); mem. Am. Fedn. Clin. Rsch., Am. Assn. Immunologists, Am. Soc. Exptl. Pathology, Soc. Clin. Investigation, Soc. Clin. Surgery, Soc. Univ. Surgeons, Soc. Surg. Chmn. (sec. 1985-87, pres. 1987-88), Am. Surg. Assn. (pres. 1989-90), Internat. Cardiovascular Soc. (recorder N.Am. chpt. 1973-76, pres. N.Am. chpt. 1991-92, v.p. 1993), Soc. Vascular Surgery (pres. 1981), N.E. Surg. Soc., New Eng. Soc. Vascular Surgery (pres. 1994-95), So. Surg. Assn., So. Soc. Vascular Surgery, Surg. Infection Soc., Halstead Soc., Phi Beta Kappa. Home: 81 Bogle St Weston MA 02193-1056 Office: 75 Francis St Boston MA 02115-6195

MANNIELLO, JOHN BAPTISTE LOUIS, research scientist; b. N.Y.C., Oct. 31, 1923; s. George and Susan Manniello; m. Rosa Ann Gulotta; children: George, John, Stephen. B of Mech. Engring., Poly. Inst. N.Y., 1953; cert. with honors, Indsl. Coll. Armed Forces, 1962; DSc (hon.), N.Y. Inst. Tech., 1989, DMS, 1991. Engring. exec. Fairchild Camera, N.Y. 1946-60; lab. div. CBS, Stamford, Conn., 1960-73, v.p. govt. ops. labs. div., 1973-77; diplomat State Dept., Rome, 1977-78; chief Am. scientist NATO Labs., 1978-79; with Office of Chmn. Western Union, Mahwah, N.J., 1978-79; v.p. N.Y. Inst. Tech., N.Y.C., 1979-91; exec. v.p. Artificial Intelligence Techs., Inc., N.Y.C., 1991-94; mem. adv. bd. CUNY, 1968-70; advisor to pres. Staten Island (N.Y.) C.C., 1970-72; permanent chair Inst. Mech. Studies, Trieste, Italy, 1975—; vis. prof. Med. Coll., U. Rome, 1977—, Hahnemann Med. Ctr., 1967—, U. Naples; pres., chief exec. officer San Marino (Italy) Telecom., 1958-59; instr. physics and engring. Hofstra U.; mem. governing bd. Clinica Moscati, Rome; apptd. mem. Commn. on Application Am. Sci. and Tech. to Improvement of Italian med. care delivery, sci. advisor Nat. Rsch. Coun., Presidency of Italy; chmn. various confs., symposiums and workshops; active Office Naval Intelligence Adv. Com., 1991—, Def. Intelligence Agy. Adv. Com., 1990-91; sci. advisor Vatican, 1994; with info. sci. divsn. Argonne Nat. Labs. Author: Marketing Research and Development for the Government, vols. 1 and 2, 1972, The NATO Market, 1978; mem. adv. panel Electronics Mag.; contbr. to books, papers and publs. Chmn. N.Y. Civic Assn. 1962-63; co-chmn. Cerebral Palsy Assn., N.Y., 1965-66; counselor Eagle Scouts; mem. VITA; founder Arnaldo Maria Angelini Scholarship Fund, John Manniello Scholarship Fund; sponsor Lennard Perrosts Intelligence Rsch. Fellowship, William Doyle Internat. Rels. Award; bd. dirs. Office Teleport. With USAAF, 1942-46, ETO, prisoner of war. Decorated Purple Heart with three oak leaf clusters, Air medal with three oak leaf clusters, DFC, Ordine Merito, Republic of Italy, 1977, comdr. and knight Cavaliere di Gran Croce-Etoile de la Paix, Order of St. John; recipient Presdl. Service award, ECO Gold Medal award. Mem.

Am. Astron. Soc. (sr.), Soc. Photo-Optical Instrumentation Engrs., Soc. Photographic Scientists and Engrs., Am. Soc. Photogrammetry, Soc. for Info. Display, Am. Mgmt. Soc., Mus. Holography (bd. dirs.), N.Y. Acad. Scis., Internat. Innovation Group, Exec. Service Corps, Pan Am. Med. Assn., Acad. Incammenatti, Acad. Gentium Pro Pace, Marconi Inst. (mem. telecommunications commn.), Tau Beta Pi, Pi Tau Sigma, Sigma Alpha. Republican. Roman Catholic. Clubs: Army and Navy (Washington), Caterpillar (N.J.), Pres.'s (N.Y.), Goldfish. Achievements include implementation of ultrasound for medical diagnosis, compass link system for transmission and reception of hi-resolution photography between Vietnam and the U.S., color TV on the moon, pioneer wireless TV, videoconferencing. Home: 5 Horizon Rd Apt 2007 Fort Lee NJ 07024-6641

MANNING, ALTHA, education commissioner; b. Bradenton, Fla., Aug. 23, 1939; d. William D. and Aldonia (Hadley) Flowers; m. George R. Manning, June 24, 1967; 1 child, George Russell II. BA in Sociology, Fla. A&M U., 1961; MS in Sociology, Ill. Inst. Tech., 1971; postgrad., U. N.C., 1969, 73-74, Fla. State U., 1989—. Tchr. social studies Marion County Sch. Bd., Ocala, Fla., 1961-66; tchr. sociology Dade County Sch. Bd., Miami, Fla., 1966-67; program assoc. Learning Inst. N.C., Durham, 1968-70; tchr. sociology, physiology, Am. history High Point (N.C.) Ctrl. High Sch., 1971-72; regional coord. early childhood N.C. Edn. Dist. 5, Greensboro, 1972-75; instr. child devel. Daytona Beach (Fla.) Community Coll., 1976-78, coord. spl. svc. program, 1978-80, coord. learning supv. ctr., 1980-83; coord. Gadsden Demo Models program, program dir. dropout Fla. Dept. Edn., Quincy & Tallahassee, 1983-87; deputy commr. Fla. Dept. Edn., Tallahassee, 1992—; chief bur. edn. Fla. Dept. Edn., 1987-91, chief bur. studnet support, 1991-92; chmn. Fla. Mcpl. Task Force, Tallahassee, 1991-92. Press Links, Inc., Tallahassee, 1988-92; mem. Planned Parenthood, Tallahassee, 1990—, Women's Resource Ctr., Tallahassee Meml. Hosp., 1992, NAACP, Tallahassee, 1992, Urban League, Tallahassee, 1992. Mem. Am. Assn. Sch. Adminstrs., Fla. Assn. Sch. Adminstrs., Fla. Assn. Supervision and Curriculum Devel., Fla. Assn. Alternative High Schs., Tchrs. English to Speakers of Other Langs., Assn. Supervision and Curriculum Devel. Democrat. Episcopalian. Avocations: reading, antiquing, nature observation, writing poetry, organizing groups. Home: 1222 Lucy St Tallahassee FL 32308 Office: Fla Dept Edn 325 W Gaines St Tallahassee FL 32399

MANNING, BRENT V., lawyer; b. Preston, Idaho, Jan. 18, 1950; s. Leon W. and Gwen (Briscoe) M.; m. J. Christine Coffin, Oct. 25, 1969; children: Justin, Britten, John. BA, Idaho State U., 1972; JD, Harvard U., 1975. Bar: Colo. 1975, Utah 1981, U.S. Ct. Appeals (10th cir.) 1978. Assoc. Holme Roberts & Owen, Denver, 1975-80, ptnr., 1980—; ptnr. Holme Roberts & Owen, Salt Lake City, 1981—; cooperating atty. ACLU, Denver, 1979-81, Salt Lake City, 1987-91; mem. panel mediators and arbitrators U.S. Dist. Ct. Utah, 1993—. Trustee Bountiful (Utah) Davis Art Found., 1985-91, Utah Tibetan Resettlement Project. Mem. ABA, Utah Bar Assn. (chmn. continuing legal edn. com. 1988, mem. disciplinary com. 1991-93, cts. and judges com. 1993—), Am. Inns of Ct. (master of bench 1989—), Sierra Club, Am. Alpine Club (N.Y.C.). Democrat. Avocations: climbing, bicycling, running. Home: 2079 Maple Grove Way Bountiful UT 84010 Office: Holme Roberts & Owen 111 E Broadway Ste 1100 Salt Lake City UT 84111-5233

MANNING, BURT, advertising executive; b. 1931. Chmn., chief exec. officer J. Walter Thompson Co., Worldwide, N.Y.C., 1987—. Bd. dirs. nat. Assn. for Depressive Illness, Nat. Players Co., Advt. Edn. Found.; trustee Neuroscis. Inst., New Sch. for Social Rsch. Mem. Lotus Club. Office: J Walter Thompson Co 466 Lexington Ave New York NY 10017-3140

MANNING, CHARLES TERRILL, retired lawyer; b. Empress, Alta., Can., Mar. 27, 1925; s. N. Folsom and Mary E. (Terrill) M.; m. H. Joyce Johnson, 1946; children—A. Terrill, Timothy F., Heather J., Annabelle H. B.A., Bishop's U., 1946; B.C.L., McGill U., 1949. Bar: Que. Ptnr. Hackett-Mulvena-Hackett, Montreal, Que., Can., 1946-56; gen. counsel, v.p. Brit. Newfoundland Corp., Montreal, Que., Can., 1956-69; v.p., sec., chief legal officer Royal Trust, Montreal and Toronto, Can., 1970-85; counsel McMaster Meighen, Montreal, Que., Can., 1985-90; assoc. Meighen Demers, Toronto, Ont., Can., 1991-94; ret., 1994. Served with Royal Can. Navy, 1944-45. Named to Queen's Counsel, Minister of Justice, Que., Can., 1968. Mem. Can. Bar Assn., Que. Bar Assn. Anglican. Home: 1000 King Sr W 703, Kingston, ON Canada K7M 8H3

MANNING, DANIEL RICARDO, professional basketball player; b. Hattiesburg, Miss., May 17, 1966; s. Ed Manning. Student, U. Kans. Basketball player L.A. Clippers, 1988-94, Atlanta Hawks, 1994, Phoenix Suns, 1994—. Recipient Bronze medal U.S. Olympic Basketball Team, 1988; named Most Outstanding Player NCAA Divsn. I Tournament, 1988, Naismith award, 1988, Wooden award, 1988; named to Sporting News NCAA All-Am. first team, 1987, 88, NBA All-Star Team, 1993-94. First pick overall NCAA draft, 1988; mem. NCAA Divsn. I Championship team, 1988. Office: Phoenix Suns 201 E Jefferson Phoenix AZ 85004*

MANNING, DARRELL V., national guard officer; b. Preston, Idaho, July 17, 1932; s. Virgil and Olive Ann (Jenks) M.; m. Rochelle Manning, June 4, 1954; children: David Scott, Michael Alan. BS, Utah State U., 1955; postgrad., Idaho State U., 1969. Enlisted USAF, 1955, pilot, 1955-60, advanced through grades to maj. gen.; v.p. Manning Inc., Pocatello, Idaho, 1960-71; dir. Idaho Dept. Aeronautics, Boise, 1971-74, Idaho Dept. Transp., Boise, 1974-85; adjutant-gen., chief Idaho N.G., Boise, 1985—; chmn. Trans Research Bd. Nat. Acad. Scis., 1982. State rep., Boise, 1960-63; Idaho sen., 1970-71. Mem. Am. Assn. State Hwy. and Transp. Officials (nat. pres. 1978, Disting. Service award 1985, MacDonald Meml. award 1985), Western Assn. State Hwy. and Transp. Officials, Adjutant-Gens. Assn. U.S., N.G. Assn. U.S., Air Force Assn., Assn. U.S. Army, VFW, Rotary. Home: 8260 Golse Cir Boise ID 83704-4455 Office: Mil Dept Gowen Field PO Box 45 Boise ID 83707-4530

MANNING, DAVID LEE, health care executive; b. Birmingham, Ala., Jan. 30, 1950; s. William L. and Lula L. (Lively) M.; m. Donna H. Holley, Dec. 29, 1972; children: Emily Anne, Laura Elizabeth. BA, U. Ala., Tuscaloosa, 1973, MPA, 1974. Budget analyst State of Tenn., Nashville, 1974-79, asst. state treas., 1979-87, commr. fin. and administrn., 1987-95; v.p. Columbia/HCA Healthcare Corp., 1995—. So. Regional Tng. Program in Pub. Adminstrn. fellow, 1973. Democrat. Baptist. Office: Columbia/HCA Healthcare Corp One Park Plz PO Box 550 Nashville TN 37202-0550

MANNING, DEBORAH A., physician, health facility administrator; b. Clinton, N.C., Dec. 21, 1952; d. George A. and Virginia M. (McLaurin) M. BS, George Washington U., 1974; MD, Howard U., 1977. Diplomate Am. Bd. Internal Medicine. Intern Harbor Gen. Hosp., Torrance, Calif., 1977-78; resident Martinez (Calif.) VA Hosp., 1978-79, Providence Hosp., Washington, 1979-80; physician United Neighborhood Health Svcs., Nashville, 1980-82; pvt. practice Nashville, 1982-93; physician State of Tenn. Corrections, Nashville, 1993-94; med. dir. Matthew Walker Comp. Health Ctr., Nashville, 1994—. mem. task force Meharry-Gen. merger Nashville C. of C., 1991; chair nat. trends Music City Links, Nashville, 1992—. Mem. ACP, Tenn. Women Medicine (mem. exec. com. 1992-94). Office: Matthew Walker Comp Health Ctr 1501 Herman St Nashville TN 37208

MANNING, DONALD O., protective services official. Fire chief L.A. Office: Los Angeles Fire Dept Office of the Fire Chief 200 N Main St Los Angeles CA 90012-4110

MANNING, ERIC, computer science and engineering educator, university dean, researcher; b. Windsor, Ont., Can., Aug. 4, 1940; g. George Gorman and Eleanor Katherine (Koehler) M.; m. Betty Goldring, Sept. 16, 1961; children: David, Paula. BSc, U. Waterloo, Ont., 1961, MSc, 1962; PhD, U. Ill., 1965. Registered profl. engr., B.C. Various positions MIT and Bell Telephone Labs., 1965-68; prof. computer sci. U. Waterloo, 1968-86, founding dir. computer comms. networks group, 1973-82; founding dir. Inst. for Computer Rsch., 1982-86; prof., dean engring. U. Victoria, Can., 1986-92, prof. computer sci., elec. engring., 1993—; trustee B.C. Advanced Systems Found., 1986-93; dir. Sci. Coun. B.C., 1988-91; bd. dirs. Can. Microelectric Corp.; mem. adv. coun. on artificial intelligence NRC, 1987-91; IBM chair computer sci. Keio U., Yokohama, 1992-93; hon. prof. South East

U., Nanjing People's Rep. of China. Author: Fault Diagnosis of Digital Systems, 1970; also numerous articles. Fellow IEEE, Engring. Inst. Can.; mem. Assn. Profl. Engrs. B.C., Soc. for Computer Simulation, Can. Inst. for Advanced Rsch. (adv. com. on artificial intelligence and robotics 1986), Can. Soc. for Fifth Generation Rsch. (trustee 1987-88), B.C. Microelectronics Soc. (bd. dirs. 1986-87). Avocations: squash, scuba diving, sailing, flying, music. Home: 2909 Phyllis St, Victoria, BC Canada V8N 1Y8 Office: U Victoria Faculty Engring, PO Box 3055, Victoria, BC Canada V8W 3P6

MANNING, FARLEY, investment company executive; b. Shelburne, Mass., Oct. 30, 1909; s. John Farley and Bessie (Learmont) M.; m. Ruth Fulton Koegel, 1932 (div. 1968); 1 child, Toni Ruth; m. Jean Yeager, Nov. 17, 1982. Student Northeastern U., 1927-29, Boston U., 1929-31. Reporter, editor various newspapers, New Eng., 1931-42; acct. exec. Dudley Anderson Yutzy, N.Y.C., 1946-54; pres., chmn. Manning Selvage & Lee, N.Y.C., 1954-79; chmn. G. & M. Creative Svcs., 1958-81; treas. Cascade Olympic Corp., Olympia, Wash., 1982—; dir. Cascade Olympic Corp., Capital Cascade Inc., Capitol Ctr. Inc. Contbr. articles on dog care and tng. to nat. mags. Maj. USAF, 1943-46. Mem. Pub. Rels. Soc. Am., Olympia Yacht Club, N.Y. Yacht Club, Beaverkill Fly Fishers Club, Overseas Press Club, Thunderbird Country Club, Comm. 25 Club, Rotary. Home and Office: 5510 Cooper Point Rd NW Olympia WA 98502-3646

MANNING, FREDERICK JAMES, insurance company executive; b. Chgo., Oct. 20, 1947; s. Herbert and June Betty (Cohen) M.; m. Gail Hilary Phillips, Feb. 9, 1980; children: Elizabeth Sarah, David Charles. BS, U. Pa., 1969; JD, Harvard U., 1972. Treas. The Marmon Group, Inc., Chgo., 1973-77; chmn. bd. dirs., chief exec. officer Celtic Life Ins. Co., Chgo., 1978—; also chmn. bd. dirs., pres., chief exec. officer Celtic Group, Inc., Chgo.; bd. overseers bus. sch., co-chmn. curriculum adv. com. Ill. Inst. Tech.; bd.dirs. Engineered Controls, Inc. Trustee, treas., chmn. bd. trustees Michael Reese Found.; trustee, v.p., asst. sec. Pritzker Family Philanthropic Fund.; mem., pres. coun. U. Pa.; mem. adv. com. Dispute Resolution Rsch. Ctr., Kellogg Grad. Sch. Mgmt., Northwestern U., Evanston, Ill.; trustee, mem. planning and mktg. com., mem. budget com. Children's Meml. Hosp. Mem. AICPA (chmn. Chgo. chpt.), Young Presidents Orgn., Standard Club, East Bank Club, Met. Club, Northmoor Country Club (Highland Park, Ill.). Home: 442 W Wellington Ave Chicago IL 60657-5804 Office: Celtic Life Ins Co 233 S Wacker Dr Ste 700 Chicago IL 60606-6393

MANNING, FREDERICK WILLIAM, retired retail executive; b. Youngstown, Ohio, Aug. 15, 1924; s. John Carroll and Mary Matilda Manning; m. Martha Ann Gross, May 9, 1953 (dec. Feb. 1992); children: William, Patricia, Joan, Donna, David. BS, Youngstown U., 1948; LLB, Case Western Res. U., 1951. With F.W. Woolworth Co., N.Y.C., 1951-88, dir. real estate N.Y. office, 1960-79, v.p., 1980-88, ret., 1988. 2nd lt. USAAF, 1943-45. Mem. Ohio State Bar. Roman Catholic. Home: 77 Huron Dr Chatham NJ 07928-1205

MANNING, GEORGE TAYLOR, lawyer; b. June 27, 1948; s. Howard M.; m. Carol Gronquist, Feb. 17, 1980; children: Nell, Taylor. BA, U. N.C., 1970; JD, Columbia U., 1973. Assoc. Chadbourne, Parke & Whiteside, N.Y.C., 1973-78; ptnr. Chadbourne, Parke & Whiteside, N.Y.C. and Washington, 1982-85; asst. U.S. Atty. So. Dist., N.Y.C., 1978-82; ptnr. Jones, Day, Reavis & Pogue, Washington, 1985—. Office: Jones Day Reavis & Pogue Met Sq 1450 G St NW Ste 600 Washington DC 20005-2088

MANNING, HENRY EUGENE, hospital administrator; b. Moresburg, Tenn., May 19, 1935; s. Henry Barnett and Lillian Pearl (Spradling) M.; m. Hope Snider Henneke, Aug. 3, 1976; 1 child by previous marriage, Henry Eugene. B.S., L.I. U., 1960; M.S., Columbia U., 1962. Asst. adminstr. Cumberland Hosp., N.Y.C., 1962-64, adminstr., 1964-67; dep. commr. N.Y.C. Dept. Hosps., 1967-70; pres., chief exec. officer MetroHealth System, Cleve., 1970—. Office: MetroHealth System 2500 Metrohealth Dr Cleveland OH 44109-1998

MANNING, JACK, photographer, columnist, author; b. N.Y.C., Nov. 21, 1920; s. Mathew and Sally (Markowitz) Mendelsohn; m. Marie Louise Koch, Oct. 9, 1970; 1 child, Sarah-Jeanne. Student, CCNY. Free-lance photographer for nat. mags., 1941-63; staff photographer N.Y. Times, N.Y.C., 1964—, photographic columnist, 1976—. Author: Venezuela, 1958, Young Puerto Rico, 1966; Young Spain, 1967, Young Ireland, 1968, Young Brazil, 1969, Portrait of Spain, 1970, The Fine 35mm Portrait, 1979, 82; photographs represented in permanent collections Mus. Modern Art, Met. Mus. Art, Nat. Gallery Arts, Toronto. Recipient numerous photog. awards. Mem. Nat. Press Photographers, N.Y. Press Photographers. Home: 75 Pearce Pky Pearl River NY 10965-1923 Office: NY Times 229 W 43rd St New York NY 10036

MANNING, JAMES FORREST, computer executive; b. Washington, July 31, 1929; s. James Forrest and Marguerite (Wise) M.; m. Joan Morris, Nov. 5, 1955; children: Katherine W., James Forest IV, Robert M. Student in Math., Dayton U., 1951-53; B.A. in Econs., Williams Coll., 1955. With IBM Corp., 1954—, sales rep. data processing div., Pittsfield, Mass., 1954-57, branch mgr., Erie, Pa., from 1957, custom systems mgr., systems devel. div., 1965-66, systems mgr., intermediate systems, 1966-68, dir. intermediate/medium systems, systems devel. div., 1968-69, v.p. mktg., data products div., 1969-71, group dir. operational programs, data processing group, 1971-72, v.p. plans and controls, gen. products div., 1972-78, v.p. plans and controls, systems products div., 1978-81, asst. group exec., from 1981, corp. v.p., asst. group exec. business info. systems group, 1985-87; pvt. practice cons., 1987—. Served to tech. sgt. USAF, 1950-53. Avocations: reading; sports. Home: Hilltop Rd Wilson Pt Norwalk CT 06854

MANNING, JEROME ALAN, lawyer; b. Bklyn., Dec. 31, 1929; s. Emanuel J. and Dorothy (Levine) M.; m. Naomi Jacobs, Oct. 31, 1954; children: Joy, Stephen, Susan. B.A., NYU, 1950, LL.B., 1952; LL.M., Yale U., 1953. Bar: N.Y. 1953, Fla. 1977. Assoc. Joseph Trachtman, N.Y.C., 1956-61; ptnr. Stroock & Stroock & Lavan, N.Y.C., 1961—; prof. NYU Sch. Law, 1956—. Editor: NYU Law Review; author: Estate Planning, 1980, new edit. 1991, Estate Planning for Laymen, 1992. Trustee Jewish Communal Fund, N.Y. Capt. USAF, 1953-56. Mem. ABA, N.Y. State Bar Assn., Am. Coll. Trust & Estate Counsel, Internat. Acad. Estate and Trust Law. Home: 35 E 75th St New York NY 10021-2761 Office: Stroock & Stroock & Lavan 7 Hanover Sq New York NY 10004-2616

MANNING, JOHN WARREN III, retired surgeon, medical educator; b. Phila., Nov. 24, 1919; s. John Warren Jr. and Edith Margaret (Reagan) M.; m. Muriel Elizabeth Johnson, Oct. 11, 1944; children: John, Melissa, Susan. BS in Chemistry with honors, Ursinus Coll., 1940; MD, U. Pa., 1943; postgrad., 1978. Diplomate Am. Bd. Surgery. Naval intern Pa. Naval Hosp., 1946; resident Saginaw (Mich.) Gen. Hosp., 1947-50; preceptor Dr. H.M. Bishop, 1950-52; pvt. practice Saginaw, 1950—; sr. staff mem. Saginaw Gen. Hosp., St. Luke's Hosp., Saginaw; past chief of surgery, chmn. tissue com. St. Mary's Hosp., Saginaw; cons. VA Hosp., Saginaw; assoc. clin. prof. surgery Mich. State U., assoc. prof. surgery, 1976-92, prof. emeritus, 1992—; mem. search com. Saginaw Coop. Hosp. Contbr. articles to profl. publs. Lt. USN, 1942-46, PTO. Fellow ACS; mem. AMA, Mich. State Med. Soc., Saginaw Surg. Soc., Soc. Abdominal Surgeons, Am. Coll. Angiology, Am. Gastrointestinal Endoscopic Surgeons. Home: PO Box 3236 Key Largo FL 33037 Office: 140 Camelot Apt i-11 Saginaw MI 48603

MANNING, JOHN WILLARD, lawyer; b. Miles City, Mont., Mar. 8, 1950; s. Frank Willard Manning and Mary Kathryn (Williams) Murphy; m. Margaret Jean Connors, Dec. 11, 1987; children: Dan Marsh, Sean Marsh, Megan Marsh, Molly Manning. AB, Dartmouth Coll., 1972; JD, Stanford U., 1975. Bar: N.Y. 1977, Mont. 1983. Assoc. Davis Polk & Wardwell, N.Y.C., 1975-80; assoc. Dorsey & Whitney, Great Falls, Mont., 1980-83, ptnr., 1984—. Bd. dirs. Neighborhood Housing Services, Great Falls, 1986—, Native Am. Ctr., Great Falls, 1987-90, Mont. Overthrust Energy Found., Great Falls, 1983—. Mem. Mont. Securities Task Force, Mont. Venture Capital Network. Avocations: skiing, golf, other sports. Office: Dorsey & Whitney PO Box 1566 507 Davidson Bldg 83rd St N Great Falls MT 59401

MANNING, KENNETH PAUL, food company executive; b. N.Y.C., Jan. 18, 1942; s. John Joseph and Edith Helen (Hoffmann) M.; m. Maureen Lambert, Sept. 12, 1964; children: Kenneth J., John J., Elise, Paul, Caroline, Jacqueline. BMechEngring., Rensselaer Poly. Inst., 1963; postgrad. in Statistics George Washington U., 1965-66; M.B.A. in Ops. Research, Am. U., 1968. With W.R. Grace & Co., N.Y.C., 1973-87, v.p. European consumer div., 1975-76, pres. ednl. products div., 1976-79, pres. real estate div., 1979-81, v.p. corp. tech. group, 1981-83, pres., chief exec. officer Ambrosia Chocolate Co. div., Milw., 1983-87; with Universal Foods Corp., Milw., 1987—, group v.p. 1987-89, exec. v.p., dir., 1989-92, pres., COO, dir., 1992—; bd. dirs. Firstar Trust Co., Milw.; chmn. bd. trustees Cardinal Stritch Coll. Served as lt. USN, 1963-67; rear adm., USNR, (ret.). Decorated Legion of Merit, Nat. Def. medal, Armed Forces Res. medal. Mem. Greater Milw. Com., Navy League, US. Naval Inst., Naval Res. Assn. Republican. Roman Catholic. Clubs: Union League (N.Y.C.), Milw. Club. Home: 2914 E Newberry Blvd Milwaukee WI 53211-3429 Office: Universal Foods Corp 433 E Michigan St Milwaukee WI 53202-5106

MANNING, MERVYN H., automobile manufacturing company executive; b. 1932; married. BA, U. Mich., 1954; MBA, Harvard U., 1956. Various positions Ford Motor Co., Dearborn, Mich., 1956-67, controller Ford Tractor div., 1967-70, gen. mgr. indsl. equipment ops., 1970-72, asst. gen. mgr. indsl. products, 1972-73, asst. gen. mgr. constrn. equipment, Europe, 1974-77, corp. v.p., gen. mgr. Ford Tractor div., 1977-84, corp. v.p., pres. Ford Asia-Pacific, Inc., 1984—. Office: Ford Motor Co The American Rd Dearborn MI 48126-2798

MANNING, MICHAEL C., lawyer; b. Kansas City, Mo., July 17, 1949. BA, Emporia State U., 1971; postgrad., U. Kans.; JD cum laude, Washburn U., 1977. Bar: Mo. 1977, Kans. 1978, D.C. 1988, U.S. Dist. Ct. Ariz. 1990. Ptnr. Morrison & Hecker, Phoenix; spl. asst. to Gov. Kans., 1974-75. Editor-in-chief Washburn Law Jour., 1976-77. Mem. Phi Kappa Phi. Office: Morrison & Hecker 2800 N Central Ste 1600 Phoenix AZ 85004-1047

MANNING, NOEL THOMAS, publishing company executive; b. Ayden, N.C., Oct. 10, 1939; s. James Samuel and Tinie (McGlohon) M.; m. Edith Joyce Reagan, Jan. 1, 1964 (div. Jan. 1973); 1 son, Noel Thomas. BS in Intermediate Edn., East Carolina U.; student, Free Will Bapt. Coll., 1960. Cert. tchr. reading diagnosis, Eng., lang. arts, social studies and art. Staff illustrator Free Will Bapt. Press, Ayden, 1959-61, 1963-68; editor Free Will Bapt. Press Found., 1968-80; tchr. creative wrtiting Pitt Community Coll., Greenville, N.C., 1972-80; instr. piano, 1974-80; tchr. composition and creative writing Greenville Recreational Dept., 1974—; mng. editor The Christian Jew Found., San Antonio, Tex., 1980—. Youth dir. Cragmont Assembly Religious Camp, Black Mountain, N.C., 1968-80; musician Reedy Br. Free-Will Bapt. Ch., organist, 1968-80; choir dir. Good Shepherd Presbyn. Ch., San Antonio, 1983—. East Carolina U. honor scholar, Columbus (Ohio) Sch. Art scholar, 1959; recipient nat. awards for poetry. Democrat. Baptist. Composer church music. Home: Apt 409 2503 Jackson Keller Rd San Antonio TX 78230-5255 Office: Christian Jew Found 611 Broadway St San Antonio TX 78215-1885 *How be it so? I have the choice to live or die—and in my hands I hold the tools to make life good—or to make it bad…One abbreviates his life when he dissociates himself from others and their concerns. In order to relate meaningfully, one must share both the sorrows and the joys of his fellowman. Identifying thus has certainly made life for me more beneficial. Accordingly, each day I live, I try to make life more livable for at least one person—be it a needed pat on the back or an extended word of greeting. I am convinced that the manner in which one approaches all situations will determine the outcome. I further believe that a smile communicates all messages best and receives in like measure.*

MANNING, PATRICK JAMES, veterinarian, experimental pathologist, educator; b. St. Paul, Sept. 4, 1938; s. Hugh Barry and Violet Margaret (West) M.; m. Patricia Lorraine Lynch, Feb. 27, 1960; children: Laura, Jennifer, Lisa. BS, U. Minn., 1963, DVM, 1965; MS, Wake Forest U., 1970. Lic. veterinarian, Minn. Postdoctoral fellow in lab. animal medicine Bowman Gray Sch. of Medicine, Winston-Salem, N.C., 1966-70; asst. prof. pathology U. Mo., Columbia, 1970-73, assoc. prof. pathology, 1974, assoc. prof. lab. medicine and pathology, 1974-90, prof. lab. medicine and pathology, 1991—; vet. med. officer VA Med. Ctr., Mpls., 1980—; mem. animal resources rev. com. NIH, Bethesda, Mo., 1981-85; sci. adv. bd. FDA-Nat. Ctr., Jefferson City, Ark., 1982-85. Author: Pasteurella and Pasteurellosis, 1989; author publs. Pasteurellosis in Lab. Animals, Diseases of Lab. Animals, Bacterial IGA Proteases; editor: Biology of the Laboratory Guinea Pig, 1976. Mem. Ednl. Adv. Coun., White Bear Lake, Minn., 1978-80. Recipient Lab. Animal Disease Rsch. & Diagnosis award NIH, 1980-90. Mem. AAAS, Am. Assn. Pathologists, Am. Soc. Microbiology, Am. Assn. for Lab. Animal Scis. (trustee 1978-81, C.A. Griffin award 1985), Am. Coll. Lab. Animal Medicine (diplomate, bd. dirs. 1974-76, pres. 1987-88). Office: U Minn Lab of Medicine & Pathology Box 351 420 Delaware St SE Minneapolis MN 55455-0374

MANNING, PETER KIRBY, sociology educator; b. Salem, Oreg., Sept. 27, 1940; s. Kenneth Gilbert and Esther Amelia (Gibbard) M.; m. Victoria Francis Shaughnessy, Sept. 1, 1961 (div. 1981); children—Kerry Patricia, Sean Peter, Merry Kathleen; m. Betsy Cullum-Swan, Aug. 4, 1991. B.A., Willamette U., 1961; M.A., Duke U., 1963, Ph.D., 1966; M.A. (hon.), Oxford U., Eng. 1983. Instr. sociology Duke U., 1964-65; asst. prof. sociology U. Mo., 1965-66, Mich. State U., East Lansing, 1966-70; assoc. prof. sociology and psychiatry Mich. State U., 1970-74, prof., 1974—; prof. criminal justice, 1993—; Beto Chair lectr. Sam Houston State U., 1990, Ameritech lectr. East Ky. U., 1993; cons. Nat. Inst. Law Enforcement and Criminal Justice (now Nat. Inst. Justice), U.S. Dept. Justice, Research Triangle Inst., NSF, Nat. Health and Med. Rsch. Coun., Australia, 1980—, Social Sci. Rsch. Coun. Eng., AID (Jamaica), 1991, Sheehy com. Police Pay and Performance, Eng., 1993; mem. nat. neighborhood foot patrol adv. coun. Sch. Criminal Justice, Mich. State U., 1982—. Author: Sociology of Mental Health and Illness, 1975, Police Work, 1977, The Narcs' Game, 1980, Semiotics and Fieldwork, 1987, Symbolic Communication, 1988, Organizational Communication, 1992, other books; also book chpts., articles in profl. jours.; cons. editor series: Principal Themes in Sociology; co-editor Sage Series in Qualitative Methods, Communications and Social Order Aldine/deGruyter; adv. editor, mem. editorial bd. numerous jours. in social scis. Recipient Bruce Smith Sr. award Acad. Criminal Justice Scis., 1993, Charles H. Cooley award Mich. Sociol. Assn., 1994; NDEA fellow, 1962-64, NSF fellow, 1965, fellow Balliol Coll., Oxford U., 1982-83, vis. fellow Wolfson Coll., Oxford U., 1981, 82-83, fellow, 1984-86. Mem. Am. Soc. Criminology, Am. Sociol. Assn., Brit. Soc. Criminology, Internat. Sociol. Assn., Midwest Sociol. Assn., Soc. Study of Social Problems, Soc. for the Study of Symbolic Interaction (spl. recognition award 1990, v.p. 1992-93, program chair 1993), Internat. Soc. for Semiotics and Law. Office: Mich State U 516 Baker Hall East Lansing MI 48824

MANNING, PRESTON, political organization worker; b. Edmonton, Alta., Canada, June 10, 1942; s. Ernest Charles and Muriel Aileen (Preston) M.; m. Sandra Beavis; children: Andrea, Avryll, Mary Joy, Nathan, David. BA, U. Alta., 1964. Owner, operator Manning Cons. Ltd., 1968-88; leader Reform Party of Canada, 1987—. Author: (book) The New Canada, 1992. Avocations: travelling, shopping, fishing, horseback riding with family. Office: Office of Leader Reform Party, 155 Qeuun St #900, Ottawa, ON Canada K1P 6L1

MANNING, RICHARD DALE, writer; b. Flint, Mich., Feb. 7, 1951; s. Harold J. Manning and Juanita Mayo; m. Margaret B. Saretsky, June 5, 1971 (div.); 1 child, Joshua; m. Tracy M. Stone, Sept. 8, 1990. AB in Polit. Sci., U. Mich., 1973. News dir. Sta. WATZ, Alpena, Mich., 1975-79; reporter Alpena News, 1977-79; city editor Post-Register, Idaho Falls, Idaho, 1979-81; columnist Wood River Jour., Hailey, Idaho, 1981-82; city editor, columnist Times-News, Twin Falls, Idaho, 1982-85; reporter, columnist Missoulian, Missoula, Mont., 1985-89; John S. Knight fellow in journalism Stanford (Calif.) U., 1994-95. Author: Last Stand: Timber, Journalism and the Case for Humility, 1991, A Good House, 1993, Grassland, 1995. Recipient Blethen award for investigative reporting Allied Newspapers, 1986-87.

MANNING, ROBERT JOSEPH, editor; b. Binghamton, N.Y., Dec. 25, 1919; s. Joseph James and Agnes Pauline (Brown) M.; m. Margaret Marinda Raymond, Dec. 28, 1944 (dec. 1984); children: Richard Raymond, Brian Gould, Robert Brown; m. Theresa M. Slomkowski, July 11, 1987. Nieman fellow, Harvard, 1945-46; LittD (hon.), Tufts U., 1966; LHD, St. Lawrence U., 1971. Reporter Binghamton (N.Y.) Press, 1936-41, AP, 1942; State Dept. and White House corr. UPI, 1944-46; chief UN corr. United Press, 1946-49; writer Time mag., 1949-55, sr. editor, 1955-58; chief London bur. Time, Life, Fortune, Sports Illus. mags., 1958-61; Sunday editor N.Y. Herald Tribune, 1961-62; asst. sec. state for pub. affairs Washington, 1962-64; exec. editor Atlantic Monthly, 1964-66, editor-in-chief, 1966-80; v.p. Atlantic Monthly Co., 1966-80; editor-in-chief Boston Pub. Co., 1981-87; pres., editor-in-chief Bobcat Books Inc., Boston, 1987—. Served with AUS, 1942-43. Fellow Kennedy Inst. Politics, Harvard U., 1980. Mem. AAAS, Century Assn. (N.Y.C.), Tavern Club, St. Botolph Club. Home and Office: 191 Commonwealth Ave Boston MA 02116-2210

MANNING, ROBERT THOMAS, physician, educator; b. Wichita, Kans., Oct. 16, 1927; s. Thomas Earl and Mary Francis (Schlegel) M.; m. Jane Bell, July 29, 1949; children: Mary Kay Travers, Phillip Trenton, Susan Ann Shiba. A.B., Wichita U., 1950; M.D., Kans. U., 1954; DHL, Med. Coll. Hampton Rds., 1991. Diplomate Am. Bd. Internal Medicine. Intern Kansas City (Mo.) Gen. Hosp., 1954-55; resident Kans. U., Kansas City, 1955-58; from assoc. prof. to prof. Kans. U. Med. Ctr. Sch. of Medicine, Kansas City, 1958-71; assoc. dean students Kans. U. Med. Ctr. Sch. of Medicine, 1969-71; dean Eastern Va. Med. Sch., Norfolk, Va., 1971-74; chmn., prof. internal medicine Eastern Va. Med. Sch., 1974-77; prof. internal medicine U. Kans. Sch. of Medicine, Wichita, 1977-93; prof. emeritus U. Kans. Sch. Medicine, Wichita, 1993-94; assoc. dean, clin. affairs U. Kans. Sch. of Medicine, Wichita, 1985-89; chmn. internal medicine U. Kans. Sch. Medicine, Wichita, 1991-93; pres. Wesley Med. Rsch. Inst., 1992-94. Author: Major's Physical Diagnosis, 9th edit., 1982; contbr. articles to profl. jours. Served with USAF, 1945-47. Recipient Advanced Achievement award Am. Bd. Internal Medicine, 1987. Fellow ACP (bd. govs. Kans. 1984-88); mem. Am. Fedn. Clin. Rsch., Cen. Soc. Clin. Rsch., Am. Assn. Study Liver Disease, Sigma Xi, Alpha Omega Alpha. Presbyterian. Avocations: hunting, fishing. Home: 156 N Maize Rd # 31 Wichita KS 67212-4649 Office: U Kans Sch Medicine 1010 N Kansas St Wichita KS 67214-3124

MANNING, SYLVIA, English studies educator; b. Montreal, Que., Can., Dec. 2, 1943; came to U.S., 1967; d. Bruno and Lea Bank; m. Peter J. Manning, Aug. 20, 1967; children—Bruce David, Jason Maurice. B.A., McGill U., 1963; M.A., Yale U., 1964, Ph.D. in English, 1967. Asst. prof. English Calif. State U.-Hayward, 1967-71, assoc. prof., 1971-75, assoc. dean, 1972-75; assoc. prof. U. So. Calif., 1975-94, prof., assoc. dir. Ctr. for Humanities, 1975-77, assoc. dir. Ctr. for Humanities, 1975-77, chmn. freshman writing, 1977-80, chmn. dept. English, 1980-83, vice provost, exec. v.p., 1984-94; prof. English U. Ill., 1994—, v.p. for acad. affairs, prof. English, 1994—. Author: Dickens as Satirist, 1971; Hard Times: An Annotated Bibliography, 1984. Contbr. essays to mags. Woodrow Wilson fellow, 1963-64, 66-67. Mem. MLA, Dickens Soc. Office: U of Ill 377 Henry Adm Bldg 506 S Wright St Urbana IL 61801

MANNING, THOMAS ALLEN, publishing company executive; b. Cleve., Oct. 17, 1951; children: Jack, Grace. BA, Marshall U., 1974, MA, 1975; MBA, Lindenwood Coll., 1983. V.p., pub. Mosby, St. Louis, 1975-90; pres. Manning Co., St. Louis, 1990-93; v.p., pub. Little Brown & Co. Inc., Boston, 1993—. Office: Little Brown & Co Inc 34 Beacon St Boston MA 02108-1415

MANNING, WALTER SCOTT, accountant, former educator, consultant; b. nr. Yoakum, Tex., Oct. 4, 1912; BBA, Tex. Coll. Arts and Industries, 1932; MBA, U. Tex., 1940; m. Eleanor Mary Jones, Aug. 27, 1937; children: Sharon Frances, Walter Scott, Robert Kenneth. Asst. to bus. mgr. Tex. Coll. Arts and Industries, Kingsville, 1932; tchr. Sinton (Tex.) High Sch., 1933-37, Robstown (Tex.) High Sch., 1937-41; prof. Tex. A&M U., College Station, 1941-77; cons. C.P.A., Tex. Walter Manning Outstanding Jr. and Outstanding Sr. awards at Coll. Bus. Adminstrn., Tex. A&M U. named in his honor. Mem. AICPA, AAUP, Am. Acctg. Assn., Tex. Soc. CPAs, College Station C. of C. (past pres.), Tex. Assn. Univ. Instrs. Acctg. (pres. 1963-64), SAR (independence chpt. past pres.), Knights York Cross of Honor, Alpha Chi, Beta Gamma Sigma, Beta Alpha Psi. Democrat. Presbyterian (elder). Clubs: Masons, (32 degree), Shriners, K.T., Kiwanis (past pres., past lt. gov. div. IX Tex. Okla. dist., Kiwanis Internat. Legion of Honor). Home: 405 Walton Dr College Station TX 77840-2224

MANNING, WHIPPLE HALL, savings and loan executive, real estate finance consultant; b. Oakland, Calif., Oct. 23, 1936; s. John Hudson and Anne Crellin (Hall) M.; m. Jacqueline Long, Sept. 5, 1963; children: Thomas Crellin, Elizabeth Anne. BS in Bus., U. Ariz., 1961. Trainee to regional mgr. Pacific Mut. Life Ins. Co., various cities, 1961-78; sr. v.p. Calif. Fed. Savs. & Loan, Los Angeles, 1978-83; exec. v.p. Coast Savs. and Loan, Los Angeles, 1983—; bd. dirs. Coast Fed. Properties, Beverly Hills, Calif., Nat. Ptrnship. Investment Co., Los Angeles, Coast Mortgage & Realty Investors, Los Angeles; mem. Los Angeles adv. bd. Chgo. Title Co. Past trustee Orme Sch., Mayer, Ariz., 1984-86; past bd. dirs. Calif. Bus. Properties Assn., Sacramento, 1984-87, mem. adv. bd., 1987—; past officer, dir. Flintridge Aquatics, La Canada, Calif., 1976-82. Mem. Urban Land Inst., Internat. Coun. of Shopping Ctrs., So. Calif. Mortgage Bankers, Nat. Assn. Indsl. and Office Parks. Republican. Episcopalian. Clubs: Los Angeles Athletic, Annandale Golf (Pasadena). Avocations: fishing, hunting, golf. Office: Coast Savs & Loan Assn 1000 Wilshire Blvd Fl 22D Los Angeles CA 90017-2457

MANNING, WILLIAM DUDLEY, JR., retired specialty chemical company executive; b. Tampa, Fla., Mar. 7, 1934; s. William Dudley and Rebecca (Reid) M.; m. Carol Randolph Gillis, June 30, 1962; children: Carol Randolph, Rebecca Barrett, Anne Gillis. BA in Chemistry, Fla. State U., 1957. Sales rep. Amoco Chem. Co., St. Louis and Cleve., 1959-63; sales engr. The Lubrizol Corp., Tulsa, 1963-64, southwestern regional sales mgr., 1964-66; mgr. chem. product sales The Lubrizol Corp., Wickliffe, Ohio, 1966-72, sales mgr., western U.S., 1972, gen. sales mgr., asst. head-sales, 1972-79, mktg. mgr., asst. div. head-sales, 1979-80, v.p. mktg., 1980-81, v.p. bus. devel. div., 1981-85, sr. v.p. sales and mktg., 1985-87; pres. Lubrizol Petroleum Chems. Co., Wickliffe, 1987-94; sr. v.p., asst. to pres. The Lubrizol Corp., 1994; cons., investor, 1994—; bd. dirs. Fletcher Paper Co., Alpena, Mich., Lubrizol TransArabian, Inc., Jeddah Kingdom of Saudi Arabia, Robbins and Myers, Dayton, Ohio. Trustee Vocat. Guidance Svcs., Cleve., 1991—. Served with USAR, 1957-63. Mem. Soc. Automotive Engrs. (assoc.), Am. Petroleum Inst., Nat. Petroleum Refiners Assn., Soc. of Chem. Industry. Republican. Roman Catholic. Clubs: Kirtland Country (Ohio) (v.p. 1986-88, pres. 1988-89); Tavern (Cleve.) (trustee 1986—); Chagrin Valley Hunt (Gates Mills, Ohio), Firestone Country (Akron). Office: 2550 5OM Center Rd Ste 100 Willoughby OH 44094

MANNING, WILLIAM FREDERICK, wire service photographer; b. Gardner, Mass., Aug. 18, 1920; s. Seth Newton and Jennie May (Bennett) M.; m. Yvonne J.C. Winslow, Feb. 29, 1964; children: Pamela Ann, Jeffrey Newton. A.A., Boston U., 1950, B.S. in Communications, 1952. With AP, Boston, 1951-53; photographer UPI, Boston, 1953-88, ret. Contbr. photos to books, mags., newspapers throughout the world. Served with USN, 1940-46, PTO. Recipient Look 1st Prize All Sports award, 1958; Pictures of the Yr. award U. Mo., 1964, 74; Nat. Headliners Club award for outstanding syndicate photography, 1974. Mem. Boston Press Photographers Assn., Delta Kappa Alpha. Congregationalist. Club: Nat. Headliners. Home: 23 Sunset Dr Beverly MA 01915-2319 Office: One Herald Sq 300 Harrison Ave Boston MA 02118-2297

MANNING, WILLIAM HENRY, lawyer; b. Dallas, Feb. 5, 1951. BA, Creighton U., 1973; JD, Hamline U., 1978. Bar: Minn. 1978, U.S. Dist. Ct. Minn. 1978, U.S. Ct. Appeals (8th cir.) 1979; cert. civil trial specialist. Spl. asst. atty. gen. Minn. Atty. Gen.'s Office, St. Paul, 1980-83; dir. tort litigation div., 1984-86; ptnr. Robins, Kaplan, Miller & Ciresi, Mpls., 1986—. Office: Robins Kaplan Miller & Ciresi 800 LaSalle Ave Minneapolis MN 55402-2015

MANNING, WILLIAM JOSEPH, lawyer; b. N.Y.C., Aug. 11, 1926; s. Joseph Michael and Eileen Johanna (Walsh) M.; m. Maryanne Cullen, June 23, 1956; children—William Joseph, Michael P., Maura G., Marian T., John A., Mary E. B.B.A. magna cum laude, St. John's U., N.Y.C., 1949, LL.B. magna cum laude, 1952. Bar: N.Y. 1952. Assoc. firm Simpson Thacher & Bartlett, N.Y.C., 1952-62; ptnr. Simpson Thacher & Bartlett, 1962—, sr. ptnr., 1968-88, of counsel, 1989—; dir. Brascan Ltd.: Toronto, Ont., Can., 1970-79; bd. dirs. N.Y. Lawyers for Public Interest, 1977-88. Notes editor: St. John's Law Rev, 1951-52. Trustee Inst. for Muscle Disease, N.Y.C., 1963-70; bd. dirs. Mercy Hosp., Rockville Centre, N.Y., 1975-87. Served with inf. U.S. Army, 1944-46. Fellow Am. Coll. Trial Lawyers, Am. Law Inst., Am. Bar Found.; mem. ABA (chmn. sect. litigation 1977-78, founding mem. coun. 1973), Assn. Bar City N.Y., N.Y. State Bar Assn., N.Y. County Lawyers Assn., Am. Judicature Soc., Downtown Assn., Garden City Golf Club, Westhampton Country Club (pres. 1989—), Cherry Valley Club. Roman Catholic. Home: 64 1st St Garden City NY 11530-4321 also: 156 Dune Rd Westhampton Beach NY 11978-3003 also: 15865 Westerly Ter Jupiter FL 33477-1337 Office: Simpson Thacher & Bartlett 425 Lexington Ave New York NY 10017-3903

MANNING, WILLIAM RAYMOND, retired state official; b. Vancouver, C., Can., May 17, 1920; came to U.S., 1922; s. William and Mary (Gysels) M.; m. Louise B. Graham, Mar. 11, 1982. B.A., San Jose (Calif.) State Coll., 1941; M.A., U. Pacific, 1949; Ed.D., Stanford U., 1956. Tchr. Galt, Calif., 1946-49; prin. Lodi, Calif., 1949-50; supt. schs. Orangevale, Calif., 1950-58, Petaluma, Calif., 1958-64, Lansing, Mich., 1964-67, Washington, 1967-70; chmn. ednl. bd. Xerox Edn. Pubis., 1969-73; pres. BFE Ednl. Consultants, 1973—; city mgr. Bel Air, Md., 1973-79; dir. adminstrn. Va. Housing Devel. Authority, Richmond, 1980-92; ret., 1992; vis. prof. U. Hawaii, Sacramento State Coll., San Francisco State Coll., No. Mich. U., Mich. State U. Contbr. to books and profl. jours. Served with USAAF, 1942-46. Recipient community and profl. awards. Home: 11807 Goodwick Sq Richmond VA 23233-3424

MANNING, WINTON HOWARD, psychologist, educational administrator; b. St. Louis, Feb. 9, 1930; s. Winton Harry and Jane (Swanson) M.; m. Nancy Mercedes Groves, Aug. 1, 1959; children: Cecelia Groves Tazelaar, Winton H. III. AB with honors, William Jewell Coll., 1947; PhD in Psychology, Washington U., St. Louis, 1959. Instr. psychology William Jewell Coll., Liberty, Mo., 1954-55, asst. prof., acting head dept. psychology, 1955-56; rsch. psychologist Washington U., St. Louis, 1956-58, rsch. assoc., 1958-59; vis. lectr. Washington U., summer, 1961, 62; asst. prof. psychology Tex. Christian U., Fort Worth, 1959-61, assoc. prof., 1961-64, prof., 1964-65, assoc. dir. univ. honors program, 1962-65; assoc. dir. rsch. Coll. Entrance Examination Bd., N.Y.C., 1965-66, dir. program devel., 1966-68, exec. dir. rsch.and devel., 1968-69; dir. devel. rsch. div. Ednl. Testing Svc., Princeton, N.J., 1969-70, v.p., 1970-77, sr. v.p. devel. and rsch., 1977-83, sr. scholar, 1983-93; pres. Ednl. Devel. Svc., Princeton, 1993—; vis. fellow Princeton U., 1982-83; cons. Gallup Internat. Inst., 1990—, Applied Ednl. Rsch., 1993—; cons. Grad. Mgmt. Admissions Coun., 1992—, Carnegie Found., 1993—. Author: The Pursuit of Fairness in Admissions to Higher Education, 1977; Student Manual for Essentials of Psychology, 1960. Contbr. articles on ednl. measurement and psychology of learning to profl. publs. Patentee in field U.S. and Europe. Trustee, Nat. Chicano Coun. on Higher Edn., 1977-85, Assn. for Advancement of Handicapped People, 1975-78, N.J. Arts Festival, 1980-85; vice-chair Found. for Books to China, 1980—; chair bd. trustees Princeton Day Sch., 1981-93; trustee Princeton Area Found., 1991-95, Our House Found., 1992-94, The Princeton Singers, 1992—, Creed, 1992-94, (Christian Renewal Effort in Emerging Democracies), 1992—, George H. Gallup Internat. Inst., 1992—, Trinity-All Saints' Cemetery, 1993—; chair Affordable Housing Bd. of Princeton Borough, 1987-89; sr. warden All Saints Epis. Ch., 1987-89; chair ins. com. Diocese N.J., 1993—; adv. coun. U. Okla. Ctr. for Rsch. on Minority Edn., 1987-92, Ind. Sch. Chmn. Assn., 1987-92; cons. Carnegie Found. for Advancement of Teaching., 1987-94, Coll. Bd., 1988—; spl. cons. Commn. on Admission to Grad. Mgmt. Edn., 1987-89; commr. Pub. Housing Princeton, N.J., 1995—; trustee Friends of Princeton Open Space, 1995—. Gallup scholar in edn. George H. Gallup Internat. Inst., 1994; recipient Alumni Achievement citation William Jewell Coll., 1970. Fellow Am. Psychol. Soc. (charter), Eastern Psychol. Assn., Psychometric Soc., Am. Ednl. Rsch. Assn., Nat. Coun. on Measurement in Edn. (mem. com. on legal issues in measurement 1977-79), N.Y. Acad. Scis., Nassau Club, Pendragon Club, Oratory of Good Shepherd, Phi Beta Kappa, Sigma Xi. Home: 12 Morven Pl Princeton NJ 08540-3024 Office: Ednl Devel Svc PO Box 441 Princeton NJ 08542-0441

MANNINO, EDWARD FRANCIS, lawyer; b. Abington, Pa., Dec. 5, 1941; s. Sante Francis and Martha Anne (Hines) M.; m. Mary Ann Vigilante, July 17, 1965 (div. 1990); m. Antoinette K. O'Connell, June 25, 1993; children: Robert John, Jennifer Elaine. B.A. with distinction, Pa. U., 1963, LL.B. magna cum laude, 1966. Bar: Pa. 1967. Law clk. 3d cir. U.S. Ct. Appeals, 1966-67; assoc. firm Dilworth, Paxson, Kalish & Kauffman, Phila., 1967-71; ptnr. Dilworth, Paxson, Kalish & Kauffman, 1972-86, co-chmn. litigation dept., 1980-86, sr. ptnr., 1982-86; sr. prin. Elliott, Mannino & Flaherty, P.C., Phila., 1986-90; chmn. Mannino Griffith P.C., Phila., 1990—; sr. ptnr. Wolf, Block, Schorr & Solis-Cohen, Phila., 1995—; hearing examiner disciplinary bd. Supreme Ct. Pa., 1986-89; lectr. Temple U. Law Sch., 1968-69, 71-72; mem. Phila. Mayor's Sci. and Tech. Adv. Com., 1976-79; mem. adv. com. on appellate ct. rules Supreme Ct. Pa., 1989-95; project mgr. Pa. Environ. Master Plan, 1973; chmn. Pa. Land Use Policy Study Adv. Com., 1973-75; chmn. adv. com., hon. mem. faculty history dept. U. Pa., 1980-85. Author: Lender Liability and Banking Litigation, 1989, Business and Commercial Litigation: A Trial Lawyer's Handbook, 1995; mem. editl. bd. Litigation mag., 1985-87, Lender Liability News, 1988—, Bank Bailout Litigation News, 1989-93, Bus. Torts Reporter, 1988—, Practical Litigator, 1989—, Civil RICO Report, 1991—; contbr. articles to profl. jours. Pres. parish coun. Our Mother of Consolation Ch., 1977-79; bd. overseers U. Pa. Sch. Arts and Scis., 1985-89, chmn. recruitment and retention of faculty com.; commonwealth trustee Temple U., 1987-90, mem. audit, bus. and fin. coms. Named one of Nation's Top Litigators Nat. Law Jour., 1990. Fellow Am. Bar Found.; mem. ABA (fellow young lawyers 1977—, co-chmn. bus. torts litigation com. 1985-88, mem. spl. RICO coord. com. 1986—, chair 1991—, chair spl. rev. com. Fed. Rules Civil Procedure 1988-92, litigation divsn. dir. 1988-90, litigation coun. 1990-93), Pa. Bar Assn., Phila. Bar Assn. (gov. 1975), Am. Law Inst., Hist. Soc. U.S. Dist. Ct. Ea. Dist. Pa. (bd. dirs.), Justinian Soc., Pyramid Club, Sharswood Law Club, Order of Coif, Phi Beta Kappa, Phi Beta Kappa Assocs. Democrat. Office: Packard Bldg 12th fl 15th & Chestnut Sts Philadelphia PA 19102

MANNIX, KEVIN LEESE, lawyer; b. Queens, N.Y., Nov. 26, 1949; s. John Warren Sr. and Editta Gorrell M.; m. Susanna Bernadette Chiocca, June 1, 1974; children: Nicholas Chiocca, Gabriel Leese, Emily Kemper. BA, U. Va., 1971, JD, 1974. Bar: Oreg. 1974, U.S.Ct. Appeals (9th cir.) 1976, U.S. Supreme Ct. 1978, Guam 1979. Law clk. to judge Oreg. Ct. Appeals, Salem, 1974-75; asst. atty. gen. Oreg. Dept. Justice, Salem, 1975-77, Govt. of Guam, Agana, 1977-79; judge adminstrv. law Oreg. Workers' Compensation Bd., Salem, 1980-83; assoc. Lindsay, Hart, Neil & Weigler, Portland, Oreg., 1983-86; pres. Kevin L. Mannix Profl. Corp., Salem, 1986—. Chmn. St. Joseph Sch. Bd., Salem, 1981-86; pres. Salem Cath. Schs. Corp., 1985; v.p. Salem Cath. Schs. Found., 1985-88, pres. 1988-90, 91-94, state rep., 1989—. Mem. Marion Bar Assn., Rotary (bd. dirs. East Salem 1985-89, pres. 1987-88), KC. Democrat. Avocations: photography, scuba diving, travel. Home: 375 18th St NE Salem OR 97301-4307 Office: 2003 State St Salem OR 97301-4349

MANNO, VINCENT PAUL, engineering educator; b. N.Y.C., Dec. 4, 1954; s. Paul Thomas and Jennie (Toia) M.; m. Mariann Margaret Montine, Feb. 16, 1980; children: Elizabeth Ellen, Michael Vincent, Christopher Lawrence. BS, Columbia U., 1976; MS, MIT, 1978, ScD, 1983. Engr. Am. Electric Power Co., N.Y.C., 1978-81; engr. Stone & Webster Corp., Boston, 1981-82; postdoctoral assoc. MIT, Cambridge, 1983-84; assoc. prof. Tufts U., Medford, Mass., 1984—; chmn. mech. engring. dept., 1993—; cons. high tech. and power industry, 1983—. Contbr. articles to engring. sci. and energy jours.; reviewer for tech. jours. and pub. cos.; guest editor tech. jours. Recipient Student award Am. Nuclear Soc., Ralph R. Teetor award, 1986; U.S. Dept. Energy fellow, 1983, sr. faculty fellow USN, 1988. Mem. AAAS, Am. Soc. Engring. Edn., AAUP, ASME, IEEE (chair conf. and program com.), Am. Nuclear Soc. (tech. conf. session chmn.), Sigma Xi. Roman Catholic. Office: Tufts U Dept Mech Engring Medford MA 02155

MANNY, CARTER HUGH, JR., architect, foundation administrator; b. Michigan City, Ind. Nov. 16, 1918; s. Carter Hugh and Ada Gage (Barnes) M.; m. Mary Alice Kellett, Dec. 6, 1942 (dec. Jan. 1994); children: Elizabeth, Carter Hugh III. A.B. magna cum laude, Harvard U., 1941, Indsl. Adminstr., 1942; Taliesin fellow, Scottsdale, Ariz., 1946; B.S. in Architecture, Ill. Inst. Tech., 1948. With Murphy/Jahn (name formerly Naess & Murphy and C.F. Murphy Assocs.), Chgo., 1948-83; partner Murphy/Jahn (name formerly Naess & Murphy and C.F. Murphy Assocs.), 1957-61; dir. 1st Citizens Bank, Michigan City, Ind., 1970-86; sr. v.p. Murphy/Jahn (name formerly Naess & Murphy and C.F. Murphy Assocs.), 1978-83; mem. adv. com. on architecture Art Inst. of Chgo., 1982—; oversight com. Ill. Inst. Tech. Sch. of Architecture, Chgo., 1989—; trustee Graham Found. Advanced Studies in Fine Arts, 1956-74, exec. dir., 1972-93, hon. trustee, 1994—. Projects include O'Hare Internat. Airport, Chgo., FBI Hdqrs, Washington, First Nat. Bank Chgo, Chgo. Civic Center, Chgo. Bd. Trade. Fellow AIA (pres. Chgo. chpt. 1973, dir. Ill. council 1972-73), Soc. Archtl. Historians (dir. 1982-85), Chgo. Bldg. Congress (dir. 1978-83); mem. Phi Beta Kappa, Pottawattomie Country Club, Mich. City Yacht Club, Tavern Club, Arts Club, Cliff Dwellers Club (Chgo., hon.). Home: 200 Lake Ave Michigan City IN 46360 also: 1448 N Lake Shore Dr Chicago IL 60610-1625 Office: Graham Found 4 W Burton Pl Chicago IL 60610-1405

MANOFF, DINAH BETH, actress; b. N.Y.C., Jan. 25, 1958; d. Arnold and Lyova (Rosenthal) (Lee Grant) M. Student public schs., N.Y. and Calif. Appeared in: TV series Soap, 1977-78, Empty Nest, 1989-95; TV movie appearances include Raid on Entebbe, 1977, High Terror, 1977, The Possessed, 1977, For Ladies Only, 1981, A Matter of Sex, 1984, The Seduction of Gina, 1984, Celebrity, 1984, Flight #90, 1984, Classified Love, 1986, The Cover Girl and The Cop, 1989, Babies, 1990, (also co-exec. prodr.) Maid for Each Other, 1992; stage performances include I Ought To Be In Pictures, 1980 (Tony award, Theatre World award), Leader of the Pack, 1985, Alfred and Victoria: A Life, Los Angeles Theatre Ctr., 1986-87; films include Grease, 1977, Ordinary People, 1979, I Ought To Be in Pictures, 1981, Gifted Children, 1983, Child's Play, 1988, Staying Together, 1989, Bloodhounds of Broadway, 1989, Welcome Home Roxy Carmichael, 1990. Mem. Screen Actors Guild, Actors Equity, AFTRA. Jewish. Office: The Gersh Agy 232 N Canon Dr Beverly Hills CA 90210 So far, so good.•

MANOFF, RICHARD KALMAN, advertising executive, nutrition policy consultant; b. Bklyn., June 24, 1916; s. Kalman and Sarah (Glatman) M.; m. Lucy B. Deutscher, Nov. 27, 1942; children: Robert K., Gregory P. B.S., CCNY, 1937, M.S., 1940. Asst. regional dir. War Manpower Commn., 1942-45; marketing dir. Welch Grape Juice Co., 1949-53; v.p. Kenyon & Eckhardt Advt., N.Y.C., 1953-56; pres., chmn. bd. Richard K. Manoff Inc. Advt., N.Y.C., from 1956; now pres. Manoff Internat. Inc.; spl. adv. mktg. and communications to exec. dir. UNICEF, 1980—; dir. Thomas J. Lipton, Inc.; adj. prof. dept. health Scis. Sargent Coll. Allied Health Professions, Boston U., 1978—; lectr. pub. health Columbia U. Sch. Medicine, 1982-83; Mem. U.S. del. FAO World Conf., Rome, Italy, 1966; spl. advisor UNICEF and WHO, 1968-78; cons. spl. mission to Food and Agr. Ministry, Govt. India, AID, 1969; Ford Found. offices Pub. Edn. Pub. Broadcasting for children's TV; participant 1st World Conf. on Social Communication for Devel. Mass Communications, Mexico, 1970, 7th Asian Advt. Congress, Delhi, 1970, 3d Western Hemisphere Nutrition Congress, Fla., 1971, Internat. Conf. Nutrition, Nat. Devel. and Planning, Mass. Inst. Tech., 1971, Symposium Eating Patterns and Their Influence on Purchasing Behavior and Nutrition, Nev., 1971, Nutrition Workshop, AID, 1971, 9th Annual Summer Workshop Family Planning, 1971, 4th & 5th Seminar Workshop on Mgmt. and Planning of Population Family Planning Programs, 1971, New Products Symposium, 1971, Communication Seminar series Cornell U., 1971, Exploration The Frontiers of Nutritional Edn. Seminar, 1972, 9th Internat. Congress of Nutrition, Mexico, 1972, East-West Center Comml. Resources Conf. on Family Planning, Hawaii, 1972; Protein adv. group UN Systems Annual Mtg., 1973; mem. panel White House Conf. Food, Nutrition and Health, 1969; mem. Sec.'s Adv. Com. on Population Affairs, Dept. HEW, 1971-76; mem. adv. com. Population Reference Bur., Washington, 1977—, Population Inst., 1980—; mem. Nelson A. Rockefeller's Commn. on Critical Choices for Ams.; cons. HRSA Healthy Start Campaign to reduce infant mortality, 1991; bd. dirs. Population Comm. Internat.; Martin J. Forman Meml. lectr., Washington, 1993. Author: Social Marketing: New Imperative for Public Health, 1985. Bd. dirs. Planned Parenthood World Population, Pathfinder Fund, Boston, 1977-80, United Nutrition Edn. Found., Alexandria, Va., 1978—; mem. com. on internat. nutrition programs NAS-NRC, 1973; founder, mem. Com. for Shakespeare Festival, N.Y.C.; bd. visitors Grad. Sch. and Univ. Ctr., CUNY; mem. adv. bd., cons. to the pres. Henry J. Kaiser Family Found., 1987-91. Recipient 5th Ann. Global award for media excellence Population Inst., China, 1985, Townsend Harris medal Alumni Assn. CCNY, 1986. Mem. Am. Assn. Advt. Agys. (gov. 1967—, sec.-treas. 1975—), City Club, City Coll. Club, Friars Club, Harmonie Club (N.Y.C.), Century Club. Home: 14 Donahue Rd Litchfield CT 06759 also: 322 E 57th St New York NY 10022 Office: 950 3d Ave New York NY 10022

MANOOGIAN, ALEX, manufacturing company executive; b. 1901. With Providence Screw Machine Co., Brown-McLoren Screw Products Co., Packard Motor Car Co., 19924-28; ptnr. Masco Screw Products Co., 1928-29; chmn., pres., chief exec. officer Masco Corp., Taylor, Mich., 1929—, chmn. emeritus, 1985—, also bd. dirs. Office: Masco Corp 21001 Van Born Rd Taylor MI 48180-1340

MANOOGIAN, JOHN A., manufacturing engineer. Gen. mgr. rsch. and engring. Ford Motor Co., Dearborn, Mich. Recipient SME Albert M. Sargent Progress award Soc. Manufacturing Engrs., 1991. Office: Ford Motor Co Rsch & Engring Ctr/ALPHA American Rd Dearborn MI 48121-1899•

MANOOGIAN, RICHARD ALEXANDER, manufacturing company executive; b. Long Branch, N.J., July 30, 1936; s. Alex and Marie (Tatian) M.; children: James, Richard, Bridget. B.A. in Econs, Yale U., 1958. Asst. to pres. Masco Corp., Taylor, Mich., 1958-62, exec. v.p., 1962-68, pres., 1968-85, chmn. bd., CEO, 1985—, chmn., dir. Mascotech, Inc., Trimas Corp.; dir. NBD Bancorp, Inc., Detroit Renaissance, Am. Bus. Conf. Trustee U. Liggett Sch., State Dept. Fine Arts Comsn., Nat. Gallery Art, Founder's Soc., Detroit Inst. Arts, Center for Creative Studies. Mem. Young Presidents Orgn., Yale Alumni Assn. Clubs: Grosse Pointe Yacht, Grosse Pointe Hunt, Country Club Detroit, Detroit Athletic. Office: Masco Corp 21001 Van Born Rd Taylor MI 48180-1340•

MANOR, ANDREA JOAN, nursing administrator; b. Milw., Apr. 27, 1951; m. William Phillip Manor, Nov. 11, 1978; children: Arianne, Adam, Ashley, Alexis. BSN, Valparaiso (Ind.) U., 1973; MS in Nursing, Marquette U., 1986. Staff nurse St. Michael Hosp., Milw., 1976-77; devel. dir. Mt. Sinai Med. Ctr., Milw., 1977-88; dir. nursing svcs. Waukesha (Wis.) Meml. Hosp., 1989—. Capt., Nurse Corps, U.S. Army, 1973-76. Mem. ANA, Am. Orgn. Nurse Execs., Wis. Orgn. Nurse Execs. Home: 10504 N Magnolia Dr Mequon WI 53092-5533 Office: Waukesha Meml Hosp 725 American Ave Waukesha WI 53188-5099

MANOS, JOHN, editor-in-chief. Editor-in-chief Consumer's Digest, Chgo. Office: Consumer's Digest 5705 N Lincoln Ave Chicago IL 60659•

MANOS, JOHN M., federal judge; b. 1922. BS, Case Inst. Tech., 1944; JD, Cleve.-Marshall Coll. Law, 1950. Bar: Ohio. Judge Ohio Ct. Common Pleas, 1963-69, Ohio Ct. Appeals, 1969-76, U.S. Dist. Ct. (6th dist.) Ohio, Cleve., 1976—. Mem. ABA, Fed. Bar Assn., Ohio Bar Assn. Office: US Dist Ct US Courthouse 201 Superior Ave E Cleveland OH 44114-1203

MANOS, PETE LAZAROS, supermarket executive; b. Washington, Dec. 29, 1936; s. George and Ardemecia (Saranides) M.; m. Barbara Lorraine Isper, July 16, 1960; children—Helene Deborah, Cynthia Denise. B. Comml. Sci., Benjamin Franklin U., Washington, 1956, M. Comml. Sci., 1962. C.P.A., Md. Buyer Giant Food Inc., Washington, 1961-63, sr. buyer, 1963-70, mgr., 1970-74, dir., 1974-77, v.p., 1977-81, sr. v.p., 1981-92, pres., 1992—; pres. Giant Food Fed. Credit Union, Greenbelt, Md., 1980-86. Mem. Prince George's Environ. Trust, Prince George's County, Md., 1969-70; mem. U.S. Selective Svc. bd., Prince George's County, 1974-76; mem.

Prince George's Solid Waste Disposal Task Force, 1972-73; chmn. Balt.-Washington Food Industry Friends of Children's Cancer Found., 1988—. With USN, 1956-59. Recipient disting. alumni award Ben Franklin U., 1993, George Washington U., 1994. Mem. United Fresh Fruit and Vegetable Assn. (bd. dirs. 1983-86), Product Mktg. Assn. Democrat. Greek Orthodox. Lodge: Masons. Home: 947 Coachway Annapolis MD 21401-6409 Office: Giant Food Inc 6300 Sheriff Rd Hyattsville MD 20785-4392

MANOSEVITZ, MARTIN, psychologist; b. Mpls., June 22, 1938; s. Julius and Ethel (Cohen) M.; m. Carolyn Heather Margulius, Sept. 17, 1959; children—Bradley, Jason. B.A., U. Minn., Mpls., 1960, Ph.D., 1964. Diplomate in clin. psychology Am. Bd. Profl. Psychology. Asst. prof. psychology Rutgers U., 1964-67; asst. prof. psychology U. Tex., Austin, 1967-69; assoc. prof. U. Tex., 1969-75, prof., 1975-87; pvt. practice clin. psychology Austin, 1975—; adj. prof. psychology U.Tex., 1987—; dir. psychol. svcs. CPC Capital Hosp., Austin, 1987-93; dir. psychol. svcs. Shoal Creek Hosp., Austin, 1994—; pres. Austin Soc. for Psychoanalytic Psychology, 1994—. Trustee Austin-Travis County Mental Health-Mental Retardation Center, 1978-80. Fellow Am. Psychol. Assn.; Am. Orthopsychiatric Assn.; mem. Soc. Research and Child Devel., Tex. Psychol. Assn., Capital Area Psychol. Assn. Home: 3703 Kennelwood Rd Austin TX 78703-2008 Office: Ste 245 8140 MoPac Expressway Bldg # 1 Austin TX 78759-8858

MANOUKIAN, NOEL EDWIN, lawyer, former state supreme court chief justice; b. Livingston, Calif., Jan. 1, 1938. B.A., U. Pacific, 1961; J.D., U. Santa Clara, 1964. Bar: Nev. 1964, U.S. Supreme Ct. 1971. Law clk., bailiff to judges Washoe County (Nev.) Dist. Ct., 1964-65; dep. dist. atty. Douglas County (Nev.), 1965-66; asso. firm Manoukian & Manoukian, Carson City, Nev., 1965-70; individual practice law Carson City, Lake Tahoe and Carson Valley, 1971-74; judge 1st Jud. Dist. Ct., Carson, Churchill, Douglas, Lyon and Storey counties, Minden, Nev., 1974-77; judge multiple ct. dist. 9th Jud. Dist. Ct., 1976-77; justice Nev. Supreme Ct., 1977-85, chief justice, 1983-85; ptnr. Thorndal, Backus, Maupin & Manoukian, Gardnerville, Nev., 1985-87; sole practice Noel E. Manoukian, Ltd.; Gardnerville, 1987—; lectr. numerous schs., profl. orgns.; mem. Conf. Chief Justices, 1983-85, chmn. alt. dispute standing com., 1983-85. Mem. Nev. div. Am. Cancer Soc., 1966-69, bd. dirs., 1969-80, vice chmn. bd. dirs., 1970, chmn. bd. chmn. exec. com., 1973-74, 74-75; now hon. life mem.; vice chmn. Nev. Small County Allocation Com., 1974-77; mem. Nev. State Personnel Adv. Commn., Nev. Commn. Crime, Delinquency and Corrections, 1979-80, Nev. State Planning and Allocations Com., 1979-80; vice chmn. drug and alcohol abuse com. Nev. Task Force, 1980-81. Contbr. articles to profl. jours. Recipient Lawyer of Yr. award Santa Clara Law Sch., 1978. Mem. ABA, Nev. Bar Assn., Am. Judicature Soc. (bd. dirs. 1983-87), Nev. Dist. Judges Assn. (chmn. bd.; pres. 1975-76, 76-77). Office: 1466 Hwy 395 Gardnerville NV 89410

MANOUSOS, JAMES WILLIAM See MANN, JIM

MANOV, LESLIE JOAN BOYLE, radiologist, medical administrator; b. White Plains, N.Y., Aug. 23, 1948; d. Myles Joseph and Harriet Geib (Warburton) Boyle; m. Gregory A. Manov; children from previous marriage: Jay Alexander Bronn, Natasha Nisa Bronn; children from current marriage: John Joseph Manov, Ann Esther Manov. BS, Ohio State U., 1970, MD, 1976. Diplomate Am. Bd. Radiology. Intern internal medicine Ohio State U. Hosp., Columbus, 1976-77, resident internal medicine, 1977-78, resident diagnostic radiology, 1978-81; chief radiology service VA Outpatient Clinic, Columbus, 1981-86; chief diagnostic radiology service Allen Park (Mich.) VA Hosp. Med. Ctr., 1986-87, chief nuclear medicine and diagnostic radiology services, 1987-94; chief radiology svc Miami (Fla.) VA Med. Ctr., 1994—; clin. asst. prof. radiology Ohio State U. Coll. Medicine, 1981-86, Wayne State U. Sch. Medicine, 1986-94, U. Miami Sch. Medicine, 1995—, mem. Am. Coll. Radiology, Radiol. Soc. N.Am., Assn. VA Chiefs of Radiology, Am. Assn. Women Radiologists, Am. Inst. Ultrasound in Medicine, Phi Beta Kappa, Alpha Lambda Delta. Office: Miami VA Med Ctr Radiology Svc Miami FL 33146

MANSBERGER, ARLIE ROLAND, JR., surgeon; b. Pitts., Oct. 13, 1922; s. Arlie Rol and Mayme (Smith) M.; m. Anna Ellen Piel, July 27, 1946; children—Ellen Lynn, John Arlie, Leigh Ann. B.A., Western Md. Coll., 1943, D.Sc. (hon.), 1974; M.D., U. Md., 1947, D.Sc. (hon.), 1978. Diplomate: Am. Bd. Surgery (dir., vice chmn.). Intern U. Md. Hosp., 1947-49, resident in surgery, 1947-54; chief wound shock br. biophysics div. Army Chem. Center, 1954-56; instr. surgery U. Md., 1956-59, asst. prof., 1959-61, asso. prof., 1961-69, prof. surgery, 1969-73; clin. dir. shock-trauma unit, 1962-73; prof. surgery, chmn. dept. Med. Coll. Ga., Augusta, 1973-91; prof. surgery emeritus, chmn., 1991—; cons. surgeon Dwight David Eisenhower Army Med. Center, VA Hosp. Editor: Essence of General Surgery, 1975; chmn. editorial bd.: Bull. U. Md. 1971-73; editor-in-chief: The Am. Surgeon, 1973-89; surg. editor: Resident and Staff Physician, 1979-91; contbr. articles to profl. jours., chpts. to books. Trustee Western Md. Coll., 1971—, Med. Research Found. Ga., 1973-91; bd. dirs. Nicholas J. Pisican Found., 1993—. Served to col. U.S. Army, 1943-46, 54-56. Recipient Man of Yr. award U. Md., 1970, 72, Golden Apple teaching award U. Md., 1968, 72, Disting. Faculty award Med. Coll. Ga., 1979, Gold Medal Alumni award U. Md., 1989, Disting. Svc. award (medal) Southeastern Surg. Congress, 1990. Fellow A.C.S. (gov.); mem. Am. Surg. Assn., Soc. Univ. Surgeons, So. Surg. Assn., Soc. Internationale de Chirurgie, Am. Assn. Surgery of Trauma, Southeastern Surg. Congress, Soc. Surgery of Alimentary Tract, AMA, Soc. Consultants to Armed Forces, Med. Assn. Ga. (editorial bd. 1987-92), Am. Bd. Family Practice (bd. dirs. 1987-92), 29th Div. Assn., Alpha Omega Alpha. Episcopalian. Home: 3128 Walton Way Augusta GA 30909-3265 Office: Dept Surgery Med Coll Ga Augusta GA 30912

MANSBRIDGE, JOHN B., art director, production designer. Prodn. designer: (films) The Love Bug, 1969, Bedknobs and Broomsticks, 1971 (Academy award nomination best art direction 1971), Deliverance, 1972, (with Mark Mansbridge) Amy, 1981, (with Leon Harris) The Devil and Max Devlin, 1981, Baby: Secret of the Lost Legend, 1985, Stone Cold, 1991; art dir.: (films) The Island at the Top of the World, 1974 (Academy award nomination best art direction 1974), No Deposit, No Return, 1976, The Shaggy D.A., 1976, Treasure of Matecumbe, 1976, Freaky Friday, 1976, Herbie Goes to Monte Carlo, 1977, Pete's Dragon, 1977, Hot Lead and Cold Feet, 1978, Return from Witch Mountain, 1978, The North Avenue Irregulars, 1979, The Last Flight of Noah's Ark, 1980, Midnight Madness, 1980, Herbie Goes Bananas, 1980, Tex, 1982, Tron, 1982, Something Wicked This Way Comes, 1983, Trenchcoat, 1983, Splash, 1984, Country, 1984, The River Wild, 1994, (TV movies) The Man Who Fell to Earth, 1987, (TV series) Beauty and the Beast, 1988 (Emmy award outstanding art direction 1989). Office: care Art Directors Guild 11365 Ventura Blvd #315 Studio City CA 91604*

MANSBRIDGE, MARK, art director, production designer. Art dir.: (films) Smokey and the Bandit, 1977, Amy, 1981, The Man with Two Brains, 1983, 8 Million Ways to Die, 1986, The Witches of Eastwick, 1987, The War of the Roses, 1989, Ghost, 1990, Chaplin, 1992 (Academy award nomination best art direction 1992), Fire in the Sky, 1993; prodn. designer: (films) Say Anything, 1989, (TV movies) Dream Breakers, 1989. Office: care Art Directors Guild 11365 Ventura Blvd #315 Studio City CA 91604*

MANSELL, DARREL LEE, JR., English educator; b. Canton, Ohio, Apr. 9, 1934; s. Darrel Lee and Virginia (Shepherd) M.; m. Elizabeth Meihack, Jan. 1957 (div. July 1970); 1 child, Benjamin Lloyd; m. Adriana Saviane, July 16, 1983. BA, Oberlin Coll., 1956; student, Oxford U., 1961-62; PhD, Yale U., 1963; MA (hon.), Dartmouth Coll., 1975. Instr. Dartmouth Coll., Hanover, N.H., 1962-64, asst. prof., 1964-68, assoc. prof., 1968-74, prof., 1974—. Author: The Novels of Jane Austen, 1973; contbr. articles to scholarly jours. Mem. Victorian Lit. Soc., Internat. Assn. for Phenomenology and Lit., Soc. for Literature and Sci., Jane Austen Soc. N.Am. (founding patron), Phi Beta Kappa. Home: 2 Dana Rd Hanover NH 03755-2227 Office: Dartmouth Coll Dept English Hanover NH 03755

MANSFIELD, CARL MAJOR, radiation oncology educator; b. Phila., Dec. 24, 1928; m. Sarah Lynn Flower; children: Joel, Kara. AB in Chemistry, Lincoln U., 1951; postgrad., Temple U., 1952; MD, Howard U., 1956; ScD (hon.), Lincoln U., 1991. Diplomate Am. Bd. Radiology, Am. Bd. Nuclear

Medicine. Rotating intern Episcopal Hosp., Phila., 1956-57, resident in radiology, 1957-58, 60, 61-62; resident in radiation therapy and nuclear medicine Thomas Jefferson Med. Coll. Hosp., Phila., 1960-61, NIH fellow in radiation therapy and nuclear medicine, 1962-63; instr. radiology, chief div. nuclear medicine, 1964-65, Chernicoff fellow in pediatric radiation therapy, 1964-66, assoc. in radiology, chief div. nuclear medicine, 1966-67, asst. prof. radiology, chief div. nuclear medicine, 1967-69, assoc. prof. dept. radiation therapy and nuclear medicine, chief sect. of ultrasound, 1970-74, prof., chief div. nuclear medicine and sect. of ultrasound, 1974-76, prof., chmn. dept. radiation therapy and nuclear medicine, 1983-95; assoc. dir. divsn. cancer treatment Nat. Cancer Inst. NIH, Bethesda, Md., 1995—; NIH postdoctoral fellow in radiation therapy Middlesex Hosp. and Med. Sch., London, 1963-64; lectr. in radiology U. Pa. Sch. Medicine, Phila., 1967-73; vis. prof. radiation therapy and nuclear medicine Hahnemann Med. Coll. Hosp., 1971; sabbatical leave Myerestein Inst. Radiotherapy, Middlesex Hosp. and Med. Sch., London, 1972-73; mem. grad. faculty in radiation biophysics U. Kans. Med. Ctr., Kansas City, 1977-83, prof., chmn. dept. radiation therapy, 1976-83; chmn. dept. radiation therapy Menorah Med. Ctr., Kansas City, Mo., 1977-83. Author 2 books, also author or co-author over 120 articles in med. jours. Served with USAF, 1958-60. Fellow Am. Coll. Radiology, Coll. Physicians of Phila.; mem. AMA, Am. Coll. Nuclear Medicine, mem. AMA, Am. Coll. Radiology, Am Cancer Soc. (dir.-at-large, nat. bd. dirs. 1981—, med. and sci. com. 1981-88, profl. edn. com. 1981-88, pres. Phila div., 1989), Am. Radium Soc. (pres. 1988), Sigma Xi. Office: NIH Bldg EPN Rm 800 Bethesda MD 20892

MANSFIELD, CHRISTOPHER CHARLES, insurance company legal executive; b. 1950; married. BA, Boston Coll., 1972, JD, 1975. With Liberty Mut. Ins. Co., Boston, 1975—, v.p., 1983, sr. v.p., gen. counsel, 1983—; underwriter Liberty Lloyds of Tex. Ins. Co., 1984—; v.p., dir. Liberty Ins. Corp., 1985—; v.p. Liberty Mut. Fire Ins. Co., 1985—, Stein Roe Svcs. Co., 1986—; v.p., gen. counsel LEXCO Ltd., 1986—, Liberty Mut. Capital Corp., 1986—; bd. dirs. Liberty Fin. Cos., Liberty Mut. Bermuda, Liberty Internat. Office: Liberty Mut Ins Co PO Box 140 175 Berkeley St Boston MA 02117

MANSFIELD, EDWARD PATRICK, JR., advertising executive; b. Warren, Pa., Oct. 29, 1947; s. Edward Patrick and Frieda (Dahler) M.; m. Norma L. Johnson, Apr. 17, 1971. AS in Acctg., Jamestown Bus. Coll., 1967; BS in Mktg. Advt., Dyke Coll., 1970. Promotion mgr., ad dir. The News-Herald, Lake County, Ohio, 1973-77; dir. advt. The Eagle, Butler, Pa., 1977-78; dir. mktg. Baltimore Mag., 1978-79; dir. advt. The Washingtonian, Washington, 1979—. Founder, chmn. Warm-A-Heart Fund, 1988—; bd. dirs. Columbia Lighthouse for Blind, 1988—, chmn., 1988-93. Avocations: amateur radio operator gen. class, sailing. Home: 347 Cottswold Pl Riva MD 21140-1528 Office: Washingtonian Mag 1828 L St NW Ste 200 Washington DC 20036-5104

MANSFIELD, EDWIN, economist, educator; b. Kingston, N.Y., June 8, 1930; s. Raymond and Sarah M.; m. Lucile Howe, Feb. 21, 1955; children: Edward, Elizabeth. AB, Dartmouth Coll., 1951; MA, Duke U., 1953, PhD, 1955; cert. diploma, Royal Statis. Soc., 1955; MA (hon.), U. Pa., 1971. Asst. prof., assoc. prof. econs. Carnegie-Mellon U., 1955-60, 62-63; vis. assoc. prof. econs. Yale U., New Haven, 1961-62; vis. prof. econs. Harvard U., Cambridge, Mass., 1963-64, Calif. Inst. Tech., Pasadena, 1967-68; prof. econs. U. Pa., Phila., 1964—; dir. Ctr. Econs. and Tech. U. Pa., 1985—; guest prof. Chalmers U. Tech., Gothenburg, Sweden, 1983, Nat. Technological U., 1989—; cons. Exec. Office Pres. of U.S., U.S. Dept. Commerce, U.S. Dept. Labor, U.S. Gen. Acctg. Office, HHS, NSF, Nat. Inst. Edn., Fed. Power Commn., Inst. for Defense Analysis, SBA, FTC, U.S. Army, Ford Found., RAND Corp., Can. Royal Commn., New Zealand Rsch. Inst., Internat. Fin. Corp., World Bank and others; cons. U.S.-U.S.S.R. Working Party on Sci. and Tech., 1974-75; mem. panel for Nat. Bur. Stds. NAS, 1974-76; mem. bd. examiners Grad. Record Exam., 1975-76; mem. econ. adv. com. U.S. Bur. Census, 1982-85; mem. Nat. Tech. Medal Com., 1984-87; chmn. vis. com. Rensselaer Poly. Inst., 1986-91; mem., bd. dirs. Am. Productivity Ctr., 1988-89. Author: The Economics of Technological Change, 1968, Industrial Research and Technological Innovation, 1968, Defense, Science and Public Policy, 1968, Research and Innovation in the Modern Corporation, 1971, The Production and Application of New Industrial Technology, 1977, Monopoly Power and Economic Performance, 4th edit., 1978, Technology Transfer, Productivity and Economic Policy, 1982, Managerial Economics and Operations Research, 5th edit., 1987, Economics, 7th edit., 1992, Economics USA, 4th edit., 1995, Managerial Economics, 1990, 2d edit., 1993, Microeconomics, 8th edit., 1994, Statistics, 5th edit., 1994, (with Elizabeth Mansfield) The Economics of Technical Change, 1993, Applied Microeconomics, 1994, Leading Economic Controversies, 1995, Innovation, Technology, and the Economy, 1995, others; editor Jour. of the Am. Statistical Assn., 1964-67, Am. Economist, 1969-90, Jour. of Econ. Edn., 1982-90, Review of Industrial Organization, 1984—; IEEE Transactions on Engring. Mgmt., 1985—; Managerial and Decision Econs., 1988-92, Univ. Wis. series on tech. change, 1984-88, Pub. Rsch. Quar., 1993—, and others. Fulbright fellow, 1954-55; Ford. Found research fellow, 1960-61; Ctr. for Advanced Study in Behavioral Scis. fellow, 1971-72; NSF grantee, 1962—; recipient cert. appreciation U.S. Sec. Commerce, 1979, Publ. award Patent Law Assn., 1984, Honor award Nat. Tech. U., 1992, Citation Classic award Inst. for Sci. Info., 1992, Spl. Creativity award NSF, 1994. Fellow Econometric Soc., Am. Acad. Arts and Scis.; mem. AAAS (sci., engring. and pub. policy com. 1981-84), Am. Econ. Assn., Royal Statis. Soc. (cert.), Phi Beta Kappa. Home: 202 Plush Mill Rd Wallingford PA 19086-6021 Office: Dept Econs U Pa Philadelphia PA 19104

MANSFIELD, JOHN H., legal educator; b. 1928. AB, Harvard U., 1952, LLB, 1956. Bar: Calif., Mass. Law clk. to presiding justice U.S. Supreme Ct., 1956-57, Justice Felix Frankfurter, 1957-58; prof. law Harvard U., Cambridge, Mass. Mem. Assn. for Asian Studies (com. on Asian law). Editor: (with Weinstein, Abrams and Berger) Cases and Materials on Evidence, 1988; book rev. editor Harvard U. Law Rev. Office: Sch Law Harvard U Cambridge MA 02138

MANSFIELD, KENNETH EUGENE, retail executive; b. Nashville, Feb. 25, 1946; s. Jack and Roberta (Corlew) M. BA in Polit. Sci., Vanderbilt U., 1971, MBA, 1985. Export sales mgr. Genesco Inc., Nashville, 1971-74, dir. world licensing, 1976-81; dir. mktg., 1981-84, dir. ops. (retail group), 1984-86; Pacific regional sales mgr. J.K. Kealy Co., Honolulu, 1974-76; pres. retail group Endicott Johnson, Endicott, N.Y., 1986-88; pres. retail div. G.H. Bass and Co., Falmouth, Maine, 1988—. Mem. Vanderbilt U., Nashville, alumni bd. dirs., 1988—. Avocations: running, water and snow skiing. Office: G H Bass & Co 360 Us Route 1 Falmouth ME 04105

MANSFIELD, LOIS EDNA, mathematics educator, researcher; b. Portland, Maine, Jan. 2, 1941; d. R. Carleton and Mary (Bowdish) M. BS, U. Mich., 1962; MS, U. Utah, 1966, PhD, 1969. Vis. asst. prof. computer sci. Purdue U., 1969-70; asst. prof. computer Sci. U. Kans., Lawrence, 1970-74, assoc. prof., 1974-78; assoc. prof. math. N.C. State U., Raleigh, 1978-79; assoc. prof. applied math. U. Va., Charlottesville, 1979-83, prof., 1983—; mem. adv. panel computer sci. NSF, 1975-78; cons., vis. scientist Inst. Computer Applications in Sci. and Engring., Hampton, Va., 1976-78. Contbr. articles to profl. jours. Grantee NSF and DOE. Mem. Am. Math. Soc., Soc. Indsl. and Applied Math. (mem. editorial bd. Jour. Sci. Statis. Computing, 1979-88), Assn. Computing Machinery (bd. dirs. SIGNUM 1980-83). Office: U Va Dept Applied Math Thornton Hall Charlottesville VA 22903

MANSFIELD, MARC LEWIS, chemist, research scientist; b. Vernal, Utah, Mar. 30, 1955; s. Henry A. and Mildred (Lind) M.; m. Susan G. Bratton, Mar. 19, 1977; children: Katharine, Heather, Eric. BA, U. Utah, 1977; PhD, Dartmouth Coll., 1980. Postdoctoral assoc. Colo. State U., Ft. Collins, 1980-83; asst. prof. U. Md., College Park, 1983-85; rsch. scientist Mich. Molecular Inst., Midland, 1985—. Recipient Presdl. Young Investigator award NSF, 1985, Initiatives in Rsch. award NAS, 1988. Mem. Am. Chem. Soc., Am. Phys. Soc. Mem. LDS Ch. Office: Mich Molecular Inst 1910 W St Andrews Rd Midland MI 48640-2657

MANSFIELD, MAYNARD JOSEPH, computer science educator, academic dean; b. Marietta, Ohio, Jan. 28, 1930; s. Walter Orville and Lessie Helena (Ullmann) M.; m. Gloria Suzanne Goe, June 7, 1953 (div. June 1975);

m. Sharon Kay Slack, July 19, 1975; children: Pamela, Nancy. BA, Marietta Coll., 1952; MS, Purdue U., 1954, PhD, 1956. Instr. math. Purdue U., West Lafayette, Ind., 1956-57; asst. prof. math. Washington and Jefferson Coll., Washington, Pa., 1957-60, assoc. prof., 1960-63; assoc. prof. math. Ind. U.-Purdue U., Ft. Wayne, 1963-65, prof., 1965-88, prof. computer sci., 1988—, chair dept., 1988-90, chair dept. math. scis., 1964-88, dean Sch. Engring. and Tech., 1990—. Author: 6 textbooks; contbr. articles to profl. jours. Mem. IEEE, Math. Assn. Am. (sec.-treas. 1967-70, bd. govs. 1975-78), Assn. for Computing Machinery (conf. chair, mem. conf. planning com. 1988), Am. Assn. for Engring. Edn., Phi Beta Kappa (pres. Pa. chpt. 1961-63), Sigma Xi. Avocations: flying, computer music, photography. Office: Ind U-Purdue U Sch Engring and Tech 2101 E Coliseum Blvd Fort Wayne IN 46805-1499

MANSFIELD, MICHAEL JOSEPH, former ambassador, former senator; b. N.Y.C., Mar. 16, 1903; s. Patrick and Josephine (O'Brien) M.; m. Maureen Hayes, Sept. 13, 1932; 1 dau., Anne Mansfield Marris. Student, Mont. Sch. Mines, 1927-28; A.B., U. Mont., 1933, A.M., 1934; student, U. Calif., 1936, 37. Seaman U.S. Navy, 1918-19; with U.S. Army, 1919-20, U.S. Marines, 1920-22; miner and mining engr., 1922-1931; prof. history and polit. sci. U. Mont., 1933-42; mem. 78th-82d Congresses from 1st Dist. Mont., 1943-53; U.S. Senator from Mont., 1953-77, asst. majority leader, 1957-61, majority leader, 1961-77; mem. Com. on Fgn. Relations, Appropriations Com.; chmn. Dem. Conf., Policy Com., Steering Com.; ambassador to Japan Tokyo, 1977-89; Presdl. rep. in, China, 1944; U.S. del. IX Inter-Am. Conf., Colombia, 1948, 6th UN Assembly, Paris, 1951-52, Southeast Asia Conf., Manila, 1954, 13th UN Gen. Assembly, 1958; Presdl. assignment, West Berlin, Southeast Asia, Vietnam, 1962, Europe, Southeast Asia, 1965, 69, visited People's Republic of China on invitation of Premier Chou-En-lai, 1972, on invitation of Govt. of People's Republic of China, 1974, 76, 77, 78. Recipient Nelson Rockefeller Pub. Service award, 1988. Office: Ste 900 1101 Pennsylvania Ave NW Washington DC 20004-2514

MANSFIELD, STEPHEN W., judge; b. Brookline, Mass., Aug. 21, 1952; s. Clarence E. and Mary Ann (Zeyer) M.; divorced; children: Eric, Mark, Greg. BA cum laude, Tufts U., 1974; JD, Boston U., 1977. Bar: Tex., Mass. Assoc. gen. counsel Corbel & Co., Jacksonville, Fla., 1984-86; sr. counsel VALIC, Houston, 1986-94; pvt. practice Houston, 1994; judge Tex. Ct. of Criminal Appeals, Austin, 1995—. Republican. Avocations: numismatics, rugby, running. Office: Ct Criminal Appeals Box 12308, Capital Sta Austin TX 78711

MANSHIP, DOUGLAS, broadcast and newspaper executive; b. Baton Rouge, Nov. 3, 1918; s. Charles P. and Leora (Douthit) M.; m. Jane French, Jan. 31, 1942 (div. 1981); children—Douglas Lewis, Richard French, David Charles, Dina. Student, La. State U., 1936-41, U. Heidelberg, 1937, U. Colo., 1938-39. Reporter State Times and Morning Advocate, 1945-47, pub., 1970—; with Baton Rouge Broadcasting Co., 1947—, pres., 1948—; pres., chmn. bd. La IV Broadcasting Corp., 1953—; vice chmn. bd. Radio Free Europe/Radio Liberty, 1978—; chmn. Mobile Video Tapes, Inc., 1960; pres. Capital City Press, 1970; bd. dirs. City Nat. Bank, TV Stas. Inc. Campaign chmn. Community Chest, 1950, bd. dirs., 1950-52, pres., 1951. With USAAF, World War II. Mem. Baton Rouge C. of C. (pres. 1963), La. C. of C. (v.p.), Assn. for Profl. Broadcasting Edn., Council for A Better La., Assn. La. Chambers Commerce, So. Newspaper Pubs. Assn. (pres. 1977-78), Kappa Alpha, Sigma Delta Chi. Episcopalian. Office: Capital City Press 525 Lafayette St Baton Rouge LA 70802-5494

MANSI, JOSEPH ANNEILLO, public relations company executive; b. Oct. 8, 1935; s. Joseph C. and Vinnie (Chirico) M.; m. Mary P. Fusco, Aug. 1, 1959; children: Karen M. D'Attore, Jeanine V. Dimenna. B.S., NYU, 1957. Newsman Internat. News Service, UPI, 1953-58; mem. pub. relations staff Lawrence Orgn., N.Y.C., 1960-63; acct. supr. Philip Lesly Co., N.Y.C., 1963-67; dir. corp. communications Ward Foods, Inc., N.Y.C., 1967-72; dir. pub. relations Metromedia Inc., N.Y.C., 1973-75; pres. Corp. Relations Network, Inc., N.Y.C., 1975-80; mng. ptnr. KCSA Pub. Rels., N.Y.C., 1980—. Served with AUS, 1958-60. Mem. Pub. Rels. Soc. Am. (accredited). Home: 10 Beatrice Ln Glen Cove NY 11542-1202 Office: KCSA Pub Rels 820 2nd Ave New York NY 10017

MANSKE, PAUL ROBERT, orthopedic hand surgeon, educator; b. Ft. Wayne, Ind., Apr. 29, 1938; s. Alfred R. and Elsa E. (Streufert) M.; m. Sandra H. Henricks, Nov. 29, 1975; children: Ethan Paul, Claire Bruch, Louisa Hendricks. BA, Valparaiso U., 1960, DSc (hon.), 1985; MD, Washington U., St. Louis, 1964. Diplomate Am. Bd. Surgery. Surg. intern U Wash., Seattle, 1964-65, surg. resident, 1965-66; orthopedic surg. resident Washington U. St. Louis, 1969-72; hand surgery fellow U. Louisville, 1971; instr. orthopedic surgery Washington U. Med. Sch., St. Louis, 1972-76, asst. prof. orthopedic surgery, 1976-83, prof., 1983—, chmn. dept., 1983-95. Contbr. more than 215 articles and abstracts to profl. jours. Lt. comdr. USN, 1966-69, Vietnam. Fellow AMA, Am. Acad. Orthopaedic Surgery, Am. Orthopaedic Assn.; mem. Am. Soc. Surgery of the Hand, Alpha Omega Alpha. Lutheran. Office: Washington U Dept Surgery 1 Barnes Hosp Plz Saint Louis MO 63110

MANSKI, WLADYSLAW JULIAN, microbiology educator, medical scientist; b. Lwow, Poland, May 15, 1915; came to U.S. 1958, naturalized, 1964; s. Julian and Helena (Lewicka) M.; m. Anna Z. Artymowicz, June 20, 1941; children: Chris, Louis. M.Phil., U. Warsaw, Poland, 1939, D.Sc., 1951. Instr. U. Warsaw, 1936-39; rsch. asst. Inst. Lwow, 1940-41, Inst. Lwow (Inst. Agr.), Pulawy, Poland, 1942-44; instr. U. Lublin, Poland, 1944-45; instr. dept. microbiology Med. Sch., Wroclaw, Poland, 1945-49; Rockefeller fellow Columbia U. N.Y.C., 1949-50; head immunochemistry lab. Inst. Immunology and Exptl. Therapy, Polish Acad. Sci., Wroclaw, 1951-55; head Macromolecular Biochemistry Lab. Inst. Immunology and Exptl. Therapy, Polish Acad. Sci. Warsaw, 1955-57; head dept. virology Biochemistry Lab. State Inst. Hygiene, Warsaw, 1955-57; research worker Coll. Physicians and Surgeons, Columbia U., 1958-62, rsch. assoc., 1962-64, asst. prof., 1964-67, assoc. prof. microbiology, 1967-74, prof. microbiology, 1974-85; dir. rsch. Harkness Eye Inst., Columbia U., N.Y.C., 1985-90. Contbr. articles to profl. jours. NIH grantee, 1960-86. Mem. AAAS, Am. Assn. Immunologists, AAUP, Research in Vision and Ophthalmology Assn., Am. Chem. Soc., Brit. Biochemical Soc. N.Y. Acad. Scis., Soc. Exptl. Biology and Medicine, Soc. Study of Evolution, Internat. Soc. Eye Research, Harvey Soc., Transplantation Soc. Home: 10 Downing St New York NY 10014 Office: 630 W 168th St New York NY 10032-3702

MANSMANN, CAROL LOS, federal judge, law educator; b. Pittsburgh, Pa., Aug. 7, 1942; d. Walter Joseph and Regina Mary (Pilarski) Los; m. J. Jerome Mansmann, June 27, 1970; children: Casey, Megan, Patrick. B.A., J.D., Duquesne U., 1964, 67; LL.D., Seton Hill Coll., Greensburg, Pa., 1985; PhD, La Roche Coll., 1990. Asst. dist. atty. Allegheny County, Pitts., 1968-72; assoc. McVerry Baxter & Mansmann, Pitts., 1973-79; assoc. prof. law Duquesne U., Pitts., 1973-82; judge west dist. U.S. Dist. Ct. Pa., Pitts., 1982-85; judge U.S. Ct. Appeals (3rd cir.), Phila., 1985—; Mem. Pa. Criminal Procedural Rules Com., Pitts., 1972-77; spl. asst. atty. gen. Commonwealth of Pa., 1974-79; bd. dirs. Pa. Bar Inst., Harrisburg, 1984-90; adj. prof. law U. Pitts., 1987—. Mem. adv. bd. Villanova U. Law Sch., 1985-91; bd. dirs. Duquesne U., 1987—; Sewickley Acad., 1988-91. Recipient St. Thomas More award, Pitts., 1983, Phila., 1984. Mem. ABA, Nat. Assn. Women Judges, Pa. and Fed. Judges Assn., Am. Judicature Soc., Allegheny County Bar Assn., Phi Alpha Delta. Republican. Roman Catholic. Office: US Ct Appeals US PO & Courthouse 7th and Grant Sts Pittsburgh PA 15219

MANSMANN, J. JEROME, lawyer; b. Pitts., Aug. 14, 1942; s. C. Rex and Margaret G. (McArdle) M.; m. Carol M. Los, June 27, 1970; children: Kathleen, Megan, Patrick. BA, U. Dayton, 1963; JD, Duquesne U., 1967. Bar: Pa., U.S. Dist. Ct. (we. dist.) Pa., U.S. Ct. Appeals (3d cir.), U.S. Supreme Ct. Assoc. Law Offices of P.J. McArdle, Pitts., 1969-70; ptnr. Mansmann & Mansmann, Pitts., 1970-72; Gondelman, Baxter, Mansmann McVerry & Cindrich, Pitts., 1972-81; Mansmann Cindrich & Titus, Pitts., 1981-91; shareholder Buchanan Ingersoll, P.C., Pitts., 1991—; spl. asst. Atty. Gen. Commonwealth of Pa., Pitts., 1974-80. Bd. dirs. SSM Health Care System, St. Louis; past mem. legal svcs. com. Cath. Health Assn. St. Louis. With USAF, 1967-68. Mem. Pa. Bar Assn., Allegheny County Bar Assn.

Home: Backbone Rd Sewickley PA 15143 Office: Buchanan Ingersoll PC 600 Grant St Fl 57 Pittsburgh PA 15219

MANSON, BRUCE MALCOLM, construction company executive; b. Chgo., July 16, 1944; s. William Donald and Evelyn Florence (Drinnen) M.; m. Mary Jane Romans, July 30, 1966; children—Jennifer Lyn, Scott Lindsay. C.E., Bradley U., 1966. Field engr. E.W. Corrigan Constrn. Co., Chgo., 1966-68, estimator, 1968-73; project mgr. Pepper Constrn. Co., Chgo., 1973-77, v.p. div., 1977-78, v.p. engring., 1978-80, exec. v.p., 1980-85; exec. v.p. chief operating officer Inland Constrn. Co., Chgo., 1985—; adv. bd. C.E. Const. Ind. Assoc. trustee Bradley U. With AUS, 1966-71. Mem. Internat. Council Shopping Ctrs. Builders Assn. Chgo. (sr. v.p.), Assoc. Gen. Contractors, Barrington C. of C. Contbr. articles to profl. jours. Club: Chgo. Athletic Assn. Home: 73 N Saddle Tree Ln Barrington IL 60010-2428 Office: Inland Constrn Co One Graycor Dr Homewood IL 60430

MANSON, JOSEPH LLOYD, III, lawyer; b. Richmond, Va., May 5, 1949; s. Joseph Lloyd Jr. and Nan Smith (Copley) M.; m. Martha Forman Foltz, Sept. 8, 1973; children: Martha Stuart, Joseph Scott, Rachel Smith. BS, U. Va., 1970; JD, Emory U., 1974. Assoc. Verner, Liipfert, Bernhard & McPherson, Washington, 1974-80; ptnr. Verner, Liipfert, Bernhard, McPherson & Hand, Washington, 1981—. Founder Alexandria Youth Sports Found., 1993. 2d lt. U.S. Army, 1973. Mem. ABA (ry. and airline labor law com., co-chmn. mgmt. 1993-94), D.C. Bar Assn. Republican. Episcopalian. Avocations: music, tennis, theatre, movies. Office: Verner Liipfert Bernhard McPherson & Hand Ste 700 901 15th St NW Washington DC 20005

MANSON, LEWIS AUMAN, energy research executive; b. Cleve., July 12, 1918; s. Lewis Frederick and Ina Josephine (Auman) M.; m. Alva Ave London, Sept. 3, 1960 (div. 1982); children: Anita, Howard; m. Shirley Anne Traeger, Jan. 27, 1982; children: Lewis, Jean, Phillip, Edward. Student, Gen. Motors Tech. U., 1944, Purdue U., 1942-43, Rice U., 1950-54. Cons. numerous oil, gas, and mining cos., 1951-57; cons. The Space Agy., Washington, 1958-59, Douglas Aircraft, El Segundo, Calif., 1964; dir. Copper Range Mines, Wyo., 1965; dir. explorations, cons. Nico Internat., S.A. de C.V., Mex., 1968-71; builder Spring, Tex., 1971-74; dir. conductor explorations Minerals of the Sun, S.A. de C.V., Honduras, 1975; dir. Asheville Petroleum Corp., Ill., 1976; conductor explorations Neozoic Minerals & Petroleum, Ltd., Colo., N.Mex., Tex., 1976-77; conductor explorations, dir. Primal Energy Rsch. Found., Houston, 1982—; pres. Transzoic Orebody Locators, Ltd., Vancouver, B.C., Pleiades Petroleum Corp., Lexington, Tenn. and Houston; lectr. grade schs., high schs., Kiwanis, and Rotary, 1962—. Author: The Primal Energy Transverter, 1966, Birth of the Moon, 1978, Origins of Solar Flares and Keys to Predicting Them, 1978, Automatic Recording of Deep Space (Interplanetry) Gravity, 1978, Arriving Ionospheric High Energy (Solar Generated), 1978, Out of the Grey Mist, 1992, Life's Continuum, 1992, The Real Origin of Stellar Energy, 1993, The Great Mystery, 1994; patentee in field; inventor Quakaster, Affinity Sys., Cradle equipment prevents and/or cures decubitus ulcers by Ocean Motion. Scoutmaster Boy Scouts Am., Houston, 1956-63; cubmaster Cub Scouts, Pasadena, Calif., 1962. With mil. NG, 1942-43. Republican. Avocations: mineral and fossil collecting, mountaineering, boating, metal and wood working. Office: Primal Energy Rsch Found Ste 1 2222 Westland Dr Houston TX 77063-2211

MANSON, MALCOLM HOOD, educational administrator; b. Melton Mowbray, Leicester, Eng., May 31, 1938; s. James Milne and Williamina (Hood) M.; m. Snowden Sandra Johnson. BA, Oxford U., Eng., 1961, MA, 1964. Tchr. The Choate Sch., Wallingford, Conn., 1961-63, adminstr., 1963-69; headmaster Marin Country Day Sch., Corte Madera, Calif., 1969-82, Ore. Episcopal Sch., Portland, Oreg., 1982-90; canon headmaster Cathedral Sch. for Boys, San Francisco, 1990—. Mem. Calif. Assn. Ind. Schs. (bd. dirs., v.p. 1976-80), Pacific N.W. Assn. Ind. Schs. (pres. 1985-86). Episcopal. Office: Cathedral Sch for Boys 1275 Sacramento St San Francisco CA 94108-1910

MANSON, PAUL DAVID, retired military officer, electronics executive; b. Trail, B.C., Can., Aug. 20, 1934; s. Robert Edwin and Mary Leonora (McLeod) M.; m. Margaret Nickel, May 11, 1957; children: Robert, Catherine, Peter, Karen. Diploma, Royal Roads Mil. Coll., Victoria, B.C., Can., 1954, Royal Mil. Coll., Kingston, Ont., Can., 1956; BS, Queen's U., 1957; D Mil. Sci. honoris causa, Royal Roads, 1990. Joined RCAF, 1957; advanced through grades to gen. Can. Armed Forces, 1989; various squadron duties Can. Armed Forces, France and Federal Republic of Germany, 1957-62, 67-72; ops. research, Hqrs. Can. Armed Forces, Ottawa, 1963-66; exec. asst. to chief of def. staff Nat. Def. Hdqrs., Can. Armed Forces, Ottawa, 1972-73, chief of air doctrine and ops., 1982-83, asst. dep. minister personnel, 1985-86, chief of def. staff, 1986-89; student Nat. Def. Coll., Kingston, 1973-74; base comdr. Can. Forces Base, Chatham, 1974-76; program mgr. New Fighter Aircraft Program, Ottawa, 1977-80; comdr. 1 Can. Air Group, Fed. Republic of Germany, 1980-81, Air Command, Winnipeg, Man., Can., 1983-85; pres. Loral Can., Inc., Montreal, Que., Can. Recipient Order of Mil. Merit Govt. of Can., 1981, Comdr. Legion of Merit U.S., 1989, C.D. Howe award for achievements in aeronatics and space, 1992. Mem. Aerospace Industries Assn. Can. (past chmn.). Anglican. Avocations: astronomy, music, golfing, home computing. Office: Loral Can Inc, 6111 Royalmount Ave, Montreal, PQ Canada H4P 1K6

MANSON-HING, LINCOLN ROY, dental educator; b. Georgetown, Guyana, May 20, 1927; m. Joyce Louise Chin, Aug. 21, 1949; children: Collin James, Jennifer Lynn, Jeffrey Neal. D.M.D. cum laude, Tufts U., 1948; M.S., U. Ala., 1961. Practice dentistry Kingston, Jamaica; also dir. Schs.' Dental Clinic, St. Mary Parish, Jamaica, 1948-56; asst. prof. dentistry U. Ala., 1956-59, assoc. prof., 1959-68, prof. dentistry, 1968-88, chmn. dept. dental radiology, 1962-88, prof. emeritus dentistry, 1988—; Cons. Am. Dental Assn., Am. Standards Assn., VA Hosp., Birmingham, Ala., Tuskegee, Ala.; cons. USAF, Ala. State Crippled Children Cleft Palate Clinic, 1957-69; Fulbright-Hays lectr., Egypt., 1964-65. Author: (with A.H. Wuehrmann) Dental Radiology, 1965, Panoramic Dental Radiology, 1975, Fundamentals of Dental Radiology, 1979; also articles, textbook chpts.; sect. editor: Jour. Oral Surgery, Oral Medicine and Pathology, 1967-80. Mem. ADA, Am. Acad. Dental Radiology (pres. 1967, editor 1967-80), Internat. Assn. Dento-maxillofacial Radiology (v.p. 41977—), Internat. Assn. Dental Research, AAAS, Sigma Xi, Omicron Kappa Upsilon. Home: 205 Mecca Ave Birmingham AL 35209-3459 Office: 1919 7th Ave S Birmingham AL 35233-2005

MANSOOR, JOHN JIRIUS, sports management executive; b. New Ulm, Minn., July 13, 1955; s. Khalil Azali Mansoor and Audre Helen (Woebke) McGranahan. AA, Am. River Jr. Coll., Sacramento, 1975; BA, Ohio State U., 1978; MA, U. Calif., Davis, 1979. Coach U. Calif., Davis, 1979-81; exec. dir. Sacramento Long Distance Running Assn., 1984—; chmn. Pacific Assn./The Athletics Congress, Sacramento, 1980—. Bd. dirs. Am. River Parkway Commn., Sacramento, 1984-85, Save the Am. River Assn., 1986-88. Avocations: fishing, hunting. Home: 800 Bonita Dr El Dorado Hills CA 95762

MANSOUR, GEORGE P., Spanish language and literature educator; b. Huntington, W.Va., Sept. 4, 1939; s. Elia and Marie (Yazbek) M.; m. Mary Ann Rogers, Dec. 27, 1961; children: Alicia, Philip. AB, Marshall U., 1961; MA, Mich. State U., 1963, PhD, 1965. Assoc. prof. Mich. State U., East Lansing, 1968-77, prof., 1977—, chmn. dept. Romance and Classical langs., 1982—; cons. Mich. Dept. Edn., Lansing, 1984-85. Contbr. articles to profl. jours. Mem. Am. Assn. Tchrs. Spanish and Portuguese (v.p. 1969-71), Mich. Fgn. Lang. Assn. (pres. 1982-84). Democrat. Mem. Eastern Orthodox Ch. Avocations: Pysanky, golf. Home: 1515 Pershing Dr Lansing MI 48910-1846 Office: Mich State U Dept Romance & Classical Langs East Lansing MI 48824

MANSOUR, TAG ELDIN, pharmacologist; b. Belkas, Egypt, Nov. 6, 1924; came to U.S., 1951, naturalized, 1956; s. Elsayed and Rokaya (Elzayat) M.; m. Joan Adela MacKinnon, Aug. 6, 1955; children—Suzanne, Jeanne, Deanine. DVM, Cairo U., 1946; PhD, U. Birmingham, Eng., 1949, DSc, 1974. Lectr. U. Cairo, 1950-51; Fulbright instr. physiology Howard U., Washington, 1951-52; sr. instr. pharmacology Case Western Res. U., 1952-54; asst.

prof., assoc. prof. pharmacology La. State U. Med. Sch., New Orleans, 1954-61; assoc. prof., prof. pharmacology Stanford U. Sch. Medicine, 1961—, chmn. dept. pharmacology, 1977-91, Donald E. Baxter prof., 1977—; cons. USPHS, WHO, Nat. Acad. Scis.; Mem. adv. bd. Med. Sch., Kuwait U.; Heath Clarke lectr. London Sch. Hygiene and Tropical Medicine, 1981. Contrbr. sci. articles to profl. jours. Commonwealth Fund fellow, 1965; Macy Found. scholar NIMR, London, 1982. Fellow AAAS; mem. Am. Soc. Pharmacology and Exptl. Therapeutics, Am. Soc. Biol. Chemists, Am. Heart Assn., Am. Soc. Parasitology, Sierra Club, Stanford Faculty Club. Office: 300 Pasteur Dr Palo Alto CA 94304-2203

MANSOURI, LOTFOLLAH, opera stage director; b. Tehran, June 15, 1929; arrived in Can., 1976; s. Hassan and Mehri (Jalili) M.; m. Marjorie Anne Thompson, Sept. 18, 1954; 1 child, Shireen Melinda. AB, UCLA, 1953. Asst. prof. UCLA, 1957-60; resident stage dir. Zurich Opera, 1960-65; chief stage dir. Geneva Opera, 1965-75; gen. dir. Can. Opera Co., Toronto, Ont., 1976-88, San Francisco Opera, 1988—; dramatic coach Music Acad. West, Santa Barbara, Calif., 1959; dir. dramatics Zurich Internat. Opera Studio, 1961-65, Centre Lyrique, Geneva, 1967-72; artistic adviser Tehran Opera, 1973-75; opera adviser Nat. Arts Centre, Ottawa, Ont., 1977; v.p. Opera America, 1979—; operatic cons. dir. Yes, Giorgio, MGM, 1981; dir. opera sequence for film Moonstruck (Norman Jewison), 1987. Guest dir. opera cos. including Met. Opera, San Francisco Opera, N.Y.C. Opera, Lyric Opera of Chgo., Houston Grand Opera, La Scala, Covent Garden, Australian Opera, Vienna Staatsoper, Vienna Volksoper, Salzburg Festival, Amsterdam Opera, Holland Festival, Nice (France) Opera, Festival D'Orange, France; co-author: An Operatic Life, 1982 (initiated above-stage projection of Surtitles (a simultaneous transl. of opera) 1983). Mem. Am. Guild Mus. Artists, Can. Actors Equity Assn.

MANTEGNA, JOE ANTHONY, actor, playwright; b. Chgo., Nov. 13, 1947; s. Joseph Anthony and Mary Ann (Novelli) M.; m. Arlene Vrhel, Oct. 3, 1975; children: Mia Marie, Gina Cristine. Student, Goodman Sch. of Drama, Chgo., 1967-69. Author: (play) Bleacher Bums, 1979 (Emmy award 1979); appeared in plays including Glengarry Glen Ross, 1984-86 (Tony award, Jeff award), Speed-the-Plow; appeared in films Compromising Positions, 1984, Offbeat, 1985, Money Pit, 1986, 3 Amigos, 1986, Critical Condition, 1986, House of Games, 1987, Suspect, 1987, Weeds, 1987, Things Change, 1988 (Best Actor award Venice Film Festival 1988), Wait Until Spring Bandini, 1990, Alice, 1990, The Godfather Part III, 1990, Queens Logic, 1991, Homicide, 1991, Bugsy, 1991, Body of Evidence, 1992, Family Prayers, 1993, Searching for Bobby Fischer, 1993, Airheads, 1994, Baby's Day Out, 1994, Stranger Things, 1995, Above Suspicion, 1995, Forget Paris, 1995; TV films include Elvis, 1979, Comrades of Summer, 1992, The Water Engine, 1992, State of Emergency, 1994. Recipient Drama Desk Award N.Y. Drama Desk, 1984. Mem. Actors Equity, Screen Actors Guild, Am. Fedn. TV and Radio Artists. Office: care Peter Strain 1501 Broadway #2900 New York NY 10036-4015

MANTEL, SAMUEL JOSEPH, JR., management educator, consultant; b. Indpls., Nov. 17, 1921; s. Samuel Joseph and Beatrice Smith (Talmas) M.; m. Dorothy Jean Friedland, June 28, 1950; children—Michael Lee, Samuel Joseph, III, Margaret Irene, Elizabeth Baer. A.B., Harvard U., 1948, M.P.A., 1950, Ph.D., 1952. Asst. prof. social sci. Ga. Inst. Tech., 1953-56; asst. prof., then assoc. prof. econs., dir. Econs.-in-Action program, Case Western Res. U., 1956-69; prof. mgmt. and quantitative analysis U. Cin., 1969-89, prof. emeritus quantitative analysis and info. systems, 1989—; Joseph S. Stern prof. mgmt., 1973-89, emeritus, 1989, exec. dir. Grad. Ctr. for Mgmt. of Advanced Tech. and Innovation, 1987-89, emeritus, 1989; mgmt. cons., condr. mgmt. seminars. Author: Cases in Managerial Decisions, 1964, Project Management: A Managerial Perspective, 1985, 2d edit. 1989, 3d edit. 1995, Operations Management for Pharmacists: Strategy and Tactics, 1992; co-author several books; mem. editl. bd. Technovation; contbr. articles to profl. jours. Vice pres. Jewish Fedn. Cin., 1978-80; past pres., life mem. Cin. Hillel Found., Cleve. Hillel Found.; historian Rockdale Temple, 1969-77; mem. mgmt. and adminstrn. com. Anti-Defamation League, B'nai B'rith, 1976; trustee Jewish Hosp., Cin., 1975-84, Sarah Marvin Found. for Performing Arts, 1990—; mem. mgmt. adv. com. Cin. Police Dept., 1991-92. Maj. USMCR, 1942-46, 51-53. Decorated D.F.C. with 3 oak leaf clusters, Air medal with 11 oak leaf clusters; Econs.-in-Action fellow, 1955; fellow Inst. Policy Research, 1980; named Prof. of Year, Delta Sigma Pi, 1974. Mem. Project Mgmt. Inst., Iota Epsilon, Beta Gamma Sigma. Home: 608 Flagstaff Dr Cincinnati OH 45215-2525 Office: Univ Cin Cincinnati OH 45221

MANTELL, LESTER J., financial business executive; b. Bklyn., Apr. 30, 1937; s. Abraham and Phyllis (Margolies) M.; m. Joanne Ellen Margolin, Dec. 5, 1970. B.S., Bklyn. Coll., 1958; J.D., NYU, 1963, LL.M., 1966. CPA, N.Y. V.p., dir. taxes City Investing Co., N.Y.C., 1968-85; treas. City Investing Found., N.Y.C., 1979-85, City Investing Polit. Action Com., N.Y.C., 1981-85; sr. v.p. AmBase Corp., 1985-91, 93-94, exec. v.p., 1994-95, asst. v.p., 1995—; treas. AmBase Found., 1985-87, dir., 1991—; treas. AmBase Polit. Action Com., 1985-87; trustee City Investing Co. Liquidating Trust, 1985—. Mem. ABA, N.Y. Bar Assn., AICPAs, N.Y. State Soc. CPAs. Office: 832 Broadway New York NY 10003

MANTELL, SUZANNE, editor; b. West Orange, N.J., Nov. 26, 1944; d. Milton A. and Florence B. M.; m. Peter Gray Friedman, 1985; 1 child, Erica Mantell Friedman. Student, U. Chgo., 1962; B.F.A., Pratt Inst., 1967. Formerly assoc. editor Harper's mag., N.Y.C., exec. editor, 1977-80; editor Harper's Bookletter, 1974-77, Learning Mag., 1980-81, Family Learning Mag., 1983-84; reader Book of the Month Club, 1985-87, 91—; editor Travel Bookstore Catalogue, Banana Republic, 1985-87; assoc. editor The N.Y. Observer, N.Y.C., 1987-91; acting Book News editor Publishers Weekly, 1992-93, contbg. editor, 1993—; also lectr. mag. writing Stanford U., U. Calif. at Santa Cruz. Consulting editor Spelman Coll. Messenger, 1994—. Mem. PEN, Nat. Book Critics Circle. Home: 601 W 113th St 2B New York NY 10025

MANTHEI, RICHARD DALE, lawyer, health care company executive; b. Olivia, Minn., Dec. 23, 1935; s. Alvin R. and Sidonia (Klatt) M.; m. Karen J. Peterson, Sept. 6, 1959 (dec. Mar. 1985); children: Steven, Jana, Kari, John, Rebecca; m. Lynn E. Graham, Aug. 9, 1986. B.S. in Pharmacy (Rexall award 1960), S.D. State U., 1960; J.D., U. Minn., 1967. Bar: Ind. 1967, Ill. 1970, D.C. 1987, U.S. Supreme Ct. 1987. Sales rep. Eli Lilly & Co., Indpls., 1962-64, atty., 1967-70; atty., then asst. corp. sec., dir. regulatory affairs Am. Hosp. Supply Corp., Evanston, Ill., 1970-79, corp. sec., dep. gen. counsel, 1979-85; assoc. gen. counsel Baxter Travenol Labs., Deerfield, Ill., 1986-87; ptnr. Burditt, Bowles & Radzius, Washington, 1987-90, McKenna & Cuneo, Washington, 1990—. Author articles in field.; Editorial adv. staff: Med. Devices and Diagnostic Industry, 1979. Mem. bd. edn. Libertyville High Sch., 1984-87; mem. governing bd. Spl. Edn. Dist. of Lake County, Ill., 1985-87. Served with AUS, 1954-56. Mem. ABA, Health Industry Mfrs. Assn. (chmn. law sect. 1976), Health Industry Assn. (chmn. legal com. 1973), Am. Soc. Corp. Secs. (corp. practices com. 1983-88, group pres. 1985-86, Chgo. regional group 1987), Ill. Bar Assn., Ind. Bar Assn., D.C. Bar Assn., Univ. Club (Evanston, Ill., bd. dirs. 1984-86), Hidden Creek Country Club (Reston, Va.). Home: 3845 N Tazewell St Arlington VA 22207-4544 Office: McKenna & Cuneo 1575 I St NW Washington DC 20005-1105

MANTHEY, ROBERT WENDELIN, retired educator; b. N.Y.C., Dec. 23, 1935; s. Frank A.J. and Josephine (Roth) M.; m. Marcia Christine Dampman; Dec. 27, 1958; children: Catherine, A. David, Jeffrey R. BA, SUNY, Albany, 1957; MA in Teaching, Brown U., 1962. Cert. secondary, sci. tchr., N.Y. Tchr. high sch. Croton-on-Hudson, N.Y., 1957-94. Coord. Boy Scouts Am., Peekskill, N.Y., 1974-90; chmn. Conservation Adv. Coun., Peekskill, 1987. Recipient Excellence award Math. Soc. Am., 1953; fellow NSF, 1962; Rsch. Participation grantee Boyce Thompson Inst., Yonkers, N.Y., 1963-64. Mem. Sci. Tchrs. Assn. N.Y. State, N.Y. State Tchrs. Assn., Croton Tchrs. Assn. (v.p. 1972-74, treas. 1976-93, exec. com. 1972-94), Lions (pres. Peekskill chpt. 1992-93), Elks, KC. Republican. Roman Catholic. Avocation: running. Home: 419 Union Ave Peekskill NY 10566-4704 also: PO Box 103 92 Fremont Ave Daytona Beach FL 32114-5509

MANTHEY, THOMAS RICHARD, lawyer; b. St. Cloud, Minn., May 5, 1942; s. Richard Jesse and Dolores Theresa (Terhaar) M.; m. Janet S. Barth, Dec. 18, 1965; children: Molly, Andrew, Luke. BA cum laude, St. John's U., Collegeville, Minn., 1964; JD cum laude, Harvard U., 1967. Bar: Minn. 1967. Assoc. Dorsey and Whitney, Mpls., 1967-73; ptnr. Dorsey & Whitney, Mpls., 1974—; mem. Dorsey and Whitney's Indian and Gaming Law Practice Group. Contbr. articles to profl. jours. Capt. U.S. Army, 1968-70. Mem. Minn. State Bar Assn. (real estate sect.), Hennepin County Bar Assn. (real estate sect.). Roman Catholic. Avocations: volleyball, golf, fishing. Home: 1834 Summit Ave Saint Paul MN 55105-1427 Office: Dorsey & Whitney 220 S 6th St Minneapolis MN 55402-4500

MANTLE, JOHN EDWARD, newspaper publisher; b. London, June 18, 1940; came to U.S., 1975; s. Arthur Edward and Margaret Ruth (Powell) M.; m. Carol Rose; children: Victoria, Emma Kate. With UPI, 1960-86; photographer UPI, USSR, 1964-67, London, 1967-69; newspictures editor S.Am. UPI, Buenos Aires, 1969-75; regional sales exec. UPI, Chgo., 1975-79; gen. sales exec. UPI, Washington, 1979-80; v.p., gen. mgr. Pacific div. UPI, San Francisco, 1980-83; sr. v.p. dir. newspaper services UPI, Washington, 1983-85, exec. v.p., gen. mgr. newspaper div., 1985-86; pres., pub. Alexandria (Va.) Gazette, 1986-87; pres., pub., co-owner (with Carol Rose-Mantle) Mantle Publs., Inc., Ft. Mill, S.C., 1988—. Mem. Ch. of Eng. Home: 1682 Maple Ridge Ln Fort Mill SC 29715-8818 Office: Mantle Publs Inc 116 Main St Fort Mill SC 29715-1739

MANTLE, MICKEY CHARLES, former baseball player, marketing consultant; b. Spavinaw, Okla., Oct. 20, 1931; s. Elvin Clark and Lovell (Richardson) M.; m. Merlyn Louise Johnson, Dec. 23, 1951; children: Mickey Elvin, David Harold, Billy Giles (dec.), Danny Merle. Grad. high sch. Signed with N.Y. Yankees, 1949, played with Independence (Mo.) farm team, 1949, played with Joplin (Mo.) farm team, 1950, 1st baseman, outfielder, 1951-68, appeared in World Series games, 1951-53, 55-64. Inducted into Baseball Hall of Fame Cooperstown, N.Y., 1974. Office: Roy J True 8080 N Central Expy Ste 800 Dallas TX 75206-1806

MANTLE, RAYMOND ALLAN, lawyer; b. Painesville, Ohio, Oct. 15, 1937; s. Junius Dow and Ada Louise (Stinchcomb) M.; m. Judith Ann LaGrange, Nov. 26, 1967; children: Amanda Lee, Rachel Ann, Leah Amy. BSBA summa cum laude, BA summa cum laude Kent State U., 1961; LLB cum laude, NYU, 1964. Bar: N.Y. 1964, N.J. 1976, U.S. Supreme Ct. Asst. counsel Gov. Nelson A. Rockefeller, N.Y., 1964-65; assoc. Paul Weiss Rifkind Wharton & Garrison, 1967-69; mem. firm Varet & Fink P.C. (formerly Milgrim Thomajan & Lee, P.C.), N.Y.C., 1969-95; ptnr. Peper & Marbury L.L.P., N.Y.C., 1995—; lectr. in computer law field. Contbg. author Doing Business in China. Served to capt. U.S. Army, 1965-67. Mem. N.Y. State Bar Assn., N.J. Bar Assn. Republican. Methodist. Office: Piper & Marbury LLP 53 Wall St New York NY 10005-2834

MANTON, EDWIN ALFRED GRENVILLE, insurance company executive; b. Earls Colne, Essex, Eng., Jan. 22, 1909; came to U.S., 1933; s. John Horace and Emily Clara (Denton) M.; m. Florence V. Brewer, Feb. 1, 1936; 1 child, Diana H. Manton Morton. Student, London (Eng.) U., 1925-27, N.Y. Ins. Soc., 1933-35. With B.W. Noble Ltd., Paris, 1927-33; casualty underwriter Am. Internat. Underwriters Corp., N.Y.C., 1933-37, sec., 1937-38, v.p., 1938-42, pres., 1942-69, chmn., 1969-75; sr. advisor Am. Internat. Group, Inc.; hon. dir. C.V. Starr & Co., Inc. Trustee St. Luke's-Roosevelt Hosp., N.Y.C. Mem. Salmagundi Club, City Midday Drug and Chem. Club, Mendelssohn Glee Club, Williams Club, St. George's Soc. Episcopalian. Home: 40 Fifth Ave New York NY 10011-8843 Office: Am Internat Group Inc 70 Pine St New York NY 10270-0199

MANTON, THOMAS JOSEPH, congressman; b. N.Y.C., Nov. 3, 1932; m. Diane Schley; children: Cathy, Tom, John, Jeanne. BBA, St. John's U., 1958, LLB, 1962. Mem. N.Y.C. Police Dept., 1955-60; mktg. rep. IBM, 1960-64; practice law, 1964-84; mem. 99th-104th Congresses from 9th (now 7th) N.Y. Dist., Washington, 1984—; mem. commerce com., Dem. steering and policy com. Mem. N.Y.C. Council, 1970-84. Served with USMC, 1951-53. Democrat. Office: US Ho of Reps 2235 Rayburn HOB Washington DC 20515*

MANTONYA, JOHN BUTCHER, lawyer; b. Columbus, Ohio, May 26, 1922; s. Elroy Letts and Blanche (Butcher) M.; m. Mary E. Reynolds, June 14, 1947 (dec. 1987); children: Elizabeth Claire, Mary Kay, Lee Ann; m. Carole L. Lugar, Sept. 28, 1989. A.B. cum laude, Washington and Jefferson Coll., 1943; postgrad., U. Mich. Law Sch., 1946-47; J.D., Ohio State U., 1949. Bar: Ohio 1949. Assoc. A.S. Mitchell (Atty.), Newark, Ohio, 1949-50, C.D. Lindrooth, Newark, 1950-57; partner firm Lindrooth & Mantonya, Newark, 1957-74; firm John B. Mantonya, 1974-81, John B. Mantonya, L.P.A., 1981—. Mem. North Fork Local Bd. Edn., 1962-69; adv. com. Salvation Army, Licking County, 1965—; Mayor of Utica, Ohio, 1953-59. Served with AUS, 1943-45. Mem. Am. Bar Assn., Ohio Bar Assn., Licking County Bar Assn. (pres. 1967), Phi Delta Phi, Beta Theta Pi. Home: 11055 Reynolds Rd Utica OH 43080-9549 Office: 3 N 3rd St Newark OH 43055-5506

MANTSCH, HENRY HORST, chemistry educator; b. Mediasch, Transylvania, Romania, July 30, 1935; emigrated to Can., 1968; s. Heinrich Johann and Olga Augusta (Gondosch) M.; m. Amy Emilia Kory, Nov. 2, 1959; children: Monica, Marietta. B.Sc., U. Cluj, Transylvania, 1958, Ph.D., 1964. Research scientist Romanian Acad. Scis., Cluj, 1958-65; Humboldt fellow Tech. U. Munich, W.Ger., 1966-68; research assoc. NRC, Ottawa, Ont., Can., 1968-72; prof. biochemistry U. Cluj, 1973-74; prof. biophys. chemistry Liebig U., Giessen, W.Ger., 1975-76; sr. rsch. officer, head molecular spectroscopy sect. NCR, Ottawa, 1977—; adj. prof. Carleton U., Ottawa, 1978-90, U. Ottawa, 1990—, U. Manitoba, Winnipeg, 1992—. Contbr. articles to profl. jours.; patentee in field. Recipient medal Ministry of Edn., Bucharest, 1972; recipient Humboldt Found. award and medal Bonn, 1980; Chem. Inst. Can. fellow, 1979; Royal Soc. Can. fellow, 1982; recipient Herzberg award, 1984. Mem. Am. Biophys. Soc., Soc. Applied Spectroscopy, Chem. Inst. Can. (chmn. biol. chem. div. 1980-81), Can. Spectroscopy Soc. (mem. nat. exec. com. 1981-90). Home: 2222 W Taylor Blvd, Winnipeg, MB Canada R3P 2J5 Office: NRC Can, 435 Ellice Ave, Winnipeg, MB Canada R3B 1Y6

MANTYLA, KAREN, sales executive; b. Bronx, N.Y., Dec. 31, 1944; d. Milton and Sylvia (Diamond) Fischer; m. John A Mantyla, May 30, 1970 (div. 1980); 1 child, Michael Alan. Student, Rockland Community Coll., Suffern, N.Y., 1962, NYU, 1967, Mercer U., 1981. Mktg. coordinator Credit Bur., Inc., Miami, Fla., 1973-79; dist. mgr. The Research Inst. Am., N.Y.C., 1979-80, regional dir., 1980-85, field sales mgr., 1985-86, nat. sales mgr., 1986-87; dir. mktg. TempsAmerica, N.Y.C., 1987-88; nat. accounts mgr. The Rsch. Inst. Am., N.Y.C., 1989; v.p. sales Bur. Bus. Practice/Paramount Comm., Inc., Waterford, Conn., 1989-93; pres. Quiet Power, Inc., Washington, 1993—. Mem. ASTD, Sales and Mktg. Execs. (past bd. dirs. N.Y. chpt., v.p. Ft. Lauderdale chpt. 1979), U.S. C. of C., Women Entrepreneurs. Avocations: antiques, tennis, writing, swimming. Home: 5449 Grove Ridge Way Rockville MD 20852 Office: Quiet Power Inc Ste 300 655 15th St NW Washington DC 20005

MANTZAVINOS, ANTHONY G., banker; b. Athens, Greece, May 9, 1928; s. George and Irene (Papaleonardos) M.; m. Anita Boukydis; children—George, Irene. B.A., Royal Bd., U., 1951, M.A., 1952. Fin. mgr. Powder & Cartridge Co. Ltd., Athens, 1955-60; dir. for capital investments Hellenic Indsl. Devel. Bank, Athens, 1960-64; various assignments Citibank, Chgo., 1964—, Spain, Portugal, Canada, N.Y.; now group exec. Citicorp/Citibank, N.Y.C.; also dir. Citibank, N.Y.C. Dep. minister of econ. coordination Greek Govt., Athens, 1966-67. Served to 2d lt. Greek Coast Guard. Mem. Pres.'s Coun. Asia Soc. (trustee 1982-88), Alexander S. Onassis Found. (dir. 1982—); Alexander S. Onassis Public Benefit Found. (dir. 1982—). Mem. Greek Orthodox Ch.

MANUEL, BERNARD M., investment banker; b. Paris, June 9, 1947; s. Andre Alexis and Jeanine (Steel) M.; m. Isabelle L. Courvoisier; came to U.S., 1971; M.S. cum laude in Mathematics, U. Paris, 1968, cum laude in Econs., 1970, M.B.A. with high distinction (Baker scholar), Harvard U.,

1973; children—Gregory, Vladimir, Severine, Olivier, Laurent. Lectr. econs. U. Paris, 1968-70; investment analyst Louis-Dreyfus S.A., Paris, 1970-71, asst. to pres. Louis-Dreyfus Corp., N.Y.C., 1973-77; pres. Portescap U.S. Inc., N.Y.C., 1977-83; pres. Amvent Inc., N.Y.C., 1983—. French Govt. scholar, 1971-73, Loeb Rhodes fin. fellow, 1971-72; Melvin T. Copeland awardee, 1971-72. Clubs: Meadow Brook, Hasty Pudding (Boston); Travellers, St. Germain des Pres, Morfontaine (Paris). Home: 25 E 86th St New York NY 10028-0553 Office: Cygne Designs Inc 1372 Broadway Fl 2 New York NY 10018

MANUEL, RALPH NIXON, private school executive; b. Frederick, Md., Apr. 21, 1936; s. Ralph Walter and Frances Rebecca (Nixon) M.; m. Sarah Jane Warner, July 22, 1960; children: Mark, David, Stephen, Bradley. A.B., Dartmouth Coll., 1958; M.Ed., Boston U., 1967; Ph.D., U. Ill., 1971. Assoc. dean Dartmouth Coll., Hanover, N.H., 1971-72, dean of freshmen, 1972-75, dean, 1975-82; pres. Culver (Ind.) Acad. and Culver Edn. Found., 1982—. Bd. dirs. Ind. Sch. Cen. States, 1986—, chair, 1993-95. NDEA fellow, 1968-69. Mem. Assn. Mil. Colls. and Schs. of U.S. (pres., bd. dirs.), Nat. Assn. Ind. Schs. (bd. dirs. 1995—). Office: Culver Acads 1300 Academy Rd Culver IN 46511

MANULIS, MARTIN, film producer; b. N.Y.C., May 30, 1915; s. Abraham and Anne (Silverstein) M.; m. Katharine Bard, June 14, 1939; children: Laurie, Karen, John Bard. BA, Columbia, 1935. Mng. dir. Bahamas Playhouse, 1951-52; exec. head TV prodn. Twentieth Century Fox, 1958-60, ind. motion picture producer, 1960—; artistic dir. Ahmanson Theatre, Music Ctr., Los Angeles, 1987-89; dir. Am. Film Inst. West, 1974-76. Producer, dir. (with John C. Wilson) Broadway; dir. Private Lives, Laura, Made in Heaven, The Show Off, Westport Country Playhouse, 1946-50, (CBS-TV shows) Suspense, Studio One, Best of Broadway, Climax, Playhouse 90, 1952-58, Requiem for a Heavyweight (Emmy award Best Show 1956-57), Miracle Worker (Emmy Best Show 1957-58); producer films Dear Heart, Days of Wine and Roses, Luv and Duffy; producer TV miniseries Chiefs, James Michener's Space, Grass Roots. Served as lt. USNR, 1942-45. Recipient spl. Svc. award Crusade for Freedom, 1954, Look TV award for Best Dramatic Series, 1955, 56, 57, eleven TV Emmy awards for Playhouse 90 Nat. Acad. TV Arts and Scis., 1956, 57; named to Producers Guild of Am. Hall of Fame for Playhouse 90, 1992. Office: Martin Manulis Prodns Ltd PO Box 818 Beverly Hills CA 90213-0818

MANVEL, ALLEN DAILEY, fiscal economist; b. Spokane, Wash., June 29, 1912; s. Arthur Orlando and Agnes Louise (Johnson) M.; m. Helen Louise de Werthern, Oct. 9, 1937; children: Sarah Katherine, Bennet. AB in Econs., Occidental Coll., 1934; postgrad., U. Chgo. 1935-36, Harvard U., 1939-40; DSc (hon.), Ohio State U., 1976. Rsch. assoc. Ill. Dept. Fin., Springfield, 1936-41; rsch. dir. Ill. Agrl. Assn., Chgo., 1941-42; state budget supr. Ill. Dept. Fin., Springfield, 1942-43; adminstrv. analyst U.S. Bur. Budget, Washington, 1943-46; chief govts. div. U.S. Bur. Census, Washington, 1946-67; assoc. dir. Nat. Com. on Urban Problems, Washington, 1967-68; asst. dir. Adv. Com. on Intergovt. Rels., Washington, 1968-71; rsch. asst., sr. fellow The Brookings Instn., Washington, 1972-75; econ. cons. Tax Analysts, Inc., Arlington, Va., from 1976; now ret.; lectr. in pub. adminstrn. George Washington U., Washington, 1946-48; cons. Fiscal Div. UN, N.Y.C., 1953, N.Y.C. Commn. on Statis. Programs, 1954-55. Author: (book) Paying for Civilized Society, 1986; co-author: (books) Measuring Fiscal Capacity and Effort, 1971, Monitoring Revenue Sharing, 1975; contbr. numerous articles to profl. jours. Recipient Louis Brownlow award, Nat. Mcpl. League, 1966. Mem. Nat. Tax Assn. (past. bd. dirs.), Nat. Acad. Pub. Administrn., Cosmos Club, Washington. Democrat. Unitarian. Avocations: reading, travel. Home and Office: 10450 Lottsford Rd Unit 3009 Mitchellville MD 20721

MANVILLE, STEWART ROEBLING, archivist; b. White Plains, N.Y., Jan. 15, 1927; s. Leo and Margaret (Roebling) M.; m. Ella V. Grainger, Jan. 19, 1972 (dec.). Student U. Wyo., 1944-46; BS, Columbia U., 1962. Various office positions, N.Y.C., 1947-51, 56-58; asst. stage dir. several European opera houses, 1951-55; editor Jas. T. White & Co., N.Y.C., 1959-63; archivist, curator Percy Grainger Library, White Plains, N.Y., 1963—. Mem. CAP. Mem. SAR, Hist. House Assn. Am., Nat. Trust Hist. Preservation, Victorian Soc. in Am. (past dir. N.Y. chpt.), Société des Antiquaires de Picardie, Soc. Archtl. Historians, Westchester County Hist. Soc., Titanic Hist. Soc., White Plains Battle Monument Com., Appalachian Trail Conf., Westchester Trails Assn. (past dir.), St. Nicholas Soc. N.Y., Quaker. Author: The Manville/Manvel Families in America; contbr. articles and revs. on music to mags. and newspapers. Office: 7 Cromwell Pl White Plains NY 10601-5005

MANWORREN, DONALD B., church administrator; b. Galesburg, Ill., Jan. 25, 1937; m. Elaine K. Jensen, June 15, 1957; children: Julia, Susan, John. BA, Drake U., 1957, BD, 1961, DD (hon.), 1981; STM, Yale U., 1962; postgrad., Sch. Theology, Claremont, Calif., 1977, Assumption Coll., 1980. Pastor 1st Christian Ch., Keota, Iowa, 1962-64, Convenant Christian Ch., Urbandale, Iowa, 1965-71, Ctrl. Christian Ch., Waterloo, Iowa, 1971-77; exec. coord. Iowa Inter-Ch. Forum, Des Moines, 1977-85; dep. gen. min., pres. Christian Ch. (Disciples of Christ) U.S. and Can., 1986—; mem. gen. bd. Christian Ch. (Disciples of Christ) U.S. and Can., 1975-83, mem. adminstrv. com., 1975-81, mem. regional commn. witness and Svc., 1979-81, mem. Upper Midwest regional bd., parliamentarian, 1981-85; mem. Disciples Ecumenical Consultative Coun., Jamaica, 1979; bd. dirs. Coun. Christian Unity, 1979-85. Commr. Iown Commn. Aging, 1976-80; bd. dirs. Ramsey Meml. Home, Des Moines, 1975-85; trustee Christian Theol. Sem., Indpls., 1976-87, 89—. Rsch. fellow Yale U., 1983. Mem. NCCC-USA (chmn. commn. regional and local ecumenism 1985-87), Nat. Coun. Chs. (mem. governing bd. 1979-87, mem. study panel ecumenical commitment and purposes 1979-87), Phi Beta Kappa. Home: 783 Woodview N Dr Carmel IN 46032 Office: Box 1986 Indianapolis IN 46206

MANZ, CHARLES C., management educator. Prof. mgmt. Ariz. State U., Tempe. Author: The Art of Self Leadership: Achieving Personal Effectiveness in Your Life and Work, 1983, Mastering Self-Leadership: Enpowering Yourself for Personal Excellence, 1991; co-author: Superleadership, 1990, Business Without Bosses: How Self-Managing Teams Are Building High-Performance Companies, 1993. Office: Ariz State U Dept Mgmt Tempe AZ 85287*

MANZER, LEO E., chemicals executive. BSc in Chemistry, U. Waterloo, Ont., Can., 1970; PhD in Chemistry, U. Western Ont., London, Ont., Can. Dir. corp. catalysis ctr. Dupont, Inc., Wilmington, Del.; assoc. dir. ctrl. sci. & engring. labs. Dupont, Inc. Recipient Earle B. Barnes award for leadership in chem. rsch. mgmt. Am. Chem. Soc., 1995. Mem. N.Am. Catalysis Soc., Japanese Catalysis Soc. Office: Dupont Inc 1007 Market St Wilmington DE 19898*

MANZI, JIM, computer software company executive; b. N.Y.C., Dec. 22, 1951; s. Walter Edward and Ann (Smirka) M.; m. Glenda Baugh, May 20, 1978. B.A., Colgate U., 1973; M.A.L.D., Fletcher Sch., Tufts U., 1979. Editorial asst. Nat. Rev. Mag., N.Y.C., 1973-74; news reporter Gannet Newspapers, Port Chester, N.Y., 1974-77; cons. McKinsey & Co., Los Angeles, Boston and N.Y.C., 1979-83; v.p. mktg. and sales Lotus Devel. Corp., Cambridge, Mass., 1983-84, pres., 1984-86, 89—, chmn., chief exec. officer, 1986—. Recipient In-Depth Reporting award AP, N.Y., 1976, 77, Investigative Reporting award N.Y. State Pubs. Assn., 1976, 77. Office: Lotus Devel Corp 55 Cambridge Pky Cambridge MA 02142-1234

MANZIONE, ARTHUR P., parochial schools administrator; b. Bklyn., May 20, 1943; s. Peter Anthony and Concetta Maria (Moscato) M. BA in Social Studies, St. Francis Coll., Bklyn., 1969; MS in Edn., Fordham U., 1978; postgrad., St. John's U., Queens, N.Y., 1977; postgrad. Catechical Inst., St. Joseph's Sem., 1978-79. Deacon, Roman Cath. Ch. Tchr. 6th grade, St. Mary's Star of the Sea Sch., Bklyn., 1965-67; tchr. 7th grade Assumption Sch., S.I., 1967-72; asst. prin. Our Lady of Good Counsel Sch., S.I., 1972-74; prin. Sacred Heart Sch., Newburgh, N.Y., 1974-83; edn. specialist U.S. Army, West Point, N.Y., 1983-88; prin. Holy Family Sch., Bronx, N.Y., 1988-91; dist. supt. Archdiocese of N.Y., White Plains, 1991—; mem. parish bd. edn. Sacred Heart Sch., Newurgh, N.Y., 1974-83; parish coun. Holy Family Parish, Bronx, 1988-91. Named Support Person of

Yr., U.S. Recruiting Bn. Newburgh, 1986. Republican. Avocations: reading, baseball, travel. Home: 427 Grand St Newburgh NY 12550 Office: Dist Supt Sch 950 Mamaroneck Ave White Plains NY 10605

MANZULLO, DONALD A, congressman, lawyer; b. Rockford, Ill., 1944; s. Frank A. Sr. and Kathryn M.; m. Freda Teslik; children: Neil, Noel, Katie. BA in Polit. Sci./Internat. Rels., American U., 1967; JD, Marquette U. Law Sch. Atty., 1970—; mem. 104th Congress from 16th Ill. Dist., 1993—; mem. House Com. on Internat. Rels., subcom. econ. policy, trade and environ., subcom. on Asia and the Pacific, House Com. on small bus., chmn. on subcom. on procurement exports and bus. opportunity, Joint Econ. Commn. Mem. No. Ill. Alliance for Arts, Friends of Severson Dells, Citizens Against Govt. Waste, Rep. Nat. Com. Recipient George Washington honor medal for excellence in pub. comm. Freedoms Found., Valley Forge, Pa., 1991. Mem. ABA, Ill. Bar Assn., Ogle County Bar Assn. (pres. 1971, 73), Nat. Legal Found., Acad. Polit. Sci., Ill. Press Assn., Ill. C. of C., Oregon City C. of C., Nat. Land Inst., Nat. Fedn. Ind. Bus., Ogle County Hist. Soc., Aircraft Owners and Pilots Assn., Ogle County Pilots Assn., Ill. Farm Bur., Ogle County Farm Bur. Office: US Ho of Reps 426 Cannon House Office Bld Washington DC 20515-1316

MAPEL, WILLIAM MARLEN RAINES, retired banking executive; b. Maryville, Mo., Sept. 17, 1931; s. William and Evelyn (Raines) M.; m. Gail Manchee, June 21, 1958; children: Daniel B., Susan L., Stephen W. B.A., Yale U., 1953. Indsl. relations asst. Union Carbide Corp., N.Y.C., 1953-57; with Citibank (N.A.), N.Y.C., 1957-88; asst. cashier Citibank (N.A.), 1959-62, asst. v.ps, 1962-64, v.p., 1964-69, sr. v.p., 1969-88; chmn. Merc. & Gen. Reins Co. Am.; bd. dirs. Merc. & Gen. Life Reassurance Co. Am., Brundage, Story & Rose Investment Trust, Worldway Corp., Churchill Ptnrs., Galey & Lord, NSC Corp., U.S. Life Income Fund, Inc., Atlantic Salmon Fedn., Que.-Labrador Found. Mem. U.S. Srs. Golf Assn., Woodway Country Club, Anglers Club, Pine Valley Golf Club, Links, Wolf's Head, Delta Kappa Epsilon. Home: 18 Stephanie Ln Darien CT 06820-2723

MAPELLI, ROLAND LAWRENCE, food company executive; b. Denver, June 10, 1922; s. Herman M. and Ella (Borelli) M.; m. Neoma Robinson, Apr. 1942; children: Terralyn Mapelli DeMoney, Geraldine Mapelli Gustafson. Student, Regis Coll., 1959-61; Doctorate (hon.), Regis U., 1994. Owner, operator Mapelli Farms and Ranches, Eaton, Colo., 1960-90; chmn. bd., sr. v.p. Monfort of Colo., Inc., Greeley, 1971-89, pres. energy div., 1983-90, also bd. dirs.; sr. v.p. ConAgra Red Meat Cos., Greeley, 1990—; bd. dirs. Norwest Banks Colo., Norwest Bank Greeley; bd. dirs., exec. com., 2d v.p. Nat. Western Stock Show; mem. Colo. Agrl. Adv. Com., 1966-73. Chmn. Denver Off-Street Parking Commn., 1960-72; mem. Denver City Coun., 1955-59, Colo. Ho. of Reps., 1961-62, Colo. State Senate, 1962-66; mem. adv. bd. Ft. Logan Mental Health Ctr., 1961-64, St. Anthony's Hosp., 1960-65; bd. dirs. N. Denver Civic Assn., 1955-65, Better Bus. Bur., 1966-69; mem. bd. Ambassadors Loretto Heights Coll., 1960-65; bd. dirs., exec. com. Nat. Western Stock Show, 1966—; dir. land coun. Colo. State U., 1984—; mem. Colo. Bus. HIgher Edn. Consortium. 2d lt. USAF, 1942-46, ETO; with USAFR, 1946-55. Recipient Knute Rockne award, 1961, Water for Colo. Conservation award, 1985, Man of Yr. award Colo. Meat Dealers Assn., 1975; named Disting. Citizen of 1994, Long Peak coun. Boy Scouts Am., Colo. Bus. Leader of Yr., 1990. Mem. Nat. Cattlemens Assn., Mountain/Plains Meat Assn. (founder, pres. 1968-69), Colo. Cattle Feeders Assn., Cherry Hills Country Club, Greeley Country Club, Thunderbird Country Club, Denver Athletic Club, Rotary. Roman Catholic. Home: 1357 43rd Ave Apt 5 Greeley CO 80634 Office: Con Agra Red Meat Cos PO Box G Greeley CO 80632-0350

MAPES, GLYNN DEMPSEY, newspaper editor; b. N.Y.C., July 15, 1939; s. John George and Dorothy (Glynn) M.; m. Elizabeth Adlum, Apr. 13, 1963; children—Timothy Glynn, Susannah Glynn. B.A., Williams Coll., 1961. Reporter Wall St. Jour., San Francisco, 1965-67; bur. chief Wall St. Jour., Phila., 1967-70; fgn. editor Wall St. Jour., N.Y.C., 1970-71, bur. chief, 1971-75, Page One editor, 1975-88, Reports editor, 1988-89; bur. chief Wall St. Jour., London, 1989-93; money and investing editor Wall St. Jour., N.Y.C., 1993—. Served to lt. (j.g.) USN, 1961-65. Democrat. Club: Collegiate Chorale, London Concert Choir. Home: 570 1st St Brooklyn NY 11215-2353 Office: Wall St Jour 200 Liberty St New York NY 10281-1099

MAPES, JEFFREY ROBERT, journalist; b. San Francisco, Nov. 21, 1954; s. James Robert and Phyllis June (Bloemker) M.; m. Karen Jane Minkel, Aug. 20, 1978; children: Katharine, James. BA, San Jose State U., 1976. Reporter Napa (Calif.) Register, 1976-79; Washington corr. Scripps League Newspapers, 1979-83; reporter The Oregonian, Portland, 1984-87, chief polit. reporter, 1987—. Office: The Oregonian 1320 SW Broadway Portland OR 97201

MAPES, PIERSON, television broadcasting company executive; m. Patricia Carlson. Grad. Norwich Univ. With NBC, 1963-72; account exec., sales mgr., v.p. Blair TV, 1972-79; v.p. NBC TV Network, 1979-82, now pres., NBC TV Network, NBC-TV, N.Y.C., 1982—; bd. dirs. Ramapo Land Co., Sloatsbury, N.Y.; bd. dirs. Broadcast Pioneers, Broadcast Pioneers Library. Trustee Norwich Univ. Capt. U.S. Army, 1959-63. Mem. Internat. Radio and TV Soc., Network TV Assn. (exec. com., bd. advt. coun.). Office: NBC-TV Network 30 Rockefeller Plz New York NY 10112-0001

MAPLE, JOHN E., protective services official; b. N.Y.C., Sept. 23, 1952; s. George and Grace (Cassedla) M.; children: Jaqueline, Brendan. Police officer N.Y.C. Transit Police, detective, patrol supr., detective supr., detective squad commdr., spl. asst. for ops. to chief of dept.; spl. asst. to police commr. Boston Police Dept.; dep. police commr. for crime control strategies N.Y.C. Police Dept. Recipient Disting. Svc. award N.Y. Shields, 1994. Mem. N.Y. Police Dept. Honor Legion, N.Y. Transit Police Dept. Honor Legion. Avocations: fishing, military strategy. Office: New York City Police Dept 1 Police Plaza New York NY 10038

MAPLES, DAN, golf course designer; b. Pinehurst, N.C., 1947. Degree in landscape architecture, U. Ga. Golf. profl., supt. Palmetto Country Club, Aiken, S.C.; prin. Dan Maples Design, Inc., Pinehurst, N.C. Prin. works include Marsh Harbor, Oyster Bay, The Pit. Mem. Am. Soc. Golf Course Archs. (pres. 1990). Office: Dan Maples Design Inc PO Box 5769 77 Cherokee Rd Pinehurst NC 28374

MAPLES, WILLIAM ROSS, anthropology educator, consultant; b. Dallas, Tex., Aug. 7, 1937; s. William Hunter and Agnes Ross (Bliss) M.; m. Margaret Jane Kelley, Dec. 20, 1958; children: Lisa Linda, Cynthia Lynn. BA, U. Tex., 1959, MA, 1962, PhD, 1967. Diplomate Am. Bd. Forensic Anthropology. With Darajani (Kenya East Africa) Primate Rsch. Sta., 1962-63; teaching asst. U. Tex., Austin, 1963-64; mgr. S.W. Primate Rsch. Ctr., Nairobi, Kenya, East Africa, 1964-66; asst. prof. Western Mich. U., Kalamazoo, 1966-68; from asst. prof. to prof. anthropology U. Fla., Gainesville, 1968—; with Fla. Mus. Natural History, Gainesville, 1972-78, chmn. dept. social scis., 1973-87, curator in charge human indentificaion lab., 1986—; Disting. Svc. prof. Fla. Mus. Natural History, 1994—; cons. Armed Forces Graves Registration Office, Honolulu, 1986—, Armed Forces Inst. Pathology, 1989, N.Y. State Police Forensic Unit, Albany, 1987—; cons. in residence U.S. Army Ctrl. Identification Lab., Honolulu, 1986-87; post mortem examination in hist. cases includes: Don Francisco Pizarro, Lima, Peru, The Elephant Man, Joseph Merrick, London, Pres. Zachary Taylor, Louisville, Czar Nicholas II and family, Ekaterinburg, Russia. Author: (with Michael Browning) Dead Men Do Tell Tales, 1994; contbr. articles to profl. jours. Recipient Disting. Tchr. Cert., U. Fla., 1973, Cert. of Honor, City of Lima, Peru, 1985. Fellow Am. Anthropol. Assn., Am. Assn. Physics Anthropologists; mem. Am. Acad. Forensic Scis. (v.p. 1986-87, bd. dirs. 1989-93), Forensic Scis. Found. (trustee, treas. 1988—), Am. Bd. Forensic Anthropology (treas. 1984-87, pres. 1987-89). Avocations: photography, sailing. Office: U Florida Florida Museum Natural History Gainesville FL 32611

MAPOTHER, DILLON EDWARD, physicist, university official; b. Louisville, Aug. 22, 1921; s. Dillon Edward and Edith (Rubel) M.; m. Elizabeth Beck, June 29, 1946; children: Ellen, Susan, Anne. B.S. in Mech. Engring. U. Louisville, 1943; D.Sc. in Physics, Carnegie-Mellon U., 1949. Engr.

Westinghouse Research Labs., East Pittsburgh, Pa., 1943-46; instr. Carnegie Inst. Tech., Pitts., 1946; mem. faculty U. Ill., Urbana, 1949-94; prof. physics U. Ill., 1959-94, dir. acad. computing services, 1971-76, assoc. vice chancellor for research, 1976-94, acting dean grad. coll., vice chancellor research, 1977-78, assoc. dean grad. coll., 1979-94, assoc. vice chancellor for rsch. emeritus, assoc. dean emeritus grad. coll., prof. emeritus physics, 1995—; cons. in field. DuPont fellow, 1947-49; Alfred P. Sloan fellow, 1958-61; Guggenheim fellow, 1960-61. Fellow Am. Phys. Soc.; mem. AAAS, Assn. Univ. Tech. Mgrs., Am. Assn. Physics Tchrs., Sigma Xi. Research on ionic mobility in alkali halides, thermodynamic properties of superconductors, calorimetric study of critical points, adminstrn. of univ. research, commercialization of academic research technology. Home: 1013 Ross Dr Champaign IL 61821-6631 Office: U Ill Office Vice Chancellor Research Swanlund Bldg 601 E John St 4th Fl E Champaign IL 61820

MAPOTHER, TOM CRUISE, IV See CRUISE, TOM

MAPP, ALF JOHNSON, JR., writer, historian; b. Portsmouth, Va., Feb. 17, 1925; s. Alf Johnson and Lorraine (Carney) M.; m. Hartley Lockhart, Mar. 28, 1953; 1 son, Alf Johnson III; m. Ramona Hartley Hamby, Aug. 1, 1971. A.A., Coll. William and Mary, 1945, A.B. summa cum laude, 1961. Editorial writer Portsmouth Star, 1945-46, asso. editor, 1946-48, editorial chief, 1948-54; news editor, editorial writer Virginian-Pilot, Norfolk, 1954-58; free-lance writer, 1958—; lectr. Old Dominion U., 1961-62, instr., 1962-67, asst. prof. English and history, 1967-73, asso prof. English, journalism, creative writing, history, 1973-79, prof., 1979-82, eminent prof., 1982-89, eminent scholar, 1989-92, eminent scholar emeritus, 1992—, Louis I. Jaffe prof. English, 1990-92; Louis I. Jaffe prof. emeritus, 1992—; profl. lectr., 1984—. Host: TV series Jamestown to Yorktown, 1975-77; author: The Virginia Experiment, 1975, 3d edit., 1987, Frock Coats and Epaulets, 1963, 4th edit., 1990, America Creates Its Own Literature, 1965, Just One Man, 1968, The Golden Dragon: Alfred the Great and His Times, 1974, 4th edit. 1990, Thomas Jefferson: A Strange Case of Mistaken Identity, 1987, 4th edit., 1994 (Book-of-Month Club feature selection 1987), Thomas Jefferson: Passionate Pilgrim, 1991, 3rd edit., 1993 (Book-of-Month Club feature selection 1991), Bed of Honor, 1995; co-author: Chesapeake Bay in the Revolution, 1981, Portsmouth: A Pictorial History, 1989, Constitutionalsim: Founding and Future, 1989, Constitutionalism and Human Rights, 1989, Constitutionalsim and Human Rights, 1991, Great American Presidents, 1993. Mem. Portsmouth-Norfolk County Savs. Bond Com., 1948-51, Va. Com. on Library Devel. 1949-50; mem. publs. com. 350th Anniversary of Rep. Govt. in the Western World, 1966-69, War of Independence Commn., 1967-83; mem. editorial bd. Jamestown Found., 1967—; chmn. Portsmouth Revolutionary Bicentennial Com., 1968-81; chmn. awards jury Baruch award United Daus. Confederacy-Columbia U., 1976, mem., 1980; chmn. Portsmouth Mus. and Fine Arts Commn., 1983-85, Southeastern Va. Anglo-Am. Friendship Day, 1976, Bicentennial Commemoration of Cornwallis' Embarkation for Yorktown, 1981, World Premiere of Mary Rose Marine Archeol. Exhibit, 1985; mem. grant rev. com. Va. Commn. for the Arts, 1986-87; bd. dirs. Portsmouth Pub. Library, 1948-58, v.p., 1954-56; bd. dirs. Va. Symphony, 1986-87, trustee, 1987—; mem. taxes and mandates com. City of Portsmouth, 1982—; mem. adv. com. City Mgr. of Norfolk, 1988-94; bd. dirs. Portsmouth Area Community Chest, 1948-52, Va. YMCA Youth and Govt. Found., 1950-52; mem. All-Am. cities com. for award-winning city Nat. League Municipalities, 1976; bd. advisors Ctr. Study Interactive Learning, Pasadena, Calif., 1993—; mem. steering com. Old Dominion U. Friends of the Libr.,1994—; trustee Coun. for Am.'s First Freedom, 1994—. Named Portsmouth Young Man of Year, 1951; recipient honor medal Freedoms Found., 1951, Disting. Rsch. award Old Dominion U., 1987, Great Citizen award Hampton Roads 8 Cities, 1987, Notable Citizen award Portsmouth, Va., 1987; English award Old Dominion Coll., 1961; Troubadour, Great Tchr. award, 1969; Outstanding Am. Educator award, 1972, 74; Nat. Bicentennial medal Am. Revolution Bicentennial Adminstrn., 1976; medal Comité Francais du Bicentenaire de I'Independence des Etats-Unis, France, 1976; (with Ramona Mapp) Nat. Family Svc. award Family Found. Am., 1980; Laureate award Commonwealth of Va., 1981; Disting. Alumnus award Old Dominion U., 1982; Liberty Bell award Portsmouth Bar Assn., 1985; Old Dominion U. Triennial Phi Kappa Phi Scholar award, 1986, 91; History medal Nat. Soc. Daus. Am. Revolution; Portsmouth Downtown Merchants award, 1984, 85; Old Dominion U. Outstanding Achievement award, 1995, nat. Patriots and Founders award, 1995; named to Order of the Crown of Charlemagne, 1993. Mem. Am. Hist. Assn., Va. Hist. Soc., Portsmouth Hist. Soc. (historiographer 1975-82, v.p. 1982-84, pres. 1985), Norfolk Hist. Soc. (dir.-72), No. Neck Hist. Soc., Hist. Socs. Eastern Va. (dir. 1971—), SAR, Am. Assn. U. Profs., Authors Guild, Va. Library Assn. (legislative com. 1950-51), Poetry Soc. Va. (pres. 1974-75, adv. com. 1976—), Va. Writers Club, Assn. Preservation of Va. Antiquities, Order of Cape Henry (dir. 1970—, nat. pres. 1975-76), Jamestowne Soc. (chief historian 1975-77, internat. sec. state 1978-79), English Speaking Union (dir. 1976-77), Modern Lang. Assn., Order of First Families Va. 1607-1624, Nat. Historians Circle, Phi Theta Kappa, Delta Phi Omega (chpt. pres. 1961), Phi Kappa Phi. Baptist. Home: Willow Oaks 2901 Tanbark Ln Portsmouth VA 23703-4828 Reared in an intellectual family with high ethical standards, enthusiasm for the arts, and firm belief in hard work, I also had impressed on me that advantages conferred obligations. In an historic environment, I became aware of my generation's responsibility to those that had preceded it (to preserve the good they had created) and to those that would follow (to create things that would enrich their lives). This concept, with personal ambition, imbues my professional life.

MAPP, KENNETH E., lieutenant governor. Lt. gov. St. Thomas, V.I. Office: 1131 King St #101 Christiansted VI 00820-4970*

MAPSTONE, BARBARA J., nursing administrator; b. Cleve., Oct. 12, 1946; d. Edward and Mildred (Bednar) Italian; m. Timothy B. Mapstone, Oct. 12, 1979; children: Todd, Terre. AD, Cuyahoga Community Coll., Cleve., 1975; BSN, Ursuline Coll., Cleve., 1983; MBA, Case Western Res. U., 1989. Unit mgr. med. ICU Metro Health Med. Ctr., Cleve., adult nurse practitioner, unit mgr., med. clinics, dir. nursing. Recipient award for outstanding achievement in mental health studies Mental Health Assn. Ohio. Mem. Am. Assn. Ambulatory Nurse Adminstrs., Am. Mgmt. Assn., Soc. Care Profl. Ambulatory.

MAQUET, JACQUES JEROME PIERRE, anthropologist, writer; b. Brussels, Belgium, Aug. 4, 1919; came to U.S., 1967, naturalized, 1974; s. Jerome and Jeanne (Lemoine) M.; m. Emma de Longrée, June 17, 1946; children: Bernard, Denis; m. Gisèle Cambresier, Nov. 13, 1970. JD, U. Louvain, Belgium, 1946, D.Phil., 1948; student, Harvard, 1946-48; PhD, U. London, Eng., 1952; Dr. ès-lettres, Sorbonne, France, 1973. Field anthropologist Inst. Sci. Research in Central Africa, 1949-51; head Inst. Sci. Research in Central Africa (Social Scis. Center), 1951-57; prof. State U. of Congo, Elisabethville, 1957-60; research dir. Ecole pratique des Hautes Etudes, U. Paris, 1961-68; prof. anthropology Case Western Res. U., 1968-71; prof. UCLA, 1971-91, chmn. dept. anthropology, 1978-83, prof. emeritus anthropology, 1991—; vis. prof. Northwestern U., 1956, Harvard, 1964, U. Montreal, 1965, U. Pitts., 1967; extraordinary prof. U. Brussels, 1963-68. Author: The Sociology of Knowledge, 1951, Aide-mémoire d'ethnologie africaine, 1954, Ruanda, 1957, (with others) Elections en Société féodale, 1957, The Premise of Inequality in Ruanda, 1961, Power and Society in Africa, 1971, Civilizations of Black Africa, 1972, Africanity, The Cultural Unity of Black Africa, 1972, Introduction to Aesthetic Anthropology, 1979, The Aesthetic Experience, 1986; co-editor: (with others) Dictionary of Black African Civilization, 1974. Recipient Waxweiler award Royal Acad. Belgium, 1961; First World Festival of Negro Arts award Dakar, 1966. Mem. Am. Anthrop. Assn., Internat. Assn. Buddhists Studies, Pali Text Soc., AAUP, Fedn. Am. Scientists. Office: UCLA Dept Anthropology Los Angeles CA 90024

MAQUIPOUR, IRAJ, consulting company executive; b. Tehran, Iran, Mar. 17, 1942; came to U.S., 1963; s. Abbas and Maman (Mahdavi) M.;m. Shirin Baygan (div. 1982); m. Giti Maquipour, Mar. 11, 1991; stepchildren: Ali Amir Khosravi, Iman Khosravi. BA, San Diego State U., 1965, MA in Internat. Rels. and Geopolitics, 1971. Sales mgr. and trainer J.C. Penney Dept. Store, San Diego, 1966-72; dept. credit mgr. Goldwater Bank, Tehran, 1973-75; dep. mng. dir., sales mgr. Meli Shoes, Tehran, 1975-76; mng. dir. Ardel Trading Co., Tehran, 1976-77; v.p., mktg. and credit officer Crocker

Nat. Bank, Beverly Hills, Calif., 1978-84; v.p., mgr. internat. private banking Security Pacific Nat. Bank, Beverly Hills, 1984-91; pres. Maquipour Cons. E&A Inc., Brentwood, Calif., 1991—; bd. dirs. Commerce Internat. Inc., London, Petro-Indelcom, II Unocal Middle East, L.A.; cons. Iran Consumer Coop. Union, Tehran, 1992, Pederson Mgmt. Inc., L.A., 1990. Author: Pre-Conditions and Political Consequences of Land Reform in Iran, 1971. Mem. Phi Sigma Alpha, Delta Sigma Phi, Rotary. Moslem. Avocations: tennis, swimming, travel, reading. Home: 29435 Weeping Willow Dr Agoura Hills CA 91301-4136

MARA, JOHN K., professional sports team executive. Exec. vp., general manager New York Giants, East Rutherford, N.J. Office: NY Giants Giants Stadium East Rutherford NJ 07073

MARA, JOHN LAWRENCE, veterinarian, consultant; b. Whitesboro, N.Y., May 17, 1924; s. William Edward and Olive Pearl (Brakefield) M.; m. Kathleen Keefe, 1946 (div. 1958); children: William, Michael, Daniel, Patrick; m. Patricia Louise Paulk, 1970 (div. 1994); children: Jennifer Lee, Kennon. DVM, Cornell U., 1951. Diplomate Am. Coll. Vet. Nutrition. Intern N.Y. State Coll. Vet. Medicine, Cornell U., Ithaca, 1951-52; assoc. veterinarian L.W. Goodman Animal Hosp., Manhasset, N.Y., 1952-55; owner, pres. Mara Animal Hosp., Huntington, N.Y., 1955-79; profl. rep. Hills Pet Products, Topeka, Kans., 1979-80, mgr. profl. rels., 1980-81, dir. profl. affairs, 1981-88, dir. vet. affairs, 1988-94, sr. fellow profl. and acad. affairs, 1994—. V.p. Huntington United Fund; chmn. Huntington Taxpayers Party, 1968-78, Ch. in the Garden, Garden City, N.Y., 1975-77, trustee, 1975-77. Sgt. U.S. Army, 1943-45, ETO. Recipient Disting. Svc. award We. Vet. Conf., 1988; named hon. alumnus Coll. Vet. Medicine, Wash. State U. Mem. AVMA (Pres.'s award), L.I. Vet. Medicine Assn., N.Y. State Vet. Medicine Assn., Am. Animal Hosp. Assn., Kans. Vet. Medicine Assn. Republican. Baptist. Avocations: gardening, swimming, reading. Home: 6439 SW Castle Ln Topeka KS 66614-9999

MARA, VINCENT JOSEPH, college president; b. Worcester, Mass., Sept. 19, 1930; s. Edward Stephan and Mary Stephanie (Kavanaugh) M.; m. Clare Owens, Feb. 15, 1958; children: John, Kevin, Maryellen, Thomas, Clare. B.S. in Edn., Ed.M, Worcester State Coll.; Ph.D., U. Conn. Asst., then assoc. prof. Framingham (Mass.) State Coll., 1960-63, dir. admissions, 1963-69, acad. dean, 1969-76; acting pres. Salem (Mass.) State Coll., 1974-75; pres. Fitchburg State Coll., 1976—; corporator Fitchburg Savs. Bank, 1976-85; mem. Montachusett Region Pvt. Industry Council, 1983—; dir. Safety Fund Nat. Bank. Contbr. articles to profl. jours. Trustee Notre Dame Prep. Sch., Fitchburg, 1985-86; trustee Worcester Pub. Libr., 1967-70, pres. bd. trustees, 1970; bd. dirs Fitchburg Civic Ctr., 1977-80, Cushing Acad., 1978-80, North Ctrl. Mass. Mental Health Assn., 1979-81, United Way, 1981-87, Montachusett Region Pvt. Industry Coun., 1983-93; bd. dirs. Thayer Symphony Orch., 1987-90, pres., 1994-95; mem. Mass. Commn. Edn. Telecomm., 1983-90, Fitchburg Bd. Health, 1982-93. With U.S. Army, 1952-53. Named Outstanding Young Man of Yr. Worcester C. of C., 1960; recipient Disting. Citizen award City of Fitchburg, 1989. Mem. NEA, Am. Conf. Acad. Deans, Am. Assn. State Colls. and Univs., N.Am. C. of C. (bd. dirs. 1984-91), Fitchburg C. of C. (bd. dirs. 1977-83), Phi Delta Kappa, Kappa Delta Pi. Democrat. Roman Catholic. Club: Fay (Fitchburg). Home: 242 Pearl Hill Rd Fitchburg MA 01420-2036 Office: Fitchburg State Coll 160 Pearl St Fitchburg MA 01420-2697

MARA, WELLINGTON T., professional football team executive; b. Aug. 8, 1916. Pres. N.Y. Giants, East Rutherford, N.J., also co-chief exec. officer. Office: NY Giants Giants Stadium East Rutherford NJ 07073 also: Nat Football League 410 Park Ave New York NY 10022-4407*

MARAFINO, VINCENT NORMAN, aerospace company executive; b. Boston, June 8, 1930; m. Doris Marilyn Vernall, June 15, 1958; children: Marli Ann, Sheri Louise, Wendi Joan. A.B. in Acctg. and Econs., San Jose State Coll., 1951; M.B.A., Santa Clara U., 1964. Chief acct. Am. Standard Advance Tech. Lab., Mountain View, Calif., 1956-59; with Lockheed Missiles & Space Co., Sunnyvale, Calif., 1959-70, asst. dir. fin. ops., 1968-70; asst. controller Lockheed Corp., Burbank, Calif., 1970-71, v.p., controller, 1971-77, sr. v.p. fin., 1977-83, exec. v.p., chief fin. and administrv. officer, 1983-88, vice chmn. bd., chief fin. and adminstrv. officer, 1988—, also dir.; bd. dirs. Lockheed Missiles & Space Co., Inc.; chmn. bd. dirs. Lockheed Fin. Corp. Trustee Holy Cross Med. Ctr., Mission Hills, Calif. Served with USAF, 1953-55. Mem. Fin. Execs. Inst., AICPAs, North Ranch Country Club. Office: Lockheed Corp 4500 Park Granada Blvd Calabasas CA 91399-0105

MARALDO, PAMELA JEAN, nursing association executive, lecturer, consultant; b. Wilmington, Del., Oct. 27, 1947; d. Ernest and Helen Cecelia (Antonini) M. B.S., Adelphi U., 1970; M.A., NYU, 1976, Ph.D., 1985; LHD (hon.), Worcester State U., 1989. Registered nurse, N.Y. Cardiovascular nurse NYU Med. Ctr., N.Y.C., 1970-74; research assoc. Nat. Health Council, N.Y.C., 1975-78; dir. pub. policy Nat. League for Nursing, N.Y.C., 1978-83, chief exec. officer, 1983-92; pres. Planned Parenthood Fed. of Am., N.Y.C., 1992—; mem. health care faculty Am. Express, N.Y.C., 1982—; N.Y.C. Bd. Health, 1988—. Contbr. articles to profl. jours., chpts. to books. Mem. legis. com. Village Reform Democrats, N.Y.C., 1985; bd. dirs. Nurses for Polit. Action, N.Y.C., 1978—, Nurses Ednl. Fund, Nurses Houses. Recipient Disting. Alumna award Adelphi U., 1985, Disting. Recent Alumna award NYU, 1989; named one of 12 top execs. of non-profit orgns. Saavy Mag., 1985. Fellow Am. Acad. Nursing; mem. Am. Nurses Assn., Women's Econ. Roundtable, Am. Soc. Assn. Execs., Nat. Health Coun. (v.p. 1989—), bd. dirs. 1987—), Epsilon Phi Tau, Sigma Theta Tau. Democrat. Avocations: tennis; swimming; horseback riding. Home: 61 Jane St New York NY 10014-5107 Office: Planned Parenthood Fed of Am 810 7th Ave New York NY 10019

MARAM, BARRY S., lawyer; b. Chgo., Mar. 21, 1946. BA, U. Ill., 1967; MA with honors, U. Chgo., 1985; JD, Ill. Inst. Tech., 1971. Bar: Ill. 1971, Fla. 1973, U.S. Dist. Ct. (no. dist.) Ill. 1971, U.S. Dist. Ct. (so. dist.) Fla. 1974. Ptnr. Winston & Strawn, Chgo.; instrs. bus. law Triton Coll., 1983-85; assoc. dir. Ill. Dept. Health, 1985; exec. dir. Ill. Health Facilities Authority, 1986-89. Pub. Policy fellow. Mem. Ill. State Bar Assn., Fla. Bar. Office: Winston & Strawn 35 W Wacker Dr Chicago IL 60601-1614

MARAMOROSCH, KARL, virologist, educator; b. Vienna, Austria, Jan. 16, 1915; came to U.S., 1947, naturalized, 1952; s. Jacob and Stefanie Olga (Schlesinger) M.; m. Irene Ludwinowska, Nov. 15, 1938; 1 dau., Lydia Ann. M.S. magna cum laude in Entomology, Agrl. U., Warsaw, Poland, 1938; student, Poly. U. Bucharest, Rumania, 1944-46; fellow, Bklyn. Bot. Garden, 1947-48; Ph.D. (predoctoral fellow Am. Cancer Soc. 1948-49), Columbia, 1949. Civilian internee in Rumania, 1939-46; asst., then assoc. Rockefeller Inst., N.Y.C., 1949-61; sr. entomologist Boyce Thompson Inst., Yonkers, N.Y., 1961-74, program dir. virology and insect physiology, 1962-74; prof. microbiology Waksman Inst., Rutgers U., New Brunswick, N.J., 1974-85; prof. entomology Cook Coll., Rutgers U., New Brunswick, 1985—, Robert L. Starkey prof., 1983—; vis. prof. agr. U. Wageningen, Netherlands, 1953, Cornell U., 1957, Rutgers U., 1967-68, Fordham U., 1973, Sapporo U., Japan, 1980, Justus Liebig U., Giessen, Ger., 1983; Mendel lectr. St. Peters Coll., Jersey City, 1963; virologist FAO to Philippines, 1960; Disting. Vis. prof. Fudan U., Shanghai, 1982; cons. FAO-UN, World-wide survey, 1963; chmn. U.S.-Japan Coop. Seminar, 1965, 74, 85; mem. panel food and fiber Nat. Acad. Scis., 1966; cons. rice virus diseases AID-IRRI, Hyderabad, India, 1971; cons. UNDP, Bangalore, India, 1978-79; virologist FAO/UNDP, Sri Lanka, 1981, 82, 83, Mauritius, 1985; AIBS lectr., 1970-72, Found. Microbiology Nat. lectr., 1972-73, Fulbright Disting. prof., Yugoslavia, 1972, 78; mem. tropical medicine and parasitology study sect. NIH, 1972-76; chmn. 1st-3d Internat. Confs. Comparative Virology, 1969, 73, 76. Author: Comparative Symptomatology of Coconut Diseases of Unknown Etiology, 1964; editor: Biological Transmission of Disease Agents, 1962, Insect Viruses, 1968, Viruses, Vectors and Vegetation, 1969, Comparative Virology, 1971, Mycoplasma Diseases, 1973, Viruses, Evolution and Cancer, 1974, Invertebrate Immunity, 1975, Legume Diseases in the Tropics, 1975, Invertebrate Tissue Culture: Research Applications, 1976, Invertebrate Tissue Culture: Applications in Medicine, Biology and Agriculture, 1976, Aphids as Virus Vectors, 1977, Insect and Plant Viruses: An Atlas, 1977, Viruses and Environment, 1978, Practical Tissue Culture Applications, 1979,

Leafhopper Vectors and Plant Disease Agents, 1979, Vectors of Plant Pathogens, 1980, Invertebrate Systems in Vitro, 1980, Vectors of Disease Agents, 1981, Mycoplasma Diseases of Trees and Shrubs, 1981, Mycoplasma and Allied Pathogens of Plants, Animals and Human Beings, 1981, Plant Diseases and Vectors: Ecology and Epidemiology, 1981, Invertebrate Cell Culture Applications, 1982, Pathogens, Vectors and Plant Diseases: Approaches to Control, 1982, Subviral Pathogens of Plants and Animals, 1985, Viral Insecticides for Biological Control, 1985, Biotechnology Advances in Insect Pathology and Cell Culture, 1987, Mycoplasma Diseases of Crops, 1988, Invertebrate and Fish Tissues Culture, 1988, Biotechnology for Biological Controls of Pests and Vectors, 1991, Viroids and Satellites: Molecular Parasites at the Frontier of Life, 1991, Plant Diseases of Uncertain Etiology, 1992, Insect Cell Biotechnology, 1994, Arthropod Cell Culture Systems, 1994; Methods in Virology, 1964—, Advances in Virus Research, 1972—, Archives of Virology, 1973-78, Intervirology, 1973-77, Advances in Cell Culture, 1979—; editor in chief Jour. N.Y. Entomol. Soc, 1972-84; assoc. editor: Virology, 1964-68, 75-79. Recipient Sr. Research award Lalor Found., 1957; Nat. Ciba-Geigy award in agr., 1976; Wolf prize in agr., 1980; Jurzykowski prize in biology, 1980; Disting. Service award Am. Inst. Biol. Scis., 1983. Fellow AAAS (Campbell award 1958), Entomol. Soc. Am., N.Y. Acad. Scis. (A. Cressy Morrison prize natural sci. 1951, chmn. div. microbiology 1956-60, rec. sec. 1960-61, v.p. 1962-63), Nat. Acad. Scis. India (hon.); mem. Harvey Soc., Growth Soc., Phytopath. Soc., Indian, Japan, Can. phytopath. socs. Leopoldina Acad., Internat. Com. Virus Nomenclature, Electron Microscope Soc., Am. Soc. Microbiology (Waksman award 1978), Tissue Culture Assn. (pres. N.E. br. 1978-81, pres. history br. 1988-90), Soc. Invertebrate Pathology (founder's lectr., Adelaide 1990), Internat. Assn. Medicinal Forest Plants (pres. 1989—), Sigma Xi (pres. Rugers chpt. 1978). Home: 17 Black Birch Ln Scarsdale NY 10583-7456 Office: Rutgers U Dept Entomology New Brunswick NJ 08903

MARAN, STEPHEN PAUL, astronomer; b. Bklyn., Dec. 25, 1938; s. Alexander P. and Clara F. (Schoenfeld) M.; m. Sally Ann Scott, Feb. 14, 1971; children: Michael Scott, Enid Rebecca, Elissa Jean. B.S., Bklyn. Coll., 1959; M.A., U. Mich., 1961, Ph.D., 1964. Astronomer Kitt Peak Nat. Obs., Tucson, 1964-69; project scientist for orbiting solar observatories NASA-Goddard Space Flight Center, Greenbelt, Md., 1969-75; head advanced systems and ground observations br. NASA-Goddard Space Flight Center, 1970-77; mgr. operation Kohoutek, 1973-74, sr. staff scientist, 1977—; Cons. Westinghouse Rsch. Labs., 1966; vis. lectr. U. Md., College Park, 1969-70; sr. lectr. UCLA, 1976; A. Dixon Johnson lectr. in sci. communication, Pa. State U., 1990; lectr. on astronomy cruises and eclipse tours. Author: (with John C. Brandt) New Horizons in Astronomy, 1972, 2d edit., 1979, Arabic edit., 1979, The Gems of Hubble, 1993; editor: Physics of Nonthermal Radio Sources, 1964, The Gum Nebula and Related Problems, 1971, Possible Relations Between Solar Activity and Meteorological Phenomena, 1975, New Astronomy and Space Science Reader, 1977, A Meeting with the Universe, 1981, Astrophysics of Brown Dwarfs, 1986, The Astronomy and Astrophysics Encyclopedia, 1991; assoc. editor: Earth, Extraterrestrial Scis, 1969-79; editor: Astrophys. Letters, 1974-77, assoc. editor, 1977-85; contbg. editor Air & Space/Smithsonian, 1990—; contbr. articles on astronomy, space to popular mags. Named Disting. Visitor Boston U., 1970; recipient Group Achievement awards NASA, 1969, 74, Exceptional Achievement medal, 1991. Mem. AAAS, Internat. Astron. Union (editor daily newspaper 1988), Am. Astron. Soc. (Harlow Shapley vis. lectr. 1981—), press. officer 1985—), Royal Astron. Soc., Am. Phys. Soc., Am. Geophys. Union. Office: NASA Goddard Space Flight Ctr Code # 680 Greenbelt MD 20771

MARANDA, GUY, oral maxillofacial surgeon, Canadian health facility executive, educator; b. Paris, May 9, 1936; arrived in Canada, 1937; s. Emilien and Lucille (Fortin) M.; married; children: Lucille, Jean, Isabelle. BA, U. Ottawa, Ont., Can., 1957; DDs, U. Montreal, Can., 1962; cert. oral surgeon, U. Pa., 1965. Pvt. practice Quebec, 1965-70; mem. faculty U. Laval, Ste. Foy, Que., Can., 1970—, asst. prof., 1987-94, prof., 1994—; bd. dirs. Ordre Dentistes du Quebec; pres. Quebec Assn. Oral Surgeons, 1985; cons. Quebec Health Bd., Assurance Auto Quebec, various law firms. Mem. Royal Coll. Dentists Can. (diplomate, pres. 1991), Internat. Assn. Oral Surgeons, Can. Assn. Orala Surgeons, Am. Assn. Oral Surgeons, Can. Dental Assn. Ordre Dentistes que. Roman Catholic. Home: 822 Bellevue, Sainte Foy, PQ Canada G1V 2R5 Office: U Laval, Faculty Dental Medicine, Sainte Foy, PQ Canada G1V 7P4

MARANDA, PIERRE JEAN, anthropologist, writer; b. Quebec, Que., Can., Mar. 27, 1930; s. Lucien and Marie Alma (Rochette) M.; m. Elli Köngäs, Mar. 12, 1963 (dec.); children: Erik Pierre, Nicolas Martin. B.A., U. Laval, Quebec, 1949, M.A., U Montreal, Que., 1953; Ph.D., Harvard U., 1966; Dr. honoris causa, Meml. U. Nfld., 1984. Asst. prof. anthropology U. Laval, 1955-58, research prof., 1975—, prof., 1976—, dept. head, 1989—; tutor Harvard U., 1964-65, research fellow, 1966-70; dir. studies Ecole Pratique des Hautes Etudes, 6th Sect., Paris, 1968-69; assoc. prof. U. B.C. (Can.), Vancouver, 1969-73; prof. U. B.C. (Can.), 1973-75; prof. étranger College de France, Paris, 1975; bd. dirs. several internat. research insts.; vis. prof. Universidade Federal, Rio de Janeiro, 1983. Author: (with Köngäs Maranda) books, including Structural Models in Folklore and Transformational Essays, 1962, 2d rev. edit., 1970, Introduction to Anthropology: A Self-Guide, 1972, French Kinship: Structure and History, 1974, Soviet Structural Folkloristics, 1974, Dialogue Conjugal, 1985; DiscAn: A Computer System for Contents and Discourse Analysis, 1989, (with Fidèle Nze-Guema) L'Unité culturelle dans la diversité: Une Geste bantu, 1990; contbr. numerous articles to profl. jours. Pres. Comité des Citoyens de Belvedere, Que., 1976-83. Recipient Medaille du College de France, 1975. Fellow Royal Soc. Can., Am. Anthrop. Assn.; mem. Internat. Semiotics Assn., Internat. Center Linguistics and Semiotics, Can. Inst. Advanced Research (council), Can. Ethnol. Soc. (former pres.), Can. Anthropology and Sociology Assn. (former pres.), Can. Semiotics Research Assn. (bd. dirs.), Can. Folklore Studies Assn.

MARANDAS, SUSAN MARGARET, secondary education educator; b. Portland, Oreg., Sept. 11, 1942; d. Phil Huth and Sue Louise (Pringle) Bushnell; children: Stephanie, John J., Jason. BA in Liberal Arts, Willamette U., 1964; MA in Polit. Sci., Portland State U., 1987. Cert. secondary edn. tchr. Tchr. Twality Jr. High., Tigard, Oreg., 1964-68, Franklin High Sch., Portland, 1969, Lakeridge High Sch., Lake Oswego, Oreg., 1986, St. Mary's Acad., Portland, 1986—. NEH fellow, 1992. Mem. ASCD, Nat. Coun. Social Studies, Oreg. Coun. Social Studies (tchr. of yr. 1992, sec./jour. editor, 1993, sec. 1994, 95). Office: St Mary's Acad 1615 SW 5th Ave Portland OR 97201-5496

MARANISS, DAVID, reporter; b. 1949. Reporter The Washington Post. Author: First in His Class: A Biography of Bill Clinton, 1995. Recipient Pulitzer Prize for nat. reporting, 1993. Office: Washington Post 1150 15th St NW Washington DC 20071-0002

MARANO, ANGELINE MARIE, hospital administrator; b. Indiana, Pa., Apr. 28, 1957; d. Salvatore A. and Elizabeth L. (Pagliaro) M. BS, U. Pitts., 1979; MHA/MBA, U. S.C., 1983. Resident Providence Hosp., Columbia, S.C., 1982-83; asst. exec. dir. Humana Hosp.-Ft. Walton Beach, Fla., 1983-84; assoc. exec. dir. Humana Hosp.-South Broward, Hollywood, Fla., 1985, Humana Hosp.-Palm Beaches, West Palm Beach, Fla., 1985-87; adminstr. Humana Hosp.-Biscayne, Miami, Fla., 1987—; adj. prof. Fla. Internat. U., Miami, 1988—. Mem. Big Bros./Big Sisters, Palm Beach/Broward. Andrew W. Mellon scholar U. Pitts., 1975-79, USPH scholar U. S.C., 1981-83. Mem. Am. Coll. Healthcare Execs. Office: Humana Hosp Biscayne 20900 Biscayne Blvd Miami FL 33180-1495

MARANO, ANTHONY JOSEPH, cardiologist; b. White Plains, N.Y., Apr. 14, 1934; s. Anthony Joseph and Mary Antoinette (Perrotta) M.; m. Mary Regina Marbach, Aug. 23, 1958; children—Thomas, Kathryn, Michele. B.A., Williams Coll., 1956; M.D., Cornell Med. Coll., 1960. Diplomate Am. Bd. Internal Medicine, Am. Bd. Cardiovascular Disease. Intern Bellevue Hosp., N.Y.C., 1960-61; resident St. Luke's Hosp., N.Y.C., 1961-63; NIH fellow in cardiology Mt. Sinai Hosp., N.Y.C., 1963-64, research assoc., 1964-75; clin. assoc. in medicine Coll. Physicians and Surgeons, N.Y.C., 1970-86; pres. med. staff White Plains Hosp., 1984-86, chief cardiology, 1985-91, chief cardiology emeritus, 1991—; bd. dirs., 1983-88; cons. in cardiology Burke Rehab. Ctr.; med. dir.; founder Paramedic

Ambulance, White Plains, 1976-82. Contbr. articles to med. jours. Trustee Pace U., N.Y.C., 1975—, Home Savs. Bank, White Plains, 1973-90; bd. dirs. YMCA, White Plains, 1978-82 ; team physician White Plains High Sch., 1967—; cons. physician Dept. Pub. Safety, White Plains, 1968—; cons. physician City of White Plains Sch. System, 1994—; bd. dirs. Westchester County Sports Hall of Fame, 1993—; alumni trustee Tyng Found., Williams Coll., 1994—. Tyng scholar Williams Coll., 1952-59; recipient Outstanding Achievement award Emergency Med. Services Council, 1982. Fellow ACP, Am. Coll. Cardiology; mem. AMA, Am. Coll. Sports Medicine, Am. Heart Assn., N.Y. State Heart Assn. (bd. dirs. 1982-85), Westchester Heart Assn. (v.p. 1983-86, pres. 1987-90), Phi Beta Kappa. Clubs: University (White Plains) (pres. 1970-71); Westchester Country (Harrison, N.Y.). Avocations: tennis, skiing, gardening. Home: 9 Fairway Dr White Plains NY 10605-4107 Office: 20 Old Mamaroneck Rd White Plains NY 10605

MARANO, ROCCO JOHN, telephone company executive; b. West Haverstraw, N.Y., 1928; B.S., Fordham U., 1953, LL.B., 1957; married. Admitted to N.Y. bar, 1958; with Irving Trust Co. to 1953; comptroller, exec. v.p. ops. and chief operating officer N.Y. Bell Telephone Co., 1953-65, 72-74, 76-78, v.p.-staff parent co. AT&T, Basking Ridge, N.J., 1979-80, v.p., 1982-83; with N.J. Bell Telephone Co., 1968-71, 74-76, 80-82, v.p.-acctg., comptroller, 1968-71, v.p.-indsl. relations, then v.p.-personnel, 1971, v.p. ops., 1974-76, pres., 1980-82; pres. Bell Communications Research Inc., Livingston, N.J., 1983—; dir. First Fidelity Bank N.A., N.J., First Fidelity Bancorp., Mut. Benefit Life Ins. Co., Blue Cross Blue Shield of N.J. Office: Blue Cross & Blue Shield of NJ 33 Washington St Newark NJ 07102

MARANS, J. EUGENE, lawyer; b. Butte, Mont., May 26, 1940; s. Edward and Florence M.; m. Anne Marie Borger, Sept. 3, 1978; children: Julia C., John E. A.B., Harvard U., 1962, LL.B., 1965. Bar: N.Y. 1966, D.C. 1971. Law clk. to Judge John M. Wisdom U.S. Ct. Appeals (5th cir.), New Orleans, 1965-66; assoc. Cleary, Gottlieb, Steen & Hamilton, N.Y.C., 1966-70, Paris, 1970-71; assoc. Cleary, Gottlieb, Steen & Hamilton, Washington, 1971-74, ptnr., 1975-90, 93—; ptnr. Cleary, Gottlieb, Steen & Hamilton, Hong Kong, 1990-93; mem. N.Y. State adv. com. U.S. Commn. Civil Rights, 1969-70; mem. nat. eval. com. on. simplified method of determining eligibility in pub. assistance HEW, 1969-70; sec., counsel Bipartisan Com. on Absentee Voting, 1973—. Contbr. articles to legal jours. Bd. dirs. New Leadership Fund, chmn. 1977-79; mem. Sabre Found., pres. 1990. Mem. Assn. Ams. Resident Overseas, Ripon Soc. (nat. governing bd. 1962—, chmn. 1969-70), Council on Fgn. Relations, ABA, D.C. Bar (chmn. internat. sect. 1978-79), Assn. of Bar of City of N.Y., Am. Soc. Internat. Law, Union Internat. des Avocats, Washington Fgn. Law Soc. (pres. 1985-86), Am. Law Inst. Office: 1752 N St NW Washington DC 20036-2806

MARANS, ROBERT WARREN, architect, planner, educator; b. Detroit, Aug. 3, 1934; s. Albert and Anne Rose (Siegel) M.; m. Judith Ann Bloomfield, Jan. 24, 1956; children: Gayl Elizabeth, Pamela Jo. BArch, U. Mich., 1957; M in Urban Planning, Wayne State U., 1961; PhD, U. Mich., 1971. Reg. architect, Mich. Archtl. engr., planner Detroit City Planning Comn., 1957-61; planning cons. Blair & Stein Assocs., Providence, 1961-64; architect-urban designer Artur Glikson, Architect, Tel Aviv, Israel, 1964-65; regional planner Detroit Area Transp. Land Use Study, 1965-67; asst. prof. Fla. State U., Talahassee, 1967; rsch. assoc., sr. study dir. Inst. Social Rsch., Ann Arbor, Mich., 1968-74, program dir., 1974—; from lectr. to assoc. prof. Coll. Architecture Urban Planning, Ann Arbor, 1971-78; prof. architecture and urban planning U. Mich., Ann Arbor, 1978—; cons. TVA, 1972, UN, 1974; chmn. urban and regional planning program, 1987—. Co-author: Planned Residential Environments, 1970, Quality of NonMetropolitan Living, 1978, Evaluating Built Environments, 1981, Retirement Communities: An American Original, 1984; co-editor: Methods of Environmental and Behavioral Research, 1987, Advanced Monograph Series on Environment, Behavior and Design, 1990, Environmental Simulation: Research and Policy Perspectives, 1993; contbr. articles to profl. jours. and tech. reports. Sec. Washtenaw County Parks Recreation Commn., Ann Arbor, 1972—; chmn. Huron-Clinton Met. Parks Authority, Brighton, Mich., 1986—. Recipient fellow Social Sci. Rsch. Coun., 1969-70; Fulbright Rsch. award Coun. Internat. Exchange Scholars, Israel, 1977; Progressive Architecture Applied Rsch. award Progressive Architecture Mag., 1982; Design Rsch. Recognition award Nat. Endowment for Arts, 1983. Mem. Am. Planning Assn., Nat. Recreation Pk. Assn., Environ. Design Rsch. Assn. Avocations: swimming, stamp collecting. Office: 3136 Inst Social Rsch Univ of Mich Ann Arbor MI 48106

MARANZANO, MIGUEL FRANCSICO, engineer; b. Buenos Aires, Argentina, Aug. 14, 1941; came to U.S., 1977; s. Miguel and Nelida (Pizzini) M.; m. Ana Isabel Carranza, Mar. 25, 1978; children: Cynthia, Rossana, Giancarlo, Gabriel. BS, SUNY, 1982; MS, Rensselaer Poly., 1985. Field engr. Johnson Controls, Phila., 1978-82; sr. rsch. engr. Hi-G Rsch., Bloomfield, Conn., 1979-82; engr. mgr. Locknetics, Hamden, Conn., 1982-85; group leader Superior Elec., Bristol, Conn., 1985-86; mgr. elec. testing Springborn Labs., Enfield, Conn., 1986-88; sr. product engr. Skinner Valve, New Britain, Conn., 1988-89, Kip, Inc., Farmington, Conn., 1989—; mem. adj. faculty dept. math. and sci. Manchester C.C., 1986-88; presenter 39th internat. conf. Nat. Assn. Relay Mfrs. Contbr. articles to profl. jours. Mem. Hispanic-Am. Cultural Coun., New Britain, Conn., 1990. Achievements include patent on electronic game and solenoid valve. Home: 110 Pheasant Run Bristol CT 06010-4891 Office: Kip Inc 72 Spring Ln Farmington CT 06032-3140

MARASCO, FRANCIS ANTHONY, human resources executive; b. Punxsutawney, Pa., Jan. 23, 1943; s. Reese and Josephine (Serriani) M.; m. Marilyn Kay Mastro, Aug. 17, 1968; children: Matthew, Lauren. BS, St. Vincent Coll., 1964; postgrad., W.Va. U., 1964-67. Personnel asst. PPG Industries, Inc., Harmar Twp., Pa., 1968-69; successively staff asst., mgr. personnel relations, dir. personnel, v.p. personnel Thrift Drug Co., Pitts., 1969-87, sr. v.p., 1987—. Div. chmn. Literacy Task Force United Way, 1986—, sect. campaign chair 1984, 88; sec. RIDC Park Assn., 1986—; bd. dirs. Arthritis Found. Western Pa., 1987. Sgt. USMC Res. 1967-73. Mem. Pitts. Personnel Assn., Nat. Assn. Chain Drug Stores (chair human resource com. 1982-84). Roman Catholic. Home: Box 153 RD # 8 Greensburg PA 15601 Office: Thrift Drug Co 615 Alpha Dr Pittsburgh PA 15238-2876

MARASH, STANLEY ALBERT, consulting company executive; b. Bklyn., Dec. 18, 1938; s. Albert Samuel and Esther (Cunio) M.; m. Muriel Sylvia Sutchin, June 24, 1961; children: Judith Ilene, Alan Scott. Student, Bklyn. Coll., 1956-58; BBA, CCNY, 1961; student, U. Idaho, 1962-63, Boston U., 1964-66; MBA, Baruch Coll., 1970. Registered profl. engr., Calif.; cert. quality engr., reliability engr. Statistician Electric Boat Gen. Dynamics, Groton, Conn., 1961-62; statistician Idaho Nat. Energy Lab. Electric Boat Gen. Dynamics, Idaho Falls, 1962-63; mgr. quality assurance memory product ops. RCA, Needham, Mass., 1963-65; cons. engr. astroelectronics div. RCA, Princeton, N.J., 1965-66; corp. mgr. quality assurance Ideal Corp., Bklyn., 1966-68; mgr. quality assurance Gen. Instrument, Signalite, Neptune, N.J., 1968; pres. STAT-A-MATRIX Inc., Edison, N.J., 1968-90; chmn. bd. STAT-A-MATRIX Inst., Edison, N.J., 1975—; chmn., CEO STAT-A-MATRIX Group, Edison, N.J., 1990-94, The SAM Group - STAT-A-MATRIX, Edison, N.J., 1994—; trustee Ellis R. Ott Found., Edison, 1982-95; chmn. Quality N.J., 1989-94, chmn. emeritus, 1994—; advisor quality tech. Middlesex County Coll., Edison, 1970-94; vis. prof. U. Sao Paulo, Brazil, 1974, 75, 77, Madrid Poly. U., 1976; expert cons. Internat. Atomic Energy Agy., Vienna, 1974-77; cons. various govt. agys. and pub. and pvt. cos., 1972—; mem. indsl. adv. com. dept. stats. Rutgers U., 1977-78; mem. exec. stds. coun. Am. Nat. Stds. Inst., N.Y.C., 1979-80. Author: (tab. manual) Statistically Aided Management: What Every Executive Needs to Know, 1987; contbr. numerous articles, manuals and tng. texts. Examiner Malcolm Baldridge Nat. Quality Award, 1990, 91. Fellow Am. Soc. Quality Control (chmn. met. sect. 1966-68, Ellis R. Ott award 1981, chmn. internat. cooperation com. 1989—); mem. IEEE (sr.) (ASTM, ASME, Am. Stats. Assn., Am. Soc. Tng. Devel., Am. Nuclear Soc. Office: The SAM Group/Stat-A-Matrix One Quality Pl Edison NJ 08820-1059

MARAYNES, ALLAN LAWRENCE, filmmaker, television producer; b. N.Y.C., Apr. 26, 1950; s. Harry and Dorothy (Kaufman) M.; m. Bitsy Healy, Oct. 14, 1978; children: Sean, Megan, Matthew. BA, Queens Coll., 1972; MA, Loyola U., L.A., 1974. Assoc. producer CBS News, N.Y.C.,

1976-77; producer CBS News-60 Minutes, N.Y.C., 1974-88; pres. Northern Films, N.Y.C., 1988—; exec. producer ABC "SST" program, 1989; producer 20/20 ABC News, N.Y.C., 1990-93; sr. investigative prodr. ABC News 20/20, 1994—; lectr. New Sch., N.Y.C., 1979, Columbia U., N.Y.C. Writer, dir. CBS News, 60 Minutes, 1976-88; author: (play) A Straight Line to the Market Place, 1975, (screenplay) Warp, 1991. Recipient Emmy award NATAS, 1981, 85, 89, 91, 93, George Foster Peabody award, 1989. Mem. NATAS, Writers Guild Am. Avocations: N.Y. Yankees. Office: ABC News 157 Columbus Ave New York NY 10023-5907

MARBLE, DUANE FRANCIS, geography educator, researcher; b. Seattle, Dec. 10, 1931; s. Francis Augustus and Beulah Belle (Simmons) M.; m. Jacquelynne Hardester, Aug. 18, 1957; children: Kimberley Eileen, Douglas Craig. BA, U. Wash., 1953, MA, 1956, PhD, 1959. Asst. prof. real estate U. Oreg., Eugene, 1959; asst. prof. regional sci. U. Pa., Phila., 1960-63; from assoc. prof. geography to prof. geography Northwestern U., Evanston, Ill., 1963-73; prof. geography and computer sci. SUNY at Buffalo, Amherst, N.Y., 1973-87; prof. geography and natural resources Ohio State U., Columbus, 1987—; chmn. com. geog. data sensing and processing Internat. Geog. Union, 1980-88; dir. Castlereagh Enterprises, Phoenix.; founder Internat. Symposium Spatial Data Handling. Editor: Intro Readings in GIS, 1990, Taylor & Francis, 1990-95; author computer program (best software award Assn. Am. Geogs. 1990). Mem. AAAS, Assn. Computing Machinery, Assn. Am. Geographers (honors 1993), IEEE Computer Soc. Home: 1310 Langston Dr Upr Arlington OH 43220-3900 Office: Dept Geography Ohio State Univ Columbus OH 43210-1361

MARBURGER, JOHN HARMEN, III, university president, physics educator; b. S.I., N.Y., Feb. 8, 1941; s. John H., Jr. and Virginia A. (Smith) M.; m. Carol Preston Godfrey, June 12, 1965; children: John Harmen, Alexander Godfrey. B.A. in Physics magna cum laude, Princeton U., 1962; Ph.D. in Applied Physics (NASA trainee), Stanford U., 1967. Physicist Goddard Space Flight Center, NASA, 1962-63; asst. prof. physics and elec. engring. U. So. Calif., Los Angeles, 1966-69, assoc. prof., 1969-75, prof., 1975-80, chmn. physics dept., 1972-75, interim dean Coll. Letters, Arts and Scis., 1976-77, dean Coll. Letters, Arts and Scis., 1977-80; prof. physics and elec. engring., pres. SUNY, Stony Brook, 1980-94; cons. laser fusion program Lawrence Livermore Labs., 1972-75; chmn. N.Y. State fact finding panel on Shoreham Nuclear Power Facility, 1983; chmn. bd. trustees Universities Rsch. Assn., 1988-94; co-chair NASULGC Bd. on Oceans and Atmosphere, 1992-93; bd. dirs. N.Y. State Edn. and Rsch. Network, Inc., 1986-88, L.I. Rsch. Inst., 1992, L.I. High Tech. Incubator Corp., 1990—. Contbr. articles to tech. publs. Bd. dirs. Mus. at Stony Brook, 1980-92, L.I. Assn., Inc., 1983-93, Action Com. for L.I., 1980-83, L.I. Forum for Tech., Inc., 1980—. Rsch. Found. SUNY, 1990—; bd. trustees Princeton U., 1985-89; chmn. N.Y. State Energy Office Rev. Commn., 1980-81, Suffolk County (N.Y.) Task Force on Priorities in Fin., 1980-81; campaign chmn. United Way of L.I., 1991-92. Recipient Shuichi Kusaka Meml. Prize Princeton U., 1962. Mem. Assn. of Colls. and Univs. State of N.Y. (pres. 1988-89), Coleman Chamber Music Assn. (bd. dirs. 1969-80). Office: SUNY Office of Pres Stony Brook NY 11794-0701

MARBURY, RITCHEY MCGUIRE, III, engineering executive, surveyor; b. Albany, Ga., May 18, 1938; s. Ritchey McGuire and Shirley Kathryn (VanHouten) M.; m. Fonda Gayle Starnes, June 16, 1962; children: Mary Kathryn, Ritchey McGuire IV. BCE, Ga. Tech. Inst., 1960, M in City Planning, 1966. Registered profl. engr., Ga., Fla., Idaho, Ala.; land surveyor, Ga. V.p. Marbury Engring. Co., Albany, Ga., 1965-78, pres., chmn. bd., 1981—; pres. Marbury, Ritter, Scott & Turner, Inc., Albany, 1970-78, 81-92, Marbury Assocs., Inc., 1991—, Idaho Boise Mission of Latter-day Saints Ch., 1978-81; presenter seminars on total quality mgmt. to nat. convs. of Am. Cons. Engrs. Coun., Design Constrn. Quality Inst., Sml. Firm Coalition of Cons. Engrs., Assn. for Project Mgrs. Exec. bd. Boy Scouts Am., Southwest Ga., 1982— Served to 1st lt. U.S. Army, 1963-65. Mem. NSPE (South Ga. chpt. pres. 1993-95), Am. Cons. Engrs. Coun., Surveying and Mapping Soc. of Ga. (bd. dirs. 1966-78), Ga. Planning Assn., Home Builders Assn. (bd. dirs. 1985-86), Rotary. Mem. LDS Ch. Avocations: fishing, writing, music, computer, golf. Home: 1824 Green Valley Dr Albany GA 31707-3116 Office: 2334 Lake Park Dr Albany GA 31707-3132

MARBUT, ROBERT GORDON, communications, cable and broadcast executive; b. Athens, Ga., Apr. 11, 1935; s. Robert Smith and Laura Gordon (Powers) M.; m. Margo Susan Spitz, Sept. 24, 1989; children: Robert Gordon, Laura Dodd, Michael Powers, Marcy Lizbeth. B.Indsl. Engring., Ga. Inst. Tech., 1957; M.B.A. with distinction, Harvard U., 1963. Registered profl. engr., Calif. Engr. Esso Standard Oil Co., Baton Rouge, 1957; mgmt. trainee Copley Newspapers, Los Angeles, 1963; engring. services coordinator Copley Newspapers, La Jolla, Calif., 1965, corp. dir. engring. and plans, 1966-70; v.p. named changed to Harte-Hanks Communications, Inc., San Antonio, 1970-71, pres., chief exec. officer, 1971-91, mem. exec. com., 1974-91, also dir.; founder, chmn., CEO Argyle Comm., Inc, San Antonio, 1991—; CEO Argyle TV Holding Inc, San Antonio, 1993—; v.p. Argyle TV Ops, San Antonio; dir. A.P.; chmn., dir. Newspaper Advirtising Bur.; Interfirst Corp., Diamond Shamrock, Inc., Premark Internat., Inc., Tracor and Ultrafish, Inc., Advanced Tobacco Prod., Inc.; instr. Armstrong Coll., 1951, Calif. State, Los Angeles, 1964, Woodbury Coll., 1964; Pres. adv. bd. U. Ga. Henry W. Grady Sch. Journalism, 1975—; mem. adv. Found. for Communications Sch. U. Tex., 1975—; mem. nat. adv. bd. Up With People, Ga. Inst. Tech.; bd. dirs. Tex. Research League, 1975— Salzburg Seminar in Am. Studies. Author: (with Healy, Henderson and others) Creative Collective Bargaining, 1965; also articles in mags., jours.; frequent speaker. Bd. dirs. Up with People, United Way of San Antonio; Tex. select com. on Tax Equity and Revenues; Tex. World Trade Council. Served with USAF, 1958-61. Recipient Isaiah Thomas award Rochester Inst. Tech., 1980; EXCEL award in comm., 1987, People of Vision award, 1991. Mem. Newspaper Advt. Bur. (exec. com., dir. 1974-81), Am. Newspaper Pubs. Assn. Research Inst. (exec. com. 1973—), Am. Newspaper Publs. Assn. (chmn. task group on future, chmn. telecommunications com. 1974—), bd. dirs. 1976—, chmn. future task group), So. Newspaper Pubs. Assn. (pres. 1978-80, dir. 1975-81, treas. 1977, chmn. bus. and adminstrn. com. 1976), Am. Newspaper Pubs. Assn. Found. (trustee 1976—), Tex. Daily Newspaper Assn. (pres. 1979), Greater San Antonio C. of C. (chmn. long range planning task force, dir. 1979—, exec. com. 1981—), Delta Tau Delta, Omicron Delta Kappa, Phi Eta Sigma. Protestant. Club: Oaks Hills Country. Office: Argyle Communications Ste 1400 100 NE Loop 410 San Antonio TX 78216

MARCA-RELLI, CONRAD, artist; b. Boston, June 5, 1913; m. Anita Gibson, 1951. Student, Cooper Union, 1930. Associated with artists such as Willem DeKooning, Jackson Pollack, Franz Kline; joined easel and mural divs. WPA Fed. Art Project, 1935-38; co-founder Eighth St. Club, N.Y.C., 1949; guest critic Yale U., 1954-55, 59-60; guest prof. U. Calif.-Berkeley, 1958; artist in residence New Coll., Sarasota, Fla., 1966. One man shows include Whitney Mus. (restrospective), N.Y.C., 1967, Albright-Knox Mems. Gallery, Buffalo, 1968, Seattle Art Mus., 1969, Marlborough Gallery, N.Y.C., 1970, 79, Galerie Schmela, Dusseldorf, Germany, 1971, Galeria Carl Van der Voort, Ibiza, Spain, 1972, Marlborough Gallery, Zurich, Switzerland, 1974, Marlborough Goddard Gallery, Toronto, Ont., Can., 1975, Cordier and Ekstrom, N.Y.C., 1977, Galeria Joan Prats, Barcelona, Spain, 1978, (retrospective) Mus. Art, Ft. Lauderdale, Fla, 1979, (retrospective) Ringling Mus., Sarasota, Fla., 1980, Alex Rosenberg Gallery, N.Y.C., 1983, Riva Yares Gallery, Scottsdale, 1990; group shows include Whitney Mus., N.Y.C., at regular intervals 1953-69, Kunsthalle, Kassel, Germany, 1959, Segunda Bienal Interamericana de Mexico, Mexico City, 1960, Mus. Modern Art, N.Y.C., 1961, Hans der Kunts, Munich, Germany, 1981, Phoenix II Gallery, Washington, 1982; represented in permanent collections Albright-Knox Art Gallery, Buffalo, Chgo. Art Inst., Brandeis U., Walthm, Mass., represented, Carnegie Inst., Pitts., Mus. Art, Cleve., Detroit Inst. Arts, Fogg Art Mus., Harvard U., Guggenheim Mus., N.Y.C., High Mus. Art, Atlanta, County Mus., Los Angeles, Met. Mus. Art, N.Y.C., Mus. Modern Art. N.Y.C., Mus. Art, San Francisco, Wadsworth Atheneum, Hartford, Conn., Whitney Mus. Am. Art., N.Y.C., Walker Art Ctr., Mpls.; now represented Marisa Del Re Gallery, N.Y.C., 1985, 87. Served to pfc. U.S. Army, 1941-45. Recipient Logan medal Art Inst. Chgo., 1954, purchase prize, 1960, Kohnstamm prize, 1963; Ford Found. grantee, 1959.

MARCEAU, MARCEL, pantomimist, actor, director, painter, poet; b. Strasbourg, France, Mar. 22, 1923; s. Charles and Anne (Werzberg) Mangel. Student, Sch. Dramatic Art, Sarah Bernhardt Theatre, Paris, 1946; D (hon.), Linfield Coll., Princeton U., U. Mich. Dir. artistique Ecole De Mimodrame de Paris Marcel Marceau. Performer role of Arlequin, pantomime Baptiste; Praxitele and the Golden Fish, Sarah Bernhardt Theatre; creator character Bip, 1947; performer Maggio Musicale in Florence and Edinburgh festivals; organizer, Pantomime Co., Paris; producer: The Overcoat, The Three Wigs, 14th of July, The Pawn Shop, Pierrot de Montmartre,Paris qui rit Paris qui pleure, Don Juan; performer extensive tours U.S., S.Am., Africa, Australia, China, Japan, South East Asia, Russia, Europe, 1950—; performer worldwide TV shows; appeared in motion pictures: Barbarella, 1967, Shanks, 1974, Silent Movie, 1976; appeared as Scrooge in TV film A Christmas Carol, 1973; author, illustrator: The Story of Bip, Pimporello; lithographer The 7 Deadly Sins, The Third Eye. Decorated Officier Legion d'Honneur; comdr. Order Arts and Letters; Commandeur de Merit (France); recipient Emmy awards, 1956, 68, Medaille Vermeil de la ville de Paris, 1978. Mem. Acad. Fine Arts Berlin, Acad. Fine Arts Munich, Academie Des Beaux Arts France. Office: Ecole Internat Mimodrame Paris, 17 Rue Rene Boulanger, 75010 Paris France

MARCEAU, YVONNE, ballroom dancer. Ballet dancer Ballet West; ptnr. with Pierre Dulaine, 1976; founder, artistic dir. Am. Ballroom Theatre, N.Y.C., 1984—; guest tchr. Sch. Am. Ballet, N.Y.C.; tchr. ballroom dancing Juilliard Sch. Appearances include The Smithsonian Inst., JFK Ctr. for Performing Arts, N.Y. State Theater, N.Y.C., Sadlers Wells, London, (Broadway and London show) Grand Hotel, 1989-92; toured with Pierre Dulaine and Am. Ballroom Theatre worldwide. Recipient Brit. Theatrical Arts Championships 4 times, Spl. Astaire award, Dance Educator awards, Outstanding Achievement in Dance award Nat. Coun. Dance Am., 1992, Dance Mag. award, 1993. Office: Am Ballroom Theatre 305 E 24th St Ste 7T New York NY 10010

MARCELLINO, JAMES J., lawyer; b. Hartford, Conn., Apr. 20, 1943. BS, Coll. Holy Cross, 1965; JD, Boston Coll., 1968; MBA, Boston U., 1976. Bar: Mass. 1968. Ptnr. McDermott, Will & Emery, Boston; chair City of Boston Dept. Health and Hosps., Boston City Hosps., 1991—; vis. prof. law Boston Coll. Mem. Boston Bar Assn. Office: McDermott Will & Emery 75 State St Ste 1700 Boston MA 02109-1812

MARCELLUS, JOHN ROBERT, III, trombonist, educator; b. Overton, Tex., Sept. 17, 1939; s. John Robert and Grace (Stockman) M.; children: Robert Gray, John Frederick. B.S., U. Md., 1964; Mus.M., Catholic U. Am., 1970, D.Mus. Arts, 1972. Adj. prof. trombone Cath. U. Am., dir. trombone choir and brass ensembles, 1966-78; prof. NC Sch. Arts, 1965-68; mem. rotating faculty Inst. Advanced Mus. Studies, Montreux, Switzerland, 1974, Am. U., 1970-78; prof. trombone Eastman Sch. Music, Rochester, N.Y., 1978—, acting chmn. woodwind, brass and percussion, 1981, dir. internat. trombone workshop, 1991; co-dir. Ea. Trombone Workshop, Towson, Md., 1974-80, Internat. Trombone Workshop, 1991; guest condr. Chautauqua Symphony Orch., Penfield Symphony Orch., Chautauqua Wind Ensemble, U.S. Naval Acad. Band, Nat. Music Camp, Interlochen. Trombonist USN Band, Washington, 1960-64, Balt. Symphony, 1964-65; trombonist Nat. Symphony, Washington, 1965-78, prin. trombone, 1970-78; prin. trombone Chautauqua Symphony Orch., 1978; mem. Eastman Brass Quintet; clinician, soloist King Benge Mus. Instruments; solo tours to Scandinavia, Japan, Germany, Australia, England, France; performer with Art Mooney, Ray Eberle, Charlie Spivak, Vaughn Monroe, Henry Mancini Orchs.; music dir. Brighton Symphony Orch., 1980—; contbr. articles to Music Educators Jour., Instrumentalist, Accent, Internat. Trombone Assn. Jour. Mem. Internat. Trombone Assn. (founder, bd. dirs., pres. 1988-90), Am. Fedn. Musicians, Nat. Assn. Wind and Percussion Instruments, Music Educators Nat. Conf., Phi Mu Alpha. Office: Eastman Sch Music 26 Gibbs St Rochester NY 14604-2599 *Dedication, drive and determination to the art of music has been center front on my career in music.*

MARCH, BERYL ELIZABETH, animal scientist, educator; b. Port Hammond, B.C., Can., Aug. 30, 1920; d. James Roy and Sarah Catherine (Wilson) Warrack; m. John Algot March, Aug. 31, 1946; 1 dau., Laurel Allison. B.A., U. B.C., Vancouver, 1942, M.S.A., 1962; D.Sc., U. B.C., 1988. Mem. indsl. research staff Can. Fishing Co. Ltd., 1942-47; mem. research staff, faculty U. B.C., 1947—, prof. animal sci., 1970—. Recipient Poultry Sci. Assn.-Am. Feed Mfrs. award, 1969, Queen's Jubilee medal, 1977, Earle Willard McHenry award Can. Soc. Nutritional Sci., 1986, 125th Can. Confederation Annv. medal, 1993. Fellow Agrl. Inst. Can., Royal Soc. Can., Poultry Sci. Assn.; mem. Profl. Agrologists, Agr. Inst. Can., Can. Soc. Nutritional Sci., Poultry Sci. Assn., Am. Soc. Exptl. Biology and Medicine, Am. Inst. Nutrition, Can. Soc. Animal Sci., Aquaculture Assn. Can. Avocation: researching poultry and fish nutrition and physiology. Office: U BC Dept Animal Sci, Vancouver, BC Canada V6T 2A2

MARCH, JAMES GARDNER, social scientist, educator; b. Cleve., Jan. 15, 1928; s. James Herbert and Mildred (MacCorkle) M.; m. Jayne Mary Dohr, Sept. 23, 1947; children: Kathryn Sue, Gary Clifton, James Christopher, Roderic Gunn. BA, U. Wis., 1949; MA, Yale U., 1950, PhD, 1953; hon. doctorate, Copenhagen Sch. Econs., 1978, Swedish Sch. Econs., 1979, U. Wis., Milw., 1980, U. Bergen, 1980, Uppsala U., 1987, Helsinki Sch. Econs., 1991, Dublin City U., 1994. From asst. prof. to prof. Carnegie Inst. Tech., 1953-64; prof., dean Sch. Social Scis., U. Calif.-Irvine, 1964-70; prof. mgmt., higher edn., polit. sci. and sociology Stanford U., 1970—; adj. prof. U. Bergen, 1989-92; cons. in field, 1954—; mem. Nat. Council Ednl. Research, 1975-78; mem. Nat. Sci. Bd., 1968-74; mem. sociol.-social psychology panel NSF, 1964-66; social sci. tng. com. NIMH, 1967-68; mem. math. social sci. com. Social Sci. Research Council, 1958-60; mem. Assembly Behavioral and Social Sci., NRC, 1973-79, chmn. com. on aging, 1977-82, chmn. com. on math., sci., tech. edn., 1984-86. Author: (with H.A. Simon) Organizations, 1958, 2nd edit., 1993, (with R.M. Cyert) A Behavioral Theory of the Firm, 1963, 2nd edit., 1992, Handbook of Organizations, 1965, (with B.R. Gelbaum) Mathematics for the Social and Behavioral Sciences, 1969, (with M.D. Cohen) Leadership and Ambiguity, 1974, 2nd edit., 1986, Academic Notes, 1974, (with C.E. Lave) An Introduction to Models in the Social Sciences, 1975, (with J.P. Olsen) Ambiguity and Choice in Organizations, 1976, Aged Wisconsin, 1977, Autonomy as a Factor in Group Organization, 1980, Pleasures of the Process, 1980, Slow Learner, 1985, (with R. Weissinger-Baylon) Ambiguity and Command, 1986, Decisions and Organizations, 1988, (with J.P. Olsen) Rediscovering Institutions, 1989, Minor Memos, 1990, A Primer on Decision Making, 1994, Fornuft og Forandring, 1995, (with J.P. Olsen) Democratic Governance, 1995; contbr. articles to profl. jour. Fellow Center Advanced Study in Behavioral Scis., 1955-56, 73-74; recipient Wilbur Lucius Cross medal Yale U., 1968. Mem. NAS, Nat. Acad. Edn., Accademia Italiana di Economia Aziendale, Royal Swedish Acad. Scis., Norwegian Acad. of Sci. and Letters, Am. Acad. Arts and Scis., Am. Econ. Assn., Am. Polit. Sci. Assn. (v.p 1983-84), Am. Psychol. Assn., Am. Sociol. Assn., Acad. Mgmt., Russell Sage Found. (trustee 1985-94, chmn. 1990-93), Finnish Soc. Scis. and Letters, Phi Beta Kappa, Sigma Xi. Home: 837 Tolman Dr Palo Alto CA 94305-1025 Office: Stanford U 509 Ceras Stanford CA 94305-3084

MARCH, KATHLEEN PATRICIA, federal judge; b. May 18, 1949; married; 2 children. BA, Colo. Coll., 1971; JD, Yale U., 1974. Bar: N.Y. 1975, Calif. 1978. Law clk. to hon. judge Thomas J. Griesa U.S. Dist. Ct. (so. dist.) N.Y., 1974-75; assoc. Cahill, Gordon & Reindel, N.Y.C., 1975-77; asst. U.S. atty. criminal div. Office of U.S. Atty. Cen. Dist. Calif., L.A., 1978-82; assoc. Adams, Duque & Hazeltine, L.A., 1982-85; ptnr. Demetriou, Del Guercio & Lovejoy, L.A., 1985-88; judge U.S. Bankruptcy Ct. Cen. Dist. Calif., L.A., Calif., 1988—. Bd. editors Yale U. Law Jour. Mem. ABA, Fed. Bar Assn., L.A. County Bar Assn., Women Lawyers Assn., Nat. Assn. Women Judges, Phi Beta Kappa. Avocations: horseback riding, scuba diving, photography. Office: Roybal Fed Ct Bldg 255 E Temple St Ste 1460 Los Angeles CA 90012

MARCH, RALPH BURTON, retired entomology educator; b. Oshkosh, Wis., Aug. 5, 1919; s. Albert Harold and Vanita Ida Cora (Siewert) M.; m. Robinetta Tompkin, Dec. 26, 1942; children: John S., Janice A., Susan E. Student, Oshkosh State Tchrs. Coll., 1937-38; B.A., U. Ill., 1941, M.A. (Grad. scholar 1941-42), 1946, Ph.D. (Grad. fellow 1947-48), 1948. Faculty

U. Calif. at Riverside, 1948—, entomologist, 1957—, prof. entomology, 1961-83, prof. entomology emeritus, 1983—, dean grad. div., 1961-68, head div. toxicology and physiology dept. entomology, 1968-72, chmn. dept. entomology, 1978-83. Served with USAAF, 1942-46. Mem. Entomol. Soc. Am., Am. Chem. Soc., AAAS, Phi Beta Kappa, Sigma Xi, Phi Kappa Phi, Phi Sigma. Home: 300 Deer Valley Rd # 4A San Rafael CA 94903-5514

MARCH, XAVIER, systems analyst; b. Guayaquil, Ecuador, Mar. 13, 1932; came to U.S., 1953; s. Francscio and Nieves (Hernández) M.; m. Carol ann Heiser, Sept. 29, 1962; children: Gregory Fancis, Christopher John. BA, Dartmouth Coll. 1957; MS in Computer Sci., Iona Coll. 1985. Applied scientist IBM Corp., Caracas, Venezuela, 1957-61; data ctr. rep. IBM Corp., N.Y.C., 1961-63; scientific developer IBM Corp., White Plains, N.Y., 1963-70; advisory programmer IBM Corp., White Plains, 1972-80; project leader IBM Corp., Croydon, U.K., 1970-72; systems assurance rep. IBM Corp., Sterling Forest, N.Y., 1980-86; sr. programmer IBM Corp., Norwalk, Conn., 1986-88; application devel. auditor IBM Corp., Southbury, Conn., 1988-93, ad effectiveness cons., 1993—. Author/editor: Application Development Guide, 1986 (IBM award 1987), Application Development Process, 1991, Testing of Boject-Oriented Methods, Calsses and Systems, 1994; author: (software tools) Risk Assessment Expert System, 1987 (IBM award 1989), Ad Maturity Audit Expert System, 1989 (IBM award 1990). Mem. Assn. Computing Machinery, IEEE Computer Soc. Home: 12 Painter Ridge Rd Washington CT 06793 Office: IBM Consulting Group 150 Kettletown Rd Southbury CT 06488

MARCHAK, MAUREEN PATRICIA, anthropology and sociology educator; b. Lethbridge, Alta., Can., June 22, 1936; d. Adrian Ebenezer and Wilhelmina Rankin (Hamilton) Russell; m. William Marchak, Dec. 31, 1956; children: Geordon Eric, Lauren Craig. BA, U. B.C., Vancouver, Can., 1958, PhD, 1970. Asst. prof. U. B.C., Vancouver, 1972-75, assoc. prof., 1975-80, prof., 1980—, head dept. anthropology and sociology, 1987-90, dean faculty arts, 1990—. Author: Ideological Perspectives on Canada, 1975, 2d edit., 1981, 3d edit., 1988, In Whose Interests, 1979, Green Gold, 1983 (John Porter award 1985), The Integrated Circus, The New Right and The Restructuring of Global Markets, 1991, Logging The Globe, 1995; author, co-editor: Uncommon Property, 1987; mem. editorial bd. Can. Rev. Sociology and Anthropology, Montreal, Que., 1971-74, Studies in Polit. Economy, Ottawa, Ont., Can., 1980-87, Current Sociology, 1980-86, Can. Jour. Sociology, 1986-90, B.C. Studies, 1988-90. Bd. dirs. U.B.C Hosp., 1992-93; chair ethics com. Cedar Lodge Trust Soc., 1989-92; adv. coun. Ecotrust, 1993, bd. dirs. B.C. Bldgs. Corp. Fellow Royal Soc. Can. (v.p. Acad. II 1994—); mem. Can. Sociology and Anthropology Assn. (pres. 1979-80, other offices), Internat. Sociol. Assn., Can. Polit. Sci. Assn., Assn. for Can. Studies, Forest History Soc. (mem. exec. com. 1991-92). Mem. New Dem. Party (Can.). Avocations: hiking, swimming, traveling. Home: 4455 W 1st Ave, Vancouver, BC Canada V6R 4H9 Office: U BC Faculty Arts Office of Dean, 1866 Main Mall, Vancouver, BC Canada V6T 121

MARCHAND, J. C. DE MONTIGNY, Canadian public servant; b. St. Jérome, Qué., Can., Mar. 19, 1936; s. Jean-Charles and Françoise (Magnan) M.; children—Julie, Charles, Emmanuelle. B.A., U. Montré, Que., Can., 1955; LL.L., U. Montreal, 1959; postgrad. Sch. Comm., Boston U. Bar: Que. 1960; cr. Q.C. 1978. Asst. to dir. pub. rels. U. Montreal, 1960-64, asst. to sec. gen., 1964-65, exec. asst. to pres., 1965-67, sec. gen., 1967-69; dir. research, co-sec. telecommission Dept. Comm., Can., 1969-71; asst. dep. min. (ops.) Dept. Comm., 1971-74; sr. asst. dep. min. (policy) 1974-75; dep. sec. to cabinet (ops.) Privy Council Office, Can., 1975-79; on spl. assignment to Western Europe Can. govt., Paris, 1979-80; assoc. under-sec. of state for external affairs Dept. External Affairs, Can., 1980-82; dep. min. polit. affairs Dept. External Affairs, 1982-85; dep. min. comm. Dept. Comm., Ottawa, Ont., Can., 1985; dep. min. Dept. Energy, Mines & Resources, Can., 1985-86; sr. advisor Privy Coun. Office, Can., 1986-87; amb., permanent rep. to UN, Geneva, 1987-90; rep. Conf. on Disarmament, Geneva, 1987-90; undersec. Dept. External Affairs, Can. 1990-91; amb. to Italy with additional accreditation to Malta and San Marino Can. Govt., 1991—; head Can. del. to Third Plenary Session Intelsat, Washington, 1971, World Adminstrn. Radio Conf. on Space Communications, Geneva, 1971, Fourth, Fifth and Sixth Session UN Working Group Direct Broadcasting by Satellite, N.Y. and Geneva, 1972, 73, 74; dep. head Can. del. to ITU Plenipotentiary Conf., Malaga-Torremolinos, 1973; pres. Inst. canadien des Affaires publiques, 1967-68; dir. Canadian Overseas Telecom. Corp., 1971-75, Uranium Canada Ltd., 1975-79. Bd. dirs. Nat. Film Bd., 1978-79, 82-85; bd. govs. U. Ottawa, 1980-83; personal rep. to P.M. for preparation of Versailles Summit, 1982, Williamsburg Summit, 1983, London Summit, 1984; chmn. bd. Internat. Energy Agy., 1986-87. Club: Five Lakes Fishing. Avocations: fishing; tennis; reading. Home: Via di Porta Latina 11, 00179 Rome Italy Office: The Candian Embassy, Via G.B. de Rossi 27, 00161 Rome Italy

MARCHAND, LESLIE ALEXIS, language educator, writer; b. Bridgeport, Wash., Feb. 13, 1900; s. Alexis and Clara Adele (Buckingham) M.; m. Marion Knill Hendrix, July 8, 1950. B.A., U. Wash., 1922, M.A., 1923; Ph.D., Columbia U., 1940; postgrad., Sorbonne, Paris, 1927-28, U. Munich, Germany, summer 1932; L.H.D. hon., U. Alaska, 1976; Litt.D. (hon.), Rutgers U., 1981. Asst. in English U. Wash., Seattle, 1920-23; instr., summer U. Wash., 1924, vis. prof., 1925, 58; prof. English and French Alaska Agrl. Coll. and Sch. Mines (now U. Alaska), 1923-27, 34-35; extension tchr. English Columbia U., 1928-34, instr., summers 1929-31, vis. prof., summers 1945-46, 65; lectr. Columbia U. (Coll. Pharmacy), 1936-37; instr. Rutgers U., 1937-42, asst. prof., 1942-46, asso. prof., 1946-53, prof., 1953-66, emeritus, 1966—; Fulbright prof. U. Athens, Greece, 1958-59; lectr. English Hunter Coll., 1960-62; Berg vis. prof. N.Y. U., 1962-63; vis. prof. Ariz. State U., 1966-67; Adams chair English Hofstra U., 1967-68; vis. prof. U. Calif. at Los Angeles, summer 1949, U. Ill., summer 1954, Harvard U., summer 1969. Author: The Atheneaum: A Mirror of Victorian Culture, 1941, Byron: A Biography, 1957, Byron's Poetry: A Critical Introduction, 1965, Byron: A Portrait, 1970; editor: Letters of Thomas Hood, 1945, Selected Poetry of Lord Byron, 1951, Lord Byron: Don Juan, 1958, Byrons's Letters and Jours., Vols. 1-12, 1973-82, supplementary vol., 1994, Lord Byron: Selected Letters and Jours., 1982; editl. bd.: Keats-Shelley Jour.; contbr. articles to profl. jours. Recipient Ivan Sandrof award Nat. Book Critics Circle, 1982; Guggenheim fellow, 1968-69, 79-80; Nat. Endowment for Humanities grantee, 1972-73, 74-75, 76-79. Fellow Royal Soc. Lit. (Eng.); mem. PEN, MLA (James Russell Lowell prize), Keats-Shelley Assn. Am. (dir.), Byron Soc., Phi Beta Kappa. Home: 570 Foxwood Blvd Englewood FL 34223-6100

MARCHAND, NATHAN, electrical engineer, corporation president; b. Shawinigan Falls, Que., Can., June 20, 1916; came to U.S., 1917; s. Harry and Rebecca (Shapiro) M.; m. Ernesta Jaros, Sept. 30, 1938; children: Mary Ann Marchand McLure, Anthony, Babette Marchand Pachence, Bonnie Jean Marchand Thomas. BEE, CCNY, 1937; MEE, Columbia U., 1941; postgrad., Poly. Inst. N.Y., 1949-51. Profl. engr., Conn. Sr. engr. Internat. Tel. & Tel., Nutley, N.J., 1941-45; lectr. Columbia U., N.Y.C., 1943-47; cons. to industry Sylvania, Internat. Tel. & Tel., U.S. Army, USAF, 1945-49; pres. Marchand Electronic Labs., Inc., Greenwich, Conn.; cons. U.S. Army R & D Command, St. Louis, 1976-86, U.S. Army Troop Support and Aviation Readiness Command, 1976-86, USAF, Cape Kennedy, Fla., 1951-54, various others.; chmn. spl. com. for micro-navigation and position location systems U.S. Army Lab, Ft. Monmouth, N.J. Author: Ultra High Frequency Techniques, 1942, Ultrahigh Frequency Transmission and Radiation, 1947, Frequency Modulation, 1948; author Antenna Section, bd. editors Data for Radio Engrs., Internat. Tel. & Tel. publ. 1st-5th edits., 1943-68—; contbr. numerous tech. papers and articles to profl. jours.;. Lt. (j.g.) USN, 1943. Fellow IEEE (founder, 1st chmn. Info.-Theory Group); mem. Sigma Xi, Eta Kappa Nu, Tau Beta Pi. Republican. Avocations: pvt. pilot, sailing. Office: Marchand Electronic Labs 311 Riversville Rd Greenwich CT 06831-3227

MARCHAND, RUSSELL DAVID, II, fire chief; b. Lafayette, Ind., May 14, 1950; s. Russell David and Mable May (Gean) M.; m. Sandra Green, June 12, 1951 (div. Nov. 1986); 1 child, Russell David III; m. Carol Bella Flashenburg, May 31, 1987. AA in Fire Sci., Clark County Community Coll., Las Vegas, Nev., 1979. Cert. fire service instr., supr. instr. Firefighter North Las Vegas Fire Dept., 1973-78, engr., 1978-82, capt., 1982-95, divsn.

chief, officer-in-charge bldg. and constrn., 1990—; pres. Local 1607 Internat. Assn. Fire Fighters, Las Vegas, 1980— (v.p. 1976-80); instr. N. Las Vegas Fire Dept., 1986. Chmn. N. Las Vegas Firefighters Polit. Action Com., 1980—, Muscular Dystrophy Assn., 1980-83, 85. Sgt. USMC, 1968-72, South Vietnam. Named Fireman of Yr., Optimist Club, 1981, Lions Club Nev., 1989, Profl. Ins. Agts. of Am.; received citation of merit Muscular Dystrophy Assn., 1982, commendation City of N. Las Vegas, 1980, 83, 85. Mem. Fed. Firefighters Nev. (received commendation 1982), Nat. Assn. Miniature Enthusiasts, Internat. Assn. Fire Fighters (local 1607 pres. emeritus 1990). Avocations: sailing, computers. Office: 2626 E Carey Ave North Las Vegas NV 89030-6215

MARCHANT, DAVID J., lawyer; b. Oakland, Calif., Jan. 12, 1939; s. Luther Brusie and Mariam Hand (Fisher) M.; m. Susan Robbins (div. 1980); children: Michael Hilton, Robbins Fisher, Lauren Payton. BA, U. Calif., Berkeley, 1961; JD, U. Calif., San Francisco, 1967. Bar: Calif. Atty. Calif. Pub. Utilities Commn. San Francisco, 1967-68; ptnr. Graham & James, San Francisco, 1968—. Mem. ABA (pub. utility law sect.), Bohemian Club. Office: Graham & James 1 Maritime Plz Ste 300 San Francisco CA 94111-3492

MARCHANT, MAURICE PETERSON, librarian, educator; b. Peoa, Utah, Apr. 20, 1927; s. Stephen C. and Beatrice (Peterson) M.; m. Gerda VaLoy Hansen, June 3, 1949; children: Catherine, Barrie, Alan, Roxanne, Claudia, David, Theresa. BA, U. Utah, 1949, MS, 1953; AM in Libr. Sci., U. Mich., 1966, MA, 1968, Ph.D., 1970. Tchr. area h.s. Altamont, Utah, 1949-50; libr. area h.s. Salt Lake City and Preston, Idaho, 1950-53; chief tech. libr. Dugway (Utah) Proving Ground, 1953-58; libr. Carnegie Free Libr., Ogden, Utah, 1958-66; mem. faculty Brigham Young U., Provo, Utah, 1969-92, prof. libr. and info. scis., 1976-92, dir. Sch. Libr. and Info. Scis., 1975-82; prof. emeritus libr. and info. scis. Brigham Young U. (Sch. Library and Info. Scis.), Provo, Utah, 1992—; exec. dir. Nat. Libr. Week, Utah, 1961-62. Author: Participative Management in Academic Libraries, 1976, SPSS as a Library Research Tool 1977, Books That Made a Difference in Provo, 1989, Why Adults Use the Public Library, 1994, also articles. Served with USN, 1945-46. Mid-career fellow Coun. Libr. Resources, 1972. Mem. AAUP, ALA (rsch. paper award Libr. Rsch. Round Table 1975), Utah Libr. Assn. (pres. 1964-65, Disting. Svc. award 1986). Address: 2877 N 220 E Provo UT 84604 *Man has the potential of learning to love or exploit, to become wise or remain ignorant. God intends us to become charitable and wise, preparing us to contribute to human progress. My measure of success as a librarian and educator must reflect my commitment to lifelong learning and to honest respect of others.*

MARCHANT, TRELAWNEY ESTON, national guard officer, lawyer; b. Columbia, S.C., Dec. 9, 1921; s. Trelawney Eston and Lila (Cave) M.; m. Caroline Melton Bristow, Nov. 10, 1951; children—Trelawney Eston, III, Walter Bristow, Caroline M., Nancy Lila. B.S., U. S.C., 1942, LL.B., 1947; grad. various USMC and U.S. Army schs. Bar: S.C. 1947. Pvt. practice Columbia, 1948-78; mem. U.S. N.G., 1947-95, maj. gen., 1979; comdr. Palmetto Mil. Acad., 1968-71; adj. gen. State of S.C., 1978-95. Mem. bd. visitors The Citadel, Charleston, S.C., 1979-95; trustee U. S.C., 1965-70, chmn., 1970-78, mem. devel. adv. coun., 1963-77; chmn. Nat. Found., 1953-60; v.p. U. S.C. Ednl. Found., 1957-77; chmn. Richland County Dem. Party, 1964-68. Served as officer USMCR, 1942-46. Mem. Am. Judicature Soc., 4th Cir. Jud. Conf., Adjs. Gen. Assn. U.S. (pres. 1989-91), Acad. Polit. Sci., S.C. Bar Assn., Richland County Bar Assn. (pres. 1970-71), Mil. Order World Wars (past chpt. pres.), Am. Legion, N.G. Assn. S.C. (past pres.), U. S.C. Alumni Assn. (past pres.), Order of Palmetto (S. Carolinian of Yr. 1990), Sigma Nu, Omicron Delta Kappa. Episcopalian. Clubs: Columbia Cotillion (pres. 1991-92), Columbia Ball, Tarantella, Summit, Forest Lake. Home: 5046 Courtney Rd Columbia SC 29206-2909

MARCHELLO, JOSEPH MAURICE, mathematics and physical science educator; b. East Moline, Ill., Oct. 6, 1933; s. Anton Joseph and Katherine Margaret (Scavarda) M.; m. Mary Louise Coulson, Jan. 27, 1960; children—Sara Leigh, Katherine C. B.S. in Chem. Engring, U. Ill., 1955; Ph.D., Carnegie-Mellon U., 1959. Asst. prof. chem. engring. Okla. State U., 1959-61; asst. prof. U. Md., 1961-62, assoc. prof., 1962-66, prof., 1966-78, chmn. dept. chem. engring., 1967-73, provost div. math. and phys. scis. and engring., 1973-78; chancellor U. Mo.-Rolla, 1978-85; pres. Old Dominion U., Norfolk, Va., 1985-88; prof., 1985—; Pres. Mo. Council Pub. Higher Edn. 1981-82. Author: Control of Air Pollution Sources, 1976; editor: (with John J. Kelly) Gas Cleaning for Air Pollution Control, 1975, (with Albert Gomezplata) Gas-Solids Handling in the Process Industry, 1976; contbr. numerous articles to profl. jours. Mem. Md. Air Quality Control Adv. Council, 1966-78, chmn., 1971-78; mem. Md. Adv. Commn. on Atomic Energy, 1973-78; chmn. Md. Power Plant Siting Com., 1978. Mem. AAAS, NSPE, Air Pollution Control Assn., Am. Inst. Chem. Engrs., Am. Chem. Soc., Mo. Soc. Profl. Engrs., N.Y. Acad. Sci., Mo. Acad. Sci., Cosmos Club. Presbyterian. Home: 6 Rhoda Ct Hampton VA 23664-1769 Office: Coll Engring Old Dominion Norfolk VA 23508

MARCHESANO, JOHN EDWARD, electro-optical engineer; b. N.Y.C., Aug. 20, 1927; s. John R. and Maria J. (Mollino) M.; divorced; children: Pamela, Debra, Scott, Neal. B of Elec. Engring., CCNY, 1951; postgrad., U. Pa., 1951-52. Project engr. Philco Rsch., Pa., 1951-56; sr. engr. Am. Bosch Arma, Garden City, N.Y., 1956-60; pres. Automation Labs. Inc., Mineola, N.Y., 1960-66; pres., CEO Decilog, Inc., Melville, N.Y., 1966—. Achievements include development and design of wide angle lens for aircraft collision avoidance, of modulation transfer system for low light level TV evaluation, long wavelength infared missile research. Office: Decilog Inc 555 Broadhollow Rd Melville NY 11747-5001

MARCHESE, RONALD THOMAS, ancient history and archaeology educator; b. Fresno, Calif., Mar. 17, 1947; s. John Anthony and Julie Rita (Ferrarese) M.; m. Marcia Lynn Schneider, Apr. 6, 1974 (div. Apr. 1980); children: Stephanie Jo, Kayla Marie. BA summa cum laude, Calif. State U., Fresno, 1970; MA, N.Y.U., 1972, PhD with distinction, 1976; postgrad., Columbia U., 1972-73. Asst. prof. Va. Poly. Inst., Blacksburg, 1976-77; asst. to assoc. prof. ancient history and archaeology U. Minn., Duluth, 1977-87, prof., 1987—; mem. numerous univ. coms.; rsch. assoc. dept. classics N.Y.U., 1972-74; lectr. in field; evaluator grant proposals NEH, HSF; excavator numerous sites, Israel and Turkey, So. Russia, Black Sean/Ancient Anapa. Author 3 books; contbr. articles to profl. jours. Recipient Fulbright-Hays Sr. Research fellowship, Turkey, 1984-85, 91-92, The Am. Council Learned Socs. fellowship, 1977-78, NDEA Title VI Fgn. Languages fellowship, 1972-75, Spl. Commendation for Excellence award Phi Alpha Theta, 1979; grantee NEH, 1978, 80, nat. Geographic Soc., 1974, Andrew Mellon Found., NSF, Ford Found., 1971-72, U. Minn., others. Mem. NEH, Nat. Assn. Scholars, Coun. for Internat. Exchange, Am. Coun. Learned Socs., Fulbright Alumni Assn., Phi Alpha Theta, Sigma Xi. Roman Catholic. Avocations: tennis, golf, dressage. Home: 5789 220th St N Forest Lake MN 55025-9607

MARCHI, JOHN JOSEPH, state senator, lawyer; b. S.I., May 20, 1921; s. Louis B. and Alina M. (Marchi-Girardello) M.; m. Maria Luisa Davini, Nov. 14, 1948; children: Joan, Aline. BA, Manhattan Coll., 1942, LLD (hon.); JD, St. John's U., 1950, LLD (hon.); JSD, Bklyn. Law Sch., 1953; LLD (hon.) Wagner Coll., 1985. Bar: N.Y. 1951, U.S. Dist. Ct., (ea. and so. dists.) N.Y., U.S. Supreme Ct. Mem. N.Y. State Senate, 1957—, dep. maj. leader Intergovtl. Affairs, NY. Senate, chair Corp. Authorities and Commn.; of counsel Whitman, Breed, Abbott & Morgan, N.Y.C. Staten Island Del. N.Y. State Constl. Conv., 1967, chair Staten Island Charter Commn.; past chmn. Coun. State Govts. Lt. col. U.S. Army. Decorated comdr. Order of Merit, (Italy); recipient Charles Carroll award Guild Cath. Lawyers, 1991. Mem. Am. Legion, VFW, Urban League, B'nai B'rith, Holy Name Soc., K.C. Home: 79 Nixon Ave Staten Island NY 10304-2209 Office: NY State Senate Rm 416cap Albany NY 12247

MARCHI, LORRAINE JUNE, association executive; b. San Francisco, June 5, 1923; d. Leopold Pulverman and Josephine Lillian (Treiber) Heiman; m. Gene Marchi, Apr. 10, 1943 (div. 1973); children—Gene, Jeffrey, Debra, Beth; m. Robert L. Fastie, Oct. 21, 1973. Student Stanford U., 1941-42, U. Calif.-Berkeley, 1942-43. Founder Com. To Aid Visually Handicapped Children, San Francisco, 1954-57; pres. Aid to Visually Handicapped, San

Francisco, 1957-59; founder, exec. dir. Nat. Assn. for Visually Handicapped, San Francisco, 1972—; sec. Calif. Conf. for Exceptional and Rehab. Needs, San Francisco, 1955-66; chmn. bd. Langley Porter Neuropsychiat. Inst., San Francisco, 1966-73. Recipient spl. service award Los Angeles County Soc. Ophthalmology, 1971; honor award Am. Acad. Ophthalmology and Otolaryngology, 1971, Lifetime Achievement award NAVH, 1989; cert. of appreciation Am. Acad. Ophthalmology, 1978; named Woman of Yr. San Francisco sect. Nat. Council Jewish Women, 1957, one of Ten Disting. Women San Francisco Examiner Bay Area, 1959. Home: 305 E 24th St New York NY 10010

MARCHI, SERGIO SISTO, Canadian government official; b. Buenos Aires, May 12, 1956; s. Ottavio and Luisa (D'Agostinis) M.; m. Laureen Storozuk, Oct. 1, 1983. BA with honors, York U., Toronto, 1979. Exec. asst. to Ron Irwin and Hon. Jim Flemming, 1980-82; alderman City of North York, 1982-84; M.P. from York West dist. Ho. of Commons, Ottawa, 1984—, min. citizenship and immigration, 1993—. Vice chmn. North York Planning Bd., Toronto, 1982-84, Standing Com. on Transport, Ottawa, 1990-93; chmn. Nat. Liberal Caucus, Ottawa, 1990-93. Mem. Liberal Party. Roman Catholic. Avocations: reading, walking, fishing, skiing. Office: Ho of Commons, 103-S Centre Block, Ottawa, ON Canada K1A 0A6

MARCHIBRODA, TED (THEODORE JOSEPH MARCHIBRODA), professional football coach; b. Mar. 15, 1931; m. Henrietta Marchibroda; children: Jodi, Teddy, Lonni, Robert. Student, St. Bonaventure Coll., 1950-51, U. Detroit, 1952. Football player Pitts. Steelers, 1953-54, 55-56, Chgo. Cardinals, 1957-58; asst. coach Washington Redskins, 1961-65, offensive coord., 1971-74; asst. coach L.A. Rams, 1966-70; head coach Balt. Colts, 1975-79; offensive coord., quarterbacks coach Chgo. Bears, 1981; offensive coord. Detroit Lions, 1982-83; offensive coord., quarterbacks coach Phila. Eagles, 1984-85; quarterbacks coach Buffalo Bills, 1987-88, offensive coord., 1989-92; head coach Indpls. Colts, 1992—. Served with U.S. Army, 1954-55. Office: Indianapolis Colts PO Box 535000 Indianapolis IN 46253*

MARCHIDO, WILLIAM F., finance executive, accountant; b. Muskegon, Mich., Nov. 7, 1950; s. Fabian William and Ila Belle (Deater) M.; m. Nancy May Steele, Aug. 22, 1970; 1 child, Mary Lynn. ABA in Acctg., Davenport Bus. Coll., 1976; BBS in Acctg. and Fin., Grand Valley U., 1978, MBA in Fin. and Econs., 1984. Cost acctg. Kelvinator, Inc., Grand Rapids, Mich., 1972-76; cost acctg. Lescoa, Inc., Grand Rapids, 1976-78, cost mgr., 1978-79; acctg. mgr. Haven-Busch Corp., Grandville, Mich., 1979-82, controller, 1982-85, v.p. fin., 1985-88; controller Rapistan Corp., Grand Rapids, 1988, v.p. fin., 1988—. Project div. tchr. Jr. Achievement, Grand Rapids, 1986-87. USNG, 1971-77. Mem. Cert. Mgmt. Accts. Republican. Roman Catholic. Office: Rapistan Corp 507 Plymouth Ave NE Grand Rapids MI 49505-6029

MARCHIONI, ALLEN, publishing company executive. Pres., CEO Wililam Morrow & Co. Inc., N.Y.C. Office: William Morrow & Co Inc 1350 Avenue of the Americas New York NY 10019-4701

MARCHMAN, ROBERT L., III, lawyer, pecan farmer; b. Ft. Valley, Ga., Jan. 10, 1925; s. Robert L. Jr. and Lois Gregory (Anderson) M.; m. Helen Chantler Thomas, Nov. 25, 1950 (div. July 1992); children: Lee, Franklin, Holmes, Granger; m. Mary E. Arnold, Nov. 21, 1992. AB, Emory U., 1947; LLB, Harvard U., 1950. Bar: Ga. 1950. Assoc. Hansell & Post, Atlanta, 1950-53, ptnr., 1953-89; of counsel Jones, Day, Reavis & Pogue, Atlanta, 1989-91; ret., 1992; bus. cons.; investor; bd. dirs., sec. Benning Constrn. Co., Atlanta, Adams Indsl. Hose, Inc., Augusta, Ga., M.D. Hodges Enterprises, Inc., Atlanta, LeConte Holdings, Inc., Augusta. Trustee Schenck Sch., Atlanta, 1974—, chmn. 1974-83; bd. dirs. Nat. Interfrat. Conf., Indpls., 1984-93, pres. 1991-92; chmn. Nat. Interfrat. Conf. Found., Indpls., 1992-93. Mem. ABA, State Bar Ga., Atlanta Bar Assn., Lawyers Club Atlanta, Peachtree Golf Club, Commerce Club, Cherokee Town and Country Club, Sigma Nu (nat. pres. 1978-80, pres. Ednl. Found. 1986—, Hall of Honor award 1976). Republican. Methodist. Avocations: sailing, birdshooting. Home: 324 Persons St Fort Valley GA 31030

MARCIALIS, ROBERT LOUIS, planetary astronomer; b. N.Y.C., Sept. 14, 1956; s. Louis Angelo and Joan Regina (Dippolito) M. SB in Aero. and Astronautical Engring., MIT, 1978, SB in Earth and Planetary Scis., 1980; MS in Physics and Astronomy, Vanderbilt U., 1983; PhD in Planetary Scis., U. Ariz., 1990. Teaching asst. dept. earth and planetary scis. MIT, Cambridge, 1976-80; lab. instr. dept. physics and astronomy Vanderbilt U., Nashville, 1981, 82-83, rsch. asst. Arthur J. Dyer Obs., 1981-82; rsch. asst. Lunar and Planetary Lab. U. Ariz., Tucson, 1983-86, rsch. assoc., 1986-90; JPL postdoctoral fellow Jet Propulsion Lab., Pasadena, Calif., 1990—; founding mem. Pluto/Charon Mut. Eclipse Season Campaign. Contbr. articles to Info. Bull. on Variable Stars, Bull. Am. Astron. Soc., Astron. Jour., Minor Planet Circular, Lunar and Planetary Sci., Sci. Jour. Brit. Astron. Assn., Astrophys. Jour., Icarus. also others. Instr. water safety ARC, 1981-82; ednl. counselor MIT, 1983—; fastpitch softball umpire, 1975—. Rsch. fellow NASA, 1986-89. Mem. AAAS, Am. Astron. Soc., Am. Geophys. Union, Astron. Soc. Pacific, Internat. Occultation Timing Assn., Sigma Pi Sigma. Roman Catholic. Achievements include discovery of water ice on surface of Pluto's moon Charon; construction of an albedo map for surface of Pluto; research on Pluto, Charon and Triton, icy satellites, outer solar system formation and evolution, solar system photometry, occultation astronomy, RS Canum Venaticorum binary stars. Office: Lunar & Planetary Lab U Ariz Tucson AZ 85721

MARCIL, WILLIAM CHRIST, SR., publisher, broadcast executive; b. Rolette, N.D., Mar. 9, 1936; s. Max L. and Ida (Fuerst) M.; m. Jane Black, Oct. 15, 1960; children: Debora Jane, William Christ Jr. BSBA, U. N.D. 1958. Br. mgr. Community Credit Co., Mpls., 1959-61; with Forum Comms. Co., Fargo N.D., 1961—, pres., pub. CEO, 1969—. Pres. Forum Comm. Found.; past bd. dirs. North Ctrl. region Boy Scouts Am. With U.S. Army, 1958-59. Mem. Inland Newspaper Press Assn., N.D. Press Assn., Am. Newspaper Pubs. Assn. (past dir., chmn.), Fargo and Morehead C. of C., N.D. State C. of C. (past pres.), U.S. C. of C. (past chmn.), Sigma Delta Chi, Lambda Chi Alpha. Republican. Lodges: Masons, Shriners, Elks, Rotary. Home: 1618 8th St S Fargo ND 58103-4240 Office: Forum Comm Co 101 5th St N Fargo ND 58102-4826

MARCINEK, MARGARET ANN, nursing educator; b. Uniontown, Pa., Sept. 29, 1948; d. Joseph Hugh and Evelyn (Bailey) Boyle; m. Bernard Francis Marcinek, Aug. 11, 1973; 1 dau., Cara Ann. R.N., Uniontown Hosp., 1969; B.S. in Nursing, Pa. State U., 1970; M.S.N., U. Md., 1973; Ed.D., W.Va. U., 1983. Staff nurse Presbyn. U., Pitts., 1970-71; instr. nursing W.Va. U., Morgantown, 1973-77, asst. prof., 1977-80, assoc. prof., 1980-83; assoc. prof. California U. of Pa., 1983-87, prof., 1987—, dept. chmn., 1985—. Contbg. author: Critical Care Nursing. Contbr. articles to profl. jours. Mem. adv. coun. In Home Health, Inc.; mem. adv. coun. Albert Gallatin VNA. Mem. Am. Nurses Assn., Am. Assn. Critical Care Nurses, Nat. League for Nurses, Sigma Theta Tau, Phi Kappa Phi.

MARCINIAK, THADDEUS J., lawyer; b. Chgo., Nov. 6, 1950. BA, U. Notre Dame, 1972, JD, 1975. Bar: Ill. 1975, Calif. 1986, U.S. Dist. Ct. (no. dist.) Ill. 1975. Ptnr. Mayer, Brown & Platt, L.A. Office: Mayer Brown & Platt 355 S Grand Ave Los Angeles CA 90071-1503

MARCO, GUY ANTHONY, library educator; b. N.Y.C., Oct. 4, 1927; s. Gaetano Mongelluzzo and Evelyn Capobianco; m. Karen Csontos, July 23, 1949; 1 son, Howard William. Student, DePaul U., 1947-50; B.Mus., Am. Conservatory Music, Chgo., 1951; M.A. in Music, U. Chgo., 1952, M.L.S., 1955, Ph.D. in Musicology, 1956. Librarian, instr. musicology Chgo. Mus. Coll., 1953-54; asst. prof. classics library U. Chgo., 1954; asst. librarian, instr. music Wright Jr. Coll., Chgo., 1954-56; librarian, instr. music Amundsen Jr. Coll., Chgo., 1957-60; assoc. prof. library sci., chmn. dept. Kent State U., 1960-66; prof., dean Kent State U. (Sch. Library Sci.), 1966-77; chief gen. reference and bibliography div. Library of Congress, Washington, 1977-78; dir. for N.Am., Library Devel. Coms.'s, London, 1979-81; prof., dir. div. library sci. San Jose State U., 1981-83; exec. dir. Global Research Services, Washington, 1984-85; chief libr. activities U.S. Army, Ft. Dix, N.J., 1985-89; sr. fellow, adj. prof. libr. sci., editor Third World Librs. Rosary Coll., River Forest, Ill., 1989—; vis. lectr. library sci. U. Wis., summer 1955; reference

librarian Chgo. Tchrs. Coll., summer 1957; vis. prof. library sci. N.Y. State Coll. Tchrs., Albany, summer 1956, 58; guest lectr. library sci. U. Denver, summer 1959; vis. prof. U. Okla., summer 1960, Coll. Librarianship, Wales, summer 1974, 76, 77, U. Md., summer 1978. Author: The Earliest Music Printers of Continental Europe, 1962, An Appraisal of Favorability in Current Book Reviewing, 1959, (with Claude Palisca) The Art of Counterpoint, 1968, Information on Music, vol. I, 1975, vol. II, 1977, vol. III, 1984, Opera: A Research and Information Guide, 1984, Ency. of Recorded Sound in the United States, 1993; contbr. 150 articles to profl. jours., also book revs. Served with AUS, 1946-47. Mem. ALA, Am. Musicological Soc. Home: 3450 N Lake Shore Dr Apt 3508 Chicago IL 60657-2864 Office: Rosary Coll Libr Sch River Forest IL 60305

MARCOCCIA, LOUIS GARY, accountant, university administrator; b. Syracuse, N.Y., Nov. 6, 1946; s. George A. and Rose J. (Misita) M.; m. Susan Evelyn Miller, June 21, 1974; 1 child: Rachel Kathryn. BS, Syracuse U., 1968, MS, 1969. CPA, N.Y. Acct. Price Waterhouse & Co., Syracuse, N.Y., 1969-75; dir. internal audit Syracuse U., 1975-76, comptroller, 1976-82, v.p., controller, 1982-85, sr. v.p. bus. and fin., 1985—; bd. dirs. Syracuse Bd. Chase Lincoln First Bank N.A., Univ. Hill Corp.; speaker Harvard U. Inst. Ednl. Mgmt., 1984-88, 90-91. Pres. parish coun. St. Michael's Ch., Syracuse, 1985-88, Syracuse U. Theatre Corp., 1987—; bd. dirs. Friends of Burnet Park Zoo, 1987-93, Syracuse U. Press, 1982—, Syracuse Sports Corp., 1990-91. Mem. AICPA, N.Y. Soc. CPAs, Nat. Assn. Accts., Fin. Execs. Inst., Inst. Internal Auditors. Republican. Roman Catholic. Clubs: Drumlins (pres. 1976—); Century. Avocations: swimming, golf. Home: Hedge Ln Cazenovia NY 13035 Office: Syracuse U Skytop Rd Syracuse NY 13244

MARCOPOULOS, GEORGE JOHN, history educator; b. Salem, Mass., June 30, 1931; s. John George and Urania Christou (Moustakis) M. BA, Bowdoin Coll., 1953; MA, Harvard U., 1955, PhD, 1966. Instr. Tufts U., Medford, Mass., 1961-66, asst. prof., 1966-71, assoc. prof., 1971-92, prof., 1992—. Contbr. articles to Ency. Americana, Ams. Ann. Yearbook, also to profl. jours. Bd. dirs., treas. Gerondelis Found., Inc., Lynn, Mass., 1987—. Recipient Mellon Faculty Devel. grant Tufts U., 1983. Mem. AAUP, Am. Assn. Advancement Slavic Studies, Am. Hist. Assn., New Eng. Hist. Assn., Danforth Assocs. New Eng., Modern Greek Studies Assn., Phi Beta Kappa. Greek Orthodox. Avocations: music, films, reading, performing arts, excursions. Office: Tufts U Dept History East Hall Medford MA 02155

MARCOSSON, THOMAS I., service company executive; b. N.Y.C., Jan. 31, 1936; s. Mark and Mollie (Schreiber) M.; m. Carla F. Hunt, May 15, 1988; children: Mark, Susan, Samuel, Jill. Student, Union Coll., Schenectady, 1953-55; B.S., NYU, 1959. CPA, N.Y. Mgr. Touche Ross & Co., N.Y.C., 1959-63; v.p. fin., dir. Superior Surg. Mfg. Co., Inc., Huntington, N.Y., 1964-66; dir. pres., gen. mgr. OEI div. Vernitron Corp., Great Neck, N.Y., 1967-71; controller Allied Maintenance Corp., N.Y.C., 1972-75; v.p. fin. Allied Maintenance Corp., 1975-82; chief fin. officer Remco Maintenance Corp., N.Y.C., 1982-84; exec. v.p., chief operating officer Remco Maintenance Corp., 1984-88; pres. MBW Advt. Network Inc., N.Y.C., 1988-89; founder, pres. Dunmarc Assocs., Inc., N.Y.C., 1989—; exec. v.p. Greater Talent Network, Inc., 1991—. Office: 150 Fifth Ave Ste 900 New York NY 10011-4311

MARCOUX, CARL HENRY, former insurance executive, writer, historian; b. San Francisco, Jan. 6, 1927; s. Henry Roderick and Margaret (Carlin) M.; m. Ana Virginia Penate-Melara, Nov. 11, 1967; children: Eric Henry, Grant Reynold. B.A., Stanford U., 1950; M.B.A., Golden Gate U., San Francisco, 1958; M.A. in Latin Am. History, U. Calif., Irvine, 1988; PhD in Latin Am. History, U. Calif., Riverside, 1994. Gen. mgr. Nat. Union Ins. Co., Pitts., 1953-68; exec. v.p. Transam. Ins. Co., 1968-85. Served with U.S. Mcht. Marine, 1944-46; USAF, 1951-53. Mem. Stanford Alumni Assn. Republican. Home: 1967 Port Cardigan Pl Newport Beach CA 92660-5347

MARCOUX, JULES EDOUARD, physicist, educator, writer; b. Charny, Que., Can., Jan. 26, 1924; s. Romeo Joseph and Atala (Fontaine); m. Hermina Mary, July 2, 1955; children: Daniel, Edouard, Elise, Vincent, Pierre, Paul. B.A., Laval U., 1946, B.S., 1952; M.A., Toronto U., 1952, Ph.D. (Burton fellow), 1956. Research assoc. U. Montreal, Que., 1957; assoc. prof. physics U. Laval, Quebec, Que., 1962-64; prof. physics Royal Mil. Coll., St.-Jean, Que., 1958-62, 64-90, ret., 1990. Author in French: (with A. Ares) Physics Textbook, 6 vols, 1970-76, Astronauts and Astronautics, 1975, Energy: Its Sources, Its Future, 1982, Mechanics for Engineers, 1983; contbr. articles to profl. publs. Exec. com. bd. dirs. College de St.-Jean-sur-Richelieu, Que., 1981—. Postdoctoral fellow NRC Can., 1957. Mem. Am. Assn. Physics Tchrs., Can. Assn. Univ. Tchrs., Can. Mil. Colls. Faculty Assn. (pres. 1980-82). Home: 29 rue de Tilleuls, Saint Luc, PQ Canada J2W 1B4

MARCOUX, JULIA A., midwife; b. St. Helens, England, Aug. 7, 1928; d. Robert Patrick and Margaret Mary Theresa (White) Ashall; m. Albert Marcoux, Apr. 23, 1955; children: Stephen, Ann Marie, Richard, Michael, Maureen, Patrick, Margaret, Julie. Diploma, Withington Hosp., Manchester, England, 1950; grad., Cowley Hill Hosp., St. Helens, England, 1952; BS in Pub. Adminstrn., St. Joseph's Coll. RN, Conn.; lic. midwife, Conn. Nurse, labor, delivery rm. and nursery Day Kimbal Hosp., Putnam, Conn.; sch. nurse Marianapolis Prep. Sch., Thompson, Conn.; occupational nurse U.S. Post Office, Hartford, Conn.; pvt. duty and gerontology nurse Conn. Contbr. articles to profl. jours. Named Internat. Cath. Family of Yr., 1982.

MARCOUX, WILLIAM JOSEPH, lawyer; b. Detroit, Jan. 20, 1927; s. Lona J. and Anna (Ransom) C.; m. Kae Marie Sanborn, Aug. 23, 1952; children: Ann K., William C. BA, U. Mich., 1949, LL.B. 1952. Bar: Mich. 1953. Pvt. practice Pontiac, Mich., 1953; assoc. McKone, Badgley, Domke and Kline, Jackson, Mich., 1953-65, ptnr., 1965-75; pres. Marcoux, Allen, Abbott, Schomer & Bower, P.C., Jackson, Mich., 1975-93. Mem. exec. bd. Great Sauk Trail council Boy Scouts Am., pres., 1965-66; bd. dirs. Jackson County United Way, pres., 1983-84. Served with USNR, 1945-46. Recipient Silver Beaver award Boy Scouts Am., 1969, Disting. Citizen award Land O'Lakes coun. Boy Scouts Am., 1991. Fellow Am. Coll. Trial Lawyers; mem. ABA, Mich. Bar Assn., Jackson County Bar Assn. (pres. 1979-80). Methodist (chmn. adminstrv. bd., chmn. bd. trustees 1976-78, chmn. fin. com. 1986-89). Clubs: Rotarian (pres. 1963-64), Country, Clark Lake Yacht (hon. mem.; commodore 1959). Home: 1745 Malvern Dr Jackson MI 49203-5378 Office: Marcoux Allen Abbott Schomer & Bower PC 145 S Jackson St Jackson MI 49201-2293

MARCOUX, YVON, financial executive, lawyer; b. St. Lambert, Que., Can., Mar. 26, 1941; s. Henry Marcoux and Irène Simard; m. Odette Marcoux, Sept. 5, 1964; children: Stéphane, Sylvain, Sébastien, Valérie. BA, Université Laval, Que., Can., 1960, LL.L, 1963, postgrad., 1966; LL.M., U. Toronto, Can., 1965. Prof. Université Laval, Faculty Law, 1966-70; asst. sec. treasury bd., asst. dep. min. mcpl. affairs Govt. Que., 1970-78; v.p., sec. Nat. Bank Can., Montréal, 1978-81; sr. v.p. adminstrn. Laurentian Bank, Montréal, 1981-86; pres., chief exec. officer Trust La Laurentienne, Montréal, 1985-86; chmn., chief exec. officer Groupe SGF, Montréal, 1986-88; exec. v.p. adminstrn. Provigo, Montreal, 1988—; bd. dirs. Groupe LGS, Montreal, Corp. d'assurance de personnes La Laurentienne. Pres. Inst. for Pub. Adminstrn. Can., 1977-78, Fondation U. Laval, 1992-93, 93-94, Que. C. of C., 1992-93, Montreal C. of C., 1985-86; bd. dirs. La Fondation Jean Duceppe, Inst. de design de Montréal, Fondation Paul Gérin-Lajoie. Mem. Can. Bar Assn., Bar Que., Club St. Denis. Office: Provigo, 1611 Crémazie Blvd E, Montreal, PQ Canada H2M 2R9

MARCOVICH, MIROSLAV, classics educator; b. Belgrade, Yugoslavia, Mar. 18, 1919; came to U.S., 1969; s. Svetozar and Mila (Sakich) M.; m. Verica Tosich, May 30, 1948; 1 son, Dragoslav. B.A., U. Belgrade, 1942; DLitt (hon.), U. Ill., 1994. Lectr. in classics U. Belgrade, 1946-55; prof. Los Andes U., Merida, Venezuela, 1955-69; prof. classics U. Ill., Urbana, 1969-89, chmn. dept., 1973-77, prof. classics, prof. humanities, 1987. Author: M. Maruli Davidias, 1957, Fr. Natalis Carmina, 1958, Bhagavadgita, 1958, Heraclitus, 1967, Eraclito: Frammenti, 1978, Three-Word Triniter in Greek Tragedy, 1984, Hippolytus Elenchos, 1986, Studies in Gnosticism, 1988, Alcestis Barcinonensis, 1988, Prosper of Aquitaine, De providentia Dei, 1989,

Athenagoras, Legatio pro Christianis, 1990, Ps.-Justin, Cohortatio, 1990, Studies in Greek Poetry, 1991, Theodorus Prodromus, Rhodanthe and Dosicles, 1992, Justin Martyr, Apologies, 1994, Tatian, Oratio, 1994, Patristic Textual Criticism I, 1994, Theophilus, Ad Autolycum, 1995, Clementis Alexandrini Protrepticus, 1995, others.; founder, editor Illinois Classical Studies, 1976—; contbr. numerous articles to profl. jours. Recipient Premio Sesquicentenario Gold medal Venezuela, 1962, 64, Silver Cross Mt. Athos, Greece, 1963, Disting. Scholarship award U. Ill., 1973, Sr. Scholarship award U. Ill., 1986, Beckman award, 1991, 94-95; Guggenheim fellow, 1980, 83; Sackler scholar Tel Aviv U., 1990-91, NEH fellow 1990. Mem. Am. Philol. Assn. (mem. adv. com. Thesaurus Linguae Graecae 1973-80). Home: 2114 S Vine St Urbana IL 61801-6616

MARCOVITZ, LEONARD EDWARD, retail executive; b. Bismarck, N.D., Sept. 6, 1934; s. Jacob and Frieda M. Asst. mgr. Greengard's Clothing, Mandan, N.D., 1955-58; mgr. K-G Men's Stores, Inc., Bismarck, 1958-61, Billings, Mont., 1961-69; v.p. store ops. K-G Men's Stores, Inc., 1969-73; pres. Leonard's Men's Stores, Yakima, Wash. and Billings, Mont., 1973-77; chief exec. officer K-G Retail div. Chromalloy Am. Corp., Englewood, Colo., 1977-81; pres. DeMarcos Men's Clothing, Casper, Wyo., 1982—, Idaho Falls, Idaho, 1984—, Billings, Mont., 1986—. Mem. Menswear Retailers Am. (past dir.), Billings Petroleum Club, Order of Demolay (Degree of Chevalier 1952, Internat. Master Councilor 1953, Demolay Dad 1959), Elks. Home: PO Box 23344 Billings MT 59104-3344

MARCUCCIO, PHYLLIS ROSE, association executive, editor; b. Hackensack, N.J., Aug. 25, 1933; d. Filippo and Rose (Henry) M. AB, Bucknell U., 1955; MA, George Washington U., 1976. Trainee Time, Inc., 1956-57; art prodn. for mags. of Med. Econs., Inc., 1958-60; mem. staff Nat. Sci. Tchrs. Assn., Washington, 1961—; assoc. editor Sci. and Children, 1963-65, editor, 1965—, dir. div. elem. edn., 1974-78, dir. div. program devel. and continuing edn., 1978-83; dir. publs. Nat. Sci. Tchrs. Assn., 1983—, assoc. exec. dir., 1990—; lectr., cons. in field. Author, photographer, illustrator numerous articles; co-author: Investigation in Ecology, 1972; editor: Science Fun, 1977, 2d edit., 94; illustrator: Selected Readings for Students of English as a Second Language, 1966; compiler: Opportunities for Summer Studies in Elementary Science, 1968, 2d edit., 1969. Apptd. commr. Rockville (Md.) Housing Authority, 1981-91, chairperson, 1984-86; bd. dirs. Nat. Sci Resource Ctr., Nat. Acad. Sci., 1986—, Hands on Sci. Outreach, Inc., 1988—. Recipient Citizenship medal DAR, 1951; hon. life mem. Ohio Council Elem. Sch. Sci., 1974. Life mem. Nat. Sci. Tchrs. Assn.; mem. Council Elem. Sci. Internat. (Internat. award outstanding contbns. sci. edn. 1971, 72, 86, 94), Am. Nature Study Soc., Soil Conservation Soc. Am., Nat. Free Lance Photographers Assn., Photog. Soc. Am., Nat. Wildlife Fedn., Nat. Audubon Soc., Nat. Geog. Soc., Wilderness Soc., AAAS, Washington Edn. Press Assn. (treas. 1966-67, pres. 1975-76), Ednl. Press Assn. Am. (regional dir. 1969-71, sec. 1979—, Disting. Achievement award 1969, 71-74, 76, 77, 80, 88, 93, 95, Eleanor Fishburn award 1978), Sci. Teaching Assn. N.Y. (Outstanding Service to Sci. Edn. award 1987), Nat. Assn. Industry Edn. Coop. (bd. dirs. 1980-86), Pocono Environ. Edn. Ctr. (bd. dirs. 1989—), Nat. Press Club, Theta Alpha Phi, Phi Delta Gamma, Phi Delta Kappa, Sigma Delta Chi. Home: 406 S Horners Ln Rockville MD 20850-1556 Office: Nat Sci Tchrs Assn 1840 Wilson Blvd Arlington VA 22201-3000

MARCUM, DEANNA BOWLING, library administrator; b. Salem, Ind., Aug. 5, 1946; d. Anderson and Ruby (Mobley) Bowling; m. Thomas P. Marcum, June 13, 1974; 1 child, Ursula. BA, U. Ill., 1964; MA, So. Ill. U., 1969; MLS, U. Ky., 1971; PhD, U. Md., 1991. Tchr. Deland-Weldon (Ill.) High Sch., 1967-68; instr. English U. Ky., Lexington, 1969-70, cataloging librarian, 1970-73, asst. to dir., 1973-74; asst. dir. pub. svcs. Joint U. Librs., Nashville, 1974-77; mgmt. tng. specialist Assn. Rsch. Librs., Washington, 1977-80; sr. cons. Info. Systems Cons., Inc., Washington, 1980-81; v.p. Coun. on Libr. Resources, Washington, 1981-89; dean Sch. Libr. and Info. Sch. Cath. U., Washington, 1989-92; dir. pub. svcs. and collections mgmt. Libr. of Congress, Washington, 1993-95; pres. Coun. on Libr. Resources, Washington, 1995—; adv. bd. So. Edn. Found., Atlanta, 1986-91; chmn. grants com. Coun. on Libr. resources, Washington, 1990-94. Author: Good Books in a Country Home, 1993; co-author: (with Richard Boss) The Library Catalog, 1980, On-Line Acquisitions Systems, 1981; contbr. articles to profl. jours. Mem. ALA, Am. Studies Assn., Orgn. Am. Historians, Am. Antiquarian Soc. (adv. bd. 1989—), Beta Phi Mu, Phi Kappa Phi. Home: 911 Malta Ln Silver Spring MD 20901-1136 Office: Coun on Libr Resources 1400 16th St NW # 510 Washington DC 20036

MARCUM, JAMES BENTON, college dean; b. Cedar County, Mo., June 25, 1938; s. Ralph Emerson and Mary Amanda (Barrett) M.; m. Carol Marlene Brewer, Dec. 26, 1964; children: Eric Bentley, Lara Beth, Sara Bethany. BSAgr, U. Mo., 1960; MS, Cornell U., 1961; MDiv, Midwest Bapt. Sem., 1965; PhD, U. Mo., 1969. Lectr. U. Libya, Tripoli, 1969-71; asst. prof. U. Mass., Amherst, 1971-77, assoc. prof., 1977-85, dept. chmn., 1979-85, prof., assoc. dean Coll. Food and Nat. Resources, 1985—; bd. dirs Mass. Agr. in the Classroom, Inc., 1985—; adv. bd. Mass. Faculty Devel. Consortium, 1993—. Deacon North Leverett (Mass.) Bapt. Ch., 1973—, chmn. deacons, 1975-76, 78-79, 83-84, 87-88, 91-93, choir dir., 1972—. Mem. Am. Assn. Higher Edn., Nat. Assn. Colls. and Tchrs. Agr., Profl. and Orgn. Devel. Network in Higher Edn., Amherst Camera Club (pres. 1977-79), Hampshire Bird Club (pres. 1988-91), Sigma Xi, Gamma Sigma Delta, Alpha Zeta. Office: U Mass 113 Stockbridge Hall Amherst MA 01003-7230

MARCUM, JOSEPH LARUE, insurance company executive; b. Hamilton, Ohio, July 2, 1923; s. Glen F. and Helen A. (Stout) M.; m. Sarah Jane Sloneker, Mar. 7, 1944; children: Catharine Ann Marcum Lowe, Joseph Timothy (dec.), Mary Christina Marcum Manchester, Sarah Jennifer Marcum Shuffield, Stephen Sloneker. B.A., Antioch Coll., 1947; M.B.A. in Fin, Miami U., 1965. With Ohio Casualty Ins. Co. and affiliates, 1947—, now chmn. bd., also bd. dirs.; bd. dirs. First Nat. Bank S.W. Ohio; bd. dirs., chmn. exec. com. First Fin. Bancorp., Monroe, Ohio. Chmn. bd. trustees Miami U., Oxford, Ohio. Capt., inf. U.S. Army. Mem. Soc. CPCU, Queen City Club, Bankers Club, Princeton Club N.Y., Little Harbor club, Walloon Lake Country Club, Mill Reef Club. Presbyterian. Home: 475 Oakwood Dr Hamilton OH 45013-3466 Office: Ohio Casualty Corp 136 N 3rd St Hamilton OH 45025

MARCUM, WALTER PHILLIP, oil company executive; b. Bemidji, Minn., Mar. 1, 1944; s. John Phillip and Johnnye Evelyn (Edmiston) M.; m. Barbara Lynn Maloof, Apr. 17, 1976. BBA, Tex. Tech U., 1967. Researcher Collins Securities, Denver, 1968-70, Hanifin Imfoff, Denver, 1970-71; cons. Marcum-Spillane, Denver, 1971-76; with MGF Oil Corp., Midland, Tex., 1976-87, sr. v.p., 1978, exec. v.p., 1979-83, pres., chief exec. officer, 1983-87; sr. v.p. corp. fin. Boettcher & Co., Denver, 1987-90; pres., chief exec. officer Marcum Natural Gas Svcs., Inc., Denver, 1991—; dir. Homefree Village Resorts, Hydrologic Inc., Asheville, N.C., Well Tech., Inc., Houston. Republican. Presbyterian. Home: 676 Monroe St Denver CO 80206-4451 Office: 1675 Broadway Ste 2200 Denver CO 80202-4622

MARCUS, ALAN C., public relations consultant; b. N.Y.C., Feb. 26, 1947; s. Percy and Rose (Fox) M.; m. Judith Lamel, June 21, 1979; 1 child, Allison. Student Hun Sch., Princeton, 1966. Dir. pub. relations Bergen County Rep. Com., Hackensack, N.J., 1968; clk. N.J. Gen. Assembly, Trenton, 1969, sec. to majority party of assembly, 1970; pres. The Marcus Group, Inc., Secaucus, 1971—; adj. prof. Rutgers U. Grad. Sch., 1986-88. Trustee Nat. Leukemia Assn., 1976-82, Hun Sch. of Princeton, 1977-88, Passaic River Coalition, 1980-82. Recipient Youth Enterprise award Jim Walter Corp., 1972. Mem. Pub. Relations Soc. Am. (N.J. chpt. pres.'s award 1975, past pres. and bd. dirs. N.J. chpt. 1976-77), N.J.C of C. N.J. Bus. and Industry Assn., N.J. Press Assn., Apple Ridge Country Club, Capitol Hill Club, Fed. City Club (Washington). Office: 500 Plaza Dr PO Box 3309 Secaucus NJ 07096-3309 also: 50 W State St Trenton NJ 08608 also: 370 Lexington Ave New York NY 10017

MARCUS, BARRY PHILIP, lawyer; b. Mount Vernon, N.Y., July 25, 1953; m. Jean Kytt Jacobs, Sept. 4, 1977. BA, Cornell U., 1974; JD, U. Va., 1977. Bar: N.Y. 1978. Assoc. Debevoise & Plimpton, N.Y.C., 1977-80; assoc., ptnr. Kaye, Scholer, Fierman, Hays & Handler, N.Y.C., 1980—. Mem. ABA, N.Y.C. Bar Assn. Home: 420 E 72nd St New York NY 10021-

4615 Office: Kaye Scholer Fierman Hays & Handler 425 Park Ave New York NY 10022-3506

MARCUS, BERNARD, lawyer; b. Wilkes-Barre, Pa., Mar. 10, 1924; m. Frances Frank; children: Kate, Aaron, Charles, Mary. Student, U. Pa., 1941-43, Carnegie-Mellon U., 1943-44; LL.B., Harvard U., 1948; postgrad. Loyola U. of South, New Orleans, 1958. Bar: D.C. 1949, La. 1958. Atty. legis. reference service Library of Congress, 1949-50; acting counsel small bus. com. Ho. of Reps., 1950; atty. NLRB, Washington, Cin., Buffalo and New Orleans, 1950-57; assoc. Deutsch, Kerrigan & Stiles, New Orleans, 1957-58; ptnr. Deutsch, Kerrigan & Stiles, 1958-95, mng. ptnr., 1985-89, emeritus ptnr., 1995—; cons. Dept. State, 1965-69; labor arbitrator Am. Arbitration Assn., Fed. Mediation and Conciliation Svc., USDA, U.S. Dept. Def., U.S. Dept. Transp., City of Houston, Fla. Power and Light, Internat. Paper Co., Celotex, Mead Paper, ADM Corp., GTE, SW Bell, Ingalls Shipbuilding, Gulf States Utilities, others. Author: Congress and the Monopoly Problem, 1950; contbr. to casebooks. Pres. New Orleans Jewish Community Center, 1973-75; mem. Nat. Jewish Welfare Bd., 1974-83; bd. dirs. New Orleans Jewish Welfare Bd., Jewish Family and Children's Service, New Orleans, Communal Hebrew Sch.; v.p. New Orleans Home for Jewish Aged, 1978-80, Florence Heller Rsch. Found. Served U.S Army, 1943-46. Mem. ABA, Fed. Bar Assn., La. Bar Assn., New Orleans Bar Assn. (exec. com. 1971-74), D.C. Bar Assn. Home: 630 Burdette St New Orleans LA 70118-3937 Office: 755 Magazine St New Orleans LA 70130-3629

MARCUS, BERNARD, retail executive; b. 1929; married. BS, Rutgers U., 1954. V.p. Vornado Inc., 1952-68; pres. Odell Inc., 1968-70; v.p. Daylin Inc., 1970-73; with Handy Dan Home Improvement, Los Angeles, 1972-78; with Home Depot Inc., Atlanta, 1978—, now chmn., chief exec. officer, sec., also bd. dirs. Office: Home Depot Inc 2727 Paces Ferry Rd NW Atlanta GA 30339-4053*

MARCUS, BETH E., religious organization administrator. Moderator Gen. Synod Council of the Reformed Ch. in Am., N.Y.C. Office: Reformed Church in Am 475 Riverside Dr Rm 1811 New York NY 10115

MARCUS, CLAUDE, advertising executive; b. Paris, Aug. 28, 1924; s. Jacques and Louise (Bleustein) M.; m. Claudine Pohl, May 27, 1948; children: Michele, Pierre, Anne-Marie, Isabelle. Diploma in Econs., U. Paris, 1947; Lic., Paris Law Sch., 1947. Sec. gen. Publicis, Paris, 1948-55, dir. comml. to dir. gen. adjoint, 1961, dir. gen., 1962-68; mng. dir. Publicis Conseil, Paris, 1968-83; pres. Publicis Internat., Paris, 1984-88; vice-chmn. Publicis Communication, Paris, 1988—, Publicis FCB Communication, Paris, 1989; dir. Publicis SA, Paris, 1988—; chmn. Publicis N.Y., 1986—; chmn. supervisory bd. FCA, Paris; vice chmn. Metrobus Publicities, Paris, 1994. Decorated Chevalier de la Legion d'Honneur, 1970. Mem. Conseil Nat. de la Cosommation, Bur. de Verification de la Publicite (vice chmn.), Racing Club (France). Home: 12 Rue Felicien David, 75016 Paris France Office: Publicis, 133 Champs Elysees, 45008 Paris France also: 304 E 45th St New York NY 10017

MARCUS, CRAIG BRIAN, lawyer; b. Boise, Idaho, May 30, 1939; s. Claude Virgil and Marie Louise M.; m. Lynne Merryweather, Sept. 3, 1960; children: Shawn, Brian, Trent. Student, Boise Jr. Coll., 1958, U. Pa., 1958-59, Mexico City Coll., 1959-60; JD, U. Idaho, 1963. Bar: Idaho 1963, U.S. Dist. Ct. Idaho 1963. Ptnr. Marcus, Merrick & Montgomery, predecessors, Boise, 1963—. Ada County dir. Rep. Congl. Campaigns, Boise, 1964-66; Ada County coord. Rep. Senatorial Campaigns, 1969; chmn. jud. campaign Idaho Ct. of Appeals, 1984, 90. Mem. ABA, Idaho Bar Assn. (peer rev. com. 1971-73), 4th Dist. Bar Assn. (treas. 1967-68, ct. trial procedural rules com. 1973-74), Lincoln Day Banquet Assn. (pres. 1975), Elks. Avocations: fishing, hunting, golf, skiing, trap shooting. Home: 7711 Apache Way Boise ID 83703-1903 Office: Marcus Merrick & Montgomery 737 N 7th St Boise ID 83702-5595

MARCUS, DONALD HOWARD, advertising agency executive; b. Cleve., May 16, 1916; s. Joseph and Sarah (Schmitman) M.; m. Helen Olen Weiss, Feb. 12, 1959; children: Laurel Kathy Heifetz, Carol Susan Greene, James Randall (dec.), Jonathan Anthony. Student, Fenn Coll., 1934-35. Mem. publicity dept. Warner Bros. Pictures, Cleve., 1935-37; mem. advt. dept. RKO Pictures, Cleve., 1937-40; mem. sales dept. Monogram Pictures, Cleve., 1940-42; pres. Marcus Advt. Inc., Cleve., 1946-85, chmn., 1986—. Mem. Ohio Democratic exec. com., 1969-70, del. nat. conv., 1968; vice-chmn. communication div. Jewish Welfare Fund Appeal Cleve., 1964-70, chmn., 1971-72; trustee Jewish Community Fedn., 1973-74; trustee Cleve. Jewish News, 1974—, v.p. 1983-85; trustee No. Ohio regional office Anti Defamation League of B'nai B'rith, 1986—, Jewish Community Ctr., 1988-90; bd. dirs. Cuyahoga County unit Am. Cancer Soc., 1979—, Cleve. State U. Devel. Found., 1987—, Achievement Ctr. for Children, 1991—. Served to 1st lt. USAAF, 1942-46. Mem. Nat. Acad. TV Arts and Scis. (Silver Circle award 1994), Ohio Commodores, Cleve. Advt. Club (elected to Hall of Fame), Cleve. Growth Assn., Mensa, Union Club of Cleve., Beechmont Country Club (past pres.). Jewish (temple trustee). Home: 22449 Shelburne Rd Cleveland OH 44122-2053 Office: Marcus Advt Inc 25700 Science Park Dr Cleveland OH 44122-7312

MARCUS, EDWARD, economist, educator; b. Bklyn., Apr. 29, 1918; s. Herman and Rose (Marayna) M.; m. Mildred Rendl, Aug. 10, 1956. B.S., Harvard, 1939, M.B.A., 1941; student, King's Coll., Cambridge (Eng.) U., 1946-47; Ph.D., Princeton, 1950. Economist Fed. Res. Bd., 1950-52; prof. econs. Bklyn. Coll., 1952-81, chmn. dept., 1979; cons. Nat. Acad. Scis., 1959, UN Conf. Trade and Devel., 1966; dir. Syracuse U. Maxwell Sch. Nigerian Project, 1961; participant Internat. Econometrics Assn., Amsterdam, Holland, 1968. Author: Canada and the International Business Cycle, 1927-1938, 1954, (with Mildred Rendl Marcus) Investment and Development Possibilities in Tropical Africa, 1960, International Trade and Finance, 1965, Monetary and Banking Theory, 1965, Economic Progress and the Developing World, 1971, Economics, 1978. Served with AUS, 1941-42; Served with USCGR, 1942-46. Grantee Merrill Found., 1953. Mem. Am. Econ. Assn., Canadian Econ. Assn., N.Y. Met. Econ. Assn. (pres. 1966-67), Am. Finance Assn., Royal Econ. Soc., Econ. Soc. S. Africa, Am. Assn. U. Profs., New Canaan Hist. Soc. Treas. 1983—), Phi Beta Kappa. Home: PO Box 814 New Canaan CT 06840-0814

MARCUS, ERIC PETER, lawyer; b. Newark, Aug. 31, 1950; s. John J. and Alice M. (Zeldin) M.; m. Terry R. Toll, Oct. 9, 1983. BA, Brown U., 1972; JD, Stanford U., 1976. Bar: N.Y. 1977, N.J. 1977. Assoc. Kaye, Scholer, Fierman, Hays & Handler, N.Y.C., 1976-84, ptnr., 1985—. Contbr. articles to profl. jours. Mem. Phi Beta Kappa. Office: Kaye Scholer Fierman Hays & Handler 425 Park Ave New York NY 10022-3506

MARCUS, ERIC ROBERT, psychiatrist; b. N.Y.C., Feb. 16, 1944; s. Victor and Pearl (Maddow) M.; m Eslee Samberg, Nov. 24, 1985; children: Max Thomas, Pia. AB, Columbia U., 1965; MD, U. Wis., 1969. Diplomate Am. Bd. Psychiatry and Neurology. Intern NYU Med. Ctr. Bellevue Hosp., 1969-70; resident Columbia Presbyn. Med. Ctr.-N.Y. State Psychiatric Inst., 1972-75; dir. St. Marks Free Clinic, N.Y.C., 1971-75; from co-dir. to dir. neuropsychiatric/diagnostic treatment unit Columbia-Presbyn. Med. Ctr., N.Y.C., 1975-84; dir. med. student edn. in psychiatry Columbia U. Coll. Physicians and Surgeons, N.Y.C., 1981—; clin. prof. psychiatry and social medicine, 1995—; mem. Columbia U. Ctr. for Psychoanalytic Tng. and Rsch., 1987—, tng. and supervising psychoanalyst, 1994—; bd. govs. student health Columbia U., 1986—. Author: Psychosis and Near Psychosis, 1992; mem. editorial bd. The Psychoanalytic Study of Society, 1989-94; contbr. articles to profl. jours. Recipient Weber rsch. award Columbia U. Psychoanalytic Ctr., 1991. Fellow Am. Psychiat. Assn. (Roeske award 1991), Am. Psychoanalytic Assn., Am. Coll. Psychoanalysts, N.Y. Acad. Medicine. Avocations: classical music, photography, swimming, reading. Office: Columbia U Dept Psychiatry 722 W 168th St New York NY 10032-2603

MARCUS, FRANK, biochemist; b. Berlin, July 27, 1933; came to U.S., 1974; s. Heinz and Feiga (Wolf) M.; m. Marietta Munoz, Sept. 12, 1959; children: Claudio, Daniel, Andres. Pharm. chemist, U. Chile, 1958. Rockefeller Found. postdoctoral fellow dept. biochemistry Australian Nat. U.,

1962-63, U. Wis, 1964; asst. prof. biochemistry U. Chile, Santiago, 1965-68; prof. biochemistry and chmn. Inst. Biochemistry Southern U., Valdivia, Chile, 1968-74; vis. prof. Inst. Enzyme Research U. Wis., Madison, 1974-77; assoc. prof. biochemistry Univ. Health Scis. Chgo. Med. Sch., 1977-81, prof. biochemistry, 1981-87, vice chmn. Dept. Biol. Chemistry and Structure, U. Health Scis., 1982-87; dir. protein chemistry Chiron Corp., Emeryville, Calif., 1988-94; sr. dir. vaccine protein purification and analytical devel., 1994-95, sr. dir. protein purification, R&D, 1995—. Contbr. articles to profl. jours. Recipient Morris L. Parker rsch. award Chgo. Med. Sch., 1982; Fulbright travel awardee, 1968; grantee NIH, 1977-89, USDA, 1983-89. Mem. AAAS, Am. Soc. Biol. Chemists, Protein Soc., Alpha Omega Alpha. Home: 43 Remington Ct Danville CA 94526-3730 Office: Chiron Corp 4560 Horton St Emeryville CA 94608-2900

MARCUS, FRANK ISADORE, physician, educator; b. Haverstraw, N.Y., Mar. 23, 1928; s. Samuel and Edith (Sattler) M.; m. Janet Geller, June 30, 1957; children: Ann, Steve, Lynn. Ba, Columbia U., 1948; MS, Tufts U., 1951; MD cum laude, Boston U., 1953. Diplomate Am. Bd. Internal Medicine, subspecialty cardiovascular diseases. Intern Peter Bent Brigham Hosp., Boston, 1953-54; asst. resident Peter Bent Brigham Hosp., 1956-57, research fellow in cardiology, 1957-58; clin. fellow in cardiology Georgetown U. Hosp., 1958-59, chief med. resident, 1959-60; chief of cardiology Georgetown U. Med. Service, D.C. Gen. Hosp., Washington, 1960-68; instr. medicine Georgetown U. Sch. Medicine, 1960-63, asst. prof., 1963-68, assoc. prof., 1968; prof. medicine, chief cardiology sect. U. Ariz. Coll. Medicine, Tucson, 1969-82, disting. prof. internal medicine (cardiology), 1982—, dir. electrophysiology, 1982—; cons. cardiology VA Hosp., Tucson, 1969, USAF Regional Hosp., Davis-Monthan AFB, Tucson, 1969; mem. courtesy staffs Tucson Med. Ctr., St. Mary's Hosp., Tucson; panel drug efficacy study, panel on cardiovascular drugs Nat. Acad. Scis.-NRC, 1967-68; chmn. undergrad. cardiovascular tng. grant com. HEW-NIH, 1970. Editor Modern Concepts of Cardiovascular Disease, 1982-84; mem. editorial bd. Circulation, 1976-81, Current Problems in Cardiology, 1976-80, Cardiocascular Drugs and Therapy, 1986—, New Trends in Arrythmias, 1984—, Jour. Am. Coll. Cardiology, 1984-87, Am. Jour. Cardiology, 1984—, Jour. Cardiovascular Drugs and Therapy, 1994—, Jour. Cardiovascular Pharmacology and Therapeutics, 1994—; contbr. numerous articles to med. jours. Chmn. Washington Heart Assn. High Sch. Heart Program, 1966-68. Served to capt. USAF, 1954-56. Recipient Career Devel. award NIH, 1965, Student AMA Golden Apple award Georgetown U. Sch. Medicine, 1968; Mass. Heart Assn. fellow, 1957-58; John and Mary Markle scholar, 1960-65. Fellow Coun. on Clin. Cardiology Am. Heart Assn., ACP (Ariz. laureate award 1987), Am. Coll. Cardiology (bd. govs. Ariz. 1984-87, asst. sec. 1987-89, trustee); mem. Am. Fedn. Clin. Rsch., Am. Soc. Pharm. and Exptl. Therapeutics, Assn. Univ. Cardiologists, Inc. (v.p. 1989-90, pres. 1990-91), Ariz. Heart Assn. (dir. 1970, v.p. 1972-73, chmn rsch. com. 1970-72), So. Ariz. Heart Assn. (dir. 1969), N.Am. Soc. for Pacing and Electrophysiology, Alpha Omega Alpha. Home: 4949 E Glenn St Tucson AZ 85712-1212 Office: U Ariz Univ Med Ctr 1501 N Campbell Ave Tucson AZ 85724-0001

MARCUS, GEORGE E., anthropologist; b. Brownsville, Pa., Oct. 17, 1946; s. Samuel Marcus and Rose Schreiber; m. Patricia Seed, June 22, 1984; children: Rachel, Avery. BA, Yale U., 1968; PhD, Harvard U., 1976. Asst. prof. Rice U., Houston, 1975-80, assoc. prof., 1980-86, chair dept. anthropology, 1980—, prof., 1986—. Author: Anthropology as Cultural Critique, 1986, Lives in Trust, 1992; editor: Writing Culture, 1986, Rereading Cultural Anthropology, 1992, Cultural Anthropology, 1986-92; also numerous editorial bds. Office: Rice U 6100 S Main Houston TX 77005

MARCUS, GEORGE MATHEW, real estate executive; b. Limni, Greece, Aug. 15, 1941; s. John and Mary (Moutsanas) M.; m. Judy A. Otten, June 26, 1965; children: Mary Jane, John, Demetra, Alexandria. BA in Econ., San Francisco State U., 1965. Founder, chmn. Marcus & Millichap, Inc. and affiliate cos., Palo Alto, Calif.; founder Plaza Bank of Commerce, San Jose, Calif.; bd. dirs. Mid Peninsula Bank. Bd. dirs. San Jose Cleve. Ballet, Modern Greek Studies Found., Ctr. for Study Dem. Instns., Greek Orthodox Fellowship Santa Clara County; mem. policy adv. bd. Ctr. for Real Estate and Urban Econs., U. Calif., Berkeley; mem. San Francisco Host Com. Mem. Urban Land Inst., Nat. Multi Housing Coun., Nat. Realty Com. (bd. dirs.), Fremont Hills Country Club, Los Altos Country Club. Office: Marcus & Millichap 2626 Hanover St Palo Alto CA 94304-1102

MARCUS, GREIL GERSTLEY, critic; b. San Francisco, June 19, 1945; s. Gerald Dodd and Eleanore (Hyman) M.; m. Jenelle Bernstein, June 26, 1966; children: Emily Rose, Cecily Helen. BA, U. Calif.-Berkeley, 1967, MA, 1968. Record editor Rolling Stone mag., San Francisco and N.Y.C., 1969-70; book columnist Rolling Stone mag., 1975-80, Calif. Mag., L.A., 1982-83, 88-90; pop music columnist Music Mag., Tokyo, 1978-94, New West mag., L.A., 1978-82, Artforum mag., N.Y.C., 1983-87, 90—, Village Voice newspaper, N.Y.C., 1986-90, Interview Mag., N.Y.C., 1992—; dir. Pagnol et Cie, operators Chez Panisse restaurant, Berkeley, Calif. Author Mystery Train: Immages of American in Rock 'n Roll Music, 1975, U.S. rev. edits., 1982-90 (Brit., German, Greek, Dutch and Japanese edits.), Lipstick Traces: A Secret History of the 20th Century 1989 (Brit., Italian, Spanish, and German edits.), Dead Elvis: A Chronicle of a Cultural Obsession, 1991 (Brit., Japanese and German edits.), Ranters and Crowd Pleasers: Punk in Pop Music, 1977-1992, 1993 (Brit. and German edits. in the Fascist Bathroom: Writings on Punk, 1977-92), Real Life Rock (Japanese only), 1994, The Dustbin of History (Brit. edit.), 1995; editor: Stranded, 1979, Psychotic Reactions and Carburetor Dung (Lester Bangs), 1987; contbr. criticism to numerous publs., including N.Y. Times, N.Y. Times Book Rev., Creem, New Yorker, Express-Times, Triquar., Boston Phoenix, New Mus. Express, Another Room, L.A. Times, Newday, IT, New Formations, RAW, Rock and Roll Confidential, Threepenny Rev., South Atlantic Quar., Common Knowledge.

MARCUS, HAROLD, physician, health facility administrator; b. N.Y.C., May 28, 1915; s. Abraham and Yetta (Salb) M.; m. Beatrice Falk, Apr. 27, 1943; children: Robert Michael, Alan David. BS, Columbia U., 1935; BS in Medicine, W.Va. U., 1936; MD cum laude, Boston U., 1939. Diplomate Nat. Bd. Med. Examiners, Am. Bd. Internal Medicine. Intern Maimonides Med. Ctr., Bklyn., N.Y., 1939-41; resident in pathology Nassau County Med. Ctr., Hempstead, N.Y., 1941, 46, resident in internal medicine, 1947-48; resident in neurology Kingsbrook Med. Ctr., Bklyn., 1948-49; pvt. practice Bklyn., 1949-88; chief medicine Internat. Ladies Garment Workers Union Health Ctr., N.Y.C., 1953—. Contbr. articles to profl. jours. Lt. col. U.S. Army, 1941-46. Decorated Bronze Star; recipient Merit Citation Gen. Chiang Kai Shek, China, 1945. Mem. ACP, Phi Delta Epsilon. Avocations: golf, tennis, leather work. Home: 180 Marlborough Rd Brooklyn NY 11226-4510

MARCUS, HARRIS LEON, mechanical engineering and materials science educator; b. Ellenville, N.Y., July 5, 1931; s. David and Bertha (Messite) M.; m. Leona Gorker, Aug. 29, 1962; children: Leland, M'Risa. BS, Purdue U., 1963; PhD, Northwestern U., 1966. Registered profl. engr., Tex. Tech. staff Tex. Instruments, Dallas, 1966-68; tech. staff Rockwell Sci. Ctr., 1968-70, group leader, 1971-75; prof. mech. engring. U. Tex., Austin, 1975-79, Harry L. Kent Jr. prof. mech. engring., 1979-90, Cullen Found. prof., 1990-95, dir. ctr. for Materials Sci. and Engring., dir. program, 1979-95; prof. metallurgy, dir. Inst. of Material Sci. U. Conn., 1995—; cons. numerous orgns. Contbr. numerous articles to profl. publs. Recipient U. Tex. faculty U. Tex. Engring. Found., 1983; Krengel lectr. Technion, Israel, 1983; Alumni Merit medal Northwestern U., 1988, Disting. Purdue Univ. Engring. Alumnus award, 1994. Fellow Am. Soc. Metals; mem. ASTM, ACS, AIME (bd. dirs. Metall. Soc. 1976-78, 84-86), Materials Rsch. Soc., Univ. Materials Coun. Achievements include 15 patents. Home: 4102 Hyridge Dr Austin TX 78759-8022 Office: U Tex Ctr Rsch Mat Sci & Engring ETC 9 104 Austin TX 78712-1063

MARCUS, HYMAN, business executive; b. Roumania, May 3, 1914; s. Morris and Fannie M.; m. Sydelle Allen, June 29, 1935; children: Beverly Faith, Carole Ann. BA, Columbia U., 1932; MA, CCNY, 1993. Math instr., 1932-39; Empire Designing Corp., 1939-46, Manhattan Capital Co., 1946-54; pres., chmn. U.S. Hoffman Machinery Corp., 1954-58; pres. Van Alstyne Noel & Co., 1956-59; chmn. bd. Artloom Industries, 1958—, pres., 1959—; chmn. bd. Hoffman Internat., 1957-59; pres., chmn. bd. Trans-

United Industries, 1958; chmn. First Capital Corp., 1968—, Maralco Enterprises Inc., 1969—. Chmn. planning commn. Village of Atlantic Beach; trustee Riverside Sch. Jewish Meml. Hosp. Home: 159 W 53rd St New York NY 10019-6050 Office: 200 W 51st St New York NY 10019-6208

MARCUS, JACOB RADER, history educator; b. Connellsville, Pa., Mar. 5, 1896; s. Aaron and Jennie (Rader) M.; m. Antoinette Brody, Dec. 30, 1925 (dec.); 1 dau., Merle Judith (dec.). AB, U. Cin., 1917, LLD, 1950; rabbi, Hebrew Union Coll., 1920; PhD, U. Berlin, 1925; attended, Lane Theol. Sem., 1914, U. Chgo., 1915, U. Kiel, 1923; spl. study, Paris and Jerusalem, 1925-26; LLD (hon.), Dropsie Coll., 1955; DHL (hon.), Spertus Coll. Judaica, Chgo., 1977, Brandeis U., 1978, Gratz Coll., Phila., 1978, Xavier U., Cin., 1985, Wayne State U., 1989, Jewish Theological Seminary, 1992. Instr. Bible, rabbinics Hebrew Union Coll., 1920, asst. prof. Jewish history, 1926-29, assoc. prof., 1929-34, prof. Jewish history, 1934-59, apptd. Adolph S. Ochs prof. Jewish history, 1946, Adolph S. Ochs prof. Am. Jewish history, 1959-65, Milton and Hattie Kutz Distinguished Service prof. Am. Jewish history, 1965—; dir. Am. Jewish Archives, 1947—, Am. Jewish Periodical Center, 1956—; v.p. Central Conf. Am. Rabbis, 1947, pres., 1949, hon. pres., 1978. Author: The Rise and Destiny of the German Jew, 1934, An Index to Jewish Festschriften, 1937, The Jew in the Medieval World-a Source Book, 1938, Communal Sick-Care in the German Ghetto, 1947, Early American Jewry, 2 vols., 1951-53, Memoirs of American Jews 1775-1865, 3 vols., 1955-56, American Jewry Documents Eighteenth Century, 1959, On Love, Marriage, Children...and Death, Too, 1966, Studies in American Jewish History, 1969, The Colonial American Jew, 3 vols., 1970, Critical Studies in American Jewish History, 3 vols., 1971, Israel Jacobson: The Founder of the Reform Movement in Judaism, 1972, The American Jewish Woman 1654-1980, The American Jewish Woman: A Documentary History, 2 vols., 1981, United States Jewry, Vol. I, 1989, Vol. II, 1991, Vol. III, 1993, Vol. IV, 1993, To Count a People, 1990, This I Believe, 1990; editor: The American Jewish Archives, The Concise Dictionary of American Jewish Biography, 2 vols., 1994. Served as 2d lt., 145th Inf. U.S. Army, 1917-19. Recipient Frank L. Weil award Nat. Jewish Welfare Bd., 1955; Lee M. Friedman medal for disting. svc. to history, 1961; honored with publ. Essays in American Jewish History, on 10th anniversary of founding of Am. Jewish Archives, 1958, A Bicentennial Festschrift for Jacob Rader Marcus, 1976, The Writings of Jacob Rader Marcus, A Bibliographic Record, 1978. Mem. Jewish Publ. Soc. Am., Am. Jewish Hist. Soc. (hon. pres.), Am. Acad. Jewish Research, B'nai B'rith, Phi Beta Kappa. Home: 401 Mcalpin Ave Cincinnati OH 45220-1532 Office: Am Jewish Archives 3101 Clifton Ave Cincinnati OH 45220-2404 *The most important thing in life is integrity.*

MARCUS, JAMES STEWART, investment banker; b. N.Y.C., Dec. 15, 1929; s. Bernard Kent and Libby (Phillips) M.; m. Barbara Ellen Silver, July 18, 1962 (dec. Nov. 1970); m. Ellen Mary Friedman, June 21, 1974. AB magna cum laude, Harvard U., 1951, MBA with distinction, 1953. Assoc. Goldman, Sachs and Co., N.Y.C., 1956-64, gen. ptnr., 1964-82, ltd. ptnr., 1982—; bd. dirs. Kellwood Co., St. Louis, Am. Bilrite Inc., Wellesley, Mass. Bd. dirs. Met. Opera Assn., N.Y.C., 1973—, chmn., 1986-93, Met. Opera Guild, Met. Opera Club; mem. exec. com. Lincoln Ctr. for the Performing Arts, N.Y.C., 1982-93; trustee Lincoln Hill Hosp., N.Y.C., 1985—, chmn. bd. dirs., 1993—, Guild Hall, East Hampton, N.Y., 1977—, Am. Composers Orch., N.Y.C., 1984—, WNET Channel 13, Regenstrief Found., Alex Hillman Family Found., Animal Med. Ctr., Manhattan Theatre Club, The Juilliard Sch.; former trustee Nat. Opera Inst., Brazilian Cultural Found. Served with U.S. Army, 1953-55. Recipient U.S. Presdl. Recognition award, 1986. Mem. Century Assn., Phi Beta Kappa. Republican. Jewish. Office: Goldman Sachs & Co 85 Broad St New York NY 10004-2434

MARCUS, JOSEPH, child psychiatrist; b. Cleve., Feb. 27, 1928; s. William and Sarah (Marcus) Schwartz; m. Cilla Furmanovitz, Oct. 3, 1951; children: Oren, Alon. B.Sc., Western Res. U., 1963; M.D., Hebrew U., 1958. Intern Tel Hashomer Govt. Hosp., Israel, 1956-57; resident in psychiatry and child psychiatry Ministry of Health, Govt. of Israel, 1958-61; acting head dept. child psychiatry Ness Ziona Rehab. Ctr., 1961-62; sr. psychiatrist Lasker dept. child psychiatry Hadassah U. Hosp., 1962-64; research asso. Israel Inst. Applied Social Research, 1966-69; practice medicine specializing in psychiatry Jerusalem, 1966-72; assoc. dir. devel. neuropsychiatry Jerusalem Infant and Child Devel. Ctr., 1969-70; dept. head Eytanim Hosp., 1970-72; cons. child psychiatrist for Jerusalem Ministry of Health, 1970-72; dir. dept. child psychiatry and devel. Jerusalem Mental Health Ctr., 1972-75; prof. child psychiatry, dir. unit for research in child psychiatry and devel. U. Chgo., 1975-85; prof. emeritus, co-dir. unit for research in child psychiatry and devel., 1986—; vis. research psychiatrist UCLA Dept. Psychiatry, 1987—. Chief editor: Early Child Devel. and Care, 1972-76; mem. editorial bd.: Israel Annals of Psychiatry and Related Disciplines, 1965-70, Internat. Yearbook of Child Psychiatry and Allied Professions, 1968-74; contbr. articles to med. jours. Mem. Am. Acad. Child Psychiatry (com. on research, com. on psychiat. aspects of infancy), Soc. Research in Child Devel., Internat. Assn. Child Psychiatry and Allied Professions (asst. gen. sec. 1966-74), European Union Paedopsychiatry (hon.), World, Israel psychiat. assns., Internat. Coll. Psychosomatic Medicine, Israel Center Psychobiology. Home: 910 Chelham Way Santa Barbara CA 93108-1049 Office: 5841 S Maryland Ave MC 30077 Chicago IL 60637-1470

MARCUS, LARRY DAVID, broadcasting executive; b. N.Y.C., Jan. 27, 1949; s. Oscar Moses and Sylvia (Ackerman) M.; m. Noreen Mary Marcus, Dec. 24, 1975; children: Julia Ilene, Barbara Maureen. BBA, CUNY, 1970, postgrad. studies Bus. Admstrn., 1970-72. Acctg. mgr. Sta. WPLG-TV, Miami, Fla., 1974-75; v.p., bus. mgr. Sta. KPLR-TV-Koplar Communications, Inc., St. Louis, 1976-82; chief fin. officer Koplar Communications, Inc., St. Louis, 1982-88, River City Broadcasting Co., St. Louis, 1988—. Mem. Broadcast Cable Fin. Mgmt. Assn. (bd. dirs. 1976-89, treas. 1989-90, sec. 1990-91, v.p. 1991-92, pres. 1992-93). Jewish. Avocations: sports, skiing, golf. Office: KDNL TV 1215 Cole St Saint Louis MO 63106-3897

MARCUS, LAURENCE RICHARD, state official; b. Brookline, Mass., July 23, 1947; s. Herbert M. and Joyce (Chaban) M.; m. Maureen Flanagan; children: Yvette, Christina Ann. BA in Polit. Sci., U. Mass., Amherst, 1969; MEd, 1972, EdD, 1976. Staff asst. U. Mass., Amherst, 1970-76; asst. to v.p. acad. affairs Stockton State Coll., Pomona, N.J., 1976-79, interim dean gen. studies, 1977; asst. to chancellor N.J. Dept. Higher Edn., Trenton, 1979-81, dir. state colls., 1981-87; dir. N.J. Fund for Improvement of Collegiate Edn., 1984-87, Div. Faculty Devel. and Ednl. Policy, 1987-89, dep. asst. chancellor, 1989-91, asst. chancellor for academic and fiscal affairs, 1991-94; prof. ednl. policy and planning Rowan Coll. of N.J., Glassboro, 1994—; tchr. U. Mass., Stockton State Coll.; cons. race relations, ednl. administrn.; trustee Glassboro State Coll., 1986-87, Trenton State Coll., 1986-87, 89-94, Montclair State Coll., 1989-91, Kean Coll. of N.J., 1990-94; trustee, N.J. Marine Scis. Consortium, 1990-94, exec. com., 1990-94. Mem. Amherst Town Meeting, 1971-73, Franklin-Hampshire Council for Children, 1974-76, N.J. Commn. Future of State Colls., 1982-84; adv. Commn. on Investing in State Colls., 1993-94. Mem. Assn. Study of Higher Edn., Coll. and Research Assn. (chair div. J govt. relations com., 1986-88, chair div. J comm. on publs. 1988-89), Am. Polit. Sci. Assn., Policy Studies Orgn., Spl. Interest Group Futures Rsch. and Strategic Planning (chair 1995—), Adelphia (past pres.). Co-author: (with Benjamin D. Stickney) Race and Education: The Unending Controversy, 1981; (with A. Leone, E. Goldberg) The Path to Excellence, 1983; (with Benjamin D. Stickney) The Great Education Debate-Washington and the Schools, 1984, (Choice's award as Outstanding Academic Book, 1985-86), (with Janet Johnson) Blue Ribbon Commissions and Higher Education: Changing Academe from the Outside, 1986, (with Benjamin D. Stickney) Politics and Policy in the Age of Education, 1990; mem. editorial bd. Review of Higher Edn., 1991-95, On the Horizon, 1994—; consulting editor: ASHE/ERIC Higher Edn. Report Series, 1994—; contbr. numerous articles to profl. jours. Home: 33 Forest Ave Medford NJ 08055-3447 Office: Rowan Coll NJ Dept Ednl Adminstrn Glassboro NJ 08028-1701

MARCUS, LEONARD, retail company executive. Sr. v.p. Abraham & Strauss, Bklyn.; pres. COO Abraham & Strauss, Cincinnati, Ohio, 1993—. Office: Abraham & Straus 7 W 7th St Cincinnati OH 45202-2424

MARCUS, MARVIN, mathematician, educator; b. Albuquerque, July 31, 1927; s. David Clarence and Esther (Rosenthal) M.; m. Arlen Ingrid

Sahlman, Sept. 14, 1951; children: Jeffrey Thomas, Karen Melissa; m. Rebecca Elizabeth Michael, Oct. 12, 1965. B.A., U. Calif. at Berkeley, 1950, Ph.D., 1953. Instr., then asst. prof. U. B.C., 1954-56, assoc. prof., 1957-62; postdoctoral research fellow Nat. Bur. Standards, Washington, 1956-57; prof. U. Calif. at Santa Barbara, 1962—; dir. Inst. for Interdisciplinary Applications of Algebra and Combinatorics, 1973-79, chmn. dept. math., 1963-68, dean research devel., 1978, assoc. vice-chancellor research and acad. devel., 1979-86; vis. distinguished prof. U. Islamabad, West Pakistan, 1970; Cons. Bur. Naval Ordnance, Pasadena, Calif. Author books and articles in field.; Editor: Linear and Multilinear Algebra. Served with USN, 1945-46. Mem. Am. Math. Soc., Math. Assn. Am., Soc. Indsl. and Applied Math. Assn. for Computing Machinery, Sigma Xi, Pi Mu Epsilon. Home: 2937 Kenmore Pl Santa Barbara CA 93105-2223

MARCUS, NORMAN, lawyer; b. N.Y.C., Aug. 31, 1932; s. David and Evelyn (Freed) M.; m. Maria Eleanor Lenhoff, Dec. 23, 1956; children: Valerie, Nicole, Eric. BA, Columbia U., 1953; LLB, Yale U., 1957. Bar: N.Y. 1958, U.S. Dist. Ct. (so. dist.) 1960, U.S. Supreme Ct. 1964. Assoc. LaPorte & Meyers, N.Y.C., 1957-61; gen. counsel Stanley Warner Corp., N.Y.C., 1961-63; gen. counsel N.Y.C. Planning Commn. and Dept. of City Planning, 1963-85; ptnr. Finley, Kumble, Wagner, Heine, Underberg, Manley, Myerson & Casey, N.Y.C., 1985-87; counsel Bachner, Tally, Polevoy & Misher, N.Y.C., 1987—; adj. prof. Pratt Inst., Bklyn., 1965-85, NYU Law Sch., 1977—, Benjamin N. Cardozo Sch. Law, N.Y.C., 1983-85, NYU Wagner Sch. Pub. Svc., 1986—; Princeton (N.J.) U. Sch. Architecture, 1990-91. Contbr. articles to profl. jours. Recipient Meritorious Achievement award Am. Planning Assn., 1986. Mem. N.Y. State Bar Assn., Assn. of Bar of City of N.Y., N.Y. County Lawyers Assn. (bd. dirs., chmn. com. on urban devel. and land use), Am. Coll. Real Estate Lawyers, The Fine Arts Fedn. N.Y. (bd. dirs.), Century Club. Avocations: antique books, swimming, drama criticism. Home: 91 Central Park West New York NY 10023 Office: Bachner Tally Polevoy & Misher 380 Madison Ave New York NY 10017-2513

MARCUS, PAUL, lawyer, educator; b. N.Y.C., Dec. 8, 1946; s. Edward and Lillian (Rubin) M.; m. Rebecca Nimmer, Dec. 22, 1968; children: Emily, Beth, Daniel. AB, UCLA, 1968, JD, 1971. Bar: Calif. 1971, U.S. Dist. Ct. (cen. dist.) Calif. 1972, U.S. Ct. Appeals (D.C. cir.) 1972, U.S. Ct. Appeals (7th cir.) 1976. Law clk. U.S. Ct. Appeals (D.C. cir.), 1971-72; assoc. Loeb & Loeb, L.A., 1972-74; prof. law U. Ill., Urbana, 1974-83; dean Coll. Law U. Ariz., Tucson, 1983-88, prof., 1988-92; Haynes prof. law Coll. William and Mary, Williamsburg, Va., 1992—; reporter, cons. Fed. Jud. Ctr. Commn. Author: The Entrapment Defense, 1989, 2d edit., 1995, The Prosecution and Defense of Criminal Conspiracy, 1978, 3d edit., 1992, Gilbert Law Summary, 1982, 4th edit., 1991, Criminal Law: Cases and Materials, 1982, 2d edit., 1989, 3d edit., 1995. Mem. accreditatio com. Am. Assn. Law Schs., 1978-81; nat. reporter on criminal law Internat. of Comparative Law, 1978-94. Office: Coll of William and Mary Williamsburg VA 85721

MARCUS, PHILIP IRVING, virology educator, researcher; b. Springfield, Mass., June 3, 1927; s. Julius and Marley Amelia (Speir) M.; m. Angela Joan Francis, Dec. 4, 1953; children: Craig F., Wendy L., Valerie L. BS, U. So. Calif., 1950; M.S., U. Chgo., 1953; Ph.D., U. Colo., 1957. Asst. prof. biophysics U. Colo. Sch. Medicine, Denver, 1957-60; assoc. prof. microbiology Albert Einstein Coll. Medicine, Bronx, N.Y., 1961-66; prof. Albert Einstein Coll. Medicine, 1967-69; prof. microbiology U. Conn., Storrs, 1969-75, head dept., 1969-75, prof. virology, 1969—, dir. Biotech. Ctr., 1990-95; dir. Nat. Cancer Inst. Program Project, 1973-83; cons. NIH, NSF; mem. sci. adv. coun. Damon Runyon-Walter Winchell Cancer Fund, 1970-74, Am. Cancer Soc., 1986-88, Am. Found. for AIDS Rsch., 1990—. Editor Jour. Cellular Physiology, 1969—; editor in chief Jour. Interferon Rsch., 1984—, Jour. Interferon & Cytokine Rsch., 1995—; contbr. numerous articles to profl. jours. Served with USAAC, 1945-47. Recipient USPHS rsch. career devel. award, 1960-70, excellence in rsch. award U. Conn. Alumni Assn., 1987; NIH grantee, 1960-94, NSF, USDA grantee. Mem. AAAS, Am. Soc. Microbiology, Am. Soc. Cell Biology, Am. Soc. Virology, Brit. Soc. Microbiology, Internat. Soc. Interferon and Cytokine Research, Tissue Culture Assn., Conn. Acad. Sci. and Engring. Home: 24 Thompson Rd Storrs Mansfield CT 06268-1806 Office: U Conn Dept Molecular And Bio # U-44 Storrs CT 06269-3044

MARCUS, RICHARD ALAN, lawyer, distribution company executive; b. N.Y.C., Aug. 25, 1933; s. Berthold and Dorothy (Kerstin) M.; m. Davys Kay Weisberg, June 4, 1961 (dec. 1992); children: Barbara Jo, Kimberly Ellen, Scott Arak. B.A., CCNY, 1954; J.D., U. Va., 1959. Bar: Va. 1959, N.Y. 1960, Fla. 1960, Minn. bar 1962. Asso. Bernard C. Fuller, Miami Beach, Fla., 1960-62; asso. firm Robbins, Davis, Lyons, Mpls., 1962-64; gen. counsel Napco Internat., Inc., Hopkins, Minn., 1964-86, 68-88, sr. v.p., 1968-86; sec. Napco Internat., Inc., 1980-86; dir. Napco Internat. Ltd.; dir. officer Inter-Ad Inc., Internat. Aircraft Sales and Support, Inc., Ordnance Corp. Am., Napco Export Corp., Napco Internat. (S.A.), Belgium, GmgH, W. Ger.; bd. govs., exec. com. Am. League for Export and Security Assistance, now ret. Served with AUS, 1954-56. Mem. Am. Soc. Corp. Secs., Nat. Soc. Corp. Planning, Am. Mgmt. Assn., Am. Bar Assn., Sigma Nu Phi, Pi Delta Epsilon. Club: Mpls. LaCrosse. Home: 4900 N Ocean Blvd Apt 621 Fort Lauderdale FL 33308-2932

MARCUS, RICHARD LEON, lawyer; b. San Francisco, Jan. 28, 1948; s. Irving Harry and Elizabeth (McEvoy) M.; m. Andrea June Saltzman, Apr. 26, 1981; 1 child, Ruth Emily. BA, Pomona Coll., 1969; JD, U. Calif. Berkeley, 1972. Bar: Calif. 1973, U.S. Dist. Ct. (no. dist.) Calif. 1976, U.S. Dist. Ct. (cen. dist.) Calif. 1978, U.S. Ct. Appeals (9th cir.) 1981. Law clk. to judge Calif. Supreme Ct. San Francisco, 1972; assoc. Boalt Hall U. Calif., 1973-74; law clk. to judge U.S. Dist. Ct. Calif., San Francisco, 1974-75; from assoc. to ptnr. Dinkelspiel, Pelavin, Steefel & Levitt, San Francisco, 1976-81; assoc. prof. law U. Ill., Champaign, 1981-84, prof. law, 1984-89; prof. law U. Calif., Hastings, 1989—; vis. prof. law U. Mich., 1986-87, U. Calif., Hastings, 1988; assoc. reporter Fed. Cts. Study Com., 1989-90; reporter com. civil motions Ill. Jud. Conf., Chgo., 1984, com. on evidence, 1985; cons. Nat. Commn. on Judicial Discipline and Removal, 1992-93; reporter Civil Justice Reform Act Adv. Group, No. Dist. of Calif., 1992—, chair local rules adv. com., 1994—. Rsch. editor U. Calif. Law Rev., 1971-72; author Complex Litigation, 1985, 2d edit., 1992, Civil Procedure: A Modern Approach, 1989, 2d edit., 1995, Federal Practice and Procedure, vols. 8 and 8A, 2d edit., 1994; contbr. articles to profl. jours. Named Order of Coif. Mem. ABA, Am. Law Inst., Am. Assn. Law Schs. (chmn. sect. civil procedure 1988, chmn. complex litigation com. 1991). Democrat. Home: 70 Domingo Ave Berkeley CA 94705-2436 Office: U Calif Coll Law 200 Mcallister St San Francisco CA 94102-4707

MARCUS, ROBERT, aluminum company executive; b. Arlington, Mass., Feb. 24, 1925; s. Hymen David and Etta (Arbetter) M.; m. Emily Patricia Ulrich, 1988; children: Lawrence Brian, Janie Sue, Clifford Scott, Emily. AB, Harvard U., 1947; MBA, U. Mich., 1949; MEd, Tufts U., 1950. Market analyst Govt. Commodity Exch., N.Y.C., 1952-54; market rsch. analyst Gen. Electric Co., 1954-55; corp. market analyst Amax Inc., N.Y.C., 1955-62, staff market mgr. aluminum group, 1962-65, pres. internat. aluminum div., 1965-70, v.p. 1970-71; exec. v.p. Amax Pacific Corp., San Mateo, Calif., 1971-72; exec. v.p., dir. Alumax Inc., San Mateo, 1973-82, pres., chief exec. officer, dir., 1982-86; ptnr. Am. Indsl. Ptnrs., San Francisco, 1987-92; dir. Saybrook Inst., 1992—; dir. Domtar, Montreal, 1984-90, Kaiser Aluminum Corp., 1990—. Trustee Mex. Mus., 1988-93. With USN, 1943-46. Mem. Japan Soc. (bd. dirs.). Clubs: Harvard (N.Y.C.); University, Commonwealth, (San Francisco). Home: 2700 Scott St San Francisco CA 94123-4637

MARCUS, ROBERT D., historian, educator; b. Bklyn., Jan. 14, 1936; s. Leonard Roger and Dorothy (Zimmerman) M.; m. Deborah Irene Weisstein, Aug. 13, 1961 (div. 1970); children: Anthony Allen, Elizabeth Sarah; m. Grania Bolton, Mar. 14, 1971 (div. 1989); children: Abigail Whitney, Benjamin Luke; m. Jill Gussow, Dec. 3, 1989; 1 child, Zora Marcus Gussow. B.A., Columbia U., 1957, M.A., 1963; postgrad. Oriel Coll., Oxford U., 1957-58; Ph.D., Northwestern U., 1967. Lectr. in history U. Bloomington, 1964-67; assist. prof. history SUNY-Stony Brook, 1967-71, assoc. prof., 1971-80, dean undergrad. studies, 1974-80; v.p. acad. affairs Rol-

lins Coll., Winter Park, Fla., 1980-83; v.p. acad. affairs SUNY-Brockport, 1983-92, prof. history, 1992—. Author: Grand Old Party, 1971, A Giant's Strength, 1971, A Brief History of the United States Since 1945, 1975, (with others) America: A Portrait in History, 1978, American Voices, 1992, American Firsthand, 3d edit., 1994. Social Sci. Research Council Faculty Research fellow, 1970; NEH grantee, 1969; Euretta J. Kellett fellow, 1957-58. Mem. Am. Hist. Assn., Orgn. Am. Historians, Phi Beta Kappa. Democrat. Office: State Coll Dept History Brockport NY 14420

MARCUS, RUDOLPH ARTHUR, chemist, educator; b. Montreal, Que., Can., July 21, 1923; came to U.S., 1949, naturalized, 1958; s. Myer and Esther (Cohen) M.; m. Laura Hearne, Aug. 27, 1949; children: Alan Rudolph, Kenneth Hearne, Raymond Arthur. BSc in Chemistry, McGill U., 1943, PhD in Chemistry, 1946, DSc (hon.), 1988; DSc (hon.), U. Chgo., 1983, Poly. U., 1986, U. Göteborg, Sweden, 1987, U. N.B., Can., 1993, Queens U., Can., 1993. Rsch. staff mem. RDX Project, Montreal, 1944-46; postdoctoral rsch. assoc. NRC of Can., Ottawa, Ont., 1946-49, U. N.C., 1949-51; asst. prof. Poly. Inst. Bklyn., 1951-54, assoc. prof., 1954-58, prof., 1958-64; prof. U. Ill., Urbana, 1964-78; Arthur Amos Noyes prof. chemistry Calif. Inst. Tech., Pasadena, 1978—; hon. prof. Fudan U., Shanghai, China, 1994—; hon. fellow U. Coll., Oxford, England, 1995—; mem. Courant Inst. Math. Scis., NYU, 1960-61; trustee Gordon Rsch. Confs., 1966-69, chmn. bd., 1968-69, mem. coun., 1965-68; mem. rev. panel Argonne Nat. Lab. 1966-72, chmn., 1967-68; mem. rev. panel Brookhaven Nat. Lab., 1971-74; mem. rev. com. Radiation Lab., U. Notre Dame, 1975-80; mem. panel on atmospheric chemistry climatic impact com. NAS-NRC, 1975-78, mem. com. kinetics of chem. reactions, 1973-77, chmn., 1975-77, mem. com. chem. scis., 1977-79, mem. com. to survey opportunities in chem. scis., 1982-86; adv. com. for chemistry NSF, 1977-80, external adv. bd. NSF Ctr. Photoinduced Charter Transfer, 1990—; vis. prof. theoretical chemistry U. Oxford, Eng., IBM, 1975-76; also professorial fellow Univ. Coll., 1995—. Former mem. editorial bd. Jour. Chem. Physics, Ann. Rev. Phys. Chemistry, Jour. Phys. Chemistry, Accounts Chem. Rsch., Internat. Jour. Chem. Kinetics Molecular Physics, Theoretica Chimica Acta, Chem. Physics Letters; mem. editorial bd. Laser Chemistry, 1982—, Advances in Chem. Physics, 1984—, World Sci. Pub., 1987—, Internat. Revs. in Phys. Chemistry, 1988—, Faraday Trans., Jour. Chem. Soc., 1990—, Progress in Physics, Chemistry and Mechanics (China), 1989—, Perkins Transactions 2, Jour. Chem. Soc., 1992—, Chem. Physics Rsch. (India), 1992—, Trends in Chem. Physics Rsch. (India), 1992—. Alfred P. Sloan fellow, 1960-61, sr. postdoctoral fellow NSF, 1960-61; sr. postdoctoral fellow NSF, 1960-61, sr. Fulbright-Hays scholar, 1972; recipient Sr. U.S. Scientist award Alexander von Humboldt-Stiftung, 1976, Electrochem. Soc. Lecture award Electrochem. Soc., 1979, Robinson medal Faraday divsn. Royal Soc. Chemistry, 1982, Centenary medal Faraday divsn., 1988, Chandler medal Columbia U., 1983, Wolf prize in Chemistry, 1985, Nat. Medal of Sci., 1989, Evans award Ohio State U., 1990, Nobel prize in Chemistry, 1992, Hirshfelder prize in Theoretical Chemistry, U. Wis., 1993, Golden Plate award Am. Acad. Achievement, 1993, Lavoisier medal French Chem. Soc., 1994; named Hon. Citizen, City of Winnipeg, 1994. Fellow AAAS (hon.), Am. Acad. Arts and Scis. (hon., exec. com. western sect., co-chmn. 1981-84, rsch. and planning com. 1989-91), Am. Phys. Soc., Internat. Soc. Electrochemistry (hon.), Royal Soc. Chemistry (hon.), Royal Soc. London (hon.), Internat. Acad. Quantum Molecular Sci. (hon.), Royal Soc. Can. (hon.); mem. NAS (hon.), Am. Philos. Soc. (hon.), Am. Chem. Soc. (past divsn. chmn., mem. exec. com., mem. adv. bd. petroleum rsch. fund, Irving Langmuir award Chem. Physics 1978, Peter Debye award Phys. Chemistry 1988, Williard Gibbs medal Chgo. sect. 1988, S.C. Lind Lecture, East Tenn. sect. 1988, Theodore William Richards medal Northeastern sect. 1990, Edgar Fahs Smith award Phila. sect. 1991, Ira Remsen Meml. award Md. sect. 1991, Pauling medal Portland, Oreg. and Puget Sound sect. 1991), Internat. Acad. Quantum Molecular Sci. Achievements include responsibility for the Marcus Theory of electron transfer reactions in chemical systems and RRKM theory of unimolecular reaction rates. Home: 331 S Hill Ave Pasadena CA 91106-3405

MARCUS, RUTH BARCAN, philosopher, educator, writer, lecturer; b. N.Y.C.; d. Samuel and Rose (Post) Barcan; divorced; children: James Spencer, Peter Webb, Katherine Hollister, Elizabeth Post. BA, NYU, 1941; MA, Yale U., 1942, PhD, 1946; LHD (hon.), U. Ill., 1995. Rsch. assoc. in anthropology Inst. for Human Relations, Yale U., New Haven, Conn., 1945-47; AAUW fellow, 1947-48; vis. prof. (intermittently) Northwestern U., 1950-57, Guggenheim fellow, 1953-54; asst. prof., assoc. prof. Roosevelt U., Chgo., 1957-63; NSF fellow, 1963-64; prof. philosophy U. Ill. at Chgo., 1964-70, head philosophy dept., 1963-69; fellow U. Ill. Center for Advanced Study, 1968-69; prof. philosophy Northwestern U., 1970-73; Reuben Post Halleck prof. philosophy Yale U., 1973—; fellow Ctr. Advanced Study in Behavioral Sci., Stanford, Calif., 1979; vis. fellow Inst. Advanced Study, U. Edinburgh, 1983, Wolfson Coll., Oxford U., 1985, 86; vis. fellow Clare Hall, Cambridge U., 1988, lifetime mem. common room, 1989—; past or present mem. adv. coms. Princeton U., MIT, Calif. Inst. Tech., Cornell U. Humanities Ctr., Columbia U., UCLA, others. Author: Modalities, 1993; editor: The Logical Enterprise, 1975, Logic Methodology and Philosophy of Science VII, 1986; mem. editorial bd. Past or Present Metaphilosophy, Monist, Philos. Studies, Signs, Jour. Symbolic Logic, The Philosophers Annual; editor, contbr. to profl. jours. and books. Recipient Machette prize for contbn. to profession; Medal, College de France, 1986; Mellon sr. fellow Nat. Humanities Ctr., 1992-93; vis. disting. prof. U. Calif., Irvine, 1994; fellow Conn. Acad. Arts & Scis. Fellow Am. Acad. Arts and Scis.; mem. Coun. on Philos. Studies (pres. 1988—), Assn. for Symbolic Logic (past exec. coun., exec. com. 1973-83, v.p. 1980-82, pres. 1981-83, coun. 1983-85, pres. 1982-85), Am. Philos. Assn. (past sect., treas., nat. bd. dirs. 1967-83, pres. ctrl. divsn. 1975-76, chmn. nat. bd. officers 1977-83), Philosophy of Sci. Assn., Institut Internat. de Philosophie (past exec. com., v.p. 1983-86, pres. 1990-93, pres. hon. 1994—), Fedn. Internat. de Philosophie (exec. com., steering com. 1985—), Elizabethan Club (v.p. 1989, pres. 1989-90), Phi Beta Kappa (professorial lectr. 1993). Office: Yale U Dept Philosophy PO Box 3650 New Haven CT 06525-0650

MARCUS, SHELDON, social sciences educator; b. N.Y.C., Aug. 4, 1937; s. Manny and Sarah (Lande) M.; m. Phyllis Knight; children: Beth, Jonathan, Evan. B.A., CCNY, 1959, M.S., 1960; Ed.D., Yeshiva U., 1970. Tchr. N.Y.C. Pub. Schs., 1959-68; lectr. social sci. CUNY, 1965-68; mem. faculty Fordham U., N.Y.C., 1968-70, chmn. div. urban edn., 1970-76, assoc. dean grad. edn. Tarrytown campus, 1976-93, prof., 1993—; mem. exec. bd. tchr. corps program U.S. Office Edn., 1974-82; trustee Doctoral Assn. N.Y., 1973-82; co-dir. Fordham Inst. for Rsch. on Supervision and Teaching, 1992-94. Author or co-author: Conflicts in Urban Education, 1970; Urban Education: Crisis or Opportunity?, 1972; Father Coughlin: The Tumultuous Life of the Priest of the Little Flower, 1973, (nominated for Pulitzer Prize); The Urban In-Service Education Experience, 1977; Administrative Decision Making in Schools: A Case Study Approach to Strategic Planning, 1986, Strategic Planning: A Case Study Approach to Administrative Decision Making. Case Teaching Notes, 1987; contbr. articles to profl. jours. Recipient Scanlon award for contbns. to edn., 1992, Admnstr. of Yr. award Phi Delta Kappa, 1993. Mem. Am. Ednl. Rsch. Assn. (proposal reviewer 1992—). Home: 36 Pocantico River Rd Pleasantville NY 10570-3510 Office: Fordham U Sch Edn Tarrytown Campus Tarrytown NY 10591

MARCUS, STANLEY, federal judge; b. 1946. BA, CUNY, 1967; JD, Harvard U., 1971. Assoc. Botein, Hays, Sklar & Herzberg, N.Y.C., 1974-75; asst. atty. U.S. Dist. Ct. (ea. dist.) N.Y., 1975-78; spl. atty., dep. chief U.S. organized crime sect. Detroit Strike Force, 1978-79, chief U.S. organized crime sect., 1980-82; U.S. atty. So. Dist. of Fla., Miami, 1982-85; judge U.S. Dist. Ct. (so. dist.) Fla., Miami, 1985—. Office: US Dist Ct 301 N Miami Ave Miami FL 33128-7701

MARCUS, STEPHEN A., lawyer; b. Chgo., Nov. 25, 1943. BS, U. Ill., 1965; JD, Northwestern U., 1968. Bar: Ill. 1968. Ptnr. Holleb & Coff, Chgo. Mem. ABA (mem. bus. law sect.), Chgo. Bar Assn. (mem. securities law com.), Chgo. Coun. Lawyers. Office: Holleb & Coff 55 East Monroe St Ste 4100 Chicago IL 60603

MARCUS, STEPHEN HOWARD, hospitality and entertainment company executive; b. Mpls., May 31, 1935; s. Ben D. and Celia Marcus; m. Joan Glasspiegel, Nov. 3, 1962; children: Greg, David, Andrew. B.B.A., U. Wis. Madison, 1957; LL.B., U. Mich., 1960. Bar: Wis. 1960. V.p. Pfister Hotel

Corp., Milw., 1963-69; exec. v.p. Pfister Hotel Corp., 1969-75; pres. Marcus Hotel Corp., Milw., 1975-91; chmn., chief oper. officer Marcus Corp., Milw., 1980—; chief oper. officer Marcus Corp., 1988, also dir.; exec. v.p. Marc Plaza Corp.; v.p. Wis. Big Boy Corp., Marcus Theatres Corp.; dir. Med. Coll. Wis., 1986—; dir. Preferred Hotels Assn., 1972—, chmn. bd., 1979; dir. Bank One N.A. Pres. Milw. Conv. and Visitors Bur., 1970-71, bd. dirs. mem. exec. com., 1968—; chmn. Wis. Gov.'s Adv. Council on Tourism, 1976-81; bd. dirs. Multiple Sclerosis Soc. Milw., 1965-67, Milw. Jewish Fedn., 1968-76, Milw. Jewish Chronicle, 1973-76, Children's Hosp. Found., Inc., Competitive Wis.; assoc. chmn. bus. div. United Fund Campaign, Milw. 1971; co-chmn. spl. gifts com. United Performing Arts Fund, Milw., 1972-74, bd. dirs., 1973-81, chmn. maj. gifts, 1982, co-chmn., 1983—; bd. dirs. Friends of Art, Milw., 1973-74; pres. Summerfest, 1975; bd. dirs. MECCA, Milw., 1975-82, mem. exec. com., 1977; bd. dirs. Jr. Achievement, Milw. 1976—; trustee Mt. Sinai Med. Center, 1977—, Nat. Symphony Orchestra, 1985; bd. govs. Jewish Community Campus; co-chmn. Ann. Freedom Fund Dinner, NAACP, 1980-81; chmn. Icebreaker Festival, 1989. Served with U.S. Army, 1960-61. Recipient Ben Nickoll award Milw. Jewish Fedn., 1969, Headliner award Milw. Press Club, 1986, Humanitarian award NCCJ, 1988, Lamplighter award Greater Milw. Conv. and Visitors Bur., 1991. Mem. Am. Hotel and Motel Assn. (dir. 1976-79, exec. com. 1978-79), Greater Milw. Hotel and Motel Assn. (pres. 1967-68), Wis. Innkeepers Assn. (pres. 1972-73), Variety Club, Milw. Assn. Commerce (bd. dirs. 1982-85), Downtown Assn., Young Pres.'s Orgn., Wis. Assn. Mfrs. and Commerce (dir. 1978-82), Greater Milw. Com. (dir. 1981). Office: The Marcus Corporation 250 E Wisconsin Ave Ste 1170 Milwaukee WI 53202-4208

MARCUS, STEVEN, dean, English educator; b. N.Y.C., Dec. 13, 1928; s. Nathan and Adeline Muriel (Gordon) M.; m. Gertrud Lenzer, Jan. 20, 1966; 1 son, John Nathaniel. Ph.D., Columbia U., 1961; D.H.L. (hon.), Clark U., 1985. Prof. English Columbia U., 1966—, George Delacorte prof. humanities, 1976—, chmn. dept. English and comparative lit., 1977-80, 85-90; v.p. Sch. of Arts and Scis., 1993—; dean Columbia Coll., 1993—; dir. planning Nat. Humanities Center, 1974-76; chmn. exec. com. bd. dirs. Nat. Humanities Ctr., 1976-80, also bd. dirs.; chmn. Lionel Trilling Seminars, 1976-80. Author: Dickens: From Pickwick to Dombey, 1965, The Other Victorians, 1966, Engels, Manchester and the Working Class, 1974, Representations, 1976, Doing Good, 1978, Freud and The Culture of Psychoanalysis, 1984; Assoc. editor: Partisan Rev. Co-dir. Heyman Ctr. for the Humanities. With AUS, 1954-56. Guggenheim Found. fellow, 1967-68; Nat. Humanities Ctr. fellow, 1980-82; Rockefeller Found. fellow in humanities, 1980-81; fellow Ctr. Advanced Studies in the Behavioral Scis., 1972-73. Fellow Am. Acad. Arts and Scis., Acad. Lit. Studies; mem. Columbia Soc. Fellows in Humanities (co-chmn.), Am. Psychoanalytic Assn. (hon.), Inst. for Psychoanalytic Tng. and Rsch. (hon.), Am. Acad. Psychoanalysis (sci. assoc.). Home: 39 Claremont Ave New York NY 10027-6824

MARCUS, STEVEN IRL, electrical engineering educator; b. St. Louis, Apr. 2, 1949; s. Herbert A. and Peggy L. (Polishuk) M.; m. Jeanne M. Wilde, June 4, 1978; children: Jeremy A., Tobin L. BA, Rice U., 1971; SM, MIT, 1972, PhD, 1975. Research engr. The Analytic Scis. Corp., Reading, Mass., 1973; asst. prof. U. Tex., Austin, 1975-80, assoc. prof., 1980-84, prof., 1984-91, assoc. chmn., dept. elec. and computer engring., 1984-89, L.B. Meaders prof. engring., 1987-91; prof. elec. engring., dir. Inst. for Systems Rsch. U. Md., College Park, 1991—; cons. Tracor Inc., Austin, 1977, 90. Assoc. editor Math. of Control Signals and Systems, 1987—, Jour. on Discrete Event Dynamic Systems, 1990—, Acta Applicandae Mathematicae, 1983—. NSF fellow, 1971-74; Werner W. Dornberger Centennial Teaching fellowship in engring., U. Tex., Austin, 1982-84. Fellow IEEE (prize paper awards com. 1985-88, field awards com. 1989-90, assoc. editor Transactions Info. Theory 1990-92), IEEE Control Systems Soc. (bd. govs. 1985-90, chmn. conf. on decision and control program com. 1983, chmn. working group on stochastic control and estimation 1984-87, assoc. editor Transactions Automatic Control 1980-81); mem. Am. Math. Soc., Soc. Indsl. and Applied Math. (editor Jour. Control and Optimization 1990—), Soc. Applicandae Math., 1983—, Eta Kappa Nu, Tau Beta Pi. Home: 9516 Thornhill Rd Silver Spring MD 20901-4836 Office: U Md Inst for Systems Rsch 2167 Av Williams Bldg 115 College Park MD 20742

MARCUS, WALTER F., JR., state supreme court justice; b. New Orleans, July 26, 1927; married; children: Walter III, Adam, Barbara Ann. B.A., Yale U.; J.D., Tulane U. Bar: La. 1955. Mem. New Orleans City Council, 1962-66; judge Civil Dist. Ct., 1966-73; assoc. justice Supreme Ct. La., 1973—. Mem. ABA. Office: Supreme Ct La 301 Loyola Ave New Orleans LA 70112-1800

MARCUS, WILLIAM MICHAEL, rubber and vinyl products manufacturing company executive; b. Boston, Jan. 31, 1938; s. Richard and Diana (Litch) M.; m. Cynthia Steinman, Dec. 9, 1962; children: Melanie, Daniel, Richard. B.S. in Bus. Administrn., Babson Inst., 1959. With Am. Biltrite Inc., Wellesley Hills, Mass., 1960—; exec. v.p., treas. Am. Biltrite Inc., 1983—, also dir.; bd. dirs. Reebok Internat. Inc., Congoleum Corp. Served with U.S. Army, 1960-61. Office: Am Biltrite Inc 57 River St Wellesley MA 02181-2006

MARCUSA, FRED HAYE, lawyer; b. Paterson, N.J., Jan. 31, 1946; s. Harry and Alice Marcusa; m. Andrea Disario, Jun. 28, 1986; children: Michael, Daniel. A.B., Dartmouth Coll., 1967; J.D., U. Pa., 1970. Bar: N.Y. 1971. Assoc. Davis, Polk & Wardwell, N.Y.C., 1970-79; v.p., gen. counsel The Coca-Cola Bottling Co. of N.Y., Inc., N.Y.C., 1979-81; ptnr. Kaye, Scholer, Fierman, Hays & Handler, N.Y.C., 1981—. Office: Kaye Scholer Fierman Hays & Handler 425 Park Ave New York NY 10022

MARCUSE, ADRIAN GREGORY, college administrator; b. N.Y.C., Mar. 25, 1922; s. Maxwell Frederick and Mildred Ann (Hitter) M.; m. Janet Constance Radlo, Oct. 28, 1945 (dec. Mar. 22, 1980); children: Nancy Ruth Marcuse Marshall, Sally Ann Marcuse Crawford, Elizabeth Susan; m. Betty Jane Lieberman Bergman, Jan. 11, 1985; 1 stepchild, Amy Beth Rossman Schurtz. BS, MIT, 1942, MS, 1946; LLD (hon.), Lab Inst. Merchandising, 1992. Registered profl. engr. N.Y., Fla. Rsch. assoc. MIT, Cambridge, Mass., 1945-46; rsch. scientist United Aircraft Co., E. Hartford, Conn., 1946-47; application engr. Westinghouse Electric Corp., Boston, N.Y.C., 1947-60; consulting engr. pvt. practice, N.Y.C., 1955-62; v.p. mktg. and sales Corrosion Control Corp., N.Y.C., 1960-62; sales & merchandising mgr. B. Altman & Co., N.Y.C., 1962; v.p-c., chief operating officer Lab. Inst. of Merchandising, N.Y.C., 1962-72, pres., chief exec. officer, 1972—; pres. LIM Fashion Edn. Found., N.Y.C., 1978—; chmn. Assn. Regionally Accredited Prvt. Colls. and Univs., Washington, 1990-93. Charter commr. City of Glen Cove, N.Y., 1964, chmn. bd. engrs., 1964-68, mem. planning bd., 1980-87; past treas. Community Concert Assn., Glen Cove; past trustee and budget chmn. North Country Reform Temple, Glen Cove; past mem: YMCA Fund-Raising Coun., Glen Cove. 1st lt. USAAF, 1942-45, PTO. Mem. Am. Assn. Higher Edn., Nat. Assn. Coll. Admissions Counselors, Assn. Proprietary Colls. (former pres., chmn.), N.Y. State Assn. Two-Yr. Colls., N.Y. State Counselors Assn., Soc. Sigma Xi. Republican. Avocations: sailing, bicycling, travel, theater. Office: Lab Inst of Merchandising 12 E 53rd St New York NY 10022-5208

MARCUSE, DIETRICH, retired physicist; b. Koenigsberg, East Prussia, Germany, Feb. 27, 1929; came to U.S., 1957; s. Richard and Gertrud (Solty) M.; m. Haide Schwarz, Jan. 13, 1959; children: Christina, Mikel. Diplom Physiker, Freie Universität, Berlin, 1954; Doktor Ingenieur, Karlsruhe Universität, 1962. Mem. tech. staff Siemens and Halske, Berlin, 1954-57; mem. tech. staff AT&T Bell Labs., Holmdel, N.J., 1957-94, dist. mem. tech. staff, 1982-94; ret., 1994. Author: Principles of Quantum-Electronics, 2d edit., 1980, Light Transmission Optics, 2d edit., 1982, Theory of Dielectric Optical Wave-guides, 1972, 2nd edit., 1991, Principles of Optical Fiber Measurements, 1981; also over 200 articles. Fellow IEEE (Quantum Electronics award 1981), Optical Soc. Am. (Max Born award 1989).

MARCUSE, MANFRED JOACHIM, paper products executive; b. Berlin, Apr. 17, 1927; came to U.S., 1947, naturalized, 1951; s. Bruno and Hedwig Elisabeth (Ettling) M.; m. Charlotte Kraemer, Sept. 23, 1950. Grad. high sch., Berlin. Export clk. ERICO Corp., N.Y.C., 1947-49; sales rep. Roseda Mills, Buffalo, 1950, various companies, 1953-58; systems engr. Nebr. Salesbook Co., Lincoln, 1958-64; prin., owner, pres. Marc Bus. Forms Inc.,

Chgo., 1964—. Contbr. articles to profl. jours. Supporting mem. Selfhelp Home for the Aged, Chgo., 1988—, Chgo. Symphony, Lyric Opera, Chgo. United Jewish Appeal. With U.S. Army, 1951-52. Jewish. Office: Marc Business Forms Inc 2722-26 W Peterson Ave Chicago IL 60659

MARCUSS, STANLEY JOSEPH, lawyer; b. Hartford, Conn., Jan. 24, 1942; s. Stanley Joseph and Anne Sutton (Leone) M.; m. Rosemary Daly, July 6, 1968; children: Elena Daly, Aidan Stanley. BA, Trinity Coll., 1963, Cambridge U., 1965; MA, Cambridge U., 1968; JD, Harvard U., 1968. Bar: D.C., N.Y., Conn., U.S. Supreme Ct. Staff atty. office of gen. counsel HUD, Washington, 1968; atty. firm Hogan and Hartson, Washington, 1968-73; counsel to internat. fin. subcom. U.S. Senate Com. on Banking, Housing and Urban Affairs, 1977-78; dep. asst. sec. for trade regulation Dept. Commerce, Washington, 1977-78; sr. dep. asst. sec. for industry and trade Dept. Commerce, 1978-79, acting asst. sec. for industry and trade, 1979-80, acting asst. sec. for trade regulation, 1980; mem. firm Milbank, Tweed, Hadley & McCloy, Washington, 1980-93, Bryan Cave, 1993—; former adj. prof. Am. U. Law Sch. Author: Effective Washington Representation, 1983; mem. bd. overseers U. Calif. Berkeley Law Jour.; contbr. articles to profl. jours. Former trustee Trinity Coll., Hartford. Marshall scholar. Mem. ABA, D.C. Bar (former chmn., steering com. internat. law div.), Phi Beta Kappa. Home: 4616 29th Pl NW Washington DC 20008-2105

MARCUVITZ, NATHAN, electrophysics educator; b. Bklyn., Dec. 29, 1913; s. Samuel and Rebecca (Feiner) M.; m. Muriel Spanier, June 30, 1946; children—Andrew, Karen. B.E.E., Poly. Inst. Bklyn., 1935, M.E.E., 1941, D.E.E., 1947; Laurea Honoris Causa, Politecnico Di Torino, 1993. Engr. RCA Labs., 1936-40; research assoc. Radiation Lab., Mass. Inst. Tech., 1941-46; asst. prof. elec. engring. Poly. Inst. Bklyn., 1946-49, asso. prof., 1949-51, prof., 1951-65; dir. Poly. Inst. Bklyn. (Microwave Research Inst.), 1957-61; v.p. research, acting dean Poly. Inst. Bklyn. (Grad. Center), 1961-63, prof. electrophysics, 1961-66, dean research, dean, 1964-65; asst. dir. def. research and engring. Dept. Def., Washington, 1963-64; prof. applied physics N.Y.U., 1966-73; prof. electrophysics Poly. Inst. N.Y., 1973—, prof. emeritus, 1978—; vis. prof. Harvard U., spring 1971. Author: Waveguide Handbook, Vol. 10, 1951, (with L. Felsen) Radiation and Scattering of Waves, 1973; also numerous articles. Recipient Microwave Career award IEEE Microwave Theory and Techniques Soc., 1985. Fellow IEEE (Heinrich Hertz medal 1989); mem. Nat. Acad. Engring., Am. Phys. Soc., Sigma Xi, Tau Beta Pi, Eta Kappa Nu. Home: 7 Ridge Dr E Great Neck NY 11021-2806 Office: Polytech U RR 11 Farmingdale NY 11735

MARCY, CHARLES FREDERICK, food products company executive; b. Buffalo, Aug. 25, 1950; s. Charles and Mary Jane (Frederick) M.; m. Helen Jean Shank, May 6, 1972 (div. Dec. 1986); children: Michelle Catherine, Adam Charles; m. Cynthia Louise Shockey, June 17, 1989; 1 child, Brooke Allison. BA, Washington and Jefferson Coll., Washington, Pa., 1972; MBA, Harvard U., 1974. Various mktg. and strategic planning positions Gen. Foods Corp., White Plains, N.Y., 1974-84; v.p. mktg. Sara Lee Bakery, Deerfield, Ill., 1984-86; v.p., gen. mgr. Wolferman's Inc., (Divsn. of Sara Lee Corp.), Lenexa, Kans., 1987-89; v.p. strategy and mktg. Kraft Gen. Foods Frozen Products, Glenview, Ill., 1989-90; pres. Kraft Gen. Foods Nat. Dairy Products Corp., Phila., 1991-92, Golden Grain Co., Pleasanton, Calif., 1993—. Bd. dirs. Phila. Police Athletic League, 1991-92, Boys and Girls Club of Kansas City, Mo., 1987-90, Lake Forest (Ill.) Symphony, 1984-87. Office: Golden Grain Co 4576 Willow Rd Pleasanton CA 94588

MARDAR, DIANNA, reporter; b. Phila., May 1, 1948. BA in Journalism summa cum laude, Temple U., 1984. Reporter city desk The Philadelphia Inquirer, 1985—; instr. Temple U., Phila., 1992. Recipient George Polk award Long Island U., 1990, Nat. Headliners award Atlantic City Press Assn., investigative, 1990, Investigative Editors and Reporters award reporting call, 1990. Office: Phila Inquirer 400 N Broad St Philadelphia PA 19101

MARDEN, JOHN NEWCOMB, lawyer; b. N.Y.C., Feb. 14, 1935; s. Orison S. and Virginia (McAvoy) M.; children: Cynthia, Elizabeth; m. Anne Roberts. BA, Yale U., 1957; LLB, Cornell U., 1960. Bar: N.Y. 1960. Assoc. Curtis, Mallet Prevost Colt & Mosle, N.Y.C., 1960-69, ptnr., 1969—. Republican. Office: Curtis Mallet Prevost Colt & Mosle 101 Park Ave New York NY 10178-0061

MARDEN, KENNETH ALLEN, advertising executive; b. Englewood, N.J., Dec. 12, 1928; s. Allen H. and Doris (Littlefield) M.; m. Julia Lee Black, June 11, 1949; children—Priscilla Anne, Emily Gage. B.A., U. Maine, 1950. Hosp. salesman Johnson & Johnson, New Brunswick, N.J., 1959-61, product dir. hosp. div., 1962-68, advt., pub. relations mgr. hosp. div., 1969-71, group product dir., patient care div., 1972-74, advt. dir. patient care div., 1974-78; v.p. E.J. Axelrod, Inc., N.Y.C., 1978-80; v.p. account mgmt. Vicom/FCB, Phila., 1980-87; pres. Am. Kennel Club, N.Y., 1987-90, cons. on dog legislation, 1990—, also bd. dirs.; pres. Crossing Creek Communications, 1991—. 1st lt. U.S. Army, 1951-53. Mem. DogWriters Assn. Am. Republican. Episcopalian. Clubs: German Shorthaired Pointer of Am. (del. 1976—, v.p. 1985-86), Denver; Eastern German Shorthaired Pointer (pres. 1972-74), Millville, N.J., Jersey Rag Racers, Middletown, Del., (pres. 1994—), Kennel Club Phila. (bd. dirs.), Hunterdon Hills Kennel, Flemington, N.J., Nat. Animal Interext Alliance, Portland, Oreg., (bd. dirs. 1994—). Home: Crossing Creek Farm 53 Nedsland Ave Titusville NJ 08560 Office: Crossing Creek Communications 53 Nedsland Ave Titusville NJ 08560-1715

MARDEN, PHILIP AYER, physician, educator; b. Newport, N.H., Oct. 31, 1911; s. Albion Sullivan and Laura Isobel (McEchern) M.; m. Magdalen Rekus, Aug. 5, 1950. A.B., Dartmouth, 1933; student, Med. Sch., 1933-34; M.D., U. Pa., 1936. Intern Presbyn. Hosp., Phila., 1936-38; chief resident Delaware County Hosp., Drexel Hill, Pa., 1938-39; fellow otolaryngology U. Pa. Hosp., 1939-40, chief otolaryngology, 1959-72; mem. faculty U. Pa. Med. Sch., 1940—, prof. dept. otolaryngology, 1959—; chief otolaryngology, div. A Phila. Gen. Hosp., 1959-94; emeritus prof. dept. otolaryngology U. Pa. Med. Sch., 1994—; cons. Presbyn. Hosp., Phila., VA Hosp., Phila., Phila. Gen. Hosp. Served to maj., M.C. AUS, 1942-46, CBI. Mem. AMA, Am. Acad. Ophthalmology and Otolaryngology, A.C.S., Coll. Physicians Phila., Phi Beta Kappa, Sigma Xi. Home: 163 Vassar Rd Bala Cynwyd PA 19004-2135

MARDENBOROUGH, LESLIE A., newspaper publishing company executive. V.p. human resources The New York Times Co. Office: The New York Times Co 229 W 43d St New York NY 10036-3959*

MARDER, JOHN G., real estate investor, marketing consultant, corporate director; b. N.Y.C., Dec. 27, 1926; s. Joseph T. and Rhea (Greenspun) M.; m. Barbara Sand, 1956 (div. 1971); children: Jonathan Allen, Susan Beth, Jane Allison; m. Joan Kron, 1971. Student, Cornell, 1944-45; B.S., Columbia U. Sch. Bus., 1950. Merchandising exec. Macy's, N.Y.C., 1951-56; exec. v.p. Grey Advt. Inc., N.Y.C., 1956-86; real estate investor-developer Miami Beach, Anguilla B.W.I., 1986—; bd. dirs. several profit, not-for-profit and ednl. corps. Served as radio officer U.S. Maritime Service, U.S. Army Transport Service, 1945-46; 2d lt. Q.M.C. U.S. Army, 1951-53. Home: 205 E 63rd St New York NY 10021 also: 18 Hedges Banks Dr East Hampton NY 11937-3505

MARDER, MICHAEL ZACHARY, dentist, researcher, educator; b. N.Y.C., Aug. 30, 1938; s. Joseph Theodore and Rhea (Greenspun) M.; (widowed); children: Sherri Ellen, Robert Whitney. Student, Tufts U., 1959; D.D.S., Columbia U., 1963. Diplomate: Am. Bd. Oral Medicine. Practice dentistry N.Y.C., 1963-66, 68—; asst. Sch. Dental and Oral Surgery, Columbia U., N.Y.C., 1963-66, instr., 1968, asst. clin. prof., 1968-72, assoc. clin. prof., 1972-76, clin. prof. dentistry, 1976—, researcher, 1963—; dir. oral medicine, 1972-84, dir. clin. cancer tng., 1993—; asst. attending dental surgeon Presbyn. Hosp., 1972-76; assoc. attending dentist, 1976-82, attending dentist, 1982—; cons. Good Samaritan Hosp., Suffern, N.Y.; lectr. in field. Author 2 textbooks in dental medicine; contbr. chpts. to med. and dental textbooks, articles to profl. jours. Served to capt. U.S. Army, 1966-68. Recipient Cert. of Achievement U.S. Army, 1968. Fellow N.Y. Acad. Dentistry; mem. ADA, Internat. Assn. Dental Rsch., Am. Acad. Oral

Medicine, Frist Dist. Dental Soc. N.Y., Omicron Kappa Upsilon, Sigma Xi. Office: 119 W 57th St New York NY 10019-2303

MARDIAN, DANIEL, construction company director; b. Pasadena, Calif., Apr. 10, 1917; s. Samuel and Akabe (Lekerian) M.; m. Katherine Evkhanian, Jan. 30, 1942; children: Daniel Jr., Tom, John, Paul, Scott. Student, Pasadena City Coll., 1937; diploma, U.S. Army Engring. Sch., Ft. Belvoir, Va., 1944, U.S. Army Command and Gen. Staff Coll., 1961. Commd. U.S. Army, 1942, advances through grades to lt. col., 1962, ret., 1970; ptnr. Mardian Constrn. Co., Phoenix, 1945-47, exec. v.p., 1947-66, pres., 1966-78, also bd. dirs.; past chmn., mem. Nat. Joint Apprenticeship/Tng. Commn. Oper. Engrs., Washington, 1975-78; mem. adv. bd. constrn. programs Ariz. State U., Tempe, 1957—, mem. adv. bd. coll. engring., 1957—; bd. dirs. Citibank, Phoenix, 1962-87. Pres. Am. Coun. Constrn. Edn., Monroe, La., 1991-93; past pres., bd. dirs. Fiesta Bowl, Tempe, 1986-92; gen. campaign chmn. United Way, Phoenix, 1967; pres. Met. Phoenix C. of C., 1967-68. Capt. C.E., U.S. Army, 1942-46, PTO, 1970—. Recipient Hall of Fame Award Ariz. State U., 1990, Excellence in Constrn. Award Am. Subcontractors Assn., 1988, Hall of Fame Award Nat. Football Found., 1987, Brotherhood Award Ariz. chpt. Nat. Conf. Christians and Jews, 1981. Mem. Associated Gen. Contractors Am. (life bd. dirs., chmn. yr. award 1970, mem. manpower tng. com., laborers tng. com., 1969—), Sun Angel Found. (chmn. 1989-91), Ariz. Acad., Phoenix Country Club (bd. dirs., pres. 1985-86), Phoenix Kiwanis Club (past dir.). Republican. Mem. United Ch. Christ. Avocations: golfing, fishing. Home: 7215 N 3rd St Phoenix AZ 85020-4904 Office: Perini Building Co 360 E Coronado Rd Phoenix AZ 85004-1524

MARE, ROBERT DENIS, sociology educator, demography researcher. BA in Sociology, Reed Coll., 1973; MA in Sociology, U. Mich., 1974, PhD, 1977. Rsch. asst.- trainee Populations Study Ctr. U. Mich., Ann Arbor, 1973-77; from asst. prof. to prof. dept. sociology U. Wis., Madison, 1977—; dir. Ctr. Demography and Ecology, 1988-94; fellow Ctr. Advanced Study in Behavioral Scis., 1983-84; project assoc. Ctr. for Demography and Ecology, U. Wis., 1977-83; site visitor Nat. Inst. Child Health and Human Devel., 1991, 93; mem. panel Nat. Rsch. Coun., 1993—; vis. sr. sociologist RAND, Santa Monica, Calif., 1994—; presenter in field. Dep. editor Demography, 1978-81; mem. editl. bd. Am. Jour. Sociology, 1978-80, Sociology of Edn., 1982-84, Sociol. Methodology, 1983-87, Sociol. Methods and Rsch., 1984-87, Jour. Am. Statis. Assn., 1984-85; contbr. articles to profl. jours. John Simon Guggenheim Meml. fellow, 1994—; Rsch. grantee NSF, U.S. Dept. Labor, Nat. Inst. Child and Human Devel., U.S. Dept. Def., Nat. Inst. Aging, Dept. Health and Human Svcs., William and Flora Hewlett Found., Russell Sage Found. Mem. Am. Sociol. Assn. (rep. to sect. U of AAAS 1993—), Population Assn. Am. (mem. Dorothy Swaine Thomas Award com. 1994—), Sociol. Rsch. Assn., Phi Beta Kappa. Office: U Wis Madison 4412 Social Sci Bldg 1180 Observatory Dr Madison WI 53706

MARECEK, JEANNE ANN, psychologist; b. Berwyn, Ill., May 28, 1946; d. Frank J. and Josephine (Serio) M. BS, Loyola U., Chgo., 1968; MS, Yale U., 1971, PhD, 1973. From asst. prof. to prof. psychology Swarthmore (Pa.) Coll., 1972—, chmn. dept., 1986-91, 94-95; Fulbright sr. lectr., Sri Lanka, 1988. Co-author: Making a Difference: Psychology and the Construction of Gender; contbr. numerous articles to profl. jours. and chpts. to books. Bd. dirs. Women in Transition, Phila., 1980-86; vice patron Nest, Hendala, Sri Lanka. Various fed. research grants. Mem. APA, Ea. Psychol. Assn., Assn. for Asian Studies. Office: Swarthmore Coll Dept Psychology 500 College Ave Swarthmore PA 19081

MAREE, WENDY, painter, sculptor; b. Windsor, Eng., Feb. 10, 1938. Student, Windsor & Maidenhead Coll., 1959; studied with Vasco Lazzlo, London, 1959-62. Exhibited at Windsor Arts Festival, San Bernardino (Calif.) Mus.; exhibited in one woman show Lake Arrowhead (Calif.) Libr., 1989, Amnesty Internat., Washington, 1990, Phyllis Morris Gallery, Many Horses Gallery, L.A., 1990, Nelson Rockefeller, Palm Springs, Calif., 1992, Stewart Gallery, Rancho Palos Verdes, Calif., Petropavlovsk (Russia) Cultural Mus., Kamchatka, Russia, 1993, Nelson Rockefeller Gallery, Palm Springs, Calif., 1994, Coyle-Coyle Gallery, Blue Jay, Calif., 1995, La Quinta Sculpture Park, Calif, 1995; numerous others; represented in pvt. collections His Royal Highness Prince Faisal, Saudi Arabia, Gena Rowlands, L.A., John Cassavetes, L.A., Nicky Blairs, L.A., Guilford Glazer, Beverly Hills, Calif., June Allyson, Ojai, Calif., Amnesty Internat., Washington. Recipient award San Bernardino County Mus., 1988, Gov. Kamchatka of Russia, 1993. Mem. Artist Guild of Lake Arrowhead. Address: 246 Saturmino Dr Palm Springs CA 92262

MAREK, VLADIMIR, ballet director, educator; b. Uzhorod, Czechoslovakia, Sept. 26, 1928; came to U.S., 1969; s. Jaroslav and Julia (Valkova) Sourek. Student Bus. Acad., Czechoslovakia, ballet schs., Czechoslovakia, 1945-47. Soloist Nat. Theater Ballet, Prague, Czechoslovakia, 1947-50, prin. dancer, Bratislava, Czechoslovakia, 1950-69, ballet master, 1958-68; ballet tchr. Our Lady of Lake U., San Antonio, 1970-78; owner, tchr. V. Marek Ballet Acad., San Antonio, 1970—; founder, artistic dir. San Antonio Ballet, 1970—. Home: 212 E Mulberry Ave San Antonio TX 78212 Office: San Antonio Ballet 212 E Mulberry Ave San Antonio TX 78212-3041

MARELLA, PHILIP DANIEL, broadcasting company executive; b. Italy, Sept. 9, 1929; came to U.S. 1930; s. T Joseph and Julia (Santolina) M.; m. Lucinda Minor, Dec. 30, 1955; children: Philip Daniel, Laura Ann, William Scott. BS, Calif. State U., 1955; MS, Syracuse U., 1956. Account exec. WGR-TV, Buffalo, 1956-57; account exec., sales mgr. WIIC-TV, Pitts., 1957-66; gen. mgr. WCHS-TV, Charleston, W.va., 1966-68; v.p. radio and television Rollins, Inc., Atlanta, 1968-70; pres. WAVY-TV, Inc., Tidewater, Va., 1970—; v.p. ops. Lin Broadcasting, Inc., N.Y.C.; also dir.; pres., owner WMGC-TV, Binghamton, N.Y., 1978—; chief exec. officer, pres. Pinnacle Communications, Inc., 1987—; chief exec. officer Pinnacle Broadcasting Co., 1987; owner radio stas. WFXC-FM/WDUR, Raleigh, N.C., WRNS-AM-FM, Coastal, N.C., WYAV-FM, Myrtle Beach, S.C., KAMZ-FM/KAMA, El Paso, Tex., KLLL-AM-FM, Lubbock, Tex., WYNG-FM, Evansville, Ind., WSOY-AM-FM, Decatur, Ill. Bd. dirs. Salvation Army, 1966-68; bd. dirs., v.p. United Fund; bd. dirs. Portsmouth chpt. ARC, Tidewater Regional Health and Planning Commn.; bd. dirs., v.p. Binghamton Symphony. Served with USMC, 1948-49, 50-52. Mem. Nat. Assn. Broadcasters (v.p.), Va. Assn. Broadcasters, Variety Club Pitts., Radio and TV Club, Portsmouth C. of C. (pres. elect), Norfolk C. of C., Newport News C. of C. Clubs: Cavalier Golf and Yacht (Virginia Beach, Va.); N.Y. Athletic. Home: 2073 Cheshire Rd Binghamton NY 13903-3107 also: Central Pk Pl 301 W 57th St #43C New York NY 10019 Office: 331 W 57th St Ste 288 New York NY 10019-3101

MARELLI, SISTER M. ANTHONY, secondary school principal. Prin. Boylan Ctrl. Cath. High Sch. Rockford, Ill. Recipient Blue Ribbon Sch. award U.S. Dept. Edn., 1990-91. Office: Boylan Ctrl Cath High Sch 4000 Saint Francis Dr Rockford IL 61103-1699

MARES, MICHAEL ALLEN, ecologist, educator; b. Albuquerque, Mar. 11, 1945; s. Ernesto Gustavo and Rebecca Gabriela (Devine) M.; m. Lynn Ann Brusin, Aug. 27, 1966; children: Gabriel Andres, Daniel Alejandro. BS in Biology, U. N.Mex., 1967; MS, Ft. Hays Kans. State U., 1969; PhD, U. Tex.-Austin, 1973. Adj. prof. U. Nacional de Cordoba, Argentina, 1971-72; adj. prof. U. Nacional de Tucuman, Argentina, 1972, vis. prof., 1974; from asst. to assoc. prof. U. Pitts., 1973-81; vis. scientist U. Ariz., Tucson, 1980-81; assoc. prof., curator mammals U. Okla., Norman, 1981-83, dir. Okla. Mus. Nat. Hist., 1983—, assoc. prof. zoology 1983-85, prof., 1985—; NUS cons., Venezuela, 1980-81; cons. Argentine Nat. Sci. Found. Inst. Arid Zone Research, Mendoza, 1983; World Wildlife Fund cons., Brazil, 1986; mem. Council Internat. Exchange of Scholars, Am. Republics Bd., Fulbright Commn., 1983-86, 88-91; bd. dirs. Coun. Internat. Exchange of Scholars, 1988-91; Okla. rep. to U.S. Fish and Wildlife Service Endangered Mammal Species Commn., 1987—; co-chair Internat. Programs Com. Systematics 2000, 1991—; sci. cons. interim working group White House Biodiversity, Ecology, and Ecosystems, 1992-94; apptd. adv. bd. Ctr. Biol. Diversity, Dept. Interior; mem. Commn. on Future of Smithsonian Instns., 1993—. NSF grantee, 1974-79, 82-93; Nat. Fulbright research fellow, 1994; Nat. Geog. Soc. grantee, 1992—. Active Chicano Council on Higher Edn. research fellow, 1978; Ford Found. Minority Research fellow, 1980-81;

Brazilian Nat. Acad. Sci. research award, 1975-78. Mem. AAAS (Western Hemispheric coop. com 1989—), Am. Soc. Mammalogists (1st v.p. 1990-94), Am. Ecol. Soc., Interam. Assn. Advancement Sci., Am. Inst. Biol. Sci., Am. Soc. Naturalists, Soc. Study of Evolution, Southwestern Assn. Naturalists (Donald W. Tinkle rsch. excellence award), Paleontol. Soc., Sigma Xi, Phi Kappa Phi, Beta Beta Beta. Contbr. articles to profl. jours. Home: 3930 Charing Cross Ct Norman OK 73072 Office: U Okla Okla Mus Natural History 1335 Asp Ave Norman OK 73019-0606

MARESCA, DANIEL G., retail executive; b. Jersey City, N.J., Aug. 6, 1952; s. Daniel Angelo and Ann (Cellucci) M.; m. Pamela Germaine Clark Maresca, Oct. 13, 1973; children: David Paul, Steven Gary. Student, St. Bridgets, No. Bergen, N.J., 1958-61; diploma, Horace Mann Sch., No. Bergen, N.J., 1961-66, No. Bergen High Sch., 1966-70; attended, U. Conn., 1972. Buyer Petrie Stores Corp., Secaucus, N.J., 1972-83, v.p., 1982-84, sr. v.p., 1984-85; assoc. mdse. mgr., sr. v.p., gen. mdse. mgr. Winkleman Stores (div. of Petrie), Plymouth, Mich., 1985-89, pres., gen. mdse. mgr., 1989-92; exec. v.p., elected to bd. dirs. Petrie Stores Corp., 1992. Republican. Roman Catholic. Avocation: tennis. Office: Winkelman Stores Inc 45000 Helm St Plymouth MI 48170

MARFIAK, THOMAS FLETCHER, career officer; b. Torrington, Conn., Feb. 2, 1944; s. Valentine Andrew and Eileen Gertrude (Kiely) M.; m. Patricia Hurwrey; children: Jennifer Garland, Thomas M., Sarah. BS, U.S. Naval Academy, 1966; MA, Institut D'Etudes Politiques, Paris, 1975, Tufts U., 1976; MALD, Tufts U., 1977. Commd. ensign USN, advanced through grades to rear adm.; chief engr. USS Biddle, 1977-80; exec. officer USS Conyngham, 1980-81; with strategic concepts group Office of Chief of Naval Ops., Washington, 1981-83; speechwriter Office of SECDEF, Washington, 1983-84; commdg. officer USS Doyle, Mayport, Fla., 1985-87, USS Bunker Hill, Yokosuka, Japan, 1990-92; dep. dir. CNO Exec. Panel, Washington, 1987-89; head Surface Warfare Plans/Programs/Requirements, Washington, 1992—. Decorated Legion of Merit with 2 gold stars and combat V; scholar George Olmsted Found. Mem. U.S. Naval Inst. Office: CNO (N863) 2000 Navy Pentagon Washington DC 20350-2000

MARGARITIS, JOHN PAUL, public relations executive; b. N.Y.C., June 8, 1949; s. George H. and Mary (Liakos) M.; m. Charlene Corenman, Feb. 21, 1982. BA in English, Washington and Jefferson Coll., 1971; MA in Media Studies, New Sch. Social Rsch., 1977. Account exec. Hank Boerner & Assocs., Uniondale, N.Y., 1974-76; account exec. Manning, Selvage & Lee, N.Y.C., 1976-77; account supr. Gen. Electric Co., N.Y.C., 1977-79, Burson-Marsteller, Inc., Los Angeles, 1980-82; exec. v.p., gen. mgr., sr. ptnr. Fleishman-Hillard, Inc., Los Angeles, 1982-88; chmn., chief exec. officer Ogilvy & Mather Pub. Relations, N.Y.C., 1988-92; pres., COO Ogilvy Adams and Rinehart, N.Y.C., 1992-94, pres., CEO, 1994—; also bd. dirs. Ogilvy Adams and Rinehart; bd. dirs. Rsch. Am., Young Press. Orgn., Arthur Ashe Found. 2nd lt. U.S. Army, 1972-74. Mem. Pub. Rels. Soc. Am. (hons. and awards com. 1986-89, counselors acad. 1985—), Alpine Country Club. Republican. Greek Orthodox. Home: 38 Hidden Ledge Rd Englewood NJ 07631-5125 Office: Ogilvy Adams and Rinehart 708 3rd Ave New York NY 10017

MARGE, MICHAEL, disability prevention specialist; b. Albany, N.Y., Oct. 26, 1928; s. Charles and Victoria (Arwady) M.; m. Dorothy Kunsevilch, July 9, 1960; children: Lisa Ann, Michael Charles. BA, Emerson Coll., 1952; MAT, Harvard U., 1953, EdD, 1959. Dir. speech therapy project N.Y. State Assn. for Crippled Children, Glens Falls, 1953-55; dir. speech therapy Glens Falls and Hudson Falls (N.Y.) Pub. Schs., 1955-57; co-chmn. speech and hearing grad. program Seton Hall U., South Orange, N.J., 1960-64; program specialist Office of Edn. Dept. HEW, Washington, 1964-68, dep. asst. sec. Office Edn., 1968-71; dep. bur. chief Office Edn. Bur. Internat. Studies, Washington, 1971-74; dean Coll. for Human Devel. Syracuse (N.Y.) U., 1974-79, prof. spl. edn. and rehab., 1979—, dir. Ctr. for the Prevention of Disabilities, 1985—; cons. Orgn. Am. States, Washington, 1976—; intergovtl. profl. cons. Ctrs. for Disease Control, Atlanta, 1994-95; disabilities prevention scientist ctrs. for disease control and prevention Dept. of Health and Human Svcs., Atlanta, 1994-95; mem. Nat. Coun. on Disability, Washington, 1982-87, cons., 1987-92; expert UN Devel. Program, N.Y.C., 1977—. Co-author: Principles of Childhood Language Disabilities, 1972; creator in field. Mem. interagy. com. HHS, Washington, 1986-89, Nat. Coun. on the Handicapped, Washington, 1982-87; mem. prevention task force N.Y. State Devel. Disabilities Planning Coun., Albany, 1986, Disability Prevention Coun., N.Y. State Dept. Health, Albany, 1989—; bd. dirs. Laubach Literacy Inc., Syracuse, 1986, Eye Rsch. Inst. Cen. N.Y., Syracuse, 1988-91; mem. com. on transp. disadvantaged Transport. Rsch. Bd. NAS, Washington, 1989-92; mem. adv. bd. on prevention Minorities Health Professions Found., 1993—. Served as cpl. U.S. Army, 1946-48. Recipient Nat. Eagle award Nat. Coun. on Disability, 1987; J.M. Found. grantee, 1985. Fellow Am. Speech-Language-Hearing Assn. (exec. bd. 1968-70, Cert. Appreciation 1975, 85); mem. Am. Psychol. Assn., Am. Pub. Health Assn., N.Y. State Speech-Language-Hearing Assn., N.J. Speech and Hearing Assn. (Honor of the Assn. 1965), Nat. Rehabilitation Assn. (Mary E. Switzer fellow 1980). Club: Harvard (Syracuse, admissions com. 1984-87). Avocations: bicycling, hiking, classical music. Office: Syracuse U 805 S Crouse Ave Syracuse NY 13210-1714

MARGELLO, MARGARET ANN, healthcare executive; b. Des Moines, June 1, 1943; d. William R. and Helen A. (Roth) Hilling; m. Ronald A. Margello, Feb. 4, 1982. BSN, Capital U., Columbus, Ohio, 1965; MS in Hosp. Adminstrn., Ohio State U., 1978. Pub. health nurse Columbus Health Dept., 1965-69; continuity of care coord. Grant Hosp., Columbus, 1969-73, social svcs. dir., 1973-76; program mgr. OHMS Health Mgmt. Svcs., Columbus, 1978-82; asst. exec. dir. Children's Hosp., Columbus, 1982-93; exec. dir. League Against Child Abuse, Columbus, 1993, Columbus Cancer Clinic, Columbus, 1994—. Grad. Leadership Columbus, 1988. Fellow Am. Coll. Healthcare Execs. (membership com. chair 1992-93, regent's adv. coun. 1989—); mem. Ctrl. Ohio Health Adminstrs. Assn. (treas. 1982-84, pres. 1985-86). Lutheran. Avocations: scuba diving, gardening, antique automobiles. Home: 7918 Sethwick Rd Dublin OH 43016 Office: Columbus Cancer Clini 65 Ceramic Dr Columbus OH 43214-3063

MARGERISON, RICHARD WAYNE, diversified industrial company executive; b. Phila., Nov. 5, 1948; s. Kenneth Hilton and Edythe (Helmuth) M.; m. Leah Blythe Creed, July 18, 1970; children: Andrew Kenneth, Ashley Creed. BA in Econs., U. N.C., 1970; MBA with distinction, Harvard U., 1977. Mgr. So. Bell Telephone Co., Greensboro, N.C., 1972-75; mgr. sub. liaison Atlas Powder Co. subs. Tyler Corp., Dallas, 1978-79, dir. mktg. svcs., 1979-80; exec. v.p. Micro-Term, Inc., St. Louis, 1980-83, pres., chief exec. officer, 1983-85; mgr. acquisitions Tyler Corp., Dallas, 1977-78, v.p., 1985-88, sr. v.p., 1988-89, exec. v.p., 1989-94, pres., COO, 1994—, also bd. dirs. Mem. Northway Christian Ch., Dallas, 1985—; coach Youth Soccer, Dallas, 1987—; advisor YMCA Indian Princess and Indian Guides, 1987-89; adult leader Boy Scouts Am., 1988-93; active Dallas United Way, 1990. Love fellow Harvard Grad. Sch. Bus., 1975-77. Mem. Harvard Bus. Sch. Club of Dallas, Lakewood Country Club, Order of Old Well, Phi Beta Kappa. Avocations: golf, youth soccer, running. Office: Tyler Corp 2121 San Jacinto St Ste 3200 Dallas TX 75201-2788

MARGERUM, DALE WILLIAM, chemistry educator; b. St. Louis, Oct. 20, 1929; s. Donald C. and Ida Lee (Nunley) M.; m. Sonya Lora Pedersen, May 16, 1953; children: Lawrence Donald, Eric William, Richard Dale. B.A., S.E. Mo. State U., 1950; Ph.D., Iowa State U., 1955. Research chemist Ames Lab., AEC, Iowa, 1952-53; instr. Purdue U., West Lafayette, Ind., 1954-57; asst. prof. Purdue U., 1957-61, assoc. prof., 1961-65, prof., 1965—, head dept. chemistry, 1978-83; inorganic-analytical chemist, vis. scientist Max Planck Inst., 1963, 70; vis. fellow U. Kent, Canterbury, Eng., 1970; mem. med. chem. study sect. NIH, 1965-69; mem. adv. chem. Research Corp., 1973-78; mem. chemistry evaluation panel Air Force Office Sci. Research, 1978-82. Cons. editor McGraw Hill, 1962-72; mem. editorial bd. Jour. Coordination Chemistry, 1971-81, Analytical Chemistry, 1967-69, Inorganic Chemistry, 1985-88. Recipient Grad. Rsch. award Phi Lambda Upsilon, 1954, Alumni Merit award S.E. Mo. State U., 1991, Sagamore of the Wabash, State of Ind., 1994; NSF sr. postdoctoral fellow, 1963-64. Fellow AAAS; mem. AAUP, Am. Chem. Soc. (chmn. Purdue sect. 1965-66,

com. on profl. tng. 1993—), Sigma Xi, Phi Lambda Upsilon. Office: Dept Chemistry Purdue U West Lafayette IN 47907

MARGERUM, J(OHN) DAVID, chemist; b. St. Louis, Oct. 20, 1929; s. Donald Cameron and Ida Lee (Nunley) M.; m. Virginia Bolen, June 5, 1954; children: John Steven, Kris Alan, Julie Ellen. A.B., S.E. Mo. State Coll., 1950; Ph.D., Northwestern U., 1956. Rsch. chemist Shell Oil Co., Wood River, Ill., 1954-55; chief spectoscopy sect. U.S. Army QMR&E Center, Natick, Mass., 1957-59; research specialist Sundstrand Corp., Pacoima, Calif., 1959-62; with Hughes Research Labs., Malibu, Calif., 1962—, sr. scientist, head chemistry sect., 1967—, head material scis. sect., 1988—, asst. dept. mgr. exploratory studies dept., 1989—, mgr. dept. materials sci., lab. chief scientist, 1991—; prin. rsch. scientist, 1993—. Contbr. articles to profl. jours.; patentee in field. Served with U.S. Army, 1955-57. Recipient Holley medal ASME, 1977. Fellow AAAS; mem. Am. Chem. Soc., Electrochem. Soc., Soc. Info. Display, Inter-Am. Photochem. Soc., Internat. Liquid Crystal Soc., Sigma Xi. Democrat. Unitarian. Home: 5433 Rozie Ave Woodland Hills CA 91367-5760 Office: 3011 Malibu Canyon Rd Malibu CA 90265-5760

MARGERUM, ROGER WILLIAMS, JR., architect; b. Chgo., May 14, 1930; s. Roger William Sr. and Juanita (Cloyd) M.; m. Frances L. Esnault, July 13, 1971. BArch., U. Ill., 1956. Designer Skidmore, Owings & Merrill, Chgo., 1957-60, Perkins & Wills Assocs., Chgo., 1960-62; ptnr. Morrison & Margerum, Chgo., 1962-65; asst. to bd. chmn. Smith, Hinchman & Grylls, Detroit, 1965-73; pres. Roger Margeram Inc. Architects, Mich., 1973—. Fellow Am. Inst. Architects; mem. Am. Inst. Architects, Nat. Orgn. Minority Architects (founding dir. 1972, v.p. 1986—), Detroit Inst. Architects (sec. 1971), Mich. Soc. Architect (pres. 1983). Address: 2111 Woodward Ave Detroit MI 48201-3421 Address: Roger Margerum Inc Arch 2111 Woodward Ave Detroit MI 48201-3421

MARGETON, STEPHEN GEORGE, law librarian; b. Elizabeth, N.J., Mar. 22, 1945; s. Louis George and Josephine A. (Bednarik) M.; m. Margaret Mary Salter, May 14, 1977; children: Catherine Ann, Elizabeth Ann. AB, Mt. St. Mary's Coll., 1967; JD, George Washington U., 1970; MLS, Cath. U., 1973. Reference librarian Am.-Brit. law div. Library of Congress, Washington, 1968-72; head law librarian Steptoe & Johnson, Washington, 1972-85; librarian Supreme Ct. of U.S., Washington, 1985-88; dir. Judge Kathryn J. DuFour Law Libr. The Cath. Univ. Am., 1988—; instr. George Mason Law Sch., Arlington, Va., 1977-80. Mem. Am. Assn. Law Libraries, Internat. Assn. Law Libraries. Office: Cath U Am Kathryn J DuFour Law Libr 620 Michigan Ave NE Washington DC 20017-1556

MARGETTS, W. THOMAS, automobile parts company executive, lawyer; b. Passaic, N.J., May 16, 1936; s. Walter T. Jr. and Josephine (Sharon) M.; m. Donna D. Ditman, July 21, 1962; children—Melissa, Sharon, Robert, James. A.B., Dartmouth Coll., 1959; LL.B., U. Va., 1962; LL.M., George Washington U., 1964. Bar: N.Y., N.J., Va. Assoc. Lord Day & Lord, N.Y.C., 1965-67; atty. Standard Brands, N.Y.C., 1967-70; counsel Purolator Courier Corp., Basking Ridge, N.J., 1970-71; sec. counsel, 1971-80, v.p., 1980-83, sr. v.p., 1983-88; adminstrn. sr. v.p., gen. counsel Stant Inc., Richmond, Ind., 1988—; of counsel Crummy, Del Deo, Dolan, Griffinger & Vecchione, Newark, 1988-92; dir. Komline-Sanderson Enging. Corp.; trustee N.J. Delta Dental Plan, Inc., Parsippany, 1985—. Mem. twp. com. Harding Twp., N.J., 1972-83, mayor, 1976-83; trustee, chmn. County Coll. of Morris; trustee, v.p. Morris Mus., 1992-95; trustee, v.p. N.J. Camp for Blind Children, 1992—. Served as 1st lt. U.S. Army. Home: PO Box 18 New Vernon NJ 07976-0018

MARGILETH, ANDREW MENGES, physician, former naval officer; b. Cin., July 17, 1920; s. Elmer C. and Bertha (Menges) M.; m. Catherine Lanier, Oct. 31, 1994; children: R. Lynn, Andrew C., Ellee C. B.A., Washington and Jefferson Coll., 1943; B.S., Mass. Inst. Tech., 1944; M.D., U. Cin., 1947. Commd. ensign USN, 1943, advanced through grades to capt., 1963; intern, resident pediatrics Nat. Naval Med. Center, 1947-49; resident pediatrics Johns Hopkins Hosp., 1949-50; chief pediatrics U.S. Naval Hosps., Corona, Calif., 1953-57, Chelsea, Mass., 1957-63, Bethesda, Md., 1963-67; prof. pediatrics Uniformed Svcs. U. Health Scis., 1979-90; clin. prof. pediatrics U. Va. Health Scis. Ctr., 1990—; council mem. Nat. Inst. Child Health and Human Devel., 1963-67; sr. attending physician Childrens Hosp., Washington; assoc. clin. prof. pediatrics Med. Sch., Howard U.; adj. prof. pediatrics Med. Sch., George Washington U. Contbr. chpt. to Current Pediatric Therapy, 1970, 72, 74, 76, 80, 83, 85, 90, 93, 95; contbr.: (textbooks) Neonatology, 1975, 81, 86, 94, Pediatrics, 1977, 81, 86, 91, 94, Medicine, 1978, 82, 86, 88, 91, Pediatric Dermatology, 1978, 86, 88, also articles to profl. jours.; co-editor Clin. Procs. of Children's Hosp. Nat. Med. Ctr., 1970-79. Fellow Am. Acad. Pediatrics, ACP; mem. Assn. Mil. Surgeons, Am. Pediatric Soc., Soc. Pediatric Dermatologists, Soc. Pediatric Infectious Diseases, Alpha Omega Alpha. Address: 20 Kingston Rd Hilton Head Island SC 29928

MARGO, KATHERINE LANE, physician; b. Buffalo, June 3, 1952; d. Warren Wilson and Virginia (Penney) Lane; m. Geoffrey Myles Margo, Apr. 20, 1980; 1 child, Benjamin; stepchildren: Jenny, Judy. BA, Swarthmore Coll., 1974; MD, SUNY Health Sci. Ctr., Syracuse, 1978. Resident physician St. Joseph's Hosp., Syracuse, 1979-82; attending physician Health Svcs. Assn., Syracuse, 1982-90, asst. med. dir. for quality assurance, 1985-90; asst. prof. family medicine SUNY-HSC at Syracuse, 1990-94; residency faculty Harrisburg (Pa.) Hosp., 1994—. Contbr. articles to profl. jours. Bd. of trustees Pt. Choice, Syracuse, 1993-94, Planned Parenthood, Syracuse, 1984-94, Friends of Chamber Music, Syracuse, 1988-94. Mem. Soc. Tchrs. of Family Medicine, Am. Acad. of Family Practitioners (v.p. Syracuse chpt.), Am. Acad. Ortho. Medicine. Home: 4705 Maple Shade Dr Harrisburg PA 17110

MARGOL, IRVING, personnel consultant; b. St. Louis, May 28, 1930; s. William and Dora (Karsh) M.; m. Myrna Levy, Dec., 1959; children—Bradley, Lisa, Cynthia. B.A., Washington U., St. Louis, 1951. M.A., 1952. Employment mgr. Am. Car & Foundry div. ACF, St. Louis, 1955-59; asst. personnel dir. Vickers Inc. div. Sperry-Rand, St. Louis, 1959-60; instr. personnel mgmt. Washington U. (St. Louis), 1960-62; personnel dir. Energy Controls div. Bendix Corp., South Bend, Ind., 1962-69; exec. v.p. community/employee affairs group, community rels. dept., employee assistance program Security Pac. Nat. Bank, L.A., 1969-92; mng. dir. Southern Calif. Jannotta, Bray & Assocs., Inc., 1992—; pres. Security Pacific Found., L.A., 1989-94; mng. dir. Jannotta Bray & Assocs., L.A., 1992-94, Right and Assocs., L.A., 1995—; instr. UCLA Extension Div., Los Angeles; Grad. Sch. Banking, Rutgers U., Notre Dame U. Bd. dirs. L.A. chpt. ARC, Am. Heart Assn., Am. Cancer Soc., Nat. Conf. Christians & Jews, Braille Inst.; bd. overseers Southwestern U. Law. Mem. Am. Bankers Assn. (exec. com. 1979—), Am. Soc. Tng. and Devel., Am. Soc. Personnel Adminstrs., Am. Inst. Banking, Washington U. Alumni Assn. Democrat. Jewish. Office: Right and Assocs 5320 Pacific Councourse Dr Los Angeles CA 90045

MARGOLIASH, EMANUEL, biochemist, educator; b. Cairo, Feb. 10, 1920; s. Wolf and Bertha (Kotler) M.; m. Sima Beshkin, Aug. 22, 1944; children: Reuben, Daniel. BA, Am. U., Beirut, 1940, MA, 1942, MD, 1945. Rsch. fellow, lectr., acting head cancer rsch. labs. Hebrew U. Jerusalem, 1945-58; rsch. fellow Molteno Inst. Cambridge (Eng.) U., 1951-53; Dazian fellow Nobel Inst. 1958; rsch. assoc. U. Utah, Salt Lake City, 1958-60, McGill U., Montreal, Que., Can. 1960-62; rsch. fellow Abbott Labs., North Chicago, Ill., 1962-69; sr. rsch. fellow Abbott Labs., 1969-71, head protein sect., 1962-71; prof. biochemistry and molecular biology Northwestern U., Evanston, Ill., 1971-90, prof. chemistry, 1985-90, Owen L. Coon prof. molecular biology, 1988-90, Owen L. Coon prof. molecular biology emeritus, 1990—; prof. biol. scis. U. Ill., Chgo., 1989—, coord. lab. for molecular biology, 1990-93; mem. com. on cytochrome nomenclature Internat. Union Biochemistry, 1962—; mem. adv. com. Plant Research Lab., Mich. State U./AEC, 1967-72; co-chmn. Gordon Research Conf. on Proteins, 1967. Editl. bd. Jour. Biol. Chemistry, 1966-72, Biochem. Genetics, 1966-80, Jour. Molecular Evolution, 1971-82, Biochemistry and Molecular Biology Internat., 1981—, Jour. Protein Chemistry, 1982-86, Chemtracts, Biochem. Molecular Biology, 1990—; contbr. over 275 articles and revs. to sci. jours. Rudi Lemberg fellow Australian Acad. Sci., 1981; Guggenheim fellow, 1983.

Fellow Am. Acad. Arts and Scis., Am. Acad. Microbiology; mem. Nat. Acad. Scis., Biochem. Soc. (Keilin Meml. lectr. 1970), Harvey Soc. (lectr. 1970-71), Am. Soc. Biochem. Molecular Biology (publs. com. 1973-76), Am. Chem. Soc., Can. Biochem. Soc., Soc. Developmental Biology, Biophys. Soc. (exec. com. U.S. bioenergetics group 1980—), N.Y. Acad. Sci., Ill. Acad. Sci., Am. Soc. Naturalists, Sigma Xi (nat. lectr. 1972-73, 74-77). Home: 353 Madison Ave Glencoe IL 60022-1809 Office: U Ill Chgo LMB-Biol Scis (M/C 067) 840 W Taylor St Chicago IL 60607-7020

MARGOLIES, JAY OWEN, transportation company executive; b. N.Y.C., Apr. 13, 1951. Asst. mgr. Canteen Corp., N.Y.C., 1974-75; mgr. Nat. Restaurants, N.Y.C., 1975-77; asst. to pres. Shortway Lines, Inc., Toledo, 1978-82; pres. Shortway Lines, Inc., 1982-86; exec. v.p. Holland Industries, Inc., Toledo, 1980-87, pres., 1987—; mem. Gov.'s Adv. Coun. on Travel/Tourism, Columbus, Ohio, 1983-87. Mem. Am. Ground Transp. Assn. Am. Bus Assn. Office: Holland Industries Inc 1 Keeshin Pl Toledo OH 43612-1247

MARGOLIES, RAYMOND, management consulting company executive; b. N.Y.C., Feb. 27, 1920; s. Isadore Moris and Nettie (Herskowitz) M.; m. Ellen Lombard, Nov. 14, 1942; children: Peter, Joan Margolies Kiernen, Lynn Margolies Colvin, Philip. BA, Principia Coll., Elsah, Ill., 1942; grad., U. Notre Dame Midshipman Sch., 1943. Salesman Bard & Margolies Inc., Bklyn., 1945-52, pres., 1952-59; exec. analyst George S. May Internat. Co., Park Ridge, Ill., 1959-62, chief exec. survey svc., 1962-64, mng. dir., 1964-68, v.p. ops., 1968-71, pres., chief exec. officer, 1971-90, pres. emeritus, 1990—, also bd. dirs.; bd. dirs. George S. May Internat. Pres. Riverwoods (Ill.) Resident Assn.; mem. Riverwoods Plan Commn. With USN, 1942-45. Mem. Am. Mgmt. Assn., Indsl. Engrs., Mill Creek Hunt Club (Wadsworth, Ill.). Avocations: horses, swimming. Office: George S May Internat Co 303 S Northwest Hwy Park Ridge IL 60068

MARGOLIN, ARTHUR STANLEY, distillery company executive; b. N.Y.C., Aug. 7, 1936; s. Samuel and Belle (Gelb) M.; m. Barbara Jane Lester, June 27, 1965; children: Sarah Jennifer, Julie Ellen, Carolyn Leigh. BA in Econs., NYU, 1957, postgrad. in bus., 1961. Analyst, sr. analyst Asch Market Research (div. JES), N.Y.C., 1961-63; field asst. to eastern div. mgr. Calvert Distillers, N.Y.C., 1963-64, asst. to asst. and met. N.Y. mgr., 1964-72, asst. to exec. v.p. sales, asst. to pres., 1972-78; exec. asst. to pres. House of Seagram, N.Y.C., 1978-80; dir. U.S. ops. Seagram Europe, London, 1980-82; asst. to pres. Seagram Internat. Joseph E. Seagram & Sons Inc., N.Y.C., 1982, asst. to office of chmn. and pres., 1982-85, v.p. spl. asst. to office of chmn. and pres., 1985—; bd. dirs. Forhan Forwarding and Handling Co., N.V., Antwerp, Belgium. Mng. editor Heights Daily News, 1956-57. Bd. dirs. Fifth Ave. Assn., N.Y.C., 1987. Capt. USAF, 1957-60. Republican. Jewish. Avocations: collecting stamps and coins, baseball. Office: Joseph E Seagram & Sons Inc 375 Park Ave New York NY 10152-0001

MARGOLIN, HAROLD, metallurgical educator; b. Hartford, Conn., July 12, 1922; s. Aaron David and Sonia (Krupnikoff) M.; m. Elaine Marjorie Rose, July 4, 1946; children: Shelley, Deborah, Amy. B in Engring., Yale U., 1943, M in Engring., 1947, DEng, 1950. Rsch. assoc./scientist divsn. rsch. NYU, N.Y.C., 1949-56, assoc. prof. metall. engring., 1956-62, prof., 1962-73; prof. phys. metallurgy Poly. U. N.Y., Bklyn., 1973-93, disting. rsch. prof., 1993—; cons. in field. Contbg. author books; contbr. articles to profl. publs. With USNR, 1944-46. Named Theodore W. Krengel vis. prof. Technion, Haifa, Israel, 1983. Fellow Am. Soc. Metals (edn. award N.Y. chpt. 1967); mem. AAAS, Metall. Soc. (honoree symposium in his name San Francisco 1994), Am. Soc. Materials, Sigma Xi. Democrat. Jewish. Patentee in field. Home: 19 Crescent Rd Larchmont NY 10538-1733 Office: 333 Jay St Brooklyn NY 11201-2907 *Achievement, work, and refusal to accept defeat are intimately intertwined.*

MARGOLIS, BERNARD ALLEN, library administrator, antique book merchant and appraiser; b. Greenwich, Conn., Oct. 2, 1948; s. Sidney S. and Rose (Birkenfeld) M.; m. Amanda Batey, Nov. 2, 1973. BA in Polit. Sci., U. Denver, 1970, MLS, 1973. Cert. libr., Mich. Libr. asst. Denver Pub. Libr., 1970-72; br. head Virginia Village Libr., Denver Pub. Libr., 1972-73; dep. dir. Monroe County Libr. Sys., Mich., 1973-75; dir. Raisin Valley Libr. Sys., Monroe, 1976-78, S.E. Mich. Regional Film Libr., Monroe, 1976-88, Monroe County Libr. Sys., 1976-88, Pikes Peak Libr. Dist., Colorado Springs, Colo., 1988—; pres. Colo. Ctr. for Books, 1989-92, Colo. Ctr. for the Book, 1993—; cons. in libr. pub. rels., 1976—; founding trustee United Colo. Investment Trust, 1993—; chmn. Colo. Gov.'s Conf. on Libr. and Info. Svcs., 1990; lectr. Western Mich. U., Kalamazoo, 1978-81; appraiser rare books, Monroe, Colorado Springs, 1970—. Contbr. articles to profl. jours; mem. editl. bd. Bottom Line Mag. Fin. Mgmt. for Librs., 1986—. Bd. dirs. Monroe Sen. Citizens Ctr., 1976-80, Monroe Fine Arts Coun., 1978-81, Am. the Beautiful Centennial Celebration, Inc., 1993, The Libr. Consortium, 1993—, Downtown Colo. Springs, Inc., 1994—; Care & Share, Inc., 1994—, vice chmn., 1995; chmn. Blue Cross-Blue Shield Consumer Coun., Detroit, 1984-88; mem. adv. bd. Access Colo. Libr. and Info. Network (ACLIN), 1991—; Mercy Meml. Hosp., Monroe, 1984-86, 5th Congl. Art Competition Com., 1992—; Dem. candidate for Mich. Senate, 1986; mem. allocations com. Pikes Peak United Way, 1988-91, chmn., 1990-91, bd. dirs. 1990-91, 94—; chmn. Great Pikes Peak Cowboy Poetry Gathering, 1990, 91, 92, 94; del. White House Conf. on Libr. and Info. Scs. Recipient Mayoral Cert. Commendation award Denver, 1972, 73; named Mich. Libr. of Yr., 1985, Colo. Libr. of Yr., 1990; commendation John F. Kennedy Ctr. for Performing Arts, 1993. Mem. ALA (governing coun. 1986—, endowment trustee 1993-99, sr. endowment trustee 1993—, chmn. resolutions com. 1991-92, cons. ann. swap and shop 1979-84, John Cotton Dana award 1977, 91, Libr. Awareness Idea Search award Washington 1982), Colo. Libr. Assn. (mem. legis. com., Intellectual Freedom award 1993), Libr. Adminstrv. Mgmt. Assn., Pub. Libr. Assn. Democrat. Jewish. Home: 10640 Hungate Rd Colorado Springs CO 80908-4312 Office: Pikes Peak Libr Dist 5550 N Union Blvd PO Box 1579 Colorado Springs CO 80901-1579

MARGOLIS, DANIEL HERBERT, lawyer; b. Montgomery, W.Va., Feb. 11, 1926; s. Morris Abraham and Miriam (Finkelstein) M.; m. Anabel Tendler, Dec. 23, 1951 (dec.); children—Peter, Beth, Laura, James; m. Sidney Millman Moore, Feb. 5, 1983. B.A., Johns Hopkins U., 1948; LL.B., Harvard U., 1951. Bar: D.C. 1951, U.S. Supreme Ct. 1959. Atty adv. Office Price Stblzn., Washington, 1951-52; trial atty. Antitrust div. Dept. Justice, Washington, 1952-56; sr. ptnr. Bergson, Borkland, Margolis & Adler, Washington, 1956-86; ptnr. McGuire, Woods, Battle & Boothe, 1986-89, Patton, Boggs & Blow, 1989—. Contbr. articles to profl. jours. Mem. adv. bd. Internat. Human Rights Law Group, 1989—. Served with USN, 1945-46, PTO. Fellow ABA (chmn. spl. com. on jury comprehension, litigation sect. 1983-90), Washington Lawyers for Civil Rights, Internat. Club. Democrat. Avocations: sailing, skiing. Office: Patton Boggs & Blow 2550 M St NW Washington DC 20037-1301

MARGOLIS, DAVID I(SRAEL), corporate executive; b. N.Y.C., Jan. 24, 1930; s. Benjamin and Celia (Kosofsky) M.; m. Barbara Schneider, Sept. 7, 1958; children: Brian, Robert, Peter, Nancy. BA, CCNY, 1950, MBA, 1952; postgrad., NYU, 1952-55. Security analyst Josephthal Co., 1952-56; asst. treas. Raytheon Co., 1956-59; treas. IT&T, N.Y.C., 1959-62; with Coltec Industries Inc., N.Y.C., 1962-95, pres., 1968-91, CEO, 1984-95, chmn. bd. dirs., 1988-95; bd. dirs. Burlington Industries, Ft. Howard Corp., Offitbank. Trustee Presbyn. Hosp. City N.Y.; bd. overseers NYU Stern Sch. Bus. Mem. Coun. Fgn. Rels. Office: Coltec Industries Inc 430 Park Ave New York NY 10022-3505

MARGOLIS, EMANUEL, lawyer, educator; b. Bklyn., Mar. 18, 1926; s. Abraham and Esther (Levin) M.; m. Edith Cushing; m. Estelle Thompson, Mar. 1, 1959; children: Elizabeth Margolis-Pineo, Catherine, Abby Margolis Newman, Joshua, Sarah. BA, U. N.C., 1947; MA, Harvard U., 1948, PhD, 1951; JD, Yale U., 1956. Bar: Conn. 1957, U.S. Dist. Ct. Conn. 1958, U.S. Sup. Ct. 1969. Instr. dept. govt. U. Conn. 1951-53; assoc. Silberberg & Silverstein, Ansonia, Conn. 1956-60; assoc. Wofsey Rosen Kweskin & Kuriansky Stamford, Conn. 1960-66, ptnr. 1966—; arbitrator State of Conn. 1984-85; trial referee, 1985—; spl. master fed. cts. 1987—; adj. prof. Quinnipiac Coll. Sch. Law, 1986—. Sr. editor Conn. Bar Jour., 1971-80, 83—, editor-in-chief, 1980-83; contbr. to legal jours. Mem. nat. bd. ACLU, 1975-

79; mem. Westport (Conn.) Planning & Zoning Commn., 1971-75; chmn. Conn. CLU, 1988-95, legal advisor, 1995—. Served with U.S. Army, 1944-46. Decorated Purple Heart; recipient First Award for Disting. Service to Conn. Bar, Conn. Law Tribune, 1987. Mem. ABA, Conn. Bar Assn. (chmn. human rights sect. 1970-73), Nat. Assn. Criminal Def. Lawyers. Home: 72 Myrtle Ave Westport CT 06880-3512 Office: 600 Summer St Stamford CT 06901-1403

MARGOLIS, EUGENE, lawyer, government official; b. Bronx, N.Y., Dec. 19, 1935; s. Louis and Minnie (Kaplan) M.; m. Sally Fay Gellman, Sept. 22, 1962; children—Judith Miriam, Linda Aileen, Aaron Keith, Pamela June. BME, Rensselaer Poly. Inst., 1957; JD, Georgetown U., 1960, M in Patent Law, 1962. Bar: N.Y. 1961, U.S. Supreme Ct. 1969; cert. exec. U.S. Office Personnel Mgmt., 1983. Patent examiner U.S. Patent Office, Washington, 1957-60; trial atty. antitrust div. U.S. Dept. Justice, Washington, 1960-66, N.Y.C., 1966-67; chief consumer protection div. N.Y.C. Dept. Law, 1967-71; gen. counsel Mayor's Interdeptl. Com. on Pub. Utilities, N.Y.C., 1972-73; spl. counsel to commr. N.Y.C. Dept. Gen. Services, 1974-79; dir. N.Y.C. Office of Energy Conservation, 1975-79; sr. legal adviser U.S. Dept. Energy, Washington, 1979—; adj. prof. Cooper Union, 1978-79; adj. assoc. prof. Grad. Sch., CUNY, 1974-80. Mem. editorial bd. Georgetown Law Jour., 1958-60. Chmn. govtl. relations and grants com. Village of Larchmont, N.Y., 1977-79, mem. cable TV com., 1977-79, mem. tax base com., 1974-79; chmn. Larchmont Democratic Com., 1976-77; vice chmn. Mamaroneck Dem. Com., 1979; mem. Westchester County Dem. Com., 1975-77, 79; bd. dirs. Jewish Community Coun. Greater Washington, 1986-94; mem. adv. bd. Dept. Volunteerism, Commonwealth Va., 1987-91; mem. pub. social policy com. United Jewish Appeal-Fedn. Greater Washington, 1988—, mem. No. Va. steering com., 1990—; bd. govs. B'nai Brith Internat., 1992-94, internat. coun., 1992-94, Hillel com., 1991-94, mem. nat. fund raising cabinet, 1987-90, com. on community vol. svcs., 1985-89, pres. dist. 5, 1993-94, pres. Va. State Assn., 1986-87, Va. Hillel Found., 1985-86. Recipient Cert. of Appreciation U.S. Dept. Energy, 1984, Sec. of Energy's Award, Outstanding Community Svc. Vol., 1990. Mem. N.Y. State Bar Assn., ASME, Phi Delta Phi, Pi Delta Epsilon, Tau Epsilon Phi. Jewish. Clubs: Rensselaer Alumni (sec. chpt. 1976-77), U. Va. Fund Parents, Town and Village Synagogue Men's (pres. 1970-71). Lodge: B'nai Brith (pres. Mcpl. lodge 1976-78, Larchmont-Mamaroneck lodge 1978-80, Masada lodge 1984-85, Internat. Lodge Col. Elliot A. Niles Community Svc. award 1984, Dist. 5 Outstanding Ben Brith award 1988, Outstanding State Pres. award 1987, Hillel award 1986, Community Vol. Svc. award 1984, Va. State Assn. Herman G. Koplen Meml. award 1987, Sherry B. Rose Leadership award 1984). Home: 6504 Sparrow Point Ct Mc Lean VA 22101-1638 Office: US Dept Energy Forrestal Bldg 1000 Independence Ave SE Washington DC 20585-0001

MARGOLIS, GEORGE, pathologist, medical educator; b. Montgomery, W.Va., Dec. 12, 1914; s. Simon and Sara Reba (Blumberg) M.; m. Anne Maria McCabe, Sept. 23, 1950; children: Susan, George McCabe, Joshua David, Dan Leo. A.B., Johns Hopkins U., 1936; M.D., Duke U., 1940, M.A. (hon.), Dartmouth, 1966. Cert. Am. Bd. Neuropathology, Am. Bd. Pathologic Anatomy, Am. Bd. Clin. Pathology. Intern pathology Duke Med. Sch., 1940-41, instr. pathology, 1940-44, asst. resident pathology, then resident, 1941-44, from asst. prof. to assoc. prof. pathology, 1947-55, prof. pathology, 1955-59; prof. pathology, chmn. dept. Med. Coll. Va., Richmond, 1959-63; prof. pathology Dartmouth Med Sch., 1963-82, prof. emeritus, 1982—, minority affairs officer, 1969-82, founding and sr. editor alumni mag., 1975-85; v.p. exec. dir., dir. Prescription for Survival Prodns., 1983—; founder neuropathology Dartmouth U., Med. Coll. Va., Duke U.; creator Donald Love Meml. (Citation), Duke U. Med. Sch., 1994. Emeritus exec. dir. Prescription for Survival; steering com. Nuclear Arms Forum, Westport-Weston, Conn.; regional rep. Duke U. Med. Sch., 1964-90; mem. alumni schs. com. Johns Hopkins U., 1963—, class agt.; bd. dirs. A Better Chance, Ridgefield, Conn., Nuclear Arms Freeze, Ridgefield chpt.; trustee chairperson rsch. and devel. dept. Falk Found. Excellence; co-founder, bd. dirs., treas. West Conn. chpt. Nat. Adv. Council Veterans for Peace; former bd. dirs. Planned Parenthood, Upper Valley, N.H., N.H. Civil Liberties Union, Parents and Tchrs. for Social Responsibility; co-founder N.H. chpt. Physicians for Social Responsibility, 1979, chmn., 1979-82, nat. bo. of dels., 1982-85, mem. steering com. Fairfield County, Conn. chpt., 1985—; mem. cerebrovascular disease coun. Am. Heart Assn.; mem. editorial bd. Archives of Pathology, 1960-65; mem. cerebrovascular disease subcom. Nat. Inst. Neurolog. Diseases and Blindness, 1962-64; mem. cerebral aneurysm subcom., 1960-64; mem. pathology study sect., Nat. Inst. Gen. Med. Scis., 1956-59. Served to maj. M.C., AUS, 1944-47, ETO. Recipient Disting. Alumni award Duke U. Med. Ctr., 1983, citation for svc. A Better Chance, 1993; Collection for Cross-Cultural Medicine and Minority Affairs named in his honor, Dartmouth med. Sch., 1993. Home: 66 Bloomer Rd Ridgefield CT 06877-6006 *It is my belief that in the long run these humanistic and humanitarian commitments will have a greater and more lasting impact on society than any contributions I have been able to make as a scientist in the narrower sense.*

MARGOLIS, GERALD JOSEPH, psychiatrist, psychoanalyst; b. Bronx, N.Y., May 7, 1935; s. Max and Sophie (Siegel) M.; A.B., U. Rochester, 1957; M.D., U. Chgo., 1960; postgrad. Inst. Phila. Assn. Psychoanalysis, 1972; m. June Edelman Greenspan, July 13, 1976; children: David J., Peter S., Steven J. Intern, psychiat. resident, Upstate Med. Center, SUNY, Syracuse, 1960-64, instr. psychiatry, 1966-67; from instr. to clin. prof. psychiatry Med. Sch., U. Pa., Phila., 1967—; practice medicine specializing in psychiatry and psychoanalysis, Cherry Hill, N.J.; tng. and supervising analyst Inst. of Phila. Assn. for Psychoanalysis. Served with M.C., USAF, 1964-66. Diplomate Am. Bd. Psychiatry and Neurology. Mem. Am. Psychoanalytic Assn. (cert.), Am. Psychiat. Assn., AMA, Phila. Assn. for Psychoanalysis (tng. and supervising analyst), Phi Beta Kappa. Club: B'nai B'rith. Contbr. articles to profl. publs. Home: 408 Park Lane Moorestown NJ 08057 Office: One Cherry Hill Ste 930 Cherry Hill NJ 08002

MARGOLIS, HAROLD STEPHEN, epidemiologist; b. Tucson, Ariz., Feb. 22, 1946; s. Maurice H. and Helen (Letz) M.; m. Susan Helen Quinn, July 3, 1971; children: Ellis, Leah, Amber. BS, U. Ariz., 1968, MD, 1972. Diplomate Am. Bd. Med. Examiners. Resident in pediatrics U. Colo. Health Scis. Ctr., Denver, 1972-75; med. epidemiologist Ctrs. for Disease Control, Anchorage, 1975-79, Phoenix, Ariz., 1981-83; dep. chief hepatitis br. Ctrs. for Disease Control, Atlanta, 1983-87, chief, 1987—; rsch. fellow Nat. Jewish Hosp., Denver, 1979-81; dir. WHO Collaborative Ctr. for Rsch. and Reference in Viral Hepatitis, Atlanta, 1987—; cons. WHO, 1988, 89, Agy. for Internat. Devel.; guest advisor Inst. Medicine, 1989, 92. Editor: Viral Hepatitis and Liver Disease, 1991; contbr. articles to profl. jours. Capt. USPHS, 1975—. Fellow Am. Acad. Pediats., Infectious Disease Soc. Am.; mem. Alpha Omega Alpha, Sigma Xi. Achievements include development of strategies to prevent viral hepatitis through immunization; research in characterization of hepatitis A viruses and molecular pathogenesis of viral hepatitis. Office: Nat Ctr for Infectious Diseases Hepatitis Branch 1600 Clifton Rd NE Atlanta GA 30333

MARGOLIS, JAMES DAVID, political consulting and advertising executive; b. Albuquerque, Apr. 30, 1955; s. Elizabeth Hayes (Rieger) M. BA, Oberlin Coll., 1978. Campaign mgr. Howard Wolpe for Congress Campaign, Kalamazoo, 1978; chief staff Congressman Howard Wolpe, Washington, 1978-83; dep. dir. comm. Mondale for Pres. Campaign, Washington, 1983-84; sr. assoc. Greer & Assocs., Washington, 1985-86; chief staff Hon. Kent Conrad U.S. Senate, Washington, 1987; ptnr. Greer, Margolis, Mitchell, Burns & Assocs., Washington, 1988—. Democrat. Office: Greer Margolis Mitchell Burns & Assoc 1010 Wisconsin Ave NW Ste 800 Washington DC 20007-3603

MARGOLIS, JEREMY, lawyer. BA History, U. Ill., 1970; JD cum laude, Northwestern U., 1973. Bar: Ill. 1973. Exec. asst. U.S. Atty., chief Fin. Crimes unit, Deputy chief, Spl. Prosecutions divsn., spl. asst. to U.S. Atty. Office of U.S. Atty., Chgo., 1973-81, 1973-84; inspector gen. State of Ill., 1984-87; dir. Ill. State Police, 1987-90; ptnr. Altheimer & Gray, Chgo., 1990—; bd. dirs. Nat. Ctr. Missing and Exploited Children, Chgo. Crime commn.; lectr. in field. Author (with Fred E. Inbau, Marvin E. Aspen) Criminal Law for the Layman, 2d edit., 1977; contbr. articles to profl. jours. Recipient Dept. Justice commendation award, 1976, Chgo. Crime commn. award Merit, 1981, U.S. Secret Svc. Honor award, 1984, Chgo. Assn. Commerce

and Industry award for Outstanding Professionalism, 1984, Disting. Svc. award Chgo. Assn. Commerce and Industry, 1989; named one of Ten Outstanding Young Citizens Chgo. Jr. Assn. Commerce, 1985. Office: Altheimer & Gray 350 W Hubbard St # 3 Chicago IL 60610-4011

MARGOLIS, JULIUS, economist, educator; b. N.Y.C., Sept. 26, 1920; s. Sam and Fannie (Weiner) M.; m. Doris Lubetsky, Oct. 30, 1942; children—Jane S., Carl W. B.S.S., City Coll. N.Y., 1941; Ph.M. in Econs, U. Wis., 1943; M.P.A. in Econs, Harvard, 1947, Ph.D., 1949. Instr. econs. Tufts Coll., 1947-48; asst. prof. econs. and planning U. Chgo., 1948-51; asst. prof. econs. Stanford, 1951-54; prof. bus adminstrn. U. Calif. at Berkeley, 1954-64; prof. econs. and engring. econ. systems Stanford, 1964-69; prof., dir. Fels Center of Govt., U. Pa., 1969-76; prof. econs. U. Calif. at Irvine, 1976—; dir. Ctr. on Global Peace and Conflict Studies, 1985—; cons. to govt. and industry, 1958—. Author: (with others) The Public Economy of Urban Communities, 1965, The Northern California's Water Industry, 1966, Public Economics, 1969, Public Expenditure and Policy Analysis, 1984; also articles. Served with AUS, 1943-46. Mem. Am. Econ. Assn., Royal Econ. Soc. Home: 45 Whitman Ct Irvine CA 92715-4059 Office: U Calif Dept Econ Irvine CA 92717

MARGOLIS, KARL L., retail company executive. BA, Bklyn. Coll., 1938; MBA, Harvard U., 1940. Now vice chmn. McCrory Corp., N.Y.C., also bd. dirs. Served to capt. AUS, 1942-46. Office: McCrory Corp 941 Park Ave # 7C New York NY 10028-0318

MARGOLIS, LAWRENCE STANLEY, federal judge; b. Phila., Mar. 13, 1935; s. Reuben and Mollie (Manus) M.; m. Doris May Rosenberg, Jan. 30, 1960; children: Mary Aleta, Paul Oliver. B.S.M.E., Drexel U., 1957; J.D., George Washington U., 1961. Bar: D.C. 1963. Patent examiner U. S. Patent Office, Washington, 1957-62; patent counsel Naval Ordnance Lab., White Oak, Md., 1962-63; asst. corp. counsel D.C., 1963-66; atty. criminal div., spl. asst. U.S. atty. Dept. of Justice, Washington, 1966-68; asst. U.S. atty. for D.C., 1968-71; U.S. magistrate judge U.S. Dist. Ct., Washington, 1971-82; judge U.S. Ct. Fed. Claims, Washington, 1982—; chmn. task force on discovery reform U.S. Claims Ct., Washington, chmn. alt. dispute resolution; mem. faculty Fed. Jud. Ctr. Editor-in-chief The Young Lawyer, 1965-66, D.C. Bar Jour., 1967-73; bd. editors The Dist. Lawyer, 1978-82. Trustee Drexel U., 1983-89; bd. govs. George Washington U. Alumni Assn., 1978-85, 93—. Recipient contbn. award D.C. Jaycees, 1966, svc. award Boy Scouts Am., 1970; Alumni Svc. award George Washington U., 1976, Disting. Alumni Achievement award, 1985; Disting. Alumni Achievement award Drexel U., 1988, Drexel 100 award, 1992; Alt. Dispute Resolution award Ctr. for Pub. Resources, 1988. Fellow Inst. Jud. Adminstrn., Am. Bar Found.; mem. ABA (chmn. jud. adminstrn. div., Disting. Svc. award 1981), ABA Nat. Conf. Spl. Ct. Judges (chmn., Disting. Svc. award 1978), D.C. Jud. Conf., Bar Assn. D.C. (bd. dirs. 1970-72, editor-in-chief contbn. award, award young lawyers sect. 1983), Fed. Bar Assn., George Washington U. Nat. Law Assn. (pres. D.C. chpt. 1974-76, pres. 1983-84), Univ. Club., Rotary (bd. dirs. Washington, 1984-90, pres. 1988-89, dist. gov. 1991-92, Rotarian of Yr. 1984,. Office: US Ct Fed Claims 717 Madison Pl NW Ste 703 Washington DC 20005-1086

MARGOLIS, LEO, marine biologist; b. Montreal, Que., Can., Dec. 18, 1927; m. Ruth Anne Lall; children: Rhonda Lee, Robert Allan, Murray Howard, Conrad Anton. B.Sc., McGill U., 1948, M.Sc., 1950, Ph.D., 1952. Rsch. scientist Pacific Biol. Sta., Can. Dept. Fish and Oceans, Nanaimo, B.C., 1952-67, head various rsch. divs., 1967-81, head fish health and parasitology sect., 1981-90, sr. scientist, 1990—; co-chmn. Can. Com. on Fish Diseases, 1970-73; mem. com. on biology and rsch. Internat. North Pacific Fisheries Commn., 1971-93, sr. Can. scientist, 1976-93, advisor Can. sect., 1956-93, sr. scientist advisor Can. sect., 1976-93; adviser Fed.-Provincial Fish Com., 1969, 70, 72; mem. Can. Del. North Pacific Anadromous Fish Commn., 1993—, chmn. com. sci. rsch. and stats., 1993—; mem. editorial referees com. Bull. Internat. North Pacific Fisheries Commn., 1976-84; mem. adv. bd. sci. info. publs. Fisheries and Oceans Can., 1979-83; mem. aquatic sci. research evaluation com. Sci. Council B.C., 1979-88, chmn. 1986-88; adj. prof. Simon Fraser U., 1983—; cons. Internat. Devel. Research Ctr., 1986; mem. nat. tech. com. Can. Fish Health Protection Regulations, 1990—; mem. sci. adv. com. N.B. Aquaculture Consortium, 1991—; mem. external adv. com. Biology program Malaspina Coll., 1992—. Assoc. editor Can. Jour. Zoology, 1971-81, Jour. World Aquaculture Soc., 1986—; mem. editl. bd., editl. cons. Jour. of Parasitology, 1977-93; mem. adv. bd. Amphipacifica, Jour. of Systematic Biology, 1993—; editl. advisor Diseases of Aquatic Organisms Jour., 1994—; author 2 books; editor 5 books; contbr. articles on parasites and diseases of fishes and other aquatic animals, and on biology of salmon to various profl. jours. Pres. B.C. Amateur Hockey Assn., 1963-66, hon. v.p., 1968-88, life mem. 1988—, Diamond Stick award, 1989, Can. Amateur Hockey Assn. Order of Merit, 1990. Decorated officer Order of Can.; recipient Commemorative medal 125th Anniversary Confedn. Can., 1992. Fellow Royal Soc. Can.; mem. Can. Soc. Zoologists (coun. mem. parasitology sect. 1977-78, recognition com. 1985-88, 93—, 2d v.p. 1988-89, 1st v.p. 1989-90, pres. 1990-91, recognition com. 1991-94, chmn. 1991-93; bd. trustees Zool. Edn. Trust 1988-93, chmn. 1990-91, R.A. Wardle lectr. award 1982), Atlantic Can. Soc. Parasitologists (hon.), Am. Soc. Parasitologists (in memoriam com. 1982, pub. responsibilities com. 1988, chmn. nominating com. 1992-93, coun. 1994—), Can. Fedn. Biol. Socs. (bd. dirs. 1990-91), Am. Fisheries Soc. (awards com. 1975-76), Wildlife Disease Assn., Aquaculture Assn. Can., World Aquaculture Soc., Asian Fisheries Soc., Brit. Soc. for Parasitology (hon.). Office: Pacific Biol Sta, Nanaimo, BC Canada V9R 5K6

MARGOLIS, LOUIS IRVING, financial executive; b. N.Y.C., Apr. 18, 1944; s. Morris and Frieda (Wactler) M.; m. Robyn Radow, July 25, 1970; children: Elizabeth, David, Matthew. BS in Econs., Columbia U., 1967. V.p options Donaldson, Lufkin & Jenerelle, N.Y.C., 1974-79; mng. dir. Salomon Bros., N.Y.C., 1979-91; Normura Securities Internat Inc, N.Y.C., 1991-93; Fin. advisor Commodity Futures Trading; bd. govs. Chgo. Merc. Exchange, Chgo., 1987-89. Vice chmn. United Jewish Appeal, N.J. Mem. Nat. Com. Options and Futures Soc. (bd. dirs.), Mountain Ridge County Club. Avocations: ski, jogging, golf, tennis. Home: 12 Chapel Hill Rd Short Hills NJ 07078-1210 Office: Normura Securties Internat Inc 2 World Financial Ctr Bldg B New York NY 10281-1001

MARGOLIS, MILTON JOSEPH, marketing executive; b. Dayton, Ohio, Oct. 13, 1925; s. Jacob and Fannie (Frankel) M.; m. Magda Lippner, July 31, 1964. BA, U. Cin., 1939; MBA, Harvard U., 1941. V.p. Hart Schaffner & Marx, N.Y.C., 1947-53, Kenyon & Eckhardt, N.Y.C., 1953-65; pres., vice chmn. Host Apparel, Inc., N.Y.C., 1965—. Former mem. econ. advisors com. to Mayor of N.Y.C., 1970-72; pres. Men's Wear Council, N.Y.C., 1985—, Father's Day Coun., 1980—; bd. dirs. YMCA, 1978, Asphalt Green Sport-Art Ctr., 1980, Civic Asphalt Green, N.Y.C., 1987—, NCCJ, 1991—. Comdr. USCGR, 1942-46. Recipient Recognition award Sales Promotion Execs. Assn., 1965, award Am. Cancer Soc., 1990, Lifetime Achievement award Men's Apparel Industry, 1992. Mem. Mktg. Comms. Execs. Assn. (pres. 1967-68), Am. Mktg. Assn. (pres. 1975-77), Harvard Club of N.Y.C., Phi Beta Kappa (bd. dirs. 1987—), Phi Beta Kappa Assocs. (nat. pres. 1994-95). Democrat. Jewish. Avocations: tennis, philately, reading, theater. Home: 180 E End Ave New York NY 10128 Office: 1430 Broadway New York NY 10018

MARGOLIS, NATALIE, nursing administrator, educator; b. Pitts., June 14, 1930; d. Philip and Evelyn (Fingeret) Wekselman; m. Gerald Margolis; children: Anne Elizabeth, Daniel Wayne, Ruth Ellen, Rachel Mary, Jonathan Aaron. Diploma, Montefiore Hosp., 1949; BSN, U. Pitts., 1953; MA, Wright State U., 1953, EdS, 1985. Acting dir. Sch. of Nursing Sinclair Community Coll., Dayton, Ohio, coord. staff devel.; dir. Sch. of Nursing Community Hosp., Springfield, Ohio, Meml. Hosp., Albany, N.Y. Contbr. articles to profl. jours. mem. ANA, Nat. League of Nursing, NCSPOP (Northeastern v.p., John Fry Individual Merit award 1984-85, 90, Glen Schmitz award Outstanding Svc.). Home: 551C Sand Creek Rd Albany NY 12205-2431

MARGOLIS, PHILIP MARCUS, psychiatrist, educator; b. Lima, Ohio, July 7, 1925; s. Harry Sterling and Clara (Brunner) M.; m. Nancy Nupuf, July 26, 1959; children: Cynthia, Marc, David, Laurence. B.A. magna cum

laude, U. Minn., 1945, M.D., 1948. Diplomate Am. Bd. Psychiatry and Neurology (examiner 1973—). Intern Milw. County Hosp., 1948-49; resident VA Hosp. and U. Minn., 1949-52, Mass. Gen. Hosp. and Harvard U., Boston, 1952-54; instr. U. Minn., Milw., 1953-55; asst. prof. psychiatry Med. Sch., U. Chgo., 1955-60, assoc. prof., 1960-66; prof. psychiatry Med. Sch., U. Mich., 1966—, prof. community mental health, 1968—; chief psychiat. inpatient service U. Chgo. Hosps. and Clinics, 1956-66; cons. Forensic Psychiat. Ctr., State of Mich., 1972—, coord. med. student edn. program, 1975-78, dir., 1978-82; cons. Turner Geriatric Clin., 1978-86, cons. Breast Cancer Clinic, 1988, Powertrain subs. Gen. Motors, 1984—, Dept. Mental Health, U.S. Dept. Justice; assoc. chief clin. affairs U. Mich. Hosps., 1981-85, chmn. ethics com.; bd. dirs., mem. profl. rev. com. PSRO Area VII, 1982-86; mem. Mich. State Bd. Medicine, 1986—; mem. bd. of Medicine chmn., 1992—, senate adv. com. Viral Hepatitis; bd. dirs. Fedn. of State Med. Bds., 1994—, Mich. del., 1988—, FLEX Com. Nat. Bd. Med. Examiners; mem. coun. Med. Edn. and Career Devel., 1993—; cons. Steering Com. on Practice Guidlines, 1991—. Author: Guide for Mental Health Workers, 1970, Patient Power: The Development of a Therapeutic Community in a General Hospital, 1974; also articles; cons. editor: Community Mental Health jour, 1967—. Recipient Commonwealth Fund fellow award, 1964, Career Svc. award, 1992, Resident Appreciation award, 1991. Fellow Am. Coll. Psychiatrists, Am. Psychiat. Assn. (life, chmn. membership com. 1979-83, coms. ethics com. 1983-86, trustee 1985-88, sec. 1989-91, mem. assembly 1992—, coun. med. edn. and career devel. 1993—, budget com. 1991—, chmn. ethics appeals bd. 1989—, pres. Lifers 1994—); mem. Washtenaw County Med. Soc. (exec. coun. 1982—, chmn. ethics com. 1983-87, pres. 1987-88, editl. bd. 1995—), Mich. Psychiat. Soc. (pres. 1980-81, chmn. ethics com. 1983-86), Internat. Assn. Social Psychiatry, World Fedn. Mental Health, Am. Acad. Psychoanalysis, Am. Acad. Psychiatry and Law (com. on psychoanalytic edn. 1995—). Home: 228 Riverview Dr Ann Arbor MI 48104-1846 Office: 900 Wall St Ann Arbor MI 48105-1910

MARGOLIS, RICHARD MARTIN, photographer, educator; b. Lorain, Ohio, June 10, 1943; s. Harold and Claudine (Martin) M.; m. Sherry Lynn Phillips. BS, Kent State U., 1969; MFA, Rochester Inst. Tech., 1978. Asst. prof. SUNY-Brockport, 1981-88; presenter Bridge Project, Stories about Bridges, Soc. for Indsl. Archeology Nat. Conf., 1995. One-man shows include Foto, N.Y.C., 1976, 79, 81, 83, Carpenter Ctr., Harvard U., 1978, George Eastman House, Rochester, N.Y., 1978, Camden Arts Ctr., London, 1981, NAS, Washington, 1990, Magic Powers, Rochester, 1991, Bridges: Symbols of Progress, catalog and exhbn. on nat. tour, 1991-94, Rochester's Landmarks Airport Art Project Permanent Installation; group shows 130 Years of Ohio Photography, Columbus, 1978, Contemporary Expression, Catskill Ctr. for Photography, Woodstock, N.Y., 1979; curator (exhbns.), 1980, 82; curator: Photography Art of State, 1983, Computers and Photography, 1989. Creative Artists Pub. Service Found. grantee N.Y. State Council on Arts, 1977-78; N.Y. State Council on Arts grantee to photograph N.Y. bridges, 1985, 90; SUNY Research Found. incentive grantee, 1983; Lift grantee, 1989. Mem. Soc. for Photog. Edn. (chmn. 1982-83), Photog. Heritage Assn. (founder, steering coun.), Soc. for Indsl. Archaeology. Office: 225 Barrington St Rochester NY 14607-2903

MARGOLIS, SIDNEY O., textile and apparel company executive; b. Boston, Dec. 13, 1925; s. Joseph and Lillian (Frank) M.; m. Phyllis Teichberg, June 24, 1950; children: Jonathan S., Dean F., Brian B. BS in Indsl. Engring. Ohio State U., 1949. Indsl. engr. ACME Backing Corp., Bklyn., 1949-53; purchasing agt. Flexible Barriers Inc., Stamford, Conn., 1953-57; office mgr. United Mchts. and Mfrs. Inc., N.Y.C., 1957-69, comptroller merchandising, 1970-77, v.p. adminstrn., 1977-80, sr v.p. adminstrn., 1980—, exec. v.p. adminstrn., 1984—; also bd. dirs.; bd. dirs. 10 West 86th Street Corp., N.Y.C. Cpl. USAAF, 1943-44. Mem. Inst. Indsl. Engrs. (recipient 25 yr. disting. svc. award N.Y.C. chpt. 1985), Am. Inst. Indsl. Engrs. (Svc. award 1984), Adminstrv. Mgmt. Soc., Textile Distbrs. Assn., Am. Textile Mfrs. Inst. Avocations: sports, travel, reading, water skiing, tennis. Office: United Mchts & Mfrs Inc 1650 Palisade Ave Teaneck NJ 07666-3630

MARGOLIS, STUART W., computer science and engineering educator; b. Bklyn., June 29, 1953; m. Jane Margolis; children: Joshua, Leah. AB in Math., Rutgers U., 1974; PhD in Math., U. Calif., Berkeley, 1979. Asst. prof. math. U. Vt., 1979-82, asst. prof. computer sci., 1982-84; assoc. prof. computer sci. U. Nebr., Lincoln, 1984-88, prof. computer sci., 1988—, dir. Ctr. for Comm. and Info. Sci., 1992—; vis. rschr. Inst. de Programmation, U. Paris VI, 1983; maitre de recherche U. Paris VI, 1988, U. Paris VII, 1990; vis. prof. Monash U. Clayton, Australia, 1990, U. Calif., Berkeley, 1991 U. Lisbon, Portugal, 1992; mem. Math. Scis. Rsch. Inst., Berkeley, Calif., 1990; computer sci. chmn. search com., mem. curriculum com. Coll. Engring., U. Nebr., Lincoln, 1988-90, curriculum com., promotion and tenure com., 1990-91, mem. curriculum com. dept. computer sci., 1984-86, mem. math PhD com., 1984-88, mem. adv. com., 1985-91, head curriculum com., 1986-91, head faculty search com., 1989-90; lectr. in field. Mng. editor: Internat. Jour. Algebra and Computation; reviewer: NSF, Math. Revs.; referee Jour. Pure and Applied Algebra, Semigroup Forum, Theoretical Computer Sci., Jour. Algebra; contbr. articles to profl. jours. U. Vt. summer rsch. fellow, 1983; NSF grantee. Mem. Am. Math. Soc., European Assn. for Theoretical Computer Sci. Achievements include research in automata and formal languages; algebra, logic and applications to theory of computation; word problems for inverse monoids. Office: U Nebr Lincoln Ctr Comm & Info Sci 214B Ferguson Hall Lincoln NE 68588-0115

MARGOLIUS, HARRY STEPHEN, pharmacologist, physician; b. Albany, N.Y., Jan. 29, 1938; s. Irving Robert and Betty (Zweig) M.; m. Francine Rockwood, May 22, 1964; children: Elizabeth Anne, Craig Matthew. BS, Union U., 1959, PhD, 1963; MD, U. Cin., 1968. Diplomate Nat. Bd. Med. Examiners, 1969, chmn. pharmacology test com., 1990-94. Intern, resident Harvard Med. Svc. Boston City Hosp., 1968-70, pharmcology rsch. assoc., 1970-72; sr. clin. investigator NHLBI NIH, Bethesda, 1972-74; assoc. prof. pharmacology, asst. prof. medicine Med. U. S.C., Charleston, 1974-77, prof. pharmacology, assoc. prof. medicine, 1977-80, prof. pharmacology, prof. medicine, 1980—, chmn. pharmacology, 1989—; cons. NIH, FDA, VA, NSF, Washington, Bethesda, 1975—; mem. editorial bd. Am. Heart Assn., Dallas, 1980—. Editor: Kinins IV, 1986, Renal Function, Hypertension and Kallikrein-Kinin System, 1988; contbr. numerous articles to profl. jours. Commdr. USPHS, 1967-74. Recipient S.C. Gov.'s award for sci. S.C. Acad. Scis., 1988, Burroughs-Wellcome scholar, 1976; vis. scholar U. Cambridge, Eng., 1980-81; NIH grantee, 1975—. Fellow Coun. for High Blood Pressure Rsch., Am. Heart Assn.; mem. Am. Soc. for Pharmacology and Exptl. Therapeutics, Am. Soc. for Clin. Investigation and 10 additional med., sci. socs. Jewish. Achievements include studies of the role of kallikreins and kinins in human and animal forms of hypertension; discovery of abnormalities which signify roles in causing high blood pressure. Office: Medical Univ of SC College of Medicine 171 Ashley Ave Charleston SC 29425-0727

MARGON, BRUCE HENRY, astrophysicist, educator; b. N.Y.C., Jan. 7, 1948; s. Leon and Maxine E. (Margon) Siegelbaum; m. Carolyn J. Bloom, May 8, 1976; 1 dau., Pamela. A.B., Columbia U., 1968; M.A., U. Calif.-Berkeley, 1971, Ph.D., 1973. Asst. rsch. astronomer U. Calif.-Berkeley, 1973-76; assoc. prof. astronomy UCLA, 1976-80; prof. astronomy U. Wash., Seattle, 1980—, chmn., 1981-87, 90—; chmn. bd. govs. Astrophys. Rsch. Consortium, Inc., Seattle; chmn. bd. dirs. AVRA, Inc., Washington; co-investigator space telescope NASA, Washington, 1977—. NATO postdoctoral fellow, 1973-74; Sloan Found. research fellow, 1979-83. Fellow AAAS, Am. Phys. Soc.; mem. Internat. Astron. Union, Am. Astron. Soc. (Pierce Prize 1981), Royal Astron. Soc. Office: Astronomy Dept Univ Wash Seattle WA 98195

MARGRAVE, JOHN LEE, chemist, educator, university administrator; b. Kansas City, Kans., Apr. 13, 1924; s. Orville Frank and Bernice J. (Hamilton) M.; m. Mary Lou Davis, June 11, 1950; children: David Russell, Karen Sue. BS in Engring. Physics, U. Kans., 1948, Ph.D. in Chemistry, 1950. AEC postdoctoral fellow U. Calif. at Berkeley, 1951-52; from instr. to prof. chemistry U. Wis., Madison, 1952-63; prof. chemistry Rice U., 1963—, E.D. Butcher chair, 1986—, chmn. dept., 1967-72, dean advanced studies and research, 1972-80, v.p. research, 1980-86; v.p. for research Houston Advanced Research Ctr., 1986-89, chief sci. officer, 1989—; dir. Materials Sci. Ctr., 1986-93; vis. prof. chem. Tex. So. U., 1993—; dir. Council for Chem.

Research, 1985-88; Reilly lectr. Notre Dame, 1968, Phi Lambda Upsilon lectr. Kans. State U., 1995; vis. distinguished prof. U. Wis., 1968, U. Iowa, 1969, U. Colo., 1975, Ga. Inst. Tech., 1978, U. Tex. at Austin, 1978, U. Utah, 1982; Seydel-Wooley lectr. Ga. Inst. Tech., 1970; Dupont lectr. U. S.C., 1971; Abbott lectr. U. N.D., 1972; Cyanamid lectr. U. Conn., 1973; Sandia lectr. U. N.Mex., 1981; R.A. Welch lectr., 1985; NSF-Japan Joint Thermophys. Properties Symposium, 1983; chmn. com. on chem. processes in severe nuclear accidents NRC, 1987-88; mem. Wilhelm und Else Heraeus Stiffung Found. Symposium on Alkali Metal Reactions, Fed. Republic Germany, 1988; various nat. and internat. confs. on chem. vapor deposition of thin diamond films, 1989, 90, 91, 92, 93, 94; orgnl. com. First, Second Third and Fourth World Superconductivity Congresses, 1989, 90, 92, 94, NATO Conf. on Supercooled Metals, Il Ciocio, Italy, 1993; mem. adv. coms. chem., materials sci., rsch. U. Tenn. Knoxville, Ohio State U., Tex. So. U., La. Bd. Regents, sci. adv. bd. SI Diamond Tech., 1992—; BioNumerik, 1993—; Intrepid Tech., 1994—; cons. to govt. and industry, 1954—; pres. Mar Chem., Inc., 1970—; High Temperature Sci., Inc., 1976—; dir. Rice Design Center, Houston Area Research Ctr.; U. Kans. Research Found., Gulf Univs. Research Consortium, Energy Research and Edn. Found., Spectroscopic Assocs., World Congress on Superconductivity; advisor NROTC Assn., 1984—. Editor: Modern High Temperature Sci., 1984; contbg. editor Characterization of High Temperature Vapors, 1967, Mass. Spectrometry in Inorganic Chemistry, 1968; editor High Temperature Sci., 1969—, Procs. XXIII and XXIV Confs. on Mass Spectrometry, 1975, 76; author: (with others) Bibliography of Matrix Isolation Spectroscopy, 1950-85, 87; contbr. articles to profl. jours. Served with AUS, 1943-46; capt. Res. ret. Sloan research fellow, 1957-58; Guggenheim fellow, 1960; recipient Kiekhofer Teaching award U. Wis., 1957; IR-100 award for CFX lubricant powder, 1970, IR-100 award for Cryolink, 1986; Tex. Honor Scroll award, 1978; Disting. Alumni citation U. Kans., 1981, Sci. and Tech. award North Harris Montgomery Cmty. Coll., 1994. Fellow AAAS, Am. Inst. Chemists, Am. Phys. Soc., Tex. Acad. Sci.; mem. AAUP, NAS, Am. Chem. Soc. (Inorganic Chemistry award 1967, S.W. Regional award 1978, Fluorine Chemistry award 1980, S.E. Tex. Sect. award 1993), Am. Ceramic Soc., Am. Soc. Mass Spectrometry (dir.), Am. Soc. Metals, Electrochem. Soc., Chem. Soc. (London), Tex. Philos. Soc., Materials Rsch. Soc., Sigma Xi (Disting. Svc. award 1994), Omicron Delta Kappa, Sigma Tau, Tau Beta Pi, Alpha Chi Sigma. Methodist. Patentee in field. Home: 5012 Tangle Ln Houston TX 77056-2114 Office: Rice University PO Box 1892 6100 South Main Houston TX 77251

MARGULIES, JAMES HOWARD, editorial cartoonist; b. Bklyn., Oct. 8, 1951; s. Henry Norman and Miriam Margulies; m. Martha Anne Golub, May 21, 1978; children: Elana, David. BFA, Carnegie-Mellon U., 1973. Editorial cartoonist Jour. Newspapers, Springfield, Va., 1980-84, Houston Post, 1984-90, The Record, Hackensack, N.J., 1990—; syndicated cartoonist various newspapers, 1985—. Author: My Husband is Not a Wimp, 1988; contbr. columns to profl. jours.; cartoons featured on TV programs. Mem. leadership com. Jewish Community Ctr., Houston, 1987, 88. Recipient Best Cartoon award Population Inst., 1985, Global Media award, 1985, 2d Place Editorial award Pavillion of Humor, 1985, Judges award World Hunger Media awards, 1986, Katie award Press Club of Dallas, 1989, Best Black and White Illustration in Advt. and Graphic Arts Addy award Houston Advt. Fedn., 1990, John Peter Zenger award N.Y. State Bar Assn., 1992; named one of Texans Who Made the Eighties winter Ultra Mag., 1990. Mem. Assn. Am. Editorial Cartoonists. Avocation: running. Office: The Record 150 River St Hackensack NJ 07601-7110

MARGULIES, JEFFREY J., lawyer; b. Sioux Falls, S.D., 1946. BA magna cum laude, U. Iowa, 1968, JD with high distinction, 1973. Bar: Ohio 1973. Ptnr. Squire, Sanders & Dempsey, Cleve. Mem. ABA, Ohio Bar Assn., Cleve. Bar Assn. Office: Squire Sanders & Dempsey 4900 Society Ct 127 Public Sq Cleveland OH 44114

MARGULIES, LEE, newspaper editor. Television editor Los Angeles Times, Calif. Office: Los Angeles Times Times Mirror Sq Los Angeles CA 90053*

MARGULIES, MARTIN B., lawyer, educator; b. N.Y.C., Oct. 6, 1940; s. Max N. and Mae (Cohen) M.; m. Beth Ellen Zeldes, July 26, 1981; children: Max Zeldes, Adam Zeldes. AB, Columbia Coll., 1961; LLB, Harvard U., 1964; LLM, NYU, 1966. Bar: N.D. 1968, N.Y. 1974, Mass. 1977, U.S. Dist. Ct. Mass. 1977, U.S. Ct. Appeals (2d cir.) 1984, Conn. 1988. Asst. prof. law U. N.D., Grand Forks, 1966-69; editor-in-chief Columbia Coll. Today, Columbia U., N.Y.C., 1969-71; assoc. editor Parade Mag., N.Y.C., 1971-72; assoc. prof. law Western New Eng. Law Sch., Springfield, Mass., 1973-76; Bernard Hersher prof. law U. Bridgeport, Conn., 1977-92; prof. law Quinnipiac Coll., 1992—. Author: The Early Life of Sean O'Casey, 1970. Contbr. articles to profl. jours. Cooperating atty. Conn. Civil Liberties Union, Hartford, 1979—, bd. dirs., 1982-94; bd. dirs. Conn. Attys. for Progressive Legislature, New Haven, 1982—; bd. dirs. ACLU, 1987-94, mem. free speech-assn. and poverty constitutional rights com. 1988-94; chmn. bd. dirs. Fairfield County Civil Liberties Union, 1982-87, Hampden County Civil Liberties Union, 1976-78; bd. dirs. Civil Liberties Union Mass., Boston, 1975-78, Greater Springfield Urban League, 1976-78, Conn. Civil Liberties Union, 1982-94, ACLU, 1987-94. Ctr. for First Amendment Rights, Inc., 1993—. Recipient Media award N.Y. State Bar Assn., 1972, Gavel award ABA, 1973, Outstanding Tchr. award U. Bridgeport Law Sch., 1986, 87. Mem. Mass. Bar Assn., N.Y. State Bar Assn. Jewish. Home: 79 High Rock Rd Sandy Hook CT 06482-1623 Office: Quinnipiac Coll Sch Law 303 University Ave Bridgeport CT 06604-5795

MARGULIS, ALEXANDER RAFAILO, physician, educator; b. Belgrade, Yugoslavia, Mar. 21, 1921; came to U.S., 1944; s. Rafailo and Olga (Weiss-Belic) M.; m. Hedvig Hricak, Feb. 26, 1983; 1 son, Peter Hricak-Margulis. Student, U. Belgrade, 1939-41, 45-46; MD, Harvard U., 1950; hon. doctorates, Aix-Marseille U. Sch. Medicine, 1980, Med. Coll. Wis., 1986, Cath. U. Louvain, 1986, Karolinska Inst., Stockholm, 1986, U. Munich, 1987, U. Toulouse, 1987, U. Montpellier, 1993. Diplomate Am. Bd. Radiology. Intern Henry Ford Hosp., Detroit, 1950-51; resident in radiology U. Mich. Hosps., 1951-53; jr. clin. instr. U. Mich., 1953-54; instr., then asst. prof. U. Minn., 1954-59; asst. prof. sch. medicine Washington U., St. Louis, 1959-60, assoc. prof. to prof., 1960-63; prof. radiology, chmn. dept. U. Calif., San Francisco, 1963-89, dir. magnetic resonance Sci. Ctr., assoc. chancellor spl. projects, 1989-93; spl. cons. to vice chancellor U. Calif.; radiologist in chief U. Calif. Hosps., 1963-89; cons. VA Hosp., Letterman Gen. Hosp., San Francisco, U.S. Naval Hosp., Oakland, Calif.; cons. in radiology Office Surgeon Gen., 1967-71. Author (with others) Roentgen Diagnosis of Abdominal Tumors in Childhood, 1957; co-editor Alimentary Tract Roentgenology; editorial bd. Calif. Medicine, 1964-74, Radiology, 1975-93; assoc. editor Investigative Radiology, 1980-89; editor Opinion in Radiiology, 1988-91. Served to capt. AUS, 1957-59. Recipient J.P. Allyn medal P. Roberts Rsch. Inst., 1989. Fellow Faculty Radiologists (hon.); sr. mem. Nat. Acad. Scis-Inst. Medicine; mem. AMA (cons. drugs 1961—), Royal Coll. Radiologists, Roentgen Ray Soc., Assn. Univs Radiologists (pres. 1966-67, chmn. adv. com. acad. radiology 1971), Am. Gastroenterology Assn., Soc. Chmn. Acad. Radiology Depts. (pres. 1968-69), Radiol. Soc. N.Am., San Francisco Radiol. Soc. (pres. 1973-74), Rocky Mountain Radiol. Soc. (hon.), Calif. Acad. Medicine (pres. 1978), Soc. Magnetic Resonance in Medicine (pres. 1983), Serbian Acad. Scis. (fgn.), Russian Acad. Med. Scis. (fgn.). Home: 8 Tara Hill Rd Belvedere Tiburon CA 94920-1544 Office: Univ Calif Ste 16 3333 California St San Francisco CA 94143-0292

MARGULIS, LES, advertising executive; b. Granite City, Ill., July 13, 1948; s. Manuel and Fay (Taylor) M.; m. Deborah Margulis. BS, U. of the Pacific, 1970; MS, Syracuse U., 1975. Asst. media mgr. Young & Rubicam, N.Y.C., 1975-76; media planner DMB&B, N.Y.C., 1976-77; media supr. BBDO, N.Y.C., 1977-83, v.p., 1983-88, sr. v.p., 1988—; advisor Newhouse Sch. Comm., Syracuse U., 1992—. Recipient Creative Media award Advertising Age Mag., 1986, Media award Media Week, 1990. Mem. Internat. Advt. Assn. (pres. U.S. chpt. 1991-93, v.p. N.Am. chpt. 1994—), Internat. Radio and TV Soc. Avocations: cooking, traveling. Office: BBDO NY 1285 Avenue Of The Americas New York NY 10019-6028

MARGULOIS, DAVID See MERRICK, DAVID

MARHIC, MICHEL EDMOND, engineering educator, entrepreneur, consultant; b. Ivry, Seine, France, June 25, 1945; came to U.S., 1968; s. Jean-Marie and Yvonne Marie (Nenez) M. Ingenieur, Ecole Sup. D'Electricite, Paris, 1968; MS, Case Western Res. U., 1970; PhD, UCLA, 1974. Asst. prof. Northwestern U., Evanston, Ill., 1974-79, assoc. prof., 1980-84, prof., 1985—; vis. asst. prof. U. So. Calif., L.A., 1979-80; vis. prof. Stanford U., 1984-85, 93-94; bd. dirs. Holicon Corp., Evanston, Holographic Industries, Lincolnshire, Ill. Contbr. and co-contbr. over 120 jour. articles and conf. publs.; holographic portrait Ronald Reagan. Mem. IEEE (sr.), Optical Soc. Am., Midwest Bio-Laser Inst., Tau Beta Pi. Achievements include 8 patents in field. Office: Northwestern U Dept Elec Engring 2145 Sheridan Rd Evanston IL 60208-0002

MARIELLA, RAYMOND P., chemistry educator, consultant; b. Phila., Sept. 5, 1919; s. Angelo Raphael and Sophia (Peel) M.; m. Miriam Margaret McMahon, Nov. 26, 1943; children: Miriam Margaret, Raymond P., Anne Marie, Patricia Sue. B.S., U. Pa., 1941; M.S., Carnegie Inst. Tech., 1942, D.Sc., 1945; postdoctoral fellow, U. Wis., 1946. Instr., then asst. prof. chemistry Northwestern U., 1946-51; mem. faculty Loyola U., Chgo., 1951-77; prof. chem. Loyola U., 1955-77, chmn. dept., 1951-70; asso. dean Loyola U. (Grad. Sch.), dir. grad. sci. programs, 1968-69, dean, 1969-77, sci. cons. indsl. orgns., 1951-77; assoc. exec. dir. Am. Chem. Soc., 1977, exec. dir., 1978-82; Sec.-treas. Midwestern Assn. Grad. Schs., 1972-77; exec. com. Council of Grad. Schs., 1972-74; Scientific adviser to gov. Ill. Producer, performer sci. TV shows Chgo. networks, 1956-65; Author: Laboratory Manual of Organic Chemistry and Biochemistry, 1953, Inorganic Qualitative Analysis, (with J. L. Huston), 1958, Chemistry of Life Processes, (with Rose Blau), 1968, Selected Laboratory Experiments for Chemistry of Life Processes, 1968, also articles. Recipient McCormack Freud Hon. lectr. award chemistry and chem. engring. Omicron chpt. Phi Lambda Upsilon, 1961; Merit award Chgo. Tech. Socs. Council, 1962. Mem. Am. Chem. Soc. (chmn. Chgo. 1960-61, nat. councilor 1956-82, chmn. bd. com. on profl. relations 1974-75, cons. to chmn. bd.), AAAS, N.Y. Acad. Scis., Sigma Xi (pres. Loyola chpt. 1956-57), Phi Kappa Phi, Alpha Chi Sigma, Phi Lambda Upsilon, Lambda Chi Sigma, Sigma Delta. Home and Office: 21215 N 123rd Dr Sun City West AZ 85375-1944

MARIENTHAL, GEORGE, telecommunications company executive; b. Kansas City, Mo., Nov. 15, 1938; s. George and Sadie (James) M.; children: Shawn Ann Capon, Patrick James, Shannon Lee Van Winter. B.S., U.S. Naval Acad., 1962; M.S., Stanford U., 1963; M.B.A., Am. U., 1974. Sr. rsch. assoc. Logistics Mgmt. Inst., Washington; dir. regional ops. EPA, 1971-75, dir. water policy, 1984-85; dep. asst. sec. def. Dept. Def., Washington, 1975-81; v.p. Survival Tech., Inc., Bethesda, Md., 1981-84; dep. asst. sec. agr. Dept. Agr., Washington, 1985-86; dep. adv. programs Titan Systems, Inc., 1986-87; mgr. mktg. Computer Scis. Corp., Falls Church, Va., 1987-89; exec. mgr. nat. accounts MCI Communications Corp., Arlington, Va., 1989—; bd. dirs. 1st Security Fed. Savs. Bank. Served with USAF, 1962-67. Mem. Inst. Indsl. Engrs., Am. Def. Preparedness Assn., Armed Forces Communications and Electronics Assn., Internat. Telephone Pioneers Assn. Republican. Episcopalian. Club: Masons. Home: 10202 Parkwood Dr Kensington MD 20895-4130

MARIETTA, MICHAEL, biochemistry and medicinal chemistry educator; b. Rochester, N.Y., Feb. 12, 1951. AB, SUNY, Fredonia, 1973; PhD, U. Calif., San Francisco, 1978. Prof. U. Mich., Ann Arbor. MacArthur fellow, 1995. Research focuses on the biosynthesis of nitric oxide; findings have influenced the treatment of toxic shock syndrome, inflammation and carcinogenesis. Office: Univ MI Ann Arbor MI 48109*

MARIMOW, WILLIAM KALMON, journalist; b. Phila., Aug. 4, 1947; s. Jay and Helen Alma (Gitnig) M.; m. Diane K. Macomb, Oct. 18, 1969; children: Ann Esther, Scott Macomb. B.A., Trinity Coll., Conn., 1969. Asst. editor Comml. Car Jour., Chilton Co., Bala Cynwyd, Pa., 1969-70; asst. to econ. columnist Phila. Bull., 1970-72; staff writer Phila. Inquirer, 1972—, city hall bur. chief, 1979-81, editor Main Line Neighbors, 1986-87, N.J. editor, 1987-89, city editor, 1989-91; city editor, asst. to pub. Phila. Inquirer and Daily News, 1991-93; met. editor The Balt. Sun, 1993, assoc. mng. editor, 1993—; instr. urban studies U. Pa., 1979; instr. English Rutgers U., Camden, N.J., 1981; mem. nominating jury Pulitzer Prize, 1991-92. Recipient 1st place award for deadline reporting Press Assn., 1977; 1st place award for deadline reporting AP Mng. Editors of Pa., 1977; 1st place award for best news story Sigma Delta Chi of Phila., 1977; 2d place award for deadline reporting, 1980; Pulitzer prize for disting. public service, 1978, Pulitzer prize for investigative reporting, 1985; Silver Gavel award Am. Bar Assn., 1978, 82; Roy W. Howard Public Service award Scripps-Howard Found., 1978; Robert F. Kennedy Journalism award, 1978; Nat. Public Service award Sigma Delta Chi, 1978; Public Service awards AP Mng. Editors of Pa., 1978, 85; Public Service awards Sigma Delta Chi of N.J., 1978; Public Service awards Sigma Delta Chi of Phila., 1978, 85; 2d place award for investigative reporting Keystone Press Assn., 1978, 85; 1st place award for best news story Keystone Press Assn., 1982; Media Achievement award Phila. Bar Assn., 1982; William Schnader award Pa. Bar. Assn., 1982; Nat. Headliners award, 1985; Trinity Coll. Alumni Achievement award, 1984; Nieman fellow Harvard U., 1982-83. Mem. Pen and Pencil Club, Investigative Reporters and Editors, Inc. Home: 1025 Winding Way Baltimore MD 21210-1232 Office: The Baltimore Sun PO Box 1377 501 N Calvert St Baltimore MD 21202-3604

MARIN, CHEECH (RICHARD ANTHONY MARIN), actor, writer, director; b. L.A., July 13, 1946; s. Oscar and Elsa Mesa M.; m. Patti Heid, Apr. 1, 1986. BS, Calif. State U., Northridge. Co-founder improvisational group, City Works, Vancouver; formed comedy duo with Tommy Chong called Cheech and Chong; appeared in clubs throughout U.S., Can., Europe and Australia including Carnegie Hall, JFK Ctr.; recs. include Sleeping Beauty, Cheech and Chong, Big Bamba, Los Cochinos (Grammy award best comedy), The Wedding Album, Get Out of My Room, Born in East L.A., (films) Up in Smoke, 1978, Cheech & Chong's Next Movie, 1980, Nice Dreams, 1981, It Came from Hollywood, 1982, Yellow Beard, 1983, Things Are Tough All Over, 1982, Still Smokin', 1983, The Corsican Brothers, 1984, After Hours, 1984 (Best Film award Havanna Film Festival 1987, Best Screenplay), Echo Park, 1985, Fatal Beauty, 1987, Rude Awakening, 1988, Oliver and Company (voice only), 1988, Troop Beverly Hills, 1989, Ghost Busters II, 1989, Shrimp on the Barbie, 1990, Fern Gully: The Last Rainforest, (voice only) 1993, The Lion King, 1994 (voice only), A Million to Juan, 1994, Ring of the Muscateers, 1994, Mr. Payback, 1995; (video) Get Out of My Room, 1986 (Gold Cert. award); writer, dir., star (movie) Born in East L.A., 1987 (Grammy nomination 1986, Best Art Direction); co-writer title song Up in Smoke; producer, writer, actor, dir. (TV series) Culture Clash, 1991; actor: Golden Palace, 1992, (TV movie) The Cisco Kid, 1994—; concerts USA, Can., Europe and Australia. Recipient Grammy award for Los Cochinos, Best Comedy Rec., 1973. Office: CAA 9830 Wilshire blvd Beverly Hills CA 90212*

MARINACCIO, CHARLES LINDBERGH, lawyer; b. Stratford, Conn., Dec. 10, 1933; m. Meta Leupin; children: Louisa, Heidi. BA, U. Conn., 1957; JD with honors, George Washington U., 1962. Bar: Conn. 1962, D.C. 1982. Trial lawyer U.S. Dept. Justice, Washington, 1963-69; advisor supervisory and regulation div. Fed. Res. Bd., Washington, 1969-73; dir., exec. sec. law enforcement asstistance adminstrn. U.S. Dept. Justice, Washington, 1973-75; gen. counsel banking housing and urban affairs com. U.S. Senate, Washington, 1975-84; commr. SEC, Washington, 1984-85; ptnr. Kelley, Drye & Warren, Washington, 1985—. Mem. Fed. Bar Assn. (banking law com.). Home: 4911 Massachusetts Ave NW Washington DC 20016-4310 Office: Kelley Drye & Warren 2300 M St NW Washington DC 20037-1434

MARINACCIO, PAUL JOHN, JR., marketing executive, writer; b. Oceanside, N.J., Sept. 1, 1957; s. Paul J. and Jeanette (Romanescu) M. AB, Rutgers U., 1979. Polit. writer The N.J. Herald, Newton, 1979-82; reporter, bur. chief The Star Ledger, Newark, 1982-85; staff writer Newsday, Melville, N.Y., 1985-87; nat. econs. writer, bus. writer Newsday, N.Y. Newsday, N.Y.C., 1987-91; exec. dir. Econ. Policy Mktg. Group City of N.Y., 1991-94; mktg. exec. Deloitte and Touche, Wilton, Conn., 1994—; contbg. editor N.J. Monthly, Princeton, N.J., 1979-82; cons. Ctr. for Capital Studies CUNY, N.Y.C., 1994. Editor: New York City 1991: the World's Capital in Transi-

tion, 1991, Strong Economy, Strong City: Jobs for New Yorkers, 1993. Recipient 1st place award for deadline reporting Press Club L.I., 1986, for bus. writing N.Y. State AP, 1988, for labor reporting Newspaper Guild N.Y., 1989, Golden Quill award Garden State Scholastic Press Assn., 1991; Davenport fellow U. Mo. Sch. Journalism, 1990.

MARINACE, KENNETH ANTHONY, financial advisor; b. N.Y.C., May 2, 1944; s. Anthony and Hilda Marinace; children: Steven Joseph, Douglas Anthony. Student, Am. Inst. Fin., 1962-63, Am. Coll., 1975; CLU, Coll. Fin. Planning, 1981. CFP. Owner, CEO Comprehensive Fin. Svcs., Burbank, Calif., 1967—; bd. dirs. Life Underwriters Assn. L.A., 1980-82. Host radio series You and Your Money, 1988-90, TV series You and Your Money, 1990—. Bd. dirs. San Gabriel coun. Girl Scouts U.S., Arcadia, Calfi., 1987, Burbank Family YMCA, 1989, Econ. Coun., Mus. Sci. and Industry, L.A., 1990-93; mem. adv. panel Royal Alliance Assocs., Inc., N.Y.C., 1989-91; pres. Burbank Cmty. Healthcare Found., 1989. Recipient Bus. Person of Yr. award Profl. Econs. Svcs., 1974, Outstanding Citizen Commendations, City of Burbank, 1988, City of L.A., 1988, County of L.A., 1993. Mem. Internat. Assn. Fin. Planning, Inst. CFP, Am. Soc. CLU and ChFC, Kiwanis (bd. dirs. Burbank Found. 1989—), Oakmont Country Club, Jonathan Club. Avocations: golf, music, travel. Office: Comprehensive Fin Svcs 3811 W Burbank Blvd Burbank CA 91505-2116

MARINAKOS, PLATO ANTHONY, medical center administrator; b. Pitts., Dec. 26, 1935; m. Vaselia Pecunis; children—Plato, Constantine, Theodore, Alexia. B.S., U. Pitts., M.S. in Hosp. Adminstrn. with honors; postgrad. Sch. Law, Duquesne U. Adminstrv. asst. Homestead Gen. Hosp. Pa., 1960-61; asst. exec. dir. Allegheny Gen. Hosp., Pitts., 1961-65, assoc. exec. dir., 1965-68, exec. dir., 1968-73; pres. Conemaugh Valley Meml. Hosp., Johnstown, Pa., 1973-77; exec. v.p. Mercy Catholic Med. Ctr., Phila., 1977—; chmn. planning bd. Eastern Mercy Health Systems, Phila., 1983—. Contbr. articles to profl. jours. Bd. dirs. YMCA, Pitts., 1975-78, Better Bus. Bur. of S.E. Pa., Phila., 1977, Pa. Trauma Systems Found., 1985—; bd. dirs., mem. exec. com. West Phila. Corp., 1981—, Delaware Valley Hosp. Council, 1984—. Mem. Am. Hosp. Assn. (ho. of dels. 1984—), Assn. Am. Med. Colls., Hosp. Assn. Pa. (bd. dirs. 1984—). Republican. Greek Orthodox. Avocations: reading; skiing. Home: 1116 Beech Rd Bryn Mawr PA 19010-1648 Office: Mercy Health Corp SE PA 1 Bala Plz Ste 402 Bala Cynwyd PA 19004-1401

MARINARI, DONALD J., advertising executive; b. 1944. With BCE Telecom Corp., Montreal, Que., Can., 1964-92; with Nat. Telephone Directory, Somerset, N.J., 1993—; now pres. Office: Nat Telephone Directory 3 Executive Dr Somerset NJ 08873

MARINARO, EDWARD FRANCIS, actor; b. Mar. 31, 1950; s. Louis John and Rose Marie (Errico) M. B.S., Cornell U. Football player Minn. Vikings; football player N.Y. Jets, N.Y.C., Seattle Seahawks. Television appearences include (TV series) Laverne and Shirley, Hill Street Blues, 1980-86, Sisters, 1991—; (TV guest appearances) Falcon Crest; (films) Mace, 1987, Tonight's the Night, 1987, Sharing Richard, 1987, Amy Fisher: My Story, 1992, The Diamond Trap, 1988. Avocations: golf; racquetball; cooking; traveling. *

MARINE, CLYDE LOCKWOOD, agricultural business consultant; b. Knoxville, Tenn., Dec. 25, 1936; s. Harry H. and Idelle (Larue) M.; m. Eleanor Harb, Aug. 9, 1958; children: Cathleen, Sharon. B.S. in Agr., U. Tenn., 1958; M.S. in Agrl. Econs., U. Ill., 1959; Ph.D. in Agrl. Econs., Mich. State U., 1963. Sr. market analyst Pet Milk Co., St. Louis, 1963-64; mgr. market planning agr. chems. div. Mobile Chem. Co., Richmond, Va., 1964-67; mgr. ingredient purchasing Central Soya Co., Ft. Wayne, Ind., 1970-73, corp. economist, 1967-70, v.p. ingredient purchasing, 1973-75, sr. v.p., 1975-90; pres. Marine Assocs., Ft. Wayne, 1991—; bd. dirs. SCAN, 1992—; mem. agrl. policy adv. com. U.S.D.A. Bd. dirs. Ft. Wayne Fine Arts Found., 1976-79; bd. dirs. Ft. Wayne Hub. Transp. Corp., 1975-83; v.p. Ft. Wayne Philharm., 1974-76. Served with U.S. Army, 1959-60. Mem. Nat. Soybean Processors Assn. (chmn.), U.S.C. of C., Am. Agrl. Econs. Assn., Am. Feed Mfrs. Assn. (chmn. purchasing coun.). Episcopalian. Club: Ft. Wayne Country. Office: Marine Assocs 4646 W Jefferson Blvd Fort Wayne IN 46804-6832

MARINEAU, PHILIP ALBERT, food company executive; b. Chgo., Oct. 4, 1946; s. Philip Albert and Bernice (Collins) M.; m. Susan Anne Graf, June 28, 1969; children: Philip Albert III, Anne Elizabeth. AB in History, Georgetown U., 1968; MBA, Northwestern U., 1970. Coordinator sales research The Quaker Oats Co., Chgo., 1972-73, mktg. asst., 1973-74, asst. brand mgr., then brand mgr., 1974-78, product group mgr., 1978-80, dir., then v.p. product mgmt., 1980-85, pres. grocery specialties div., 1985-87, exec. v.p. grocery specialties and market devel., 1987-88, exec. v.p. internat. grocery products, 1988, exec. v.p., U.S. grocery products, 1989-93, pres., COO, 1993—. Bd. dirs. Travelers and Immigrant Aid, Chgo., 1987—; trustee Northlight Theatre, Evanston, Ill., 1985—. Mem. Am. Mktg. Assn. (Steuart Henderson Britt award 1987), Westmoreland Country Club (Wilmette, Ill.). Office: Quaker Oats Co Quaker Tower 321 N Clark St Chicago IL 60610-4714*

MARINELLI, JOSEPH JOHN, educational administrator; b. Mt. Vernon, N.Y., Aug. 8, 1943; s. Joseph and Antoinette (Valentino) M.; m. Rebekah Slavis, Feb. 21, 1981. BS in Psychology, U. Fla., 1965, MEd in Counseling, 1967; PhD in Ednl. Adminstrn., U. Wis., Madison, 1976. Counselor, dir. guidance, then dir. adminstrv. support svcs. Union County Pub. Schs., Lake Butler, Fla., 1967-72; project, rsch. asst., coord. cost-effectiveness Wis. Rsch. and Devel. Ctr. Individualized Learning, Madison, 1972-74; intern Coun. Exceptional Children, Reston, Va., 1974-75; fed. liaison Fla. Dept. Edn., Washington, 1975-77; sch. system adminstr. Orange County Pub. Schs., Orlando, Fla., 1977-89; assoc. supt. planning and govtl. rels. Orange County Pub. Schs., 1983-89; supt. schs. Livonia (Mich.) Pub. Schs., 1989—; dir. curriculum devel. project for educable mentally retarded, Baker, Bradford and Union County Pub. Schs., Lake Butler, 1971-72; cons. Nat. Conf. State Legislatures, Washington, 1975, Biscayne Coll., Miami, Fla., 1982-83; exec. dir. Orange County Pub. Schs. Found., Orlando, 1987-88; mem. state adv. com. Southeastern Edn. Improvement Lab., Research Triangle, N.C., 1987-89; mem. task force on testing,task force on edn. of exceptional students in least restrictive environment, Fla. Commr. Edn., 1988-89. Co-author: Toward Equality, Equity and Excellence, 1981, The Principal and Individually Guided Education: Concepts, Cases and Competencies, 1976, Public Policy and Education of Exceptional Children, 1976; contbr. articles to profl. jours. Treas. Orlando Leadership Coun., 1980-87; mem. steering com. Orlando Exec. Coun., 1987-89; bd. dirs. Livonia Symphony, 1990-91; chmn. Livonia Prayer Breakfast, 1989-91. Mem. Nat. Assn. Fed. Edn. Program Adminstrs. (pres. 1986-88), Fla. Assn. Sch. Adminstrs. (pres. 1988-89), Fla. Assn. Instrnl. Suprs. and Adminstrs. (pres. 1984-86), Fla. Assn. State and Fed. Ednl. Program Adminstrs. (pres. 1980-82), Am. Assn. Sch. Adminstrs., Am. Ednl. Rsch. Assn., Greater Orlando C. of C., Livonia C. of C., Fla. Ednl. Leaders Forum, Wayne County Assn. Sch. Adminstrs. (v.p. 1991—), Mich. Assn. Sch. Adminstrs. (coun. 1991—), Nat. Sch. Bd. Assn., U. Fla. Gator Club Cen. Fla. (pres. 1980-82), U. Fla. Nat. Alumni Assn. (exec. com.), Delta Upsilon Alumni Club (pres. 1971-72). Democrat. Roman Catholic. Avocations: tennis, antiques, travel. Office: Livonia Pub Schs 15125 Farmington Rd Livonia MI 48154-5413

MARINELLI, LYNN M., county official; b. Akron, Ohio, Aug. 4, 1962; d. Michael and Christine (Golonka) Madden; divorced; 1 child, Jessica. BA in English, Daemen Coll., 1985. Pub. rels. coord. Bison Baseball Inc., Buffalo, 1985-86; exec. asst. to Assemblyman William B. Hoyt N.Y. State Assembly, Buffalo, 1986-92; exec. dir. Erie County Commn. on Status of Women, Buffalo, 1992—; chair Erie County Coalition Against Family Violence, 1992-95; co-chair domestic violence com. Multidisciplinary Coordinating Coun., 1992—; mem. adv. bd. Dept. Social Svcs., Erie County, 1992—. Sec. dem. com. Town of Tonawanda, 1991—; active Dem. Jud. Adv. Com. Erie County, 1990—, Reapportionment Com., Erie County, 1991, Ct. Case Project, 1992—, Compass House, Erie County, 1993—, Women for Downtown, 1993—, Citizens Com. on Rape and Sex Assault, 1993—, Leadership Buffalo, 1994, United Way Family Support and Safety, 1994—. Recipient Disting. Svc. award Coalition Against Family Violence, 1992; named Young Careerist, Bus. and Profl. Women, 1991; named to 40 Under

Forty list, Bus. First, 1993. Roman Catholic. Avocations: skiing, reading. Office: Erie County Commission on Women 95 Franklin St # 1655 Buffalo NY 14202

MARINETTI, GUIDO V., biochemistry educator; b. Rochester, N.Y., June 26, 1918; s. Michael and Nancy (Lippa) M.; m. Antoinette F. Francione, Sept. 19, 1942; children: Timothy D., Hope L. B.S., U. Rochester, 1950, Ph.D., 1953. Research biochemist Western Regional Lab., Albany, Calif., 1953-54; instr. U. Rochester, N.Y., 1954-57; asst. prof. U. Rochester, 1957-60, assoc. prof., 1960-66, prof. sch. medicine and dentistry, 1966—; cons. Eastman Kodak, 1978, Rochester Gas & Electric, 1979. Author: Disorders of Lipid Metabolism, 1990; editor: Lipid Chromatographic Analysis, 3 vols., 1969, 2nd edit., 1976; contbr. 160 pub. articles in sci. jours. Served with USAAF, 1942-46. Recipient Nat. Infantile Paralysis award, 1952; recipient Glycerine Research award, 1957; NSF grantee, 1953; recipient Lederle Med. Faculty award, 1955, 56. Mem. Am. Soc. Biol. Chemists, Am. Chem. Soc., AAAS, Sigma Xi, Phi Beta Kappa. Rsch. area: membrane structure and function, biochemistry of phospholipids, phosphatidyinositol metabolism in isolated synaptomsomes. Office: Univ Rochester Med Ctr 601 Elmwood Ave Rochester NY 14642-0001

MARINI, ELIZABETH ANN, civilian military executive; b. Dubuque, Iowa, Feb. 8, 1940; d. Cletus Nicholas and Catherine Margaret (Blasen) Freiburger; m. John J. Marini, Jan. 12, 1980. BA, Carinal Stritch Coll., 1962; MPA, George Washington U., 1982. Claims examiner Social Security Adminstrn., Chgo., 1962-64; supply systems analyst Navy Electronic Supply Office, Great Lakes, Ill., 1964-67; investment rep. Investors Planning Corp. Am., N.Y.C., 1967; supply systems analyst Naval Electronic Systems Command, Washington, 1968-76, head Saudi naval expansion program, 1976-80, head def. security assistance office internat. program, 1979-80; chief East Asia/Latin Am. divsn. Office of Sec. of Def. Def. Security Assistance Agy., Washington, 1980-84; chief East Asia Pacific divsn. Office of the Sec. of Def., DSAA, Washington, 1984-90; chief arms coop. and policy analysis divsn. Office of the Sec. of Def., Def. Tech. Security Adminstrn., Washington, 1990—. Tchr. religion classes Blessed Sacrament Ch., Alexandria, Va., 1972-73. Mem. Kappa Gamma Pi, Pi Alpha Alpha. Roman Catholic. Avocations: reading, walking. Office: Def Tech Security Adminstrn # 210 400 Army Navy Dr Arlington VA 22202-2700

MARINI, FRANK NICHOLAS, public administration and political science educator; b. Melrose Park, Ill., June 18, 1935; s. Joseph and Lillian Lee (Stuart) M.; m. Elsie B. Adams; children: Lisa M., Katherine D. B.A., Ariz. State U., 1960, M.A., 1961; Ph.D., U. Calif., Berkeley, 1966. Instr. U. Mo., Columbia, 1963-64; asst. prof. polit. sci. U. Ky., 1966-67; asst. prof. Syracuse U., 1967-70; assoc. prof., asso. dean Syracuse U. (Maxwell Sch.), dir. public adminstrn. programs, 1970-73; dean Coll. Arts and Letters, San Diego State U., 1973-80; provost, v.p. acad. affairs Calif. State U., Fullerton, 1980-84; sr. adviser chancellor's office Calif. State U., 1984-85; sr. v.p., provost U. Akron, Ohio, 1985-90, prof. pub. adminstrn., urban studies, polit. sci., 1990—. Author pamphlets; contbr. numerous articles to profl. jours; editor: Toward a New Public Administration, 1971; mng. editor: Public Administrn. Rev, 1967-77; editor-in-chief Jour. Pub. Adminstrn. Edn., 1994—. Served with USAF, 1954-58. Mem. Am. Soc. Pub. Adminstrn., Am. Polit. Sci. Assn. Office: U Akron Dept Pub Adminstrn Urban St Akron OH 44325-7904

MARINI, ROBERT CHARLES, environmental engineering executive; b. Quincy, Mass., Sept. 29, 1931; s. Larry and Millie (Cirillo) M.; m. Myrna Lydia Pellegrini, June 26, 1955 (div. June 1994); children: Debra, Robert Charles, Larry. B.S.C.E. with honors, Northeastern U., 1954; S.M.S.E., Harvard U., 1955. registered. Advanced Mgmt. Program, 1985. Registered profl. engr., Mass., N.Y., Maine, R.I., N.H., Conn., Vt., Calif., N.C., Wash., Colo., Mich., Fla., Wis., Tenn., La., Ariz., Ohio, Ill., Va. Jr. engr. Camp Dresser & McKee Inc., Boston, 1955-56, project engr., 1958-64, assoc., 1964-67, ptnr., sr. v.p., 1967-77, pres. environ. engring. div., 1977-82, exec. v.p., 1982-84, pres., 1984-90, chief exec. officer, 1989—, also chmn. bd. dirs.; mem. civil engring. adv. com. Worcester (Mass.) Poly. Inst., 1985-90, U. Mass., 1986-90, U. Tex., Austin, 1989-91, chmn., 1991-92, mem. engring. found. adv. coun., 1991—. Contbr. articles to profl. jours. Dir. nat. coun. Northeastern U., Boston, 1983—, mem. corp. bd., 1983—, bd. overseers, 1985-89, trustee, 1989—; chmn. Leadership Phase Century II Fund, 1989-91, chmn. devel. com., 1991—; corporator Weymouth Savs. Bank, 1988—, trustee, 1991—; bd. dirs. Mass. Bus. Round Table, 1991—, vice chmn., 1995—. Recipient Disting. Eagle Scout award Boy Scouts Am., 1986, W. Erwin Story award, 1991, Outstanding Civil Engring. Alumni award Northeastern U., 1992, Outstanding Alumni award, 1993. Fellow ASCE, NAE, Instn. Engrs. Australia; mem. Am. Pub. Works Assn. (Man of the Yr. award New Eng. chpt. 1981), Am. Water Works Assn., Mass. Soc. Profl. Engrs. (Young Engr. of Yr. award 1966), Am. Acad. Environ. Engrs. (diplomate, trustee at large 1989-92, v.p. 1992-93, pres.-elect 1993-94, pres. 1994—, Stanley E. Kappe award 1992), Water Environment Fedn. (hon.), Internat. Assn. Water Pollution Rsch. and Control (hon.), Engring. Soc. New Eng. (New Eng. award 1994), Tau Beta Pi, Phi Kappa Phi. Roman Catholic. Home: 1 Nevin Rd Weymouth MA 02190-1610 Office: Camp Dresser & McKee Inc 1 Cambridge Ctr Cambridge MA 02142-1601

MARINIS, THOMAS PAUL, JR., lawyer; b. Jacksonville, Tex., May 31, 1943; s. Thomas Paul and Betty Sue (Garner) M.; m. Lucinda Cruse, June 25, 1969; children—Courtney, Kathryn, Megan. B.A., Yale U., 1965; LL.B. U. Tex., 1968. Bar: Tex. Assoc. Vinson & Elkins, Houston, 1969-76, ptnr., 1977—. Served with USAR, 1968-74. Fellow Tex. Bar Found; mem. ABA (sec. taxation sect. 1984-85), Tex. Bar Assn. (chmn. taxation sect. 1986-87). Clubs: Houston Country, Houston Ctr., Coronado.

MARINO, DANIEL CONSTANTINE, JR., professional football player; b. Pittsburg, Penn., Sept. 15, 1961. BA, communications, U. Pitts., 1983. Profl. football player Miami Dolphins, NFL, 1983—. Named All-America team quarterback, The Sporting News, 1981; Rookie of the Year, The Sporting News, 1983, NFL All-Pro team, The Sporting News, 1984-86, MVP, Nat. Football League, 1984-85; named to Pro Bowl Team, 1983-87, 91-92. NFL career record for most games (10) with 400 or more yards passing; NFL records for most seasons (5) with 4,000 or more yards passing, most seasons (9) with 3,000 or more yards passing, 1984-1992, most consecutive games (4) with four or more touchdown passes, 1984; NFL record for lowest percentage (2.03) of passes intercepted by a rookie, 1983; NFL record for most games (17) with four or more touchdown passes, 1984. Office: care Miami Dolphins Joe Robbie Stadium 2269 NW 199th St Opa Locka FL 33056-2602*

MARINO, EUGENE LOUIS, publishing company executive; b. N.Y.C., Jan. 7, 1929; s. Salvatore A. and Florence M. (Casabona) M.; student Columbia U., 1945-48; m. Patricia Ryan, Mar. 11, 1948; children—Jeanette, Anthony, John, Eugene III. Credit mgr. Sears, Roebuck Inc., L.I., N.Y., 1951-60; gen. credit mgr. Davison-Paxon div. R.H. Macy, Inc., Atlanta, 1960-63, Grand-Way div. Grand Union Co., N.Y.C., 1963-66; v.p., gen. credit mgr. Consumer Products div. Singer Co., N.Y.C., 1966-75, Grolier, Inc., Danbury, Conn., 1975-90, ret.; officer, v.p., gen. credit mgr., dir. numerous subsidiaries. Recipient Quarter Century cert. Internat. Consumer Credit Assn., 1981. Mem. Mchts. Research Council, Internat. Consumer Credit Assn., Nat. Assn. Credit Mgmt., Alpha Sigma Phi. Home: 4858 Tivoli Ct Sarasota FL 34235-3653

MARINO, JOSEPH ANTHONY, retired publishing executive; b. Geneva, N.Y., Apr. 1, 1932; s. Anthony Rocco and Antoinette (DePalma) M.; m. Catherine Colville, Dec. 18, 1953; children: Joseph, Michael, Paul. B.S., Tri-State U., 1959; M.B.A., Mich. State U., 1960. Mgr. Gillette Co., Boston, 1960-82; pres., chief exec. officer Liquid Paper Corp. div. Gillette, Dallas, 1979-82, Western Pub. Co., Inc., Racine, Wis, 1982-89; mem. adv. bd. Heritage Bank, Racine, 1983—; bd. dirs. Wickes Furniture Co., Aerosol Svcs. Co., Inc. Mem. bus. alumni adv. bd. Mich. State U., 1987. Served with USAF, 1951-54. Recipient award of Honor Fedn. Jewish Philanthropies, 1973. Mem. Racine Country Club (Wis.).

MARINO, MICHAEL, church administrator. Asst. gen. overseer Christian Ch. of N. Am. Office: Christian Church of North Am 25595 Chardon Rd Richmond Heights OH 44143

MARINO, MICHAEL FRANK, lawyer; b. Little Falls, N.Y., Feb. 19, 1948; s. Michael Frank and Betty (Roberts) M.; m. Catherine Viladesau, Aug. 31, 1970; children: Michael John, Lisa Kathryn, Matthew Christopher. BS, Cornell U., 1971; JD, Syracuse U., 1974; LLM, Georgetown U., 1982. Bar: D.C. 1975, U.S. Dist. Ct. D.C. 1975, U.S. Ct. Mil. Appeals 1975, N.Y. 1976, U.S. Dist. Ct. (ea. and we. dists.) Va. 1977, U.S. Dist. Ct. Md. 1980, U.S. Ct. Appeals (4th cir.) 1982, Va. 1982, U.S. Ct. Appeals (9th cir.) 1994. Civilian employee head rels. br. Office of the Judge Adv. of the Navy, Washington, 1975-76; spl. asst. to the gen. counsel Office of Sec. of Navy, Washington, 1977; asst. gen. counsel labor and employment Office of the Gen. Counsel of the Navy, Washington, 1978; assoc. Pierson, Ball & Dowd, Washington, 1978-81; ptnr. Boothe, Prichard & Dudley, Fairfax and Mc Lean, Va., 1981-87, McGuire, Woods, Battle & Boothe, Mc Lean, 1987-89, Reed, Smith, Shaw & McClay, Mc Lean, 1989—; labor group head, Washington, Va.; mng. ptnr. McLean Office. Author: Virginia Employer's Guide to Labor Law, 1982; co-author: New York Employer's Guide, 1989, 92-94, Fla. Labor and Employment Law, 1994, Labor Employment Law in Pa., 1994. Mem. planning com. SMU Multi State labor Law Conf., Dallas; chmn. Arlington (Va.) Chamber Employee Rels. Com.; bd. dirs. Arlington Chamber Bd. of Dirs.; mem. Va. Chamber Mgmt. Rels. Com. Richmond, 1989—. Capt. USMC, 1971-78. Named Best Lawyer in Am., 1986-95. Mem. ABA (labor law com. 1974—), D.C. Bar Assn. (labor law com. 1974—), Va. Bar Assn. (labor law com. 1974—, sec.-treas. labor law sect. 1995), N.Y. Bar Assn. (labor law com. 1974—), Westwood Country Club. Roman Catholic. Avocations: jogging, fitness, hunting, fishing. Office: Reed Smith Shaw & McClay 8251 Greensboro Dr Ste 1100 Mc Lean VA 22102-3844

MARINO, PETER ANDREW, electronics company executive; b. Englewood, N.J., Feb. 3, 1942; s. Peter Marino and Elda Rossi; m. Jan Collins, May 11, 1944; children: Andrew, Dewey, Molly. BS, Rollins Coll., Winter Pk., Fla., 1963; MS, Penn State U., 1970. Sr. engr. Pratt & Whitney Aircraft, Jupiter, Fla., 1963-67; rsch. assoc.applied rsch. lab. Penn State U., State College, 1967-70; dir. tech. svc. CIA, Washington, 1970-86; exec. v.p. Lockheed Electronics, Plainfield, N.J., 1986-87; pres. Lockheed Electronics, 1987-88; sr. v.p. Fairchild Industries, Chantilly, Va., 1988-91, E-Systems, Dallas, 1991—; Bd. overseers N.J. Inst. Tech., Newark, 1987; bd. trustees Polytechnic Inst. N.Y., Bklyn., 1988; mem. blue ribbon panel on sci. & math. in secondary schs., 1986—. Contbr. articles to profl. jours.; inventor low frequent sound absorbing device. Bd. trustees Indl. Coll. Fund, Trenton, N.J., 1987. Mem. Nat. Security Industrial Assn. (trustee 1988—), Defense Intelligence Agency (cons. 1987—), Nat. Security Telecommunications Adv. Coun. (cons. 1989—), N.J. State C. of C. (bd. dirs. 1987). Roman Catholic. Office: E-Systems Dallas TX 76134

MARINO, SHEILA BURRIS, education educator; b. Knoxville, Nov. 24, 1947; d. David Paul and Lucille Cora (Maupin) Burris; m. Louis John Marino, Dec. 19, 1969; children: Sheila Noelle, Heather Michelle. BS, U. Tenn., 1969, MS, 1971, EdD, 1976; postgrad, W.Va. U. Elem./early childhood tchr. Knoxville City Schs., 1969-71; cooperating tchr. U. Tenn., Knoxville, 1969-71; dir. early childhood edn./tchr. Glenville (W.Va.) State Coll., 1971-72, Colo. Women's Coll., Denver, 1972-73; asst. prof. edn. Lander U., Greenwood, S.C., 1973-75; instr., spl. asst. coordinator of elem./ early childhood edn. U. Tenn., 1975-76; prof. edn., dir. clin. experiences, asst. dean Sch. Edn. Lander U., 1976-95, dean sch. edn., 1993-94; cons. in field; dir. Creative Activities Prog. for Children, Lander U., 1979—; mem. W.Va. Gov.'s Early Childhood Adv. Bd., 1971-72, Gov.'s Team of Higher Edn. Profls. on Comprehensive Plan for S.C. Early Childhood Edn., 1982. Contbr. articles to profl. jours.; author: International Children's Literature 1989. Bd. dirs. Greenwood Lit. Coun., v.p., 1990, pres., 1991; bd. dirs. St. Nicholas Speech and Hearing Ctr., Greenwood, pres., 1992; bd. dirs. Old Ninety-Six coun. Girl Scouts U.S.A., 1987-92; vol. March of Dimes Program, Greenwood, 1987. Mem. AAUW (pres. 1990—), AAUP, SNEA (state advisor 1981-88), S.C. Student Edn. Assn., Piedmont Assn. Children and Adults with Learning Disabilities (pres. 1986—, exec. bd.), Learning Disabilities Assn. S.C. (pres. 1990-94), S.C. Edn. Assn., S. C. Assn. for Children Under Six, So. Assn. for Children under Six, S.C. Assn. Tchr. Educators, Piedmont Reading Coun. (v.p. 1985-86, 90-91), pres. 1986-88, 91-92), S.C. Coun. Internat. Reading Assn. (exec. bd. 1986-88, 91—), Delta Kappa Gamma (pres. Epsilon chpt. 1984-88, 92-94, mem. exec. bd.), Pi Lambda Theta, Kappa Delta Pi (pres. U. Tenn. chpt. 1974-75), Phi Delta Kappa (v.p. 1988-90, pres. Lander U. chpt. 1990-91, 94—). Democrat. Presbyterian. Avocations: reading, gardening, swimming, music, arts and crafts. Home: 103 Essex Ct Greenwood SC 29649-9561 Office: Lander U Stanley Avenue Greenwood SC 29649

MARIO, ERNEST, pharmaceutical company executive; b. Clifton, N.J., June 12, 1938; s. Jerry and Edith (Meijer) M.; m. Mildred Martha Daume, Dec. 10, 1961; children: Christopher Bradley, Gregory Gerald, Jeremy Konrad. B.S. in Pharmacy, Rutgers U., 1961; M.S. in Phys. Scis., U. R.I., 1963, Ph.D. in Phys. Scis., 1965. Registered pharmacist, R.I., N.Y. Vice pres. mfg. Smith Kline Corp., Phila., 1975-77; v.p. mfg. ops. U.S. Pharm. Co. (divsn. E. R. Squibb), New Brunswick, N.J., 1977-79; v.p., gen. mgr. chem. div. E. R. Squibb, Princeton, N.J., 1979-81; pres. chem. and engring. div., sr. v.p. Squibb Corp., Princeton, 1981-84; v.p. Squibb Corp., 1984-86; pres., COO Glaxo Inc., 1986-88, chmn., CEO, 1988, chmn., 1989-91; CEO Glaxo Holdings plc, 1989-93, dep. chmn., 1991-93; co-chmn., CEO, Alza Corp., Palo Alto, Calif., 1993—; grad. asst., instr. U. R.I., Kingston, 1961-66; research fellow Inst. Neurol. Diseases, Bethesda, Md., 1963-65. Contbr. articles to profl. jours. Trustee Duke U., Rockefeller U., U. R.I. Found.; mem. president's coun. U. R.I.; chmn. Am. Found. for Pharm. Edn., Nat. Found. Infectious Diseases. Office: Alza Corp 950 Page Mill Rd Palo Alto CA 94304

MARION, DANIEL J(OSEPH), hospital executive; b. N.Y.C., Aug. 19, 1947; s. Sidney and Mildred (Eichenbaum) M.; m. Nancy Vogel, Oct. 5, 1974; 1 dau., Stacey Frances. B.S., Cornell U., 1969, M.H.A., 1974; M.S. Syracuse U., 1972. Lic. nursing home adminstr., Ill. Adminstrv. resident Fairfield Hills Hosp., Newtown, Conn., 1973; adminstrv. asst. Oak Forest (Ill.) Hosp., 1974-75; adminstr. Louise Burg Hosp., Chgo., 1975-77; asst. adminstr. Community Hosp. Ottawa (Ill.), 1977-81; exec. dir. Gibson Community Hosp., Gibson City, Ill., 1981-86; v.p. Cottage Hosp. of Grosse Pointe (Mich.), 1986-88; corp. v.p. St. Joseph's Health Sys., Atlanta, 1988-92; dir. provider rels. Med. Rev. Sys., 1992-93; v.p. Preferred Payment Sys., 1993—; former mem. Ill. Provider Trust Bd.; former mem. Ill. Compensation Trust; former mem. Ford County (Ill.) Mental Health Bd.; former mem. Champaign/Ford County Emergency Med. Services Bd. Fellow Am. Coll. Healthcare Execs., Am. Hosp. Assn. Office: Preferred Payment Systems 1771 W Diehl Rd Ste 200 Naperville IL 60563

MARION, DOUGLAS WELCH, magazine editor; b. Des Moines, May 9, 1944; s. Francis Orville and Alice Virginia (Welch) M.; m. Patricia Fisher, Sept. 2, 1967; children—Douglas Welch, Anne Welch. B.A., Parsons Coll., 1970; postgrad., Fresno State U., 1970. Staff editor Argus Publs., Los Angeles, 1974—, editor Super Chevy Mag., 1979-89; sr. editor Argus Pubs. Corp., L.A., 1989-94; asst. dir., bus. mgr. Super Chevy Show Events, 1994—; editor Popular Hot Rodding mag., L.A., 1994—; cons. in field. Contbr. articles to profl. jours. Named Man of Yr., Classic Chevy Club, Dearborn, Mich., 1981; named to Hall of Fame, Nat. Nostalgic Nova Club, 1990. Republican. Avocations: sports; golf; music; auto racing; photography. Office: Argus Pubs Corp 12100 Wilshire Blvd Ste 250 Los Angeles CA 90025

MARION, JOHN LOUIS, fine arts auctioneer and appraiser; b. N.Y.C., Nov. 27, 1933; s. Louis John and Florence Adelaide (Winters) M.; children: John L., Deborah Mary, Therese Marie, Michelle Marie; m. Anne Burnett Windfohr, May 26, 1988. BS, Fordham U., 1956; postgrad, Columbia U., 1960-61. With Sotheby Parke Bernet Inc., N.Y.C., 1960—, dir., 1965—, v.p., 1966-70, exec. v.p., 1970-72, pres., 1972-87; chmn. bd. Sotheby's Inc., N.Y.C., 1975—; bd. dirs. Sotheby Holdings Inc., London. Chmn. fine arts N.Y.C. div. Am. Cancer Soc., 1983—; vice chmn. bldg. steering com. Dobbs Ferry (N.Y.) Hosp., 1975; bd. dirs. Internat. Found. Art Research, Ctr. for Hope. Served as lt. (j.g.) USN, 1956-60. Mem. Appraisers Assn. Am., Lotos Club, Eldorado Club, Shady Oaks, Vintage Club. Home: 1400 Shady Oaks Ln Fort Worth TX 76107-3538 Office: Sotheby's Inc 1334 York Ave New York NY 10021-4806*

MARION, MARJORIE ANNE, English educator; b. Winterset, Iowa, May 6, 1935; d. Virgil Arthur and Marilyn Ruth (Sandy) Hammon; m. Robert H. Marion, Dec. 20, 1964; 1 dau., Kathryn Ruth. BA, Colo. Coll., 1958; MA, Purdue U., 1969; postgrad., Inst. Mgmt. Lifelong Edn. Harvard U., 1981. Chairperson English dept. Lincoln-Way High Sch., New Lenox, Ill., 1964-68; dir. pub. rels. Coll. St. Francis, Joliet, Ill., 1968-70, chairperson English dept., 1971-75, chairperson div. humanities and fine arts, 1975-79, coord. instructional devel., 1979-80, dir. continuing edn., 1980-84, acting v.p. for acad. affairs, 1984-85, dean of faculty, 1985-89, assoc. prof. English, 1989—; dir. Freshman Core Program, 1993—; mem. vis. team North Cen. Assn., Joliet & Lockport, Ill, 1975-79; lectr. at ednl. workshops and insts.; TV and radio appearances regarding lifelong edn., Chgo., St. Louis, Albuquerque, Pheonix, 1982-85. Drama critic Joliet Herald News, 1970-82. Recipient Pres.'s award Coll. St. Francis, 1975. Mem. Am. Assn. Higher Edn., Nat. Coun. Tchrs. of English. Roman Catholic. Office: Coll St Francis 500 Wilcox St Joliet IL 60435-6169

MARIONI, TOM, artist; b. Cin., May 21, 1937; s. John D. and Jennie (Geiss) M.; m. Kathan Brown, June 14, 1983; children by previous marriage: Marino, Anthony, Miles. MFA, Cin. Art Acad., 1959. Curator, Richmond Art Ctr. (Calif.), 1968-71; founding dir. Mus. Conceptual Art, San Francisco, 1970-84. Exhibited one-man shows: Galeria Foksal, Warsaw, Poland, 1975, DeYoung Mus., San Francisco, 1977, Modern Art Gallery, Vienna, Austria, 1979, Crown Point Press, San Francisco, 1993, Margarete Roeder Gallery, N.Y.C., 1994; group shows include: Tate Gallery, London, 1982, Belca House, Kyoto, Japan, 1982, Mus. Contemporary Art, L.A., 1995; editor, designer Vision, 1975-81. Mem. tech. assistance com. San Francisco Redevel. Agy., 1982—. Served with U.S. Army, 1960-63. W.Ger. Nat. Endowment Arts grantee, 1980; Guggenheim Found. fellow, 1981; Awards in Visual Arts grantee, 1984. Address: 657 Howard St San Francisco CA 94105

MARIOTTI, JAY ANTHONY, journalist; b. Ellwood City, Pa., June 22, 1959; s. Geno Anthony and Dolores Virginia (Lordi) M.; m. Dana Lynne Barnard, Apr. 19, 1985; children: Karina, Allison. Student, Ohio U., 1976-80. Sports writer The Detroit News, 1980-85; sports columnist The Cin. Post, 1985-87, The Rocky Mountain News, Denver, 1987-89, The Denver Post, 1989-90, The Nat. Sports Daily, N.Y.C., 1990-91, The Chgo. Sun-Times, 1991—. Recipient AP Sports Editors award, 1987, 1993, Crain's Forty under 40 award Crain's Chgo. Bus., 1992, Peter Lisagor award Chgo. Headline Club, 1992. Avocations: reading, tennis, golf, travel. Office: Chicago Sun-Times 401 N Wabash Ave Chicago IL 60611-3532

MARIOTTI, JOHN LOUIS, plastics & rubber manufacturing company executive; b. Toluca, Ill., Apr. 12, 1941; s. Faustino L. and Lillian E. (Gallagher) M.; m. Maureen, Aug. 22, 1964; children: Lisa, Michael, Susan. BSME, Bradley U., Peoria, Ill., 1963; MSME, U. Wis., 1964. Process engr., staff engr., staff supr. Automatic Electric Co., 1964-67; mfg. mgr. L.R. Nelson Corp., Peoria, Ill., 1967-76, v.p. planning and devel., 1976-79; pres., gen. mgr. Okla. Bicycle Div., Ponca City, 1979-83, Huffy Bicycle Co., Dayton, Ohio, 1983—. Chmn. bd. Productivity Communication Ctr., Chapel Hill, N.C.; chmn. bd. Goodwill Industries Dayton, 1990-93. Mem. Bicycle Inst. Am. (pres. 1991-92). Republican. Roman Catholic. Avocations: tennis, music, reading, painting. Office: Huffy Corp 7701 Byers Rd Miamisburg OH 45342

MARIS, HUMPHREY JOHN, physicist, educator; b. Ipswich, Eng., Apr. 25, 1939. B.S., Imperial Coll., London, 1960, Ph.D., 1963. Research assoc. Case Inst., Cleve., 1963-65; asst. prof. Brown U. Providence, 1965-71; assoc. prof. Brown U., 1971-76, prof. physics and engring., 1976—; sr. vis. fellow U. East Anglia, Eng., 1972-73; vis. fellow Chalmers Inst., Göteborg, Sweden, 1973; vis. scientist CNRS, Grenoble, France, 1973; sr. vis. fellow Japanese Soc. Promotion of Sci., 1982; vis. prof. Centro Atomicó de Bariloche, Argentina, 1983, U. Paris, 1984, 93, 94. Editor: Phonon Scattering in Condensed Matter, 1980. Recipient Senior Humboldt award, 1989. Fellow Am. Phys. Soc. Office: Brown U Dept Physics Providence RI 02912

MARIS, STEPHEN S., lawyer, educator; b. Dallas, Dec. 19, 1949; m. Bronwyn Holmes; children: Shane, Kara. BS, Stephen F. Austin State, 1971; JD, So. Meth. U., 1975. Bar: U.S. Dist. Ct. (no. dist.) Tex. 1975, U.S. Dist. Ct. (ea. dist.) Tex. 1986, U.S. Dist. Ct. (so. dist.) Tex. 1992, U.S. Ct. Appeals (5th cir.) 1980, U.S. Ct. Appeals (11th cir.) 1981, U.S. Supreme Ct. Tex. 1975. Assoc. Passman & Jones, Dallas, 1975-80, ptnr., 1980-87; ptnr. Fulbright & Jaworski, Dallas, 1987—; prof. So. Ill. U., 1979-80, So. Meth. U., Dallas, 1980—; mem. faculty Nat. Inst. Trial Advocacy, 1980—. Editor: Southwest Law Journal, 1973-75. Mem. ABA, State Bar Tex., Dallas Bar Assn., Barristers, Order Coif, Phi Delta Phi. Office: Fulbright & Jaworski 2200 Ross Ave Ste 2800 Dallas TX 75201-2784

MARISOL (MARISOL ESCOBAR), sculptor; b. Paris. Ed., Ecole des Beaux-Arts, Paris, 1949, Art Students League, N.Y.C., 1950, New Sch. for Social Research, 1951-54; Hans Hofmann Sch., N.Y.C., 1951-54; DFA (hon.), Moore Coll. Arts, Phila., 1969, R.I. Sch. Design, 1986, SUNY, Buffalo, 1992. One-woman shows include Leo Castelli Gallery, 1958, Stable Gallery, 1962, 64, Sidney Janis Gallery, N.Y.C., 1966, 67, 73, 75, 81, 84, 89, Hanover Gallery, London, 1967, Moore Coll. Art, Phila., 1970, Worcester (Mass.) Art Mus., 1971, N.Y. Cultural Center, 1973, Columbus (Ohio) Gallery of Fine Arts, 1974, Makler Gallery, Phila., 1982, Boca Raton Mus. Art, Fla., 1988, Galerie Tokoro, Tokyo, 1989, Hasagawa Gallery, Tokyo, 1989, Nat. Portrait Gallery, Washington, 1991, numerous others; exhibited in group shows including Painting of a Decade, Tate Gallery, London, 1964, New Realism, Municipal Mus., The Hague, 1964, Carnegie Internat., Pitts., 1964, Art of the U.S.A., 1670-1966, Whitney Mus. Am. Art, N.Y.C., 1966, American Sculpture of the Sixties, Mus. of Art, Los Angeles, 1967, Biennale, Venice, 1968, Art Inst. Chgo., 1968, Boymans-van Beuningen Mus., Rotterdam, The Netherlands, 1968, Inst. Contemporary Art, London, 1968, Fondation Maeght, Paris, 1970, Hirshhorn Mus. and Sculpture Garden, 1984, Nat. Portrait Gallery, Washington, 1987, Heckscher Mus., Huntington, N.Y., 1987, Whitney Mus. at Philip Morris, N.Y.C., 1988, Rose Art Mus., Waltham, Mass., 1990, Nat. Portrait Gallery, London, 1993; represented in permanent collections at Mus. Modern Art, N.Y.C., Whitney Mus. Am. Art, Albright-Knox Gallery, Buffalo, Hakone Open Air Mus., Tokyo, Nat. Portrait Gallery, Washington, Harry N. Abrams Collection, N.Y.C., Yale U. Art Gallery, Art Inst. Chgo., Met. Mus., N.Y.C., numerous others; pub. installation Am. Mcht. Mariner's Meml., Promenade Battery Pk. Pier A., Port of N.Y., N.Y.C. Mem. Am. Acad. and Inst. Arts and Letters (v.p. art 1984-87). Address: Marlborough Gallery 40 W 57th St New York NY 10019

MARITZ, WILLIAM E., communications company executive; b. St. Louis; m. Phyllis Mesker; 4 children. Grad., Princeton U., 1950. With Maritz Inc., St. Louis, now pres., chmn. bd. Bd. dirs. Community Sch., John Burroughs Sch., Princeton U., Sta. KETC, Mo. Bot. Garden, St. Luke's Hosp., Washington U., Brown Group, Am. Youth Found., Camping and Edn. Found., Cystic Fibrosis, others; founder, chmn. bd. Laclede's Landing Devel. Corp., St. Louis; chmn. bd. VP Fair Found. Recipient Levee Stone award Downtown St. Louis; Right Arm of St. Louis award, Regional Commerce and Growth Assn. Served with USN. Home: 10 Upper Ladue Rd Saint Louis MO 63124-1630 Office: Maritz Inc 1375 N Highway Dr Fenton MO 63099-0002*

MARK, ALAN SAMUEL, lawyer; b. N.Y.C., Mar. 13, 1947; s. Stanley M. and Miriam (Gordon) M.; m. Jean Mark, Aug. 1972 (div. 1976); m. Paula Calimafde, Oct. 14, 1978; children: Ilana, Clifford. Student, Johns Hopkins U., 1965-66; BA, NYU, 1969; JD cum laude, Am. U., 1973; LLM in Taxation, George Washington U., 1977. Bar: D.C. 1973, Maryland 1975. Ptnr. Verner, Liipfert, Bernhard, McPherson, Washington, 1982-85, Finley, Kumble, Wagner et al, Washington, 1986-88, Laxalt, Washington, Perito & Dubuc, Washington, 1988—; adj. prof. law Georgetown U. Law Sch. With U.S. Army. 1969-75. Mem. ABA, City Club of Washington. Avocation: tennis. Office: Laxalt Washington Perito & Dubuc 1120 Connecticut Ave NW Washington DC 20036-3902

MARK, HANS MICHAEL, aerospace engineering educator, physicist; b. Mannheim, Germany, June 17, 1929; came to U.S., 1940, naturalized, 1945; s. Herman Francis and Maria (Schramek) M.; m. Marion G. Thorpe, Jan. 28, 1951; children: Jane H., James P. A.B. in Physics, U. Calif. at Berkeley,

1951; Ph.D., MIT, 1954; Sc.D. (hon.), Fla. Inst. Tech., 1978; D. Eng. (hon.), Poly. U. N.Y., 1982; DEng (hon.), Milw. Sch. Engring., 1991; LHD (hon.), St. Edward's U., 1993. Research assoc. MIT, 1954-55, asst. prof., 1958-60; research physicist Lawrence Radiation Lab., U. Calif. at Livermore, 1955-58, 60-69, exptl. physics div. leader, 1960-64; assoc. prof. nuclear engring. U. Calif. at Berkeley, 1960-66, prof., 1966-69, chmn. dept. nuclear engring. 1964-69; lectr. dept. applied sci. U. Calif. at Davis, 1969-73; cons. prof. engring. Stanford, 1973-84; dir. NASA-Ames Research Center, 1969-77; undersec. Air Force, Washington, 1977-79; sec. Air Force, 1979-81; dep. adminstr. NASA, Washington, 1981-84; chancellor U. Tex. System, Austin, 1984-92; prof. aerospace engring. and engring. mechanics U. Tex., Austin, 1988—; mem. Pres.'s Adv. Group Sci. and Tech., 1975-76; bd. dirs. BDM Internat. Corp., Astronautics Corp. Am., MAC Equipment Co., Tex. Biotech. Corp.; trustee Poly. U., 1984—, MITRE Corp., 1985-88. Author: (with N.T. Olson) Experiments in Modern Physics, 1966 (with E. Teller and J.S. Foster, Jr.) Power and Security, 1976, (with A. Levine) The Management of Research Institutions, 1983, The Space Station-A Personal Journey, 1987; also numerous articles.; Editor: (with S. Fernbach) Properties of Matter Under Unusual Conditions, 1969, (with Lowell Wood) Energy in Physics, War and Peace, 1988. Recipient Disting. Svc. medal NASA, 1972, 77, medal for exceptional engring. achievement, 1984, Exceptional Civilian Svc. award USAF, 1979, Disting. Pub. Svc medal, Dept. Def., 1981. Fellow AIAA (Von Karmen Lectr. Astronautics 1992), Am. Phys. Soc.; mem. Nat. Acad. Engring., Am. Nuclear Soc., Am. Geophys. Union, Coun. Fgn. Rels., Cosmos Club. Achievements include research on nuclear energy levels, nuclear reactions, applications, nuclear energy for practical purposes, atomic flourescence yields, measurement X-rays above atmosphere, spacecraft and experimental aircraft design. Office: U Tex Dept Aerospace Engring & Engring Mechs Austin TX 78712-1085

MARK, JAMES B. D., surgeon; b. Nashville, June 26, 1929; s. Julius and Margaret (Baer) M.; m. Jean Rambar, Feb. 5, 1957; children: Jonathan, Michael, Margaret, Elizabeth, Katherine. B.A., Vanderbilt U., 1950, M.D. 1953. Intern, resident in gen. and thoracic surgery Yale-New Haven Hosp., 1953-60; instr. to asst. prof. surgery Yale U., 1960-65; asso. prof. surgery Stanford U., 1965-69, prof., 1969—, Johnson and Johnson prof. surgery, 1978—, head div. thoracic surgery, 1972—, assoc. dean clin. affairs, 1988-92; chief staff Stanford U. Hosp., 1988-92; governing bd. Health Systems Agy., Santa Clara County, 1978-80; sr. Fulbright-Hays fellow, vis. prof. surgery U. Dar es Salaam, Tanzania, 1972-73. Mem. editorial bd. Jour. Thoracic and Cardiovascular Surgery, 1986-94; contbr. over 130 articles to sci. jours. Bd. dirs. Stanford U. Hosp., 1992-94. With USPHS, 1955-57. Fellow ACS (pres. No. Calif. chpt. 1980-81), Am. Coll. Chest Physicians (pres. 1994-95); mem. Am. Assn. Thoracic Surgery, Am. Surg. Assn., Western Surg. Assn., Pacific Coast Surg. Assn., Halsted Soc. (pres. 1984), Western Thoracic Surg. Assn. (pres. 1992-93), Calif. Acad. Medicine (pres. 1978), Santa Clara County Med. Soc. (pres. 1976-77). Home: 921 Casanueva Pl Stanford CA 94305-1001 Office: Stanford U Med Ctr CVRB Stanford CA 94305

MARK, JAMES EDWARD, physical chemist; b. Wilkes-Barre, Pa., Dec. 14, 1934; married, 1964; married, 1990; 2 children. BS, Wilkes Coll., 1957; PhD in Physical Chemistry, U. Pa., 1962. Rsch. chemist Rohm & Haas Co., 1955-56; rsch. asst. Stanford U., 1962-64; asst. prof. chemistry Polytechnic Inst. Brooklyn, N.Y., 1964-67; from asst. prof. to prof. chemistry U. Mich., Ann Arbor, 1967-77; prof. chemistry, chmn. physical chemistry divsn., dir. polymer rsch. ctr. U. Cincinnati, 1977—; cons. various industries, 1963—; vis. prof. Stanford U., 1973-74; spl. rsch. fellow NIH, 1975-76; lectr. short course program Am. Chem. Soc., 1973—. Mem. AAAS, Am. Chem. Soc. (Am. Chem. Soc. award in applied polymer sci. 1994), Am. Phys. Soc., N.Y. Acad. Sci. Research in statistical properties of chain molecules; elastic properties of polymer networks. Office: U Cincinnati Dept Chemistry Cincinnati OH 45221*

MARK, JOHN, film company executive. With John Mark Film Co., L.A., 1971—; chmn., ceo John Mark Film Co., Beverly Hills, Calif., 1992—. Office: John Mark Film Corp 421 N Rodeo Dr # 1500 Beverly Hills CA 90210-4500

MARK, JONATHAN L, lawyer; b. N.Y.C., Oct. 18, 1947; s. Sandor and Ruth (Weiss) M.; m. B. Kathleen Munguia, May 25, 1986; children: Ramona G., Sandor A. AB, Dartmouth Coll., 1969; JD, Columbia U., 1974. Bar: N.Y., Calif., U.S. Dist. Ct. (so. and ea. dists.) N.Y., U.S. Ct. Appeals (2d cir.) Law clk. to presiding justice U.S. Dist. Ct. (so. dist.) N.Y., N.Y.C., 1974-75; assoc. Cahill Gordon & Reindel, N.Y.C., 1975-82, ptnr., 1982—. Office: Cahill Gordon & Reindel 80 Pine St New York NY 10005-1701

MARK, LAURENCE MAURICE, film producer; b. N.Y.C., Nov. 22; s. James Mark and Marion Lorraine (Huebner) Green. BA, Wesleyan U., 1971; MA, NYU, 1973. Exec. dir., publicity Paramount Pictures, N.Y.C., 1978-80; v.p., West Coast mktg. Paramount Pictures, L.A., 1980-82, v.p., prodn., 1982-84; exec. v.p., prodn Twentieth Century Fox, L.A., 1984-86; pres. Laurence Mark Prodns., L.A., 1986—. Exec. prodr.: (films) Black Widow, 1987, My Stepmother is an Alien, 1988, Working Girl, 1988, Sister Act 2: Back in the Habit, 1993, (TV) Sweet Bird of Youth, 1989, Mr. Destiny, 1990; prodr.: (films) Cookie, 1989, True Colors, 1991, One Good Cop, 1991, The Adventures of Huck Finn, 1993, Cutthroat Island, 1995. Mem. Acad. Motion Pictures Arts and Scis. Home: 7888 Woodrow Wilson Dr West Hollywood CA 90046-1256 Office: Hollywood Pictures Walt Disney Studios 500 S Buena Vista St Burbank CA 91521-0001

MARK, MARY ELLEN, photographer; b. Phila., Mar. 20, 1940; d. A. DeRoy and Beatrice (Silverman) M.; m. Frank Anthony Macaoge, 1963 (div. 1964); m. Martin Bell. BA, U. Pa., 1962; MA, Annenberg Sch. Communication, 1964. lectr.; presenter workshops in field. One-woman shows include Photographers Gallery, London, 1976, Castelli Graphics, N.Y.C., 1978, Olympus Gallery, London, 1981, Seson Art Gallery, U. Calif-Santa Cruz, Calif. Mus. Photography, Riverside, Drew U., N.J., 1982, Gallery of Fine Arts, Daytona Beach Community Coll., Fla., Friends of Photography, Carmel, Calif., 1983, Allen Street Gallery, Dallas, 1985, Birmingham (Ala.) Mus. of Art, 1989, numerous others; exhibited in group shows at Photokina, Cologne, 1973, Sidney Janis Gallery, N.Y.C., 1976, Internat. Ctr. of Photography, N.Y.C., 1979, Bibliotheque Nationale, Paris, 1979, Corcoran Gallery of Art and George Eastman House, N.Y., U. Colo., 1982, Eaton Shoen Gallery, San Francisco, 1983, Barbican Art Gallery, London, 1985, Munich Stadt Mus., 1985, Walker Art Ctr., Mpls., 1986, Portland (Maine) Mus. Art, 1986, Castle Gallery, New Rochelle, N.Y., Hillwood Art Gallery, Greenvale, N.Y., UN 40th Anniversary Photography Exhibit, 1985, Paris Opera, 1988, Zeitgensichss Photography, Frankfurt, 1989, numerous others; contbr. articles, photographs to profl. publs., mags., 5 books. Fulbright scholar, 1965-66; grantee USIA, 1975, NEA, 1977, 80, N.Y. State Coun. for Arts, 1977, NEA, 1979-80; recipient Page One award The Newspaper Guild of N.Y., 1979, First Pl. Feature Picture Stroy U. Mo., 1980, Canon Photo Essayist award Life Mag., 1983, 1st prize Robert F. Kennedy Journalism, 1985, Philippe Halsman award ASMP, Photojournalism award George W. Polk, 1988. Mem. Assn. Soc. Mag. Photographers.

MARK, MELVIN, consulting mechanical engineer, educator; b. St. Paul, Nov. 15, 1922; s. Isadore William and Fannye (Abrahamson) M.; m. Elizabeth J. Wyner, Sept. 9, 1951; children: Jonathan S., David W., Peter B. B.M.E., U. Minn., 1943, M.S., 1946; Sc.D. (Teaching, Research Fellow), Harvard, 1950. Registered profl. engr., Mass., Minn. Instr. N.D. State U., 1943-44, U. Minn., 1945-47; project mgr. Gen. Electric Co., Lynn., Mass., 1950-52; mgr. Raytheon Co., Wayland, Mass., 1952-56; cons. engr., 1956—; prof. Lowell Technol. Inst., 1957-59, dean faculty, 1959-62; prof. mech. engring. Northeastern U., Boston, 1963-84; dean engring. Northeastern U., 1968-79, provost, sr. v.p. for acad. affairs, 1979-84; vis. prof. Mass. Inst. Tech., 1955, Brandeis U., 1958; vis. prof. U. Mass., 1984-86; mem. Mass. Bd. Registration of Profl. Engrs. and Land Surveyors, 1990—. Author: Thermodynamics: An Auto-Instructional Text, 1967, Concepts of Thermodynamics, 1975, Thermodynamics: Principles and Applications, 1979, Engineering Thermodynamics, 1985. Contbr. articles to profl. jours. Served with USAAF, 1944-45. Recipient prize Lincoln Arc Welding Found., 1947. Hon. fellow ASME (fellow 1948-50); mem. Am. Soc. Engring. Edn., Sigma Xi, Tau Beta Pi, Pi Tau Sigma, Phi Kappa Phi. Patentee in field. Home: 17 Larch Rd Newton MA 02168-1413 Office: 93 Union St Suite 400 Newton Center MA 02159

MARK, MICHAEL LAURENCE, music educator; b. Schenectady, N.Y., Dec. 1, 1936; s. David and Ruth (Garbowitz) M.; m. Lois Nitekman, Jan. 28, 1942; children: Michelle, Diana. BM, The Cath. U. of Am., 1958, DMA, 1969; MA, George Washington U., 1960; M in Music Edn., U. Mich., 1962. Tchr. Prince George's County, Md. Pub. Schs., 1958-60, 61-66; assoc. prof. music Morgan State U., Balt., 1966-70; supr. music Auburn (N.Y.) Enlarged Sch. Dist., 1970-72; dir. music Elmira (N.Y.) Enlarged Sch. Dist., 1972-73; assoc. prof., sch. music Cath. U. Am., Washington, 1973-81; dean grad. sch., prof. music Towson (Md.) State U., 1981-95, prof. music, 1995—. Author: Contemporary Music Education, 1978, 2d edit., 1986, Source Readings in Music Education History, 1982; co-author: A History of American Music Education, 1992. Mem. Music Educators Nat. Conf. (numerous coms.), Am. Fedn. Musicians, Coll. Music Soc., Council for Research in Music Edn. (editorial com.), Nat. Assn. Acad. Affairs Adminstrs., Am. Assn. Higher Edn. Avocations: travel, woodworking. Office: Music Dept Towson State U Towson MD 21204

MARK, PETER, director, conductor; b. N.Y.C., Oct. 31, 1940; s. Irving and Edna M.; m. Thea Musgrave, Oct. 2, 1971. B.A. (Woodrow Wilson fellow), Columbia U., 1961; M.S., Juilliard Sch. Music, 1963. Prof. music and dramatic art U. Calif., Santa Barbara, 1965—; fellow Creative Arts Inst., U. Calif., 1968-69, 71-72; guest condr. Wolf Trap Orch., 1979, N.Y.C. Opera, 1981, L.A. Opera Theater, 1981, Royal Opera House, London, 1982, Hong Kong Philharm. Orch., 1984, Jerusalem Symphony Orch., 1988, Tulsa Opera, 1988, Compania Nacional de Opera, Mexico City, 1989, 92, N.Y. Pops, Carnegie Hall, 1991. Concert violist U.S., S.Am., Europe, 1961-67; artistic dir., condr. Va. Opera, Norfolk, 1975—, gen. dir., 1978—; condr.: Am. premier of Mary, Queen of Scots (Musgrave), 1978; world premier of A Christmas Carol (Musgrave), 1979, of Harriet, The Woman Called Moses (Musgrave), 1985, Porgy & Bess, Buenos Aires, Mexico City, Sao Paulo, 1992, Orlando Opera Co., 1993, Richmond Symphony, 1993. Recipient Elias Lifchey viola award Juilliard Sch. Music, 1963; named hon. citizen of Norfolk (Va.). Mem. Musicians Union, Phi Beta Kappa. Office: Va Opera PO Box 2580 Norfolk VA 23501-2580*

MARK, REUBEN, consumer products company executive; b. Jersey City, N.J., Jan. 21, 1939; s. Edward and Libbie (Berman) M.; m. Arlene Slobzian, Jan. 10, 1964; children: Lisa, Peter, Stephen. AB, Middlebury Coll., 1960; MBA, Harvard U. 1963. With Colgate-Palmolive Co., N.Y.C., 1963—; pres., gen. mgr. Colgate-Palmolive Co., Venezuela, 1972-73, Can., 1973-74, v.p., gen. mgr. Far East div. Colgate-Palmolive Co., 1974-75, v.p., gen. mgr. household products div., 1975-79, group v.p. domestic ops., 1979-81, exec. v.p., 1981-83, chief operating officer, 1983-84, pres., 1983—, chief exec. officer, 1984—, chmn. bd., 1986—; lectr. Sch. Bus. Adminstrn., U. Conn., 1977. Served with U.S. Army, 1961. Mem. Soap and Detergent Assn. (bd. dirs.), Grocery Mfrs. Am. (dir.), Nat. Exec. Service Corp. Office: Colgate-Palmolive Co 300 Park Ave New York NY 10022-7499*

MARK, SHELLEY MUIN, economist, educator, government official; b. China, Sept. 9, 1922; came to U.S., 1923, naturalized, 1944; s. Hing D. and S. (Wong) M.; m. Janet Chong, Sept. 14, 1946 (dec. Mar. 1977); children—Philip, Diane, Paul, Peter, Steven; m. Tung Chow, July 8, 1978. B.A. U. Wash., 1943, Ph.D., 1956; M.S., Columbia, 1944; postgrad. (Ford Found. fellow), Harvard, 1959-60. Fgn. news reporter CBS, N.Y., 1945-46; instr. U. Wash., 1946-48; asst. prof. Ariz. State Coll., 1948-51; territorial economist OPS, Honolulu, 1951-53; prof. econs. U. Hawaii, 1953-62, dir. econ. rsch. ctr., 1959-62; dir. planning and econ. devel. State of Hawaii, 1962-74, state land use commr., 1962-74, state energy coord., 1973-74; dir. Office Land Use Coordination EPA, Washington, 1975-77; prof. econs. U. Hawaii, 1978—; rsch. fellow East-West Ctr., Inst. Econ. Devel. and Policy, 1984-94; Asian advisor Internat. Ctr. Econ. Growth, 1992—; sr. advisor Dept. Bus., Econ. Devel. and Tourism, Hawaii, 1995—; vis. scholar Harvard U., 1986; vis. faculty Grad. Sch. People's Bank of China, 1988; also econ. cons. Philippines Inst. Studies, Devel. Rsch. Ctr. State Coun., China, also other orgns.; mem. Gov.'s Adv. Com. Sci. and Tech., 1963-74, Oahu Transp. Policy Com., 1964-74, Regional Export Expansion Coun., 1964-74;. Author: Economics in Action, 4th edit., 1969, Macroeconomic Performance of Asia-Pacific Region, 1985, Development Economics and Developing Economies, 1990, Aspects of Chinese Economic Development, 1991; editor: Economic Interdependence and Cooperation in Asia-Pacific, 1993; contbr. articles to profl. jours. Bd. dirs. U. Hawaii Rsch. Corp.; bd. dirs. Coun. State Planning Agys., pres., 1973-74, hon. mem., 1975—; governing bd. Coun. State Govts., 1972-74. Recipient Sackett Meml. award Columbia, 1944. Mem. Hawaii Govt. Employees Assn. (pres. univ. chpt., dir. 1958-59), Am. Econ. Assn. Royal Econ. Soc., Western Regional Sci. Assn. (pres. 1974-75, dir.), Phi Beta Kappa, Sigma Delta Chi. Mem. United Ch. of Christ. Home: 2036 Keeaumoku St Honolulu HI 96822-2526 Office: Dept Bus Econ Devel and Tourism Inst Econ Devel & Policy Honolulu HI 96813

MARK, SHEW-KUEY TOMMY, physics educator; b. Canton, China, Aug. 8, 1936; emigrated to Can., 1952, naturalized, 1952; s. Yook Sue and Nuey (Fong) M.; m. Yan Chu Woo, Sept. 9, 1961; children: Bethany Mark, Terence Mark. BSc, McGill U., 1960, MSc, 1962, PhD, 1965. Postdoctoral fellow NRC of Can., U. Man., 1965-66; asst. prof. McGill U., Montreal, 1966-70; assoc. prof. McGill U., 1970-75, prof. physics, 1975—; dir. McGill U. (Foster Radiation Lab.), 1971-79; chmn. dept. physics McGill U., 1982-90. Contbr. articles to profl. jours. Grantee Natural Scis. and Engring. Research Council of Can., 1965—. Mem. Canadian Assn. Physicists, Am. Phys. Soc., Canadian Assn. Univ. Tchrs. Home: 660 Victoria Ave, Westmount, PQ Canada H3Y 2R9 Office: 3600 University St, Montreal, PQ Canada H3A 2T8

MARKE, JULIUS JAY, law librarian, educator; b. N.Y.C., Jan. 12, 1913; s. Isidore and Anna (Taylor) M.; m. Sylvia Bolotin, Dec. 15, 1946; 1 child, Elisa Hope. BS, CCNY, 1934; LLB, NYU, 1937; BS in Lib. Sci., Columbia U., 1942. Bar: N.Y. 1938. Reference asst. N.Y. Pub. Libr., 1937-42; prt. practice law N.Y.C., 1939-41; prof. law, law libr. NYU, 1949-83, prof. law emeritus, 1983—, interim dean of librs., 1975-77; disting. prof., dir. Law Libr. St. John's U. Sch. Law, 1983—; lectr. Columbia Sch. Library Service, 1962-78, adj. prof., 1978-85; cons. Orientation Program Am. Law, 1965-68, Found. Overseas Law Libraries Am. Law, 1968-79, copyright Ford Found., law libraries, Coun. Fgn. Rels., 1990—, Shubert Archives, 1991, others. Author: Vignettes of Legal History, 1965, 2d series, 1977, Copyright and Intellectual Property, 1967, (with R. Sloane) Legal Research and LawLibrary Management, rev. edit., 1990, 95; editor: Modern Legal Forms, 1953, The Holmes Reader, 1955, The Docket Series, 1955—; Bender's Legal Business Forms, 4 vols., 1962; compiler, editor: A Catalogue of the Law Collection at NYU with Selected Annotations, 1953, Dean's List of Recommended Reading for Pre-Law and Law Students, 1958, 84, and others; chmn. editorial bd. Oceana Group, 1977—, Index to Legal Periodicals, 1978—; columnist N.Y. Law Jour., 1970—; contbr. articles to profl. jours. Mem. publs. coun. N.Y.U., 1964-80. Sgt. AUS, 1943-45. Decorated Bronze Star. Mem. ABA (editorial bd. Experience), Am. Assn. Law Librs. (pres. 1962-63, Disting. Svc. award 1986), Assn. Am. Law Schs., Coun. of Nat. Libr. Assns. (exec. bd., v.p. 1959, 60), Law Libr. Assn. Greater N.Y. (pres. 1949, 50, chmn. joint com. on libr. edn. 1950-52, 60-61), NYU Law Alumni Assn. (Judge Edward Weinfeld award 1987, mem. exec. bd. 1988—), Columbia Sch. Libr. Svc. Alumni Assn. (pres. 1973-75), Order of Coif (pres. NYU Law Sch. br. 1970-83), NYU Faculty Club (pres. 1966-68), Field Inn, Phi Delta Phi. Home: 4 Peter Cooper Rd Apt 8F New York NY 10010-6746

MARKEE, KATHERINE MADIGAN, librarian, educator; b. Cleve., Feb. 24, 1931; d. Arthur Alexis and Margaret Elizabeth (Madigan) M. AB, Trinity Coll., Washington, 1953; MA, Columbia U., 1962; MLS, Case Western Res. U., 1968. Employment mgr., br. store tng. supr. The May Co., Cleve., 1965-67; assoc. prof. libr. sci., data bases libr. Purdue U. Libr., West Lafayette, Ind., 1968—. Contbr. articles to profl. jours. Mem. ALA, AAUP, Spl. Libres Assn., Med. Libr. Assn., Ind. Online Users Group, Sigma Xi (Rsch. Support award 1986). Avocations: photography, sailing, gardening. Office: Purdue U Libr West Lafayette IN 47907-1530

MARK, ROBERT THOMAS, mayor; b. Wilmington, Del., Apr. 4, 1943; s. Robert H. and Margaret T. (Dillon) M.; m. Mary C. Alby, Aug. 5, 1967; children: Robert J. Katharine C. BA, Notre Dame U., 1965, PhD, 1975. Assoc. prof. Am. Internat. Coll., Springfield, Mass., 1969-92; city councillor City of Springfield, 1978-92, mayor, 1992—; mem. Springfield Conservation

Commn., 1976-78, Springfield Preservation Trust, 1982—, local govt. adv. commn. Commonwealth of Mass., Boston, 1982-90; bd. dirs. World Affairs Coun. Western Mass., 1979—, Mass. Mcpl. Assn., Boston, 1981-88; pres. Springfield City Coun., 1986. Bd. dirs. Stage West Resident Theatre, 1987—. Mem. Am. Polit. Sci. Assn. Democrat. Roman Catholic. Avocations: skiing, fishing, running. Home: 53 Florentine Gdns Springfield MA 01108-2507 Office: Office of Mayor Adminstrn Bldg 36 Court St Springfield MA 01103-1699

MARKELL, ALAN WILLIAM, linguistic company executive; b. Boston, June 6, 1933; s. Edward and Frances B. Markell; m. Carol Markell (div. Apr. 1978); children: Jennifer, Adam. AB, Bowdoin Coll., 1954; MBA, Columbia U. 1956. Fin. analyst RCA Corp., Camden, N.J. and N.Y.C., 1956-58; controller Jenkins Spirits Corp., Somerville, Mass., 1958-60, Marum Knitting Mills, Lawrence, Mass., 1960-63; pres. Norfolk Fluoridation Corp., Dedham, Mass., 1963-65, Car Mark Inc., Brookline, Mass., 1965-78; v.p. Linguistic Systems Inc., Cambridge, Mass., 1978-90, also bd. dirs.; pres. Cambridge Inst. Inc., Boston, 1979-86, instr. in mgmt.; ptnr. Moss Roberts and Co., Cambridge, 1978-90, bd. dirs. Miami Chamber Symphony, 1991—. Home: 200 Ocean Lane Dr Key Biscayne FL 33146

MARKEN, GIDEON ANDREW, III, advertising and public relations executive; b. Hampton, Iowa, June 24, 1940; s. Gideon Andrew Jr. and Cleone (Marie Riss) M.; m. Jeannine Gay Hill, Dec. 28, 1963; children: Tracy Lynn, Gideon Andrew. BS, Iowa State U., 1962; MBA, Hamilton Inst., 1967. Pub. relations mgr. Fairchild Instrumentation, Mountain View, Calif., 1967-68; pub. relations dir. Barnes-Hind Pharms., Sunnyvale, Calif., 1968-69; v.p. acct. supr. Hal Lawrence, Inc., Palo Alto, Calif., 1969-74, Bozell-Jacobs, Palo Alto, 1974-77; pres. Marken Communications, Sunnyvale, Calif., 1977—. Contbr. articles to profl. jours. Served as sgt. USAF, 1963-67. Mem. Pub. Relations Soc. of Am., Peninsula Mktg. Assn., Bus. Publishing Advt. Assn., Am. Mgmt. Assn., Am. Electronics Assn., Am. Med. Writers Assn. (pres. 1968-70, 72-74). Republican. Methodist. Club: San Rafael Yacht. Home: 1428 Bellingham Ave Sunnyvale CA 94087-3811 Office: Marken Comm 3375 Scott Blvd # 108 Santa Clara CA 95054

MARKEN, WILLIAM RILEY, magazine editor; b. San Jose, Calif., Sept. 2, 1942; s. Harry L. and Emma Catherine (Kraus) M.; m. Marilyn Tonascia, Aug. 30, 1964; children—Catherine, Elizabeth, Michael, Paul. Student, Occidental Coll., 1960-62; B.A., U. Calif.-Berkeley, 1964. Writer, mng. editor, now editor-in-chief and v.p. Sunset Mag., Menlo Park, Calif., 1964—. Bd. dirs. Calif. Tomorrow, 1979-83; pres. League to Save Lake Tahoe, 1994—. Democrat. Avocations: tennis; skiing; basketball. Office: Sunset Mag 80 Willow Rd Menlo Park CA 94025-3661

MARKER, DAVID GEORGE, university president; b. Atlantic, Iowa, Mar. 20, 1937; s. Calburt D. and Vera (Smith) M.; children—Paul C., Elizabeth A. A.B., Grinnell Coll., 1959; M.S., Pa. State U., 1962, Ph.D., 1966; L.H.D. (hon.), Hope Coll., 1984; ScD (hon.), Grinnell Coll. 1993. Instr., asst. prof., assoc. prof., prof. physics Hope Coll., Holland, Mich., 1965-84, adminstrv. dir. Computer Ctr., 1969-74, chmn. dept. computer sci., 1973-79, assoc. dean acad. affairs, 1973-74, provost, 1974-84; pres. Cornell Coll., Mount Vernon, Iowa, 1984-94, U. of Osteo. Medicine and Health Scis., Des Moines, 1994—; bd. dirs. Des Moines Gen. Hosp., Firstar, Des Moines,; cons. in field. Contbr. articles to profl. jours. Bd. dirs. St. Luke's Hosp., 1987-90; mem. adv. com. NSF Project Kaleidoscope, 1990-94. Recipient Bishop's Service Cross. Mem. NCAA (pres. commn. 1989-93), Nat. Assn. Colls. and Univs. (chmn. commn. on policy analysis 1991), Iowa Assn. Ind. Colls. and Univs. (exec. com. 1986-93, chmn. 1991-92), Iowa Coll. Found. (exec. com. 1987-92, chmn. 1990-91), Rotary, Phi Beta Kappa, Sigma Xi. Episcopalian. Avocations: cycling; music; photography. Home: Apt 601 3131 Fleur Dr Des Moines IA 50321 Office: Univ Osteo Medicine Health 3200 Grand Ave Des Moines IA 50312

MARKER, MARC LINTHACUM, lawyer, investor; b. Los Angeles, July 19, 1941; s. Clifford Harry and Voris (Linthacum) M.; m. Sandra Yocom, Aug. 29, 1965; children: Victor, Gwendolyn. BA in Econs. and Geography, U. Calif-Riverside, 1964; JD, U. So. Calif., 1967. Asst. v.p., asst. sec. Security Pacific Nat. Bank, L.A., 1970-73; sr. v.p., chief counsel, sec. Security Pacific Leasing Corp., San Francisco, 1973-92; pres. Security Pacific Leasing Svcs. Corp. San Francisco, 1977-83, dir., sec. Voris, Inc., 1973-86; bd. dirs. Refiners Petroleum Corp., 1977-81, Security Pacific Leasing Singapore Ltd., 1983-85, Security Pacific Leasing Can. Ltd., 1989-92; lectr. in field. Served to comdr. USCGR. Mem. ABA, Calif. Bar Assn., D.C. Bar Assn., Am. Assn. Equipment Lessors. Republican. Lutheran. Club: Univ. (L.A.). Office: 471 B Magnolia Ave Larkspur CA 94939

MARKER, ROBERT SYDNEY, management consultant; b. Nashville, July 27, 1922; s. Forest M. and Lassie (Weatherford) M.; m. Elizabeth Davis, Oct. 27, 1943; children—Christopher, Andrew. B.A., Emory U., 1946. Account exec. Griswold-Eshleman, 1949-51; advt. mgr. B.F. Goodrich Co., 1947-49; copy group head Maxon, Inc., 1951-56; sr. v.p., dir. creative services McManus, John & Adams, 1956-63; v.p. McCann-Erickson, Inc., 1963-64, sr. v.p., 1964-67; mgr. McCann-Erickson, Inc. (Detroit office), 1964-68; exec. v.p. McCann-Erickson, Inc. (Detroit office), 1967-68; pres. McCann-Erickson, Inc. (Detroit office), 1968-71, chmn. bd., chief exec. officer, 1971-74, also bd. dirs., mem. exec. com.; chmn. exec. com. Needham, Harper & Steers, Inc., 1975-80; mng. ptnr. Robert S. Marker, Inc., Tequesta, Fla. and N.Y.C., 1980-90; bd. dirs. Am. Assn. Advt. Agys., Detroit Adcraft Club, 1965, Detroit Advt. Assn., 1965, N.Y. Bd. Trade. Mem. Mayor's Council on Environment. Served with USAAC, 1943-46. Recipient Creative Advt. awards N.Y. Art Dirs. Club, Creative Advt. awards Detroit Advt. Club, Creative Advt. awards Chgo. Copy Club, Creative Advt. awards Alpha Delta Sigma. Mem. Am. Assn. Advt. Agys. (dir., chmn. Eastern region), Alpha Delta Sigma, Sigma Delta Chi. Clubs: Turtle Creek (Fla.); Winged Foot (Mamaroneck, N.Y.). Home: 10555 SE Terrapin Pl Jupiter FL 33469-1571

MARKERT, CLEMENT LAWRENCE, biology educator; b. Las Animas, Colo., Apr. 11, 1917; s. Edwin John and Sarah (Norman) M.; m. Margaret Rempfer, July 29, 1940; children—Alan Ray, Robert Edwin, Betsy Jean. B.A. summa cum laude, U. Colo., 1940; M.A., UCLA, 1942; Ph.D., Johns Hopkins U., 1948. Merck-NRC fellow Calif. Inst. Tech., 1948-50; asst. prof. zoology U. Mich., 1950-56, assoc. prof., 1956-57; prof. biology Johns Hopkins, 1957-65; chmn. dept. biology Yale U., 1965-71, prof. biology, 1965-86, dir. Center for Reproductive Biology, 1974-86; Disting. Univ. Research prof. N.C. State U., 1986-93, disting. univ. prof. emeritus, 1993—; panelist NSF, 1959-63; panelist subcom. on marine biology President's Sci. Adv. Com., 1965-66; mem. council Am. Cancer So., 1976-78; co-chmn. devel. biology interdisciplinary cluster Pres.' Biomed. Research Panel, 1975; mem. com. on animal models and genetic stocks NRC, 1979-85; trustee Bermuda Biol. Sta. for Research, 1959-83, life trustee, 1983—; bd. sci. advisers La Jolla Cancer Research Found.; mem. bd. sci. advs. Jane Coffin Childs Meml. Fund for Med. Research, 1979-86; chmn. bd. trustees BIOSIS, 1981, mem. 1976-81. Editor Prentice-Hall Series in Developmental Biology, Procs. 3d, 5th, 6th, 7th Internat. Congress Isozymes, 1974, 86, 89, 92; assoc. editor The Physiology of Reproduction; mng. editor Jour. Exptl. Zoology, 1963-85; mem. editl. bd. Archives of Biochemistry and Biophysics, 1963-81, Sci. mag. 1979-83, Differentiation, 1973—, Developmental Genetics, 1979-92, Cancer Rsch., 1982-85, Tansgenics, 1993—; mem. spl. adv. bd. Jour. Reprodn. and Devel., 1992—. Served with Internat. Brigades, 1938, Spain; with Mcht. Marine, 1944-45. Mem. Am. Inst. Biol. Scis. (pres. 1965), NAS (governing council 1970-71, 77-80), Inst. Medicine, Am. Soc. Biochemistry and Molecular Biology, Internat. Soc. Developmental Biologists, Am. Soc. Developmental Biology (pres. 1963-64), Soc. Study of Reprodn., Am. Acad. Arts and Scis. (governing council 1980-84), Am. Genetic Assn. (pres. 1980), Am. Soc. Naturalists (v.p. 1967), Am. Soc. Zoologists (pres. 1967), Genetics Soc. Am., Am. Soc. Animal Sci., Phi Beta Kappa, Sigma Xi. Home: 4005 Wakefield Dr Colorado Springs CO 80906-4324

MARKESBERY, WILLIAM R., neurology and pathology educator, physician; b. Florence, Ky., Sept. 30, 1932; s. William M. and Sarah E. (Tanner) M.; m. Barbara A. Abram, Sept. 5, 1958; children—Susanne Hartley, Catherine Kendall, Elizabeth Allison. B.A., U. Ky., 1960; M.D. with distinction, U. Ky. Med. Coll., 1964. Diplomate Am. Bd. Neurology and Psychiatry Diplomate Am. Bd. Pathology. Intern U. Hosp., Lexington, KY,

1964-65; resident neurology Presbyn. Hosp., N.Y.C., 1965-67; fellow neuropathology Coll. Physicians and Surgeons, Columbia U., N.Y.C., 1967—; asst. prof. pathology, neurology U. Rochester, N.Y., 1969-72; assoc. prof. pathology, neurology U. Ky., Lexington, 1972-77, prof. neurology, pathology, anatomy, 1977—, dir. Ctr. on Aging, 1979—, prof. neurology, pathology, dir., 1977—; mem. pathology study sect. NIH, Washington, 1982-85, nat. adv. coun. NIH, 1990-94; chmn. Med. Sci. Adv. Bd., Chgo. 1989-94, Nat. Alzheimer's Assn., Chgo., 1985-86, adv. panel on dementia U.S. Congress of Tech., Washington, 1985-86; dir. Alzheimer's Disease Research Ctr., 1985—, Alzheimer's Diseases Program Project Grant, 1984—. Mem. editorial bd. Jour. Neuropathology and Exptl. Neurology, 1983-86, 89—, Neurobiology of Aging, 1986—, Ann. Neurology, 1990—; contbr. numerous articles to profl. jours. With U.S. Army, 1954-56. Recipient Disting. Achievement award Ky. Research Found., Lexington, 1978; named U. Ky. Disting. Alumni prof., 1985, Disting. Research prof., U. Ky., 1977, Disting. Alumni U. Ky. Coll. Medicine, 1993; inductee U. Ky. Disting. Alumni, 1989; prin. investigator NIH, Washington, 1977—. Mem. Am. Acad. Neurology, Am. Assn. Neuropathologists (exec. com. 1984-86, pres1991—), Soc. Neurosci., Am. Neurol. Assn., Alpha Omega Alpha. Home: 1555 Tates Creek Rd Lexington KY 40502-2229 Office: U Ky Coll Med Dept Neurology & Pathology 800 Rose St Lexington KY 40536-0001

MARKEY, ANDREW JOSEPH, health care products company executive; b. Bayonne, N.J., May 23, 1931; s. Andrew Joseph and Mae Clara (Clark) M.; m. Elizabeth Kissak, Aug. 24, 1957; children: Timothy, Kevin, Mary Ellen, Michael, Jean Marie. B.S. in Econs., Villanova U., 1952. Auditor Lybrand, Ross Bros. & Montgomery, N.Y.C., 1954-58; various acctg. positions Johnson & Johnson Products, New Brunswick, N.J., 1958-72, v.p. fin., 1973-77; v.p. fin. Johnson & Johnson Internat., New Brunswick, 1977-80, corp. treas., 1981—. Home: 84 Bullion Rd Basking Ridge NJ 07920-2423 Office: Johnson & Johnson 1 Johnson Johnson Plz New Brunswick NJ 08933

MARKEY, EDWARD JOHN, congressman; b. Malden, Mass., July 11, 1946; s. John E. and Christine M. (Courtney) M. B.A., Boston Coll., 1968, J.D., 1972. Bar: Mass. Mem. Mass. Ho. of Reps., 1973-76, 94th-104th Congresses from 7th Mass. Dist., 1975—, New Eng. Congl. Caucus, N.E.-Midwest Econ. Advancement Coalition, Dem. Study Group, Environ. Study Conf. Freshman Caucus, now chmn. subcom. telecomm. and fin.; ranking minority mem., mem. commerce subcom. on telecomm. and fin. Mem. editorial staff: Boston Coll. Law Rev. Served with USAR, 1968-73. Mem. Mass. Bar Assn. Mass. (Mass. Legislator of Year 1975). Club: K.C. Home: 7 Townsend St Malden MA 02148-6322 Office: US Ho of Reps 2133 Rayburn HOB Washington DC 20515-2107*

MARKEY, ROBERT GUY, lawyer; b. Cleve., Feb. 25, 1939; s. Nate and Rhoda (Gross) M.; children: Robert Jr., Randolph; m. Nanci Louise Brooks, Aug. 25, 1990. AB, Brown U., 1961; JD, Case Western Res., 1964. Bar: Ohio 1964. Assoc., ptnr. Kahn and Kleinman, Cleve., 1964-75; ptnr. Arter & Hadden, Cleve., 1975-83, Baker & Hostetler, Cleve., 1983—; dir., sec. Blue Coral, Inc., Cleve.; bd. dirs. Matrix Essentials, Inc., Cleve., McKay Chem. Co., L.A. Chmn. attys. div. United Way Svcs., Cleve., 1978; trustee Fedn. Community Planning, Cleve., 1980-87, Cleve. Ctr. Contemporary Art, 1993—. Mem. ABA, Cleve. Bar Assn. (chmn. securities law com. 1974-75), Ohio State Bar Assn., Union Club, Chagrin Valley Hunt Club. Republican. Jewish. Office: Baker & Hostetler 3200 National City Ctr 1900 E 9th St Cleveland OH 44114

MARKEY, WILLIAM ALAN, health care administrator; b. Cleve., Dec. 29, 1927; s. Oscar Bennett and Claire (Feldman) M.; m. Irene Nelson, Oct. 31, 1954; children—Janet Ellen Markey-Hisakawa, Suzanne Katherine Markey-Johnson. Student, Case Inst. Tech., 1945-48; BA, U. Mich., 1950; MS, Yale U., 1954. Resident hosp. adminstrn. Beth Israel Hosp., Boston, 1953-54; asst. dir. Montefiore Hosp., Pitts., 1954-56; asst. adminstr. City of Hope Med. Ctr., Duarte, Calif., 1956-57; adminstrv. dir. City of Hope Med. Ctr., 1957-66; assoc. dir. cancer hosp. project, instr. pub. health U. So. Calif. Sch. Medicine, 1966-67, asst. clin. prof. pub. health and community medicine, 1968-70, asst. prof., 1970-75, dep. dir. regional med. programs, 1967-71; adminstr. Health Care Agy., County of San Diego, 1971-74; health services cons. Health Care Agy., 1974-75; dir. Maricopa County Dept. Health Services, Phoenix, 1975-79; cons. Maricopa County Dept. Health Services, 1979-80; adminstr. Sonoma Valley Hosp., Calif., 1980-83;; lectr. pub. health Sch. Pub. Health, UCLA, 1969-74; lectr. community medicine Sch. Medicine, U. Calif.-San Diego, 1973-75; cons. L.A. County Dept. Hosps., 1966-71, cons. Hosp./Health Svcs., 1983—; CEO Chinese Hosp., San Francisco, 1985-86, 90-91; adj. instr. Golden Gate U., 1992—. Mem. bd. edn. Duarte Unified Sch. Dist., 1967-72, pres., 1970-72; bd. dirs. Hosp. Coun. So. Calif., 1963-67, sec. 1966-67; bd. dirs. Duarte Pub. Libr. Assn., 1965-72, Duarte-Bradbury chpt. Am. Field Svc., 1967-72, Duarte-Bradbury Cmty. Chest, 1961-68, Cen. Ariz. Health Svcs. Agy., 1975-80, Vis. Nurse Assn. The Redwoods, Santa Rosa, Calif., 1985-86, Sonoma Greens Homeowners Assn., 1990-91, Sonoma City Opera, 1987, 93, United Way, Sonoma, 1995—; com. chmn. Sonoma County Bd. Realtors, 1990-92; active Sonoma County Multiple Listing Svc., 1987—. Served with AUS, 1950-52. Fellow Am. Coll. Health Care Execs. (life); mem. Am. Hosp. Assn. (life), Am. Pub. Health Assn., Royal Soc. Health, Calif. Hosp. Assn. (trustee 1966-69, dir. 1966-69), Internat. Fedn. Hosps., Hosp. Coun. No. Calif. (dir. 1981-83), Kiwanis, Rotary (past pres. Duarte). Home: 866 Princeton Dr Sonoma CA 95476-4186 Office: PO Box F Sonoma CA 95476-0370

MARKEY, WINSTON ROSCOE, aeronautical engineering educator; b. Buffalo, Sept. 20, 1929; s. Roscoe Irvin and Catherine L. (Higgins) M.; m. Phoebe Anne Sproule, Sept. 10, 1955; children: Karl Richard, Katherine Ilse, Kristina Anne. BS, MIT, 1951, Sc.D., 1956. Engr. MIT, 1951-57, asst. prof., 1957-62, assoc. prof., 1962-66, prof., 1966—, chmn. undergrad. com., 1988—, dir. Measurement Systems Lab., 1961-89; chief scientist USAF, 1964-65, mem. sci. adv. bd., 1966-69. Author: (with J. Hovorka) The Mechanics of Inertial Position and Heading Indication, 1961; Assoc. editor: AIAA Jour, 1963-66. Recipient Exceptional Civilian Service award USAF, 1965. Mem. Sigma Xi, Tau Beta Pi, Gamma Alpha Rho. Home: 11 Edgewood Rd Lexington MA 02173-3501 Office: MIT Bldg 33-208 Cambridge MA 02139

MARKGRAF, J(OHN) HODGE, chemist, educator; b. Cin., Mar. 16, 1930; s. Carl A. and Elizabeth (Hodge) M.; m. Nancy Hart, Apr. 4, 1957; children: Carrie G, Sarah T. A.B., Williams Coll., 1952; M.Sc., Yale U., 1954, Ph.D., 1957; postgrad., U. Munich, W. Ger., 1956-57. Research chemist Procter & Gamble Co., Cin., 1958-59; asst. prof. chemistry Williams Coll., Williamstown, Mass., 1959-65; assoc. prof. Williams Coll., 1965-69, prof., 1969—, Ebenezer Fitch prof. chemistry, 1977-85, 94—, provost, 1980-83, v.p. for alumni relations and devel., 1985-94; vis. prof. U. Calif., Berkeley, 1964-65, 68-69, 76-77, Duke U., 1983-84. Contbr. articles to profl. jours. NSF fellow; Sci. Faculty fellow; grantee NSF; grantee Am. Chem. Soc. Petroleum Research Fund; grantee Research Corp.; grantee Merck & Co. Mem. Am. Chem. Soc., Phi Beta Kappa, Sigma Xi. Patentee in field. Home: 104 Forest Rd Williamstown MA 01267-2029 Office: Williams College Williamstown MA 01267

MARKHAM, CHARLES BUCHANAN, lawyer; b. Durham, N.C., Sept. 15, 1926; s. Charles Blackwell and Sadie Helen (Hackney) M. A.B., Duke U., Durham, N.C., 1945; postgrad., U. N.C. Law Sch., Chapel Hill, 1945-46; LL.B., George Washington U., Washington, 1951. Bar: D.C. 1951, N.Y. 1961, N.C. 1980, U.S. Ct. Appeals (2d cir.) 1962, U.S. Ct. Appeals (D.C. cir.) 1955, U.S. Supreme Ct. 1964. Reporter Durham Sun, N.C. 1945; asst. state editor, editorial writer Charlotte News, N.C. 1947-48; pol. publicity and research Young Democratic Clubs Am., Washington, 1948-49, exec. sec., 1949-50; polit. analyst Dem. Senatorial Campaign Com., Washington, 1950-51; spl. atty. IRS, Washington and N.Y.C., 1952-60; assoc. Battle, Fowler, Stokes and Kheel, N.Y.C., 1960-65; dir. research U.S. Equal Employment Opportunity Commn., Washington, 1965-68; dep. asst. sec. U.S. Dept. Housing and Urban Devel., Washington, 1969-72; asst. dean Rutgers U. Law Sch., Newark, 1974-76; assoc. prof. law N.C. Central U., Durham, 1976-81, prof. law, 1981-83; mayor City of Durham, N.C., 1981-85; ptnr. Markham and Wickham, Durham, 1984-86; Trustee Hist. Preservation Soc. Durham, 1982-86; bd. dirs. Stagville Ctr., 1984-86; mem. Gov.'s Crime Commn., Raleigh, 1985; dep. commr. N.C. Indsl. Commn., Raleigh, 1986-93. Editor: Jobs, Men and Machines: The Problems of Automation, 1964. Mem.

Carolina Club, Phi Beta Kappa, Omicron Delta Kappa, Phi Delta Phi, Phi Delta Theta. Republican. Episcopalian. Home: 204 N Dillard St Durham NC 27701-3404

MARKHAM, JESSE WILLIAM, economist; b. Richmond, Va., Apr. 21, 1916; s. John James and Edith (Luttrell) M.; AB, U. Richmond, 1941; postgrad. Johns Hopkins U., 1941-42, U.S. Fgn. Service Sch., 1945; MA, Harvard U., 1947, PhD, 1949; m. Penelope Jane Anton, Oct. 15, 1944; children: Elizabeth Anton Markham McLean, John James, Jesse William. Accountant, E.I. duPont de Nemours Co., Richmond, 1935-38; teaching fellow Harvard U., 1946-48; asst. prof. Vanderbilt U., 1948-52, asso. prof., 1952-53; chief economist FTC, Washington, 1953-55; asso. prof. Princeton U., 1955-57, prof. econs., 1957-68; prof. Harvard Grad. Sch. Bus. Adminstrn., 1968-72, Charles Edward Wilson prof., 1972-82, prof. emeritus, 1982—; prof. Harvard U. Extension Svcs., 1984—; vis. prof. Columbia U., 1958; Ford Found. vis. prof. Harvard Grad. Sch. Bus. Adminstrn., 1965-66; rsch. prof. Law and Econs. Ctr., Emory U., 1982-84; rsch. staff, mem. bd. editors Patent Trademark Copyright Rsch. Inst., George Washington U., 1955-70; econs. editor Houghton Mifflin Co., 1961-71; U.S. del. commn. experts on bus. practices European Productivity Agy., OEEC, 1956, 57, 58, 59, 61; vis. prof. Harvard U., 1961-62; dir. Ford Found. Seminar Region II, 1961; adv. com. mktg. to sec. commerce, 1967-71; mem. Am. Bar Assn. Commn. to study FTC, 1969. Del. People to People Diplomacy Mission to USSR, 1989; active Boy Scouts Am.; chmn. Harvard Parents Com., 1969-72. Served as lt. USNR, World War II. Ford Found. research prof., 1958-59. Mem. Am. Econ. Assn., U.S.C. of C. (econ. policy com.), Harvard Club (N.Y.C., Sarasota, Fla.), The Cedars Club. Episcopalian. Author: Competition in the Rayon Industry, 1952; The Fertilizer Industry: Study of an Imperfect Market, 1958; The American Economy, 1963; (with Charles Fiero and Howard Piquet) The European Common Market: Friend or Competitor, 1964; (with Gustav Papanek) Industrial Organization and Economic Development, 1970; Conglomerate Enterprise and Public Policy, 1973 (with Paul Teplitz) Baseball Economics and Public Policy, 1982; sect. on oligopoly Internat. Ency. Social Scis.; contbr. articles to econ. jours. Mem. Phi Beta Kappa. Home: 663 Martin Rd Friendship ME 04547 Office: Harvard U Grad Sch Bus Adminstrn 300 Cumnock Boston MA 02163

MARKHAM, JORDAN J., physicist, retired educator; b. Samokov, Bulgaria, Dec. 25, 1916; s. Reuben Henry and Mary (Gall) M.; m. Lillian Cagnon, Feb. 6, 1943; children—Linda C., Roger H. B.S., Beloit (Wis.) Coll., 1938; M.S., Syracuse U., 1940; Ph.D., Brown U., 1946. With div. war research Columbia U., 1942-45; trainee Clinton Lab., Oak Ridge, 1946-47; instr. physics U. Pa., 1947-48; asst. prof. Brown U., 1948-50; physicist Applied Physics Lab., Johns Hopkins U., 1950-53; research lab. Zenith Radio Corp., 1953-60; sci. adv. Armour Research Found., 1960-62; prof. physics Ill. Inst. Tech., 1962-81, ret., 1981; vis. prof. Phys. Inst. U. Frankfurt, Germany, summer 1965; sabbatical leave U. Reading, Eng., 1977. Author: F-centers in Alkali Halides, 1966, also articles. Home and Office: Villa 128 Carolina Meadows Chapel Hill NC 27514

MARKHAM, RICHARD GLOVER, research executive; b. Pasadena, Calif., June 18, 1925; s. Fred Smith and Maziebelle (Glover) M.; m. Jonne Louise Pearson, Apr. 29, 1950; children: Janet B., Fred S., Charles R., Richard G., Marilyn A. Student, Stanford U., 1943; BS, Calif. Inst. Tech., Pasadena, 1945; MS, Stanford U., 1947. Pres., owner Aquarium Pump Supply, Prescott, Ariz., 1957-78; 1st v.p., dir. Bank of Prescott, 1981-87; also v.p., bd. dirs. Oxycal Labs., Prescott, 1981—. Mem. Ariz. Dept. Econ. Planning and Devel., 1967-72; treas. Ariz. State Rep. Com., 1970-72; active Ariz. Acad., 1974—; trustee Orme Sch., Mayer, Ariz., 1970-83, Prescott Coll., 1979-83. Office: Oxycal Labs 533 Madison Ave Prescott AZ 86301-2432

MARKHAM, WILLIAM E., timber and logging company owner; b. Chehalis, Wash., Oct. 9, 1922; s. John Howard and Grace (Young) M.; m. L. Jean Eddins, Sept. 25, 1943; children: William Jr., Michael, Patrick. BS in Bus., U. Wash., 1946. Owner Markham & Son Lumber Co., Riddle, Oreg., 1947-93; mem. Oreg. Legis., Riddle, 1969—, speaker pro tem, 1990—; bd. dirs. Douglas Nat. Bank, Rosebury, Oreg., Pacific State Bank, Reedsport, Oreg. Bd. dirs. Umpqua Coll., Rosebury, 1964-88. Lt. USAF, 1942-45. Mem. Lions, VFW, Am. Legion, Masons, Elks. Republican. Episcopalian. Avocation: hunting. Home: PO Box 300 Riddle OR 97469

MARKIN, DAVID ROBERT, motor company executive; b. N.Y.C., Feb. 16, 1931; s. Morris and Bessie (Markham) M.; children: Sara, John, Christopher, Meredith. B.S., Bradley U., 1953. Foreman Checker Motors Corp., Kalamazoo, 1955-57, factory mgr., 1957-62, v.p. sales, 1962-70, pres., 1970—, dir.; bd. dirs. Jackpot Inc. Trustee Kalamazoo Coll. Served to 1st lt. USAF, 1953-55. Mem. Alpha Epsilon Pi. Clubs: Standard (Chgo.); Park (Kalamazoo). Home: 2121 Winchell Ave Kalamazoo MI 49008-2205 Office: Internat Controls Corp 2016 N Pitcher St Kalamazoo MI 49007-1894

MARKINSON, MARTIN, theatre owner, producer; b. Bklyn., Dec. 23, 1931; s. Abraham and Dora (Rosenthal) M.; m. Arlene Francis Gefand, Apr. 15, 1962; children: Brett, Keith, Sydney. Owner, operator Helen Hayes Theatre, N.Y.C.; bd. assos. Am. League of Theatre and Producers, N.Y.C Producer Broadway plays including: Poor Murderer, Some of My Best Friends, Cheaters, Whoopee, Ned and Jack, Snoopy, Torch Song Trilogy (Tony award 1983), Passion, And a Nightingale Sang, Corpse, Dusky Sally, Last Minstral Show and Daddy Goodness. Sgt. USAF, 1951-53, Korea.

MARKKULA, A. C., JR., entrepreneur, computer company executive. Co-founder, former pres., chief exec. officer Apple Computer Inc., now chmn. bd. dirs.; founder, chmn. Echelon Inc., Los Gatos, Calif. Office: Apple Computer Inc 20525 Mariani Ave Cupertino CA 95014

MARKLAND, FRANCIS SWABY, JR., biochemist, educator; b. Phila., Jan. 15, 1936; s. Francis Swaby Sr. and Willie Lawrence (Averritt) M.; m. Barbara Blake, June 27, 1959; children: Cathleen Blake, Francis Swaby IV. B.S., Pa. State U., 1957; Ph.D., Johns Hopkins U., 1964. Postdoctoral fellow UCLA, 1964-66, asst. prof. biochemistry, 1966-73; vis. asst. prof. U. So. Calif., Los Angeles, 1973-74, assoc. prof., 1974-83, prof., 1983—, acting chmn. dept. biochemistry, 1986-88, vice-chmn., 1988-92; cons. Clin. Lab. Med. Group, L.A., 1977-88, Cortech, Inc., Denver, 1983-88.; mem. biochem., endocrinology study sect. NIH, 1986-90. Editorial bd. Toxicon., Internat. Jour. of Toxinology; contbr. articles, chpts. and abstracts to profl. publs.; patentee in field. Mem. Angeles Choral, Northridge, Calif. Served to capt. USNR. Recipient NIH rsch. career devel. award USPHS, NIH, 1968-73; rsch. grantee Nat. Cancer Inst., 1979-86, 91-93, Nat. Heart Lung and Blood Inst., 1984-88. Mem. Am. Soc. Biochem. and Molecular Biology, Am. Chem. Soc., Internat. Soc. on Toxinology, Internat. Soc. on Thrombosis and Haemostatis (subcom. exogenous hemostatic agts.), Am. Assn. Cancer Rsch., Am. Soc. Hematology, The Protein Soc., Sigma Xi, Alpha Zeta. Avocations: singing, skiing, aerobics. Office: U So Calif Medicine Cancer Rsch Lab Rm 106 1303 N Mission Rd Los Angeles CA 90033-1020

MARKLE, CHERI VIRGINIA CUMMINS, nurse; b. N.Y.C., Nov. 22, 1936; d. Brainard Lyle and Mildred (Schwab) Cummins; m. John Markle, Aug. 26, 1961 (dec. 1962); 1 child, Kellianne. RN, Ind. State U. and Union Hosp., 1959; BS in Rehab. Edn., Wright State U., 1975; BSN, Capital U., 1987; postgrad. in nursing adminstrn., Wright State U., 1987-89; postgrad., Calif. Coll. Health Sci. Administration, 1994, Columbia Pacific U., 1995—. Cert. clin. hypnotherapist Nat. Guild Hypnotherapists. Coordinator Dayton (Ohio) Children's Psychiat. Hosp., 1962-75; dir. nursing Stillwater Health Ctr., Dayton, 1975-76; rehab. cons. Fairborn, Ohio, 1976-91; sr. supr. VA, Dayton, 1977-85, nurse coord. alcohol rehab., 1985-86; DON Odd Fellows, Springfield, Ohio, 1987-88, Miami Christel Manor, Miamisburg, Ohio, 1988—; DON, rehab. cons. NMS Tng. Sys., Dayton, 1989-91; rehab. cons., N.Y.C., 1991—; psychiat. rsch. unit nurse VA Med. Ctr., N.Y. Rehab. 1991, mem. com. women vets., 1991-93. Newspaper columnist Golden Times, Clark County. Bd. dirs. Temple Universal Judaism. 1st lt. USAF, 1959-61. Mem. ANA (cert. adminstrn. 1983, cert. gerontology 1984), NAFE, AAUW, Nat. Rehab. Nursing Soc., Nurse Mgrs. Assembly, Gerontol. Nurse Assembly, Rehab. Soc., Nat. Guild Hypnotherapists, Wright State U. Alumni Assn., Am. Legion, Womens' City Club N.Y., Gilbert & Sullivan Soc., Alpha Sigma Alpha, Sigma Theta Tau. Jewish. Avocations: cats, reading, music, needlework, swimming. Office: VA Med Ctr 423 E 23rd St New York NY 10010

MARKLE, DAVID A., optical engineer. With Ultratech Stepper, San Jose, Calif. Recipient David Richardson medal Optical Soc. Am., 1994. Office: Ultratech Stepper 3050 Vanker Rd San Jose CA 95134*

MARKLE, GEORGE BUSHAR, IV, surgeon; b. Hazleton, Pa., Oct. 29, 1921; s. Alvan and Gladys (Jones) M.; m. Mildred Donna Umstead, July 3, 1944; children: Donna Markle Partee, Melanie Jones Markle, George Bushar, Christian. B.S., Yale U., 1943; M.D., U. Pa., 1946. Diplomate Am. Bd. Surgery. Intern Geisinger Med. Ctr., Danville, Pa., 1946-47, resident, 1947-49; surg. fellow Mayo Clinic, Rochester, Minn., 1949-52; chief surgery U.S. Army Hosp., Ft. Monroe, Va., 1952-54; practice gen. surgery Carlsbad, N.Mex., 1954-94; surg. staff Carlsbad Regional Med. Ctr., 1954-77, Guadalupe Med. Ctr., 1977-94; ret., 1994; panelist Voice of Am. Author: Ill Health and Other Foolishness, 1966, How to Stay Healthy All Your Life, 1968, The Teka Stone, 1983, How to Be Healthy, Wealthy and Wise, 1991, Donna's Story, 1991; contbr. articles to profl. jours., radio health series. Mem. Eddy County Cen. Rep. Com. Served with M.C. U.S. Army, 1952-54. Recipient Distinguished Service award Jr. C. of C., 1956. Fellow Internat. Coll. Surgeons (regent, Regent of Yr. 1991), Southwestern Surg. Congress, Priestley surg. Soc., Western Surg. Assn.; mem. Eddy County Med. Soc., Ogden Surg. Soc., Kiwanis. Presbyterian. Home: 1003 N Shore Dr Carlsbad NM 88220-4635 Office: 911 N Canal St Carlsbad NM 88220-5109 Those blest in family and fortune, things not of their own making, ought, I believe, to strive, as they are able, to deserve those blessings through service to God and Man. Even the least of us has some power to influence others through our examples and attitudes, and through each we influence, for good or bad, we may affect sequentially many others, like ever widening ripples on the water.

MARKLE, JOHN, JR., lawyer; b. Allentown, Pa., July 20, 1931; s. John Markle II and Pauline (Powers) Mulligan; m. Mary B. McLean, Apr. 19, 1952 (div. Apr. 1990); children: Ellen, John III, Patricia, Stephen, Mary; m. Kathryn E. Wheeler, July 14, 1990. Grad., The Hill Sch., Pottstown, Pa., 1949; BA, Yale U., 1953; LLB, Harvard Law Sch., 1958. Assoc. Drinker Biddle & Reath, Phila., 1958-64, ptnr., 1964—. Contbg. editor: The Developing Labor Law, 1976—. Bd. dirs. Main Line Health Sys., Inc., Radnor, Pa., 1987—, The Hill Sch., 1970—; treas., bd. dirs. Paoli (Pa.) Meml. Hosp., 1982—, The Found. at Paoli, 1995—. Lt. col. USMCR, 1951-73. Named Most Outstanding Young Rep. (Pa.), 1966. Mem. ABA, Pa. Bar Assn., Am. Arbitration Assn. Republican. Clubs: Union League of Phila., Yale of Phila., Merion Golf. Avocations: golf, photography. Home: 205 Cambridge Chase Exton PA 19341-3137 Office: Drinker Biddle & Reath Ste 300 1000 Westlakes Dr Berwyn PA 19301

MARKLE, ROGER A(LLAN), retired oil company executive; b. Sidney, Mont., Dec. 12, 1933; s. Forrest William and Mary Elizabeth (Hartley) M.; m. Mary Elizabeth Thompson, Jan. 13, 1967. B.S. in Mining Engring, U. Alaska, 1959; M.S., Stanford U., 1965; M.B.A., U. Chgo., 1972. Mgr. mine devel. Amoco Minerals, Inc., Chgo., 1973-74; pres. western div. Valley Camp Coal Co., Salt Lake City, 1974-78; pres., chief exec. officer Valley Camp Coal Co., Cleve., 1979-82; pres. Quaker State Corp., Oil City, Pa., 1982-86, chief operating officer, 1986-88, also bd. dirs.; vice chmn. Quaker State Corp., Oil City, 1988-89; pres. Nerco Oil & Gas, Vancouver, Wash., 1990-92; dir. U.S. Bur. Mines, Washington, 1978-79. Served with USN, 1951-54. Mem. AIME.

MARKLEY, JOHN LUTE, biochemistry educator; b. Denver, Mar. 6, 1941; s. Miles Russell and Winnifred Farrar (Lute) M.; m. Diane Sheehan, Aug. 9, 1975; children—Jessamyn Sheehan, Andrew Lute. B.A., Carleton Coll., 1963; student U. Munich, Fed. Republic Germany, 1960-61; Ph.D., Harvard U., 1969. Sr. research chemist Merck Inst., Rahway, N.J., 1966-69; NIH postdoctoral fellow U. Calif.-Berkeley, 1970-71; asst. prof. biochemistry Purdue U., West Lafayette, Ind., 1972-75, assoc. prof., 1975-81, prof., 1981-84, adj. prof., 1984—; dir. Biochem. Magnetic-Resonance Lab., 1975-84; prof. biochemistry U. Wis.-Madison, 1984—, dir. Nat. Magnetic Resonance Facility at Madison 1984; mem. adv. com. Resource for Biomed. Nuclear Magnetic Resonance Spectroscopy, Carnegie-Mellon U., 1975-92. Mem. editorial bd. Bull. Magnetic Resonance, 1983—, Biochemistry and Biophysics, 1988—, Jour. of Biomolecular NMR, 1990—, Biophysical Jour., 1991—, Jour. of Magnetic Resonance, 1993—. Contbr. research articles to profl. jours. Recipient Research Career Devel. award USPHS, 1975-80; sr. Fogarty fellow USPHS, Montpellier, France, 1980-81; grantee USPHS, U.S. Dept. Agr., NSF. Mem. Soc. Magnetic Resonance in Medicine, Internat. Soc. Magnetic Resonance, Am. Chem. Soc., Am. Soc. Biol. Chemists, Biophys. Soc., Phi Beta Kappa, Sigma Xi. Avocations: travel; gardening; photography. Home: 3452 Crestwood Dr Madison WI 53705-1445 Office: U Wis Dept of Biochemistry 420 Henry Mall Madison WI 53706-1569

MARKMAN, HOWARD J., psychology educator; b. Oct. 27, 1950; s. Arnold J. and Claire (Fox) M.; m. Fran Dickson, June 29, 1980; children: Mathew Lee, Leah Deborah. BA, Rutgers U., 1972; MA in Clin. Psychology, Ind. U., 1976, PhD in Clin. Psychology, 1977. Lic. clin. psychologist, Colo. Assoc. instr. psychology Ind. U., 1973-75; psychology trainee, consultation team Monroe County Community Mental Health Ctr., Bloomington, Ind., 1975-76; clin./community psychology intern U. Colo. Sch. Medicine, Denver, 1976-77; asst. prof. psychology Bowling Green (Ohio) U., 1977-80, U. Denver, 1980-83; dir. Denver Ctr. for Marital and Family Studies, U. Denver, 1980—; dir. clin. tng. U. Denver, 1983-86, assoc. prof. psychology, 1983-89, prof. psychology, 1989—; presenter in field. Author: Couples' Guide to Communication, 1976, Prevention and Relationship Enhancement Program, 1980, We Can Work it Out, Fighting for your Marriage; mem. editorial bd. Jour. Consulting and Clin. Psychology, 1988-90, Behavioral Assessment, Jour. Family Psychology, Contemporary Psychology, Am. Assn. for Marriage and Family Therapy, Am. Jour. Family Therapy; guest assoc. editor Behavioral Assessment, 1989, Human Communication Rsch.; contbr. articles and reviews to profl. jours. Bd. dirs. Assn. Children and Youth, Boulder, Colo., 1985-86. NIMH grantee, 1980-82. Fellow APA; mem. NIMH (adhoc reviewer 1980—), NSF (adhoc reviewer 1980—), APA, Internat. Soc. Social and Personal Relationships (world conf. planning com. 1990—), Colo. Psychol. Assn. (co-chmn. 1990—), Nat. Coun. on Family Rels., Am. Assn. Marriage and Family Therapy (clin. mem.), Rocky Mountain Conf. Family Rels. (bd. dirs.). Democrat. Jewish. Avocations: softball, photography, tennis, hockey, skiing. Office: Ctr for Marital & Family Studies 2155 S Race St Frontier Hall Denver CO 80208

MARKMAN, RAYMOND JEROME, marketing executive; b. Bklyn., Dec. 26, 1927; s. Julius and Celia (Schroeder) M.; m. Frances Pauline Heyman, June 4, 1949; children: Leslie Jane Stern, Janet Beth Meyer, Thomas Irion. BJ in Advt., U. Mo., 1949; postgrad., U. Chgo., 1955-58. Creative dir. Chicago Tribune, 1949-53; pres., founder Salespower Inc., Chgo., 1953-55; brand dir. Helene Curtis Industries, Chgo., 1955-58; account supr. Leo Burnett Co., Chgo., 1958-63; v.p. mktg. GRI Corp., Chgo., 1971-74; exec. v.p. mktg. Ency. Britannica, Chgo., 1974-83; pres., founder Heritage Home Video, Chgo., 1983-86, Magic Video Pub. Co., Chgo., 1986—, Life Planning Co., Chgo., 1988—; bd. dirs., founder Seago Realty Co., Chgo., 1970-86; bd. dirs. Chgo. City Bank; pres. Raymond J. Markman Assocs., Chgo., 1983—. Author: Handbook of Direct Marketing, 1983. Mem. Chgo. Crime Commn., 1951, Park Board Sports Coun., Highland Park, Ill., 1971-77, Mayor's Com. Highland Park, 1980-82; organizer Little League, Highland Park, 1965-70. Mem. Direct Mail Mktg. Assn., Chgo. Direct Mktg. Assn. (lectr. 1977-85, chmn. echos com.), Execs. Club. Home and Office: Life Planning Co 424 Lakeside Manor Rd Highland Park IL 60035-5040

MARKMAN, RONALD, artist, educator; b. Bronx, N.Y., May 29, 1931; s. Julius and Mildred (Berkowitz) M.; m. Barbara Miller, Sept. 12, 1959; 1 dau., Ericka Elizabeth. B.F.A., Yale U., 1957, M.F.A., 1959. Instr. Art Inst. Chgo., 1960-64; prof. fine arts Ind. U., 1964—; color. cons. Hallmark Card Co., 1959-60. One-man shows Kanegis Gallery, 1959, Reed Coll., 1966, Terry Dintenfass Gallery, 1965, 66, 68, 70, 76, 79, 82, 85, The Gallery, Bloomington, Ind., 1972, 79, Indpls. Mus., 1974, Tyler Sch. Art, Phila., 1976, Franklin Coll., 1980, Dart Gallery, Chgo., 1981, Patrick King Gallery, Indpls., 1983, 86, John Heron Gallery, Indpls., 1985, New Harmony Gallery, 1985; two-man show Dintenfass Gallery, 1984; group shows include Kanegis Gallery, Boston, 1958, 60, 61, Boston Arts Festival, 1959, 60, Mus. Modern

Art, 1959, 66, Whitney Mus., N.Y.C., 1960, Art Inst. Chgo., 1964, Gallery 99, Miami, Fla., 1966, Ball State Coll., 1966, Butler Inst., 1967, Indpls. Mus., 1968, 69, 72, 74, Phoenix Gallery, N.Y.C., 1970, Harvard U., 1974, Skidmore Coll., 1975, Am. Acad. Arts and Letters, 1977, 89, Tuthill-Gimprich Gallery, N.Y.C., 1980, Patrick King Gallery, 1988, numerous others; represented in permanent collections Met. Mus. Art, Mus. Modern Art, Art Inst. Chgo., Library of Congress, Cin. Art Mus., Bklyn. Mus., Ark. Art Center, others; commns. include 5 murals Riley Children's Hosp., Indpls., 1986; installation Evanston (Ill.) Art Ctr., 1989, 2-part installation Ortho Child Care Ctr., Raritan, N.J., 1991; illustrator Acid and Basics-A Guide to Acid-Base Physiology, 1992. Served with U.S. Army, 1952-54. Recipient Ind. Arts Commn. award, 1990, 93; Fulbright grantee, Italy, 1962, grantee Ctr. for New TV, Chgo., 1992; Lilly Endowment fellow, 1989. Home: 719 S Jordan Ave Bloomington IN 47401-5123 Office: Ind U Dept Fine Arts Bloomington IN 47401

MARKO, ANDREW PAUL, school system administrator; b. Kingston, Pa., Aug. 16, 1936; s. Andrew Paul and Anna (Stragis) M.; m. Janet Thimm, Aug. 10, 1988; 1 child, Danielle. BA, Kings Coll., Wilkes-Barre, Pa., 1962; MA, Scranton U., 1968, prin.'s cert., 1971; postgrad., Oxford (Eng.) U., 1988, Lehigh U., 1991, Widener U., 1991—. Cert. tchr., secondary prin., supt.'s letter of eligibility, Pa. Elem. tchr. Dundalk Elem. Sch., Balt., 1963-64; English tchr. Kingston (Pa.) High Sch., 1964-66; English tchr. Wyoming Valley West High Sch., Plymouth, Pa., 1966-90, vice prin. 1980, 89; secondary curriculum adminstr. Wyoming Valley West Sch. Dist., Kingston, 1990, dir. instrnl. svcs. and pupil svcs., 1991—; wrestling coach Kingston High Sch., 1964-69; jr.-sr. class advisor Wyoming Valley West High Sch., Plymouth, 1968-88, newspaper advisor, 1970-90, literary mag. advisor, 1970-90, publs. bus. mgr., 1988-90. Councilman Kingston Borough Coun., 1969-77; pres. Holy Name Soc.; ward capt. Heart Fund and March of Dimes. With USN, 1954-57. Mem. ASCD, Pa. Assn. Student Assistance Profls., Pa. Assn. for Supervision and Curriculum Devel., Pa. Assn. Pupil Svcs. Adminstrs., Nat. Assn. Pupil Svcs. Adminstrs., Pa. Staff Devel. Coun., Nat. Mid. Sch. Assn., Ptnrs. for Quality Learning, VFW, Am. Legion, KC. Democrat. Roman Catholic. Avocations: sports, gardening, building, reading. Home: Box 108 Harvey's Lake PA 18618 Office: Wyoming Valley West Sch Dist 450 N Maple Ave Kingston PA 18704

MARKO, HAROLD MEYRON, diversified industry executive; b. Detroit, Oct. 29, 1925; s. Louis Meyron and Mae (Goldberg) M.; m. Barbara Soss, July 2, 1951; children—Clifford S., Neil L., Matthew P. B.A., U. Mich., 1948. Salesman Core Industries Inc (formerly SOS Consol. Inc.), Bloomfield Hills, Mich., 1951-57; v.p. sales Core Industries Inc (formerly SOS Consol. Inc.), 1957-60, pres., 1961-90; chmn. emeritus, chmn. exec. com. Core Industries Inc. (formerly SOS Consol. Inc.), 1991—; also dir. Core Industries Inc (formerly SOS Consol. Inc.), chmn. bd. dirs., chief exec. officer, 1986. Editorial adv. bd. Fin. World mag.; contbr. chpt. to book. Mem. Founders' Soc., Detroit Inst. Arts; trustee Nat. Jewish Hosp., Denver, Mich. Opera Theatre; bd. dirs. Detroit Symphony Orch.; mem. adv. bd. Greater Detroit Round Table; bd. govs. Cranbrook Acad. Art. Served with AUS, 1943-45. Club: Bloomfield Open Hunt. Home: 1132 Woburn Green Bloomfield Hills MI 48302 Office: Core Industries Inc 500 N Woodward Ave Bloomfield Hills MI 48304-2961

MARKOE, FRANK, JR., lawyer, business and hospital executive; b. Balt., Sept. 5, 1923; s. Frank and Margaret (Smith) M.; m. Margaret McCormack (div.); children: Andrée Markoe Caldwell, Ritchie Harrison Markoe Scribner. AB, Washington and Lee U., 1947; LLB, U. Md., 1950. Bar: Md. 1950. Pntr. Karl F. Steinmann, Balt., 1948-50, 50-53, Cable & McDaniel, Balt., 1954-55; gen. counsel, dir. Emerson Drug Co., Balt., 1955-56; adminstrv. v.p. Emerson Drug Co., 1957-58; v.p., sec., dir., gen. counsel Warner-Lambert Pharm. Co., 1958-67, exec. com., sr. v.p., dir., gen. counsel, sec., 1967-69, exec. asst. chmn. bd., 1970-71, v.p., 1971-73; exec. v.p. Warner-Lambert Co., Morris Plains, N.J., 1973-77; vice chmn. bd. Warner-Lambert Co., 1977-81; vice chmn. adv. bd. N.Y. Hosp.-Cornell Med. Ctr., 1987—, also chmn. major gifts com. Capital Campaign; hon. holder Alfred E. Driscoll chair Fairleigh Dickinson U. Trustee Morristown Meml. Hosp., Morris County Soc. for Crippled Children and Adults; bd. dirs. N.J. Coll. Medicine and Dentistry, Bd. Internat. Broadcasting, Radio Free Europe/Radio Liberty, Kips Bay Boys; bd. dirs., exec. com., pres. N.J. Ballet. With USAAF, 1942-45, PTO. Mem. U.S.C. of C., Proprietary Assn. (chmn., bd. dir., exec. com.), Pharm. Mfrs. Assn. (bd. dir., exec. com.), N.J. State C. of C. (bd. dir.), Phi Beta Kappa. Home and Office: 201 Grenville Rd Hobe Sound FL 33455-2414 also: Peacock Point Locust Valley NY 00001

MARKOPOULOS, ANDREW JOHN, retail executive; b. Toledo, Mar. 23, 1931; s. John G. and Maria (Paraskevopoulos) M.; m. Joanne Valassis; children: Maria, Nicole. Diploma, Woodward High Sch., Toledo. With Macy's, Toledo and Kansas City, Mo., 1953-73, Gimbels, Phila., 1973-80; sr. v.p. visual merchandising and design Dayton Hudson Dept. Store Co., Mpls., 1980—; guest lectr. Drexel U., U. Wis. Bd. dirs. Friends of Goldstein Gallery, U. Minn. Cpl. U.S. Army, 1951-53. Mem. Nat. Retail Merchants Assn. (chmn. bd. dirs. 1983-84, Silver Plaque 1986, Visual Merchandiser of Yr. award 1981), Soc. Visual Merchandisers (bd. dirs.), Nat. Assn. Display Industries (Hall of Fame 1980), Western Assn. Visual Merchandising (adv. bd.), Am. Hellenic Ednl. Progressive Assn. Republican. Greek Orthodox. Home: 10950 Spoon Rdg Eden Prairie MN 55347-2956 Office: Dayton Hudson Corp Dept Store Divsn 700 On The Mall Minneapolis MN 55402-2065

MARKOS, CHRIS, real estate company executive; b. Cleve., Nov. 25, 1926; s. George and Bessie (Papathatou) M.; m. Alice Zaharopoulos, Dec. 11, 1949; children: Marilyn, Irene, Betsy. BA, Case Western Reserve, Cleve., 1960; LLB, LaSalle U., Chgo., 1964. Cert. gen. real estate appraiser, Ohio. Vice-pres. Herbert Laronge Inc., Cleve., 1963-76; v.p. Calabrese, Racek and Markos Inc., Cleve., 1976-83; v.p. Herbert Laronge Inc., Cleve., 1983-87, pres., 1987-88; v.p. Cragin Lang, Inc., Cleve., 1989-91; sr. cons. Grubb & Ellis, Cleve., 1991-93; sr. v.p. Realty One Appraisal Divsn., Independence, Ohio, 1993—; pres. Alcrimar Inc., 1989—. Co-author: Ohio Supplement to Modern Real Estate Practice, 5th-7th edits.; cons. editor, co-author: Modern Real Estate Practice in Ohio, 12th & 13th edits. Bd. dirs. Dyke Coll., Cleve. 1984—. With U.S. Army, 1945-46. Named Realtor of the Year, Cleve. Bd Realtors, 1976. Mem. Am. Soc. Appraisers (sr., pres. 1973, state dir. 1976), Cleve. Bd. Realtors (pres. 1974, Realtor of Yr. 1976). Republican. Greek Orthodox. Home: 6731 Hidden Lake Trail Brecksville OH 44141-3189 Office: Realty One 6000 Rockside Woods Blvd Cleveland OH 44131

MARKOSKI, JOSEPH PETER, lawyer; b. Floral Park, N.Y., Nov. 7, 1948; s. Stephen Nicholas and Josephine Veronica (Lapkofsky) M.; m. Julie Ann Angus, June 30, 1979; children: Katherine, Caroline, Peter. BSFS, Georgetown U., 1970, JD, 1973. Bar: D.C. 1973. Law clk. Hon. Thomas A. Flannery U.S. Dist. Ct., Washington, 1973-74; assoc. Wilkinson, Cragun & Barker, Washington, 1975-80, ptnr., 1980-82; ptnr. Squire, Sanders & Dempsey, Washington, 1982—, mng. ptnr., 1991—; co-chmn. task force on open network initiatives Strategic Planning Group of US CCITT Nat. Com., 1988-92. Author: (with others) Internat. Telecommunications Handbook, 1986; contbr. articles to profl. jours. Active Fed. City Coun. Capt., USAR, 1970-78. Mem. ABA (vice-chmn. common carrier com. sci. and tech. sect. 1986-88, internat. common carrier project 1980-86), Fed. Comm. Bar Assn. (com. common carrier practice and procedure, 1980—), Computer Law Assn. (chmn. telecom. bar liaison com. 1994—, bd. dirs., 1995—), Econ. Club Washington. Democrat. Roman Catholic. Office: Squire Sanders & Dempsey 1201 Pennsylvania Ave NW PO Box 407 Washington DC 20044

MARKOU, PETER JOHN, economic developer; b. Keene, N.H., Apr. 11, 1940; s. Peter John and Zoe Nicholas (Kussku) M.; m. Ann Corcoran Gibbons, June 25, 1983; 1 child, Justin Peter. BSBA cum laude, Suffolk U., 1964, MSBA, 1965; cert. in taxation, U. Hartford, 1977; PhD in Econ. Devel., Am. U. London, 1993. Purchasing apt. Fed. Prison Industries, Danbury, Conn., 1965; instr. Becker Jr. Coll., Worcester, Mass., 1967-70; assoc. prof. Post Coll., Waterbury, Conn., 1976-77; asst. prof. Hous. North Adams (Mass.) State Coll., 1970-76, assoc. prof., 1977-84, prof., 1984-94; exec. dir. Green Mountain Econ. Devel. Corp., White River Junction, Vt., 1994—. Contbr. articles to small bus. and econ. devel. proc. Pres. North Adams Community Devel. Corp., 1985-91, Hardman Indsl. Pk. Corp., North Adams, 1989-91;

mem. North Adams Mgmt. Improvement Com., 1987-88; mem., sec. Mass. Mus. Contemporary Art Cultural Commn., North Adams, 1988—; bd. dirs. No. Berkshire Community Action, North Adams, 1989-91; mem. adv. bd. Salvation Army, North Adams, 1988-90. Recipient Mass. Pride in Performance award Commonwealth of Mass., 1989. Mem. Nat. Soc. Pub. Accts. (educator mem.), Am. Econ. Devel. Coun., N.E. Indsl. Developers Assn. Home: 34 Deerfield Dr Montpelier VT 05602 Office: Green Mountain Econ Devel Corp Gates-Briggs Bldg White River Junction VT 05001

MARKOVITS, INGA, law educator; b. 1937. Referendar, Free U. Berlin, 1960, JD, 1966; LLM, Yale U., 1969. Attachee German Fgn. Svc., 1963-66; resident assoc., lectr. Hoover Inst. and polit. sci dept. Stanford U., 1969-71, lectr., 1971-76; asst. prof. U. Tex., Austin, 1976-80, prof., 1980—. Ford Internat. fellow Cornell U., 1962-63, Fgn. Area fellow London Sch. Econs., 1967-68. Mem. Am. Acad. Fgn. Law, Law and Soc. Assn. Office: U Tex Sch Law 727 E 26th St Austin TX 78705-3224

MARKOVITS, RICHARD SPENCER, lawyer, educator, consultant; b. Middletown, N.Y., Mar. 30, 1942; s. William Benjamin and Dorothy Susan (Franzos) M.; m. Inga Schulthes, Mar. 22, 1967; children: Daniel, Stefanie, Benjamin, Julia, Rebecca. B.A., Cornell U., 1965; Ph.D., U. London, 1966; LL.B., Yale U., 1968; M.A. (hon.), Oxford U., 1981. Bar: Tex. 1978. Lectr. econs. Yale U., New Haven, 1966-68; asst. then assoc. prof. Stanford Law Sch., Calif., 1968-75; mem. law faculty Oxford U., Eng., 1981-83; dir. Ctr. for Socio-Legal Studies, Oxford, 1981-83; prof. U. Tex. Law Sch., Austin, 1975-82, Lloyd M. Bentsen prof. law, 1983-85, Marrs McLean prof. law, 1985—; Baker & Botts Regents Research prof., 1988-89; panel mem. NSF, Washington, 1978-80; mem. econ. affairs com. Social Sci. Research Council, London, 1982-83; trustee Law and Soc. Assocs., 1979-80. Contbr. articles to profl. jours.; author collections of essays. Fellow Ctr. for Advanced Studies, Berlin, 1985-86; Guggenheim fellow, 1988. Home: 3112 Wheeler St Austin TX 78705-2816 Office: U Tex Law Sch 727 E 26th St Austin TX 78705-3224

MARKOVITZ, ALVIN, molecular biologist, geneticist, educator; b. Chgo., May 30, 1929; s. Raymond and Fannie (Rudich) M.; m. Harriet June Porter, Aug. 24, 1952; children—Diane (dec.), Paula, Ellen, Nancy. B.S., U. Ill., 1950, M.S., 1952; Ph.D., U. Wash., 1955. Instr., U. Chgo., 1957-59; asst. prof., 1959-64, assoc. prof. microbiology, 1964-74, prof. microbiology, 1974-84, prof. biochemistry and molecular biology, 1984—. Contbr. articles to sci. publs. Grantee NIH, 1964-88. Mem. Am. Soc. for Microbiology, Am. Soc. for Biochemistry and Molecular Biology, AAAS. Jewish. Avocations: piano, sports.

MARKOWICZ, JOHN C., engineering consulting company executive; b. 1944. Pres., COO Sonalysts, Inc., Waterford, Conn., 1976—. Office: Sonalysts Inc 215 Parkway N PO Box 280 Waterford CT 06385*

MARKOWICZ, VICTOR, video company executive; b. Tynda, USSR, July 6, 1944; s. Szymon and Gustawa (Goldstain) M.; m. Monica A. Minkiewicz, July 10, 1971; children: Clara, Daniela. Student, U. Warsaw, Poland, 1962-64; BS in Maths, Technion U., Haifa, Israel, 1966. Software mgr. Elbit Computers, Ltd., Haifa, 1966-69; tech. dir., co-founder System Ops., Inc., Princeton, N.J., 1970-76; pres., co-founder Gaming Dimensions, Providence, 1976-78; v.p. Datatrol Inc., Hudson, Mass., 1978-80; chmn., dir., co-founder GTech Corp., Providence, 1981—; bd. dirs. Intervoice, Dallas, Nat. TV Network Mgmt., Pasadena. Designer of state lottery games, 1970—; exec. producer (movie) South of Reno, 1987. Jewish. Avocations: bridge, skiing, tennis. Office: Gtech Corp 55 Technology Way West Greenwich RI 02817

MARKOWITZ, ALAN LARRY, hospital administrator; b. N.Y.C., June 10, 1943; s. Seymour and Lillian (Burr) M.; children: Michele, Glenn. BA in Biology, NYU, 1965; MHA, Med. Coll. Va., 1969; PhD in Health Svcs. Adminstrn., Columbia Pacific U., 1980. Asst. adminstr. Beth Sholom Home Va., Richmond, 1969-71; assoc. adminstrv. for support svcs. Cook County Hosp., Chgo., 1971-73; with Hosp. Affiliates Internat., Inc., Nashville, 1973-78; exec. v.p., chief operating officer Westchester Gen. Hosp., Miami, Fla., 1978-80; exec. dir. corp. acquisitions Charter Med. Corp., Macon, Ga., 1981-86; chief exec. officer Highland Park Hosp., Miami, 1986-87; v.p. ops. Vanguard Healthcare Corp., St. Petersburg, Fla., 1988-89; dir. mental and behavioral health svcs. Our Lady of Lake Regional Med. Ctr., Baton Rouge, 1989-90; CEO Goodlark Med. Ctr., 1991-92, Cheatham Med. Ctr., 1991-92, Town and Country Home Health; adminstr., CEO DeKalb General Hosp., 1992—; former mem. La. Bd. Cert. Substance Abuse Counselors; speaker in field. Contbr. articles to profl. jours. and newspapers. Former mem. Baton Rouge Mayor's Task Force on Drugs; bd. dirs. United Way Dickson. 1st lt. Med. Svc. Corps, U.S. Army, 1965-67, Vietnam. Fellow Am. Coll. Healthcare Execs.; mem. Am. Cancer Soc., Humane Soc. (bd. dirs.), Diversified Svcs. Corp. Tenn. Hosp. Assn., Rotary. Jewish. Avocations: golf, reading. Home: PO Box 737 Smithville TN 37166-0737 Office: DeKalb Gen Hosp 520 W Main St Smithville TN 37166-1138

MARKOWITZ, ARTHUR WALTER, food brokerage executive; b. Bklyn., Sept. 21, 1935; s. Harry Lewis and Mildred (Pincus) M.; m. Estelle Weiner, Aug. 20, 1960 (div. 1986); children—Gary D., Karen E., Steven M. B.S. NYU, 1957. C.P.A., N.J., N.Y. Jr. acct. Howard Listander & Berkower, Perth Amboy, N.J., 1957-59; sr. acct. Rich & Rubenstein, Union, N.J., 1959-60; ptnr. J.H. Cohn & Co., Newark, 1960-73; sr. v.p. Pezrow Companies, Ramsey, N.J., 1973—. Chmn. Planning Bd. Montvale, 1983-85; arbitrator Better Bus. Bur., Bergen, Passaic, and Rockland counties, 1984. Served with N.J. NG, 1959-65. Mem. Met. Food Brokers (treas. N.Y.S. 1983-88), Montvale Bus. Assn. (pres. 1984), Nat. Food Broker Assn. (office adminstrn. and ops. com. 1984-88), Am. Inst. CPAs, N.J. Soc. CPAs, N.Y. State Soc. CPAs, Republican. Jewish. Clubs: NYU Alumni of Bergen County, Temple Beth Or Couples (co-pres. 1981-82), Beta Gamma Sigma. Lodge: Food Industry B'nai B'rith. Office: Ken J Pezrow Corp 535 E Crescent Ave Ramsey NJ 07446-1219

MARKOWITZ, HARRY M., finance and economics educator; b. Chicago, Ill., Aug. 24, 1927; s. Morris and Mildred (Gruber) M.; m. Barbara Gay. PhB, U. Chgo., 1947, MA, 1950, PhD, 1954. With research staff Rand Corp., Santa Monica, Calif., 1952-60, 61-63; tech. dir. Consol. Analysis Ctrs., Inc., Santa Monica, 1963-68; prof. UCLA, Westwood, 1968-69; pres. Arbitrage Mgmt. Co., N.Y.C., 1969-72; pvt. practice cons. N.Y.C., 1972-74; with research staff T.J. Watson Research Ctr. IBM, Yorktown Hills, N.Y., 1974-83; Speiser prof. fin. Baruch Coll. CUNY, N.Y.C., 1982—; dir. rsch. Daiwa Securities Trust Co, Jersey City, N.J., 1990—; v.p. Inst. Mgmt. Sci., 1960-62. Author: Portfolio Selection: Efficient Diversification of Investments, 1959, Mean-Variance Analysis in Portfolio Choice, 1987; co-author: SIMSCRIPT Simulation Programming Language, 1963; co-editor: Process Analysis of Economic Capabilities, 1963. Recipient John von Neumann Theory prize Ops. Rsch. Soc. Am. and Inst. Mgmt. Sci., 1989, Nobel Prize in Econs., 1990. Fellow Econometric Soc., Am. Acad. Arts and Scis.; mem. Am. Fin. Assn. (pres. 1982—). Office: CUNY Baruch Coll Bus Sch 155 E 24th St New York NY 10010-5526 also: Daiwa Securities 1 Evertrust Plz Jersey City NJ 07302-3051

MARKOWITZ, SAMUEL SOLOMON, chemistry educator; b. Bklyn., Oct. 31, 1931; s. Max and Florence Ethel (Goldman) M.; children: Michael, Daniel, Jonah. B.S. in Chemistry, Rensselaer Poly. Inst., 1953, M.A., Princeton U., 1955, Ph.D., 1957; postgrad. Brookhaven Nat. Lab., 1955-57. Asst. prof. chemistry U. Calif.-Berkeley, 1958-64, assoc. prof., 1964-72, prof., 1972—; faculty sr. scientist Lawrence Berkeley Lab., 1958—; vis. prof. nuclear physics Weizmann Inst. Sci., Rehovoth, Israel, 1973-74. Mem. Bd. Edn. of Berkeley Unified Sch. Dist., 1969-73, pres. bd., 1971-72. Recipient Elizabeth McCray fellow Princeton U., 1955; Charlotte Elizabeth Proctor fellow Princeton U., 1956; NSF postdoctoral fellow Faculte des Scis. L'Universite de Paris at Orsay, Laboratoire Joliot-Curie de Physique Nucleaire, 1964-65. Fellow AAAS; mem. Am. Chem. Soc. (bd. dirs. Calif. sect., chmn. 1991, 93-94), Am. Phys. Soc., Am. Inst. Chemists, N.Y. Acad. Scis., Calif. Inst. Chemists, Sigma Xi. Home: 317 Tideway Dr Alameda CA 94501-3540 Office: U Calif Dept Chemistry Berkeley CA 94720

MARKS, ANDREW H., lawyer; b. N.Y.C., May 5, 1951; s. Theodore and Rosalie Ruth (Goldman) M.; m. Susan G. Esserman, Aug. 3, 1975; children: Stephen Matthew, Clifford Michael, Michael David. AB, Harvard Coll., 1973; JD, U. Mich., 1976. Law clerk for Hon. Charles R. Richey U.S. Dist. Ct. D.C., Washington, 1976-78; exec. asst. to personal rep. of Pres. to Middle East Peace negotiations, Washington, 1979-81; assoc. Shea & Gardner, Washington, 1978-79, 81-84, ptnr., 1984-86; ptnr. Crowell & Moring, Washington, 1986—. Mem. D.C. Bar (gen. counsel 1987-89, bd. govs. 1989—, chmn. task force civility in the profession 1993—), Harvard Club Washington (pres. 1994—). Office: Crowell & Moring 1001 Pennsylvania Ave NW Washington DC 20004-2595

MARKS, ARNOLD, journalist; b. Phila., Aug. 4, 1912; s. Morris M. and Esther (Joel) M.; m. Isabelle Ruppert, Oct. 3, 1942 (dec.); 1 son, Rupert William Joel (dec.); m. Emi Seligman Simon. B.A., U. Wash., 1935; M.S., Columbia U., 1939. Editor Pasco (Wash.) Herald, 1946; with Oreg. Jour., Portland, 1946-78; drama, TV, entertainment editor Oreg. Jour., 1948-58, entertainment editor, 1958-78, ret., 1978, freelance writer. Served with AUS 1942-46. Mem. Sigma Delta Chi, Sigma Alpha Mu. Club: University (Portland). Home: PO Box 590 Gleneden Beach OR 97388-0590 also: 2393 SW Park Pl Portland OR 97205-1056 *In retrospect, there is great satisfaction in the thought that the years seem more loaded with heartwarming memories than with disappointments.*

MARKS, BARBARA HANZEL, publishing executive; b. Providence, Sept. 8, 1955; d. Albert and Pearl (Garfinkel) Hanzel; m. Alan D. Marks, Apr. 3, 1982; 1 child, Harrison Douglas. B.A. in English and Am. Lit., Harvard U., 1977, M.B.A., 1980. Circulation mgr. New Age Mag., Brookline, Mass., 1977-78; dir. planning Leisure Mags., N.Y.C., 1980-81; dir. planning ABC Pub., N.Y.C., 1981-82, v.p. strategic planning, 1982-83, v.p. ops., fin., 1984-88, v.p. ops. and fin., 1988-89. Class fund agt. Harvard U. Sch. Bus., 1987—. Honoree, ABC Pub., N.Y.C., 1985; named to City YWCA Acad. Women Achievers. Mem. Mag. Pubs. Assn., Am. Bus. Press. Club: Harvard (N.Y.C.). Home: 20 Kensington Rd Scarsdale NY 10583-2217 Office: ABC Pub 1330 Ave Of The Americas New York NY 10019-5422

MARKS, BERNARD BAILIN, lawyer; b. Sioux City, Iowa, Sept. 6, 1917; s. Meyer A. and Beulah (Bailin) M.;m. Betty L. Marks; 1 child, Susan E. BA, Harvard U., 1939, JD, 1942. Bar: Iowa 1942. With firm Shull, Marshall & Marks, Sioux City, 1946-85, ptnr., 1949-85; ptnr. Marks & Madsen, Sioux City, 1985—; sec., asst. treas., dir. Flavorland Industries, Inc. (formerly Needham Packing Co., Inc.), Sioux City, 1962-81; sec., dir. KTIV-TV Co., Sioux City, 1965-74; bd. dirs. First Nat. Bank, Firstar Bank, Sioux City, 1963-91. Bd. dirs. Iowa Heart Assn., 1960, Woodbury County chpt., 1958-64, pres., 1962-64; bd. dirs. Sioux City Art Center, 1952-54, Sioux City United Fund, 1965-71, Sioux City Community Appeals Bd., 1965-68; trustee Briar Cliff Coll., Sioux City, 1968-74. Served with USAAF, 1942-46. Fellow Iowa Bar Assn. Found.; mem. ABA, Iowa Bar Assn., Woodbury County Bar Assn. (prews. 1958), Am. Coll. Trust and Estate Counsel, Sioux City C. of C. (bd. dirs. 1964-67, treas. 1965-66), Sioux City Lawyers Club (pres. 1951), Sioux City Country Club (bd. dirs. 1963-64). Clubs: Sioux City Lawyers (pres. 1951), Sioux City Country (bd. dirs. 1963-64). Office: Marks & Madsen 303 United Federal Plaza Bldg PO Box 3226 Sioux City IA 51102

MARKS, BRUCE, artistic director, choreographer; b. N.Y.C., Jan. 23, 1937; s. Albert and Helen (Kosersky) M.; m. Toni Pihl Petersen, Jan. 27, 1966 (dec. May 1985); children: Erik Antony, Adam Christopher, Kenneth Rikard. Student, Brandeis U., 1954-55, Juilliard Sch., 1955-56; DFA (hon.), Wheaton Coll., 1986, Franklin Pierce Coll., 1990, U. Mass., 1995. Prof. U. Utah, 1981, 84-86; now artistic dir. Boston Ballet Co., 1985—; mem. dance adv. panel Nat. Endowment for Arts, 1979, chmn. internat. selection com., 1979, chmn. dance adv. panel, 1981, mem. nat. adv. bd. on arts and edn., 1989; bd. dirs., mem. exec. com., Dance/USA 1989, 92—, chmn., 1990-92, chmn. govt. affairs, 1992—; mem. U.S.-USSR Commn. on Dance and Theatre Studies, Am. Coun. Learned Socs./IREX; mem. jury Internat. Moscow Internat. Ballet Competition, 1989. Prin. dancer Met. Opera, 1956-61, Am. Ballet Theatre, 1961-72, Royal Swedish Ballet, 1963, Festival Ballet, London, 1965, Royal Danish Ballet, 1971-76; artistic dir. Ballet West, Salt Lake City, 1976-85; choreographer Eliot Feld Ballet Co., 1970, Royal Danish Ballet, 1972-73, Netherlands Dance Theatre, 1974, Ballet West, 1976-85; artistic fellow Aspen Inst. for Humanistic Studies, 1979—. Bd. dirs. Am. Arts Alliance, 1983-85, Am. Coun. for Arts, 1985—; bd. dirs. Dance U.S.A., 1988-94, chmn., 1990-92; chmn. U.S.A. Internat. Ballet Competition, Jackson, Miss., 1990—, vice chair jury, Helsinki, Finland, 1991; mem. nat. adv. bd. on arts and edn. NEA, 1989-91; mem. internat. jury 1st Japan Internat. Ballet Competition, Nagoya, Japan, 1993, Am. jury for Prix de Lausanne, 1994; mem. Brandeis Creative Arts Awards Commn., 1993, chmn. Brandeis Creative Arts Awards Dance, 1994; chair Grants to Dance Cos. panel NEA, 1993, overview panel, 1994. Recipient Disting. Svc. award for artistic prodn. Nat. Govs. Assn., 1994, Capezio award Balletmakers, Inc., 1995. Office: Boston Ballet 19 Clarendon St Boston MA 02116-6100

MARKS, CHARLES CALDWELL, retired investment banker, retired industrial distribution company executive; b. Birmingham, Ala., June 1, 1921; s. Charles Pollard and Isabel (Caldwell) M.; m. Jeanne Vigeant, Jan. 12, 1945; children: Randolph C., Margaret Marks Porter, Charles P. Student, Birmingham U., 1930-38; BS in Physics, U. of South, 1942; grad. mgmt. seminar, Harvard U., 1957; DCL (hon.), U. of the South, 1989; LLD (hon.), U. Ala., Birmingham, 1990. With Owen-Richards Co. (name changed to Motion Industries, Inc. 1970), Birmingham, 1946—; chmn. bd. Owen-Richards Co. (name changed to Motion Industries, Inc. 1970), 1952-73, pres., 1973-83; vice chmn. bd. Porter White & Yardley Cos., Inc., 1984-92, ret., 1992; bd. dirs. emeritus Genuine Parts Co., BE & K Inc.; bd. dirs., chmn. Birmingham br. Fed. Res. Bank of Atlanta. Bd. dirs. Sioux City Rsch. Inst., exec. com., 1987-95, dir. emeritus, 1995—; bd. govs. Indian Springs Sch., dir. emeritus, 1995—; pres., bd. dirs. Workshop for Blind, Birmingham, 1958-61, Children's Aid Soc. Birmingham, 1962; chmn. Com. of 100, Birmingham, 1963; co-chmn. United Appeals of Jefferson County, 1963; trustee, regent U. of South; pres. St. Vincent's Found., 1987; bd. dirs. U. Ala.-Birmingham Rsch. Found., Exec. Svcs. Corps of Birmingham, 1984—. Lt. USNR, WWII, ATO, MTO. Mem. Navy League, The Club, Redstone Club, John's Island Club, Mountain Brook Club, Willow Point Club, Ala. Newcomen Soc., Blue Key, Phi Beta Kappa, Sigma Alpha Epsilon. Episcopalian. Home: 2828 Cherokee Rd Birmingham AL 35223-2607 Office: 2160 Highland Ave Suite 301 Birmingham AL 35205

MARKS, CHARLES DENNERY, insurance salesman; b. New Orleans, Nov. 22, 1935; s. Sidney Leroy Marks and Melanie Dennery; m. Gillian E. Otter, Sept. 1, 1963; children: Elizabeth Dennery, Richard Dennery. BA, Yale U., 1957. CLU, ChFC. With Charles Dennery, Inc., 1959-63; sales rep. Prudential Ins. Co., New Orleans, 1964—; v.p. Mgmt. Compensation Group, New Orleans, 1985—. Past bd. dirs. Boys Club Greater New Orleans, Big Bros. Greater New Orleans, United Way; past pres. Goodwill Rehab. Ctr.; vice chmn. Jr. Achievement; active Temple Sinai Synagogue. 1st lt. U.S. Army, 1957-59. Recipient award Volunteer Activist, 1983. Mem. Am. Soc. CLU and ChFC (pres. New Orleans chpt. 1984-85), Am. Advanced Life Underwriting, Life Underwriters Pol. Action Com. (diplomat, sec./treas. 1982-87), La. Assn. Life Underwriters (Life Underwriter of Yr. 1985, 87, pres. 1986-87), New Orleans Estate Planning Coun. (pres. 1986-87), New Orleans Life Underwriters Assn. (Life Underwriter of Yr. 1981, pres. 1982-83), Million Dollar Round Table (Top of the Table 1986-89, exec. com. 1990-94, pres. 1993), Nat. Assn. Life Underwriters (vice chmn. fin. com. 1993—), Life and Health Found. for Edn. (life, chmn.- elect 1994—). Republican. Home: 1525 Eleonore St New Orleans LA 70115-4242 Office: Mgmt Compensation Group Ste 325 1250 Poydras Plz New Orleans LA 70113-1826

MARKS, CRAIG, management educator, consultant, engineer; b. Salt Lake City, Oct. 9, 1929; s. Elmer Lester and Louie Thelma (Marks) M.; m. Lois Marie Brinkman, June 11, 1950 (div. 1972); children—Gary C., Diane Marks White, Marian Marks Deming; m. Anne Mary Crowe, Oct. 28, 1972. B.S.M.E., Calif. Inst. Tech., 1950, M.S.M.E., 1951, Ph.D. in Mech. Engring., 1955. Instr. Calif. Inst. Tech., Pasadena, 1953-55; supr. Ford Motor Co., Detroit, 1955-56, Gen. Motors Research Labs., Warren, Mich., 1956-57; asst. engr.-in-charge engring. staff Gen. Motors Corp., Warren, 1957-67; engr.-in-charge Gen. Motors Corp., 1967-72, exec. asst. to v.p.,

1972-79, exec. dir. environ. activity staff, 1979-83; v.p. engring. and tech. TRW Inc., Cleve., Ohio, 1983-88; v.p. tech. and productivity Allied Signal Inc., Southfield, Mich., 1988-91; prof. U. Mich., 1991—; pres. CMS-Creative Mgmt. Solutions, Bloomfield Hills, Mich., 1991—; co-dir. Tauber Mfg. Inst. U. Mich., 1995—. Contbr. articles to profl. jours.; patentee in field. Speaker civic leaders meetings Gen. Motors Corp., 1977-82. Fellow Soc. Automotive Engrs. (bd. dirs.); mem. NAE, ASME, Engring. Soc. Detroit (bd. dirs.), Sigma Xi, Tau Beta Pi. Christian Scientist. Avocations: flying; tennis; golf. Home and Office: 174 Kirkwood Ct Bloomfield Hills MI 48304-2926

MARKS, DAVID HUNTER, civil engineering educator; b. White Plains, N.Y., Feb. 22, 1939; s. Sidney M. and Jean (Berger) M.; div.; 1 child, Joanna. BCE, Cornell U., 1962, MS in Environ. Engring., 1964; PhD, Johns Hopkins U., 1969. Registered profl. engr., N.Y., Mass.; registered hydrologist, Am. Inst. Hydrology. Sr. sanitary engr. USPHS, Phila., 1964-66; asst. prof. civil engring. MIT, Cambridge, Mass., 1969-72, assoc. prof., 1972-75, prof., 1975—, head dept., 1985-92, dir. program in environ. engring. edn. and rsch., 1991—; James Mason Crafts Prof., 1992—; bd. dirs. Camp Dresser and McKee, Environ. Engrs., Boston. Office: MIT Rm 48-305 Dept Civil & Environ Engring Cambridge MA 02139

MARKS, DENNIS A., lawyer; b. Akron, Ohio, Nov. 25, 1946. BBA, Loyola U., 1969; JD, John Marshall Law Sch., 1974. Bar: Ill. 1974. Ptnr. Querrey & Harrow Ltd., Chgo. Mem. Ill. State Bar Assn., Chgo. Bar Assn., West Suburban Bar Assn., Trial Lawyers Club Chgo. Address: 2 Prudential Plz 180 N Stetson Ste 3500 Chicago IL 60601

MARKS, EDWARD B., international social service administrator; b. N.Y.C., Apr. 22, 1911; s. Edward B. and Miriam (Chuck) M.; m. Margaret Levi (dec. 1980); 2 children; m. Vera J. Barad, 1987. BA cum laude, Dartmouth Coll., 1932; MA in Sociology, Columbia U., 1938. Assoc. editor Am. Wine and Liquor Jour., N.Y.C., 1933-36; mng. editor Better Times mag. Welfare Coun. N.Y.C., 1937-38; dir. div. for social and cultural adjustment Nat. Refugee Svc., N.Y.C., 1938-42; refugee program officer War Relocation Authority, Dept. Interior, Washington, 1942-46; chief of mission for Greece UN Internat. Refugee Orgn., Geneva and Athens, 1947-50; chief of mission successively for Greece, N.Y., and Yugoslavia Internat. Migration Orgn., 1951-58; exec. dir. U.S. Com. for Refugees, N.Y.C., 1958-62; dep. chief office cen. African affairs AID, Washington, 1962-65; asst. dir. for relief and rehab., Vietnam AID, 1965-66, aid coordination officer, Am. Embassy, U.K., 1966-68, asst. dir. for relief and rehab., Nigeria, 1969-71, voluntary agy. liaison officer for Asia, 1973-75; various emergency liaison assignments UNICEF, N.Y.C., Paris, Geneva, 1971-73; dep. dir. secretariat Internat. Yr. of Child UNICEF, N.Y.C., 1976-80, liaison bur. for UN Yr. for Disabled, 1981-82, internat. cons., 1983-85; interim pres. U.S. Com. for UNICEF, N.Y.C., 1985, bd. dirs., mem. exec. com., chmn. nominating com., 1986-92; pres. then chmn. Immigration and Refugee Svcs. Am., 1985—; instr. Boston U. Sch. Social Work, 1988, 89. Contbr. articles to The New Yorker, N.Y. Times Mag., other jours. Recipient First Disting. Career award AID, 1976. Address: 333 E 46th St New York NY 10017-7401 also: 4 Channing St Cambridge MA 02138

MARKS, EDWIN S., investment company executive; b. N.Y.C., June 3, 1926; s. Carl and Edith R. (Smith) M.; m. Nancy Lucille Abeles, June 21, 1949; children: Carolyn Gail, Linda Beth, Constance Ann. Student, Princeton U., 1944-45; BS, U.S. Mil. Acad., 1949. V.p. Carl Marks & Co., N.Y.C., 1958-61, pres., 1961—, also bd. dirs.; dir., exec. v.p. CMNY Capital Co. Inc., 1962—. Author: What I Know about Foreign Securities, 1958. Trustee Lincoln Ctr. Fund, 1966-77, Hofstra U., 1974-79, Sarah Lawrence Coll., 1979-81, North Shore Univ. Hosp., Manhasset, N.Y.; chmn. bd. overseers Rsch. Lab., North Shore Univ. Hosp.; bd. dirs. Chief Execs. Orgn. Cold Spring Harbor Labs., 1992, Smith New Court PLC, London, 1988-94; bd. dirs., exec. com. Lincoln Ctr. for the Performing Arts. Mem. West Point Soc., N.Y. Bd. Trade, Harmonie Club. Office: Carl Marks & Co 135 E 57th St New York NY 10022-2050

MARKS, ELAINE, French language educator; b. N.Y.C., Nov. 13, 1930; d. Harry and Ruth (Elin) M. BA, Bryn Mawr Coll., 1952; MA, U. Pa., 1953; PhD, NYU, 1958. Asst. prof. French NYU, N.Y.C., 1958-60; assoc. prof. U. Wis., Milw., 1963-65; prof. U. Wis., Madison, 1967-68, prof. French, Italian and women's studies, 1980—; prof. French U. Mass., Amherst, 1965-66; dir. Women's Studies Rsch. Ctr., 1977-85. Author: Colette, 1960, 2nd edit., 1981, Simone de Beauvoir: Encounters with Death, 1973; co-editor: Homosexualities and French Literature, 1979, 2nd edit., 1990, New French Feminisms, 1980, 81; editor: Critical Essays on Simone de Beauvoir, 1987. Decorated officier Ordre Palmes Académiques (France), 1994; recipient Disting. Alumni award NYU Grad. Sch. Arts and Sci. Alumni Assn., 1994; Wis. Alumni Rsch. Found. U. House Professorship, 1988; Fulbright fellow, France, 1956-57, Guggenheim fellow, 1992. Mem. MLA (pres. 1993), Midwest MLA, Am. Assn. Tchrs. French, Nat. Women's Studies Assn. Home: 2040 Field St Madison WI 53713-1159

MARKS, ESTHER L., metals company executive; b. Canton, Ohio, Oct. 3, 1927; d. Jacob and Ella (Wisman) Rosky; m. Irwin Alfred Marks, June 29, 1947; children: Jules, Howard, Marilyn. Student, Ohio State U., 1945-46, Youngstown State U., 1946-47. V.p. Steel City Iron & Metal, Inc., Youngstown, Ohio. Pres. Jr. Hadassah, Youngstown, 1943-45, Pioneer Women, Youngstown, 1951, Anshe Emeth Sisterhood, Youngstown, Broadway Theatre League, Youngstown, 1958, B'nai B'rith Women, Youngstown, 1962, Dist. 2 B'nai B'rith Women, Cleve., 1969-70, Jewish Community Ctr., Youngstown, Youngstown Area Jewish Fedn., 1988-90; v.p. United Way, Youngstown, 1991; grad. Leadership Youngstown., 1991. Named Guardian of the Menorah B'nai B'rith, Youngstown, 1978; recipient BBG Alumna award B'nai B'rith Girls, Washington, 1989. Mem. LWV, YWCA, Ohio Hist. Soc. Democrat. Jewish. Avocations: knitting, organizational work. Home: 3511 5th Ave Youngstown OH 44505-1907 Office: 703 Wilson Ave Youngstown OH 44506-1445

MARKS, FLORENCE CARLIN ELLIOTT, nursing informaticist; b. Louisville, Ky., Oct. 15, 1928; d. David Carlin and Anna Marie (Lance) Elliott; m. George Edward Marks, Mar. 18, 1961; children: Mary Ellen Marks Fox, Ruth Ann, Charles Douglas. BS in Chemistry, Zoology, U. Cin., 1949; BSN, U. Minn., 1953, M of Nursing Adminstrn., 1956. RN, Minn. From staff nurse to asst. head nurse U. Minn. Hosps., Mpls., 1953-54; staff nurse Marseilisbog Hosp., Aarhaus, Denmark, 1954-55; nursing supr. U. Minn. Hosps., Mpls., 1956-61, spl. asst. to dir. of nursing svc., 1962; rsch asst. Hill Family Found. Nursing Rsch. Project, Mpls., 1966-69; writer U. Minn. Sch. of Nursing, Mpls., 1976; cons. U. Minn. Sch. of Nursing, 1976, 1978; nursing program specialist Hennepin County Med. Ctr., Mpls., 1978-84; nursing info. systems dir., cons., 1987—; nursing utilization system coord. U. Minn. Hosps., Mpls., 1984-87; cons. Creative Nursing Mgmt., 1992—; speaker, lectr. various nursing confs. in U.S. Contbr. articles to profl. publs., chpts. to profl. books, posters, abstracts; co-author: (with Joan Williams) (TV series) TLC, 1953 (McCall's award 1954); editor: Tomorrow's Nurse, 1966; Minn. Nursing Accent (commemorative issue 60th anniversary) May, 1965. Prin. flutist St. Anthony Civic Orch., 1975—, bd. dirs., 1988-92, adminstrv. bd. Hennepin Ave. United Meth. Ch., Mpls., 1977-81, 1966-83 intentionality cmty. outreach ministry, chair adv. com. 1992—; mem. U. Minn. Sch. Nursing Densford Recognition Com., 1992—; troop leader Mpls. Coun. Girl Scouts of U.S., 1971-85, bd. dirs. 1977-79, svc. unit mgr. 1973-77, Cub Scout Webelo den leader Viking Coun. Boy Scouts Am., 1977-79; v.p. Wilshire Park PTSA, 1975-76, pres. 1976-77. Recipient Thanks Badge Greater Mpls. Girl Scout Coun. Mem. Minn. Nurses Assn. (various coms., bd. dirs. 1965-67), Minn. League for Nursing, Minn. Heart Assn. (profl. edn. com. 1959-61), Nursing Info. Discussion Group (chmn. Twin City program com. 1985-91), U. Minn. Sch. Nursing Alumni Assn. (bd. dirs. 1963-67, pres. 1965-66), Mortar Bd., Zeta Tau Alpha, Tau Beta Sigma, Sigma Theta Tau (bd. dirs. 1986-91, sec. 1989-91, pres. 1972-73, heritage com. 1990). Home: 3424 Silver Lake Rd NE Minneapolis MN 55418-1605

MARKS, HERBERT EDWARD, lawyer; b. Dayton, Ohio, Nov. 3, 1935; s. I.M. and Sarah S. M.; m. Marcia Frager; children: Jennifer L., Susan E. A.B. with high distinction, U. Mich., 1957; J.D., Yale U., 1960; post-grad., George Washington U. Law Sch., 1965-67. Bar: Ohio 1960, D.C. 1964, U.S. Supreme Ct. 1965. Law clk. to chief judge U.S. Ct. Claims, 1964-

65; assoc. Wilkinson, Cragun & Barker, Washington, 1965-69, ptnr., 1969-82; ptnr. Squire, Sanders & Dempsey, Washington, 1982—; assoc. gen. counsel Presdl. Inaugural Coms., 1969, 73, 81; chmn. U.S. State Dept. Adv. Panel on Internat. Telecomm. Law, 1987-91; mem. adv. com. on internat. comm. and info. policy U.S. State Dept., 1988-91; mem. U.S. del. ITU European Telecomm. Devel. Conf., 1991. Contbr. articles to legal jours. Served to capt. JAG USAF, 1960-64. Mem. ABA (chair sci. and tech. sect. 1990-91, chmn. communications div. 1986-88), D.C. Bar Assn., Computer Law Assn. (pres. 1975-77, bd. dirs. 1972-85, adv. bd. 1985—), Fed. Communications Bar Assn., Cosmos Club, Kenwood Golf & Country Club, Phi Beta Kappa. Office: Squire Sanders & Dempsey 1201 Pennsylvania Ave NW PO Box 407 Washington DC 20004 also: 5317 Cardinal Ct Bethesda MD 20816

MARKS, JAMES FREDERIC, pediatric endocrinologist, educator; b. Pitts., Dec. 18, 1928; s. Alfred Mozelle and Cecil (Cuff) M.; m. Mary Fay Clement, Jan. 29, 1959; 1 child, Roland Phillip. BA, Princeton U., 1950; MD, Harvard U., 1954; MPH, U. Pitts., 1984. Intern Montefiore Hosp., Pitts., 1954-55; resident in pediatrics Children's Hosp. of Pitts., 1955-57; rsch. fellow in pediatric endocrinology U. Pitts., 1959-61; asst. prof. dept. pediatrics U. Tex. Southwestern Med., Dallas, 1961-68, assoc. prof. pediatrics, 1968—; bd. dirs. State Newborn Screening Program, Tex., 1980—. Contbr. articles to profl. publs., chpts. to med. textbooks. Capt. U.S. Army, 1957-59. Sr. rsch fellow USPHS, 1983-84. Mem. Am. Diabetes Assn. (bd. dirs. Tex. affiliate 1992—), Am. Acad. Pediatrics, Endocrine Soc., Soc. for Pediatric Rsch. Achievements include research in thyroid function in infancy, delineation of early clinical course in Lesch-Nyhan disease, observations on the possible genetic factors in diabetic microvascular disease. Office: U Tex Southwestern Med 5323 Harry Hines Blvd Dallas TX 75235-9063

MARKS, JEROME, lawyer; b. N.Y.C., June 24, 1931; s. Leon and Ida (Weiner) M.; children: Susan Marks Schmetterer, David J., Ilyse Marks Kelly, Laurence K. BA, Northwestern U., 1952, JD summa cum laude, 1955. Bar: Ill. 1955. Assoc. Friedman & Koven, Chgo., 1956-63, ptnr., 1963-86; ptnr. Rudnick & Wolfe, Chgo., 1986—. Asst. editor-in-chief Northwestern U. Law Rev., 1954-55. Co-chmn. No. Suburbs div. Operation Breadbasket, Chgo. and Highland Park (Ill.), 1968-72. Mem. Chgo. Bar Assn., Chgo. Coun. Lawyers, Order of Coif. Democrat. Avocations: walking, swimming, horse racing. Office: Rudnick & Wolfe 203 N La Salle St Ste 1800 Chicago IL 60601-1293

MARKS, JOHN HENRY, Near Eastern studies educator; b. Denver, Aug. 6, 1923; s. A. Emil E. (Dralle) M.; m. E. Aminta Willis, July 21, 1951; children: Peter A., Fleur A., John B. B.A., U. Denver, 1946; B.D. (O.T. fellow), Princeton Theol. Sem., 1949; Th.D., U. Basel (Switzerland), 1953. Instr. Princeton Theol. Sem., 1953-54; instr. Princeton U., 1954-55, asst. prof. to assoc. prof. Near Eastern studies, 1955-61, prof., 1979-93; dir. Am. Schs. Oriental Research, Jerusalem, 1966-67; pres. Am. Ctr. Oriental Research, Amman, Jordan, 1969-79; trustee Am. Schs. Oriental Research, Phila, 1971-86 ; Acting dean Princeton U. Chapel, 1980. Author: Der Textkritische Wert des Psalterium Hieronymi iuxta Hebraeos, 1956, Visions of One World, Legacy of Alexander, 1985; also translator. Pres. Sch. Bd. Princeton, 1969-71; mem. Planning-Zoning Bds. Princeton, 1964-66. Served with U.S. Army, 1943-45. Mem. Soc. Bibl. Lit. Democrat. Presbyterian. Home: 107 Moore St Princeton NJ 08540 Office: 110 Jones Princeton NJ 08544-0001

MARKS, LAWRENCE EDWARD, psychologist; b. N.Y.C., Dec. 28, 1941; s. Milton and Anne (Parnes) M.; m. Joya Ellen Cazes, Dec. 24, 1963; children: Liza, Laura. AB, Hunter Coll., N.Y.C., 1962; PhD, Harvard U., Cambridge, Mass., 1965; PhD honoris causa, Stockholm U., 1994. Rsch.-assoc. prof. Yale U., New Haven, 1966-84; asst.-assoc. prof. John B. Pierce Lab., New Haven, 1966-84; prof. psychology Yale U., New Haven, 1984—; fellow John B. Pierce Lab., New Haven, 1984—. Author: Sensory Processes: The New Psychophysics, 1974, The Unity of the Senses, 1978. Named to Hall of Fame, Hunter Coll., N.Y.C., 1985; recipient Jacob Javits award NIH, Washington, 1987. Fellow AAAS, Am. Psychol. Assn., Am. Psychol. Soc., N.Y. Acad. Sci. Democrat. Jewish. Achievements include elucidation of common principles underlying sensory processes in various sense modalities; development of validational scheme for quantifying magnitudes of sensory experience; indication of role of cross-modal (synesthetic) perception in relation to language and literature. Home: 48 Maplevale Dr Woodbridge CT 06525-1118 Office: John B Pierce Lab 290 Congress Ave New Haven CT 06519-1403

MARKS, LEONARD, JR., retired corporate executive; b. N.Y.C., May 22, 1921; s. Leonard M. and Laura (Colegrove) Rose; m. Antonia Saldaña Riley, July 19, 1986; children from previous marriage: Linda, Patricia Anne, Peter K. A.B. in Econs., Drew U., 1942; M.B.A., Harvard U., 1948, D.B.A., 1961. Asst. prof. bus. adminstrn. Harvard U., 1949-55; prof. fin. Stanford U., 1955-64; asst. sec. USAF, Washington, 1964-68; v.p. Gen. devel. Times Mirror Co., Los Angeles, 1968-69; sr. v.p. Wells Fargo Bank, San Francisco, 1969-72; exec. v.p. Castle & Cooke Inc., San Francisco, 1972-85; gen. ptnr. Marks-Hoffman Assocs., Venture Capital, 1985-92; ind. dir., 1992—; bd. dirs. Airlease Mgmt. Svcs., Alexion Pharm. Inc., No. Trust Bank of Ariz. Co-author: Case Problems in Commercial Bank Management, 1962; contbg.: Credit Management Handbook, 1958. Capt. AUS, 1942-46, ret. brig. gen. USAFR.

MARKS, LEONARD HAROLD, lawyer; b. Pitts., Mar. 5, 1916; s. Samuel and Ida (Levine) M.; m. Dorothy Ames, June 3, 1948; children: Stephen Ames, Robert Evan. B.A., U. Pitts., 1935, LL.B., 1938. Bar: Pa. 1938, D.C. 1946. Asst. prof. law U. Pitts. Law Sch., 1938-42; prof. law Nat. U., 1943-55; asst. to gen. counsel FCC, 1942-46, ops. counsel, 1986—; ptnr. Cohn & Marks, Washington, 1946-65, 69-86; head USIA, 1965-68; chmn. exec. com Nat. Savs. and Trust Co., 1977-85; chmn. Internat. Conf. on Communications Satellites, 1968-69; Am. del. Internat. Broadcasting Confs., 1948-69; pres. Internat. Rescue Com., 1973-79, Honor Am. Com., 1976-78; chmn. U.S. Adv. Commn. on Internat. Ednl. and Cultural Affairs, 1973-78, Fgn. Policy Assn., 1981—; head U.S. del. Internat. Telecommunication Union 1983, 87; chmn. U.S. del. to London Info. Forum, Commn. on Security and Cooperation in Europe, 1989. Mem. ABA (ho. of dels. 1962-64), Fed. Communications Bar Assn. (pres. 1959-60), Bar Assn. D.C., World Affairs Council Washington (chmn.), Phi Beta Kappa, Order of Coif, Omicron Delta Kappa, Sigma Delta Chi. Clubs: Cosmos, Metropolitan, Federal City, Broadcasters, (pres. 1957-59), Alfalfa (Washington). Home: 2833 Mcgill Ter NW Washington DC 20008-2749 Office: 1333 New Hampshire Ave NW Washington DC 20036-1500

MARKS, MARTHA ALFORD, author; b. Oxford, Miss., July 27, 1946; d. Truman and Margaret (Parnell) Alford; m. Bernard L. Marks, Jan. 27, 1968. BA, Centenary Coll., 1968; MA, Northwestern U., 1972, PhD, 1978. Tchr. Notre Dame High Sch. for Boys, Niles, Ill., 1969-74; teaching asst. Northwestern U., Evanston, Ill., 1974-78, lectr., lang. coord., 1978-83; asst. prof. Kalamazoo (Mich.) Coll., 1983-85; writer Riverwoods, Ill., 1985—; cons. WGBH Edn. Found., Boston, 1988-91. Am. Coun. on the Teaching of Fgn. Langs., 1981-92, Ednl. Testing Svcs., 1988—, Peace Corps, 1993—. Co-author: Destinos: An Introduction to Spanish, 1991, Al corriente, 1989, 93, Que tal?, 1986, 90; author: (workbook) Al corriente, 1989, 93; contbr. articles to profl. jours. Mem. Lake County (Ill.) Forest Preserve Commn., 1992—, Lake County Conservation Alliance; vice chmn. Friends of Ryerson Conservation Area Bd. Mem. AAUW. Home: 2940 Cherokee Ln Riverwoods IL 60015 Office: County Bd Office County Bldg Rm 1001 18 N County St Waukegan IL 60085

MARKS, MERTON ELEAZER, lawyer; b. Chgo., Oct. 16, 1932; s. Alfred Tobias and Helene Fannie (Rosner) M.; m. Radee Maiden Feiler, May 20, 1966; children: Sheldon, Elise Marks Vazelakis, Alan, Elaine Marks Ianchiou. BS, Northwestern U., 1954, JD, 1956. Bar: Ill. 1956, U.S. Ct. Mil. Appeals 1957, Ariz. 1958, U.S. Dist. Ct. Ariz. 1960, U.S. Ct. Appeals (9th cir.) 1962, U.S. Supreme Ct. 1970. Assoc. Moser, Compere & Emerson, Chgo., 1956-57; ptnr. Morgan, Marks & Rogers, Tucson, 1960-62; asst. atty. gen. State of Ariz., Phoenix, 1962-64, counsel indsl. commn., 1964-65; from assoc. to ptnr. Shimmel, Hill, Bishop & Greunder, Phoenix, 1965-74; ptnr. Lewis & Roca, Phoenix, 1974—; lectr. on pharm., health care, product liability, ins. and employers' liability subjects; Judge Pro Tempore Ariz. Ct.

Appeals, 1994. Contbr. more than 35 articles to various tort and ins. subjects to profl. jours. Capt. JAGC, USAR, 1957-64. Mem. ABA (tort and ins. practice sect., chmn. spl. com. on fed. asbestos legislation 1987-89, chmn. workers' compensation and employers liability law com. 1983-84), Am. Bd. Trial Advocates, Am. Coll. Legal Medicine, Internat. Bar Assn., Am. Soc. Pharmacy Law, State Bar Ariz. (chmn. workers' compensation sect. 1969-73), Nat. Coun. Self Insurers, Ariz. Self Insurers Assn., Fedn. Ins. and Corp. Counsel (chmn. pharm. litigation sect. 1989-91, chmn. workers' compensation sect. 1977-79, v.p. 1978-79, 81, bd. dirs. 1981-89), Internat. Assn. Defense Counsel, Ariz. Assn. Defense Counsel (pres. 1976-77), Maricopa County Bar Assn., Defense Rsch. Inst. (mem. drug and device com., chmn. workers' compensation com. 1977-78). Office: Lewis & Roca 40 N Central Ave Phoenix AZ 85004-4424

MARKS, MICHAEL J., corporate executive, lawyer; b. 1938. AB, Cornell U., 1960; JD, U. Chgo., 1963. Assoc. Stroock & Stroock & Lavan, 1964-70, Chun, Kerr & Dodd, 1970-72; counsel Kelso, Spencer, Snyder & Stirling, 1972-75; asst. gen. counsel Alexander & Baldwin Inc., Honolulu, 1975-80, v.p., gen. counsel, 1980-84, v.p., gen. counsel, sec., 1984-85, sr. v.p., gen. counsel, sec., 1985—. Office: Alexander & Baldwin Inc 822 Bishop St Honolulu HI 96813-3925

MARKS, PAUL ALAN, oncologist, cell biologist, educator; b. N.Y.C., Aug. 16, 1926; s. Robert R. and Sarah (Bohorad) M.; m. Joan Harriet Rosen, Nov. 28, 1953; children: Andrew Robert, Elizabeth Susan Marks Ostrer, Matthew Stuart. AB with gen. honors, Columbia U., 1945, MD, 1949. D in Biol. Sci. (hon.), U. Urbino, Italy, 1982; PhD (hon.), Hebrew U., Jerusalem, Israel, 1987, U. Tel Aviv, 1992. Fellow Columbia U. Coll. Physicians and Surgeons, 1952-53, assoc., 1955-56, mem. faculty, 1956-82, dir. hematology tng., 1961-74, prof. medicine, 1967-82, prof. human genetics and devel., 1969-82, dean faculty of medicine, v.p. med. affairs, 1970-73, dir. Comprehensive Cancer Ctr., 1972-80, v.p. health scis., 1973-80, Frode Jensen prof. medicine, 1974-80; prof. medicine and genetics Cornell U. Coll. Medicine, N.Y.C., 1982—; prof. medicine Grad. Sch. Med. Scis., 1983—; instr. Sch. Medicine, George Washington U., 1954-55; cons. VA Hosp., N.Y.C., 1962-66; attending physician Presbyn. Hosp., N.Y.C., 1967-82; pres., CEO Meml. Sloan-Kettering Cancer Ctr., 1980—; attending physician Meml. Hosp. for Cancer and Allied Diseases, 1980—; mem. Sloan-Kettering Inst. for Cancer Rsch., 1980—; adj. prof. Rockefeller U., 1980—; vis. physician Rockefeller U. Hosp., 1980—; hon. staff N.Y. Hosp., 1981—; bd. sci. counselors divsn. cancer treatment Nat. Cancer Inst., 1980-83; mem. steering com. Frederick Cancer Rsch. Facility Nat. Cancer Inst., 1982-86; chmn. program adv. com. Robert Wood Johnson Found., 1983-89; mem. Gov.'s Commn. on Shoreham Nuclear Plant, 1983; mem. Mayor's Commn. Sci. and Tech. City of N.Y., 1984-87; mem. adv. com. on NIH to Sec. HHS, 1989-90, 93—, external adv. com. Intramural Rsch. Program Rev. NIH; mem. coun. biol. scis. Pritzker Sch. Medicine U. Chgo., 1977-88; first lectr. Nakasone Program for Cancer Control U. Tokyo, 1984; Ayrey fellow, vis. prof. Royal Postgrad. Med. Sch. U. London, 1985; William Dameshek vis. prof. hematology Mt. Sinai Med. Ctr., 1985; nat. vis. com. CUNY Med. Sch., 1986-89; trustee Feinberg Grad. Sch. Weizmann Inst. Sci., Rehovot, Israel, 1986—; William H. Resnick lectr. in medicine Stamford Hosp., 1986; disting. faculty lectr. M.D. Anderson Hosp. U. Tex., 1986; Maurice C. Pincoffs lectr. U. Md., Balt., 1987; Japan Soc. Hematology Disting. lectr., 1989; vis. prof. Coll. de France, 1988; Alpha Omega Alpha vis. prof. N.Y. Med. Coll., 1990; Mario A. Baldini vis. prof. Harvard Med. Sch., 1991; mem. sci. adv. bd. City of Hope Nat. Med. Ctr., Duarte, Calif., 1987-92; Raymond and Beverly Sackler Found. Inc., 1989, Jefferson Cancer Inst., Phila., 1989, Hong Kong Cancer Inst., U. Hong Kong, 1994; mem. Found. Biomed. Rsch., 1989—; advisor Third World Acad. Sci.; mem. sci. adv. com. Imperial Cancer Rsch. Fund, 1994; mem. bd. govs. Friends of Sheba Med. Ctr., Tel Hashomer. Editor: Monographs in Human Biology, 1963; author 9 books; contbr. over 350 articles to profl. jours.; mem. editorial bd. Blood, 1964-71, assoc. editor, 1976-77, editor-in-chief, 1978-82; editor-in-chief Jour. Clin. Investigation, 1967-71; mem. editorial bd. Cancer Treatment Revs., 1981—, Cancer Preventions, 1989, Sci., 1990; guest editorial bd. Japanese Jour. Cancer Rsch., 1985—; assoc. editor Molecular Reprodn. and Devel., 1988—; expert analyst Chemistry and Molecular Biology edit. of Chemtracts, 1990-92; mem. adv. bd. Internat. Jour. Hematology, 1992, bd. contrib. editors Blood Cells, Molecules and Diseases, 1994. Trustee St. Luke's Hosp., 1970-80, Presbyn. Hosp., 1972-80, Metpath Inst. Med. Edn., 1977-79; mem. jury Albert Lasker Awards, 1974-82; bd. govs. Weizmann Inst., 1976—, Friends of Sheba Med. Ctr., Tel Hashomer, Israel; bd. dirs. Revson Found., 1976-91, Am. Found. for Basic Rsch. Israel, Israel Acad. Scis., 1991; mem. tech. bd. Milbank Meml. Fund, 1978-85. Recipient Charles Janeway prize Columbia U., 1949, Joseph Mather Smith prize, 1959, Stevens Triennial prize, 1960, Swiss-Am. Found. award in med. rsch., 1965, Columbia U. Coll. Physicians and Su achievement medal, 1980, Centenary Inst. Pasteur medal, 1987, Disting. Oncological award Hipple Cancer Ctr. and Kettering Ctr., 1987, Found. for Promotion of Cancer Rsch. medal, 1984 (Japan), Disting. Svc. medal Robert Wood Johnson Found., 1989, Outstanding Achievement award in Hematopoiesis U. Innsbruck, 1991, Nat. Medal Sci., 1991, NSF, Gold Medal for Disting. Acad. Accomplishments, Coll. Physicians and Surgeons, 1994; Commonwealth Fund fellow Pasteur Inst., 1961-62. Master ACP, Coll. Phys. Surgeons; fellow Royal Soc. Medicine, Am. Acad. Arts and Scis., AAAS, Pasteur Inst. Paris; mem. NAS (chmn. sect. med. genetics, hematology and oncology 1980-83, chmn. Acad. Forum Adv. Com. 1980-81, mem. coun. 1984-87, coun. on internat. affairs 1985-87, del. biol. warfare com. Internat. Security and Arms Control 1986-89), Royal Soc. Med. (London), Inst. Medicine (mem. coun. 1973-76, chmn. com. study resources clin. investigation with NAS 1988), Red Cell Club (past chmn.), Am. Fedn. Clin. Rsch. (past councillor Eastern dist.), Am. Soc. Clin. Investigation (pres. 1972-73), Am. Soc. Biol. Chemists, Am. Soc. Human Genetics (past mem. program com.), Am. Assn. Cancer Rsch., Assn. Am. Cancer Insts. (bd. dirs. 1983-88), Soc. Cell Biology, Am. Soc. Hematology (pres.-elect 1983, pres. 1984, chmn. adv. bd. 1985), Assn. Am. Physicians, Econ. Club (N.Y.C.), Harvey Soc. (pres. 1973-74), Internat. Soc. Devel. Biologists, Italian Assn. Cell Biology and Differentiation (hon.), Chinese Anti-Cancer Assn. (hon.), Soc. for Devel. Biology, Japanese Cancer Assn. (hon.), Japan Soc. Hematology (Disting. lectr. 1989), Internat. Leadership Ctr. on Longevity and Soc., Interurban Clin. Club, Soc. for Study Devel. and Growth, Third World Acad. Scis., Sci. adv. Hong Kong Cancer Inst., U. Hong Kong, Sci. Adv. Com. Imperial Cancer Rsch. Fund, Health Scis. Adv. Counc. Columbia U., Century Assn., Econ. Club, N.Y.C., Univ. Club N.Y.C., Alpha Omega Alpha. Home: PO Box 1485 Washington CT 06793-0485 Office: Meml Sloan-Kettering Cancer 1275 York Ave New York NY 10021

MARKS, RICHARD, film editor; b. N.Y.C., Nov. 10, 1943; s. Ben and Irene (Epstein) Marks; m. Barbara Joan Fallick, Jan. 15, 1967; 1 child, Leslie Sharon. Student, NYU; BA, CCNY. Freelance film editor N.Y.C. and Los Angeles, 1964—. Mem. Motion Picture Acad. Arts and Scis., American Cinema Editors.

MARKS, RICHARD DANIEL, lawyer; b. N.Y.C., June 21, 1944; s. Morris Andrew and Dorothy (Schill) M.; m. Cheryl L. Hoffman, Nov. 13, 1971. BA, U. Va., 1966; JD, Yale U., 1969. Bar: D.C., U.S. Ct. Appeals (3rd, 4th, 11th and D.C. cir.), U.S. Supreme Ct. Assoc. Dow, Lohnes & Albertson, Washington, 1972-78, ptnr., 1978—. Co-author: Legal Problems in Broadcasting, 1974. Capt. U.S. Army, 1970-72. Mem. ABA (chmn. contracting for computer com., sect. for sci. and tech., computer law div., chmn. computer law div. 1994), Fed. Comms. Bar Assn., Capital Area Assn. Flight Instrs. (pres. 1989-90), UVA Club of Washington (pres. 1991-92). Avocations: aviation, skiing. Office: Dow Lohnes & Albertson 1255 23rd St NW Ste 500 Washington DC 20037

MARKS, ROBERT ARTHUR, lawyer; b. Dayton, Ohio, Oct. 9, 1952; s. Arthur Kenneth and Patricia Marks; m. Victoria Scurlock, Oct. 21, 1978; two sons. BA, U. Wis., 1974; JD, U. Cin., 1977. Bar: Ohio 1977, Hawaii 1978, U.S. Ct. Appeals (6th cir.) Ohio 1977, U.S. Ct. Appeals (9th cir.) Hawaii 1978, U.S. Supreme Ct. 1992. Pvt. practice Honolulu, 1978-84; dep. atty. gen. State of Hawaii, Honolulu, 1984-87, supervisory atty. gen., 1987-92, 1st dep. atty. gen., 1992, atty. gen., 1992—. Office: Hawaii Dept Atty Gen 425 Queen St Honolulu HI 96813-2903

MARKS, ROBERT L. (BOB MARKS), treasurer ex-officio, rancher; b. Clancy, Montana; m. Barbara Marks; 6 children. Student, U. Mont., Mont.

State U. Rancher Clancy; mem. Mont. Ho. of Reps., Helena, 1968-89; with State Dept. Adminstrn., Helena, 1993—; treasurer State of Mont., 1993—; minority whip, 1975; minority leader, 1977; speaker of the house, 1981-82, 1987-88; Rep. house leader, 1985-86; served numeous regional, nat. coms. Office: Mont Ho of Reps Sam W. Mitchell Bldg rm 155 State Capitol Helena MT 59620

MARKS, RUSSELL EDWARD, JR., management consultant; b. Sparrows Point, Md., July 6, 1932; s. Russell Edward and Edna Elizabeth (Johnson) M.; m. Patricia Mary Hunt, June 12, 1954; children—Tamara Elizabeth, Melissa. A.B., Princeton U., 1954; P.M.D., Harvard U., 1969. With W.R. Grace & Co., 1954-70; mem. staff W.R. Grace & Co., Bolivia, 1957-58, Peru, 1960-68; v.p. Latin Am. Group W.R. Grace & Co., N.Y.C., 1969-70; exec. v.p. Marine Internat. Corp., 1971-72; with Phelps Dodge Internat. Corp., N.Y.C., 1973-78; v.p., group v.p. Phelps Dodge Internat. Corp., Coral Gables, Fla., 1978-81; sr. v.p., pres., dir.; sr. v.p. Haley Assocs. Inc., N.Y.C., 1985-87, exec. v.p., 1988; v.p. A.T. Kearney Inc., 1988-90; dir. Webb, Johnson & Klemmer, 1990—; dir. Coun. of the Ams., N.Y.C., 1978-85, pres., 1981-85; dir. Ctr. for Inter-Am. Rels., N.Y.C., 1980-85, pres., 1981-85; dir., pres. Ams. Soc., N.Y.C.; pres., dir. Pan Am. Soc., N.Y.C., 1983-85; pres., dir. Caribbean/Cen. Am. Action, Washington, 1984-85; mem. U.S. del. to observe elections, El Salvador, 1982. Dir. Accion Internat., Boston, 1983-86, Bolivarian Soc., N.Y.C., 1982-85, Fla. Philharm. Orch., Miami, 1979; trustee Am. Acad. Dramatic Arts, N.Y., 1985-90; mem. adv. bd. internat. internship program James Madison U., 1989-90; mem. Princeton U. Alumni Coun., 1987-92, exec. com. 1991-92. With U.S. Army, 1955-57. Mem. Coun. on Fgn. Rels.

MARKS, THEODORE LEE, lawyer; b. N.Y.C., Oct. 18, 1935; s. Irving Edward and Isabel (Goodman) M.; m. Benita Cooper, July 13, 1958; children: Eric, Robert, Jennifer. B.S., NYU, 1956, LL.B., 1958. Bar: N.Y. 1959, U.S. Dist. Ct. (so. dist.) N.Y. 1963, U.S. Supreme Ct. 1964, U.S. Ct. Appeals (2d cir.) 1975, U.S. Dist. Ct. (ea. dist.) N.Y. 1978. Assoc. Silver, Bernstein, Seawell & Kaplan, N.Y.C., 1959-65; sole practice N.Y.C., 1965-70; ptnr. Lee, Cash & Marks, N.Y.C., 1970-76, Vogel, Marks & Rosenberg, N.Y.C., 1976-79, Bromberg, Gloger, Lifschultz & Marks, N.Y.C., 1979-85, Epstein Becker Borsody & Green, P.C., N.Y.C., 1985-86, Gelberg & Abrams, 1986-87, Morrison Cohen Singer & Weinstein, 1987—; speaker at meetings of profl. assns. Contbr. articles to profl. jours. Served with Army N.G., 1958-61. Mem. Larchmont Bd. Assessment Rev., 1994—. Mem. N.Y. State Bar Assn. (mem. real property, banking, corp. and bus. law sects.), N.Y. County Lawyers Assn., Fed. Bar Coun. Office: Morrison Cohen Singer & Weinstein 750 Lexington Ave New York NY 10022-1200

MARKS, TOBIN JAY, chemistry educator; b. Washington, Nov. 25, 1944; s. Eli Sidney and Miriam (Heller) M.; m. Indrani Mukharji, May 19, 1985. B.S., U. Md., 1966; Ph.D., MIT, 1970. Asst. prof. Northwestern U., Evanston, Ill., 1970-74, assoc. prof., 1974-78, prof. chemistry, 1978—, Morrison prof. chemistry, 1986—, prof. materials sci. and engring., 1987—. Editor: Organometallics of the F-Elements, 1979; assoc. editor Organometallics, 1986—; editor: Fundamental and Technological Aspects of Organo-F-Element Chemistry, 1985. Sloan Found. fellow, 1974, Guggenheim fellow, 1989—; Dreyfus Found. scholar, 1975; recipient Nat. Fesenius award Phi Lambda Upsilon, 1979, Mack award Ohio State U., 1987. Fellow Am. Acad. Arts and Scis.; mem. NAS, Am. Chem. Soc. (A.K. Doolittle award 1984, award in Organometallic Chemistry 1989, award in Inorganic Chemistry 1994), Soc. for Applied Spectroscopy, Materials Rsch. Soc., Phi Beta Kappa. Home: 2300 Central Park Ave Evanston IL 60201-1810

MARKS, WALTER, school system administrator. Supt. Kansas City (Mo.) Sch. Dist. 33. Office: Kansas City SD 33 1211 McGee St Kansas City MO 64106

MARKUN, RACHEL, lawyer; b. Des Moines, Sept. 7, 1957; d. Ray O. and Marjorie (Campbell) Brandenburg; m. Paul Markun, Sept. 24, 1983; children: Peter Ryan, Leslie Caitlin, David Campbell. B.A., U. Chgo., 1977; JD, U. Calif., San Francisco, 1981. Bar: Calif., 1981. Ptnr. Morrison & Foerster, San Francisco, 1981—; adj. prof. taxation U. San Francisco, 1984-89; lectr. taxation sect. Bar Assn. San Francisco, 1984; Calif. Continuing Edn. of Bar, 1984; tax cons. San Francisco Commn. on Status Women, San Francisco, 1984-85. Co-author: Attorneys' Guide to Pension and Profit Sharing Plans, 1992; editor-in-chief Hastings Law Jour., 1980-81. Mem. ABA, Calif. Bar Assn. (exec. com. taxation sect.), Western Pension & Benefits Conf. (treas., Bar Assn. San Francisco. Home: 613 Eucalyptus Way Mill Valley CA 94941-3905 Office: Morrison & Foerster 345 California St San Francisco CA 94104

MARKUS, KENT RICHARD, lawyer; b. Cleve., Feb. 1, 1959; s. Kent Richard and Carol (Slater) M.; m. Susan Mary Gilles, Apr. 15, 1987. BS, Northwestern U., 1981; JD with honors, Harvard U., 1984. Bar: Ohio 1984, U.S. Dist. Ct. (no. dist.) Ohio 1984, U.S. Ct. Appeals (6th cir.) 1986. Jud. clk. to Hon. Alvin I. Krenzler U.S. Dist. Ct. (no. dist.) Ohio, Cleve., 1984-86; litigation assoc. Gold, Rotatori, Schwartz & Gibbons, Cleve., 1986-89; transition dir. Ohio Atty. Gen. Office, Columbus, Ohio, 1990-91, first asst. atty. gen., chief of staff, 1991-93; counsel to dep. atty. gen. U.S. Dept. Justice, Washington, 1994, dep. assoc. atty. gen., 1994-95, acting asst. atty. gen., 1995—; adj. prof. law Cleveland-Marshall Coll. Law, 1987-88. Co-editor: Trial Handbook for Ohio Lawyers, 2nd edit., 1988; contbn. editor for law Webster's New World Dictionary, 3d edit., 1988. Bd. dirs., former legis. chair Handgun Control Fedn. of Ohio, 1984—; mem. adv. coun. Northwestern U. Sch. Speech, 1985—; spl. projects dir. Celeste for Gov. Com., Cleve., 1986; campaign mgr. Lee Fisher for Atty. Gen., Cleve. and Colombus, 1989-90; bd. dirs., trustee Cleve. NAACP, 1986—; chief of staff Dem. Nat. Com., Washington, 1993-94. Named Rising Star of Dem. Party, Campaigns and Elections mag., 1991. Mem. ATLA, Cleve. Bar Assn., Ohio State Bar Assn. (chair young lawyers divsn.), Ohio Legal Needs Implementation Com. (chair fin. resources subcom.), Cuyahoga County Bar Assn. (mem. grievance com.). Home: 7215 MacArthur Blvd Bethesda MD 20816 Office: US Dept Justice Rm 1143 10th & Constitution Ave NW Washington DC 20530

MARKUS, LAWRENCE, retired mathematics educator; b. Hibbing, Minn., Oct. 13, 1922; s. Benjamin and Ruby (Friedman) M.; m. Lois Shoemaker, Dec. 9, 1950; children: Sylvia, Andrew. BS, U. Chgo., 1942, MS, 1946, PhD, Harvard U., 1951. Instr. meteorology U. Chgo., 1942-44; rsch. meteorologist Atomic Project, Hanford, 1944; instr. math. Harvard U., 1951-52; instr. Yale U., 1952-55; lectr. Princeton U., 1955-57; asst. prof. U. Minn., Mpls., 1957-58, assoc. prof., 1958-60, prof. math., 1960-93, assoc. chmn. dept. math., 1961-63, dir. control scis., 1964-73, Regents' prof. math., 1980-93, Regents' prof. emeritus, 1993—; dir. Control Sci. and Dynamical Systems Ctr. U. Minn., 1980-89; Leverhulme prof. control theory, dir. control theory centre U. Warwick, Eng., 1970-73, Nuffield prof. math., 1970-85, hon. prof., 1985—; regional conf. lectr. NSF, 1969; vis. prof. Yale U., Columbia U., U. Calif., U. Warsaw, 1980, Tech. Inst. Zurich, 1983, Peking U. (China), 1983; vis. prof. U. Tokyo, 1976, Tech. U., Denmark, 1979; mem. panel Internat. Congress Mathematicians, Helsinki, 1978; sr. vis. fellow Sci. Rsch. Coun., Imperial Coll., London, 1978; mem. UNESCO sci. adv. com. Control Symposium, U. Strasbourg, France, 1980; IEEE Plenary lectr., Orlando, Fla., 1982; Sci. and Engring. Rsch. Coun. vis. prof. U. Warwick, Eng., 1982-90; Neustadt Meml. lectr. U. So. Calif., 1985, prin. lectr. symposium U. Minn., 1988, dir. NSF workshop, 1989; mem. adv. bd. Office Naval Rsch., Air Force Office Sci. Rsch. Author: Flat Lorentz Manifolds, 1959, Flows on Homogeneous Spaces, 1963, Foundations of Optimal Control Theory, 1967, rev. edit., 1985, Lectures on Differentiable Dynamics, 1971, rev. edit., 1980, Generic Hamiltonian Dynamical Systems, 1974, Distributed Parameter Control System, 1991; editor Internat. Jour. Nonlinear Mechanics, 1965-73, Jour. Control, 1963-67; mem. editorial bd. Proc. Georgian Acad. Sci. Math., 1993—; contbr. articles to profl. jours. Lt. (j.g.) USNR, 1944-46. Recipient Rsch. prize Internat. Conf. Nonlinear Oscillations, Ukrainian Acad. Sci., Kiev, 1969, Festschrift volume, 1993; Fulbright fellow Paris, 1950; Guggenheim fellow Lausanne, Switzerland, 1963. Mem. Am. Math. Soc. (past mem. nat. coun.), Am. Geophys. Soc., Soc. Indsl. and Applied Math. (past nat. lectr.), Phi Beta Kappa, Sigma Xi. Office: U Minn Math Dept 127 Vincent Hall Minneapolis MN 55455

MARKUS, RICHARD M., lawyer; b. Evanston, Ill., Apr. 16, 1930; s. Benjamin and Ruby M.; m. Carol Joanne Slater, July 26, 1952; children: Linda, Scott, Kent. BS magna cum laude, Northwestern U., 1951; JD cum laude, Harvard U., 1954. Bar: D.C. 1954, Ohio 1956, Fla. 1994. Appellate atty., civil div. Dept. Justice, Washington, 1954-56; ptnr. civil litigation law firms Cleve., 1956-76, 89—; judge Cuyahoga County (Ohio) Common Pleas Ct., 1976-80, Ohio Ct. Appeals, 1981-88; instr. M.I.T., 1952-54; adj. prof. Case Western Res. U. Law Sch., 1972-78, 84-87, Cleve. State U. Law Sch., 1960-80; prof. Harvard Law U., 1980-81; mem. Nat. Commn. on Med. Malpractice, 1971-73; chmn. Nat. Inst. Trial Advocacy, 1978-81, trustee 1971—. Author: Trial Handbook for Ohio Lawyers, 1973, 3d edit., 1991; contbr. articles to profl. jours.; editor Harvard U. Law Rev, 1952-54. Republican nominee Justice of Ohio Supreme Ct., 1978; co-founder Nat. Advocacy Coll., 1970; bd. dirs. Lutheran Coun. Greater Cleve., 1979-81, Fairview Luth., Hosp., 1985—. Mem. Ohio State Bar Assn. (pres. 1991-92), Cuyahoga County Bar Assn., Greater Cleve. Bar Assn. (trustee 1967-70, 85-90), Assn. Trial Lawyers Am. (nat. pres. 1970-71), Ohio Acad. Trial Lawyers (pres. 1965-66), Phi Beta Kappa, Pi Mu Epsilon, Delta Sigma Rho, Phi Alpha Delta. Home: 3903 N Valley Dr Cleveland OH 44126-1716 Office: Porter Wright Morris & Arthur 925 Euclid Ave Cleveland OH 44115-1408

MARKUS, ROBERT MICHAEL, journalist; b. Chgo., Jan. 30, 1934; s. David White and Anna (Tonkonogy) M.; m. Leslie Winnifred Ator, Aug. 25, 1962; children—Catherine Mary, Patricia Anne, Michael Hughes. B.J., U. Mo., 1955. Gen. assignment reporter Moline (Ill.) Dispatch, 1955-59; successively copy editor, sports columnist, feature writer, baseball writer, coll. sports writer Chgo. Tribune, 1959—. Mem. Northbrook (Ill.) Caucus, 1967. Served with U.S. Army, 1956-58. Recipient Nat. Headliner award as best columnist, 1973; named Ill. Sports Writer of Year, 1970, 71, 72. Mem. Football Writers Assn. Am., Baseball Writers Assn. Am., Am. Auto Racing Writers and Broadcasters Assn. Home: 402 Willow Rd Winnetka IL 60093-4132 Office: Chgo Tribune PO Box 25340 Chicago IL 60625-0340

MARKWARDT, KENNETH MARVIN, former chemical company executive; b. St. Paul, Mar. 6, 1928; s. Rudy A. and Kathryn M. (Thell) M.; m. Bernice M. Kimmel, Aug. 5, 1950; children: Ronald, Mary Ellen, Gary, Thomas, Jean. BBA, Coll. St. Thomas, 1950. With Ecolab, Inc., St. Paul, 1951-83, contr., 1961-69, v.p., contr., 1968-73, v.p., treas., sr. v.p. fin., 1973-83, also bd. dirs.; bd. advisors 1st Trust Co., St. Paul. Treas. St. Patrick's Guild, bd. dirs., 1951—; bd. dirs. sec. Health East, St. Paul. Served with AUS 1946-47. Mem. Cath. Athletic Assn. (pres. 1956-57, dir. 1953-80, trustee 1980—), Tax Execs. (pres. Minn. chpt. 1962-63), K.C. Home: 100 Imperial Dr W Apt 304 West Saint Paul MN 55118-2244

MARKWART, PAUL MARTIN, architect; b. Buffalo, Feb. 4, 1942; s. Herbert Martin and Irene Josephine (Pawlak) M.; m. Nancy Ott, June 29, 1964; children: Anton Martin, Heather Elizabeth. BS in Bldg. Sci., Rensselaer Poly. Inst., 1964. Registered architect, N.Y. Ohio, Pa. Draftsman Cannon Partnership, Niagara Falls, N.Y., 1966-67; office mgr. Highland & Highland Architects, Buffalo, 1967-72; dir. design Caldwell Devel. Corp., Williamsville, N.Y., 1972-74; dir. planning and design McIntosh & McIntosh P.C., Lockport, N.Y., 1974-76; chmn. Trautman Assocs., Buffalo, 1976—. Prin. works include Chem. Loading Facility, 1978. House designer Habitat for Humanity, Buffalo, 1989—. 1st lt. U.S. Army Corps Engrs., 1964-66. Mem. AIA (dir. Buffalo Western N.Y. chpt. 1976—), N.Y. State Assn. Architects, Buffalo Canoe Club, Western N.Y. Preservation Coalition. Democrat. Presbyterian. Avocation: sailing. Home: 53 Berkley Pl Buffalo NY 14209-1001 Office: Trautman Assocs 470 Franklin St Buffalo NY 14202-1389

MARLAND, ALKIS JOSEPH, leasing company executive, computer science educator, financial planner; b. Athens, Greece, Mar. 8, 1943; came to U.S., 1961, naturalized, 1974; s. Basil and Maria (Pervanides) Mouradoglou; m. Anita Louise Malone, Dec. 19, 1970; children: Andrea, Alyssa. BS, Southwestern U., 1963; MA, U. Tex., Austin, 1967; MS in Engring. Adminstrn., So. Meth. U., 1971. Cert. in data processing, enrolled agt., fund specialist, ChFC, CLU, CFP, RFC, CTP. With Sun Co., Richardson, Tex., 1968-71, Phila., 1971-76; mgr. planning and acquisitions Sun Info. Svcs. subs. Sun Co., Dallas, 1976-78; v.p. Helios Capital Corp. subs. Sun Co., Radnor, Pa., 1978-83; pres. ALKAN Leasing Corp., Wayne, Pa., 1983—; prof. dept. computer scis. and bus. adminstrn. Eastern Coll., St. David's, Pa., 1985-87; prof. math. Villanova (Pa.) U., 1987-89; bd. dirs. Alkan Leasing Corp., 1983—. Bd. dirs. Radnor Twp. Sch. Dist., 1987-91, Delaware County Intermediate Unit, 1988-91, Phila. Fin. Assn., 1989-92, Delaware Valley Soc. ICFP, 1993—. Mem. IEEE, Assn. Computing Machinery, Data Processing Mgmt. Assn., Internat. Assn. Fin. Planners, Am. Soc. CLUs and ChFC, Am. Assn. Equipment Lessors, Inst. Cert. Fin. Planners (bd. dirs. Del. Valley Soc. 1993—, v.p. mem. 1994—), Nat. Assn. Enrolled Agts., Nat. Assn. Tax Practitioners, Nat. Assn. Pub. Accts., Fin. Analysts Phila., Phila. Fin. Assn. (sec. 1989-92, mem. award 1988, bd. dirs. 1989-92), Fgn. Policy Rsch. Inst., World Affairs Coun. Phila., Phila. Union League, Main Line C. of C., Assn. Investment Mgmt. and Rsch., Rotary (pres. Wayne club 1989-90, gov.'s rep. dist. 7450, 1990-91, 93-94), Masons (32 degree). Republican. Home: 736 Brooke Rd Wayne PA 19087-4709 Office: PO Box 8301 Radnor PA 19087-8301

MARLAS, JAMES CONSTANTINE, holding company executive; b. Chgo., Aug. 22, 1937; s. Constantine J. and Helen (Cotsirilos) M.; m. Kendra S. Graham, 1968 (div. 1971); m. Glenn Close, 1984 (div. 1987); m. Marie Nugent-Head, 1993. A.B. cum laude, Harvard U., 1959; M.A. in Jurisprudence, Oxford (Eng.) U., 1961; J.D., U. Chgo., 1963. Bar: Ill. 1963, N.Y. 1966. Assoc. firm Baker & McKenzie, London and N.Y.C., 1963-66; exec. v.p. South East Commodity Corp., N.Y.C., 1967-68; chmn. bd. Union Capital Corp., N.Y.C., 1968—; vice chmn. bd. Mickelberry's Food Products Co., N.Y.C. 1970-71; pres., dir. Mickelberry Comm. Corp., N.Y.C., 1972—; chief exec. officer Mickelberry Comm. Corp., 1973—; chmn. bd. Mickleberry Commn. Corp., 1984—; chmn. bd., chief exec. officer Mickelberry Comm. Corp., 1976—; chmn. bd. dirs. Bowmar Instrument Corp., chmn. exec. com., 1983-92. Co-editor: Univ. Chgo. Law Rev, 1962-63; Contbr. articles to profl. jours. Bd. dirs. N.Y.C. Opera, Commanderie de Bordeaux, Brasenose Coll. Charitable Found. Mem. Am. Fgn. Law Assn., Young Pres.'s Orgn. Clubs: Boodle's (London); Racquet and Tennis (N.Y.C.). Office: Mickelberry Comm Corp 405 Park Ave New York NY 10022-4405

MARLATT, JERRY RONALD, lawyer; b. Vancouver, B.C., Can., Apr. 13, 1942; s. Edgerton Myron and Marion Christina (MacLeod) M.; m. Linda Susan Vaughn, Nov. 25, 1972 (div. 1985); children: Catherine Anne, Lindsey Alexandra, Christopher David. BA, U. So. Calif., 1967; JD, Southwestern U., 1977. Bar: Calif. 1977, D.C. 1979, N.Y. 1985. Systems analyst U. So. Calif., Los Angeles, 1964-72, City of Los Angeles, 1972-73, Rand Corp., Santa Monica, Calif., 1973-78; staff atty. SEC, Washington, 1978-81, spl. counsel, 1981, legal asst. to commr. P.A. Loomis, 1981-82, to commr. J.C. Treadway, 1982-84, asst. gen. counsel, 1984, assoc. Seward & Kissel, N.Y.C., 1984-87; assoc. Skadden, Arps, Slate, Meagher & Flom, N.Y.C., 1987-88; ptnr. Hunton & Williams, N.Y.C., 1988—. Assoc. editor Law Rev., 1976-77. Mem. ABA, Assn. Bar City of New York.

MARLEAU, DIANE, Canadian government official; b. Kirkland Lake, Ont., Can., June 21, 1943; d. Jean-Paul and Yvonne (Desjardins) LeBel; m. Paul C. Marleau, Aug. 3, 1963; children: Brigitte, Donald, Stéphane. Student, U. Ottawa, Ont., 1960-63; BA in Econs., Laurentian U., Sudbury, Ont., 1976. With Donald Jean Acctg. Svcs., Sudbury, 1971-75; receiver mgr. Thorne Riddell, Sudbury, 1975-76; treas. No. Regional Residential Treatment Program for Women, Sudbury, 1976-80, Com. for the Industry and Labour Adjustment Program, Sudbury, 1983; mem. transition team Ont. Premier's Office, Toronto, 1985; firm adminstr. Collins Barrow-Maheu Noiseux, Sudbury, 1985-88; M.P. from Sudbury House of Commons, Ottawa, 1988—; minister of health for Can., 1993—; councilor Regional Municipality of Sudbury, 1980-85, chair fin. com., 1981; alderman City of Sudbury, 1980-85; mem. No. Devel. Coun., Sudbury, 1986-88; vice chair Nat. Liberal Standing Com. on Policy, 1989; chair Ont. Liberal Caucus 1990; apptd. nat. exec. Liberal Party Can., 1990, assoc. critic Govt. Ops., 1990, Dep. Opposition Whip, 1991, assoc. critic Fin., 1992; vice chair standing com. fin., 1992. Chmn. fund-raising Canadian Cancer Soc., Sudbury, 1987-88; co-chmn. Laurentian Hosp. Cancer Care Svcs. fund-raising campaign, Sudbury, 1988; chair bd. govs. Cambrian Coll., 1987-88,

bd. govs., 1983-88; mem. Sudbury and Dist. Health Unit Bd., 1981-82; mem. fin. com., bd. dirs. Laurentian Hosp., 1981-85; chair Can. Games for the Physically Disabled, 1983; apptd. Ont. Adv. Coun. Women's Issues, 1984. Mem. Sudbury Bus. and Profl. Women Club. (named Woman of the Day 1989). Avocations: playing piano, gardening, cooking. Office: House of Commons, Confederation Bldg Rm 613, Ottawa, ON Canada K1A 0A6 also: 36 Elgin St, Sudbury, ON Canada P3C 5B4

MARLEAU, ROBERT, parliamentary clerk; b. Cornwall, Ont., Can., Apr. 27, 1948; m. Ann Spilsbury; children: Stéphane, Kristian. Grad., Cornwall Classic Coll., 1967, U. Ottawa, 1969. French high sch. tchr., 1969-70; com. clk. Coms. and Pvt. Legis. Br., 1970-74, prin. clk., 1981-83; dep. sec. gen., Parliamentary Relations Secretariat Can. Ho. Commons, Ottawa, 1974-81, clk. asst., 1983-87, clk., 1987—; adv. bd. faculty of adminstrn. U. Ottawa. Mem. Can. Study Parliament Group, Can. Soc. Clks. at the Table, Assemblée Sec. Gen. Parlements Membres l'Assemblée internationale des parlementaires de langue française, Sovereign Mil. Order Malta (knight magistral grace, dir. Forum for Young Canadians, Can. 125th medal 1992). Office: Ho of Commons, Ottawa, ON Canada K1A 0A6

MARLEN, JAMES S., chemical-plastics-building materials manufacturing company executive; b. Santiago, Chile, Mar. 14, 1941; came to U.S., 1961; grad. in Chem. Engring. (tennis athletic scholar), U. Ala., 1965; MBA, U. Akron, 1971; m. Carolyn S. Shields, Jan. 23, 1965; children: James, Andrew, John. With GenCorp, Akron, Ohio, 1965-93, engring., marketing and gen. mgmt. positions domestic and internat. ops., 1965-76; divsn. pres. GTR Coated Fabrics Co., 1977-80, group pres. 1980-87; pres., GenCorp Polymer Products, Akron, Ohio, 1988—, v.p., GenCorp, Akron, 1988-93; pres., CEO Ameron, Inc., Pasadena, Calif., 1993—, bd. dirs., Ameron, Inc., chmn. bd. dirs., pres. and CEO, 1995—, Tamco Steel, Gifford-Hill, gen., hon. chmn. Nat. Inventors Hall of Fame Induction, 1993. Bd. dirs. YMCA Met. L.A.; bd. dirs. The Employers Group of Calif. (dir.), Town Hall of L.A. (gov.); mem. The Beavers; mem. L.A. Sports Coun. Mem. Am. Mgmt. Assn. (mem. pres. assn.), Chem. Mfrs. Assn. (past pres.), Assocs. Caltech, Calif. C of C., L.A. C of C (dir.), Rotary Club Pasadena, Portage Country Club (Akron, Ohio), Calif. Club. (L.A.), Annandale Golf Club (Pasadena). Office: Ameron Inc 245 S Los Robles Ave Pasadena CA 91101-2830

MARLER, LARRY JOHN, private investor; b. Chgo., Sept. 22, 1940; s. Walter William and Lena Inez (Killen) M.; m. Katy Jo Hibbits, Oct. 17, 1962 (div. Apr. 1971); 1 child, Preston Scott; m. Linda Lee Sorg, Sept. 2, 1982. BA, Christian Coll. Am., 1987; MA, Houston Grad. Sch. Theology, 1988; PhD, U.S. Internat. U., San Diego, 1992. Acct. Shell Oil Co., New Orleans and Houston, 1964-73; acctg. supr. We. Geophys. Co. Am., Houston, 1974; payroll supr. Olsen Inc., Houston, 1975-77; corp. credit mgr. Grant Corps., Houston, 1977-82; rschr., student contractor Navy Pers. R&D Ctr., San Diego, 1990-92; entrepreneur Denver, 1995—. Served with USCG, 1959-62. Mem. Am. Psychol. Soc., Am. Soc. Quality Control, Toastmasters Internat. Republican. Protestant. Avocations: reading, jogging, swimming, hiking, downhill skiing.

MARLER, PHILLIP LYNN, healthcare administrator; b. Bremerton, Wash., Apr. 2, 1948; s. Charles Henry and Ruth Ann (McGinley) M.; m. Regina Ann Alford, May 18, 1970 (div. July 1980); children: M. Lance, Amy Lynn; m. Ruth Janet Miller, June 4, 1983. BBA, Tex. Christian U., 1970; MHA, Med. Coll. Va., 1978. Commd. 2d lt. USAF, 1970, advanced through grades to lt. col.; assoc. adminstr. USAF Hosp. Tyndall, Panama City, Fla., 1973-76, David Grand USAF Med. Ctr., Fairfield, Calif., 1989-91; med. manpower analyst Surgeon Gen.'s Office, Hdqs. USAF, Washington, 1978-83; adminstr. USAF Hosp. Lajes, Lajes Field, Azores, 1983-85; assoc. dir. med. manpower Office Asst. Sec. Def., Washington, 1985-89; ret., 1991; asst. adminstr. support svc. Woodland (Calif.) Meml. Hosp., 1991-93; exec. dir. integrated svc. Woodland Healthcare, 1993—. Bd. dirs. Yolo Fed. Credit Union, Woodland, 1992-95, v.p., 1994-95. Fellow Am. Coll. Healthcare Execs.; mem. Healthcare Execs. Greater Sacramento Valley (pres. 1994-95). Republican. Avocation: restoring old Volkswagens. Home: 890 Purdue Dr Woodland CA 95695 Office: Woodland Healthcare 1325 Cottonwood St Woodland CA 95695-5199

MARLETT, DE OTIS LORING, retired management consultant; b. Indpls., Apr. 19, 1911; s. Peter Loring and Edna Grace (Lombard) M.; m. Ruth Irene Pillar, Apr. 10, 1932 (dec. Feb., 1969); children: De Otis Neal, Marilynn Ruth; m. Marie Manning Ostrander, May 1, 1970 (dec. Apr. 1982); m. Peggie P. Whittlesey, Jan. 15, 1983 (dec. Oct., 1993); m. Estelle B. Brewer, Sept. 23, 1994. B.A., M.A., U. Wis., 1934; postgrad., Northwestern U., (part time), 1934-39, Harvard U.; postgrad. (Littauer fellow in econs. and govt.), 1946-47. CPA, Wis. 1935. Staff mem. Ill. Commerce Commn., 1934-39; lectr. in econs. and pub. utilities Northwestern U., (part time), 1936-39; staff mem. Bonneville Power Adminstrn., U.S. Dept. Interior, 1939-45, asst. adminstr., 1945-52; acting adminstr. Def. Electric Power Adminstrn., 1950-51; asst. to v.p., gen. mgr. Dicalite and Perlite divs. Great Lakes Carbon Corp., 1952-53; v.p., also gen. mgr. Dicalite, Perlite, Mining and Minerals divs. Gt. Lakes Carbon Corp., 1953-62, v.p. property investment dept., 1962-81; pres., chief exec. officer Great Lakes Properties, Inc., 1981-83, ret. 1983; past pres., dir. Rancho Palos Verdes Corp., G.L.C. Bldg. Corp., Del Amo Energy Co., Torrance Energy Co.; former mem. L.A. arbitration panel N.Y. Stock Exch. Contbr. articles and reports on public utility regulation, operation and mgmt. to profl. jours. Past bd. dirs. United Cerebral Palsy Assn. Los Angeles County; bd. dirs., past co-chmn. So. Calif. region NCCJ; mem. nat. trustee, mem. nat. exec. bd., nat. protestant co-chmn., 1987-90; past mem. Orthopaedic Hosp. Adv. Coun.; past trustee City of Hope; past pres., The Los Angeles area coun., past chmn. relationships com., past pres. Sunshine area, pres. Western region Boy Scouts Am., 1978-81, nat. exec. bd., 1978-88, past mem. nat. exec. com., past chmn. properties com., chmn. logistics for world jamboree delegation to Australia, 1987-88; past trustee Nat. Scouting Mus.; mem. internat. com. Baden Powell fellow World Scouting Found., 1984; past mem. Western Govs. Mining Adv. Coun., Calif. State Mining Bd.; bd. govs. Western div. Am. Mining Congress, chmn., 1962-63; incorporator, past pres., bd. dirs. Torrance Meml. Med. Center Health Care Found.; capt fin. com., mem. corp. adminstrn. and fin. com., Los Angeles United Way. Recipient Disting. Service medal U.S. Dept. Interior, 1952; named knight Order of Crown Belgium; commd. Ky. Col.; recipient Silver Beaver, Silver Antelope, Silver Buffalo awards Boy Scouts Am., 1984. Mem. AIME, AICPA, Fin. Execs. Inst., L.A. World Affairs Coun., Wis. Alumni Assn., Perlit Inst. (past pres., dir.), L.A. C of C. (past dir., chmn. mining com.), Mining Assn. So. Calif. (past pres., dir.), Calif. Mine Operators Assn. (past dir.), Bldg. Industry Assn. So. Calif., Calif. Club, Portuguese Bend Club (past pres.), Palos Verdes Bay Club (past v.p.), Phi Kappa Phi, Beta Gamma Sigma, Phi Beta Kappa, Beta Alpha Psi, Lambda Alpha Internat. Democrat. Home: 32759 Seagate Dr Apt 204 Rancho Palos Verdes CA 90275

MARLETT, JUDITH ANN, nutritional sciences educatr, researcher; b. Toledo. BS, Miami U., Oxford, Ohio, 1965; PhD, U. Minn., 1972; postgrad., Harvard U., 1973-74. Registered dietitian. Therapeutic and metabolic unit dietitian VA Hosp., Mpls., 1966-67; spl. instr. in nutrition Simmons Coll., Boston, 1973-74; asst. prof. U. Wis., Madison, 1975-80, assoc. prof. dept. nutritional scis., 1981-84, prof. dept. nutritional scis., 1984—; cons. U.S. AID, Leyte, Philippines, 1983; acting dir. dietetic program dept. Nutritional Scis. U. Wis., 1977-78, dir., 1985-89; cons. grain, drug and food cos., 1985—, adv. bd. U. Ariz. Clin. Cancer Ctr., 1987-95; sci. bd. advisors Am. Health Found., 1988—; reviewer NIH, 1982—. Mem. editorial bd. Jour. of Sci. of Food and Agrl., 1989—, Jour. Food Composition and Analysis, 1994; contbr. articles to profl. jours. Mem. AAAS, NIH (Diabetes and Digestive and Kidney Disease spl. grant rev. com. 1992—), Am. Inst. Nutrition, Am. Dietetic Assn., Am. Soc. for Clin. Nutrition, Inst. of Food Technologists, Am. Assn. Cereal Chemists. Achievements include rsch. and internat. speaker on dietary fiber and gastrointestinal function. Office: U Wis Dept Nutritional Sci 1415 Linden Dr Madison WI 53706-1571

MARLETTE, DOUGLAS NIGEL, editorial cartoonist, comic strip creator; b. Greensboro, N.C., Dec. 6, 1949; m. Melinda Hartley; 1 child, Jackson Douglas. Student, Fla. State U. Editorial cartoonist The Charlotte (N.C.) Observer, 1972-87, The Atlanta Constn., 1987-89, N.Y. Newsday, N.Y.C., 1989—; syndicated to over 200 newspapers through Creators Syndicate, Inc., L.A., 1988—. Creator syndicated comic strip Kudzu; works reproduced in

Time, Newsweek, Christian Century, Rolling Stone, Der Spiegel, Esquire mags., also textbooks and encys.; author: The Emperor Has No Clothes, If You Can't Say Something Nice, Drawing Blood, Kudzu, 1982, Preacher, The Wit and Wisdom of Will B. Dunn, 1984, Just A Simple Country Preacher, 1985, It's a Dirty Job But Somebody Has To Do It, There's No Business Like Soul Business, 1987, Chocolate is My Life, Shred This Book, I Am Not a Televangelist, Doublewide with a View, 1989, In Your Face, A Cartoonist At Work, 1991, (children's book) The Before and After Book, Even White Boys Get the Blues, 1992, Gone With the Kudzu, 1995; co-wrote screenplay "EX"; TV appearances include ABC's Nightline, Good Morning Am Today Show, CBS Morning News, Nat. Pub. Radio's Morning Edition; syndicated animated editorial cartoons NBC Today Show. Nieman fellow, 1st for editorial cartoonist, Harvard U.; recipient Nat. Headliners award 1983, 88, Robert F. Kennedy Meml. award 1984, Sigma Delta Chi Disting. Service award 1986, First Amendment award, 1986, 1st Pl. award John Fischetti Editorial Cartoon Competition, 1986, The Golden Plate Acad. of Achievement award, 1991; named to Register of Men and Women Who Are Changing Am., Esquire Mag., 1984; recipient Pulitzer Prize for editorial cartooning Newsday, 1988; 1st Prize, John Fischetti Editorial Cartoon Competition, 1992. Office: NY Newsday 2 Park Ave New York NY 10016-5603 also: care Creators Syndicate Inc 5777 W Century Blvd Ste 700 Los Angeles CA 90045

MARLEY, EVERETT ARMISTEAD, JR., lawyer; b. Memphis, June 15, 1933; s. Everett Armistead and Elizabeth (Alexander) M.; m. Carolyn Marie McKay, June 21, 1958; children: Elizabeth Ann, Jill Marie. B.A. in Econs., Rice Inst., 1955; LL.B., U. Tex.-Austin, 1959. Bar: Tex.; cert. specialist in estate planning State Bar of Tex., 1977. C.P.A., Tex. Assoc. Butler & Binion L.L.P., Houston, 1959-68; ptnr. Butler & Binion, L.L.P., 1968—. Trustee Schreiner Coll., Kerrville, Tex., 1980-88, San Francisco Theol. Sem., San Anselmo, Calif., 1991—; elder St. Philip Presbyn. Ch., Houston. Fellow Am. Coll. Trust and Estate Counsel; mem. ABA. Presbyterian. Avocation: bass fishing. Office: Butler & Binion LLP 1600 First Interstate Bank Pl Houston TX 77002

MARLEY, JAMES EARL, manufacturing company executive; b. Marietta, Pa., Mar. 18, 1935; s. Earl W. and Elsie H. (Fahringer) M.; m. Kathleen Y. Robinson, Nov. 22, 1974; children—Kathy L., Robert B., Kimberly J., Lora B. BS in Aero. Engring., Pa. State, 1957; MS in Mech. Engring., Drexel Inst., 1963. Group dir. automachine AMP Inc., Harrisburg, Pa., 1969-70, v.p. automachine group, 1970-79, v.p. mfg. resources, 1979-80, v.p. mfg., 1980-81, corp. v.p. mfg., 1981-83, corp. v.p. ops., 1983-86, pres., 1986—, COO, 1990—, chmn. bd., 1993—, also bd. dirs. Inventor and patentee in field. Mem. IEEE, Am. Soc. Mech. Engrs., Am. Mgmt. Assn., Mfg. Council of the Machinery and Allied Products Inst., Harrisburg C. of C. Republican. Club: Harrisburg Country (Pa.) (bd. govs. 1983—). Home: 1230 Mountain Rd Dauphin PA 17018-9706 Office: AMP Inc PO Box 3608 470 Friendship Rd Harrisburg PA 17105*

MARLIN, JENESTA, banker; b. Phila., Jan. 6, 1940; d. Charles David and Rebecca (Shoemaker) Rutherford; divorced; children: John, Elizabeth. BS, U. So. Calif., 1960; MBA, U. Pa., 1962. Buyer, merchandiser United Trading Stamp Corp., 1962-64; asst. pub. relations dir. Phila. Gas Works, 1964-68; v.p. Assoc. Mortgage Cons., Inc., Camden, 1968-72; cons. in field Phila., 1972-76; v.p. Citibank, N.A., N.Y.C., 1977-87; first sr. v.p. The Dime Savs. Bank, N.Y.C., 1987—; lectr. L.I. Bd. Realtors, Huntington, N.Y., 1984-85. Gov. sch. banking Adelphi U., Garden City, N.Y., 1980-86; bd. dirs., treas., chair annual benefit Friends of the Arts, Locust Valley, N.Y., 1985-87; mem. adv. bd. Women's Ednl. Ctr. NYU, Stonybrook, 1984-86. Mem. Nat. Assn. of Bank Women, L.I. Ctr. for Bus. Women (Bus. Woman of Yr. 1985). Avocations: golf, theater, art. Office: Dime Savs Bank NY 1225 Franklin Ave Ste 235 Garden City NY 11530-1659

MARLIN, RICHARD, lawyer; b. N.Y.C., June 1, 1933; s. Edward and Lillian (Milstein) M.; m. Merrel Pincus, June 12, 1955 (div. 1972); children: John F., Elizabeth; m. Jenesta Rutherford, July 29, 1974 (div. 1981); m. Caroline Mary Hirsch Magnus, Nov. 1, 1981. BA magna cum laude, Yale U., 1955, LLB, 1958; LLM, NYU, 1964. Bar: N.Y. 1959, Fla. 1978. Law clk. to presiding justice U.S. Dist. Ct. Conn., New Haven, 1958-59; assoc. Cleary, Gottlieb, Steen & Hamilton, N.Y.C., 1959-62, Wien Lane & Klein, N.Y.C., 1962-64; ptnr. Mnuchin Moss & Marlin, N.Y.C., 1964-66, Marshall, Bratter, Greene, Allison & Tucker, N.Y.C., 1966-79; sr. ptnr. Kramer, Levin, Naftalis, Nessen, Kamin & Frankel, N.Y.C., 1979—. Bd. editors Yale Law Jour. Mem. ABA, N.Y. State Bar Assn., Assn. of Bar of City of N.Y. (corp. law com., chmn. subcom.), N.Y. County Lawyers' Assn, Glen Oaks Club (Old Westbury, N.Y.) (bd. govs. 1979-85, 92—), Phi Beta Kappa. Office: Kramer Levin Naftalis et al 919 3rd Ave New York NY 10022

MARLIN, STERLING, professional race car driver. Winner Daytona 500, 1994, 1995. Office: NASCAR PO Box 2875 Daytona Beach FL 32120-2875*

MARLING, LYNWOOD BRADLEY, lawyer; b. Cin., Apr. 17, 1944; s. John Bertron Marling and Florence Mary (Kelly) Lyman;m. Patricia Lynne Coté, June 13, 1981; children: Burke, Brady, Dustin. B Ceramic Engring., Ga. Inst. Tech., 1967; MBA, Stanford U., 1969; JD, Tex. Tech U., 1976. Bar: Tex. 1976, U.S. Dist. Ct. (no. dist.) Tex. 1977; cert. in family law Tex. Bd. Legal Specialization. Distbn. cons. Jos. Schlitz Brewing Co., Milw., 1969-71; pres., owner Marling Industries, Lubbock, Tex., 1971-74; pvt. practice, Hurst, 1981-88; ptnr. Caston and Marling, Hurst, Tex., 1976-81, 88—; legal cons. St. John the Apostle Sch., Ft. Worth, 1982—. Contbr. articles to legal jours. Mem. St. John the Apostle Sch. Bd., 1982-84; campaign mgr. Robert Caston for State Rep., Tarrant County, Tex., 1980, Rick Barton for Mayor, Bedford, Tex., 1992. Recipient svc. award St. John the Apostle Sch., 1988. Mem. ABA, State Bar Tex. (coll. 1987—), Tarrant County Bar Assn., N.E. Tarrant County Bar Assn. (pres. 1990-92), Soto Grande Tennis Club (Outstanding Mem. award 1980). Avocations: snow skiing, tennis, officiating high school football, public speaking. Office: 1848 Norwood Plz Ste 214 Hurst TX 76054

MARLOWE, EDWARD, research company executive; b. N.Y.C., May 5, 1935; s. Meyer and Jeanette (Sokoloff) M.; m. Marjorie Deitz, Dec. 20, 1959; children—Shari Marlowe Kasten, Steven Richard. B.S., Columbia U., 1956, M.S., 1958; Ph.D. U. Md.-Balt., 1962. Research assoc. Merck, Sharp & Dohme Research Lab., West Point, Pa., 1962-64; sr. scientist Ortho Pharm. Corp. div. Johnson & Johnson, Raritan, N.J., 1964-67; dir. research and devel. Whitehall Labs. div. Am. Home Products Corp., Hammonton, N.J., 1967-72; v.p. research and devel. Plough Products div. Schering-Plough Corp., Memphis, 1972-81; v.p. research and devel., consumer products group Warner-Lambert Co., Morris Plains, N.J., 1981-83, pres. consumer products div. rsch. and devel., 1983-91, v.p., 1984-91, v.p. parent Co.; pres. The Marlowe Group, Short Hills, N.J., 1991-92; v.p. Rsch. and Devel. Clairol Inc., Stamford, Conn., 1992-94. Contbr. articles to profl. publs. Bd. dirs. Lowenstein Found., Overlook Hosp., 1985-94. Recipient award Skin Cancer Found., 1979; Pfizer fellow, 1962-65; Robert Lincoln McNeil fellow, 1961. Mem. Am. Pharm. Assn., Acad. Pharm. Scis., Soc. Cosmetic Chemists, Indsl. Rsch. Inst., Cosmetic, Fragrance and Toiletry Assn. (sci. affairs com. 1976-79), Non-Prescription Drug Mfrs. Assn. (sci. affairs com. 1976-91, policy planning subcom. 1977-91, bd. dirs. 1981-83), N.Y. Acad. Sci., Sigma Xi, Rho Chi. Home: 56 Kean Rd Short Hills NJ 07078-1430 Office: Clairol Inc 2 Blachley Rd Stamford CT 06902-4149

MARLOWE, HOWARD DAVID, lobbyist, public affairs company executive; b. N.Y.C., Apr. 20, 1943; s. Leon and Anne (Cohen) M.; m. Cherie A. DeSouza, July 15, 1967 (div. 1977); children: Jennifer Elizabeth, Catherine Anne, Anne-Louise; m. Sarah Cowan Coviello, Mar. 25, 1982. BS in Econs., U. Pa., 1964; JD, NYU, 1969. Asst. prof. Briarcliff Coll., Briarcliff Manor, N.Y., 1969-71; chief legis. asst. Sen. Vance Hartke, Washington, 1971-75; govt. affairs rep. Ruttenberg Kilgallon & Assocs., Washington, 1975-80; assoc. dir. legislation AFL-CIO, Washington, 1980-84; pres. Marlowe & Co., Washington, 1984—. Editor, pub. Tax Exempt News, Washington, 1976-86. Pres. Young Dems., New Rochelle, N.Y., 1965-71, N.Y. State, 1970-71, Westchester County, 1970-71; Dem. precinct capt., Westchester County, N.Y., 1966-71. Mem. Am. League of Lobbyists (pres. 1989-90). Jewish. Office: Marlowe & Co 1667 K St NW Ste 480 Washington DC 20006-1605

MARMADUKE, JOHN H., retail executive; b. Amarillo, Tex., May 6, 1947; m. Martha Ann Harter, July 29, 1975; children: Margaret, Owen, Samuel. Student, Amarillo Coll., 1965-67; BBA in Fin., U. Tex., Austin, 1969. Advt. mgr., salesman Western Merchandisers, Inc., Amarillo, 1969-73; pres., dir., chief exec. officer Western Merchandisers, Inc., Amarillo, 1982-94; v.p. Hastings Books & Records, Inc., Amarillo, 1973-76; pres., dir., chief exec. officer Hastings Books & Records, Inc., 1976—; pres., Gift of Music Found., 1982-84. Past bd. dirs. Amarillo Art Ctr.; bd. dirs. Ctr. for Non-Profit Mgmt., Amarillo, 1988—, Amarillo Area Found., 1989; chmn. Don & Sybil Harrington Cancer Ctr., Amarillo, 1988-91. Recipient spl. merit award, Internat. Music Industry Conf., Berlin, 1982, Golden Nail award, Amarillo, 1987; named Vol. of Yr., Panhandle chpt. Tex. Multiple Sclerosis assn., 1988. Mem. Nat. Assn. Recording Merchandisers (pres. 1981-82). Republican. Roman Catholic. Avocations: skiing, fly fishing, cooking, travel, racquetball. Office: Hastings Books Music & Video Inc PO Box 35350 Amarillo TX 79120

MARMAS, JAMES GUST, retired businees educator, retired college dean; b. Virginia, Minn., July 11, 1929; s. Gust George and Angela (Fatili) M.; m. Ruth Phyllis Leinonen, May 23, 1952; children—James Matthew, Lynn Marie, Brenda Kay. B.S., St. Cloud (Minn.) State Coll., 1951; M.A., U. Minn., 1956; Ed.D., Stanford, 1961. Tchr. bus. Littlefork (Minn.) High Sch., 1951-53, Lake City (Minn.) High Sch., 1953-55, Austin (Minn.) High Sch., 1955-59; asst. prof. bus. edn. Los Angeles State Coll., 1961-62; chmn. dept. bus. edn., dir. Center Econ. Edn., St. Cloud State Coll., 1962-66; dean Coll. of Bus. St. Cloud State Coll. (Sch. Bus.), 1966-87; bd. dirs. Ins. and Savs. and Loan. Author articles in field. Bd. dirs., mem. exec. com. Minn. Council Econ. Edn.; bd. dirs. St. Cloud (Minn.) Econ. Devel. Ptnrship., chmn. research and planning com. (sec., bd. dirs.). Mem. Nat. Bus. Edn. Assn., Minn. Bus. Edn. Assn., N. Central Bus. Edn. Assn. (2d v.p.), Midwest Bus. Adminstrn. Assn., St. Cloud C. of C., Phi Delta Kappa, Delta Pi Epsilon (nat. research com.), Rotary (pres. St. Cloud). Home: 13215 County Rd 4 N Nisswa MN 56468

MARMER, ELLEN LUCILLE, pediatrician; b. Bronx, N.Y., June 29, 1939; d. Benjamin and Diane (Goldstein) M.; m. Harold O. Shapiro, June 5, 1960; children: Cheri, Brenda. BS in Chemistry, U. Ala., 1960; MD, U. Ala., Birmingham, 1964. Cert. Nat. Bd. Med. Examiners; diplomate Am. Bd. Sports Medicine, Bd. Pediatrics, Bd. Qualified and Eligible Pediatric Cardiology, Bd. cert. sports medicine. Intern Upstate Med. Ctr., Syracuse, N.Y., 1964-65, resident, 1965-66; fellow in pediatric cardiology Columbia Presbyn. Med. Ctr.-Babies Hosp., N.Y.C., 1967-69; pvt. practice Hartford, Vernon, Conn., 1969—; examining pediatrician child devel. program Columbia Presbyn. Med. Ctr.-Babies Hosp., N.Y.C., 1967, instr. pediatrics, 1967-69; dir. pediatric cardiology clinic St. Francis Hosp., Hartford, 1970-80; asst. state med. examiner, Tolland County, Conn., 1974-79; sports physician Rockville (Conn.) High Sch., 1976—; advisor Cardiac Rehab. com., Rockville, 1984-90; mem. bd. examiners Am. Bd. Sports Medicine, 1991—, chmn. credentials com., 1991—. Mem. Vernon Town Coun., 1985-89; bd. dirs. Child Guidance Clinic, Manchester, Conn., 1970—; life mem. Tolland County chpt. Hadassah, v.p., 1969-70, pres., 1970-72, bd. dirs., 1973-74; mem. B'nai Israel Congregation and Sisterhood, Vernon, 1969—, chmn. youth commn., 1970-72. Recipient Outstanding Svc. award Indian Valley YMCA, 1985. Fellow Am. Acad. Pediatrics, Am. Coll. Cardiology, Am. Coll. Sports Medicine (bd. examiners 1991—, chmn. credentials com. 1991—); mem. Conn. Med. Soc., Am. Heart Assn. (mem. coun. cardiovascular disease in young 1969—, chmn. elect New Eng. regional heart com. 1990-91), Conn. Heart Assn. (bd. dirs. 1974-75, 83-84, pres. 1986-88), Heart Assn. Greater Hartford (bd. dirs. 1970-89, mem. exec. com. 1972-73, 79-84, pres. 1982-84), Tolland County Med. Assn. (sec. 1971-72), Vis. Nurse and Community Care Tolland County, LWV (state program chairperson Vernon chpt. 1971-73). Democrat. Jewish. Avocation: sports. Office: 520 Hartford Tpke Vernon Rockville CT 06066-5037

MARMET, PAUL, physicist; b. Levis, Que., Can., May 20, 1932; s. Albert and Corinne (Filteau) M.; m. Jacqueline Cote, June 6, 1959; children—Louis, Marie, Nicolas, Frederic. B.Sc., Laval U., Quebec, Que., 1956, D.Sc., 1960. Research asst. Commonwealth Sci. and Inds. Research Orgn., Melbourne, Australia, 1960-61; asst. prof. physics Laval U., 1961-66, asso. prof., 1966-70, prof., 1970-84; sr. research officer Herzberg Inst. Astrophysics, 1984-91; prof. physics dept. U. Ottawa, 1991—; vis. prof. U. Liège, Belgium, 1967; com. mem. NRC Can.; bd. dirs. Atomic Energy Control Bd. of Can., 1979-84. Author: (with others) Case Studies in Atomic Physics I, 1969, A New Non-Doppler Redshift, 1981, Absurdities in Modern Physics: A Solution, 1993; contbr. (with others) numerous articles to internat. sci. jours. Recipient Sci. prize Province Que., 1962; Royal Soc. Can. Rutherford Meml. fellow Melbourne, 1960; decorated officer Order of Can. Fellow Royal Soc. Can.; mem. AAAS, Can. Assn. Physicists (pres. 1981-82, Herzberg medal 1971), Am. Phys. Soc., Royal Astron. Soc. Can. (Svc. award 1977), Assn. canadienne-francaise pour l'avancement des scis. (Parizeau medal 1976). Patentee energy analyser of charged particules. Office: Univ Ottawa, Physics Dept, Ottawa, ON Canada K1N 6N5

MARMION, WILLIAM HENRY, retired bishop; b. Houston, Oct. 8, 1907; s. Charles Gresham and Katherine (Rankin) M.; m. Mabel Dougherty Nall, Dec. 28, 1935; children: William Henry, Roger Mills Nall. B.A., Rice U., 1929; M.Div., U. Theol. Sem., 1932, D.D. (hon.), 1954. Ordained to ministry Episc. Ch., 1932. Priest-in-charge St. James, Taylor, Tex., and Grace Ch., Georgetown, Tex., 1932-35; asso. rector St. Mark's Ch., San Antonio, 1935-38; rector St. Mary's-on-the-Highlands, Birmingham, Ala., 1938-50, St. Andrew's Ch., Wilmington, Del., 1950-54; bishop Episcopal Diocese of Southwestern Va., Roanoke, 1954-79, ret., 1979; Former dir. diocesan camps for young people in, Tex. and Ala., headed diocesan youth work, several yrs; dep. to Gen. Conv. Episcopal Chs., 1943, 46, alternate dep., 1949, 52; del. to Provincial Synod; mem. exec. council Episcopal Ch., 1963-69; chmn. Ala. Com. on Interracial Cooperation, 4 yrs. Trustee Va. Theol. Sem., Va. Episc. Sch., St. Paul's Coll.; pres. Appalachian Peoples Svc. Orgn.; interim warden Coll. of Preachers, 1981-82, diocesan coord. of pastoral ministry to retired clergy and families, 1990—. Home: 2730 Avenham Ave SW Roanoke VA 24014-1527

MARMOR, JUDD, psychiatrist, educator; b. London, May 1, 1910; came to U.S., 1911, naturalized, 1916; s. Clement K. and Sarah (Levene) M.; m. Katherine Stern, May 1, 1938; 1 son, Michael Franklin. AB, Columbia U., 1930, MD, 1933; DHL, Hebrew Union Coll., 1972. Diplomate: Am. Bd. Psychiatry and Neurology, Nat. Bd. Med. Examiners. Intern St. Elizabeth Hosp., Washington, 1933-35; resident neurologist Montefiore Hosp., N.Y.C., 1935-37; psychiatrist Bklyn. State Hosp., 1937; psychoanalytic tng. N.Y. Psychoanalytic Inst., N.Y.C., 1937-41; pvt. practice psychiatry, psychoanalysis and neurology N.Y.C., 1937-46, L.A., 1946—; instr. assoc. in neurology Columbia Coll. Physicians and Surgeons, 1938-40; adj. neurologist, neurologist-in-charge clinic Mt. Sinai Hosp., N.Y.C., 1939-46; lectr. New Sch. Social Rsch., N.Y.C., 1942-43; instr. Am. Inst. Psychoanalysis, N.Y.C., 1943; lectr. psychiatry N.Y. Med. Coll., 1944-46; lectr. social welfare UCLA, 1948-49, vis. prof. social welfare, 1949-64, clin. prof. psychiatry sch. medicine, 1953-80, adj. prof. psychiatry, 1980—; vis. clin. prof. psychology U. So. Calif., 1946-49; tng. analyst, also pres. So. Calif. Psychoanalytic Inst., 1955-57; sr. attending psychiatrist L.A. County Gen. Hosp., 1954—; dir. divs. psychiatry Cedars-Sinai Med. Ctr., L.A., 1965-72; Franz Alexander prof. psychiatry U. So. Calif. Sch. Medicine, 1972-80, emeritus, 1980—; sr. cons. regional office social svc. Va., L.A., 1946-50; cons. psychiatry Brentwood VA Hosp., Calif., 1955-65; mem. Coun. Mental Health of Western Interstate Commn. Higher Edn., 1966-72. Editor: Sexual Inversion-The Multiple Roots of Homosexuality, Modern Psychoanalysis: New Directions and Perspectives, Psychiatry in Transition: Selected Papers of Judd Marmor, Homosexual Behavior: A Modern Reappraisal, (with S. Woods) The Interface Between the Psychodynamic and Behavioral Therapies, Psychiatrists & Their Patients: A National Study of Private Office Practice, (with S. Elsenstein and N.A. Levy) The Dyadic Transaction: An Investigation into the Nature of the Psychotherapeutic Process; mem. editl. bd. Am. Jour. Psychoanalysis, Contemporary Psychoanalysis, Archives Sexual Behavior; contbr. articles in field to profl. jours. Served as sr. attending surgeon USPHS USNR, 1944-45. Fellow Am. Psychiat. Assn. (life mem. pres. 1975-76), N.Y. Acad. Medicine (life mem.), Am. Acad. Psychoanalysis (pres. 1965-66), Am. Orthopsychiat. Assn. (dir. 1968-71), AAAS, Am. Coll. Psychiatrists; mem. AMA, Calif. Med. Assn., Group for Advancement Psychiatry (dir. 1968-70, pres. 1973-75), Am. Fund for Psychiatry (dir. 1955-57), So. Calif. Psychiat. Soc., So.

Calif. Psychoanalytic Soc. (pres. 1960-61), Am. Psychoanalytic Assn., Los Angeles County Med. Soc., Phi Beta Kappa, Alpha Omega Alpha. Home: 655 Sarbonne Rd Los Angeles CA 90077-3214 Office: 1100 Glendon Ave Ste 921 Los Angeles CA 90024-3513

MARMOR, MICHAEL FRANKLIN, ophthalmologist, educator; b. N.Y.C., Aug. 10, 1941; s. Judd and Katherine (Stern) M.; m. C. Jane Breeden, Dec. 20, 1968; children: Andrea K., David J. AB, Harvard U., 1962, MD, 1966. Diplomate Am. Bd. Ophthalmology. Med. intern UCLA Med. Ctr., 1967; resident in ophthalmology Mass. Eye and Ear Infirmary, Boston, 1970-73; asst. prof. ophthalmology U. Calif. Sch. Medicine, San Francisco, 1973-74; asst. prof. surgery (ophthalmology) Stanford (Calif.) U. Sch. Medicine, 1974-80, assoc. prof., 1980-86, prof., 1986—, head. div. ophthalmology, 1984-88, chmn. dept., 1988-92, dir. Basic Sci. Course Ophthalmology, 1993—; mem. assoc. faculty program in human biology Stanford U., 1982—; chief ophthalmology sect. VA Med. Ctr., Palo Alto, Calif., 1974-84; mem. sci. adv. bd. No. Calif. Soc. to Prevent Blindness, 1984-92, Calif. Med. Assn., 1984-92, Nat. Retinitis Pigmentosa Found., 1985—. Editor: The Retinal Pigment Epithelium, 1975, The Effects of Aging and Environment on Vision, 1991; editor-in-chief Doc. Ophthalmologica, 1995—; mem. editl. bd. Healthline, Lasers and Light in Ophthalmology; contbr. more than 175 articles to sci. jours., 25 chpts. to books. Mem. affirmative action com. Stanford U. Sch. Medicine, 1984—. Sr. asst. surgeon USPHS, 1967-70. Recipient Svc. award Nat. Retinitis Pigmentosa Found., Balt., 1981, Rsch. award Alcon Rsch. Found., Houston, 1989; rsch. grantee Nat. Eye. Inst., Bethesda, Md., 1974-94. Fellow Am. Acad. Ophthalmology (bd. councillors 1982-85, pub. health com. 1990-93, rep. to NAS com. on vision 1991-93, Honor award 1984); mem. Internat. Soc. Clin. Electrophysiology of Vision (v.p. 1990—), Assn. Rsch. in Vision and Ophthalmology, Internat. Soc. for Eye Rsch., Macula Soc. (rsch. com.), Retina Soc. Democrat. Avocations: tennis, race-walking, chamber music (clarinet), art, medical history. Office: Stanford U Sch Medcine Dept Ophthalmology Stanford CA 94305

MARMOR, THEODORE RICHARD, political science and public management educator; b. Bklyn., Feb. 24, 1939; s. James and Mira Bernice (Karpf) M.; m. Jan Schmidt, Oct. 20, 1961; children—Laura Carleton, Sarah Rogers. B.A., Harvard U., Cambridge, Mass., 1960, Ph.D., 1966; postgrad., Wadham Coll., Oxford U., Eng., 1961-62. Asst. and assoc. prof. polit. sci. U. Wis.-Madison, 1967-69; assoc. prof. pub. affairs U. Minn.-Mpls., 1970-73; prof. U. Chgo., 1973-79; prof. polit. sci. Yale U., New Haven, 1979—, chmn. Ctr. Health Studies, 1979—; prof. pub. mgmt. Yale U. Sch. Orgn. & Mgmt., New Haven, 1983—; vis. fellow Russell Sage Found., 1987-88; cons., lectr. in field. Author: The Politics of Medicare, 1970, 73, Political Analysis & American Medical Care, 1983; co-author: Health Care Policy, 1982; editor: Poverty Policy, 1971, National Health Insurance, 1980, Social Security: Beyond the Rhetoric of Crisis, 1988; editor Jour. Health Politics Policy and Law, 1980-84; contbr. articles to profl. jours. Mem. Council on Fgn. Relations, N.Y.C., 1979-80, Pres.' Commn. on 1980s, 1980; social policy adviser Walter Mondale Presdl. Campaign, 1984. Can. Inst. Advanced Rsch. fellow, 1987-91; fellow Adlai Stevenson Inst.; J.F.K. Inst. Politics. Fellow Inst. of Medicine, Nat. Acad. Social Ins.; mem. U.S. Squash Racquets Assn. (bd. dirs. 1983—). Democrat. Jewish. Clubs: Century Assn. (N.Y.C.), United Oxford and Cambridge (London); Lawn Club (New Haven); Yale (N.Y.C.). Home: 139 Armory St Hamden CT 06517-4005 Office: Yale Univ Sch of Mgmt 135 Prospect New Haven CT 06520

MARNANE, JOSEPH PETER, maritime center executive; b. Bklyn., Apr. 30, 1937; s. Joseph Patrick and Evelyn Jane (Brett) M.; m. Kate M. Martin, Sept. 22, 1962; children: Brian, Dena, Daragh. BA, U. Dayton, 1960; MA, Am. U., 1965. Commd. officer USN, 1961, advanced through grades to capt., 1980; exec. asst. to asst. sec. of def. The Pentagon, Dept. of Def., Washington, 1978-80; commdg. officer USS Miller, Newport, R.I., 1980-82, USS Edson, 1983; dir. naval staff coll. Naval War Coll., Newport, R.I., 1983-85; chief of staff Naval Edn. and Tng. Ctr., Newport, 1985-87; dean of adminstrn. Naval War Coll., Newport, 1987-90; pres., chief exec. officer The Maritime Ctr., South Norwalk, 1990—; mem. State of Conn. Tourism Task Force, 1991—, Norwalk (Conn.) State Heritage Pk. Commn., 1991—; commr. Conv. and Visitors Commn., Norwalk, 1991—. Bd. dirs. Armed Svcs. YMCA, Newport, 1987-90. Decorated Bronze Star medal Chief of Naval Ops., Washington, 1969, Def. Superior Svc. medal Sec. of Def., Washington, 1980, Legion of Merit, Sec. of the Navy, Washington, 1990, various Meritorious Svc. medals. Mem. South Norwalk Bus. Assn., N.Y. Yacht Club, Navy Yacht Club (Newport, commodore 1983-84), Greater Norwalk C. of C. Avocations: sailing, skiing. Home: 250 Wolfpit Ave Norwalk CT 06851-2647 Office: Maritime Center at Norwalk 10 N Water St Norwalk CT 06854-2269

MAROCKIE, HENRY R., state school system administrator. Instr., rsch. assoc., asst. to dean W.V. Univ., Morgantown, 1968; asst. supt. Fin., Secondary Schs., Parkersburg, W.V., 1971; supt. Ohio County Schs., Wheeling, W.V., 1972-89; state supt. schs. Charleston, W.V., 1989—; chair Nat. gov. bd. Project Use It, W.V. Literacy Coun.; co-chair Learning Techs. com. Coun. Chief State Sch. Officers; pres. W.V. Sch/ Bldg. Authority; exec. com. mem. W.V. Edn. Fund; past officer W.V. Bd. dirs; dir. reorgn. W.V. Dept. Edn., new evaluation systems tchrs., adminstrs.; launched Tobacco Control Policy W.V. schs.; est. Student, Tchr. Code Conduct, policies to modernize curriculum to State Bd., Gov's. am. 2000 goals. Contbr. articles to profl. jours. Officer W.Va. Bd. Dirs., W.Va. Bd. Trustees, W.Va. Gov.'s Honors Acad., W.Va. Profl. Devel. Ctr., W.Va. Joint Commn. Vocat., Tech., Occupational Edn. Recipient W.Va. Supt. Yr. award, W.Va. Leader Learning award Dept. Edn., 1984, Supt. Yr. award W.Va. Assn. Music Educators, 1986, Leadership award Coll. Human Resources and Edn., W.Va. U., 1988, Alumni Achievement award West Liberty State Coll., 1985, citation edn. excellence W.Va. Ho. of Dels., 1982, Disting. Svc. award Nat. Alliance Health/Phys. Edn. Mem. W.V. Bd. Pub. Works, Ednl. Broadcasting Authority, Labor Mgmt. Coun., Tchrs. Retirement Bd., Drug Control Policy Bd., State Job Tng. Coord. Coun., Private Ind. Coun. W.V. Inc. Office: State Dept Edn Rm 358 Bldg 6 Capitol Complex 1900 Kanawha Blvd E Charleston WV 25305-0330

MAROLDA, ANTHONY JOSEPH, management consulting company executive; b. Winthrop, Mass., Sept. 7, 1939; s. Daniel Arthur and Rose Marie (Pagliarulo) M.; m. Maria Theresa Rizzo, Oct. 10, 1970; children: Matthew, Ria. BS in Physics, Northeastern U., 1962; MS in Physics, Northeastern U., 1968; MBA, Harvard U., 1970. Rsch. physicist High Voltage Engring. Corp., Burlington, Mass., 1962-65; sr. scientist E.G. & G. Inc., Wellsley, Mass., 1965-68; v.p Arthur D. Little, Inc., Cambridge, Mass., 1970-85; pres. The Winbridge Group, Inc., Cambridge, Mass., 1985—; bd. dirs. Daetwyler N.Am., Burlington, N.J., Altdorf, Switzerland. Inventor Apparatus High Density Plasma, 1965; co-author: Business Problem Solving, 1980, Modern Marketing, 1986. Adv. Waterbury-Leningrad. Intersport, Waterbury, Conn., 1988-92. Recipient Hayden Meml. Scholarship, Northeastern U., 1957. Mem. Harvard Club, Harvard Bus. Sch. Alumni Assn. Republican. Roman Catholic. Avocations: hiking, sailing, tennis. Office: The Winbridge Group Inc University Place 124 Mt Auburn St Cambridge MA 02138

MARON, MELVIN EARL, philosopher, educator; b. Bloomfield, N.J., Jan. 23, 1924; s. Hyman and Florence (Goldman) M.; m. Dorothy Elizabeth Mastin, Aug. 16, 1948; children—Nadia, John. B.S. in Mech. Engring. U. Nebr., 1945, B.A. in Physics, 1947; Ph.D. in Philosophy, U. Calif. at Los Angeles, 1951. Lectr. philosophy UCLA, 1951-52; tech. engr. IBM Corp., San Jose, Calif., 1952-55; mem. tech. staff Ramo-Wooldridge Corp., 1955-59; mem. sr. staff, computer scis. dept. RAND Corp., 1959-66; prof. Sch. Libr. and Info. Studies U. Calif., Berkeley. Served with AUS, 1943-46. Fellow AAAS; mem. Assn. Computing Machinery, Am. Soc. Info. Sci., Philosophy Sci. Assn. Home: 63 Ardilla Rd Orinda CA 94563-2201 Office: U Calif Sch Libr & Info Studies Berkeley CA 94720

MARONDE, ROBERT FRANCIS, internist, clinical pharmacologist, educator; b. Monterey Park, Calif., Jan. 13, 1922; s. John August and Emma Florence (Palmer) M.; m. Yolanda Cerda, Apr. 15, 1970; children—Robert George, Donna F. Maronde Varnau, James Augustus, Craig DeWald. B.A., U. So. Calif., 1941, M.D., 1944. Diplomate: Am. Bd. Internal Medicine. Intern L.A. County-U. So. Calif. Med. Ctr., 1943-44, resident, 1944-45, 47-48; asst. prof. physiology U. So. Calif., L.A., 1948-49, asst. clin. prof.

medicine, 1949-60, assoc. clin. prof. medicine, 1960-65, assoc. prof. medicine and pharmacology, 1965-67, prof. medicine and pharmacology, 1968-90, emeritus, 1990—; prof. emeritus, 1990—; spl. asst. v.p. for health affairs, 1990—; cons. FDA, 1973, Medco Containment Co. Inc., 1991—, State of Calif. Dept. Health Svcs., 1993. Served to lt. (j.g.) USNR, 1945-47. Fellow ACP; mem. Am. Soc. Clin. Pharmacology and Therapeutics, Alpha Omega Alpha. Home: 785 Ridgecrest St Monterey Park CA 91754-3759 Office: U So Calif 2025 Zonal Ave Los Angeles CA 90033-4526 *Scientific integrity, objectivity, concern for the quality of life and adherence to the ethics of Nuremberg are ingredients for the evaluation of therapy for human illness. This is the ultimate objective of the practice of medicine.*

MARONI, DONNA FAROLINO, science administrator, retired; b. Buffalo, Feb. 27, 1938; d. Enrico Victor and Eleanor (Redlinska) Farolino; m. Gustavo Primo Maroni, Dec. 16, 1974. BS, U. Wis., 1974. Project assoc. U. Wis., Madison, 1960-63, 68-74; Alexander von Humboldt fellow Inst. Genetics U. Cologne, Fed. Republic Germany, 1974-75; Hargitt fellow Duke U., Durham, N.C., 1975-76, rsch. assoc., 1976-83, rsch. assoc. prof., 1983-87; sr. program specialist N.C. Biotech. Ctr., Research Triangle Park, 1987-88, dir. sci. programs div., 1988-92, v.p. for sci. programs, 1992-94, ret., 1995; mem. adv. com. MICROMED at Bowman Gray Sch. Medicine, Winston-Salem, N.C., 1988—, Minority Sci. Improvement Alliance for Instrn. and Rsch. in Biotech. Ala. A & M U., Normal, 1990-91. Contbr. over 20 articles and revs. to profl. jours. Grantee NSF, 1977-79, NIH, 1979-82, 79-83, 82-87. Mem. Am. Soc. Cell Biology, Genetics Soc. Am., N.C. Acad. Sci., Inc. (bd. dirs. 1983-86), Sigma Xi (mem. exec. com. Duke U. chpt. 1989-90). Achievements include research in electron microscopy, evolution of chromosomes, chromosome structure, evolution of mitosis, and mitosis and fungal phylogeny.

MARONI, PAUL L., finance executive; b. Scranton, Pa., June 20, 1947; s. L. Paul and Mary M. (Manzo) M.; m. Margaret Garretson Bronner, Apr. 27, 1985; 1 child, Emily Garretson. BA, U. Scranton, 1969; MLS, Rutgers U., 1972; MBA, Cornell U., 1980. Reference libr. SUNY Coll., Oneonta, 1972-78; fin. analyst Continental Grain Co., N.Y.C., 1980-82; asst. treas. Newmont Mining Corp., N.Y.C., 1982-88; treas. Newmont Mining/Newmont Gold, N.Y.C., Denver (Colo.), 1988-93; v.p. Newmont Mining/Newmont Gold, Denver, 1990-91, sr. v.p., chief fin. officer, 1991-93; sr. v.p. fin. Consolidated Hydro, Inc., Greenwich, Conn., 1994—. Mem. Fin. Execs. Inst., Nat. Assn. Corp. Treas. Office: Consolidated Hydro Inc 1 Greenwich Plz Greenwich CT 06830

MAROTTA, JOSEPH THOMAS, medical educator; b. Niagara Falls, N.Y., May 28, 1926; emigrated to Can., 1930; s. Alfred and Mary (Montemuro) M.; m. Margaret Hughes, Aug. 31, 1953; children: Maureen, Patricia, Margaret, Fred, Thomas, Jo Anne, Michael, Martha, John, Virginia. M.D., U. Toronto, 1949. Trainee in internal medicine U. Toronto, 1949-52; trainee in neurology Presbyn. Hosp., N.Y.C., 1952-55, U. London, Eng., 1955-56; mem. faculty U. Toronto, 1956—, prof. medicine, 1969—; former assoc. dean clin. affairs U. Toronto (Faculty of Medicine), 1981-89; hon. prof. of neurology U. Western Ontario, 1990—; consulting staff Dept. of Neurol. Scis. Victoria Hosp., U. Hosp., London. Fellow Royal Coll. Physicians (Can.); mem. Acad. Medicine (Toronto), Alpha Omega Alpha, Phi Chi. Home and Office: 46 Carnforth Rd, London, ON Canada M6G 4P6

MAROVICH, GEORGE M., federal judge; b. 1931. AA, Thornton Community Coll., 1950; BS, U. Ill., 1952, JD, 1954. Atty. Chgo. Title & Trust Co., 1954-59; mem. firm Jacobs & Marovich, South Holland, Ill., 1959-66; v.p., trust officer South Holland Trust & Savs. Bank, 1966-76; judge Cir. Ct. Cook County, Ill., 1976-88; dist. judge U.S. Dist. Ct. (no. dist.) Ill., Chgo., 1988—; adj. instr. Thornton Community Coll., 1977-88. Mem. Ill. Judges Assn., Ill. Jud. Conf., Chgo. Bar Assn., South Suburban Bar Assn. Office: US Dist Ct Chambers 1956 219 S Dearborn St Chicago IL 60604-7206

MAROVITZ, ABRAHAM LINCOLN, judge; b. Oshkosh, Wis., Aug. 10, 1905; s. Joseph and Rachel (Glowitz) M. J.D., Chgo.-Kent Coll. Law, 1925; L.H.D., Lincoln (Ill.) Coll., 1956; LL.D., Winston Churchill Coll., 1968; H.H.D., Chgo. Med. Sch., 1984; LL.D (hon.), Ill. Inst. Tech., 1988, Roosevelt U., 1989, Nat.-Louis U., 1991. Bar: Ill. bar 1927. Asst. state's atty. Cook County, Ill., 1927-33; practiced in Chgo., 1933-50; judge Superior Ct. Cook County, 1950-63; chief justice Cook County Criminal Ct., 1958-59; U.S. judge No. dist. Ill., 1963-75, sr. judge, 1975-89; ret., 1989; chmn. bd. Lincoln Nat. Bank, 1946-63; Past nat. chmn. Nat. Conf. State Ct. Trial Judges; past mem. lawyer's adv. council U. Ill. Law Forum. Mem. Ill. Senate, 1938-50; bd. dirs. Hebrew Theol. Coll.; mem. adv. bd. YMCA Met. Chgo.; trustee Chgo.-Kent Coll. Law, Chgo. Med. Sch.; former trustee Ill. Hist. Library; past mem. Jewish Bd. Edn. Served to sgt. maj. USMCR, 1943-46. Named outstanding legislator Ind. Voters Ill., 1949; named to Wisdom Hall of Fame, 1979; recipient Founders' Day award Loyola U. in Chgo., 1967; annual award merit Decalogue Soc. Lawyers, 1968; awards Chgo. Press Club; awards Chgo. Press Photographers Assn., 1968; Man of Year awards Jewish Nat. Fund; Man of Year awards Israel Bond Orgn., 1973; Horatio Alger award, 1979; Nat. Americanism medal D.A.R., 1980; Citizens' awards Chgo. Police Dept., 1982, Lincoln The Lawyer award, 1985; Chgo. Park Dist. Sr. Citizen of Year award, 1985; Spirit of Lincoln award Anti-Defamation League, 1989; Celtic Man of Yr. award Celtic Legal Soc. Chgo. 1989. Mem. Chgo. Bar Assn. (past mgr.), Jewish War Vets. U.S. (past dept. comdr.), Am. Legion (comdr. Marine post Chgo.). Jewish religion (bd. dirs. synagogue). Home: 3260 N Lake Shore Dr Apt 8A Chicago IL 60657-3913 Office: U S Dist Ct 219 S Dearborn St Apt 1900 Chicago IL 60604-1801

MAROVITZ, JAMES LEE, lawyer; b. Chgo., Feb. 21, 1939; s. Harold and Gertrude (Luster) M.; m. Gail Helene Florsheim, June 17, 1962; children: Andrew, Scott. BS, Northwestern U., 1960, JD, 1963. Bar: Ill. 1963, U.S. Dist. Ct. (no. dist.) Ill. 1963, U.S. Ct. Appeals (7th cir.) 1990. Assoc. Leibman, Williams, Bennett, Baird & Minow, Chgo., 1963-70, ptnr., 1970-72; ptnr. Sidley & Austin, Chgo., 1972—; bd. dirs. Cobra Elec. Corp., Chgo. Plan commr. Village of Deerfield, Ill., 1972-79, trustee, 1983-93. Mem. ABA, Ill. Bar Assn., Chgo. Bar Assn. Club: Univ. (Chgo.). Office: Sidley & Austin 1 First Nat Plz Chicago IL 60603

MAROVITZ, WILLIAM A., state senator, lawyer; b. Chgo., Sept. 29, 1944; s. Sidney Robert and Jane (Chulock) M.; B.A., U. Ill., 1966; J.D., DePaul U., 1969. Admitted to Ill. bar, 1970; tchr. Chgo. Bd. Edn., 1969-70; partner firm Marovitz & Edelstein, Chgo., 1970—; asst. corp. counsel City of Chgo. 1973-74; mem. Ill. State Ho. of Reps., 1975-80; mem. Ill. State Senate, 1981—; chmn. Exec. Com. Mem. Young Men's Jewish Council; chmn. Spanish Speaking Peoples' Study Commn. in Ill., 1976—; High-Rise Fire Commn. Mem. Ill. Bar Assn., Chgo. Bar Assn., Decalogue Soc. Lawyers. Recipient Chgo. Met. Outstanding Citizen award, 1976; named Best Freshman Legislator, Ill. Young Democrats, 1975; Best Freshman Senator, 1981, Chgo. Jaycees, 1976 (Young Citizens award). Jewish. Office: 180 N La Salle St Ste 3300 Chicago IL 60601-2802

MAROZSAN, JOHN ROBERT, publishing company executive; b. Trenton, N.J., Oct. 25, 1941; s. John Nichols and Anna Mary (Lacko) M.; m. Anne Marie Gousha, Mar. 18, 1983; children—Andre J., Marc J., Carl B. A.S., Trenton Jr. Coll., 1965; B.A., Trenton State Coll., 1967; M.A., Harvard U., 1969. Tchr. Princeton Pub. Sch., N.J., 1967-68; coordinator secondary pub. Ginn and Co., Boston, 1969-72; program mgr. Ginn and Co., Lexington, Mass., 1972-75; v.p. editor-in-chief Aspen Publishers, Inc., Rockville, Md., 1975-80, v.p. pub., 1980-85; pres. Aspen Pubs., Inc., Rockville, 1986—. Bd. dirs. Hospice Caring; bd. examiners Henry B. Betts Found.; bd. gov. WUSA One and Only Award. With USAF, 1959-63. Recipient Sci. award NSF, 1968. Mem. Newsletter Assn. Am., Rotary. Home: 9713 Lookout Pl Gaithersburg MD 20879-2158 Office: Aspen Pubs Inc 200 Orchard Ridge Dr Gaithersburg MD 20878-1978

MARPLE, DOROTHY JANE, retired church executive; b. Abington, Pa., Nov. 24, 1926; d. John Stanley and Jennie (Stetler) M. A.B., Ursinus Coll., 1948; M.A., Syracuse U., 1950; Ed.D., Columbia U. Tchrs. Coll., 1969; L.H.D., Thiel Coll., 1965, Gettysburg Coll., 1979, Ursinus Coll., 1981; D Humanitarian Services, Newberry Coll., 1977; DD, Trinity Luth. Sem., 1987. Counselor, asst., office dean undergrad. women Women's Coll., Duke, 1950-53; dean women, fgn. student adv. Thiel Coll., 1953-61; asst. social dir.

Whittier Hall, Columbia Tchrs. Coll., 1961-62; exec. dir. Luth. Ch. Women, Luth. Ch. Am., Phila., 1962-75; asst. to bishop Luth. Ch. Am., 1975-85; coord. Transition Office Evang. Luth. Ch. Am., 1986-87; asst. gen. sec. ops. Nat. Coun. Chs. of Christ in U.S., N.Y.C., 1987-89; coordinator Luth. Ch. in Am. commn. on function and structure, 1970-72. Home: 8018 Anderson St Philadelphia PA 19118-2936

MARPLE, GARY ANDRE, management consultant; b. Mt. Pleasant, Iowa, Feb. 22, 1937; s. Kenneth Lowry and Truma Janice (Cook) M.; m. Ellen I. Metcalf, May 29, 1971 (div. 1981); m. Meredith Ann Rutter, July 23, 1988; children: Brian Edward, Stephen Lowry. BS, Drake U., 1959; MBA, Mich. State U., 1962, DBA, 1963. Postdoctoral fellow mgmt. MIT, 1963; cons. Arthur D. Little Inc., Cambridge, Mass., 1963-82; pres. Commonwealth Strategies, Inc., Acton, Mass., 1982—; Oceanus Holding, Ltd., S.W. Harbor, Maine, 1985—; treas. Bramar, Inc., Stow, Mass., 1988—. Editor, author: Grocery Manufacturing in the U.S., 1968; contbr. to Conquering Government Regulation, 1982. Mem. Arthur D. Little Alumni Assn. (bd. dirs., pres. Lexington, Mass. 1992—).

MARPLE, STANLEY LAWRENCE, JR., electrical engineer, signal processing researcher; b. Tulsa, Sept. 7, 1947; s. Stanley Lawrence and Geraldine Doris (Van Duyne) M.; m. Suzanne Eileen Stevens, Aug. 31, 1974; children: Darci Leah, Rebecca Anne, Matthew Lawrence. BA, Rice U., 1969, MEE, 1970; DEng, Stanford U., 1976. Staff engr. Argo Systems, Inc., Sunnyvale, Calif., 1972-78; sr. staff engr. Advent Systems, Inc., Mountain View, Calif., 1978-79, The Analytic Scis. Corp., Mc Lean, Va., 1980-82; sr. devel. engr. Schlumberger Well Svcs., Houston, 1983-85; mgr., devel. engr. Martin Marietta Aero & Naval Systems, Balt., 1986-88; chief scientist Orincon Corp., San Diego, 1989-93, Acuson Corp., Mountain View, Calif., 1993—. Author: Digital Spectral Analysis, 1987, Digital Time, Frequency, and Space Analysis, 1995. Capt. Signal Corps, U.S. Army, 1972-80. Fellow IEEE; mem. IEEE Signal Processing Soc. (editor Trans. on Signal Processing 1982-86, Sr. Paper award 1984, adminstrv. com. 1985-88, chmn. spectral estimation and array processing com. 1989-91). Avocations: stamp collecting, hiking, writing. Office: Acuson Corp 1220 Charleston Rd Mountain View CA 94043-1330

MARQUARD, WILLIAM ALBERT, diversified manufacturing company executive; b. Pitts., Mar. 6, 1920; s. William Albert and Anne (Wild) M.; m. Margaret Thoben, Aug. 13, 1942; children: Pamela, Suzanne, Stephen. BS, U. Pa., 1940; HHD (hon.), U. Puebla (Mex.). With Westinghouse Electric Corp., Pitts. and Mexico City, 1940-52; with Mosler Safe Co., Hamilton, Ohio, 1952-67, sr. v.p., 1961-67, pres., 1967-70; with Am. Standard, Inc., N.Y.C., 1967—, sr. exec. v.p., 1970, pres., chief exec. officer, 1971-85, also chmn., 1971-86, chmn. exec. com., from 1985; now chmn. Am. Standard, Inc. subs. ASI Holding Corp., N.Y.C.; bd. dirs. Chem. N.Y. Corp., Chem. Bank, N.Y. Life Ins. Co., Shell Oil Co., N.L. Industries, Inc., Allied Stores; chmn., bd. dirs. Arkansas Best Corp. Trustee U. Pa., N.Y.C. Citizens Budget Commn., N.Y. Infirmary-Beekman Downtown Hosp., Washington Opera, Found. of U. Ams., Com. Econ. Devel.; bd. overseers Wharton Sch. Bus., Bus. Com. for Arts, Brit.-N. Am. Com.; mem. Com. Corp. Support Pvt. Univs.; bd. dirs. Nat. Minority Purchasing Council. Mem. Conf. Bd. (sr.). Address: Ark Best Corp 1000 S 21st St Fort Smith AR 72901

MARQUARDT, CHRISTEL ELISABETH, lawyer; b. Chgo., Aug. 26, 1935; d. Herman Albert and Christine Marie (Geringer) Trolenberg; children: Eric, Philip, Andrew, Joel. BS in Edn., Mo. Western Coll., 1970; JD with honors, Washburn U., 1974. Bar: Kans. 1974, Mo. 1992, U.S. Dist. Ct. Kans. 1974, U.S. Dist. Ct. (we. dist.) Mo. 1992. Tchr. St. John's Ch., Tigerton, Wis., 1955-56; pers. asst. Columbia Records, L.A., 1958-59; ptnr. Cosgrove, Webb & Oman, Topeka, 1974-86, Palmer & Marquardt, Topeka, 1986-91, Levy and Craig P.C., Overland Park, Kans., 1991-94; sr. ptnr. Marquardt and Assocs., L.L.C., Fairway, Kans., 1994—; mem. atty. bd. discipline Kans. Supreme Ct., 1984-86. Mem. editorial adv. bd. Kans. Lawyers Weekly, 1992—; contbr. articles to legal jours. Bd. dirs. Topeka Symphony, 1983-92, Arts and Humanities Assn. Johnson County, 1992—, Brown Found., 1988-90; hearing examiner Human Rels. Com., Topeka, 1974-76; local advisor Boy Scouts Am., 1973-74; bd. dirs., mem. nominating com. YWCA, Topeka, 1979-81; bd. govs. Washburn U. Law Sch., 1987—, v.p., 1994-95; mem. dist. bd. adjudication Mo. Synod Luth. Ch., Kans., 1982-88. Names Woman of Yr., Mayor, City of Topeka, 1982; Obee scholar Washburn U., 1972-74. Fellow Am. Bar Found., Kans. Bar Found. (trustee 1987-89); mem. ABA (labor law, family and litigation sects., mem. ho. dels. 1988—, state del. 1995—, specialization com. 1987-93, chmn. 1989-93, lawyers referral com. 1993—, constrn. law), Kans. Bar Assn. (sec., treas. 1981-82, 83-85, v.p. 1985-86, pres. 1987-88, bd. dirs.), Kans. Trial Lawyers Assn. (bd. govs. 1982-86, lectr.), Topeka Bar Assn., Am. Bus. Women's Assn. (lectr., corr. sec. 1983-84, pres. career chpt. 1986-87, named one of Top 10 Bus. Women of Yr. 1985). Home: 8572 Hauser Ct Lenexa KS 66215 Office: 4330 Shawnee Mision Pky Ste 107 Fairway KS 66205

MARQUARDT, KATHLEEN PATRICIA, association executive; b. Kalispell, Mont., June 6, 1944; d. Dean King and Lorraine Camille (Buckmaster) Marquardt; m. William Wewer, Dec. 6, 1987; children: Shane Elizabeth, Montana Quinn. Purser, Pan Am. World Airways, Washington, 1968-75; info. specialist Capital Systems Group, Kensington, Md., 1979-81; dir. pub. affairs Subscription TV Assn., Washington, 1981-83, exec. dir., 1983-86; pres. Internat. Policy Studies Group, 1983-90; pres., designer Elizabeth Quinn Couture; lectr. in field. Chmn. bd. Friends of Freedom, 1982-90, Putting People First, 1990—; bd. dirs. Tex. Sportsman's Legal Fund, 1992—; treas. Yes on Caps, 1994—. Author: Animal Scam-The Beastly Abuse of Human Rights, 1993, (national newpaper column) From the Trenches; contbr. articles to syndicated newspapers and mags.; host Grass Roots radio. Recipient Citizen Achievement award Ctr. fo Def. Free Enterprise, 1992, Gold Medal award Pa. State Fish and Game Protective Assn., 1993. Mem. Outdoor Writers Assn. Am. Home: 533 5th Ave Helena MT 59601 Office: Putting People First 21 N Last Chance Gulch Helena MT 59601

MARQUARDT, SANDRA MARY, activist, lobbyist, researcher; b. Dhahran, Saudi Arabia, Mar. 5, 1959; parents Am. citizens; d. Donald Edward and Mary Eleanor (Lindsay-Rea) M. BA, U. Wis., 1982. Editor, organizer Nat. Coalition Against the Misuse of Pesticides, Washington, 1983-87; rschr., author Environ. Policy Inst., Washington, 1987-88; organizer, lobbyist Greenpeace, Washington, 1988—; mem. steering com., former chmn. Pesticide Action Network, San Francisco, 1984-89, 92—. Author reports; editor, author newsletter Pesticides and You, 1983-87. Avocation: bicycling, frisbee (ultimate), running, stained glass, photography. Office: Greenpeace USA 1436 U St NW Washington DC 20009-3997

MARQUARDT, STEVE ROBERT, library director; b. St. Paul, Sept. 7, 1943; s. Robert Thomas and Dorothy Jean (Kane) M.; m. Judy G. Brown, Aug. 4, 1968; 1 child, Sarah. BA in History, Macalester Coll., 1966; MA in History, U. Minn., 1970, MLS, 1973, PhD in History, 1978. History instr. Macalester Coll., St. Paul, 1968-69; original monographic cataloger N.Mex. State U. Libr., Las Cruces, 1973-75; acting univ. archivist, acting dir. Rio Grande Hist. Collections N. Mex. State U. Libr., Las Cruces, 1973-74; acquisitions librarian Western Ill. U. Libr., Macomb, 1976-77, head cataloger, Online Computer Libr. Ctr. coord., 1977-79; asst. dir. resources & tech. svcs. Ohio U. Libr., Athens, 1979-81; dir. libs. U. Wis., Eau Claire, 1981-89; dir. univ. libs. No. Ill. U., DeKalb, 1989-90; dir. libs. U. Wis., Eau Claire, 1990—. Editor Jour. Rio Grande History, 1974; contbr. articles to profl. jours. Coord. Amnesty Internat. Adoption Group 275, Eau Claire, 1985-88; pres. Chippewa Valley Free-net, 1994—. Mem. ALA, Assn. Coll. and Rsch. Librs. (chmn. performance measures in acad. librs. com. 1985-89). Lutheran. Avocations: tennis, bicycling. Office: Univ Wis McIntyre Libr Eau Claire WI 54702

MARQUEZ, ALFREDO C., federal judge; b. 1922; m. Linda Nowobilsky. B.S., U. Ariz., 1948, J.D., 1950. Bar: Ariz. Practice law Mesch Marquez & Rothschild, 1957-80; asst. atty. gen. State of Ariz., 1951-52; asst. county atty. Pima County, Ariz., 1953-54; adminstrv. asst. to Congressman Stewart Udall, 1955; judge U.S. Dist. Ct. Ariz., Tucson, 1980—. Served with USN, 1942-45. Office: US Dist Ct US Courthouse Rm 327 55 E Broadway Blvd Tucson AZ 85701-1719

MARQUEZ, JOAQUIN ALFREDO, lawyer; b. Humacao, P.R., Aug. 1, 1942; s. Joaquin and Emelina (Tudela) M.; m. Jocelyn Christiansen, Mar. 27, 1967; children: Joaquin A. Jr., Julian A. BS in Econs., U. Pa., 1964; LLB, U. P.R., 1967; LLM in Taxation, Georgetown U., 1974. Bar: P.R. 1967, U.S. Dist. Ct. P.R. 1968, U.S. Ct. Appeals (lst cir.) 1968, D.C. 1972, U.S. Dist. Ct. D.C. 1972. Assoc. Goldman, Antonetti & Subira, San Juan, P.R., 1967-68; adminstrv. asst. to resident commr. for P.R. Washington, 1971-72, 77-78; sr. atty.-advisor AID U.S. Dept. State, Washington, 1973-76; dir. P.R. Fed. Affairs Adminstrn., Washington, 1978-81; ptnr. Hopkins & Sutter, Washington, 1981-94, Drinker, Biddle & Reath, Washington, 1994—; mem. P.R. Export Promotions Coun., San Juan, 1979-81; staff dir. So. Govs.' Assn., Washington, 1980-81. Capt. U.S. Army, 1968-70, Vietnam. Decorated Bronze Star. Mem. ABA, P.R. Bar Assn., D.C. Bar Assn. Republican. Roman Catholic. Avocations: sailing, reading. Office: Drinker Biddle & Reath 901 15th St NW Washington DC 20005-2503

MARQUIS, CHRISTOPHER HOLLIDAY, newspaper correspondent; b. Kentfield, Calif., Nov. 13, 1961; s. Harold H. and Nancy J. Marquis. Student, U. Seville, Spain, 1981-82; BA in Comparative Lit., U. Calif., Berkeley, 1984; MS in Journalism, Columbia U., 1985. Freelance journalist Pitts., 1985-86; city desk reporter The Miami Herald, 1987-90, Latin Am. corr., 1989-90, diplomatic corr., 1991—. Recipient Citation for Excellence, Overseas Press Club, 1991, Pedro Joaquin Chamorro award Inter-Am. Press Assn., 1992; fellow Inter-Am. Press Assn., 1986; scholar Scripps-Howard Found., 1984. Office: 700 Nat Press Bldg Washington DC 20045

MARQUIS, ROLLIN PARK, retired librarian; b. Badin, N.C., Nov. 29, 1925; s. Rollin Howard and Carmen (Park) M.; m. Marian Horton Bonstein, Aug. 21, 1954; children—Rollin Hilary, Jeffrey Perrin, Anne-Louise. B.A., Columbia, 1948; postgrad. linguistics, St. Catherines Soc. U. Oxford, 1948-50; painting, Art Students League N.Y., 1950-52; M.L.S., Carnegie Inst. Tech., 1958. Catalog asst. Columbia Med. Library, 1952-53; adminstrv. asst. Nat. Council Chs. Christ in U.S.A., N.Y.C., 1953-56, Friends Com. on Nat. Legislation, Washington, 1956-57; reference asst. Carnegie Library, Pitts., 1957-58; dir. Citizens Library, Washington, Pa., 1958-59, River Edge (N.J.) Free Pub. Library, 1959-63, Allegany County Library, Cumberland, Md., 1963-64; city librarian Dearborn (Mich.) Dept. Libraries, 1964-89, ret., 1989. Active Fine Arts Assocs., U. Mich., Dearborn. With AUS, 1944-46. Mem. ALA, Better Edn. through Simplified Spelling, Dearborn Orchestral Soc. Fair Lane Music Guild., Schoolcraft Coll. Community Choir, Soc. Friends. Democrat. Club: Torch (Detroit). Lodge: Rotary (Dearborn). Home: 23849 Lloyd Ct Dearborn MI 48124-2505 *The things obtained through cooperation, sharing and mutual goodwill are the achievements which satisfy—as significantly for public and business life, as for private life.*

MARR, CARMEL CARRINGTON, lawyer, retired state official; b. Bklyn.; d. William Preston and Gertrude Clementine (Lewis) Carrington; BA, Hunter Coll., 1945; JD, Columbia U., 1948; m. Warren Marr, II, Apr. 11, 1948; children: Charles Carrington, Warren Quincy III. Bar: N.Y. 1948, U.S. Dist. Ct. (ea. dist.) N.Y. 1950, U.S. Dist. Ct. (so. dist.) N.Y. 1951; clk. Dyer & Stevens, N.Y.C., 1948-49; pvt. practice, N.Y.C., 1949-53; adviser legal affairs U.S. mission to UN, N.Y.C., 1953-67, sr. legal officer Office Legal Affairs, UN Secretariat, 1967-68; mem. N.Y. State Human Rights Appeal Bd., 1968-71; mem. N.Y. State Pub. Svc. Commn., 1971-86; cons. Gas Rsch. Inst., 1987-91; lectr. N.Y. Police Acad., 1963-67. Contbr. articles to profl. jours. Mem. N.Y. Gov.'s Com. Edn. and Employment of Women, 1963-64; mem. Nat. Gen. Svcs. Pub. Adv. Council, 1969-71; mem., former chmn. adv. council Gas Rsch. Inst.; mem., chmn. tech. pipeline safety standards com. Dept. Transp., 1979-85; former mem. task force Fed. Energy Regulatory Commn. and EPA to examine PCBs in gas supply system; past chmn. gas com. Nat. Assn. Regulatory Utility Commrs.; past pres. Great Lakes Conf. Pub. Utilities Commrs., mem. exec. com.; mem. UN Devel. Corp., 1969-72; bd. dirs. Amistad Rsch. Ctr., New Orleans, 1970—, chmn. bd. dirs., 1981-94; bd. dirs. Bklyn. Soc. Prevention Cruelty to Children, Nat. Arts Stblzn. Fund, 1984-93, Prospect Park Alliance, 1987—; bd. visitors N.Y. State Sch. Girls, Hudson, 1964-71; mem. exec. bd. Plays for Living, N.Y.C., 1968-75; pres. bd. dirs. Billie Holiday Theatre, 1972-80; mem. nat. adv. coun. Hampshire Coll.; pres.'s. coun. Tulane U., 1988—. Mem. Phi Beta Kappa, Alpha Chi Alpha, Alpha Kappa Alpha. Republican. Episcopalian.

MARR, DAVID FRANCIS, television announcer, former professional golfer, journalist; b. Houston, Dec. 27, 1933; s. David Francis and Grace Anne (Darnell) M.; m. Caroline Elizabeth Dawson, Sept. 25, 1972; children by previous marriage: Elizabeth S., David Francis III, Anthony J. Student, Rice U., 1950-51, U. Houston, 1951-52. Profl. golfer, 1953—; tour player, 1960-72, part-time tour player, 1973—; golf announcer ABC Sports, 1970-91, BBC Sports, 1992—; dir. Nabisco-Dinah Shore Tournament, 1981-86. Elected to Coll. golf Hall of Fame, 1981, Tex. Golf Hall of Fame, 1981; named to Ryder Cup Team, 1965. Mem. Profl. Golfers Assn. (nat. champion 1965, Player of Year 1965), AFTRA. Roman Catholic. Clubs: Lochinvar Golf (Houston), Houston City; Champions Golf (Houston); Brae-Burn Country. Capt. Ryder Cup Team, 1981. Office: care Riviere-Marr 2100 W Loop S Ste 800 Houston TX 77027 also: care Hans Kramer IMG One Erieview Pla Ste 1300 Cleveland OH 44114*

MARR, DAVID FRANKLIN, nurse, administrator; b. Cleveland, Tenn., Jan. 11, 1953; s. Bobby D. and Margaret (Snyder) M.; m. Lynn Marie Stoneking, Aug. 3, 1974; children: Andrew, Katherine. AS, Cleveland State Community Coll, 1974; BS, Med. Coll. Ga., 1976, MS, 1977. RN, Tenn. Staff nurse Bradley Meml. Hosp., Cleveland, 1974-75, St. Joseph Hosp., Augusta, Ga., 1975-77; instr. nursing Cleveland State Community Coll., 1977-81; asst. dir. nursing Cleveland Community Hosp., 1981-82; IV team mgr. HPI Health Care Svcs., Cleveland, 1981-83; dir. nursing Fentress County Gen. Hosp., Jamestown, Tenn., 1983-85; group dir. nursing Nat. Health Care, Inc., Dothan, Ala., 1985-86; v.p. nursing South Fulton Med. Ctr., East Point, Ga., 1986—. Trustee, Cleveland State Community Coll. Foudn., 1983—. Mem. Am. Nurses Assn., Ga. Nurses Assn. Baptist. Home: 114 Cloister Dr Peachtree Cty GA 30269-1440 Office: South Fulton Med Ctr 1170 Cleveland Ave Atlanta GA 30344-3600

MARR, JO ANN, special education educator; b. Deadwood, S.D., July 13, 1945; d. James A. and Frances M. (Yonker) M.; divorced; children: Seth P. Hawken, Tyler U. Hawken, Sara F. Hawken. BS in Edn., Black Hills State U., 1966, postgrad., 1968-69, 86; postgrad., U. Wyo., 1970—. Social studies tchr. Cheyenne-Eagle Butte (S.D.) High Sch., 1966-67; elem. tchr. Wakpala (S.D.) Pub. Sch., 1968-69, Moorcroft (Wyo.) Elem. Sch. 1969-79; substitute tchr. Riverton (Wyo.) Sch. Dist., 1984-86; spl. edn. tchr. Wyo. State Tng. Sch., Lander, 1986-88, Wind River Sch. Dist., Kinnear, Wyo., 1988-90; spl. edn. tchr., case mgr. Converse County Sch. Dist., Glenrock, Wyo., 1990—; local hostess, facilitator CCLD/CDE sponsored Odyssey Program, Glenrock, 1992—; Crook County rpe. Wyo. Right to Read Program, Moorcroft, 1978-79; coord. Crook and Weston County drug edn. program Wyo. State Dept. Edn., Moorcroft, 1973-77. Sec., bd. dirs. Sundance (Wyo.) Kids Day Care Ctr., 1971-75; county officer, mem. state com. Nat. Cattlewomen, Crook County, 1970-75. Mem. NEA, Wyo. Edn. Assn., Nat. Coun. Learning Disabilities, GEA, Colo. Coun. Learning Disabilities. Home: PO Box 104 Glenrock WY 82637-0104

MARR, LUTHER REESE, communications executive, lawyer; b. Kansas City, June 23, 1925; s. Luther Dow and Aileen (Shimfessel) M.; m. Christelle Lois Taylor, July 12, 1956; children—Michelle Lois, Stephen Luther, Christelle Elizabeth. A.B., U. Calif. at Los Angeles, 1946; J.D., U. So. Calif., 1950. Bar: Calif. 1951. With firm Hasbrouck & Melby, Glendale, 1952-54; atty. The Walt Disney Co., Burbank, Calif., 1954-92; corp. sec. The Walt Disney Co., 1957-78, v.p. corp. and shareholder affairs, 1978-87, v.p. shareholder svc., 1987-92. Trustee Le Lycée Français de Los Angeles. Served with USNR, 1946-47. Mem. Am. Soc. Corp. Secs., Calif., Los Angeles Bar Assns., Phi Beta Kappa, Phi Alpha Delta. Republican. Methodist. Home: 1785 Cielito Dr Glendale CA 91207-1023

MARR, ROBERT BRUCE, physicist, educator; b. Quincy, Mass., Mar. 25, 1932; s. Ralph George and Ethel (Beals) M.; m. Nancy Rosa Parkes, June 12, 1954; children: Richard, Jonathan, Rebecca. B.S., MIT, 1953; M.A., Harvard U., 1955, Ph.D., 1959. Research asso. Brookhaven Nat. Lab., Upton, N.Y., 1959-61; asso. physicist Brookhaven Nat. Lab., 1961-64, physicist, 1964-68, sr. physicist, 1968—, assoc. chmn. applied math. dept.,

1974-75, 83-88, chmn., 1975-78; adj. assoc. prof. Columbia U., 1969; lectr. SUNY at Stony Brook, 1969-70, vis. prof. dept. computer sci., 1979; guest mathematician U. Colo., 1970; vis. mathematician Lawrence Berkeley Lab., 1978; cons. NSF, NIH, 1969—. Contbr. articles to profl. jours. Served with U.S. Army, 1958-59. NSF grantee, 1974. Mem. Am. Math. Soc., Soc. for Magnetic Resonance in Medicine (trustee 1982-87, sec.-treas. 1984-86, treas. 1986-87), Sigma Xi. Home: 368 Private Rd Patchogue NY 11772-5827 Office: Brookhaven Nat Lab Applied Sci Dept Upton NY 11973

MARRAM, EDWARD P., engineering company executive; b. 1937; married. BS, U. Mass., 1959, MS, 1961; PhD, Tufts U., 1965. Staff asst. Arthur D. Little, Co., Cambridge, Mass.; with Avco Corp., Wilmington, Mass., 1960-69, EG&G Inc., Bedford, Mass., 1969-73; with Geo-Ctrs. Inc., Newton, Mass., 1973—, pres., treas., CEO, clk. Office: Geo-Centers Inc 7 Wells Ave Newton MA 02159-3212

MARRETT, MICHAEL MCFARLENE, chaplain; b. Greenwich Town, Surrey, Jamaica, Oct. 7, 1935; s. Kenneth Louis and Ivy Lynmae (McFarlane) M.; m. Margery Eva Mugford, Jan. 29, 1984. Cert. gen. ordination, Oxford (Eng.) U., 1961; cert. edn. in English lang., London U., 1967; MDiv, Gen. Theol. Sem., 1969, STM, 1970; STM, N.Y. Theol. Sem., 1972; postgrad., Princeton Theol. Sem., 1972-73, Columbia U., 1973-75; BA, Fordham U., 1974; postgrad., The Coll. of Preachers, 1979, Yale U., 1979-81; PhD, NYU, 1980; MS, So. Conn. State U., 1982. Lic. pastoral counselor, Md.; cert. profl. mental health clergy, chaplain and fellow of Coll. Chaplains. Staff chaplain St. Elizabeths Hosp., Washington, 1986—. Author: The Lambeth Conferences and Women Priests, 1981. Appointed commissary Diocese of Akoko, West Africa, 1984, appointed hon. canon St. Stephens Cathedral, 1987. Mem. Assn. Clin. Pastoral Edn. (clin.), Nat. Interfaith Coalition on Aging, Am. Assn. Christian Counselors, Am. Assn. Family Counselors. Home: PO Box 48232 1902 C St NE Washington DC 20002

MARRIE, THOMAS PHILLIP, bank executive; b. N.Y.C., Feb. 13, 1938; s. Thomas P. Marrie; m. Elizabeth Marrie Schneeman; 1 child, Crystal. BEE, Manhattan Coll., 1960; MS in Engring., Yale U., 1962; MS in Indsl. Mgmt., MIT, 1964. Various positions Am. Express Co., Fireman's Fund Ins. Co., Rockwell Internat. Corp, W.R. Grace Co., N.Y.C., 1964-78; sr. v.p., chief fin. officer Am. Express Bank, N.Y.C., 1979-81; treas., chief fin. officer No. Trust Co., Chgo., 1981-84; exec. v.p., chief fin. officer First Interstate Bank of Calif., L.A., 1984-88; exec. v.p., chief fin. officer, First Interstate Bancorp, L.A., 1988—. Office: 1st Interstate Bancorp 707 Wilshire Blvd # 2512W Los Angeles CA 90017-3501

MARRINER, SIR NEVILLE, orchestra conductor; b. Lincoln, Eng., Apr. 15, 1924; s. Herbert Henry and Ethel May (Roberts) M.; m. Elizabeth Sims, Dec. 20, 1957; children: Susan Frances, Andrew Stephen. Ed., Royal Coll. Music, Paris Conservatory. Violinist Martin String Quartet, 1946-53, Virtuoso String Trio, 1950, Jacobean Ensemble, 1952, London Symphony Orch., from 1956; condr. L.A. Chamber Orch., 1969-77; music dir. Minn. Orch., 1979-86, Stuttgart (Germany) Symphony Orch., 1986-89; dir. South Bank Festival Music, 1975-78, Meadow Brook Festival, Detroit, 1979-84. Condr. Béatrice et Bénédict, Festival Hall, 1989; recs. include CDs of Dvořák Serenades, Haydn Violin Concerto in C, Mozart Serenade K361, Il Barbiere di Siviglia, Schubert 4th and 5th Symphonies, Baroque Favourites, with Yehudi Menuhin, The English Connection (Vaughan Williams The Lark Ascending, Elgar Serenade and Tippett Corelli Fantasia), Trumpet Concertos, with Håkan Hardenberger, Mendelssohn Piano Works with Murray Perahia, Mozart Haffner Serenade, 200 other recordings include Bach Concertos, Suites and Die Kunst der Fuge, Vivaldi, The Four Seasons and other concertos, Concerti Grossi by Corelli, Geminiani, Torelli, Locatelli and Manfredini, Mozart Symphonies, Concertos, Serenades and Divertimenti, Handel Messiah, Opera overtures and Water and Fireworks music, Die Zauberflöte, Handel Arias with Kathleen Battle, Il Turco in Italia and Don Giovanni. Bd. dirs., founder Acad. of St. Martin-in-the Fields, 1959—. Decorated Comdr. of Brit. Empire, KBE; recipient Grand Prix du Disque, Edison award, Mozart Gemeinde prize, Tagore prize, Grammy award, Shakespeare prize, KT of Polar Star, others. Fellow Royal Coll. Music, Royal Acad. Music. Office: care IMG, Media House, 3 Burlington Ln, London W4, England also: Acad St Martin Fields Raine House, 109 Boundary Rd, Raine St, London E1 9RG, England*

MARRINGA, JACQUES LOUIS, manufacturing company executive; b. Rotterdam, The Netherlands, Aug. 8, 1928; came to U.S., 1965; s. Jakob and Christine Antoinette (Vandervalk) M.; m. Joan Kathryn Potter, Oct. 23, 1965; children—Jack, Bob, Katy. student, Erasmus U. Rotterdam, 1946-49, Doctors in Econs., 1954, Advanced Mgmt. Program Harvard U., 1984. Rsch. asst. Chem. Projects, N.Y.C., 1955; product mgr. Philips, N.V. Eindhoven, Netherlands, 1956-61; product line mgr. ITT, Brussels and N.Y.C., 1961-70; v.p. Elco Corp., Willow Grove, Pa., 1970-72, v.p. Crouse-Hinds, Syracuse, N.Y., 1972-77; group v.p. Sta-Rite Industries, Milw., 1977-94; pres. Marringa Internat. Corp, 1994—. Mem. Milw. Country Club, Rotary (Milw.). Home: 2520 W Dean Rd Milwaukee WI 53217-2019

MARRINGTON, BERNARD HARVEY, retired automotive company executive; b. Vancouver, B.C., Can., Nov. 9, 1928; s. Fredrick George and Constance Marie (hall) M.; m. Patricia Grace Hall, Sept. 3, 1953 (div. 1993); children: Jodie Lynn, Stacey Lee. Student, U. Pitts., 1982, Bethany Coll., W.Va., 1983; BS in Mktg. Mgmt., Pacific Western U., 1985. V.p., sales mgr. W & L of La Mesa, Calif., 1960-66; pres., gen. mgr. W & L of La Mesa, 1966-68; regional mgr. PPG Industries, Inc., L.A., 1977-88, regional mgr. profit ctr., 1988-91; cons. L.A. Unified Sch. Dist., 1992, South Coast Air Quality Mgmt. Dist., El Monte, Calif., 1987-91; adv. com. So. Calif. Regional Occupational Ctr., Torrance, 1978-91. Contbr. articles to profl. jours. Sustaining sponsor Ronald Reagan Presdl. Found., Simi, 1987—; sustaining mem. Rep. Nat. Com., L.A., 1985-92, Rep. Presdl. Legion of Merit, 1986-94; del. Rep. Platform Planning com., L.A., 1992; charter mem. Nat. Tax Limitation Com., Washington, 1988, Jarvis Gann Taxpayers Assn., L.A., 1979-94; sponsor Reagan Presdl. Libr., 1986. Recipient Award for Outstanding Community Support, So. Calif. Regional Occupational Ctr., 1986. Episcopalian. Avocations: rose gardening, circus culture, golf, sailing, classical music.

MARRIOT, SALIMA SILER, state legislator, social work educator; b. Batl., Dec. 5, 1940; d. Jesse James and Cordie Susie (Ayers) Silver; m. David Small Mariott, Sept. 24, 1964 (div. 1972); children: Terrex Siler, Patrice Kenyatta. BS, Morgan State Coll., 1964; M in Social Work, U. Md., 1972; D in Social Work, Howard U., 1988. Tchr. Balt. City Pub. Sch., 1964-65; social worker N.Y.C. Social Svcs., 1965-67, Balt. City Social Svcs., 1968-72; instr., asst. prof. Morgan State U., Balt., 1972—; now also mem. Md. Ho. of Dels.; chair Park Heights Devel. Corp., Balt., 1976-92, Nat. Black Women's Health Project, 1993-94. Co-editor: U.S. Policy Toward Southern Africa, 1984. Cons. Balt. City Head Start, 1985-94; del. Dem. Conv., Atlanta, 1988; active Md. Dem. Ctrl. Com., 1988-90; bd. dirs. Nat. Black Women's Health Project, Atlanta, 1991-94. Mem. Nat. Polit. Cong. Black Women, Nat. Coun. Negro Women, Delta Sigma Theta. Office: Md House of Dels 4515 Homer Ave Baltimore MD 21215-6302

MARRIOTT, ALICE SHEETS (MRS. JOHN WILLARD MARRIOTT), restaurant chain executive; b. Salt Lake City, Oct. 19, 1907; d. Edwin Spencer and Alice (Taylor) Sheets; m. John Willard Marriott, June 9, 1927; children—John Willard, Richard Edwin. AB, U. Utah, 1927, LHD (hon.) 1974; LHD (hon.), Mt. Vernon Coll., 1980. Ptnr. Marriott Corp. (formerly Marriott-Hot Shoppees, Inc.), Washington, 1927, v.p., dir., 1929. Chmn. adv. com. on arts John F. Kennedy Center for Performing Arts, 1970-76; mem. adv. com. Nat. Child Abuse, 1976—; mem. adv. council Nat. Arthritis and Musculoskeletal and Skin Diseases NIH, 1987—; bd. dirs. Washington Ballet Guild, Washington Home Rule Com., Arthritis and Rheumatism Found. of Met. Washington; trustee John F. Kennedy Center, 1972—; hon. trustee Nat. Arthritis Found., 1987—; mem. exec. com., vice chmn. Rep. Nat. Com., 1965-76, mem.; officer numerous state coms.; treas. Rep. Nat. Conv., 1964, 68, 72, mem. Arrangements com., 1960, 64, 68, 72; mem. coord. com. Women's Nat. Rep. Club. Recipient 1st ann. Marriott Lifetime Achievement award Arthritis Found. Model Washington Area, 1987. Mem. League Rep. Women D.C. (treas. 1955-57, v.p. 1957-59), Nat. Symphony Orch. Assn., Am. Newspaper Womens Club (asso. mem.), Capitol Speakers

Club (membership chmn.), Welcome to Washington Internat. Clubs (treas., dir.), Chi Omega (Women of Achievement award 1989), Phi Kappa Phi. Mem. Ch. of Jesus Christ of Latter-Day Saints. Clubs: Washington, Capitol Hill, 1925 F Street. Home: 4500 Garfield St NW Washington DC 20007-1131 Office: Marriott Dr Washington DC 20058

MARRIOTT, DAVID M., public relations executive; b. Port Townsend, Wash., Oct. 1, 1943. BA in Radio and TV Comm., U. Wash., 1966. Reporter Sta. KVI, Seattle, 1966-68; gen. assignment and city hall reporter Sta. KIRO-TV, Seattle, 1968-72; press sec. Mayor of Seattle, 1972-77; dir. corp. comm. Alaska Airlines, 1977-82; area dir. Sheraton Corp. N.Am., 1982-84; v.p. Corp. Comm., Inc., 1984-86; ptnr. Bean/Marriott Pub. Rels., 1986; eec. v.p., gen. mgr. Evans/Kraft/Bean Pub. Rels., 1986-90; sr. v.p., mng. dir. pub. rels. Elgin Syferd, 1990—. Office: Elgin Syferd/DDB Needham 1008 Western Ave Ste 601 Seattle WA 98104

MARRIOTT, JOHN WILLARD, JR., hotel and food service chain executive; b. Washington, Mar. 25, 1932; s. John Willard and Alice (Sheets) M.; m. Donna Garff, June 29, 1955; children: Deborah, Stephen Garff, John Willard, David Sheets. B.S. in Banking and Fin, U. Utah, 1954. V.p. Marriott Hot Shoppes Inc., 1959-64, exec. v.p., bd. dirs., 1964; pres. Marriott Corp., 1964—, chief exec. officer, 1972—, chmn. bd., 1985—; bd. dirs. Outboard Marine Corp., Waukegan, Ill., GM, U.S.-Russia Bus. Coun., Host Marriott Corp. (formerly Marriott Corp.). Trustee Mayo Found., Nat. Geog. Soc., Eisenhower Med. Ctr., Exec. Coun. on Fgn. Diplomats; mem. nat. adv. bd. Boy Scouts Am.; mem. conf. bd. Bus. Coun., Bus. Roundtable. Lt. USNR, 1954-56. Recipient Bus. Leader of Yr. award, Georgetown U. Sch. Bus. Adminstrn., 1984, Svc. Above Self award, Rotary Club at JFK Internat. Airport, 1985, Am. Mgr. of Yr. award, Nat. Mgmt. Assn., 1985, Golden Chain award, Nation's Restaurant News, 1985, Hall of Fame award, Consumer Digest Mag., 1985, Citizen of Yr. award, Boy Scouts of Am., 1986, Restaurant Bus. Leadership award, Restaurant Bus. Mag., 1986, Gold Plate award, Am. Acad. Achievement, 1986, Hall of Fame, Am. Hotel and Motel Assn., 1986, Hall of Fame award Culinary Inst. of Am., 1987, Hospitality Exec. of Yr. award, Pa. State U., 1987, Bronze winner in Fin. World's Chief Exec. Officers award, 1988, Silver Plate award Lodging Hospitality Mag., 1988, Chief Exec. Officer of Yr. Chief Exec. Officer Mag., 1988, Signature award CA chpt. Nat. Multiple Scelerosis, 1988, named Outstanding Mktg. Exec. Gallagher Report, 1988. Mem. Conf. Bd., U.S.C. of C., Sigma Chi. Mem. LDS Ch. Clubs: Burning Tree (Washington), Met. (Washington). Office: Marriott Hotels Resorts & Suites Marriott Dr Washington DC 20058*

MARRIOTT, RICHARD EDWIN, hotel and contract services executive; b. Washington, Jan. 9, 1939; s. John Willard and Alice Taylor (Sheets) M.; m. Nancy Peery, Mar. 20, 1962; children: Julie Ann, Sandra, Karen, Mary Alice. BS, U. Utah, 1963; MBA, Harvard U., 1965. With Marriott Corp., Washington, 1965—; group v.p. restaurant ops., 1976-78, corp. group v.p. restaurant and theme park ops., 1979-84, exec. v.p., 1984, vice chmn., 1986—, also bd. dirs.; chmn. bd. dirs. Media Corp., 1973—; bd. dirs. Riggs Nat. Bank of Washington. Mem. Nat. Commn. Against Drunk Driving; trustee Boys Clubs Am., Dole Found. for Employemnt of Persons with Disabilities. Mem. Nat. Restaurant Assn., Sigma Chi. Mem. LDS Ch. Office: Marriott Corp Marriott Dr Dept 97701 Washington DC 20058

MARRO, ANTHONY JAMES, newspaper editor; b. Middlebury, Vt., Feb. 10, 1942; s. Francis James and Esther Martha (Butterfield) M.; m. Jacqueline Helen Cleary, June 5, 1965; 1 child, Alexandria. B.A. in History, U. Vt., 1965; M.S. in Journalism, Columbia U., 1968. Reporter Rutland (Vt.) Herald, 1964-67; Reporter Newsday, L.I., N.Y., 1968-74, chief Washington bur., 1979-81, mng. editor, 1981-86, exec. editor, 1986-87, editor, 1987—; reporter Newsweek, Washington, 1974-76, N.Y. Times, Washington, 1976-79. Co-recipient Pulitzer prizes for Pub. Service Reporting, 1970, 74. Office: Newsday 235 Pinelawn Rd Melville NY 11747

MARRON, DONALD BAIRD, investment banker; b. Goshen, N.Y., July 21, 1934; m. Catherine D. Calligar. Student, Baruch Sch. Bus., 1949-51, 55-57. Investment analyst N.Y. Trust Co., N.Y.C., 1951-56, Lionel D. Edie Co., N.Y.C., 1956-58; mgr. research dept. George O'Neill & Co., 1958-59; pres. D.B. Marron & Co. Inc., N.Y.C., 1959-65; pres. Mitchell Hutchins & Co. Inc. (merger with D.B. Marron & Co. Inc. 1965), N.Y.C., 1965-69, pres., chief exec. officer, 1969-77; pres. PaineWebber Inc. (merger with Mitchell Hutchins & Co. Inc. 1977), N.Y.C., 1977-88, chief exec. officer, 1980—, chmn. bd., 1981—, also bd. dirs.; co-founder, former chmn. Data Resources, Inc.; former dir. N.Y. Stock Exchange. Vice chmn. bd. trustees Mus. of Modern Art; bd. overseers and mgrs. Meml. Sloan-Kettering; trustee for cultural resources N.Y.C., trustee Dana Found.; bd. dirs. N.Y.C. Partnership; bd. dirs. Bus. Com. for the Arts, Inc.; mem. Govs.'s Sch. and Bus. Alliance Task Force, N.Y.; mem. Coun. on Fgn. Rels., Inc.; mem. pres.'s com. on The Arts and The Humanities, Inc. Office: PaineWebber Group Inc 1285 Ave of the Americas New York NY 10019-6028 also: Mus Modern Art 11 W 53rd St New York NY 10019*

MARROW, TRACY See ICE-T*

MARRS, JAMES F., JR., author, journalist, educator; b. Ft. Worth, Dec. 5, 1943; s. James Marrs; m. Carol Ann Worcester, May 25, 1968; children: Cathryn Nova Ayn, Jayme Alistar. BA in Journalism, North Tex. State U., 1966; postgrad., Tex. Tech. Coll., 1967-68. Editor/owner Magpie Mag., 1963-64; sports/news writer, cartoonist Denton (Tex.) Record Chronicle, 1965-66; reporter, copy editor, cartoonist and photographer Lubbock (Tex.) Avalanche-Jour., 1967-68; news and feature writer, cartoonist, photographer Lubbock Sentinel, 1968; reporter, feature writer, photographer, cartoonist Ft. Worth Star-Telegram, 1968-80; prodr. "Texas Roundup" Sammons Cable TV, Ft. Worth, 1982-83; scriptwriter Spindletop Prodns., Dallas, 1982-83; pub. rels. cons. The Mktg. Group, Dallas, 1982-83; pubr., co-owner The Springtown (Tex.) Current, 1983-84; comm. dir. Continental State Bank, Springtown, 1985—; editl. page editor Campus Chat, North Tex. State U., 1965-66; part-time copywriter, pub. rels. dir., cartoonist Jerre R. Todd & Assocs., 1972-74, dir. spl. projects, account exec., pub. rels. dir., 1980-81; editor/pub. and co-owner Cowtown Trails, Ft. Worth, 1983-84; faculty Office Continuing Edn. U. Tex., Arlington, 1976—; comm. dir. N E. Health-Care Ctr., Hurst, Tex., 1985-86. Contbr. articles to profl. jours.; author: Crossfire: The Plot That Killed Kennedy, 1992; scriptwriter, dir. video: Fake, 1991, The Many Faces of Lee Harvey Oswald, 1992; author: The Enigma Files: The True Story of America's Psychic Warfare Program, 1995. Prodr. Tex. Gridiron Show, Ft. Worth, 1978-79, dir., 1980; chmn. pub. info. subcom. Ft. Worth Mayor's Com. on Employment of Handicapped, 1979-82; co-chmn. Springtown Centennial Com., 1984; workshop tchr. Operation CLASP, Neighborhood Adv. Coun., Community Devel. Block Grant, City of Ft. Worth, 1984; community rels. cons. All Church Home for Children, Ft. Worth, 1984—. With USAR, 1969-70. Recipient White Helmet award Ft. Worth Fire dept., 1969, 71, Assoc. Press writing awards, 1969-76, Nat. Writing award Aviation/Aerospace Writers Assn., 1972, Human Rights Leadership award Freedom Mag., 1993; named Arts and Entertainment Newsmaker of the Yr., Tex. Gridiron Club, Soc. Profl. Journalists, 1991. Mem. Tex. Mil. Hist. Soc., Springtown Optimist Club, Delta Sigma Phi, Sigma Delta Chi. Libertarian. Methodist. Avocation: civil war reenactor. Home and Office: Wise Comms PO Box 189 Springtown TX 76082

MARRS, RICHARD E., insurance company executive; married. BS, W.Va. Wesleyan Coll., 1955; JD, U. Md., 1959. Bar: Md. 1959. Sr. v.p. Travelers Corp., 1984—, Travelers Indemnity Co., Hartford, Conn., 1984—; also sr. v.p. Phoenix Ins. Co.; sr. v.p. Travelers Life and Annuity Co.; bd. dirs. Bankers & Shippers Ins. Co.; bd. dirs., mem. fin. com. Ins. Info. Inst.; ins. adv. com. Ctr. for Pub. Resources; lawyers com. Nat. Ctr. for State Cts. Mem. ABA, Md. Bar Assn., Internat. Assn. Def. Counsel, Am. Ins. Assn. (claim adminstrn. com.). Office: The Travelers Corp 1 Tower Sq Hartford CT 06183-0001

MARRS, RICHARD PRESTON, gynecologist, obstetrician; b. Paducah, Tex., Dec. 6, 1947; s. Benjamin Verne and Mary Angela (Mattei) M.; m. Joyce Marie Vargyas, Nov. 1, 1980; children: Ashley Marie, Austen Michael. AA, Schreiner Inst., Kerrville, Tex., 1968; BA, U. Tex., Austin, 1970; MD, U. Tex., Galveston, 1974. Lic. MD Tex, 1974, Calif., 1977; diplomate Am. Bd. Ob-Gyn, Am. Bd. Reproductive Endocrinology. Re-

sident in Ob-Gyn U. Tex. Med. Br., Galveston, 1974-77, asst. prof., 1979-82; fellow in reproductive endocrinology U. So. Calif. Sch. Medicine, L.A., 1977-79, clin. instr. dept Ob-Gyn, 1977-79, from asst. to assoc. prof. dept. Ob-Gyn, 1979-86; dir. div. reproductive endocrinology and infertility Cedars-Sinai Med. Ctr., L.A., 1986-88; prof. dept. Ob-Gyn UCLA Sch. Medicine, 1986-88; dir. inst. for reproductive tech. Hosp. Good Samaritan, L.A., 1988—; Mem. Outpatient Surgery com., Hosp. Good Samaritan, L.A., 1986-88; pres. Marrs/Vargyas Corp., 1983; mem. sci. adv. bd. IVF Australia, 1988—, Serono Pharm., 1989—; mem. physician's adv. bd. Resolve, Inc. 1989—. Mem. editorial bd. Jour. In Vitro Fertilization and Embryo Transfer, Jour. Clin. Endocrinology and Metabolism; contbr. over 75 articles to med. jours.; contbr. chpts. to books. Recipient Squibb prize Pacific Coast Fertility Soc., 1979, Sci. Exhibit award Am. Coll. Ob-Gyn, 1980, Mem. Found. award 49th Ann. Mtg. Pacific Coast Ob-Gyn Coc., 1982, sr. residents award for excellence in teaching, 1980. Fellow Am. Coll. Obstetrics and Gynecology, Jeanne Kemper Found.; mem. In Vitro Fertilization Spl. Interest Group (chmn. 1986-88, pres. 1987-88), Los Angeles Obstetrics and Gynecology Soc., Salerni Collegium, AMA, Soc. for Gynecol. Investigation, Endocrine Soc., Soc. for Study of Reproduction, Am. Inst. Ultrasound In Medicine. Avocations: tennis, racquetball, horseback riding. Office: Marrs/Vargyas Corp 1245 16th St Ste 220 Santa Monica CA 90404-1240

MARRS, SHARON CARTER, librarian; b. Andover, Va., May 7, 1943; d. Wallace Ralph and Dorothy (Stout) Carter; m. Glenn Robert Marrs, July 3, 1965. BS, East Tenn. State U., 1965; MLS, U. Pitts., 1974, postgrad., 1983—. Cert. libr. sci. and English, Pa. Tchr. English grades 8 and 10 Powell Valley H.S., Big Stone Gap, Va., 1964-65; libr. Coeburn (Va.) Elem., 1967-68, tchr. grade 2, 1968; libr. Wise (Va.) Elem., 1968-69; tchr. English grade 7 Christiansburg (Va.) Elem. Sch., 1969-70, libr., 1970-71; libr. Myrtle, Vernridge and Kelton Schs., Pitts., 1972—; apptd. to serve on Microcomputer in the Media Ctr. Award com., Am. Assn. Sch. Librs.; presenter workshops in field. Inventor games for children on use of card catalog, the Dewey Decimal System, various ref. books. Mem. ALA, Pa. State Libr. Assn. (mem. tech. com.), Internat. Assn. Sch. Librarianship, Beta Phi Mu. Home: 620 Broughton Rd Bethel Park PA 15102-3775

MARS, FORREST E., JR., candy company executive; s. Forrest Mars Sr.; married. Grad., Yale U., 1953. Co-pres., CEO Mars Inc. Office: Mars Inc 6885 Elm St Mc Lean VA 22101-3881

MARS, JOHN F., candy company executive; b. 1935; married. Student, Yale U., 1957. Chmn. Kal Kan Foods Inc.; co-pres., CEO Mars Inc., 1973—. Office: Mars Inc 6885 Elm St Mc Lean VA 22101-3881*

MARSALA, THERESA CLARK, nurse, administrator; b. Tulsa, Aug. 5, 1952; d. Robert Earl and Mary Louise (Pettigrew) Clark; m. Thomas A. Marsala, Aug. 17, 1974; children—Thomas, Leslie, Robert, Catherine. B.S. in Nursing, Northeast La. U., 1975, MEd in Counseling. Cert. advanced cardiac life support provider. Staff nurse St. Francis Med. Ctr., Monroe, La., 1975-78, head nurse dialysis, 1976-78, registered nurse instr., 1979-80, dir. edn. and tng., 1980-83, dir. nursing service, 1983-84, asst. adminstr. nursing service, 1984-92, v.p. patient care svcs., 1992—; CPR instr. Am. Heart Assn., 1979—, trainer, 1980—, advanced cardiac life support instr. provider, 1982—. Named Outstanding Young Woman Am., 1984. Mem. ANA, La. Orgn. Nurse Execs. (bd. dirs. 1990-93), Monroe Dist. Nurses Assn., Am. Heart Assn., Nat. Kidney Found., La. Soc. for Nursing Service Adminstrs., Progressive Men's Club Aux. (treas. Monroe, La. 1978-79), Sigma Theta Tau. Roman Catholic. Office: St Francis Med Ctr Nursing Adminstrn 309 Jackson St Monroe LA 71201-7498

MARSALA-CERVASIO, KATHLEEN ANN, medical/surgical nurse; b. Mar. 22, 1955; d. James Patrick and Kathleen (McLoughlin) Waters. AAS with honors, S.I. Coll., 1974, BS in Nursing with honors, 1984; MS in Nursing with honors, CUNY, 1986; student, NYU. RN, N.Y.; cert. CS, CCRN, CNAA. Staff nurse USPHS Hosp., S.I., 1974-80; head nurse MICU-critical care unit-surg. ICU Bayley Seton Hosp., N.Y., 1980-82; staff nurse surg. ICU, MICU, critical care unit East Orange (N.J.) VA Med. Ctr., 1982-86, critical care nurse specialist; clin. specialist, cons. Med Ctr. Bklyn. VA Med. Ctr., 1989-95; dep. dir. nursing svcs. U. Hosp./SUNY Health Sci. Ctr., Bklyn., 1990—; asst. clin. prof. UMDNJ and SUNY Health Sci. Ctr. Mem. ANA (coun. clin. nurse specialists), AACN (no. N.J. chpt., N.J. chpt.), Am. Coll. Healthcare Execs. (assoc.), N.Y. Orgn. Nurse Execs., Nat. League for Nursing, Sigma Theta Tau. Home: 8898 16th Ave Brooklyn NY 11214

MARSALIS, BRANFORD, musician; b. New Orleans, Aug. 26, 1960; s. Ellis Marsalis. Student, So. U., 1978, Berklee Coll. Music, 1979-81. Mem. Art Blakey Group, 1981, Wynton Marsalis Quintet, 1982; ind. saxophonist, 1983—; bandleader The Tonight Show, L.A. 1992-95. Rec. Artist: (with Wynton Marsalis) Wynton Marsalis, Think of One, Hot House Flowers, Black Codes (From the Underground), (with Art Blakey) Keystone 3, (with Kevin Eubanks) Opening Nights, (with Dizzy Gillespie) New Faces, Closer to the Source, (with Andy Jaffe) Manhattan Projects, (with Sting) Dream of the Blue Turtles, Bring on the Night; (solo albums) Romances for Saxophone, 1986, Royal Garden Blues, 1986, Renaissance, 1987, Random Abstract, 1988, Tio Jeepy, 1989, Crazy People Music, 1990, The Beautiful Ones Are Not Yet Born, 1991, Bloomington, 1993, Scenes in the City, I Heard You Twice the First Time, (Guru) Jazzmatazz, 1993; composer various pieces including No Backstage Pass, Solstice, Waiting for Rain, (video) David and Goliath, 1993, (film) Mo' Better Blues, 1990. Winner Down Beat magazine's readers' poll, best soprano sax player, 1991-92; Grammy award, Best Pop Instrumental 1994 for "Barcelona Mona" with Bruce Hornsby. Address: care NBC-TV Tonight Show 3000 W Alameda Burbank CA 91523 also: PO Box 55398 Washington DC 20040-5398*

MARSALIS, WYNTON, musician; b. New Orleans, Oct. 18, 1961; s. Ellis and Dolores Marsalis. Studied with John Longo; student, New Orleans Ctr. for Performing Arts, Berkshire Music Ctr., Juilliard Sch. Music, 1979-81. Trumpet soloist with New Orleans Philharm. Orch., 1975; recitalist with New Orleans Ctr. for Creative Arts, 1979; played with various New Orleans and N.Y.C. orchs.; with Art Blakey's Jazz Messengers, 1980-81, Herbie Hancock's V.S.O.P. quartet; formed own group, 1981; albums include Fathers and Sons, 1982, Hummel/Haydn/L. Mozart Trumpet Concertos, 1983 (Grammy award), Wynton Marsalis (Best Jazz Record, Downbeat readers' poll 1982), Think of One, 1983 (Grammy award), Handel, purcell, Torelli, Fasch, Moler (Grammy award), Trumpet Concertos, 1983, Hot House Flowers, 1984, Black Codes from the Underground, 1985 (2 Grammy awards), J Mood, 1986, Carnaval, 1987, Marsalis Standard Time, Vol. I, 1987 (Grammy award), Majesty of the Blues, 1989, Standard Time, Vol. 3, 1990, Intimacy Calling Standard Time, Soul Gestures in Southern Blue, Vols. 1, 2, 3, 1991, Blue Interlude, 1992, Citi Movement, 1993, In This House, On This Morning, 1994. Named Jazz Musician of Yr., Downbeat readers' poll, 1982, 84-86, 89, Best Trumpet Player, Downbeat critics' poll, 1984, Acoustic Jazz Group of Yr., 1984, Best Trumpet Player, Downbeat readers' poll, 1985; recipient Grammy award for best solo jazz instrumental, 1983-85, Grammy award for best jazz instrumental performance with group, 1985, 87; musician of the Year, Down Beat Readers' poll, 1992. Office: care Agy for Performing Arts 9000 W Sunset Blvd West Hollywood CA 90069-5801*

MARSAN, JEAN-CLAUDE, architect, urban planner, educator; b. St-Eustache, Que., Can., Oct. 7, 1938; s. Aimé and Gertrude (Bolduc) M.; children: Jean-Sébastien, Marc-Aurèle. BA, U. Montreal, Que., 1960, BArch, 1965; MSc in Urban Planning, U. Edinburgh, Scotland, 1968, PhD in Urban Planning, 1975. Assoc. prof. Sch. Architecture U. Montreal, 1975-84, prof., 1984—, dean Faculté de l'Aménagement, 1984-93, dir. Sch. architecture, 1975-79; rsch. prof. Inst. québécois de recherche sur la culture 1980-82; pres. Com. to Study the Future of Olympic Installations, Montreal, 1977. Author: Montréal en évolution, 1974, Montreal une esquisse du futur, 1983, Sauver Montréal, 1990; contbr. articles to profl. jours. and newspapers, chpts. to books. Founding mem. Save Montreal, 1973-78, Mcpl. Action Group, 1978; pres. Heritage Montreal, 1983-88; bd. dirs. Mus. Fine Arts Montreal, 1975-87, v.p., 1978-87. Mem. Ordre des Architectes du Que. (Prix Paul-Henry Lapointi 1984, 85, 87, Prix Gérard Morisset, 1992, govt. of Que.). Royal Soc. Can., Corp. Profl. des Urbanistes du Qué. Office: U Montreal Box 6128 Sta A, Faculté de l'Aménagement, Montreal, PQ Canada H3C 3J7

MARSCHER, FRAN HEYWARD (FRAN SMITH), editor; b. Charleston, S.C., Dec. 10, 1941; d. Daniel H. Jr. and Margaret (Zorn) Hegward; m. Elmer Haineswoth Smith Jr., July 30, 1961 (div. Feb. 1987); children: Georgia Leigh Smith Horan, Margaret Daniel Smith McCarthy; m. William Frederick Marscher, Nov. 26, 1994. BA in Journalism, U. S.C., 1963. Feature writer Savannah (Ga.) News Press, 1963-65; English tchr. Bluffton (S.C.) H.S., 1968-70; reporter The Island Packet, Hilton Head Island, S.C., 1978-80, 81-85, assoc. editor, 1985-87, editor, 1987—; reporter Daily News Sun, Sun City, Ariz., 1980-81; workshop chmn. S.C. Press Assn., Columbia, 1991-92, mem. com., 1987-91. Bd. dirs. Vol. Action Ctr., Hilton Head Island, 1988-90, Literacy Vols., Hilton Head Island, 1988-92; founding bd. dirs. Bluffton (S.C.) Libr., 1985-88, Hilton Head Mus., 1985-87. Recipient 1st place Pub. Svc. award S.C. Press Assn., 1991-92, 1st place award Inst. for So. Studies, 1991-92, Harry Hampton award for Journalism, S.C. Wildlife Fedn., 1983. Mem. S.C. Coastal Conservation League. Episcopalian. Avocations: reading, gardening, birdwatching, music. Home: 23 Big Oak St Hilton Head Island SC 29926 Office: The Island Packet 1 Pope Ave Park Hilton Head Island SC 29928

MARSCHING, RONALD LIONEL, lawyer, former precision instrument company executive; b. N.Y.C., Mar. 30, 1927; m. Marjory Fleming Duncan, Dec. 31, 1964; children: Christine, Jane. BA cum laude, Princeton U., 1950; JD, Harvard U., 1953. Bar: N.Y. 1954. Assoc. White & Case, N.Y.C.; vice chmn., gen. counsel Timex Corp., Waterbury, Conn., 1967-86, also bd. dirs. Served with U.S. Army, 1953-55. Mem. ABA, Nat. Assn. Dirs., University Club (N.Y.C. chpt.). Home: 41 E Hill Rd Woodbury CT 06798-3017

MARSDEN, BRIAN GEOFFREY, astronomer; b. Cambridge, Eng., Aug. 5, 1937; came to U.S., 1959; s. Thomas and Eileen (West) M.; m. Nancy Lou Zissell, Dec. 26, 1964; children: Cynthia Louise, Jonathan Brian. Ba, Oxford U., U.K., 1959, MA, 1963; PhD, Yale U., 1965. Rsch. asst. Yale U., New Haven, 1959-65; lectr. astronomy Harvard U., Cambridge, Mass., 1966-83; astronomer Smithsonian Astrophys. Obs., Cambridge, 1965-86; assoc. dir. planetary scis. Harvard-Smithsonian Ctr. for Astrophysics, Cambridge, 1987—; dir. Cen. Bur. Astron. Telegrams, 1968—, Minor Planet Ctr. Internat. Astron. Union, 1978—. Editor: The Earth-Moon System, 1966, The Motion, Evolution of Orbits and Origin of Comets, 1972, Catalogue of Cometary Orbits, 1992, Catalogue of Orbits of Unnumbered Minor Planets, 1992. Recipient Merlin medal Brit. Astron. Assn., 1965, Goodacre medal, 1979; Van Biesbroeck award U. Ariz., 1989, Camus-Waitz prize Société astronomique de France, 1993. Fellow Royal Astron. Soc.; mem. Am. Astron. Soc. (chmn. div. on dynamical astronomy 1976-78), Internat. Astron. Union (pres. commn. 1976-79), Astron. Soc. Pacific, Sigma Xi. Office: Harvard-Smithsonian Ctr Astrophysics 60 Garden St Cambridge MA 02138-1596

MARSDEN, CHARLES JOSEPH, financial executive; b. N.Y.C., Dec. 18, 1940; s. David Joseph and Louise (Noell) M.; m. Marilyn Weber, Nov. 12, 1988; children from previous marriage: Anne Brewer, George David. A.B. cum laude, Amherst Coll., 1962; M.B.A. with distinction, Harvard U., 1965. Credit analyst Irving Trust Co., N.Y.C., 1962-63; with W.R. Grace & Co., 1965-81; treas. Polyfibron Div. W.R. Grace & Co., Cambridge, Mass., 1969-72; v.p. fin. adminstrn. Cryovac Div. W.R. Grace & Co., Duncan, S.C., 1972-78; v.p. fin. Indsl. Chems. Group W.R. Grace & Co., N.Y.C., 1978-81; exec. v.p., chief fin. officer The Grand Union Co., Elmwood Park, N.J., 1981-83; also dir. The Grand Union Co.; v.p. fin. Pan Am. World Airways, Inc., 1984-85; v.p. fin., chief fin. officer Crompton & Knowles Corp., 1985—; also dir. Mem. Harvard Club. Office: Crompton & Knowles Corp 1 Station Pl Stamford CT 06902-6800

MARSDEN, HERCI IVANA, classical ballet artistic director; b. Omis-Split, Croatia, Dec. 2, 1937; came to U.S., 1958; d. Ante and Magda (Smith) Munitic; m. Myles Marsden, Aug. 10, 1957 (div. 1976); children—Ana, Richard, Mark; m. Dujko Radovnikovic, Aug. 27, 1977; 1 child, Dujko. Student, Internat. Ballet Sch., 1955. Mem. corps de ballet Nat. Theatre, Split, 1954-58; founder Braecrest Sch. Ballet, Lincoln, R.I., 1958—; founder State Ballet of R.I., Lincoln, 1960—, artistic dir., 1976—; artistic dir. U. R.I. Classical Ballet, Kingston, 1966—, lectr., 1966—.

MARSDEN, LAWRENCE ALBERT, retired textile company executive; b. Mpls., May 28, 1919; s. Lawrence N. and Carrie Elizabeth (Ross) M.; m. Millicent Irene Snyder, Mar. 24, 1941; children: Millicent Carrie, Andrea Leigh, Lawrence Stewart, John Daniel. B.S. in Law, U. Minn., 1941; LL.B, George Washington U., 1946. Bar: D.C. 1946. Ptnr. Onion, Marsden & New, Washington, 1947-48; pres. Marsden-Slate, Inc., High Point, N.C., 1949-68; v.p. Guilford Mills, Inc., Greensboro, N.C., 1968-72; sr. v.p., 1973-84; chmn. Marcor, Inc., High Point, 1980—; ptnr. SPM Investments. Author: Attack Transport, 1946; bd. dirs. U. Minn. Law Rev. Served to lt. comdr. USN, 1941-46, PTO. Mem. Am. Assn. Textile Chemists and Colorists, Sportsman Pilots Assn. (past pres.), Aircraft Owners and Pilots Assn., Rolls Royce Owner's Club, Quiet Birdmen, High Point Country Club, Willow Creek Golf Club (High Point), Isla Del Sol Yacht and Country Club (St. Petersburg, Fla.), Phi Delta Phi, Phi Delta Theta. Republican. Home: 1706 Maryfield Ct High Point NC 27260-2684

MARSDEN, WILLIAM, government official; b. Cambridge, Eng., Sept. 15, 1940; s. Christopher Alexander Marsden and Ruth Kershaw; m. Kaia Collingham, Sept. 9, 1964; children: Inge, Thomas. BSc in Econs., London U., 1973; MA, Cambridge U., 1962. 3d sec. U.K. Del. to NATO, Paris, 1964-66; 2d sec. Brit. Embassy, Rome, 1966-70; 1st sec. Brit. Embassy, Moscow, 1976-78; min. trade Brit. Embassy, Washington, 1992-94; asst. under sec. of state For the Americas Fgn. Office, London, 1994—; asst. to gen. mgr. Joseph Lucas Elec. Co., 1970-71; 1st sec. sci. and tech. Fgn. Office, London, 1971-75; asst. head European community dept., 1978-81; head African dept., commr. Brit. Indian Ocean Ter. Fgn. Office, 1985-89; counsellor U.K. Representation to EEC, Brussels, 1981-85; amb. to Costa Rica and Nicaragua, 1989-92. Named Companion of Order St. Michael and St. George by Her Majesty the Queen. Mem. Brit. Inst. Mgmt., The City London (freeman), The Grocers' Co. London (freeman), The Univ. Club, The Lansdowne Club. Office: Americas Fgn & Commonwealth Office, Asst Under-Sec, London SW1A 2AH, England

MARSEE, STUART (EARL), educational consultant, retired; b. Gardener, Oreg., Sept. 30, 1917; s. William and Clare (Grimes) M.; m. Audrey Belfield, June 1, 1940; children: Frederic, Jeffrey, Wayne. B.S., U. Oreg., 1939, M.S., 1942; Ed.D., U. So. Calif., 1947; LL.D., Pepperdine U., 1977. Asst. supt. for bus. Pasadena City Schs., Calif., 1949-57, acting supt., 1957-58, asst. supt., 1949-58; pres. El Camino Coll., 1958-82, cons., 1982—; lectr. UCLA, 1965, U. So. Calif., 1956-57; adj. prof. Pepperdine U., 1978-79. Author: History of the Rotary Club of Torrance, 1962-74, 1974; contbr. articles to profl. jours. Recipient Disting. Service award Los Angeles County Bd. Suprs., 1958, Disting. Service Leadership award Kiwanis Internat., 1970; named Citizen of Yr., Torrance, Calif., 1981, Redondo Beach, Calif., 1986. Mem. Am. Assn. Community and Jr. Colls. (pres. 1968), Nat. Commn. Accrediting (dir. 1970-74), Council Postsecondary Accreditation (dir. 1974-78), Western Coll. Assn. (exec. com. 1978-81). Lodge: Rotary (Torrance). Office: 358 Camino De Las Colinas Redondo Beach CA 90277-6435

MARSEE, SUSANNE IRENE, lyric mezzo-soprano; b. San Diego, Nov. 26, 1941; d. Warren Jefferson and Irene Rose (Wills) Dowell; m. Mark J. Weinstein, May, 1987; 1 child, Zachary. Student, Santa Monica City Coll., 1961; BA in History, UCLA, 1964. Mem. voice faculty Am. Mus. and Dramatic Acad., N.Y.C., 1994—; assoc. prof. La State U. Appeared with numerous U.S. opera cos., 1970—, including N.Y.C. Opera, San Francisco Opera, Boston Opera; appeared with fgn. cos., festivals, Mexico City Bellas Artes, 1973, 78, Canary Islands Co., 1976, Opera Metropolitana, Caracas, Venezuela, 1977, Spoleto (Italy) Festival, 1977, Aix en Provence Festival, France, 1977, Calgary, Alta., Can., 1986; recorded Tales of Hoffman, ABC/Dunhill Records; TV appearances include Live from Lincoln Center, Turk in Italy, Cenerentola, 1980, Live from Wolftrap, Roberto Devereux's Rigoletto, 1988, A Little Night Music, 1990, Marriage of Figaro, 1991, (PBS TV) Rachel, La Cubana; recs. and CDs Anna Bolena with Ramey Scotto, Roberto Devereux with Beverly Sills, Roberto Devereux with Monserat Caballé, Tales of Hoffman with Beverly Sills, Rigoletto with Quilico and Carreras; videotape Roberto Devereux with Beverly Sills. Recipient 2d place award Met. Opera Regional Auditions, 1968, San Francisco Opera Regional

Auditions 1968; named winner Liederkranz Club Contest, 1970; Gladys Turk Found. grantee, 1968-69; Corbett Found. grantee, 1969-73; Martha Baird Rockefeller grantee, 1969-70, 71-72. Mem. AFTRA, Am. Guild Mus. Artists (past bd. dirs.), Nat. Assn. Tchrs. of Singing (bd. dirs.). Democrat.

MARSH, BENJAMIN FRANKLIN, lawyer; b. Toledo, Apr. 30, 1927; s. Lester Randall and Alice (Smith) M.; m. Martha Kirkpatrick, July 12, 1952; children: Samuel, Elizabeth. BA, Ohio Wesleyan U., 1950; JD, George Washington U., 1954. Bar: Ohio 1955. Pvt. practice law Toledo, 1955-88, Maumee, Ohio, 1988—; assoc., ptnr. Doyle, Lewis & Warner, Toledo, 1955-71; ptnr. Ritter, Boesel, Robinson & Marsh, Toledo, 1971-88, Marsh & McAdams, Maumee, 1988—; personnel officer AEC, 1950-54; asst. atty. gen. State of Ohio, 1969-71; asst. solicitor City of Maumee, 1959-63, solicitor, 1963-92; mem. U.S. Fgn. Claims Settlement Commn., Washington, 1990-94; counsel N.W. Ohio Mayors and Mgrs. Assn., 1993—; mem. regional bd. rev. Indsl. Commn. Ohio, Toledo, 1993-94. U.S. rep. with rank spl. amb. to 10th Anniversary Independence of Botswana, 1976; past pres. Toledo and Lucas County Tb Soc., citizens for metro pks.; past mem. Judges Com. Notaries Pub.; formerly mem. Lucas County Bd. Elections; former chmn. bldg. commn. Riverside Hosp., Toledo; past trustee Com. on Rels. with Toledo, Spain; past chmn. bd. trustee Med. Coll., Ohio; past treas. Coglin Meml. Inst.; chmn. Lucas County Rep. Exec. Com., 1973-74; precinct committeeman, Maumee, 1959-73; legal counsel, bd. dirs. Nat. Coun. Rep. Workshops, 1960-65; pres. Rep. Workshops, Ohio, 1960-64; alt. del. Rep. Nat. Conv., 1964; candidate 9th dist. U.S. Ho. of Reps., 1968; adminstrv. asst. to Rep. state chmn. Ray C. Bliss, 1954; chmn. Lucas County Bush for Pres., 1980; co-chmn. Reagan-Bush Com. for Northwestern Ohio, 1980, vice chmn. fin. com. Bush-Quayle, 1992; co-chmn. Ohio steering com. Bush for Pres., mem. nat. steering com., 1988; del. Rep. Nat. Conv., 1988; past bd. dirs. Ohio Tb and Respiratory Disease Assn.; apptd. Ohio chmn. UN Day, 1980, 81, 82; adminstrv. asst. Legis. Svc. Commn., Columbus, 1954-55; mem. Lucas County Charter Commn., Toledo, 1959-60; vice-chmn. U.S. Nat. Commn. for UNESCO, mem. legal com., del. 17th gen. conf., Paris, 1972, U.S. observer meeting of nat. commns., Africa, 1974, Addis Ababa, Ethiopia; past mem. industry functional adv. com. on standards trade policy matters; mem. nat. def. exec. res. Dept. Commerce; active Am. Bicentennial Presdl. Inauguration, Diplomatic Adv. Com. With USNR, 1945-46. Named Outstanding Young Man of Toledo, 1962. Mem. ABA, Maumee C. of C., Ohio Bar Assn., Toledo Bar Assn., Nat. Inst. Mcpl. Law Officers, Ohio Mcpl. League (past pres.), Am. Legion, Maumee Valley Hist. Soc., George Washington Law Assn., Internat. Inst. Toledo, Ohio Mcpl. Attys. Assn. (past pres.), Ohio Hist. Soc., Am. Canal Soc., Canal Soc. Ohio, Toledo Mus. Art, Ohio Wesleyan U. Alumni Assn. (past pres.), Toledo C. of C, Rotary, Ohio State Bar Found., Laurel Hill Swim and Tennis Club, Faculty Club Med. Coll., Toledo Country Club, Press Club, Omicron Delta Kappa, Delta Sigma Rho, Theta Alpha Phi, Phi Delta Phi. Presbyterian. Home: 124 W Harrison St Maumee OH 43537-2119 Office: 312 Conant St Maumee OH 43537-3358

MARSH, BRUCE DAVID, geology educator; b. Munising, Mich., Jan. 4, 1947; s. William Roland and Audrey Jane (Steinhoff) M.; m. Judith Anne Congdon, Jan. 24, 1970; children: Hannah Eyre, William Noah. BS, Mich. State U., 1969; MS, U. Ariz., 1971; PhD, U. Calif.-Berkeley, 1974. Geologist, geophysicist Anaconda Co., Tucson, 1969-71; asst. prof. dept. earth/planet sci. Johns Hopkins U., Balt., 1974-78, assoc. prof., 1978-81, prof., 1981—; chmn., 1989-93; vis. prof. Calif. Inst. Tech., Pasadena, 1985, U. Maine, 1992-93; co-chmn. Gordon Rsch. Conf. on Inorganic Geochemistry, Holderness, N.H., 1983-84; advisor NASA, Washington, 1975-84, NSF, Washington, 1978-90, NRC, 1985-91; Hallimond lectr. Mineral. Soc. Great Britain and Ireland, 1995. Assoc. editor Geology, 1981-83, Jour. Volcanology and Geothermal Rsch., 1978—, Jour. Petrology, 1986—. Fellow Geol. Soc. Am. (assoc. editor Bulletin 1986-92), Royal Astron. Soc.; mem. Am. Geophys. Union (sec. sect. on volcanology, geochemistry and petrology 1984-86, pres. elect 1988-90, pres. 1990-92, Bowen award 1993), New Eng. Historic and Geneol. Soc., Model A Ford Club Am. Office: Johns Hopkins U Dept Earth & Planetary Scis 34th Charles St Baltimore MD 21201-3707

MARSH, CARYL AMSTERDAM, curator, psychologist; b. N.Y.C., Mar. 9, 1923; d. Louis and Kitty (Weitz) Amsterdam; m. Michael Marsh, Sept. 3, 1942; children: Susan E., Anna L. B.A., Bkln. Coll., 1942; M.A., Columbia U., 1946; Ph.D., George Washington U., 1978. Lic. psychologist, D.C. Asst. cultural attache Am. Embassy, Paris, 1946-48; psychologist D.C. Recreation Dept., 1957-69; spl. asst. Smithsonian Instn., Washington, 1966-73; curator exhbns. Nat. Archives, Washington, 1978-85, sr. exhbns. specialist, 1985-86; dir. traveling psychology exhbn. Am. Psychol. Assn., 1986-93, sr. advisor, 1993—; chair humanities seminars in sci. mus. Assn. Sci. Tech. Ctrs., 1994; rsch. fellow exptl. gallery Smithsonian Instn., 1992; rsch. cons. Nat. Zoo, 1981-92, Smithsonian Folk Life Festival, Nat. Mus. Am. History, 1977-78; organizer Discovery Room Nat. Mus. Natural History, 1969-73; cons. Meyer Found., 1964-66. Editor: Exhibition: The American Image, 1979. Organizer Anacostia Neighborhood Mus., Washington, 1967, bd. dirs., 1974—, v.p. 1993; sec. D.C. Commn. on Arts and Humanities, 1969-72; pres. Pre-Sch. Parents Coun., Washington, 1956-57. Fellow Nat. Mus. Am. Art, 1975-77; vis. scholar Nat. Mus. Am. Art, 1978—; grad. fellow CUNY, 1945-46; scholar George Washington U.; noted for Disting. Contbn. to Pub. Understanding of Psychology, APA, 1993. Mem. AAAS, APA (Outstanding Svc. award 1992, Disting. Contbn. to Pub. Understanding of Psychology award 1993), D.C. Psychol. Assn., Am. Assn. Mus., Mus. Edn. Roundtable (bd. dirs. 1983-87). Home and Office: 3701 Grant Rd NW Washington DC 20016-1819

MARSH, CARYL GLENN, career officer; b. Ky., Oct. 12, 1939; m. Claire Boudrias, Sept. 11, 1961; children: Jeffrey, Regina, John. BS in Agr., U. Ky., 1961; MPA, Auburn U., 1973. Commd. 2d lt. U.S. Army, 1962, advanced through grades to lt. gen.; various ops. officer, then dep. brigade comdr. Berlin Brigade, 1979-81, brigade comdr., 1987-89; div. chief staff 9th Inf. Divsn. Inf. Div., Ft. Lewis, Wash., 1981-82; brigade comddr., 1982-84; chief staff I Corps, Ft. Lewis, 1984-85; asst. div. comdr. Air Assault Div., Ft. Campbell, Ky., 1985-87; comddg. gen. 2d Inf. Div., Camp Casey, Republic of Korea, 1989-91; dep. comdr.-in-chief, chief staff Hdqrs. Forces Command, Ft. McPherson, Ga., 1991-94; comdr. I Corps and Ft. Lewis (Wash.), 1994—. Mem. Kiwanis. Roman Catholic. Avocation: hunting. Office: DCINC/Cofs I Corps & Ft Lewis Fort Lewis WA 98433

MARSH, DAVE RODNEY, writer, publisher, editor; b. Pontiac, Mich., Mar. 1, 1950; s. Oliver Kenneth and Mary A. (Evon) M.; m. Barbara E. Carr, July 21, 1979; stepchildren: Sasha J. Carr, Kristen A. Carr (dec.). Student, Wayne State U., 1968-69. Editor Creem Mag., Detroit and Birmingham, Mich., 1969-73; music critic Newsday, Garden City, N.Y., 1973, 74-75; assoc. editor Rolling Stone Mag., N.Y.C., 1975-78, contbg. editor, 1978-85; contbg. editor The Record, N.Y.C., 1982-84; editor, pub. Rock & Rap Confidential, L.A., 1983—; music critic Playboy, 1985—, Rock Today (syndicated radio), 1987-92; contbg. editor Entertainment Weekly, 1991-93. Author: Born to Run: The Bruce Springsteen Story, 1979, The Book of Rock Lists, 1981, Elvis, 1982, Before I Get Old, 1983, Fortunate Son, 1985, Michael Jackson and the Crossover Dream, 1985, Glory Days: Bruce Springsteen in the 1980s, 1987;The Heart of Rock and Soul, 1989, 50 Ways to Fight Censorship, 1991, Louie, Louie, 1993, Merry Christmas Baby, 1993, The New Book of Rock Lists, 1994; editor: Rolling Stone Record Guide, 1979, The First Rock and Roll Confidential Report, 1985, Pastures of Plenty (Woody Guthrie, Harper and Row), 1990, (with Don Henley) Heaven Is Under Our Feet: Essays for Walden Woods, 1991, Mid-Life Confidential: The Rock Bottom Remainders Tour America, 1994; host Radio Mafia, Finland, 1990—. Trustee Kristen Ann Car Fund; active The Critics Chorus, Rock Bottom Remainders, 1992-94. Office: Rock & Rap Confidential PO Box 341305 Los Angeles CA 90034-9305

MARSH, DON ERMAL, supermarket executive; b. Muncie, Ind., Feb. 2, 1938; s. Ermal W. and Garnet (Gibson) M.; m. Marilyn Faust, Mar. 28, 1959; children: Don Ermal, Jr., Arthur Andrew, David Alan, Anne Elizabeth, Alexander Elliott. BA, Mich. State U., 1961. With Marsh Supermarkets, Inc., Indpls., 1961—, pres., 1968—, chmn. CEO; also dir. Marsh Supermarkets, Inc.; chmn. FoodPAC, Washington, 1991; bd. dirs. Nat. City Bank, Indpls., Ind. Energy, Inc., Indpls.; gov. World Econ. Forum—Food & Agro, Geneva. Bd. dirs. Corp. Community Coun., Culver Fathers Assn., Food Industry Crusade Against Hunger, Charlene S. Lugar Birth Defects Grant Fund; mem. adv. com. on food distbn. Western Mich.

U.; mem. Conner Prairie Pioneer Settlement Adv. Coun.; mem. Indpls. Mus. Art. Mem. Am. Mgmt. Assn., Gen. Mgmt. Coun., Internat. Food Congress, Assn. of Publicly Traded Cos. (bd. dirs., past chmn.), Food Mktg. Inst. (bd. dirs.), Indpls. C. of C., Ind. State C. of C. (bd. dirs.), Ind. Retail Coun. (bd. dirs.), Ind. Soc. Chgo., Chief Execs. Orgn., World Bus. Coun., Newcomen Soc. N.Am., Internat. Ctr. for Cos. of Food Trade and Industry (past chmn., bd. dirs.), Food Merchandisers Edn. Coun., Nat. Assn. Convenience Stores, Nat. Assn. Food Rsch., World Pres.' Orgn., Young Pres.' Orgn. Alumni, Am. Bus. Club, Ind. Fiscal Policy Inst., Ind. Soc. Chgo., Ind. U. Varsity Club, Crooked Stick Golf Club, Columbia Club, Delaware Country Club, The Hundred Club Indpls., Indpls. Athletic Club, Marco Polo Club, Meridian Hills Country Club, Skyline Club, Masons, Elks, Pi Sigma Epsilon, Lambda Chi Alpha Found. Republican. Presbyterian. Office: Marsh Supermarkets Inc 9800 Crosspoint Blvd Indianapolis IN 46256-3300

MARSH, DON SEAGLE, retired newspaper editor; b. Cherry Tree, W.Va., Aug. 23, 1927; s. Roy Jackson and Blanche (Marcum) M.; m. Geraldine L. Braden, Aug. 9, 1957; children—Clay B., Samuel D. B.S. in Journalism, W.Va. U., 1950. Sports editor Bluefield Daily Telegraph, 1950-51; reporter Parkersburg News, 1951, Charleston (W.Va.) Daily Mail, 1951-52; with Charleston Gazette, 1952—, city editor, 1970-76, editor, 1976-92, ret., 1992. Served as seaman USN, 1945-46. Nieman fellow Harvard U., 1956. Democrat. Home: 3807 Venable Ave Charleston WV 25304-1531 Office: Charleston Gazette 1001 Virginia St E Charleston WV 25301-2895

MARSH, DONALD JAY, college dean, medical educator; b. N.Y.C., Aug. 5, 1934; m. Wendy G. Clough; 2 children. AB, U. Calif., Berkeley, 1955; MD, U. Calif., San Francisco, 1958. Intern in medicine UCLA Hosp., 1958-59; postdoctoral fellow dept. physiology NYU, 1959-60, instr. dept. physiology, 1960-61, asst. prof. physiology and biophysics, 1963-67, assoc. prof. physiology and biophysics, 1967-71; prof. biomed. engring. U. So. Calif., 1971-92, prof. dept. physiology and biophysics, 1978-92, prof. medicine, 1982-92, rsch. prof. physiology and biophysics, 1992—; prof. physiology Brown U., Providence, 1992—, dean medicine and biol. scis., 1992—; mem. engring. in medicine and biology tng. com. NIH, 1973, cardiovascular renal study sect., 1983-86, ad hoc mem. med. lab. scis. rev. com., 1976, inst. gen. med. scis. adv. com., 1982; ad hoc reviewer NSF; mem. rsch. com. Am. Heart Assn., 1979-82, rev. com. for grants-in-aid, pub. affairs com., 1986-88; cons. com. interdisciplinary rsch. Nat. Rsch. Coun.- Inst. of Medicine, 1989; mem. med. schs. sect. task force AMA, 1994—; lectr. in field. Mem. editorial bd. Annals of Biomed. Engring., 1972-74, mng. editor, 1974-78; mem. editorial bd. Am. Jour. Physiology and Jour. of Applied Physiology, 1972-76, Am. Jour. Physiology: Regulatory, Integrative and Comparative Physiology, 1977-79, Am. Jour. Physiology: Renal, Fluid and Electrolyte Physiology, 1977-82, 88-94, Am. Jour. Physiology: Modelling Methodology Forum, 1984-91; guest reviewer Biophys. Jour., Circulation Rsch., Jour. Clin. Investigation, Jour Theoretical Biology, Kidney Internat., Sci., Pfluegers Archiv European Jour. Physiology; contbr. articles to profl. jours., chpts. to books. Named Career Scientist, Health Rsch. Coun. N.Y., 1964-71; Spl. fellow NIH, 1970-71, grantee, 1990-94, 91—. Fellow AAAS; mem. Assn. Am. Med. Colls. (coun. of deans), Am. Soc. Nephrology, Am. Physiol. Soc. (com. on cons. 1980-83, chmn. renal sect. 1982-83, long range planning com. 1990-93), Biophys. Soc., Microvascular Soc., Soc. Gen. Physiologists, Soc. Math. Biology (nominating com. 1983, publs. com. 1984-85, bd. dirs. 1986-88), Alpha Omega Alpha. Home: 148 Pratt St Providence RI 02906 Office: Brown U Sch of Medicine Box G-A1 Providence RI 02912

MARSH, ERNESTINE PEASE, nursing administrator, medical-surgical nurse; b. St. Louis, June 24, 1935; d. Clifford Robert and Ernestine Arnecia (Washington) Pease; children: Ann, Clifford. Diploma in nursing, Homer G. Phillips Hosp., St. Louis, 1955; BSN, St. Louis U., 1972; postgrad., So. Ill. U. RN, Calif., Pa., Va. Asst. chief nurse San Diego VA Med. Ctr.; chief nursing svc. Coatesville (Pa.) VA Med. Ctr., McGuire VA Med. Ctr., Richmond, Va., University Drive VA Med. Ctr., Pitts. Named Fed. Woman of Yr., 1989; recipient Hon. Alumnus award U. Pitts. Sch. Nursing, 1990. Mem. Pa. Nurses Assn. (fund raising chmn. dist. 6), Western Pa. Nursing Adminstrs. Assn., Sigma Theta Tau.

MARSH, FRANK (IRVING), former state official; b. Norfolk, Nebr., Apr. 27, 1924; s. Frank and Delia (Andrews) M.; m. Shirley Mac McVicker, Mar. 5, 1943; children: Sherry Anne Marsh Tupper, Corwin Frank, Stephen Alan (dec.), Mitchell Edward, Dory Michael, Melissa Lou. BS, U. Nebr., 1950; hon. degree in commerce and bus., Lincoln Sch. Commerce, 1975. Builder, businessman, part-time instr. Lincoln Sch. System, 1946-52; sec. of state State of Nebr., Lincoln, 1953-71, lt. gov., 1971-75, state treas., 1975-81, 87-91; state dir. Farmers Home Adminstrn., Lincoln, 1981-85; with Tabitha, Inc., Lincoln, 1986; ptnr. Lincoln Landscaping and Landscape Interiors Inc., 1983—; organizer, CEO Lincoln FoodNet, Inc. Ops., 1985—; U.S. State Dept. escort, interpreter, cons. Ctr. Continuing Edn., U. Nebr., 1986-87; mem. Foodchain Assn. (prepared perishable food rescue programs); bd. dirs. Ultras Pharmaceuticals. Bd. dirs. Lincoln Mayor's Com. Internat. Friendship, 1967—; affiliate mem., past pres. Nat. Coun. Internat. Visitors, Washington, 1967; bd. dirs. Nebraskaland Found., Inc., Lincoln, 1970—, Lincoln-Lancaster Food and Hunger Coalition, Good Neighbor Ctr.; hunger coord. Lincoln Dist. United Meth. Ch.; port insp., past fleet adm. Soc. Nebr. Adms. With AUS, 1943-46, ETO. Recipient Gov.'s Citation, State of Nebr., 1984, Outstanding Svc. award U.S. Info. Agy., 1990, Lincoln Parks and Recreation award, 1991, Mayor's Waste and Recycling award 1993, Lincoln Dist. Outstanding Laity award United Meth. Ch., 1993, Citation of Achievement, Nebr. Game and Parks Commn., 1993. Mem. VFW (life), Internat. Livestock Identification Assn. (life), Am. Legion, Disabled Am. Vets. (life), Nebr. Alumni Assn. (Outstanding Alumni award 1975, life), Nebr. Nut Growers Assn., Nebr. Hist. Soc. (life), Alpha Phi Omega (life), Sertoma (past pres. Gateway Club). Republican. Methodist. Home: 2701 S 34th St Lincoln NE 68506-3211 Office: 1911 R St Lincoln NE 68503

MARSH, HARRY DEAN, journalism educator; b. Marfa, Tex., Feb. 28, 1928; s. Samuel Ferguson and Susanna Flora (Martie) M.; m. Ellie Elizabeth Bruton, Sept. 3, 1967; children: William Lawrence, Marti Christian. BA, Baylor U., 1949; MS, Columbia U., 1957; PhD, U. Tex., 1974. Reporter, news editor Hillsboro (Tex.) Evening Mirror, 1949-51, Delta Democrat-Times, Greenville, Miss., 1954-60; Miss. correspondent Birmingham (Ala.) News, 1960-61; asst. to editorial page editor N.Y. Herald Tribune, N.Y.C., 1961-66; telegraph desk staff N.Y. News, N.Y.C., 1966-67; asst. to assoc. prof. journalism Baylor U., Waco, Tex., 1967-75; chmn. dept. journalism U. Ark., Fayetteville, 1975-80; head. dept. journalism and mass communication Kans. State U., Manhattan, 1980-86, prof. journalism, 1986—. Author: Creating Tomorrow's Mass Media, 1995; co-author: Excellence in Reporting, 1987. Pres. SW Journalism Congress, Waco, 1973-74. Served with U.S. Army, 1951-53. Recipient Advanced Internat. Reporting fellowship Columbia U., N.Y.C., 1966-67. Mem. Soc. Profl. Journalists, Assn. Edn. in Journalsim and Mass Communication, Kappa Tau Alpha. Democrat. Presbyterian. Avocation: photography. Home: 1739 Fairchild Ave Manhattan KS 66502-4037 Office: Kans State U Dept of Journalism 104 Kedzie Manhattan KS 66506

MARSH, HELEN UNGER, retired educational administrator; b. Grenada, Miss., May 4, 1925; d. John Waugh and Hortense (Baker) Unger; m. Loren C. Marsh, Sept. 4, 1950 (div. Dec. 1981); children: Keith S., Douglas L., Charlene M., Margaret Marsh Woods. AB, Bob Jones U., 1947; MA, Northwestern U., 1950; EdD, Ball State U., 1975. Cert. profl. adminstr., supr., secondary tchr., supt., Ind. Intermittent instr. speech and English Ball State U., Muncie, Ind., 1961-83, mem. adv. bd. for lab. expts., 1987-93; tchr. lang. arts Southside High Sch., Muncie, 1963-74, dept. chmn., 1974-76, dir. guidance, 1976-83; supr. lang. arts and guidance Muncie Community Schs., 1983-87, dir. rsch. and univ. rels., 1987-93; ret., 1993, 1994; judge nat. writing contest Nat. Coun. Tchrs. English, 1974-80; proposal writer Eli Lilly Found.; student placement coord., rschr. coord. Ball State U. and Muncie Community Schs.; community projects coord. Muncie Community Schs.; cons. Brainbow Learning Ctr. Writer, editor, coord. Muncie Community Schs. publs. Bd. dirs. univ. div. Ind. U., Bloomington, 1984-87; bd. dirs. East Ctrl. Ind. Area Libr. Svc., 1987—; chmn. edn. div. Shakespeare Festival, Ind. Com. for Humanities, Muncie, 1987; chair Mayor's Steering Com. for Muncie/Delaware County History, 1994—; cons. Brainbow, Inc., 1993-94; assoc. Minn. Cultural Ctr.. Mem. AAUW, Am. Econ. Rsch. Assn., Assn. for Lifelong Learning, Muncie Bus. and Profl. Women's Club (treas.

1980-82, pres. 1982-84), Delaware County Ret. Tchrs. Assn. (sec. 1993-94). Republican. Methodist. Avocations: investing, reading. Home: 606 N Alden Rd Muncie IN 47304-3827

MARSH, JAMES C., JR., secondary school principal. Headmaster Westminster Christian Acad., St. Louis. Recipient Blue Ribbon Sch. award U.S. Dept. of Edn., 1990-91. Office: Westminster Christian Acad 10900 Ladue Rd Saint Louis MO 63141-8496

MARSH, JEAN LYNDSEY TORREN, actress, writer; b. London, July 1, 1934; d. Henry Charles John and Emmeline Susannah Nightingale Poppy (Bexley) M.; m. Jon Devon Roland Pertwee, Apr. 2, 1955 (div. 1960). Student in dance, voice and mime; DHL (hon.), Marymount Coll. photographers' model; with repertory cos.; Broadway debut in Much Ado About Nothing, 1959; other theatrical appearances include Travesties, The Importance of Being Earnest, 1977, Too True to Be Good, 1977, My Fat Friend, Whose Life Is It Anyway?, 1979, Hamlet, Blithe Spirit, Habeas Corpus, Uncle Vanya, Pygmalion, The Chalk Garden; movie appearances include Cleopatra, 1963, Frenzy, 1972, Dark Places, The Eagle Has Landed, 1977, The Limbo Line, 1969, The Changeling, 1980, Return To Oz, Willow, 1988; artistic dir. Adelphi U. Theatre, 1981; co-creator, story coms., starred in I.T.V. series Upstairs, Downstairs, 1974-77, The House of Elliot, 1992, also starred The Grover Monster/Jean Marsh Cartoon Special, 1975, A State Dinner for Queen Elizabeth II, 1976, Mad About the Boy: Noel Coward— A Celebration, 1976; other TV appearances include (series) Nine to Five, (film) Jane Eyre, Master of the Game, Act of Will, A Connecticut Yankee at the Court of King Arthur, Dr. Who, Tomorrow People, Adam Bede, Carlton Lives, Fatherland (HBO). Named Most Outstanding New Actress of 1972; Recipient Emmy award, 1975. Office: Fifi Oscard Agy Inc 24 W 40th St New York NY 10018-3904

MARSH, JEANNE CAY, social welfare educator, researcher; b. Madison, Wis., July 9, 1948; d. Herbert Louis and Helen Irene (Moeckly) M.; m. Steven King Shevell, Oct. 3, 1976; children: Lee Catherine Marsh, Lauren Elisabeth Marsh. BA, Mich. State U., 1969; MSW, U. Mich., 1972, PhD, 1975. Postdoctoral fellow Inst. for Social Rsch., U. Mich., Ann Arbor, 1975-77; asst. prof. Sch. Social Adminstrn., U. Chgo., 1978-83, assoc. prof., 1983-88, prof., dean, 1988—; acad. vis. London (Eng.) Sch. Econ.; vis. fellow Clare Hall U. Cambridge, Eng., 1987-88. Author: (with N. Caplan and A. Geist) Rape and the Limits of Law Reform, 1982, (with S. Berlin) Informing Practice Decisions, 1993; editor (with others) spl. issues of Jour. Social Issues, 1982, Evaluation and Program Planning, 1991; chair editorial bd. Social Svc. Rev.; mem. editorial bd. Social Work Rsch. and Abstracts, 1982-92, Internat. Applied Social Svc. Index, 1988—. Trustee Chgo. Theol. Sem., 1988—. Recipient Disting. Alumna award Sch. Social Work, U. Mich., 1987; Leadership Greater Chgo. fellow, 1985-86. Mem. NASW, Am. Psychol. Assn., Am. Evaluation Assn., Leadership Fellows Assn., Phi Beta Kappa. Office: U Chgo Sch Social Svc Adminstrn 969 E 60th St Chicago IL 60637-2640

MARSH, JOHN, research chemist. BS in Chemistry, U. Coll., London; PhD in Chemistry, Manchester U.; postgrad., U. N.H. Lubricant chemist Exxon Chem. Co., Houston, 1961—. Patentee in fuel and lubricants technology. Recipient Thomas Midgley award Am. Chem. Soc., 1994. Office: Exxon Chemical Company 13501 Katy Freeway Houston TX 77079*

MARSH, JOHN S., JR., newspaper editor; b. Niagara Falls, N.Y., Apr. 23, 1949; s. John S. and Muriel (MacLaren) M.; m. Elizabeth Poreda, July 10, 1971; children: Beth, Colleen. BA in Gov., Baldwin-Wallace Coll., 1971. Reporter, then various editing positions Times-Union, Rochester, N.Y., 1971-82; mng. editor Daily Press, Utica, N.Y., 1982-84; exec. editor Observer-Dispatch, Utica, 1984-91; pub., pres. Daily Jour., Vineland, N.J., 1991-92; exec. editor Argus Leader, Sioux Falls, S.D., 1992—. Bd. dirs. Forward Sioux Falls. Mem. Am. Soc. Newspaper Editors, AP Mng. Editors, S.D. Assc. Press Mng. Editors Assn. (pres. 1994095), Rotary. Office: Argus Leader PO Box 5034 Sioux Falls SD 57117-5034

MARSH, JOSEPH FRANKLIN, JR., emeritus college president, educational consultant; b. Charleston, W.Va., Feb. 24, 1925; s. Joseph Franklin and Florence (Keller) M. Student, Concord Coll., 1941-42; W.Va. U., 1942-43; A.B., Dartmouth Coll., 1947; student, Nat. Inst. Pub. Affairs, Washington, 1947-48; M.P.A., Harvard U., 1949; LL.D., Davis and Elkins Coll., 1968; L.H.D., Alderson-Broaddus Coll., 1982. Cons. Hoover Commn., Washington, 1948; instr. in gt. issues Dartmouth, 1952-54, instr. econs., 1953-55, asst. prof., 1955-59; pres. Concord Coll., Athens, W.Va., 1959-73, pres. emeritus, 1985—; ednl. cons., 1973-74; pres. Waynesburg (Pa.) Coll., 1974-83, pres. emeritus, 1983—; v.p. The Armand Hammer United World Coll. of the Am. West, Montezuma, N. Mex., 1984-85; pres. Marsh Edn Cons., Athens, W.Va., 1985—; Dir. One Valley Bank of Mercer County. Author articles. Mem. State Dept. Ednl. Mission to U.A.R., 1964, Mercer County (W. Va.) Planning Commn., 1964-74, 83—; vice chmn. W.Va. Com. for Constnl. Amendments, 1966; mem. regional council Internat. Edn. Study Mission to Europe, 1970; bd. dirs. Am. Assn. State Colls. and Univs., 1972-73, Regional Council for Internat. Edn., 1973, Hospice Care Mercer County, W.Va., 1987-91, Faculty Merit Found. W.Va., 1990—; bd. dirs. Pa. Assn. Colls. and Univs., 1974-83, exec. com., 1980-82; bd. dirs. Pa. Commn. for Ind. Colls. and Univs., 1974-83, sec.-treas. 1976-77, vice chmn., 1977-80, chmn., 1980-82; trustee Found. Ind. Colls. Pa., 1974-83, mem. exec. com., 1979-82; bd. visitors Midway Coll., Ky., 1979-93; adv. com. Pa. State Council Higher Edn., 1980-82; trustee Concord Coll. Found., 1986, bd. dirs., 1987—; active Town of Athens Planning Commn., 1986-94, pres. commn. 1987-94; vice chmn. bd. trustees, Princeton (W.Va.) Community Hosp. Found., 1989—; Gov's appointee to bd. dirs. State Coll. System W.Va. 1989—, chmn. adminstrv. com., 1990-91, vice chmn. of bd., 1991—. Served as gunnery officer USNR, 1943-46. Named Outstanding Young Man, W.Va. Jr. C. of C., 1960; recipient Alumnus of Yr. award Concord Coll., 1973, Golden Alumnus award, 1992; Outstanding Citizen award Athens Woman's Club, 1992; Rotary fellow Oxford (Eng.) U., 1950-52. Mem. AAUP, Am. Assn. Univ. Adminstrs., Am. Econ. Assn., Royal Inst. Pub. Adminstrn., Oxford Union Debating Soc. (life), Oxford Soc. (life), Pa. Soc., Duquesne Club (Pitts.), Univ. Club (Bluefield), Masons, Rotary (dist. gov. 1992-93), Phi Beta Kappa, Phi Tau, Phi Delta Pi, Phi Sigma Kappa, Alpha Kappa Psi (hon.). Methodist. Home: 106 First Ave Athens WV 24712 Office: PO Box 734 Athens WV 24712-0734

MARSH, MALCOLM F., federal judge; b. 1928. BS, U. Oreg., 1952, LLB, 1954, JD, 1971. Ptnr. Clark & Marsh, Lindauer & McClinton (and predecessors), Salem, Oreg., 1958-87; judge U.S. Dist. Ct. Oreg., Portland, 1987—. With U.S. Army, 1946-47. Fellow Am. Coll. Trial Lawyers; mem. ABA. Office: US Dist Ct 114 US Courthouse 620 SW Main St Portland OR 97205-3023

MARSH, MICHAEL, track and field athlete. Olympic runner Barcelona, Spain, 1992. Recipient 200m Track and Field Gold medal Olympics, Barcelona, 1992. Office: US Olympic Com 1750 E Boulder St Colorado Springs CO 80909-5746*

MARSH, MILES L., holding company executive. Pres. Kraft Gen. Foods div. Gen. Foods USA, Glenview, Ill., until 1989; pres., chief oper. officer Whitman Corp., Chgo., 1989-91; chmn, chief exec. officer Pet Inc., St. Louis, MO, 1991—. Office: Pet Inc 400 S 4th St Saint Louis MO 63102

MARSH, QUINTON NEELY, banker; b. Omaha, July 1, 1915; s. Arthur J. and Rose L. (Baysel) M.; m. Thelma May Beck, Nov. 24, 1944. B.C.S., Benjamin Franklin U., Washington, 1949, M.C.S., 1950; student, Am. U., 1950-51; diploma, Sch. Bank Adminstrn., U. Wis., 1959. Chartered bank auditor; cert. internal auditor; cert. protection profl. V.p., gen. auditor Am. Security & Trust Co., Washington, 1972, sr. officer auditing and security, 1972-77; sr. v.p., cashier Bank of Columbia N.A., Washington, 1977-79; sr. v.p. United Nat. Bank of Washington, 1979-80. Mem. Bank Adminstrn. Inst. (prs. D.C. 1966-67, auditing commn. 1968-70), Inst. Internal Auditors (pres. D.C. 1962-63), Am. Soc. Indsl. Security. Lodges: Masons, Shriners. Home: # 312 4801 Connecticut Ave NW Washington DC 20008-2207

MARSH, RICHARD J., strategic management consultant; b. Bklyn., Dec. 7, 1933; s. Thomas and Claire (Mangi) M.; m. Catherine Monahan, Sept. 24, 1960; children: Amy E., Jamie P. B.S. in Bus., U. Conn., 1955; M.S. in Human Resources, U. Bridgeport, 1974. Regional mgr. Student Mktg. Inst., N.Y.C., 1955-58; project mgr. bus. devel. Harvey Research Co., Rochester, N.Y., 1958-60; account exec. Rumrill-Hoyt Mktg./Advt., Inc., N.Y.C. and Rochester, N.Y., 1960-67; dir. mktg. services Burlington Hosiery Co., 1967-71; v.p. Innotech Corp., Trumbull, Conn., 1972-78; mng. dir. Nordic ops. Innotech, 1978-81; cons. Strategic Bus. Devel. Services Internat., Mount Kisco, N.Y., and Hillsboro, N.H., 1981—; course leader Am. Mgmt. Assn., 1976—; lectr. Tech-Transfer Conf., Hanover, Germany, 1994. Contbr. articles to profl. jours. Pres. PTA, Bedford, N.Y., 1976-77; bd. dirs. Property Owners Assn. Hillsboro, N.H., 1977-78. Mem. Am. Mktg. Assn., Licensing Execs. Soc., Comml. Devel. Assn., Internat. Assn. Product Innovation (v.p.). Republican. Clubs: American (Stockholm), Chemists (N.Y.C.), Royal Commonwealth (U.K.), Tech. Innovation and Info. (Luxembourg). Avocations: skiing; canoeing; touring. Office: Strategic Bus Devel Svcs Internat 367 Bog Rd PO Box 567 Hillsboro NH 03244-0657

MARSH, ROBERT CHARLES, writer, music critic; b. Columbus, Ohio, Aug. 5, 1924; s. Charles L. and Jane A. (Beckett) M.; m. Kathleen C. Moscrop, July 4, 1956 (div. 1985); m. Ann Noren, Feb. 25, 1987; 1 child, James MacArtain. BS, Northwestern U., 1945, AM, 1946; postgrad., U. Chgo., 1948; EdD, Harvard U., 1951; postgrad., Oxford U., 1952-53, Cambridge U., 1953-56. Instr. social sci. U. Ill., 1947-49; lectr. humanities Chgo. City Jr. Coll., 1950-51; asst. prof. edn. U. Kansas City, 1951-52; vis. prof. edn. SUNY, 1953-54; humanities staff U. Chgo., 1956-58, lectr. in social thought, 1976; music critic Chgo. Sun-Times, 1956-91; dir. Chgo. Opera Project, Newberry Libr., 1983—. Author: Toscanini and the Art of Orchestral Performance, 1956, rev. edit., 1962, The Cleveland Orchestra, 1967, Ravinia, 1987, James Levine at Ravinia, 1993; editor: Logic and Knowledge, 1956. Co-recipient Peabody award for ednl. broadcasting, 1976; Ford Found. fellow, 1965-66. Mem. Harvard U. Faculty Club. Roman Catholic. Home and Office: 1001 7th St New Glarus WI 53574-0790

MARSH, ROBERT MORTIMER, sociologist, educator; b. Everett, Mass., Jan. 22, 1931; s. Henry Warren and Ruth (Dunbar) M.; children: Eleanor L., Christopher S.H., Diana E. Student, Boston U., 1948-50; A.B., U. Chgo., 1952; M.A., Columbia, 1953, Ph.D. 1959. Fellow Ford Found., Japan, Taiwan, Hong Kong, 1956-58; instr. sociology U. Mich., 1958-61; asst. prof. sociology Cornell U., 1961-65; assoc. prof. Duke, 1965-67; mem. faculty Brown U., 1967—; prof. sociology, 1968—, chmn. dept., 1971-75; manpower personnel and tng. rsch. prof. U.S. Naval Acad., Annapolis, 1987-88; vis. prof. Nat. Tsing Hua U., Taiwan, 1991. Author: The Mandarins: The Circulation of Elites in China, 1961, Comparative Sociology: A Codification of Cross-Societal Analysis, 1967; (with H. Mannari) Modernization and the Japanese Factory, 1976, Organizational Change in Japanese Factories, 1988; also articles. Assoc. editor: Adminstrv. Sci. Quar, 1963-67; assoc. editor: Jour. Comparative Family Studies, 1970-74; co-editor: (with J. Michael Armer) Comparative Sociological Research in the 1960s and 1970s. East Asian Inst. summer fellow Chinese Columbia, 1955; Ford Found. and Guggenheim Found. fellow Japan, 1969-70; Japan Soc. Promotion Sci. fellow, 1976, 83; Chiang Ching Kuo Found. and Nat. Sci. Coun. fellow (Taiwan, Republic of China). 1991-93. Mem. Am. Sociol. Assn., Ea. Sociol. Assn., Assn. Asian Studies, Internat. Studies Assn. (exec. com. comparative interdisciplinary studies sect. 1971-76), Japan Human Rels. Assn. (councilor 1970—). Office: Dept Sociology Brown Univ Providence RI 02912

MARSH, ROBERT THOMAS, corporate executive, retired air force general; b. Logansport, Ind., Jan. 3, 1925; m. Joan Spears, June 7, 1949; children: Kathy, Teri, Debi. Student, Wabash Coll., 1943; B.S., U.S. Mil. Acad., 1949; M.S. in Engring. U. Mich., 1956; postgrad., Air Command and Staff Coll., 1960, Air War Coll., 1965. Commd. 2d lt. USAF, 1949, promoted to gen., 1970; space systems project officer, Hdqrs. Space Systems div. Los Angeles Air Force Sta., USAF, Calif., 1960-64; staff officer Directorate of Reconnaissance & Electronic Warfare, USAF; chief Projects Div., Directorate of Space, Office of Dep. Chief of Staff for Research and Devel., Hdqrs. USAF, Washington, 1965-67; exec. officer to dep. chief of staff Research & Devel., Hdqrs. USAF, Washington, 1967-69; dep. for reconnaissance, strike and electronics warfare Aero. Systems Div., Wright-Patterson AFB, Ohio, 1969-73; dep. chief of staff, devel. plans Hdqrs. Air Force Systems Command, Andrews AFB, Md., 1973, dep. chief of staff, Systems, 1973-75, vice comdr., 1975-77; comdr. Electronic Systems Div., Hanscom AFB, Mass., 1977-81, Air Force Systems Command, Andrews AFB, 1981-84; ret., 1984; bd. dirs. Thiokol Corp., Teknowledge Corp., CAE-Link Corp., ITHACO Inc., Comverse Govt. Systems Corp.; trustee Mitre Inc. Served with U.S. Army, 1943-45. Decorated Legion of Merit, Disting. Service medal with 2 oak leaf clusters. Office: Thiokol Corp 6327 Manchester Way Alexandria VA 22304 *I realized early in my military career some 40 plus years ago that all jobs—no matter how small—should be handled with equal determination, persistence, and dedication. Just as important to doing a job well is the need for leadership. That means professionally—able to stand alone with decision-making responsibility; and organizationally—being sensitive to the needs of one's people and motivating them toward getting the job done.*

MARSH, ROBERTA REYNOLDS, educator, consultant; b. Kokomo, Ind., June 2, 1939; d. Elwood Bert and Mildred Bell (Wolford) Reynolds; m. Ronald Dean Marsh Sr., Apr. 5, 1958; children: Ronald Jr., Bryan William, Joel Allen. BEd, Ind. U., Kokomo, 1970; MEd, Ind. U., Bloomington, 1971. Cert. tchr., spl. edn. tchr., Ind.; cert. tchr., spl. edn. tchr., Ariz. Tchr. spl. edn. Kokomo Ctr. Schs., 1970-77; tchr. spl. edn. Tempe (Ariz.) Elem. Dist. #3, 1978-86, tchr. civics, geography, English/lit., 1986—. Local dir. Spl. Olympics, Kokomo, 1974-77, Tempe Assn. Retarded Citizens, 1978-88; den mother Boy Scouts Am., Kokomo, 1967-73; leader 4-H Club, Kokomo, 1974-77. Recipient Excellence in Edn. award Tempe Diablo, 1991, Mem. Coun. for Exceptional Children (state pres. 1986-87, Tempe chpt. pres. 1994-95, Outstanding Leader 1985), Internat. Reading Assn., Assn. for Children with Learning Disabilities, Ind. U. Alumni Assn., Alpha Delta Kappa (corr. sec. 1986-88, Theta pres. 1990-92). Democrat. Avocations: bridge, traveling, reading, collecting apples and bells. Home: 4113 E Emelita Circle Mesa AZ 85206 Office: Hudson Sch 1325 E Malibu Dr Tempe AZ 85282

MARSH, STEPHEN F., production designer; b. Bouremouth, Dorset, Eng., Mar. 17, 1948; came to U.S., 1975; s. Daniel John and Jean Elizabeth (Lang) M.; m. Ellen Suzanne Surrey; 1 child, Evan Andrew. Prodn. designer Lyons/Sheldon Agy., L.A. Recipient Emmy nomination for art direction of Citizen Cohn, NATAS, 1993, cable ace nomination for Citizen Cohn, Acad. Cable Programming, 1993. Mem. Acad. Motion Picture Arts and Scis. Office: The Lyons/Sheldon Agency 8344 Melrose Ste 20 Los Angeles CA 90069

MARSH, TERENCE, production designer. Prodn. designer: (films) (with John Box) Doctor Zhivago, 1965 (Academy award best art direction 1965), (with Box) A Man for All Seasons, =1966, (with Wallis Smith) The Wild Affair, 1966, (with Box) Oliver!, 1968 (Academy award best art direction 1968), (with Robert Laing) Perfect Friday, 1970, The Looking Glass War, 1970, (with Robert Cartwright) Scrooge, 1970, (with Cartwright) Mary, Queen of Scots, 1971 (Academy award nomination best art direction 1971), (with Cartwright) The Public Eye, 1972, Follow Me!, 1972, (with Alan Tomkins) The Mackintosh Man, 1973, (with Tomkins) A Touch of Class, 1973, (with Tomkins) Juggernaut, 1974, The Abdication, 1974, The Adventures of Sherlock Holmes' Smarter Brother, 1975, (with Tomkins) Royal Flash, 1975, A Bridge Too Far, 1977, (with Richard Lawrence) Magic, 1978, (with Marvin March) The Frisco Kid, 1979, (with others) Sunday Lovers, 1980, Absence of Malice, 1981, (with Peter Lamont and Gil Parrondo) Sphinx, 1981, (with J. Dennis Washington) To Be or Not to Be, 1983, (with Tomkins) Haunted Honeymoon, 1986, (with Fernando Ramirez, El Polo, George Richardson, and Craig Edgar) Miracles, 1987, (with Harold Michelson) Spaceballs, 1987, (with Dianne Wager) Bert Rigby, You're a Fool, 1989, (with Richardson) Havana, 1990, (with Wager, Donald Woodruff, and William Cruse) The Hunt for Red October, 1990, Basic Instinct, 1992, The Shawshank Redemption, 1994, Forget Paris, 1995, (TV movies) Great Expectations, 1974; prodn. designer, prodr.: (films) (with Steve Sardanis) The World's Greatest Lover, 1977; prodn. designer, co-prodr. (with Washington), co-screenwriter (with Ronny Graham and Charles Dennis): (films) Finders

Keepers, 1984. Office: Sandra Marsh Mgt 9150 Wilshire Blvd Ste 220 Beverly Hills CA 90210*

MARSH, WILLIAM LAURENCE, retired research pathology executive; b. Cardiff, Wales, Great Britain, Apr. 21, 1926; came to U.S., 1969; s. William and Violet (Hill) M.; m. Jean Beryl Margaret Hill, June 6, 1952; children: Christine Margaret, Nicholas John. Fellow, Inst. Med. Lab. Sci., London, 1954, Inst. Biology, London, 1969; PhD, Columbia Pacific U., 1968; fellow, Royal Coll. Pathologists, London, 1985. Lab. chief Regional Blood Transfusion Ctr., Brentwood, Eng., 1955-69; assoc. investigator N.Y. Blood Ctr., N.Y.C., 1969-79, investigator, 1980-83, sr. investigator, 1984-87; sr. v.p. rsch. Lindsley Kimball Rsch. Inst. of N.Y. Blood Ctr., N.Y.C., 1987-94; ret.; editorial bd. Transfusion jour., 1979-91, Blood Transfusion and Immunohematology jour., 1980-86; sci. reviewer various jours. Author chpts. on human blood groups in textbooks, 1965-91; contbr. over 250 articles to profl. jours. Recipient Blood Donors award of merit Blood Donor Assn., Eng., 1961. Fellow Inst. Med. Lab. Sci. (Race prize 1976), Inst. Biology, Royal Coll. Pathologists; mem. Internat. Soc. Blood Tranfusion, Am. Assn. Blood Banks (Dunsford Meml. award 1975, Emily Cooley award 1988, Grove-Rasmussen award 1990, Karl Landsteiner award 1995), Am. Soc. Clin. Pathologists (Philip Levine Outstanding Rsch. award 1993), Brit. Soc. Hematology, Brit. Soc. Blood Transfusion. Avocations: sailing, flying, photography. Home: 101 Hillcrest Dr Moneta VA 24121-3003 Office: NY Blood Ctr S310 E 67th St New York NY 10021-6204

MARSHAK, ALAN HOWARD, electrical engineer, educator; b. Miami Beach, Fla., Mar. 21, 1938; s. Jerome and Yetta (Feiner) M.; children: Jerry Brian. B.Sc.E.E., U. Miami, 1960; M.S., La. State U., 1962; Ph.D., U. Ariz., 1969. Asst. prof. elec. engring. La. State U., Baton Rouge, 1969-73; assoc. prof. La. State U., 1973-78, prof., 1978—, chmn. dept. elec. and computer engring., 1983—; vis. prof. Electron Device Rsch. Ctr. U. Fla., Gainesville, 1979-80; tech. reviewer NSF, 1976—, panelist, 1993—, NRC, 1993; mem. Southeastern Ctr. Elec. Engring. Edn., 1984—, chmn. and CEO, 1992—; speaker profl. confs. Tech. referee various jours. including Solid-State Electronics, Jour. Applied Physics; assoc. editor IEEE Trans. Electron Devices, 1991—; author: (with D. J. Hamilton and F. A. Lindholm) Principles and Applications of Semiconductor Device Modeling, 1971, Basic Experiments in Electronics: A Laboratory Manual, 1978, also tech. papers. NSF grad. trainee, 1967-69; grantee, 1970, 73, 75, 78; named F.H. Coughlin/CLECO prof. of elec. engring., 1993. Fellow IEEE; mem. Electron Devices Soc., Sigma Xi, Eta Kappa Nu. Home: 320 Misty Creek Dr Baton Rouge LA 70808-8174 Office: La State U Elec And Computer Dept Baton Rouge LA 70803

MARSHAK, MARVIN LLOYD, physicist, educator; b. Buffalo, Mar. 11, 1946; s. Kalman and Goldie (Hait) M.; m. Anita Sue Kolman, Sept. 24, 1972; children: Rachel Kolman, Adam Kolman. AB in Physics, Cornell U., 1967; MS in Physics, U. Mich., PhD in Physics, 1970. Rsch. assoc. U. Minn., Mpls., 1970-74, asst. prof., 1974-78, assoc. prof., 1978-83, prof. physics, 1983—, dir. grad. studies in physics, 1983-86, prin. investigator high energy physics, 1982-86, head sch. of physics and astronomy, 1986—. Contbr. articles to profl. jours. Trustee Children's Theater Co., 1989-94. Mem. Am. Phys. Soc. Home: 2855 Ottawa Ave S Minneapolis MN 55416-1946 Office: U Minn Dept Physics 116 Church St SE Minneapolis MN 55455-0149

MARSHAK, ROBERT REUBEN, former university dean, medical educator, veterinarian; b. N.Y.C., Feb. 23, 1923; s. David and Edith (Youselovsky) M.; m. Ruth Emilie Lyons, Dec. 4, 1948; children: William Lyons, John Ball, Richard Best.; m. Margo Post Marshall, June 25, 1983. Student, U. Wis., 1940-41; D.V.M., Cornell U., 1945; D.V.M. (hon.), U. Bern, 1968; M.A. (hon.), U. Pa., 1971. Diplomate: Am. Coll. Vet. Internal Medicine (charter). Practice vet. medicine Springfield, Vt., 1945-56; prof., chmn. dept. medicine Sch. Vet. Medicine, U. Pa., Phila., 1956-58; prof. medicine Grad. Sch. Medicine, 1957-64; chmn. dept. clin. studies Sch. Vet. Medicine, 1958-73; dir. Bovine Leukemia Research Center, 1965-73; dean Sch. Vet. Medicine, 1973-87; co-dir. Center on Interactions Animals and Soc., 1975-79, also mem. grad. group com. in comparative med. scis.; prof. medicine, chief sect. epidemiology and pub. health Sch. Vet. Medicine U. Pa., 1990-93, prof. medicine emeritus, 1993—; mem. adv. bd. Pa. Dept. Agr., 1973-87; chmn. Gov.'s Study Group on Horse Racing Industry in Pa., 1979; mem. del. to evaluate vet. med. and rsch. Chinese Ministry Agr.; mem. adv. com. Stroud Water Rsch. Ctr., 1992—; mem. adv. coun. Coll. Vet. Medicine, Cornell U., 1993—. Sr. co-editor Advances in Veterinary Science and Comparative Medicine; contbr. numerous articles to sci. jours. Bd. dirs. Humane Soc. U.S., 1978-82, Bide-a-wee Home Assn., 1980-85; sci. adv. bd. mem. Sch. Vet. Medicine The Hebrew U., Jerusalem, 1984—; chmn. external com. Sch. Vet. Medicine Tuskegee U.; trustee Upland Country Day Sch., 1988-91; mem. animal adv. com. City of Phila., 1989-93. Served with AUS, 1943-44. Recipient Disting. Veterinarian award Pa. Vet. Med. Assn., 1984, Barnraiser award Pa. Farmers Assn., 1987. Fellow Phila. Coll. Physicians; mem. AAAS, John Morgan Soc. (pres. 1967-68), Am. Assn. Cancer Rsch., Am. Vet. Med. Assn., Pa. Vet. Med. Assn, NAS Inst. Medicine (sr.), Pa. Livestock Assn. (dir.), Westminster Kennel Club, James A. Baker Inst. for Animal Health (mem. adv. coun. 1977—), Phila. Soc. for Promoting Agr., Pa. Friends of Agr. Found., Phila. Zool. Soc. (bd. dirs. 1986-87), Sigma Xi, Phi Zeta.

MARSHALEK, EUGENE RICHARD, physics educator; b. N.Y.C., Jan. 17, 1936; s. Frank M. and Sophie (Weg) M.; m. Sonja E. M. Lennhart, Dec. 8, 1962; children: Thomas, Frank. BS, Queens Coll., 1957; PhD, U. Calif., Berkeley, 1962. NSF postdoctoral fellow Niels Bohr Inst., Copenhagen, Denmark, 1962-63; rsch. assoc. Brookhaven Nat. Lab., Upton, N.Y., 1963-65; asst. prof. U. Notre Dame, Ind., 1965-69, assoc. prof., 1969-78, prof., 1978—. Contbr. articles to profl. jours. Recipient Alexander van Humboldt sr. scientist award, 1985. Mem. AAAS, Am. Phys. Soc., Sigma Xi. Office: U Notre Dame Dept Physics Notre Dame IN 46556

MARSHALL, ALAN GEORGE, chemistry and biochemistry educator; b. Bluffton, Ohio, May 26, 1944; s. Herbert Boyer Marshall Jr. and Cecile (Mogil) Rosser; m. Marilyn Gard, June 13, 1965; children: Gwendolyn Scott, Brian George. BA in Chemistry with honors, Northwestern U., 1965; PhD in Phys. Chemistry, Stanford U., 1970. Instr. II U. B.C., Vancouver, Can., 1969-71, asst. prof., 1971-76, assoc. prof., 1976-80; prof. chemistry and biochemistry Ohio State U., Columbus, 1980-93; prof. chemistry Fla. State U., Tallahassee, 1993—; cons. Extrel FTMS, Madison, Wis., 1989-92, Oak Ridge (Tenn.) Nat. Lab., 1990—; dir. Ion Cyclotron Resonance Program Nat. High Magnetic Field Lab., 1993—. Author: Biophysical Chemistry, 1978, Fourier Transforms in Spectroscopy, 1990; editor: ICR/ION Trap newsletter, 1986—; N.Am. editor Rapid Comm. in Mass Spectrometry, 1988—; mem. editl. bd. Analytical Chemistry, 1990-92, Internat. Jour. Mass Ion Proc., 1987—, Jour. Am. Soc. Mass Spectrometry, 1989—, Mass Spectrometry Rev., 1994—; contbr. more than 200 articles to profl. jours. Recipient Disting. Scholar award Ohio State U. Fellow AAAS, Am. Phys. Soc.; mem. Am. Chem. Soc. (award in chem. instrumentation, Akron sect. award, award in analytical chemistry Ea. Analytical Symposium 1991, Field-Franklin award 1995), Soc. Applied Spectroscopy (chmn. local sect. 1990-91), Am. Soc. Mass Spectroscopy (bd. dirs. 1991-92). Office: Fla State Univ Nat High Magnetic Field Lab 1800 East Paul Dirac Dr Tallahassee FL 32310

MARSHALL, ALTON GARWOOD, real estate counselor; b. Flint, Mich., Sept. 19, 1921; s. William Robert and Lela Christine (Brabon) M.; m. Mary Lee Golden, June 22, 1945 (div. July 1971); children: William A., Stephen B., Bruce S., Mary Ann Marshall Trebian, John L.; m. Sarah Elizabeth DeLand, Sept. 4, 1971; 1 child, Sarah Graham. BA, Hillsdale Coll. 1942; MS, Syracuse U., 1948, LLD (hon.), 1974; D Pub. Service & Bus. Adminstrn. (hon.), Hillsdale Coll., 1980. Sec. utility regulations pub. svc. commn. N.Y. State, Albany, 1953-61, dep. dir. div. budget, 1961-65, exec. officer, then sec. to gov., Office of Gov., 1965-70; pres., bd. dirs. Rockefeller Ctr., N.Y.C., 1971-81; pres. A.G. Marshall Assocs., N.Y.C., 1981—; chmn., pres., chief exec. officer Lincoln Savs. Bank, N.Y.C., 1984-88, chmn., chief exec. officer, 1988-91, also bd. dirs.; mem. exec. com. Nat. Realty Com., Washington, 1970—; bd. dirs. N.Y. State Electric & Gas Corp., 1971—; ind. gen. ptnr. Equitable Capital Ptnrs. and Equitable Capital Ptnrs. Retirement Fund, 1989—; bd. dirs. Equitable Life Assurance Soc., N.Y. Prism and Equitable Trusts, 1977-91; trustee Hudson River Trust, 1991—. Mem. exec. com., steering com. Assn. for a Better N.Y., 1971—; mem. exec., landmarks and

MARSHALL, continued — polit. action coms. Real Estate Bd. N.Y., sec. bd. dirs., 1973—; chmn. Nat. Assn. on Drug Abuse Problems, 1990-92. Sr. fellow The Nelson A. Rockefeller Inst. Govt., 1991-94. Mem. Am. Soc. Real Estate Counselors. Office: Alton G Marshall Assocs Inc 136 E 79th St New York NY 10021

MARSHALL, ANDREW WALTER, federal official; b. Detroit, Sept. 13, 1921; s. John Pollach and Katherine (Last) M.; m. Mary Katherine Speer, July 18, 1919. MA, U. Chgo., 1949; DSc (hon.), Ohio State U., 1989. Economist Rand Corp., Santa Monica, Calif., 1949-53, sr. economist, 1954-72; vis. prof. U. Chgo., 1953-54; dir. net assessment Nat. Security Council, Washington, 1972-73, Office Sec. of Def., Washington, 1973—. Co-author: (with Herbert Goldhamer) Psychosis and Civilization, 1950. Recipient Medal for Disting. Pub. Svc., Sec. Def., 1975, 76, 80, 88. Mem. Internat. Inst. Strategic Studies, Coun. of Fgn. Rels., Inst. Math. Stats., Am. Statis. Assn. Republican. Home: 2450 Virginia Ave NW Apt 614 Washington DC 20037-2654 Office: Office of Sec Def Pentagon Washington DC 20301

MARSHALL, ARTHUR K., lawyer, judge, arbitrator, educator, writer; b. N.Y.C., Oct. 7, 1911. BS, CUNY, 1933; LLB, St. John's U., N.Y.C., 1936; LL.M., U. So. Calif., 1952. Bar: N.Y. State 1937, Calif. 1947. Practice law N.Y.C., 1937-43, Los Angeles, 1947-50; atty. VA, Los Angeles, 1947-50; tax counsel Calif. Bd. Equalization, Sacramento, 1950-51; inheritance tax atty. State Controller, Los Angeles, 1951-53; commr. Superior Ct. Los Angeles County, 1953-62; judge Municipal Ct., Los Angeles jud. dist., 1962-63, Superior Ct., Los Angeles, 1963-81; supervising judge probate dept. Superior Ct., 1968-69, appellate dept., 1973-77; presiding judge Appellate Dept., 1976-77; pvt. practice, arbitrator, referee, judge pro tem, 1981—; acting asst. prof. law UCLA, 1954-59; grad. faculty U. So. Calif., 1955-75; lectr. Continuing Edn. of the Bar; mem. Calif. Law Revision Commn., 1984—, chmn., 1986-87, 92-93; chmn. com. on efficiency and econs. Conf. Calif. Judges, past chmn. spl. action com. on ct. improvement; past chmn. probate law cons. group Calif. Bd. Legal Specialization. Author: Joint Tenancy Taxwise and Otherwise, 1953, Branch Courts, 1959, California State and Local Taxation Text, 2 vols., 1962, rev. edit., 1969, supplement, 1979, 2d edito., 1981, Triple Choice Method, 1964, California State and Local Taxation Forms, 2 vols., 1961-75, rev. edit., 1979, California Probate Procedure, 1961, 5th rev. edit., 1994, Guide to Procedure Before Trial, 1975; contbr. articles to profl. jours. Mem. Town Hall; mem. Com. on Fgn. Affairs. With AUS, 1943-46; lt. col. JAGC Res. (ret.). Named Judge of Yr. Lawyers Club L.A. County, 1975; first recipient Arthur K. Marshall award established by estate planning, trust and probate sect. L.A. Bar Assn., 1981, Disting. Jud. Career award L.A. Lawyers Club, award L.A. County Bd. Suprs., 1981. Fellow Am. Bar Found.; mem. Am. Arbitration Assn. (mem. nat. panel), Internat. Acad. Estate and Trust Law (academician, founder, 1st pres., now chancellor), ABA (probate litigation com. real property, probate and trust sect.), Calif. State Bar (advisor to exec. com. real property, probate and trust sect. 1970-83), Santa Monica Bar Assn. (pres. 1960), Westwood Bar Assn. (pres. 1959), L.A. Bar Assn., Am. Legion (comdr. 1971-72), U. So. Calif. Law Alumni Assn. (pres. 1969-70), Phi Alpha Delta (1st justice alumni chpt.). Office: 300 S Grand Ave 28th fl Los Angeles CA 90071

MARSHALL, BRYAN EDWARD, anesthesiologist, educator; b. London, Oct. 24, 1935; came to U.S., 1965, naturalized, 1979; m. Carol Davies, Sept. 1957; children—Leisa, David. M.D., Leeds U., 1959. Diplomate: Am. Bd. Anesthesiology. Rotating intern Hereford (Eng.) Gen. Hosps., 1959-60; sr. house officer anesthesia United Cambridge Hosps., 1960-61; registrar anesthesia United Cambridge Hosps., 1961-63; research scholar Cambridge U., 1963-65; research fellow U. Pa. Med. Sch., 1965-66, mem. faculty, 1966—, prof. anesthesia, 1972—; prof. comparative anesthesia U. Pa. Vet. Sch., 1973—, Horatio C. Wood prof. research in anesthesia, dir. anesthesia research, 1982; vis. prof., U.K., Can., Europe, Asia, Australia; lectr. throughout, U.S.; mem. merit rev. bd. VA; study sect. NIH. Author textbooks and numerous articles in field.; editor: Anesthesiology, 1975—; Circulatory Shock; mem. editorial bds. profl. jours. Recipient Career Devel. award NIH, 1971-76. Fellow Am. Coll. Anesthesiologists, Royal Coll. Physicians; mem. Assn. Univ. Anesthetists, Am. Soc. Anesthesiologists, Am. Physiol. Soc., Am. Soc. Exptl. Biology and Medicine, Assn. Anesthesiologists Gt. Britain and Ireland (Research prize 1964), Anesthesia Research Group Gt. Britain, AAUP, AAAS, Shock Soc., Phila. Med. Soc., Pa. Soc. Anesthesiologists, Phila. Physiol. Soc., Pa. Thoracic Soc., Laennec Soc. Phila., Circanes Soc., John Morgan Soc., Sigma Xi. Home: 119 Adrienne Ln Wynnewood PA 19096-1205 Office: Hosp U Pa 773 Dudley St Bldg Philadelphia PA 19148-2423

MARSHALL, BURKE, law educator; b. Plainfield, N.J., Oct. 1, 1922. A.B., Yale U., 1944, LL.B., 1951, M.A., 1970. Bar: D.C. bar 1952. Assoc., then partner firm Covington and Burlington, Washington, 1951-61; asst. atty. gen. U.S., 1961-65; gen. counsel IBM Corp., Armonk, N.Y., 1965-69; sr. v.p. IBM Corp., 1969-70; prof. law Yale U. Law Sch., 1970—, Nicholas deB. Katzenbach prof.; chmn. Nat. Adv. Commn. SSS, 1967; bd. dirs. State Farm Mut. Author: Federalism and Civil Rights, 1965; co-author: The Mylai Massacre and Its Cover-up, 1975; editor: The Supreme Court and Human Rights, 1982, A Workable Government?, 1989; contbr. articles, revs. to legal publs. Bd. dirs. Ctr. Community Change, Washington, 1968—, Robert F. Kennedy Meml., 1969—, Vera Inst. Justice, N.Y.C., 1965—. Home: Castle Meadow Rd Newtown CT 06470 Office: Yale U Sch Law 127 Wall St New Haven CT 06511-6636

MARSHALL, C. TRAVIS, manufacturing executive, government relations specialist; b. Apalachicola, Fla., Jan. 31, 1926; s. John and Estelle (Marks) M.; m. Katherine Rose Lepine; children: Melanie, Monica, Katharine. BS, U. Notre Dame, 1948. Chief clk. Firestone Tire & Rubber Co., Detroit, 1948-51; gen. sales mgr. The Hallicrafters, Chgo., 1952-65; v.p. mktg. E. F. Johnson, Waseca, Minn., 1965-70; v.p. mktg. ops. Motorola, Inc., Schaumburg, Ill., 1970-72, dir. govt. relations, communications div., 1972-74; v.p.; dir. govt. relations Motorola, Inc., Washington, 1974-85, sr. v.p., dir., gov. relations, 1985-92; telecomm. cons., 1992—; bd. dirs. Iridium, Inc. Appointed amb. by Pres. Bush to Internat. Telecomm. Union Conf.; trustee Md. Youth Symphony Orch. Recipient Disting. Service award Electronics Industries Assn., Washington, 1987. Mem. Electronics Industries Assn. (treas. 1982-92, treas. emeritus 1992—, v.p. 1975-88), Burning Tree Country Club (Bethesda), Columbia Country Club (Chevy Chase), Met. Club (Washington), Crystal Downs Country Club (Frankfort, Mich.). Republican. Roman Catholic. Avocations: sailing, golf. Office: Motorola Inc 1350 I St NW Washington DC 20005-3305

MARSHALL, CAROLYN ANN M., church official, consultant; b. Springfield, Ill., July 18, 1935; d. Hayward Thomas and Isabelle Bernice (Hayer) McMurray; m. John Alan Marshall, July 14, 1956 (dec. Sept. 1990); children: Margaret Marshall Bushman, Cynthia Marshall Kyrouac, Clinton, Carol. Student, De Pauw U., 1952-54; BSBA, Drake U., 1956; D of Pub. Svc. (hon.), De Pauw U., 1983; LHD (hon.), U. Indpls., 1990. Corp. sec. Marshall Studios, Inc., Veedersburg, Ind., 1956-89, exec. cons., 1989-93; sec. Gen. Conf., lay leader South Ind. conf. United Meth. Ch., 1988—; Carolyn M. Marshall chair in women studies Bennett Coll., Greensboro, N.C., 1988; fin. cons. Lucille Raines Residence, Indpls., 1977—. Pres. Fountain Ctrl. Band Boosters, Veedersburg, 1975-77; del. Gen. Conf. United Meth. Ch., 1980, 84, 88, 92, pres. women's divsn. Gen. Bd. Global Ministries, 1984-88; bd. dirs. Franklin (Ind.) United Meth. Home. Home: 204 N Newlin St Veedersburg IN 47987-1358

MARSHALL, CHARLES, communications company executive; b. Vandalia, Ill., Apr. 21, 1929; s. William Forman and Ruth (Corson) M.; m. Millicent Bruner, Jan. 2, 1953; children: Ruth Ann, Marcia Kay Marshall Rinek, William Forman, Charles Tedrick. B.S. in Agr, U. Ill., 1951. With Ill. Bell Telephone Co., 1953-59, 61-64, 65-70, 71-72, 77-81; pres., chief exec. officer Ill Bell Telephone Co., Chgo., 1977-81; with AT&T, 1959-61, 64-65, 70-71, 76-77, 81-89; chmn., chief exec. officer Am. Bell, Morristown, N.J., 1983-84, AT&T Info. Systems, 1984-85; vice chmn. AT&T, N.Y.C., 1985-89; bd. dirs. Ceridian, GATX, Sundstrand, Zenith, Sonat, Hartmarx; trustee U. Chgo., U. Ill. Found., Newberry Libr. Served to 1st lt. USAF, 1951-53. Mem. Econ. Club Chgo., Comml. Club Chgo., Club of Pelican Bay, Tavern Club, Chgo. Club. Avocations: fishing, golfing, reading. Home: Ph-B 6001 Pelican Bay Blvd Naples FL 33963-8166

MARSHALL, CHARLES BURTON, political science consultant; b. Catskill, N.Y., Mar. 25, 1908; s. Caleb Carey and Alice (Beeman) M.; m. Betty Louise O'Brien, Aug. 1, 1958 (dec. July, 1991); children (by previous marriage) Charles Richard, Jean Marshall Vickery. BA, U. Tex., 1931, MA, 1932; PhD, Harvard U., 1939; LHD, Johns Hopkins U., 1987. With newspapers in El Paso and Austin, Tex., 1925-31; With newspapers in Detroit, 1934-38; instr., tutor govt. Harvard U. and Radcliffe Coll., 1938-42; vis. lectr. Harvard U., summer 1963; cons. Intergovtl. Com. Refugees, 1946-47; staff cons. com. fgn. affairs U.S. Ho. of Reps., 1947-50; mem. policy planning staff State Dept., 1950-53; advisor to prime minister Pakistan, 1955-57; research assoc. Washington Center Fgn. Policy Research, 1957-74, acting dir., 1969-70; vis. prof. Sch. Advanced Internat. Studies, Johns Hopkins, 1965-66, prof., 1966-67, Paul H. Nitze prof. internat. politics, 1967-75; Alumni prof. internat. studies U. N.C., 1960-61; Centennial vis. prof. Tex. A&M U., 1976; cons. in field, 1961—; U.S. govt. rep. XIV Conf. Internat. Red Cross, Toronto, Can., 1952; mem. Gen. Adv. Com. Arms Control and Disarmament, 1982-92. Author: The Limits of Foreign Policy, 1954, The Exercise of Sovereignty, 1965, The Cold War: A Concise History, 1965, Crisis Over Rhodesia: A Skeptical View, 1967; Cons. editor: New Republic, 1959-64; contbg. editor: Nat. Rev, 1979-83. Served to lt. col. AUS, 1942-46. Fellow Carnegie Endowment Internat. Peace, 1934-35; vis. scholar, 1958-59. Mem. Coun. Fgn. Rels., Washington Inst. Fgn. Affairs, Cosmos Club. Home: 4106 N Randolph St Arlington VA 22207-4808

MARSHALL, CHARLES NOBLE, railroad executive; b. Phila., Feb. 18, 1942; s. Donnell and Cornelia Lansdale (Brooke) M.; m. Ann Shaw Donovan, Jan. 12, 1971; children—Elizabeth, Caroline, Cornelia, Edward. B.S. in Engring., Princeton U., 1963; J.D., U. Mich., 1967. Bar: Pa., Md., D.C. Atty. Balt. & Ohio R.R., Balt. and Cleve., 1967-73; gen. atty. So. Ry., Washington, 1973-78; gen. counsel commerce Conrail, Phila., 1978-83, v.p. mktg., 1983-85, sr. v.p. mktg. and sales, 1985-89, sr. v.p. devel., 1989—; bd. dirs. Pa. Chamber and Bus. Industry, Phila Reg. Port Authority; adv. bd. PNC Bank, Phila. Republican. Episcopalian.

MARSHALL, CLIFFORD WALLACE, mathematics educator; b. N.Y.C., Mar. 11, 1928; s. Clifford Wallace and Virginia (Roe) M.; m. Adele Kentoffio, Nov. 21, 1955; children: Wallace F., James A. B.A., Hofstra U., 1949; M.A., Syracuse U., 1950; M.S., Poly. Inst. Bklyn., 1954; Ph.D., Columbia U., 1961. Staff mem. Inst. Def. Analyses, Washington, 1958; prin. engr. Inst. Def. Analyses, 1959-60, cons. summer staff mem., 1965-68; specialist operations analyst Republic Aviation Corp., Farmingdale, N.Y., 1963; cons. USN Strategic Systems Project Office, Washington, 1968-69; assoc. prof. math. Polytechnic U., Brooklyn, 1963-68, prof. math., 1968—; Cons. Urban Inst., 1971-77, U.S. Dept. Energy, 1977-80, U.S. Dept. Energy (Simulation Systems Div., Gould Inc.), 1976-80. Author: Applied Graph Theory, 1971; assoc. editor Naval Rsch. Logistics, 1977—. Mem. Math. Assn. Am., Am. Math. Soc., Sigma Xi. Home: 264 N Ocean Ave Patchogue NY 11772-2010 Office: Rt 110 Farmingdale NY 11735

MARSHALL, CODY, bishop. Bishop No. Ill. Ch. of God in Christ, Chgo. Office: Ch of God in Christ 8836 S Blackstone Ave Chicago IL 60619-7105

MARSHALL, CONRAD JOSEPH, entrepreneur; b. Detroit, Dec. 23, 1934; s. Edward Louis Fedak and Maria Magdalena Berzsenyi; m. Dorothy Genieve Karnafil, Dec. 1, 1956 (div. 1963); children: Conrad Joseph Jr., Kevin Conrad, Lisa Marie; m. Beryle Elizabeth Callahan, June 15, 1965 (div. 1972); children: Brent Jasmer, Farah Elizabeth. Diploma, Naval Air Tech. Tng. Ctr., Norman, Okla., 1952; student, Wayne State U., 1956-59; Diploma, L.A. Police Acad., 1961. Dir. mktg. Gulf Devel., Torrance, Calif., 1980-83; sales mgr. Baldwin Piano Co., Santa Monica, Calif., 1977-80; dir. mktg., v.p. Western Hose, Inc., L.A., 1971-76; city letter carrier U.S. Post Office, L.A. 1969-71; writer freelance L.A., 1966—; police officer L.A. Police Dept., 1961-66; asst. sales mgr. Wesson Oil Co., Detroit, 1958-60; agt. Life Ins. Co. of Va., Wayne, Mich., 1956-58; pres. Am. Vision Mktg., L.A., 1990—, Con-Mar Prodns., L.A., 1983—; sr. v.p. Pacific Acquisition Group, 1992—, Invest. Admin. HealthCom., Int., 1993—; pres. Midway TV Co., 1994—; tech. advisor Lion's Gate Films, Westwood, Calif., 1970-74, Medicine Wheel Prodns., Hollywood, Calif., 1965-75; mng. gen. ptnr. Encino Wireless #1, 1994—; CEO Midway TV Co., 1995. Author: (series) "Dial Hot Line", 1967, (screenplay) "Heads Across the Border", 1968, "The Fool Card", 1970, "Probable Cause", 1972; co-author: The Fedak File, 1995; albums include Song Shark, 1992, Conrad Marshall Quintet, 1991. Campaign vol. Dem. Party, L.A., 1976; vol. Amanda Found., Beverly Hills, Calif., 1992. With USN, 1952-56. Mem. Screen Actors Guild, Internat. Platform Assn. Avocations: poetry, song writing, club singing, philosophy, theology. Home: 11853 Kling Ste 17 Valley Village CA 91607 Office: Con-Mar Prodns 2026 Holly Hill Terr Hollywood CA 90068

MARSHALL, CONSUELO BLAND, federal judge; b. Knoxville, Tenn., Sept. 28, 1936; d. Clyde Theodore and Annie (Brown) Arnold; m. George Edward Marshall, Aug. 30, 1959; children: Michael Edward, Laurie Ann. A.A., Los Angeles City Coll., 1956; B.A., Howard U., 1958, LL.B. 1961. Bar: Calif. 1962. Dep. atty. City of L.A., 1962-67; assoc. Cochran & Atkins, L.A., 1968-70; commr. L.A. Superior Ct., 1971-76; judge Inglewood Mcpl. Ct., 1976-77, L.A. Superior Ct., 1977-80, U.S. Dist. Ct. Central Dist. Calif., L.A., 1980—; lectr. U.S. Information Agy. in Yugoslavia, Greece and Italy, 1984, in Nigera and Ghana, 1991, in Ghana, 1992. Contbr. articles to profl. jours.; notes editor Law Jour. Howard U. Mem. adv. bd. Richstone Child Abuse Center. Recipient Judicial Excellence award Criminal Cts. Bar Assn., 1992; research fellow Howard U. Law Sch., 1959-60;. Mem. State Bar Calif., Calif. Women Lawyers Assn., Calif. Assn. Black Lawyers, Calif. Judges Assn., Black Women Lawyers Assn., Los Angeles County Bar Assn., Nat. Assn. Women Judges, NAACP, Urban League, Beta Phi Sigma. Office: US Dist Ct 312 N Spring St Los Angeles CA 90012-4701

MARSHALL, DALE ROGERS, college president, political scientist, educator; b. Mar. 22, 1937; m. Donald J. Marshall; children: Jessica, Cynthia, Clayton. BA in Govt., Cornell U., 1959; MA in Polit. Sci., U. Calif., Berkeley, 1960; PhD in Polit. Sci. with distinction, UCLA, 1969. Lectr. in polit. sci. UCLA, 1969-70, U. Calif., Berkeley, 1970-72; from asst. prof. to prof. U. Calif., Davis, 1972-86, faculty asst. to vice chancellor acad. affairs, 1980-82, assoc. dean Coll. Letters and Scis., 1983-86; acting pres. Wellesley (Mass.) Coll., 1987-88, dean of coll., prof. polit. sci., 1986-92, pres., 1992—; mem. exec. bd. Calif. Assembly Fellowship Program, 1980-86; mem. vis. com. polit. sci. dept. Brown U., Providence, 1990; bd. trustees, bd. overseers Newton-Wellesley Hosp., 1989-93; bd. trustees Cornell U., Ithaca, N.Y., 1983-93, chair Cornell Fund, co-chair Coll. Arts and Scis. Capital Campaign, 1990—; bd. trustees New Eng. Zenith Fund, New Eng. Mut. Life Ins. Co., 1995—; bd. dirs. Am. Student Assistance Guarantor, Am. Student Assistance Corp. Author: (with John C. Bollens) Guide to Participation: Field Work, Role Playing Cases and Other Forms, 1973, (with Roger Montgomery) Housing Policy for the 80s, 1980, (with Rufus P. Browning and David H. Tabb) Protest is Not Enough: The Struggle of Blacks and Hispanics for Equality in Urban Politics, 1984 (Ralph J. Bunche award for best book on ethnic rels. 1985, Gladys Kammerer award for best book in Am. policy 1985); editor: Urban Policy Making, 1979, (with David K. Leonard) Institutions of Rural Development for the Poor: Decentralization and Organizational Linkages, 1982, Racial Politics in American Cities, 1990; mem. editl. bd. Am. Polit. Sci. Rev., 1972-76, Pub. Adminstrn. Rev., 1985-86; contbr. articles to profl. jours. Woodrow Wilson fellow, 1959-60, Calif. Regents fellow, 1966-67, 67-68; NSF grantee, 1976-78, 79-80; recipient Significant Contbn. to Status of Women citation Chancellor's Com. on Status of Women at U. Calif. at Davis, 1978. Mem. Am. Polit. Sci. Assn. (mem. exec. coun. 1974-76, v.p. 1985-86, mem. nominating com. 1988-90), Western Polit. Sci. Assn. (mem. exec. coun. 1973-75, pres. 1983-85), Nat. Acad. Pub. Adminstrn., Phi Beta Kappa, Phi Kappa Phi. Office: Wheaton Coll Office of Pres Norton MA 02766

MARSHALL, DANIEL STUART, advertising executive; b. London, Eng., Nov. 14, 1930; came to U.S., 1964; s. Leslie Stuart and Jessie (Morrison) M.; m. Solange Goohier, Sept. 2, 1985. Student, St. Johns Coll., Hassocks, Eng., 1944. Dir. art J. Walter Thompson, Santiago, Chile, 1958-61, San Paulo, Brazil, 1961-64, N.Y.C., 1964-75; exec. v.p., creative dir. Marshall Jacomma & Mitchell, N.Y.C., 1978—. Artist, designer (book) The Dream Theatre, 1975, In a Monastery Kitchen, 1982. Office: Marshall Jacomma & Mitchell 41 Madison Ave New York NY 10010-2202

MARSHALL, DAVID LAWRENCE, freight forwarding and mining company executive; b. Orange, N.J., Mar. 10, 1939; s. Lawrence Clark and Sylvia (Hitch) M.; m. Lucy Smith, June 17, 1961; children: Lucy, Jennifer, Christopher, Stephen. B.A., Princeton U., 1961; M.S., Yale U., 1962. Vice pres. Freeport of Australia, Melbourne, 1969-71, pres., 1971-73; v.p. Freeport Minerals Co., N.Y.C., 1973-79, sr. v.p., 1979-81, exec. v.p., 1981-84; with Pittston Co., 1984—; chief fin. officer, exec. v.p. Pittston Co., until 1990, now vice-chmn. bd., CEO; chmn. bd. Burlington Air Express, Irvine, Calif. Republican. Episcopalian. Clubs: Wee Burn (Darien, Conn.); Sky.

MARSHALL, DONALD GLENN, English language and literature educator; b. Long Beach, Calif., Sept. 9, 1943; s. Albert Louis and Margaret Corinne (Morrison) M.; m. Kathleen Bonann, June 21, 1975; children—Stephanie Deborah, Zachary Louis. A.B. summa cum laude, Harvard U., 1965; M.Phil., Yale U., 1969, Ph.D., 1971. Asst. prof. English UCLA, 1969-75; assoc. prof. English U. Iowa, Iowa City, 1975-79; prof. English U. Iowa, 1979-90, honors dir. Coll. Liberal Arts, 1981-85; prof., head English dept. U. Ill., Chgo., 1990—. Editor: Philosophy as Literature/Literature as Philosophy, 1986; compiler: Contemporary Critical Theory: A Selective Bibliography, 1993; translator: (with Joel Weinsheimer) Truth and Method by Hans-Georg Gadamer, 1989; contbr. articles and revs. to profl. jours. Recipient Bell prize Harvard U., 1965, Webster prize Yale U., 1967; NEH Younger Humanist fellow, 1973-74; grantee UCLA, U. Iowa. Mem. MLA, Internat. Assn. Philosophy and Lit., Soc. Values in Higher Edn., Ill. Humanities Coun. (bd. dirs. 1994—). Democrat. Roman Catholic. Office: U Ill Dept English Univ Hall 601 S Morgan St Chicago IL 60607-7100

MARSHALL, DONALD STEWART, computer systems company executive; b. Saskatoon, Sask., Can., Nov. 18, 1938; s. Arthur Stewart and Helen Margaret (Pederson) M.; children: Douglas Stewart, Andrew Christopher. B Applied Sci. in Civil Engring., Queen's U., Kingston, Ont., Can., 1962. Registered profl. engr., Ont. Progressed from computer systems analyst to branch mgr. Honeywell, IBM and AGT Data Systems, 1962-71; pres. Ventek Ltd., London, 1971-80; v.p. CDC Data Systems Ltd., Toronto, Ont., 1980-83; exec. v.p. Meridian Techs. Inc., Toronto, 1983-93; pres. Atelco Ltd., Richmond Hill, Ont., 1993—; bd. dirs. Incontext Sys. Inc., Halzone Tech. Inc., Alteco Ltd. Mem. Assn. Profl. Engrs. Ont. Avocations: golf, squash, tennis. Home: 54 Anderson Ave, Toronto, ON Canada M5P 1H7 Office: Atelco Ltd, Unit 7, Richmond Hill, ON Canada L4B 3H6

MARSHALL, DONALD TOMPKINS, industrial distribution executive; b. Schenectady, N.Y., Oct. 29, 1933; s. Allen Edward and Margaret (Leahy) M.; m. Susan Fisher, July 25, 1959; m. Anna Marie Pikes O'Brien, Feb. 14, 1987; children: Amy, Scott, Jennifer. BS in Math., St. Lawrence U., 1956; BS in Mech. Engring., Columbia U., 1957. With Union Carbide Corp., N.Y.C., 1958-70; pres. airco cryo plants div. Air Reduction Corp., Murray Hill, N.J., 1970-76; pres. Gen. Energy Corp., Willingboro, N.J., 1976-78; v.p. Sun Distbrs. div. Sun Co., Phila., 1978-82, pres., 1982-86; chmn., chief exec. officer Sun Distbrs. Co.- N.Y. Stock Exch., Phila., 1986—. Mem. ASME, Riverton Golf Club (treas. 1979-85), Seabrook Island Club, Pine Valley Golf Club. Avocations: golf, hunting, fishing. Office: Sun Distbrs Inc 1 Logan Sq Philadelphia PA 19103-6901

MARSHALL, DOYLE, real estate executive; b. Frederick, Okla., July 22, 1932; s. Dallas H. and Sally Vada (Hicks) M.; m. Glenda Ruth Pawley, May 7, 1955; children: William Donald, Sheryl Ruth, David Weston. AS, U. Tex., Arlington, 1957. Realty specialist Corps Engrs., Ft. Worth, 1955-70; realty officer Gen. Svcs. Adminstrn., Ft. Worth, 1971—, dep. dir. real estate sales, 1981—; pub. Annetta Valley Farm Press, Aledo, Tex., 1987—. Author: Aledo Country Sketchbook, 1987, A Cry Unheard, 1990, The Liveoak Tree School, 1994; contbr. articles to mags. and newspapers. Scoutmaster Boy Scouts Am., Ft. Worth, 1969-72. Mem. Tex. State Hist. Assn., West Tex. Hist. Assn., various county hist. assns. Baptist. Avocations: Texas history, collecting Texana books, raising cattle, collecting for private farm and ranch museum, writing.

MARSHALL, E. G., actor; b. Owatonna, Minn., June 18, 1910; s. Charles G. and Hazel Irene (Cobb) M.; m. Helen Wolf, Apr. 26, 1939 (div. 1953); children: Jill, Degen. Student, Carlton Coll., 1930, U. Minn., 1932. Began profl. career on radio stas. St. Paul, Mpls., Chgo., 1932. Featured on radio program Eugene O'Neill's The Iceman Cometh, Theatre Guild on the Air, 1946-47; actor: (films) including Bachelor Party, 1957, House on 92d Street, 13 Rue Madeleine, Swamp Angel, Caine Mutiny, 1954, Pushover, 1954, Bamboo Prison, 1954, Broken Lance, 1954, Silver Chalice, 1954, Left Hand of God, 1955, Scarlet Hour, 1956, Call Northside 777, Twelve Angry Men, 1957, Compulsion, 1959, The Journey, 1959, Town Without Pity, 1961, The Chase, 1966, The Bridge at Remagen, 1969, Tora! Tora! Tora!, 1970, Pursuit of Happiness, 1971, Interiors, 1978, Superman II, 1980, Creepshow, 1982, Power, 1986, My Chauffer, 1986, La Gran Fiesta, 1987, National Lampoon's Christmas Vacation, 1989, Two Evil Eyes (The Black Cat), 1991, Consenting Adults, 1991, (plays) The Gang's All Here, 1959, The Crucible, Red Roses for Me, Waiting for Godot, (TV movies) Vampire, 1979, Disaster on the Coastliner, 1979, The Phoenix, 1981, John Steinbeck's The Winter of Our Discontent, 1983, Under Siege, 1986, At Mother's Request, 1987, Emma, Queen of the South seas, 1988, The Hijacking of the Achille Lauro, 1989, Ironclads, 1991, Stephen King's The Tommyknockers, 1993, (TV miniseries) Eleanor: First Lady of the World, 1982, Kennedy, 1983, At Mother's Request, 1987, Ike, 1987, Oldest Living Confederate Widow Tells All, 1994, (TV series) The Defenders, 1961-65 (2 Emmy awards), The Bold Ones (The Doctors), 1969-73, Chicago Hope, 1994. Recipient Emmy award for best actor in Defenders series, 1961, 62. Office: Paradigm Talent Agy 10100 Santa Monica Blvd 125th Flr Los Angeles CA 90067*

MARSHALL, ELLEN RUTH, lawyer; b. N.Y.C., Apr. 23, 1949; d. Louis and Faith (Gladstone) M. A.B, Yale U., 1971; JD, Harvard U., 1974. Bar: Calif. 1975, D.C. 1981, N.Y. 1989. Assoc. McKenna & Fitting, Los Angeles, 1975-80; ptnr. McKenna, Conner & Cuneo, Los Angeles and Orange County, Calif., 1980-88, Morrison & Foerster, Orange County, Calif., 1988—. Mem. ABA (bus. law sect., savs. inst. com., asset securitization com., tax sect., employee benefits com.), Orange County Bar Assn. Club: Center (Costa Mesa, Calif.). Office: Morrison & Foerster 19900 Macarthur Blvd Irvine CA 92715-2445

MARSHALL, ERIC C., lawyer; b. Oak Park, Ill., June 21, 1958; s. Marvin W. and Erika K. M.; m. Deborah A. Claflin. BA, Yale U., 1980; JD, U. Mich., 1984. Bar: Ill. 1984. Assoc. Katten, Muchin & Zavis, Chgo., 1984-87; atty. Amoco Corp., Chgo., 1987—. Office: Amoco Corp MC2102 PO Box 81235 Chicago IL 60681-0235

MARSHALL, F. RAY, public affairs educator. BA, Millsaps Coll., 1949; MA, La. State U., 1950; PhD, U. Calif., Berkeley, 1954. Pres. Indsl. Rels. Rsch. Assn., 1976-77; U.S. sec. of labor, 1977-81; pres. Internat. Labor Rights Rsch. and Edn. Fund; Audre and Bernard Rapoport Centennial chair in econs. and pub. affairs, Lyndon B. Johnson Sch. Pub. Affairs U. Tex., Austin; bd. dirs. German Marshall Fund, Aurora Nat. Life Assurance, USX Corp., Nat. Ctr. on Edn. and Economy, Inst. for the Future; mem. Coun. on Fgn. Rels. Office: U Tex Sch of Pub Affairs Austin TX 78713-7450

MARSHALL, FRANCIS JOSEPH, aerospace engineer; b. N.Y.C., Sept. 5, 1923; s. Francis Joseph and Mary Gertrude (Leary) M.; m. Joan Eager, June 14, 1952; children—Peter, Colin, Stephen, Dana. BS in Mech. Engring., CCNY, 1948; M.S., Rensselaer Poly. Inst., 1950; Dr. Eng. Sci., N.Y. U., 1955. Engr. Western Union Co., N.Y.C., 1948, Gen. Electric Co., Schenectady, 1948-50; engr. Wright-Aero Corp., Woodridge, N.J., 1950-52; group leader Lab. for Applied Scis., U. Chgo., 1955-60; instr. Ill. Inst. Tech., 1957-59; prof. Sch. Aeros. and Astronautics, Purdue U. West Lafayette, Ind., 1960—; engr. U.S. Naval Underseas Warfare Center, Pasadena, Calif., 1966-68; faculty fellow NASA-Langley, 1969-70; vis. prof. Inst. Tech. Mara-Midwest Univs. Consortium for Internat. Activities, Malaysia, 1989. Contbr. articles to profl. jours. Served with U.S. Army, 1943-46. Decorated Combat Inf. badge.; NASA research grantee, 1970, 76; Fulbright scholar, Turkey, 1988-89. Fellow AIAA; mem. Am. Soc. Engring. Edn., AAUP. Home: 120 Leslie Ave West Lafayette IN 47906-2410 Office: Sch Aeros and Astronautics Purdue U West Lafayette IN 47907

MARSHALL, FRANK W., film producer, director. Student, UCLA. Location mgr.: The Last Picture Show, 1971, What's Up Doc?, 1972; assoc. prodr.: Paper Moon, 1973, Daisy Miller, 1974, At Long Last Love, 1975. Nickelodeon, 1976, The Driver, 1978; line prodr.: Orson Welles' The Other Side of the Wind (unreleased), Marin Scorsese's The Last Waltz, 1977; prodr.: (films) Raiders of the Lost Ark, 1981 (Academy award nomination for best picture 1981), Noises Off, 1992; (with Steven Spielberg) Poltergeist, 1982; (with Spielberg, Quincy Jones, and Kathleen Kennedy) The Color Purple, 1985 (Academy award nomination for best picture 1985); (with Spielberg and Kennedy) Empire of the Sun, 1987, Always, 1989; (with Robert Watts) Who Framed Roger Rabbit, 1988; (with Kennedy and Gerald R. Molen) Hook, 1991; (with Kennedy) Milk Money, 1994; exec. prodr.: (films) The Warriors, 1979, Twilight Zone-The Movie, 1983; (with George Lucas) Indiana Jones and the Temple of Doom, 1984; (with Kennedy and Spielberg) Gremlins, 1984, The Goonies, 1985, Back to the Future, 1985, Young Sherlock Holmes, 1985, *batteries not included, 1987, Dad, 1989, Back to the Future Part II, 1989, Gremlins 2: The New Batch, 1990, Back to the Future Part III, 1990, Joe Versus the Volcano, 1990, Cape Fear, 1991, We're Back! A Dinosaur's Story, 1993; (with Kennedy) Fandango, 1985; (with Kennedy, Spielberg, and David Kirschner) An American Tail, 1986; (with Kennedy and Art Levinson) The Money Pit, 1986; (with Kennedy, Spielberg, Peter Guber, and Jon Peters) Innerspace, 1987; (with Kennedy, Lucas, and Spielberg) The Land Before Time, 1988; (with Kennedy and Lucas) Indiana Jones and the Last Crusade, 1989; (with Kennedy and Kirschner) An American Tail: Fievel Goes West, 1991; (with Chris Meledandri) Swing Kids, 1993; (with Kennedy and Molen) A Far Off Place, 1993; exec. prodr. (with Spielberg, Robert W. Cort, and Ted Field), dir.: Arachnophobia, 1990; dir.: Alive, 1993, Congo, 1995; exec. producer: TV Roger Rabbit and the Secret of Toontown; prodr., dir. TV Johnny Bago. Office: Kennedy/Marshall Co Clinton # 100 650 N Bronson Ave Los Angeles CA 90004-1404

MARSHALL, GARLAND ROSS, biochemist, biophysicist, medical educator; b. San Angelo, Tex., Apr. 16, 1940; s. Garland Ross and Jewel Wayne (Gray) M.; m. Suzanne Russell, Dec. 26, 1959; children: Chris, Keith, Melissa, Lee. BS, Calif. Inst. Tech., 1962; PhD, Rockefeller U., 1966; DSc (hon.), Politechnika, Lodz, Poland, 1993. Instr. Washington U., St. Louis, 1966-67, asst. prof., 1967-72, assoc. prof., 1972-76, prof. biochemistry, 1976—, prof. pharmacology, 1985—, dir. Ctr. for Molecular Design, 1988—; vis. prof. Massey U., Palmerston North, New Zealand, 1975; vis. prof. chemistry U. Florence, Italy, 1991; pres. Tripos Assocs., Inc., St. Louis, 1979-87; chmn. 10th Am. Peptide Symposium, St. Louis, 1986-88; councilor Am. Peptide Soc., 1990-93; established investigator Am. Heart Assn., Washington, 1970-75. Editor: Peptides: Chemistry and Biology, 1988, Peptides: Chemistry, Structure and Biology, 1990; editor-in-chief Jour. Computer-Aided Molecular Design, 1986—. Recipient medal XL-Lecia Tech. U., Lodz, Poland, 1987, Vincent de Vigneaud award Am. Peptide Soc., 1994. Mem. Am. Chem. Soc. (Medicinal Chemistry award 1988), Am. Soc. for Biochemistry and Molecular Biology, Am. Soc. for Pharmacology and Exptl. Therapeutics, Biophys. Soc., Am. Peptide Soc. (Vincent du Vigneaud award 1994). Office: Washington U Ctr for Molecular Design One Brookings Dr Saint Louis MO 63130-4899

MARSHALL, GARRY, film producer, director, writer; b. N.Y.C., Nov. 13, 1934. B.S., Northwestern U. Writer I Spy, Jack Paar Show, Joey Bishop Show, Danny Thomas Show, Lucy Show, Dick Van Dyke Show; writer, creator Hey Landlord; exec. producer The Odd Couple, 1968; creator, exec. producer Evil Roy Slade, 1972, Happy Days, Laverne and Shirley, Mork and Mindy, Angie, Joanie Loves Chachi; writer, producer films, How Sweet It Is, 1968, The Grasshopper, 1970: dir. Young Doctors in Love, 1982; screenwriter, dir. Flamingo Kid, 1984; dir. films Nothing in Common, 1987, Overboard, 1987, Beaches, 1988, Pretty Woman, 1990, Frankie & Johnny, 1991, Exit to Eden, 1994; film appearance includes Psych-out, 1968, Lost in America, 1985, Soapdish, 1991, A League of Their Own, 1992, Hocus Pocus, 1993.

MARSHALL, GEOFFREY, university administrator; b. Lancaster, Pa., Feb. 6, 1938; s. Ray Ardell and Mary (Elsen) M.; m. Mary Gale Beckwith, June 17, 1961; children: Eden Elizabeth, Erin Elizabeth. BA, Franklin and Marshall Coll., 1959; MA, Rice U., 1961, PhD, 1965; LHD (hon.), Mansfield State Coll., 1980, Ursinus Coll., 1990. Assoc. prof. English U. Okla., Norman, 1964-74; asst. provost U.Okla., Norman, 1973-74; dir. div. state programs Nat. Endowment for Humanities, Washington, 1974-78; dir. div. edn. programs, 1978-80, dep. chmn., 1981-85; assoc. provost and dean for acad. affairs Grad. Sch. CUNY, 1985-92, acting provost and v.p. for acad. affairs, 1992-94, provost, sr. v.p., 1994—; bd. dirs. Ursinus Coll., 1986—. Author: Restoration Serious Drama, 1975; contbr. articles to profl. jours. Trustee Norman Pub. Library, 1970-74; chmn. Okla. Humanities Com., 1971-74; mem. Norman Human Rights Commn., 1972-73. Assoc. Danforth Found., 1968-74; recipient Couch Scholars award for excellence in undergrad. edn. U. Okla., 1967. Mem. MLA, Nat. Council Tchrs. English, Am. Soc. 18th Century Studies, Nat. Collegiate Honors Council (exec. com. 1972-74). Home: 125 Cypress Dr Hightstown NJ 08520-2315 Office: CUNY Grad Sch and Univ Ctr 33 W 42rd St New York NY 10036

MARSHALL, GEORGE DWIRE, supermarket chain executive; b. Washington, Feb. 7, 1940; s. Joseph Paul and Jane Schouler (Dwire) M.; m. Sharon Ruth Carter, Nov. 17, 1968; children: Sarah Dwire, Benjamin Carter. Ba, Amherst Coll., 1962; JD, U. Calif., Berkeley, 1965. Bar: Calif. 1966. Atty., then sr. atty. legal div. Safeway Inc., Oakland, Calif., 1970-79, v.p., mgr. labor rels. divsn., 1979—; employer trustee UFCW Internat. Union-Industry Pension Fund, 1980—. Served to lt. USNR, 1966-70, Korea, Vietnam. Mem. State Bar Calif., Bar Assn. San Francisco, Psi Upsilon, Phi Delta Phi. Republican. Presbyterian. Office: Safeway Inc 201 4th St Oakland CA 94660-0001

MARSHALL, GERALD FRANCIS, optical engineer, consultant, physicist; b. Seven Kings, Eng., Feb. 26, 1929. BSc in Physics, London U., 1952. Physicist Morganite Internat., London, 1954-59; sr. research devel. engr. Ferranti Ltd., Edinburgh, Scotland, 1959-67; project mgr. Diffraction Limited Inc., Bedford, Mass., 1967-69; dir. engring. Medical Lasers, Inc., Burlington, Mass., 1969-71; staff cons. Speeding Systems, Troy, Mich., 1971-76; dir. industrial engring. Energy Conversion Devices, Inc., Troy, Mich., 1976-87; sr. tech. staff specialist Kaiser Electronics, San Jose, Calif., 1987-89; cons. in optics design and engring., 1989—. Editor, contbg. author: Laser Beam Scanning, 1985, Optical Scanning, 1991; patentee in field. Fellow Inst. Physics, Internat. Soc. Optical Engring. (symposia chair 1990), bd. dirs. 1991-93, exec. chair Internat. Symposium on Electronic Imaging Device Engring., Munich 1993); mem. Optical Soc. Am. (program chair 1979-80, pres. Detroit sect. 1980-81, bd. dirs. No. Calif. sect. 1990-92).

MARSHALL, GORDON BRUCE, construction company executive; b. Hamilton, Ont., Can., Sept. 26, 1943; s. J. Gordon and Mae J. (Tucker) M.; m. Rita J. Penca, Apr. 22, 1979. BSBA, Northwestern U., 1965; MBA, U. Chgo., 1970; AAS, Coll. Lake County, 1975. CPA, Mo., Ill. Comptrollership trainee Continental Ill. Nat. Bank, Chgo., 1967-68; profit analyst Morton Salt Co., Chgo., 1968-70; sr. fin. specialist Abbott Labs., North Chicago, Ill., 1970-76; treas. Pott Industries Inc., St. Louis, 1976-81; v.p. fin. and adminstrn. Pepper Constrn. Co., Chgo., 1981-84; v.p. fin., chief fin. officer The Pepper Cos. Inc., Chgo., 1989—, v.p. fin., treas., 1989—; instr. Coll. Lake County, Grayslake, Ill., 1975-76; pres. Blue Jay Ventures Inc., West Dundee, Ill., 1988—. Served to lt. (j.g.) USNR, 1965-67. Recipient Eagle Scout honor Boy Scouts Am. Mem. AICPA, Ill. CPA Soc., Constrn. Fin. Mgmt. Assn. (bd. dirs., pres. 1987-88), Nat. Constrn. Industry Coun. (bd. dirs. 1987-88), Am. Coun. for Constrn. Edn. (trustee 1989—, treas. 1991-93, v.p. 1993—). Office: The Pepper Cos Inc 411 Lake Zurich Rd Barrington IL 60010-3141

MARSHALL, HAROLD D., leasing and financial services company executive; b. 1936; married. Student, U. Fla., Nat. Installment Banking Sch., U. Colo. Mgmt. trainee Family Fin., 1959-61; with Assocs. Corp. N.Am., 1961—, regional v.p. N.W. zone, 1969-73, sr. v.p. Ea. ops., 1973-74, exec. v.p., 1974-79, pres. v.p., now vice chmn., 1979—; then sr. exec. v.p., now vice chmn.; exec. v.p. Assocs. Comml. Corp., 1976-79, past sr. exec. v.p., now vice chmn., 1979—. With USAR, 1959-65. Office: Assocs Comml Corp PO Box 650363 Dallas TX 75265-0363*

MARSHALL, HERBERT A., lawyer; b. Clinton, Ill., Aug. 20, 1917; s. Harry A. and Andrea (Pederson) M.; m. Helen Christman, May 3, 1941; children—James A., Thomas O., Mary (Mrs. William Nichols). A.B., Washburn U., 1940, LL.B., J.D., 1943. Bar: Kans. bar 1943. Law clk. U.S. Ct. Appeals, 1943-44; asst. county atty. Shawnee County, Kans., 1944-50; practiced in Topeka, 1944—; instr. practice ct. Washburn U. Law Sch., 1963—; mem. Kans. Supreme Ct. Nominating Commn., 1968-79. Trustee, elder Presbyn. Ch. Fellow Am. Bar Found. (life), Kans. Bar Found. (life); Am. Coll. Trial Lawyers; mem. ABA, Kans. Bar Assn. (exec. council 1968—, v.p. 1977, pres. 1979), Am. Judicature Soc., Topeka Bar Assn. (pres. 1968), Topeka C. of C., Optimist Club, Masons, Elks. Home: 4722 Brentwood St Topeka KS 66606

MARSHALL, HOWARD LOWEN, music educator, musicologist; b. Nokesville, Va., July 21, 1931; s. Howard Hampton and Florence Annie (Nash) M.; m. Doris Mae Rosencranz, July 14, 1962. B of Music Edn., Shenandoah U., 1952; MusM, U. Cin., 1958; PhD, U. Rochester, 1968. Asst. prof. music Lake Forest (Ill.) Coll., 1966-73; Charles B. Thompson prof. music, chmn. music dept. Mercer U., Macon, Ga., 1974—. Author: The Four-Voice Motets of Thomas Crecquillon, Symbolism in Schubert's Winterreise in Studies in Romanticism. Lt. comdr. USNR, ret. Mem. Am. Musicological Soc., AAUP, Phi Mu Alpha, Phi Kappa Lambda. Avocation: photography. Home: 1324 Maplewood Dr Macon GA 31210-3106 Office: Mercer U Music Dept 1400 Coleman Ave Macon GA 31207-0001

MARSHALL, IRL HOUSTON, JR., residential and commercial cleaning company executive; b. Evanston, Ill., Feb. 28, 1929; s. Irl H. and Marjorie (Greenleaf) M.; m. Barbara Favill, Nov. 5, 1949; children: Alice Louise Vogler, Irl Houston III, Carol Marshall Allen. AB, Dartmouth Coll., 1949; MBA, U. Chgo., 1968; cert. franchise exec., La. State U., 1991. Gen. mgr. Duraclean Internat., Deerfield, Ill., 1949-61; mgr. Montgomery Ward, Chgo., 1961-77; pres., chief exec. officer Duraclean Internat., 1977—. Inventor/patentee in field. Pres. Cliff Dwellers, Chgo., 1977; exec. com., treas., dir. Highland Park Hosp., 1971-80; dir. Continential Ill. Bank Deerfield, 1982-90; bd. dirs. Better Bus. Bur. Chgo. & No. Ill., Chgo., 1988—. Mem. Internat. Franchise Assn. (bd. dirs. 1981-90, pres. 1985, chmn. 1985-86), Econ. Club Chgo., Exmoor Country Club, Univ. Club Chgo. Presbyterian. Home: 1248 Ridgewood Dr Northbrook IL 60062

MARSHALL, J. HOWARD, II, lawyer; b. Phila., Jan. 24, 1905; s. S. Furman and Annabelle (Thompson) M.; m. Eleanor Pierce, June 20, 1931; children: J. Howard III, Pierce; m. Bettye M. Bohanan, Dec. 10, 1961. AB, Haverford Coll., 1926, LLD, 1985; JD magna cum laude, Yale U., 1931. Instr. and asst. cruise dir. Floating Univ., 1926-27, cruise dir., 1928-29; asst. dean, asst. prof. law Yale U., 1931-33; mem. Petroleum Adminstrv. Bd., U.S. Dept. Interior, 1933-35; spl. asst. to U.S. atty. gen. and asst. solicitor Dept. Interior, 1933-35; spl. counsel Standard Oil Co. Calif., 1935-37; partner Pillsbury, Madison & Sutro, San Francisco, 1938-44; chief counsel Petroleum Adminstrn. for War, 1941-44, asst. dep. adminstr., 1943-44; gen. counsel U.S. del. to Allied Commn. on Reparations, 1945; ptnr. Meyers, Marshall & Meyers, Washington; Mem. Mil. Petroleum Adv. Bd. to joint chiefs staff, 1944-50, 54-59; pres., dir. Ashland Oil & Refining Co. (and subs. corps.), 1944-51; v.p., dir. Signal Oil & Gas Co., 1952-59, exec. v.p., dir., 1959-60, also subs. and affiliated corps.; pres., dir. Union Texas Natural Gas Corp., 1961-62; dir. Allied Chem. Corp., 1962-68; pres. Union Tex. Petroleum div., exec v.p. Allied Chem. Corp., 1965-67; dir. Tex. Commerce Bank Nat. Assn., Houston; dir., mem. exec. com. M-K-T R.R.; dir. Koch Industries, Inc., Wichita; chmn., dir. Petroleum Corp.; chmn. exec. com., dir. Coastal Corp.; dir. Presidio Oil Co., 1987; cons. sec. interior petroleum def. program, 1950-52. Author (with N.L. Meyers); series monographs Yale Law Jour., 1931, 33. Vice-pres., bd. mgrs. Haverford Coll. Mem. 25 Year Club, Am. Petroleum Inst. (v.p., dir.). Nat. Petroleum Council, Soc. Petroleum Engrs., Am., Calif., Ky. bar assns., AIME, Order of Coif, Beta Rho Sigma. Mem. Soc. of Friends. Clubs: Bohemian (San Francisco), Pacific-Union (San Francisco); 29 (N.Y.C.); River Oaks Country (Houston). Home: 11100 Meadowick Dr Houston TX 77024-7503 Office: 7600 W Tidwell Rd Ste 800 Houston TX 77040-5719

MARSHALL, JANE PRETZER, newspaper editor; b. Chase County, Kans.; married; 2 children. BS in Home Econs. and Journalism, Kans. State U., 1967; student, Tex. A&M U. Mo., Tex. Christian U., Brite Divinity Sch. Asst. editor dept. agr. info. Tex. Agrl. Ext. Sta. Tex. A&M U., College Station, 1967-70; staff writer Gazette-Telegraph, Colorado Springs, Colo., 1970-72; editor corporate publ. Colorado Interstate, Colorado Springs, 1972-75; co-editor The Pampa (Tex.) News, 1975-78; exec. features editor Ft. Worth Star-Telegram, 1978-84; features editor Denver Post, 1984-88, Houston Chronicle, 1988—. Recipient 1st place for feature writing Tex. AP Mng. Editors Assn., 1978. Mem. Am. Assn. Sunday and Features Editors (bd. dirs., founding chairperson Features First), Women's Found. Health Edn. and Rsch. (bd. dirs.), Journalism and Women Symposium (1st pres.). Office: Houston Chronicle 801 Texas St Houston TX 77002-2907

MARSHALL, JEAN MCELROY, physiologist; b. Chambersburg, Pa., Dec. 31, 1922; d. Frank Lester and Florence (McElroy) M. A.B., Wilson Coll., 1944; M.A., Mt. Holyoke Coll., 1946; Ph.D., U. Rochester, 1951. Instr. Johns Hopkins U. Med. Sch., Balt., 1951-56; asst. prof. Johns Hopkins U. Med. Sch., 1956-60; research postdoctoral fellow Oxford (Eng.) U., 1954-55; asst. prof. Harvard U. Med. Sch., Boston, 1960-66; assoc. prof. physiology Brown U., Providence, 1966-69; prof. Brown U., 1969-88, prof. emerita, 1988, E. Brintznehof Prof. Med. Sci., 1987—; mem. physiology study sect. NIH, 1967-71, mem. tng. com. engring. in biology and medicine, 1971-74, mem. tng. com. lab. medicine, 1976-77; physiol. test com. Nat. Bd. Med. Examiners, 1972-76, neurobiology adv. com., 1977-80. Editor: The Initiation of Labor, 1964; mem. editorial bd. Jour. Pharmacology and Exptl. Therapeutics, 1963-69, Am. Jour. Physiology, 1969-73, Circulation Research, 1973-81; contbr. articles to profl. jours. Mem. Am. Physiol. Soc., Am. Pharmacol. Soc., N.Y. Acad. Scis., Soc. Reproductive Biology, Soc. Gen. Physiologists, Phi Beta Kappa, Sigma Xi. Home: 14 Aberdeen Rd Weston MA 02193-1733 Office: R I Hosp/Brown Univ Dept Medicine Providence RI 02903

MARSHALL, JEFFREY SCOTT, mechanical engineer, educator; b. Cin., Feb. 10, 1961; s. James C. and Norma E. (Everett) M.; m. Marilyn Jane Patterson, July 16, 1983; children: Judith K., Eric G., Emily J. BS summa cum laude, UCLA, 1983, MS, 1984; PhD, U. Calif., Berkeley, 1987. Asst. rsch. engr. U. Calif., Berkeley, 1988; engr. Creare, Inc., Hanover, N.H., 1988-89; from asst. to assoc. prof. dept. ocean engring. Fla. Atlantic U., 1989-93; assoc. prof. dept. mech. engring., rsch. scientist Iowa Inst. Hydraulic Rsch. U. Iowa, Iowa City, 1993—. Contbr. articles to profl. jours. Rsch. grantee Am. Soc. Engring. Edn./USN Summer Faculty Rsch. Programs, 1991-94. ARO Young Investigator Program, 1992-95. Mem. ASME (assoc., Henry Hess award 1992), Am. Phys. Soc. , Tau Beta Pi. Achievements include research in fluid mechanics, three-dimensional vortex dynamics and geophysical flows. Office: U Iowa Iowa Inst Hydraulic Rsch Dept Mech Engring Iowa City IA 52242

MARSHALL, JOHN, association administrator; b. Sandwich, Mass., June 30, 1917; s. Walton H. and Vira F. (Stowe) M.; m. Anna Silk, May 11, 1961. BA cum laude, Williams Coll., 1939; Diploma, Sorbonne U., Paris. Trainee Am. Tobacco C., Va., 1939-41; asst. to sr. v.p. European dept. Singer Sewing Machine Co., Europe, Near East and Africa, 1946-56; past pres. Amateur Astronomers Assn., CEO; lectr. in field. Contbr. articles to profl. jours. Lt. comdr. USN, 1941-45, ETO. Recipient Excellence in French Studies award Govt. of France, 1939, Amateur Astronomers medal, 1985. Mem. N.Y. Acad. Scis. Home: 1 Gracie Ter New York NY 10028

MARSHALL, JOHN ALOYSIUS, bishop; b. Worcester, Mass., Apr. 26, 1928; s. John A. and Katherine T. (Redican) M. A.B. cum laude, Holy Cross Coll., Worcester, 1949; postgrad., Sem. de Philosophie, Montreal, Can., 1949-50; S.T.L., Pontifical Gregorian U., Rome, 1954; M.A. in Guidance and Psychology, Assumption Coll., Worcester, 1964. Ordained priest Roman Catholic Ch., 1953, consecrated bishop, 1972; parish priest in Mass., 1954-57; asst. vice rector Pontifical N. Am. Coll., 1957-61; instr. Acad. Sacred Heart, Worcester, 1961-62, St. Vincent Hosp. Sch. Nursing, Worcester, 1961-62; headmaster St. Stephen Cath. High Sch., Worcester, 1962-68; spiritual dir. Pontifical N. Am. Coll., 1968-71, bus. mgr., 1969-71;

bishop of Burlington Vt., 1972-91; bishop Diocese of Springfield, Springfield, Mass., 1992—; chmn. com. priestly formation Nat. Conf. Cath. Bishops, 1975-78. Bd. dirs. Champlain Coll., Burlington, from 1974, Wadhams Hall, Ogdensburg, N.Y., from 1974. Office: PO Box 1730 76 Elliott St Springfield MA 01101

MARSHALL, JOHN DAVID, lawyer; b. Chgo., May 19, 1940; s. John Howard and Sophie (Brezenk) M.; m. Marcia A. Podlasinski, Aug. 26, 1961; children: Jacquelyn, David, Jason, Patricia, Brian, Denise, Michael, Catherine. BS in Acctg., U. Ill., 1961; JD, Ill. Inst. Tech., 1965. Bar: Ill. 1965, U.S. Tax Ct. 1968, U.S. Dist. Ct. (no. dist.) Ill. 1971; CPA, Ill. Ptnr. Mayer, Brown & Platt, Chgo., 1961—. Bd. dirs. Levinson Ctr. for Handicapped Children, Chgo., 1970-75. Fellow Am. Coll. Probate Counsel; mem. Ill. Bar Assn., Chgo. Bar Assn. (agribus. com. 1978—, trust law com. 1969—, probate practice com. 1969—, com. on coms. 1983—, vice chmn. 1988-89, chmn. 1989-90, legis. com. of probate practice com. 1983—, chmn. and vice chmn. legis. com. of probate practice com. 1983-84, chmn. exec. com. of probate practice com. 1982-83, vice chmn. exec. com. 1981-82, sec. exec. com. 1980-81, div. chmn. 78-79, div. vice chmn. 1977-78, div. sec. 1976-77, Appreciation award 1982-83), Chgo. Estate Planning Council. Roman Catholic. Club: Union League (Chgo.). Home: 429 Willow Wood Dr Palatine IL 60067-3831 Office: Mayer Brown & Platt 190 S La Salle St Chicago IL 60603-3410

MARSHALL, JOHN DONALD, JR., lawyer; b. Spartanburg, S.C., Oct. 17, 1950. BA in Polit. Sci. with high honors, Clemson (S.C.) U., 1972; JD, Emory U., 1975. Bar: Ga. 1975, U.S. Dist. Ct. (no. dist.) Ga., U.S. Supreme Ct. Pvt. practice Atlanta, 1975; cons. atty. Treatment Alternatives to Street Crime program, Atlanta, 1975-76; asst. contract officer Ga. State U., Atlanta, 1976-78, atty., asst. to exec. v.p. and provost, 1979-86, asst. v.p. legal affairs, 1986—; speaker in field; mem. Gov.'s Commn. on Criminal Justice Standards and Goals, 1974, 1975; asst. prof. polit. sci. and ednl. adminstrn., 1979-86. Cons. editor Ashe-Eric Higher Edn. Reports. Chmn. heart fund steering com. Fulton County Heart Assn., 1984, sec.-treas. bd., 1982-83, chmn. spl. events com., 1981-83, v.p., 1986-88, pres. 1988—, bd. dirs., bd. dirs. Hemophilia of Ga. Mem. ABA, Nat. Assn. Coll. and Univ. Attys. (bd. dirs. 1986-87), Am. Judicature Soc., Phi Kappa Phi (past pres. Ga. State U. chpt.). Home: 1237 Cumberland Rd NE Atlanta GA 30306-2219 Office: U System Ga Bd Regents Ga State U Asst Vp Legal Affairs Atlanta GA 30303

MARSHALL, JOHN ELBERT, III, foundation executive; b. Providence, July 2, 1942; s. John Elbert Jr. and Millicent Edna (Paige) M.; m. Diana M. Healy, Aug. 16, 1968; children: Nelson John, Priscilla Anne. B.A., Brown U., 1964. Advt. mgr. U.N. Alloy Steel Corp., Boston, 1968-70; assoc. dir. devel. Brown U., 1970-74; exec. dir. R.I. Found., Providence, 1974-79; v.p. Kresge Found., Troy, Mich., 1979-82, exec. v.p., 1982-87, pres., 1987—, trustee, 1991—; CEO, 1993—; bd. dirs., former chmn. Coun. Mich. Founds.; chmn. Mich. Cmty. Found. Youth Project. Bd. dirs. Southeastern Mich. chpt. United Way, Mich. Campus Compact; former bd. dirs., vice chmn. Family Svc. Detroit and Wayne County; past pres. Bloomfield Village Assn.; former trustee Coun. on Founds., Washington. Office: Kresge Found PO Box 3151 Troy MI 48007-3151

MARSHALL, JOHN L., III, construction company executive; b. 1934. Grad., Brown U., 1957. With Marshall Contractors, Inc., Rumford, R.I., 1957-63, pres., treas., 1963—. Office: Marshall Contractors Inc 75 Newman Ave Rumford RI 02916-1960

MARSHALL, JOHN PATRICK, lawyer; b. Bklyn., July 3, 1950; s. Harry W. and Mary Margaret (Kelly) M.; m. Cheryl J. Garvey, Aug. 10, 1975; children: Kelly Blake, Logan Brooke. BA, Rutgers U., 1972; JD cum laude, N.Y. Law Sch., 1976. Bar: N.Y. 1977, N.J. 1977, U.S. Dist. Ct. N.J. 1977, U.S. Dist. Ct. (so. and ea. dists.) N.Y. 1978, U.S. Ct. Appeals (3rd cir.) 1982, U.S. Dist. Ct. (no. dist.) N.Y. 1991. Assoc. Kelley Drye & Warren, N.Y.C., 1976-84; ptnr. Kelley Drye & Warren, N.Y.C. and Parsippany, 1985—; bd. dirs. Am. Foreign Shipping Co., Inc., Westfield, N.J. Editorial bd. N.Y. Law Sch. Law Rev., 1975-76, staff mem., 1974-75; contbr. articles to profl. jours. Mem. jud. screening com. N.Y. County Dem. Com., N.Y. County New Dem. Coalition, 1988; v.p. Humanitarian Found. for Nicaragua, 1991. Fellow Am. Bar Found.; mem. ABA, N.Y. State Bar Assn. (sec. com. on cts. and the cmty. 1993—), N.Y. County Lawyers' Assn. (sec. 1984-87, mem. com. on Supreme Ct. 1984-94, mem. legal edn., admission to bar and lawyer placement com. 1983-93), Am. Arbitration Assn. (nat. panel of arbitrators, N.Y. and N.J. regions 1991—, mem. corp. counsel com. 1993—), Assn. of Bar of City of N.Y. (sec. judiciary com. 1989-92, mem. com. on arbitration 1994—). Office: Kelley Drye & Warren 101 Park Ave New York NY 10178-0062 also: 5 Sylvan Way Parsippany NJ 07054-3805

MARSHALL, JOHN PAUL, broadcast engineer; came to U.S., 1967; Degree, U. Grenoble, France, 1963; student, U. Munich, 1964-65, San Francisco State, 1969-71, John O'Connell Tech. Inst., 1973-74. Mem. faculty law and econ. scis. U. Grenoble, 1963-64; mem. Expo '67 staff City of Montreal, Que., Can., 1967; filmmaker Cinemalab, San Francisco, 1970; engr. film and TV Able Studios, San Francisco, 1971-73; radio and TV engr. Sta. KALW-FM (Nat. Pub. Radio), San Francisco, 1973-74; broadcast engr. Sta. KRON-TV (NBC), San Francisco, 1974-91; intern Centre d'Informatique et de Maintenance Automatisme, Tunisia, 1993; founder Marshall U.S.A., San Francisco, 1994; freelance audio visual tech. advisor, San Francisco area, 1975—, lectr. radio, TV, motion pictures, 1975—, cons. customized electronic effects. Translator tech. pubs. and manuals, 1975—. Mus. dir., participant in theater prodns., 1950-59; active Boy Scouts Am. Govt. of France scholar, 1960-63. Mem. Rolls Royce Owners Club Found. (life), Internet Soc. 1995—. Avocations: classical pianist, polyglot, world traveler. Office: 298 4th Ave Ste 419 San Francisco CA 94118-2468 *Personal philosophy: (French proverb) Aide toi, le ciel t'aidera–Use your own resources and you will always receive a helping hand from heaven.*

MARSHALL, JOHN STEVEN, artist, educator, museum administrator. Spl. studies, U. of the South, 1979-80; AA, Motlow State Community Coll., Tullahoma, Tenn., 1981; BFA, Middle Tenn. State U., 1983; MFA, U. N.C., 1985. Registrar, curatorial asst. Weatherspoon Art Gallery, U. N.C. Greensboro, 1983-85, asst. curator, lectr., 1985, acting curator, 1986; instr./curator Meridian C.C., 1986—; dir. Meridian Mus. Art, 1986-89; represented by Artworks Gallery Laurel, Miss.; lectr. art various Tenn. and Miss. orgns.; curator, jury mem. various exhbns. One-man shows include Meridian Mus. Art, 1989, Miss. State U., 1990, 92, Miss. U. for Women, 1990, Tusculum Coll., 1992, Gen. Art Gallery, Miss., 1993; 2-person show Winfield Gallery, 1991; exhibited in group shows Elliot U. Ctr. Gallery, Brentwood and Nashville, 1984, Weatherspoon Art Gallery, Greensboro, 1985, 86, Waterworks Gallery, Winston-Salem, N.C., 1985, Meridian Mus. Art, 1987, 89, Casteel Art Gallery, Meridian, 1987, U. So. Miss., 1988, Greenville Art Gallery, 1988, Space One-Eleven Gallery, 1990, Birmingham-So. Coll., 1990, Winfield Gallery, 1991; represented in pvt. collections. Office: Meridian Community Coll 910 Hwy 19 N Meridian MS 39307-5890

MARSHALL, JOHN TREUTLEN, lawyer; b. Macon, Ga., Nov. 1, 1934; s. Hubert and Gladys (Lucas) M.; m. Katrine White, May 1, 1959; children: Allison, Rebecca, Paul, Mary Anne. BA, Vanderbilt U., 1956; LLB, Yale U., 1962. Bar: Ga. 1962, U.S. Dist. Ct. (no., mid. and so. dists.) Ga. 1962, U.S. Ct. Appeals (5th cir.) 1962, U.S. Supreme Ct. 1978, U.S. Ct. Appeals (11th cir.) 1982. Ptnr. Powell, Goldstein, Frazer & Murphy, Atlanta, 1962—; adj. prof. law Emory U. Sch. Law, 1968-86, mem. coun.; chmn. No. Dist. Ga. Bar Coun., 1989; chmn. Ga. State Commn. on Continuing Lawyer Competency, 1991-93. Bd. editors: Yale Law Jour. Bd dirs. Atlanta Legal Aid, 1972-73; trustee Ga. Inst. Continuing Legal Edn., 1984. Recipient S. Phillip Heiner award Atlanta Vol. Lawyers Assn., 1992, A. Gus Cleveland award Ga. State Commn. on Continuing Edn. Fellow Am. Coll. Trial Lawyers (state chmn. 1985-86), Am. Bar Found., Ga. Bar Found.; mem. ABA (ho. dels. 1976-86, Harrison Tweed award 1986), Atlanta Bar Assn. (pres. 1974-75, Charles E. Watkins Jr. award 1983), Ga. Inst. Trial Advocacy (chmn. 1982-83), Cherokee Town and Country Club, 191 Club, Lawyers Club. Office: Goldstein Frazer & Murphy 191 Peachtree St NE Fl 16 Atlanta GA 30303-1740

MARSHALL, JOSEPH FRANK, electronic engineer; b. Wyoming, Pa., Mar. 2, 1917; s. Anthony Marchel and Mary (Moosic) M.; m. Margaret Mary Kennedy, June 17, 1961. BSEE, Pa. State Coll., 1941; MSEE, Harvard U., 1951. Registered profl. engr., Mass. N.J. Devel. engr., project mgr. Stromberg Carlson Co., Rochester, N.Y., 1941-49; design engr., staff engr. Bell Aircraft Corp., Buffalo, 1952-60; fellow engr. Electronics div. Westinghouse, Balt., 1961-62; sr. staff engr. Avco Corp., Wilmington, Mass., 1962-64; rsch. electrical engr. Cornell Lab., Buffalo, 1964-65; systems engr. Radio div. Bendix, Balt., 1966-67, Raytheon Corp., Sudbury, Mass., 1967-69, Astro Electronics div. RCA, Princeton, N.J., 1969-72; broadcast engr. N.J. Pub. TV, Princeton, 1972-74; sr. staff engr. Office of Engring. Tech. FCC, Washington, 1974-92; with Luthier Acoustic Rsch., Pittsford, N.Y.; IRE subcom. mem. Industry Audio Amplifier Standards, 1944-46; served on EIA TR-8 ad hoc com. Nationwide Cellular Mobile Radio Standards, 1979-80. Violinist Pa. State Coll. Symphony Orch., 1937-40. Fellow Radio Club of Am., Inc.; mem. Inst. Elec./Electronics Inc. (life), Radio Club of Washington, Violin Soc. Am., Catgut Acoustical Soc. Inc., Harvard Club of Rochester, Eta Kappa Nu, Sigma Tau, Tau Beta Pi, Pi Mu Epsilon. Democrat. Roman Catholic. Achievements include patents for selective tuning and damping of partials of rods and method of clamping tunable rods for electronic carillons, for critical components employed in a Navy secure missile command guidance system. Home: 9 Kimberly Rd Pittsford NY 14534-1505

MARSHALL, KATHRYN SUE, lawyer; b. Decatur, Ill., Sept. 12, 1942; d. Edward Elda and Frances M. (Minor) Lahniers; m. Robert S. Marshall, Sept. 5, 1964 (div. Apr. 1984); m. Robert J. Arndt, June 25, 1988; children: Stephen Edward, Christine Elizabeth. BA, Lake Forest Coll., 1964; JD, John Marshall Law Sch., 1976. Intern U.S. Atty.'s Office, Chgo., 1974-76; mng. ptnr. Marshall and Marshall Ltd., Waukegan, Ill., 1976-84; pvt. practice Waukegan, 1984-93. Contbr. articles to profl. jours. Cert. jud. candidate Dem. party, Lake County, Ill.; bd. mem. Camerata Soc., Lake Forest; bd. mem. v.p. Lake Forest (Ill.) Fine Arts Ensemble. Fellow ABA (gov. 1993—), Ill. State Bar Assn., Coll. Law Practice Mgmt.; mem. Navy League (life). Avocations: boating, reading, travel.

MARSHALL, MARGARET HILARY, lawyer; b. Newcastle, Natal, South Africa, Sept. 1, 1944; came to U.S., 1968; d. Bernard Charles and Hilary A.D. (Anderton) M.; m. Samuel Shapiro, Dec. 14, 1968 (div. Apr. 1982); m. Anthony Lewis, Sept. 23, 1984. BA, Witwatersrand U., Johannesburg, 1966; MEd, Harvard U., 1969; JD, Yale U., 1976; LHD (hon.), Regis Coll., 1993. Bar: Mass. 1977, U.S. Dist. Ct. Mass., U.S. Dist. Ct. N.H., U.S. Dist. Ct. D.C., U.S. Dist. Ct. (ea. dist.) Mich., U.S. Tax Ct., U.S. Ct. Appeals (1st, 11th and D.C. cirs.), U.S. Supreme Ct. Assoc. Csaplar & Bok, Boston, 1976-83, ptnr., 1983-89; ptnr. Choate, Hall & Stewart, Boston, 1989-92; v.p., gen. counsel Harvard U., Cambridge, Mass., 1992—; mem. jud. nominating coun., 1987-90, 92; chairperson ct. rules subcom. Alternative Dispute Resolution Working Group, 1985-87; mem. fed. appts. commn., 1993; mem. adv. com. Supreme Judicial Ct., 1989-92. mem. gender equality com., 1989-94; mem. civil justice adv. group U.S. Dist. Ct. Mass., 1991-93; spl. counsel Jud. Conduct Commn., 1988-92; trustee Mass. Continuing Legal Edn., Inc., 1990-92. Trustee Africa News, Africa Fund, Regis Coll., 1993—; bd. dirs. Internat. Design Conf., Aspen, 1986-92, Boston Mcpl. Res. Bur., 1990—, Supreme Judicial Ct. Hist. Soc., 1990-94, sec., 1990-94. Fellow Am. Bar Found. (state chair); mem. Boston Bar Assn. (treas. 1988-89, v.p 1989-90, pres.-elect 1990-91, pres. 1991-92), Internat. Women's Forum, Mass. Women's Forum, Boston Club, Phi Beta Kappa (hon.). Home: 8 Lowell St Cambridge MA 02138-4726 Office: Harvard U Massachusetts Hall Cambridge MA 02138

MARSHALL, MARGO, artistic director; b. Louisville, Nov. 3, 1934; d. Irving Robert and Elizabeth (Greenleaf) Sidney; m. Jay C. Marshall, 1952 (div. 1971); 1 child, Dennis. BA, U. Houston, 1953. Pvt. tchr. dance Houston, 1950-58, owner, operator pvt. dance sch., 1958—; guest tchr. Joffrey Sch., N.Y., Internat. Acad. Dance, Portugal, Louisville Ballet, Boston Ballet's Summer Workshops, 1981-85, The Place, London, and others; parttime faculty mem. High Sch. for the Performing and Visual Arts, Houston; tchr. dance U. Houston, Sam Houston State U. Artistic dir. City Ballet Houston, 1967—; mem. dance panel Cultural Arts Coun. Houston; advisor Tex. Commn. on the Arts. Recipient Adjudicator award Mid-States Regional Ballet Assn., 1986. Mem. Southwestern Regional Ballet Assn. (officer 1965—). Office: City Ballet 9902 Long Point Rd Houston TX 77055-4199

MARSHALL, MARTIN VIVAN, business administration educator, business consultant; b. Kansas City, July 22, 1922; s. Vivan Dean and Marie (Church) M.; m. Rosanne Borden, Sept. 5, 1951 (dec. Feb. 8, 1986); children: Martin Dean, Michael Borden, Neil McNair; m. Hildegard Meyer, June 24, 1988. A.B., U. Mo., 1943; M.B.A., Harvard U., 1947, D.C.S., 1953. Instr. mktg. and advt. U. Kans., 1947-48; mem. faculty Harvard U., 1948—, Henry R. Byers prof. bus. adminstrn., 1960—, chmn. mktg. area faculty, 1962-66, chmn. Smaller Co. Mgmt. Program, 1981-84; chmn. Owner/Pres. Mgmt. Program, 1985-94; mem. faculty Inst. Ednl. Mgmt. Harvard U., 1981-90; cons. U.S. and internat. bus., 1950—; dir. ann. seminar mktg. and advt. Am. Advt. Fedn., 1958-78; vis. prof. mktg. IMEDE Mgmt. Inst., Lausanne, 1965-66; sr. prof., ednl. dir. Internat. Mktg. Inst., 1967-71; vis. prof. Indian Inst. Mgmt., Agra, 1968, IPADE, Mexico City, 1969, U. Melbourne, Australia, 1977, 79. Author: Automatic Merchandising, 1954, (with N.H. Borden) Advertising Management, 1960, Notes on Marketing, 1983, 88, 90, 92, 93. Bd. dirs. Youth Svcs. Internat., Inc., 1994—. Served to lt. (s.g.) USNR, 1943-46. Home: 130 Mount Auburn St Apt 309 Cambridge MA 02138-5779 Office: Harvard U Cumnock Hall Boston MA 02163

MARSHALL, MARVIN GIFFIN, real estate company executive; b. Linn County, Kans., July 4, 1937; m. Patricia Jean Hellman, July 29, 1978; children: Taylor Alexandra, Maxwell Giffin, Morgan D. Doran, Edwin M. Dir. real estate Crown Ctr., Kansas City, Mo.; pres., CEO Cullen Ctr. Inc., Houston, 1986-90; pres., CEO Bramalea Inc. Toronto, Ont., Can., 1990—, also bd. dirs.; bd. dirs. Can. Inst. Pub. Real Estate Cos., Inter-City Products Corp.; bd. dirs. adv. bd. 1st Am. Title Ins. Co. Office: Bramalea Inc, 1 Queen St E Ste 2300, Toronto, ON Canada M5C 2Y9

MARSHALL, NANCY HAIG, library administrator; b. Stamford, Conn., Nov. 3, 1932; d. Harry Percival and Dorothy Charlotte (Price) Haig; m. William Hubert Marshall, Dec. 28, 1953; children—Bruce Davis, Gregg Price, Lisa Reynolds, Jeanine Haig. BA., Ohio Wesleyan U., 1953; M.A.L.S., U. Wis., 1972. Dir. Wis. Inter Libr. Svcs., Madison, 1972-79; Reference librarian U. Wis., Madison, 1972, assoc. dir. univ. libraries, 1979-86; dean univ. librs. Coll. William and Mary, Williamsburg, Va., 1986—; mem. adv. com. Copyright Office, Washington, 1978-82; dir. USBE, Inc., Washington, 1983-86; trustee OCLC, Inc., Dublin, Ohio, 1982-88. Contbr. articles to profl. jours. Mem. ALA (coun. 1980-88, 90-93), Wis. Libr. Assn. (Libr. of the Yr. award 1982), Va. Libr. Assn., Beta Phi Mu. Office: Coll William and Mary E G Swem Libr Williamsburg VA 23185

MARSHALL, NATALIE JUNEMANN, economics educator; b. Milw., June 13, 1929; d. Harold E. and Myrtle (Findlay) Junemann; m. Howard D. Marshall, Aug. 7, 1954 (dec. 1972); children: Frederick S., Alison B.; m. Phillip Shatz, May 27, 1988. AB, Vassar Coll., 1951; MA, Columbia U., 1952, PhD, 1963, JD, 1994. Instr. Vassar Coll., Poughkeepsie, N.Y., 1952-54, 59, 60-63, dean studies, prof. econs., 1973-75, v.p. for student affairs, 1975-80, v.p. for adminstrn. and student services and prof. econs. 1980-91, prof. econs., 1991-94; teaching fellow Wesleyan U., Middletown, Conn., 1955-56; from asst. prof. to prof. SUNY, New Paltz, 1964-73; prof. econs. Vassar Coll., Poughkeepsie, N.Y., 1973-94; of counsel Anderson, Banks, Curran and Donoghue, Mt. Kisco, N.Y., 1994—. Editor: (with Howard Marshall) The History of Economic Thought, 1968; Keynes, Updated or Outdated, 1970; author: (with Howard Marshall) Collective Bargaining, 1971. Trustee St. Francis Hosp., 1979-88, Area Fund Dutchess County, 1981-87, Coll. New Rochelle, 1994—, Hudson Valley Philharm., 1985-92, pers., 1989-91. Mem. AAUP, Am. Assn. Higher Edn., Am. Econ. Assn., AAUW (v.p. N.Y. State div. 1964-66), Poughkeepsie Vassar Club (pres. 1965-67). Home: PO Box 2470 Poughkeepsie NY 12603-8470

MARSHALL, PAUL MACKLIN, oil company executive; b. Toronto, Ont., Can., Sept. 21, 1923; s. Griffith Macklin and Josephine Angela (Hodgson) M.; m. Carol Ann Dickie; children: Blake, Gregory, Jonathan, Kirk. B.C.L.,

McGill U., Montreal, Que., Can., 1949. Bar: called to bar Que. 1949. Legal asst. Sun Life Assurance Co., Montreal, 1949-52; exec. asst. to Canadian minister nat. def., Ottawa, Ont., 1952-54; with Canadian Chem. & Cellulose Ltd. Co., Montreal, 1955-69; v.p. Canadian Chem. & Cellulose Co. Ltd., 1958-59; v.p. sec.-treas. Chemcell Ltd., 1959-67, chmn. bd., 1967-69; v.p. treas. Columbia Cellulose Co. Ltd., 1959-62, pres., chief exec. officer, 1962-66; v.p., treas. Can. Chem. Co. Ltd., Celgar Ltd., 1959-62; v.p. Hamilton Bros. Petroleum Corp., 1969-72; pres. Hamilton Bros. Exploration Co., Denver, 1972; exec. v.p. Hamilton Bros. Oil Co., 1972; pres. Canadian Hydrocarbons Ltd., Calgary, Alta., 1972-77, Westmin Resources, Ltd., 1978-90; vice chmn. Brascan Ltd., 1987—; pres., dir. Brascade Resources, Inc.; dir. Brascan Ltd.; Noranda Mines Inc.; chmn. Norcen Energy Resources Ltd.; bd. dirs. Westinghouse Can. Inc., Journey's End Corp., M.A. Hanna Co. Lt. Royal Can. Army, 1943-45. Club: Toronto; Petroleum (Calgary). Office: Brascan Ltd, BCE Pl, Ste 4400 181 Bay St PO Box 762, Toronto, ON Canada M5J 2T3*

MARSHALL, (C.) PENNY, actress, director; b. N.Y.C., Oct. 15, 1943; d. Anthony W. and Marjorie Irene (Ward) M.; m. Michael Henry (div.); 1 child, Tracy Lee; m. Robert Reiner, Apr. 10, 1971 (div. 1979). Student, U. N.Mex., 1961-64. Appeared on numerous television shows, including The Odd Couple, 1972-74, Friends and Lovers (co-star), 1974, Let's Switch, 1974, Wives (pilot), 1975, Chico and the Man, 1975, Mary Tyler Moore, 1975, Heaven Help Us, 1975, Saturday Night Live, 1975-77, Happy Days, 1975, Battle of Network Stars (ABC special), 1976, Barry Manilow special, 1976, The Tonight Show, 1976-77, Dinah, 1976-77, Mike Douglas Show, 1975-77, Merv Griffin Show, 1976-77, Blansky's Beauties, 1977, Network Battle of the Sexes, 1977, Laverne and Shirley (co-star), 1976-83; TV films More Than Friends, 1978, Love Thy Neighbor, 1984; appeared in motion pictures How Sweet It Is, 1967, The Savage Seven, 1968, The Grasshopper, 1970, 1941, 1979, Movers and Shakers, 1985, The Hard Way, 1991, Hocus Pocus, 1993; dir. films: Jumpin' Jack Flash, 1986, Big, 1988, Awakenings, 1990, A League of Their Own, 1992, Renaissance Man, 1994; co-exec. prodr. TV series A League of Their Own, 1993 (also dir. episodes). Office: care CAA/Todd Smith 9830 Wilshire Blvd Beverly Hills CA 90212-1825*

MARSHALL, PHILIPS WILLIAMSON, insurance agency executive; b. Orange, N.J., Aug. 28, 1935; s. Herbert Jr. and Evelyn Lenore (Philips) M.; m. Sandra Richards Vose, Mar. 29, 1958; children: Tracy Anne Marshall Santa Florentina, Laurie Williamson Marshall Holbrook. BS in Econs., U. Pa., 1957. Enlisted U.S. Army, 1958, advanced through grades to capt., 1964, resigned, 1970; underwriter Continental Ins. Co., N.Y.C., 1957-60; salesman A.W. Marshall & Co., Newark, 1960-65; spl. agt. Aetna Ins. Co., Millburn, N.J., 1965-66; v.p. Woodward & Williamson, Jersey City, 1966-88; pres. Woodward & Williamson, 1988—; pres. Ind. Ins. Agts. Hudson County, Jersey City, 1979-80. Chmn. ARC-Millburn (N.J.)-Short Hills, 1971-74, Harriman Div. coun. ARC, N.Y.C., 1977; chief Millburn Aux. Police, Millburn, 1976-81. Mem. Ind. Ins. Agts. N.J. (exec. com. 1982-86, Presdl. Citation 1986), Ducks Unltd. (chmn. State of N.J. 1990-92), Short Hills Club. Republican. Episcopalian. Avocations: tennis, fishing, hunting. Home: 24 Meadowview Ln Berkeley Heights NJ 07922-1370 Office: Woodward & Williamson 25A Hanover Rd Florham Park NJ 07932

MARSHALL, PHILOMENA ANN, health care administration; b. Oak Park, Ill., Mar. 21, 1949; d. John and Marie (Desmond) Piscopo; m. Robert Paul Marshall, June 17, 1972. BS in Nursing, Loyola U., 1972; postgrad., U. Minn., 1989—. Registered Nurse. Staff nurse Rush Pres. St. Luke's Med. Ctr., Chgo., 1972-73; pub. health nurse Vis. Nurse Assn., Chgo., 1973-75, Lake County Health Dept., Waukegan, Ill., 1975-76; mem. faculty St. Francis Hosp. Sch. Nursing, Evanston, Ill., 1976-78; dir. home care and hospice St. Joseph Med. Ctr., Brainerd, Minn., 1978-83; dir. family home care Empire Health Svcs., Spokane, Wash., 1983-87; dir. sr. svcs. West Suburban Hosp. Med. Ctr., Oak Park, 1987-89, v.p nursing, 1989—. Bd. dirs. United Way, Brainerd, 1980-82, Spokane, 1985-86; chmn. Ideal Community Svc. Orgn., Pequot Lakes, Minn., 1981-82. Mem. Am. Soc. Aging, Nat. Council on Aging, Nat. Assn. Home Care, Ill. Council Home Health Services, Alumni Assn. Minn. Roman Catholic. Avocations: camping, handmade crafts. Office: St Margaret Hosp 5454 Hohman Ave Hammond IN 46320

MARSHALL, PRENTICE H., JR., lawyer; b. Oak Park, Ill., Sept. 5, 1952. BA, U. Ill., 1974; JD magna cum laude, U. Iowa, 1977. Bar: Ill. 1977, U.S. Ct. Appeals (7th cir.) 1978, U.S. Dist. Ct. (no. dist.) Ill. 1978. Law clk. to Hon. Philip W. Tone U.S. Ct. Appeals (7th cir.), 1977-78; ptnr. Sidley & Austin, Chgo.; adj. prof. law John Marshall Law Sch., 1979-82, ITT, Chgo., 1985-88. Office: Sidley & Austin 1 First Nat Plz Chicago IL 60603

MARSHALL, PRENTICE HENRY, federal judge; b. 1926. B.S., 1949; J.D., U. Ill. 1951. Bar: Ill. bar 1951. Judge U.S. Dist. Ct. (no. dist.) Ill., 1973—; assoc. firm Johnston Thompson Raymond & Mayer, Chgo., 1953-60; ptnr. Raymond Mayer Jenner & Block, Chgo., 1961-67; spl. asst. atty. gen. State of Ill., 1964-67; hearing officer Ill. Fair Employment Practices Commn., 1967-72; faculty Am. Law Inst.; adj. prof. law Ill. Inst. Tech.-Chgo.-Kent Coll. Law, 1975—; prof. law U. Ill., 1967-73. Served with USN, 1944-46. Mem. ABA, Am. Coll. Trial Lawyers, Am. Law Inst., Am. Judicature Soc., Chgo. Bar Assn., Bar Assn. of 7th Cir., Order of the Coif, Phi Kappa Phi. Office: US Dist Ct 111 N Canal St Bldg 6 Chicago IL 60606-7206

MARSHALL, RICHARD, art historian, curator; b. L.A., 1947. B.A. Calif. State U., Long Beach, 1969; postgrad. U. Calif., Irvine, 1969-70, study program Whitney Mus. Am. Art, 1973-74. Advisor Mus. Modern Art, N.Y., 1974-77, Whitney Mus. Am. Art, curator, 1974-93. Art editor Paris Rev. mag., 1977-94.

MARSHALL, RICHARD TREEGER, lawyer; b. N.Y.C., May 17, 1925; s. Edward and Sydney (Treeger) M.; m. Dorothy M. Goodman, June 4, 1950; children—Abigail Ruth Marshall Bergerson, Daniel Brooks; m. 2d, Sylvia J. Kelley, June 10, 1979. B.S., Cornell U., 1948; J.D., Yale U., 1951. Bar: Tex. 1952, U.S. Ct. Appeals (5th cir.) 1966, U.S. Ct. Appeals (10th cir.) 1980, U.S. Supreme Ct., 1959. Sole practice, El Paso, Tex., 1952-59, 61-79; assoc. Fryer & Milstead, El Paso, 1952; sr. ptnr. Marshall & Wendorf, El Paso, 1959-61; sr. ptnr. Marshall & Volk, El Paso, 1979-81; sr. atty. Richard T. Marshall & Assocs., P.C., El Paso, 1981-85; sr. ptnr. Marshall, Thomas & Winters, El Paso, 1985-87; sr. atty. Marshall & Winters, 1987-88; sr. atty. Marshall, Sherrod & Winters, 1988-90, pvt. practice law, 1990—; instr. polit. sci. U. Tex., El Paso, 1961-62; instr. ins. law C.L.U. tng. course Am. Coll.; officer, dir. Advance Funding, Inc., El Paso. Mem. ABA, Coll. State Bar Tex., El Paso Bar Assn., El Paso Trial Lawyers Assn. (pres. 1965-66), Tex. Trial Lawyers Assn., Assn. Trial Lawyers Am. (sec. personal injury law sect. 1967-68, nat. sec. 1969-70, sec.-treas. environ. law sect. 1970-71, vice chmn. family law litigation sect. 1971-72); Roscoe Pound-Am. Trial Lawyers Found. (Commn. on Profl. Responsibility 1979-82). Editor: El Paso Trial Lawyers Rev., 1973-80; contbr. articles to legal jours. Office: 6070 Gateway Blvd E Ste 508 El Paso TX 79905-2031

MARSHALL, ROBERT CHARLES, computer company executive; b. Berwyn, Ill., June 19, 1931; s. Joseph H. and Rose M.; m. Sarane Virruso, Aug. 1, 1954; children—Joseph, Lisa, Jim. B.S.E.E., Heald Engring. Coll., 1956; M.B.A., Pepperdine U., 1976. Engr. Lawrence Radiation Lab., Livermore, Calif., 1956-64; systems engr. Electronics Assos., Palo Alto, Calif., 1964-69; v.p. mfg. Diablo Systems, Hayward, Calif., 1969-75; with Tandem Computers, Inc., Cupertino, Calif., 1975—; sr. v.p., chief operating officer, dir. Tandem Computers, Inc., 1979—. Served with U.S. Army, 1952-54. Office: Tandem Computers Inc 19333 Vallco Pky Cupertino CA 95014-2506

MARSHALL, ROBERT GERALD, language educator; b. Houston, Feb. 19, 1919; s. Luther Pierce and Nancy (May) M.; m. Kathryn Keller, Aug. 27, 1949; children—Christoph Patton, Ann Patterson, Philip Sanburn. B.A. Rice U., 1941, M.A., 1946; Ph.D., Yale, 1950; diploma, U. Siena, Italy, 1954. Asst., then instr. French Yale, 1947-49; asst. prof. fgn. langs. Tex. Women's U., 1949-51; mem. faculty Wells Coll., Aurora, N.Y., 1951—; prof. Romance langs. Wells Coll., 1958—, chmn. dept., 1956-72, coordinator summer programs, 1963-67; dir. NDEA Inst. Advanced Study French, 1963-67;

prof.-in-charge Sweet Briar Coll. Jr. Year In Paris, France, 1967-68; dir. Jr. Year in France, 1972-84. Contbr. to profl. jours.; editor-in-chief: Catalogue of 16th Century Italian Books in American Libraries, 1970; editor: (with F. C. St. Aubyn) Les Mouches (Sartre), 1963, Trois Pièces Surréalistes, 1969, Abraham de Vermeil in Textes et Contexts, 1986, American, French, Italian Relationships in Mélanges André Bordeaux, 1988; contbr. to Columbia Dictionary of Modern European Lit., 18th Century Bibliography. Commr. Historic Area Commn., St. Michaels, Historic Preservation Commn., Talbot County, Md. Served to capt. AUS, 1942-46. Decorated chevalier dans L'Ordre des Palmes Academiques France); R.G. Marshall scholarship named in his honor Sweet Briar Coll.; grantee Am. Council Learned Socs., 1953; Fulbright research grantee Rome, Italy, 1959-60. Mem. Am. Assn. Tchrs. French (v.p. Central N.Y. chpt. 1967-68, pres. 1979-84), South Atlantic Modern Lang. Assn., Soc. Profs. français à l'Etranger. Episcopalian. Home: PO Box 1059 Saint Michaels MD 21663-1059

MARSHALL, ROBERT HERMAN, economics educator; b. Harrisburg, Pa., Dec. 6, 1929; s. Mathias and Mary (Bubich) M.; m. Billie Marie Sullivan, May 31, 1958; children: Mellisa Frances, Howard Hylton, Robert Charles. A.B. magna cum laude, Franklin and Marshall Coll., 1951; M.A., Ohio State U., 1952, Ph.D., 1957. Teaching asst. Ohio State U., 1952-57; mem. faculty, then prof. econs. U. Ariz., Tucson, 1957—, head dept., 1967-69; dir. Internat. Bus. Studies Project, 1969-71; research observer Sci.-Industry Program, Hughes Aircraft Co., Tucson, summer 1959. Author: Commercial Banking in Arizona: Structure and Performance Since World War II, 1966, (with others) The Monetary Process, 2d edit, 1980. Bd. dirs. Com. for Econ. Opportunity, Tucson, 1968-69. Faculty fellow Pacific Coast Banking Sch., summer 1974. Mem. Am. Econ. Assn., Phi Beta Kappa, Beta Gamma Sigma, Pi Gamma Mu, Phi Kappa Phi, Delta Sigma Pi. Democrat. Roman Catholic. Home: 6700 N Abington Rd Tucson AZ 85743-9795

MARSHALL, ROBERT LEWIS, musicologist, educator; b. N.Y.C., Oct. 12, 1939; s. Saul and Pearl (Shapiro) M.; m. Traute Maass, Sept. 9, 1966; children—Eric, Brenda. A.B., Columbia U., 1960; M.F.A., Princeton U., 1962, Ph.D., 1968; postgrad., U. Hamburg, W. Ger., 1965. Instr. dept. music U. Chgo., 1966-68, asst. prof. 1968-71, assoc. prof., chmn. dept., 1972-78, prof., 1978-83; prof. Brandeis U., 1983—, chmn. dept., 1985-93, incumbent endowed chair Louis, Frances and Jeffrey Sachar prof. music, 1986—; vis. assoc. prof. Princeton U., 1971-72; endowed prof. Univ. Ala., 1994; mem. rev. bd. rsch. materials program NEH, 1982, rev. bd. edits., 1991. Author: The Compositonal Process of J.S. Bach, 2 vols, 1972, The Music of Johann Sebastian Bach: The Sources; The Style; The Significance, 1989, Mozart Speaks: Views on Music, Musicians and the World, 1991; editor New Bach Edit., Eighteenth Century Keyboard Music, 1994; contbr. articles to musical jours. in U.S., Gt. Brit., Germany. Mem. music adv. bd. Ill. Arts Council, 1977-79. Recipient Deems Taylor award ASCAP, 1990; NEH fellow, 1978-79; Hon. Harold Spivacke consultantship Library of Congress. Mem. Am. Musicol. Soc. (bd. dirs. 1974-75, v.p. 1985-86, editl. bd. jour. 1975-80, rev. editor 1986-89, chmn. publs. com. 1991-94, Otto Kinkeldey prize 1974), New Bach Soc. (chmn. Am. chpt. 1977-80), Phi Beta Kappa. Home: 100 Chestnut St Newton MA 02165-2538 Office: Music Dept Brandeis U Waltham MA 02254

MARSHALL, RUSSELL FRANK, research company executive; b. Fort Madison, Iowa, Sept. 10, 1941; s. William Frank and Dorothy Eleanor (Mikels) M.; m. Mary Jean Bailey, June 19, 1966; children: William Russell, Robert Scott, Gregory Howard. AB, Monmouth Coll., 1963; MS, U. Ill., 1965, PhD, 1971. Rsch. engr. Materials Rsch. Lab, Urbana, Ill., 1970-75; mgr. acad. computing Drake U., Des Moines, 1975-80; v.p. GMI Ltd., Des Moines, 1980-83; sr. v.p., treas. Communication Devel. Co., West Des Moines, 1983—. Contbr. articles to profl. jours. Active Boy Scouts Am., 1982—; mem. Des Moines Coummunity Theatre. Grantee AEC, 1964-71. Mem. Assn. Computing Machinery, Am. Phys. Soc., Assn. for Systems Mgmt., Sigma Xi. Presbyterian. Avocations: music, reading. Home: 1625 19th St West Des Moines IA 50265-1622 Office: Communication Devel Co 2910 Westown Pky Ste 100 West Des Moines IA 50266-1341

MARSHALL, SCOTT, advertising agency executive. V.p. Ogilvy & Mather, N.Y.C., sr. v.p., 1986-88; pres. Cole & Weber, Inc., Seattle, 1988—. Office: Cole & Weber Inc 308 Occidental Ave S Seattle WA 98104-2840

MARSHALL, SHEILA HERMES, lawyer; b. N.Y.C., Jan. 17, 1934; d. Paul Milton and Julia Angela (Meagher) Hermes; m. James Josiah Marshall, Sept. 30, 1967; 1 child, James J.H. BA, St. John's U., N.Y.C., 1959; JD, NYU, 1963. Bar: N.Y. 1964, U.S. Ct. Appeals (2d, 3d, 5th and D.C. cirs.), U.S. Supreme Ct. 1970. Assoc. LeBoeuf, Lamb, Greene & MacRae, N.Y.C., 1963-72, ptnr., 1973—; specialist in field. Mem. ABA, N.Y. State Bar Assn., Assn. of Bar of City of N.Y. Republican. Home: 1035 Park Ave New York NY 10028-0912 Office: LeBoeuf Lamb Greene & MacRae 125 W 55th St New York NY 10019-4513

MARSHALL, SHERRIE, newspaper editor. Metro editor Star Tribune, Mpls. Office: Star Tribune 425 Portland Ave Minneapolis MN 55488-0001*

MARSHALL, STANLEY, former educator, business executive; b. Cheswick, Pa., Jan. 27, 1923; s. Walter W. and Mildred (Crawford) M.; m. Ruth Cratty, June 13, 1944 (div. 1966); children: David, Sue, John; m. Shirley Ann Slade, Sept. 10, 1966; children: Kimberly, James Andrew. B.S., Slippery Rock (Pa.) State Tchrs. Coll., 1947; M.S., Syracuse U., 1950, Ph.D., 1956. Tchr. sci. Mynderse Acad., Seneca Falls, N.Y., 1947-52; asst. prof. sci. State U. N.Y. Coll. Edn., Cortland, 1953-55; asso. prof. State U. N.Y. Coll. Edn., 1956-57, prof., 1957-58; instr. Syracuse U., 1955-56; prof., head dept. sci. edn. Fla. State U., Tallahassee, 1958; asso. dean Fla. State U. (Sch. Edn.), 1965-67; dean Fla. State U. (Coll. Edn.), 1967-69, pres., 1969-76; pres. Sonitrol of Tallahassee, Inc., 1978-87, COMSAFE Inc. 1981-84; pres. James Madison Inst. for Pub. Policy Studies, 1987-90, chmn. bd. dirs., 1990—; pres. Marshall Land Co. 1989—; pres. So. Scholarship and Research Found., 1968-69. Author: (with E. Burkman) Current Trends in Science Education, 1966, (with I. Podendorf and C. Swartz) The Basic Science Program, 1965; Editor: Jour. of Research in Sci. Teaching, 1962-66; Mem. editorial bd.: Science World, 1962-65; Contbr. articles to profl. jours. Mem. U.S. Navy Sec.'s adv. bd. edn. and tng. U.S. Army adv. panel ROTC, 1975-79; bd. regents Nat. Libr. Medicine, 1970-75; bd. dirs. Tallahassee Meml. Regional Med. Ctr., 1980-86; mem. Citizens Commn. on the Fla. Cabinet, 1995—. Served with U.S. Army, 1943-46, ETO. Fellow AAAS; mem. Am. Inst. Physics, Nat. Sci. Tchrs. Assn., Fla. Acad. Scis., Fla. Assn. Sci. Tchrs., So. Assn. State Univs. and Land-Grant Colls (pres. 1971-72), Nat. Assn. Research Sci. Teaching, NEA, Fla. Edn. Assn., Sigma Xi, Phi Delta Kappa, Kappa Delta Pi. Home: 5000 Brill Pt Tallahassee FL 32312-5600

MARSHALL, SUSAN, artistic director; b. Hershey, Pa.. Student, Juilliard Sch. Founder, artistic dir. Susan Marshall and Co., N.Y.C., 1982—. Recipient Dance Mag. award, 1995. Office: Susan Marshall & Co 2130 Broadway New York NY 10023*

MARSHALL, TERRELL, lawyer; b. Little Rock, July 14, 1908; s. J. C. and Jenice (Thomas) Marshall-Small; m. Lourie Darland, Jan. 2, 1927; 1 son, Terrell. LL.B., Ark. Law Sch., 1931, J.D., 1979. Bar: Ark. 1931, U.S. Supreme Ct. 1938. Pvt. practice in Little Rock, 1931-85; atty. Pulaski County Legal Aid Bur., 1938-42. Contbr. to: Birds of Ark, 1951. Bd. dirs. Ark. Property Owners Found.; trustee Ark. Law Sch. Fellow Ark. Bar Found.; mem. ABA, Ark. Bar Assn. (past pres., mem. exec. com.). Pulaski County Bar Assn. (past pres.), Am. Judicature Soc. Club: Lakeside Country (Saline County, Ark.) (past pres.). Address: 372 Skyline Dr North Little Rock AR 72116-9226

MARSHALL, THOM, columnist. Columnist The Houston Chronicle, Tex. Office: Houston Chronicle 801 Texas St Houston TX 77002-2996

MARSHALL, THOMAS, chemical company executive; b. Pitts., 1929. Grad., U. Pitts., 1957. With USX Corp., 1949-86, pres. U.S. Diversified Group, 1986; chmn., chief exec. officer Aristech Chem. Corp., Pitts., 1986—, also bd. dirs. With USN, 1946-49. Office: Aristech Chem Corp 600 Grant St Pittsburgh PA 15219-2702

MARSHALL, THOMAS CARLISLE, applied physics educator; b. Cleveland, Ohio, Jan. 29, 1935; s. Stephen Irby and Bertha Marie (Bieger) M.; children—Julian, John. B.Sc., Case Inst. Tech., 1957; M.Sc., U. Ill., 1958, Ph.D., 1960. Asst. prof. elec. engring. U. Ill., 1961-62; mem. faculty Columbia U., 1962—, asst. prof. elec. engring., 1962-65, assoc. prof., 1965-70, prof. engring. sci., 1970-78, prof. applied physics, 1978—. Author: Free Electron Lasers, 1985, Book of the Toade, 1992; contbr. over 100 articles to profl. jours. Research grantee Dept. Energy, Office Naval Research, NSF. Fellow Am. Phys. Soc. (study group on directed energy weapons 1985-87). Office: Columbia U 213 Mudd Bldg New York NY 10027

MARSHALL, THOMAS DAVID, judge; b. Wainfleet, Ont., Can., Feb. 23, 1939; s. Albert Haydow Marshall and Ora Colback); m. Jill Smith, 1961; children: Jillian, Julie, Albert, Tom, David Jr. MD, U. Toronto, 1963; LLB, Osgoode Hall, Toronto, 1970. Cert. LMCC barrister and solicitor, judge. Prof. law U. Windsor, Ont., 1981-82; justice Supreme Ct. N.T., 1983-88; dir. Nat. Judicial Inst., Ottawa, 1988-92; hon. prof. law Ottawa U., 1988; justice Ont. Ct. Justice, Hamilton, 1992—; chmn. com. ethics med. rsch. coun. of Can., Ottawa, 1984-93. Author: Canadian Law of Inquests, 1988, Canadian Physician and the Law. Lt. col. Can. Armed Forces Reserve, 1988-93. Mem. Can. Bar Assn., Can. Medieval Assn. Avocations: farming, flying. Office: Court House, 50 Main St, Hamilton, ON Canada

MARSHALL, THOMAS OLIVER, JR., lawyer; b. Americus, Ga., June 24, 1920; s. Thomas Oliver and Mattie Louise (Hunter) M.; m. Angie Ellen Fitts, Dec. 20, 1946; children: Ellen Irwin Marshall Beard, Anne Hunter Marshall Peagler, Mary Olivia Marshall Hodges. BS in Engring., U.S. Naval Acad., 1941; JD, U. Ga., 1948. Bar: Ga. 1947. Pvt. practice law Americus, Ga., 1948-60; judge S.W. Judicial Circuit, Americus, 1960-74, Ga. Ct. Appeals, Atlanta, 1974-77; justice Ga. Supreme Ct., Atlanta, 1977-86, chief justice, 1986-89; pvt. practice Atlanta, 1989—; chmn. bd. visitors U. Ga. Law Sch., 1970. Trustee Andrew Coll., So. Ga. Meth. Home for Aged; active ARC, 1948-60, United Givers Fund, 1948-54. Served with USN, World War II, Korean War. Decorated Bronze Star; named Young Man of Yr. Americus, 1953. Mem. ABA, Ga. Bar Assn. (bd. govs. 1958-60), Atlanta Bar Assn., State Bar Ga., Am. Judicature Soc., Nat. Jud. Coll., Jud. Coll. Ga., VFW, Am. Legion. Methodist. Lodges: Kiwanis, Masons, Shriners. Home: 238 15th St NE Condominium 3 Atlanta GA 30309 Office: 230 Peachtree St NW Ste 1100 Atlanta GA 30303-1533

MARSHALL, VICTOR FRAY, physician, educator; b. Culpeper, Va., Sept. 1, 1913; s. Otis and Marie Josephine (Riton) M.; m. Barbara Walsh, Dec. 11, 1943; children—Fray F., Victor R., Philip S. M.D., U. Va., 1937; D.Sc., Washington and Lee U., 1975. Diplomate: Am. Bd. Urology (past pres.). Intern N.Y. Hosp., 1937-38; tng. in gen. surgery and urology Cornell U. Med. Coll.-N.Y. Hosp., 1938-43, staff mem., 1943-88; attending-in-charge urology James Buchanan Brady Found., 1949-78; faculty Med. Coll., Cornell U., 1938-81, assoc. prof. clin. surgery urology, 1947-57, prof. clin. surgery (urology), 1957-78, James J. Colt prof. urology in surgery, 1970-78, head service urology, 1946-78, emeritus, 1978-88; prof. urology U. Va., Charlottesville, 1979-83; cons., 1983-88, ret., 1988; asst. attending surgeon Meml. Center for Cancer and Allied Diseases, 1943-52, assoc. attending, 1952-67, attending surgeon, 1967-83, emeritus, 1983—. Contbr. articles to med. jours. Fellow ACS, N.Y. Acad. Medicine (Valentine medal 1974); mem. AAAS, N.Y. Urol. Soc. (past pres.), Am. Urol. Assn. (Guiteras award 1975), N.Y. Cancer Soc. (past pres.), Soc. Pelvic Surgeons (past pres.), Mexican Acad. Surgery, Am. Surg. Assn., Am. Acad. Pediatrics, Soc. Pediatric Urology, Clin. Soc. Genito-Urinary Surgeons (pres. 1976), Surg. Soc. Venezuela, Mexican Urol. Soc., Brit. Assn. Urol. Surgeons, Venezuelan Soc. Urology, Am. Assn. Genito-Urinary Surgeons (Barringer medal 1970, Keyes medal 1994), Canadian Urol. Assn. (hon.), Royal Coll. Surgeons Ireland (hon.), Alpha Omega Alpha, Pi Kappa Alpha, Nu Sigma Nu. Home: The Colonades C8 2600 Barracks Rd Charlottesville VA 22901

MARSHALL, VINCENT DE PAUL, industrial microbiologist, researcher; b. Washington, Apr. 5, 1943; s. Vincent de Paul Sr. and Mary Frances (Bach) M.; m. Sylvia Ann Kieffer, Nov. 15, 1986; children from previous marriage: Vincent de Paul III, Amy. BS, Northeastern State Coll., Tahlequah, Okla., 1965; MS, U. Okla. Health Sci. Ctr., Oklahoma City, 1967, PhD, 1970. Rsch. assoc. U. Ill., Urbana, 1970, postdoctoral fellow, 1971-73; rsch. scientist The Upjohn Co., Kalamazoo, Mich., 1973-74, rsch. head, 1975, sr. rsch. scientist, 1976-91, sr. scientist, 1991—. Mem. editorial bd. Jour. of Antibiotics, 1990—, Jour. Indsl. Microbiology, 1989—, Devels. in Indsl. Microbiology, 1990; contbr. numerous articles to profl. jours., chpts. to books; patentee in field. Served with U.S. Army Nat. Guard, 1960-65. NIH predoctoral fellow, 1967-70; NIH postdoctoral fellow, 1971-73. Fellow Am. Acad. Microbiology; mem. Soc. for Indsl. Microbiology (membership com. 1988-90, co-chair elem. 1989-93, local sects. com. 1991—, chair nominating com. 1993-94, co-chair program com. 1993-94, dir. 1994—, pres. Indsl. sect. 1992-95), Am. Soc. Microbiology, Am. Soc. Biochemistry and Molecular Biology, Internat. Soc. for Antimicrobial Activity of Non-Antibiotics (sci. adv. bd.), Sigma Xi. Republican. Episcopalian. Home: 203 Paisley Ct Kalamazoo MI 49006-4359 Office: Upjohn Co Chem & Biol Screening Dept 301 Henrietta St Kalamazoo MI 49007-4940

MARSHALL, WILLIAM, architect; b. Ashland, Ky., Nov. 24, 1925; s. William and Lee (Powers) M.; m. Joan Goodyear Ellington, June 16, 1951; children—William III, Jenefer, Charles, Elizabeth, Christopher. Student, Va. Mil. Inst., 1943-44; B.S., U. Va., 1949; postgrad., Columbia, 1949-50. Designer, draftsman, 1950-53; architect Lublin, McGaughy & Assos. (Architects and Cons. Engrs.), Norfolk, Washington, 1953-55; architect, partner Lublin, McGaughy & Assos. (Architects and Cons. Engrs.), 1955-60; pres. MMM Design Group, Architects and Cons. Engrs., Norfolk, Va., Washington, Houston, Frankfort, Germany, Athens, Greece, 1960-84, William Marshall Assocs. Ltd., 1984—. Prin. works include United Va. Bank, Norfolk, 1970, Kirn Meml. Library, Norfolk, 1962, Ministry of Def. Hdqrs, Riyadh, Saudi Arabia, 1976, New City of Brega, Libya, 1980, Kuwait Ministry of Def. Interior Design Project, 1976. Mem. profl. unit United Comty. Fund, Norfolk, 1962-71, mem. ad hoc com. to establish city planning dept., Norfolk, 1961-62, mem. citizens adv. com. to mayor, 1962-68, chmn. codes sub-com., 1962-68, mem. exec. com., 1962-68; mem. adv. com. bldg. constrn. curriculum Norfolk State Coll., 1968—; trustee Hermitage Found., 1974—, pres., 1985-95; trustee AIA Rsch. Corp., 1075. With AUS, 1944-46. Fellow AIA (pres. Tidewater sect. Va. chpt. 1964-65, pres. Va. chpt. 1969-70, v.p. nat, pres. Va. chpt. 1971, mem. exec. com. 1974-75, bd. dirs. 1974-75, chmn. commn. govt. affairs 1972-73, commr. spl. assessment program 1973-74, 1st v.p 1974, chmn. planning com. 1974, pres. 1975—); mem. Am. Inst. Steel Construction (archtl. awards of excellence jury 1974), Am. Iron and Steel Inst. (honor awards jury 1975), Prestressed Concrete Inst. (chmn. honor awards jury 1975), Va. Am. Professions (bd. dirs. 1970-71, regional v.p. 1970), Downtown Norfolk Assn. (bd. dirs. 1966-72).

MARSHALL, WILLIAM EDWARD, historical association executive; b. St. Paul, Apr. 19, 1925; s. William Edward and Louise (White) M.; m. Ruth Marie Winner, Sept. 3, 1947 (div.); children: Michael Scott, Terry Lee, Sharon; m. Loretta E. Slota, Nov. 6, 1976; children: Marc William, Matthew Ryan. B.A., Mont. State U., 1950; B.F.A., Wittenberg U., 1951; postgrad., Ohio State U., 1951-52. Owner, operator Public Library Public Relations Service, 1952-55, Specialized Press, 1952-60; graphic and exhibits designer Ohio Hist. Soc., 1952-60, State Historic Soc. Colo., Denver, 1960-61; dep. exec. dir. State Historic Soc. Colo., 1961-63, exec. dir., 1963-79; cons. to hist. agys., author, 1979—; founding mem. Little Kingdom Hist. Found.; condr. historic interpretation seminars and workshops. Author historic TV and film prodns., books, fiction and non-fiction in nat. publs.; editor: Humboldt Historian, 1990-91, CEO MediFacts, 1992—; illustrator, photographer books and periodicals; contbr. articles to profl. jours. Bd. dirs. Rocky Mountain Center on Environment, 1967-72, Trinidad Mus. Soc., 1986-89; chmn. Colo. Humanities Program Com., 1971, 75. With USMCR, 1943-45. Mem. Am. Assn. Museums (exec. com. 1973-74, mus. accreditation evaluator), Am. Assn. State and Local History (mem. council 1966-72, awards com. 1966-80, com. on fed. programs in history), Orgn. Am. Historians (hist. sites com. 1974-75). Presbyterian. Home: Moonstone Heights 719 Driver Rd Trinidad CA 95570-9722

MARSHALL, WILLIAM EMMETT, biotechnology company executive, biochemistry researcher; b. Chgo., July 21, 1935; s. William E. and Margaret (Fitzgerald) M.; m. Bonnie M. Dallman, June 10, 1961; children: Elizabeth, Stephanie, William. BS, U. Ill., 1957, MS, 1959, PhD, 1961. Asst. prof. U. Minn. Med. Sch., Mpls., 1961-67; dir. tech. devel. Gen. Foods Corp., White Plains, N.Y., 1967-83; pres. Microbial Genetics div. Pioneer Hi-Bred Internat. Inc., Johnston, Iowa, 1983-91, pres. Microbial Environ. Svcs. div., 1989-91; pres. Immunom Techs. Inc., Bedford Hills, N.Y., 1991—; mem. Grace Commn. U.S. Govt., 1982-83; chmn. adv. bd. Nat. Agrl. Research and Extension Users, Washington, 1983-88; mem. panel on new devel. in biotech. Office of Tech. Assessment, Washington, 1986-90; vice-chmn bd. dirs. Rodale Inst., Emmaus, Pa., Keystone (Colo.) Adv. Panel on Biotech.; mem. adv. com. on intellectual property matters to Gen. Agreement on Trade and Tariffs; mem. adv. bd. NSF Ctr. for Microbial Ecology, Mich. State U., 1990—; adj. assoc. prof. dept. microbiology N.Y. Med. Coll., Valhalla, 1992—. Contbr. articles to profl. jours.; patentee in field. Recipient award of Merit U. Ill., 1994. Mem. AAAS, Iowa Acad. Sci. (awards and recognition com.). Club: Univ. (Washington). Office: 112 Succabone Rd Bedford Hills NY 10507-2221

MARSIK, FREDERIC JOHN, microbiologist; b. Camden, N.J., June 22, 1943; s. Ferdinand Vincent and Helen (Reidl) M.; children: Terri Jean, Kristi Ann Marsik McCann. BA, Lebanon Valley Coll., 1965; MS, U. Mo., 1970, PhD, 1973. Diplomate Am. Bd. Med. Microbiology. Asst. prof. Sch. Medicine, U. Va., Charlottesville, 1976-80; tech. dir. microbiology and serology Children's Hosp. Wis., Milw., 1980-84; assoc. prof. microbiology and internal medicine Sch. Medicine, Oral Roberts U., Tulsa, 1984-87; dir. microbiology Crozer-Chester Med. Ctr., Upland, Pa., 1987-88; mgr. media systems Becton Dickinson Microbiology Systems, Cockeysville, Md., 1988—; mem. adv. com. Milw. Area Tech. Coll., Milw., 1983-84, Tulsa Jr. Coll., 1985-87; mem. rev. bd. Clin. Lab. Sci. Publ., Washington, 1990—. Contbr. chpts. to textbooks. Treas. Rose Fire Co. and Ambulance Svc., New Freedom, Pa., 1989—; bd. govs. New Freedom Community Ctr., 1989—; mem. adult edn. com. So. York County Sch. Dist., Glen Rock, Pa., 1989—. Lt. col. USAR. Recipient Best Rsch. Project award S.W. Assn. for Clin. Microbiology, 1984. Mem. Am. Soc. Microbiology (mem. lab. practices com. 1990—), Am. Soc. Med. Tech., N.Y. Acad. Scis. Congregationalist. Avocations: fishing, camping, basketball. Home: 6 Keesey Rd New Freedom PA 17349-9638 Office: Becton Dickinson 250 Schilling Cir Cockeysville MD 21031-1103

MARSOLAIS, HAROLD RAYMOND, association executive; b. Troy, N.Y., Mar. 10, 1942; s. Harold George and Viola Marie (Chamberlain) M.; m. Susan Lemieux, Jul. 5, 1964; children: Michelle, Harold R. BS, U. So. Miss., 1974; MS, Webster Coll., 1979. Officer US Army, 1961-82; CEO Minn. Bad. Hardware Assn., Mpls., 1982-84, Penn. ATL. Sbd. Hardware Assn., Harrisburg, Pa., 1984-87; v.p. sales Natl. Retail Hardware Assn., Indpls., Ind., 1987-89; CEO Nat. Retail Hardware Assn., Indpls., 1989-94; exec. dir. Russell Mueller Found. 1989, Home Center Inst. 1987. Author: Guide to FAA Reg., 1971, In Store Merchandising, 1987, Doing the Right Thing: An Environmental Guide, 1994. Dir. Jr. Chamber, Hattiesburg, Pa., Rotary Intl., Harrisburg, Pa. Recipient W.B. Harlan Business award U. So. Miss., 1974, Outstanding Young Man Jaycees, Hattiesburg, 1974. Decorated Distinguished Flying Cross. Mem. Am. Soc. Assn. Exec. Avocations: golf, boating, flying. Office: Marsolais and Assocs 115 S Lake Cir Saint Augustine FL 32095

MARSTERS, GERALD FREDERICK, retired aerospace science and technology executive; b. Summerville, N.S., Can., Dec. 18, 1932; s. Ralpha Roland and Madge Thelma (Harvey) M.; m. Lorena May Gunter, Oct. 23, 1954; children: Mariko Collette, Cynthia Denise. BS, Queens U., Kingston, Ont., Can., 1962; PhD, Cornell U., 1967. Registered profl. engr., Ont., Can. Prof. mech. engring. Queen's U., 1967-82; dir. airworthiness Dept. of Transport, Ottawa, 1982-87; dir. gen. Inst. for Aerospace Rsch., Nat. Rsch. Coun., Ottawa, 1987-94; ret., 1994; proprietor, owner. AeroVations: Aerospace Tech. Specialists; nat. del. adv. group Aerospace Rsch. (NATO), Paris, 1987-94. Flying officer Royal Can. Airforce, 1953-58. Recipient Gold medal for Extraordinary Svc. FAA, 1986. Fellow AIAA, Can. Aero. and Space Inst. (past pres. 1992-93), Can. Acad. Engring., Can. Soc. for Mech. Engring.; mem. SAE (aerospace coun. 1985). Avocations: recreational flying, model railroads. Home: 39 Westpark Dr, Gloucester, ON Canada K1B 366

MARSTON, CHARLES, state education official. Commr. edn. New Hampshire. Office: Dept Edn 101 Pleasant St Concord NH 03301-3852

MARSTON, EDGAR JEAN, III, lawyer; b. Houston, July 5, 1939; s. Edgar Jr. and Jean (White) M.; m. Graeme Meyers, June 21, 1961; children: Christopher Graham, Jonathan Andrew. BA, Brown U., 1961; JD, U. Tex., 1964. Bar: Tex. 1964. Law clk. to presiding justice Supreme Ct. Tex., Austin, 1964-65; assoc. Baker & Botts, Houston, 1965-71; ptnr. Bracewell & Patterson, Houston, 1971-89, of counsel, 1990—; exec. v.p., gen. counsel Southdown, Inc., Houston, 1987—, also bd. dirs. Mem. ABA, Tex. Bar Assn., Tex. Bar Found., Houston Bar Assn., Houston Country Club, Coronado Club. Episcopalian. Avocations: hunting, fishing, philately, reading. Office: Southdown Inc 1200 Smith St Ste 2200 Houston TX 77002-4401

MARSTON, MICHAEL, urban economist, asset management executive; b. Oakland, Calif., Dec. 4, 1936; s. Lester Woodbury and Josephine (Janovic) M.; m. Alexandra Lynn Geyer, Apr. 30, 1966; children: John, Elizabeth. BA, U. Calif., Berkeley, 1959; postgrad. London Sch. Econs., 1961-63. V.p Larry Smith & Co., San Francisco, 1969-72, exec. v.p urban econ. div., 1969-72; chmn. bd. Keyser Marston Assocs., Inc., San Francisco, 1973-87; gen. ptnr. The Sequoia Partnership, 1979-91; pres. Marston Vineyards and Winery, 1982—, Marston Assocs., Inc., 1982—. Cert. rev. appraiser Nat. Assn. Rev. Appraisers and Mortgage Underwriters, 1984—. Chmn., San Francisco Waterfront Com., 1969-86; chmn. fin. com., bd. dirs., mem. exec. com., treas. San Francisco Planning and Urban Rsch. Assn., 1976-87, Napa Valley Vintners, 1986—, mem. gov. affairs com.; trustee Cathedral Sch. for Boys, 1981-82, Marin Country Day Sch., 1984-90; v.p. St. Luke's Sch., 1986-91; pres. Presidio Heights Assn. of Neighbors, 1983-87; chmn. Presidio Com. 1991—; v.p., bd. dirs., mem. exec. com. People for Open Space, 1972-87, chmn. adv. com., 1988—; mem. Gov.'s Issue Analysis Com. and Speakers Bur., 1966; mem. speakers bur. Am. Embassy, London, 1961-63; v.p., bd. dirs Dem. Forum, 1978-82; v.p., trustee Youth for Service. Served to lt. USNR. Mem. Napa Valley Vintners, Napa Grape Growers, Urban Land Inst., World Congress Land Policy (paper in field), Order of Golden Bear, Chevalier du Tastevin, Commanderie de Bordeaux, Bohemian Club, Pacific Union Club, Lambda Alpha. Contbr. articles to profl. jours. Home: 3375 Jackson St San Francisco CA 94118-2018 *Personal philosophy: Success is what you do with what you have not what others think or what is in vogue.*

MARSTON, ROBERT ANDREW, public relations executive; b. Astoria, N.Y., Aug. 6, 1927; s. Frank and Lena (DiDomenico) M.; m. Maryann Doherty, Sept. 23, 1990. BA, Hofstra U., 1959. Sr. v.p Rowland Co., N.Y.C., 1959-68, Rogers & Cowen, Inc., 1968-70; founder, chmn., CEO Robert Marston And Assocs., Inc., N.Y.C., 1970—. Contbr. articles and photographs to profl. jours. and popular mags. Mem. Pub. Rels. Soc. Am. (counselors sect.), Marco Polo Club, Doubles Club, Southampton Bath & Tennis Club. Roman Catholic. Home: 570 Park Ave New York NY 10021-7370 also: 130 Captains Neck Ln Southampton NY 11968 Office: Robert Marston And Assocs 485 Madison Ave New York NY 10022-5803

MARSTON, ROBERT QUARLES, university president; b. Toano, Va., Feb. 12, 1923; s. Warren and Helen (Smith) M.; m. Ann Carter Garnett, Dec. 21, 1946; children: Ann, Robert, Wesley. B.S., Va. Mil. Inst., 1943; M.D., Med. Coll. Va., 1947; B.Sc. (Rhodes scholar 1947-49), Oxford (Eng.) U., 1949; B.Sc. 6 hon. degrees. Intern Johns Hopkins Hosp., 1949-50; resident Vanderbilt U. Hosp., 1950-51; resident Med. Coll. Va., 1953-54, asst. prof. medicine, 1954; asst. prof. bacteriology and immunology U. Minn., 1958-59; assoc. prof. medicine, asst. dean charge student affairs Med. Coll. Va., 1959-61; dean U. Miss. Sch. Medicine, 1961-66; dir. U. Miss. Med. Medicine (Med. Center), 1961-65, vice chancellor, 1965-66; assoc. dir. div. regional med. programs NIH, 1966-68; administr. Fed. Health Services and Mental Health Adminstrn., 1968; dir. NIH, Bethesda, Md., 1968-73; scholar in residence U. Va., Charlottesville, 1973-74; Disting. fellow Inst. of Medicine, Nat. Acad. Scis., 1973-74; pres. U. Fla., 1974-84, pres. emeritus, emeritus prof. medicine, emeritus prof. fish and aquaculture; bd. dirs.

Johnson and Johnson, Nat. Bank Alachua, Wackenhut Corp.; chmn. bd. dirs. Cordis Corp.; chmn., mem. Fla. Marine Fisheries Commn. Author articles in field. Chmn. Commn. on Med. Edn. for Robert Wood Found.; chmn. Safety Adv. Bd. Three Mile Island; chmn. adv. com. med. implications of nuclear war NAS; exec. coun. Assn. Am. Med. Coll., 1964-67; past chmn. exec. com. Nat. Assn. State Univs. and Land Grant Colls., chmn., 1982. 1st lt. AUS, 1951-53. Decorated Knight of North Star (Sweden); Markle scholar, 1954-59; hon. fellow Lincoln Coll. Oxford U. Fellow Am. Pub. Health Assn.; mem. Inst. Medicine of NAS, AAAS, Am. Hosp. Assn. (hon.), Nat. Med. Assn. (hon.), Assn. Am. Rhodes Scholars, Assn. Am. Physicians, Assn. Am. Med. Colls. (disting. mem.), Am. Clin. and Climatol. Assn., Soc. Scholars Johns Hopkins, Alpha Omega Alpha. Episcopalian. Home: RR 1 Box 20A Alachua FL 32615-9707

MARSTON-SCOTT, MARY VESTA, nurse, educator; b. St. Stephen, N.B., Can., Apr. 5, 1924; d. George Frank and Betsey Mildred (Babb) M.; m. John Paul Scott, June 30, 1979. B.A., U. Maine, 1946; M.N., Yale U., 1951; M.P.H., Harvard U., 1957; M.A., Boston U., 1964, Ph.D., 1969. Research asst. Roscoe B. Jackson Meml. Lab., Bar Harbor, Maine, 1946-48; nurse, 1952-54; instr. Yale U. Sch. Nursing, 1955-56; nurse cons. Div. Nursing, Washington, 1957-62; asso. prof. Frances Payne Bolton Sch. Nursing, Case-Western Res. U., Cleve., 1969-74; prof. grad. program community health nursing Boston U., 1974-86; assoc. prof. Coll. Nursing U. Ill., Chgo., 1986-94; cons. in field. Contbr. articles to profl. jours. Served with USPHS, 1957-62. Fellow Am. Acad. Nursing; mem. Am. Psychol. Assn., Am. Public Health Assn., Am. Nurses Assn., Sigma Theta Tau. Office: U Ill Coll Nursing 845 S Damen Ave Chicago IL 60612-7350

MARTEKA, VINCENT JAMES, JR., magazine editor, writer; b. Uxbridge, Mass., Jan. 29, 1936; s. Vincent James and Genevieve (Ramian) M.; m. Janet Littler, May 26, 1962; children—Andrew, Peter, Katherine. B.S. in Geology, U. Mass., 1958; M.S., Rensselaer Poly. Inst., 1959. Editor U.S. Geol. Survey, Washington, 1959-60; sci. writer, news editor Sci. Service, Washington, 1961-63; sci. editor My Weekly Reader, children's newspaper, Middletown, Conn., 1964-65; editor Current Sci., sci. mag. jr. high sch. students, Middletown, 1966—. Author: Bionics, 1965, Mushrooms: Wild and Edible, 1980, also numerous articles (writing awards Edn. Press Assn.); series editor: Our Living World, 12 books, 1993-94. Served with AUS, 1960. Mem. Nat. Assn. Sci. Writers, Mycological Soc. Am., N.Am. Mycological Assn., Nat. Audubon Soc., Mattabeseck Audubon Soc. (pres. 1976). Home: 239 Jobs Pond Rd Portland CT 06480-1712 Office: Weekly Reader Corp 245 Long Hill Rd Middletown CT 06457-4056

MARTEL, EUGENE HARVEY, engineering company executive; b. Webster, Mass., Sept. 15, 1934; s. Eugene P. and Rose A. (Lemay) M.; m. Audrey Renee Ballou, Sept. 1, 1958; children: Neil A., Denise M., Kevin E., Lisa A. B.S. in Chem Engring., U. R.I., 1956. Registered profl. engr., Mass. Process engr. Badger, Cambridge, 1956-71; v.p. Badger Tomoe, Tokyo, 1971-73; pres. China Badger, Taipei, Taiwan, 1973-75; v.p. Asia/Pacific The Badger Co., Inc., Cambridge, Mass., 1975-81, sr. v.p. bus. devel., 1981-83; sr. v.p Western hemisphere and Far East Lummus Crest, 1984-87, exec. v.p., 1987—. Served to 2d lt. U.S. Army, 1957-63. Mem. Am. Inst. Chem. Engrs. Office: ABB Lummus Crest Inc 12141 Wickchester Ln Houston TX 77079-1207 also: ABB Lummus Crest Inc 1515 Broad St Bloomfield NJ 07003

MARTEL, JACQUES G., entineer, administrator. PhD. Dir. Gen. Indsl. Materials Inst. Nat. Rsch. Coun. Can., Boucherville, PQ, Canada. Office: Indsl Materials Rsch Inst, 75 De Mortagne Blvd, Boucherville, PQ Canada J4B 6Y4

MARTEL, PETRA JEAN HEGSTAD, elementary school educator; b. Oakland, Calif., May 27, 1944; d. Lorentz Reginald and Hazel Dorothy (Danielson) Hegstad; m. Curtis Wayne Martel, Apr. 30, 1966 (div. 1989); children: Christopher W., Peter L., Loren R. BS in Elem. Edn. and German, Concordia Coll., Moorhead, Minn., 1966; MS in Elem. Edn., Bemidji (Minn.) State U., 1989. Cert. elem. edn., reading cons., German remedial and devel. reading tchr. K-12, Minn. 2d grade tchr. Rice Creek and Hayes Elem. Schs., Fridley, Minn., 1966-72; chpt. 1 reading tchr. Chief Bug-O-Nay-Ge-Shig Sch., Cass Lake, Minn., 1986-92; tchr. English and reading Rochester (Minn.) Pub. Schs., 1992-93; tchr. reading Moorhead (Minn.) Pub. Schs., 1993—. Vol. den mother Cub Scouts, Bismarck, N.D., 1976-77; vol. com. to establish kindergarten Bismarck Pub. Schs., 1974-75; vol. com. to help refugees relocate Bismarck, 1976; vol. Bemidji Sch. System, 1985. Mem. NEA, Northland Reading Coun. (pres. 1985-86, honor coun. 1986), Minn. Reading Assn. (sec. 1993—), Internat. Reading Assn., Minn. Edn. Assn., Kappa Delta Pi. Avocations: skiing, golf, music, art, travel. Home: 2333 Calihan Ave NE Bemidji MN 56601-2333

MARTEL, WILLIAM, radiologist, educator; b. N.Y.C., Oct. 1, 1927; s. Hyman and Fanny M.; m. Rhoda Kaplan, Oct. 9, 1956; children: Lisa, Pamela, Caryn, Jonathan, David. M.D., NYU, 1953. Intern, Kings County Hosp., N.Y., 1953-54; resident in radiology Mt. Sinai Hosp., N.Y.C., 1954-57; instr. radiology U. Mich., 1957-60, asst. prof., 1960-63, asso. prof., 1963-67, prof., 1967—, Fred Jenner Hodges prof., 1984—, chmn. dept. radiology, 1981-92, dir. skeletal radiology, 1970-81. Contbr. articles to Radiol. Diagnoses of Arthritic Diseases. Served with USAAF, 1945-46. Recipient Amoco U. Mich. Outstanding Teaching award, 1980. Mem. Radiol. Soc. N.Am., Am. Roentgen Ray Soc., Assn. Univ. Radiologists. Home: 2972 Parkridge Dr Ann Arbor MI 48103-1737 Office: Univ Mich Hosps Dept Radiology 1500 E Med Ctr Dr Ann Arbor MI 48109

MARTELL, ARTHUR EARL, chemistry educator; b. Natick, Mass., Oct. 18, 1916; s. Ambrose and Dorina (Lamoureaux) M.; m. Norma June Saunders, Sept. 2, 1944; children: Stuart A., Edward S., Janet E., Judith S., Jon V., Elaine C.; m. Mary Austin, 1965; children: Helen E., Kathryn A. B.S., Worcester Poly. Inst., 1938, D.Sc. (hon.), 1962; Ph.D., NYU 1941. Instr. Worcester Poly. Inst., 1941-42; mem. faculty Clark U., 1942-61, prof. chemistry, 1951-61, chmn. dept., 1959-61; prof. chemistry, chmn. dept. Ill. Inst. Tech., 1960-66; prof. chemistry Tex. A&M U., College Station, 1966—; Disting. prof. Tex. A&M U., 1973—, dept. head, 1966-80, adv. to pres., 1980-82; rsch. on chem equilibria, kinetics, catalysis, metal chelate compounds in solution. Author: (with M. Calvin) Chemistry of the Metal Chelate Compounds, 1952, (with G.L Sillen) Stability Constants, 1964; supplement, 1971; (with M.M. Taqui Khan) Homogeneous Catalysis by Metal Complexes, 2 vols, 1973; (with R.M. Smith) Critical Stability Constants, Vol. 1, 1974, Vol. 2, 1975, Vol. 3, 1977, Vol. 4, 1976, Vol. 5, 1982, Vol. 6, 1989, (with R.J. Motekaitis) Determination and Use of Stability Constants, 1989, 2nd edit, 1992; editor: ACS Monograph on Coordination Chemistry, Vol. 1, 1973, Vol. 2, 1978, ACS Symposium Series 140, Inorganic Chemistry in Biology and Medicine, 1980, Inorg. Coordination Chemistry, 1970-80; mem. editorial bd. Bioinorganic Chemistry, Jour. Inorganic and Nuclear Chemistry, Inorganic Chemistry; contbr. articles to profl. jours. Mem. sci. adv. bd. Northborough, Mass., 1958-61, chmn., 1959-61. Research fellow U. Calif. at Berkeley, 1949-50; Guggenheim fellow U. Zurich, Switzerland, 1954-55; NSF sr. postdoctoral fellow, also fellow Sch. Advanced Studies Mass. Inst. Tech., 1959-60; NIH Spl. fellow U. Calif. at Berkeley, 1964-65. Fellow N.Y. Acad. Scis. (hon. life); mem. AAAS, Am. Chem. Soc. (chmn. cen. Mass. sect. 1957-58, chmn. Tex. A&M sect. 1990-91, S.W. Regional award 1976, Nat. award for Disting. Svc. 1980), Am. Acad. Arts and Scis., Jap. Soc. for Analytical Chemistry (hon.), Sigma Xi, Phi Lambda Upsilon (hon.). Home: 9742 Myrtle Dr College Station TX 77845

MARTELLI, JENNIFER A., social welfare administrator; b. Pawtucket, R.I., Jan. 24, 1970; d. Frank Paul III and Valerie Ann (Vecchio) M. BA in Polit. Sci., U. Mass., North Dartmouth, 1992. Mem. R.I. Ho. of Reps., Providence, 1992-94; cmty. edn. coord. R.I. Coalition Against Domestic Violence, Warwick, 1994—; bd. dirs. Reform Watch; mem. health, edn. and welfare com., 1992-94, mem. waste reutilization commn., 1992-94, mem. welfare reform commn., 1992-94. Mem. Sons of Italy (trustee). Home: 19 Warren Ave Johnston RI 02919

MARTEN, GORDON CORNELIUS, research agronomist, educator, federal agency administrator; b. Wittenberg, Wis., Sept. 14, 1935; s. Clarence George and Cora Levina (Verpoorten) M.; m. Lynette Joy Hanson, Sept. 9,

1961; 1 dau., Kimberly Joy. BS, U. Wis., 1957; MS, U. Minn., 1959, PhD, 1961; postgrad., Purdue U., 1962. Rsch. agronomist U.S. Dept. Agr., U. Minn., St. Paul, 1961-72; supervisory rsch. agronomist, rsch. leader, 1972-89; adj. prof. agronomy U. Minn., St. Paul, 1971—; assoc. dir. USDA-Agr. Rsch. Svc., Beltsville, Md., 1989—; mem. governing body and U.S. rep. to OECD Biol. Resource Mgmt. Program, Paris, 1990—; adminstrv. coun. USDA Sustainable Agrl. Rsch. and Edn. Program, 1993—. Consulting editor: Crop Sci., 1972-74; sr. editor USDA Handbook Near Infrared Reflectance Spectroscopy: Analysis of Forage Quality, 1985, rev. edit., 1989; mem. edit. bd. Sci. of Food and Agriculture, 1985-90; contbr. numerous articles to profl. jours. Recipient Merit award Am. Forage and Grassland Coun., 1976, Outstanding Svc. award, 1981, Civil Servant of Yr. award Twin Cities, Minn., 1976; NSF grad. fellow, 1959-61; numerous cert. merit USDA Agrl. Rsch. Svc., Northrup King Faculty Outstanding Performance award U. Minn., 1986, Superior Svc. award USDA, 1987. Fellow Am. Soc. Agronomy, Crop Sci. Soc. Am. (bd. dirs. 1975-77); mem. Am. Forage and Grassland Coun. (bd. dirs. 1977-80), Coun. Agr. Sci. and Tecch. (bd. dirs. 1985-90), Agronomic Sci. Found. (trustee 1984-89), Biol. Club, Sigma Xi, Gamma Sigma Delta (Adminstrn. award of merit/Nat. Capital Area 1994), Alpha Zeta, Delta Theta Sigma. Lutheran. Office: USDA Agr Rsch Svc Office of Dir BARC-W Bldg 003 Rm 223 Beltsville MD 20705

MARTENS, DON WALTER, lawyer; b. Darlington, Wis., Mar. 25, 1934; s. Walter W. and Geraldine A. (McWilliams) M.; children: Kim Martens Cooper, Diane Martens Reed. BS in Petroleum Engring., U. Wis., 1957; JD with honors, George Washington U., 1963. Bar: Supreme Ct. Calif. 1964, U.S. Ct. Appeals (9th cir.) 1964, U.S. Dist. Ct. (no. and cen. dists.) Calif. 1964, U.S. Supreme Ct. 1973, U.S. Dist. Ct. (so. dist.) Calif. 1977, U.S. Ct. Appeals (fed. cir.) 1982, U.S. Dist. Ct. (ea. dist.) 1984. Examiner U.S. Patent and Trademark Office, Washington, 1959-63; patent lawyer Standard Oil of Calif., San Francisco, 1963-65; ptnr. Knobbe, Martens, Olson & Bear, Newport Beach, Calif., 1965—; mem. appellate adv. comm. Fed. Cir. Ct. Appeals, 1991—. Author: (with others) Attorney's Guide to Trade Secrets, 1978. Lt. USN, 1957-60. Mem. Orange County Bar Assn. (pres. 1975), Orange County Legal Aid Soc. (pres. 1969), Orange County Patent Law Assn. (pres. 1984), L.A. Patent Law Assn. (pres. 1989), State of Calif. Jud. Coun., State Bar of Calif. (bd. govs. 1984-87, v.p. 1986-87), Am. Intellectual Property Law Assn. (bd. dirs. 1989—, 1st v.p. 1993—), State Bar Intellectual Property Assn. (chmn. 1977), Ninth Cir. Jud. Conf. (del. 1985-88), Big Canyon Country Club. Republican. Roman Catholic. Office: 620 Newport Center Dr Fl 16 Newport Beach CA 92660-6420

MARTENS, ERNESTO, glass products company executive. CFO Vitro Sociedad Anonima; CEO, chmn. Anchor Glass Container Corp., 1989—. Office: Anchor Glass Container Corp 4343 Anchor Plz Pky Tampa FL 33634

MARTENS, LYLE CHARLES, state education administrator; b. Wausau, Wis., June 22, 1935; s. Norman Theodore and Eloise Loretta (Kreger) M.; m. Darlene Carrol Pyatt, Dec. 22, 1956; children: William Lyle, Robert Michael. BS in Indsl. Edn., Stout State U., 1957, MS in Indsl. Tech., 1962. Tchr. indsl. arts Mercer (Wis.) Pub. Schs., 1957-62; high sch. prin. Seymour (Wis.) Community Schs., 1962-65, supt. schs., 1965-87; supt. schs. Green Bay (Wis.) Area Pub. Schs., 1987-89; asst. state supt. State Dept. Edn., Madison, Wis., 1989-90, dep. state supt., 1990—. Chair United Way Edn. Fund Dr., Brown County, Wis., 1989; mem. bd. dirs. Green Bay C. of C., Good Shepherd Nursing Home, Seymour, Wis., 1975-87; mem. Econ. Devel. Corp., Outagamie County, Wis., 1985-86. Mem. Am. Assn. Sch. Adminstrs., Wis. Assn. Sch. Dist. Adminstrs. (pres. 1978-79), Assn. Svc./Curriculum Devel., North Cen. Regional Ednl. Lab., Fox Valley Tech. Inst., Masons, Phi Delta Kappa. Lutheran. Avocations: fishing, hunting, flying, woodworking, raising and showing dogs. Home: 1301 Manchester E Waunakee WI 53597 Office: State Dept Pub Instrn 125 S Webster St Madison WI 53702-0001

MARTENSON, EDWARD ALLEN, theater manager; b. Paris, Ky., May 4, 1949; s. Milton A. and Bettye (Hudnall) M.; m. Gina Franz, Mar. 18, 1979; children: Benn, Hallie. AB, Princeton U., 1971. Mgr. McCarter Theater, Princeton, N.J., 1973-79; mng. dir. Yale Repertory Theater, New Haven, 1979-82; dir. theater program NEA, Washington, 1982-86; exec. dir. Guthrie Theater, Mpls., 1986—; adj. assoc. prof. Sch. Drama Yale U., New Haven, 1979-82, co-chmn. adminstrn., 1979-82. Home: 102 Farmdale Rd W Hopkins MN 55343-7183 Office: Guthrie Theater 725 Vineland Pl Minneapolis MN 55403-1187*

MARTENSTEIN, THOMAS EWING, lawyer; b. Phila., Mar. 5, 1949; s. Austin Walrath and Nancy (Ewing) M.; m. Constance Samsonoff Martenstein, Dec. 31, 1971; children: Justin Thomas, Charles Alexander, Sarah Weatherly Ewing. BA, Va. Mil. Inst., 1971; JD, U. Richmond, 1978. Bar: Va. 1978. Various banking and ins. positions, until 1986; sr. v.p., gen. counsel, corp. sec. Blue Cross & Blue Shield Va., Richmond, 1986—; sec.-treas. Va. Life, Accident & Sickness Ins. Guaranty Assn., Richmond, 1990-94, also bd. dirs. Active various ch. groups, youth orgns. and sch. adv. panels, also others; mem. Am. Corp. Counsel Assn. exec. edn. for sr. corp. attys. Duke U., Durham, N.C., 1988. Capt. U.S. army, 1971-78. Mem. ABA, Va. Bar Assn., Richmond Bar Assn., Am. Corp. Counsel Assn., Nat. Health Lawyers Assn., Am. Soc. Corp. Secs., Bull & Bear Club. Episcopalian. Avocations: reading, gardening. Office: Trigon Blue Cross & Blue Shield PO Box 27401 2015 Staples Mill Rd Richmond VA 23230

MARTH, ELMER HERMAN, bacteriologist, educator; b. Jackson, Wis., Sept. 11, 1927; s. William F. and Irma A. (Bublitz) M.; m. Phyllis E. Menge, Aug. 10, 1957. BS, U. Wis., 1950, MS, 1952, PhD, 1954. Registered sanitarian, Wis. Teaching asst. bacteriology U. Wis., Madison, 1949-51; research asst. U. Wis., 1951-54, project asso., 1954-55, instr. bacteriology, 1955-57, assoc. prof.food sci., bacteriology and food microbiology and toxicology, 1966-71, prof., 1971-90, prof. emeritus, 1990—; vis. prof. Swiss Fed. Inst. Tech., Zurich, 1981; with Kraft Foods, Inc., Glenview, Ill., 1957-66, rsch. bacteriologist, 1957-61, sr. rsch. bacteriologist, 1961-63, group leader microbiology, 1963-66, assoc. mgr. microbiology, 1966; mem. Intersoc. Coun. on Std. Methods for Exam. Dairy Products, 1968-84, chmn., 1972-78. Contbg. author books; editor: Jour. Milk and Food Tech, 1967-76, Jour. Food Protection, 1977-87; contbr. articles to profl. publs. Sec. Luth. Acad. Scholarship, 1961-71; WHO travel fellow, 1975. Recipient Nordica award for rsch. Am. Cultured Dairy Products Inst., 1979, Meritorious Svc. award APHA, 1977, 83, Sanitarian of Yr. award Wis. Assn. Milk and Food Sanitarians, 1983, Meritorious Svc. award Nat. Confectioners Assn., 1987, Joseph Mityas Meml. Laboratorian of Yr. award Wis. Lab. Assn., 1989, Quality of Comm. award Am. Agrl. Econs. Assn., 1992. Fellow Inst. Food Technologists (Nicholas Appert award 1987, Babcock-Hart award 1989); mem. Am. Soc. Microbiology, Am. Dairy Sci. Assn. (Pfizer rsch. award 1975, Dairy Rsch. Found. award 1980, Borden award 1986, Kraft Inc. teaching award 1988), Internat. Assn. Milk, Food, and Environ. Sanitarians (hon. life, Educator award for rsch. and teaching food hygiene 1977, citation award 1984), Coun. Biology Editors, Inst. Food Technologists, Sigma Xi, Alpha Zeta, Kappa Eta Kappa, Phi Sigma, Phi Tau Sigma, Delta Theta Sigma, Gamma Sigma Delta, Gamma Alpha. Patentee in field. Office: U Wis Dept Food Sci 1605 Linden Dr Madison WI 53706-1565

MARTI, KURT, chemistry educator; b. Berne, Switzerland, Aug. 18, 1936; came to U.S., 1965; s. Werner Marti and Emma H. (Habegger) M.; children: Andres Niklaus, Stefan Kurt, Lorenz Roman. MS, U. Berne, 1963, PhD, 1965. Postgrad. research chemist U. Calif-San Diego, La Jolla, 1965-68, asst. prof., 1969-74, assoc. prof., 1974-80, prof., 1980—; vis. scientist phys. research lab. Ahmedabad, India, 1977, U. Berne, Switzerland, 1977; vis. prof. U. Bordeaux, France, 1983; mem. rev. panel Lunar Sci. Inst., Houston, 1971-74, 91-93; lunar sample analysis planning team mem. Johnson Space Ctr., Houston, 1975-78; lectr. in field. Assoc. editor Geochim. Cosmochim. Acta, 1985—. Grantee NASA, 1971—; Guggenheim fellow, 1976. Fellow Meteoritical Soc.; mem. AAAS, Am. Geophys. Union, Am. Chem Soc. Home: 13424 Calais Dr Del Mar CA 92014-3524 Office: U Calif San Diego Dept Chemistry La Jolla CA 92093-0317

MARTIMUCCI, RICHARD ANTHONY, engineering company executive; b. N.Y.C., Sept. 25, 1934; s. Dominic Ernest and Angela (Gentile) M.; m. Claudia Frances Reagan, Nov. 2, 1957; 1 child, Lisa Felice. Student,

CCNY, 1952-57; AB, Syracuse U., 1960. Registered profl. engr., Conn., N.Y., N.J., Calif., Pa. Sales engr. Morse-Boulger Inc., N.Y.C., 1960-62; project engr. Nichols Research and Engring., N.Y.C., 1962-65; mgr. ops. Dorr-Oliver, Inc., Stamford, Conn., 1965-72; v.p. Environgenics Systems Chemico div. Aerojet-Gen., El Monte, Calif., 1972-75; pres. RAM Engring., Inc., Wilton, Conn., 1975—. Served with USAF, 1957-59. Mem. ASME, Nat. Soc. Profl. Engrs., Water Pollution Control Assn. Office: 9 Hollyhock Ln Wilton CT 06897-4414

MARTIN, AGNES, artist; b. Maklin, Sask., Can., 1912; came to U.S., 1932, naturalized, 1950; Student, Western Wash. State Coll., 1935-38; BS, Columbia U., 1942, MFA, 1952. One-woman shows include Betty Parsons Gallery, N.Y.C., 1958, 59, 61, Robert Elkon Gallery, N.Y.C., 1961, 63, 72, 76, Nicolas Wilder Gallery, Los Angeles, 1963-66, 67, Visual Arts Ctr., N.Y.C., 1971, Kunstraum, Munich, 1973, Inst. Contemporary Art U. Pa., Phila., 1973, Pace Gallery, N.Y.C., 1975, 76, 77, 78, 79, 80-81, 81, 83, 84, 85, 86, 89, 91, 92, Mayor Gallery, London, 1978, 84, Galerie Rudolf Zwirner, Cologne, Fed. Republic Germany, 1978, Harcus/Krakow Gallery, Boston, 1978, Margo Leavin Gallery, Los Angeles, 1979, 85, Mus. N.Mex., Santa Fe, 1979, Richard Gray Gallery, Chgo., 1981, Garry Anderson Gallery, Sydney, Australia, 1986, Waddington Galleries Ltd., London, 1986, Stedelijk Mus., Amsterdam, 1991, Whitney Mus. Am. Art, N.Y.C., 1992; exhibited in group shows at Carnegie Inst., Pitts., 1961, Whitney Mus. Am. Art, N.Y.C., 1962, 66, 67, 74, 77, 92, Tooth Gallery, London, 1962, Gallery Modern Art, Washington, 1963, Wadsworth Atheneum, Hartford, Conn., 1963, Solomon R. Guggenheim Mus., N.Y.C., 1965, 66, 76, Mead Corp., 1965-67, Mus. Modern Art, N.Y.C., 1967, 76, 85, Inst. Contemporary Art, Phila., 1967, Detroit Inst. Art, 1967, Corcoran Gallery Art, Washington, 1967, 81, Finch Mus., N.Y., 1968, Phila. Mus., 1968, Zurich Art Mus., Switzerland, 1969, Ill. Bell Telephone Co., Chgo., 1970, Mus. Contemporary Art, Chgo., 1971, Inst. Contemporary Art U. Pa., Phila., 1972, Randolph-Macon Coll., N.C., 1972, Kassel, Fed. Republic Germany, 1972, Stedelijk Mus., Amsterdam, 1975, U. Mass., Amherst, 1976, Venice Biennale, Italy, 1976, 80, Cleve. Mus. Art, 1978, Albright-Knox Gallery, Buffalo, 1978, Inst. Contemporary Art, Boston, 1979, Art Inst. Chgo., 1979, San Francisco Mus. Modern Art, 1980, ROSC Internat. Art Exhbn., Dublin, Ireland, 1980, Marilyn Pearl Gallery, N.Y.C., 1983, Kemper Gallery, Kansas City Art Inst., 1985, Am. Acad. and Inst. Arts and Letters, N.Y.C., 1985, Charles Cowles Gallery, N.Y.C., 1986, Moody Gallery Art U. Ala., Birmingham, 1986, Butler Inst. Am. Art, 1986, Art Gallery Western Australia, Perth, 1986, Mus. Contemporary Art, Los Angeles, 1986, Boston Fine Arts Mus., 1989; represented in permanent collections Mus. of Modern Art, N.Y.C., Albright-Knox Gallery, Aldrich Mus., Ridgefield, Conn., Art Gallery Ont., Can., Australian Nat. Gallery, Canberra, Grey Art Gallery and Study Ctr., N.Y.C., Solomon R. Guggenheim Mus., High Mus. Art, Atlanta, Hirshhorn Mus. and Sculpture Garden, Washington, Israel Mus., Jerusalem, La Jolla (Calif.) Mus. Contemporary Art, Los Angeles County Mus. Art, Mus. Art R.I. Sch. Design, Providence, Mus. Modern Art, Neuegalerie der Stadt, Aachen, Fed. Republic Germany, Norton Simon Mus. Art at Pasadena, Calif., Stedelijk Mus. Amsterdam, The Netherlands, 1992, Mus. Modern Art, paris, 1992, Tate Gallery, London, Wadsworth Atheneum, Walker Art Ctr., Mpls., Whitney Mus. Am. Art, 1993, Sofia, Madrid, 1993, Huosten, 1993, Worcester (Mass.) Art Mus., Yale U. Art Gallery, New Haven; subject of various articles. Office: care The Pace Gallery 32 E 57th St New York NY 10022-2513

MARTIN, ALBERT CAREY, architect; b. Los Angeles, Aug. 3, 1913; s. Albert Carey and Carolyn Elizabeth (Borchard) M.; m. Dorothy Virginia Dolde, Nov. 15, 1937; children—Albert Carey III, David Charles, Mary Martin Marquardt, Claire, Charles Dolde. B.Arch. cum laude, U. So. Calif., 1936. Registered architect, Calif. Architect Albert C. Martin and Assocs., Los Angeles, 1937-42; ptnr. Albert C. Martin and Assocs., 1942—; dir. Rancho Los Alamitos Found. Prin. works include Los Angeles Dept. Water and Power, ARCO Twin Towers, St. Basil's Ch., Union Bank Sq. Trustee Los Angeles Orthopaedic Hosp.; bd. dirs. Long Beach Mus. Art Found. Recipient Annual Spirit of Los Angeles award Los Angeles Hdqrs. City Assn., 1980, Brotherhood award NCCJ, 1980, Asa V. Call Achievement award U. So. Calif. Alumni Assn., 1984, Boy Scouts Am. Good Scout award L.A. Area Coun., 1989; named Constrn. Man of Yr. Los Angeles C. of C. 1971. Fellow AIA (past dir., pres. So. Calif. chpt., past v.p. Calif. Coun.); mem. U. So. Calif. Archtl. Guild (advisor, disting. alumnus 1990), L.A. C. of C. (past pres.), Calif. C. of C. (past dir.), Lambda Alpha, Automobile Club of So. Calif. Republican. Roman Catholic. Clubs: California, Jonathan (Los Angeles). Avocation: sailing. Office: Albert C Martin and Assocs 811 W 7th St Los Angeles CA 90017-3408

MARTIN, ALBERT CHARLES, manufacturing executive, lawyer; b. San Lucido, Italy, Sept. 20, 1928; s. Joseph and Carmela M.; m. Jean Perrin, Aug. 22, 1953; children: Lynne, Ken. B.S., Mich. State U., 1952; M.S., U. Mich., 1953; J.D., Detroit Coll. Law, 1962. Bar: Mich. 1962. Corp. counsel, sec. Udylite Corp., Detroit, 1963-68; corp. counsel Hooker Chem. Corp., N.Y.C., 1968-70, Grow Chem. Co., N.Y.C., 1970-71; group v.p. Leeds & Northrup Internat., North Wales, Pa., 1971-79, pres., 1979—. Served with U.S. Army, 1946-48. Mem. Mich. Bar Assn.

MARTIN, ALLEN, lawyer; b. Manchester, Conn., Aug. 12, 1937; s. Richard and Ruth Palmer (Smith) M.; m. Bonnie Reid, Sept. 8, 1979; children: Elizabeth Palmer, Samuel Bates. B.A., Williams Coll., 1960, Oxford U., 1962; LL.B., Harvard U. 1965. Ptnr. firm Downs, Rachlin and Martin, Burlington, Brattleboro and St. Johnsbury, Vt., 1971—; chmn. bd. dirs. Elcon Inc., 1991—; bd. dirs. Union Mut. Ins. Co., New Eng. Guaranty Ins. Co.; mem. Vt. Judicial Responsibility Bd.; vice chmn., 1978-80. Chmn. Vt. Bd. Edn., 1978-83; chmn. Vt. Rep. Party, 1991-95; mem. Rep. Nat. Com., 1991-95. Mem. Am. Law Inst., Am., Vt. bar assns. Republican. Home: 283 S Union St Burlington VT 05401 Office: PO Box 190 199 Main St Burlington VT 05402-0190

MARTIN, ALVIN CHARLES, lawyer; b. Bklyn., Oct. 25, 1933; s. George and Dora (Gitlin) M.; m. Susan Goldman, Sept. 3, 1959 (div. Jan. 1980); children: Robert, Peter; m. Gail Leichtman, Oct. 25, 1985; stepchildren: Hilary Macht, Timothy Macht. BBA, CCNY, 1954; JD, Harvard U., 1957; LLM in Taxation, NYU, 1963. Bar: N.Y. 1958, N.J. 1977, Fla. 1991. Pvt. practice N.Y.C., 1958-76, Newark and Morristown, N.J., 1977—; with Office of Regional Counsel, IRS, 1959-64; assoc. Curtis Mallet-Prevost Colt & Mosle, 1964-66; ptnr. Zissu, Halper & Martin, 1966-76; ptnr. Shanley & Fisher, 1977-88, counsel, 1988—; of counsel Ruden, Barnett, McClosky, Smith, Schuster & Russell P.A., Ft. Lauderdale, Fla., 1990—; sec. Vornado, Inc., 1966-79, exec. v.p., asst. to chmn. bd., 1971-76, also bd. dirs.; adj. prof. taxation NYU, 1972-86; mem. taxation faculty Pace Coll. Grad. Sch. Bus. Adminstrn., 1964-70, Baruch Sch. Bus. and Pub. Adminstrn., 1959-62. Author: New Jersey Estate Planning, Will Drafting and Estate Administration Forms, 1988, 94. Bd. dirs. Met. Jewish Geriatric Ctr., 1980-84. With U.S. Army, 1957. Fellow Am. Coll. Trust and Estate Counsel. Clubs: Boca West (Fla.). Home: 20179 Fairfax Dr Boca Raton FL 33434 Office: 131 Madison Ave Morristown NJ 07960-6097 also: 200 E Broward Blvd Fort Lauderdale FL 33301

MARTIN, ANDREA LOUISE, actress, comedienne, writer; b. Portland, Md., Jan. 15, 1947. Grad. Emerson Coll. Appearances include (plays) Hard Shell, 1980 (off-Broadway debut), Sorrows of Stephen, 1980, What's a Nice Country Like You Doing in a State Like This?, 1974, She Loves Me, My Favorite Year, 1993 (Tony award, Featured Actress in a Musical), (films) Cannibal Girls, 1973, Black Christmas, 1974, Wholly Moses!, 1980, Soup for One, 1982, Club Paradise, 1986, Innerspace, 1987, Martha Ruth and Eddie, 1988, Worth Winning, 1989, Boris and Natasha, 1989, Rude Awakening, 1989, Too Much Sun, 1991, Stepping Out, 1991, All I Want for Christmas, 1991; (TV) Second City TV 1977-81, That Thing on ABC, 1978, Torn Between Two Lovers, 1979, The Robert Klein Show, 1981, Kate and Allie, 1982, The Comedy Zone, 1984, Late Night Film Festival, 1985, Second City Twenty-Fifth Anniversary, 1985, Martin Short Concert for the North Americas, 1985, The Smothers Brothers Comedy Hour, 1988, Poison, 1988, and numerous others; TV host Women of the Night II, 1988, Second City Fifteen Anniversary Special, 1988, Andrea Martin: Together Again, 1989; actress/writer: TV series SCTV Network 90, 1981-83 (2 Emmy awards 1982, 83), TV pilot From Cleveland, 1980; also The Completely Mental Misadventures of Ed Grimley, 1988-90 (voice of Mrs. Freebus). Office: care William Morris Agy 1350 Avenue of the Americas New York NY 10019*

MARTIN, ANN MATTHEWS, writer, juvenile; b. Princeton, N.J., Aug. 12, 1955; d. Henry R. and Edith Aiken (Matthews) M. BA cum laude, Smith Coll., 1977. Elem. sch. tchr. Plumfield Sch., Noroton, Conn., 1977-78; editorial asst. Simon & Schuster, N.Y.C., 1978-80; copywriter Teenage Book Club, Scholastic Books, Inc., N.Y.C., 1980-81; assoc. editor Scholastic Books, Inc., N.Y.C., 1981-83, editor, 1983; sr. editor Bantam Books, N.Y.C., 1983-85; free lance writer, editor N.Y.C., 1985—. Author: (novels) Bummer Summer, 1983, Just You and Me, 1983, Inside Out, 1984, Stage Fright, 1984, Me and Katie (the Pest), 1985, With You and Without You, 1986, Missing Since Monday, 1986, Just a Summer Romance, 1987, Slam Book, 1987, Yours Turly, Shirley, 1988, Ten Kids, No Pets, 1988, Fancy Dance in Feather Town, 1988, Ma and Pa Dracula, 1989, Moving Day in Feather Town, 1989, Eleven Kids, One Summer, 1991, Rachel Parker, Kindergarten Show-off, (novels in series) The Baby-sitters Club, Baby-sitters Little Sister, Baby-sitters Club/Mysteries. Mem. PEN, Authors Guild, Soc. Children's Book Writers and Illustrators. Democrat. Avocations: sewing, needlework. Office: Scholastic Inc c/o Bethany Buck 555 Broadway New York NY 10012-3999

MARTIN, ARTHUR MEAD, lawyer; b. Cleveland Heights, Ohio, Mar. 29, 1942; s. Bernard P. and Winifred (Mead) M. AB, Princeton U., 1963; LLB, Harvard U., 1966. Bar: Ill. 1966, U.S. Dist. Ct. (no. dist.) Ill. 1969, U.S. Ct. Appeals (7th cir.) 1970, U.S. Supreme Ct. 1980. Instr. law U. Wis., Madison, 1966-68; assoc. Jenner & Block, Chgo., 1968-74, ptnr., 1975—; co-trustee Dille Family Trust, 1982—; bd. dirs. Sleepeck Printing Co. Author: Historical and Practice Notes to the Illinois Civil Practice Act and Illinois Supreme Court Rules, 1968-88. Mem. ABA, Am. Law Inst., Ill. Bar Assn., Chgo. Bar Assn. (bd. editors 1972-86), Am. Arbitration Assn. (panel), Lake Mich. Fedn. (bd. dirs. 1993—, exec. com. 1994—), Law CLub Chgo., Legal Club Chgo. Office: Jenner & Block 1 Ibm Plz Chicago IL 60611-3608

MARTIN, BARBARA JEAN, elementary school principal; b. Mt. Vernon, Tex., May 17, 1940; d. Billy Earl and Wilene (Dawson) Dade; m. J.B. Martin III, Aug. 29, 1959; children: J.B. IV, Mark Anthony. Ba, Fisk U., Nashville, 1961; MEd, U. Ill., Chgo., 1979, PhD, 1992. Cert. tchr. kindergarten to 3rd grade, type 75 adminstr., Ill. Tchr. Chgo. Pub. Schs., 1969-93, prin., 1993—. Mem. Nat. Alliance Black Sch. Educators, Delta Kappa Gamma (sec. 1992—), Pi Lambda Theta, Alpha Kappa Alpha. Home: 825 E Drexel Sq Chicago IL 60615-3705 Office: O W Holmes Sch 955 W Garfield Blvd Chicago IL 60621-2240

MARTIN, BERNARD LEE, former college dean; b. Dayton, Ohio, May 29, 1923; s. Harley L. and Clare (Murphy) M.; m. Mary Patricia McDonald, Nov. 23, 1950; children: Joseph, Mary, David, Patrick, Paul, Timothy, Michael, Christopher. B.A., Athenaeum of Ohio, 1941-45; M.A. in History, Xavier U., 1950, M.B.A., 1955; Ph.D. in Econs, U. Cin., 1963; Ph.D. honoris causa, Canisius Coll., 1978. Mem. faculty Xavier U., Cin., 1948-65; asst. prof. bus. adminstrn. Xavier U., 1955-62, assoc. prof. mktg., 1962-65, chmn. mktg. deptt., 1961; chmn., prof. mktg. Eastern Mich. U., Ypsilanti, 1965-66; dean Sch. Bus. Adminstrn. Canisius Coll., Buffalo, 1966-71, 1973-78, acting acad. v.p. of coll., 1971-73; dean McLaren Coll. Bus. Adminstrn., U. San Francisco, 1978-86, prof. mktg., 1986-91; prof. emeritus U. San Francisco, 1992. Author: (with others) Contemporary Economic Problems and Issues, 3d edit, 1973. Ford Found. grantee Harvard, 1964. Mem. Am. Mktg. Assn., Am. Econ. Assn. Home: 224 Greenview Dr Daly City CA 94014-3458

MARTIN, BETSY, magazine publishing executive. Sales rep. Money mag., N.Y.C., 1981; then mgr. New Eng. sales group Money mag., Boston, until 1986; head sales dept. Women's Sports and Fitness mag., 1986-87; nat. advt. sales dir. Working Woman mag., 1987-88; advt. sales dir. Money mag., N.Y.C., 1988-94, assoc. pub., 1993-94, pub., 1994—. Office: Money Time Inc Rockefeller Ctr. New York NY 10020-1393*

MARTIN, BETTY CAROLYN, library director; b. Louisville, Nov. 2, 1933; d. Earl Francis and Marie Dorothy (Baertich) Snyder; m. Charles Frank Martin, Aug. 18, 1956. BS, Ind. U., 1956, MLS, 1982. Sch. libr. Decatur Twp. Schs., Indpls., 1955-57; tchr. Indpls. Schs., 1957-58; libr. libr. dir. Vigo County Pub. Libr., Terre Haute, Ind., 1958—; exec. bd. Ind. State Libr. Adv. Coun., Indpls., 1989—. Contbr. articles to profl. jours. Bd. dirs. State Student Assistance Commn., Indpls., 1991—, United Way Wabash County, Terre Haute, 1989—, Alliance for Growth and Progress, Sec., 1989; bd. dirs. LWC, pres., 1980; bd. dirs. Pres. Adv. Bd. St. Mary of Woods Coll., Salvation Army, pres., 1990-92; sec. bd. dirs. Work Force Devel. Commn. Western Ind., Terre Haute, 1990—. Recipient Louise Maxwell award SLIS-IU Alumni Assn., Bloomington, Ind., 1991; named Outstanding Woman of COmmunity, Bus. & Profl. Womens Club, Terre Haute, 1990. Mem. ALA, Ind. Libr. Fedn. (bd. dirs., pres. 1989-90, Assn. Leadership award 1990), Ind. U. Libr. Sch. Alumni Assn. (pres.-elect 1992-94), C. of C. (terre award 1989). Democrat. Roman Catholic. Avocations: reading, travel, gardening. Home: 5351 N 13th St Terre Haute IN 47805-1613 Office: Vigo County Public Lib 1 Library Sq Terre Haute IN 47807-3609

MARTIN, BILL, artist, art educator; b. South San Francisco, Calif., Jan. 22, 1943; s. Gordon and Zelia (Sonderman) M.; m. Shelley Persistence Balaban, Feb. 22, 1975. B.F.A., San Francisco Art Inst., 1968, M.F.A., 1970. instr. Acad. Art, San Francisco, 1970-71, U. Calif., Berkeley, 1972, San Francisco Art Inst., 1972, Calif. State U., San Jose, 1973, Coll. Marin, Kentfield, Calif., 1975-78, Coll. of the Redwoods, Mendocino, Calif., 1983—. One-man shows, San Francisco Mus. Art, 1973, Nancy Hoffman Gallery, N.Y.C., 1977, 79, 82, Zara Gallery, San Francisco, 1978, 80, Joseph Chowning Gallery, 1983, 85, 87, 89, 92, 94, U. Nev., 1988, Clatsop Coll., Oreg., 1989, Joseph Chowning Gallery, San Francisco, 1989, Chabot Coll., Hayward, Calif., 1990, Kabutoya Gallery, Tokyo, 1991; Joseph Chowning Gallery, San Francisco, 1992, Atrium Galley, San Francisco, 1992; group shows include, San Francisco Art Inst., 1966, 68, 70, 71, Unicorn Gallery, San Francisco, 1969, Sun Gallery, San Francisco, 1969, Richmond (Calif.) Art Center, 1970, Pioneer Mus., Stockton, Calif., 1970, U. So. Calif., Los Angeles, 1971, Whitney Mus. Am. Art, N.Y.C., 1972-73, U. Pa., 1972, Calif. State U. San Jose, 1973, Nancy Hoffman Gallery N.Y.C., 1974, State U. Albany, 1974, Milw. Arts Center, 1974, Chgo. Art Inst., 1974, Mus. Modern Art, Paris, 1975, Tri-Ann. Invitational of India, 1978, European traveling exhbn. organized by New Mus., N.Y.C., 1979-81, Zara Gallery, 1979, 80, Western Assn. Arts Mus., 1980-81, Joseph Chowning Gallery, 1983, 85, 87, Mendocino (Calif.) Art Gallery, 1987, Cheney Cowles Mus., Spokane, Wash., 1988, Humbolt State Univ., 1988, Muscarelle Mus. Art Coll. William & Mary Coll., 1988, Salt Lake City, 1988, Mus. of Rockies, Bozeman, Mont., 1988, Lancaster (Calif.) Mus., 1988, Humboldt State U., Arcata, Calif. 1988, City Coll. San Francisco, 1988, Medocino (Calif.) Art Ctr., 1989, So. Utah State U., 1989, Springfield (Mo.) Art Mus., 1989, From the Studio: Recent Painting and Sculpture by 20 California Artists, Oakland (Calif.) Mus., 1992; painting and sculptures represented in permanent collections, Neue Gallerie der Stadt Acchen, Germany, AT&T, San Francisco Internat. Airport, Oakland Mus., Calif., Owens Corning, Vesti Corp., Boston, Varney Collection, San Francisco, Ohio, Capital Group Inc., Los Angeles, McDermott, Will & Emery, N.Y.C., Clayton E. Michael CPA., San Fancisco, Police Data Systems, Dublin, Calif., John F. Kennedy U., Orinda, Calif., Madison (Wis.) Art Ctr.; author: Visions, Bill Martin Paintings 1969-1979, Composition In Painting Drawing, Joy of Drawing, Lost Legends, 1995, (videotape series) Principles of Painting. Home: PO Box 511 Albion CA 95410-0511

MARTIN, BOBBY L, retail corporation executive; b. Gidden, Mo., Dec. 24, 1948; s. Billie Jean (Skaggs) M.; m. Margie L. Martin, Dec. 9, 1950; children: Lori, Christy. Student, South Tex. U., 1969; hon. doctorate. S.W. Bapt. U., 1989. Mgr. data processing Dillard Dept. Stores, Little Rock, 1969-76, dir. data processing, 1976-84; v.p. Wal-Mart Stores, Inc., Bentonville, Ark., 1984-85; exec. v.p. N000, Bentonville, Ark., 1985-93; pres., CEO Wal-Mart Internat., Bentonville, 1993—; chmn. VICS, 1986—; exec. dir. Gen. Mdse. Adv. coun., 1987—; mem. Wal-Mart exec. com., 1985—; bd. dirs. Western Merchandising, World Wide Distbn., Inc.; mem. The Rsch. Bd., 1991, exec. bd. I/5 Adv. Group IBM, 1988-92. Recipient Don Percival award Automated Identification Mfrs. Am., 1989, Excellence award Internat. Mass Retailer Assn., 1990, Achievement Info. Tech. award Carnegie-Mellon U., 1992. Mem. DPQA Univ. Ark. Baptist. Home: 1415

Concord Dr Lowell AR 72745-9648 Office: Wal-Mart Stores Inc 702 SW 8th St Bentonville AR 72712-6299

MARTIN, BOE WILLIS, lawyer; b. Texarkana, Ark., Oct. 6, 1940; s. E. H. and Dorothy Annette (Willis) M.; m. Carol J. Edwards, June 12, 1965; children—Stephanie Diane, Scott Andrew. B.A., Tex. A&M U., 1962; LL.B., U. Tex., 1964; LL.M., George Washington U., 1970. Bar: Tex. 1964. Law clk. Tex. Supreme Ct. 1966-67; assoc. Snakard, Brown & Gambill, Fort Worth, 1967-69; asst. counsel U.S. Senate Labor and Pub. Welfare Com., 1969; legis. asst. U.S. Senator Ralph W. Yarborough, 1969-71; assoc., ptnr. Snakard, Brown & Gambill, Fort Worth, 1971-72; assoc., ptnr. Stalcup & Johnson, Dallas, 1972-77; assoc., ptnr. Coke & Coke, Dallas, 1977-80; ptnr., shareholder Johnson & Gibbs, Dallas, 1981—; vis. prof. law So. Meth. U. Sch. Law, 1972, 73, 75, 88, 89, U. Tex. Sch. Law, 1977, 79. Mem. Carter-Mondale Campaign staff, 1976, 1980; cons. to Vice-Pres. of U.S., 1977-80; cons. Mondale for Pres. Campaign, 1983-84, Dukakis for Pres. campaign, 1988, State of Minn., for visit of Pres. Mikhail Gorbachev, 1990. Served to capt. U.S. Army, 1964-69. Mem. ABA, Tex. Bar Assn., Dallas Bar Assn. Democrat. Methodist. Contbr. articles to legal jours. Home: 4435 Arcady Ave Dallas TX 75205-3604 Office: Johnson & Gibbs Founders Sq Suite 100 900 Jackson St Dallas TX 75202-4404

MARTIN, BOYCE FICKLEN, JR., federal judge; b. Boston, Mass., Oct. 23, 1935; s. Boyce Ficklen and Helen Artt M.; m. Mavin Hamilton Brown, July 8, 1961; children: Mary V. H., Julia H.C., Boyce Ficklen III, Robert C. G. II. A.B., Davidson Coll., 1957; J.D., U. Va., 1963. Bar: Ky. 1963. Law clk. to Shackelford Miller, Jr., chief judge U.S. Ct. Appeals for 6th Circuit, Cin., 1963-64; asst. U.S. atty. Western Dist. Ky., Louisville, 1964; U.S. atty. Western Dist. Ky., 1965; pvt. practice law Louisville, 1966-74; judge Jefferson Circuit Ct., Louisville, 1974-76; chief judge Ct. Appeals Ky., Louisville, 1976-79; judge U.S. Ct. Appeals (6th cir.), Cin. and Louisville, 1979—. Mem. vestry St. Francis in the Fields Episc. Ch., Harrods Creek, Ky., 1979-83; bd. visitors Davidson (N.C.) Coll., 1980-86, trustee, 1994—; trustee Isaac W. Bernheim Found., Louisville, 1981—, chmn., 1982-95; trustee Blackacre Found., Inc., Louisville, 1983-94, chmn., 1986-94; trustee Hanover Coll., Inc., 1983—, vice chmn., 1992—; mem. exec. bd. Old Ky. Home coun. Boy Scouts Am., 1968-72; pres. Louisville Zool. Commn., 1971-74. Capt. JAGC U.S. Army, 1958-66. Fellow Am. Bar Found.; mem. Inst. Jud. Adminstrn., Am. Judicature Soc., Fed Bar Assn., ABA (com. effective appellate advocacy Conf. Appellate Judges), Ky. Bar Assn., Louisville Bar Assn. Office: US Ct Appeals 209 US Courthouse 601 W Broadway St Louisville KY 40202

MARTIN, BOYD ARCHER, political science educator emeritus; b. Cottonwood, Idaho, Mar. 3, 1911; s. Archer Olmstead and Norah Claudine (Imbler) M.; m. Grace Charlotte Swingler, Dec. 29, 1933; children: Michael Archer, William Archer. Student, U. Idaho, 1929-30, 35-36, B.S., 1936; student, Pasadena Jr. Coll., 1931-32, U. Calif. at Los Angeles, summer 1934; A.M., Stanford, 1937, Ph.D., 1943. Rsch. asst. Stanford U., 1936-37, teaching asst., 1937-38; instr. polit. sci. U. Idaho, 1938-39; acting instr. polit. sci. Stanford U., 1939-40; John M. Switzer fellow, summer 1939-40; chief personnel officer Walter Butler Constrn. Co., Farragut Naval Tng. Center, summer 1942; instr. polit. sci. U. Idaho, 1940-43, asst. prof. polit. sci., 1943-44, asso. prof. polit. sci., 1944-47; prof., head dept. social sci., asst. dean coll. letters and sci. U. Idaho, 1947-55, dean, 1955-70, Borah Distinguished prof. polit. sci., 1970-73, prof., dean emeritus, 1973—; vis. prof. Stanford U., summer 1946, spring 1952, U. Calif., 1962-63; affiliate Center for Study Higher Edn., Berkeley, 1962-63; mem. steering com. N.W. Conf. on Higher Edn., 1960-67, pres. conf., 1966-67; mem. bd. Am. Assn. of Partners of Alliance for Progress; chmn. Idaho Adv. Coun. on Higher Edn.; del. Gt. Plains UNESCO Conf., Denver, 1947; chmn. bd. William E. Borah Found. on Causes of War and Conditions of Peace, 1947-55; mem. Commn. to Study Orgn. Peace; dir. Bur. Pub. Affair Rsch. 1959-73, dir. emeritus, 1973—; dir. Martin Peace Inst., 1970—. Author: The Direct Primary in Idaho, 1947, (with others) Introduction to Political Science, 1950, (with other) Western Politics, 1968, Politics in the American West, 1969, (with Sydney Duncombe) Recent Elections in Idaho (1964-70), 1972, Idaho Voting Trends: Party Realignment and Percentage of Voters for Candidates, Parties and Elections, 1890-1974, 1975, In Search of Peace: Starting From October 19, 1980, 1980, Why the Democrats Lost in 1980, 1980, On Understanding the Soviet Union, 1987; editor: The Responsibilities of Colleges and Universities, 1967; contbr. to: Ency. Britannica, 1990, 91; also articles. Mem. Am. Polit. Sci. Assn. (exec. council 1952-53), Nat. Municipal League, Am. Soc. Pub. Adminstrn., Fgn. Policy Assn., UN Assn., AAUP, Western Polit. Sci. Assn. (pres. 1950), Phi Beta Kappa, Pi Gamma Mu, Kappa Delta Pi, Pi Sigma Alpha. Home: PO Box 38 Kamiah ID 83536-0038 *Attempt to contribute to society to the maximum of your ability. Assume responsibility in positions commensurate with the obligations and accountability of the position. In making decisions, first gather all factual data, interpret it fairly, make the decision, and assume responsibility for the decision. In dealing with people, whether family, friends, professionals, or adversaries, try to remember the sensitivity of personal feelings and personal pride. Commend people who achieve and contribute. Be completely honest; when you don't know, admit it.*

MARTIN, BRUCE DOUGLAS, university official, chemist; b. Rochester, N.Y., Apr. 8, 1934; s. Frederic and Harriet Emily (Krieger) M.; m. Geraldine Ann Coughlin, July 6, 1957 (div. 1980); children: James Scott, Robert Douglas; m. Marilyn Frances Harris, Aug. 15, 1984. B.S. in Pharmacy, Albany Coll. Pharmacy, 1955; M.S. in Pharm. Chemistry, U. Ill., 1959, Ph.D., 1962. Asst. prof. Sch. Pharmacy, Duquesne U., 1961-64, asso. prof., 1964-68, prof., chmn. dept. pharm. chemistry, 1968-71, dean, 1971-81, acting dean health professions, 1979-80, acting v.p. acad. affairs, 1981-82, assoc. v.p. acad. affairs, 1982—; acting dean Grad. Sch., Duquesne U., 1984-86; state dir. Pa. Sci. Talent Search, 1989—. Fulbright lectr. U. Sci. and Tech. Kumasi, Ghana, 1968-69. Mem. Pa. Pharm. Assn., Allegheny County Pharm. Assn. (exec. bd. 1971—), Am. Pharm. Assn., Am. Chem. Soc., Pa. Acad. Sci. (pres. 1980-82), Inst. for German-Am. Rels. (founder, chmn. bd. dirs. 1990—), AAUP, Sigma Xi, Kappa Psi, Rho Chi, Sigma Pi Sigma, Alpha Epsilon Delta, Phi Delta Chi, Omicron Delta Kappa, Phi Lambda Sigma, Phi Kappa Phi. Home: 5340 Pocussett St Pittsburgh PA 15217-1909 Office: Duquesne U 502 Adminstrn Bldg Pittsburgh PA 15282

MARTIN, BRUCE JAMES, newspaper editor; b. Pontiac, Mich., Sept. 2, 1956; s. James Patrick and Patricia Ann (Taylor) M.; m. Elizabeth Hartley Nutting, July 30, 1988. BJ, U. Mo., 1982. Reporter Spinal Col. Newsweekly, Union Lake, Mich., 1982; sports editor Northville (Mich.) Record/Novi News, 1982-85; news editor Novi News, Northville, 1984-85; copy editor Kalamazoo Gazette, 1985-89; copy editor Ann Arbor (Mich.) News, 1989-91, homes editor, 1991, arts and entertainment editor, 1991—. Recipient 1st Place in Sports Writing in Circulation Category, Mich. Press Assn., 1993. Avocations: songwriting, playing piano and guitar. Office: Ann Arbor News 340 E Huron Ann Arbor MI 48106

MARTIN, CHARLES NEIL, JR., health care management company executive; b. Florence, Ala., Dec. 11, 1942; s. Charles Neil Sr. and Hazel Lucy (Hawkins) M. BS, So. Coll., Chattanooga, 1964. Adminstr. El Reposo Nursing Home, Florence, 1964-66, Parkwood Convalescent Ctr., Chattanooga, 1966-67; project dir. Tenn. Hosp. Assn., Nashville, 1967-68, asst. dir., 1968-69; v.p. Gen. Care Corp., Nashville, 1969-76, exec. v.p., 1976-79, pres., chief operating officer, 1979-80; exec. v.p. HCA, Nashville, 1980-85, exec. v.p., 1985-87, also bd. dirs.; pres., chief operating officer HealthTrust, Inc. - The Hosp. Co., Nashville, 1987—; bd. dirs. Equicor, Nashville, 1986—. Bd. dirs. Cystic Fibrosis Found., Nashville, 1987. Office: Ornda Healthcorp 3401 W End Ave Ste 700 Nashville TN 37203

MARTIN, CHARLES RAYMOND, chemist, educator; b. Cin., Nov. 20, 1953; s. Samuel James and Flora Joy (Clifton) M.; m. Deborah Susan Greco, May 2, 1987. BS, Centre Coll., Danville, Ky., 1975; PhD, U. Ariz., 1980. Asst. prof. chemistry Tex. A&M U., College Station, 1981-85, assoc. prof., 1985-87, prof., 1987-90; prof. chemistry Colo. State U., Ft. Collins, 1990—; cons. Dow Chem. Co., Midland, Mich., 1983—. Editor: Functional Polymers, 1990; contbr. peer-reviewed rsch. articles to sci. publs. Mem. AAAS, Am. Chem. Soc., Electrochem. Soc., Materials Rsch. Soc. Achievements include fundamental research in membrane science, electronically conductive polymers, electrochemistry.

MARTIN, CHARLES WALLACE, travel executive, retired university administrator; b. Columbia, S.C., Feb. 1, 1916; s. Earle Purkerson and Caroline Louise (Keenan) M.; m. Nancy Miles Chisolm, Sept. 30, 1944; children: Nancy Miles, Charles Wallace, Louise Elizabeth. B.A., U. S.C., 1936. Br. office employee N.Y. Life Ins. Co., Columbia, 1936-38; mgr. Palmetto Theatre Co., Columbia, 1938-42, Reamer Appliance Co., Columbia, 1946-47; local sales mgr. WIS Radio, Columbia, 1947-50; pres., gen. mgr. WMSC Radio, Columbia, 1950-60; dir. devel. U. S.C., Columbia, 1960-66; exec. dir. ednl. found. U. S.C., 1960-77, v.p. for devel., 1966-77, instr. English, 1948-52; chmn. Carolina V.I.P. Tours, 1977—; adv. bd. Bankers Trust S.C., Columbia, 1960-78. Chmn. United Way Columbia, 1954; pres. Columbia Philharm. Orch., 1967-68; commr. Columbia Housing Authority, 1971-76, chmn., 1974-76; bd. dirs. Bus. Ptnrs. Found., 1969-77, Providence Hosp. Found., 1977-82; trustee Columbia Mus. Arts and Sci., 1977-80, 88-94, life mem.; co-chmn. S.C. Gov.'s Mansion Found., 1979-83; vestryman Trinity Cathedral, Columbia; chmn. Trinity Found. Lt. USNR, 1942-45. Named Young Man of Year Columbia, 1951. Mem. Columbia Stage Soc. (dir. 1947-59, 66-69), Greater Columbia C. of C. (pres. 1959), S.C. Broadcasters Assn. (pres. 1954), Am. Coll. Pub. Relations Assn. (dir., treas. Mason-Dixon dist. 1967-72), English-Speaking Union U.S. (pres. Columbia br. 1973-75, nat. dir. 1972-75), Sigma Nu, Omicron Delta Kappa, Pi Gamma Mu. Episcopalian. Clubs: Kiwanian (pres. 1957), Forest Lake, Pine Tree Hunt (pres. 1985-86) Centurion Soc., Columbia Ball (pres. 1959), Forum (pres. 1989-90), Palmetto. Home: 1424 Heatherwood Rd Columbia SC 29205-1422

MARTIN, CHESTER Y., sculptor, painter; b. Chattanooga, Nov. 2, 1934; s. Woodfin Ballenger and Mabel Willett (Young) M.; m. Patricia Ann Parnell, Aug. 15, 1963; 1 child, Sharon Elizabeth (Mrs. Christopher Pruitt). Student, U. Chattanooga, 1952-55, 60-61, Internat. Medallic Workshop-Pa. State U., 1984. Freelance artist Chattanooga, 1967-86; sculptor, engraver U.S. Mint, Phila., 1986-92. One-man shows include Hunter Mus. Art, Chattanooga, 1979; group shows: Kottler Galleries, N.Y.C., 1966; Internat. Exposition Contemporary Medals, Italy, 1983, Sweden, 1985, Finland, 1990; U.S. Dept. State, 1984, Nat. Sculpture Soc., N.Y.C., 1984, 85, Cast Iron Gallery, N.Y.C., 1992, Internat. Exhbn. of Contemporary Medals, Brit. Mus., London, 1992, Hungarian Nat. Gallery, Budapest, 1994, numerous others; permanent collections: British Mus., London; Smithsonian Instn.; Food and Agrl. Orgn., Rome; Am. Numismatic Soc., N.Y.C.; Julius Wile Sons and Co., N.Y.C.; Brookgreen Gardens, S.C., U.S. Mint, Phila.; major comms.: World Food Day Medal, UN, 1984, others; other major works: History of Chattanooga Mural, 1974; Centennial Mural for Chattem Inc., Chattanooga, 1980; sculptured Congl. Bicentennial Silver Dollar, 1989, Eisenhower Centennial Dollar reverse, Mt. Rushmore Dollar obverse, 1991; designer Andrew Wyeth Congl. medal, 1989, George Bush Presdl. medal reverse; designer Yosemite Nat. Park Centennial Congressional Medal, 1991, Gen. Colin L. Powell Congressional Medal, 1992, White House Bicentennial Dollar reverse, 1992. Served with USAF, 1956-60. Recipient numerous art awards, most recent being Purchase award Benedictine Art Competition, 1975, Medallic Sculpture award Am. Numismatic Assn., 1993. Mem. Fedn. Internationale de la Medaille (Am. del.), Am. Medallic Sculpture Assn. (v.p. 1987). Methodist. Avocations: modern languages. Mailing Address: 4110 Sunbury Ave Chattanooga TN 37411-5232

MARTIN, CHRISTINA MARIE, public relations executive; b. Shawnee Mission, Kans., June 28, 1966; d. Rafael Luis and Rebecca Barbara (Bunck) M. BA in Econs., U. Kans., 1988. Dep. asst. to chief speechwriter, rschr., dep. asst. to the asst. to the president The White House, Washington, 1989-93; chief of staff, press sec. Rep. Michael Huffington, Washington, 1993-94; press sec. Gov. Branstad, Des Moines, 1994—; spl. asst. Office Pres. Elect., Washington, 1988-89. Staff asst. Bush-Quayle 88, Washington, 1988. Republican. Roman Catholic. Avocation: travel. Home: 300 Walnut St # 87 Des Moines IA 50309 Office: Office of the Gov State Capitol Bldg Des Moines IA 50319

MARTIN, CHRYS ANNE, lawyer; b. Portland, Oreg., June 18, 1953; d. Richard Keith and Doris Glenna (Osborne) M.; m. Jack Pessia, Oct. 18, 1987. BA with honors, Oreg. State U., 1975; JD cum laude, Northwestern U., Portland, 1981. Bar: Oreg. 1981, U.S. Dist. Ct. (we. dist.) Oreg. 1981. Adminstrv. asst. City of Portland, 1975-76, Multnomah County Dist. Atty., Portland, 1976-80; assoc. Bullivant, Houser, Bailey, Pendergrass & Hoffman, Portland, 1981—, ptnr., 1987—; bd. dirs., v.p. State Mortuary and Cemetary Bd., 1987—. Contbr. articles to profl. jours. Mem. ABA (chair com. on health ins. 1992-93, spl. labor and employment law 1985—), Def. Rsch. Inst. (chair life, health and disability com. 1990-93), Oreg. State Bar (chair affirmative action com. 1988, chair civil rights com. 1989), Inst. Managerial and Profl. Women (pres. 1983-85), City Club of Portland. Democrat. Avocations: snow and water skiing. Office: Bullivant Houser Bailey Pendergrass & Hoffman 300 Pioneer Tower 888 SW 5th Portland OR 97204

MARTIN, CLAUDE RAYMOND, JR., marketing consultant, educator; b. Harrisburg, Pa., May 11, 1932; s. Claude R. and Marie Teresa (Stapf) M.; m. Marie Frances Culkin, Nov. 16, 1957; children: Elizabeth Ann, David Jude, Nancy Marie, William Jude, Patrick Jude, Cecelia Marie. B.S., U. Scranton, 1954, M.B.A., 1963; Ph.D., Columbia U., 1969. Newsman Sta. WILK-TV, Wilkes-Barre, Pa., 1953-55; news dir. Sta. WNEP-TV, Scranton, Pa., 1955-60; dir. systems Blue Cross & Blue Shield Ins., Wilkes-Barre, 1960-63; lectr. mktg. St. Francis Coll., Bklyn., 1964, U. Mich., Ann Arbor, 1965-68; asst. prof. U. Mich., 1968-73, asso. prof., 1973-77, prof., 1977-80, Isadore and Leon Winkelman prof. retail mktg., 1980—, chmn. mktg. dept., 1986-90; bd. dirs. Perry Drug Stores, Inc., Nashville, early, 1983-89; spl. cons. on rsch. changes in U.S. currency Fed. Res. Sys., 1978—; pub. mem. Nat. Advt. Rev. Bd., 1989-94. Contbr. articles on mktg. analysis, consumer research to profl. publs. Served with USNR, 1955-57. Mem. Acad. Mktg. Sci., Am. Mktg. Assn., S.W. Mktg. Assn., Bank Mktg. Assn., Assn. Consumer Research, Am. Collegiate Retailing Assn., Am. Acad. Advt. Roman Catholic. Home: 1116 Aberdeen Dr Ann Arbor MI 48104-2812

MARTIN, CLYDE VERNE, psychiatrist; b. Coffeyville, Kans., Apr. 7, 1933; s. Howard Verne and Elfrieda Louise (Moehn) M.; m. Barbara Jean McNeilly, June 24, 1956; children: Kent Clyde, Kristin Claire, Kerry Constance, Kyle Curtis. Student Coffeyville Coll., 1951-52; AB, U. Kans., 1955; MD, 1958; MA, Webster Coll., St. Louis, 1977; JD, Thomas Jefferson Coll. Law, Los Angeles, 1985. Diplomate Am. Bd. Psychiatry and Neurology. Intern, Lewis Gale Hosp., Roanoke, Va., 1958-59; resident in psychiatry U. Kans. Med. Ctr., Kansas City, 1959-62, Fresno br. U. Calif.-San Francisco, 1978; staff psychiatrist Neurol. Hosp., Kansas City, 1962; practice medicine specializing in psychiatry, Kansas City, Mo., 1964-84; founder, med. dir., pres. bd. dirs. Mid-Continent Psychiat. Hosp., Olathe, Kans., 1972-84; adj. prof. psychology Baker U., Baldwin City, Kans., 1969-84; staff psychiatrist Atascadero State Hosp., Calif., 1984-85; clin. prof. psychiatry U. Calif., San Francisco, 1985—; chief psychiatrist Calif. Med. Facility, Vacaville, 1985-87; pres., editor Corrective and Social Psychiatry, Olathe, 1970-84, Atascadero, 1984-85, Fairfield, 1985—. Contbr. articles to profl. jours. Bd. dirs. Menn. Youthville, Newton, Kans. 1965-75, Spofford Home, Kansas City, 1974-78. Served to capt. USAF, 1962-64, ret. col. USAFR. Oxford Law & Soc. scholar, 1993. Fellow Am. Psychiat. Assn., Royal Soc. Health, Am. Assn. Mental Health Profls. in Corrections, World Assn. Social Psychiatry, Am. Orthopsychiat. Assn.; mem. AMA, Assn. for Advancement Psychotherapy, Am. Assn. Sex Educators, Counselors and Therapists (cert.), Assn. Mental Health Adminstrs. (cert.), Kansas City Club, Masons, Phi Beta Pi, Pi Kappa Alpha. Methodist (del. Kans. East Conf. 1972-80, bd. global ministries 1974-80). Office: PO Box 3365 Fairfield CA 94533-0587

MARTIN, CRAIG LEE, engineering company executive; b. Dodge City, Kans., Nov. 23, 1949; s. Ray N. and Nadia C. (Chandler) M.; m. Diane E. Hensley, Mar. 19, 1977. BS in Civil Engring., U. Kans., 1971; MBA, U. Denver, 1982. Project mgr. Martin K. Eby Constrn. Co., Wichita, Kans., 1972-83; exec. v.p., COO CRSS Constructors, Inc., Denver, 1983-89; exec. v.p. CRSS Comml. Group, Houston, 1989-90; sr. v.p. CRSS Capital, Houston, 1990-92, CRSS Inc., Houston, 1992-94; pres. CRSS Architects, Inc., Houston, 1992-94; sr. v.p. ops. Jacobs Engring. Group Inc., 1994—; pres. Jacobs Constructors, Inc., 1994—; mem. adv. bd. Constrn. Bus. Rev., 1993—; bd. dirs. Meridian Engrs. Mem. ASCE, Am. Mgmt. Assn. Avocations: golf, clay shooting, fishing. Home: 2524 Stanmore Dr Houston TX

77019-3426 Office: Jacobs Engring Group Inc 251 S Lake Ave Pasadena CA 91101

MARTIN, DALE, vocational rehabilitation executive; b. N.Y.C., May 10, 1935; d. Byron Pink Molter and Ruth (Nobel) Gestram; m. Robert A. Wishart, Dec. 13, 1985; children by previous marriage: Elizabeth, Devon. BS, U. Conn., 1957. RN, cert. case mgr., ins. rehab. specialist, lic. rehab. counsellor, Mass. Dental asst. Hempstead, N.Y., 1951; with Wesson Maternity Hosp., Springfield, Mass., 1957-58, Huntington Hartford Meml. Hosp., Pasadena, Calif., 1958-59; office mgr. Indsl. By Products Inc., Kalamazoo, Mich., 1969-72; controller Indsl. By Products Inc., Chgo., 1970-74; cons. Mgmt. Resources Inc., Broomall, Pa., 1978-81; cons., owner Martin-Collard Assocs., Inc., Monmouth Beach, N.J., 1980-84; cons., owner, chmn. bd. dirs. MCA, Inc., Boston, 1984—; bd. dirs. Consortium Advantage, Inc., Boston; cons. Viewfinder, Old Chatham, N.Y., 1987—, Phoenix Inc., Global Explorations, Inc. Contbr. articles to profl. jours.; painter, sculptor. Bd. govs. Rumson-Fair Haven H.S., N.Y., 1976-78. Mem. Nat. Assn. Rehab. Profls. in Pvt. Sector (forensic sect., past rep. region I to bd. dirs.), Nat. Rehab. Assn. (pvt. sector group), Internat. Assn., Psychosocial Rehab. Specialists, New Eng. Claims Assn., Individual Case Mgmt. Assn., Mass. Nurses Assn. (chmn. image com. 1984-85), Town Club (v.p.), Mountain Lakes Ski Club (founder), Jewel Way Internat., Jr. Women's Club, Jr. League, Sigma Theta Tau, Alpha Delta Pi. Avocations: painting, tennis, N.J. state girls gymnastic judge. Office: MCA Inc PO Box 5438 Boston MA 02102-5438 also: MCA Inc PO Box 789 Port Salerno FL 34992-0789

MARTIN, DANIEL RICHARD, pharmaceutical company executive; b. Lima, Peru, June 9, 1937; s. James Marion and Clemmy Caroline (Valencia) M.; m. Barbara Artemis Cyrus, June 23, 1962; children: Daniel Richard Jr., John Alexander, Christopher Andrew. BA, Cornell U., 1958; MS, Columbia U., N.Y.C., 1959. Area sales supr. Schering Corp., Bloomfield, N.J., 1960-64; assoc. McKinsey & Co., N.Y.C., 1964-69; treas. Harper & Row, Pubs., N.Y.C., 1969-72; mng. dir. Merck & Co., Rahway, N.J., 1972-77; group v.p. Bell & Howell Co., Chgo., 1977-80; pres. Howland Martin Corp., N.Y.C., 1980-85; pres. Sterling Europe, Middle East, Africa Sterling Drug, Inc., N.Y.C., 1986-89; pres., CEO E-Z-EM, Inc., Westbury, N.Y., 1990—. Pres. Accion Internat., Cambridge, Mass., 1988—; trustee Bangor (Maine) Theol. Sem., 1991—; dir. Americas Found.; bd. dirs., fin. com. White Plains (N.Y.) Hosp. Decorated Order of Merit (Ecuador). Mem. Coun. on Fgn. Rels., Americas Soc., Univ. Club (N.Y.C., Chgo.), Cornell Club (N.Y.C.). Republican. Congregationalist. Home: 2 Dolma Rd Scarsdale NY 10583-4506 Office: E-Z-EM Inc 717 Main St Westbury NY 11590-5021

MARTIN, DANIEL WILLIAM, acoustical physicist; b. Georgetown, Ky., Nov. 18, 1918; s. Dean William and Ethel (Weigle) M.; m. Martha Elizabeth Parker, June 9, 1941; children: Mary Elizabeth, David William, Nancy Jane, Donald Warren. A.B., Georgetown Coll., 1937, Sc.D., 1981; M.S., U. Ill., 1939, Ph.D., 1941. Asst. physics U. Ill. at Urbana, 1937-41; with RCA, 1941-49, tech. coordinator, 1946-49; acoustical research supr. Baldwin Piano Co., Cin., 1949-57; research dir. D.H. Baldwin Co., Cin., 1957-70, 74-83; chief engr. D.H. Baldwin Co., 1970-74; acoustical cons., 1983—; extension instr. math. Purdue U., 1941-46; asst. prof. mus. acoustics U. Cin., 1964-73, assoc. prof., 1973-75. Author/Editor: I.R.E. Trans. on Audio, 1953-55; assoc. editor: Sound, 1961-63; patent reviewer Jour. Acoustical Soc. Am, 1950—, assoc. editor, 1977-85, editor-in-chief, 1985—. Trustee Pikeville Coll., 1976-82; mem. theology and worship ministry unit Presbyn. Ch. (U.S.A.), 1987-93, vice-chair, 1987-89, 91-92, vice-chmn. Presbyn. Assn. for Sci., Tech. and Christian Faith, 1992—. Recipient Ohio Engr. of Yr. award Nat. Soc. Profl. Engrs., 1972. Fellow Acoustical Soc. Am. (exec. council 1957-60, pres.-elect 1983-84, pres. 1984-85), Audio Engring. Soc. (pres. 1964-65), IEEE (nat. chmn. audio group 1956-57); mem. Engring. Soc. Cin. (dir. 1964-67, pres. 1969-70), Tech. and Sci. Assn. Council Cin. (pres. 1967-68, Cin. Engr. Year 1972), Nat. Council Presbyn. Men. (1977). Republican. Patentee in field. Home and Office: 7349 Clough Pike Cincinnati OH 45244-3745 *A Christian home, economic need, and early choice of profession gave me momentum. Generous personal assistance and teaching, professional opportunity and family stability sustained my efforts. The byproducts of striving for goals are just as valuable as the realization of goals. Building bridges between disciplines is difficult but intellectually stimulating. Great are the rewards of service to profession, people and the church.*

MARTIN, DARNELL, medical care products corporation executive. V.p. Baxter Internat., Inc., Deerfield, Ill. Office: Baxter Healthcare Corp 1430 Waukegan Rd Waukegan IL 60085

MARTIN, DAVID ALAN, law educator; b. Indpls., July 23, 1948; s. C. Wendell and Elizabeth Bowman (Meeker) M.; m. Cynthia Jo Lorman, June 13, 1970; children: Amy Lynn, Jeffrey David. BA, DePauw U., 1970; JD, Yale U., 1975. Bar: D.C. Law clk. Hon. J. Skelly Wright U.S. Ct. Appeals (D.C. cir.), 1975-76; law clk. Hon. Lewis F. Powell U.S. Supreme Ct., Washington, 1976-77; assoc. Rogovin, Stern & Huge, Washington, 1977-78; spl. asst. human rights and humanitarian affairs U.S. State Dept., Washington, 1978-80; from asst. prof. sch. law to assoc. prof. U. Va., Charlottesville, 1980-86, prof., 1986-91, Henry L. & Grace Doherty prof. law, 1991—; F. Palmer Weber Rsch. prof. civil liberties and human rights, 1992-95; cons. Adminstrv. Conf. U.S., Washington, 1988-89, 91-92, U.S. Dept. Justice, 1993—. Author: Immigration: Progress and Policy, 1985, 2d edit., 1991, 3d. edit., 1995, Asylum Case Law Sourcebook, 1994, The Endless Quest: Helping America's Farm Workers, 1994; editor: The New Asylum Seekers, 1988; contbr. numerous articles to profl. jours. Mem. nat. governing bd. Common Cause, Washington, 1972-75; elder Westminster Presbyn. Ch., Charlottesville, 1982-84, 89-92. German Marshall Fund Rsch. Fellow, Geneva, 1984-85. Mem. Am. Soc. Internat. Law (annual book award 1986), Am. Immigration Lawyers Assn., Internat. Law Assn. Democrat. Office: U Va Sch Law 580 Massie Rd Charlottesville VA 22903-1738

MARTIN, DAVID BRITON HADDEN, JR., lawyer; b. Beverly, Mass., Dec. 9, 1946; s. David Briton Hadden and Mary Louise (Ward) M.; m. Martha Bacon, June 21, 1969; children: Charlotte, Jessica, Benjamin Ward. BA, Yale U., 1969; JD, U. Va., 1976. Bar: Va. 1976, D.C. 1977. Assoc. Dunnells, Duvall, Bennett & Porter, Washington, 1976-79, Dickstein, Shapiro & Morin, Washington, 1979-80; spl. counsel SEC, Washington, 1980-84, spl. counsel to chmn., 1984-85; assoc. Hogan & Hartson, Washington, 1985-87, ptnr., 1987—. Mng. editor U. Va. Law Review, 1975-76. Chair The Washington Revels, 1993—; mem. corp. action com. Jubilee Jobs, 1993—; bd. dirs. First Night Alexandria, Va., 1995—, Alexandria Indsl. Devel., 1980-82. Mem. Metro. Club. Office: Hogan & Hartson 555 13th St NW Washington DC 20004

MARTIN, DAVID EDWARD, health sciences educator; b. Green Bay, Wis., Oct. 1, 1939; s. Edward Henry and Lillie (Luckman) M. B.S., U. Wis., 1961, M.S., 1963, Ph.D., 1970. Ford Found. research trainee Wis. Regional Primate Ctr., Madison, 1967-70; asst. prof. health scis. Ga. State U., Atlanta, 1970-74, assoc. prof., 1974-80, prof., 1980-91, regents prof., 1992—; affiliate scientist Yerkes Primate Rsch. Ctr., Emory U., Atlanta, 1970—; U.S. rep. to Internat. Olympic Acad., 1978; sports medicine rsch. assoc. U.S. Olympic Com., 1981-84; chmn. sports scis. U.S.A. Track and Field; coaching staff U.S. teams to world championships in distance running, Rome, 1982, Gateshead, Eng., 1983, Budapest, 1994, head coach, Paris, 1980, Madrid, 1984, Hiroshima, 1985, Warsaw, Poland, 1987, Antwerp, 1991; mem. Olympic med. support group Atlanta Olympic Games. Author: Laboratory Experiments in Human Physiology, 4th edit., 1980, The Marathon Footrace, 1979, La Corsa Di Maratona, 1982, The High Jump Book, 1982, 2d edit., 1987, Respiratory Anatomy and Physiology, 1987, Training Distance Runners, 1991; contbr. articles to profl. jours. Trustee Ga. Found. for Athletic Excellence. Recipient fed. and univ. grants for physiol. research; named Disting. prof. Ga. State U., 1975, 81, 85. Fellow Am. Coll. Sports Medicine; mem. Internat. Soc. Olympic Historians, Am. Physiol. Soc., Internat. Primatological Soc., Atlanta Track Club. Home: 510 Coventry Rd Apt 13A Decatur GA 30030-5038 Office: Ga State U Dept Cardiopulmonary S Atlanta GA 30303

MARTIN, DAVID HUBERT, physician, educator; b. Detroit, Mar. 24, 1943; s. Hubert Cillis and Mable Anita (Stewart) M.; m. Jane Ellen

Schlichtemeier, Nov. 22, 1970; children: Jennifer, Jason. BA with distinction, U. Kans., 1965; MD cum laude, Harvard Coll., 1969. Diplomate Nat. Bd. Med. Examiners, Am. Bd. Internal Medicine, Infectious Disease Subspecialty Bd. Am. Bd. Internal Medicine. Intern Bronx (N.Y.) Mcpl. Hosp. Ctr., 1969-70; staff assoc. Nat. Inst. Allergy and Infectious Diseases, Mid. Am. Rsch. Unit, NIH, Panama Canal Zone, 1970-73; med. resident U. Wash. Affiliated Hosps., 1973-75; sr. fellow in infectious disease U. Wash., 1976-78; chief resident in medicine USPHS Hosp., Seattle, 1975-76, staff internal medicine clinic, 1975, attending physician internal medicine, 1976-78; staff dept. internal medicine USPHS Hosp., New Orleans, 1979-81; staff Hotel Dieu Hosp., New Orleans, 1982-94; clin. asst. prof. medicine La. State U. Med. Sch., New Orleans, 1979-81, asst. prof. medicine divsn. infectious diseases, 1981-82, assoc. prof. medicine divsn. infectious diseases, 1982-88, assoc. prof. microbiology, 1986-88, prof. internal medicine and microbiology, 1988, asst. chief sect. infectious diseases, 1988-89, chief sect. infectious diseases, 1990—, Harry E. Dascomb M.D. prof. of medicine, 1990—; instr. dept. medicine U. Wash. Sch. Medicine, Seattle, 1975-78, acting asst. prof. medicine, 1978-79; chmn. infection control com., chmn. instnl. rev. bd. human rsch. com., chmn. antibiotic utilization com., sec. rsch. and editl. com., sec. animal welfare com. USPHS Hosp., New Orleans, 1979-81, dep. chief clin. rsch. dept., 1979-81, chmn. credentials com., 1980-81; mem. infection control com. Hotel Dieu Hosp., New Orleans, 1983-84, chmn. pharmacy and therapeutics com., 1988-94, mem. infection control com., 1990-94; vis. physician Charity Hosp. (now Med. Ctr. of La. at New Orleans), New Orleans, 1982—, chmn. antibiotics com., 1982—, dir. infection control program, 1993—, chmn. infection control com., 1993—, vice chmn. pharmacy and therapeutics com., 1995—; cons. sexually transmitted diseases control program Dept. Health and Human Resources, State of La., 1985—; staff physician Jefferson Parish Venereal Disease Clinic, 1986-90, New Orleans (La.) Sexually Transmitted Disease Clinic, 1992—; cons. pharmacy and therapeutics com. Mercy Hosp., New Orleans, 1989-91; cons. La. AIDS Cmty. Rsch. Project, 1989-92; chmn. comprehensive medicine head search com. La. State U. Med. Sch., 1989-90, dept. medicine faculty promotion com., 1988—, AIDS policy com., 1992; mem. La. State Labs. Adv. Bd., 1993—, State La. Pub. Health Lab. Adv. Com., 1994—, U.S. Pub. Health Region 6 Infertility Prevention Adv. Com., 1995—; lectr., workshop presenter and rschr. in field; others. Peer reviewer various jours. including Sexually Transmitted Diseases, The Jour. of Infectious Diseases, The Am. Jour. of the Med. Scis., Archives of Internal Medicine, Clin. Infectious Diseases, New Eng. Jour. Medicine, Annals Internal Medicine, Jour. AMA; contbr. chpts. to books and articles to profl. jours. With USPHS, 1970-82. Achievements include established the first chlamydia laboratory in the Gulf South. Fellow ACP (La. chpt. program chmn. 1994-95), Infectious Diseases Soc. Am.; mem. Internat. Soc. for Sexually Transmitted Disease Rsch. (bd. dirs. 1991—, chmn. 1995 meeting organizing com. 1993-95), Am. Fedn. for Clin. Rsch., Am. Venereal Disease Assn. (v.p. 1992-94, pres. 1994—), Am. Soc. for Microbiology, European Soc. for Clin. Microbiology and Infectious Diseases, So. Soc. for Clin. Investigation, La. Miss. Infectious Diseases Soc. (bd. dirs., sci. program chmn. 1993), Phi Beta Kappa. Achievements include research in the effect of sexually transmitted microorganisms on pregnancy outcome; antibiotic treatment of sexually transmitted diseases and in particular C. trachomatis; the epidemiology of C. trachomatis in normal populations; Chancroid and other genital ulcer diseases. Office: Sch 1542 Tulane Ave New Orleans LA 70112

MARTIN, DAVID R., oil company executive; b. 1931. BA, UCLA, 1957, MA, 1958. With Mobil Oil Corp., N.Y.C., 1959-61; with Occidental Oil & Gas Corp., 1969—, v.p. Latin Am. ops., 1969-85, pres., 1986—; exec. v.p. Occidental Petroleum Corp., 1986—. Served with USAF, 1950-53. Office: Occidental Oil & Gas Corp 10889 Wilshire Blvd Los Angeles CA 90024-4200

MARTIN, DAVID S., educator, administrator; b. N.Y.C., May 14, 1941; s. Perry Johnson and Polly Edith (Shedlov) M.; m. Florence E. Martin, Jan. 14, 1989; children: Drew Michael, Amy Davida. BA, Adelphi Coll., 1962, MA, 1966; profl. cert., Hofstra U., 1969. Cert. secondary tchr., sch. dist. adminstr., N.Y. Adj. assoc. prof. Pace U., White Plains, N.Y., 1978—; tchr., computer coord. Jericho (N.Y.) Pub. Schs., 1962—. Author: Teachers Manual for Introduction to Pascal; co-author: How To Prepare for SAT II: Physics, 6th edit.; also author other books; contbr. articles to profl. jours. Fulbright-Hays grantee, 1967-68; recipient Grand award L.I. Sci. Congress, 1958, Disting Achievement award Electronic Learning, 1983, Outstanding Accomplishment award RITEC, 1984. Mem. IEEE (sr.). Internat. Soc. for Technology in Edn., Am. Assn. Physics Tchrs., Assn. Computing Machinery, Authors Guild, Jericho Tchrs. Assn., N.Y. State United Tchrs., Flambeau, Phi Delta Kappa, Sigma Pi Sigma. Home: 16 Elm Pl Sea Cliff NY 11579-1634 Office: Jericho Pub Schs Cedar Swamp Rd Jericho NY 11753

MARTIN, DEAN (DINO CROCETTI), actor, singer; b. Steubenville, Ohio, June 17, 1917; m. Elizabeth Ann McDonald, 1940 (div. 1949); children: Craig, Claudia, Gail, Deanna; m. Jeanne Bieggers, 1949 (div.); children: Dean Paul (dec.), Ricci, Gina; m. Cathy Hawn, 1973. Ed. high sch. Successively employed odd jobs, Weirton, W.Va.; welterweight boxer, appeared with Jerry Lewis on stage and in films. Amateur dance band singer; singer with Ernie McKay's band, later in night clubs; formed comedy team with Jerry Lewis, 1946; appeared in night clubs, theatres, radio and TV programs, also motion pictures; former star weekly TV show, NBC; appeared in motion pictures including: My Friend Irma Goes West, 1949, At War with the Army, 1950, That's My Boy, 1951, The Stooge, 1952, Jumpin' Jacks, The Caddy, 1953, Scared Stiff, 1953, Money From Home, 1953, Living It Up, 1954, Three Ring Circus, 1954, You've Never Too Young, 1955, Artists and Models, 1955, Pardners, 1956, Hollywood or Bust, 1956, Ten Thousand Bedrooms, 1957, Sailor Beware, 1957, Young Lions, 1958, Rio Bravo, 1959, Some Came Running, Career, 1959, Who Was That Lady?, 1960, Bells Are Ringing, 1960, Ocean's 11, 1960, Ada, 1961, Who's Got the Action, 1962, Who's Sleeping in my Bed, 1963, Toys in the Attic, 1963, What A Way to Go, 1964, Robin and the Seven Hoods, 1964, Kiss Me, Stupid, 1964, Son of Kate Elder, 1965, Rough Night in Jericho, 1967, Silencers, 1966, Murderers Row, 1966, The Ambushers, 1967, How to Save a Marriage, 1968, The Wrecking Crew, 1969, Airport, 1970, Texas Across The River, Something Big, 1972, Showdown, 1973, Mr. Ricco, 1975, Cannonball Run, 1981, Cannonball Run II, 1984; TV shows include: Dean Martin Celebrity Roasts, 1976, 78, Dean Martin Christmas Specials, 1975, 78, 80, Dean's Place, 1976; recorded albums including Memories Are Made of This. Recipient Golden Globe award. Office: 8942 Wilshire Blvd Beverly Hills CA 90211*

MARTIN, DEANNA COLEMAN, university director; b. Kansas City, Mo., Feb. 6, 1939; d. Olaf Arthur and Dolores Augustine (Judd) Coleman; m. Robert Allan Blanc, Apr. 28, 1982; children: Chris Robert Martin, Coleman O'Brian Martin. BA in English, U. Kansas City, 1960; MA in Reading Edn., U. Mo., Kansas City, 1974, PhD in Reading Edn., 1976. Cert. tchr., Mo. Tchr. Raytown (Mo.) H.S., 1964-74, Lee's Summit (Mo.) H.S., 1964-74; coord. learning resources U. Mo., Kansas City, 1974, dir. student learning ctr., 1978, dir. ctr. for acad. devel., 1980—, assoc. prof. sch. edn.; cons., presenter in field. Cons. editor Unit for Rsch. into Higher Edn.—Ctr. for Sci. Devel. of the South African Human Scis. Rsch. Coun.; co-author: Supplemental Instruction: A Guide to Student Retention, 1983, Study Guide and Readings for Abnormal Psychology: Current Perspectives, 1984, Supplemental Instruction: Improving First-Year Student Success in High Risk Courses, 1992, Supplemental Instruction: Increasing Student Achievement and Persistence, 1994, also book chpts., monographs; contbr. articles to profl. pubs. Trustee Multi-Media Network Trust, Johannesburg, South Africa. Grantee HEW, 1976, 81, Kansas City Assn. Trusts and Founds., 1977, 84, 85, U. Mo.-Kansas Coty, 1978, 79, 80, Nat. Basic Skills Improvement Schs. Program, 1980, Nat. Assn. State Univs. and Land-Grant Colls. 1984-85, Center Sch. Dist., 1994, Sch. Dist. of City of Independence, Mo., Ft. Osage Sch. Dist., 1984, Consol. Sch. Dist. Raytown, 1984, Kansas City pub. Sch. Dist., 1984, Coalition of 100 Black Women, 1985, U.S. Dept. Edn. 1989—, Nat. Diffusion Network, Office Edn., 1984—; recipient Retention Excellence award Noel/Levitz Nat. Ctr. for Student Retention, 1990, Cert. of Recognition NASPA, 1981. Mem. Nat. Assn. for Developmental Edn., Am. Assn. for Higher Edn. Avocations: skiing, biking, reading. Office: U Mo Kansas City Ctr Acad Devel 5100 Rockhill Rd SASS 210 Kansas City MO 64110

MARTIN, DON P., lawyer; b. Roanoke, Va., Jan. 9, 1949. BA with distinction, U. Va., 1972, JD, 1975. Bar: Ariz. 1975, Nev. 1992. Ptnr. Streich

Lang, Phoenix, 1975—. Echols scholar, Dupont scholar. Office: Streich Lang Renaissance One Two N Central Ave Phoenix AZ 85003-2391

MARTIN, DONALD RAY, chemist, educator, consultant; b. Marion, Ohio, Oct. 21, 1915; s. Royal Frederick and Goldia Ferne (Gelbaugh) M.; m. Katherine Gertrude Newton, Feb. 4, 1939; children: Donald Ray II, Thomas Newton. A.B., Otterbein Coll., 1937; M.S., Western Res. U., 1940, Ph.D. in Inorganic Chemistry, 1941. Lectr. chemistry Western Res. U., 1940-42; lab. mgr. Naval research project, 1941-43; instr., then asst. prof. chemistry U. Ill., 1943-51; head chem. metall. br., metall. div. U.S. Naval Research Lab., 1951-52; lab. mgr. govt. research. Mathieson Chem. Corp., 1952-56; mgr. chem. research, aviation div. Olin Mathieson Chem. Corp., 1956-57, assoc. dir. fuels research, energy div., 1957-60; dir. research Libbey-Owens-Ford Glass Co., 1960-61; with Harshaw Chem. Co., 1961-68, v.p. research and devel., 1967-68; prof. inorganic chemistry U. Tex. at Arlington, 1969-86, prof. emeritus, 1986—, chmn. dept. chemistry, 1969-76; mem. Coll. Chemistry Cons. Service, 1971-76; mem. com. examiners Grad. Record Exam. for Advanced Chemistry, 1962-70; mem. chem. tech. adv. com. Cuyahoga Community Coll., 1965-70. Author: (with H.S. Booth) Boron Trifluoride and Its Derivatives, 1949. Adv. bd. Euclid (Ohio) Orch. and Chorus, 1965-68, pres., 1966; trustee Otterbein Coll., 1962-72. Recipient Disting. Sci. Achievement award Otterbein Coll., 1970. Life fellow AAAS; mem. Am. Chem. Soc. (emeritus, chmn. div. inorganic chemistry 1962), Royal Soc. Chemistry (life), Electrochem. Soc. (emeritus), Sigma Xi (chpt. v.p 1975-77, chpt. pres. 1978-80), Phi Lambda Upsilon, Sigma Zeta, Alpha Chi Sigma. Presbyterian (elder). Lodge: Kiwanis (Arlington) (hon., life, pres. 1970-71, disting. lt. gov. 1973-74, dist. sec. 1976-77, Kiwanian of Yr. award Euclid (Ohio) club 1966). Home: 16916 Hierba Dr Apt 267 San Diego CA 92128-2679

MARTIN, DONALD WILLIAM, psychiatrist; b. Columbus, Ohio, Aug. 13, 1921; s. Olin R. and Clara (Jahraus) M.; m. Clara Jane Jones, June 23, 1951; children: Jennifer Christine, David Lawrence. B.A., Ohio State U., 1942, M.D., 1944. Diplomate: Am. Bd. Psychiatry and Neurology. Intern Met. Hosp., N.Y.C., 1944-45; resident psychiatrist Kings Park (N.Y.) State Hosp., 1945-46, sr. psychiatrist, 1948-49; supervising psychiatrist Central Islip (N.Y.) State Hosp., 1950-56; staff psychiatrist Summit County Receiving Hosp. (name now Fallsview Psy. Hosp.), Cuyahoga Falls, Ohio, 1956-59; supt. Summit County Receiving Hosp. (name now Fallsview Psy. Hosp.), 1959-63; dir. Pontiac (Mich.) State Hosp. (name now Clinton Valley Center), 1963-79; pvt. practice cons. psychiatry, 1979-90, ret., 1990. Served from 1st lt. to capt. M.C., U.S. Army, 1946-48. Fellow Am. Psychiat. Assn. (life). Home: 2091 Chapel Dr Fairborn OH 45324 My experiences over the years have only strengthened my belief that our happiness and growth as human beings derives above all else from our relationships with others. The life's theme I have evolved is: becoming and being a loving person.

MARTIN, DONNA LEE, publishing company executive; b. Detroit, Aug. 7, 1935; d. David M. Paul and Lillian (Paul); m. Rex Martin, June 5, 1956; children: Justin, Andrew. B.A., Rice U., 1957. Mng. editor trade dept. Appleton-Century-Crofts Co., N.Y.C., 1961-62; dir. publs. Lycoming Coll., Williamsport, Pa., 1966-68; editor Univ. Press of Kans., Lawrence, 1971-74; mng. editor Andrews & McMeel, Kansas City, Mo., 1974-80, v.p., editorial dir., 1980—; v.p. Universal Press Syndicate, Kansas City, 1980—; lectr. U. Mo., Kansas City. Author: (adaptation) Charles Dickens' A Christmas Carol: Adapted for Theatre; contbr. articles to profl. jours. Named Disting. Alumna Rice U., 1990. Mem. Women in Comms., The Groucho Club (London), Phi Beta Kappa. Office: Universal Press Syndicate 4900 Main St 9th Fl Kansas City MO 64112

MARTIN, EDGAR THOMAS, telecommunications consultant, lawyer; b. Princeton, W.Va., May 1, 1918; s. Edgar Frank and Delia Florence (Nowlin) M.; m. Hannelore Elisabeth Trucksaess, Jan. 12, 1952. BS, Va. Poly. Inst., 1938, MS, 1953; MA, Am. U., 1957; JD, George Washington U., 1957, M of Forensic Sci., 1977; LLM, Georgetown U., 1959; grad., U.S. Army Command and Gen. Staff Coll., 1963, Indsl. Coll. Armed Forces, 1963. Bar: Va. 1958, U.S. Ct. Mil. Appeals 1959; registered profl. engr., Va. Elec. engr. Radford Ordnance Works, 1940-41, chief radio sect., 1946-48, chief telecommunications br., 1948-49; with office of mil. govt. for Germany; communications specialist Office High Commr., Germany, 1949-52; chief cen. frequency staff, 1952-54, chief engr., 1954-58; engring mgr., Broadcasting Svc. (Voice of Am.) USIA, 1958-75; telecomm. cons., 1975—. 2d lt. USAR, 1940, U.S. Army, 1941-46, lt. col. USAR, 1946, col. USAR, 1961, col. AUS ret. 1978. Fellow IEEE; mem. ABA, Am. Acad. Forensic Sci., Am. Soc. Internat. Law, Va. Trial Lawyers Assn., Soc. Bibl. Lit., Am. Soc. for Legal History, Soc. for Mil. History, U.S. Commn. on Mil. History, Nat. Lawyers Club, Army Navy Club. Home: 922 26th Pl S Arlington VA 22202-2412

MARTIN, EDWARD BRIAN, electrical engineer; b. Lawrence, Kans., Feb. 9, 1936; s. Edward Brian and Dorothy Irene (Dowers) M.; m. Sharon Anne Zimmerman, Dec. 21, 1955; children: Terry Brian, Ricky Lynn, Mindy Anne, Timothy Alan. BSEE, U. Kans., 1958; MSEE, St. Louis U., 1969. Registered profl. engr., Mo. Program mgr. McDonnell Douglas, St. Louis, 1980-85, mgr. avionics, 1985-86, dir. engring., 1986-88, dir. electronics, 1988-89, sr. dir. tech. processes, 1989-91, sr. dir. avionics tech., 1991-92, dir. advanced missile systems, 1992—; chmn. bd. dirs. Martin Internat., Ltd. Contbr. numerous articles to profl. jours. Mem. PTA, St. Louis, 1972; founder Martin Family Found. Mem. AIAA. Avocations: running, mountain climbing, writing. Home: 5 Baron Ct Florissant MO 63034-1203

MARTIN, EDWARD CURTIS, JR., landscape architect, educator; b. Albany, Ga., Aug. 21, 1928; s. Edward Curtis and Mildred Lee (Tyler) M.; m. Roberta Inman Parker, Mar. 18, 1967; children: Edward Curtis III, Andrew Parker. BFA, U. Ga., 1950, M of Landscape Architecture, 1969. Registered landscape architect, Miss. Landscape architect Norman C. Butts Landscape Contractor, Altanta, 1950; M.T. Brooks Office, Birmingham, Ala., 1950-56; univ. landscape architect, horticulturalist Miss. State U., Mississippi State, 1956-70, prof. landscape architecture, 1970-92, Disting. prof., 1988, prof. emeritus, 1992—, part-time prof., 1992—; originator, chmn. Miss. Landscape Design Sch., Mississippi State, 1957—; guest lectr. U. San Luis Potosi, Mex., 1990, U. Mexico, Mex. City, 1991, La. State U., 1990, 91, 92, 94, Biendenharn Found., Monroe, La., 1991, Longue Vue Found., New Orleans, 1991, So. Garden Symposium, 1993, St. Francisville, La., 1993, Southern Regional Meeting Garden Writers Assn. Am., Memphis, 1993, Rotary Internat. Dist. Conf., Memphis, 1993, Deep S. Regional Conf. Nat. Coun. State Garden Clubs, Lafayette, La., 1993; guest instr. Nat. Landscape Design Study Courses Nat. Coun. State Garden Clubs, Inc., U.S., Mex., 1960—; originator, lectr. Garden Design Workshops, Miss. State U., 1988—; host Flower and Garden Tour of British Isles, Southland Travel Svcs., 1985, Flower and Garden Tour of Europe, 1981, 82; photographic landscape architecture rsch. study: Europe, 1958, 66, 74, 85, S.Am., 1960, Israel, 1993; vis. prof. La. State U., 1990-93, vis. landscape architecture prof., 1994; host, lectr. historic southern gardens on Miss. River, New Orleans to Vicksburg, Delta Queen Steamboat; host Chelsea Flower Show and English Gardens Tour, 1994, Nat. Coun. State Garden Clubs, 1994, Fla. Wild Flower Conf. Fla. Fedn. Garden Clubs, Inc., 1994; instr. ecology tour Copper Canyon, Mex., 1994. Author: Landscape Plants in Design, A Photographic Guide, 1983; co-author: Home Landscapes, Planting Design and Management, 1994; invited to participate in Attingham Summer Program in Historic Preservation (English country houses and gardens) Eng., 1985; author/photographer of 80-captioned slide series, one on Home Landscapes, another on Urban Landscape Design for use by Nat. Coun. State Garden Clubs, Inc., 1994. Mem. Miss. State Bd. Landscape Architects for Profl. Registration, 1973-74; mem. Starkville (Miss.) Park and Recreation Bd., 1973-79. Recipient Silver Seal award Nat. Coun. State Garden Clubs 1969, Landscape Heritage award Fraser Found. Calif. 1986. Fellow Am. Soc. Landscape Architects (chmn. edn. com. 1960-61, pres. Miss. sect. S.W. chpt. 1975, chmn. S.W. chpt. am. awards com. 1976, trustee Miss. chpt. 1977-81); mem. Nat. Trust for Historic Preservation, So. Garden History Soc., Coun. of Educators in Landscape Architecture, Nat. Coun. State Garden Clubs (chmn. landscape design 1993—), Garden Clubs Miss. (bd. dirs. 1958—, Silver Trophy 1961, Spl. Silver award 1980, Gold trophy 1993). Presbyterian. Home: 1335 Ridgewood Rd Starkville MS 39759-9177 Office: Dept Landscape Architecture Box 9725 Mississippi State MS 39762

MARTIN, EDWIN J(OHN), psychologist; b. Washington, Mar. 14, 1934; s. Richard Edwin and Florence (Johnson) M.; m. Helen Onis Tilley, Aug. 22, 1959; children—Theresa, John Charles. B.S. in Math, N.Mex. State U., 1960; Ph.D. in Psychology, U. Iowa, 1963. Mem. faculty dept. psychology U. Mich., Ann Arbor, 1963-74; asso. prof. U. Mich., 1967-71, prof., 1971-74; prof. dept. psychology U. Kans., Lawrence, 1974—, chmn. dept., 1979-93. Editor: Jour. Verbal Learning and Verbal Behavior, 1972-76, (with A.W. Melton) Coding Processes in Human Memory, 1972. Served with USN, 1953-57. Fellow AAAS, APA, Am. Psychol. Soc.; mem. Psychonomic Soc., Sigma Xi. Home: 848 E 1259 Road Lawrence KS 66047*

MARTIN, EDWIN WILLIAM, JR., pharmaceutical marketing consultant, copywriter; b. St. Louis, July 3, 1924; s. Edwin W. and Grace (Lenden) M.; married, 1951. BJ, U. Mo., 1949; postgrad., Fairleigh Dickinson U., 1959-61. Salesman Carroll Dunham Smith, Inc., St. Louis, 1949-53; advt. mgr. Hoffmann-LaRoche Inc., Nutley, N.J., 1954-66; mktg. mgr. Neisler Lab. div. Union Carbide, N.Y.C., 1966-68; v.p., account supr. Kallir, Philips Ross, Inc., N.Y.C., Arthur Wilk, Inc., Chgo., 1973-74; v.p., creative dir. Dimensional Mktg., 1974-81; creative dir. Grant-Jacoby, 1981-82, pres., 1982—; instr. Columbia Coll. Chgo., 1987—. Cpl. US Army 1943-46. Mem. Ind. Writers, Midwest Pharm. Advt. Coun. Roman Catholic.

MARTIN, ELLIOT EDWARDS, theatrical producer; b. Denver, Feb. 25, 1924; s. William Harrison and Elma Abigale (Harvey) M.; m. Marjorie Cuesta, Oct. 7, 1949; children: Richard, Linda Lisa. Student, U. Denver, 1943-46. Actor, singer, stage mgr., assoc. producer Theatre Guild, N.Y.C. and London, 1947-53; prodn. stage mgr. 20 Broadway plays and musicals, 1953-61; theatrical producer Never Too Late, Nobody Loves an Albatross, N.Y.C., 1962-66; theatre producer London, 1963; mng. dir. Center Theatre Group, Music Ctr., Los Angeles, 1966-71; producer Elliot Martin Prodns., N.Y.C., 1972—; mem. exec. bd. Nat. Theatre of the Deaf, Chester, Conn., 1981—, Westport-Weston Arts Council, 1976—. Prodns. on Broadway include: Dinner at Eight, 1966, More Stately Mansions, 1967, Abelard and Heloise, 1971, Emperor Henry IV, 1973, A Moon for the Misbegotten, 1973 (spl. Tony award), When You Comin' Back, Red Rider, 1974 (Outer Critics award), Of Mice and Men, 1975, Touch of the Poet, 1976, Dirty Linen and New Found Land, 1977, Caesar and Cleopatra, 1977, Kingfisher, 1979, Clothes for a Summer Hotel, 1980, Kingdoms, 1981, American Buffalo, 1981, Angels Fall, 1983, Glengarry Glen Ross, 1984 (Pulitzer prize), Woza Albert, 1984, American Buffalo, 1984, Harrigan 'n' Hart, 1985, Arsenic and Old Lace (Broadway and nat. tour), 1986-87, Joe Turner's Come and Gone (7 Tony nominations, N.Y. Drama Critic's award best play), 1988, Steel Magnolias (nat. tour), 1989, The Circle, 1989-90, Shadowlands, 1990-91, Breaking Legs, 1991-92, She Loves Me (9 Tony noms.). Mem. bd. assocs. U. Bridgeport, 1978-83. Recipient Tony award for most innovative revival, 1977-78, Larry Tajiri award for outstanding contbn. to arts Denver Post, 1970, Congl. commendation, 1970, Profl. Achievement award U. Denver, 1987. Mem. Platform Speakers Am., League N.Y. Theatres and Producers. Republican. Club: N.Y. Athletic (N.Y.C.). Office: Elliot Martin Prodns 152 W 58th St New York NY 10019-2139

MARTIN, EMILY, anthropologist, educator. Mary Garrett prof. dept. anthropology Johns Hopkins U., Balt. Office: Johns Hopkins U Dept Anthropology Baltimore MD 21218

MARTIN, ERNEST H., theatrical and motion picture executive; b. Pitts., Aug. 28, 1919; s. Samuel and Cecilia (Sklar) Markowitz; m. Nancy Frank (div.); m. Nancy Guild (div.); children: Elizabeth, Cecilia Martin Ford, Polly; m. Twyla Elliott.. A.B., U. Calif. at Los Angeles, 1942. Producer: (with Cy Feuer) stage plays Where's Charley?, 1948, Guys and Dolls, 1950, Can-Can, 1953, The Boy Friend, 1954, Silk Stockings, 1955, Whoop-Up, 1958, How to Succeed in Business Without Really Trying, 1961 (Pulitzer prize for drama), Little Me, 1962, Skyscraper, 1965, Walking Happy, 1966, The Goodbye People, 1968, The Act, 1977; (with Cy Feuer) motion picture Cabaret, 1972 (winner 8 Acad. awards); (motion pictures) Piaf, 1975, A Chorus Line, 1985. Inducted into the Theater Hall of Fame, 1994. Office: 1369 Londonderry Pl Los Angeles CA 90069

MARTIN, FRANK KIEFFER, mayor, lawyer; b. Columbus, Ga., Nov. 4, 1938; s. Frank Callier and Jean Louise (Kieffer) M.; m. Sandra Katherine Tally, June 8, 1964 (div. 1980); children: Frank K. Jr., John T., Katherine Lee; m. Katherine Ellis, Aug. 16, 1986. BBA, U. Ga., 1961, JD, 1964. Assoc. Cartledge & Cartledge, Columbus, Ga., 1964-65; ptnr. Young, Dicus & Martin, Columbus, Ga., 1966; asst. dist. atty. Chattahoochee Jud. Cir., Columbus, Ga., 1966-70; pvt. practice Columbus, Ga., 1971, 76-90; ptnr. Martin & Kilpatrick, Columbus, Ga., 1972-73, Martin, Kilpatrick & Davidson, Columbus, Ga., 1974-75; mayor, pub. safety dir. City of Columbus, 1991—. Chmn. Columbus Govt. Employee Pension, 1991—; bd. dirs. Columbus Water Works, 1991—, Columbus Conv. and Visitors Bur., 1991—, Columbus Bd. Health, 1991—, Columbus Transp. and Planning Bd., 1991—; mem. exe. com. State Dem. Orgn. Ga., Columbus, 1994—, mcpl. liaison chmn., 1994—. Recipient Congl. Medal of Honor Soc., Columbus, 1993; named one of Best Lawyers in Am., Woodward/White, Inc., 1991-92. Fellow ABA, Nat. Assn. Criminal Def. Lawyers, Ga. Assn. Criminal Def. Lawyers, Nat. Bd. Trial Advocacy; mem. Am. Bd. Criminal Lawyers (pres., v.p., dir. 1982-89). Avocations: reading, jogging, environmental activities. Office: City of Columbus PO Box 1340 Columbus GA 31993

MARTIN, FRED, artist, college administrator; b. San Francisco, June 13, 1927; s. Ernest Thomas and Leona (Richey) M.; m. Genevieve Catherine Fisette, Jan. 29, 1950 (dec.); children: T. Demian, Fredericka C., Anthony J.; m. Stephanie Zuperko Dudek, 1992. B.A., U. Calif.-Berkeley, 1949, M.A., 1954; postgrad. Calif. Sch. Fine Arts, 1949-50. Registrar Oakland (Calif.) Art Mus., 1955-58; dir. exhbns. San Francisco Art Inst., 1958-65, dir. coll., 1965-75, dean acad. affairs, 1983-92, dean acad. affairs emeritus. Exhibited one man shows, Zoe Dusanne Gallery, Seattle, 1952, M.H. deYoung Meml. Mus., San Francisco, 1954, 64, Oakland Art Mus., 1958, San Francisco Mus. Modern Art, 1958, 73, Dilexi Gallery, San Francisco, 1961, Minami Gallery, Tokyo, 1963, Royal Marks Gallery, N.Y.C., 1965-70, Hansen Fuller Gallery, San Francisco, 1974, 75, 76, Quay Gallery, San Francisco, 1979, 81, 84, Natsoulas Gallery, Davis, Calif., 1991, Belcher Studios Gallery, San Francisco, 1994; represented in permanent collections, Mus. Modern Art, N.Y.C., San Francisco Mus. Modern Art, Oakland Art Mus., Whitney Mus., Fogg Mus.; Author: Beulah Land, 1966, Log of the Sun Ship, 1969, Liber Studiorum, 1973, A Travel Book, 1976, From an Antique Land, 1979; Bay area corr.: Art Internat; contbg. editor Art Week, 1976-93. Recipient prizes Oakland Art Mus., 1951, 58, prizes San Francisco Mus. Art, 1957, 58, prizes Richmond (Calif.) Art Center, 1962, prizes Nat. Found. for Arts, 1970. Home: 232 Monte Vista Ave Oakland CA 94611-4922 Office: San Francisco Art Inst 800 Chestnut St San Francisco CA 94133-2206

MARTIN, FRED, retired municipal official; b. Detroit, Oct. 21, 1925; s. Fred McKinley and Eva Irene (Agnew) M.; m. Ernestine Robinson, Sept. 20, 1947 (div. 1980); children: Robin K. Turner, Keith R. Ba, Wayne State U., 1953, MEd, 1954, postgrad., 1970-74. Tchr. Detroit Schs., 1953-61, asst. prin., 1961-63, personnel adminstr., 1963-67, asst. to supt., 1967-74, exec. dir., 1974-78, pers. dir., dep. supt., 1978-81; pers. dir. City of Detroit, 1981-82, chief exec. asst. to mayor, 1981-92, personnel dir., 1992—; instr. Wayne State U., 1968-75, U. Mich., Detroit, 1972; cons. U. Detroit, 1968. Author: Corrective Discipline - Management Grade, 1978. Bd. dirs. Greater Detroit Resource Recovery Authority, 1985, Detroit Sci. Ctr., 1987; pres. Northwest Activities Ctr., Detroit, 1987; mem. library commn. Detroit Pub. Library, 1987; trustee Detroit Med. Ctr.. With U.S. Army, 1944-46, ETO, PTO. Mem. Forum Black Pub. Adminstrs. (bd. dirs. 1984—), Your Heritage House, Detroit Inst. Arts. (Founders Soc.), Kappa Alpha Psi. Democrat. Baptist. Avocations: reading, music, sports. Home: 1300 E Lafayette St Apt 1401 Detroit MI 48207-2921

MARTIN, FREDDIE ANTHONY, agronomist, educator; b. Raceland, La., Nov. 17, 1945; s. of Abraham and Flossie Margarette (Foret) M.; m. Rose Ann Hill, Aug. 23, 1969; children: Samson, Jonathan, Robert. BS, Francis T. Nicholls State Coll, Thibodaux, La., 1966; MS, Cornell U., 1968, PhD, 1970. Asst. prof. Plant Pathology Dept. La. State U., Baton Rouge, 1971-76; assoc. prof. Plant Pathology Dept. La. State U., 1976-80, prof. Plant Pathology Dept., 1980, prof. Agronomy Dept., 1980—, head Sugar Sta./Audubon Sugar, 1988—. Editor Am. Soc. Sugar Cane Technologists jour.,

1980-94; author profl. manuscripts, jours. Recipient Rsch. Excellence Award, La. Agricultural Experimental Sta., 1984, Svc. Award, St. James Sugar Growers, 1989. Mem. Am. Soc. Agronomy, Crop Sci. Soc. Am., Am. Soc. Sugarcane Tech., Gamma Sigma Delta. Office: Louisiana State Univ Sugar Station Audobon Sugar Inst Baton Rouge LA 70803

MARTIN, FREDERICK NOEL, audiologist; b. N.Y.C., July 24, 1931; s. Philip and Mildred Ruth (Austin) M.; m. Mary Catherine Robinson, Apr. 4, 1954; children: David C., Leslie Anne. B.A., Bklyn. Coll., 1957, M.A., 1958; Ph.D., CUNY, 1968. Audiologist, Lenox Hill Hosp., N.Y.C., 1957-58; Audiologist Ark. Sch. for the Deaf, Little Rock, 1958-60; dir. audiology Bailey Ear Clinic, Little Rock, 1960-66; mem. faculty Bklyn. Coll., 1966-68; mem. faculty U. Tex., Austin, 1968—, endowed prof. audiology, 1982—. Author: Introduction to Audiology, 1975, 5th edit., 1994, Basic Audiometry, 1986, Medical Audiology, 1981, Pediatric Audiology, 1978; editor: Remediation of Communication Disorders 12 vol., 1978, Hearing Disorders in Children, 1986, Effective Counseling in Audiology, 1994; contbr. over 100 articles to profl. jours. Served with USAF, 1951-55. Fellow Am. Speech-Language Hearing Assn.; mem. Am. Acad. Audiology; mem. Tex. Speech-Lang.-Hearing Assn., Am. Auditory Soc. Home: 8613 Silver Ridge Dr Austin TX 78759-8144 Office: U of Tex Austin TX 78712

MARTIN, GARY O., film company executive; b. Santa Monica, Calif., Aug. 14, 1944; s. Ivan C. and Helen M. (Werner) M.; m. Susan Alden Seaton, Sept. 2, 1967; 1 child, Sean Robert. Student, Calif. State U., Northridge, 1962-65. V.p. prodn. Columbia Pictures, Burbank, Calif., 1984-86, exec. v.p prodn., exec. prodn. mgr., 1986-88; pres. prodn. adminstrn. Columbia Pictures and Tri Star Pictures, Culver City, Calif., 1988—. Mem. Motion Picture Acad. Arts and Scis., Dirs. Guild. Republican. Home: 8605 Amestoy Ave Northridge CA 91325-3405 Office: Columbia Pictures 10202 Washington Blvd Culver City CA 90232-3119

MARTIN, GARY WAYNE, lawyer; b. Cin., Feb. 14, 1946; s. Elmer DeForrest and Nellie May (Hughes) M.; m. Debra Lynn Goldsmith, June 25, 1982; children: Christopher, Jeremy, Joie, Casey. BA, Wilmington Coll., 1967; JD, U. Cin., 1974. Bar: Fla. 1974. Head casualty dept. Fowler White Gillen Boggs Villareal & Banker, Tampa, Fla., 1974—, also bd. dirs. Lt. USNR, 1967-71. Mem. The Tampa Club, Harbour Island Athletic Club. Republican. Avocation: tennis. Office: Fowler White Gillen Boggs Villareal & Banker 501 E Kennedy Blvd Ste 1600 Tampa FL 33602

MARTIN, GEORGE COLEMAN, aeronautical engineer; b. Everett, Wash., May 16, 1910; s. Walter Franklin and Minnie (Coleman) M.; m. Mary Sturart Patrick, June 29, 1935; children: Marian Coleman, Edith Patrick. B.S. cum laude, U. Wash., 1931. With Boeing Airplane Co., Seattle, 1931—; successively chief of stress, staff engr. stress and power plant, XB-47 project engr., preliminary design chief, B-47 project engr., chief project engr Boeing Airplane Co., 1951-53; chief engr. Boeing Airplane Co. (Seattle div.), 1953-58, v.p., 1958-64, v.p. engring., 1964-72, cons., 1972—. Recipient Disting. Alumnus award Dept. Aeros. and Astronautics, Coll. of Engring. of U Wash., 1983, Pathfinders award Mus. of Flight, 1987. Fellow Am. Inst. Aeros. and Astronautics; mem. Aerospace Industries Assn. (chmn. aerospace tech. council 1969), Phi Beta Kappa, Tau Beta Pi. Club: Seattle Yacht. Home: 900 University St Apt 5P Seattle WA 98101-2728

MARTIN, GEORGE CONNER, pomology educator; b. San Francisco, Sept. 15, 1933; s. Henry B. and Doris E. (Brockman) M.; m. C. Patricia Thayer, June 28, 1951; children: Steven P., Pamela J. MS, Purdue U., 1960, PhD, 1962. Plant physiologist USDA, Wenatchee, Wash., 1962-67; assoc. prof. dept. pomology U. Calif., Davis, 1967-73, prof. dept. pomology, 1973—. Contbr. over 240 articles to scholarly and profl. jours. 1st Lt. USMC, 1955-58. Fellow Am. Soc. Hort. Sci. (pres. 1989-90, chmn. bd. 1990-91, Gourley award 1971, Membership award 1976, 81, 83, 85, Stark award 1980, Miller award 1981, Popenoe award 1982, Rschr. of Yr. award 1987, Fruit Publ. award 1992). Office: U Calif Dept Pomology Davis CA 95616-5224

MARTIN, GEORGE FRANCIS, lawyer; b. Yuba City, Calif., July 7, 1944; s. John Severd and Albaina Marie M.; m. Linda Louise D'Aoust, Mar. 17, 1968; children: Brandon, Bry. BA in Govt., Calif. State U., Sacramento, 1968; JD, U. Calif., Davis, 1971. Bar: Calif. Adminstr. asst. Assemblyman E. Richard Barnes, Sacramento, 1967-68; with Borton, Petrini & Conron, Bakersfield, Calif., 1971—; mng. gen. ptnr. Borton, Petrini & Conron, Bakersfield, 1977—; holdings numerous ventures, partnerships including Golden Empire Land and Devel., Inc.; lectr. in field; founder, owner theatrical bus. Mgmt. by Martin, Inc., Shower of Stars, Frantic Records, 1962-67. Editor-in-chief Verdict Jour. of Law, Calif. Def. Mag.; newspaper reporter Appeal Democrat, Marysville, Calif., 1959-62. Former vice chmn. Kern County Rep. Ctrl. Com.; past pres. So. Calif. Def. Counsel; past chmn. Ctrl. Calif. Heart Inst.; bd. dirs. Calif. State U, at Bakersfield Found., Kern County Food Bank, Calif. Coun. Partnerships, Bakersfield Meml. Hosp., Kern Hospice, Kern Econ. Devel. Corp. Mem. Greater Bakersfield C. of C. (bd. dirs., past pres.). Offic: Borton Petrini & Conron 1600 Truxtun Ave Bakersfield CA 93301-5111

MARTIN, GEORGE J, JR., lawyer; b. Port Chester, N.Y., June 7, 1942; s. George J. and Eileen Ann (Buckley) M.; m. Joanne L. Frost, Aug. 21, 1965 (div. May 1986); children: Amy Anne, Ryan Frost; m. Anna Marie Cipriati, June 21, 1986; children: Marissa McCreay, Jill McCreay. BA, Georgetown U., 1964, JD, 1967. Bar: N.Y. 1969; conseil juridique, France, 1977. From assoc. to ptnr. Mudge Rose Guthrie Alexander & Ferdon, N.Y.C., 1967—; chmn. Corp. Dept., 1994—. Mem. Friends Vieilles Maisons Francaises Inc. (dir.-exec.). Roman Catholic. Home: 165 State St Brooklyn NY 11201-5609 Office: Mudge Rose Guthrie Alexander & Ferdon 180 Maiden Ln New York NY 10038-4925

MARTIN, GEORGE REILLY, federal agency administrator; b. Boston, Jan. 20, 1933. BS, Colgate U., 1955; PhD, U. Rochester, 1958. Rsch. asst. U. Rochester, N.Y., 1955-58; guest researcher LCP, Nat. Heart Inst., NIH, Bethesda, Md., 1958-59; pharmacologist Nat. Inst. Dental Rsch., NIH, Bethesda, 1959-66, Weizmann Inst. Sci., Rehovet, Israel, 1966-67; chief CTS/LBC Nat. Inst. Dental Rsch., NIH, Bethesda, 1967-74, acting chief LBC/LDBA, 1972-74; with Max Planck Institut fur Biochemie, Munich, 1975-76; lab. chief Lab. Devel. Biol. and Anomalies, NIDR, NIH, Bethesda, 1974-88; sci. dir. Nat. Inst. on Aging, NIH, Balt., 1988—. Office: NIH Gerontology Rsch Ctr 4311 Buchanan Ave Baltimore MD 21211-1202

MARTIN, GEORGE (WHITNEY), writer; b. N.Y.C., Jan. 25, 1926; s. George Whitney and Agnes Wharton (Hutchinson) M. B.A., Harvard U., 1948; student, Trinity Coll., Cambridge (Eng.) U., 1950; LL.B., U. Va., 1953. Bar: N.Y. 1955. With firm Emmet, Marvin & Martin, N.Y.C., 1955-59; engaged in writing, 1959—. Author: The Opera Companion, A Guide for the Casual Operagoer, 1961, 4th edit., 1994, The Battle of the Frogs and Mice, An Homeric Fable, 1962, 2d edit., 1987, Verdi, His Music, Life and Times, 1963, 4th edit., 1992, The Red Shirt and The Cross of Savoy, The Story of Italy's Risorgimento, 1748-1871, 1969, Causes and Conflicts, The Centennial History of the Association of the Bar of the City of New York, 1870-1970, 1970, Madam Secretary: Frances Perkins, 1976, The Companion to Twentieth Century Opera, 1979, 3d edit., 1989, The Damrosch Dynasty, America's First Family of Music, 1983, Aspects of Verdi, 1988, 2nd edit., 1993, Verdi at the Golden Gate, San Francisco in the Golden Years, 1993; contbr. articles to profl. jours., mags. Home: 21 Ingleton Cir Kennett Square PA 19348-2000

MARTIN, GEORGE WILBUR, association executive; b. Oklahoma City, Aug. 24, 1930; s. Jeff Frank and George Mullineaux (Bullard) M.; m. Maryellen Brokaw, June 20, 1953; 1 son, Michael Blake. Student, Okla. A&M Coll., 1951. Real estate salesman Washington, 1955-59; jr. analyst CIA, Washington, 1953-55; advt. mgr. Guns and Ammo Mag., Petersen Pub. Co., Los Angeles, 1959-66; editor Guns and Ammo Mag., Petersen Pub. Co., 1967-73; pub. Petersen's Hunting, Guns and Ammo and shooting splty. books, 1974-78; exec. dir. publs. NRA, Washington, 1978-93, exec. dir. industry rels., 1993—; cons. White House Com. Firearms Legis., 1971—. Served with USAF, 1951-52. Named hon. lt. gov. State of Okla.; recipient Anschutz-Precision Sales Internat. Outstanding Writer award, 1988. Mem.

NRA (endowment mem.), Internat. Profl. Hunters Assn., Alaska Profl. Hunters Assn., Hunting Hall of Fame Found. (charter, life), Am. Handgunner Awards Orgn. (endowment), Outdoor Writers Assn. Am., Wildflower Assn. Scotland. Home: 1021 Farm Haven Dr Rockville MD 20852-4247 Office: NRA 11250 Waples Mill Rd Fairfax VA 22030-7400

MARTIN, GORDON MATHER, physician, educator, administrator; b. Brookline, Mass., Mar. 2, 1915; s. Harry O. and Mary Alice (Mather) M.; m. Neva M. Cocklin, June 14, 1940; children—Richard, Lawrence, Douglas. Student, U. N.H., 1932-34; A.B., Nebr. Wesleyan U., 1936; M.D., U. Nebr., 1940; M.S. (fellow in phys. medicine Mayo Found.), U. Minn., 1944. Diplomate Am. Bd. Phys. Medicine and Rehab. (asst. sec. 1974-77, exec. sec.-treas. 1977-85, exec. dir. 1985-92, asst. exec. dir. 1992—). Intern U. Nebr. Hosp., Omaha, 1940-41; 1st asst. phys. medicine Mayo Clinic, 1943-44, cons. phys. medicine and rehab., 1947-65, chmn. dept. phys. medicine and rehab., 1965-73, sr. cons., 1973-81, emeritus cons., 1981—; asst. prof. phys. medicine, dir. dept. U. Kans. Sch. Medicine, 1944-47, dir. sch. phys. therapy, 1944-47; asso. prof. phys. med. and rehab. Mayo Grad. Sch. Med., U. Minn. Grad. Sch.; prof. Mayo Med. Sch., 1973-81, prof. emeritus, 1981—; chmn. sub-com. phys. medicine and rehab. Gov.'s Adv. Council Mental Health for Minn., 1956-60; cons. chronic diseases program USPHS, 1959-62; chmn. residency rev. com. phys. medicine and rehab., 1975-81, ex-officio, 1981—. Author chpts. to med. books. Recipient Alumni Achievement award Nebr. Wesleyan U., 1957. Fellow ACP; mem. AAAS, AMA (sec. phys. medicine and rehab. sect., coun. 1963-69, chmn. 1970-76), Nat. Rehab. Assn., Am. Congress Rehab. Medicine (pres. 1955-56, mem. exec. coun., Gold Key award 1985), Am. Bd. Med. Spltys., Am. Acad. Phys. Medicine and Rehab. (v.p.), Am. Coll. Rheumatology, Minn. Rehab. Assn. (pres. 1970), Assn. Acad. Physiatrists, Internat. Rehab. Med. Assn., Am. Guild of Organists, Rochester C. of C., Sigma Xi, Alpha Omega Alpha. Home: Charter House 211 2nd St NW Apt 2116 Rochester MN 55901 Office: Mayo Clinic 200 1st St SW Rochester MN 55905-0001

MARTIN, GREGORY S., air force officer; b. Ft. Meyer, Va., Apr. 24, 1948; m. Wendy Bliss; children: Tracie, Todd, Tyler. BS, USAF Acad., 1970; M in Bus. Mgmt., Ctrl. Mich. U., 1977; attended, Nat. War Coll., 1985-86. Commd. 2d lt. USAF, 1970, advanced through grades to brig. gen., 1993; student, pilot tng. USAF, Laredo AFB, Tex., 1970-71; student F-4 replacement tng. USAF, George AFB, Calif., 1971-72; f-4 fighter pilot 388th tactical fighter wing USAF, Korat Royal Thair Air Base, Thailand, 1972; F-4 flight leader 421st tactical fighter squadron USAF, Udorn Royal Thai Air Base, Thailand, 1972-73; F-4 instr. pilot 49th tactical fighter wing USAF, Holloman AFB, N.Mex., 1973-76; air staff tng. assignment officer, Pentagon USAF, Washington, 1976-77; aide to chief of staff of air force, Pentagon USAF, 1977-78; F-15 instr. pilot and flight comdr. 461st tactical fighter tng. squadron USAF, Luke AFB, Ariz., 1978-81; chief of wing tng. 12th tactical fighter squadron ops. officer, then comdr. 67th tactical fighter squadron 18th tactical fighter wing USAF, Kadena Air Base, Japan, 1981-85; divsn. chief CONUS bases, units, then divsn. chief tactical programs for Air Staff's directorate programs and resources, Pentagon USAF, Washington, 19986-88; vice comdr. 49th tactical fighter wing USAF, Holloman AFB, 1988-89; exec. officer to comdr., then asst. dep. chief of staff of plans tactical air command USAF, Langley AFB, Va., 1989-90; comdr. 479th tactical tng. wing USAF, Holloman AFB, 1990-91; comdr. 33d fighter wing USAF, Eglin AFB, Fla., 1991-93; comdr. 1st fighter wing USAF, Langley AFB, 1993—. Decorated Legion of Merit with 1 oak leaf cluster, DFC, Meritorious Svc. medal with 3 oak leaf clusters, Air medal with 11 oak leaf clusters, Air Force Commendation medal. Office: 1 FW/CC 159 Sweeney Blvd Ste 200 Langley AFB VA 23665-2292

MARTIN, GUY, lawyer; b. Los Angeles, Jan. 22, 1911; s. I.G. and Mary Pearl (Howe) M.; m. Edith Kingdon Gould, Oct. 12, 1946; children—Guy III, Jason Gould, Christopher Kingdon, Edith Maria Theodosia Burr. A.B., Occidental Coll., 1931; B.A. (1st class hons.), Oxford U., 1934, M.A., 1944; LL.B., Yale, 1937. Bar: N.Y. 1938, D.C. 1947. Practiced with Donovan, Leisure, Newton & Lumbard, N.Y.C., 1938-41; gen. counsel Am Am. Aviation, Inc., 1942, Am Mexican Claims Commn., U.S. Dept. State, 1945-47; ptnr. Martin, Whitfield, Smith & Bebchick (and predecessors), Washington, 1952-80; counsel Martin and Smith (and predecessors), 1981-86; pres., vice chmn. bd., dep. chief exec. officer Internat. Bank, 1981-86; with Law Office of Saltzstein & Martin, 1988—. Served with USN; sea duty 1942-45. Mem. ABA, Assn. of Bar of City of N.Y., Bar Assn. D.C, Phi Beta Kappa, Sigma Alpha Epsilon. Episcopalian. Clubs: Yale, Brook, Knickerbocker (N.Y.C.); Metropolitan, City Tavern (Washington). Home: 3300 O St NW Washington DC 20007-2813

MARTIN, HAROLD CLARK, humanities educator; b. Raymond, Pa., Jan. 12, 1917; s. Henry Floyd and Anna May (Clark) M.; m. Elma Hicks, Dec. 21, 1939; children—Thomas, Joel, Ann, Rebecca. A.B., Hartwick Coll., Oneonta, N.Y., 1937, LL.D. (hon.), 1965; A.M., U. Mich., 1941; Ph.D., Harvard, 1954; student, U. Wis., 1936, Columbia, 1947; L.H.D. (hon.), Elmira Coll., 1967, Siena Coll., 1968, Concord Coll., 1968; D.H.L. (hon.), Trinity Coll., Conn., 1970; Litt.D. (hon.), Skidmore Coll., 1974; L.H.D (hon.), Coll. St. Rose, 1974, Union Coll., 1975. High sch. tchr. English and French langs. Adams, N.Y., 1937-39; high sch. tchr. English Goshen, N.Y., 1939-44; prin. high sch., 1944-49; mem. faculty Harvard U., 1951-65, dir. gen. edn., 1951-63, lectr. comparative lit., 1954-65; chancellor Union U.; also pres. Union Coll. Schenectady, 1965-74; pres. Am. Acad., Rome, Italy, 1974-76; Margaret Bundy Scott prof. Williams Coll., 1977; Charles A. Dana prof. humanities Trinity Coll., Conn., 1977-82, prof. emeritus, 1982—; sr. lectr. humanities 1982—. Author: Logic and Rhetoric of Exposition, 1958, Spanning Three Centuries, 1984, Outlasting Marble and Brass, 1986. Editor: Inquiry and Expression (with Richard Ohmann), 1958, Style in Prose Fiction, 1959. Chmn. Mass. Com. Fulbright Awards, 1955-65, Coll. Bd. Com. English, 1959-64; Trustee Hartwick Coll., Siena Coll., Franklin Coll., Switzerland, Wenner-Gren Found. Served with USNR, 1945-46. Home: 1317 W Meadowlark Ln Corrales NM 87048-9691

MARTIN, HAROLD EUGENE, publishing executive, consultant; b. Cullman, Ala., Oct. 4, 1923; s. Rufus John and Emma (Meadows) M.; m. Jean Elizabeth Wilson, Nov. 25, 1945; children: Brian, Anita. B.A. in History with honors, Howard Coll., Birmingham, Ala., 1954; M.A. in Journalism, Syracuse U., 1956. Asst. gen. mgr. Birmingham News Newhouse Newspapers, 1960-63, asst. prodn. mgr. St. Louis Globe-Democrat, 1958-60, asst. bus. mgr. Syracuse Herald Jour., 1957-58; pub. Montgomery Advertiser and Ala. Jour., Ala., 1963-70; pres. Multimedia Newspapers, editor and pub. Montgomery Advertiser and Ala. Jour. Multimedia, Inc., 1970-78, v.p., mem. mgmt. bd., 1973-78, also corp. dir.; exec. v.p., chief exec. officer So. Baptist Radio and TV Commn., Ft. Worth, 1979; pres. Jefferson Pilot Publs., Inc., Beaumont, Tex., 1980-85; pres., pub. Beaumont Enterprise, 1981-85; owner, pub. Herald Citizen daily newspaper, Cookeville, Tenn., 1970-78, News-Observer, Crossett, Ark., 1970-78; co-owner, pub Baxter Bull., Mountain Home, Ark., 1970-78; disting. vis. prof. Sch. Journalism, U. Fla., 1979-80; adj. prof. Samford U., 1961; juror Pulitzer Prize, 1971-72; dir. exec. Svc. Corp. Ft. Worth. Contbr. articles to newspapers. Bd. dirs. Billy Graham Evangelistic Assn., Mpls.; coun. Samford U. Study Ctr. London. Recipient awards for articles; recipient citation Howard Coll, 1965, award of Outstanding Merit Ala. Dental Assn. 1966, Community Service award AP Assn., 1969, 72, 73, Pulitzer prize, 1970, First Place Newswriting award AP, 1971, Newswriting award for Best Stories of Yr. by Ala. Reporters AP, 1974, 75, Canon award, 1972, Ann. award for outstanding contbn. to health care Ala. State Nurses's Assn., 1973, News award Ala. State Nurses' Assn., 1976, Ala. Bapt. Communications award Ala. Bapt. State Conv., 1975; named Alumnus of Yr. Samford U., 1970. Mem. Alumni Assn. Samford U. (pres. 1967, 92, 93, adv. bd. Samford London Centre), Sigma Delta Chi (Green Eye Shade citation for Reporting 1969). Baptist. Home: 4958 Overton Woods Ct Fort Worth TX 76109-2433

MARTIN, HARRY CORPENING, state supreme court justice, retired; b. Lenoir, N.C., Jan. 13, 1920; s. Hal C. and Johnsie Harshaw (Nelson) M.; m. Nancy Robiou Dallam, Apr. 16, 1955; children: John, Matthew, Mary. A.B., U. N.C., 1942; LL.B., Harvard U. 1948; LL.M., U. Va., 1982. Bar: N.C. 1948. Sole practice Asheville, N.C., 1948-62; judge N.C. Superior Ct., Asheville, 1962-78, N.C. Ct. Appeals, Raleigh, 1978-82; justice N.C. Supreme Ct., 1982-92; ptnr. Martin & Martin, Attys., Hillsborough, N.C.,

1992—; adj. prof. U. N.C. Law Sch., 1983-92, Dan K. Moore disting. vis. prof., 1992—; sr. conf. atty. U.S. Ct. Appeals 5th cir., 1994—; adj. prof. Duke U., 1990-91. Served with U.S. Army, 1942-45, South Pacific. Mem. N.C. Supreme Ct. Hist. Soc. (pres.). Democrat. Episcopalian. Home: 702 E Franklin St Chapel Hill NC 27514-3823 Office: Univ NC Law Sch Van Hecke-Wettach Hall Chapel Hill NC 27599

MARTIN, HARRY STRATTON, III, law librarian; b. 1943. AB, Harvard U., 1965; JD, U. Minn., 1968; MLS, U. Pitts., 1971. Instr. U. Liberia, Monrovia, 1969-71; asst. librarian U. Tex., Austin, 1972-74, assoc. librarian, 1975-76; librarian, asst. prof. Georgetown U., Washington, 1976-81; librarian, prof. Harvard U., Cambridge, Mass., 1981—. Office: Harvard University Law School Library Langdell Hall Cambridge MA 02138

MARTIN, HENRY ALAN, lawyer; b. Nashville, Sept. 5, 1949; s. James Alvin and Mary Elizabeth (Long) M.; m. Gloria B. Rullard, May 9, 1975; children: Nathan Daniel, Anna Elizabeth. BA, Vanderbilt U., 1971, JD, 1974. Bar: Tenn. 1975, U.S. Dist. Ct. (mid. dist.) Tenn. 1975, U.S. Ct. Appeals (6th cir.) 1976, U.S. Supreme Ct. 1979. Pvt. practice Nashville, 1975-76; ptnr. Haile & Martin, P.A., Nashville, 1976-82; assoc. firm Barrett & Ray, P.C., Nashville, 1982-85; fed. pub. defender U.S. Dist. Ct. (mid. dist.) Tenn., Nashville, 1985—; bd. dirs. Capital Case Resource Ctr. Tenn., 1988—; mem. adv. com. on rules criminal procedure U.S. Judicial Conf., 1994—. CO-author, co-editor trial manual, Tools for the Ultimate Trial, 1985, 2d edit., 1988; contbr. articles to profl. jours. Del., Witness for Peace, Managua, Nicaragua, 1987. Mem. ABA (criminal justice sect. coun. 1993—), Nat. Assn. Criminal Def. Lawyers, Nat. Lawyers Guild, Napier Looby Bar Assn., Nashville Bar Assn., Nat. Legal Aid and Def. Assn., Tenn. Assn. Criminal def. Lawyers (bd. dirs. 1978-94, pres. 1984-85; pres.'s award 1984). Democrat. Avocations: jogging, swimming. Home: 3802 Whitland Ave Nashville TN 37205-2432 Office: Fed Pub Defender 810 Broadway Ste 200 Nashville TN 37203-3805

MARTIN, J. LANDIS, manufacturing company executive, lawyer; b. Grand Island, Nebr., Nov. 5, 1945; s. John Charles and Lucile (Cooley) M.; m. Sharon Penn Smith, Sept. 23, 1978; children: Mary Frances, Sarah Landis, Emily Penn. BS in Bus. Adminstrn., Northwestern U., 1968, JD cum laude, 1973. Bar: Ill. 1974, D.C. 1978, Colo. 1982. Assoc. Kirkland & Ellis, Chgo., 1973-77; ptnr. Kirkland & Ellis, Washington, 1978-81; mng. ptnr. Kirkland & Ellis, Denver, 1981-87, firm com. mem., Chgo., 1983-87; pres., CEO NL Industries Inc., Houston, 1987—; also bd. dirs. NL Industries Inc.; chmn., CEO Baroid Corp., Houston, 1987-94; chmn. bd., pres., CEO Tremont Corp., 1990—, also bd. dirs.; dir. Dresser Industries, Dallas, Aimco. Editor-in-chief: Exchange Act Guide to SEC Rule 144, 1973; articles editor Northwestern U. Law Rev., 1972-73. Pres. Ctrl. City Opera House Assn., Denver, 1986-88, chmn., 1987—; pres. Ctrl. City Opera House Assn. Endowment Fund, 1992—; vis. com. Northwestern U. Sch. Law, 1987—; sr. v.p. devel. Houston Grand Opera, 1992—, pres., 1994—; exec. com., 1991—; bd. trustees Denver Art Mus., 1994—, Graland Country Day Sch., 1992—. Served with U.S. Army, 1969-71. Mem. ABA, Ill. Bar Assn., Colo. Bar Assn., D.C. Bar Assn. Clubs: Chevy Chase (Md.), John Evans (Evanston, Ill.), Denver, Denver Country, Castle Pines Golf. Office: NL Industries Inc 16825 Northchase Dr Ste 1200 Houston TX 77060-2544

MARTIN, JAMES ALFRED, JR., religious studies educator; b. Lumberton, N.C., Mar. 18, 1917; s. James Alfred and Mary (Jones) M.; m. Ann Bradsher, June 1, 1936 (dec. 1982); m. Nell Gifford, Jan. 6, 1984. AB, Wake Forest Coll., 1937, LittD, 1965; MA, Duke U., 1938; PhD, Columbia U., 1944; student, Union Theol. Sem., 1940-43; M.A. (hon.), Amherst Coll., 1950. Ordained to ministry Bapt. Ch., 1944; asst. pastor Roxboro (N.C.) Ch., 1937-38; instr. philosophy and psychology Wake Forest Coll., 1938-40; asst. philosophy religion Union Theol. Sem., N.Y.C., 1941-44; Danforth prof. religion in higher edn. Union Theol. Sem., 1960-67, adj. prof. philosophy religion, 1967-82; prof. religion Columbia U., 1967-82, prof. emeritus, 1982—; chmn. dept., 1968-77; asst. prof. religion Amherst Coll., 1946-47, asso. prof., 1947-50, prof., 1950-54, Marquand and Stone prof., 1954-57, Crosby prof. religion, 1957-60; ordained deacon P.E. Ch., 1953; vis. prof. Cornell U., summer 1948, Mt. Holyoke Coll., 1949-50, 52-53, 59-60, State U. Iowa, summer 1959, U. N.C., summer 1964; Union prof. Wake Forest U., 1984—; vis. prof. religious studies U. Va., 1984; asso. mem. East-West Philosophers Conf., U. Hawaii, 1949. Author: Empirical Philosophies of Religion, 1944, (with J.A Hutchison) Ways of Faith, 1953, rev., 1960, Fact, Fiction, and Faith, 1960, The New Dialogue between Philosophy and Theology, 1966, Beauty and Holiness, 1990; contbr. articles to profl. jours. and encys., chpts. to books. Chmn. bd. visitors Wake Forest Coll., 1981-83. Served as lt. chaplain USNR, 1944-46, PTO. Recipient Disting. Alumnus award Wake Forest U., 1971. Mem. Soc. Values in Higher Edn. (Kent fellow, pres. 1964-69), Am. Theol. Soc. (v.p. 1981-82, pres. 1982), Soc. Theol. Discussion, Soc. Philosophy of Religion, Phi Beta Kappa, Omicron Delta Kappa, Pi Kappa Alpha. Home: PO Box 6746 Winston Salem NC 27109-6746 *My experience of life has increasingly underscored the central importance of honesty-in understanding of oneself, and in perceptions of and relations to others. The quest for honesty entails a relentless and often painful search for truth. Acceptance of truth, and of others as they truly are, requires grace. The goal is to speak the truth in love.*

MARTIN, JAMES CULLEN, chemistry educator; b. Dover, Tenn., Jan. 14, 1928; s. Joseph Emmett and Myrtle (Futrell) M.; m. June Echols, Aug. 25, 1951; children: Joseph Vinson, Bruce Thomas, Kendall James, Steven Echols, Christopher Cullen. BA, Vanderbilt U., 1951, MS, 1952; PhD, Harvard U., 1956. Instr. organic chemistry U. Ill., Urbana, 1956-59, asst. prof., 1959-62, assoc. prof., 1962-65, prof. chemistry, 1965-85; Disting. prof. chemistry Vanderbilt U., Nashville, 1985—; mem. adv. com. on chemistry NSF, Washington, 1986-89. Served with U.S. Army, 1946-48. Recipient Alexander von Humboldt U.S. Sr. Scientist award Humboldt Stiftung, Bonn, Fed. Republic of Germany, 1979, 88; Alfred P. Sloan fellow, 1962, Guggenheim fellow, 1966. Fellow AAAS, Japan Soc. for Promotion Sci.; mem. Am. Chem. Soc. (com. publs. 1978-87, chem. abstracts svc. com. 1988-90, chmn. organic div. 1981-82, editorial adv. bd. 1986-87, Buck-Whitney medal Ea. N.Y. chpt. 1979), Internat. Union Pure and Applied Chemistry (U.S. nat. com. Washington, 1985-88, observer Commn. on Nomenclature of Organic Chemistry 1991—). Avocations: camping, singing. Home: 5031 Lakeview Dr Nashville TN 37220-1407

MARTIN, JAMES FRANCIS, state legislator, lawyer; b. Atlanta, Aug. 22, 1945; s. Joseph Grant and Helen (Hester) M.; m. Joan Vohryzek, Jan. 30, 1970; children: Morgan, Rebecca, James, Frank. AB, U. Ga., 1967, JD, 1969, LLM, 1972; MBA, Ga. State U., 1980. Bar: Ga. 1972. Asst. legis. counsel Ga. Gen. Assembly, Atlanta, 1972-77; staff atty. Atlanta Legal Aid and Ga. Legal Svc. Programs, 1977-80; ptnr. Martin and McDuffie, 1980-86; of counsel Martin and Wilkes, 1986—, Martin Bros. P.C., 1986—; mem. Ga. Ho. of Reps., 1983—. Chmn. Ethics Com., 1993—. 1st lt. U.S. Army, 1969-71, Vietnam. Democrat. Presbyterian. Office: Legislative Office Bldg Ste 613 E Atlanta GA 30334

MARTIN, JAMES FRANKLIN, physician, lawyer; b. Chattanooga, Feb. 22, 1929; s. Delbert Chester and Doshia (Locke) M.; m. Mary Edna Connelly, June 5, 1950; children: Samuel Franklin, Mary Karen, John Delbert, Molly Frances. MD, U. Tenn., Memphis, 1960; LLB, U. Tenn., Knoxville, 1952. Bar: Tenn. 1952, U.S. Ct. Mil. Appeals 1953. Engring. draftsman Combustion Engring. Co., Chattanooga, 1947-48; engr. mech. Combustion Engring. Co., Chattanooga, 1952; lawyer Harold Stone Law Firm, Knoxville, 1955-60; atty. Tenn. Valley Authority, Knoxville, 1955-56; intern James Walker Meml. Hosp., Wilmington, N.C., 1960-61; attending staff mem., 1962-66; pvt. practice in family practice Wilmington, N.C., 1961-66, Yuma, Ariz., 1968—; med. dir. Provident Life Accident Ins. Co., Chattanooga, 1966-68; instr. medicine James Walker Meml. Hosp., 1962-64; bd. dirs. Yuma Regional Med. Ctr., Mutual Ins. Co. of Ariz., Phoenix. Editor Tenn. Law Rev., 1951-52; author: Principal Security Devices in Tennessee, 1952. Capt. U.S. Army, 1952-55. Fellow Am. Acad. Family Practice, Am. Coll. Legal Medicine; mem. AMA, Ariz. Med. Assn., Am. Coll. Legal Medicine. Democrat. Avocations: reading, Southwest pottery history, Spanish language, quail hunting, tennis. Home: 1733 W Arcadia Ln Yuma AZ 85364-5064 Office: 2451 S Avenue A Ste 4 Yuma AZ 85364-7133

MARTIN, JAMES GILBERT, university provost emeritus; b. Paris, Ill., Dec. 10, 1926; s. James and Ruth Ann (Gilbert) M.; m. Doris E. Edmonson, Aug. 23, 1969; children—Bradley Keith, Philip Roger. B.A., Ind. State Coll., 1952, M.A., 1953; Ph.D., Ind. U., 1957. Instr. Ind. State Coll., Terre Haute, 1952-53; lectr. Ind. U., Bloomington, 1953-56; instr. sociology Okla. U., Norman, 1956-57; asst. prof. sociology No. Ill. U., DeKalb, 1957-65; asso. prof. No. Ill. U., 1959-64; asst. dean Coll. Arts and Scis., Ohio State U., Columbus, 1965-68; asso. dean Coll. Arts and Scis., Ohio State U. (Coll. Social and Behavioral Scis.), 1968-70, acting dean, 1970-71; v.p., provost U. No. Iowa, Cedar Falls, 1971-89, provost emeritus, 1989—; intern academic adminstrn. E.L. Phillips Found., 1963-64. Author: The Tolerant Personality, 1964, Minority Group Relations, 1973. Mem. Iowa Peace Inst. Bd., 1989-92. With AUS, 1945-48. Home: 749 Hidden Cir Dayton OH 45458-3317

MARTIN, JAMES GRUBBS, medical research executive, former governor; b. Savannah, Ga., Dec. 11, 1935; s. Arthur Morrison and Mary Julia (Grubbs) M.; m. Dorothy Ann McAulay, June 1, 1957; children: James Grubbs, Emily Wood, Arthur Benson. BS, Davidson Coll., 1957; PhD, Princeton U., 1960. Assoc. prof. chemistry Davidson (N.C.) Coll., 1960-72; mem. 93d to 98th Congresses from N.C., 1973-85; gov. State of N.C., 1985-92; chmn. James G. Cannon Med. Rsch. Ctr., Charlotte, N.C., 1993—; mem. Mecklenburg (N.C.) Bd. County Commrs., 1966-72, chmn., 1967-68, 70-71; v.p. Nat. Assn. Regional Couns., 1971-72; pres. N.C. Assn. County Commrs., 1970-71; mem., tuba player Charlotte Symphony, 1961-66. Danforth fellow, 1957-60. Mem. Beta Theta Pi (v.p., trustee 1966-69, pres. 1975-78), Masons (33 deg.), Shriners. Presbyterian. Office: PO Box 32861 Charlotte NC 28232-2861

MARTIN, JAMES JOHN, JR., retired consulting research firm executive, systems analyst; b. Paterson, N.J., Feb. 3, 1936; s. James John and Lillian (Lea) M.; m. Lydia Elizabeth Bent, June 11, 1954; children: David, Peter, Laura, Daniel, Lucas. B.A., U. Wis.-Madison, 1955; postgrad., Div. Sch., Harvard U., 1955-57; M.S., Navy Postgrad. Sch., 1963; Ph.D., MIT, 1965. Commd. ensign USN, 1957, advanced through grades to comdr., 1971, ret., 1977; sector v.p. Sci. Applications Internat. Corp., La Jolla, Calif., 1977-95. Author: Bayesian Decision Problems and Markov Chains, 1967; editor: On Not Confusing Ourselves, 1991; author articles on nat. security. Bd. dirs. Mil. Conflict Inst., 1986-92. Decorated Legion of Merit. Mem. Internat. Inst. Strategic Studies, Ops. Research Soc. Am., Mil. Ops. Research Soc. (bd. dirs. 1974-77). Republican. Avocation: cooking. Home: 6603 Aranda Ave La Jolla CA 92037-6216

MARTIN, JAMES KIRBY, historian, educator; b. Akron, Ohio, May 26, 1943; s. Paul Elmo and Dorothy Marie (Garrett) M.; m. Karen Wierwille, Aug. 7, 1965; children: Darcy Elizabeth, Sarah Marie, Joelle Kathryn Garrett. B.A. summa cum laude, Hiram Coll., 1965; M.A., U. Wis., 1967, Ph.D., 1969. Asst. prof. history Rutgers U., New Brunswick, N.J., 1969-73, assoc. prof., 1973-79, prof., 1979-80, asst. provost, 1972-74, v.p. acad. affairs, 1977-79; vis. Rutgers Ctr. of Alcohol Studies, 1978-88; prof. history U. Houston, 1980—, chmn. dept., 1980-83; vis. prof. history Rice U, 1992; chmn. bd. sponsors Papers of Thomas Edison Project, 1977-80; mem. editorial adv. bd. Papers of William Livingston Project, 1973-80. Author: Men in Rebellion, 1973, In the Course of Human Events, 1979, (with M.E. Lender) A Respectable Army: The Military Origins of the Republbic, 1982, Drinking in America: A History, 1982, new. edit., 1987, (with others) America and Its People, 1989, 2d edit., 1993, Interpreting Colonial America, 1973, 2d. edit. 1978, The Human Dimensions of Nationmaking, 1976, (with K. Stubaus) The American Revolution, Whose Revolution?, 1977, 81, (with M. E. Lender) Citizen-Soldier: The Revolutionary War Journal of Joseph Bloomfield, 1982. Mem. Tex. Assn. for Advancement History (bd. dirs. 1981-93, v.p. 1986-90), Inst. for Internat. Bus. Analysis (adv. coun. 1982-86), Am. Hist. Assn. (Beveridge-Dunning prize com. 1990-93), Orgn. Am. Historians, So. Hist. Assn., So. Historians Early Am. Republic (adv. coun. 1985-88), Phi Beta Kappa, Phi Kappa Phi, Pi Gamma Mu, Omicron Delta Kappa, Phi Alpha Theta. Office: U Houston Dept History 4800 Calhoun Rd Houston TX 77204-3785

MARTIN, JAMES ROBERT, plastics company executive; b. Indpls., Mar. 31, 1943; s. Walter and Helen (Snider) M.; m. Jan. 24, 1970 (div. Dec. 1990); children: Julia, Justin; m. Tamara Hicks, Dec. 21, 1991; stepchildren: Hunter Hoskins, Laura Hoskins. BA, DePauw U., 1965; MBA, Ind. U., 1967. Bus. analyst TRW, Inc., Redondo Beach, Calif., 1967-70; fin. analyst Internat. Industries, Beverly Hills, Calif., 1970; v.p. fin., treas. A & E Plastik Pak Co., Inc., Industry, Calif., 1970-75; pres. Plasti-Line, Inc., Knoxville, Tenn., 1975-92, chmn., CEO, 1992—; bd. dirs. 1st Am. Corp., Nashville, Signal Thread Co., Chattanooga, Tenn. Bd. dirs. Knoxville Symphony Soc., 1976, Fort Sanders Health System, Knoxville United Way; bd. dirs., vice-chmn. Am. Symphony Orch. League, Washington, Webb Sch., Knoxville, 1986; bd. dirs., chmn. fin. com. Thompson Cancer Survival Ctr., Knoxville, 1985; bd. mem. Knoxville Mus. Art. Mem. Chief Execs. Orgn., World Pres. Orgn., Club LeConte (bd. dirs.), East Tenn. Automobile Club (bd. dirs.), St. Francis Yacht Club, Cherokee Country Club. Republican. Episcopalian. Home: 1029 Scenic Dr Knoxville TN 37919-7641 Office: Plasti-Line Inc PO Box 59043 Knoxville TN 37950-9043

MARTIN, JAMES RUSSELL, lawyer; b. Columbus, Ohio, June 24, 1947; s. Robert Wells and Gwendolyn (Collins) M.; m. Susan Virginia Jarman, Aug. 4, 1973; children: James Russell Jr., Elizabeth Collins. BA in History, Denison U., 1969; JD, U. Denver, 1972. Bar: Colo. 1972, U.S. Dist. Ct. Colo. 1972. Sole practice Denver, 1972-74, 76-78, 1983-85; asst. atty. gen. State of Colo., Denver, 1974-76; v.p. Butterwick Enterprises Ltd., Denver, 1978-81, pres., 1981-83; ptnr. Baker & Hostetler, Denver, 1985—. Mem. ABA, Colo. Bar Assn., Denver Bar Assn. Club: Hiwan Golf (Evergreen, Colo.). Avocations: skiing, tennis, golf, cycling. Office: Baker & Hostetler 303 E 17th Ave Ste 1100 Denver CO 80203-1264

MARTIN, JAMES SMITH, insurance executive; b. Hartford, Conn., Mar. 10, 1936; s. John G. and Elis (Parsons) M.; student Loomis Inst., 1954; BS, Yale U., 1958; MBA, Columbia U., 1961; m. Ann Louise Willem, Feb. 11, 1961; children: James Smith, Lawrence Hedrick. With Chase Manhattan Bank, N.Y.C., 1961-74, v.p., 1969-74; with Tchrs. Ins. & Annuity Assn. Am., N.Y.C., 1974—, exec. v.p., 1979-83, chmn. fin. com., 1984—; trustee Coll. Retirement Equities Fund; United Kingdom Fund, Europe Fund. Office: Tchrs Ins & Annuity Assn Am 730 3rd Ave New York NY 10017-3206

MARTIN, JAY HERBERT, psychoanalysis and English educator; b. Newark, Oct. 30, 1935; s. Sylvester K. and Ada M. (Smith) M.; m. Helen Bernadette Saldini, June 9, 1956; children: Helen E., Laura A., Jay Herbert. AB with honors, Columbia U., 1956; MA, Ohio State U., 1957, PhD, 1960; PhD in Psychoanalysis, So. Calif. Psychoanalytic Inst., 1983. Instr. Franklin Pa. State U., 1957-58; instr., then asst. to assoc. prof. English and Am. Studies Yale U., New Haven, Conn., 1960-68; prof. English and comparative culture U. Calif., Irvine, 1968-79; asst. prof. psychiatry and human behavior, clin. supr. residency program Calif. Coll. Medicine U. So. Calif., Irvine, 1978—, Leo S. Bing prof. English and Am. lit., 1979—, dir. undergrad. program in Am. studies, 1968-69, dir. program in comparative culture, 1970-71, dir. edn. abroad program, 1971-75, dir. grad. studies dept. English, 1980-83; instr. psychoanalysis So. Calif. Psychoanalytic Inst., 1984—; Bicentennial prof. Am. lit. and culture Moscow State U., USSR, 1976; vis. Parmenter lectr. Children's Hosp., San Francisco, 1989, Ann. William Faulkner Lecture, 1991, Herman Serota Found. lecture, 1992; cons. to pub. houses; lectr. USSR, Poland, Norway, France, Costa Rica, Fed. Republic Germany, Brazil, Can., U. London, Hebrew U., Jerusalem, Seoul, Rep. Korea; dir. NEH summer sems., 1976, 77; mem. evaluation com. dept. pvt. post-secondary edn. State of Calif., 1986; cons. numerous univs., pubs., NEH, NEA, J.S. Guggenheim Found., Calif. Coun. for Humanities and Pub. Policy, U.S. Congress Com. on Edn. and Labor; faculty assoc. Coun. Internat. Exch. of Scholars; frequent speaker profl. orgns. and sems., univs., confs., hosps. Author: (criticism and biography) Conrad Aiken: A Life of His Art, 1962, Harvests of Change: American Literature 1865-1914, 1967, Nathanael West: The Art of His Life, 1970 (U. Calif. Friends Libr. award), Robert Lowell, 1970, Always Merry and Bright. The Life of Henry Miller, 1978, (U. Calif. Friends of Libr. award, Phi Kappa Phi Best Faculty Publ. prize U. So. Calif.; transl. in French, Japanese and German), (fiction) Winter Dreams: An American in Moscow, 1979, Who Am I This Time, Uncovering the Fictive Personality, 1988 (Burlington No. Found. award 1989); author one hour radio drama, William Faulkner. Sound Portraits of Twentieth-Century Humanists, starring Tennessee Williams, Glenn Close, Colleen Dewhurst, Nat. Pub. Radio, 1980; author sects. 24 books including most recently American Writing Today, vol. I, 1982, The Haunted Dusk: American Supernatural Fiction, 1820-1902, 1983, Frontiers of Infant Psychiatry, vol.II, 1986, Centenary Essays on Huckleberry Finn, 1985, Robert Lowell: Essays on the Poetry, 1987, William Faulkner: The Best from American Literature, 1989, The Homosexualities: Reality, Fantasy and the Arts, 1991, Life Guidance Through Literature, 1992, Biography and Source Studies, 1995, William Faulkner and Psychology, 1995; contbr. numerous articles and revs. to profl. jours., bulls., L.A. Times Book Rev., Partisan Rev., N.Y. Times Book Rev., Internat. Rev. Psycho-Analysis, Am. Lit.; editor: Winfield Townley Scott (Yale series recorded poets), 1962, Twentieth Century Interpretations of the Waste Land: A Collection of Critical Essays, 1968, Twentieth Century Views of Nathanael West, 1972, A Singer in the Dawn: Reinterpretations of Paul Laurence Dunbar (with intro.), 1975, Economic Depression and American Humor (with intro.), 1986, The Theory and Practice of the Contemporary American Short Story, 1993; mem. editorial bd. Am. Lit., 1978-81, Humanities in Society, 1979-1983; editor-in-chief Psychoanalytic Edn., 1984-89; appearances on TV and radio including Connie Martinson Talks Books, Barbara Brunner Nightline, Sonya Live in L.A., Oprah Winfrey Show, 1988-89. Pres. Friends of Irvine Pub. Libr., 1974-75; mem. Com. for Freud Mus. Recipient Fritz Schmidl Meml. prize for rsch. applied psychoanalysis Seattle Assn. Psychoanalysis, 1982, Marie H. Briehl prize for child psychoanalysis,82, Franz Alexander prize in psychoanalysis, 1984; Morse rsch. fellow, 1963-64, Am. Philos. Soc. fellow, 1966, J.S. Guggenheim fellow, 1966-67, Rockefeller Found.humanities sr. fellow, 1975-76, Rsch. Clin. fellow So. Calif. Psychoanalytic Soc. 1977-81, Rockefeller fellow, Bellagio, Italy, 1983, NEH sr. fellow, 1983-84. Mem. So. Calif. Am. Studies Assn. (pres. 1969-71), Am. Studies Assn. (exec. bd. 1969-71, del. to MLA Assembly 1974, chmn. Ralph Gabriel prize com. 1975-77), MLA (chmn. prize com. Jay B. Hubbell Silver medal in Am. lit. 1978-84), Nat. Assn. Arts and Letters (prize com. 1987-88), Nat. Humanities Faculty (advisor to Valhalla High Sch., El Cajon, Calif. 1979-81), Nat. Am. Studies Faculty, Internat. Psychoanalytic Assn., Internat. Assn. Empirical Aesthetics, Internat. Assn. U. Profs. English, Internat. Karen Horney Soc., Phi Beta Kappa. Home: 18651 Via Palatino Irvine CA 92715-3445

MARTIN, JEAN CLAUDE, health management educator; b. Montreal, Que., Can., Dec. 12, 1929; s. Lorenzo and Alice May (Baillargeon) M.; m. Yvette Leclerc, June 30, 1956; children: Denis, Diane, Benoit, Vincent. B. Pharmacy, U. Montreal, 1956, M.H.A., 1962. Pharmacist Pharmacy Centre, Dorval Shopping Centre, Que., 1956; resident in hosp. adminstrn. The Montreal Children's Hosp., 1961, adminstrv. asst., 1962-63, asst. exec. dir., 1963-65, adminstr. svcs., 1969-71; sr. lectr. Inst. Hosp. Adminstrn. U. Montreal, 1965-69; exec. dir. Montreal Joint Hosp. Inst., 1971-75, Hôpital du Sacre-Coeur, Montreal, 1975-77; pres. Can. Hosp. Assn., Ottawa, Ont., 1977-89, spl. advisor, 1990-91; prof. health adminstrn. program U. Ottawa, 1990-92; exec. dir. Assn. Pharm. Établissements Santé, Montreal, 1992-95; health mgmt. cons. C.G.O. Inc., 1995—; dir. Can. Council Hosp. Accreditation, 1981-89. Editor: Magazine Dimension in Health Services, 1977-89; contbr. articles in field to profl. jours. Served with RCAMC, 1956-60. Mem. Can. Coll. Health Svc. Execs., Am. Coll. Hosp. Adminstrs., Internat. Hosp. Fedn. (bd. dirs.), Internat. Hosp. Assn. (London) (past pres.), Am. Hosp. Assn. (hon.), Can. Assn. Hosp. Auxs. (hon.). Roman Catholic. Home: 4874 Ave Grosvenor, Montreal, PQ Canada H3W 2M1 Office: CGO Inc, 800 Carré Victoria Ste 2211, Montreal, PQ Canada H4Z 1C8

MARTIN, JERRI WHAN, public relations executive; b. Aurora, Ill., Oct. 21, 1931; d. Forest Livings and Geraldeane Jeanette (Cutler) Whan; m. Charles L. Martin (div.); children: Vicki, Bill, Erica, Kevin. BMus, Wichita State U., 1952. Co-owner Sta. KCNY, San Marcos, Tex., 1957-70; correspondent Austin Am.-Statesman, 1959-85; co-owner Sta. KWFT, Wichita Falls, Kans., 1965—; cons. U.S. Office Econ. Opportunity, Austin, 1966-68, Tex. Ednl. Found., Inc., San Marcos, 1975—, State Bank and Trust Co., San Marcos, 1985—. Mem. ethics com. Hays Meml. Hosp., 1985—; pres. Hays County Women's Polit. Caucus, Tex., 1985-89; officer Tex. Women's Polit. Caucus, 1990; del. State Dem. Convs., Dallas, Houston, 1982, 84; bd. dirs. Cen. Tex. Higher Edn. Authority, San Marcos, 1982—, Scheib Opportunity Ctr., San Marcos 1983—, Edwards Underground Water Dist., San Antonio 1985—, sec.; trustee Tex. Ednl. Found., Inc., 1991—. Named Outstanding Reporter in Tex., Tex. Legis., 1960; inducted into San Marcos Hall of Fame, 1993; recipient Extraordinary Svc. award Trust for Pub. Land, 1994. Mem. Bus. and Profl. Women, Jr. Service League (sustaining), San Marcos C. of C. Office: Tex Ednl Found Inc PO Box 1108 San Marcos TX 78667-1108

MARTIN, JERRY C., oil company executive; b. Indpls., May 10, 1932; s. Joel C. and Blanche J. (Traubel) M.; m. Marilyn L. Brock, Sept. 7, 1952 (div. 1976); children: Cathy J., Kiefer, Douglas E.; m. Connie B. Young, May 8, 1979 (div. 1988); m. Rachel M. Fulgieri, Aug. 22, 1990. BS in Acctg., Butler U., 1953. Acct. Allison div. Gen. Motors, Indpls., 1953-57; acctng. and budget mgr. Standard Oil, Indpls., 1957-60; budget dir. Inland Container Corp., Indpls., 1960-71; corp. controller Storm Drilling and Marine Co., Chgo., 1971-75; v.p. Scottsman Norwood, Houston, 1975-76; corp. controller Internat Systems and Controls, Houston, 1976-79; v.p. controller Global Marine Drilling Co., Houston, 1979-85; sr. v.p., chief fin. officer Global Marine, Inc., Houston, 1985—. Bd. dirs. Global Marine Inc., 1993—. Mem. Fin. Execs. Inst., Mensa, Westlake Club, Westside Tennis Club, Houstonian Club. Republican. Avocation: tennis. Office: Global Marine Inc 777 N Eldridge Pky Houston TX 77079-4425

MARTIN, JERRY K., engineering company executive; b. 1944. Pres. Enercon svcs., Inc., Tulsa, Okla., 1982—. Office: Enerson Svcs Inc 10820 E 45th St Ste 100 Tulsa OK 74146*

MARTIN, JERRY L., federal agency administrator; b. Turkey, Tex., Oct. 16, 1941. Student, San Diego State Coll., 1961; BA in Polit. Sci., U. Calif., Riverside, 1963; MA in Philosophy and Polit. Sci., U. Chgo., 1966; PhD in Philosophy, Northwestern U., 1970. Asst. prof. U. Colo., Boulder, 1967-74, chmn. dept. philosophy, 1979-81, assoc. prof., 1974-84, adjunct prof., 1984—; rsch. analyst House Rep. Rsch. Com., 1982-87; legis. asst. Congressman Hank Brown, 1982-87; dir. divsn. edn. programs NEH, Washington, 1987-88, asst. chmn. studies and evaluation, 1988-89, asst. chmn. programs and policy, 1989—, acting chmn., 1993; sr. vis. scholar Georgetown U., 1993—; dir. Ctr. Study Values and Social Policy, U. Colo., Boulder, 1981-82; founding mem. Organized Rsch. Program, State of Colo., 1981-82; mem. exec. com. faculty adv. coun. Colo. Commn. Higher Edn., 1980-82. Contbr. articles to profl. jours.; speaker in field; panelist TV sta., Washington. Andrew W. Mellon Found. Congl. fellow, 1992-93. Mem. AAUP (state pres. 1977-79), Am. Philos. Assn., Soc. Historians of Early Am. Republic, Am. Polit. Sci. Assn., Soc. Social Polit., Legal Philosophy, Am. Enterprise Inst. Avocations: tennis, baseball, hist. tours. Office: NEH 1100 Pennsylvania Ave NW Washington DC 20506 Home: 5902 Mount Eagle Dr Apt 108 Alexandria VA 22303

MARTIN, JIM G., church renewal consultant; b. Mannington, W.Va., Nov. 16, 1933; s. Jacob Calvin and Dona Marie (Edgel) M.; m. R. Carolyn Holdman, Dec. 28, 1957; children: Susan Diane Martin Fenker, Stephen Glen. Pastor Bloom Ctr. Ch. of God, Bloomdale, Ohio, 1955-57, Esther (Mo.) Ch. of God, 1957-61, Silver Creek Ch. of God, Silver Lake, Ind., 1961-69, Oak Grove Ch. of God, Columbia City, Ind., 1969-77, Enola (Pa.) Ch. of God, 1977-81; sr. pastor Chambersburg (Pa.) Ch. of God, 1985-92; renewal assoc. Chs. of God Gen. Conf., Findlay, Ohio, 1992—. Office: Churches of God PO Box 926 700 E Melrose Ave Findlay OH 45840-4417

MARTIN, JOAN CALLAHAM, psychologist, educator; b. N.Y.C., June 9, 1930; d. Jack Alfred and Mary Louise (Williams) Callaham; m. Donald Charles Martin, Aug. 15, 1959; children: Walter Michael, Steven Raymond. B.A., U. Fla., 1959; M.S., Fla. State U., 1962, Ph.D., 1965. Postdoctoral trainee Duke U. Med. Center, Durham, N.C., 1965-67; postdoctoral fellow Duke U. Med. Center (Center for Aging and Human Devel.), 1967-69, asst. prof. psychiatry and research assoc. anatomy, 1969-71; adminstrv. fellow NIH, Bethesda, Md., 1971-72; asso. prof. psychiatry and behavioral sci. U. Wash., Seattle, 1972-79; asso. dean U. Wash. (Grad. Sch.), 1977-80, research coordinator psychiatry and behavioral scis., 1979-; clinical psychologist, 1990—; mem. gen. research support review com., div. research resources NIH, 1980—; cons. Nat. Cancer Inst., NIH, 1971-79; lectr. Mem. editorial bd. Neurobehavioral Toxicology and Teratology; contbr. articles to profl. jours.; referee: Sci., Physiology and Behavior, Pharm. Biochem. and Behavioral Psychopharmacology. Mem. Am. Psychol. Assn., N.Y. Acad. Sci., Teratology Soc., Psychonomic Soc., Assn. Women in Sci., Am. Assn. Univ. Profs. (pres. 1993-95), Sigma Xi. Office: U Wash Dept Psychiatry & Behavioral Sci Seattle WA 98195

MARTIN, JOANNE, business educator; b. Salem, Mass., Sept. 25, 1946; d. Richard Drake and Nathalie (Ashton) M.; m. Beaumont A. Sheil, July 9, 1977; 1 child, Beaumont Martin Sheil. BA, Smith Coll., 1968; PhD in Social Psychology, Harvard U., 1977. Assoc. prof. McBer & Co. (formerly Behavior Sci. Ctr. of Sterling Inst.), 1968-70, dir. govt. mktg., 1970-72; asst. prof. orgnl. behavior and sociology Grad. Sch. Bus., Stanford (Calif.) U., 1977-80; assoc. prof. grad. sch. bus. Stanford (Calif.) U., 1980-91, prof. grad. sch. bus., 1991—, dir. doctoral programs, grad. sch. bus., 1991—; vis. scholar Australian Grad. Sch. of Mgmt., U. N.S.W., Dept. Psychology, Sydney (Australia) U., 1989-90; Ruffin lectr. on bus. and ethics Darden Grad. Sch. of Bus. Adminstrn., U. Va., 1990. Author/co-author four books; contbr. over four dozen articles to profl. jours. Lena Lake Forrest Rsch. fellowship Bus. and Profl. Women's Found., 1978, James and Doris McNamara Faculty fellowship Grad. Sch. of Bus., Stanford U., 1990-91. Fellow APA (dissertation award), Acad. of Mgmt. (western divsn. promising young scholar award 1982, rep.-at-large 1983-85, divsn. program chair 1985-87, divsn. chair 1987-89, nat. bd. govs. 1992-95), Am. Psychol. soc., Consulting Psychologists Press (bd. dirs.). Office: Stanford U Grad Sch Bus Stanford CA 94305

MARTIN, JOEL JEROME, physics educator; b. Jamestown, N.D., Mar. 27, 1939; s. Clarence and Marian (Stelter) M. BS in Physics, S.D. State U., 1961, MS in Physics, 1962; PhD in Physics, Iowa State U., 1967. Postdoctoral fellow Ames Lab. Iowa State U., Ames, 1967-69; asst. prof. Okla. State U., Stillwater, 1969-73, assoc. prof., 1973-79, prof., 1979—. Contbr. articles to profl. jours. Mem. Am. Phys. Soc., Am. Assn. Physics Tchrs., Am. Assn. for Crystal Growth. Office: Okla State U Dept Physics Stillwater OK 74078

MARTIN, JOHN A., engineering company executive. Chmn. bd. dirs. Martin Assoc Group, Inc., L.A., 1953—. Office: Martin Assoc Group Inc 1800 Wilshire Blvd Los Angeles CA 90057*

MARTIN, JOHN BRUCE, chemical engineer; b. Auburn, Ala., Feb. 2, 1922; s. Herbert Marshall and Lannie (Steadham) M.; m. Mildred Jane Foster, Aug. 7, 1943 (dec. Nov. 1960); children—Shirlie Martin Briggs, John Bruce; m. 2d, Phyllis Barbara Rodgers, June 25, 1963; 1 child, Richard Kipp. B.S., Ala. Poly. Inst.; 1943; M.Sc., Ohio State U., 1947, Ph.D., 1949. Registered profl. engr., Ohio. With Procter & Gamble Co., Cin., 1949-82, coordinator orgn. devel., research and devel., 1967-77, mgr. indsl. chem. market research, 1977-82; sr. assoc. Indumar Inc., Cin., 1982-86, sr. v.p., 1986-87; lectr. U. Cin., 1982-88; adj. assoc. prof. Auburn U., 1983-88. Contbr. articles to profl. jours.; patentee in field. Served with AUS, 1943-46. Decorated Air Medal, Bronze Star with oak leaf cluster; recipient Disting. Alumnus award Coll. Engring., Ohio State U., 1970, Disting. Engr. award Tech. Socs. Council Cin., 1982. Fellow Am. Inst. Chem. Engrs. (Chem. Engr. of Yr. award Ohio Valley 1971; bd. dirs. 1968-70, chmn. mktg. div. 1985, named to Mktg. Hall of Fame 1988); mem. Am. Chem. Soc., Am. Soc. Engring. Edn., Engring. Soc. Cin. (pres. 1972-73), Tech. and Sci. Socs. Cin. (pres. 1972-73), Chem. Mgmt. & Resources Assn., Sigma Xi, Tau Beta Pi, Phi Kappa Phi, Phi Lambda Upsilon. Republican. Mem. Disciples of Christ Ch. Club: Clifton Track. Home: 644 Doepke Ln Cincinnati OH 45231-5045

MARTIN, J(OHN) EDWARD, architectural engineer; b. L.A., Oct. 23, 1916; s. Albert C. and Carolyn Elizabeth (Borchard) M.; m. Elizabeth Jane Hines, May 27, 1944; children: Nicolas Edward, Peter Hines, Sara Jane McKinley Reed, Christopher Carey, Elizabeth Margaret Ferguson. Student, U. So. Calif. 1934-36; BS in Archtl. Engring., U. Ill., 1939. Registered profl. engr., Calif., Ill. Structural engr. Albert C. Martin & Assocs., L.A., 1939-42, ptnr., 1945-75, mng. ptnr., 1975-86. Founding mem. Bd. trustees Thomas Aquinas Coll., Santa Paula, Calif., 1971—. Lt. USNR, 1942-45. Fellow ASCE; mem. Structural Engrs. Assn. Calif., Cons. Engrs. Assn. Calif., Jonathan Club (bd. dirs. 1978-81), Calif. Club (Ranchero Visitadores), Valley Hunt Club, Flintridge Riding Club, West Hills Hunt Club (Master of Fox Hounds 1975-88). Republican. Roman Catholic. Avocation: horsemanship. Office: Albert C Martin & Assocs 811 W 7th St Los Angeles CA 90017-3408

MARTIN, JOHN GUSTIN, investment banker; b. Bay Port, Mich., Dec. 25, 1928; s. Rig and Phoebe (Ballard) M.; m. Patricia Jean Martell, Nov. 16, 1957; children: James Martell, John Douglas. BA, Mich. State Coll., 1952; student, U. Detroit Law Sch., 1952-54. With First of Mich. Corp., Detroit, 1952—; sr. v.p. First of Mich. Corp., 1966-69, exec. v.p., 1969, pres., 1970—, dir., 1966—; trustee Renaissance Assets Trust; mem. regional firms adv. com. N.Y. Stock Exch. Chmn. bd. Bon Secours Health System Found., Grosse Pointe, Mich. Mem. Bond Club Detroit (pres. 1961), Security Traders Detroit (pres. 1963), Investment Bankers Am. (nat. com. 1969—), Nat. Assn. Security Dealers (nat. com. 1973), Security Industry Assn. (bd. dirs. 1986-89), Mich. State U. Bus. Alumni Assn. (dir., recipient Outstanding Alumni award 1974). Clubs: Detroit, Grosse Pointe Yacht, Renaissance. Home: 794 N Saint Joseph St # 44 Suttons Bay MI 49682-9755 Office: First of Michigan Corp 26th fl 100 Renaissance Ctr Fl 26 Detroit MI 48243-1003

MARTIN, JOHN HUGH, lawyer, retired; b. Los Angeles, Apr. 19, 1918; s. John Hume and Carrie Suzanne (Hatcher) M.; m. Jean Morrison Park, Sept. 17, 1945; 1 dau., Suzanne L. B.S., Monmouth Coll., 1939; J.D., U. Chgo., 1942. Bar: Ill. 1943, Calif. 1962. Practice law Chgo., 1943-52; sec., gen. counsel Am. Community Builders, Park Forest, Ill., 1952-54; dep. counsel Bur. Aero., Dept. Navy, Washington, 1954-57; with Lockheed Aircraft Corp., Burbank, Calif., 1957-79; European counsel Lockheed Aircraft Corp., 1960-61, div. counsel, 1961-71, asst. sec., chief counsel, 1971-77, corp. adv., 1977-79; pvt. practice law, 1980-94, retired, 1994. Mem. Am., Fed., Internat., Los Angeles County bar assns., Phi Alpha Delta. Democrat. Episcopalian. Club: Legal (Chgo.);. Home: 1611 Arboles Dr Glendale CA 91207-1127

MARTIN, JOHN JOSEPH, journalist; b. N.Y.C., Dec. 3, 1938; s. John and Marie Agnes (Jacobsen) M.; children from previous marriage: Sophie Suzanne, Claire Catherine; m. Katherine Fitzhugh, Feb. 14, 1987. Student, San Diego State U., 1956-62. Copy editor, reporter San Diego Union, 1959-62; copy editor Augusta (Ga.) Chronicle, 1963, N.Y. Times Internat. Edit., Paris, 1964-65; editorial asst. Temple Fielding Pubs., Mallorca, Spain, 1965-66; reporter, producer Sta. KCRA-TV News, Sacramento, 1966-75; corr. ABC-TV News, 1975—. Served with U.S. Army, 1962-64. Recipient Nat. Headliner awards, 1980, 89, NSPE award, 1982, Nat. Assn. Home Care award, 1992, 95, Emmy award, 1993, George Polk award, 1994. Mem. AFTRA, U.S. Tennis Assn., Coffee House Club N.Y.C., Nat. Press Club. Office: 1717 Desales St NW Washington DC 20036-4401

MARTIN, JOHN L., state legislator; b. Eagle Lake, Maine, June 5, 1941; s. Frank and Edwidge (Raymond) M. BA in History and Govt., U. Maine, 1963, postgrad., 1963-64. Tchr. Am. govt. and history Ft. Kent (Maine) Community High Sch., 1966-72; instr. U. Maine, Ft. Kent, 1972—; asst. prof. U. Maine, 1989—; mem. from Eagle Lake and St. Francis dist. Maine Ho. of Reps., 1964—, minority fl. leader, 1970-74, speaker of ho. 1975-94, chmn. com. on energy & natural resources, 1994—; adj. lectr.; mem. intergovtl. rels. com. Nat. Legis. Conf., 1970—; chmn. Maine Land Use Regulation Commn., 1972-73, Maine Bur. Human Rels., 1972, State Legis. Leaders Found., 1979—; mem. exec. bd. Nat. Conf. State Legislatures, chmn. state-fed. assembly, 1985-86, chair task force on reapportionment, 1987-88, vice chmn. budget, fiscal and rules com., 1986-87, v.p., 1988-89, pres.-elect, 1989-90, pres., 1990-91, immediate past pres., 1991-92; mem. exec. com. New Eng. Caucus of State Legislatures, 1978—, chmn., 1982; mem. regional exec. com. Nat. Dem. State Legis. Leaders Assn., 1991—, chmn., 1987—; bd. dirs. Found. for State Legislatures, 1988—; mem. exec. com. Dem. Nat. Com., 1991— Trustee Eagle Lake Water and Sewer Dist., 1966—, No. Maine Gen. Hosp., Ft. Kent, Ea. Maine Health Care, 1991—; mem. rural health steering com. Nat. Acad. for State Health Policy; advisor White House Task Force on Health Care Reform; dir. intergovtl. affairs Nat. Health Care Campaign, 1994—. Mem. New Eng. Polit. Sci. Assn. Home: PO Box 250 Eagle Lake ME 04739-0250 Office: Maine Ho of Reps State House Augusta ME 04333

MARTIN, JOHN S., JR., federal judge; b. Bklyn., May 31, 1935. BA, Manhattan Coll., 1957; LLB, Columbia U., 1961. Law clk. to Hon. Leonard P. Moore U.S. Ct. Appeals (2d cir.), 1961-62; asst. U.S. atty. U.S. Dist. Ct. (so. dist.) N.Y., 1962-66; chief appellate atty. Criminal Divsn., 1964-65, asst. chief, 1965-66; ptnr. Johnson, Hekker & Martin, Nyack, N.Y., 1966-67; asst. to solicitor gen., 1967-69, atty., 1969-72; ptnr. Martin, Obermaier & Morvillo, 1972-79, Schulte, Roth & Zabel, 1979-80; U.S. atty. U.S. Dist. Ct. for So. Dist. N.Y., N.Y.C., 1980-83; atty. Schulte, Roth & Zabel, 1983-90; judge U.S. Dist. Ct. for So. Dist. N.Y., N.Y.C., 1990—. Fellow Am. Coll. Trial Lawyers; mem. Assn. Bar City N.Y. Office: US Dist Ct US Courthouse Rm 420 Foley Square New York NY 10007-4728

MARTIN, JOHN WILLIAM, JR., lawyer, automotive industry executive; b. Evergreen Park, Ill., Sept. 1, 1936; s. John William and Frances (Hayes) M.; m. Joanne Cross, July 2, 1966; children: Amanda Hayes, Bartholomew McGuire. AB in History, DePaul U., 1958, JD, 1961. Bar: Ill. 1961, D.C. 1962, N.Y. 1964, Mich. 1970. Antitrust trial atty. Dept. Justice, Washington, 1961-62; assoc. Donovan, Leisure, Newton & Irvine, N.Y.C., 1962-70; sr. atty. Ford Motor Co., Dearborn, Mich., 1970-72, assoc. counsel, 1972-74, counsel, 1974-76, asst. gen. counsel, 1976-77, assoc. gen. counsel, 1977-89, v.p., gen. counsel, 1989—; trustee Ford Motor Co. Fund, 1989—. Contbr. articles to profl. jours. Mem. Assn. Gen. Counsel, Am. Law Inst. Coun., Nat. Legal Aid and Defender Assn. (bd. dirs.), Nat. Assn. for Pub. Interest Law Fellowships (bd. dirs. 1991-94), Ctr. for Social Gerontology, Inc. (pres. 1991—), Little Traverse Yacht Club. Republican. Roman Catholic. Office: Ford Motor Co The American Rd Dearborn MI 48121

MARTIN, JOSEPH, JR., lawyer, former ambassador; b. San Francisco, May 21, 1915; m. Ellen Chamberlain Martin, July 5, 1946; children: Luther Greene, Ellen Myers. AB, Yale U., 1936, LLB, 1939. Assoc. Cadwalader, Wickersham & Taft, N.Y.C., 1939-41; ptnr. Wallace, Garrison, Norton & Ray, San Francisco, 1946-55, Pettit & Martin, San Francisco, 1955-70, 73-95; gen. counsel FTC, Washington, 1970-71; ambassador, U.S. rep. Disarmament Conf., Geneva, 1971-76; mem. Pres.'s Adv. Com. for Arms Control and Disarmament, 1974-78; bd. dirs. Astec Industries, Inc. Pres. Pub. Utilities Commn., San Francisco, 1956-60; Rep. nat. committeeman for Calif., 1960-64; treas. Rep. Party Calif., 1956-58; bd. dirs. Patrons of Art and Music, Calif. Palace of Legion of Honor, 1958-70, pres., 1963-68; bd. dirs. Arms Control Assn., 1977-84; pres. Friends of Legal Assistance to Elderly, 1983-87. Lt. comdr. USNR, 1941-46. Recipient Ofcl. commendation for Outstanding Service as Gen. Counsel FTC, 1973, Distinguished Honor award U.S. ACDA, 1973, Lifetime Achievement award Legal Assistance to the Elderly, 1981. Fellow Am. Bar Found. Clubs: Burlingame Country, Pacific Union. Home: 2879 Woodside Rd Woodside CA 94062 Office: # 2280 Three Embarcadero Ctr San Francisco CA 94111

MARTIN, JOSEPH BOYD, neurologist, educator; b. Bassano, Alta. Can. Oct. 20, 1938; s. Joseph Bruce and Ruth Elizabeth (Ramer) M.; m. Rachel Ann Wenger, June 18, 1960; children: Bradley, Melanie, Douglas, Neil. B.Sc., Eastern Mennonite Coll., Harrisonburg, Va., 1959; M.D., U. Alta., 1962; Ph.D., U. Rochester, N.Y., 1971; M.A. (hon.), Harvard U., 1978; ScD (hon.), McGill U., 1994. Resident in internal medicine Univ. Hosp., Edmonton, Alta., 1962-64; resident in neurology Case-Western Res. U. Hosps., 1964-67; rsch. fellow U. Rochester, N.Y., 1967-70; mem. faculty McGill U. Faculty Medicine, Montreal, Que., Can., 1970-78; prof. medicine and neurology, neurologist-in-chief Montreal Neurol. Inst., 1976-78; chmn. dept. neurology Mass. Gen. Hosp., Boston, also Dorn prof. neurology Harvard U. Med. Sch., 1978-89; dean Sch. Medicine U. Calif., San Francisco, 1989-93; chancellor U. Calif., San Francisco, 1993—; mem. med. adv. bd. Gairdner Found., Toronto, 1978-83; adv. council neurol. disorders program Nat. Inst. Neurol., Communicative Disorders and Stroke, 1979-82. Co-author: Clinical Neuroendocrinology, 1977, The Hypothalamus, 1978, Clinical Neuroendocrinology: A Pathophysiological Approach, 1979, Neurosecretion and Brain Peptides: Implications for Brain Functions and Neurological Disease, 1981, Brain Peptides, 1983; editor Harrison's Principles of Internal Medicine, Clin. Neuroendocrinology 2d edit., 1987. Recipient Moshier Meml. gold medal U. Alta. Faculty Medicine, 1962, John W. Scott gold med. award, 1962; Med. Research Council Can. scholar, 1970-75. Mem. Internat. Soc. Neuroendocrinology (coun. 1980—), Am. Neurol. Assn., Am. Physiol. Soc. (pres. 1990, Bowditch lectr. 1978), Royal Coll. Phys. and Surg. Can., Endocrine Soc., Soc. Neurosci., Am. Soc. Clin. Investigation, Am. Physicians, Am. Acad. Arts and Scis., Inst. of Medicine, Nat. Acad. Scis., Nat. Adv. Coun., Nat. Inst. Aging. Office: U Calif 513 Parnassus Ave Ste 126 San Francisco CA 94143-0001

MARTIN, J(OSEPH) PATRICK, lawyer, arbitrator, educator; b. Detroit, Apr. 19, 1938; s. Joseph A. and Kathleen G. (Rich) M.; m. Denise Taylor, June 27, 1964; children: Timothy J., Julie D. AB magna cum laude, Notre Dame U., 1960; JD with distinction, U. Mich., 1963. Bar: Mich. 1963, U.S. Dist. Ct. (ea. dist.) Mich. 1963, U.S. Ct. Appeals (6th cir.) 1967, U.S. Supreme Ct. 1979, U.S. Dist. Ct. (we. dist.) Mich. 1981. Assoc. Dykema, Wheat, Spencer, et. al., Detroit, 1963-66; assoc., then ptnr. Poole Littell Sutherland, Detroit, 1966-76; sr. atty., ptnr., then shareholder Butzel Long, Detroit, Birmingham, Mich., 1976-94; shareholder Vicko, Lane, Payne & Broder, Bingham Farms, Mich., 1994—; adj. prof. law U. Detroit Law Sch., 1989-92; arbitrator Am. Arbitration Assn., Southfield, Mich., 1986—; Nat. Assn. Security Dealers, 1988—; NYSE, 1991—; mediator Oak Co. Circuit Ct., Pontiac, Mich., 1985—; Lex Mundi Coll. Mediators, Dallas, 1992—; spl. regional and nat. panelist large complex case program Am. Arbitration Assn., 1992—. Author; editor: Laches-Oak County Bar Assn. Legal Jour., 1984, 92, Real Property Rev., 1989-90, Mich. Law Weekly, 1990. Mem. ABA, Fed. Bar Assn., Mich. Bar Assn., Detroit Bar Assn., Oakland County Bar Assn., Oakland Hills Country Club (Birmingham, Mich.). Roman Catholic. Avocations: gardening, golf, platform tennis, walking, bridge. Home: 1663 Hoit Tower Dr Bloomfield Hills MI 48302 Office: Vicko Lane Payne & Broder Ste 200 32100 Telegraph Rd Bingham Farms MI 48025-2454

MARTIN, JOSEPH PAUL, human rights administrator; b. Liverpool, Eng., June 28, 1936; m. Joseph and Winifred (Austin) M.; m. Roberta Martin, Aug. 7, 1971; children: Christopher, Elizabeth. PhL, Angelicum, Rome, 1960, STL, 1964; PhD, Columbia U., 1973. Cert. comparative and internat. edn. Missionary Oblate Fathers, Lesotho, 1964-67; dir. Earl Hall Ctr. Columbia U., N.Y.C., 1972-86, exec. dir. ctr. study of human rights, 1977—. Lt. Brit. Artillery, 1954-56. Mem.ACLU (ch.-state com. 1987—), African Studies Assn., Amnesty Internat. Office: Columbia U Ctr Human Rights 1108 International Affairs Bldg New York NY 10027

MARTIN, JOSEPH RAMSEY, philosophy educator; b. Paducah, Ky., Oct. 15, 1930; s. J. Ramsey and Mary Terry (Burnett) M.; m. Barbara Bench, Sept. 17, 1955 (dec. Jan. 1992); children: Joseph Ramsey III, Mary Case; m. Joan Garland, Oct. 8, 1993. B.A., U. Va., 1952, M.A., 1958, PhD, 1967. Master, head lower sch. Brooks Sch., North Andover, Mass., 1958-62; asst. prof. Transylvania Coll., Lexington, Ky., 1967-68; prof. philosophy Washington and Lee U., Lexington, Va., 1968—, chmn. dept., 1989—. Mem. Piedmont Environ. Coun., Warrenton, Va., 1973-76; bd. dirs. Va. Found. for Humanities and Pub. Policy, Charlottesville, 1982-89. Lt. USN, 1952-56. Mem. Am. Philos. Assn., Va. Philos. Assn., Airplane Owners and Pilots Assn. Home: PO Box 285 Ivy VA 22945-0285 Office: Washington and Lee U Dept Philosophy Lexington VA 24450

MARTIN, JOSEPH ROBERT, financial executive; b. Phila., Dec. 9, 1947; s. Robert and Elva Ruth (Griffen) M.; m. Catherine Marie Kelly, Sept. 5, 1970; children: Joseph Robert Jr., Jennifer H., Patrick F., Kathleen K., Mariah E. BS, Embry Riddle U., 1974; MBA, U. Maine, 1976. Sr. corp. fin. analyst Keyes Fibre Co., Waterville, Maine, 1976-80; mgr. fin. analysis and planning Schlumberger, Fairchild, South Portland, Maine, 1980-83; div. contr. Schlumberger, Factron, Clifton Park, N.Y., 1983-84; corp. contr. VTC, Inc., Bloomington, Minn., 1984-87; v.p. fin., chief fin. officer VTC, Inc., Bloomington, 1987-88, sr. v.p., chief fin. officer, 1989-90; dir. fin. Nat.

Semiconductor, South Portland, Maine, 1990-91; v.p. fin. Nat. Semiconductor Standard Products Group, Santa Clara, Calif., 1991—. Served to capt. U.S. army, 1967-72, Vietnam. Decorated D.F.C., Purple Heart, Bronze Star medal, Air medal. Home: 1 Beechtree Ln Yarmouth ME 04096-1062 Office: Nat Semiconductor 1090 Kifer Rd Santa Clara CA 95051

MARTIN, JUDITH SYLVIA, journalist, author; b. Washington, Sept. 13, 1938; d. Jacob and Helen (Aronson) Perlman; m. Robert Martin, Jan. 30, 1960; children: Nicholas Ivor, Jacobina Helen. Ba, Wellesley Coll., 1959; DHL (hon.), York Coll., 1985, Adelphi U., 1991. Reporter-critic, columnist Washington Post, 1960-83; syndicated columnist United Feature Syndicate, N.Y.C., 1978—; critic-at-large Vanity Fair, 1983-84. Author: The Name on the White House Floor, 1972, Miss Manners' Guide to Excruciatingly Correct Behavior, 1982, Gilbert, 1982, Miss Manners' Guide to Rearing Perfect Children, 1984, Common Courtesy, 1985, Style and Substance, 1986, Miss Manners' Guide for the Turn-of-the-Millennium, 1989; mem. editorial bd. The American Scholar. Bd. dirs. Washington Concert Opera; mem. nat. adv. coun. Inst. Govtl. Studies, U. Calif., Berkeley. Mem. Cosmos Club (bd. mgmt.). Office: United Feature Syndicate 200 Park Ave New York NY 10166-0001

MARTIN, JUDSON PHILLIPS, retired education educator; b. Butler, Wis., Feb. 4, 1921; s. Darwin H. and Emma (Phillips) M.; m. June Ruth Elletson, June 19, 1948 (div.); children: Christopher Alan, Karen Marie; m. Mary Belle Jepson, Sept. 23, 1971; stepchildren: Stephen, Susan, Sandra, Christopher. BS, U. Wis., 1942, MA, 1946, PhD, 1955. Registrar, acad. dean Bemidji (Minn.) State U., 1946-68; dean grad. study, prof. edn. N.E. Mo. State U., 1968-71, prof. edn., 1971-80, 82-85, head div. edn. and head tchr. edn., 1980-82; substitute tchr. Seminole County, Fla., 1990—. Dist. officer Minn. Boy Scouts Am.; mem. Bemidji City Coun., 1951; pres. Red Barn Cmty. Arts Coun.; sch. vol. Seminole County, Fla., 1994—; newspaper reader for the blind Sta. WMFE, Orlando, Fla. With AUS, 1942-45. Decorated Bronze Star; Croix de Guerre (France) avec etoille. Mem. NEA, Am. Legion, Minn. Edn. Assn. (past pres. higher edn. sect.), Mo. Edn. Assn., Am. Assn. Higher Edn., Mo. Fiber Artists Assn., Weavers of Orlando, Handweavers of Am. Tropical Weavers of Fla., Masons, K.T., Elks, Kiwanis (dist. lt. gov. 1974-75), Phi Delta Kappa. Methodist. Home: 802 Live Oak Ln Oviedo FL 32765-9533

MARTIN, KATHLEEN MINDER, lawyer; b. Ludlow, Mass., Mar. 16, 1957; d. Norbert F. and Gladys Minder; m. Thomas O. Martin, May 21, 1982; children: Matthew Thomas, Andrew William. BA, U. Minn., 1978, JD cum laude, 1981. Bar: Minn. 1981, U.S. Dist. Ct. Minn. 1981, U.S. Ct. Appeals (8th cir.) 1982. Sr. atty. Popham, Haik, Schnobrich & Kaufman, Ltd., Mpls., 1981—. Mem. ABA, Minn. Bar Assn., Hennepin County Bar Assn. Leage: Mpls. Women's Rotary (pres. 1986—, v.p. 1985-86). Home: 440 Pheasant Ridge Rd Wayzata MN 55391-9581 Office: Popham Haik Schnobrich & Kaufman Ltd 4344 Ids Ctr Minneapolis MN 55402

MARTIN, KEITH, lawyer; b. Mpls., May 5, 1953; s. L. John and Lois Ann (Henze) M.; m. Linda Harvill, 1977 (div. 1985). BA, Wesleyan, 1974; JD, George Washington U., 1977; MSc, London Sch. Econs., 1978. Bar: D.C. 1978, N.Y. 1985. Legis. asst. Sen. Henry M. Jackson Washington, 1974-77, legis. counsel Sen. Daniel Patrick Moynihan, 1977-82; ptnr. Chadbourne & Parke, Washington, 1983—, mng. ptnr., 1989-93. Democrat. Office: Chadbourne & Parke 1101 Vermont Ave NW Washington DC 20005

MARTIN, KENNETH DOUGLAS, consumer products company executive; b. Fort Thomas, Ky., Mar. 13, 1940; s. George Kenneth and Edith (Caudell) M.; m. Ann Helm Hoffmann, Sept. 1, 1962; children: Mark Thomas, Scott Douglas, Edith Louise. B.S., Washington and Lee U., 1962; M.B.A., U. N.C., 1963. With The Gillette Co., 1963-78; v.p. PaperMate div. The Gillette Co., Boston, 1975-78; pres., chief exec. officer Scripto/Wilkinson Sword, Inc., Atlanta, 1978-84; also dir. Scripto, Inc.; pres. Tupperware Home Parties, N.Am., 1985-91; vice chmn., chief ops. officer Primerica Fin. Svcs., 1991-93; vice chmn., pres., CEO Nest Entertainment, Dallas, 1994—; dir. Lowe's Inc., Barnett Bank; founding dir. Security Nat. Bank. Mem. nat. adv. bd., Ga. Inst. Tech.; bd. dirs. Fla. Symphony, Econ. Devel. Commn. Cen. Fla.; bd. visitors U.N.C., Chapel Hill; trustee United Arts Cen. Fla. Mem. Interlachen Country Club (Winter Park, Fla.), Cherokee Town and Country Club (Atlanta), Eastward Ho Country Club (Chatham, Mass.). Home: 3446 Habersham Rd NW Atlanta GA 30305-1157 Office: Nest Entertainment 6100 Colwell Blvd Irving TX 75093

MARTIN, LE ROY, accounting firm executive; b. 1941. With Mc Gladrey & Pullen, Mpls., 1962—, now mng. ptnr., CEO. Office: Mc Gladrey & Pullen 1300 Midwest Plz E Minneapolis MN 55402*

MARTIN, LEE, mechanical engineer; b. Elkhart, Ind., Feb. 7, 1920; s. Ross and Esther Lee (Schweitzer) M.; m. Geraldine Faith Fitzgarrald, July 20, 1945; children: Jennifer L., Casper, Rex, Elizabeth L. SBME, SMME, MIT, 1943. With GE, 1940-42; with NIBCO Inc., Elkhart, 1943—, pres., 1957-76, chmn., 1975—. Chmn. Samaritan Inst., Denver, 1980-86; dir. Interlochen (Mich.) Ctr. for Arts, 1983-94; trustee Tri-State U., Angola, Ind., 1973-88. Mem. Union League Club.

MARTIN, LEO G., educational administrator. Commr. edn. dept. State of Maine, Augusta. Office: Edn Dept State House Sta 23 Augusta ME 04333

MARTIN, LLOYD WAYNE, research agriculturist; b. Ada, Okla., Jan. 5, 1934; s. Jess A. and Gladys E. (Asselstine) M.; m. Sharon Louise Wessel, Jan. 24, 1957; children: Mitch Wayne, Mike Scott, Monty Jay, Maria Louise. BS, Okla. State U., 1958, MS, 1961; PhD, Mich. State U., 1967. Supt., Ea. Okla. field sta. Okla. State U., Stilwell, 1959-63; extension specialist Oreg. State U., Corvallis, 1967-70, assoc. dir. Agrl. Expt. Sta., 1986-87; supt. North Willamette Expt. Sta., Aurora, Oreg., 1970-89; supt. and extension chmn. North Willamette Rsch. and Extension Ctr., Aurora, 1989—; Dean's adv. com. Coll. Agrl. Scis., Oreg. State U., Corvallis, 1986-89; crop adv. com. Nat. Germplasm Repository, Corvallis, 1987—. Contbr. articles to profl. jours. Sgt. USMC, 1952-56, Korea. Mem. Am. Soc. Hort. Sci., Soil and Crop Socs. Am., Am. Soc. Agronomy, Coun. for Agrl. Sci. and Tech., Sigma Xi, Epsilon Sigma Phi. Achievements include research in cultural production and mechanical harvesting of small fruits. Home: 3240 N Maple St Canby OR 97013-2112 Office: North Willamette Rsch & Extension Ctr 15210 NE Miley Rd Aurora OR 97002-9543

MARTIN, LOUIS EDWARD, retired library director; b. Detroit, Sept. 16, 1928; s. Emerick G. and Irene Rose (Fuhrman) M.; m. Barbara Hilda Heinrich, Apr. 7, 1951; children: Paul Emerique, Clare Ellen, Ann Maureen. PhB, U. Detroit, 1951, MA, 1954; MLS, U. Mich., 1960. Instr. in English U. Detroit, 1953-58, circulation librarian, 1958-60; asst. librarian Oakland U., Rochester, Mich., 1960-62; asst. dir. libraries U. Rochester, N.Y., 1962-65, assoc. dir. libraries, assoc. prof. bibliography, 1965-68; assoc. exec. dir. Assn. Research Libraries, 1968-72; librarian Harvard Coll., Cambridge, Mass., 1972-79; univ. librarian Cornell U., Ithaca, N.Y., 1979-85; dir. Linda Hall Library, Kansas City, Mo., 1985-93; cons. library bldgs. and mgmt. Served with USMCR.

MARTIN, LUCY Z., public relations executive; b. Alton, Ill., July 8, 1941; d. Fred and Lucille J. M. BA, Northwestern U., 1963. Adminstrv. asst., copywriter Batz-Hodgson-Neuwoehner, Inc., St. Louis, 1963-64; news reporter, Midwest fashion editor Fairchild Publs., St. Louis, 1964-66; account exec. Milici Advt. Agy., Honolulu, 1967; publs. dir. Barnes Med. Ctr. St. Louis, 1968-69; communications cons. Fleishman-Hillard, St. Louis, 1970-74; communications cons., chief exec. officer, pres. Lucy Z. Martin & Assocs. Portland, Oreg., 1974—; Speaker Healthcare Assn. Hawaii, 1993, Oreg. Assn. Healthcare, 1992, Healthcare Fin. Mgmt. Assn., 1993, Healthcare Communicators Oreg., 1994; bd. dirs. Am. Mktg. Assn. Oreg. chpt. 1992-93. Featured in Entrepreneurial Woman mag.; contbr. articles to profl. jours. Chmn. women's adv. com. Reed Coll., Portland, 1977-79; mem. Oreg. Commn. for Women, 1984-87; bd. dirs. Ronald McDonald House Oreg. 1986, Oreg. Sch. Arts & Crafts, 1989—, Inst. Managerial and Profl. Women, 1992—, Northwestern U. Alumni Coun., 1992—; chmn. bd. Good Samaritan Hosp. Assocs., 1991—; mem. alumni coun. Northwestern U., 1992—; mem. pub. policy com. YMCA. Oreg. 1993—; mem. adv. bd. Jr. League, 1994—.

Recipient MacEachern Citation Acad. Hosp. Pub. Relations, 1978, Rosey awards Portland Advt. Fedn., 1979, Achievement award Soc. Tech. Communications, 1982, Disting. Tech. Communication award, 1982, Exceptional Achievement award Council for Advancement and Support Edn., 1983, Monsoon award Internat. Graphics, Inc., 1984; named Woman of Achievement Daily Jour. Commerce, 1980. Mem. Pub. Rels. Soc. Am. (pres. Columbia River chpt. 1984, bd. 1980-84, Oreg. del. 1984-86, judicial panel N. Pacific dist 1985-86, exec. bd. health care sect. 1986-87, mem. Counselors Acad., Spotlight awards 1985, 86, 87, 88, nat. exec. com. 1987-91), Portland Pub. Rels. Roundtable (chmn. 1985, bd. dirs. 1983-85), Assn. Western Hosps. (editorial adv. bd. 1984-85), Best of West awards 1978, 80, 83, 87), Oreg. Hosp. Pub. Relations Orgn. (pres. 1981, chmn. bd. 1982, bd. dirs. 1992-93), Acad. Health Service Mktg., Am. Hosp. Assn., Am. Mktg. Assn. (Oreg. chpt. bd. dirs. 1992-93), Am. Soc. Hosp. Mktg. & Pub. Relations, Healthcare Communicators Oreg. (conf. keynote speaker 1994), Internat. Assn. Bus. Communicators (18 awards 1981-87), Oreg. Assn. Hosps. (keynote speaker for trustee, 1991, speaker, 1993, bd. dirs. 1992-93), Oreg. Press Women, Nat. and Oreg. Soc. Healthcare Planning and Mktg., Women in Communications (Matrix award 1977), Inst. Managerial and Profl. Women (bd. dirs. 1992—), City Club Portland. Office: 1881 SW Edgeware Rd Portland OR 97201-2235

MARTIN, MALCOLM ELLIOT, lawyer; b. Buffalo, Dec. 11, 1935; s. Carl Edward and Pearl Maude (Elliot) M.; m. Judith Hill Harley, June 27, 1964; children—Jennifer, Elizabeth, Christina, Katherine. A.B., U. Mich., Ann Arbor, 1958, J.D., 1962. Bar: N.Y. 1963, U.S. Ct. Appeals (2d cir.) 1966, U.S. Supreme Ct. 1967. Assoc., Chadbourne, Parke, Whiteside & Wolff, N.Y.C., 1962-73, ptnr., 1974—, now Chadbourne & Parke, 1986; dir., sec. Carl and Dorothy Bennett Found., Inc.; sec., treas. Jute Carpet Backing Council, Inc., Burlap and Jute Assn. Served with U.S. Army, 1958-60. Mem. ABA, N.Y. State Bar Assn., Assn. Bar City N.Y., St. Andrew's Soc. of State of N.Y., Met. Opera Guild. C-lubs: Oratamin (Blauvelt, N.Y.), Nyack (N.Y.) Field, Nyack Boat, Rockefeller Center, Copper (N.Y.C.). Home: 74 S Highland Ave Nyack NY 10960-3602 Office: Chadbourne & Parke 30 Rockefeller Plz New York NY 10112

MARTIN, MARGARET ANNE See STEELE, ANITA MARTIN

MARTIN, MARILYN JOAN, library director; b. Golden Meadow, La., Jan. 17, 1940; d. Marion Francis Mobley and Audrey Virna (Goza) Sapaugh; m. James Reginald Martin, Dec. 16, 1958; children: James Michael, Linda Jill Michaels. BA in History, U. Wash., 1975, MLS, 1976; MA in Pub. History, U. Ark., 1992; PhD in Libr. Sci., Tex. Woman's U., 1993. Cataloger, reference librar. St. Martin's Coll., Lacey, Wash., 1976-78; asst. reference libr. Pacific Luth. U., Tacoma, 1978-85; serials libr. Henderson State U., Arkadelphia, Ark., 1985-86, collection devel. libr., 1987-88, dir. learning resources, 1989—. Contbr. articles to profl. jours. Pres. Ark. United Meth. Hist. Soc., 1994—, also bd. dirs.; chmn. Little Rock Conf., Commn. on Archives and History, United Meth. Ch., 1993—, sec., mem. exec. bd. Gen. Commn. on Archives and History, 1984-92. Mem. ALA (rsch. com. 1993-94, stds. com. 1994-95), Assn. Coll. and Rsch. Librs., Ark. Libr. Assn. (chmn. future conf. site com. 1993-94), Ark. Hist. Assn. (awards com. 1992-940. Republican. Avocations: walking, reading, collecting names. Office: Henderson State U Huie Libr Box 7540 Arkadelphia AR 71999-0001

MARTIN, MARK EDWARD, molecular biologist, biochemist; b. Slater, Mo., July 28, 1958; s. Donald Eugene and Jeannine Lucille (Gerhard) M.; m. Brenda Mae Chiles, May 31, 1980; children: Daniel Mark, Robert Anthony. BA in Biology, Ctrl. Meth. Coll., 1980; PhD in Microbiology, U. Miss., Jackson, 1985. Rsch. lab. tech. II dept. microbiology U. Miss. Med. Ctr., Jackson, Miss., 1983-85; postdoctoral fellow dept. microbiology Am. Cancer Soc., U. Tex., Austin, 1986-88; rsch. asst. prof. dept. biochemistry U. Mo., Columbia, 1989—, asst. prof., 1993—; investigator Am. Heart Assn., 1993. Contbr. articles to Jour. Bacteriology, Jour. Biol. Chemistry, Molecular and Cellular Biology, procs. NAS. Recipient Rsch. Coun. award U. Mo., 1990. Mem. AAAS, Am. Soc. Microbiology, Sigma Xi. Home: 2404 Lynnwood Dr Columbia MO 65203 Office: U Mo Dept Biochemistry Columbia MO 65211-0002

MARTIN, MARY, secondary education educator; b. Detroit, Mich., May 17, 1954; d. Enos and Sara (Evans) M. AS, Highland Park C.C., 1975; BA, Wayne State U., 1975, MA in Teaching, 1981; postgrad. So. Calif. Sch. Ministry, Detroit, 1992—. Dietary aide Allan Dee Nursing Home, Detroit, 1972; dietary aide Harper Hosp., Detroit, 1973, 74, nurse aide, 1974-75, respiratory technician, 1975-80; respiratory technician Dr.'s Hosp., Detroit, 1980; head cook, supr. Focus Hope, Detroit, 1981; substitute tchr. Detroit Bd. Edn., 1984-90, tchr. adult edn., 1990-93, tchr., 1993—; interim advisor student coun. Wayne State U., Detroit, 1985. Sunday sch. teaching trainer People's Missionary Bapt. Ch., Detroit, 1986, del., 1984-87, mem. All Aid, 1984-87, mem. choir, 1984, usher, 1984; precinct del. 13th Congl. Dist., 1986-88, 90-92, model, 1985. Recipient Spirit of Detroit award Detroit City Coun., 1993, Spl. Congl. cert. Hon. Barbara Rose Collins, 1994, Proclamation, Wayne County Commr. George Cushingberry, 1994. Mem. Nat. Sociol. Honor Soc. Democrat. Avocations: reading, shopping, movies, golf, driving.

MARTIN, MARY COATES, genealogist, writer; b. Gloucester County, N.J.; d. Raymond and Emily (Johnson) Coates; m. Lawrence O. Kupillas (dec.); m. Clyde Davis Martin (dec.); 1 child, William Raymond. Contbg. editor Md. & Del. Genealogist, St. Michaels, Md., 1985—. Author: The House of John Johnson (1731-1802) Salem County, N.J. and His Descendants, 1979, Fifty Year History of Daughters of Colonial Wars in the State of New York, 1980, 350 Years of American Ancestors: 38 Families: 1630-1989, 1989, Colonial Families: Martin and Bell Families and Their Kin: 1657-1992, Clifton--Coates Kinfolk and 316 Allied Families, 1995. Pres. Washington Hdqrs. Assn., 1970-73, bd. dirs., 1962—; Centennial pres. Sorosis, Inc., 1966-68; bd. dirs. Soldiers Sailors Airmen's Club, N.Y.C. 1976-81, Yorkville Youth Coun., N.Y.C., 1954-60; co-chmn. Colonial Ball, N.Y.C., 1965-67; rec. sec. Parents League of N.Y., Inc., 1954-57; mem. coun. Internat. Debutante Ball, N.Y.C., 1977-81; mem. Am. Flag Inst., N.Y.C., 1963-72. Mem. Hereditary Order of Descendants of Colonial Govs. (gov. gen. 1981-83), Nat. Soc. Colonial Dames of Seventeenth Century (N.Y. State pres. 1977-79, parlimentarian 1979-81), Nat. Soc. Daus. of Colonial Wars (N.Y. State pres. 1977-80), Nat. Soc. DAR (regent 1962-65, pres. roundtable 1964-65, N.Y. State chaplain 1968-71, parliamentarian 1980-83, nat. platform com. 1970-76, certificate of award 1971, nat. vice chmn. lineage rsch. com. 1977-80, geneal. com. 1980-83), Nat. Soc. New Eng. Women (dir. gen. 1972-77, nat. vice chmn. helping hand disbursing fund 1968-71), Order of Crown of Charlemagne U.S.A. (corr. sec. gen. 1985-88, 3rd v.p 1988-89, 2nd v.p. 1989-91), Nat. Soc. Children Am. Revolution, Nicasius de Sille Soc. (pres. 1960-62), Order Ams. of Armorial Ancestry (1st v.p. gen. 1985-88, councillor gen. 1988—), Nat. Gavel Soc., Nat. Soc. Magna Carta Dames, Descendants of Soc. of Colonial Clergy, Huguenot Soc. Am., Descendants of a Knight of Most Noble Order Garter, Nat. Soc. Daus. Am. Colonists, Nat. Soc. U.S. Daus. 1812, Order of Descendants of Colonial Physicians and Chirurgiens, Plantagenet Soc., Vt. Soc. Colonial Dames, Del. Geneal. Soc., Huguenot Hist. Soc., DuBois Family Assn. (1st v.p.), Cumberland County N.J. Hist. Soc., Gloucester County N.J. Hist. Soc., Md. Hist. Soc., Hist. Soc. Del., Salem County N.J. Hist. Soc., Mayflower Descendants, Swedish-Pilesgrove N.J. Hist. Soc., Hereditary Order First Families of Mass., Inc. Avocation: travel. Home: Hague Towers # 1815 330 W Brambleton Ave Norfolk VA 23510-1307

MARTIN, MARY-ANNE, art gallery owner; b. Hoboken, N.J., Apr. 26, 1943; d. Thomas Philipp and Ruth (Kelley) M.; m. Henry S. Berman, June 9, 1963 (div. 1976); 1 child, Julia Berman. Student, Smith Coll., 1961-63; BA, Barnard Coll., 1965; MA, NYU, 1967. Head dept. painting Sotheby Parke Bernet, N.Y.C., 1971-78; sr. v.p. Sotheby's, N.Y.C., 1978-82; pres. Mary-Anne Martin, Fine Art, N.Y.C., 1982—; founder Latin Am. dept. Sotheby's, 1977. Mem. Art Dealers Assn. Am. (v.p., bd. dirs.). Avocations: art collecting, scuba diving. Office: 23 E 73rd St New York NY 10021-3522

MARTIN, MAURICE JOHN, psychiatrist; b. Tuscola, Ill., July 6, 1929; s. Daniel Ambrose and Mary Alta (Payne) M.; m. Ada Himma, Aug. 15, 1953; children: Daniel, Mark, Matthew, Tina, Lisa. BS, U. Ill., 1951, MD, 1954; MS, U. Minn., 1960. Diplomate Am. Bd. Internal Medicine, Am. Bd.

Psychiatry and Neurology (bd. dirs. 1984-92, treas. 1988-90, v.p. 1991), Am. Bd. Emergency Medicine (bd. dirs. 1990-94), Am. Bd. Med. Spltys. (v.p. 1992, pres. elect 1993, pres. 1994—), Am. Bd. Med. Spltys. Edn. Rsch. Found. (pres. 1992-94). Intern Presbyn. Hosp., Chgo., 1954-55; resident Mayo Grad. Sch. Medicine, Rochester, Minn., 1955-57, 59-62; cons. in adult psychiatry Mayo Clinic, Rochester, 1962—; head adult psychiatry Mayo Clinic, 1968-74, sr. cons. adult psychiatry, 1985—; chmn. dept. psychiatry and psychology Mayo Clinic and Mayo Med. Sch., 1974-85, asst. prof. psychiatry and psychology, 1965-70, assoc. prof., 1970-75, prof., 1975—; pres. staff Mayo Clinic, 1981-82; mem. Minn. Bd. Med. Practice, 1989, v.p., 1995; pres., pres. com. ABMS. Contbr. articles on psychiatry and psychosomatic medicine to profl. jours. Served to col., M.C. USAR, 1955—. Decorated Order Mil. Med. Merit; recipient H.V. Jones award Mayo Found., 1960, Burlingame award Inst. of Living, 1994. Fellow Am. Psychiat Assn. (life), Am. Coll. Psychiatrists (regent 1980-83, v.p. 1986-89, pres.-elect 1988, pres. 1989-90, sec. gen. 1993—, Bowls award 1992), Acad. Psychosomatic Medicine (pres. 1974-75, Prestigious Achievement award 1986), Fedn. State med. Bds. (exam com. 1992—); mem. Minn. Psychiat. Soc. (pres. 1977-79), Benjamin Rush Soc. (sec.-treas. 1993—), Minn. Med. Ass. (Pres. award, 1994), Sigma Xi (chpt. pres. 1981-82), Alpha Omega Alpha. Home: 914 Sierra Ln NE Rochester MN 55906-4232 Office: 200 1st St SW Rochester MN 55905 *Diligence, perseverance, and hard work —all virtues learned on the farm in Illinois, along with a strong desire for excellence in the altruistic service of sick patients have led to accomplishment. The jump from horse-drawn farm equipment to professor and chairman of a large department of psychiatry in 25 years required the above factors in addition to being in the right place at the right time.*

MARTIN, MELISSA CAROL, radiological physicist; b. Muskogee, Okla., Feb. 7, 1951; d. Carl Leroy and Helen Shirley (Hicks) Paden; m. Donald Ray Martin, Feb. 14, 1970; 1 child, Christina Gail. BS, Okla. State U., 1971; MS, UCLA, 1975. Cert. radiol. physicist, Am. Bd. Radiology, radiation oncology, Am. Bd. Med. Physics. Asst. radiation physicist Hosp. of the Good Samaritan, L.A., 1975-80; radiol. physicist Meml. Med. Ctr., Long Beach, Calif., 1980-83, St. Joseph Hosp., Orange, Calif., 1983-92, Therapy Physics, Inc., Bellflower, Calif., 1993—; cons. in field. Editor: (book) Current Regulatory Issues in Medical Physics, 1992. Fund raising campaign div. mgr. YMCA, Torrance, Calif., 1988-92; dir. AWANA Youth Club-Guards Group, Manhattan Beach, Calif., 1984—. Named Dir. of Symposium, Am. Coll. Med. Physics, 1992. Fellow Am. Coll. Med. Physics (chancellor western region 1992-95); mem. Am. Assn. Physicists in Medicine (profl. coun. 1990-95), Am. Coll. Radiology (econs. com. 1992-95), Calif. Med. Physics Soc. (treas. 1991-95), Am. Soc. for Therapeutic Radiology and Oncology, Health Physics Soc. (pres. So. Calif. chpt. 1992-93), Am. Brachytherapy Soc. Baptist. Avocations: Christian youth group dir. Home: 507 Susana Ave Redondo Beach CA 90277 Office: Therapy Physics Inc 9156 Rose St Bellflower CA 90706-6420

MARTIN, MICHAEL J., university administrator, consultant; b. Ceresco, Nebr., June 8, 1945; s. John H. and Phyllis L. (Peterson) M.; m. Anne G. Hammel, Aug. 3, 1968; children: Daniel J., Robert R. BSChemE, U. Detroit, 1968; MBA, U. Del., 1970. Chem. engr. E.I. DuPont, Wilmington, Del., 1968-70; market mgr. Sybron, Paramus, N.J., 1970-72; mgr. bus. devel. PPG Industries, Pitts., 1972-84; mgr. nat. sales Ciba-Geigy, East Lansing, Mich., 1984-85; dir. indsl.devel. inst. Mich. State U., East Lansing, Mich., 1985-92, mgr. tech. transfer, 1993—; v.p. Performance Assocs., East Lansing, 1992—; bd. dirs. Access Bioco, Lansing, Mich., Biomechanical Design, Inc., Lansing, Electronic Tracking, Inc., Okemos, Mich.; with tech. transfer Mich. Biotechnology Inst., Lansing, 1993—. Contbg. author: Design for Manufacturing, 1991; contbr. articles to profl. jours., papers to proceedings. Vice chair Ingham County Econ. Devel., Lansing, 1991; pres. Capital Enterprise Forum, Lansing, 1991; strategic planner Am. Cancer Soc., Lansing., 1992. Grantee Rsch. in Excellence Fund, 1987-91, Small Bus. Administrn., 1989, Mich. Chem. Coun., 1991, EPA, 1991. Mem. Composite Mfg. Assn. (chair-elect 1992—), Engring. Soc. Detroit (organizing com. 1987—). Roman Catholic. Avocations: tennis, jogging, golf. Office: Mich State U 452 N Business Complex East Lansing MI 48824

MARTIN, MURRAY SIMPSON, librarian, writer, consultant; b. Lower Hutt, N.Z., July 21, 1928; came to U.S., 1966, naturalized, 1974; s. Francis Roy and Sarah Isabel (Mitchell) M.; m. Noelene Phyllis Ax, Aug. 28, 1954. B.A., U. New Zealand, Auckland, 1948; M.A., U. New Zealand, 1949; B.Comm., U. New Zealand, Auckland and Wellington, 1958; Diploma, New Zealand Library Sch., Wellington, 1950. Cert. pub. acct., N.Z. With New Zealand Nat. Library Service, Wellington, 1951-63; br. serials librarian U. Sask., Saskatoon, Can., 1963-66; acquisitions-collections devel. librarian Pa. State U., University Park, 1967-73; assoc. head of libraries Pa. State U., 1973-81; univ. librarian, prof. library sci. Tufts U., Medford, Mass., 1981-89, prof. libr. sci. emeritus, univ. libr. emeritus, 1990—, spl. asst. to provost for libr. planning and devel., 1989-90; sr. acad. library planner Aaron Cohen Assocs., 1990-91; interim exec. sec. Coll. and Univ. Librs. Assn., 1990-92; treas. Universal Serials and Book Exchange Washington, 1979-80, 82-84, v.p., 1985, pres. 1986; pres. Pitts. Regional Library Ctr., 1980-81, Boston Library Consortium, 1984-85; mem. adj. faculty Simmons Coll., 1989—. Author: Budgetary Control in Academic Libraries, 1979, Issues in Personnel Management in Academic Libraries, 1981, Academic Library Budgets, 1993, Collection Development and Finance, 1995; editor: Financial Planning in Libraries, 1983, Library Finance: New Needs, New Models, 1994; assoc. editor: Bottom Line, 1990—, Guide to Reference Books, 1993-94; column editor: Technicalities, 1995—; mng. editor: JAI Press, Inc., 1990—; contbr. articles and revs. to profl. and lit. publs. Mem. ALA, Can. Libr. Assn., N.Z. Libr. Assn. (chmn. fiction com. 1960-63, assoc.), Am. Comparative Lit. Assn., Am. Australian Lit. Studies, MLA, NELA, Soc. for Scholarly Pub. Democrat. Avocations: bird-watching; stamp-collecting; conservation; travel.

MARTIN, NATHANIEL FRIZELL GRAFTON, mathematician, educator; b. Wichita Falls, Tex., Oct. 10, 1928; s. James Thelbert and Ethel Elizabeth (Nycum) M.; m. Joan Bowman, Apr. 10, 1954; children: Nathaniel Grafton, Jonathan Bowman. BS, North Tex. State U., 1948, MS, 1950; PhD, Iowa State U., 1958. Instr. Midwestern U., Wichita Falls, 1950-52; teaching asst. Iowa State U., Ames, 1955-59; from instr. to prof. math. U. Va., Charlottesville, 1959—, assoc. dean Grad. Sch. Arts and Scis., 1976-82; rsch. assoc. U. Calif., Berkeley, 1965-66; guest lectr. U. Copenhagen, 1969-70. Author: Mathematical Theory of Entropy, 1981; editor: McGraw-Hill Dictionary of Physics & Math, 1978, Sci. & Tech. Terms, 1974. Lt. USNR, 1952-55. Mem. Am. Math. Soc., Math. Assn. Am., Sigma Xi, Pi Mu Epsilon. Office: Univ Va Dept Math Kerchof Hall Charlottesville VA 22903

MARTIN, NEAL ANDERSON, library director; b. Aug. 15, 1946; s. Arthur Morrison and Mary Julia (Grubbs) M.; m. Charlotte Salley Berry, Sept. 6, 1969 (div. Oct. 1989); children: Jennifer Berry, Amanda Fleming; m. Mary Alice Sherlock, Apr. 7, 1990. AB, Davidson Coll., 1968; MLS, Emory U., 1969. Libr. spl. projects Presbyn. Coll., Clinton, S.C., 1969; ref. libr. Francis Marion Coll., Florence, S.C., 1971-88; dir. libr. Coker Coll., Hartsville, S.C., 1988—; state dir. (S.C.) for U.S. Acad. Decathlon, 1990-94. Bd. dirs. Alston Wilkes Soc., Columbia, S.C., 1986-91. Lt. U.S. Army Signal Corps, 1969-71. Mem. S.E. Libr. Assn. (exec. bd. rep. S.C. 1984—), S.C. Libr. Assn., ALA, Alpha Psi Omega. Presbyterian. Office: Coker Coll Libr College Ave Hartsville SC 29550

MARTIN, NED HAROLD, chemistry educator; b. New Brunswick, N.J., May 18, 1945; s. Harold and Gertrude (Link) M.; m. Lynda Susan Blackadar, June 14, 1980; 1 child, Tara Elizabeth. BA, Denison U., 1967; PhD, Duke U., 1972. NDEA trainee Duke U., Durham, N.C., 1967-69; rsch. chemist Research Triangle Inst., Research Triangle Park, N.C., 1969-70; rsch. asst. Duke U., Durham, 1970-72; lectr., 1971-72; asst. prof. U. N.C. Wilmington, 1972-77, assoc. prof., 1977-82, prof., 1982—; chair chemistry dept., 1992—; cons. Corning Glass, Wilmington, 1979-80, LaQue Ctr. for Corrosion Tech., Wrightsville Beach, N.C., 1983-87, Condux, Inc., Newark, Del., 1989-90, Trinity Mfg., Inc., 1991; postdoctorate researcher U. Geneva, 1980-81. Co-author: Organic Chemistry Lab Manual with Waste Management and Molecular Modeling, 1993, Chemistry 211/212 Lab Manual, 1987. Mem. N.C. Acad. Sci. (v.p. 1988-90, pres.-elect 1989-90, pres. 1990-91, past pres. 1991-92), Am. Chem. Soc., Sigma Xi (assoc.), Phi Beta Kappa,

Omicron Delta Kappa, Phi Soc., Phi Eta Sigma, Phi Lambda Upsilon. Office: UNCW 601 S College Rd Wilmington NC 28403-3297

MARTIN, NEIL, lawyer; b. Centralia, Ill., Oct. 9, 1942; s. Robert Floyd and Virginia Dare (Rice) M.; m. Judy Ann Parker, Aug. 29, 1964; children: Lori Ann, Brett Tyson. BBA, Baylor U., 1964, JD, 1967. Bar: Tex. 1967, U.S. Dist. Ct. (no., so. and we. dists.) Tex. 1967, U.S. Ct. Appeals (5th cir.) 1971, U.S. Supreme Ct. 1972. Spl. agent FBI, Birmingham, Ala., 1968-69, St. Louis, 1969-70; assoc. Fulbright & Jaworski, Houston, 1970-77, ptnr., 1977-93; Gardere & Wynne, Houston, 1993—. Mem. ABA, Tex. Bar Assn., Houston Bar Assn., Baylor Alumni Assn, Baylor Law Sch. Alumni Assn. (counselor). Baptist. Office: Gardere & Wynne LLP 600 Travis St Ste 5000 Houston TX 77002-3006

MARTIN, NOEL, graphic design consultant, educator; b. Syracuse, Ohio, Apr. 19, 1922; s. Harry Ross and Lula (Van Meter) M.; m. Coletta Ruchty, Aug. 29, 1942; children—Dana, Reid. Cert. in Fine Arts, Art Acad. Cin. Doctorate (hon.), 1994. Designer Cin. Art Mus., 1947-93, asst. to dir., 1947-55; freelance designer for various ednl., cultural and indsl. orgns., 1947—; instr. Art Acad. Cin., 1951-57, artist-in-residence, 1993—; design cons. Champion Internat., 1959-82, Xomox Corp., 1961—, Federated Dept. Stores, 1962-83, Hebrew Union Coll., 1969—; designer-in-residence U. Cin., 1968-71, adj. prof., 1968-73; mem. adv. bd. Carnegie-Mellon U., R.I. Sch. Design, Cin. Symphony Orch., Am. Inst. Graphic Arts; lectr. Smithsonian Instn., Libr. of Congress, Am. Inst. Graphic Arts, Aspen Design Conf., various additional schs. and orgns. nationally. One man shows include Contemporary Arts Ctr., Cin., 1954, 71, Addison Gallery Am. Art, 1955, R.I. Sch. Design, 1955, Soc. Typographic Arts, Chgo., 1956, White Mus. of Cornell U., 1956, Cooper & Beatty, Toronto, Ont., Can., 1958, Am. Inst. Graphic Arts, 1958, Ind. U., 1958, Ohio State U., 1971; exhibited in group shows at Mus. Modern Art, N.Y.C., Library of Congress, Musee d'Art Moderne, Paris, Grafiska Inst., Stockholm, Carpenter Ctr., Cambridge, Gutenberg Mus., Mainz, U.S. info. exhbns. In Europe, South America and USSR; represented in permanent collections Mus. Modern Art, Stedelijk Mus., Amsterdam, Cin. Art Mus., Boston Mus. Fine Arts, Cin. Hist. Soc., Library of Congress; served to sgt. U.S. Air Force, 1942-45. Recipient Art Directors medal, Phila., 1957, Sachs award, Cin., 1973, Lifetime Achievement award Cin. Art Dirs., 1989.

MARTIN, PATRICK, business equipment company executive; b. N.Y.C., Mar. 16, 1941; s. Michael and Theresa (Devaney) M.; children: Julia, Margaret, Brendan, Patrick, Sean Patrick. BS in Math., Iona Coll., 1962; MS in Math., George Washington U., 1965, PhD in Elec. Engring. and Computer Sci., 1971. Sr. scientist Research Analysis Corp., 1962-64; sr. mgr. Informatics Inc., 1964-66; pres. NCS Computing Corp., 1966-72; assoc. prof. George Washington U., 1966-77; dep. asst. sec. USDA, 1972-77; v.p., gen. mgr. China bus. devel. Xerox Corp., Rochester, N.Y., 1977-91; pres., gen. mgr. Am. Customer Ops., Stamford, Conn., 1991—. Contbr. numerous articles and research papers in computer sci. and mgmt. jours. Avocations: squash, skiing, reading, ethnic dances. Home: 74 Maple Ave S Westport CT 06880-6336 Office: Xerox Corp 200 First Stamford Pl Stamford CT 06904

MARTIN, PAUL, Canadian government official; b. Windsor, Ont., Can., Aug. 28, 1938; s. Paul Joseph and Eleanor (Adams) M.; m. Sheila Ann Cowan, Sept. 11, 1965; children—Paul William James, Robert James Edward, David Patrick Anthony. BA in Philosophy and History, U. Toronto, Can., 1962, LLB, 1965; LLB, U. Toronto, Can., 1965. Bar: Ont. 1966. Exec. asst. to pres. Power Corp. Can. Ltd., 1966-69, v.p., 1969-71; v.p. spl. projects Consol.-Bathurst Ltd., 1971-73; v.p. planning and devel. Power Corp., Can., 1973-74; pres. Can. S.S. Lines Ltd., Montreal, 1974-80, chief exec. officer, 1976-80; pres., chief exec. officer CSL Group Inc., 1980-88; M.P. Ho. of Commons, 1988-93; min. of finance Dept. of Finance Canada, 1993—. Former mem. C.D. Howe Inst. Policy Analysis Com., Birt, N.Am. Com., Ctr. Rsch. Action on Race Rels.; fromer bd. dirs. Can. Coun. Christians and Jews; founding dir. emeritus North-South Inst., Can. Coun. Native Bus.; bd. govs. Concrodia U., coun., v.p., past mem. bd. advs. Liberal. Avocations: sports, reading. Office: Dept of Finance Canada, 140 O'Connor St, Ottawa, ON Canada K1A 0G5*

MARTIN, PAUL CECIL, physicist, educator; b. Bklyn., Jan. 31, 1931; s. Harry and Helen (Salzberger) M.; m. Ann Wallace Bradley, Aug. 7, 1957; children: Peter, Stephanie Glennon, Daniel. A.B., Harvard U., 1952, Ph.D., 1954. Mem. faculty Harvard U., Cambridge, Mass., 1957—, prof. physics 1964-82, J. H. VanVleck prof. pure and applied physics 1982—, chmn. dept. physics, 1972-75, dean div. applied scis., 1977—, assoc. dean Faculty Arts and Scis., 1981—; vis. prof. Ecole Normale Superieure, Paris, 1963, 66, U. Paris, Orsay, 1971; mem. materials rsch. adv. coun. NSF, 1986-89; bd. dirs. Mass. Tech. Pk. Corp., 1990—, exec. com., 1992-94. Bd. editors: Jour. Math Physics, 1965-68, Annals of Physics, 1968-82, Jour. Statis. Physics, 1975-80. Bd. dirs. Assoc. Univs. for Rsch. in Astronomy, 1979-85; trustee Assoc. Univs., Inc., 1981—, exec. com., 1986-90, 92—. NSF postdoctoral fellow, 1955; Sloan Found. fellow, 1959-62; Guggenheim fellow, 1966, 71. Fellow AAAS (chair physics sect. 1986), NAS, Am. Acad. Arts and Scis., Am. Phys. Soc. (councillor-at-large 1982-84, panel on pub. affairs 1983-86, chmn. nominating com. 1994), N.Y. Acad. Scis. Office: Harvard U Dept Physics Cambridge MA 02138*

MARTIN, PAUL EDWARD, retired insurance company executive; b. Santa Claus, Ind., Sept. 10, 1914; s. James F. and Anna (Singer) M.; m. Pauline Peva, Dec. 22, 1939 (dec. Feb. 1982); 1 child, Peter McDowell; m. Ann Parker, Oct. 14, 1983. B.A., Hanover Coll., 1936. With actuarial dept. State Life Ins. Co., Indpls., 1936-42; asst. actuary Ohio Nat. Life Ins. Co., Cin., 1946-48; asso. actuary Ohio Nat. Life Ins. Co., 1948-49, actuary, 1949-55, actuarial v.p., 1955-56, adminstrv. v.p., 1956-67, sr. v.p. ins. adminstrn., 1967-71, pres., 1971-72, chmn. bd., chief exec. officer, 1972-79, also dir.; former dir. First Nat. Cin. Corp. Trustee Hanover (Ind.) Coll. Served to maj. F.A. AUS, 1942-46, PTO. Fellow Soc. Actuaries, Acad. Actuaries; mem. Masons, Shriners, Comml. Club, Skyline Club, Gamma Sigma Pi, Beta Theta Pi. Presbyterian. Clubs: Mason (Shriner), Commercial, Ventana Canyon Country. Home: 7146 N Finger Rock Pl Tucson AZ 85718-1406

MARTIN, PAUL EGLEY, investment banker; b. St. Louis, Mar. 25, 1958; s. Frederick William and Dorothy Jean (Egley) M.; m. Georgia Remington, July 31, 1982; children: Katherine Remington, Charles Powell Whitehead. AB in Econs., Princeton U., 1980; MBA in Fin., U. Chgo., 1984. Fin. analyst Blythe Eastman Paine Webber, N.Y.C., 1980-82; asst. to chmn. Farley Inds., Chgo., 1983-84; assoc. Paine Webber, N.Y. & San Francisco, 1984-85, Smith Barney, Harris & Upham, San Francisco, 1986; v.p. Smith, Barney, Harris & Upham, San Francisco, 1987—. Bd. dirs. ARC Golden Gate Chpt., San Francisco, 1988—. Mem. Princeton Club of No. Calif. (pres. 1989-91). Republican. Home: 201 Magellan Ave San Francisco CA 94116-1452 Office: Smith Barney et al 350 California St San Francisco CA 94104-1402

MARTIN, PAUL JOSEPH, biomedical engineer, cardiology researcher, educator, consultant; b. Hammond, Ind., May 22, 1936; s. Joseph Edwin and Verna Catherine (Heidgerken) M.; m. Jeanne Therese Oubre, Sept. 10, 1960 (div. 1992); children: Mary Kay, Barry James, Craig Anthony, Colleen Therese; m. Marjie Anne Prentice, June 19, 1993. BSEE, U. Tex., 1960; MS in Biomed. Engring., Drexel U., 1961; PhD in Biomed. Engring., Case Western Res. U., 1967. Rsch. fellow Latter Day Sts. Hosp., Salt Lake City, 1961-62; biomed. rsch. engr. Tech., Inc., Dayton, Ohio, 1962-63; rsch. assoc. Mt. Sinai Med. Ctr., Cleve., 1967-75, head bioengring. sect., div. investigative medicine, 1975-89, assoc. chief, div. investigative medicine, 1989—, chmn. instl. rev. bd., 1973—; asst. prof. physiology, biophysics and biomed. engring. Case Western Res. U. Sch. Medicine and Engring., Cleve., 1967-76, assoc. prof., 1976-83, prof., 1983—; physiology cons. Artificial Heart Program of Cleve. Clinic, 1963-70; computer cons. Acad. Medicine of Cleve., 1987-92; cons. various rsch. labs.; mem. study sect. NIH, NSF, EPA, Washington, 1973—; treas. G & R Sports, Inc. Contbr. numerous articles, book chpts. to profl. publs.; assoc. editor Am. Jour. Physiology, Heart and Circulatory Physiology, 1976-81; mem. editorial bd. Circulation Rsch., 1975-80. Mem. campaign com. Cleveland Heights Dems., 1970-84. With USN, 1954-57. NIH Spl. fellow, Bethesda, Md., 1961-62, 64-67; rsch. grantee Am. Heart Assn., Cleve., 1966-74, NIH, 1979—. Fellow Am. Heart Assn. (chmn. rsch. study sect. N.E. Ohio 1975-79), Am. Physiol. Soc.; mem. IEEE

(sr.), Biomed. Engring. Soc. (sr.), Royal Scottish Country, Dance Soc. (treas. 1988-93). Avocations: woodworking, classical guitar, Scottish country dancing. Home: 3611 Runnymede Blvd Cleveland Heights OH 44121-1333 Office: Mt Sinai Med Ctr University Circle Cleveland OH 44106

MARTIN, PETER WILLIAM, lawyer, educator; b. Cin., Apr. 11, 1939; s. Wilfred Samuel and Elizabeth (Myers) M.; m. Ann Wadsworth, Nov. 28, 1964; children: Leah, Elliot, Isaac. B.A., Cornell U., 1961; J.D., Harvard U., 1964. Bar: Ohio 1964. Atty. AF Gen. Counsel's Office, 1964-67; asso. prof. law U. Minn., 1967-71; vis. asso. prof. law Cornell U., 1971-72, prof. law, 1972—, dean, 1980-88, Edward Cornell prof. law, 1989-92, Jane Foster prof. law, 1992—; co-dir. Legal Info. Inst., 1992—; pres. Ctr. for Computer Assisted Legal Instrn., 1986-88; cons. Adminstrv. Conf. U.S., 1977-79; reporter Am. Bar Assn. Task Force on Lawyer Competency and the Role of the Law Schs. Author: The Ill-Housed, 1971, (with others) Social Welfare and the Individual, 1971, Cases and Materials on Property, 1974, 3d edit., 1992, Social Security Law, 1990, Basic Legal Citation, 1992, Social Security Plus, 1994; editor Jour. Legal Edn., 1985. Chmn. Ithaca Bd. Zoning Appeals, 1974-79. Served to capt. USAF, 1964-67. Mem. ABA (task force on law schs. and legal profession 1990-92), Am. Bar Found. (vis. com.), Am. Assn. Law Schs. (chmn. law and computers sect. 1987-88, 93-94). Office: Cornell U Law Sch Myron Taylor Hall Ithaca NY 14853

MARTIN, PHILLIP DWIGHT, banking consulting company executive, mayor; b. Nevada, Mo., Jan. 4, 1943; s. E. Dwight and Berniece E. (Leedy) M. BS, U. Mo., 1964, MBA, 1965, cert. math. and bus. edn., 1966. Tchr. Warson (Mo.) Pub. Schs., 1966-68; investment analyst Bus. Men's Assurance Co., Am. Kansas City, Mo., 1968-70; exec. v.p. Farmer's Bank Walker, Mo., 1970-71; banking cons. Howard J. Blender Co., Dallas, 1971-84; chmn. Profit Motivators Internat., Inc., Boulder, Colo., 1984—; mayor City of Walker, 1986—. Home: 214 E Marvin Ave Walker MO 64790-0069 Office: Profit Motivators Internat 2146 Linden Dr Boulder CO 80304

MARTIN, PHILLIP HAMMOND, lawyer; b. Tucson, Jan. 4, 1940; s. William P. and Harriet (Hammond) M.; m. Sandra S. Chandler, June 17, 1961 (div. Mar. 1989); children: Lisa, Craig, Wade, Ryan; m. Erika Zetty, May 9, 1990. BA, U. Minn., 1961, JD, 1964. Bar: Minn. 1964, U.S. Tax Ct. 1967, U.S. Dist. Ct. Minn. 1968, U.S. Ct. Appeals (8th cir.) 1973, U.S. Supreme Ct. 1981, U.S. Claims Ct. 1983, U.S. Ct. Appeals (fed. cir.) 1988, U.S. Ct. Appeals (7th cir.) 1989. Assoc. Dorsey & Whitney, Mpls., 1964-69, ptnr., 1970—. Home: 487 Portland Ave Saint Paul MN 55102-2216 Office: Dorsey & Whitney 220 S 6th St Minneapolis MN 55402-1498

MARTIN, QUINN WILLIAM, lawyer; b. Fond du Lac, Wis., Mar. 12, 1948; s. Quinn W. and Marcia E. (Petrie) M.; m. Jane E. Nehmer; children: Quinn W., William J. BSME, Purdue U., 1969; postgrad., U. Santa Clara, 1969-70; JD, U. Mich., 1973. Bar: Wis. 1973, U.S. Dist. Ct. (ea. dist.) Wis. 1973, U.S. Ct. Appeals (7th cir.) 1973. Sales support mgr. Hewlett-Packard, Palo Alto, Calif., 1969-70; assoc. Quarles & Brady, Milw., 1973-80, ptnr., 1980—; bd. dirs. Associated Bank Milw., Martin Communications, Inc. Kaukauna, Wis., Gen. Timber and Land, Inc., Fond du Lac. Active McCallum for Lt. Gov., Wis., U. Mich. Law Sch. Fund; bd. dirs. Milw. Zool. Soc., Found. for Wildlife Conservation. Mem. ABA, Wis. Bar Assn., Milw. Bar Assn., Univ. Club, Milw. Club, Ozaukee Country Club, Chaine des Rottiseurs, Delta Upsilon (sec.), Milw. Alimni Club. Office: Quarles & Brady 411 E Wisconsin Ave Milwaukee WI 53202-4409

MARTIN, R. EDEN, lawyer; b. Sullivan, Ill., May 17, 1940. BA, U. Ill., 1962; LLB, Harvard U., 1967. Bar: Ill. 1967, U.S. Supreme Ct. 1972, D.C. 1982. Ptnr. Sidley & Austin, Chgo. Office: Sidley & Austin 1 First Nat Plz Chicago IL 60603

MARTIN, R. KEITH, business and information systems educator, consultant; b. Seattle, Sept. 5, 1933; s. Jerome Milton and Winifred (Gifford) M.; m. Carolyn Joanne Carosella, June 15, 1957; children: Jefferson, Sean, Jennifer, Katherine. AB, Whitman Coll., 1955; MBA with high honors, CCNY, 1965; PhD, U. Wash., 1973. Registered profl. engr.; cert. data processing, cert. systems profl., cert. computer profl. Div. mgr. Campus Merchandising Bur., Inc., N.Y.C., 1955-56; sales rep IBM, Seattle, 1956, Service Bur. Corp. subs. IBM, N.Y.C., 1957-58; specialist mgmt. adv. services Price Waterhouse & Co., N.Y.C., 1959-65; specialist mgmt. adv. services Price Waterhouse & Co., Seattle, 1965-66, mgr., 1966-67; dir. mgmt. systems dept. U. Wash., 1967-71, lectr. dept. acctg. Sch. Bus. Adminstrn. 1971-73; asst. prof. dept. accountancy Baruch Coll., CUNY, 1973-76, assoc. prof., 1977-79; prof. acctg. and info. systems Fairfield U., 1979—, assoc. dean Sch. Bus., 1980-82, dean, 1982-93, acting dean grad. Sch. of Communications, 1988-90; v.p. Eastalco Systems, 1971-72; faculty fin. div. mem. Marquis Am., 1963-64; part-time lectr. Bellevue Community Coll., 1967-69, Shoreline Community Coll., 1968-72, Seattle U., 1971-72. Co-author: Management Control of Electronic Data Processing, 1965; author: Management Information Systems in Higher Education: Case Studies at Three Universities, 1973, Effective Business Communications, 1976, 79, 91, Systems Development and Computer Concepts, 1977; assoc. editor: Industry Guides for Accountants and Auditors, 2 vols., 1980; mem. editorial rev. bd. Dickenson Pub. Co., 1974-75, Prentice-Hall, Inc., 1977-78, 87-88, 90-91, Reston Pub. Co., 1977-78, Jour. Acctg. Edn., 1981-83; contbr. monographs and articles. Mem. Citizens' Legis. Rev. Com., 1968-69; mem. City of Seattle EDP Adv. Com., 1968-71, chmn., 1968-69; vice chmn. subcom. Citizens Adv. Com. Licensing and Consumer Affairs, 1970-73; chmn. indsl. engring. adv. com. Shoreline Community Coll., 1968-72; mem. mgmt. info. systems data element task force Western Interstate Commn. Higher Edn., 1968-70, adv. council 1969-71; mem. com. for non-partisan nomination and election of Bronxville Sch. Bd. Trustees, 1976-78, chmn., 1977, chmn. mgmt. policies and procedures com., 1981-82, mem. fin. com., chmn. audit subcom., 1985-86; cons. to Urban Acad., City N.Y., 1974-78; chmn., pres. Loft Film and Theatre Ctr., Inc., 1977-78, mem. adv. bd., 1982-83; v.p. Normandy Homeowners Assn., 1978-80, pres., 1983, treas., 1989-91; sec.-treas. governing mem., mem. of policy com. The Com. on Developing American Capitalism, 1982—; bd. dirs. Intelligent Communications Network, 1982-86, chmn. audit com. 1983-86, mem. compensation com., 1982-86; trustee Conn. Joint Council Econ. Edn., 1982-93; trustee Ctr. Fin. Studies, 1983—, vice chmn. audit com. 1983—, mem. exec. com., 1985-94; cons. examiner and mem. com. bus. Charter Oak Coll., 1984-92, co-chmn., 1987-91, com. on degrees, 1987-92, core curriculum com., 1989-91, vice chmn., 1991-92; bd. advisers Econ. Club of Conn., Nat. Assn. Economists, 1985-86; mem. adv. com. regional vocat. mgmt. program, City of Bridgeport, 1987-87; mem. adv. bd. So. Conn. Bus. Jour., 1987-88; mem. Am. Assembly of Collegiate Schs. of Bus. Task Force on Faculty Renewal, 1985-87, nominating com., 1989-90; adv. bd. So. Conn. Bus. Jour., 1987-88; mem. bd. eden. Village of Bronxville, 1987-90, mem. fin. com., 1987-88, v.p., 1989-90, chmn. pers. com., 1988-90; acad. policy and standards com. Inst. for Fin. Planning, 1987-92, sec.-treas., 1988-89, v.p., 1989-90, pres., 1990-91; cons. TRI Corp., 1991—. Recipient cert. of appreciation Am. Mgmt. Assn., 1966, cert. of merit for disting. service to Mgmt. Scis., 1969, for disting. service to info. systems profession, 1973; Merit award Assn. Systems Mgmt., 1971, Achievement award, 1972; cert. for service City of Seattle, 1973; named Outstanding Young Man Am., 1970, One of0 Outstanding Alumni, Whitman Coll., 1979; Kellogg fellow, 1971-72, Price Waterhouse faculty fellow, 1976. Mem. Am. Inst. Indsl. Engrs. (dir. Seattle chpt. 1967-70, chmn. regional conf. 1969), Inst. Mgmt. Accts. (assoc. dir. N.Y. chpt. 1963-64, 75-85 Seattle chpt. 1967-70), Assn. Systems Mgmt. (sec. 1968-69, v.p. 1969-70, pres. Pacific N.W. chpt. 1970-71), Data Processing Mgmt. Assn., Assn. Computing Machinery, Soc. Cert. Data Processors, NSPE, N.Y. Soc. Profl. Engrs., Soc. Mgmt. Info. Systems, AAUP, Am. Acctg. Assn., Phi Delta Theta (province pres. 1986-87), Mu Gamma Tau, Phi Delta Kappa, Beta Alpha Psi. Club: Bronxville Field. Home: 2 Normandy Rd Bronxville NY 10708-4808

MARTIN, RALPH GUY, writer; b. Chgo., Mar. 4, 1920; s. Herman and Tillie (Charno) M.; m. Marjorie Jean Pastel, June 17, 1944; children: Maurice Joseph, Elizabeth, Tina. B.J., U. Mo., 1941. Reporter, mng. editor Box Elder News Jour., Brigham, Utah, 1940-41; contbr. mags. including Sunday N.Y. Times, Look, Harpers mag., 1945-53; assoc. editor New Republic mag., 1945-48; assoc. editor charge spl. reports Newsweek mag., 1953-55; exec. editor House Beautiful mag., 1955-57; pub., pres. Bandwagon, Inc. Author: Boy From Nebraska, 1946, The Best is None Too Good, 1948, Ballots and

Bandwagons: Five Key Conventions since 1900, 1964, Skin Deep, 1964, The Bosses, 1964, President from Missouri, 1964, Wizard of Wall Street, 1965, World War II, Pearl Harbor to V-J Day, 1966, The GI War, 1967, A Man for All People, 1968, Jennie: The Life of Lady Randolph Churchill, The Romantic Years, 1969, vol. II, The Dramatic Years, 1971, Lincoln Center for the Performing Arts, 1971, The Woman He Loved: The Story of the Duke and Duchess of Windsor, 1974, Cissy, The Extraordinary Life of Eleanor Medill Patterson, 1979; A Hero For Our Time, An Intimate Study of the Kennedy Years, 1983, Charles and Diana, 1985, Golda, Golda Meir: The Romantic Years, 1988, Henry and Clare: An Intimate Portrait of the Luces, 1991; co-author: Stevenson Speeches, 1952, Eleanor Roosevelt: Her Life in Pictures, 1958, The Human Side of FDR, 1960, Front Runner, Dark Horse, 1960, Money, Money, Money, 1960, Man of Destiny: Charles DeGaulle, 1961, Man of the Century: Winston Churchill, 1961, The Three Lives of Helen Keller, 1962, World War II: From D-Day to VE-Day, 1962; Contbr. to: Yank The GI History of The War, Social Problems in America, 1955, Democracy in Action, 1962, others. Dep. dir. pub. relations Nat. Vols. for Stevenson-Kefauver, 1956; mem. Dem. Nat. Campaign Com. Combat corr. Stars and Stripes, Yank mag., 1941-45. Mem. Author's League Am., Author's Guild, English-Speaking Union, Tenn. Squires, Dramatist's Guild. Clubs: Century, Overseas Press, Princeton. Home: 135 Harbor Rd Westport CT 06880-6918

MARTIN, RANDI CHRISTINE, psychology educator; b. Salem, Oreg., May 24, 1949; d. Harold Raymond and Maxine Constance (Torgeson) M.; m. Lawrence P. Chan, Aug. 30, 1974. BA, U. Oreg., 1971; MA, Johns Hopkins U., 1977, PhD, 1979. Lectr. U. Calif., Santa Cruz, 1979-80; assoc. rsch. scientist Johns Hopkins U., Balt., 1980-82; asst. prof. Rice U., Houston, 1982-87, assoc. prof., 1987-93, prof., 1993—. Assoc. editor Psychonomic Bulletin & Rev., Austin, Tex., 1995—; editl. bd. mem. Cognitive Neuropsychology, London, 1994—, Jour. Neurolinguistics, Cambridge, Eng., 1994—; contbr. articles to profl. jours. Recipient Claude Pepper award NIH Deafness and Comm. Disorders Inst., 1995—. Mem. APA, Psychonomic Soc. (sec./treas. 1993-95), Acad. Aphasia (program com. 1990-93). Achievements include research in short term memory deficits in brain damaged patients. Office: Rice U Psychology Dept 6100 Main St Houston TX 77005

MARTIN, RAY, banker; b. Nogales, AZ, 1936. With Coast Savs. and Loan Assn. (now Coast Fed. Bank), L.A., 1959—, pres., 1980-84, pres., chief exec. officer, from 1984, now chmn. bd., chief exec. officer, also bd. dirs. Office: Coast Svgs Fin Inc 1000 Wilshire Blvd Los Angeles CA 90017-2457

MARTIN, REBECCA REIST, librarian; b. Princeton, N.J., Mar. 2, 1952; d. Benjamin A. and Harriet (Nold) Reist; m. Joseph M. Lubow; 1 child, Benjamin R. Martin. BA, U. Calif., Santa Cruz 1973; MA, San Jose State U., 1975; DPA, U. So. Calif., 1992. Med. libr. VA Med. Ctr., San Francisco, 1975-77, chief libr. svc., 1977-81; head biology libr. U. Calif., Berkeley, 1981-85; assoc. libr. dir. San Jose (Calif.) State U., 1985-90; dir. librs. and media svcs. U. Vt., Burlington, 1990—. Author: Libraries and the Changing Face of Academia, 1994; contbr. articles to profl. jours., chpts. in books. Mem. Libr. Commn. San Jose, 1989-90. Mem. ALA, New England Libr. Assn., Am. Soc. Pub. Adminstrn., Am. Assn. Coll. and Rsch. Librs., Libr. Adminstrn. and Mgmt. Assn. (bd. dirs. 1987-89). Office: U Vt Bailey/ Howe Libr Burlington VT 05405

MARTIN, RICHARD HARRISON, curator, art historian; b. Bryn Mawr, Pa., Dec. 4, 1946; s. Frank Harrison and Margaret Dever M. BA, Swarthmore Coll., 1967; MA, Columbia U., 1969, M.Phil., 1971. Instr. William Paterson Coll. of N.J., Wayne, 1972-73; editor Arts Mag., N.Y.C., 1974-88; prof. Fashion Inst. Tech., SUNY, N.Y.C., 1973-93, Ednl. Found. for the Fashion Industries, 1991-93; exec. dir. Shirley Goodman Resource Center, 1980-93; critic-in-residence Md. Inst. Coll. Art, 1985-87; editor, pub. Textile & Text, 1989-93; curator The Costume Inst., Met. Mus. Art, N.Y.C., 1993—; adj. faculty Sch. Visual Arts, N.Y.C., 1975-80, 93—; adj. prof. NYU, 1977—, Columbia U., 1987-89, 95—, Vt. Coll., 1991-93. Author: Fashion and Surrealism, 1987, Jocks and Nerds, 1989, The Historical Mode, 1989, The New Urban Landscape, 1990, Giorgio Armani: Images of Man, 1990, Flair: Fashion Collected by Tina Chow, 1992, Infra-Apparel, 1993, Diana Vreeland: Immoderate Style, 1993, Waist Not, 1994, Madame Grès, 1994, Orientalism: Visions of the East in Western Dress, 1994, Bloom, 1995, Contemporary Fashion, 1995. Mem. Coll. Art Assn., Victorian Soc. Am. (dir. 1980-84, chpt. dir. 1981-83), Soc. Archtl. Historians, Am. Soc. for Aesthetics, Art Libraries Soc. N.Am., N.Y. Hist. Soc., Soc. for History of Tech., Costume Soc. Am. (dir. 1983-89, Region II pres. 1984-87). Home: 225 E 79th St New York NY 10021 Office: Met Mus Art The Costume Inst 1000 5th Ave New York NY 10028-0113

MARTIN, RICHARD JAY, medical educator; b. Detroit, May 16, 1946; s. Peter Aaron and Tillie Jean (Munch) M.; m. Helene Iris Horowitz, Dec. 23, 1967; children: Elizabeth Hope, David Evan. BS, U. Mich., 1967, MD, 1971. Diplomate Am. Bd. Internal Medicine and Pulmonary Disease. Intern Ariz., 1971-72; resident Tulane U., New Orleans, 1974-76; asst. prof. medicine U. Okla., Okla. City, 1978-80; asst. prof. medicine U. Colo., Denver, 1980-85, assoc. prof., 1985-92, prof., 1992—; dir. Cardiorespiratory Sleep Disorders Ctr. and Cardiorespiratory Sleep Rsch., Nat. Jewish Ctr. for Immunology and Respiratory Medicine, Denver, 1980-89, staff physician, 1980—, head divsn. pulmonary medicine, 1993—. Author: Cardiorespiratory Disorders During Sleep, 1984, 2d edit., 1990, (with others) Current Therapy in Internal Medicine, 1984, Clinical Pharmacology and Therapeutics in Nursing, 1985, Interdisciplinary Rehabilitation of Multiple Sclerosis and Neuromuscular Disorders, 1984, Drugs for the Respiratory System, 1985, Current Therapy in Pulmonary Medicine, 1985, Abnormalities of Respiration During Sleep, 1986, Cardiorespiratory Disease: Hemodynamics, 1986, Mitchell's Synopsis of Pulmonary Medicine, 1987; editor: Nocturnal Asthma: Mechanisms and Interventions, 1993; author, editor: Nocturnal Asthma: Mechanisms and Treatment, 1993; contbr. articles, reviews, reports on respiratory and neuromuscular diseases to profl. jours. Pres. Congregation Rodef Shalom, Denver, 1984-85; regional v.p. United Synagogues of Am., Denver, 1988-89. Pulmonary fellow Am. Lung Assn., 1977-79; James F. Hammarsten Outstanding fellow U. Okla. Health Scis. Ctr., 1978; grantee Purdue-Frederick Co., Winthrop-Breon Labs. Inc., Werner-lambert Co., VA, U. Okla. Lung Assn., NIH, Parker B. Francis Found.; recipient Best Paper in Internal Medicine award Okla. Soc. Interna. Medicine, 1977, 78, U. Okla. Gastroenterology sect, 1977. Mem. Am. Thoracic Soc., Am. Fedn. for Clin. Rsch., Am. Coll. Chest Physicians (rep. to Young Pulmonary Physician Conf., St. Charles, Ill. 1979), ACP, Colo. Trudeau Soc., Western Soc. Clin. Investigation. Avocations: biking, golf, karate. Office: Nat Jewish Ctr Immunology & Respiratory Medicine 1400 Jackson St Denver CO 80206-2762

MARTIN, RICHARD KELLEY, lawyer; b. Tulsa, June 30, 1952; s. Richard Loye and Maxine (Kelley) M.; m. Reba Lawson, June 12, 1993; children from previous marriage: R. Kyle, Andrew J. BA, Westminster Coll., 1974; JD, So. Meth. U., 1977. Bar: Tex. 1977, U.S. Tax Ct. 1979. Ptnr. Akin, Gump, Strauss, Hauer & Feld, LLP, Dallas, 1977-95; prnt. Haynes and Boone LLP, Dallas, 1995—. Bd. dirs. Goodwill Industries, Dallas, 1986—, v.p., 1986-91; bd. dirs. Greater Dallas Youth Orchs., 1987-90; bd. dirs., v.p., pres. Big Bros. and Sisters Met. Dallas, 1988-91, bd. dir. Girl Scout of U.S. Tejas Divsn.   ). Mem. Tex. Bar Assn., Salesmanship Club Dallas. Republican. Methodist. Office: Haynes and Boone LLP 3100 NationsBank Plz 901 Main St Dallas TX 75202

MARTIN, RICHARD L., insurance executive; b. Franklin, N.J., Feb. 2, 1932; s. Richard Lewis and Elizabeth (Roe) M.; m. Susan Mazuy, June 20, 1970; children: David Cory, Scott Mazuy. BEd, U. Miami, 1958; MA, Columbia U., 1963. Chartered Property Casualty Underwriter. Educator Franklin (N.J.) Sch. Dist., 1958-60; mng. dir. Sparta (N.J.) Sch. Dist., 1960-66; adminstr. Orange (N.J.) Sch. System, 1966-71; chief exec. officer Montague (N.J.) Sch. Dist., 1971-72, Stanhope (N.J.) Sch. System, 1972-73; v.p. Selective Ins. Group, Branchville, N.J., 1973-87; pres., chief exec. officer Medl. Malpractice Ins. Assn., N.Y.C., 1987—; chmn. N.J. Assn of Hlth Care Com., Trenton, 1980-87; treas. N.J. Ins. News Svc., Newark, 1982-87; chmn. AIA-N.J. State Conf., Trenton, 1983-87. Contbr. several articles to mags. With USMC, 1952-54. Mem. CPCU, Am. Mgmt. Assn., Soc. Ins. Research, Soc. for Corp. Planning, City Midday, Newton Country, Branchville Rotary,

Sons of Am. Revolution, Mayflower Soc. Presbyterian. Avocations: golf, hunting. Home: 230 E 48th St Apt 4A New York NY 10017-1511 Office: Med Malpractice Ins Assn 110 William St New York NY 10038-3997

MARTIN, RICHARD OTTO, medical device company executive; b. Chgo., Jan. 28, 1940; s. Richard and Barbara (Hildner) M.; divorced; children: Michelle Marie, Richard Michael, Bryan Joseph. BS in Elec. Engring., Christian Bros. Coll., Memphis, 1962; MSin Elec. Engring., Notre Dame U., 1964; PhD, Duke U., 1970. Registered prof. engr., Tenn. Research instr. dept. of medicine U. Tenn., Memphis, 1970-75; assoc. prof., head elec. engring. dept. Christian Bros. Coll., 1970-75; dir. U.S. Tech. Ctr. and Adv. Lead Devel. Medtronic, Inc., Mpls., 1975-78; v.p. clin. engring. Intermedics, Inc., Freeport, Tex., 1978-83; exec. v.p. Intermedics, Inc., 1983-85, pres., chief operating officer, 1985-87; pres., chief operating officer Positron Corp., 1988-89; v.p. bus. devel. Cardiovascular Sulzermedica, 1989—. Contbr. articles to profl. jours. NIH fellow, 1967-70. Mem. IEEE (assoc. editor Transactions on Biomed Engring. 1976-87), Am. Soc. Engring. Edn., Assn. for Advancement of Med. Instrumentation, N.Am. Soc. Pacing and Electrophysiology, Tau Beta Pi. Roman Catholic. Office: Physio-Control Corp 11811 Wollows Rd NE Redmond WA 98052

MARTIN, ROBERT A., electronics company executive. Chmn., pres. NES, Inc., Carpentersville, Ill. Office: NES Inc 16900 Foltz Industrial Pky Strongsville OH 44136-5520

MARTIN, ROBERT BRUCE, chemistry educator; b. Chgo., Apr. 29, 1929; s. Robert Frank and Helen (Woelffer) M.; m. Frances May Young, June 7, 1953. B.S., Northwestern U., 1950; Ph.D., U. Rochester, 1953. Asst. prof. chemistry Am. U., Beirut, Lebanon, 1953-56; research fellow Calif. Inst. Tech., 1956-57, Harvard U., 1957-59; asst. prof. chemistry U. Va., Charlottesville, 1959-61, assoc. prof., 1961-65, prof., 1965—, chmn. dept., 1968-71; spl. fellow Oxford U., 1961-62; Program dir. Molecular Biology Sect., NSF, 1965-66. Author: Introduction to Biophysical Chemistry, 1964. Fellow AAAS; mem. Am. Chem. Soc. Office: Univ of Va Dept Chemistry Charlottesville VA 22901

MARTIN, ROBERT DAVID, judge, educator; b. Iowa City, Oct. 7, 1944; s. Murray and G'Ann (Holmgren) M.; m. Ruth A. Haberman, Aug. 21, 1966; children: Jacob, Matthew, David. A.B., Cornell Coll. Mt. Vernon, Iowa, 1966; J.D., U. Chgo., 1969. Bar: Wis. 1969, U.S. Dist. Ct. (we. dist.) Wis. 1969, U.S. Dist. Ct. (ea. dist.) Wis. 1974, U.S. Supreme Ct. 1973. Assoc. Ross & Stevens, S.C., Madison, Wis., 1969-72, ptnr., 1973-78; chief judge U.S. Bankruptcy Ct. We. Dist. Wis., 1978—; instr. gen. practice course U. Wis. Law Sch., 1974, 76, 77, 80, lectr. debtor/creditor course, 1981-82, 83, 85, 87, farm credit seminar, 1985, advanced bankruptcy problems, 1989; co-chmn. faculty Am. Law Inst.-ABA Fin. and Bus. Planning for Agr., Stanford U., 1979; faculty mem. Fed. Jud. Ctr. Schs. for New Bankruptcy Judges, 1985—; chmn. Ann. Continuing Legal Edn. Wis. Debtor Creditor Conf., 1981—. Author: Bankruptcy: Annotated Forms, 1989; co-author: Secured Transactions Handbook for Wisconsin Lawyers and Lenders, Bankruptcy-Text Statutes Rules and Forms, 1992, Bankruptcy (with Ginsberg) 3d edit., 1992. Bd. dirs., exec. com. Luth. Social Svcs. for Wis. and Upper Mich. Mem. Wis. State Bar, Am. Coll. Bankruptcy, Am. Judicature Soc., Nat. Conf. Bankruptcy Judges (bd. govs. 1989-91, sec. 1993-94, v.p. 1994-95, pres. 95—), Nat. Bankruptcy Conf. Office: 120 N Henry Rm 340 PO Box 548 Madison WI 53701-0548

MARTIN, ROBERT EDWARD, architect; b. Dodge City, Kans., Mar. 17, 1928; s. Emry and Alice Jane (Boyce) M.; m. Billie Jo Lange, Aug. 16, 1952 (div. Feb. 1970); m. Kathryn M. Arvanitis, June 26, 1971; children: Lynn, Amy, Blaine. Student, McPherson Coll., 1946-48; BArch, U. Cin., 1954. Registered architect, Ohio. Architect Samborn, Steketee, Otis & Evans, Inc., Toledo, 1956-58; prin. Schauder & Martin, Toledo, 1958-72, The Collaborative, Inc., Toledo, 1972-93; mem. Bd. Examiners Archs., Ohio, 1985—, pres., 1989-94; bd. examiners Nat. Coun. Archtl. Registration Bds., 1986—, edn. com., 1992; chmn. site design divsn. Archtl. Registration Exam., 1989, 90, 91; mem. Nat. Coun. Archtl. Registration Bds. Grading, 1987-94; chmn. study of Toledo Fire & Rescue Dept., Corp. for Effective Govt., 1994. Artist numerous paintings. Mem. Toledo Planning Commn., 1971-74, Toledo Zoning Appeals Bd., 1973, Toledo Bd. Bldg. Stds., 1967-84, Citizens Fire Adv. Commn., 1974-80, Citizens Urban Area Adv. Commn., 1962, Toledo Area Coun. Govts., 1977-80, Com. of 100, Toledo, 1987-89, Spectrum Friends Fine Arts, Inc., Toledo; chmn. bd. Toledo Area Govtl. Rsch. Assn., 1981-90; chmn. Corp. for Effective Govt., Study of Toledo Fire and Rescue Dept., 1994; chmn. Cystic Fibrosis, Toledo. 1985. Seved to capt. USAF, 1954-56. Recipient numerous watercolor awards. Fellow AIA (pres. Toledo chpt. 1966, Arch. of Yr. 1993), Archs. Soc. Ohio (pres. 1975), Ohio Watercolor Soc., N.W. Ohio Watercolor Soc., Toledo Fedn. Art Socs. (pres. 1989, 90), Spectrum, Tile Club, Toledo Artists Club, Toledo Artists Club, Sylvania Country Club, Rotary, Masons, Shriners, Jesters. Mem. Ch. of Brethren. Avocation: painting. Home: 5119 Regency Dr Toledo OH 43615-2946 Office: 1700 N Reynolds Rd Toledo OH 43615

MARTIN, ROBERT FINLAY, JR., retired judge; b. Akron, O., May 4, 1925; s. Robert Finlay and Olive (Dexter) M.; m. Eleanor A. Gunn, Sept. 3, 1948; children—Roberta C. (Mrs. Bobby P. Grimes), Craig J., Scott D. B.A., Kent State U., 1949; J.D., U. Akron, 1954. Bar: Ohio bar 1955, Okla. bar 1963, U.S. Supreme Ct. bar 1974, Supreme Ct. Okla. bar 1963, Supreme Ct. Ohio bar 1955, U.S. Dist. Ct. Northeastern Dist. Okla. bar 1971. Claims atty. Ohio Farmers Ins. Cos., LeRoy, 1951-59; claims supr. Selman & Co., Tulsa, 1959-63; practiced in Tulsa, 1963-66; judge Common Pleas Ct., Tulsa, 1967-69, Dist. Ct., Tulsa, 1969-88. City solicitor City of Seville, Ohio, 1958-59; Trustee Bd. Pub. Affairs, LeRoy, 1957-59, Ct. Fund Trustees Tulsa County, 1971-74. Served with USNR, 1943-46. Lodge: Masons. Home: 2315 S Fulton Pl Tulsa OK 74114-3746

MARTIN, ROBERT LESLIE, physician; b. Abilene, Tex., Oct. 28, 1934; s. Leslie Resa and Garnet Iva (Brown) M. m. Henrietta Montgomery, 1956; children: Randal, Christopher. BA, U. Kans., 1956, MD, 1960. Diplomate in clin. pathology Am. Bd. Pathology; diplomate Nat. Bd. Med. Examiners; lic. physician, Calif., Fla. Intern U. Kans., 1960-61, resident and fellow in pathology, 1964-67; asst. prof. pathology Case We. Res. U., Cleve., 1967-78; dir. clin. labs. Univ. Hosps. of Cleve., 1972-76; assoc. prof. pathology U. South Fla., Tampa, 1978-82; chief clin. pathology James A. Haley Vets. Hosp., Tampa, 1978-82; project mgr. Scott Sci. & Tech., Albequerque, N.Mex., 1982-83; physician advisor Profl. Found. for Health Care Inc., Tampa, 1984-89; primary care physician Tampa, Fla., 1986—. Contbr. articles to profl. jours. Fellow Coll. Am. Pathologists; Alpha Omega Alpha, Phi Gamma Delta. Republican. Episcopalian. Home: 15840 Sanctuary Dr Tampa FL 33647

MARTIN, ROBERT RICHARD, emeritus college president, former senator; b. McKinney, Ky., Dec. 27, 1910; s. Henry Franklin and Annie Frances (Peek) M.; m. Anne French Hoge, May 31, 1952. AB, Eastern Ky. U., 1934; MA, U. Ky., 1940; EdD, Columbia U., 1951. Tchr., prin. pub. schs. Mason and Lee counties, Ky., 1935-48; with Ky. Dept. Edn., 1948-59, beginning as auditor, successively dir. finance, head bur. adminstrn. and finance, 1948-55, supt. pub. instrn., 1955-59; commr. finance Commonwealth Ky., 1959-60; pres. Eastern Ky. U., Richmond, 1960-76; pres. emeritus Eastern Ky. U., 1976—; mem. Ky. Senate, 1977-86; chmn. health and welfare com.; assisted devel. found. program for financing of edn. in Ky.; bd. dirs. Bank One; chmn. health and welfare com.; assisted devel. found. program for financing edn. in Ky. Bd. dirs. Pattie A. Clay Hosp., Telford Community Center, Ky. Diabetes Assn.; bd. mem. Ky. Cancer Commn.; bd. dirs. Jud. Form Retirement; hon. chmn. United Way Madison County, 1978—; trustee, elder Presbyn. ch. Tech. sgt. USAAF, 1942-46; meteorologist. Recipient Outstanding Alumnus award Eastern Ky. State Coll., 1966; named Kentuckian of Yr. Ky. Press Assn., 1964; recipient Service award Joint Alumni Council Ky., 1970, Civilian Service award Dept. Army, 1971; Danforth Found. grantee, 1971. Mem. NEA, Am. Assn. Sch. Adminstrs., English-Speaking Union, Civil War Roundtable (bd. dirs.), Ky. Hist. Soc. (pres. 1974—), Ky. Edn. Assn., Am. Assn. State Colls. and Univs. (pres. 1971-72), Phi Delta Kappa, Kappa Delta Pi. Democrat. Presbyterian. Lodge: Masons (Shriners), Rotary, Filson. Home: 300 Summit St Richmond KY 40475-2134

MARTIN, ROBERT WILLIAM, former utilities company executive; b. Toronto, Ont., Can., June 7, 1936; s. William George and Evelyn Irene (Phillips) M.; m. Patricia Lorraine Norris, June 27, 1959; children: Stephen Gregory, Robert Scott, Adrienne Christine Teron. B.A.Sc., U. Toronto, 1958. V.p. ops. Consumers Gas, Toronto, 1973-80, pres., dir., 1981-92, CEO, ret., 1981-92; chmn. Silcorp. Ltd.; bd. dirs. IPL Energy Inc., Cara Ops. Ltd., Peoples Jewellers Ltd., ACC TeleEnterprises Ltd., Reed Stenhouse Cos., Guildfarb Corp. Bd. dirs. York U.; campaign chmn. United Way Toronto, 1988; chmn. Toronto Symphony Orch.; pres. West Park Hosp. Found. Recipient Meritorious Svc. award U. Toronto, 1983. Mem. Assn. Profl. Engrs. Ont., Can. Gas Assn. (past chmn.), Ont. Natural Gas Assn. (past pres.), Mad River Golf Club, Mississauga Golf and Country Club, Toronto Club. Home: 118 Farnham Ave, Toronto, ON Canada MHW 1HH

MARTIN, ROBLEE BOETTCHER, retired cement manufacturing executive; b. St. Louis, Apr. 21, 1922; s. Henry W. and Esther (Boettcher) M.; m. Lillian Seegraves, July 15, 1940; children: Mary Katherine, Bruce Daniel, Amy Lee. B.S. in Chem. Engring., Columbia U., 1943, M.S. in Chem. Engring., 1947; D.Sc. in Bus. Adminstrn. (hon.), Cleary Coll., 1962. Prodn. supr. Monsanto Chem. Co., St. Louis, 1946-49; dir. research and devel. Miss. Lime Co., Ste. Genevieve, Mo., 1949-59; pres. Dundee Cement Co., Mich. 1959-69; v.p. Fruehauf Corp.; gen. mgr. (Fruehauf Bldgs. div.), Detroit, 1969-72; pres. Presidents Assn. div. Am. Mgmt. Assn., N.Y.C., 1972-74; pres. insulation div. Keene Corp., Princeton, N.J., 1974-76; chmn., chief exec. officer Keystone Cement Co., Bath, Pa., 1976-89, Giant Cement Co., Harleyville, S.C., 1985-89; sr. v.p., dir. Giant Group Ltd., Beverly Hills, Calif., 1985-89. Served to lt. (j.g.) USNR, 1944-46, PTO. Mem. Sigma Xi, Tau Beta Pi, Phi Lambda Upsilon. Baptist. Home: 2151 Palermo Pl Charleston SC 29406-9231

MARTIN, ROGER BOND, landscape architect, educator; b. Virginia, Minn., Nov. 23, 1936; s. Thomas George and Audrey (Bond) M.; m. Janis Ann Kloss, Aug. 11, 1962; children: Thomas, Stephen, Jonathan. BS with high distinction, U. Minn., 1958; M. Landscape Arch., Harvard U., 1961. Asst. prof. U. Calif.-Berkeley, 1964-66; assoc. prof. U. Minn., Mpls., 1966, prof., 1968—, chmn. dept. landscape architecture, 1966-77, 83-87, dir. grad. studies in landscape architecture, 1983-84, dir. undergrad. studies, 1987-94, dir. profl. studies, 1994—; owner Roger Martin & Assoc., site planners and landscape architects, Mpls., 1966-68; prin. InterDesign, Inc., Mpls. 1968-84, Martin & Pitz Assocs., Inc., 1984—; vis. prof. U. Melbourne, 1979-80. Prin. works include Minn. Zool. Gardens, 1978 (merit award Am. Soc. Landscape Archs. 1978), Mpls. Pky. Restorations, 1972-87 (merit award 1978, Minn. Classic award Am. Soc. Landscape Archs. 1994), South St. Paul Ctrl. Sq., 1978 (merit award 1978), Festival Park, Chisholm, Minn., 1986, Miss. Wildlife Refuge (visual image assessment merit award 1985), Nicollet Island Park (merit award 1989), Hennepin Avenue Master Plan, 1995 (merit award 1995). Recipient Fredrick Mann award for svc. to edn. U. Minn., 1990, Disting. Educator award Sigma Lambda Alpha, 1990; fellow Am. Acad. in Rome, 1962-64. Fellow Am. Soc. Landscape Archs. (pres. Minn. chpt. 1970-72, trustee 1980-84, nat. pres. 1987, chmn.-elect coun. fellows 1991, chmn. 1992-94, past chmn.-elect 1991, chmn. 1992-94, past chmn. 1992-94, Pub. Svc. award 1985); mem. Nat. Coun. Instrs. Landscape Architecture (pres. 1973-74), Can. Soc. Landscape Archs. (hon.). Home: 2912 45th Ave S Minneapolis MN 55406-1829 Office: Martin & Pitz Assocs Inc 1409 Willow St Minneapolis MN 55403-2249

MARTIN, ROGER HARRY, college president; b. N.Y.C., June 26, 1943; s. Edwin Diller and Emma (Neuenburg) M.; m. Susan Bradford, Aug. 29, 1970; children: Katherine R., Emily G. BA, Drew U., 1965; BD, Yale U., 1968, STM, 1969; DPhil, Oxford (Eng.) U., 1974. Program officer Edn. Incentive Program, N.Y.C., 1969-70; devel. officer NYU, 1970-71, 75-76; asst. dir. devel. Rensselaer Polytech Inst., Troy, N.Y., 1974-75; asst. prof. history, exec. asst. to pres. Middlebury (Vt.) Coll., 1976-80; assoc. dean Harvard Div. Sch., Cambridge, Mass., 1980-86; prof. history, pres. Moravian Coll., Bethlehem, Pa., 1986—. Author: Evangelicals United: Ecumenical Stirrings in Pre-Victorian Britain, 1795-1830, 1983. Chmn. bd. assocs. Yale Divinity Sch.; trustee Moravian Acad. Mem. Harvard Club (N.Y.C.), Saucon Valley Country Club. Mem. Soc. of Friends. Avocations: skiing, running. Home: Frueauff House 79 W Church St Bethlehem PA 18018-5821 Office: Moravian Coll Office of President 1200 Main St Bethlehem PA 18018-6650

MARTIN, ROGER JOHN, computer scientist, computer systems analyst; b. Ft. Atkinson, Iowa, Sept. 11, 1947; s. Raymond Charles and Linda R. (Kuennen) M.; m. Jane Degnan, Nov. 21, 1970; children: John, Kathryn, Susan, Jacquelyn. BS in Computer Sci., Iowa State U., 1969, MS in Computer Sci., 1971. Computer specialist Naval Ship R & D Ctr., Bethesda, Md., 1971-76; supervisory systems analyst Exec. Office of Pres., Washington, 1976-82; computer scientist, mgr. software engring. group Inst. for Computer Scis. and Tech., Nat. Inst. Standards and Tech., Washington, 1982-92, chief System and Software Technology Divsn., 1993—; program co-chmn. Conf. on Software Maintenance, 1985, gen. chair, 1987; gen. chair Computer Standards Conf. 1988. Coach soccer Montgomery County Recreation Dept., Rockville, Md., 1979-83; treas., del. Mill Creek Towne Elem. Sch. PTA, Rockville, 1981-84, pres. 1986-87; Magruder cluster PTA coordinator, 1984-86; leader Cub Scouts, Rockville, 1983-84, asst. scoutmaster troop, 1984-92. Recipient Outstanding Performance award Naval Ship R & D Ctr., 1976; Outstanding Performance award Exec. Office of Pres., 1979, Spl. Achievement award, 1981; cert. of recognition Nat. Bur. Standards, 1983; Dept. Commerce Bronze medal award, 1984, Silver Medal award, 1989. Mem. Assn. for Computing Machinery, IEEE Computer Soc. (chmn. working group on test methods for POSIX 1986-93, tech. com. on operating system steering com. on conformance testing 1989—, cert. recognition 1987, tech. com. on operating system project mgmt. com. 1991-93, Meritorious Svc. award 1991, Standards Medallion, 1992). Home: 7413 Cliffbourne Ct Rockville MD 20855-1101 Office: NIST/NCSL Sys and Software Tech Divsn Bldg 225 Rm B266 Gaithersburg MD 20899

MARTIN, RON, newspaper editor in chief. Editor Atlanta Journal-Constitution, Ga. Office: Atlanta Jour-Constn 72 Marietta St PO Box 4689 Atlanta GA 30302-5501*

MARTIN, RON, adult basic education coordinator, superintendent of schools, consultant, minister; b. Rock Island, Tenn., Aug. 5, 1942; s. Houston and Bernie (Gribble) M.; m. Carolyn J. Odineal, Oct. 5, 1969. AA, Freed-Hardeman Coll., Henderson, Tenn., 1963; BA with honor, David Lipscomb Coll., 1973; MEd with highest honors, Mid. Tenn. State U., 1983. Entered ministry Ch. of Christ, 1963. Cons. Tenn. Dept. Edn., Nashville, 1977-82; tchr. remedial reading Warren County Schs., McMinnville, Tenn., 1972-74, elem. prin., 1974-77; tchr. Warren County Schs., Viola, Tenn., 1981-82; asst. prin. sr. high sch. Warren County Schs., McMinnville, 1982-85, supt. schs., 1987-92, editor newsletter, 1989—; min. Bible tchr. Warren County Chs. of Christ, McMinnville, 1963—; announcer, news reporter Cumberland Valley Broadcasting, McMinnville, 1963-90. Vice chmn. Warren County Dem. com., 1984-86; mem. bd. rev. Eagle Scouts, Boy Scouts Am., McMinnville, 1986—; pres. Warren County Drug Task Force, 1987, 92. Named Young Educator of Yr., Warren County Jaycees, 1976, Leader of Yr., 4-H Club, Warren County, 1974-76, Leadership award Tenn. Acad. Sch. Leaders, 1983. Mem. NEA, ASCD, Am. Adult Edn. Coun., Nat. Assn. Secondary Sch. Prins., Nat. Adult Devel. Coun., Am. Assn. Sch. Adminstrs., Coun. Adult Basic Edn. (Southeastern regional rep. 1993-95, nat. sec. 1995), Tenn. Edn. Assn. (pres. 1995), Tenn. Adult Edn. Coun., Tenn. Literary Coun., Warren County Edn. Assn. (rep. assembly 1976, 83, Leadership award), Warren County Aviators and Navigators (sec.), Kiwanis (bd. dirs.), Kappa Delta Pi. Avocations: reading, working on community projects, visiting outstanding school systems, teaching young people, developing educational ideas. Home: 4200 Crisp Springs Rd Mc Minnville TN 37110-9056 Office: Warren County Schs 109 Lyon St Mc Minnville TN 37110-2545

MARTIN, RONALD LAVERN, physicist; b. Devereaux, Mich., Sept. 13, 1922; s. Frank Deforest and Marian Maude (Elmer) M.; m. Margaret M. Cooper, June 11, 1949; children: Diane, Karen, Terry, Lynn, Kim, Jill. Student, U. Mich., 1940-41; BS, US Naval Acad., 1944; MS in Physics, Mich. State U., 1948; PhD in Physics, U. Chgo. 1952. AEC doctoral fellow U. Chgo., 1952, rsch. assoc., 1952-53; rsch. assoc. Cornell U., 1953-56; staff mem. Bell Telephone Labs., Murray Hill, N.J., 1956-59; asst.

dept. head TRG, Inc., Syosset, L.I., 1959-62; assoc. dir. accelerator div. Argonne (Ill.) Nat. Lab., 1962-67, dir., 1967-79, rsch. mgr. heavy ion fusion, 1976-81; pres. Acctek Assoc. Inc., 1984—, Martin Energy System, Inc., 1990—; guest lectr. U. Ill., 1980. With USN, 1944-47. Recipient prize for math. VFW, 1944. Fellow Am. Phys. Soc.; mem. AAAS, IEEE. Rsch. on heavy ion fusion, 1976-81, proton radiography, 1974-76. Home: 901 S Kensington Ave La Grange IL 60525-2712 Office: 9700 Cass Ave Argonne IL 60439

MARTIN, ROSEMARY SCARBROUGH, public library administrator; b. Cumberland, Miss., Feb. 12, 1935; d. James Eurel Scarbrough and Jessie (Hood) Scarbrough Brooks; m. Tilden S. Holley, July 7, 1956 (div. Nov. 1962); m. Gary Frank Martin, Nov. 27, 1962; 1 child, Caitlin. B.S., Miss. Women's U., 1961; M.S.L.S., U. Wis., 1973. Asst. coordinator children's services Memphis Pub. Library, 1972-73, coordinator children's services, 1974-76; zone mgr. Dallas Pub. Library, 1977-78; dir. Central Ark. Library System, Little Rock, 1978—; trustee Amigos Bibliographic Council, Inc., Dallas, 1985—; treas. trustee Amigos Bibliographic Council, Inc., Dallas, 1987, 88, v.p. 1988—; mem. users council Online Computer Library Ctr., Inc., Columbus, Ohio, 1983-85, 86—. Mem. ALA (pub. library rep. 1987—), Pub. Library Assn. (rep. to ALA Coun. 1987-90), Ark. Library Assn. Democrat. Avocations: flower gardening; knitting; sewing; reading. Home: 556 E 5th Ave Lancaster OH 43130-3105 Office: Cen Ark Libr System 700 Louisiana St Little Rock AR 72201-4698

MARTIN, ROY BUTLER, JR., museum director, retired broker; b. Norfolk, Va., May 13, 1921; s. Roy Butler and Anne (Holman) M.; m. Louise Eggleston, Apr. 17, 1948; children: Roy Butler III, Anne Beverly Martin Sessoms. Student, William and Mary Coll., Norfolk, 1939-40; BS in Commerce, U. Va., 1943. Chmn. bd. Commonwealth Brokers Inc., 1955-88; mayor City of Norfolk, 1962-74; pres. Chrysler Mus., Norfolk, 1989—; pres. U.S. Conf. Mayors, Washington, 1973-74; trustee Sentara Health System. Chmn. Douglas MacArthur Found., 1963—, Civic Facilities Commn., Norfolk, 1986—; bd. dirs. Norfolk Forum; exec. com., pres. Va. Mcpl . League, 1968-69; past mem. Va. State Water Control Bd.; past mem. exec. com., adv. bd. Nat. League of Cities, com. on community devel., U.S. Conf. Mayors, Southeastern Va. Planning Dist. Commn; chmn. Southeastern Tidewater Area Manpower Planning System, Mayor's Youth Commn.; Gov.'s Com. on Youth; past bd. dirs. Norfolk Urban Coalition; past mem. VALC Zoning Procedures Com.; past bd. dirs. Norfolk Symphony Orch., Boys Club Norfolk, Old Dominion U. Edns. Found.; past mem. Norfolk Cerebral Palsy Tng. Ctr., vestry Ch. of Good Shepherd, Norfolk. Lt. USNR, 1943-46, USNR, 1948-52. Decorated officer in Order of the Crown (Belgium); recipient Outstanding Alumni award Old Dominion U., 1964, Sales of Yr. award Sales and Mktg. Club Tidewater, 1971, Meritorious Pub. Svc. citation Dept. Navy, 1974, Community Svc. award Jewish Community Ctr., 1974, Cert. Appreciation Va. Food Dealers Assn., 1974, Fall Guy award Saints and Sinners, 1974, Brotherhood award NCCJ, 1976. Mem. Norfolk Yacht and Country Club (pres. 1990-92), Va. Club (bd. dirs. 1991-93), Chi Phi, Alpha Kappa Psi. Episcopalian. Home: 1519 Commonwealth Ave Norfolk VA 23505

MARTIN, SAM See MOSKOWITZ, SAM

MARTIN, SAMUEL ELMO, linguistics educator; b. Pittsburg, Kans., Jan. 29, 1924. AB, U. Calif., 1947, AM, 1949; PhD, Yale U., 1950. Instr. to asst. prof. Japanese and Korean Yale U., New Haven, 1950-58, assoc. prof. Far Ea. linguistics, 1958-62, prof., 1962—, chmn. dept. East and South Asian langs., 1963-65; chmn. dept. linguistics Yale U., New Haven, Conn., 1966-80; vis. prof. Georgetown U., 1955, U. Mich., 1956, U. Alta. (Can.) 1959, U. Wash., 1962-63; vis. prof. linguistics and dir. Pacific and Asian Linguistics Inst. U. Hawaii, 1965-66; sec. com. Uralic and Altaic studies Am. Coun. Learned Socs., 1958-64. Author: Korean-English Dictionary, 1968, Beginning Korean, 1969, A Reference Grammar of Japanese, 1975, Advanced Japanese Conversation, 1976; contbr. articles to profl. publs. Mem. Linguistic Soc., Am. Am. Orient Soc., Assn. Asian Studies. Rsch. in phonemics, morphophonemics and hist. phonology of Japanese, Korean and Chinese. Office: Yale U Dept of Linguistics New Haven CT 06520

MARTIN, STANLEY A., lawyer; b. Logansport, Ind., Apr. 9, 1955; s. Richard James and Helen Elizabeth (Newburn) M.; m. Kellie Lea McCabe, Aug. 14, 1988. BS, MIT, 1977; JD, Boston Coll., 1984. Bar: Mass. 1985, U.S. Dist. Ct. Mass. 1985, U.S. Ct. Appeals (1st cir.) 1985, N.H. 1986, U.S. Dist. Ct. N.H. 1987. Prin. Stan Martin, Designer/Builder, Andover, Mass., 1977-84; assoc. Gadsby & Hannah, Boston, 1984-91, ptnr., 1992—; lectr. Northeastern Univ., Boston, 1989—. Author: Mechanic's Liens, Performance and Payment Bonds under Massachusetts Law, 1989, 3d rev. edition 1992; co-author: Architect-Engineer Liability under Massachusetts Law, 1985, 5th rev. edition 1990; contbr. articles to profl. jours. Bd. dirs. Andover Com./A Better Chance-ABC, 1981-84. Mem. ABA (pub. contract sect., chair region I 1990—), Am. Arbitration Assn. Constrn. Industry Panel, Mass. Bar Assn. (chair pub. law sect. 1993-94), Internat. Bar Assn., N.H. Bar Assn. Home: 13 Brown St Andover MA 01810-5302 Office: Gadsby & Hannah 125 Summer St Ste 1500 Boston MA 02110-1620

MARTIN, STEPHEN JAMES, lawyer; b. Montclair, N.J., Mar. 20, 1930; s. Willis Elwin and Katherine Elizabeth M.; m. Kathleen Ellen Lyons, May 10, 1958; children: Christopher John, Therese Marie. Ph.B., U. Notre Dame, 1951; J.D., Mich., 1954; LL.M., NYU, 1959. Bar: Mich. 1954, Calif. 1960; diplomate: CPA-CA, Calif. Mem. pub. acctg. staff Touche, Ross, Bailey & Smart, Detroit, 1954-58; assoc. Pillsbury, Madison & Sutro, San Francisco, 1959-66, ptnr., 1965—. Contbr. articles to profl. jours. Mem. ABA (sect. taxation council 1981-83), State Bar Calif., Am. Bar Found., Am. Coll. Tax Counsel, Am. Inst. C.P.A.s, Calif. Soc. C.P.A.s. Clubs: San Francisco (sec.-treas.) (1982-83); World Trade (San Francisco), Bankers (San Francisco). Home: 60 Denise Dr Burlingame CA 94010-7150 Office: Pillsbury Madison & Sutro 225 Bush St San Francisco CA 94104-4207

MARTIN, STEVE, comedian, actor; b. Waco, Tex., 1945; s. Glenn and Mary Lee Martin; m. Victoria Tennant, Nov. 20, 1986 (div. 1994). Student, Long Beach State Coll., UCLA. Exec. prodr. TV show Domestic Life, 1984. TV writer for Smothers Bros. (co-winner Emmy award 1969), Sonny and Cher, Pat Paulsen, Ray Stevens, Dick Van Dyke, John Denver, Glen Campbell; nightclub comedian; guest and host appearances NBC's Saturday Night Live, Tonight Show; appeared on Carol Burnett Show; starred in TV spls. Steve Martin: A Wild and Crazy Guy, 1978, Comedy is Not Pretty, 1980, Steve Martin's Best Show Ever, 1981; rec. comedy albums Let's Get Small, 1977 (Grammy award 1977), A Wild and Crazy Guy, 1978 (Grammy award 1978), Comedy is Not Pretty, 1979, The Steve Martin Brothers, 1982; actor, screenwriter (films) The Absent Minded Waiter, 1977 (Academy award nomination best short film 1977), The Jerk, 1979, Pennies From Heaven, 1981, Dead Men Don't Wear Plaid, 1982, The Man With Two Brains, 1983, All of Me, 1984 (Nat. Soc. Film Critics award best actor 1984, New York Film Critics' Circle award best actor 1984), Three Amigos, 1986, Roxanne, 1987, (Nat. Soc. Film Critics award best actor 1986, Los Angeles Film Critics' award best actor 1988), L.A. Story, 1991; actor (films) Sergeant Pepper's Lonely Hearts Club Band, 1978, The Muppet Movie, 1979, The Kids Are Alright, 1979, The Lonely Guy, 1984, Little Shop of Horrors, 1986, Planes, Trains and Automobiles, 1987, Dirty Rotten Scoundrels, 1988, Parenthood, 1989, My Blue Heaven, 1990, Father of the Bride, 1991, Grand Canyon, 1991, Housesitter, 1992, Leap of Faith, 1993, Mixed Nuts, 1994, Twist of Fate, 1994; (theatre) Waiting For Godot, 1988; (television) And the Band Played On, 1993; screenwriter (films) Easy Money, 1983; author Cruel Shoes, 1977; playwright Picasso at the Lapin Agile, 1993. Recipient Georgie award Am. Guild Variety Artists 1977, 78; Grammy award 1978. Office: care ICM 8942 Wilshire Blvd Beverly Hills CA 90211 also: Rogers & Cowan c/o Michelle Bega 1888 Century Park E # 500 Los Angeles CA 90067

MARTIN, SUSAN KATHERINE, librarian; b. Cambridge, Eng., Nov. 14, 1942; came to U.S., 1950, naturalized, 1961; d. Egon and Jolan (Schonfeld) Orowan; m. David S. Martin, June 30, 1962. BA with honors, Tufts U., 1963; MS, Simmons Coll., 1965; PhD, U. Calif., Berkeley, 1983. Intern libr. Harvard U., Cambridge, Mass., 1963-65, systems libr., 1965-73; head systems office gen. libr. U. Calif., Berkeley, 1973-79; dir. Milton S. Eisenhower Libr. Johns Hopkins U., Balt., 1979-88, exec. dir. Nat. Commn. on Libraries and Info. Sci., 1988-90; univ. libr. Georgetown U., Washington, 1990—;

mem. libr. adv. com. Princeton (N.J.) U., 1987—; mem. vis. com. Harvard U. Libr., 1987-93, 94—; bd. overseers for univ. libr. Tufts U., 1986—; mem. libr. adv. com. Hong Kong U. Sci. Tech., 1988—; mem. acad. libr. adv. group U. Md. sch. of Librs. and Info. Sci., 1994—; cons. to various librs. and info. cos., 1975—; mem. adv. bd. ERIC, 1990-92, History Assocs., Inc., 1990-92. Author: Library Networks; Libraries in Partnership, 1986-87; editor; Jour. Libr. Automation, 1972-77; mem. editorial bd. Advanced Tech./Librs., 1973-93, Jour. Libr. Adminstrn., 1986—, Libr. Hi-Tech., 1989-93, Jour. Acad. Librarianship, 1994—; contbr. articles to profl. jours. Trustee Phila. Area Libr. Network, 1980-81; bd. dirs. Universal Serials and Book Exch., 1981-82, v.p., 1983, pres., 1984; trustee Capital Consortium, 1992-95. Recipient Simmons Coll. Disting. Alumni award, 1977; Council on Library Resources fellow, 1973. Mem. ALA (coun. 1988-92), Rsch. Librs. Group (gov., exec. com. 1985-87), Libr. and Info. Tech. Assn. (pres. 1978-79), Assn. Rsch. Librs., Libr. of Congress (optical disk pilot project adv. com. 1985-89), Coalition for Networked Info. (leader working group 1990-92), Assn. Coll. and Rsch. Librs. (pres. 1994-95), Cosmos Club, Grolier Club, Phi Beta Kappa. Home: 4709 Blagden Ter NW Washington DC 20011-3719 Office: Georgetown U Lauinger Libr Washington DC 20057

MARTIN, SUSAN TAYLOR, newspaper editor; b. N.Y.C., Aug. 3, 1949; d. Lewis Randolph and Carolyn Emmons (Douthat) Taylor; m. James Addison Martin Jr., Nov. 15, 1975; 1 child, Steven Randolph. BA in Polit. Sci., Duke U., 1971. Reporter Ft. Myers (Fla.) News Press, 1972-75, Tampa (Fla.) Tribune, 1975-77, Associated Press, Detroit, 1977-78; bur. chief Detroit News, 1978-81; asst. city editor Orlando (Fla.) Sentinel, 1981-82; exec. bus. editor St. Petersburg (Fla.) Times, 1982-86, city editor, 1986-87, nat. corr., 1987-91, asst. mng. editor, 1991-93, dep. mng. editor, 1993—. Trustee Poynter Fund, St. Petersburg, 1992—. Recipient Non-Deadline Reporting award Soc. Profl. Journalists, 1990, Investigative Reporting award, 1991, Feature, Depth Reporting award Fla. Soc. Newspaper Editors, 1990, Depth Reporting award, 1991. Mem. Suncoast Figure Skating Club. Democrat. Episcopalian. Avocations: figure skating, travel, antiques, reading. Home: 1312 51st Ave NE Saint Petersburg FL 33703 Office: St Petersburg Times 490 1st Ave S Saint Petersburg FL 33731

MARTIN, SUZANNE CAROLE, health facility administrator; b. Columbus, Ohio, Aug. 29, 1945; d. John Fredrick and Clairmae (Kelley) Belknap; m. Daniel C. Martin, Mar. 16, 1968 (div. Apr. 1974); m. Richard Wayne Shadburn, Sept. 10, 1986. Diploma in nursing, Mount Carmel Sch. Nursing, Columbus, Ohio, 1977; BA in Sociology, Ohio Dominican Coll., 1976; JD cum laude, Capital U., 1983. Bar: Ohio 1983. From staff nurse to unit dir., med. dir. medicine Mount Carmel Med. Ctr., Columbus, 1966-77; dir. nursing McNamara-Mercy Hosp., Fairplay, Colo., 1977-78; staff nurse Nurse Pro Nurses Registry, San Diego, 1978-80; from dir. ambulatory care to asst. v.p., quality assurance to v.p. quality, utilization and risk mgmt. to v.p. patient care svcs. Mount Carmel Med. Ctr., Columbus, 1981-92; sr. cons. Deloitte & Touche, 1992-93; v.p. patient care svcs. Santa Rosa Health Care, San Antonio, 1993—; bd. dirs. United Ostomy Assn. Ctrl. Ohio, Columbus; com. mem. Franklinton Health Ctr., Columbus, 1985-92; mem. ethics com. Cath. Conf., Columbus, 1989-92; lectr. various group and orgns. on nursing and legal aspects. Mem. Columbus Zoo, 1990-93, Friends of Sta. WOSU, Columbus, 1990-93. Mem. Am. Acad. Hosp. Attys., Am. Soc. Hosp. Risk Mgrs.; Am. Orgn. Nurse Execs., Ohio Soc. Nurse Execs., Ohio Soc. Risk Mgrs., Wilderness Soc., Mount Carmel Alumni Assn., Capital U. Alumni Assn. Roman Catholic. Home: 20210 Bat Cave Rd Garden Ridge TX 78266-2300 Office: Santa Rosa Health Care 519 W Houston St San Antonio TX 78207-3108

MARTIN, SUZANNE GABRIELLE, health facility administrator; b. Phila., Mar. 24, 1954; d. George Thomas and Patricia Ann (Connor) M.; m. John Earl Forgione, Oct. 21, 1978. BS in Psychology, St. Josephs U., 1977, MS in Health Adminstrn., 1982; postgrad., Immaculata Coll., 1992—. Unit mgr. Albert Einstein Med. Ctr., Phila., 1981-84, dir. unit mgmt., 1984-87, dir. adminstrv. svcs., 1989—; adminstr. emergency svcs. U. Pa., Phila., 1987-89. Mem. Am. Hosp. Assn., Greater Phila. Health Assembly, Am. Psychol Assn. (student mem.), Phila. Soc. of Clin. Psychologists (student mem.). Democrat. Roman Catholic. Home: 1 E Windermere Ter Lansdowne PA 19050 Office: Albert Einstein Med Ctr 5501 Old York Rd Philadelphia PA 19141-3098

MARTIN, THEODORE KRINN, former university administrator (deceased); b. Blue Mountain, Miss., Jan. 2, 1915; s. Thomas Theodore and Ivy (Manning) M.; m. Lorene Garrison, Sept. 6, 1947; children: Glenn Krinn, Mary Ann, Janet Kay. A.B., Georgetown (Ky.) Coll., 1935; M.A., La. State U., 1941; Ph.D., George Peabody Coll., 1949. Tchr. Consol. Sch., Dumas, Miss., 1935-36; prin. Mississippi Heights Acad., 1936-39; tchr. Murphy High Sch., Mobile, Ala., 1940-41; registrar Miss. State U., 1949-53, registrar, adminstrv. asst. to pres., 1953-56, dean Sch. Edn., 1956-61, exec. asst. to pres., 1961-66, v.p., 1966-85, dir. Summer Sch., 1956-70, ret., 1985. Served as capt. AUS, 1941-46. Mem. Masons, Kappa Alpha, Phi Kappa Phi, Omicron Delta Kappa, Kappa Delta Pi, Phi Delta Kappa. Home: 1151 East Dr Starkville MS 39759-9216

MARTIN, THOMAS E., motel chain executive; b. Jackson, Mich., Apr. 13, 1942; s. Clarence A. and Olive Martin; m. Maureen D. Hunt, Feb. 7, 1975; 1 child, Anne Marie; children by previous marriage: Julie, Laurie, Kathy, Cindy. BS in Acctg., Mich. State U., 1964; MBA, Western Mich. U., 1971. Cert. mgmt. acct. Jr. acct. Ernst & Ernst, Grand Rapids, Mich., 1964; various acctg. positions Consumers Power Co., Jackson, 1965-69, mgr. acctg., 1969-73; dir. acctg. Ramada Inns, Inc., Phoenix, 1973-75, domestic controller, 1975-76, v.p., controller, 1976-79, sr. v.p., chief fin. officer, 1979-82, exec. v.p. fin. and adminstrn., from 1982, now exec. v.p. restaurants, 1979-90, also dir., until 1990; pres., dir. Elsinore Corp., Las Vegas, 1990—; pres. Four Queens Inc., Las Vegas, 1993—. Mem. minority relations com. Dean's Council of 100, Ariz. State U.; bd. dirs., mem. fin. and long range planning coms. Ariz. Zool. Soc. Mem. Nat. Assn. Accts., Am. Mgmt. Assn., Inst. Mgmt. Acctg. (bd. regents, chmn. examination policy com.), Fin. Execs. Inst., Beta Alpha Psi. Office: Four Queens Inc 202 Fremont St Las Vegas NV 89101

MARTIN, THOMAS LYLE, JR., university president; b. Memphis, Sept. 26, 1921; s. Thomas Lyle and Malvina (Rucks) M.; m. Helene Hartley, June 12, 1943 (dec. Sept. 1983); children: Michele Marie, Thomas Lyle; m. Mildred L. Moore, June 5, 1984. B.E.E., Rensselaer Poly. Inst., 1942, M.E.E., 1948, D.Eng., 1967; Ph.D., Stanford U., 1951. Prof. elec. engring. U. N.Mex., 1948-53; prof. engring. U. Ariz., 1953-63, dean engring., 1958-63; dean engring. U. Fla., Gainesville, 1963-66, So. Meth. U., Dallas, 1966-74; pres. Ill. Inst. Tech., Chgo., 1974-87, pres. emeritus, 1987—; bd. dirs. Cherry Corp. Capt. Signal Corps AUS, 1944-46. Fellow IEEE; mem. Nat. Acad. Engring. Home and Office: PO Box 167845 Irving TX 75016-7845

MARTIN, THOMAS STEPHEN, lawyer; b. N.Y.C., Aug. 31, 1946; s. Stephen Paul and Kathleen Mary (Redmond) M.; m. Lynne Kathryn Mallory, Oct. 2, 1968; children: Laura Kathryn, Mallory Anne. B.A. maxima cum laude, King's Coll., 1968; J.D., U. Chgo., 1972. Bar: D.C. 1973. Assoc. Steptoe & Johnson, Washington, 1972-75; spl. asst. to asst. atty. gen., civil div. Dept. Justice, Washington, 1975-76, asst. to solicitor gen., 1976-78, dep. asst. atty. gen. civil div., 1978-80, acting asst. atty. gen. civil div., 1981-82; ptnr. Venable, Baetjer, Howard & Civiletti, Washington, 1982-83, Jenner & Block, Washington, 1983-90, Shearman & Sterling, Washington, 1990—; mem. adv. com. fed. rules of civil procedure, 1980-84; chmn. com. admissions and grievances U.S. Ct. Appeals (D.C. cir.), 1991—. Comment editor: U. Chgo. Law Rev., 1971-72. Mem. D.C. Bar Assn., Am. Law Inst. Office: Shearman & Sterling 801 Pennsylvania Ave NW Washington DC 20004

MARTIN, TONY, foundation administrator; b. Oklahoma City, Feb. 27, 1953; s. Tony Jr. and Rebecca (Yargee) M.; m. Sherry Jean Berryhill, Oct. 12, 1952. Respiratory therapist Okmulgee (Okla.) Meml. Hosp., 1980-82, Creek Nation, Okemeh, Okla., 1986-88; mgr. smoke shop Okemeh Indian Comty., 1990-94; archivist, rschr. Kialegee Tribal Town, Wetumka, Okla, 1994, acting adminstr., 1994—. Town king Kialegee Tribal Town, Wetumka, 1991—; 1st warrior, 1991-92. Avocation: tracing history of Kialegee Tribal Town. Office: Kialegee Tribal Town 318 S Wahita PO Box 332 Wetumka OK 74883

MARTIN, VERNON EMIL, librarian; b. Guthrie, Okla., Dec. 15, 1929; s. Vernon E. Sr. and Marian (Brandon) M.; m. Arlan Stone, June 30, 1956 (div. 1977); children: Vernon Martin III, Jeffrey Martin; m. Elizabeth Jean Chapin, June 16, 1979; 1 child, Amy Chapin Hathaway. MA in Music, Columbia U., 1959, MS in Libr., 1965. Libr. Lincoln Ctr. Libr. Mus., N.Y.C., 1964-66; music libr. North Tex. State U., Denton, 1966-70; dir. Morningside Coll., Sioux City, Iowa, 1970-74; head art dept. Hartford (Conn.) Pub. Libr., 1974-93, ret., 1993. Composer operas including Ladies Voices, 1956, Waiting For the Barbarians, 1956, Fables By Thurber, 1986. CHmn. Cultural Affairs Commn., Hartford, 1984-86. Mem. ASCAP (Standard award 1969-72). Home: 7 Tamarack Dr Bloomfield CT 06002-3022

MARTIN, VINCENT FRANCIS, JR., real estate investment executive; b. Waterbury, Conn., Oct. 20, 1941; s. Vincent Francis and Mary Elizabeth (Fugilese) M.; m. Kathy Sue Plummer, May 26, 1979; children: Christopher, Paige, Vincent Francis III. B.S., Boston Coll., 1963; M.B.A., Harvard U., 1968. Auditor, Peat Marwick Mitchell, Waterbury, 1964-65; exec. v.p. EFM, Inc., Boston, 1968-70, Coldwell Banker, Los Angeles, 1970-82; mng. ptnr. TCW Realty Advisors, Los Angeles, 1982—. Bd. dirs. Nat. Realty com., Los Angeles Entrepreneur Acad. Author articles in fin. jours. Active Lowman Club, Los Angeles. Mem. Urban Land Inst., Soc. Rev. Appraisers (sr.), Internat. Found. Employee Benefit Plans, Pension Real Estate Assn. (bd. dirs.), Nat. Realty Com. Roman Catholic. Clubs: Jonathan, Los Angeles Athletic. Home: 1551 Sorrento Dr Pacific Palisades CA 90272-2746 Office: TCW Realty Advisors 865 S Figueroa St Ste 3500 Los Angeles CA 90017-5447

MARTIN, VINCENT GEORGE, management consultant; b. N.Y.C., Feb. 9, 1922; s. Joseph R. and Mae B. (Mulligan) M.; m. Alice Ann McGovern, June 8, 1946; children—Kathleen (Mrs. Michael Greiner), Joseph F. Student, Pace Coll., 1948-49, Am. Internat. Coll., 1950. Salesman Lavigna Jewels, N.Y.C., 1945-47; indsl. engr. Barton Watchase Mfg., N.Y.C., 1948-49; office procedures Local Loan Co., N.Y.C., 1950-51; sr. time study engr. Perkins Machine & Gear Co., West Springfield, Mass., 1951-52; with Milton Bradley Co., East Longmeadow, Mass., 1952-79; mgr. mfg. Milton Bradley Co., 1962-64, v.p. mfg., 1964-69, exec. v.p., 1969—, dir., 1971—, gen. mgr., 1972-79; with Vincent G. Martin Assos. (Mgmt. Consultants), 1979—; trustee Springfield Inst. for Savs., 1978-81; dir. Armoury Corp., Stockbridge Corp., 1978-80. Past pres. Springfield Speech and Hearing Center; mem. East Longmeadow Indsl. Park Steering Com.; gen. campaign chmn. United Fund Pioneer Valley, 1976; bd. dirs. Springfield Symphony Orch.; operator Springfield Coll., 1976-79, Wesson Meml. Hosp., 1976-80. Served with AUS, 1942-45. Decorated Bronze Star. Mem. Soc. Advancement Mgmt. (pres. Western Mass. chpt. 1954-56), Am. Mgmt. Assn., Toy Mfrs. Am. (dir. 1973-75), Springfield C. of C. (dir. 1974-78), Newcomen Soc. N.Am., East Longmeadow C. of C. (pres., dir. 1965-68). Club: Rotarian (dir. 1970-72). Office: 8 Flume Ave PO Box 505 Marstons Mills MA 02648

MARTIN, VINCENT LIONEL, manufacturing company executive; b. Los Angles, June 29, 1939; s. Arthur Seymon and Alice Maria (Miller) M.; m. Janet Ann Dowler, Mar. 25, 1961; children: Jennifer Lynn, Karen Arlene, Timothy Paul. B.S., Stanford U., 1960; M.B.A., Harvard U., 1963. Various staff positions FMC Corp, Chgo, 1966-74; gen. mgr. Crane and Excavator div. FMC Corp, Cedar Rapids, Iowa, 1974-79; pres. Equipment Systems div. AMCA Internat. Corp., Houston, 1979-81; group v.p. AMCA Internat. Corp., Brookfield, Wis., 1981-85; pres. Jason Inc., Milw., 1986—. Mem. Phi Beta Kappa, Tau Beta Pi. Republican. Presbyterian. Home: 9440 N Range Line Rd Milwaukee WI 53217-2861 Office: Jason Inc 411 E Wisconsin Ave Milwaukee WI 53202-4409

MARTIN, W. TERRY, librarian; b. Tuscaloosa, Ala., Sept. 5, 1948; s. W. Harry and Eleanor (Ambrose) M.; m. Carol Prewitt, May 25, 1973; 1 child, W. Brian. AB, Samford U., 1970; MA, SAmford U., 1977; MLS, U. Ala. 1973. Libr. tech. svcs. Samford U., Birmingham, Ala., 1973-79; circulation and tech. svcs. libr. Southeastern Bapt. Theol. Sem., Wake Forest, N.C., 1979-85; dir. libr. svcs. Georgetown (Ky.) Coll., 1985-93; dir. libr. La. Coll., Pineville, 1993—. Contbr. articles to profl. jours. Mem. So. Bapt. Libr. Assn. (pres. 1990-91), Ky. Libr. Assn., Southeastern Libr. Assn., La. Libr. Assn. Baptist. Avocations: camping, travel, genealogy, local history. Office: La Coll Coll Station Norton Libr Pineville LA 71359

MARTIN, WALTER EDWIN, biology educator; b. DeKalb, Ill., Jan. 14, 1908; s. Walter Sylvester and Tillie Lula (Secora) M.; m. Ruth Virginia Butler, June 16, 1934; children: Carol Ann, John Walter, Judith Kathryn, David Butler. B.E., No. Ill. State Tchrs. Coll., 1930; M.S., Purdue U., 1932, Ph.D., 1937. Asst. Purdue U., 1930-34, instr., 1934-37; instr. No. Ill. State Tchrs. Coll., summers 1930-31; mem. sci. exped. Honduras, summer 1934; mem. staff Marine Biol. Lab., summers 1935-42; asst. prof. DePauw U., 1937-41, assoc. prof., 1941-46, prof., 1946-47; assoc. prof. U. So. Calif., 1947-48, prof., 1948—, head zoology dept., 1948-54, head biology dept., 1954-58; naval technician to Egypt, summer 1953, 55, Japan, Taiwan and Philippines, 1957; sabbatical leave Marine Lab., U. Hawaii, 1956-57; sabbatical year Neuchatel, Switzerland, 1963-64, U. Queensland, Brisbane, Australia, 1970-71. Fellow Ind. Acad. Sci., AAAS, So. Calif. Acad. Sci.; mem. Am. Soc. Zoologists, Am. Soc. Parasitologists, Am. Micros. Soc., Western Soc. Naturalists, Phi Sigma, Alpha Epsilon Delta. Home: 2185 Warmouth St San Pedro CA 90732-4530 Office: U of Southern California Los Angeles CA 90007

MARTIN, WILFRED WESLEY FINNY, psychologist, property owner and manager; b. Rock Lake, N.D., Dec. 3, 1917; s. William Isaac and Anna Liisa (Hendrickson-Juntunen) M.; m. Stella Helland, Sept. 25, 1943; children: Sydney Wayne, William Allan. BA, Jamestown Coll., 1940; army specialized tng. program, Hamilton Coll., 1944; MS, EdD, U. So. Calif., 1956. Highsch. prin., coach pub. sch., Nekoma, N.D., 1940-42; contact rep., psychologist VA, L.A., 1946-49, psychologist, chief rehab., 1972-77; from intern to resident Fargo (N.D.) VA Hosp., 1953-58; guidance dir., instr. Concordia Coll., Moorhead, Minn., 1951-53; psychologist VA, Fargo, N.D., 1953-57; assoc. Rsch. Assoc./IBM, Boulder, Colo., 1957-65; regional dir. Sci. Rsch. Assoc./IBM, L.A., 1966-72; owner, mgr. Martin Investments, Huntington Beach, Calif., 1977—; adjutant U. Miss., Oxford, 1942; trustee Wilfred W. and Stella Martin Trust, Huntington Beach, 1991. Author: Veterans Administration Work Simplification, 1948, 57. Charter mem. Rep. Presdl. Task Force, 1980; adv. sr. ptnrs. bd. dirs. U. Calif. Med. Sch., Irvine, 1990; donor Dr. and Mrs. W.W. Martin Endowment, Jamestown Coll., N.D., 1985. With U.S. Army, 1942-45. Mem. Am. Psychol. Assn., Cardinal & Gold U. So. Calif., Jamestown Coll. Heritage Circle (charter), Suomi Coll. Second Century Soc., Elks. Republican. Lutheran. Avocations: reading, Finnish heritage, swimming, sports, card playing. Home: PO Box 5445 Huntington Beach CA 92615

MARTIN, WILLIAM AUBERT, law association executive, lawyer, retired air force officer; b. Warren, Ark., Dec. 7, 1931; s. Aubert and Anna Christine (Joiner) M.; m. Mary Lou Mauderly, Mar. 31, 1963; children: Kathryn G., Karen E., Michael W. J.D., U. Ariz., 1955; MBA., Ariz. State U., 1969. Bar: Ark. 1955. Commd. 2d lt. U.S. Air Force, 1955, advanced through grades to col.; chief claims and tort litigation div., U.S. Air Force Hdqrs., Washington, 1973-77; staff judge adv. Oklahoma City Air Logistics Ctr., Tinker AFB, Okla., 1977-79, Hdqrs. 5th Air Force, Yokota AFB, Tokyo, 1979-81, Hdqrs. Air Tng. Command, Randolph AFB, Tex., 1981-83; ret. 1983; exec. dir. Ark. Bar Assn., Little Rock, 1983—. Treas. Ark. Iolta Found., Inc.; trustee Nat. Conf. Bar Founds. Mem. ABA, Ark. Bar Assn., Fed. Bar Assn., Pulaski County Bar Assn., Judge Advocates Assn, Am. Soc. Assn. Execs., Ark. Alumni Assn. (meas. capital chpt.), Rotary. Methodist. Office: Ark Bar Assn 400 W Markham St Little Rock AR 72201-1408

MARTIN, WILLIAM EDWIN, government official; b. Bowling Green, Ky., Oct. 16, 1943; s. John Edwin and Bess Carolyn (Matherly) M.; children: Anne Whitson, William Whitson; m. Jean Clinton Nelson, Aug. 1, 1981. BA, Vanderbilt U., 1965, JD, 1968. Bar: Tenn. 1968. Ptnr. Waller Lansden Dortch & Davis, Nashville, 1968-75; sr. ptnr. Harwell Martin & Stegall, Nashville, 1975-93; dep. asst. sec. for internat. affairs U.S. Dept. Commerce-NOAA, Washington, 1993—. Contbr. articles to newspapers and law revs. Dir. polar programs Wilderness Soc., Washington, 1990-92; pres.

Environ. Action Fund, Nashville, 1982; bd. dirs. Tenn. Environ. Coun., Nashville, 1992, So. Appalachian Highland Conservancy, Johnson City, Tenn., 1988-90. Mem. Nashville Bar Assn. (bd. dirs. 1979-80). Democrat. Episcopalian. Avocations: mountain climbing, photography, running, tennis. Office: Nat Oceanic and Atmospheric Admn 14th & Constitution Ave NW Washington DC 20230

MARTIN, WILLIAM GIESE, lawyer; b. Canton, Ohio, Nov. 4, 1934; s. George Denman and Emily (Giese) M.; m. Martha Justice, June 14, 1958; children: William E.J., Peter J.D., George F.D. BA, Yale U., 1956; LLB, Harvard U., 1959. Bar: Ohio 1959, U.S. Dist. Ct. (so. dist.) Ohio 1963. Assoc. Porter, Stanley, Treffinger & Platt, Columbus, Ohio, 1963-68; ptnr. Porter, Wright, Morris & Arthur, Columbus, 1968—. Lt. USNR, 1959-63. Mem. ABA, Ohio State Bar Assn., Columbus Bar Assn., Capital Club, Rocky Fork Hunt and Country Club, Yale Club of N.Y. Home: 6169 Havens Corners Rd Blacklick OH 43004-9676 Office: Porter Wright Morris & Arthur 41 S High St Columbus OH 43215-6101

MARTIN, WILLIAM ROYALL, JR., association executive; b. Raleigh, N.C., Sept. 3, 1926; s. William Royall and Edith Ruth (Crocker) M.; m. Betty Anne Rader, June 14, 1952; children: Sallie Rader Martin Busby, Amy Kemp Martin Bass. AB, U. N.C., 1948, MBA, 1964; BS, N.C. State U., 1952. Chemist Stamford (Conn.) rsch. labs. Am. Cyanamid Co., 1952-54; chemist Dan River Mills, Danville, Va., 1954-56, Union Carbide Corp., South Charleston, W.Va., 1956-59; rsch. assoc. Sch. Textiles N.C. State U. 1959-63; tech. dir. Am. Assn. Textile Chemists and Colorists, Research Triangle Park, N.C., 1963-73, exec. dir., 1974—; adj. assist. prof. Coll. Textiles, N.C. State U., 1966-88, adj. assoc. prof., 1989—; del. Internat. Orgn. Standardization, Pan Am. Standards Commn. With USNR, 1944-46. Fellow Am. Inst. Chemists, Soc. Dyers and Colourists, Textile Inst.; mem. Am. Chem. Soc., Coun. Engring. and Sci. Soc. Execs. (past pres. 1992-93), Fiber Soc., Am. Assn. Textile Chemists and Colorists, Masons, Rotary, Phi Kappa Phi, Phi Gamma Delta. Methodist. Home: 224 Briarcliff Ln Cary NC 27511-3901 Office: AATCC PO Box 12215 Research Triangle Park NC 27709

MARTIN, WILLIAM RUSSELL, nuclear engineering educator; b. Flint, Mich., June 2, 1945; s. Carl Marcus and Audrey Winifred (Rosene) M.; m. Patricia Ann Williams, Aug. 13, 1967; children: Amy Leigh, Jonathn William. B.S.E. in Engring. U. Mich., 1967; MS in Physics, U. Wis., 1968; M.S.E. in Nuclear Engring., U. Mich., 1975, PhD in Nuclear Engring., 1976. Prin. physicist Combustion Engring., Inc., Windsor, Conn., 1976-77; asst. prof. nuclear engring. U. Mich., Ann Arbor, 1977-81, assoc. prof. nuclear engring., 1981-88, prof. nuclear engring., 1988—; dir. lab. for sci. computation, 1986—, chmn. nuclear engring., 1990-94, assoc. dean acad. affairs, 1994—; cons. Lawrence Livermore Nat. Lab., Livermore, Calif., 1982—, Los Alamos (N.Mex.) Nat. Lab., 1980-89, IBM, Inc., Kingston, N.Y., 1984, Rockwell Internat., Pitts., 1985. Author: Transport Theory, 1979; author tech. and conf. papers. Recipient Glenn Murphy award Am. Soc. for Engring. Edn., 1993; Disting. scholar U. Mich. Coll. Engring., 1967; vis. fellow Royal Soc., London, 1989. Mem. Am. Nuclear Soc., Am. Phys. Soc., Soc. for Indsl. and Applied Math., IEEE. Avocations: running, reading, skiing, sailing. Home: 1701 Crestland St Ann Arbor MI 48104-6329 Office: U Mich Dept Nuclear Engring Ann Arbor MI 48109

MARTIN, WILLIAM TRUETT, oral surgeon, state legislature; b. Throckmorton, Tex., Oct. 23, 1924; s. Olin O. and Marie (Gautier) M.; m. C. Maxine Almond, Aug. 31, 1946; children: Dawne, Sally, William C. BS, North Tex. State U., 1947; DDS, U. Mo., Kansas City, 1952; MS in Oral Surgery, U. Iowa, 1959. Diplomate Am. Bd. Oral and Maxillofacial Surgery. Pvt. practice, Warrensburg, Mo., 1952-56; resident in oral surgery U. Iowa, Iowa City, 1956-59; pvt. practice oral surgery, Colorado Springs, Colo. 1959-88; mem. Colo. Ho. of Reps., Denver, 1988—. 1st lt., pilot USAAF, 1942-45. Fellow Am. Assn. Oral and Maxillofacial Surgeons, Am. Coll. Dentists, Internat. Coll. Dentists; mem. ADA, Colo. Dental Assn. (pres. 1984). Republican. Avocations: golf, tennis, flying, fishing. Office: Colo Ho of Reps State Capital Denver CO 80203

MARTIN, WILLIE PAULINE, elementary school educator, illustrator; b. Pendleton, Tex., May 27, 1920; d. Lester B. and Stella (Smith) M.; m. Charles M., June 23, 1946; 1 child, Charles Jr. BS, Middle Tenn. State U., Murfreesboro, 1944; MS, U. Tenn., 1965; postgrad., U. Ga., 1980. Cert. tchr., Tenn., Tex., Ga. Elem. tchr. Bd. Edn., Sparta, Tenn., 1940-44; home econs. tchr. Bd. Edn., Salado, Tex., 1944-46; rsch. technician Oak Ridge (Tenn.) Nat. Lab., 1946-50; art, gen. sci. tchr. Bd. Edn., State of Tenn., 1965-69; art, reading, elem. tchr. Bd. Edn., State of Ga., 1970-83; elem. tchr. Bd. Edn., Augusta, Ga., 1984-86; tchr. aerospace edn. workshop Middle Tenn. State U., 1969; spkr. in field. Contbr. articles in field to profl. jours. Exhibitor Oak Ridge (Tenn.) Festival. Mem. Nat. Art Edn. Assn. (del. conv. Washington 1989, Balt. 1994), Ga. Art Edn. Assn. (del. state conv. dist. pres. 1974, del. conv. Savannah 1986, Augusta 1993, del. state conv. Athens 1994), Tenn. Edn. Assn. Methodist. Avocations: art, crafts, music, singing, reading. Home: 1406 Flowing Wells Augusta GA 30909

MARTIN, WINN FARRAR, banking executive; b. Birmingham, July 29, 1939; s. Winn Edwin Martin; m. Kathryn Bohnert Stovall, July 29, 1961 (div. Sept. 1969); children: John, Kathryn; m. Patricia Van Wezel, Mar. 15, 1971; children: Winn, David. BSEE, Mass. Inst. Tech., 1962; MBA, U Pa., 1964. Data processing salesman IBM, Atlanta, 1964-66; cons. Arthur Young & Co., N.Y.C., 1966-68; owner Winn F. Martin & Assocs., Atlanta, 1969-71; sys. mgr. Bendix Home Sys., Inc., Atlanta, 1971-74; mgmt. cons. Price, Waterhouse & Co., Memphis, 1975-77; CEO, chmn. Southland Bank, Dothan, Ala., 1977—; lectr. Ga. Inst. Tech., Atlanta, 1970-71, Troy State U., Dothan, 1993—. Vice chmn. Lakeside Sch. bd. trustees, Eufaula, Ala., 1982; chmn. Barbour County Sch. Bd., Clayton, Ala., 1979-81; sys. mgr. Rep. Nat. Com., Washington, 1968. Methodist. Avocation: tennis. Home: 117 Lakeview Ln Headland AL 36345 Office: Southland Bank 3299 Ross Clark Cir NW Dothan AL 36303

MARTIN-BOWEN, (CAROLE) LINDSEY, freelance writer; b. Kansas City, Kans., Aug. 4, 1949; d. Lawrence Richard and V. Marie (Schaffer) Pickett; m. Frederick E. Nicholson, July 3, 1971 (div. 1977); 1 child, Aaron Frederick; m. Edwin L. Martin, June 18, 1980 (div. 1987); 1 child, Ki Elise; m. Michael L. Bowen, Dec. 23, 1988. BA in English Lit., U. Mo., Kansas City, 1972, MA in English and Creative Writing, 1988, postgrad., 1991—. Tech. editor Office Hearings and Appeals, U.S. Dept. Interior, Washington, 1976-77; reporter, photographer Louisville Times, 1982-83; reporter, features editor Sun Newspapers, Overland Park, Kans., 1983-84; assoc. editor Modern Jeweler, Overland Park and N.Y.C., 1984-85; writer Coll. Blvd. News, Overland Park, 1985-89, KC View, Kansas City, Mo., 1988-89; editor Number One, Kansas City, Mo., 1986-88, cons., 1988-89; copywriter Sta KXEO/KWWR Radio, Mexico, Mo., 1989; editorial asst. New Letters, 1985—; features writer, columnist The Squire, Prairie Village, Kans., 1990—; instr. English U. Mo., Kansas City, 1986-88, Johnson County C.C., 1988—; tchr. English and fiction Longview C.C., 1988—; instr. writing and mass comm. Webster U., 1990—; instr. world lit., women in lit. and creative writing Penn Valley C.C., 1993—; faculty sponsor The Penn (Penn Valley C.C. lit. mag.); owner, writer Paladin Freelance Writing Svc., Kansas City, 1988—; prodn. editor, staff writer Nat. Paralegal Reporter, 1992—; judge New Letters lit. mag. writing contest, 1987—. Author: (novel) The Dark Horse Waits in Boulder, 1985, (poetry) Waiting for the Wake-Up Call, 1990, Second Touch, 1990, (fiction) Cicada Grove and Other Stories, 1992; contbr. poems, book revs., features, cartoon artwork, and photographs to numerous publs. including New Letters, Lip Service and Contemporary Lit. Criticism. Campaigner McGovern for Pres. Campaign, Kansas City, 1971-72. Regents scholar, 1967; GAF fellow, 1986. Mem. U. Mo.-Kansas City Alumni Assn. (media com. 1983-84), Phi Kappa Phi. Roman Catholic. Avocations: acrylic and oil painting, downhill skiing, music, Greek cooking, paralegal work. Home: 7109 Pennsylvania Ave Kansas City MO 64114-1316 Office: Penn Valley CC 3201 Southwest Trafficway Kansas City MO 64111-2764

MARTINDALE, CATHERINE ANN, editor; b. Dayton, Ohio, Nov. 9, 1946; d. Belden Dewitt and Ruth Elizabeth (Milas) M.; m. John D. Felton, Apr. 1972 (div. Aug. 1977); m. Dave C. Wohlfarth, May 3, 1991. BS in Journalism, Ohio U., 1969. Reporter, city editor, copy editor Dayton (Ohio) Jour. Herald, 1969-83; copy desk chief Fla. Times-Union, Jacksonville, 1983-

86, Wichita (Kans.) Eagle, 1986-88; exec. editor Amarillo (Tex.) Globe-News, 1988—; bd. dirs. Freedom of Info. Found. of Tex., Dallas, 1989—. Bd. dirs. United Way, Amarillo, 1991—, Winners Circle Equitherapy, 1991—. Recipient Career Achievement award Amarillo Womens Network, 1989. Mem. Nat. Cutting Horse Assn., Panhandle Press Assn. (bd. dirs. 1990—). Amarillo Exec. Women. Avocation: showcutting horses. Office: Amarillo Globe-News 900 S Van Buren St Amarillo TX 79101-3330

MARTINDALE, LARRY, hotel executive. BS in Bus. Adminstrn., U. Miss. Divsn. mgr. Waffle House Restaurants, Inc.; with W.B. Johnson Properties, 1976-78; pres. Northlake Foods subs W.B. Johnson Properties, 1978-84, J.P. Hotels subs W.B. Johnson Properties, 1984-86; exec. v.p., Coo Ritz Carlton Hotel Co. subs. W.B. Johnson Properties, 1986-88, vice chmn., 1988—. With USMC. Office: The Ritz-Carlton Hotel Co 3414 Peachtree Rd NE Atlanta GA 30326

MARTINEN, JOHN A., travel company executive; b. Sault St. Marie, Mich., June 26, 1938; s. John Albert and Ina Helia (Jarvi) M.; B.S. with highest honors, Mich. State U., 1960; LL.B., N.Y.U., 1963. With Grace Line, N.Y.C., 1963-69; cons. Empresa Turistica Internat., Galapagos Cruises, Quito, Ecuador, 1969-70; regional mgr. Globus & Cosmos (Group Voyagers Inc.), N.Y.C., 1971-73, v.p., 1974-76, exec. v.p., 1977-78, pres., CEO, 1979-92, Littleton, Colo., 1993—. Bd. dirs. Colo. Fedn. Arts. Mem. U.S. Tour Operators Assn. (bd. dirs.), Am. Soc. Travel Agts., Tour Operator Plan Com. (bd. dirs.), Denver Acad. Travel & Tourism, Lotos, Sky and Wings Club (N.Y.), Columbine Country Club, Denver Athletic Club. Democrat. Home: 1450 Wynkoop St Denver CO 80202-1116 Office: 5301 S Federal Cir Littleton CO 80123-2980

MARTINES, LAURO, historian, writer; b. Chgo., Nov. 22, 1927; m. Julia O'Faolain, Nov. 20, 1957; 1 child, Lucien. A.B., Drake U., 1950; Ph.D., Harvard, 1960. Asst. prof. history Reed Coll., 1958-62; fellow Villa I Tatti, Harvard Center for Italian Renaissance Studies, Florence, Italy, 1962-65; prof. history UCLA, 1966-92; vis. prof. Warburg Inst., U. London, 1985; vis. dir. studies Ecole des Hautes Etudes en Sces Sociales, Paris, spring 1992, 94. Author: The Social World of the Florentine Humanists, 1963, Lawyers and Statecraft in Renaissance Florence, 1968, Power and Imagination: City-States in Renaissance Italy, 1979, Society and History in English Renaissance Verse, 1985, An Italian Renaissance Sextet: Six Tales in Historical Context, 1994; co-author: Not in God's Image: Women in Western Civilization, 1973; Editor: Violence and Civil Disorder in Italian Cities 1200-1500, 1972. Served with AUS, 1945-47. Fellowships include Am. Council Learned Socs., 1962-63, Harvard U. Ctr. Italian Renaissance Studies, Villa i Tatti, Florence, Italy, 1962-65, Guggenheim Meml. Found. 1964-65;, sr. fellow Nat. Endowment for Humanities, 1971, 78-79; resident fellow Rockefeller Found. Bellagio Ctr., Italy, 1990. Fellow Mediaeval Acad. Am., Italian Deputation for History Tuscany (fgn.); mem. Am. Hist. Assn., Renaissance Soc. Am. Home: 8 Gloucester Crescent, London NW1 7DS, England

MARTINEZ, AL, journalist, screenwriter; b. Oakland, Calif., July 21, 1929; s. Alfredo Martinez and Mary (Larragoite) Lehmann; m. Joanne Cinelli, July 30, 1949; children: Cinthia, Linda, Allen. Student. San Francisco State U., 1949-50, U. Calif., Berkeley, 1952-53, Contra Costa Jr. Coll., Walnut Creek, Calif., 1953-54. Reporter, feature writer Richmond (Calif.) Ind ., 1952-55; reporter, feature writer Oakland Tribune, 1955-71, columnist, 1963-71; profilist, feature writer L.A. Times, 1972-84, columnist, 1984—; screenwriter CBS, ABC, NBC, L.A., 1975—; tech. advisor Lou Grant TV Series, CBS, Los Angeles, 1979-80. Author: Rising Voices, 1974, Jigsaw John, 1976, Ashes in the Rain, 1989, Dancing Under the Moon, 1992, Rising Voices: A New Generation, 1993, City of Angels, 1995; screenwriter TV movie That Secret Sunday, 1988, Out on the Edge, 1990 (nominated for Emmy Best Screenplay 1990), other TV movies, pilots, 1975—. Recipient Nat. Headliner award Atlantic City Press Club, 1987, 88, Best Columnist award Nat. Soc. News Columnist, St. Louis, 1986, Pulitzer prize (shared Gold medal to L.A. Times) Columbia U., 1984, Nat. Ernie Pyle award, 1991. Mem. PEN, Writers Guild Am. Office: Los Angeles Times Editorial Dept Times Mirror Sq Los Angeles CA 90053

MARTINEZ, ALBERT, computer peripherals company executive; b. Ft. Benning, Ga., Aug. 9, 1945; s. Seledon and Josephine (Martinez) M.; m. Gay Hugo, July 14, 1990; children: Katherine, Naomi. BS in Math., No. Ariz. U., 1967; BSEE, Ariz. State U., 1969, MSEE, 1974, postgrad., 1975. Reliability engr. Motorola, Mesa, Ariz., 1969-70, design engr., 1970-73, product engring. mgr., 1973-75, product mgr., 1975-77, ops. mgr., 1977-80; v.p. Burr-Brown, Tucson, 1980-82, exec. v.p. and chief oper. officer, 1982-86; v.p., gen. mgr. TRW-LSI, San Diego, 1986-87; pres., chief exec. officer Applied Micro Circuits Corp., San Diego, 1987—; bd. dirs. Micro Chip, Phoenix, 1990—. Bd. dirs. U. Calif. Cancer Ctr., San Diego. Roman Catholic. Avocations: bicycling, motorcycle riding. Office: Applied Micro Circuits Corp 6195 Lusk Blvd San Diego CA 92121-2793

MARTINEZ, ANDREW TREDWAY, lawyer; b. New Orleans, Oct. 24, 1930; s. Andrew Richmond and Mary Leslie (Tredway) M.; m. Margaret Leslie Buchan, June 7, 1952; children: Andrew, Leslie, Margaret. BA, Tulane U., 1952, LLB, 1956. Bar: La. 1956, U.S. Dist. Ct. (ea. dist.) La. 1956, U.S. Ct. Appeals (5th cir.) 1962, U.S. Supreme Ct. 1971. Ptnr. Terriberry, Carroll and Yancey, New Orleans, 1956—. Assoc. editor Am. Maritime Cases, 1989—; adv. editor Tulane Maritime Jour., 1976—. Lt. (j.g.) USN, 1952-54. Mem. ABA, Maritime Law Assn. U.S. Assoc. Average Adjusters U.S., La. Bar Assn., New Orleans Bar Assn. Home: 1500 Jefferson Ave New Orleans LA 70115-4121 Office: Terriberry Carroll Yancey 3100 Energy Ctr New Orleans LA 70163

MARTINEZ, ARTHUR C., retail company executive; b. N.Y.C., Sept. 25, 1939; s. Arthur F. and Agnes (Caulfield) M.; m. Elizabeth Rusch, July 30, 1966; children: Lauren, Gregory. BSME, Polytech. U., 1960; MBA, Harvard U., 1965. Dir. planning Internat. Paper Co., N.Y.C., 1967-69; asst. to pres. Talley Industries, Mesa, Ariz., 1969-70; dir. fin. RCA Corp., N.Y.C., 1970-73, v.p., 1973-80; sr. v.p., CFO Saks Fifth Ave., N.Y.C., 1980-84, exec. v.p., 1984-87, vice chmn., 1990-92; sr. v.p. Batus Inc., Louisville, 1987-90; chmn., CEO Sears Merchandise Group, Chgo., 1992—; bd. dirs. Sears, Roebuck and Co., Sprout Venture Capital Group, N.Y.C., 1987—. Bd. dirs. Defenders of Wildlife, 1992—; chmn. bd. trustees Polytech. U., 1990—, chmn. devel. com. 1st lt. U.S. Army, 1961-63. Mem. Nat. Retail Fedn. (bd. dirs.). Avocations: tennis, golf, gardening. Home: 1420 Lake Shore Dr Chicago IL 60611-2601 Office: Sears Merchandise Group 3333 Beverly Rd Hoffman Estates IL 60179-0002

MARTINEZ, ARTURO, newspaper editor. Entertainment editor The Star-Ledger, Newark. Office: The Star-Ledger One Star Ledger Plz Newark NJ 07102-1200*

MARTINEZ, EDGAR, professional baseball player; b. N.Y.C., Jan. 2, 1963. Student, American Coll., Puerto Rico. Baseball player Seattle Mariners, 1987—. Named: to Am. League All-Star Team, 1992, Am. League Silver Slugger Team, 1992. Am. League Batting Champion, 1992. Office: Seattle Mariners PO Box 4100 411 1st Ave S Seattle WA 98104*

MARTINEZ, GUSTAVE See SOLOMONS, GUS, JR.

MARTINEZ, HERMINIA S., banker, economist; b. Havana, Cuba; came to U.S., 1960, naturalized, 1972; d. Carlos and Amelia (Santana) Martinez Sanchez; B.A. in Econs. cum laude, Am. U., 1965; M.S. in Fgn. Service (Univ. fellow), M.S. in Econs., Georgetown U., 1967, PhD in Econs., 1969; postgrad. Nat. U. Mex. Instr. econs. George Mason Coll., U. Va., Fairfax, 1967-68; researcher World Bank, 1967-69, indsl. economist, industrialization div., 1969-71, loan officer, Central Am., 1971-79, loan officer, economist, Mex., 1973-74, Venezuela and Ecuador, 1973-77, sr. loan officer in charge of Panama and Dominican Republic, Washington, 1977-81, sr. loan officer for Middle East and North Africa, 1981-84, sr. loan officer for Western Africa region, 1985-87, sr. economist Africa Region, 1988-91, prin. ops. officer Africa region, 1991—. Mid-Career fellow Princeton U., 1988-89. Mem. Am. Econ. Assn., Soc. Internat. Devel., Brookings Inst. Latin Am. Study Group. Roman Catholic. Contbg. author: The Economic Growth of Colombia:

Problems and Prospects, 1973. Home and Office: 5145 Yuma St NW Washington DC 20016-4336

MARTINEZ, JULIO J., chemical company executive; b. 1932; came to U.S., 1961; With Chemtex Inc., Old Greenwich, Conn., 1961-89; with Chemtex Internat., N.Y.C., 1989—, pres., CEO. Office: Chemtex Internat Inc 560 Lexington Ave New York NY 10022

MARTINEZ, JULIO J., mayor; b. Havana, Cuba, June 26, 1965; m. Diane Rhodes, 1965; children: Christopher, Jennifer, Sean, Jo Ellen. USAF Inst., 1962, Ft. Lauderdale Bus. Coll., 1971. With J and H Aluminum Products, 1971-90; owner Julio Martinez Boxing Promotions, 1982-85; with East Side Boxing Gym, 1982-85; councilman City of Hialeah, Fla., 1989-90, mayor, 1990—. With US Army, 1961-67. Recipient Pub. Ofcl. Of Month award Spotlite Club, 1986. Mem. Dade County League of Cities, Hialeah-Miami Springs C. of C. (past dir.), Latin C. of C. (past dir.), Miami Lakes Jaycees (past v.p., 19th dist. progress of yr. award), Am. legion Post 229 (past vice comdr.), Half Track Conservation Club (mem. of yr. award, 1987-88, legislator of yr. award, 1988-89), Palm Springs Optimists, Hialeah Old Town Optimists (past pres.). Office: Office of Mayor 501 Palm Ave Hialeah FL 33010-4719

MARTÍNEZ, LUÍS OSVALDO, radiologist, educator; b. Havana, Cuba, Nov. 27, 1927; came to U.S., 1962, naturalized, 1967; s. Osvaldo and Felicita (Farinas) M.; children: Maria Elena, Luis Osvaldo, Alberto Luis; m. Nydia M. Ceballos. MD, U. Havana, 1954. Intern Calixto García Hosp., Havana, 1954-55; resident in radiology Jackson Meml. Hosp., Miami, Fla., 1963-65, fellow in cardiovascular radiology, 1965-67; instr. radiology U. Miami, 1965-68, asst. prof., clin. asst. prof., 1968-70, assoc. prof., 1970-76, prof., 1976-91, clin. prof., 1991-94; chief radiol. svcs. VA Med. Ctr., 1991—; assoc. dir. dept. radiology Mt. Sinai Med. Ctr., Miami Beach, Fla., 1969-91, chief div. diagnostic radiology, 1970-91, dir. residency program in diagnostic radiology; dir. Spanish Radiology Seminar. Reviewer Am. Jour. Radiology, Radium Therapy and Nuclear Medicine, 1978; contbr. articles to profl. jours. Former pres. League Against Cancer. Recipient Medaille Antoine Beclere ICR-89, 1989, Carlos J. Finlay Gold medal Cuban Med. Congress in Exile, 1990. Mem. AMA, AAUP, Radiol. Soc. France (hon. 1991), Internat. Soc. Lymphology, Interam. Coll. Radiology (pres.), Internat. Coll. Surgeons, Internat. Coll. Angiology, Internat. Soc. Radiology, Interam. Coll. Radiology (Gold medal 1975), Cuban Med. Assn. in Exile, Am. Coll. Chest Physicians (assoc.), Radiol. Soc. N.Am., Am. Coll. Radiology, Am. Roentgen Ray Soc., Am. Assn. Fgn. Med. Grads., Am. Profl. Practice Assn., Am. Thoracic Soc., Pan Am. Med. Assn., Am. Assn. Univ. Radiologists, Brit. Inst. Radiology, Am. Heart Assn. (mem. council cardiovascular radiology), Faculty Radiologists, Soc. Gastrointestinal Radiologists, Am. Geriatrics Soc., Am. Coll. Angiology, Royal Coll. Radiologists, Am. Soc. Therapeutic Radiologists, Assn. Hosp. Med. Edn., Am. Coll. Med. Imaging, Interasma, So. Med. Assn., N.Y. Acad. Scis., Fla. Thoracic Soc., Fla. Radiol. Soc., Dade County Med. Assn., Greater Miami Radiol. Soc., Cuban Radiol. Soc. (sec.), Can. Assn. Radiologists, Soc. Thoracic Radiologists (founding mem.), Emeritus mem., Am. Coll. of Angiology, 1989, Emeritus mem., Am. Heart Assn., 1992; hon. mem. numerous med. socs. of Mex., Cen. and S.Am. Roman Catholic. Office: 1201 NW 16th St Miami FL 33125-1624

MARTINEZ, MATTHEW GILBERT, congressman; b. Walsenburg, Colo., Feb. 14, 1929; children: Matthew, Diane, Susan, Michael, Carol Ann. Cert of competence, Los Angeles Trade Tech. Sch., 1959. Small businessman and bldg. contractor; mem. 97th-103rd Congresses from 30th (now 31st) Calif. dist., 1982—; mem. edn. and labor com., fgn. affairs com. Mem. Monterey Park Planning Commn. 1971-74; mayor City of Monterey Park, 1974-75; mem. Monterey Park City Council, 1974-80, Calif. State Assembly, 1980-82; bd. dirs. San Gabriel Valley YMCA. Served with USMC, 1947-50. Mem. Congl. Hispanic Caucus, Hispanic Am. Democrats, Nat. Assn. Latino Elected and Apptd. Ofcls., Communications Workers Am., VFW, Am. Legion, Latin Bus. Assn., Monterey Park C. of C., Navy League (dir.). Democrat. Lodge: Rotary. Office: US Ho of Reps 2239 Rayburn House Ofc Washington DC 20515

MARTINEZ, PETE R., beverage company executive; b. San Antonio, July 8, 1937; m. Aurora Valadez; children: Shirley Jeanne, Peter Roland, Frieda Ann, Ruben Jay and Lynn Virginia (twins). A in Mgmt., San Antonio Coll., 1974. Various positions Coca-Cola Bottling Co. of S.W., San Antonio, 1952-79, v.p., 1979, BEVTEX gen. mgr., 1979-84, spl. events/concessions/youth market depts. mgr., 1984-86, spl. events/concessions/ice/youth market/cold drink telephone sales and cooler depts. mgr., 1986-87, v.p. govt. and cmty. rels., 1987—; chmn. U.S. Hispanic Bus. Bilateral Commn. on Free Trade Agreement, 1990—. Vol. United Way San Antonio, 1979, bd. dirs. 1989-94; mem. adv. com. San Antonio Coll. Mgmt. 1984-91; bd. dirs. Leukemia Soc. Am., 1985, v.p., 1986, pres. S.W. Tex. chpt., 1987, 88, 89; chmn. nat. hispanic leukemia televent, 1990, treas., 1990-91, nat. bd. trustee class A, 1988-92; bd. dirs. Goodwill Industries of San Antonio, 1985-90, vice chmn., 1991-94; bd. dirs. Jr. Achievement South Tex., 1985-94, chmn., 1995, Keep San Antonio Beautiful, 1987-94, chmn. legis. com., 1990, chmn. found. bd. dirs. Alamo Cmty. Coll. Dist., 1985, 94, vice chmn., 1986-94; commr. San Antonio Fiesta Commn./Ann. Fiesta Week, 1986-91, v.p., chmn. pub. rels. com., 1989, mem. exec. bd. presdl. appointee, 1990, mem. exec. bd. treas. and chmn. finance com., 1991, mem. exec. bd. sr. v.p-chmn., 1992, mem. pers. com., pres. 1993, mem. exec. bd. cmty. rels. and nominating com., 1994; mem. distribution com. San Antonio Area Found., 1985-92, treas. exec. com., 1994; so. sector task force chmn. City of San Antonio, 1985-86, bd. dirs. Citizens for Dome, 1988-89, bd. dirs. Inst. Ams.; mem. fgn. trade and transp. com. San Antonio Target Commn. 1983-84; mem. awards selection panel J.C. Penny Golden Rule Awards, Bexar County, Tex., 1988, 89; bd. dirs. North San Antonio Chamber, 1988-91, vice chmn. cmty. devel., 1989, 91, YMCA of San Antonio & Hill Country, 1989-90, vice chmn. pub. policy 1990, vice chmn. bd. devel., 1991, vice chmn. ptnrs. in youth 1992-94, bd. chmn. 1993, 94; mem. pub. policy com. YMCA of Tex., 1989-94, bd. dirs. YMCA of U.S.A., 1994; Assumption Sem. Press area chmn. Papal Visit Pope John Paul II, 1989; mem. corporate adv. coun. to sch. bd. Ursuline Acad., 1989-91. Recipient Leadership award Jr. Achievement San Antonio, 1989, Corporate Sponsor of Yr. award Keep San Antonio Beautiful, 1989. Mem. San Antonio Mex.-Am. Profl. Men's Assn. (bd. dirs. 1985, 86, v.p. 1987), U.S. Hispanic C. of C. (bd. dirs. 1980, mem. adv. bd. 1981, Member of Yr. award 1984, Corporate Advocate of Yr. award 1990), Tex. Assn. Mex. C. of C. (San Antonio rep. 1976-92, chmn. conv. 1980, 92, state chmn. bd. dirs. 1980-81, 86-87, 87-88, spl. advisor to chmn. 89-92, Press award 1980), San Antonio Hispanic C. of C. (bd. dirs. 1975-77, 81, 82, 84, 1st v.p. 1978, 3d v.p. 1979, 2nd v.p. 1980, co-chmn. conv. 1985, 86, adv. to chmn. bd. dirs. 1987-91, bd. historian 1992), Greater San Antonio C. of C. (mem. Internat./Mex. Day Stock Show com. 1976-93, chmn. com. 1980-85, mem. steering com. exec. devel coun. 1980, 81. Office: Coca-Cola Bottling Co SW 1 Coca Cola Pl San Antonio TX 78219-3712

MARTINEZ, RAUL L., mayor, publisher; b. Santiago, Oriente, Cuba, Mar. 6, 1949; came to U.S., 1960; s. Chin and Aida Martinez; m. Angela Callava, Jan. 10, 1970; children—Aida, Raul. AA, Miami Dade Coll.; BS in Criminal Justice, Fla. Internat. U., Miami. Pub., founder El Sol de Hialeah, Fla., 1969—; mem. city council City of Hialeah, 1977-81, mayor, 1981—; Mem. Dem. Policy Commn.'s Roundtable on Defense and Fgn. Policy, State Comprehensive Plan Com., Dade Clean Inc.; past vice chmn. Beacon Council; chmn. Dade County Council Mayors, So. Fla. Employment and Tng. Consortium, Hialeah Dade Devel. Inc.; bd. dirs. Hialeah Pk. racecourse; mem. franchise and environ. rev. com. High Speed Rail, 1987; mem. Gov.'s Commn. on Statewide Prosecution Function, 1984-85, Fla. State Commn. on Hispanic Affairs, 1979-82;pres. Fla. League of Cities. Mem. Dade County Assn. Chiefs Police, Little Havana Nutrition and Activities Ctr., State Fla. Planning Commn., United Way of Dade County (community devel. com.), Little Havana Activity Ctrs. Commn., St. John Home Health Care Inc.; adv. bd. Barry U.; hon. adviser Miami Dade Community Coll., North Campus-Hialeah Ctr. Fedn. Hispanic Students; chmn. So. Mcpl. Conf.; bd. dirs. Nat. League of Cities; former pres. Fla. League of Cities. Recipient Legion of Honor award, 1977, Citizen Involvement award Crime Commn. of Greater Miami, 1977, Over the Top award Hialeah-Miami Springs YMCA, 1979, Pub. Adminstr. of Yr. award South Fla. chpt. Am. Soc. Pub. Adminstrn., 1984. Mem. U.S. Conf. of Mayors, Hialeah-Miami Springs-N.W. Dade Area C. of C., Nat. League Cities, Fla.

League Cities (pres.), Dade County League (past. pres.), Hialeah Latin C. of C., Kiwanis. Lodge: Kiwanis. Office: City of Hialeah 501 Palm Ave Hialeah FL 33010-4719

MARTINEZ, ROMAN, IV, financial executive; b. Santiago, Cuba, Dec. 29, 1947; came to U.S., 1960, naturalized, 1971; s. Roman and Virginia G. (Gomez) M.; B.S., Boston Coll., 1969; MBA, U. Pa., 1971; m. Helena Hackley, Dec. 20, 1974; children—Roman, Helena Catalina. Asso., Kuhn Loeb & Co., N.Y.C., 1971-73, v.p., 1974-77; corp. v.p. Lehman Bros. Kuhn Loeb Inc., N.Y.C., 1977, mng. dir., 1978-84; mng. dir. Lehman Bros. (formerly Shearson Lehman Bros. Inc.), N.Y.C., 1984—. Republican. Roman Catholic. Clubs: Racquet and Tennis, Links, River, Piping Rock. Home: 555 Park Ave New York NY 10021-8166 Office: Lehman Bros 3 World Fin Ctr New York NY 10285

MARTINEZ, WALTER BALDOMERO, architect; b. Havana, Cuba, Sept. 21, 1937; came to U.S., 1961; s. Baldomerò and Maria J. Amparo (Rodriguez) M.; m. Olga Justa Sardina, July 23, 1961; children: Teresita Maria, Gabriel Jose. Cert. in civil constrn., Arts and Craft Vocat. Sch., Havana, 1957; student Sch. Architecture, U. Havana, 1958-60, U. Miami, 1963-64; cert. fallout shelter analyst, U. Miami, 1970. Registered architect, Fla.; cert. gen. contractor, Fla. Job capt. Tony Sherman Architect, Miami, Fla., 1961-63; project mgr. Ken Miller Architect, Miami, 1968-69; designer, project mgr. Russell-Melton & Assocs., Miami, 1969-70; head archtl. dept. Sanders & Thomas, Miami, 1971-72; assoc. Russell-Wooster & Assoc., Miami, 1973-77; prin. Russell-Martinez & Holt, Miami, 1977-84; prin., pres. The Russell Partnership, Miami, 1985—. Contbr. articles to Constrn. mag. Bd. dirs. Biscayne Nature Ctr., Miami, 1982—; vice chmn. Latin Quarters Rev. Bd., Miami, 1989. Fellow AIA (nat. chmn. minority resources com. 1985, pres. Miami chpt. 1982, Silver medal 1981); mem. Nat. Assn. Cuban Architects (bd. dirs. Miami chpt. 1986-87, Gold medal 1984), Latin Builders Assn., Fla. Bd. Architects (chmn. 1991), NCARB, Greater Miami C. of C. (Hispanic affairs com. 1988-93, chmn. affordable housing com. 1989), Nat. Architectural Accrediting Bd., Inc. (accreditation team mem. 1992-94). Republican. Roman Catholic. Avocations: boating, photography. Home: 223 Grand Canal Dr Miami FL 33144-2529 Office: Russell Partnership Inc 2733 SW 3rd Ave Miami FL 33129-2330

MARTINEZ-CARRION, MARINO, biochemist, educator; b. Felix, Almeria, Spain, Dec. 2, 1936; came to U.S., 1957; naturalized, 1961.; s. Juan Martinez and Maria Carrion; m. Ana J. Iriarte, Apr. 20, 1987; children: Victoria, Marino Juan. BA, U. Calif, Berkeley, 1959, MA, 1961, PhD, 1964. NIH postdoctoral fellow U. Rome, 1964-65; asst. prof. U. Notre Dame, Ind., 1965-68, 1968-74, prof., 1974-77; chmn. Va. Commonwealth U., Richmond, 1977-86; dean Sch. Biol. Sci. U. Mo., Kansas City, 1986—; dir. Ctr. for Innovative Tech. Inst. Biotech., Richmond, 1984-86; chmn. biophys. chemistry study sect. NIH, Washington, 1977-82; mem. cell neurobiol. panel NSF, Washington, 1985-89. Contbr. numerous articles on biochem. subjects to profl. jours.; mem. Jour. Protein Chemistry; mem. editorial bd. Archives Biochemistry and Biophysics, Jour. Biol. Chemistry. Rsch. grantee NIH, 1965—, NSF, 1974—, Am. Heart Assn., 1974-77, career devel. grantee NIH, 1972-77. Fellow N.Y. Acad. Scis.; mem. Am. Chem. Soc., Am. Soc. Biochemistry and Molecular Biology, Pan Am. Assn. Biochem. Socs. (treas. 1987-90, vice chmn. 1990-93, chmn. 1993—), Internat. Soc. Neurochemistry, Biophys. Soc. Democrat. Roman Catholic. Office: U Mo Sch Biol Scis Kansas City MO 64110

MARTINEZ-MALDONADO, MANUEL, medical service administrator, physician; b. Yauco, P.R., Aug. 25, 1937; s. Manuel Martinez and Josefa Maldonado; m. Nivia Elena Rivera, Dec. 18, 1959; children: Manuel, David, Ricardo, Pablo. BS, U. P.R., 1957; MD, Temple U., 1961. Diplomate Am. Bd. Internal Medicine (assoc. mem. nephrology com. 1982-86), Am. Bd. Nephrology. Intern St. Charles Hosp., Toledo, 1961-62; resident VA Hosp., San Juan, PR, 1962-65, chief resident, 1964-65; instr. U. Tex. Southwestern Med. Sch., Dallas, 1967-68; asst. prof. medicine Baylor Coll. Medicine, Houston, 1968-71, assoc. prof. medicine, 1971-73, prof. medicine, dir. renal sect., 1973; prof. medicine U. P.R. Sch. Medicine, 1973-90, prof. physiology, 1974-90; prof. medicine U. Caribbean, Bayamon, P.R., 1980-90; chief med. services VA Hosp., San Juan, P.R., 1973-90; dir. renal metabolic lab VA Hosp., San Juan, PR, 1973-90; prof., vice chmn. dept. medicine Emory U. Sch. Medicine, 1990—; chief med. svc. Atlanta VA Hosp.; mem. nat. adv. bd. gen. medicine, B study sect. Nat. Inst. Arthritis, Metabolism and Digestive Diseases NIH; mem. bd. sci. counselors, sci. advisors com. Nat. Heart, Lung and Blood Inst., Nat. Insts. Health. Author: La Voz Sostenida, 1984, Palm Beach Blues, 1986, Por Amor al Arte, 1989; film critic for El Reportero, 1983-86, El Mundo, 1987-90; contbr. over 100 med. rsch. articles to sci. jours.; editor or co-editor of 11 books on renal pharmacology, nephrology, physiology; mem. editorial bd. U. P.R. Press, numerous profl. jours.; editor-in-chief Am. Jour. of Med. Scis., 1994-99. Mem. health com. Poplar Dem. Com., P.R., 1982-84; mem. Com. 500th Anniversary of Discovery Am., P.R., 1987-92; mem. com. on human rights Inst. of Medicine, Washington, 1987-92. Recipient Lederle Internat. award, 1966-67, Scholar award Macy Faculty, 1979-80, Grand Mobil prize medicine Mobil Oil Corp., 1981, Disting. Alumnus award Temple Med. Sch., 1988, Presdl. award Nat. Kidney Found, 1988, Donald W. Seldin medal 1994, Disting. Physician award P.R. Hosps. Assn., 1988, Orden del Cafetal award Municipality of Yauco, 1989; named one of Outstanding Med (medicine) P.R. C. of C., 1976, Fed. Supr. Employee of Yr., Fed. Execs. Assn., P.R., 1977. Fellow ACP, AAAS, Coun. for High Blood Pressure Rsch., Am. Heart Assn. (hypertension rsch. coun.; mem. Inst. Medicine NAS, Am. Soc. Nephrology (legis. liaison com., chmn. audit com. 1988), So. Soc. Clin. Investigation (sec.-treas. 1983-85, pres. 1985-86, Founders medal 1990), Am. Soc. for Clin. Investigation, Nat. Kidney Found. (chmn. sci. adv. bd. 1987-89, Donald W. Seldin medal, chmn. pub. policy com. 1992-94, pub. svc. medal), Latin Am. Soc. Nephrology (v.p. 1987-91, pres. elect 1991-94, pres. 1994—), Inter-Am. Soc. Hypertension Assn. (bd. govs., chmn. 8th Sci. Congress 1989), U.S. Pharmacopeial Convention Cardio Renal Drugs Com., Assn. Am. Physicians, Inst. Medicine, Alpha Omega Alpha. Achievements include contributions in field of kidney physiology and pathophysiology; contributions in treatment of clinical disturbances of blood composition, clinical use of diuretics, mechanisms of the development of hypertension. Office: VAMC Med Svc 1670 Clairmont Rd Decatur GA 30033-4004

MARTINEZ-TABONE, RAQUEL, school psychologist supervisor; b. Santurce, P.R., Mar. 28, 1944; d. Santos and Amelia (Guzman) Gonzalez; m. Fernando Martinez, Oct. 13, 1962 (div. Mar. 1968); 1 child, Stuart Andrew; m. Francis J. Tabone, July 9, 1980; children: Francis N., Christopher M.; grandchildren (wards): Amanda Marie Martinez, Andrea Amelia Martinez. BA, Lehman Coll., 1973, MS, 1977; PD, Fordham U., 1985; MA, Yeshiva U., 1988; MEd, Bank Street Coll., 1990; PhD, Yeshiva U., 1994. Cert. elem. tchr., sch. psychologist, supr. and sch. administr., N.Y.; ordained interfaith minister, 1990. Elem. sch. tchr. N.Y.C. Bd. Edn., Bronx, 1973-84, sch. psychologist, com. on spl. edn., 1985-94, supr. sch. psychologists, 1994—; adj. prof. NYU, 1992—. Mem. Nat. Assn. Sch Psychologists (cert.), Coun. Exceptional Children, Orthopsychiat. Assn. Home: 17 Ritchie Dr Yonkers NY 10705-2543 Office: NYC Bd Edn 1887-95 Bathgate Ave Bronx NY 10457-8308

MARTING, MICHAEL G., lawyer; b. Cleve., Nov. 5, 1948. BA summa cum laude, Yale U., 1971, JD, 1974. Bar: Ohio 1974. Assoc. Jones, Day, Reavis & Pogue, Cleve., 1974-83, ptnr., 1984—. Mem. ABA, Union Club, Cleve. Racquet Club, Kirtland Country Club, Tavern Club (treas., sec., trustee local chpt. 1985-88). Avocations: fly fishing, birdshooting, big game hunting, squash, golf. Office: Jones Day Reavis & Pogue N Point 901 Lakeside Ave E Cleveland OH 44114-1190

MARTINI, ROBERT EDWARD, wholesale pharmaceutical and medical supplies company executive; b. Hackensack, N.J., 1932. BS, Ohio State U., 1954. With Bergen Brunswig Corp., Orange, Calif., 1956-92, v.p., 1962-69, exec. v.p., 1969-81, pres., 1981-92, CEO, 1990—; chmn. Bergen Brunswig Corp., Orange, 1992—. chmn. exec. com. Bergen Brunswig Corp. Capt. USAF, 1954. •

MARTINI, WILLIAM J., congressman; b. Passaic, N.J.; m. Gloria Martini; children: William Jr., Marissa. Degree, Villanova U., 1968; JD, Rutgers U., 1972. Elected mem. City Coun. of Clifton, N.J., Passaic County Bd. Chosen

Freeholders, U.S. House of Reps., 1994—. Pres. Nicholas Martini Found.; trustee United Way of Passaic County, Ctr. Italian Am. Culture, Passaic Valley Coun. Boys Scouts of Am. Office: US House Reps 1728 Longworth House Office Bldg Washington DC 20515-3008•

MARTIN-NAGLE, CAROL RENEE, lawyer; b. Balt., Jan. 21, 1955; d. Guy and Barbara Geraldine (Wigington) Martin; m. Ronald Nagle, Jan. 26, 1974 (div. Aug. 1976); 1 child, Tanya. AA, Mt. Aloysius Jr. Coll., 1979; BA, St. Francis Coll., Loretto, Pa., 1981; JD, U. Pitts., 1984. Bar: Tex. 1984, U.S. Claims Ct. 1988. Internal tax acct. Arthur Young, Dallas, 1984-86; gen. counsel Aerospatiale Helicopter Corp., Grand Prairie, Tex., 1986—; sec. Aerospatiale Gen. Aviation, Grand Prairie, 1987—; sec. SFIM, Inc., 1989—. Author: Injunctions of Letters of Credit, 1984, U.S. Aviation Accident Law, 1988. Sec. Alliance Francaise, Dallas, 1986—. Mem. ABA, Dallas Bar Assn. (pres. internat. sect. 1988, chmn. law day com. 1989), Tex. State Bar, Helicopter Assn. Internat. (sec. legal com. 1989). Democrat. Avocations: movies, water skiing, travel. Home: 593 Herndon Pky Ste 300 Herndon VA 22070-5242 Office: Aerospatiale Helicopter Corp 2701 Forum Dr Grand Prairie TX 75052-7027

MARTINO, DONALD JAMES, composer, educator; b. Plainfield, N.J., May 16, 1931; s. James Edward and Alma Ida (Renz) M.; m. Mari Rice, Sept. 5, 1953 (div. June 1968); 1 child, Anna Maria; m. Lora Harvey, June 5, 1969; 1 child, Christopher James. B.Mus., Syracuse U., 1952; M.F.A., Princeton, 1954; MA (hon), Harvard U., 1983. Instr. music Princeton, 1957-59; asst. prof. theory music Yale, 1959-66, assoc. prof., 1966-69; chmn. dept. composition New Eng. Conservatory Music, Boston, 1969-80; Irving Fine prof. music Brandeis U., 1980-82; prof. music Harvard U., 1983—, Walter Bigelow Rosen prof. music, 1989-93; Walter Bigelow Rosen prof. emeritus, 1993—; tchr. composition and theory Yale Summer Sch. of Music and Art, summers 1960-63; tchr. composition Berkshire Music Ctr., summers, 1965-67, 69; composer in residence Berkshire Music Ctr., 1973; vis. lectr. Harvard U., 1971; composer in residence Composers' Conf., Johnson, Vt., summer 1979, May in Miami, 1994; Maurice Abravanel vis. disting. composer U. Utah, 1994, Mary Duke Biddle disting. composer Duke U., 1995. Composer: Separate Songs, 1951; for high voice and piano, Sonata for Clarinet and Piano, 1951, The Bad Child's Book of Beasts, 1952, Suite of Variations on Medieval Melodies, 1952; cello solo, A Set for Clarinet, 1954, Quodlibets for Flute, 1954, Three Songs, 1955, Portraits; a secular cantata for chorus, soloists and orch., 1955, Sette Canoni Enigmatici, 1956, Contemplations for Orch. (commd. by Paderewski Fund), 1956, 24 Tin Pan Alley Tunes, 1956, Quartet for Clarinet and Strings, 1957, Canon Ball, Three Way, MacFugal, Cathy, Lover Come Bach, 1957, Piano Fantasy, 1958, Trio for violin, clarinet and piano, 1959, Cinque Frammenti, 1961, Two Rilke Songs, 1961, Fantasy-Variations for violin, 1962, Concerto for Wind Quintet (commd. by Fromm Found. and Berkshire Music Center), 1964, Parisonatina Al'Dodecafonia; for cello solo, 1964, Concerto for Piano and Orch. (commd. by New Haven Symphony), 1965, B, a, b, b, it, t; for clarinet, 1966, Strata; for bass clarinet, 1966, Mosaic for grand orch. (commd. by U. Chgo.), 1967, Pianississimo; sonata for piano, 1970, Seven Pious Pieces, 1971, Concerto for Violoncello and Orch., 1972, Augenmusik, 1972, Notturno, 1973 (Naumburg Chamber Music award commn., Pulitzer prize in music 1974), Paradiso Choruses for Chorus, Soloists, Orch. and Tape, 1974 (Paderewski Fund commn., Classical Critics citation Record World mag. 1976), Ritorno for Orch. (Plainfield Symphony commn.), 1975, Triple Concerto for Clarinet, Bass Clarinet and Contrabass Clarinet with Chamber Ensemble (N.Y. State Council on Arts and Andrew W. Mellon Found. commn.), 1977, Impromptu for Roger; piano solo, 1977, Quodlibets II; flute solo, 1980, Fantasies and Impromptus, piano solo (Koussevitzky Found. commn.), 1981, Divertisements for Youth Orch. (Groton, Mass. Arts Ctr. Commn.), 1981, Suite in Old Form, piano solo, 1982, String Quartet (Elizabeth Sprague Coolidge Commn., winner 1st prize Kennedy Ctr. Friedheim Awards 1985), 1983, Canzone e Tarantella, clarinet and cello, 1984, The White Island, for chorus and chamber orchestra (Boston Symphony Centennial Commn.), 1985, Concerto for Alto Saxophone and Chamber Orch. (Nat. Endowment Consortium commn.), 1987, From the Other Side, Divertimento for Flute, Cello, Percussion and Piano (commd. by Flederman New Music Ensemble for the Australian Bicentennial, 1988), 12 Preludes (commd. Meet the Composer-Readers Digest), 1990, 15, 5, '92 AB for Carinet solo, 1992, Three Sad Songs, 1993; numerous others; contbr. articles to prof. jours. Recipient BMI Student Composer awards, 1952, 53; Bonsall fellow, 1953-54; Kosciuszko scholar, 1953-54; Nat. Fedn. Music Clubs award, 1953; Kate Neal Kinley fellow U. Ill., 1954-55; Fulbright grantee Florence, Italy, 1954-56; Pacifica Found. award, 1961; Creative Arts citation Brandeis U., 1963; Morse Accad. fellow, 1965; Nat. Inst. Arts and Letters grantee, 1967; Guggenheim fellow, 1967-68, 73-74, 82-83; Nat. Endowment on Arts grantee, 1973, 76, 79, 89; Mass. Council on Arts grantee, 1973, 79, 89; Pulitzer prize in music, 1974; recipient Kennedy Ctr. Friedheim Awards 1st prize, 1985, Mark M. Horblit award Boston Symphony Orch., 1987, Paul Revere award for mus. autography Music Publ. Assn., 1990, 91, 92. Mem. AAAS, AAAL, Coll. Music Soc., Am. Composers Alliance, Broadcast Music Inc., Am. Music Ctr., Internat. Soc. Contemporary Music (a founder New Haven chpt. 1966, dir. U.S. sect. 1961-64), Am. Soc. U. Composers (founding mem., exec. com. 1965-66, trustee 1965—), Internat. Clarinet Soc. (bd. dirs.). Office: Harvard U Dept Music Cambridge MA 02138

MARTINO, JOSEPH PAUL, research scientist; b. Warren, Ohio, July 16, 1931; s. Joseph and Anna Elizabeth (Kubina) M.; m. Mary Lou Bouquot, May 18, 1957; children: Theresa, Anthony, Michael. A.B., Miami U., Ohio, 1953; M.S., Purdue U., 1955; Ph.D., Ohio State U., 1961. Commd. 2d lt. USAF, 1953, advanced through grades to col., 1973; project engr. armament lab. USAF, Wright-Patterson AFB, Ohio, 1955-58; mathematician Office Sci. Rsch. USAF, Washington, 1961-62; staff scientist Avionics Lab. USAF, Wright-Patterson AFB, 1972-73; dir. engring. standardization Def. Electronics Supply Ctr. USAF, Dayton, Ohio, 1973-75; ret. USAF, 1975; sr. scientist, rsch. inst. U. Dayton, 1975-93. Author: Technological Forecasting for Decisionmaking, 1972, rev. edit., 1983, 3d edit., 1992, A Fighting Chance-The Moral Use of Nuclear Weapons, 1988, Science Funding: Politics and Porkbarrel, 1992, Research and Development Project Selection, 1995; assoc. editor: Tech. Forecasting and Social Change Jour., 1968—. Fellow IEEE, AAAS, AIAA (assoc.); mem. Inst. Mgmt. Scis., Am. Soc. Engring. Mgmt. Roman Catholic. Office: U Dayton Rsch Inst Rsch Inst 300 College Park Ave Dayton OH 45469-0120

MARTINO, MICHAEL CHARLES, entertainer, musician; b. Philadelphia, Pa., Sept. 10, 1950; s. Salvatore Joseph and Marie Angela (Langone) M. Grad. high sch., Upper Darby, Pa. Spokesperson/rep. Petosa Accordion Co., Seattle, 1979—; featured TV entertainer Mike Martino Show, Delaware County, Pa., 1987-89; accordion tchr. Drexel Hill, Pa., 1989—; entertainer/host/producer St. Jude's Children's Hosp. Marathon, King of Prussia, Pa., 1973; opening act comedian Morty Gunty Downingtown, Pa., 1973, opening act comedian Morty Gunty, 1973, Pat Cooper, Phila., 1981; guest artist/entertainer Internat. Platform Assn. Conv., Washington, 1979; nite club performer Glen Mills, Pa., 1989; actor TV commls., Elkton, Md., 1979, Halloween Spl. KYW-TV, Phila., 1986; performed radio contest jingle Sta. KISS 100 radio, Media, Pa., 1992. Author: (movie script) Forever Fiftys, 1990; composer popular songs; directed, produced, starred video Forever Fiftys; composed theme song Forever Fiftys, (movie theme) That First September; creator, performer Suspended Triple Bellows Shake Technique for the Accordion, 1994; composer (ballad) Through the Music, Through the Words I Sing, 1995. Recipient citation U.S. Ho. Reps., 1989, Proclamation Mike Martino Day Mayor Ward, Del. County, 1988, Danny Thomas Hon. award St. Jude's Hosp., Del. County, 1973, Mayor's Svc. award Upper Darby, Pa., 1994. Roman Catholic. Avocations: antique cars, dogs. Home: 2530 Stoney Brook Ln Drexel Hill PA 19026

MARTINO, ROBERT LOUIS, computational scientist and engineer, researcher; b. Derby, Conn.; s. Pasquale Theodore and Louise Mary (Bartomioli) M.; m. Alfreda Helen Guarente, Aug. 28, 1971. BS, Northeastern U., 1971; MS, U. Md., 1973, PhD, 1982. Elec. engr. Goddard Space Flight Ctr., NASA, Greenbelt, Md., 1971-76; electronics engr. NIH, Bethesda, Md., 1973-89; mem. adj. grad. sch. faculty Johns Hopkins U., Balt., 1982—; chief computational sci. and engring. sect. NIH, 1989-93, chief computational bioscience and engring. lab., 1993—; mem. computer sci. program com. Johns Hopkins U., 1985—; NIH rep. Nat., Multi-Agy. High-Performance Computing and Comm. Program, Bethesda, 1992—; mem. program com. Symposium on Frontiers of Massively Parallel Computing,

1993-95. Author: (with others) Parallel and Distributed Computing Handbook, 1995; contbr. articles to profl. jours. Recipient Disting Svc. award HHS, 1994; Grad. fellow U. Md., 1971-73. Mem. IEEE, Sigma Xi, Tau Beta Pi, Eta Kappa Nu. Achievements include the adaptation of high-performance parallel supercomputing to computationally intensive problems in basic and clinical biomedical research; application of concepts and technology of computer science and electrical engineering to biomedical applications for the advancement and understanding of the fundamentals of biological systems and medical practices and for the development of new and improved methods of health care. Home: 7996 Aladdin Dr Laurel MD 20723 Office: NIH Bldg 12A Rm 2033 12 South Dr MSC 5624 Bethesda MD 20892-5624

MARTINO, ROBERT SALVATORE, orthopedic surgeon; b. Clarksburg, W.Va., May 31, 1931; s. Lenord L. and Sarafina (Foglia) M. AB, W.Va. U., 1953, postgrad., 1955-56, BS in Medicine, 1958; MD, Northwestern U., 1960. Diplomate Am. Bd. Orthopaedic Surgery; lic. Ill., Calif., Ind. Intern Chgo. Wesley, 1960-61; resident dept. orthopaedic surgery Northwestern U., 1961-65, Chgo. Wesley Meml., 1961-62, Am. Legion Hosp. for Crippled Children, 1962-63, Cook County Hosp., Chgo., 1964, 64-65; orthopaedic surgeon Gary, Ind., 1965-67; orthopaedic surgeon Merrillville, Ind., 1967—; fellow Nat. Found. Infantile Parralysis, 1956, Office of Vocat. Rehab., Hand Surgery, 1965; chief of staff St. Mary Med. Ctr., 1976, chief of surgery, 1974-85; chief of staff Gary Treatment Ctr./Ind. Crippled Children's Svcs., 1974-84; adj. asst. prof. anatomy Ind. U., 1978, clin. asst. prof. orthopaedic surgery, 1980, others; mem. Zoning Bd., 1989-90. Chmn. Planning Bd., Town of Dune Acres, 1992—; bd. dirs. St. Mary's Med. Ctr., Hobart, Ind., 1980-86. Capt. U.S. Army, 1953-56. Mem. Ind. Med. Soc., Ill. Med. Soc., Chgo. Med. Soc., Lake County Med. Soc., AMA, Ill. Orthopaedic Soc., Ind. Orthopaedic Soc., Mid-Am. Orthopaedic Assn., Tri-State Orthopedic Soc., Clin. Orthopaedic Soc. Home: 22 Oak Dr Chesterton IN 46304-1016

MARTINO, ROCCO LEONARD, computer systems executive; b. Toronto, Ont., Can., June 25, 1929; s. Domenic and Josephine (DiGiulio) M. BSc, U. Toronto, 1951, MA, 1952; PhD, Inst. Aerospace Studies, 1955, DSc, Neumann Coll., 1993; m. Barbara L. D'Iorio, Sept. 2, 1961; children: Peter Domenic, Joseph Alfred, Paul Gerard, John Francis. Dir.. Univac Computing Svc. Ctr., Toronto, 1956-59; pres. Mauchly Assos. Can. Ltd., Toronto, 1959-62, v.p. Mauchly Assocs., Inc., Ft. Washington, Pa., 1959-61; mgr. advanced systems Olin Mathieson Chem. Corp., N.Y.C., 1962-64; dir. advanced computer systems Booz, Allen & Hamilton, N.Y.C., 1965-70; pres., chmn. bd. Info. Industries, Inc. and subs.'s, Wayne, Pa., 1965-70; chmn. bd., chief exec. officer XRT, Inc., Wayne, Pa., 1970—; chmn. bd. MBF Computer Ctr. for Handicapped Children; mem. bd. St. Joseph's U., Phila., Gregorian U. Found., N.Y., vice chmn. bd., 1990—; mem. exec. com. Gregorian U., N.Y. and Rome, 1987—; bd. dirs. 1984—; pontifical circle 1985—, active, 1982—; assoc. prof. math. U. Waterloo, 1959-62, prof. engring., dir. Inst. Systems and Mgmt. Engring., 1964-65; adj. assoc. prof. NYU, 1963-64, adj. prof. math., 1966-56, lectr. on computers mgmt.; chmn. Gov. Ill. Task Force, 1970-71, Ill. Bd. Higher Edn. Task Force, 1971-72, Computer-Use Task Force FCC, 1972-73, Computer-Use Planning Task Force U.S. Postal Svc., 1973-74. Trustee Gregorian Found., N.Y.C. and Rome, 1984—; bd. dirs. St. Joseph's U., 1987—, Cath. League Religious and Civil Rights, 1988-91; chmn. bd. dirs. MBF Ctr. Disabled Children, 1985—; founder Vatican Observatory, 1988—, bd. dirs. Tucson, Rome, 1990—. Mem. Assn. Computing Machinery, Ops. Rsch. Soc. Am., Nat. Italian Am. Found. (bd. dirs. 1991—), Profl. Engrs. Ont., Computing Soc. Can., ITEST (bd. dirs.), Union League Phila., Lions, Overbrook Golf and Country Club, Yacht of Sea Isle City Club (commodore 1973-74, trustee 1975-86, chmn. 1983-86), Commodores Club, Mid-Atlantic Yacht Racing Assn. (commodore 1979-81, sec. 1981-83, officer 1983—), Order St. Gregory the Great (papal knight 1991—), Legatus (bd. dirs. 1988, ea. regional v.p. 1992), Equestrian Order Holy Sepulchre (knight 1986, knight commdr. 1989), KC, Order of Malta, Knights of Malta (knight 1988, knight commdr. 1989), Cath. Campaign for Am. (nat. coun. 1992). Author: Resources Management, 1968, Dynamic Costing, 1968, Project Management, 1968, Information Management: The Dynamics of MIS, 1968, MIS-Management Information Systems, 1969, Decision Patterns, 1969, Methodology of MIS, 1969, Personnel Information Systems, 1969, Integrated Manufacturing Systems, 1972, APG-Virtual Application Systems, 1981; contbr. numerous articles on mgmt., computers and planning in profl. publs.; designer, developer Application Program Generator computer system, 1974-75, integrated treasury systems; developer cash mgmt. and on-line internat. trading systems, 1984, local area network systems fault tolerant and disaster tolerant systems for real-time fin. transactions, commd. paper trading systems for global networks. Office: 989 Old Eagle School Rd Wayne PA 19087-1704

MARTINS, HEITOR MIRANDA, foreign language educator; b. Belo Horizonte, Brazil, July 22, 1933; came to U.S., 1960; s. Joaquim Pedro and Emilia (Miranda) M.; m. Teresomja Alves Pereira, Nov. 1, 1958 (div. 1977); children—Luzia Pereira, Emilia Pereira; m. Marlene Andrade, Jan. 11, 1984. A.B., U. Federal de Minas Gerais, 1959; Ph.D., U. Federal de Minas Gerais, 1962. Instr. U. N.M., Albuquerque, 1960-62; asst. prof. Tulane U., New Orleans, 1962-66; assoc. prof. Tulane U., 1966-68; prof. dept. Spanish and Portuguese Ind. U., Bloomington, 1968—; chmn. dept. Ind. U., 1972-76; vis. prof. U. Tex., Austin, 1963, Stanford U. 1968. Author: poetry Sirgo nos Cabelos, 1961; essay Manuel de Galhegos, 1964; essays Oswald de Andrade e Outros, 1973; critical anthology Neoclassicismo, 1982; Essays Do Barroco a Guimarães Rosa, 1983; editor: essays Luso-Brazilian Literary Studies. Social Sci. Research Council grantee, 1965; Fulbright-Hays Commn. grantee, 1966; Ford Found. grantee, 1970, 71. Mem. MLA, Renaissance Soc. Am., Am. Comparative Lit. Assn., Am. Assn. for 18th Century Studies. Home: 1316 S Nancy St Bloomington IN 47401-6050 Office: Indiana U Dept Spanish and Portuguese Bloomington IN 47405

MARTINS, NILAS, dancer; b. Copenhagen, 1967. Tng., Royal Danish Ballet Sch. Featured in ballets (John Neumaier) Romeo and Juliet, (August Bourronville) Conservatoriet, A Folk Tale, Napoli, (Glen Tetley) Firebird, (Robbins) The Concert, Conservatoriet, Dances at a Gathering, Fanfare, The Four Seasons, Glass Pieces, The Goldberg Variations, Mother Goose, Opus 19, The Dreamer, Robbins with Twyla Tharp) Brahms/ Handel, (Balanchine) Cortege Hongrois, Who Cares?, Apollo, Chaconne, Coppelia, Divertimento No. 15, Duo Concertant, The Four Temperaments, Haieff Divertimento, Jewels, A Midsummer Night's Dream, The Nutcracker, Scotch Symphony, Serenade, Sonatina, La Sonnambula, Stars and Stripes, Stravinsky Violin Concerto, Swan Lake, Symphony in Three Movements, Tschaikovsky Suite No. 3, Union Jack, Vienna Waltzes, Western Symphony, Orpheus, (Martins) Delight of the Muses, Fearful Symmetries, Jazz, Jeu de Cartes, Sleeping Beauty, Tanzspiel, The Waltz Project, X-Ray; also appeared in Ray Charles in Concert with the N.Y.C. Ballet, N.Y.C. Ballet's Balanchine Celebration, 1993. Office: New York City Ballet NY State Theater Lincoln Ctr Plz New York NY 10023

MARTINS, PETER, ballet master, choreographer, dancer; b. Copenhagen, Oct. 27, 1946; came to U.S., 1967, naturalized, 1970; m. Lise La Cour (div. 1973); 1 child, Nilas; m. Darci Kistler, 1991. Pupil of Vera Volkova and Stanley Williams with Royal Danish Ballet. With N.Y.C. Ballet, 1967—, tchr., 1975, ballet master, 1981-83, co-ballet master-in-chief, 1983-89; ballet master-in-chief, 1989—; Tchr. Sch. Am. Ballet, 1975; artistic adviser Pa. Ballet, 1982—. Mem. Royal Danish Ballet, 1965-67, prin. dancer (including Bournonville repertory), 1967; guest artist N.Y.C. Ballet, 1967-70, prin. dancer, 1970-83; guest artist regional ballet cos. U.S., also Nat. Ballet Can., Royal Ballet, London, Grand Theatre Geneva, Paris Opera, Vienna State Opera, Munich State Opera, London Festival Ballet, Ballet Internat., Royal Danish Ballet; TV appearance in series of Balanchine works, 1974; also has appeared on PBS Dance in America series including A Choreographer's Notebook: Stravinsky Piano Ballets by Peter Martins, 1984; choreographed Broadway musicals including Dream of the Twins (co-choreographer) 1982, On Your Toes, 1982, Song and Dance, 1985; works choreographed include Calcium Light Night, 1977, Tricolore (Pas de Basque sect.), 1978, Rossini Pas de Deux, 1978, Tango-Tango (ice ballet), 1978, Dido and Aeneas, 1979, Sonate di Scarlatti, 1979, Eight Easy Pieces, 1980, Lille Suite, 1980, Suite from Histoire du Soldat, 1981, Capriccio Italien, 1981, The Magic Flute, 1981, Symphony No. 1, 1981, Delibes Divertissement, 1982, Piano-Rag-Music, 1982, Concerto for Two Solo Pianos, 1982, Waltzes, 1983, Rossini Quartets, 1983, Tango, 1983, A Schubertiad, 1984, Mozart Violin Concerto, 1984, Poulenc Sonata, 1985, La Sylphide, 1985, Valse Triste, 1985, Eight

More, 1985, We Are the World, 1985, Eight Miniatures, 1985, Ecstatic Orange, Tanzspiel, 1988, Jazz, 1993, Symphonic Dances, 1994, Barber Violin Concerto, 1994, Mozart Paino Concerto (No. 17), 1994, X-Ray, 1995; author: (autobiography) Far from Denmark, 1982. Recipient Dance mag. award 1977, Cue's Golden Apple award 1977, award of merit Phila. Art Alliance, 1985, Liberty award N.Y.C., 1986, H.C. Andersen Ballet prize, Royal Danish Theatre, 1988. Office: NY State Theater NYC Ballet Lincoln Ctr Plz New York NY 10023*

MARTINSON, IDA MARIE, nurse, physiologist, educator; b. Mentor, Minn., Nov. 8, 1936; d. Oscar and Marvel (Nelson) Sather; m. Paul Varo Martinson, Mar. 31, 1962; children—Anna Marie, Peter. Diploma, St. Luke's Hosp. Sch. Nursing, 1957; B.S., U. Minn., 1960, M.N.A., 1962; Ph.D., U. Ill., Chgo., 1972. Instr. Coll. St. Scholastica and St. Luke's Sch. Nursing, 1957-58, Thornton Jr. Coll., 1967-69; lab. asst. U. Ill. at Med. Ctr., 1970-72; lectr. dept. physiology U. Minn., St. Paul, 1972-82; asst. prof. Sch. Nursing U. Minn., 1972-74, assoc. prof. rsch., 1974-77, prof., dir. rsch., 1977-82; prof. dept. family health care U. Calif., San Francisco, 1982—; chmn. dept., 1982-90; vis. rsch. prof. Nat. Taiwan U., Def. Med. Ctr., 1981; vis. prof. nursing Sun Yat-Sen U. Med. Scis., Guang Zhou, Republic of China, Ewha Women's U., Seoul, Korea, vis. prof. nursing Frances Payne Bolton Sch. of Nursing, Case Western U., Cleve., 1994—. Author: Mathematics for the Health Science Student, 1977; editor: Home Care for the Dying Child, 1976, Women in Stress, 1979, Women in Health and Illness, 1986, The Child and Family Facing Life Threatening Illness, 1987, Family Nursing, 1989, Home Health Care Nursing, 1989; contbr. chpts. to books, articles to profl. jours. Active Am. Cancer Soc. Recipient Book of Yr. award Am. Jour. Nursing, 1977, 80, 87, 90, Children's Hospice Internat. award, 1988, Humanitarian award for pediatric nursing, 1993; Fulbright fellow, 1991. Mem. Council Nurse Researchers, Nat. League for Nursing, Am. Acad. Nursing, Am. Nurses Assn., Inst. Medicine, Sigma Xi, Sigma Theta Tau. Lutheran. Office: U Calif Family Health Care Nursing San Francisco CA 94143-0606 *The challenge of quality health care to all of society and the critical role nursing has to play in order to achieve this goal has motivated me throughout my professional life. The richness of talent in this country spurs me on.*

MARTINSON, JACOB CHRISTIAN, JR., university president; b. Menomonie, Wis., Apr. 15, 1933; s. Jacob Christian and Matilda Kate (Wisner) M.; m. Elizabeth Smathers, Apr. 29, 1962; children—Elizabeth Anne, Kirsten Kate. BA, Huntingdon Coll., Ala., 1954; MDiv, Duke U., 1957; DDiv, Vanderbilt U., 1972; grad., Inst. Ednl. Mgmt., Harvard U., 1981; LLD (hon.), Huntingdon Coll., 1993. Ordained elder United Methodist Ch. Minister Trinity United Meth. Ch., Lighthouse Point, Fla., 1960-67; sr. minister First United Meth. Ch., Winter Park, Fla., 1967-71; supervising instr. Vanderbilt U. Div. Sch., Nashville, 1971-72; pres. Andrew Coll., Cuthbert, Ga., 1972-76, Brevard Coll., N.C., 1976-85, High Point (N.C.) U., 1985—; bd. dirs. First Union Nat. Bank, High Point, chmn. 1989; lectr. St. Mary's Theol. Soc., U. St. Andrews, Scotland. Bd. advisors Uwharrie coun. Boy Scouts Am. Glen Slough scholar Vanderbilt U., 1971; Z. Smith Reynolds grantee Harvard U. Inst. Ednl. Mgmt., 1981; hon. fellow Westminster Coll., Oxford, Eng., 1994. Mem. Nat. Assn. Schs. and Colls. United Meth. Ch. (bd. dirs. 1982-85, 87-90, chmn. fin. com.), So. Assn. Colls. and Schs. (commn. on colls.), Ind. Coll. Fund. N.C. (trustee), N.C. Ctr. Ind. Higher Edn. (bd. dirs.) Brevard C. of C. (pres. 1979), High Point C. of C. (chmn. 1992), Piedmont Ind. Coll. Assn. (chmn. 1991-93), Carolinas Intercollegiate Athletic Conf. (pres. 1991-93), Rotary, Phi Theta Kappa. Methodist. Avocation: mountain hiking. Home: 1109 Rockford Rd High Point NC 27262-3607 Office: High Point U Office of Pres High Point NC 27262-3598

MARTINUZZI, LEO SERGIO, JR., banker; b. Newton, Mass., Aug. 1, 1928; s. Leo Sergio and Jessica (Stewart) M.; m. Helen Renfrew Gibson, Oct. 26, 1957; children: John James, Georgiana Gibson, Samuel Stewart. B.A., Harvard U., 1950; B.Litt., Oxford U., 1952. With Chase Manhattan Bank, N.Y.C., 1956-81; asst. treas. Chase Manhattan Bank, 1960, asst. v.p. Japanese brs., 1961-64, v.p Japanese brs., 1964-68, marketing exec. internat. staff, 1968-72, sr. v.p., 1971-81; corporate devel. officer Chase Manhattan Corp., 1972-75, group exec. info. services, 1975-81; chmn. Chase Econometric Assocs. Inc., 1975-80; sr. v.p. strategic planning Squibb Corp., 1981-87, cons., 1988-91; chmn. Strategic Dimensions, Inc., 1991—. Trustee Internat. Found. for St. Catherine's Coll., Oxford. Lt. (j.g.) USNR, 1952-56. Mem. Coun. on Fgn. Rels. Home: 336 Galleon Dr Naples FL 33940-7638

MARTO, PAUL JAMES, mechanical engineering educator, researcher; b. Flushing, N.Y., Aug. 15, 1938; s. Peter Joseph and Natalie Janet (Verrinoldi) M.; m. Mary Virginia Indence, June 10, 1961; children: Terese V. Marto Sanders, Paul J. Jr., Wayne T., Laura C. BS, U. Notre Dame, 1960; SM, MIT, 1962, ScD, 1965. Asst. prof. Naval Postgrad. Sch., Monterey, Calif., 1965-69, assoc. prof., 1969-77, prof., 1977-85, Disting. prof., 1985—, chmn. dept. mech. engring., 1978-86, dean of rsch., 1990—; cons. Modine Mfg. Co., Racine, Wis., 1986—. Editor: Power Condenser Heat, 1981; regional editor N.Am. Jour. of Enhanced Heat Transfer, 1993—; contbr. articles to profl. jours. Lt. USN, 1965-67. Recipient Rear Adm. John J. Schieffelin award Naval Postgrad. Sch., 1976, Alexander von Humboldt U.S. Sr. Scientist award Humboldt Stiftung, Fed. Republic Germany, 1989-90. Fellow ASME (assoc. tech. editor Jour. of Heat Transfer 1984-90); mem. Am. Soc. Naval Engrs., Am. Soc. for Engring. Edn., Sigma Xi. Avocations: walking, tennis, music. Office: Naval Postgrad Sch Dept Mechanical Engring Code ME/MX Monterey CA 93943

MARTON, BERNARD ANTHONY, headmaster, priest, educator; b. Budapest, Hungary, Apr. 3, 1941; came to U.S., 1957; s. Istvan and Maria (Zirig) M. STB, St. Anselm, Rome, 1965, STL, 1967, STD, 1968; MA, So. Meth. U., 1971. Tchr. Cistercian Prep Sch., Irving, Tex., 1968-71, asst. headmaster, 1971-81, headmaster, 1981—. Mem. Ind. Schs. Assn. S.W. (chair standards 1985-87). Roman Catholic. Avocations: photography, video, computers, skiing, foreign languages. Home and Office: Cistercian Prep Sch 1 Cistercian Rd Irving TX 75039-4599

MARTON, EVA, opera singer; b. Budapest, Hungary, June 18, 1943; m. Zoltan Marton; children: Zoltan, Diana. Student, Liszt Acad., Budapest. Debut Budapest State Opera, 1968-72; performed with Frankfurt Opera, 1972-77, Hamburg State Opera, 1977-80, Maggio Musicale Fiorentino, Vienna State Opera, La Scala Milan, Met. Opera, N.Y., Lyric Opera, Chgo., Grand Opera, Houston, San Francisco Opera, Convent Garden, London, Teatro Liceo, Barcelona, Munich State Opera, Berlin, Paris, Sydney, Teatro Colon Buenos Aires, Bayreuth Festival, Salzburg Festival, Area of Verona, others; roles include Manon Lescaut, Tosca, Turandot, Aida Elisabetta in Don Carlo, Leonora in Forza del destino and in Il Trovatore, Fedora, Maddalena in A Chenire, Wally, Gioconda, Leonore in Fidelio, Salome, Ariadne, Helene in Agyptische Helene, Chrysothemis in Electra, Empress in Die Frau ohne Schatten, Vensu and Elisabeth in Tannhäuser, Elsa and Ortrud in Lohengrin, Sieglinde and Bruünnhilde in the Ring, Isolde, others; rec. include Turandot, Tosca, La Fanciulla del West, A Chenier, Fedora, La Gioconda, Violanta, Tiefland, La Wally, Semiramla, Bluebeards Castle, Mefistofele, Electra, Salome, Die Walkuere, Sieglfrid, Götterdämmerung, Gurrelider, Forza del destino, Tristan und Isolde, Puccini Arias, Wagner arias, Songs by Bartok and Liszt, others. Office: Orgn Int Opera et Concert, 19 rue Vignon, F-75008 Paris France

MARTON, LAURENCE JAY, clinical pathologist, educator, researcher; b. Bklyn., Jan. 14, 1944; s. Bernard Dov and Sylvia (Silberstein) M.; m. Marlene Lesser, June 27, 1967; 1 child, Eric Nolan. B.A., Yeshiva U., 1965; M.D., Albert Einstein Coll. Medicine, 1969. Intern Los Angeles County-Harbor Gen. Hosp., 1969-70; resident in neurosurgery U. Calif.-San Francisco, 1970-71, resident in lab. medicine, 1973-75, asst. research biochemist, 1973-74, asst. clin. prof. depts. lab. medicine and neurosurgery, 1974-75, asst. prof., 1975-78, assoc. prof., 1978-79, prof., 1979-92, asst. dir. div. clin. chemistry, dept. lab. medicine, 1974-75, dir. div., 1975-79, acting chmn. dept., 1978-79, chmn. dept., 1979-92; dean med. sch. U. Wis., 1992-95, prof. pathology, lab. medicine, and oncology depts., 1992—; prof. dept. human oncology U. Wis., Madison, 1993—. Co-editor: Polyamines in Biology and Medicine, 1981; Liquid Chromatography in Clinical Analysis, 1981; Clinical Liquid Chromatography, vol. 1, 1984, vol. 2, 1984. Served with USPHS, NIH, 1971-73. Recipient Research Career Devel. award Nat. Cancer Inst. Mem. Am. Assn. Cancer Rsch., AAAS, Acad. Clin. Lab.

Physicians and Scientists, Am. Investigative Pathology, Am. Soc. Clin. Pathologists, Soc. Analytical Cytology, Alpha Omega Alpha. Jewish. Avocations: photography; art; music; travel; sports. Home: 5810 Tree Line Dr Fitchburg WI 53711-5826 Office: McArdle Lab Cancer Rsch 1400 University Ave Madison WI 53706

MARTONE, PATRICIA ANN, lawyer; b. Bklyn., Apr. 28, 1947; d. David Andrew and Rita Mary (Dullmeyer) M. BA in Chemistry, NYU, 1968, JD, 1973; MA in Phys. Chemistry, Johns Hopkins U., 1969. Bar: N.Y. 1974, U.S. Dist. Ct. (so. and ea. dists.) N.Y. 1975, U.S. Ct. Appeals (2d cir.) 1975, U.S. Ct. Appeals (1st cir.) 1981, U.S. Ct. Appeals (fed. cir.) 1984, U.S. Patent and Trademark Office 1983, U.S. Supreme Ct. 1984, U.S. Dist. Ct. (ea. dist.) Mich. 1985, U.S. Dist. Ct. (no. dist.) Calif. 1995. Tech. rep. computer timesharing On-Line Systems, Inc., N.Y.C., 1969-70; assoc. Kelley Drye & Warren, N.Y.C., 1973-77; assoc. Fish & Neave, N.Y.C., 1977-82, ptnr., 1983—; adj. prof. NYU Sch. Law, 1990—; participating atty. Cmty. Law Offices, N.Y.C., 1974-78; atty. Pro Bono Panel U.S. Dist. Ct. (so. dist.) N.Y., 1982-84; lectr. Practising Law Inst., N.Y.C., 1995, Prentice Hall Law & Bus., 1990—, Franklin Pierce Law Sch., 1992—; mem. panel arbitration Am. Arbitration Assn.; dir. N.Y. Lawyers for the Pub. Interest, 1987—; exec. com., 1989—, treas., 1992-94; dir. Legal Svcs. N.Y.C., 1991-95. Mng. editor NYU Law Sch. Rev. Law and Social Change, 1972-73. Contbr. articles to profl. jours. Recipient Founder's Day award NYU Sch. Law, 1973; NSF grad. trainee John Hopkins U., 1968-69; NYU scholar, 1964-68. Mem. ABA, Assn. Bar City N.Y. (mem. environ. law com. 1978-83, trademarks, unfair competition com. 1983-86), Fed. Bar Council, Fed. Cir. Bar Assn., Am. Chem. Soc., Licensing Execs. Soc., Intellectual Property Law Assn., N.Y. University Club. Office: Fish & Neave 1251 Ave of the Americas New York NY 10020-6250

MARTONOSI, ANTHONY NICHOLAS, biochemistry educator, researcher; b. Szeged, Hungary, Nov. 7, 1928; came to U.S., 1957; s. Antal and Anna (Zsoter) M.; m. Mary Alice Gouvea, May 2, 1959; children: Mary Anne, Anthony, Margaret, Susan. MD, U. Med. Sch. Szeged, 1953. Asst. prof. dept. physiology Med. Sch., Szeged, 1955-57; rsch. fellow Mass. Gen. Hosp., Boston, 1957-59; rsch. assoc. Retina Found., Boston, 1959-62, asst. dir. dept. muscle rsch., 1962-65; assoc. prof. biochemistry St. Louis U. Sch. Medicine, 1965-69, prof., 1969-79; prof. biochemistry SUNY Health Sci. Ctr., Syracuse, 1979—; Albert Szent-Gyorgyi Prof., U. Med. Sch., Szeged, Hungary, 1994; adj. prof. Kwangju Inst. of Sci. and Tech., Korea, 1995—; vis. scientist dept. biochemistry U. Birmingham, Eng., 1963-64. Editor: The Enzymes of Biological Membranes, Vols. 1-4, 1976, 2d edit., 1985; Membranes and Transport, Vols. 1-2, 1982; contbr. over 180 articles to sci. publs.; mem. editorial adv. bd. Jour. Muscle Rsch. and Cell Motility, 1980—, Biochimica et Biophysica Acta, 1984—. Recipient Established Investigator award Am. Heart Assn., 1961-66; rsch. grantee USPHS, NIH, 1959—, NSF, 1963—, Muscular Dystrophy Assn., 1975—. Mem. Am. Soc. Biochemists and Molecular Biologists, Biophys. Soc. Roman Catholic. Home: 110 Stanwood Ln Manlius NY 13104-1412 Office: SUNY Health Sci Ctr 766 Irving Ave Syracuse NY 13210-1605

MARTORANA, SEBASTIAN VINCENT, educational consultant; b. Farnham, N.Y., Jan. 7, 1919; s. Francis and Jennie (Mancuso) M.; m. Carrie Mae Stephenson, Sept. 20, 1947; children: Vincenne (Mrs. Alfred Kirmss), Francis Stephen, John Charles. B.S., N.Y. State Coll. at Buffalo, 1939; postgrad., U. Buffalo, 1940; M.A., U. Chgo., 1946, Ph.D., 1948. Prof. Wash. State Coll., 1948-53; dean Ferris State Inst., 1953-55; specialist community colls. U.S. Office Edn., Washington, 1955-57; chief state and regional orgns. U.S. Office Edn., 1957-63; asst. commr. for higher edn. planning N.Y. State Bd. Regents, 1963-65; vice-chancellor for community colls., provost tech. edn. SUNY, 1965-72; sr. rsch. assoc. Ctr. Study Higher Edn., prof. higher edn. Pa. State U., 1972-89, prof. emeritus, 1989; mem. nat. bd. inservice edn. project Edn. Commn. States, 1976-82; pres., chmn. bd. Assoc. Cons. in Edn., 1976—; lectr. in field. Author: (with D Grant Morrison) Criteria for Establishing Two Year Colleges, 1961, State Formulas for the Support of Public Two Year Colleges, 1962, (with E. Hollis) State Boards Responsible for Higher Education, 1960, College Board of Trustees, 1963, (with C. Blocker, L. Bender) The Political Terrain of American Postsecondary Education, 1975, (with E. Kuhns) Managing Academic Change, 1975, (with Gary McGuire) State Legislation Relating to Community and Junior Colleges, 1975, (with L. Nespoli), 1976, Regionalism in American Postsecondary Education: Concepts and Practices, 1978, Regionalism: Study, Talk, and Action, 1978, (with E. Kuhns) Quality Beyond the Campus, 1983, (with W. D. Smutz) State Legislation Relating to Community and Junior Colleges, 1979, (with W. Piland) Designing Programs for Community Groups, 1984; editor: (with W. Toombs, D. Breneman) Graduate Education and Community Colleges, 1976, (with E. Kuhns) Qualitative Methods for Institutional Research, 1982, (with J. Broomall) State Legislation on Affecting Community, Jr. and 2-Year Technical Colleges, 1981, (with P. Corbett) State Legislation Affecting Community, Jr. and 2-Year Technical Colleges, 1982, (with P. Garland) State Legislation Affecting Community, Jr. and Two-Year Technical Colleges, 1985, 86, 87, 88, 89, (with T. Kelley and L.A. Nespoli) Politics, Law and Economics of Higher Education, 1987; mem. editorial bd. Community Coll. Rev., 1972-86; mem. editorial adv. bd. Jour. Edn. Finance, 1972-86. Pres. Wakefield Forest Civic Assn., Annandale, Va., 1958-59, Pearse Rd. Civic Assn., Schenectady, 1966-67; Trustee Coll. Entrance Exam. Bd., 1966-70, Washington Internat. Coll., 1974-80; lay adv. bd. Notre Dame High Sch., Schenectady, 1968-72; bd. human resources Nat. Acad. Scis., 1971-72; mem. Pres. Nat. Adv. Commn. on Higher Edn., 1969. Served with USAAF, 1942-45. Decorated Legion of Merit; recipient Distinguished Alumnus award State U. N.Y. Coll. at Buffalo, 1959, Distinguished Service award HEW, 1960, Award of Merit N.Y.S. Jr. Coll. Assn., 1972, Outstanding Reservist, Air Univ., 1974, Outstanding Publ. award Nat. Council Univ. and Coll. Profs./Am. Assn. Community and Jr. Colls., 1982, 86, Disting. Svc. award Nat. Coun. Univ. and Coll. Profs./Am. Assn. Community and Jr. Coll Assn., 1985; named to Community Coll. Founders Hall of Fame, 1984. Danforth Found. grantee, 1974; Ford Found. grantee, 1978; grantee Fund for Improvement of Postsecondary Edn., 1982. Mem. NEA, Nat. Coun. State Dirs. Community and Jr. Colls. (founding mem. pres. 1968, 72), Am. Assn. Higher Edn., Am. Ednl. Rsch. Assn., Assn. Instl. Rsch., Am. Assn. Community and Jr. Colls. (founding mem. 1977-80, Nat. Leadership award 1988), Nat. Soc. Study Edn., Am. Acad. Polit. and Social Sci., Nat. Assn. Coll. and Univ. Attys. (founding mem.), Nat. Coun. coll. and Univ. Profs. Community and Jr. Colls. (pres. 1979, bd. dirs. 1987-89), Pa. Higher Edn. Assn., Res. Officers Assn., Air Force Assn., Knights of Columbus, Sons of Itlay, Italic Studies Inst. (adv. coun. mem.), Reserve Officers Assn., Retired Officers Assn., Phi Delta Kappa. Home: Bo 256 Rural Delivery 1 Centre Hall PA 16828 Office: 322 Pond Lab University Park PA 16802-6107

MARTORI, JOSEPH PETER, lawyer; b. N.Y.C., Aug. 19, 1941; s. Joseph and Teresa Susan (Fezza) M. BS summa cum laude, NYU, 1964, MBA, 1968; JD cum laude U. Notre Dame, 1967. Bar: D.C. 1968, U.S. Dist. Ct. D.C. 1968, U.S. Dist. Ct. Ariz. 1968, U.S. Ct. Appeals (9th cir.) 1969, U.S. Supreme Ct. 1977. Assoc. Sullivan & Cromwell, N.Y.C., 1967-68, Snell & Wilmer, Phoenix, 1968-69; pres. Goldmar Inc., Phoenix, 1969-71; ptnr. Martori, Meyer, Hendricks & Victor, P.A., Phoenix, 1971-85; ptnr. Brown & Bain, P.A., Phoenix, 1985-94; chmn. corp. banking & real estate dept.; bd. dirs. Firstar, Met. Bank, Phoenix, Red Rock Collection Inc., Phoenix; chmn., pres. ILX Inc. Author: Street Fights, 1987; also articles, 1966-70. Bd. dirs. Men's Arts Council, Phoenix, 1972—; trustee Boys' Clubs Met. Phoenix, 1974—; consul for Govt. of Italy, State of Ariz., 1987—. Mem. ABA, State Bar Ariz., Maricopa County Bar Assn., Lawyers Com. for Civil Rights Under Law (trustee 1976—), Phoenix Country Club, Plaza Club (founding bd. govs. 1979-90). Republican. Roman Catholic. Office: ILX Inc 2777 E Cammelback Rd Phoenix AZ 85016

MARTUCCI, WILLIAM CHRISTOPHER, lawyer; b. Asbury Park, N.J., Mar. 10, 1952; s. Frank and Evelyn (Gerrity) M.; m. Julie Sessions, Aug. 2, 1980; children: Daniel Robert, William Sessions, John Andrew, James Christopher, Andrew Michael. AB magna cum laude, Rutgers U., 1974; JD with honors, U. Ark., 1977; LLM, Georgetown U., 1981. Bar: Mo. 1977. Law clk. to presiding justice Mo. Ct. Appeals, Kansas City, 1977-78; assoc. Spencer, Fane, Britt & Browne, Kansas City, 1981-86, ptnr., 1987—; mem. practice and procedure com. Nat. Labor Relations Act; adj. prof. employment law U. Mo. Law Sch., Kansas City, 1988—, chair minority affairs com. 1992—. Editor-in-chief Ark. Law Rev., 1976-77; contbr. articles to profl. jours. Chmn. adv. coun. Urban League Greater Kansas City Tng. Ctr.,

chmn. mentor program, 1988—; mem. Kansas City Civic Coun.; mem. Kansas City Tomorrow Leadership Program, 1992-93; adv. bd. Boys and Girls Club Kansas City. Served to lt. JAGC, USN, 1978-81. Mem. ABA, Mo. Bar Assn. (exec. com. continuing legal edn. 1987—, chair 1993—), Kansas City Bar Assn. (chmn. continuing legal edn. 1984-86, mem. exec. com. 1985-87, leadership award 1985, chmn. labor and employment law com. 1988-90, Pres. award 1992), Lawyers Assn. Kansas City (mem. exec. com. young lawyers sect. 1981-82), Nat. Inst. Mcpl. Law Officers (vice-chmn. labor rels. and pers. law com. 1988-90), Kansas City Club, Homestead Country Club, Rotary. Republican. Roman Catholic. Club: Kansas City. Home: 1251 W 59th St Kansas City MO 64113-1148 Office: Spencer Fane Britt & Browne 1400 Commerce Bank Bldg 1000 Walnut St Kansas City MO 64106-2123

MARTY, JOHN, state senator, writer; b. Evanston, Ill., Nov. 1, 1956; s. Martin E. and Elsa Louise (Schumacher) M.; m. Connie Jaarsma, Nov. 29, 1980; children: Micah. BA in Ethics, St. Olaf Coll., 1978. Researcher Minn. Ho. of Reps., St. Paul, 1980-82, com. adminstr. com. criminal justice, 1982-84; corp. found. grant adminstr., 1984-86; mem. Minn. State Senate, St. Paul, 1987—. Dem. Farm Labor gubernatorial candidate, 1994. Office: Minn State Senate 9 State Capitol Saint Paul MN 55155-1002

MARTY, LAWRENCE A., magistrate, lawyer; b. Leigh, Nebr., June 17, 1926. Student Wayne State U., 1944-46, Creighton Sch. Law, 1946-48; J.D., U.Wyo., 1954. Bar: Wyo. 1954. Sole practice, Green River, Wyo., 1954-67; ptnr. Mart & Clark, Green River, 1967-74; ptnr. Marty & Ragsdale, Green River, 1975—; judge Green River Mcpl. Ct., 1956-58; U.S. Magistrate Dist. Wyo., 1958—. Alt. del. Rep. Nat. Conv., 1964. Mem. ABA, Wyo. Bar Assn., Sweetwater County Bar Assn. Office: 20 E Flaming Gorge Way Green River WY 82935-4210

MARTY, MARTIN EMIL, religion educator, editor; b. West Point, Nebr., Feb. 5, 1928; s. Emil A. and Anne Louise (Wuerdemann) M.; m. Elsa Schumacher, 1952 (dec. 1981); children: Frances, Joel, John, Peter, James, Micah, Ursula; m. Harriet Lindemann, 1982. MDiv, Concordia Sem., 1952; STM, Luth. Sch. Theology, Chgo., 1954; PhD in Am. Religious and Intellectual History, U. Chgo., 1956; LittD (hon.), Thiel Coll., 1964; LHD (hon.), W.Va. Wesleyan Coll., 1967, Marian Coll., 1967, Providence Coll., 1967; DD (hon.), Muhlenberg Coll., 1967; LittD (hon.), Thomas More Coll., 1968; DD (hon.), Bethany Sem., 1969; LLD (hon.), Keuka Coll., 1972; LHD (hon.), Willamette U., 1974; DD (hon.), Wabash Coll., 1977; LLD (hon.), U. So. Calif., 1977, Valparaiso U., 1978; LHD (hon.), St. Olaf Coll., 1978, De Paul U., 1979; DD (hon.), Christ Sem.-Seminex, 1979, Capital U., 1980; LHD (hon.), Colo. Coll., 1980; DD (hon.), Maryville Coll., 1980, North Park Coll. Sem., 1982; LittD (hon.), Wittenberg U., 1983; LHD, Rosary Coll., 1984; LHD (hon.), Rockford Coll., 1984; DD (hon.), Va. Theol. Sem., 1984; LHD (hon.), Hamilton Coll., 1985, Loyola U., 1986; LLD (hon.), U. Notre Dame, 1987; LHD (hon.), Roanoke Coll., 1987, Mercer U., 1987, Ill. Wesleyan Coll., 1987, Roosevelt U., 1988, Aquinas Coll., 1988; LittD (hon.), Franklin Coll., 1988, U. Nebr., 1993; LHD (hon.), No. Mich. U., 1989, Muskingum Coll., Coe Coll., Lehigh U., 1989, Hebrew Union Coll. and Governors State U., 1990, Whittier Coll., 1991; Calif. Luth. U., 1993; DD (hon.), St. Xavier Coll. and Colgate U., 1990, Mt. Union Coll., 1991, Tex. Luth. Coll., 1991, Aurora U., 1991, Baker U., 1992; LittD (hon.), U. Nebr., 1993; LHD (hon.), Luth. U., 1993; Litt.D, U. Nebr., 1993; LHD, Calif. Luth. U., 1993; DD, Hope Coll., 1993, Northwestern Coll., 1993; LHD (hon.), George Fox Coll., 1994, Drake U., 1994, Centre Coll., 1994. Ordained to ministry Luth. Ch., 1952. Pastor Washington, 1950-51; asst. pastor River Forest, Ill., 1952-56; pastor Elk Grove Village, Ill., 1956-63; prof. history of modern Christianity Div. Sch. U. Chgo., 1963—, Fairfax M. Cone Disting. Service prof., 1978—; assoc. editor Christian Century mag., Chgo., 1956-85, sr. editor, 1985—; co-editor Ch. History mag., 1963—; pres. Park Ridge (Ill.) Ctr.: An Inst. for Study of Health, Faith and Ethics, 1985-89; dir. fundamentalism project Am. Acad. Arts & Scis., 1988—. Author: A Short History of Christianity, 1959, The New Shape of American Religion, 1959, The Improper Opinion, 1961, The Infidel, 1961, Baptism, 1962, The Hidden Discipline, 1963, Second Chance for American Protestants, 1963, Church Unity and Church Mission, 1964, Varieties of Unbelief, 1964, The Search for a Usable Future, 1969, The Modern Schism, 1969, Righteous Empire, 1970 (Nat. Book award 1971), Protestantism, 1972, You Are Promise, 1973, The Fire We Can Light, 1973, The Pro and Con Book of Religious America, 1975, A Nation of Behavers, 1976, Religion, Awakening and Revolution, 1978, Friendship, 1980, By Way of Response, 1981, The Public Church, 1981, A Cry of Absence, 1983, Health and Medicine in the Lutheran Tradition, 1983, Pilgrims in Their Own Land, 1984, Protestantism in the United States, 1985, Modern American Religion. The Irony of It All, Vol. 1, 1986, An Invitation to American Catholic History, 1986, Religion and Republic, 1987, Modern American Religion. The Noise of Conflict, Vol. 2, 1991, (with R. Scott Appleby) The Glory and the Power, 1992; contbr. articles to religious publs.; editor: Context, 1969—. Second Opinion, 1990; sr. editor: The Christian Century, 1956—. Chmn. bd. regents St. Olaf Coll. Sr. scholar-in-residence The Park Ridge Ctr., 1989—. Fellow Am. Acad. Arts and Scis. (dir. fundamentalism project 1988-94), Soc. Am. Historians; mem. Am. Phil. Soc., Am. Soc. Ch. History (pres. 1971), Am. Cath. Hist. Assn. (pres. 1981), Am. Acad. Religion (pres. 1987-88), Am. Antiquarian Soc. Home: 239 Scottswood Rd Riverside IL 60546-2223 Office: U Chgo Div Sch 1025 E 58th St Chicag37-1509

MARTYAK, JOSEPH J., lawyer; b. Hazleton, Pa.; s. Gabriel S. and Catherine A. (Cranston) M.; m. Vicki Jean Love, July 12, 1980; children: J. Winston, Marisa Love. B.A. cum laude, Georgetown U.; student, Institut d'Etudes Europeennes, Paris; J.D., Georgetown U. Bar: Pa. 1975, D.C. 1975. Legis. asst. to Rep. Daniel Flood, Pa., 1973-75; legis. asst. House Com. on Interstate and Fgn. Commerce, 1975-77; legis. rep. AGA, 1977-79; sr. Washington rep. Union Carbide Corp., 1979-85; prin. dep. under sec. Dept. Interior, Washington, 1985-87; v.p. corp. affairs Rhone-Poulenc Inc., Washington, 1987—. Mem. ABA, Pa. Bar Assn., D.C. Bar Assn., Club at Franklin Sq., Pisces Club, Capitol Hill Club, Congl. Country Club. Office: Rhone-Poulenc Inc 1401 I St NW Ste 200 Washington DC 20005-2225

MARTYL (MRS. ALEXANDER LANGSDORF, JR.), artist; b. St. Louis, Mar. 16, 1918; d. Martin and Aimee (Goldstone) Schweig; m. Alexander Langsdorf, Jr., Dec. 31, 1941; children: Suzanne, Alexandra. A.B., Washington U., St. Louis, 1938. instr. art dept. U. Chgo.; artist in residence Tamarind Inst., U. N.Mex., Albuquerque, 1974. One-man shows include Calif. Palace of Legion of Honor, 1956, Chgo. Art Inst., 1949, 76, Feingarten Galleries, N.Y.C., Beverly Hills and Chgo., 1961, 62, 63, St. Louis, 1962, Feingarten Gallery, N.Y.C., 1963, Los Angeles, 1964, Kovler Gallery, Chgo., 1967, Washington U., St. Louis, 1967, U. Chgo. Oriental Inst. Mus., 1970, Deson&Zaks Gallery, 1973, Fairweather-Hardin Gallery, 1977, 81, 83, Ill. State Mus., 1978, Fermilab, 1985, 91, Bklyn. Mus., 1986, Oriental Inst. Mus., 1987, Gibbes Art Mus., Charleston, S.C., 1988, Fairweather-Hardin Gallery, 1988, Tokyo Internat. Art Expo, 1990, State of Ill. Art Gallery, Chgo., 1990, Expo Navy Pier, Chgo., 1993, Printworks Gallery Ltd., Chgo., 1995; represented in permanent collections, Met. Mus. Art, Chgo. Art Inst., Pa. Acad. Fine Arts, Ill. State Mus., Bklyn. Mus., DuSable Mus., Chgo., Los Angeles County Mus., Whitney Mus. Am. Art, Davenport (Iowa) Municipal Mus., St. Louis Art Mus., Washington U., U. Ariz., Arnot Gallery, Elmira, N.Y., Greenville (S.C.) Mus., Nat. Coll. Fine Arts, Hirshhorn Mus. and Sculpture Gallery, Rockford (Ill.) Mus. Recipient 1st prize City Art Mus. St. Louis, 1943, 44; Armstrong prize Chgo. Art Inst., 1947; William H. Bartels award, 1953; Frank Logan medal and prize, 1950; Walt Disney purchase award Los Angeles Mus.; purchase prize Portrait of America competition, Colo. Springs Fine Arts Center, 1961; honor award for mural AIA, 1962, Outstanding Achievement award in the Arts YWCA, 1986; named Artist of Year Am. Fedn. Arts, 1958. Mem. Chgo. Network, Arts Club (Chgo.), Quadrangle Club (Chgo.). Unitarian. *To be an artist means devoting a lifetime to an intensely difficult activity—one that requires concentration and skill. I've spent my time learning the power of color, line, shape and meaning. I like to think that I have opened out experiences people cannot reveal by themselves.*

MARTZ, CLYDE OLLEN, lawyer, educator; b. Lincoln, Nebr., Aug. 14, 1920; s. Clyde O. and Elizabeth Mary (Anderson) M.; m. Ann Spieker, May 29, 1947; children: Robert Graham, Nancy. AB, U. Nebr., 1941; LLB, Harvard U., 1947. Bar: Colo. 1948, U.S. Ct. Appeals (D.C. cir.) 1968, U.S.

Supreme Ct. 1969. Prof. U. Colo., Boulder, 1947-58, 60-62; jud. adminstr. State of Colo., Denver, 1959-60; ptnr. Davis, Graham & Stubbs, Denver, 1962-67, 69-80, 81-87, of counsel, 1988—; asst. atty. gen. U.S. Dept. Justice, Washington, 1967-69; solicitor U.S Dept. Interior, Washington, 1980-81; exec. dir. dept. natural resources State of Colo., 1987; adj. prof. U. Denver, 1961-79, U. Colo., Boulder, 1988—; cons. Pres. Materials Policy Commn., 1951; mem. Colo. Adv. Bd. Bur. Land Mgmt., 1967-69. Author: Cases and Materials on Natural Resources Law, 1951, Water for Mushrooming Populations, 1954; co-author: American Law of Property, 1953, Water and Water Rights, 1963; editor, co-author: American Law of Mining, 1960. Co-chmn. Jud. Reorganization Commn., 1961-63; elder Presbyn. Ch., Boulder; pres. Rocky Mountain Mineral Found., 1961-62, others. Comdr. USN, 1942-58, PTO, with Res. Decorated Silver Star, Bronze Star, Letter of Commendation. Mem. ABA (chmn. natural resources sect. 1985-86), Fed. Bar Assn., Colo. Bar Assn. (chmn. water sect. 1957, chmn. mineral sect. 1961, award of merit 1962), Order of Coif, Phi Beta Kappa. Democrat. Avocations: horticulture, woodworking, mountaineering, skiing. Home: 755 6th St Boulder CO 80302-7416 Office: Davis Graham & Stubbs 370 17th St Ste 4700 Denver CO 80202-5601

MARTZ, JOHN ROGER, lawyer; b. Buffalo, June 13, 1937; s. George Albert and Dorothy (Dinsbier) M.; m. Charlotte Gail Lemberes, July 22, 1966; children: Teresa Gail, Nicole Jackie. BS, U.S. Mil. Acad., 1960; MS in Engring., Purdue U., 1964; JD, U. San Francisco, 1980. Bar: Nev. 1980. Commd. 2d lt. U.S. Army, 1960; nuclear engr. Army Nuclear Power Program, 1964-66; with Spl. Forces in Okinawa, Vietnam, Thailand, Korea, Taiwan,, Philippines, 1966-72; elec. engr. Armed Forces Radiobiology Rsch. Inst. and Def. Nuclear Agy., 1972-75; advisor N.G., Calif. and Nev., 1975-80; ret. U.S. Army, 1980; atty. Henderson & Nelson, Reno, 1980-85; pvt. practice Reno, 1985—. Decorated Bronze Star, Combat Inf. badge; recipient Joint Svc. Commendation medal U.S. Dept. Def., 1975. Mem. Nev. State Bar Assn., Washoe County Bar Assn. Avocations: running, hiking, fishing, motorcycling. Office: 440 Ridge St Reno NV 89501

MARTZ, LOUIS LOHR, English literature educator; b. Berwick, Pa., Sept. 27, 1913; s. Isaiah Louis Bower and Ruth Alverna (Lohr) M.; m. Edwine Montague, June 30, 1941 (dec. 1985); children: Frederick, Louis, Ruth Anne; m. Barbara Stuart, May 5, 1990; 1 child, Olivia. AB, Lafayette Coll., 1935, LittD (hon.), 1960; PhD, Yale U., 1939; LHD (hon.), De Pauw U., 1983; LittD (hon.), Siena Coll., 1984. Instr. English Yale U., 1938-44, asst. prof., 1944-48, assoc. prof., 1948-54, prof., 1954-57, Douglas Tracy Smith prof. English and Am. lit., 1957-71, Sterling prof. English, 1971-84, prof. emeritus, 1984—, chmn. dept., 1956-62, 64-65, dir. div. humanities, 1959-62, 80, dir. Beinecke Rare Book and Manuscript Libr., 1972-77, acting master Saybrook Coll., 1978-79, chmn. coll. seminar program, 1968-71, acting dir. Ctr. Brit. Art, 1981; vis. prof. English Georgetown U., 1985-91; vis. prof. English Emory U., 1986-88. Author: The Later Career of Tobias Smollett, 1942, The Poetry of Meditation, 1954, The Paradise Within, 1964, The Poem of the Mind, 1966, The Wit of Love, 1969, Poet of Exile (Milton) 1980, Thomas More: The Search for the Inner Man, 1990, From Renaissance to Baroque: Essays on Literature and Art, 1991; editor: Pilgrim's Progress, 1949, The Meditative Poem, 1963, Milton: Critical Essays, 1966, Anchor Anthology of 17th Century Verse, Vol. I, 1969 (with R. Sylvester) Thomas More's Prayer Book, 1969, Marlowe's Hero and Leander, 1972, (with F. Manley) Thomas More's Dialogue of Comfort, 1976, (with Aubrey Williams) The Author in His Work, 1978, H.D. (Hilda Doolittle) Collected Poems, 1912-1933, 1983, George Herbert and Henry Vaughan, 1986, H.D. Selected Poems, 1988, Quetzalcoatl (D.H. Lawrence), 1994, George Herbert, 1994, Henry Vaughan, 1995; mem. editl. bd. Yale Editl. Prose Works of John Milton; chmn. Yale Editl. Works of Thomas More; contbr. articles, revs. to Brit. and Am. jours. Recipient Christian Gauss prize, 1955; Guggenheim fellow, 1948-49, 81, Rockefeller fellow, 1966-67, NEH fellow, 1977-78. Mem. Am. Acad. Arts and Sci., Amici Thomae Mori, Renaissance Soc. Am., Brit. Acad., Elizabethan Club, Yale Club (N.Y.C.), Athenaeum Club (London), Phi Beta Kappa, Kappa Delta Rho. Home: 60 Old Quarry Rd Guilford CT 06437 Office: 200994 Yale Sta New Haven CT 06520

MARUMOTO, WILLIAM HIDEO, management consultant; b. L.A., Dec. 16, 1934; s. Harry Y. and Midori Mary (Koyama) M.; m. Jean Masako Morishige, June 14, 1959; children: Wendy H. Vlahos, Todd M., Lani M. Moore, J. Tamiko Smith. BA, Whittier Coll., 1957; postgrad., U. Oreg., 1957-58. Dir. alumni rels. Whittier (Calif.) Coll., 1958-65; assoc. dir. alumni and devel. UCLA, 1965-68; v.p. planning and devel. Calif. Inst. of the Arts, L.A., 1968-69; sr. cons. Peat, Marwick & Mitchell, L.A., 1969; asst. to sec. HEW, Washington, 1969; spl. asst. Pres. of U.S., Washington, 1970-73; pres. The Interface Group Ltd., Washington, 1973-89, chmn., 1989—; lectr. on career strategy and planning, 1973—; mem. White House Pers. Task Force, 1981-88, White House Conf. on Small Bus., 1986. Trustee Whittier Coll., 1978—, Japanese Am. Nat. Mus., 1989—, Mex. Am. Legal Def. and Ednl. Fund, 1989-93, Wolf Trap Found. for the Performing Arts, 1995—; active Coun. for the Advancement and Support of Edn., 1980-84; chmn. Nat. Japanese Am. Meml. Found., 1994—, Leadership Edn. for Asian Pacifics, Inc., 1993—. Named one of Am.'s Top 150 Exec. Recruiters, Harper & Rowe Pubs., 1990, 92, 94. Mem. Assn. Exec. Search Cons. (bd. dirs. 1994—), U.S. Nat. Assn. Corp. and Profl. Recruiters, Employment Mgmt. Assn., Congl. Country Club. Republican. Methodist. Home: 8808 Brook Rd Mc Lean VA 22102-1509 Office: The Interface Group Ltd/ Boyden Ste 305 2828 Pennsylvania Ave NW Washington DC 20007-5201

MARUSKA, EDWARD JOSEPH, zoo administrator; b. Chgo., Feb. 19, 1934; s. Edward M.; m. Nancy; children—Donna, Linda. Student, Wright Coll., Chgo., 1959-61; D.Sc. (hon.), Xavier U., 1986, U. Cin., 1989. Keeper hoofed animals Lincoln Park Zoo, Chgo., 1961-62; head keeper Children's Zoo, 1959-62; gen. curator Cin. Zoo, 1962-68, dir., 1968—; lectr. biol. sci. U. Can.; numerous TV appearances. Recipient Cin. Conservation Man of Year award, 1973, Ambassador award Cin. Conv. and Visitors Bur., 1974. Fellow Am. Assn. Zool. Parks and Aquariums (pres. 1978-79); mem. Am. Soc. Ichthyologists and Herpetologists, Whooping Crane Conservation Assn., Internat. Union Zoo Dirs., Langdon Club, Cin. Naturalists Soc. Office: Zool Society of Cin 3400 Vine St Cincinnati OH 45220-1333*

MARUVADA, PERESWARA SARMA, engineering executive, researcher; b. Rajahmundry, India, Jan. 1, 1938; emigrated to Can., 1964; s. Ramakrishnamma and Meenakshi (Karra) M.; m. Kamakshi Karra, Nov. 28, 1963; children: Venkata Rao, Siva Prasad. B.E. with honors, Coll. Engring., Kakinada, India, 1958; M.E. with distinction, Indian Inst. Sci. (Bangalore), 1959; M.A.Sc., U. Toronto, 1966, Ph.D., 1968. Sr. teaching fellow Indian Inst. Tech., Kharagpur, India, 1959-61; lectr. M.A. Coll. Tech., Bhopal, India, 1961-64; researcher Institute de Recherche d'Hydro-Que., Varennes, Que., 1969-75, program mgr., 1975-81, group mgr., 1981-83, research mgr., 1983-87, sr. researcher, 1987—. Contbr. articles to profl. jours.; patentee in field. Recipient Platinum Jubilee Alumni award Indian Inst. Sci., 1985. Fellow IEEE; mem. Internat. Conf. on Large High Voltage Electric Systems (chmn. study com. 36 on power sys. electromagnetic compatibility), Que. Order Engrs. Home: 817 de Serigny, Boucherville, PQ Canada J4B 5C5 Office: Institut de Recherche d'Hydro-Que, 1800 Montee Sainte-Julie, Varennes, PQ Canada J3X 1S1

MARVEL, THOMAS STAHL, architect; b. Newburgh, N.Y., Mar. 15, 1935; s. Gordon Simis and Madelyn Emigh (Jova) M.; m. Lucilla Wellington Fuller, Apr. 19, 1958; children—Deacon Simis, Jonathan Jova, Thomas Stahl. A.B., Dartmouth Coll., 1956; M.Arch., Harvard U., 1962. Registered architect, N.C., P.R., Mass., N.Y. Designer Synergetics, Inc., Raleigh, N.C., 1958; designer IBEC Housing, N.Y.C., 1959; ptnr.-architect Torres-Beauchamp-Marvel, San Juan, P.R., 1960-85, Marvel-Flores-Cobian, San Juan, P.R., 1985—; prof. Sch. Architecture, U. P.R., Rio Piedras, 1967-89. Author: Antonin Nechodoma, Architect, 1994; co-author: Parish Churches of Puerto Rico, 1984. Works include Am. Embassy, Guatemala, 1973, U.S. Courthouse and Fed. Office Bldg., V.I., 1976, City Hall, Bayamon, P.R., 1978, Mcpl. Baseball Stadium, Bayamon, 1975, Am. Embassy, Costa Rica, 1986. Bd. dirs. St. John's Sch., San Juan, 1976-93. Recipient 1st award for regional coll. design U. P.R., Utuado, 1983; Harvard Grad. Sch. Design Julia Amory Appleton travelling fellow, 1962, Henry Klumb prize, 1991. Fellow AIA (awards for design Fla. Caribbean region 1981, 84-85, 90-91); mem. P.R. Coll. Architects, Acad. Arts and Scis. Roman Catholic. Club: Harvard

(N.Y.C.). Home: Del Valle 450 San Juan PR 00915 Office: Marvel-Flores-Cobian 1555 Calle Francia Santurce San Juan PR 00911-1934

MARVIN, DAVID KEITH, international relations educator; b. Lincoln, Nebr., Apr. 8, 1921; s. Henry Howard and Alma (Wright) M.; m. Frances Parks Cash, Dec. 14, 1946; children: Margaret Elaine, Keith Wright, Martha Jean. B.A. U. Nebr., 1943; M.A., Northwestern U., 1955, Ph.D., 1957. Mem. UNRRA, Austrian Mission, 1946; vice consul Am. Fgn. Service, Peiping. 1947-50; 2d sec. London, 1950-53; consul Dar-es-Salaam, 1953; Ford Found. fellow Tanganyika, 1956-58; vis. asst. prof. Northwestern U., 1958; asst. prof. San Francisco State U., 1958-62, assoc. prof., 1962-67, prof., 1967—, asst. chmn. social sci. div., 1960-64, chmn. dept. internat. relations, 1964-70, 77-78, 80-84, prof. emeritus, 1986—; vis. prof. U. Calif. at Berkeley, 1967. Author: Emerging Africa in World Affairs, 1965. Chmn. North Coastside Community Council, 1962-64; Bd. dirs. Diablo Valley Edn. Project. Served with inf. AUS, 1943-46. Fellow African Studies Assn.; mem. Phi Beta Kappa. Office: 467 Urbano Dr San Francisco CA 94127-2862

MARVIN, DOUGLAS RAYMOND, lawyer; b. E. Stroudsburg, Pa., Aug. 20, 1947; s. Lester Daniel and Merle Catherine (Loeb) M.; m. Judith Ann; children: Douglas R. Jr., Drew, Carrie, Jill. A.B., Lafayette Coll., 1969; J.D., U. Va., 1972. Bar: Va. 1972, Pa. 1972, D.C. 1977, U.S. Supreme Ct. 1977. Atty.-adv. office of legal counsel U.S. Dept. Justice, Washington, 1972-74; counsel subcom. on criminal laws and procedure Senate Jud. Com., U.S. Senate, Washington, 1974; counsel Senate Jud. Com., 1974; counselor to Atty. Gen. U.S., 1975-77; ptnr. firm Williams & Connolly, Washington, 1977—. Bd. dirs. Braddock Rd. Youth Club. Recipient spl. commendation for outstanding service Atty. Gen., Dept. Justice, 1973. Mem. Am. Law Inst., Am. Bar Assn. (litigation sect.), Va. Bar Assn., Pa. Bar Assn., D.C. Bar Assn., Order of Coif. Home: 4501 Demby Dr Fairfax VA 22032-1728 Office: 839 17th St NW Washington DC 20006-3902

MARVIN, EUGENE L., civil engineer; b. Three Rivers, Mich., Mar. 4, 1935; s. John William and Evangelene (Rahn) M.; m. Isobel Anne Mathieson, Aug. 17, 1957; children: Charles W., James L. BCE, U. Mich., 1957; MS in Mechanics, Mich. State U., 1968, PhD in Mechanics, 1971. Registered prof. engr., Mich. Bridge designing engr. Mich. Dept. Transp., Lansing, 1960-66, phys. rsch. engr., 1966-71; rsch. civil engr. U.S. Army Constrn. Engrs. Rsch. Lab., Champaign, Ill., 1971-80; phys. rsch. scientist U.S. Army Corps of Engrs., Washington, 1980-85; divsn. chief Cold Regional Rsch. Engring. Lab. Corps of Engrs., Hanover, N.H., 1985—; mem. Transp. Rsch. Bd., 1980. Editor: Cold Region Engr. Jour., 1991-95; contbr. articles to profl. jours. Lt. USN, 1957-60. Mem. ASCE, Tech. Coun. for Cold Regions Engring., Chi Epsilon. Avocations: golf, sailing, skiing. Home: PO Box 798 Grantham NH 03753 Office: US Army Cold Regions Rsch & Engring Lab 72 Lyme Rd Hanover NH 03755-1290

MARVIN, JAMES CONWAY, librarian, consultant; b. Warroad, Minn., Aug. 3, 1927; s. William C. and Isabel (Carlquist) M.; m. Patricia Katharine Moe, Sept. 8, 1947; children: Heidi C., James Conway, Jill C., Jack C. B.A., U. Minn., 1950, M.A., 1966. City librarian Kaukauna, Wis., 1952-54; chief librarian Eau Claire, Wis., 1954-56; dir. Cedar Rapids (Iowa) Pub. Library, 1956-67, Topeka Pub. Library, 1967-92; Am. Library Assn.-Rockefeller Found. vis. prof. Inst. Library Sci. U. Philippines, 1964-65; vis. lectr. dept. librarianship Emporia (Kans.) State U., 1970-80; chmn. Kans. del. to White House Conf. on Libraries and Info. Services, Gov.'s Com. on Library Resources, 1980-81; mem. Kans. State Libr. Adv. Commn., 1992—. Served with USNR, 1945-46. Mem. ALA, Iowa Libr. Assn. (past pres.), Kans. Libr. Assn., Philippine Libr. Assn. (life), Mountain Plains Libr. Assn. Home: 40 SW Pepper Tree Ln Topeka KS 66611-2055

MARVIN, OSCAR MCDOWELL, retired hospital administrator; b. Statesville, N.C., Apr. 12, 1924; s. Oscar McDowell and Gladys (Early) M.; m. Jane Everitt Krauss, June 16, 1951 (div. 1975); children: Frederick McDowell, Elizabeth Anne, Robert Doyle; m. Marcia Ann Benefiel Jackson, Dec. 2, 1977; children: Jonathan Paul, Katherine Susanne. A.B., U. N.C. 1948; M.B.A., U. Chgo., 1953; M.S., U. Louisville, 1971. Foreman Hanes Dye & Finishing Co., Winston-Salem, N.C., 1948-51; adminstrv. resident N.C. Bapt. Hosp., Winston-Salem, 1952-53; asst. adminstr. City Meml. Hosp., Winston-Salem, 1953-55, N.C. Med. Care Commn., Raleigh, 1955-57; hosp. adminstr., missionary Bd. World Missions, Presbyn. Ch. U.S., Yodogawa Christian Hosp., Osaka, Japan, 1957-60; asst. adminstr. City Memphis Hosp., 1960-62, adminstr., 1962-68; exec. dir. Louisville Med. Ctr., Inc., 1968-93, Med. Ctr. Commn. Jefferson County, 1982-93; lectr. dept. preventive medicine U. Tenn., 1963-68; assoc. prof. Coll. Pharmacy, 1965-68; organizer N.C. chpt. Hosp. Accts., 1954 pres., 1955-56; treas. Memphis Hosp. Coun., 1963, v.p., 1964, pres., 1965; sec. Memphis Inst. Medicine and Religion, 1966-68; sec.-treas. Assn. Coop. Hosp. Laundries, 1970-71; bd. dirs. Nat. Assn. Hosp. Hospitality Houses, Inc., 1986-93, v.p. 1990-91; sec., bd. dirs. Louisville Med. Ctr. Fed. Credit Union, 1974-92, Med. Ctr. Hospitality House, Inc., 1988-93. Contbr. articles to profl. jours. Mem. Memphis Mayor's Com. to Employ Handicapped, 1963; chmn. hosp. divsn. Shelby United Neighbors, Memphis, 1965; trustee Med. Benevolence Found., 1971; pres. Jefferson County Assn. Children with Learning Disabilities, 1973-74, Ky. Assn. Children with Learning Disabilities, 1974-78; sec., bd. dirs. Butchertown Neighborhood Assn., 1992—. Served with AUS, 1942-45. Mem. Am. Coll. Health Care Execs., Sigma Nu. Presbyterian (deacon, elder). Clubs: Rotary, Belles 'n Beau's Square Dance (pres. 1983-84). Home: 225 Bramton Rd Louisville KY 40207-3419

MARVIN, ROBERT EARLE, landscape architect; b. Colleton County, S.C., Feb. 10, 1920; s. William Robert and Alta Elise (Marvin) M.; m. Anna Lou Carrington, Nov. 8, 1947; children: Earle Robert, Alta Mae. BS in Horticulture, Clemson U., 1942; graduate work in Landscape Architecture, U. Ga., 1947. Registered landscape architect, Ala., Ga., N.C., S.C., Tenn., Va. Pres., owner Robert E. Marvin & Assocs., Walterboro, S.C., 1948—; mem. coun. S.C. Landscape Architecture Bd. Registration; cons. Walterboro-Colleton Planning Commn.; lectr. Landscape Architects Corp. Engrs., Seattle, Pa. State U., Making Cities Liveable Conf., Charleston, S.C., 1989, Nat. Holly Soc. Pa., Nat. Critics Coun. of the Garden Club of Am., Garden Club of Am. Nat. Convention, Univs. across Am., Am. Soc. of Landscape, Architects Nat. Convention. Mem. editorial policy bd. Gardens Design Mag., 1988-89; SC-ETV half-hour Profile Documentary. Trustee Nat. Hort. Rsch. Inst.; apptd. mem. S.C. Arts Commn., S.C. Beautification and Community Improvement Bd., Am. Assembly Future Growth S.C.; mem. adv. com. on turf, floriculture and ornamentals Clemson U., bd. dirs Clemson Bot. Gardens; founding mem. S.C. Landscape Critics Coun. Capt. U.S. Army, World War II, PTO. Recipient Slater Wright award So. Nurseryman Assn., 1967; Community Svc. award City of Walterboro, 1968, Svc. award Walterboro Planning Commn., 1980; Disting. Alumni award Clemson U., 1975, Coll. Agr., Clemson U., 1989, Coll. Environ. Design, U. Ga., 1988; Silver Seal award Nat. Coun. of State Garden Club, Inc., 1980, Elizabeth O'Neill Verner award S.C. Gov., 1986, Friend award Landscape Architect Found., 1987, Landscape Design award Am. Hort. Soc., 1991, numerous others; named to S.C. Jaycees Hall of Fame; Profile Documentary on SC-ETV, 1976; recipient of 11 Nat. Design Awards, presented at White House by First Ladies; numerous Nat. and regional awards. Fellow Am. Soc. Landscape Architects (conv. lectr., Orlando, FLa. 1989); mem. AIA (assoc. S.C. chpt.), S.C. Garden Club (life), Tau Sigma Delta (Silver medal 1983). Methodist. Home: 622 Hampton St Walterboro SC 29488 Office: Robert E Marvin & Assocs PA Rte 7 Box 10 Walterboro SC 29488 *Professional philosophy: The dominant reason for the existence of Robert E. Marvin and Associates shall be to create and design an environment in which each individual can grow and develop to be a full human being as God intended him to be.

MARVIN, ROY MACK, foundry executive; b. Aberdeen, Wash., May 4, 1931; s. Merrill McKinley and Jennie Marie (Larsen) M.; B.S., Lewis and Clark Coll., 1954; A.S., Grays Harbor Coll., 1951; m. Diane Valeri MacKenzie, Nov. 26, 1955. Acct., Pope, Loback & Co., Portland, Oreg., 1953-54, 56-59; controller Ranch Homes, Inc., Beaverton Oreg., 1959-61; controller, Precision Castparts Corp., Portland, Oreg., 1961-70, treas., 1967-93, dir., 1967—, v.p. fin., 1970-80, v.p. adminstrn., 1980—, sec., 1983—; dir. Physicians Assn. Clackamas County, Providence, Milwaukie, Oreg. Bd. dirs. Dwyer Hosp., 1970-79, 84-86; mem. exec. com. Greater Portland Bus. Group on Health; mem. Clackamas County Econ. Devel. Commn., 1984-91, dep.

Oreg. Bus. Coun., 1982-90; bd. dirs Boys and Girls Aid Soc. Oreg., 1990—. Served with U.S. Army, 1954-56. C.P.A., Oreg. Mem. Nat. Assn. Accts. (past pres. Portland chpt.), Planning Execs. Inst. (past pres. Portland chpt.), AICPA, Fin. Execs. Inst., Oreg. Soc. C.P.A.s, Associated Oreg. Industries (bd. dirs., vice chmn. 1992-94), Assoc. Oreg. Indus. Pol. Action Com., (pres. 1991, trustee), North Clackamas Co. of C. (pres. 1973), Oreg. Metals Industry Coun. (pres. 1991-94). Republican. Presbyterian. Club: Multnomah Athletic. Office: Precision Castparts Corp 4600 SE Harney Dr Portland OR 97206-0898

MARVIN, URSULA BAILEY, geologist; b. Bradford, Vt., Aug. 20, 1921; d. Harold Leslie and Alice Miranda (Bartlett) Bailey; m. Lloyd Burton Chaisson, June 28, 1944 (div. 1951); m. Thomas Crockett Marvin, Apr. 1, 1952. BA, Tufts Coll., 1943; MA, Harvard/Radcliffe Coll., 1946; PhD, Harvard U., 1969. Rsch. asst. dept. geology U. Chgo., 1947-50; mineralogist Union Carbide Corp., N.Y.C., 1952-58; instr. dept. geology Tufts U., Medford, Mass., 1958-61; geologist, sr. staff Smithsonian Astrophys. Obs., Cambridge, Mass., 1961—, fed. womens program coord., 1974-77; vis. prof. dept. geology Ariz. State U., Tempe, 1978; lectr. geology Harvard U., 1974-92; trustee Tufts U., 1975—, U. Space Rsch. Assn., Columbia Md., 1979-84, chair 1982-83. Author: Continental Drift, 1973; contbr. chpt.: Astronomy from Space, 1983, The Planets, 1985; assoc. editor Earth in Space, Am. Geophys. Union, 1988-90; contbr. articles to profl. jours. Mem. Lunar and Planetary Sci. Coun., Houston, 1987-91; chair antarctic meteorite working group Lunar and Planetary Inst., Houston, 1993—. Recipient Antarctic Svc. medal NSF, 1983, Group Achievement award NASA, 1984; Sustained Superoir Achievement award SAO, 1988; Asteroid Marvin named in her honor, Minor Planet Bur. of Internat. Astron. Union, 1991, Marvin Nunatak (mountain peak rising through the Antarctic ice sheet) named in her honor U.S. Bd. on Geog. Names, 1992. Fellow AAAS, Meteoritical Soc. (pres. 1975-76), Geol. Soc. Am. (History of Geology award 1986); mem. Assn. Women in Sci., Am. Geophys. Union, History of Earth Scis. Soc. (pres. 1991), Internat. Commn. on History Geol. Scis. (sec.-gen. 1989—), Sigma Xi (pres. Harvard-Radcliffe chpt.1971-72). Avocations: birding. Office: Harvard-Smithsonian Ctr for Astrophysics 60 Garden St Cambridge MA 02138-1516

MARVIN, WILLIAM GLENN, JR., former foreign service officer; b. Dobbs Ferry, N.Y., Oct. 30, 1920; s. William Glenn and Charlotte (Linden) M.; m. Sheila Wells, June 6, 1945 (dec.); children: Sally Marvin Lockhart, William Glenn III, Wells.; m. Suzanne Franzon, Oct. 16, 1982. Student, U. Calif., Berkeley, 1938-40; B.S., Harvard U., 1942; M.A., Stanford U., 1948. European rep. Hoover Instn., 1948-49; polit. scientist Stanford Research Inst., 1949-52; commd. fgn. service officer Dept. State, 1952; vice consul Algiers, 1952-55; consul Berlin, 1955-60; consul, prin. officer Fort de France, Martinique, 1964-66; econ. sec. CENTO, Ankara, Turkey, 1974-76; consul gen. Bordeaux, France, 1977-80; ret., 1980. Served to capt. U.S. Army, 1942-46. Mem. U.S. Fgn. Service Assn., Assn. Bordeaux-L.A. Clubs: Connetablie de Guyenne, Ordre de Tursan.

MARVIT, ROBERT CHARLES, psychiatrist; b. Lynn, Mass., Jan. 23, 1938. BS summa cum laude, Mass. Coll. Pharmacy, 1960; MD, Tufts U., 1964; M.Sc., Harvard U., 1970. Intern New Eng. Med. Ctr., Pratt Diag. Hosp., 1964-65; resident in psychiatry, neuropsychol. medicine Mass. Gen. Hosp., Boston, 1967-70; pvt. practice medicine, specializing psychiatry Honolulu, 1970—; prof. pub. health U. Hawaii, Honolulu, 1974-78, adj. prof. Sch. Pub. Health, 1978—; forensic advisor Hawaii Mental Health Div., 1977—; dir. Health Info. Sys. Office, Dept. Health, 1976-80; cons. in field; lectr. in field. Contbr. articles to profl. jours. Served with USPHS, 1965-67 to lt. comdr. Recipient Alpha Omega Alpha Research award Tufts U., 1963. Fellow Am. Coll. Preventive Medicine, Internat. Soc. Social Psychiatry of Am. Pub. Health Assn., Am. Psychiat. Soc.; mem. Am. Acad. Psychiatry and the Law, Hawaii Psychiat. Soc., AAAS, Harvard Med. Soc., Boston Soc. Neurology and Psychiatry, Hawaii Neurol. Soc., Internat. Soc. Neurosci., Am. Acad. Forensic Psychiatry, Alpha Omega Alpha. Home: 929 Pueo St Honolulu HI 96816-5234 Office: 1314 S King St Ste 759 Honolulu HI 96814-2004

MARWEDEL, WARREN JOHN, lawyer; b. Chgo., July 3, 1944; s. August Frank and Eleanor (Wolgamot) M.; m. Marilyn Baran, Apr. 12, 1975. BS in Marine Engring., U.S. Merchant Marine Acad., 1966; JD, Loyola U., Chgo., 1972. Bar: Ill. 1972, U.S. Dist. Ct. (no. dist.) Ill. 1972, U.S. Supreme Ct. 1974. With U.S. Merchant Marines, 1966-70; ptnr. Keck, Mahin & Cate, Chgo. Served to lt. (j.g.) USNR. Mem. ABA (Ho. of Dels. 1989—), Ill. Bar Assn., Chgo. Bar Assn., Maritime Law Assn. Club: Propellor (Chgo.) (pres. 1982). Avocations: boating, reading, history. Office: Keck Mahin & Cate 77 W Wacker Dr Chicago IL 60601-1629

MARWELL, GERALD, sociology educator, research consultant; b. NYC, Feb. 12, 1937; s. Hilton M. and Pearl (Berman) M.; m. Barbara Epstein, June 16, 1957. B.S., MIT, 1957; M.A., NYU, 1959, Ph.D., 1964. Asst. prof. U. Wis., Madison, Wis., 1963-68, assoc. prof., 1968-71, prof., 1971—, chmn. dept. sociology, 1982-85; vis. rsch. assoc. Internat. Peace Rsch. Inst., Oslo, 1969-70; vis. prof. U. Oslo, 1970, U. Essex, Colchester, Eng., 1978-79, Columbia U., 1989; chief cons. radio programs Sound Studies in Sociology, 1982-84 (recipient Ohio State award 1985). Author: Dynamics of Idealism, 1971; Cooperation: An Experimental Analysis, 1975, Self-Esteem: Its Conceptualization and Measurement, 1976, The Critical Mass in Collective Action, 1993; editor Am. Sociol. Rev., 1990-93; contbr. articles to profl. jours. Vol. cons. Madison Metro Sch. System, 1984; coach Madison Youth Soccer Assn. Avocation: baseball. Home: 3509 Blackhawk Dr Madison WI 53705-1477 Office: U Wis Sociology Dept 1180 Observatory Dr Madison WI 53706-1393 Office: Am Sociological Assn Am Sociological Review 1722 N St NW Washington DC 20036-2983

MARX, ANNE (MRS. FREDERICK E. MARX), poet; came to U.S., 1936, naturalized, 1938; d. Jacob and Susan (Weinberg) Loewenstein; m. Frederick E. Marx, Feb. 12, 1937; children: Thomas J., Stephen L. Student, U. Heidelberg, U. Berlin. mem. staffs N.Y.C. Writers Conf., 1965, Iona Coll., 1964, 65, 70, Wagner Coll., 1965, Poetry Workshop, Fairleigh Dickinson U., 1962, 63, 64, Poetry Soc. Am. Workshop, 1970-71, 78-79; Bronxville Adult Sch. Lecture Series, 1972; bd. dir. poetry series Donnell Library Ctr. (N.Y. Pub. Library) 1970-74; poetry day chmn. Westchester County, 1959—; Poetry Day Workshop, Ark., 1966, 70, Ark. Writers Conf., 1971, South and West Conf., Okla., 1972; vis. poet So. U., 1979; tchr., poetry readings, Jakarta, Indonesia, summer 1979; poetry workshop leader Scarsdale Cultural Ctr., 1981-82; conv. speaker Nat. Fedn. State Poetry Socs., 1974, 81, 82; condr. symposium Immigrant Voices, Pa. State U., 1986; judge Chapbook Award, 1994; judge various nat. poetry contests. Poet; more than 1500 poems published in nat. mags., anthologies, lit. jours. and newspapers; Author: Ein Buechlein, 1935, Into the Wind of Waking, 1960, The Second Voice, 1963, By Grace of Pain, 1966, By Way of People, 1970, A Time to Mend; selected poems, 1973, A Conversation with Anne Marx; 2 hour talking book for blind, 1974; Hear of Israel and Other Poems, 1975, 40 Love Poems for 40 Years, 1977, Face Lifts for All Seasons, 1980, 45 Love Poems for 45 Years, 1982, Holocaust: Hurts to Healings, 1984, German edit. Wunden und Narben, 1986; A Further Semester, 1985, Love in Late Season (New Poems by Anne Marx), 1993; co-editor: Pegasus in the Seventies, 1973; contbr. to American Women Poets Discuss Their Craft, 1983, The Courage to Grow Old, 1989, A Collection of Essays by Ballantine Books, 1989; nat. editor poetry recs., Lamont Library at Harvard, stas. WFAS, WRNW, WEVD, WRVR, Voice of Am., The Pen Woman, 1986-88, Christian Sci. Monitor Anthology of Poems, 1989, Canadian Anthology, 1991, Irish Anthology, 1991. Recipient Am. Weave Chapbook award 1960, Nat. Sonnet 1959, 67, 81, award World Order Narrative Poets, 1981-85 1959, 67, prizes Nat. Fedn. Women's Clubs 1959, 60, Nat. Fedn. State Poetry Socs. 1962, 65, 66, 73, 80-83, South and West Publn. award 1965, Greenwood prize Eng. 1966, 2d Ann. Viola Hayes Parsons award 1977, award Delbrook Center Advanced Studies 1978, 1st prize Nat. Essay Competition, 1990, N.Y. State Outstanding Writer award, 1991; named Poet of the Year N.Y. Poetry Forum, 1981; winner Chapbook competition Crossroads Press, 1984, Am. Writer's Digest award, 1983-90. Mem. Poetry Soc. Am. (life, exec. bd. 1965-70, v.p. 1971-72, two fellowships, Cecil Hemley Meml. award 1974), Poetry Soc. Gt. Britain, Nat. League Am. Pen Women (pres. Westchester County br. 1962-64, North Atlantic regional chmn. 1964-66, nat. letters bd. 1972-74, biennial poetry workshop leader nat. poetry editor 1974-78, N.Y. State lit.

chmn. 1979-80, N.Y. state pres. 1982-84, 2d nat. v.p. 1984-86, nat. editor Pen Woman mag. 1986-88, contbg. editor 1990—, Biennial book award 1976, Biennial awards (4) 1982, (2) 1984, (3) 1986, (2) 1987, (2) 1988, (3) 1989, (2) 1990, Writer of Yr. award 1991), Acad. Am. Poets, Poet Soc. Pa., Composers, Authors and Artists Am., Inc. (poetry editor mag. 1973-78), Poets and Writers, Inc., N.Y. Poetry Forum (life mem.). Subject of story "An American by Choice, A Poet's Credo" pub. in The PEN Woman mag., Nov. 1988, The Courage to Grow Old, 1989, N.Y. Times interview "Finding Poetry in All of Life's Events," 1993; collected works N.Y. Pub. Libr.: Anne Marx Archives, 1992, early German material added to collection, 1994. *To be undeterred is the key to any achievement that is important to our lives. Undeterred by detractors asserting that one's goal is impossible to reach. Undeterred by blame or praise. Undeterred by demands of custom and fashion. Undeterred by all but the most essential bonds of family and friends. Undeterred even by the knowledge that there will be no greatness at the end of the long climb - only the satisfaction that we have tried to bring out the best that is in us, that we have added to our years that special ingredient we needed most to add zest to existence.*

MARX, ARTHUR, author, playwright, director; b. N.Y.C., July 21, 1921; s. Groucho and Ruth (Johnson) M.; m. Irene Kahn, Feb. 27, 1943 (div. 1960); children: Steve, Andy; m. Lois Goldberg, June 27, 1961. Student, U. So. Calif., 1939-40. Copywriter Hal Horne Agy., 1941. Radio comedy writer Milton Berle Show, 1942, Sealtest Show, 1942, Edgar Bergen Show, 1948; writer: (films) Blondie in the Dough, 1947, A Global Affair, 1964, I'll Take Sweden, 1965, Eight on the Lam, 1967, Cancel My Reservation, 1972, (TV series) Pete Smith Specialties, 1949-50; free-lance mag. writer for Parade, N.Y. Times Mag., Sports Illustrated, Cosmopolitan, Los Angeles Mag., others; Broadway playwright: The Impossible Years, 1965, Minnie's Boys, 1970, My Daughter's Rated X, 1971, Groucho: A Life in Review, 1986; musical adaptation of The Ghost and Mrs. Muir, 1987; dir.: Groucho: A Life in Review; author: (books) The Ordeal of Willie Brown, 1950, Life With Groucho, 1954, Not as a Crocodile, 1958, Son of Groucho, 1972, Everybody Loves Somebody Sometime, 1974, Goldwyn, 1976, Red Skelton, 1979, The Nine Lives of Mickey Rooney, 1986, My Life With Groucho, 1988, Set To Kill, 1993, The Secret Life of Bob Hope, 1993; exec. story editor, writer: (TV series) Alice, 1977-81. Served with USCG, 1942-45, PTO. Mem. Dramatists Guild, Authors Guild, Writers Guild Am., West, Acad. Motion Picture Arts and Scis., Internat. Assn. Crime Writers. Jewish. U.S. Intercollegiate Freshman Tennis Champion, 1940. *

MARX, DAVID, JR., lawyer; b. Chgo., Nov. 15, 1950. BA cum laude, Amherst Coll., 1972; JD, Syracuse U., 1975. Bar: N.Y. 1976, Ill. 1986. Ptnr. McDermott, Will & Emery, Chgo. Mem. ABA, Chgo. Bar Assn. Office: McDermott Will & Emery 227 W Monroe St Chicago IL 60606-5016

MARX, GERTIE FLORENTINE, anesthesiologist; b. Frankfurt am Main, Germany, Feb. 13, 1912; came to U.S., 1937, naturalized, 1943; d. Joseph and Elsa (Scheuer) M.; m. Eric P. Reiss, Sept. 26, 1940 (dec. 1968). Student, U. Frankfurt, Germany, 1931-36; M.D., U. Bern, Switzerland, 1937. Diplomate: Nat. Bd. Med. Examiners, Am. Bd. Anesthesiology. Intern, resident in anesthesiology Beth Israel Hosp., N.Y.C., 1939-43; adj. anesthesiologist Beth Israel Hosp., 1943-50, assoc. anesthesiologist, 1950-55; attending anesthesiologist Bronx Municipal Hosp. Center, 1955-95; attending anesthesiologist Bronx VA Hosp., 1966-72; cons., 1972-84; asst. prof. anesthesiology Albert Einstein Coll. Medicine, 1955-60, assoc. prof., 1960-70, prof., 1970-95, prof. emeritus, 1995—. Author: (with Orkin) Physiology of Obstetric Anesthesia, 1969; assoc. editor: Survey Anesthesiology, 1957-83; editor: Parturition and Perinatology, 1973, Clinical Management of Mother and Newborn, 1979, (with G. M. Bassell) Obstetric Analgesia and Anesthesia, 1980, Obstetric Anesthesia Digest, 1981—; cons. editor Internat. Jour. Obstetric Anesthesia, 1991—; contbr. articles to profl. jours. Recipient Nils Lofgren award, 1990, Coll. medal Royal Coll. Anaesthetists, 1993. Fellow Am. Coll. Anesthesiology, N.Y. Acad. Medicine, Am. Coll. Obstetricians and Gynecologists; mem. AMA, Am. Soc. Anesthesiologists (Disting. Svc. award 1988), N.Y. State Soc. Anesthesiologists, Am. Soc. Regional Anesthesia (Disting. Svc. award 1990), Bronx County Med. Soc., N.Y. Acad. Scis. Home: 642A Heritage Vlg Southbury CT 06488-1551 Office: Albert Einstein Coll Medicine Dept Anesthesiology Bronx NY 10461 *I have devoted my professional life to easing the discomfort of childbirth and dare to hope that my efforts have helped to improve the outcome of pregnancy for mother and baby.*

MARX, LEO, retired American cultural history educator; b. N.Y.C., Nov. 15, 1919; s. Leo and Theresa (Rubinstein) M.; m. Jane T. Pike, Aug. 14, 1943; children: Stephen P., Andrew R., Lucy T. S.B. magna cum laude, Harvard U., 1941, Ph.D. in History Am. Civilization, 1950; M.A. (hon.), Amherst Coll., 1959. Teaching fellow, tutor Harvard U., 1946-49; asst. prof. English U. Minn., Mpls., 1949-53; assoc. prof. U. Minn., 1953-58; prof. English and Am. studies Amherst (Mass.) Coll., 1958-76; William R. Kenan, Jr. prof. Am. cultural history MIT, Cambridge, 1976-90, prof. emeritus, 1990—; Fulbright lectr. U. Nottingham, Eng., 1956-57, U. Rennes, France, 1965-66; chmn., adv. coun. Ctr. for Study Am. Culture, Coll. William and Mary. Author: The Machine in the Garden: Technology and the Pastoral Ideal in America, 1964, The Pilot and the Passenger: Essays on Literature, Technology, and Culture in the United States, 1988; editor: The Americanness of Walt Whitman, 1960, Henry Thoreau, Excursions, 1962, Adventures of Huckleberry Finn (Mark Twain), 1966, Anthology of American Literature, 1974, F.B. Sanborn, Life of Henry David Thoreau, 1980, The Railroad in American Art, 1988, Does Technology Drive History?, 1994; editor Literature and Society, 1991—; reviewer: N.Y. Rev. of Books. Served with USNR, 1941-45. Guggenheim fellow, 1962-63, 65-66; Rockefeller humanities fellow, 1983-84. Fellow Am. Acad. Arts and Scis.; mem. MLA, Am. Studies Assn. (pres. 1975-77), Am. Antiquarian Soc., Mass. Hist. Soc., Mass. Found. for Humanities (v.p.), Signet Soc., Phi Beta Kappa (Bicentennial fellow). Home: 19 Joy St Boston MA 02114-4149 Office: MIT E-51 E 211th Cambridge MA 02139

MARX, MORRIS LEON, academic administrator; b. New Orleans, May 21, 1937. BS in Math., Tulane U., 1959, MS in Math., 1963, PhD, 1964. Asst. prof. math. Vanderbilt U., 1966-69, assoc. prof., 1972, dir. grad. studies in math., 1970-72; prof. math., chmn. dept. U. Okla., 1977-81, assoc. dean coll. of arts and scis., 1981-84, interim dean coll. of arts and scis., 1984-85; vice chancellor acad. affairs, prof. math. U. Miss., 1985-88; pres., prof. math. U. West Fla., Pensacola, 1988—. 1st lt. U.S. Army, 1956-64, capt., 1965-66. Office: U West Fla Office of President Pensacola FL 32514-0101

MARX, NICKI D., sculptor, painter; b. L.A., Oct. 3, 1943; d. Donald F. and Ruth H. (Ungar) M. Undergrad., U. Calif., Riverside, 1965, U. Calif., Santa Cruz, 1973. Represented by Tally Richards Gallery, Taos, N.Mex. One-woman shows include Palm Springs Desert Mus., 1977, Julie Artisans Gallery, N.Y.C., 1975, Phoenix Art Mus., 1975, Weston Gallery, Carmel, Calif, 1981, Kirk de Gooyer Gallery, L.A., 1982, Rocklands Gallery, Monterey, Calif., 1983, Fetish Gallery, Taos, 1988, Fenix Gallery, Taos, 1991, Stables Gallery, Taos, 1995, others; group exhbns. include E.P. Smith Gallery, Santa Cruz, 1994, Lumina Gallery, Taos, 1994, Cafe Gallery, Albuquerque, 1991, Bareiss Gallery, Taos, 1990, Ctr. for Contemporary Art, Santa Fe, 1989, Jordan Gallery, Taos, N.Mex., 1988, 89, Stables Art Gallery, Taos, 1988, 94, Albuquerque State Fair Grounds, 1986, San Francisco Mus. Modern Art, 1977, 78, The Elements Gallery, Greenwich, Conn., 1977, Pacific Design Ctr., L.A., 1976, Lester Gallery, Inverness, Calif., 1976, numerous others; work included in sixteen invitational shows; represented in pub. collections IBM, Milford, Conn., N.Y.C., San Jose, Calif., Bank of Am., San Francisco, The Continental Group, Inc., Stamford, Conn., Cedars-Sinai Hosp., L.A., Farm Bur. Fedn., Sacramento, Calif., Sherman Fairchild Sci. Ctr., Stanford, Calif., Palm Springs (Calif.) Desert Mus., Univ. Mus., Ariz. State U. at Tempe, Mills Coll. Art Gallery, Berkeley, Calif.; exhibited in pvt. collections of Estate of Eugene Klein, Estate of Louise Nevelson, Estate of Georgia O'Keeffe, Fritz Scholder, Ray Graham, Bunny Horowitz, Sue and Otto Meyer, Burt Sugarman, Craig Moody, Paul Pletka, others; subject of numerous articles in jours. and mags. MacDowell Colony fellow, 1975; recipient Adolph and Esther Gottlieb Found. grant, 1985. Studio: PO Box 1135 Ranchos De Taos NM 87557-1135

MARX, OWEN COX, lawyer; b. Grosse Pointe, Mich., Oct. 17, 1947; s. Leo A. and Anne (Cox) M.; m. Patricia Windschill, Aug. 14, 1971; children:

Patrick Cox, Molly Simser, Anne Windschill. BA, Coll. of St. Thomas, St. Paul, 1969; JD, Cath. U., Washington, 1972. Bar: Minn. 1972, N.Y. 1973. Law clk. to presiding justice Minn. Supreme Ct., St. Paul, 1972-73; assoc. Mudge, Rose, Guthrie & Alexander, N.Y.C., 1973-75; assoc. Dorsey & Whitney, Mpls., 1975-78, ptnr., 1979-86; ptnr., head London office Dorsey & Whitney, 1986-90; ptnr. Dorsey & Whitney, N.Y.C., 1990—; bd. dirs. Bush Mfg. Co., Detroit, Silver Lake Bancorporation, Hutchinson, Minn., OFLA Receivables Corp., San Diego. Mem. Internat. Bar Assn., Minn. Bar Assn., Mpls. Athletic Club, N.Y. Athletic Club. Republican. Roman Catholic. Home: 136 E 79th St New York NY 10021 Office: Dorsey & Whitney 350 Park Ave New York NY 10022-6022

MARX, PAUL BENNO, author, social service administrator, missionary; b. Saint Michael, Minn., May 8, 1920; s. George and Elizabeth Marx. PhD in Family Sociology, Cath. U. Am., 1957. Ordained priest Roman Cath. Ch., 1947. Worldwide prolife missionary; founder, exec. dir. Human Life Ctr., 1972-80; founder, pres. Human Life Internat., 1980—; prof. sociology St. John's U., Collegeville, Md., 1957-80. Author: Virgil Michel and the Liturgical Movement, 1957, The Mercy Killers, 1971, The Death Peddlers: War on the Unborn, 1972, Japanese edit., 1972, Spanish edit., 1973, Death without Dignity: Killing for Mercy, 1983, And Now Euthanasia. . . , 1985, Confessions of a Prolife Missionary, 1988, Fighting for Life, 1989, The Flying Monk, 1991; contbr. numerous chpts. to books and articles to jours.; founder (quars.) The Internat. Rev. Natural Family Planning, Human Life Issues, Sorrow's Reward, (bi-monthlies) Escoge la Vida!, Seminarians for Life International; (monthly) Pro-Family Parish Notes. Mem. Internat. Fedn. for Family Life Promotion, Japan Found. for Family Life Promotion. Home: 7845 Airpark Rd Gaithersburg MD 20879-4124

MARX, THOMAS GEORGE, economist; b. Trenton, N.J., Oct. 25, 1943; s. George Thomas and Ann (Szymanski) M.; m. Arlene May Varga, Aug. 23, 1969; children: Melissa Ann, Thomas Jeffrey, Jeffrey Alan. B.S. summa cum laude, Rider Coll., 1969; Ph.D., Wharton Sch., U. Pa., 1973. Fin. analyst Am. Cyanamid Co., Trenton, 1968; economist FTC, Washington, 1973; econ. cons. Foster Assocs. Inc., Washington, 1974-77; sr. economist GM, Detroit, 1977-79, mgr. indsl. econs., 1980-81, dir. econs. policy studies, 1981-83; dir. corp. strategic planning group GM, 1984-86, gen. dir. market analysis and forecasting, 1986-88, gen. dir. econ. analysis, 1988-90, gen. dir. issues mgmt. on industry govt. rels. staff, 1990—; mem. faculty Temple U., 1972-73, U. Pa., 1972-73; adj. prof. Wayne State U., 1981—, U. Detroit, 1988—. Assoc. editor Bus. Econs., 1980—; mem. editorial bd. Akron Jour. Bus. and Econs., 1981-90; contbr. articles to profl. jours. Served with USAF, 1961-65. Mem. Nat. Econs. Club, Am. Econ. Assn., Nat. Assn. Bus. Economists, Detroit Area Bus. Economists (v.p.), Econ. Soc. Mich., So. Econ. Assn., Western Econ. Assn., Planning Forum, Assn. Pub. Policy Analysts, Pi Gamma Mu, Beta Gamma Sigma. Roman Catholic. Home: 3312 Bloomfield Park Dr West Bloomfield MI 48323-3514 Office: GM Corp 3044 W Grand Blvd Detroit MI 48202-3091

MARX, WILLIAM B., JR., telecommunications industry executive; b. 1939. BME, Union Coll., 1961; MS, Stanford U., 1978. With AT&T, 1961—; formerly exec. v.p. for network systems mktg. and customer svc.; pres. AT&T Network Systems Group, 1989—. Office: AT&T 1 Oak Way Berkeley Heights NJ 07922-2724

MARZETTI, LORETTA A., government agency executive, policy analyst; b. N.Y., Mar. 13, 1943; d. Lawrence Arthur and Josephine (Palazzo) M.; m. Gerald Oren Miller, July 12, 1986. AB in Sociology, Cath. U. Am., 1965. Chief info. svcs. br., OARM EPA, Washington, 1985-88, dir. comm., analysis and budget divsn., office of solid waste, 1988—. Avocations: aerobics, exercise, walking, European travel. Home: 3088 S Woodrow St Arlington VA 22206 Office: Environmental Protection Agency Solid Waste 5305 401 M St SW Washington DC 20460

MARZILLI, LUIGI GAETANO, chemistry educator, consultant; b. Providence, Sept. 23, 1943; s. Luigi and Modesta (Mignanelli) M.; m. Patricia Ann Selby, Aug. 14, 1965; children: Alan Stewart, Veronica Gina, Alisa Francesca. ScB in Chemistry, Brown U., 1965; PhD in Inorganic Chemistry, Australian Nat. U., Canberra, 1969. Rsch. assoc. U. Chgo., 1969-70; asst. prof. chemistry Johns Hopkins U., Balt., 1970-76, assoc. prof., 1976-80; prof. chemistry Emory U., Atlanta, 1980-86, Samuel Candler Dobbs prof. chemistry, 1986—; prof. Winship Cancer Ctr., 1988—; permanent mem. Bioanalytical & Metallobiochemistry Study Sect. NIH, 1980-84, Biomed. Scis. Study Sect., 1988-92; cons. Centocor, 1986-90. Editor: Advances in Inorganic Biochemistry (10 vols.), 1979—; editor (jour.) Comments on Inorganic Chemistry, 1990—; contbr. articles to profl. jours.; co-inventor 3 patents. Japan Soc. for Promotion of Sci. fellow, Hiroshima, 1992; recipient Sr. U.S. Scientist award Alexander von Humboldt Found., Munich, 1983-84; grantee NIH, 1971—. Fellow AAAS; mem. Am. Chem. Soc. (chair bioinorganic divsn. 1993-94). Home: 2221 Randolph Ct Atlanta GA 30345 Office: Emory U Dept Chemistry 1515 Pierce Dr Atlanta GA 30322

MARZIO, PETER CORT, museum director; b. Governor's Island, N.Y., May 8, 1943; s. Francis and Katherine (Mastroberte) M.; m. Frances Ann Parker, July 2, 1979; children: Sara Lon, Steven Arnold. B.A. (Neva Miller scholar), Juniata Coll., Huntingdon, Pa., 1965; M.A., U. Chgo., 1966, Ph.D. (univ. fellow, Smithsonian Instn. fellow), 1969. Research asst. to dir., then historian Nat. Mus. History and Tech., Smithsonian Instn., 1969-73, asso. curator prints, 1977-78, chmn. dept. cultural history, 1978; dir., chief exec. officer Corcoran Gallery Art, Washington, 1978-82; dir. Mus. Fine Arts, Houston, 1982—; instr. Roosevelt U., Chgo., 1966-68; assoc. prof. U. Md., 1976-77u; adv. coun. Anthrop. Film Ctr., Archives Am. Art; mem. adv. bd. Smithsonian Inst. Press; bd. dirs. First Interstate Bank of Tex. Author: Rube Goldberg: His Life and Works, 1973, The Art Crusade, 1976, The Democratic Art: An Introduction to the History of Chromolithography in America, 1979; editor: A Nation of Nations, 1976. Mem. adv. council Dumbarton Oaks, 1979-86; trustee, mem. exec. com., pres. Texart 150, Tex. Commn. on the Arts, Tex. Assn. for Promotion of Art, 1990-91. Sr. Fulbright fellow Italy, 1973-74. Mem. Print Council Am., Am. Print Council, Dunlap Soc., Assn. Art Mus. Dirs. (pres. 1988-89), Am. Assn. Mus. (exec. com.), Am. Fedn. of the Arts (trustee), Young Pres. Orgn. Club: Cosmos (Washington). Home: 101 Westcott St Houston TX 77007-7044 Office: Mus Fine Arts PO Box 6826 1001 Bissonet St Houston TX 77005

MARZLUF, GEORGE AUSTIN, biochemistry educator; b. Columbus, Ohio, Sept. 29, 1935; s. Paul Bayhan and Opal Faun (Simmons) M.; children: Bruce, Julie, Philip, Glenn. BS, Ohio State U., 1957, MS, 1960; PhD, Johns Hopkins U., 1964. Postdoctoral fellow U. Wis., Madison, 1964-66; asst. prof. biochemistry Marquette U., Milw., 1966-70; assoc. prof. Ohio State U., Columbus, 1970-75, prof., 1975—, chmn. dept. biochemistry, 1985—. Contbr. articles to profl. jours. Mem. Genetics Soc. Am., Am. Soc. Microbiology, AAAS, Am. Soc. Biochemists and Molecular Biologists. Office: Ohio State U Dept of Biochemistry 484 W 12th Ave Columbus OH 43210-1292

MARZULLA, ROGER JOSEPH, lawyer; b. Glendale, Calif., Aug. 12, 1947; m. Nancie George. Student, U. Calif., Berkeley, 1964-66; BA in Polit. Sci., U. Santa Clara, 1968, JD magna cum laude, 1971. Bar: Calif. 1971, U.S. Dist. Ct. (no. dist.) Calif. 1971, U.S. Ct. Apls. (9th cir.) 1971, U.S. Supreme Ct. 1979, U.S. Ct. Apls. (10th cir.) 1981, Colo. 1982, U.S. Dist. Ct. Colo. 1982, U.S. Ct. Apls. (D.C. cir.) 1982, D.C. 1985. Assoc. Mager and Matthews, San Jose, Calif., 1971-74; ptnr. Matthews & Marzulla, San Jose, 1974-81; pres. Mountain States Legal Found., Denver, 1981-82; spl. litigation counsel Land and Natural Resources div. U.S. Dept. Justice, Washington, 1983-84, dep. asst. atty. gen., 1984-87, asst. atty. gen., 1987-89; instr. internat. law San Jose State U., 1975; instr. real estate law San Jose City Coll., 1976-81; judge pro tem Calif. Mcpl. Ct., 1978-81, Superior Ct., 1978-81. Named Jaycees Young Man Yr. 1982. Mem. ABA, State Bar Calif., State Bar Colo., D.C. Bar Assn. Presbyterian. Office: Akin Gump et al Ste 400 1333 New Hampshire Ave NW Washington DC 20036-1500

MARZULLI, JOHN ANTHONY, JR., lawyer; b. Orange, N.J., Jan. 3, 1953; s. John Anthony Sr. and Ruth Eileen (Dyer) M.; m. Penelope Bennett, Dec. 13, 1986; children: Emily Mooers, John A. III, Peter Bennett. BA magna cum laude, Middlebury Coll., 1975; JD, NYU, 1978. Bar: N.J. 1978, N.Y. 1979. Law clk. to chief judge U.S. Dist. Ct., N.J., 1978-80; assoc. atty.

Shearman & Sterling, N.Y.C., 1980-87, pntr., 1988—. Contbg. author: Corporate Restructuring, 1990, European Corporate Finance Law, 1990. Mem. ABA, N.Y. State Bar Assn., N.J. Bar Assn., Order of Coif, Phi Beta Kappa. Office: Shearman & Sterling 599 Lexington Ave New York NY 10022 also: Shearman & Sterling, 199 Bishopsgate, London EC2M 3TY, England

MASAMUNE, SATORU, chemistry educator, consultant; b. Fukuoka, Japan, May 24, 1928; came to U.S., 1953; s. Hajime and Chikako (Kondo) M.; m. Takako Nozoe, July 25, 1956; children: Hiroko, Tohoru. BS, Tohoko U., Sendai, Japan, 1953; PhD, U. Calif. at Berkeley, 1957. Postdoctoral fellow U. Wis., Madison, 1957-59, lectr., 1959-61; rsch. fellow Mellon Inst., Pitts., 1961-64; assoc. prof. U. Alta., Edmonton, Can., 1964-67; prof. U. Alta, Edmonton, Can., 1967-79; prof. MIT, Cambridge, 1978-91, A.C. Cope prof., 1991—; cons. Abbott Labs., North Chicago, Ill., 1982-88, Kao Corp., Tokyo, 1983—, Toyo Akuzo, Tokyo, 1987—. Editor: Reaction Intermediate, 1976, Organic Synthesis, 1970-78; contbr. 220 sci. articles to profl. jours. Recipient Hamilton award U. Nebr., 1984. Fellow Am. Acad. Arts and Scis., Royal Soc. Can.; mem. Am. Chem. Soc. (Organic Synthesis award 1978, A.C. Cope scholar 1987), Chem. Soc. of London (Centenary lectr. 1980). Home: 182 Brookline St Newton MA 02159-2803 Office: MIT Dept Chemistry 77 Massachusetts Ave # 18311 Cambridge MA 02139-3594

MASCARA, FRANK, congressman; b. Belle Vernon, Pa., Jan. 19, 1930; married; 4 children. BS, Calif. U. Pa., 1972. Pub. acct., 1956-75; contr. Washington County, 1974-79; comm. Wash. Bd. County Commrs., 1980—; mem. 104th Congress 20th Pa. dist., 1994—. Office: US House Reps 2210 Rayburn House Office Bldg Washington DC 20515-3820*

MASCETTA, JOSEPH ANTHONY, principal; b. Canonsburg, Pa., Sept. 2, 1931; s. Joseph Alphonso and Amalia (Ciavarra) M.; m. Jean Vernone, June 18, 1960; children: Lisa Marie, Linda Jo, Lori Jean. BS, U. Pitts., 1954; MS, U. Pa., 1963; cert. advanced study, Harvard U., 1970. Cert. tchr. math., phys. scis., adminstr. secondary sch., Pa. Tchr. chemistry Canonsburg High Sch., 1956-59; tchr. chemistry Mt. Lebanon High Sch., Pitts., 1959-75, chair sci. dept., 1967-75; coord. secondary curriculum Mt. Lebanon Sch. Dist., Pitts., 1975-81; prin. Mt. Lebanon Sr. High Sch., Pitts., 1981-91; ret., 1991; vis. team mem. Mid. States Assn. Colls. and Schs., Phila., 1967-78, chair vis. teams, 1981—, Pa. state adv. com., 1988-91; mem. sch. bd. and edn. commn. St. Patrick Sch., Canonsburg, 1972-85; regional dir. Pa. Jr. Acad. Sci., Pitts., 1976-82. Author: Modern Chemistry Review, 1968, Chemistry the Easy Way, 1989, revised, 1995, Barron's SAT II, Chemistry, 1994; contbg. author: (ency.) Barron's Student Concise Ency., 1988, rev. 1994, Barron's New Student's Concise Ency., 1993. Recipient Outstanding Tchr. award Spectroscopy Soc., 1973; grantee NSF, 1961, 62-63, 63, 67, 69-70, 73; sci. fellow GE, 1959. Mem. ASCD, Nat. Assn. Secondary Sch. Prins. (Cert. of Recognition 1991), Pa. Assn. for Curriculum and Supervision (exec. bd. dirs. 1985-87, regional pres. 1987), Western Pa. Assn. for Curriculum and Supervision (v.p. 1983-85, pres. 1985-87), Phi Delta Kappa. Roman Catholic. Avocations: painting, writing. Home: 451 Mcclelland Rd Canonsburg PA 15317-2258

MASCHO, GEORGE LEROY, education educator emeritus; b. Warsaw, N.Y., Feb. 5, 1925; s. Clayton Leroy and Dorothy Emma (Bailey) M. B.Ed., SUNY, Geneseo, 1948; M.A., Stanford U., 1950; Ed.D., Ind. U., 1961. Tchr. Ontario (N.Y.) Jr. High Sch., 1948-49, Burris Lab. Sch., Muncie, Ind., 1950-61; mem. faculty Ball State U., Muncie, 1961-85; prof. edn. Ball State U., 1967-85, prof. emeritus, 1985—. Contbr. articles to profl. jours. Bd. dirs., treas. United Day Care Center, 1977—; mem. nat. com. developing Head Start program, 1965-66; vol. tutor Hui Malama Adult Literacy Svcs., 1988—; corr. sec. Maui Sr. Citizen Planning and Coordinating Coun., 1987-88; chmn. community ctr. planning com. Pukalani Community Assn., 1989. With inf. U.S. Army, 1943-46. Mem. Nat. Assn. Edn. Young Children, Ind. Assn. Edn. Young Children (chmn. legis. com. 1968-70), Assn. Childhood Edn., Hawaii State Ret. Tchrs. Assn. (chmn. planning com. conv. 1991), Maui Ret. Tchrs. Assn. (dir. 1985—, v.p. 1987-88, 88-89), Maui Sr. Citizen Planning/Coordinating Coun. (corr. sec. 1987-89), AARP, Hawaii, Hawaii State Ret. Tchrs. Assn. (Maui rep. 1989-90), Ind. Arabian Horse Assn. (dir. 1968-73), Am. Contract Bridge League, Pukalani Bridge Club (treas. 1993—), Phi Delta Kappa. Home: 2792 Aina Lani Dr Makawao HI 96768-8404 *To educate is to work with the future. All educators attempt to motivate, provide stimulating environments, prod and inspire students to reach just a bit higher than they would have reached had such contact not been made. If I attain that goal, my life is worthwhile.*

MASCITELLI, JOEL, oil industry executive. With Ultramar Group, Tarrytown, N.Y., 1978-1989; sr. v.p.-operations Ultramar Inc., Hanford, Calif., 1989—. Office: Can Ultramar Ltd, 1 Valleybrook Dr, Don Mills, ON Canada M3B 2S8 Office: Ultramar Inc 525 W 3rd St Hanford CA 93230-5016

MASCOTTE, JOHN PIERRE, insurance executive; b. Ft. Wayne, Ind., May 19, 1939; s. Leo Cyril and Mary Harriet (Rowen) M.; m. Sarah Ann Foret, Apr. 23, 1966; children: Leo Rowen, Mark Foret and Matthew Foret (twins), Mary Marcella. BA in Philosophy, St. Joseph's Coll., Rensselaer, Ind., 1961, BS in Acctg., 1961; LLB, U. Va., 1964. Bar: Ind. 1964. Clk. Tax Ct. U.S., Washington, 1964-66; tax specialist Coopers & Lybrand, Ft. Wayne, 1966-67; exec. v.p. Peoples Trust Bank, Ft. Wayne, 1967-69; sr. v.p. Lincoln Nat. Corp., Ft. Wayne, 1969-74; exec. v.p. Mut. Benefit Life Ins. Co., Kansas City, Mo., 1974-81; pres. Continental Corp., N.Y.C., 1981—, also chmn., chief exec. officer, 1982—; bd. dirs. Continental Corp., Hallmark Cards, Inc., Chemical Bank, Bus. Men's Assurance Co. of Am. Democrat. Roman Catholic. *

MASELLI, JOHN ANTHONY, food products company executive; b. N.Y.C., Feb. 18, 1929; s. Anthony and Livia M.; m. Brigitta Degenkolb, Dec. 26, 1948; children: Elisa, John A. Jr. BS in Chemistry, CCNY, 1947; MS in Chemistry, Fordham U., 1949, PhD in Chemistry, 1952. Dir. research and devel. Standard Brands, Stamford, Conn., 1952-64; mgr. product devel. M&M/Mars, Hackettstown, N.J., 1964-67; pres. OZ Food Corp., Chgo., 1967-79; v.p. tech. Nabisco Brands, East Hanover, N.J., 1979-85; v.p. corp. research and devel. RJR Nabisco, Winston-Salem, N.C., 1985-87; sr. v.p. tech. Planters LifeSavers Co., Winston-Salem, 1987-91, cons., 1991—; bd. dirs. Cultor U.S., Xyrofin (Finland), N.C. Biotech. Ctr. Patentee in field. Bd. dirs. Chgo. Boy's Club, 1975-79, YMCA, Wilton, Conn, 1980-84. Mem. AAAS, ACS, Inst. Food Tech., Am. Soc. Bakery Engrs., Indsl. Biotechnology Assn., Indsl. Research Inst. Republican. Avocations: sailing, photography, music. Home: 529 Knob View Pl Winston Salem NC 27104-5107

MASER, FREDERICK ERNEST, clergyman; b. Rochester, N.Y., Feb. 26, 1908; s. Herman A. and Clara (Krumm) M.; m. Anne S. Spangeberg, Aug. 3, 1933; m. Mary L. Jarden, Dec. 25, 1959. AB, Union Coll., Schenectady, N.Y., 1930; MA, Princeton U., 1933; MDiv, Princeton Theol. Sem., 1933; DD, Dickinson Coll., 1957; LL.D. (hon.), McKendree Coll., 1964. Ordained to ministry Methodist Ch., 1933. Pastor Alice Focht Meml. Ch., Birdsboro, Pa., 1933-38; pastor Central Ch., Frankford, Phila., 1938-45, St. James Ch., Olney, Phila., 1945-53; dist. supt. Northwest dist. Phila. Meth. Ann. Conf., 1953-58; pastor Old St. George's Ch., Phila., 1958-67; on sabbatical leave Europe, 1967-68; acting dean students Conwell Sch. Theology, 1968-69; dir. pub. relations Eastern Pa. Conf. United Meth. Ch., 1969-72; exec. sec. World Meth. Hist. Soc., 1971-74; commn. on archives and history United Meth. Ch., 1974—; Tipple lectr. Drew U., Madison, N.J., 1977; spl. lectr. N.Am. sect. World Meth. Hist. Soc., Ashbury Sem., Wilmore, Ky., 1984—; rep. from Northeast Jurisdiction to TV Radio and Film Commn. Meth. Ch., 1952-60; exec. com. Am. Hist. Socs. of Meth. Ch., 1952-68; vice chmn. N.E. Jurisdictional Hist. Socs., 1948; chmn. div. evangelism Pa. Council Chs., 1953-58; mem.-at-large TV, Radio and Film Commn. Meth. Ch., 1960-64; del. Phila. Ann. Conf. to Jurisdictional Conf. of Meth. Ch., 1952; leader ministerial del. to Gen. Conf. Meth. Ch., Mpls., 1956; del. 9th World Conf. of Methodism, Lake Junaluska, 1956, 10th Conf., Oslo, 1961, 12th Conf., Denver, 1971, 13th Conf., Dublin, 1976, 14th Conf., Hawaii, 1981; dir. pub. relations Phila. Meth. ann. conf., 1961-68; exec. sec. World Meth. Hist. Soc., 1971-74. Author: The Dramatic Story of Early American Methodism, 1965, The History of Methodism in Central Pennsylvania, 1971, Challenge of Change: The Story of a City's Central Church, 1982, Robert Strawbridge,

First American Methodist Circuit Rider, 1983, The Story of John Wesley's Sisters or Seven Sisters in Search of Love, 1988, The Wesley Sisters, 1990, Unfolding the Secret of History, 1991, Theories of the Atonement and the Final Solution, 1993, Sara Teasdale, A Returning Comet, 1993, The Human Side of the Mother of Methodism, 1993; co-author: Proclaiming Grace and Freedom, 1984, Christina Rossetti, 1991, United Methodism in America, A Compact History, 1992; mem. editorial bd. Meth. History, 1971-75; editor in chief Jour. Joseph Pilmore, 1968; mem. editorial bd., author History American Methodism, 1964, Ency. World Methodism, 1974, Second Thoughts on John Wesley, 1977, Affectionately, your Brother, 1994; contbr. articles to religious jours. Trustee George Ruck Trust, 1958-82; mem. adv. council Wesley Theol. Sem., Washington, 1960-72. Recipient St. George's Gold medal award for disting. svc. to Meth. Ch., 1967, Citation Temple U., 1971, (with Mary L. Maser) Phyllis Goodhart award Bryn Mawr Coll. Libr., 1988, cert. appreciation for disting. contbns. to field of Meth. history Commn. on Archives and History of United Meth. Ch., honoree for life-long commitment to Wesley studies The Charles Wesley Soc., 1992. Mem. Pa. Acad. Fine Arts, Colonial Phila. Hist. Soc. (bd. dirs. 1956-64), Ch. History Soc., Union League, Wesley Soc. (life, honored for disting. contbn. in field of rsch.), Philobiblon Club, Princeton Club, Phi Beta, Phi Alpha. Home: Heritage Towers Apt 634 200 Veterans Ln Doylestown PA 18901 *Life offers many honors but the older I grow, the more I realize that the highest honor is to have one's name written in the Lamb's Book of Life.*

MASEY, JACK, exhibition designer; b. N.Y.C., June 10, 1924; s. Max and Anna Masey; m. Mary Lou Leach, Dec. 27, 1959. Student, Cooper Union, 1941-43; B.F.A., Yale, 1950. Pres. MetaForm Inc., N.Y.C., 1979—; co. project mgr. for design of La. Pavilion, World Expo., New Orleans, 1984, Statue of Liberty Exhibit, N.Y.C., 1986, Johnstown (Pa.) Flood Mus., N.Y.C., 1988, Nat. D-Day Mus., New Orleans, 1994, Harry S. Truman Mus., Independence, Mo., 1994; lectr. Sch. Art and Architecture, Yale U., 1968-69. Cartoonist Esquire mag, 1946; exhibits officer, USIS, New Delhi, 1951-55; designer U.S. Pavilion, Kabul Internat. Fair, 1956; dir. design Am. Nat. Exhbn., Moscow, 1959, chief, East-West exhibits br. USIA, Washington, 1960-67; chief design U.S. Pavilion, Montreal (Que., Can.) World's Fair, 1967, dep. commr. gen. for planning and design Osaka (Japan) World Expn., 1970; dir. design Am. Revolution Bicentennial Commn., Washington, 1971-73; dir. design and exhbns. Am. Revolution Bicentennial Adminstrn., 1974-77, design dir. Internat. Communication Agy., Washington, 1977—; designer: Medicine-U.S.A. exhbn. for, USSR exchange program, 1962, Tech.-Books exhbns., 1963. Served with AUS, 1943-45, ETO. Recipient Meritorious Service award USIA, 1959, Superior Service award, 1964, Superior Honor award, 1967, 75; award of excellence Fed. Design Council, 1975; Outstanding Achievement award, 1979; award of excellence Soc. Fed. Artists and Designers, 1971; Gold medal Art Dirs. Club, 1965; cert. of excellence Am. Inst. Graphic Arts, 1964; two Fed. Design Achievement awards for Contributions to Excellence in Design, U.S. Govt., 1984, Presdl. awards for Statue of Liberty Exhibit, 1986, for Ellis Island Immigration Mus., 1990. Home: 131 E 66th St Apt 3A New York NY 10021-6129 Office: 15 E 26th St New York NY 10010-1501

MASH, DONALD J., college president; b. Oct. 12, 1942; m. Julia Larson; children: Maria, Christina. BS in Edn., Ind. U. Pa., 1960; MA in Geography, U. Pitts., 1966; PhD, Ohio State U., 1974. Teaching fellow U. Pitts., 1964-65; instr. geography U. Pitts.-Bradford, 1965-68; dean for student svcs. Ohio Dominican Coll., 1968-75; v.p. for student affairs George Mason U., Fairfax, Va., 1975-85, exec. v.p. adminstrn., 1985-88; pres. Wayne (Nebr.) State Coll., 1988—. Office: Wayne State Coll Office of Pres Wayne NE 68787

MASHAW, JERRY L., lawyer, educator; b. 1941. B.A., Tulane U., 1962, LL.B., 1964; Ph.D., U. Edinburgh, 1969. Bar: La. 1964, Va. 1975. Asst. prof. Tulane U., 1966-68; asst. prof. U. Va., 1968-69, assoc. prof., 1969-72, prof., 1972-76; prof. Yale U. Law Sch., 1976—, William Nelson Cromwell prof., 1983—; cons. Ctr. Adminstrn. Justice. Mem. Order of Coif, Phi Beta Kappa. Author: (with Merrill) Introduction to the American Public Law System, 1975; (with others) Social Security Hearings and Appeals, 1978, Bureaucratic Justice, 1983, Due Process in the Administrative State, 1985; past editor-in-chief Tulane Law Rev. Office: Yale U Law Sch PO Box 401A New Haven CT 06520-7397

MASHBERG, GREGG M., lawyer; b. Peekskill, N.Y., Dec. 4, 1951; s. edward and Mildred (Weinstein) M.; m. Amy Lee Garfinkel, Aug. 1, 1976; children: Jenny, Emily. BA, Case Western Res. U., 1973; JD, NYU, 1977. Bar: N.Y. 1978, U.S. Dist. Ct. (so. and ea. dists.) N.Y. 1978, U.S. Ct. Appeals (2nd cir.) 1979, U.S. Supreme ct. 1988. Assoc. corp. counsel Law Dept., City of N.Y., 1978-83; assoc./ptnr. Schwartz Klink & Schreiber, P.C., N.Y.C., 1983-87; ptnr. Proskauer Rose Goetz & Mendelsohn, N.Y.C., 1987—. Bd. dirs. Children's Day Treatment Ctr. and Sch., N.Y.C., 1987—; founder, mem. New Rochelle (N.Y.) Coalition for Excellence in Pub. Schs., 1992. Mem. Assn. Bar City of N.Y. (Award for Excellence Com. on Mcpl. Affairs 1981), N.Y. Bar Assn., Anti-Defamation League (nat. com. legal affairs). Avocations: jogging, skiing, clarinet. Home: 21 Arbor Dr New Rochelle NY 10804 Office: Proskauer Rose Goetz et al 1585 Broadway New York NY 10036

MASHECK, JOSEPH DANIEL, art critic, educator; b. N.Y.C., Jan. 19, 1942; s. Joseph Anthony and Dorothy Anna (Cahill) M. A.B., Columbia U., 1963, M.A., 1965, Ph.D., 1973. Editorial researcher Bollingen Found.-Princeton U. Press, 1967-69; lectr. liberal studies Maidstone Coll. Art, Kent, Eng., 1968-69; preceptor in art history Columbia U., 1970-71; instr. art history Barnard Coll., 1971-73, asst. prof., 1973-83; lectr. visual and environ. studies Harvard U., Cambridge, Mass., 1983-86; assoc. prof. art history Hofstra U., Hempstead, N.Y., 1987-94, prof., 1994—; coord. grad. program in humanities, curatorial cons. Hofstra Mus., Hempstead, N.Y. Author: Historical Present: Essays of the 1970s, 1984, Smart Art (Point 1), 1984, Modernities: Art-Matters in the Present, 1993, Building-Art: Modern Architecture Under Cultural Construction, 1993; editor: Marcel Duchamp in Perspective, 1975; contbg. editor: Art in Am. mag., 1987—; contbr. articles to profl. publs. Nat. Endowment Arts fellow, 1972-73, 75-76; Guggenheim fellow, 1977-78. Mem. AAUP, Coll. Art Assn., Internat. Assn. Art Critics. Roman Catholic. Democrat. Office: Hofstra U Dept Fine Arts and Art History Calkins Hall Hempstead NY 11550

MASI, DALE A., research company executive, social work educator; b. N.Y.C.; d. Alphonse E. and Vera Avella; children: Eric, Renee, Robin. BS, Coll. Mt. St. Vincent; MSW, U. Ill.; D Social Work, Cath. U. Lectr. Sch. Social Svcs., Ipswitch, Eng., 1970-72; project dir. occupational substance abuse program, asso. prof. Boston Coll. Grad. Sch. Social Work, 1972-79; dir. Office Employee Counseling Svc., Dept. Health/Human Svcs., Washington, 1979-84; pres. Masi Research Cons., Inc.,, 1984—; prof. U. Md. Grad. Sch. Social Work, 1980—; adj. prof. U. Md. Coll. Bus. and Mgmt., 1980—; mem. IBM Mental Health Adv. Bd., 1990—; cons. IBM, Toyota, Mobil Chem., The Washington Post, U.S. Ho. Reps., White House, WHO, Bechtel Corp., other orgns. in pub. and pvt. sector; bd. advisors Employee Assistance mag. and Nat. Security Inst.; USIA AmPart lectr. on alcohol, drugs and AIDS in the workplace. Author: Human Services in Industry, Organizing for Women, Designing Employee Assistance Programs, Drug Free Workplace, AIDS Issues in the Workplace: A Response Model for Human Resource Management, The AMA Handbook for Developing Employee Assistance and Counseling Programs, Evaluating Your Employee Assistance and Managed Behavioral Care Program; also over 40 articles. Fulbright fellow, 1969-70; AAUW postdoctoral fellow; NIMH fellow, 1962-64; recipient award Employee Assistance Program Digest; named to Employee Assistance Program Hall of Fame. Mem. AAUW, NASW (Internat. Rhoda G. Sarnat award 1993), Acad. Cert. Social Workers, Employee Assistance Profls. Assn. (nat. individual achievement award 1983), Fulbright Assn. (nat. bd.). Democrat. Roman Catholic. Office: 2301 E St NW Ste 209A Washington DC 20037-2829

MASI, EDWARD A., computer company executive; b. Medford, Mass., May 7, 1947; s. Joseph Carl and Rita Olivine (Metras) M.; m. Kristine Ann Lauderbach Masi, Jan. 24, 1970. BSME, Tufts U., 1969. Mktg. sales IBM, Boston, 1969-76; commercial analysis IBM, Westchester, N.Y., 1976-78; mktg. mgr. IBM, Bethesda, Md., 1978-80; region mgr. mktg. sales Cray Rsch., Calverton, Md., 1980-87; exec. v.p. mktg. Mpls., 1988-92; corp. v.p.

and pres. Intel Corp., Beaverton, Oreg., 1992. Mem. Am. Electronics Assn. (vice chair 1991-92). Avocations: tennis, scuba diving. Office: Intel Scalable Systems Divsn 5200 NE Elam Young Pkwy Beaverton OR 97124

MASIELLO, ANTHONY M. (TONY MASIELLO), mayor; b. 1947; s. Dan and Bridget M.; married; 1 child, Kimberly; m. Kathleen McCue; 1 child, Ariel Lynn. BS, Canisius Coll.; LHD (hon.), Medaille Coll. Mem. North Dist. Buffalo Common Coun., councilman-at-large, coun. majority leader; mem. N.Y. State Senate, 1980—; mayor City of Buffalo. Office: Office of the Mayor 201 City Hall 65 Niagara Sq Buffalo NY 14202*

MASIELLO, ROCCO JOSEPH, airlines and aerospace manufacturing executive; b. N.Y.C., Jan. 9, 1922; s. Joseph and Armanda (Mansueti) M.; m. Rita Elizabeth Amoruso, Feb. 19, 1945; children: Richard, Robin, Janet. Student, CCNY, 1946-48, Hofstra U. 1951-54. Registered profl. engr., Maine. With Pan. Am. World Airways, N.Y.C., 1950-59; v.p. maintenance and engring. U.S. Air Group, Pitts., 1959-72, Am. Airlines, Tulsa, 1973-82; sr. v.p. ops. Am. Airlines, Dallas, 1982-86; founder, exec. v.p. USAfrica Airways 1990—, also bd. dirs; aerospace cons., prin. R.J. Masiello and Assocs. Mem. Soc. Automotive Engr., Royal Aero. Soc. Roman Catholic.

MASIN, MICHAEL TERRY, lawyer; b. Montreal, Jan. 28, 1945; came to U.S., 1994. s. Frank J. and Sonia (Ellmann) M.; m. Joanne Elizabeth Combé, June 4, 1966; 1 child, Courtney. BA, Dartmouth U., 1966; JD, UCLA, 1969. Bar: Calif. 1969, D.C. 1970. Assoc. O'Melveny & Myers, Los Angeles, 1969-76; ptnr. O'Melveny & Myers, Washington, 1976-91; mng. ptnr. O'Melveny & Myers, N.Y.C., 1991—; bd. dirs. Trust Co. West, L.A., GTE Corp., Stamford, Conn., Contel Cellular, Inc., Atlanta. Trustee Am. U., 1982—. Mem. ABA, Coun. on Fgn. Rels., The Brook, Calif. Club. Republican. Methodist. Office: O'Melveny & Myers 153 E 53d St New York NY 10022

MASINTER, EDGAR MARTIN, lawyer; b. Huntington, W.Va., Jan. 2, 1931; s. Ralph Leon and Gazella (Schlossberg) M.; m. Margery Flocks, July 8, 1962; children: Robert Andrew, Catherine Diane. BA, Princeton U., 1952; LLB, Harvard U., 1955. Bar: D.C. 1955, N.Y. 1958. Assoc. Simpson Thacher & Bartlett, N.Y.C., 1957-65, ptnr., 1966—; bd. dirs. Grand Cen. Partnership, Inc. Vice pres. bd. dirs. Grand St. Settlement, N.Y.C., 1980—; mem. bd. regents, The Mercersburg (Pa.) Acad. With U.S. Army, 1955-57. Mem. ABA, Assn. of Bar of City of N.Y. Office: Simpson Thacher & Bartlett 425 Lexington Ave New York NY 10017-3903

MASKALERIS, STEPHEN NICHOLAS, lawyer; b. Newark, June 23, 1927; s Nicholas S. and Kalliope Pappas; m. Corinne, Dec. 27, 1953; children—Carol Christine, Susan Corinne. B.S. in Acctg., Seton Hall U., 1949; J.D., Rutgers U., 1953. Bar: N.J. 1953, N.Y. 1980, U.S. Ct. Appeals (3d cir.) 1963, U.S. Supreme Ct. 1957. Assoc. Van Riper and Belmont, Newark, 1953-69; prin. Maskaleris & Assocs., Newark, Athens, Greece; prin. Maskaleris & Berowitz, Morristown, N.J., 1977-82; prin. Maskaleris & Assoc., Morristown, N.J., 1982—; Far Hills, N.J., N.Y.C.; lectr. Inst. Continuing Legal Edn. Rutgers U., N.J., 1962—; project chmn. Indigent Defender Project, Essex County, Newark, 1964; spl. rate counsel N.J. Pub. Utilities Commn. Author (with others): Defense of the Poor in Criminal Cases in American State Courts, 1965; Defending Persons Accused of Crime, 1966; contbr. articles to profl. jours. trustee Essex-Newark Legal Services, 1983—. Served with USAAF, 1944-46. Mem. N.J. State Bar Assn. (chmn. jr. sect. 1959-61, trustee 1961-62, gen. council 1970—; chmn. Pub. Defender Study Commn. 1978-81), Essex County Bar Assn. (chmn. criminal law sect. 1979), Morris County Bar Assn., ABA (chmn. Jr. Bar Conf. client's security fund com. 1961-62, co-reporter spl. com. on def. of indigent persons accused of crime 1963-64, chmn. law office structure and orgn. commn. 1978-82, council mem., excoms. of law sect. 1980-82, standing com. retirement of lawyers 1980-85, chmn. 1983—, sr. lawyers div. founding mem. 1985), Fed. Bar Assn., Advocates Soc., Comml. Law League, Am. Judicature Soc., Nat. Assn. Def. Lawyers in Criminal Cases, Assn. Trial lawyers Am. (v.p. N.J. bd. 1971-73, exec. council 1973—), U.S. China Law League (founding mem.), Am. Arbitration Assn. (arbitrator). Greek Orthodox. Avocations: music; composition. Home: 2 Farley Rd Short Hills NJ 07078-2135 Office: Maskaleris & Assocs 30 Court St Morristown NJ 07960-5188

MASKE, MONICA, newspaper editor. Religion editor The Star Ledger, Newark. Office: The Star-Ledger 1 Star Ledger Plz Newark NJ 07102-1200*

MASKET, EDWARD SEYMOUR, television executive; b. N.Y.C., Mar. 3, 1923; s. Isadore and Jennie (Bernstein) M.; m. Frances Ellen Rees, June 11, 1958 (div.); children: Joel Daniel, Johanna Rees Ettaeib, Kate Isobel Smiley. BS, CCNY, 1942; LLB, JD, Harvard U., 1949. Bar: N.Y. 1949. Atty., dir. bus. affairs, v.p. bus. affairs ABC, 1951-68; v.p. to exec. v.p. Columbia Pictures TV, Burbank, Calif., 1968-81; sr. v.p. adminstrn. Universal TV, 1982-86, exec. v.p. adminstrn., 1986-90; exec. v.p. adminstrn. MCA TV Group, 1990-93; TV cons., 1993—. Served as 2d lt. AUS, 1942-46, PTO. Mem. ABA, Acad. TV Arts and Scis., Motion Picture Pioneers, Hollywood Radio and TV Soc., Phi Beta Kappa. Avocation: tennis, golf. Office: MCA TV Group 100 Universal City Plz Universal City CA 91608-1002

MASKIN, ARVIN, lawyer; b. Bklyn., Mar. 27, 1954; s. Robert and Clair (Diamond) M.; m. Debra Ann, 1979; children: Daniel Chase, Andrew Noah, Sophie Leah. BA, Georgetown U., 1975, JD, 1978. Bar: N.Y. 1978, Pa. 1984, D.C., U.S. Ct. Appeals (2d, 3d and fed. cirs.), U.S. Supreme Ct. Dep. atty. gen. Office of Atty. Gen., Pa., Dept. Justice, Phila., 1978-82; trial atty. civil div. U.S Dept Justice, Washington, 1982-86; assoc. Weil, Gotshal & Manges, N.Y.C., 1987-88, counsel, 1988-90, ptnr., 1990—; bd. dirs. Civil Trial Manual, Bureau Nat. Affairs, Toxics Law Reporter, reporter Product Safety and Liability; lectr. Yale U., Columbia U., Fordham U. Founder, editor-in-chief Product Liability Perspective; contbr. articles to profl. jours. Mem. ABA (nat. inst. subcom., torts and ins. com., litigation com.), U.S.C. of C. (mass tort task force). Jewish. Office: Weil Gotshal & Manges 767 Fifth Ave New York NY 10153-0002

MASLACH, CHRISTINA, psychology educator; b. San Francisco, Jan. 21, 1946; d. George James and Doris Ann (Cuneo) M.; m. Philip George Zimbardo, Aug. 10, 1972; children: Zara, Tanya. B.A., Harvard-Radcliffe Coll., 1967; Ph.D., Stanford U., 1971. Prof. psychology U. Calif.-Berkeley, 1971—. Author: Burnout: The Cost of Caring, 1982; co-author: Influencing Attitudes and Changing Behavior, 1977, Maslach Burnout Inventory (rsch. scale), 1981, 2d edit., 1986, Experiencing Social Psychology, 1979, 2d edit., 1984, 3d edit., 1993, Professional Burnout, 1993. Recipient Disting. Teaching award, 1987. Fellow AAAS, APA, Am. Psychol. Soc., Soc. Clin. and Exptl. Hypnosis (Henry Guze rsch. award 1980), We. Psychol. Assn. (pres. 1989); mem. Soc. Exptl. Social Psychology. Democrat. Office: U Calif Dept Psychology Tolman Hall # 1650 Berkeley CA 94720-1650

MASLACH, GEORGE JAMES, former university official; b. San Francisco, May 4, 1920; s. Michael J. and Anna (Pszczolkowska) M.; m. Doris Anne Cuneo, Mar. 12, 1943; children: Christina, James, Steven. A.A., San Francisco Jr. Coll., 1939; B.S., U. Calif., 1942. Staff mem. radiation lab. Mass. Inst. Tech., 1942-45, Gen. Precision Labs., 1945-49; research engr. Inst. Engring. Research, 1949-52, asst. dir., 1956-58; assoc. prof. U. Calif., Berkeley, 1952-58, prof., 1959-72, dean Coll. Engring., 1963-72, provost profl. schools and colls., 1972-81, vice-chancellor research and acad. services, 1981-83; internat. cons. edn. and econ. devel., 1982—; adv. aeros. research and devel. NATO, 1960-78, U.S. Naval Acad. Rev. Bd., 1966-75, Dept. Commerce Tech. Adv. Bd., 1964-69, Ford Found. and Am. Soc. Engring. Edn., 1966-78. Mem. ASME, AAAS, Sigma Xi. Home: 265 Panoramic Way Berkeley CA 94704-1831

MASLEN, STEPHEN HAROLD, research engineer, consultant; b. Cleve., Jan. 28, 1926; s. Harold Carpendale and Ethel (Canavan) M.; m. Lee Howeth, July 28, 1951 (dec. 1970); children: Paul, Catherine, Eric; m. Andree Amy Karlak, July 16, 1983. B Aero. Engring., Rensselaer Poly. Inst., 1945, M Aero. Engring., 1947; PhD, Brown U., 1952. Rsch. scientist NASA-Lewis Rsch. Ctr., Cleve. 1947-1955, chief plasma physics br., 1955-60; rsch. group head Martin Marietta, Balt., 1960-67; assoc. dir. Martin

Marietta Labs., Balt., 1967-90; cons. Dept Energy, Oak Ridge, Tenn., 1961-88. Contbr. articles to profl. jours. Fellow Am. Inst. Aeros. and Astronautics; mem. Nat. Acad. Engrs. Democrat. Unitarian. Avocations: traveling, camping, reading. Home: 1315 Margarette Ave Baltimore MD 21286

MASLIN, HARVEY LAWRENCE, staffing service company executive; b. Chgo., Oct. 22, 1939; s. Jack and Shirley Maslin; m. Marcia Silberman, Aug. 23, 1960; children: Elaine, Shelley, Bonnie. BS, U. Ariz., 1961, JD, 1964. Bar: Ariz., 1964, Calif., 1966, U.S. Dist. Ct., 1964, 66. Ptnr. Maslin, Rotundo & Maslin, Sherman Oaks, Calif., 1966-67; gen. counsel Western Temporary Svcs., Inc., San Francisco, 1967-71, v.p., 1972-78, sr. v.p., sec., 1979-84; pres., chief oper. officer Western Staff Svcs., Inc., Walnut Creek, Calif., 1985—; dir. Western Staff Svcs., USA, Western Staff Svcs., U.K. Ltd., London, Western Staff Svcs. Pty Ltd., Melbourne, Australia, Western Staff Svcs. (N.Z.) Ltd., Auckland, Western Svc. A/S, Copenhagen, Denmark, Western Svc./Kontorsvc. A/S Oslo, Western Svc., Inc., Zurich, Western Video Images, Inc., San Francisco. Mem. Rep. Presidential Task Force, Washington, 1981. Mem. Nat. Assn. Temporary and Staffing Svcs. (bd. dirs.), Calif. Bar Assn., Ariz. Bar Assn., World Trade Club, Phi Alpha Delta. Home: 2300 Deer Valley Ln Walnut Creek CA 94598-5005 Office: Western Staff Svcs Inc Exec Offices 301 Lennon Ln Walnut Creek CA 94598

MASLIN, JANET, film critic; b. N.Y.C., Aug. 12, 1949; d. Paul and Lucille (Becker) M.; m. Benjamin Cheever; children: John, Andrew. BA in Math., U. Rochester, 1970. Film and music critic The Boston Phoenix, 1972-76; film critic Newsweek, N.Y.C., 1976-77; dep. film critic The N.Y. Times, N.Y.C., 1977-93, chief film critic, 1993—. Office: The NY Times 229 W 43rd St New York NY 10036-3913

MASLOW, MELANIE JANE, physician; b. N.Y.C., Mar. 11, 1952; d. Morris and Rosalie (Kaufman) Schwartz; m. James Edward Maslow, June 11, 1973 (div. 1977); m. David Tice, Sept. 12, 1985. B.A., Barnard Coll., 1973; M.D., NYU, 1977. Diplomate Am. Bd. Internal Medicine. Intern NYU Med. Ctr.-Manhattan VA Hosp., N.Y.C., 1977-78, resident, chief resident, 1978-81, fellow, 1981-83; co-physician-in-charge infectious disease L.I. Coll. Hosp., Bklyn., 1983-87, co-chief infectious diseases, 1987-92; asst. chief infectious diseases VA Med Ctr., N.Y.C., 1992—; clin. asst. prof. medicine NYU Med. Sch., 1992—. Fellow ACP; mem. Am. Soc. for Microbiology, Infectious Diseases Soc. Am., N.Y. Acad. Sci. Democrat. Jewish. Office: VA Med Ctr 423 E 23rd St New York NY 10010

MASLOW, WILL, lawyer, association executive; b. Kiev, Russia, Sept. 27, 1907; came to U.S., 1911, naturalized; 1924; s. Saul and Raeesa (Moonves) M.; m. Beatrice Greenfield, Dec. 21, 1933; children: Laura, Catha. A.B., Cornell U., 1929; J.D., Columbia U. 1931. Bar: N.Y. 1932, U.S. Supreme Ct. 1932. Reporter N.Y. Times, 1929-31; assoc. Arthur Garfield Hays, 1931-34; assoc. counsel Dept. Investigation, N.Y.C., 1934-36; trial atty., trial examiner NLRB, 1937-43; dir. field operations Pres.'s Com. Fair Employment Practice, 1943-45; gen. counsel Am. Jewish Congress, 1945—, exec. dir., 1960-72; Faculty N.Y. Sch. Social Research, 1948-60; adj. prof. Coll. City N.Y., 1965-84. Editor: Boycott Report, 1977-94. Trustee Meml. Found. for Jewish Culture; bd. dirs. Interracial Council for Bus. Opportunity, A. Philip Randolph Inst. Mem. World Jewish Congress (exec. com.), ACLU (dir. 1963-72), Am. Jewish Congress (Stephen Wise laureate 1972), Phi Beta Kappa. Home: 401 E 86th St New York NY 10028 Office: 15 E 84th St New York NY 10028-0458

MASNARI, NINO ANTONIO, electrical engineer, educator; b. Three Rivers, Mich., Sept. 20, 1935; s. Antonio and Giovanna (Lupato) M.; m. Judy E. Guild, June 29, 1957; children: Michael A., Jeffrey P., Maria L. BSEE, U. Mich., 1958, MSEE, 1959, PhD, 1964. Lectr., rsch. assoc. U. Mich., Ann Arbor, 1964-67; electronics engr. R&D ctr. GE, Schenectady, N.Y., 1967-69; assoc. prof. elec. engring. U. Mich., 1969-76, prof., 1976-79, dir. elec. physics lab., 1975-79; prof. elec. engring. N.C. State U., Raleigh, 1979—; dept. head N.C. State U., 1979-88, dir. AEMP Ctr., 1988—; cons. in field. Raytheon predoctoral fellow 1962. Fellow IEEE; mem. Am. Soc. Engring. Edn., Matl. Rsch. Soc., Sigma Xi, Phi Kappa Phi, Tau Beta Pi, Eta Kappa Nu. Achievements include patent for Process for Manufacturing Inertial Confinement Fusion Targets and Resulting Product.

MASO, MICHAEL HARVEY, managing director; b. N.Y.C., Aug. 9, 1951; s. James and Goldie (Aronowitz) M.; m. Lisa Marie Coady, Sept. 13, 1987; children: Alexander Peter, Graham Emanuel. BA, SUNY, Stony Brook, 1972; postgrad., Cornell U., 1973-76. Gen. mgr. Roundabout Theatre Co., N.Y.C., 1972-73; bus. mgr. P.A.F. Playhouse, Huntington, N.Y., 1976-78; pres. Taos (N.Mex.) Arts Mgmt., 1978-80; mng. dir. Ala. Shakespeare Festival, Anniston, 1980-82, Huntington Theatre Co., Boston, 1982—; sec. League of Resident Theatres, 1985-88, v.p., 1988-93; trustee, treas. StageSource, Boston, 1986—; trustee Mass. Advocates for Arts, Scis. and Humanities, Boston, 1992—; trustee Arts Boston, 1995—. Chair theater advancement panel NEA, Washington, 1988, panelist/challenge grant, 1989; chair Cultural & Sci. Dirs. Group, Boston, 1993—; trustee Arts Boston, 1995—. Avocations: reading, running. Office: Huntington Theatre Co 264 Huntington Ave Boston MA 02115-4606

MASON, ANTHONY HALSTEAD, lawyer, corporate executive; b. N.Y.C., Dec. 23, 1938; s. Anthony Taylor and Margaret Adams (Halstead) M.; children: Linda Gaye, David Anthony. BA, U. Denver, 1961, JD, 1965. Bar: Colo. 1965, Ariz. 1966. Atty. Ariz. Atty. Gen.'s Office, Phoenix, 1966-67, Maricopa County Atty.'s Office, Phoenix, 1967-69; ptnr. McCall & Mason, Phoenix, 1969-71, Mason, McCall & Ross, Phoenix, 1971-74, Mason & Ross, Phoenix, 1974-77, Carmichael, McClue, Stephens, Mason & Toles, Phoenix, 1977-78, Levy, Mason, Spector & Sherwood, Phoenix, 1978-84, Deltacor, Phoenix, 1984-91, Morrison and Hecker, Phoenix, 1991-93; CEO Emerald Biosystems, LLC, Phoenix, 1993-94; pres., CEO Inc. Corp., 1995—; guest lectr., moot ct. judge Ariz. State U., Tempe; lectr. continuing legal edn. State Bar Ariz., 1978, Crittenden Real Estate Conf., 1984-87. Chmn. City of Phoenix Planning Commn., 1974-76, Mayor's Task Force on Drug Abuse, Phoenix, 1987-88; pres. bd. dirs. Phoenix Symphony Assn., 1981-84; mem. steering com. Phoenix 40, 1988-90; candidate for Gov. Ariz., 1986; co-chmn. Ariz. Bus. Leadership for Edn., Inc., 1989-90. Named Best Land Use Planner in U.S. Am. Soc. Planning Ofcls., 1975, Valley Leadership Visionary of the Yr., 1992. Mem. Ariz. Bar Assn., Maricopa County Bar Assn. (pres. 1975-76), Plaza Club, Univ. Club, Ariz. Club. Democrat. Avocation: racquetball. Office: Inc Corp Ste 2250 2400 E Arizona Biltmore Cir Phoenix AZ 85016-2107

MASON, BARRY JEAN, retired banker; b. Big Spring, Tex., June 3, 1930; s. Vernon E. and Irene E. (Owen) M.; m. Alexana Petroff, Aug. 31, 1958; children: Scott Alexander, Claire Laire. B.S., U. Tex., 1957; B.F.T., Am. Inst. Fgn. Trade, 1958; postgrad., Advanced Mgmt. Program Harvard, Auspices U. Hawaii, 1968. Trainee First Nat. City Bank, N.Y., Hong Kong, 1959-60; asst. accountant First Nat. City Bank, N.Y., Toyko, Japan, 1960-63; asst. mgr. First Nat. City Bank, N.Y., 1963-66; mgr. First Nat. City Bank, N.Y., Hong Kong, 1966-67; resident v.p. First Nat. City Bank, N.Y., 1967-68, Tokyo, 1968-69; v.p. First Nat. City Bank, N.Y., Japan, Korea, Okinawa, 1969; v.p. Republic Nat. Bank Dallas, 1969-70, sr. v.p., 1970-72, exec. v.p., 1972-83; chmn., chief exec. officer Republic Bank Las Colinas, 1983-87; sr. advisor Sumitomo Trust and Banking Co. Ltd., 1989-91; mem. adv. bd. PEFCO. Trustee Am. Sch. Japan; bd. advisers Internat. Sch. Hong Kong. Served with AUS, 1948-49; Served with USNR, 1952-53; Served with USMCR, 1953-55. Mem. Bankers Assn. for Fgn. Trade (past dir.), Am. Bankers Assn. Clubs: Hong Kong, T Bar M Racquet. Home: 7730 Yamini Dr Dallas TX 75230-3231

MASON, BENJAMIN LINCOLN, museum director; b. Boston, Jan. 13, 1940; s. Charles Ellis and Ada Brooks (Trafford) M.; A.B., Harvard U., 1963, M.Ed., 1975; m. Anne Silliman Brown, Aug. 5, 1978; children—Benjamin Silliman, Alexander Borden. Various positions in industry, 1963-71; exec. dir. Historic Harrisville (N.H.), 1971-72; staff cons. to bd. trustees SPNEA, Boston, 1972-73; asst. dir. Boston Zool. Soc., 1973-74; pres. ELEEMOS, Inc., Boston, 1975-79; dir. Shelburne (Vt.) Mus., 1979—. Served in USCGR, 1958-64. Office: Shelburne Mus US Rte 7 Shelburne VT 05482

MASON, BERT E., podiatrist; b. Ryderwood, Wash., Mar. 17, 1944; s. Jean Grenette and Bette Evelyn (Phillips) M.; m. Rachel Nell Hall, May 17, 1991; children: Michelle Renee, Samantha Dell Yarbrough. BA with honors, U. Calif., San Diego, 1971; B in Basic Med. Sci., Calif. Coll. Podiatric Medicine, 1975; D Podiatric Medicine, Calif. Coll. Podiatric Med., 1977. Diplomate Am. Bd. Podiatric Surgery, Am. Bd. Podiatric Orthopedics. Pvt. practice Fairfield, Calif., 1977-79; chief podiatry sect., dir. podiatric residency VA Med. Ctr., Huntington, W.Va., 1983-87; pvt. practice San Diego, 1979-; chief podiatry svc., dir. podiatric residency program VA Med. Ctr., Huntington, W.Va., 1993-; asst. prof. podiatric surgery Ohio Coll. Podiatric Medicine, Cleve., 1984-87; asst. prof. dept. surgery and community medicine Marshall U. Sch. Medicine, Huntington, 1985-87; v.p. Smith Hanna Med. Group. Alumni mem. scholarship com., U. Calif., San Diego, 1988—. Maj. U.S. Army, 1979—, chief Podiatry Sect. Ft. Knox, Ky., Ireland Army Hosp. 1980-83, Individual Augmentee Health Svcs. Command, 1983—. Luth. Hosp. Soc. scholar, 1968. Fellow Am. Coll. Foot Surgeons, Am. Coll. Foot Orthopedics, Am. Assn. Hosp. Podiatrists; mem. Am. Podiatric Med. Assn., AAAS, U. Calif. San Diego Alumni Assn. (bd. dirs.). Republican. Avocations: mountain climbing, golf. Home: 350 Grand Blvd Huntington WV 25705-3612 Office: VA Med Ctr Huntington WV 25704

MASON, BOBBIE ANN, novelist, short story writer; b. Mayfield, Ky., May 1, 1940; d. Wilburn A. and Christianna (Lee) M.; m. Roger B. Rawlings, April 12, 1969. BA, U. Ky., 1962; MA, SUNY, Binghamton, 1966; PhD, U. Conn., 1972. Asst. prof. English Mansfield (Pa.) State Coll., 1972-79. Author: Nabokov's Garden, 1974, The Girl Sleuth: A Feminist Guide to the Bobbsey Twins, Nancy Drew and Their Sisters, 1976, 2d edit., 1995, Shiloh and Other Stories, 1982 (Ernest Hemingway award, Nat. Book Critic's Circle award nominee, Am. Book award nominee, PEN Faulkner award nominee), In Country, 1985, Spence Lila, 1988, Love Life, 1989, Feather Crowns, 1993 (Nat. Book Critic's Circle award nominee, So. Book award); contbr. regularly to The New Yorker, 11980—; contbr. fiction to The Atlantic, Redbook, Paris. Rev., Mother Jones, Harpers, N.Am. Rev., Va. Quar. Rev., Story, Ploughshares, So. Rev., Crazyhorse; contbr. works Best American Short Stories, 1981, The Pushcart Prize: Best of the Small Presses, 1983, Best American Short Stories, 1983. Recipient O. Henry Anthology awards, 1986, 88; grantee Pa. Arts Coun., 1983, 89, Nat. Endowment Arts, 1983, Am. Acad. and Inst. Arts and Letters, 1984; Guggenheim fellow, 1984. Address: care Amanda Urban Internat Creative Mgmt 40 W 57th St New York NY 10019

MASON, BRIAN HAROLD, geologist, curator; b. N.Z., Apr. 18, 1917; came to U.S., 1947, naturalized, 1953; s. George Harold and Catherine (Fairweather) M. M.Sc., U. New Zealand, 1938; Ph.D., U. Stockholm, 1943. Lectr. geology Canterbury Coll., N.Z., 1944-47; prof. mineralogy Ind. U., 1947-53; chmn. dept. mineralogy Am. Mus. Natural History, N.Y.C., 1953-65; research curator Dept. Mineral Scis. Smithsonian Instn., Washington, 1965—. Author: Principles of Geochemistry, 3d edit, 1967, Meteorites, 1962, The Literature of Geology, 1958, (with L. G. Berry) Mineralogy, 1959, (with W.G. Melson) The Lunar Rocks, 1970, Victor Moritz Goldschmidt: Father of Modern Geochemistry, 1992. Fellow Mineral. Soc. Am., Geol. Soc. Am.; mem. Geochem. Soc., Royal Soc. N.Z., Swedish Geol. Soc. Office: Dept Mineral Scis Smithsonian Instn Washington DC 20560

MASON, BRUCE, advertising agency executive; b. Chgo., Dec. 20, 1939; s. William G. and Maryellen (Robb) M.; m. Diana Albery, Sept. 14, 1963; children: Jennifer, Kristin, Amy. BA, St. John's U., 1961; MBA, U. Chgo., 1963. Account exec. Leo Burnett, Chgo., 1965-69; with Foote Cone & Belding, Chgo., 1969—; dir. account mgmt., 1979-81, gen. mgr., 1981-87, pres. cen. region, 1987-88, chmn. cen. region, 1988, chmn. bd., chief exec. officer, 1991—; bd. dirs. Foote, Cone & Belding, 1987—. Capt. U.S. Army, 1963-65. Mem. Am. Assn. Advt. Agys. (reg. bd. 1987—). Office: Foote Cone & Belding Commns Inc Corporate Hdqrs 101 E Erie St Chicago IL 60611-2897*

MASON, CHARLES ELLIS, III, magazine editor; b. Boston, Oct. 31, 1938; s. Charles Ellis, Jr. and Ada Brooks (Trafford) M. B.A., Yale U., 1960. Loan officer State St. Bank, Boston, 1963-68; asso. editor Sail mag., Boston, 1968-74; exec. editor Sail mag., 1974—. Author: (with Buddy Melges) Sailing Smart, 1983; editor: Best of Sail Trim, 1976, Best of SAIL Navigation, 1981. Mem. exec. com. Sierra Club Greater Boston Group, 1992. Served with USNR, 1960-62. Home: 16 Joy St Boston MA 02114-4140 Office: Sail Publs 275 Washington St Newton MA 02158

MASON, CHERYL WHITE, lawyer; b. Champaign, Ill., Jan. 16, 1952; d. John Russell and Lucille (Birden) White; m. Robert L. Mason, Oct. 9, 1972; children: Robert L. II and Daniel G. BA, Purdue U., 1972; JD, U. Chgo., 1976. Bar: Calif. 19767. Assoc. O'Melveny & Myers, L.A., 1976-81, 84-86, ptnr., 1987—; exec. dir. Public Counsel, L.A., 1981-84. Chmn. State Bar, Legal Svcs. Trust Fund, 1987; trustee L.A. County Bar, 1985-88; bd. dirs. Challengers Boys and Girls Club, L.A., 1990—, Western Ctr. Law and Poverty, L.A., 1991—. Mem. ABA (co-chair environ. litigation commn 1992—, lawyer rep. 9th cir. jud. conf. 1993—), Calif. Women Lawyers, L.A. County Bar Assn., Women Lawyers L.A., Black Women Lawyers L.A., Langston Bar Assn. Democrat. Office: O'Melveny & Myers 400 S Hope St Los Angeles CA 90071-2899

MASON, DAVID DICKENSON, statistics educator; b. Abingdon, Va., Jan. 22, 1917; s. William Thomas and Eva (Dorton) M.; m. Virginia Louise Pendleton, Oct. 28, 1944; children: Marjorie F., David P. B.A., King Coll., 1936; M.S. (Acad. Merit fellow), Va. Poly. Inst., 1938; postgrad., Ohio State U., 1939-40; Ph.D., N.C. State U., 1948. Asst. soil scientist Va. Poly. Inst., 1938-39; asst. prof. soils Ohio State U., 1947-49; prin. biometrician Dept. Agr., Beltsville, Md., 1949-53; prof. stats. N.C. State U., 1953-62, prof. and head dept. stats., 1962-81, emeritus prof. and head, 1981—; head Inst. Stats., 1962-81, emeritus head, 1981—; Sr. cons. United Fruit Co., Boston, 1957-71. Contbr. articles to profl. jours. Instl. rep. to Regional Edn. Bd. com statistics, 1963-81, chmn., 1973-75; Bd. dirs. Triangle Univs. Computation Center Corp., chmn., 1968-70. Served with AUS, 1941-45. Fellow Am. Statis. Assn., Am. Soc. Agronomy, Soil Sci. Soc. Am.; mem. Biometric Soc., Sigma Xi, Phi Kappa Phi, Gamma Sigma Delta. Presbyn. (elder, deacon). Club: Rotarian. Home: 4212 Arbutus Dr Raleigh NC 27612-3702 Office: Inst Stats PO Box 8203 Raleigh NC 27695

MASON, DEAN TOWLE, cardiologist; b. Berkeley, Calif., Sept. 20, 1932; s. Ira Jenckes and Florence Mabel (Towle) M.; m. Maureen O'Brien, June 22, 1957; children: Kathleen, Alison. B.A. in Chemistry, Duke U., 1954, M.D., 1958. Diplomate: Nat. Bd. Med. Examiners, Am. Bd. Internal Medicine (cardiovascular diseases). Intern, then resident in medicine Johns Hopkins Hosp., 1958-61; clin. assoc. cardiology br., asst. surgeon USPHS, Nat. Heart Inst., NIH, 1961-63, asst. sect. dir. cardiovascular diagnosis, attending physician, sr. investigator cardiology br., 1963-68; prof. medicine, prof. physiology, chief cardiovascular medicine U. Calif. Med. Sch., Davis-Sacramento Med. Center, 1968-82; dir. cardiac ctr. Cedars Med. Ctr., Miami, Fla., 1982-83; physician-in chief Western Heart Inst., San Francisco, 1983—; chmn. dept. cardiovascular medicine St. Mary's Med. Ctr., San Francisco, 1986—; co-chmn. cardiovascular-renal drugs U.S. Pharmacopeia Com. Revision, 1970-75; mem. life scis. com. NASA; med. rsch. rev. bd. VA, NIH; vis. prof. numerous univs., cons. in field; mem. Am. Cardiovascular Splty. Cert. Bd., 1970-78. Contbr. numerous articles to profl. pubs. Recipient Research award Am. Therapeutic Soc., 1965; Theodore and Susan B. Cummings Humanitarian award State Dept.-Am. Coll. Cardiology, 1972, 73, 75, 78; Skylab Achievement award NASA, 1974; U. Calif. Faculty Research award, 1978; named Outstanding Prof. U. Calif. Med. Sch., Davis, 1972. Fellow Am. Coll. Cardiology (pres. 1977-78), A.C.P., Am. Heart Assn., Am. Coll. Chest Physicians, Royal Soc. Medicine; mem. Am. Soc. Clin. Investigation, Am. Physiol. Soc., Am. Soc. Pharmacology and Exptl. Therapeutics (Exptl. Therapeutics award 1973), Am. Fedn. Clin. Research, N.Y. Acad. Scis., Am. Assn. U. Cardiologists, Am. Soc. Clin. Pharmacology and Therapeutics, Western Assn. Physicians, AAUP, Western Soc. Clin. Research (past pres.), Phi Beta Kappa, Alpha Omega Alpha. Republican. Methodist. Club: El Marcero Country. Home: 44725 Country Club Dr El Macero CA 95618-1047 Office: Western Heart Inst St Mary's Med Ctr 450 Stanyan St San Francisco CA 94117-1079

MASON, DONALD ROGER, protective services official, city official; b. Kalamazoo, June 30, 1942; s. Donald R. and Mary Jane (Anderson) M.; m. Judith Gay Thompson, Feb. 24, 1964 (div. July 1981); children: Chad A., Bredt P.; m. Katherine M. Compton, Nov. 25,1981; children: Meg E. Krueger, Stephanie Shepherd. BS in Criminal Justice, Nazareth Coll., Kalamazoo, 1980; grad., FBI Acad., Quantico, Va., 1988. Cert. EMT, police officer, firefighter, Mich.; lic. bldg. contractor, Mich.; reg. bldg. inspector, Mich. Police officer City of Otsego, Mich., 1966, City of Plainwell, Mich., 1977, City of Battle Creek, Mich., 1970-71; youth officer Portage (Mich.) Police Dept., 1971-78; chief police City of Mendon, Mich., 1978-80; chief police, dir. emergency med. svcs. City of Belding, Mich., 1980-92, dir. pub. safety, 1992—; advisor criminal justice program Grand Valley State U., Allendale, Mich., 1984—; chmn. Emergency Dispatch Fire and Emergency Med. Svcs. Com., Ionia, Mich., 1990—. Trustee Belding Bd. Edn., 1988—; chmn., founder Miss Belding Pageant, 1988—. Sgt. USAF, 1966-70. Recipient Chief's Achievement award City of Belding, 1984, achievement award Mich. Mcpl. League, 1985. Mem. Internat. Assn. Chiefs Police, Mich. Assn. Chiefs Police (rep. 1985), West Mich. Assn. Chiefs Police (chmn. 1987), Mich. Assn. Sch. Bds., Belding Area C. of C. (pres. 1984-85, 87, 92), FBI Acad. Assocs., Masons. Republican. Methodist. Avocations: computer programming, residential building. Home: 207 W Congress St Belding MI 48809 Office: Belding Police Dept 120 S Pleasant St Belding MI 48809

MASON, EARL LEONARD, steel company executive; b. Jersey City, July 12, 1947; s. Herman E. and Marguerite (Rondeau) M.; m. Patricia Fladung (div. 1976); children: Holly Ann, Wendy Lynn; m. Bonita L. Blair, Dec. 11, 1976. BS, Fairleigh Dickinson U., 1969, MBA, 1984. With AT&T, N.J., 1969-79, dir. mktg., 1979-81; corp. contr. ATT Info. Systems, 1981-85; dir. fin. mgmt. and planning AT&T, N.J., 1985-87; controller mfg. Digital Equipment Corp., Maynard, Mass., 1987-91; European CFO Digital Equipment Corp., Geneva, 1991—; v.p. fin., CFO Inland Steel Industries, Chgo., 1991—; dir. Family Inn, Boston, 1992—, dir. Family Inn, Boston, 1992—, State of Ill. Mem. Am. Iron and Steel Inst., Fin. Execs. Inst., Univ. Club, East Bank Club, City of Chgo. C. of C. (bd. dirs.). Avocations: squash, racquetball, tennis, golf, boating. Office: Inland Steel Ind Inc 30 W Monroe St Chicago IL 60603

MASON, EDWARD EATON, surgeon; b. Boise, Idaho, Oct. 16, 1920; s. Edward Files and Dora Bell (Eaton) M.; m. Dordana Fairman, June 18, 1944; children—Daniel Edward, Rose Mary, Richard Eaton, Charles Henry. B.A., U. Iowa, 1943, M.D., 1945; Ph.D. in Surgery, U. Minn., 1953. Intern, resident in surgery Univ. Hosps., Mpls., 1945-52; asst. prof. surgery U. Iowa, 1953-55, asso. prof., 1956-60, prof., 1961-91, prof. emeritus, 1991—, chmn. gen. surgery, 1978-91; cons. VA Hosp.; trainee Nat. Cancer Inst., 1949-52. Author: Computer Applications in Medicine, 1964, Fluid, Electrolyte and Nutrient Therapy in Surgery, 1974, Surgical Treatment of Obesity, 1981; developer gastric bypass and gastroplasty for treatment of obesity; contbr. articles profl. jours. Served to lt. (j.g.) USNR, 1945-47. Fellow ACS; mem. AMA, Am. Surg. Assn., Western Surg. Assn., Soc. Univ. Surgeons, Internat. Soc. Surgery, Ctrl. Surg. Assn., Soc. Surgery Alimentary Tract, Am. Thyroid Assn., Am. Soc. Bariatric Surgery, Sigma Xi, Alpha Omega Alpha. Republican. Presbyterian. Home: 5 Melrose Cir Iowa City IA 52246-2013 Office: Dept of Surgery University Hospitals Iowa City IA 52242 *Continuity of interest and planning weaves the daily decisions into a whole cloth that does more than cover one's imperfections.*

MASON, ELLSWORTH GOODWIN, librarian; b. Waterbury, Conn., Aug. 25, 1917; s. Frederick William and Kathryn Loretta (Watkins) M.; m. Rose Ellen Maloy, May 13, 1951 (div. Oct. 1961); children: Kay Iris, Joyce Iris; m. Joan Lou Shinew, Aug. 16, 1964; 1 son, Sean David. B.A., Yale U., 1938, M.A., 1942, Ph.D., 1948; L.H.D., Hofstra U., 1973. Reference asst. Yale Library, 1938-42; export license officer Bd. Econ. Warfare, 1942-43; instr. English Williams Coll., 1948-50; instr. humanities Marlboro (Vt.) Coll., 1951-52; serials libr. U. Wyo. Libr., 1952-54; reference libr. Colo. Coll. Libr., Colorado Springs, 1954-58; lectr., libr. Colo. Coll., 1958-63; prof., dir. libr. svcs. Hofstra U., Hempstead, N.Y., 1963-72; prof., dir. U. Colo. Librs., Boulder, 1972-76; adj. prof. U. Ill., Urbana, 1968; pres. Mason Assocs., Ltd., 1977—; rsch. assoc. U. Calif.-Berkeley, 1965; vis. lectr. Northwestern U., 1961, Colo. Coll., 1965, Syracuse U., 1965-68, Elmira Coll., 1966, Columbia U., 1966-68, U. Ill., 1972, Lincoln U., 1969, U. B.C. (Can.), 1969, U. Toronto, 1970, U. Tulsa, 1971, 76, Rutgers U., 1971, Colgate U., 1972, Simmons Coll., 1972, U. Oreg., 1973, Hofstra U., 1974, U. N.C., 1976, U. Ala., 1976, Ball State U., 1977, U. Lethbrige, Can., 1977, U. Ariz., 1981, Ariz. State U., 1981, Victoria U., New Zealand, 1983, U. Canterbury, New Zealand, 1983, U. Nev. Las Vegas, 1992, Remember Pearl Harbor Assn., 1993, 94; libr. cons., 1958—, libr. value engr., 1992—. Editor: (with Stanislaus Joyce) The Early Joyce, 1955, Xerox U.M. edit., 1964, (with Richard Ellmann) The Critical Writings of James Joyce, 1959, 2d edit., 1989, Critical Commentary on A Portrait of the Artist as a Young Man, 1966; translator: Recollections of James Joyce (S. Joyce), 1950, Essais de J. Joyce, 1966, Escritos Criticos de James Joyce, (Portuguese edit.), 1967, (Spanish edit.), 1973, 75, James Joyce's Ulysses and Vico's Cycle, 1973, Kritische Schriften v. James Joyce, 1975, Mason on Library Buildings, 1980, (with Walter and Jean Shine) A MacDonald Potpourri, 1988, The University of Colorado Library and Its Makers, 1876-1972, 1994; contbr. Contemporary Authors, 1988—; editor: Colorado College Studies, 1959-62; editor and compiler: Focus on Robert Graves, 1972-88; adv. editor: Focus on Robert Graves and His Contemporaries, 1988—; editor: The Booklover's Bounty, 1977—; mem. editorial bd. Serial Slants, 1957-59, The Serials Librarian, 1977—, Choice, 1962-65, Coll. and Rsch. Librs., 1969-72. Mem. exec. bd. U. Ky. Libr. Assocs., 1991—. Served with USNR, 1943-46. Recipient Harry Bailly spkr.'s award Assn. Colls. of Midwest, 1975; fellow Coun. on Libr. Resources, 1969-70; grantee Am. Coun. Learned Socs., Edn. Facility Labs., Hofstra U., U. Colo.; named Ky. Coll. 1993. Mem. ALA (councillor-at-large 1961-65), Colo. Libr. Assn. (pres. so. dist. 1960-61), Bibliog. Soc. Am., Libr. Assn. (London), N.Z. Libr. Assn., MLA, Pvt. Librs. Assn., Alcuin Soc. Vancouver, Conf. Editors Learned Jours., N.Z. Royal Forest and Bird Protection Soc., Colo. Book Collectors (founder, pres. 1975—), Inst. Vico Studies, James Joyce Found. (chmn. sect. on translation from Joyce, 2d Internat. James Joyce Symposium, Dublin 1969), Black America's PAC, Caxton Club, Archons of Colophon, Ghost Town Club, Alpha Sigma Lambda, Sigma Kappa Alpha (pres. 1969-70). Home: 736 Providence Rd Lexington KY 40502-2267 also: 39 Discovery Dr, Whitby New Zealand

MASON, FRANK HENRY, III, automobile company executive, leasing company executive; b. Paris, Tenn., Nov. 16, 1936; s. Frank H. and Dorothy (Carter) M.; children—Robert C., William C. B.E.E., Vanderbilt U., 1958; M.S. in Indsl. Mgmt., MIT, 1965. With Ford Motor Co. 1965-71, asst. controller Ford Brazil, Sao Paulo, Brazil, 1971-74, mgr. overseas financing dept., Dearborn, Mich., 1974-76, asst. controller engine div., 1976-78, mgr. facilities and mgmt. services, 1978-81; controller Ford Motor Credit Co., Dearborn, 1981-87; dir. finance Ford Fin. Services Group, Dearborn, 1987-89; exec. v.p., chief fin. officer U.S. Leasing, Internat., San Francisco, 1989-92; ret. 1992. Served to lt. USN, 1958-63.

MASON, FRANKLIN ROGERS, automotive executive; b. Washington, June 16, 1936; s. Franklin Allison and Jeannette Morgan (Rogers) M.; m. Aileen Joan Larson, July 29, 1961; children: William Rogers, Elisa Ellen. BS in Engring. Princeton U., 1958; MBA, Northwestern U., 1960. With Ford Motor Co. 1960-75, finance mgr., Portugal, 1969-72; fin. analysis mgr. Ford subs. Richier S.A., France, 1972-75; sr. v.p. finance Raymond Internat. Inc., Houston, 1975-86; chief fin. officer Quanex Corp., Houston, 1986-87; group v.p., chief fin. officer Gulf States Toyota, Inc., Houston, 1987—. With arty. U.S. Army, 1960. Mem. Princeton U. Alumni Assn., Univ. Club, Racquet Club. Republican. Episcopalian. Home: 5765 Indian Cir Houston TX 77057-1302 Office: Gulf States Toyota Inc 7701 Wilshire Place Dr Houston TX 77040-5346 *Business is people, and success is dependent on good communication with people. Effective communication must be accompanied by fairness, consistency, patience, and a willingness to compromise.*

MASON, GEORGE H., business educator, consultant; b. Chgo., Sept. 11, 1929; s. Robert De Main and Dorothy Wills (Belden) M.; m. Constance Eleanor Wolcott, May 14, 1960. AB, Kenyon Coll., 1955; MBA, Cornell U., 1957; MF, Duke U., 1983. CFA. Investment officer Travelers Ins. Co., Hartford, Conn., 1957-88; exec.-in-residence U. Hartford, West Hartford,

1989—; mng. dir. Heaphy Trust Group, Springfield, Mass.; mem. bus. bd. advisors Sustainable Forest Systems Corp., Incline Village, Nev. Co-author: Timberland Investments, 1992. Mem. Assn. Investment Mgmt. & Rsch., Soc. Am. Foresters, Hartford Soc. Fin. Analysts, Cornell Club. Republican. Avocations: skiing, golf, writing. Office: U Hartford 200 Bloomfield Ave West Hartford CT 06117

MASON, GEORGE ROBERT, surgeon, educator; b. Rochester, N.Y., June 10, 1932; s. George Mitchell and Marjorie Louise (Hooper) M.; m. Grace Louise Bransfield, Feb. 4, 1956; children: Douglas Richard, Marcia Jean, David William. BA, Oberlin Coll., 1955; MD with honors, U. Chgo., 1957; PhD in Physiology, Stanford U., 1968. Diplomate: Am. Bd. Surgery (examiner 1977-80, dir. 1980-86), Bd. Thoracic Surgery. Teaching asst. pathology U. Chgo., 1954-56; rotating intern U. Chgo. Clinics, 1957-58; tchg. asst. surgery, NIH postdoctoral fellow, USPHS fellow surgery Stanford U., 1960-62; from asst. resident in surgery to sr. and chief resident in surgery Stanford U. Hosps., 1962-66; mem. faculty Stanford Med. Sch., 1965-71, asso. prof., 1970-71; prof., chmn. dept. surgery U. Md. Med. Sch., Balt., 1971-80; also prof. physiology; prof., chmn. dept. surgery U. Calif., Irvine, 1980-89; chief surgical svc. Hines (Ill.) VA Hosp., 1990—; prof. surgery and thoracic cardiovascular surgery Loyola U. Med. Ctr., 1990—; mem. residency review com. for surgery, 1981-87. Contbr. to profl. jours., med. textbooks. Served to capt. M.C., USAF, 1958-60. Giannini fellow Stanford U., 1966-67; recipient Markle scholarship in acad. medicine, 1968-74. Mem. ACS, Am. Assn. Thoracic Surgeons, Am. Coll. Chest Physicians, Am. Physiol. Soc., Assn. Program Dirs. in Surgery (exec. com. 1987-89), Am. Gastroent. Assn., Pacific Coast Surg. Assn., Assn. Acad. Surgery, Chgo. Surg. Soc., Am. Surg. Assn., Western Surg. Assn., Soc. Thoracic Surgeons, Ill. Thoracic Surg. Soc., Halsted Soc., Chesapeake Vascular Soc., Soc. Internat. Chirurgie, Soc. Clin. Surgery, Soc. for Surgery Alimentary Tract, Soc. Univ. Surgeons, Sigma Xi. Home: PO Box 3877 Oak Brook IL 60522-3877 Office: Hines VAH Chief Surgical Svc Hines IL 60141

MASON, HENRY LLOYD, political science educator; b. Berlin, Germany, Nov. 4, 1921; came to U.S., 1940, naturalized, 1943; s. Hugo L. and Maria (Werner) M.; m. Mathilde Jessé, Jan. 23, 1946; children—Monica (Mrs. Robert Mimeles), Paul. B.A., Johns Hopkins, 1942; Ph.D., Columbia, 1951. Mem. faculty Tulane U., New Orleans, 1952—; prof. polit. sci., 1961—; chmn. dept., 1966-75, 87-88; vis. assoc. prof. Columbia, 1958; Fulbright prof. U. Innsbruck, 1958-59, Free U. Berlin, 1965; vis. prof. U. Amsterdam, 1973-74. Author: The Purge of Dutch Quislings, 1952, The European Coal and Steel Community, 1955, Toynbee's Approach to World Politics, 1959, Mass Demonstrations Against Foreign Regimes, 1966, University Government, 1972. Bd. dirs. Urban League Greater New Orleans, 1961-69. Served to 1st lt., M.I. AUS, 1942-46, ETO. Mem. AAUP (mem. nat. council 1966-69 1st nat. v.p. 1984-86), Internat. Studies Assn. (pres. so. region 1972-73), So. Polit. Sci. Assn. (mem. exec. council 1973-76). Home: 1821 Upperline St New Orleans LA 70115-5547

MASON, HENRY LOWELL, III, lawyer; b. Boston, Feb. 10, 1941; s. Henry Lowell and Fanny Crowninshield (Homans) M.; m. Elaine Bobrowicz, June 7, 1969. A.B., Harvard U., 1963, LL.B., 1967. Bar: Ill. 1967. Assoc. Leibman, Williams, Bennett, Baird & Minow, Chgo., 1967-72; assoc. Sidley & Austin, 1972-73, ptnr., 1973—. Mem. Chgo. Bar Assn. Republican. Office: Sidley & Austin 1 First Nat Plz Chicago IL 60603

MASON, HERBERT WARREN, JR., religion and history educator, author; b. Wilmington, Del., Apr. 20, 1932; s. Herbert Warren and Mildred Jane (Noyes) M.; m. Jeanine Young, June 25, 1982; children from previous marriage: Cathleen, Paul, Sarah. AB, Harvard U., 1955, AM, 1965, PhD, 1969. English tchr. Am. Sch. Paris, 1955-60; asst. prof. St. Joseph's Coll., Gorham, Maine, 1960-62; vis. lectr. Simmons Coll., Boston, 1962-63; vis. lectr. in Islamic Hist. Tufts U., Medford, Mass., 1965-66; teaching fellow in English Harvard U., Cambridge, Mass., 1962-66, teaching fellow in Islamic Hist., 1966-67; translator Bollingen Found., N.Y.C., 1968-72; prof. History and Religion Boston U., 1972—. Author: Reflections on the Middle East Crisis, 1970, Two Statesmen of Medieval Islam, 1971, Gilgamesh, 1971 (Nat. Book award nomination), The Death of al-Hallaj, 1979, Moments in Passage, 1979, (novel) Summer Light, 1980; translator: La Passion d'al-Hallaj, 4 vols., Bollingen Series (Louis Massignon), 1983, abridged 1 vol., 1994, A Legend of Alexander, 1986, Memoir of a Friend: Louis Massignon, 1988, Testimonies and Reflections, 1989, Hallaj, 1995; co-editor Humaniora Islamica; contbr. articles, essays, reviews, fiction, reviews and poetry to popular fiction mags. Sec. Inter-racial Riverside Assn., Cambridge, Mass., 1965-67; trustee Bd. Charity of Edward Hopkins, Boston Athenaeum. Fellow Soc. for Values in Higher Edn.; mem. PEN (bd. dirs. Delos chpt.), Medieval Acad. Am., Am. Oriental Soc., Am. Acad. Religion, Mark Twain Soc., Inst. Internat. des Recherches Louis Massignon in Paris (dir. edn.). Home: 30 The Common Phillipston MA 01331 Office: Boston U 745 Commonwealth Ave Boston MA 02215-1401

MASON, JACKIE, comedian, actor; b. Sheboygan, Wis., June 9, 1934. Stand-up comedian; performances include (theater) A Teaspoon Every Four Hours, 1969, The World According to Me! (one man show, Tony, Emmy and Ace awards 1987), Brand New, Politically Incorrect, 1994; (films) Operation Delilah, 1966, The Stoolie, 1972, The Jerk, 1979, History of the World Part I, 1981, The Perils of P.K., 1986, Caddyshack II, 1988; TV appearances in Steve Allen, Ed Sullivan, Jack Paar, Garry Moore, Perry Como and Merv Griffin Shows, Johnny Carson, Arsenio Hall, Late Night with David Letterman; (TV series) Chicken Soup, The Jackie Mason Show; (TV movies) The Best of Times; (TV specials) Jackie Mason on Broadway (Emmy award for writing in a variety or music program 1988); records include The World According to Me!, Brand New. Recipient special Tony award, 1987, Emmy award for The Simpsons, 1991. Office: csre William Morris Agy 1350 Ave of the Americas New York NY 10019

MASON, JAMES ALBERT, museum director, university dean; b. Eureka, Utah, 1929; married, 1956; 3 children. BA, Brigham Young U., 1955, MA, 1957; EdD, Ariz. State U., 1970. Cons., clinician in fine arts, 1955—; former chmn. dept. music Brigham Young U., Provo, dean Coll. Fine Arts and Communications; now dir. Mus. of Art Brigham Young U. vis. prof., lectr. Ind. U., Northwestern U., Cin. Coll.-Conservatory, U. Tex., Central Conservatory, Beijing, Internat. Soc. Music Edn., Warsaw; chmn. nat. symposium Applications of Psychology to the Teaching and Learning of Music; chmn., bd. dirs. The Barlow Endowment for Music Composition; co-founder, 1st pres. Utah Valley Symphony Orch.; past condr. Utah Valley Youth Orch.; bd. trustees Utah Opera Co.; commr. Utah Centennial of Statehood. Editor: The Instrumentalist, Orch. News, Utah Music Educator, Research News column, Jour. Research in Music Edn. Bd. dirs. Presser Found. Mem. Music Educators Nat. Conf. (past nat. pres., council), Nat. Music Council (past bd. dirs.), Am. Music Conf. (past bd. dirs.). Office: Brigham Young U Coll Fine Arts and Communications A410 Harris Fine Arts Ctr Provo UT 84602-1026

MASON, JAMES MICHAEL, biomedical laboratories executive; b. Kingsport, Tenn., Mar. 19, 1943; s. William Tilson and Mary Thelma (Epperson) M; m. Linda Kaye Hussung, June 14, 1969. BS, Memphis State U., 1966; PhD, U. Tenn., 1972. Intern: Health Sci. Ctr., U. Tenn.-Memphis, 1972-74, asst. prof. pathology, 1974-84, assoc. prof. pathology, 1984-89; dir. paternity evaluation and histocompatibility testing Roche Biomed. Labs., Inc., Burlington, N.C., 1989—; asst. v.p., pathologist 'HLA cons. Roche Biomed. Labs., Burlington, 1986-89; blood bank dir. Regional Med. Ctr. at Memphis, 1977-89. Contbr. articles to profl. jours. Rsch. grantee NIH, U. Tenn., 1973-76; recipient Astra Pharm. award Soc. of Perinatal Obstetrics. Fellow Assn. of Clin. Scientists; mem. Am. Assn. of Blood Banks (chmn. transp. immunology com. 1989-92), Internat. Soc. Forensic Hemogenetics, Nat. Child Support Enforcement Assn., Am. Soc. for Histocompatibility and Immunogenetics, Human Identity Trade Assn. (pres. 1993, chmn. stds. com. 1994—), Kiwanis. Presbyterian. Achievements include patent for cry-opreservation of platelets; research in T-lymphocyte counting in neoplastic disease, pathogenesis of SIDS, automated reading of HLA reactions for paternity testing, innovative approaches to DNA analysis in parentage and identity testing. Home: 50 Driftwood Ct Gibsonville NC 27249 Office: Roche Biomedical Labs Inc 1447 York Ct Burlington NC 27215

MASON, JAMES OSTERMANN, public health administrator; b. Salt Lake City, June 19, 1930; s. Ambrose Stanton and Neoma (Thorup) M.; m. Lydia Maria Smith, Dec. 29, 1952; children: James, Susan, Bruce, Ralph, Samuel, Sara, Benjamin. BA, U. Utah, 1954, MD, 1958; MPH, Harvard U., 1963, DPH, 1967. Diplomate Am. Bd. Preventive Medicine. Intern Johns Hopkins Hosp., Balt., 1958-59; resident in internal medicine Peter Bent Brigham Hosp.-Harvard Med. Service, Boston, 1961-62; chief infectious diseases Latter-day Saints Hosp., Salt Lake City, 1968-69; commr. Health Services Corp., Ch. of Jesus Christ of Latter-day Saints, 1970-76; dep. dir. health Utah Div. Health, 1976-78, exec. dir., 1979-83; chief epidemic intelligence service Ctr. Disease Control, Atlanta, 1959, chief hepatitis surveillance unit epidemiology br., 1960, chief surveillance sect. epidemiology br., 1961, dep. dir. bur. labs., 1964-68, dep. dir. of Ctr., 1969-70; dir. Ctrs. for Disease Control, Atlanta; adminstr. Agy. for Toxic Substances and Disease Registry, 1983-89; acting asst. sec. health HHS, Washington, 1985, asst. sec. for health, acting surgeon gen., 1989-90, asst. sec. for health, 1990-93; asst. prof. dept. medicine and preventive medicine U. Utah, Salt Lake City, 1968-69; assoc. prof., chmn. div. community medicine, dept. family and community medicine U. Utah, 1978-79; v.p. planning, devel., prof. preventive medicine and biometrics Uniformed Svcs. U. Health Scis., 1993-94; 2nd quorum of Seventy LDS Ch., 1994—; physician, cons. to med. services Salt Lake VA Hosp., 1977-83; clin. prof. dept. family and community medicine, U. Utah. Coll. Medicine, 1979-83, clin. prof. dept. pathology, 1980-83; clin. prof. community health Emory U. Sch. Medicine, 1984-86; chmn. joint residency com. in preventive medicine and pub. health Utah Coll. Medicine, 1975-80; mem. Utah Cancer Registry Research Adv. Com., 1976-83; mem. adv. com. Utah Ctr. Health Stats., 1977-79; chmn. bd. Hosp. Coop. Utah, 1977-79; chmn. exec. com. Utah Health Planning and Resource Devel. Adv. Group, 1977-79; chmn. Utah Gov.'s Adv. Com. for Comprehensive Health Planning, 1975-77; mem. recombinant DNA adv. com. NIH, 1979-83; mem. Gov.'s Nuclear Waste Repository Task Force, 1980-83, chmn., 1980-82; bd. dirs. Utah Health Cost Mgmt. Found., 1980-83; mem. adv. com. for programs and policies Ctrs. for Disease Control, 1980; mem. com. on future of local health depts., Inst. Medicine, 1980-82; mem. exec. com., chmn. tech. adv. com. Thrasher Research Found., 1980-89; mem. Robert Wood Johnson Found. Program for Hosp. Initiatives in Long-Term Care, 1982-84; mem. sci. and tech. adv. com. UNDP-World Bank-WHO Spl. Programme for Research and Tng. in Tropical Diseases, 1984-89; mem. Utah Resource for Genetic and Epidemiologic Research, 1982-85, chmn. bd., 1982-83; U.S. rep. WHO Exec. Bd., 1990-93. Author: (with H.L. Bodily and E.L. Updyke) Diagnostic Procedures for Bacterial, Mycotic and Parasitic Infections, 5th edit., 1970; (with M.H. Maxell, K.H. Bousfield and D.A. Ostler) Funding Water Quality Control in Utah, Procs. for Lincoln Inst., 1982; contbr. articles to profl. jours. Mem. nat. scouting com. Boy Scouts Am., 1974-78. Recipient Roche award U. Utah, 1957, Wintrobe award U. Utah, 1958, Disting. Alumni award U. Utah, 1973, Adminstr. of Yr. award Brigham U., 1980, spl. award for outstanding pub. svc. Am. Soc. Pub. Adminstrn. 1984, Disting. Svc. medal USPHS, 1988, LDS Hosp. Deseret Found. Legacy of Life award, 1992, Gorgas Medal and Scroll, 1993. Mem. Inst. Medicine of NAS, AMA, Am. Pub. Health Assn. (task force for credentialing of lab. personnel 1976-78, program devel. bd. 1979-81), Utah State Med. Assn. (trustee 1979-83), Utah Acad. Preventive Medicine (pres. 1982-83), Utah Pub. Health Assn. (pres. 1980-82, Beatty award 1979), Sigma Xi, Alpha Epsilon Delta, Phi Kappa Phi, Alpha Omega Alpha, Delta Omega. Mem. LDS Ch. Lodge: Rotary. Office: LDS ChThe 70 47 E South Temple St Salt Lake City UT 84150 also: Africa Area Adminstrv Office, POBox 1218, Lonehill 2062, South Africa

MASON, JAMES TATE, surgeon; b. Seattle, June 17, 1913; s. James Tate and Laura (Whittlesey) M.; m. Margaret Elisabeth Thomas, Jan. 10, 1942; children—Laura Mason Foster, Anne Mason Curti, James Tate, Mary Mason, Paul. Student, U. Wash., 1936; M.D., U. Va., 1940. Diplomate: Am. Bd. Urology (trustee 1974-80, pres. 1979-80, exec. sec. 1980-84). Intern Bellevue Hosp., N.Y.C., 1940-41; resident Lahey Clinic, Boston, 1942-43, U. Mich., 1946-49; practice medicine, specializing in urologic surgery Seattle, 1949-83; staff Mason Clinic, Virginia Mason, Univ., Harborview hosps., all Seattle; clin. prof. urology U. Wash., Seattle, 1974-83, emeritus clin. prof., 1983—. Contbr. articles to profl. jours. Bd. dirs. Virginia Mason Hosp., 1956-79, pres., 1975-78; trustee Virginia Mason Research Found., Seattle, 1960-79, King County (Wash.) chpt. Boys' Clubs Am., 1965-76, Seattle Art Mus., 1978-88, Seattle Hist. Soc., 1979-86. Served to comdr. M.C., USNR, 1941-46. Fellow A.C.S.; Mem. Am. Urol. Assn. (pres. Western sect. 1968-69, exec. com. assn. 1973-76, nat. pres. 1984-85), Am. Assn. Clin. Urologists, AMA, Am. Assn. Genitourinary Surgeons, Pacific Coast Surg. Assn., SAR (pres. chpt. 1957-58). Clubs: University, Seattle Tennis. Home: 3825 E Mcgraw St Seattle WA 98112-2428 Office: U Wash Med Sch Seattle WA 98195 *Family and friends are the greatest treasures a person may have. One must try in every way to live up to their expectations.*

MASON, JOHN LATIMER, engineering executive; b. Los Angeles, Nov. 8, 1923; s. Zene Roberts and Edna Ella (Watkins) M.; m. Frances Howe Draeger, Sept. 1, 1950 (dec. June 1951); m. Mary Josephine Schulte, Nov. 26, 1954; children: Andrew, Peter, Mary Anne, John Edward. B.S. in Meteorology, U. Chgo., 1944; B.S. in Applied Chemistry, Calif. Inst. Tech., 1947, M.S. in Chem. Engring., 1948, Ph.D., 1950. Registered profl. engr., Calif. Engr. AiResearch Mfg. Co., Los Angeles, 1950-60; dir. engring. AiResearch Mfg. Co. div. Garrett Corp., Los Angeles, 1960-72; v.p. engring. Garrett Corp., Los Angeles, 1972-87; v.p. engring. and tech. Allied-Signal Aerospace Co., Los Angeles, 1987-88, cons., 1989—; chmn. tech. adv. com. Indsl. Turbines Internat., Inc., Los Angeles, 1972-81, bd. dirs., 1980-88; adj. profl. engring. Calif. State U., Long Beach, 1992—; mem. tech. adv. bd. Tex. Ctr. for Superconductivity, U. Houston, 1989—; chair Calif. Coun. Sci. and Tech. Panel on Ranspt. R&D Cr., 1993-94; bd. dirs. San Juan Capistrano Rsch. Inst. Patentee in field. Chmn. energy and environment com. FISITA Coun., 1990-94. 1st lt. USAAF, 1943-45, PTO. Fellow AIAA (assoc.), pres. 1990-91), Performance Rev. Inst. (chmn. 1990-91, bd. dirs 1992-93); mem. NAS (com. on alternative energy R&D strategies 1989-90), Office Sci. and Tech. Policy (Nat. Critical Techs. panel 1992-93), Inst. Medicine of NAS (com. on health effects of indoor allergens 1992-93), NAE, U.S. Advanced Ceramics Assn. (chmn. tech. com., bd. dirs. 1985-88), Am. Soc. Com., Am. Ceramic Soc., Caltech Assocs., Sigma Xi. Office: Allied Signal Automotive 3201 W Lomita Blvd Torrance CA 90505-5064

MASON, JOHN MILTON (JACK MASON), judge; b. Mankato, Minn., Oct. 31, 1938; s. Milton Donald and Marion (Dailey) M.; m. Vivian McFerran, Aug. 25, 1962; children: Kathleen, Peter, Michael. BA cum laude, Macalester Coll. 1960; JD, Harvard U., 1963. Bar: Minn. 1963, U.S. Supreme Ct. 1970. Assoc. Dorsey & Whitney, Mpls., 1963-68, ptnr., 1969-71, 73-95; solicitor gen. State of Minn., St. Paul, 1971, chief dep. atty. gen., 1972-73; U.S. magistrate judge Dist. of Minn., St. Paul, 1995—. Bd. dirs. Macalester Coll., St. Paul, 1971-77, St. Paul Chamber Orch., 1979-88, U. Minn. Hosps. and Clinics, St. Paul, 1979-83, Mpls. Bd. Edn., 1973-80, Minn. Chorale, 1990—, MacPhail Ctr. for Arts, 1990—, Ordway Music Theatre, 1991—. With USAF, 1957, with Res., 1957-65. Mem. Harvard Law Sch. Assn. (pres. Minn. sect. 1980-81). Democrat. Avocations: classical piano, bicycling, German, French and Italian lang. Home: 2849 Burnham Blvd Minneapolis MN 55416-4331 Office: Warren E Burser Fed Bldg 316 N Robert St Saint Paul MN 55401

MASON, JOSEPH See BUSHINSKY, JAY

MASON, LEON VERNE, financial planner; b. Lawrence, Kans., Jan. 13, 1933; s. Thomas Samuel and Mabel Edith (Hyre) M.; divorced; children: Mark Verne, Kirk Matthew, Erik Andrew. BS in Engring. with honors, U. Kans., 1955; MS in Mgmt. with honors, U. Colo., 1970. Engr., Pittsburg Des Moines Steel Co., 1955-56; with IBM, 1958—, sr. engr., San Jose, Calif., 1975-77, Boulder, Colo., 1977—; sr. engr. on loan dir. capital campaign Vols. of Am., 1980-81; with exec. mgmt. IBM, 1985-87, cons. 1988—. Pres., Boulder Interfaith Housing; dir. Golden West Manor, 1978-84, pres., 1983-84; dir. Ret. Sr. Vol. Program, 1979-86; chmn. elders 1st Christian Ch., Boulder, 1977-79. Served with USAF, 1955-57; col. Res. Cert. fin. planner; registered profl. engr.; chmn. trustees 1st Christian Ch., 1959, 93; supervisory faculty Regis U., 1988—. Mem. Internat. Assn. Fin. Planners, Am. Soc. Quality Control, Soc. Mfg. Engrs. Club: Kiwanis. Home: 5577 N Fork Ct Boulder CO 80301

MASON, MARILYN GELL, library administrator, writer, consultant; b. Chickasha, Okla., Aug. 23, 1944; d. Emmett D. and Dorothy (O'Bar) Killebrew; m. Carl L. Gell, Dec. 29 1965 (div. Oct. 1978); 1 son, Charles E.; m. Robert M. Mason, July 17, 1981. B.A., U. Dallas, 1966; M.L.S., N. Tex. State U., Denton, 1968; M.P.A., Harvard U., 1978. Libr. N.J. State Libr., Trenton, 1968-69; head dept. Arlington County Pub. Libr., Va., 1969-73; chief libr. program Metro Washington Coun. Govts., 1973-77; dir. White House Coun. on Libra. and Info. Svcs., Washington, 1979-80; exec. v.p. Metrics Rsch. Corp., Atlanta, 1981-82; dir. Atlanta-Fulton Pub. Libr., Atlanta, 1982-86, Cleve. Pub. Libr., 1986—; trustee Online Computer Library Ctr., 1984—; Evalene Parsons Jackson lectr. div. librarianship Emory U., 1981. Author: The Federal Role in Library and Information Services, 1983; editor: Survey of Library Automation in the Washington Area, 1977; project dir.: book Information for the 1980's, 1980. Bd. visitors Sch. Info. Studies, Syracuse U., 1981-85, Sch. of Libr. and Info. Sci. , U. Tenn.-Knoxville, 1983-85; trustee Coun. on Libr. Resources, Atlant, 1992—. Recipient Disting. Alumna award N. Tex. State U., 1979. Mem. ALA (mem. council 1986—), Am. Assn. Info. Sci., Ohio Library Assn., D.C. Library Assn. (pres. 1976-77). Home: 12427 Fairhill Rd Cleveland OH 44120 Office: Cleve Pub Libr 325 Superior Ave E Cleveland OH 44114-1271

MASON, MARSHA, actress, director, writer; b. St. Louis; d. James and Jacqueline M.; m. Gary Campbell, 1965 (div.); m. Neil Simon, Oct. 25, 1973 (div.). Grad., Webster (Mo.) Coll. Performances include cast Broadway and nat. tour Cactus Flower, 1968; other stage appearances include The Deer Park, 1967, The Indian Wants the Bronx, 1968, Happy Birthday, Wanda June, 1970, Private Lives, 1971, You Can't Take It With You, 1972, Cyrano de Bergerac, 1972, A Doll's House, 1972, The Crucible, 1972, The Good Doctor, 1973, King Richard III, 1974, The Heiress, 1975, Mary Stuart, 1982; one-woman show off-Broadway, The Big Love, Perry St. Theatre, 1988, Lake No Bottom, Second Stage, 1990, Escape From Happiness, With the Naked Angels, 1994; film appearances include Blume in Love, 1973, Cinderella Liberty, 1973 (recipient Golden Globe award 1974, Acad. award nominee), Audrey Rose, 1977, The Goodbye Girl, 1977 (recipient Golden Globe award 1978, Acad. award nominee), The Cheap Detective, 1978, Promises in the Dark, 1979, Chapter Two, 1979 (Acad. award nominee), Only When I Laugh, 1981 (Acad. award nominee), Max Dugan Returns, 1982, Heartbreak Ridge, 1986, Stella, 1988, Drop Dead Fred, 1990, I Love Trouble, 1994; TV appearances include PBS series Cyrano de Bergerac, 1974, The Good Doctor, 1978, Lois Gibbs and the Love Canal, 1981, Surviving, 1985, Trapped in Silence, 1986, The Clinic, 1987, Dinner At Eight, 1989, The Image, 1990, Broken Trust, 1994, series Sibs, 1991; dir. (plays) Juno's Swans, 1987, Heaven Can Wait; dir. ABC Afternoon Spl. Little Miss Perfect, 1988. Office: care Internat Creative Mgmt 8942 Wilshire Blvd Beverly Hills CA 90211

MASON, MARSHALL W., theater director; b. Amarillo, Tex., Feb. 24, 1940; s. Marvin Marshall and Lorine (Chrisman) M. B.S. in Speech, Northwestern U., 1961. prof. Ariz. State U., 1994; chief drama critic New Times, Phoenix, Ariz., 1994—. Founder, artistic dir. Circle Repertory Co., 1969-87, guest artistic dir., Ctr. Theater Group, 1988; dir. Broadway prodns. Redwood Curtain, 1993, The Seagull, 1992, Solitary Confinement, 1992, Burn This, 1987, As Is, 1985 (Drama Desk award, Tony nomination), Passion, 1983, Angels Fall, 1983 (Tony nomination), Fifth of July, 1981 (Tony nomination), Talley's Folly, 1980, (Pulitzer Prize, N.Y. Drama Critics Circle award, Tony nomination), Murder at the Howard Johnsons, 1979, Gemini, 1977, Knock Knock, 1976 (Tony nomination); Off-Broadway prodns. A Poster of the Cosmos/The Moonshot Tape, 1994, The Destiny of Me, 1992, Sunshine, 1989, Talley and Son, 1985, Childe Byron, 1980, Hamlet, 1979, Serenading Louie, 1976 (Obie award), Knock Knock, 1976 (Obie award), The Mound Builders, 1975 (Obie award), Battle of Angeles, 1974 (Obie award), The Sea House, 1974, The Hot L Baltimore, 1973 (Obie award); dir. numerous prodns. including Who's Afraid of Virginia Woolf?, Tokyo, 1985, Talley's Folly, 1982, London, Home Free! and The Madness of Lady Bright, 1968, London, Nat. Tour Sleuth, 1988, Summer and Smoke, 1988, Whisper in the Mind, 1990; dir. numerous TV prodns. including Picnic, 1986, Kennedy's Children, 1982, The Fifth of July, 1983. Recipient Vernon Rice award, 1975, Drama Desk award, 1977, Margo Jones award, 1977, Outer Critics Circle award, 1978, Theatre World award, 1979, Shubert's Vaughan award, 1980, Obie award for Sustained Achievement, 1983, Inge Festival award for lifetime achievement, 1990. Mem. Soc. Stage Dirs. and Choreographers (pres. 1983-85), Dirs. Guild Am., Actors Equity Assn. Office: care Chandler Warren 7803 W Sunset Blvd Los Angeles CA 90046-3305

MASON, NANCY TOLMAN, state agency director; b. Buxton, Maine, Mar. 14, 1933; d. Ansel Robert and Kate Douglas (Libby) M. Grad., Bryant Coll., Providence, R.I., 1952; BA, U. Mass., Boston, 1977; postgrad., Inst. Governmental Services, Boston, 1985, The Auditor's Inst., 1988. Asst. to chief justice Mass. Superior Ct., Boston, 1964-68; community liaison Action for Boston Community Devel., Boston, 1968-73; mgmt. cons. East Boston Community Devel. Assn., Boston, 1973-78; asst. dir. Mass. Office of Deafness, Boston, 1978-86; dir. of contracts Mass. Rehab. Commn., Boston, 1986—; cons. Jos. A Ryan Assocs., Boston and Orleans, Mass., 1981-86, Radio Sta. WFCC, Chatham, Mass., 1987-91. Author: Bromley-Heath Security Patrols, 1974, Reorganization of East Boston Community Development Corporation, 1976, How to Start Your Own Small Business, 1981. Bd. dirs. Deaf-Blind Contact Ctr., Boston, 1988-91; vol. Am. Cancer Soc., Winchester, Mass., 1986-93, Tax Equity Alliance Mass. 1994. Recipient Good Citizen award DAR, 1950, Community Svc. award Northeastern U., 1986, Gov.'s citation for outstanding performance, 1993; named to Outstanding Young Women of Am., 1965. Mem. NOW, NAFE, Mass. State Assn. Deaf, MRC Statewide Cen. Office Dirs. (chair 1995-96). Democrat. Episcopalian. Avocations: reading, music, bridge, swimming, sign language. Office: Mass Rehab Commn 27-43 Wormwood St Boston MA 02210

MASON, PERRY CARTER, philosophy educator; b. Houston, Sept. 24, 1939; s. Lloyd Vernon and Lorraine (Carter) M.; m. Judith Jane Fredrick, June 11, 1960; children—Gregory Charles, Nicole Elizabeth. B.A., Baylor U., Waco, Tex., 1961; B.D., Harvard U., 1964; M.A., Yale U., 1966, Ph.D., 1968. Asst. prof. philosophy Carleton U., Northfield, Minn., 1968-73, assoc. prof. philosophy, 1973-80, prof. philosophy, 1980—, v.p. for planning and devel., 1988-89, v.p. for external rels., 1989-91. Contbr. articles to profl. publs. Fellow Soc. for Values in Higher Edn.; mem. Minn. Philos. Soc., Am. Philos. Assn. Democrat. Home: 8629 Hall Ave Northfield MN 55057-4884 Office: Carleton College One North College St Northfield MN 55057

MASON, PHILLIP HOWARD, aircraft company executive, retired army officer; b. Cash, Va., Mar. 13, 1932; s. Phillip Howard and Mary Armfried (Hogg) M.; m. Frances Murray Gallogly, Mar. 3, 1962; children: Mary Catherine, Patrick Howard, Susan Frances, Sheryl Ann. B.S in B.A., magna cum laude, St. Benedicts, 1966; M.B.A., Shippensburg State Coll., 1976; postgrad., U.S. Army Command and Gen. Staff Coll., 1965-66, U.S. Army War Coll., 1975-76. Enlisted in U.S. Army, 1948, advanced through grades to brig. gen., 1980; bn. comdr. 1st Bn. 1st ADA U.S. Army, Ger., 1971-73, sec. gen. staff 32d Army Air Def. Command, 1974; systems coordinator ODCSRDA, Dept Army U.S. Army, Washington, 1975; project mgr. AD Command and Control Redstone Arsenal, Ala., 1976-78; comdr. 11th ADA Bde Fort Bliss, Tex., 1978-79; project mgr. STINGER Redstone Arsenal, 1979-83; dir. combat support system ODCSRDA, Dept. Army Washington; ret. U.S. Army, 1983; v.p. bus. devel. Sanders Assocs., Nashua, N.H., 1984-90; project mgr. Hughes Aircraft Co., 1990—. Decorated Disting. Svc. medal, Legion of Merit with oak leaf cluster, Bronze star, Meritorious Svc. medal with two oak leaf clusters, Joint Svcs. Commendation medal, Army Commendation medal. Home: 20 Winterberry Dr Amherst NH 03031-1605 Office: 1100 Wilson Blvd Ste 2000 Arlington VA 22209

MASON, RAYMOND ADAMS, brokerage company executive; b. Lynchburg, Va., Sept. 28, 1936; s. Raymond Watsi and Marion (Adams) M.; married; children: Paige Adams, Pamela Ann, Carter Meade, Morgan Rand. BA in Econs., Coll. William and Mary, 1959. Rep. Mason & Lee Inc., Richmond, Va., 1960-62; founder, pres. Mason & Co. Inc., Newport News, Va., 1962-70; pres. Legg, Mason & Co., Inc., Washington, 1970-73; pres. Legg, Mason Wood Walker, Inc., Balt., 1978—; chmn. bd. dirs. pres., chmn., chief exec. officer Legg Mason, Inc., 1981—; bd. dirs. Environ. Elements Corp.; chmn. regional firms com. N.Y. Stock Exchange, 1978-81; bd. dirs. Legg Mason Value Trust, Howard Weil Fin., Western Asset Mgmt. Trustee emeritus Endowment Assn., Coll. William and Mary; bd. dirs. emeritus William and Mary Sch. Bus. Adminstrn. Sponsors, Inc.; former trustee Balt. Mus. Art; former bd. dirs. Nat. Aquarium, Balt.; bd. dirs., exec. com., chair fin. com. Johns Hopkins Hosp.; mem. exec. com., chair endowment funds, fin. com. Johns Hopkins U.; former chmn. bd. sponsors Sch. Bus. & Mgmt. Loyola Coll., Balt., 1980-88; bd. dirs. Greater Balt. Com., 1982—, chmn., 1987-89; chmn. United Way Ctrl. Md. Mem. Nat. Assn. Securities Dealers (bd. govs. 1971-75, chmn. bd. govs. 1974-75), Securities Industry Assn. (bd. dirs. 1982—, chmn. 1985-86, bd. govs. 1984-88, chmn. bd. govs. 1987). Clubs: Ctr., Md., Balt. Country, L'Hirondelle, Caves Valley, New Orleans Country Club. Home: 1832 Circle Rd Baltimore MD 21204-6415 Office: Legg Mason Inc 111 S Calvert St Baltimore MD 21202-6174

MASON, RICHARD CLYDE, landscape architect; b. Omaha, Mar. 20, 1948; s. Raymond C. and Sue (Elmore) M. Student Austin Coll., 1966-70; B.B.A., So. Meth. U., 1971; postgrad N. Tex. State U., 1971-72; MLA Tex. A&M U., 1989. Auditor, Dallas Fed. Res. Bank, 1972-73; br. office mgr. Neuhaus & Taylor, archs., 1974-76; auditor Lawhon, Thomas, Holmes & Co., Dallas, 1976-78; controller, dir. Mason Johnston & Assocs., Inc., Dallas, 1979-89; exec. dir. Springside Landscape Restoration, Poughkeepsie, N.Y., 1990-91; dist. landscape arch. Tex. Dept. Transp., 1992—. Mem. Nat. Assn. Accts. (past pres. North Dallas chpt., nat. com. cmty. rels.), Tex. State Hist. Assn., Tex. Hist. Found. (life mem.), Dallas Hist. Soc., Dallas Mus. Art, Am. Soc. Landscape Archs. Methodist. Home: 6412 La Cadena Dr El Paso TX 79912 Office: 212 N Clark Dr El Paso TX 79905

MASON, ROBERT JOSEPH, automotive parts company executive; b. Muskegon, Mich., Nov. 17, 1918; s. Robert J. and Delora (Houle) M.; m. Kathleen Carr, June 24, 1944 (dec. Nov. 1965); children: Marcia (Mrs. Richard Dwyer), Eileen A. (Mrs. Thomas Wilhelm); m. Carol F. Fales, Jan. 31, 1967. M.B.A., U. Chgo. 1941. Accounting analyst Carnegie-Ill. Steel Corp., Gary, Ind., 1941-45; with Sealed Power Corp., Muskegon, 1945-83; sec.-treas. Sealed Power Corp., 1959-70, v.p. finance, 1970-83, dir., 1972-92. Bd. dirs. Muskegon County United Appeal, Muskegon Area C. of C.; adv. bd. Mercy Hosp. Mem. C. of C., Fin. Execs. Inst., Am. Soc. Corp. Secs. Clubs: Century (pres., dir.), Muskegon Country (past bd. dirs.). Home: 320 W Circle Dr Muskegon MI 49445

MASON, ROBERT MCSPADDEN, technology management educator, consultant; b. Sweetwater, Tenn., Jan. 16, 1941; s. Paul Rankin and Ruby May (McSpadden) M.; m. Betty Ann Durrence (div. 1980); children: Michael Dean, Donald Andrew; m. Marilyn Killebrew Gell, July 17, 1981. SB, MIT, 1963, SM, 1965; PhD, Ga. Inst. Tech., 1973. Tech. staff mem. Sandia Labs., Livermore, Calif., 1965-68; rsch. scientist Ga. Inst. Tech., Atlanta, 1971-75, sr. rsch. scientist, 1975; prin. Metrics, Inc., Atlanta, 1975-80; pres. Metrics Rsch. Corp., Atlanta, 1980-86, Cleve., 1986—; adj. prof. Weatherhead Sch. Mgmt. Case Western U., 1987-88, vis. prof., 1988-91, prof. for practice of tech. mgmt., 1991—; dir. Ctr. Mgmt. Sci. and Tech., 1988—. Editor: Library Micro Consumer; co-editor: Information Services: Economics, Management, and Technology, 1981; co-author: The Impact of Office Automation on Clerical Employment, 1985-2000, 1985; contbr. articles series "Mason on Micros" to Libr. Jour., 1983-86; contbr. articles to other profl. jours. Mem. Internat. Assn. for Tech. Mgmt. (newsletter editor 1992-93, program chair intenat. conf., pres.-elect.). Republican. Presbyterian. Avocations: flying, skiing, sailing, scuba diving, photography. Home: 12427 Fairhill Rd Cleveland OH 44120-1015 Office: Ctr Mgmt Sci & Tech Weatherhead Sch Mgmt Case Western Res U Cleveland OH 44106-7235

MASON, RONALD LEONARD, architect; b. Winnipeg, Man., Can., June 14, 1938; came to U.S., 1952; s. Arthur Hater and Lillian Eileen (Pennock) M.; m. Joan Louise Irwin, July 19, 1958 (div. 1976); children: Mark, Susan, Jeffrey; m. Kimberly Kay Wood, June 1, 1988. Student, U. Colo., 1958-62. Registered architect, Colo., S.D.; cert. Nat. Coun. Archtl. Registration Bds., value engr. Archtl. draftsman Charles S. Sink Arch., Denver, 1961-70; archtl. draftsman and assoc. ABR Partnership Arch., Denver, 1970-75, John D. Anderson & Assocs., Denver, 1975-80; arch. Anderson Archs., Denver, 1980-85; pres. Anderson Mason Dale, P.C., Denver, 1985—; mem. Creekfront Project adv. com. Denver Partnership, mem. 16th Street Mall sign code com.; spl. design cons. Platte River Greenway Com. Prin. works include Western Wyo. Coll. expansion, Rock Springs Wyoming, Joint Inst. for Lab. Astrophysics bldg. and addition, U. Colo., Boulder, master plan and new visitor facilities Mt. Rushmore Nat. Meml., S.D., Brighton (Colo.) H.S., Scis. and Industries Bldg. and South City Campus expansion Salt Lake C.C., New Meeting Bldg., Denver Botanic Gardens, Biomed. Rsch. Facility, U. Colo. Health Scis. Ctr., Denver, also schs. in Colo. Chmn. urban follies competition Urban Design Forum, Denver, 1991, also bd. dirs. Fellow AIA (Denver city and county design rev. group, mem. design awards jury Dallas 1989, Ky. and Wyo. 1994, Ariz. 1992, chmn. Colo. design conf. 1993). Avocations: kayaking (3d place nat. kayak championships 1973, nat. freestyle champion 1974), hiking, travel, drawing. Office: Anderson Mason Dale 1615 17th St Denver CO 80202-1293

MASON, SCOTT MACGREGOR, entrepreneur, inventor, consultant; b. N.Y.C., Feb. 11, 1923; s. Gregory Mason and Mary Louise Turner; m. Mildred Davidson, Mar. 13, 1949 (div. 1970); children: Alan Gregory, Phoebe Louise, Caleb; m. Virginia Frances Perkins, May 5, 1970 (dec. 1990). AB, Princeton U., 1943; MS, NYU, 1947. Control chemist Firestone Tire & Rubber Co., Akron, Ohio, 1943-44; R & D chemist Am. Cyanamid Co. Rsch. Labs., Stamford, Conn., 1944-52; mgr. stearate dept. Warwick Chem. div. Sun Chem. Corp., Wood River Junction, R.I., 1952-58; cons., Stonington, Conn., 1958-59; instr. Williams Meml. Inst., New London, Conn., 1959-63; NSF fellow Brown U., Providence, 1963-64; tchr. Moses Brown Sch., Providence, 1964-70; owner, mgr. Innoventures, Wakefield, R.I., 1970—; cons. Greene Plastics Corp., Canonchet, R.I., 1972-80, Dorette Inc., Pawtucket, R.I., 1982-83. Patentee in field. Trustee Pine Point Sch., Stonington, 1956-62, pres. bd., 1959-61. With AUS 1944-46, ETO. Named Tchr. of Week, Sta. WICE, Providence, 1967; summer rsch. fellow NSF, U. R.I., 1960. Mem. AAAS, N.Y. Acad. Scis. Avocations: tennis, fishing, snorkeling, photography, music. Office: Innoventures PO Box 369 Wakefield RI 02880-0369

MASON, STEPHEN OLIN, academic administrator; b. Fresno, Calif., July 11, 1952; s. Olin James and Mary Edna (Moyer) M. BA, Bridgewater (Va.) Coll., 1974; MEd, James Madison U., 1979; PhD, Loyola U., Chgo., 1991. Asst. to the dir. student ctr. Bridgewater Coll., 1974-76; guidance counselor Woodlawn Elem. Sch., Sebring, Fla., 1976-77; asst. dean for student devel. Bridgewater Coll., 1977-81; dir. student life Roger Williams Coll., Bristol, R.I., 1981-83; assoc. dean for residential svcs. Dickinson Coll., Carlisle, Pa., 1983-84; v.p., dean student affairs Westmar Coll., LeMars, Iowa, 1984; rsch. assoc. to pres. Elmhurst (Ill.) Coll., 1986-87; v.p. student affairs Felician Coll., Chgo., 1987-88; dean students Huntingdon Coll., Montgomery, Ala., 1988-90; dir. devel. McPherson (Kans.) Coll., 1990-94, v.p. fin. svcs., 1994—. Coord. Bridgewater Coll. ARC Blood Dr., 1978-79; mem. allocatons com. United Way, Carlisle, 1984; mem. adv. bd. LeMars chpt. Siouxland Coun. for Alcoholism and Drug Abuse, 1984; site coord. for coat dr. Mental Health Greater Chgo., 1985; dir.-at-large Bridgewater Coll. Alumni Bd., 1987-93; v.p. McPherson Habitat for Humanity, 1993, 94, bd. dirs., 1993—, pres., 1994; bd. dirs. McPherson Mus. and Arts Found., 1993-94; mem. bd. dirs. Assn. Brethren Caregivers, 1993—. Mem. Am. Assn. for Higher Edn., Assn. for Study of Higher Edn., Coun. for Advancement and Support of Edn. Avocations: calligraphy, community theatre, barbershop singing, spelunking. Home: 1502 E Sharp St Mc Pherson KS 67460-3851 Office: McPherson Coll 1600 E Euclid St Mc Pherson KS 67460-3899

MASON, STEVEN CHARLES, forest products company executive; b. Sarnia, Ont., Can., Feb. 22, 1936. B.S., MIT, 1957. Pres. div. Mead Corp., Dayton, Ohio, 1978-79, group v.p., 1979-82, sr. v.p. ops. 1982, pres., chief oper. exec., 1990-92, vice chmn., 1992—, chmn., CEO, 1992—. Office: Mead Corp Courthouse Plz NE Dayton OH 45463

MASON, STEVEN JUDE, wholesale company executive; b. New Orleans, Mar. 4, 1944; s. Henry Lee and Mildred (Griffin) M.; m. Linda Lauve; children: Steven Jr., Michael, David. BA, La. State U., 1966; JD, Loyola U., New Orleans, 1969. Bar: La. 1969, Tenn. 1981. Atty. FTC, New Orleans, 1969-70, Ingram Corp., New Orleans, 1970-78; v.p., gen. counsel Ingram

Industries Inc., Nashville, 1978-83; pres. Ingram Book Co, LaVergne, Tenn., 1983—, Ingram Book Co., La Vergne, 1989—; vice chmn. Ingram Book Co., 1990—; bd. dirs. So. Festival of Books. Bd. dirs. Nashville Opera Assn., 1985—; mem. bd. trust Tenn. Repertory Theatre. Recipient Am. Legion Award, New Orleans, 1962. Mem. La. State Bar Assn., Tenn. Bar Assn. Home: 1318 Chickering Rd Nashville TN 37215-4522 Office: Ingram Book Co 1125 Heil Quaker Blvd La Vergne TN 37086-3610

MASON, THEODORE W., lawyer; b. June 17, 1943. AB, Yale U., 1965; JD, U. Pa., 1972. Bar: Pa. 1972, Fla. 1987. Ptnr. Morgan, Lewis & Bockius, Phila. Mem. Nat. Assn. Bond Lawyers. Office: Morgan Lewis & Bockius 2000 One Logan Sq Philadelphia PA 19103

MASON, THOMAS ALBERT, lawyer; b. Cleve., May 4, 1936; s. Victor Lewis and Frances (Speidel) M.; m. Elisabeth Gun Sward, Sept. 25, 1965; children: Thomas Lewis, Robert Albert. AB, Kenyon Coll., 1958; LLB, Case-Western Res. U., 1961. Bar: Ohio 1961. Assoc. Thompson, Hine and Flory, Cleve., 1965-73, ptnr., 1973—. Trustee Cleve. YMCA, 1975-94. Capt. USMCR, 1962-65. Mem. Am. Coll. Real Estate Lawyers, Am. Land Title Assn. (lender's counsel group), Mortgage Bankers Assn. of Met. Cleve., ABA, Ohio Bar Assn., Cleve. Bar Assn., Am. Coll. Mortgage Attys., Nat. Assn. Indsl. and Office Pks., Country Club, Union Club of Cleve., Masons. Republican. Episcopalian. Avocations: tennis; golf. Home: 23375 Duffield Rd Cleveland OH 44122-3101 Office: Thompson Hine & Flory 1100 Nat City Bank Bldg 629 Euclid Ave Cleveland OH 44114

MASON, VIVIAN LEE CONWAY, elementary education educator; b. Richmond, Va., Jan. 16, 1942; d. Edward Gordon and Raconia (Boyd) Conway; m. Eugene Albertis Mason Jr., June 30, 1962; children: Eugene Albertis III, Yevette Matrease. BS, Va. Commonwealth U., 1976; postgrad., U. Richmond, 1979, Va. Union U., 1982, Hampton U., 1985. Cert. collegiate profl., Va. Tchr. Richmond (Va.) Pub. Schs., 1976—; chairperson Am. Bus. Women's Assn., Richmond, 1990-91; trainer, cons. Project Head Start, 1987-89. Mem. Richmond Dem. Party, 1991-92, Alpha Kappa Alpha Sorority, Richmond, 1986-92. Mem. NEA, AAUP, Va. Edn. Assn., Richmond Edn. Assn. (bd. dirs. 1993), Nat. Edn. Assn. Women's Caucus, Am. Bus. Women's Assn. (Inner Circle award 1992). Democrat. Avocations: writing children's literature, painting, jogging, working with youth and families. Home: 6319 Windcroft Rd Richmond VA 23225 Office: Richmond Pub Schs 301 N Ninth St Richmond VA 23219

MASON, WILLIAM A(LVIN), psychologist, educator, researcher; b. Mountain View, Calif., Mar. 28, 1926; s. Alvin Frank and Ruth Sabina (Erwin) M.; m. Virginia Joan Carmichael, June 27, 1948; children—Todd, Paula, Nicole, Hunter. B.A., Stanford U., 1950, M.S., 1952, Ph.D., 1954. Asst. prof. U. Wis.-Madison, 1954-59; research assoc. Yerkes Labs. Primate Biology, Orange Park, Fla., 1959-63; head dept. behavioral sci. Delta Primate Research Ctr., Tulane U., Covington, La., 1963-71; prof. psychology, research psychologist U. Calif., Davis, 1971—; leader behavioral biology unit Calif. Primate Rsch. Ctr., 1972—; bd. dirs. Jane Goodall Inst., 1978-92, Karisoke Rsch. Ctr., 1980-86. Mem. Editorial bd. Animal Learning and Behavior, 1973-76, internat. Jour. Devel. Psychobiology, 1980-92, Internat. Jour. Primatology, 1980-90; contbr. numerous articles to profl. jours., chpts. to books. With USMC, 1944-46. USPHS spl. fellow, 1963-64. Fellow AAAS, APA (pres. div. 6 1982), Am. Psychol. Soc., Animal Behavior Soc.; mem. Internat. Primatological Soc. (pres. 1976-80, 81-84), Am. Soc. Primatologists (pres. 1988-90, disting. primatologist award), Internat. Soc. Devel. Psychobiology (pres. 1971-72, Best Paper of Yr. award 1976), Sigma Xi. Home: 2809 Anza Ave Davis CA 95616-0257 Office: U Calif Regional Primate Rsch Ctr Davis CA 95616

MASON, WILLIAM CORDELL, III, hospital administrator; b. Montgomery, Ala., June 7, 1938; s. William C. and Sibyl (Evans) M.; m. Mona Holloway, Jan. 5, 1957 (div. June 1992); children: Michael C., Rebecca Mason Malone, Stephen E., Holly M.; m. Juliette Baldwin Woodruff, Apr. 17, 1993. B.S., U. Southwestern La., 1961; M. Hospital and Health Care, Trinity U., 1971. Hosp. rep. Eaton Labs., Norwich, N.Y., 1962-66; fgn. service officer U.S. Dept. State, Manila and Saigon, 1966-69; chief exec. officer Bapt. Hosp. of East Africa, Mbeya, Tanzania, 1971-74, Bapt. Hosp., Bangalore, India, 1974-78; chief operating officer Bapt. Med. Ctr., Jacksonville, Fla., 1978-84, pres., chief exec. officer, 1984-95; pres., CEO Bapt./St. Vincent's Health Sys. Inc., Jacksonville, Fla., 1995—; mem. adj. faculty U. No Fla. Jacksonville, 1985—; cons. So. Bapt. Fgn. Mission Bd., Richmond, Va., 1980-85; bd. dirs. Sun Bank of North Fla., N.A., SunHealth Corp., sec. exec. com., 1990-94. Contbr. articles to profl. jours. Chmn. deacons Hendricks Ave. Bapt. Ch., Jacksonville, 1984-85, Calvary Bapt. Ch., Bangalore, 1976-77; treas. Karnataka State Bapt. Conv., Bangalore, 1975-77; trustee Jacksonville Symphony Orch.; bd. dirs. U. No. Fla.Assn. Vol. Hosps., 1986, Med. Assistance Program Internat., 1986-87, United Way, 1990; chmn. Greater Jacksonville Area Hosp. Coun., 1985, Mayor's Health Econ. Devel. Coun., 1986-87, Greater Jacksonville U.S. Savs. Bond Campaign, 1987; mem. adv. coun. Jacksonville U. Sch. Bus., 1986-88; chmn. area devel. coun. So. Bapt. Fgn. Mission Bd., 1987-91. Fellow Am. Coll. Hosp. Execs.; mem. Am. Hosp. Assn., Fla. Hosp. Assn. (trustee 1982, 83-85, 86), Fla. Hosp. Assn. (chmn. 1992-93, trustee 1994—), Healthcare Exec. Study Soc., Jacksonville C. of C. (vice chmn. exec. com. 1988-89, chmn. health econ. devel. 1992-95, chmn. cornerstone econ. devel. initiative), Epping Forest Yacht Club (bd. govs. 1990—), Beta Sigma Gamma, Rotary. Avocations: golf, boating, reading. Home: 947 Greenridge Rd Jacksonville FL 32207-5203 Office: Bapt/St Vincent's Health Sys Inc 800 Prudential Dr Jacksonville FL 32207-8203

MASON, WILLIAM RANDY, sales executive; b. Quantico, Va., Aug. 10, 1944; s. Wilbur Randall and Anne (Kelly) M.; m. Maureen Middlecamp, Feb. 22, 1969; children: Erin, Shannon. Student, Roanoke Coll., 1963-65. Technician Gen. Electric, Salem, Va., 1965-70; sales rep. Am. Greetings, Roanoke, Va., 1970-72; field mgr. Am. Greetings, Raleigh, N.C., 1972-74; dist. mgr. Am. Greetings, Atlanta, 1974-76; regional dirs. Am. Greetings, Cleve., 1976-78; regional v.p. Am. Greetings, San Francisco, 1978-80; nat. sales mgr. Am. Greetings, Cleve., 1980-81, sone v.p., 1981-83, v.p., mgr. gen. sales, 1983—. Served with USMC. Named Eagle Scout with gold palm Boy Scouts Am. Mem. Internat. Mass Retail Assn., Nat. Assn. Chain Drug Stores, Food Market Inst. Republican. Roman Catholic. Avocations: hunting, fishing, archery, golf.

MASONER, PAUL HENRY, counseling educator; b. Middletown, Ohio, Mar. 25, 1908; s. Paul and Emma Martha (Hayes) M.; m. Lorraine Carr, 1983; children: Paul, David, Linda; stepchildren: Elisabeth Carr-Jones, Phillip Carr, Jr. Student, Capital U., 1926-28; B.A. in English, Ohio State U., 1930, M.A. in Sociology, 1931; postgrad., Wilmington Coll., summer 1931; Ph.D. in Counseling, U. Pitts., 1949; postgrad., U. London, Eng., summers 1964, 66; D.Litt. (hon.), Hanyang U., Seoul, Korea, 1978. Tchr. English Central High Sch., Uhrichsville, Ohio, 1930-32; tchr. social scis. Bellevue High Sch., Pitts., 1932-34; counselor, vice prin. Bellevue High Sch., 1934-43, acting prin., 1943-44; adminstrv. head Engring. and Sci. Mgmt. War Tng. Center, Bellevue, Pa., 1942-44; sr. analyst Nat. Def. Research Com., U. Pa., 1944-45; counselor, lectr. psychology Vets. Counseling Center, U. Pitts., 1945-46; instr. Vets. Counseling Center, U. Pitts. (Sch. Edn.), 1946-48, asst. prof., 1948-50, asso. prof., 1950-51, prof., 1953—, asst. dean, 1952-54, acting dean, 1954, dean, 1955-73, dean emeritus, 1973—, Univ. prof., 1973—; Mem. adv. com. Learning Research and Devel. Center, Pitts., 1965-73; cons. scholarship aid programs; ednl. cons. to sch. systems, colls., univs., ednl. orgns.; govt. agys., others; mem. accreditation teams Middle States Assn. and Nat. Council for Accreditation of Tchr. Edn., 1954-75; mem. adv. com. Pa. Grad. Tchr. Edn., 1964-70; mem. Pa. Curriculum Commn., 1964-70, Com. of One Hundred Citizens for Better Edn., 1963-67; mem. council Nat. Council Accreditation Tchr. Edn., 1966-70; mem. Nat. Adv. Council Edn. Professions Devel., 1970-73; mem. exec. bd. Nat. Reading Center, Washington, 1970-73; Extensive fgn. travel and study. Contbg. author: Standards for the 60's, 1962, Counseling: Selected Readings, 1964, Changes in Teacher Education: An Appraisal, 1964; author: Design for Teacher Education, 1964, An Imperative: A National Policy for Teacher Education, 1972, Evaluación de Sistemas de Communicación Educativa, 1980. Bd. dirs. Falk Elementary Sch., Pitts., 1955-73, Westminster Found., 1964-66, Pitts. Council of Chs., 1964-66; pres. bd. trustees Robert Morris Coll. Recipient Outstanding Service to Edn. award Commonwealth of Pa., 1962, Effective

Leadership to Tchr. Edn. award, 1964. Fellow Coll. Preceptors (hon.) (Eng.); mem. Western Pa. Scholarship Assn. (exec. sec. 1950-70), NEA, Pa. State Edn. Assn. (exec. council 1966-68), Western Pa. Edn. Conf. (chmn. 1955-70), Pa. Schoolman's Club (pres. 1963), Pa. Assn. Liberal Arts Colls. for Advancement of Teaching (pres. 1959), AAUP, Am. Personnel and Guidance Assn., Nat. Vocat. Guidance Assn. (profl.), Am. Assn. Sch. Adminstrs. (profl.), Internat. Council Edn. for Teaching (trustee 1972-76, pres. 1976—), Am. Assn. Colls. Tchr. Edn. (pres. 1970-71), AAAS, Civic Club Allegheny County (Pa.), Allegheny Roundtable (pres. 1964-70), Omicron Delta Kappa, Delta Pi Epsilon (hon.), Iota Lambda Sigma (hon.), Phi Delta Kappa, Kappa Phi Kappa. Conglist. Clubs: Cosmos (Washington); University (Pitts.). Office: 44 Oxford Ct Pittsburgh PA 15237

MASORO, EDWARD JOSEPH, JR., physiology educator; b. Oakland, Calif., Dec. 28, 1924; s. Edward Joseph and Louise Elizabeth (DePaoli) M.; m. Barbara Weikel, June 25, 1947. AB, U. Calif., Berkeley, 1947, PhD, 1950. Asst. prof. physiology Queen's U., Kingston, Ont., Can., 1950-52; asst. prof., then asso. prof. Tufts U. Sch. Medicine, 1952-62; research asso. prof., then research prof. physiology and biophysics U. Wash., 1962-64; prof. physiology and biophysics, chmn. dept. Med. Coll. Pa., 1964-73; prof. physiology, chmn. dept. U. Tex. Health Sci. Center, San Antonio, 1973-91, prof., 1991—; dir. Aging Rsch. and Edn. Ctr., 1992—; cons. coun. basic sci. Am. Heart Assn., 1965-67; chmn. metabolic discussion group Fed. Am. Soc. Exptl. Biology, 1969-73; mem. aging rev. com. Nat. Inst. on Aging, 1981-84, chmn. bd. sci. counselors, 1985-89; chmn. Gordon Conf. on Biology of Aging, 1983; mem. bd. sci. advisors Human Nutrition Inst., Internat. Life Sci. Inst., 1989-92; mem. rsch. com. Am. Fedn. Aging Rsch., 1988—; vis. prof. U. Pisa, 1993; Wellcome vis. prof. basic med. scis., 1992-93. Author: Physiological Chemistry of Lipids in Mammals, 1967; co-author: Acid-Base Regulation: Its Physiology and Pathophysiology, 1971, 2d edit., 1977; editor sect. 24 Internat. Ency. Pharmacology and Therapeutics, 1974; mem. editorial bd. Jour. Lipid Rsch., 1967-83, Jour. Gerontology, 1979-91, Exptl. Gerontology, 1984—, Proc. Soc. Exptl. Biol. Medicine, 1986-92, Physiol. Rev., 1988—; editor Jour. Gerontology: Biol. Scis., 1991—, Handbook Physiol. Aging, 1990—; editor for biol. scis. Exptl. Rsch. Aging, 1980-88; co-editor Aging: Clinical and Experimental Research, 1989—; contbr. articles to profl. jours. Served with USNR, 1943-46. Recipient Christian R. and Mary F. Lindback Distinguished Teaching award Med. Coll. Pa., 1967, Golden Apple award Student Am. Med. Assn., 1966, 71, Achievement award Allied Signal, 1989, Rsch. Achievements in Gerontology, U. Pisa, 1991, Irving Wright award Am. Fedn. Aging Rsch., 1995. Fellow AAAS (coun. 1970—), Gerontol. Soc. Am. (chmn. biol. sci. sect. 1978-79, v.p. 1978-79, Kleemeir award 1990, pres.-elect 1992-93, pres. 1994-95); mem. AAUP, Am. Physiol. Soc. (chmn. endocrinology and metabolism sect. 1981-82), Soc. Exptl. Biology and Medicine (coun. 1987-91), Am. Soc. Biochemistry and Molecular Biology, N.Y. Acad. Scis., Phila. Physiol. Soc. (pres. 1966-67). Office: U Tex Dept Physiology Health Sci Ctr San Antonio TX 78284

MASOTTI, LOUIS HENRY, management educator, consultant; b. N.Y.C., May 16, 1934; s. Henry and Angela Catherine (Turi) M.; m. Iris Patricia Leonard, Aug. 28, 1958 (div. 1981); children: Laura Lynn, Andrea Anne; m. Ann Randel Humm, Mar. 5, 1988. AB, Princeton U., 1956; MA, Northwestern U., 1961, PhD, 1964. Fellow Nat. Ctr. Edn. in Politics, 1962; asst. prof. polit. sci. Case Western Res. U., Cleve., 1963-67, assoc. prof., 1967-69, dir. Civil Violence Research Ctr., 1968-69; sr. Fulbright lectr. Johns Hopkins U. Ctr. Advanced Internat. Studies, Bologna, Italy, 1969-70; assoc. prof. Northwestern U., Evanston, Ill., 1970-72, prof. polit. sci. and urban affairs, 1972-83, prof. mgmt. and urban devel. Kellogg Sch. Mgmt., 1983-94, dir. Ctr. Urban Affairs, 1971-80, dir. Program in Pub. and Not-for-Profit Mgmt., Kellogg Sch. Mgmt., 1979-80, dir. Real Estate Research Ctr., 1986-88; cons. to numerous publs., govt. agys. real estate devels. and corps.; vis. assoc. prof. U. Wash., summer 1969; exec. dir. Mayor Byrne Transition Com., Chgo., 1979; vis. prof. Stanford Sch. Bus., 1989-92, UCLA Sch. Mgmt., 1989-92; prof., dir. real estate mgmt. program U. Calif. Grad. Sch. Mgmt., Irvine, 1992—, dir. NHC, Inc., dir. Tucker Properties Corp., 1993; dir. Facilities Mgmt. Internat., 1994—, MCH, Inc., 1993—, Tucker Properties Corp. (REIR), 1993—. Author: Education and Politics in Suburbia, 1967, Shootout in Cleveland, 1969, A Time to Burn?, 1969, Suburbia in Transition, 1973, The New Urban Politics, 1976, The City in Comparative Perspective, 1976, co-editor: Metropolis in Crisis, 1968, 2d edit., 1971, Riots and Rebellion, 1968, The Urbanization of the Suburbs, 1973, After Daley: Chicago Politics in Transition, 1981, Downtown Development, 1985, 2d edit., 1987; editor Edn. and Urban Soc., 1968-71, Urban Affairs Quar., 1973-80; sr. editor Econ. Devel. Quar., 1986-92; vice chmn. bd. Illinois Issues jour., 1986-92. Rsch. dir. Carl Stokes for Mayor of Cleve., 1967; mem. Cleveland Heights Bd. Edn., 1967-69; devel. coordinator for high tech. State of Ill.-City Chgo., 1982-83; advisor to various congl., gubernatorial and mayoral campaigns, Ohio, Ill., N.J., Calif.; cons. urban devel. issues Corps. developers, govt. agys. and news media. Lt. USNR, 1956-59. Fellow Homer Hoyt Inst. for Advanced Real Estate Studies; recipient Disting. Service award Cleve. Jaycees, 1967; numerous fed. and found. research grants, 1963—. Mem. Urban Land Inst., Nat. Coun. Urban Econ. Devel., Internat. Assn. Corp. Real Estate Execs., Internat. Devel. Rsch. Coun., Nat. Assn. Indsl. Office Properties (bd. dirs.), Lambda Alpha Internat. Home: 2810 Villa Way Newport Beach CA 92663-4022

MASOVER, GERALD KENNETH, microbiologist; b. Chgo., May 12, 1935; s. Morris H. and Lillian (Perelgut) M.; m. Bonnie Blumenthal, Mar. 30, 1958 (dec. 1992); children: Steven, Laurie, David; m. Lee Haskins Tower, Mar. 25, 1995. BS, U. Ill., Chgo., 1957, MS, 1970; PhD, Stanford U., 1973. Registered pharmacist, Calif., Ill. Owner, operator Ropert Pharmacy, Chgo., 1960-68; rsch. assoc. Stanford U. Med. Sch., Palo Alto, Calif., 1974-80; assoc. rsch. cell biologist Children's Hosp., Oakland, Calif., 1980-83; rsch. microbiologist Hana Biologics, Berkeley, Calif., 1983-86; pharmacist various locations, 1970—; quality control sect. head Genentech, Inc., South San Francisco, 1986-90, quality control sr. microbiologist, 1990—. Contbr. articles to profl. jours., chpts. to books. 1st Lt. USAR, 1957-66. NSF predoctoral fellow, 1970-73; NIH rsch. grantee, 1974-78. Mem. Tissue Culture Assn., Internat. Orgn. for Mycoplasmology, Parenteral Drug Assn., Am. Soc. for Microbiology, Sigma Xi. Jewish. Achievements include patents on triphasic mycoplasmatales detection method; triphasic mycoplasmatales detection device. Home: 4472 24th St San Francisco CA 94114 Office: Genentech Inc 460 Point San Bruno Blvd South San Francisco CA 94080-4990

MASRI, MERLE SID, biochemist, consultant; b. Jerusalem, Palestine, Sept. 12, 1927; came to U.S., 1947; s. Said Rajab and Fatima (Muneimné) M.; m. Maryjean Loretta Anderson, June 28, 1952 (div. 1974); children: Kristin Corinne, Allan Eric, Wendy Joan, Heather Anderson. BA in Physiology, U. Calif., Berkeley, 1950; PhD in Mammalian Physiology and Biochemistry, U. Calif., Berkeley, 1953. Rsch. asst. dept. Physiology, Univ. Calif., Berkeley, 1950-53; predoctoral fellow Baxter Labs., Berkeley, 1952-53; rsch. assoc. hematology Med. Rsch. Inst., Michael Reese Hosp., Chgo., 1954-56; sr. rsch. biochemist Agrl. Rsch. Svc., USDA, Berkeley, 1956-87; supervisory rsch. scientist Agrl. Rsch. Svc., USDA, N.D. State U. Sta., Fargo, N.D., 1987-89; pvt. practice as cons. Emeryville, Calif., 1989—; lectr. numerous confs. Contbr. over 130 articles to profl. jours. Recipient Spl. Svc. and Merit awards USDA, 1966, 76, 77, Superior Svc. award USDA, 1977. Fellow Am. Inst. Chemists; mem. AAAS, Am. Chem. Soc., Am. Oil Chemists Soc., Am. Assn. Cereal Chemists, N.Y. Acad. Scis., Sigma Xi. Achievements include patents for detoxification of aflatoxin in agrl. crops, new closed-circuit raw wool scouring technology to conserve water and energy and control pollution, synthesis and use of polymers for water treatment, and for enzyme immobilization, toxic heavy metals removal and textile finishing treatment: discovered new methods and reagents for protein and amino acid residue modification and analysis, new metabolic pathways; patent for inactivation of aflatoxins in crops; methods of treating fabrics for desired textile products of improved dyeability, wrinkle recovery, laundering shrinkage control, flameproofing and insect resistance; developed other non-polluting textile finishing treatments. Home: 9 Commodore Dr Emeryville CA 94608

MASRI, SAMI F(AIZ), civil and mechanical engineering educator, consultant; b. Beirut, Dec. 9, 1939; came to U.S., 1956; B.S. in Aerospace Engring., U. Tex., 1960, M.S. in Aerospace Engring., 1961; M.S. in Mech. Engring., Calif. Inst. Tech., 1962, Ph.D. in Mech. Engring., 1965. Research fellow Calif. Inst. Tech., Pasadena, 1965-66; asst. prof. civil and mech. engring. U. So. Calif., Los Angeles, 1966-69; assoc. prof. U. So. Calif., 1969-76,

prof., 1976—. Contbr. articles to profl. jours. Research grantee NSF, NASA, NRC. Mem. AIAA, ASME, ASCE, IEEE, AAAS, Sigma Xi. Office: U So Calif Dept Civil Engring Mc # 2531 Los Angeles CA 90089

MASS, M. F., allergist, immunologist; b. Phila., Feb. 24, 1945; s. Edward I. and Pearl (Markovitz) M.; m. Marilyn Halpern, June 12, 1966; children: Ellis, David. Student, U. Fla., 1963; BA, Brandeis U., 1966; MD, U. Fla., 1970; postgrad., U. Colo., Albany, N.Y., 1972, U. Colo., Denver, 1975. Intern Albany (N.Y.) Med. Ctr., 1970-71, residency, 1971-72; sr. residency U. Colo. Med. Ctr., Denver, 1972-73, postgrad. fellow/allergy-immunology, 1973-75; assoc. clin. professor of medicine U. Fla., Jacksonville, Fla., 1977—; dir. Osteoporosis Diagnostic Lab. Meml. Med. Ctr., Jacksonville; sec. Duval County Environ. Protection Bd.; past chmn. dept. medicine, Meml. Med. Ctr., Jacksonville; sec. S.E. Regional Am. Coll. Rheumatology. Inventor skin chamber. Maj. USAF, 1975-77. Health Professions scholar U. Fla. Fellow Am. Coll. Physicians, Am. Acad. Allergy and Immunology, Am. Coll. Allergy; mem. Am. Coll. Rheumatology (sec. S.E. region), N.E. Fla. Arthritis Found. (bd. dirs., past pres.). Office: 3636 University Blvd S Ste B2 Jacksonville FL 32216-4223 also: 1895 Kingsley Ave # 401 Orange Park FL 32073

MASSA, CONRAD HARRY, religious studies educator; b. Bklyn., Oct. 27, 1927; s. Harry Frederick and Josephine W. (Lepold) M.; m. Anna W. Rossi, Aug. 19, 1951; children: Stephen Mark, Barbara Ann. A.B. with honors, Columbia U., 1951; M.Div., Princeton Theol. Sem., 1954, Ph.D., 1960; HHD, Lafayette Coll., 1987. Ordained to ministry Presbyn. Ch., 1954. Pastor Elmwood Presbyn. Ch., East Orange, N.J., 1954-57; asst. prof. homiletics Princeton Theol. Sem., 1957-61; sr. pastor Old First Ch., Newark, 1961-66, Third Presbyn. Ch., Rochester, N.Y., 1966-78; dean acad. affairs Princeton Theol. Sem., 1978-94, dean emeritus, 1994—, Charlotte W. Newcombe prof., 1978-95, Charlotte W. Newcombe prof. emeritus, 1995—; 1st moderator Synod of the Northeast, United Presbyn. Ch.; vis. prof. St. Bernard's Roman Cath. Sem., Rochester, 1968-70; keynote speaker 11th ann. conf. Inst. Theology, Yonsei U., Seoul, Republic of Korea, 1991. Author articles and book revs. Trustee Lafayette Coll., Easton, Pa., 1982-93. Served with U.S. Army, 1946-47. Mem. Acad. Homiletics, Assn. Theol. Field Edn., Am. Assn. for Higher Edn., Am. Acad. Religion. Home: RR 5 21 Maple Ln Lake Ariel PA 18436 *I have learned to try to understand all events and persons in terms of their relationships to other things, persons and events. While it is sometimes fruitful to isolate a particular and study it in its solitude, nothing and no one really exists in such isolation. This has become a guiding principle in my continued research and growth in those areas of greatest interest - religion, education and society.*

MASSA, PAUL PETER, publisher; b. Hammond, Ind., Aug. 20, 1940; s. Paul Peter and Frances (Ferrara) M.; m. Susan W. Olsgard, Sept. 13, 1969; children: Katherine Alice, Karen Elizabeth. B.S., Ind. U., 1962, postgrad., 1962. Instr. Ind. U. Lab. Sch., 1962, 64-65; with Harcourt Brace Jovanovich Inc., 1965-73; bus. mgr. sch. div. Harcourt Brace Jovanovich Inc., N.Y.C., 1969-73; v.p., gen. mgr., div. Congl. Quar. Inc., Washington, 1973-80; exec. v.p., chief oper. officer, bd. dirs. Congl. Info. Svc., Inc., Washington, 1980-81, pres., chief exec. officer, bd. dirs., 1981—; chmn. Elsevier Realty Info., Inc., 1988—, also bd. dirs.; chmn. Greenwood Pub. Group, Inc., 1985-91, also bd. dirs.; pres. Elsevier Investment Corp., 1987-88, also bd. dirs.; mem. info. industry adv. coun. GPO. Mem. bd. visitors Sch. Edn. Ind. U., 1987—, adv. panel for assessment of tech., pub. policy and changing nature of fed. info. dissemination U.S. Congress Office of Tech. Assessment; mem. Friends of the Law Libr. of Congress. 1st lt. USAR, 1962-64, Korea. Mem. ALA (mem. commn. freedom and equality of access to info.), Info. Industry Assn. (dir. 1993—), Assn. Am. Pubs., Soc. Scholarly Pub., Washington Pubs. Assn., Nat. Press Club. Office: Congressional Info Service 4520 E West Hwy Bethesda MD 20814-3319

MASSA, SALVATORE PETER, psychologist; b. Queens, N.Y., Aug. 5, 1955; s. Joseph and Marie Massa; AAS, Orange County Community Coll., 1975; BA in Psychology, Queens Coll., 1977; MA, St. John's U., 1978, profl. diploma, 1979, PhD, 1985; m. Patricia Louise Kathryn Kelley, Mar. 12, 1979; children: Kathryn Kelley, Kristopher Kelley, KayLynn Kelley, Patrick Kelley, Grace Kelley. Lic. psychologist, N.Y.; nat. cert. sch. psychologist. Intern psychologist Sagamore Children's Psychiat. Hosp., Melville, N.Y., 1978-79; habilitation supr. Suffolk Child Devel. Center, Smithtown, N.Y., 1979; staff psychologist Cumberland Mental Health Center, Bklyn., 1979-81; asst. program dir., dir. clin. services Rhinebeck (N.Y.) Country Sch., 1981-87; cons. psychologist Brookwood Ctr., 1985-86, Anderson Sch., 1987-89, Rensselaer Columbia Greene, 1987—; chmn. Com. on Spl. Edn., 1991—, Com. on Presch. Edn., 1991—; sch. psychologist Red Hook Cen. Sch. Dist., Rhinebeck Cen. Sch. Dist., 1986-90, chmn. profl. conf. com., 1986-87, Anderson Sch., 1987-88; cons. Columbia County Assn. for Retarded Citizens, Rehab. Programs, Inc., 1989; adj. prof. Marist Coll., Poughkeepsie, N.Y., 1989—. Head football coach YMCA winter league, 1979-81; asst. football coach Rhinebeck Country Sch., 1982; coach Germantown Little League, Germantown Winter Basketball League. Recipient public service award for vol. work Middletown State Hosp., 1975; spl. recognition award Internat. Council Psychology, 1981; cert. sch. psychology, N.Y. Mem. Am. Psychol. Assn. (divs. pediatric psychology, psychotherapy, sch. psychology, clin. psychology, evaluation), Eastern Psychol. Assn., Internat. Council Psychologists, Hudson Valley Psychol. Assn., Nat. Assn. Sch. Psychologists, Nat. Soc. Autistic Children. Democrat. Roman Catholic. Contbr. papers to profl. confs.; co-author study on relaxation tng. in residential treatment.

MASSAD, STEPHEN ALBERT, lawyer; b. Wewoka, Okla., Dec. 20, 1950; s. Alexander Hamilton and Delores Jean (Razook) M.; m. Amy S. Massad, Jan. 13, 1979; children: Caroline, Sarah, Margaret. AB, Princeton U., 1972; JD, Harvard U., 1975. Bar: Tex. 1975. Assoc. Baker & Botts, Houston, 1975-82, ptnr., 1983—. Office: Baker & Botts 3000 One Shell Plz 910 Louisiana St Houston TX 77002

MASSALSKI, THADDEUS BRONISLAW, material scientist, educator; b. Warsaw, Poland, June 29, 1926; came to U.S., 1959; s. Piotr and Stanislawa (Andrukaniec) M.; m. Sheila Joan Harris, Sept. 19, 1953; children: Irena, Peter, Christopher. B.Sc., Birmingham (Eng.) U., 1952, Ph.D., 1954, D.Sc., 1964; fellow, Inst. Study Metals, U. Chgo., 1954-56; D.Sc. (h.c.), Warsaw (Poland) U., 1973. Lectr. Birmingham U., 1956-59; head. metal physics group Mellon Inst., Pitts., 1959-75; staff fellow Mellon Inst., 1961—; prof. metal physics and materials sci. Carnegie-Mellon U., 1968—; vis. prof. U. Buenos Aires, 1962, Calif. Inst. Tech., 1962, Stanford, 1963, U. Calif., 1964, 66, Inst. Physics, Bariloche Argentina, 1966, 70, Harvard, 1969; exchange prof. Krakow (Poland) U., 1968; vis. scientist Nat. Bur. Standards, 1980-81; NAVSEA prof. Naval Postgrad. Sch., Monterey, Calif; chmn. bd. govs. Acta Metallurgica, Inc., 1992—. Co-author: Structure of Metals, 3d edit, 1966, Advanced Physical Metallurgy, 1965; co-editor Progress in Materials Science, 1969—, Metall. Transactions, 1991—; editor-in-chief ASM/NIST Phase Diagram Program, 1980—; author papers and articles on alloy theory, crystallography, metal physics, meteorites. Guggenheim fellow Oxford U., 1965-66; recipient Alexander von Humboldt prize, 1991. Fellow Am. Soc. Metals (gold medal 1993), Am. Phys. Soc., The Metals Soc. (gold medal 1995), Brit. Inst. Metals, Brit. Inst. Physics, AIME (Hume-Rothery prize 1989); mem. Polish Acad. Sci. (fgn.), German Acad. Sci. (fgn.). Phys. Soc. Home: 900 Field Club Rd Pittsburgh PA 15238-2127 Office: Carnegie Mellon U 3303 Wean Hall Pittsburgh PA 15213

MASSARE, JOHN STEVE, medical association administrator, educator; b. Rochester, N.Y., Feb. 16, 1949; s. Peter Anthony and Clara Marie (Skill) M.; 1 child. John Simon. BA in Biol. Scis., SUNY, Oswego, 1970; MS in Physiology, SUNY, Brockport, 1973; postgrad., Ind. U., 1976-80. With Carnation Co., 1970-71; lab. instr. SUNY, Brockport, 1972-73; sales rep. Bausch and Lomb Corp., Rochester, 1973-76; assoc. instr. Ind. U., Bloomington, 1976-80; with CIBA Vision Corp., Atlanta, 1981-91, mgr. profl. svcs., 1986-91; exec. dir. Contact Lens Assns. Ophthalmologists, New Orleans, 1992—; adj. instr. Tulane U. Sch. Medicine, New Orleans, 1994—. Contbr. articles to profl. jours. Recipient Assoc. Instr. of Yr. award Ind. U., 1978, 79, Silver Javal Pin Internat. Contact Lens Coun., 1994; Robert C. Ezell fellow, 1979. Mem. Am. Assn. Soc. Execs., Contact Lens Soc. Am. (assoc., v.p. edn. fund com. 1990-92, bd. dirs. 1990-91). Avocations: reading, golf, personal computers, swimming. Office: Contact Lens Assn Ophthalmologists 523 Decatur St Ste 1 New Orleans LA 70130-1057

MASSÉ, LAURENCE RAYMOND, personnel search firm executive; b. Holland, Mich., July 27, 1926; s. Lawrence Joseph and Gladys Lucille (Tidd) M.; m. Barbara Anne Kranendonk, Dec. 23, 1948 (div. 1970); children: Laurel, Babette; m. Pamela Bateman, Feb. 3, 1982; children: Heather, Edward. BA in English, Hope Coll., 1950. Tchr. Pub. Sch. System, Holland, 1950-53; cons. Gen. Motors Corp., Flint, Detroit, Mich., 1953-56; dir. personnel Gen. Foods Corp., White Plains (N.Y.), London, Paris, 1956-66; dir. adminstrn. & personnel Internat. Telephone & Telegraph Co., Brussels, 1966-68; cons. Heidrick & Struggles, N.Y.C., 1968-69; v.p. indsl. relations REA Express Inc., N.Y.C., 1969-72; sr. ptnr. Ward Howell Internat., N.Y.C., Chgo., 1972—. Dir. Ridgefield (Conn.) Community Ctr., 1960-63. With U.S. Navy, 1945-46. Mem. AMA, Chgo. Council Fgn. Relations, Nat. Indsl. Conf. Bd., U.S. C. of C. Republican. Presbyterian. Avocations: reading, music, gardening, swimming, antique collecting. Home: 400 Westwood Dr Barrington IL 60010-4152 Office: Ward Howell Internat Inc 1300 S Grove Ave Ste 100 Barrington IL 60010-5246

MASSÉ, MARCEL, Canadian government official; b. Montreal, June 23, 1940; m. Josee M'Baye; 4 children. B.A., U. Montreal, 1958; LL.B., McGill U., 1961; B.Phil. in Econs., Oxford U., 1966; Diploma in Internat. Law, U. Warsaw, Poland, 1962. Dep. minister fin. N.B., Can., 1973-74; chmn. Cabinet Secretariat, N.B., Can., 1974-77; dep. sec. to Cabinet Fed.-Provincial Relations, Ottawa, Ont., Can., 1977-79; Privy Council Office, 1979; sec. to Cabinet and clk. Privy Council, Ottawa, 1979-80; pres. Can. Internat. Devel. Agy., 1980-82, 89-93; undersec. state for external affairs Dept. External Affairs, Ottawa, 1982-85; exec. dir. IMF, Washington, 1985-89; sec. Cabinet Intergovtl. Affairs, 1993; pres. Queen's privy coun. for Can., min. intergovtl. affairs, min. pub. svc. renewal Govt. of Can., Ottawa, Ont. World Univ. Service scholar in internat. law, 1961; Rhodes scholar, 1963; Nuffield Coll. scholar in econs. Oxford U., 1966. Office: 155 Queen St 5th Fl, Ottawa, ON Canada K1P 6LI

MASSENGALE, MARTIN ANDREW, agronomist, university president; b. Monticello, Ky., Oct. 25, 1933; s. Elbert G. and Orpha (Conn) M.; m. Ruth Audrey Klingelhofer, July 11, 1959; children: Alan Ross, Jennifer Lynn. BS, Western Ky., 1952; MS, U. Wis., 1954, PhD, 1956; LHD (hon.), Nebr. Wesleyan U., 1987. Cert. profl. agronomist, profl. crop scientist. Research asst. agronomy U. Wis., 1952-56; asst. prof., asst. agronomist U. Ariz., 1958-62, assoc. prof., assoc. agronomist, 1962-65, prof. agronomist, 1965-76, head dept., 1966-74, assoc. dean Coll. Agr. assoc. dir. Ariz. Agr. Expt. Sta., 1974-76; vice chancellor for agr. and natural resources U. Nebr., 1976-81; chancellor U. Nebr.-Lincoln, 1981-91, interim pres., 1989-91; pres. U. Nebr., Lincoln, 1991-94, pres. emeritus, 1994, found. prof. and dir. Ctr. for Grassland Studies, 1994—; chmn. pure seed adv. com. Ariz. Agrl. Expt. Sta.; past chmn. bd., pres. Mid-Am. Internat. Agrl. Consortium; mem. EPA-Dept. Agr. Land Grand Univ. Coordinating Com. Environ. Quality; mem., past chmn. bd. dirs. Am. Registry Cert. Profls. in Agronomy, Crops and Soils; past bd. dirs. Nat. Merit Scholarship Corp., Lincoln Found.; bd. dirs. Ctr. for Human Nutrition, U. Nebr. Found. Chmn. NCAA Pres.'s Commn., 1988-91; mem. distbn. of revenue com., standing com. on appointments North Ctrl. Assn. Commn. on Insts. of Higher Edn., 1991; trustee Nebr. State Hist. Soc.; mem. Knight Found. Commn. on Intercollegiate Athletics. Named Midlands Man of Yr., 1982, to We. Ky. U. Hall of Disting. Alumni, 1992, Outstanding Educator of Am., 1970; recipient faculty recognition award Tucson Trade Bur., 1971, Ak-Sar-Ben Agrl. Achievement award, 1986, Agrl. Builders Nebr. award, 1986, Walter K. Beggs award, 1986, hon. state farmer degrees Ky., Ariz., Nebr. Future Farmers of Am. Assns. Fellow Crop Sci. Soc. Am. (past dir., pres. 1972-73, past assoc. editor), Am. Soc. Agronomy (past dir., vis. scientist program, past assoc. editor Agronomy Jour., past chmn bd. dirs., Disting. Service award 1984), AAAS (sect. chmn.); mem. Am. Grassland Council, Agrl. Crop Improvement Assn. (dir.), Am. Soc. Plant Physiology, Nat. Assn. Colls. and Tchrs. of Agr., Soil and Water Conservation Soc. Am., Ariz. Acad. Sci., Nebr. Acad. Sci., Agrl. Council Am. (dir., mem. issues com.), Council Agrl. Sci. and Tech. (bd. dirs. 1982-94), Nat. Assn. State Colls. and Land-Grant Univs. (chmn. com. on info. tech. 1987-94, exec. com. 1990-92, bd. dirs. 1992-94), Edn. Engring. Professions (mem. commn.), Coll. Football Assn. (chmn. 1986-88), Am. Assn. of State Coll. and Univs. (task force instl. resource allocation), Assn. Am. Univs. Rsch. Libs. (steering com. 1992—), Nebr. C. of C. and Industry, Nebr. C.C. Assn. (hon.), Lincoln C. of C., Sigma Xi, Phi Kappa Phi, Gamma Sigma Delta, Alpha Zeta, Phi Kappa Phi, Phi Sigma, Gamma Alpha, Alpha Gamma Rho, Phi Beta Delta, Golden Key Nat. Hon. Soc. Office: U Nebr 220 Kern Hall Lincoln NE 68583

MASSEY, ANDREW JOHN, conductor, composer; b. Nottingham, Eng., May 1, 1946; came to U.S., 1978; s. Henry Louis Johnson and Margaret (Park) M.; m. Sabra Ann Todd, May 29, 1982; children: Colin Sebastian, Robin Elizabeth. BA, Oxford U., 1968, MA, 1981; MA, Nottingham U., 1969. Asst. condr. The Cleve. Orch., 1978-80; assoc. condr. New Orleans Symphony, 1980-86, San Francisco Symphony, 1985-88; music dir. Fresno (Calif.) Philharmonic, 1986-93, R.I. Philharmonic, Providence, 1986-91; music dir. Toledo Symphony Orch., 1991—, also condr.; vis. scholar Brown U., Providence, 1986—. Composer incidental music (stage prodns.) Murder in the Cathedral, 1968, King Lear, 1971, A Midsummer Night's Dream, 1972. Avocations: trees, computers, astrology, philosophy of Karl Popper. Office: care Toledo Symphony Two Maritime Plz Toledo OH 43604*

MASSEY, CHARLES KNOX, JR., advertising agency executive; b. Durham, N.C., Jan. 16, 1936; s. Charles Knox and Louise (Southerl) M.; m. Mary Ann Keith, Aug. 27, 1960; children: Elizabeth, Knox, Louise. BS in Bus. Adminstrn, U. N.C., 1959. Vice pres. C. Knox Massey & Assoc., Inc., advt. agy., Durham, N.C., 1959-64; account exec. Tucker Wayne & Co., advt. agy., Atlanta, 1964-78; exec. v.p., gen. mgr. Tucker Wayne & Co., advt. agy., 1975-78, pres., 1978-93; pres. Tucker Wayne/Luckie & Co., Atlanta, 1988-93, chmn., CEO, 1994—. Trustee The Lovett Sch., Atlanta, Inst. for the Arts and Scis., U. N.C., Chapel Hill. Mem. Atlanta C. of C. (bd. dirs.), Piedmont Driving Club (pres. 1990-92), Peachtree Club, Coral Beach and Tennis Club (Bermuda). Episcopalian. Home: 67 Brighton Rd NE Atlanta GA 30309-1518 Office: Tucker Wayne/Luckie & Co 1100 Peachtree St NE Ste 1800 Atlanta GA 30309-3696

MASSEY, DONALD WAYNE, microfilm consultant, small business owner; b. Durham, N.C., Mar. 7, 1938; s. Gordon Davis and Lucille Alma (Gregory) M.; m. Violet Sue McIlvain, Nov. 2, 1958; children: Kimberly Shan (dec.), Leon Dale, Donn Krichele, Anthony Donn Prestarri. Student, U. Hawaii, 1959, U. Ky., 1965, 66, U. Va., 1970, Piedmont C.C., 1982. Head microfilm sect. Ky. Hist. Soc., Frankfort, 1961; dir. microfilm ctr. U. Ky., Lexington, 1962-67; dir. photog. svcs. and graphics U. Va., Charlottesville, 1967-73; pres. Micrographics II, Charlottesville, Va. & Charleston, S.C., 1973—; owner Roseraie Nursery Ctr., 1988—; instr. U. Va. Sch. Continuing Edn., 1971-72, Central Va. Piedmont Community Coll., 1976; cons. Microform Systems and Copying Centers; owner Massland Farm, Shadwell, Va.; basketball coach Rock Hill Acad., 1975-77; chaplain Cedars Nursing Home, Charlottesville, 1992-94; chaplain Colonnades Charlottesville, Va., 1994—. Pub.: Micropublishing Series, 18th Century Sources for Study of English Lit. and Culture, Women Authors 18th and 19th Centuries, 1993, Va. Colonial History, 1994—, Theology in the 18th and 19th Centuries, 1995; author: Episcopal Churches in the Diocese of Virginia, 1989, A Catechism for Children, 1995, A Guide to Colonial Churches in Virginia, 1995. Chmn. bd. dirs. Park St. Christian Ch., 1970-75; pres., Rock Hill Acad. Aux., 1975-76; pres. bd. Workshop V for handicapped, Charlottesville, Va., 1972-73; bd. chmn. Park St. Christ Ch. 1969-73; mem. Emmanuel Episc. Ch., Greenwood, Va., Grace Episc. Ch., Cismont, Va.; pres. region XV Episc. Diocese of Va.; chalice bearer St. Luke's Chapel Simeon, Va., Christ Ch., Charlottesville, 1992, lay eucharistic min., 1993—; lay reader eucharistic minister Christ Episcopal Ch., Charlottesville, Va.; chaplain Cedars Nursing Home, Charlottesville, 1991—; rep. Senatorial Inner Circle, 1990, George Bush Rep. Task Force, 1990; eucharistic min. Grace Episc. Ch., Cismont, 1995—. With USMCR, 1957-63. Named Ky. Col.; recipient Key award Workshop V. Mem. Am. Libr. Assn., Va. Libr. Assn. Soc. Reprodn. Engrs., Nat. Microfilm Assn. (libr. rels. com. 1973—), Va. Microfilm Assn. (pres. 1971-72, v.p. 1973-74, program chmn. ann. conf. 1974, Pioneer award 1973, Fellow award 1976), Ky. Microfilm Assn. (Outstanding award 1967, pres.

1964-67), Assn. for Info. and Image Mgmt., Va. Gamebird Assn., Thoroughbred Owners and Breeders Assn., Am. Rose Soc., Thomas Jefferson Rose Soc. (charter), Nat. Rifle Assn. Contbg. editor Va. Librarian, 1970-71, Micro-News Va. Microfilm Assn., 1970-71, Plant & Print Jour., 1983-85; contbr. articles to profl. publs. Home and Office: RR 2 Box 44 Keswick VA 22947-9317

MASSEY, GERALD J., philosophy educator. BA maxima cum laude, U. Notre Dame, 1956, MA in Philosophy, 1960; MA in Philosophy, Princeton U., 1962, PhD, 1964. Instr. philosophy Mich. State U., 1963-68, prof. philosophy, 1968-69; prof. philosophy U. Pitts., 1970—, chmn. dept. philosophy, 1970-77, dir. Ctr. for Philosophy of Sci., 1988—, Disting. Svc. prof. philosophy, 1992—; vis. lectr. U. Mich., 1968; vis. Truax prof. of philosophy Hamilton Coll., 1980. Author: Understanding Symbolic Logic, 1970; co-editor: Thought Experiments in Science and Philosophy, 1991, Philosophical Problems of the Internal and External World, 1993; mng. editor Philosophy of Sci., 1964-70; contbr. articles to profl. jours. Arty. officer USMC, 1958-61. Danforth fellow, 1956, Woodrow Wilson fellow, 1956, Fulbright fellow U. Louvain, Belgium, 1956-57, Chancellor Green fellow, 1962-64, Mellon Postdoctoral fellow U. Pitts., 1969-70. Mem. Philosophy of Sci. Assn. (sec.-treas. 1964-70). Office: U Pitts Ctr Philosophy of Sci 817 Cathedral of Learning Pittsburgh PA 15260

MASSEY, IKE, newspaper publishing executive; b. San Angelo, Tex.. Staff and mgmt. positions in adv., circulation, prodn., editorial, bur. chief Odessa, Tex. San Angelo Standard-Times, to 1978; pub. Tulsa (Okla.) Suburban Newspapers Park Newspapers, Inc., 1979-85, head Western Divsn., 1983-85; v.p. MediaNews Group, 1986-88; pres., chief oper. officer DTH Media, Inc., Dallas, 1988-91; pub., chief exec. officer Houston Post, 1991—. Dir. Better Bus. Bur.; Sam Houston Area Coun. Boy Scouts Am., Houston Symphony, Houston Bus. Com. Edn. Excellence; trustee United Way Tex. Gulf Coast; mem. adv. coun. Sch. Comm. U. Houston, adv. com. Lombardi Award, adv. bd. Houston Proud, Houston Livestock Show and Rodeo, life. Recipient 3 Mng. Editor awards Tex. AP, 1978; honored Outstanding Tex. leader John Ben Shepperd Leadership Found. LBJ Sch. Pub. Affairs, Austin, 1988. Mem. Tex. Daily Newspaper Assn., Forum Club, Houston Rotary Club. Office: The Houston Post PO Box 4747 Houston TX 77210*

MASSEY, JAMES D., bank holding company executive. Student, Butler U., U. Wis., Harvard U. With Mchts. Nat. Bank & Trust Co., Indpls., 1957—, mgmt. trainee, 1957-60, mgr. auto loan dept., 1960-63, br. mgr., 1963-66, v.p., 1966-70, v.p., br. adminstrn. officer, 1970-77, sr. v.p., 1977-79, exec. v.p., 1979-83, pres., chief exec. officer, 1983-86, chmn., chief exec. officer, 1986—; also pres., chief oper. officer Mchts. Nat. Corp., Indpls. Office: Mchts Nat Corp 1 Merchants Plz Ste 415E Indianapolis IN 46204-3022

MASSEY, JAMES L., investment banker; b. Cairo, Ga., Feb. 9, 1943; s. Robert L. and Grace P. (Pinson) M.; m. Sue Ann Jameson, Oct. 9, 1971; children—Vaughn Elizabeth, Lee Jameson. BA, Fla. State U., 1965; MBA, Emory U., 1967. With Salomon Bros. Inc., 1967—; instnl. sales rep. N.Y.C., 1967-74; regional mgr. Atlanta, 1974-79; nat. sales mgr., gen. ptnr. N.Y.C., 1979-82, exec. com., 1982—, vice chmn., 1988—; chmn., CEO Salomon Bros. Europe Ltd., London, 1988—; honorary managing dir. Salomon Bros., N.Y.C., 1992—. Trustee Greenwich Acad., 1984—, vice chmn. bd.; bd. dirs. Film Soc. of Lincoln Ctr., N.Y.C. Republican. Episcopalian. Avocations: tennis, shooting. Home: 99 Round Hill Rd Greenwich CT 06831-3722 Office: Salomon Bros Inc 2 Greenwich Plz Greenwich CT 06830

MASSEY, LEON R., association executive; b. Grand Island, Nebr., Jan. 16, 1930; s. James Moore and Iva Pearl (Richardson) M.; m. Jean M. Nielsen, June 17, 1951; children: Dean R., Maureen L. Student, U. Colo., 1948-49; BA, U. Nebr., 1955; postgrad., N.Y. Inst. Fin., 1963. Salesman consumer products Union Carbide Corp., Memphis, 1956-57, Greenville, Miss., 1957-58, Albuquerque, 1958-61, Dallas, 1962-63; regional sales mgr. GC Electric div. Textron Corp., Dayton, Ohio, 1963-64; account exec. Merrill Turben Co., Dayton, 1964-66; with Nat. Electric Contractors Assn., Dayton, 1967-72, Denver, 1972-83, exec. sec., 1967-83, also bd. dirs. Rocky Mountain chpt.; pres. RLM's Assocs., Englewood, Colo., 1983—; instr. adult edn. Wayne State U., Dayton, 1964-66. City councilman City of Greenwood Village, Colo., 1986-90; pres. Cherry Creek Civic Assn., 1979-80, bd. dirs. 1973-74; bd. dirs. Assn. Operating Rm. Nurses, Cherry Creek Village Water Dist., 1992—; bd. dirs. Goldsmith Gulch Sanitation Dist., 1990—, pres., 1992—; active Dem. Party, 1960. With USAF, 1950-54, Korea. Mem. Am. Soc. Assn. Execs. (cert., bd. dirs.), Colo. Soc. Assn. Execs. (life, pres. 1979), Civitan Club, Masons, Phi Kappa Psi. Office: RLM Assocs 5031 S Beeler St Englewood CO 80111-1313

MASSEY, MARILYN CHAPIN, academic administrator. BA in English and Philosophy, Marquette U., 1963, MA in History of Religion, 1965; MA in Interdisciplinary Religious Studies, U. Chgo., 1969, PhD Philosophy Religion with distinction, 1973. Instr. and asst. prof. religious studies Mundelein Coll., 1966-73, chair dept. religious studies, 1972-73; adj. prof. religious and women's studies U. Louisville, 1974-77; adj. prof. history Christianity Louisville Presbyn. Seminary, 1974-76; asst. prof. dept. religion Duke U., 1977-81, dir. undergrad studies dept. religion, 1980-81; assoc. prof. history Christianity Sch. Div. Harvard U., 1981-84, co chair dept. ch. history Sch. Div., 1982-84; prof. divsn. history, philosophy, and religion, dean sch. arts and scis. Coll. New Rochelle, 1984-87; prof. divsn. humanities, v.p. acad. affairs, dean faculty Marymount Manhattan Coll., 1987-92; pres. Pitzer Coll., Claremont, Calif., 1992—; mem. community edn. study group sch. edn. Harvard U., 1985-87; rep. nat. identification program Am. Coun. on Edn., N.Y.C., 1989-92, mem. commn. on govtl. rels., 1993—. Author: Christ Unmasked: The Meaning of "The Life of Jesus" in German Politics, 1983 (Outstanding book Choice, 1983), The Feminine Soul: The Fate of an Ideal, 1985; contbng. author Beyond Androcentrism: New Essays of Women and Religion, 1977; translator: In Defense of My "Life of Jesus" Against the Hegelians, 1983; contbr. articles to profl and religious jours.; lectr. in field. Carnegie Faculty fellow Bunting Inst. Radcliffe Coll., 1983; named alumna of yr. Trinity High Sch., 1989, U. Chgo. Div. Sch., 1989. Mem. Am. Acad. Religion (sec. so. region 1980-84). Office: Pitzer Coll Office of Pres 1050 N Mills Ave Claremont CA 91711

MASSEY, RAYMOND LEE, lawyer; b. Macon, Ga., Sept. 25, 1948; s. Ford B. and Juanita (Sapp) M.; m. Lynn Ann Thielmeier, Aug. 23, 1967; children: Daniel, Caroline. BA, U. Mo., St. Louis, 1971; JD, U. Louisville, 1974. Bar: Mo. 1974, Ill. 1976, U.S. Dist. Ct. (ea. and we. dists.) Mo. 1974, U.S. Dist. Ct. (so. dist.) Ill. 1976. Assoc. Thompson & Mitchell, St. Louis, 1974-79, ptnr., 1979—. Mem. Maritime Law Assocs. (chmn. ocean and river towing). Home: 3 Wild Rose Dr Saint Louis MO 63124-1465 Office: Thompson & Mitchell 1 Mercantile Ctr Ste 3300 Saint Louis MO 63101-1622

MASSEY, RICHARD WALTER, JR., investment counselor; b. Birmingham, Ala., May 19, 1917; s. Richard Walter and Elizabeth (Spencer) M.; m. Ann Hinkle, Sept. 4, 1959; children—Richard Walter, Dale Elizabeth. B.S., U. Va., 1939; M.A., Birmingham-So. Coll., 1954; Ph.D., Vanderbilt U., 1960. Owner, mgr. Massey Bus. Coll., Birmingham, Ala., 1946-56; asst. to chancellor Vanderbilt U., 1959-60; chmn. dept. econs. Birmingham-So. Coll., 1960-66; investment trust officer 1st Nat. Bank of Birmingham, 1966-67; prof. econs. U. Ala., Tuscaloosa, 1967-68; v.p., dir. investment rsch. Sterne, Agee & Leach, Inc., Birmingham, 1968-75; pres. Richard W. Massey & Co., Inc., Investment Counsel, Birmingham, 1975—. Served to maj. U.S. Army, 1941-46. Mem. Country Club of Birmingham. Home and Office: 1304 Kingsway Ln Birmingham AL 35243-2174

MASSEY, ROBERT JOHN, telecommunications executive; b. Montclair, N.J., July 12, 1945; s. William A. and Elizabeth (Grissing) M.; m. Sue A. Lavallee, July 26, 1968; children: Mary Beth, Michelle, Megan. BA, Holy Cross Coll., Worcester, Mass., 1967; MBA, Syracuse U., 1969. Mktg. rep. IBM, Washington, 1969-70, Boston, 1971-73; mktg. rep. Control Data Corp., Greenwich, Conn., 1974-75, mktg. mgr., N.Y.C., 1975-76; area mgr. CompuServe Inc., Eastern area, 1976-78, v.p. sales, Stamford, Conn., 1979-83, exec. v.p. bus. svcs., Columbus, Ohio, 1984-86, exec. v.p. software products, 1987-90, exec. v.p. network svcs., 1990—; bd. dirs. CompuServe. Coach Dublin (Ohio) Youth Athletics, 1978-85; parents coun. St. Mary's

Coll., Notre Dame, Ind., 1988—. Mem. Dublin C. of C., Ohio State Fastbreakers, Holy Cross Alumni Assn., Syracuse U. Bus. Alumni Assn., Country Club of Muirfield Village (golf. com.). Avocations: golf, tennis. Office: CompuServe Inc 5000 Arlington Centre Blvd Columbus OH 43220-5439

MASSEY, ROBERT UNRUH, physician, university dean; b. Detroit, Feb. 23, 1922; s. Emil Laverne and Esther Elisabeth (Unruh) M.; m. June Charlene Collins, May 28, 1943; children: Robert Scott, Janet Charlene. Student, Oberlin Coll., 1939-42, U. Mich. Med. Sch., 1942-43; M.D., Wayne State U., 1946. Intern, resident in internal medicine Henry Ford Hosp., Detroit, 1946-50; assoc. Lovelace Clinic, Albuquerque, 1950-68; chmn. dept. medicine Lovelace Clinic, 1958-68, bd. govs., 1957-68; dir. med. edn. Lovelace Found. for Med. Edn. and Research, 1960-68; clin. assoc. U. N.Mex. Sch. Medicine, 1961-68; prof. medicine U. Conn. Sch. Medicine, Farmington, 1968—; assoc. dean for grad edn. U. Conn. Sch. Medicine, 1968-71, dean Sch. Medicine, 1971-84, currently prof. emeritus dept. community medicine and health care, acting univ. v.p. for health affairs, 1975-76; chief staff Newington (Conn.) VA Hosp., 1968-71; trustee Am. Assn. Med. Clinics, 1966-68; exec. com., regional adv. group Conn. Regional Med. Program, 1971-76; trustee, v.p. Capitol Area Health Consortium, 1974-78, pres., 1980-81. Editor-in-chief Conn. Medicine, 1986—; editor Jour. of the History of Medicine and Allied Scis., 1987-91. Bd. dirs Health Planning Coun., Inc., 1974-76; bd. dirs. Hartford Inst. for Criminal and Social Justice, 1976-80, Conn. Easter Seal Soc., 1977-85, Hospice Inst. Edn., Tng. and Rsch., 1979-81. With AUS, 1955-57; maj. Res. Fellow ACP; mem. Am. Group Practice Assn. (accreditation commn. 1968-78), Assn. Am. Med. Colls., Am. Assn. History of Medicine, Hartford County Med. Assn., AMA, Conn., Hartford med. socs., Am. Osler Soc., Beaumont Med. Club, Soc. Med. Adminstrs., Twilight Club (Hartford), Sigma Xi, Alpha Omega Alpha. Episcopalian. Office: U Conn Sch Medicine Farmington CT 06032

MASSEY, STEPHEN CHARLES, auctioneer; b. London, May 9, 1946; s. Charles Dudley and Sheila Florence (Browne) M.; divorced; 1 child, Sarah Louise. Grad. high sch., U.K. Cataloguer books and manuscripts Christie's, London, 1964-75; head book and manuscript dept. Christie's, N.Y.C., 1975—. Fellow Pierpont Morgan Libr.; mem. The Grolier Club, The Old Book Table. Avocations: cinema, reading, running, music, forestry. Office: Christie Manson & Woods Internat Inc 502 Park Ave New York NY 10022-1108

MASSEY, THOMAS BENJAMIN, educator; b. Charlotte, N.C., Sept. 5, 1926; s. William Everard and Sarah (Corley) M.; m. Bylee Hunnicutt Massey, July 10, 1968; children: Pamela Ann, Caroline Forest. A.B., Duke U., 1948; M.S., N.C. State U., 1953; Ph.D., Cambridge U., 1968. Assoc. dean students Ga. Inst. Tech., Atlanta, 1950-58; lectr. U. Md. Univ. Coll., 1960-66, asst. dir. London, 1966-69, dir. Toyko, 1969-71, dir. Heidelberg (Fed. Republic of Germany), 1971-76, vice chancellor, 1976-78, chancellor, 1978-88, pres., 1988—; bd. dirs. Internat. Univ. Consortium for Telecommunications in Learning, 1983—. Served with USN, 1943-46. Mem. Am. Assn. Adult and Continuin Edn., Soc. Rsch. in Higher Edn., Nat. Univ. Continuing Edn. Assn., Am. Psychol. Assn., Am. Assn. Higher Edn., Internat. Confs. on Improving Univ. Teaching (chmn. 1975—). Office: U Md Univ Coll University Blvd at Adelphi Rd College Park MD 20742-1600

MASSEY, VINCENT, biochemist, educator; b. Berkeley, New South Wales, Australia, Nov. 28, 1926; s. Walter and Mary Ann (Mark) M.; m. Margot Grunewald, Mar. 4, 1950; children: Charlotte, Andrew, Rachel. BSc with honors, U. Sydney, Australia, 1947; PhD, U. Cambridge, Eng., 1953; DSc, U. Tokushima, 1994. Mem. research staff Henry Ford Hosp., Detroit, 1955-57; lectr. to sr. lectr. U. Sheffield, 1957-63; prof. Med. Sch. U. Mich., Ann Arbor, 1963-95, J. Lawrence Oncley Disting. U. prof., 1995—; mem. biochemistry-biophysics rev. panel NSF, 1980-84; mem. fellowship rev. panel NIH, 1965-69, mem. biochemistry study sect. NIH, 1972-76, chmn. 1974-76. Contbg. author numerous books.; co-editor Flavins and Flavoproteins, 1982; contbr. numerous articles, chiefly on oxidative enzymology, to profl. jours. Recipient Alexander Von Humboldt U.S. Sr. Scientist award, 1973-74, 86; Imperial Chem. Industries Research fellow, 1953-55. Fellow Royal Soc. London; mem. NAS, Biochem. Soc., Am. Soc. Biochemistry and Molecular Biology (membership com. 1970, nominating com. 1978-80, chmn. 1979-80, chmn. program com. 1992-93), Am. Chem. Soc. (exec. bd. divsn. biol. chemistry 1975-77). Home: 2536 Bedford Rd Ann Arbor MI 48104-4008 Office: U Mich Med Sch Dept Biol Chemistry Ann Arbor MI 48109

MASSEY, WALTER EUGENE, physicist, science foundation administrator; b. Hattiesburg, Miss., Apr. 5, 1938; s. Almar and Essie (Nelson) M.; m. Shirley Streeter, Oct. 25, 1969; children: Keith Anthony, Eric Eugene. BS, Morehouse Coll., 1958; MA, Washington U., St. Louis, 1966, PhD, 1966. Physicist Argonne (Ill.) Nat. Lab., 1966-68; asst. prof. physics U. Ill., Urbana, 1968-70; assoc. prof. Brown U., Providence, 1970-75, prof., dean of Coll., 1975-79; prof. physics U. Chgo., 1979—, v.p. for rsch., 1983-84; dir. Argonne Nat. Lab., 1979-84; v.p. for rsch. and for Argonne Nat. Lab. U. Chgo., 1984—; dir. NSF, Washington, 1990-93; sr. v.p. acad. affairs U. Calif. System, 1993—; mem. NSB, 1978-84; cons. NAS, 1973-76. Contbr. articles on sci. edn. in secondary schs. and in theory of quantum fluids to profl. jours. Bd. fellows Brown U., 1980-90, Mus. Sci. and Industry, Chgo., 1980-89, Ill. Math. and Sci. Acad., 1985-88; bd. dirs. Urban League R.I., 1973-74. NAS fellow, 1961, NDEA fellow, 1959-60, AAAS fellow, 1962. Mem. AAAS (bd. dirs. 1981-85, pres.-elect 1987-88, pres. 1988-89, chmn. 1989-90), Am. Phys. Soc. (councillor-at-large 1980-83, v.p. 1990), Sigma Xi. Office: 300 Lakeside Dr 22nd Fl Oakland CA 94612

MASSEY, WILLIAM LLOYD, federal agency administrator, lawyer; b. Malvern, Ark., Oct. 19, 1948. BA cum laude, Ouachita Bapt. U., 1970; JD, U. Ark., 1973; ML, Georgetown U., 1985. Bar: Ark. 1973, D.C. 1992, U.S. Supreme Ct. 1985, U.S. Ct. Appeals (8th cir.) 1973, U.S. Ct. Appeals (D.C. cirs. 1985), U.S. Dist. Ct. (ea. and we. dists.) Ark. 1973. Assoc. Youngdahl & Larrison, Little Rock, 1973-76; chief atty. Ctr. Ark. Legal Svcs., Little Rock, 1976-77, dir., 1977-78; law clk. to Hon. Richard S. Arnold U.S. Ct. Appeals (8th cir.), 1978-80; legis. asst. U.S. Senator Dale Bumpers, Washington, 1980-81, chief counsel, legis. dir., 1989-91; ptnr. Mayer, Brown & Platt, Washington, 1991-93; commr. FERC, Washington, 1993—. Contbr. articles to profl. publs. Mem. ABA, D.C. Bar Assn., Ark. Bar Assn., Fed. Energy Bar Assn. Democrat. Presbyterian. Office: Commr FERC 825 N Capitol St NE Washington DC 20426

MASSEY, WILLIAM S., mathematician, educator; b. Granville, Ill., Aug. 23, 1920; s. Robert R. and Alma (Schumacher) M.; m. Ethel Heap, Mar. 14, 1953; children—Eleanor, Alexander, Joan. Student, Bradley U., 1937-39; B.S., U. Chgo., 1941, M.S., 1942; Ph.D., Princeton, 1948. Mem. research dept. Princeton, 1948-50; from asst. prof. to prof. Brown U., 1950-60; prof. math. Yale, 1960—, Erastus L. Deforest prof. math, 1964-82, Eugene Higgins prof. math., 1983-91, Eugene Higgins prof. math. emeritus, 1991—, chmn. dept. math., 1968-71. Author: Algebraic Topology: An Introduction, 1967, Homology and Cohomology Theory, 1978, Singular Homology Theory, 1980, A Basic Course in Algebraic Topology, 1991; mem. editorial staff math. jours. Served as officer USNR, 1942-46. Fellow Am. Acad. Arts and Scis.; mem. Am. Math. Soc. Achievements include research in algebraic topology, differential topology, homotopy theory, fibre bundles. Home: 64 N Lake Dr Hamden CT 06517 Office: Yale U Math Dept PO Box 208283 New Haven CT 06520

MASSEY, WILLIAM WALTER, JR., sales executive; b. Lawrenceburg, Tenn., Sept. 21, 1928; s. William Walter and Bess Ann (Brian) M.; m. Virginia Claire Smith, Aug. 16, 1952; children: William Walter III, Laura Ann, Lynn Smith, Lisa Claire. BBA, U. Miami, Fla., 1949; BFA, U. Fla., 1969. Exec. v.p., dir. Massey Motors, Inc., Jacksonville, Fla., 1950—; v.p., dir. Atlantic Discount Co. Inc., Jacksonville, 1954-64; pres. Owners Surety Corp., Jacksonville, 1959—, General Svcs. Corp., Jacksonville, 1960-69, Owners Guaranty Life, Phoenix, Ariz., 1960-64, Securities Guaranty Life, Phoenix, Ariz., 1961-64, Fla. Properties, Inc., Jacksonville, 1961-66, Chi-Cha, Inc., Jacksonville, 1965-70, Univ. Square Properties, Jacksonville, 1969-80; v.p., bd. dir. Southside Country Day School, Jacksonville, 1963-68; bd. dirs. Southside Atlantic Bank, Jacksonville, 1970. Served as officer group shows at Internat., N.Y., 1970, Ball State U. 1972. Lt. USAF, 1950-1952. Mem. Ponte Vedra Club, River Club, Epping Forest Club, Sigma Chi. Methodist.

Avocations: music, painting, writing. Office: 6000 San Jose Blvd Jacksonville FL 32217-2381

MASSIE, EDWARD LINDSEY, JR., retired publishing company executive; b. Louisville, Sept. 16, 1929; s. Edward Lindsey and Ruth Sarah (Walts) M.; m. Betty Ann Hart, June 13, 1953; children: Steven, Cornelia, Diana. B.S., U. Ky., 1953. Trainee GE, Louisville, 1953-54; sales profl. Commerce Clearing House, 1954-80, exec. v.p., 1980-91, pres., CEO, 1991-95; retired, 1995. Served to 1st lt. USAF, 1955-56. Presbyterian.

MASSIE, LOWELL DAVID, aeronautical engineer. Ret. chief power components branch USAF Wright Labs., Dayton, Ohio. Recipient Aerospace Power Syss. award AIAA, 1994. Office: USAF Wright Labs Propulsion & Power Directorate 1950 5th St Bldg 18 Dayton OH 45433-7251*

MASSIE, MICHAEL EARL, lawyer; b. Stambaugh, Mich., Aug. 12, 1947; s. Glen E. and Bernice L. (Lambert) M.; m. Vicki L. Colmark, June 11, 1977; children: Christopher, Adam. B.A., U. Ill., 1969, JD, 1972. Bar: Ill. 1972, U.S. Dist. Ct. (cen. dist.) Ill. 1989, U.S. Ct. Appeals (7th cir.) 1989. Pvt. practice Galva, Ill., 1972—; atty., sec. Community State Bank Galva, 1980—. Fellow Am. Bar Found.; mem. ABA (coun. mem. gen. practice sect. 1989—, chmn. programs com. gen. practice sect. 1987—, chmn. agrl. law com. gen. practice sect. 1985—), Ill. STate Bar Assn. (chmn. gen. practice sect. 1980, chmn. agrl. law com. gen. practice sect. 1980—), Ill. Farm Legal Assistance Found. (chmn. bd. 1985—). Republican. Avocations: tennis, handball. Office: 115 NW 3rd Ave Galva IL 61434

MASSIE, NOEL DAVID, lawyer; b. Bessemer, Mich., Sept. 23, 1949; s. Leo Oliver and Ann Matilda (Salmi) M.; m. Diane Soubly, June 16, 1978; 1 child, Courtney Alimine. BS, Mich. State U., 1970; JD, U. Mich., 1978. Bar: Mich. 1978, U.S. Ct. Appeals (6th cir.) 1982. Rsch. atty. Mich. Ct. Appeals, Lansing, 1978-79; law clk. Mich. Supreme Ct., Lansing, 1979-81; assoc. Dickinson, Wright, Moon, Van Dusen & Freeman, Detroit, 1981-84, ptnr., 1985—. Mem. ABA (com. on employee rights and responsibilities), State Bar Mich., Ctr. for Pub. Resources (com. on employment dispute resolution 1992—). Office: Dickinson Wright Moon Van Dusen & Freeman 500 Woodward Ave Ste 4000 Detroit MI 48226-3423

MASSIE, ROBERT JOSEPH, publishing company executive; b. N.Y.C., Mar. 19, 1949; s. Franklin Joseph and Genevieve Helen (Savarese) M.; m. Barbara Ellen Batchelder, Apr. 16, 1982; children—David Chance, Caroline Courtenay, Laura Brett. B.A., Yale U., 1970; M.B.A., Columbia U., 1974, J.D., 1974; Diploma, U. d'Aix en Provence, France, 1969. Bar: D.C. 1974. Assoc. Covington & Burling, Washington, 1975-79; mgmt. cons. McKinsey & Co., N.Y.C., 1979-82; v.p. Harlequin Enterprises, Toronto, Ont., Can., 1982-84, exec. v.p. overseas div., 1984-89; exec. v.p. Direct Mktg., 1989-90; pres., chief exec. officer Gale Rsch., Inc., Detroit, 1990-92; dir. Chmn. Abstracts Svc., Columbus, Ohio, 1992—; chmn. bd. dirs. Harlequin Mondadori, Milan, Italy, 1985-88; bd. dirs. Harlequin Hachette, Paris, Cora Verlag, Hamburg, Fed. Republic Germany, Mills & Boon, Sydney, Australia, Harlenik Ltd., Athens, Greece. Contbr. articles to law jours. Bd. dirs. Columbus Symphony Orch., Ctr. of Sci. and Industry, Columbus. Harlan Fiske Stone scholar, 1974. Office: Am Chem Soc Chem Abstracts Srvcs PO Box 3012 Columbus OH 43210-0012

MASSIE, ROBERT KINLOCH, author; b. Lexington, Ky., Jan. 5, 1929; s. Robert K. and Mary (Kimball) M.; m. Suzanne L. Rohrbach, 1954 (div. 1990); children: Robert Kinloch, Susanna, Elizabeth; m. Deborah L. Karl, 1992; 1 child, Christopher. BA, Yale U., 1950; BA (Rhodes scholar), Oxford U., 1952. Reporter Collier's mag., N.Y.C., 1955-56; writer, corr. Newsweek mag., N.Y.C., 1956-62; writer USA-1 mag., N.Y.C., 1962, Sat. Eve. Post, N.Y.C., 1962-65; Ferris prof. journalism Princeton U., 1977, 85; Mellon prof. humanities Tulane U., 1981. Author: Nicholas and Alexandra, 1967, Journey, 1975 (Christopher award 1976), Peter the Great: His Life and World, 1980 (Am. Book award nomination 1981, Pulitzer Prize for biography 1981), Dreadnought: Britain, Germany, and the Coming of the Great War, 1991, Unt on Romanovs, 1995. Served to lt. (j.g.) USNR, 1952-55. Mem. Authors, Guild Am. (v.p. 1985-87, pres. 1987—), PEN, Soc. Am. Historians. Address: 60 W Clinton Ave Irvington NY 10533*

MASSIE, SAMUEL PROCTOR, JR., chemistry educator; b. North Little Rock, Ark., July 3, 1919; s. Samuel Proctor M. and Earlee Lillian (Jacko) Taylor; m. Gloria B. Thompkins, Aug. 23, 1947; children: Herbert and James (twins), Samuel III. A.A., Dunbar Jr. Coll., 1936; B.S., A.M.N. Coll., 1938; M.A., Fisk U., 1940; Ph.D., Iowa State U., 1946; LL.D. (hon.), U Ark., 1970; D.Sc., Lehigh U., Pa., 1985; D.H.L. (hon.), Bowie State U., 1990; D.Sc. (hon.), The Coll. of Wooster, 1992. Asst. prof., acting chmn. math and physics dept. A.M.N. Coll., Pine Bluff, Ark., 1940-41; instr. chemistry Fisk U., Nashville, 1946-47; prof., chmn. chemistry dept. Langston U., Okla., 1947-53, Fisk U., Nashville, 1953-60; assoc. program dir. NSF, Washington, 1960-63; prof., chmn. pharm. chemistry dept. Howard U., Washington, 1961-63; pres. N.C Coll., Durham, 1963-66; prof. chemistry U.S. Naval Acad., Annapolis, Md., 1966-94, chmn. dept., 1977-81; v.p. of edn. Bingwa Multicultural Software Co., 1994—; eminent resident scholar Va. State U., Petersburg, fall 1981-82; mem. Md. State Bd. for Community Colls., Annapolis, 1968-89, chmn., 1978-89; chmn. Gov.'s Sci. Adv. Bd., Annapolis, 1981-89; trustee Coll. of Wooster, Ohio, 1966-87; trustee emeritus 1987—; spkr. in field Martin Luther King Jr. address, Econ. Club, Detroit, 1990; Prof. Emeritus Status award, U.S. Naval Acad. Co-author invention and antibacterial drugs; contbr. articles on chemistry to profl. jours; permanent exhbns. "Science in American Life", Smithsonian Inst., portrait in Nat. Acads. of Sci.; portrait in Nat. Acads. of Sci. Gallery, 1995. Pres. A.A. County Community Services, Annapolis, 1976-79; bd. dirs. A.A. County ARC, 1978-83; mem. exec. bd. Boy Scouts Am., Washington, 1975-78. Recipient numerous awards; recipient MCA award for excellence in coll. chemistry teaching, 1961, Freedom Funds award Anne Arundel County chpt. NAACP, Md., 1975, Laurel Wreath Kappa Alpha Psi, 1976, Disting. Alumni Achievement award Iowa State U., 1981; named Outstanding Prof. Nat. Orgn. Black Profl. Chemists and Chem. Engrs., 1980; recipient Lifetime Achievement award, White House Initiative, 1988; named in Nat. Black Coll. Alumni Hall of Fame in Sci., 1989; recipient J.F. Norris, Am. Chem. Soc. award, 1994; grantee U.S. Naval Acad., 1966, 1967-68, 1968-74, 1975-77, 1979—, others. Fellow Okla. Acad. Sci. (pres. 1953), Am. Inst. Chemists; mem. Am. Chem. Soc. (chmn. com. on vis. scientists in chemistry 1958-60, chmn. div. chem. edn. 1973-74), Nat. Inst. Sci. (regional dir. 1953-56), Tenn. Acad. Sci., Am. Council on Edn. (mem. commn. on acad. affairs), NEA, N.C. Tchrs. Assn., AAAS, Sigma Xi (pres. Tenn. A.L.-Fisk-Meharry Club 1955), hon. alumnus mem. USNA Alumni, 1993—, Phi Lambda Upsilon, Beta Kappa Chi (nat. pres. 1956-59), Rho Chi. Democrat. Episcopalian. Endowment Fund in name established, USNA Alumni, 1992; nine Massie chairs of Excellence in Environ. Scis. in nine HBCU Engring. Schs., Dept. of Energy, 1994. Home: 12203 Brittany Pl Laurel MD 20708-2522 Office: US Naval Acad Dept of Chemistry Annapolis MD 21402 *An African proverb tells the story of the sparrow, who hearing thunder fell to the ground with his two legs extended. An eagle asked, "What's happening?" Replied the sparrow, "The sky is falling." Mocked the eagle, "What are you going to do Hold it up with your two legs?" Replied the sparrow, "One does what one can with what one has." This is my story and guideline. I have sought to do what I could with what I had.*

MASSIMINO, ROLAND V., former university basketball coach; b. Hillside, N.J., Nov. 13, 1934; s. Salvatore and Grace (Alberti) M.; m. Mary Jane Reid, Aug. 13, 1958; children—Thomas, Lee Ann, Michele, R.C., Andrew. Degree in Bus., U. Vt., 1956; M.P.E., Rutgers U., 1959; guidance cert., Tufts U., 1969. Asst. coach Cranford High Sch., N.J., 1956-59; coach Hillside High Sch., N.J., 1959-63, Lexington High Sch., Mass., 1963-69; head coach SUNY-Stony Brook, 1969-71; asst. coach U. Pa., 1971-73; head coach Villanova U., Pa., 1973-92, U. Nev., Las Vegas, 1992-95. Winning coach NCAA Nat. Basketball Championship, 1985; named Coach of Yr., Phila. Big 5, 1976-76, 77-78, 81-82, 82-83, 84-85, Eastern Athletic Assn., 1976-77, Eastern 8 Conf., 1979-79, 79-80, Widmer Cup Eastern Coach of Yr., 1981-82, Coach of Yr., Big East Conf., 1981-82, Eastern Basketball Eastern Coach of Yr., 1984-85, Harry Latwick/Herb Good Phila. Mem. Nat. Assn. Basketball Coaches. *

MASSION, WALTER HERBERT, anesthesiologist, educator; b. Eitorf, Ger., June 4, 1923; came to U.S., 1954; s. Rudolf and Margarethe (Polch) M.; m. Rose Marie Kumin, July 15, 1956; children: Birgit, Stuart, Iris. BS, U. Cologne, Ger., 1948; MD, U. Heidelberg, 1951, U. Bonn, 1951. Diplomate German Bd. Anesthesiology. Intern U. Zurich Hosps., 1951-52; trainee WHO Anesthesiology Centre, Copenhagen, 1952-53; asst. prof. physiology U. Basel, Switzerland, 1953-54; postdoctoral fellow U.S. Nat. Acad. Sci., Rochester, N.Y., 1954-56; asst. prof. anesthesiology U. Okla. Med. Ctr., Oklahoma City, 1957-61, assoc. prof., 1961-67; prof. anesthesiology, physiology and biophysics U. Okla. Health Sci. Ctr., Oklahoma City, 1967-88, prof. emeritus, 1988; prin. investigator NATO Collaborative Rsch. Project, Oklahoma Cityand Homburg, 1988-95. Editor: Hemorrhage/Anesth. Requirements, 1974, Multiple Trauma, 1984, Critical Care Cardiology, 1988; contbr. over 125 articles to profl. jours. Hon. consul Federal Republic Germany, Oklahoma City, 1980—. Grantee WHO, 1953, U.S. Nat. Acad. Scis., 1954, NIH, 1959-88; Fulbright scholar, 1985; named Newsmaker of the Yr., Okla. Press Assn., 1964, Alexander von Humboldt prize, 1974; decorated Order of Merit 1st class Fed. Republic Germany, 1990. Avocations: gardening, chamber music, travel. Office: Univ Okla Health Sci Ctr PO Box 26901 Oklahoma City OK 73126-0901

MASSLER, HOWARD ARNOLD, lawyer, corporate executive; b. Newark, July 22, 1946; s. Abraham I. and Sylvia (Botwin) M.; m. Randee Elyce Karch, July 1, 1977; children: Justin Scott, Jeremy Ross. BA, U. Pa., 1969; JD, Rutgers U., 1973; LLM in Taxation, NYU, 1977. Bar: N.J. 1974, U.S. Dist. Ct. N.J. 1974, D.C. 1975, U.S. Ct. Appeals (D.C. cir.) 1975, N.Y. 1977, U.S. Dist. Ct. (we. dist.) N.Y. 1977, U.S. Tax Ct. 1977. Counsel house banking, currency and housing com., chmn. sub-com. U.S. Ho. Reps., Washington, 1974-76; tax atty. Lipsitz, Green, Fahringer, Roll, Schuller & James, N.Y.C. and Buffalo, 1977-79; pvt. practice Mountainside, N.J., 1979-89; pres. Bestway Products Inc., A.A. Records Inc., Servor Corp., 1979-85; pres., chief exec. officer, chmn. bd. Bestway Group Inc., Dover, Del., 1985-91; gen. ptnr. 26/27 Law Drive Assocs., 1988—; ptnr. Shonageri, Pearce & Massler, Hackensack, N.J., 1989-90, Mott, Pearce, Williams & Lee, Hackensack and Washington, 1990-91, Pearce & Massler, Hackensack, N.J., 1991—; prodn. staff asst. DECCA House Ltd., London, 1968; chief exec. officer Basura Pub., Inc. (affiliated with BMI), 1974-80; arbitrator U.S. Dist. Ct. N.J., 1985—; adj. prof. law Seton Hall U., Newark, N.J., 1988-89, N.J. Inst. for Continuing Legal Edn., 1986; lectr. N.J. Inst. for Continuing Legal Edn., 1986—; assoc. dir. United Jersey Bank/Franklin State Bank, 1987—; del. adv. com. on indsl. trade and econ. devel. U.S./China Joint Sessions, Beijing, People's Republic of China, 1988. Author: QDROs (Tax and Drafting Considerations), 1986, 2nd. ed., 1987; contbr. West's Legal Forms, Vol. 7, 2d edit., 1987, 3d edit., Domestic Relations with Tax Analysis, Contemporary Matrimonial Law Issues: A Guide to Divorce Economics and Practice; tax author: Matthew Bender, NYCP-Matrimonial Actions and Equitable Distribution Actions, 1988; tax author, tax editor: Matthew Bender, Alimony, Child Support & Counsel Fees-Award, Modification and Enforcement, 1988, 2d edit., 1989, 3d edit., 1991, Matthew Bender, Valuation & Distribution of Marital Property, 1988, 89, 91; contbg. author: How to Make Legal Fees Tax Deductible, 1988, Closely Held Corporations, Forms and Checklists, Buy-Sell Agreement Forms with Tax Analysis, 1988, The Encyclopedia of Matrimonial Practice, 1991; author: New York Practice Guide: Negligence, Tax Law of Compensation for Sickness and Injury, 2d edit., 1992; contbg. editor Pensions and Ins. Problems, 1984—, Taxation, 1984—, Fair$hare, 1984—, Law & Bus., Inc., 1984—; staff contbr., N.J. Law Jour., 1986—; contbr. articles to law revs. and profl. jours. Bd. dirs., legal counsel western N.Y. chpt. Nat. Handicapped Sports and Recreation Assn., 1977-79; counsel Union County, N.J., 1984-85; candidate Springfield (N.J.) Twp. Commn., 1986. Mem. ABA, N.J. Bar Assn. (vice chmn. taxation comm. family law section 1987—), N.Y. Bar Assn. (taxation com., subcom. on criminal and civil penalties), D.C. Bar Assn., Erie County Bar Assn. (sec. taxation com. 1977-79, continuing edn. lectr. taxation 1977—), Essex County Bar Assn. (tax com. 1981—), Union County Bar Assn. (chmn. tax com. 1984—). Republican. Avocation: Sports Car Club Am. (formula Ford racing. Home: 4 Overlook Dr Warren NJ 07059-5144 Office: 25 Main St Hackensack NJ 07601-7025

MASSMAN, RICHARD ALLAN, lawyer; b. Beaumont, Tex., Aug. 19, 1943; s. Irwin Massman and Sylvia (Schidmt) Schwartz; m. Barbara Elaine Kessler; children: Jason Todd, Karen Faye. BS cum laude, U. Pa., 1965; JD cum laude, Harvard U., 1968. Bar: Tex. 1968; cert. in taxation, Tex. Bd. Legal Specialization. Assoc. Coke & Coke, Dallas, 1968-70; assoc. Johnson & Wortley, P.C. (formerly Johnson & Gibbs, P.C.), Dallas, 1970-71, ptnr., 1971-88, shareholder, 1988-94; of counsel Johnson & Wortley P.C., Dallas, 1994-95; sr. v.p., gen. counsel Hunt Consolidated Inc., Dallas, 1994—; lectr. So. Meth. U., Dallas, 1973. Bd. dirs. Martin Luther King Jr. Community Ctr., Dallas, 1979-81, Jewish Fedn. Greater Dallas, 1980-83, 89—; mem. exec. com. Dallas regional bd. Anti-Defamation League, 1979—, chmn., 1990-92; chmn. Dallas Civil Svc. Bd., 1983; trustee Greenhill Sch., Dallas, 1985-92, vice chmn., 1990-92. Mem. Tex. State Bar (chmn., sec. taxation 1983-84), Dallas Bar Assn. (chmn., sec. taxation 1978), Dallas Petroleum Club, Columbian Club. Office: Hunt Consolidated Inc Fountain Pl 20th Fl 1445 Ross at Field Dallas TX 75202-2785

MASSOF, ROBERT W., neuroscientist, educator; b. Minn., Jan. 2, 1948; m. Darcy Rood; children: Eric, Allison. BA, Hamline U., 1970; PhD, Ind. U., 1975. Postdoctoral fellow in ophthalmology Johns Hopkins U. Sch. Medicine, Balt., 1975-76, from instr. ophthalmology to assoc. prof., 1976-91, prof., 1991-93, prof. neurosci., 1993—; vis. prof. Taiwan U., Taipei, 1983, Warsaw Acad. Medicine, Poland, 1987, Robert Y. Garrett Meml. Lecture, Lancaster, Pa., 1988, Albert Einstein Coll. Medicine, N.Y.C., 1989, Ohio State U., Columbus, 1991, Mayo Clinic, Rochester, Minn., 1993; guest lectr. in field. Mem. editorial bd. Clin. Vision Scis., N.Y.C., 1985—, Eye Care Technology/Computers in Eye Care, Folsom, Calif., 1992—; patentee in field (3); contbr. articles to profl. jours. Recipient Manpower award, 1989, Technology Transfer award NASA, 1993. Mem. Optical Soc. Am. (chmn. edn. coun. 1993—, bd. dirs. 1993—), Am. Acad. Opthalmology, Assn. Rsch. in Vision and Ophthalmology. Office: Johns Hopkins Univ Lions Vision Ctr 550 N Broadway 6th Fl Baltimore MD 21205

MASSOLO, ARTHUR JAMES, banker; b. N.Y.C., July 21, 1942; s. Silvio Libro and Josephine Louise (Oneto) M.; A.B., Hamilton Coll., 1964; J.D., U. Chgo., 1967; m. Karen Irene Clasen, Mar. 7, 1970; 1 son, Arthur Reab. Vol. Peace Corps, 1967-68; with 1st Nat. Bank of Chgo., 1969—; beginning as trainee, sucessively rep. in Indonesia, gen. mgr. Italy, area head Latin Am. in Panama, sr. v.p. and head corp. personnel, 1979-81, sr. v.p., head Internat. Banking div., 1981-85; pres., chief exec. officer Banco Denasa de Investimento S.A., Brazil, 1985-87; also bd. dirs.; sr. v.p. Internat. Asset Enhancement, 1987-89, corp. sr. v.p. asset mgmt., 1990-94, corp. sr. v.p. of Latin Am., 1995—; founding dir. Banco Latino Americano de Exportaciones Panama; chmn., bd. dirs. Link Unlimited. Trustee Hamilton Coll. Mem. Ill. Bar Assn., Phi Beta Kappa. Office: One 1st National Pla Ste 0556 Chicago IL 60670

MASSON, GAYL ANGELA, airline pilot; b. L.A., Feb. 5, 1951; d. Jack Watson and Margaret Jean (Evans) M.; 1 child, Athena. BFA, U. So. Calif., 1970, MA, 1972, MPA, 1975, PhD, 1976. Lic. airline transport, seaplane, glider pilot, flight instr., flight engr. Pilot Antelope Valley Land Investment Co., Century City, Calif., 1972; ROTC flight instr. Claire Walters Flight Acad., Santa Monica, Calif., 1973; flight instr. Golden West Airways, Santa Monica, 1974; co-pilot Express Airways, LaMoore Naval Air Sta., Calif., 1975-76; charter pilot, instr. Shaw Airventure, Orange County Airport, Calif., 1976; flight engr. Am. Airlines, Dallas, 1976-79, co-pilot, 1979-86, capt., 1986—; accident prevention counselor FAA, 1993—. Contbr. articles to profl. publs. Participant Powder Puff Derby, Angel Derby, Pacific Air Race and others. First woman type-rated on Boeing 747, also type-rated on DC-10, DC-9, Boeing 767, Boeing 757, Airbus-310. Mem. Airline Pilots Assn., Internat. Soc. Women Airline Pilots (charter), Ninety-Nines (past v.p. Smo Bay chpt.), Aerospace Med. Assn., Aerospace Human Factors Assn. Avocations: oil paint, viticulture.

MASSON, ROBERT HENRY, paper company executive; b. Boston, June 27, 1935; s. Robert Louis and Henrietta Hill (Worrell) M.; m. Virginia Lee Morton, Dec. 28, 1957; children: Linda Anne, Kenneth Morton, Robert Louis, II. B.A. in Econs. (Travis and Woods award), Amherst Coll., 1957;

M.B.A., Harvard U., 1964. Fin. staff Ford Motor Co., Dearborn, Mich., 1964-68; mktg. services div. controller Ford Motor Co., 1968-70; pres. Knutson Constrn. Co., Mpls., 1970-72; v.p. fin., treas. Ellerbe, Inc., Bloomington, Minn., 1972-77; fin. dir. CirTech, Inc., Mpls., 1973-77; v.p. fin. transp. div. PepsiCo., Inc., Tulsa, 1977; corp. v.p., treas. PepsiCo., Inc., Purchase, N.Y., 1978-80; v.p., treas. Combustion Engring., Inc., Stamford, Conn., 1981-86, v.p. fin. and venture devel., 1986-87, v.p. venture fin. and internat. ops., 1988-90; v.p., CFO Parsons & Whittemore, Inc., Rye Brook, N.Y., 1990—; adv. bd. Shawmut Bank, 1988—. Author: (with others) The Management of Racial Integration in Business, 1964. Pres. North Georgtown Homeowner's Assn., Birmingham, Mich., 1968-70, U.S. Presdl. Advance Man, 1972-76; trustee Naval Aviation Mus. Found., 1987—; Hebron Acad., 1993—; elder Presbyn. Ch. of Old Greenwich, 1992—. Served to lt. USN, 1957-62; lt. comdr. Res. Mem. Am. Forest and Paper Assn. (fin. com. 1991—), Fin. Execs. Inst. (com. on corp. fin. 1981—), Fairchester Treas. Group (pres. 1986), Lucas Point Homeowner's Assn. (pres. 1986-87), Theta Delta Chi. Clubs: Wayzata Yacht (dir.-treas. 1973-77), Riverside Yacht (asst. treas. 1985-87). Office: Parsons & Whittemore Inc 4 International Dr Rye Brook NY 10573-1064

MASSURA, EDWARD ANTHONY, accountant; b. Chgo., July 1, 1938; s. Edward Matthew and Wilma C. (Kussy) M.; m. Carol A. Barber, June 23, 1962; children: Edward J., Beth Ann, John B. BS, St. Joseph's Coll., Rensselaer, Ind., 1960; JD, DePaul U., 1963. Bar: Ill. 1963; CPA, Mich., Ill., others. Tax acct. Arthur Andersen & Co., Chgo., 1963—, ptnr., 1973—; dir. tax div. Arthur Andersen & Co., Detroit, 1974-84, dep., co-dir. internat. tax, 1983-84, ptnr.-in-charge internat. trade customs practice, 1983-88. Co-author: West's Legal Forms, 2d. edit.; 1984; contbr. numerous articles to bus. jours. Bd. dirs. Arts Found. of Mich., Detroit, 1982-95, treas., 1982-93; bd. dirs. Ctr. for Internat. Bus. Edn. and Rsch., Wayne State U. Mem. AICPA, Internat. Fiscal Assn. (coun.), Assn. for Corp. Growth, Mich. Assn. CPAs, Mich. Dist. Export Coun. (chmn. 1985-92), Mich. Ptnrs. Am., Detroit Internat. Tax Group (founder, co-moderator), Licensing Exec. Soc., World Trade Club of Detroit, Econ. Club of Detroit, Orchard Lake Country Club, Renaissance Club Detroit, Skyline Club, Fairlane Club. Office: Arthur Andersen & Co 1 Detroit Ctr Ste 2700 500 Woodward Ave Detroit MI 48226-3407

MASSURA, EILEEN KATHLEEN, family therapist; b. Chgo., July 25, 1925; d. John Wellsun and Loretta (Feil) Stratemeier; m. Edmund Karamanski, July 24, 1948 (dec.); children: John, Kathleen; m. Alfred Massura, Aug. 30, 1963; children: Michael, Kathryn, Mark. BS in Nursing, DePaul U., 1963; MS in Nursing, St. Xavier Coll., 1971. RN; cert. family therapist. Dir. nurses Franklin Blvd. Hosp., Chgo., 1958-62; adminstr. Mich. Ave Hosp., Chgo., 1962-64; instr. St. Xavier Coll., Chgo., 1972-74, Joliet (Ill.) Jr. Coll., 1972-81; family therapist Oak Lawn (Ill.) Family Svc., 1978-88; prof. nursing Govs. State U., University Park, Ill., 1981-89; family therapist McCarthy & Assocs., Oak Lawn, 1982-93, Massura & Assocs., Oak Lawn, 1994—; preceptor to grads. St. Xavier Coll., 1980-90, Govs. State U., 1980-89; co-leader Clin. Study Med./Surg. Nursing, Moscow, 1984; presenter Am. Nursing Rev., Ala., Fla., Va., Pa., Tex., Md., 1985-86. Leader Campfire Girls, Oak Lawn, 1964-74; co-leader Orient/Am. Med./ Surg. Nursing, 1987; mem. Marist Women's Bd., Chgo., 1978-82, Bro. Rice Women's Bd., Chgo., 1969-72; Luth. Family Svc. Bd. Day Care for Srs., 1988-89. Grantee HEW, 1969-71; named Disting. Nurse Alumnae, St. Xavier Coll., 1985; named Nursing Prof. of Yr., Govs. State U., 1983. Mem. Am. Nurses Assn. (nominating com. 1982-87), Ill. Nurses Assn. (program com. 1980-84), Am. Assn. Marital and Family Therapists, Cath. Order Foresters, Sigma Theta Tau (v.p. 1971-75). Roman Catholic. Avocations: crewel, needlepoint, watercolor, travel. Office: 5660 W 95th St Oak Lawn IL 60453-2380

MASSY, WILLIAM FRANCIS, education educator, academic administrator; b. Milw., Mar. 26, 1934; s. Willard Francis and Ardys Dorothy (Digman) M.; m. Sally Vaughn Miller, July 21, 1984; children by previous marriage: Willard Francis, Elizabeth. BS, Yale U., 1956; SM, MIT, 1958, PhD in Indsl. Econs., 1960. Asst. prof. indsl. mgmt. MIT, Cambridge, 1960-62; from asst. prof. to prof. bus. adminstrn. Stanford U., Calif., 1962—; assoc. dean Grad. Sch. Bus., 1971, vice provost for research, 1971-77, v.p. for bus. and fin., 1977-88, v.p. fin., 1988-91; prof. edn., dir. Stanford Inst. Higher Edn. Research, Calif., 1988—; bd. dirs. Diebold, Inc., Bijur Lubricating Corp.; mem. univ. grants com., HongKong, 1990—; mem. coun. Yale U., 1980-95; mgmt. cons.; mem. Stanford Mgmt. Co., 1991-93. Author: Stochastic Models of Buying Behavior, 1970, Marketing Management, 1972, Market Segmentation, 1972, Planning Models for Colleges and Universities 1981, Endowment, 1991; mem. editorial bd. Jour. Mktg. Research, 1964-70, Harcourt, Brace Jovanovich, 1965-71; contbr. articles to profl. jours. Bd. dirs. Palo Alto-Stanford chpt. United Way, 1978-80, Stanford U. Hosp., 1980-91, MAC, Inc., 1969-84, EDUCOM, 1983-86. Ford Found. faculty research fellow, 1966-67. Mem. Am. Mktg. Assn. (bd. dirs. 1971-73, v.p. edn. 1976-77), Inst. Mgmt. Scis. Republican. Club: Yale N.Y. Office: Stanford U 508 Ceras Bldg Stanford CA 94305

MAST, FREDERICK WILLIAM, construction company executive; b. Quincy, Ill., Jan. 3, 1910; s. Christian Charles and Jessie Minnie (Pape) M.; B.S., U. Ill., 1933; m. Kathryn Mary Boekenhoff, Sept. 15, 1932 (dec. Jan. 17, 1975); children—Robert Frederick, Janet (Mrs. James Austin Jones), Susan (Mrs. Edward Hoskins Wilson), Linda (Mrs. William Frederick Bohlen), Teresa Ann (Mrs. Charles Edward Connell); m. 2d, Elaine Ellen Thies Driver, Feb. 14, 1976. Hwy. engr. Adams County (Ill.) Hwy. Dept., Quincy, 1929-33; jr. engr. Ill. Div. Hwys. Rd. Office, Springfield, 1933-35, asst. hwys. architect, 1935-39; estimator Jens Olesen & Sons Constrn. Co., Waterloo, Iowa, 1939-41, v.p., 1941-54, exec. v.p., 1954-65, pres., 1965-76, chmn. bd., 1970-80; owner Frederick W. Mast & Assos., Waterloo, 1946-60; pres. Broadway Bldg. Co., 1951—, Kimball Shopping Center, Inc., 1964-78; dir. First Fed. Savs. Bank of Waterloo, 1957-78, Nat. Bank of Waterloo, 1958-79. Mem. Council Constrn. Employers, Washington, 1968-72, chmn., 1969; ofcl. U.S. del. to Soviet Union under U.S./USSR Exchanges Agreement, 1968-69; del. 8th and 9th sessions bldg., civil engring. and public works com. ILO, Geneva, 1971, 77; sr. builder specialist Tech. for the Am. Home Exhibit USIA, USSR, 1975; mem. Nat. Def. Exec. Res., assigned to Fed. Emergency Mgmt. Agy., 1969-89. Mem. Iowa Bldg. Code Council, Des Moines, 1947-50; mem. Bd. Zoning Adjustment, Waterloo, 1947-59; mem. City Plan and Zoning Commn., Waterloo, 1955-78; chmn. Community Devel. Bd., City of Waterloo, 1959-70; fin. chmn. Black Hawk County Republican Central Com., 1958-60; chmn. Waterloo-Cedar Falls Symphony Orch. endowment fund dr., 1977-79, St. Francis Health Care Found., 1980-86; chmn. bd. dirs. St. Francis Hosp., 1976-78; chmn. contractors adv. com. Iowa Coll. Found., 1972-73. Served to col., C.E., AUS, 1941-46. Decorated Legion of Merit; recipient Disting. Service award Waterloo C. of C., 1962; Ky. Col. Registered architect, Ill., Iowa. Mem. Asso. Gen. Contractors Am. (dir. 1956—, mem. exec. com. 1959-62, 66-72, nat. pres. 1968, SIR award Nev. chpt. 1970), Master Builders Iowa (pres. 1952, hon. mem. 1983), Am. Inst. Constructors, Contractors Mut. Assn. Washington (dir. 1971-83, chmn. exec. com. 1971-73), Iowa Engring. Soc., Nat. Soc. Profl. Engrs., Soc. Am. Mil. Engrs., Waterloo Tech. Soc., Amvets, Am. Legion, Phi Eta Sigma, Sigma Phi Epsilon, Tau Beta Pi, Tau Nu Tau, Theta Tau. Roman Catholic. Clubs: Sunnyside Country. Lodges: Elks, Kiwanis. Home: 3309 Inverness Rd Apt F Waterloo IA 50701-4650 Office: PO Box 575 Waterloo IA 50704-0575

MAST, STEWART DALE, retired airport manager; b. Kalamazoo, May 10, 1924; s. Virgil S. and S. Louise (Rippey) M.; m. Judy Jo Bolton; children: Peter S., Frances Ann Mast Adams; m. May 20, 1979. Student, U. Mich., 1942-43; grad. Spartan Sch. Aerospace, Tulsa, 1946, Argubright Bus. Coll., Battle Creek, Mich. 1947. Mgr. Mcpl. Airport, Battle Creek, 1948-60; airport dir. Mitchell Field, Milw., 1961-66; mgr. Tampa (Fla.) Internat. Airport, 1966-89, ret.; pres. Mich. Airport Mgrs., 1958; bd. dirs. The Summit Ministries Inc., Manitou Springs, Colo., 1980. Past mem. aviation coun. Milw. . of C; past mem. bd. rev. Boy Scouts Am., Milw.; bd. dirs. Sun'n Fun Aviation Found., Inc., Lakeland, Fla., 1992—, Sun'n Fun EAA Fly-in, Inc., Lakeland, Fla., 1994—. 1st lt. USAAF, 1943-45. Recipient Community Leadership award Greater Tampa C. of C., 1979. Mem. Am. Assn. Airport Execs. (past bd. dirs., pres.'s award 1979), Southeastern Airport Mgrs. Assn., Fla. Assn. Airport Mgrs. Avocations: antique/classic aircraft, photography.

MASTALER, RICHARD MICHAEL, healthcare executive; b. Miami, Fla., Jan. 31, 1946; s. Michael George and Margaret (Jeren) M.; m. Sherilyn Eileen Sullestad, Oct. 4, 1972; children: Jason R., Brett R.. BS, Fla. State U., 1968; MA, George Washington U., 1972. Adminstrn. resident Samaritan Health Services, Inc., Phoenix, 1971-72; asst. adminstr. U. N.Mex. Hosp., Albuquerque, 1972-75; adminstr. Beverly Glen Hosp., Los Angeles, 1975-76; exec. dir. Humana Hosp.-West Hills, Canoga Park, Calif., 1976-79, Humana Hosp., Phoenix, 1979-83; v.p. mktg. and sales Humana-Group Health div., Louisville, Ky., 1983-87; pres., chief exec. officer Preferred Health Network, Los Angeles, 1987—. Served to 1st lt. U.S. Army, 1968-70. Mem. Am. Coll. Health Care Execs., Am. Assn. Preferred Provider Orgns. Republican. Mem. Ch. of Christ. Club: Hunting Cree Country (Louisville, Ky.). Avocations: racquetball, tennis, golf, phototography. Office: Preferred Health Network 301 E Ocean Blvd Ste 900 Monterey Park CA 90802

MASTEN, CHARLES C., federal agency administrator; b. Albany, Ga., Apr. 20, 1943; s. Charles C. and Sophia L. (Wynn) M.; m. Betty Dodson, June 25, 1966; children: Deborah Denise, Maria Tereon, Kelle Marie, Stephan John. BS Bus. Adminstrn., Albany State Coll., 1965; MBA, U. Ark., 1976; degree mgmt. law enforcement execs., FBI Exec. Devel. Inst., 1991. Asst. nat. bank examiner comtroller of currency U.S. Treasury, Atlanta, 1969-71; cashier Citizens Trust Bank, Atlanta, 1971-72; spl. agt. FBI, Memphis, 1973-77; supervisory spl. agent FBI, Little Rock, 1978-85; supervisory spl. agent FBI, Washington, 1985-87, unit chief, 1987-91; dep. inspector gen. U.S. Dept. Labor, Washington, 1991-94, inspector gen., 1994—. Lt. USN, 1966-69, Vietnam. Mem. Assn. Govt. Accts. Roman Catholic. Avocations: jogging, gardening. Office: Dept of Labor Office of the Inspector General 200 Constitution Ave NW Ste S Washington DC 20210

MASTEN, JEFFREY A., English educator; b. Bryan, Ohio, June 10, 1964. BA in English, Denison U., 1986; AM, U. Pa., 1987, PhD, 1991. Asst. prof. English Harvard U., Cambridge, Mass., 1991—; exec. sec. English Inst. Nat. Mellon fellow Woodrow Wilson Fellowship Found., 1986-88, Mellon Dissertation fellow, 1990-91. Mem. MLA, Shakespeare Assn. Am., Phi Beta Kappa.

MASTER-KARNIK, PAUL JOSEPH, art museum director; b. N.Y.C., Nov. 20, 1948; s. Charles Oldrich and Evelyn Donnelly (Donnelly) K.; m. Susan Irene Master, Aug. 19, 1973. BA, Rutgers U., 1970, MA, 1971, PhD, 1978. Cert. in mus. studies, 1979. Faculty Rutgers U., New Brunswick, N.J., 1974-78; art critic Newhouse Publs., N.Y.C., 1976-80; faculty NYU, N.Y.C., 1980-83; dir. N.J. Ctr. for Visual Arts, Summit, 1981-84, DeCordova Mus. & Sculpture Pk., Lincoln, Mass., 1984—; bd. dirs. UrbanArts, Inc., Boston, 1988—, Mus. Coun. of N.J., Trenton, 1982-84; adv. bd. Archives of Am. Art, Boston, 1985—; vis. com. Sch. Mus. Fine Arts, Boston, 1987-90. Author: Exhibition Catalogues, 1982—. Recipient Outstanding Svc. award Inst. Mus. Svcs., 1988; Art Critic fellow NEA, 1980, Burns-Marvin fellow Rutgers U., 1971-73. Mem. Assn. Art Mus. Dirs. Office: DeCordova Mus & Sculpture 51 Sandy Pond Rd Lincoln MA 01773-2600

MASTERMAN, JACK VERNER, insurance company executive; b. Calgary, Alta., Can., Aug. 8, 1930; s. Lawrence Arthur and Mary F.G. (Robinson) M.; m. Isabel Christine Kaitting, June 25, 1954 (dec. 1990); children: Christine, Lawrence, Sheila, Keith. B.Com. with honors, U. Man., Can., 1953. With Mut. Life Assurance Co. Can., Waterloo, Ont., 1953—, v.p. ops., 1972-75, v.p. individual ins. and annuities, 1975-78, exec. v.p., 1978-82, pres., chief operating officer, 1982-85, pres., chief exec. officer, 1985-89, chmn., chief exec. officer, 1989-92, also bd. dirs., 1980—. Mem. United Ch. of Can. Office: Mut Life Assurance Co Can, 227 King St S, Waterloo, ON Canada N2J 4C5

MASTERS, BEDA DORIS, elementary educator; b. McComb, Miss., Feb. 14, 1942; d. Robert C. and Selma Doris (Barksdale) Moak; m. Terry Labe Masters Sr., Oct. 12, 1940; children: Terry Labe Jr., Karen Denise Masters Ishee. AS, S.W. Miss. Jr. Coll., 1971; BS, U. So. Miss., 1975; M in Edn., William Carey Coll., 1981. Cert. elem. educator, Miss. Teller 1st Nat. Bank, McComb, 1971-72, Laurel, Miss., 1972-73; tchr. Jones County Schs., Laurel, 1975—; presenter Miss. Reading Assn. Conf., 1986, 94. Mem. Internat. Reading Coun., Miss. Reading Coun., Laurel-Jones County Reading Coun. (pres. 1980-81, membership dir. 1988-89), Assn. for Excellence in Edn., PhiTheta Kappa, Phi Kappa Phi, Kappa Delta Pi, Delta Kappa Gamma (corr. sec. state Zeta Mu chpt. 1986-88, chmn. world fellowship 1990-92). Baptist. Avocations: swimming, sewing, cooking, travel, interior design. Home: RR 12 Box 590 Laurel MS 39440-8401

MASTERS, CHARLES DAY, geologist; b. Pawhuska, Okla., Aug. 4, 1929; s. Alan Dunning and Maxine Lueretta (Day) M.; m. Anna Ruth Sandin, June 6, 1953; children—Cynthia Ruth, Eric Alan, Carolyn Frances. BS, Yale U., 1951, Ph.D., 1965; M.S., Colo. U., 1957. Exploration geologist Pan Am. Petroleum Corp., Denver, 1957-62, 65-68; research geologist Pan Am Petroleum Corp., Tulsa, 1968-70; chmn. div. sci. and math., asso. prof. geology W. Ga. Coll., Carrollton, 1970-73; chief Office Energy Resources; also acting chief Office Marine Geology, Geol. Div., U.S. Geol. Survey, Reston, Va., 1973-80; pub. law research scientist branch of petroleum geology, chief The World Energy Resources Program, 1980-95; ret., 1995; Pecora fellow in U.S. Geol. Survey for continued world energy studies. Activities chmn. Tulsa YMCA, 1968-70; founder pres. W. Ga. chpt. Ga. Conservancy, 1971-73. Served with USNR, 1951-55. Fellow Geol. Soc. Am.; mem. Am. Assn. Petroleum Geologists, Sigma Xi. Democrat. Unitarian. Home: 1028 Walker Rd Great Falls VA 22066-1928

MASTERS, EDWARD E., association executive, former foreign service officer; b. Columbus, Ohio, June 21, 1924; s. George Henry and Ethel Verena (Shaw) M.; m. Allene Mary Roche, Apr. 2, 1956; children: Julie Allene, Edward Ralston. Student, Denison U., 1942-43; BA with distinction, George Washington U., 1948; MA, Fletcher Sch. Law and Diplomacy, 1949. Joined U.S. Fgn. Service, 1950; intelligence research analyst Near East Dept. State, 1949-50; resident officer Heidelberg, Germany, 1950-52; polit. officer embassy Karachi, Pakistan, 1952-54; Hindustani lang. and area tng. U. Pa., 1954-55; consul, polit. officer Madras, India, 1955-58; intelligence research specialist South Asia Dept. State, 1958-60; chief Indonesia-Malaya br. Dept. State (Office Research Asia), 1960-61, officer-in-charge Thailand affairs, 1961-63; grad. Nat. War Coll., 1964; counselor for polit. affairs Am. embassy, Djakarta, 1964-68; country dir. for Indonesia Dept. State, 1968-70; dir. Office East Asian Regional Affairs, 1970-71; minister Am. embassy, Bangkok, Thailand, 1971-75; ambassador to Bangladesh, 1976-77, to Indonesia, 1977-81; adj. prof. diplomacy Fletcher Sch. Law and Diplomacy, 1981-82; sr. v.p. Natomas Co., 1982-84; pres. Nat. Planning Assn., 1985-92, Edward Masters & Assocs., Washington, 1992—, U.S.-Indonesia Soc., 1994—. Mem. Am. Fgn. Svc. Assn., Phi Beta Kappa, Omicron Delta Kappa, Pi Gamma Mu, Delta Phi Epsilon, Cosmos Club. Home: 4525 Garfield St NW Washington DC 20007-1165

MASTERS, IAN, metallurgical engineer. With Sherritt Gordon Ctr., Ft. Saskatchewan, Alberta, Can. Recipient Sherritt Hydormetallurgy award Can. Inst. Mining, Metallurgy & Petroleum, 1992. Address: Sherritt Inc, 10111 114th St Bag 9, Fort Saskatchewan, AB Canada T8L 2P2*

MASTERS, JACK GERALD, mayor; b. Ft. William, Ont., Can., Sept. 27, 1931; s. John and Janet Mary (Winn) M.; m. Kathleen Jean Whatley, Sept. 4, 1953; children: Susan, Diane, Gerald, Scott. From sales mgr. to nat. sales mgr. and v.p. Sta. CKPR-CHFD-TV, Thunder Bay, Ont., 1952-77; gen. mgr., account exec. Thunder Bay Ins., 1977-80; mem. Can. Parliament, Ottawa, 1980-84; mayor City of Thunder Bay, 1985—. Mem. Liberal Party. Roman Catholic. Home: 153 Whalen St, Thunder Bay, ON Canada P7A 7H9

MASTERS, JOHN CHRISTOPHER, psychologist, educator, writer; b. Terre Haute, Ind., Oct. 25, 1941; s. Robert William and Lillian Virginia (Decker) M.; m. Mary Jayne Capps, June 6, 1970; children—Blair Christopher, Kyle Alexander. A.B., Harvard Coll., 1963; Ph.D., Stanford U., 1967. Asst. prof. Ariz. State U., Tempe, 1968-69; from asst. prof. to prof. U. Minn., Mpls., 1969-79; assoc. dir. Inst. Child Devel., 1974-79; Luce prof. pub. policy and the family, prof. psychology Vanderbilt U., Nashville, 1979-

87, interim chair dept. psychology, 1986-88; pres. Profl. Mgmt. Group, Inc., 1991—; dir. Master Ventures, 1989—, Master Travel, 1989—. Assoc. editor: Child Development, 1973-76, Behavior Therapy: Techniques and Empirical Findings, 1974, 79, 88; editor: Psychol. Bull., 1987-89. Fellow Am. Psychol. Assn.; mem. Soc. for Research in Child Devel., Internat. Soc. for Study of Behavioral Sci., Assn. for Public Policy and Mgmt. Home: 963 Overton Lea Rd Nashville TN 37220-1521

MASTERS, JON JOSEPH, lawyer; b. N.Y.C., June 20, 1937; s. Arthur Edward and Esther (Shady) M.; m. Rosemary Dunaway Cox, June 16, 1962; children: Brooke Alison, Blake Edward. B.A., Princeton U., 1958; J.D., Harvard U., 1964. Bar: N.Y. 1965, U.S. Dist. Ct. (so. dist.) N.Y. 1965, U.S. Ct. Appeals (2d cir.) 1965. Cons. asst. to under sec. Dept. Army, 1961; mem. policy planning staff asst. sec. for internat. security affairs Dept. Def. Washington, 1962; mem. Pres. Johnson's Spl. Polit. Research Staff, Washington, 1964; assoc. Shearman & Sterling, N.Y.C., 1965-68, 69; mem. staff Bedford-Stuyvesant D & S Corp., Bklyn., 1968-69; v.p.; sec., gen. counsel, dir. Baker, Weeks & Co., Inc., N.Y.C., 1969-76; prtnr. Christy & Viener, N.Y.C., 1976—; mem. SEC adv. com. broker-dealer compliance, 1972-74; legal advisor NACD Blue Ribbon Commn. on CEO and Dir. Performance Evaluation, 1994; chmn. bd. Clear and Present Prodns., 1992-93; bd. dirs. Harris & Harris Group Inc., 1992—. Mem. implementation com. Econ. Devel. Task Force of N.Y. Urban Coalition, 1968; mem. bd. Internat. Social Service, Am. Br., Inc., 1978-83, pres., 1979-83; bd. dirs. The Arts Connection, 1979-85; mem. steering com. N.Y. Lawyers Alliance for Nuclear Arms Control, 1983—. Served with USN, 1958-61. Mem. ABA, Assn. Bar City N.Y. (com. mcpl. affairs 1977-80), N.Y. State Bar Assn. Home: 530 E 86th St New York NY 10028-7535 Office: 620 5th Ave New York NY 10020-2402

MASTERS, ROGER DAVIS, government educator; b. Boston, June 8, 1933; s. Maurice and S. Grace (Davis) M.; m. Judith Ann Rubin, June 6, 1956 (div. 1984); children—Seth J., William A., Katherine R.; m. Susanne R. Putnam, Aug. 25, 1984. B.A., Harvard U., 1955; M.A., U. Chgo., 1958, Ph.D., 1961; M.A. (hon.), Dartmouth Coll., 1974. Instr. dept. polit. sci. Yale U., 1961-62, asst. prof., 1962-67; assoc. prof. dept. govt. Dartmouth Coll., Hanover, N.H., 1967-73; prof. Dartmouth Coll., 1973—, John Sloan Dickey Third Century prof., 1980-85, chmn. dept., 1986-89, Nelson A. Rockefeller prof., 1991—; cultural attache Am. embassy, Paris, 1969-71; chmn. France-Am. Commn. Ednl. and Cultural Exch., 1969-71; vis. lectr. Yale U. Law Sch., 1988-89, Vt. Law Sch., 1993, 94; sect. editor Social Sci. Info., 1971—. Author: The Nation Is Burdened, 1967, The Political Philosophy of Rousseau, 1968, The Nature of Politics, 1989, Beyond Relativism, 1993; editor: Rousseau's Discourses, 1964, Rousseau's Social Contract, 1978; co-editor: Ostracism: a Social and Biological Phenomenon, 1986, Collected Writings of J.J. Rousseau, 1990—, Primate Politics, 1991, The Sense of Justice, 1992, The Neurotransmitter Revolution, 1994; editor Gruter Inst. Reader in Biology, Law, and Human Social Behavior, 1992—. Served with AUS, 1955-57. Fulbright fellow Institut d'Etudes Politiques, Paris, 1958-59; joint Yale U.-Social Sci. Rsch. Coun. fellow, 1964-65; Guggenheim fellow, 1967-68; fellow Hastings Ctr. for Ethics and Life Scis., 1973-78. Mem. AAAS, Am. Polit. Sci. Assn., Assn. Polit. and Life Sci. (coun.), Am. Soc. for Legal and Polit. Philosophy, Gruter Inst. for Law and Behavioral Rsch. (adv. bd.), Internat. Soc. Human Ethology, Human Behavior Evolution Soc. Home: PO Box 113 South Woodstock VT 05071-0113 Office: Dartmouth Coll Dept Govt Hanover NH 03755

MASTERS, WILLIAM HOWELL, physician, educator; b. Cleve., Dec. 27, 1915; s. Francis Wynne and Estabrooks (Taylor) M.; children: Sarah Worthington, William Howell III. BS, Hamilton Coll., 1938, ScD (hon.), 1973; MD, U. Rochester, 1943; ScD (hon.), 1975. Diplomate Am. Bd. Obstetricians and Gynecologists; cert. Am. Assn. Sex Educators, Counselors and Therapists. Intern obstetrics and gynecology St. Louis Maternity and Barnes Hosp., 1943, asst. resident, 1944; intern pathology Washington U. Sch. Medicine, St. Louis, 1944; asst. resident gynecology Barnes Hosp., 1944, intern internal medicine, 1945, resident gynecology, 1945-46; resident obstetrics St. Louis Maternity Hosp., 1946-47; mem. faculty Washington U. Sch. Medicine, 1947—, assoc prof. clin. obstetrics and gynecology, 1964-69, prof., 1969—; dir. Reproductive Biology Research Found., 1964-73; co-dir. Masters & Johnson Inst. (formerly Reproductive Biology Research Found.), 1973-80, chmn. bd., 1981—; asso. physician St. Louis Maternity Barnes and St. Louis Children's hosps.; asso. physician Washington U. Clinics; asst. attending physician Jewish Hosp., St. Louis. Meml. Hosp. Author: (with Virginia E. Johnson) Human Sexual Response, 1966, Human Sexual Inadequacy, 1970, The Pleasure Bond, 1975, Homosexuality in Perspective, 1979, (with Kolodny et al) Textbook of Sexual Medicine; editor: (with V.E. Johnson and R.C. Kolodny) Ethical Issues in Sex Therapy and Research, Vol. 1, 1977, Vol. 2, 1980. Bd. dirs. St. Louis Family and Childrens Service, Planned Parenthood Assn., St. Louis Health and Welfare Council. Served to lt. (j.g.) USNR, 1942-43. Recipient Paul H. Hoch award Am. Psychopathol. Assn., 1971, award SECUS, 1972, Disting. Svc. award Am. Assn. Marriage and Family Counselors, 1976, award fo rdisting. achievement N=Modern Medicine, 1977, award Am. Assn. Sex. Educators, Counselors and Therapists, 1978; Paul Harris fellow, 1976. Mem. Gerontol. Soc., Am. Fertility Soc., Internat. Fertility Assn., Endocrine Soc., Am. Coll. Obstetricians and Gynecologists, N.Y. Acad. Sci., Soc. Sci. Study Sex, AAAS, Comprehensive Med. Soc., Pan Am. Med. Assn., Internat. Soc. for Research in Biology Reprodn., Am. Geriatric Soc., Am. Soc. Cytology, Soc. for Study Reprodn., AMA, Eastern Mo. Psychiat. Soc. (hon.), Authors Guild, Alpha Omega Alpha, Alpha Delta Phi. Episcopalian. Office: Masters & Johnson Inst 1 Campbell Plz Ste 4B 59th and Arsenal Saint Louis MO 63139*

MASTERSON, CARLIN See GLYNN, CARLIN

MASTERSON, CHARLES FRANCIS, retired social scientist; b. N.Y.C., Nov. 3, 1917; s. Frank Joseph and Harriett Geneva (Whittaker) M.; m. Vivian Ethel Reppke, May 8, 1954; children by previous marriage: Michael Charles, Susan Masterson Forrest. A.B., L.I. U., 1938; M.A., Columbia U., 1939, Ph.D., 1952. Dir. pub. relations Poly. Prep., Bklyn., 1946-49, Bklyn. C. of C., 1949-50, N.Y.C. Mission Soc., 1950-53; spl. asst. White House, Washington, 1953-56, Rumbough Co., N.Y., 1957-60, Nat. Safety Council, 1960-62; exec. dir. Office of Trustees, 1962-77; sr. assoc. Clark, Phipps, Clark & Harris, 1978-80; now ret. Author: World History, 1949, History of Asia, 1950. Mem. Pub. Rels. Soc. Am., Nat. Inst. Social Scis., N.Y.C. Mission Soc. (bd. dirs.), U.S. Com. for UN (bd. dirs.), Phi Delta Kappa. Presbyterian (elder). Club: Internat. Lawn Tennis. Home: 9801 Shore Rd Brooklyn NY 11209-7650

MASTERSON, JAMES FRANCIS, psychiatrist; b. Phila., Mar. 25, 1926; s. James Francis and Evangeline (O'Boyle) M.; m. Patricia Cooke, Jan. 28, 1950; children: James F., Richard K., Nancy. BS, U. Notre Dame, 1947; MD, Jefferson Med. Sch., Phila., 1951. Diplomate Am. Bd. Psychiatry, Am. Bd. Neurology. Intern Phila. Gen. Hosp., 1951-52; resident in psychiatry Payne Whitney Clinic, N.Y. Hosp., N.Y.C., 1952-55, chief resident, 1955-56, dir. adolescent OPD, 1956-66, head adolescent program, 1968-75, asst. attending psychiatrist, 1956-60, assoc. attending psychiatrist, 1960-70, attending psychiatrist, 1970—, dir. The Symptomatic Adolescent Research Project, 1957-67; dir. Masterson Group, P.C. for Study and Treatment Personality Disorders, 1977—. Author: Psychotherapy of the Borderline Adolescent, Psychotherapy of the Borderline Adult, Countertransference, Narcissistic Personality Disorder, The Real Self, The Psychiatric Dilemma of Adolescence, The Test of Time: From Borderline Adolescent to Functioning Adult; contbr. articles to profl. jours. Fellow Am. Psychiat. Assn., Am. Coll. Psychoanalysts; mem. AMA, Am. Coll. Psychoanalysis, N.Y. Soc. Adolescent Psychiatry (founder, past pres.), N.Y. County Med. Soc. Office: 60 Sutton Pl S New York NY 10022-4168

MASTERSON, JOHN PATRICK, retired English language educator; b. Chgo., Mar. 15, 1925; s. Michael Joseph and Delia Frances (Dolan) M.; m. Jean Frances Wegrzyn, Aug. 18, 1956; children: Mary Beth, Michael, Maureen, Laura. B.A., St. Mary of the Lake; 1947; M.A., De Paul U., 1952; Ph.D., U. Ill., 1961. Chmn. English dept. De Paul U., Chgo., 1964-67, head humanities div., 1967-70, prof. English, 1970, dean Coll. Liberal Arts and Scis., 1970-76, prof. emeritus, 1976-80, 82-87, prof. emeritus, 1988—, dean Grad. Sch., 1980-82; cons. in field. Recipient award Shell Oil Co., 1968, Via Sapientiae award De Paul U., 1987; fellow adminstrn. program Am. Coun.

Edn. Roman Catholic. Home: 1922 Belleview Ave Westchester IL 60154-4345

MASTERSON, KLEBER SANDLIN, former organization executive, retired naval officer; b. San Jon, N.Mex., July 12, 1908; s. John Patrick and Lela (Johnson) M.; m. Charlotte Elizabeth Parker, Oct. 3, 1931 (dec. 1986); 1 son, Kleber Sandlin, Jr. Student, U. N.Mex., 1925-26; B.S., U.S. Naval Acad., 1930; grad., U.S. Naval Postgrad. Sch., 1939, Naval War Coll., 1953. Commd. ensign U.S. Navy, 1930, advanced through grades to vice adm., 1964; assigned various ships, 1930-41; main battery asst. U.S.S. Arizona, Pearl Harbor; gunnery officer U.S.S. Pennsylvania, to 1944; staff research and devel. div., bur. ordnance Navy Dept., Wash., 1944-46; mem. staff CINCLANT FLT, 1946-47; comdr. Destroyer Div. 102, 1947-48; head ammunition br. Bur. Naval Ordnance, 1950-52; comdr. officer U.S.S. Lenawee, 1953-54; comdr. Naval Adminstrv. Unit, also asst. comdr. operations, field command Armed Forces Spl. Weapons Project, 1954-56; comdg. officer U.S.S. Boston, 1956-57; dir. guided missile div. Office Chief Naval Operations, exec. mem. navy ballistic missile com., 1958-60; comdr. Cruiser Div. 1, 1960-61; asst. chief naval operations devel. Office Chief Naval Operations, 1961; dep. chief Bur. Naval Weapons, 1961-62, chief, 1962-64; comdr. 2d Fleet and comdr. Striking Fleet Atlantic, 1964-66; dir. Weapons Systems Evaluation Group. Office of Sec. of Def., Washington, 1966-69; ret. Weapons Systems Evaluation Group. Office of Sec. of Def., 1969; pres. Navy Relief Soc., 1969-73. Decorated D.S.M., Legion of Merit, Navy Commendation; commandeur de l'Ordre National du Mérite (France). Mem. U.S. Naval Acad. Alumni Assn., U.S. Naval Inst. Navy Hist. Found. Club: Army Navy Country (Arlington, Va.). Home: 3440 S Jefferson St Apt 915 Falls Church VA 22041-3128

MASTERSON, KLEBER SANLIN, JR., physicist; b. San Diego, Sept. 26, 1932; s. Kleber Sandlin and Charlotte Elizabeth (Parker) M.; m. Sara Ann Cooper, Dec. 21, 1957; children: Thomas Marshall, John Cooper. BS in Engring., U.S. Naval Acad., 1954; MS in Physics, USN Postgrad. Sch. 1960; PhD in Physics, U. Calif., San Diego, 1963; student Advanced Mgmt. Programs, Harvard Bus. Sch., 1981-82. Commd. ensign USN, 1954, advanced through grades to rear adm., 1979; comdg. officer USS Preble, Pearl Harbor, Hawaii, 1969-71; mgr. antiship missile def. project USN, Washington, 1974-77, exec. asst. to sec. of Navy, 1977-79, asst. dep. comdr. Naval Sea Systems Command, 1979-81, chief Studies, Analyses and Gaming Agy., 1981-82; ret. USN, 1982; prin. Booz, Allen and Hamilton, Inc., Arlington, Va., 1982-87; v.p. Booz, Allen and Hamilton, Inc., Arlington, 1987-92; sr. v.p. Sci. Applications Internat. Corp., 1992-94; pres. The Riverside Group, Ltd., 1994—; bd. control U.S. Naval Inst., Annapolis, Md., 1971-82; bd. dirs. Mil. Ops. Rsch. Soc., 1984-90, pres., 1988-89. Editor: Book of Navy Songs, 1954; contbr. articles on plasma and theoretical nuclear physics, computer science, radars, ops. rsch. to profl. publs. Mem. Am. Phys. Soc., U.S. Naval Acad. Alumni Assn. (pres. Washington chpt. 1989-90), U.S. Naval Acad. Found. (trustee 1991—), Sigma Xi. Achievements include development of NELIAC computer program and Strategic Simulation Methodology. Home: 101 Pommander Walk Alexandria VA 22314-3844 Office: The Riverside Group Ltd 101 Pommander Walk Alexandria VA 22314-3844

MASTERSON, MARY STUART, actress; b. N.Y.C., June 29, 1966; d. Peter and Carlin Glynn Masterson. Theatre appearances include Alice in Wonderland, 1982, Been Taken, 1985, The Lucky Spot, 1987, Lily Dale, 1987; TV movies include Love Lives On, 1985, City in Fear; films: The Stepford Wives, 1975, Heaven Help Us, 1984, At Close Range, 1985, My Little Girl, 1986, Gardens of Stone, 1987, Some Kind of Wonderful, 1987, Mr. North, 1988, Chances Are, 1989, Immediate Family, 1989, Funny About Love, 1990, Fried Green Tomatoes, 1991, Married To It, 1993, Benny and Joon, 1993, Bad Girls, 1994, Radioland Murders, 1994, Heaven's Prisoners, 1994. Office: David Lewis Paul Matins Internat Creative Mgmt 8942 Wilshire Blvd Beverly Hills CA 90211*

MASTERSON, MICHAEL RUE, journalist, educator, editor; b. Harrison, Ark., Dec. 10, 1946; s. Rue B. and Elaine H. (Hammerschmidt) M.; m. Ruthie Louette Laws; children: Brandon Lee, Anna Kathleen. Student, U. N.Mex., 1965-68; BA, U. Cen. Ark., 1971. Editor The Daily Independent, Newport, Ark., 1971-73; exec. editor Sentinel-Record, Hot Springs, Ark., 1973-80; staff writer L.A. Times, 1980; investigative reporter Chgo. Sun-Times, 1981; spl. projects editor WEHCO Media (daily newspapers), Little Rock, 1982-86; investigative team leader Ariz. Republic, 1986-89; Kiplinger Program chair, prof. journalism Ohio State U., Columbus, 1989-94; investigative projects editor The Asbury Park (N.J.) Press, 1994—; isntr. journalism Garland Community Coll., 1974-75. Co-author: (text) Excellence in Reporting, 1987; contbg. editor, cons. Two River Times, Monmouth, N.J., 1993—. With USCGR, 1968-73. Recipient Nat. Headliner awards Press Club Atlantic City, 1971, 89, Robert F. Kennedy awards, 1972, 74, 77, 80, Freedom of Info. and Investigative Reporting awards Ark. chpt. Soc. Profl. Journalists, 1974, honor awards, 1975, award for editorial Freedom Found. Valley Forge, 1974, Mass Media Gold Medallion NCCJ, 1974, Paul Tobenkin Meml. awards Columbia Grad. Sch. Journalism, 1975, 85, 88, 89, Disting. Svc. awards Sch. Journalism U. Ark. Little Rock, ann. 1979-84, citation Roy Howard Pub. Svc. Awards, 1978, Cert. of Merit ABA, 1980, 84, Nat. Assn. Black Journalists reporting prize, 1985, Don Bolles award for outstanding investigative reporting, 1987, 88, Best of West Journalism awards, 1987, 88, Congl. Achievement award Nat. Congress Am. Indians, 1987, Clarion journalism award, 1988, George Polk award for nat. reporting, 1989, Heywood Broun Meml. awards, 1984, 87, hon. mention, 1975; finalist Pulitzer Prize Nat. Reporting 1988, Specialized Reporting 89; named one of Outstanding Young Men Am., 1973, Ark. Journalist of Yr., 1986; Alicia Patterson journalism fellow, 1976-77; teaching fellow Poynter Inst. Media Studies, 1993; finalist First Journalist in Space Program, 1986. Mem. Investigative Reporters and Editors (Nat. Journalism awards 1979, 82, IRE Bronze Medallion 1979, Disting. Teaching honors Ohio State 1994, bd. dirs. 1982-87), Sigma Delta Chi, Nat. Headliners Club. Home: 242 W 18th Ave Columbus OH 43210-1107 Office: Ohio State U Dept Journalism Columbus OH 43210 *To call attention to the events, predicaments and inequities in the neighborhood in hopes at least one person who follows will somehow benefit from my having once been here.*

MASTERSON, PETER, actor, director; b. Houston, June 1, 1934; s. Carlos Bee and Josephine Seager (Smith) M.; m. Carlin Glynn, Dec. 29, 1960; children: Carlin Alexandra, Mary Stuart, Peter Carlos. BA in History, Rice U., 1957. Appeared on Broadway Marathon '33, 1963, Blues For Mr. Charlie, 1964; title role in Trial of Lee Harvey Oswald, 1967; appeared in The Great White Hope, 1968, That Championship Season, 1974, The Poison Tree, 1975, (films) The Exorcist, 1972, Man On A Swing, 1973, The Stepford Wives, 1974; playwright The Best Little Whorehouse in Texas, 1978; (Broadway prodns.) dir. The Best Little Whorehouse in Texas, 1978 (Drama Desk award for best dir. of musical 1978), co-dir., co-writer The Best Little Whorehouse Goes Public, 1994; dir. (off-Broadway) The Cover of Life, 1994, The Young Man From Atlanta (winner Pulitzer prize 1995); screenwriter (film) The Best Little Whorehouse in Texas, 1980; producer (TV film) City in Fear, 1980; dir. (films) The Trip to Bountiful, 1985, Blood Red, 1986, Full Moon in Blue Water, 1987, Night Game, 1988, Convicts, 1989, Arctic Blue, 1993. Mem. Actors Equity Assn., Screen Actors Guild, Soc. Stage Dirs. and Choreographers, AFTRA, Writers Guild Am., Actors Studio, Dirs. Guild Am. Episcopalian. Clubs: Seawanhaka Corinthian Yacht, Tex. Corinthian Yacht.

MASTERSON, THOMAS A., lawyer; b. Phila., Dec. 10, 1927; s. James F. and Evangeline O. Masterson; m. Louise M., Apr. 27, 1982. A.B. magna cum laude, Harvard U., 1949; LL.B. cum laude, U. Pa., 1952. Bar: Pa. 1953, U.S. Dist. Ct. Pa., U.S. Ct. Appeals (3d cir.) 1953. Asst. dist. atty., 1954-56; dep. city solicitor City of Phila., 1956-60; ptnr. Morgan, Lewis & Bockius, Phila., 1960-67, 1973—; judge U.S. Dist. Ct. Eastern Dist. Pa., 1967-73. Mem. Phila. Human Relations Commn., 1960-64; mem. Phila. Sch. Bd., 1964-67. Mem. Am. Coll. Trial Lawyers, ABA. Office: Morgan Lewis & Bockius 2000 Logan Sq Philadelphia PA 19103-6993

MASTNY-FOX, CATHERINE LOUISE, administrator, consultant; b. New Rochelle, N.Y., June 4, 1939; d. Louis Francis and Catherine Marie (Haage) Kacmarynski; m. Vojtech Mastny, July 25, 1964 (div. 1987); m. Richard K. Fox, Oct. 10, 1993; children: Catherine Paula (dec.), John

Adalbert (dec.), Elizabeth Louise. BA magna cum laude, Coll. New Rochelle, 1961; MA, Columbia U., 1963, PhD, 1968. Lectr. in history various colls. N.Y. and Calif., 1968-71; researcher, writer H. W. Wilson Co., N.Y.C., 1971-81; contbg. editor Columbia U. Press, N.Y.C., 1972-74; v.p., exec. dir. Internat. Mgmt. and Devel. Inst., Washington, 1978-84, exec. dir. spl. asst. to chmn., 1986-91; v.p. Meridian House Internat., Washington, 1984-85; dir. corp. devel. Washington Music Ensemble, 1991—, also bd. dirs.; cons. in field; panelist NEH, Washington, 1983; internat. advisor Global Nomads, Washington, 1990—. Contbg. author: The American Book of Days, 1978, World Authors, 1970-1971, 1980; contbg. editor: Columbia Ency., 3d edit., 1975. Fulbright Found. grantee, 1961-62; fellow Woodrow Wilson Found., 1962-63, Walter L. Dorn, 1963-64, Konrad Adenauer fellow, 1965-66. Democrat. Roman Catholic. Avocations: travel, classical music, hiking, art collecting, gardening. Home: 5102 Wyoming Rd Bethesda MD 20816-2267

MASTRANGELO, REGINA MARY, nursing administrator, dean; b. Olyphant, Pa., July 9, 1938; d. Michael and Julia (Pilch) Bausher; m. John T. Mastrangelo, Apr. 23, 1960; children: Gina Julie, Christine, John. BSN, Villanova (Pa.) U., 1959; MSN, U. Pa., 1964; EdD, Nova U., 1989. Instr. in nursing Our Lady of Lourdes Sch. of Nursing, Camden, N.J.; instr. in rehab. U. Pa., Phila.; dean Helene Fuld Sch. of Nursing, Camden. Mem. Sigma Theta Tau, Pi Lambda Theta.

MASTRANTONIO, MARY ELIZABETH, actress; b. Lombard, Ill., Nov. 17, 1958; d. Frank A. and Mary D. (Pagone) M. Student, U. Ill., 1976-78. Actress: (stage prodns.) Copperfield, 1981, Oh, Brother, 1981, Amadeus, 1982, Sunday in the Park with George, 1983, The Human Comedy, 1984, Henry V, 1984, Measure for Measure, 1985, The Knife, 1987, Twelfth Night, (feature films) Scarface, 1983, The Color of Money, 1986 (Acad. award nomination 1986), The January Man, 1989, The Abyss, 1989, Fools of Fortune, 1990, Class Action, 1991, Robin Hood: Prince of Thieves, 1991, Consenting Adults, 1992, Three Wishes, 1995; (TV movie) Mussolini: The Untold Story, 1985. Office: Internat Creative Mgmt 8942 Wilshire Blvd Beverly Hills CA 90211*

MASTRIANA, ROBERT ALAN, architect; b. Youngstown, Ohio, July 6, 1949; s. Fred Paul and Rose L. (Fusco) M.; m. Kathy Ann Peloe, June 26, 1971; children: Robert Byron, Kathryn Olivia. BArch, Kent State U., 1972, U. D'Florence (Italy), 1972. Registered profl. architect, Fla., N.J., Ohio, Pa., Tenn., Tex., W.Va., Va.; cert. gen. contractor, Fla. Project architect Allan M. Sveda, Architect, Cuyahoga Falls, Ohio, 1972-75; pvt. practice architect Poland, Ohio, 1976-78; ptnr., architect 4M Co., Youngstown, 1978—; mem., past chmn. City of Youngstown Design Rev. Bd.; past chmn. Poland Village Design Rev. Bd.; past asst. chmn. Poland Bd. Appeals; tchr. archtl. awareness class to realtors for continuing edn. Trustee Circle of Butler Art; past trustee Poland Twp. Hist. Soc.; patron Youngstown Symphony Soc.; past asst. chmn. bd. trustees 1st Covenant Ch.; mem. adv. bd. YMCA, Kent State U. Sch. Arch.; mem. Nat. Trust Histo. Preservation. Recipient Builder award Poland Masonic Lodge, 1988, Charles Marr award Archtl. Soc. Ohio Found., 1990, Barvikski Meml. award, 1983; Paul Harris fellow Boardman Rotary, 1988. Mem. AIA (past pres. Ohio chpt., past treas., state conv. chmn., design awards chmn., past pres. Ea. Ohio chpt., past v.p., bd. dirs.), Am. Archtl. Found., Ohio Archtl. Found. (bd. dirs.), Youngstown Warren Region C. of C. (civic improvements award com.), Dover Club, Rotary, Fellowship Christian Athletes, Phi Gamma Delta. Avocations: running, golf, tennis, antique cars, Karate. Home: 34 Botsford St Youngstown OH 44514-1755 Office: 4M Company 4251 Glenwood Ave Ste 3 Youngstown OH 44512-1062

MASTRION, GUY, secondary school principal. Prin. Longwood Mid. Sch., Middle Island, N.Y. Recipient Blue Ribbon Sch. award U.S. Dept. Edn., 1990-91. Office: Longwood Mid Sch Middle Island-Yaphank Rd Middle Island NY 11953

MASTRO, A. F., chemical company executive; b. 1939. Student, LoyolaU. With USX Corp., 1961-86, v.p. acctg. and fin. U.S. Diversified Group, 1986; exec. v.p. Aristech Chem. Corp., 1986—, now also chief fin. officer, bd. dirs. Office: Aristech Chem Corp 600 Grant St Pittsburgh PA 15219-2701

MASTROIANNI, LUIGI, JR., physician, educator; b. New Haven, Nov. 8, 1925; s. Marion (Dallas) M.; m. Elaine Catherine Pierson, Nov. 4, 1957; children: John James, Anna Catherine, Robert Luigi. AB, Yale U., 1946; MD, Boston U., 1950, DSc (hon.), 1973; MA (hon.), U. Pa., 1970. Diplomate Am. Bd. Ob-gyn. and Reproductive Endocrinology and Infertility. Intern, then resident ob.-gyn. Met. Hosp. N.Y., 1950-54; fellow rsch. Harvard Med. Sch. and Free Hosp. for Women, Boston, 1954-55; instr. dept. ob-gyn. Sch. of Medicine Yale U., New Haven, 1955-56, asst. prof. ob-gyn. dept., 1956-61; prof. U. Calif., L.A., 1961-65; chief ob-gyn Harbor Gen. Hosp., L.A., 1961-65; William Goodell prof. ob.-gyn., chmn. dept. U. Pa. Sch. of Medicine, Phila., 1965-87, William Goodell prof. ob.-gyn. dept., dir. human reproduction div., 1987—. Contbr. numerous articles to profl. jours. Recipient Squibb prize Pacific Coast Fertility Soc., 1965, Christian R. and Mary Lindback award, 1969, Gold medal Barren Found., 1977, King Faisal prize in medicine, 1989, Pub. Recognition award Ass. Profls. of Gynecology and Obstets., 1990, Disting. Svc. award Soc. Study of Reproduction, 1992. Mem. ACS, Am. Gyneol. and Ostet. Soc., Am. Gynecol. Club, Am. Fertility Soc., Am. Physiol. Soc., Am. Coll. Obs.-Gyns., Inst. Medicine of NAS, Soc. Gynecology Investigation, Soc. for Exptl. Biology and Medicine, Endocrine Soc., Soc. for Study Reproduction (Disting. Svc. award 1992), Pacific Coast Fertility Soc. (hon.), Cen. Assn. Ob.-Gyns. (hon.), Tex. Assn. Ob.-Gyns. (hon.), N.C. Gynecol. Soc. (hon.), Assn. Profs. Ob.-Gyns., Brazilian Fertility Soc. (hon.), Italian Soc. Ob-Gyns. (hon.), Argentina Fertility Soc. (hon.), Peruvian Fertility Soc. (hon.), Sociedad Espanola de Fertilidad (hon.), Israel Soc. Ob-Gyn. (hon.), Uruguan Soc. Sterility and Fertility (hon.), Inst. Medicine, Sigma Xi, Alpha Omega Alpha. Home: 561 Ferndale Ln Haverford PA 19041-1614 Office: Hosp U Pa 3400 Spruce St Philadelphia PA 19104-4378

MASTROIANNI, MARCELLO, actor; b. Fontana Liri, Italy, Sept. 28, 1924; s. Ottone and Ida (Irolle) M.; ed. U. Rome; m. Flora Carabella, 1950; 1 child, Barbara. Cashier, Eagle Lion Films, Rome, 1944; debut U. Rome stage prodn. Angelica, 1948; appeared in films including: Una Domenica d'Agosto, 1949, Le Notti Bianche, 1957, I Soliti Ignoti, 1958, Bella' Antonio, 1960, La Dolce Vita, 1960, La Notte, 1961, A Very Private Affair, 1961, Divorce—Italian Style, 1961, 8 1/2, 1963, Family Diary, 1963, Yesterday, Today and Tomorrow, 1964, Fantasmi a Roma, 1964, Casanova 70, 1965, Marriage—Italian Style, 1965, The Organizer, 1965, The 10th Victim, 1965, Ciao Rudy, 1966, Lo Straniera, 1967, Viaggio di G. Mastorna, 1967, Shout Louder, I Don't Understand, L'Etranger, 1967, The Man with the Balloons, 1968, Diamonds for Breakfast, 1968, Leo the Last, 1970, The Priest's Wife, 1970, Drama of Jealousy, (prize for best actor Cannes 1970), 1970, Sunflower, 1970, The Pizza Triangle, 1970, What?, 1972, La Grande Bouffe, 1973, Salut L'Artiste, 1973, Massacre in Rome, 1973, T7uche Pas la Femme Blanche, 1974, Allonsanfan, 1975, Gangster Doll, 1975, Down the Ancient Stairs, 1975, The Sunday Woman, 1976, A Special Day, 1977, Bye Bye Monkey, 1978, Stay as You Are, 1979, La Cite des Femmes, 1979, Blood Feud, 1981, The New World, 1981, Gabriella, 1982, Nuit de Varennes, 1983, Allonsanfan, 1985, Macaroni, 1985, Ginger and Fred, 1986, Dark Eyes (best actor Cannes Film Fest.), 1987, Intervista, 1987, The Beekeeper, 1988, The Two Lives of Martin Pascal, Splendor, 1989, What's the Time (Best Actor Venice Film Festival), 1989, The Hesitant Step of the Stork, 1991, Everybody's Fine, 1991, A Fine Romance, Used People, 1992, The Beekeeper, 1993, The Children Thief, 1994, I Don't Want To Talk About It, 1994. Recipient Silver ribbon Italian Film Critics, 1958, 61, European Film award, 1988.*

MASTROMONACO-ADLER, ELLEN G., publishing company executive. Pub. N.Am. and S.Am. Berlitz Pub. Co., Inc. (subs: Berlitz Internat. Inc.), N.Y.C. Office: Berlitz Pub Co Inc 257 Park Ave South New York NY 10010

MASUDA, GOHTA, physician, educator; b. Tokyo, Nov. 21, 1940; s. Ryota and Chiyo (Ikeuchi) M.; m. Mitsuko Taguchi, May 14, 1983. MD, Keio U., 1966, PhD, 1972. Intern, Keio Univ. Hosp., Tokyo, 1966-67; instr. Keio U., Tokyo, 1967-74, 76-78; asst. prof. Kitasato Med. Coll., Kanagawa-Ken,

Japan, 1974-76; chief dept. infectious diseases Tokyo Met. Komagome Hosp., 1978—; asst. prof. Toho U., Tokyo, 1985—, Keio U., 1986—, Gunma U., 1989—. Contbr. articles to profl. jours. Mem. Japanese Assn. for Infectious Diseases, Japan Soc. Chemotherapy, Am. Soc. Microbiology, Brit. Soc. for Antimicrobial Chemotherapy, N.Y. Acad. Scis. Buddhist. Home: 1-14-12-305 Komagome, Toshima-ku 170 Tokyo Japan Office: Tokyo Met Komagome Hosp Dept Infectious Diseases, 3-18-22 Honkomagome, Bunkyo-ku 113 Tokyo Japan-

MASUR, KURT, conductor; b. Brieg, Silesia, Germany, July 18, 1927. Grad., Nat. Music Schule, Breslau, Germany, 1944, Leipzig Conservatory, 1946-48; hon. degree, U. Mich., Cleve. Inst. Music, Leipzig U., Westminster Choir Coll., Hamilton Coll. Repetiteur and conductor Halle Nat. Theatre, 1948-51; conductor Erfurt City Theatre, 1951-53, Leipzig City Theatre, 1953-55, Dresden Philharm., 1955-58; gen. music dir. Mecklenburg Staatstheater, 1958-60; mus. dir. Komische Oper Berlin, 1960-64; chief conductor Dresden Philharm., 1967-72; conductor Leipzig Gewandhaus Orch., since 1970; mus. dir. New York Philharmonic, N.Y.C., since 1991; conductor London Philharm. Orch., 1989-92; prof. Leipzig Acad. Music, 1975—; hon. guest conductor The Israel Philharm. Orch., 1992. Tours include Europe, South Am., Japan, U.S., Can., Middle East; recordings include: Symphonies by Mendelssohn, Brahms, Bruckner, Beethoven, Schumann, Tchaikovsky, Prokofiev's Piano Concertos, Beethoven's Missa Solemnis. Office: care NY Philharmonic Avery Fischer Hall 132 W 65th St New York NY 10023-6903 also: Gewandhaus zu Leipzig, Augustusplatz 8, O-7010 Leipzig Germany*

MASUREL, JEAN-LOUIS ANTOINE NICOLAS, investment company executive; b. Cannes, France, Sept. 18, 1940; s. Antoine and Anne-Marie (Gallant) M.; children: Anne-Sophie, Aude. Grad., Ecoles des Hautes Etudes Commerciales, 1962; M.B.A., Harvard U., 1964. With Morgan Guaranty Trust Co., N.Y.C., 1964-80; v.p., gen. mgr. Morgan Guaranty Trust Co., Paris, 1975-78; sr. v.p Morgan Guaranty Trust Co., 1978-80; sr. exec. v.p. Banque de Paribas, 1980-82; dep. pres. Banque Pays-Bas, 1982-83; mng. dir. Moët-Hennessy, 1983-87, Moët-Hennessy-Louis Vuitton, 1987-89; pres. Arcos Investissement S.A., 1989—, Hediard S.A., 1991-95; bd. dirs. Peugot S.A., Paris Said Holdings, Bermuda Société des Bains d Mor (SBM) Monalo. Bd. govs. Am. Hosp., Paris; hon. chmn., dir. Harvard Bus. Sch. Club France. Address: 31 rue Raynouard, 75016 Paris France

MASYS, DANIEL RICHARD, medical school director; b. Columbus, Ohio, Mar. 6, 1949; s. Paul John and Jane Marie (Mollenauer) M.; m. Linda Suzanne Bross, June 2, 1974; 1 child, Christopher. AB in Biochemistry, Princeton U., 1971; MD, Ohio State U., 1974. Diplomate Am. Bd. Internal Medicine. Staff hematologist, oncologist U.S. Naval Hosp., San Diego, 1980-84; chief ICRDB br. NIH, Bethesda, Md., 1984-86; dir. Lister Hill Nat. Ctr. Nat. Libr. Medicine, Bethesda, Md., 1986-94; dir. informatics Sch. Medicine U. Calif., San Diego, 1994—. Assoc. editor Acad. Medicine jour., 1988-91. Mem. high performance computing White House Office of Sci., Washington, 1991-94; rep. Fed. Networking Coun., Washington, 1991-94. Capt. USPHS, 1984-94. Fellow Am. Coll. Physicians, Am. Coll. Med. Informatics (exec. com. 1989-92); mem. Am. Med. Informatics Assn. (bd. dirs. 1991—, assoc. editor jour. 1993—, Pres.'s award 1992), Alpha Omega Alpha. Office: Univ of Calif San Diego Sch of Medicine 9500 Gilman Dr Rm 1317 La Jolla CA 92093-0602

MATALIN, MARY, political consultant; d. Steven and Eileen Matalini; m. Artie Arnold (div.); m. James Carville, Nov. 25, 1993. Grad., Western Ill. Univ.; student, Hofstra Univ. With the Rep. Nat. Com., since the early 80's; polit. dir. George Bush's 1992 re-election campaign. Co-host, CNBC talk show Equal Time, 1993—; author: (with James Carville) All's Fair, 1994. Office: Equal Time 825 K St NW Ste 917 Washington DC 20006-1202

MATALON, VIVIAN, theatrical director; b. Manchester, Eng., Oct. 11, 1929; came to U.S., 1977; s. Moses and Rose (Tawil) M. Student, Munro Coll., Jamaica (W.I.) Coll., Neighborhood Playhouse, N.Y.C. Prof. acting Brandeis U., 1977-78; prof. acting and direction SUNY, Stony Brook, 1985-86. Dir. Broadway prodns. After the Rain, Noel Coward in Two Keys, P.S. Your Cat is Dead, Morning's at Seven (Tony award, Drama Desk award 1980), Brigadoon, The American Clock, The Corn is Green, The Tap Dance Kid (Tony nomination 1984); London West End Prodns. include Season of Goodwill, The Chinese Prime Minister, The Glass Menagerie, Suite in Three Keys, After the Rain, Two Cities, Girlfriend, I Never Sang for My Father, Small Craft Warnings, The Gingerbread Lady, Bus Stop, Morning's at Seven; dir. Ah Wilderness, Stratford (Ont., Can.) Festival, The Heiress, Chichester (Eng.) Festival; television prodns. Private Contentment, Am. Playhouse, Morning's at Seven, Showtime. Office: 259 W 45th St New York NY 10036-3903

MATARAZZO, JOSEPH DOMINIC, psychologist; b. Caiazzo, Italy, Nov. 12, 1925; (parents Am. citizens); s. Nicholas and Adeline (Mastroianni) M.; m. Ruth Wood Gadbois, Mar. 26, 1949; children: Harris, Elizabeth, Sara. Student, Columbia U., 1944; BA, Brown U., 1946; MS, Northwestern U., 1950, PhD, 1952. Fellow in med. psychology Washington U. Sch. Medicine, 1950-51; instr. Washington U., 1951-53, asst. prof., 1953-55; research assoc. Harvard Med. Sch., assoc. psychologist Mass. Gen. Hosp., 1955-57; prof., head med. psychol. dept. Oreg. Health Scis. U., Portland, 1957—; mem. nursing research and patient care study sect., behavioral medicine study sect. NIH, nat. mental health adv. bd. NIMH; mem. bd. regents Uniformed Services U. Health Scis., 1974-80. Author: Wechsler's Measurement and Appraisal of Adult Intelligence, 5th edit., 1972, (with A.N. Wiens) The Interview: Research on its Anatomy and Structure, 1972, (with Harper and Wiens) Nonverbal Communication, 1978; editor: Behavioral Health: A Handbook of Health Enhancement and Disease Prevention, 1984; editorial bd.: Jour. Clin. Psychology, 1962—; cons. editor: Contemporary Psychology, 1962-70, 80—, Jour. Community Psychology, 1974-81, Behavior Modification, 1976-91, Intelligence: An Interdisciplinary Jour, 1976-90, Jour. Behavioral Medicine, 1977—, Profl. Psychology, 1978—, Jour. Cons. and Clin. Psychology, 1978-85; editor: Psychology series Aldine Pub. Co, 1964-74; psychology editor: Williams & Wilkins Co, 1974-77; contbr. articles to psychol. jours. Ensign USNR, 1943-47; capt. Res. Recipient Hofheimer prize Am. Psychiat. Assn., 1962. Fellow AAAS, APA (pres. divsn. health psychology 1991-92, mem. Coun. of Reps. 1982-91, bd. dirs 1986-90, pres. 1989-90); mem. Western Psychol. Assn., Oreg. Psychol. Assn., Am. Assn. State Psychology Bds. (pres. 1963-64, 86-87), Nat. Assn. Mental Health (bd. dirs.), Oreg. Mental Health Assn. (bd. dirs., pres. 1962-63), Internat. Coun. Psychologists (past pres. 1972-74, pres. 1976-77), Assn. Advancement of Psychology (trustee 1980-84, chmn. bd. trustees 1983-85). Home: 1934 SW Vista Ave Portland OR 97201-2455 Office: Oreg Health Scis U Sch of Medicine 3181 SW Sam Jackson Park Rd Portland OR 97201-3011

MATARAZZO, RUTH GADBOIS, psychology educator; b. New London, Conn., Nov. 9, 1926; d. John Stuart and Elizabeth (Wood) Gadbois; m. Joseph D. Matarazzo, Mar. 26, 1949; children: Harris, Elizabeth, Sara. A.B., Brown U., 1948; M.A., Washington U., St. Louis, 1952, Ph.D., 1955. Diplomate in clin. psychology and clin. neuropsychology Am. Bd. Examiners in Profl. Psychology. Rsch. fellow pediatrics Washington U. Med. Sch., 1954-55; rsch. fellow psychology Harvard U. Med. Sch., 1955-57; asst. prof. med. psychology Oreg. Health Scis. U., Portland, 1957-63, assoc. prof., 1963-68, prof., 1968—; woman liaison officer to Assn. Am. Med. Colls., 1979-90. Author: (with E. Greif) Behavioral Approaches to Rehabilitation: Coping with Change, 1982; contbr. chpts. to books and articles to profl. jours. Fellow Am. Psychol. Assn. (bd. ednl. affairs, del. to coun. reps., vice chmn. accreditation com., chmn. accreditation task force); mem. AAAS, Western Psychol. Assn. (bd. dirs.), Oreg. Psychol. Assn. (past pres.), Portland Psychol. Assn. (past pres.), Sigma Xi. Home: 1934 SW Vista Ave Portland OR 97201-2455

MATASAR, ANN B., former dean, business and political science educator; b. N.Y.C., June 27, 1940; d. Harry and Tillie (Simon) Bergman; m. Robert Matasar, June 9, 1962; children—Seth Gideon, Toby Rachel. AB, Vassar Coll., 1962; MA, Columbia U., 1964, PhD, 1968; M of Mgmt. in Fin., Northwestern U., 1977. Assoc. prof. Mundelein Coll., Chgo., 1965-78; prof. dir. Ctr. for Bus. and Econ. Elmhurst Coll., Elmhurst, Ill., 1978-84; dean Roosevelt U., Chgo., 1984-92; prof. Internat. Bus. and Fin. Walter E. Heller Coll. Bus. Adminstrn. Roosevelt U., 1992—; dir. Corp. Responsibility Group, Chgo., 1978-84; chmn. long range planning Ill. Bar Assn., 1982-83; mem. edn. com. Ill. Commn. on the Status of Women, 1978-81. Author: Corporate PACS and Federal Campaign Financing Laws: Use or Abuse of Power?, 1986; (with others) Research Guide to Women's Studies, 1974. Contbr. articles to profl. jours. Dem. candidate 1st legis. dist. Ill. State Senate, no. suburbs Chgo., 1972; mem. Dem. exec. com. New Trier Twp., Ill., 1972-76; rsch. dir., acad. advisor Congressman Abner Mikva, Ill., 1974-76; bd. dirs. Ctr. Ethics and Corp. Policy, 1985-90. Named Chgo. Woman of Achievement Mayor of Chgo., 1978. Fellow AAUW (trustee ednl. found. 1992—, v.p. fin.); mem. Am. Polit. Sci. Assn., Midwest Bus. Adminstrn. Assn., Acad. Mgmt., Women's Caucus for Polit. Sci. (pres. 1980-81), John Howard Assn. (bd. dirs. 1986-90), Am. Assembly of Coll. Schs. of Bus. (bd. dirs. 1989-92, chair com. on diversity in mgmt. edn. 1991-92), North Ctrl. Assn. (commr. 1994—), Beta Gamma Sigma. Democrat. Jewish. Avocations: jogging, biking, tennis, opera, crosswords. Office: Roosevelt U Coll Bus Adminstrn Dept Fin 430 S Michigan Ave Chicago IL 60605-1301

MATATHIA, IRA LESLIE, advertising agency executive; b. N.Y.C., Dec. 26, 1949; s. Morris and Eleanor (Sussman) M.; m. Julie Lawrence, Dec. 12, 1970 (div. 1980); 1 child, David Reed; m. Kathie Ellen Strauss, Jan. 1, 1984; children: Lily Elizabeth, Nicholas Joseph. BA, Queens Coll., CUNY, 1969, MA, 1971. Asst. advt. exec., mgmt. supr. Grey Advt., N.Y.C., 1971-82; sr. v.p., mgmt. supr. Kurtz & Tarlow/Geers Gross, N.Y.C., 1982-84; group mgmt. supr. Chiat/Day, N.Y.C., 1984-89; dir. client svc. Chiat/Day/Mojo, N.Y.C., 1989-90; pres., chief exec. officer Chiat/Day/Mojo, Toronto, Ont., Can., 1990—. Office: Chiat/Day/Toronto, 10 Lower Spadina Ave, Toronto, ON Canada M5V 2Z1

MATAXIS, THEODORE CHRISTOPHER, consultant, lecturer, writer, retired army officer, educator; b. Seattle, Aug. 17, 1917; s. Chris P. and Edla (Osterdahl) M.; m. Helma Mary Jensen, Aug. 27, 1940; children: Shirley Jeanne (Mrs. J. L. Slack), Theodore Christopher, Kaye Louise (Mrs. Vernon P. Isaacs, Jr.). B.A., U. Wash., 1940; student, Def. Services Staff Coll., India, 1950-51, Army War Coll., 1957-58; M.A. in Internat. Relations, George Washington U., 1965. Commd. 2d lt. U.S. Army, 1940, advanced through grades to brig. gen., 1967; inf. bn. comdr. Europe, World War II; regt. comdr. Korea, 1952-53; mem. Gov. Harriman's Presdl. Mission to Establish Mil. Aid Program India, 1962; mil. asst., speech writer for chmn. Joint Chiefs of Staff, 1962-64; sr. adviser II Vietnamese Army Corps. Pleiku, 1964-65; dep. comdr. 1st Brigade, 101st Airborne Div., 1966, asst. div. comdr. 82d Airborne Div., 1967; chief army sect. Army Mission/MAAG Iran, 1968-70; asst., acting div. comdr. Americal Div. Vietnam, 1970; chief mil. equipment delivery team Cambodia, 1971-72; ret., 1972; ednl. and systems mgmt. cons. Republic of Singapore, 1972-74; asst. supt., comdt. cadets Valley Forge Mil. Acad., Wayne, Pa., 1975-83; dir. AZED Assocs., Ltd., Southern Pines, N.C., 1983—; faculty Am. Mil. U., 1993—. Author: (with Seymour Goldberg) Nuclear Tactics, 1958, (chpt.) International Affairs in South West Asia, 1984, American Military Encyclopedia; also numerous mil. and hist. articles. Mem. adv. council Com. for Free Afghanistan. Decorated D.S.M., Silver Star, D.F.C., Bronze Star with 3 oak leaf clusters with V, Commendation medal with 3 oak leaf clusters and V, Joint Services Commendation medal, Purple Heart with oak leaf cluster, Legion of Merit with 2 oak leaf clusters, Air medal with V and 30 oak leaf clusters, Combat Inf. Badge with 2 stars (U.S.); Nat. Order 5th class; Distinguished Service Order; 4 Gallantry crosses; Honor medal 1st class; Air medal Vietnam; Def. medal Order of Republic Cambodia; Chapel of Four Chaplains-Legion of Honor. Mem. Oral History Assn., Soc. Study Mil. History, U.S. Commn. on Mil. History, Mil. Order World Wars (life), Am. Coun. for Study Islamic Socs., The Federalist Rsch. Inst. (bd. dirs.), Am. Legion, VFW, Airborne Assn. (life), 70th Divsn. Assn. (life), Assn. U.S. Army, Nat. Rifle Assn. (endowment mem.), 82d Airborne Divsn. Life Assn. (life), Am. Security Coun. (spkrs. bur.), Ends of the Earth, Scabbard and Blade (adv. coun. nat. soc.), Freedom Medicine (adv. bd.), Def. Policy Coun., Nat. Policy Forum, Am. Immigration Control (mem. adv. bd.), Clubs: Elks (Southern Pines), Army Navy (Washington); Tanglin (Singapore). Office: AZED Assocs Ltd PO Box 1643 Southern Pines NC 28388-1643

MATCHAR, DAVID BRUCE, internist, educator; b. Balt., Sept. 29, 1955; s. Joseph Charles and Evelyn (Wegman) M.; m. Barbara Fran Goldfinger, May 4, 1980; children: Emily Ruth, Benjamin Jacob, Daniel William. AB, Princeton U., 1976; MD cum laude, U. Md., 1980; postgrad., Duke U. Diplomate Am. Bd. Internal Medicine. Statistician Ctr. for Environ. Studies, Princeton, N.J., 1975; asst. statistician Ctr. for Disease Control, Atlanta, 1977; intern dept. medicine U. Md. Hosp., Balt., 1980, jr.; asst. resident dept. medicine, 1981; rsch. assoc. health svcs. rsch. and edn. VA Med. Ctr., Durham, N.C., 1985—; staff physician ambulatory care, 1985—, med. dir. hosp. home care, 1985-87; dir. Ctr. for Health, Policy Rsch and Edn. Duke U., Durham, N.C., 1988—, assoc. prof. Fellow ACP, Soc. Gen. Internal Medicine (pres. so. sect. 1988); mem. Am. Fedn. Clin. Rsch., Soc. for Med. Decision Making (editorial bd., chair 1993 ann.meeting, trustee). Am. Acad. Neurology. Office: Duke U Ctr Health Policy Rsch and Edn Durham NC 27708

MATCHETT, JANET REEDY, psychologist; b. Chgo., Sept. 2, 1926; d. Joseph Franklin and Minnie Mae (Burr) Reedy; m. Russell W. Kemerer, Jan. 20, 1949 (div. Aug. 1974); children: Brian Lee, Pamela Ann, Patricia Lynn, Bruce Reed, Bryce Jason; m. Charles Ernest Matchett, Nov. 17, 1984. BS summa cum laude, U. Pitts., 1974; MEd, Indiana U. of Pa., 1977, Ednl. Specialist, 1978; postgrad., U. Akron, U. Pitts., Pa. State U. Lic. psychologist; cert. sch. psychologist, Pa., Ohio, W.Va. Tchr. adult edn. Greensburg (Pa.)-Salem Sch. 1963-70; teaching cons. Peterson Systems, Inc., Greensburg, 1967-75, Ednl. Self-Devel., Inc., Greensburg, 1975-78; sch. psychologist Columbiana Bd. Edn., Lisbon, Ohio, 1979, Struthers (Ohio) City Schs., 1979-80; instr. Monroeville (Pa.) Sch. Bus., 1983; sch. psychologist Community Mental Health Ctr. of Beaver County, Rochester, Pa., 1983-84, South Side Area Sch. Dist., Hookstown, Pa., 1984-87, Blackhawk Sch. Dist., Beaver Falls, Pa., 1984—; instr. Pa. State U., New Kensington, 1984-86; substitute tchr. Greensburg (Pa.)-Salem Sch. Dist., 1975-83, long range planning com. 1981-82; cons. Allegheny East Mental Health/Mental Retardation Ctr., Monroeville, Pa., 1981-83, Westmoreland County Community Coll, Youngwood, Pa., 1981-83; sch. psychologist Wetzel County Schs., New Martinsville, W.Va., 1981; com. action team, strategic planning com. Blackhawk Sch. Dist., Beaver Falls, 1991—. Vol. Adelphi House, 1978; chmn. drug/alcohol abuse prevention program, City of Greensburg, 1981; troop leader Girl Scouts Am.; asst. den mother Boy Scouts Am.; ch. sch. tchr. United Meth. Ch., Greensburg; Bible sch. program vol. United Ch. of Christ, Greensburg; chmn. PTO, Greensburg. Mem. NEA, Nat. Assn. Sch. Psychologists, We. Pa. Assn. Sch. Psychologists, Assn. Sch. Psychologists Pa., Beaver County Sch. Psychologists Assn., Blackhawk Edn. Assn., Alpha Sigma Lambda. Republican. Avocations: reading, swimming, sewing, hiking, motorcycling, lecturing. Home: 48 W Manilla Ave Pittsburgh PA 15220-2838 Office: Blackhawk Sch Dist 635 Shenango Rd Beaver Falls PA 15010-1498

MATCHETT, WILLIAM H(ENRY), English literature educator; b. Chgo., Mar. 5, 1923; s. James Chapman and Lucy H. (Jipson) M.; m. Judith Wright, June 11, 1949; children: David H., Katherine C., Stephen C. BA with highest honors, Swarthmore Coll., 1949; MA, Harvard U., 1950, PhD, 1957. Teaching fellow Harvard U., Cambridge, Mass., 1953-54; instr. English lit. U. Wash., Seattle, 1954-56, asst. prof., 1956-61, assoc. prof., 1961-66, prof., 1966-82, prof. emeritus, 1982—. Author: The Phoenix and the Turtle, 1965, Fireweed, 1980; numerous poems; co-author: Poetry: From Statement to Meaning, 1965; editor: Modern Lang. Quar., Seattle, 1962-83. Mem. Soc. Friends. Home: 1017 Minor Ave Apt 702 Seattle WA 98104-1303

MATE, MARTIN, bishop; b. Port Rexton, Nfld., Can., Nov. 12, 1929; s. John and Hilda (Toope) M.; m. Florence Mabel Hooper, Nov. 12, 1962; children: Carolyn, Elizabeth, Phyllis, John, Carl. L.Th., Queens Coll., St. John's Nfld., 1953; B.A. with honors, Bishop's U., Que, 1966, M.A. with honors, 1967. Ordained deacon Anglican Ch. of Can., 1952, priest, 1953, elected bishop, 1980, consecrated, 1980. Curate Anglican Cathedral, St. John's, 1952-53; rector Pushthrough Parish, Nfld., 1953-58; incumbent St. Anthony Mission, Nfld., 1958-64; rector Cooksshire Parish, Que, 1964-67, Catalina Parish, Nfld., 1967-72, Pouch Cove Parish, Nfld., 1972-76; treas. Diocese of Eastern Nfld. and Labardor, St. John's, 1976-80; bishop Diocese of Eastern Nfld. and Labrador, St. John's, 1980—; mem. liturgical, programme, exec. and fin. coms. Anglican Diocese of Nfld. and Diocese of Eastern Nfld. and Labrador, 1972—; mem. provincial synod and provincial council Anglican Province of Can., 1975—; mem. gen. synod, nat. exec and adminstrn. and fin. com. Anglican Ch. of Can., 1975—. Home: 25 E Meadows Ave, Saint John's, NF Canada A1A 3M6 Office: Diocese of Eastern Nfld, & Labrador Anglican Ch, 19 Kings Bridge Rd, Saint John's, NF Canada A1C 3K4

MATEJU, JOSEPH FRANK, hospital administrator; b. Cedar Rapids, Iowa, Oct. 18, 1927; s. Joseph Frank and Adeline (Smid) M. B.A., U. N.Mex., 1951; M.A., N.Mex. State U., 1957. Sr. juvenile probation officer San Diego County, 1958-64; adminstr. Villa Solano State Sch., Hagerman, N.Mex., 1965-67; state coordinator on mental retardation planning N.Mex. Dept. Hosps. and Instns., Santa Fe, 1969-70; adminstr. Los Lunas (N.Mex.) Hosp. and Tng. Sch., 1968-69, 70-85. Bd. dirs. Mountain-Plains region Deaf-Blind Program. Served with USAAF, 1946-47. Fellow Am. Assn. Mental Deficiency; fellow Am. Coll. Nursing Home Adminstrs.; mem. Nat. Assn. Supts. Residential Facilities for Mentally Retarded, Assn. Mental Health Adminstrs., Am. Assn. Retarded Children, Albuquerque Assn. Retarded Citizens (1st v.p.), N.Mex. Hosp. Assn., Pi Gamma Mu. Home: 405 Fontana Pl NE Albuquerque NM 87108-1168 Office: PO Box 1269 Los Lunas NM 87031-1269

MATEKER, EMIL JOSEPH, JR., geophysicist; b. St. Louis, Apr. 25, 1931; s. Emil Joseph and Lillian (Broz) M.; m. Lolita Ann Winter, Nov. 25, 1954; children: Mark Steven, Anne Marie, John David. BS in Geophys. Engring., St. Louis U., 1956, MS in Rsch. Geophysics, 1959, PhD in Seismology, 1964. Registered geologist and geophysicist, Calif. Assoc. prof. geophysics Washington U., St. Louis, 1966-69; mgr. geophys. rsch. Western Geophys. Co. of Am., Houston, 1969-70; v.p. R & D Western Geophys. Co. of Am., 1970-74; pres. Litton Resources Sys., Houston, 1977, Litton Westrex, Houston, 1974-79; pres. Aero Svc. div. Western Geophys. Co. of Am., 1974-87, v.p. 1974-90; v.p. Western Atlas Internat., Inc., Houston, 1987—; pres. Aero Svc. div. Western Atlas Internat., Inc., Houston, 1987-90; v.p. tech. Western Geophys. div. Western Atlas Internat., Inc., Houston, 1990-93; pres. Western Atlas Software Divsn. Western Atlas Internat. Inc., Houston, 1993-94; sr. vice pres. Tech. We. Atlas Internat., Inc., 1994—; mem. State of Calif. Bd. Registration for Geophysicists, Sacramento, 1974—, State of Calif. Bd. Registration for Geologists, Sacramento, 1974—. Author: A Treatise on Modern Exploration Seismology, 2 vols., 1965; contbr. articles to profl. jours.; asst. editor Geophysica, 1969-70. Baseball mgr. Westchester High Sch., 1969-74; soccer coach Spring Forest Jr. High Sch., Houston, 1974; bd. dirs. St. Agnes Acad., Houston, 1977-82; pres. Strake Jesuits Booster Club, Houston, 1977-78. 2nd lt. U.S. Army, 1951-54. Recipient St. Louis U. Alumni award, 1976. Mem. AAAS, Am. Geophys. Union, Seismological Soc. Am., Geophys. Soc. Houston, European Assn. Exploration Geophysicists, Soc. Exploration Geophysicists (chmn. 1974). Roman Catholic. Avocations: racquetball, golf, literature, running, fishing. Home: 419 Hickory Post Ln Houston TX 77079-7430 Office: Western Atlas Software Div Western Atlas Internat 10205 Westheimer Rd Houston TX 77042-3115

MATELES, RICHARD ISAAC, biotechnologist; b. N.Y.C., Sept. 11, 1935; s. Simon and Jean (Phillips) M.; m. Roslyn C. Fish, Sept. 2, 1956; children: Naomi, Susan, Sarah. BS, MIT, 1956, MS, 1957, DSc, 1959. USPHS fellow Laboratorium voor Microbiologie, Technische Hogeschool, Delft, The Netherlands, 1959-60; mem. faculty MIT, 1960-70, assoc. prof. biochem. engring., 1965-68; dir. Fermentation unit MIT, Jerusalem, 1968-77; prof. applied microbiology Hebrew U., Hadassah Med. Sch., Jerusalem, 1968-80; vis. prof. dept. chem. engring. U. Pa., Phila., 1978-79; asst. dir. rsch. Stauffer Chem. Co., Westport, Conn., 1980, dir. rsch., 1980-81, v.p. rsch, 1981-88; sr. v.p. applied scis. IIT Rsch. Inst., Chgo., 1988-90; proprietor Candida Corp., Chgo., 1990—. Editor: Biochemistry of Some Foodborne Microbial Toxins, 1967, Single Cell Protein, 1968, Jour. Chem. Tech. and Biotech., 1972—; contbr. articles to profl. jours. Mem. Conn. Acad. Sci. Engring., 1981—; mem. vis. com., dept. applied biol. sci. MIT, 1980-88; mem. exec. com. Coun. on Chem. Rsch., 1981-85. Fellow Am. Inst. Med. and Biol. Engring.; mem. AICE, AAAS, SAR, Am. Chem. Soc., Am. Soc. Microbiology, Soc. for Gen. Microbiology U.K., Inst. Food Technologists, Soc. Chem. Ind. (U.K.) Union League, Sigma Xi. Home: 150 W Eugenie St # 46 Chicago IL 60614-5839 Office: 175 W Jackson Blvd Chicago IL 60604-2601

MATELIC, CANDACE TANGORRA, museum studies educator, consultant, museum director; b. Detroit, Aug. 21, 1952; d. Paul Eugene and Madeline Marie (Tangora) M.; m. Steven Joseph Mrozek, Sept. 17, 1983 (div. Sept. 1989); 1 child, Madeline Rose. BA, U. Mich., 1974; MA, SUNY, Oneonta, 1977. Interpretive specialist Living History Farms, Des Moines, 1978-80; mgr. adult edn. Henry Ford Mus./Greenfield Village, Dearborn, Mich., 1981-82, mgr. interpretive tng., 1982-84; dir., prof. mus. studies Cooperstown grad. program SUNY, Oneonta, 1986-94; exec. dir. Mission Houses Mus., Honolulu, 1994—; cons. history mus., 1979—; lectr., tchr. nat. and regional confs., workshops, seminars, 1979—; grant reviewer Nat. Endowment for the Humanities and Inst. for Mus. Svcs., Washington, 1982—. Author: (with others) Exhibition Reader, 1992; co-author: A Pictorical History of Food in Iowa, 1980, Survey of 1200-Plus Museum Studies Graduates, 1988; contbr. articles and videos on mus. interpretation and tng., 1979—; author conf. proceedings. Mem. Am. Assn. State and Local History (sec., bd. dirs. 1988—, program chmn. ann. meeting 1988), Assn. Living Hist. Farms and Agrl. Mus. (bd. dirs. 1980-88, pres. 1985), Midwest Open Air Mus. Coordinating Coun. (founder, bd. dirs., pres. 1978-80), Am. Assn. Mus. (mus. studies com. 1986—), Internat. Coun. Mus., Nat. Trust for Hist. Preservation. Democrat. Roman Catholic. Office: Mission Houses Mus 553 S King St Honolulu HI 96813

MATER, GENE P., communications consultant; b. N.Y.C., Nov. 27, 1926; s. Albert and Anne (Lande) M.; m. Jeanne M. Blanc, Mar. 7, 1947; children: Richard L., Gene A., Philip E. Student, Bklyn. Poly. Inst., 1943-44. Editor news agy., various newspapers Fed. Republic of Germany, 1946-48; reporter, county editor, city editor San Bernardino (Calif.) Sun-Telegram, 1949-53; copy editor, makeup editor, asst. night editor, news editor N.Y. World-Telegram & Sun, N.Y.C., 1953-59; news dir. Radio Free Europe, Munich, 1959-65; exec. v.p., sec. Radio Free Europe Fund, Inc., N.Y.C., 1965-70; spl. asst. to pres. Broadcast Group, CBS, Inc., N.Y.C., 1970-72, v.p., asst. to pres., 1972-80, sr. v.p., 1981-83; sr. v.p. CBS News, N.Y.C., 1983-84, v.p. internat. affairs, 1984-85; spl. asst. to dir. Commn. Bicentennial U.S. Constn., 1986; cons. communications, 1987—; v.p. broadcasting Internat. Media Fund, 1990—; guest columnist on communications issues Washington Journalism Rev., other pubs.; mem. U.S. Commn. on Broadcasting to the People's Republic of China, 1992. Mem. adv. bd. World Press Freedom Com., Ohio State Awards, Ctr. for the Book, Libr. of Congress, 1981-85; trustee Radio and Television News Dirs. Found. With AUS, 1944-46. Home: 4001 N 9th St # 708 Arlington VA 22203

MATERA, RICHARD ERNEST, minister; b. Hartford, Conn., July 13, 1925; s. Charles Carlo and Philomena Antoinette Cecile (Liberatore) M.; m. Marylynn Olga Beuth, Sept. 3, 1949; children: Thomas Charles, Nancy Jean Matera Dye. Student, Trinity Coll., Hartford, 1943, Biarritz Am. U. France, 1945; BA magna cum laude, Colgate U., 1949; MDiv, Andover Newton Theol. Sch., 1953; DD, Calif. Christian U., 1981. Ordained to ministry Bapt. Ch., 1952. Dir. youth work Quincy Point (Mass.) Congl. Ch., 1949-50; pastor, dir. vacation ch. sch. Panton and Addison (Vt.) chs., 1950; min. Thompson (Conn.) Hill Ch., 1950-51, Waldo Congl. Ch., Brockton, Mass., 1951-54, Cen. Congl. Ch., Orange, Mass., 1954-59; sr. min. 1st Congl. United Ch. of Christ, Berea, Ohio, 1959-71, St. Paul Community Ch., Homewood, Ill., 1971-76; interim min. United Ch. Christ, Chgo., 1978—; pres. Millers River Coun. Chs., 1957-58; mem. dept. ch. world responsibility Mass. Coun. Chs., 1957-59; chmn. internat. affairs com. of state social action com. United Ch. of Christ, 1962-63, del. Gen. Synod, Chgo., mem. peace priority task force Western Res. Assn., 1967-70, mem. commn. on ch. and ministry Ohio conf., 1968-71, chmn. dept. ch. and community Western Res. Assn. Coun., Cleve., 1969-70, mem. peace and internat. rels. com., 1973; mem. ad hoc com. on Vietnam Greater Cleve. Coun. of Chs. of Christ, 1966-68; probation officer DuPage County Probation Dept., Wheaton, Ill., 1985-86; interim min. Chgo. area, 1978—; Sauk Village United Ch. of Christ, 1978-80, Steger 1st Congregation, 1981-83, Forest Park, 1986-88, River

Grove Grace, 1989-91, Mont Clare Congregation, 1990-92, St. Nicolai, 1992—. Contbr. poetry to anthologies including Tears of Fire, 1994, A Break in the Clouds, 1994. Capt. Cleve. United Fund, 1961-63, Colgate Fund Dr., 1963; trustee Cleve. Union, 1961-63, Berea United Fund, 1963-69; mem. Berea Coun. on Human Rels., 1965-71, U.S. com. Christian Peace Conf., Prague, Czechoslovakia, 1967—, Nat. Arbor Day Found.; del. Action Conf. on Nat. Priorities, Washington, 1969; bd. dirs., mem. ecumenical mission com. Community Renewal Soc., Chgo., 1972-76; bd. dirs. Respond Now, Chicago Heights, Ill., 1972-78; mem. Pres.'s Coun., Chgo. Theol. Sem., 1973-81; pres. Mended Hearts Inc., Downers Grove, Ill., 1989-90. With U.S. Army Med. Corps., 1943-46, ETO. Austen Colgate scholar, 1946-49; recipient Harvard Book prize, 1942; name inscribed on The Wall of Liberty, Battle of Normandy Found., Normandy, France, 1994. Fellow Profl. Assn. Clergy, Acad. Parish Clergy; mem. Smithsonian Instn., Audubon Soc., Internat. Fellowship of Reconciliation, Internat. Soc. Poets, Nat. Libr. Poetry, Steinway Soc. Chgo., Planetary Soc., Jacques Cousteau Soc., Antique Automobile Club, Hupmobile Club, Cadillac Club, Phi Beta Kappa, Beta Theta Pi. Democrat. Avocations: drawing, poetry, astronomy, piano, working out at health club. Home and Office: 5 E Memorial Rd Bensenville IL 60106-2541 *From world philosophers, I have gleaned this: While borders stand, we are in prehistory. When all borders are gone, human history will begin.-Yevtushenko A person only has the right to do that which he agrees should become universal law.-Kant To do others as you want them to do to you.-Hebrew tchg. The human race is now capable of and ready for the above.*

MATERNA, THOMAS WALTER, ophthalmologist; b. Passaic, N.J., Oct. 24, 1944; s. Anthony and Ann (Popowich) M.; m. Jorunn Pauline Aronsen, Aug. 18, 1973; children: Richard C., Barbara L. BA, Coll. Holy Cross, Worcester, Mass., 1966; MD, SUNY, N.Y.C., 1971; MBA, Rutgers U., Newark, 1990. Diplomate Am. Bd. Ophthalmology. Intern N.Y. Hosp.-Cornell U. Med. Ctr., N.Y.C., 1971-72; resident N.Y. Eye and Ear Infirmary, N.Y.C., 1975-78; pvt. practice ophthalmology San Francisco, 1986; ophthalmologist N.J. Eye Physicians & Surgeons, Newark; pres., CEO US Try Zub Ent., Inc., Newark, Bizmore Internat., Inc., Luiv, Ukraine. Com. mem. N.J. Sch. for the Arts, Montclair, 1991—. Lt. USN, 1972-74, comdr. USNR, 1974—. Fellow ACS, Am. Acad. Ophthalmology; mem. Rotary, Army-Navy Club. Democrat. Roman Catholic. Avocations: coin collecting, rare document collecting, tennis, art history. Home: 87 Lorraine Ave Montclair NJ 07043-2304 Office: NJ Eye Physicians and Surgeons 20 Ferry St Newark NJ 07105-1420

MATEUS, LOIS, manufacturing executive; b. 1946. Grad., U. Ky., 1968. Asst. mgr. advt. Begley Drug, 1969-70; staff writer Commonwealth of Ky., 1970-72; dir. pub. rels. Ky. Dem. Party, 1973-75; exec. dir. Hist. Events Celebration Commn., 1976; free-lance writer, 1977-79; press sec., various other adminstrv. positions Gov. John Y. Brown of Ky., 1979-82; sr. v.p. corp. communications and corp. svcs. Brown-Forman Corp., Louisville, 1982—. Office: Brown-Forman Corp 850 Dixie Hwy Louisville KY 40210-1038

MATHAY, JOHN PRESTON, elementary education educator; b. Youngstown, Ohio, Jan. 27, 1942; s. Howard Ellsworth and Mary Clara (Siple) M.; m. Sandra Elizabeth Rhoades, June 9, 1973 (div. Jan. 1986); children: Elizabeth Anne, Sarah Susannah; m. Judith Anne Matthy, June 19, 1988; 1 child, Andrew Micah. B History, Va. Mil. Inst., Lexington, 1964; Cert. Teaching, Cleve. State U., 1972; postgrad., Mich. State U., 1964-65; MEd, Westminster Coll., New Wilmington, 1986. Cert. asst. supt., elem. tchr., elem. prin., high sch. prin. Cabinet maker Artisian Cabinet, Orwig Cabinets, Cleve. and Howland, Ohio, 1970-72; tchr. Urban Community Sch., Cleve., 1972-73, Pymatuning Valley Sch., Andover, Ohio, 1973—; cross country coach, 7th and 8th grade track coach, Andover. Bd. mem. Badger Sch. Bd., Kinsman, Ohio; trustee Kinsman Libr.; trustee, elder Kinsman Presbyn. Ch. Capt. U.S. Army Res., 1966-69. Martha Holden Jennings Found. scholar, Cleve., 1976. Mem. ASCD, Pymatuning Valley Edn. Assn. (pres. 1975-76, 91-92, 94-95), Ohio Edn. Assn., Am. Legion, Rotary (pres. 1991-92, sec. 1992-93, Paul Harris fellow), Masons (jr. deacon 1984-85, 32d deg., York Rite commandery), Ashtabula County Antique Engine Club, Phi Delta Kappa. Republican. Presbyterian. Avocations: sailing, skating, ham radio, fishing, reading. Home: 8424 Main St Kinsman OH 44428-9409 Office: Pymatuning Valley Schs W Main St Andover OH 44003

MATHENY, CHARLES WOODBURN, JR., retired army officer, retired civil engineer, former city official; b. Sarasota, Fla., Aug. 7, 1914; s. Charles Woodburn Sr. and Virginia (Yates) M.; m. Jeanne Felkel, July 12, 1942; children: Virginia Ann, Nancy Caroline, Charles Woodburn III. BSCE, U. Fla., 1936; grad., Army Command and Gen. Staff Coll., 1944. Lic. commi. pilot. Sanitary engr. Ga. State Dept. Health, 1937-39; civil engr. Fla. East Coast Ry., 1939-41; commd. 2d lt. F.A., USAR, 1936, 2d lt. F.A. U.S. Army, 1942, advanced through grades to col, 1955; field arty. bn. comdr., Fed. Republic of Germany, 1945-46, staff officer, 1947; gen. staff G-3 Plans Dept. Army, 1948-51; qualified Air Force liaison pilot, 1951; qualified Army aviator, 1952; aviation officer 25th Inf. Div., Korea, 1952-53; sr. Army aviation advisor Korean Army, 1953; dep. commdt., dir. combat devel. Army Aviation Sch., 1954-55; dep. dir. research, dep. dir. dept. tactics Arty. Sch., 1955-57; aviation officer 7th U.S. Army, Germany, 1957-58; Munich sub area comdr. So. Area Command, Europe, 1958-59, qualified sr. army aviator, 1959, dep. chief staff for info. So. Area Command, 1960; Mich. sector comdr. VI Army Corps, 1961-62; ret., 1962; asst. dir. Tampa (Fla.), Dept. Pub. Works 1963-77, asst. to dir., 1977-81, ret., 1981. Initiator tact. use of helicopters in Army and army warrant officer aviator program, 1949, army combat units equipped with helicopter mobility, 1950; pilot 1st combat observation mission in army helicopter, Korea, 1952; organizer, comdr., helicopter pilot 1st Army combat ops. using helicopter mobility to support inf. and engr. front line units 25th Inf. Div., Korea, 1952; pilot 100 combat observation missions, Korea, 1952-53; author 1st state legis. to establish profl. sch. civil engring. for state of Fla., 1974. Contbr. numerous articles on tactical use of helicopter aerial vehicles to mags. Mem. troop com. Boy Scouts Am., 1965-73; active various community and ch. activities; patron Tampa Art Mus., 1965-83, Tampa Community Concert Series, 1979-82; bd. dirs. Tampa YMCA, 1967-71, Fla. Easter Seal Soc., 1978, Easter Seal Soc. Hillsborough County, 1971-84, hon. bd. dirs. 1984—, treas., 1973-76, pres., 1977. Decorated Bronze Star with oak leaf cluster, Air medal with three oak leaf clusters; named to U. Fla. Student Hall of Fame, 1936. Mem. ASCE (pres. West Coach br., Fla. sect. 1973, Engr. of Yr. award West Coast br. Fla. sect. 1979, life mem. 1980), Am. Soc. Profl. Engrs., Fla. Engring. Soc., Am. Pub. Works Assn. (pres. West Coast br. Fla. chpt. 1972, exec. com. Fla. chpt 1972-77, v.p. 1977, pres. 1978), Ret. Officers Assn., Army Aviation Assn., SAR, Fla. Blue Key, Alpha Tau Omega. Episcopalian. Lodge: Kiwanis. Home: 4802 W Beachway Dr Tampa FL 33609-4836

MATHENY, EDWARD TAYLOR, JR., lawyer; b. Chgo., July 15, 1923; s. Edward Taylor and Lina (Pinnell) M.; m. Marion Elizabeth Shields, Sept. 10, 1947; children: Nancy Elizabeth, Edward Taylor III.; m. Ann Spears, Jan. 14, 1984. B.A., U. Mo., 1944; J.D., Harvard, 1949. Bar: Mo. 1949. Pvt. practice Kansas City, 1949-91; ptnr. firm Blackwell, Sanders, Matheny, Weary & Lombardi, 1954-91, of counsel, 1991—; pres. St. Luke's Hosp. Found., Kansas City, 1980-95. Pres. Cmty. Svc. Broadcasting of Mid-Am., Inc., 1971-72; chmn. Citizens Assn. Kans City, 1958; chmn. bd. dirs. St. Luke's Found., Kansas City, 1980-95; trustee U. Kansas City., Kansas City Cmty. Found., 1983-94, Eye Found. Kansas City. Served to lt. (j.g.) USNR, 1944-46. Mem. Kansas City Bar Assn., Mo. Bar, River Club, Mission Hills Country Club, Phi Beta Kappa, Sigma Chi (Balfour Nat. award 1944). Episcopalian (chancellor Diocese West Mo. 1971-89). Home: 2510 Grand Ave Kansas City MO 64108-2626 Office: 2300 Main St Kansas City MO 64108-2415

MATHENY, ROBERT LAVESCO, history educator, former university president; b. Lubbock, Tex., Jan. 15, 1933; s. Samuel Worth and Elsie Jane (Jones) M.; m. Sandra Hansen, July 6, 1973; children: Nelda, Monica, Cali. B.A., Eastern N.Mex. U., 1961, M.A., 1962; Ph.D., U. Ariz., 1975. Asst. prof. Eastern N.Mex. U., Portales, 1968-72, assoc. prof., 1972-76, v.p Clovis campus, 1977-80, exec. v.p, 1981-83, pres., 1983-89, prof. dept. history, 1989—, dir. devel. and govt. rels., 1989—; dean continuing edn. Ft. Hays State U., Hays, Kans., 1980-81. Rockfellow Found. fellow, 1967-68. Mem. Western History Assn. Club: N.Mex. Amigos. Lodge: Rotary

(Portales). Office: Eastern New Mexico U Office of Devel Portales NM 88130

MATHENY, RUTH ANN, editor; b. Fargo, N.D., Jan. 17, 1918; d. Jasper Gordon and Mary Elizabeth (Carey) Wheelock; m. Charles Edward Matheny, Oct. 24, 1960. B.E., Mankato State Coll., 1938; M.A., U. Minn., 1955; postgrad., Universidad Autonoma de Guadalajara, Mex., summer 1956, Georgetown U., summer, 1960. Tchr. in U.S. and S.Am., 1938-61; asso. editor Charles E. Merrill Pub. Co., Columbus, Ohio, 1963-66; tchr. Confraternity Christian Doctrine, Washington Court House, Ohio, 1969-70; assoc. editor Jr. Cath. Messenger, Dayton, Ohio, 1966-68; editor Witness Intermediate, Dayton, 1968-70; editor in chief, assoc. pub. Today's Cath. Tchr., Dayton, 1970—; editor in chief Catechist, Dayton, 1976-89, Edn. Dealer, Dayton, 1976-80; v.p. Peter Li, Inc., Dayton, 1980—. Editorial collaborator: Dimensions of Personality series, 1969—; co-author: At Ease in the Classroom; author: Why a Catholic School?, Scripture Stories for Today: Why Religious Education?. Mem. Bd. Friends Ormond Beach Library. Mem. Nat. League Am. Pen Women, Nat. Coun. Cath. Women, Cath. Press Assn., Nat. Cath. Edni. Assn.; 3d Order St. Francis (eucharistic minister 1990—). Home: 26 Reynolds Ave Ormond Beach FL 32174-7043 Office: Peter Li Inc 330 Progress Rd Dayton OH 45449-2322 *In a world that is constantly changing, a strong religious faith is a dependable compass through which we are able to stay on a positive, forward course.*

MATHENY, TOM HARRELL, lawyer; b. Houston; s. Whitman and Lorene (Harrell) M. BA, Southeastern La. U., 1954; JD, Tulane U., 1957; LLD (hon.), Centenary Coll., 1979, DePauw U.; LHD (hon.), Oklahoma City U. Bar: La. 1957. Ptnr. Matheny & Pierson, Hammond, La., 1957—; gen. counsel First Guaranty Bank, 1960-83; trust counsel, chmn. bd. 1st Guaranty Bank, Hammond; v.p. Edwards & Assocs., So. Brick Supply, Inc.; faculty Southeastern La. U., 5 yrs., Holy Cross Coll., New Orleans, 3 yrs.; lectr. Union Theol. Sem., Law Sci. Acad.; mem. com. on conciliation and mediation of disputes World Peace through Law Ctr. Chmn. advancement com. Boy Scouts Am., Hammond, 1960-64, mem. dist. coun., 1957-66, mem. exec. bd. Istrouma coun., 1966—, adv. com. to dist. area coun.; past pres. Tangipahoa Parish Mental Health Assn.; pres. La. Mental Health Assn., 1989—; mem. La. Mental Health Advocacy Svc.; co-chmn. La. Mental Health Advocacy Bd.; sec. Chep Morrison Scholarship Found.; mem. men's com. Japan Internat. Christian U. Found.; chmn. speakers com., mem. com. on community action and crime prevention, La. Commn. on Law Enforcement and Adminstrn. Criminal Justice; campaign mgr. for Dem. gov. La., 1959-60, 63-64; bd. dirs. La. Moral and Civic Found., Tangipahoa Parish ARC, 1957-67, Hammond United Givers Fund, 1957-68, La. Coun. Chs., Southeastern Devel. Found., La. Mental Health Assn.; bd. dirs. Wesley Found., La. State U., 1965-68, 70—, chmn. bd.; trustee Centenary Coll., 1964-70, Scarritt Coll., 1975-81; pres., bd. trustees Lallie Kemp Hosp. Found., 1994—; hon. trustee John F. Kennedy Coll.; del. world conf. Nat. Assn. Conf. Lay Leaders, London, 1966, Denver, 1971, Dublin, 1976, Hawaii, 1981, del. to gen. confs., 1968, 70, 72; mem. Common Cause. Recipient Man of Yr. award Hammond, 1961, 64, also La. Jaycees, 1964, Layman of Yr. award La. Ann. Conf. United Meth. Ch., 1966, 73, Disting. Alumnus award Southeastern La. U., 1981, W.L. "Bill" May Outstanding Christian Bus. award La. Moral and Civic Found., 1986. Fellow Harry S. Truman Libr. Inst (hon.); mem. ABA (com. on probate), La. Bar Assn. (past gen. chmn. com. on legal aid, com. prison reform), 21st Jud. Dist. Bar Assn. (past sec.-treas., v.p. 1967-68, 71), Comml. Law League Am. (past mem. com. on ethics), La. Alumni Coun. (pres. 1963-65), Acad. Religion and Mental Health, La. Assn. Claimant Compensation Attys., Southeastern La. U. Alumni Assn. (dir., pres. 1961-62, dir. spl. fund 1959-62, dir. Tongipahoa chpt.), Tulane Sch. Law Alumni Assn., Assn. Trial Lawyers Am., Am. Judicature Soc., Law-Sci. Inst., World Peace Through Law Acad. (com. on conciliation), Acad. Polit. Sci., Am. Acad. Polit. and Social Sci., Internat. Acad. Law and Sci., Internat. Platform Assn., UN Assn. Am. Trial Lawyers Assn., La. Hist. Assn., Friends of Cabildo, Gideons Internat., Hammond Assn. Commerce (dir. 1960-65), Intern Soc. Barristers, Intern Assn. Valuers, La. Mental Health Assn. (pres.-elect), Masons (33 degree), Demolay (dist. dep. to supreme coun. 1964—, Legion of Honor), Kiwanis (v.p., dir., Layman of Yr. award 1972), Rotary, Phi Delta Phi, Phi Alpha Delta. Democrat. Methodist. Lodges: Masons, Scottish Rite (33 degree), Demolay (dist. dep. to supreme council 1964—, Legion of Honor), Kiwanis (v.p., dir., Layman of Yr. award for La., Miss. and West Tenn. 1972), Rotary. Home: PO Box 221 Hammond LA 70404-0221 Office: PO Box 1598 401 E Thomas St Hammond LA 70404

MATHER, ALLEN FREDERICK, lawyer; b. Kansas City, Mo., Apr. 28, 1922; s. William Frederick and Alberta (Stephenson) M.; m. Patricia T. Mitchell, June 23, 1972; children—Allen Frederick, Nathaniel J., J. Miles Mitchell. A.B., Colgate U., 1943; LL.B., Harvard, 1949. Bar: Calif. bar 1953. With Agrl. Council of Calif., Sacramento, 1950-57; exec. sec. Agrl. Council of Calif., 1954-57; gen. counsel Sunkist Growers, Los Angeles, 1958-66; pres. Sun-Maid Raisin Growers of Calif., Kingsburg, 1966-72, Sunland Marketing, Inc., Menlo Park, Calif., 1971-72, First Nat. Bank Fresno, Calif., 1973-77; mem. firm Wild, Carter, Tipton & Oliver, 1977-84; mng. partner Agribus. Group, 1977—. Mem. Calif. Industry and World Trade Commn., 1969—; pres. Sequoia council Boy Scouts Am., 1969—. Served with USNR, 1943-46. Mem. Dried Fruit Assn. (dir.), Fresno C. of C. (dir.). Club: Sunnyside Country (Fresno). Home: 5962 E Hamilton Ave Fresno CA 93727-6228 Office: 1713 Tulare St Ste 107 Fresno CA 93721-2528

MATHER, BARBARA W., lawyer; b. Lancaster, Pa., 1944. BA with high honors, Swarthmore Coll., 1965; JD, U. Chgo. 1968. Bar: Pa. 1969. City solicitor City of Phila., 1984-85; mng. ptnr. Pepper, Hamilton & Scheetz, Phila. Fellow Am. Coll. Trial Lawyers. Office: Pepper Hamilton & Scheetz 3000 Two Logan Sq 18 Arch St Philadelphia PA 19103

MATHER, BETTY BANG, musician, educator; b. Emporia, Kans., Aug. 7, 1927; d. Read Robinson and Shirley (Smith) Bang; m. Roger Mather, Aug. 3, 1973. MusB, Oberlin Conservatory, 1949; MA, Columbia U., 1951. Instr. U. Iowa, Iowa City, 1953-58, asst. prof., 1959-65, assoc. prof., 1965-73, prof., 1973—; editor Romney Press; vis. instr. U. Iowa, Iowa City, 1952-53. Rec. artist; author: Interpretation of French Music from 1675-1775, 1973, (with David Lasocki) Free Ornamentation for Woodwind Instruments from 1700-1775, 1976, (with David Lasocki) The Classical Woodwind Cadenza, 1978, (with David Lasocki) The Art of Preluding, 1985, (with Dean Karns) Dance Rhythms of the French Baroque, 1987; editor: 30 Virtuosic Selections in the Gallant Style for Unaccompanied Flute, 1975, others; contbr. articles to profl. publs. Mem. Nat. Flute Assn. (v.p. 1986-87, pres. 1987-88, chmn. bd. dirs. 1988-89). Home: 308 4th Ave Iowa City IA 52245

MATHER, BRYANT, research administrator; b. Balt., Dec. 27, 1916; s. Leon Bryant and Julia (Ferguson) M.; m. Katharine Selden Kniskern, Mar. 27, 1940 (dec. Feb. 1991). Grad., Balt. City Coll., 1934; A.B. in Geology, Johns Hopkins, 1936, postgrad., 1936-38; postgrad., Am. U., 1938-39; D.Sc. (hon.), Clarkson U., 1978. Curator mineralogy Chgo. Mus. Natural History, 1939-41; with U.S. Army Corps Engrs., 1941—; geologist Central Concrete Lab., U.S. Mil. Acad., 1941-42, Mt. Vernon, N.Y., 1942-43; supervisory research civil engr., chief engring. scis. br., concrete lab. (Waterways Expt. Sta.), Vicksburg, Miss., 1946-65; asst. chief concrete lab. (Waterways Expt. Sta.), 1965-66, chief, 1966-76, acting chief structures lab., 1978-80, chief lab., 1980-92, dir. structures lab., 1992—; rsch. assoc. Fla. Dept. Agr. and Consumer Svcs., 1968—, Miss. Mus. Natural Scis., 1979—, Miss. Ent. Mus. Miss. State U., 1985—, Am. Mus. Natural History, N.Y.C., Fla. Dept. Agrl. and Consumer Svcs., Gainesville; charter mem. U.S. Sr. Exec. Svc., 1979—; mem. Sr. Exec. Assn., 1980—; mem. U.S. Com. of Internat. Commn. Large Dams, 1959—; lectr. Purdue U., 1961, Old Master lectr. 1991; lectr. U. Notre Dame, 1964, MIT, 1966, Clemson U., 1967; Henry M. Shaw lectr. N.C. State U., 1967, U. Wis., 1978—, U. of Tex., 1987, Okla. State U., 1987, Johns Hopkins U., 1991, Utah State, 1995; Stanton Walker lectr. U. Md., 1969; Edgar Marburg lectr. ASTM, 1970; mem. 4th, 5th, 6th and 7th Internat. Symposia Chemistry Cement, Internat. Symposium Movement Water in Porous Bodies, Paris, 1964. Co-author: Butterflies of Mississippi, 1958; Editor: Handbook for Concrete and Cement, 1942, 49, also quar. supplements, 1949—. Recipient Meritorious Civilian Svc. award, 1965, Exceptional Civilian Svc. award, 1968, with laurel-leaf cluster, 1991, Civilian of Yr. award C.E., 1992, Disting. Rsch. award Aggregates Found. for Tech., Rsch. and Engring., 1995. Fellow AAAS, ASTM (sec. com. C-9 1952-60, chmn.

1960-66, chmn. com. C-1 1968-74, chmn. com. E-39 1973-75, dir. 1970-73, v.p. 1973-75, pres. 1975-76, Award of Merit 1959, Sanford E. Thompson award 1961, Frank E. Richart award 1972, William T. Cavanaugh award 1990), Transp. Rsch. Bd., NAS-NRC (chmn. Concrete Divsn. 1963-69, chmn. Curing com. 1970-76, Roy W. Crum Disting. Svc. award 1966, 2nd Disting. Lectr. 1993), Inst. Concrete Technologists (Eng.) (hon. 1982); mem. NAE, ASCE (hon. mem. 1988), AIME, Entomol. Soc. Am., Am. Concrete Inst. (pres. 1964, Henry C. Turner medal 1973, Charles S. Whitney medal 1974, Robert E. Philleo award 1992, Delmar L. Bloem award 1990, hon. mem.), Entomol. Soc. Md., Mich. Entomol. Soc., Meteoretical Soc. Md., Mich. Entomol. Soc., Meteoretical Soc., Natural Hist. Soc. Md., Orleans County (Vt.) Hist. Soc., Lepidopterists Soc., Miss. Acad. Sci., Miss. Gem and Mineral Soc., Am. Mus. Natural History (hon. mem. 1968, hon. patron 1974, rsch. assoc. 1979—), So. Lepidopterists Soc., Soc. Ky. Lepidopterists, Metall. and Petroleum Engrs. (Legion of Honor), Mencken Soc., Phi Beta Kappa, Sigma Xi. Home: 213 Mount Salus Dr Clinton MS 39056-5007 Office: US Army Engr Waterways Expt Sta Structures Lab 3909 Halls Ferry Rd Vicksburg MS 39180-6133 *The production of hydraulic-cement concrete—a synthetic sedimentary rock, may be the human race's most successful attempt to reproduce an activity previously engaged in only by God; and we have done it better; there are more varieties and there is better uniformity.*

MATHER, ELIZABETH VIVIAN, health care executive; b. Richmond, Ind., Sept. 19, 1941; d. Willie Samuel and Lillie Mae (Harper) Fuqua; m. Roland Donald Mather, Dec. 26, 1966. BS, Maryville (Tenn.) Coll., 1963; postgrad., Columbia U., 1965-66. Tchr. Richmond Community Schs., 1963-67, Indpls. Pub. Schs., 1967-68; systems analyst Ind. Blue Cross Blue Shield, Indpls., 1968-71, Ind. Nat. Bank, Indpls., 1971; med. cons. Ind. State Dept. Pub. Welfare, Indpls., 1971-78, cons. supr., 1978-86; systems analyst Ky. Blue Cross Blue Shield, Louisville, 1988-89; contracts specialist Humana Corp., Louisville, 1989—. Active Rep. Cen. Com. Montgomery County, Crawfordsville, 1976-86, Centenary Meth. Ch., adminstrv. bd., 1990. Mem. DAR (treas. 1963-66, sec. 1978-86). Avocations: designing and sewing clothes. Home: 6106 Partridge Pl Floyds Knobs IN 47119-9427 Office: Humana Corp 500 W Main St Louisville KY 40201-1438

MATHER, JOHN CROMWELL, astrophysicist; b. Roanoke, Va., Aug. 7, 1946; s. Robert Eugene and Martha Belle (Cromwell) M.; m. Jane Anne Hauser, Nov. 22, 1980. BA, Swarthmore (Pa.) Coll., 1968; PhD, U. Calif., Berkeley, 1974; DS (hon.), Swarthmore Coll., 1994. NAS/NRC rsch. assoc. NASA/Goddard Inst. for Space Studies, N.Y.C., 1974-76; lectr. in astronomy Columbia U., N.Y.C., 1975-76; astrophysicist NASA/Goddard Space Flight Ctr., Greenbelt, Md., 1976—, head infrared astrophysics br., 1988-89, 90-93, sr. scientist, 1989-90, 93—, study scientist Cosmic Background Explorer Satellite., 1976-82, project scientist COBE, 1982—, prin. investigator FIRAS on COBE, 1976—; chmn. external adv. bd. Ctr. for Astrophys. Rsch. in the Antarctic, U. Chgo., 1992—; mem. lunar astrophysics mgmt. ops. working group NASA Hdqrs., Washington, 1992. Contbr. over 50 articles to profl. jours. Recipient Space Sci. award AIAA, 1993, Nat. Space Achievement award Rotary, 1991, Laurels award Aviation Week and Space Tech., 1992, Goddard fellow, 1994—. Mem. Am. Astron. Soc. (Dannie Heineman prize astrophysics 1993), Am. Phys. Soc., Internat. Astron. Union, Sigma Xi. Democrat. Unitarian. Achievements include proposed Cosmic Background Explorer Satellite, led team to successful launch in 1989, measured spectrum of cosmic microwave background radiation to unprecedented accuracy. Office: NASA/Goddard Space Flight Code G85 Greenbelt MD 20771

MATHER, JOHN NORMAN, mathematics educator; b. L.A., June 9, 1942; s. Norman Wells and Mary Adele (Clark) M.; m. Naomi W. Shelley; children: Mara, Thomas, Franklin, Emily. Ba, Harvard U., 1964; PhD, Princeton U., 1967. Vis. prof. Inst. des Hautes Etudes, Bures-sur-Yvette, France, 1967-69; assoc. prof. Harvard U., Cambridge, Mass., 1969-71, prof. mathematics, 1971-74; prof. Princeton (N.J.) U., 1974—. Contbr. articles to profl. jours. Mem. Am. Math. Soc., NAS (John J. Carty award 1976). Achievements include proved R. Thom's conjectures concerning structural stability of differentiable mappings; contributions to the theory of foliations; discovery of action minimizing orbits in the theory of dynamics of area preserving mappings. Office: Princeton U Washington Rd Princeton NJ 08540-6431

MATHER, JOHN RUSSELL, climatologist, educator; b. Boston, Oct. 9, 1923; s. John and Mabelle (Russell) M.; m. Amy L. Nelson, 1946; children: Susan, Thomas, Ellen. BA, Williams Coll., 1945; BS in Meteorology, MIT, 1947, M.S., 1948; Ph.D. in Geography-Climatology, Johns Hopkins U., 1951. Rsch. assoc., climatologist Lab. Climatology, Seabrook, N.J., 1948-54; prin. rsch. scientist Lab. Climatology, Centerton, N.J., 1954-63; pres. Lab. Climatology, C.W. Thornthwaite Assoc., Centerton, 1963-72; asst. prof. Johns Hopkins U., 1951-53; assoc. prof. climatology Drexel Inst. Tech., Phila., 1957-60; prof. geography U. Del., Newark, 1963—; chmn. dept. geography U. Del., 1966-89; state climatologist Del., 1978-92; vis. lectr. geography U. Chgo., 1957-61; vis. prof. U.S. Mil. Acad., 1989. Author 2 books on applied climatology, 1 book on water resources; U.S. editor joint U.S.-USSR book on global change; contbr. numerous articles to tech. jours. Fellow AAAS; mem. Am. Meteorol. Soc., Assn. Am. Geographers (v.p. 1990-91, pres. 1991-92), Am. Geog. Soc. (councilor 1981—, sec. 1982—), Am. Water Resources Assn., Tau Beta Pi, Phi Kappa Phi. Contributed to concept of potential evapotranspiration, its measurement, use in climatic water balance; moisture factor in climate; application of climatic water balance to studies in agr., hydrology, applied climatology. Home: 378 Daretown Rd Elmer NJ 08318 Office: U Del Dept Geography Newark DE 19716

MATHER, MILDRED EUNICE, retired archivist; b. Washington, Iowa, July 25, 1922; d. Hollis John and Delpha Irene (Cummings) Whiting; m. Stewart Elbert Mather, Aug. 7, 1955; children: Julie Marie, Thomas Stewart (dec.). Cert. bus sch., Burlington and Des Moines (Iowa), 1941, 1947; cert., Stenotype Inst., 1948. Typist Burlington Willow-Weave, 1941-42, Burlington Basket Co., 1942; clk. typist U.S. Dept. War, Washington, 1942-43; supr. internat. cont. Dept. State, Washington, 1949-52; bookkeeper Iowa Wesleyan Coll., Mt. Pleasant, 1952-55; clk. typist Herbert Hoover Presdl. Libr., West Branch, Iowa, 1964-69; archives technician Herbert Hoover Presdl. Libr., West Branch, 1964-72, archivist, 1972-92. WAC, 1943-46. Mem. Order of Eastern Star (worthy matron). Republican. Home: 79 Eisenhower St West Branch IA 52358-9403

MATHER, RICHARD BURROUGHS, retired Chinese language and literature educator; b. Baoding, Hebei, China, Nov. 11, 1913; s. William Arnot and Grace (Burroughs) M.; m. Virginia Marjorie Temple, June 3, 1939; 1 dau., Elizabeth Temple. B.A., Princeton U., 1935; B.Th., Princeton Theol. Sem., 1939; Ph.D. in Oriental Langs., U. Calif., Berkeley, 1949. Ordained to ministry United Presbyterian Ch. U.S., 1939; pastor Belle Haven (Va.) Presbyterian Ch., 1939-41; asst. prof. Chinese U. Minn., Mpls., 1949-57; assoc. prof. Chinese U. Minn., 1957-64, prof., 1964-84; mem. Am. Council Learned Socs. Com. on Study of Chinese Civilization, 1979-81. Author: Shih-shuo hsin-yu, A New Account of Tales of the World, 1976, The Poet Shen Yueh (441-513), the Reticent Marquis, 1988; contbr. articles on medieval Chinese lit. and religion. Guggenheim fellow, 1956-57; Fulbright Hays grantee, 1956-57, 63-64; Am. Council Learned Socs. grantee, 1963-64. Mem. Am. Oriental Soc. (pres. 1980-81), Assn. Asian Studies, Chinese Lang. Tchrs. Assn. Democrat. Home: 2091 Dudley Ave Saint Paul MN 55108-1415

MATHER, ROGER FREDERICK, music educator, freelance technical writer; b. London, England, May 27, 1917; came to U.S., 1938; s. Richard and Marie Louise (Schultze) M.; m. Dorothea Meinen, Sept. 11, 1943 (div. Sept. 1971); children: Arielle Diane, Christopher Richard; m. Betty Louise Bang, Aug. 3, 1973. BA with honors, Cambridge U., 1938; MSc, MIT, 1940; MA in Metallurgy, U. Cambridge, 1941. Registered profl. engr., Ohio, Mich., Pa. Rsch. metallurgist Inland Steel Co., East Chicago, Ind., 1940-42; chief metallurgist Willys-Overland Motors, Toledo, 1942-46, Kaiser-Frazer Corp., Willow Run, Mich., 1946-50; project mgr. U.S. Steel Corp., Pitts., 1950-61; dir. rsch. engring. Mine Safety Appliances Co., Pitts., 1961-62; rsch. staff Du Pont Co., Wilmington, Del., 1962-63; chief nuclear power tech. br. NASA, Cleve., 1963-73; adj. prof. music U. Iowa, Iowa City, 1973—; instr.

pub. speaking and stage fright U. Iowa, 1983—, Kirkwood C.C., Iowa City, 1983—; cons. Miyazawa Flutes, U.S.A., Coralville, Iowa, 1985-90; lectr. U. Toledo; Mich. state examiner Registration of Profl. Engrs.; condr. numerous workshops, clinics, classes, and flute recitals regionally, nationally, and abroad. Author: The Art of Playing the Flute, 1980, 2d vol., 1981; author chpts. in Woodwind Anthology and Fluting and Dancing; pub., exec. editor The Romney Press, 1980—; contbr. numerous articles to sci. and music jours. Mem. Nat. Flute Assn. (life, cons.), Nat. Assn. Coll. Wind and Percussion Instrs., Am. Mus. Instrument Soc., Nat. Assn. Mus. Instruments Techs., Am. Recorder Soc., Galpin Soc., Brit. Flute Soc., Soc. Automotive Engrs., AIME, Am. Soc. Metals, ASTM, ASME, AIAA, Soc. Experimental Stress Analysis, Air Force Assn., Army Ordnance Assn., NAM (rsch. com.), The Pa. Assn., Mensa. Episcopalian. Avocations: high fidelity sound reproduction, photography. Home: 308 4th Ave Iowa City IA 52245-4613 Office: U Iowa Sch Music Iowa City IA 52242

MATHER, ROLAND DONALD, judge; b. New Albany, Ind., Oct. 1, 1939; s. Howard Milton and Elizabeth Ann (Fisher) M.; m. Elizabeth Vivian Fuqua, Dec. 26, 1966. BS, Ind. State U., 1963; MA, Ball State U., 1967; JD, Ind. U., 1972; postgrad., Nat. Jud. Coll., 1977-92; grad., Ind. Jud. Coll., 1981. Bar: Ind. 1972, U.S. Dist. Ct. 1972. Tchr. Richmond (Ind.) Community Schs., 1963-67, Indpls. Pub. Schs., 1967-68; asst. dir. consumer protection div. Ind. Atty. Gen., Indpls., 1970-72, asst. atty. gen., dir. consumer protection div., 1972-75; county judge Montgomery County, Crawfordsville, Ind., 1976-84; U.S. adminstrv. law judge Office of Hearing and Appeals, Pitts., 1986-88, Louisville, 1988—. Mem. ABA, Ind. Bar Assn., Assn. Adminstrv. Law Judges. Republican. Methodist. Home: 6106 Partridge Pl Floyds Knobs IN 47119-9427 Office: Office Hearing Appeals SSA 332 W Broadway Ste 1402 Louisville KY 40202-2119

MATHER, STEPHANIE J., lawyer; b. Kansas City, Mo., Dec. 5, 1952; d. Edward Wayne and H. June (Kunkel) M.; m. Miles Christopher Zimmerman, Sept. 23, 1988. BA magna cum laude, Okla. City U., 1975, JD with honors, 1980. Lawyer Pierce, Couch, Hendrickson, Johnston & Baysinger, Okla. City, Okla., 1980-88, Manchester, Hiltgen & Healy, P.C., Okla. City, 1989-90; sr. staff counsel Nat. Am. Ins. Co., Chandler, Okla., 1990—; asst. v.p. Lagere & Walkingstick Ins. Agy., Inc., Chandler, Okla., 1993—. Co-chair Lincoln County Dem. Party, 1991-92, 95—; v.p. Lincoln Co. Dem. Women, 1992—; dir. Lincoln County Partnership for Children, 1994—. Mem. Okla. Bar Assn.(editor bd. of editors, 1992—), Lincoln County Bar Assn. (mem. library bd. 1990—), Lincoln County Profl. Women. Democrat. Avocations: reading, genealogy, ranching, cooking. Home: PO Box 246 Chandler OK 74834 Office: Nat Am Ins Co PO Drawer 9 Chandler OK 74834

MATHERLEE, THOMAS RAY, health care and financial services executive; b. Dayton, Ohio, Sept. 18, 1934; s. Dennis R. and Eleanor E. Matherlee; B.S. in Bus. Adminstrn. Findlay Coll., 1958; M.B.A., U. Chgo., 1960; m. Ann Deverka; children: Michael, Jennifer, Craig, Brent, Brian. Adminstrv. resident Shannon Hosp., San Angelo, Tex., 1959-60; asst. adminstr. Richland Meml. Hosp., Olney, Ill., 1960-61; adminstrv. asst., then adminstr. Forsyth Meml. Hosp., Winston-Salem, N.C., 1961-68; exec. dir. Gaston County (N.C.) Hosp., Gastonia, N.C.; exec. dir. Gaston Meml. Hosp., Inc., Gastonia, 1970-80, pres., 1981-85; sr. v.p. Vol. Hosps. of Am. Inc., Washington, 1986-87, exec. v.p., Irving, Tex., 1987-90; pres. AMA Svcs., Inc., 1990-94; sr. v.p. The Hunter Group, 1991—; cons. Sch. Pastoral Care N.C. Bapt. Hosp., Winston-Salem, 1967-68; mem. sub-area adv. coun. Health Systems Agy., 1975-80; adj. faculty Sch. Community and Allied Health, U. Ala.-Birmingham, 1980-85; bd. dirs. Joint Commn. on Accreditation of Healthcare Orgns., 1986-90, treas., audit and fin. com. chmn., mem. exec. com. Dir. Olney Ill. CD, 1960-61; mem. fin. com. Piedmont coun. Boy Scouts Am., 1970; mem. adv. bd. Gastonia Wesleyan Youth Chorus, 1972; mem. joint com. nursing edn. N.C. State Bd. Edn. and Bd. Higher Edn., 1969-71; mem. adminstrv. bd. First United Meth. Ch., Gastonia, 1972-74; bd. dirs. Gaston County Heart Assn., 1968-70, Forsyth County Cancer Soc., 1964-65; trustee N.C. Hosp. Edn. and Research Found., 1966-71, pres., 1970-71; trustee N.C. Blue Cross and Blue Shield, Inc., 1971-77, Southeastern Hosp. Conf., 1971-72, 73-81, mem. edn. com., 1978—, mem. program com., 1975-76. Named Boss of Yr., Nat. Secs. Assn., 1970-71. Fellow Am. Coll. Healthcare Execs.; mem. MGMA, N.C. Hosp. Assn. (life; trustee 1966-72, pres. 1970-71, chmn. council govt. liaison 1978-81, Disting. Service award 1985), N.C. League Nursing, Am. Hosp. Assn. (ho. of dels. 1973-78, 83-85, speaker ho. of dels. 1985, trustee 1975-78, 83-85, chmn. bd. trustees 1984), Gastonia C. of C. (health affairs com. 1969-72). Lodge: Kiwanis. Contbr. articles on hosp. adminstrn. to profl. jours.

MATHERN, TIM, state senator, social worker; b. Edgeley, N.D., Apr. 19, 1950; s. John J. and Christina (Wolf) M.; m. Lorene Randall Mathern, Feb. 12, 1971; children: Rebecca, Tonya, Joshua, Zachary. BA, N.D. State U., 1971; MSW, U. Nebr., Omaha, 1980. Dir. family life Cath. Family Svc., Fargo, N.D., 1972—; senator State of N.D., Bismarck, 1986—; chmn. health and comms. com., 1993—; mem. Capitol Ground Planning Commn., 1987-93. Mem. Juvenile Justice Adv. Group, Fargo-Cass County Econ. Devel. Corp., 1993—, Nat. Family Life Ministries; asst. majority leader N.D. Senate, 1992—. Named Legislator of Yr., Red River Valley Mental Health Assn., 1989, 91, Legislator of Yr., N.D. Children's Caucus, 1993. Mem. NASW (Social Worker of Yr. award 1987). Democrat. Roman Catholic. Home: 406 Elmwood Fargo ND 58103-4315 Office: 2537 S University Fargo ND 58103-5736

MATHERS, THOMAS NESBIT, financial consultant; b. Bloomington, Ind., Apr. 22, 1914; s. Frank Curry and Maud Esther (Bowser) M.; m. Helen M. Curtis, Oct. 23, 1943 (dec.); children: Mary, Abigail. A.B., Ind. U., 1936, LL.B., 1939; M.B.A., Harvard U., 1941. Bar: Ind. 1939. Research asst. No. Trust Co., 1941-43; legal asst. Chgo. Ordnance Dist., 1943-44; employee to ptnr. Woodruff Mays & Co., Chgo., 1944-51; pres. Security Counselors, Inc., Chgo., 1951-62; pres. Mathers & Co., Chgo., 1962-75, chmn. bd., 1975-85, vice chmn. 1985-91; bd. dirs. Lincoln Income Fund, 1978—, Lincoln Convertible Securities Fund, 1986—; pres. Mathers Fund, 1965-75, chmn. bd., 1975-85, vice chmn., 1985-91; v.p., bd. dirs. OFC Corp. Meadowood Project, 1991—. Trustee Beloit Coll., 1970—. Recipient Disting. Alumni Service award Ind. U., 1979. Mem. Ind. U. Disting. Alumni Assn. (past pres.). Republican. Presbyterian. Clubs: Union League, Econ. of Chgo, Westmoreland Country, Mich. Shores, Investment Analysts Chgo. (past pres.). Home: 115 Bertling Ln Winnetka IL 60093-4202

MATHERS, WILLIAM HARRIS, lawyer; b. Newport, R.I., Aug. 27, 1914; s. Howard and Margaret I. (Harris) M.; m. Myra T. Martin, Jan. 17, 1942; children: William Martin, Michael Harris, John Grinnell, Myra Tutt, Ursula Fraser. A.B., Dartmouth Coll., 1935; J.D., Yale U., 1938. Bar: N.Y. 1940. With Milbank, Tweed & Hope, 1938-48; mem. Milbank, Tweed, Hope & Hadley, 1948-57; v.p., sec., dir. Yale & Towne Mfg. Co., Stamford, Conn., 1957-60; ptnr. Chadbourne & Parke, 1960-75, counsel 1983—; exec. v.p., gen. counsel, sec., dir. United Brands Co., 1975-82. Mayor, trustee Village of Cove Neck, N.Y., 1950-82; trustee Barnard Coll., 1958-69. Served as pvt. to maj. U.S. army, 1942-46. Mem. ABA, N.Y. State Bar Assn., Nassau County Bar Assn., Assn. of Bar of City of N.Y., New Eng. Soc. in City of N.Y., Casque and Gauntlet, Corbey Court, Piping Rock Club, Seminole Golf Club, N.Y. Yacht Club, Cold Spring Harbor Beach Club, Phi Beta Kappa, Psi Upsilon. Home: Gordon Farm RR 1 Box 83 Sutton VT 05867-9721 Office: 30 Rockefeller Plz New York NY 10112-0127

MATHES, CARYN G., broadcast executive; b. Terre Haute, Ind., Jan. 10, 1955; d. Robert Nathaniel and Carcelia James (Rudy) M.; m. Charles David Stanley, Oct. 18, 1975 (div. June 1980), m. Phillip James Lesky, Jan. 9, 1993. BS in Print Journalism, Ind. State U., 1976. News anchor, reporter Sta. WTHI-TV, Terre Haute, 1974-78, Sta. WCKY-AM, Cin., 1978-80, Sta. WJR-AM, Detroit, 1980-82; news dir. Sta. WDET-FM, Detroit, 1982-84, gen. mgr., 1984—. Sec. Mich. Corp. for Pub. Broadcasting, 1986—; pres. Mich. Pub. Radio Network. Recipient Minority Achievement award Detroit YMCA, 1986. Baptist. Avocations: travel, cooking, gardening. Office: Sta WDET-FM 6001 Cass Ave Fl 1 Detroit MI 48202-3400

MATHES, SORRELL MARK, investment banker; b. Cin., Jan. 21, 1936; s. Irving and Sylvia (Jasper) M.; m. Barbara Goldstein, April 8, 1962; children: Emily, Richard. Ba, Cornell U., 1957; MBA, Columbia U., 1959. Assoc. The Conf. Bd., N.Y.C., 1959-67; assoc. N.Y. Securities, Inc., N.Y.C., 1968-

70, v.p., 1970-73, pres., 1973-75, also bd. dirs.; v.p., bd. dirs. Moseley, Hallgarten, Estabrook & Weeden, N.Y.C., 1975-80; v.p. Warburg, Paribas, Becker, N.Y.C., 1980-81, mng. dir., 1981-84; mng. dir. Merrill Lynch Capital Markets, N.Y.C., 1984-91; mng. dir., head corp. fin. Prudential Securities Inc., N.Y.C., 1991—. Clubs: India House (N.Y.C.), Metropolis Country, (White Plains, N.Y.), Cornell (N.Y.C.). Office: Prudential Securities Inc 1 New York Plz New York NY 10292

MATHES, STEPHEN JOHN, plastic and reconstructive surgeon; educator; b. New Orleans, Aug. 17, 1943; s. John Ernest and Norma (Deutsch) M.; m. Jennifer Tandy Woodbridge, Nov. 26, 1966; children: David, Brian, Edward. BS, La. State U., 1964; MD, La. State U., New Orleans, 1968. Diplomate Am. Bd. Surgery, Am. Bd. Plastic Surgery (dir. 1993—). Asst. prof. surgery Wash. U., St. Louis, 1977-78; assoc. prof. U. Calif., San Francisco, 1978-84, prof. surgery, 1984, prof. surgery, anatomy and cell biology, 1984-85, also bd. dirs. craniofacial anomalies; head plastic surgery sect. U. Mich., Ann Arbor, 1984-85, prof. surgery, 1984-85; prof. surgery, head plastic and reconstructive surgery div. U. Calif., San Francisco, 1985—. Author: (textbook) Clinical Applications for Muscle and Musculocutaneous Flaps, 1983 (Best Med. Book award Physician's category, Am. Med. Writer's Assn., 1983); contbr. articles to profl. jours. Recipient 1st prize plastic surgery scholarship contest, Plastic Surgery Edn. Found., 1981, 83, 84, 86; grantee NIH, 1982-85, 86—. Fellow ACS; mem. Am. Assn. Plastic Surgery, Plastic Surgery Research Council (pres.-elect 1986), Am. Soc. Surgery of Hand, Soc. Univ. Surgeons. Republican. Episcopalian. Avocations: gardening, tennis. Home: 30 Trophy Ct Burlingame CA 94010-7434 Office: U Calif San Francisco Dept Surgery San Francisco CA 94143-0932

MATHES, STEPHEN JON, lawyer; b. N.Y.C., Mar. 18, 1945; s. Joseph and Beatrice M.; m. Michele Marshall, Oct. 22, 1972 (div. 1992); children: Aaron, Benjamin; m. Maria McGarry, Dec. 19, 1992. BA, U. Pa., 1967, JD, 1970. Bar: N.Y. 1971, Pa. 1972, U.S. Dist. Ct. (ea. dist.) Pa. 1971. U.S. Ct. Appeals (3d cir.) 1972, U.S. Ct. Appeals (5th cir.) 1985, U.S. Ct. Appeals (4th cir.) 1985, U.S. Supreme Ct. 1978. Law clk. U.S. Ct. Appeals (3d cir.), Phila., 1970-71; asst. dist. atty. Office of Phil. Dist. Atty., Phila., 1975; assoc. Dilworth, Paxson, Kalish & Kauffman, Phila., 1971-74, 76-77, sr. ptnr., 1977-91, mem. exec. com., 1987-90, co-chmn. litigation dept., 1987-91; ptnr., mem. mng. com. Hoyle, Morris & Kerr, Phila., 1992—; bd. dirs. The Levitt Found., 1990—, sec., 1991—. Bd. dirs. Acad. Vocal Arts, 1993—. Mem. ABA, Pa. Bar Assn., Phila. Bar Assn. (arbitrator), Thanatopsis Soc., Racquet Club, Germantown Cricket Club. Home: 199 Lynnebrook Ln Philadelphia PA 19118 Office: Holye Morris & Kerr One Liberty Pl Ste 4900 Philadelphia PA 19103

MATHESON, ALAN ADAMS, law educator; b. Cedar City, Utah, Feb. 2, 1932; s. Scott Milne and Adele (Adams) M.; m. Milicent Holbrook, Aug. 15, 1960; children—Alan, David Scott, John Robert. B.A., U. Utah, 1953, M.S., 1957, J.D., 1959; postgrad. asso. in law, Columbia U. Bar: Utah 1960, Ariz. 1975. Asst. to pres. Utah State U., 1961-67; mem. faculty Ariz. State U., Tempe, 1967—; prof. law Ariz. State U., 1970—, dean, 1978-84; bd. dirs Ariz. Center Law in Public Interest, 1979-81; bd. dirs. DNA Navajo Legal Services, 1984—. Pres. Tri-City Mental Health Citizens Bd., 1973-74. Served with AUS, 1953-55. Mem. Utah Bar Assn., Ariz. Bar Assn., Maricopa County Bar Assn., Phi Beta Kappa, Order of Coif. Democrat. Mormon. Home: 720 E Geneva Dr Tempe AZ 85282-3737 Office: Coll Law Ariz State U Tempe AZ 85287

MATHESON, KENT D., school system administrator. Supt. Highline Sch. Dist. 401, Seattle. Named state finalist Nat. Supt. of Yr. award, 1992. Office: Highline Sch Dist 401 15675 Ambaum Blvd SW Seattle WA 98166-2523

MATHESON, RICHARD BURTON, author, scriptwriter; b. Allendale, N.J., Feb. 20, 1926; s. Bertolf and Fanny M.; m. Ruth Ann Woodson, July 1, 1952; children: Richard, Alison, Christian, Bettina. BA, U. Mo., 1949. Author: (novels) Fury on Sunday, 1954, I Am Legend, 1954, Someone is Bleeding, 1954, The Shrinking Man, 1956, A Stir of Echoes, 1958, Ride the Nightmare, 1959, The Beardless Warriors, 1960, Hell House, 1971, Bid Time Return, 1975 (World Fantasy award best novel 1976), What Dreams May Come, 1978, Journal of the Gun Years, 1991, Seven Steps to Midnight, 1992, The Gun Fight, 1993, By the Gun, 1994, Earthbound, 1994, Shadow on the Sun, 1994, (short stories) Born of Man and Woman, 1954, The Shores of Space, 1957, Shock: Thirteen Tales to Thrill and Terrify, 1961, Shock II, 1964, Shock III, 1966, Shock Waves, 1970, Richard Matheson: Collected Stories, 1989; screenwriter: (films) Ransom, 1955, The Incredible Shrinking Man, 1957 (Hugo award World Sci. Fiction Conv. 1958), The Beat Generation, 1959, The House of Usher, 1960, Master of the World, 1961, The Pit and the Pendulum, 1961, Tales of Terror, 1962, Burn, Witch, Burn, 1962, The Raven, 1963, The Comedy of Terrors, 1964, Die! Die! My Darling!, 1965, The Young Warriors, 1967, The Devil's Bride, 1968, De Sade, 1969, Legend of Hell House, 1973, Somewhere in Time, 1980, Twilight Zone-The Movie, 1983, Jaws 3-D, 1983, Loose Cannons, 1990, (teleplays) Duel, 1971, Ghost Story, 1972, The Night Stalker, 1972, The Night Strangler, 1973, Dying Room Only, 1973, Scream of the Wolk, 1973, Dracula, 1974, Trilogy of Terror, 1974, The Stranger Within, 1974, The Morning After, 1974, Dead of Night, 1975, The Strange Possession of Mrs. Oliver, 1977, The Martian Chronicles, 1980, The Dreamer of Oz, 1990, (TV episodes) Lawman, The Twilight Zone, Star Trek, The Girl from U.N.C.L.E., Chrysler Playhouse, (plays) Now You See It; editor: Twilight Zone: The Original Stories, 1985. Named Guest of Honor, World Sci. Fiction Conv., 1958, 76. Mem. Writers Guild (Best Anthology Adapted from Another Medium award 1973), Dramatists Guild. Office: ICM David Greenblatt 8942 Wilshire Blvd Los Angeles CA 90211*

MATHESON, WILLIAM LYON, lawyer, farmer; b. Coeburn, Va., Dec. 5, 1924; s. Julius Daniel and Ruth Steele Lyon M.; m. Katrina B. Hickox; children: Katherine, William Lyon, Alline, Thornton; m. Marjorie H. Anderson, Nov. 26, 1977. Student, Emory U., 1946-47; AB, Mercer U., 1944; LLB, U. Va., 1950. Bar: N.Y. 1951. Assoc. firm Patterson, Belknap & Webb, N.Y.C., 1950-57; assoc. Wertheim & Co. (investments), N.Y.C., 1957-58; ptnr. Webster & Sheffield, N.Y.C., 1959-65; pvt. practice N.Y.C. 1965-92; chmn. bd. Mich. Energy Resources Co., Monroe, 1959-89, Mercom Inc. (cable TV), 1984-91. Bd. dirs. Madison Sq. Boys' Club, N.Y.C., 1958-76, assoc. mem. bd. dirs., 1977-91; trustee Police Athletic League, N.Y.C., 1962—. Served to lt. (j.g.) USN, 1942-46. Mem. Links Club (N.Y.C.), Piping Rock Club (Locust Valley, N.Y.), Meadow Brook Club (Jericho, N.Y.), Seminole Golf (North Palm Beach, Fla.), Island Club (Hobe Sound, Fla.). Democrat. Home: 430 S Beach Rd Hobe Sound FL 33455-2702 also: Sunset Hill Heather Ln Mill Neck NY 11765

MATHEU, FEDERICO MANUEL, university chancellor; b. Humacao, P.R., Mar. 17, 1941; s. Federico Matheu-Baez and Matilde Delgado-Vazquez; m. Myrna Delgado-Miranda, May 30, 1963; children: Federico Antonio, Rosa Myrna, Alfredo Javier, David Reinaldo. B.S. in Chem. Engring., U. P.R., 1962; Ph.D. in Phys. Chemistry, U. Pitts., 1971. Chem. engr. Commonwealth Oil Refining Co., 1962-63; mem. adminstrv. staff and faculty U. P.R., 1963-78, dir. Humacao Coll., 1976-78; chancellor San German campus Inter Am. U. P.R., 1978-91; exec. dir., gen. coun. on edn. Commonwealth of P.R., Hato Rey, 1991—; cons. in field. Author papers, reports in field. Named Disting. Educator P.R. Jaycees, 1974. Mem. Colegio de Quimicos P.R., Am. Chem. Soc., Sci. Tchrs. Assn. P.R. (pres. 1975-76), P.R. Acad. Arts and Scis., Phi Delta Kappa, Phi Tau Sigma. Home: Parque de Villa Caparra Zuania St G-4 Guaynabo PR 00966 Office: Gen Coun on Edn PO Box 5429 San Juan PR 00919

MATHEW, MARTHA SUE CRYDER, retired education educator; b. Hallsville, Ohio, Feb. 21, 1928; d. Earl and Minnie Ada (Hough) Cryder; m. Guy Wilbur Mathew, Mar. 25, 1949; children: John G., Jeffrey Bruce. BS, Ohio No. U., 1966. Cert. tchr., Ohio. Tchr. Immaculate Conception Sch., Celina, Ohio, 1961-64, Zane Trace Local Sch., Chillicothe, Ohio, 1964-93, ret., 1993; mem. Juvenile Ct. Rev. Bd., Ross County, Chillicothe. Named Educator of Yr., Zane Trace Local, Ross County, 1993. Mem. Order Ea. Star (Worthy Matron 1976, 88, Evergreen chpt. 169, Adelphi), Ladies Oriental Shrine (treas., sec., v.p., pres.), Delta Kappa Gamma (com.). Republican. Methodist. Home: 8995 State Route 180 Kingston OH 45644-9546

MATHEWS, ANNE JONES, international consultant, library director; b. Phila., Feb. 5, 1928; d. Edmond Fulton and Anne Ruth (Reichner) Jones; m. Frank Samuel Mathews, June 16, 1951; children: Lisa Anne Bingham, David Morgan, Lynne Elizabeth Beitenhader, Alison Fulton Sawyer. AB, Wheaton Coll., 1949; MA, U. Denver, 1965, PhD, 1977. Mem. field staff Intervarsity Christian Fellowship, Chgo., 1949-51; Interviewer supr. Colo. Market Rsch. Svcs., Denver, 1952-64; reference libr. Oreg. State U., Corvallis, 1965-67; program dir. Ctrl. Colo. Libr. System, Denver, 1969-70; inst. dir. U.S. Office of Edn., Inst. Grant, 1979; dir. pub. rels. U. Denver Grad. Sch. Librarianship & Info. Mgmt., 1970-76, dir. continuing edn., 1977-80, asst. prof., 1970-77, assoc. prof., 1977-79, prof., 1979-85; dir. Office Libr. Programs U.S. Dept. Edn., Washington, 1986-91; dir. Nat. Libr. Edn., Washington, 1992-94; cons. Acad. Ednl. Devel., Washington, 1994—; vis. lectr. Simmons Coll. Sch. Libr. Sci., Boston, 1977; cons. USIA, 1984-85, mem. book and libr. adv. com., 1981-91; faculty assoc. Danforth Found., 1974-84; speaker in field; mem. secondary sch. curriculum com. Jefferson County Pub. Schs., Colo., 1976-78; mem. adv. com. Golden H.S., 1973-77; mem. adv. coun. White House Conf. on Librs. and Info. Svs., 1991; del. Internat. Fedn. Libr. Assns. Author, editor 3 books; contbr. articles to profl. jours., numerous chpts. to books. Mem. rural libs. and humanities program Colo. planning and resource bd. NEH, 1982-83; bd. mgrs. Friends of Denver Pub. Libr., 1976-82; pres. Faculty Women's Club, Colo. Sch. Mines, 1963-64. Mem. ALA (visionary leaders com. 1987-89, coun. mem 1979-83, com on accreditation 1984-85, orientation com. 1974-77, 83-84, pub. rels. com.), Am. Soc. Info. Sci. (pub. rels. chmn. 1971), Mountain Plains Libr. Assn. (profl. devel. com. 1979-80, pub. rels. and publs. com. 1973-75, continuing edn. com. 1973-76), Colo. Libr. Assn. (pres. 1973-74, bd. dirs. 1973-75, continuing edn. com. 1976-80), Assn. Libr. & Info. Sci. Edn. (communication com. 1978-80, program com. 1977-78), Cosmos Club (Washington). Avocations: travel, reading, antique collecting, mus. & gallery activities. Home: 492 Mount Evans Rd Golden CO 80401

MATHEWS, BARBARA BAILEY, special education educator; b. Cambridge, Mass., Apr. 20, 1943; d. Herbert Sternbergh and Inez (Wells) Bailey; m. J.D. Mathews, Aug. 20, 1966 (div. 1987); children: David Herbert, Diana Grace. AB, Syracuse U., 1965, MS, 1992; postgrad., SUNY, Brockport, 1965-66, SUNY, Oswego, 1968-70. Cert. spl. edn. tchr., German tchr., sci. tchr., N.Y. Jr. high sch. German tchr. Phoenix, N.Y., 1965-68; high sch. German tchr. Parish, N.Y., 1968-71; sci. and German tchr. North Syracuse, N.Y., 1984-91; spl. educator resource room North Syracuse Cen. Schs., 1992-94; spl. educator Westmoreland Ctrl. Schs., N.Y., 1994—; steering com. and sci. fair North Syracuse Schs., 1985-87. Bd. mgrs. North Area YMCA, Liverpool, N.Y., 1982-84. Mem. Delta Phi Alpha, Chi Omega (past pres. alumnae, treas. 1966—). Home: 8100 Maple Rd Clay NY 13041-8908 Office: Westmoreland HS Rt 233 Westmoreland NY 13000

MATHEWS, BARBARA EDITH, gynecologist; b. Santa Barbara, Calif., Oct. 5, 1946; d. Joseph Chesley and Pearl (Cieri) Mathews; AB, U. Calif., 1969; MD, Tufts U., 1972. Diplomate Am. Bd. Ob-Gyn. Intern, Cottage Hosp., Santa Barbara, 1972-73, Santa Barbara Gen. Hosp., 1972-73; resident in ob-gyn Beth Israel Hosp., Boston, 1973-77; clin. fellow in ob-gyn Harvard U., 1973-76, instr., 1976-77; gynecologist Sansum Med. Clinic, Santa Barbara, 1977—; faculty mem. ann. postgrad. course Harvard Med. Sch.; bd. dirs. Sansum Med. Clinic; dir. ann. postgrad course UCLA Med. Sch. Bd. dirs. Meml. Rehab. Found., Santa Barbara, Channel City Club, Santa Barbara, Music Acad. of the West, Santa Barbara; mem. citizen's continuing edn. adv. council Santa Barbara C.C.; moderator Santa Barbara Cottage Hosp. Cmty. Health Forum. Fellow ACS, Am. Coll. Ob-gyn.; mem. AMA, Am. Soc. Colposcopy and Cervical Pathology (dir. 1982-84), Harvard U. Alumni Assn., Tri-counties Obstet. and Gynecol. Soc. (pres. 1981-82), Phi Beta Kappa. Clubs: Birnam Wood Golf (Santa Barbara). Author: (with L. Burke) Colposcopy in Clinical Practice, 1977; contbg. author Manual of Ambulatory Surgery, 1982. Home: 2105 Anacapa St Santa Barbara CA 93105-3503 Office: 317 W Pueblo St Santa Barbara CA 93105-4365

MATHEWS, BYRON BURNETT, JR., lawyer; b. Andalusia, Ala., Aug. 24, 1948; s. Byron Burnett and Georgia Ruth (Lowman) M.; m. Carol Ann Mathews, June 19, 1971 (div.); children: Wiley, Ann. BA, Birmingham-So. Coll., 1970; JD, U. Ala., 1975. Bar: Ala. 1975, Fla. 1976. Law clk. to presiding justice U.S. Ct. Appeals 5th cir., Montgomery, Ala., 1975-76; assoc. Merson, Sawyer et al, Miami, Fla., 1976-78, Lane, Mitchell & Harris, Miami, 1978-80; ptnr. McDermott, Will & Emery, Miami, Tallahassee, 1980—. Served with U.S. Army, 1970-72. Mem. Gov.'s Club, Capital City Country Club (Tallahassee), Riviera Country Club, City Club Miami. Democrat. Methodist. Avocations: golf, cinema, travel. Home: 3769 Main Hwy Coconut Grove FL 33133-9999 Office: McDermott Will & Emery 201 S Bicayne Blvd Miami FL 33131

MATHEWS, CARMEN SYLVA, actress; b. Phila., May 8, 1918; d. Albert Barnes and Matilde (Keller) M. Student, Bennett Jr. Coll., 1936-38, Royal Acad. Dramatic Art, Eng., 1938, 39. Appeared numerous stage plays; roles include Ophelia in Hamlet, Queen in Richard II, Lady Mortimer in Henry IV, Varya in Cherry Orchard, 1943, Violet in Man and Superman, 1945, Mrs. Sullen in Beaux Strategem, 1945, Miss Ronberry in The Corn is Green, 1946, Miss Neville in She Stoops to Conquer, 1946, Madame Ducotel in My Three Angels, 1952, Mary in Holiday for Lovers, 1957, Candida in Shaw's Candida, 1958, Eileen in Man in Dogsuit, 1958, Lady Utterword in Heartbreak House, 1959-60, Contessa in mus. adapted from Candide, Voltaire, 1956, Ceil in Night Life, 1962, Maria in Lorenzo, 1963, Louise in Zenda, 1963, Queen in Hamlet, 1964, Grandma Hutto in mus. adaptation The Yearling, 1965, Edna in A Delicate Balance, 1966, Bathsheeba in mus. adaptation I'm Solomon, 1967-68, Constance in mus. adaptation Dear World, 1968, Rabbit Run, 1969, Fraulein Schneider in mus. adaptation Cabaret, 1970, Wife in All Over, 1970, Grandma in Ring around the Bathtub, 1971, Gloriani in mus. Ambassador, 1972, Mrs. Aigreville in mus. In Fashion, 1973, Mamita in mus. Gigi, 1974, Arietta in Mornings at Seven, 1974, Mrs. Higgins in Pygmalion, 1975, Mother in Children, 1976, Mrs. Ellis in The Autumn Garden, 1976, Madame Arcati in Blithe Spirit, 1977, Mrs. Tilford in The Children's Hour, Catherine in Arms and the Man, 1979, Fanny Farrelly in Watch on the Rhine, 1980, Cornelia in The Bat, 1980, Betsy Trotwood in mus. David Copperfield, 1981, Cora in Mornings at Seven, 1981, Sarah Delano Roosevelt in Sunrise at Campobello, 1982, Old Lady in Sunday in the Park with George, 1983, Helen in The Road to Mecca, 1984, Mother in Night, Mother, 1985, Grandmother in A Grand Romance, 1985, Mrs. Hardcastle in She Stoops to Conquer, 1986, Cecelia in Autumn Elegy, 1989, Dowager Empress in The Anastasia Game, 1989, Mme. Armfeldt in A Little Night Music, 1990; movie appearances include Butterfield 8, A Rage To Live, Mrs. Boatwright in Sounder, 1971, Fanny Ascher in Daniel, 1983; also in various dramatic TV shows, and other TV show including Judge in TV after sch. spl. To Take A Stand, 1988, role of Lil in MASH, HBO spl. The Last Day in the Life of Brian Darling, 1990, The Best Year of My Life, 1990; recording books for Am. Found. for Blind. Named one of Conn. Outstanding Women United Nations, 1987. Mem. Actors Equity, Screen Actors Guild, AFTRA. Home: New Pond Farm Redding CT 06896

MATHEWS, DAN, animal rights activist; s. Ray and Perry Mathews. Grad., Am. U., 1985. With People for the Ethical Treatment of Animals, 1985—, receptionist, dir. internat. campaigns. Office: care PETA PO Box 42516 Washington DC 20015*

MATHEWS, DAVID, foundation executive; b. Grove Hill, Ala., Dec. 6, 1935; s. Forrest Lee and Doris (Pearson) M.; m. Mary Chapman, Jan. 24, 1960; children: Lee Ann Mathews Hester, Lucy Mathews Heegaard. A.B., U. Ala., 1958; Ph.D., Columbia U., 1965; LL.D., U. Ala., 1969, Mercer U., 1976; L.H.D., William and Mary Coll., 1976, Med. U. S.C., 1976, Samford U., 1978, Transylvania U., 1978, Stillman Coll., 1980, Miami U., 1982; H.H.D., Birmingham-So. Coll., 1976, Wash. U. St. Louis, 1984; L.H.D., Ctr. Coll., 1985; LL.D., Ohio Wesleyan U., 1987, Lynchburg Coll., 1987; L.H.D., U. New Eng., 1988. Exec. v.p. U. Ala., 1968-69, pres., 1969-80, prof. history, 1977-81; pres., chief exec. officer Charles F. Kettering Found., Dayton, Ohio, 1981—; sec. HEW, Washington, 1975-77; dir. Birmingham br. Fed. Res. Bank of Atlanta, 1970-72, chmn., 1973-75; mem. council SRI Internat., 1978-85; chmn. Council Public Policy Edn., 1980—. Contbr. articles to profl. jours. Trustee Judson Coll., 1973-75, Am. Univs. Field Staff, 1969-80; bd. dirs. Birmingham Festival of Arts Assn., Inc., 1969-75;

mem. Nat. Programming Council for Public TV, 1970-73, So. Regional Edn. Bd., 1969-75, Ala. Council on Humanities, 1973-75; vice chmn. Commn. on Future of South, 1974; mem. So. Growth Policies Bd., 1974-75; mem. nat. adv. council Am. Revolution Bicentennial Adminstrn., 1975; mem. Ala. State Oil and Gas Bd., 1975, 77-79; bd. dirs. Acad. Ednl. Devel., 1975—, Ind. Sector, 1982-88, ; chmn. Pres.'s Com. on Mental Retardation, 1975-77; chmn. income security com. aging com. Health Ins. Com. of Domestic Council, 1975-77; bd. govs. nat. ARC, 1975-77; bd. govs., bd. visitors Washington Coll., 1982-86 ; trustee John F. Kennedy Center for Performing Arts, 1975-77, Woodrow Wilson Internat. Center for Scholars, 1975-77; fed. trustee Fed. City Council, 1975-77; bd. dirs. A Presdl. Classroom for Young Americans, Inc., 1975-76; trustee Tchrs. Coll., Columbia U., 1977—, Nat. Found. March of Dimes, 1977-83, Coun. om Learning, 1977-84, Miles Coll., 1978—; mem. nat. adv. bd. Nat. Inst. on Mgmt. Lifelong Edn., 1979-84; mem. Ala. 2000, 1980—; spl. adviser Aspen Inst., 1980-84; mem. bd. trustees Gerald R. Ford Found., 1988—, bd. visitors Mershon Ctr. Ohio State U., 1988-91. Served with U.S. Army, 1959-60. Recipient Nicholas Murray Butler medal Columbia U., 1976, Ala. Adminstr. of Year award Am. Assn. Univ. Adminstrs., 1976, Educator of Year award Ala. Conf. Black Mayors, 1977, Brotherhood award NCCJ, 1979. Mem. Newcomen Soc. Am., Phi Beta Kappa, Phi Alpha Theta, Omicron Delta Kappa, Delta Theta Phi. Home: 6050 Mad River Rd Dayton OH 45459-1508 Office: Charles F Kettering Found 200 Commons Rd Dayton OH 45459-2799

MATHEWS, HARRY BURCHELL, poet, novelist, educator; b. N.Y.C., Feb. 14, 1930; s. Edward James and Mary (Burchell) M.; m. Niki de Saint Phalle, June 6, 1949 (div. 1964); 2 children; m. Marie Chaix, July 29, 1992. BA cum laude, Harvard Coll., 1952. Faculty Bennington (Vt.) Coll., 1978-80; vis. lectr. Hamilton Coll., Clinton, N.Y., 1979, Columbia Coll., N.Y.C., 1982-83; vis. writer Brown U., Providence, R.I., 1988, Temple U., Phila., 1990, Magdalene Coll., Cambridge, U.K., 1992; founding dir. Shakespeare & Co., Lenox, Mass.; lectr. in field, nat., internat. colls, art ctrs., instns. Author: The Conversions, 1962, Tlooth, 1964, The Sinking of the Odradek Stadium, 1975, Country Cooking and Other Stories, 1980, Cigarettes, 1987, 20 Lines A Day, 1988, The Orchard, 1988, The Way Home, 1988, The American Experience, 1991, Singular Pleasures, 1993, The Journalist, 1994; (poetry) The Ring, Poems 1956-69, 1970, The Planisphere, 1974, Trial Impressions, 1977, Selected Declarations of Dependence, 1977, Armenian Papers: Poems 1954-84, 1987, Out of Bounds, 1989, A Mid-Season Sky: Poems 1954-89, 1991, (in French) Le savoir des rois: poèmes à perverbes, 1976, Ecrits français, 1990; (essays) Immeasurable Distances: The Collected Essays, 1981; trans.: A Man in a Dream (Georges Perec) 1975, The Laurels of Lake Constance (Marie Chaix) 1977, The Life: Memoirs of a French Hooker (Jeanne Cordelier), 1978, Blue of Noon (Georges Bataille), 1978, Chronicles of Ellis Island (Georges Perec) 1981, The Dust of Suns (Raymond Roussel) 1991, various jour. articles; pub., co-editor Locus Solus, 1960-62; Paris editor The Paris Review, 1989—; contbr. poems, stories to anthologies, articles, criticisms, reviews to profl. jours. Recipient award Fiction Writing Am. Acad. Inst. Arts and Letters, N.Y., 1991; grantee Deutsche Akademische Austausch Dienst, Berlin, 1991; fiction writing grantee NEA, 1982. Mem. Ouvroir de Littérature Potentielle (Paris). Avocations: music making, back-country skiing, hiking, cooking.

MATHEWS, JACK WAYNE, journalist, film critic; b. L.A., Dec. 2, 1939; s. Walter Edwin and Dorothy Helen (Friley) M.; m. Lucinda Lucille Herbert, Nov. 5, 1971; children: Darren Brady, Shelby Kay. BA, San Jose (Calif.) State Coll. 1965; MS, UCLA, 1966. Reporter Riverside (Calif.) Press, 1967-69; mktg. exec. Riverside Raceway, 1969-75; columnist, editor Rochester (N.Y.) Democrat & Chronicle, 1975-78; columnist, film critic Detroit Free Press, 1978-82, USA Today, L.A., 1982-85; columnist L.A. Times, 1985-89, film editor, 1989-91; film critic N.Y. Newsday, N.Y.C., 1991—; juror Montreal World Film Festival, 1993. Author: The Battle of Brazil, 1987. Mem. N.Y. Film Critics Cir. Democrat. Office: NY Newsday 2 Park Ave New York NY 10016-5603 also: Newsday Inc 235 Pinelawn Rd Melville NY 11747-4226

MATHEWS, JESSICA TUCHMAN, policy researcher, columnist; b. N.Y.C., July 4, 1946; d. Lester Reginald and Barbara (Wertheim) Tuchman; m. Colin D. Mathews, Feb. 25, 1978; children: Oliver Max Tuchman, Jordan Henry Morgenthau; stepchildren: Zachary Chase, Hilary Dustin. AB magna cum laude, Radcliffe Coll., 1967; PhD, Calif. Inst. Tech., 1973. Congrl. sci. fellow AAAS, 1973-74; profl. staff mem. Ho. Interior Com. on Energy and Environment, Washington, 1974-75; dir. issues and rsch. Udall Presdl. campaign, 1975-76; dir. Office of Global Issues NSC staff, Washington, 1977-79; mem. editorial bd. The Washington Post, 1980-82; v.p., dir. rsch. The World Resources Inst., Washington, 1982-92; dep. to undersec. for global affairs U.S. Dept. State, Washington, 1993; sr. fellow Coun. on Fgn. Rels., Washington, 1993—; columnist Washington Post, 1991—; mem. numerous adv. panels Office Tech. Assessment, NAS, AAAS, EPA; bd. dirs. Population Ref. Bur., Washington, 1988-93. Bd. dirs. Joyce Found., Chgo., 1984-91, Radcliffe Coll., 1992—, Carnegie Endowment for Internat. Peace, Washington, 1992—, Rockefeller Bros. Fund, N.Y.C., 1992—, Inter-Am Diaogue, 1991—, Surface Transp. Policy Project. Disting. fellow Aspen Inst. Mem. Coun. Fgn. Rels., Fedn. Am. Scientists (bd. dirs. 1985-87, 88-92), Inst. for Internat. Econs. (adv. com.). Democrat. Jewish. Office: Council on Fgn Relations 2400 N St NW Washington DC 20037

MATHEWS, JOHN, bishop. Bishop Apostolic Overcoming Holy Ch. of God Inc., Dayton, Ohio. Office: Apostolic Overcoming Holy Church of God Inc 12 College St Dayton OH 45407-2934

MATHEWS, JOHN DAVID, electrical engineering educator, consultant; b. Kenton, Ohio, Apr. 3, 1947; s. John Joseph and Mary (Long) M.; children: John Todd, Debra Juanita, Alex David. BS in Physics with honors, Case Western Res. U., 1969, MS in Elec. Engring. and Applied Physics, 1972, PhD in Elec. Engring. and Applied Physics, 1972. Lectr. dept. elec. engring. and applied physics Case Western Res. U., Cleve., 1969-72, asst. prof., 1975-79, assoc. prof., 1979-85, prof., 1985-87; prof. dept. elec. engring. Pa. State U., University Park, 1987—; dir. Comm. & Space Scis. Lab. Ctr. of Excellence, Coll. Engring., 1988-94; dir. Comm. & Space Scis. Lab. Ctr. of Excellence, Coll. Engring., University Park, Pa., 1994—; vis. scientist Nat. Astronomy and Ionosphere Ctr., Case Western Res. U., Arecibo, P.R., 1972-75; adj. asst. prof. dept. elec. engring. Pa. State U., 1978-86, dir. artist-in-residence program Coll. Engring., 1990-92; mem. Arecibo adv. bd. and visiting com. Cornell U., 1989-92, chmn., 1991-92; cons. to engring. svc. group and laser engring. group Lawrence Livermore Nat. Labs., 1979-87; cons. Nat. Astronomy and Ionosphere Ctr. Arecibo Obs., 1980—; cons. engr., 1975—; presenter, speaker numerous profl. meetings. Contbr. articles to profl. jours. including Jour. Atmos. Terr. Physics, Jour. Geophys. Rsch., Radio Sci. Leonardo, Icarus and numerous others. Achievements include research on observations of narrow sodium and narrow ionization layers using both lidar and incoherent scatter radar techniques, on tides and acoustic-gravity waves as observed in the motions of ionospheric E region meteoric ion layers, on electron concentration configurations during geomagnetic storms, and on detection and correction of coherent interference in incoherent scatter radar data processing meteor physics. Office: Pa State U Communications & Space Scis Lab 316 Electrical Engineering E University Park PA 16802-2707

MATHEWS, KENNETH PINE, physician, educator; b. Schenectady, N.Y., Apr. 1, 1921; s. Raymond and Marguerite Elizabeth (Pine) M.; m. Alice Jean Elliott, Jan. 26, 1952 (dec.); children: Susan Kay, Ronald Elliott, Robert Pine; m. Winona Beatrice Rosenburg Nov. 8, 1975. A.B., U. Mich., 1941, M.D., 1943. Diplomate Am. Bd. Internal Medicine, Am. Bd. Allergy and Immunology (past sec.). Intern, asst. resident, resident in medicine Univ. Hosp., Ann Arbor, Mich., 1943-45, 48-50; mem. faculty dept. medicine med. sch. U. Mich., 1950—, assoc. prof. internal medicine, 1956-61, prof., 1961-86, prof. emeritus, 1986—, head div. allergy, 1967-83; adj. mem. Scripps Clinic and Research Found., La Jolla, Calif., 1986—; past chmn. residency rev. com. for allergy and immunology, past chmn. allergy and immunology rsch. com. NIH. Co-author: A Manual of Clinical Allergy, 2d edit, 1967; editor: Jour. Allergy and Clin. Immunology, 1968-72; contbr. numerous articles in field to profl. jours. Served to capt. M.C. AUS, 1946-48. Recipient Disting. Service award Am. Acad. Allergy, 1976; Faculty Disting. Achievement award U. Mich., 1984. Fellow Am. Acad. Allergy (past pres.), A.C.P. (emeritus); mem. AMA, Assn. Immunologists (emeritus), Ctrl. Soc. Clin. Rsch. (emeritus), Am. Fedn. Clin. Rsch., Alpha Omega Alpha, Phi

Beta Kappa. Home: 7080 Caminito Estrada La Jolla CA 92037-5714 Office: Scripps Clinic & Rsch Found Dept Molecular & Exptl Medicine 10666 N Torrey Pines Rd La Jolla CA 92037

MATHEWS, LINDA MCVEIGH, newspaper editor; b. Redlands, Calif., Mar. 14, 1946; d. Glenard Ralph and Edith Lorene (Humphrey) McVeigh; m. Thomas Jay Mathews, June 15, 1967; children:—Joseph, Peter, Katherine. B.A., Radcliffe Coll., 1967; J.D., Harvard U., 1972. Gen. assignment reporter Los Angeles Times, 1967-69, Supreme Ct. corr., 1972-76, corr., Hong Kong, 1977-79, China corr., Peking, 1979-80, op-ed page editor, 1980-81, dep. nat. editor, 1981-84, dep. fgn. editor, 1985-88, editorial writer, 1988-89, editor L.A. Times mag., 1989-92; sr. producer ABC News, 1992-93; nat. editor N.Y. Times, 1993—; corr. Wall St. Jour., Hong Kong, 1976-77; lectr.; freelance writer. Author: (with others) Journey Into China, 1982; One Billion: A China Chronicle, 1983. Mem. Women's Legal Def. Fund, 1972-76; co-founder, pres. Hong Kong Montessori Sch., 1977-79; bd. dirs. Ctr. for Childhood. Mem. Fgn. Corrs. Club Hong Kong. Office: NY Times 229 W 43rd St New York NY 10036-3913

MATHEWS, PAUL JOSEPH, allied health educator; b. Washington, Aug. 17, 1944; s. Paul Joseph and Ruth Irene (O'Malley) M.; m. Loretta Jeanne Calvo; children: Heather Marie, Amy Elizabeth, Timothy Hunter. AS, Quinnipiac Coll., 1971, BS, 1975; MPA, U. Hartford, 1978; EdS, U. Mo., Kansas City, 1989. Registered respiratory therapist; lic. respiratory therapist, Kans. Instr., clin. coord. New Britain (Conn.) Gen. Hosp., 1971-74; instr. Quinnipiac Coll., Hamden, Conn., 1974-76; chief respiratory therapy dept. Providence Hosp., Holyoke, Mass., 1974-80, dir. cardiology/neurology, 1977-80, asst. dir. planning, 1980-81; asst. prof. U. Kans. Sch. Allied Health, Kansas City, 1981-88, assoc. prof., 1988—, chmn. dept. respiratory care edn., 1981-93, assoc. prof. grad. sch., 1992—; assoc. prof. phys. therapy edn. U. Kans. Sch. Allied Health, 1992—; adj. assoc. prof. Ctr. on Aging, U. Kans. Med. Ctr., 1987—; hon. prof. U. Costa Rica, San Jose, 1987—; cons. FDA, 1988, NIH, 1988, 89, SUNY, Stony Brook, 1990, U.S. Pub. Health Svc., 1994, 95, Costa Rican Soc. Sec. Dept., Crit. Care and Emergency Med. System Couns. 1991-92, USPHS/NIH, 1994, 95. Mem. editl. bd. Neonatal Intensive Care, 1990—, Nursing, 1991, Disting. Abstracts, 1991—, Respiratory Therapy, 1992—, Respiratory Therapy Internat., 1993—; author audio tapes in field, 5 book chpts., 1 textbook in field; contbr. articles to profl. jours., chpts. to books. Recipient Creative Achievement award Puritan-Bennett Corp., 1984, 85, A. Gerald Shapiro award N.J. Soc. for Respiratory Care, 1990; fellow Intert. Project HOPE, 1987, 92. Fellow Soc. Crit. Care Medicine; mem. Am. Assn. Respiratory Care (life, bd. dirs. 1984-90, pres. 1988-89), Am. Assn. for Cardiovascular and Pulmonary Rehab., Kans. Soc. Respiratory Care (recognition award 1982-84), Coun. Pulmonary Svc. Mgmt. (life, treas. 1978), Phillipine Soc. Respiratory Care (hon. mem.), N.Y. Acad. Sci., Sigma Xi, Lambda Beta, Pi Lambda Theta. Avocations: scuba diving, reading, travel. Home: 8844 Hemlock Dr Overland Park KS 66212-2946 Office: U Kans 39th and Rainbow Blvd Kansas City KS 66103

MATHEWS, ROBERT EDWARD, banker; b. Columbus, Ohio, Dec. 30, 1909; s. John Sherman and Mary (Stump) M.; m. Alice Nelleny, Sept. 10, 1934; children: Marianne, Robert Edward. Student, Ohio State U., 1931. With Ohio Nat. Bank, Columbus, 1929—; v.p. Ohio Nat. Bank, 1951-66, v.p., cashier, 1966-67, sr. v.p., dir., 1967—; dir. Franklin Industries Ohio. Pres. Franklin County chpt. Am. Cancer Soc., also chmn. bd. trustees Ohio div.; bd. dirs. Ohio Regional Med. Program, Health Careers Ohio, Consumer Credit Counseling Service of Central Ohio; mem. Cancer Research Center. Mem. Columbus C. of C., Res. City Bankers Assn., Am. Inst. Banking, Nat. Assn. Accountants, Bank Adminstrv. Inst. (past pres. Central Ohio chpt.), Aquinas, Ohio State U. alumni assns., Am. Mgmt. Assn. Roman Catholic. Clubs: Brookside Country (Worthington, Ohio) (past pres.); Columbus Athletic (Columbus), Columbus Maennerchor (Columbus), Ambassadors National (Columbus); Scioto Country (Upper Arlington, Ohio). Home: 2299 Abington Rd Columbus OH 43221-3113 Office: 51 N High St Columbus OH 43215-3031

MATHEWS, RODERICK BELL, lawyer; b. Lawton, Okla., Mar. 12, 1941; s. James Malcolm and Sallie Lee (Bell) M.; m. Karla Kurbjin, Apr. 26, 1980; children: Roderick Bell Jr., Andrew Crittenden, Malcolm Timothy. BA, Hampden Syndey Coll., 1963; LLB, U. Richmond, 1966; postgrad., U. Mich., 1991. Bar: Va. 1966. Assoc. Christian, Barton, Parker, Epps & Brent, Richmond, Va., 1966-72; ptnr. Christian, Barton, Epps, Brent & Chappell, Richmond, 1972-88; sr. v.p., corp. legal and govt. affairs officer Trigon Blue Cross & Blue Shield, 1989—. Trustee Children's Hosp., Richmond, 1980—. Mem. ABA (house of dels. 1984-88, state del. Va. 1988-93, bd. govs. 1993—), am. Bar Found., Am. Judicature Soc. (bd. dirs. 1992—), Va. Bar Found., Va. State Bar (pres. 1987-88), Cen. Richmond Assn. (bd. dirs. 1994—). Avocations: travel, fly fishing, photography, skiing. Home: 1516 Park Ave Richmond VA 23220-3538 Office: Mail Drop 02H 2015 Staples Mill Rd Richmond VA 23230

MATHEWS, SHARON WALKER, artistic director, secondary school educator; b. Shreveport, La., Feb. 1, 1947; d. Arthur Delmar and Nona (Frye) Walker; m. John William (Bill) Mathews, Aug. 14, 1971; children: Rebecca, Elizabeth, Anna. BS, La. State U., 1969, MS, 1971. Dance grad. asst. La. State U., Baton Rouge, 1969-71, choreographer, 1975-76; 6th grade tchr. East Baton Rouge Parish, 1971-72, health phys. edn. tchr., 1972-74; dance instr. Magnet High Sch., Baton Rouge, 1975—; artistic dir. Baton Rouge Ballet Theatre, 1975—; dance dir. Dancers' Workshop, Baton Rouge, 1971—; choreographer Baton Rouge Opera, 1989-94. Named Dance Educator of Yr., La. Alliance for Health, Physical Edn., Recreation and Dance, 1986-87. Mem. Southwestern Regional Ballet Assn. (bd. dirs. 1981—, treas., exec. bd. dirs. 1989-92), La. Assn. for Health, Phys. Edn., Recreation and Dance (dance chairperson 1995). Republican. Baptist. Office: Baton Rouge Ballet Theater 10689 Perkins Rd Ste C Baton Rouge LA 70810-1608

MATHEWS, W. GARRET, columnist; b. Covington, Va., Sept. 23, 1949; s. Kenneth G. and Betsy (Waid) M.; m. Maryanne Mathews, June 24, 1978; children: Colin, Evan. BS in Econs., Va. Poly. Inst. and State U., 1971. News editor/columnist Daily Telegraph, Bluefield, W.Va., 1972-87; columnist Evansville (Ind.) Courier, 1987—. Author: Folks I, 1979, Folks II, 1984. With U.S. Army, 1971-77. Avocations: juggling, coaching boys baseball. Home: 7954 Elna Kay Dr Evansville IN 47795 Office: Evansville Courier 300 E Walnut Evansville IN 47715

MATHEWS, WILLIAM HENRY, geologist, educator; b. Vancouver, B.C., Can., Feb. 2, 1919; s. Thomas Mathews and Jean Wilson; m. Laura Lu Tolsted, June 17, 1948; children: Thomas William, Margaret Jean, Janet Marian. BASc, U. B.C., Vancouver, 1940, MASc, 1941; PhD, U. Calif., Berkeley, 1948. Registered profl. engr., B.C. Assoc. mining engr. B.C. Dept. Mines, Victoria, 1942-49; asst. prof. U. Calif., Berkeley, 1949-51; assoc. prof. geology U. B.C., 1951-59, prof., 1959-84, head dept., 1964-71, prof. emeritus, 1984—; cons. in field. Contbr. over 150 articles to profl. jours. Recipient of Willet G. Miller Medal, 1989, Royal Soc. Can. Fellow Geol. Soc. Am. (vice chmn., chmn. Cordilleran sect. 1980-82), Royal Soc. Can. (Willet G. Miller medal 1989); mem. Geol. Soc. Can. (hon., v.p., pres. Cordilleran sect. 1978-80, 94, Career Achievement medal volcanology and igneous geology divsn. 1994), Can. Assn. for Quaternary (Johnston medal 1991), Alpine Club Can. (chmn. Vancouver sect. 1942). Office: U BC, Dept Geol Sci, Vancouver, BC Canada V6T 2B4

MATHEWSON, CHARLES NORMAN, manufacturing company executive; b. Huntington Park, Calif., June 12, 1928; s. Alfred C. and Mildred (Niquette) M.; m. Lucille Linkowitz (div. June 1975); children: Gail P., Robert A., Curtis N.; m. Barbara Martin (div. June 1982); 1 child, Christina Easter; m. Ann Ballinger; 1 child, Miles Carlton. BS in Fin., U. So. Calif., 1953; postgrad., UCLA, 1961. Office mgr., v.p. Hill Richards & Co., L.A., 1953-59; pres. Fradelis Frozen Foods, L.A., 1959-61; account exec. Morgan & Co., L.A., 1961-62; sales mgr. R.J. Henderson & Co., L.A., 1962-63; sr. v.p. Jefferies & Co., L.A., 1963-71; chmn. Arden-Mayfair, Inc., L.A., 1971-75, Wagenseller & Durst, L.A., 1979-80; ind. mgr. pvt. investments Laguna Beach, Calif., 1980-86; chmn. Internat. Game Tech., Reno, 1986—; bd. dirs. Baron Asset Fund, N.Y.C. With U.S. Army, 1946-48. Named Exec. of Yr., Internat. Gaming Bus. Expn., 1990. Mem. Prospectors Club. Republican. Roman Catholic. Avocations: bridge, golf, tennis, hiking. Office: Internat Game Tech 5270 Neil Rd Reno NV 89502-4169

MATHEWSON, CHRISTOPHER COLVILLE, engineering geologist, educator; b. Plainfield, N.J., Aug. 12, 1941; s. George Anderson and Elsa Rae (Shrimpton) M.; m. Janet Marie Olmsted, Nov. 2, 1968; children: Heather Alexis, Glenn George Anderson. BSCE, Case Inst. Tech., 1963; MS in Geol. Engring., U. Ariz., 1965, PhD in Geol. Engring., 1971. Registered profl. engr., Tex., Ariz., geologist, Oreg., Alaska. Officer, lt. Nat. Ocean Survey, 1965-71; prof. Tex. A&M U., College Station, 1981—; cons., speaker in field. Author: Engineering Geology, 1981 (C.P. Holdredge award); contbr. articles to profl. publs. Chmn. College Station Planning and Zoning Commn., 1973-81. Fellow Geol. Soc. Am. (chmn. engring. geology divsn. 1986-87, Meritorious Svc. award 1991); mem. Assn. Engring. Geologists (editor bull. 1981-88, pres. 1988-89), Am. Geol. Inst. (pres. 1991-92), Nat. Coal Coun., Internat. Assn. Engring. Geologists (chmn. U.S. nat. com. 1995-99). Office: Dept Geology Tex A&M Univ College Station TX 77843-3115 *Commitment and dedication to the mission will lead to its successful completion regardless of the odds.*

MATHEWSON, HUGH SPALDING, anesthesiologist, educator; b. Washington, Sept. 20, 1921; s. Walter Eldridge and Jennie Lind (Jones) M.; m. Dorothy Ann Gordon, 1943 (div. 1952); 1 child, Jane Mathewson Holcombe; m. Hazel M. Jones, 1953 (div. 1978); children: Geoffrey K., Brian E., Catherine E. Brock, Jennifer A. Jehle; m. Judith Ann Mahoney, 1979 (div. 1990). Student, Washburn U., 1938-39; A.B., U. Kans., 1942, M.D., 1944. Intern Wesley Hosp., Wichita, Kans., 1944-45; resident anesthesiology U. Kans. Med. Ctr., Kansas City, 1946-48; pvt. practice specializing in anesthesiology Kansas City, Mo., 1948-69; chief anesthesiologist St. Luke's Hosp., Kansas City, 1953-69; med. dir., sect. respiratory therapy U. Kans. Med. Ctr., 1969-92, assoc. prof., 1969-92, prof., 1975-92, prof. anesthesiology emeritus, respiratory care edn., 1992—; examiner schs. respiratory therapy, 1975—; oral examiner Nat. Bd. Respiratory Therapy; mem. Coun. Nurse Anesthesia Practice, 1974-78; prof. phys. therapy edn., 1993—. Author: Structural Forms of Anesthetic Compounds, 1961, Respiratory Therapy in Critical Care, 1976, Pharmacology for Respiratory Therapists, 1977; contbr. articles to profl. publs.; mem. editorial bd. Anesthesia Staff News, 1975-84; assoc. editor: Respiratory Care, 1980—, cons. editor, 1980—, editor-in-chief Respiratory Mgmt., 1989-92. Trustee Kansas City Mus., Kansas City Conservatory of Music, 1993—. Served to lt. comdr. USNR, 1956. Recipient Bird Lit. prize Am. Assn. Respiratory Therapists, 1976. Mem. Mo. Soc. Anesthesiologists (pres. 1963), Kans. Soc. Anesthesiologists (pres. 1974-77), Kans. Med. Soc. (council), Phi Beta Kappa, Sigma Xi, Lambda Beta (hon.). Office: Kans Med Ctr 39th and Rainbow St Kansas City KS 66103

MATHIAS, CHARLES MCCURDY, lawyer, former senator; b. Frederick, Md., July 24, 1922; s. Charles McCurdy and Theresa McElfresh (Trail) M.; m. Ann Hickling Bradford, Nov. 8, 1958; children: Charles Bradford, Robert Fiske. B.A., Haverford Coll., 1944; student, Yale U., 1943-44; LL.B., U. Md., 1949. Bar: Md. 1949, U.S. Supreme Ct. 1954. Asst. atty. gen. of Md., 1953-54; city atty. City of Frederick, 1954-59; mem. Md. Ho. of Dels., 1958, 87th-90th Congresses from 6th Dist. Md., U.S. Senate from Md., 1969-87; ptnr. Jones Day Reavis and Pogue, Washington, 1987-93; chmn. bd. First Am. Bankshares, 1993—; Milton Eisenhower vis. prof. Johns Hopkins U., 1987—. Served from seaman to capt. USNR. Decorated Order of Merit (Federal of Republic Germany), Legion of Honor (France), Order of Orange Nassau (The Netherlands), Order of Brit. Empire (Eng.). Republican. Episcopalian. Office: 1450 G St NW Ste 700 Washington DC 20005-2088

MATHIAS, EDWARD JOSEPH, merchant banker; b. Camden, N.J., Nov. 11, 1941; s. Edward Joseph and Zelma (Pollack) M.; m. Ann Robyn Rafferty, Aug. 3, 1968; 1 child, Ellen Susannah. BA, U. Pa., 1964; MBA, Harvard U., 1971. Mng. dir. T. Rowe Price Assocs., Inc., Balt., 1971-93; mng. dir., co-founder Carlyle Group Merchant Bank, Washington, 1994—; bd. dirs. Fresh Fields, Ovation, Inc. U.S. Office Supply SIRROM Capital; spl. ltd. ptnr. Trident Capital. Bd. overseers Sch. Arts and Scis. U. Pa.; chmn. bd. visitors Kogod Sch. Bus. Adminstrn., Am. Univ. Lt. USN, 1964-69. Mem. Harvard Club, Univ. Club (N.Y.C.), Columbia Country Club (Chevy Chase, Md.), Robert Trent Jones Golf Club (Manassas, Va.), Coral Beach Club (Bermuda), The Brook (N.Y.C.), Ctr. club (Balt.), Met. Club. Republican. Home: 5120 Cammack Dr Bethesda MD 20816-2902 Office: The Carlyle Group 1001 Pennsylvania Ave NW Washington DC 20004-2505

MATHIAS, JOHN JOSEPH, federal administrative law judge; b. Frostburg, Md., July 13, 1929; s. James Maxwell and Mary Genevieve (McGuire) M.; m. Rosemary Povanda, May 30, 1959; children: John Joseph, Terese, Susan. BS, Georgetown U., 1951, JD, 1953. Bar: Md. 1954, D.C. 1954. Ptnr. Lippel & Mathias, Cumberland, Md., 1960-62; adminstrv. law judge CAB, Washington, 1978-79; trial atty. U.S. FTC, Washington, 1956-60, 1962-78, adminstrv. law judge, 1979-84; adminstrv. law judge U.S. Internat. Trade Commn., Washington, 1984-90; chief adminstrv. law judge U.S. Dept. Transp., Washington, 1990—. With U.S. Army, 1954-56. Home: 8812 Connecticut Ave Chevy Chase MD 20815-6737 Office: US Dept Transp 400 7th St SW Washington DC 20590-0001

MATHIAS, JOSEPH SIMON, metallurgical engineer, consultant; b. Bombay, India, Oct. 28, 1925; came to U.S., 1948, naturalized, 1954; s. Pascal Lawrence and Dulcine Applina (De Souza) M.; m. Anna Katherine Elliott, Nov. 10, 1956. BS, U. Bombay, 1944, BA, 1946; PhD, Lehigh U., Bethlehem, Pa., 1954; M in Engring., U. Calif., Berkeley, 1951. Rsch. assoc. Lehigh U., 1951-54; chief metallurgist Superior Metals, Inc., Bethlehem, Pa., 1954-56; mgr. process metall. rsch. Foote Mineral Co., Easton, Pa., 1956-59; mgr. materials rsch., then group mgr. physics and materials Sperry Univac Co., Blue Bell, Pa., 1959-67; dir. rsch. Sperry Univac Co., 1967-79, dir. mfg. and systems hardware rsch., 1979-86, v.p. rsch. and tech., 1986-93; program dir. NSF, Washington; cons. NIST/ATP, Gaithersburg, Md., 1993—; mem. program com. Internat. Magnetic Conf., 1969, 70; cons. in field. Author: Fellow Am. Inst. Chemists, N.Y. Acad. Scis.; mem. IEEE (sr.), Coun. Arts and Sci. Franklin Inst., Riverton Country Club, Rotary (bd. dirs.), Sigma Xi. Club: Riverton Country. Lodge: Rotary (dir.). Patentee in field. Home: 105 Thomas Ave Riverton NJ 08077-1134 Office: NIST/ATP Bldg A 101 Rm 309 Gaithersburg MD 20899

MATHIAS, LESLIE MICHAEL, electronic manufacturing company executive; b. Bombay, Dec. 17, 1935; came to U.S., 1957; s. Paschal Lawrence and Dulcine (D'Souza) M.; m. Vivian Mae Doolittle, Dec. 16, 1962. BSc, U. Bombay, 1957; BS, San Jose (Calif.) State U., 1961. Elec. engr. Indian Standard Metal, Bombay, 1957; sales engr. Bleisch Engring. and Tool, Mt. View, Calif., 1958-60; gen. mgr. Meadows Terminal Bds., Cupertino, Calif., 1961-63; prodn. mgr. Sharidon Corp., Menlo Park, Calif., 1963-67, Videx Corp., Sunnyvale, Calif., 1967-68, Data Tech. Corp., Mt. View, 1968-69; pres. L.G.M. Mfg., Inc., Mt. View, 1969-83; pvt. practice plating cons. Los Altos, Calif., 1983-87; materials mgr. Excel Cirs., Santa Clara, Calif., 1987-91, 93—, acct. mgr., 1991-93, materials mgr., 1993—. Social chmn. Internat. Students, San Jose, 1958-59. Mem. Nat. Fedn. Ind. Bus., Calif. Cirs. Assn., Better Bus. Bur., Purchasing Assn., U.S.C. of C. Roman Catholic. Avocations: computer hacker, electronics, reading, med. jours. Home: 20664 Mapletree Pl Cupertino CA 95014-0449

MATHIAS, REUBEN VICTOR (VIC MATHIAS), real estate executive, investor; b. Coppers Cove, Tex., Mar. 5, 1926; s. Alvin E. and Ella L. (Teinert) M.; m. Helen I. Thoresen, Jan. 28, 1950; children: Mona, Mark, Matt. B.B.A., U. Tex., 1950. Cert. Chamber Exec. Dist. mgr. W.A. Shaeffer Pen Co., Youngstown, Ohio, 1950-51; mgr. Cen-Tex Fair, Temple, Tex., 1951-52; dir. info. Tex. Assn. Soil Conservation Suprs., Temple, 1952-53; mgr. membership dept. Austin (Tex.) C. of C., 1953-56, chief exec. officer, 1956-82; dir. corp. devel. Hardin Corp., Austin, 1983-86; real estate and investments, 1987-92; pres. Tex. Travel Industry Assn., Austin, 1992—; v.p. Austin Tours, Inc.; sec. Longhorn Caverns, Inc.; chmn. bd., instr. Inst. for Orgn. Mgmt., U. Houston. Contbr. monthly editorial Thoughts While Thinking to Austin Mag., 1961-82. Pres. Austin USO Council, 1958-59; v.p. Beautify Tex. Council, 1975-77; founding pres. Discover Tex. Assn., 1969-70; chmn. Central Tex. Blood Donor Fund, 1979. Served with U.S. Army, 1944-46. Mem. Am. C. of C. Execs., Tex. C. of C. Execs. (pres. 1965), Rotary (pres. Austin 1985-86). Lutheran. Home: 3100 Mistywood Cir Austin TX 78746-7861 Office: 400 W 15th St Ste 711 Austin TX 78701-1648 *You can find happiness only by giving it to others. Much of my life has been devoted to community building through voluntary action. The fact that my career has*

---

allowed me to stay in one community has made it possible for me to make and carry out long-term plans, both for the community and personally.

MATHIAS, SEAN GERARD, author, director; b. Swansea, South Wales, U.K., Mar. 14, 1956; s. John Frederick and Anne Josephine (Harding) M. Author: (plays) Cowardice, 1983, Infidelities, 1985, A Prayer for Wings, 1985, Poor Nanny, 1989, Swansea Boys, 1990, Language, 1991, (film) The Lost Language of Cranes, 1990, (novel) Manhattan Mourning, 1988; dir. (plays) Exceptions, 1988, Bent, 1990, Talking Heads, 1991, Noel and Gertie, 1991, Uncle Vanya, 1991, Indiscretions, 1995 (Tony nomination - Direction of a Play). Bd. mem. West End Cares, 1990; trustee Ian Charleson Trust, London, 1990. Recipient Gold medal Lamda, 1972, Fringe First award Edinburgh Festival, 1985. Office: Jonathan Altaras Assocs Ltd 2, Goodwins Ct, London WC2 4LL, England*

MATHIASON, GARRY GEORGE, lawyer; b. Great Falls, Mont., Aug. 6, 1946; s. George Herman and Cora Sylvia M.; m. Karla Jeanne Borud, Aug. 16, 1968; children: Jessica Lee, Tiffany Anne Cora. BS, Northwestern U., 1968; JD, Stanford U., 1971. Bar: Calif., U.S. Dist. Ct. (no. and ea. dists.) Calif. 1972, U.S. Ct. Appeals (9th cir.) 1972, U.S. Ct. Appeals (5th cir.) 1987, U.S. Supreme Ct. 1976. Atty. NLRB, San Francisco, 1971-72; shareholder Littler, Mendelson, Fastiff, Tichy & Mathiason, San Francisco, 1972—; faculty Am. Law Inst. ABA, 1989—, Continuing Edn. of Bar, Calif., 1991—; lectr. Practicing Law Inst., Calif. C. of C., Fed. Pubs., Am. Mgmt. Assns.; gen. counsel Inst. Advancement Japanese-Am. Employment Rels., 1991—. Contbg. author, editor, founder Nat. Employer & Calif. Supplement, 1984-94; contbg. author The Pub. Sch. Employer, 1977; author, creator, presenter Bringing Arbitration into Workplace 2000, 1992; co-author Employee Handbook: How to Write One for your Company, 1992, 93. Mem. nat. adv. bd. sch. speech Northwestern U., Evanston, Ill., 1990—. Mem. ABA (chair labor law divsn. construction industry forum com. 1984-86). Office: Littler Mendelson Fastiff Tichy & Mathiason 650 California St Fl 20 San Francisco CA 94108-2702

MATHIES, ALLEN WRAY, JR., physician, hospital administrator; b. Colorado Springs, Colo., Sept. 23, 1930; s. Allen W. and Esther S. (Norton) M.; m. Lewise Austin, Aug. 23, 1956; children: William A., John N. BA, Colo. Coll., 1952; MS, Columbia U., 1956, PhD., 1958; MD, U. Vt., 1961. Rsch. assoc. U. Vt., Burlington, 1957-61; intern L.A. County Hosp., 1961-62; resident in pediatrics L.A. Gen. Hosp., 1962-64; asst. prof. pediatrics U. So. Calif., L.A., 1964-68, assoc. prof., 1968-71, prof., 1971—, assoc. dean, 1969-74, interim dean, 1974-75, dean, 1975-85; head physician Communicable Disease Svc. U. So. Calif., Los Angeles, 1975—; pres., chief exec. officer Huntingtom Meml. Hosp., Pasadena, Calif., 1985-94; pres., CEO So. Calif. Healthcare Sys., Pasadena, 1992—; bd. dirs. Pacific Mut. Contbr. articles to med. jours. Bd. dirs. Occidental Coll. With U.S. Army, 1953-55. Mem. Am. Acad. Pediatrics, Infectious Disease Soc. Am., Am. Pediatric Soc., Soc. Pediatric Rsch. Republican. Episcopalian. Home: 314 Arroyo Dr South Pasadena CA 91030-1623 Office: Huntington Meml Hosp PO Box 7013 Pasadena CA 91109

MATHIES, RICHARD ALFRED, chemistry educator; b. Seattle, Sept. 20, 1946; s. James Crosby and Liuba (Ivanoff) M.; m. Jo Anne Johnson, Jan. 20, 1979; children: Christopher James, Jennifer Lane. B.S., U. Wash.-Seattle, 1968; M.S., Cornell U., 1970, Ph.D., 1974. Researcher, teaching asst. chemistry dept. Cornell U., Ithaca, N.Y., 1969-73; postdoctoral fellow Yale U., New Haven, 1973-76; asst. prof. chemistry U. Calif.-Berkeley, 1976-82, assoc. prof. chemistry, 1982-86, prof., 1986—. Contbr. articles to profl. jours. Helen Hay Whitney fellow Yale U., 1974-76; A.P. Sloan fellow, 1979-81; NIH Research Career Devel. award, 1981-86; Harold Lamport award N.Y. Acad. Sci., 1983. Mem. Biophys. Soc., Am. Chem. Soc., AAAS. Office: Chemistry Dept U Calif Berkeley CA 94720

MATHIESON, ANDREW WRAY, investment management executive; b. Pitts., June 11, 1928; s. Andrew Russell and Margaret (Wray) M.; m. Helen Fricke, Dec. 5, 1953; children—Margaret Adele Conver, Andrew Fricke, Peter Ferris. B.S. in Mech. Engring. Bucknell U., 1950; M.S. in Indsl. Adminstrn, Carnegie-Mellon U., 1952. With elevator div. Westinghouse Electric Corp., 1955-63; dist. mgr. Westinghouse Electric Corp., Cleve., 1960-62; asst. group v.p. constrn. group Westinghouse Electric Corp., Pitts., 1962-63; with T. Mellon and Sons, Pitts., 1963-71; v.p., gov. T. Mellon and Sons, 1967-71; v.p. Richard K. Mellon and Sons, Pitts., 1971-78; exec. v.p. Richard K. Mellon and Sons, 1978—; dir. Gen. Re Corp., Mellon Nat. Corp. Trustee, vice-chmn. Richard King Mellon Found., R.K. Mellon Family Found.; bd. dirs. St. Margaret Meml. Hosp., Pitts., 1966—, pres., 1976-81; exec. com. Allegheny Conf. Cmty. Devel., 1976. With USNR, 1952-55. Episcopalian. Clubs: Duquesne (Pitts.) (bd. dirs. 1986, pres. 1989), Fox Chapel Golf (Pitts.) (dir. 1974); Laurel Valley Golf (Ligonier, Pa.), Rolling Rock (Ligonier, Pa.) (v.p., gov.); Unversity (N.Y.C.), Links (N.Y.C.). Home: 14 The Trillium Pittsburgh PA 15238-1929 Office: Richard K Mellon and Sons PO Box 3030 Pittsburgh PA 15230-3030

MATHIESON, J. DOUGLAS, engineering association executive. BA, Denison U., 1955; D in Philosophy and Letters, U. Madrid; degree in assn. mgmt., Mich. State U. Mem. pub. rels. staff GM, from 1955; mgr. seminars, edn. and membership devel. Soc. Mfg. Engrs.; dir. membership and confs. and expns. Engring. Soc. Detroit-The Engring. Soc., 1964-72, exec. v.p., 1972—. Active various environ. orgns. Mem. Coun. Engring. and Sci. Soc. Execs. (past pres.), Mich. Soc. Assn. Execs. (past pres.). Office: Engring Soc Detroit The Engring Soc 100 Farnsworth Detroit MI 48202

MATHIEU, HELEN M., state legislator; b. Newport, R.I., May 8, 1940; m. Roger E. Mathieu, 1964. Grad., Salve Regina Coll. Mem. R.I. State Senate, dist. 46. Mem. Kappa Gamma Pi. Democrat. Roman Catholic. Home: 160 Lawrence Dr Portsmouth RI 02871-4063 Office: R I State Senate State Capital Providence RI 02903

MATHIEU, HENRI DONAT See SAINT LAURENT, YVES

MATHILE, CLAYTON LEE, corporate executive; b. Portage, Ohio, Jan. 11, 1941; s. Wilbert and Helen (Good) M.; m. Mary Ann Maas, July 7, 1962; children: Cathy, Tim, Mike, Tina, Jennie. BA, Ohio No. U., 1962, DBA (hon.), 1991; postgrad., Bowling Green State U., 1964. Acct. GM, Napoleon, Ohio, 1962-63; acct. Campbell Soup Co., Napoleon, 1963-65, buyer, 1965-67, purchasing agt., 1967-70; gen. mgr. The Iams Co., Dayton, Ohio, 1970-75, v.p., 1975-80, chief exec. officer, 1980-90, chmn., chief exec. officer, 1990—, also dir.; mem. Pet Food Inst.; bd. dirs. Midwest Group, Cin., Bush Bros. Co., Knoxville, Tenn. Author: A Business Owner's Perspective on Outside Boards. Trustee Chaminade-Julienne High Sch., Dayton, 1987—, U. Dayton; mem. adv. bd. coll. bus. Ohio No. U., Ada, 1987—, also trustee. Named Best of Best Ctr. for Values Rsch., Houston, 1987. Mem. Am. Mgmt. Assn., Am. Agt. Assn. Roman Catholic. Avocations: traveling, swimming, golf. Officer: The Iams Company 7250 Poe Ave Dayton OH 45414-2572*

MATHIS, ALLEN WASHINGTON, JR., manufacturing executive; b. Gadsen, Ala., Apr. 29, 1920; s. Allen Washington and Ola Gertrude (Davis) M.; m. Gloria Beverly Taylor, Oct. 26, 1942; children: Caryl Lynn Mathis Cusick, Beverly Gayle Mathis Hargrave, Allen Washington III. BS, Harvard U., 1942, MBA, 1947. 2nd v.p. Continental Ill. Bank, Chgo., 1947-52; pres. and chief exec. officer Club Aluminum Products Co., La Grange Park, Ill., 1952-65, The Presidents Assn., N.Y.C., 1965-70, The Kershaw Cos., Montgomery, Ala., 1971-73; chmn. and chief exec. officer Mathis & Mathis, Inc., Montgomery, 1973—; chmn. Griffin Corp., Valdosta, Ga., 1975-90; also bd. dirs. Griffin Corp., Valdosta; chmn. CEO Internat., Inc., Dallas, 1987-89; bd. dirs. Bell Packaging Corp, Marion, Ind., Winona (Minn.) Knitting Mills, Inc., Colonial Bancgroup, Montgomery; adj. prof. mgmt. Auburn U., Coll. of Bus., 1988—. Author (with others) Handbook for Corporate Directors, 1985. Mem. exec. bd. Nat. Coun. Boy Scouts Am., Dallas, 1968-80, adv. com. to exec. bd., 1980-91; bd. dirs. Montgomery YMCA, 1994—; trustee Christian Workers Found., Montgomery, 1970—; pres. Four Way Test Assn., 1979—. Capt. Field Artillery U.S. Army, 1942-45, PTO. Decorated Bronze Star, U.S. Army, Japan, 1945; recipient Silver Beaver Boy Scouts Am., 1960, Silver Antelope 1966, Silver Buffalo, 1968, Disting. Eagle, 1974; named to Disting. Bd. Visitors Air Univ., U.S. Air

---

Force, 1984-87. Mem. Chgo. Club, Montgomery Country Club, Harvard Bus. Sch. Club, Birmingham, Ala. Republican. Presbyterian. Avocations: boating, swimming.

MATHIS, DAVID B., financial services and insurance company executive; b. Atlanta, Ga.. BA, Lake Forest Coll., 1960. Formerly exec. v.p. ins. ops. Kemper Corp., Long Grove, Ill., pres., chief oper. officer, 1990-92; chmn., chief exec. officer Kemper Corp., 1992—, also bd. dirs. Office: Kemper Corp 1 Kemper Dr Long Grove IL 60047-9108*

MATHIS, JACK DAVID, advertising executive; b. La Porte, Ind. Nov. 27, 1931; s. George Anthony and Bernice (Bennethum) M.; student U. Mo., 1950-52; BS, Fla. State U., 1955; m. Phyllis Dene Hoffman, Dec. 24, 1971; children: Kane Cameron, Jana Dene. With Benton & Bowles, Inc., 1955-56; owner Jack Mathis Advt., 1956—; cons. films, including That's Action!, 1977, Great Movie Stunts: Raiders of the Lost Ark, 1981, The Making of Raiders of the Lost Ark, 1981, An American Legend: The Lone Ranger, 1981; Heroes and Sidekicks: Indiana Jones and the Temple of Doom, 1984, The Republic Pictures Story, 1991, The Making of The Quiet Man, 1992, Roy Rogers: King of the Cowboys, 1992, Cliffhangers: Adventures from the Thrill Factory, 1993, The Making of Sands of Iwo Jima, 1993, Gene Autry: Melody of the West, 1994. Mem. U.S. Olympic Basketball Com. Recipient citation Mktg. Research Council N.Y., inducted Ill. Basketball Hall of Fame. Mem. Alpha Delta Sigma. Author: Valley of the Cliffhangers, Republic Confidential. Office: PO Box 3580 Barrington IL 60011-3580

MATHIS, JAMES FORREST, retired petroleum company executive; b. Dallas, Sept. 28, 1925; s. Forrest and Martha (Godbold) M.; m. Frances Ellisor, Sept. 4, 1948; children: Alan Forrest (dec.), Lisa Lynn Lambeth. BS in Chem. Engring., Tex. A&M U., 1946; MS, U. Wis., 1951, PhD, 1953. Rsch. engr. Humble Oil & Refining Co., Baytown, Tex., 1946-49, 53-61, mgr. rsch. and devel., 1961-63, mgr. Splty. products planning, 1963-65; v.p. Exxon Rsch. & Engring. Co., Linden, N.J., 1966-68; sr. v.p., dir. Imperial Oil Ltd., Toronto, Ont., Can., 1968-71; v.p. tech. Exxon Chem. Co., Florham Park, N.J., 1971-80; v.p. sci. and tech. Exxon Corp., N.Y.C., 1980-84; ret., 1984; cons. Arthur D. Little, 1985-92, ChemShare Corp., 1989-92; chmn. N.J. Commn. Sci and Tech., 1988—; dir. Laser Recording Systems, Inc., 1989-93, N L Industries, 1985-86, Hanlin Corp., 1989—. Bd. dirs. Chem. Industry Inst. Toxicology, 1975-83, treas., 1977-80, chmn., 1980-83; trustee Wis. Alumni Rsch. Found., 1989—, pres. 1993—; bd. chem. sci. and tech. of Nat. Rsch. Coun., 1987-89. Served with AC, USNR, 1944-45. Recipient Disting. Alumni award Coll. Engring. Tex. A&M U., 1982, Disting. Svc. citation Coll. Enring. U. Wis., 1969. Fellow Am. Inst. Chem. Engrs. (interim exec. dir., sec., 1987-88, Robert L. Jacks award in Mgmt. 1985, Van Antwerpen award for Svc. to Inst. 1989); mem. AAAS, NAE, Am. Chem. Soc. (Earle B. Barnes award for Chem. Rsch. Mgmt. 1984), Sigma Xi, Phi Lambda Upsilon, Tau Beta Pi. Presbyterian. Achievements include 2 patents in field. Home: 96 Colt Rd Summit NJ 07901-3042 Office: PO Box 3 Summit NJ 07902-0003

MATHIS, JOHNNY, singer; b. San Francisco, Sept. 30, 1935; s. Clem and Mildred Mathis. Student, San Francisco State Coll. Recordings include It's Not for Me to Say, Chances are, Someone, Twelfth of Never, There Goes My Heart, My One and Only Love, Let Me Love You; albums include Johnny Mathis, 1956, Wonderful, Wonderful, 1957, Warm, 1957, Good Night, Dear Lord, 1958, Johnny's Greatest Hits, 1958, Swing Softly, 1958, Merry Christmas, 1958, Open Fire, Two Guitars, 1959, More Johnny's Greatest Hits, 1959, Heavenly, 1959, Faithfully, 1960, The Rhythms and Ballads of Broadway, 1960, Johnny's Mood, 1960, I'll Buy You a Star, 1961, Portrait of Johnny, 1961, Live It Up, 1962, Rapture, 1962, Johnny's Newest Hits, 1963, Johnny, 1963, Romantically, 1963, I'll Search My Heart, 1964, Tender is the Night, 1965, The Wonderful World of Make Believe, 1965, This is Love, 1966, Ole, 1966, The Sweetheart Tree, 1967, Up, Up and Away, 1967, Love is Blue, 1968, Those Were the Days, 1968, People, 1969, The Impossible Dream, 1969, Raindrops Keep Fallin' On My Head, 1970, Close To You, 1970, Bacharach & Kaempfert, 1970, Love Story, 1970, You've Got a Friend, 1971, The First Time Ever I Saw Your Face, 1972, Song Sung Blue, 1972, Me and Mrs. Jones, 1973, Killing Me Softly With Her Song, 1973, I'm Coming Home, 1973, The Heart of a Woman, 1974, Feelings, 1975, I Only Have Eyes for You, 1976, Hold Me, Thrill Me, Kiss Me, 1977, You Light Up My Life, 1978, Mathis Magic, 1979, Different Kinda Different, 1980, Friends in Love, 1982, A Special Part of Me, 1984, Johnny Mathis Live, 1984, Right From the Heart, 1985, Christmas Eve With Johnny Mathis, 1986, In The Still of the Night, 1989, In a Sentimental Mood: Mathis Sings Ellington, 1990, Better Together, 1991, How do you Keep the Music Playing, 1992, Music of Johnny Mathis: A Personal Collection, 1993; appeared in films Lizzie, 1957, A Certain Smile, 1958; tours of Europe, Africa, Australia, S.Am., Orient, Can.; rec. artist, Columbia Records, Mercury Records, 1964-67. Avocations: cooking, golf. Office: care Rojon Prodns Inc PO Box 2066 Burbank CA 91507*

MATHIS, LARRY LEE, health care administrator; b. Lincoln, Nebr., May 29, 1943; s. Henry William George and Berneta Lucille (Van Laningham) M.; children—Julie, Jennifer. B.A. in Social Scis., Pittsburg State U., Kans., 1965; M.H.A., Washington U., St. Louis, 1972; postgrad. health systems mgmt., Harvard U., 1978, advanced mgmt. program, 1982. Adminstrv. resident Meth. Hosp., Houston, 1971-72, adminstrv. asst., 1972, asst. to pres., 1972-74, v.p. 1974-78, sr. v.p., 1978-80, exec. v.p., chief operating officer, 1980-83, pres., CEO, 1983—. Contbr. articles to profl. jours. Health svcs. chair U.S. Savs. Bond Vol. Com. Gulf Coast, Diagnostic Ctr. Hosp., Houston, 1972—; mem. bd. global ministries Tex. Conf. United Meth. Ch., 1984—; chmn., bd. dirs. Greater Houston Hosp. Coun. Rsch. and Edn. Found., 1985—. Capt. U.S. Army, 1965-70, Vietnam. Decorated Bronze Star, Vietnamese Cross of Gallantry; recipient Alumni Meritorious Achievement award Pittsburg State U., 1984. Fellow Am. Coll. Healthcare Execs. (gov. 1990-94); mem. Am. Hosp. Assn. (chmn. 1993, spkr. Ho. Dels. 1994), Healthcare Execs. Study Soc., Assn. Univ. Programs in Health Adminstrn., Assn. Am. Med. Colls. (various coms. coun. on tchg. hosps.), Tex. Hosp. Assn. (trustee 1984-90, chmn. 1988-89), Washington U. alumni Assn. (pres. 1988-90), Houston C. of C., Greater Houston Hosp. Coun. (chmn. bd. dirs. 1983-84), Petroleum Club, Ramada Club, Drs. Club, Harvard Bus. (bd. dirs. 1986-87), Houston City. Avocations: sailing; reading; hunting; traveling. Home: 3037 Reba Houston TX 77019 Office: Meth Hosp Sys 6565 Fannin St Houston TX 77030-2707

MATHIS, LUSTER DOYLE, college administrator, political scientist; b. Gainesville, Ga., May 5, 1936; s. Luster and Fay Selena (Wingo) M.; m. Rheba Burch, June 5, 1958; children—Douglas James, Deborah Jane. A.B., Berry Coll., 1958; M.A., U. Ga., 1958, Ph.D. (Univ. Alumni Found. fellow), 1966. Asst. prof. polit. sci. Brenau Coll., Gainesville, 1960-61; asso. prof. Calif. Baptist Coll., 1961-62, Belmont Coll., Nashville, 1962-64; asso. prof., head dept. polit. sci. W.Ga. Coll., Carrollton, 1965-68; prof. W.Ga. Coll., 1969-75, head dept., 1969-71, chmn. div. grad. studies, 1970-73; assoc. dean, 1972-75; research asso., asst. editor Papers of Thomas Jefferson Princeton U., 1968-69; v.p., dean of coll. Berry Coll., Mt. Berry, Ga., 1975-93, v.p. acad. affairs, 1993—; cons. Citizens Com. on Ga. Gen. Assembly. Co-author: Courts as Political Instruments, 1970. Mem. Ga. Democratic Charter Commn., 1974-75; mem. consumer adv. com. Floyd Med. Center, 1978-80. Nat. Hist. Publs. Commn. fellow, 1968-69. Mem. Am. Assn. Higher Edn., Am. Conf. Acad. Deans, Ga. Polit. Sci. Assn. (pres. 1968-69), Conf. Acad. Deans of the So. States, Kiwanis. Democrat. Baptist. Office: Berry Coll Mount Berry GA 30149

MATHIS, MARK JAY, lawyer; b. N.Y.C., Aug. 25, 1947; s. Meyer and Beulah (Nechemias) M.; m. Marylin Gail Goodman, Aug. 14, 1971; children: Alison Leigh, Brian Todd. BS, MIT, 1969; JD, U. Pa., 1972. Bar: D.C. 1973. Assoc. Arent, Fox, Kintner, Plotkin & Kahn, Washington, 1972-75; minority counsel Com. on D.C. U.S. Ho. of Reps., 1975-76; atty. Chesapeake & Potomac Telephone Cos., Washington, 1977-81, gen. atty., 1982-83, v.p., gen. counsel, 1984-89, v.p., assoc. gen. counsel Bell Atlantic Network Svcs., Washington, 1988-89, v.p., gen. counsel, 1990-91; v.p., dep. gen. counsel, sec. Bell Atlantic Corp., Phila., 1992; v.p., gen. counsel Bell Atlantic NSI, Arlington, Va., 1993—. Office: Bell Atlantic NSI 8th Fl 1320 N Court House Rd Arlington VA 22201

MATHIS, SHARON BELL, author, elementary educator, librarian; b. Atlantic City, Feb. 26, 1937; d. John Willie and Alice Mary (Frazier) Bell; m. Leroy F. Mathis, July 11, 1957 (div. Jan. 1979); children: Sherie, Stacy, Stephanie. B.A., Morgan State Coll., 1958; M.L.S., Catholic U. Am., 1975. Interviewer Children's Hosp. of D.C., Washington, 1958-59; tchr. Holy Redeemer Elementary Sch., Washington, 1959-65; Charles Hart Jr. High Sch., Washington, 1965-72; spl. edn. tchr. Stuart Jr. High Sch., Washington, 1972-74; librarian Benning Elementary Sch., Washington, 1975-76, Friendship Ednl. Center, 1976—; writer-in-charge children's lit. div. D.C. Black Writers Workshop; writer-in-residence Howard U., 1972-73. Author: Brooklyn Story, 1970, Sidewalk Story, 1971 (Council on Interracial Books for Children award 1970), Teacup Full of Roses, 1972 (Outstanding Book of Yr. award New York Times 1972), Ray Charles, 1973 (Coretta Scott King award 1974), Listen for the Fig Tree, 1974, The Hundred Penny Box, 1975 (Boston Globe-Horn Book Honor book 1975, Newbery Honor Book 1976), Cartwheels, 1977, Red Dog Blue Fly: Football Poems, 1991 (Children's Book of Yr. award Bank St. Coll. 1992). Mem. bd. advisers lawyers com. D.C. Commn. on Arts, 1972. Nominated Books for Brotherhood list NCCJ, 1970; recipient D.C. Assn. Sch. Librs. award 1976, Arts and Humanities award Archdiocese of Washington Black Secretariat, 1978; Weekly Reader Book Club fellow Bread Loaf Writers Conf., 1970, MacDowell Colony fellow, 1978. Roman Catholic. *My success is due to the glorious African blood which flows throughout my body—and to the dignity, intelligence, strength, pride, efforts, and faith of my very creative parents—and all other Black people who have helped me.*

MATHIS, WILLIAM LOWREY, lawyer; b. Jackson, Tenn., Dec. 19, 1926; s. Harry Fletcher and Syrene (Lowrey) M.; m. Marilyn Jayne Cason, Sept. 10, 1949; children—Amanda Jayne, Amy Susan, Peter Andrew, Perry Alexander, Anne Lowrey. B.M.E., Duke U., 1947; J.D., George Washington U., 1951. Bar: D.C. bar 1951, Fla. bar 1972, Va. bar 1977. Examiner U.S. Patent Office, 1947-52; mem. firm Swecker & Mathis, Washington, 1952-61, Burns, Doane, Swecker & Mathis, Alexandria, Va., 1961—; adj. prof. law Georgetown U. Law Center, 1974—. Co-author: Trademark Litigation in the Trademark Office and Federal Courts, 1977; also chpt. in Handbook of Modern Marketing, 2d edit., 1986. Mem. Am., D.C. bar assns., Am. Intellectual Property Law Assn., Order of Coif. Roman Catholic. Home: 3709 Chanel Rd Annandale VA 22003-2024 Office: George Mason Bldg Washington and Prince Sts Alexandria VA 22313

MATHIS, WILLIAM WALTER, career officer; b. Washington, Apr. 18, 1939; s. Oliver Bennette and Sara Jane (Miles) M.; m. Patricia Lee Winter, May 22, 1959; children: Lisa S., Lauren L. BA, U. Md., 1962. Commd. ensign USN, 1962, advanced through grades to rear adm., 1990; student Naval Justice Sch., Newport, R.I., 1963; officer USS Blue (DD 744), 1963-65; student Naval Destroyer Sch., Newport, 1965; Officer USS Haverfield (DER 393), 1965-67; student Naval Mine Warfare Schs., Charleston, S.C., 1967; officer USS Adroit (MSO 509) (XO), 1967-69; assignment officer Bur. Naval Pers., 1969-71; officer Officer of Chief Naval Officer, 1972-73; student Armed Forces Staff Coll., 1973-74, Naval Destroyer Sch., Newport, 1974; officer USS Koelsch (DE 1049), 1974-75; joint short range plans officer Office of Chief Naval Officer, 1975-78; surface warfare officer Schs. Command, Newport, 1978; student Naval Amphibious Sch, Little Creek, 1978; commdg. officer USS Robert E. Peary (FF 1073), 1978-80; surface ops. officer Comdr. Carrier Group Seven, 1980-82; fleet plans and policy officer Staff CINCPACFLT, 1984-86; comdg. officer USS Fox (CG 33), 1986-88; dir. surface officer Naval Mil. Pers., Distbn. Div., 1099-89; comdr. Mine Warfare Command, 1989-91, U.S. Naval Forces, Dem. People's Republic of Korea, 1991—. Decorated Legion of Merit with two gold stars, Meritorious Svc. medal with three gold stars, Battle Efficiency ribbon, Meritorious Unit citation, Navy Expeditionary medal, others. Republican. Avocations: golf, photography, woodworking, water sports. Home and Office: US Naval Forces WNY Bldg 210 901 M St SE Washington DC 20398-5540

MATHISON, IAN WILLIAM, chemistry educator, academic dean; b. Liverpool, Eng., Apr. 17, 1938; came to U.S., 1963; s. William and Grace (Almond) M.; m. Mary Ann Gordon, July 20, 1968; children: Mark W., Lisa A. B. Pharm., U. London, 1960, Ph.D., 1963, D. Sci., 1976. Lic. pharmacist, Gt. Britain. Research assoc. U. Tenn. Ctr. for Health Scis., Memphis, 1963-65, asst. prof., 1965-68, assoc. prof., 1968-72, prof., 1972-76; medicinal chemistry prof. Ferris State U., Big Rapids, Mich., 1977—, dean, prof., 1977—; external examiner U. Sci., Malaysia, 1978-79; mem. Mich. Dept. Mental Health Pharmacy Facilities Rev. Panel, Lansing, 1978—; Quality Assurance Commn., 1979—; cons. in field. Mem. editorial bd.: Jour. Pharm. Sci., 1981-86; contbr. articles to profl. jours.; sr. inventor, patentee in field. Marion Labs. awardee, 1965-74; NSF grantee, 1968-72; Beecham Co. grantee, 1974-79. Fellow Royal Inst. Chemistry, Royal Soc. Chemistry; mem. Am. Pharm. Soc., Am. Chem. Soc., Am. Assn. Coll. Pharmacy. Bd. dirs. 1988-90), Nat. Assn. Retail Druggists (edn. adv. com. 1989-94), Royal Pharm. Soc. Gt. Britain, Nat. Assn. Chain Drug Stores (ednl. adv. com. 1993—). Home: 820 Osborn Cir Big Rapids MI 49307-2536 Office: Ferris State U 901 S State St Big Rapids MI 49307-2251

MATHOG, ROBERT HENRY, otolaryngologist, educator; b. New Haven, Apr. 13, 1939; s. William and Tiby (Gans) M.; m. Deena Jane Rabinowitz, June 14, 1964; children: Tiby, Heather, Lauren, Jason. AB, Dartmouth Coll., 1960; MD, NYU, 1964. Diplomate Am. Bd. Facial Plastic and Reconstructive Surgery. Intern Duke Hosp., Durham, N.C., 1964-65; resident surgery Duke Hosp., 1965-66, resident otolaryngology, 1966-69; practice medicine, specializing in otolaryngology Mpls., 1971-77, Detroit, 1977—; chief of otolaryngology Hennepin County Med. Center, Mpls., 1972-77; asst. prof. U. Minn., 1971-74, asso. prof., 1974-77; prof., chmn. dept. otolaryngology Wayne State U. Sch. Medicine, 1977—; chief otolaryngology Hennepin County Hosp., Mpls., 1972-77, Harper-Grace Hosps., Detroit, 1977—, Detroit Receiving Hosp., 1977-92; cons. staff VA Hosp., Allen Park, Minn., 1977—, Children's Hosp., Detroit, 1977—, Hutzel Hosp., Detroit, 1966; mem. adv. coun. Nat. Inst. Deaf and Other Communicable Disorders NIH, 1992—; chief otolaryngology, head and neck surgery June Hosp., 1994-95. Author: Otolaryngology Clinics of North America, 1976, Textbook of Maxillofacial Trauma, 1983; editor in chief Videomed. Edn. Systems, 1972-75; editor: Atlas of Craniofacial Trauma, 1992; contbr. articles to med. jours. Bd. dirs. Bexer County Hearing Soc., 1969-71; adv. coun. WIDCB, 1993. Maj. USAF, 1969-71. Recipient Valentine Mott medal for proficiency in anatomy, 1961, Recognition award Wayne State Bd. Govs. Faculty, 1993; Deafness Rsch. Found. grantee, 1979-81, NIH grantee, 1986, 92. Fellow ACS, Am. Acad. Otolaryngology, Head and Neck Sugery (cert. award 1976, cert. Appreciation 1978); Am. Soc. Head and Neck Surgery, Triological Soc. (v.p. 1995—), Am. Otol. Soc., Am. Acad. Facial Plastic and Reconstructive Surgery (v.p. 1980), Am. Neurotology Soc.; mem. AMA, Am. Laryngol. Soc. (coun. 1995—), Am. Laryngol. Assn., Mich. Med. Soc., Am. Head and Neck Soc., Am. Soc. Univ. Otolaryngologists (pres. elect 1994), Assn. Acad. Depts. Otolaryngology, Assn. Rsch. Otolaryngology (pres. 1981), Soc. U. Otolaryngology-Head Neck Surgery (pres. 1994—). Home: 27115 Wellington Rd Franklin MI 48025-1329 Office: Otolaryngology 27117 Lahser Rd Ste 203 Southfield MI 48034-8468 Office: Wayne State U Sch Medicine 540 E Canfield St Detroit MI 48201-1928

MATHUES, THOMAS OLIVER, retired automobile company executive; b. Dayton, Ohio, Jan. 26, 1923; s. John Leslie and Florence (Killen) M.; m. Patricia McFarland, May 20, 1944 (dec. Feb. 1992); children: Thomas P., Rebecca, John, Jennifer; m. Mary Nell Galloway, Apr. 15, 1993. Student, Grove City Coll., 1944-45, U. Ill., 1945-46; B.M.E., Gen. Motors Inst., 1947; postgrad., Harvard U. Bus. Sch., 1976. With Inland div. Gen. Motors Corp., Dayton, 1940-78; gen. mgr. Inland div. Gen. Motors Corp., 1966-78; v.p. mfg. staff Gen. Motors, Warren, Mich., 1978-81, v.p. current engring. and mfg. services staff, 1981-85. Served with USNR, 1944-46. Mem. Soc. Automotive Engrs., Commonwealth Yacht Club (Grand Rivers, Ky.), Phi Gamma Delta. Mem. Christian Ch. (Disciples of Christ). Patentee in field. Home: 1930 Sledd Creek Rd Gilbertsville KY 42044-9402

MATHUR, RUPA AJWANI, state official, risk management consultant; b. Khairpur, Sind, India, Nov. 2, 1939; came to U.S., 1980; d. Mehnghraj Lalchand and Giani Ajwani; m. Ramesh Saran Mathur, Mar. 2, 1967; children: Sanjay Saran, Seema. BA with honors, Bombay U., 1962, LLB, 1965. CPCU. Lawyer High Ct., Bombay; with GM, U.K., Lindus & Horton, U.K.; welfare staff Brit. High Commn., Africa, 1977-78; English tchr. Thai-

land, 1978-80; ins. specialist, analyst Met. Transit Authority, Houston, 1980-83; ins. analyst Coastal Corp., Houston, 1983-84; dir. ins. and employee benefits Houston Ind. Sch. Dist., 1984-88; dir. risk mgmt. and benefits Harris County, Houston, 1988-94; dir. State Risk Mgmt., Austin, 1994—; owner Health Environ. and Risk Mgmt. Co. (HER Inc.); team leader risk mgmt. del. People to People, Ea. Europe and Russia, 1993, China, 1994; instr. CPCU and accredited advisor ins. courses U. Houston Sch. Inst. Mktg. and Fin., 1985-88; speaker in field. Author: Managing Occupational Injury Costs, 1993; contbr. articles to profl. jours. Chmn. Multi Cultural Soc., Ft. Bend County, Tex., 1992, Indian Cmty.-Equal Opportunity, Houston, 1990; bd. dirs. Children at Risk, Ft. Bend Sch. Dist., 1990, mem. task force Multi Culture Ctr., 1993; co-founder Internat. Gourmet Club, 1976; sec.-treas. Internat. Ladies Club, 1976; tchr. English, YMCA, Thailand, 1976; founder Indian Am. Orgn. for Equal Opportunity; bd. dirs. India Culture Ctr., 1993-94. Recipient Honor award Tex. Safety Assn., 1993, Woman on the Move award Houston Post and KPRC/Channel 2, 1993. Mem. Profl. Women in Govt., Risk and Ins. Mgrs. Soc. (com.), Pub. Risk and Ins. Mgmt. Assn. (past pres. Tex. chpt.), World Safety Orgn. (cert. safety exec., appreciation award 1991, Concerned Safety Profl. award 1993), CPCU's (edn. com.), State and Local Govt. Benefits Assn., Nat. Safety Coun. (safety awards), Profl. Devel. Inst. (past officer). M. Avocations: travel, reading, writing, painting, fishing. Home: 3802 Point Clear Missouri City TX 77459 Office: Harris County 1310 Prairie Houston TX 77002

MATHWICH, DALE F., insurance company executive; b. 1934. Student, U. Wis., 1954. With Am. Family Mutual Ins. Co., Madison, Wis., 1955—; state dir. Am. Family Mutual Ins. Co., Rockford, Ill., 1970-79; mktg. dir. Am. Family Mutual Ins. Co., 1979-82, v.p. mktg., 1982-85, exec. v.p., 1985-86, pres., chief oper. officer, from 1986, now chmn. bd., CEO. Office: Am Family Ins Group 6000 American Pky Madison WI 53783

MATIA, PAUL RAMON, federal judge; b. Cleve., Oct. 2, 1937; s. Leo Clemens and Irene Elizabeth (Linkert) M.; m. Nancy Arch Van Meter, Jan. 2, 1993. BA, Case Western Res. U., 1959; JD, Harvard U., 1962. Law clk. Common Pleas Ct. of Cuyahoga County, Cleve., 1963-66, judge, 1985-91; asst. atty. gen. State of Ohio, Cleve., 1966-69; adminstrv. asst. to atty. gen. State of Ohio, Columbus, 1969-70; senator Ohio State Senate, Columbus, 1971-75, 79-83; ptnr. Hadley, Matia, Mills & MacLean Co., L.P.A., Cleve., 1975-84; judge U.S. Dist. Ct. (no. dist.) Ohio, 1991—. Candidate Lt. Gov. Rep. Primary, 1982, Ohio Supreme Ct., 1988; vice chmn. exec. com. Cuyahoga County Rep. Orgn., Cleve., 1971-84. Named Outstanding Legislator, Ohio Assn. for Retarded Citizens, 1974, Watchdog of Ohio Treasury, United Conservatives of Ohio, 1979; recipient Heritage award Polonia Found., 1988. Mem. ABA, Ohio Bar Assn., Clev. Bar Assn. (Pres.'s award 1988), Cuyahoga County Bar Assn., Athletic Club of Columbus, The Club at Soc. Ctr. Avocations: skiing, gardening, travel. Office: US Dist Ct 201 Superior Ave E Cleveland OH 44114-1204

MATIJEVIC, EGON, chemistry educator, researcher, consultant; b. Otocac, Croatia, Apr. 27, 1922; came to U.S., 1957; s. Grgur and Stefica (Spiegel) M.; m. Bozica Biscan, Feb. 27, 1947. Diploma in chem. engring., U. Zagreb, 1944, PhD in Chemistry, 1948, Dr. Habil. in Phys. Chemistry, 1952; DSc (hon.), Lehigh U., 1977, M. Curie-Sklodowska U., Lublin, Poland, 1990; DSc. (hon.), Clarkson U., 1992. Instr. chemistry U. Zagreb, Yugoslavia, 1944-47; sr. instr. phys. chemistry U. Zagreb, 1949-52, privat dozent in colloid chemistry, 1952-54, dozent in phys. and colloid chemistry, 1955-56, on leave, 1956-59; rsch. assoc. Inst. Cinematography, Zagreb, 1948; rsch. fellow dept. colloid sci. U. Cambridge, Eng., 1956-57; vis. prof. Clarkson Coll. Tech., Potsdam, N.Y., 1957-59; assoc. prof. chemistry Clarkson Coll. Tech., Potsdam, N.Y., 1960-62; prof. Clarkson U., Potsdam, 1962-86, disting. univ. prof., 1986—; assoc. dir. Inst. Colloid and Surface Sci. Clarkson Coll. Tech., 1966-68; dir. inst., 1968-81, chmn. dept. chemistry, 1981-87; vis. prof. Japan Soc. for Promotion Sci., 1973, U. Melbourne, Australia, 1976, Sci. U. Tokyo, 1979, 84; vis. scientist U. Leningrad, USSR, 1977; Internat. Atomic Energy Agy. adviser Buenos Aires, Argentina, 1978, 80; fgn. guest Inst. Colloid and Interface Sci. Sci. U. Tokyo, 1982; lectr. in field; mem. adv. com. Univs. and Space Research Assn.; referee NATO Advanced Study Inst. Author: (with M. Kesler) General and Inorganic Chemistry for Senior High Schools, 11 edits., including Croatian, Macedonian, Hungarian, Italian, 1943-63; translator: Einfuhrung in die Stochiometrie (Nylen and Wigern), 1948; editor: (with Alter J. Weber) Adsorption from Aqueous Solution, 1968, Surface and Colloid Science, vols. 1-15, 1969-92; contbr. numerous articles to profl. publs. Recipient Gold medal Am. Electrolaters Soc., 1976; guest of honor 56th and 63rd Colloid and Surface Sci. Symposiums, Blacksburg, Va., 1982, Seattle, 1989. Mem. Am. Chem. Soc. (councilor div. colloid and surface chemistry 1982-87, chmn. 1969-70, Kendall award 1972, Langmuir Disting. Lectureship award 1985, Ralph K. Iler award 1993), Kolloid Gesellschaft (hon. life, Thomas Graham award 1985), Internat. Assn. Colloid Interface Sci. (pres. 1985-87), Chem. Soc. Japan, Inst. Colloid and Interface Sci. of Sci. of Tokyo (hon.), Phalanx Soc., Croatian Acad. Scis. and Arts (fgn.), Am. Ceramic Soc. (hon.), Materials Rsch. Soc. Japan (hon.), Acad. Ceramics (Italy), Croatian Chem. Soc. (Bozo Tezak medal 1991), Sigma Xi (Clarkson Coll. Tech. chpt. award 1972, nat. lect. 1987-89). Roman Catholic. Office: Clarkson U Dept Chemistry Ctr Advanced Materials Proc Potsdam NY 13699-5814

MATIS, NINA B., lawyer; b. N.Y.C., June 23, 1947. AB cum laude, Smith Coll., 1969; JD, NYU, 1972. Bar: Ill. 1973. Ptnr. Katten Muchin & Zavis, Chgo.; adj. prof. law Northwestern U., 1984-87. Mem. Am. Coll. Lawyers, Urban Land Inst. Office: Katten Muchin & Zavis 525 W Monroe St Ste 1600 Chicago IL 60661

MATISOFF, SUSAN, cultural research organization administrator. Dir. Ctr. East-Asian Studies, Stanford U., Calif. Office: Stanford University Ctr E-Asian Studies 300 Lasuen St Stanford CA 94305-5013

MATKOWSKY, BERNARD JUDAH, applied mathematician, educator; b. N.Y.C., Aug. 19, 1939; s. Morris N. and Ethel H. M.; m. Florence Knobel, Apr. 11, 1965; children: David, Daniel, Devorah. B.S., CCNY, 1960; M.E.E., NYU, 1961, M.S., 1963, Ph.D., 1966. Fellow Courant Inst. Math. Scis., NYU, 1961-66; mem. faculty dept. math. Rensselaer Poly. Inst., 1966-77; John Evans prof. applied math., mech. engring. & math. Northwestern U., Evanston, Ill., 1977—, chmn. engring. sci. and applied math. dept., 1993—; vis. prof. Tel Aviv U., 1972-73; vis. scientist Weizmann Inst. Sci., Israel, summer 1976, summer 1980, Tel Aviv U., summer 1980; cons. Argonne Nat. Lab., Sandia Labs., Lawrence Livermore Nat. Lab., Exxon Research and Engring. Co. Editor Wave Motion-An Internat. Jour., 1979—, Applied Math. Letters, 1987—, SIAM Jour. Applied Math., 1976-95, European Jour. Applied Math., 1989—, Random and Computational Dynamics, 1991—, Internat. Jour. SHS, 1992—, Jour. Materials Synthesis and Processing, 1992—; mem. edit. adv. bd. Springer Verlag Applied Math. Scis. Series; contbr. chpts. to books, articles to profl. jours. Fulbright grantee, 1972-73; Guggenheim fellow, 1982-83. Fellow Am. Acad. Mechanics; mem. AAAS, Soc. Indsl. and Applied Math., Am. Math. Soc., Combustion Inst., Am. Phys. Soc., Am. Assn. Combustion Synthesis, Conf. Bd. Math. Scis. (coun., com. human rights of math. scientists), Com. Concerned Scientists, Soc. Natural Philosophy, Sigma Xi, Eta Kappa Nu. Home: 3704 Davis St Skokie IL 60076-1745 Office: Northwestern U Technological Institut Evanston IL 60208

MATLACK, GEORGE MILLER, radiochemist; b. Pitts., June 14, 1921; s. Allyn Wolcott and Mildred Narcissa (Miller) M.; m. Meredith Mildred Madsen, Sept. 4, 1943; children—Nancy, Christine, Martin, Allyn. AB, Grinnell Coll., 1943; MS, State U. Iowa, 1947, PhD, 1949. Prin. chemist Iowa Geol. Survey, Iowa City, 1943-46; rsch. asst. State U. Iowa, 1946-49; sect. leader, analytical chemistry Los Alamos (N.Mex.) Nat. Lab., 1949-82, assoc. group leader analytical chemistry div., 1983-90, mem. team for devel. remote sensing of dinosaur bones by radiometric methods, 1988—, sr. adv. analytical chemistry divsn., 1990—. Contbr. articles to profl. jours. Pres., Los Alamos Choral Soc., 1961-62, Los Alamos Sinfonietta, 1967-69. Fellow Am. Inst. Chemists, AAAS; mem. Am. Chem. Soc., Am. Nuclear Soc., N.Y. Acad. Scis., Iowa Acad. Scis., Four-Fifths Mus. Soc. Lodges: Masons, Eastern Star. Home: 254 San Juan St Los Alamos NM 87544-2635 Office: Los Alamos Nat Lab Chemistry Div MS-G740 PO Box 1663 Los Alamos NM 87545-0001

MATLEY, BENVENUTO GILBERT (BEN MATLEY), computer engineer, educator, consultant; b. Monroe, La., Sept. 8, 1930; s. Welcome Gilbert and Lucette Marie (Renaud) M.; m. Patricia Jean McWilliams, June 21, 1959; children: Elizabeth, Katherine, John, Stephen, Richard, David. AB, San Diego State U., 1960; MBA, U. So. Calif., 1964; EdD, Nova U., 1980. Cert. data processor. Mathematician, engr. various data processing and computing firms, San Diego and L.A., 1956-64; sr. computer systems engr. Nortronics div. Northrop Corp., Hawthorne, Calif., 1964-69; prof. data processing and math. Ventura (Calif.) Coll., 1969—; lectr. in mgmt. and computer sci. West Coast U., L.A., 1982—; software cons, ednl. cons., Ventura, 1972—. Author: Principles of Elementary Algebra: A Language and Equations Approach, 1991; sr. author: National Computer Policies, 1988; contbr. chpts. to books, articles to profl. jours. Active Ventura County coun. Boy Scouts Am., 1979-82; cons. Calif. Luth. U., Thousand Oaks, Calif., 1989. Lt. (j.g.) USNR, 1952-55, Europe. Mem. IEEE Computer Soc. (Disting. Visitor 1988-91), Assn. for Computing Machinery, Spl. Interest Group-the Ada Lang. Avocation: writing. Office: Ventura Coll 4667 Telegraph Rd Ventura CA 93003-3899

MATLIN, MARLEE, actress; b. Morton Grove, Ill., Aug. 24, 1965; m. Kevin Grandalski, Aug. 29, 1993. Attended William Rainey Harper Coll. Appeared in films Children of a Lesser God (Acad. award for best actress), 1986, Walker, 1987, Linguini Incident, 1990, The Player, 1992, Hear No Evli, 1993; TV film: Bridge to Silence, 1989, Against Her Will: The Carrie Buck Sotry, 1994; TV series: Reasonable Doubts, 1991-93; guest of Picket Fences, 1993 (Emmy nomination, Guest Actress-Drama Series, 1994), Seinfeld, 1993 (Emmy nomination Guest Actress-Comedy Series, 1994). Recipient Golden Globe award Hollywood Fgn. Press Assn., 1987, named Best Actress. Office: care ICM 8942 Wilshire Blvd Beverly Hills CA 90211*

MATLOCK, CLIFFORD CHARLES, retired foreign service officer; b. Whittier, Cal., Nov. 6, 1909; s. William Holl and Clara Louisa (Wallace) M.; m. Nina Stolypin, Nov. 6, 1934 (dec. Dec. 1969); m. Elisabeth Thompson Scobey, May 3, 1971. A.B., Stanford U., 1932; A.M., Harvard U., 1940, certificate pub. adminstrn. (Littauer fellow), 1940. Economist USDA, 1938-41, U.S. Treasury, 1941-42; economist, adminstr. Bd. Econ. Warfare, Fgn. Econ. Adminstrn., 1942-45; econ., polit. officer Dept. State, 1946-62; polit. adviser European coordinating com. Dept. State, London, 1949-50; polit. officer U.S. delegation North Atlantic Council, London, 1950-52; polit. officer, then dir. plans and policy staff Office U.S. spl. rep. in Europe, Paris, 1952-53; spl. asst. Am. ambassador, Tehran, 1955-57; spl. asst. econ. affairs asst. sec. state for Far Eastern affairs, also alternate to Dep. Asst. Sec., 1959-62, ret.; acting dep. asst. Sec. of State, 1959; spl. asst. for polit. and econ. affairs to asst. adminstr. East Asia AID, Dept. of State, 1962-68; dir. East Asia tech. adv. staff, 1966-68, cons. Bur. for East Asia, 1968-71; coordinator interdisciplinary Devel. Cycles Research Project, 1971-76, prin., 1977-84; U.S. del. Econ. Commn. for Asia and Far East (UN), Tokyo, Japan, 1962; U.S. del. to devel. assistance com. Orgn. for Economic Cooperation and Devel., Paris, France, 1962; Member U.S. delegation Colombo Plan Consultative Com., Seattle, 1958, London, 1964; Member Development Assistance Group, Orgn. Econ. Coop. and Development, Washington, 1960; U.S. alternate rep. UN Econ. Commn. for Asia and Far East, Bangkok, 1960; adviser, mem. U.S. del. bds. govs. Internat. Monetary Fund, Internat. Bank for Reconstrn. and Devel., Tokyo, Japan, 1964; exec. com. SE Asia Devel. Adv. Group, 1965-70. Author: Man and Cosmos: A Theory of Endeavor Rhythms, 1977; draftsman of American Credo (in support of Truman Doctrine, now in U.S. Archives, H.S. Truman Libr.), 1947. Recipient Superior Honor award AID, 1968. Mem. Fgn. Service Assn., Diplomatic and Consular Officers Ret., Phi Beta Kappa. Clubs: Metropolitan (Washington), Harvard (Washington); Harvard of Western N.C. Home: Rte 1 Box 388 Lowry Rd Balsam Heights Waynesville NC 28786

MATLOCK, (LEE) HUDSON, civil engineer, educator; b. Floresville, Tex., Dec. 9, 1919; s. Lee Hudson Sr. and Charlie Mary (Stevenson) M.; m. Harriett Nadine Kidder, Nov. 28, 1942; children: John Hudson, David Kidder. BSCE, U. Tex., 1947, MSCE, 1950. Registered profl. engr., Tex. From instr. to prof. U. Tex., Austin, 1948-78, chmn. dept. civil engring., 1972-76, prof. emeritus civil engring., 1995—; v.p. R & D Earth Tech. Corp., Long Beach, Calif., 1978-85; civil engring. cons. Kerrville, Tex., 1985—; cons. Shell, Mobil, Chevron, Conoco and others, 1958—. Contbr. numerous tech. papers and sponsored rsch. reports to profl. publs. 1st lt. AC, U.S. Army, 1941-45. Recipient Disting. Achievement award Offshore Tech. Conf., Houston, 1985; named Disting. Engring. Grad. Coll. Engring. U. Tex.-Austin, 1986. Fellow ASCE (J. James R. Croes medal 1968), Tau Beta Pi; mem. NAE. Methodist. Avocations: flying, fishing, gardening. Home and Office: HC 5 Box 574-655 Kerrville TX 78028-9034

MATLOCK, JACK FOUST, JR., diplomat; b. Greensboro, N.C., Oct. 1, 1929; s. Jack Foust and Nellie (McSwain) M.; m. Rebecca Burrum, Sept. 2, 1949; children: James, Hugh, Nell, David, Joseph. A.B. summa cum laude, Duke U., 1950; M.A., Columbia U., 1952; cert., Russian Inst., 1952; LLD (hon.), Greensboro Coll., 1989, Albright Coll., 1992, Conn. Coll., 1993. Instr. Dartmouth, 1953-56; fgn. service officer Dept. State, 1956-91; assigned Washington, 1956-58, Am. Embassy, Vienna, Austria, 1958-60; Am. consul. gen. Munich, Germany, 1960-61; assigned Am. Embassy, Moscow, 1961-63, Accra, Ghana, 1963-66; assigned Am. Consulate, Zanzibar, 1967-69, Am. Embassy, Dar es Salaam, Tanzania, 1969-70, Sr. Seminar in Fgn. Policy, Dept. State, 1970-71; country dir. for USSR State Dept., 1971-74; minister-counselor, dep. chief mission Am. Embassy, Moscow, 1974-78; diplomat-in-residence Vanderbilt U., Nashville, 1978-79; dep. dir. Fgn. Service Inst., Washington, 1979-80; chargé d'affaires ad interim Am. Embassy, Moscow, 1981; ambassador to Czechoslovakia, 1981-83; spl. asst. to pres., sr. dir. European and Soviet Affairs Nat. Security Council, 1983-87; U.S. ambassador to the Soviet Union, Moscow, 1987-91; sr. rsch. fellow Columbia U., N.Y.C., 1991-93, Kathryn and Shelby Collum Davis prof. Practice Internat. Diplomacy, 1993—. Compiler, editor: Index to J.V. Stalin's Works, 2d edit, 1971. Home: 2913 P St NW Washington DC 20007-3069 also: 448 Riverside Dr Apt 1 New York NY 10027 Office: Columbia U 420 W 118th St Rm 1325 New York NY 10027-7213

MATLOCK, JOHN HUDSON, science administrator, materials engineer; b. San Angelo, Tex., Nov. 23, 1941; s. Lee Hudson Jr. and Harriett (Kidder) M.; m. Kathe Lynne Reep, Sept. 3, 1966; children: Michelle, Joseph. B. Engring. Sci., U. Tex., 1967, MSME, 1969, PhD in Material Sci. and Engring., 1970; MBA, So. Ill. U., Edwardsville, 1976. Registered profl. engr., Mo., Wash., Oreg. Sr. rsch. engr. Monsanto Co., St. Peters, Mo., 1970-72, rsch. specialist, 1972-74, supt. rsch. svcs., 1974-79; sr. staff engr. Mostek Corp., Carrollton, Tex., 1979-80, mgr. material tech. group, 1980-83; v.p. tech. SEH Am., Inc., Vancouver, Wash., 1983-90, exec. v.p., 1990—; bd. dirs. Wash. Tech. Ctr., 1991—; mem. vis. com. U. Wash. Engring. Coll., Seattle, 1985-94; mem. engring. adv. bd. Wash. State U., Pullman, 1984—; bd. dirs. Wash. Higher Edn. Telecomms., 1985-90; adj. prof. mech. engring., mem. grad. faculty Oreg. State U., Corvallis, 1985-90; adj. asst. prof. physics So. Ill. U., Edwardsville, 1973-76; adj. lectr. Wash. State U., Pullman, 1985. Contbr. approximately 40 articles on silicon crystal growing and the effect of silicon properties on electronic devic performance to profl. and trade jours. Mem. bd. trustees 1st Ch. of God, Vancouver, 1988-91, tchr. adult ch. sch., 1986-91; mem. sch. bd. Kingsway Christian Sch., Vancouver, 1990-91. Mem. Electrochem. Soc., Metall. Soc., AIME, Am. Soc. for Materials, Materials Rsch. Soc., ASTM, Tau Beta Pi, Pi Tau Sigma, Phi Kappa Phi, Beta Gamma Sigma. Home: 10916 NE 30th Ave Vancouver WA 98686-4346 Office: SEH Am Inc 4111 NE 112th Ave Vancouver WA 98682-6776

MATLOCK, KENNETH JEROME, building materials company executive; b. Oak Park, Ill., May 30, 1928; s. Harvey and Lillian (Sivertsen) Samuelson; m. Dorothy Belowski, Nov. 3, 1956; children—Geoffrey, Barbara, Gail, Paul. Student, James Millikin U., 1946-48; B.S. in Accountancy, U. Ill., 1950; postgrad., Northwestern U. Inst. Mgmt., summer 1963. C.P.A., Ill., Fla. Sr. audit mgr. Price Waterhouse & Co., Chgo., 1950-64; with Celotex Corp., Chgo., 1964-65; v.p. fin. ops. Celotex Corp., Tampa, Fla., 1965-74; asst. to v.p. Jim Walter Corp., Tampa, 1966-69, controller, 1970-72, v.p., 1972-74, v.p., chief acctg. officer, 1974-88, v.p., v.p. CFO, 1987-91; v.p., CFO Walter Industries, Inc., Tampa, 1987-88; Walter Industries, Inc.; exec. v.p., bd. dirs. Walter Industries, Inc., Tampa, 1991—; exec. v.p., CFO, also bd. dirs. Walter Industries, Inc. Adviser Jr. Achievement, Chgo., 1958-60; active Heart Fund, United Fund, 1956-58. Served with USNR, 1945-46. Mem.

AICPA, Ill. Soc. CPAs. Fla. Soc. CPAs, Fin. Execs. Inst. Home: 1401 87th Ave N Saint Petersburg FL 33702-2931 Office: Walter Industries Inc 1500 N Dale Mabry Hwy Tampa FL 33607-2551

MATON, ANTHEA, education consultant; b. Burnley, Lancashire, England, Feb. 1, 1944; d. William Douglas Newton-Dawson and Beatrice Joan (Simpson) Bateman; m. K.F. Edward Asprey, Nov. 13, 1965 (div. 1978); children: George William Edward, Mariana Alexandra Beatrice; m. Paul Nicholas Maton, Mar. 23, 1978; 1 child, Petra Beatrice Suzanne. Diploma, tchg. cert., higher diploma, tchg. diploma; postgrad., U. Okla. Clin. instr. radiotherapy Hammersmith Hosp., London, 1970-75; prin. sch. radiotherapy Royal Free Hosp., London, 1977-80, acting supt., 1979-80; head of careers Putney High Sch. for Girls, London, 1981-83; head of physics St. Andrews Episc. High Sch., Bethesda, Md., 1984-88; vis. fellow Am. Assn. Physics Tchrs., 1988-89; nat. coord. project scope, sequence, and coordination Nat. Sci. Tchrs. Assn. 1989-91; exec. dir. Edn. Commections, Oklahoma City, 1991—, dir. exhbn. on art and physics, 1994—; organizer U.S.-Soviet High Sch. Physics Student Exch. and Visit, 1989; conducted numerous workshops on sci. curriculum reform and assessment reform, 1987—; faculty USA Physics Olympiad Team, 1986, 89; physics tchr. St. Andrews Episc. High Sch., 1984-88, Putney High Sch. for Girls, 1980-83, tchr. med. ethics, 1982-83; tchr. physics, anatomy and physiology, radiobiology Royal Free Hosp., 1977-80, contemporary physics edn. project, 1989—; vis. faculty Oklahoma Sch. of Sci. and Math., 1995-96; vis. faculty physics Western Washington U. Lead author Prentice Hall Sci., 1993; contbr. articles to profl. jours. Mem. Nat. Mus. Women Arts (charter), Women's Philharm. (charter); apptd. to scientific adv. bd. OMNIPLEX Sci. Mus., Okla. City; cons. Sta. WGBH, Boston, Smithsonian, Am. Mus. of Moving Image, UCLA, Del. Edn. Dept., Ark. Project Advise, Newcastle (Del.) Sch. Dist. Named one of Today's Leaders Okla. Edn. Equity Roundtable, 1992. Mem. NAFE, ASCD, AAUW (pub. policy chair Oklahoma City chpt. 1995—), NOW (coord. metro chpt. 1992-95, treas. Okla. state chpt. 1993-95), Assn. for Women in Sci., Nat. Sci. Tchrs. Assn., Am. Assn. Physics Tchrs., N.Y. Acad. Scis., Assn. for Sci. Edn., Soc. Radiographers U.K. Avocations: gender and science, drawing, writing poetry, singing, making wood cuts. Home and Office: 1804 Dorchester Dr Oklahoma City OK 73120

MATOY, ELIZABETH ANNE, personnel executive; b. Stillwater, Okla., Sept. 11, 1946; d. Ray Roland and Helen Louise (Springer) Matoy; m. Michael D. Banks; children: Heather Anne, Kirsten Sue, Aaron Christian, Kendra Jeanne Carlson. BA, U. Ill., Chgo., 1968; MSM, Frostburg (Md.) State Coll., 1975. Publs. mgr. Forum Press, Stillwater, Okla., 1982-84; editor centennial histories project Okla. State U., 1984-88, assoc. pers. dir., 1988-91, pers. dir., 1991—; owner, pub. Prairie Imprints, Stillwater, 1985-92; cons. Active Corps of Execs., Frostburg, Md., 1975-77. Editor: DAC in Oklahoma, 1984; also editor for Payne County (Okla.) Historical Soc., 1980-90. Pres. LaVale (Md.) Vol. Fire Dept. Aux., 1972-77; bd. dirs. Morgantown, W.Va. Shawnee Girl Scouts Council, 1975-77; mem. allocations com. Cumberland, Md. United Way, 1975-77; bus. mgr. Stillwater Sylvia Stapley Day Camp Girl Scouts, 1982-84. Recipient Bronze Pelican award Archdiocese of Tulsa, 1990, Sr. Profl. Human Resources award Human Resources Cert. Inst., 1992. Mem. Payne County Hist. Soc. (sec. 1980-82, historian 1986), Okla. Colls. Univs. Pers. Assn., Stillwater Rotary Club. Republican. Methodist. Home: 210 E Greenvale Ct Stillwater OK 74075-1662 Office: Okla State U Stillwater OK 74076-0481

MATSAKIS, STEVEN C., bank executive, retail executive; b. Rutherford, N.J., May 1, 1958; s. Constantinos Demetrios and Victoria (Lucas) M.; m. Mary Louise Finlayson, July 2, 1988; 1 child, Louise Victoria. BA, NYU, 1980, MBA, 1982. V.p. Bankers Trust Co., N.Y.C., 1980-89, Corestates Fin., Phila., 1989-90; exec. v.p. Atlantic Bank N.Y., N.Y.C., 1992—; CEO Super Video Mgmt. Co., Woodridge, N.J., 1990—. Republican. Avocations: movies, tennis, politics. Home: 749 New York Ave Lyndhurst NJ 07071 Office: Atlantic Bank of N Y 960 Avenue Of The Americas New York NY 10001-2107

MATSCH, RICHARD P., federal judge; b. 1930. A.B., U. Mich., 1951, J.D., 1953. Bar: Colo. Asst. U.S. atty. Colo., 1959-61; dep. city atty. City and County of Denver, 1961-63; judge U.S. Bankruptcy Ct., Colo., 1965-74, U.S. Dist. Ct. for Colo., 1974—. Served with U.S. Army, 1953-55. Mem. ABA, Am. Judicature Soc. Office: US Dist Ct 1929 Stout St Denver CO 80294-2900

MATSCHULLAT, DALE LEWIS, lawyer; b. Ft. Sill, Okla., May 1, 1945; s. Wayne Emil and Harriet Jane (Bowman) M.; m. Eileen Joanne Davidson, Aug. 26, 1967; children—Robert Charles, Stephen Francis. A.B., Stanford U., 1967, J.D., 1970. Bar: N.Y., Wis. Law clk. U.S. Dist. Ct. (ea. dist.) N.Y., Bklyn., 1970-71; assoc. firm Davis, Polk & Wardwell, Manhattan, N.Y., 1972-77; former sector counsel Allis Chalmers Corp., Milw., from 1977; former gen. counsel Allis Chalmers Corp.; now gen. counsel Newell Co., Freeport, Ill. Roman Catholic. Office: Newell Co 29 E Stephenson St Freeport IL 61032-4235

MATSLER, FRANKLIN GILES, higher education educator; b. Glendive, Mont., Dec. 27, 1922; s. Edmund Russell and Florence Edna (Giles) M.; m. Lois Josephine Hoyt, June 12, 1949; children—Linda, Jeanne, David, Winfield. B.S., Mont. State U., Bozeman, 1948; M.A., U. Mont., Missoula, 1952; Ph.D., U. Calif. at Berkeley, 1959. Tchr. Missoula County (Mont.) High Sch., 1949-51, Tracy (Calif.) Sr. Elem. Schs., 1952-53, San Benito County (Calif.) High Sch. and Jr. Coll., 1953-55; grad. asst. U. Calif. at Berkeley, 1955-58; asst. prof. Humboldt State Coll., Arcata, Calif., 1958-62; asso. prof. Humboldt State Coll., 1962-63, asst. acad. dean, 1958-63; chief specialist higher edn. Calif. Coordinating Council for Higher Edn., Sacramento, 1963-68; exec. dir. Ill. Bd. Regents, Springfield, 1968-84; prof. higher edn. Ill. State U., Normal, 1968—, Regency prof. higher edn., 1984—; chancellor Ill. Bd. Regents, 1995—. Bd. dirs. Ill. Edn. Consortium, 1972-76; bd. dirs. Central Ill. Health Planning Agy., 1970-76, Springfield Symphony Orch. Assn.; pres. Bloomington/Normal Symphony Soc., 1988-90. Served to 1st lt. AUS, 1943-46. Mem. Nat. Assn. Sys. Heads (exec. v.p. 1985-92), Am. Assn. State Colls. and Univs. Assn. for Instl. Rsch., Phi Delta Kappa, Lambda Chi Alpha. Home: 2005 Woodfield Rd Bloomington IL 61704-2427 Office: Illinois State U 539 DeGarmo Hall Normal IL 61761

MATSON, MERWYN DEAN, educational consultant; b. Forest City, Iowa, Aug. 6, 1937; s. Archie Alvin and Henrietta (Wittgreve) M.; m. Audrey Christine Gaydos, Apr. 9, 1988; children: Candace, Kevin, Shaunna, Dan, Cathy, Mindy, Lisa, Matthew. AB, Northwest Nazarene Coll., 1959; MEd, Oreg. State U., 1963; EdM, U. Oreg., 1962. Cert. tchr., sch. counselor, sch. psychologist, Iowa. Elem. sch. guidance coord. Pottawattami County Schs., Council Bluffs, Iowa, 1969-70; sch. psychologist Hancock County Schs., Garner, Iowa, 1970-71; dir. career edn. Mason City (Iowa) Pub. Schs., 1971-73; regional dir. Am. Coll. Testing Program, Springfield, Mo., 1973-84; Midwest regional dir. career planning svcs. Am. Coll. Testing Program, Lincolnshire, Ill., 1984-86; Mountains/Plains regional dir. career planning svcs. Am. Coll. Testing Program, Aurora, Colo., 1994-96; west region dir. elementary/secondary svcs. Am. Coll. Testing Program, 1995—. Mem. AARP, Am. Counseling Assn., Rotary Club of Univ. Hills (Denver). Lutheran. Home: 831 E Phillips Ln Littleton CO 80122-2982 Office: Am Coll Testing Program 3131 S Vaughn Way Ste 218 Aurora CO 80014-3507 *Personal philosophy: Service above self. He profits most who serves best.*

MATSON, PAMELA ANNE, environmental science educator; b. Eau Claire, Wis., Aug. 3, 1953. BS, U. Wis., 1975; MS, Ind. U., 1980; PhD, Oreg. State U., 1983. Prof. U. Calif., Berkeley, 1993—. MacArthur fellow, 1995. Mem. Am. Acad. Arts & Scis., Nat. Acad. Sci. Specializes in the interactions between the biosphere and the atmosphere; pioneered research into the role of land-use changes on global warming, analyzing the effects of greenhouse gas emissions resulting from tropical deforestation; investigating the effects of intensive agriculture on the atmosphere, especially the effects of tropical agriculture and cattle ranching, and is finding ways in which agricultural productivity can be expanded without increasing the level of greenhouse gasses. Office: U California Dept Environ Science Berkeley CA 94720*

MATSON, ROBERT EDWARD, leadership educator, consultant; b. Chauncey, Ohio, Dec. 2, 1930; s. William I. and Mary Royal (Rivers) M.; m.

Mary Athearn, June 27, 1954; children—Laurie, Jeanne, Scott. B.S., Ohio U., 1956, M.Ed., 1957; Ed.D, Ind. U., 1961. Dean of Men Carroll Coll., Wis., 1961-65; v.p. student affairs Kent State U, Ohio, 1965-70; pres. Ricker Coll., 1970-74; sr. prof. Fed. Exec. Inst., Charlottesville, Va., 1974-80, acad. dean, 1980-82, dir., 1982-87, sr. prof., dir. emeritus, 1987-89; prof., dir. exec. devel. & mgmt. svcs. Ctr. Pub. Svc. U. Va., 1989-94; prof., dir. Inst. Govt. U. Va., 1994—. Served to 1st. lt. U.S. Army, 1953-55; Korea. Mem. Am. Soc. Pub. Adminstrn., Am. Assn. Higher Edn., Internat. City/County Mgrs. Assn. (Sweeney Acad. award 1993), Am. Personnel and Guidance Assn. Methodist. Office: Ctr for Pub Svc 918 Emmet St N Charlottesville VA 22903-4832

MATSON, WESLEY JENNINGS, educational administrator; b. Svea, Minn., June 25, 1924; s. James and Ettie (Mattson) M.; m. Doris Cragg; 1 child, James Jennings. BS with distinction, U. Minn., 1948; MA, U. Calif., Berkeley, 1954; EdD, Columbia U., 1960. High sch. tchr. Santa Barbara County Pub. Schs., Santa Maria, Calif., 1948-50; instr. U. Calif., Berkeley, 1950-54, Columbia U. N.Y.C., 1954-55; lectr. Fordham U., N.Y.C., 1955-56; asst. prof. U. Md., College Park, 1956-59; prof., asst. dean U. Wis., Milw., 1959-72; dean emeritus Winona (Minn.) State U., 1972-88; vis. prof. U. P.R., Rio Peidras, Western Wash. U., Bellingham, San Diego State U., U. Minn., Mpls., U. Hawaii, St. Olaf Coll., Northfield, Minn.; cons. U.S. Dept. Edn., Washington, Ill., Wis.; bd. regents Wis. Dept. Pub. Instruction; examiner Nat. Coun. Accreditation of Tchr. Edn., N. Ctrl. Assn., Chgo. Editorial bd.: Jour. Instructional Psychology; contbr. articles to profl. jours. Exec. com. Minn. Alliance of the Arts, Mpls.; mem. Minn. Com. Certification Stds., St. Paul; bd. dirs. F. Snelling Meml. Chapel Found. Served to capt. USAAF, 1943-46, ETO. Decorated Bronze star; recipient Disting. Service award Wis. Assn. for Tchr. Edn., 1972. Mem. Minn. Assn. Colls. for Tchr. Edn. (pres. 1983-85, hon. life award of merit 1985), Nat. Assn. Tchr. Educators (exec. com. 1970-72), Nat. Edn. Assn. (life), Assn. Higher Edn., Minn. Edn. Assn., Minn. Hist. Soc., U. Minn. Alumni Soc. (Outstanding Educator award 1984), Rotary, Phi Delta Kappa, Kappa Delta Pi, Alpha Sigma Phi. Home: #605 6615 Lake Shore Dr Minneapolis MN 55423

MATSUDA, FUJIO, institute president; b. Honolulu, Oct. 18, 1924; s. Yoshio and Shimo (Iwasaki) M.; m. Amy M. Saiki, June 11, 1949; children: Bailey Koki, Thomas Junji, Sherry Noriko, Joan Yuuko, Ann Mitsuyo, Richard Hideo. B.S. in Civil Engring., Rose Poly. Inst., 1949; D.Sc., Mass. Inst. Tech., 1952; D. Engring. (hon.), Rose Hulman Inst. Tech., 1975. Rsch. engr. MIT, 1952-54; rsch. asst. prof. engring. U. Ill., Urbana, 1954-55; asst. prof. engring. U. Hawaii, Honolulu, 1955-57; assoc. prof. U. Hawaii, 1957-62, chmn. dept. civil engring., 1960-63, prof., 1962-65, 74-84, dir. engring. expt. sta., 1962-63, v.p. bus. affairs, 1973-74, pres., 1974-84, exec. dir. Rsch. Corp. Japan-Am. Inst. Mgmt. Sci., Honolulu, 1994—; dir. Hawaii Dept. Transp., Honolulu, 1963-73; v.p. Park & Yee, Ltd., Honolulu, 1956-58; pres. SMS & Assocs., Inc.; 1960-63; pvt. practice as structural engr., 1958-60; bd. dirs. C. Brewer & Co., Ltd., UAL Corp., 1975-94, First Hawaiian Bank, First Hawaiian Inc., Pacific Internat. Ctr. for High Tech. Rsch., Rehab. Hosp. of Pacific, Kuakini Health Sys., Japanese Cultural Ctr. of Hawaii, Hawaii Cmty. Found., Japan-Am. Inst. Mgmt. Sci.; mem. Airport Ops. Coun. Internat., 1968-73; pres. Pacific Coast Assn. Port Authorities, 1969; mem. sci. bd. Dept. Army, 1978-80; mem. U.S. Army Civilian Adv. Group, 1978—; mem. exec. com. transp. rsch. bd. NRC, 1982-86; mem. vis. com. on sponsored rsch. MIT; mem. Rose-Hulman Inst. Tech. Com. on the Future, 1992-94. Bd. dirs. Aloha United Way, 1973-76, Kuakini Med. Ctr., 1987-89; trustee Kuakini Health Systems, 1984-86, bd. dirs., 1986-89; trustee Nature Conservancy, 1984-89. Recipient Honor Alumnus award Rose Poly. Inst., 1971, Disting. Svc. award Airport Ops. Coun. Internat., 1973, Disting. Alumnus award U. Hawaii, 1974, 91; named Hawaii Engr. of Yr., 1972. Mem. NAE, NSPE, ASCE (Parcel-Sverdrup Engring. Mgmt. award 1986), Social Sci. Assn., Western Coll. Assn. (exec. com. 1977-84, pres. 1980-82), Japan-Am. Soc. Honolulu (trustee 1976-84, adv. council 1984—), Japan-Hawaii Econ. Coun., World Sustainable Agr. Assn., Beta Gamma Sigma, Sigma Xi, Tau Beta Pi. Office: Japan Am Inst Mgmt Sci 6660 Hawaii Kai Dr Honolulu HI 96825

MATSUI, ROBERT TAKEO, congressman; b. Sacramento, Sept. 17, 1941; s. Yasuji and Alice (Nagata) M.; m. Doris Kazue Okada, Sept. 17, 1966; 1 child, Brian Robert. AB in Polit. Sci, U. Calif., Berkeley, 1963; JD, U. Calif., San Francisco 1966. Bar: Calif. 1967. Practiced law Sacramento, 1967-78; mem. Sacramento City Council, 1971-78, vice mayor, 1977; mem. 96th-104d Congresses from 5th Calif. dist., 1979—; ranking minority mem., mem. ways and means subcom. on oversight; chmn. profl. bus. forum Dem. Congl. Campaign Com.; congl. liaison nat. fin. council Dem. Nat. Com.; mem. adv. council on fiscal policy Am. Enterprise Inst. chmn. Profl. Bus. Forum of the Dem. Congl. Co. and Com.; congl. liaison Nat. Fin. Council, Dem. Nat. Com.; mem. Am. Enterprise Inst. Adv. Council on Fiscal Policy. Named Young Man of Yr. Jr. C. of C., 1973; recipient Disting. Service award, 1973. Mem. Sacramento Japanese Am. Citizens League (pres. 1969), Sacramento Met. C. of C. (dir. 1976). Democrat. Clubs: 20-30 (Sacramento) (pres. 1972), Rotary (Sacramento). Office: US Ho of Reps 2311 Rayburn HOB Washington DC 20515-0505*

MATSUMOTO, ATSUSHI, electronics executive; b. 1936. Pres. Maxell Corp. Am., Fair Lawn, N.J., 1984—. Office: Maxell Corp Am 22-08 State Rt 208 Fair Lawn NJ 07410*

MATSUMOTO, GEORGE, architect; b. San Francisco, July 16, 1922; s. Manroku F. and Ise (Nakagawa) M.; m. Kimi Nao, Dec. 15, 1951; children—Mari-Jane, Kiyo-Ann, Kei-Ellen, Kenneth Manroku, Miye-Eileen. Student, U. Calif. at Berkeley, 1938-42; B.Arch., Washington U., 1944; M.Arch., Cranbrook Acad. Art, 1945. Designer Heathers Garden Devel. Co., Calif., 1941-42; designer with George F. Keck, Chgo., 1943-44; sr. designer, planner Saarinen & Swanson, Birmingham, Mich., 1945-46; sr. designer Skidmore, Owings & Merrill, Chgo., 1948; partner Runnells, Clark, Waugh, Matsumoto, Kansas City, Mo., 1946-47; practice architecture Okla., N.C., 1948-61, San Francisco, 1962-92; pres. George Matsumoto and assocs., San Francisco, 1992-93; retired, 1993; instr. U. Okla., 1947-48; prof. N.C. State Coll., 1948-61, U. Calif. at Berkeley, 1961-67. Important works include libraries, office bldgs., schs., recreation ctrs., chs., govt. bldgs., pvt. residences, med. research labs. and offices. Bd. dirs. Young Audiences, Oakland Mus. Assn., Oakland Art Council. Recipient over 50 archtl. awards and prizes. Fellow AIA (dir. chpt.), Internat. Inst. Arts and Letters; mem. Mich. Soc. Architects, Assn. Coll. Sch. Architecture, Raleigh Council Architects, San Francisco Planning and Urban Renewal Assn., Nat. Council Archtl. Registration Bds., Calif. Assn. Architects, Bldg. Research Inst., Japanese-Am. Citizens League. Home: 1170 Glencourt Dr Oakland CA 94611-1405

MATSUMOTO, TERUO, surgeon, educator; b. Fukuoka City, Japan, Jan. 2, 1929; came to U.S., 1956, naturalized, 1964; s. Yoshinari and Fumie (Hayashi) M.; m. Mary L. Cousino, July 29, 1961; children: Louisa Michi, Maria Chieko, Monica Mieko, Nelson Tateru. M.D., Kyushu U., 1953, Ph.D., 1956. Diplomate: Am. Bd. Surgery, Am. Bd. Gen. Vascular Surgery. Intern Cook County Hosp., Chgo., 1956-57; surg. resident Med. Coll. Ohio, Toledo, 1957-61; commd. capt. U.S. Army, 1961, advanced through grades to lt. col., 1965; gen. surgeon U.S. Army Camp Zama Hosp., Japan, 1961-65; chief surg. service U.S. Army Camp Zama Hosp., 1962-65, chief gen. surgery sect., 1962-65; chief dept. exptl. surgery Walter Reed Army Inst. Research, 1965-68, dir. U.S. Army Surg. Research, Pacific, 1968; assoc. prof. surgery Hahnemann Med. Coll. and Hosp., Phila., 1969-72; prof. surgery Hahnemann U., Phila., 1973—; chmn. dept. surgery Hahnemann U., 1975-90, dir. divsn. vascular surgery, 1990—; pres. med. staff Hahnemann Med. Coll. and Hosp., 1979-81; mem. sci. rev. com. NIH, cons. field reader for Office of Orphan Products Devel., FDA, 1986. Editor Emergency Surgery, Jour. Internat. Surgery, Jour. Critical Care Medicine, Jour. Internat. Cardiovascular Surgery; contbr. to profl. jours. and books. Recipient Sir Henry Wellcome medal and prize, 1965, gold medal Southeastern Sug. Congress, 1968, Outstanding Achievement award U.S. Army Sci. Conf., 1969, Golden Apple award Student AMA, 1972. Fellow Southeastern Surg. Congress, ACS, Am. Coll. Angiology, Am. Assn. for Surgery of Trauma, Pan Am. Med. Assn., Assn. Surgery for Alimentary Tract, AMA, Japanese Coll. Surgeons, Internat. Cardiovascular Surgery, Soc. Vascular Surgery, AOA, Phila. Acad. Surgery, Pan Pacific Surg. Congress, Soc. Surg. Chairmen; mem. Council Cardiovascular Surgery, Soc. Surg. Oncology. Home: 1116 San-

dringham Rd Bala Cynwyd PA 19004-2023 Office: Hahnemann U Med Sch Philadelphia PA 19102

MATSUO, FUMISUKE, physician, educator; b. Iida, Japan, Dec. 24, 1942; came to U.S., 1969; s. Riichi and Utako (Sasaki) M.; m. Ruth Ann Smith, May 24, 1975; children: Jocelyn, Bryan. MD, Kyoto (Japan) Prefectural U. Medicine, 1968. Assoc. prof. U. Iowa, Iowa City, 1975; asst. prof. U. Utah, Salt Lake City, 1975-79, assoc. prof., 1979-87, prof., 1987—; dir. EEG Lab. Univ. Hosp., Salt Lake City, 1975—. Contbr. articles to profl. jours. Fellow Am. Acad. Neurology, Am. EEG Soc.; mem. AMA, Soc. Neuroscis., Am. Epilepsy Soc., Epilepsy Assn. Utah (bd. dirs. 1978-81, 87-89), Western EEG Soc. (bd. dirs. 1983-86, sec.-treas. 1989-90, pres. 1991-92). Home: 1353 S 1900 E Salt Lake City UT 84108-2219 Office: U Utah Med Ctr 50 N Medical Dr Salt Lake City UT 84132-0001

MATSUURA, TERUO, chemistry educator; b. Osaka, Japan, Dec. 19, 1925; s. Takeo and Fumi (Nakata) M.; m. Fumi Ohshiro, Oct. 28, 1956; children: Masato, Jiro. BSc, Osaka U., 1949, DSc, 1956. Rsch. asst. dept. chemistry Osaka City U., 1949-57; vis. scientist NIH, Bethesda, Md., 1957-58; rsch. assoc. dept. chemistry MIT, Cambridge, Mass., 1958-59; asst. prof. dept. chemistry Osaka City U., 1959-63; assoc. prof. dept. synthetic chemistry Kyoto (Japan) U., 1963, prof. dept. synthetic chemistry, 1963-89; prof. dept. materials chemistry Ryukoku U., Otsu, Japan, 1990—; prof. emeritus Kyoto U., 1989—. Author: Organic Photochemistry, 1970, Oxygenation Reactions, 1977; contbr. about 400 articles to profl. jours. including Organic Photochemistry, Reactive Oxygen Species, Bioorganic Chemistry; mem. editorial bd. Jour. Photochemistry and Photobiology, 1984—, Bioorganic Chemistry, 1983—. Pres. Photobiology Assn. Japan, 1989-90, Japanese Photochemistry Assn., Japan, 1989-91. Fogarty scholar NIH, 1985; recipient Chem. Soc. Japan prize, 1987, Soc. prize Japan Soc. Synthetic Organic Chemistry, 1974. Mem. Am. Chem. Soc., Royal Soc. Chemistry (London). Home: 21-26 Kawashima Gondencho, Saikyoku Kyoto 615, Japan Office: Ryukoku U Faculty Sci Tech, Seta, Otsu 520-21, Japan

MATTA, RAM KUMAR, aeronautical engineer; b. Karachi, India, May 9, 1946; came to U.S., 1967; s. Madhavdas Lalchand and Damyanti (Ahuja) M.; m. Renee M. Verhoff, Dec. 1988. B.Tech., Indian Inst. Tech., New Delhi, 1967; M.S., U. Minn., 1969, Ph.D., 1973. Grad. asst. mechanics U. Minn., Mpls., 1967-68, research asst., 1968, teaching assoc., 1968-69, research assoc., 1969, research fellow, 1969-73; acoustics engr. advanced engring. and tech. program dept. engring. div. Aircraft Engine Group, Gen. Electric Co., Evendale, Ohio, 1973-75, mgr. turbomachinery acoustics, 1975-76, mgr. component tech., 1976-77, sr. engr. cycle systems analysis, 1977-78; bus. interface Gen. Electric Corp. R & D, Evendale, Ohio, 1979-80; mgr. new engine design support Aircraft Engine Group, Gen. Electric Co., Evendale, Ohio, 1980-83, mgr. advanced programs, 1983-84, mgr. CFM56-5 systems engring. and product improvement, 1984-87, gen. mgr. CFM56-5C and advanced programs, 1988-92; program gen. mgr. GE45/CFMXX, dir. CFM advanced programs Gen. Electric Co., Evendale, Ohio, 1992-93; bus. interface Gen. Electric Corp. Rsch. and Devel., 1993—. Contbr. articles to profl. publs.; patentee in field. Exec. mem., vol. Minn. Internat. Ctr., Mpls., 1970-72; chmn. Citizens Com. for Community Devel., Forest Park, Ohio, 1975-76. Recipient Dir.'s Gold medal Indian Inst. Tech., 1967, Profl. Performance award, 1975, Mgmt. award, 1979; Merit scholar Indian Inst. Tech., 1967; Sloan fellow Stanford U., 1987-88. Mem. AIAA, Sigma Gamma Tau. Home: 1010 Lamplighter Rd Schenectady NY 12309-1159 Office: GE CR&D MD K-1/3A59 PO Box 8 # 59 Schenectady NY 12301-0008

MATTAR, EDWARD PAUL, III, academic administrator; b. Buffalo, Mar. 15, 1939. JD, U. Balt., 1964; MBA, Boston U., 1975; postgrad., U. Mass. Staff mem. Nelson H. Rockefeller, N.Y.C., 1964; tchr. Arlington (Va.) Pub. Schs., 1965-66; dean of students Ea. Coll., Balt., 1966-67; exec. asst. pres. Mullin-Kille Co., Chillicothe, Ohio, 1967-68; pres. Mattar, Bork & Mattar, Buffalo, 1969, Century 21 Internat. Ltd., Washington, 1964-77, Cen. New Eng. Coll., Worcester, Mass., 1977—; chmn. Northbanke Group, Matheson Apts. Inc., Worcester, Nasson Learning Systems; chief exec. officer Mass. Edn. Network, Inc., 1987—. Author: Barry Goldwater - A Political Indictment, 1964, The Manager's Tool Box, 1987, Management Success Secrets, 1987, Effective Management Techniques, 1987; editor: Handbook for Corporate Directors, 1985; contbr. articles to profl. jours. Mem. Worcester Consortium of Higher Edn., Am. Assn. Coll. Pres., Am. Assn. U. Adminstrs., Ctr. Entrepreneurial Mgmt., Am. Mgmt. Assn. Home: 251 Salisbury St Worcester MA 01609-1669

MATTAUCH, ROBERT JOSEPH, electrical engineering educator; b. Rochester, Pa., May 30, 1940; s. Henry Paul and Anna Marie (Mlinarcik) M.; m. Frances Sabo, Dec. 29, 1962; children: Lori Ann, Thomas J. BS, Carnegie Inst. Tech., Pitts., 1962; MEE, N.C. State U., Raleigh, 1963, PhD, 1967. Asst. prof. elec. engring. U. Va., Charlottesville, 1966-70, assoc. prof. elec. engring., 1970-76, prof. elec. engring., 1976-83, Wilson prof. elec. engring., 1983-86, Standard Oil Co. prof. sci. and tech., 1986-89, chmn. dept. elect. engring., 1987—; BP Am. prof. sci. and tech., 1989—; cons. The Rochester Corp., Culpeper, Va., 1983-88, Milltech Corp., Deerfield, Mass., 1985. Patentee: infrared detector; solid state switching capacitor; thin wire pointing method, whiskerless Schottky diode, controlled in-situ etch back growth technique. Bd. dirs. U. Va. Patent Found. Recipient Excellence in Instruction of Engring. Students award Western Electric, 1980. Fellow IEEE (Centennial medal 1984); mem. Eta Kappa Nu (recipient Oustanding Prof. in Elec. Engring. 1975), Sigma Xi, Tau Beta Pi. Office: U Va Dept Elec Engring Thornton Hall Charlottesville VA 22903-2442

MATTAUSCH, THOMAS EDWARD, public relations consultant, business owner; b. Davenport, Iowa, Dec. 4, 1944; s. Carl Henry and Luverna Ann (Koch) M.; B.A. in Journalism, U. Iowa, 1967; M.A. in Social Psychology Ball State U., 1974; children—Jason Paul, Laura Anne. Asst. to dir. public relations Gen. Telephone Co. Midwest, Grinnell, Iowa, 1968-71; mgr. public relations Midwestern div. Am. Water Works Service Co., Inc., Richmond, Ind., 1971-74; with IBM, 1974-82, sr. communications specialist, White Plains and Armonk, N.Y., 1974-79, mgr. communications and community relations IBM Info. Systems Center, Sterling Forest, N.Y., 1979-82; dir. communication programs, communication products group GTE, Stamford, Conn., 1982-84, dir. communication programs, diversified products and services group, 1984-87, dir. communication programs Products and Systems group, 1987-89; dir. pub. rels. svcs. corp. hdqrs., 1989-92; prin. T.E. Mattausch Pub. Rels. and Communications, 1993—; owner Serenities, 1994—. Mem. Iowa adv. com. to U.S. Commn. on Civil Rights, 1969-71; bd. dirs. Orange County (N.Y.) C. of C., 1979-82, Central Orange County United Way, 1979-82, Metro Pool, Inc., Stamford, Ct., 1992-93. Served with USNR, 1967-68. Mem. Public Relations Soc. Am. (dir. tech. sect.), Am. Mgmt. Assn., Am. Assn. Counseling and Devel., Internat. Communications Assn., Internat. Platform Assn., Internat. Assn. Bus. Communicators (dir. Iowa chpt. 1969-70, chpt. Best Employee Newsletter award 1970), Internat. Assn. of Bus. Communications ACE award of merit for annual report design, 1990, IABC ACE award of merit for Crisis Communications, 1990, Spl. Publs. 1991, Pub. rels. soc. of Am. (N.Y. chpt.), Big Apple award for annual reports, 1992, Ridgefield C. of C. Office: 23 Danbury Rd Ridgefield CT 06877-4027

MATTEA, KATHY, vocalist, songwriter; m. Jon Vezner, Feb. 14, 1988. Student, W.Va. U. Former mem. bluegrass band. Albums include Walk the Way the Wind Blows, 1986, Untasted Honey, 1987, Willow in the Wind, 1989, Kathy Mattea: A Collection of Hits, 1990, Time Passes By,

1991 (Best country video award Houston Internat. Film Festival 1991), Lonesome Standard Time, 1992, Good News, 1993 (Grammy award, Best Southern Gospel, Country Gospel or Bluegrass Gospel album, 1994), Walking Away a Winner, 1994. Recipient Best Single award, 1988 (Eighteen Wheels and a Dozen Roses), Song of the Yr. award, 1988 (Eighteen Wheels and a Dozen Roses), Top Female Vocalist award, 1989, Song of the Yr. award., 1989 (Where've You Been) Acad. Country Music, Best Female Vocalist award Country Music Assn., 1989, 90, Best Female Vocalist Radio & Records Country Readers Poll, 1990, Song of the Yr. award (Where've You Been) Country Music Assn., 1990, Best Country Vocal Female Grammy award, 1991, Grammy nomination, Best Country Vocal Collaboration for "Romeo" with Dolly Parton, Tanya Tucker, Billy Ray Cyrus, Pam Tillis & Mary-Chapin Carpenter, 1994. Address: care Robert R Titley 706 18th Ave S Nashville TN 37203*

MATTEI, CHARLES A., oil company executive; b. 1930. With Gulf Oil Corp., Houston, 1951-85; chmn., pres. Cit-Can Oil Corp. subs. Citgo Petroleum Corp., Lake Charles, La., 1985—, also bd. dirs. Office: Cit-Con Oil Corp 6100 S Yale Ave Tulsa OK 74136

MATTER, EDITH ANN, religion educator; b. Ft. Smith, Ark., Dec. 29, 1949; d. Robert Allen and Faye Bert (Overton) M. AB, Oberlin Coll., 1971; MA in Religious Studies, Yale U., 1975, PhD, 1976. Prof. religious studies U. Pa., Phila., 1976—. Author: The Voice of My Beloved: The Song of Songs in Western and Medieval Christianity, 1990; editor: De Partu Virginis, 1985. Tchr., lectr. Pa. Humanities Coun., 1984. Faculty fellow Van Pelt Coll. House, 1981-86, summer rsch. fellow ACLS, 1978, rsch. fellow NEH, 1979, 88; grantee Am. Philos. Soc., 1977, 81, 84. Mem. Medieval Acad. Am., Am. Acad. Religion, Delaware Valley Medieval Assn. Democrat. Home: 941 Annin St Philadelphia PA 19147-4612 Office: U Pa Dept Religious Studies PO Box 36ch Philadelphia PA 19105

MATTERN, DONALD EUGENE, association executive; b. Mapleton Depot, Pa., Feb. 11, 1930; s. John Franklin and Lizzie May (Fiss) M.; m. Anna Mae Bard, Nov. 24, 1951; children: Debra Jeanne, Cynthia Ann, James Franklin. BA, Pa. State U., 1951; MBA, U. Pa., 1965. Exec. trainee Fed. Res. Bank Phila., 1953-55; from asst. cashier to cashier Cumberland County Nat. Bank, New Cumberland, Pa., 1955-63; v.p. 1st Nat. Bank State Coll., Pa., 1963-64; asst. v.p., v.p., sr. v.p., sec. Hamilton Bank, Lancaster, Pa., 1964-86; sec., v.p. Nat. Cen. Fin. Corp., 1972-83; exec. dir. Mfr.'s Assn. Berks County, 1986-95; mem. adv. bd. Berks campus Pa. State U., 1987-92. Treas., bd. dirs. Reading-Berks Human Rels. Coun., 1967-70, v.p. bd. dirs. local chpt. Ams. Competitive Enterprise System, 1970-92; past bd. dirs., past pres. and gen. campaign chmn. United Way Berks County; bd. dirs. Nat. Coun. Alcoholism, 1967-68; chmn. bd. trustees Cmty. Gen. Hosp., Reading; bd. dirs. Reading Ctr. City Devel. Fund, Greater Berks Devel. Fund, 1984-89, Reading Mus. Found., 1985—, Luth Home Topton, Berkshire Health Plan, Congregation Coun. Advent Luth. Ch., Reading New Futures Project, Inc., 1988-91, Pub. Edn. Found. for Berks County, 1991—; mem. exec. bd. Hawk Mountain coun. Boy Scouts Am.; mem. N.E. Pa. Synod Endowment Investment Fund Com.; treas., bd. dirs. Housing Opportunities in Met. Environment, 1968-73. 1st lt. USAF, 1951-53. Mem. Masons, Shriners. Republican. Lutheran. Home: 20 Birchwood Rd Reading PA 19610-1908 Office: PO Box 1539 Reading PA 19603-1539

MATTERN, KEITH EDWARD, lawyer; b. Savanna, Ill., Apr. 24, 1931; s. Harvey and Caroline (Miller) M.; m. Sue D. Cuquet, Oct. 12, 1963; children—Scott, David, Melissa. B.S. in Mgmt., U. Ill., 1953; J.D., U. Mo., 1958. Bar: Mo. 1958, U.S Supreme Ct. 1971. Sole practice, St. Louis, 1958-66; atty. Interco, Inc., St. Louis, 1966-69, asst. gen. counsel, 1969-80, assoc. gen. counsel, 1980-82, gen. counsel, 1982—. Served to capt. USAF, 1953-55. Mem. St. Louis Bar Assn. Roman Catholic. Office: Interco Inc 101 S Hanley Rd Saint Louis MO 63105-3406

MATTERS, CLYDE BURNS, former college president; b. Fargo, N.D., Nov. 10, 1924; s. Lester H. and Pearl Lila (Burns) M.; m. Anna R. Skeels, Mar. 24, 1948; children—Cynthia (Mrs. Charles V. Carroll), Richard B. B.S., Whitworth Coll., Spokane, Wash., 1950, M.Ed., 1951; Ph.D. U. Wash., 1960; L.H.D. (hon.), Hastings Coll., 1985. Tchr. Spokane Pub. Schs., 1950-51; prof. Whitworth Coll., 1950-57, 70-72; research assoc. U. Wash., 1957-60; asst. supt. schs. King County, Wash., 1960-63; program adviser Ford Found., West Africa, 1963-70; pres. Hastings (Nebr.) Coll., 1972-83; pres. Nebr. Ind. Coll. Found.; mem. nexus com. Presbyn. Coll. Union; pres. Assn. Ind. Colls. and Univs. Nebr. Resident camp dir. Spokane YMCA, 1952-57, bd. dirs., 1970-72; bd. dirs. United Good Neighbors, Spokane County, 1969-70; trustee Synod of Alaska N.W. Found., 1995—. With AUS, 1943-46. Decorated Bronze Star. Mem. Assn. Ind. Colls. and Univs. (pres. Nebr. 1979-80), Phi Delta Kappa. Presbyterian (elder). Lodge: Kiwanis. Home: E 4415 51st Ln Box # 3 Spokane WA 99203

MATTES, HANS GEORGE, communications system design scientist, researcher; b. Washington, Jan. 27, 1943; s. Hans Adam and Marion Jane (Burge) M.; m. Martha Jean Throneburg, July 3, 1968; children: Sarah Jane Anne, Kirsten Anne Marie. BS, Calif. Inst. Tech., 1964; MS, U. So. Calif., 1966, PhD, 1968. Mem. tech. staff Bell Labs., Allentown, Pa., 1968-70; vis. assoc. prof. Nat. Taiwan U., Taipei, Republic of China, 1970-71; mem. tech. staff Bell Labs., Holmdel, N.J., 1972-79; dept head Bell Labs., Indpls., 1979-82; dir. data communications lab. Bell Labs., Liberty Corner, N.J., 1986-89; dir. software devel. lab. Bell Labs., 1989-91; devel. v.p. wireless transmission Bell Labs., Whippany, N.J., 1991—. Inventor, patentee in field. Home: 120 Intervale Rd Mountain Lakes NJ 07046-1450

MATTES, MARTIN ANTHONY, lawyer; b. San Francisco, June 18, 1946; s. Hans Adam and Marion Jane (Burge) M.; m. Catherine Elvira Garzio, May 26, 1984; children: Nicholas Anthony, Daniel Joseph, Thomas George. BA, Stanford U., 1968; postgrad., U. Chgo., 1968-69, U. Bonn, Fed. Republic Germany, 1971; JD, U. Calif., Berkeley, 1974. Bar: Calif. 1974, U.S. Ct. Appeals (D.C., 5th and 9th cirs.) 1978, U.S. Dist. Ct. (no. dist.) Calif. 1979, U.S. Dist. Ct. (ea. dist.) Calif. 1991. Asst. legal officer Internat. Union Conservation of Nature and Natural Resources, Bonn, 1974-76; staff counsel Calif. Pub. Utilities Commn., San Francisco, 1976-79, legal advisor to pres., 1979-82, adminstrv. law judge, 1983, asst. chief adminstrv. law judge, 1983-86; ptnr. Graham & James, San Francisco, 1986—; mem. adv. group. to Calif. Senate Subcom. on Pub. Utilities Commn. Procedural Reform, 1994. Mng. editor Ecology Law Quar., 1973-74; contbr. articles to profl. publs. Mem. Conf. Calif. Pub. Utility Counsel (treas. 1988-90, v.p. 1990-91, pres. 1991-92), Internat. Coun. Environ. Law, San Francisco Bar Assn. Office: Graham & James 1 Maritime Plz Ste 300 San Francisco CA 94111

MATTESON, LAWRENCE JAMES, business educator; b. Schenectady, Aug. 23, 1939; s. Parley Lewis and Helen Elizabeth (Panas) M.; m. Mary Kay Myers, June 23, 1962; children: Margaret, Michael. BS in Elec. Engring., Union Coll., 1961; MS in Elec. Engring., Rensselaer Poly. Inst., 1965; MBA, U. Rochester, 1979. Devel. engr. Gen. Electric Co., Syracuse, N.Y., 1961-64; devel. and mfg. engr. Eastman Kodak Co., Rochester, N.Y., 1965-77, consumer products mgr., 1977-81, asst. gen. mgr., 1981-82; exec. prof. bus. policy and ops. U. Rochester, Rochester, N.Y., 1992—; gen. mgr. comml. and info. group Eastman Kodak Co., Rochester, N.Y., 1984-92; mem. tech. adv. bd. Microelectronic and Computer Corp., Austin, Tex., 1984—. Patentee in field. Mem. capital campaign Roberts Wesleyan, Rochester, 1984, endowment com. U. Rochester, 1984; mem. founders com. Rensselaer Poly. Inst., Troy, N.Y., 1983—; trustee Rochester Inst. Tech. Recipient Hugh Whitney award U. Rochester, 1979. Mem. Rochester C. of C., Beta Gamma Sigma, Delta Upsilon. Republican. Roman Catholic. Home: 23 Sesqui Dr Rochester NY 14624-4053 Office: U Rochester Rochester NY 14627

MATTESON, THOMAS T., academic administrator; s. Ruth (Cole) M.; m. Dorothy Johnston, Apr. 10, 1965; children: Juliet M., Jeffrey C. BS, U.S. Coast Guard Acad., 1957; MS, Naval Post Grad. Coll., 1969; postgrad., Air War Coll., 1976-77. Tng. officer USCG Air Sta., Miami, Fla., 1962-63; RCC contr. 9th dist. U.S. Coast Guard Acad. Cleve., 1963-65; asst. ops. officer air sta. U.S. Coast Guard Acad., Port Angeles, Wash., 1965-68; exec. officer Aviation Tng. Ctr. hdqrs. U.S. Coast Guard Acad., Washington, 1973-76; commdg. officer air sta. USCG, Borinquen, P.R., 1977-79; chief aviation br.

hdqrs. USCG, Washington, 1979-81; chief, officer pers. div. hdqrs. U.S. Coast Guard Acad., Washington, 1981-82; chief ops. div. 8th dist. U.S. Coast Guard Acad., New Orleans, 1982-84, chief staff 8th dist., 1984-85, chief pub. and congl. affairs office of boating safety hdqrs., 1985-87, chief office pers. hdqrs., 1987-89; supt. U.S. Coast Guard Acad., New London, Conn., 1989-93, U.S. Merchant Marine Acad., Kings Point, N.Y., 1993—. Office: Dept Transp Merchant Marine Acad Kings Point NY 11024-1699

MATTESON, WILLIAM BLEECKER, lawyer; b. N.Y.C., Oct. 20, 1928; s. Leonard Jerome and Mary Jo (Harwell) M.; m. Marilee Brill, Aug. 26, 1950; children: Lynn, Sandra, Holly. B.A., Yale U., 1950; J.D., Harvard U., 1953. Bar: N.Y. 1954. Clk. to judge Augustus N. Hand U.S. Ct. Appeals, 1953-54; clk. to U.S. Supreme Ct. Justice Harold H. Burton, 1954-55; asso. firm Debevoise & Plimpton (and predecessors), N.Y.C., 1955-61; partner Debevoise & Plimpton (and predecessors), 1961—, Debevoise & Plimpton (European office), Paris, 1973-78; presiding ptnr., 1988-93; lectr. Columbia U. Law Sch., 1972-73, 78-80. Trustee Peddle Sch., Hightstown, N.J., 1968-73, Kalamazoo Coll., 1972-77, Miss Porter's Sch., Farmington, Conn., 1977-83, N.Y. Inst. Spl. Edn., 1981—, Salk Inst., La Jolla, Calif., 1994—; chmn. USA Bus. and Industry Adv. Com. to the Orgn. for Econ. Coop. and Devel., Paris, 1986—; chmn. Worldwide Bus. and Industry Adv. Com., 1994—; vice chmn. U.S. Coun. for Internat. Bus., 1990—. Mem. ABA, Internat. Bar Assn. (sect. on bus. law coun.), Fed. Bar Assn., N.Y. State Bar Assn., Assn. of Bar of City of N.Y. (chmn. securities regulation com. 1968-71), Harvard U. Law Sch. Assn. N.Y.C. (trustee 1968-73), Coun. Fgn. Rels., Union Club, River Club, Sky Club, Links Club, Sankaty Head Club (Nantucket, Mass.). Home: 201 E 62nd St New York NY 10021-7627 Office: Debevoise & Plimpton 875 Third Ave New York NY 10022

MATTESSICH, RICHARD VICTOR (ALVARUS), business administration educator; b. Trieste, Venezia-Julia, Italy, Aug. 9, 1922; s. Victor and Gertrude (Pfaundler) M.; m. Hermine Auguste Mattessich, Apr. 12, 1952. Mech. engr., Engring. Coll., Vienna, Austria, 1940; Diplomkaufmann, Hochschule für Welthandel, Vienna, 1944; Dr.rer.pol., Hochschule für Welthandel, 1945; Accademico Ordinario, Accademia Italiana di Economia Aziendale, Bologna, 1980—; Austrian Acad. Scis., Vienna, 1984—. Research fellow Austrian Inst. Econ. Research, Vienna, 1945-47; instr. Rosenberg Coll., St. Gallen, 1947-52; dep. head Mt. Allison U., Sackville, Can., 1953-59; assoc. prof. U. Calif.-Berkeley, 1958-67; prof. econs. Ruhr U., Bochum, W. Ger., 1966-67; prof. indsl. administrn. U. Tech., Vienna, 1976-78; prof. bus. adminstrn. U. B.C., Vancouver, 1967-87, Arthur Andersen & Co. Disting. chair, 1980-87, prof. emeritus, 1988—; Vis. prof. Free U., Berlin, 1965, U. Social Scis., St. Gallen, Switzerland, 1965-66, U. Canterbury, 1970, Austrian Acad. Mgmt., 1971, 73; mem. bd. nominations Acctg. Hall of Fame, Columbus, Ohio, 1978-87; bd. govs. Sch. Chartered Accountancy, Vancouver, 1981-82; bd. dirs. Can. Cert. Gen. Accts. Research Found., 1984-90; internat. adv. bd. CGA Rsch. Found., 1993—. Author: Accounting and Analytical Methods, 1964, Simulation of the Firm through a Budget Computer Program, 1964, Instrumental Reasoning and Systems Methodology, 1978; editor: Modern Accounting Research: History, Survey and Guide, 1984, 89, 92, Accounting Research in the 1980s and Its Future Influence, 1991, French transl., 1993: Critique of Accounting, 1995, Foundational Research in Accounting: Professional Memoirs and Beyond, others; mem. editl. bds. Theory and Decision Libr., The Acctg. Historians Jour., Jour. Bus. Adminstrn., Economia Aziendale, Praxiology, Acctg., Bus. and Fin. History. Sec.-treas. Internat. House, U. B.C., 1969-70; bd. dirs. Can. Cert. Gen. Accts. Research Found., 1984-90. Served to lt. Orgn. Todt., 1944-45. Recipient Gold medal and Lit. award AICPA, 1972, Haim Falk award Can. Acad. Acctg. Assn., 1991; Ford Found. fellow, 1961-62; Disting. Erskine fellow U. Canterbury, 1970; Killam sr. fellow U. B.C., 1971-72. Fellow Accademia Italiana di Economia Aziendale (accademico ordinario 1980—); mem. Inst. Chartered Accts., Am. Acctg. Assn. (lit. award 1972, 73), Schmalenbach Gesellschaft, Verb. d. Hochschullehrer für Betriebswirtschaft (exec. adv. council 1976-78), Inst. Chartered Accts. of B.C. (bd. of govs. 1981-82), Austrian Acad. Scis. (corr.), Acad. Acctg. Historians (life). Club: Faculty U. B.C. (Vancouver). Office: U BC, Vancouver, BC Canada V6T 1Z2 *Cautious optimism is the best long-run optimization strategy.*

MATTHAU, WALTER, actor; b. N.Y.C., Oct. 1, 1920; s. Milton and Rose (Berolsky) M.; m. Carol Grace Marcus, Aug. 21, 1959; children—David, Jenny, Charles. Ed. pub. schs., N.Y.C. Broadway appearances include: Anne of a Thousand Days, 1948, The Liar, 1949, Season in the Sun, 1950, Fancy Meeting You Again, 1951, Twilight Walk, 1951 (N.Y. Drama Critics award), One Bright Day, 1951, In Any Language, 1952, The Grey-Eyed People, 1952, The Ladies of the Corridor, 1953, Will Success Spoil Rock Hunter, 1955, Once More with Feeling, 1958 (N.Y. Drama Critics award), Once There Was a Russian, 1960, A Shot in the Dark, 1961 (Antoinette Perry award), My Mother, My Father and Me, 1963, The Odd Couple, 1964 (Antoinette Perry award); motion pictures include A Guide for the Married Man, Secret Life of An American Wife, Mirage, Charade, The Kentuckian, 1955, The Indian Fighter, 1955, Slaughter on Tenth Avenue, 1957, Ride A Crooked Trail, A Face in the Crowd, 1957, No Power on Earth, Middle of the Street, Onion Head, 1958, Voice in the Mirror, 1958, Bigger Than Life, King Creole, 1958, Island of Love, Strangers When We Meet, 1960, The Gangster Story, 1960, Where's The Action, 1962, Lonely Are the Brave (Film Daily award), 1962, Fail-Safe, 1964, Goodbye Charlie, 1964, The Odd Couple, 1966, The Fortune Cookie (Academy award), 1966, Candy, 1968, Hello Dolly!, 1968, Cactus Flower, 1969, A New Leaf, Plaza Suite, Kotch, 1971, Pete 'n Tillie, 1972, Charley Varrick, Laughing Policeman, The Front Page, The Sunshine Boys, 1975, The Bad News Bears, The Taking of Pelham, One Two Three, California Suite, 1978, Casey's Shadow, 1978, House Calls, 1978, I Ought To Be In Pictures, Little Miss Marker, 1979, Hopscotch, 1979, First Monday in October, 1981, Buddy Buddy, 1981, The Survivors, Movers and Shakers, 1984, Pirates, 1986, Couch Trip, 1987, The Little Devil, 1988, J.F.K., 1991, Dennis the Menace, 1993, Grumpy Old Men, 1993, I.Q., 1994; TV films include: Incident in a Small Town, 1994. Served with USAAF, 1941-45, ETO. Office: care Ernst & Young 1999 Avenue Of The Stars # 210 Los Angeles CA 90067

MATTHEI, EDWARD HODGE, architect; b. Chgo., Dec. 21, 1927; s. Henry Reinhold and Myra Beth (Hodge) M.; m. Mary Nina Hoffmann, June 30, 1951; children: Edward Hodge, Suzanne Marie, Christie Ann, Laura Jean, John William. B.S. in Archtl. Engring, U. Ill., 1951. Registered architect, Ariz., Calif., Colo., Fla., Ga., Ill., Ind., Iowa, Mich., Minn., Nev., N.Mex., N.Y., Ohio, Pa., Wis., Md. Dir. health facilities planning and constrn. Child & Smith (architects and engrs.), Chgo., 1951-60; sr. v.p. health facilities planning Perkins & Will, Chgo., 1960-74; ptnr. firm Matthei & Colin Assoc., Chgo., 1974—; com. chmn. Am. Nat. Standards Inst., 1983-89; lectr. 1st Internat. Conf. on Rehab. of Handicapped, Beijing, 1986, Design USA, Novosbirsk and Moscow, USSR, 1990. Editor: Inland Architect, 1956-58; prin. works health facilities projects, med. ctr. master plans including Augustana Hosp. and Health Care Ctr., Chgo., Mercy Hosp., Davenport, Iowa, Westlake Community Hosp., Chgo., Highland Park (Ill.) Hosp., Ctrl. DuPage Hosp., Winfield, Ill., Nebr. Meth. Hosp., Omaha, Rockford (Ill.) Meml. Hosp., U. Ala. Med. Ctr., Birmingham, U. Calif. Sch. Medicine, Irvine, Kent Hall, U. Chgo., Holy Cross Hosp., Mass., West Mich. Cancer Ctr. Second v.p. Nat. Easter Seal Soc., 1978; mem. bd. dirs. St. Scholastica High Sch., Chgo., 1973-83, 86—; mem. Welfare Council Greater Met. Chgo., 1965-72; chair profl. adv. coun. Nat. Easter Seal Soc. 1988-89. Served with AUS, 1946-47. Recipient Leon Chatelain award for barrier-free environ. Nat. Easter Seals Soc., 1979, Disting. Svc. award, 1990, Am. Nat. Standards Inst., 1989, Speedy award Paralyzed Vets. Am., 1993. Fellow AIA (Disting. Svc. award Chgo. chpt. 1988); mem. Am. Hosp. Assn., Am. Assn. Hosp. Planning, Internat. Hosp. Fedn., Nat. Center Barrier Free Environ. (dir.), Builders Assn. Chgo., Chgo. Assn. Commerce and Industry. Clubs: Monroe (Chgo.). Home: 1437 W Glenlake Ave Chicago IL 60660-1801 Office: Matthei & Colin Assocs 332 S Michigan Ave Chicago IL 60604-4301

MATTHEI, WARREN DOUGLAS, investment company executive; b. N.Y.C., Apr. 14, 1951; s. Warren Everrett and Helen (Riewerts) M.; m. Susan Kelley, June 12, 1976 (div. 1992); children: Anne E., Kathryn M. Warren Douglas Jr. BA, Princeton U., 1973; MBA, Harvard U., 1977. Asst. treas. Chase Manhattan Bank, N.Y.C., 1973-75; with Kidder Peabody, N.Y.C., 1977-82; dir. Salomon Bros., L.A., 1982-87; mng. dir. Merrill Lynch, L.A., 1987-93; with Mansfield Coll., U. Oxford, 1994—; dir. CFOMoscow, Russia Fedn. Health Care Ltd., 1995—. Trustee Am. Ch. in London.

Recipient John Loeb award Harvard U. Faculty, Boston, 1977, Steinneck prize Princeton U., 1972. Mem. Winged Foot Club (Mamaroneck, N.Y.), Princeton Club (N.Y.C.), Baltusrol Club (Springfield, N.J.), Annandale Club (Pasadena, Calif.), The Queen's Club (London). Republican. Lutheran.

MATTHES, GERALD STEPHEN, advertising agency executive; b. Hamburg, Germany, Aug. 31, 1938; Brit. subject; came to U.S., 1964, naturalized 1977; s. Stanley Rutter and Gerda Elena (Spiro) M.; m. Betsy Durkin (div. 1981); 1 child, Peter Charlton; m. Margaret Emily Secher; children: Christopher Stanley, Lydia Janet. Undergrad. edn., Gt. Britain; M. in Communications, Advt. and Mktg., London Coll., 1963. Acct. exec. Press and Gen. Publicity, Ltd., London, 1959-61, Dudley, Turner and Vincent, Ltd., London, 1961-64; v.p., mgmt. supr. Doyle, Dane, Bernbach, N.Y.C., 1964-79; sr. v.p. internat. Bozell, N.Y.C., 1980—; coun. Robert P. Gersin Assoc., 1979. Contbr. articles to profl. jours. Recipient Gold Medal award Direct Mail Assn. Great Britain, 1963. Democrat. Episcopalian. Home: 709 Kensington Ln Bloomfield Hills MI 48304-3743 Office: Bozell Worldwide Inc 1000 Town Ctr Ste 1500 Southfield MI 48075-1241

MATTHEW, KATHRYN KAHRS, museum director; b. Charleston, S.C., Mt. Holyoke Coll., 1976; PhD, U. Pa., 1981; MBA, U. Minn., 1988. Collection asst., mgr. Acad. Natural Scis., Phila., 1979-82; curator sci. Cranbrook Inst. of Sci., Bloomfield Hills, Mich., 1983-85; asst. dir. Santa Barbara (Calif.) Mus. Natural History, 1988-89; dep. dir. Va. Mus. Natural History, Martinsville, 1989-91; dir. N.Mex. Mus. Natural History, Albuquerque, 1991—; prin. sci. adviser Omnimax film Sci. Mus. Minn., Mpls., 1988-92. Bd. dirs. Albuquerque Conv. and Visitors Bur., 1992—; mem. steering com. Magnifico Arts Festival, 1992; mem. govs. coun. Advance Math and Sci. Edn., 1992—; mem. rsch. com. N.Mex. First, 1992—. Mem. N.Mex. Women's Forum. Office: NM Mus Natural History & Sci 1801 Mountain Rd NW Albuquerque NM 87104-1375

MATTHEWS, BETTY PARKER, special education educator; b. Port Arthur, Tex., Dec. 9, 1929; d. Clarence G. and Florence (Sudduth) Parker; m. Paul A. Matthews, Mar. 25, 1955; children: Michael A., Scott P., Lisa M. Alexander. B.S. La. Coll., 1975; MEd, Northwestern U., 1981. Specialist in edn. La., 1984; cert. elem. tchr., mentally retarded, learning disabled, ednl. cons., generic mild/moderate, assessment tchr., ednl. diagnostician, La. 3d grade tchr. Rapides Parish Sch. Bd., Alexandria, La., 1975-76, tchr. spl. edn., 1976-81, assessment tchr., ednl. diagnostician, 1981—; ednl. diagnostician Rapides Parish Sch. Bd., Alexandria, 1993—; ednl. cons. Briarwood Psychiatric Hosp., Alexandria, La., 1986-93, Crossroads Psychiat. Hosp., Alexandria, 1993—; adj. prof. La. State U. Alexandria, 1990—. Dir. children's Bible study 1st Bapt. Ch., Pineville, La., 1985—. Mem. La. Edn. Assessment Tchrs. Assn. (regional rep. 1987-88, treas. 1988-90, Pres.'s Svc. award 1990-91, La. Assessment Tchr. of Yr. 1993), La. Edn. Diagnostician Assn., Coun. Exceptional Children, Reading Coun., Alpha Delta Kappa, Phi Delta Kappa, Epsilon Sigma Alpha (state pres., regional sec.). Home: 3050 Rigolette Rd Pineville LA 71360

MATTHEWS, BRIAN W., molecular biology educator; b. Mount Barker, Australia, May 25, 1938; came to U.S., 1967; s. Lionel A. and Ethlinda L. (Harris) M.; m. Helen F. Denley, Sept. 7, 1963; children—Susan, Kristine. B.S., U. Adelaide, Australia, 1959, B.S. with honors, 1960, Ph.D., 1964, D.Sc., 1986. Mem. staff Med. Research Council, Cambridge, Eng., 1963-66; vis. assoc. NIH, Bethesda, Md., 1967-69; prof. molecular biology U. Oreg., Eugene, 1969—, chmn. dept. physics, 1985-86, dir. Inst. Molecular Biology, 1980-83, 90-92; advisor NSF, Washington, 1975-77; investigator Howard Hughes Med. Inst., 1989—; mem. U.S. Nat. Commn. for Crystallography, Washington, 1980-86, 88-90. Rsch. fellow Alfred P. Sloan Found., 1971, Guggenheim fellow, 1977; recipient Career Devel. award NIH, 1973, Faculty Excellence award Oreg. Bd. Edn., 1984, Discovery award Med. Rsch. Found. Oreg., 1987, Reed Coll. Vollum award, 1994. Mem. NAS, AAAS, Crystallographic Assn., Am. Chem. Soc., Protein Soc. (pres. 1995—). Office: U Oreg Inst Molecular Biology Eugene OR 97403

MATTHEWS, BRUCE RANKIN, professional football player; b. Arcadia, Calif., Aug. 8, 1961. BS in Indsl. Engring., U. So. Calif., 1983. Center, guard Houston Oilers, 1983—. Named NFL All-Pro Team Guard by Sporting News, 1988-90, 92, Leader, 1993. Played in Pro Bowl, 1988-93. Office: Houston Oilers 6910 Fannin St Fl 3 Houston TX 77030-3875*

MATTHEWS, CARI PINEIRO, lawyer, author; b. Nov. 16, 1942; d. Calixto R. and Dionisia G. Pineiro; m. Frederic Lawrence Matthews III, Mar. 20, 1964 (dec. Apr. 1981); children: Barbara C., Christopher James. BA, Hunter Coll., 1964; JD, U. Miami, 1975. Bar: Fla. 1975. Assoc. Cramer & Matthews, Miami, 1975-77; asst. U.S. atty. U.S. Justice Dept., So. Dist. Fla., 1977-79; mem. Civil Rights Reviewing Authority, U.S. Dept. Edn., Washington, 1983-84; assoc. dep. atty. gen. U.S. Justice Dept., Washington, 1984-86; asst. gen. counsel fed. litigation U.S. Def. Dept. Navy, Washington, 1986-88; gen. counsel, v.p. ICN Pharms., Costa Mesa, Calif., 1988-89. Author: Federal Civil Trialbook, 1991; co-author: West's Federal Practice Manual, rev. 2d edit., vol. 8, 1993. Mem. women's com. Nat. Symphony Orch., Washington, 1985—. Mem. Fed. Bar Assn. (mem. continuing legal edn. bd. 1994, Outstanding Legal Edn. Programs award 1987), Fla. Bar Assn.

MATTHEWS, CHARLES SEDWICK, petroleum engineering consultant, research advisor; b. Houston, Mar. 27, 1920; s. Charles James and Zadoc Coleman (Sedwick) M.; m. Miriam Loraine Ormerod, June 2, 1945; children—Joan Gail, Wendy Loraine. B.S. in Chem. Engring., Rice U., 1941, M.S. in Chem. Engring., 1943, Ph.D. in Chemistry, 1944. Registered profl. engr., Tex. Engr. Shell Devel. Co., San Francisco, 1944-48; research engr. Shell Devel. Co., Houston, 1948-56; dir. research Shell Devel. Co., 1967-72; chief reservoir engr. Shell Oil Co., Houston, 1965; mgr. engring. Shell Oil Co., 1972-73, sr. petroleum engring. cons., 1973-89; mem. engring. adv. com. Rice U., Houston, 1973-77; cons. Dept. Energy, Washington, 1974-78, mem. adv. com., 1975-79; spl. asst. Nat. Petroleum Council, Washington, 1981-83; mem. reserves com. Am. Petroleum Inst. Author: Pressure Buildup and Flow Tests in Wells, 1967; contbr. articles to profl. jours.; patentee in field. Chmn. Tex. Engrs. for Conservation, Houston, 1973. Recipient Disting. Alumnus award Rice U., 1994. Mem. NAE, Soc. Petroleum Engrs. (hon. mem., Lester Uren award 1975, disting. author, disting. lectr. 1968, Disting. lectr. emeritus 1986), Phi Beta Kappa, Sigma Xi, Tau Beta Pi, Phi Lambda Upsilon. Republican. Methodist. Clubs: Houston, Meyerland (treas. 1982-85). Avocations: swimming; fishing. Home: 5307 S Braeswood Blvd Houston TX 77096-4149

MATTHEWS, CLARK J(IO), II, retail executive, lawyer; b. Arkansas City, Kans., Oct. 1, 1936; s. Clark J. and Betty Elizabeth (Stewart) M.; children: Patricia Eleanor, Pamela Elaine, Catherine Joy. B.A., So. Meth. U., 1959, J.D., 1961. Bar: Tex. 1961. Trial atty. Ft. Worth Regional Office, SEC, 1961-63; law clk. to chief U.S. dist. judge No. Dist. Tex., Dallas, 1963-65; atty. Southland Corp., Dallas, 1965-73; v.p., gen. counsel Southland Corp., 1973-79, exec. v.p., chief fin. officer, 1979-83, sr. exec. v.p., chief fin. officer, 1983-87, exec. v.p., chief fin. officer, 1987-91, pres., chief exec. officer, 1991—. Mem. ABA, Tex., Dallas, Bar Assns., Am. Judicature Soc., Alpha Tau Omega, Pi Alpha Delta. Methodist. Club: DeMolay. Home: 7005 Stefani Dr Dallas TX 75225-1747 Office: Southland Corp 2711 N Haskell Ave Dallas TX 75204-2910

MATTHEWS, CRAIG GERARD, gas company executive; b. Bklyn., Mar. 8, 1943; m. Carol O. Olsen, Sept. 10, 1971; children: Kenneth C., Bradford P., Melinda M. BCE. Rutgers U., 1965; MS in Indsl. Mgmt., Polytech. Inst. Bklyn., 1971. Trainee Bklyn. Union Gas Co., 1965, exec. v.p., 1988—. Bd. dirs. Bklyn. Philharm., Salvation Army, Inform, Prospect Park Alliance, Regional Planning Assn., Greater Jamaica Devel. Corp., Pub. Utility Reports, Neighborhood Housing Svcs. Mem. Bklyn. C of C. (bd. dirs.), Am. Gas Assn. (bd. dirs.). Republican. Presbyterian. Home: 17 Wynwood Rd Chatham NJ 07928-1755 Office: Bklyn Union Gas Co 195 Montague St Brooklyn NY 11201-3684

MATTHEWS, DALE SAMUEL, information scientist, media futurist; b. Van Nuys, Calif., Oct. 30, 1954; s. Dale Lionel Mandall and Helen Adeline (Pierce) M. AA cum laude, Coll. of Redwoods, 1974; BA magna cum laude,

San Francisco State U., 1976. With physics dept. Georgetown U., Washington; dir., Advanced Projects Neural Network rsch. facility Georgetown U.; founder Exec. Briefing Technology Alliance; speaker in field. Author: The Biological Future of Computing, World At Risk-Key Indicators of The Inevitability of Change, Executive Briefing System For The National Science Highway To The White House, New Concepts For A Three-Screen Digital Environment Utilizing Super-Saturated Communications Techniques, High Technology and the Future of Barbados, Say Goodbye To The World As You Know It, Shift Happens-Predicting Tomorrow's Paradigm Challenges, Tools And How They Shape Us, Surfers On The Third Wave. Achievments include originating the concept of consensual reality and supersaturated communications. Office: Georgetown U Dept Physics Washington DC 20057-0995

MATTHEWS, DAN GUS, lawyer; b. Jacksonville, Tex., Feb. 6, 1939; s. Agustus Newcomb and Charlie (Morton) M.; m. Mary Ellen Whittredge, Dec. 12, 1959; children: Mark Henderson, Daniel William. BS in History and English, Stephen F. Austin U., 1960; LLB, U. Houston, 1964. Bar: Tex. 1964, U.S. Dist. Ct. (so. dist.) Tex. 1964, U.S. Ct. Appeals (5th cir.) 1965, U.S. Ct. Appeals (11th cir.) 1981, U.S. Supreme Ct. 1967, U.S. Dist. Ct. (ea. dist.) Tex. 1990. Briefing clk. Fed. Judge Ben C. Connally, Houston, 1964-66; assoc. firm Fulbright & Jaworski, Houston, 1966-73; ptnr. Fulbright & Jaworski, Houston and San Antonio, 1973—. Bd. dirs., exec. com., chmn. membership coun. Los Compadres de San Antonio, Missions Nat. Hist. Pk., 1988—; deacon, elder Presbyn. Ch. Mem. ABA, State Bar Tex., Houston Bar Assn., San Antonio Bar Assn. Avocations: hunting, fishing. Office: Fulbright & Jaworski 300 Convent St Ste 2200 San Antonio TX 78205-3792

MATTHEWS, DANIEL GEORGE, editorial consultant; b. Lawrenceville, Va., Dec. 18, 1932; s. George Daniel and Evelyn (Goodrich) M.; student George Washington U., 1956-64, U.S. Fgn. Service Inst., 1960-64; m. Linda L. Fink, Oct. 25, 1975; children: Strelka Jamila, Francesca Alina. Analyst, VA, Washington, 1953-54; libr. asst. cataloging U.S. Dept. State, Washington, 1954-63, intelligence and rsch. specialist, 1964-66; editor-in-chief African Bibliog. Ctr., Washington, 1963-83, exec. dir., 1966-83; v.p. Afritec cons. firm, 1983-85; ptnr. The Matthews Assocs., editor Africa Insider, biweekly newsletter on U.S.-African rels., 1984—; editor African Fgn. Affairs, 1985—; editorial cons. Greenwood Press, N.Y.C., 1967—; pres. Washington Task Force on African Affairs, 1969-79, African Communications Liaison Svc., 1979-84; mem. exec. com. coordinating coun. Internat. Ednl. Exch., 1969-87; program dir. So. African Devel. Documentation and Info. Exch., 1979-83; acting Am. dir. U.S./S. Africa Leader Exch. program, 1987-88; dir. Congl. African program Internat. Ctr. for Dynamics of Devel., 1989-90; lectr., cons. to acad. instns. on Africana collections and U.S. fgn. policy toward Africa; N.Am. liaison Orgn. African Unity/UN; mem. Econ. Commn. on Africa's Pan African Devel. Info. System, 1979-82. Bd. dirs. U.S.-South Africa Leader Exch. Program, 1980-90, chmn. exec. com., 1985-87; bd. dirs. Internat. Ctr. for Dynamics Devel., 1985-90; dir. ICDD Congressional Africa Program, 1989-90; pres. Internat. Ctr. for Devel. Initiatives, 1991-93; exec. dir. Operation Hunger, 1992-93. With AUS, 1950-53. Mem. ALA, African Studies Assn. (publs. com. 1974), African Heritage Studies Assn. (assoc.; award for outstanding contbn. to Africa 1975). Internat. Inst. Edn. (South African program bd. 1983—). Author: Soviet View of Africa, 1957; A Current Bibliography on Ethiopian Affairs, 1967, 72; editor-in-chief A Current Bibliography on African Affairs, 1963-84, editor emeritus, 1984—; editor: African affairs for General Reader, 1967; Current Themes in African Historical Studies, 1970; editorial bd. African Books in Print, Ife, Nigeria. Home: 1001 Rockville Pike 509 Rockville MD 20852

MATTHEWS, DAVID, clergyman; b. Indianola, Miss., Jan. 29, 1920; s. Albert and Bertha (Henderson) M.; m. Lillian Pearl Banks, Aug. 28, 1951; 1 dau., Denise. A.B., Morehouse Coll., Atlanta, 1950; student, Atlanta U., 1950, Memphis Theol. Sem., 1965, Delta State U., Cleveland, Miss., 1969, 71, 72; D.D. (hon.), Natchez (Miss.) Jr. Coll., 1973, Morris Booker Meml. Coll., 1988. Ordained minister Nat. Baptist Conv. U.S.A., 1946; pastor chs. in Miss., 1951—, Bell Grove Baptist Ch., Indianola, 1951—, Strangers Home, Greenwood, 1958—; tchr., chmn. dept. social sci. Gentry H.S., Indianola, 1958-83; moderator Sunflower Bapt. Assn., 1957—; v.p. Gen. Bapt. Conv. Miss., 1958—; former lectr., conv. congress religious edn.; v.p. Nat. Bapt. Conv. U.S.A., 1971-94; del. to Nat. Coun. Chs., 1960, supr. oratorical contest, 1976; pres. Gen. Missionary Bapt. State Conv. Miss., 1974—. Mem. Sunflower County Anti-Poverty Bd., 1965-71, Indianola Bi-Racial Com., 1965—; mem. Gov.'s Advisory Com.; col. on staff Gov. Finch, 1976-80; mem. budget com. Indianola United Fund, 1971—; chmn. bd. Indianola FHA, 1971—; trustee Natchez Jr. Coll.; mem. Miss. Gov.'s Research and Devel. Council, 1984—; apptd. mem. So. Govs. Ecumenical Coun. Infant Mortality, 1987. Served with U.S. Army, 1942-45, PTO. Recipient citation Morehouse Coll., 1950, citation Miss. Valley State Coll., 1956; J.H. Jackson Preaching award Midwestern Baptist Laymen Fellowship, 1974; Gov.'s Merit award, 1975. Mem. NEA, Miss., Indianola Tchrs. Assns., Am. Bible Soc. (adv. coun. 1991—, student reform theol. sem. centennial edn. 1990—). Democrat. Home: PO Box 627 Indianola MS 38751-0627 *I have learned not to seek honors and success but to become so involved in worthwhile works that I lose myself and by such actions success and honors have come.*

MATTHEWS, DONALD ROWE, political scientist, educator; b. Cin., Sept. 14, 1925; s. William Procter and Janet Burch (Williams) M.; m. Margie C. Richmond, June 28, 1947 (div.); children: Mary, Jonathan; m. Carmen J. Onstad, July 7, 1970 (div.); children: Christopher, Amy. Student, Kenyon Coll., 1943, Purdue U., 1944-45; A.B. with high honors, Princeton, 1948, M.A., 1951, Ph.D., 1953; Dr. hon. causa, U. Bergen, 1985. Instr. Smith Coll., Northampton, Mass., 1951-53; asst. prof. govt. Smith Coll., 1953-57; lectr. polit. sci. U. N.C., Chapel Hill, 1957-58; assoc. prof. U. N.C., 1958-63, prof., 1963-70; research prof. Inst. for Research in Social Sci., 1963-70; sr. fellow in govtl. studies Brookings Instn., Washington, 1970-73; prof. polit. sci. and research assoc. Inst. for Research in Social Sci., U. Mich., Ann Arbor, 1973-76; prof. polit. sci. U. Wash., Seattle, 1976—, chmn. dept. polit. sci., 1976-83; guest prof. U. Bergen, Norway, 1980-81, 93; fellow Ctr. for Advanced Study in the Behavioral Scis., 1964-65; cons. to U.S. Commn. on Civil Rights, 1958-60, NBC News, 1966-68, Ford Found., 1967-68, U.S. Ho. of Reps., 1970-72, others; faculty lectr. U. Wash., 1989. Author: The Social Background of Political Decision-Makers, 1954, U.S. Senators and Their World, 1960, (with James Prothro) Negroes and the New Southern Politics, 1966, Perspectives on Presidential Selection, 1973, (with William Keech) The Party's Choice, 1976, (with James Stimson) Yeas and Nays: A Theory of Decision-Making in the U.S. House of Representatives, 1975; Contbr. articles to profl. jours. Served with USNR, 1943-46. Recipient Sr. Award for Research in Govtl. Affairs Social Sci. Research Council, 1962; Ford Found. fellow, 1969-70; Guggenheim fellow, 1980-81. Fellow Am. Acad. Arts and Scis.; mem. Am. Polit. Sci. Assn. (treas. 1970-72, v.p. 1985-86), Pacific N.W. Polit. Sci. Assn. (pres. 1977-78), Western Polit. Sci. Assn. (pres. 1979-80), So. Polit. Sci. Assn., Midwestern Polit. Sci. Assn., Inter-Univ. Consortium for Polit. Research (exec. com. 1970-72). Democrat. Home: Houseboat B 3125 Fairview Ave E Seattle WA 98102-3063 Office: U Wash Polit Sci Do # 30 Seattle WA 98195

MATTHEWS, EDWARD E., insurance company executive; b. 1931. AB, Princeton U., 1953; MBA, Harvard U., 1957. With Morgan Stanley & Co., 1957-73; exec. v.p. fin., vice chmn. bd. dirs. Am. Internat. Group, Inc., N.Y.C., from 1973, now vice chmn. bd. dirs. With U.S. Army, 1953-55. Office: Am Internat Group Inc 70 Pine St New York NY 10270-0001

MATTHEWS, EDWIN SPENCER, JR., lawyer; b. Spokane, Wash., May 31, 1934; s. Edwin Spencer and Dorothy Chace (Ehrhardt) M.; m. Marie-Claude Paris, Dec. 19, 1959 (div. 1982); children: Nadia, Sylvie, Clarissa; m. Patricia L. Sills Barnes, Aug. 22, 1983; children: Paxton, Gillian. AB magna cum laude, Harvard U., 1956; Diplome d'Etudes Francaises, Institut de Tourraine, Tours, France, 1958; LLB, Yale U., 1962. Bar: N.Y. 1963, Calif. 1979, U.S. Supreme Ct. 1992; Conseil Juridique (France) 1965-79. Assoc. Coudert Bros., N.Y.C., 1962-65; assoc. Coudert Freres, Paris, 1965-69, ptnr., 1969-79; ptnr. Coudert Bros., San Francisco, 1979-80, N.Y.C., 1980—. Trustee Sierra Club Legal Def. Fund, San Francisco, 1984—; bd. dirs. Friends of Earth Found., N.Y.C., 1979-90; bd. dirs. Friends of Earth Inc., Washington, 1970-90, pres., 1979-80. With U.S. Army, 1957-58. Mem. Assn. of Bar of City of N.Y. (com. on housing and urban devel. 1964-65), Am. Alpine Club, Harvard Club (N.Y.C.), Coffie House, N.Y. Athletic

Club. Democrat. Avocations: ocean sailing, carpentry, mountain climbing, sculling. Home: 11 Harrison St New York NY 10013-2888 also: PO Box 493 Washington Depot CT 06794-0493 Office: Coudert Brothers 1114 Avenue of the Americas New York NY 10036-7703

MATTHEWS, ELIZABETH WOODFIN, law librarian, law educator; b. Ashland, Va., July 30, 1927; d. Edwin Clifton and Elizabeth Frances (Luck) Woodfin; m. Sidney E. Matthews, Dec. 20, 1947; 1 child, Sarah Elizabeth Matthews Wiley. BA, Randolph-Macon Coll., 1948, LLD (hon.), 1989; MS in Libr. Sci., U. Ill., 1952; PhD, So. Ill. U., 1972; LLD, Randolph-Macon Coll., 1989. Cert. law libr., med. libr., med. libr. III. Libr. Ohio State U., Columbus, 1952-59; libr., instr. U. Ill., Chicago, 1962-63, lectr. Grad. Sch. Libr. Sci., 1964; libr. instr. Morris Libr. So. Ill. U., Carbondale, 1964-67, classroom instr. Coll. Edn., 1967-70, med. libr., asst. prof. Morris Libr., 1972-74, law libr., assoc. prof., 1974-79, law libr., assoc. prof., 1979-85, law libr., prof., 1985-93; prof. emeritus, 1993—. Author: Access Points to Law Libraries, 1984, 17th Century English Law Reports, 1986, Law Library Reference Shelf, 1988, 2d edit., 1992, Pages and Missing Pages, 1983, 2d edit., 1989, Lincoln as a Lawyer: An Annotated Bibliography, 1991. Mem. AAUW (pres. 1976-78, corp. rep. 1978-88), Am. Assn. Law Librs., Mid Am. Assn. Law Librs., Beta Phi Mu, Phi Kappa Phi. Methodist. Home: 811 S Skyline Dr Carbondale IL 62901-2405 Office: So Ill U Law Libr Carbondale IL 62901

MATTHEWS, EUGENE EDWARD, artist; b. Davenport, Iowa, Mar. 22, 1931; s. Nickolas Arthur and Velma (Schroeder) M.; m. Wanda Lee Miller, Sept. 14, 1952; children: Anthony Lee, Daniel Nickolas. Student, Bradley U., 1948-51; BFA, U. Iowa, 1953, MFA, 1957. Prof. fine arts grad. faculty U. Colo., Boulder, 1961—, dir. vis. artists program, 1985—; vis. artist Am. Acad. Rome, 1989. Exhibited in one-man shows U. Wis., Milw., 1960, Brena Gallery, Denver, 1963, 65, 67, 70, 74, 76, 78, 80, 83, 88, Colorado Springs Fine Arts Ctr., 1967, Sheldon Art Gallery, U. Nebr., 1968, Denver Art Mus., 1972, James Yu Gallery, N.Y.C., 1973, 77, Dubins Gallery, L.A., 1981, Galeria Rysunku, Poznan, 1983; exhibited numerous group shows U.S., Europe, Africa, Asia, internat. watercolor exhbn. New Orleans, 1983, Louvre, Paris, Met. Mus. of Art, N.Y.C., Internat. Art Ctr., Kyoto, Japan, Mus. of Modern Art, Rijeka, Yugoslavia, Taipei Fine Arts Mus., Taiwan, Republic of China; represented in permanent collections Nat. Mus. Am. Art, Washington, Denver Art Mus., Butler Inst. Am. Art, Chrysler Art Mus., others. Recipient Penello d'Argento award Acitrezza Internazionale, 1958, S.P.Q.R. Cup of Rome, Roma Olimpionica Internazionale, 1959, Gold medal of honor Nat. Arts Club, N.Y.C., 1969, Bicentennial award Rocky Mountain Nat. Watercolor Exhbn., 1976, Am. Drawings IV Purchase award, 1982, others; fellow in painting Am. Acad. Rome, 1957-60, U. Colo. Creative Rsch. fellow, 1966-67. Mem. Watercolor U.S.A. Honor Soc. (charter). Home: 720 Hawthorn Ave Boulder CO 80304-2140

MATTHEWS, FRANCIS RICHARD, lawyer; b. Calgary, Alta., Can., Aug. 19, 1920; s. Charles Curtice and Grace (Cathro) M.; m. Joyce Winter Jarvis, Nov. 10, 1944; children: James Richard, Frances Elizabeth, Michael John. B.Com., U. Alta., 1941, LL.B., 1948. Bar: Called to Alta. bar 1949, created Queen's Counsel 1963. Assoc. firm Mackimmie, Matthews, Calgary, 1949-54; ptnr. Mackimmie, Matthews, 1954-87, of counsel, 1987—; dir. Murphy Oil Co. Ltd., Ranger Oil Ltd. Served to lt. Royal Canadian Naval Vol. Res., 1941-45. Mem. Calgary Philharmonic Orchestra Soc. (bd. govs., pres. 1955-56, 61-62), Calgary C. of C., Can., Alberta bar assns., Soaring Assn. Can., Delta Kappa Epsilon. Mem. Anglican Ch. Clubs: Calgary Petroleum, Ranchmen's. Home: 720 13th Ave SW Apt 1810, Calgary, AB Canada T2R 1M5 Office: Gulf Canada Sq 7th Fl Calgary, AB Canada T2P 2M2

MATTHEWS, GEORGE TENNYSON, history educator; b. Bklyn., May 27, 1917; s. George Tennyson and Olive Beulah (Richardson) M.; m. Mildred G. Byars (dec. 1962); m. Margie R. Kresge (dec. 1989); 1 child, Mildred Matthews Hershey; 1 stepchild, Christopher J. Kresge. AB, Columbia U., 1939, MA, 1941, PhD, 1953. Instr., then asst. prof. history Columbia U., 1946-59, chmn. contemporary civilization staff, 1953-59, asst. to dean Columbia Coll., 1951-59; mem. faculty Oakland U., Rochester, Mich., 1959—; prof. history Oakland U., 1960-85, prof. emeritus, 1985—, dist. prof. emeritus, 1988—, chmn. dept., 1960-62, assoc. dean humanities, then dean Coll. Arts and Scis., 1962-73, vice provost, 1973-79, pres., 1979-81; dir. honors coll. Oakland U., Rochester, Mich., 1991; Hill Family Found. lectr. MacAlister Coll., St. Paul, 1954. Author: Royal General Farms in 18th Century France, 1958, News and Rumor in Renaissance Europe, 1959; also articles, revs.; Editor: Man in Contemporary Society, 2 vols, 1957, Contemporary Civilization in the West, 2 vols, 1956. Served with USAAF, 1941-45. Mem. Soc. French Hist. Studies (treas. 1967-74), Am. Hist. Assn., Phi Beta Kappa (past chpt. treas.). Democrat. Home and Office: 2900 Heidelberg Dr Rochester Hills MI 48309-2301

MATTHEWS, GERTRUDE ANN URCH, retired librarian, writer; b. Jackson, Mich., July 16, 1921; d. Charles P.A. and Amy (Granville) Urch; student Albion Coll., 1940-41; AA, Jackson Jr. Coll., 1939; BS, MS in Library Arts, U. Mich., 1959; m. Geoffrey Matthews, June 30, 1942 (dec.). Adult services librarian Jackson, Mich., 1959-63; asst. dir. librarian Franklin Sylvester Library, Medina, Ohio, 1963-81, dir. older adults facility library, 1977-93. Pres., Hist. Soc., 1966-67; active Dollars for Scholars Com., 1966-86; mem. Bicentennial Com.; officer diocesean leval Episcopal Ch.; mem. vestry St. Paul's Ch., Medina, 1981-84. Mem. ALA, Ohio Library Assn., AAUW (dir., Community Service award 1985, Woman of Yr.), LWV (dir.). Republican. Contbr. articles to profl. and popular publs.; weekly newspaper columnist, 1958-81; bookreviewer The Nat. Librarian. Home: 750 Weymouth Rd Medina OH 44256-2038

MATTHEWS, GILBERT ELLIOTT, investment banker; b. Brookline, Mass., Apr. 24, 1930; s. Martin W. and Charlotte (Cohen) M.; m. Anne Lisbeth Barnett, Apr. 20, 1958 (div. 1975); children: Lisa Joan, Diana Kory; m. Elaine Rita Siegal Pulitzer, Jan. 2, 1978; 1 dau., Jennifer Rachel. A.B., Harvard U., 1951; M.B.A., Columbia U., 1953. Chartered fin. analyst. Dept. mgr. Bloomingdale's, N.Y.C., 1953, 56-60; security analyst Merrill Lynch, N.Y.C., 1960; investment banker Bear, Stearns & Co., N.Y.C., 1960—, gen. ptnr. 1979-85; mng. dir. Bear, Stearns & Co. Inc., 1985-86, sr. mng. dir., 1986—; bd. dirs. Oak Industries, Inc., Waltham, Mass. Served as lt. (j.g.) USN, 1953-56. Mem. N.Y. Soc. Security Analysts, Noyac Golf and Country Club, Old Westbury Golf and Country Club. Democrat. Jewish. Home: 3 Long Ridge Ln Old Brookvl NY 11545-2505 Office: 245 Park Ave New York NY 10167-0001

MATTHEWS, HAROLD DOWNS, author, consultant; b. Waco, Tex., Mar. 24, 1925; s. Harold Jackson and Sophie Grace (Downs) M.; m. Mary Byers Riley, Nov. 22, 1948 (div. Oct. 1971); children: Mark Allen, Elizabeth Ann Matthews Inman; m. Marianne Reeder, Nov. 22, 1971. BA in Journalism, U. Tex., 1947. Coord. employee comm. Schlumberger Well Svcs., Houston, 1948-68; editor Exxon USA mag. Exxon Co., U.S.A., Houston, 1968-86; freelance writer, cons., Houston, 1986—. Author: How to Manage Business Publications, 1987, Polar Bear Cubs, 1989, Skimmers, 1990, Arctic Summer, 1992, Wetlands, 1993, Polar Bear, 1993, Arctic Foxes, 1994; contbr. numerous feature articles to publs. Fellow Internat. Assn. Bus. Communicators; mem. Travel Journalists Guild, Outdoor Writers Assn. Am., Am. Soc. Journalists and Authors, Am. Orchid Soc. Avocation: photography. Home and Office: 3501 Underwood Houston TX 77025

MATTHEWS, JACK, psychologist, speech pathologist, educator; b. Winnipeg, Man., Can., June 17, 1917; s. Samuel and Ellen (Walker) M.; m. Hannah Miriam Polster, Aug. 16, 1942; children: Rachel Sophia, Rebecca. A.B., Heidelberg Coll., 1938, D.Sc., 1976; M.A., Ohio U., 1940; Ph.D., Ohio State U., 1946; student, Vanderbilt U., 1942-43. Asst. dir. speech clinic Purdue U., 1946-48; dir. speech clinic, asst. prof. psychology and speech U. Pitts., 1948-55, dir. speech clinic, dir. div. psychol. services, asso. prof. psychology, 1950-55, prof., chmn. speech dept., 1955—; dean humanities, 1967-68, pres. univ. senate, 1969-72; bd. dirs. Community Hearing Coun., Pitts. Hearing Soc.; pres. Am. Bd. Examiners Speech Pathology and Audiology, 1966-67; sec. Speech and Hearing Found., 1964-68; mem. Edn. Commn. States, Nat. Adv. Com. on Handicapped Children; bd. trustees Clay Theatre, 1985—, Western Pa. Sch. for Deaf, 1980—, v.p. 1982-92. Asst. editor: Jour. Speech and Hearing Disorders, 1952-54; editorial bd., 1965-69,

Speech Monographs, 1951-53; 56-65, Jour. Communications, 1961-64, Deafness, Speech and Hearing pubs.; cons. editor: Today's Speech, 1968- 70, ERIC, 1975—; Contbr. articles to profl. jours. Served as sgt. AC Psychol. Research Unit USAAF, 1942-45. Mem. AAAS, APA, AAUP, Am. Speech and Hearing Assn. (pres. 1963-64, assoc. editor jours. 1959-62), Am. Assn. Cleft Palate Rehab. (pres. 1957-59), Speech Assn. (adminstrv. coun., rsch. bd. 1966-69, chmn. 1967-69), Am. Assn. Mental Deficiency, Soc. Psychol. Study Social Issues, Pa. Speech Assn. (pres. 1959-60), Assn. for Comm. Adminstrn. (exec. com. 1978-81), Sigma Xi, Pi Kappa Delta, Alpha Psi Omega, Tau Kappa Alpha, Sigma Alpha Eta. Home: Longwood at Oakmount Ch 53 500 Rt 909 Verona PA 15147

MATTHEWS, JACK (JOHN HAROLD MATTHEWS), English educator, writer; b. Columbus, Ohio, July 22, 1925; s. John Harold and Lulu Emma (Grover) M.; m. Barbara Jane Reese, Sept. 16, 1947; children: Cynthia Ann Matthews Warnock, Barbara Ellen Matthews, John Harold. B.A., Ohio State U., 1949, M.A., 1954. Clk. U.S. Post Office, Columbus, 1950-59; prof. English Urbana Coll., Ohio, 1959-64; prof. English Ohio U., Athens, 1964-77, disting. prof., 1977—. Author: Bitter Knowledge, 1964 (Ohioana fiction award 1964), Hanger Stout, Awake!, 1967, The Charisma Campaigns, 1972 (nominee NBA Fiction award), Sassafras, 1983, Crazy Women, 1985, Booking in the Heartland, 1986 (Ohioana non-fiction award 1986), Ghostly Populations, 1986, Memoirs of a Bookman, 1989, Dirty Tricks, 1990, On The Shore of That Beautiful Shore (play), 1991, An Interview with the Sphinx (play), 1992, Storyhood As We Know It and other Tales (stories), 1993, others. Served with USCG, 1943-45. Recipient numerous bd. artist awards Ohio Art Council, Major Artist award, 1989-90; Guggenheim fellow, 1974-75. Mem. Phi Beta Kappa. Home: 4314 Fisher Rd Athens OH 45701-1301 Office: Ohio U Dept English Athens OH 45701

MATTHEWS, JAMES GORDON, JR., obstetrician, gynecologist; b. Bridgeport, Conn., Jan. 22, 1916; s. James G. and Sue Gay (Short) M.; m. Gladyce Lorraine Carlberg, Apr. 4, 1942; children: Suzanne, James III, Barbara, William, Christine, Thomas. BS, Ea. Mich. U., 1937; DO, Kirksville Coll Osteo Mecidine, 1942. Diplomate ob-gyn. Am. Osteo. Bd. Intern-resident ob-gyn. Detroit Osteo. Hosp., Highland Park, Mich., 1942-45, sr. ob-gyn., chmn., 1947-68; chmn. ob-gyn. Bicounty Community Hosp., Warren, Mich., 1970; sr. attending ob-gyn. Doctor's Hosp., Columbus, Ohio, 1971-75; chair ob-gyn. Doctor's Hosp., Columbus, 1974-75, Dallas Ft. Worth Med. Ctr., Grand Prairie, Tex., 1975-90; clin. prof. ob-gyn. Tex. Coll. Osteo. Medicine, Ft. Worth, 1975—, Okla. State U. Coll. Osteo. Medicine, Tulsa, 1984—; dir. resident tng. ob-gyn. Dallas Ft. Worth Med. Ctr., Grand Prairie, 1984-94; retired, 1994; lectr. in field; cons. sex edn. Bd. Edn., Berkley, Mich. Contbr. articles to profl. jours. Mem. Grand Prairie YMCA Bd. Mgmt., 1977—; sustaining campaign chmn. YMCA, Grand Prairie, 1989; pres. Rotary Club, Grand Prairie, 1988-89. Named Pub. Servant of Yr., Grand Prairie C. of C., 1988, Vol. of Yr., Dallas Met. YMCA, 1989, Physician of Yr., Dallas/Ft. Worth Med. Ctr. Found., 1990. Fellow Am. Coll. Osteo. Ob-Gyn. (disting., pres. 1964); mem. Am. Osteo Assn. (life), Am. Menopause Soc., Am. Bd. Sexology (diplomate), Tex. Osteo. Med. Assn. (life). Assn. Reproductive Health Profls., Grayline Game Club (pres.), Red Run Golf Club (life), Mich. Inter-Club Swimming Assn. (pres.), Rotary Internat. (Paul Harris fellow). Methodist. Avocations: golf, sailing, skiing.

MATTHEWS, JAMES SHADLEY, lawyer; b. Omaha, Nov. 24, 1951; s. Donald E. and Lois Jean (Shadley) M.; m. Mary Kvaal, May 3, 1991; 1 child, Katherine. BA cum laude, St. Olaf Coll., 1973; JD, U. Ill., 1976; MBA, U. Denver, 1977. Bar: Minn. 1976, U.S. Dist. Ct. Minn. 1978. With Northwestern Nat. Life Ins. Co., Mpls., 1978-89; v.p., asst. gen. counsel Northwestern Nat. Life Ins. Co., 1985-89; ptnr. Lindquist & Venum, Mpls., 1990—; sr. v.p., gen. counsel Washington Square Capital, Inc., 1989; bd. dirs., sec. NWNL Health Network, Inc., St. Paul, 1987-89; pub. bd. Minn. Health Resns. Assn., 1992-94; speaker to profl. orgns., 1984—. Chmn. benevolence com. Colonial Congl. Ch., Edina, Minn., 1981-82. Mem. ABA, Nat. Health Lawyers Assn., Am. Acad. Hosp. Attys., Minn. Bar Assn. (chmn. health law sect. 1986-87). Office: Lindquist & Vennum 4200 IDS Ctr 80 S 8th St Minneapolis MN 55402-2113

MATTHEWS, JAY ARLON, JR., publisher, editor; b. St. Louis, Apr. 13, 1918; s. Jay Arlon and Mary (Long) M.; student San Jose State Coll., 1939-41, U. Tex., 1946-47; BLS St. Edward's U., 1994; m. May Clark McLemore, Jan. 16, 1944; children—Jay Arlon III, Emily Cochrane, Sally McLemore. Asst. dir. personnel Adj. Gen.'s Dept. Tex., 1947-53, dept. adj., 1957-65, mil. support plans officer, 1965-69, chief emergency operations, 1965-71; pub. Presidial Press, Mil. History Press. Past Dir. Civil Def., Austin; mem. adv. bd. Confrad. Research Center, Hill Jr. Coll.; mil. historian 65th Legislature, Tex., 1977-78. Served with AGC, Tex. N.G., 1946—, brig. gen. ret., 1973. Named to Tex. Nat. Guard Hall of Honor, 1990. Fellow Co. Mil. Historians (gov. 1981-84); mem. Austin (state v.p. 1951-52), U.S. Jaycees (chmn. nat. security com. 1952-53), N.G. Assn. U.S. (chmn. publicity 81st Gen. Conf.), Instituto Internationale de Historia Militar (hon. life), Mil. Order World Wars (comdr. Austin chpt. 1980). Episcopalian. Club: Exchange (pres. Austin chpt. 1982-83). Editor: Mil. History of Tex. and S.W. Quar., 1961-88; editor emeritus Mil. Hist. of the West, 1989. Home: 1807 Stamford Ln Austin TX 78703-2939 also: PO Box 5248 Austin TX 78763

MATTHEWS, JOHN CARROLL, manufacturing executive; b. Galax, Va., Dec. 25, 1933; m. Freida Felts; children: Jason, Justin. BSBA, Appalachian State U., 1959. Plant employee Carolina Mirror Co., North Wilkesboro, N.C., 1959-60, scheduling employee, 1960-66, salesman, 1967-77, sales promotion profl., 1978-88, nat. sales mgr., 1989-90, v.p., 1991—; bd. dirs. First Citizens Bank, seminar spkr., trade show mgr. Nat. Assn. Mirror Mfrs., Potomac, Md. Contbr. articles to profl. jours. Mem. YMCA; mem. adminstrv. bd. First United Meth. Ch., North Wilkesboro; mem. PTA, North Wilkesboro; chmn. Wilkes County Cancer Soc., North Wilkesboro; coach YMCA Little League, North Wilkesboro. With U.S. Army, 1956-58. Mem. Nat. Glass Assn. (bd. dirs., seminar spkr.), Appalachian State U. Alumni Assn., Rotary (charter, past pres. North Wilkesboro chpt.), Oakwoods Country Club. Avocations: golf, hunting. Office: Carolina Mirror Co Hwy 268 E North Wilkesboro NC 28659

MATTHEWS, JOHN FLOYD, writer, educator; b. Cin., Apr. 8, 1919; s. Floyd L. and Helen (Orth) M.; m. Maurine Zollman, Mar. 4, 1945 (dec. 1959); children—Lauralee Alice, Caroline Elaine (dec.); m. Brenda Martin, Aug. 27, 1966. Student, Wooster Coll., 1935-37, Northwestern U., 1937; B.A., U. Cin., 1940, postgrad., 1940-41; postgrad., Columbia U., 1943, New Sch. for Social Research, 1944-45. Lectr. New Sch. for Social Research, 1948-50; lectr., chmn. faculty Dramatic Workshop and Tech. Inst., N.Y.C., 1950-52; lectr. in playwriting CCNY, 1947-63; asst. prof. dramatic lit. and history Brandeis U., 1952-59, assoc. prof., 1959-67, Schulman prof., 1967-71, chmn. dept. theatre, 1955-58, prof. Am. studies, 1971—, chmn. dept. Am. studies, 1973-74, Richter prof. Am. Civilization and Instns., 1972-84, prof. emeritus, 1984—; vis. critic Yale Sch. Drama, 1965; mem. Seminar in Am. Studies, Circle Cultural de Royaumont, France, 1965; founding mem. Brandeis Creative Arts Awards Commn. Network radio actor, writer, producer, 1939-45, screenwriter, Warner Bros., 1945; author: plays, including The Scapegoat, 1950, Michael and Lavinia, 1956, Barnum, 1962; books The Old Vic In America, 1946, El Greco, 1952, Shaw's Dramatic Criticism, 1959, George Bernard Shaw, 1969, Reflections on Abortion, 1976; contbr. fiction to lit. mags.; cons., play doctor for script and prodn. problems of numerous Broadway and off-Broadway plays and musicals including Anastasia, The First Gentleman, others; TV scriptwriter for maj. networks, 1955-64; screenwriter, MGM, United Artists, Also. Screen Prodns., Toronto, Ont. Can., 1958-64; Contbg. editor: Library of Living Painters, 1949-51, Dictionary of the Arts, 1946, Ency. World Biography, 1970. Mem. Westport (Conn.) Democratic Town Com., 1959-64; mem. Newton (Mass.) Republican City Com., 1977—, Mass. Rep. Platform Com., 1978; bd. dirs. Newton Taxpayers Assn., 1979-81, 86-91. Recipient Arts of the Theatre Found. award, 1950. Mem. Brit. Drama League, The Nat. Trust, English Speaking Union, Trustees of Reservations. Episcopalian. Home: 5 Tudor Close, Dean Court Rd, Rottingdean BN1 7DF, England

MATTHEWS, JOHN LOUIS, retired military officer, educator; b. Copperton, Utah, June 27, 1932; m. Darlene Davis, 1956 (dec.); 3 children; m. Janice Holbrook, June 27, 1990. BS in Geology, Brigham Young U., 1955, MEd in Ednl. Adminstrn., 1967; grad. Air War Coll., 1976. Commd. 2d lt.

USAF, 1954, advanced through grades to maj. gen., 1984; instr. pilot, Laredo, Tex., 1955-58; with Utah Air N.G., 1959-94, Colo. Air N.G., 1961-62, comdr. 151st Air Refueling Group, adj. gen. State of Utah, 1982-94; prin. Dixon Jr. H.S., Provo, Utah, 1967-73; prin. Timpview H.S., Provo, 1976-79. Mem. Steering Com. Pres. Sixth Quadrennial Rev. of Mil. Compensation, Washington; former chmn. Air Res. Forces Policy com.; mem. Res. Forces Policy Bd. Sec. of Def., Washington; commn. on Rolls and Mission of the Armed Forces. Decorated Disting. Svc. medal, Legion of Merit, Vietnam Svc. medal, Nat. Def. Svc. medal, AE Disting. Svc. medal, others. Mem. N.G. Assn. of U.S. (pres. 1992-94), Adjs. Gen. Assn. of U.S. (pres. 1987-89), Commn. on Rolls and Missions, Air Force Assn., Assn. U.S. Army, Rotary.

MATTHEWS, JULIE, performing arts company director; b. Cleve., Mar. 3, 1957; d. Daniel Louis Harb and Diane Louise (Salem) Mack; m. Guo Ming, Dec. 24, 1993. Student, Cuyahoga C.C., Cleve., 1975-77, HB Studio, N.Y.C., 1977, Lee Strassberg Actors Studio, N.Y.C., 1977. Acting coach Huntington Playhouse, Cleve., 1978-82; children's theatre dir. Chagrin Valley Little Theatre, Cleve., 1978-82; acting coach Independence Theatre, Cleve., 1982; host, dir. pub. rels. Cleveland Rocks TV Show, 1986-91; dir. on-camera casting/agt. Powers Internat., Cleve., 1991-92; casting dir. Motion Picture/"Babe Ruth", 1991; acting coach, casting dir., talent scout, founder/dir. Am. Performing Arts Network, Cleve., 1992—; cons. in field, 60 Minutes, Australian TV, 1994, Sally Jesse Raphael, CBS TV, 1994, Danny Bonaduce, Loop Radio/Chgo., 1994. Author: (manual) How to Get Into Show Business . . . The Right Way, 1993; film credits include: A Christmas Story, Major League, The Light of Day, Bob Roberts; leading stage role credits include: South Pacific, Cinderella, Fiddler on the Roof, Grease; studio vocalist various recording artists. Recipient Emmy for PSA comml., Am. Fedn. TV Arts and Scis., Cleve., 1974. Home: 17113 Neff Rd Cleveland OH 44119 Office: Am Performing Arts Network 3130 Mayfield Rd Cleveland OH 44118

MATTHEWS, KATHLEEN SHIVE, biochemistry educator; b. Austin, Tex., Aug. 30, 1945; d. William and Gwyn Shive; m. Randall Matthews. BS in Chemistry, U. Tex., 1966; PhD in Biochemistry, U. Calif., Berkeley, 1970. Post doctoral fellow Stanford (Calif.) U., 1970-72; mem. faculty Rice U., Houston, 1972—, chair dept., 1987—, Wiess prof., 1989—; mem. BBCB study sect. NIH, Bethesda, Md., 1980-84, 86-88, BRSG adv. com., 1992-94; mem. adv. com. on rsch. programs Tex. Higher Edn. Coord. Bd., Austin, 1987-92; mem. udnergrad. edn. initiative rev. panel Howard Hughes Rsch. Inst., Bethesda, 1991. Mem. editorial bd. Jour. Biol. Chemistry, 1988-93, assoc. editor, 1994—; contbr. 100 reviewed papers. Mem. Am. Soc. Biochemistry and Molecular Biology (nominating com. 1993-94), Phi Beta Kappa. Office: Rice Univ Dept Biochemistry & Cell Biology PO Box 1892 Houston TX 77251

MATTHEWS, L. WHITE, III, railroad executive; b. Ashland, Ky., Oct. 5, 1945; s. L. White and Virginia Carolyn (Chandler) M.; m. Mary Jane Hanser, Dec. 30, 1972; children: Courtney Chandler, Brian Whittlesey. BS in Econs, Hampden-Sydney Coll., 1967; MBA in Fin. and Gen. Mgmt, U. Va., 1970. Cons. fin. Chem. Bank, N.Y.C., 1970-72, asst. sec., 1972-74, asst. v.p., 1974-75, v.p., 1976-77; treas. Mo. Pacific Corp., St. Louis, 1977-79, v.p. fin. Mo. Pacific R.R. Co. subs. Mo. Pacific Corp., St. Louis, 1979-82; v.p. treas. Union Pacific Corp. and Union Pacific R.R. Co., N.Y.C., 1982-87; sr. v.p. fin. Union Pacific corp., Bethlehem, Pa., 1987-92, exec. v.p. fin., 1992—; mem. coun. of fin. execs. The Conf. Bd.; mem. nat. adv. bd. Chem. Bank of N.Y.; bd. dirs. Union Pacific Corp., Bethlehem, Pa. Trustee Pilot Funds, St. Louis; bd. dirs. Moravian Coll., Bethlehem, Pa.

MATTHEWS, LARRYL KENT, mechanical engineering educator; b. Lubbock, Tex., Sept. 18, 1951; s. Morrison Arliss and Juanita Ruby (Parr) M.; m. Marie Elizabeth Twist, May 15, 1972. MS, N.Mex. State U., 1975; PhD, Purdue U., 1982. Test engr. Sandia Nat. Labs., Albuquerque, 1976-81; rsch. dir., educator N.Mex. State U., Las Cruces, 1982—; cons. Sandia Nat. Labs., 1985-89, ISOTEC, Santa Fe, N.Mex., 1986-88; bd. dirs. Waste-Mgmt. Edn. Rsch. Consortium, Las Cruces, 1990—; mem. mgmt. bd. Ctr. for Space Power. Author: (with Gade Garcia) Laser and Eye Safety in the Laboratory; contbr. articles to Jour. Solar Energy, Internat. Jour. Exptl. Heat Transfer, ASME Jour. Solar Engring., internat. Jour. Heat and Mass Transfer, Intech mag. Mem. AAAS, ASME, Am. Astron. Soc., Soc. de Ingenieros (founder), Pi Tau Sigma. Democrat. Methodist. Achievements include development of multiple-head radiometer for large pool-fire environments, of CSMP (Circum Solar Measurement Package) for concentrating solar applications. Office: NMex State U Engring Rsch Ctr PO Box 30001 Las Cruces NM 88003-3449

MATTHEWS, LEONARD SARVER, advertising executive, consultant; b. Glendean, Ky., Jan. 6, 1922; s. Clell and Zetta Price (Sarver) M.; m. Dorothy Lucille Fessler; children: Nancy, James, Douglas. B.S. summa cum laude, Northwestern U., 1948. With Leo Burnett Co., Inc., Chgo., 1948-75; v.p., dir. Leo Burnett Co., Inc., 1958-59, v.p. charge mktg. services, 1959-61, exec. v.p., 1961-69, pres., 1970-75; asst. sec. commerce for domestic and internat. bus., 1976; pres., exec. com., dir. Young and Rubicam, 1977-78; pres. Am. Assn. Advt. Agys., 1979-89; co-founder Matthews & Johnston, Stamford, Conn., 1989-92; chmn. Next Century Media, 1992—; bd. dirs. Digital Gen. Systems, San Francisco, Propiview Interactive, Boston. Served as ensign USCGR, 1942-46. Mem. Advt. Coun. (bd. dirs.), Delta Sigma Pi, Beta Gamma Sigma. Republican. Lutheran. Clubs: Sky (N.Y.C.), Pine Valley Golf (N.J.), Rancho Santa Fe Golf (Calif.). Office: PO Box 2036 Rancho Santa Fe CA 92067-2036

MATTHEWS, MILDRED SHAPLEY, scientific editor, freelance writer; b. Pasadena, Calif., Feb. 15, 1915; d. Harlow and Martha (Betz) Shapley; m. Ralph Vernon Matthews, Sept. 25, 1937; children:: June Lorrain, Bruce Shapley, Melvin Lloyd, Martha Alys. AB, U. Mich., 1936. Rsch. asst. Calif. Inst. Tech., Pasadena, 1950-61; bilingual editor, rsch. asst. Astron. Obs. Merate-Milan and Trieste, Italy, 1960-70; rsch. asst. Lunar-Planetary Lab., editor space sci. series U. Ariz., Tucson, 1970—. Contbr. articles to Sky and Telescope, Astronomia. Recipient Masursky Meritorious Svc. award div. planetary sci. Am. Astron. Soc., 1993. Avocation: classical music concerts, especially opera. Home: 1600 Milvia St Berkeley CA 94709 Office: U Arizona Lunar & Planetary Lab Tucson AZ 85721

MATTHEWS, NORMAN STUART, department store executive; b. Boston, Jan. 13, 1933; s. Martin W. and Charlotte (Cohen) M.; m. Joanne Banks, June 11, 1956; children: Gary S., Jeffrey B., Patricia A. B.A., Princeton U.; M.B.A., Harvard U. Ptnr. Beacon Mktg. and Advt. Assocs., N.Y.C., 1956-71; sr. v.p. Broyhill Furniture Co., Lenoir, N.C., 1971-73, E.J. Korvettes, N.Y.C., 1973-78; chmn., chief exec. officer Gold Circle Stores, Columbus, Ohio, 1978-82; vice chmn. Federated Dept. Stores, Cin., from 1982, pres., chief oper. officer, 1987-88, retail cons., 1988—; dir. Progressive Corp., Cleve., Loehmann's, N.Y.C., Finley Fine Jewelry, N.Y.C., Lechters Inc., N.J., Hills Dept. Stores, Boston. Office: 650 Madison Ave New York NY 10022-1004

MATTHEWS, PATRICK JOHN, consumer products company executive; b. Winnipeg, Manitoba, Can., Mar. 17, 1942; m. Clarice Marie Carstens; children: Brian, Richard. B of Commerce, U. Manitoba, 1968. Chartered acct., Manitoba. Various positions Peat, Marwick, Mitchell & Co., Winnipeg, Manitoba, 1968-75, ptnr., 1975-79; v.p. corp. planning Gendis Inc., Winnipeg, Manitoba, 1979-82, v.p. fin., 1982—; dir. Chauvco Resources Ltd. Mem. Inst. Chartered Accts. Manitoba, Fin. Exec. Inst. Office: Gendis Inc, 1370 Sony Pl PO Box 9400, Winnipeg, MB Canada R3C 3C3

MATTHEWS, PETER F., electrical contracting company executive; b. N.Y., 1928; married. Grad., Manhattan Coll., 1950. V.p. Lord Electric Co., N.Y.C., 1961-74, pres., 1974-86, chief exec. officer, 1982-86, also dir.; now pres., chief exec. officer, dir. Leco Enterprises, Inc. (parent), N.Y.C. Lodge: KC. Office: Leco Enterprises Inc 230 Park Ave New York NY 10169-0004

MATTHEWS, RICHARD J., pharmaceutical research company executive; b. Scranton, Pa., Apr. 11, 1927; s. Richard John and Ruth (Duffy) M.; m. Sally Griffith (Aug. 8, 1953); children: Todd (dec.), Nanette Matthews Field, Pamela Matthews Otto, Wesley, Richard. BS, Phila. Coll. Pharmacy & Sci., 1951; MS, PhD, Jefferson Med. Coll., 1955. Head neuropharmacology rsch.

The Upjohn Co., Kalamazoo, 1956-62; owner Pharmakon Labs., Scranton, 1962-66; dir. pharmacology Union Carbide Corp., Tuxedo, N.Y., 1966-69; pres. Pharmakon Rsch. Internat., Waverly, Pa., 1969—. Bd. dirs. Pa. State U., Scranton, Community Med. Ctr., Scranton, 1974-89. Served with U.S. Army, 1945-46. Mem. Am. Soc. Pharmacology and Exptl. Therapeutics. Republican. Presbyterian. Avocations: golf, gun collecting. Office: Pharmakon Rsch Internat Inc PO Box 609 Waverly PA 18471-0609

MATTHEWS, ROGER HARDIN, lawyer; b. Greensboro, N.C., Sept. 16, 1948; s. Shuford Roger and Jacqueline (Hardin) M.; m. Jane Elizabeth Dougan, Aug. 7, 1982; children: Christopher Hardin, Marielle Aimée. AB, Harvard U., 1970, JD, 1974. Bar: Mass. 1974. Assoc. Ropes & Gray, Boston, 1974-84, ptnr., 1984—. Mem. ABA (employee benefits com., tax sect.), Boston Bar Assn. (co-chmn. Employee Retirement Income Security Act com. 1985-88). Avocation: piano. Office: Ropes & Gray One International Place Boston MA 02110-2624

MATTHEWS, ROWENA GREEN, biological chemistry educator; b. Cambridge, Eng., Aug. 20, 1938 (father Am. citizen); d. David E. and Doris (Cribb) Green; m. Larry Stanford Matthews, June 18, 1960; children: Brian Stanford, Keith David. BA, Harvard U., 1960; PhD, U. Mich., 1969. Instr. U. S.C., Columbia, 1964-65; postdoctoral fellow U. Mich., Ann Arbor, 1970-75, asst. prof., 1975-81, assoc. prof. biol. chemistry, 1981-86, prof. 1986—, assoc. chmn., 1988-92, Robert Greenberg disting. prof., 1993—; mem. phys. biochemistry study sect. NIH, 1982-86; mem. adv. coun. Nat. Inst. Gen. Med. Scis., NIH, 1991-94; adv. bd. NATO, 1994— mem. editorial adv. bd. Biochem. Jour., 1984-92, Biochemistry, 1993—, Jour. Bacteriology, 1995—. Contbr. articles to profl. jours. Recipient Faculty Recognition award U. Mich., 1984, Merit award Nat. Inst. Gen. Med. Scis., 1991; NIH grantee, 1978—; NSF grantee, 1992—. Mem. AAAS, Am. Soc. Biochemical & Molecular Biol. (program chair 1995), Am. Chem. Soc. (program chmn. biochemistry div. 1985, sec. biochemistry div 1990-92, chair elect 1992-94, chair 1994—), Phi Beta Kappa, Sigma Xi. Avocations: bicycling, snorkeling, cross country skiing, cooking. Home: 1609 S University Ave Ann Arbor MI 48104-2620 Office: U Mich Biophysics Rsch Divsn 1055 Chem Bldg 930 N University Ann Arbor MI 48109-1055

MATTHEWS, STEVE ALLEN, lawyer; b. Columbia, S.C., Oct. 11, 1955; s. Philip Garland and Vernecia Neely (Wilson) M.; m. Caroline Elizabeth FitzSimons, Sept. 26, 1987; children: Philip Garland II, Nathalie Fitz-Simons. BA in History, U. S.C., 1977; JD, Yale U., 1980. Bar: S.C. 1980, D.C. 1982. Assoc. Boyd, Knowlton, Tate & Finlay, Columbia, 1980-81, Dewey, Ballantine, Bushby, Palmer & Wood, Washington, 1981-85; spl. counsel to asst. atty. gen. Civil Rights Div. U.S. Dept. Justice, Washington, 1985-86, dep. asst. atty. gen. for jud. selection, Office of Legal Policy, 1986-88; exec. asst. to U.S. Atty. Gen., 1988; mem. Sinkler & Boyd P.A., Columbia, 1988—. Mem. Federalist Soc., Party of the Right, Euphradian Soc., Nat. Assn. Bond Lawyers (chmn. profl. responsibility com.). Office: Sinkler & Boyd PA 1426 Main St Columbia SC 29201-2834

MATTHEWS, SIR STUART, aviation industry executive; b. London, May 5, 1936; came to U.S., 1974; s. Bernard De Lides and Daisy Vera (Woodcock) M.; chartered engr., Hatfield Coll. Advanced Tech., 1958; m. Kathleen Hilary Adams, Jan. 12, 1974; children: Anthony, Caroline, Joanna. Chartered engr. Apprentice, de Havilland Aircraft Ltd., Hatfield, 1952-53; aircraft project design engr. Hawker Siddeley Aviation Ltd., Hatfield, 1953-64; with mktg. dept. Brit. Aircraft Co., Bristol, 1964-67; gen. mgr. planning Brit. Caledonian Airways, London, 1967-74; v.p. N.Am. div. Fokker-VFW Internat., Washington, 1974-80; pres., chief exec. officer Fokker Aircraft USA, Alexandria, Va., 1980-93, chmn. 1993-94, Aircraft Fin. and Trade, Alexandria, 1984-94; pres., CEO Flight Safety Found., Arlington, Va., 1994—; chmn. assoc. mem. group Commuter Airlines Assn. Am. 1979-80. Chmn. Flight Safety Found.; mem. adv. bd. Am. Security Bank. Fellow Royal Aero. Soc., Inst. Transp., AIAA, Royal Order of Orange Nassau (The Netherlands) (knight), Netherlands/Am. C. of C. (bd. dirs.), Alexandria C. of C. (bd. dirs.). Clubs: Aero, Nat. Aviation (Washington); Wings (N.Y.C., mem. bd. govs.); Lions (pres. Engleside, Va. 1977-78); Rotary Internat. Home: 9439 Mt Vernon Cir Alexandria VA 22309-3221 Office: Flight Safety Found 2200 Wilson Blvd Arlington VA 22201

MATTHEWS, THOMAS MICHAEL, energy company executive; b. Luling, Tex., May 20, 1943; s. Chester Raymond and Mary Lucille (Stutts) M.; m. Sherry Dianne Klein, May 25, 1968; children: Stephanie Dianne, Leslie Michelle. BSCE, Tex. A & M U., 1965; postgrad., U. Okla., 1967, UCLA, 1975, Stanford U., 1988, Columbia U., 1993. Staff engr. Exxon Co. USA, Houston, New Orleans, 1965-69; project engr. Exxon Co. USA, L.A., 1974-76; div. engr. Exxon Co. USA, Houston, 1969-74; engring. mgr. Exxon Co. USA, Anchorage, 1976-78; v.p. Exxon Gas, Houston, 1978-81, Tenn. Gas/Tenneco, Houston, 1981-86; pres. Tenn. Gas/Tenneco, 1986-89; v.p., gen. mgr. Texaco USA, Houston, 1989—; pres. Texaco Gas, 1990-93; pres., CEO Texaco Refining & Mktg., Inc.; v.p. Texaco, Inc.; dir. Offshore Tech. Ctr., Tex. A & M U., 1987-89, adv. coun.; bd. dirs. Inroads, Inc. Contbr. articles to profl. jours.; inventor in field. Pres., chmn. Ponderosa Forest Community Council, Houston, 1980-85; mem. PTO, Scenic Pk. Sch., Anchorage, 1976-78. Mem. NSPE (bd. dirs.), Soc. Petroleum Engrs., Soc. Ga. Assn., Am. Petroleum Inst., Natural Gas Supply Assn., Gas Rsch. Inst., Petroleum Club, Northgate Forest Country Club. Republican. Lutheran. Avocations: snow skiing, golf, reading, running, singing. Home: 17402 Ridge Top Dr Houston TX 77090-2021 Office: Texaco USA 1111 Bagby St Houston TX 77210

MATTHEWS, WANDA MILLER, artist; b. Barry, Ill., Sept. 15, 1930; d. Harry Leonard and Gladys (Smith) Miller; m. Eugene Edward Matthews, Sept. 14, 1952; children: Anthony Lee, Daniel Nicholas. BFA, Bradley U., Peoria, Ill., 1952; MFA, U. Iowa, 1957. Spl. services artist U.S. Army, Ft. Riley, Kans., 1954-55; research asst. printmaking U. Iowa, 1956-57; travel Italy and Europe, 1957-60. Producing and exhibiting printmaker, Boulder, Colo., 1961—; one-woman exhbns. include, Lehigh U., Bethlehem, Pa., 1973, Gettysburg (Pa.) Coll., 1973, U. Colo., 1976, U. N.D., 1976, Jane Haslem Gallery, Washington, 1982, Am. Ctr. Gallery, Belgrade, Yugoslavia, 1982, Oxford Gallery (Eng.), 1982, U. Colo., Boulder, 1985, U. Northern Colo., Greeley, 1985, The Printerly Image: Wanda Miller Matthews 1951-1991, Arvada (Colo.) Ctr. for the Arts and Humanities, 1991, Jane Haslem Gallery, Washington, 1990; group exhbns. include USIS Gallery, Naples, Italy, 1960; Nat. Invitational Print Exhbn., Otis Art Inst., L.A., 1962, 63, Brit. Internat. Print Biennale, Bradford, Eng., 1970, 79, Invitational Graphics, Minot (N.D.) State Coll., 1972, Printmaking Now, W. Tex. Mus., Lubbock, 1973, ColorPrint U.S.A., Tex. Tech U., Lubbock, 1974, 78, Nat. Invitational Print Show, Central Wash. State Coll., Ellensburg, 1975, 11th Internat. Exhbn. Graphic Art, Ljubljana, Yugoslavia, 1975, 6th, 7th, 8th, 10th Internat. Print Biennales, Cracow, Poland, 1976, 78, 80, 84, Internat. Book Fair, Leipzig, E.Ger., 1977, New Talent in Printmaking, 1980, Associated Am. Artists, N.Y.C. and Phila., 1980, Rockford Internat. Biennale, Ill., 1985, Western States Invitational, Portland Art Mus., Oreg., 1985, 40th Am. Colorprint Soc. Exhbn., Jenkintown, Pa., 1985, Premio Internzionale Biella per l'incisione, Italy, 1976, 80, 87, Small Graphic Forms, Poland, 1987, 4X4X4: Sixteen Contemporary Printmakers from the Four Corner States, Utah State U., 1987, 3d Internat. Biennial Print Exhbt.: 1987, Taipei, Taiwan, 1987-88, CSP Exch. Show, Brandts Klaedefabrik, Odense, Denmark, 1989, Am. Self Portraits in Prints (traveling exhbn.) Ind. U., Bloomington, 1990, Am. Prints: Last Half of 20th Century Jane Haslem Gallery, Washington, 1993, Juniper Gallery, Napa, Calif., 1993, Boston Archtl. Ctr., 1994, Am. Inst. Architecture, Washington, 1994, U. N.H. (Nw), others; represented in permanent collections, Portland Art Mus. (Oreg.); Boston Pub. Library, Bytow Nat. Museum (Poland), LA County Mus., Nat. Collection Fine Arts, Washington, Phila. Mus. Art, Library of Congress, Coll. Bd. Collection of Prints by Am. Artists, N.Y.C., Honolulu Acad. Art, others. Recipient numerous awards including: Purchase prize Prints 1962 Nat. Exhbn., State U. Coll., Potsdam, N.Y., 1962, Prints 10th ann. print exhbn., 1970; purchase prize Dulin Nat. Print and Drawing competition Dulin Gallery Art, Knoxville, Tenn., 1968, 81, 22d ann. nat. exhbn. Boston Printmakers, 1970; recipient purchase award Graphics '71, Nat. Print and Drawing Exhbn., Western N.Mex. U., Silver City, 1971, Soc. Am Graphic Artists, Nat. Exhibition, N.Y.C., 1979, Benton Spruance prize Print Club Phila., 1971, Am. Colorprint Soc. Drabkin Meml. award and medallion, 1981, 1st Place in Color Prints Ybor Nat. Print Competition, 1985, Leila

Sawyer Meml. award 97th ann. exhibition Nat. Assn. Women Artists, 1986, Tiffany grantee, 1957-58, 58-59. Mem. Calif. Soc. Printmakers, Print Club Phila., Soc. Am. Graphic Artists, The Boston Printmakers. Home: 720 Hawthorn Ave Boulder CO 80304-2140

MATTHEWS, WESTINA L., finance and banking executive; b. Chillicothe, Ohio, Nov. 8, 1948; d. Wesley Smith and Ruth (Fields) M. BS, U. Dayton, 1970, MS, 1974; PhD, U. Chgo., 1980. Tchr. Mills Lawn Elem. Sch., Yellow Springs, Ohio, 1970-75; program officer The Chgo. Community Trust, sr. program officer, 1983-85; v.p. philanthropic programs, sec. Merrill Lynch Found., N.Y.C., 1985—, trustee, 1993—; bd. dirs. Women's Forum. Bd. dirs. Coalition of 100 Black Women, N.Y.C., 1991—, Arthur Ashe Inst., N.Y. Theol. Sem.; trustee Wilberforce U. Postdoctoral fellow Northwestern U., 1980-81, U. Wis., 1981-82. Office: Merrill Lynch & Co 225 Liberty St New York NY 10080-0001

MATTHEWS, WILBUR LEE, lawyer; b. Big Spring, Tex., Jan. 20, 1903; s. Robert D. and Sallie (Bourland) M.; m. Mary LeNoir Kenney, June 22, 1932 (dec. Oct. 1972); children: Wilbur Lee, John Kenney; m. Helen P. Davis, May 28, 1976. LL.B. with highest honors, U. Tex., 1926. Bar: Tex. 1926. Since practiced in San Antonio; with Matthews & Branscomb (and predecessors firms), 1926—, partner, 1930—. Contbr. articles to legal publs.; author: San Antonio Lawyer, 1983. Mayor City of Terrell Hills, 1939-41; mem. Tex. Finance Adv. Commn., 1960; trustee, chmn. San Antonio Med. Found. Fellow Am. Coll. Trial Lawyers; mem. Am. Law Inst., Am. Judicature Soc., ABA. Clubs: San Antonio Country, Argyle, San Antonio. Home: 200 Patterson Ave # 806 San Antonio TX 78209-6268 Office: One Alamo Ctr 106 S Saint Mary's St San Antonio TX 78205

MATTHEWS, WILLIAM D(OTY), lawyer, consumer products manufacturing company executive; b. Oneida, N.Y., Aug. 25, 1934; s. William L. and Marjorie L. (Doty) M.; m. Ann M. Morse, Aug. 4, 1956; children: Judith Anne, Thomas John. A.B., Union Coll., 1956; LL.B., Cornell U., 1960. Bar: N.Y. 1960, D.C. 1962. Atty. div. corp. fin. SEC, Washington, 1960-62; assoc. Whitlock, Markey & Tait, Washington, 1962-69; gen. counsel Oneida (N.Y.) Ltd., 1973-86, v.p., 1977-78, sr. v.p., 1978-86, exec. v.p., 1986, also dir., chmn., chief exec. officer, 1986—; bd. dirs. N.Y. State Bus. Coun. Alderman City of Oneida, 1972-79; mem. Madison County Bd. Suprs., 1984-86. Presbyterian. Home: 621 Patio Circle Dr Oneida NY 13421-1820 Office: Oneida Ltd Adminstrn Bldg Kenwood Station Oneida NY 13421-2808

MATTHEWS, WILLIAM ELLIOTT, IV, gas company executive; b. Birmingham, Ala., Sept. 11, 1929; s. William Elliott and Julia Lovett (Murfee) M. III; m. Wahwiece Coe, Feb. 17, 1962; children—Martha Wahwiece, William Elliott V, Julia Lovett, Mary Elizabeth. B.E.E., Ga. Inst. Tech., 1950; postgrad. Advanced Mgmt. Program, Harvard U., 1977. With So. Natural Gas Co., Birmingham, 1950—, pres., 1984—, chmn. bd. dirs., 1989—; sr. v.p. Sonat Inc., Birmingham, 1987—. Bd. dirs. YMCA, Birmingham, Jefferson-Shelby div. Am. Heart Assn., 1982-85. Served to lt. USN, 1954-56. Mem. Am. Gas Assn., Interstate Natural Gas Assn. Am., So. Gas Assn. (bd. dirs. 1979-82), Newcomen Soc. N.Am. Presbyterian. Lodge: Kiwanis. Avocations: golf; hunting. Office: So Natural Gas Co First Nat-So Nat Bldg PO Box 2563 Birmingham AL 35202-2563 also: Sonat Inc 1900 5th Ave N Birmingham AL 35203-2610

MATTHEWS, WILLIAM PROCTER, English educator; b. Cin., Nov. 11, 1942; s. William P. and Mary Elizabeth (Sather) M.; m. Marie Murray Harris, May 4, 1963 (div. 1973); children: William, Sebastian. B.A., Yale U., 1965; M.A., U. N.C., Chapel Hill, 1966. Instr. English Wells Colls., Aurora, N.Y., 1968-69; asst. prof. Cornell U., 1969-74; asso. prof. U. Colo., 1974-78; prof. English U. Wash., Seattle, 1978-83, CCNY, 1983—; bd. dirs. Asso. Writing Programs, 1977-80, pres., 1979-80; mem. lit. panel Nat. Endowment Arts, 1976-79, chmn., 1978-79. Author: Ruining the New Road, 1970, Sleek For the Long Flight, 1972, Sticks and Stones, 1975, Rising and Falling, 1979, Flood, 1982, A Happy Childhood, 1984, Foreseeable Futures, 1987, Blues If You Want, 1989, Curiosities, 1989, Selected Poems and Translations, 1992. Fellow Nat. Endowment Arts, 1974, 83, Guggenheim Found., 1980-81. Mem. Poetry Soc. Am. Office: CCNY Dept English New York NY 10038

MATTHEWS, ZAKEE, psychiatrist, educator. Prof. psychiatry sch. medicine Stanford U., Palo Alto, Calif. Recipient Presdl. Scholar award Am. Acad. Child and Adolescent Psychiatry, 1993. Office: Stanford U School of Medicine Divsn Child Psychiatry & Child Devel 725 Welch Rd Palo Alto CA 94304*

MATTHIAS, JOHN EDWARD, English literature educator; b. Columbus, Ohio, Sept. 5, 1941; s. John Marshall and Lois (Kirkpatrick) M.; m. Diana Clare Jocelyn, Dec. 27, 1967; children—Cynouai, Laura. BA, Ohio State U., 1963; MA, Stanford U., 1966; postgrad., U. London, 1967. Asst. prof. dept. English U. Notre Dame, Ind., 1966-73, assoc. prof., 1973-80, prof., 1980—; vis. fellow Clare Hall, Cambridge U., 1966-77, assoc., 1977—; vis. prof. dept. English, Skidmore Coll., Saratoga Springs, N.Y., 1975, U. Chgo., 1980. Author: Bucyrus, 1971, Turns, 1975, Crossing, 1979, Five American Poets, 1980, Introducing David Jones, 1980, Contemporary Swedish Poetry, 1980, Bathory and Lermontov, 1980, Northern Summer, New and Selected Poems, 1984, The Battle of Kosovo, 1989, David Jones: Man and Poet: A Gathering of Ways, 1991, Reading Old Friends, 1991, Swimming at Midnight, 1995, Beltane at Aphelion, 1995. Recipient Columbia U. Transl. award, 1978, Swedish Inst. award, 1981, Poetry award Soc. Midland Authors, 1984, Ingram Merrill Found. award, 1984, 90, Woodrow Wilson fellow, 1963, Lily Endowment fellow, 1993; Fulbright grantee, 1966. Mem. AAUP, PEN, Poets and Writers, Poetry Soc. Am. (George Bogin Meml. award 1990), London Poetry Secretariat. Office: U Notre Dame Dept English Notre Dame IN 46556

MATTHIES, FREDERICK JOHN, architectural engineer; b. Omaha, Oct. 4, 1925; s. Fred J. and Charlotte Leota (Metz) M.; m. Carol Mae Dean, Sept. 14, 1947; children—John Frederick, Jane Carolyn Matthies Goding. BSCE, Cornell U., 1947; postgrad., U. Nebr., 1952-53. Diplomate Am. Acad. Environ. Engrs.; registered profl. engr., Iowa, Nebr. Civil engr. Hennigson, Durham & Richardson, Omaha, 1947-50, 52-54; sr. v.p. devel. Leo A. Daly Co., Omaha, 1954-90; cons. engr., 1990—; lectr. in field; mem. dist. export coun. U.S. Dept. Commerce, 1981-83. Contbr. articles to profl. publs. Mem. Douglas County Rep. Cen. Com., Nebr., 1968-72; bd. regents Augustana Coll., Sioux Falls., S.D., 1976-89; bd. dirs. Orange County Luth. Hosp. Assn., Anaheim, Calif., 1961-62, Nebr. Humanities Coun., 1988—, Omaha-Shizuoka City (Japan) Sister City Orgn.; trustee Luth. Med. Ctr., Omaha, 1978-82; mem. adv. bd. Marine Mil. Acad., Harlingen, Tex. 1st lt. USMCR, 1943-46, 50-52, Korea. Fellow ASCE, Instn. Civil Engrs. (London, Euro Engr. European Econ. Commn.); mem. NSPE, Am. Water Works Assn. (life), Air Force Assn., Am. Legion, VFW, The Omaha Club. Lutheran. Home: 337 S 127th St Omaha NE 68154-2309

MATTHIESEN, LEROY THEODORE, bishop; b. Olfen, Tex., June 11, 1921; s. Joseph A. and Rosa (Englert) M. BA, Josephinum Coll. Columbus, Ohio, 1942; MA, Cath. U., Washington, 1961; LittD, Register Sch. Journalism., Denver, 1962. Ordained priest Roman Cath. Ch., 1946. Editor West Tex. Cath., Amarillo diocese, from 1948; prin. Alamo Cath. High Sch, from 1969; pastor St. Francis parish, from 1972; ordained bishop of Amarillo, Tex., 1980—. Office: PO Box 5644 Amarillo TX 79117-5644*

MATTHIESSEN, PETER, author; b. N.Y.C., May 22, 1927; s. Erard A. and Elizabeth (Carey) M.; m. Patricia Southgate, Feb. 8, 1951 (div.); m. Deborah Love, May 8, 1963 (dec. June 1972); children: Lucas C., Sara C., Rue, Alexander F.L.; m. Maria Eckhart, Nov. 28, 1980. Student, The Sorbonne, Paris, 1948-49; B.A., Yale U., 1950. Author: Race Rock, 1954, Partisans, 1955, Wildlife in America, 1959, Raditzer, 1960, The Cloud Forest, 1961, Under the Mountain Wall, 1963, At Play in the Fields of the Lord, 1965, The Shorebirds of North America, 1967, Oomingmak: The Expedition to the Musk Ox Island in the Bering Sea, 1967, Sal Si Puedes, 1969, Blue Meridian, 1971, The Tree Where Man Was Born, 1972, Far Tortuga, 1975, The Snow Leopard, 1978 (Nat. Book award), Sand Rivers, 1981 (John Burroughs medal), In the Spirit of Crazy Horse, 1983, Indian Country, 1984, Nine-Headed Dragon River, 1986, Men's Lives, 1986, On the River Styx & Other Stories, 1989, Killing Mister Watson, 1990, African Silences, 1991, Baikal, 1992, African Shadows, 1992. Trustee N.Y. Zool. Soc., 1965-78. AAAL grantee, 1963. Mem. Am. Acad. Arts and Letters.

MATTHIS, EVA MILDRED BONEY, college official; b. Magnolia (Waycross), N.C., Aug. 18, 1927; d. James Horace and Eva Alice (Merritt) Boney; m. George Clifton Matthis, Aug. 31, 1949; 1 child, George Clifton Jr. AA, Louisburg Coll., 1946; BS, East Carolina U., 1969, MLS, 1971. Advt. mgr. Efirds, Wilmington, N.C., 1946-49; advt. acct. Lenoir Co. News, 1950; syn. aviation instrument instr. Serv-Air Aviation, Kinston, N.C., 1951-57; advt. account exec. Kinston Free Press, 1959-64; libr. Caswell Ctr., 1965-66; history tchr. North Lenoir High Sch., 1969-70; libr. Sampson Elem. Sch. 1970-72; head libr. media program Lenoir C.C., Kinston, 1972-76, dean, learning resources, 1976-89, dean, mktg. instl. devel., learning resources, 1989-91, dean, instl. advancement, 1991, v.p. instrnl. svcs.; alumni rep. East Carolina U. LS SACS Self-study, Greenville, 1987-89. Family editor: Heritage of Lenoir County, 1981. Developer Heritage Place, local history mus., 1988; pres. Jr. Women's Club, Kinston, 1960; dist. dir. N.C. Jr. Women's Club, 1961; mem. Kinston Mayor's All-Am. City Com., 1988; rep. Lenoir County Bicentennial Com., Kinston, 1987; parish chmn. Queen Street United Meth. Ch., 1984-90, mem. bishop's coun., 1988-90, com. chmn., 1988-90, chmn. fin. com., 1992—, bldg. com., 1992-94, Sunday Sch. tchr., mem. adminstrv. bd., 1984—; mem. Kinston Mus. com., 1990-92, Fireman Mus. com., 1992-93; chair archtl. survey, Lenoir county, 1993. Named Scouting Family of Yr., 1970; recipient merit award N.C. Hist. Soc., 1989, Excellence award Kinston C. of C., 1985, Educators Office Pers. Lenoir C.C., Adminstr. of Yr. award, 1990. Mem. N.C. C.C. Learning Resources Assn. (life, pub. info. officer 1989-92, exec. bd., dir. dist. II 1986-89, Achievement award 1992, Hon. Mention Libr. Jour. LIbr. of Yr. 1991), Librs. of Lenoir County (pres. 1985, 92), Lenoir County Hist. Assn. (v.p., exec. bd.), Coun. on Resource Devel., Hist. Lenoir County-Kinston Celebration, East Carolina U. Alumni Assn., Phi Beta Kappa, Delta Kappa Gamma (yearbook editor). Avocations: basketmaking, reading, gardening, grandmothering. Home: PO Box 6340 Kinston NC 28501-1440 Office: Lenoir C C PO Box 188 Kinston NC 28502-0188

MATTIA, FRANK J., secondary school principal. Prin. Incarnation Cath. Schs., Centerville, Ohio. Recipient Elem. Sch. Recognition award U.S. Dept. Edn., 1989-90. Office: Incarnation Cath Sch 45 Williamsburg Ln Centerville OH 45459

MATTIELLO, BRIAN EDWARD, state legislator; b. Torrington, Conn., Oct. 15, 1965; s. Arthur Edward and Joyce Ann (Leonard) M. BA, Conn. State U., 1988; MA, Trinity Coll., 1992. State rep. 65th Dist., City of Torrington, 1992—. Bd. dirs. Purple Heart Mus., Brooker Meml. Inc. Cath. Family Svcs.; mem. Torrington Rep. Town Com. Mem. CCSU Alumni Assn. (bd. dirs.), Unico (Torrington chpt.), Order Sons of Italy (Torrington chpt.). Avocations: swimming, golf, reading, music, comedy. Home: 79 Maple St Torrington CT 06790 Office: Legis Offic Bldg Capitol Ave Hartford CT 06106

MATTINGLY, DONALD ARTHUR, professional baseball player; b. Evansville, Ind., Apr. 20, 1961; m. Kim Sexton; children: Taylor Patrick, Preston Michael. Baseball player N.Y. Yankees, 1979—. Named Most Valuable Player South Atlantic League, 1980, Am. League Most Valuable Player, Baseball Writer's Assn., 1985, Am. League Player of Yr., Sporting News, 1984-86, All-Star Team, 1984-89, Major League Player of the Yr. Sporting News, 1985; recipient Gold Glove award, 1985-89, 91-94, Silver Slugger award, 1985-87, Am. League batting champion, 1984. Office: NY Yankees Yankee Stadium Bronx NY 10451*

MATTINGLY, J. VIRGIL, JR., federal lawyer; b. Leonardtown, Md., Oct. 18, 1944. BBA in Acctg., George Washington U., JD. Sr. atty. Fed. Res. Bd., Washington, 1974-79, asst. gen. counsel, 1979-81, assoc. gen. counsel, 1981-85, dep. gen. counsel, 1985-89, gen. counsel, 1989—. With JAGC, U.S. Army, 1970-74. Office: Fed Res Bd Bd Govs 20th & C Sts NW Washington DC 20551

MATTINGLY, MACK F., former US ambassador, former US senator, entrepreneur; b. Anderson, Ind., Jan. 7, 1931; m. Carolyn Longcamp, 1957; children: Jane, Anne. BS, Ind. U., 1957. Acct. supr. IND, Arvin, Ind., 1957-59; mktg. mgr. IBM Corp., Ga., 1959-79; owner/pres. M's Inc., Ga. 1975-80; US senator Rep. Ga., 1981-87; assoc. sr. gen. def. support NATO, Brussels, 1987-90; US Ambassador Seychelles, 1992-93; speaker/author econ., def., fgn. policy, entrepreneur, 1990-92; mem. U.S. Sen. Com. Appropriations, chmn. legis. and mil. constrn. subcoms.mem. energy and water devel., agr. rural devel., treasury, postal svc. and gen. govt., mil. constrn. legis. subcoms., U.S. Sen. com. Banking, Housing and Urban affairs, chmn. rural housing, econ. policy subcoms.; mem. select com. ethics 1981-83, joint econ. com. 1983-87; chmn. Rep. com. on Coms., mem. Rep. Senate Leadership, Holocaust commn.; U.S. Del. GATT, Geneva, 1982; del. alt. at arms Rep. Nat. Convention, Del. Georgian rep. party convs., 1964-90, task force econ. policy, 1978-80; chmn. 8th Dist. Goldwater for pres., 1964; mem. Ge. Rep. State centennial com., state exec. com., vice chmn. state party, 1968-75;. Author 40 U.S. Sen. Bills, Amendments and Resolutions. Del. Alt. Sgt. at Arms, Rep. Nat. Convs., Del. Georgian Rep. Party Convs., 1964-90; chmn. 8th Dist. Goldwater for Pres., 1964, Ga. 8th Congl. Dist., Cand. U.S. Congress, 8th Dist., 1966; mem. Ga. Rep. Party State Cen. Com., State Exec. Com., vice-chmn. state party, 1968-75, chmn. state party, 1975-77; elected 1st Rep. U.S. Sen. from Ga. since 1871, 1980; co-chmn. Bush/Quayle Campaign, Bush/Quayle Fund Raising Dinner, del. Rep. State and Nat. Convs., 1992; bd. dirs. U.S. Nat. Chamber Found., 1990; hon. me. bd. dirs. M.L. King Jr. Fed. Holiday commn., 1990. With USAF, 1951-57. Recipient Southeast Father of Yr. award 1984, Ga. Wildlife Fed. Conservationist of Yr. award 1985, Selective Svc. System Disting. Svc. Gold medal 1985, Watchdog of Treasury award 1981-86, Nat. Taxpayers Union Taxpayers Best Friend award 1981-86, NFIB's Guardian of Small Bus. award 1981-86, Am. Security Coun. award 1981-86, Sec. Def. medal for Outstanding Pub. Svc. 1988. Mem. Brunswick Golden Isle C. of C., Am. Legion. Episcopalian.

MATTINGLY, PATTI JANE, educational administrator; b. Caddo Mills, Tex., May 21, 1936; d. Raymond Edward and Marjorie (Glass) M.; B.S., North Tex. State U., 1957, M.Ed., 1962; postgrad. Nova U., 1973-75. Elem. tchr. Richardson (Tex.) Public Schs., 1957-62, U. Tex. Lab Sch., Austin, 1962-67; cons. Tex. Edn. Agy., Austin, 1967-68; instr. edn., dir. materials-learning center Austin Coll., Sherman, Tex., 1968-70, asst. prof. edn., dir. Texoma Coop. Tchr. Center, 1971-74; asst. prof. edn. Tex. Christian U., Ft. Worth, 1970-71; asso. dir. Lamplighter Sch., Dallas, 1974-75, dir., 1975—. Delta Kappa Gamma scholar, 1973. Mem. Ind. Schs. Assn. S.W. (pres.), Nat. Assn. Ind. Schs. (bd. dirs.), Assn. for Supervision and Curriculum Devel., Tex. Assn. for Supervision and Curriculum Devel., Assn. for Childhood Edn. Internat., Dallas Mus. Art Presbyterian. Office: Lamplighter Sch 11611 Inwood Rd Dallas TX 75229-3098

MATTINGLY, PAUL R., lawyer; b. Cin., Feb. 1, 1950; s. Richard Ralph and Mary Catherine (Wunderlich) M.; m. Elizabeth Baringhaus, May 1, 1976; children: Anne Marie, Michael, David, Stephen. BA magna cum laude, U. Dayton, 1972; JD, U. Notre Dame, 1975. Bar: Ohio 1975, Ind. 1976; cert. secondary edn. tchr., Ohio. Ptnr. Dinsmore & Shohl, Cin., 1975—. Mem. Neighborhood Svcs. Allocations com. United Way, Community Chest; Juvenile Ct. referee Colerain Township; vol. Catholic Inner City Schs. Ednl. Fund, Athenaeum Bus. Campaign, Archbishop's Advancement com.; trustee Hamilton County Resource Svcs.; mem. Leadership Cin. Capt. USAR. Mem. Ohio State Bar Assn., Cin. Bar Assn., Hamilton County Ohio Bd. Mental Retardation and Developmental Disability, Notre Dame Law Assn. (trustee), Notre Dame Club Greater Cin., Cin. Inst. Small Enterprise, Cin. C. of C. Roman Catholic. Avocations: antique autos. Office: Dinsmore & Shohl 1900 Chemed Ct 255 E 5th St Cincinnati OH 45202-4700

MATTINGLY, ROBERT KERKER, entrepreneur; b. Zanesville, Ohio, Mar. 12, 1921; s. John Clement and Olive (Kerker) M.; m. Bette Louise Allen, Dec. 27, 1941; 1 child, Barbara Kay. Grad., High Sch., Zanesville, 1939. Pres. Mattingly Foods, Inc., Zanesville, 1945—. Bd. dirs. Goodwill Industries, Zanesville, 1970-76, Zanesville Trace, 1981—; trustee Muskingum County Found., 1989—. Served to 1st lt. U.S. Army, 1942-45. Named So.

Ohio Gentleman Farmer, Bob Evans, 1979, Ohio Commodore, Gov. Rhodes, 1979; recipient Pres.'s award, Syracuse China, 1978-85. Mem. Internat. Foodsvc. Distbrs. Assn. (bd. dirs. 1990—), Zanesville C. of C. (pres. 1976-77). Avocations: reading, swimming, golf, travel. Home: PO Box 2668 Zanesville OH 43702-2668 Office: Mattingly Foods Inc 302 State St Zanesville OH 43701-3200

MATTINGLY, THOMAS K., astronaut; b. Chgo., Mar. 17, 1936; s. Thomas K. Mattingly; separated; 1 child, Thomas K. III. BS in Aero. Engring., Auburn U., 1958; attended, Air Force Aerospace Rsch. Pilot Sch. Commd. officer USN, 1958; comdr. assigned to space shuttle ops. NASA; astronaut NASA Manned Spacecraft Ctr., Houston; crew mem. Apollo 16, 1972, 4th Test Mission, Columbia, 1982, Shuttle Mission 51-C, 1985; rear admiral in charge Space Sensor Systems, Dept. Navy, Washington, 1986-93; div. v.p. and program dir. Atlas Program of Martin-Marietta Astronautics Space System, San Diego, 1993—. Decorated NASA Disting. Svc. Medals (2), JSC Cert. Commendation, 1970, JSC Group Achievement award, 1972, Navy Disting. Svc. Medal, Navy Astronaut Wings; recipient SETP Ivan C. Kincheloe award, 1972, Delta Tau Delta Achievement award, 1972, Outstanding Achievement award Auburn Alumni Engrs. Coun., 1972, AAS Flight Achievement award, 1972, Fedn. Aeronautique Internationale V.M. Komarov Diploma, 1973, Disting. Svc. Medal Dept. Def., 1982. Fellow AIAA (assoc., Haley Astronautics award 1973), Am. Astronautical Soc.; mem. Socl Exptl. Test Pilots, U.S. Naval Inst. Office: Martin Marietta PO Bos 85990 MZ K4-7010 San Diego CA 92186

MATTINGLY, WILLIAM EARL, lawyer; b. Decatur, Ill., Mar. 6, 1948; s. Woodrow W. and Lena (Dayhuff) M.; children: Claire, Henry, Grace. BS in Indsl. Engring., Purdue U., 1971, MSE, 1972; JD cum laude, Ind. U., Indpls., 1975. Bar: Ind. 1975, Ill. 1978, Okla. 1980. Assoc. Sonnenschein, Carlin, Nath & Rosenthal, Chgo., 1978-80, Hall, Estill, et al, Tulsa, 1980-83; sr. ptnr. employee benefits dept. Katten, Muchin & Zavis, Chgo., 1984—; lectr. tax inst. conf. U. So. Calif., 1985, U. Ill. Conf. on Employee Stock Ownership Plans, 1987, Inst. for Health Law Loyola U., Chgo., 1987. Contbr. articles to profl. jours. Mem. ABA (chmn. 2 subcoms. banking and bus. law sects.), Chgo. Bar Assn., Ill. State Bar Assn.

MATTIS, LOUIS PRICE, pharmaceutical and consumer products company executive; b. Balt., Dec. 12, 1941; s. Louis Wadsworth and Sara Helene (Myers) M.; m. Patricia Diane Brown, Nov. 29, 1963; children—Louis Wadsworth, Deborah Cook. A.B. in Internat. Affairs, Lafayette Coll., Easton, Pa., 1962; M.B.A. Tulane U., 1964. V.p., gen. mgr. Warner Lambert Co., Manila, 1971-74; regional dir. Warner Lambert Co., Hong Kong, 1974-76; region pres. Warner Lambert Co., Sydney, Australia, 1976-79; exec. v.p. Americas-Far East Richardson-Vicks, Inc., 1979-81, pres. Americas-Far East, 1981-84, exec. v.p., 1985-87; group v.p. Sterling Winthrop Inc., N.Y.C., 1987-88, pres., CEO, 1988-94, chmn., 1989-94; dir. Sterling Winthrop Inc., Solomon Bros. Fund, 1992—. Mem. Gov. Ctr. for Creative Leadership, 1989—. Mem. Union League of N.Y., New Canaan (Conn.) Country Club, Sea Island (Ga.) Golf Club, Skek-o club, Snowmass Club. Republican. Episcopalian. Clubs: Union League of N.Y., New Canaan (Conn.) Country; Sea Island (Ga.) Golf; Skek-o. Avocations: skiing; tennis; woodworking. Home: 156 Kemble Dr Sea Island GA 31561 Office: PO Box 31073 Sea Island GA 31561

MATTISON, DONALD ROGER, dean, physician, military officer; b. Mpls., Apr. 28, 1944; s. Milford Zachary and Elizabeth Ruth (Davey) M.; m. Margaret Rose Libby, Jan. 28, 1967; children: Jon, Amy. BA cum laude in Chemistry and Math., Augsburg Coll., Mpls., 1966; MS in Chemistry, MIT, 1968; MD, Columbia U., 1973. Resident in ob-gyn Presbyn. Hosp., N.Y.C., 1973-75, 77-78; commd. rsch. assoc. USPHS, 1975, advanced through grades to comdr., 1984; rsch. assoc. Nat. Inst. Child Health and Human Devel., NIH, Bethesda, Md., 1975-77, med. officer then chief pregnancy rsch. br., 1978-84; assoc. prof. ob-gyn. U. Ark., Little Rock, 1984-87; prof. U. Pitts., 1987-90, assoc. prof. toxicology, 1984-88, prof., 1988-90, dean Grad. Sch. Pub. Health, prof., 1990—; mem. Bd. Environ. Studies and Toxicology, NRC, NAS, 1988—; mem. sci. adv. bd. Hawaii Heptachlor Edn. and Rsch. Found., 1987—; mem. sci. adv. panel Semicondr. Industry Assn., 1987—; mem. portfolio team United Way Allegheny County and Western Pa., 1990—; mem. pre-screening com. Magee-Women's Hosp., Pitts., 1990—; mem. steering com. Pa. Dept. Health, Harrisburg, 1990—, mem. com. Inst. Medicine, NAS, 1989-91; cons. Women's Vietnam Health Study Protocol Devel., New England Rsch. Inst., 1986-90. Mem. editorial bd. Pediatric Pharmacology, 1980-87, Reproductive Toxicology, 1987—, Devel. Pharmacology and Therapeutics, Switzerland, 1987—, Reproductive Scis., The Info. Netork, 1989—, Methods in Toxicology, 1989—; guest editor Jour. Symposium on Reproductive Toxicology, Am. Jour. Indsl. Medicine, 1983; contbr. numerous articles, abstracts, letters and editorials to profl. pubs. Recipient Am. Chem. Soc. medal Minn. sect. Am. Chem. Soc., 1966, Assn. Am. Publs. award, 1983. Mem. APHA, Soc. Risk Analysis (editorial bd. jour. 1988—), Pitts. chpt. Soc. Risk Analysis, Am. Assn. Cancer Rsch., N.Y. Acad. Sci., Am. Coll. Toxicology, Am. Fertility Soc., Soc. Gynecologic Investigation, Soc. Toxicology. Avocations: photography, computer sciences, house restoration, cross country skiing. Office: U Pitts Grad Sch Pub Health 130 DeSoto St Pittsburgh PA 15261

MATTISON, HARRY D., utility company executive; b. 1936. BS, Univ. Ark., 1959. Asst. mgr. Southwestern Electric Power Co., 1957-68, asst. mgr. indsl. sls, 1968-70, mgr. indsl. sls, 1970-78, div. mgr. La., 1978-82, asst. div. mgr. East Tex., 1982-83, v.p East Tex. div., 1983-86, v.p. div. ops., 1986-87, v.p. adminstrn., 1987-88, exec. v.p., 1988-90; exec. v.p., COO Ctrl. and SW Corp., Dallas, 1990—. Office: Ctrl and SW Corp 1616 Woodall Rodgers Fwy Dallas TX 75202

MATTISON, RICHARD, psychiatry educator; b. Bradford, Pa., Nov. 14, 1946. BA in Biology magna cum laude, Lafayette Coll., Easton, Pa., 1968; MD, Cornell U., 1970. Diplomate Am. Bd. Psychiatry and Neurology (examiner child psychiatry); cert. Nat. Bd. Med. Examiners; bd. cert. psychiatry, 1980, child psychiatry, 1981; lic. physician, Mo., registered DEA. Intern Buffalo Children's Hosp., 1972-73; residency in adult psychiatry Cornell U. Medical Coll., White Plains, N.Y., 1975-77; rsch. fellow UCLA Ctr. for the Health Scis. Neuropsychiatric Inst., 1977-79, chief psychiatrist, 1979-80; from asst. prof. to assoc. prof. dept. psychiatry Pa. State U., Hershey, 1980-90, dir. children's diagnostic clinic, 1980-90, dir. child psychiatry inpatient unit, 1983-84, dir. sch. consultation, 1988-90; dir. divsn. child psychiatry Washington U. Sch. Medicine, St. Louis, 1990—, Blanche F. Ittleson assoc. prof., 1990—; cons. Hyperkinetic Children Clinic Gateway Hosp., L.A., 1976-78, Mental Health/Mental Retardation Program, Harrisburg (Pa.) Hosp., 1980-89; sch. psychiatric cons. Capital Area Intermediate Unit, Harrisburg, 1980-90, Lincoln Intermediate Unit, York, Pa., 1986-90, Lancaster-Lebanon Intermediate Unit, Lancaster, Pa., 1988-90, Spl. Sch. Dist., St. Louis, 1990—; psychiatrist-in-chief St. Louis Children's Hosp., 1990—, med. exec. com., 1990—, child abuse subcom., 1991-92; dir. child psychiatry fellowship training program, Washington U. Sch. Medicine, 1990—; staff Barnes Hosp., St. Louis, 1990—, exec. com. dept. psychiatry, 1990—, clin. affairs com., 1992—; vis. cons. Brown U. Sch. Medicine, Providence, 1986; vis. prof. U. Rochester (N.Y.) Sch. Medicine, 1986; cons., speaker in field. Co-author: Child and Adolescent Mental Health Consultation in Hospitals, Schools, and Courts, 1993; editor: Child Psychopathology; Diagnostic Criteria and Assessment, 1992, Developmental Disorders: Diagnostic Criteria and Clinical Assessment, 1992; editor Jour. Abnormal Child Psychology, Contemporary Child; contbr. numerous articles to profl. jours., chpts. to books. Fellow UCLA Ctr. for the Health Scis., 1975-77; recipient Faculty Devel. award ALCOA Found., 1981-82. Mem. Am. Psychiatric Assn., Am. Acad. Child and Adolescent Psychiatry (program com. 1987-89, editor jour.), Nat. Assn. Sch. Psychologists, Coun. for Exceptional Children, Soc. for Rsch. in Child and Adolescent Psychiatry (mem. com. 1992—), Soc. Profs. Child and Adolescent Psychiatry (Peter Henderson Mem. award com. 1993), Phi Beta Kappa. Home: 14725 Westerly Pl Chesterfield MO 63017-7918 Office: Washington U Sch Medicine Dept Psychiatry 4940 Childrens Pl Saint Louis MO 63110-1002

MATTOCH, IAN L., lawyer. BA, Occidental Coll., 1965; JD, Northwestern U., 1968. Prin. Law Offices Ian L. Mattoch, Honolulu; instr. law and soc. Punahou Sch., 1970-92; lectr. in field. Editor-in-chief Hawaii Bar Journal, 1970-72; contbr. articles to profl. jours. Bd. dirs. PREVENT Child

Abuse Hawaii, Make-A-Wish Hawaii, past pres. Fellow Hawaii Trial Lawyers Assn. (founding mem. bd. govs.); mem. ABA, Assn. Trial Lawyers Am., Nebr. Bar Assn., Hawaii State Bar Assn. Office: 737 Bishop St Ste 1835 Honolulu HI 96813-3209 also: 688 Kinoole St Ste 202 Hilo HI 96720-3869 also: 75-170 Hualalai Rd Ste D211 Kailua Kona HI 96740-1737 also: Spencer House Kamuela HI 96743 also: 45-781 Kamehameha Hwy Kaneohe HI 96744-2949

MATTONE, VINCENT J., investment banker; b. 1945. With Bear Stearns & Co., Inc., N.Y.C., 1966—, exec. v.p., sr. mng. dir., 1987—. Office: 245 Park Ave New York NY 10167-0001

MATTOON, HENRY AMASA, JR., advertising and marketing consultant, writer; b. Waterbury, Conn., Jan. 14, 1914; s. Henry A. and Sarah Currie (Hallock) M.; m. Dorothy Ann Teeter, Sept. 13, 1934; children: Ann Brooks Wofford, David Scott, Sara Halsey, Judith Scott Conn. BS, Yale U., 1935. Mail boy, then copywriter, copy supr. Compton Advt. Inc., N.Y.C., 1935-44; v.p., creative dir. Compton Advt. Inc., 1944-50; v.p., chmn. plans bd. Ruthrauff & Ryan, Inc., 1950-52; v.p., creative dir. Dancer-Fitzgerald-Sample, Inc., 1952-54; pres., dir. Reach, Yates & Mattoon, Inc., 1954-56; v.p., mktg. plans bd. McCann-Erickson, Inc., 1956-57, v.p., assoc. creative dir., 1957-62; v.p., gen. mgr. McCann-Erickson, Inc., Los Angeles, 1962-65; sr. v.p. and mgr. McCann-Erickson, Inc., Houston, 1965-68; v.p., dir. advt., pub. relations and sales promotion Yardley of London, Inc., 1968-69; ptnr. Walter Weintz & Co., Inc., Stamford, Conn., 1969-70; prin. Otto Man Assocs., Inc., Weston, Conn., 1970-93; exec. v.p. Mktg. Lab, Inc., Danbury, Conn., 1985—, also bd. dirs. Contbr., columnist profl. jours. and mags. Mem. Yale Club of N.Y., Crow Canyon Country Club, Knights of Malta, Chi Phi. Republican. Episcopalian. Home: 675 Doral Dr Danville CA 94526

MATTOON, PETER MILLS, lawyer; b. Bryn Mawr, Pa., Oct. 22, 1931; s. Harold Gleason and Marguerite Jeanette (Mills) M.; m. Mary Joan Henley, June 27, 1953; children: Pamela M. Zisselman, R. Stephen, Peter H., Philip P. AB, Dartmouth Coll., 1953; LLB, Harvard U., 1959. Bar: Pa. 1960. Assoc. Ballard Spahr Andrews & Ingersdoll, Phila., 1959-67, ptnr., 1967—; mem. adv. bd. PNC Bank, Phila. Emeritus trustee The Episcopal Acad., Merion, Pa., 1970—, former chmn.; trustee, v.p. Widener Meml. Found., Lafayette Hill, Pa., 1972—; trustee, vice chmn. Widener U., Chester, Pa., 1984—; trustee Thomas Jefferson U. Phila, 1989—; chmn., overseer Widener U. Law Sch., Wilmington, 1979—. Served to lt USN, 1953-56. Mem. Greater Phila. C. of C. (dir.). Office: Ballard Spahr Andrews & Ingersoll 1735 Market St 51st fl Philadelphia PA 19103

MATTOS NETO, SEBASTIAO DE SOUZA, lawyer; b. San Paulo, Brazil, Apr. 29, 1951. LLB, Facultad de Direito da Universidade, San Paulo, Brazil, 1974; MCL, U. Ill., 1976; JD, Chgo. Kent Coll. Law, 1980. Bar: Brazil 1974, Ill. 1980, Portugal 1989. Ptnr. Baker & McKenzie, San Paulo, 1984-85, Chgo. Office: Baker & McKenzie One Prudential Plz 130 E Randolph St Chicago IL 60601

MATTOX, KENNETH LEON, surgeon, educator, medical scientist; b. Ozark, Ark., Oct. 25, 1938. BS, Wayland Coll., 1960; MD, Baylor U., 1964. Diplomate Am. Bd. Surgery, Am. Bd. Thoracic Surgery. Intern surgery VA Hosp., Houston, 1964-65; resident in gen. surgery, asst. instr. Baylor U., Houston, 1967-71, resident in thoracic surgery, 1971-72, asst. instr. thoracic surgery, 1971-73, instr. surgery, 1973-74, asst. prof. surgery, 1974-78, assoc. prof. surgery, 1978-84, prof. surgery, 1984—; aeromed. cons. Dept. Army, Natick (Mass.) Labs., 1967-70; dep. surgeon in chief, dir. emergency surg. services, chief thoracic surgery service Ben Taub Gen. Hosp., Houston, 1973-90, chief surgery 1990—, surg. tech. adv. bd. 1982—; physician com. 1984—, chief of staff, 1990—; surg. cons. Tex. Inst. for Research and Rehab., Houston, 1973—; attending surgeon VA Hosp., Houston, 1973—, active staff Meth. Hosp., Houston, 1973—, Women's Hosp., Houston, 1973-82; courtesy staff St. Luke's Hosp., Houston, 1973—, Tex. Children's Hosp., Houston, 1973—; clin. prof. Uniformed Services U. for the Health Scis., Bethesda, Md., 1983—; sr. cardiac surgeon Baylor heart team King Faisal Specialist Hosp. and Research Ctr., Riyadh, Saudi Arabia, 1979, 80, 81, 83; active various coms. Baylor Coll. Medicine, Houston, vice chmn. dept. surgery; operating room com., profl. activities tng. fund com., critical care com., others Harris County Hosp. Dist., 1979—; adv. com. regional emergency med. services tng. program Health Sci. Ctr., U. Tex., 1978—; Curtis Artz Meml. lectr. Am. Coll. Surgeons, 1985; emergency med. services adv. council Tex. Dept. Health, 1983—; mem. task force for state health coordinating council for regionalization specialized health services State of Tex., 1985-86; chmn. categorization subcom. emergency med. services com. Houston-Galveston Area Council, 1978-82. Sr. editor Trauma, 1987; editor Complications in Trauma, 1993; edtl. cons. Chest, Med. Instrumentation, JAMA, Jour. Trauma; edtl. adv. bd. Emergency Medicine, 1975-92, Emergency Medicine Ann., Emergency Dept. News; assoc. editor thoracic trauma Current Concepts in Trauma Care, 1975-87; edtl. com. Tex. Medicine; reviewer Ann. Surgery, Ann. Thoracic Surgery, Am. Jour. Surgery; referee Med. Principles & Practice, contbr. over 400 sci. articles, chpts. and editorials to med. books and jours. Disaster physician Harris County Sheriff's Dept., 1973-82; pres. Emergency Medicine Found., 1982-83; mem. Houston area disaster and emergency med. system com. Greater Houston Hosp. Council, 1985—; trustee Wayland Bapt. U., 1984—; bd. dirs. Child Abuse Prevention Ctr., 1982-85. Served to capt. U.S. Army, 1965-67. Named one of Outstanding Young Men of Am., 1968; recipient Disting. Alumni award Wayland Bapt. U., 1986. Mem. Am. Assn. for the Surgery Trauma (bd. mgrs. 1985—, recorder, program chmn. 1990-93, pres.- elect 1995), Am. Assn. Thoracic Surgery, Am. Coll. Cardiology (chmn. tech. exhibitor 1979-80), Am. Coll. Chest Physicians (bd. govs. 1986-90, gov. from Tex. 1986-91, Most Outstanding Motion Picture 1975, pulmonary surgery com. 1978, postgrad. med. edn. com. 1979—), Am. Coll. Emergency Physicians (bd. dirs. Tex. div. 1973-78, Cert. Appreciation 1975), Am. Coll. Surgeons (med. device com. 1980-85, chmn. 1983-85, com. on trauma 1983-89, bd. govs. 1985-91, others), AMA (Physician Recognition award 1972, 73), Am. Surg. Assn., Am. Trauma Soc. (founder, sec. 1974, v.p. 1975, Harris unit pres. Tex. div. 1975-76, state bd. dirs., nat. bd. dirs. 1973-82, 1988—, others), Assn. for Acad. Surgery, Assn. for the Advancement Med. Instrumentation (bd. dirs. 1980-86, chmn. bd. standards 1979-84, pres. elect 1987-88, pres. 1988-89), Am. Nat. Standards Inst. (rep. med. device standards bd.), Harris County Med. Soc. (alt. del. Tex. Med. Assn. 1982—), emergency med. services com. 1973—, chmn. hosp. subcom. 1973-75, disaster subcom. 1973-78), Houston Surg. Soc., Internat. Cardiovascular Soc., Internat. Coll. Angiology, Michael Surg. Soc. (program chmn. 1980, 82, 84, bd. dirs. 1978—, sec.-treas. 1987—, others), Pan Am. Med. Assn. (v.p. trauma sect.), Pan Pacific Surg. Assn., Soc. Thoracic Surgery, Soc. Univ. Surgeons, Soc. Vascular Surgery, So. Surg. Assn., So. Thoracic Surg. Assn., Am. Coll. Surgeons (1st v-p south Tex. chpt. 1983-84, pres. 1984-85), SW Surg. Congress (budget and fin. com. 1976-80), Tex. Med. Assn. (trauma com. 1975—, interspecialty com. 1985—, alt. del. 1982—), Tex. Surg. Soc., Univ. Assn. for Emergency Medicine (program. chmn. 1976-79, pres. 1979-80, exec. com. 1976-83, pres. 1979-80, emergency dept. design and function 1974-75, James Mackenzie award 1980), Tex. Collegiate Acad. Sci., Tex. Acad. Sci., Aerospace Med. Assn., Tex. Inst. Rehabilitation and Research (utilization rev. com.), TexPac (Harris County Med. Soc. exec. com. 1983), Alpha Chi, Sigma Tau Delta. Office: 1 Baylor Plz Houston TX 77030-3411

MATTRAN, DONALD ALBERT, management consultant, educator; b. Chgo., July 8, 1934; s. George Charles and Lucille Alice (Boule) M.; m. Betty Elena Flores, July 18, 1953 (div. Mar. 1988); children: Donald, Julie, Kimberly, Guy, Christy; m. Rose Lynn Castellano, May, 1988. B.Mus., U. Mich., 1957, M.Mus., 1960. Tchr. Van Buren Schs., Belleville, Mich., 1957-61; asst. prof. U. N.H., Durham, 1961-65, Boston U., 1965-66; assoc. prof. Hartt Sch. Music, West Hartford, Conn., 1966-82, dean, 1971-80; dir. Syracuse U. Sch. Music, N.Y., 1982-83; dean Sch. Fine and Performing Arts Montclair State Coll, Upper Montclair, N.J., 1983-87; pres. Sales Consultants of Sarasota (Fla.) Inc., 1987—; cons. Music div. Kaman Corp. Bloomfield, Conn.; evaluator Nat. Assn. Schs. of Music and Joint Commn. Theater and Dance Accreditation; guest condr. Hartford Symphony Orch., Hartt Opera Theatre, All-State Festivals, 1976-83, Soc. New Music, Syracuse, N.Y. Sch. Arts Orch., 1985-87. Co-author (with Mary Rasmussen) A Teacher's Guide to the Literature of Woodwind Instruments, 1966; condr.: rec. Concerto for Cello and Jazz Band, 1972. Chmn. adv. com. Prodigy Inc.,

Syracuse, 1982-86; trustee Conn. Opera Assn., 1977-80; bd. advs. Watkinson Sch. Creative Arts Program, Hartford, 1977-80; mem. humanities adv. com. N.J. Dept. Higher Edn., 1984—; mem. multi-disciplinary panel N.J. State Council on Arts, 1985-87; mem. adv. com. on auditions Met. Opera Nat. Council, 1984-87; mem. adv. com. Frank and Lydia Bergen Found., 1986-87. Mem. Nat. Assn. Schs. Music (exec. bd., sec. 1978-81). Home: 888 Blvd Of The Arts Apt 204 Sarasota FL 34236 Office: 1343 Main St Ste 600 Sarasota FL 34236-5630

MATTSON, FRANCIS OSCAR, retired librarian and rare books curator; b. Boston, Aug. 17, 1931; s. Frans Oscar and Catherine (Carr) M. BA, Boston U., 1957, MA, 1959; MS, Sch. Library Sci., Simmons Coll., 1967. Cert. librarian. Teaching fellow Boston U., 1958-60; instr. Tufts U., Medford, Mass., 1960-64, State Coll. at Salem, Mass., 1964-65; librarian Boston Pub. Library, 1965-68, N.Y. Pub. Library, N.Y.C., 1969-95; curator rare books N.Y. Pub. Library, 1981-88, chief spl. collections cataloging unit, 1988-93, curator Berg Collection of English and Am. Lit., 1991-95; mem. adv. com. Small Press Ctr., 1984-88; mem. adv. bd. Biblion, 1990—. Book rev. editor Printing History, 1983-86, contbg. editor Am. Book Collector, 1984-88. Staff sgt. USAF, 1952-56. Mem. ALA, Biblog. Soc. Am., Biblog. Soc. (London), Biblog. Soc. of U. Va. (life), Printing Hist. Soc., Am. Printing History Assn. (program chmn. ann. confs. 1983, 84, bd. dirs. 1985-90); Manuscript Soc. (trustee 1977-80, 83-86), Am. Coll. and Research Libraries (rare books and manuscripts sect.), Assn. Internationale de Bibliophilie, Browning Inst. (sec. bd. dirs. 1975-90), Soc. for Preservation New Eng. Antiquities (life), Grolier Club. Home: PO Box 515 Midtown Sta New York NY 10018

MATTSON, GEORGE ARTHUR, architect; b. Knoxville, Tenn., Oct. 4, 1936; s. Frank Emil and Hildur Augusta (Freeberg) M.; m. Beverly Joanne Bruegger, Feb. 25, 1960; children: Steven, Susan. BArch, Mont. State Coll., 1959. Assoc. Paffard Clay Architect San Francisco, 1964-70; pvt. practice Bozeman, Mont., 1971-77, 92—; ptnr. Mattson, Prugh & Lenon Architects, Bozeman, 1978-91. Prin. works include Bozeman Pub. Libr., 1980, Bozeman Fire Sta. No. 2, 1984, Mus. of Rockies, 1987. Founding bd. mem. Sweetpea Arts Festival, Bozeman, 1977-86; bd. dirs. Loft Community Theater, Bozeman, 1980-85, Gallatin Performing Arts Ctr., Bozeman, 1989—; founding mem. Beall Park Art Ctr., Bozeman, 1984. Lt. USN, 1960-62. Mem. Quest for Knowledge Club, AIA. Democrat. Avocations: cross country skiing, tennis, sailing. Home: 47 Hitching Post Rd Bozeman MT 59715-9241 Office: 17 W Main St Bozeman MT 59715-4642

MATTSON, JAMES STEWART, lawyer, environmental scientist, educator; b. Providence, July 22, 1945; s. Irving Carl and Virginia (Lutey) M.; m. Carol Sandry, Aug. 15, 1964 (div. 1979); children: James, Birgitta; m. Rana A. Fine, Jan. 5, 1983. BS in Chemistry, U. Mich., 1966, MS, 1969, PhD, 1970; JD, George Washington U., 1979. Bar: D.C. 1979, Fla. 1983, U.S. Dist. Ct. D.C. 1979, U.S. Dist. Ct. (so. dist.) Fla. 1984, U.S. Ct. Appeals (D.C. cir.) 1979, U.S. Ct. Claims 1985, U.S. Supreme Ct. 1985, U.S. Ct. Appeals (11th cir.) 1985, U.S. Ct. Appeals (5th cir.) 1987, U.S. Ct. Appeals (fed. cir.) 1990. Staff scientist Gulf Gen. Atomic Co., San Diego, 1970-71; dir. R & D Ouachita Industries, Inc., Monroe, La., 1971-72; asst. prof. chem. oceanography Rosenstiel Sch. Marine & Atmospheric Sci., U. Miami (Fla.), 1972-76; phys. scientist NOAA, Washington, 1976-78; mem. profl. staff & congl. liaison Nat. Adv. Commn. on Oceans and Atmosphere, 1978-80; ptnr. Mattson & Pave, Washington, Miami and Key Largo, Fla., 1980-86, Mattson & Tobin, Key Largo, 1987—; adj. prof. law U. Miami, 1983—; cons. Alaska Dept. Environ. Conservation, 1981—. Author: (with H.B. Mark) Activated Carbon: Surface Chemistry and Adsorption from Solution, 1971; editor (with others): Computers in Chemistry and Instrumentation, 8 vols., 1972-76; The Argo Merchant Oil Spill: A Preliminary Scientific Report, 1977, (with H.B. Mark) Water Quality Measurement: Modern Analytical Techniques, 1981; contbr. articles to profl. jours. Candidate dist. 120 Fla. Ho. of Reps., 1994. Fellow Fed. Water Pollution Control Adminstrn., 1967-68; recipient Spl. Achievement award U.S. Dept. Commerce, 1976-77; Regents Alumni scholar U. Mich., 1963. Mem. ABA, Am. Chem. Soc. (chmn. Symposium on Oil Spill Indentification 1971), Am. Trial Lawyers Assn., Order of Coif. Office: Mattson & Tobin PO Box 586 Key Largo FL 33037-0586

MATTSON, MARLIN ROY ALBIN, health facility administrator, psychiatry educator; b. Bellingham, Wash., Apr. 25, 1939; s. Conrad Roy and Ruth Viola (Thompson) M. BA, U. Wash., 1961, MD, 1965. Diplomate Am. Bd. Psychiatry and Neurology. Intern and resident in medicine Cornell U. program at Bellevue and Meml. Hosps., N.Y.C., 1965-67; resident in psychiatry Payne Whitney Clin. The N.Y. Hosp., N.Y.C., 1967-70, chief resident in psychiatry, 1972-73, asst. med. dir., 1973-89, assoc. med. dir., 1989—; asst. med. dir. quality assurance Westchester Div. The N.Y. Hosp., White Plains, 1979-89, assoc. med. dir. quality assurance, 1989-93; head of quality assurance program Dept. Psychiatry The N.Y. Hosp., N.Y.C., 1979-94; asst. prof. psychiatry Cornell U. Med. Coll., N.Y.C., 1973-79, assoc. prof. clin. psychiatry, 1979—; bd. visitors Manhattan Psychiat. Ctr., 1991—; bd. dirs. N.Y. County Health Svcs. Rev. Organ., N.Y.C., 1983-95. Editor Manual of Psychiat. Quality Assurance, 1992; contbr. numerous articles to profl. jours. Capt. U.S. Army Med. Corps., 1967-69, Korea. Fellow Am. Psychiat. Assn. (mem. nat. com. on quality assurance 1988—, chmn. 1992—; mem. com. champus peer review program 1984-86, sec. N.Y. County dist. br. 1987-91, pres.-elect 1991-92, pres. 1992-93), N.Y. Acad. Medicine (com. pub. health 1984-92, sec. sect. on psychiatry 1993-94, chmn. 1994-95); mem. N.Y. State Psychiat. Assn. (chmn. peer rev. com. 1982-95, mem. com. econ. affairs 1995—). Republican. Episcopalian. Avocations: piano, European travel, theater, Swedish-American organizations. Home: 501 E 87th St Apt 4J New York NY 10128-7609 Office: NY Hosp Payne Whitney Psychiat Clinic 525 E 68th St New York NY 10021-4873

MATTSON, STEPHEN JOSEPH, lawyer; b. Abilene, Tex., Oct. 11, 1943; s. Joseph Martin and Dorothy Irene (Doyle) M.; m. Lynn Louise Mitchell, Mar. 13, 1965; children: Eric, Laura. BA (hon.), U. Ill., 1965, JD (hon.), 1970. Bar: Ill., 1970, U.S. Dist. Ct. (no. dist.) Ill. 1970. Assoc. Mayer, Brown & Platt, Chgo., 1970-77, ptnr., 1978—. Mem. ABA, Ill. State Bar Assn., Chgo. Bar Assn., Fed. Energy Bar Assn., Order of Coif. Office: Mayer Brown & Platt 190 S La Salle St Chicago IL 60603-3410

MATTSON, WALTER EDWARD, retired publishing company executive; b. Erie, Pa., June 6, 1932; s. Walter Edward and Florence Evelyn (Anderson) M.; m. Geraldine Anne Horsman, Oct. 10, 1953; children: Stephen, William, Carol. B.S., U. Maine, 1955; A.S., Northeastern U., 1959. hon. doctorate, 1980; postgrad., Harvard U. Advanced Mgmt. Program, 1973. Printer various cos., 1948-53; advt. mgr. Anderson Newspapers Co., Oakmont, Pa., 1954; asst. prodn. mgr. Boston Herald Traveler, 1955-58; cons. Chas. T. Main Co., Boston, 1959; with N.Y. Times Co., N.Y.C., 1960—, sr. v.p., 1972-74, exec. v.p., 1974-79, pres., 1979-93, COO, 1979-93, also bd. dirs. Bd. dirs. nat. council Northeastern U. Served with USMC, 1951-52. Named Distinguished Alumni Northeastern U., 1974. Mem. Neus. Adv. Bur. (chmn. 1991), Advt. Coun. (chmn. 1987-88). Office: NY Times Co 229 W 43rd St New York NY 10036-3913

MATTSON, WILLIAM ROYCE, JR., health care consulting company executive; b. Decatur, Ill., Nov. 24, 1946; s. William Royce Sr. and Mary Carolyn (Olsen) M.; m. Carol Sue Eichel, June 8, 1968; children: Todd Kennedy, Nicole Maureen. BS in Acctg., Bradley U., 1968; MBA in Mktg., Loyola U., Chgo., 1972. Mgr. fin. analysis Abbott U.S.A., Chgo., 1970-74; bus. devel. mgr. Abbott Internat., Chgo., 1974-76; dir. mktg. Abbott Philippines, Manila, 1976-77; gen. mgr. Abbott Iran, Teheran, 1977-79; dir. internat. div. Abbott Labs., Chgo., 1979-82, group dir. hosp. products, 1982-83; dir. mktg. Monsanto, St. Louis, 1983-85; area v.p. G.D. Searle, Chgo., 1985-86; pres. Mattson Jack Group, St. Louis, 1986—; chief exec. officer Medstrategy, Inc., St. Louis, 1986—. Author: Thrombolytic Therapy to the Year 2000, 1986; producer film The Misconception, 1981 (5 film festival awards). With USAF, 1968-69. Mem. Licensing Execs. Soc., Fgn. Rels. Coun. St. Louis, Midwest Pharm. Advt. Coun., Biomed. Mktg. Soc. Republican. Lutheran. Office: Mattson Jack Group 9 The Pines Ct Ste A Saint Louis MO 63141

MATTSSON, AKE, psychiatrist, physician; b. Stockholm, May 30, 1929; came to U.S. 1956, naturalized, 1964; s. Erik H. and Thyra (Bergtsson) M.;

m. Margareta Fürst, Jan. 5, 1953; children: Erik, Peter, Nicholas. B.M. Karolinska Inst., Stockholm, 1950, M.D., 1955. Intern Vanderbilt U. Med. Sch., Nashville, 1955-56; resident in pediatrics and child psychiatry Karolinska Hosp., Stockholm, 1958-60; fellow in child devel. Case Western Res. U. Med. Sch., 1957-58, resident in psychiatry and child psychiatry, 1960-64, asst. prof. psychiatry, 1964-70; prof. psychiatry and pediatrics U. Va. Med. Sch., 1970-77, U. Pitts Med. Sch., 1977-78; prof. psychiatry and pediatrics, dir. div. child and adolescent psychiatry N.Y. U. Med. Sch., 1978-85, rsch. prof. psychiatry, 1985—; prof. psychiatry U. Va. Med. Sch., 1985-91; prof. psychiatry and pediatrics, dir. div. child and adolescent psychiatry Med. Sch., East Carolina U., Greenville, N.C., 1991—. Contbr. numerous articles to med. jours. Served with Swedish Navy, 1948-59. Fulbright-Hays grantee, 1975. Mem. Am. Psychiat. Assn., Am. Psychoanalytical Assn., Am. Psychosomatic Soc., N.Y. Psychiat. Soc., Am. Soc. Adolescent Psychiatry, Am. Acad. Child Adolescent Psychiatry, N.Y. Acad. Scis. Office: East Carolina U Med Sch Dept Psychiatry Greenville NC 27858

MATULA, RICHARD A(LLAN), academic administrator; b. Chgo., Aug. 22, 1939; s. Ludwig A. and Leone O. (Dufeck) M.; m. Brenda C. Mather, Sept. 5, 1959; children: Scott, Kristopher, Daniel, Tiffiny. BS, Purdue U., 1961, MS, 1962, PhD, 1964. Instr. Purdue U., 1963-64; asst. prof. mech. engring. U. Calif., Santa Barbara, 1964-66, U. Mich., 1966-68; assoc. prof. mech. engring. Drexel U., Phila., 1968-70; prof. Drexel U., 1970-76, chmn. thermal and fluid sci. advanced study group, 1969-72; chmn. Drexel U. (Environ. Studies Inst.), 1972-73, chmn. dept. mech. engring. and mechanics, 1973-76; dean Coll. Engring.; prof. mech. engring. La. State U., Baton Rouge, after 1976; pres. Inst. Paper Chemistry, Appleton, Wis., 1986-89, Inst. Paper Sci. and Tech., Atlanta 1989—. Contbr. articles to profl. jours. Treas., bd. dirs. Wexford Leas Swim and Racquet Club, Inc., 1968-73; v.p. Wexford Leas Civic Assn., 1969-71. Mem. Air Pollution Control Assn., Am. Soc. Engring. Edn., ASME, AAAS, Combustion Inst., Soc. Automotive Engrs., Sigma Xi, Pi Kappa Phi, Pi Tau Sigma, Sigma Pi Sigma, Tau Beta Pi. Roman Catholic. Home: 3143 St Ives Country Club Pky Duluth GA 30136-2001 Office: Inst Paper Sci and Tech 500 10th St NW Atlanta GA 30318-5714

MATURI, RAYMOND ROCKNE, healthcare information services company executive; b. Duluth, Minn., Aug. 16, 1938; s. Alfred J. and Gwynn (Eklund) M.; m. Carolyn D. Zobitz, Mar. 16, 1962; children: Paul R., Sara Ann. BBA, U. Notre Dame, 1960. Systems engr., sales rep. IBM, Mpls., 1962-67; account mgr., sales rep., sales mgr. EDS, Dallas, 1967-78; sales mgr. MCSI, Dallas, 1978-80; sr. v.p. software div. Systematics, Inc., Little Rock, 1980-83, pres., 1983-88, sr. exec. v.p. mktg. and sales, 1988-90; pres. Cycare Systems, Inc., Phoenix, 1990—. Office: Cycare Systems Inc 7001 N Scottsdale Rd Ste 1000 Scottsdale AZ 85253-3664

MATUSKA, JOHN E., hospital administrator; b. Elizabeth, N.J., May 22, 1945; married. B, Seton Hall U., 1968; M, NYU, 1977. Dir. fin. svcs. Perth Amboy (N.J.) Gen. Hosp., 1971-77; v.p. fin., treas. St. Peter's Med. Ctr., New Brunswick, N.J., 1977-83, sr. v.p., treas., 1983-86, exec. v.p., 1986-89, pres., 1989—. Home: 833 Clawson Ave Neshanic Station NJ 08853-3313 Office: St Peter's Med Ctr PO Box 591 New Brunswick NJ 08903-0591

MATUSOW, ALLEN JOSEPH, history educator, academic administrator; b. Phila., May 18, 1937; m. Rosalynn Revis; children: Eric, Adam, Cathy, Joseph. BA, Ursinus Coll., 1958; MA, Harvard U., 1959, PhD, 1963. Asst. prof. history Rice U., Houston, 1963-66, assoc. prof., 1966-70, prof., 1970-83, dean humanities, 1981-95, William Gaines Twyman prof., 1983—. Author: Farm Policies and Politics in the Truman Years, 1967, The Unraveling of America: A History of Liberalism in the 1960s, 1984; co-editor: The Truman Administration: A Documentary History, 1966, Twentieth Century America: Recent Interpretations, 1969. Mem. Tex. Commn. on Standards for the Teaching Profession, 1985-88. NEH grantee; fellow Lyndon Baines Johnson Library, Austin, 1974; recipient Minnie Stevens Piper Found. award, San Antonio, 1980. Mem. Am. Hist. Assn., So. Hist. Assn., Orgn. Am. Historians., ACLU. Office: Rice U PO Box 1892 Houston TX 77251-1892

MATUSZAK, ALICE JEAN BOYER, pharmacy educator; b. Newark, Ohio, June 22, 1935; d. James Emery and Elizabeth Hawthorne (Irvine) Boyer; m. Charles Alan Matuszak, Aug. 27, 1955; children: Matthew, James. BS summa cum laude, Ohio State U., 1958, MS, 1959; postgrad., U. Wis., 1959-60; PhD, U. Kans., 1963. Registered pharmacist, Ohio, Calif. Apprentice pharmacist Arensberg Pharmacy, Newark, 1953-58; rsch. asst. Ohio State U., Columbus, 1958, lab. assist., 1958-59; rsch. asst. U. Wis., Madison, 1959-60, U. Kans., Lawrence, 1960-63; asst. prof. U. of the Pacific, Stockton, Calif., 1963-67, assoc. prof., 1971-78, prof., 1978—; vis. prof. Kobe-Gakuin U., Japan, 1992. Contbr. articles to profl. jours. Recipient Disting. Alumna award Ohio State U. Coll. Pharmacy, 1994; NIH grantee, 1965-66. Mem. Am. Assn. Colls. of Pharmacy (chmn. chemistry sect. 1979-80, bd. dirs. 1993-95), Am. Pharm. Assn. (chmn. basic scis. 1990), Am. Inst. History of Pharmacy (exec. coun. 1984-88, 90-92, 92-95, chmn. contributed papers 1990-92, pres.-elect 1995—, Cert. of Commendation 1990), Am. Chem. Soc., Internat. Fedn. Pharmacy, Acad. Pharm. Rsch. Sci. (pres. 1993-94), Coun. Sci. Soc. Pres., U.S. Adopted Names Coun. U.S Pharmacopeial Convention, Sigma Xi, Rho Chi, Phi Kappa Phi, Kappa Epsilon (Unicorn award), Lambda Kappa Sigma, Delta Zeta. Democrat. Episcopalian. Avocation: collecting historical pharmacy artifacts. Home: 1130 W Mariposa Ave Stockton CA 95204-3021 Office: U of the Pacific Sch of Pharmacy Stockton CA 95211

MATUSZKO, ANTHONY JOSEPH, research chemist, administrator; b. Hadley, Mass., Jan. 31, 1926; s. Joseph Anthony and Katherine (Narog) M.; m. Anita Colley, Oct. 26, 1956; children—Martha, Mary, Stephen, Richard. BA, Amherst Coll., 1946; MS in Chemistry, U. Mass., 1951; PhD in Chemistry, McGill U., 1953. Demonstrator in chemistry McGill U., Montreal, Que., Can., 1950-52; from instr. to assoc. prof. chemistry Lafayette Coll., Easton, Pa., 1952-58; head fundamental process div. Naval Propellant Lab., Indian Head, Md., 1958-62; program mgr. in chemistry Air Force Office Sci. Research, Washington, 1962-89; cons., Annandale, Va., 1989—. Contbr. articles to tech. jours. Patentee in field. Pres. Forest Heights PTA, Md., 1967. Served with U.S. Army, 1946-48. Named Hon. Fellow in Chemistry, U. Wis.-Madison, 1967-68; recipient Superior Performance award USAF, Outstanding Career Svc. award U.S. Govt. Fellow AAAS, Am. Inst. Chemists (life); mem. Am. Chem. Soc., Cosmos Club, Sigma Xi. Home: 4210 Elizabeth Ln Annandale VA 22003-3654

MATYJASZEWSKI, KRZYSZTOF, chemistry educator; b. Konstantynow, Poland, Apr. 8, 1950; came to U.S., 1985; s. Henryk and Antonina (Styss) M.; m. Malgorzata Kowalska, July 15, 1972; children: Antoni, Maria. BS, MS, Tech. U., Moscow, 1972; PhD, Polish Acad. Scis., Lodz, 1976; DSc, Lodz Poly., 1985. Postdoctoral fellow U. Fla., 1977-78; rsch. assoc. Polish Acad. Scis., CNRS, France, 1984-85; asst. prof. chemistry Carnegie Mellon U., Pitts., 1985-89, assoc. prof., 1989-93, prof., 1993—, interim head dept. chemistry, 1994—; invited prof. U. Paris, 1985; vis. prof. U. Freiburg, 1988, U. Paris, 1990, U. Bayreuth, 1991, U. Strasbourg, 1992; cons. Down Corning, Midland, Mich. 1988-89, Arco, Phila., 1990-92, Gen. Electric, Schenectady, 1992—, Amoco, Naperville, Ill., 1994—. Mem. editorial bd. Macromolecules, Macromolecular Synthesis, Jour. Polymer Sci., Jour. Macromolecular Sci.-Pure and Applied chemistry, Jour. Inorganic and Organometallic Polymers, Macromolecular Reports. Recipient award Polish Acad. Sci., 1981, Presdl. Young Investigator award NSF, 1989. Mem. Am. Chem. Soc. (Carl S. Marvel award 1994). Achievements include research in synthesis of well defined macromolecules via living and controlled polymerizations; organometallic polymers. Home: 9 Queens Ct Pittsburgh PA 15238 Office: Carnegie Mellon U 4400 5th Ave Pittsburgh PA 15213

MATZ, ROBERT, physician, educator; b. N.Y.C., Aug. 5, 1931; s. Milton and Celia (Wachovsky) M.; m. Lita Selma Freed, Dec. 24, 1955 (dec. July 1982); children: Jessica, Jonathan, Daniel; m. Bette Lynn Becker, Aug. 4, 1983. BA cum laude, NYU, 1952, MD, 1956. Diplomate Am. Bd. Internal Medicine. Intern Bronx (N.Y.) Mcpl. Hosp. Ctr., 1956-57, resident, 1957-60; assoc. dir. medicine Morrisania Hosp., Bronx, 1964-71; dir. medicine North Cen. Bronx Hosp., 1977-91, pres. med. bd., 1987-89, med. dir., 1989-91; med. dir. quality assurance and risk mgmt. Mt. Sinai Med. Ctr., N.Y.C., 1991—; attending physician St. Sinai Med. Ctr., N.Y.C., 1991—; prof.

medicine Mt. Sinai Sch. Medicine, N.Y.C., 1991—; asst. prof. Albert Einstein Coll. Medicine, Bronx, 1967-71, assoc. prof., 1971-79, prof., 1979-91; cons. N.Y.C. Health and Hosp. Corp., 1983-91; mem. health adv. com. to pres. Borough of Bronx, 1987-91. Dept. editor Cardiovascular Revs. and Reports, 1985—; contbr. articles to med. jours., chpts. to books. Mem. physicians action network Amnesty Internat., 1979—. Capt. M.C., U.S. Army, 1960-62, Korea. Fellow ACP; mem. AMA, N.Y. Heart Assn., N.Y. Diabetes Assn. (v.p. 1977-83), Soc. Urban Physicians, Am. Diabetes Assn. (pres. elect chpt. 1987-89, pres. N.Y. downstate affiliate 1989-91), Harvey Soc., Hastings Hist. Soc., Phi Beta Kappa, Beta Lambda Sigma. Democrat. Jewish. Avocations: collecting antique postcards, coins, philately, travel. Home: 32 Buena Vista Dr Hastings Hdsn NY 10706-1104 Office: Mt Sinai Hosp 19 E 98th St New York NY 10029-6501

MATZEK, RICHARD ALLAN, library director; b. Milw., Nov. 18, 1937; s. Robert Edward and Alice Elizabeth (Mudroch) M.; m. Ann Lynne Erickson, Aug. 24, 1963; 1 child, John Kensel. BA, Marquette Univ., 1959; MALS, U. Wis., 1960. Asst. libr. Marquette U., Milw., 1962-63; asst. libr. dir. Sacred Heart Univ., Bridgeport, Conn., 1963-66, libr. dir., 1966-77; libr. dir. Nazareth Coll., Rochester, N.Y., 1977—. Editor (book rev. sect.) Religious Book Rev., 1968-80, (publ. series) Libr. Adminstrn. and Mgmt. Assn., 1988-92; contbr. articles to profl. jours. Bd. trustees St. Bernard's Inst., Rochester, 1989—. Fellow Rotary Internat., 1974; recipient Cert. Spl. Thanks Libr. Adminstrn. and Mgmt. Assn., 1992. Mem. ALA, N.Y. Libr. Assn. (councilor-at-large, Spirit of Librarianship award 1994), Rochester Regional Libr. Coun. (chair, coun. 2000). Avocations: golf, tennis, bridge, travel. Office: Nazareth Coll of Rochester 4245 East Ave Rochester NY 14618-3790

MATZICK, KENNETH JOHN, hospital administrator; b. Chgo., May 31, 1943; married. B, U. Iowa, 1965, MHA, 1967. Adminstrv. resident VA Med. Ctr., Iowa City, 1966; adminstrv. resident Morristown (N.J.) Meml. Hosp., 1967-68, asst. to exec. v.p., 1968-69; asst. dir. William Beaumont Hosp., Royal Oak, Mich., 1969-76; dir. William Beaumont Hosp., Troy, Mich., 1976-83; v.p., hosp. dir. William Beaumont Hosp., Royal Oak, 1983—. Home: 1811 Campus Ct Rochester MI 48309-2159 Office: William Beaumont Hosp 3601 W 13 Mile Rd Royal Oak MI 48073-6769

MATZKE, FRANK J., architect, consultant; b. Akron, Ohio, Jan. 28, 1922; s. Frank G. and Erna (Weibel) M.; m. Shirley Elizabeth Hall, Nov. 27, 1952 (div. Dec. 1966); children: Kim Elizabeth, Karla Jo. Student, State Tchrs. Coll. at Buffalo, 1940-41; B.Arch., Rensselaer Poly. Inst., 1951. Registered architect, N.Y., Md. Field rep., project architect W. Parker Dodge Assos., Rensselaer, N.Y., 1951-54; sr. architect div. architecture N.Y. State Dept. Pub. Works, Albany, 1954-58; assoc. architect State U. N.Y., Albany, 1958-62; dep. mgr. planning State U. Constrn. Fund, Albany, 1962-68; dep. gen. mgr. State U. Constrn. Fund, 1968-72; assoc. commr. for project mgmt. Pub. Bldgs. Service, GSA, Washington, 1972-75; acting asst. commr. for constrn. mgmt. Pub. Bldgs. Service, GSA, 1974-75; exec. dir. Ill. Capital Devel. Bd., 1975-76; v.p. for tech. and programs Nat. Inst. Bldg. Scis., Washington, 1978-83; mem. Bldg. Research Adv. Bd., Washington, 1976-79; chmn. Mgmt. Resource Council, 1974-75; cons. to pub. agys., colls. and univs. on methods to expedite design and constrn. of phys. facilities. Contbr. articles to profl. jours. Chmn. Johnsburg Planning Bd., 1962-65; nat. ski patrolman, 1953-73, past patrol leader O.C. Ski Club Ski Patrol; bd. dirs. Bldg Rsch. Inst., 1973-75, Town Ctr. Coop., Inc., 1980-82. 1st lt. inf., AUS, 1942-46, PTO. Decorated Bronze Star. Fellow AIA (pres. Ea. N.Y.- chpt 1959-60, dir. 1960-63, mem. nat. commn. on architecture for education 1966-72, chmn. nat. com. on architects in govt. 1975, medal for excellence 1951), N.Y. State Assn. Architects (dir. 1966-69); mem. VFW, Wilderness Soc., Cousteau Soc., Sierra Club, Smithsonian Assocs., Natural Resources Def. Coun., Am. Rivers, Nature Conservancy, Environ. Def. Fund, Mil. Order of Caraboa, Nat. Order of Battlefield Commissions, 31st Infantry "Dixie" Divsn. Soc., Am. Legion, North Fla. Cruising Club, Sigma Xi (ret. assoc.). Tau Beta Pi, Sigma Phi Epsilon. Address: 24 Andalusia Ct Saint Augustine FL 32086-7647

MATZKE, GARY ROGER, pharmacologist, educator, researcher; b. Sturgeon Bay, Wis., July 13, 1950; s. Erwin Walter and Alice (Logerquist) M.; m. Cindy Claire Boxwell, Apr. 11, 1981; children: Megan, Jonathan, Jason. BS in Pharmacy, U. Wis., 1973; PharmD, U. Minn., 1977. Asst. prof. Coll. Pharmacy & Allied Health Wayne State U., Detroit, 1977-80; asst. prof. U. Minn., Mpls., 1980-84, assoc. prof., 1984-87, prof., 1987-89; prof., vice chmn. U. N.C., Chapel Hill, 1989-91; prof., dir. clin. scientist program Sch. of Pharmacy U. Pitts., 1991—; co-dir. The Drug Evaluation Unit, Mpls., 1981-89. Editor Pharmacotherapy: A Pathophysiologic Approach and Internat. Jour. Antimicrobial Agts.; contbr. over 125 articles to profl. jours. Fellow Am. Coll. Clin. Pharmacy, Am. Coll. Clin. Pharmacology; mem. Am. Soc. for Clin. Pharmacology and Therapeutics, Am. Soc. Hosp. Pharmacists, Am. Soc. Nephrology, Am. Soc. Microbiology. Avocations: golf, running. Office: U Pitts Sch Pharmacy 1019 Salk Hall Pittsburgh PA 15261-1910

MATZNER, RICHARD ALFRED, physicist, educator; b. Ft. Worth, Tex., Jan. 2, 1942; s. Alfred John and Theresa (Wangler) M.; m. Sara Pitt, June 1, 1967; children: Christopher, Deborah. BS in Physics, U. Notre Dame, 1963; PhD in Physics, U. Md., 1967. Prof. of physics U. Tex., Austin, 1980—, dir. ctr. for relativity, 1987—; mem. editorial bd. Computers in Physics, Am. Inst. Physics, N.Y.C., 1988—. Co-author (with Futterman and F. Handler) Scattering from Black Holes, 1988, (with L. Shepley) Classical Mechanics, 1991; editor (with L. Shepley) Spacetime and Geometry, 1982; editor Tex. Symposium on 3 Dimensional Numerical Relativity. Recipient Univ. medal Helsinki (Finland) Univ., 1982, Univ. Silver medal Univ. Nat. Autonoma de Mexico, 1990. Mem. Am. Physical Soc., Internat. Soc. of Gravitation and Gen. Relativity (sci. nominating com.). Office: U Tex Physics Dept R L Moore Hall Rm 9 224 Austin TX 78712

MAU, DWAYNE HOLGER, minister; b. Chgo., June 17, 1942; s. John Arthur and Leona An (Plummer) M.; m. Janice Barter, June 20, 1971; children: Joy Lyn, David John. AA, Concordia Coll., Milw., 1962; BA, Concordia Sr. Coll., Ft. Wayne, Ind., 1964; MDiv, Concordia Sem. Coll., St. Louis, 1968; M in Christian Edn., Presbyn. Sch. Christian Edn., 1969; LLD (hon.), Concordia Coll., Bronxville, N.Y., 1991. Ordained to ministry Luth. Ch.-Mo. Synod, 1969. Asst. pastor Good Shepherd Luth. Ch., Plainview, N.Y., 1969-74; pastor St. John Luth. Ch., Flushing, N.Y., 1974-80; staff exec. mission and edn., Atlantic Dist. The Luth. Ch.-Mo. Synod, 1980—; adminstr. Luth. Sch. of Flushing, 1975-80; chmn. Task Force-Urban Ministry, St. Louis, 1987—; bd. dirs. Wartburg Luth. Svcs.; v.p. Conf. of Edn. Exec., 1985-88. Contbr. articles to profl. jours. Mem. Plainview Against Drug Abuse, 1970-73; bd. dirs. adminstrv. com. Queens (N.Y.) Citizen Orgn., 1977-81, pres., 1979-81. Mem. Luth. Edn. Assn., Luth. Schs. Assn. (bd. dirs. 1978—, Educator of Yr. 1988), N.Am. Mission Enablers. Home: 47-42 157th St Flushing NY 11355 Office: The Luth Ch Mo Synod Atlanta Dist 171 White Plains Rd Bronxville NY 10708-1998

MAUBERT, JACQUES CLAUDE, headmaster; b. Provins, France, May 19, 1932; s. Jean Pierre and Simone Jeanne (Bocqueho) M.; m. Micheline Josephine Lathuille, June 16, 1956; children: Eric, Sandrine. MA, Dakar U., Senegal, 1969; CAPES, U. Bordeaux (France), 1971. Tchr. French Ministry Edn., Morocco, 1952-62; tchr. French Ministry Edn., Senegal, 1962-73, councellor, 1973-75; councellor French Ministry Edn., Togo, 1975-77; headmaster French Ministry Edn., LeMans, France, 1977-79; headmaster Lycee Francais of San Francisco French Ministry Edn., 1979-85; headmaster French Ministry Edn., Sannois, France, 1985-86; headmaster Lyceum Kennedy French Ministry Edn., N.Y.C., 1986—; mem. Comm. Reform for Teaching French in Africa, Dakar, 1973-78; pedagogic councellor U. Benin, Togo, 1975-77. Author: French Literature for 11th Grade, 1975. Pres. Union des Francais de l' Etranger, San Francisco, 1983-85. Decorated officer The Acad. Palms (France). Roman Catholic. Avocations: swimming, tennis, classical music, jazz, opera. Home: Apt 28R 245 E 54th St New York NY 10022-4707 Office: Lyceum Kennedy 20 W 44th St New York NY 10036-6694

MAUCH, JEANNINE ANN, elementary education educator; b. Scribner, Nebr., Apr. 17, 1944; d. Oscar Herman Frederick and Viola Fredricka (Backhus) M. BS in Luth. Teaching, Concordia Coll., 1966, MEd, 1988.

Cert. tchr., Nebr. Tchr. 1st, 2d, 3d and 4th grades St. Paul Luth. Ch., Perham, Minn., 1966-68; tchr. 3d and 4th grades Wheat Ridge (Colo.) Luth. Ch., 1968-70; tchr., prin. St. Mark Luth. Ch., Yonkers, N.Y., 1970-86; tchr. 3d, 4th and 5th grades Zion Luth. Ch., Plainview, Nebr., 1987—. Recipient 25-Yr. Svc. plaque Zion Luth. Ch., Plainview, 1992, others. Mem. Luth. Edn. Assn. Avocations: travel, craft shows, punch embroidery. Home: PO Box 218 Plainview NE 68769-0218

MAUCH, ROBERT CARL, gas industry executive; b. Cleve., Dec. 7, 1939; s. Otto Herman and Clara (Lapple) M.; m. Rita Marie Szucs, Aug. 25, 1964 (div. Jan. 1980); children: David Otto, Martin Leslie, Karolyn Leigh; m. Drusilla Ann Tesch, Feb. 18, 1989. AMP, Harvard U., 1983; MS, U. Calif., Berkeley, 1965; BSChemE. Cleve. State U., 1962. V.p., gen. mgr., LP gas divsn. Amerigas Inc., Valley Forge, Pa., 1978-83; v.p. UGI Corp., Valley Forge, 1978-87, sr. v.p., 1987-90; dir. Ansutech, Inc., Valley Forge, 1981-82, Matheson Gas Products, Inc., Valley Forge, 1981-82; pres., dir. AP Propane Inc., Valley Forge, 1983-90, Amerigas Propane, Valley Forge, 1983—; pres., CEO, dir. AmeriGas Inc., Valley Forge, 1991—, Petrolane, Inc., Valley Forge, 1993—, Amerigas, Inc. subs. UGI Corp., Valley Forge, 1990—, AmeriGas Propane Inc. (gen. ptnr. AmeriGas Ptnrs. L.P.). Bd. govs. Pa. Economy League, Phila., 1985-91; mem. World Affairs Coun., Phila., 1980-95. Mem. Nat. Propane Gas Assn. (pres. 1978-95), Waynesborough C. of C., Propane Vehicle Coun. (chmn. 1994—). Lutheran. Avocations: tennis, reading, skiing, weight training. Office: Amerigas Inc PO Box 965 Valley Forge PA 19482

MAUCK, HENRY PAGE, JR., medical and pediatrics educator; b. Richmond, Va., Feb. 3, 1926; s. Henry Page and Harriet Hutcheson (Morrison) M.; m. Janet Garrett Horsley, May 14, 1955; children—Henry Page III, John Waller. B.A., U. Va., 1950, M.D., 1952. Diplomate: Am. Bd. Internal Medicine. Intern Henry Ford Hosp., Detroit, 1952-53; resident Med. Coll. Va., Richmond, 1953-56; asst. prof. medicine and pediatrics Med. Coll. Va., 1961-66, assoc. prof., 1966-72, prof., 1972—; fellow in cardiology Am. Heart Assn., 1956-57; cons. cardiology Langley Field Air Force Hosp., Hampton, Va., McGuire's VA Hosp., Richmond. Contbr.: chpt. to Autonomic Control of Cardiovascular System, 1972; contbr. articles to sci. jours. Served with U.S. Army, 1944-46. Fellow ACP, Am. Coll. Cardiology (former gov.); mem. Am. Physiol. Soc., So. Soc. Clin. Investigation, Am. Fedn. Clin. Research, So. Soc. Clin. Research. Presbyterian. Home: 113 Oxford Cir W Richmond VA 23221-3224 Office: Med Coll Va PO Box 281 Richmond VA 23202-0281

MAUCK, WILLIAM M., JR., executive recruiter, small business owner; b. Cleve., Mar. 30, 1938; s. William M. and Elizabeth Louise (Stone) M.; m. Paula Jean Mauck, Aug. 15, 1969 (div. Mar. 1983); children: Brian, David; m. Jeanne Lee Mauck, May 21, 1987. BS in Bus., Ind. U., 1961. Sales engr. Inland Container Corp., Louisville, 1964-69; sales mgr. Dixie Container Corp., Knoxville, Tenn., 1969-70, gen. mgr., 1970-75; v.p., ptnr. Heidrick & Struggles, Inc., Houston, 1975-81; pres. Booker & Mauck, Inc., Houston, 1981-85; ptnr. Ward Howell Internat. Inc., Houston, 1985-88; prin. William M. Mauck, Jr., Houston, 1988—; owner Pepe Engring., Inc., Houston, 1990—; mem. adv. bd. Women's Sports Found., N.Y.C., 1985—. Mem. Plaza Club (Houston) (chmn. bd. govs. 1987-88), Sertoma Club (Knoxville 1972-75) (pres. 1974-75). Republican. Methodist. Home: 5203 Norborne Ln Houston TX 77069-1537 Office: 9950 Cypresswood Dr Ste 300 Houston TX 77070-3400

MAUCKER, EARL ROBERT, newspaper editor, newspaper executive; b. St. Louis, Sept. 20, 1947; s. Robert Buffem and Linette (Meloy) M.; m. Betsy Ann Johnson, May 21, 1977; children: Eric Robert, Michael Earl. BA in Mass Communications, So. Ill. U., 1972. Reporter Alton (Ill.) Telegraph, 1969-73; reporter, city editor, news editor, asst. mng. editor Rockford (Ill.) Morning Star, 1973-79; mng. editor Springfield (Mo.) Daily News, 1979-80; mng. editor Ft. Lauderdale (Fla.) Sun-Sentinel, 1990-95, v.p. editorial, 1995—. Sgt. SUAF, 1966-69. Mem. Am. Soc. Newspapers Editors, Fla. Soc. Newspapers Editors, Associated Press Mng. Editors Assn. (bd. dirs. 1989-93). Home: 11160 SW 1st St Coral Springs FL 33071-8175 Office: Sun-Sentinel 200 E Las Olas Blvd Fort Lauderdale FL 33301-2248*

MAUDERLY, JOE LLOYD, pulmonologist; b. Strong City, Kans., Aug. 31, 1943; s. Joseph Park and Violet May (Cox) M.; m. Cheryl Gaines, Jan. 31, 1965; children: Laurie Jean, Jameson Lynn. BS, Kans. State U., 1965, DVM, 1967. Respiratory physiologist Inhalation Toxicology Research Inst., Albuquerque, 1967-89, supr. pathophysiology group, 1976-89, dir., 1989—; rsch. prof. medicine U.N.Mex., Albuquerque, 1988—; clin. prof. pharmacy, 1990—; cons. in field. Assoc. editor Fundamental Applied Toxicology, 1989-94; contbr. articles to profl. jours., chpts. to books. Served to capt. USAF, 1967-69. Mem. Am. Thoracic Soc. (chmn. assembly of environ. and occupational health 1991-93, long-range planning com. 1991-94), sci. adv. com. 1993—, editl. bds., inhalation toxicology and exptl. lung rsch.), Am. Physiol. Soc., Am. Vet. Med. Assn., N.Mex. Vet. Med. Assn., Soc. of Toxicology, Exptl. Aircraft Assn. Republican. Home: 4517 Banff Dr NE Albuquerque NM 87111-2829 Office: Inhalation Toxicology Rsch Inst PO Box 5890 Albuquerque NM 87185

MAUDLIN, ROBERT V., economics and government affairs consultant; b. Washington, June 8, 1927; s. Cecil V. and Eva Jane (Wright) M.; m. Carole M. Jackson, Sept. 3, 1949; children: Lynda C., David V., Tim W.E. Student, MIT, 1945; BS, Am. U., 1951. Ptnr. C.V. & R.V. Maudlin, Washington, 1952-72, owner, 1972—; mng. dir. Bur. Applied Econs., Washington, 1960—; sec. Nat. Assn. Scissors and Shears Mfrs., 1970—; exec. dir. Joint Govt. Liaison Com., 1973-81; mem. Industry Sector Adv. Com. U.S. Dept. Commerce and U.S. Trade Rep., Washington, 1975—. Author econ. and statis. reports. Pres. Forest Hills Citizens Assn., Washington, 1964; chmn. Boy Scouts Am., Washington, 1972. 2nd lt., Corps of Engrs., USN, 1945-47. Republican. Home: 2906 Ellicott Ter NW Washington DC 20008-1023 Office: CV & RV Maudlin 1511 K St NW Washington DC 20005-1401

MAUER, ALVIN MARX, physician, medical educator; b. LeMars, Iowa, Jan. 10, 1928; s. Alvin Milton and Bertha Elizabeth (Marx) M.; m. Theresa Ann McGivern, Dec. 2, 1950; children: Stephen James, Timothy John, Daria Maureen, Elizabeth Claire. B.A., State U. Iowa, 1950, M.D., 1953. Intern Cin. Gen. Hosp., 1953-54; resident in pediatrics Children's Hosp. Cin., 1954-56; fellow in hematology dept. medicine U. Utah, Salt Lake City, 1956-59; dir. div. hematology Children's Hosp. Cin.; prof. dept. hematology, 1959-73; prof. dept. pediatrics U. Cin. Coll. Medicine, 1959-73; prof. pediatrics U. Tenn. Coll. Medicine, Memphis, 1973—; prof. medicine, 1983—; chief med. oncology/hematology; dir. cancer program U. Tenn. Coll. Health Scis.; dir. St. Jude Children's Research Hosp., Memphis, 1973-83; mem. hematology study sect. NIH; mem. clin. cancer investigation rev. com. Nat. Cancer Inst.; mem. com. on maternal and infant nutrition NRC. Author: Pediatric Hematology, 1969; editor: The Biology of Human Leukemia, 1990. Served with U.S. Army, 1946. Mem. Am. Soc. Hematology (pres. 1980-81), Assn. Am. Cancer Insts. (pres. 1980), am. Acad. Pediatrics (com. on nutrition), Am. Assn. Cancer Edn., Am. Soc. Clin. Investigation, Am. Fedn. Clin. Rsch., Assn. Am. Physicians, Am. Pediatric Soc., Cen. Soc. Clin. Investigation, Cen. Soc. Clin. Rsch., Internat. Soc. Hematology (pres. 1988-90, chmn. 1992—), bd. councilors 1992—), Am. Cancer Soc. (pres. Tenn. divsn. 1992-93), Midwest Soc. Pediat. Rsch., N.Y. Acad. Scis., Soc. Pediat. Rsch., Am. Assn. Cancer Rsch., Phi Beta Kappa, Sigma Xi, Alpha Omega Alpha. Democrat. Roman Catholic. Office: U Tenn Memphis Cancer Ctr N327 Van Vleet Bldg 3 N Dunlap St Memphis TN 38103-2802

MAUER, MICHAEL LEONARD, banker; b. Flint, Mich., Mar. 20, 1940; s. Leonard A. and Julia R. (Vamos) Mauer; m. Patricia Ann Grace, June 15, 1963; children: Eric M., Todd M., Ryan M. BA, U. Mich., 1963, MBA, 1964. Trainee Mfrs. Nat. Bank, Detroit, 1964-67; asst. v.p. Nat. Bank Alaska, Anchorage, 1967-69, v.p., 1969-73, sr. v.p., 1973-79; v.p. Seattle-First Nat. Bank, 1979-84, exec. v.p., mgr. northwest nat. div., 1984—. Bd. dirs. YMCA, Seattle, 1989—, Hospice of Seattle, 1989—. Mem. U. Mich Club. Republican. Roman Catholic. Avocations: outdoor activities, skiing, sailing. Office: Seattle First Nat Bank 701 5th Ave Seattle WA 98104-7016

MAUGANS, EDGAR HURLEY, utility company executive; b. Harrisburg, Pa., Jan. 14, 1935; s. Edgar Hurley and Grace Lenore (English) M.; m. Fern Shaw, Sept. 3, 1955 (div. Dec. 1982); children: Edgar Hurley, Todd D.,

Elizabeth, Jennifer; m. Barbara Nickerson Schulte, Dec. 28, 1982. BS, Findlay Coll., 1956; grad. advanced mgmt. program, Harvard U., 1987. With Cleve. Electric Illuminating Co., 1956-86, supt., 1972-73, controller, 1973-79, v.p., 1977-79, v.p. fin., chief fin. officer, 1979-86; sr. v.p. fin., chief fin. officer Centerior Energy Corp., 1986-90, exec. v.p. fin. and adminstrn., CFO, 1990-93, exec. v.p., 1993—. Trustee Great Lakes Theater Festival, 1979-90, Friends of Cleve. Pub. Libr., 1982-88, U. Findlay (Ohio), 1988—; trustee Health Cleve., Nuclear Electric Insurers Ltd., 1990-93. Mem. Am. Statis. Assn., Edison Electric Inst., Fin. Execs. Inst. (chpt. pres. 1991-92). Republican. Lodge: Lakewood-Rocky River Rotary. Home: 12550 Lake Ave Apt 1407 Cleveland OH 44107-1570 Office: Centerior Service Corp 55 Public Sq Rm 550 Cleveland OH 44101

MAUGHAN, DERYCK C., investment banker. Degree earned, King's Coll., Univ. of London, 1969. With Treasury Dept., United Kingdom, from 1970, Salomon Bros. Inc., 1983—; mng. dir. Salomon Bros. Inc, 1985-91, Tokyo, until 1991; chief oper. officer Salomon Bros. Inc, N.Y.C., 1991-92, chmn., chief exec. officer, 1992—. Office: Salomon Bros Inc 7 World Trade Ctr New York NY 10048-1100

MAUGHAN, WILLARD ZINN, dermatologist; b. Riverside, Calif., Apr. 21, 1944; s. Franklin David and Martha Charlotte (Zinn) M.; m. Rona Lee Wilcox, Aug. 20, 1968; children: Julie Anne, Kathryn Anita, Willard Wilcox, Christopher Keith. Student, Johns Hopkins U., Balt., 1962-64; BS, U. Utah, 1968, MD, 1972. Diplomate Am. Bd. Dermatology. Intern Walter Reed Army Med. Ctr., Washington, 1972-73; fellow Mayo Clinic, Rochester, Minn., 1976-79; pvt. practice Ogden, Utah, 1979—. Contbr. articles to profl. jours. Commr. Boy Scouts Am., Weber County, Utah, 1980-84, dist. chmn., 1993-94; pres. Am. Cancer Soc., Weber County, 1985-86. Maj. U.S. Army, 1971-76. Recipient Dist. award of merit Boy Scouts Am., 1985, Silver Beaver award 1994. Fellow ACP, Am. Acad. Dermatology, Royal Soc. Medicine (London); mem. N.Y. Acad. Scis., Kiwanis Club. Republican. Mormon. Avocations: woodcarving, camping. Home: 2486 W 4550 S Roy UT 84067-1944 Office: 3860 Jackson Ave Ogden UT 84403-1956

MAUGHMER, JOHN TOWNSEND, federal judge; b. St. Joseph, Mo., Nov. 26, 1954; s. Norman Earl and Bette Jean (Townsend) M.; m. Jan L. Schroeder, June 30, 1979; children: Drew Townsend, Amy Veronica. BS magna cum laude, U. Mo., 1977, JD with distinction, 1980. Bar: Mo. 1980, U.S. Dist. Ct. (we. dist.) Mo. 1980. Law clk. Hon. Elmo B. Hunter, Kansas City, 1980-82; assoc., ptnr. Lathrop, Koontz & Norquist, Kansas City, 1982-88; U.S. Magistrate judge U.S. Dist. Ct. (we. dist.) Mo., 1988—. Mem. Mo. Bar Assn., Kansas City Met. Bar Assn., Assn. Magistrate Judges. Office: 221 US Courthouse 811 Grand Ave Kansas City MO 64106

MAUKE, OTTO RUSSELL, retired college president; b. Webster, Mass., Jan. 26, 1924; s. Otto G. and Florence (Giroux) M.; m. Leah Louison, June 18, 1950. A.B., Clark U., 1947, A.M., 1948; Ph.D. (Kellogg fellow), U. Tex., 1965. Tchr. history, acad. dean Endicott Jr. Coll., Beverly, Mass., 1948-65; acad. dean Cumberland County Coll., Vineland, N.J., 1966-67; pres. Camden County Coll., Blackwood, N.J., 1967-87, pres. emeritus. Served with U.S. Army, 1943-46, PTO. Home: 2119 E Lakeview Dr Sebastian FL 32958-8519

MAULDEN, JERRY L., utility company executive; b. North Little Rock, Ark., 1936; married. B.S., U. Ark., Little Rock, 1963. Acct. Dyke & Assocs., Inc., 1959-61; sr. auditor Madigan James & Co., C.P.A.'s, 1961-62; asst. controller Dillard Dept. Stores, Inc., 1962-65; asst. to treas. Ark. Power & Light Co. a company of Middle South Utilities, Inc., Little Rock, 1965-68, asst. controller, 1968-71; controller, asst. sec., asst. treas. and later spl. asst. to pres. Ark. Power & Light Co., Little Rock, 1971-73, sec.-treas., 1973-75, v.p. fin. svcs., sec., treas., 1975-79, pres., chief exec. officer, 1979-89, chmn. bd., chief exec. officer, 1989—, also dir.; former sr. v.p. Entergy Corp., Little Rock; now pres., chief operating officer Entergy Corp., New Orleans; sr. v.p. Mid. South Utilities, 1990; chmn., chief exec. officer Miss. Power & Light, also dir. Office: Ark Power & Light PO Box 551 Little Rock AR 72203-0551 Office: Entergy Corp 225 Baronne St New Orleans LA 70112*

MAULDIN, ROBERT RAY, banker; b. China Grove, N.C., Jan. 15, 1935; s. Raymond Ray and Hazel Inez (Luther) M.; m. Patricia Crain Jarman, Aug. 29, 1959; children—John Clayton, Patricia Crain, Elizabeth Jarman, Anne Luther, Katherine Purnell. Student, N.C. State U., 1953-54; B.S., U. N.C., 1959. Trainee, asst. trust officer Nations Bank, Charlotte, 1959-62; cashier Bank of York, S.C., 1962-65; v.p. Colonial Am. Nat. Bank, Roanoke, Va., 1965-69; exec. v.p. Peoples Bank & Trust Co., Rocky Mount, N.C., 1969-81; pres. Peoples Bank & Trust Co., 1981-85, chmn., chief exec. officer, 1985-90; chmn., CEO Centura Banks Inc., 1993—. Pres. Rocky Mount Untied Cmty. Svcs., 1974-75; mem. Rocky Mount City Schs. Bd., 1979-83; trustee N.C. Wesleyan Coll., 1993—; bd. dirs. N.C. Citizens Assn., 1993—, N.C. Pub. TV Found., 1993—; trustee Va. Episcopal Sch., 1993—; mem. Commn. for Competive N.C., 1994—; bd. dirs. Global Tranpark Found, 1994—; mem. adv. bd. Kenan Flaglar Bus. Sch. U. N.C., 1994—. Mem. N.C. Young Bankers (pres. 1974-75), am. Inst. Banking, Robert Morris Assocs., N.C. Bankers Assn. (dir. 1984-92), Rocky Mount C. of C. (dir. 1975-80, pres. 1978-79), Kiwanis (pres. Rocky Mount 1976-77), Chi Phi. Presbyn. Home: 109 Essex Ct Rocky Mount NC 27803-1207 Office: Centura Bank 134 N Church St Rocky Mount NC 27804-5401

MAULDIN, WILLIAM H. (BILL MAULDIN), cartoonist; b. Mountain Park, N.Mex., Oct. 29, 1921; s. Sidney Albert and Edith Katrina (Bemis) M.; m. Norma Jean Humphries, Feb. 28, 1942 (div. 1946); children—Bruce Patrick, Timothy; m. Natalie Sarah Evans, June 27, 1947 (dec. Aug. 1971); children—Andrew, David, John, Nathaniel; m. Christine Ruth Lund, July 29, 1972; children: Kaja Lisa, Samuel Lund. Ed. pub. schs. and high schs., N.Mex. and Ariz.; studied art, Chicago Acad. of Fine Arts; M.A. (hon.) Conn. Wesleyan U., 1946; Litt.D. (hon.), Albion Coll., 1970, N.Mex. State U., Las Cruces, 1972; L.H.D. (hon.), Lincoln Coll., 1970, Wash. U., St. Louis, 1984, Coll. of Santa Fe, 1986. Cartoonist St. Louis Post-Dispatch, until 1962, Chgo. Sun-Times, 1962-85. Tech. adviser, actor film Teresa, 1950; actor film The Red Badge of Courage, 1950; author or cartoonist: Star Spangled Banter, 1941, Sicily Sketch Book, 1943, Mud, Mules and Mountains, 1943, This Damn Tree Leaks, 1945, Up Front (Book of the Month selection), 1945, Back Home (Book of the Month selection), 1947, A Sort of a Saga, 1949, Bill Mauldin's Army, 1951, Bill Mauldin in Korea, 1952, What's Got Your Back Up?, 1961, I've Decided I Want My Seat Back, 1965, The Brass Ring, 1971 (Book of Month Club selection), Mud and Guts, 1978; Let's Declare Ourselves Winners and Get the Hell Out, 1985; author: Bradley: A Soldier's Story, 1978; author, illustrator numerous articles Sports Illus., Life, Collier's. Served with U.S. Army, 1940-45, 45th Inf. Div. and Stars and Stripes; campaigns Sicily, Italy, France, Germany. Decorated Purple Heart, Legion of Merit; recipient Pulitzer prize for cartoons 1944, 59, Sigma Delta Chi award for cartoons 1963, 69, 72; Prix Charles Huard de dessin de presse Fondation pour l'Art et la Recherche Paris, 1974, Walter Cronkite award for journalistic excellence Ariz. State U., 1985. Fellow Sigma Delta Chi. Home: 1110 Old Santa Fe Trail Santa Fe NM 87501*

MAULDING, BARRY CLIFFORD, lawyer; b. McMinnville, Oreg., Sept. 3, 1945; s. Clifford L. and Mildred (Fisher) M.; m. Reva J. Zachow, Dec. 27, 1965; children: Phillip B., John C. BA in Psychology, U. Oreg., 1967, JD, 1970. Bar: Oreg. 1970. Sec., gen. counsel Alaska Continental Devel. Corp., Portland, also Seattle, 1970-75; gen. counsel Alaska Airlines, Seattle, 1975-84; dir. legal services, corp. sec. Univar Corp., Seattle, 1984-91; gen. counsel, corp. sec. Momentum Distbn., Bellevue, Wash., 1991—; dir. Alaska N.W. Properties, Inc., Seattle. Mem. editorial bd. Oreg. Law Rev. Trustee Good Neighbor Found., Seattle. Republican. Office: Univar Corp 1600 Norton Bldg 801 2nd Ave Seattle WA 98104-1509

MAULIN, JACK DOOLIN, construction company executive; b. Buffalo, Mo., Nov. 7, 1934; s. George Washington and Gussie Dean (Doolin)M.; m. Jane Lois Eason, Sept. 1, 1957 (div. 1979); children: Debra, John, Robert; m. Stpehanie Anne Liesk, Oct. 25, 1980. BS, U. Mo., 1957. Asst. project engr. Morrison-Knudsen, Calif., Mo. and Wyo., 1959-63; project engr./project mgr. multiple constrn. projects Morrison-Knudsen, Wyo., N.D. and Calif., 1963-66; ea. regional engr. Morrison-Knudsen, N.Y., 1966-71; project mgr. multiple constrn projects Morrison-Knudsen, N.D. and Calif., 1970-73; v.p. corp. mktg. and planning Morrison-Knudsen, Boise, Idaho, 1973-83, sr. v.p.

corp. mktg. and planning, 1983-87, sr. v.p. constrn., 1987—. 1st lt. U.S. Army, 1957-59. Republican. Home: 1727 Trout Rd Eagle ID 83616-5660 Office: Morrison-Knudsen M-K Plaza Boise ID 83729

MAULL, GEORGE MARRINER, music director, conductor; b. Phila., Oct. 14, 1947; s. Frederick Dunlap and Helen Norbury (Jordan) M.; m. Marcia Eileen Korn, Aug. 13, 1984. MusB, U. Louisville, 1970, MusM, 1972; postgrad., Julliard Sch. Music, 1976-78. Condr. Louisville Ballet Co., 1971-75; asst. condr. Opera Orch. N.Y., N.Y.C., 1976-78, N.J. Symphony Orch., Newark, 1979-80; music dir., condr. Bloomingdale Chamber Orch., N.Y.C., 1980-83, N.J. Youth Symphony, Summit, 1980—, Philharm. Orch. N.J., Warren, 1987—. Conducting debut Carnegie Hall, N.Y.C., 1989; condr. in Eng., Belgium, The Netherlands, Poland, Romania, Hungary, Germany; featured in WNET mini-documentary Art Effects: Young and Noteworthy, 1988. Named Disting. Alumnus, U. Louisville, 1994. Mem. Am. Fedn. Musicians, Am. Symphony Orch. League (conducting fellow 1978, Nat. Cert. Merit 1980), Condr's. Guild. Episcopalian. Home: 79 Stone Run Rd Bedminster NJ 07921-1711 Office: Philharm Orch of NJ PO Box 4064 Warren NJ 07059

MAULSBY, ALLEN FARISH, lawyer; b. Balt., May 21, 1922. A.B., Williams Coll., Williamstown, Mass., 1944; LL.B., U. Va., 1946. Bar: Md. 1947, N.Y. 1950. Law clk. to judge U.S. Circuit Ct. Appeals 4th Circuit, 1946-47; assoc. firm Cravath Swaine & Moore, N.Y.C., 1947-57; partner Cravath Swaine & Moore, 1958—. Vestryman St. James' Episcopal Ch., N.Y.C., 1962-68, 80-85, warden, 1986-87; trustee Greer-Woodycrest Child Care, 1961-82; bd. dirs. Episc. Ch. Found., 1973-86. Mem. Am. Bar Found., N.Y. Bar Found., Am. Coll. Trial Lawyers, Am. Bar Assn., N.Y. State Bar Assn., Fed. Bar Assn., Assn. Bar City N.Y., N.Y. County Lawyers Assn. Office: Cravath Swaine & Moore Worldwide Pla 825 8th Ave New York NY 10019-7475

MAUNDER, ADDISON BRUCE, agronomic research company executive; b. Holdrege, Nebr., May 13, 1934; s. Addison Haynes and Marie Sophia (Luebs) M.; m. Katherina Marlene Blum, Sept. 8, 1978; children: Lynda Diane, Christopher Allen. B.Sc., U. Nebr., 1956; M.Sc., Purdue U., 1958, Ph.D., 1960; DSc (hon., U. Nebr., 1991. With DeKalb AgResearch, Inc., Lubbock, Tex., 1960—, sorghum breeder, 1960-61, dir. sorghum research, 1961-76, v.p. sorghum research, 1976-78; v.p. DeKalb-Pfizer Genetics, DeKalb, Ill., 1982-89; v.p. agronomic research DeKalb Plant Genetics, DeKalb, Ill., 1989-91; sr. v.p. DeKalb Genetics Corp., DeKalb, Ill., 1991—; bd. dirs. Diversity Mag., Washington; adj. prof. Tex. Tech U., 1992—. Contbr. 10 chpts. to books and more than 72 articles to profl. jours. Mem. deans adv. com. Tex. Tech U., Lubbock, 1983-86; chmn. external rev. INTSORMIL of AID, Lincoln, Nebr., 1980—; bd. dirs. Tex., Tech U. Rsch. Found., 1986-92; mem. Nat. Plant Genetic Resources Bd., 1991-92, Nat. Plant Variety Protection Bd., 1991—. Recipient Gerald Thomas award Tex. Tech U., 1974, Prodn. award Grain Sorgnum Producers Assn., 1985, Genetics and Plant Breeding award for Industry, 1987, Indsl. Agronomy award, 1988. Fellow AAAS, Am. Soc. Agronomy (bd. dirs. 1991-92), Crop Sci. Soc. Am. (bd. dirs. 1991-92, pres. 1995—); mem. Sigma Xi, Alpha Zeta. Republican. Achievements include development of plant products (130 hybrids) emphasizing improved drought and insect resistance as well as nutritional quality. Office: DeKalb RR 2 Box 56 Lubbock TX 79415-9717

MAUPIN, ARMISTEAD JONES, lawyer; b. Raleigh, N.C., Nov. 10, 1914; s. Alfred McGhee and Mary Armistead (Jones) M.; m. Diana Jane Barton, May 16, 1942 (dec.); children: Armistead Jones, Anthony Westwood, Jane Stuart; m. Cheryl Leigh Erhard, July 31, 1982. A.B., U. N.C., 1936; J.D., George Washington U., 1940. Bar: N.C. 1939. Ptnr. Maupin, Taylor & Ellis., Raleigh. Pres. Occoneechee coun. Boy Scouts Am., 1962-64; pres. Carolina Charter Corp., 1976-80, 93—; former chancellor Episcopal Diocese of N.C.; former sr. warden Christ Ch. Parish; vice chmn. Am. Battle Monuments Commn., 1981-90. Comdr. USNR, WWII, PTO. Decorated chevalier French Legion of Honor. Fellow Am. Bar Found.; mem. ABA (ho. of dels. 1960-72), N.C. State Bar (coun. 1955-60, pres. 1959-60), Soc. of Cincinnati (v.p. gen. 1968-70, pres. gen. 1971-74, pres. N.C. soc. 1964-67), Carolina Country Club, Circle Club, Triangle Fox Hounds Club. Republican. Episcopalian. Home: 2005 Banbury Rd Raleigh NC 27608-1121 Office: Highwoods Tower One 3200 Beech Leaf Ct Raleigh NC 27604-1064

MAUPIN, ARMISTEAD JONES, JR., writer; b. Washington, May 13, 1944; s. Armistead Jones and Diana Jane (Barton) M. BA, U. N.C., 1966. Reporter News and Courier, Charleston, S.C., 1970-71, AP, San Francisco, 1971-72; account exec. Lowry Russom and Leeper, Pub. Rels., San Francisco, 1973; columnist Pacfic Sun mag., San Francisco, 1974; publicist San Francisco Opera, 1975; serialist San Francisco Chronicle, 1976-77, 81, 83; commentator Sta. KRON-TV, San Francisco, 1979; serialist San Francisco Examiner, 1986. Author: (novels) Tales of the City, 1978, More Tales of the City, 1980, Further Tales of the City, 1982, Babycakes, 1984, Significant Others, 1987, Sure of You, 1989, (omnibus) 28 Barbary Lane, 1990, (omnibus) Back to Barbary Lane, 1991, Maybe the Moon, 1992; librettist musical Heart's Desire, 1990; exec. prodr. (TV program) Armistead Maupin's Tales of the City, 1993; contbr. articles to N.Y. Times, L.A. Times, others. Lt. (j.g.) USN, 1967-70, Vietnam. Recipient Freedom Leadership award Freedoms Found., Valley Forge, Pa., 1972, Comms. award Met. Elections Com. L.A., 1989, Exceptional Achievement award ALA, 1990, Best Dramatic Serial award Royal TV Soc., 1994, Peabody award 1994, Outstanding Miniseries award, Gay and Lesbian Alliance Against Defamation, 1994, Best Miniseries award Nat. Bd. of Rev., 1994. Office: Harper Collins 10 E 53rd St New York NY 10022

MAUPIN, ELIZABETH THATCHER, theater critic; b. Cleve., Oct. 21, 1951; d. Addison and Margaret (Thatcher) M. BA in English, Wellesley (Mass.) Coll., 1973; M in Journalism, U. Calif., Berkeley, 1976. Editorial asst. Houghton-Mifflin Co., Boston, 1973-74; intern Washington bureau McClatchy Newspapers, 1975; reporter, movie critic Times-Standard, Eureka, Calif., 1976-78; theater and movie critic Chronicle-Telegram, Elyria, Ohio, 1978-79; movie and restaurant critic Ledger-Star, Norfolk, Va., 1979-82; feature writer Va.-Pilot and Ledger-Star, Norfolk, 1982-83; sr. theater critic Orlando (Fla.) Sentinel, 1983—. Fellow Nat. Critics Inst.; mem. Am. Theatre Critics Assn. (exec. com. 1993—). Office: Orlando Sentinel 633 N Orange Ave Orlando FL 32801

MAURA, MARIANO A., library and information science educator; b. S.P. Macoris, Dominican Republic, Sept. 9, 1949; s. Mariano and Edita (Sardó) M.; m. Luccy Pérez, Dec. 14, 1973; children: Jordi, Gabriel. BA in Edn., U. P.R., 1971, MLS, 1972, cert. computer applications programmer, 1982, cert. computer operator, 1982; MSc of Info. Sci., U. Pitts., 1985, PhD in Libr. and Info. Sci., 1993. Reference libr. Natural Sci. Libr. Rio Piedras campus U. P.R., 1973-74; circulation libr. Natural Sci. Libr., 1974-83, coord. online searching svcs., Main Libr., 1983-85, coord. libr. sys. automation project, 1986; coord. integrated automation project for libr. sys. U. P.R., 1987-88; from asst. prof. to assoc. prof. Grad. Sch. Libr./Info. Sci. U. P.R., San Juan, 1986-91, acting dir. Grad. Sch. Libr./Info. Sci., 1991-92, assoc. prof. Grad. Sch. Libr./Info. Sci., 1992-94, dir. Grad. Sch. Libr./Info. Sci., 1994—; lectr. in field The Expert Sys., J.M. Lázaro Libr., 1986, CompuCampus IV, Caribe Hilton Hotel, 1987, Humacao U. Coll., 1987, Mayaguez campus U. P.R., 1991, Ponce Univ. Coll., 1992, Pontifical Cath. U. Libr., Ponce, P.R., 1994, others; cons. in field. Contbr. articles to profl. jours. Mem. Assn. for Libr. and Info. Sci. Edn., Nat. Assn. to Promote Libr. Svcs. to Spanish Speaking, P.R. Libr. Assn. (Lauro a la Investigación Aplicada a Servicios de Información 1994), P.R. Assn. Univ. Profs. (chmn. cultural activities com. 1976-77), Nat. Fedn. Librs. (sec. 1977-83), Grad. Sch. Librarianship Alumni Assn. Home: PO Box 22008 San Juan PR 00931-2008 Office: Grad School of Lib & Info Sci PO Box 21906 UPR Sta Rio Piedras PR 00931

MAURER, ADAH ELECTRA, psychologist; b. Chgo., Oct. 26, 1905; d. Frank Ulysses and Mary Louise (Meng) Bass; m. Harry Andrew Maurer, June 14, 1937 (div. 1947); children: Douglas, Helen. BS, U. Wis., 1927; MA, U. Chgo., 1957; PhD, Union Inst., 1976. Lic. sch. psychologist, Calif. Tchr. pub. schs. Chgo., 1927-61; psychologist pub. schs. Calif., 1962-75; pvt. practice marriage, family and child counselor Berkeley, Calif., 1965-75; organizer, chief exec. officer End Violence Against the Next Generation, Berkeley, 1972—; lectr. U. Calif. Davis, 1965-68; bd. dirs. Nat. Ctr. for Study Cpl. Punishment & Alternatives in Schs. Temple U., Phila.; liaison People Opposed to Paddling Students, Houston, 1981—; v.p. Nat. Coalition to Abolish Cpl. Punishment in Schs., Columbus, Ohio, 1987—; cons. Calif. State Dept. Social Svcs., 1988. Author: Paddles Away, 1981, 1001 Alternatives, 1984, (with others) The Bible and the Rod, 1983, Think Twice, 1985; editor: (newsletter) The Last? Resort, 1972—; contbr. numerous articles to profl. jours. Sponsor End Phys. Punishment of Children Worldwide. Recipient Disting. Humanitarian award Calif. State Psychol. Assn., Presdl. award Nat. Assn. Sch. Psychologists, 1988, Donna Stone award Nat. Commn. for Prevention of Child Abuse, 1988, commendation Giraffe Project, 1988, award in recognition of pioneering efforts in banning corporal punishment in nation's schs. Nat. Coalition to Abolish Corporal Punishment in Schs., Achievement award Child, Youth and Family Svcs. Am. Psychol. Assn., 1994. Mem. Am. Psychol. Assn. (Lifetime Career Achievement award 1995), Hemlock Soc. Avocations: hiking, gardening. Home and Office: 977 Keeler Ave Berkeley CA 94708-1498

MAURER, BARBARA GLEE, educational administrator; b. Coopeville, Wash., May 21, 1945; d. James Clifton and Roberta Margaret (Torrison) Lawrence; m. Paul Gerry Maurer, June 3, 1984; children: Karl Norsen, Curtis Norsen. BS in Edn., U. Idaho, 1967; MA in Edn. Adminstrn., U. Wash., 1982. Cert. tchr. K-12, Wash. Tchr. Seattle Pub. Schs., 1968-70, 76-78, 85-86, program mgr., 1978-83, curriculum specialist, 1983-85; curriculum specialist Highline Sch. Dist., Seattle, 1986-87, curriculum coord., 1988—; curriculum cons. Sch. Dists., Seattle, 1980—; bd. dirs., sec. Wash. Coun. Honors and Advanced Placement, 1990—; cons. MacMillan McGraw Hill, N.Y.C., 1992-93; editor newsletter Gifted Unltd., 1985-88; cert. trainer Lead Devel. Project; liaison administr. Project Leadership; adj. prof. Seattle Pacific U. Contbr. articles to profl. jours. Precinct com. chmn. Rep. Party, 1980-85. Recipient Outstanding Project award Nat. Diffusion Network, 1981, Project Leadership award Wash. Assn. Sch. Administrs., 1992, Leadership in Profl. Devel. award Wash. State ASCD, 1992. Mem. ASCD, Nat. Assn. Social Studies, Wash. Assn. Edn. Talented and Gifted (award 1990), Wash. Coalition for Gifted and Talented (sec. 1991-92), Rotary (bd. dirs. 1993—), Nat. Coun. Tchrs. English, Nat. Assn. for Gifted. Avocations: sailing, skiing, gardening, cooking. Office: Highline Sch Dist 15675 Ambaum Blvd SW Seattle WA 98166

MAURER, BEVERLY BENNETT, school administrator; b. Bklyn., Aug. 23, 1940; d. David and Minnie (Dolen) Bennett; m. Harold M. Maurer, June 12, 1960; children: Ann Maurer Rosenbach, Wendy Maurer Rausch. BA, Bklyn. Coll., 1960, postgrad., 1961; postgrad., U. Richmond, 1980-90, Va. Commonwealth U., 1980-90. Cert. tchr., N.Y., Va. Math. tchr. Col. David Marcus Jr. High Sch., Bklyn., 1960-61, Pomona (N.Y.) Jr. High Sch., 1967-68; math. tchr. Hebrew day sch. Rudlin Torah Acad., Richmond, Va., 1969-80, asst. prin., 1980-86, prin., 1986-89; dir. edn. Jewish Community Day Sch. Ctrl. Va., Richmond, 1990-93; pvt. practice, ednl. cons.; prin. East Coast Antiques. Developed talented and gifted program, pre-admission program for children at Med. Coll. Va., 1982. Bd. dirs. Jewish Comty. Ctr., Richmond, 1980s; bd. dirs. Aux. to Med. Coll. Va., Richmond, 1980s, Aux. to U. Nebr. Med. Ctr., 1994—, Uta Hallee, 1994—. Recipient Master Tchr. award Rudlin Torah Acad., 1983. Mem. Jewish Community Day Sch. Network, Anti-Defamation League, Jewish Women's Club. Republican. Avocations: collecting contemporary and art nouveau glass, world travel.

MAURER, DAVID L., lawyer; b. Evansville, Ind., Oct. 31, 1945; s. John G. Jr. and Mildred M. (Lintzenich) M.; m. Diane M. Kaput, Aug. 11, 1973; children: Eric W., Kathryn A. BA magna cum laude, U. Detroit, 1967, Cert. in Teaching, 1971; JD, Wayne State U., 1975. Bar: Mich., U.S. Dist. Ct. (ea. dist.) Mich., U.S. Ct. Appeals (6th cir.) Cin. Law clk. Mich. Ct. Appeals, Detroit, 1976, Supreme Ct. Mich., Lansing, 1977-78; asst. U.S. atty. civil div. U.S. Dept. Justice, Detroit, 1978-81; assoc. to ptnr. Butzel, Long, Gust, Klein & Van Zile, Detroit, 1981-85; ptnr. Pepper, Hamilton & Scheetz, Detroit, 1986—; guest lectr. Practicing Law Inst., 1988—, Nat. Bus. Inst., 1989—, U. Mich. Law Sch., U. Detroit Law Sch., 1990, Hazardous Waste Super Conf., 1986-87. Contbr. articles and chpt. to profl. jours. Mem. Energy & Environ. Policy Com., 1988—, chairperson, 1989-90; mem. Great Lakes Water Resources Commn., 1986. Mem. State Bar Mich. (environ. couns. 1986-91, sec., treas., chairperson-elect, chairperson 1991-93). Office: Pepper Hamilton & Scheetz 100 Renaissance Ctr Ste 3600 Detroit MI 48243-1157

MAURER, EVAN MACLYN, art museum director; b. Newark, Aug. 19, 1944; s. Myron P. and Belle (Cloth) M.; m. Naomi E. Maurer; children: Noah, Aaron. BA, Amherst Coll., 1966, MA, U. Minn., 1968; PhD, U. Pa., 1974. Asst. dir. Mpls. Inst. Arts, 1971-73; curator Art Inst. Chgo., 1973-81; dir. Mus. Art, prof. U. Mich., Ann Arbor, from 1981; now dir., chief exec. officer Minneapolis Inst. of Arts. Author: The Native American Heritage, 1977; co-author: Rising of the New Moon: A Century of Tabwa Art, 1986, Max Ernst: Beyond Surrealism, 1986, The Intelligence of Forms: An Artist Collect African Art, 1992, Visions of the People: A Pictorial History of Plains Indian Life, 1992. Office: Mpls Inst Arts 2400 3rd Ave S Minneapolis MN 55404-3506

MAURER, GERNANT ELMER, metallurgical executive, consultant; b. Sayre, Pa., May 5, 1949; s. Elmer L. and Joyce F. (Fox) M.; m. Suzanne Walker Berry, Aug. 19, 1972. BES, Johns Hopkins U., 1971; PhD, Rensselaer Poly. Inst., 1976. Materials engr. Spl. Metals Corp., New Hartford, N.Y., 1976-80, mgr. R & D, 1981-84, dir. R & D, 1985-87, v.p. tech., 1987—; founding v.p. Specialty Metals Processing Consortium, pres. 1992-93; chmn. Internat. Symposium on Superalloys, 1984-88. Co-editor: Superalloys, 1980, 2d edit., 1988; contbr. tech. papers to profl. jours.; inventor various superalloys. Dir. devel. com. Maxon William Proctor Inst., Utica, N.Y., 1988-89. Fellow Am. Soc. for Metals (trustee 1992-95); mem. The Metall. Soc., Am. Vacuum Soc. (bd. dirs. metall. div. 1988), Utica Area C. of C. (bd. dirs. 1986-89), Wash. State U. (adv. materials engring. adv. bd. 1993—), Yahnundasis Club. Avocations: golf, fly fishing, art, photography, metal working. Home: 27 Sherman Cir Utica NY 13501-5808 Office: Spl Metals Corp Middle Settlement Rd New Hartford NY 13413

MAURER, GILBERT CHARLES, media company executive; b. N.Y.C., May 24, 1928; s. Charles and Mildred (Petite) M.; m. Ann D'Espinosa. A.B., St. Lawrence U., 1950; M.B.A., Harvard U., 1952. With Cowles Communications, Inc., N.Y.C., 1952-71, Look Mag., 1952-62; pub. Venture mag., 1963-67; pres. Family Circle mag., 1967-69, v.p., dir. corporate planning, exec. com., 1969-71; also dir.; sr. v.p. dir. F.A.S. Internat., Inc., 1971-73; v.p mag. div. Hearst Corp., 1973-74, exec. v.p., 1974-76, pres. mag. div., 1976-90, also dir.; exec. v.p. The Hearst Corp., 1985—; chief operating officer, 1990—. Mem. N.Y. adv. bd. Salvation Army, 1979—; trustee Whitney Mus. Am. Art, 1983—, pres., 1994—; mem. vis. com. Medill Sch. Journalism Northwestern U., 1985-94, chmn., 1989-94; bd. dirs. Boys Club Am., 1986—; mem. bd. mgrs. N.Y. Bot. Garden, 1989. Mem. Mag. Pubs. Assn. (bd. dirs., chmn. 1979-81). Clubs: Harvard (N.Y.C.), Metropolitan (N.Y.C.). Office: The Hearst Corp 959 8th Ave New York NY 10019-3737

MAURER, HAROLD MAURICE, pediatrician; b. N.Y.C., Sept. 10, 1936; s. Isador and Sarah (Rothkowitz) M.; m. Beverly Bennett, June 12, 1960; children: Ann Louise, Wendy Sue. A.B., N.Y. U., 1957; M.D., SUNY, Bklyn., 1961. Diplomate Am. Bd. Pediatrics, Am. Bd. Pediatric Hematology-Oncology. Intern pediatrics Kings County Hosp., N.Y.C., 1961-62; resident in pediatrics Babies Hosp., Columbia-Presbyn. Med. Center, N.Y.C., 1962-64; fellow in pediatric hematology/oncology Columbia-Presbyn. Med. Center, 1966-68; asst. prof. pediatrics Med. Coll. Va., Richmond, 1968-71; assoc. prof. Med. Coll. Va., 1971-75, prof., 1975—; chmn. dept. pediatrics, 1976-93; dean U. Neb. Coll. Medicine, Omaha, 1993—; chmn. Intergroup Rhabdomyosarcoma Study; exec. com. Pediatric Oncology Group; mem. cancer clin. investigation rev. com. NIH. Editor: Pediatrics, 1983, Rhabdomyosarcoma and Related Tumors in Children and Adolescence, 1991; mem. editorial bd. Am. Jour. Hematology, Med. and Pediat. Oncology, 1984—; contbr. articles to profl. jours. Mem. Youth Health Task Force, City of Richmond., Gov.'s Adv. Com. on Handicapped.; mem. nat. com. on childhood cancer Am. Cancer Soc., bd. dirs. Va. div. Served to lt. comdr. USPHS, 1964-66. NIH grantee, 1974—. Mem. Am. Acad. Pediatrics (com. oncology-hematology), Am. Soc. Hematology, Soc. Pediatric Rsch., Am. Pediatric Soc., Va. Pediatric Soc. (exec. com.), Assn. Med. Sch. Pediatric Dept. Chmn., Internat. Soc. Pediatric Oncology, Am.

Soc. Clin. Oncology, Va. Hematology Soc., Am. Assn. Cancer Rsch., Am. Cancer Soc., Am. Soc. Pediatric Hematology (v.p. 1990-91, pres. 1991-93), Sigma Xi, Alpha Omega Alpha. Republican. Jewish. Home: 9822 Ascot Dr Omaha NE 68114-3848 Office: U Neb Coll Medicine 600 S 42nd St Omaha NE 68108-6545

MAURER, JEFFREY STUART, finance executive; b. N.Y.C., July 9, 1947; s. Herbert and Phoebe Maurer; m. Wendy S. Nemerov. BA, Alfred U., 1969; MBA, NYU, 1975; JD, St. John's U., 1976. With U.S. Trust Co. N.Y., 1970—, pres., 1990; COO U.S. Trust Co., N.Y.C., 1994—. Trustee Alfred (N.Y.) U., 1984; mem. adv. bd. Salvation Army Greater N.Y., 1987; bd. dirs., treas. Children's Health Fund, N.Y.C., 1988; bd. dirs. Hebrew Home Aged, Riverdale, N.Y., 1992; mem. Citizens Budget Commn. and Bankers Roundtable. Mem. ABA, N.Y. State Bar Assn., Nassau County Bar Assn., N.Y. State Bankers Assn. (chmn. trust div. 1987-88), Am. Bankers Assn. (chmn. trust div. 1992-93), Glen Head Country Club. Jewish. Avocations: skiing, golf. Office: US Trust Co NY 114 W 47th St New York NY 10036-1510

MAURER, JOHAN FREDRIK, religious denomination administrator; b. Oslo, Mar. 23, 1953; came to U.S., 1957; s. Harald and Erika Elfreide (Schmitz) M.; m. Judith Marshall Van Wyck, Aug. 9, 1980; children: Luke Van Wyck, Eliot Heyerdahl. BA in Russian, Carleton U., Ottawa, Ont. Can., 1976; postgrad., Earlham Coll., 1983—. Asst. dir., dir. Beacon Hill Friends House, Boston, 1977-80; field sec. Friends World Com. for Consultation, Wilmington, Ohio, Richmond, Ind., 1983-93; coord. Right Sharing of World Resources, Wilmington and Richmond, 1986-93; gen. sec. Friends United Meeting, Richmond, 1993—; mem. Europe com. Nat. Coun. Chs., N.Y.C., 1985—; recorded min. Ind. Yearly Meeting of Friends, Muncie, 1989—; mem. U.S. Ch. Leaders, Chgo., 1993—; mem. bd. advisors Earlham Coll. Sch. Religion, Richmond, 1993—; keynote speaker numerous denominational events, 1982—. Editor Quaker Life, 1994—; contbr. numerous articles to religious publs. Mem., mem. steering com. Social Action Ministries Greater Boston, 1978-80; mem. Boston 350 Com., 1979-80; bilingual vol. Jewish Family and Children's Svcs., Boston, 1978-80. Mem. Quaker U.S.-USSR Com., Soc. for Internat. Devel., Bible Assn. Friends, World Hunger Edn. Svc. (assoc.), Richmond Ministerial Assn., Evangs. for Social Action. Avocations: correspondence, computers, reading, walking. Office: Friends United Meeting 101 Quaker Hill Dr Richmond IN 47374

MAURER, LAWRENCE MICHAEL, acting school administrator, educator; b. Bklyn., Oct. 2, 1935; s. Charles and Ethel (Ryan) M.; married Mar. 20, 1970 (div. 1971); 1 child, Lalaine; m. Carol Schneider, July 27, 1971. B of Vocat. Edn., San Diego State U., 1976; MS in Sch. Adminstrn., Nat. U., 1981. Cert. sch. adminstr., tchr., c.c. educator, Calif. Commd. ensign USN, 1953; advanced through grades to chief, 1969, ret., 1972; tchr. San Diego County Office Edn., 1972—, acting vice prin., 1989—; bd. dirs. Multi-cultural Affairs Com., San Diego, 1991—, Self Esteem Devel. C.C., San Diego, 1990—, Vocat. Edn. Comm. San Diego County, 1986—; cons. Vocat. Edn. in Ct. Schs., San Diego, 1986—. Organizer Dem. party. Named Excellent Tchr. of Yr. Corp. for Excellence in Pub. Edn., 1992; vocat. grantee, 1988. Mem. ASCD (bd. dirs.), Nat. Vocat. Educators, Calif. Reading Assn., Calif. Ct. Sch. Adminstrs. Avocation: civil rights activist. Home: 98-80 Magnolia Ave Santee CA 92071 Office: San Diego County Office Edn 6401 Linda Vista Rd San Diego CA 92111

MAURER, LUCILLE DARVIN, state treasurer; b. N.Y.C., Nov. 21, 1922; d. Joseph Jay and Evelyn (Levine) Darvin; m. Ely Maurer, Apr. 29, 1945; children: Stephen Bennett, Russell Alexander, Edward Nestor. Student, U. N.C., Greensboro, 1938-40; BA, U. N.C., Chapel Hill, 1942; MA, Yale U., 1945; DH (hon.), Hood Coll., 1984; HLD (hon.), U. Coll., U. Md., 1990. Economist U.S. Tariff Commn., 1942-43; econ. and market research for pvt. firms, 1957-60; cons. Nat. Center for Ednl. Stats., 1969-70; mem. Md. House of Dels., 1969-87, mem. ways and means coms., 1971-87, chmn. joint com. on fed. relations 1983-87; state treas. State of Md., 1987—; mem. intergovtl. adv. coun. U.S. Dept. Edn., 1980-82. Del., Md. Constl. Conv., 1967-68; mem. Montgomery County Bd. Edn., 1960-68; trustee Montgomery Community Coll., 1960-68; vice chmn. nat. planning com., advanced leadership program of seminars on edn. and ednl. policy for state legislators Edn. Commn. of States, 1979-81; mem. exec. com. of edn. com. Nat. Conf. of State Legislatures, 1975-84, chmn., 1978-79, chmn. com. on taxes, trade and econ. devel., 1985-86; mem. Servicemems. Opportunity Colls., 1978-82; mem. nat. adv. bd. Inst. for Ednl. Leadership, 1979-81; mem. Nat. Com. on Postsecondary Accreditation, 1974-1979; bd. dirs. Montgomery United Way, 1971-76, 84-94; mem. Commn. Higher Edn. of Middle States Assn., 1982-85; mem. Gov.'s Employment and Tng. Coun., 1983-91. Recipient Legislator of Yr. award Md. Assn. for Retarded Children, 1972, John Dewey award Montgomery County Fedn. Tchrs., 1972, Hornbook award Montgomery County Edn. Assn., 1972, Legislator of Yr. award Md. Assn. Counties, 1984, Willis award for outstanding service Md. Assn. Bds. Edn., 1984, Louis B. Brandeis Justice in Govt. award Am. Jewish Congress, 1988, Judge Sarah T. Hughes award for disting. pub. svc. Goucher Coll., 1989, Disting. Pub. Svc. award Md. C. of C., 1989, Nat. Identification Program award Am. Coun. Edn., 1993; named Energy Warrior of Yr., Md. Energy Adminstrn., 1990; inductee Md. Women's Hall of Fame, 1990. Mem. LWV (past dir. Montgomery County, past dir. Md.), AAUW (Internat. Women's Yr. award Silver Spring 1975), NOW (Legis. Excellence award 1981), Bus. and Profl. Women's Club (Woman of Yr. 1984), Nat. Assn. State Treas. (v.p. 1989-90, chmn. legis. com. 1989-91, sr. v.p. 1991-92, pres. 1992-93, Jesse M. Unruh award 1994), Nat. Assn. State Auditors, Comptrs. and Treas. (exec. com. 1988-91, fed./state cash mgmt. reform task force 1988-92), Women Execs. State Govt. (bd. dirs. 1988-92), Women's Equity Action League, Women's Polit. Caucus, Montgomery County Hist. Soc., Order Women Legislators, Delta Kappa Gamma. Jewish. Office: State Treas Office Goldstein Treasury Bldg Annapolis MD 21401

MAURER, MARC MORGAN, federation administrator, lawyer; b. Des Moines, June 3, 1951; s. Fred V. and June Jeraldine (Davis) M.; m. Patricia Ann Schaaf; children: David Patrick, Dianna Marie. Student, Orientation and Adjustment Ctr. of Iowa Commn. Blind; grad. cum laude, U. Notre Dame, 1974; JD, U. Ind., 1977. Bar: Ind. 1977, Ohio 1978, Iowa 1978, Md. 1979, U.S. Supreme Ct. 1981. Former auto mechanic; dir. a legal assistance project Advocates for Basic Legal Equality, Toledo, Ohio, 1977-78; lawyer rates and routes div. Office of Gen. Counsel CAB, Washington, 1978-81; pvt. practice Balt., 1981—; v.p. Nat. Fedn. of the Blind Ind., 1971, elected pres., 1973, 75, Nat. Fedn. of the Blind Md., 1984-86; pres. Nat. Fedn. of the Blind, 1986—. Bd. dirs. various tenants and community assns. Avocations: oenology, books, barbecue. Office: Nat Fedn Blind 1800 Johnson St Baltimore MD 21230-4940

MAURER, PAUL HERBERT, biochemist, educator; b. N.Y.C., June 29, 1923; s. Joseph and Clara (Vogel) M.; m. Miriam Esther Merdinger, June 27, 1948; children—Susan Gail, David Mark, Philip Mitchell. B.S., City Coll. N.Y., 1944; Ph.D., Columbia, 1950. Research biochemist Gen. Foods Corp., Hoboken, N.J., 1944-46; instr. City Coll. N.Y., 1946-51; research asso. Coll. Phys. and Surg., Columbia, 1950-51; asst. research prof. Sch. Medicine, U. Pitts., 1951-54, asso. prof. immunochemistry, 1954-60; asso. prof. microbiology Seton Hall Coll. Medicine, 1960-62; prof. microbiology N.J. Coll. Medicine, 1962-66; prof., chmn. dept. biochemistry Jefferson Med. Coll., Phila., 1966-93, prof. pathology, biochemistry and molecular biology emeritus, 1993—; mem. allergy and infectious diseases tng. grant com. NIH, 1961-66; mem. commn. on albumin Protein Fedn.; mem. NRC com. on plasma; chmn. Transplantation Biology and Immunology Com. NIAID, 1986—. Asso. editor: Immunochemistry, 1964, Science, 1966; Contbr. profl. jours. Served with USNR 1946-48. Recipient Research Career award Nat. Inst. Allergy and Infectious Diseases, 1962-66, Chemistry medal City Coll. N.Y., 1944. Mem. Am. Chem. Soc., N.Y. Acad. Scis., Biochem. Soc. (London), Harvey Soc., Am. Assn. Immunologists, Am. Soc. Biol. Chemistry, AAAS, Societe de Chimie Biologique (France), Soc. Exptl. Biology and Medicine, Sigma Xi. Home: 8470 Limekiln Pike Apt B517 Wyncote PA 19095-2704 Office: Jefferson Med Coll Dept Pathology 1020 Locust St Philadelphia PA 19107-6731

MAURER, RICHARD MICHAEL, investment company executive; b. Bethlehem, Pa., June 4, 1948; s. Richard Thomas and Anna Theresa (Bold) M.; m. Karen Coe, June 13, 1970; children: Christopher Coe, Mark Emer-

son. Student, Pa. State U., 1966-68; BS, Point Park Coll., 1971; MBA, U. Pitts., 1982. CPA Pa. Staff acct. Price Waterhouse, Pitts., 1972-74, tac acct., 1974, sr. tax acct., 1974-77, tax mgr., 1977-78; dir. taxes The Hillman Co., Pitts., 1978-85; pres. Maurer Ross & Co., Inc., Pitts., 1985—; co-mng. ptnr. Wesmar Ptnrs., Pitts., 1985—; bd. dirs. Gateway Additive Co., Inc., Pitt Penn Oil Co., Pitt Penn Distbn. Co., Springdale Specialty Plastics, Inc., New Horizons Baking Co., M & R Distbn. Co., The KoolVent Group, Inc., S2 Golf Inc., Maurer Ross & Co., Inc., Maurer & Ross, Inc. With U.S. Army, 1970-76. Mem. AICPA, Assn. Corp. Growth, Pa. Inst. CPAs, Rotary (past dir., past pres.). Clubs: Oakmont Country, Duquesne, Lake Nona Golf, Rivers, Gateway Ctr. Office: Three Gateway Ctr Pittsburgh PA 15222

MAURER, ROBERT DISTLER, retired industrial physicist; b. St. Louis, July 20, 1924; s. John and Elizabeth J. (Distler) M.; m. Barbara A. Mansfield, June 9, 1951; children: Robert M., James B., Janet L. B.S., U. Ark., 1948, LL.D., 1980; Ph.D., MIT, 1951. Mem. staff MIT, 1951-52; with Corning Glass Works, N.Y., 1952-89; mgr. physics research Corning Glass Works, 1963-78, research fellow, 1978-89. Contbr. articles to profl. jours., chpts. to books. Served with U.S. Army, 1943-46. Recipient Indsl. Physics prize Am. Inst. Physics, 1978, L.M. Ericsson Internat. prize in telecommunications, 1979, Indsl. Rsch. Inst. Achievement award, 1988, Optical Soc. Am./IEEE Leos Tyndall award, 1987, Disting. Alumni award U. Ark., 1994. Fellow IEEE (Moris N. Liebmann award 1978), Am. Ceramic Soc. (George W. Morey award 1976); mem. NAE, Am. Phys. Soc. (New Materials prize 1989), Nat. Inventors Hall of Fame. Patentee in field. Home: 6 Roche Dr Painted Post NY 14870-1225 Office: Corning Inc Sullivan Park Corning NY 14830

MAURICE, DON, personal care industry executive; b. Peoria, Ill., Aug. 29, 1932; s. Imajean (Webster) Crayton; m. Cindalu Jackson, Aug. 31, 1990. Student, Loma Linda U., 1984-86; cert. paralegal studies, Calif. State U., San Bernardino, 1994. Lic. hair stylist, skin therapist. Owner 2 schs. in advanced hair designs, San Diego, 1962-64, D & M Enterprises, Advt. Agy., 1964-78; now cons. D&M Enterprises Advt. Agy.; dist. mgr. AqRo Matic Co. Water Purification Systems, San Diego, 1972-75; profl. sales educator Staypower Industries, San Diego, 1972-76, 3d v.p., 1975-76; regional bus. cons. Estheticians Pharmacology Rsch., Garden Grove, Calif., 1975-81; owner, operator Don Maurice Hair Designs, Hemet, Calif., 1980-83; dir., operator Hair Sytles by Maurice, Loma Linda, Calif., 1984-88; owner, pres. Grooming Dynamics, Redlands, Calif., 1988—; bus. cons. Yogurt Place, Paradise Valley, Ariz., 1978-79, others; regular guest Channel 6/Channel 8, San Diego, 1968-78; cons. infomercial Pre-Paid Legal Svcs., Inc., 1994—. Author: The New Look For Men, 1967, The Art of Men's Hair Styling, 1968 (accepted by Library of Congress), Baldness, To Be or Not To Be, 1989. Promoter Spl. Olympics, Hemet, 1981. Sgt. U.S. Army, 1950-53, Korea. Decorated Purple Heart, 1952; named Leading Businessman in His Profession, Union and Evening Tribune, 1969. Mem. Internat. Platform Assn., Christian Businessmen's Assn. Avocations: writing, sculpting, art, sports, music. Office: Grooming Dynamics PO Box 1279 Loma Linda CA 92354

MAURICIO, LILIA D(UJUA), pathologist; b. Manila, Aug. 14, 1943; d. Fernando and Nieves (de Guzman) Dujua; children—Dino, Ditas. M.D., U. Santo Tomas, 1965. Diplomate Am. Bd. Pathology. Intern, Westmoreland Hosp., Greensburg, Pa., 1966-67; resident Bapt. Hosp., Nashville, 1967-68, pathologist, 1976-79; resident in pathology Vanderbilt U., Nashville, 1968-72, instr. pathology, 1972-73; dir. cytopathology Vanderbilt Hosp., Nashville, 1973-74, asst. prof. pathology, 1974-76, asst. clin. prof., 1976—; chief pathologist, lab. dir. Crockett Gen. Hosp., Lawrenceburg, Tenn., 1979—, Giles County Hosp., Pulaski, Tenn., 1983—; med. examiner Giles County. Fellow Am. Soc. Clin. Pathologists, Coll. Am. Pathologists, Internat. Acad. Pathology; mem. AMA, Tenn. Med. Assn., Tenn. Soc. Pathologists, Lawrence County Med. Soc. Republican. Roman Catholic. Office: PO Box 784 Lawrenceburg TN 38464-0784

MAURO, RICHARD FRANK, lawyer, investment manager; b. Hawthorne, Nev., July 21, 1945; s. Frank Joseph and Dolores D. (Kreimeyer) M.; m. LaVonne M. Madden, Aug. 28, 1965; 1 child, Lindsay Anne. AB, Brown U., 1967; JD summa cum laude, U. Denver, 1970. Bar: Colo. 1970. Assoc. Dawson, Nagel, Sherman & Howard, Denver, 1970-72; assoc. Van Cise, Freeman, Tooley & McClearn, Denver, 1972-73, ptnr., 1973-74; ptnr. Hall & Evans, Denver, 1974-81, Morrison & Forester, Denver, 1981-84; of counsel Parcel, Mauro, Hultin & Spaanstra, P.C., Denver, 1984—, pres., 1988-90, of counsel, 1992—; pres. Sundance Oil Exploration Co., 1985-88; exec. v.p. Castle Group, Inc., 1992—; adj. prof. U. Denver Coll. Law, 1981-84. Symposium editor: Denver Law Jour., 1969-70; editor: Colorado Corporation Manual; contbr. articles to legal jours. Pres. Colo. Open Space Coun., 1974; mem. law alumni coun. U. Denver Coll. Law, 1991. Francis Wayland scholar, 1967; recipient various Am. jurisprudence awards. Mem. ABA, Colo. Bar Assn., Denver Bar Assn., Colo. Assn. Corp. Counsel. (pres. 1974-75), Am. Arbitration Assn. (comml. arbitrator), Order St. Ives, Denver Athletic Club (bd. dirs. 1986-89). Home: 2552 E Alameda Ave No 128 Denver CO 80209-3320 Office: 475 17th St Ste 750 Denver CO 80202-4017

MAUSEL, PAUL WARNER, geography educator; b. Mpls., Jan. 2, 1936; s. Paul George and Esther Victoria (Sundstrom) M.; m. Jean Frances Kias, July 2, 1966; children: Paul Brandon, Catherine Suzanne, Justin Thomas. BA in Chemistry and Geography, U. Minn., 1958, MA in Geography, 1961; PhD, U. N.C., 1966. Asst. prof. geography Eastern Ill. U., Charleston, 1965-70, assoc. prof., 1970-71; assoc. prof. geography Ind. State U., Terre Haute, 1971-75, prof., 1975—; dir. Remote Sensing Lab., 1975-89, Geog. Inf. Systems, 1989—; research geographer Lab. Applications of Remote Sensing Purdue U., West Lafayette, Ind., 1972-73; soils geographer cons. U. Mo. at Columbia, summer 1974; lectr. in field; grants, contracts with EPA, NSF, Nat. Park Svc., Dept. of Energy, Stennis Space Ctr/ITD, Oak Ridge Nat. Lab., U.S. Forest Svc, NASA, USDA. Contbr. articles to profl. jours., Chpts. to textbooks. NSF fellow, 1978; recipient research award Ind. State U., 1983. Mem. Assn. Am. Geographers, Am. Soc. Photogrammetry and Remote Sensing. Home: 7400 E Old Maple Ave Terre Haute IN 47803-9627

MAUSKOPF, SEYMOUR HAROLD, history educator; b. Cleve., Nov. 11, 1938; s. Philip and Dora (Trompeter) M.; m. Josephine Mary Album, Aug. 9, 1964; children: Deborah, Philip, Alice. A.B., Cornell U., 1960; Ph.D., Princeton U., 1966. Instr. history Duke U., Durham, N.C., 1964-66, asst. prof., 1966-72, assoc. prof., 1972-80, prof., 1980—, dir. program in sci. tech. and human values, 1979-84. Author: Crystals and Compounds, Molecular Structure and Composition in Nineteenth Century French Science, 1976, (with M.R. McVaugh) The Elusive Science; Origins of Experimental Physical Research, 1915-1940, 1980; editor: The Reception of Unconventional Science by the Scientific Community, 1979, Chemical Sciences in th e Modern World, 1993. NSF postdoctoral fellow, 1971-72; NSF grantee, 1974, 92-93; Am. Philos. Soc. travel grantee, 1979; Nat. Endowment for Humanities summer stipend, 1982; Edelstein internat. fellow in history chem. scis. and tech. Beckman Ctr. U. Pa. and Hebrew Univ., Jerusalem, 1988-89. Mem. History Sci. Soc. (exec. com. treas. 1979-83, coun. 1993-95). Jewish. Office: Duke U PO Box 90719 Bldg Durham NC 27708-0719

MAUTNER, HENRY GEORGE, chemist; b. Prague, Czechoslovakia, Mar. 30, 1925; came to U.S., 1941, naturalized, 1946; s. Frank Thomas and Maria (Neumann) M.; m. Dorothea Johanna Barkemeyer, Nov. 21, 1967; children—Monica Ann, Matthew Erich, Andrea Christina. B.S., U. Calif. at Los Angeles, 1946; M.S., U. So. Calif., 1950; Ph.D., U. Calif., Berkeley, 1955; M.A. (hon.), Yale U., 1967. Teaching asst. U. Calif., 1951-55; rsch. chemist Productol Co., Santa Fe Springs, Calif., 1950; faculty Yale U., New Haven, 1955-70; prof. dept. pharmacology Yale U., 1967-70, head sect. medicinal chemistry, 1962-70; prof. biochemistry and pharmacology Tufts U. Sch. Medicine, 1970-90, prof. emeritus, 1990—, chmn. depts., 1970-85; vis. scholar Dept. Fine Arts, Harvard U., Cambridge, Mass., 1991-92, vis. fellow, 1992—; vis. fellow dept. organic chemistry U. Uppsala, Sweden, 1962; vis. prof. biochemistry Max Planck Inst. Biochemistry, Munich, 1967-68; vis. prof. biochemistry Bio-Ctr., U. Basel, Switzerland, 1985; mem. med. chemistry study sect. NIH, 1964-72, chmn., 1971-72; mem. neurobiology panel NSF, 1977-80; vis. prof. biophys. chemistry U. Bielefeld, Germany, 1987; mem. sci. adv. com. City of Cambridge; sci. chmn. Children's Sch. Sci., Woods Hole, Mass., 1991-94; mem. corp. Marine Biol. Lab., Woods Hole. Editorial bd. Jour. Med. Chemistry, 1967-70, 76-81; contbr. articles to profl.

jours., chpts. to books. Mem. Am. Chem. Soc., Chem. Soc. (London), Am. Assn. Pharmacology, Am. Assn. Cancer Research, Biophys. Soc., Am. Soc. Biol. Chemists. Home: 183 Ward St Newton Center MA 02159

MAUTZ, ROBERT BARBEAU, lawyer, educator; b. Marion, Ohio, Jan. 22, 1915; s. Albert Edward and Bessie (Barbeau) M.; m. Esther Guthery, Feb. 22, 1947 (dec. Sept. 1993). BA, Miami U., Oxford, Ohio, 1937; JD, Yale U., 1940; postgrad., 1949-50; hon. degrees, 1 Miami U. Fla., Miami U., Oxford U., Jacksonville U., Fla. Inst. Tech., U. South Fla., Flagler Coll. Bar: N.Y. 1941. Assoc. Root, Clark, Buckner & Ballantine, N.Y.C., 1940-41; atty. Pan Am. Airways, Brit. W. Africa, 1941-42; exec. officer legal div. Office Mil. Govt., Berlin, 1945-48; dep. legal dir. Hesse, 1948-49; prof. law, asst. dean U. Fla., Gainesville, 1950-58, dean acad. affairs, 1958-63, v.p. acad. affairs, 1963-68; chancellor State Univ. System of Fla., 1968-75; Regent's prof., dir. Inst. Learned Scholars, Gainesville, 1975-80; spl. advisor for higher edn. Fla. Commr. of Edn., 1981-83; mem. Post-Secondary Edn. Planning Commn. of Fla., 1983—. Author legal and other articles. Former commr. Edn. Commn. of States; mem. exec. bd. So. Regional Edn. Bd.; bd. dirs. Am. Coll. Testing Program, Nat. Ctr. for Higher Edn. Mgmt. Systems; adv. coun. Nat. Ctr. for Edn. Stats, Def. Systems Mgmt. Coll.; exec. com. Yale Law Sch. Served to col. USAAF, 1942-45; maj. gen. USAF, ret. Decorated D.S.M.; chevalier Swedish Royal Order North Star; Star of Yugoslavia with gold wreaths; named Man of Yr. by several orgns. Mem. Phi Beta Kappa, Beta Theta Pi, Omicron Delta Kappa, Phi Alpha Delta, Order of Coif. Home: 5027 SW 9th Ln Gainesville FL 32607-3869 Office: U Fla 401 Seagle Bldg Gainesville FL 32611

MAUZ, HENRY HERRWARD, JR., retired naval officer; b. Lynchburg, Va., May 4, 1936; s. Henry Herrward and Rene C. (Ball) M.; m. Margaret Catherine O'Neill, June 6, 1959; children: Sheila, David, Lynn, Daniel. BS, U.S. Naval Acad., 1959; BSEE, U.S. Naval Postgrad. Sch., 1965; MBA, Auburn U., 1970. Commd. ensign USN, 1959, advanced through grades to adm., 1992, various ships and shore duty assignments, 1977-80; strategy and concepts officer Office of Chief Naval Ops. Washington, 1980-82; comdg. officer USS England, San Diego, 1980-82, chief of staff Carrier Group One, 1982-83; ops./readiness officer SHAPE Belgium, 1983-85; comdr. Cruiser/Destroyer Group 12 Mayport, Fla., 1985-86; ops./plans officer to comdr. in chief Pacific Fleet, Pearl Harbor, Hawaii, 1986-88; comdr. Seventh Fleet Yokosuka, Japan, 1988-90; dep. chief Office Naval Op.s, Washington, 1991-92; comdr. in chief U.S. Atlantic Fleet, 1992-94; ret. USN, 1994. Decorated D.S.M. with four gold stars, Def. Superior Svc. medal, Legion of Merit, Bronze Star with combat V device. Mem. U.S. Naval Inst., U.S. Naval War Coll. Found., Naval Hist. Found., Monterey Peninsula Country Club, Army-Navy Country Club. Avocations: golfing, skiiing. Home: PO Box 1465 Pebble Beach CA 93953-1465

MAUZERALL, DAVID CHARLES, biophysics educator, research scientist; b. Sanford, Maine, July 22, 1929; s. David James and Jeannette (Morin) M.; m. Miriam I. Jacob, July 31, 1959; children—Denise, Michele. B.S., St. Michael's Coll., 1951; Ph.D. (NSF fellow), U. Chgo., 1954. Mem. faculty Rockefeller U., N.Y.C., 1954-65, 67-69, 69—; prof. biophysics Rockefeller U.; vis. assoc. prof. U. Calif.-San Diego, 1966, now adj. prof. Guggenheim fellow, 1966. Mem. Am. Soc. Biol. Chemists, Biophys. Soc., Am. Chem. Soc. Home: 36 Belden Ave Dobbs Ferry NY 10522-1102 Office: Rockefeller U 1230 York Ave New York NY 10021-6399

MAUZY, OSCAR HOLCOMBE, lawyer, retired state supreme court justice; b. Houston, Nov. 9, 1926; s. Harry Lincoln and Mildred Eva (Kincaid) M.; m. Anne Rogers; children: Catherine Anne, Charles Fred, James Stephen. BBA, U. Tex., 1950, JD, 1952. Bar: Tex. 1951. Practiced in Dallas, 1952-87; pres. Mullinax, Wells, Mauzy & Baab, Inc. (P.C.), 1970-78; mem. Tex. Senate from 23d Dist., 1967-87, chmn. edn. com., 1971-81, chmn. jurisprudence com., 1981-87, pres. pro tempore, 1973; justice Tex. Supreme Ct., 1987-93; pvt. practice Austin, 1993—; Mem. Tex. Adv. Commn. Intergovtl. Relations, Nat. Conf. State Legislators, Edn. Commn. of the States, Am. Edn. Finance Assn., 1971-87. Vice chmn. judiciary com. Tex. Constl. Conv., 1974; nat. committeeman Young Democrats, 1954. Served with USNR, 1944-46. Home: 5000 Crestway Dr Austin TX 78731-5404

MAVROVIC, IVO, chemical engineer; b. Fiume, Italy, Dec. 5, 1927; came to U.S., 1959; s. Janko and Milica (Gregorina) M.; m. Erna Gallian, oct. 14, 1955; 1 child, Paul. BSChemE, U. Zagreb, Yugoslavia, 1952, MSChemE, 1955. Registered profl. engr, N.Y. Chem. engr. Dorr-Oliver, Milan, Italy, 1956-59, Chemico, N.Y.C., 1960-65; cons. UTI/UTI Constrn. Inc., Hackensack, N.J., 1977—. Patentee in field; contbr. articles to profl. jours. Mem. AICE. Roman Catholic. Office: UTI/UTI Constrn Inc 2 University Pla Hackensack NJ 07601

MAW, SAM H., restaurant chain executive; b. Easley, S.C., 1933. Grad., Wofford Coll., Spartanburg, S.C., 1956. Formerly v.p. for r & d Spartan Food Systems Inc., Spartanburg, S.C.; pres., chief exec. officer Denny's Inc., La Mirada, Calif., 1988—. Address: TW Services Inc 203 E Main St Spartanburg SC 29302 Office: Denny's Inc PO Box 25320 Santa Ana CA 92799-5320

MAWARDI, OSMAN KAMEL, plasma physicist; b. Cairo, Dec. 12, 1917; came to U.S., 1946, naturalized, 1952; s. Kamel Ibrahim and Marie (Wiennig) M.; m. Betty Louise Hosmer, Nov. 23, 1950. B.S., Cairo U., 1940, M.S., 1945; A.M., Harvard U., 1947, Ph.D., 1948. Lectr. physics Cairo U., 1940-45; asst. prof. Mass Inst. Tech., 1951-56, asso. prof., 1956-60; prof. engring., dir. plasma research program Case Inst. Tech., Cleve., 1960-88; dir. Energy Research Office, Case Western Res. U., 1977-82; pres. Collaborative Planners, Inc.; mem. Inst. Advanced Study, 1969-70; also cons. Contbr. articles to profl. jours. Trustee Print Club Cleve., Cleve. Inst. Art. Recipient Biennial award Acoustical Soc. Am., 1952; CECON medal of achievement, 1979. Fellow AAAS, Acoustical Soc. Am., Am. Phys. Soc., IEEE (Edison lectr. 1968-69, Centennial award 1984, Cleve. sect. Engr. of Yr. 1994); mem. N.Y. Acad. Scis., Sigma Xi, Eta Kappa Nu. Home: 15 Mornington Ln Cleveland OH 44106 Office: 2490 Lee Rd Cleveland OH 44118-4125 *I never cease to be amazed that the goals I really believe in invariably materialize.*

MAWBY, RUSSELL GEORGE, foundation executive; b. Grand Rapids, Mich., Feb. 23, 1928; s. Wesley G. and Ruby (Finch) M.; m. Ruth E. Edison, Dec. 16, 1950; children: Douglas, David, Karen. B.S. in Horticulture, Mich. State U., 1949, Ph.D. in Agrl. Econs., 1959, LL.D. (hon.), 1972; M.S. in Agrl. Econs, Purdue U., 1951, D.Agr. (hon.), 1973; L.H.D. (hon.), Luther Coll., Decorah, Iowa, 1972, Alma (Mich.) Coll., 1975, Nazareth Coll., 1976, Madonna Coll., 1983, N.C. Central U., 1986; LL.D. (hon.), N.C. A&T State U., Greensboro, 1974, Tuskegee Inst., 1978, Kalamazoo Coll. 1980; D.P.A. (hon.), Albion Coll., 1976; D.C.L. (hon.), U. Newcastle, Eng. 1977; D.Sc. (hon.), Nat. U. Ireland, 1980; D.Pub. Service (hon.), No. Mich. U., 1981; D.H.L. (hon.), So. Utah State Coll., 1983; HHD (hon.), Grand Valley State U., 1988; ScD (hon.), Calif. State U., 1989; LLD (hon.), Adrian Coll., 1990; LHD (hon.), Olivet Coll., 1991. Extension specialist Mich. State U., East Lansing, 1952-56; asst. dir. coop. extension service Mich. State U., 1956-65; dir. div. agr. W.K. Kellogg Found., Battle Creek, Mich., 1965-66; mem., trustee W.K. Kellogg Found., 1966—; v.p. programs, 1966-70, pres., 1970-82, chmn., chief exec. officer, 1982—; dir. Kellogg Co., 1974—; Detroit br. Fed. Res. Bank Chgo., 1980-85, J.M. Smucker Co., 1983—; fellow Inst. for Children, Youth and Families Mich. State U., 1993; hon. fellow Rewley House U. Oxford, Eng., 1990; mem. chancellor's ct. of benefactors U. Oxford, Eng., 1991. Trustee Arabian Horse Trust, 1978—, chmn. bd. trustees, The Starr Commonwealth Schs., 1987—; chmn. bd. trustees, Found. Ctr., 1988—, chmn. bd., 1989—; bd. dirs. Council on Founds., 1978-84; mem. Joint Council on Food and Agrl. Scis., USDA, 1984-88; mem. Com. on Agrl. Edn. in Secondary Schs., NRC, 1985-88, Gov.'s Task Force on Revitalization of Agr. Through Research and Edn. 1986; mem. rural bus. partnership adv. bd. Mich. Dept. Commerce, 1989—; Mich. Coop. Extension Svc. Study Com., 1989; mem. pres.'s adv. coun. Clemson U., 1987—; bd. trustees Mich. Nonprofit Forum, 1990—, chmn. bd. trustees, 1990—; bd. trustees Mich. State U., 1992—. With AUS, 1953-55. Decorated knight 1st class Royal Order St. Olaf Norway; knight's cross Order of Dannebrog 1st class Denmark; comdr.'s medal Order of Finnish Lion Finland; recipient Disting. Service award U.S. Dept. Agr., 1963, Disting. Alumni award Mich. State U., 1971, Nat. Alumni award 4-H Clubs,

1972, Disting. Eagle Scout award Boy Scouts Am., 1973, Meritorious Achievement award Fla. A&M U., 1973, Nat. Ptnr. in 4-H award Dept. Agr. Extension Service, 1976; named hon. fellow Spring Arbor (Mich.) Coll., 1972; recipient Walter F. Patenge medal for pub. service Coll. Osteo. Medicine, Mich. State U., 1977, Disting. Service award Coll. Agr. and Natural Resources, 1980, Seaman A. Knapp Meml. lectr. U.S. Dept. Agr., 1983; recipient George award for community service City of Battle Creek, 1986, Disting. Service award Rural Sociol. Soc., 1986, Centennial Alumnus award for Mich. State U. Nat. Assn. State Univs. and Land Grant Colls., 1988, Pres.'s award Clemson U., 1989, Disting. Citizen award Southwest Mich. Coun. Boy Scouts Am., 1989, Disting. Svc. award 1890 Land-Grant Colls. and Univs., 1990, Vol. of Yr. award Clemson U., 1990, Disting. Grantmaker award Coun. on Founds., 1992, Disting. Svc. award Nat. Assn. Homes and Svcs. for Children, 1992, Merit award Nat. Soc. Fund Raising Execs. West Mich. chpt., 1992, Red Rose award Rotary Club of Battle Creek, 1993, George W. Romney award Nat. Soc. Fund Raising Execs. Greater Detroit chpt., 1993. Mem. Mich. Soc. Architects (hon.), Am. Agrl. Econ. Assn., Mich. State U. Alumni Assn. (bd. dirs. 1984-88), Alpha Gamma Rho (dir. 1976-82, grand pres. 1980-82, Man of Year Chgo. Alumni chpt. 1976, Hall of Fame 1986), Alpha Zeta, Phi Kappa Phi (Disting. Mem. award Mich. State U. 1978), Epsilon Sigma Phi (certificate of recognition 1974, Nat. Friend of Extension 1982), Gamma Sigma Delta. Office: W K Kellogg Found One Michigan Ave E Battle Creek MI 49017-3398

MAX, CLAIRE ELLEN, physicist; b. Boston, Sept. 29, 1946; d. Louis William and Pearl (Bernstein) M.; m. Jonathan Arons, Dec. 22, 1974; 1 child, Samuel. AB, Harvard U., 1968; PhD, Princeton U., 1972. Postdoctoral researcher U. Calif., Berkeley, 1972-74; physicist Lawrence Livermore (Calif.) Nat. Lab., 1974—; dir. Livermore br. Inst. Geophysics and Planetary Physics, 1984-93, dir. of insts., phys. sci. dept., 1993—; mem. Math.-Sci. Network Mills Coll., Oakland, Calif.; mem. com. on fusion hybrid reactors NRC, 1986, mem. com. on internat. security and arms control, 1986-89, mem. com. on phys. sci., math. and applications, 1991-94, mem. policy and computational astrophys. panels, astron. and astrophys. survey, 1989-91. Editor: Particle Acceleration Mechanisms in Astrophysics, 1979; contbr. numerous articles to sci. jours. Fellow Am. Phys. Soc. (exec. com. div. plasma physics 1977, 81-82); mem. AAAS, Am. Astron. Soc. (exec. com. div. high energy astrophysics 1975-76), Am. Geophys. Union, Internat. Astron. Union, Phi Beta Kappa, Sigma Xi. Avocations: violin, skiing. Office: Lawrence Livermore Nat Lab PO Box 808 7000 East Ave L-413 Livermore CA 94550-9900

MAX, HERBERT B., lawyer; b. Newark, May 24, 1931; children: Adam, Eric, Daniel. BA, Columbia U., 1952, LLB, 1954. Bar: N.Y. 1958. Assoc. Delson & Gordon, N.Y.C., 1959-65; pvt. practice N.Y.C., 1965-85; ptnr. Mayer, Brown & Platt, N.Y.C., 1985-89; of counsel Spengler, Carlson, N.Y.C., 1989-92, Reid & Priest, N.Y.C., 1992—. Author: Raising Capital: Private Placement Forms and Techniques, 2nd edit. 1987; assoc. editor N.Y. State Legislative Annual, 1958-59. With USN, 1955-57. Mem. ABA, N.Y. State Bar Assn., Assn. of Bar of City of N.Y. Office: Reid & Priest 40 W 57th St New York NY 10019

MAX, PETER, artist; b. Germany, Oct. 19, 1937; came to U.S., 1953; s. Jacob and Salla (Zeisel) Finkelstein; children: Adam, Libra. Student, Art Students League, Sch. Visual Arts. Artist, pres. Peter Max Enterprises, N.Y.C. Publisher 29 books, 160 posters, 310 ltd. edit. graphics, TV spls., designs for 52 corps.; over 70 nat. mag. covers; commd. to design U.S. postage stamp; commd. by U.S. govt. to create 235 murals at border sta. points between U.S./Can. and U.S./Mexican borders; commd. to create 10-panel mural in honor of 200th anniversary Am. Constitution; commd. by Sony for painting and poster commemorating 20th anniversary Apollo II, Air Space Smithsonian Instn.; commd. stage designer Moscow Music Fest.; commd. murals World's Fair Seville, 1992; designer various items Pres. Clinton's inauguration, 1993; ann. series Statue of Liberty painting; over 147 exhbns. of paintings in numerous galleries and museums, U.S. and abroad. Recipient numerous arts and humanitarian awards. Office: ViaMax 37 W 65th St New York NY 10023-6610

MAX, THEODORE CONRAD, surgeon; b. Langhorne, Pa., Apr. 29, 1929; s. Theodore Louis and Marian (Smith) M.; m. Melva Sholenberg, June 17, 1950; children: Christopher, Steven, Melva, Theodore, Erica. BS, Hobart Coll., 1950; MD, U. Rochester, 1954. Diplomate Am. Bd. Surgery. Resident in surgery Strong Meml. Hosp., Rochester, N.Y., 1954-60; instr. surgery U. Rochester Sch. Medicine, 1961-63; pvt. practice gen. and vascular surgery Utica, N.Y., 1963—; chief surgery, pres. med. staff St. Luke's Meml. Hosp., Utica; chief surgery, pres. med. staff St. Elizabeth Hosp., Utica, dir. surgery family practice residency program, 1976—; mem. bd. profl. conduct N.Y. State Dept. Health, 1978-86; dir. Med. Liability Ins. Co., N.Y.C., 1986—. Dir., chpt. pres. Am. Heart Assn., 1976-78. Capt. USAF, 1957-59. Fellow Am. Coll. Surgeons (pres. chpt. 1977-78, gov. 1982-88); mem. N.Y. Soc. Surgeons (pres. 1974-76), Med. Soc. State of N.Y. (del. for surgery 1974-94). Home: 238 W Main St Holland Patent NY 13354 Office: 2206 Genesee St Utica NY 13502

MAXA, RUDOLPH JOSEPH, JR., journalist; b. Cleve., Sept. 25, 1949; s. Rudolph Joseph and Christine Marie (Kimpel) M.; m. Kathleen Ann Zolciak, June 19, 1971 (div. 1988); children: Sarah Lynn, Alexander. B.S. in Journalism cum laude, Ohio U., 1971. Reporter Washington Post, 1971-82; sr. writer The Washingtonian, 1983-92; daily commentator Cable News Network, 1980-82; chief Washington bur. Spy mag., 1992-94; talk show host sta. WRC-AM; lectr. on journalism. Author: Dare to be Great, 1977, Public Trust, Private Lust, 1977, (TV script) Capital News, ABC-TV, 1990; travel commentator Pub. Radio Internat. Marketplace, 1990—. Recipient John Hancock award for excellence in bus. and financial writing, 1972. Office: 1746 N St NW Washington DC 20036-2907

MAXEINER, CLARENCE WILLIAM, lawyer, construction company executive; b. Sioux City, Iowa, Mar. 24, 1914; s. Frank A. and Dora A. (Olson) M.; m. Julie Frazer, Sept. 8, 1937; children: Mary Jane, Jay Frank, Mary Katherine, Nancy Carol; m. Rosalie F. Steele, May 29, 1974. Student, Columbia Coll., 1933-34, Columbia U. Law Sch., 1938-39; A.B., Grinnell Coll., 1936; J.D., U. Calif.-Berkeley, 1941. Bar: Calif. 1941. Ptnr. Thelen, Marrin, Johnson & Bridges, San Francisco and Los Angeles, 1941-60; sr. v.p., gen. counsel, dir. J.H. Pomeroy & Co., Inc. (and affiliated cos.), San Francisco, 1959-65; v.p., gen. counsel Dillingham Corp. (and affiliated cos.), Honolulu, 1966—; sr. v.p., gen. counsel, sec., dir., mem. exec. com. Dillingham Corp. (and affiliated cos.), 1968-71, spl. counsel, 1971—. Chmn. equipment fund com. Somona State Hosp., 1956-65; Bd. overseers Grinnell Coll., 1964; bd. dirs. Del Monte Forest Found. Mem. ABA, San Francisco Bar Assn., State Bar Calif., Am. Judicature Soc., Hawaii State Bar (assoc.), Columbia, U. Calif. law schs. assns., Phi Beta Kappa, Phi Delta Phi. Congregationalist. Clubs: Commonwealth of Calif. (San Francisco), The Family (San Francisco). Home: 4071 Sunset Ln Pebble Beach CA 93953-3049

MAXEY, DAVID WALKER, lawyer; b. Scranton, Pa., May 17, 1934; s. Paul Harold and Margaret (Walker) M.; m. Catharine Eglin, June 6, 1968; children: Paul Eglin, Margaret Wilson. AB, Harvard U., 1956, LLB cum laude, 1960. Bar: Pa. 1961, U. S. Dist. Ct. (ea. dist.) Pa. 1961, U.S. Ct. Appeals (3d cir.) 1963. Assoc. Drinker Biddle and Reath, Phila., 1960-66, ptnr., 1967—, chmn. real estate dept., 1970-88, mng. ptnr., 1977-91, co-chmn., 1988-91; bd. dirs. Ikea Property, Inc., Plymouth Meeting, Pa.; vis. faculty mem. Villanova U., U. Pa. Law Sch., 1987—. Contbr. articles to profl. jours. Sec., bd. dirs. Greater Phila. Internat. Network, 1981-95; bd. dirs. Young Audiences Ea. Pa., Phila., 1985—, Gladwyne (Pa.) Libr., 1991—, Libr. Co., Phila., 1993—; chmn. bd. dirs. Hist. Soc. Pa., 1991-93; chmn. internat. adv. com. Greater Phila. First. Recipient Hughes-Gossett award U.S. Supreme Ct. Hist. Soc., Washington, 1991. Mem. ABA, Pa. Bar Assn., Phila. Bar Assn., Am. Coll. Real Estate Lawyers, Harvard Club Phila. (pres. 1970-72), Franklin Inn Club, Merion Cricket Club, Sunday Breakfast Club (mem. steering com.). Avocation: historical research and publication. Home: 829 Black Road Rd Gladwyne PA 19035 Office: Phila Nat Bank Bldg 1345 Chestnut St Philadelphia PA 19107-3496

MAXEY, THOMAS F., advertising agency executive; b. Scranton, Pa., Mar. 6, 1937; s. Paul and Margaret (Walker) M.; m. Anne Watkins Barette, Sept.

19, 1964; children: Christopher, Jack, Elizabeth, Kathleen. B.A., Yale U., 1959. Account exec. N.W. Ayer, Inc., Phila., 1964-71; v.p. internat. N.W. Ayer, Inc., London, 1971-72; v.p N.W. Ayer, Inc., Phila., 1972-73; sr. v.p. N.W. Ayer, Inc., N.Y.C., 1973-81, exec. v.p., 1981-87, pres. internat., 1987-89, vice chmn., 1989—, also bd. dirs. Republican. Roman Catholic. Clubs: Merion Golf (Ardmore, Pa.); Yale (N.Y.C.); Cotton Bay (Eleuthera, Bahamas). Home: 559 Watford Rd Berwyn PA 19312-1746 Office: N W Ayer Inc Worldwide Plz 825 8th Ave New York NY 10019-7498

MAXFIELD, GUY BUDD, lawyer, educator; b. Galesburg, Ill., May 4, 1933; s. Guy W. and Isabelle B. Maxfield; m. Carol Tunick, Dec. 27, 1970; children—Susan, Stephen, Kim. A.B. summa cum laude, Augustana Coll., 1955; J.D., U. Mich., 1958. Bar: N.Y. 1959. Assoc. White & Case, N.Y.C., 1958-63; prof. law NYU, 1963—. Mem. ABA, Am. Law Inst., N.Y. State Bar Assn. Author: Tennessee Will and Trust Manual, 1982, Federal Estate and Gift Taxation, 6th edit. 1990, Florida Will and Trust Manual 1984, Tax Planning for Professionals, 1986; contbr. articles to profl. jours. Trustee Acomb Found., Newark, 1974—. Served with U.S. Army, 1958-64. Fellow Am. Coll. Tax Counsel; mem. ABA, Am. Law Inst., N.Y. State Bar Assn., Phi Beta Kappa, Order of Coif. Office: NYU Sch Law 40 Washington Sq S New York NY 10012-1005

MAXFIELD, JOHN EDWARD, retired university dean; b. Los Angeles, Mar. 17, 1927; s. Chauncey George and Rena Lucile (Cain) M.; m. Margaret Alice Waugh, Nov. 24, 1948; children—Frederick George (dec.), David Glen, Elaine Rebecca, Nancy Catherine, Daniel John. B.S., Mass. Inst. Tech., 1947; M.S., U. Wis., 1949; Ph.D., U. Oreg., 1951. Instr. U. Oreg. 1950-51; mathmatician U.S. Naval Ordnance Test Sta., China Lake, Calif., 1949-56, head computing br., 1956-57, head math. div., 1957-60; lectr. UCLA, 1951-60; head prof. dept. math. U. Fla., 1960-67; prof., chmn. dept. math. Kans. State U., 1967-81; dean Grad. Sch. and univ. research La. Tech. U., 1981-92, dean emeritus, 1992—; ret. La. Tech. U., 1992. Mem. Am. Math. Soc., Math. Assn. Am., Soc. Indsl. and Applied Math., Sigma Xi. Home: 209 E Louisiana Ave Ruston LA 71270-4417

MAXFIELD, KENNETH WAYNE, transportation company executive; b. Leo, Ind., Oct. 26, 1924; m. Jean; 2 children. Student, Loyola U., Chgo., 1946-48; LL.B., De Paul U., 1950. Bar: Ind., Ill. bars 1950. With North Am. Van Lines Inc., Ft. Wayne, Ind., 1950-89, exec. v.p. corp. world hdqrs., 1966-77, pres., chief oper. officer, chmn. bd., 1977-89, ret.; chmn. Am. Movers Conf., 1989; vice chmn. litigation sect. Am. Trans. Assn., 1987-89. Pres. bd. Jr. Achievement, Ft. Wayne, 1976-77. Served with U.S. Army, 1943-46. Mem. Ft. Wayne C. of C. (pres. 1974), Summit Club (dir.)

MAXFIELD, MICHAEL GERALD, forest products and restaurant company executive; b. Pontiac, Mich., Feb. 27, 1954; s. Gerald E.L. and Mildred (Lewis) M. BS, Mich. State U., 1973, MBA, 1975. CPA, Mich. Mgr. Deloitte, Haskins & Sells, Detroit and Grand Rapids, Mich., 1975-86; exec. v.p. The Universal Cos., Inc., Grand Rapids, 1986-94, treas., 1986-89. Treas. Kent County Rep. Com., Grand Rapids, 1991—, chmn. 1992—, 5th dist. fin. chmn.; mem. state com. Mich. Rep. Party, 1990—; bd. dirs. Kent Community Hosp., 1988-92. Mem. AICPA, Mich. Assn. CPAs, Grand Rapids C. of C. (chmn. 1984-88), Fin. Execs. Inst. Republican. Home: 7737 Kenrob Dr SE Grand Rapids MI 49546-9122

MAXFIELD, PETER C., state legislator, law educator, lawyer; b. 1941. AB, Regis Coll., 1963; JD, U. Denver, 1966; LLM, Harvard U., 1968. Bar: Colo. 1966, Wyo. 1969. Trial atty. Dept. Justice, 1966-67; assoc. Hindry, Erickson & Meyer, Denver, 1968-69; asst. prof. U. Wyo. Coll. Law, 1969-72, assoc. prof., 1972-76, prof., 1976—, dean, 1979-87; vis. assoc. prof. U. N.Mex., 1972-73; Raymond F. Rice Disting. prof. U. Kans., 1984; Chapman Vis. Disting. prof., U. Tulsa, 1987; vis. prof. U. Utah, 1992. Coord. Wyo. State Planning, 1988-89; adj. asst. Gov. Wyo. 1989-90; Dem. nominee U.S. Ho. Reps., 1990; mem. Wyo. Environ. Quality Coun., 1991-93; mem. Wyo. Senate, Laramie, 1993—. Mem. Order St. Ives, Omicron Delta Kappa, Pi Delta Phi. Author: (with Bloomenthal) Cases and Materials on the Federal Income Taxation of Natural Resources, 1971, 72, 77; (with Houghton) Taxation of Mining Operations, 1973, 76; (with Trelease and Dietrich) Natural Resources Law on American Indian Lands, 1977. Home: 3501 Grays Gable Rd Laramie WY 82070 Office: U Wyo Coll Law PO Box 3035 Laramie WY 82071-3035

MAXFIELD, THOMAS H., lawyer; b. Scottsbluff, Nebr., Feb. 20, 1944. BA, U. Wyo., 1966, JD, 1970; LLM, NYU, 1971. Bar: Wyo. 1970, Colo. 1971. Ptnr. Baker & Hostetler, Denver. Mem. ABA, Colo. Bar Assn., Denver Bar Assn., Wyo. State Bar. Office: Baker & Hostetler 303 E 17th Ave Ste 1100 Denver CO 80203-1264

MAXHEIM, JOHN HOWARD, utility executive; b. Clinton, Iowa, Oct. 4, 1934; s. Vincent J. and Dorothy F. M. B.S. in Indsl. Engring., Iowa State U., 1958. Indsl. sales engr. Mobil Oil Co., Chgo., 1958-59; indsl. sales engr. and mgr. Milw. Gas Light Co., 1959-62; asst. to pres. United Cities Gas Co., Nashville, 1962-65, v.p., 1965-66, exec. v.p., 1966-70, pres., chief exec. officer, 1970-78, also bd. dirs., 1970-78; pres., chief operating officer Piedmont Natural Gas Co., Inc., Charlotte, N.C., 1978-80, also bd. dirs., 1979—, chief exec. officer, chmn., 1980—, now also pres.; dir. Wachovia Bank & Trust Co., Univ. Research Park. Past chmn. Charlotte Auditorium-Coliseum Conv. Ctr. Authority; trustee Inst. Gas Tech., N.Y. Mercantile Exchange; mem. Nat. Gas Adv. Com.; adv. bd. Fuqua Sch. Bus., Duke U.; trustee Ind. Coll. Fund N.C.; bd. visitors Johnson C. Smith U.; U. N.C., Charlotte; bd. dirs. Found. U. N.C. Mem. Am. Gas Assn. (bd. dirs.), So. Gas Assn. (past chmn.), Southeastern Gas Assn. (past dir.), Tenn. Gas Assn. (past pres.), Greater Charlotte C. of C. (bd. dirs., Nashville City Club, Carolina Ambassadors, Capital City Club, Carmel Country Club, Quail Hollow Country Club, Alpha Tau Omega. Home: 4100 Beresford Rd Charlotte NC 28211-3810 Office: Piedmont Natural Gas Co Inc PO box 33068 1915 Rexford Rd Charlotte NC 28233

MAXIMOS (MAXIMOS DEMETRIOS AGHIORGOUSSIS), bishop; b. Callimassia, Chios, Greece, Mar. 5, 1935; s. Evanghelos G. and Lemonia G. (Rythianou) A. Licentiate, Patriarchal Sch. Theology, Halki, 1957; Baccalaureate, U. Louvain, Belgium, 1964, Th.D., 1964. Ordained to ministry Greek Orthodox Ch., 1957; chaplain U. Louvain, 1957-64; pastor chs. Brussels, Rome, Brookline, Mass., Manchester and Newport, N.H., 1960-78; observer-del. II Vatican Council, 1964-65; chaplain Holy Cross Sem., Brookline, 1967-76; prof. systematic theology Holy Cross Sch. Theology, Brookline, 1967-79, Christ Savior Sem., Johnstown, Pa., from 1979; bishop Greek Orthodox Diocese Pitts., 1979—; mem. Orthodox-Roman Cath. Consultation, from 1967; v.p. Nat. Council Chs. Christ U.S., 1979-81; ecumenical officer Greek Orthodox Archdiocese N. and S. Am., 1978-79, chmn. synodal coms. ecumenical affairs, spiritual renewal and youth, from 1979. Author articles in field. Mem. Orthodox Theol. Soc. Am., AAUP, Christian Assos. Pitts., Pa. Council Chs., W.Va. Council Chs., Helicon Cultural Soc. Office: Greek Orthodox Diocese Pittsburgh 5201 Ellsworth Ave Pittsburgh PA 15232-9913 *My ministry is such that it requires a total commitment to its goals, but first of all a total commitment to Christ. In my childhood, I was fortunate to be guided by excellent parents and grandparents, who gave me not only the necessary security and stability, but also the inspiration to imitate their personal commitment to the Lord. I fully trust in the grace of the Lord, but I also have always accepted my responsibility for everything I have done.*

MAXIMOVICH, MICHAEL JOSEPH, chemist, consultant; b. Akron, Ohio, Mar. 3, 1932; s. Michael Stephen and Josephine Anna (Salzwimner) M. BS, Kent State U., 1958, MS, 1964. Rsch. chemist PPG Industries, Barberton, Ohio, 1964-69; sr. devel. engr. Goodyear Chems., Akron, 1969-80; sr. rsch. chemist Polymer Industries, Stanford, Conn., 1980-82, Mooney Chems., Cleve., 1982-84; cons. All-Chem Techs., Lakewood, Ohio, 1984—. Pres. St. Mary Holy Name Soc., Akron, 1978-80, Akron Deanery Holy Name Soc., 1978-80; del. Cleve. Holy Name Soc., 1978-80. With USN, 1950-54. Mem. Am. Chem. Soc., Assn. Cons. Chemists and Chem. Engrs. Republican. Roman Catholic. Achievements include patents for liquid phase hydrofluorination of alkynes; for polyglycol carbonates using CO_2 and catalysts, for water borne styrene-acrylates; first proof of the mechanism of the Schmidt Reaction of Substituted Acetophenones. Home and Office: 1224 Elbur Ave Cleveland OH 44107-2716

MAXMAN, SUSAN ABEL, architect; b. Columbus, Ohio, Dec. 30, 1938; d. Richard Jack Abel and Gussie (Brenner) Seiden; children: Andrew Frankel, Thomas Frankel, Elizabeth Frankel; m. William H. Maxman; children: Melissa, Abby, William Jr. Student, Smith Coll., 1960; MArch., U. Pa., 1977; HHD, Ball State U., 1993. Registered profl. architect, Pa., Ohio, N.J., Md., W.Va., Va. Project designer Kopple Sheward & Day, Phila., 1978-80; ptnr. Maxman & Sutphin, Phila., 1980-83; prin. Susan Maxman Architects, Phila., 1984—. Works include design of Women's Humane Soc. Animal Shelter, Bensalem, Pa. (Northeastern Sustainable Energy Assn.'s Comml. Bldg. award, 1994), Camp Tweedale-Freedom Valley, Girl Scouts USA (AIA honor award, 1991), restoration Vernon House (honorable mention Remodeling Mag.), Germantown, Robert Lewis House (McArthur award 1985), Phila., interior architecture Criminal Justice Ctr., Phila., Julia DeBurgos Bilingual Middle Sch., Phila., Feasibility Study and renovations Old Main Complex, Kutztown U., Pa., Chestnut Hill Nat. Bank, Phila. Participant community leadership seminars, Phila., 1986-87; bd. overseers Grad. Sch. Fine Arts U. Pa., trustees coun. Penn Women U. Pa.; bd. dirs. Alliance to Save Energy, Found. for Architecture, Phila. Hist. Preservation Corp., Pa. Women's Forum, Forum of Exec. Women. Recipient Benjamin Franklin Bridge Lighting honor award, Phila., 1986, Am. Wood Coun., Citation of Excellence Engring. News Record, Shattering the Glass Ceiling award Women's Nat. Demo. Club, Mayor's Commendation City of Phila., Citation Commonwealth of Pa. Ho. of Reps. Mem. AIA (Phila. chpt. bd. dirs. 1984-87, Pa. Soc. Architects bd. dirs. 1983-87, sec. 1984-85, v.p. 1986, pres. 1987, Nat. bd. dirs. 1988—, v.p. 1991, 1st v.p., pres.-elect 1992, nat. pres.-first woman pres. 1993), Am. Inst. Architects, Am. Archtl. Found. (bd. regents), Carpenters' Co. of Phila., Eco-Efficiency Task Force Pres.'s Coun. on Sustainable Devel. Avocations: swimming, gardening. Office: 123 S 22nd St Philadelphia PA 19103-4335

MAXNER, JOYCE KAREN, family therapist, author; b. Lynn, Mass., Oct. 23, 1929; d. Arthur Martin Leopold and Mary Grace Meyerson; married, 1951 (div. 1968); children: m. Joseph Maxner, Mar. 7, 1970 (div. 1976). AA, Centenary Coll. for Women, 1949; BA, Harvard U., 1976; MS, Villanova U., 1979. Copywriter Advt. Agys., Boston, 1949-64, Sta. WLYN, Lynn, 1950-52; advt. exec., writer Unicorn Studio, Marblehead, Mass., 1964-69; mgr. advt., writer Am. Art Guild, N.Y.C., 1972-73; asst. pub. Bergen News, Cliffside Park, N.J., 1974; artists' rep., pub. rels. rep. Ft. Lee, N.J., 1975-76; juvenile probation officer Del. County Juvenile Ct., Media, Pa., 1979-82; family therapist Family Inst. Va., Richmond, 1982-84; pvt. practice Newtown Square, Pa., 1984—. Author: Nicholas Cricket, 1989 (selected for permanent collection Delta Blues Mus., Best Design for Children's Book award N.Y. Bookbinders Guild 1990), Lady Bugatti, 1991. Pres. Women's Am. Ogn. for healing. through Tng., Marblehead, 1957-58; troop leader Girl Scouts USA, Marblehead, 1960-61. Mem. AACD, Pen Am. Ctr., Phila. Children's Reading Roundtable, Soc. Children's Book Writers, Harvard Alumni Assn., Author's Guild. Home and Office: 269 Green Briar Ct Newtown Square PA 19073-2125

MAXON, DON CARLTON, construction company executive, mining company executive; b. Downers Grove, Ill., Dec. 23, 1914; s. Norman T. and Agnes M. (Matteson) M.; m. Mary T. Quirk, June 14, 1941; children: Maureen, Don, Paul, Anne, Lee; m. Ella Luanne Roy, Dec. 10, 1971; 1 stepchild, Tom Roy. Student pub. schs., Barrington, Ill. Founder, pres. Maxon Constrn. Co., Barrington, 1936, Gen. Mining & Devel. Co., Santa Fe, N.Mex., 1967—; U.S. Communities S.A. Panama, 1974, Taipei, Taiwan, 1986—, Carson City, NA, 1989—, Bonanza Mines Internat., Carson City, NA, 1987; rancher; internat. fin. cons. Fiduciary Banks, London, Paris, Geneva, mem. pres.'s club. Pres. Johnson and Kennedy; mem. Pockets of Poverty Commn.; founder City of Streamwood, Ill., 1954, City of Green Valley, Ariz., 1963. With Seabees, USN, 1942-45. Recipient awards for designing family communities of Streamwood, Barrington Woods, Ill. and Trout Valley, Ill., Parents' mag., 1953, 59, 60; Tenn. Squire. Mem. Nat. Assn. Home Builders (Nat. Homes Pres.'s Land Planning first place award 1954), Gov.'s Club Ariz. Democrat. Roman Catholic. Rsh. on methods for testing and extracting gold from complex ores and rsch. to create the finest possible environment for quality of life and sci. applications of all disciplines needed for a self contained city of 150,000 population; builder U.S. Gypsum Co. Rsch. Village, Barrington. Home: 2586 E Avenida De Maria Tucson AZ 85718-3056

MAXSON, LINDA ELLEN, biologist, educator; b. N.Y.C., Apr. 24, 1943; d. Albert and Ruth (Rosenfeld) Resnick; m. Richard Dey Maxson, June 13, 1964; 1 child, Kevin. BS in Zoology, San Diego State U., 1964, MA in Biology, 1966; PhD in Genetics, U. Calif. and San Diego State U., 1973. Instr. biology San Diego State U., 1966-68; tchr. gen. sci. San Diego Unified Sch. Dist., 1968-69; instr. biochemistry U. Calif., Berkeley, 1974; asst. prof. zoology, dept. genetics and devel. U. Ill., Urbana-Champaign, 1974-76, asst. prof. dept. genetics, devel. and ecology, ethology & evolution, 1976-79, assoc. prof., 1979-84, prof., 1984-87, prof. ecology, ethology and evolution, 1987-88; prof., head dept. biology Pa. State U., State College, 1988-94; assoc. vice chancellor acad. affairs, dean undergrad affairs U. Tenn., Knoxville, 1995—; exec. officer biology programs Sch. Life Scis., U. Ill., 1981-86, assoc. dir. acad. affairs, 1984-86, dir. campus honors program, 1985-88; vis. prof. ecology and evolutionary biology U. Calif., Irvine, 1988; mem. adv. panel rsch. tng. groups behavioral biol. scis. NSF, 1990-94. Author: Genetics: A Human Perspective, 3d edit., 1992; edtl. bd. Molecular Biology Evolution, Amphibia/Reptilia; exec. editor Biochem. Sys. & Ecology, 1993—; contbr. numerous articles to scientific jours. Recipient Disting. Alumna award San Diego State U., 1989. Fellow AAAS (Disting. Herpetologist award 1993); mem. Am. Men and Women in Sci., Am. Genetics Assn. (mem. coun., 1994—), Soc. for Study of Amphibians and Reptiles (pres. 1991), Internat. Herpetol. Com., Soc. Study Evolution, Soc. Systematic Biology, Soc. Molecular Biology and Evolution (sec. 1992—, treas. 1992-94), Soc. Ichthyologists and Herpetologists, Am. Soc. Zoologists, Herpetologists League, Soc. Euroeaea Herpetologica, European Soc. Evolutionary Biology. Home: 5201 Western Ave Apt 522 Knoxville TN 37921 Office: U Tenn 505 Andy Holt Twr Knoxville TN 37996-0154

MAXSON, M. FINLEY, lawyer; b. Toledo, Ohio, Aug. 9, 1934. AB, Duke U., 1956; LLB, Harvard U., 1962. Bar: Ill. 1962. Ptnr. Winston & Strawn, Chgo. Mem. ABA, Ill. State Bar Assn., Chgo. Bar Assn. Office: Winston & Strawn 35 W Wacker Dr Chicago IL 60601-1614

MAXWELL, ANDERS JOHN, corporate executive; b. San Francisco, Oct. 3, 1946; s. John L. and Deborah A. Maxwell; m. Alexis S. Collins, June 14, 1975; children: Lauren A., Colin A., Ian W., Erin C. BArch, U. Calif.-Berkeley, 1969; MBA, U. Pa., 1971. Analyst Gen. Electric Co., 1971-73; v.p. Gen. Electric Credit Corp., Stamford, Conn., 1973-83; mng. dir. Dean Witter Reynolds Inc., N.Y.C., 1983-87; v.p. Kidder Peabody & Co., Inc., N.Y.C., 1987-88; prin. L.F. Rothschild & Co., N.Y.C., 1988; v.p. Smith Barney, Harris Upham & Co., Inc., 1989-91, Lazard Frères & Co., N.Y.C., 1991-92; ptnr. Benedetto, Gartland & Greene, N.Y.C., 1992-94; v.p., gen. mgr. GE Capital Corp., Stamford, Conn., 1994—; bd. dirs. Rymer Foods, Inc. Served to capt. U.S Army, 1971. Office: GE Capital Corp 260 Long Ridge Rd Stamford CT 06927-5000

MAXWELL, ARTHUR EUGENE, oceanographer, marine geophysicist, educator; b. Maywood, Calif., Apr. 11, 1925; s. John Henry and Nelle Irene (Arnold) M.; m. Colleen Oleary, July 1, 1988; children: Delle, Eric, Lynn, Brett, Gregory, Sam Wade, Henry Wade. BS in Physics with honors, N.Mex. State U., 1949; MS in Oceanography, Scripps Instn. Oceanography, 1952, PhD in Oceanography, 1959. Jr. rsch. geophysicist Scripps Instn. Oceanography, La Jolla, Calif., 1950-55; head oceanographer Office Naval Rsch., Washington, 1955-59, head br. geophysics, 1959-65; assoc. dir. Woods Hole (Mass.) Oceanographic Instn., 1965-69, dir. rsch., 1969-71, provost, 1971-81; prof. dept. geol. scis., dir. Inst. Geophysics U. Tex., Austin, 1982-94, prof. emeritus dept. geol. sci., 1994—; bd. dirs. Palisades Geophys. Inst. Corp; chmn. bd. govs. Joint Oceanographical Instns., 1985-86. Planning com. deep earth sampling, 1968-70, chmn. exec. com. deep earth sampling, 1971-72, 78-79, 91-92; mem. joint U.S./USSR com. for coop. studies of the world ocean NAS/NRC, 1973-80, chmn. U.S. nat. com. to Internat. Union Geodesy and Geophysics, 1976-80, vice chmn. outer continental shelf/environ. studies rev. com., 1986-93; chmn. U.S. nat. com. on geology NAS, 1979-83, chmn. geophysics rsch. bd. geophysics study com., 1982-87; nat. sea grant review panel NOAA, 1982-85, 90—; mem. vis. com. Rosenstiel Sch. Marine and Atmospheric Studies U. Miami, 1982-86, dept. physics N.Mex. State U., 1986-94; acad. adv. com. Com. Exchanges CIA, 1983—; mem. Gulf of Mexico Regional Marine Rsch. Bd., 1992—. Editor: The Sea, Vol. 4, Parts I and II, 1970; editorial adv. bd. Oceanus, 1981-92; contbr. articles to profl. jours. Chmn. tech. adv. com. Navy Thresher Search, 1963; mem. Mass. Gov's. Adv. Com. on Sci. and Tech., 1965-71. With USN, 1942-46, PTO. Recipient Meritorious Civilian Svc. award Chief Naval Rsch., 1958, Superior Civilian Svc. award Asst. Sec. of Navy, 1963, Disting. Civilian Svc. award Sec. of Navy, 1964, Disting. Alumni award N.Mex. State U., 1965, Bruun Meml. Lecture award Intergovtl. Oceanographic Commn., 1969, Outstanding Centennial Alumnus award N.Mex. State U., 1988. Fellow Am. Geophys. Union (pres. 1976-78, pres. oceanography sect. 1970-72); mem. Marine Tech. Soc. (charter, pres. 1981-82), Cosmos Club. Achievements include research in heat flow through the ocean floor, in structure and tectonics of the sea floor. Home: 8115 Two Coves Dr Austin TX 78730-3122 Office: U Tex Inst for Geophysics 8701 N Mo Pac Expy Austin TX 78759-8345

MAXWELL, BRYCE, engineer,educator; b. Glen Cove, N.Y., July 26, 1919; s. Howard W. and Helen (Young) W.; m. Margurite Kulsar, June 5, 1953 (dec. 1974); children: Bryce Jr., Margaret H., Stephen H. B.S. in Engring, Princeton, 1943, M.S. in Engring, 1948. Rsch. assoc. Princeton U., 1948-53, asst. prof., 1953-57, assoc. prof., 1957-66, asst. dean Sch. Engring., 1962-66, prof. chem. engring. Sch. Engring., 1966-68, prof. chem. engring. for polymer studies, chmn. polymer materials program, 1968-85, prof. emeritus, 1985—; pres. Maxwell Instrument Inc., 1992—; bd. dirs. U.S. Rubber Reclaiming Co., Inc., Vicksburg, Miss., 1962-80; cons. several chem. cos. Trustee Plastics Inst. Am. Served with USNR, 1943-46. Recipient Honor Scroll N.J. Inst. Chemists, 1981. Mem. ASME (life), ASTM, Soc. Rheology, Soc. Plastics Engrs. (gold medal and internat. award in plastics sci. and engring. 1976, fellow 1992), Sigma Xi. Achievements include research and publication in polymer viscoelastic behavior, polymer melt rheology; inventor elastic melt extruder, orthogonal rheometer, melt elasticity tester, 12 U.S. patents, 14 foreign patents. Home: Rossmoor 686A Yarborough Way Jamesburg NJ 08831-2012

MAXWELL, CARLA LENA, dancer, choreographer, educator; b. Glendale, Calif., Oct. 25, 1945; d. Robert and Victoria (Carbone) M. Student, Bennington Coll., 1963-64; B.S., Juilliard Sch. Music, 1967. Mem. Jose Limón Dance Co., N.Y.C., 1965; prin. dancer Jose Limón Dance Co., 1969—, acting artistic dir., 1977-78, artistic dir., 1978—; lectr., tchr. in field. Soloist, Louis Falco Dance Co., 1967-71, Harkness Festival at N.Y.C. Delacorte Theater, from 1964, artist-in-residence, Gettysburg Coll., 1970, Luther Coll., Decorah, Iowa, 1971, U. Idaho, 1973, guest tchr., performer, Centre Internat. de la Danse, Vichy, France, 1976; choreographer: Function, 1970, Improvisations on a Dream, 1970, A Suite of Psalms, 1973, Homage to José Linón, Place Spirit, 1975, Aadvark Brothers; Schwartz and Columbo Present Please Don't Stone The Clowns, 1975, Blue Warrier, 1975, Sonata, 1980, Keeping Stil, Mountain, 1987; featured in Carlota, Dances For Isadora, La Malinche, Comedy, The Moor's Pavane, The Winged, There Is A Time, The Shakers, Brandenburg Concerto No. 4, Trnaslucence, Caviar, Missa Brevis, Day on Earth, Two Ecstatic Themes, A Choreographic Offering, The Exiles, Sacred Conversations; toured East and West Africa, 1969. N.Y. State Cultural Council grantee, 1971; recipient Dance Mag. award, 1995. Home: 7 Great Jones St New York NY 10012-1135 Office: Jose Limon Dance Ctr 622 Broadway Fl 5 New York NY 10012-2617*

MAXWELL, CLYDE EDWIN, JR., hospital administrator; b. Athens, Ga., July 31, 1940; s. Clyde Edwin and Viva Kate (Cole) M.; m. Nancy H. King, June 24, 1972; children: Nancy Katheryne, Elizabeth Cole. BS, U. Miss., 1962; MHA, Baylor U., 1971. Assoc. adminstr. U.S. Army Gen. Hosp., Augusta, Ga., 1971-73; adminstr. Computerized Ambulatory Triage System, Washington, 1973-76, U.S. Army Health Services Command, San Antonio, 1976-78, U.S. Army Hosp., Livorno, Italy, 1978-81, U.S. Army Ambulatory Care Ctr., Atlanta, 1981-84; pres., chief exec. officer South Fulton Hosp., East Point, Ga., 1985—. Author: Quick Reaction Hospital, 1981. Bd. dirs. Jesse Draper Boys Club, East Point, 1987. Served to lt. col. U.S. Army MSC, 1964-84. Fellow Am. Coll. Healthcare Execs.; mem. Vol. Hosp. Am. Adminstrs. Ga. (bd. dirs.), Am. Hosp. Assn., Ga. Hosp. Assn., Southcare Med. Alliance (bd. dirs. 1985—), Leukemia Soc. Am. (bd. dirs. Ga. chpt. 1987—). Club: Atlanta Airport (East Point, Ga.) (pres. 1984-85). Lodge: Rotary. Avocations: deep sea fishing, golf, tennis, hunting, jogging. Home: 7553 Raleigh Ln Jonesboro GA 30236-2623 Office: HealthCrest Mgt Group PO Box 897 Snellville GA 30278

MAXWELL, D. MALCOLM, college president; b. Watford/Herts, Eng., Apr. 6, 1934; came to U.S., 1936; s. Arthur S. and Rachel Elizabeth (Joyce) M.; m. Eileen J. Bolander, Aug. 25, 1955; children: Wendy Henderson, Kevin. BA in Theology and Bibl. Langs., Pacific Union Coll., Calif., 1956; M.A., Andrews U., Mich., 1958; Ph.D., Drew U., N.J., 1965. Pastor Seventh-Day Adventist Ch., No. Calif. Conf., 1956-64; instr. Union Coll., Lincoln, Neb., 1964-65; prof. Walla Walla Coll., College Place, Wash., 1965-78, v.p. acad. affairs, 1978-83; pres. Pacific Union Coll., Angwin, Calif., 1983—; bd. trustees St. Helena Hosp., Deer Park, Calif., 1983—, Rio Linda Acad., Healdsburg, Calif., 1983—; Adventist Health Systems West Membership Bd., Roseville, Calif., 1983—. Contbr. articles to profl. jours. Drew U. scholar, Rockefeller fellow, 1967-68; named Tchr. of Yr., Wash. State Auto Dirs. Assn., 1971. Mem. Soc. Bibl. Lit., Rotary (St. Helena). Adventist. Avocations: Golf; boating; gardening. Home: PO Box 711 Angwin CA 94508-0711 Office: Pacific Union Coll Office of Pres Angwin CA 94508

MAXWELL, DAVID E., academic executive, educator; b. N.Y.C., Dec. 2, 1944; s. James Kendrick and Gertrude Sarah (Bernstein) M.; children: Justin Kendrick, Stephen Edward. BA, Grinnell Coll., Iowa, 1966, MA, Brown U., 1968, PhD, 1974. Instr. Tufts U., Medford, Mass., 1971-74, asst. prof., 1974-78, assoc. prof. Russian lang. and lit., 1978-89, dean undergrad. studies, 1981-89; pres. Whitman Coll., Walla Walla, Wash. 1989-93; dir. Nat. Fgn. Lang. Ctr., Washington, 1993—; chmn. steering com. Coop. Russian Lang. Program, Leningrad, USSR, 1981-86, chmn. 1986-90; cons. Coun. Internat. Ednl. Exchange, 1974—, bd. dirs., 1988-92, 93-94, vice chair, 1991-92, cons. Internat. Rsch. Exchanges, 1976—; mem. adv. bd. Israeli Lang. Policy Inst. Contbr. articles to scholarly jours. Fulbright fellow, 1970-71, Brown U., 1966-67, NDEA Title IV, 1967-70; recipient Lillian Leibner award Tufts U., 1979; citation Grad. Sch. Arts & Scis., Brown U., 1991. Mem. MLA, Am. Coun. Edn. (commn. on internat. edn., pres.'s coun. on internat. edn.), Am. Assn. Advancement of Slavic Studies, Am. Assn. Tchrs. Slavic and E. European Langs., Assn. Am. Colls., Am. Assn. Higher Edn., Am. Coun. Tchg. Fgn. Langs., Brown U. Alumni Assn. Democrat. Avocations: tennis, running, music. Office: Nat Fgn Lang Ctr 1619 Massachusetts Ave NW Washington DC 20036-2213

MAXWELL, DAVID OGDEN, government official, financial executive; b. Phila., May 16, 1930; s. David Farrow and Emily Ogden (Nelson) M.; m. Joan Clark Paddock, Dec. 14, 1968. BA, Yale U., 1952; LLB, Harvard U. 1955. Bar: Pa. 1955, D.C. 1955. Assoc. Obermayer, Rebmann, Maxwell & Hippel, Phila., 1959-67, ptnr., 1963-67; ins. commr. State of Pa., 1967-69, adminstrn. and budget sec. 1969-70; gen. counsel HUD, Washington, 1970-73; pres., chief exec. officer Ticor Mortgage Ins. Co., 1973-81; chmn. bd., chief exec. officer Fed. Nat. Mortgage Assn., Washington, 1981-91; bd. dirs. Corp. Ptnrs., L.P., Hechinger Co., Kaufman and Broad Home Corp., Potomac Electric Power Co., SunAm. Inc.; trustee The Enterprise Found., The European Inst., The Urban Inst., The Brookings Instn. Dir. Czech & Slovak Am. Enterprise Fund; chmn. Sta. WETA-TV; trustees coun. Nat. Gallery Art. With USNR, 1955-59. Home: 3525 Springland Ln NW Washington DC 20008-3119 Office: 5335 Wisconsin Ave NW Ste 440 Washington DC 20015-2030

MAXWELL, DONALD STANLEY, publishing executive; b. L.A., May 30, 1930; s. Harold Stanley and Margaret (Trenam) M.; m. Martha Helen Winn, Dec. 5, 1952; children: Sylvia Louise, Cynthia Lynn, Bruce Stanley, Bradley Erl, Walter James, Wesley Richard, Amy Bernice. Student, Long Beach City Coll., 1948-50; BBA, Woodbury Coll., 1956; D of Bus. Adminstrn. (hon.), Woodbury U., 1991. CPA. Ptnr. Robert McDavid & Co. (CPAs), L.A., 1955-61; controller Petersen Pub. Co., L.A., 1961-68; v.p. fin. Petersen Pub. Co., 1969; controller L.A. Times, 1969-79; v.p. Los Angeles Times,

1977-79, v.p. fin., 1979-81; asst. treas. Times Mirror Co., 1971-82, v.p., controller, 1982-87, v.p., chief acctg. officer, 1987-93, v.p., 1993, exec. dir. fin. program, 1993-95; ret., 1995. Trustee Woodbury U., 1981—, chmn. bd. trustees, 1984-87. Served with AUS, 1950-52. Mem. Fin. Execs. Inst. (dir. 1979-82, pres. L.A. chpt. 1973-74), Internat. Newspaper Fin. Execs. (dir. 1978-82, pres. 1980-81), Am. Inst. CPAs, Calif. Soc. CPAs, Am. Horse Council, Internat. Arabian Horse Assn., Arabian Horse Assn. So. Calif., Friendly Hills Country Club. Republican. Baptist. Home: 2160 Le Flore Dr La Habra Heights CA 90631-8020 Office: Times Mirror Co Times Mirror Sq Los Angeles CA 90012-3816

MAXWELL, HAMISH, diversified consumer products company executive; b. 1926. BA, Cambridge U., Eng., 1949. With Thomas Cook Sons & Co., 1949-54, Philip Morris, Inc., 1954-85; salesman Philip Morris, Inc., Richmond, Va., 1954-69; v.p. Philip Morris, Inc., 1969-76, sr. v.p., 1976-78, exec. v.p., 1978-83, pres., chief operating officer, 1983-84, chmn., chief exec. officer, 1984-85, also bd. dirs.; with Philip Morris Internat., 1961-83, advt. dir., 1961-63, v.p. mktg., 1963-65, regional v.p., Asia/Pacific region, 1965-73, exec. v.p. Canadian & Asia/Pacific regions, 1973-75, exec. v.p. Can./Asia & Europe/Middle East/Asia regions, 1975-78, pres., chief exec. officer, 1978-85; chmn., chief exec. officer Philip Morris Cos. Inc., 1985-91, chmn. exec. com., 1991—, also bd. dirs., 1985—. Served with RAF, 1944-47. Office: Philip Morris Cos Inc 120 Park Ave New York NY 10017-5523*

MAXWELL, J. DOUGLAS, JR., chemical service company executive; b. Glen Cove, N.Y., Sept. 26, 1941; s. John Douglas M. and Marie Elise (Powers) Cummings; m. Hanne Agnete Kristensen, June 6, 1970; children: Scott Rogers, Samuel Douglas, Whitney Bodil. BA, Williams Coll., 1963; MBA, L.I.U., 1970. With Photocircuits Corp., Glen Cove, 1963-70; mgr. epuipment mktg. Chemco Techs., Inc., Glen Cove, 1970-76, treas., 1976-79, mng. dir., 1979-84, pres., 1984-89, also bd. dirs.; chmn. bd. dirs., chief exec. officer Empower Inc., Glen Cove, 1990—; dir. Kellmorgen Corp., Stamford, Conn., Slater Electric Corp., Glen Cove, First Nat. Bank L.I., Glen Head. Bd. dirs., v.p. Glen Cove Boys & Girls Club, 1970; bd. dirs., treas. L.I. Coun. on Alcoholism, Mineola, 1980; trustee Green Wood Cemetery, Bklyn., 1984, Green Vale Sch., Glen Head, 1986. Home: Cherry Ln Glen Head NY 11545-2216 Office: Chemco Tech Inc Charles St Glen Cove NY 11542-2957

MAXWELL, JACK ERWIN, manufacturing company executive; b. Cleve., July 17, 1926; s. Fred A. and Gertrude F. (Haug) M.; m. Martha Jane Miller, Dec. 28, 1966; children by previous marriage: Laura Jane, Fredric, Elizabeth Grant, Carla Moore, Linda Hanson. B.S., Case Inst. Tech., 1949; M.B.A., Harvard U., 1952. Indsl. engr. Lincoln Electric Co., Cleve., 1952-53; mgr. purchase analysis Ford Motor Co., Dearborn, Mich., 1953-57; v.p. Booz, Allen & Hamilton, Inc., Detroit, 1957-69; v.p. corp. devel. Am. Motors Corp., Detroit, 1969-71; v.p. adminstrn. Am. Motors Corp., 1971-76, v.p. non-automotive subsidiaries, 1976-79, v.p. diversified ops., 1979-80; chmn., pres. Wheel Horse Products, Inc., South Bend, Ind., 1974-80; chmn. Ingersoll Products Corp., Chgo., 1980-86; pres. Wellmax, Inc., 1976—; Served with USNR, 1944-46. Mem. Case Inst. Tech. Alumni Assn., Harvard Bus. Sch. Alumni Assn., Tau Beta Pi, Theta Tau. Clubs: Detroit Athletic, Economics, Chicago, Old Club. Home: 3541 Bradway Blvd Bloomfield Village MI 48301 Office: Ste 330 6905 Telegraph Rd Bloomfield Hills MI 48301

MAXWELL, JOE, state representative, lawyer; b. Kirksville, Mo., Mar. 17, 1957; s. Robert E. and Molly B. Maxwell; m. Sarah Maxwell; children: Megan, Elizabeth. BS in Secondary Edn., Social Studies, U. Mo., 1986, JD, 1990. Farmer Rush Hill, Mo., 1976-78; ptnr., operator Maxwell Svc., Laddonia, Mo., 1978-84; rural mail carrier U.S. Postal Svc., Rush Hill, 1980-84; outstate field coord. Travis Morrison's Campaign for State Auditor, Mo., 1986; Mo. state field coord. Richard Gephardt for Pres., 1986-87; atty. Mexico, Mo., 1992—; state rep. State of Mo., 1991—; vice chmn. budget com. Mo. Ho. of Reps., mem. agri-bus. com., elem. and secondary com., energy and environ. com., social svcs., Medicaid and the elderly com., co-chmn. joint com. ADA, co-chmn. joint com. welfare reform, show me health reform. Assoc. editor-in-chief Mo. Jour. of Dispute Resolution, 1989, candidate, 1988. Mem. Am. Legion, 1982—; adj. Post 510, 1982-84; mem. Young Dem. Clubs Mo., 1982—, jud. coun. young dems. Am., 1985, pres., 1984-87, 9th congl. dist. chmn., 1982; mem. Laddonia Bapt. Ch., 1975—, Sunday sch. tchr., 1990-91, pulpit com.; bd. dirs. Handi-Shop Inc., Mexico, 1981-84, mimeo. and mktg. com., 1982-84; bd. dirs. Boy Scouts Am., Troop 94, 1980-82. 1st sgt. Mo. N.G., 1986—. Recipient St. Louis Globe Dem. award for outstanding achievement, 1979, Cert. of Appreciation, Troop 94, Boy Scouts Am., 1982, Mo.'s Outstanding Male Young Dem. award, 1987, George B. Freeman award for outstanding svc., 1987, Appreciation award Mo. Bar, 1992, Mo. Ho. of Reps. Resolution # 624 for exceptional svc. Mo., 1987, Mo. State Senate Resolution # 382 for exceptional svc. Mo., 1987; named one of Outstanding Young Men of Am., 1983, 85. Mem. Moose, Jaycees (Laddonia chpt. pres. 1978-79, coord. Laddonia Area Blood Drive, coord. Laddonia City Clean-up Day, chmn. Mexico Soybean Festival 1989, chmn. Lenten Breakfast 1990, Presdl. award of honor 1979), Kappa Delta Pi, Golden Key Nat. Honor Soc. Home: PO Box 517 Mexico MO 65101 Office: State Rep Rm 235B State Capitol Bldg Jefferson City MO 65101

MAXWELL, JOHN RAYMOND, artist; b. Rochester, N.Y., Nov. 3, 1909; s. Herbert F. and Esther Helen (Donovan) M.; m. Phyllis Mitchell Custer, Sept. 9, 1968. Student, Rochester Inst. Tech., U. Rochester, Provincetown Workshop; studied with nationally known artists including V. Candell, L. Manso, C. Peters, and A. Clements. Past pres. Nat. Advt. Agy., Phila., N.Y.C., L.A. Arts in oil, watercolor, acrylic. Exhbns. include Nat. Acad. of Design, Am. Watercolor Soc., Toledo Mus., Ohio, Richmond Mus., Va., Norfolk Mus., Va., Smithsonian Instn., Art Inst. Chgo., Lehigh U., San Francisco Palace Legion Honor, Corcoran Gallery, Rutgers U., U. Pa., William Penn Mus., Harrisburg, Pa.; represented in permanent collections Phila. Mus. Art, Nat. Acad. Design, Butler Inst. Am. Art, Wichita State U., Allentown (Pa.) Art Mus., U. Pa. Sci. Ctr., Lehigh U., Am. Coll., Phila., Woodmere Mus., Phila.; represented in pvt. collections in U.S., Can. and abroad; work featured in several books on contemporary painting; works reviewed in newspapers and jours.; contbr. articles on art and artists to nat. mags. Recipient Dana medals Pa. Acad. Fine Arts, Soc. Painters Casein and Acrylic, Purchase prizes Butler Inst. Am. Art, Woodmere Mus. Mem. NAD (Altman prize), Am. Watercolor Soc. (silver and bronze honor medals, other prizes), Audubon Artists, Allied Artists Am., Nat. Soc. Painters in Watercolor & Acrylic, Phila. Sketch Club (Gold medals). Studio: 415 Holly Ln Wynnewood PA 19096

MAXWELL, MALCOLM, college president, minister; b. Watford, Eng., Apr. 6, 1934; s. Rachel Elizabeth (Joyce) M.; m. Eileen J. Bolander, Aug. 25, 1955; children: Wendy E. Maxwell Henderson, D. Kevin. BA in Theology and Biblical Langs., Pacific Union Coll., 1956; MA in Systematic Theology, Andrews U., 1958; PhD in Biblical Studies New Testament, Drew U., 1968. Pastor No. Calif. Conf. Seventh-Day Adventists, Oakland, Calif., 1956-64; instr. in religion Union Coll., Lincoln, Nebr., 1964-65; prof. in religion Walla Walla Coll., College Place, Wash., 1965-78, v.p. acad. affairs, 1978-83; pres. Pacific Union Coll., Angwin, Calif., 1983—. Bd. trustees St. Helena Hosp., Deer Park, Calif., 1983—, Rio Linda Acad., Healdsburg, Calif., 1983—; bd. dirs. Adventist Health Sys./West, Roseville, Calif., 1983—. Rockefeller fellow, 1967-68; Drew U. scholar, 1967-68; named Tchr. of Yr., Wash. State Auto Assn., 1971. Mem. Soc. Biblical Lit., Rotary. Avocations: golf, boatings, gardening. Office: Pacific Union Coll 1 Angwin Ave Angwin CA 94508

MAXWELL, NEAL A., church executive; m. Colleen Hinckley; four children. B in Polit. Sci., M in Polit. Sci., U. Utah, LLD (hon.); LLD (hon.), Brigham Young U.; LittD (hon.), Westminster Coll.; HD (hon.), Utah State U., Ricks Coll. Legis. asst. U.S. sen. Wallace F. Bennett, Utah; exec. v.p. U. Utah, Salt Lake City; various ch. positions including bishop Salt Lake City's Univ. Sixth Ward, mem. gen. bd. youth orgn., adult correlation com. and one of first Regional Reps. of the Twelve; dept. Ch. Jesus Christ Latter Day Sts., Asst. to the Council of Twelve, 1974-76, mem. of Presidency of First Quorum of the Seventy, 1976-81, mem. of Council of Twelve Apostles, 1981—; bd. dirs. Quester Corp., Deseret News Pub. Co. Mem. Quorum of the Twelve Ch. of Jesus Christ of Latter-day Saints, Salt Lake City. Recipient Liberty Bell award Utah State Bar, 1967; named Pub.

Adminstr. of Yr. Inst. Govt. Service Brigham Young U., 1973. Office: LDS Church Quorum of the Twelve 47 E South Temple Salt Lake City UT 84150

MAXWELL, RAYMOND ROGER, accountant; b. Parmer County, Tex., Jan. 7, 1918; s. Frederick W. and Hazel Belle (Rogers) M.; m. Jeanne Hollarn, June 16, 1945 (dec. Dec. 1987); children: Donald R., Bruce Edward, Sabrina G. Spiering Warren Kleinecke. Ed.B., Western Ill. State Tchrs Coll., 1941; MBA in Acctg., U. Fla., 1949; postgrad., UCLA, 1965-68. CPA, Fla., Calif. Asst. to bus. mgr. Western Ill. State Tchrs. Coll., Macomb, 1939-41; apprentice acct. Charles H. Lindfors, CPA, Ft. Lauderdale, Fla., 1946-48; acct./auditor Frederic Dunn-Rankin & Co. CPA, Miami, Fla., 1948-49; CPA staff Charles Costar, CPA, Miami, 1951; resident auditor/CPA prin. Raymond R. Maxwell CPA, Ft. Lauderdale, 1951-56; supt. pub. instrn. Broward County, Ft. Lauderdale, 1956-61; staff asst. in fin. North Am. Aviation, Inc., El Segundo, Calif., 1961-65; tchr. Calif. Polytechnic, 1967; acctg. prin. Raymond R. Maxwell, CPA, Whittier, Calif., 1968—; tchr. Calif. State U., Fullerton, 1989; part-time rsch. asst. UCLA, 1965, teaching asst., 1966, 67; instr. Calif. Poly., 1967. Active precinct election bds., Whittier, L.A. County, 1989; 1st reader First Ch. of Christ, Scientist, Whittier, 1990-92, exec. bd., 1989, exec. bd. chmn., 1993, participant Bible Explorations, 1991-92. 1st lt. USAAF, 1942-46. Republican. Avocations: dancing, swimming. Office: Unit # C 13217 Whittier Blvd Whittier CA 90602-3050

MAXWELL, RICHARD CALLENDER, lawyer, educator; b. Mpls., Oct. 7, 1919; s. Bertram Wayburn and Blossom (Callender) M.; m. Frances Lida McKay, Jan 27, 1942; children—Richard Callender, John McKay. B.S.L., U. Minn., 1941, LL.B., 1947; LL.D. (hon.), Calif. Western U., 1983; LLD (hon.), Southwestern U., 1993. Assoc. prof. U. N.D., 1947-49; assoc. prof. U. Tex., 1949-51, prof., 1951-53; counsel Amerada Petroleum Corp., 1952-53; prof. UCLA, 1953-81; dean UCLA (Sch. Law), 1959-69, Connell prof., 1979-81, Connell prof. emeritus, 1981—; Chadwick prof. Duke U. Sch. Law, 1981-89, Chadwick prof. emeritus, 1989—; vis. prof. Columbia U., 1955; vis. Alumni prof. U. Minn., 1970-71; Fulbright lectr. Queen's U., No. Ireland, 1970; vis. Ford Found. prof. U. Singapore, 1971; Thompson prof. U. Colo., 1982; vis. prof. Hastings Coll. Law, 1976, Duke U., 1979-80, U. Tex., 1985; pres. Minn. Law Rev., 1946; chmn. Council Legal Edn. Opportunity, 1971-72; pres. Assn. Am. Law Schs., 1972; chmn. adv. com. law Fulbright Program, 1971-74, chmn. adv. com. U.K., 1974-77; mem. com. on gas prodn. opportunities NRC, 1977-78; mem. law sch. editorial and adv. bd. West Pub. Co., 1971-94. Author: (with S. A. Riesenfeld) Cases and Materials on Modern Social Legislation, 1950, (with H.R. Williams and C.J. Meyers) Cases on Oil and Gas Law, 1956, 6th edit., (with Stephen F. Williams, Patrick H. Martin, Bruce M. Kramer), 1992, (with S. A. Riesenfeld) California Cases on Security Transactions, 1957, 4th edit. (with S.A. Riesenfeld, J.R. Hetland, W.D. Warren), 1991; West Coast editor Oil and Gas Reporter, 1953—. Mem. Los Angeles Employee Relations Bd., 1971-74; bd. dirs. Constl. Rights Found., 1963-81; trustee Calif. Western U., 1979-81; bd. visitors Duke U. Sch. Law, 1973-79, chmn. bd. Pvt. Adjudication Ctr., 1984-89; bd. visitors Southwestern U. Sch. Law, 1981—. Served to lt. comdr. USNR, 1941-46. Recipient Disting. Tchg. award UCLA, 1977, Duke Law Sch., 1986, UCLA medal, 1982, Clyde O. Martz Tchg. award Rocky Mountain Mineral Law Found., 1994. Mem. ABA (com. on youth edn. for citizenship 1975-79, spl. com. on public understanding about the law 1979-84), Order of Coif. (nat. exec. com. 1980-86). Office: Duke U Sch Law Durham NC 27708-0362

MAXWELL, ROBERT EARL, federal judge; b. Elkins, W.Va., Mar. 15, 1924; s. Earl L. and Nellie E. (Rexstrew) M.; m. Ann Marie Grabowski, Mar. 29, 1948; children—Mary Ann, Carol Lynn, Ellen Lindsay, Earl Wilson. Student, Davis and Elkins Coll., LLD (hon.), Elkins, W.Va. U., 1949; LLD (hon.), Davis and Elkins Coll., 1984. Bar: W.Va. 1949. Practiced in Randolph County, 1949, pros. atty., 1952-61; U.S. atty. for No. Dist. W.Va., 1961-64; judge U.S. Dist. Ct. (no. dist.) W.Va., Elkins, 1965—; Temp. Emergency Ct. of Appeals, 1980-89; past chmn. budget com. Jud. Conf. U.S.; former mem. exec. com. Nat. Conf. Fed. Trial Judges; former mem. adv. bd. W.Va. U. Mem. bd. advisors W.Va. U., past chmn.; bd. advisors Mary Babb Randolph Cancer Ctr. Recipient Alumni Disting. Svc. award Davis and Elkins Coll., 1969, Religious Heritage Am. award, 1979, Outstanding Trial Judge award W.Va. Trial Lawyers Assn., 1988, Order of Valdalia award W.Va. U., Outstanding Alumnus award, 1992, Tenured Faculty Mem. Recognition award Bd. Govs., Def. Trial Coun., W.Va., 1992, Cert. of Merit, W.Va. State Bar, 1994, Justitia Officium award Coll. of Law, W.Va. U., 1994. Mem. Nat. Conf. Federal Trial Judges, Dist. Judges Assn. 4th Cir. (past pres.), Moose (life), Lions (life), Beta Alpha Beta (merit award), Elkins-Randolph County C. of C. (citizen of yr. 1994). Office: US Dist Ct No Dist PO Box 1275 Elkins WV 26241-1275

MAXWELL, ROBERT HAWORTH, agriculture educator, college dean; b. Earlham, Iowa, Oct. 8, 1927; s. Charles Erich and Mildred Grace M.; m. Betty Ruth Michener, Dec. 24, 1950; children: Robert Steven, Daniel Guy, Timothy Charles, Kristen Kimuli. Student, Earlham Coll., 1946-48; BS in Farm Ops., Iowa State U., 1950, MS in Agrl. Edn., 1964; PhD in Agrl. Edn., Cornell U., 1970. Cert. tchr., Iowa. Farm operator Iowa, 1952-60; instr. Earlham Coll., Richmond, Ind., 1960-62; tchr. vocat. agr. Earlham (Iowa) Community Sch., 1963-64; asst. prof. agrl. edn. W.Va. U., Morgantown, 1964-68, assoc. prof. agrl. edn., 1970-75, prof. agrl. edn., 1975-79, asst. dean coll. agr. & forestry, acting chmn. divsn. animal & vet. scis., 1980, assoc. dean coll. agr. & forestry, chmn. divsn. internat. agr. & forestry, 1980-84, interim dean coll. agr. & forestry, interim dir. W.Va. agrl. & forestry experiment sta., 1984-85, dean coll. agr. & forestry, dir. W.Va. agrl. & forestry experiment sta., 1985-93; prof. agrl., coord. internat. agrl. U. W.Va., Morgantown, 1994—; vocat. agr. tchr. Dexfield Community Schs., Redfield, Iowa, 1958-60; grad. asst. dept. edn. Cornell U., 1969-70; contract AID agrl. edn. advisor Kenya Ministry Edn., 1960-62, 64-68, spl. asst. dir. manpower devel. divsn. Tanzania Ministry Agr., 1975-79; dir. Allegheny Highlands Project, 1970-75; bd. dirs. Northeast Regional Ctr. Rural Devel., W.Va. U. Rsch. Corp.; lectr. in field. Author: (with others) Agriculture for Primary School series, 1979, 82, 85; editor Empire State Vo-Ag Teacher Jour., 1969-70; pub. papers and reports; contbr. articles to profl. jours. Unit leader United Way, Elkins, W.Va., 1970-75, Morgantown, 1979-93. With U.S. Army, 1950-52. Named W.Va. Agr. and Forestry Hall of Fame, 1995, Disting. West Virginian, Gov. W.Va., 1993; recipient Commemorative medal U. Agr., Nitra, Slovakia, 1993. Mem. AAAS, Am. Assn. Agrl. Edn., Am. Farmland Trust (life), Am. Soc. Agrl. Conss. (Meritorious Svc. award 1994), Am. Soc. Agrl. Conss. Internat. (cert., bd. dirs.), Nat. Assn. Colls. and Tchrs. Agr., Nat. Peace Inst., World Future Soc., Soc. Internat. Devel., Assn. Internat. Agrl. and Extension Educators (pres.-elect, pres. 1994, Outstanding Svc. 1991), Assn. Internat. Agr. and Rural Devel. (Outstanding Svc. 1992), Coun. Agrl. Sci. and Tech., Northeast Regional Assn. Agrl. Experiment Sta. Dirs. (Svc. Commendation 1993), UN Assn. of the USA, Soil and Water Conservation Soc. (life), Kenya Assn. Tchrs. Agr. (life), Tanzanian Soc. Agr. Edn. and Extension (life), W.Va. Shepherd's Fedn., W.Va. Poultry Assn., W.Va. Cattlemen's Assn., W.Va. Farm Bur., Iowa Farm Bur., W.Va. Grassland Coun., W.Va. Horticultural Soc., Agriculture and Forestry Hall of Fame Found. W.Va. (past pres.), Upshur Livestock Assn. (life), Morgantown Rotary Club, Iowa State U. Alumni Assn. (life), Cornell U. Alumni Assn. (life), W.Va. U. Alumni Assn. (life), FFA Alumni Assn. (life), Phi Delta Kappa, Gamma Sigma Delta, Alpha Zeta, Phi Mu Alpha (life). Mem. Soc. of Friends. Home: 4009 Cedar Ct Morgantown WV 26505 Office: W Va Univ Coll Agriculture & Forestry Evansdale Campus PO Box 6108 Morgantown WV 26506-6108

MAXWELL, ROBERT OLIVER, insurance company executive; b. Sioux City, Iowa, Sept. 23, 1940; s. Lyle Charles and Corinne Zenobia (Knudson) M.; m. Carol Marie Lejchar, June 23, 1973; 1 child, Todd Robert. BS in Mktg., Drake U., 1962. Office mgr. Occidental Life Ins. Co. L.A., 1962-68; sales rep. William Volker & Co., L.A., 1968-70; mgr. sales office State Farm Ins. Co., Palos Verdes, Calif., 1970-71; pres., CEO Congress Life Ins. Co., Mpls., 1971—; also bd. dirs. Congress Life Ins. Co.; pres., CEO Security Ins. Co., Mpls., 1971—; also bd. dirs. Security Ins. Co. With U.S. Army, 1963-69. Mem. Hazeltine Golf Club. Republican. Lutheran. Home: 15034 Boulder Pointe Rd Eden Prairie MN 55347-2410 Office: Security Life Ins Co 10901 Red Circle Dr Minnetonka MN 55343

MAXWELL, ROBERT WALLACE, II, lawyer; b. Waynesburg, Pa., Sept. 6, 1943; s. Robert Wallace and Margaret M.; m. Mamie Lee Payne, June 18, 1966; children—Robert William. B.S. magna cum laude, Hampden-Sydney Coll., 1965; J.D. with honors, Duke U., 1968. Bar: Ohio 1968. Assoc. Taft, Stettinius & Hollister, Cin., 1968-75, ptnr., 1975-88; ptnr. Keating Muething & Klekamp, 1988—; part-time instr. U. Cin. Sch. Law, 1975-76. Bd. dirs. Contemporary Arts Ctr. of Cin; bd. dirs. Cin. Ballet Co.; elder Wyoming First Presbyterian Ch. Mem. ABA, Am. Assn. Mus. Trustees. Republican. Home: 535 Larchmont Dr Cincinnati OH 45215-4215 Office: Keating Muething & Klekamp 1 E 4th St Cincinnati OH 45202-3717

MAXWELL, W(ILBUR) RICHARD, management consultant; b. Troy, Ohio, June 20, 1920; s. Wilbur D. and Gertrude (McDowell) M.; m. Roberta Mae Kennedy, June 29, 1942; children: Douglas R., Jean Ann. Student, Ohio Wesleyan U., 1938-41; BS, Richmond Profl. Inst. of Coll. William and Mary, 1955. Sec. Troy C. of C., 1948-50, Va. C. of C., 1950-55; asst. to pres./chmn. bd. Reynolds Metals Co., 1955-64; v.p., dir. Reynolds Fgn. Sales Inc., 1964-68; pres. Nat. Better Bus. Bur., 1968-70; pres., chief exec. officer Jr. Achievement, Inc., Stamford, Conn., 1970-82; instr. Richmond Profl. Inst., part-time 1955-57; sponsor-trustee U. Va. Grad. Bus. Sch., 1963-72. Pres., Lancaster County Libr., 1984-85, Rappahannock Gen. Hosp. Found., 1989-90, Northern Neck Vocat.-Tech. Edn. Ctr., 1991-93; bd. dirs. Rappahannock Gen. Hosp., 1988-90, Richmond (Va.) Cmty. H.S., 1989-91; chmn. Northumberland County (Va.) Econ. Devel. Commn., 1994—. With USAAF, USN, 1942-45. Recipient Albert Schweitzer award Hugh O'Brien Youth Fedn., 1982; inducted Jr. Achievement Profl. Hall of Fame, 1986. Mem. Indian Creek Yacht and Country Club (v.p., 1991-93, bd. dirs. 1991-93). Home: PO Box 1090 Kilmarnock VA 22482-1090

MAXWELL, WILLIAM, writer; b. Lincoln, Ill., Aug. 16, 1908; s. William Keepers and Eva Blossom (Blinn) M.; m. Emily Gilman Noyes, May 17, 1945; children: Katharine Farrington, Emily Brooke. Student, U. Ill., 1926-30, 31-33, D.Litt., 1973; student, Harvard U., 1930-31. Mem. English faculty U. Ill., 1931-33; editorial staff New Yorker mag., 1936-76. Author: Bright Center of Heaven, 1934, They Came Like Swallows, 1937, 88, The Folded Leaf, 1945, 81, The Heavenly Tenants, 1946, Time Will Darken It, 1948, 83, (with Jean Stafford, John Cheever, Daniel Fuchs) Stories, 1956, The Chateau, 1961, 85, 95, The Old Man at the Railroad Crossing, 1966, 87, Ancestors, 1971, 85, 94, Over by the River, 1977, 84, Editor: The Garden and the Wilderness, by Charles Pratt, 1980, So Long, See You Tomorrow, 1979, 89, The Outermost Dream, 1989, Billie Dyer 1992, 93, All the Days and Nights, 1995; also stories, book reviews.; editor: Letters of Sylvia Townsend Warner, 1982. Recipient William Dean Howells medal Am. Acad. Inst. Arts and Letters, 1980; Am. Book award, 1982; Brandeis U. Creative arts award medal for fiction, 1984; Ivan Sandrof award Nat. Book Critics Circle, 1994. Mem. Nat. Inst. Arts and Letters (pres. 1969-72), Am. Acad. of Arts and Letters. Club: Century Assn. (N.Y.C.). Home: 544 E 86th St New York NY 10028-7536

MAXWELL, WILLIAM HALL CHRISTIE, civil engineering educator; b. Coleraine, County Londonderry, Northern Ireland, Jan. 25, 1936; came to U.S., 1958, naturalized, 1967; s. William Robert and Catherine Dempsey (Christie) M.; m. Mary Carolyn McLaughlin, Sept. 28, 1960; children: Katrina, Kevin, Wendy, Liam. B.Sc., Queen's U., Belfast, No. Ireland, 1956; M.Sc., Queen's U., Kingston, Ont., Can., 1958; Ph.D. U. Minn., 1964. Registered profl. engr., Ill. Site engr. Motor Columbus AG, Baden, Switzerland, 1956; teaching asst. Queen's U., 1956-58; research asst. to instr. U. Minn., Mpls., 1959-64; asst. prof. civil engring. U. Ill., Urbana, 1964-70, assoc. prof., 1970-82, prof., 1982—. Editor: Water Resources Management in Industrial Areas, 1982; Water for Human Consumption, Man and His Environment, 1983; Frontiers in Hydrology, 1984. Vestryman, Emmanuel Meml. Episcopal Ch., Champaign, Ill., 1977-80. State exhibitor Ministry Edn., Stormont, No. Ireland 1953-56; Queen's U. Found. scholar, Belfast, 1954-56; R.S. McLaughlin travelling fellow Queen's U., 1958-59. Fellow ASCE (com. chmn. 1982-83), Internat. Water Resources Assn. (editor-in-chief Water Internat. 1986-93, sr. editor 1994—, mem. publs. com. 1980—, v.p. U.S. geog. com. 1986-91, chmn. awards com. 1995—, bd. dirs. 1995—, Editl. award 1994), mem. Internat. Assn. for Hydraulic Research, Am. Geophys. Union. Avocations: camping, fishing, home construction, oil painting. Home: 1210 Devonshire Dr Champaign IL 61821-6527 Office: Univ Illinois Dept Civil Engring 205 N Mathews Ave Urbana IL 61801-2352

MAXWELL, WILLIAM LAUGHLIN, industrial engineering educator; b. Phila., July 11, 1934; s. William Henry and Elizabeth (Laughlin) M.; m. Judith Behrens, July 5, 1969; children: Deborah, William, Judith, Keely. BMechE, Cornell U., 1957, PhD, 1961. Andrew Schultz Jr. prof. dept. indsl. engring. Cornell U., Ithaca, N.Y., 1961—. Author: Theory of Scheduling, 1967. Recipient Disting. Teaching award Cornell Soc. Engrs., 1968. Fellow Inst. Indsl. Engrs.; mem. Ops. Rsch. Soc., Soc. Mfg. Engrs. Home: 106 Lake Ave Ithaca NY 14850-3537 Office: Cornell U Dept Indsl Engring Ithaca NY 14850

MAXWELL, WILLIAM STIRLING, retired lawyer; b. Chgo., May 2, 1922; s. W. Stirling and Ethel (Bowes) Maxwell Reineke. A.B. with distinction, U. Mich., 1947, postgrad., 1946-49, J.D., 1949. Bar: Ill. 1949, U.S. Ct. Mil. Appeals 1951, U.S. Supreme Ct. 1952. Assoc. Sidley & Austin, Chgo., 1949-60, 61, ptnr., 1962-84; now ret.; sr. legis. counsel U.S. Treasury, Washington, 1960-61. Trustee Mid-North Animal Shelter Found., Chgo., 1971—. Mem. Order of Coif, Phi Beta Kappa. Republican. Episcopalian. Clubs: Law, Legal (Chgo.). Home: PO Box 1776 Brookings OR 97415-0058

MAXWORTHY, TONY, mechanical and aerospace engineering educator; b. London, May 21, 1933; came to U.S., 1954, naturalized, 1961; s. Ernest Charles and Gladys May (Butson) M.; m. Emily Jean Parkinson, June 20, 1956 (div. 1974); children: Kirsten, Kara; m. Anna Barbara Parks, May 21, 1979. BS in Engring., U. London, 1954; MSE, Princeton U., 1955; PhD, Harvard U., 1959. Research asst. Harvard U., Cambridge, Mass., 1955-59; sr. scientist, group supr. Jet Propulsion Lab., Pasadena, Calif., 1960-67, cons., 1968—; assoc. prof. U. So. Calif., Los Angeles, 1967-70, prof., 1970—. Smith Internat. prof. mech. and aero. engring.; 1988—, chmn. dept. mech. engring., 1979-89; cons. BBC Rsch. Ctr., Baden, Switzerland, 1972—, J.P.L., Pasadena, Calif., 1968—; lectr. Woods Hole Oceanographic Inst., Mass., summers 1965, 70, 72, 83; Forman vis. prof. in aeronautics Tech. Haifa, 1986; vis. prof. U. Poly, Madrid, 1988, Inst. Sop. Tech., Lisbon, 1988, E.T.H., Zürich, 1989, E.P.F., Lausanne, 1989—. Mem. editorial bd. Geophys. Fluid Dynamics, 1973-79, 88—, Dynamic Atmospheric Oceans, 1976-83, Phys. Fluids, 1978-81, Zeitschrift fuer Angewandte Mathematik und Physik, 1987—; contbr. articles to profl. jours. Recipient Humboldt Sr. Scientist award 1981-83; fellow Cambridge U., 1974, Australian Nat. U., 1978, Nat. Ctr. Atmospheric Research, 1976, Glennon fellow U. Western Australia, 1990, Sr. Queen's fellow in Marine Scis., Commonwealth of Australia, 1984; recipient Halliburton award U. So. Calif., 1980, Otto Laporte award Am. Physics Soc., 1990. Fellow Am. Phys. Soc. (chmn. exec. com. fluid dynamics div. 1974-79); mem. NAE, Am. Meteorol. Soc., Am. Geophys. Union, ASME (fluid mechs. com.), European Geophys. Soc. Office: U So Calif Dept Mech Engring Exposition Park Los Angeles CA 90089-1453

MAY, ADOLF DARLINGTON, civil engineering educator; b. Little Rock, Mar. 25, 1927; s. Adolf Darlington and Inez (Shelton) M.; m. Margaret Folsom, Dec. 23, 1948; children—Dolf, Barbara, David, Larry. B.Sc. in Civil Engring. So. Meth. U., 1949; M.Sc., Iowa State U., 1950; Ph.D, Purdue U., 1955. Asst. prof., then assoc. prof. Clarkson Coll. Tech., 1952-56; assoc. prof. Mich. State U., 1956-59; research engr. Thompson-Ramo Wooldridge, 1959-62; project dir. Ill. Div. Hwys., 1962-65; mem. faculty U. Calif., Berkeley, 1965—, prof. civil engring., 1965-91, prof. emeritus, 1991—; guest prof. numerous univs., 1965—, cons. to industry, 1965—. Contbr. to profl. jours.,books. Served with USNR, 1944-47. Recipient Disting. Engring. Alumnus award Purdue U., 1978; Fulbright scholar to Netherlands, 1977; German Humboldt Scholarship awardee, 1980. Mem. ASCE (Turner award 1994), Transp. Rsch. Bd. (Disting. Lectr. award 1994), Nat. Acad. Engring. (Matson Transp. Rsch. award 1992), AAm. Soc. Engring. Edn., Inst. Traffic Engrs., Sigma Xi, Tau Beta Pi. Home: 1645 Julian Dr El Cerrito CA 94530-2011 Office: U Calif Dept of Civil Engring 114 McLaughlin Hall Berkeley CA 94720

MAY, ARTHUR W., former Canadian government official, educator; b. St. John's, Nfld., Can., June 29, 1937; s. William J. and Florence (Dawe) M.; m. Sonia Susan Streeter, Aug. 18, 1958; children—Stephen J., Heather E., Maria S., Douglas W. BSc with honors, Meml. U., St. John's, 1958; MSc, Meml. U., 1964; PhD, McGill U., Montreal, Que., Can., 1966; D of Univ. (hon.), U. Ottawa, 1988; DSc (hon.), Meml. U. Nfld., 1989; LLD (hon.), Brock U., 1992. Sci. adviser internat. fisheries Dept. Fisheries, Ottawa, Ont., Can., 1971-73; dir. Nfld. biol. sta. Dept. Fisheries, St. John's, 1973-75; dir. gen. resource services Dept. Fisheries, Ottawa, 1975-78; asst. dep. minister Atlantic Dept. Fisheries and Oceans, Ottawa, 1978-82; dep. minister Dept. Fisheries and Oceans, 1982-86; pres. Natural Sci. and Engring. Rsch. Coun. Canada, 1986-90; pres., vice chancellor Meml. U. Nfld., St. Johns, 1990—; v.p. Internat. Coun. for Exploration of Seas, Copenhagen, 1977-79; mem. Task Force on Atlantic Fisheries, Ottawa, 1982; mem. Nat. Adv. Bd. Sci. and Tech., 1988-90. Contbr. articles to profl. jours. Served to sub. lt. Can. Navy, 1955-58. Recipient Gov.-Gen.'s medal Nfld. Dept. Edn., St. John's, 1954, Gov.-Gen.'s medal Meml. U. of Nfld., 1958; named Alumnus of Yr., Meml. U., 1983. Mem. N.W. Atlantic Fisheries Orgn. (pres. 1977-80). Anglican. Avocations: gardening; philately. Home: 20 Baker St, Saint John's, NF Canada A1A 5A7 Office: Meml Univ Nfld, Saint John's, NF Canada A1C 5S7

MAY, BRUCE BARNETT, lawyer; b. Portland, Oreg., Apr. 16, 1948; s. Ralph Barnett May and Barbara (Newton) Evans; m. Deborah Sue Wright, Jan. 22, 1972; children: Alexander, Christopher, Elizabeth, Andrew. BA, Princeton U., 1971; JD, U. Oreg., 1978. Bar: Ariz. 1978. Ptnr. Streich Lang, Phoenix, 1978—; lectr. various bar and trade assns. Contbr. articles to profl. jours. Dir Phoenix Mountain Preservation Coun., 1985-89; mem. Paradise Valley Urban Village Planning Com., Phoenix, 1985-87; mem. Men's Art Coun., 1987-91. Lt. (j.g.) USN, 1972-75. Mem. ABA (chmn. land sales regulation com., vice chair div. CLE), Am. Coll. Real Estate Lawyers, Order of Coif. Republican. Episcopalian. Avocations: book collecting, running. Home: 4616 E Shadow Rock Rd Phoenix AZ 85028-6106 Office: Streich Lang 100 W Washington Ste 2100 Phoenix AZ 85003-0471

MAY, CHARLES KENT, lawyer; b. Pitts., Nov. 28, 1939; s. Charles Leroy and Nora Margaret (Brown) M.; m. Valerie Lynne Harrell, May 18, 1981; children: C. Kent, Kerry Elizabeth, Kathryn Lynn, Andrew John, James Davis, Grant Stevens. BA, Dickinson Coll., 1961; LLB, U. Pitts., 1964. Bar: Pa. 1965, U.S. Dist. Ct. (we. dist.) Pa. 1965. Assoc. Eckert Seamans Cherin & Mellott, Pitts., 1964-70, ptnr., 1971—, chmn. corp. bus. dept., 1986-91, mng. ptnr., 1991—, mem. exec. com., 1986-91, chmn., 1991-92; treas. BBB, Western Pa., Inc.; bd. dirs., v.p. The Pilot Group Co., Ltd.; bd. dirs. Consumers Packaging, Inc. Bd. dirs., mem. exec. com. Pitts. Pub. Theatre; bd. dirs. Mendelssohn Choir, Main St. Capital, Children's Home Pitts., 1978-79. Mem. ABA, Pa. Bar Assn., Allegheny County Bar Assn., Duquesne Club. Republican. Home: 137 Old Mill Rd Pittsburgh PA 15238-1941 Office: Eckert Seamans Cherin & Mellott 600 Grant St Pittsburgh PA 15219-2702

MAY, CLIFFORD DANIEL, newspaper editor, journalist; m. Lou Ann Brunwasser; 1 child, Miranda Rose. Cert. in Russian lang. and lit., U. Leningrad, 1972; BA, Sarah Lawrence Coll., 1973; M Journalism, Columbia U., 1975, M Internat. Affairs, 1975. Assoc. editor Newsweek, 1977-78; roving fgn. corr. Hearst Newpapers, 1978-79; sr. editor Am. edit. Geo mag., 1979-80; gen. editor Sunday Mag., Washington corr. N.Y. Times, 1980-89; chief West Africa bur. N.Y. Times, Abidjan, Ivory Coast, 1984; assoc. editor Rocky Mountain News, Denver, 1989—; spl. corr. CBS Radio News, Bill Moyers' Jour./Internat. Report-PBS-TV, 1970's; host, prodr. Roundtable, Sta. KRMA, Colo.; freelance writer, 1979-89. Contbg. editor World Press Rev. Mag.; host, prodr. roundtable Sta. KRMA, Denver, 1994—. Avocations: downhill skiing, outdoor activities. Office: Rocky Mountain News 400 W Colfax Ave Denver CO 80204-2694

MAY, DAVID L., JR., architectural firm executive. Degree in architecture, Va. Tech. U., 1975. Registered arch., Va. Founding ptnr. CMSS Archs., Virginia Beach, Va., 1982—; mem. com. for study of wind resistive design Commonwealth of Va. Dept. Housing and Cmty. Devel.; lectr. Va. Hurricane Conf., USN, City of Virginia Beach Dept. Codes and Permits, Constrn. Specifications Inst., numerous others; guest lectr. Regent U. Law Sch., 1992, 93; panelist Hurricane Aftermath Conf., Ocean City, Md., 1994. Active Cmty. Assn. Inst., Hampton Rds. United Way. Mem. AIA (bd. dirs. Hampton Rds. chpt., Soc. Am. Mil. Engrs., Hampton Rds. C. of C. Office: CMSS Archs 5041 Corp Woods Dr 200 Virginia Beach VA 23462

MAY, DONALD ROBERT LEE, ophthalmologist, retina and vitreous surgeon, educator, academic administrator; b. Spring Valley, Ill., Nov. 26, 1945; s. Reo Georg and Edna Antoinette (Klein) M.; m. Jane N. Sakauye, Nov. 12, 1988. BS in Liberal Arts and Scis. with high honors, U. Ill., 1968, MD, 1972. Diplomate Am. Bd. Ophthalmology, Nat. Bd. Med. Examiners. Med. student rsch. fellow Dept. Ophthalmology U. Ill. Eye and Ear Infirmary, Chgo., 1971-72; intern rotating internal medicine Northwestern U. Sch. Medicine Meml. Hosps., Chgo., 1972-73; resident ophthalmology U. Ill. Eye and Ear Infirmary, Chgo., 1973-76, instr. dept. Ophthalmology, 1974-77, attending surgeon dept. Ophthalmology, 1976-77; fellow in Diabetic Retinopathy study, Diabetic Retinopathy Vitrectomy study, and Retina and Vitreous Surgery U. Ill. Eye and Ear Infirmary, 1976-77; founder and dir. Retina/Vitreous/Ocular Trauma Svc of the USAF dept. Ophthalmology, Wilford Hall USAF Medical Ctr., Lackland AFB, Tex., 1977-79; asst. prof. Ophthalmology, founder, dir. Retina/Vitreous/Ocular Trauma Svc. U. Calif. Davis Sch. Medicine, Calif., 1979-81; assoc. prof. of Ophthalmology, dir. Retina/Vitreous/Ocular Trauma Svc. U. Calif. Sch. Medicine, Davis, 1981-84; prof. Ophthalmology Tulane U. Sch. Medicine, New Orleans, 1984-89, dir. med. student edn., dept. of Ophthalmology, 1985-89; dir. Ophthalmology Tulane U. Sch. Medicine div., Charity Hosp., New Orleans, 1985-89; prof. Tex. Tech. U. Health Scis. Ctr., Lubbock, Tex., 1989—; chmn. dept. ophthalmology and visual scis. Tex. Tech. U. Health Scis. Ctr., Lubbock, 1989-94; prof. dept. health ope. mgmt. Tex. Tech U Health Scis. Ctr., Lubbock, 1993—, assoc. dean Sch. Medicine, 1994—; co-investigator in the Intraocular Gentamicin Prophylaxis Study, Govt. Erskine Hosp. Madurai, So. India, 1975, Dept. Ophthalmology, Audie Murphy VA Hosp., San Antonio, 1977-79, Martinez VA Hosp., Calif., 1979-84, VA Hosp., New Orleans, 1984-89, VA Med. Ctr., Alexandria, La., 1985-89, VA Med. Ctr., Big Spring, Tex., 1989—, VA Ctr., Lubbock, Tex., 1989-92; cons. People's Republic China, 1980, 82, 85, Japan, 1982, 83, 85; vis. prof. Germany, 1984, Switzerland, 1987; 1st v.p. U.S. Eye Injury Registry, 1990-92, pres.-elect, 1992-94, pres., 1994—; med. dir., Tex. Eye Injury Registry. Contbg. editor Ocutome/Fragmatome Newsletter, 1978-81; assoc. editor Vitreoretinal Surgery and Tech., 1989—; contbr. articles to profl. jours.; appeared in numerous TV and radio programs. Mem. coms. Sch. Medicine, U. Calif., Davis, Tulane U. Sch. Medicine, New Orleans, Am. Acad. Ophthalmology, San Francisco, Sch. Medicine Tex. Tech. U. Health Scis. Ctr., U. Med. Ctr., Lubbock. Maj. USAF, 1973-80. Decorated Air Force Commendation medal. Mem. Am. Acad. Ophthalmology (com. on internat. ophthalmology, bylaws and rules com.), Am. Coll. of Surgeons, Am. Med. Assn., Assn. for Rsch in Vision and Ophthalmology, Chinese Am. Ophthalmological Soc. (charter mem.), Christian Med. Soc., Lubbock-Crosby-Garza County Med. Soc., Southern Med. Assn., So. Retina Study Group (steering com. 1987-89), Tex. Med. Assn. (continuing edn. 1993—), Tex. Ophthalmological Assn. (chair edn. com. 1990-93, coun. 1990-93, mem. nominating com., 1991-93), Tex. Tech Rsch. Found. (bd. dirs. 1993—), The Pan-Am. Assn. of Ophthalmology, The Retina Soc., The Vitreous Soc. (charter mem.), World Eye Found. (bd. dirs. 1982—), Soc. Med. Consultants to Armed Forces, Sigma Xi (sec. Tex. Tech chpt 1990-91). Republican. Lutheran. Avocations: farming, travel, photography, cycling, hiking. Home: PO Box 1678 Lubbock TX 79408-1678 Office: Tex Tech U Health Scis Ctr Sch Medicine Office of Dean Lubbock TX 79430 *If we are to survive as a free society, we must each accept responsibility. The individual must function on the premise that personal rewards come with the investment of hard, honest work and not as a right mediated by government at the expense of others. Our legislative bodies must enact laws for the common good and not for individual self-interest. Our judicial systems must provide for the just enforcement of our laws. Our leadership must be the watchdog to ensure the indivdual has the opportunity to life without unreasonable danger, the freedom to follow one's dreams, and the ability to pursue happiness through* *individual achievement. Security comes with the contribution of all who are able.*

MAY, EDGAR, former state legislator, nonprofit administrator; b. Zurich, Switzerland, June 27, 1929; came to U.S., 1940, naturalized, 1954; s. Ferdinand and Renee (Bloch) M. B.J. with highest distinction, Northwestern U., 1957. Reporter, acting editor Bellows Falls (Vt.) Times, 1951-53; reporter Fitchburg (Mass.) Sentinel, 1953; part time reporter Chgo. Tribune, 1955-57; reporter Buffalo Evening News, 1958-61; dir. pub. welfare projects State Charities Aid Assn., 1962-64; mem. President's Task Force on War Against Poverty, 1964; spl. asst. to dir., asst. dir. Office Econ. Opportunity, 1964; spl. adviser to Ambassador Sargent Shriver, 1968-70; cons. Ford Found., 1970-75; mem. Vt. Ho. of Reps., 1975-82; mem. Vt. Senate, 1983-91, chmn. com. appropriations; project dir. Vt. Jud. Mgmt. Study, 1992; COO Spl. Olympics Internat., Washington, 1993—. Author: The Wasted Americans, 1964. With AUS, 1953-55. Recipient Page One award Buffalo Newspaper Guild, 1959, Walter O. Bingham award, 1959; Pulitzer prize for local reporting, 1961; Merit award Northwestern U. Alumni Assn., 1962. Office: 1325 G St NW Washington DC 20005

MAY, ELAINE, actress, theatre and film director; b. Phila., Apr. 21, 1932; d. Jack Berlin; m. Marvin May (div.); 1 child, Jeannie Berlin; m. Sheldon Harnick, Mar. 25, 1962 (div. May 1963). Ed. high sch., studied Stanislavsky method of acting with Marie Ouspenskaya. Stage and radio appearances as child actor; performed with Playwright's Theatre, in student performance Miss Julie, U. Chgo.; appeared with improvisational theatre group in night club The Compass, Chgo., 1954-1957, (with Mike Nichols) appeared N.Y. supper clubs, Village Vanguard, Blue Angel, also night clubs other cities; TV debut on Jack Paar Show, 1957; also appeared in Omnibus, 1958, Dinah Shore Show, Perry Como Show, Laugh Line, Laugh-In, TV spls.; comedy albums include Improvisations to Music, An Evening with Mike Nichols and Elaine May, Mike Nichols and Elaine May Examine Doctors; weekly appearance NBC radio show Nightline; appeared (with Mike Nichols) NBC radio show, N.Y. Town Hall, 1959, An Evening with Mike Nichols and Elaine May, Golden Theatre, N.Y.C., 1960-61; theater appearances include The Office, N.Y.C., 1966, Who's Afraid of Virginia Woolf?, Long Wharf Theatre, New Haven, Conn., 1980; dir. plays The Third Ear, N.Y.C., 1964, The Goodbye People, Berkshire Theater Festival, Stockbridge, Mass., 1971, various plays at Goodman Theatre, Chgo., 1983; dir., author screenplay, actress film A New Leaf, 1972; dir. films The Heartbreak Kid, 1973, Mikey and Nicky, 1976 (writer, dir. remake 1985), Ishtar, 1987 (also writer); appeared in films Luv, 1967, California Suite, 1978 (Acad. award Best Supporting Actress 1978), In The Spirit, 1990; co-author screenplay Heaven Can Wait, 1978; author plays A Matter of Position, 1962, Not Enough Rope, 1962, Adaptation, 1969, Hot Line, 1983, Better Part of Valor, 1983, Mr. Gogol and Mr. Preen, 1991, (one act) Death Defying Acts, 1995; stage revue: (with Mike Nichols) Telephone, 1984; co-recipient (with Mike Nichols) Grammy award for comedy performance, Nat. Acad. Recording Arts & Scis., 1961. Office: care Julian Schlossberg Castle Hill Productions 1414 Ave of the Americas New York NY 10019*

MAY, ERNEST MAX, charitable organization official; b. Newark, July 24, 1913; s. Otto Bernard and Eugenie (Morgenstern) M.; m. Harriet Elizabeth Dewey, Oct. 12, 1940; children: Ernest Dewey, James Northrup, Susan Elizabeth. BA, Princeton, 1934, MA, 1935; PhD in Organic Chemistry, U. Chgo., 1938; LittD (hon.), Montclair State Coll., 1989. With Otto B. May, Inc., Newark, 1938-73; successively chemist, gen. mgr. Otto B. May, Inc., 1938-52, pres., 1952-73; trustee Youth Consultation Service Diocese of Newark, 1952-59, 61-66, 68—; pres., 1971-75; dir. Cone Mills Corp., 1961-73, mem. exec. com., 1968-71; tech. adviser to spl. rep. trade negotiations, 1964-67. Councilman, Summit, N.J., 1963-70; mem. Summit Environ. Com., 1971-75, chmn., 1974-75; pres. Family Svc. Assn. Summit, 1959-61, Mental Health Assn. Summit, 1954, Summit Coun. Chs. Christ, 1962-63; mem. exec. com. Christ Hosp., Jersey City, 1971—, v.p., chmn., 1974—; chmn. Summit Hwy. Adv. Com., 1976-94; trustee, organizer Summer Organic Chemistry Inst., Choate Sch., Wallingford, Conn.; mem. Union County Mental Health Bd., 1973-76; bd. dirs. N.J. Mental Health Assn., 1974-81; trustee Montclair (N.J.) State Univ., 1975-85, vice-chmn., 1976-80, chmn., 1980-83; adviser applied prof. psychology Rutgers U., 1976—; mem. Nat. Commn. on Nursing, 1980-83; adviser dept. music Princeton U.; trustee Assn. for Children in N.J., 1975—; Citizen's Com. on Biomed. Ethics in N.J., 1984—; advisor Nat. Exec. Svcs. Corps Health Care Consulting Group, 1994—. Fellow Am. Inst. Chemists; mem. Am. Chem. Soc., Swiss Chem. Soc., German Chem. Soc., Synthetic Organic Chem. Mfrs. Assn. (bd. govs. 1952-54, 63070, v.p 1966-68, chmn. internat. comml. rels. com. 1968-73, hon. mem.), Vol. Trustees Not-for-Profit Hosps. (trustee 1986-88, 94—), N.J. Hosp. Assn. (coun. on edn. 1990-91), Nat. Exec. Svc. Corps (health adviser 1994—), Sigma Xi. Republican. Episcopalian (vestry 1950-60). Clubs: Metropolitan Opera (N.Y.), Chemists (N.Y.); Beacon Hill (Summit, N.J.); Nassau (Princeton). Home: 57 Colt Rd Summit NJ 07901-3004 also: State Rd Chilmark MA 02535 *To live right and help others live right too, each in his own way.*

MAY, ERNEST RICHARD, historian, educator; b. Ft. Worth, Tex., Nov. 19, 1928; s. Ernest and Rachel (Garza) M.; m. Nancy Caughey, Dec. 15, 1950; children: John Ernest, Susan Rachel, Donna LaRee. A.B., UCLA, 1948, M.A. (Native Sons of Golden West fellow in history), 1949, Ph.D. (Univ. fellow), 1951; M.A. (hon.), Harvard U., 1959. Lectr. history Los Angeles State Coll., 1950; mem. hist. sect. Joint Chiefs of Staff, 1952-54; instr. history Harvard U. 1954-56, asst. prof., 1956-59, assoc. prof., 1959-63, prof., 1963—, Charles Warren prof. history, 1981—; Allston Burr sr. tutor Harvard U. (Kirkland House), 1960-66; mem. Harvard U. (Inst. Politics), 1967—, dir. inst., 1971-74, dean of coll., 1969-71; mem. Council on Fgn. Relations. Author: The World War and American Isolation, 1914-17, 1959, The Ultimate Decision, The President as Commander in Chief, 1960, Imperial Democracy, The Emergence of America as a Great Power, 1961, The American Image, 4 vols, 1963, (with John W. Caughey) A History of the United States, 1964, (with editors of Life) The Progressive Era, 1964, War, Boom and Bust, 1964, From Isolation to Imperialism, 1898-1919, 1964, (with John W. Caughey and John Hope Franklin) Land of the Free, 1966, American Imperialism; A Speculative Essay, 1968, Lessons of the Past: The Use and Misuse of History in American Foreign Policy, 1973, The Making of The Monroe Doctrine, 1975, (with Dorothy G. Blaney) Careers for Humanists, 1981; author: A Proud Nation, 1983, Knowing One's Enemies: Intelligence Assessment before the Two World Wars, 1984, (with Richard E. Neustadt) Thinking in Time; The Uses of History for Decision Making, 1986; Author also numerous articles. Chmn. bd. control John Anson Kittredge Trust. Served as lt. (j.g.) USNR, 1951-54. Guggenheim fellow, 1958-59; faculty research fellow Social Sci. Research Council, 1959-61; fellow Center for Advanced Study Behavioral Scis., 1963-64; fellow Woodrow Wilson Internat. Center, 1983. Mem. Mass. Hist. Soc., Am. Hist. Assn., Soc. Historians Am. Fgn. Relations (pres. 1982-83), AAUP, Am. Acad. Arts and Scis. Episcopalian. Club: Belmont Hill. Office: History Dept Harvard U Cambridge MA 02138

MAY, FELTON EDWIN, bishop; b. Chgo., Apr. 23, 1935; s. James Albert May and Florine C. (Felton) May Caruthers; m. Phyllis Elizabeth Henry, June 22, 1963; children: Daphne Bredena, Felton II. B.A., Judson Coll., 1962; M.Div., Crozer Theol. Sem., 1970; DD, Lycoming Coll., 1989, Lebanon Valley Coll., 1989, Wesley Coll., Dover, Del., 1990. Ordained deacon United Meth. Ch., 1962, elder, 1970. Assoc. pastor St. James Meth. Ch., Chgo., 1961-63; pastor Maple Park United Meth. Ch., Chgo., 1963-68; assoc. exec. dir. Meth. Action Program, Wilmington, Del., 1968-70, Ezion-Mt. Carmel United Meth. Ch., Wilmington, 1970-75; dist. supt. Peninsula Conf., United Meth. Ch., Easton, Md., 1975-81; coun. dir. Peninsula Conf., United Meth. Ch., Dover, 1981-84; bishop United Meth. Ch., Harrisburg, Pa., 1984-90; spl. assignment Coun. of Bishops, Washington, 1990-91; bishop United Meth. Ch., Harrisburg, 1991—; chairperson United Meth. Ch. Shalom Communities Com., 1992, Pan Meth. Commn., 1993; co-chair Coalition of Religious Leaders, Harrisburg, Pa. Author: Developmental Evangelism (workbook), 1979; co-author. articles to mags.; co-author church sch. curriculum. Mem. Atty.'s Grievance Com., Annapolis, 1979-81; bd. govs. Wesley Sem., Washington, 1975—; bd. dirs. Boy Scouts Am., Dover, 1981-83, Wesley Coll., 1972-83, Wilmington Parking Authority, 1974, Del. Health and Social Svc. Commn., Dover, 1977; mem. Del. Civil Rights Com., Wilmington, 1970; trustee Lycoming Coll., Lebanon Valley Coll., Camp David Chapel; com. Camp David, Md. With U.S. Army, 1957-59. Avocations: oil

painting; tennis; plants; travel. Home: PO Box 239 Harrisburg PA 17108-0239 Office: United Meth Ch Harrisburg Area 900 S Arlington Ave Harrisburg PA 17109-5024

MAY, FRANCIS HART, JR., retired building materials manufacturing executive; b. Dunkirk, Ind., Apr. 2, 1917; s. Francis Hart and Agnes (Elabarger) M.; m. June Breen, Aug. 31, 1940; children: Francis Hart, John Joseph, Marcia Ann. A.B., U. Notre Dame, 1938; M.B.A., Harvard, 1940. Mgr. war contracts div. Owens-Ill. Glass Co., Toledo, 1940-44; v.p. sec. Glass Fibers, Inc., Toledo, 1946-54; v.p., sec., treas. L-O-F Glass Fibers Co., Toledo, 1955-58; v.p., gen. mgr. Johns-Manville Fiber Glass, Inc., 1959-60; asst. v.p. finance Johns-Manville Corp., N.Y.C., 1960-61; v.p. fin., dir. Johns-Manville Corp., 1962-70, exec. v.p. fin. and adminstrn., 1971-79, vice-chmn. bd., 1979-80, spl. projects, 1980-82, ret., 1982. Served with inf. AUS, 1944-46. Mem. Fin. Execs. Ins., Dolphin Head Golf Club (Hilton Head Island, S.C.). Home: 8330 E Quincy Ave J-103 Denver CO 80237 Home (summer): PO Box 955 Cooperstown NY 13326-5955 Home (winter): 29 China Cockle Ln Hilton Head Island SC 29926-1908

MAY, GERALD WILLIAM, university administrator, educator, civil engineering consultant; b. Kenya, Jan. 2, 1941; s. William and Ruth (Koch) M.; m. Mary Joyce Pool, July 27, 1963; children: Erica Ruth, Christian William, Heidi Clara. B.S., Bradley U., 1962; M.S., U. Colo., 1964, Ph.D., 1967. Registered profl. engr., N.Mex. Civil engr. Ill. Hwy. Dept., Peoria, summer 1959-63; instr. U. Colo., Boulder, 1964-67; from asst. to prof. engring. U. N.Mex., Albuquerque, 1967-77, prof. of civil engring, 1977—; dean Coll. Engring., U. N.Mex., Albuquerque, 1980-86; pres. U. N.Mex., Albuquerque, 1986-90; dir. accident study program, Albuquerque, 1970-75, cons. to corps., govtl. agys. Contbr. articles to profl. jours., chpts. to books. Recipient Borden Freshman award Bradley U., 1958. Mem. ASCE (sec. N.Mex. sect. 1982-83), Am. Soc. Engring. Edn. (Outstanding Young Faculty award 1973), Nat. Soc. Profl. Engrs., Sigma Xi, Chi Epsilon, Tau Beta Pi, Phi Eta Sigma. Office: Univ N Mex Civil Engring Dept Albuquerque NM 87131

MAY, GITA, French language and literature educator; b. Brussels, Sept. 16, 1929; came to U.S., 1947, naturalized, 1950; d. Albert and Blima (Sieradzka) Jochimek; m. Irving May, Dec. 21, 1947. BA magna cum laude, CUNY-Hunter Coll., 1953; MA, Columbia U., 1954, PhD, 1957. Lectr. French CUNY-Hunter Coll., 1953-56; instr. Columbia U., 1956-58, asst. prof., 1958-61, assoc. prof., 1961-68, prof., 1968—, chmn., 1983-93, mem. senate, 1979-83, 86-88, chmn. Seminar on 18th Century Culture, 1986-89; lecture tour English univs., 1965. Author: Diderot et Baudelaire, critiques d'art, 1957, De Jean-Jacques Rousseau à Madame Roland: essai sur la sensibilité préromantique et révolutionnaire, 1964, Madame Roland and the Age of Revolution, 1970 (Van Amringe Disting. Book award), Stendhal and the Age of Napoleon, 1977; co-editor: Diderot Studies III, 1961; mem. editl. bd. 18th Century Studies, 1975-78, French Rev., 1975-86, Romanic Rev., 1959—; contbg. editor: Ouevres complètes de Diderot, 1984, 95; gen. editor: The Age of Revolution and Romanticism: Interdisciplinary Studies, 1990—; contbr. articles and revs. to profl. jours. Decorated chevalier and officier Ordre des Palmes Acad.; recipient award Am. Coun. Learned Socs., 1961, award for outstanding achievement CUNY-Hunter Coll., 1963; Fulbright rsch. grantee, 1964-65; Guggenheim fellow, 1964-65, NEH fellow, 1971-72. Mem. AAUP, MLA (del. assembly 1973-75, mem. com. rsch. activities 1975-78, mem. exec. coun. 1980-83), Am. Assn. Tchrs. of French, Am. Soc. 18th Century Studies (pres. 1985-86, 2nd v.p. 1983-84, 1st v.p. 1984-85), Soc. Française d'Etude du Dix-Huitième Siècle, Soc. Diderot, Am. Soc. French Acad. Palms, Phi Beta Kappa. Home: 404 W 116th St New York NY 10027-7202

MAY, GREGORY EVERS, lawyer; b. Harrisonburg, Va., Sept. 17, 1953; s. Russell J. and Arlene Virginia (Ringgold) M. AB, Coll. of William and Mary, 1975; JD, Harvard U., 1978. Bar: Va. 1978, U.S. Dist. Ct. (ea. dist.) Va. 1979, U.S. Ct. Appeals (4th cir.) 1979, U.S. Claims Ct. 1981, U.S. Tax Ct. 1981, D.C. 1985, N.Y. 1988. Law clk. to Judge Butzner U.S. Ct. Appeals (4th cir.), Richmond, Va., 1978-79; law clk. to Justice Powell U.S. Supreme Ct., Washington, 1979-80; assoc. Hunton & Williams, Richmond, 1980-83; assoc. Hunton & Williams, Washington, 1984-86, ptnr., 1986-89; ptnr. Milbank, Tweed, Hadley & McCloy, Washington, 1989—. Articles editor Harvard Law Rev., 1977-78. Mem. ABA, Va. State Bar, D.C. Bar, N.Y. State Bar. Office: Milbank Tweed Hadley & McCloy 1825 I St NW Ste 1100 Washington DC 20006-5492

MAY, HAROLD EDWARD, chemical company executive; b. N.Y.C., Oct. 18, 1920; s. Charles Edward and Mollie (Flax) M.; m. Margaret June Hochman, June 27, 1943; children: Charles S., Michael E., Suzanne E. A.B., Columbia U., 1941, B.S. in Mech. Engring, 1942. With E.I. duPont de Nemours & Co., Inc., 1942—; v.p. materials and logistics E.I. duPont de Nemours & Co., Inc., Wilmington, Del., 1977-82, sr. v.p. corp. staff, 1982-85; ret. E.I. duPont de Nemours & Co., Inc., 1985. Recipient Illig medal Columbia U., 1942. Mem. Phi Beta Kappa, Tau Beta Pi. Jewish. Home: 36 Southridge Dr Kennett Square PA 19348-2714

MAY, J. JOEL, health care management consultant; b. Allentown, Pa., Dec. 21, 1935; s. J. Melville and Marian B. (Fegley) M.; m. Helen Parr; children: Douglas, Kathleen. BS, Albright Coll., 1957; MBA, U. Chgo. 1963. Lectr. U. Chgo., 1963-70, dir. grad. program in health adminstrn., 1970-77; exec. v.p. Health Research and Ednl. Trust, Princeton, N.J., 1977-81; pres. Health Research and Ednl. Trust, Princeton, 1981-84; sr. cons. The Pennington Group, Titusville, N.J., 1984—; bd. dirs. New Hope Found., Marlboro, N.J., 1988-91; mem. N.J. Citizens' Com. on Biomed. Ethics, 1989—. Contbr. articles to profl. jours. Cpl. U.S. Army, 1959-61. Fellow Am. Coll. Healthcare Execs.; mem. Am. Hosp. Assn., Am. Econ. Assn., Hosp. Mgmt. and Info. Systems Soc., Internat. Assn. for Healthcare Tech. Assessment. Republican. Roman Catholic. Avocations: computers, science fiction, jogging. Office: The Pennington Group 230 Jacobs Creek Rd Titusville NJ 08560-1403

MAY, J. PETER, mathematics educator; b. N.Y.C., Sept. 16, 1939; s. Siegmund Henry and Jane (Polachek) M.; m. Maija Bajars, June 8, 1963; children: Anthony D., Andrew D. BA, Swarthmore Coll., 1960; PhD, Princeton U., 1964. Instr. Yale U., New Haven, 1964-65, asst. prof., 1965-67; assoc. prof. U. Chgo., 1967-70, prof., 1970—, chmn. dept. math., 1985-91, chmn. coun. on teaching, 1991—; mem. Inst. Advanced Study, Princeton, 1966; vis. prof. Cambridge U., Eng., 1971-72, 1977. Author: Simplicial Objects in Algebraic Topology, 1967, The Geometry of Iterated Loop Spaces, 1972, E-infinity Ring Spaces and E-infinity Ring Spectra, 1977; co-author: The Homology of Iterated Loop Spaces, 1976, H-infinity Ring Spectra and Their Applications, 1986, Equivariant Stable Homotopy Theory, 1986; also 80 articles and monographs. NSF grantee, 1967—; Fulbright fellow, 1971-72; fellow Nat. Research Council, Eng., 1977. Mem. AAUP, Am. Math. Soc. Office: U Chgo Dept Math 5734 S University Ave Chicago IL 60637-1546

MAY, JAMES WARREN, JR., plastic surgeon, medical association executive; b. Lexington, Ky., 1943. MD, Northwestern U., 1969. Intern Mass. Gen. Hosp., Boston, 1969-70, resident, 1974-75, resident plastic surgeon, 1975—; fellow U. Louisville, 1975; assoc. prof. clin. surgery Harvard Med. Sch., Boston; chmn. Am. Bd. Plastic Surgery. Office: Harvard Med Sch Mass Gen Hosp 15 Parkman St Fl 453 Care Boston MA 02114-3139

MAY, JERRY RUSSELL, psychologist; b. Seattle, Apr. 24, 1942; s. Harold Russell May and Anne Margret (Jones) DeGolier; m. Carolyn Marlene May; children: Darin, Christopher, Laurel. Student, Sorbonne U., Paris, 1961-62; BA, Western Wash. U., 1966; PhD, Bowling Green State U., 1974. Prof. psychiatry sch. medicine U. Nev., Reno, 1974-90, dean admissions and student affairs sch. medicine, 1977—; cons. VA Med. Ctr., Reno, 1974-90, U.S. Olympic Sports Medicine Program, Colorado Springs, Colo., 1977—; pvt. practice clin. psychology, mgmt. cons., Reno, 1977—; team psychologist U.S. Ski Team, Park City, Utah, 1977-92; chmn. U.S. Olympic Psychology Com., Colorado Springs, 1985-92; mem. U.S. Olympic Sports Medicine Coun., Colorado Springs, 1985-92; team psychologist U.S. Sailing Team, 1992—. Author/editor: Sports Psychology: The Psychological Health of the Athlete, 1987; contbr. articles to profl. jours., chpts. to books. Pres. West Coast Group on Student Affairs, 1981-82. Served to lt. USN, 1968-71. Mem. APA, No. Nev. Assn. Cert. Psychologists (pres. 1979-82), Am. Assn.

Med. Colls., Western Psychol. Assn., Nev. Psychol. Assn. Office: U Nev Sch Medicine Reno NV 89557

MAY, JOSEPH LESERMAN (JACK), lawyer; b. Nashville, May 27, 1929; s. Daniel and Dorothy (Fishel) M.; m. Natalie McCuaig, Apr. 12, 1957 (dec. May 1990); children: Benjamin, Andrew, Joshua, Maria; m. Lynn Hewes Lance, June 10, 1994. BA, Yale U., 1951; JD, NYU, 1958; postgrad., Harvard Bus. Sch., 1969. Bar: Tenn. 1959. With CIA, 1951-55; pres. Nuweave Socks, Inc., N.Y.C., 1955-59; May Hosiery Mills, Nashville, 1960-83, Athens Hosiery Mills, Tenn., 1966-83; v.p. Wayne-Gossard Corp., Chattanooga, 1972-83; pvt. practice law Nashville, 1984—; bd. dirs. Convertible Holdings, Princeton, N.J., World Income Fund, Princeton, Merrill Lynch Growth Fund; adv. group Civil Justice Reform Act U.S. Dist. Ct., 1991; adv. bd. Asian Strategies Group, 1994. Mem. Eagle Scout Assn.; bd. dirs. Vanderbilt Cancer Ctr., 1994—. With USN, 1947-53, U.S. Army, 1954. Mem. Tenn. Bar Assn., Nashville Bar Assn., Shamus Club, Old Oak Club, Yale Club of N.Y., Jewish Cmty. Ctr. (pres. 1969), Guardianship and Trust Corp. (chmn. 1994), Nashville Rotary (pres. 1971). Home: 2136 Golf Club Ln Nashville TN 37215-1224 Office: Box 190628 424 Church St Ste 2000 Nashville TN 37219-0628

MAY, KENNETH NATHANIEL, food industry consultant; b. Livingston, La., Dec. 24, 1930; s. Robert William and Mary Hulda (Caraway) M.; m. Patsy Jean Farr, Aug. 4, 1953; children: Sherry Alison (dec.), Nathan Elliott. BS in Poultry Sci., La. State U., 1952, MS in Poultry Sci., 1955; PhD in Food Tech., Purdue U., 1959, DAgr, 1988. Asst. prof. U. Ga., Athens, 1958-64, assoc. prof., 1964-67, prof., 1967-68; prof. Miss. State U., State College, 1968-70; dir. rsch. Holly Farms Poultry, Wilkesboro, N.C., 1970-73, v.p., 1973-85, pres., 1985-88, chmn., chief exec. officer, 1989; bd. dirs. Hudson Foods, Inc., Embrex, Inc.; adjunct prof. N.C. State U., 1975. Contbr. over 60 articles to profl. jours.; patentee treatment of cooked poultry. Bd. trustees Appalachian State U., 1987-94, chmn., 1989-90. Recipient Industry Service award Poultry and Egg Inst. Am., 1971, Meritorious Service award, Ga. Egg Commn., 1964, Disting. Service award Agribus. N.C., 1986; named to Am. Poultry Hall of Fame, 1992. Fellow Poultry Sci. Assn.; mem. Nat. Poultry Hist. Soc. (bd. dirs. 1982-83), Inst. Food Technologists. Methodist. Avocations: reading, stained glass.

MAY, MELANIE ANN, theologian; b. Washington, Jan. 6, 1955; d. Russell Junior and Arlene Virginia (Ringgold) May. AB, Manchester Coll., 1976; MDiv., Harvard U., 1979, AM, 1982, PhD, 1986. Teaching fellow div. sch. Harvard U., Cambridge, Mass., 1981-83, asst. head tutor, 1983-84; staff program for women Ch. Brethren Gen. Bd., Elgin, Ill., 1985-87, ecumenical officer, 1985-91, assoc. gen. sec. human resources, 1987-91; adj. faculty Bethany Theol. Sem., Oak Brook, Ill., 1986-92, Garrett-Evang. Theol. Sem., 1991-92; dean program in the study of women and gender in ch. and soc., prof. theology Colgate Rochester Div. Sch., Bexley Hall, Crozer, 1992—. Author: Bonds of Unity, Women, Theology and Worldwide Church, 1989, Women and Church: A Challenge of Solidarity in an Age of Alienation, 1991, For All The Saints: The Practice of Ministry in the Church, 1990, A Body Knows: A Theopoetics of Death and Resurrection, 1995; assoc. editor Jour. Ecumenical Studies. Quality Ministerial candidates, 1987—, chmn. commn. Faith and Order, Nat. Council, N.Y., 1988; mem. standing commn. Faith and Order, World Coun. Chs., 1991—. Mem. N.Am. Acad. Economists, Am. Acad. Religion. Avocations: reading, gardening, swimming. Home: 309 Rugby Ave Rochester NY 14619-1219

MAY, MELVIN ARTHUR, computer software company executive; b. Cortez, Colo., Oct. 22, 1940; s. Everett James and Viola Christina (Lair) M.; m. Dale Charlene Kelly, Oct. 3, 1963; children: Diana, Michael. A.A., Pueblo Coll., 1959; B.S., U. Colo., 1961. Accountant Haskins & Sells (C.P.A.'s), San Diego, Denver, and Colorado Springs, Colo., 1961-68; asst. to v.p., treas. Holly Sugar Corp., Colorado Springs, 1968-69, asst. treas., 1970-71, treas., 1972-82, v.p., 1977-82; v.p. fin. Cibar, Inc., Colorado Springs, 1982-86, chief operating officer, 1983-86, sr. v.p. fin., 1986-87; ret., 1987. Served with USMCR, 1963-64. Mem. NRA. Home: 637 Dexter St Colorado Springs CO 80911-2539

MAY, PETER WILLIAM, business executive; b. N.Y.C., Dec. 11, 1942; s. Samuel D. and Isabel (Meyer) M.; m. Leni Finkelstein, Aug. 16, 1964; children: Jonathan Paul, Leslie Ann. AB, U. Chgo., 1964, MBA, 1965. CPA, N.Y. Mgr. Peat, Marwick, Mitchell & Co., N.Y.C., 1965-72; exec. v.p. Flagstaff Corp., N.Y.C., 1972-78; pres., chief operating officer Trian Group. L.P. (formerly Triangle Industries, Inc.), N.Y.C., 1978—, also bd. dirs.; pres., COO Triar Cos., Inc., N.Y.C. Trustee Mt. Sinai Hosp., N.Y.C., exec. com., founding mem. Laura Rosenberg Meml. Fund for Pediatric Leukemia Rsch.; alumni dir. U. Chgo. Grad. Sch. Bus.; bd. dirs. 92d St. YMCA, United Jewish Appeal, Operation Exodus campaign. Mem. Am. Inst. CPA's, N.Y. Soc. of CPA's. Office: Triarc Cos Inc 700 Third Ave Miami FL 10022*

MAY, RICHARD EDWARD, lawyer; b. Austin, Tex., Feb. 5, 1946; s. Howard Curtis and Gertrude E. (Wallace) M.; m. Tracey C. May; 1 child, Elynor Lee. AB, U. Md., 1967; JD, Georgetown U., 1973. Bar: D.C. 1973, Va. 1984. Assoc. Steptoe & Johnson, Washington, 1973-79; spl. asst. to chief counsel IRS, Washington, 1979-81; ptnr. Jenkens & Gilchrist, Dallas, 1981-83, Hunton & Williams, Washington, 1983—. Served to lt. USN, 1968-71. Mem. ABA (taxation sect., chmn. reorganization subcom. 1981-83, vice chmn. corp. stockholder relationships com. 1983-85, chmn. 1985-87, tax sect. asst. sec. 1988-89, tax sect. sec. 1989-91, coun. dir. 1991—). Episcopalian. Clubs: Metropolitan (Washington); Commonwealth (Richmond). Office: Hunton & Williams PO Box 19230 2000 Pennsylvania Ave NW Washington DC 20006-1812

MAY, ROBERT GEORGE, dean, accounting educator; b. Detroit, Nov. 11, 1943; s. George Joseph and Winifred Marie (Donnelly) M.; m. Carol Ann Rogers, June 18, 1965; children: Gregory Charles, Lynn Marie. B.B.A., Mich. State U., 1965, Ph.D., 1970. Asst. prof. U. Wash., Seattle, 1970-73, assoc. prof., 1973-79; prof. acctg. U. Tex., Austin, 1979—, chmn. dept. acctg., 1988-92, assoc. dean, 1992-95, interim dean, 1995—; vis. assoc. prof. Stanford U., 1972-73; dir. Fedn. Schs. Accountancy, Athens, Ga., 1982. Co-author: Accounting, 1995, Financial Accounting, 1995, Managerial Accounting, 1995, Corporate Financial Accounting, 1995; assoc. editor: the Accounting Review. Recipient Notable Contbn. to Acctg. Lit. award AICPAs, 1976; named Outstanding Alumnus, Mich. State U. Dept. Acctg., 1995. Mem. Am. Acctg. Assn. (chmn. audit sect. 1988-89, pres., adminstrs. of acctg. programs 1993-94, Innovation in Acctg. Edn. award 1991, 93). Home: 7137 Valburn Dr Austin TX 78731 Office: U Tex Austin TX 78712

MAY, ROBERT MCCREDIE, biology educator; b. Sydney, Australia, Jan. 8, 1936; s. Henry W. and Kathleen (McCredie) M.; m. Judith Feiner, Aug. 3, 1962; 1 dau., Naomi Felicity. B.Sc., Sydney U., 1956, Ph.D., 1959; D.Sc. (honoris causa), City U. London, 1989, Uppsala U. 1990; DSc (hon.), Yale U., 1993, Heriot-Watt U., 1994, U. Edinburgh, 1994, U. Sydney, 1995. Gordon Mackay lectr. applied math Harvard U., Cambridge, Mass., 1959-61, mem. vis.-faculty, 1966; theoretical physics lectr. Sydney U., 1962-64, reader, 1964-69, personal chair, 1969-73; prof. biology Princeton U., N.J., 1973-88; Royal Soc. rsch. prof. U. Oxford, 1989-95, fellow Merton Coll., 1989-95; chief scientific advisor to Prime Minister John Major, 1995—; head Office of Science and Tech., 1995—; vis. faculty Calif. Inst. Tech., 1967; vis. prof. Imperial Coll., Eng., 1975—, UKAEA Culham Lab., 1971, Magdalen Coll., 1971, bd. trustees, Nat. Hist. Mus., London. Editor: Stability and Complexity in Model Ecosystems, 1973, Population Biology of Infectious Diseases, 1982, Theoretical Ecology: Principles and Applications, 1976, Perspectives in Ecological Theory, 1989, Infectious Diseases of Humans: Dynamics and Control, 1991. Fellow Royal Soc., Am. Acad. Arts and Scis.; mem. NAS, Athenaeum Club. Home: 3 Upland Park Rd, Oxford OX2 7RU, England Office: Oxford U Dept Zoology, S Parks Rd, Oxford OX1 3PS, England

MAY, RONALD ALAN, lawyer; b. Waterloo, Iowa, Sept. 8, 1928; s. John W. and Elsie (Finlayson) M.; m. Naomi Gray, Aug. 18, 1950 (div. Feb. 1974); children: Sarah, Jonathan, Andrew, Rachel; m. Susan East Gray, May 9, 1975. B.A. U. Iowa, 1950; LL.B, Vanderbilt U., 1953. Bar: Ark. 1953. Atty. Daggett & Daggett, Marianna, 1953-57, Wright, Lindsey & Jennings, Little Rock, 1957-84; sr. ptnr. Wright, Lindsey & Jennings, 1986—. Editor: Automated Law Research, 1972, Sense and Systems in Automated Law

Research, 1975; contbg. editor Fifty State Construction Lien and Bond Law, 1992; assoc. editor: Jour. Irreproducible Results. Pres. Spl. Com. on Pub. Edn., Ark. Assn. for Mental Health, Friends of Library, Central Ark. Radiation Therapy Inst.; chmn. Ark. Cancer Research Ctr., 1990-92; bd. dirs. Nat. Assn. for Mental Health, Ark. State Hosp., Gaines House, State Bd. Architects; bd. dirs. State Bd. Bar Examiners, chmn. 1987-88, Ark. ethics com., 1991-93; trustee Mus. Sci. and Natural History, Little Rock, chmn., 1973; mem. profl. adv. bd. sch. architecture U. Ark., 1990—, mem. profl. adv. bd. sch. urban studies and design, 1993—. Served with AUS, 1946-47. Mem. ABA (chmn. sci. and tech. sect. 1975-76), Ark., Pulaski County Bar Assns., Internat. Assn. Def. Counsel, Am. Inns of Ct. (Master of the Bench), Assn. for Computing Machinery, Order of Coif, Phi Beta Kappa. Republican. Episcopalian. Clubs: Capital, Little Rock Country. Home: 821 N Ash St Little Rock AR 72205-2051 Office: Wright Lindsey & Jennings 2200 Worthen Bank Bldg Little Rock AR 72201

MAY, STEPHEN, writer, former government official; b. Rochester, N.Y., July 30, 1931; s. Arthur J. and Hilda (Jones) M. Grad., Wesleyan U., 1953; LL.B., Georgetown U., 1961. Bar: N.Y. 1963. Exec. asst. to Rep. and Senator Kenneth B. Keating, 1955-64; asso., mem., then ptnr. Branch, Turner & Wise, Rochester, 1965-81; city councilman-at-large Rochester, 1966-73; mayor, 1970-73; chmn. and commr. N.Y. State Bd. Elections, Albany, 1975-79; asst. sec. for legis. and Congl. relations Dept. Housing and Urban Devel., 1981-88; lectr. and freelance writer for newspapers and mags., 1988—; Vice chmn. Temporary State Commn. on Powers of Local Govt., 1970-73; mem. 20th Century Fund Task Force on Future of N.Y.C., 1979, Nat. Adv. Commn. Higher Edn. for Police Officers, 1977-79, Joint Com. Assn. Bar City N.Y. and Drug Abuse Council on N.Y. Drug Law Evaluation, 1977-78; chmn. Rochester Interfaith Com. on Israel, 1973-81; del.-at-large Republican Nat. Conv., 1972; mem. N.Y. State Crime Control Planning Bd., 1970-73. Contbr. numerous articles on Am. art, culture and hist. preservation to newspapers and periodicals. Bd. dirs. Police Found., 1970-81, Nat. Com. for Labor Israel, 1977-81, Empire State Report, 1974-81, Inst. Mediation and Conflict Resolution, 1973-81. Served with U.S. Army, 1953-55. Mem. Phi Beta Kappa. Home and Office: 4101 Cathedral Ave NW Washington DC 20016-3585

MAY, STERLING RANDOLPH, health association executive; b. Muskogee, Okla., Dec. 27, 1946; s. William Sterling and Mary Catherine (Griffith) M.; m. Sharon Louise McDonald, July 3, 1987. BA with honors, U. Kans., 1968; MS, U. Mich., 1969, PhD, 1977; M in Bus., Johns Hopkins U., 1995. Coord. Skin Bank St. Agnes Med. Ctr., Phila., 1977-79, assoc. dir. Burn Rsch., 1980, dir. Burn Rsch., 1981-83; dir. Southeastern Burn Rsch. Inst., Augusta, Ga., 1983-87; v.p. LifeCell Corp., The Woodlands, Tex., 1987-91; nat. head tissue svcs. ARC Nat. Hdqs., Arlington, Va., 1991—; rsch. asst. prof. Hahnemann U. Sch. Medicine, Phila., 1979-82, rsch. assoc. prof., 1983; assoc. clin. prof. Med. Coll. Ga., 1984-87; adj. prof. U. Tex. Med. Sch., Houston, 1987-91. Editor: Care of the Burn Wound, 1985; author 84 published articles in biomed. lit., 1974—; mem. editorial bd. Jour. Burn Care and Rehab., 1982-90, Burns, 1985-92, Cryobiology, 1987-93. Mem. Soc. for Cryobiology (pres. 1989-91, chmn. 23d ann. meeting, 1986), Am. Burn Assn. (chmn. rsch. com. 1990-93), Internat. Soc. For Burn Injuries (mem. gen. coun. 1982-90), Am. Assn. Tissue Banks (sec. 1991-93, bd. govs. 1989-93), Nat. Trust for Hist. Preservation. Avocations: antique furniture, music, archaeology. Home: 1501 Crystal Dr Apt 825 Arlington VA 22202-4125 Office: ARC Nat Hdqs Tissue Svcs 2025 E St NW Washington DC 20006-5009

MAY, TIMOTHY JAMES, lawyer; b. Denver, Aug. 3, 1932; s. Thomas Henry and Helen Frances (O'Conner) M.; m. Monica Anita Gross, Aug. 24, 1957; children: Stephanie, Maureen, Cynthia, Timothy, Anthony. BA, Cath. U. Am., 1954; LLB, Georgetown U., 1957, LLM, 1960. Bar: D.C. 1957, U.S. Supreme Ct. 1961. Law clk. to judge U.S. Ct. Appeals, D.C. Cir., 1957-58; assoc. Covington & Burling, Washington, 1958-61; cons. Exec. Office of Pres. U.S., Washington, 1961-62; chief counsel subcom. on stockpile Armed Svcs. Com., U.S. Senate, Washington, 1962-63; mng. dir. Fed. Maritime Commn., Washington, 1963-66; gen. counsel U.S. Post Office Dept., Washington, 1966-69; mng. ptnr. Patton, Boggs & Blow, Washington, 1969—. Bd. dirs. Legal Aid Soc. D.C., 1986—, Coun. for Ct. Excellence, Washington, 1985—; chmn. bd. regents Cath. U. Am., 1988-93, trustee, 1993—. Fellow Am. Bar Found.; mem. ABA (House of Dels.), Fed. Bar Assn., Bar Assn. of D.C. (pres. 1991-92), Congl. Country Club (bd. govs. 1992—, sec. 1994—), Met. Club, Indian Creek Country Club, Bal Harbour Club, Knight of Malta. Democrat. Roman Catholic. Home: 3828 52nd St NW Washington DC 20016-1924 Office: Patton Boggs Patton Boggs LLP 2550 M St NW Washington DC 20037

MAY, WALTER GRANT, chemical engineer; b. Saskatoon, Sask., Can., Nov. 28, 1918; came to U.S., 1946, naturalized, 1954; s. George Alfred and Abigail Almira (Robson) M.; m. Mary Louise Stockan, Sept. 26, 1945 (dec. 1977); children: John R., Douglas W., Caroline O. m. Helen Dickerson, 1988. B.Sc., U. Sask., Saskatoon, 1939, M.Sc., 1942; Sc.D., M.I.T., 1948. Registered profl. engr., Ill. Chemist British Am. Oil Co., Moose Jaw, Sask., 1939-40; asst. prof. U. Sask., 1943-46; with Exxon Research & Engring. Co., Linden, N.J., 1948-83; sr. sci. adv., 1976-83; profl. U. Ill., 1983-90, prof. emeritus, 1990—; with Advanced Research Projects Agy., Dept. Def., 1959-60; industry based prof. Stevens Inst. Tech., 1968-74, Rensselaer Poly. Inst., 1975-77. Recipient Process Indsl. Div. award ASME, 1972. Fellow Am. Inst. Chem. Engrs.; mem. Am. Inst. Chem. Engrs. (Chem. Engring. Practice award 1989), Nat. Acad. Engring. Home: 916 W Clark St Champaign IL 61821-3328 Office: U Ill Dept Chem Engring 1209 W California Ave Urbana IL 61801-3731

MAY, WILLIAM FREDERICK, manufacturing executive; b. Chgo., Oct. 25, 1915; s. Arthur W. and Florence (Hartwick) M.; m. Kathleen Thompson, June 14, 1947; children: Katherine Hartwick (Mrs. Edward W. Bickford), Elizabeth Shaw. BS, U. Rochester, 1937; grad. Advanced Mgmt. Program, Harvard, 1950; D in Engring., Clarkson U.; LLD, Okla. Christian Coll.; LHD, Livingstone U.; LLD, Lafayette U. Research worker E.I. Du Pont de Nemours Co., 1937-38; with Am. Can Co., 1940-80, mgr., 1957-58, v.p., 1958-64, exec. v.p., 1964-65, vice chmn. bd. dirs., 1965, chmn. bd. dirs., chief exec. officer, 1965-80; mem. exec. com. Am. Can Co., Greenwich, Conn., 1960—; bd. dirs. U.S. Surgical & Catalyst Energy Corp., Phibro-Salomon Corp.; dean Grad. Sch. Bus. Adminstrn., NYU, 1980-84; chmn. and chief exec. officer Statue of Liberty Found., 1984—. Bd. dirs. Lincoln Ctr.; trustee Am. Ditchley Found., Am. Mus. Natural History, Taft Inst. Govt., Columbia-Presbyn. Hosp., U. Rochester; mem. corp. Poly. Inst. N.Y.; chmn. pub. policy council Advt. Council. Mem. Nat. Order of Merit (France, officier), River Club, Econ. Club, Round Hill Club, Megunticook Golf Club, Golf Phi Beta Kappa, Alpha Delta Phi. Episcopalian. Home: 35 Lauder Ln Greenwich CT 06831-3707 Office: Statue of Liberty Found 52 Vanderbilt Ave New York NY 10017-3808

MAY, WILLIAM HATHAWAY, instrument corporation executive, lawyer. BSME, Va. Poly. Inst., 1964; MS, U. So. Calif., 1970; LLB, U. Va., 1972. Bar: Calif. 1973. Assoc. Fowler Knobbe & Martens, 1972-76; div. staff atty. Beckman Instruments, Inc., Fullerton, Calif., 1976-79, sr. div. staff atty., 1979-82, litigation counsel, 1982-83, counsel litigation and corp. affairs, 1983-84, gen. counsel, sec., 1984-85, v.p., gen. counsel, sec., 1985—. Trustee Santa Ana Sch. Dist., 1982-83; mem. Santa Ana Pers. Bd., 1973-76, 81-82. Capt. USAF, 1966-70. Mem. L.A. Patent Law Assn. (chmn. corp. practice sect. 1977-78, bd. dirs. securities 1978-80). Office: Beckman Instruments Inc 2500 N Harbor Blvd Fullerton CA 92635-2600

MAYALI, LAURENT, legal history educator; b. 1956. LLB, 1976, DEA, 1978, habilitation; 1985; doctorat d'Etat, U. Montpellier, France, 1985. Prof. legal history Roman and comparative law U. Calif., Berkeley, 1989—; dir. Robbins Religious and Civil Law Collection. Office: U Calif Sch Law Boalt Hall Berkeley CA 94720

MAYBERRY, JULIUS EUGENE, realty company owner, investor; b. Qulin, Mo., July 3, 1935; s. Julius E. and Mabel L. (Gunnells) M.; m. Nettie Sue Burden, Dec. 8, 1953; children: Michael Eugene, Cynthia E. Copeland, Karen Sue Mayberry-Lee. AS, Ga. Mil. Acad., 1973; postgrad., Augusta Coll., 1976. Enlisted U.S. Army, 1957, advanced through grades to first sgt., 1973, ret., 1979; salesperson TIPS Realty Co., Augusta, Ga., 1979—, owner,

---

broker, 1984—. Scoutmaster Boy Scouts of Am., Ft. Gordon, Ga., 1961-67. Decorated Bronze medal, Purple Heart. Mem. Augusta Bd. Realtors, Multiple Listing Service Augusta. Republican. Baptist. Lodge: Optimist (v.p. 1987). Avocation: golf. Home: 2327 Lupkin Ct Augusta GA 30906 Office: TIPS Realty Co 2327 Lupkin Ct Augusta GA 30906-3090

MAYCOCK, IAN DAVID, oil executive; b. St. Helens, Lancashire, Eng., Dec. 8, 1935; s. Joseph and Lilian (Hewitt) M.; m. Katherine Ella Bennett, May, 1968; children: Alison, Fiona, Colin, Andrew. BSc in Geology with honors, St. Andrews (Scotland) U., 1957; MSc in Geology, Queens U., Kingston, Ont., Can., 1959; PhD in Geology, Reading (Eng.) U., 1962. Field geologist Ont. Dept. Mines, 1957, Texaco Can., 1958-59; subsurface rsch. geologist Sask. (Can.) Dept. Mineral Resources, 1962-64; geologist Conoco, U.K., U.S., Middle East, 1964-73; exploration mgr. Zapata Exploration, London, 1973-80; pres. Hunt United, London, 1980-86; v.p. exploration Yemen Hunt Oil Co., Dallas, 1986-88; sr. v.p. exploration Hunt Oil Co., Dallas, 1989—. Queens/St. Andrews exchange scholar St. Andrews U., 1957; Thayer Linsdley rsch. fellow Queens U., 1958. Mem. Am. Assn. Petroleum Geologist, Soc. Econ. Paleontologists and Mineralogists, Dallas Petroleum Club. Avocations: fishing, photography. Office: Hunt Oil Co Fountain Pl 1445 Ross Ave Dallas TX 75202-2711

MAYCOCK, JOSEPH FARWELL, JR., lawyer; b. Buffalo, June 8, 1930; s. Joseph Farwell and Annie (Richmond) M.; m. Margaret Shaw, May 25, 1968; children—Suzannah, Mary, John. B.A., Hamilton Coll., 1952; J.D., U. Mich. Law Sch., 1955. Bar: Mich. Assoc. Miller, Canfield, Paddock & Stone, Detroit, 1958-68, ptnr., 1968—. Contbr. articles to profl. jours. Trustee Greater Detroit Soc. for Blind, 1984—; mem. adv. bd. Small Bus. Council of Am., Columbia Ga., Washington, 1983—. Served with U.S. Army, 1955-57. Mem. ABA, Mich. Bar Assn., Detroit Bar Assn., Mich. Employee Benefits. Republican. Episcopalian. Clubs: Country of Detroit. Office: Miller Canfield Paddock & Stone 150 W Jefferson Ave Detroit MI 48226-4429

MAYDA, JARO, lawyer, educator, author, consultant; b. Brno, Czechoslovakia; came to U.S., 1949, naturalized, 1955; s. Francis and Maria (Hornova) M.; m. Maruja del Castillo, 1967; children by previous marriage: Jaro II, Maria Raquel, Pavel. Dr. Juris Utriusque, Masaryk U., Brno, 1945; J.D. (Rockefeller fellow 1955-56), U. Chgo., 1957. Legal counsel export div. Skodaworks, Pilsen-Prague, 1946-48; vis. prof. polit. sci. Denison U., Granville, Ohio, 1949-50, Ohio State U. Columbus, 1950-51; asst. prof. law and polit. sci. U. Wis-Madison, 1951-56; mem. faculty U. P.R., Rio Piedras, 1957—; prof. law and public policy U. P.R., 1958-85, research prof., 1985-89; dir. Inst. Policy Studies and Law, 1972-75, spl. asst. to pres., 1972; Fulbright research prof. Inst. Comparative Law, U. Paris, 1967-68; fellow Woodrow Wilson Internat. Ctr. for Scholars (Smithsonian Instn.), 1971; Bailey lectr. La. State U., 1969; lectr. Am. specialist program Dept. State, 1960, Fed. Office of Environ., Berlin, 1983, UN Ctr. for Formation in Environ. Scis., Madrid, 1983, Grad. Sch. Bus. Adminstn., IESA, Caracas, Venezuela, 1987, U.S. Info. Agy. (German Democratic Republic, Czechoslovakia, Poland), 1988; Fulbright prof. Sch. Applied Econs., Dakar, Senegal, 1980; dep. sec. gen. 42d Conf. Internat. Law Assn., 1947; cons. Internat. Assn. Legal Sci., UNESCO, 1972—, FAO, 1974—, UN Environ. Program, 1977—, UN Econ. and Social Commn. for Asia and Pacific, 1977-78, UN Econ. Commn. for Europe, 1981, World Bank, 1994; mem. adv. com. Internat. Juridical Orgn., Rome, 1991—; Govt. of Columbia, 1974, Govt. of Honduras, 1977; cons. Govt. of St. Vincent and the Grenadines, 1983, AID, Haiti, 1985, Mozambique, Guinea-Bissau, 1991, Chile, 1992, China, 1993, São Tomé & Príncipe, 1994; mem., policy adv. Gov.'s Study Group P.R. and Sea, 1972; research assoc. Ctr. Energy and Environ. Research, U. P.R.-U.S. Dept. Energy, 1977-88; adviser P.R. Environ. Quality Bd., 1984-86; mem. com. environ. policy and law Internat. Union Conservation Nature, 1972-78; adv. panel on Ecosystem Data Handbook, NSF, 1976-77; mem. Internat. Council Environ. Law, Bonn, Ger., 1974—; U.S. rapporteur X Internat. Congress, Budapest, 1978; reporter on comparative legislation Congress on Forest Mgmt. and Environment, Madrid, 1984, Environ. Penal Law Internat. Symposium, San Juan, P.R., 1991, Globalization and Environment Conf. on Wider Caribbean, San Juan, 1994; lectr. Academia Istropolitana, U. Bratislava, 1994. Author: Introduction to Law, 1959, 74, Environment and Resources: From Conservation to Ecomanagement, 1967, Francois Geny and Modern Jurisprudence, 1978, Policy Research and Development: Outline of a Methodology, 1979, UNEP Manual on Environ. Legis., 1979; also articles, manuals; translator: law treatises; mem. editorial bd.: Am. Jour. Comparative Law, 1958-78; dir.: U. P.R. Law Rev, 1958-62; contbr. to Ency. Environ. Law, Berlin, 1987, 93. Home: R Pedro de Ornelas 12-B, P-9050 Funchal Madeira, Portugal

MAYDEN, BARBARA MENDEL, lawyer; b. Chattanooga, Sept. 18, 1951; d. Eugene Lester Mendel and Blanche (Krugman) Rosenberg; m. Martin Ted Mayden, Sept. 14, 1986. AB, Ind. U., 1973; JD, U. Ga., 1976. Bar: Ga. 1976, N.Y. 1980. Assoc. King & Spalding, Atlanta, 1976-79, Willkie Farr & Gallagher, N.Y.C., 1980, Morgan Lewis & Bockius, N.Y.C., 1980-82, White & Case, N.Y.C., 1982-89; spl. counsel Skadden, Arps, Slate, Meagher & Flom, N.Y.C., 1989—. Mem. U. Ga. Bd. Visitors, Athens, 1986-89. Fellow Am. Bar Found. (life); mem. ABA (chairperson young lawyers div. 1985-86, house of dels. 1986—, commr. commn. on women 1987-91, commr. commn. opportunities for minorities in profession 1986-87, chmn. assembly resolutions com. 1990-91, select com. of the house 1989-91, membership com of the house 1991-92, bd. govs. 1991-94, chair bd. govs. ops. com., exec. com. 1993-94, mem. task force long range fin. planning 1993—), Nat. Assn. Bond Lawyers (bd. dirs. 1985-86), Bond Attys.' Workshop (chmn. 1986), N.Y. State Bar Assn. (mem. ho. of dels. 1993—), Assn. of Bar of City of N.Y. (internat. human rights com. 1989-89, 2d century com. 1986-90, com. women in the profession, 1989-92), N.Y. County Lawyers Assn. (com. spl. projects, chair com. rels with other bars). Democrat. Jewish. Home: 465 West End Ave New York NY 10024-4926 Office: Skadden Arps Slate Meagher & Flom 919 3d Ave 43d Fl New York NY 10022

MAYER, ARNO JOSEPH, history educator; b. Luxembourg, June 19, 1926; came to U.S., 1941, naturalized, 1944; s. Frank J. and Ida (Lieben) M.; m. Nancy Grant, June 19, 1955 (div. Dec. 1965); children: Carl, Daniel. BBA, CCNY, 1949; MA, Yale U., 1950, PhD, 1953. Asst. prof. politics Brandeis U., 1954-58; asst. prof. history Harvard U., 1958-61; prof. history Princeton U., 1961—; vis. prof. Columbia U., 1966-71, NYU, 1971-72; research assoc. Ecole Pratiques des Hautes Études, Paris, 1973. Author: Political Origins of the New Diplomacy, 1959, Politics and Diplomacy of Peacemaking, 1967, Dynamics of Counterrevolution, 1971, The Persistence of the Old Regime, 1981; Why Did the Heavens Not Darken?, 1988. With intelligence service AUS, 1944-46. Recipient Herbert Baxter Adams prize Am. Hist. Assn., 1968, Isaac Teuscher prize, 1991; Am. Council Learned Socs. fellow, 1960-61, Soc. Sci. Research Council fellow, 1961-62, Rockefeller Found. fellow, 1963-64, Guggenheim fellow, 1967-68, Research fellow Inst. War and Peace Columbia, 1971-72, Research fellow Lehrman Inst., 1976-77. Fellow PEN, Am. Acad. Arts and Scis. Home: 58 Battle Rd Princeton NJ 08540-4902

MAYER, CARL JOSEPH, lawyer, town official; b. Boston, Apr. 23, 1959; s. Arno Joseph and Nancy Sue (Grant) M. AB magna cum laude, Princeton U., 1981; JD, U. Chgo., 1986; LLM, Harvard U., 1988. Bar: N.J. 1986, Mass. 1988, N.Y. 1989, D.C. 1989. Writer for Ralph Nader Washington, 1981-83; law clk. to presiding justice U.S. Dist. Ct., Wilmington, Del., 1986-87; asst. prof. Hofstra Law Sch., Hempstead, N.Y., 1989-94; atty. Milberg Weiss, Bershad, Hynes and Lerach, N.Y.C., 1995—; cons. U.S. Senate Com., Washington, 1988-89. Co-author: Public Domain, Private Dominion, 1985; contbr. articles to profl. jours. Town committeeman, Princeton, N.J. NYU fellow, 1988-89. Mem. ABA, N.Y. Bar Assn., N.J. Bar Assn., Mass. Bar Assn. Avocations: marathon running, squash, tennis. Home: 58 Battle Rd Princeton NJ 08540-4902 Office: Milberg Weiss Bershad Hynes & Lerach One Pennsylvania Plz New York NY 10019

MAYER, DENNIS THOMAS, biochemist, educator; b. Lexington, Mo., Jan. 3, 1901; s. August John and Agatha (Gavin) M.; m. Virginia Louise Miller, May 8, 1937; children—Dennis T., David R., Michael J. Student, U. Ill., 1923-25; A.B., U. Mo., 1931, M.A., 1933, Ph.D., 1938. Agt. U.S. Dept. Agr., 1937-42; mem. faculty U. Mo. at Columbia, 1937—, prof. agrl. biochemistry, 1952—, dir. research in physiology and biochemistry reprodn.,

---

1942—, dir. interdisciplinary reproductive biology tng. program, 1966, chmn. dept. agrl. chemistry, dir. grad. studies, 1968-71, prof. emeritus, 1971—. Contbr. articles to profl. jours. Mayer lecture series designated by U. Mo. in his honor, 1987. Mem. Am. Soc. Biol. Chemists, Soc. for Exptl. Biology and Medicine, Am. Soc. Animal Sci., N.Y. Acad. Scis., Mo. Acad. Sci., Phi Beta Kappa, Sigma Xi, Gamma Sigma Delta. Home: 3812 Cedar Ln Columbia MO 65201-6502

MAYER, ENRIQUE JOSÉ, anthropology educator; b. Huancayo, Peru, June 11, 1944; came to U.S., 1981, naturalized; s. Guillermo and Elizabeth Mayer; m. Helaine I. Silverman, Aug. 15, 1975. BSc in Econs., London Sch. Econs.-Polit. Sci., 1966; MA in Anthropology, Cornell U., 1968, PhD in Anthropology, 1974. Lectr. anthropology Cath. Pontificia U. Peru, 1970-71; asst. prof. Pontificia Cath. U. Peru, 1972-74, assoc. prof., 1974-78, coord. masters program in anthropology, 1972-77; head rsch. dept. Inst. Indigenísta Interamericano, Mexico City, 1978-81; vis. assoc. prof. U. Tex., Austin, 1981; asst. prof. anthropology U. Ill., Urbana-Champaign, 1982-85, assoc. prof., 1985-90, prof., 1990—, dir. Ctr. for L.Am. and Caribbean Studies, 1985—; vis. prof. Yale U., New Haven, spring 1990-91; mem. joint com. on L.Am. studies Social Sci. Rsch. Coun., N.Y.C., 1989-91; participant numerous symposia and seminars, 1982—; guest lectr. numerous univs., including U. Ill., Princeton U., U. Calif., Berkeley, U. Chgo., Hunter Coll., CUNY, George Mason U., U. Wis., Yale U., Brandeis U.; reviewer rsch. proposals NSF, Nat. Geog. Soc., Wenner Gren Anthrop. Found., rsch. bd. U. Ill.; book reviewer various univ. presses; cons. in field, 1975-92. Author: Reciprocity, Self-Suffiency and Market Relations in a Contemporary Community in the Central Andes of Peru, 1974, (with Martel) Comunidad y Producción en la Agricultura Andina, 1988, (with de la Cadena) Cooperació y Conflicto en las Communidades Andinas, 1989; co-editor: Reciprocidad e Intercambio en los Andes Peruanos, 1974, Andean Kinship and Marriage, 1977; contbr. articles and book revs. to profl. jours., chpts. to books, also monographs. Grantee Am. Coun. Learned Socs. and Social Sci. Rsch. Coun., 1974-75, Cath. Pontificia U. Peru, 1976-77, U. Ill., 1982, 84, 85, 87, 88, NSF, 1984-86; Hewlett fellow U. Ill. Office Internat. Programs and Studies, 1984. Mem. L.Am. Studies Assn., Am. Anthrop. Assn., Soc. for Econ. Anthropology. Office: U Ill Dept Anthropology 607 S Mathews St Urbana IL 61801

MAYER, FOSTER LEE, JR., toxicologist; b. Fletcher, Okla., Nov. 17, 1942; s. Foster Lee Sr. and Annis Lucille (Edwards) M.; m. Anita June Poarch, Aug. 31, 1962 (div. Nov. 1981); children: Sunie K., Carolyn Elizabeth; m. Kathleen Joyce Stecher, July 14, 1983. BS in Biology and Chemistry, Southwestern Okla. State U., 1965; MS in Wildlife Biology, Utah State U., 1967, PhD in Toxicology, 1970. Instr. Utah State U., Logan, 1969-70; research sect. leader U.S. Fish and Wildlife Service Columbia (Mo.) Fish Research Lab., 1970-73, asst. chief biologist, 1973-74, chief biologist, 1974-80, research scientist, 1980-84; sect. chief U.S. EPA, Gulf Breeze, Fla., 1984-85; br. chief EPA, Gulf Breeze, Fla., 1985-91, sr. rsch. scientist, 1991—; expert witness U.S. Fish and Wildlife Service, 1973-84. Author: Manual of Acute Toxicity-Freshwater, 1986, Acute Toxicity Handbook-Estuarine, 1987, also book chpts.; editor: Aquatic Toxicity and Hazard Evaluation, 1977; contbr. numerous articles to profl. jours. Instr. 4-H Club, Columbia, Mo., 1978-80. Mem. Am. Chem. Soc., Am. Fisheries Soc. (chpt. pres. 1976, sect. pres. 1979), Soc. Environ. Toxicology and Chemistry (editor 1982-87, bd. dirs. 1985-88), Soc. Toxicology (editorial bd. 1981-90), Am. Inst. Fishery Rsch. Biologists, Am. Soc. for Testing and Materials, NRA, Sigma Xi. Republican. Baptist. Avocations: hunting, fishing, boating, wood carving, scrimshawing. Office: EPA Sabine Island Gulf Breeze FL 32561

MAYER, FRANK D., JR., lawyer; b. Dec. 23, 1933. BA, Amherst Coll., 1955; student, Cambridge U.; JD, U. Chgo., 1959. Bar: Ill. 1959. Ptnr. Mayer, Brown & Platt, Chgo. Mem. ABA, Chgo. Bar Assn., Order of Coif, Phi Beta Kappa. Office: Mayer Brown & Platt 190 S La Salle St Chicago IL 60603-3410

MAYER, GEORGE MERTON, elementary education educator; b. Ellisburg, N.Y., July 11, 1936; s. Carlton Scott and Florence Geraldine (Allen) M.; m. Charlotte Anne Dawley, Aug. 31, 1963; children: Linda Sue Mayer Randall, Brian Keith, Amanda Leanne. AA, Erie County Tech. Inst., 1957; BA in Edn., SUNY, Buffalo, 1966, MEd, 1973. Cert. tchr., N.Y. Lab. tech. Sylvania Electric Co., Buffalo, 1957-58; driver, mechanic Ransomville (N.Y.) Bus Lines, 1959-66; coach driver Lockport (N.Y.) and Grand Island Transit Bus Lines, 1966-87; tchr. Thomas Marks Sch., Wilson, N.Y., 1965-82; tchr. remedial math. Wilson Sch. Dist., 1982—; coach wrestling Wilson High Sch., 1977-88, coach jr. varsity football, 1972. Lay leader, mem. choir Ransomville United Meth. Ch., 1960-90; co-chmn. Niagara County Foster Parents, 1980—; bd. dirs. Town of Porter Recreation Commn. With USNG, 1955-58, USAR, 1958-62. Mem. Wilson Tchrs. Assn., N.Y. State United Tchrs. Assn., N.Y. State Foster and Adoptive Assn. Republican. Avocations: music, electronics, sports, woodworking. Home: 2470 Youngstown Lockport Rd Ransomville NY 14131-9644 Office: W H Stevenson Elem Sch 3745 Ransomville Rd Ransomville NY 14131-9768 also: Thomas Marks Elem Sch PO Box 648 Wilson NY 14172-0648

MAYER, HALDANE ROBERT, federal judge; b. Buffalo, N.Y., Feb. 21, 1941; s. Haldane Rupert and Myrtle Kathleen (Gaude) M.; m. Mary Anne McCurdy, Aug. 13, 1966; children: Anne Christian, Rebecca Paige. B.S., U.S. Mil. Acad., 1963; J.D., Coll. William and Mary, 1971. Bar: Va. 1971, U.S. Ct. Appeals (4th cir.) 1972, U.S. Dist. Ct. (ea. dist.) Va. 1972, U.S. Ct. Mil. Appeals, U.S. Army Ct. Mil. Rev. 1973, D.C. 1980, U.S. Supreme Ct. 1977, U.S. Ct. Claims 1984. Law clk. U.S. Ct. Appeals (4th cir.), Richmond, Va., 1971-72; atty. McGuire Woods & Battle, Charlottesville, Va., 1975-77; spl. asst. to chief justice U.S. Supreme Ct., Washington, 1977-80; atty. Baker & McKenzie, Washington, 1980-81; dep. acting spl. counsel U.S. Merit Systems Protection Bd., Washington, 1981-82; judge U.S. Claims Ct., Washington, 1982-87, U.S. Ct. Appeals (Fed. cir.), Washington, 1987—; lectr. U. Va. Sch. Law, 1975-77, 92—, George Washington U. Law Sch., 1992—. Bd. dirs. William and Mary Law Sch. Assn., 1979-85. Served to maj. AUS, 1963-75, lt. col. res. ret. Decorated Bronze Star, two Army Commendation medals, Meritorious Service medal. Mem. West Point Assn. Grads., Army Athletic Assn., West Point Soc. D.C., Omicron Delta Kappa. Office: US Ct Appeals 717 Madison Pl NW Washington DC 20439-0002*

MAYER, HENRY MICHAEL, mass transit consultant; b. Wauwatosa, Wis., Oct. 20, 1922; s. Henry and Rose (Daas) M.; m. Colleen C. Reisner, July 25, 1944; children: Michael, Michele, David, Jennifer. B.S. in Bus. Adminstrn., Marquette U., 1947. With Milw. Transit System, 1947-83, exec. asst., 1959-67, v.p., pres., mng. dir. Milw. Transport Services, Inc., 1975-83; cons., 1983—; lectr., cons., author, mass transit. Lt. USNR, 1943-46, PTO. Named to Pub. Transit Hall of Fame. Mem. Inst. Transp. Engrs., Alpha Sigma Nu. Originator bus service using pvt. shopping centers as park-ride lots for freeway express service to downtown. Home: 1620 N 124th St Milwaukee WI 53226-2910

MAYER, JAMES HOCK, mediator, lawyer; b. Neptune City, N.J., Nov. 1, 1935; s. J. Kenneth and Marie Ruth (Hock) M.; m. Carol I. Keating, Sept. 20, 1958 (div. Feb. 1981); children: Craig, Jeffrey; m. Patrisha Renk, Mar. 28, 1981. AB with distinction, Dartmouth Coll., 1957; JD, Harvard U., 1964. Bar: Calif. 1965, U.S. Dist. Ct (no. dist., so. dist.) Calif. 1965, U.S. Ct. Appeals (9th cir.) 1965, U.S. Supreme Ct. 1974. Assoc. Pillsbury, Madison & Sutro, San Francisco, 1964-72, ptnr., 1973—; ind. mediator, 1992—. Rear adm. USNR, 1957-93. Rufus Choate scholar Dartmouth Coll., 1956-57. Mem. Newcomen Soc., Navy League, Naval Order of U.S., Harvard Club. Office: 101 W Broadway Ste 1800 San Diego CA 92101-8201

MAYER, JAMES JOSEPH, retired corporate lawyer; b. Cin., Nov. 27, 1933; s. Cletus Joseph and Berna Mae (Schroeder) M.; m. Margaret Ann Hobbs, Oct. 24, 1964; children: Kimberly, Susanne, Terri. BEE, U. Cin., 1961; JD, No. Ky. U., 1969. Registered profl. engr.: Ohio. Bar: Ohio 1969, Ky. 1975. Engr. Cin. Gas & Electric Co. 1961-69, atty., 1969-85, gen. counsel, Sigma Xi, v.p., gen. counsel, 1991-95, ret., 1995. Served with USAFR, 1961-64. Mem. Ohio Bar Assn., Ky. Bar Assn., Cin. Bar Assn. Republican. Roman Catholic. Club: Bankers. Avocations: home remodeling, sports, golf.

MAYER, JAMES WALTER, materials science educator; b. Chgo., Apr. 24, 1930; s. James Leo and Kathleen (Engels) M.; m. Elizabeth Billmire, June

27, 1952; children: James Leo, John William, Frank Charles, Helen Kathleen, William Andrew. BSME, Purdue U., 1952, PhD in Physics, 1960; DSc (hon.), SUNY, Albany, 1988. Tech. staff Hughes Research Lab., Malibu, Calif., 1959-67; prof. Calif. Inst. Tech., Pasadena, 1967-80; master of student houses Calif. Inst. Tech., 1975-80; F. Norwood Bard prof. materials sci. Cornell U., Ithaca, N.Y., 1980-92, Bard prof. emeritus, 1992—; dir. Ctr. for Solid State Sci., Regents' prof. Ariz. State U., Tempe, 1992—; scuba instr. Nat. Assn. Underwater Instrs. 1970-80. Author: Backscattering Spectrometry, 1978, Ion Implantation in Semiconductors, 1970, Materials Analysis by Ion Channeling, 1982, Fundamentals of Surface and Thin Film Analysis, 1986, Electronic Materials Science, 1990, Electronic Thin Film Science, 1992; editor: Laser Annealing of Semiconductors, 1982. Served to 1st lt. U.S. Army, 1952-54. Recipient Von Hippel award, Materials Research Soc., Boston, 1981, Silver Medal of U. Catania, Italy, 1986. Fellow Am. Phys. Soc., IEEE; mem. Bohmische Physical Soc., Am. Vacuum Soc., Nat. Acad. Engring. Home: 3355 N Valencia Ln Phoenix AZ 85018-6610 Office: Ariz State U Ctr for Solid State Sci Tempe AZ 85287-1704

MAYER, JOHN, lawyer; b. Beatrice, Nebr., Aug. 25, 1948; m. Kathleen A. Slaydon, Mar. 8, 1986; children: Amelia, Holly. BA, U. N.Mex., 1970; JD, U. Tex., 1973. Bar: Tex. 1973; cert. Tex. Bd. Civil Trial Advocacy. Assoc. Ross, Banks, May, Cron & Cavin, Houston, 1973-80, ptnr., 1980—. Mem. Assn. Trial Lawyers Am., Tex. Assn. Bank Counsel, Comml. Law League Am. Home: 725 E Creekside Dr Houston TX 77024-3239 Office: Ross Banks May Cron & Cavin 2 Riverway # 700 Houston TX 77056

MAYER, MARGERY WEIL, publishing executive; b. Beaufort, S.C., Feb. 11, 1952; d. Warren Burke Weil and Elise Jean (Schiff) Rubel; m. Theodore Van Huysen Mayer, Dec. 28, 1975; children: Lily, Henry. BA, Middlebury Coll., 1974; MS, MIT, 1976. Planning analyst Digital Equipment Corp., Maynard, Mass., 1976-77; editor-in-chief sch. pub. sect. Holt, Rinehart & Winston, N.Y.C., 1977-87; pres. Ginn div. Silver, Burdett & Ginn, Needham, Mass., 1987-90; exec. v.p. Scholastic Inc., N.Y.C., 1990—. Editor Sloan Mgmt. Rev., 1975-76. Trustee program Read With Me, Dedham, Mass., 1989; mem. rev. panel U.S. Dept. Edn. Sch. Recognition Program. Mem. Phi Beta Kappa. Office: Scholastic Inc 555 Broadway New York NY 10012-9511*

MAYER, MORRIS LEHMAN, marketing educator; b. Demopolis, Ala., Dec. 14, 1925; s. Lehman M. and Anne (Rochotsh) M.; m. Judith Marian Morton, Dec. 22, 1957; children: Susan Morton, Elizabeth Anne. B.S. in Bus. Adminstrn, U. Ala., 1949, DHL (hon.), 1994; M.S. in Retailing, N.Y. U., 1950; Ph.D. in Bus. Orgn, Ohio State U., 1961. Buyer Goldblatts Dept. Store, Chgo., 1951-55; mem. faculty U. Ala., 1955—, prof., 1960—, chmn. dept. mktg., 1969-74, dir. Hess Inst. Retailing, 1985-92, Bruno prof. mktg., 1986-92; Bruno prof. mktg. emeritus, 1992—; instr. Ohio State U., Columbus, 1956-60; cons. Mgmt. Horizons Co., Columbus, 1966-70, N.C.R. Co., Dayton, Ohio, 1967-75. Co-author: Modern Retailing, 1978, 6th edit., 1993, Retailing, 1981, 5th edit., 1993. Served with AUS, 1944-46, 50-51. Recipient Teaching Excellence award Burlington No. Found., 1986; Ford Found. fellow, 1962-63, So. Mktg. fellow, 1986; Morris Mayer Endowed scholarship estab. 1992; Morris L. Mayer award estab. U. Ala., 1993; Morris L. Mayer Outstanding Student award estab. Sales and Mktg. Execs., 1993, others. Mem. Am. Mktg. Assn. (Morris L. Mayer Outstanding Mem. award estab. Birmingham chpt. 1993), So. Mktg. Assn. (pres.), Ala. Retail Assn. (bd. dirs.), Am. Coll. Retail Assn. (pres., Hall of Fame 1992, Mortar Bd., Beta Gamma Sigma, Eta Mu Pi, Pi Sigma Epsilon, Omicron Delta Kappa, Zeta Beta Tau (chpt. trustee). Jewish (temple trustee). Home: 1321 Montclair Cir Tuscaloosa AL 35404-4241 Office: U Ala PO Box 870225 Tuscaloosa AL 35487-0225

MAYER, NANCY J., state official; b. Phila., June 9, 1937; d. Benjamin and Florence Hannah (Altshuler) Rosenstein; m. Edward C. Leand, Sept. 6, 1958 (div. 1970); children: Judith, Marjorie; m. William L. Mayer, June 16, 1971. BA in Am. Hist., Barnard Coll., 1958; MAT in Am. Hist., Brown U., 1972; JD, Northeastern U., 1982. Assoc. firm Tillinghast, Collins & Graham, Providence, 1982-84; chief legal counsel R.I. Dept. Bus. Regulation, Providence, 1986-92; treas. State of R.I., 1992—; candidate R.I. Senate, 1978, 80. Mem. R.I. adv. com. U.S. Commn. on Civil Rights; mem. R.I. Partnership of Sci. and Tech.; mem. AGing 2000 Health Care for Srs. Com., adv. com. U.S. Com. on Civil Rights (R.I. Chpt.). Mem. Nat. Assn. State Treas. (v.p.). Republican. Jewish. Avocations: tennis (former nationally and regionally ranked player), cycling, jogging, writing, duplicate bridge. Office: Treasury Dept 102 State House Providence RI 02903

MAYER, PATRICIA JAYNE, financial officer, management accountant; b. Chgo., Apr. 27, 1950; d. Arthur and Ruth (Greenberger) Hersh; m. William A. Mayer Jr., Apr. 30, 1971. AA, Diablo Valley Coll., 1970; BSBA, Calif. State U., Hayward, 1975. Cert. mgmt. acct. Staff acct., auditor Elmer Fox Westheimer and Co., Oakland, Calif., 1976; supervising auditor Auditor's Office County of Alameda, Oakland, 1976-78; asst. acctg. mgr. CBS Retail Stores doing bus. as Pacific Stereo, Emeryville, Calif., 1978-79; contr. Oakland Unified Sch. Dist., 1979-84; v.p. fin., chief fin. officer YMCA, San Francisco, 1984—; instr. acctg. to staff YMCA San Francisco, 1984—, CBS Retail Stores, 1978-79. Draft counselor Mt. Diablo Peace Ctr., Walnut Creek, Calif., 1970-72; dep. registrar of voters Contra Costa County Registrar's Office, Martinez, Calif., 1972-77. Mem. Fin. Execs. Inst. (bd. dirs. San Francisco chpt.), Inst. Mgmt. Accts. (pres.- elect Diablo Valley chpt. 1995—), Dalmatian Club No. Calif., Dalmatian Club Am. Democrat. Jewish. Avocations: showing and breeding Dalmatians. Home: 2395 Lake Meadow Cir Martinez CA 94553-5475 Office: YMCA of San Francisco 44 Montgomery St Ste 770 San Francisco CA 94104

MAYER, PETER, publisher; b. London, 1936. Grad., Columbia Coll., Oxford U., Eng. CEO Penguin Books, London, N.Y.C., 1978—; now chmn. Penguin USA, N.Y.C. Recipient grad. fellowship Ind. Univ.; Fulbright scholar Univ. Berlin. Office: Penguin Books Ltd, 27 Wrights Ln, London W8 5TZ, England also: Penguin USA 375 Hudson St New York NY 10014-3658

MAYER, RAYMOND RICHARD, business administration educator; b. Chgo., Aug. 31, 1924; s. Adam and Mary (Bogdala) M.; m. Helen Lakowski, Jan. 30, 1954; children: Mark, John, Mary, Jane. B.S., Ill. Inst. Tech., 1948, M.S., 1956, Ph.D., 1957. Indsl. engr. Standard Oil Co., Whiting, Ind., 1948-51; orgn. analyst Ford Motor Co., Chgo., 1951-53; instr. Ill. Inst. Tech., Chgo., 1953-56; asso. prof. Ill. Inst. Tech., 1958-60; asst. prof. U. Chgo., 1956-58; Walter F. Mullady prof. bus. adminstrn. Loyola U., Chgo., 1960—. Author: Financial Analysis of Investment Alternatives, 1966, Production Management, 1962, rev. edit., 1968, Production and Operations Management, 1975, rev. edit., 1982, Capital Expenditure Analysis, 1978. Served with USNR, 1944-46. Ingersoll Found. fellow, 1955-56; Machinery and Allied Products Inst. fellow, 1954-55; Ford Found. fellow, 1962. Mem. Acad. Mgmt., Am. Econ. Assn., Am. Statis. Assn., Am. Inst. for Decision Scis., Nat. Assn. Purchasing Mgmt., Polish Inst. Arts and Scis. in Am., Alpha Iota Delta, Alpha Kappa Psi, Beta Gamma Sigma. Home: 730 Green Bay Rd Winnetka IL 60093-1912 Office: 820 N Michigan Ave Chicago IL 60611-2103

MAYER, RICHARD DEAN, mathematics educator; b. Ft. Wayne, Ind., May 26, 1930; s. Lester Blyle and Velma Lucille (Maulsby) M.; m. Patsy Jean Hartwell, Aug. 31, 1952; children—Susan, Joann, John. B.S., Purdue U., 1952, M.S., 1954; Ph.D., U. Wash., 1959. Teaching asst. Purdue U., 1952-54, U. Wash., 1954-59; asst. prof. math. Idaho State U., 1959-61, assoc. prof. math., chmn. dept., 1961-67; prof. math. SUNY, Oswego, 1967-91, prof. math. emeritus, 1991—, chmn. dept., 1967-74; rsch. engr. Boeing Airplane Co., Seattle, summer, 1959, Carter Oil Co., Billings, Mont., summer, 1960. Mem. The Planetary Soc., Math. Assn. Am., Am. Math. Soc., Sigma Xi, Sigma Pi Sigma, Delta Rho Kappa, Pi Mu Epsilon, Kappa Mu Epsilon. Avocations: handball. Home: 23040 Chisholm Trl Bend OR 97702-9664

MAYER, RICHARD EDWIN, psychology educator; b. Chgo., Feb. 8, 1947; s. James S. and Bernis (Lowy) M.; m. Beverly Linn Pastor, Dec. 19, 1971; children: Kenneth Michael, David Mark, Sarah Ann. BA with honors, Miami U., Oxford, Ohio, 1969; MS in Psychology, U. Mich., 1971, PhD in Psychology, 1973. Vis. asst. prof. Ind. U., Bloomington, 1973-75; asst. prof. psychology U. Calif., Santa Barbara, 1975-80, assoc. prof., 1980-85, prof.,

pres., 1985—, chmn. dept., 1987-90; vis. scholar Learning Rsch. and Devel. Ctr., U. Pitts., 1979, Ctr. for Study of Reading, U. Ill., 1984. Author: Foundations of Learning and Memory, 1979, The Promise of Cognitive Psychology, 1981, Thinking, Problem Solving, Cognition, 1983, 2d edit., 1992, BASIC: A Short Course, 1985, Educational Psychology, 1987; editor: Human Reasoning, 1980, Teaching and Learning Computer Programming, 1988; editor jours. Instructional Sci., 1983-87, Educational Psychologist, 1983-89. Sch. bd. officer Goleta (Calif.) Union Sch. Dist., 1981—. NSF grantee, 1975-88. Fellow APA (divsn. 15 officer 1987—, G. Stanley Hall lectr. 1988); mem. Am. Ednl. Rsch. Assn. (divsn. C officer 1986-88), Psychonomic Soc., Soc. Computers in Psychology. Democrat. Jewish. Avocations: computers, hiking, bicycling, reading, dogs. Office: U Calif Dept Of Psychology Santa Barbara CA 93016

MAYER, RICHARD PHILIP, food executive; b. Bloomfield, N.J., Feb. 13, 1940; s. Richard R. and Margaret (Kernan) M.; m. Diane Marie Krouse; children: Margaret, Catherine. B.S., Rutgers U., 1962, M.B.A., 1965. Dir. group prodns. Gen. Foods Corp., 1962-72; dir. bus. devel. Heublein, Inc., Farmington, Conn., 1973-75; v.p. mktg. planning Heublein Grocery Prodn., Farmington, Conn., 1975-77; v.p. planning and program integration Kentucky Fried Chicken, Louisville, 1977-78, sr. v.p. mktg., planning and devel., 1978-79, pres., 1979-80, chmn., chief exec. officer, 1980-89; pres. Gen. Foods USA (divsn. Kraft Gen. Foods), White Plains, N.Y., 1989-91; chmn. bd., CEO Kraft Gen. Foods, Northfield, Ill., 1991—. Chmn. Louisville Fund for Arts, 1984-85; bd. dirs. Northwestern Meml. Hosp., Chgo., Lyrice Opera of Chgo., Nat. City Bank, Louisville, Brown-Forman Corp., Louisville. Served with U.S. Army, 1964-70. Recipient Gold Medal award Am. Mktg. Assn. Mem. First Ky. Nat. Corp. (bd. dirs.). Office: Kraft Gen Foods 3 Lakes Dr Northfield IL 60093

MAYER, ROBERT ANTHONY, art institute executive; b. N.Y.C., Oct. 30, 1933; s. Ernest John and Theresa Margaret (Mazura) M.; m. Laura Wiley Christ, Apr. 30, 1960. BA magna cum laude, Fairleigh Dickinson U., 1955; MA, NYU, 1967. With N.J. Bank and Trust Co., Paterson, 1955-61; mgr. advt. dept. N.J. Bank and Trust Co., 1959-61; program supr. advt. dept. Mobil Oil Co., N.Y.C., 1961-62; asst. to dir. Latin Am. program Ford Found., N.Y.C., 1963-65; asst. rep. Ford Found., Brazil, 1965-67; asst. to v.p. adminstrn. Ford Found., 1967-73, officer in charge logistical services, 1968-73; asst. dir. programs N.Y. Community Trust, N.Y.C., 1973-76; exec. v.p. N.Y. State Council on the Arts, N.Y.C., 1976-79; mgmt. cons. N.Y.C., 1979-80; dir. Internat. Mus. Photography, George Eastman House, Rochester, N.Y., 1980-89, mgmt. cons., 1989-90; pres. Cleve. Inst. of Art, 1990—. Mem. editorial adv. bd.: Grants mag., 1978-80; author: (plays) La Borgia, 1971; Alijandru, 1971, They'll Grow No Roses, 1975. mem. state programs adv. panel Nat.Endowment Arts, 1977-80; mem. Mayor's Com. on Cultural Policy, N.Y.C., 1974-75; mem. pres.'s adv. com. Bklyn. campus Ll. U., 1978-79; bd. dirs. Fedn. Protestant Welfare Agys., N.Y.C., 1977-79, Arts for Greater Rochester, 1981-83, Garth Fagan's Dance Theatre, 1982-86; trustee Internat. Mus. Photography, 1981-89., Lacoste Sch. of Arts, France, 1991—, sec., 1994—; mem. dean's adv. com. Grad. Sch. Social Welfare, Fordham u., 1976; mem. N.Y. State Motion Picture and TV Devel. Adv. Bd., 1984-87, N.Y. State Martin Luther King Jr. Commn., 1985-90, Cleve. Coun. for Cultural Affairs, 1992-94; chmn Greater Cleve. Regional Transit Authority Arts in Transit Com., 1990—. Recipient Nat. award on advocacy for girls Girls Clubs Am., 1976. Mem. Nat. Assembly Art Agys. (bd. dirs. 1977-79, 1st vice chmn. 1978-79), Alliance Ind. Colls. Art (bd. dirs. 1983-91, vice chmn. 1986-87, sec. 1987-89), N.Y. State Assn. Museums (bd. councilors 1983-86, pres. 1986-89), Assn. Ind. Colls. Art and Design (bd. dirs. 1991—, exec. com. 1991-93). Home: 20201 N Park Blvd Apt 101 Shaker Heights OH 44118-5024 Office: Cleve Inst Art 11141 East Blvd Cleveland OH 44106-1700

MAYER, ROBERT WALLACE, emeritus finance educator; b. Mt. Pulaski, Ill., Apr. 17, 1909; s. Edward Otto and Minnie Laura (Clark) M.; m. Nella Coryell DeAtley, AUg. 2, 1933 (dec.); children: nancy (Mrs. Donald G. Wyatt), Anne (Mrs. Robert M. Shannon, dec.), Caroline (Mrs. Chester R. Keller), Melinda (Mrs. Thomas Martinez). B.S., U. Ill., 1930, M.S., 1931, Ph.D., 1933. Cert. ofcl. U.S. Track and Field Fedn. Statistician Libby McNeill & Libby, Chgo., 1929, Commonwealth Edison Co., Chgo., 1930; from instr. to asst. prof. Lehigh U., 1933-42; sr. economist WPB, Washington, 1942-45; asso. prof. econs. U. Ill., Urbana, 1945-52; prof. U. Ill., 1952-57, prof. finance, 1957-77, prof. emeritus, 1977—, vice chmn. dept. econs., 1953-57; vis. prof. fin. Ill. State U., Normal, 1978-79; Exec. sec. Combined (Brit.-Am.) Steel Com., 1943-45; cons. Rand Corp., 1951-53. Author Stemma, 1984m Bios Didaskalos, 1991; contbr. articles to profl. jours. Mem. Am. Finance Assn., Midwest Finance Assn. (pres. 1967-68), Am. Econ. Assn., Chgo. Fin. Writers Assn., SAR, U. Ill. Varsity Assn. (hon.), Beta Gamma Sigma, Phi Kappa Phi, Alpha Kappa Psi, Tau Kappa Epsilon. Republican. Presbyterian. Club: Kiwanian (pres. 1969-70). Home: 17 Greencroft Dr Champaign IL 61821-5117 Office: U Ill Urbana IL 61801

MAYER, SUSAN MARTIN, art educator; b. Atlanta, Oct. 25, 1931; d. Paul McKeen and Ione (Garrett) Martin; m. Arthur James Mayer, Aug. 9, 1953; 1 child. Melinda Marilyn. Student, Am. U., 1949-50; BA, U. N.C., Greensboro, 1953; postgrad., U. Del., 1956-58; MA, Ariz. State U., 1966. Artist-in-residence Armed Forces Staff Coll., Norfolk, Va., 1968-69; coord. of edn. Huntington Art Gallery U. Tex., Austin, 1970—, mem. art faculty, 1971—. Co-editor: Museum Education: History, Theory and Practice, 1989; author various mus. publs.; contbr. articles to profl. jours. Recipient award Austin Ind. Sch. Bd., 1985. Mem. Nat. Art Edn. Assn. (bd. dirs. 1983-87, award 1987, 91), Tex. Art Edn. Assn. (mus. edn. chair 1982-83, legis. rep. 1988—, Mus. Educator of Yr. 1986), Tex. Assn. Mus. (mus. edn. chair), Austin Visual Arts Assn., Am. Assn. Mus. Office: U Tex Art/Art History Dept Art Dept Austin TX 78712

MAYER, THEODORE V.H., lawyer; b. Waltham, Mass., Sept. 30, 1952; s. Jean and Elizabeth (Van Huysen) M.; m. Margery Weil, Dec. 28, 1975; children: Lily, Henry. BA, Yale U., 1974; JD, Harvard U., 1977. Bar: N.Y. 1978, Mass. 1988, U.S. Ct. Appeals (2d, 3d, fed. and 7th cirs.), U.S. Supreme Ct., numerous U.S. Dist. Cts. Assoc. Hughes, Hubbard & Reed, N.Y.C., 1978-85, ptnr., 1985—. Contbr. articles to profl. jours. Bd. dirs. New Media Repertory Co., N.Y.C., 1991—. Office: Hughes Hubbard & Reed One Battery Park Pla New York NY 10004

MAYER, VICTOR JAMES, geological science educator; b. Mayville, Wis., Mar. 25, 1933; s. Victor Charles and Phyllis (Bachhuber) M.; m. Mary Jo Anne White, Nov. 25, 1965; children: Gregory, Maribeth. BS in Geology, U. Wis., 1956; MS in Geology, U. Colo., 1960, PhD in Sci. Edn., 1966. Tchr. Colo. Pub. Schs., 1961-65; asst. prof. SUNY Coll., Oneonta, 1965-67; asst. prof. Ohio State U., Columbus, 1967-70, assoc. prof., 1970-75, prof. ednl. studies, geol. scis. and natural resources, 1975—; coord. Earth Systems Edn. Program, 1991—; research fellow Am. Geol. Inst., Alexandria, Va., 1987; co-organizer of symposium at 29th Internat. Geol. Congress; internat. sci. edn. assistance to individuals and orgns. in Japan, Korea, Taiwan, Russia and Venezuela; dir. NSF Insts., program for leadership Earth Systems Edn., 1990-95; dir. Korean Sci. Tchrs. Insts., 1986-88; keynote spkr. U.S.A. rep. Internat. Conf. on Geoscis. Edn., Southampton, Eng., 1993; Disting. vis. prof. SUNY, Plattsburgh, 1994. Contbr. articles to profl. jours. Served with USAR. Named Disting. Investigator, Ohio Sea Grant Program, 1983. Fellow AAAS (chmn. edn. 1988-89), Ohio Acad. Sci. (v.p. 1978-79, exec. com. 1993-94); mem. Nat. Sci. Tchrs. Assn. (bd. dirs. 1984-86), Nat. Assn. Geol. Teachers (pres. 1987-88), Sigma Xi, Phi Delta Kappa. Roman Catholic. Avocation: photography. Home: 111 W Dominion Blvd Columbus OH 43214-2607 Office: Ohio State U Coll of Edn 1945 N High St Columbus OH 43210-1120

MAYER, WALTER GEORG, physics educator; b. Silberbach, Bohemia, Czech Republic, Mar. 13, 1927; came to U.S., 1949; s. Karl and Berta *Guldan) M.; m. Gretl Anna König, Mar. 21, 1959. AB, Hope Coll., 1953; MS, Mich. State U., 1955, PhD, 1958. Rsch. scientist Siemens Corp., Erlangen, Germany, 1958-59; asst. rsch. prof. Mich. State U., East Lansing, 1959-65; asst. prof. Georgetown U., Washington, 1965-69, assoc. prof., 1969-72, prof. physics, 1972—; dir. Ultrasonics Rsch. Lab., 1988—; vis. prof. U. Saarbruecken, Germany, 1980-81, U. Solidstate, Paris, 1990. Editor Ultrasonics, 1989; contbr. articles to profl. jours. Recipient Humboldt prize Humboldt Found., 1980, Medaille d'Argent, Acoutsical Soc. France, 1990.

Fellow Acoustical Soc. Am., Inst. Acoustics U.K. Office: Georgetown U Physics Dept 37th and O Sts NW Washington DC 20057

MAYER, WILLIAM DIXON, pathologist, educator; b. Beaver Falls, Pa., Oct. 5, 1928; s. Emil Leroy and Elizabeth (Townsend) M.; m. Donna S. Dashiell; children: Elizabeth Ann, David Dixon, William Dixon, Kathy Dashiell. A.B., Colgate U., 1951; M.D. with honor, U. Rochester, 1957; D.Sc. (hon.), U. Osteopathic Medicine and Health Scis., 1988. Intern, then resident pathology Strong Meml. Hosp., Rochester, N.Y., 1957-61; instr., mem. faculty U. Mo. Sch. Medicine, 1961-76, dir. Univ. Med. Center, 1967-74; dean U. Mo. Sch. Medicine (Sch. Medicine), 1967-74, prof. pathology, 1967-76; asst. chief med. dir. for acad. affairs VA, Washington, 1976-79; pres. Med. Coll. Hampton Roads, Norfolk, Va., 1979-87; assoc. dir. div. regional med. programs NIH, 1966-67; mem. exec. com. Nat. Bd. Med. Examiners, 1969-81, treas., 1975-79, vice-chmn., 1979-81, hon. mem., 1981—, fin. com., 1987-93; bd. regent Nat. Libr. of Medicine, 1980-84, chmn., 1982-84. Bd. dirs., 1st v-p. Future of Hampton Rds., 1983—; bd. dirs. Greater Norfolk Corp., 1987-91, exec. v.p., 1989-90; founding mem. bd. dirs. Town Point Club, 1983-91. With USMC, 1946-48. Markle scholar acad. medicine, 1962-67. Fellow Coll. Am. Pathologists; mem. AMA, Assn. Am. Med. Colls. (Disting. Service mem.), C. of C. (bd. dirs. 1986-91), Sigma Xi, Alpha Omega Alpha. Episcopalian. Home: 223 Ocean Hills Rd Virginia Beach VA 23451-2601

MAYER, WILLIAM EMILIO, dean; b. N.Y.C., May 7, 1940; s. Emilio and Marie Mayer; m. Katherine Mayer, May 16, 1964; children: Kristen Elizabeth, William Franz. BS, U. Md., 1966, MBA, 1967. Pres., chief exec. officer First Boston Corp., N.Y.C., 1967-91; dean Coll. Bus. & Mgnt. U. Maryland, College Park, 1992—; bd. dirs. Am. Med. Internat., Inc., Chart House Enterprises, Inc., TechnoServe, Riverwood Interant., Hambrecht & Quist, Inc., Colonial Mut. Fund Group. Bd. dirs. U. Md. Found., College Park; bd. adminstrs. Tulane U.; trustee Cancer Rsch. Inst. 1st lt. USAF, 1961-65. Mem. Bond Club N.Y., Investment Assn. of N.Y., Annapolis Yacht Club, Manhasset Bay Club (N.Y.), Univ. Club (N.Y.C.), Mashomack Fish & Game Club. Home: 172 Long Neck Point Rd Darien CT 06820-5816 Office: U Maryland Coll Bus & Mgnt Van Munching Hall College Park MD 20742

MAYERON, CAROL ANN, cantor; b. Mpls., Jan. 14, 1951; d. Phillip Jerome and Shirley (Shapiro) Richter; m. Robert Charles Mayeron, May 27, 1973; children: Jennifer Lynn, Molli Beth. BS magna cum laude, U. Minn., 1973. Mem. choir Adath Jeshurun Synagogue, Mpls., 1967-74; cantorial soloist, dir. music Bet Shalom Congregation, Hopkins, Minn., 1981-95; del. Joint Commn. on Synagogue Music, Paramus, N.J., 1987-95; tutor B'nai Mitzvah Temple Israel, Mpls., 1988-90. Active Mpls. Children's Health Ctr. Aux., 1977—; coach Golden Valley (Minn.) Girls Jr. Softball, 1987-88, 90-91; co-chair Meadowbrook Parent Coun., Golden Valley, 1988. Recipient Shomer Shirah award Guardian Jewish Music, 1992. Mem. Am. Conf. Cantors (bd. dirs. 1989-92), Nat. Coun. Jewish Women, Minn. Cantor's Assn., Guild Temple Musicians (sec. 1987-89, pres. 1989-92), Hadassah (life, various offices).

MAYERS, BARBARA W., lawyer; b. Chgo., Nov. 28, 1940. BA, Roosevelt U., 1970; JD magna cum laude, DePaul U., 1975. Bar: Ill. 1975. Ptnr. McDermott, Will & Emery, Chgo. Mem. Ill. State Bar Assn., Chgo. Bar Assn., Nat. Health Lawyer's Assn., Group Health Assn. Am. Office: McDermott Will & Emery 227 W Monroe St Chicago IL 60606-5016*

MAYERS, DANIEL KRIEGSMAN, lawyer; b. Scarsdale, N.Y., July 10, 1934; s. Chauncey Maurice and Helen P. (Kriegsman) M.; m. Karen E. Silverman, Sept. 30, 1956, children—Peter D. Leslie H. Shroyer. A.B., Harvard U., 1955, LL.B., 1960. Bar: D.C. 1961, U.S. Supreme Ct. 1961. Law clk. to Justice Felix Frankfurter, U.S. Supreme Ct., Washington, 1960-61; spl. asst. U.S. Dept. Justice, Washington, 1961-62; assoc. Wilmer Cutler & Pickering, Washington, 1962-65, ptnr., 1967—; exec. asst. to undersec. U.S. State Dept., Washington, 1965-66; mem. vis. com. Harvard Law Sch., Cambridge, Mass., 1982-89, chmn., 1986-89; bd. dirs. Legal Action Ctr., N.Y.C., 1982—; chmn. Washington Ednl. TV Assn., 1993—. Pres. Nat. Symphony Orch., Washington, 1987-89; chmn. Sidwell Friends Sch., Washington, 1979-81; mem. Ams. for Peace Now, 1991—, Fed. City Coun., Washington, 1981—; counsel, dir. Ctr. for Nat. Policy, Washington, 1984-93. With U.S. Army, 1955-57. Recipient Sears prize Harvard Law Sch., 1959. Mem. ABA, Met. Club, Woodstock Country Club. Democrat. Jewish. Avocations: tennis; fishing. Home: 3222 Woodland Dr NW Washington DC 20008-3547 Office: Wilmer Cutler & Pickering 2445 M St NW Washington DC 20037-1435

MAYERS, EUGENE DAVID, philosopher, educator; b. N.Y.C., July 30, 1915; s. Sylvester and Estelle (Weinstein) M.; m. Odette Julia Marguerite Gilchriest, Dec. 30, 1950; children: David Allan, Marilyn Anne, Judith Odette, Peter Michael. A.B., Yale U., 1936, LL.B., 1940; Ph.D., Columbia U., 1956. Bar: N.Y. State bar 1941. With Nat. Bur. Econ. Research, N.Y.C., 1941, Office Gen. Counsel, Navy Dept., 1946; mem. faculty Carleton Coll., Northfield, Minn., 1950-61, Columbia, 1959-60, Mills Coll., Oakland, Calif., 1961-63; prof. philosophy Calif. State U., Hayward, 1963-92, prof. emeritus, 1992—; chmn. dept. philosophy Calif. State U., 1963-73, acting head div. humanities, 1966-67. Author: Some Modern Theories of Natural Law, 1957; Contbr. articles to profl. jours. Served to capt. AUS, 1941-46, 51-52; lt. col. USAR ret. Fellow Soc. Values in Higher Edn.; mem. Am. Philos. Assn. (chmn. conf. dept. chmn. Pacific div. 1973-75, Pacific div. exec. com. 1976-80, chmn. exec. com. 1978-80), Am. Soc. Polit. and Legal Philosophy, Pacific Coast Theol. Soc. (sec. 1984-86), Internat. Assn. Philosophy Law and Social Philosophy, AAUP, Am. Acad. Religion, Soc. Advancement Am. Philosophy, Soc. Study Process Philosophies. Home: 3191 Frye St Oakland CA 94602-4040 Office: Calif State U Hayward CA 94542

MAYERS, JEAN, aeronautical engineering educator; b. N.Y.C., June 8, 1920; s. Lou and Ida (Edrich) M.; m. Reva Lee Bookbinder, May 20, 1945; children: Eileen, Laurence. B.Aero. Engring., Poly. Inst. Bklyn., 1942, M.Aero. Engring., 1948. Research asst. aero. engring. Poly. Inst. Bklyn., 1946-48; aero. research scientist, structures research div. NACA, Langley Field, Va., 1948-56; successively prin. engr., engring. sec. head, engring. dept. head Sperry Utah Co. div. Sperry Rand Corp., 1956-61; vis. asso. prof. Stanford U., 1961-63, mem. faculty, 1963—, prof. aero. engring., 1967-83, prof. emeritus, 1984—, vice chmn. dept. aero. and astronautics, 1966-71; vis. prof. Technion-Israel Inst. Tech., Haifa, 1970; Naval Air Systems Command Research prof. U.S. Naval Acad., 1978-79; Sci. adviser U.S. Army, 1962-74; cons. to govt. and industry, 1962—; mem. ad hoc vis. com. on aero. engring. curricula Engrs. Council for Profl. Devel., 1969-70. Author articles, reports in field. ARC vol. USN Hosp., Bethesda, Md., 1992—. Lt. comdr. USNR, 1942-46. Recipient U.S. Army Outstanding Civilian Service medal, 1972. Asso. fellow Am. Inst. Aero. and Astronautics (asso. editor jour. 1967-70); mem. Aircraft Owners and Pilots Assn., Naval Res. Assn., Ret. Officers Assn., Am. Soc. Engring. Edn., Sigma Xi. Home: 4550 N Park Ave Apt 909 Chevy Chase MD 20815-7238

MAYERS, ROY, publishing executive; Mgr. Globe Book Co., Inc., N.Y.C., 1962-66, asst. to pres., 1966-69, gen. mgr., 1969-71, v.p. gen. mgr. 1971-75; pres. Modern Curriculum Press divsn. Esquire, Inc., 1975-85, v.p., group exec., 1982-85; pres., founder Schoolhouse Prcss. divsn. Simon and Schuster, 1985; elementary group pres. Coronet Media, Ginn and Co., Modern Curriculum Press, Schoolhouse Press divsns., Simon and Schuster Internat. divsns. Simon and Schuster, Boston, 1985-86; group pres. numerous divsns. Simon and Schuster, 1986-87; pres. CEO Steck-Vaughn Co., Austin, 1987—; mem. found. adv. coun. U. Tex. Coll. Edn. Bd. dirs. Travis County Adult Literacy Coun. Mem. Internat. Reading Assn., Austin C. of C. Office: Steck-Vaughn Co 8701 N MoPac Austin TX 78759 also: Berrent Pubs 1025 Northern Blvd Roslyn NY 11576

MAYERS, STANLEY PENROSE, JR., public health educator; b. Phila., Nov. 9, 1926; s. Stanley Penrose and Margaret Amelia (Thorpe) M.; m. Virginia Lee Lytle, Aug. 25, 1951 (dec. Oct. 1990); children: Douglas Lytle, Kenneth Stanley, Daniel John, andrew William; m. Patricia Ann Harne Hulsey, Mar. 6, 1993. BA, U. Pa., 1949, MD, 1953; MPH, Johns Hopkins

U., 1958. Diplomate Am. Bd. Preventive Medicine. Intern Phila. Gen. Hosp., 1953-54; resident Arlington County Health Dept., Va., 1954-55; health dir. Henry-Martinsville-Patrick Health Dist., Martinsville, Va., 1955-57; regional dir. Va. State Health dept., Richmond, 1958-59; dist. state health officer N.J. State Dept. of Health, Trenton, 1959-62; asst. prof. and asst. dean Johns Hopkins Sch. Hygiene and Pub. Health, Balt., 1962-65; dir. Arlington County Dept. of Human Resources, Arlington, Va., 1965-71; prof. Health Planning and Adminstrn. Program Pa. State U., Univ. Pk., Pa., 1971-74, 88—; prof. in charge Pa. State U., Univ. Park, Pa., 1974-78; chmn. Pa. State U., Univ. Pk., Pa., 1979-88; assoc. dean undergrad. studies Coll. Health and Human Devel. Pa. State U., Univ. Pk., 1989-92, assoc. dean acad. studies Coll. Health and Human Devel., 1992—; faculty assoc. Johns Hopkins U. Sch. Medicine, Balt., 1965-75; clin. assoc. prof. Georgetown U. Sch. Medicine, Washington, 1965-71; cons. VA, 1985—. Author numerous reports, articles and surveys on pub. health. Mem. Arlington Optimist Club, 1979-72, pres. 1970-71; bd. dirs. Centre County Family Planning Svcs., Bellefonte, Pa., 1972-79. With USN, 1945-46. Recipient Outstanding Achievement award Dept. Community Medicine, Georgetown U. Sch. Medicine, 1968, Saubel award Coll. of Human Devel., Pa. State U., 1985. Fellow Am. Coll. Preventive Med., Am. Pub. Health Assn. (chmn. membership com. health officer's sect. 1968-70, mem. nominating com. health adminstrn. sect. 1970-72, chmn. com. to draft a statement on local health agy. responsibilities 1973-74); mem. AMA, Arlington County Med. Soc. (Wellborn award 1971), Centre County Med. Soc. (pres. 1978), Med.¹ Soc. Va., Met. Washington Health Officers Assn. (sec. 1967-71), Am. Assn. Pub. Health Physicians (pres. Va. chpt. 1970-71), Pa. Med. Soc. (mem. Ho. of Dels. for Centre County 1974-76, 81—; treas. 1973-74, 85—, sec. 1974-76, v.p. 1976, pres. elect 1977, pres. 1978), University Club (State College, Pa.), Phi Beta Kappa. Episcopalian. Avocations: fishing, boating, hiking. Home: 648 Wiltshire Dr State College PA 16803-1450 Office: Pa State U Human Devel Bldg Rm 201 University Park PA 16802

MAYERSON, HY, lawyer; b. Phila., June 29, 1937; s. Henry and Gertrude Mayerson; m. June 13, 1964 (div. 1973); children: Merrie Joy, Benjamin, Erin Megan, Stephnie Dawn; m. Colleen Koos. BS, Temple U., 1958, JD, 1961. Bar: Pa. 1961, Phila. Ct. Common Pleas 1962, Pa. Supreme Ct. 1968, U.S. Ct. Appeals (3d cir.) 1980, U.S. Ct. Appeals (4th cir.) 1984, U.S. Dist. Ct. (ea. dist.) Pa. Pvt. practice law Phila., 1961-65; sr. ptnr. Hy Mayerson Law Offices, 1965-81, Mayerson, Schniper & Gerasimowicz, Spring City, Pa., 1981-87, Mayerson, Gerasimowicz & Munsing, Spring City, 1987-91, Mayerson, Munsing, Corchin & Rosato, P.C., Spring City and Norristown, 1991—; coord. Nat. Forklift Litigation, 1978-91; lead counsel Agent Orange Product Liability Litigation. Contbr. articles to profl. jours. Mem. Am. Trial Lawyers (chmn. sect. on Indsl. & Agrl. Eqipment, Product Liability adv.bd.), Pa. Trial Lawyers Assn. Home: Sky Farm Birchrunville PA 19421 Office: RR 72 Spring City PA 19475 also: 701 Dekalb St Norristown PA 19401-3945

MAYERSON, PHILIP, classics educator; b. N.Y.C., May 20, 1918; s. Theodore and Clara (Fader) M.; m. Joy Gottesman Ungerleider, Nov. 25, 1976; children—Miriam Mayerson, Clare Mayerson, Peter Ungerleider, Steven Ungerleider, Jeanne Ungerleider, Andrew Ungerleider. AB, NYU, 1947, PhD, 1956. With Purian Fed. Clothing Stores, N.Y.C., 1935-42; instr. NYU, 1948-56, asst. prof., 1956-60, assoc. prof., 1960-66, prof. classics, 1966—, vice dean, 1969-71, acting dean, 1971-73, dean Washington Sq. and U. Coll. Arts and Scis., 1973-78. Author: The Ancient Agricultural Regime of Nessana and the Central Negeb, 1961, Classical Mythology in Literature, Art and Music, 1971, Monks, Martyrs, Soldiers and Saracens, 1994; contbr. articles in field to profl. jours. Served with USN, 1942-45. Rockefeller Found. grantee, 1956-57; Am. Council of Learned Socs. fellow, 1961-62. Mem. Am. Philological Assn., Am. Schs. of Oriental Rsch. Home: 4 Oak Ln Larchmont NY 10538-3917 Office: 100 Washington Sq E New York NY 10003-6656

MAYERSON, SANDRA ELAINE, lawyer; b. Dayton, Ohio, Feb. 8, 1952; d. Manuel David and Florence Louise (Tepper) M.; m. Scott Burns, May 29, 1977 (div. Oct. 1978). BA cum laude, Yale U., 1973; JD, Northwestern U. 1976. Bar: Ill. 1976, U.S. Ct. Appeals (7th cir.) 1976, U.S. Dist. Ct. (no. dist.) Ill. 1977, U.S. Dist. Ct. Md. 1989. Assoc. gen. counsel JMB Realty Corp., Chgo., 1979-80; assoc. Chatz, Sugarman, Abrams et al, Chgo., 1980-81; ptnr. Pollack, Mayerson & Berman, Chgo., 1981-83; dep. gen. counsel AM Internat., Inc., Chgo., 1983-85; ptnr. Kirkland & Ellis, Chgo., 1985-87; ptnr., chmn. bankruptcy group Kelley Drye & Warren, N.Y.C., 1987-93; ptnr., chmn. N.Y. bankruptcy group McDermott, Will & Emery, N.Y.C., 1993—; bd. dirs. Jr. Med. Rsch. Inst. coun. Michael Reese Hosp., Chgo., 1981-86; mem. met. div. Jewish Guild for Blind, 1990-92; mem. nat. legal afffairs com. Anti-Defamation League, 1990—. Fellow Branford Coll., Yale U., 1993—. Mem. ABA (bus. bankruptcy com. 1976—, sec. 1990—), Ill. State Bar Assn. (governing council corp. and securities sect. 1983-86), Chgo. Bar Assn. (current events chmn. corp. sect. 1980-81), 7th Cir. Bar Assn. Democrat. Jewish. Clubs: Yale (N.Y.C.), Metropolitan (Chgo.). Office: McDermott Will & Emery 1211 Ave of the Americas New York NY 10036*

MAYES, BERNARD DUNCAN, broadcast journalist, educator, dramatist; b. London, Oct. 10, 1929; came to U.S., 1957; s. Reginald Harry and Nellie (Drew) M. BA, Cambridge (Eng.) U., 1952, MA, 1954. Ordained to ministry Eng. Episc. Ch., 1958. Reporter BBC, London, 1954-79, Hollywood, Calif., 1965-70; reporter ABC, Sydney, Australia, 1970-84, CBC, Toronto, Ont., 1970-75, Radio New Zealand, Wellington, 1970-80; mem. faculty Stanford (Calif.) U., 1970-84; mgr. Sta. KQED-FM, San Francisco, 1969-71; founding chmn. Nat. Pub. Radio, Washington, 1969-71; exec. v.p. Sta. KQED-TV, San Francisco, 1971-73; pres. Trans Pacific Consortium, San Francisco, 1980-87; mem. faculty U. Va., 1984—; dir. U. Va. Ctr. Modern Media Studies, Charlottesville, 1987—; sr. cons. Corp. for Pub. Broadcasting, Washington, 1980—. Author: Getting It Across, 1957, This is Bernard Mayes in San Francisco, 1986; audio dramatist The Odyssey, Agammemnon and Antigone; actor (audio drama prodns.) The Hobbit, Lord of the Rings; producer documentary USA 200. Founder Ctr. for Suicide Prevention, San Francisco, 1961, The Parsonage Episc. Study Ctr., San Francisco, 1981; chmn. media com. Campaign to End Homophobia, Boston, 1987; mem. bd. Heartland project; mem. Lesbian and Gay Task Force. Recipient Scripts award Nat. Endowment for Arts, Washington, 1985. Fellow Brown Coll.; mem. Bay Area Suicide Prevention Assn. (pres. 1975-77). Democrat. Avocation: writing. Home: Pavilion VIII East Lawn Charlottesville VA 22903 Office: U Va Ctr Modern Media Studies Brown Coll 4 Bryan Hall Charlottesville VA 22903-3102 also: 217 South St Sausalito CA 94965-2530

MAYES, FRANK GORR, food company executive; b. Kellogg, Idaho, Nov. 27, 1930; s. Gilford H. and Rose (Gorr) M.; m. Pamela Ruth Healy, Apr. 20, 1968; 1 child, Matthew A. B.S., Northwestern U., 1952; M.S., NYU, 1953. Supr. mdse. engring. Marshall Field & Co., Chgo., 1953-58; product mgr. Topco Assocs., Inc., Skokie, Ill., 1959-66; dir. grocery, 1966-72, v.p. grocery, 1972-80, sr. v.p. non-perishables, 1980-88, sr. v.p., planning and devel., 1989—; lectr. mktg. Northwestern U., Chgo., 1956-73. Mem. Am. Mktg. Assn. Office: Topco Assocs Inc 7711 Gross Point Rd Skokie IL 60077-2697

MAYES, HELEN, professional association administrator; b. Waycross, Ga., May 28, 1918; d. Oscar Moody Sr. and Mary Woodson Moody; m. N. H. Mayes Sr., Dec. 22, 1940; 1 child, Nathaniel H. Jr. BBA, Savannah State Coll., 1938; MA in Higher Edn., NYU, 1961. Clk. nat. youth adminstrn. Savannah State Coll., 1938-40, sub-dir. div. gen. extension, 1940-44; asst. register, dir. admissions and records Albany (Ga.) State Coll., 1944-76, emeritus dir. admissions and records, 1976—; exec. sec. Nat. Assn. Coll. Deans Registrars and Admissions Officers, 1978—; dir. fin. Semper Fidelis Nursery Sch., Inc., 1979—, fin. sec., 1982—. Chmn. div. campaigns, mem. exec. com. United Way Dougherty County, bd. dirs., 1988—, mem. venture grant com., 1982—; chmn. adv. com. Albany State Coll., 1978-80, vice chmn. social work adv. com., 1983, chmn. social com., 1983—; active HARAMBEE Women's Auxiliary, 1982—; bd. dirs. Albany Symphony Assn., 1983—. Mem. Alpha Kappa Alpha. Office: NACDRAO 917 Dorsett Ave Albany GA 31701-2956

MAYES, PAUL EUGENE, engineering educator, technical consultant; b. Frederick, Okla., Dec. 21, 1928; s. Robert Franklin and Bertha Ellen (Walter) M.; m. Lola Mae Davis, June 4, 1950; children: Gwynne Ellen,

Linda Kay, Stuart Franklin, Patricia Gail, Steven Lee, David Thomas. BS in Elec. Engring., U. Okla., 1950; MS in Elec. Engring., Northwestern U., 1952, PhD, 1955. Rsch. asst. Northwestern U., Evanston, Ill., 1950-54; asst. prof. U. Ill. Urbana, 1954-58, assoc. prof., 1958-63, prof., 1963-93, prof. emeritus, 1994—; tech. cons. TRW, Redondo Beach, Calif., GM, Warren, Mich. Author: Electromagnetics for Engineers, 1965; contbr. articles to profl. jours.; inventor in field. Fellow IEEE. Avocations: woodworking, hiking, camping. Home: 1508 Waverly Dr Champaign IL 61821-5002 Office: U Ill 1406 W Green St Urbana IL 61801-2918

MAYES, WENDELL WISE, JR., broadcasting company executive; b. San Antonio, Mar. 2, 1924; s. Wendell Wise and Dorothy Lydia (Evans) M.; m. Mary Jane King, May 11, 1946; children: Cathey, Sarah, Wendell Wise, III. Student, Schreiner Inst., 1941-42, U. Tex. at Austin, 1942, Daniel Baker Coll., 1946; B.S., Tex. Tech. Coll., 1949. Program dir., sta. mgr. Sta. KBWD, Brownwood, Tex., 1949-57; mgr. Sta. KCRS, Midland, Tex., 1957-63; pres. Sta. KCRS, 1965-84, chmn., 1984—; pres. Sta. KNOW, Austin, Tex., 1970-81; pres. Stas. KVIC and KAMG, Victoria, Tex., 1970-84, chmn., 1984—; chmn. Sta. KCRS-FM, Midland 1984—; pres. Sta. KCSW, San Marcos, 1976-81; sec.-treas. Sta. KSNY-AM-FM, Snyder, 1952-94; mem. bd. mgrs. Sta. KLBJ-AM-FM, Austin, 1991—; lectr. Coll. Communications, U. Tex., Austin, 1978-81. Pres. Tex. Broadcast Edn. Found., 1973-76; chmn. bd. Am. Diabetes Assn., 1974-77; mem. Nat. Diabetes Adv. Bd., 1977-84; v.p. Internat. Diabetes Fedn., 1980-88, pres. elect 1989-91, pres., 1991-94; mem. Tex. Diabetes Coun., 1983-85, chmn., 1983-86; bd. regents Tex. Tech. U., 1985-91, chmn., 1987-88. With USNR, 1943-46. Recipient Addison B. Scoville award Am. Diabetes Assn., 1977, first Wendell Mayes Jr. award, 1986, Josiah K. Lilly award, 1991, Harold Rifkin award, 1994, Masaji Takeda medal Kobe, Japan Colloquium Med. Sci., 1994; named to Tex. Tech. Mass Comm. Hall of Fame, 1978; named Disting. Alumnus Tex. Tech. U., 1981, Disting. Engr., 1985. Mem. Tex. Assn. Broadcasters (pres. 1964, named Pioneer Broadcaster of Year 1978), Nat. Assn. Broadcasters (dir. 1969-72), Am. Council on Edn. in Journalism (dir. 1977-80), Broadcast Edn. Assn. (dir. 1973-77), AP Broadcasters (bd. dirs. 1988-91), Tex. Tech. Elec. Engring. Acad. Episcopalian (vestryman 1966-69, 86-88; sr. warden 1988). Home: 2834 Montebello Rd #1 Austin TX 78746 Office: Wendell Mayes Stas 1907 N Lamar Blvd Austin TX 78705-4900

MAYEUX, RONALD N., school system administrator; b. Independence, La., Sept. 24, 1944; s. Paul and Eunice (Bondelon) M.; m. Margaret Lambert, Nov. 7, 1964; chldren: Eric, Jill, Toni, Kipp. BS in Agrl. Edn., La. State U., 1966, MS in Agrl. Edn., 1970, postgrad., 1973. Cert. vocat. agriculture educator, sch. prin., parish or city supt., supr. Tchr. Bordelonville (La.) High Sch., 1966-67, Hessmer (La.) High Sch., 1967-73; supr. fed. programs Avoyelles Parish Sch. Bd., Marksville, La., 1973-78, dir. spl. svc., 1978-80, supt. of schs., 1980-86; prin., tchr., coach Hessmer High Sch., 1986-88; acad. dir., tchr. La. Bus. Coll., Alexandria, La., 1988-90; supt. of schs. Cath. Diocese of Alexandria, 1990—. Mem. St. Martin of Tours Cath., Ch.; charter pres. Avoyelles Little League. Named Outstanding Young Man of Am., 1973, Outstanding Young Educator of Yr., 1973, So. Regional Young Vocat. Agriculture Tchr. of Yr., 1971, La. Tchr. of Yr., 1971. Mem. ASCD, La. Ret. Tchrs. Assn., La. Assn. Sch. Execs., La. Assn. Prins., Nat. Cath. Edn. Assn., La. Assn. Sch. Supts., La. High Sch. Athletics Assn. Exec. Coun., La. State Adv. Coun. for Vocat. Edn. Home: RR 1 Hessmer LA 71341 Office: Cath Diocese of Alexandria 4400 Coliseum Blvd Alexandria LA 71303-3513

MAYFIELD, CURTIS LEE, musician; b. Chgo., June 3, 1942; s. Kenneth and Marion (Washington) M.; children—Tracy, Curtis, Todd, Sharon, Tymphani, Kirk. co-pres. Curtom Records Inc. Performer with group Impressions, 1958-70; solo albums include Curtis, 1970, Curtis Live, Roots, 1971, Back to the World, 1973, Sweet Exorcist, 1974, America Today, 1975, Never Say You Can't Survive, 1977, Do It, We Came in Peace with a Message of Love, 1985, Give, Get, Take and Have, 1992; composer, arranger, performer soundtrack; also actor film Super Fly, 1972; now rec. artist, producer, songwriter film. Recipient: Nat. Acad. of Recording Arts & Sciences Lifetime Achievement Award, 1994. Office: care Epic Records 51 W 52nd St New York NY 10019-6119 Office: Curtom Records PO Box 724677 Atlanta GA 31139-1677*

MAYFIELD, DAVID MERKLEY, genealogy director; b. Salt Lake City, Nov. 29, 1942; s. Orson Smith and Isabell (Merkley) M.; m. Judy Rae White, Dec. 17, 1965; children: Celeste, Melody, Michael, Paul, Nathan, Heather, Christopher, Benjamin. BA in German, U. Utah, 1967, MA in German, 1969; MLS, UCLA, 1971. Instr. Brigham Young U., Provo, Utah, 1971-72; mgr., dir. hist. dept., mem. and stats. records dept., info. systems dept. Ch. of Jesus Christ of Latter-day Saints, Salt Lake City, 1972-80; dir. family history library of Ch. of Jesus Christ of Latter-day Saints, Salt Lake City, 1980-92; dir.; priesthood and area support, 1992—; v.p. Geneal. Soc. Utah, 1988—. Contbr. articles to profl. jours. Fellow NDEA, 1967, HEW Title II, 1970. Mem. Nat. Geneal. Soc., (nat. coun., 1992—), Fedn. Geneal. Socs. (adv. counc. 1988-91), Nat. Soc. Sons of Utah Pioneers (v.p. 1982-83), Phi Beta Kappa. Republican. Mormon. Office: Family History Dept 50 E North Temple Salt Lake City UT 84150-0001

MAYFIELD, RICHARD HEVERIN, lawyer; b. Washington, Sept. 29, 1921; s. Robert Edwin and Helen May (Benton) M.; m. Caroline C. Mayfield; children: Elinor D., Nancy L., Anne W. A.B., Swarthmore Coll., 1943; LL.B., Harvard U., 1948. Bar: D.C., Md. Assoc. firm McKenney, Flannery & Craighill (name later changed to Craighill, Mayfield & Fenwick & Cromelin), Washington, 1948-54; partner McKenney, Flannery & Craighill (name later changed to Craighill, Mayfield, Fenwick & Cromelin), 1954—. Editor: Will Forms and Clauses, 1969, Trust Forms and Clauses, 1975. Bd. govs. Beauvoir Sch., 1961-67, chmn., 1967. Served with AUS, 1943-46. Fellow Am. Coll. Trust and Estate Counsel; mem. Washington Estate Planning Coun., Barrister Club (sec. 1959), Lawyers Club, Columbia Country Club, Farmington Country Club, Masons, Shriners. Home: 5 E Kirke St Bethesda MD 20815-4216 Office: 4910 Massachusetts Ave NW Washington DC 20016-4300

MAYFIELD, ROBERT CHARLES, university official, geography educator; b. Abilene, Tex., Oct. 15, 1928; s. Percy Anderson and Fay (Hicks) M.; m. Loraine Poindexter, Sept. 3, 1952; children: Julie Barnes, Jennifer Manley, Mark Stanley, Malcolm Randall. B.A., Tex. Christian U., 1952; M.S., Ind. U., 1953; Ph.D., U. Wash., 1961. Chmn. geography dept. Tex. Christian U., Ft. Worth, 1960-64, U. Tex., Austin, 1967-71; Chmn. geography dept. Boston U., 1972-77, acad. v.p. external programs, 1977-83, provost, 1979-84; cons. Coun. for Econ. Action, Boston, 1980—; adj. prof. U. Tex., Austin, 1987—; U.S.I.S. lectr., Bangladesh, 1994. Editor, contbg. author: Man, Environment and Space, 1972. Served with USAF, 1946-49. Research fellow Nat. Acad. Sci. No. India, 1957-58; Fulbright-Hays fellow Office Edn., Bangalore, Mysore, India, 1966-67; research grantee Agrl. Devel. Council, 1968. Mem. Assn. Am. Geographers.

MAYFIELD, T. BRIENT, IV, media and computer executive; b. Athens, Tenn., Mar. 31, 1947; s. Thomas Brient III and Alma Ruth (Bolton) M.; m. N. Katherine Rodgers, Dec. 7, 1974 (div. Mar. 1984); children: Brittany Alexander, Blair Ashton, Katherine Thomas; m. Margaret L. Reeves, Oct. 3, 1987. BS, U. Tenn., 1969. Project mgr. Mayfield Dairy Farms, Athens, 1969-70; v.p. fin. 13-30 Corp., Knoxville, Tenn., 1970-72; exec. v.p. Computer Concepts Corp., Knoxville, 1970-77, pres., 1977-85; pres. Resource Optimization Inc., Knoxville, 1986—; co-founder Whittle Communications LP, Knoxville, 1970, v.p., pub., 1987-92. Bd. dirs. Results Edn. Fund, Washington,, 1990—. Republican. Avocations: flying, music. Home: 5108 Buckhead Trl Knoxville TN 37919-8903 Office: Resource Optimization Inc 531 S Gay St Ste 1212 Knoxville TN 37902-1520

MAYFIELD, WILLIAM STEPHEN, law educator; b. Gary, Indiana, Mar. 2, 1919; s. William Henry and Elnora Elizabeth (Williams) M.; m. Octavia Smith, Feb. 6, 1949 (dec.); children: Pamela L., William E., Stephanie K. Stokes; m. Mildred G. Harris, May 25, 1991. B.A., Detroit Inst. Tech., 1946; J.D., Detroit Coll. Law, 1949. Bar: Mich. 1949. Mem. firm Lewis, Rowlette, Brown, Wanzo and Bell, Detroit, 1949-51; atty. U.S. Office Price Stblzn., Detroit, 1951-53; referee Friend of the Court, Detroit, 1953-72; vis. prof. Law Center, La. State Univ., Baton Rouge, summer, 1979; prof. law So. U., Baton Rouge, 1972—; mem. com. sci. and tech. in cts. La. Supreme

Ct., 1978. Mem. regional bd. Boy Scouts Am., Detroit, 1961-63; Served with U.S. Army, 1942-46. Mem. Am. Bar Assn., Nat. Bar Assn., Wolverine Bar Assn., World Assn. Law Profs., Detroit Coll. Law Alumni Assn., Assn. Henri Capitanti, Comml. Law League Am., Ret. Officers Assn. (pres. Greater Baton Rouge 1985), Am. Legion, Mil. Order of the World Wars, Delta Theta Phi (Outstanding Prof. of Yr. award 1983). Office: PO Box 74301 Baton Rouge LA 70874-4301

MAYGARDEN, JERRY LOUIS, health care foundation executive; b. Pensacola, Fla., Dec. 22, 1948; s. Louis Ameal and Jean (Saxon) Maygarden; m. Rhonda Delene Fosha, June 25, 1977; children: Louis Ameal III, Morgan Lora. AA in Liberal Arts, Pensacola Jr. Coll., 1972; BA in Communications Arts, U. West Fla., 1974, MA in Communication, 1975. V.p.u. West Fla., Pensacola, 1980-83; exec. v.p. Sacred Heart Found., Pensacola, 1983-89; pres. Bapt. Health Care Found., Pensacola, 1989—; bd. dirs. Bank of Pensacola; mem. Fla. House of Reps., 1994—. City councilman Pensacola City Coun., 1985—, mayor pro tem, 1989-91, mayor, 1991—; bd. dir. C. of C. Com. 100, Pensacola, 1989—. With USN, 1968-74, Viet Nam. Recipient George Washington Honor medal, Freedoms Found. of Valley Forge, 1992, Paul Harris fellow, Rotary Found. Internat., 1993; named Cmty. Leader of Yr. C. of C., Pensacola, 1988, Outstanding Young Man Am. U.S. Jaycees, 1977, Nat. Soc. Fund Raising Execs., Assn. for Health Care Philanthropy, Rotary Internat. Mem. Fla. League Cities, Nat. League Cities, Nat. Soc. Fund Raising Execs., Assn. for Health Care Philanthropy, Rotary Internat. Democrat. Methodist. Avocations: tennis, sailing, hiking, biking, fishing. Home: 1240 Tamara Dr Pensacola FL 32504-6622 Office: Bapt Health Care Found PO Box 17500 Pensacola FL 32522-7500

MAYHALL, DOROTHY ANN, museum director, curator of art, sculptor; b. Portland, Oreg., May 31, 1925; d. Nelles Harvey and Dorothy (Gray Orton) M. BFA, U. Iowa, 1950, MFA, MA in Art History, 1952; Diplome Doctorat, Ecole Des Beaux-Arts, Paris, 1953. Exec. dir. jr. coun. Mus. Modern Art, N.Y.C., 1961-65; dir. The Aldrich Mus., Ridgefield, Conn., 1965-71, 79-83, Storm King Art Ctr., Mountainville, N.Y., 1971-75, The Nave Mus., Victoria, Tex., 1976-78; dir. of art The Stamford (Conn.) Mus. and Nature Ctr., 1984—. Bd. mem. Stamford (COnn.) Arts Coun., 1984-90, Pub. Art Commn., Stamford, 1986-91; chmn. Mayor's Art Gallery, Stamford, 1986-91; mem. art adv. com. Norwalk Community Coll. 1st lt. WAC, 1952-56. Recipient Fulbright scholar Inst. Internat. Edn., Paris, 1952-53. Avocations: gardening, pets, boating, cooking, reading. Office: Stamford Mus 39 Scofieldtown Rd Stamford CT 06903-4023

MAYHEW, AUBREY, music business executive; b. Washington, Oct. 2, 1927; s. Aubrey and Verna June (Hall) M.; m. Carol de onis, May 10, 1962 (div. 1971); children: Lawrence Aubrey, Michael Aubrey, Parris Mitchell, Casey Aran. Student, Wilson Tchs. Coll., 1948. Dir. Sta. WWVA, Wheeling, W.Va. 1947-54, Sta. WCOP, Boston, 1954-56; asst. to pres. MGM Records, N.Y.C. 1957-58; v.p. mktg. Capitol Records, Los Angeles, 1958-60; prodr., dir. Sta. KCAM-TV Prodns., Nashville, 1981—; pres., founder John F. Kennedy Meml. Ctr., 1968; authority on John F. Kennedy life and memorabilia. Author: (books) Commandants Marine Corps, 1953, World Tribute to John F. Kennedy, 1965; composer (music) Touch My Heart, 1966 (Broadcast Music, Inc. award, 1967); record producer, artist mgmt., 1947—; music pub., 1954—; developed careers numerous entertainers including Johnny Paycheck, Jeannie C. Riley, Bobby Helms. Served to cpl. U.S. Army Signal Corps, 1945-48. Named Govs. Aide, Nashville, 1978. Mem. Country Music Assn., Broadcast Music Inc., Manuscript Soc., N.Y. Numismatic Soc., Gospel Music Assn. Republican. Episcopalian. Avocations: collector, historian, author. Home: 827 Meridian St Nashville TN 37207-5856 Office: Amcorp Music Group 827 Meridian St Nashville TN 37207-5804

MAYHEW, DAVID RAYMOND, political educator; b. Putnam, Conn., May 18, 1937; s. Raymond William and Jeanie (Nicholson) M. B.A., Amherst Coll., 1958; Ph.D. (Delancey K. Jay dissertation prize 1964), Harvard U., 1964. Teaching fellow Harvard U., 1961-63; instr., then asst. prof. polit. sci. U. Mass., Amherst, 1963-67; vis. assoc. prof. Amherst Coll., 1965-66; mem. faculty Yale U., 1968—, prof. polit. sci., 1977—, chmn. dept., 1979-82, Alfred Cowles prof. govt., 1982—. Author: Party Loyalty Among Congressmen, 1966, Congress: The Electoral Connection, 1974 (Washington Monthly ann. polit. book award 1974), Placing Parties in American Politics, 1986, Divided We Govern, 1991. Recipient Richard E. Neustadt prize 1992; Woodrow Wilson fellow, 1958-59, vis. fellow Nuffield Coll., Oxford, 1978, Guggenheim fellow, 1978-79, Hoover Nat. fellow, 1978-79, Sherman Fairchild fellow, 1990-91. Fellow Am. Acad. Arts and Scis.; mem. Am. Polit. Sci. Assn. (nat. council 1976-78, Congl. fellow 1967-68), So. Polit. Sci. Assn., New Eng. Polit. Sci. Assn. Home: 100 York St Apt 5C New Haven CT 06511-5611 Office: Yale U Polit Sci Dept Box 208301 New Haven CT 06520-8301

MAYHEW, HARRY EUGENE, physician, educator; b. St. Clair, Mich., Apr. 16, 1933; s. Eugene Nelson and Viola Erma (Danneels) M; m. Eunice Yvonne Brown, June 23, 1950; children: Dawn Boers, Timothy, Stephen, Elise Couch, Betheny, Heidi Reimer. Student, Port Huron Jr. Coll., 1951-53; MD, U. Mich., 1958. Diplomate Am. Bd. Family Practice. Intern St. Joseph Hosp., Flint, Mich., 1958-59; pvt. practice St. Clair, Mich., 1959-73; asst. dir. family practice residency Sparrow Hosp., Lansing, Mich., 1974-76; asst. prof. dept. family practice Coll. Human Medicine, Mich State U., 1974-76; prof., chmn. dept. family medicine Med. Coll. Ohio, Toledo, 1976—; cons. Residency Assistance Program Acad. Family Physicians, Kansas City, Mo., 1978-95; adv. bd. Salvation Army. Co-editor: Critical Issues in Family Practice: Cases and Commentaries, 1982, Basic Procedures in Family Practice, 1984, Genital Urinary Problems in the Male Patient, 1989. Mem. AMA, Soc. Tchrs. Family Medicine, Assn. Depts. Family Medicine, Coun. Acad. Socs., Assn. Depts. Family Medicine Bd., Coun. Acad. Socs., Coun. Acad. Soc. Bd., Toledo Country Club, Alpha Omega Alpha. Baptist. Office: Med Coll Ohio Dept Family Medicine PO Box 10008 Toledo OH 43699-0008

MAYHEW, KENNETH EDWIN, JR., transportation company executive; b. Shelby, N.C., Sept. 27, 1934; s. Kenneth Edwin and Evelyn Lee (Dellinger) M.; m. Frances Elaine Craft, Apr. 7, 1957; 1 dau., Catherine Lynn Prince. A.B., Duke U., 1956. CPA, N.C. Sr. auditor Arthur Andersen & Co., Atlanta, 1956-58, 60-63; controller Trendline, Inc., Hickory, N.C., 1963-66; with Carolina Freight Corp., Cherryville, 1966-93; treas. Carolina Freight Carriers Corp., Cherryville, 1969-74, v.p., 1971-72, exec. v.p., 1972-85, pres., chief oper. officer, 1985-89, also dir., chmn., pres., CEO, 1989-93, pres., chief exec. officer, 1989-93; pres., dir. Robo Auto Wash Shelby Inc., 1967-73, Robo Auto Wash Cherryville, Inc., 1968-73; dir. Cherryville Nat. Bank, Kenmar Bus. Group, Inc. Mem. Bus. Adv. Bd., Fuqua Sch. Bus., Duke U.; bd. dirs., vice-chmn. Gaston Meml. Hosp.; trustee Pfeiffer Coll. With AUS, 1958-60. Mem. AICPA, Am. Trucking Assn. (dir., v.p.), N.C. Trucking Assn. (dir., chmn.), Gaston County C. of C. (v.p. pub. affairs), Lions (pres. Cherryville 1972-73), Phi Beta Kappa, Omicron Delta Kappa, Phi Eta Sigma. Methodist. Home: 507 Spring St Cherryville NC 28021-3540

MAYHEW, WILLIAM A., judge; b. Pueblo, Colo., July 21, 1940; s. Wilbren D. and Dorothy L. (Holloway) M.; m. Marianne J., May 8, 1971; children: Lance, Kevin, Christie. AA, Modesto Jr. Coll., 1959; BS, UCLA, 1961, JD, 1964. Bar: Calif. 1965, U.S.Ct. Appeals (9th cir.) 1965, U.S. Dist. Ct. (no., ea. dists.) Calif. 1965. Dep. atty. gen. State Calif., 1964-67; ptnr., pvt. practice Thompson, Mayhew & Michel (now Thompson & Heller), 1968-82; prof. law Miss. Coll. Sch. Law, 1982-86; atty. Sarhad & Mayhew, Turlock, Calif. 1986-88; mng. ptnr. Borton, Petrini & Conron, Modesto, Calif., 1988-94; assoc. prof. Coll. Law U. Toledo, 1975-76; judge Stanislau County Mcpl. Ct., 1994—; speaker in field. Bd. editors UCLA Law Review; contbr. articles to profl. jours. Mem. Burlock H.S. Bd. Trustees, 1989-94, pres., 1992; usher, progress com. St. Francis Episcopal Ch.; mem. standing com. Episcopal Diocese San Joaquin Diocesan Coun., 1991; vice chancelor Episcopal Bisohp of San Joaquin, 1990-94. Maj. JAGC, Calif. Army N.G., 1966-77. Mem. Am. Bd. Trial Advocates (nat. bd. dirs., advocate, chair western regional conf. 1987, Miss. chpt., sec.-treas. 1985), Turlock Rotary Club, Order of Coif. Republican. Office: Stanislau County Mcpl Ct PO Box 828 Modesto CA 95353

MAYLAND, KENNETH THEODORE, economist; b. Miami, Fla., Nov. 17, 1951; s. Herbert and Vera (Bob) M.; m. Gail Fern Bassok, Apr. 14, 1984. BS, MIT, 1973; MS, U. Pa., 1976, PhD, 1979. Econ. economist Data Resources, Inc., Lexington, Mass., 1973; economist, then chief economist First Pa. Bank, Phila., 1973-89; sr. v.p., chief economist Soc. Nat. Bank, Cleve., 1989-94; sr. v.p., chief fin. economist Key Corp., Cleve., 1994—; econs. instr., Chartered Fin. Aanalysts Assn., Phila, 1984—; econ. adv. com. Phila. Econ. Devel. Coalition, 1984-86; chmn. econ. adv. com. Pa. Bankers Assn., Harrisburg, 1982-84; mem. Gov.'s Econ. Adv. Com., Ohio, 1989—. Contbr. semi-monthly periodical Money Markets, 1981-85, quar. periodical Regional Report, 1980-89, Econ. Viewpoint biweekly periodical, 1989—, Regional Rev. quarterly periodical, 1989—. Mem. curriculum adv. com. Widener U., 1986-89. Mem. Am. Bankers Assn. (econ. adv. com. 1990-93), Internat. Econ. Roundtable (vice chmn. 1987-88, chmn. 1988-90), Nat. Assn. Bus. Economists (New Face for the Eighties award 1979), Phila. Coun. Bus. Economists (pres. 1982-84), Cleve. Bus. Economist Club (sec.-treas. 1990-91, v.p. 1991-92, pres. 1992-93). Avocations: fishing, badminton, gardening, camping. Home: 3237 Fox Hollow Dr Cleveland OH 44124-5426 Office: Key Corp 127 Public Sq Cleveland OH 44114-1216

MAYLE, PETER, writer; b. Surrey, Eng., 1939; m. Jennie Mayle. Advt. copywriter London; columnist Gentleman's Quarterly. Author: (non-fiction for children) Where Did I Come From? The Facts of Life without any Nonsense and with Illustrations, 1973, What's Happening to Me? The Answers to Some of the World's Most Embarrassing Questions, 1975, Will I Go to Heaven?, 1976, Will I Like It? Your First Sexual Experience, What to Expect, What to Avoid, and How Both of You Can Get the Most Out of It, 1977, Divorce Can Happen to the Nicest People, 1979 (revised, republished as Why Are We Getting a Divorce?, 1988), (with Paul Rice) As Dead as a Dodo, 1981, Congratulations! You're Not Pregnant: An Illustrated Guide to Birth Control, 1981, Grown-ups and Other Problems: Help for Small People in a Big World, 1982, Sweet Dreams and Monsters: A Beginner's Guide to Dreams and Nightmares and Things That Go Bump under the Bed, 1986; (non-fiction for adults) How to Be a Pregnant Father: An Illustrated Survival Guide for the First-time Father, 1977, Baby Taming, 1978, The Honeymoon Book, 1983, Chilly Billy, 1983, Man's Best Friend: Introducing Wicked Willie in the Title Role, 1984, Anything but Rover-The Art and Science of Naming Your Dog: A Breed by Breed Guide, 1985, Wicked Willie's Guide to Women: A Worm's-Eye View of the Fair Sex, 1986, Wicked Willie's Guide to Women: The Further Adventures of Man's Best Friend, 1988, (with Raffaella Fletcher) Dangerous Candy: A True Drug Story by Someone Who Did Them and Kicked Them, 1990 (republished as Dangerous Candy: A True Story about Drug Addiction, 1991); (essays) A Year in Provence, 1989, Toujours Provence, 1991, Acquired Tastes: A Beginner's Guide to Serious Pleasures, 1992, Hotel Pastis: A Novel of Provence, 1993, Provence, 1994; (novels) A Dog's Life, 1995. Office: Gentleman's Quarterly Conde Nast Pub 350 Madison Ave New York NY 10017-3704*

MAYMAN, SHLOMO ALEX, engineering executive; b. Winnipeg, Man., Can., July 16, 1933; s. Joseph and Dorothy (Fordman) M.; m. Marion Blonder, Jan. 1, 1956; children: Gadi Gershon, David. BSc, U. Man., Winnipeg, 1954; MS in Nuclear Engring., MIT, 1964. Registered profl. engr. Heavy equipment supr. Timorim, Israel, 1957-62; rsch. asst. MIT Reactor, Cambridge, Mass., 1962-64; supr. reactor physics Atomic Energy Can. Ltd./ Whiteshell Nuclear Rsch. Establishment, Pinawa, Man., 1964-67, head reactor tech., 1967-74; head rsch. Atomic Energy Can. Ltd./Whiteshell Nuclear Rsch. Establishment, Pinawa, 1974-82, mgr. engring., 1982-84; dir. Nat. Rsch. Coun. Can./Inst. for Mfct. Tech., Winnipeg, 1984-86, Nat Rsch. Coun. Can./Divsn. Elec. Engring., Ottawa, Ont., Can., 1986-90; dir. gen. NRC/IIT, Ottawa, Ont., Can., 1990—. V.p. Hillel Lodge, Ottawa, 1994; mem. Jewish Community Coun., Ottawa, 1994. Mem. IEEE (sr.). Avocations: bridge, cycling. Office: NRC/Inst for Info Tech, Montreal Rd Bldg M-50, Ottawa, ON Canada K1A 0R6*

MAYNARD, CHARLES DOUGLAS, radiologist; b. Atlantic City, Sept. 11, 1934; m. Mary Anne Satterwhite; children—Charles D., Deanne, David. B.S., Wake Forest U., 1955, M.D., 1959. Diplomate Am. Bd. Radiology (trustee, sec.-treas., v.p. 1992-94, pres. 1994—). Intern U.S. Army Hosp., Honolulu, 1959-60; resident N.C. Baptist Hosp., 1963-66; dir. Nuclear Medicine Lab., 1966-77; asst. dean admissions Bowman Gray Sch. Medicine, 1966-71, asso. dean student affairs, 1971-75, prof. radiology, chmn. dept., 1977—; guest examiner Am. Bd. Radiology. Author: Clinical Nuclear Medicine, 1969; mem. editorial bd. Academic Radiology, Yearbook of Diagnostic Radiology, Contemporary Diagnostic Radiology. Mem. Leadership Winston-Salem, Triad Leadership Network; trustee Forsyth Tech. C.C.; mem. bd. dirs. Downtown Devel. Corp., 1995—, Winston-Salem Bus., 1995—. Mem. AMA, Soc. Nuclear Medicine (past pres.), Am. Coll. Radiology (past bd. chancellors, past chmn. commn. on nuclear medicine), Radiol. Soc. N.Am. (sec.-treas.), Assn. Univ. Radiologists, Soc. Chairmen Radiology Depts. (past pres.), Acad. Radiology Rsch. (bd. dirs. 1995—), Am. Bd. Radiology (bd. trustees 1987—, pres. 1994—), Am. Bd. Med. Specialists, Greater Winston-Salem C. of C. (bd. dirs.). Office: Medical Center Blvd Winston Salem NC 27157

MAYNARD, DONALD NELSON, horticulturist, educator; b. Hartford, Conn., June 22, 1932; s. Harry Ashley and Elsie Frances (Magnuson) M.; m. Adrienne A. Taylor; 1 child, David Nelson. BS, U. Conn., 1954; MS, N.C. State U., 1956; PhD, U. Mass., 1963. Instr. plant sci. U. Mass., Amherst, 1956-62, asst. prof., 1962-67, assoc. prof., 1967-72, prof., 1972-79, asst. dean, 1974-75, prof. emeritus, 1979—; prof. vegetable crops U. Fla., Gainesville, 1979—; chmn. dept. U. Fla., 1979-85; cons. Greenleaf, Inc., Hackensack, N.J., SRD Rsch., Logan, Utah. Assoc. editor Jour. Am. Soc. Hort. Sci., 1976-80, 89-91, HortSci, 1975-80, 89—. Recipient Aid to Edn. award Gulf Oil Corp., 1965. Fellow Am. Soc. for Hort. Sci. (Environ. Quality Rsch. award 1975, Mawak W. Meadows award 1977); mem. Sigma Xi, Phi Kappa Phi, Alpha Zeta, Phi Tau Sigma. Republican. Episcopalian. Home: 5551 Contento Dr Sarasota FL 34242 Office: U Fla Gulf Coast Rsch Edn Ctr Bradenton FL 34203

MAYNARD, JOAN, education educator; b. Louisa, Ky., Oct. 18, 1932; d. Macon Scott and Jeanette (Thompson) Chambers; m. Frank Maynard Jr., June 15, 1951 (dec. Oct. 1988); children: Mark Steven, Julia Beth Maynard McFann, Robert Blake. BA, Wittenberg U., 1977; MEd, Wright State U., 1980, Wright State U., 1984. Tchr., reading specialist Mechanicsburg (Ohio) Exempted Village Schs., 1976—; pres. TOTT Publs. Inc., Bellbrook, Ohio, 1988—; rep. Career Edn., Mechanicsburg, 1981-88, mem. Thompson Grant Com., Mechanicsburg, 1987-88. Author: Mud Puddles, 1988, Mud Pies, 1989. Vol. Mechanicsburg Schs. Levy, 1980, 82, 88, Congl. Race, Campaign County, Ohio, 1982, 84, 86; cons. Urbana U., Ohio, 1989-90, 91, 92, 93; tutor Laubach Lit. Action, Urbana, 1989-90, 91-93, 94. Recipient Thompson grant, 1982, 88, 92. Mem. AAUW (bd. chmn. Champaign County chpt. 1988-89, treas. 1989-90), Internat. Reading Assn., Champaign County Reading Coun. (treas. 1990-91), Midwestern Assembly Lit. Young People (treas. 1989-93), Kappa Delta Pi. Avocations: collecting children's lit. books, travel, reading. Home: 1546 Parkview Rd Mechanicsburg OH 43044-9779 Office: Exempted Village Schs 60 High St Mechanicsburg OH 43044-1098

MAYNARD, JOHN RALPH, lawyer; b. Seattle, Mar. 5, 1942; s. John R. and Frances Jane (Mitchell) Maynard Kendryk; children: Bryce James, Pamela Ann. BA, U. Wash., 1964; JD, Calif. Western U., San Diego, 1972; LLM, Harvard U., 1973. Bar: Calif. 1972, Wis. 1973. Assoc. Whyte & Hirschboeck, Milw., 1973-78, Minahan & Peterson, Milw., 1979-91, Quarles & Brady, Milw., 1991—. Bd. dirs. Am. Heart Assn., 1979-82. Mem. Wis. Adv. Coun. to U.S. SBA, 1987-89. Served to It. USN, 1964-69. Mem. ABA, Harvard Club (Wis.), Yacht Club (Milw.). Republican. Home: 809 E Lake Forest Ave Milwaukee WI 53217-5377 Office: Quarles & Brady 411 E Wisconsin Ave Milwaukee WI 53202-4409

MAYNARD, JOHN ROGERS, English educator; b. Williamsville, N.Y., Oct. 6, 1941; s. Atherton Rogers and Olive (Fisher) M.; m. Florence Michelson, July 1, 1967 (div. 1980); 1 child, Alex Stevens; m. Ursula Krammer, Oct. 17, 1992. BA, Harvard U., 1963, Ph.D, 1970. Asst. prof. Harvard U., Cambridge, Mass., 1969-74, NYU, N.Y.C., 1974-79, assoc. prof., 1976-84, prof. English, 1984—, chmn. English dept., 1983-89; chmn. Faculty Council NYU, 1983-84; vis. prof. U. Venice, Italy, 1991. Author: Brownings Youth, 1977 (Wilson prize 1977), Charlotte Bronte and Sexuality, 1984, Victorian Discourses on Sexuality and Religion, 1993; editor: (with Lockridge and Stone) Nineteenth Century Lives, 1989, (with Bloom) Anne Thackeray Ritchie: Journals and Letters, (with Munich) Victorian Literature and Culture, 1991—. Organizer, Concord Sq. Assn., Boston, 1972-74; mem. Bklyn. Heights Assn., 1980—. NEH grantee, 1972-73; Guggenheim fellow, 1979-80. Mem. MLA, PEN, Browning Inst. (bd. dirs.), Signet Soc., Andiron Club (pres. 1983-84). Democrat. Avocation: bicycling. Home: 39 Schermerhorn St Brooklyn NY 11201-4825 Office: NYU Dept of English 19 University Pl New York NY 10003-4501

MAYNARD, JULIAN D., acoustician, physicist, educator; b. Newport News, Va., Nov. 18, 1945. Instr. physics Princeton U., 1973-74; adj. asst. prof. UCLA, 1974-77; from asst. to full prof. physics Pa. State U., 1977—. Fellow Am. Phys. Soc., Acoustical Soc. Am. (Silver medal in Phys. Acoustics and Engring. Acoustics 1994); mem. Sigma Xi. Office: Pennsylvania State University Dept Physics University Park PA 16802*

MAYNARD, KENNETH DOUGLAS, architect; b. Hackensack, N.J., Aug. 16, 1931; s. Douglas Harry and Eva (Whiting) M.; m. Myrna Myrtle James, Feb. 4, 1956; children: Colin, Vivien Regan. Cert. in Architecture, U. Natal, Durban, Republic of South Africa, 1958. Registered architect Alaska. Draftsman Morross & Graff, Johannesburg, Republic of South Africa, 1950-51, Anglo-Am. Corp., Johannesburg, Republic of South Africa, 1951-54, Moir & Llewellyn, Empangeni, Zululand, Republic of South Africa, 1955-57; architect Pearse Aneck-Hahn & Bristol, Johannesburg, 1957-60, Manley & Mayer, Anchorage, 1960-61, FAA, Anchorage, 1961-62, Crittenden Cassetta Wirum & Jacobs, Anchorage, 1962-65; prin. Schultz & Maynard, Anchorage, 1965-68, Kenneth Maynard Assocs., Anchorage, 1968-78; pres. Maynard & Partch, Anchorage, 1978—. Active Western Alaska Coun. Boy Scouts. Am., Anchorage, 1965-84; bd. dirs. Salvation Army Adv. Bd., Anchorage, 1981-87, Anchorage Mus. Assn., 1969-86, Anchorage Opera Co., 1983-90; chmn. Mayor's Comprehensive Homeless Program Strategy Group, 1992-94. Fellow AIA (pres. Alaska chpt. 1969, N.W. regional rep. for nat. com. on design 1976-89); mem. Constrn. Specification Inst. (pres. Cook Inlet chpt. 1993-94), Soc. Am. Mil. Engrs. Republican. Avocation: tennis. Home: 2237 Forest Park Dr Anchorage AK 99517-1324 Office: Maynard & Partch 4007 Old Seward Hwy Ste 800 Anchorage AK 99503-6060

MAYNARD, NANCY GRAY, biological oceanographer; b. Middleboro, Mass., Apr. 18, 1941; d. Thomas LaSalle and Clara (Gray) M.; m. Conrad Dennis Gebelein, Jan., 1969 (div. 1977); 1 child, Jennifer Lynn. BS, Mary Washington Coll., 1963; MS, U. Miami (Fla.), 1968, PhD, 1974. Rsch. assoc. Bermuda Biol. Sta., Ferry Reach, 1972-75; rsch. fellow Lamont-Doherty Geol. Obs. Columbia U. (CLIMAP), 1972-75; post-doctoral fellow Div. Engring., Applied Physics Harvard U., Cambridge, Mass., 1975-76; field coord. environ. studies Alaska Outer Continental Shelf Office U.S. Dept. Interior, Anchorage, 1976-78; with oil spills sci. support Nat. Oceanic and Atmospheric Adminstrn., Alaska and S.E. U.S., 1978-81; policy analyst Exec. Office Pres. U.S. Office Sci. and Technology Policy, Washington, 1982-83; fellow Dept. of Commerce Sci. and Tech., 1982-83; staff asst. Bd. Ocean Sci. and Policy NAS, Washington, 1983-85; resident rsch. assoc. Nat. Rsch. Coun. Scripps Instn. Oceanography and Jet Propulsion Lab NASA, 1985-87; br. head Oceans and Ice Br. Goddard Space Flight Ctr. NASA, Greenbelt, Md., 1987-88, assoc. chief rsch. Lab. for Oceans, 1988-89; asst. dir. for environment Exec. Office of Pres. Office Sci. and Tech. Policy, Washington, 1989-93; dep. dir. sci. div. NASA Mission to Planet Earth HQ, Washington, 1993—. Contbr. numerous articles profl. jours. Recipient Pub. Svc. Commendation USCG, 1979. Mem. AAAS, Assn. Women in Sci., The Oceanography Soc., Am. Geophys. Union, Women's Aquatic Network (bd. dirs.), Corp. Bermuda Biol. Sta. Rsch. Office: NASA Mission Planet Earth Sci Divsn 300 E St SW/Code YS Washington DC 20546

MAYNARD, PARRISH, ballet dancer; b. Epernay, France. Student, San Francisco Ballet Sch., 1978-80. Dancer Am. Ballet Theatre II, N.Y.C., 1983-85; soloist Joffrey Ballet, N.Y.C., 1986-88; mem. corps de ballet Am. Ballet Theatre, N.Y.C., 1988-92, soloist, 1992—; guest artist Australian Nat. Ballet, 1993, English Nat. Ballet, 1993. Created role of narrator in Ulysses Dove's Serious Pleasures; performed in dances including (with Joffrey Ballet) The Clowns, A Midsummer Night's Dream, Monotones I, (with Am. Ballet Theatre) La Bayadere, Etudes, Drink to Me Only With Thine Eyes, Giselle, Romeo and Juliet, The Sleeping Beauty, Swan Lake, Symphonic Variations, Moondance, La Sylphide, The Nutcracker. Office: Am Ballet Theatre 890 Broadway New York NY 10003*

MAYNARD, ROBERT HOWELL, lawyer; b. San Antonio, Feb. 15, 1938; s. William Simpson Sr. and Lillian Isabel (Tappan) M.; m. Joan Marie Pearson, Jan. 6, 1962; children: Gregory Scott, Patricia Kathryn, Alicia Joan, Elizabeth Simms. BA, Baylor U., 1959, LLB, 1961; LLM, Georgetown U., 1965. Bar: Tex. 1961, D.C. 1969, Ohio 1973. Trial atty. gen. litigation sect. lands div. U.S. Dept. Justice, Washington, 1964-65; spl. asst. to solicitor U.S. Dept. Interior, Washington, 1965-69; legis. asst. U.S. Senate, Washington, 1969-73; ptnr., dept. head Smith & Schnacke, Dayton, Ohio, 1973-83; dir. Ohio EPA, Columbus, Ohio, 1983-85; ptnr., environ. policy and strategy devel. Vorys, Sater, Seymour and Pease, Columbus, 1985—. Trustee Episcopal Community Svcs. Found. USNR, 1962-65. Episcopalian. Office: Vorys Sater Seymour and Pease PO Box 1008 52 E Gay St Columbus OH 43216-1008

MAYNARD, STEVEN HARRY, writer; b. San Diego, July 4, 1954; s. Harry Clark and Ruby Kristina (Odna). BA in Communications, U. Wash., 1976; MA in Theology, Fuller Theol. Seminary, 1979. Religion writer, gen. news reporter Walla Walla (Wash.) Union-Bulletin, 1979-84; religion writer Houston Chronicle, 1984-87; religion/higher edn. reporter The News Tribune, Tacoma, Wash., 1987—. Recipient Mng. Editors award Tex. Associated Press, 1984, Wilbur award Religious Pub. Relations Council, 1981. Mem. Religion Newswriters Assn. Office: 1950 S State St Tacoma WA 98405-2860

MAYNARD, TERRELL DENNIS, minister; b. Paducah, Ky., Dec. 10, 1944; s. Claude and Euda (Finley) M.; m. Mary Jacqueline Chappell, Sept. 3, 1965; children: Terrell Geoffrey, Christopher Dennis. BA, Bethel Coll., 1966; MDiv, Memphis Theol. Sem., 1969. Pastor Cumberland Presbyn. Ch., Searcy, Ark., 1969-72, Hohenwald, Tenn., 1972-76; pastor Swan Cumberland Presbyn. Ch., Centerville, Tenn., 1972-76, Elliottsville Presbyn. Ch., Alabaster, Ala., 1976-94, 1st Cumberland Presbyn. Ch., Jackson, Tenn., 1994—; pres. Bd. Christian Edn., Memphis, 1976-85; chair Gen. Assembly's Exec. Com., Memphis, 1987-93. Bd. dirs., pres. Shelby Emergency Assistance, Montevallo, Ala., 1990-94; bd. dirs. Developing Ala. Youth Found., Alabaster, 1989-94, Shelby County Hosp. Authority, Alabaster, 1993-94. Recipient Disting. Alumni award Bethel Coll., McKenzie, Tenn., 1992; named Outstanding Vol. Shelby County Chpt. ARC, Alabaster, 1989. Mem. Assn. Cumberland Presbyn. Ch. Educators. Avocations: fishing, golf, hunting, reading, college basketball. Home: 139 Paddock Pl Jackson TN 38305 Office: 1st Cumberland Presbyn Ch 1730 Hwy 45 Bypass Jackson TN 38305

MAYNE, LUCILLE STRINGER, finance educator; b. Washington, June 6, 1924; d. Henry Edmond and Hattie Benham (Benson) Stringer; children: Patricia Anne, Christine Gail, Barbara Marie. BS, U. Md., 1946; MBA, Ohio State U., 1949; PhD, Northwestern U., 1966. Instr. fin. Utica Coll., 1949-50; lectr. fin. Roosevelt U., 1961-64; lectr. fin. Pa. State U., 1965-66, asst. prof., 1966-69, assoc. prof., 1969-70; assoc. prof. banking and fin. Case-Western Res. U. 1971-76, prof., 1976-94, prof. emerita, 1994—; adjunct dean Sch. Grad. Studies, 1980-84; sr. economist, cons. FDIC, 1977-78; cons. Nat. Commn. Electronic Fund Transfer Systems, 1976; rsch. cons. Am. Bankers Assn., 1975, Fed. Res. Bank of Cleve., 1968-70, 73; cons. Pres.'s Commn. Fin. Structure and Regulation, 1971, staff economist, 1970-71; analytical statistician Air Materiel Command, Dayton, Ohio, 1950-52; asst. to promotion mgr. NBC, Washington, 1946-48; expert witness cases involving fin. instns.; bd. dirs. Cleve. Citywide Devel. Corp., 1981—, Horizon Savs. Bank, 1983-92. Assoc. editor: Jour. Money, Credit and Banking, 1980-83, Bus. Econs., 1980-85; contbr. articles to profl. jours. Vol. Cleve. Soc. for Blind, 1979—; mem. policyholders nominating com. Tchrs. Ins. and Annuity Assn./Coll. Retirement Equities Fund, 1982-84, chairperson com., 1983-84; bd. dirs. Women's Cmty. Found., 1994—. Grad. scholar Ohio State U., 1949; doctoral fellow Northwestern U., 1963-65. Mem. Midwest Fin. Assn. (pres. 1991-92, bd. dirs. 1975-79, officer 1988-93), Phi Kappa Phi, Beta Gamma Sigma. Episcopalian. Home: 3723 Normandy Rd Cleveland OH 44120-5246 Office: Case Western Res U Weatherhead Sch Mgmt U Circle Cleveland OH 44106-7235

MAYNE, THOM, architect; b. Waterbury, Conn., Jan. 19, 1944; s. Walter and Bernice (Gornall) M.; m. Susan Burnham, Sept. 10, 1964 (div. 1970); 1 child, Richard; m. Blythe Alison Mayne, Aug. 8, 1981; children: Sam, Cooper. BArch, U. So. Calif., 1968; MArch, Harvard U., 1978. Mem. faculty UCLA Sch. Art and Architecture, Santa Monica, Calif., 1972—; bd. dirs. So. Calif. Inst. Architecture, Santa Monica, Calif., 1983—; architect Morphosis, Santa Monica, Calif.; adj. prof. UCLA, 1993; mem. vis. faculty Calif. State Coll., Pomona, 1971, Miami U., Ohio, 1982, Washington U., St. Louis, 1984, U. Tex., Austin, 1984, U. Pa., 1985, Columbia U., N.Y.C., 1986, Harvard U., 1988, Clemson U., 1991, Yale U., 1991, UCLA, 1986, 92, U. Ill., Urbana-Champaign, 1992-93, Tech. U., Vienna, Austria, 1993, Berlage Inst., Amsterdam, 1993, Hochschule für Andgewandt Kunst, Vienna, 1991, 93; lectr. in field; adjudicator numerous awards. Archtl. one-man exhbns. include 2 AES Gallery, San Francisco, 1988, Cheney Cowles Mus., Spokane, Wash., 1989, Walker Arts Ctr. Mpls., 1989, Gallery of Architecture, L.A., 1989, Contemporary Arts Ctr., Cin., 1989, San Francisco Mus. Modern Art, 1990, Graham Found., Chgo., 1990, Aedes Galerie and Architecture Forum, Berlin, 1990, Fenster Architekturgalerie, Frankfurt, Germany, 1990, Gallery MA, Toyko, 1990, Laguna (Calif.) Art Mus., 1991, G201 Gallery, Ohio, 1991, 1-Space Gallery, Chgo., 1992, Sadock & Uzzan Galerie, Paris, 1992, Diane Farris Gallery, 1993; group exhbns. include Umwelt Galerie, Stuttgart, Germany, 1978, The Archtl. Gallery, Venice, Calif., 1979, La Jolla (Calif.) Mus. of Contemporary Art, 1982, Inst. Contemporary Arts, London, 1983, Archtl. Assn., London, 1983, NAD, N.Y.C., 1983, 88, Mus. Modern Art, San Francisco, 1983, Calif. Mus. Sci. and Industry, 1984, G.A. Gallery, Tokyo, 1985, 87, 90, Max Protech Gallery, N.Y.C., 1985, 86, I.D.C, N.Y.C., 1986, Axis Gallery, Tokyo, Milan, Paris, 1988, Pacific Design Ctr., L.A., 1988, Australia Ctr. for Contemporary Arts, Victoria, 1988, Cooper-Hewitt Mus., N.Y.C., 1988, Aedes Galerie für Architektur und Raum, Berlin, 1988, Kirsten Kiser Gallery, 1988, 89, Visual Arts Ontario, Toronto, 1988, Gallery Functional Art, Santa Monica, Calif., 1989, Deutsches Architektur Mus., Frankfurt, 1989, USIA, Moscow, 1989-90, Lameier Sculpture Park, St. Louis, 1989, Gwenda Jay Gallery, Chgo., 1990, Sadock & Uzzan Galerie, 1991, Bannatyne Gallery, Santa Monica, 1991, ROM Galleri for Arkitektur, Oslo, 1992, 65 Thompson Street Gallery, N.Y.C., 1992; archtl. projects include Sequoyah Edn. and Rsch. Ctr., Santa Monica, 1977 (Progressive Architecture award 1974), Flores Residence, 1979 (Progressive Architecture award 1980), Sedlak Residence, 1980 (AIA award 1981), Western Melrose Office Bldg, 1981 (Progressive Architecture award 1982), Hermosa Beach Ctrl. Bus. Dist. (Progressive Architecture award 1984), 72 Market Street Restaurant, 1983 (AIA award 1985, CCAIA award 1986), Bergren Residence, 1984 (AIA award 1985, CCAIA award 1986, Nat. AIA award 1986), Cedar Sinai Comprehensive Cancer Ctr., L.A., 1988 (Progressive Architecture award 1987, AIA award 1988, CCAIA award 1989), Arts Park Performing Pavilion, 1988, (Progressive Architecture award 1989), Leon Max Showroom, L.A., 1988 (CCAIA award 1990, Archtl. Record Interior award 1990), Club Post Nulear, Laguna Beach, Calif., 1988, Berlin Wall Competition, 1988, Expo '90 Folly, Osaka, Japan, 1989, The Emery Ctr. Performing Arts, 1989, Temple U. CCC, Phila., 1989, Politix, 1990 (AIA award 1990), Salick Health Care Corp. Hdqs., 1990 (AIA award 1992, CCAIA award 1993), Visual Performing Arts Sch. at Thomas More Coll., Crestview, N.Y., 1990, MTV Studios, L.A., 1990, Higashi Azabu Tower, Tokyo, 1991, Yuzen Vintage Car Mus., L.A., 1991 (AIA award 1993), Disney Inst. and Town Ctr. Competition, Orlando, Fla., 1991, Cranbrook Acad. Gatehouse Competition (Pilkington Planar prize 1993), Spreebogen Master Plan, Berlin, 1993, Check Point Charlie Office Bldg., Berlin, 1993; contbr. articles to profl. jours. Rome Prize fellow Am. Acad. Rome, 1987; recipient Architecture award Am. Acad. Arts and Letters, 1992. Mem. AIA, Am. Acad. Design. Democrat. Avocations: skiing, travelling. Office: Morphosis 2041 Colorado Ave Santa Monica CA 90404-3415

MAYNES, CHARLES WILLIAM, editor, former government official; b. Huron, S.D., Dec. 8, 1938; s. Charles William and Almira Rose (Summers) M.; m. Gretchen Schiele, July 17, 1965; children: Stacy Kathryn, Charles William. Ba, Harvard U., 1960; MA, Oxford (Eng.) U., 1962. UN polit. affairs ofcl. Dept. State, Washington, 1962-65; chief monetary economist AID, Laos, 1965-67; econ. officer Am. Embassy, Moscow, 1968-70; sec. Carnegie Endowment Internat. Peace, 1971-76; sr. legis. asst. to Sen. Fred R. Harris, 1972; mem. issues mgmt Sargent Shriver's Vice-Presdl. campaign, 1972; mem. Carter-Mondale Transition team, 1976-77; asst. sec. for internat. orgn. affairs Dept. State, 1977-80; editor Fgn. Policy mag., 1980—; mem. Clinton-Gore Transition team, 1992-93; mem. Coun. Fgn. Rels., Internat. Inst. Strategic Studies, Washington Inst. Internat. Affairs, UN Assn., Overseas Devel. Coun., Nat. Acad. Pub. Adminstrn.; adv. com. European Inst., Lincoln U. Ctr. Pub. Policy and Diplomacy, Overseas Devel. Coun., Nat. Inst. Citizen Participation and Negotiation, U. Calif. Inst. Global Conflict and Cooperation, UN Assn., others. Contbr. articles to profl. jours. Recipient Meritorious Service award Dept. State; congl. fellow Rep. F. Bradford Morse, 1971, Sen. Fred R. Harris, 1971; Rhodes scholar. Mem. Phi Beta Kappa. Democrat. Office: Fgn Policy Mag 2400 N St NW Washington DC 20037-1153 Home: 3914 LeLand St Chevy Chase MD 20815

MAYO, BERNIER L., secondary school principal. Headmaster St. Johnsbury (Vt.) Acad. Recipient Blue Ribbon Sch. award U.S. Dept. Edn., 1990-91. Office: St Johnsbury Acad 7 Main St Saint Johnsbury VT 05819-2699

MAYO, CLYDE CALVIN, organizational psychologist; b. Robstown, Tex., Feb. 2, 1940; s. Clyde Culberson and Velma (Oxford) M.; m. Jeanne Lynn McCain, Aug. 24, 1963; children: Brady Scott, Amber Camille. BA, Rice U., 1961; BS, U. Houston, 1966, PhD, 1972; MS, Trinity U., 1966. Lic. psychologist, Tex. Mgmt. engr. LWFW, Inc., Houston, 1966-72, sr. cons. 1972-78, prin., 1978-81; ptnr. Mayo, Thompson, Bigby, Houston, 1983-, founder Mgmt. and Personnel Systems, Houston, 1983—; counselor Interface Counseling Ctr., Houston, 1976-79; dir. Mental Health HMO Group, 1985-87; instr. St. Thomas U., Houston, 1979—, U. Houston Downtown Sch., 1972, U. Houston-Clear Lake, 1983-88, U. Houston-Central Campus, 1984—; dir. mgmt. devel. insts. U. Houston Woodlands and West Houston, 1986-1991, adj. prof. U. Houston, 1991—. Author: Bi/Polar Inventory of Strengths, 1978, LWFW Annual Survey of Manufacturers, 1966-1981. Coach, mgr. Meyerland Little League, 1974-78, So. Belles Softball, 1979-80, S.W. Colt Baseball, 1982-83, Friends of Fondren Library of Rice U., 1988—; charter mem. Holocaust Mus. Mem. Soc. Indsl. Organizational Psychologists, Tex. Indsl. Orgnl. Psychologists (founder), Houston Psychol. Assn. (membership dir. 1978, sec. 1984), Houston Area Quality Circle Soc., Tex. Psychol. Assn., Am. Psychol. Assn., Bus. Execs. for Nat. Security, Houston Area Indsl. Orgnl. Psychologists (bd. dirs. 1989-92), Forum Club. Methodist. Club: Meyerland (bd. dirs. 1988-92, pres. 1991). Home: 8723 Ferris Dr Houston TX 77096-1409 Office: Mgmt and Personnel Systems 4545 Bissonnet St Bellaire TX 77401-3121

MAYO, ELIZABETH BROOM, lawyer; b. Jackson, Miss., Aug. 20, 1948; d. Harmon W. and Elizabeth (Kehoe) Broom; m. Gerald E. Mayo, Aug. 30, 1980; stepchildren: Sharon E. Parker, Gerald E. Jr. AB, Spring Hill Coll., 1970; JD, Washington U., 1973; LLM in Taxation, Capital U., 1989. Bar: Ohio 1973, S.C. 1994. Assoc. Schottenstein, Zox & Dunn, Columbus, Ohio, 1973-75, ptnr., 1982-89; 2d v.p. underwriting Midland Mut. Life Ins. Co., Columbus, 1975-80; dir. fin. svcs. Nationwide Ins. Cos., Columbus, 1980-82; ptnr. Porter, Wright, Morris & Arthur, Columbus, 1989—, mem. directing ptnrs. com., 1989-93, chair healthcare practice group. Active Ohio Arts Coun., 1991—, vice chair, 1994—; active Franklin County Pvt. Industry Coun., Columbus, 1990—, vice chair, 1994—; active Recreation and Parks Commn., Columbus, 1990—, 1994—; active Met. Human Svcs. Commn., Columbus, 1987-94, chmn., 1991-92. Fellow Am. Coll. Trusts and Estates Counsel; mem. ABA, Ohio Bar Assn., Columbus Bar Assn., Nat. Health Lawyers Assn., Capital Club. Office: Porter Wright Morris & Arthur 41 S High St Columbus OH 43215-6101

MAYO, GEORGE WASHINGTON, JR., lawyer; b. Waycross, Ga., Dec. 23, 1946; s. George Washington Sr. and Perrie R. (Ling) M.; m. Katherine

Louise Boland, Nov. 15, 1977; children—Regan L.B., Taylor L.B. A.B., Emory U., 1967; J.D., U. Va., 1973. Bar: Va. 1973, D.C. 1974. Assoc. Hogan & Hartson, Washington, 1973-80, ptnr., 1980—. Contbr. articles to prof. jours. Bd. dirs. Vietnam Vets. Meml. Fund Inc., 1978—, Earth Conservation Corps., 1990—, dean's coun. Emory U., 1994—. Served to 1st lt., U.S. Army, 1969-71, Vietnam. Mem. ABA, D.C. Bar Assn., Order of Coif. Democrat. Methodist. Club: Met. (Washington), City (Washington). Home: 26 Holly Leaf Ct Bethesda MD 20817-2652 Office: Hogan & Hartson 555 13th St NW Washington DC 20004-1109

MAYO, GERALD EDGAR, insurance company executive; b. Boston, Aug. 12, 1932; m. Elizabeth Broom, Aug. 20, 1948; children: Sharon Elaine, Gerald Edgar. B.A. in History, Boston U., 1953; grad., Advanced Mgmt. Program, Harvard U., 1968; LHD, Ohio Dominican Coll., 1993. C.L.U., 1975. With New Eng. Mut. Ins. Co., Boston, 1956-68; 2d v.p. New Eng. Mut. Ins. Co., 1967-68; with Midland Mut. Life Ins. Co., Columbus, Ohio 1968—; exec. v.p. mktg. Midland Mut. Life Ins. Co., 1976-80, pres., chief exec. officer, 1980-86, chmn. bd., chief exec officer, 1986—; bd. dirs. Huntington Bancshares Inc., CompuServe, HBO & Co., Columbia Gas of Ohio. Chmn. Grant Med. Ctr., U.S. Health Corp.; depositor asst., corp. mem. Franklin County Conv. Facility Authority. With AUS. Mem. ACLUI (mem. local and nat. chpts.), Assn. Ohio Life Ins. Cos., Columbus Area C. of C. (sr. coun.), Columbus Club, Columbus Country Club, Capital Club (bd. govs. 1985—, chmn. 1993-94), Harvard Bus. Sch. Club, The New Albany Country Club (bd. govs. 1991—). Republican. Presbyterian. Office: Midland Mut Life Ins Co 250 E Broad St Ste 211 Columbus OH 43215-3703

MAYO, J. HASKELL, JR., bishop. Bishop African Methodist Episcopal Church 4th Dist., Chgo. Office: African Methodist Episcopal Ch PO Box 53539 400 E 41st St Ste 114 Chicago IL 60653-2757

MAYO, JOAN BRADLEY, microbiologist, epidemiologist; b. Ada, Okla., Oct. 24, 1942; d. Samuel S. and Norene (Parker) Bradley; m. Harry D. Mayo III, Sept. 30, 1967. BA, Drake U., 1964; MS in Microbiology, NYU, 1978; MBA in Mgmt., Fairleigh Dickinson U., 1989. Technologist clin. labs. St. John's Episc. Hosp., Bklyn., 1964-66; supr. Med. Tech. Sch. Bklyn.-Cumberland Med. Ctr., 1966-71; clin. instr., technologist SUNY Downstate Med. Ctr., Bklyn., 1970-73; supr. bacteriology lab. Meml. Sloan-Kettering Cancer Ctr., N.Y.C., 1972-82; dir. microbiology labs., 1982-87; dir. infection control svc. N.Y.C. Health and Hosp. Corp./Harlem Hosp. Ctr., 1987—; mem. com. for prevention of bloodborne diseases N.Y.C. Health and Hosp. Corp., 1990—. Contbr. articles to profl. publs. Active Friends of Harlem Hosp. 1988—, North Bergen (N.J.) Action Group, 1987—. Mem. Am. Soc. Microbiology, Am. Pub. Health Assn., Assn. Practitioners in Infection Control, Delta Mu Delta, Alpha Kappa Alpha. Avocations: writing, travel, reading. Home: 7855 Boulevard E North Bergen NJ 07047-5938 Office: NYC Health/Hosp Corp Harlem Hosp Ctr 506 Lenox Ave New York NY 10037-1802

MAYO, JOHN SULLIVAN, telecommunications company executive; b. Greenville, N.C., Feb. 26, 1930; s. William Louis and Mattie (Harris) M.; m. Lucille Dodgson, Apr. 1957; children: Mark Dodgson, David Thomas, Nancy Ann, Lynn Marie. BS, N.C. State U., 1952, MS, 1953, PhD, 1955. With AT&T Bell Labs., Murray Hill, N.J., 1955-95, exec. dir. toll electronic switching div., 1973-75, v.p. electronics tech., 1975-79, sr. v.p. network systems and network svcs., 1979-91, pres., 1991-95; mem. adv. bd. Coll. Engring., U. Calif., Berkeley; mem. sci. adv. group House subcom. on renewing U.S. Sci. and Tech. Policy; bd. dirs. Johnson and Johnson, Found. for Nat. Medals of Sci. and Tech. Contbr. articles to profl. jours.; patentee in field. Trustee Polytech U., The Kenan Inst. for Engring., Tech. and Sci. at N.C. State U., Liberty Sci. Ctr.; mem. bd. overseers N.J. Inst. Tech.; mem. commn. on future of Smithsonian Instn. Recipient Indsl. Rsch. Inst. medal, 1992, Navy League N.Y. Coun. Roosevelts gold medal for sci., 1993, Engring. Mgr. of Yr. award Am. Soc. for Engring. Mgmt., 1992, N.J. Sci./Tech. medal, 1994; named Outstanding Engring. Alumnus N.C. State U., 1977; Internat. Engring. Consortium fellow, 1994. Fellow IEEE (Alexander Graham Bell award 1978, Simon Ramo medal 1988, C&C prize 1988, Nat. Medal of Tech. 1990), Internat. Engring. Consortium; mem. NAE, Royal Swedish Acad. Engring. Scis., Sigma Xi, Phi Kappa Phi. Baptist. Avocations: fishing, gardening, bicycling, jogging. Office: AT&T Bell Labs 600 Mountain Ave Murray Hill NJ 07974-2008

MAYO, ROBERT PORTER, banker; b. Seattle, Mar. 15, 1916; s. Carl Asa and Edna Alberta (Nelson) M.; m. Marian Aldridge Nicholson, Aug. 28, 1942; children: Margaret Alice, Richard Carl, Carolyn Ruth (Mrs. Gregory Brown), Robert Nelson. A.B. magna cum laude, U. Wash., 1937, M.B.A. 1938. Research asst., auditor Wash. State Tax Commn., 1938-41; economist U.S. Treasury, 1941-47, asst. office of tech. staff, 1948-53, chief debt div. analysis staff, 1953-59; asst. to sec. Treasury Dept., 1959-60; v.p. Continental Ill. Nat. Bank & Trust Co. of Chgo., 1960-69; chmn. Boye Needle Co., 1963-67; staff dir. Pres. Commn. on Budget Concepts, 1967; dir. U.S. Bur. of Budget, 1969-70; counsellor to Pres. U.S., 1970; pres. Fed. Res. Bank of Chgo., 1970-81; trustee Instnl. Liquid Assets and Assoc. Goldman Sachs Funds, CNA Income Shares; dir. Chgo. Tokyo Bank, Duff and Phelps Utilities Income Fund. Trustee YMCA, Chgo.; bd. dirs. Assoc. Ve. Corps, Chgo. Mem. Comml. Club Chgo., Econ. Club Chgo., Perico Bay (Fla.) Club, Bartlett-on-the-Greens Homeowner's Assn., Phi Beta Kappa. Presbyterian.

MAYOCK, ROBERT LEE, internist; b. Wilkes-Barre, Pa., Jan. 19, 1917; s. John F. and Mathilde M.; m. Constance M. Peruzzi, July 2, 1949; children: Robert Lee, Stephen Philip, Holly Peruzzi. B.S., Bucknell U., 1938; M.D. U. Pa., 1942. Diplomate Am. Bd. Internal Medicine. Intern Hosp. U. Pa., Phila., 1943-44; resident Hosp. U. Pa., 1944-45, chief med. resident, 1945-46, attending physician, 1946—; chief pulmonary disease Phila. Gen. Hosp., 1955-72, chief pulmonary disease sect., 1959-72, sr. cons. pulmonary disease sect., 1972—; asst. prof. clin. medicine U. Pa., 1949-59, assoc. prof., 1959-70, prof. medicine, 1970-87, prof. emeritus, 1987—; mem. med. adv. com. for Tb Commonwealth of Pa., 1965-74, mem. med. adv. com. on chronic respiratory disease, 1974-92, chmn. adv. com., 1981-90; mem. subsplty bd. pulmonary disease Am. Bd. Internal Medicine, 1965-76; nat. bd. dirs. Am. Lung Assn., 1983-92, local bd. dirs., 1961, local pres., 1966-69, dir. at large, 1983—. Contbr. articles in field to med. jours. Served to capt. U.S. Army, 1952-54. Fellow ACP, Am. Coll. Chest Physicians (regent 1972-79); mem. AMA, Am. Thoracic Soc., Am. Fedn. Clin. Rsch., Am. Heart Assn., Pa. Lung Assn. (dir. 1976—), N.Y. Acad. Scis., Pa. Med. Soc., Phila. County Med. Soc., Physiology Soc. Phila., Laennec Soc. Phila., Merion Cricket Club, Westmoreland Club, Swiftwater Res., Sigma Xi, Alpha Omega Alpha. Home: 244 Gypsy Ln Wynnewood PA 19096-1113 Office: U Penn 3rd Fl Ste F Ravdin Bldg Philadelphia PA 19104

MAYOR, HEATHER DONALD, medical educator; b. Melbourne, Victoria, Australia, July 6, 1930; d. Joseph A. L. and Elizabeth Emily (Boyd) Donald; m. Richard Blair Mayor, May 28, 1956; children: Diana Boyd (Mrs. Russell Hawkins), Philip Hastings. BS, U. Melbourne, Australia, 1949; MS, U. Melbourne, 1951, DSc, 1970; PhD, U. London, 1954. Electron microscopist Nat. Inst. for Med. Research, London, 1952-55; postdoctoral fellow Walter and Eliza Hall Inst., Melbourne, 1955-56; post doctoral fellow Harvard U. Med. Sch., Boston, 1956-60; from asst. prof. to prof. Baylor Coll. Medicine, Houston, 1960—; prof., 1970—; cons. AEC, Washington, 1971—, Nat. Cancer Inst., Bethesda, Md., 1975—, U. Tex. Med. Sch., Houston, 1975—. Contbr. articles and papers to profl. jours.; artist, coordinator Life Shapes, Contemporary Arts Mus. Houston, Tex. art exhbn., 1974. Recipient Disting. award Ctr. for Interaction Man-Sci.-Soc., Houston, 1973, Sir Hiram Maxim award, 1990; named Scientist of Yr., Ency. Britannica, 1992; scholar in residence Rockefeller Inst. and Found., Bellagio, Italy, 1983. Mem. Am. Assn. Immunologists, Biophysical Soc. (program chmn.), Am. Soc. for Cell Biology (program chmn.), Doctors Club, Houstonian Club, Houston Harpsichord Soc. (bd. dirs.). Avocations: piano, harpsichord, skiing, jogging. Home: 22 N West Oaks Dr # 3 Houston TX 77056-1502 Office: Baylor Coll of Medicine 1 Baylor Plz Houston TX 77030-3498

MAYOR, RICHARD BLAIR, lawyer; b. San Antonio, Mar. 27, 1934; s. E. Allan and Elizabeth Ann (Hastings) M.; m. Heather Donald, July 28, 1956; children: Diana Boyd, Philip Hastings. BA, Yale U., 1955; postgrad., Melbourne U., Australia, 1955-56; JD, Harvard U., 1959. Bar: Tex. 1960. Assoc. Butler and Binion, Houston, 1959-67, ptnr., mem. exec. com., 1967-

82; founding, sr. ptnr. Mayor, Day, Caldwell & Keeton, L.L.P., Houston, 1982—; bd. dirs., founder Internat. Ctrs Arbitration. Trustee, chmn. exec. com. Contemporary Arts Mus., Houston, 1972-78; trustee Houston Ballet Found., 1983-88. Fulbright scholar, 1955-56. Fellow Tex. Bar Found.; mem. ABA, Am. Law Inst., Tex. Bar Assn., Ramada Club, Houstonian Club, Houston Club, Phi Beta Kappa. Office: Mayor Day Caldwell & Keeton LLP 700 Louisiana St Ste 1900 Houston TX 77002-2727

MAYORAS, DONALD EUGENE, corporate executive, speaker, consultant, educator; b. Danville, Ill., Aug. 25, 1939; s. Andrew John and Katherine Ann (Shelato) M.; m. JoAnna Marie Kacmer, June 9, 1962; children—Tyler, Stacie. B.S. in Edn., Purdue U., 1962; postgrad., Northwestern U., 1968-71; M.B.A., So. Ill. U., 1977. Regional mgr. Pacific Intermountain Express, Akron, Ohio, 1972-74; v.p. United Van Lines, Fenton, Mo., 1974-78; pres. Bekins Van Lines, L.A., 1978-83; pres., chief exec. officer Sun Carriers, Inc., Holliston, Mass., 1983-90, chmn. bd. dirs.; vice chmn., chief exec. officer Builders Transport, Camden, S.C., 1990-91; pres. D.E. Mayoras Assocs., Devon, Pa., 1992—, Tons, Inc., Devon, 1993—, Truckload Holdings, Inc.; mng. dir. Svc. & Adminstrv. Inst.; pres. Truckload Holding Inc., Devon, Pa. Trustee Ross Ade Found., West Lafayette, Ind., 1962—. Capt. U.S. Army, 1962-68; Europe, Vietnam. Decorated Bronze Star. Mem. Am. Trucking Assn. (v.p. 1983-91, trustee Found. 1983-91), Nat. Speakers Assn., Nat. Coun. Logistics, Nat. Private Truck Coun., Purdue U. Alumni Assn., Nat. Def. Transp. Assn., Aronomink Golf Club (Newtown Sq., Pa.), Haverford Tennis Club (Pa.), Delta Nu Alpha, Beta Gamma Sigma, Omicron Delta Kappa. Republican. Roman Catholic. Avocations: golf, antiques, classic automobiles, tennis.

MAYPOLE, JOHN FLOYD, real estate holding company executive; b. Chgo., May 17, 1939; s. John James and Althea Floyd M.; m. Anne White, 1961; children: Cynthia, John, Kimberly. B.A. in Econs, Yale U., 1961. With Arthur Andersen & Co., 1961-62, 65-66; mgr. corp. acctg. Interpace Corp., 1966, asst. treas., 1967-68, treas., 1968-70, treas., controller, 1970-73, v.p. fin., 1973-77, sr. v.p., 1977-80, exec. v.p., 1980-81, pres., 1981-83; pres., chief operating officer Clevepak Corp., 1983-84; mng. ptnr. Peach State Real Estate Holding Co., Toccoa, Ga., 1984—; bd. dirs. Dan River Mills, Blodgett Corp., Briggs Industries Inc., Bell Atlantic Corp., Conn. Mut. Life Ins. Co., Davies, Turner & Co., Igloo Products Corp.; mem. adv. bd. Chem. Bank N.J. Bd. adjustment Borough of Mountain Lakes, N.J., 1971-81, chmn., 1980-81. Served with USMC, 1962-65. Mem. Yale Club (N.Y.C.), Rockaway River Country Club, Laurel Oak Country Club. Republican. Office: PO Box 1223 Toccoa GA 30577

MAYR, ERNST, emeritus zoology educator, author; b. Kempten, Germany, July 5, 1904; came to U.S. 1931; s. Otto and Helene (Pusinelli) M.; m. Margarete Simon, May 4, 1935; children: Christa E., Susanne. Cand. med., U. Greifswald, 1925; Ph.D., U. Berlin, 1926; Ph.D. (hon.), Uppsala U., Sweden, 1957; D.Sc. (hon.), Yale U., 1959, U. Melbourne, 1959, Oxford U., 1966, U. Munich, 1968, U. Paris, 1974, Harvard U., 1980, Guelph U., U. Cambridge, 1982, U. Vt., 1984; DSc (hon.), U. Mass., 1993; PhD (hon.), U. Vienna, 1994; DPhil (hon.), U. Konstanz, 1994. Asst. curator zool. mus. U. Berlin, 1926-32; mem. Rothschild expdn. to Dutch New Guinea, 1928, expdn. to Mandated Ty. of New Guinea, 1928-29, Whitney Expdn., 1929-30; research asso. Am. Mus. Natural History, N.Y.C., 1931-32; asso. curator Am. Mus. Natural History, 1932-44, curator, 1944-53; Jesup lectr. Columbia U., 1941; Alexander Agassiz prof. zoology Harvard U., 1953-75, emeritus, 1975—; dir. Mus. Comparative Zoology, Harvard U., 1961-70; Messenger lectr. Cornell U., 1985; Hitchcock prof. U. Calif., 1987; hon. fellow Ctr. for Philosophy of Sci., U. Pitts. Author: List of New Guinea Birds, 1941, Systematics and the Origin of Species, 1942, Birds of the Southwest Pacific, 1945, Birds of the Philippines, (with Jean Delacour), 1946, Methods and Principles of Systematic Zoology, (with E. G. Linsley and R. L. Usinger), 1953, Animal Species and Evolution, 1963, Principles of Systematic Zoology, 1969, Populations, Species and Evolution, 1970, Evolution and the Diversity of Life, 1976, (with W. Provine) Evolutionary Synthesis, 1980, Biologie de l'Evolution, 1981, The Growth of Biological Thought, 1982, Toward a New Philosophy of Biology, 1988, One Long Argument, 1991; editor: Evolution, 1947-49. Pres. XIII Internat. Ornith. Congress, 1962. Recipient Leidy medal, 1946, Wallace Darwin medal, 1958, Brewster medal Am. Ornitologists Union, 1965, Daniel Giraud Elliot medal, 1967, Nat. Medal of Sci. 1970, Molina prize Accademia delle Sci., Bologna, Italy, 1972, Linnean medal, 1977, Gregor Mendel medal, 1980, Balzan prize, 1983, Darwin medal Royal Soc., 1987, Disting. Scientist award UCLA, 1993, Galvin Godman medal, 1994, Japan Prize, 1995. Fellow Linnaean Soc. N.Y. (past sec. editor) Am. Ornithol. Union (pres. 1956-59), New York Zool. Soc.; mem. NAS, Am. Philos. Soc., Am. Acad. Arts and Scis., Am. Soc. Zoologists, Soc. Systematic Zoology (pres. 1966), Soc. Study Evolution (sec. 1946, pres. 1950); hon. or corr. mem. Royal Soc., Royal Australian, Brit. ornithol. unions, Zool. Soc. London, Soc. Ornithol. France, Royal Soc. New Zealand, Bot. Gardens Indonesia, S. Africa Ornithol. Soc., Linnean Soc. London, Deutsche Akademie der Naturforsch Leopoldina., Accad. Naz. dei Lincei, Royal Soc., Académie des Sci. Office: Harvard U Mus of Comparative Zoology Cambridge MA 02138

MAYRON, MELANIE, actress, writer; b. Phila., Oct. 20, 1952. Ed., Am. Acad. Dramatic Arts, N.Y.C. Writer Tribeca Prodns. Appearances include (films) Harry and Tonto, 1974, Car Wash, 1976, The Great Smokey Road Block, 1976, Girl Friends (British Acad. award nomination), You Light Up My Life, 1977, Heart Beeps, 1981, Missing, 1982, Sticky Fingers (also cowriter, co-producer), 1988, Checking Out, 1989, My Blue Heaven, 1990, Drop Zone, 1994; (TV movies) Hustling, 1975, Katie: Portrait of a Centerfold, 1978, The Best Little Girl in the World, 1981, Will There Really Be a Morning?, 1983; (TV miniseries) Wallenberg: A Hero's Story, 1985, Playing for Time, The Boss's Wife, (TV series) thirtysomething (Emmy award for best supporting actress in a drama series, 1989), dir. 2 episodes; film dir.: The Baby-Sitters Club, 1995; author (anthology): Stepping Back. •

MAYS, CAROL JEAN, state legislator; b. Independence, Mo., July 16, 1933; m. Ronald H. Mays; children: Terri, Melanie, Hugh. Student, Baker U. State rep., chmn. consumer protection edn. appropriations com., mem. transp., ways & means & comm. coms. Mo. Ho. of Reps., Jefferson City; restaurant owner. Mem. Mo. Restaurant Assn., Independence C. of C., Fairmount Comml. Club, Alpha Chi Omega. Democrat. Methodist. Home: 3603 S Hedges Ave Independence MO 64052-1167 Office: Mo Ho of Reps State Capital Jefferson City MO 65101

MAYS, GEORGE WALTER, JR., educational technology educator, consultant; b. Decatur, Ill., July 1, 1926; s. George Walter Sr. and Ida May (Lookabaugh) M.; children: Richard, Steven, John, James. BS in Edn., U. Ill., Champaign, 1950, MS in Edn., 1952; BSEE, U. md., 1960; cert., Calif. State U., Carson, 1987. Tchr. math. and physics Mahomet (Ill.) High Sch., 1950-52, prin., 1952-55; br. chief engring studies Nat. Security Agy., Ft. Meade, Md., 1955-62; sr. engr. Jet Propulsion Lab., Pasadena, Calif., 1962-71; tchr. math.-sci., chair Aviation High Sch., Redondo Beach, Calif., 1971-82; tchr. math. and physics, dept. chair Redondo Union High Sch., 1982-89; cons. ednl. tech. Apple Valley, Calif., 1989—; math. coord. Sci. and Tech. Ctr., Apple Valley, Calif., 1990—; part-time instr. electronics Pasadena City Coll., 1963-72, Pepperdine U., 1975-76, math. Victor Valley Coll., 1991—. Author: Educational Technology Application Notes, 1989-90. With USN, 1944-46. Recipient Appollo Achievement award NASA, 1969. Mem. IEEE (life), Calif. Tchrs. Assn. (WHO award 1989), Nat. Coun. Tchrs. of Math., Computer Using Educators, Apple Valley Country Club, Victor Valley Aero Club. Avocations: reading, sports, computer usage, flying. Home and Office: 14070 Seminole Rd PO Box 1930 Apple Valley CA 92307-0037

MAYS, GERALD AVERY (JERRY MAYS), engineering executive, consultant; b. Dallas, Nov. 24, 1939; s. Avery and Blanche (Ponder) M.; m. Shirley Ann Pike; children: Gerald Avery, Sandra Jo, Sherrie Lynn, Sarah Elisabeth; stepchildren: Donald K. Turner, Bruce R. Turner, Barry K. Turner. B.S. in Civil Engring., So. Methodist U., 1962, postgrad., 1962-63. Registered profl. engr., Tex., Kans., Mo. Laborer, engr. Avery Mays Constrn. Co., Dallas, 1950-63; v.p. Avery Mays Constrn. Co., 1967-71, pres., 1971-84; pres. George A. Fuller Co. of Tex., 1984-87, The Mays Cos., 1987—; owner Gerald A. Mays, P.E., cons. engrs., 1988—; football player Kansas City Chiefs, 1961-70; engr. Howard, Needles, Tammen & Bergendoff

(cons. engrs.), 1964-67; partner Mays, Flowers, Grady & Burruss Ins.; pres. GAMCO Constructors, Inc., 1972-82. Campaign chmn. Greater Dallas Dimes, 1973; mem. Dallas Community Relations Bd.; Adv. bd. Dallas Opportunities Industrialization Com., 1972; bd. dirs. Kansas City chpt. ARC, 1969-70, pres. Heart of Am. chpt., 1973; bd. dirs. Baker U., 1970-73; exec. com. Met. Dallas YMCA; chmn. Met. Y Sustaining Fund Campaign, 1976; exec. com. Goodwill Industries Dallas, Goals for Dallas. Recipient football awards All Am. Football League, 1962, 64-68; All Am. Football Conf., 1970; named to All-time Am. Football League Team, All-Time Kansas City Chief Team, Kansas City Chief Hall of Fame, , Young Engr. of Month Kansas City, 1970, Alpha Tau Omega Man of Year, 1970, capt. Kansas City Chiefs, 1963-70. Mem. Salesmanship Club Dallas, Young Pres.'s Orgn., Dallas C. of C., Sigma Tau, Chi Epsilon, Alpha Tau Omega. Home: 4710 Abbot Ave #204A Dallas TX 75205-3024*

MAYS, JANICE ANN, lawyer; b. Waycross, Ga., Nov. 21, 1951; d. William H. and Jean (Bagley) M. AB (hon.), Wesleyan Coll., Macon, Ga., 1973; JD, U. Ga., 1975; LLM in Taxation, U. Georgetown, 1980. Bar: Ga. 1976. Tax counsel com. on ways and means U.S. Ho. Reps., Washington, 1975-88, chief tax counsel com. on ways and means, staff dir. subcom. select revenue measures, 1988-93, chief counsel, staff dir. com. on ways and means, 1993-95, minority chief counsel, staff dir. com. on ways and means, 1995—. Mem. Tax Coalition (past chair). Office: Ways and Means Com 1106 Longworth Office Bldg Washington DC 20515

MAYS, JOSEPH BARBER, JR., lawyer; b. Birmingham, Ala., Dec. 15, 1945; s. Joseph B. and Elizabeth (Tiller) M.; m. June Blackwell, June 13, 1970; 1 child, Mary-Elizabeth. BA, Tulane U., 1967; MA, Cornell U., 1969; JD, U. Ala., 1978. Bar: Ala. 1978, U.S. Ct. Appeals (5th, 4th, 6th, 11th cir.) Ala., U.S. Supreme Ct., U.S. Tax Ct. Ala. Tchr. Indian Springs Sch., Helena, Ala., 1969-75; assoc. Bradley, Arant, Rose & White, Birmingham, 1978-84, ptnr., 1984—; tchr. Birmingham Sch. Law, 1979—. Contbr. articles to profl. jours. Recipient Woodrow Wilson fellowship Woodrow Wilson Found., 1968-69. Mem. ABA, Nat. Assn. Criminal Def. Lawyers, Ala. State Bar Assn., Birmingham Bar Assn., Phi Beta Kappa. Episcopalian. Avocations: sailing, fly-fishing, photography. Home: 3514 Country Club Rd Birmingham AL 35213-2824 Office: Bradley Arant Rose & White 1400 Park Place Towers Birmingham AL 35203

MAYS, L. LOWRY, broadcast executive; b. Houston, July 24, 1935; s. Lester T. and Virginia (Lowry) M.; m. Peggy Pitman, July 29, 1959; children: Kathryn Mays Johnson, Linda Mays McCaul, Mark P., Randall T. BS in Petroleum Engring., Tex. A&M, 1959; MBA, Harvard U., 1962. Comml. recorder San Antonio; with KTTU TV, Tucson, KOKI/KTFO TV, Tulsa, WMPI/WJTC TV, Mobile and Pensacola, Okla., WAWS TV, Jacksonville, Fla., Sta. KSAS-TV, Wichita, Kans., KLRT/KASN TV, Little Rock, Ark., WFTC TV, Mpls.; WFTC TV, WLMT/WMTU TV, Memphis, WXXA, Albany, N.Y.; with WQUE AM/FM, New Orleans, Clear Channel Sports, Des Moines, Okla. News Network, Oklahoma City, Va. News Network, KJYO & KTOK, Oklahoma City, KEBC, Oklahoma City, WELI, New Haven, WKCI-WAVZ, New Haven, KPEZ, Austin, Tex., KHYS, KALO, KBXX, KMJQ, KPRC, KSEV, KYOK, Houston and Point Arthur, Tex., KMOD & KAKC, Tulsa, KTAM & KORA, Bryan and College Station, Tex., WHAS & WAMZ, Louisville; with radio and TV broadcasting WOAI & KAJA, San Antonio; pres., chief exec. officer Clear Channel Communications, Inc., San Antonio; past chmn. bd. CBS Radio Affiliates Bd. Bd. dirs., trustee Tex. Rsch. Park; bd. dirs., mem. exec. com. United Way; regent emeritus Tex. A&M U. System; trustee Tex. Rsch. and Tech. Found.; mem. devel. bd. U. Tex. Health Sci. Ctr.; adv. dir. Permanent Univ. Fund Tex. Mem. Nat. Assn. Broadcasters (past chmn. joint bd.), Greater San Antonio C. of C. (past chmn.), Rotary. Home: 400 Geneseo Rd San Antonio TX 78209-6127 Office: Clear Channel Comm PO Box 659512 San Antonio TX 78265-9512

MAYS, M. DOUGLAS, state legislator, financial consultant; b. Pittsburg, Kans., Aug. 18, 1950; s. Marion Edmund and Lilliemae Ruth (Norris) M.; m. Lena M. Krog, June 10, 1971; children: Jessica, Aaron. BFA, Pittsburg State U., 1972; postgrad., Washburn U., 1973—. Registered rep. Waddell & Reed, Inc., Topeka, 1981-83, Paine Webber Jackson & Curtis, Topeka, 1983-85, Columbian Securities, Topeka, 1985-87; commr. securities State of Kans., Topeka, 1987-91; pres. Mays & Assocs., Topeka, 1991—; mem. Kans. Ho. Reps., Topeka, 1993—; adminstrv. law judge various securities proceedings, 1987—; with securities and commodities fraud working group U.S. Dept. Justice, 1988-90; with penny stock task force SEC, 1988-90; del. Commonwealth Secretariat Symposium Comml. Crime, Cambridge, Eng., 1989; securities arbitrator, 1991—. Rep. precinct committeeman Shawnee County, Kans., 1976—, county chmn., 1978-82; mem. 2d Dist. Rep. State Com., Kans., 1976-86, 92—; mem. Kans. Rep. State Com., 1976-87; Senate steering com. Kassebaum for Senate campaign, 1978; chmn., mgr. Hoferer for Senate campaign, 1984; campaign coord., dir. fin. Hayden for Gov., 1986; mem. pub. bldg. commn. City of Topeka, 1985-86, bldg. and fire appeals bd. , 1986-89, dep. mayor, 1987-88; mem. Topeka City Coun., 1985-89; exec. bd. Topeka/Shawnee County Interngovtl. Coun., 1986-89; adv. bd. Topeka Performing Arts Ctr., 1989-90; active Topeka/Shawnee County Met. Planning Commn., 1992—, chmn., 1994—. Mem. North Am. Securities Adminstrs. Assn. (chmn. enforcement sect. 1988-89, pres.-elect, bd. dirs. 1989-90, pres. 1990-91), Nat. Assn. Securities Dealers, Nat. Futures Assn. (bd. arbitrators), Internat. Orgn. Securites Commns. (inter-Am. activities consultative com. 1990, pres.'s com. 1990, del. 1990). Methodist. Home: 1920 SW Damon Ct Topeka KS 66611-1926 Office: Kans Ho Reps State Capital S Topeka KS 66612

MAYS, WILLIAM FRITZ, health facility regional administrator, retired military career officer; b. Taft, Calif., Oct. 10, 1944; s. William Jesse and Cleda Bell (Shankle) M.; m. Kathleen Ann Hull, July 28, 1967; 1 child, W. Fritz Mays, Jr. BS in Indsl. Mgmt., Clemson U., 1967; MBA in Mgmt. & Orgnl. Theory, Fla. State U., 1971. Commd. 2d lt. USAF, 1967, advanced through grades to lt. col.; comdr. med. squadron Regional Hosp. USAF, Carswell AFB, Ft. Worth, Tex., 1967-70; adminstr. ops. Clinic Kadena USAF, AFB, Okinawa, Japan, 1971-74; chief fin. officer Regional Hosp. USAF, MacDill AFB, Tampa, Fla., 1974-76; adminstr. 36th Tactical Hosp. USAF, Bitburg Air Base, Germany, 1976-79; chief student mgmt. divsn. 3790th Med. Svc. Tng. Wing USAF, Sheppard AFB, Wichita Falls, Tex., 1979-81; chief tng. evaluation divsn. 3790th Med. Svc. Tng. Wing USAF, Sheppard AFB, Wichita Falls, 1981-82; chief tri-svc. support branch combat casualty care course USAF, Ft. Sam Houston, San Antonio, 1982-84; chief staffing, manpower, personnel program divsn., HQ Air Tng. Command USAF, Randolph AFB, San Antonio, 1984-87; chief exec. officer Chanute Hosp. USAF, AFB, Rantoul, Ill., 1987-90; chief wing standardization/evaluation 3790th Med. Svc. Tng. Wing USAF, Sheppard AFB, 1990-91; ret. USAF, 1991; regional adminstr. Correctional Med. Systems, Smyrna, Del., 1991—. Chmn. Areawide Hosp. Emergency Svcs. Com. Champaign, Ford Counties, Ill., 1988-90; pres. Floral Hgts. Meth. Men's Group, 1990-91; mem. Whatcoat United Meth. Ch., Camden, Del. Fellow Am. Coll. Healthcare Execs. (com. ethics 1989-92, chmn. 1991-92, chmn. elect San Antonio chpt. 1985-86, chmn. 1986-87); mem. Camden-Wyoming Lions Club (sec. 1993). Avocations: all sports, movies, travel. Office: Correctional Medical Systems 80 Monrovia Ave Smyrna DE 19977

MAYS, WILLIE HOWARD, JR. (SAY HEY KID), former professional baseball player; b. Westfield, Ala., May 6, 1931; s. William Howard and Anna M.; m. Mae Louise Allen, Nov. 27, 1971; 1 adopted son, Michael. Baseball player Birmingham Black Barons, 1948-50, Trenton Inter-State League, 1950-51, Mpls. Millers, Am. Assn., 1951, N.Y. Giants, 1951-57, San Francisco Giants, 1958-72, N.Y. Mets, 1972-73; with Bally's Park Place, Atlantic City, 1980—; pub. rels. exec. San Francisco Giants, 1986—. Author: Willie Mays: My Life In and Out of Baseball, 1966, Say Hey: The Autobiography of Willie Mays, 1988. Served with AUS, 1952-54. Named Most Valuable Player Nat. League, 1954, 65; named Player of Yr. Sporting News, 1954, Baseball Player of Decade Sporting News, 1970, Male Athlete of Yr. AP, 1954, Rookie of the Yr., 1951, Most Exciting Playin Sport Sporting News, 1954, All-Star Game, 1954-73; recipient Hickok belt, 1954, Golden Bat award to commemorate 600 home runs, Gold Glove award (12 times), 1st Commissioner's award, 1970, Golden Plate awarded to America's Captains of Achievement by Am. Acad. Achievement, 1976, Spirit of Life award City of Hope, 1988, Sportsman of Decade, Cong. Racial Equality,

1991, Legendary Star award HBO Video; inducted into Ala. Sports Hall of Fame, Baseball Hall of Fame, 1979, Black Hall of Fame, 1973, Calif. Sports Hall of Fame. Holder 3d place in major league homeruns (660); lifetime batting average of .302; signed lifetime pub. rels. contract with San Francisco Giants, 1993. Office: care San Francisco Giants Candlestick Park San Francisco CA 94124*

MAYSENT, HAROLD WAYNE, hospital administrator; b. Tacoma, Wash., June 26, 1923; s. Wayne L. Shivley and Esther Pierce M.; m. Marjorie Ellen Hodges, June 13, 1953; children: Jeffrey, Nancy, Brian, Gregory. B.A., U. Wash., 1950; M.S. in Hosp. Adminstrn. with distinction, Northwestern U., 1954. Adminstrv. resident Passavant Meml. Hosp., 1953-54, adminstrv. asst., 1954-55; research assoc. hosp. adminstrn. Northwestern U., Evanston, Ill., 1954-55; with Lankenau Hosp., Phila., 1955-72; dir. Lankenau Hosp., 1963-67, exec. dir. 1967-72; exec. v.p. Rockford (Ill.) Meml. Hosp., 1972-75, pres., 1975-91; pres. Rockford Meml. Corp., 1983-91, pres. emeritus, 1991—; pres. The Rockford Group, 1983-91; teaching assoc. Rockford Sch. Medicine, U. Ill., 1974-89, adj. assoc. prof., 1989-92; mem. Ill. Health Facility Planning Bd., 1980-92; chmn. bd. Ill. Hosp. Joint Ventures, Inc., 1977-78; chmn. bd. Vol. Hosps. Am. Midwest Partnership, 1985-89; bd. Atlantic Aviation Holdings, Inc., 1995—. Contbr. articles to profl. jours. Chmn.-elect Coll. Healthcare Execs., 1988-89, chmn., 1989; coach, adminstr. Broomal (Pa.) Little League, 1962-72; bd. dirs. Community Health Assn., 1964-70, Rockford Med. Edn. Found., 1972-87, Tri State Hosp. Assembly, 1978-80, Rockford Coun. 100, 1987-91, exec. com. 1987-91. With AUS, 1942-46. Recipient Malcolm T. MacEachern award Northwestern U., 1954, Laura G. Jackson Alumni Assn. award, 198, Disting. Svc. award Ill. Hosp. Assn., 1989. Fellow Am. Coll. Hosp. Adminstrs. (Ill. regent 1979-84, dist. bd. govs. 1984-88, gov. 1984-88, chmn. elect 1988-89, chmn. 1989-90, past chmn. 1990-91); mem. Am. Hosp. Assn. (com. on vols. 1976-80, coun. patient svcs. 1980-82, ho. of dels. 1977-84, rep. Am. Acad. Pediatrics com. on hosp. care 1983-85), Ill. Hosp. Assn. (bd. dirs. 1965-68), Ill. Hosp. Assn. (trustee 1973-79, sec. 1974-76, chmn. elect 1977, chmn. bd. trustees 1978, named Outstanding Leader in Hosp. Industry 1978, Disting. Svc. award 1989). Office: Rockford Meml 2400 N Rockton Ave Rockford IL 61103-3681

MAYTUM, HARRY RODELL, retired physician; b. Alexandria, S.D., Jan. 25, 1913; s. Wellington James and Lillian May (Syferd) M.; m. Louetta Susanna Stoltz, Apr. 27, 1937; children: James, Nancy, Joan. BS magna cum laude, U. Wis., 1936, MD, 1938. Intern Alameda County Hosp., Oakland, Calif., 1938-39, resident in surgery, 1946-47; resident in surgery Merced County Hosp., Merced, Calif., 1939-41; pvt. practice, Merced, 1947-93; ret., 1993; chief staff Mercy Hosp., Merced, Merced County Hosp. Bd. dirs. Merced County Mosquito Abatement Dist., 1954-64. Lt col. M.C., USAAF, 1941-47, ETO. Fellow Am. Geriatric Soc., Am. Acad. Family Practice (charter); mem. AMA, Calif. Med. Assn. (Plessner Meml. award 1992), Merced-Mariposa County Med. Soc. (pres., 1955), Merced C. of C. (bd. dirs. 1973-77, former chmn. health affairs com., Merced Citizen of Yr. award 1989), Kiwanis (pres. Merced 1953), Elks, Phi Beta Kappa, Alpha Omega Alpha. Republican. Avocations: wood carving, furniture restoration, lapidarist. Home: 2887 Forist Ln Merced CA 95340

MAZAIKA, ROBERT J., chemicals executive; b. 1934. BS in Chemistry, Boston U., 1956. With Uniroyal, Inc., Middlebury, Conn., 1956-85, Uniroyal Chem. Co., Inc., Middlebury, Conn., 1985—; with Uni Royal Chem. Corp., Middlebury, Conn., 1988—, now pres., CEO. Office: Uni Royal Chem Corp Benson Rd Middlebury CT 06749

MAZANEC, GEORGE L., natural gas company executive; b. Chgo., May 30, 1936; s. Charles and Catherine (Traczyk) M.; m. Elsa Weiffenbach, Oct. 1, 1960; children: Robert A., John C. AB in Econs., DePauw U., 1958; MBA, Harvard U., 1960. Various positions Enron Corp., Internorth Inc., 1964-82; exec. v.p. ETO Tex. Gas Resources Corp., Owensboro, Ky., 1982-85; CFO, v.p. fin. Duquesne Light Co., from 1985; formerly sr. v.p. Tex. Ea. Corp.; formerly pres. TETCO; group v.p. Panhandle Ea. Corp., Houston, 1989-91, exec. v.p. 1991—; bd. dirs. TEPPCO Ltd. Mem. Am. Gas Assn. (bd. dirs.), Ramada Club, Univ. Club, Old Baldy Club. Home: 302 Fall River Ct Houston TX 77024-5611 Office: Panhandle Ea Corp 5400 Westheimer Ct Houston TX 77056-5310

MAZANKOWSKI, DONALD FRANK, Canadian government official; b. Viking, Alta., Can., July 27, 1935; s. Frank and Dora (Lonowski) M.; m. Lorraine Poleschuk, Sept. 6, 1958; children: Gregory, Roger, Donald. Student, pub. schs., 1987; PhD in Engring (hon.), N.S. Inst. Tech.; LLD (hon.), U. Alta., 1993. MP Ho. of Commons, 1968—, chmn. com. transp., 1972-74, mem. com. govt. ops., 1976-77, mem. com. trans. and communication, 1977-79; min. of transp., min. responsible for Can. Wheat Bd. Govt. of Can., 1979-80, min. of transp. (re-drafted Nat. Transp. Act), 1984-86, dep. prime min., 1986—, govt. house leader, 1986-88, pres. Privy Coun., 1986-91, pres. Treas. Bd., 1987-88, min. responsible for privatization and regulatory affairs, 1988-91, min. of agriculture, 1988-91, min. of fin., 1991-93; mem. bd. govs. U. Alta.; mem. bd. dirs. The Vigoro Corp., Gulf Canada Resources, Great Wets Life Assurance, The Investors Group, Canadian Utilities Ltd., Shaw Comms. Inc., Weyerhaeuser Canada Ltd., Greyhound Lines of Canada, Golden Star Resources, Equimar Capital Inc. Mem. Royal Can. Legion (life). Roman Catholic. Club: Vegreville Rotary (past dir.). Lodge: KC.

MAZE, THOMAS H., engineering educator; b. St. Paul, June 1, 1952; s. Robert O. and Viola A.E. (Schultz) M.; m. Leslie Foster Smith, Aug. 2, 1979; children: Lauren L. Simonds, Julie W. Simonds. BS in Civil Engring., Iowa State U., 1975; M of Engring., Urban and Pub. Systems, U. Calif., Berkeley, 1977; PhD in Civil Engring., Mich. State U., 1982. Asst. prof. dept. civil engring. Wayne State U., 1979-82; assoc. prof. sch. civil engring. and environ. sci. U. Okla., Norman, 1982-87; prof. dept. civil and construction engring. Iowa State U., Ames, 1988—, prof. in-charge transp. planning program, 1987—, dir. Iowa transp. ctr., ctr. transp. rsch. and applied rsch., 1988—; assoc. dir. inst. urban transp., transp. rsch. ctr. Ind. U., Bloomington, 1987—; dir. Midwest Transp. Ctr., U.S. Dept. Transp.'s Univ. Transp. Ctr. Fed. Region VII, 1990—. Mem. ASCE, Am. Pub. Transit Assn., ITS Am. (founding instnl. issues com., CVO com.), Am. Pub. Works Assn. (adj. workshop faculty mem. 1986-91, exec. coun. inst. equipment svcs. 1991—), Coun. Univ. Transp., Transp. Rsch. Bd. (mem. various coms., chair 8th equipment mgmt. conf. 1990), Inst. Transp. Engrs. (assoc., mem. dept. 6 standing com., chmn. various coms., pres. U. Fla. student chpt. 1976-79), Chi Epsilon (faculty advisor U. Okla.. 1985-87), Sigma Xi. Office: Iowa State U Iowa Transp Ctr Ste 125 2521 Elwood Dr Ames IA 50010-8626

MAZEK, WARREN F(ELIX), academic administrator, economics educator; b. Pitts., Oct. 14, 1938; s. Felix Frank and Josephine Catherine (Sethner) M.; m. Nancy Lee Metcalfe, June 18, 1960 (div. Jan. 1982); children: Thomas W., Erika A., Laura J., Michael M.; m. Susan Chapman, Apr. 24, 1982; 1 child, Marissa C. AB, Washington and Jefferson Coll., 1960; MA, Ind. U., 1962; PhD, U. Pitts., 1965. Asst. prof. econs. Coll. Wooster, 1965-67; asst. prof. Fla. State U., 1967-70, assoc. prof., 1970-75, prof., 1975-86, dean coll. Social Scis., 1973-86; prof., asst. supt. acad. affairs U.S. Merchant Marine Acad., Kings Point, N.Y., 1986—. Cons. on econ. loss to legal firms, 1974—; vestryman Christ Ch., Manhasset, 1991—; chmn. Big Bend chpt. March of Dimes, Tallahassee, 1981-83. Recipient faculty research award Fla. State U., 1973-74; Resources of the Future dissertation fellow, 1964; Richard K. Mellon fellow Am. Council for Edn., 1975. Mem. Am. Assn. Higher Edn., Am. Econs. Assn., Regional Sci. Assn., Conf. Fed. Degree Granting Instrs., Assn. Acad. Affairs Adminstrs. Episcopalian. Home and Office: US Merchant Marine Acad Kings Point NY 11024

MAZENKO, GENE FRANCIS, physics educator; b. July 5, 1945; m. Judy Oakley, Aug. 9, 1969. BS in Physics, Stanford U., 1967; PhD in Physics, MIT, 1971. Rsch. assoc. dept. physics Brandeis U., Waltham, Mass., 1971-72; rsch. assoc. dept. nuc. engring. MIT, Cambridge, 1972-73; rsch. assoc. dept. applied physics Stanford (Calif.) U., 1973-74; asst. prof. dept. physics James Franck Inst., U. Chgo. 1975-80, assoc. prof., 1980-85, prof. Physics, inst. dir., 1985-92, physics 1993—, assoc. provost, 1993-95; vis. asst. prof. Dept. Physics U. Calif., San Diego, 1980; vis. scientist Theoretical physics Oxford U., 1985; cons. Argonne (Ill.) Nat. Lab., 1976-80; vis. scientist Service de Physique Theorique Ctr. d' Etudes Nucleaires de Saclay,

France, 1979. Contbr. over 90 articles to profl. jours. Alfred P. Sloan Found. fellow, 1977-81. Office: James Franck Inst 5640 S Ellis Ave Chicago IL 60637-1467

MAZER, NORMA FOX, writer; b. N.Y.C., May 15, 1931; d. Michael and Jean (Garlen) Fox; m. Harry Mazer, Feb. 12, 1950; children: Anne E., Joseph D., Susan R., Gina R. Author: I, Trissy, 1971, A Figure of Speech, 1973 (Nat. Book award nominee 1974); Saturday, the Twelfth of October, 1975 (Lewis Carroll Shelf award 1976); Dear Bill, Remember Me? and Other Stories, 1976 (N.Y. Times Notable Book 1976, ALA Notable Book 1976, Sch. Library Jour. Best Books of Yr. 1976, Christopher award 1976, Lewis Carroll Shelf award 1977); (with Harry Mazer) The Solid Gold Kid, 1978 (ALA Best Books for Young Adults 1978, Internat. Reading Assn. Children's Choice, 1979); Up in Seth's Room, 1979 (ALA Best Books for Young Adults 1979, SLJ Best Books of Yr. 1979, ALA Best of the Best Books, 1970-83); Mrs. Fish, Ape and Me, The Dump Queen, 1980 (German Children's Literature prize 1982, List of Honor Austrian Children's Books 1983); Taking Terri Mueller, 1981 (Edgar award 1982, Calif. Young Readers' Medal 1985), Summer Girls, Love Boys and Other Short Stories, 1982, When We First Met, 1982 (Iowa Teen award 1985); Someone to Love, 1983 (ALA Best Books for Young Adults 1983), Downtown, 1984 (ALA Best Books for Young Adults 1984, N.Y. Times Notable Book 1984), Supergirl The Novel, 1984, Three Sisters, 1986, A, My Name Is Ami (Internat. Reading Assn. Children's Choice, 1987), 1986, B, My Name is Bunny, 1987, After the Rain, 1987 (Newbery Honor Book, ALA Notable Book, Sch. Library Jour. Best Books 1987, ALA Best Books for Young Adults 1987, Canadian Children's Book Coun. Choice 1988, assn. Booksellers for Children Choice, 1988, Horn Book Fanfare Book 1988), Silver, 1988 (ALA Best Books for Young Adults, 1988, Iowa Teen award 1990-91), (with Harry Mazer) Heartbeat, 1989 (Internat. Reading Assn. Children's Choice 1990); editor: Waltzing on Water, 1989, C, My Name Is Cal, 1990, D, My Name Is Danita, 1991, Babyface, 1991 (Am. Booksellers pick of list 1991, Internat. Reading Assn. Tchr.'s Choice), E, My Name Is Emily, 1991, (with Harry Mazer) Bright Days, Stupid Nights, 1992 (Am. Bookseller Pick of List 1992), Out of Control, 1993 (Am. Booksellers Pick of the List 1993, ALA Best Books for Young Adults 1994); contbr. short stories to numerous mags. including Redbook, Playgirl, Voice, Ingenue, Young Miss. Home: Brown Gulf Rd Jamesville NY 13078-9636

MAZLISH, BRUCE, historian, educator; b. N.Y.C., Sept. 15, 1923; s. Louis and Lee (Reuben) M.; m. Neva Goodwin, Nov. 22, 1988; children from previous marriage: Anthony, Jared, Cordelia, Peter. B.A., Columbia U., 1944, M.A., 1947, Ph.D., 1955. Instr. history U. Maine, 1946-48, Columbia U., 1949- 50, Mass. Inst. Tech., 1950-53; dir. Am. Sch. in Madrid, Spain, 1953-55; mem. faculty Mass. Inst. Tech., 1955—, prof. history, 1965—, chmn. history sect., 1965-70, head dept. humanities, 1974-79. Author: (with J. Bronowski) The Western Intellectual Tradition, 1960, The Riddle of History, 1966, In Search of Nixon, 1972, James and John Stuart Mill: Father and Son in the 19th Century, 1975, 2d edition, 1988, The Revolutionary Ascetic, 1976, Kissinger, The European Mind in American Policy, 1976, The Meaning of Karl Marx, 1984, A New Science: The Breakdown of Connections and the Birth of Sociology, 1989, The Leader, the Led and the Psyche, 1990, The Fourth Discontinuity: The Co-Evolution of Humans and Machines, 1993; Editor: Psychoanalysis and History, 1963, rev. edit., 1971, The Railroad and the Space Program: An Exploration in Historical Analogy, 1965, (with Ralph Bultjens) Conceptualizing Global History, 1993. Bd. dirs. Rockefeller Family Fund, 1987—; v.p. Mount Desert Festival of Chamber Music, 1985—; bd. dirs. Toynbee Prize Found., 1992—. Served with inf. and OSS, AUS, 1943-45. Recipient Toynbee prize, 1986-87. Fellow Am. Acad. Arts and Scis. Clubs: Cambridge Tennis, Badminton and Tennis; Harbor (Seal Harbor, Maine). Home: 11 Lowell St Cambridge MA 02138-4725 Office: M.I.T. 77 Massachusetts Ave Cambridge MA 02139-4307

MAZO, MARK ELLIOTT, lawyer; b. Phila., Jan. 12, 1950; s. Earl and Rita (Vane) M.; m. Fern Rosalyn Litman, Aug. 19, 1973; children: Samantha Lauren, Dana Suzanne, Ross Elliott, Courtney Litman. AB, Princeton U., 1971; JD, Harvard U., 1974. Bar: D.C. 1975, U.S. Dist. Ct. D.C. 1975, U.S. Claims Ct. 1975, U.S. Ct. Appeals (D.C. cir.) 1976, U.S. Supreme Ct. 1979. Assoc. Jones, Day, Reavis & Pogue, Washington, 1974-79; assoc. Crowell & Moring, Washington, 1979-81, ptnr., 1981-90; ptnr. Hogan & Hartson, L.L.P., Washington and Paris, 1990—. Contbr. articles to profl. jours. White House intern Exec. Office of Pres., Washington, 1972. Capt. USAR, 1971-79. Mem. ABA, Harvard Law Sch. Assn., D.C. Bar Assn., Columbia Country Club, Princeton Club (N.Y.C.), Colonial Club, City Club, Phi Beta Kappa. Republican. Home: 3719 Cardiff Rd Chevy Chase MD 20815-5943 Office: Hogan & Hartson Columbia Sq 555 13th St NW Washington DC 20004-1109 also: Hogan & Hartson, 14 rue Chauveau-Lagarde, 75008 Paris France

MAZO, ROBERT MARC, chemistry educator; b. Bklyn., Oct. 3, 1930; s. Nathan and Rose Marion (Mazo) M.; m. Joan Ruth Spector, Sept. 5, 1954; children: Ruth, Jeffrey, Daniel. B.A., Harvard U., 1952; M.S., Yale U., 1953, Ph.D., 1955. Research assoc. U. Chgo. 1956-58; asst. prof. Calif. Inst. Tech., 1958-62; assoc. prof. U. Oreg., Eugene, 1962-65; prof. chemistry U. Oreg., 1965—, head chemistry dept., 1978-81, dir. Inst. Theoretical Sci., 1964-67, 84-87, assoc. dean Grad. Sch., 1967-71; program dir NSF, 1977-78; Alfred P. Sloan fellow, NSF Sr. Postdoctoral fellow, vis. prof. U. Libre de Bruxelles, Belgium, 1968-69; vis. prof. Technische Hochschule Aachen, Weizmann Inst., Rehovoth, Israel, 1981-82, U. New South Wales, Australia, 1989. Author: Statistical Mechanical Theories of Transport Processes, 1967; also research articles. NSF Postdoctoral fellow U. Amsterdam, Netherlands, 1955-56. Mem. Am. Chem. Soc., Am. Phys. Soc., AAAS, AAUP. Home: 2460 Charnelton St Eugene OR 97405-3214 Office: U Oreg Inst Theoretical Sci Eugene OR 97403

MAZRUI, ALI AL'AMIN, political science educator, researcher; b. Mombasa, Kenya, Feb. 24, 1933; came to U.S., 1960; s. Al'Amin Ali and Safia (Suleiman) M.; m. Molly Vickerman, 1962 (div. 1982); children: Jamal, Al'Amin, Kim Abubakar; m. Pauline Uti, Oct. 1991; children: Farid Chinedu, Harith Ekenechukwu. B.A. with distinction, U. Manchester, Eng., 1960; M.A., Columbia U., 1961; D.Phil., Oxford U., 1966. Lectr. Makerere U., Kampala, Uganda, 1963-65; prof. polit. sci., head dept. polit. sci., 1965-73; dean Faculty Social Scis., Makerere U., Kampala, Uganda, 1967-69; prof. polit. sci. U. Mich., Ann Arbor, 1974-91, prof. Ctr. Afroam. and African Studies, dept. polit. sci., 1974-91; Andrew D. White prof.-at-large Cornell U., Ithaca, 1986-92; research prof. polit. sci. U. Jos, Nigeria, 1981-86; Albert Schweitzer prof. humanities SUNY, Binghamton, 1989—; Albert Luthuli prof.-at-large U. Jos (Nigeria), 1991—; sr. scholar, Andrew D. White prof.-at-large emeritus Cornell U., Ithaca, 1992—; dir. Inst. Global Cultural Studies SUNY, Binghamton, 1991—; Reith lectr. BBC, London, 1979; vis. prof. various univs. including U. London, U. Chgo., Oxford U., U. Pa., Ohio State U., Manchester U., Harvard U. Nairobi U., UCLA, Northwestern U., U. Singapore, Colgate U., U. Australia, U. Cairo, Sussex U., U. Leeds, 1965—; mem. bank's coun. African advisers World Bank, Washington, 1988-91. Author: Towards A Pax Africana: A Study of Ideology and Ambition, 1967, The Anglo-African Commonwealth: Political Friction and Cultural Fusion, 1967, On Heroes and Uhuru-Worship: Essays on Independent Africa, 1967, Violence and Thought: Essays on Social Tensions in Africa, 1969, Cultural Engineering and Nation-Building in East Africa, 1972, World Culture and the Black Experience, 1974, The Political Sociology of the English Language: An African Perspective, 1975, Soldiers and Kinsmen in Uganda: The Making of a Military Ethnocracy, 1975; co-editor: (with Robert I. Rotberg) Protest and Power in Black Africa, 1970, (with Hasu Patel), Africa in World Affairs: The Next Thirty Years, 1973; editor: The Warrior Tradition in Modern Africa, 1978; sr. editor: (with T.K. Levine) The Africans: A Reader, 1986; author: The Trial of Christopher Okigbo, 1971; A World Federation of Cultures: An African Perspective, 1976; Africa's International Relations: The Diplomacy of Dependency and Change, 1977, Political Values and the Educated Class in Africa, 1978; The African Condition: A Political Diagnosis, 1980, (with Michael Tidy) Nationalism and New States in Africa, From About 1935 to the Present, 1984; narrator, presenter: The Africans: A Triple Heritage, 1986, Cultural Forces in World Politics, 1990; editor Africa since 1935 Volume VIII UNESCO General History of Africa, 1973-93; mem. editorial bd. various profl. jours., 1963—; contbr. articles to profl. publs. Fellow Ctr for Advanced Study in Behavioral Scis., Palo Alto, Calif., 1972-73; sr. fellow Hoover Instn. on War, Revolution and Peace, Stanford, Calif., 1973-74, Mich. Soc. Fellows, 1978-82. Fellow In-

ternat. Assn. Middle Eastern Studies, Ghana Acad. Arts and Scis. (hon.); mem. African Studies Assn. (exec. bd. 1975—, pres. 1978-79), Internat. Congress African Studies (v.p. 1978-85), Internat. Polit. Sci. Assn. (v.p. 1970-73), World Order Models Project (dir. African sect. 1968-83), Royal African Soc. (v.p.), Royal Commonwealth Soc. Clubs: United Kenya (Nairobi); Athenaeum (London). Office: SUNY Inst Global Cultural Studies Off Schweitzer Chair PO Box 6000 Binghamton NY 13902-6000

MAZUMDER, JYOTIRMOY, mechanical and industrial engineering educator; b. Calcutta, India, July 9, 1951; came to U.S., 1978; s. Jitendra Mohan and Gouri (Sen) M.; m. Aparajita, June 17, 1982; children: Debashis, Debayan. B in Engring., Calcutta U., 1973; diploma, PhD, Imperial Coll., London U., 1978. Rsch. scientist U. So. Calif., L.A., 1978-80; asst. prof. mechanical and indsl. engring. U. Ill., Urbana, 1980-84, assoc. prof., 1984-88, prof., 1988—; co-dir. ctr. laser aided material processing U. Ill., 1990—; dir. Quantum Laser Corp., Edison, N.J., 1982-89; pres. Laser Scis., Inc., Urbana, 1988—; vis. scholar physics dept. Stanford (Calif.) U., 1990. Author: (with others) Laser Welding; co-editor: Laser Materials Processing, 1984, 88; contbr. numerous articles to profl. jours. Fellow Am. Soc. of Metals and Laser Inst. of Am. (life, sr. editor Jour. Laser Application); mem. Am. Metallurgical Engrs. (phys. mets. com. 1980—), Optical Soc. Am. Achievements include non-equilibrium synthesis of Ni-Cr-Al-Hf alloy by laser; weld pool visualization system for measurement of free surface deformation. Office: U Ill Dept Mech and Ind Engring 1206 W Green St Urbana IL 61801-2906

MAZUR, ALLAN CARL, sociologist, engineer, educator; b. Chgo., Mar. 20, 1939; s. Joseph and Esther (Markowitz) M.; m. Minnette Albrecht, Jan. 21, 1968; children—Julie Elizabeth, Rachel Lee. B.S., Ill. Inst. Tech., 1961; M.S., UCLA, 1964; Ph.D., Johns Hopkins U., 1969. Research engr. North Am. Aviation Co., Los Angeles, 1961-64; instr. polit. sci. Mass. Inst. Tech., 1966-67; ops. research analyst Lockheed Missile & Space Corp., Sunnyvale, Calif., 1967-68; asst. prof. sociology Stanford U., 1968-71; mem. faculty Syracuse U., N.Y., 1971—; prof. pub. affairs Syracuse U., 1992—. Co-author: Biology and Social Behavior, 1972; author: Dynamics of Technical Controversy, 1981, Global Social Problems, 1991; contbr. articles to profl. jours. Fellow AAAS; mem. Am. Sociol. Assn. Jewish. Home: 246 Scottholm Ter Syracuse NY 13224-1738 Office: Syracuse U Maxwell School Syracuse NY 13244

MAZUR, ERIC, physicist, educator; b. Amsterdam, The Netherlands, Nov. 14, 1954; came to U.S., 1982; s. Peter and Hélène E.C. (Contamine) M.; m. Angela B. Romijn, July 14, 1984; children: Natalie I., Marc. BA in Physics and Astronomy, U. Leiden, 1975, MS in Physics, 1977, PhD, 1981. Research fellow Harvard U., Cambridge, Mass., 1982-84, asst. prof., 1984-88, assoc. prof., 1988-90; prof. physics and Gordon McKay prof. applied physics Harvard U., 1990—; cons. N.E. Rsch. Assocs., Woburn, Mass., 1985-89. Contbr. articles to profl. jours. Recipient Presidential Young Investigator award, 1988. Fellow. Am. Phys. Soc., Optical Soc. Am. Avocations: photography, gardening, sewing, coaching wrestling, dancing. Office: Harvard U 29 Oxford St Cambridge MA 02138-2901

MAZUR, JAY J., trade union official. Ba in Indsl. Relations, CUNY, 1965; MA in Labor Studies, Rutgers U., 1977. Dir. orgn. local 40 Internat. Ladies Garment Workers Union, N.Y.C., 1955-59, dir. orgn. local 23, 1959-64, asst. mgr. local 23-25, 1964-77, mgr. sec. local 23-25, 1977-83, gen. sec.-treas., 1983-86, pres., 1986—; v.p. exec. council AFL-CIO, Washington, 1986—, N.Y. State exec. council, Albany; mem. exec. council Indsl. Union Dept., Washington, 1984—; mem. exec. bd. Fiber, Fabric and Apparel Coalition, Washington, 1986—; bd. dirs. Occupational Health Legal Rights Fund, Washington. V.p. Nat. Immigration Refugee and Citizenship Forum, Washington; bd. dirs. Regional Plan Assn., N.Y.C., 1983, Spl. Contbn. Fund NAACP, Balt., 1987. Avocations: music, jogging, gardening. Office: Internat Ladies Garment Workers Union 1710 Broadway New York NY 10019-5254*

MAZUR, MICHAEL, artist; b. N.Y.C., Nov. 2, 1935; s. Burton Boris and Helen (Isaacs) M.; m. Gail Lewis Beckwith, Dec. 28, 1958; children: Daniel Isaac, Kathe Elizabeth. BA, Amherst Coll., 1958; BFA, Yale U., 1959, MFA, 1961. Asst. prof. fine arts Brandeis U., Waltham, Mass., 1965-76; instr. RISD, 1962-65; vis. prof. Yale U. Sch. Art and Arch., 1972, 81, Queens Coll., CUNY, 1973, U. Calif., Santa Barbara, 1974-75, Boston U., 1982; lectr. Mus. Fine Arts, Boston, Brown U., U. Calif., Berkeley, New Sch. for Social Rsch., Bennington Coll., U. Iowa, Boston U., 1994-95, Katonah Mus., N.Y. Studio Sch., 1994; vis. lectr. Carpenter Ctr., Harvard U., 1976, 78, 89, 92, 94, 95, others; illustrator The Inferno of Dante, Farrar, Strans & Giroux, 1994. Exhibited in one-man shows at Kornblee Gallery, N.Y.C., 1960, 63, 66, Boris Mirski, Boston, 1963, 65, Phila. Print Club, 1964, Silvermine Guild, 1964, Fla. State U., 1966, Shoemaker Gallery Juniata Coll., 1966, Alpha Gallery, Boston, 1967, 68, 74, OGL Gallery, Los Angeles, Calif., 1968, Rose Art Mus., Brandeis U., 1969, A.A.A. Gallery, 1969, Fogg Art Mus., 1969, A.A.A. Gallery, 1969, Fogg Art Mus., 1969, Contemporary Art, Boston, 1970, Terry Dintenfass, N.Y.C., 1974, 76, Alpha Gallery, Boston, 1974, Picker Gallery, Colgate U., 1973, Trinity Coll., 1976, Ohio State U., 1975, Robert Miller Gallery, N.Y.C., 1977, 80, Harkus-Krakow, Boston, 1977, 79, 80, Pace Gallery, N.Y.C., 1980, John Stoller, Mpls., 1981, 85, 88, 91, William and Mary Coll., 1981, Ronald Greenberg, St. Louis, 1981, Janus Gallery, L.A., 1982, 84, 88, Barbara Mathes Gallery, N.Y.C., 1984, 86, Barbara Krakow Gallery, Boston, 1984, 86, 89, 91, 93, 95, Art Club Chgo., 1985, Beaver Coll., 1985, Joe Fawbush, N.Y., 1987, 88, Jan Turner Gallery, L.A., 1988, Butler Gallery, Houston, 1989, Mary Ryan Gallery, N.Y.C., 1990, 94, 95; exhibited group shows at, Mus. Modern Art, 1964, 75, Bklyn. Mus., 1960, 62, 64, 66, 76, 80, 84, 86, Fogg Art Mus., 1966, 76, 94, Art. Inst. Chgo., 1964, Pa. Acad., 1966, 93, Phila. Mus., 1966, 88, Boston Mus. Fine Arts., 1967, 68, 76, 78, 80, 90-91, 92, DeCordova Mus., Lincoln, Mass., 1965-67, 75, 86, 87, Whitney Mus. Am. Art, 1965, 81, 90, 92, Nat. Inst. Arts and Letters, 1965, 74, 80, 86, Silvermine Guild, 1965, Print Biennial of Americas, Santiago, Chile, 1965, Paris Biennale, 1969, Venice Biennale, 1970, Finch Coll. Mus., 1971-72, 2d and 3d Biennial Graphic Art, Cali, Colombia, N.A.D. Ann., 1974, Butler Inst., Youngstown, Ohio, 1974, Ball State U., 1974, America-1976, Sense of Place, Met. Mus., N.Y.C., 1979, 80, Montreal Mus. Fine Arts, 1977, Palais Royale, Brussels, 1979, Claude Bernard, Paris, 1980, Alan Frumkin, N.Y.C., 1981, 82, Madison Art Ctr., 1989, Nat. Gallery of Art, Washington, 1990, Pratt Mus., N.Y.C., 1990; traveling exhbns. include, Bicentennial Exhbn., 1976, State Arts Councils, Iowa, Kans., Mo., Nebr., 1973, Am. Monotypes, Smithsonian Instn., 1977; represented in permanent collections, Met. Mus., N.Y.C., Mus. Modern Art, Smith Coll. Art Mus., Library Congress, Fogg Art Mus., Art Inst. Chgo., Whitney Mus., Los Angeles County Art Mus., Mus. R.I. Sch. Design, Oreg. Art Mus., U. Maine, Mpls. Inst., Pa. State U., Toledo Art Mus., Phila. Art Mus., U. Ohio Westminster Found., Boston Mus. Fine Arts, Boston Pub. Library, Bklyn. Mus., Addison Gallery, Andover Acad., Yale Art Gallery, Montreal Mus. Fine Arts; (Recipient 2d prize Soc. Am. Graphic Artists 1963, Nat. Inst. Arts and Letters award 1965). Co-founder Artists Against Racism and the War, 1968; bd. dirs. Mass. Arts and Humanities Found., The Artists Found., Fine Arts Work Ctr., Provincetown, Mass.; mem. Mass. Coun. on Arts and Humanities; mem. Mass. Coun. on Arts and Humanities; mem. Pennell com. Libr. of Congress, 1983-93; founder, dir. Art for Nuclear Weapons Freeze, 1983-84, New Provincetown Print Project, 1990-95. Grantee Tiffany Found., 1964, Tamarind Lithography Workshop, 1968; Guggenheim Found. fellow, 1964-65; winner numerous purchase awards. Home: 5 Walnut Ave Cambridge MA 02140-2706 also: 561 Commercial St Provincetown MA 02657-1724

MAZUR, RHODA HIMMEL, federation president; b. Bklyn., July 4, 1929; d. Morris and Nadie (Himmel) Himmel; m. Marvin Irwin Mazur, June 7, 1952; children: Jody, Amy, Leslie, Eric. Student, CCNY, CUNY. Pres. United Jewish Community Va. Peninsula Inc, Newport News, 1985-88; pres. Friends of the Homeless, Inc., 1993—, also bd. dirs.; chmn. Social Action Com. Rodef Sholom Temple, 1990-93 (com. mem. 1990—). bd. dirs. Anti-Defamation League Regional Bd., Richmond, 1985—, v.p., 1983-85, Newports News Social Services Adv. Bd, Newport News, 1979-84, Council of Jewish Fedns., 1975-85. Gov's. Commn. Status Women, Richmond, 1981-84, Nat. Council Christians and Jews, 1985—; mem. adv. bd. Friends of the Homeless, 1987—; Associated Marine Inst.. 1988—; active Newport News Task Force on Emergency Housing, 1984-85; chair fin. com. Peninsula Peace Edn. Ctr., Newport News, 1984-85. Recipient Young

Leadership award Jewish Fedn. Newport News, 1968, Brotherhood citation Nat. Conf. Christians and Jews, 1984. Democrat. Avocations: hand crafts, reading, music, photography. Home: 114 James River Dr Newport News VA 23601-3604 Office: United Jewish Community Va Peninsula Inc 2700 Spring Rd Newport News VA 23606-2514

MAZUREK, JOSEPH P., lawyer, state senator; b. San Diego, July 27, 1948; B.A., U. Mont., 1970, J.D., 1975; m. Patty Mazurek; 3 children. Bar: Mont. 1975; atty. Gough, Shanahan, Johnson, and Waterman, Helena, Mont.; mem. Mont. Senate from 23d Dist., 1981-92; Senate pres., 1992-; atty. gen., State of Mont., 1993—; mem. Revenue Oversight Com., 1983-92; chmn. Senate Judiciary Com.; assoc. editor Mont. Law Rev., 1974-75. Served with U.S. Army, 1970-72. Mem. ABA, Beta Gamma Sigma, Phi Delta Phi, Phi Delta Theta. Office: Justice Bldg PO Box 201401 215 N Sanders 3rd Fl Helena MT 59620

MAZURSKY, PAUL, screenwriter, theatrical director and producer; b. Bklyn., Apr. 25, 1930; s. David and Jean (Gerson) M.; m. Betsy Purdy, Mar. 12, 1953; children—Meg, Jill. B.A., Bklyn. Coll., 1951. Actor state, TV and films, 1951—, including film Deathwatch, Miami Rhapsody, 1995, Faithful, 1995; night club comedian, 1954-60; writer Danny Kaye Show, 1963-67; co-writer film I Love You, Alice B. Toklas, 1968; writer, dir. films Bob — Carol & Ted & Alice, 1969, Alex in Wonderland, 1970, Blume in Love, 1972, Harry & Tonto, 1973, Next Stop, Greenwich Village, 1976, An Unmarried Woman, 1977-78, Millie & Phil, 1979-80, Tempest, 1982, Moscow on the Hudson, 1984; sriter, producer, dir. films Down and Out in Beverly Hills, 1986, Moon Over Parador, 1988; co-scriptwriter, producer, dir. film Enemies, A Love Story, 1989, Scenes from a Mail, 1990, The Picke, 1992.

MAZZA, DAVID LAWRENCE, university athletic director, educator; b. Stamford, Conn., May 5, 1942; s. Dominec Lawrence and Clara Mazza; m. Deborah Lee Simpkins, June 24, 1972; 1 chld, Elizabeth Joy. BA, Carroll Coll., 1964; MEd, U. Bridgeport, 1970; MA, Fordham U., 1968; PhD, St. John's U., 1978. Athletic dir. U. Conn., Stamford, 1966—; tchr. Stamford Pub. Schs., 1964—; real estate agt. Dollar Dry Dock Real Estate, Trumbull, Conn., 1989—; mgr. Long Ridge Club, Stamford, 1978—, also bd. dirs.; cons. New Eng. Tennis Co., Cheshire, Conn., 1991—. Mem. NEA, Conn. Edn. Assn., Nat. Assn. Realtors, Conn. Assn. Realtors, KC. Avocations: fitness exercise, reading, tennis, jogging. Office: Dollar Dry Dock Real Estate 921 White Plains Rd Trumbull CT 06611-4562

MAZZA, THOMAS CARMEN, lawyer; b. Erie, Pa., Feb. 14, 1940; s. Carmen J. and Helen (Fronius) M.; m. Lois Bigbie, June 12, 1993; children: Elizabeth Williamson Burnette, Thomas Denholm. BA, Yale U., 1961, LLB, 1964. Bar: N.Y. 1965; U.S. Ct. Appeals (2nd cir.) 1965, U.S. Dist. Ct. (so. and ea. dists.) N.Y. 1976, U.S. Ct. Appeals (11th cir.) 1980, U.S. Dist. Ct. (no. dist.) N.Y. 1982, U.S. Supreme Ct. 1982. Assoc. Dewey Ballantine, N.Y.C. and Brussels, 1964-72; ptnr. Dewey Ballantine, N.Y.C., 1972—. Vestryman Trinity Parish, N.Y.C., 1976-83, 86-93, 94—; bd. dirs. St. Margaret's House Housing Corp., N.Y.C., 1977-93. Fellow Am. Coll. Investment Counsel; mem. ABA, N.Y. State Bar Assn., Assn. Bar City of N.Y., Collectors Club N.Y. (gov. 1989—, pres. 1993—). Episcopalian. Avocations: music, philately. Office: Dewey Ballantine 1301 Avenue Of The Americas New York NY 10019-6092 also: The Collectors Club Inc 22 E 35th St New York NY 10016-3806

MAZZAFERRI, ERNEST LOUIS, physician, educator; b. Cleve., Sept. 27, 1936; s. Joseph and Nanetta (Marinelli) M.; m. Florence Mildred Marolt, Nov. 23, 1957; children: Patricia Marie Herbers, Michael Louis, Sharon Lynne Brown, Ernest Louis. BS cum laude, John Carroll U., 1958; MD, Ohio State U., 1962. Diplomate: Am. Bd. Internal Medicine. Intern Ohio State U. Hosps., Columbus, 1962-63; resident Ohio State U. Hosps., 1963-64, 66-68; asst. prof. medicine Ohio State U., 1968-70, assoc. prof., 1973-76, prof., 1976-79, dir. endocrinology and metabolism, 1975-78; acting dean U. Nev., Reno, 1979-81; prof., chmn. dept. medicine U. Nev., 1978-84, prof. physiology, 1982-84; prof., chmn. dept. medicine, prof. physiology Ohio State U., Columbus, 1984—; pres. Dept. of Medicine Found., 1986—. Author: Endocrinology Case Studies, 3d edit., 1985, Internal Medicine Pearls, 1993; editor: Textbook of Endocrinology, 3d edit., 1986, Contemporary Internal Medicine, 1988, 3d edit., 1990, Advances in Endocrinology and Metabolism, Vol. 4, 1993, Endocrine Tumors, 1993; mem. sci. adv. bd. We. Jour. Medicine, 1978-84; mem. editorial bd. Jour. Lab. Clin. Medicine, 1987—; Hosp. Practice; contbr. articles to profl. jours. Chmn. Gov.'s Com. on Radiation Fallout in Nev., 1980-84, hosp. ethics com. Ohio State U.; mem. Sec. of Energy Dose Assessment Adv. Com., 1980-84, Agy. for Health Care Policy, Rsch. Cataract Guideline Com., 1991-92. Lt. col. USAF, 1964-72; col. USAR. Decorated Air Force Commendation medal, Meritorious Svc. medal. Fellow ACP (gov. for Nev. 1984-85, chmn. clin. efficacy assessment program com. 1992—; mem. health and pub. policy com., edn. policy com.); mem. AMA, Am. Thyroid Assn., Am. Diabetes Assn. (pres. Ohio affiliate 1988-89), Western Soc. Clin. Investigation, Endocrine Soc., Western Assn. Physicians, Am. Clin. and Climatol. Assn., Ctrl. Soc. Clin. Rsch., Alpha Omega Alpha. Republican. Roman Catholic. Research in treatment thyroid cancer, gastric inhibitory polypeptide and diabetes mellitus. Home: 2481 Slate Run Rd Columbus OH 43220-2850 Office: Ohio State U Means Hall 1655 Upham Dr Columbus OH 43210-1251 *Success, like every other human experience, is relative, measured against shifting standards and subject to the scrutiny of time. One must strike a fine balance—self certainty against external review—that permits the full expression of new ideas enriched by the best and time-worn thoughts of others.*

MAZZARELLA, ANDREW JAMES, automotive products executive, accountant; b. Oak Park, Ill., Aug. 12, 1950; s. Paul and Doloros (Arnold) M.; m. Christine Mildred Mengler, Aug. 13, 1972; children: Kristen, Karen, Kathryn, Paul. BS in Acctg., U. Ill., 1972. Controller Braker Parts Co., Litchfield, Ill., 1972-79, Kravex Mfg., Miami, Fla., 1979-81; group controller Echlin Inc., Branford, Conn., 1981-85, corp. controller, 1985-90; chief fin. officer Go/Dan Industries, New Haven, 1990—; bd. dirs. Friendship House, New Haven. Mem. Nat. Assn. Accts., Fin. Execs. Inst. Home: 12 Laura Rd Hamden CT 06514-1102 Office: Go/Dan Industries 100 Gando Dr New Haven CT 06513-1049

MAZZARELLA, DAVID, newspaper editor; b. 1938. With AP, Lisbon, N.Y.C., Rome, 1962-70, Daily American, Rome, 1971-75, Gannett News, D.C., 1976-77, The Bridgewater, Bridgewater, N.J., 1977-83; now editor USA Today, Arlington, Va. Office: USA Today 1000 Wilson Blvd Arlington VA 22229*

MAZZE, EDWARD MARK, marketing consultant, business educator; b. N.Y.C., Feb. 14, 1941; s. Harry Alan and Mollie (Schneider) M.; m. Sharon Sue Hastings, Sept. 7, 1967; children—Candace, Thomas. B.B.A., City U. N.Y., 1961, M.B.A., 1962; Ph.D., Pa. State U., 1966. Lectr. bus. adminstrn. CCNY, 1961-62; bus. cons., 1961—; pres., dir. JET Corp., East Orange, N.J., 1976-79; instr. bus. Pa. State U., 1963-66; assoc. prof. mktg. U. Detroit, 1966-68; assoc. prof., dir. spl. programs W.Va. U., 1968-70; prof. bus. adminstrn., coordinator mktg. program Va. Poly. Inst. and State U., Blacksburg, 1970-75; v.p. adminstrv. services, dean Sch. Bus., Seton Hall U., South Orange, N.J., 1975-79; dean sch. bus. adminstrn. Temple U., Phila., 1979-86, prof. mktg. and internat. bus., 1979-93; dean Belk Coll. Bus. Adminstrn., prof. mktg. U. N.C.-Charlotte, Charlotte, 1993—; chmn. bd. William Penn Bank, Phila., 1985-87; bd. dirs. Technitrol, Inc.; mem. dist. export coun. U.S. Dept. Commerce, 1978-80, 83-93; mem. panel trustees U.S. Bankruptcy Ct., 1984—. Author: International Business: Articles and Essays, 1963, Readings in Organization and Management, 1963, Marketing in Action, 1963, Case Histories in Sales Management, 1965, Sales Management: Theory and Practice, 1965, International Marketing Adminstration, 1967, Introduction to Marketing, 1970, Marketing in Turbulent Times: The Challenges and the Opportunities, 1975, Personal Selling: Choice Against Chance, 1976; mem. editorial bd. Jour. Access. and Bus., 1976-80, Indsl. Mktg. Mgmt., 1977—, Jour. Internat. Bus. Studies, 1978-82, Jour. Acad. Mktg. Sci., 1980-91, Jour. Mktg. Edn., 1985-94, Jour. Global Mktg., 1987—; contbr. articles to profl. and trade jours. Trustee Phila. Home Care, 1984-89, Manor Coll., 1985-92, Thomas A. Edison State Coll. Found., 1987-93, Delaware Valley Coll. Sci. and Agr., 1991—, Pa. Inst. Tech., 1992-93; chmn. econ. devel. adv. com. Village South Orange, 1977-80; mem., vice-chmn. Bd.

Suprs. Doylestown Twp., 1980-81. Ford. Found. fellow, 1962-63. Mem. Am. Mktg. Assn., Acad. Internat. Bus., Nat. Assn. Corp. Dirs., Acad. Mktg. Sci., City Club, Tower Club, Beta Gamma Sigma, Alpha Kappa Psi, Pi Sigma Epsilon, Pi Kappa Alpha. Home: 6805 Linkside Ct Charlotte NC 28277-0394 Office: Univ NC Charlotte NC 28223

MAZZE, ROGER STEVEN, medical educator, researcher; b. N.Y.C., May 14, 1943; s. Harry Alan and Mollie (Schneider) M.; m. Rochelle Linda March, Dec. 28, 1969; children—Aaron, Rebekkah. B.A., Queens Coll., 1965, M.A., 1967; Ph.D., U. Ill., 1971. Fellow in social psychiatry Brandeis U., Waltham, Mass., 1971; chmn. urban studies Fordham U., N.Y.C., 1970-75; from assoc. to full prof. epidemiology and social medicine Einstein Coll. Medicine, N.Y.C., 1975-87, exec. dir. Diabetes Research and Tng. Ctr., 1980-88; sr. v.p. research and devel. Internat. Diabetes Ctr., Mpls., 1988—; clin. prof. U. Minn. Med. Sch., 1988—; v.p. Park Nicollet Med. Found., Mpls., 1993—; adv. bd. Nat. Diabetes Info. Clearinghouse, Washington, 1980-84, Pa. Diabetes Acad., Harrisburg, 1982—; co-dir. WHO Coll. Ctr. in Diabetes Care, Edn. and Computer Sci., Mpls., 1988—. Author: Narcotics, Knowledge and Nonsense, 1977, Professional Education in Diabetes, 1983, Frontiers of Diabetes Research, 1990, Staged Diabetes Management, 1995; editor: Practical Diabetes, 1987-89; contbr. articles to profl. jours. Active Internat. Diabetes Fedn., European Assn. for Study of Diabetes; chmn. Am. Diabetes Assn. Named Disting. vis. Scientist CDC, 1983-84; Hoechst lectr. Australian Diabetes Assn., 1985, 87, Japanese Diabetes Assn., 1983, 88, 93, 94, Polish Diabetes Assn., 1993, 94, 95; named Best Spkr. of the Yr., Soc. for Clin. Chemistry, 1991; grantee NIH, 1977—, ADA, 1991—, Juvenile Diabetes Found., 1992—. Mem. Am. Diabetes Assn. (chmn.), Itnernat. Diabetes Fedn., European Assn. for Study Diabetes. Home: 5870 Boulder Bridge Ln Excelsior MN 55331-7969 Office: Internat Diabetes Ctr 3800 Park Nicollet Blvd Minneapolis MN 55416-2699

MAZZIA, VALENTINO DON BOSCO, physician, educator, lawyer; b. N.Y.C., Feb. 17, 1922; s. Alexander Lloret and Francesca (D'Alessandro) M.; m. Rosana Sgarlata, Sept. 2, 1974; children: Lisa Mitchell, Donald Mitchell, Christopher Mitchell. B.S. cum laude, CCNY, 1943; M.D., NYU, 1950; postgrad., U. So. Calif. Sch. Law, 1973-74; J.D., U. Denver, 1978. Bar: Colo. 1978, U.S. Dist. Ct. Colo. 1978, Calif. 1979, U.S. Dist. Ct. (So. dist.) Calif. 1979, U.S. Supreme Ct. 1982, Ala. 1984, U.S. Dist. Ct. Ala. 1984, N.Y. 1987; diplomate: Am. Bd. Anesthesiology, Am. Bd. Law in Medicine. Intern Kings County Hosp., Bklyn., 1950-52; resident N.Y. Hosp., N.Y.C., 1952-54; asst. prof. Cornell U. Med. Coll., N.Y.C., 1952-61; prof. anesthesiology, chmn. dept. Coll. Medicine NYU, N.Y.C., 1961-72, prof. anesthesiology, chmn. dept. Postgrad. Med. Sch., 1961-72, prof. anesthesiology Coll. Dentistry, 1962-72; dir. attending anesthesiologist Univ. Hosp., N.Y.C., 1961-72; vis.-in-charge, dir. anesthesia service Bellevue Hosp. Center, N.Y.C., 1961-72; cons. N.Y. VA Hosp., Manhattan State Hosp., 1961-72; dir. anesthesiology Los Angeles County/Martin Luther King Jr. Gen. Hosp., 1971-73; chief anesthesiology Kern County Gen. Hosp., Bakersfield, Calif., 1973; practice medicine specializing in anesthesiology Bakersfield, Los Angeles; solo practice Las Vegas; staff 35 hosps., 1973-75; prof. anesthesiology U. Colo. Health Scis. Center and Dental Sch., Denver, 1976-83; clin. prof. U. Colo. Health Scis. Center and Dental Sch., 1984-88; clin. dir. operating room for anesthesiology Univ. Hosp., 1976-82; vis. prof., chmn. anesthesiology Charles R. Drew Post Grad. Med. Sch., Los Angeles, 1971-73; vis. prof. anesthesiology UCLA, 1972; asst. med. examiner, cons. forensic anesthesiology Office of Chief Med. Examiner, N.Y.C., 1962-73; dep. coroner, asst. med. examiner County Coroner's Office, Los Angeles, 1973-82; of counsel Cunningham Bounds Yance Crowder & Brown, Mobile, Ala. Coauthor: Practical Anesthesiology, 1962—; contbr. chpts. to books, articles to profl. jours. Served with USAAF, 1943-45; med. dir. USPHS Res. Fellow Am. Coll. Anesthesiology, N.Y. Acad. Medicine, Am. Coll. Chest Physicians, Am. Osteo. Coll. Anesthesiologists, Am. Coll. Legal Medicine; mem. Harvey Soc., Assn. Trial Lawyers Am., Ala. Trial Lawyers Assn., Phi Beta Kappa, Sigma Xi, Alpha Omega Alpha. Club: New York Athletic (life). Office: 120 E 87th St Apt P14D New York NY 10128-1101 Office: 1601 Dauphin St Mobile AL 36604 *When one's progress appears to be blocked by circumstances or people, change location or vocation.*

MAZZILLI, PAUL JOHN, investment banker; b. White Plains, N.Y., Dec. 4, 1948; s. Philip Joseph and Sara (Bialick) M.; m. Sharon Pickett, May 23, 1986; children: Meredith Paige, Nicholas Parker. BS in Indsl. Engring., Syracuse U., 1970; MBA, Columbia U., 1973. Lic. real estate agt., N.Y. Budget analyst The Pentagon, Washington, 1972; mgr. planning and analysis Xerox Corp., White Plains, 1973-75; mgr. planning and analysis Morgan Stanley & Co., Inc., N.Y.C., 1975-78, dir. planning and analysis, 1979-80, exec. asst. to oper. com., 1981-82, new product specialist, 1982-83, v.p hedging products, 1984-85, prin. pension svcs. group, 1986-87, head stategy group for Employee Stock Ownership Plan, 1988-91, head of Equity Derivatives Corp. Svc. Group, 1992-93; prin. Equity Capital Markets Svcs., 1993—; pres. Wall St. Planning Group, N.Y.C., 1979-80; adj. prof. fin. Mercy Coll., Dobbs Ferry, N.Y., 1977-79; mem. tax rev. bd. Town of Greenburgh, N.Y., 1972-77. Coun. mem. Jr. Achievement N.Y., 1978-79; elected Westchester County Rep. Com., 1970-75. Capt. USAFR, 1970-76. Mem. Nat. Assn. Securities Dealers (registered rep.), Columbia U. Alumni Assn. (rep. 1979-80), Columbia Bus. Sch. Alumni Assn. (bd. dirs., v.p. 1978-81), Sleepy Hollow Country Club, Shattemuc Yacht Club (Ossining, N.Y.). Home: Tower Hill Rd Scarborough NY 10510 Office: Morgan Stanley & Co Inc 1251 Ave Of The Americas New York NY 10020-1104

MAZZO, KAY, ballet dancer, educator; b. Evanston, Ill., Jan. 17, 1946; d. Frank Alfred and Catherine M. (Hengel) M.; m. Albert C. Bellas, 1978; children: Andrew, Kathryn. Student, Sch. Am. Ballet, 1959-61. Profl. debut in ballets U.S.A. 1961, touring Europe with co., performing for Pres. Kennedy at White House, 1961, joined N.Y.C. Ballet, 1962-80, soloist, 1965-69, prin. ballerina, 1969-80, prin. roles in world premiere of ballets including Tschaikowsky Suite No: #3, 1970, PAMTGG, 1971, Stravinsky Violin Concerto, 1972, Scherzo A La Russe, 1972, Duo Concertant, 1972, Sheherazade, 1975, Union Jack, 1976, Vienna Waltzes, 1977, Davidsbundlertanze, 1980; ballet tchr. Sch. Am. Ballet, 1980—; appeared as guest artist in leading roles with numerous cos. including Boston Ballet, Washington Ballet, Berlin Ballet, Geneva Ballet; appeared on TV in U.S., Can., Fed. Republic Germany. Recipient Mademoiselle Merit award 1970. Office: Sch Am Ballet 70 Lincoln Center Plz New York NY 10023-6548*

MAZZOCCO, ANGELO, language educator; b. Cerreto di Vastogirardi, Isernia, Italy, May 13, 1936; came to U.S., 1954, naturalized, 1957; s. Giuseppe and Ida (Rotolo) M.; m. Elizabeth Hunt Davis, Oct. 7, 1990; children: Michael Ray, Marco Angelo. BS, BA, Ohio State U., 1959, MA, 1963; PhD in Romance Langs. and Lits., U. Calif., Berkeley, 1973. instr. Spanish John Carroll U., Cleve., 1962-65; teaching asst. Italian U. Calif., Berkeley, 1966-69; asst. prof. Italian No. Ill. U., DeKalb, 1970-75; asst. prof. Spanish and Italian Mt. Holyoke Coll., South Hadley, Mass., 1975-78, assoc. prof., 1978-83, prof., 1983—, chair dept. 1981-84, 93—; chair romance langs. and lits., 1989-93; assoc. Columbia U. Renaissance Seminar. Author: Linguistic Theories in Dante/Humanists, 1993; contbr. chpts. in books and articles to profl. jours. Travel grantee Am. Coun. Learned Socs., 1985, NEH Italian Humanism summer sem. fellow, 1981, Italian-Am. Traveling fellow U. Calif., 1969-70; Gladys Krieble Found. Rsch. grantee, 1993-94. Mem. MLA (exec. com. Medieval and Renaissance Italian Lit. 1981-85, assembly del. 1985-87), Am. Assn. of Tchrs. of Italian, Dante Soc. Am. (coun. assoc. 1985-90, coun. 1994—), Medieval Acad. Renaissance Soc. Am., Internat. Assn. Neo-Lating Studies, Internat. Assn. History Lang. Socs., Assn. Internat. Studi di Lingua a Letteratura Italiana, Internat. Soc. Classical Tradition, Am. Boccaccio Assn. (v.p. 1982-83), Am. Assn. Italian Studies, N.E. MLA Am. Office: Mt Holyoke Coll Dept Spanish Italian South Hadley MA 01075

MAZZOLA, ANTHONY THOMAS, editor, art consultant, designer; b. Passaic, N.J., June 13, 1923; s. Thomas and Jennie (Failla) M.; m. Michele Morgan, Nov. 18, 1967; children: Anthony Thomas II, Marc Eden, Alisa Morgan. Grad. Cooper Union Art Sch., 1948. Art dir. Street & Smith Publs., N.Y.C., 1948, Town and Country mag. (pub. by Hearst Corp.), N.Y.C., 1948-65; editor-in-chief Town and Country mag. (pub. by Hearst Corp.), 1965-72, Harpers Bazaar, 1972-92; pres. Anthony Mazzola Design Corp., N.Y.C., 1963—; creative cons. Hearst Mags., 1992—; editorial dir. 125 Great Moments of Harper's Bazaar, 1991-94, Town & Country 150th Anniversary, 1994—; cons. designer United Nations Childrens' Fund,

Assn. Jr. Leagues Am., Columbia Pictures Corp., Sells Spltys., Gen. Foods, Paramount Pictures, Princess Marcella Borghese, Inc., Huntington Hartford, Ltd., N.Y. World's Fair, 1965. Exhibited, Art Dirs. Club N.Y., ann. exhbns., 1948—. Served with AUS, 1943-46. Decorated Knight Officer of Order of Merit Italy; recipient Bronze Star, Certificate of Merit awards N.Y. Art Dirs. Club; medal Art Dirs. Club N.Y.C., 1955. Office: Town & Country 150th Anniversary 1790 Broadway New York NY 10019-5905

MAZZOLA, CLAUDE JOSEPH, physicist, small business owner; b. Newton, Mass., May 24, 1936; s. Gradinola and Anne (Cicconi) M.; m. Helen Alamanos, July 25, 1965; children: Peppina, Jean-Claude. BS in Physics, Boston Coll., 1959; postgrad. in Physics, MIT, 1961-62. Jr. engr. Lab. for Electronics, Boston, 1959-61; scientist AVCO R&D, Wilmington, Mass., 1961-62; engr. Space Scis., Waltham, Mass., 1962-63, BBN, Cambridge, Mass., 1963-72; staff engr. Edo, College Point, N.Y., 1972-82; engr. Sperry, Great Neck, N.Y., 1982-89; sole proprietor Namlak, Mamaroneck, N.Y., 1989—. Author: Active Sound Absorption, 1993; patentee Magnetic Storage Device (floppy disc), 1963; contbr. articles to profl. jours., papers to sci. confs. and meetings. Mem. IEEE. Republican. Roman Catholic. Avocations: jogging, skiing, sailing, foreign travel. Home: 106 Lawn Ter Mamaroneck NY 10543-4023 Office: Namlak PO Box 804 Mamaroneck NY 10543-0804

MAZZOLA, JOHN WILLIAM, former performing arts center executive, consultant; b. Bayonne, N.J., Jan. 20, 1928; s. Roy Stephen and Eleanor Burnett (Davis) M.; m. Sylvia Drulie, Mar. 7, 1959; children: Alison, Amy. AB, Tufts U., 1949; LLD, Fordham U., 1952. Bar: N.Y. 1956. Mem. firm Milbank, Tweed, Hadley & McCloy, N.Y.C., 1952-64; sec., exec. v.p. Lincoln Center for Performing Arts, N.Y.C., 1964-68; gen. mgr., chief exec. officer Lincoln Center for Performing Arts, 1969-70, mng. dir., chief exec. officer, 1970-77, pres., chief exec. officer, 1977-84; cons. performing arts ctrs. in U.S. and abroad, also motion pictures, non-profit orgns. Bd. dirs. various charitable orgns.; mem. adv. bd. U. S.C. Koger Arts Ctr. With CIC. U.S. Army, 1953-55. Decorated cavaliere ufficiale Ordine al Merito della Repubblica Italiana; Ordre des Arts et des Lettres France; Benjamin Franklin fellow Royal Soc. Arts. Mem. Watch Hill Yacht Club, Misquamicut Club (R.I.). Episcopalian. Home: 12 Beekman Pl New York NY 10022-8059

MAZZONE, A. DAVID, federal judge; b. Everett, Mass., June 3, 1928; s. A. Marino and Philomena M.; m. Eleanor G. Stewart, May 10, 1951; children: Margaret Clark, Andrew David, John Stewart, Jan Eleanor, Martha Ann, Robert Joseph, Carolyn Cook. B.A., Harvard U., 1950; J.D., DePaul U., 1957. Bar: Ill. 1957, Mass. 1959, U.S. Supreme Ct. 1964. Asst. dist. atty. Middlesex County, Mass., 1961; asst. U.S. atty. Mass., 1961-65; partner firm Moulton, Looney & Mazzone, Boston, 1965-75; asso. justice Superior Ct., Boston, 1975-78; U.S. dist. judge, now sr. judge Boston, 1978—. Served with U.S. Army, 1951-52. Mem. ABA, Mass. Trial Lawyers Assn., Am. Law Inst., Mass. Bar Assn., Boston Bar Assn., Middlesex Bar Assn., Fed. Bar Assn. Democrat. Roman Catholic. Office: US Dist Ct 2001 US Courthouse Boston MA 02109

MAZZOTTA, BRUNO ROBERT, hospital administrator, former military officer; b. Rome, Italy, Aug. 20, 1942; came to U.S., 1946; s. Vito and Adele (Michienzi) M.; m. Vivienne L. Mazzotta; children: Jennifer, Brian. BS in Pharmacy, Northeastern U., 1965; MA in Health Facilities Mgmt., Webster U., 1977; postgrad., St. Louis U. Registered pharmacist. Pharmacist Stevens Pharmacy, Wellesley, Mass., 1964-65; commd. 2d lt. USAF, advanced through grades to col.; asst. adminstr. USAF Hosp. USAF, Eng. AFB, La., 1965-67; adminstr. Vietnamese Provincial Hosp. USAF, Tan An, 1967-68; asst. adminstr. USAF Hosp. USAF, Wiesbaden, Ger., 1968-73; adminstr. USAF Medical Svc. Squadrons USAF, Govs. Island, N.Y., 1973-76; asst. adminstr. USAF Aeromed. Squadron USAF, Scott AFB, Ill., 1976-77; ret. USAF, 1977; asst. dir. St. Louis U. Hosp., 1977-85, dir. risk mgmt., 1985—; risk mgmt. cons. NFP Cons., St. Louis, 1992—; speaker various assns., hosps. Exec. dir. video/film: You are hereby summoned to appear, 1979 (Emmy nominee for outstanding achievement). Bd. dirs. Claimjumper Condominium Assn., Park City, Utah. Col. USAFR. Fellow Am. Coll. Healthcare Execs., Risk and Ins. Mgmt. Soc. (past pres. St. Louis chpt.), Univ. Risk Mgmt. Ins. Assn., Am. Soc. Healthcare Risk Mgmt. Avocations: enology, skiing, antique cars. Home: 8901 Foley Dr Belleville IL 62223 Office: St Louis Univ 2d flr 3500 Lindell Blvd Saint Louis MO 63103

MAZZOTTA, GIUSEPPE FRANCESCO, Italian language and literature educator; b. Curinga, Calabria, Italy, Jan. 1, 1942; s. Pasquale and Rosa (Anania) M.; m. Carol Carlson, Mar. 2, 1972; children: Rosanna, Antony, Paula. BA, U. Toronto, Can., 1965, MA, 1966; PhD, Cornell U., 1969. Asst. prof. dept. romance studies Cornell U., Ithaca, N.Y., 1969-70, assoc. prof. dept. romance studies, 1973-78, prof. romance langs., 1978-83; asst. prof. dept. romance studies Yale U., New Haven, 1970-72, prof. Italian lang. and lit., 1983—; assoc. prof. Medieval Inst. U. Toronto, 1972-73. Author: Dante, Poet of the Desert: History and Allegory in the Divine Comedy, 1979, 2d edit., 1987, The World of Play: A Study of Boccaccio's Decameron, 1986, Dante's Vision and the Circle of Knowledge, 1993, The Worlds of Petrarch, 1993; mem. editl. bd. Yale Italian Studies, Dante Studies, Yale Jour. Criticism, Yale Jour. Law and Humanities. NEH fellow Cornell U., 1977, Guggenheim Found. fellow Yale U., 1986-87. Fellow Am. Coun. Learned Socs., Soc. for the Humanities; mem. Dante Soc. Am. (assoc.). Roman Catholic. Avocations: basketball. Home: 152 Waite St Hamden CT 06517-2526 Office: Yale U 82-90 Wall St Fl 4 New Haven CT 06520

MBILA, SIMON, government official, accountant; b. Cameroon, Jan. 9, 1941; s. Samuel Mbila and Ngo Mayack Hermine; m. Marie, Nov. 15, 1968; 7 children. Student, Technium, Lucerne, Switzerland; diploma, Ecole Superieure Commerce. Profl. lic. Cameroon; head acctg. dept. Camshipping Lines, Douala; dep. Nat. Assembly Cameroon, 1992, pres. prodn. comm.; min. work and social planning Govt. Cameroon, 1992—. Named Judo Champion all categories, Cameroon, 1974, 75, 76. Office: Embassy of Cameroon 2349 Massachusetts Ave NW Washington DC 20008

MBUMBA, NANGOLO, government executive; b. Olukonda, Namibia, Aug. 15, 1941; s. Erastus and Johanna M.; m. Sustjie Van Wyk, Aug. 8, 1980; children: Matati, Mutaleni, Nameni. BS, Southern Conn. State Coll., New Haven, Conn., U.S.A., 1971; MS in Biology, U. Conn., U.S.A., 1973; cert. in distance edn., U. London, Eng., 1980. Cert. secondary school tchr., 1971. Tchr. sci. and math. Harlem Preparatory Sch., N.Y.C., 1975-78; head sci. dept. Namibia Edn. Ctr., Kwanzasul, Angola, 1979-80, sch. prin., 1980-85; dep. sec. edn. and culture SWAPO, Luanda, Angola, 1985-87, personal sec. to pres., 1987-88; asst. dir. and head dept. edn., tchr. tng. UN Inst. for Namibia, Lusaka, Zambia, 1988-89; advisor on adminstrv. matters to dir. of elections SWAPO, Windhoek, Namibia, 1989; sec. to the cabinet Republic of Namibia, Windhoek, Namibia, 1990-92; CEO for Walvis Bay and the off shore islands Joint Adminstrv. Authority, Republic of Namibia, Walvis Bay, Namibia, 1992-93; min. agrl., water and rural devel. Republic of Namibia, 1993—. Co-author: Namibia in History, Understanding History Book Series; co-editor Through the Flames. Office: Embassy Republic of Namibia 1605 New Hampshire Ave NW Washington DC 20009-2503

MCABEE, CHERYL ROSILYN, lawyer; b. Greensberg, Pa., Apr. 6, 1955; d. Charles Russel and Thelma Beatrice (White) McA. BSChemE, Carnegie-Mellon U., 1977; JD, Duquesne U., 1983. Bar: Pa. 1985, U.S. Dist. Ct. (we. dist.) 1985. Ptnr. C.R. McAbee and Assocs., Herminie, Pa., 1985—. Mem. ABA, Pa. Bar Assn., Allegheny County Bar Assn., Am. Inst. Chem. Engring., Western Pa. Engrs. Soc., AAUW, Continental Socs. Democrat. Home: 7 Keystone Rd Herminie PA 15637-1720 Office: CP McAbee and Assocs 11 Keystone Rd Herminie PA 15637-1720

MCABEER, SARA CARITA, school administrator; b. Logan, Utah, Aug. 19, 1906; d. Edward Thomas and Carrie Estelle (Martin) Harris; m. Frederick Alexander McAbeer, Dec. 24, 1929 (div. 1971); 1 child, Winifred. BA, Iowa State Tchr., Cedar Falls, 1929; postgrad., Sacramento (Calif.) Coll., 1956. Cert. high sch. administr. Clk., bookkeeper Curtis Jewelry, Kemmerer, Wyo., 1923-24; tchr. Miles High Sch., Miles, Iowa, 1929-30, Salinas (Calif.) High Sch., 1930-32; sec. supervised teaching U.

Calif., Berkeley, 1934-41; tchr. Vallejo (Calif.) Jr. High Sch., 1947-50, Napa (Calif.) Jr. High Sch., 1950-52; dean of girls Napa High Sch., 1952-72. Active mem. Napa County Dem. Party, 1950-52, St. Thomas Altar Guild, Napa, 1973—, Community Projects, Inc., Napa, 1966-67, 77—; mem., vol. tchr., bd. dirs. North Bay Suicide Prevention, Inc., Napa, 1972-91; leader Vallejo Girl Scouts, 1947-49; tchr. St. John's Cath. Ch., Napa, 1960-62. Recipient Vol. of Yr. North Bay Suicide Prevention Napa, 1986, Finalist continuing Svc. Vol. Ctr. Napa, 1988; Top Ten Ia. State Tchr. Cedar Falls scholar, 1929. Mem. AAUW, Delta Kappa Gamma. Democrat. Roman Catholic. Avocations: needlepointing, bridge, dancing.

MCADAM, WILL, electronics consultant; b. Wheeling, W.Va., Oct. 22, 1921; s. Will and Elizabeth Margaret (Wickham) McA.; m. Evelyn Virginia Warren, Sept. 22, 1945; children: Elizabeth Ruth, Margaret Evelyn. BSEE, Case Inst. Tech., 1942; MSEE, U. Pa., 1959. Registered control engr., Calif. Rsch. technologist Leeds & Northrup Co., Phila., 1945-57; head elec. sect. R&D dept. Leeds & Northrup Co., North Wales, Pa., 1957-68, assoc. dir. rsch. ops., 1968-75, mgr. devel. and engring. adv. devel., 1977-79, prin. scientist rsch. dept., 1979-82, ret., 1982; cons. in electronics, 1982—. Contbr. articles to profl. jours.; chpts. to handbooks; 30 patents in field. 1st lt. AUS, 1942-45, ETO. Decorated Bronze Star. Fellow IEEE (life; chmn. subcom. on elec. and high frequency measurements 1957-59, com. indsl. electronic and control instruments 1961-65, Prize Paper award 1958), Eta Kappa Nu, Tau Beta Pi. Republican. Presbyterian. Avocations: amateur radio, woodworking/cabinetmaking, hiking, bicycling. Home: PO Box 470 Worcester PA 19490-0470

MCADAMS, BRIAN, advertising executive; b. Camden, N.J., Apr. 20, 1942; s. Leonard J. and Harriet M. (Bissel) McM.; m. Joanne McAdams (dec. Aug. 1985); m. Louise Taylor; children: Brian, Maxwell, Georgia. BS, St. Joseph's U., Phila., 1966. Nat. bus. devel. mgr. Hunt-Wesson Foods, Fullerton, Calif., 1966-71; exec. v.p., chief oper. officer J.M. Korn Advt., Phila., 1971-76; chmn., chief exec. officer McAdams and Ong, Inc., Phila., 1976-87, Richman & Ong, Phila., 1987—; cons. Ireland Coffee & Tea, Inc., Atlantic City, 1986—; mem. adv. bd. St. Joseph's U. Bus. Sch.; bd. dirs. Nat. Media Corp., Crusader Savs. Bank. Chmn. fin. com. Boy Scouts Am., Phila., 1987-88; bd. dirs. BBB, Phila, 1978—, chmn. 1979-80, also Nat. Coun. BBB; bd. dirs. Greater Phila. Food Bank, 1987—; pres. Corporate Alliance for Drug Edn. Mem. Founders Club Acad. Food Marketers (chmn. 1977-87), Phila. Ad Club (pres. 1978-79), Poor Richard Club (pres. 1977-78) Union League Club Phila., Merion Cricket Club. Avocations: sports, hunting, fishing. Home: 117 Maple Ave Bala Cynwyd PA 19004-3016 Office: McAdams Richman & Ong One Bala Plz Bala Cynwyd PA 19004-4301

MCADAMS, HERBERT HALL, II, banker; b. Jonesboro, Ark., June 6, 1915; s. Herbert Hall I and Stella (Patrick) McA.; children by previous marriage: Judith (Mrs. Walter A. DeRoeck), Sandra (Mrs. Robert C. Connor), Herbert Hall III, Penny (Mrs. Tim Hodges); m. Shelia Wallace, Nov. 27, 1970; 1 child, Nicole Patrick. BS, Northwestern U., Evanston, Ill., 1937; postgrad., Harvard U., 1937-38, Loyola U., Chgo., 1938-39; JD with honors, U. Ark., 1940; LLD (hon.), Ark. State U., 1984. Bar: Ark. 1940, U.S. Dist. Ct. Ark., U.S. Supreme Ct. 1944, U.S. Ct. Appeals (8th cir.) 1944, U.S. Ct. Claims 1944,. Chmn. bd., CEO Citizens Bank, Jonesboro, 1958—; chmn. bd. emeritus, chief exec. officer Union Nat. Bank, Little Rock, 1970-93, Citizens Bancshares Corp., 1979-93, Union Ark. Corp., 1980-93; bd. dirs. Worthen Bank Corp., 1993-95; McAdams-Frierson chair bank mgmt. Ark. State U., 1987; bd. dirs. 1st Ark. Devel. Fin. Corp., Systematics, Inc. Pres. Jonesboro Sch. Dist., 1948-50, Bapt. Med. Ctr. Sys. Real Estate Corp., 1977—; state chmn. Citizen's Com. on Edn., 1950; mem. Ark. Indsl. Devel. Commn., 1965-73, chmn., 1967-72; trustee Ark. Children's Hosp., 1972-75, Bapt. Med. Ctr. Sys., 1975-77, Bapt. Found., 1975; bd. govs. Ark. State Fair and Livestock Show Assn., 1976; mem. Bapt. Med. Ctr. Sys. Corp., Fifty for Future; founder, chmn. bd. govs. Ark. State U. Found.; bd. dirs. Nat. Children's Eye Care Found., 1987—, numerous others. Decorated Purple Heart; recipient F. Rector Meml. award 50 for the Future, 1973-81; named outstanding alumnus U. Ark., 1984. Mem. ABA (uniform laws com. 1961-66, mem. tax sect. 1954—), Ark. Bar Assn., Am., Ark. bankers assns., Ark. Coun. Econ. Edn., Craighead (Ark) County Bar Assn. (past pres.), Pulaski (Ark) County Bar Assn., Greater Little Rock C. of C. (dir.), Sales and Mktg. Execs. (top mgmt. honoree 1972), Sigma Nu. Methodist. Clubs: Country of Little Rock, Capital, Little Rock Lodge: Rotary. Home: 47 Edgehill Rd Little Rock AR 72207-5461 Office: Union Nat Bank 124 W Capitol Ste 1700 Little Rock AR 72201 also: Citizens Bank Bldg Jonesboro AR 72401

MCADAMS, JOHN P., lawyer; b. Phila., June 5, 1949; s. Eugene P. and Mary (Miller) McA.; m. Anne Christina Connelly, Sept. 5, 1970; children: Emily Lane, Anne Connelly. BA, U. N.C., 1971; JD, Wake Forest U., 1976. Bar: Fla. 1976, N.C. 1976, U.S. Dist. Ct. (mid. dist.) Fla. 1977. Assoc. Carlton, Fields, Ward, Emmanuel, Smith & Cutler, Tampa, Fla., 1976-82, ptnr., 1982—. Contbg. editor The Developing Labor Law, 1983; contbr. articles to profl. jours. Pres. Hillsborough Community Mental Health Ctr., Tampa, 1983; trustee City of Temple Ter. (Fla.) Pension Plan, 1985-89; pres. Hyde Park Preservation, Inc., Tampa, 1993. Mem. ABA, ABA Equal Rights & Responsibilities Com., Fla. Bar Assn. (exec. coun. labor sect. 1987-89). Republican. Episcopalian. Home: 820 S Delaware Ave Tampa FL 33606 Office: Carlton Fields PO Box 3239 Tampa FL 33601

MCADAMS, ROBERT, JR., electronics executive; b. San Francisco, July 10, 1939; s. Robert Sr. and Emily Dolores (Ragozzino) McA.; m. Frances Rose Heinrich, June 24, 1961; children: Michael, Kevin, Timothy, Darin. BS in Indsl. Mgmt., San Jose State U., 1963. Various fin. positions Ampex Corp., Redwood City, Calif., 1960-71, asst. corp. controller, 1971-74, v.p., controller, 1974-80, v.p. fin., 1980-83; sr. v.p. fin. and adminstrn. Measurex Corp., Cupertino, Calif., 1983-93, sr. v.p. oper. and info. svcs., 1993—. Mem. Fin. Execs. Inst. (bd. dirs. 1978-81), Am. Electronics Assn. (chmn. acctg. and fin. com. 1986-91). Avocations: golf, coaching soccer. Office: Measurex Corp One Results Way Cupertino CA 95014

MC ADAMS, RONALD EARL, geologist; b. Tulia, Tex., Aug. 6, 1910; s. Earl A. and Laura Ann (Hutchinson) McA.; m. Lucy Grace Harris, Aug. 24, 1927; children—Elizabeth Ann, John Harris. B.A., Tex. A&M U., 1932; M.S., Tex. A. and M. Coll., 1935. Field geologist Shell Oil Co., 1936-42, dist. geologist, 1946-47; exploration mgr. Shell Oil Co., Tulsa, 1947-53, Denver, 1954; mgr. exploration and land, head office Shell Oil Co., N.Y.C., 1955-57; v.p. exploration Shell Oil Co., 1957-70; cons. petroleum geologist, 1970-76; chmn., chief exec. officer McAdams, Roux and Assocs., Inc., ind. oil and gas exploration and producing (merged with Plains Petroleum), 1977-90; ind. oil and gas operator, 1990—. Served from 1st lt. to lt. col. AUS, 1942-45, ETO. Decorated Bronze Star with oak leaf cluster. Fellow Geol. Soc. Am.; mem. Am. Assn. Petroleum Geologists, Am. Inst. Profl. Geologists, Tau Beta Pi, Cherry Hills Country Club, Champions Golf Club (Houston), Denver Petroleum Club, Castle Pines Golf Club (Castle Rock). Home: 3401 S Race St Englewood CO 80110-3137

MCADOO, CAROLYN, secondary school business educator; b. Athens, Tex., Mar. 19, 1943; d. Willie S. and Grace Lee (Dawson) Smith; m. Patrick Lee McAdoo, Sept. 9, 1962; children: Monica Lynn, Patrick Lee Jr. AA, Tex. Christian U., 1962; Coll. of SW, Coll. of S.W., 1970; MEd, Tex. Tech U., 1987. Cert. elem. and secondary tchr., Tex. Elem. tchr., adminstrv. sec. Seagraves (Tex.) Elem. Sch., 1972-80; tchr. bus. edn. Seagraves High Sch., 1980—; cons. gifted and talented, 1989—. Officer local ch. Named Tex. Dist. 17 Bus. Tchr. of Yr., 1990. Mem. ASCD, Nat. Bus. Edn. Assn., Tex. Assn. Gifted and Talented, Assn. Tex. Profl. Educators, Tex. Bus. Edn. Assn. (pres. dist. 17 1991), Tex. Bus. Edn. Assn. (curriculum com.), Delta Kappa Gamma (v.p.). Home: PO Box 824 Seagraves TX 79359-0824

MC AFEE, JERRY, retired oil company executive, chemical engineer; b. Port Arthur, Tex., Nov. 3, 1916; s. Almer McD. and Marguerite (Calfee) McA.; m. Geraldine Smith, June 21, 1940; children: Joe R., William M., Loretta M., Thomas R. B.S. in Chem Engring, U. Tex. at Austin, 1937; Sc.D. in Chem. Engring. Mass. Inst. Tech., 1940; student, Mgmt. Problems for Execs., U. Pitts., 1952. Research chem. engr., rsch. technologist Universal Oil Products Co., Chgo., 1940-43, operating engr., 1944-45; tech. specialist Gulf Oil Corp., Port Arthur, Tex., 1945-50; successively dir. chemistry, asst. dir. research, v.p., asso. dir. research subs., Gulf Research & Devel. Co.

Hamarville, Pa., 1950-55; v.p. engring. mfg. dept. of corp. Gulf Oil Corp., 1955-60, v.p., exec. tech. advisor of corp., 1960-64, also dir. planning and econs., 1962-64, sr. v.p., 1964-67, chmn. bd., chief exec. officer, 1976-81; sr. v.p. Gulf Eastern Co., London, 1964-67; exec. v.p. Brit. Am. Oil Co., Ltd. Toronto, Ont., 1967-69; pres., chief exec. officer, dir. Gulf Oil Can. Ltd., 1969-75. Bd. dirs. Am. Petroleum Inst., MIT; mem. exec. com. Alleghery Conf. Community Devel. Fellow Am. Inst. Chem. Engrs. (v.p. 1959, pres. 1960); Mem. Nat. Acad. Engring., Am. Petroleum Inst., Am. Chem. Soc. Presbyterian. Clubs: Duquesne (Pitts.); Fox Chapel Golf; Rolling Rock (Ligonier, Pa.); John's Island, Bent Pine Golf (Vero Beach, Fla.). Patentee in field. Home: 1150 Beach Rd Vero Beach FL 32963-3471

MCAFEE, JOHN GILMOUR, nuclear medicine physician; b. Toronto, Ontario, Can., June 11, 1926; came to U.S., 1952; s. Robert Duncan and Susan Jane (Damery) McA.; m. Joan Weber, Feb. 11, 1952 (dec. 1978); children: Paul Clifton, Carol Joan, David Robert. MD, U. Toronto, 1948. Rotating intern Victoria Hosp., London, Ont., Can., 1948-49; resident in radiology Victoria Hosp., London, Ont., 1950-51; resident in internal medicine Westminster Hosp., London, 1949-50; resident in radiology Johns Hopkins Hosp., Balt., 1951-52, fellow, 1952-53; instr. radiology Johns Hopkins Sch. Medicine, Balt., 1953-55, asst. prof. radiology, 1955-58, assoc. prof. radiology, 1958-65; prof., chmn. radiology SUNY Health Sci. Ctr., Syracuse, 1965-73, dir. div. nuclear medicine, 1973-78, dir. div. radiological scis., 1978-90; prof. div. nuclear medicine George Washington U. Med. Ctr., Washington, 1990-92; sect. chief, dept. nuclear medicine Clin. Ctr., NIH, Bethesda, Md., 1992—; chmn. radiology tng. com. NIH, Bethesda, Md., 1970-73; bd. dirs. Am. Bd. Nuclear Medicine, L.A., 1973-80; cons. editorial bd. Jour. Nuclear Medicine, N.Y.C., 1975—; chmn. subcom. nuclear medicine DOE, Gaithersburg, Md., 1987-88. Author; editor: (with others) Differential Diagnosis in Nuclear Medicine, 1984; assoc. editor: Year Book of Nuclear Medicine, 1993; contbr. articles to profl. jours. NIH grantee, 1961-92. Fellow Royal Coll. Physicians; mem. Soc. Nuclear Medicine (Paul C. Aebersold awad 1979, Georg Charles De Hevesy Nuclear Medicine Pioneer award 1989), Radiol. Soc. N.Am., Am. Roentgen Ray Soc., Assn. Univ. Radiologists. Avocations: sailing, jazz, organ, yachting, swimming. Home: 3303 Winnett Rd Bethesda MD 20815-3201 Office: NIH Dept Nuclear Medicine 900 Rockville Pike Rm 1 C401 Bethesda MD 20892

MCAFEE, JOHN WILSON, SR., principal; b. Hallsville, Tex., May 17, 1942; s. Howard Lawrence Sr. and Julia (Hart) McA.; m. Ruby Lee Runnels, May 31, 1966 (div.); children: Veronica Michelle, Charlotte Nichelle, John Wilson Jr.; m. Karen Walker, Nov. 23, 1993; children: Christopher Walker, Derrick Walker. BS, Bishop Coll., 1963; MEd, East Tex. State U., 1970, EdD, 1977. Tchr. Terrell (Tex.) Ind. Sch. Dist., 1963-79, prin., 1979-83, head start dir., 1979-83; head start dir. Midland (Tex.) Ind. Sch. Dist., 1983-86, prin., 1986—. Author and presenter video Coun. Minority Students, 1988. Election judge City of Terrell, 1980-82; co-chairperson Census Redistricting Com., Terrell, 1981; bd. dirs. YMCA, Midland, 1983-90; rep. Dist. Tchr. Com., Midland, 1988-93; mem. distbn. panel United Way, Midland, 1990-93; speaker achievement day Wiley Coll., 1994. Named Man of Yr. Elem. Prins. Assn. (dist. officer), Midland Prins. Assn., Renaissance Club (v.p., Achievement award 1980), Kappa Alpha Psi, Pi Lambda Theta, Phi Delta Kappa (historian 1980-81), Kappa Psi (Achievement award 1978). Mem. Ch. of Christ. Avocations: jazz music, accapella singing. Home: PO Box 9052 Midland TX 79708 also: 2401 Fairview Ln Midland TX 79705 Office: Midland Ind Sch Dist 615 W Missouri Midland TX 79701

MCAFEE, LAWRANCE WILEY, finance executive; b. Huntsville, Tex., Jan. 31, 1955; s. Raymond Mack McAfee and Moira Jean (Wiley) Attwell; m. Martha Jane O'Neal, Apr. 21, 1984. BBA, U. Tex., 1977; MBA, So. Meth. U., 1978. Analyst First Nat. Bank in Dallas, 1979, banking assoc., 1979-80, loan officer, 1980-81; corp. fin. Transco Energy Co., Houston, 1981-82; dir. fin. U.S. Home Corp., Houston, 1982-85, treas., 1985-87, v.p., treas., 1987, v.p., chief fin. officer, 1987-89; sr. v.p., chief fin. officer Stillbrooke Corp., Houston, 1989-91; chief fin. officer, dir. Waste Processor Industries, Inc., Friendswood, Tex., 1991-93; exec. v.p., CFO and sec. Air-Cure Environ, Inc., Annapolis, Md., 1993—. Mem. Assn. for Corporate Growth. Office: Air-Cure Environ Inc 275 West St #204 Annapolis MD 21401

MC AFEE, MARILYN, ambassador; b. Portsmouth, N.H., Jan. 23, 1940; m. Joel William Febel. BA in History with honors, U. Pa., 1961; MA, Johns Hopkins U., 1962. Liaison Fgn. Svc., Dept. State, Washington, 1968; served with U.S. Embassy, Guatemala, 1969-70, Nicaragua, 1970-72, Iran, 1972-77; served with Fgn. Svc., Dept. State, Washington, 1977-80; served with U.S. Embassy, Costa Rica, 1980-83, Venezuela, 1983-86, Chile, 1986-89; dep. chief of mission U.S. Embassy, Bolivia, 1989-92; amb. U.S. Embassy, Guatemala City, Guatemala, 1993—. Ford Found. fellow; recipient 4 Meritorious Honor awards, 1 Superior Honor award, 1 Presdl. Meritorious Svc. award. Office: Am Embassy Guatemala APO AA 34024-5000

MC AFEE, WILLIAM, government official; b. Port Royal, Jan. 25, 1910; s. French and Willietta (Anderson) McA. B.A., Coll. of Wooster, 1932; M.A. in Am. History, Pa. State U., 1941; student, Oxford, Eng., summer 1937. Wooster in India rep. on faculty Ewing Christian Coll., Allahabad, India, 1932-35; tchr. pub. high schs. and prep. sch. Pa., 1935-42; joined State Dept., 1946; country specialist (Office Chinese Affairs), 1946-50; coordinator current intelligence (Bur. Intelligence and Research), 1950-56, spl. asst. to dir., 1956-60, dir. ops. staff, 1960-66, asst. dep. dir. coordination, 1966-72, dep. dir. coordination, 1972-80, asst. sec. intelligence coordination, 1980—; dir. (Office of Intelligence Liaison), 1981-86, ret.; adviser Griffin Econ. Aid Mission to S.E. Asia, 1950. Served to lt. col. AUS, 1942-46, CBI. Decorated Legion of Merit; Order Brit. Empire; Precious Tripod Chinese Nationalist Govt.; recipient Superior Honor award State Dept., 1964, Disting. Honor award, 1980. Mem. Am. Fgn. Service Assn., Delta Sigma Rho. Home: 4433 Brandywine St NW Washington DC 20016-4419

MCAHREN, ROBERT WILLARD, history educator; b. Sioux City, Iowa, Dec. 3, 1935; s. Willard Calvin and Winifred Mae (Small) McA. B.A., So. Meth. U., 1958; Ph.D., U. Tex.-Austin, 1967. Instr. history Washington & Lee U., Lexington, Va., 1966-67, asst. prof. history, 1967-70, assoc. prof. history, 1970-75, prof. history, 1975—, asst. dean coll., 1971-73, assoc. dean coll., 1973-77, head dept. history, 1988—. Editor (with David V. Van Tassel) document collection with interpretive introduction; European Origins of American Thought, 1969. Mem. Phi Beta Kappa. Democrat. Avocations: orchid growing; model railroading. Office: Washington and Lee U Dept Of History Lexington VA 24450

MC ALEECE, DONALD JOHN, mechanical engineering educator; b. Detroit, May 26, 1918; s. Joseph Patrick and Kathryn (DeLeeuw) McA.; m. Margaret Ann Mull, Nov. 25, 1954; children: Stephen, Donald, Michele Denise. Diploma, machinist-toolmaker apprentice program, Gen. Electric Co., 1940; BS, Purdue U., 1952; MA, Ball State U., 1968; postgrad., U. S.C., 1990, 91. With Gen. Electric Co., Fort Wayne, Ind., 1936-66; mem. faculty Purdue U., Ft. Wayne campus, 1966-88, prof. mech. engring. tech., 1966-88, prof. emeritus, 1988—; tchr. Ind. U.-Purdue U., Fort Wayne, Ind. Vocation Tech. Coll., Fort Wayne, fall 1988; vis. prof. U. Ark., Little Rock, 1989, Trident Tech. Coll., Charleston, S.C., 1989-95; assisted devel. job tng. program and minority intro. to engring. and tech. Ind. U.-Purdue U., Ft. Wayne, summer 1986, 87; design engr., advanced safety rsch. Ford Motor Co., Dearborn, Mich., 1972; Job placement cons. Outreach office Nat. Alliance Businessmen, Fort Wayne, 1968; indsl. engr. cons. Am. Hoist & Derric Co., Ft. Wayne, 1969; cons. Franklin Electric Co., 1970, Wayne Home Equipment div. Scott & Fetzer, 1979; intern Harvester Co., 1977; engring. cons. Dana Corp., Ft. Wayne, 1984; mem. Tech. Accreditation Commn., Accreditation Bd. Engring. and Tech., 1980-82, program evaluator, 1988; statis. process control cons. Gen. Motors Corp., Ft. Wayne, 1986. Mem. editorial cons. bd. Indsl. Press, Inc., 1982-84. Scout master, com. Boy Scouts Am. With AUS, 1946-47. Ednl. Profl. Devel. Act grantee, 1971; Soc. Mfg. Engrs. grantee, 1982; named Eagle Scout Boy Scouts Am. Mem. Am. Soc. Engring. Edn., Am. Soc. Mech. Engrs., Soc. Auto Engrs., Inc. (faculty advisor student br. Trident Coll. 1995-95, elec. vehicle com. 1980-94, Svc. award 1982, Ralph R. Teetor award 1972, Outstanding Faculty Adv. Svc. award 1974), Soc. Am. Mil. Engrs., ASME (life, chmn. program com. 1971-75), ASHRAE (nat. engring. coun. prof. devel. accreditation team), S.C.

Tech. Edn. Assn. Robotics Internat. of Soc. Mfg. Engrs. (life cert.), GE Co. Qaurter Century Club (Ft. Wayne), GE Apprentice Alumni Assn., Eagle Scout (scout master, com. BSA 1968-72), Pi Tau Sigma. Baptist (deacon 1968-72). Lodges: Masons, Shriners. Home: Apt 8B 7930 Saint Ives Rd North Charleston SC 29418

MCALEER, JOHN JOSEPH, English literature educator; b. Cambridge, Mass., Aug. 29, 1923; s. Stephen Ambrose and Helen Louise (Collins) McA.; m. Ruth Ann Delaney, Dec. 28, 1957; children: Mary Alycia, Saragh Delaney, Seana Caithlin, John Joseph, Paul Bernard, Andrew Stephen. AB, Boston Coll., 1947, MA, 1949; PhD, Harvard U., 1955. Teaching fellow Boston Coll., 1947-48, English and Latin instr., 1948-50; Dexter fellow in Europe Harvard U., 1952, teaching fellow gen. edn., 1953-55; from asst. prof. to prof. Boston Coll., 1955—; vis. fellow Durham (Eng.) U., 1988-89. Author: Ballads and Songs Loyal to the Hanoverian Succession, 1962, Theodore Dreiser: A Biography, 1968, Artist and Citizen Thoreau, 1971, (with M. Tjader) Notes on Life: The Philosophical Writings of Theodore Dreiser, 1974, Rex Stout: A Biography, 1977, Justice Ends at Home: The Early Crime Fiction of Rex Stout, 1977, (with others) Rex Stout: An Annotated Primary and Secondary Bibliography, 1980, (with Billy Dickson) Unit Pride, 1981, Royal Decree: Conservations with Rex Stout, 1983, Ralph Waldo Emerson: Days of Encounter, 1984, Queens Counsel: Conversations with Ruth Stout, 1986, Coign of Vantage, 1988; editor-in-chief: Rex Stout Jour., 1979—, Thorndyke File, 1981-95, Best Sellers, 1965-85, Shakespeare newsletter, 1959-71, Armchair Detective, 1978-82; cons. editor: Dreiser Studies, 1971—. Mem. adv. bd. Walden Woods Project, 1990—, Parents Choice, 1980—. Sgt. U.S. Army, 1942-46. Recipient Cath. Press Assn. award, 1969, New Eng. Hist. Soc. award, 1985, Humanities award Boston Coll. Alumni Assn., 1991, Ignatian medal Boston Coll., 1995. Mem. Thoreau Soc. (pres. dir. 1971—), Mystery Writers Am. (v.p., dir. 1979-89, Edgar Allan Poe award 1978), R. Austen Freeman Soc. (pres. 1981—), Edith Wharton Soc., Jane Austen Soc. (Burke award 1991), Internat. Dreiser Soc. (founding mem. 1991—), Boston Authors Club (pres., dir. 1982-95), Tavern Club (Boston), Baker St. Irregulars. Democrat. Roman Catholic. Avocations: swimming, bibliopoly, genealogy, philately, gardening. Home: 121 Follen Rd Lexington MA 02173 Office: Boston Coll Dept English McGuinn 530 Chestnut Hill MA 02167

MCALEER, WILLIAM HARRISON, software company financial executive; b. Pitts., Feb. 14, 1951; s. William Kearns and Helen (Harrison) McA.; m. Colleen McGinn, Aug. 9, 1975; children: William F., Lindsay J. BS, Cornell U., 1973, MBA, 1975. CPA, Wash. Sr. acct. KPMG-Peat Marwick, Seattle, 1975-78; v.p., controller Westin Hotels, Seattle, 1978-87; v.p. finance, CFO Ecova Corp., Seattle, 1987-88; v.p. fin., CFO, sec. Aldus Corp., Seattle, 1988—; bd. dirs. Raster Ops Corp., Four Gen Corp. Pres., dir. Seattle Jr. C. of C., 1977-82; bd. dirs. Big Bros. King County, Seattle, 1994—. Mem. Fin. Execs. Ins., Software Pubs. Assn., Wash. Software Assn., Wash. Soc. CPAs, Cornell Alumni Club, Sand Point Country Club. Avocations: hiking, travel, golfing, boating, gardening. Home: 3530 W Laurelhurst Dr Seattle WA 98105 Office: Aldus Corp 411 First Ave S Seattle WA 98104

MCALESTER, ARCIE LEE, JR., geologist, educator; b. Dallas, Feb. 3, 1933; s. Arcie Lee and Alverta (Funderburk) McA.; m. Virginia Wallace Savage; children: Kirstie Martine, Archibald Keven. B.A., B.B.A., So. Methodist U., 1954; M.S., Yale U., 1957, Ph.D., 1960. Mem. faculty Yale U., 1959-74, prof. geology, 1966-74; curator invertebrate paleontology Peabody Mus., 1966-74; prof. geol. scis. So. Meth. U., Dallas, 1974—; dean Sch. Humanities and Scis. So. Meth. U., 1974-77. Author: The Earth, 1973, The History of Life, 1977, History of the Earth, 1980, Physical Geology, 1984, History of the Earth's Crust, 1984, (with V.S. McAlester) A Field Guide to American Houses, 1984, Discover Travel Guides, 1988—, Great American Houses, 1994; assoc. editor Am. Scientist, 1970-74; also articles. Served to 1st lt. USAF, 1954-56. Guggenheim fellow Glasgow U., Scotland, 1965. Office: So Meth U Dept Geol Scis Dallas TX 75275

MC ALISTER, LINDA LOPEZ, educator, philosopher; b. Long Beach, Calif., Oct. 10, 1939; d. Manuel Lee and Elena Maria (Sherwood) McAlister; AB, Barnard Coll., 1962; postgrad. Coll. City N.Y., 1963-64; PhD, Cornell U., 1969. Meritb. Coll., 1968-77, CUNY. Grad. Center, 1970-77; prof. humanities, dean campus Imperial Valley campus San Diego State U., 1977-82; prof. philosophy, campus dean U. South Fla., Ft. Myers, 1982-85; spl. asst. to vice chancellor for acad. programs State Univ. System Fla., 1985-87; prof. Women's Studies and Philosophy U. South Fla., Tampa, 1987—; Fla. state coordinator Am. Council Edn. Nat. Identification Project, 1983-86. Franz Brentano Found. grantee, 1968-72; Fulbright-Hays research grantee, 1973-74. Mem. Am. Philos. Assn., Nat. Women's Studies Assn., Soc. Women in Philosophy, Internat. Assn. von Philosophinen (founding). Author: The Development of Franz Brentano's Ethics, 1982; gen. editor Hypatia: A Journal of Feminist Philosophy, 1990—; contbr. articles to profl. jours. Editor and translator: Psychology From an Empirical Standpoint (Franz Brentano), 1973; Sensory and Noetic Consciousness (Franz Brentano), 1980; editor: The Philosophy of Brentano, 1976; translator: On Colour (Ludwig Wittgenstein), 1977, SWIP-L Electronic Mail Forum for Feminist Philosophy, 1992—, Film Criticism: Radio, Print and Electronic Media, 1990—. Office: U South Fla HMS 413 4202 E Fowler Ave Tampa FL 33620-9951

MCALISTER, MAURICE L., savings and loan association executive; b. 1925; married. Pres., dir. Downey Savs. and Loan, Newport Beach, Calif., 1957—, chmn. bd. Office: Downey Savs & Loan Assn PO Box 6000 3501 Jamboree Rd Newport Beach CA 92660-2939

MCALISTER, MICHAEL HILLIS, architect; b. Bakersfield, Calif., May 22, 1945; s. Doyle R. and Mary E. McAlister. AA, Bakersfield Coll., 1967; BArch, Calif. Polytech. U., 1971. Planning technition Bakersfield City Hall, 1963; carpenter Del Webb Corp., Kern City, Calif., 1964; architectural draftsman Goss & Choy Architects, Bakersfield, 1965-67; architect, v.p. D.G.C. & Assocs., Bakersfield, 1971-80; dir. architecture, v.p. N.B.A. & Assocs., Architects, Bakersfield, 1980-83; architect, pres. Michael H. McAlister, A.I.A., Bakersfield, 1983—; hepthology design cons. for various treatment groups and hosps., 1987—. Commr. architectural advisor Historic Preservation Commn., Bakersfield, 1986-87; bd. dirs. Camp Fire Coun., Kern County, Calif., 1980-84. Recipient Architectural Pub. Bldg. Hist. award Beautiful Bakersfield Com., City of Bakersfield's City Coun. and Hist. Preservation Commn., 1985, 87, Exterior Environ. Design Excellence Bakersfield C. of C., 1988, Comml. Design Excellence award, 1984, Design Excellence and Beautification award City of Taft, Calif., 1989, Design Excellence award State of Nev., 1992. Mem. AIA (Calif. Coun., Golden Empire chpt.). Avocations: horseback riding, art and sculpture, renovation of fine furniture and guns. Office: Ste B 5030 Office Park Dr Bakersfield CA 93309

MCALISTER, ROBERT BEATON, lawyer; b. N.Y.C., Oct. 5, 1932; s. Richard Charles and Martha Olive (Weisenbarger) McA.; widowed; children: Michael, Peter, Betsy. AB, Kenyon Coll., 1954; JD, U. Mich., 1957. Ptnr. Alexander, Ebinger, Fisher, McAlister & Lawrence, Columbus, Ohio, 1957-85; supt. Ohio Div. Savs. & Loan Assns., Columbus, 1985; ptnr. Baker & Hostetler, Columbus, 1985—, chmn. litigation dept., 1988-93. Exec. com. mem. Ohio Dem. Party, Columbus, 1967-74; active Dem. Nat. Com., Washington, 1972-76; counsel Gov. Richard F. Celeste, Columbus, 1982-90, Senator John Glenn, Washington, 1986-94. With USAF, 1968-64. Fellow Ohio Bar Found., Columbus Bar Found. Democrat. Episcopalian. Club: Capital (Columbus), The Club (Cleve.). Home: 5571 Sutterton Ln Westerville OH 43081-5228 Office: Baker & Hostetler 65 E State St Columbus OH 43215-4213

MCALLISTER, DARRELL DEAN, banker; b. Russell, Kans., July 3, 1948; s. Everett and Anna Marie (Bean) McA.; m. Connee Daughe. Apr. 23, 1988. BBA, U. Colo., 1972. CPA, Colo. Asst. nat. bank examiner Office of Comptroller of Currency, Ft. Collins, Colo., 1976-79; asst. v.p. United Bank, Ft. Collins, 1979-81, 1st Interstate Bank, Ft. Collins, 1981-82; v.p. Greeley (Colo.) Nat. Bank, 1982-83; pres., chmn. Cache Nat. Bank, Greeley, 1983—. Active United Way, Greeley, 1985-87; bd. dirs. Partners, Greeley, 1986-87. Served to 1st lt. U.S. Army, 1972-76. Club: Toastmasters. Lodges: Lions, Sertoma. Office: Cache Nat Bank 2600 11th Ave Greeley CO 80631-8441

MCALLISTER, DEE THERESA, elementary education educator; b. Islip, N.Y., Jan. 7, 1942; d. Joseph August and Victoria Harriet (Sczepaniak) Boesel. BS in Elem. Edn. and Spl. Edn., Marywood Coll., Scranton, Pa., 1963; postgrad., L.I.U., 1983-86. Cert. elem. tchr., N.Y., lic. real estate. Tchr. Our Lady of Good Counsel Parochial Sch., Inwood, N.Y., 1963-64, Elmont (N.Y.) Sch. Dist., 1964, Middle County Sch. Dist., Centereach, N.Y., 1968—; union rep. MCTA, Centereach, 1969-70. Mem. Audubon Soc., Mus. Nat. History, Nat. Geographic Soc., NCTM, Internat. Platform Assn. N.Y. State United Tchrs. Avocations: traveling, playing piano, reading, photography, bird watching, breeding English Budgies. Home: PO Box 407 Centereach NY 11720-0407 Office: Elem Sch North Coleman Rd Centereach NY 11720

MCALLISTER, GENE ROBERT, electronics company executive, electrical engineer; b. La Porte, Ind., Apr. 28, 1930; s. Leonard Leroy and Ethel May (Kellog) McA.; m. Diane Stanton, Jan. 29, 1955; children: Jean Anne, Thomas Michael. BSEE, Purdue U., 1959. Jr. engr. No. Ind. Pub. Service Co., La Porte, 1948-59; engr. Magnavox G&I Electronics Co., Ft. Wayne, Ind., 1959-60, asst. product mgr., 1960-63, product mgr., 1963-68, dir. mktg., 1968-74, v.p., gen. mgr. sensors, 1974-82; also bd. dirs. Magnavox G&I Electronics Co.; v.p., dir. ops. Magnavox Electronic Systems Co., Ft. Wayne, 1982-85, group v.p., 1985-87, exec. v.p., ops. and COO, 1987-91; pres., COO Magnavox Electronic Systems Co., 1991, pres., CEO, 1992—. Mem. Leadership Ft. Wayne, 1981—; bd. dirs. Jr. Achievement, 1982—; mem. Ft. Wayne Corp. Coun., 1991—, Ft. Wayne Community Found., 1991—. With U.S. Army, 1951-53, Korea. Mem. Nat. Security Indsl. Assn. (bd. dirs., ASW exec. com.), Machinery and Allied Products Inst. (govt. contracts council 1970—), Magnavox Mgmt. Club (bd. dirs. 1984—), Ft. Wayne C. of C. (legis. com. 1982—), Assn. U.S. Army, Navy League, Summit Club, Sycamore Hills Golf Club. Clubs: Pine Valley Country (bd. dirs. 1978-82), Ft. Wayne Racquet, Olympia (bd. dirs 1970-79). Avocations: golf, tennis, bowling, racquetball, water skiing. Office: Magnavox Electronic Systems Co 1313 Production Rd Fort Wayne IN 46808-1164

MC ALLISTER, GERALD NICHOLAS, retired bishop, clergyman; b. San Antonio, Feb. 23, 1923; s. Walter Williams and Leonora Elizabeth (Alexander) McA.; m. Helen Earle Black, Oct. 2, 1953; children—Michael Lee, David Alexander, Stephen Williams, Elizabeth. Student, U. Tex., 1939-42, Va. Theol. Sem., 1948-51; D.D. (hon.), Va. Theol. Sem., 1977. Rancher, 1946-48; ordained deacon Episcopal Ch., 1953, priest, 1954; deacon, priest Ch. of Epiphany, Raymondville, Ch. of Incarnation, Corpus Christi, St. Francis Ch., Victoria, all Tex., 1951-63; 1st canon Diocese of W. Tex., 1963-70; rector St. David's Ch., San Antonio, 1970-76; consecrated Episcopal bishop of Okla., Oklahoma City, 1977-89, ret., 1989; bishop-in-residence Episcopal Theol. Sem., Austin, Tex., 1990-93; trustee Episcopal Theol. Sem. of S.W., 1961—; adv. bd., 1974—; mem. Case Commn. Bd. for Theol. Edn., 1981-82; pres. Tex. Council Chs., 1966-68, Okla. Conf. Chs., 1980-83; bd. dirs. Presiding Bishop's Fund for World Relief, 1972-77, Ch. Hist. Soc., 1976—; chmn. Nat. and World Mission Program Group, 1973-76; mem. Structure of Ch. Standing Commn., 1979, mem. standing com. on Stewardship/Devel., 1979-85; founder Chaplaincy Program, Bexar County Jail, 1968; mem. governing bd. nat. council Ch. of Christ, 1982-85; chmn. standing commn. on stewardship Episcopal Ch., 1983-85; v.p., trustee The Episc., Episc. Theol. Sem. of Soutwest, 1987—, chmn. bd. trustees, 1993—. Author: What We Learned from What You Said, 1973, This Fragile Earth Our Island Home, 1980. Bd. dirs. Econ. Opportunity Devel. Corp., San Antonio, 1968-69; mem. exec. com. United Way, 1968-70, vice-chmn., 1970. Served with U.S. Mcht. Marines, 1942; to 1st lt. USAAF, 1942-45. Recipient Agudas Achim Brotherhood award, 1968. Address: 507 Bluffestates San Antonio TX 78216-7930

MCALLISTER, PATRICIA ANNE, retail company executive; b. Auburn, N.Y., May 18, 1951; d. C.E. and Helen (Terpening) Olmstead. BA, SUNY, Brockport. Jr. buyer Woodward & Lathrop, Washington, 1975-76, dress buyer, 1976-79, dress div. v.p., 1979-82, accessory div. v.p., 1982-86, gen. mdse. mgr., sr. v.p., 1986-87; gen. mdse. mgr., sr. v.p. Lord & Taylor, N.Y.C., 1987—; mem. Fashion Group, Washington. Democrat. Home: 6316 Chaucer View Cir Alexandria VA 22304-3545 Office: Woodward & Lothrop Inc 1025 F St NW Washington DC 20004-1409

MCALLISTER, WAYNE R., principal. Prin. Garrettford Elem. Sch., Drexel Hill, Pa. Recipient Elem. Sch. Recognition award U.S. Dept. of Edn., 1989-90. Office: Garrettford Elem Sch 3830 Garrett Rd Drexel Hill PA 19026-3598

MCALLISTER, WILLIAM HOWARD, III, newspaper reporter, columnist; b. Durham, N.C., Nov. 6, 1941; s. William Howard, Jr. and Dorothy Fisk (Tillett) McA.; m. Rena Catherine Farrell, June 13, 1965; children: William Howard IV, Christopher F., Jonathan T., Benjamin J. B.A. in Polit. Sci, U. N.C., Chapel Hill, 1964, M.A. in Journalism, 1966. Cecil Prince research asst. U. N.C., 1965; reporter The Virginian-Pilot, Norfolk, 1964-67; reporter, city editor Virginian-Pilot, 1972-75; reporter Wall St. Jour., San Francisco, 1972; reporter Washington Post, 1975-78, Va. editor, 1978-86, nat. reporter, 1986—, columnist stamp and coin sect., 1987—; TV cons. Ford Found., 1969-72. Capt. USNR, 1966-93. Decorated Navy Commendation medal, Meritorous Svc. medal, Gold Star; recipient Lidman prize for philatelic writing, 1990. Mem. Kappa Tau Alpha. Presbyterian. Home: 4140 Lenox Dr Fairfax VA 22032-1111 Office: 1150 15th St NW Washington DC 20071-5000

MCALPIN, KIRK MARTIN, lawyer; b. Newark, Sept. 14, 1923; s. Aaron Champion and Margaret (Martin) McA.; m. Sarah Frances Morgan, Dec. 14, 1951; children: Kirk Martin Jr., Philip Morgan, Margaret Champion Margeson. LLB, U. Ga., 1948; postgrad., Columbia U., 1949. Bar: Ga. 1949. Asst. solicitor gen. Ea. Jud. Cir. Ct. Ga., 1951; assoc. Bouhan, Lawrence, Williams, Levy & McAlpin, Savannah, Ga., 1952-53; ptnr. Bouhan, Lawrence, Williams, Levy & McAlpin, Savannah, 1954-63; sr. ptnr. King & Spalding, Atlanta, 1963-86; pvt. practice Savannah, 1987—; chmn. Inst. Continuing Legal Edn., 1980-81, Inst. Continuing Jud. Edn. in Ga., 1981-84, Jud. Council Ga., 1979-82. Pres. Atlanta Legal Aid Soc., 1971. Fellow Am. Bar Found., Am. Law Inst., Am. Coll. Trial Lawyers, Internat. Acad. Trial Lawyers, Internat. Soc. Barristers; mem. ABA (Jr. Bar Conf. chmn. 1958-59, chmn. gen. practice sect. 1972-73, chmn. sr. lawyers div. 1986-87, ho. of dels. 1960-90, state del. 1970-90, bd. govs. 1973-76), State Bar Ga. Assn. (chmn. Young Lawyers 1953-54, bd. govs. 1953-63, pres. 1979-80), Atlanta Bar Assn., Savannah Bar Assn. (v.p. 1960-61), Nat. Conf. Bar Pres. (exec. com. 1981-83), Ga. Def. Lawyers Assn., Ga. Trial Lawyers Assn., Fed. Bar Assn., Am. Judicature Soc., Assn. R.R. Trial Counsel, Soc. of Cin., Sons Colonial Wars, St. Andrews Soc., Capital City Club, Commerce Club, Piedmont Driving Club, Oglethorpe Club, Chatham Club, First City Club, Savannah Yacht and Country Club, Savannah Golf Club, Phi Delta Phi, Sigma Alpha Epsilon. Episcopalian. Home: 303 E 44th St Savannah GA 31405-2213 Office: PO Box 10027 Savannah GA 31412-0227

MCALPINE, ANDREW, production designer. Prodn. designer: (films) Sid and Nancy, 1986, Aria, 1987, Straight to Hell, 1987, High Season, 1988, Stormy Monday, 1988, For Queen and Country, 1989, The Rachel Papers, 1989, Slipstream, 1989, The Piano, 1993, The Tool Shed, 1993. Office: Sandra Marsh Mgt 9150 Wilshire Blvd Ste 220 Beverly Hills CA 90210*

MCALPINE, DONALD, cinematographer. Cinematographer: (films) The Adventures of Barry McKenzie, 1972, Letters, 1973, Don's Party, 1976, The Getting of Wisdom, 1977, The Odd Angry Shot, 1979, Patrick, 1979, Breaker Morant, 1979, My Brilliant Career, 1980, The Club, 1980, The Earthling, 1981, Money Movers, 1981, Don't Cry, It's Only Thunder, 1981, Tempest, 1982, Now and Forever, 1983, Puberty Blues, 1983, Blue Skies Again, 1983, Harry & Son, 1984, Moscow on the Hudson, 1984, King David, 1985, Barry McKenzie Holds His Own, 1985, Down and Out in Beverly Hills, 1986, The Fringe Dwellers, 1987, Orphans, 1987, Predator, 1987, Moon Over Parador, 1988, Moving, 1988, Parenthood, 1989, See You in the Morning, 1989, Stanley & Iris, 1990, The Hard Way, 1991, Career Opportunities, 1991, The Man Without a Face, 1993, Mrs. Doubtfire, 1993, Clear and Present Danger, 1994, Nine Months, 1995. Office: Am Soc Cinematographers PO Box 2230 Los Angeles CA 90078*

MCAMIS, EDWIN EARL, lawyer; b. Cape Girardeau, Mo., Aug. 8, 1934; s. Zenas Earl and Anna Louise (Miller) McA.; m. Malin Eklof, May 31, 1959 (div. 1979); 1 child, Andrew Bruce. AB magna cum laude, Harvard U., 1956, LLB, 1959. Bar: N.Y. 1960, U.S. Dist. Ct. N.Y., U.S. Supreme Ct. 1965, U.S. Ct. Appeals (2nd, 3rd and D.C. cirs.). Assoc. law firm Webster, Sheffield & Chrystie, N.Y.C., 1959-61, Regan Goldfarb Powell & Quinn, N.Y.C., 1962-65; assoc. law firm Lovejoy, Wasson, Lundgren & Ashton, N.Y.C., 1965-69, ptnr., 1969-77; ptnr. Skadden, Arps, Slate, Meagher & Flom, N.Y.C., 1977-90, spl. ptnr., pro bono, 1990-93; adj. prof. law Fordham U., 1984-85, Benjamin N. Cardozo Sch. Law, N.Y.C., 1985-90. Board dirs. Aston Magna Found. for Music, Inc., 1982-93, Community Rsch. Initiative N.Y., 1988-89; Lambda Legal Def. & Edn. Fund, 1991—. Mem. ABA, Selden Soc. Home: 4110 Kiaora St Coconut Grove FL 33133

MCANANAMA, JUDITH, library executive. BA in Russian and Polit. Sci., U. Man., Can., 1962; BLS, McGill U., Montreal, 1964; MBA, McMaster U., Can., 1982. From children's libr. to head of ctrl. br. Hamilton (Ont.) Pub. Libr., Can., 1965-80, CEO, 1980—. Bd. dirs. St. Peter's Hosp.; past chmn. Hamilton Gallery of Distinction; vice chmn. bd. govs. Mohawk Coll. Applied Arts and Tech., chmn. operational rev. com.; past pres. Industry-Edn. Coun. Mem. Can. Libr. Assn. (past pres., convenor copyright com., Outstanding Pub. Svc. award 1994), Ont. Libr. Assn., Hamilton and Dist. C. of C. (bd. dirs.). Office: Hamilton Pub Library, 55 York Blvd, Hamilton, ON Canada L8N 4E4

MCANDREWS, JAMES PATRICK, retired lawyer; b. Carbondale, Pa., May 11, 1929; s. James Patrick and Mary Agnes (Walsh) McA.; m. Mona Marie Steinke, Sept. 4, 1954; children: James P., George A., Catherine McAndrews Lawlor, Joseph M., Anne Marie, Michael P., Edward R., Daniel P. B.S., U. Scranton, 1949; LL.B., Fordham U., 1952; grad., Real Estate Inst., NYU, 1972. Bar: N.Y. 1953, Ohio 1974. Assoc. James F. McManus, Levittown, N.Y., 1955; atty. Emigrant Savs. Bank, N.Y.C., 1955-68; counsel Tchrs. Ins. and Annuity Assn., 1968-73; assoc. Thompson, Hine & Flory, 1973-74; ptnr. Thompson, Hine & Flory, Cleve., 1974-84, Benesch, Friedlander, Coplan & Aronoff, Cleve., 1984-94; mem. law faculty Am. Inst. Banking, N.Y.C., 1968-69. 1st lt. USAF, 1952-54. Fellow Am. Bar Found. (life); mem. ABA (past chmn. real estate financing com. 1985-87), Am. Coll. Real Estate Lawyers (gov. 1983-86, trans. 1986-88, chmn. membership devel. com. 1985-87), Ohio Bar Assn., Bar Assn. Greater Cleve. (past chmn. coun. real estate sect.), Am. Coll. Mortgage Attys. Roman Catholic. Home: 6638 Duneden Ave Cleveland OH 44139-4048

MCANIFF, EDWARD JOHN, lawyer; b. N.Y.C., June 29, 1934; s. John Edward and Josephine (Toomey) McA.; m. Jane Reiss, June 11, 1960; children: John E., Maura T., Anne T., Jane A., Peter J., Kathleen A. AB magna cum laude, Holy Cross Coll., 1956; LLB cum laude, NYU, 1961. Bar: N.Y. 1962, Calif. 1963, D.C. 1976. Law clk. to Justice A.T. Goodwin Supreme Ct. Oreg., Salem, 1961-62; assoc. then ptnr. O'Melveny & Myers, L.A., 1962—; lectr. Stanford U., 1974-75, 94, Boalt Hall Law Sch., 1992—; fgn. law counsel Freehill, Hollingdale & Page, Sydney, Australia, 1981-82; bd. dirs. Mellon Bank Corp. Trustee Mayfield Sr. Sch., 1979—, chmn. bd. trustees, 1980-81; bd. dirs. L.A. Master Chorale, 1979-81, 87—, pres., 1992—; trustee Music Ctr. Los Angeles County, 1992—, exec. com., 1992—; bd. dirs. Music Ctr. Found., 1992—. Capt. USNR, 1956-83. Mem. City Club, Valley Hunt Club. Republican. Home: 3315 San Pasqual St Pasadena CA 91107-5436 Office: O'Melveny & Myers 275 Battery St Ste 2500 San Francisco CA 94111-3305

MCANIFF, NORA P., publishing executive. BA, CUNY. Pub. People Weekly, N.Y.C., 1994—. Office: People Magazine Time Inc Rockfeller Ctr New York NY 10020-1393*

MCANINCH, HAROLD D., college president; b. Leota, Mo., May 29, 1933; s. James Loyd and Essie L. McA.; m. Karyl Kay Woodbridge, May 25, 1956; children: Michele Kay, Michael Sean. B.S., S.W. Mo. State U., 1957; M.A., U. Ark., 1958; Ed.D., U. Mo., 1967; postgrad., Loyola U., Chgo., 1972-74; D.Hum. (hon.), Lewis U., 1974. Tchr. Smith Cotton High Sch., Sedalia, Mo., 1958-61; instr. U. Mo., Columbia, 1961-64; dean Jefferson Coll., Hillsboro, Mo., 1964-68; pres. Jackson (Mich.) Community Coll., 1968-71, Joliet (Ill.) Jr. Coll., 1971-79, Coll. of DuPage, Glen Ellyn, Ill., 1979—. Contbr. articles to profl. jours. Chmn. Will County Cancer Crusade; bd. dirs. United Crusade of Will County. Served with U.S. Army, 1950-53. Mem. Council North Central Community and Jrs. Colls. (pres. 1975), Ill. Council Public Community Coll. Presidents (vice chmn. 1976, pres. 1977, past chmn. fin. com.), North Central Assn. Colls. and Secondary Schs. (evaluator, commr.), Am. Assn. Community and Jr. Colls. (chmn. President's Acad. 1979, dir. 1980-84, vice chmn. 1982, chmn. 1983), Phi Delta Kappa. Lodge: Rotary. Office: Coll of DuPage 22nd and Lambert Rds Glen Ellyn IL 60137

MCANINCH, JACK WELDON, urological surgeon, educator; b. Merkel, Tex., Mar. 17, 1936; s. Weldon Thomas and Margaret (Canon) McA.; m. Barbara B. Buchanan, Dec. 29, 1960 (div. Aug. 1972); m. Burnet B. Sumner, Dec. 29, 1987; children: David A., Todd G., Brendan J. BS, Tex. Tech U., 1958; MS, U. Idaho, 1960; MD, U. Tex., 1964. Diplomate Am. Bd. Urology (trustee 1991—). Commd. capt. U.S. Army, 1964-66, advanced through grades to col., 1977, ret., 1977; col. USAR; intern then resident Luetterman Army Med. Ctr., San Francisco, 1964-69; chief urol. surgery San Francisco Gen. Hosp., 1977—; prof. urol. surgery U. Calif., San Francisco, 1977—. Editor: Urogenital Trauma, 1985, University Clinics of North America, 1989, Smith's General Urology, 1995; section editor: Early Care of the Injured Patient, 1990. Col. US Army, 1964-72. Recipient Disting. Alumnus award Tex. Tech U., 1994. Fellow ACS (gov. 1992—); mem. Am. Urol. Assn. (pres. we. sect. 1992-93, bd. dirs. 1990—), Genitourinary Reconstructive Surgeons (pres.), Am. Assn. Surgery Trauma (v.p.), Soc. Univ. Urologists. Office: San Francisco Gen Hosp Dept Urology 1001 Potrero Ave San Francisco CA 94110-3518

MCANUFF, DES, artistic director; b. Princeton, Ill., June 19, 1952; s. John Nelson and Ellen Boyd; m. Susan Berman, Jan. 1, 1984; 1 child, Julia Violet. Artistic dir. La Jolla Playhouse, until 1994; Founding mem. Dodger Prodns.; former faculty Julliard Sch.; now adj. prof. theatre U. Calif. San Diego. Dir.: (Broadway prodns.) Big River (Tony award 1985), A Walk in the Woods (San Diego Critics Circle award), Tommy (Tony award 1993), How to Succeed in Business Without Really Trying (Tony nomination 1995); (off-Broadway prodns.) Gimme Shelter (Soho Arts award 1979), The Crazy Locomotive, Chelsea Theatre Ctr., Mary Stuart, How It All Began, Henry IV Part One, The Death of Von Richthofen as Witnessed from Earth (Villager award 1982), N.Y. Shakespeare Festival, A Mad World My Masters, Romeo & Juliet, As You Like It (San Diego Critics Circle award), The Sea Gull, Shout Up A Morning, Gillette, The Matchmaker, Two Rooms, 80 Days, Down The Road, Macbeth, The Three Sisters, A Funny Thing Happened on the Way to the Forum, Twelfth Night, La Jolla Playhouse, Macbeth, Stratford Festival Can., others; prodr.: A Walk in the Woods, My Children! My Africa!; playwright Leave it to Beaver is Dead (Soho Arts award), The Death of Von Richthofen as Witnessed from Earth (Villager and Bay Area Critics Circle awards), Troll, A Lime in the Morning, Silent Edward; contbg. editor Am. Theatre Mag. Can. Council grantee, Rockefeller grantee. Mem. Theatre Communications Group (past bd. dirs.), Soc. of Stage Dirs. and Choreographers. *

MC ANULTY, HENRY JOSEPH, university administrator; b. Pitts., Apr. 25, 1915; s. William J. and Catherine (Calpin) McA. BA, Duquesne U., 1936; BTh., St. Mary's Sem., Ferndale, Norwalk, Conn., 1941; LLD, Loyola U., Los Angeles, 1958; DEd, St. Vincent Coll., Latrobe, Pa., 1961; LHD, U. Pitts., Duquesne U., 1990. Joined Congregation of Holy Ghost, 1936; ordained priest Roman Catholic Ch., 1940; nat. sec., Pitts. Diocesan dir. Pontifical Assn. Holy Childhood, 1941-44; commd. 1st lt. chaplain USAAF 1944; advanced through grades to lt. col. USAF, resigned, 1958; brig. gen. (Res.); asst. to pres. Duquesne U., 1958-59, pres., 1959-80. Bd. dirs. Pitts. Symphony Soc., Pitts. Regional Indsl. Devel. Corp., Pitts. Conv. and Visitors Bur., Allegheny Conf. for Community Devel. Mem. Am. Legion, K.C. Office: Duquesne U Pittsburgh PA 15282

MCARDLE, JOHN, publishing company executive; b. Boston, 1928. Attended, Boston Coll., 1952, 70. Pres., chief exec. officer, dir. Fin. Pub. Co., Boston. Home: Box 201 19 Towne Hill Topsfield MA 01983 Office: Financial Pub Co 82 Brookline Ave Boston MA 02215

MCARDLE, JOHN EDWARD, management consultant; b. Evanston, Ill., Apr. 22, 1928; s. Robert Patrick and Mary Catherine (Andersen) McA.; m. Gloria T. McArdle, Oct. 1, 1955; children: John E. Jr., Mary M. Lueders. Grad., Northwestern U., 1950. Brand mgr. candy bars Curtiss Candy Co., Chgo., 1952-56; account exec., v.p. mgmt. supr. Foote Cone & Belding Advt. Agy., Chgo., 1956-81; v.p. corp. com. George S. May Internat. Co. Mgmt. Cons., Park Ridge, Ill., 1981—; grad. sch. guest lectr. Northwestern U., U. Mich., U. Tenn., Drake U., No. Ill. U. Editor May Trends mag.; contbr. articles to profl. jours. Past chmn. bd. dirs. Better Bus. Bur. of Chgo. & No. Ill., 1986—; v.p. Riverwoods (Ill.) Residence Assn. past chmn. Riverwoods Plan Commn., 1976-80, 1993—. With USN, 1950-52, Korea. Sr. mem. Econ. Club Chgo.; mem. Mill Creek Fox Hunt, Town Club. Avocations: horses, squash.

MCARDLE, PAUL FRANCIS, judge; b. Albany, N.Y., Nov. 26, 1918; s. Charles P. and Mary (Murray) McA.; m. Catherine Angela Manley, Nov. 8, 1952; children: Paul Francis, Peter M., Susan M., Mary M. B.S., Georgetown U., 1941, LL.B., 1948. Bar: D.C. 1948. Assoc. Cleary, Gottlieb, Friendly & Cox, Washington, 1948-51, Covington & Burling, Washington, 1951—; now judge Superior Ct. D.C. Active United Givers Fund, Chevy Chase, Md. Served to capt. USMCR, 1941-46. Mem. ABA, Bar Assn. D.C., Am. Bar Found. Home: 3505 Windsor Pl Bethesda MD 20815-4001 Office: Superior Ct DC Washington DC 20001

MCARDLE, RICHARD JOSEPH, academic administrator; b. Omaha, Mar. 10, 1934; s. William James and Abby Marie (Menzies) McA.; m. Katherine Ann McAndrew, Dec. 27, 1958; children: Bernard, Constance, Nancy, Susan, Richard. B.A., Creighton U., 1955, M.A., 1961; Ph.D., U. Nebr., 1969. Tchr. pub. high schs. Nebr., 1955-65; grad. asst. romance langs. U. Nebr., 1965-66, instr. fgn. lang. methods, 1966-69; chmn. dept. edn. Cleve. State U., 1969-70; chmn. dept. elem. and secondary edn. U. North Fla., 1971-75; dean Coll. Edn. Cleve. State U., 1975-87, prof. edn., 1987-89, spl. asst. to pres. for campus planning, 1989-91, vice provost for strategic planning 1991-92, acting provost, v.p. for acad. affairs, 1992-94; vice provost for strategic planning, 1994—; cons. in field. Author articles related to issues in tchr. edn. Mem. World Future Soc., Soc. Coll. and Univ. Planning, Am. Assn. Higher Edn., Phi Delta Kappa. Office: Office of Provost Academic Affairs Cleve State U Cleveland OH 44115

MCARTHUR, ELDON DURANT, geneticist, researcher; b. Hurricane, Utah, Mar. 12, 1941; s. Eldon and Denise (Dalton) McA.; m. Virginia Johnson, Dec. 20, 1963; children: Curtis D., Monica McArthur Bennion, Denise, Ted O. AS with high honors, Dixie Coll., 1963; BS cum laude, U. Utah, 1965, MS, 1967, PhD, 1970. Postdoctoral rsch. fellow, dept. demonstrator Agrl. Rsch. Coun. Gt. Britain, Leeds, Eng., 1970-71; rsch. geneticist Intermountain Rsch. Sta. USDA Forest Svc., Ephraim, Utah, 1972-75; rsch. geneticist Shrub Scis. Lab., Intermountain Rsch. Sta. USDA Forest Svc., Provo, Utah, 1975-83, project leader, chief rsch. geneticist, 1983—; adj. prof. dept. botany and range sci. Brigham Young U., Provo, 1976—. Author over 250 rsch. papers; contbr. chpts. to books; editor symposium procs. Grantee Sigma Xi, 1970, NSF, 1981, 85, Coop. State Rsch. Svc., 1986, 91. Mem. Soc. Range Mgmt. (pres. Utah sect. 1987), Botan. Soc. Am., Soc. Study Evolution, Am. Genetic Assn., Shrub Rsch. Consortium (chmn. 1983—), Intermountain Consortium for Aridlands Rsch. (pres. 1991—). Mormon. Avocations: hiking, cycling, basketball. Home: 555 N 1200 E Orem UT 84057 Office: USDA Forest Svc Shrub Scis Lab 735 N 500 E Provo UT 84606-1856

MC ARTHUR, GEORGE, journalist; b. Valdosta, Ga., July 15, 1924; s. George and Ann (Johnson) McA.; m. Eva Kim, Sept. 17, 1979. B.A. in Journalism, U. Ga., 1948. With AP, 1948-69; corr. AP, Korea, 1950-54, Paris, 1954-60; bur. chief AP, Cairo, 1960-63, Manila, 1963-65; corr. AP, Saigon, 1966-68; bur. chief AP, 1968-69; with Los Angeles Times, 1969-83; bur. chief Los Angeles Times, Saigon, 1970-75; corr. for Southeast Asia Los Angeles Times, Bangkok, 1975-79; diplomatic corr. U.S. News & World Report, 1983-85. Served with USNR, 1943-45. Recipient citation for fgn. reporting Overseas Press Club, 1973. Mem. Sigma Delta Chi. Clubs: Fgn. Corrs. (Hong Kong); Glen Arven Country (Thomasville, Ga.); River Bend Country (Gt. Falls, Va.). Address: 506 E Creek Ct Vienna VA 22180-3578

MC ARTHUR, JANET WARD, endocrinologist, educator; b. Bellingham, Wash., June 25, 1914; d. Hyland Donald and Alice Maria (Frost) McA. A.B., U. Wash., 1935, M.S., 1937; M.B., Northwestern U., 1941, M.D., 1942; ScD (hon.), Mt. Holyoke Coll., 1962. Diplomate: Am. Bd. Internal Medicine. Intern Cin. Gen. Hosp., 1941-42, asst. resident in medicine, 1942-43; asst. resident, rsch. fellow in medicine H.P. Walcott fellow clin. medicine Mass. Gen. Hosp., Boston, 1943-47, assoc. physician, 1959-84, assoc. children's svc., 1968-84; instr. Harvard U., 1955-57, asst. prof., 1960-64, assoc. prof., 1964-73, prof., 1973-84, prof. emeritus, 1984—; clin. prof. medicine Boston U. Sch. Medicine, 1984—; adj. prof. Sargent Coll. Allied Health Scis. Boston U., 1982—; mem. reproductive biology study sect. NIH, 1974-78, Com. on Population Studies, 1980-84; co-dir. Vincent Meml. Rsch. Lab., 1977-79; sr. scientist U. London, 1985-86. Author: (with others) Functional Endocrinology from Birth Through Adolescence, 1952; editor: (with Theodore Colton) Statistics in Endocrinology, 1970; contbr. articles to profl. jours. Fellow ACP; mem. AMA, AAAS, Endocrine Soc., Am. Fertility Soc., Am. Assn. Clin. Endocrinologists, Boston Obstet. Soc., Phi Beta Kappa, Sigma Xi, Alpha Omega Alpha. Home: 19 Brimmer St Boston MA 02108-1025 Office: Boston U 4th Fl 635 Commonwealth Ave Fl 4 Boston MA 02215-1605

MCARTHUR, JOHN HECTOR, university dean, business educator; b. Vancouver, B.C., Can., Mar. 31, 1934; came to U.S., 1957; s. Hector and Elizabeth Lee (Whyte) McA.; m. Netilia Ewasiuk, Sept. 15, 1956; children: Jocelyn Natasha, Susan Patricia. B in Commerce, U. B.C., 1957; MBA, Harvard U., 1959, DBA, 1962; LLD (hon.), Simon Fraser U., 1982, Queens U., 1985, Middlebury Coll., 1988, U. Western Ont., 1992; hon. degree, U. Navarra, Spain, 1989. Prof., dean Sch. Bus. Adminstrn., Sch. Bus. Adminstrn., Harvard U., Cambridge, Mass., 1980—; bd. dirs. BCE, Inc., Chase Manhattan Corp., Rohm and Haas Co., Inc., Springs Industries, Inc., Cabot Corp.; cons. numerous cos. and govt. agys. in Can., Europe and U.S. Chmn. bd. trustees Brigham and Women's Hosp., 1986, Ptnrs. Health Sys., 1994. Home: 140 Old Connecticut Path Wayland MA 01778-3202 Office: Coll Bus Adminstrn Harvard U Cambridge MA 02138

MCATEE, PATRICIA ANNE ROONEY, medical educator; b. Denver, Apr. 20, 1931; d. Jerry F. and Edna E. (Hansen) Rooney; m. Darrell McAtee, Sept. 4, 1954; 1 son, Kevin Paul. BS, Loretto Heights Coll., 1953; MS, U. Colo., 1961; PhD, Union of Univs., 1976. Supr. St. Anthony Hosp., Denver, 1952-55; pub. health nurse edn. dir. Tri-County Health Dept., Colo., 1956-58; adminstr. sch. health program Littleton (Colo.) Pub. Schs. 1958-60; asst. prof. community health, acad. adminstr. continuing edn. U. Colo., 1968-70; project dir. Western Interstate Commn. for Higher Edn., 1972-74; asst. prof. pediatrics, project co-dir. Sch. Medicine U. Colo., 1975—; mem. profl. svcs. staff Mead Johnson & Co., 1980—; cons. Colo. Safety Coun.; treas. Vista Nueva Assocs. Editor: Pediatric Nursing, 1975-77. Chmn. bd. dirs. Found. for Urban and Neighborhood Devel.; mem. Arapahoe Health Planning Coun. Mem. NAS, APHA, Inst. Medicine, Nat. Bd. Pediatric Nurse Practitioners and Assocs. (pres.), Nat. Assn. Pediatric Nurse Practitioners (v.p.), Am. Acad. Polit. and Social Scientist, Nat. League Nursing, Western Soc. Rsch., Am. Sch. Health Assn., Sigma Theta Tau. Home: 877 E Panama Dr Littleton CO 80121-2531 Office: 4200 E 9th Ave Box C-219 Denver CO 80262

MCATEER, JAMES FRANCIS, lawyer; b. Seattle, Feb. 23, 1931; s. George Henry and Irene Mary (Ethier) McA.; m. Joan Francis Fitzpatrick, July 31, 1954 (div. Aug. 1977); children: Maryjeanne, Anne, Patricia, Margaret, Kathleen, Suzanne, Heidi; m. Judith Ann Gautsch, Jan. 24, 1978. Student, Santa Clara U., 1948-51; BS, U. Wash., 1953, JD, 1954. Bar: Wash. 1954, U.S. Supreme Ct. 1976. Asst. U.S. atty. for western dist. Wash., Seattle, 1959-62; ptnr. Lenihan, Ivers & McAteer, 1964-80, Schwabe, Williamson, Ferguson & Burdell, Seattle, 1986—. Mem. Law Rev., U. Wash., 1953-54. Capt. JAGC, U.S. Army, 1954-58. Mem. Wash. State Bar Assn., Seattle-

King County Bar Assn., Wash. Athletic Club, Central Park Tennis Club, Order of Coif. Roman Catholic. Home: 2109 E Crescent Dr Seattle WA 98112 Office: Schwabe Williamson Ferguson & Burdell 1420 5th Ave Ste 3400 Seattle WA 98101

MCAULAY, DIANNE LUCY, gifted education educator; b. Brockton, Mass., Aug. 5, 1940; d. Ernest Francis and Clarissa May (Atwood) Marcotte; m. William Alexander McAulay, Apr. 22, 1960; children: Laurie Mae McAulay Cambrola, W. Scott, Lisa Dianne. BA, U. R.I., 1972; MEd, R.I. Coll., 1974, cert. Adv. Grad. Studies, 1982; PhD, U. Conn., 1987. Cert. elem. tchr., secondary English tchr., educator of gifted, R.I. Sec. Met. Life Ins., Union Mut. Ins. Providence and Barrington, R.I., 1957-62; resource tchr. gifted and talented Cranston (R.I.) Pub. Sch.s, 1972—; ednl. cons., South Kingstown, R.I., 1975—; discussion leader Great Books Found., 1976—; ednl. svcs. cons. New Eng. Power Svc., Westborough, Mass., 1978—; adj. prof. edn. and curriculum U. R.I., Kingston, 1979—, R.I. Coll., Providence, 1979—, dir. educator of gifted cert. program, 1981—; coach The Future Problem Solving Program, Ann Arbor, Mich., 1988—; adv. R.I. State Project Dirs. Gifted and Talented Programs, Providence, 1990—; lectr. Jason project, South Kingstown, 1991—; trainer Talents Unltd., 1991, ASCD's Tactics for Thinking, 1992; chairperson adv. bd. R.I. State Commr. of Edn. on Gifted and Talented, 1994—. Author: (film guides) Donald in Mathmagic Land, 1983, Powers of Ten, 1984, Current Events, 1985, Why Man Creates, 1986, (book) Type II Enrichment by Gifted/Talented Teachers, 1987. Adv. Save the Bay, Providence, 1981—; field tester, promoter R.I. Naturally Audubon Soc., Smithfield, 1978—; supporter U. R.I. Sch. Oceanography, Naragansett, 1989—; data collector, evaluator, R.I. Watershed Watch, Kingston, 1989—. Recipient 1st place R.I. Film, Video Competition Brown U., Providence, 1983; grantee Montclair (N.J.) State Coll. 1985, Nat. Sci. Found. Washington, 1993; named R.I. Tchr. of Yr. R.I. Farmers Bureau, Warwick, 1992-93. Mem. Nat. Sci. Tchrs. Assn., Assn. Supervision and Curriculum Devel. Ctr. Econ. Edn., Law Related Edn., S.E. New Eng. Marine Educators (exec. bd. 1987-91), R.I. State Advocates of Gifted Edn. (pres., v.p. 1982—), R.I. Agriculture in Classroom (advocate), Phi Kappa Phi (highest distinction 1972). Avocations: expedition travel, wild plant propagation, jazz, sailing, fitness. Home: 150 Half Moon Trl Wakefield RI 02879-7706 Office: Glen Hills Sch Glen Hills Dr Cranston RI 02920

MCAULEY, SKEET, artist; b. Monahans, Tex., Mar. 7, 1951; s. George Clifford and Thelma Lee (Martin) McA.; m. Karen Suzanne Gee, June 25, 1994. BA, Sam Houston State U., 1976; MFA, Ohio U., 1978. Instr. photography Spring Hill Coll., Mobile, Ala., 1978-79, Tyler (Tex.) Jr. Coll., 1979-81; assoc. prof. photography U. N.Tex., Denton, 1981-93; featured in numerous articles and publs. One-person exhibits include Christopher Grimes Gallery, Santa Monica, Calif., 1995, Lowinsky Gallery, N.Y.C., 1993, U.S. Golf Assn. Mus., Far Hills, N.J., 1993, Dallas Mus. Art, 1992, Moody Gallery, Houston, 1992, Tyler Mus. of Art, 1992, The Heard Mus., Amherst, Mass., 1991, Calif. Mus. Photography, Riverside, 1991, Etherton/ Stern Gallery, Tucson, Ariz., 1991, The Albuquerque Mus., 1990; group exhibits include Cleve. Mus. Art, 1994, Virginia Beach Ctr. for Arts, 1994, others; author: Sign Language: Contemporary Southwest Native Americans, 1989. Grantee Polaroid Copr., 1988, Nat. Endowment for the Arts Individual Artist fellowship, 1984, 86. Mem. Soc. Photographic Education (bd. dirs. 1990-93). Democrat. Office: 3516 Madera Ave Los Angeles CA 90039

MCAULIFFE, CLAYTON DOYLE, chemist; b. Chappell, Nebr., Aug. 18, 1918; s. John F. and Emma Elizabeth (Stenger) McA.; m. Irene Opal Pickering, Sept. 5, 1943 (dec. Dec. 1988); children: Carol Ann McAuliffe Krenek, Clifford Andrew, Douglas Clayton, Thomas Frank; m. Wilma G. Long, Oct. 2, 1993. A.B., Nebr. Wesleyan U. 1941; M.A., U. Minn., 1942; Ph.D., Cornell U., 1948. Lab. asst. Nebr. Wesleyan U., 1939-41; research chemist Manhattan Project, 1943-46; cons. Dept. Agrl., 1947-48; research assoc. Cornell U., 1948-50; research assoc. prof. chemistry N.C. State U., 1950-56; sr. research chemist Chevron Oil Field Research Co., La Habra, Calif., 1956-67, sr. research assoc., 1967-86; pres. Clayton McAuliffe and Assocs., Inc., 1986—; mem. steering com. petroleum in marine environ. Nat. Acad. Scis., 1972-75, com. energy and environ. 1974-76, com. dispersnat effectiveness, 1985-89; mem. Ocean Scis. Bd., 1975-77; cons. in field. Contbr. articles to profl. jours., chpts. to books; patentee in field. U. Minn. fellow, 1941-42; Cornell U. fellow, 1942-43, 46-48; NSF grantee; duPont Co. grantee; AEC grantee. Fellow AAAS; mem. Am. Chem. Soc., Soc. Petroleum Engrs., Am. Soc. Agronomy, Soil Sci. Soc. Am., Am. Assn. Petroleum Geologists. Republican. Methodist. Home and Office: 1220 Frances Ave Fullerton CA 92631-1807

MCAULIFFE, JANE DAMMEN, Middle Eastern and Islamic studies educator. BA in Classics and Philosophy, Trinity Coll., 1968; MA in Religious Studies, U. Toronto, 1979, PhD in Islamic Studies, 1984. Asst. prof. dept. religious studies U. Toronto, 1981-86, assoc. prof. dept. Middle East and Islamic studies, 1992—, chair dept. study of religion, dir. Ctr. Study of Religion, 1992—; from asst. prof. to assoc. prof. history of religions and Islamic studies Candler Sch. Theology Emory U., Atlanta, 1986-92, assoc. dean Candler Sch. Theology, 1990-92; appointed Vatican Commn. for Religious Rels. with Muslims, 1994. Author: Qur'anic Christians: An Analysis of Classical and Modern Exegesis, 1991, 'Abbasid Authority Affirmed: The Early Years of al-Mansur, vol. 28, 1995; contbr. articles to profl. jours. Danforth Found. fellow, 1976-80, NEH Summer fellow, 1979-80, Charles Gordon Heyd fellow, 1980-81, Social Scis. and Humanities Rsch. Coun. Doctoral fellow, 1981-84, Postdoctoral fellow, 1984-86, CASA II fellow, 1986, NEH Summer Faculty Travel fellow, 1989, NEH Rsch. fellow, 1992, Mellon fellow, 1994; Queen Elizabeth II Ont. scholar, 1983-84. Mem. Am. Soc. Study of Religion, Am. Acad. Religion, Am. Oriental Soc., Can. Soc. Study of Religion, Mid. East Studies Assn. (Thesis award 1985), Oriental Club Toronto, Soc. Values in Higher Edn. Office: U Toronto Dept & Ctr Religion, 123 Saint George St, Toronto, ON Canada M5S 2E8

MC AULIFFE, MICHAEL F., bishop; b. Kansas City, Mo., Nov. 22, 1920. Student, St. Louis Prep. Sem., Cath. U. Ordained priest Roman Cath. Ch., 1945; consecrated bishop, 1969; bishop diocese of Jefferson City Jefferson City, Mo., 1969—. Office: Chancery Office 605 Clark Ave PO Box 417 Jefferson City MO 65102*

MCAULIFFE, RICHARD L., church official; m. Janet Bettinghaus; children: Brian, Andrea Stephenson. Student, Carleton Coll.; MBA, Harvard U. Exec. v.p., treas., CFO Harris Bankcorp, Harris Trust and Savs. Bank, 1960-90; mng. agt. Resolution Trust Corp., 1990—; treas. Evang. Luth. Ch. in Am., Chgo., 1992—; pres. Grace Luth. Ch., Glen Ellyn, Ill., Evang. Luth. Ch. Am. Ch. Coun.; treas. English Synod and Christ Sem.-Seminex, AELC; bd. dirs./com. mem. Christian Century Found., Luth. Gen. Healthcare Sys.; active Luth. Social Svcs. Ill. Office: Evang Luth Ch Am 8765 W Higgins Rd Chicago IL 60631

MCAULIFFE, STEVEN JAMES, federal judge; b. 1948. BA, Va. Mil. Inst., 1970; JD, Georgetown U., 1973. Capt. appellate coun. U.S. Army Judge Advocate Gens. Corps, 1973-77; asst. atty. gen. Office N.H. Atty. Gen., 1977-80; ptnr. Gallagher, Callahan, Gartrell, P.A., Concord, N.H., 1980-92; fed. judge U.S. Dist. Ct. (N.H. dist.), Concord, 1992—. Trustee Univ. System of N.H., 1986-94; bd. dirs. N.H. Med. Malpractice Stabilization Res. Fund Trust, 1987-92, Office Pub. Guardian, 1980-92, Challenger Ctr. for Space Sci. Edn.; active N.H. Dem. Leadership Coun., 1988-92. Capt. U.S. Army, 1970-77, USAR, 1977-80, N.H. Army NG, 1980-88. Fellow N.H. Bar Found.; mem. ABA, N.H. Bar Assn. (pres. 1991-92, pres.-elect 1990-91, v.p. 1989-90, mem. ex-officio N.H. Supreme Ct. com. profl. conduct 1989-90, mem. ethics com. 1984-86), Nat. Conf. Bar Pres., Merrimack County Bar Assn., D.C. Bar Assn., U.S. Supreme Ct. Hist. Soc., N.H. Jud. Coun. (vice-chmn. 1991-92), Aircraft Owners and Pilots Assn., N.H. Hist. Soc., Concord Country Club. Office: US Dist Ct PO Box 1498 55 Pleasant St Concord NH 03302

MCAVITY, JOHN GILLIS, museum director, association executive, museologist; b. St. John, N.B., Can., Oct. 30, 1950; s. J. Patrick H. and Catharine A. (McNeil) McA. BA., U. N.B., 1972. Cert. assn. exec. Asst. curator Kings Landing Mus., Fredericton, N.B., Can., 1972-73; provincial mus. adviser N.B. Mus., St. John, Can., 1973-76; exec. dir. Ont. Mus. Assn.

Toronto, Can., 1976-81, Can. Mus. Assn., Ottawa, Ont., Can., 1981—. V.p. St. John Heritage Trust, 1974-76; exec. com. Can. Club, St. John, 1975, English Speaking Union, St. John, 1974-76; vol. fundraiser Kidney Found. Can.; bd. dirs. Centretown Citizens Corp; founding mem. Mus. Found. Can. 1994—. Mem. Am. Assn. Museums, Am. Assn. for State and Local History (awards com. 1981-84, nominations com. 1985), Mus. Found. Can. (founding dir. 1994—), Inst. Assn. Execs. (chmn. postal com., bd. dirs. Ottawa chpt., cert.), Assn. Cultural Execs. (bd. dirs. 1988-92), Quaco Hist. and Libr. Soc. (hon. life), Tourism Industry Assn. Can. (bd. dirs.), Assn. Museums N.B. (founding mem.), Ont. Assn. Art Galleries (bd. dirs. 1986-90), Can. Soc. Copyright Consumers, Can. Soc. Assn. Execs. (bd. dirs. 1993—), Can. Art Mus. Dirs. Orgn., Shefford Heritage Co-op (membership com. 1992—). Anglican. Home: Apt 41, 300 Cooper St, Ottawa, ON Canada K2P 0G7 Office: Can Museums Assn, Ste 400, 280 Metcalfe, Ottawa, ON Canada K2P 1R7

MCAVOY, BRUCE RONALD, scientist, consultant; b. Jamestown, N.Y., Jan. 30, 1933; s. George Harold and Agda Amelia (Martinson) McA. BS in Physics, U. Rochester, 1954. Jr. engr. Westinghouse Air Arm Div., Balt., 1956-57, assoc. engr., 1957-58; rsch. engr. Westinghouse Rsch. Ctr., Pitts. 1958-69; sr. rsch. engr. Westinghouse R & D Ctr., Pitts., 1969-78, fellow engr., 1978-84, adv. scientist, 1984—; adv. bd. mem. Nat. Ctr. Physical Acoustics, U. Miss., 1987-88. Editor spl. issue IEEE Trans. Microwave Theory Tech., Ultrasonics Symposium procs., 1976-93; mem. editl. bd. jour. Microwave and Guided Wave Letters, 1990. With U.S. Army, 1954-56. Fellow IEEE (awards and recognition com. 1989—, def. R&D policy com. 1989-91, Centennial medal 1984); mem. DAV (life), Ultrasonic, Rerroelectric and Frequency Control Soc. of IEEE (pres. 1986-87), Electromagnetics Acad., Microwave Theory and Techniques Soc. (chmn. microwave acoustics tech. com. 1988—). Republican. Lutheran. Home: 926 Ivy St Pittsburgh PA 15232-2651

MCAVOY, JOHN JOSEPH, lawyer; b. Worley, Idaho, June 28, 1933; s. Earl Francis and Florence Jewel (Mitchell) McA.; m. Joan Marjorie Zeldon, Sept. 20, 1964; children: Jason, Jon. B.A., U. Idaho, 1954, LL.B., 1958; LL.M., Yale U., 1959. Bar: Idaho 1958, U.S. Supreme Ct. 1962, N.Y. 1963, U.S. Tax Ct. 1969, D.C. 1976. Asst. prof. law George Washington U., Washington, 1959-62; staff atty. stockpile investigating subcom. Armed Forces Com. U.S. Senate, Washington, 1962; assoc. White & Case, N.Y.C., 1963-71, ptnr., 1972—; adj. prof. Washington Coll. Law, Am. U., Washington, 1990. Bd. dirs. N.Y. Civil Liberties Union, 1975-77; chmn. due process com. ACLU, 1971-75. Served with U.S. Army, 1954-56. Mem. Assn. of Bar of City of N.Y., D.C. Bar Assn. (ethics com. 1982-88, vice chmn. 1986-87, chmn. 1987-88), Phi Beta Kappa, Phi Alpha Delta. Democrat. Avocations: swimming, bicycling, fgn. travel. Office: White & Case 1747 Pennsylvania Ave NW Washington DC 20006-4604

MCAVOY, ROGERS, educational psychology educator, consultant; b. Webster Springs, W.Va., Dec. 28, 1927; s. Ellis McLaughlin and Carolyn (McIntosh) McA.; m. Anne T. Limpe, Dec. 19, 1956 (div.); children: Carol Ann, Philip Ellis, Karen Lynelle; m. Irma Jean Tingler, July 7, 1973. BA, Fairmont State Coll., 1951; MA, W.Va. U., 1954; PhD, Ind. U., 1966. Tchr. biology Petersburg (W.Va.) High Sch., 1951-53; asst. dir. admissions Marshall U., Huntington, W.Va., 1953-55; registrar Glenville (W.Va.) State Coll., 1955-56; rsch. asst., asst. to dean Ind. U., Bloomington, 1956-61; asst. prof. ednl. psychology W.Va. U., Morgantown, 1961-65, assoc. prof., 1967-72, prof., 1973—, chmn. dept., 1966-77; cons. state and county ednl. systems, W.Va., others, 1965-89; cons. follow through program Stanford Rsch. Inst., 1969-72. Contbr. articles to profl. jours. Mem. Phi Delta Kappa (Disting. Svc. award 1982, 25-yr. svc. award 1990). Avocations: writing, book collecting, restoring houses, photography, reading. Office: WVa U 608 Allen Hall Morgantown WV 26506

MCAVOY, THOMAS JAMES, federal judge. AB, Villanova U., 1960; JD, Union U., 1964. Bar: N.Y. 1964, U.S. Dist. Ct. (no. dist.) N.Y. 1964. Assoc. Hinman, Howard & Kattell, Binghamton, N.Y., 1964-69, Kramer, Wales, & McAvoy, Binghamton, 1969-84, McAvoy & Hickey, P.C., Binghamton, 1984-85; from judge to chief judge U.S. Dist. Ct. (no. dist.) N.Y., Binghamton, 1986—. With USMC, 1958. Office: US Dist Ct/No Dist NY 225 Fed Bldg 15 Henry St Binghamton NY 13901

MCAWARD, PATRICK JOSEPH, JR., architectural and engineering company executive; b. Flushing, N.Y., Feb. 13, 1934; s. Patrick Joseph and Lucy (Aufenanger) McA.; m. Jean Ann Schehr, Dec. 26, 1955; children: Patrick J., Michael J., Timothy J., Maura J., Kevin J. BSCE, U. Notre Dame, 1955; postgrad, CCNY, 1957. Registered profl. engr. in 20 states. With TAMS Consultants Inc., N.Y.C., 1955—; project engr. N.Y.C., 1965-68; assoc. and resident engr. Charleston, W.Va., 1968-71, head bridges and structures dept., 1968-71; project coord. for projects in Ethiopia, Kenya, Malawi, Botswana, Zaire, 1973-76; mgr. projects, L.I., Tex., N.Y., 1977-80; head transp. div., 1976-81; ops. mgr., prin. N.Y.C., 1981—. Mem. ASCE, NSPE, Am. Pub. Transit Assn., Internat. Bridge, Tunnel and Turnpike Assn. (assoc.). Roman Catholic. Home: 135 Succabone Rd Bedford Hills NY 10507-2230 Office: TAMS Consultants Inc 655 3rd Ave New York NY 10017-5617

MCBAIN, DIANE JEAN, actress, writer; b. Cleve., May 18, 1941; d. Walter George and Cleo Lida (Ferguson) McB.; m. Rodney L. Burke (div.); 1 child, Evan Andrew. Student, Antioch U., Los Angeles, 1985-87. Film, TV actress, 1957—; actress Warner Bros. Studios, 1959-64; freelance actress, 1976-81; owner Superior Interiors, 1964-68; screen writer, novelist, 1979—; treas., producer, prodn. coordinator Pied Piper Prodns., Inc., 1980-83, also bd. dirs.; freelance writer, photographer, 1982—; bd. dirs. The Response Ctr., L.A., counselor, 1985-89; treas. Theater for Youth Project, 1981; with Project Angel Food, 1989-92. Appeared in films including Ice Palace, Parrish, Claudelle Inglish, A Distant Trumpet, The Caretakers, Donner Pass, Mary, Mary, I Sailed to Tahiti, Spinout, The Delta Factor, Thunder Alley, Wicked, Wicked, The Puppet Master; TV shows include Dallas, Eight is Enough, Hawaii Five-O, Grizzly Adams Christmas Spl., Knight Rider, Air Wolf, Days of Our Lives, Marcus Welby, M.D., Police Story, Charlie's Angels, Matt Houston, Jake and the Fat Man, General Hospital; TV movie Donner Pass; theater prodns. include Who's Happy Now, The Tender Trap, The Glass Menagerie, Star Spangled Girl. Mem. exec. com. Iris Cantor Ctr. for Breast Imaging, 1990—; Stephen minister All Sts. Episcopal Ch., Beverly Hills, Calif., 1987; bd. dirs. exec. com. Justiceville, Homeless, U.S.A.; administr., project mgr. for C.Y.T./Blue Star Prodns., Paramount Studios, L.A. Democrat. Avocations: tennis, photography, traveling, aerobics.

MC BAIN, ED See HUNTER, EVAN

MCBAINE, JOHN NEYLAN, lawyer; b. San Francisco, Apr. 29, 1941; s. Turner H. and Jane Frances (Neylan) McB.; m. Alison Denny, Feb. 22, 1963 (div.); 1 child, Diana; m. Ariel Bybee, Nov. 24, 1972; 1 child, Neylan. B.A., Stanford U., 1962; J.D., U. Calif., 1967. Bar: D.C. 1968, Calif. 1970, N.Y. 1975. Assoc. law firm Covington & Burling, Washington, 1967-68; law clk. Hon. Gerhard A. Gesell U.S. Dist. Ct., D.C., 1968-69; assoc. law firm Pillsbury, Madison & Sutro, San Francisco, 1970-74; ptnr. Lord, Day & Lord, N.Y.C., 1975-86, Coudert Bros., N.Y.C., 1986—. Contbr. articles to profl. jours. Pres. Lincoln Plaza Tenants Corp., 1982-84, bd. dirs., 1982—; bd. visitors Brigham Young Law Sch., 1983-92. Served with AUS, 1963. Mem. ABA, Calif. Bar Assn., N.Y. Bar Assn. Mem. LDS Ch. Home: 44 W 62nd St New York NY 10023-7008 Office: Coudert Bros 1114 Ave of the Americas New York NY 10036

MCBATH, DONALD LINUS, osteopathic physician; b. Chgo., May 19, 1935; s. Earl and Phyllis (Michalski) McB.; m. Ruth Southerland, Jan. 18, 1956; children: Donald L. Jr., Donna Ruth McBath Bassett, Daniel P. BA in Polit. Sci., U. Fla., 1957, BS in Pre Med, 1962; DO, Kansas City (Mo.) Coll. Osteopathy and Surgery, 1969; MA, St. Leo Coll., 1981. Diplomate Nat. Bd. Examiners; cert. family practice Am. Osteo. Bd. Gen. Practice, Correctional Health Profl. Med. dir. various orgns., Dade City, Fla., 1971; chief of staff Jackson Meml. Hosp., Dade City, Fla., 1969—; past chief of staff, med. dir. East Pasco Med. Ctr., Zephyrills, Fla.; med. dir. Pasco County, Hernando County Prison Sys., Fla.; bd. dirs. East Pasco Med. Ctr., Zephrillis; adv. bd. Prudential Health Plan, Anthem Health Plan; trustee, pres., exec. com. Fla. Osteo. Med. Assn.; sports physician Pasco Com-

prehensive H.S.; med. examiner Fed. Acronautics Adminstrn.; Dade City grand marshall, past chmn. adv. coun.; pres., trustee East Pasco Med. Ctr. Found.; assoc. prof. clin. sci. Southeastern U. Health Scis., Miami, Fla. Trustee St. Leo (Fla.) Coll.; adv. dir. First Union Nat. Bank Fla., Dade City; com. chmn. Hall of Fame Bowl, Pasco County, Fla., 1987. Recipient Pump Handle award Pasco County Health Authority, 1988, Outstanding Contbn. award H.R.S. Pasco County Pub. Health Unit, 1988, Outstanding Svc. award Fla. Interscholastic Athletic Adminstrs. Assn., 1994; named Gen. Practitioner of Yr., Fla. Acad. Gen. Practice, 1990-91. Fellow Am. Coll. Osteo. Family Physicians; mem. Am. Osteo. Assn. (nat. program conv. chmn., conv. com., exhibit adv. com., mem. ho. of dels.), Fla. Soc. Am. Coll. of Gen. Practitioners (nat. conv. com., bd. dirs. 1989-90, pres. 1991-92), Rotary (Dade City chpt. past pres., Paul Harris fellow). Roman Catholic. Avocation: sports. Home and Office: McBath Med Ctr 13925 17th St Dade City FL 33525

MCBAY, ARTHUR JOHN, toxicologist, consultant; b. Medford, Mass., Jan. 6, 1919; s. Arthur and Virginia (Davito) McB.; m. Avis Louise Botsford, Aug. 24, 1946; children: John, Robert. B.S., Mass. Coll. Pharmacy, 1940, M.S., 1942; Ph.D., Purdue U., 1948. Diplomate Am. Bd. Forensic Toxicology; cert. toxicol. chemist Am. Bd. Clin. Chemistry; registered pharmacist, Mass. Asst. prof. chemistry Mass. Coll. Pharmacy, Boston, 1948-53, asst. in legal medicine, dept. legal medicine, 1953-63; lectr. legal medicine Harvard U.; toxicologist, criminalist, cons. Mass. State Police Chemistry Lab., 1955-63; instr. Northeastern U., 1962-63; assoc. prof. toxicology Law-Medicine Inst. Boston U., 1963-69, assoc. prof. pharmacology Med. Sch., 1963-69; supr. lab. Mass. Dept. Pub. Safety, Boston, 1963-69; assoc. prof. pathology and toxicology U. N.C., Chapel Hill, 1969-73, prof., 1973-89, prof. emeritus pharmacy and pathology, 1989—; chief toxicologist Office Chief Med. Examiner, Chapel Hill, 1969-89; mem. task force on alcohol, other drugs and transp. NRC; cons. toxicology resource com. Coll. Am. Pathologists, 1975—, Bur. Med. Devices and Diagnostic Products, FDA, 1975-91, N.C. Drug Authority, 1971-75; dir. Mass. Alcohol Project, 1968-69. Mem. editorial bd. Jour. Forensic Scis., 1981—; bd. editors Yearbook of Pathology, 1981-91; contbr. numerous articles on toxicology to profl. jours. Served to capt. USAAF, 1943-45. Fellow Am. Acad. Forensic Scis.; mem. Internat. Assn. Forensic Toxicologists, Nat. Safety Coun. (exec. bd. com. on alcohol and drugs 1981-91), Am. Pharm. Assn. (sec., treas. sci. sect. 1954-57), Soc. Forensic Toxicologists (dir. 1978), Am. Chem. Soc., Sigma Xi, Rho Chi, Phi Lambda Upsilon. Democrat. Roman Catholic. Home: V-306 Carolina Meadows Chapel Hill NC 27514

MCBAY, HENRY CECIL, chemist, educator; b. Mexia, Tex., May 29, 1914; s. William Cecil and Roberta (Ransom) McB.; (div. Apr. 1968); children: Michael H.C., Ronald P.W. BS in Chemistry, Wiley Coll., 1934; MS in Chemistry, Atlanta U., 1936; PhD in Chemistry, U. Chgo., 1945. Prof. Morehouse Coll., Atlanta, 1980-87; Fuller E. Callaway prof. chemistry Atlanta U., 1982-86, emeritus prof. chemistry, 1986—; vis. lectr. Howard U., 1973, Dept. Chemistry, U. Md., 1974, Dept. Chemistry, U. Atlanta, 1974, Southern U., 1976, Washington U., 1979, U. Ala., 1987, The Ala. A&M U., 1987; invited lectr. Wesleyan U., Middletown, Conn., 1993. Contbr. numerous articles to profl. jours. Recipient Elizabeth Norten prize for Excellence in Rsch. in Chemistry, The U. Chgo., 1944, 45, Outstanding Tchr. award Nat. Orgn. for Advancement Black Chemists and Engrs., 1976, The Charles H. Herty award for Outstanding Contbns. to Chemistry from Ga. sect. Am. Chem. Soc., 1976, James Flack Norris award for Outstanding Achievement in Teaching of Chemistry, Northeastern Sect. Am. Chem. Soc., 1978, Kimuel A. Huggins award in Sci., Bishop Coll., 1980, Beta Kappa Chi Sci. Soc. Lamplighter award. Mem. Am. Chem. Soc., Am. Inst. Chemists, Ga. Acad. Sci., Nat. Inst. Sci. Home: 1719 Detroit Ct NW Atlanta GA 30314 Office: Morehouse Coll Dept Chemistry 830 Westview Dr SW Atlanta GA 30314

MCBEATH, ANDREW ALAN, orthopedic surgery educator; b. Milw., Mar. 4, 1936; s. Ivor Charles and Lida McBeath; children: Craig Matthew, Drew Alan. BS, U. Wis., 1958, MD, 1961. Diplomate Am. Bd. Orthopaedic Surgery (oral examiner). Intern, resident Hartford (Conn.) Hosp., 1961-63; resident in orthopedic surgery U. Iowa, Iowa City, 1963-66; asst. prof. div. orthopedic surgery div. surgery U. Wis., Madison, 1968-72, assoc. prof., 1972-79, prof., 1979—, Frederick J. Gaenslen prof., 1980, acting chmn. div., 1972-75, chmn. div., 1975—. Contbr. over 65 articles, chpt. to books. Capt. M.C., USAF, 1966-68. Mem. AMA, Am. Acad. Orthopaedic Surgeons, Orthopaedic Rsch. Soc., Am. Orthopaedic Assn., Pico Soc., Wis. Orthopaedic Soc., Rotary, Alpha Omega Alpha. Avocations: bicycling, skiing, reading. Office: U Wis Div Orthopedic Surg G5/361 600 Highland Ave Madison WI 53792-3228

MCBEE, FRANK WILKINS, JR., industrial manufacturing executive; b. Ridley Park, Pa., Jan. 22, 1920; s. Frank Wilkins and Ruth (Moulton) McB.; m. Sue U. Brandt, Apr. 10, 1943; children: Marilyn Moore, Robert Frank. BSME, U. Tex, 1947, MSME, 1950; PhD (hon.), St. Edward's U., Austin, 1986. Instr. to asst. prof. mech. engring. U. Tex., Austin, 1946-53, supr. mech. dept. Def. Research Lab., 1950-59; co-founder Tracor, Inc., Austin, 1955, treas., sr. v.p., 1955-67, exec. v.p., 1967-70, pres., 1970-86, chief exec. officer, 1970-88, chmn. bd., 1972-88, exec. cons., 1988-91; bd. dirs. MCorp, Dallas, Radian Corp., Austin, Rsch. Applications, Inc., Austin. Sr. active mem. adv. council U. Tex. Engring. Found.; mem. chancellor's council, U. Tex.; bd. dirs. St. Edward's U.; mem., bd. dirs. Tex. Nature Conservancy, Audubon Soc., Smithsonian Inst.; chmn. adv. bd. Discovery Hall; devel. com. mem. U. Tex. Dept. Computer Scis.; hon. chmn. Allan Shivers Radiation Therapy Ctr.; past chmn. bd. trustees Laguna Gloria Art Mus; fin. council Seton Med. Ctr., Seton N.W. Corp. Campaign; past chmn. Austin Area Rsch. Orgn.; trustee emeritus Southwest Tex. Pub. Broadcasting Council; sustaining mem. Friends of Archer M. Huntington Art Gallery, Austin; contbg. mem. N.Y. Met. Mus. Art; sr. advisor Tex. Lyceum; trustee Headliners Found.; chmn. Headliners Club; patron Ctr. for Battered Women, Austin; dir. SW Rsch. Inst.; San Antonio; past dir. Paramount Theatre for Performing Arts. Served to capt. USAAF, 1944-46. Recipient Benefactor award Austin Community Found., 1980, Spl. award Austin C. of C. Econ. Devel. Council, 1982, Clara Driscoll award Laguna Gloria Art Mus., 1987, Disting. Alumnus award U. Tex. Coll. Engring., 1978, Austinite of Yr. award Austin C. of C., 1986, Disting. Alumnus award U. Tex., 1988, Hist. Preservation awards 1964, 75, Walter Bremond House, 1990, Raymond Todd Civic award Austin Community Found., 1989, Allan Shivers Jr. award Bus. Com. for the Arts, Greater Austin C. of C., 1989, Brotherhood award Nat. Conf. Christians and Jews, 1981; named to Stephen F. Austin High Sch. Hall of Honor, 1981, Tex. Bus. Hall of Fame, 1990, Bus. Stateman of Yr. Harvard Bus. Sch. Club, 1990, Man of Yr. Air Force Assn. (Austin chpt.), 1977. Mem. NAE (life), NSPE, Tex. Soc. Profl. Engrs. (Outstanding Engr. of Yr. 1983), Tex. Assn. Bus., Tex. Taxpayers Assn. (bd. dirs.), Austin Heritage Soc. (life), Austin History Ctr. Assn. (founding), Nat. Trust for Hist. Preservation (sustaining mem.), Nat. Acad. Engring., U. Tex. Bus. Hall of Fame, U. Tex. Pres.'s Assocs., Austin C. of C., U. Tex. Ex-Students Assn. (life), 100 Club, Tau Beta Pi, Sigma Xi, Pi Tau Sigma, Austin Yacht Club (former commodore, vice chmn.). Office: 705 San Antonio St Austin TX 78701-2823

MCBEE, MARY LOUISE, state legislator, former academic administrator; b. Strawberry Plains, Tenn., June 15, 1924; d. John Wallace and Nina Aileen (Umbarger) McB. BS, East Tenn. State U., 1946; MA, Columbia U., 1951; PhD, Ohio State U., 1961. Tchr. East Tenn. State U., Johnson City, 1947-51; asst. dean of women, 1952-56, 57-60, dean of women, 1961-63; dean of women U. Ga., Athens, 1963-67; world campus afloat adminstr., 1966-67, assoc. dean of students, 1967-72, dean of students, 1972-74, asst. v.p. acad. affairs, 1974-76, assoc. v.p. acad. affairs, 1976-86, v.p. acad. affairs, 1986-88; now mem. Ga. Gen. Assembly; bd. dirs. Ga. Nat. Bank, Athens, 1989—. Author: College Responsibility for Values, 1980; co-author: The American Woman: Who Will She Be?, 1974, Essays, 1979, 2d edit. 1981. Bd. dirs. Salvation Army, Athens, 1989—, United Way, Athens. Fulbright scholar, The Netherlands, 1956-57. Mem. Athens C. of C. (bd. dirs.). Democrat. Methodist. Avocations: gardening, tennis, hiking. Home: 145 Pine Valley Pl Athens GA 30606-4031 Office: GA House of Reps State Capitol Atlanta GA 30334

MCBENNETT, ROBERT JOSEPH, utility executive; b. Elmira, N.Y., Sept. 19, 1942; s. Joseph Francis and Regina Frances (Kaminski) McB.; m.

Miriam A. Feliciano, Apr. 20, 1968; children—Tara A., Cindy M. B.B.A. in Fin., U. Miami, 1965; M.S. in Fin., U. Ill., 1971. Fin. analyst, Orange and Rockland Utilities, Inc., Pearl River, N.Y., 1971-72, sr. fin. analyst, 1972-75, asst. mgr. fin. planning, 1975, asst. treas., 1975-84, treas., 1984—. Served to capt. USAF, 1966-71. Mem. Nat. Assn. Corp. Treas., Fin. Execs. Inst. Roman Catholic. Home: Sycamore Dr Newburgh NY 12553 Office: Orange and Rockland Utilities Inc One Blue Hill Plz Pearl River NY 10965

MCBETH, RUBEN JOSE, JR., retired criminal justice administrator; b. St. Louis, May 2, 1945; s. Ruben Andrew McBeth and Doris Augusta (Bell) Sweet; 1 child, Lisa Christine. BS in Criminal Justice, Pacific Western U., Los Angeles, 1980; grad., Nat. Inst. Corrections, FBI Tng. Acad.; postgrad., U. Colo., Denver, 1987—. Cert. instr. self-defense, tactical instr. With Sheriff's Dept. City of Denver, 1970-95, cpl., 1974-75, sgt., 1975-78, lt., 1978-79, capt., 1978-95, tng. capt., 1987-95, ret., 1995; instr. jail ops. Nat. Sheriffs Assn., Alexaddria, Va., 1980—, I.P.A. correctional program specialist, U.S. Dept. Justice; NIC, Nat. Acad. Corrections, Boulder, Colo., 1989-90, 91, Denver Sheriff Dept., Capt. Internal Investigations, NCIC. Served as sgt. USAF, 1965-68; Vietnam. mem. Am. Correctional Assn. (auditor, standards and accreditation com. 1986—, mem. affirmative action com. 1978-80), Am. Jail Assn., Am. Correctional Assn., Nat. Assn. Blacks in Law Enforcement, Nat. Orgn. Black Law Enforcement Execs., Nat. Sheriffs Assn., Colorado Correctional Assn., Colo. Police Protective Assn., Am. Legion. Avocations: martial arts, fishing, golf, painting. Home: 7156 E Appleton Cir Englewood CO 80112

MCBRAYER, SANDRA L., educational director, homeless outreach educator. AA, San Diego Mesa Coll., 1981; BA in Applied Arts and Scis., San Diego State U., 1986, MA in Edn., 1990. Cert. presch.-kindergarten, grs. 1-12, adult edn., Calif. Tchr. asst. group homes Oz, The Bridge, Escondido, 1984-87; tchr. Hillcrest Receiving Home, 1987-88, Juvenile Hall, 1987-88, Comprehensive Adolescent Treatment Ctr., 1987-88; head tchr. Homeless Outreach Sch., 1988—; lectr., cons. Ctrs. Careers Edn., Sch. Tchr. Edn. San Diego State U., 1990—; collaborator sch. dists. State Dept. Edn., Equity/Homeless Office, 1992—; staff devel. tng. Recipient award Exceptional Vols. Svc. Family Care Ctr., 1988, San Diego's 10 Leadership award Sta. KGTV, 1991, Celebrate Literacy award Internat. Reading Assn., 1992, Women of Vision in Edn. award LWV San Diego, 1992, Disting. Alumna of Yr.-Edn. award San Diego State U., 1992, Golden Bell award Calif. Sch. Bds. Found., 1992; named San Diego County Tchr. of Yr. by San Diego County Office of Edn., 1993, Calif. Tchr. of Yr. by State Dept. Edn., 1993; recognized by local and nat. news media. Mem. NEA, Calif. Tchrs. Assn., Assn. Educators, Nat. Dropout Prevention Network, Calif. Homeless Coalition, Phi Kappa Phi. Office: Homeless Outreach Sch Program 1245 Market St Ste A San Diego CA 92101

MCBREEN, MAURA ANN, lawyer; b. N.Y.C., Aug. 18, 1953; d. Peter J. and Frances S. (McVeigh) McB. AB, Smith Coll., 1975; JD, Harvard U., 1978. Bar: Ill. 1978. Ptnr. Kirkland & Ellis, Chgo., 1978-86, Isham, Lincoln & Beale (merged with Reuben & Proctor), Chgo., 1986-88, Baker & McKenzie, Chgo., 1988—. Mem. ABA, Chgo. Bar Assn., Midwest Pension Conf. Office: Baker & McKenzie 1 Prudential Pla 130 E Randolph St Chicago IL 60601

MCBRIDE, ANGELA BARRON, nursing educator; b. Balt., Jan. 16, 1941; d. John Stanley and Mary C. (Szcpepanska) Barron; m. William Leon McBride, June 12, 1965; children: Catherine, Kara. BS in Nursing, Georgetown U., 1962; LHD (hon.), 1993; MS in Nursing, Yale U., 1964; PhD, Purdue U., 1978; D of Pub. Svc. (hon.), U. Cin., 1983; LLD (hon.), Ea. Ky. U., 1991; DSc(hon.), Med. Coll. of Ohio, 1995. Asst. prof., rsch. asst. inst. Yale U., New Haven, 1964-73; assoc. prof., chairperson Ind. U. Sch. Nursing, Indpls., 1978-81, 80-84, prof., 1981-92, disting. prof., 1992—; assoc. dean rsch. Ind. U. Sch. Nursing, 1985-91, interim dean, 1991-92, univ. dean, 1992—. Author: The Growth and Development of Mothers, 1973, Living with Contradictions. A Married Feminist, 1976, How to Enjoy A Good Life With Your Teenager, 1987; editor: Psychiatric-Mental Health Nursing: Integrating the Behavioral and Biological Sciences, 1995. Recipient Disting. Alumna award Yale U., Disting. Alumna award Purdue U., Univ. Medallion, U. San Francisco, 1993; Kellog nat. fellow; Am. Nurses Found. scholar. Fellow Am. Acad. Nursing (pres.), Am. Psychol. Assn., Nat. Acads. Practice; mem. Midwest Nursing Rsch. Soc. (disting. Rsch. award, 1985), Soc. for Rsch. in Child Devel., Sigma Theta Tau Internat. (past pres., mentor award, 1993). Office: Ind U Sch Nursing 1111 Middle Dr Indianapolis IN 46202-5107

MCBRIDE, BARRY CLARKE, microbiology and oral biology educator, research microbiologist; b. Victoria, B.C., Can., June 22, 1940; s. Clarke Fyfe and Phyllis Frankie (Whitchelo) McB.; m. Barbara Elizabeth Insley, Oct. 12, 1963; children—Christopher, David. B.Sc., U. B.C., Vancouver, Can., 1963; M.Sc., U. B.C., 1965; Ph.D., U. Ill., 1970. Asst. prof. oral biology and microbiology U. B.C., 1970-75, assoc. prof., 1976-80, prof. head dept. oral biology, 1981-86, head dept. microbiology, 1986-89, dean faculty sci., 1990—; mem. Med. Research Council, 1973-79, vis. scientist, 1979, vis. prof. 1982-84; sci. officer Dental Scis. Grants Com., 1981-86. Assoc. editor Oral Microbiology and Immunology; contbr. articles to profl. jours. Rsch. grantee Med. Rsch. Coun., 1971—. Mem. Internat. Assn. Dental Research, Can. Assn. Dental Research (pres. 1990), Am. Soc. Microbiology, Sigma Xi. Avocations: mountaineering; kayaking; sailing. Office: U BC, Faculty of Sci, Vancouver, BC Canada V6T 1Z4

MCBRIDE, DAVID ALAN, business information services executive; b. Henryetta, Okla., Jan. 14, 1936; s. Willis Wilton and Leah Josephine (Adams) McB.; m. Geneva Cheryne Martin, June 12, 1960; 1 child, David Alan, II. Grad., Gen. Motors Inst., 1958; M.B.A., Harvard U., 1960. Cons. McKinsey & Co., N.Y.C., 1967-73; exec. v.p. Hopeman Bros. Inc., N.Y.C., 1973-76; pres. Dun & Bradstreet Plan Services, N.Y.C., 1977-83, Dun & Bradstreet Internat., N.Y.C., 1983—; exec. v.p. The Dun & Bradstreet Corp., N.Y.C., 1985—. Mem. Gov.'s Com. on Mental Health, Del., Wilmington, 1964-65; trustee Village of Bronxville, N.Y., 1973-74; bd. govs. Lawrence Hosp., Bronxville, 1973-79. Republican. Mem. Reformed Ch. Am. (elder). Clubs: Harvard Bus. Sch. (N.Y.C.) Siwanoy Country (gov., treas. 1983-85, pres. 1985-86), Bronxville Field. Home: 75 White Plains Rd Bronxville NY 10708-2411 Office: The Dun & Bradstreet Corp 299 Park Ave New York NY 10171-0001

MCBRIDE, DONNA JANNEAN, publisher; b. Kansas City, Kans., July 3, 1940; d. Donald Merle and Hazel Frances (Williams) McBride. A.B., Central Coll., 1962; M.L.S. in No.-Columbia, 1969. Tchr., Pilot Grove High Sch. (Mo.), 1961-62; corr. Bus. Men's Assurance Co., Kansas City, Mo., 1962-66; acctg. clk. Prudential of Eng., Sydney, Australia, 1966-67; head tech. processes Kansas City Pub. Library (Mo.), 1967-77; customer rep. C.L. Systems, Inc., Newtonville, Mass., 1977-80; dir. support services Leon County Pub. Library, Tallahassee, 1980-82; dir. ops. The Naiad Press, Inc., Tallahassee, 1982—; dir. The Naiad Press, 1976—, Sappho's Libr., 1983—. Mem. ALA, Nat. Gay Task Force, Am. Booksellers Assn., Nat. Women's Studies Assn., NOW. Home: RR 1 Box 3319 Havana FL Office: The Naiad Press Inc PO Box 10543 Tallahassee FL 32302-2543

MCBRIDE, ELIZABETH, costume designer. Costume designer: (films) Square Dance, 1986, True Stories, 1986, Tapeheads, 1988, Driving Miss Daisy, 1989 (Academy award nomination best costume design 1989), Thelma & Louise, 1991, Fried Green Tomatoes, 1992, Made in America, 1992, The Shawshank Redemption, 1994. Office: care Costume Designer's Guild 13949 Ventura Blvd Ste 309 Sherman Oaks CA 91423*

MC BRIDE, GUY THORNTON, JR., college president emeritus; b. Austin, Tex., Dec. 12, 1919; s. Guy Thornton and Imogene (Thrasher) McB.; m. Rebekah Jane Bush, Sept. 2, 1942; children: Rebekah Ann, William Howard, Ellen McBride McCarty. B.S. in Chem. Engring., U. Tex., 1940; Sc.D., MIT, 1948; D.P.S. (hon.), Regis Coll., 1979; D.Engring. (hon.), Colo. Sch. Mines, 1984. Registered profl. engr., Tex. La., N.Y., Colo. Instr. chem. engring. Mass. Inst. Tech., 1942-44, research assoc., 1946-48; job engr. Standard Oil Co. Calif., 1944-46; asst. prof. chem. engring Rice Inst., 1948-55, assoc. dean students, 1950-57, dean, 1957-58, assoc. prof., 1955-58; cons. Tex. Gulf Sulphur Co., 1950-58, asst. mgr. research dept., 1958-59, mgr., 1959-60, v.p., mgr. research, 1960-63; v.p. Tex. Gulf Sulphur Co. (Phosphate

div.), 1963-70, gen. mgr., 1966-70; pres. Colo. Sch. Mines, Golden, 1970-84; ret.; dir. Halliburton Co., Kerr-McGee Corp., Hercules, Inc.; hon. dir. Texasgulf Inc. Fellow Am. Inst. Chem. Engrs.; mem. Am. Chem. Soc., Nat. Soc. Profl. Engrs.; Sigma Xi, Phi Lambda Upsilon, Tau Beta Pi. Club: Mile High (Denver). Home: 2615 Oak Dr Apt 13 Lakewood CO 80215

MC BRIDE, JOHN ALEXANDER, retired chemical engineer; b. Altoona, Pa., Mar. 29, 1918; s. Raymond E. and Carolyn (Tinker) McB.; m. Elizabeth Anne Vogel, Aug. 28, 1942; children: Katherine M. Harris, Susan McBride Malick, Carolyn McBride Nafziger. A.B., Miami U., Oxford, Ohio, 1940; M.Sc., Ohio State U., 1941; Ph.D., U. Ill., 1944. Registered profl. engr., Calif. Various positions in research and devel. dept. Phillips Petroleum Co., 1944-58, 59-65; dir. chem. tech. Phillips Petroleum Co. (Atomic energy div.), 1963-65; chief applications engring. Astrodyne, Inc., 1958-59; dir. div. materials licensing AEC, 1965-70; v.p. E.R. Johnson Assocs., Inc., Fairfax, Va., 1970-92; asst. gen. mgr. Nuclear Chems. & Metals Corp., 1970-71; Adviser U.S. del. 3d Internat. Conf. Peaceful Uses Atomic Energy, 1964. Mem. AIChE (chmn. nuclear engring. divsn. 1986, Robert E. Wilson award 1991), Am. Chem. Soc., Alpha Chi Sigma, Phi Kappa Tau. Achievements include publications and patents on petrochemical products and processes, solid propellant rockets, irradiated fuel reprocessing, radioactive waste fixation and disposal. Home: 1727 Sherman Ave Canon City CO 81212-4354 Address: PO Box 1482 Canon City CO 81215-1482

MCBRIDE, JONATHAN EVANS, executive search consultant; b. Washington, June 16, 1942; s. Gordon Williams and Martha Alice (Evans) McB.; BA, Yale U., 1964; m. Emilie Evans Dean, Sept. 5, 1970; children: Webster Dean, Morley Evans. Account exec. Merrill Lynch & Co., Washington, 1968-72; v.p. dept. mgr. Lionel D. Edie & Co., N.Y.C., 1972-76; v.p., exec. search cons. Simmons Assocs., Inc., Washington, 1976-79; pres. McBride Assocs., Inc., Washington, 1979—. Bd. dirs. Yale U. Alumni Fund, 1974-79. Served to lt. USNR, 1964-68. Clubs: Yale (N.Y.C.); Met. (Washington); Chevy Chase (Md.). Office: 1511 K St NW Washington DC 20005-1497

MCBRIDE, MICHAEL FLYNN, lawyer; b. Milw., Mar. 27, 1951; s. Raymond Edward and Marian Dunne McBride; m. Kerin Ann O'Brien, Mar. 23, 1991. BS in Chem. and Biology, U. Wis., 1972, JD, 1976; MS in Environ. Engr. Sci., Calif. Inst. Tech., 1973. Bar: Wis. 1976, D.C. 1976. Assoc. LeBoeuf, Lamb, Leiby & MacRae, Washington, 1976-84, ptnr., 1985—. Mem. Fed. Energy Bar Assn., Assn. Transp. Practitioners (v.p., energy transp. law inst. com. 1990, co-chmn. 1991—, editor ATP Jour.), Chantilly Nat. Golf and Country Club (Centreville, Va.). Roman Catholic. Avocations: golf, reading, travel. Home: 6648 Byrns Pl McLean VA 22101 Office: LeBoeuf Lamb Leiby & MacRae 1875 Connecticut Ave NW Washington DC 20009

MCBRIDE, NANCY ALLYSON, child resource center administrator; b. Lakewood, Ohio, June 15, 1952; d. Harold Jackson and Mary Alice (Inman) McB. BA in Psychology magna cum laude, Oakland U., 1977. Program dir. Alternative Lifestyles, Inc., Pontiac, Mich., 1975-77; youth counselor Creative Outlooks Counseling Ctr., Pontiac, Mich., 1977-78; chief probation officer 47th Dist. Ct., Farmington Hills, Mich., 1978-80; program coord. Adam Walsh Ctr., Ft. Lauderdale, Fla., 1980-81; program coord. Adam Walsh Ctr., Ft. Lauderdale, 1981-87; regional trainer Home Box Office, Inc., Atlanta, 1987-90; exec. dir. Adam Walsh Ctr./Fla., Lake Park, Fla., 1990—; adj. instr. Nova U., Ft. Lauderdale, 1985-87, 90—, Broward C.C., Ft. Lauderdale, 1986-87; cons. 5 maj. TV prodns., Ft. Lauderdale, 1983-87; instr. Inst. for Nonprofit Orgn. and Mgmt., Denver, 1986-87, 93-94, victim svcs. cert. program Palm Beach Atlantic Coll., West Palm Beach, Fla. Author: (rsch. project) Child Abuse & Neglect: The Plight of the 2nd Class Citizens, 1977. Tutor Laubach Literacy Tng., Chgo., 1972; vol Erie Neighborhood House, Chgo., 1970, 72, student intern Macomb County Youth Svcs., Warren, Mich., 1977; family aide Family Focus, Birmingham, Mich., 1976-77. Recipient plaque 2d Conf. Missing Children, Chgo., 1987, Guardian Ad Litem Program, Ft. Lauderdale, 1982, Cmty. Svc. award Consortium for Human Devel., Troy, Mich., 1980, Spl. Plaque award John and Reve Walsh, 1992. Democrat. Avocations: swimming, reading, creative writing. Office: Adam Walsh Ctr Ste 100 9176 Alternate A1A Lake Park FL 33403

MC BRIDE, RAYMOND ANDREW, pathologist, physician, educator; b. Houston, Dec. 27, 1927; s. Raymond Andrew and Rita (Mullane) McB.; m. Isabelle Shepherd Davis, May 10, 1958 (div. 1978); children—James Bradley, Elizabeth Conway, Christopher Ramsey, Andrew Gore. B.S., Tulane U., 1952, M.D., 1956. Diplomate: Am. Bd. Pathology. Surg. intern Jefferson Davis Hosp., Baylor U. Coll. Medicine, Houston, 1956-57; asst. in pathology Peter Bent Brigham Hosp., Boston, 1957-60; sr. resident pathologist Peter Bent Brigham Hosp., 1960-61; resident pathologist Free Hosp. for Women, Brookline, Mass., 1959; asst. resident pathologist Children's Hosp. Med. Center, Boston, 1960; teaching fellow pathology Harvard Med. Sch., Boston, 1958-61; research trainee Nat. Heart Inst., NIH, HEW, 1958-61; spl. postdoctoral fellow Nat. Cancer Inst., HEW, McIndoe Meml. Research unit Blond Labs., East Grimstead, Sussex, Eng., 1961-63; asst. attending pathologist Presbyn. Hosp., N.Y.C., 1963-65; asst. prof. pathology Coll. Physicians and Surgeons, Columbia U., 1963-65; research asso. Mt. Sinai Hosp., N.Y.C., 1965-68; assoc. prof. surgery and immunogenetics Mt. Sinai Sch. Medicine, N.Y.C., 1965-68; career scientist Health Research Council City N.Y., 1967-73; attending pathologist Flower and Fifth Ave. Hosps., N.Y.C., 1968-78, Met. Hosp. Center, N.Y.C., 1968-78; prof. pathology N.Y. Med. Coll., 1968-78, Baylor Coll. Medicine, Houston, 1978—; attending pathologist Harris County Hosp. Dist., Ben Taub Gen. Hosp., Houston, 1978—; chief pathology svcs. Harris County Hosp. Dist., 1988—; assoc. staff Meth. Hosp., Houston, 1978-81, active staff, 1981—; vis. grad. faculty Tex. A & M U., College Station, 1979—; clin. prof. pathology U. Tex. Grad. Sch. Biomed. Scis., Galveston, 1982—, U. Tex. Med. Br., Galveston, 1982—; prof., chmn. dept. pathology Libero Instituto Universitario Campus Bio-Medico, Rome, 1993—; adj. prof. dept. stats. Rice U., Houston; mem. sci. com. Libero Instituto Universitario Campus Bio-Medico, Rome, 1991—; exec. dean N.Y. Med. Coll., Valhalla, 1973-75; exec. dir., COO, bd. dirs. Westchester Med. Ctr. Devel. Bd., Valhalla, 1974-76. Mem. editorial bd. Jour. Immunogenetics, Exptl. and Clin. Immunogenetics, European Jour. Immunogenetics; contbr. articles to profl. jours. Bd. dirs. Westchester Artificial Kidney Found., Inc., 1974-78, Westchester Med. Center Library, 1974-78, Westchester div. Am. Cancer Soc., 1973-78, Magnificat House, 1989—, Foundation for Life, 1989—, Tuxedo Library, 1976-78; co-chmn. Westchester Burn Center Task Force, 1975-76. Grantee Health Research Council, N.Y.C., 1963-73; Grantee Am. Cancer Soc., 1971-72; Grantee NIH, USPHS, 1964—; Grantee NSF, 1965-68. Fellow Royal Soc. Medicine; mem. Transplantation Soc., Am. Soc. Exptl. Pathology, Reticuloendothelial Soc., AAAS, Am. Assn. Pathologists and Bacteriologists, Am. Assn. Immunologists, AAUP, AMA, Tex. Med. Assn., Harris County Med. Soc., Tex. Soc. Pathologists, Coll. Am. Pathologists, Am. Assn. Clin. Pathologists, Houston Acad. Medicine, Houston Soc. Clin. Pathologists, Assn. Am. Med. Colls. Fedn. Am. Scientists, Am., N.Y. cancer socs., Soc. Health and Human Values, Am. Acad. Med. Ethics, Alpha Omega Alpha (hon. med. soc.). Republican. Roman Catholic. Club: Tuxedo (Tuxedo Park, N.Y.). Achievements include research on relationship between genes of the major histocompatibility locus and the ability to regress tumors induced by different groups of avian sarcoma retroviruses; haptencarrier relationship between erythrocyte isoantigens providing a strategy for the production of antibodies to weakly immunogenic differentiation antigens; complementation of MHC and non-MHC genes in the ability to regress avian sarcoma retrovirus induced tumors; demonstration that the induction of skin graft tolerance in adult inbred mouse strains by means of parabiosis is accompanied by lymphoid cell chimerism; development of an assay for quantitation of isoimmune plaque forming cells in a non-hemolytic system. Home: 5001 Woodway Unit 1404 Houston TX 77056 Office: Baylor Coll Medicine Tex Med Ctr Dept Pathology One Baylor Plz Houston TX 77030 Address: via Lancellotti 18, Palazzo Lancellotti, 00186 Rome Italy also: Via Zanardelli 36, Appartamento 18, 00186 Rome Italy

MC BRIDE, ROBERT DANA, steel company executive; b. Decatur, Ill., Nov. 5, 1927; s. Glen Clovis and Winifred Audrey (Spates) McB.; m. Gloria Jean Haefner, July 8, 1950; children: Scott, Dana, Kelly, Kitty. B.S., U.S. Mil. Acad., 1950; grad., Advanced Mgmt. Program, Harvard U., 1974. V.p. ops. Granite City Steel Co., Ill., from 1966; pres. Granite City Steel div. Nat.

Steel Corp., 1976-77; pres. Great Lakes Steel div. Nat. Steel Corp., Detroit, 1977-82; pres. Nat. Steel Corp., Pitts., 1983-86; sr. cons. Genix Corp., Pitts., 1987-89; pres. Trebbi Cons., Washington, 1989-90; pres., CEO McLouth Steel, Trenton, 1991-92, chmn., CEO, 1993-94, chmn., 1995—, also bd. dirs.; bd. dirs. The Drafus/Laurel Funds, Pitts., Salem Corp., Pitts.; mem. bd. visitors Marine Biol. Lab., Woods Hole, Mass. Served with U.S. Army, 1950-56. Decorated Purple Heart, Silver Star, Bronze Star. Mem. Am. Iron and Steel Inst., Assn. Iron and Steel Engrs. (dir., past pres.). Roman Catholic. Home: 15 Waverly Ln Grosse Pointe MI 48236-3039

MCBRIDE, RODNEY LESTER, investment counselor; b. Denver, Sept. 1, 1941; s. Laurence Thomas and Harriet Alvina (Primmer) McB.; m. Nancy Faye Davenport, Mar. 21, 1964 (div. June 1984); children: Douglas L., Cheryl L.; m. Judy Winslow, Nov. 7, 1992; stepchildren: Mark P. Winslow, Scott C. Winslow. BS in Mktg., U. Colo., 1963; MBA, U. Calif., Berkeley, 1976. Chartered investment counselor Investment Counsel Assn. Am., Fin. Analyst Fedn. Indsl. salesman Fibreboard Corp., San Diego and San Francisco, 1963-66; investment counselor Shuman, Agnew & Co., San Francisco, 1966-71; investment counselor, co-founder capital counseling svc. Bank of Am., San Francisco, 1971-75; investment counselor Scudder, Stevens and Clark, San Francisco, 1975-76; sr. v.p., office mgr. Crocker Investment Mgmt. Corp., Los Angeles, 1977-84; sr. v.p., dir. portfolio mgmt., chmn. equity strategy com. Crocker Investment Mgmt. Corp., San Francisco, 1984-86; mng. dir., sr. portfolio mgr., chmn. equity strategy com., chmn. core equity com., chmn. internat. asset allocation com. Chancellor Capital Mgmt., Inc. (formerly Citicorp Investment Mgmt. Corp.), N.Y.C., 1986-94; mng. dir., sr. portfolio mgr., chmn. equity strategy com. Furman Selz Capital Mgmt., N.Y.C., 1994—. Pres., coach Palos Verdes (Calif.) Basketball Assn., 1982-83; mem. 2d Congregational Ch.; bd. dirs. Greater N.Y. couns. Boy Scouts Am. Mem. L.A. Soc. Fin. Analysts (sec., bd. dirs. 1984, treas. 1983, chmn. seminar com. 1982-83), N.Y. Soc. Fin. Analysts, Assn. Investment Mgmt. and Rsch. (chartered fin. analyst), Western Pension Conf., U. Colo. Alumni Assn., U. Calif. Alumni Assn., Stanwick Country Club, Round Hill Country Club, Alpha Kappa Psi (treas. 1963). Republican. Avocations: golf, tennis, volleyball, duck hunting, fishing. Home: 148 Clapboard Ridge Rd Greenwich CT 06831 Office: Furman Selz Capital Mgmt 230 Park Ave New York NY 10169

MCBRIDE, THOMAS FRANCIS, machinery company executive; b. Essington, Pa., Oct. 22, 1931; s. Thomas F. and Margaret F. (Schuhay) McB.; B.S. in Acctg., Kings Coll., Pa., 1957; m. Marie E. Schultz, Feb. 7, 1959; children: Maureen, Thomas, Colleen, Mary Kathleen. Cost acct. Air Products Co., Allentown, Pa., 1957-59; mgr. cost acctg. Litton Industries, College Park, Md., 1961-64; mgr. ops. adminstrn. RCA, Eng., 1964-65, mgr. ops. analysis, N.J., 1965-68; v.p. fin. Singer Co., State College, Pa., 1968-71, v.p., group controller, N.Y.C., 1971-74; asst. comptroller Ingersoll-Rand, Woodcliff Lake, N.J., 1974-79, v.p., corp. comptroller, 1979-93, sr. v.p., CFO, 1993—. Bd. dirs. Bergen County council Boy Scouts Am. Served with USMC, 1959. Mem. Fin. Execs. Inst., Am. Mgmt. Assn. (fin. council). Roman Catholic. Club: K.C. Office: Ingersoll-Rand Co Inc 200 Chestnut Ridge Rd Westwood NJ 07675

MC BRIDE, THOMAS FREDERICK, lawyer, former university dean, government official; b. Elgin, Ill., Feb. 8, 1929; s. Thomas Wallace and Sarah Rosalie (Pierce) McB.; m. Catherine Higgs Mitton, Aug. 23, 1975; children: Matthew (dec.), Elizabeth, John, Raphael, Luke. Ba, NYU, 1952; LLB, Columbia U., 1956. Bar: N.Y. 1956, D.C. 1966, U.S. Supreme Ct. 1963, Calif. 1989. Asst. dist. atty. N.Y. County, 1956-59; trial atty. organized crime sect. Dept. Justice, 1961-65; adviser to Home Ministry, Govt. India, 1964; ofcl. Peace Corps, 1965-68; dep. chief counsel select com. on crime Ho. of Reps., 1969-70; assoc. dir., staff dir. Police Found., 1970-73; assoc. spl. prosecutor Watergate, 1973-75; dir. bur. enforcement CAB, 1975-77; insp. gen. U.S. Dept. Agr., Washington, 1977-81, U.S. Dept. Labor, Washington, 1981-82; assoc. dean Stanford Law Sch. (Calif.), 1982-89; mem. Pres.'s Commn. Organized Crime, 1983-86, Calif. Council on Mental Health, 1986-90; dir. environ. health and safety Stanford U., 1990-92; counselor U.S. Dept. Energy, Washington, 1993-95. Served with AUS, 1946-47. Mem. D.C. Bar Assn. Home: 837 Cedro Way Palo Alto CA 94305-1034 Office: 837 Cedro Way Stanford CA 94305

MCBRIDE, WANDA LEE, psychiatric nurse; b. Dayton, Ohio, Dec. 13, 1931; d. Owen Francis Staup and Ruby Madonna (Campbell) Inscore; m. Richard H. McBride, July 28, 1951 (div. Mar. 1966); children: Kathleen Kerns, Kimberlee Haley. Diploma, Christ Hosp. Sch., Cin., 1953; student, U. Cin., 1954-55. Cert. psychiat. mental health nursing ANA. Various healthcare positions, 1953-66; from supr. 4 acute male units to supr. outpatient dept. Cen. Ohio Psychiat. Hosp., Columbus, 1966-77; supr. hosp., head nurse urology and respiratory diseases flr. St. Anthony Hosp., Okla., 1977-83; shift supr. and coord. child program Willowview Hosp., Spencer, Okla., 1983-88; adminstr. nursing supr. Grant Ctr. Deering Hosp., Miami, 1988—. Mem. Gov.'s Com. for Mental Health and Retardation, 1963-66, Logan County Mental Health League, Ohio, 1963-66. Named Nurse of Yr., 1983-90. Mem. Nat. League for Nursing, Mental Health League (past pres.), Lioness Club (past pres.). Republican. Episcopalian. Avocations: orchid growing, classical music, cooking, fishing, camping. Home: 304 Lakeside Ct Sunrise FL 33326

MCBRIDE, WILLIAM BERNARD, treasurer; b. N.Y.C., May 22, 1931; s. William and Nora (Hughes) McB.; m. Lorraine Barry, May 27, 1956; children: Mary, William, Stephen, Anne. BS, Fordham U., 1952; MBA, Baruch Sch., 1963. CPA, N.Y. Staff auditor Touche, Ross, Bailey & Smart (CPAs), N.Y.C., 1952-58; asst. v.p. Bankers Trust Co., N.Y.C., 1959-67; treas. Kidde, Inc., Saddle Brook, N.J., 1967-87; v.p. Kidde, Inc., 1974-87; cons. Hanson Industries, other cos., Iselin, N.J., 1987—. Mem. AICPA, N.Y. State Soc. CPAs. Home and Office: 243 Sunset Ave Ridgewood NJ 07450-2420

MC BRIDE, WILLIAM LEON, philosopher, educator; b. N.Y.C., Jan. 19, 1938; s. William Joseph and Irene May (Choffin) McB.; m. Angela Barron, July 12, 1965; children: Catherine, Kara. A.B., Georgetown U., 1959; postgrad. (Fulbright fellow), U. Lille, 1959-60; M.A. (Woodrow Wilson fellow), Yale U., 1962; Ph.D. (Social Sci. Research Council fellow), 1964. Instr. philosophy Yale U., New Haven, 1964-66, asst. prof., 1966-70, assoc. prof., 1970-73; lectr. Northwestern U., Evanston, Ill., summer 1972; assoc. prof. Purdue U., West Lafayette, Ind., 1973-76, prof., 1976—; lectr. Korcula Summer Sch., Yugoslavia, 1971, 73. Author: Fundamental Change in Law and Society, 1970, The Philosophy of Marx, 1977, Social Theory at a Crossroads, 1980, (with R.A. Dahl) Demokrati og Autoritet, 1980, Sartre's Political Theory, 1991, Social and Political Philosophy, 1994; editor: (with C.O. Schrag) Phenomenology in a Pluralistic Context, 1983. Mem. AAUP (pres. Purdue chpt. 1983-86, pres. Ind. conf. 1988-89), Am. Philos. Assn. (chmn. com. on internat. coop. 1992-95, bd. dirs. 1992-95), Am. Soc. Polit. and Legal Philosophy, Soc. Phenomenology and Existential Philosophy (exec. co-sec. 1977-80), Sartre Soc. N.Am. (chmn. bd. dirs. 1985-88, 91-93), Am. Soc. Philosophy in the French Lang. (pres. 1994-96). Home: 744 Cherokee Ave Lafayette IN 47905-1872 Office: Purdue U Dept Philosophy West Lafayette IN 47907-1360

MCBRIEN, RICHARD PETER, theology educator; b. Hartford, Conn., Aug. 19, 1936; s. Thomas Henry and Catherine Ann (Botticelli) McB. AA, St. Thomas Sem., 1956; BA, St. John Sem., 1958, MA, 1962; STD, Gregorian U., 1967. Assoc. pastor Our Lady of Victory Ch., West Haven, Conn., 1962-63; prof., dean of studies Pope John XXIII Nat. Sem., Weston, Mass., 1965-70; prof. theology Boston Coll., Newton, Mass. 1970-80, dir. inst. of religious edn. and pastoral ministry., 1975-80; prof. theology U. Notre Dame, Ind., 1980—, chmn. dept., 1980-91; cons. various dioceses and religious communities in the U.S. and Can., 1965—; vis. fellow John F. Kennedy Sch. Govt. Harvard U., Cambridge, 1976-77; mem. Council on Theol. Scholarship and Research Assn. of Theol. Schs., 1987-91. Author: Do We Need Church?, 1969, Catholicism, 2 vols., 1980, new edit., 1994 (Christopher award 1981), Caesar's Coin: Religion and Politics in America, 1987, Report on the Church: Catholicism after Vatican II, 1992; editor: Encyclopedia Religion, 1987, Harper Collins Encyclopedia of Catholicism, 1995. Recipient Best Syndicated Weekly Column award Cath. Press Assn. of U.S. and Can., 1975, 77, 78, 84. Mem. Cath. Theol. Soc. of Am. (pres. 1973-74, John Courtney Murray award 1976), Coll. Theology Soc., Am. Acad.

Religion. Office: Univ of Notre Dame Dept of Theology Notre Dame IN 46556

MC BRYDE, F. WEBSTER, geographer, ecologist, consultant; b. Lynchburg, Va., Apr. 23, 1908; s. John McLaren and Flora O'N. (Webster) McB. B.A., Tulane U., 1930, LL.D. (hon.), 1967; Ph.D., U. Calif., Berkeley, 1940; postgrad. (rsch. fellow) U. Colo., 1930-31, Clark U., 1931-32; m. Frances Van Winkle, July 23, 1934; children: Richard Webster, Sarah Elva, John McLaren. Geographer-photographer 4th Tulane Expdn. across Cen. Am. Maya Area, 1927-28; geology teaching asst. Tulane U., 1929-30, U. of Utah-Smithsonian Uinta Ute Expdn., No. Utah, 1931; field fellow Clark U.-Carnegie Inst., Washington, Guatemala, 1932; rsch. fellow Middle Am. Rsch. Inst., Tulane U., 1932-33; teaching asst. geography U. Calif., Berkeley, 1933-35, 37; predoctoral field fellow social sci. Social Sci. Rsch. Coun. N.Y., Guatemala and El Salvador, 1935-36; instr. geography Ohio State U., 1937-42, UCLA, 1940; field fellow in natural scis.NRC, Washington, also Berkeley, Guatemala, Mexico, 1940-41; expert cons., sr. geographer M.I. War Dept., Washington, 1942-45; lectr. geography Western Res. U., 1944; dir. Peruvian office Inst. Social Anthropology, Smithsonian Instn., Washington, Lima, 1945-47; dir., organizer and writer of curriculum Inst. Geography, U. San Marcos, Lima, 1945-47; spl. rep. Inst. Andean Rsch., Lima, 1947-48; lectr. Fgn. Svc. Inst., Dept. State, 1949-53; prof. geography U. Md., 1948-59, cons. prof., 1959-63; chief geographer office of coord. Internat. Stats. U.S. Bur. Census, Washington and Latin Am., 1948-56; geographer, com. on 1950 Census of Ams., Inter-Am. Statis. Inst., cons. all Am. nations, 1948-51; chief U.S. Census Mission, tech. advisor 1st Nat. Census of Ecuador, Quito, 1949-51; dir. regional planning Gordon A. Friesen Assocs., Inc., San José, Costa Rica nat. master hosp. plan, 1956-58; survey dir., sr. author survey report, Greater Southeast Washington, D.C. Cmty. Hosp. 1958-59; on contract to Exec. Rsch. Inc., N.Y.C., presdl. campaign advisor Pres. Villeda Morales, Honduras, 1957; U.S. rep., electoral advisor to Pres. Ydigoras Fuentes, Guatemala, 1958-64; pres. F.W. McBryde Assocs., Inc., Washington and Guatemala, 1958-64; founder-pres. Inter-Am. Inst. Modern Langs., Guatemala, 1962-66; Latin Am. cons. Inst. Modern Langs., Washington, 1962-66; chief phys. and cultural geography br., natural resources div. Inter-Am. Geodetic Survey, U.S. Army, Fort Clayton, C.Z., 1964-65; field dir. Bioenviron. Program, Atlantic-Pacific Interoceanic Sea-Level Canal Studies in Panama and Colombia (AEC contract), 1965-70, field dir. U.S. Army, Natick, Mass., Andean ecology project, S.Am., 1967-69, dir. project devel. program, Cen. Am. and Mex., 1968-69; cons. in ecology Battelle Meml. Inst., Columbus, Ohio, 1970—; founder-dir. McBryde Ctr. for Human Ecology, 1969—; cons. in human ecology and Latin Am., Transemantics, Inc., Washington, 1970—; with UN Devel. Program, ecologist (tourism), expert Jamaica, W.I., 1971; hydrology ecologist, expert Parana River Nav. Improvement Project, Argentina, 1972; ecol. cons. Battelle Meml. Inst., Panama and Brazil, 1972; U.S. Bur. Census geography adviser to Govt. of Honduras on cartography for 1973 population census, 1972; Battelle cons., procedural analysis in internat. project devel., 1972; ecologist World Bank environ. impact analysis Bayano River Hydroelectric Project, one-man mission to Panama; Battelle cons., ecologist, prin. investigator and field coord., environ. impact study Darien Gap Hwy., Panama-Colombia for U.S. Dept. Transp., 1973; cons. Enviro Plan. Chesapeake Bay ecology; expert ecologist (biology) Engr. Agy. for Resources Inventories, C.E., U.S. Army, Washington, 1974; dir. recruitment, dir. internat. bus. intelligence, 1975-80, dir. Geog. Rsch. div. Transemantics, Inc., Washington, 1975—; cons. geographer Census Office, Govt. of Honduras, 1981; cons. ecologist UN Tech. Cooperation and Devel., Cerro Colorado Copper Mine, Panama, 1981. Mem. nat. adv. bd. Am. Security Coun.; state advisor U.S. Congl. Adv. Bd., Am. Security coun. Found.; charter founder Ronald Reagan Rep. Ctr., Washington, 1988, founder Pres. Trust Rep. Nat. Com., 1988, mem. Chmns. Coun., 1993; charter mem. Pres. Bush's Rep. Presdl. Task Force, 1989; charter mem. Rep. Presdl. Trust, 1992; mem. Rep. Senatorial Inner Circle, 1992—; at-large-del., Rep. Party Platform Planning Com., rep. Potomac area, Md., founding prodr., GOP-TV, 1994; charter sponsor Conservative TV Network; advisor U.S. Nat. Strategy Commn., 1993—; sponsor Nat. Rep. Congressional Com.; charter mem. Free Enterprise Coun. Rep. Nat. Com., 1994—. Fellow Explorers Club (life); mem. AAAS (life), Am. Anthrop. Assn., Am. Cartographic Assn., Am. Congress on Surveying and Mapping, Am. Geog. Soc., Assn. Am. Geographers (life, formerly Am. Soc. for Profl. Geographers founding pres., sec.(1 yr.), treas., meetings coord., editor publs. 1943-45, organizer 8 regional divs. in U.S., now 9 quasi-socs. in U.S. and Can.), Am. Geophys. Union (life), Am. Inst. Biol. Scis., Conf. Latin Americanist Geographers, Arctic Inst. N.A., Assn. Tropical Biology, Chesapeake Bay Found., Am. Soc. Photogrammetry and Remote Sensing, Ecuadorian Inst. Anthropology and Geography (founder dir. 1950-52, hon. dir. 1952—), Inter-Am. Coun. (organizing sec. 1953-59, pres. 1959-62), N.Y. Acad. Scis., Washington Acad. (adv. bd. 1981—), Lima Geog. Soc., Oceanography Soc. (charter mem.), Soc. Am. Archeology, Soc. Am. Mil. Engrs., Soc. for Med. Anthropology, N.Am. Cartographic Info. Soc., Guatemalan Soc. Geography and History, Internat. Oceanographic Found., Nature Conservancy Internat. Program, Mexican Soc. Geography and Stats., U.S. Naval Inst., World Wildlife Fund, Nat. Wildlife Fedn. (world assoc.), Phi Beta Kappa, Sigma Nu, others. Episcopalian. Author: Solola, 1933; Cultural and Historical Geography of Southwest Guatemala, 1947, Spanish , 1969, 2 vols. transl. by Francis Gall, Guatemala, 1969, Greenwood reprint (English), 1971; (with P. Thomas) Equal-Area Projections for World Statistical Maps, 1949; founding editor Profl. Geographer; contbr. numerous articles to profl. jours. Achievements include patent for equal-area designs and methods of constructing original projections for world maps, wherein median representations between true overall global linear scale (equidistance), true azimuth (indicated by directional bearings of intersecting graticule lines, hence shape of terrestrial features), and equivalence (or true relative size of land and water bodies on the map) are plotted to attain the closest similarity to earth features in all dimensions, which are completely true only on the spherical surface of the terrestrial globe; discovery of origin of beans (phaseolus vulgaris and p. lunatus) in western Guatemala and Chiapas; of maize varieties; development of new system of biological/ecological classification keyed to environmental factors, of new micro-geodemographic planning techniques employing data graphics plotted on thematic maps, especially useful in hospital, health, and economic surveys; research in Mayan and Andean archeology, ecology, on tectonic and seismic determinants and geomorphology. Home: 10100 Falls Rd Potomac MD 20854

MCBRYDE, JAMES EDWARD, state legislator; b. Santa Monica, Calif., Sept. 23, 1950; s. Edward James McBryde and Barbara Jean (Fowler) Mallon; m. Kimberly Anne Benoit, Nov. 28, 1987; children: Sarah Joy, Natalie Marie, Elizabeth Anne, Rebecca Christine. BS, Cen. Mich. U., 1972. Sales rep. Laconia (N.H.) Shoe Co., 1977-78, The McBryde Shoe Co., Petosky, Mich., 1978-79, The Sheboygan (Wis.) Co., 1979-85, The Timberland Co., Hampton, N.H., 1985-90; mem. Mich. Ho. of Reps., 1991—. Chmn. Isabella County Criminal Justice Com., Mt. Pleasant, Mich., 1985-86, 1989-90, 91—, Isabella County 911 Governing Bd., Mt. Pleasant, 1989-90, Campaign Search Com., Isabella County, 1988, 90, 92, 94; county commr. Isabella County Bd. Commrs., 1985-90, vice chmn., 1985-86, 89-90; first vice chmn. Isabella County Rep. Com., 1989-90; rep. Mich. Rep. State Com., Lansing, 1989-90. Named Legislator of Yr. Mich. Sheriff's Assn., 1994; recipient Star award for Legis. Achievement Mich. Dep. Sheriff's Assn. 1994. Mem. Mich. and Isabella County Right to Life, Mt. Pleasant Lions Club. Republican. Presbyterian. Avocations: reading, biking. Office: PO Box 164 Mount Pleasant MI 48804-0164

MCBRYDE, JOHN HENRY, federal judge; b. Jackson, Oct. 9, 1931; m. Betty Vinson; children: Rebecca McBryde Dippold, Jennifer, John Blake. BS in Commerce, Tex. Christian U., 1953; LLB, U. Tex., 1956. Bar: Tex. 1956, U.S. Ct. Appeals (5th cir.) 1958, U.S. Dist. Ct. (no. dist.) 1958, U.S. Dist. Ct. (ea. dist.) 1989, U.S. Supreme Ct. 1972. Assoc. Cantey, Hanger, Johnson, Scarborough & Gooch, Ft. Worth, 1956-62; ptnr. Cantey & Hanger and predecessor firm, Ft. Worth, 1962-69, McBryde, Bennett and predecessor firms, Ft. Worth, 1969-90; judge U.S. Dist. Ct. (no. dist.) Tex., Ft. Worth, 1990—. Fellow Am. Bar Found., Tex. Bar Found. (life), Am. Coll. Trial Lawyers. Office: US Dist Ct US Courthouse Rm 401 501 W 10th St Fort Worth TX 76102-3637

MCBRYDE, NEILL GREGORY, lawyer; b. Durham, N.C., Jan. 11, 1944; s. Angus M. and Priscilla (Gregory) McB., m. Margaret McPherson, Aug. 1, 1970; children: Margaret Courtauld, Neill Gregory Jr. AB cum laude, Davidson Coll., 1966; JD with high honors, U. N.C., 1969. Bar: N.C. 1969,

---

Ga. 1972. Assoc. King & Spalding, Atlanta, 1971-76; ptnr. Fleming, Robinson, Bradshaw & Hinson, Charlotte, N.C., 1977-81, Helms, Mulliss & Johnston, Charlotte, 1981-86, Smith Helms Mulliss & Moore, Charlotte, 1986-90, Moore & Van Allen PLLC, Charlotte, 1990—; lectr. in field, conducter workshops in field. Author, editor: First Union National Bank of North Carolina Will Book, 1986; contbr. to profl. jours. Elder and Deacon Myers Park Presbyn. Ch., Charlotte, 1980-86, 92—; dir. sec. Presbyn. Home for Aged, Charlotte, 1978-82; trustee Charlotte Latin Schs., Inc., 1980-86, 87-93. Fellow Am. Coll. Trust and Estate Counsel (mem. bd. regents), Am. Coll. Tax Counsel; mem. ABA, Ga. Bar Assn., N.C. Bar Assn. (probate and fiduciary law sect.), Order of Coif, Phi Beta Kappa, Omicron Delta Kappa. Republican. Avocations: tennis, golf, fishing. Office: Moore & Van Allen PLLC Nations Bank Corp Ctr 100 N Tryon St 47th Fl Charlotte NC 28202-4003

MCBRYDE, THOMAS HENRY, lawyer; b. New Albany, Miss., Oct. 26, 1925; s. Henry Thornton and Mary Catherine (Davis) McB.; m. Barbara White, Dec. 28, 1946; children: Elise, William Henry, John Thomas. B.S., U.S. Mil. Acad., 1946; LL.B., U. Va., 1952. Bar: Va. 1952, N.Y. 1959. Commd. 2d lt. U.S. Army, 1946, advanced through grades to capt.; 1950; assigned to Japan, ETO and U.S.; instr. law U.S. Mil. Acad., 1956-57; resigned, 1957; asst. counsel N.Y. State Banking Dept., 1960-61; assoc. Rogers & Wells and predecessors, N.Y.C., 1957-60, 61-65, ptnr., 1965-93, sr. counsel, 1993—; chief counsel N.Y. State Joint Legis. Com. to Revise Banking Law, 1962-65, minority counsel, 1965-66; mem. comml. panel Am. Arbitration Assn., 1976—; mem. adv. com. supervision mut. instns. Office N.Y. Banking Supt., 1966-67. Mem. Assn. Grads. U.S. Mil. Acad., N.Y. West Point Soc., Order of Coif, Am. Yacht Club, Yale Club N.Y. (assoc.). Republican. Episcopalian. Home: 15 Waters Edge Rye NY 10580-3254 Office: Rogers & Wells 200 Park Ave Ste 5200 New York NY 10166-0005

MCBURNEY, GEORGE WILLIAM, lawyer; b. Ames, Iowa, Feb. 17, 1926; s. James William and Elfie Hazel (Jones) McB.; m. Georgianna Edwards, Aug. 28, 1949; children: Hollis Lynn, Jana Lee McBurney-Lin, John Edwards. B.A., State U. Iowa, 1950, J.D. with distinction, 1953. Bar: Iowa 1953, Ill. 1954, Calif. 1985. With Sidley & Austin and predecessor, Chgo., 1953—, ptnr., 1964-1993, counsel, 1994—; resident ptnr. Singapore, 1982-84. Editor-in-chief: Iowa Law Rev., 1952-53. Mem. Chgo. Crime Commn., 1966-84; trustee Iowa Law Sch. Found., 1988—, Old People's Home of City of Chgo., 1968-83, sec., 1972-79, exec. v.p., 1969-74, pres., 1974-82, hon. life trustee, 1983—; hon. life trustee Georgian, Evanston, Ill., trustee, counsel, 1976-82, v.p., 1980-82. Served with inf. AUS, 1944-46. Fellow Am. Coll. Trial Lawyers, Am. Bar Found. (life); mem. ABA, State Bar of Calif., Los Angeles County Bar Assn., Fed. Bar Assn., Am. Judicature Soc., Bar Assn. 7th Fed. Circuit, Am. Arbitration Assn. (panelist large complex dispute resolution program), Assn. Bus. Trial Lawyers, The Ctr. for Internat. Comml. Arbitration L.A. (bd. dirs., exec. v.p.), Nat. Coll. Edn. (bd. assocs. 1967-84), U.S. C. of C. (govt. and regulatory affairs com. of council on antitrust policy 1980-82), L.A. Complex Litigation Inn of Ct., Law Soc. Singapore (hon.), Western Ctr. on Law and Poverty (bd. dirs. 1992—), L.A. Union League Club (vet.), Mid-Day Club Chgo., Law Club (life), Legal Club Chgo., Am. Club, Cricket Club, Town Club Singapore, Phi Kappa Psi, Omicron Delta Kappa, Delta Sigma Rho, Phi Delta Phi. Republican. Presbyterian. Home: Malibu Pacifica 13 3601 Vista Pacifica Malibu CA 90265-4830 Office: Sidley & Austin 555 W 5th St Ste 4000 Los Angeles CA 90013-3018

MCBURNEY, MARGOT B., librarian; b. Lethbridge, Alta., Can.; d. Ronald Laurence Maness and R. Blanche (Lott) Hart; children: Margot Elisabeth McBurney Lane, James Ronald Gordon. B.A. with honours, Principia Coll., 1953; M.Sc. in LS, U. Ill., 1969. Sec. Marshall Brooks Library, Principia Coll., Elsah, Ill., 1966-69; reference librarian Marshall Brooks Library, Principia Coll., 1969-70; systems analyst trainee in library systems U. Alta. Library, Edmonton, 1970-71; undergrad. reference librarian U. Alta. Library, 1971-72, editor periodicals holdings list 1972-73, serials cataloguer, 1973-74, head acquisitions div., 1974-77; chief librarian Queen's U. Library, Kingston, Ont., Can., 1977-90. Editor: Am. Soc. Info. Sci. Western Can. chpt. Proceedings, 1975, 76. Mem. ALA, Am. Soc. Info. Sci. (councilor-at-large 1976-79, past chmn. chpt.), Assn. Research Libraries (dir. 1978-81, chmn. task force on library edn. 1980-83), Can. Assn. Info. Sci., Can. Assn. Research Libraries, Can. Library Assn., Council on Library Resources (PETREL com. 1981-84), Phi Alpha Eta, Beta Phi Mu.

MCBURNEY, THOMAS ROSS, food company executive; b. Mpls., June 16, 1938; s. Lloyd L. and Lorna McB.; m. Barbara L. Dawson; children—Ann, Susan, Megan, Lesley. B.A., Dartmouth U., 1960; M.B.A. Amos Tuck U., 1962; postgrad., Stanford U., 1973. Vice pres., gen. mgr.; refrigerated foods Pillsbury Co., Mpls., 1977-80, v.p. gen. mgr. grocery foods, 1980-82, group v.p. frozen and refrigerated foods, 1983-85, pres. U.S. Foods, 1985-86, chmn., 1986-88, exec. v.p., 1987—; bd. dirs. Security Am. Fin. Enterprises, Valspar Corp.; chmn. Internat. Foods, 1988—. Vice chmn. Minn. Pub. Radio; St. Paul; bd. dirs. Freedom from Hunger Found., Davis (Calif.), Minn. Orch., Minn. Council on Founds., Mpls., 1985, UNICEF. Office: Pillsbury Co Pillsbury Ctr 200 S 6th St Minneapolis MN 55402-1464

MCCABE, CHARLES LAW, retired manufacturing company executive, management consultant; b. Port Deposit, Md., Oct. 13, 1922; s. Joshua Burton and Adah (Law) McC.; m. Ingrid Alice Koebel, Dec. 21, 1949; children: Chad, Sigrid Christina, Ingrid Lisa. B.S., Dickinson Coll., 1943; M.S., Carnegie Mellon U., 1947, Sc.D., 1948. Mem. faculty Carnegie Mellon U., Pitts., 1951-65, prof., 1959-65; dean Grad. Studies, Carnegie Mellon U., 1962-65, v.p. research, 1964-65; pres. Koebel Diamond Tool Co., Detroit, 1966-70, Teledyne Firth Sterling, Pitts., 1970-75; gen. mgr. v.p. High Tech. Materials div. Cabot Corp., Kokomo, Ind., 1975-82; v.p. Cabot Corp., Boston, 1982-87; pres. High St. Assocs., Boston, 1988—. Author: (with C.L. Bauer) Metals, Atoms and Alloy, 1964. Past trustee Dickinson Coll.; active fund drives United Way. Served with AUS, 1945-46. Fellow Am. Soc. Metals (Pitts. award 1961); mem. AIME, Grosse Pointe Club, Naples Yacht Club, Keewaydin Club, Pt. Royal Club (Naples). Episcopalian.

MCCABE, SISTER DANIEL MARIE, nun, religious organization executive; b. Ansonia, Conn., Sept. 30, 1924; d. Daniel J. and Delia Theresa McCabe. RN, St. Mary's Hosp., Waterbury, Conn., 1945; BS, Coll. of Mary Immaculate, Hartford, Conn., 1954; MHA, St. Louis U., 1957; LHD (hon.), Sacred Heart U., Bridgeport, Conn., 1981. Joined Sisters of St. Joseph of Chambery, Roman Cath. Ch., 1946. Asst. administr. St. Francis Hosp., Hartford, 1957-63; administr. St. Joseph Med. Ctr., Stamford, Conn., 1963-85, pres., chief exec. officer, 1985—; trustee St. Camillus Health Ctr., Conn. Cath. Hosp. Coun.; mem. adv. bd. Inst. for Religious Edn. and Pastoral Studies Sacred Heart U.; mem. New Eng. Healthcare Assembly, New Eng. Conf. Cath. Hosps. Recipient Ella T. Grasso Community Svc. award Judeo-Christian Women Fairfield County, Conn., 1984, Outstanding Woman of Yr. award Soroptomist Internat., 1984, Spl. Svc. award Fairfield Found., Inc., 1986. Fellow Am. Coll. Healthcare Execs.; mem. Conn. Hosp. Assn. (mem. com. on govt.), Alliance for Health (trustee), Northeast Hosp. Network (trustee). Home and Office: St Joseph Med Ctr 128 Strawberry Hill Ave Stamford CT 06902-2500

MCCABE, DAVID ALLEN, lawyer; b. N.Y.C., Aug. 2, 1940; s. Charles Bernard and Ruth (Starr) McC.; m. Caroline F., Nicholas D. AB, Princeton U., 1962; LLB, Columbia U., 1966. Bar: N.Y. 1967, U.S. Dist. Ct. (so. dist.) N.Y. 1967. Assoc. Shearman & Sterling, N.Y.C., 1966-74, ptnr., 1974—; bd. dirs. Kanthal Corp., Bethel, Conn., Gen. Tire Inc., Akron, Ohio, Degussa Corp., Teterboro, N.J., fin. com., 1973-87. Mem. ABA, N.Y. State Bar Assn., Assn. of Bar of City of N.Y., German-Am. C. of C. (bd. dirs. 1979-82, 83-86, sec. 1983-86). Office: 599 Lexington Ave New York NY 10022-6030

MCCABE, EDWARD AENEAS, communications company fin. executive; b. County Monaghan, Ireland, Mar. 4, 1917; came to U.S., 1928; naturalized; 1931; s. Patrick and Alice (McDonnell) McC.; m. Janet Isabel Stevens, Nov. 17, 1951, (dec. Oct. 1981); children: Thomas, Michael, Patrick, Barbara; m. Verna Ann Peterson, June 27, 1985. LLB, Columbus U., 1946; LHD (hon.), Johnson & Wales U., 1977; LLD (hon.), Allentown Coll., 1992. Bar: D.C. 1946, U.S. Supreme Ct. 1950. Exec. asst. Joint Congl. Com. Labor Mgmt. Rels., 1947-48; atty. labor rels. and trade assn. matters Wash-

---

ington, 1949-52; gen. counsel com. on edn. and labor Ho. of Reps., 1953-55; assoc., White House counsel to Pres. of U.S., 1956-58; admnstrv. asst. President Eisenhower, Washington, 1958-61; ptnr. Hamel, Morgan, Park & Saunders, Washington, 1961-71, Hamel, Park, McCabe & Saunders, Washington, 1971-82; of counsel Hamel, Park, McCabe & Saunders (now Hopkins & Sutter), Washington, 1982—; bd. dirs. USA GROUP, Inc., Indpls., First Am. Bank, Washington; chmn. bd. Student Loan Mktg. Assn.; White House cons. Presdl. transition, 1974-75, advisor, 1980-81; mem. D.C. Criminal Justice Coordinating Bd. Trustee Pub. Defender Svc. D.C., Immaculata Coll., Washington, 1965-78, Allentown Coll., Center Valley, Pa., 1969-75; bd. govs. USO; bd. advisers DeSales Sch. Theology, Washington; bd. dirs. Community Found. Greater Washington; bd. dirs., pres. Eisenhower World Affairs Inst., Washington; mem. cardinal's com. laity Archdiocese of Washington, com. for deferred gifts for Archdiocese; exec. cabinet Cath. Charities USA. With U.S. Army, 1941-45. Mem. ABA, Fed. Bar Assn., D.C. Bar Assn., Jud. Conf. D.C. Cir., Capitol Hill Club, Met. Club (Washington), Burning Tree Club (Bethesda, Md.), Kenwood Golf and Country Club (Bethesda). Republican. Roman Catholic. Home: 4940 Sentinel Dr Bethesda MD 20816-3593 Office: Hopkins & Sutter 888 16th St NW Washington DC 20006-4103

MCCABE, EDWARD ARTHUR, communications company executive; b. Chgo., Dec. 9, 1938; m. Stephanie Jane Hulton, Oct. 14, 1972 (div. 1978); 1 child, Colin Adam; 1 child from previous marriage, Mark Owen. With McCann-Erickson Co., Chgo., 1954-55; copywriter Automatic Electric Co., Northlake, Ill., 1956-58; cashier Schrafft's, N.Y.C., 1959; copywriter Benton & Bowles, N.Y.C., 1960-63, Young & Rubicam, 1963-64; assoc. copy chief Carl Ally, N.Y.C., 1964-66; pres., worldwide creative dir. Scali, McCabe Sloves, N.Y.C., 1967-87; prin. McCabe Communications, Inc., N.Y.C., 1988-89; chmn., creative ptnr. Beber, Silverstein, McCabe & Ptnrs., N.Y.C., 1989—. Author: Against Gravity, 1990. Named to Copywriters Hall of Fame Copy Club N.Y., 1974; recipient Advt. Man of Yr. award B'nai Brith Youth Svcs., 1983. First American to drive an automobile in Paris/Dakar Rallye. Office: Beber Silverstein McCabe & Ptnrs 1500 Broadway New York NY 10036-4015

MC CABE, GERARD BENEDICT, library administrator; b. N.Y.C., Jan. 22, 1930; s. Patrick Joseph and Margaret Irene (McDonald) McC.; m. Jacqueline L. Maloney, Aug. 3, 1963 (dec. 1987); children: Theresa Marie, Rebecca Mary. B.A. in English, Manhattan Coll., 1952; A.M. in Library Sci. (scholar), U. Mich., 1954; M.A. in English, Mich. State U., 1959. Asst. acquisitions dept. U. Nebr. Library, Lincoln, 1954-56; chief bibliog. acquisitions dept. Mich. State U. Library, East Lansing, 1956-58; librarian Inst. Community Devel. and Service, Mich. State U., 1958-59; acquisitions librarian U. S. Fla., Tampa, 1959-66; asst. dir. planning and devel. U. S. Fla., 1967-70; assoc. dir. U. Ark. Library, Fayetteville, 1966-67; dir. univ. libraries Va. Commonwealth U., Richmond, 1970-82; dir. libraries Clarion U. of Pa., 1982—. Editor: The Smaller Academic Library: A Management Handbook, 1988, Operations Handbook for Small Academic Library, 1989, Academic Libraries in Urban and Metropolitan Areas, 1992; co-editor ann. pub. Advances in Libr. Adminstrn. and Orgn., Insider's Guide to Libr. Automation: Essays of Prractical Experiences, 1993, Acad. Librs.: Their Rationale and Role in Am. Higher Edn., 1995; contbr. articles to profl. jours. Mem. ALA, Southeastern Library Assn., Bibliog. Soc. Am. Home: PO Box 221 Clarion PA 16214-0221 Office: Rena M Carlson Libr Clarion U of Pa Clarion PA 16214 *Consideration for others is a guiding principle for my personal and professional behavior. I, as a librarian, must have concern for those I serve. Their needs are my first and only interest, not success, not notoriety, only their service and their satisfaction.*

MCCABE, JAMES PATRICK, library director; b. Phila., May 24, 1937; s. Felix and Josephine (Murtaugh) McC. BA, Niagara U., 1963; MA, U. Mich., 1964, MA in LS, 1965, PhD, 1968. Libr. dir. Allentown Coll., Center Valley, Pa., 1968-89; acting libr. dir. Muhlenberg Cedar Crest Colls., Allentown, Pa., 1989-90; dir. univ. libr. Fordham U., N.Y.C., 1990—. Author: Critical Guide to Catholic Reference Books, 3d edit., 1989. Bd. dirs. Pa. Shakespear Festival, Center Valley, 1990—. Office: Fordham U Libr Bronx NY 10458

MCCABE, JAMES R., school system administrator. Supt. Lake County Sch. Dist. R-1, Leadville, Colo. State finalist Nat. Supt. Yr. award, 1992. Office: Lake County Sch Dist R-1 PO Box 977 107 Spruce Leadville CO 80461

MC CABE, JOHN CHARLES, III, writer; b. Detroit, Nov. 14, 1920; s. Charles John and Rosalie (Dropiewski) McC.; m. Vija Valda Zarina, Oct. 19, 1962 (dec. 1984); children—Linard Peter, Sean Cahal and Deirdre Rose (twins); m. Rosina Lawrence, June 8, 1987. Ph.B., U. Detroit, 1947; M.F.A. in Theatre, Fordham U., 1948; Ph.D. in English Lit, Shakespeare Inst., U. Birmingham, Eng., 1954. Instr. theatre Wayne State U., 1948-51, CCNY, 1955; mem. faculty N.Y. U., 1956-68, prof. dramatic art, chmn. dept., 1962-68; chmn. dept. drama and theatre arts Mackinac Coll., Mackinac Island, Mich., 1968-70; founder The Sons of the Desert (group devoted to works Laurel and Hardy), 1963. Profl. actor, 1928—; producer-dir., Milford (Pa.) Playhouse, summers 1948-53, producer, N.Y. U. Summer Theatre, Sterling Forest, N.Y., 1963-65, author-in-residence, Lake Superior State Coll., Sault Ste. Marie, Mich., 1970-86; author: Mr. Laurel and Mr. Hardy, 1961, rev. edit., 1986, George M. Cohan: The Man Who Owned Broadway, 1973, The Comedy World of Stan Laurel, 1974, Laurel & Hardy, 1975, (with G.B. Harrison) Proclaiming the Word, 1976, Charlie Chaplin, 1978, Grand Hotel: Mackinac Island, 1987, Babe: The Life of Oliver Hardy, 1990, The High, 1992; ghostwriter of James Cagney's autobiography, Cagney by Cagney, 1976; Babe: The Life of Oliver Hardy. Served with USAAF, 1943-45, ETO. Mem. Shakespeare Assn. Am., Actors Equity Assn., Catholic Actors Guild Am., Baker St. Irregulars. Clubs: The Players (N.Y.), The Lambs (N.Y.C.). Home: British Landing PO Box 363 Mackinac Island MI 49757-0363 *At fourteen I learned from the Jesuits that one who knows both the function and beauty of an English sentence will be blessed life-long.*

MCCABE, MICHAEL, broadcast executive; b. Toronto, 1938; divorced; 2 children. Honours degree Philosophy, English, U. Toronto. Exec. asst. fed. cabinet minister Ottawa, 1963-68; v.p. Helix Investments Ltd., 1968-70; dir.-gen. policy and program devel. citizenship br. Dept. State, Ottawa, 1970-74; chmn. policy and rsch. Can. Mortgage and Housing Corp., Ottawa, 1974-76; asst. dep. minister comsumer affairs Fed. Dept. Consumer and Corp. Affairs, Ottawa, 1976-78; exec. dir. Can. Film Devel. Corp. (now Telefilm Can.), Ottawa, 1978-80; pres. McCabe Comm. Ltd., Ottawa, 1981-88; pres.& CEO Can. Assn. Broadcasters, Ottawa, 1988—. Office: Can Assn Broadcasters, 350 Sparks St #306, PO Box 627 Stn B, Ottawa, ON Canada K1P 5S2

MCCABE, RICHARD LEE, real estate developer; b. Cheyenne, Wyo., June 9, 1943; s. Thomas Junior and Alice May (Vernon) McC.; m. Janet Ann Lefkow (div.); children: Bradley Samuel, Kevin Ira; m. Julianne Clements, Dec. 22, 1979; children: Thomas Durant, Claire Angela Kim. BArch., U. Colo., 1967. V.p., sec. McSan Enterprises, Inc., Boulder, 1968-72; pres. Boulder (Colo.) Design & Tool Group, Inc., 1972-74; pvt. practice R.L. McCabe & Assocs., Boulder, 1974-77; pres. R.L.M. Inc., Boulder, 1977-80, Cubit Corp., Boulder, 1980-84, Centermark Corp., Boulder, 1984-87, Cubit Constrn. Corp., Boulder, 1987-88, Core Corp., Boulder, 1988—; dir. Boulder Builders Group, 1988-89, Nat. Fastpitch Assn., Mpls., 1990—; pres. Boulder County Builders Assn., 1990-91. Co-author: (mcpl. legislation) Community Housing Assistance Plan, 1991. Mem. Affordable Housing Task Force, Boulder, 1989, Thistle Community Housing Corp., Boulder, 1991; mem. steering com. North Boulder Subcmty., 1994. Recipient Svc. award Assn. Student Chpts. of AIA, 1966, award of appreciation City Boulder Housing Authority, 1989, cert. award Dept. Housing and Human Svcs., Boulder, 1990, cert. appreciation Boulder County Safehouse, 1991. Mem. Boulder County Chpt. of the Met. Denver Home Builders Assn. (pres. 1991-92), Congress for New Urbanism. Avocations: sailing, fishing, camping, hiking, river floating. Home: 526 Arapahoe Ave Boulder CO 80302-5827 Office: Core Corp 4845 Pearl East Cir Ste 302 Boulder CO 80301-6113

MCCABE, ROBERT ALBERT, wildlife ecology educator; b. Milw., Jan. 11, 1914; s. Frank and Matilda (Guetlich) McC.; m. Marie Elinor Stanfield, July 5, 1941; children: Colleen, Richard, Thomas, Kevin. BA, Carroll Coll., 1939; MA, U. Wis., 1943, PhD, 1948; LLD (hon.), Nat. U. Ireland, 1988;

DHL (hon.), Carroll Coll., Waukesha, Wis., 1989. Arboretum biologist U. Wis., Madison, 1943-45, from instr. to full prof. wildlife ecology, 1943-84, prof. emeritus, 1984—; chmn. dept., 1952-69; cons. Office Pub. Works, Dublin, Ireland, 1970-87; mem. rsch. adv. commn. Wis. Dept. Natural Resources, Madison, 1952-86. Author: Aldo Leopold: The Professor, 1987, The Little Green Bird, 1991. Sec. Wis. Expo. Dept. Ed. West Allis, 1960-66, Wis. Dept. Resource Devel., Madison, 1961-63; mem. Dept. Interior Commn. on Lead and Iron Shot Evaluation, Washington, 1973-74; chmn. Nat. Acad. Com. on Vertebrate Pests, Washington, 1967-69. Fulbright prof., Ireland, 1969-70; recipient Aldo Leopold medal The Wildlife Soc., Washington, 1986. Fellow Am. Ornithologists Union; mem. The Wildlife Soc. (life, pres. 1976-77), Wilson Ornithol. Soc. (life), Brit. Ecol. Soc., Brit. Ornithol. Union. Club: Madison Literary. Avocations: hunting, fishing, antiques. Office: U Wis Dept Wildlife Ecology 215 Russell Lab Madison WI 53706-1598

MCCABE, ROBERT HOWARD, educator, college president; b. Bklyn., Dec. 23, 1929; s. Joseph A. and Kathryn (Greer) McC.; m. Arva Moore Parks, June 1992. BEd, U. Miami (Fla.), 1952; MS, Appalachian State U., Boone, N.C., 1959; PhD, U. Tex., Austin, 1963; LLD (hon.), Barry U., 1986, U. Miami, 1990, Fla. Internat. U., 1990. Asst. to pres. Miami-Dade Community Coll. (Fla.), 1963-65, v.p., 1965-67, exec. v.p., 1969-80, pres., 1980—; pres. Essex County Coll., Newark, 1967-69; exec. com. So. Regional Edn. Bd., Atlanta, 1981-83; trusteeColl. Bd., chmn., 1988-90; vice chair The Miami Coalition for a Drug-Free Community, 1989-93. Recipient Disting. Service award Fla. Congl. Del., 1983, Spirit of Excellence award The Miami Herald, 1988, Harold W. McGraw Jr. prize in Edn., 1991; named Outstanding Grad., Coll. Edn., U. Tex., 1982, named one of the 18 Most Effective Chief Exec. Officer in Am. Higher Edn. Bowling Green U., 1988; Disting. Service award, Dade County, Fla., 1983; Kellogg fellow, 1962-63, MacArthur fellow John D. and Catherine T. MacArthur Found., 1992. Mem. Am. Assn. Community Colls. (bd. dirs. 1991—), Am. Assn. Higher Edn. (dir. 1973-75), Am. Assn. for Environ. Edn. (pres. 1970-73), Am. Council on Edn., Commn. on Higher Edn. Issues, Higher Edn. Consortium, Am. Council Edn. (bd. dir. 1983-85, 92—), Southeast Fla. Edn. Consortium (chmn. bd. 1981-83), League for Innovation in Community Colls. (dir., exec. com. 1985—). Episcopalian. Author: Man and Environment, 1971; contbr. articles to profl. jours.; editor Jour. Environ. Edn.; contbr. editor Change Mag., 1980—. Home: 1000 Venetian Way Apt 1303 Miami FL 33139-1011 Office: Miami-Dade Community Coll Dist 300 NE 2nd Ave Miami FL 33132-2204*

MCCABE, ROBERT R., architect, city planner. BArch, U. Calif. Berkeley, 1965; postgrad., Mich. State U., 1967-68; M in Community Planning, U. Cin., 1971. Vol. Peace Corps, Colombia; city planner 5, chief planner model cities physical planning program Cin. City Planning Commn.; prin. Flatow, Moore, Shaffer, McCabe, Inc., Albuquerque, 1984—; instr. U. N.Mex. 1976-79, Grad. Dept. Community Planning, Cin., 1972, Urban Conservation Project, Cin., 1968, Mich. State U., 1968; assoc. prof. community planning Sch. Art, Architecture and Design, U. Cin., 1972. Prin. works include Albuquerque Acad. Mid. Sch., St. Joseph Rehab. Hosp., Vision of Albuquerque, among others. Mem. Environ. Planning Commn., Downtown Action Planning Com., Comprehensive Plan Oversight Com.; v.p. met. affairs, v.p. govtl. affairs, Albuquerque Mus. Found., mem. exec. com.; mem. bus. adv. coun. Gov. Garry Carruthers, chmn. long-range planning task force. Mem. AIA (com. on architecture for health), Am. Planning Assn., Nat. Coun. Archtl. Registration Bds., Greater Albuquerque C. of C. (bd. dirs.). Office: Flatow Moore Shaffer McCabe Inc PO Box 8266 Albuquerque NM 87198-8266

MCCAFFREE, BROTHER BENEDICT BRADFORD, historian; b. Nurnburg, Germany, May 31, 1958; s. Robert James McC. AA, St. Gregory's Coll., 1978; AB, St. Anselm Coll., 1981; MA in Mediaeval History, U. Notre Dame, 1983, PhD, 1994. Prof. history St. Gregory's Abbey, Shawnee, Okla., 1985-92; archivist St. Gregory's Abbey, Coll., 1987-94; dir. Mabee-Gerrer Mus. Art, Shawnee, 1990-94; internat. lectr. ethics, ecclesiastical hist., monasticism, art liberal arts. Contbr. articles to profl. jours in U.S. and Europe. Mem. Leadership Okla. Democrat. Avocations: weight training, pro-life activities. Home: 21-14 45th Ave Long Island City NY 11101 Office: Mabee-Gerrer Museum of Art 1900 W MacArthur Dr Shawnee OK 74801-2499

MCCAFFREE, BURNHAM CLOUGH, JR., retired naval officer; b. San Diego, Sept. 28, 1931; s. Burnham Clough and Elisabeth Cory (Woodhull) McC.; m. Erlend Elizabeth Carlton, June 19, 1954; children: Elizabeth Anne McCaffree Antanitus, Debora Lynn McCaffree Hagwood. BS in Naval Engring., U.S. Naval. Acad., 1954. Commd. ensign USN, 1954, advanced through grades to rear adm., 1983, served on six ships, mem. staffs Atlantic Fleet and Pacific Fleet, until 1970; comdg. officer USS Johnston, U.S. Atlantic Fleet, Charleston, S.C., 1970-72; action officer, sr. navy planner Office Chief Naval Ops., Washington, 1972-76, dir. mobile logistic support forces, amphibious, mine and spl. warfare div., 1982-84, asst. dep. chief naval logistics, 1986-87, dir. logistics plans div., 1987-88; comdg. officer USS Shreveport, U.S. Atlantic Fleet, Norfolk, Va., 1976-78; chief staff, comdr. amphibious group 2 U.S. Atlantic Fleet, Norfolk, 1978-84; comdr. amphibious squadron 2, 1980-82; comdr. amphibious force U.S. 7th Fleet, Okinawa, Japan, 1984-86; ret., 1988; cons. Inst. Defense Analyses, Alexandria, Va., Ctr. Naval Analyses, Alexandria, Va., 1989—. Decorated Legion of Merit with 4 gold stars, Meritorious Service Medal, others. Mem. U.S. Naval Inst., U.S.C. of C. (assoc.). Episcopalian. Home: 3620 Buckwood Ct Annandale VA 22003-1951

MCCAFFREY, ANNE INEZ, author; b. Cambridge, Mass., Apr. 1, 1926; d. George H. and Anne (McElroy) McC.; m. Wright Johnson, Jan. 14, 1950 (div. Aug. 1970); children: Alec Anthony, Todd, Georgeanne. B.A. cum laude, Radcliffe Coll., 1947; student, U. City of Dublin, 1970-71. Copywriter, layout designer Liberty Music Shops, N.Y.C. 1948-50; copywriter, sec. Helena Rubinstein, N.Y.C., 1950-52. Author: Restoree, 1967, Dragonflight, 1968, Decision at Doona, 1969, Ship Who Sang, 1969, Mark of Merlin, 1971, Dragonquest: Being the Further Adventures of the Dragonriders of Pern, 1971, Ring of Fear, 1971, To Ride Pegasus, 1973, Cooking Out Of This World, 1973, A Time When, 1975, Dragonsong, 1976, Kilternan Legacy, 1975, Dragonsinger, 1977, Dinosaur Planet, 1977, Get Off the Unicorn, 1977, White Dragon, 1978, Dragondrums, 1979, Crystal Singer, 1981, The Worlds of Anne McCaffrey, 1981, The Coelura, 1983, Moreta: Dragonlady of Pern, 1983, Dinosaur Planet Survivors, 1984, Stitch in Snow, 1984, Killashandra, 1985, The Girl Who Heard Dragons, 1985, The Year of the Lucy, 1986, Nerilka's Story, 1986, The Lady, 1987, People of Pern, 1988, Dragonsdown, 1988, Renegades of Pern, 1989, (with Jody-Lynn Nye) The Dragonlover's Guide to Pern, 1989, The Rowan, 1990, Pegasus in Flight, 1990, (with Elizabeth Moon) Sassinak, 1990, (with Nye) The Death of Sleep, 1990, All the Weyrs of Pern, 1991, Generation Warriors, 1991, Damia, 1991, (with Margaret Ball) The Partnership, 1991, (with Nye) Crisis at Doona, 1991, Damia, 1992, (with Mercedes Lackey) The City Who Fought, 1993, (with Elizabeth Ann Scarborough) Powers That Be, 1993, Chronicles of Pern: First Fall, 1993, Lyon's Pride, 1994, (with Nye) The Ship Who Won, 1994, (with Scarborough) Power Lines, 1994, Dolphins of Pern, 1994, (with Scarborough) Power Play, 1995; editor: Alchemy and Academe, 1970; anthology: The Girl Who Heard Dragons, 1991; dir. musical Brecks Mill Cronies, 1962-65. Recipient Hugo award, 1967, Nebula award, 1968, E.E. Smith award, 1975, Ditmar award, 1979, Gandalf award, 1979, Eurocon/Streso award, 1979, Balrog award, 1980, Golden PEN award, 1981, Sci. Fiction Book Club award, 1986, 89, 91, 92, 93. Mem. PEN (Ireland), Sci. Fiction Writers Am. (sec.-treas. 1968-70), Authors' Guild. Office: Dragonhold Underhill, Timmore Ln, Newcastle, Wicklow Ireland

MCCAFFREY, BARRY RICHARD, army officer; b. Taunton, Mass., Nov. 17, 1942; s. William Joseph and Mary Veronica (Curtin) McC.; m. Jill Ann Faulkner, June 8, 1964; children: Sean, Tara, Amy. BS, U.S. Mil. Acad., 1964; MA, Am. U., 1971; postgrad., Command and Gen. Staff Coll., Ft. Leavenworth, Kans., 1976, Army War Coll., Carlisle Barracks, Pa., 1982. Commd. 2d lt. U.S. Army, 1964, advanced through grades to maj. gen. 1990; co. comdr. 1st Cav. Div., Vietnam, 1968-69; assoc. prof. dept. social sci. U.S. Mil. Acad., West Point, N.Y., 1972-75; bn. comdr. 3d Inf. Div., Germany, 1979-83; div. chief staff, then brigade comdr. 9th Inf. Div., Ft. Lewis, Wash., 1983-86; asst. comdt. U.S. Army Inf. Sch., Ft. Benning, Ga.,

1986-88; dep. U.S. mil. rep. NATO, Brussels, 1988-89; dir. strategic plans policy Joint Staff, Washington, 1989-90; div. comdr. 24th Inf. Div., Ft. Stewart, Ga., 1990—. Contbr. articles to mil. publs. Decorated D.S.C. with oak leaf cluster, Silver Star with oak leaf cluster, Purple Heart with two oak leaf clusters. Mem. Legion of Valor. Roman Catholic. Avocations: hunting, reading military history. Office: Department of the Army Chief of Public Affairs Washington DC 20310

MCCAFFREY, CARLYN SUNDBERG, lawyer; b. N.Y.C., Jan. 7, 1942; d. Carl Andrew Lawrence and Evelyn (Back) Sundberg; m. John P. McCaffrey, May 24, 1967; children: John C., Patrick, Jennifer, Kathleen. Student, Barnard Coll., 196.; AB in Econs., George Washington U., 1963; LLB cum laude, NYU, 1967, LLM in Taxation, 1970. Bar: N.Y. 1974. Law clk. to presiding justice Calif. Supreme Ct., 1967-68; teaching fellow law NYU, N.Y.C., 1968-70; asst. prof. law, 1970-74; assoc. Weil, Gotshal & Manges, N.Y.C., 1974-80, ptnr., 1980—; prof. in residence Rubin Hall NYU, 1971-75; adj. prof. law NYU, 1975—, U. Miami, 1979-81, 83—; lectr. in field. Contbr. articles to profl. jours. Mem. ABA (chmn. generationskipping trusts 1979-81, 91—, real property probate and trust law sect.), N.Y. State Bar Assn. (exec. com. tax sect. 1979-80, chmn. estate and gift tax com. 1976-78, life ins. com. 1983-85, trusts and estates sect.), Assn. of Bar of City of N.Y. (matrimonial law com., chmn. tax subcom. 1984-86). Home: 38 Sidney Pl Brooklyn NY 11201-4607 Office: Weil Gotshal & Manges 767 Fifth Ave New York NY 10153-0002

MCCAFFREY, JUDITH ELIZABETH, lawyer; b. Providence, Apr. 26, 1944; d. Charles V. and Isadore Frances (Langford) McC.; m. Martin D. Minsker, Dec. 31, 1969 (div. May 1981); children: Ethan Hart Minsker, Natasha Langford Minsker. BA, Tufts U., 1966; JD, Boston U., 1970. Bar: Mass. 1970, D.C. 1972, Fla. 1991. Assoc. Sullivan & Worcester, Washington, 1970-76; atty. FDIC, Washington, 1976-78; assoc. Dechert, Price & Rhoads, Washington, 1978-82; McKenna, Conner & Cuneo, Washington, 1982-83; gen. counsel, corp. sec. Perpetual Savs. Bank, FSB, Alexandria, Va., 1983-91; ptnr. Powell, Goldstein, Frazer & Murphy, Washington, 1991-92, McCaffrey & Raimi, P.A., 1992—. Contbr. articles to profl. jours. Mem. edn. com. Bd. Trade, Washington, 1986-92. Mem. ABA (chairperson subcom. thrift instns. 1985-90), Fed. Bar Assn. (exec. com., banking law com. 1985-91), D.C. Bar Assn. (bd. govs. 1981-85), Women's Bar Assn. (pres. 1980-81). Episcopalian. Avocations: golf, travel, tennis, sailing, reading. Office: McCaffrey & Raimi, PA Ste 202 4501 Tamiami Trl N Naples FL 33940

MCCAFFREY, NEIL, publishing executive; b. Rye, N.Y., Aug. 29, 1925; s. Cornelius Thomas and Anastasia Frances (Waterman) McC.; m. Joan Elizabeth Melervey, Apr. 10, 1950; children: Maureen, Neil III, Eugene V., Roger A., Eileen, Susan. B.A., Fordham U., 1950. Employed various positions, 1948-55; editor Doubleday Co., N.Y.C., 1955-61; copywriter Doubleday Co., 1955-61, product mgr., 1960-61; mail order mgr. Macmillan Co., N.Y.C., 1961-64, dir. advt. 1963-64; founder, pres. Arlington House Pubs., New Rochelle, N.Y., 1964-78, Conservative Book Club, New Rochelle, 1964-78; pres. Conservative Book Club, Harrison, N.Y., 1982—; founder, pres. Nostalgia Book Club, New Rochelle, 1968-78, Arlray Advt., New Rochelle, 1972-78; pres. Movie/Entertainment Book Club, Harrison, N.Y., 1978—; pres. Harrison Assocs. (advt.), Harrison, 1979—; circulation mgr. Human Events, 1978-83; direct mail cons. Nat. Republican Congl. Com., 1963-71. Contbr. to: Nat. Rev. Bd. dirs. Am. Conservative Union, 1970-72. Served with USCGR, 1943-46. Mem. Conservation Book Club. Republican. Roman Catholic. Office: 15 Oakland Ave Harrison NY 10528-3709

MCCAFFREY, R. MICHAEL, orthopedic company executive; b. Parkersburg, W.Va., Apr. 6, 1942; s. Robert James and Margaret Rita (McDermott) McC.; m. Penny Sue Weems McCaffrey, June 5, 1965; children: Molly, Katie. BS cum laude, Xavier U., 1964, MBA, 1965. Naval officer U.S. Navy, Newport, R.I., 1966-71; v.p. Johnson & Johnson, Somerville, N.J., 1971-84; pres. DePuy Inc., Warsaw, Ind., 1984—. Lt. U.S. Navy, 1966-71. Republican. Roman Catholic. Avocation: fishing. Home: 1904 Deer Trail Warsaw IN 46580 Office: DePuy Inc 700 Orthopedic Dr Warsaw IN 46580

MCCAFFREY, ROBERT HENRY, JR., retired manufacturing company executive; b. Syracuse, N.Y., Jan. 20, 1927; s. Robert Henry and May Ann (McGuire) McC.; m. Dorothy Anne Evers, Sept. 22, 1956; children: Michael Robert, Kathleen Mary. BS, Syracuse U., 1949. Sales asst. Sealright Corp., Fulton, N.Y., 1949-50; with TEK Hughes div. Johnson & Johnson, Metuchen, N.J., 1950-67, gen. sales mgr., 1958-59, v.p. sales, 1959-62, pres., 1962-67; gen. mgr. med. div. Howmet Corp., N.Y.C., 1967-70; group v.p. Howmedica, Inc., 1970-73, sr. v.p., 1973-74, exec. v.p., also bd. dirs., 1974-76; pres., CEO C.R. Bard Inc., Murray Hill, N.J., 1976-78, chmn. bd. dirs., CEO, 1978-89, chmn. bd., 1989-91, also bd. dirs.; chmn. exec. com. C.R. Bard, Inc., Murray Hill, 1991—; bd. dirs. Summit and Elizabeth Trust, Summit Bancorp, Thomas & Betts Corp. Trustee Found. for Univ. Medicine and Dentistry N.J., 1989-90, Syracuse U., 1979—, chmn. corp. adv. council, 1974-75. With AUS, 1945-46. Mem. Orthopedic Surg. Mfrs. assn., Health Industry Mfrs. Assn. (bd. dir., chmn. 1982-83), N.Y. Sales Execs. Club, Algonquin Club (Boston), Baltusrol Golf Club (Springfield, N.J.), Oyster Harbors Club (Osterville, Mass.), Sigma Chi. Republican. Roman Catholic. Avocations: reading, skiing, golf. Office: C R Bard Inc 1200 Technology Park Dr Billerica MA 01821-4139

MCCAFFREY, SHELLYN GAE, federal official; b. Pitts., Dec. 22, 1957; d. Leo and Elizabeth (Stegman) McC. BS with high honors, Pa. State U., 1979; JD, Am. U., 1991. Press aide, fundraiser Reagan/Bush presdl. campaign, 1979-80; press sec. Reagan-Bush presidential campaign, 1981; senior staff mem. Office of Policy Devel., The White House, Washington, 1981-85; prin. dep. exec. sec. Pres.'s Econ. Policy Coun., Washington, 1985-88; assoc. dep. sec. U.S. Dept. Commerce; dep. under sec. internat. affairs U.S. Dept. Labor, 1989—; U.S. amb., rep. governing body U.N. Internat. Labor Orgn., 1989—; bd. dirs. Overseas Pvt. Investment Corp., Fgn. Svc. Bd., Am. Polish Labor Coop. Ctr., 1991—. Office: US Dept Labor Internat Affairs 200 Constitution Ave NW Washington DC 20210-0001

MC CAFFREY, THOMAS R., utilities company executive. Pres., chief oper. officer Columbus (Ohio) So. Power, 1991. Office: Columbus So Power Co 215 N Front St Columbus OH 43215-2291

MCCAFFREY, WILLIAM THOMAS, financial services company executive; b. N.Y.C., July 7, 1936; s. Daniel and Alice (Dineen) McC.; m. Mary Margaret Timms, June 25, 1960; children: Ann, William E., Christine. BS, NYU, 1970; MS in Bus., Columbia U., 1972. Dir. pub. The Equitable Fin. Cos., N.Y.C., 1968-71, asst. v.p. communications, 1972-74, v.p., office of the pres., 1975-77, v.p. corp. devel., 1977-79, v.p., personnel dir., 1980-84, sr. v.p. pers. and adminstrn., 1984-85, exec. v.p. corp., 1986-87, exec. v.p., chief adminstrv. officer, 1988—, chmn. benefits com., 1986—; bd. dirs. Equitable Variable Life Ins. Co., N.Y.C. Bd. dirs. Equitable Found., 1987—, Bronx-Lebanon Hosp.; project mgr. Grace Commn., Washington, 1982—; chmn. bd. trustees Xavier U., New Orleans, 1986—; chmn. bd. Deafness Rsch. Found., N.Y.C. Sgt. U.S. Army, 1957-58. Mem. West Side Tennis Club (Forest Hills, N.Y.) (gov. 1988—). Avocations: tennis, photography. Home: 89-25 63rd Ave New York NY 11374 Office: Equitable Fin Cos 787 7th Ave New York NY 10019-6018

MCCAGHY, CHARLES HENRY, sociology educator; b. Eau Claire, Wis., Apr. 29, 1934; s. Elmer and Anna Josephine (Soha) McC.; m. M. Dawn Ysebaert, June 10, 1961. BBusA, U. Wis., 1956, MA, 1962, PhD, 1966. Instr. sociology U. Conn., 1964-66; asst. prof. sociology Case Western Res. U., Cleve., 1966-70; assoc. prof. sociology Bowling Green State U., Ohio, 1970-76, prof., 1976-94, prof. emeritus, 1994—; vis. scholar Australian Inst. Criminology, 1984. Author: Deviant Behavior: Crime, Conflict and Interest Groups, 1976, 3d edit., 1994, Crime in American Society, 1980, 2d edit., 1987. Served to lt. (j.g.) USN, 1956-59. Mem. Am. Sociol. Assn., Am. Soc. Criminology (treas. 1978-82), Soc. for Sci. Study of Sex. Office: Bowling Green State U Dept Sociology Bowling Green OH 43403

MCCAHILL, BARRY WINSLOW, federal public affairs official; b. Glen Ridge, N.J., May 25, 1947; s. William Francis and Frances (Elliott) McC.; m. Margaret Anne Bonnes, Feb. 8, 1980; children: Jennifer, Kimberly, Erin, Meghan; 1 stepchild, Rob White. BA in English, U. Va., 1969, postgrad., 1974-76. Lic. U.S. Coast Guard capt. Account exec. Whyte Berry Price, Advt. & Pub. Rels., Washington, 1967-69; publs. mgr. Nat. Telephone Coop. Assn., Washington, 1972-74; visual info. specialist U.S. Customs Svc., Washington, 1974-76; pub. affairs specialist IRS, Washington, 1976-79; mgr. radio and TV news Nat. Hwy. Traffic Safety Adminstrn., U.S. Dept. Transp., Washington, 1979-85, dep. dir. Office Pub. and Consumer Affairs, 1985—. Loaned exec. Combined Fed. Campaign United Way, Washington, 1983. 1st lt. U.S. Army, 1969-72. Recipient Blue Pencil award Nat. Assn. Govt. Communicators, 1975, 88, Adminstrs. award for exceptional achievement Nat. Hwy. Traffic Safety Adminstrn., 1983, Sec.'s Honor award Sec. of Treasury, 1983, Sec.'s award for meritorious achievement Sec. of Transp., 1985. Mem. Am. Profl. Capts. Assn., Washington Automotive Press Assn., Old Dominion Morgan Horse Assn. (bd. dirs.), Cobbosseecontee Yacht Club (Manchester, Maine), Pi Kappa Alpha. Roman Catholic. Avocations: boating, skiing, golf. Home: 4832 Heron Neck Ln Fairfax VA 22033 Office: Nat Hwy Traffic Safety Adminstrn 400 7th St SW NOA-40 Washington DC 20590

MCCAIG, JEFFREY JAMES, transportation company executive; b. Moose Jaw, Sask., July 5, 1951; s. John Robert and Anne Shorrocks (Glass) McC.; m. Marilyn Graves, July 7, 1983; children: Robbert Angus, Scott Thomas, Christa Mae. Student, Can. Jr. Coll. Lausanne, Switzerland, 1970; AB, Harvard Coll., 1973; LLB, Osgoode Hall Law Sch., Can., 1976; MSc in Mgmt., Leland Stanford Jr. U., 1984. Assoc. MacKimmie Matthews, 1976-81; owner, sr. officer Jeffery J. McCaig Profl. Corp., 1981-83; v.p. planning and corp. devel. Trimac Ltd., Calgary, Alta., Can., 1983-87, exec. v.p., 1987-90; pres. Trimac Ltd., Clagary, Alta., Can., 1990-94, pres., CEO, 1994—; chmn. Bovar, Inc., Calgary, 1994—; bd. dirs. Bovar Inc., chmn.; bd. dirs. Trimac Ltd., Greyhound Lines Can. Ltd., 20/20 Fin. Group, Alberta Spl. Waste Mgmt. System, Richland Petroleum Corp., Conf. Bd. Can., ATA Found., Inerta. Mem. Law Soc. Alta., Young Pres.'s Orgn., Calgary Golf and Country Club, Calgary Petroleum Club, Glencoe Club, 400 Club. Home: 1201 Riverdale Ave SW, Calgary, AB Canada T2S 0Z1 Office: Trimac Ltd, 800 5 Ave SW Ste 2100, Calgary, AB Canada T2P 3T6

MCCAIG, JOHN ROBERT, transportation executive; b. Moose Jaw, Sask., Can., June 14, 1929; m. Ann McCaig; children: Jeffrey, JoAnn, Melanie. Grad. pub. sch., Moose Jaw. Various positions Maccam Transport Ltd., 1947-52, gen. mgr.; 1952-60; pres. Trimac Transp. Ltd. and H.M. Trimble & Sons Ltd., 1961-68, Westburne Internat. Industries Ltd., 1969-70; chmn. Trimac Ltd., Calgary, Alta., Can., 1970-72, 80—; pres. Trimac Ltd., Calgary, Alta., 1972-80, CEO, 1972-94; chmn. Trimac Ltd., Calgary, 1994—; bd. dirs. Banister Found., Inc., Chauvco Resources Ltd., Computalog, Inc., Pan-Alta Gas Ltd., Cameco Corp., Vencap Equities. Past pres. Jr. Achievement So. Alta, Calgary; campaign chmn. Western Orthopaedic and Arthritis Found., Calgary. Mem. Calgary Petroleum Club, Ranchmen's Club, Calgary Golf and Country Club, Glencoe Club. Avocations: golf, skiing. Office: Trimac Ltd, 800 5 Ave SW Ste 2100, Calgary, AB Canada T2P 3T6

MCCAIG, JOSEPH J., retail food chain executive; b. Bklyn., 1944. B.S. Seton Hall U., 1967. With The Grand Union Co., Elmwood Park, N.J., 1965—, gen. store mgr., 1967-68, resident trainer suburban div., 1968-69, supr. personnel, 1969-70, dist. mgr., 1970-72, supt. stores, 1972-73, asst. to sr. v.p. store ops., 1973-74, v.p. empire div. and v.p. no. region, 1974-78, v.p. no. region, 1978-80, sr. v.p., 1980-81; pres., chief operating officer The Grand Union Co, Wayne, N.J., 1981-89, 1989—. Office: Grand Union Co 52 Center St Westport CT 06880

MCCAIN, ARTHUR WILLIAMSON, JR., pension investment consultant; b. N.Y.C., Apr. 15, 1934; s. Arthur Williamson and Marion Wilmer (Vinsonhaler) McC.; m. Margaret Bain Dale, Nov. 3, 1956; children: Robert Williamson, Elizabeth Dale, Scott Lamar. BA in Philosophy magna cum laude, Washington and Lee U., 1956. Various positions as fin. mgr., auditor and trainee Gen. Electric Co., 1958-73; comptroller GE Investment Corp., Stamford, Conn., 1973-87; mgr. master custody, cons. Chase Manhattan Bank N.A., N.Y.C., 1987-90; v.p., cons. InterSec Rsch. Corp., Stamford, 1990—; speaker Investment Mgmt. Inst., Greenwich, Conn., 1990—, Inst. for Internat. Rsch., N.Y.C., 1990—. Mem. Pension East Assn., Stamford, 1982-87; founder, mem. Peer Group-Large Plan Sponsors, Stamford, 1982-87; sec. Internat. Performance Forum, 1992—; deacon Greenfield Hill. Congl. Ch., Fairfield, Conn., 1987-91, treas., 1992—. Capt. arty. U.S. Army, 1956-61. Mem. Phi Beta Kappa. Republican. Avocations: singing, tennis, reading. Home: 212 Brookbend Rd Fairfield CT 06430-3833 Office: InterSec Rsch 66 Gatehouse Rd Stamford CT 06902-7914

MCCAIN, BETTY LANDON RAY (MRS. JOHN LEWIS MCCAIN), political party official, civic leader; b. Faison, N.C., Feb. 23, 1931; d. Horace Truman and Mary Howell (Perrett) Ray; student St. Marys Jr. Coll., 1948-50; AB in Music, U. N.C., Chapel Hill, 1952; MA, in Music Columbia U., 1953; m. John Lewis McCain, Nov. 19, 1955; children: Paul Pressly III, Mary Eloise. Courier, European tour guide Ednl. Travel Assocs., Plainfield, N.J., 1952-54; asst. dir. YWCA, U. N.C., Chapel Hill, 1953-55; chmn. N.C. Democratic Exec. Com., 1976-79 (1st woman); mem. Dem. Nat. Com., 1971-72, 76-79, 80-85, chmn. sustaining fund, N.C., 1981, 88-91, mem. com. on Presdl. nominations (Hunt Commn.), 1981-82, mem. rules com., 1982-85, mem. cabinet Gov. James B. Hunt, Jr., 1981; dept. cultural resources 1993—; mem. Winograd Commn., 1977-78; pres. Dem. Women of N.C. 1971-72, dist. dir., 1969-72; pres. Wilson County Dem. Women, 1966-67; precinct chmn., 1972-76; del. Dem. Nat. Conv., 1972, 88; mem. Dem. Mid-term Confs., 1974, 78, mem. judicial council Dem. Nat. Com., 1985-89; dir. Carolina Tel. & Tel. Co., 1981— (1st woman). Sunday sch. tchr. First Presbyn. Ch., Wilson, 1970-71, 86-88, 90-92, mem. chancel choir, 1985—, deacon, 1986-92, elder, 1992—, chmn. fin. com., 1990-91; treas. Wilson on the Move, 1990-92; mem. Council on State Goals and Policy, 1970-72, Gov.'s Task Force on Child Advocacy, 1969-71, Wilson Human Relations Commn., 1975-78, chmn. Wilson-Greene Morehead scholarship com., 1986-89; mem. career and personal counseling service adv. bd. St. Andrews Coll.; charter mem. Wilson Edn. Devel. Council; active Arts Council of Wilson, Inc., N.C. Art Soc., N.C. Lit. and Hist. Assn.; regional v.p., bd. dirs. N.C. Mental Health Assn.; pres., bd. dirs. legis. chmn. Wilson County Mental Health Assn.; bd. dirs. U. N.C. Ctr. Pub. TV, 1993—, Country Doctor Mus., 1968-93, Wilson United Fund; bd. govs., sec. personnel and tenure com. U. N.C., chmn. budgets and fin. com. 1991-93; bd. regents Barium Springs Home for Children; bd. dirs., mem. N.C. Mus. History Assocs., 1982-83, membership chair, 1987-88; co-chmn. Com. to Elect Jim Hunt Gov., 1976, 80, co-chmn. senatorial campaign, 1984; mem. N.C. Adv. Budget Com., 1981-85 (1st woman); chmn. State Employees Combined Campaign N.C., 1993; bd. visitors Peace Coll., Wake Forest U. Sch. Law, U. N.C., Chapel Hill; co-chmn. fund drive Wilson Community Theatre; state bd. dirs. N.C., Am. Lung Assn., 1985-88; bd. dirs. Roanoke Island Commn. 1994—, USS/NC Battleship Commn. Recipient state awards N.C. Heart Assn., 1967, Easter Seal Soc., 1967, Community Service award Downtown Bus. Assocs., 1977, award N.C. Jaycees, 1979, 85, Women in Govt. award N.C. and U.S. Jaycettes, 1985, Flora Mac Donald Scottish Heritage award, 1995; named to Order of Old Well and Valkyries, U. N.C., 1952; named Dem. Woman of Yr., N.C., 1976, Disting. Alumna U. N.C., Chapel Hill, 1993. Mem. U. N.C. Chapel Hill Alumni Assn. (dir.), St. Marys Alumni Assn. (regional v.p.), AMA Aux. (dir., nat. vol. health services chmn., aux. liaison rep. Council on Mental Health, aux. rep. Council on Vol. Health Orgns.), N.C. (pres., dir., parliamentarian) med. auxs., UDC (historian John W. Dunham chpt.), DAR, N.C. Found. for Nursing (bd. dirs. 1989-92), N.C. Agency Pub. Telecoms.(bd. dirs. 1993—), info. Resources Mgmt. Commn. N.C. (bd. dirs. 1993—), N.C. Symphony (bd. dirs. 1993—), N.C. Soc. Internal Medicine Aux. (pres., bd. dirs. N.C. Equity), N.C. Sch. Arts (bd. trustees), Pi Beta Phi. The Book Club (pres.), Little Book Club , Wilson Country Club. Contbg. editor History of N.C. Med. Soc. Home: 1134 Woodland Dr NW Wilson NC 27893-2122

MCCAIN, JOHN SIDNEY, III, senator; b. Panama Canal Zone, Aug. 29, 1936; s. John Sidney and Roberta (Wright) McC.; m. Cindy Hensley, May 17, 1980; children: Doug, Andy, Sidney, Meghan, Jack, Bridget. Grad. U.S.

Naval Acad., 1958; grad., Nat. War Coll., 1973-74. Commd. ensign U.S. Navy, 1958, capt., navy pilot, 1977; prisoner of war Hanoi, Vietnam, 1967-73; dir. Navy Senate Liaison Office, Washington, 1977-81; mem. 98th-99th Congress from 1st Ariz. Dist.; U.S. senator from Ariz., 1987—. Bd. dirs. Community Assistance League, Phoenix, 1981-82. Decorated Legion of Merit; decorated Silver Star, Bronze Star, Purple Heart, D.F.C., Vietnamese Legion of Honor. Mem. Soc. of the Cin., Am. Legion, VFW. Republican. Episcopalian. Office: US Senate 111 Russell Senate Office Washington DC 20510

MCCAIN, NORRIE, province official. Lt. gov. Govt. New Brunswick, Fredericton, Can. Office: Office of Lt Gov, 736 King St PO Box 6000, Fredericton, NB Canada E3B 5H1*

MCCALEB, GARY DAY, university administrator; b. Anson, Tex., Nov. 2, 1941; s. Victor Earl and Vivian (Day) McC.; m. Sylvia Ravanelli, June 5, 1964; children: Cara Lee Cranford, Bryan Day. BA, Abilene Christian Coll., 1964; MBA, Tex. A&M U., 1975, PhD, 1979. Asst. dir. alumni rels. Abilene (Tex.) Christian U., 1964-65, dir. alumni rels., 1965-69, dir. coll. rels., 1969-73, asst. acad. dean, 1978-80, v.p. pub. rels., 1980-83, v.p., dean campus life, 1983-91, v.p., 1991—; asst. dir. devel. Tex. A&M U., Bryan, 1973-75; leader internat. travel and goodwill groups. Coun. mem. City of Abilene, 1985-90, mayor, 1990—; bd. dirs. Taylor County Am. Cancer Soc., 1972-73; mem. adv. bd. United Way of Abilene, 1979-83, dir. pub. svc. divsn., 1987, chmn. consortium on drug and alcohol abuse, 1989; bd. dirs. Civic Abilene, Inc., 1981-83; treas. Abilene Task Force on Drug and Alcohol Abuse, 1984-86; active March of Dimes. Recipient Polit. Courage award John Ben Shepperd Pub. Leadership Forum, Austin, Tex., 1993. Mem. Nat. League Cities (nat. steering com. on fin., administr. and intergovtl. rels. 1989-90, adv. bd. 1994, bd. dirs. 1992-94), U.S. Conf. Mayors, Internat. Mcpl. Consortium (chmn.), Tex. Mcpl. League (legis. policy com. Houston 1986, resolutions com. Dallas 1988, v.p. region 6 1988-89, bd. dirs. 1989-90, pres. 1992), Abilene C. of C. (aviation com. 1981, aviation com. 1984). Republican. Mem. Ch. of Christ. Avocations: art, baseball, jogging. Office: City of Abilene PO Box 60 Abilene TX 79604

MCCALEB, MALCOLM, JR., lawyer; b. Evanston, Ill., June 4, 1945. BA, Colgate U., 1967; JD, Northwestern U., 1971. Bar: Ill. 1971. Ptnr. Keck, Mahin & Cate, Chgo. Chmn. Northfield (Ill.) Village Caucus, 1981-82, active, 1977-82, Northfield (Ill.) Zoning Commn., 1985-88, active, 1983-88; pres. bd. dirs. Vols. Am., 1977-79, active 1972-82; active Northfield (Ill.) Sch. and Park Bd. Caucus, 1980-87. Mem. Chgo. Bar Assn., Bar Assn. 7th Fed. Cir., Patent Law Assn. Chgo., Legal Club Chgo., Internat. Trademark Assn. Office: Keck Mahin & Cate 77 W Wacker Dr Ste 4900 Chicago IL 60606

MC CALL, ABNER VERNON, law educator, retired university administrator; b. Perrin, Tex., June 8, 1915; s. Harry Vernon and Gertrude Elizabeth (Rhoades) McC.; m. Frances Laura Bortle, 1940 (dec. 1969); children: Anne, Bette, Richard, Kathleen; m. Mary W. Russell, 1970. A.B., J.D., Baylor U., 1938; LL.M., U. Mich., 1943. Bar: Tex. 1938. Instr. law Baylor U., 1938-42, prof. law, 1946-59, dean Law Sch., 1948-59, exec. v.p., 1959-61, pres., 1961-81, chancellor, 1981-85; justice Supreme Ct. Tex., 1956; spl. agt. FBI, 1943-46; mem. Tex. Civil Jud. Coun., 1954-84, pres., 1955-58. Pres. Baptist Gen. Couv. Tex., 1963-64; 1st v.p. So. Baptist Conv., 1979, 80, Tex. rep. Edn. Commn. of States, 1968-83, 87-90; pres. Tex. Scottish Rite Found.; bd. dirs. Tex. Scottish Rite Hosp. for Children, Nat. Right to Work Com.; chmn. bd. Tex. System Natural Labs., Baylor Med. Found., Leon Jaworski Found., Madison Cooper Found. Mem. State Bar Tex., Assn. Tex. Colls. and Univs. (pres. 1968-69), Ind. Colls. and Univs. Tex. (pres. 1965-71), Philos. Soc. Tex. (pres. 1982). Office: Baylor U Waco TX 76798

MCCALL, BILLY GENE, charitable trust executive; b. Ellerbe, N.C., Mar. 28, 1928; s. Arthur Hall and Letha Belle (Anderson) McC.; m. Betty Sue Berryhill, Aug. 20, 1949; children: Stephen Andrew, Kathryn Elaine McCall Manson. BS magna cum laude, Clemson U., 1950, HHD (hon.), 1991. Administrv. resident Charlotte Meml. Hosp., N.C., 1951-53; asst. administr. Anderson Meml. Hosp., S.C., 1953-54; field rep. hosp. and child care divs. The Duke Endowment, Charlotte, 1954-62, dir. mgmt. service, 1962-66, asst. exec. dir., 1966-70, assoc. exec. dir., 1970-77, exec. dir., 1977-80, asst. sec., 1966-80, dep. exec. dir., sec., 1980-86, dep. exec. dir., 1987-90, asst. dir. 1990-92; ret., 1992; bd. dirs., mem. exec. com. SunHealth Alliance, Inc.; chmn. Commn. on Profl. and Hosp. Activities, Ann Arbor, Mich., 1977-78; mem. N.C. Med. Care Commn., Raleigh, 1977-89; mem. adv. bd. Kate B. Reynolds Health Care Trust, Winston-Salem, N.C., 1977-91. Past pres. Presbyn. Home at Charlotte; bd. dirs. United Way of Cen. Carolinas, Charlotte; adv. bd. Queens Coll., Charlotte; bd. visitors Davidson Coll., N.C., Lineberger Cancer Ctr., U.N.C., Chapel Hill; past pres., bd. dirs. Charlotte-Mecklenburg Sr. Ctrs., N.C. With U.S. Army, 1946-47, 50-51, PTO. Mem. N.C. Hosp. Assn., S.C. Hosp. Assn., Carmel Country Club. Democrat. Presbyterian. Home: 7724 Cooper Ln Charlotte NC 28217

MC CALL, CHARLES BARNARD, health facility executive, educator; b. Memphis, Nov. 2, 1928; s. John W. and Lizette (Kimbrough) McC.; m. Carolyn Jean Rosselot, June 9, 1951; children: Linda, Kim, Betsy, Cathy. B.A., Vanderbilt U., 1950, M.D., 1953. Diplomate: Am. Bd. Internal Medicine (pulmonary diseases). Intern Vanderbilt U. Hosp., Nashville, 1953-54; clin. assoc., sr. asst. surgeon USPHS, Nat. Cancer Inst., NIH, 1954-56; sr. asst. resident in medicine U. Ala. Hosp., 1956-57, chief resident, 1958-59; fellow chest diseases Nat. Acad. Scis.-NRC, 1957-58; instr. U. Ala. Med. Sch., 1958-59; asst. prof., then assoc. prof. medicine U. Tenn. Med. Sch., 1959-69, chief pulmonary diseases, 1964-69; mem. faculty U. Tex. System, Galveston, 1969-75, prof. medicine med. br., 1971-73; assoc. prof. medicine Health Sci. Center, Southwestern Med. Sch., Dallas, 1973-75, also assoc. dean clin. programs, 1973-75; dir. Office Grants Mgmt. and Devel., 1973-75; dean, prof. medicine U. Tenn. Coll. Medicine, 1975-77, Oral Roberts U. Sch. Medicine, Tulsa, 1977-78; interim assoc. dean U. Okla. Tulsa Med. Coll., 1978-79; clin. prof. medicine U. Colo. Med. Sch., Denver, 1979-80; prof. medicine, assoc. dean U. Okla. Med. Sch., 1980-82; exec. dean and dean U. Okla. Coll. Medicine, 1982-85; v.p. patient affairs, prof. medicine U. Tex. M.D. Anderson Cancer Ctr., 1985-94; chief of staff VA Med. Center, Oklahoma City, 1980-82; cons. in field. Contbr. articles to med. jours. Fellow ACP, Am. Coll. Chest Physicians; mem. AMA, Am. Thoracic Soc., So. Thoracic Soc. (pres. 1968-69), Am. Fedn. Clin. Rsch., Tex. Med. Assn., Harris County Med. Soc., Sigma Xi, Alpha Omega Alpha. Baptist. Home: 17056 Crossgate Dr Jupiter FL 33477

MCCALL, CHARLES W., computer company executive; b. Oskaloosa, Iowa, Mar. 11, 1944; s. Charles W. and Esther (Horn) McC.; m. Jacqueline K. Townes, Nov. 26, 1969; 1 child, Chad. B.B.A., U. Iowa, 1966; M.B.A., Roosevelt U., 1972. With sales dept. IBM, Chgo., 1968-73; various mgmt. positions Control Data, Dallas, 1973-77; various mgmt. positions CompuServe, Inc., Columbus, Ohio, 1977-84, pres., chief exec. officer, 1984—; also dir.; bd. dirs. H&R Block, Kansas City, Midland Mut., Columbus. Avocations: running; scuba diving; sports. Home: 1004 Cherbury Ln alpharetta GA 30202-7146 Office: HBO & Co 301 Perimeter Ctr N Atlanta GA 30346

MCCALL, DANIEL THOMPSON, JR., retired justice; b. Butler, Ala., Mar. 12, 1909; s. Daniel Thompson and Caroline Winston (Bush) McC.; m. Mary Edna Montgomery, Apr. 3, 1937; children: Mary Winston McCall Laseter, Daniel Thompson III, Nancy McCall Poynor. A.B., U. Ala., 1931, LL.B., 1933, LL.D. (hon.), 1981. Bar: Ala. 1933, U.S. Supreme Ct. 1960. Practice law Mobile, 1933-60; ptnr. Johnston, McCall & Johnston, 1943-60; cir. judge Mobile County, 1960-69; assoc. justice Supreme Ct. Ala., 1969-75; dir. Title Ins. Co., 1959-69; pres. Jr. Bar Ala., 1937. Author McCall Reprot on U. Ala. Hosps. Elected to Mobile County Bd. Sch. Commrs., 1950-56, 58-60; co-founder, trustee Julius T. Wright Sch. Girls, 1953-63; mem. com. U. Ala. Hosps.; dir. U. Ala. Law Sch. Found., Ala. bar commrs., 1957-60; trustee U. Ala., 1965-79, nat. alumni pres., 1963, pres. Mobile chpt., 1961. Disting. Alumnus award, 1995. Lt. USNR, WWII. Named to Ala. Acad. of Hon.; recipient Dean's award, U. Ala. Law Sch., 1974; Julius T. Wright Sch. Disting. Svc. award, 1979, M.O. Beale Scroll Merit, 1979, U.M.S. Preparator Sch. Outstanding Alumnus award, 1980. Mem. ABA, Ala. Bar Assn. (grievance com. 1954-57), Mobile Bar Assn. (pres. 1953), Am. Judicature Soc., Farrah Law Soc. (charter), Cumberland Law Sch. Order Jurisprudence,

Inst. Jud. Adminstrn., Nat. Trust Hist. Preservation, Hist. Mobile Preservation Soc., Navy League U.S. (co-founder, pres. Mobile chpt. 1963-65), Am. Legion, Ala. Hist. Soc., Res. Officer's Assn. U.S., 40 and 8, U. Tuscaloosa Club, Omicron Delta Kappa, Phi Delta Phi, Sigma Nu. Democrat. Episcopalian. Home: 2253 Ashland Place Ave Mobile AL 36607-3242

MCCALL, DAVID BRUCE, advertising executive; b. N.Y.C., Mar. 13, 1928; s. Sydney C. and Katharine (Adams) McC.; m. Joan C. Williams, Feb. 10, 1951; children: John Percy, Peter Cortelyou, David Bruce, William Dudley, Robert Dodd, Thomas Clement; m. Susan Alder, Jan. 18, 1975 (dec.); m. Penny Mills McSweeney, Oct. 19, 1979. Student, Hotchkiss Sch., Lakeville Conn., 1942-45, Yale U., 1948-49. Copywriter Young and Rubicam, Inc., 1949-51; Hewitt, Ogilvy, Benson, and Mather, 1951-53; v.p., copy chief David J. Mahoney, Inc., 1953-56; with Ogilvy, Benson, and Mather, 1956-62; copy chief, sr. v.p., dir. Ogilvy, Benson and Mather, 1961-62; vice chmn, bd. C.J. LaRoche, Inc. (named changed to McCaffrey and McCall, Inc.), N.Y.C., 1962-64; pres., chmn. bd. McCaffrey and McCall, Inc., N.Y.C., 1964-87, chmn. bd., creative dir. Served with AUS, 1946-47. Home: 136 E 64th St New York NY 10021-7360 Office: Shepardson Stern & Kaminsky 230 Park Ave New York NY 10022-6102

MCCALL, DAVID WARREN, chemist, administrator, materials consultant; b. Omaha, Dec. 1, 1928; s. H. Bryron and Grace (Cox) McC.; m. Charlotte Marion Dunham, July 30, 1955; children—William Christopher, John Dunham. B.S., U. Wichita, 1950; M.S., U. Ill., 1951, Ph.D., 1953. Mem. tech. staff AT&T Bell Labs, Murray Hill, N.J., 1953-62; head dept. phys. chemistry AT&T Bell Labs, Murray Hill, NJ, 1962-69, asst. chem. dir., 1969-73, chem. dir., 1973-91; dir. environ. chemistry rsch. AT&T Bell Labs, Murray Hill, N.J., 1991-92; chmn. bd. trustees Gordon Rsch. Confs.; mem. adv. bd. Chem. Abstract Svcs.; chmn. Nat. Commn. on Super-conductivity; chmn. panels on advanced composites, electronic packaging, and shipboard pollution control NRC, mem. Naval Studies Bd.; bd. dirs., v.p. Randolph (Vt.) Corp. Trustee Matheny Sch. Hosp. Fellow AAAS, Am. Phys. Soc., Royal Soc. Chemistry London; mem. NAE, AICE, Am. Chem. Soc. (Barnes award 1992). Home: 12 Polo Club Rd Far Hills NJ 07931

MCCALL, DOROTHY KAY, social worker, psychotherapist; b. Houston, July 18, 1948; d. Sherwood Pelton Jr. and Kathryn Rose (Gassen) McC. BA, Calif. State U., Fullerton, 1973; MS in Edn., U. Kans., 1978; PhD, U. Pitts., 1989. Cert. alcoholism counselor, N.Y.; lic. social worker. Counselor/intern Ctr. for Behavioral Devel., Overland Park, Kans., 1976-77; rehab. counselor Niagra Frontier Voc. Rehab. Ctr., Buffalo, 1978-79; counselor/instr. dept. motor vehicles Driving While Impaired Program N.Y. State, 1979-80; alcoholism counselor Bry Lin Hosp., Buffalo, 1979-81; instr. sch. social work U. Pitts., 1984, 91; alcohol drug counselor The Whale's Tale, Pitts., 1984-86; sole practice drug and alcohol therapy Pitts., 1986—; faculty Chem. People Inst., Pitts., 1987-89; guest lectr. sch. social work U. Pitts., 1982-87, 89; educator, trainer Community Mental Health Ctr., W.Va., 1986-87, Tenn., 1986; tchr. Tri-Community Sch. System, Western Pa., 1984-87; cons. Battered Women's Shelter, Buffalo, 1980, Buffalo Youth and Alcoholism Abuse program, 1980; lectr. in field. Mem. Spl. Adv. Com. on Addiction, 1981-83; bd. dirs. Chem. People, Task Force Adv. Com., 1984-86; bd. dirs. Drug Connection Hot Line, 1984-86; mem. Coalition of Addictive Diseases, 1984—; co-founder Greater Pitts. Adult Children of Alcoholics Network, 1984; mem. adv. bd. Chem. Awareness Referral and Evaluation System Duquesne U., 1988-93. Recipient Outstanding Achievement award Greater Pitts. Adult Children of Alcoholics Network, 1987, Disting. Svc. award Pa. Assn. for Children of Alcoholics, 1993; Nat. Inst. Alcohol Abuse tng. grantee, 1981; U. Pitts. fellow, 1983. Mem. NASW, Pa. Assn. for Children of Alcoholics (bd. dirs. 1987—, v.p. 1990-94, Disting. Svc. award 1993), Employee Assistance Profls. Assn., Inc., Am. Soc. for Clinical Hypnosis (assoc.), Nat. Assn. for Children of Alcoholics, Inst. for Noetic Scis. Democrat. Avocations: perfumery, film, reading, drawing, playing the synthesizer. Office: 673 Washington Rd Pittsburgh PA 15228-1917

MC CALL, DUKE KIMBROUGH, clergyman; b. Meridian, Miss., Sept. 1, 1914; s. John William and Lizette (Kimbrough) McC.; m. Marguerite Mullinnix, Sept. 1, 1936 (dec. 1983); children—Duke, Douglas H., John Richard, Michael W.; m. Winona Gatton McCandless, Feb. 2, 1984. B.A., Furman U., Greenville, S.C., 1936; M.Div., So. Bapt. Sem., Louisville, 1938; Ph.D., So. Bapt. Sem., 1943; LL.D. (hon.), Baylor U.; D.D. (hon.), Furman U., U. Richmond, Stetson U.; Litt.D., Georgetown Coll. Ordained to ministry, Bapt. Ch., 1937. Pastor Broadway Bapt. Ch., Louisville; pres. New Orleans Bapt. Theol. Sem., 1943-46; exec. sec. So. Bapt. Exec. Com., Nashville, 1946-51; pres. So. Bapt. Theol. Sem., Louisville, 1951-82; chancellor So. Bapt. Theol. Sem., 1982-92; pres. Bapt. World Alliance, Washington, 1980-85; chmn. bd. dirs. Covenant Life Ins. Co., 1989-90. Author: God's Hurry, 1948, Passport to the World, 1951, Broadman Comments, 1957, 2d edit. 1958; editor: What is the Church. Recipient E. Y. Mullins Denominational Service award. Avocations: golf; boating. Home: 3534 Lantern Bay Dr Jupiter FL 33477

MC CALL, JERRY CHALMERS, government official; b. Oxford, Miss., June 30, 1927; s. E. Forrest and Mariada (Huffaker) McC.; m. Margaret Denton, Nov. 28, 1952; children: Betsy, Lynn, Kim. B.A., U. Miss., 1951, M.A., 1951; M.S., U. Ill., 1956, Ph.D., 1959. Teaching asst. dept. math. U. Miss., 1950-51, instr. math., 1952-53, prof. math., 1973-76, exec. vice chancellor, 1973-76; rsch. assoc. U. Ill., 1953-57; applied sci. rep. IBM, Springfield, Ill., 1957-58; mgr. IBM, Bethesda, Md., 1966-68, Huntsville, Ala., 1968-71, Owego, N.Y., 1971-72; exec. v.p. Midwest Computer Service, Inc., Decatur, Ill., 1958-59; mem. sci. staff computation lab. Army Ballistic Missile Agy., Huntsville, 1959-60; asst. to dr. Marshall Space Flight Ctr., NASA, Huntsville, 1960-63, dep. dir. rsch. and devel. ops., 1963-66; dir. info. rsch. Miss. Test Facility NASA, Bay St. Louis, 1972-73; pres. 1st State Bank and Trust Co., Gulfport, Miss., 1976-77; dir. Nat. Data Buoy Ctr., Miss., 1977—; pres. McKool, Inc., Gulfport, Miss., 1982-94, Am. Mini Storage, Gulfport, 1985—, Am Crane Rentals, Inc., 1985-89, Cool-Power, Inc., 1988-93; head math dept. St. Bernard Coll., Cullman, Ala., part-time, 1960-65; asso. prof. math. U. Ala., Huntsville, 1960-62; pub. speaker, 1960-63; chmn. incorporators First State Bank & Trust Co., Gulfport, Miss., 1973-76; tech. cons. Gen. Electric Co., 1974-75. Editor: (with Ernst Stuhlinger) Astronautical Engineering and Science, 1963, From Peenemunde to Outer Space, 1963. Mem. Miss. Criminal Justice Standards Commn., 1974-75; mem. Miss. Marine Resources Council, 1974-76; bd. dirs. U. Miss. Found.; bd. advisers Sch. Engring., U. Miss., 1965-73; mem. indsl. advisors U. New Orleans; chmn. founders U. Ala. Research Inst., Huntsville, 1960-62. Mem. Am. Judicature Soc. (lay mem.), U. Miss. Alumni Assn. (dir. 1966-73). Home: PO Box 7092 Gulfport MS 39506-7092 Office: Nat Data Buoy Ctr Bldg 1100 Stennis Space Center MS 39529

MCCALL, JOHN ANTHONY, banker; b. N.Y.C., Oct. 8, 1940; s. John Agustine and Helen Patricia (Sullivan) McC.; m. Mary Irene Burke, July 11, 1964; children: Kathleen, Stacey, Jennifer, John, Christopher, Matthew. BA, Fairfield U., Conn., 1962; postgrad., Stonier Grad. Sch. Bus., Rutgers U., 1968-70; postgrad. program of mgmt. devel., Harvard Grad. Sch. Bus., 1970. Vice pres. Irving Trust Co., N.Y.C., 1963-77; sr. v.p. E.F. Hutton & Co., Inc., N.Y.C., 1977-89; dir. Swiss Bank Corp., N.Y.C., 1989—. Mem. Pine Valley Golf Club (N.J.), Plainfield Country Club (N.J.).

MCCALL, JOHN PATRICK, college president, educator; b. Yonkers, N.Y., July 17, 1927; s. Ambrose V. and Vera E. (Rush) McC.; m. Mary-Berenice Morris, June 15, 1957; children: Claire, Anne, Ambrose, Peter. AB, Holy Cross Coll., 1949; MA, Princeton U., 1952, PhD, 1955. Instr. Georgetown U., 1955-57, asst. prof. English, 1957-62, assoc. prof., 1962-66; prof. U. Cin., 1966-82, head dept. English, 1970-76, sr. v.p., provost, 1976-82; pres. Knox Coll., 1982-93; pres. emeritus and prof. emeritus English, 1993—; vol. Peace Corps, Turkmenistan, 1993—; vis. prof. Turkmen State U., 1994—; vice chmn. Gov.'s Task Force on Rural Ill., 1986; pres. Associated Colls. Ill., 1986-88; chmn. Associated Colls. of M.W., 1991-92; mem. edn. com. Ill. Bd. Higher Edn., 1985, 90; mem. rural libr. panel, State of Ill., 1992; vis. prof. Turkmen State U., 1994—. Author: Chaucer Among the Gods: the Poetics of Classical Myth, 1979; contbr. articles to profl. jours.; research in medieval lit. and Chaucer's poetry. With Signal Corps, U.S. Army, 1952-54. Am. Coun. Learned Socs. fellow, 1962; John Simon Guggenheim Meml. Found. fellow, 1975; Fulbright grantee, 1962. Mem. Medieval Acad. Am. MLA, AAUP. Democrat. Roman Catholic. Home: care A McCall 2213 W Manor

Pkwy Peoria IL 61604 Office: US Peace Corps Cen Post Office, PO Box 258, Krugozor, Ashgabat 744000, Turkmenistan

MCCALL, JOHN RICHARD, lawyer; b. New Orleans, Sept. 18, 1943; s. Duke Kimbrough and Marguerite (Mullinnix) McC.; m. Sara Boykin Ferris, July 13, 1945; children: Sara Marguerite, Katherine Kimbrough, John Mathews. B.A., Vanderbilt U., 1965, J.D., 1967. Bar: Ky. 1967, U.S. Dist. Ct. (ea. and we. dists.) Ky. 1967, U.S. Dist. Ct. (so. dist.) Ohio 1981, U.S. Dist. Ct. Colo. 1981, U.S. Ct. Appeals (6th and 10th cirs.) 1981. Assoc., Middleton, Seelbach, Wolford, Willis & Cochran, 1970-72; ptnr. Middleton & Reutlinger, Louisville, 1972-83, chmn. mgmt. com., 1979-82; ptnr. Brown, Todd & Heyburn, Louisville, 1983—, chmn. litigation dept.; dir., sec. Ky. Wood Floors, Inc., Louisville. Mem. exec. com. So. Bapt. Conv.; chmn. Citizens for Better Judges; chmn. bd Metro United Way, 1982-83. Served to lt. USNR, 1967-70. Mem. ABA, Def. Research Inst., Ky. Def. Counsel, Louisville Bar Assn. Democrat. Baptist. Clubs: Country, Law Jefferson (Louisville). Office: Brown Todd & Heyburn 3200 Capital Holding Ctr Louisville KY 40202

MC CALL, JULIEN LACHICOTTE, banker; b. Florence, S.C., Apr. 1, 1921; s. Arthur M. and Julia (Lachicotte) McC.; m. Janet Jones, Sept. 30, 1950; children: Melissa, Alison Gregg, Julien Lachicotte Jr. BS, Davidson Coll., 1942, LLD (hon.), 1983; MBA, Harvard U., 1947. With First Nat. City Bank, N.Y.C., 1948-71, asst. mgr. bond dept., 1952-53, asst. cashier, 1953-55, asst. v.p., 1955-57 v.p., 1957-71; 1st v.p. Nat. City Bank, Cleve., 1971-72, pres., 1972-79, chmn., 1979-85, chief exec. officer, from 1979, also bd. dirs.; pres. Nat. City Corp., 1973-80, chmn., chief exec. officer, 1980-86, also bd. dirs., cons.; bd. dirs. Acme Steel Co., Brush Wellman, Inc., Russell Burdsall & Ward Corp.; mem. fed. adv. council Fed. Res. Bd., 1984-87. Trustee St. Luke's Hosp., United Way Services, Boy Scouts Am., Playhouse Sq. Found., Cleve. Mus. Natural History. Served with AUS, 1942-46, Africa, ETO. Episcopalian. Clubs: Union, Pepper Pike, Chagrin Valley Hunt, Kirtland Country (Cleve.); Rolling Rock (Ligonier, Pa.); Mountain Lake (Lake Wales, Fla.). Home: Arrowhead County Line Rd Chagrin Falls OH 44022 Office: 30195 Chagrin Blvd Ste 104W Pepper Pike OH 44124

MCCALL, MARSH, cardiologist; b. Tazewell, Va., 1903. Intern Meml. Hosp., Richmond, 1930-31; resident Episcopal Hosp., Phila., 1932-33; instr. medicine Cornell U., Ithaca, N.Y., 1934-42; chief med. svcs. Tilton Gen. Hosp., 1944-45; med. dir. Beekman Downtown Hosp., N.Y.C., 1945-65, cardiology cons., 1965-75; med. cons. City of N.Y. Fire Dept., 1975-95; med. cons. Beekman Dowtown Hosp., N.Y.C. Coll. USMC, 1942-45. Fellow ACP, ACC; mem. AMA, AHA, AFCR, Assn. Hosp. Dirs. Med. Edn., Harvey Soc., Alpha Omega Alpha, Omicron Delta Kappa. Address: 1192 Park Ave New York NY 10128-1314

MCCALL, ROBERT H., oil and chemical company executive; b. 1938. Attended, U. Colo. With McCall Oil & Chem. Corp., Portland, Oreg., 1961—, pres., 1967—, now also chief exec. officer. With USAF, 1959-60. Office: McCall Oil and Chem Corp 808 SW 15th Ave Portland OR 97205-1907

MC CALL, ROBERT R., retired oil company executive; b. Norman, Okla., June 21, 1926; s. Robert R. and Ida (Smith) McC.; m. Byrdine Grimm, June 12, 1987; children: Claudia, Michael, Melinda, Danial. B.S., U. Okla., 1951, M.S., 1952. With Texaco, Inc., 1952-88, gen. mgr. producing Eastern hemisphere, 1972-78; v.p. producing Texaco, Inc., Harrison, N.Y., 1978-80; sr. v.p. Texaco U.S.A., Houston, 1980-83, exec. v.p., 1983-88. Bd. dirs. Near East Found. Served with USNR, 1944-46. Mem. Am. Inst. Mech. Engrs., Am. Petroleum Inst., Okla. Profl. Engrs., Pi Epsilon Tau. Republican. Home: 27 Grogans Point Ct Spring TX 77380-2648 Office: Texaco USA PO Box 1404 Houston TX 77251-1404

MCCALL, TINA, critical care nurse; b. Searcy, Ark., Sept. 15, 1960; d. Junior Lee and Doris (Weaver) Barger; m. Todd McCall, Sept. 4, 1981; children: Morgan, Christian. BSN, U. Cen. Ark., Conway, 1982; student, Webster U., Little Rock. Cert. critical care nurse. Cardiac ICU staff nurse St. Vincent Infirmary, Little Rock; asst. head nurse in oncology St. Bernards Hosp., Jonesboro, Ark.; staff devel. instr. Doctors Hosp., Little Rock, nursing dir. intensive care; head nurse intermediate care unit St. paul Med. Ctr., Dallas; asst. divisional dir. med. surg. critical care Arlington (Tex.) Meml. Hosp.; staff nurse critical care. Mem. AACCN, Am. Heart Assn., Sigma Theta Tau. Home: 934 Rio Vista Ln Arlington TX 76017-1753

MCCALL, WILLIAM CALDER, oil and chemical company executive; b. Hoquiam, Wash., Feb. 1, 1906; s. Dougall Hugh and Hughena (Calder) McC.; m. Marian Hall, Mar. 22, 1946; children—Ernest, Robert. Student U. Oreg., 1924-28; LHD Lewis & Clark Coll., 1992. Asst. sales mgr. Anaconda Sales Co., Chgo., 1932-39; chmn. McCall Oil & Chem. Corp., Portland, Oreg., 1939—, Gt. Western Chem. Co., Portland, 1975—; dir. Oreg. Bank, Portland, King Broadcasting Co., Seattle. Pres. Oreg. Art Mus., Portland; trustee Lewis and Clark Coll., Portland; pres. v.p. Oreg. Symphony Soc.; dir. Oreg. Health Scis. Found., Good Samaritan Hosp. Found., Portland. Republican. Episcopalian. Clubs: Eldorado Country (Indian Wells, Calif.) (pres. 1978-79); Arlington (Portland); Pacific-Union (San Francisco); Los Angeles Country, Vintage (Palm Desert, Calif.), Waverley Country, Rainier (Seattle). Office: McCall Oil and Chem Corp 808 SW 15th Ave Portland OR 97205-1907

MCCALLA, JON P., federal judge; b. 1947; m. Mary R. McCalla; children: Marjorie Katherine, Elizabeth Clair. BS, U. Tenn., 1969; JD, Vanderbilt U., 1974. Law clk. to Hon. Bailey Brown U.S. Dist. Ct. (we. dist.) Tenn., 1974-75; assoc. Armstrong, Allen, Braden, Goodman, McBride & Prewitt, 1975-80; ptnr. Armstrong, Allen, Prewitt, Gentry, Johnson & Holmes, 1980-87, Heiskell, Donelson, Bearman, Adams, Williams & Kirsch, 1987-92; fed. judge U.S. Dist. Ct. (we. dist.) Tenn., Memphis, 1992—. Mem. Fed. Bar Assn., Tenn. Bar Assn., Memphis Bar Assn. Office: US Dist Ct 167 N Main St Ste 907 Memphis TN 38103-1828

MCCALLIE, MARSHALL F., ambassador; b. Chattanooga, June 21, 1945; m. Amye Grady; 2 children. BA, Vanderbilt U.; MA, Tufts U. Mem. staff Peace Corps, 1974; with Fgn. Svc., 1974—; polit. officer Kinshasa, 1975-76; watch officer Ops. Ctr., 1977-79; econ. officer Abu Dhabi, 1979-81; polit. counselor Monrovia, 1982-84; desk officer Nigeria, 1984-86; dir. jr. officer divsn. Bur. Pers., 1986-87; dep. chief of mission Lusaka, 1988-90, Pretoria, 1990-93; U.S. amb. to Namibia Windhoek, 1993—. With USAF, 1967-71. Mem. Am. Fgn. Svc. Assn. Office: Southern Africa Dept of State Washington DC 20521-9300

MCCALLION, HAZEL, mayor; b. Port Daniel, Can.; m. Samuel McCallion; children—Peter, Linda, Paul. Formerly office mgr. Can. Kellogg Co.; mayor City of Mississauga, Ont., Can., 1978—; mem. com. on transp. of dangerous goods Minister of Transport. Dep. reeve City of Streetsville, 1968, mayor, 1970-73; chmn. Mississauga Taxicab Authority, Mississauga Planning com., Mississauga Sign Com.; vice chmn. adv. com. on local govt. mgmt.; chmn. provincial mcpl. subcom. on transp. of dangerous goods; bd. dirs. Credit Valley Hosp.; 3d v.p. World Conf. of Mayors, 1989. Paul Harris fellow Rotary Internat., 1983. Mem. Streetsville C. of C. (former pres.), Assn. Municipalities Ont. (past pres.), Can. Fedn. Municipalities (bd. dirs.), Can. Jaycees (gov.); hon. mem. Polish Alliance Can., Mississauga Real Estate Bd. (hon.), Alpha Delta Kappa. Club: Mississauga Kinsmen (hon. mem.). Office: City of Mississauga, 300 City Centre Dr, Mississauga, ON Canada L5B 3C1

MCCALLUM, BENNETT TARLTON, economics educator; b. Poteet, Tex., July 27, 1935; s. Henry DeRosset and Frances (Tarlton) McC.; m. Sally Jo Hart, June 3, 1961. B.A., Rice U., 1957, B.S. in Chem. Engring., 1958, Ph.D., 1969. M.B.A., Harvard U., 1963. engr. Petro-Tex Chem. Corp., Houston, 1958-61; lectr. U. Sussex, Eng., 1965-66; asst. prof. to prof. U. Va., Charlottesville, 1967-80; prof. econs. Carnegie-Mellon U., Pitts., 1981-86, H.J. Heinz prof. econs., 1986—; cons. Fed. Res. Bd., Washington, 1974-75; econ. assoc. Nat. Bur. Econ. Rsch., Cambridge, Mass., 1979—; adviser Fed. Res. Bank Richmond, Va., 1981—. Author: Monetary Economics, 1989; co-editor Am. Econ. Rev., 1988-91; contbr. more than 100 articles to profl. publs. NSF grantee, 1977-86; vis. scholar Internat. Monetary Fund, Washington, 1989-90, Bank of Japan, 1993. Fellow Econometric Soc.; mem. Am. Econ. Assn. Home: 219 Gladstone Rd Pittsburgh PA 15217-1111 Office: Carnegie-Mellon U Grad Sch Indsl Adminstrn 206 Pittsburgh PA 15213

MC CALLUM, CHARLES ALEXANDER, university official; b. North Adams, Mass., Nov. 1, 1925; s. Charles Alexander and Mabel Helen (Cassidy) McC.; m. Alice Rebecca Lasseter, Dec. 17, 1955; children: Scott Alan, Charles Alexander III, Philip Warren, Christopher Jay. Student, Dartmouth Coll., 1943-44, Wesleyan U., Middletown, Conn., 1946-47; D.M.D., Tufts U., 1951; M.D., Med. Coll. Ala., 1957; D.Sc. (hon.), U. Ala., 1975, Georgetown U., 1982, Tufts U., 1988, Chulalongkorn U., Thailand, 1993, U. Medicine & Dentistry, N.J., 1993. Diplomate Am. Bd. Oral Surgery (pres. 1970). Intern oral surgery Univ. Hosp., Birmingham, Ala., 1951-52, resident oral surgery, 1952-54, intern medicine, 1957-58; mem. faculty U. Ala. Sch. Dentistry, 1956—, prof., chmn. dept oral surgery, 1959-65, dean sch., 1962-77; v.p. for health affairs, dir. U. Ala. Med. Center, Birmingham, 1977-87; pres. U. Ala., Birmingham, 1987-93, chief sect. oral surgery Sch. Dentistry, 1958-65, 68-69; prof., 1959-93, disting. prof., 1993—; mem. nat. adv. dental rsch. coun. NIH, 1968-72; mem. Joint Commn. on Accreditation of Hosps., 1980-91, vice chmn., 1985, chmn., 1987-88. Fellow Am. Coll. Dentists, Internat. Coll. Dentists; mem. ADA (council on dental edn. 1970-76), Am. Assn. Dental Schs. (pres. 1969), Ala. Acad. of Honor, AMA, Am. Soc. Oral Surgeons (trustee 1972-73, pres. 1975-76), Southeastern Soc. Oral Surgeons (pres. 1970), Inst. of Medicine of Nat. Acad. of Scis., Assn. Acad. Health Ctrs. (chmn. bd. dirs. 1984-85), Omicron Kappa Upsilon, Phi Beta Pi. Home: 2328 Garland Dr Birmingham AL 35216-3002 Office: Univ Ala at Birmingham 107 MJH Birmingham AL 35294-2010

MC CALLUM, CHARLES EDWARD, lawyer; b. Memphis, Mar. 13, 1939; s. Edward Payson and India Raimelle (Musick) McC.; m. Lois Ann Gowell Temple, Nov. 30, 1985; children: Florence Andrea, Printha Kyle, Chandler Ward, Sabra Nicole Temple. B.S., MIT, 1960; J.D., Vanderbilt U., 1964. Bar: Mich. 1964. Assoc. Warner, Norcross & Judd, Grand Rapids, Mich., 1964-69, ptnr., 1969—, mng. ptnr., 1992—; rep. assemblyman State Bar Mich., 1973-78; dir. Rsch. and Tech. Inst. West Mich., 1986—, chmn. 1989-91; lectr. continuing legal edn. programs; chmn., bd. dirs. Butterworth Ventures, 1987—; mem. West Mich. World Trade Week Com., 1988—, chmn., 1990-91; mem. Mich. Dist. Export Couns., 1990—, chmn., 1992—. Chmn. Grand Rapids Area Transit Authority, 1976-79, mem., 1972-79; regional v.p. Nat. Mcpl. League, 1978-86, mem. coun., 1971-78; pres. Grand Rapids Art Mus., 1979-81, trustee, 1976-83, 94—; chmn. Butterworth Hosp., 1979-87, trustee, 1977-87; chmn. Butterworth Health Corp., 1982-89, dir., 1982—, vice chmn., 1989-91, sec., 1991—; vice chmn. Citizens Com. for Consolidation of Govt. Svcs., 1981-82; chmn. Kent County Cultural Svcs. Consol. Com., 1984-85; edni. counselor MIT, 1974—; nat. chmn. devel. com. Vanderbilt U. Law Sch., 1977-78; trustee Kent Med. Found., 1979-82; chmn. Vol. Trustees of Not-for-Profit Hosps., 1987-89, dir., 1983-92; mem. exec. bd. The Right Place Program, 1992—; Woodrow Wilson fellow, 1960-61; Fulbright scholar U. Manchester, Eng., 1960-61. Mem. ABA (com. on law firms bus. law sect. 1982-94, chmn. com. on law firms bus. law sect. 1994—, chmn. subcom. on firm mgmt. 1988—, mem. fed. regulation of securities com. 1982—, mem. internat. bus. law com.), Tenn. Bar Assn., Mich. Bar Assn. (mem. coun. bus. law sect. 1983-89, sect. chmn. 1988-89, ex-officiao coun. bus. law sect. 1989—, chmn. takeover laws subcom. 1986-88, co-chmn. internat. bus. law com., internat. law sect. 1988-89), Grand Rapids Bar Assn., Itnernat. Bar Assn., Grand Rapids C. of C. (pres. 1975, bd. dirs. 1970-76, met. issues steering com. 1992—, downtown 21 coordinating com. 1992-93), Univ. Club, Peninsular Club, Order of Coif, Sigma Xi. Home: 110 Bittersweet Ln NE Ada MI 49301-9552 Office: 111 Lyon St NW Grand Rapids MI 49503

MC CALLUM, DAVID, actor; b. Scotland, Sept. 19, 1933; m. Katherine Carpenter; children: Peter, Sophie; children by previous marriage, Paul Jason (dec.), Valentine. Appearances include (films) The Secret Place, 1958, Hell Drivers, 1958, RobberyUnder arms, 1958, Violent Playground, 1959, A Night to Remember, 1959, The Long and Short and the Tall, 1961, Jungle Street, 1961, Billy Budd, 1962, Freud, 1962, The Great Escape, 1963, The Greatest Story Ever Told, 1965, To Trap A Spy, 1966, The Spy with My Face, 1966, Around the World Under the Sea, 1966, One Spy Too Many, 1966, Three Bites of the Apple, 1967, Sol Madrid, 1968, Mosquito Squadron, 1970, The Kingfisher Caper, 1976, Dogs, 1977, King Solomon's Treasure, 1977, Watcher in the Woods, 1980, Terminal Choice, 1985, The Wind, 1987, The Haunting of Morella, 1990, Hear My Song, 1991, Dirty Weekend, 1993, Shattered Image, 1994; (TV series) The Man From U.N.C.L.E., 1964-68, Colditz, 1972-74, The Invisible Man, 1975-76, Sapphire and Steel, Trainer, 1992; (guest appearances) Hitchcock, Murder She Wrote; (TV movies) Teacher, Teacher, Hauser's Memory, 1970, Frankenstein: The True Story, 1972, She Waits, 1972, The Return of the Man Fron U.N.C.L.E., 1983, Behind Enemy Lines, 1985, Freedom Fighters, 1985, The Man Who Lived At the Ritz, 1988, The Return of Sam McCloud, 1989, Mother Love, 1990. Address: 9229 Sunset Blvd Los Angeles CA 90069

MCCALLUM, JAMES SCOTT, lieutenant governor, former state senator; b. Fond du Lac, Wis., May 2, 1950; s. George Duncan and Marilyn Joy (Libke) McC.; m. Laurie Ann Riach, June 19, 1979; children: Zachary Scott, Rory Duncan, Cara. BA, Macalester Coll., 1972; MA, Johns Hopkins U., 1974. Mem. Wis. State Senate, Madison, 1977-87; lt. gov. State of Wis., Madison, 1987—. Chmn. Fond du Lac County Reps., 1974-76, Wis. Safe Kids Project; mem. resolutions com. Wis. State Rep. Conv., 1977; presdl. appointee to Internat. Trade Adv. Group, 1988-89, U.S. EPA Nat. Adv. Coun. for Environ. Policy and Tech., 1991—; chmn. Gov.'s Conf. on Small Bus. and Gov.'s Com. on Econ. Issues and Safe Kids Project; chair Nat. Conf. of Lt. Govs., 1991—. Named one of Outstanding Young Men Am. Jaycees, 1976; recipient Presdl. award Honor, Jaycees, 1976; Toll Fellow, 1987. Office: State of Wis Office of Lt. Gov. 22 State Capitol Madison WI 53702-0001

MCCALLUM, KENNETH JAMES, retired university dean, chemistry and chemical engineering educator; b. Scott, Sask., Can., Apr. 25, 1918; s. James Alexander and Alice (Fines) McC.; m. Christine Chorneyko, Sept. 20, 1950 (dec. 1971); children: Patricia Jean, Douglas James; m. Erika Connell, Aug. 16, 1974. B.Sc., U. Sask., 1936, M.Sc., 1939; Ph.D., Columbia U., 1942. Jr. research officer NRC Can., 1942-43; mem. faculty U. Sask., from 1943, prof. chemistry and chem. engring., from 1953, head dept. chemistry and chem. engring., from 1959, dean grad. studies, from 1974. Assoc. editor: Jour. Chem. Physics, 1947-50; research, publs. (in cement chemistry, electron affinities, radioisotope exchange reactions, chem. effects transformations, radiation chemistry). Fellow Royal Soc. Can., AAAS, Chem. Inst. Can. (dir. sci. affairs 1961-64, pres. 1968-69). Home: 1622 Park Ave, Saskatoon, SK Canada

MCCALLUM, RICHARD WARWICK, medical researcher, clinician, educator; b. Brisbane, Australia, Jan. 21, 1945; came to U.S., 1969; MD, BS Queensland U., Australia, 1968. Rotating intern Charity Hosp. La., New Orleans, 1969-70; resident in internal medicine Barnes Hosp., Washington, 1970-72; fellow in gastroenterology Wadsworth VA Hosp., L.A., 1972-74, chief endoscopic unit, dept gastroenterology, 1974-76; dir. gastrointestinal diagnostic svcs. Yale-New Haven Med. Ctr., New Haven, 1975-85; asst. prof. medicine UCLA, 1974-76; asst. prof. medicine Yale U., New Haven, 1977-82, assoc. prof., 1982-85; prof., chief div. gastroenterology, hepatology and nutrition U. Va., Charlottesville, 1985—, Paul Janssen prof. medicine, 1987—. Fellow ACP, Am. Coll. Gastroenterology, Royal Australasian Coll. Physicians, Royal Australian Coll. Surgeons; mem. Australian Gastroenterology Soc., Am. Fedn. Clin. Rsch., Am. Assn. Study Liver Diseases, Am. Soc. Gastrointestinal Endoscopy, Am. Soc. for Clin. Investigation, Am. Gastroenterology Assn., Am. Coll. Gastroenterology. Office: U Va Health Scis Ctr Dept Internal Medicine Box 145 Med Ctr Charlottesville VA 22908-0001

MCCALLUM, SCOTT, state official; b. Fond du Lac, Wis.; m. Laurie McCallum; children: Zachary, Rory, Cara. BA, Macalester Coll.; MA Internat. Studies, Johns Hopkins U. Pvt. practice property mgr. Fond du Lac; mem. Wis. State Senate; lt. gov. State of Wis.; bd. dirs. Wis. Child Care Clearinghouse; chair Repeat Offenders Task Force State of Wis., Trauma and Injury Prevention Task Force; presdl. adv. coun. EPA; past chair Conf. Lt.

Govs. Office: Lieutenant Governor Rm 22 East State Capitol Madison WI 53702

MCCALMENT, RAYMOND, junior college educator. Dean, dir. continuing edn. Tulsa Junior Coll., NE Campus, Tulsa, Okla. Recipient Regional Person of the Yr. awd., Nat. Coun. on Community Services and Continuing Education, 1993. Office: Tulsa Jr Coll NE 3727 E Apache Tulsa OK 74115-3510

MCCAMBRIDGE, JOHN JAMES, civil engineer; b. Bklyn., Oct. 27, 1933; s. John Joseph and Florence Josita (McDonnell) McC.; m. Dorothy Antoinette Cook, Mar. 17, 1962; children: Sharon J., John S., Patrick J., Kathleen C. BCE, Manhattan Coll., 1955; MS, Vanderbilt U., 1958; postgrad., UCLA, 1963-66. Civil engr. Raymond Concrete Pile Co., N.Y.C., 1955; commd. 2d lt. USAF, 1955, advanced through grades to col., 1972; exec. sec. Defense Com. On Rsch., Washington, 1971-73, DOD-NASA Supportive Rsch. Tech. Panel, Washington, 1972-74; asst. dir. Def. Rsch. and Engring. (for Life Scis.) Office Sec. Def., Washington, 1974-75; dir. Air Force Life Support Systems Program Office, Wright Patterson AFB, Ohio, 1975-79; retired USAF, 1979; prin. Booz, Allen & Hamilton, Inc., Bethesda, Md., 1979-86; v.p. Espey, Huston & Assoc., Inc., Falls Church, Va., 1986-90; mng. prin. JMC Cons. Group, McLean, Va., 1990—; chmn. air panel on NBC Def., NATO, Evere, Belgium, 1970-71; exec. sec. Def. Com. on Rsch., Washington, 1971-73; def. dept. rep. to physics survey com., Nat. Acad. Scis., Washington, 1971. Contbr. articles to profl. jours. Decorated Legion of Merit with oak leaf cluster. Fellow Aerospace Med. Assn. (exec. coun. 1972-73); mem. Inst. Hazardous Materials Mgmt. (chmn. 1988—), Acad. Cert. Hazardous Materials Mgrs. (pres. 1984-86), coun. Engring. Specialty Bds., 1995—, Survival & Flight Equipment Assn. (nat. sec. 1977-78), River Bend Golf and Country Club, Fairfax Hunt Club, Tower Club, N.C. Republican. Roman Catholic. Office: JMC Cons Group 9200 Falls Run Rd Mc Lean VA 22102-1028

MC CAMERON, FRITZ ALLEN, university administrator; b. Nacogdoches, Tex., Oct. 8, 1929; s. Leland Allen and Gladys (Turner) Mc C.; m. Jeannine Young, June 11, 1957; 1 child, Mary Hartley. B.B.A., Stephen F. Austin State Coll., 1950, M.A., 1951; Ph.D., U. Ala., 1954. C.P.A., La. Assoc. prof. U. La. State U., 1959-62, prof., 1962-67, chmn. dept. accounting, 1967-71, asst. vice chancellor, 1971-73, dean continuing edn., 1973—; cons. in field. Author: FORTRAN Logic and Programming, 1968, Cobol Logic and Programming, rev. edit, 1970, 5th edit., 1985, FORTRAN IV, 1970, rev. edit., 1974, 3d edit., 1977. Mem. Am. Inst. C.P.A.'s, La. Soc. C.P.A.'s; Am. Accounting Assn. Home: 930 Rodney Dr Baton Rouge LA 70808-5867

MCCAMLY, JERRY ALLEN, high school educator; b. Battle Creek, Mich., Mar. 15, 1940; s. Derrol John and Adelee (Harding) McC.; m. Janet Aileen Pulatie, Aug. 25, 1962; children: Ty A., Jodi. BS in Edn., Ariz. State Coll., 1963; MA in Edn., Azusa Pacific Coll., 1978. Tchr. Casa Grande (Ariz.) High Sch., 1963-64, Whittier (Calif.) High Sch., 1964-65, Norwalk (Calif.)-LaMirada Unified Sch. Dist., 1965—; cons. WASC Accrediting Assn., Burlingame, Calif., 1978—. Contbr. articles to profl. publs. Recipient Hon. Svc. award Norwalk Sch. PTA, 1986, Tchr.'s Medal Freedoms Found., 1977. Mem. L.A. Continuation Assn. (pres. 1980-81), Calf. Continuation Assn. (pres. 1981-82), World Future Soc. Republican. Methodist. Avocations: restoring classic Corvettes, bowling, golf, travel, reading. Home: 25630 Sierra Calmo Ct Moreno Valley CA 92551-2162 Office: John Glenn High Sch 13520 Shoemaker Ave Norwalk CA 90650-4598

MC CAMMON, DAVID NOEL, automobile company executive; b. Topeka, Nov. 6, 1934; s. Noel F. and Freda E. McC.; m. Valerie L. Palliaer, May 18, 1968; children: Jeff, Mark, Scott. B.S. in Bus. Adminstrn, U. Nebr., 1957; M.B.A. (Baker scholar), Harvard U., 1962. With Ford Motor Co., Dearborn, Mich., 1957—; contr. Ford div. Ford Motor Co., 1970-71, asst. corp. contr., 1971-77, exec. dir. bus. strategy, 1977-78, v.p. corp. strategy analysis, 1979-84, v.p., contr., 1984-87, v.p. fin., treas., 1987-94, v.p. fin., 1995—. Served with U.S. Army, 1957-58. Club: Harvard Bus. Sch. (Detroit). Office: Ford Motor Co The American Rd Dearborn MI 48126-2798

MCCAMMON, HELEN MARY, government administrator; b. Winnipeg, Man., Can., Aug. 16, 1933; came to U.S., 1956; d. Joseph Zaborniak and Mary Choman; m. Richard B. McCammon, Sept. 5, 1956; children—Catherine Ann, Ian David. B.S. with honors, U. Man., 1955; M.S., U. Mich., 1956; Ph.D., Ind. U., 1959. Research geologist Man. Mines Br., Winnipeg, 1952-59; lectr. U. N.D., Grand Forks, 1960-61; from lectr. to assoc. prof. U. Pitts., 1963-68; vis. assoc. prof. U. Ill.-Chgo., 1968-70; research assoc. Field Mus. Natural History, Chgo., 1970-72; from research rep. to research dir. U.S. EPA, Boston, 1972-76; from sr. oceanographer to dir. ecol. research div. U.S. Dept. Energy, Washington, 1976-91. Contbr. articles to profl. jours. Ind. U. fellow, 1959-59, Orgn. Am. States fellow, 1969-70, Commerce Science and Tech. fellow, 1991-92; NSF grantee, 1967-72. Fellow AAAS (council 1981-84, sect. sec. 1985-89); mem. Am. Geol. Inst. (chmn. edn. com. 1978-82), Am. Soc. Limnologists and Oceanographers, Am. Women in Sci., Am. Soc. Zoologists, Marine Tech. Assn., Sigma Xi. Home: 8430 Bradley Blvd Bethesda MD 20817-1914 Office: Dept Energy ER-74 Washington DC 20585

MCCAMMON, JAMES ANDREW, chemistry educator; b. Lafayette, Ind., Feb. 8, 1947; s. Lewis Brown and Jean Ann (McClintock) McC.; m. Anne Elizabeth Woltmann, June 6, 1969. BA magna cum laude, Pomona Coll., 1969; MA, Harvard U., 1970, PhD, 1976. Research fellow Harvard U., Cambridge, Mass., 1976-78; asst. prof. U. Houston, 1978-81, M.D. Anderson prof. chemistry, 1981-94, dir. Inst. for Molecular Design, 1987-94, prof. biochemistry, 1989-94, adj. prof. chemistry, 1995—; adj. prof. molecular physiology and biophysics Baylor Coll. Medicine, Houston, 1986-94, adj. prof. biochemistry, 1992-94; Joseph E. Mayer chair theoretical chemistry U. Calif., San Diego, 1995—, prof. pharmacology, 1995—. Author: Dynamics of Proteins and Nucleic Acids, 1987. Recipient Tchr.-Scholar award Camille and Henry Dreyfus Found., 1982, George H. Hitchings award Burroughs-Wellcome Fund, 1987, Breakthrough Computational Sci. award Computerworld Smithsonian, 1995; rsch. fellowship Alfred P. Sloan Found., 1980. Fellow Am. Phys. Soc.; mem. AAAS, Am. Chem. Soc., Biophys. Soc., Protein Soc., Phi Beta Kappa. Achievements include development of the molecular dynamics simulation method for proteins and nucleic acids, of the thermodynamic cycle perturbation method for studying molecular recognition, and of the Brownian dynamics method for simulating diffusion-controlled reactions. Office: U Calif San Diego Dept Chemistry La Jolla CA 92093-0365

MC CAMY, JAMES LUCIAN, former political science educator; b. Knoxville, Tenn., June 10, 1906; s. James Lucian and Ida Winfield (Mullendore) McC.; m. Julia Texie Boggess, July 17, 1931; children—Keith, Colin. B.A., U. Tex., 1929, M.A., 1932; Ph.D., U. Chgo., 1938. Reporter Austin (Tex.) Am., 1925-28; editor, publicity dir. Tex. Ex-Students Assn., Austin, 1928-32; tchr. Am. govt. U. Tex., 1932-33; fellow, research asst. dept. polit. sci. U. Chgo., 1933-34; prof. of govt Bennington Coll., 1934-39, 1941-42; asst. to sec. of agr. U.S. Dept. Agr., 1939-41; asst. to dir. Bd. Econ. Warfare, 1942-43; exec. dir. Bur. Areas, Fgn. Econ. Adminstrn., 1943-45; econ. adviser U.S. Forces, Austria, 1945; dir. Office of World Trade Policy, also dep. dir. for policy Office of Internat. Trade U.S. Dept. Commerce, 1946; prof. polit. sci. U. Wis., 1947-71; ret., 1971; Knapp vis. scholar to U. Wis. Centers, 1967-68, chmn. dept., 1948-52; Brittingham prof. Inst. for Environ. Studies, 1970-71; chmn. Wis. Seminar on Quality of Environment, 1967; distinguished vis. scholar Milton Coll., 1969; mem. Wis. Bd. Ethics, 1973-74; U.S. del. to Internat. Inst. Agr., Rome, 1940; adviser to U.S delegations at meetings of Internat. Bank and Monetary Fund, Savannah, 1946; 2d and 3d sessions of UNESCO Lake Success, 1946; staff mem. Pub. Library Inquiry, Social Sci. Research Council, 1947-48. Author: Government Publicity, 1939, Governmental Publications for the Citizen, Ivers, The Administration of American Foreign Affairs, 1950 (Freedom House-Willkie award), American Government, 1957, Science and Public Administration, 1960, Conduct of the New Diplomacy, 1964, The Quality of the Environment, 1972; assoc. editor: Am. Polit. Sci. Rev. 1952-55; Contbr. articles to profl. jours. Mem. Am. Polit. Sci. Assn. (past v.p.). Home: 1610 Adams St Madison WI 53711-2140

MCCANDLESS, BARBARA J., auditor; b. Cottonwood Falls, Kans., Oct. 25, 1931; d. Arch G. and Grace (Kittle) McCandless; m. Allyn O. Lockner, 1969. BS, Kans. State U., 1953; MS, Cornell U., 1959; postgrad. U. Minn., 1962-66, U. Calif., Berkeley, 1971-72; Cert. home economist; enrolled agt. IRS. Home demonstration agt. Kans. State U., 1953-57; teaching asst. Cornell U., 1957-58, asst. extension home economist in marketing, 1958-59; consumer mktg. specialist, asst. prof. Oreg. State U., 1959-62; instr. home econs. U. Minn., 1962-63, research asst. agrl. econs., 1963-66; asst. prof. U. R.I., 1966-67; assoc. prof. family econs., mgmt., housing, equipment dept. head S.D. State U., 1967-73; asst. to sec. Dept. Commerce and Consumer Affairs, S.D., 1973-79; tax cons., 1980-91. Mem. Nat. Council Occupational Licensing, dir., 1973-75, v.p., 1975-79. Mem. Am. Agrl. Econs. Assn., Am. Assn. Family and Consumer Scis., Am. Coun. Consumer Interests, Assn. Govt. Accts., Nat. Council on Family Relations, LWV, Kans. State U. Alumni Assn., Pi Gamma Mu. Research on profl. and occupational licensing bds. Address: 2114 Potomac Dr Topeka KS 66611

MC CANDLESS, BRUCE, II, engineer, former astronaut; b. Boston, Mass., June 8, 1937; s. Bruce and Sue (Bradley) McC.; m. Alfreda Bernice Doyle, Aug. 6, 1960; children: Bruce III, Tracy. BS, U.S. Naval Acad., 1958; MS in Elec. Engring., Stanford U., 1965; MBA, U. Houston, Clear Lake, 1987. Commd. ensign USN, 1958, advanced through grades to capt., 1979, naval aviator, 1960, with Fighter Squadron 102, 1960-64; astronaut Johnson Space Ctr., NASA, Houston, 1966-90; mem. Skylab 1 backup crew Johnson Space Center, NASA, Houston, mem. STS-11 shuttle crew, mem. STS-31 Hubble Space Telescope deployment crew; ret. USN, 1990; prin. staff engr. Martin Marietta Corp., Denver, 1990—. Decorated Legion of Merit; recipient Def. Superior Service medal, NASA Exceptional Service medal, NASA Spaceflight medal, NASA Exceptional Engring. Achievement medal, Collier Trophy, 1985, Haley Space Flight award AIAA, 1991. Fellow Am. Astron. Soc.; mem. IEEE, U.S. Naval Inst., Nat. Audubon Soc., Houston Audubon Soc. (past pres.). Episcopalian. Achievements include executing 1st untethered free flight in space using Manned Maneuvering Unit. Office: Martin Marietta Astronautic Mail System S8000 PO Box 179 Denver CO 80201-0179

MCCANDLESS, CAROLYN KELLER, entertainment, media company executive; b. Patuxent River, Md., June 6, 1945; d. Stevens Henry and Betty Jane (Bethune) Keller; m. Stephen Porter McCandless, Apr. 22, 1972; children: Peter Keller, Deborah Marion. BA, Stanford U., 1967; MBA, Harvard U., 1969. Fin. analyst Time Inc., N.Y.C., 1969-72, mgr. budgets and fin. analysis, 1972-78, asst. sec., dir. internal adminstrn., 1978-85, v.p., dir. employee benefits, 1985-90; v.p human resources and adminstrn. Time Warner, Inc., N.Y.C., 1990—; bd. dirs. LifeRe Corp. Republican. Mem. Unitarian Ch. Office: Time Warner Inc 1271 Ave Of The Americas New York NY 10020-1300

MCCANDLESS, J(ANE) BARDARAH, retired religion educator; b. Dayton, Ohio, Apr. 16, 1925; d. J(ohn) Bard and Sarah Catharine (Shuey) McC. BA, Oberlin Coll., 1951; MRE, Bibl. Sem., N.Y.C., 1953; PhD, U. Pitts., 1968. Dir. Christian edn. Wallace Meml. United Presbyn. Ch., Pitts., 1953-54, Beverly Heights United Presbyn. Ch., Mt. Lebanon, Pa., 1956-61; instr. religion Westminster Coll., New Wilmington, Pa., 1961-65, asst. prof., 1965-71, assoc. prof., 1971-83, prof. religion, 1983-94, prof. emeritus, 1994—, chair dept. religion and philosophy, 1988-92; leader Christian edn. workshops Presbytery of Shenango, Presbyn. Ch. (U.S.A.), 1961—, Synod of Trinity, 1972, 76. Author: An Untainted Saint...Ain't, 1978; contbr. articles to profl. jours., Harper's Ency. Religious Edn. Mem. session New Wilmington Presbyn. Ch., 1977-79. Mack grantee Westminster Coll., 1962-63, Faculty rsch. grantee, 1972, 78, 90. Mem. Religious Edn. Assn., Assn. Profs. and Researchers in Religious Edn. (mem. exec. com. 1978-80), Soc. for Sci. Study Religion, Phi Beta Kappa, Pi Lambda Theta.

MCCANDLES, SANDRA RAVICH, lawyer; b. Revere, Mass., Sept. 5, 1948; d. Merrill Earl and Goldie (Clayman) Ravich; m. Ross Erwin McCandless; 1 child, Phyra. BA, Radcliffe Coll., 1970; JD, Georgetown U., Washington, 1973. Bar: Calif. 1973, U.S. Ct. Appeals (1st and 7th cirs.) 1974, U.S. Ct. Appeals (6th and 9th cirs.) 1975, U.S. Dist. Ct. (no. dist.) Calif. 1976, U.S. Dist. Ct. (ea. dist.) Calif. 1978. Law clk. NLRB, Washington, 1971-73, atty. appellate ct. br., 1973-75; assoc. Pillsbury, Madison & Sutro, San Francisco, 1975-79; from assoc. to ptnr. Graham & James, San Francisco, 1979-93; atty. Sonnenschein, Nath & Rosenthal, San Francisco, 1993—; mem. faculty Nat. Inst. Appellate Advocacy, San Francisco. Mem. ABA, Bar Assn. San Francisco, San Francisco Barrister Club (co-chair com. on labor law 1977-83). Avocations: writing, cruises, theatre. Office: Sonnenschein Nath & Rosenthal 685 Market St 10th fl San Francisco CA 94105

MCCANDLESS, STEPHEN PORTER, financial executive; b. Denver, Mar. 17, 1941; s. Robert B. and Mary (Porter) McC.; m. Carolyn Keller, Apr. 22, 1972; children: Peter, Deborah. Geol. Engr., Colo. Sch. Mines, 1963; M.B.A., Harvard U., 1969. Geologist Shell Oil Co., Casper, Wyo., 1963-65; securities analyst Kidder Peabody & Co., N.Y.C., 1969-70; fin. analyst Asarco Inc., N.Y.C., 1971-72; asst. to treas., 1972-73, asst. treas., 1973-79, treas., 1979-89, v.p., 1983-89; sr. v.p. fin. The Personalized Mass Media Corp., N.Y.C., 1989—, also bd. dirs. Trustee The Town Sch., 1984-94. Served with C.E., U.S Army, 1963-65. Recipient Voice for Justice award Support Com. for Battered Women, 1994. Mem. Tau Beta Pi. Office: Personalized Mass Media Corp 110 E 42nd St New York NY 10017-5611

MCCANLES, MICHAEL FREDERICK, English language educator; b. Kansas City, Mo., Mar. 8, 1936; s. Martin and Dorothy (Kaysing) McC.; m. Penelope A. Mitchell, May 27, 1967; children—Christopher, Stephanie, Jocelyn. B.S., Rockhurst Coll., 1957; M.A., U. Kans., 1959, Ph.D., 1964. Instr. dept. English U. Cin., 1962-64; asst. prof. Marquette U., 1964-68, assoc. prof., 1968-76, prof., 1976—. Author: Dialectical Criticism and Renaissance Literature, 1975, The Discourse of Il Principe, 1983, The Text of Sidney's Arcadian World, 1989, Jonsonian Discriminations: The Humanist Poet and the Praise of True Nobility, 1992; contbr. articles to profl. jours. Guggenheim fellow, 1978-79. Home: 2640 N 89th St Milwaukee WI 53226-1808 Office: Dept English Marquette U Milwaukee WI 53233 As educator, scholar, and citizen I try to encourage in the public domain the same qualities of open-mindedness, secular tolerance of multiple viewpoints, and critical judgement of these viewpoints that I encourage among my students and colleagues.

MCCANN, CLARENCE DAVID, JR., special events coordinator, museum curator and director, artist; b. Mobile, Ala., Apr. 30, 1948; s. Clarence David and Theresa (Pope) McC.; m. Brenda Clemens (div. 1979); 1 child, Nathan; m. Robin Chiavaroli, 1980; children: Angela, John. BFA, U. South Ala., 1970; MFA, U. Cin., 1972; grad. cert., Mus. Mgmt. Inst., Berkeley, Calif., 1982. Art instr. Spring Hill Coll., Mobile, 1972-75, U. South Ala., Mobile, 1975-76; mem. staff, asst. registrar Fine Arts Mus. of South, Mobile, 1977-78, registrar, 1978-81, curator collection, 1981-84, asst. dir., 1985-86, 88-91, acting dir., 1986-88, mus. curator, 1988-91; asst. mgr. spl. events coord. City of Mobile, 1991—; adj. lectr. U.S. Ala.-1990-91, adj. lectr. Bishop State Community Coll., 1991—. Author: (catalogues) The Ripening of American Art: Duveneck and Chase, 1979, The Artists of Barbizon: The Boone Collection, 1983, Enisled Visions: The Southern Nontraditional Folk Artist, 1987, The Acquisitive Eye: Selections From The Collection of James M. Younger, 1990. Pres. Contemporary Artists Consortium of Mobile, 1979-81. Recipient various painting awards Allied Arts Coun., Mobile, 1974; U. Cin. fellow, 1972. Mem. Am. Assn. Mus., Ala. Mus. Assn., Southeastern Mus. Assn. Democrat. Home: 9080 Rawhide St Semmes AL 36575-7275 Office: Office of Spl Events 2900 Dauphin St Mobile AL 36606

MCCANN, DAVID DEWITT, motion picture company executive; b. Glendale, Calif., Apr. 1, 1943; s. DeWitt and Celia (Jeminez) McC.; m. Stephani Ryan, Aug. 25, 1978. Student, L.A. City Coll., 1961-62. Freelance 2d unit dir., editor, 1962-74; v.p. post prodn. ABC Motion Pictures-ABC Circle Films, L.A. 1974-86; sr. v.p. post prodn. Walt Disney Pictures, Burbank, Calif., 1986—. Mem. NATAS, Acad. Motion Picture Arts & Scis., Dirs. Guild Am., Editors Guild. Office: Walt Disney Studio 500 S Buena Vista St # 2 Burbank CA 91521-0001

MCCANN, DEAN MERTON, lawyer, former pharmaceutical company executive; b. Ontario, Calif., Mar. 13, 1927; s. James Arthur and Alma Anis (Hawes) McC.; m. Carol Joan Geissler, Mar. 23, 1957. AA, Chaffey Coll.,

1948; BS in Pharmacy, U. So. Calif., 1951; JD, U. Calif., San Francisco, 1954; LLM, NYU, 1955. Bar: Calif. 1955; lic. pharmacist, Calif. Pharmacist San Francisco and Ontario, 1951-54; sole practice law Los Angeles, 1955-60; ptnr. MacBeth, Ford & Brady, Los Angeles, 1960-65, McCann & Berger, Los Angeles, 1965-68; v.p., sec. and gen. counsel Allergan Pharms., Inc., Irvine, Calif., 1968-78; v.p., sec., gen. counsel Allergan, Inc., Irvine, 1978-89; pvt. practice Irvine, 1989—; instr. pharmacy law U. So. Calif., Los Angeles, 1956-68; exec. v.p. Pharm. Wholesaler Assn., Los Angeles, 1956-68. Mem., past chmn. bd. counsellors Sch. Pharmacy U. So. Calif., Los Angeles, 1975—, life mem., past chmn. QSAD centurion, 1963—. Served with USNR, 1945-46. Fellow Food and Drug Law Inst., 1954-55; recipient Outstanding Alumni Award Sch. Pharmacy U. So. Calif., 1973. Mem. Calif. Bar Assn., Orange County Bar Assn., Calif. Pharm. Assn., Orange County Pharm. Assn., U. So. Calif. Pharmacy Alumni Assn. (past pres., Outstanding Alumni award 1973), U. So. Calif. Assocs. (life), Newport Beach Country Club, Balboa Bay Club, Skull and Dagger Club, Phi Delta Chi. Republican. Home: 21 Rockingham Dr Newport Beach CA 92660-4219 Office: 2525 Dupont Dr Irvine CA 92715-1599

MCCANN, DENNIS JOHN, columnist; b. Janesville, Wis., July 25, 1950; s. Thomas G. and Jean E. (Skelly) McC.; m. Barbara Jo Bunker, Sept. 11, 1971. BA, U. Wis., 1974. Reporter WMIR Radio, Lake Geneva, Wis., 1974, Janesville (Wis.) Gazette, 1975-78, 79-83; reporter, columnist Milw. Jour., 1983—; reporter Daily Herald, Arlington Heights, Ill., 1978. Contbg. author: Best of the Rest, 1993. Recipient Writing awards Milw. Press Club, Wis. Newspaper Assn., Newspaper Farm Editors. Avocations: golf, running. Office: The Milwaukee Journal 333 W State St Milwaukee WI 53201

MCCANN, ELIZABETH IRELAND, theater, television and motion picture producer, lawyer; b. N.Y.C., Mar. 31, 1931; d. Patrick and Rebecca (Henry) McC. BA, Manhattanville Coll., 1952, PhD hon., 1983; MA, Columbia U., 1954; LLD, Fordham U., 1966; ArtsD (hon.), Manhattanville Coll., 1987; LitD (hon.), Marymount Coll., 1993. Bar: N.Y. 1966. Assoc. firm Paul, Weiss, Rifkind, Wharton & Garrison, N.Y.C., 1965-66; assoc. numerous theater mgmts. Robert Joffrey, Hal Prince, Saint Suber, Maurice Evans, 1956-68; mng. dir. Nederlander Orgn., N.Y.C., 1968-76; pres. McCann & Nugent Prodns., Inc., N.Y.C., 1976-86; bd. dirs. City Ctr. Music and Dance; exec. dir. Big Apple Circus, 1968-69. Producer: play My Fat Friend, 1975, Dracula (Tony award 1977), The Elephant Man, 1978 (Tony award), (Drama Critics award 1978, Drama Desk award 1978, Outer Critics Circle award 1978, Obie award 1978), Night and Day, 1979, Home, 1980 (Adelco award 1980), Amadeus, 1980 (Tony award 1980), (Drama Desk award 1980), Morning's At Seven, 1980 (Tony award 1980), Piaf, 1981, Rose, 1981, The Dresser, 1981, Mass Appeal, 1981, The Life and Adventures of Nicholas Nickleby, 1981 (Tony award 1981), (Drama Critics Circle award 1981), Good, 1982, All's Well That Ends Well, 1983, The Glass Menagerie, 1983, Total Abandon, 1983, Painting Churches, 1983, The Lady and the Clarinet, 1983, Cyrano de Bergerac/Much Ado About Nothing, 1984, Pacific Overtures, 1984, Leader of the Pack, 1985, Les Liaisons Dangereuses, 1987 (Drama Critics Circle award 1987), Stepping Out, 1987, Orpheus Descending, 1989, Nick & Nora, 1991, Three Tall Women, 1994; TV show Piaf, 1981, Morning's At Seven, 1982, Philobolus Dance Theatre, 1982; assoc. producer Orpheus Descending, 1990. Recipient Entrepreneurial Woman award Women Bus. Owners of N.Y., 1981, 82; recipient James J. and Jame Hoey award for Interracial Justice, 1981, Spl Drama League award for co-producing the Life and Adventures of Nicholas Nickleby on Broadway, 1982, Dr Louis M. Spadero award Fordham Grad. Sch. Bus., 1982.

MC CANN, FRANCES VERONICA, physiologist, educator; b. Manchester, Conn., Jan. 15, 1927; d. John Joseph and Grace E. (Tuttle) Mc C.; m. Elden J. Murray, Sept. 20, 1962 (dec. Nov. 1975). AB with distinction and honors, U. Conn., 1952, PhD, 1959; MS, U. Ill., 1954; MA (hon.), Dartmouth Coll., 1973. Investigator Marine Biol. Lab., Woods Hole, Mass., 1952-62; instr. physiology Dartmouth Med. Sch., Hanover, N.H. 1959-61, asst. prof., 1961-67, assoc. prof., 1967-73, prof., 1973—; adj. prof. biol. scis. Dartmouth Coll., 1974—; mem., cons. physiology study sect. NIH, 1973-77, mem. biomed. rsch. devel. com., 1978-82, chmn, 1979; cons. Hayer Inst., 1979—; cons. staff Hitchcock Hosp., Hanover, 1980—, sr. staff rsch. Norris Catton Cancer Ctr., 1980—; mem. NRC, 1982-86; chmn. Symposium on Comparative Physiology of the Heart, 1968. Editor: Comparative Physiology of the Heart: Current Trends, 1965; contbr. numerous articles to profl. jours. Trustee Lebanon Coll., 1970-73, Montshire Mus. Sic., Hanover, 1975—, Hanover Health Coun., 1976, Lebanon Coll., 1978—; incorporator Howe Libr., 1975—; active LWV, 1980—, Conservation Coun., 1983—, Hist. Soc., 1975—, N.H. Lakes Assn., 1992—; pres. Aramingo Lake Assn., 1991—. Nat. Heart Inst. fellow, 1959; NIH rsch. grantee, 1959—, Nat. Heart Inst., 1960, N.H. Heart Assn., 1964-65, Vt. Heart Assn., 1966—. Mem. AAAS, Am. Assn. Advancement of Lab. Animal Care, Am. Physiol. Soc., Soc. Gen. Physiologists, Biophys. Soc., Am. Heart Assn. (coun. basic sci., exec. coun. Dallas chpt. 1982-86), Soc. Neurosci. Marine Biol. Lab., LWV, Sigma Xi, Phi Kappa Phi. Avocations: sailing, hiking, reading, keyaking, skiing. Office: Dartmouth Med Sch Lebanon NH 03756

MCCANN, GAIL ELIZABETH, lawyer; b. Boston, Aug. 25, 1953; d. Joseph and Ruth E. (Lagerquist) McC.; m. Stanley J. Lukasiewicz. AB, Brown U., 1975; JD, U. Pa., Phila., 1978. Bar: R.I. 1978, Mass. 1984, U.S. Dist. Ct. R.I. 1978, U.S. Dist. Ct. Mass. 1990. Ptnr. Edwards & Angell, Providence, 1978—. Dir. Pembroke Ctr. Assocs. Coun., Providence, AAA South Ctrl. New Eng., Warwick; dir., immediate past pres. Associated Alumni of Brown U. Mem. R.I. Bar Assn. Avocations: hiking, travel, aerobics. Office: Edwards & Angell 2700 Hospital Trust Tower Providence RI 02903

MCCANN, JOHN FRANCIS, financial services company executive; b. South Orange, N.J., Nov. 30, 1937; s. Frank Charles and Dorothy Marie (Devaney) McC.; m. Mary Ellen Howland, Aug. 4, 1962; children: Sean Francis, Maureen Ellen, Darragh Siobain, Kevin Patrick. Student, LaSalle Mil. Acad., 1951-55, U. Notre Dame, 1955-57, Niagara U., 1959-61, U. Pa., 1984-86. V.p., sales mgr. Imco Container Co., N.Y.C., 1962-68; vice-pres., sales mgr. Eastman Dillon, Union Securities Co., N.Y.C., 1968-72; sr. v.p., sales mgr. Faulkner, Dawkins & Sullivan, N.Y.C., 1972-75; sr. v.p., br. mgr. Faulkner, Dawkins & Sullivan, Chatham, N.J., 1975-77; sr. v.p. Shearson Loeb Rhoades, Chatham, N.J., 1977-83; exec. v.p. Shearson Am. Express, N.Y.C., 1983-84; exec. v.p., dir. Shearson Lehman Bros., N.Y.C., 1984-92, divisional dir. Philanthropic Found., 1989-92; pres. Smith Barney Shearson, N.Y.C., 1993—; bd. dirs. The Robinson-Humphrey Co., Inc., South Atlantic Group, Smith Barney; pres. Great Atlantic Group, 1994—. Fund raiser Riverview Hosp. Found., Red Bank, N.J., 1983; regional dir. Am. Express Found., N.Y.C., 1985—, Shearson Lehman Bros. Philanthropic Found. Mem. N.Y. Stock Exch. (arbitrator 1982—), Securities Industry Assn., Nat. Assn. Securities Dealers (dist. com. 1988-91), Navesink Country Club, Monmouth Beach Bath and Tennis Club, Beacon Hill Club (Summit, N.J.). Republican. Roman Catholic. Avocations: golf; tennis; travel; reading. Home: 135 Bingham Ave Rumson NJ 07760-1852 Office: Smith Barney 151 Bodman Pl Red Bank NJ 07701-1070

MC CANN, JOHN JOSEPH, lawyer; b. N.Y.C., Feb. 4, 1937; s. John and Katherine (McKeon) Mc C.; m. June M. Evangelist, Oct. 16, 1965; children: Catherine Anne, John Bernard, Robert Joseph, James Patrick. AB, Fordham U., 1958; LLB, Columbia U., 1961. Bar: N.Y. 1962, N.J. 1974, Fla. 1994. Ptnr. Donovan Leisure Newton & Irvine, N.Y.C. Mem. ABA (chair bus. law sect. 1992-93), Am. Law Inst., Am. Coll. Investment Counsel (pres. 1984-85), Am. Arbitration Assn. (mem. bd. govs.), Trio A Segno Club, Canoe Brook Golf and Country Club. Roman Catholic. Office: Donovan Leisure Newton & Irvine 30 Rockefeller Plaza New York NY 10112

MCCANN, JOSEPH JOHN, JR., lawyer; b. Yonkers, N.Y., Apr. 3, 1939; s. Joseph John Sr. and Helen Joan (Farley) McC.; m. Helena Mary Hunt, June 10, 1971 (div. May 1978); children: Sean Joseph, Moira Helen, Bryan Daniel; m. Linda Schmitz, June 22, 1979; children: Kimberly Anne Craven, Keith Bryson Craven, Cassandra Lee Craven. BS, U.S. Mil. Acad., 1961; JD, Fordham U., 1967; postgrad., Stanford U., 1989. Bar: N.Y. 1967, N.J. 1974, Calif.1979. Assoc. Chadbourne, Park, Whiteside & Wolff, N.Y.C., 1967-73; v.p., gen. counsel, sec. Keyes Fibre Co., Montvale, N.J., 1973-79; asst. gen. counsel Rockwell Internat. Corp., El Segundo, Calif., 1979-87; v.p.

law TRW Inc., Redondo Beach, Calif., 1987—. Trustee emeritus U.S. Mil. Acad., West Point; mem. adv. bd. Inst. Corp. Counsel of Law Ctr., U. So. Calif.; bd. dirs. Jonsson Cancer Ctr. Found./UCLA. 1st lt. U.S. Army, 1961-64. Mem. ABA, Calif., N.Y., N.J., L.A. County, Fed. bar assns., Assn. Grads. of West Point, Bel Air Country Club. Office: TRW Inc One Space Park E2/6000 Redondo Beach CA 90278

MCCANN, NORMA REED, health facility administrator; b. Alexandria, La., Mar. 21, 1953; d. John and Eris (O'Neal) Reed; m. Clayton Leo McCann, Nov. 26, 1971; children: Chad Wesley, Tara Ainslie. AS Nursing, La. State U., 1973; BS in Health Arts, Coll. St. Francis, Joliet, Ill., 1992. Adminstrv. asst., divsn. adminstr. St. Frances Cabrini Hosp., Alexandria, La. Mem. ANA, Am. Orgn. Nurse Execs. Home: 52 Bethel Rd Deville LA 71328-9572

MCCANN, RAYMOND J., utility company executive; b. N.Y.C., Sept. 28, 1934. B.S., Fordham U., 1956; M.B.A., CUNY, 1962. Gen. auditor Consol. Edison Co. N.Y., N.Y.C., 1972-74, controller, 1974-76, v.p. acctg., treas., 1976-77, v.p. Manhattan div., 1977-80, exec. v.p. ops., 1980-87, exec. v.p. fin. and law, 1987-89, exec. v.p., CFO, trustee, 1989—. Served to capt. USAR. Office: Consol Edison Co NY Inc 4 Irving Pl New York NY 10003-3502

MCCANN, RICHARD EUGENE, lawyer; b. Billings, Mont., Aug. 14, 1939; s. Oakey O. and Edith May (Miller) McC.; m. Mona N. Miyagishima, Apr. 27, 1964; children: Tami, Todd, Jennifer. BA magna cum laude, Rocky Mountain Coll., 1965; JD with highest honors, U. Mont., 1972. Bar: Mont. 1972, Washington 1977, Ala. 1982. Law clk. to presiding justice U.S. Dist. Ct., Billings, 1972-73; assoc. Crowley, Haughey, Hanson, Toole & Dietrich, Billings, 1973-77; assoc. Perkins Coie, Seattle, 1977-80, ptnr., 1981—. Contbr. articles to profl. jours. Trustee Rocky Mountain Coll., Billings, 1973-77. Served with USMC, 1957-61. Mem. ABA, Mont. Bar Assn., Wash. Bar Assn., Alaska Bar Assn. Office: Perkins Coie 1201 3rd Ave 40th fl Seattle WA 98101

MC CANN, SAMUEL MCDONALD, physiologist, educator; b. Houston, Sept. 8, 1925; s. Samuel Glenn and Margaret (Brokaw) McC.; m. Barbara Lorraine Richardson; children: Samuel Donald, Margaret, Karen Elizabeth. Student, Rice U., Houston, 1942-44; M.D., U. Pa., 1948. Intern in internal medicine Mass. Gen. Hosp., Boston, 1948-49; resident Mass. Gen. Hosp., 1949-50; mem. faculty U. Pa. Sch. Medicine, 1952-65, prof. physiology, 1964-65, acting chmn. dept., 1963-64; prof., chmn. physiology U. Tex. Southwestern Med. Sch., Dallas, 1965-85, dir. neuropeptide div., 1985-95, prof. internal medicine, 1995—; cons. Schering Corp., Bloomfield, N.J., 1958; mem. gen. medicine B study sect. NIH, 1965-67, endocrinology study sect., 1967-69, population research com., 1974-76, reproductive biology study sect., 1978-82, chmn. reproductive biology study sect., 1980-82, neurology study sect., 1985-86. Editorial bd.: Endocrinology, 1963-68, 72-77; editorial bd. Neuroendocrinology, 1967-76, editor, 1985-92; editorial bd. Ann. Rev. Physiology, 1974-79, Soc. Exptl. Biology and Medicine, 1976-85, 91—, Am. Jour. Physiology, 1980-85; editor: Endocrine Physiology, Pioneers in Neuroendocrinology; contbr. articles to profl. jours., chpts. to books. Recipient Spencer Morris prize U. Pa. Med. Sch., 1948, Lindback award for distinguished teaching, 1965, Oppenheimer award for research in endocrinology, 1966, Hartman award Soc. Study of Reproduction, 1986. Mem. Endocrine Soc. (exec. council 1985-88, Fred Conrad Koch award 1979), Am. Physiol. Soc. (council 1979-81), Soc. for Exptl. Biology and Medicine (coun. 1979-83, pres. 1995—), Soc. Clin. Investigation, N.Y. Acad. Scis., Nat. Acad. Scis., Am. Acad. Arts and Scis., Neuroendocrine Discussion Group (chmn. 1965), Internat. Neuroendocrine Soc. (council 1972-79, pres. 1984-88), Internat. Soc. Neuroimmunomodulation (sec. gen. 1990—). Home: PO Box 45713 Dallas TX 75245-0713 Office: U Tex Southwestern Med Sch Dept Internal Medicine Dallas TX 75235

MCCANN, WILLIAM H., SR., lawyer; b. Winchester, Ky., Feb. 19, 1929; s. James Marshall McCann and Henrietta (Prewitt) Clark; m. Betty Bruce Brown, Oct. 23, 1953 (div. 1985); children: William H. Jr., Laura, Bruce, Susan, Elizabeth. LLB, U. Ky., 1952. Law clk. Ky. Ct. of Appeals, Frankfort, 1952-53; ptnr. Brown, Sledd & McCann, Attys., Lexington, Ky., 1956-85, Wyatt, Tarrant, Comas, Attys., Lexington, 1985—. Mem. Ky. Ho. of Reps., Frankfort, 1970-72; councilman Lexington-Fayette County Govt., Lexington, 1975-76; mem., chmn. Ky. Coun. on Higher Edn., Frankfort, 1975-84; mem., bd. dirs. Prichard Com. on Acad. Excellence, 1985—. 1st lt. U.S. Army, 1953-56. Fellow Am. Coll. of Trial Lawyers; mem. ABA, Ky. Bar Assn. Democrat. Avocations: golf, fishing, farming, reading. Home: 541 W Short St # 023N Lexington KY 40507-1258 Office: Wyatt Tarrant Combs 1700 Lexington Fin Ctr Lexington KY 40507

MCCARD, HAROLD KENNETH, aerospace company executive; b. Corinth, Maine, Dec. 18, 1931; s. Fred Leslie and Ada (Drake) McC.; m. Charlotte Marie Despres, June 29, 1957; children: Robert Fred, Renee Glen. BEE, U. Maine, Orono, 1959; MEE, Northeastern U., 1963; MS in Mgmt., MIT, 1977. Engr. Avco Systems div. Textron, Wilmington, Mass., 1959-60, group leader, 1960-62, section chief, 1962-65, dept. mgr., 1965-72, dir./staff dir., 1972-77, chief engr., 1977-79, v.p. ops., 1979-82, v.p., gen. mgr., 1982-85; pres. Textron Def. Systems (formerly Avco Systems div./ Avco Systems Textron), Wilmington, Mass., 1986—. Mem. Nat. Indsl. Security Assn. (bd. dirs. 1986—), AIAA (Leadership in Quality Mgmt. award 1991), Armament Research and Devel. Council, Am. Def. Preparedness Assn. (exec. com.), North Shore C. of C. (bd. dirs. 1986—). Avocations: golf, tennis, skiing. Home: 6 Lantern Ln Lynnfield MA 01940-1347 Office: Textron Def Systems 201 Lowell St Wilmington MA 01887-4113

MCCARDELL, JAMES ELTON, retired naval officer; b. Daytona Beach, Fla., Jan. 22, 1931; s. J. Elton and Margaret Almira (Payne) McC.; m. Nancy Ann Chandler, July 9, 1955; children: Jenise, Patrick. Student, U. Fla., 1948-50; B.A., U.S. Naval Postgrad. Sch., 1965. Commd. ensign U.S. Navy, 1952, advanced through grades to rear adm., 1980; exec. officer USS Forrestal, 1972-73; dep. chief of staff Air Readiness Staff, Chief Naval Res., New Orleans, 1973-76; comdg. officer NAS, Key West, Fla., 1976-78; chief of staff Staff of Chief Naval Res., New Orleans, 1978-80; def. and naval attache U.S. Embassy, Brasilia, Brazil, 1981-83; dir. Inter-Am. Def. Coll., Fort L.J. McNair, Washington, 1983-85; ret., 1985. Decorated Legion of Merit with cluster, Bronze Star medal, Air medal with 12 clusters, Def. Disting. Service medal, Def. Superior Performance medal. Republican. Roman Catholic. Home: PO Box 719 Pass Christian MS 39571-0719 *The absolute measure of successful leadership has always been reflected by performance of subordinates in the achievement of unit goals.*

MCCARDELL, JOHN MALCOLM, JR., college administrator; b. Frederick, Md., June 17, 1949; s. John Malcolm Sr. and Susan (Lane) McC.; m. Bonnie Greenwald, Dec. 30, 1976; children: John Malcolm III, James Benjamin Lee. AB, Washington and Lee U., 1971; postgrad., John Hopkins U., 1972-73; PhD, Harvard U., 1976. Asst. prof. history Middlebury (Vt.) Coll., 1976-80, assoc. prof. history, 1982-87, dean for academic devel., 1985-88, prof. history, 1987—, dean faculty, 1988-89, provost, v.p for academic affairs, 1989-91, acting pres., 1991-92, pres., 1992—; sr. rsch fellow U. S.C., Columbia, 1980-81; bd. dirs. Nat. Bank Middlebury. Author: The Idea of a Southern Nation, 1979 (Allan Nevins award 1977); editor: A Master's Due, 1985. Vestry St. Stephen's Episcopal Ch., Middlebury, 1983-85, sr. warden, 1985; bd. dirs. Sheldon Mus., Middlebury, 1988-91; chmn. bd. Addison Cen. Ednl. Endowment, Middlebury, 1988-91. Recipient Algernon Sydney Sullivan prize Washington and Lee U., 1971, Charles Eliot medal Eliot House Harvard U., 1976; Nat. Endowment for Humanities fellow, 1980; Am. Philosophical Soc. fellow, 1979. Mem. Am. Hist. Assn., Orgn. Am. Historians, So. Hist. Assn., Am. Studies Assn., Vt. Hist. Soc., Omicron Delta Kappa, Phi Beta Kappa, Lambda Chi Alpha. Office: Middlebury Coll Old Chapel Bldg Middlebury VT 05753

MCCARGAR, JAMES GOODRICH, diplomat, writer; b. San Francisco, Apr. 20, 1920; s. Jesse B. and Addie May (Goodrich) McC.; m. Geraldine Claudia Cooper-Key, Aug. 2, 1948 (div. 1954); m. Emanuela Butculescu, Dec. 22, 1973. BA, Stanford U., 1942. Joined Fgn. Svc., 1942; fgn. svc. officer Dept. State, Moscow, 1942, 43, Vladivostok, 1942-43, Santo Domingo, 1943-44; sec. of legation; chief public sect. Dept. State, Budapest, Hungary, 1946-47; vice consul Dept. State, Genoa, Italy, 1948; chief div. Southeastern European Affairs Office of Policy Coordination, Washington,

1948-50; sec. of embassy, mem. U.S. Del. to Allied Coordinating Com., Paris, 1950-53; asst. to v.p. Free Europe Com., Inc., N.Y.C., 1955; European dir. polit. ops. Free Europe Com., Inc., Paris, 1956-58; cons. to pres. Free Europe Com., Inc., 1959-60, 71-76; spl. asst. to chmn. NEH, Washington, 1978-82; U.S. del. UNESCO confs., 1978, 80, 82, Sem. on Funding of Culture, Madrid, 1982; cons. BBC-TV, London, 1984, Nat. Dem. Inst. Internat. Affairs, Washington, 1984, African-Am. Labor Ctr., Washington, 1984-85, Am. Inst. Free Labor Devel., Washington, 1985, Dept. Internat. Affairs, AFL-CIO, Washington, 1986—, Free Trade Union Inst., Washington, 1993—; editorial adv. Interco Press, Washington, 1988—; bd. dirs. Ams. for Universality of UNESCO, Washington, 1985—. Author: A Short Course in the Secret War, 1963, rev. edit., 1988, 3d edit., 1992, El Salvador and Nicaragua: The AFL-CIO Views on the Controversy, 1985; co-author: Three-Cornered Cover, 1972, Lost Victory, 1989; contbr. articles and book revs., 1940-70. Co-founder, sec. Ams. Abroad for Kennedy, Paris, 1960. Ensign USNR, 1944-46. Recipient Cert. of Appreciation Internat. Ctr. for Free Trade Unions in Exile, 1958, Fed. Outstanding Performance award NEH, 1979, 81; decorated Knight First Class Royal Norwegian Order St. Olav, 1983, Silver Medallion of the Hungarian Parliament, 1991, Officer's Cross Order of the Hungarian Republic, 1992, Officer's Cross Order of Merit of the Rep. of Poland, 1993. Mem. Polish Inst. Arts and Scis. Am. (elected), Diplomatic and Consular Officers Retired, Chevaliers du Tastevin (France), Vets. of OSS (hon.), Authors' Guild. Democrat. Home and Office: Apt 1207 W 4201 Cathedral Ave NW Washington DC 20016-4901

MCCARLEY, ROBERT EDWARD, real estate executive, real estate appraiser; b. Memphis, Apr. 19, 1943; s. Bernie Bryant and Mildred (Clark) McC.; m. Anne Weatherford Hyatt, Oct. 23, 1971; children: Hyatt, Clark, John. BS in Bus. Adminstrn., U. Ark., 1965. Pres. McCarley & Co., West Memphis/Little Rock, Ark., 1966—; v.p. The Hathaway Group, Little Rock, 1986-89; sec.-treas. The Title Co., West Memphis, 1992—. Dir. Bank of West Memphis, Ark., 1973-86. Mem. Appraisal Inst. (regional committeeperson 1990—, pres. Ark. chpt. 1989), Country Club of Little Rock. Presbyterian. Avocations: golf, travel. Home: 5614 Edgewood Rd Little Rock AR 72207-5314

MCCARRICK, EDWARD R., magazine publisher. Pub. Life Mag., N.Y.C. Office: Life Time Inc Time & Life Bldg Rockefeller Ctr New York NY 10020-1393*

MC CARRICK, THEODORE EDGAR, archbishop; b. N.Y.C., July 7, 1930; s. Theodore Egan and Margaret (McLaughlin) McC. Student, Fordham U., 1950-52; AB, St. Joseph's Sem., 1954, AM, 1958; MA, Cath. U., 1960, PhD, 1963; LLD, Mt. St. Vincent Coll., 1967; STD, Inter-Am. U., 1969; STD (hon.), Niagara U. 1982; LHD (hon.), St. John's U., 1974, St. Peter's Coll., 1987. Ordained priest Roman Cath. Ch., 1958. Asst. chaplain Cath. U. Am., Washington, 1959-61, dean students, 1961-63, asst. to rector, dir. univ. devel., 1963-65, instr. dept. sociology, 1961-65; domestic prelate, 1965; pres. Cath. U. P.R., 1965-69; assoc. dir. edn. Archdiocese of N.Y., 1969-71; sec. to Cardinal-Archbishop N.Y., 1971-77; titular bishop of Rusubisir, aux. bishop N.Y., 1977-81; 1st bishop Diocese of Metuchen, N.J., 1981-86; 4th archbishop Newark, 1986—; mem. policy bd. Washington Consortium, Peace Corps, 1962-63, Pontifical Commn. for Migrants and Refugees, 1987; chmn. U.S. Bishops Com. on Migration, 1986-89, 92—; pres. Nat. Coun. for Spanish-Speaking People, 1961-65; chmn. Gov.'s Commn. for Higher Edn. in P.R., 1968, P.R. Adv. Coun. on Tech. and Vocat. Edn., 1968-69. Mem. Fed. Commn. for Study of Migration and Econ. Devel., 1989; Episcopal promoter Apostleship of the Sea, 1989-92; chmn. com. aid to ch. in Ctrl. and Ea. Europe, Nat. Conf. Cath. Bishops, 1992—; sec.-treas. Papal Found., 1988—. Named knight grand cross Holy Sepulchre. Clubs: K.C, Am. Assn. Knights Malta (chaplain 1978-82). Office: 31 Mulberry St Newark NJ 07102-5202*

MCCARROLL, MARY BARBARA, social services adminstrator, retired; b. Canton, Ohio, May 16, 1927; d. Donald Lester and Mildred (Troll) McC. BA, Ohio Wesleyan U., 1949; MSW, U. Mich., 1959. Dir. health, phys. edn. and recreation YWCA, Canton, 1950-55, Lansing, Mich., 1955-58; br. exec. YWCA, Detroit, 1959-74, assoc. exec. dir., 1974-79; exec. dir. YWCA, San Diego, 1979-88; mem. nominating com. U.S. YWCA, 1985-88. Bd. dirs. San Diego County United Way, 1984-86, mem. Par Council, 1982-86. Mem. Nat. Assn. Social Work, Agy. Exec. Assn. (pres. 1984-86), Nat. Assn. YWCA Execs. (nominating com. 1986-88), Altrusa (pres. San Diego chpt. 1983-85). Methodist. Avocations: swimming, outdoor activities, needlework. Home: 5129 Abuela Dr San Diego CA 92124-2020 Office: YWCA San Diego County 1012 C St San Diego CA 92101-5544

MCCARRON, JOHN FRANCIS, columnist; b. Providence, Jan. 20, 1949; s. Hugh Francis and Katherine Anne (Brooks) McC.; m. Janet Ann Velsor, Sept. 3, 1971; children: Veronica, Catherine. BS in Journalism, Northwestern U., 1970, MS in Journalism, 1973. Gen. assignment reporter Chgo. Tribune, 1973-80, urban affairs writer, 1980-91, fin. editor, 1991-92, editorial bd. columnist, 1992—. Contbr. to Planning mag., World Book Ency., Preservation mag. Lt. USNR, 1970-72. Recipient Editors award AP, 1983, 84, Ann. Journalism award Am. Planning Assn., 1983, Heywood Broun award Am. Newspaper Guild, Washington, 1989, Peter Lisagor award Soc. Profl. Journalists, 1994. Home: 1425 Noyes St Evanston IL 60201-2639 Office: Chicago Tribune Chicago IL 60611

MCCARTAN, LUCY, geologist; b. Miami Beach, Fla., Oct. 4, 1942; d. Arthur Austin and Edith (Newby) McC.; m. J.P. Owens, 1981. BA, Occidental Coll., 1965; MS, Lehigh U., 1967, PhD, 1972. Rsch. geologist U.S. Geol. Survey, Reston, Va., 1973—. Author maps, books and articles on geology of U.S. Atlantic seaboard, the Fla. peninsula, New Zealand, and Antarctica. Fulbright-Hays grantee, New Zealand, 1967-68; scholar AAUW, New Zealand, 1968-69; NSF Summer Teaching fellow, Fla., 1966; recipient NSF medal for Antarctic Rsch., 1980. Fellow Geol. Soc. Am.; mem. Soc. Econ. Paleontologists and Mineralogists, Clay Minerals Soc., Assn. for Women Geoscientists (v.p. Found. 1991-93). Office: US Geol Survey 928 Nat Ctr Reston VA 22092

MC CARTAN, PATRICK FRANCIS, lawyer; b. Cleve., Aug. 3, 1934; s. Patrick Francis and Stella Mercedes (Ashton) McC.; m. Lois Ann Buchman, Aug. 30, 1958; children: M. Karen, Patrick Francis, III. AB magna cum laude, U. Notre Dame, 1956, JD, 1959. Bar: Ohio 1960, U.S. Ct. Appeals (6th cir.) 1961, U.S. Ct. Appeals (3rd cir.) 1965, U.S. Ct. Appeals (D.C. cir.) 1980, U.S. Ct. Appeals (5th cir.) 1981, U.S. Ct. Appeals (4th cir.) 1989, U.S. Ct. Appeals (7th cir.) 1992, U.S. Supreme Ct. 1970. Law clk. to Hon. Charles Evans Whittaker, U.S. Supreme Ct., 1959; asso. Jones, Day, Reavis & Pogue, Cleve., 1961-65, ptnr., 1966-93, mng. ptnr., 1993—; bd. trustees Nat. Inst. for Trial Adv., Boulder, Colo., 1987—, U. Notre Dame, Cleve. Clinic Found., Greater Cleve. Roundtable. Fellow Am. Coll. Trial Lawyers, Internat. Acad. Trial Lawyers; mem. ABA, 6th Cir. Jud. Conf. (life), U.S.-Japan Bus. Coun. (coun. fgn. rels.), Ohio Bar Assn., Bar Assn. Greater Cleve. (pres. 1977-78). Roman Catholic. Home: 7570 Thistle Ln Novelty OH 44072-9500 Office: Jones Day Reavis & Pogue North Point 901 Lakeside Ave E Cleveland OH 44114-1190

MCCARTEN, WILLIAM WEISEL, financial executive; b. Washington, Nov. 12, 1948; s. William G. and Lucille (Weisel) McC.; Shelia A. Ferguson, Feb. 3, 1968; children: Richard J., Lorna B. BS in Acctg., U. Va., 1970. Audit mgr. Arthur Andersen & Co., Washington, 1970-79; v.p., asst. corp. controller Marriott Corp., Bethesda, Md., 1979-82; v.p., controller Marriott Corp. Roy Rogers Restaurant Div., Bethesda, Md., 1982-84, v.p. fin. 1984-85, v.p. fin., corp. controller, 1985-86, sr. v.p. fin. and corp. controller, 1986—; adv. bd. McIntire Sch. of Commerce, 1980—. Mem. Am. Inst. CPA's, D.C. Inst. CPA's, Nat. Assn. Real Estate Cos. Avocations: tennis, racquetball. Home: 2008 Roundhouse Rd Vienna VA 22181-2834 Office: Marriott Corp 1 Marriott Dr Washington DC 20058-0001

MCCARTER, CHARLES CHASE, lawyer; b. Pleasanton, Kans., Mar. 17, 1926; s. Charles Nelson and Donna (Chase) McC.; m. Clarice Blanchard, June 25, 1950; children—Charles Kevin, Cheryl Ann. BA, Principia Coll., 1950; JD, Washburn U., 1953; LLM, Yale U., 1954. Bar: Kans. 1953, U.S. Supreme Ct. 1962, Mo. 1968. Asst. atty. gen. State of Kans., 1954-57; lectr. law sch. Washburn U., 1956-57; appellate counsel FCC, Washington, 1957-58; assoc. Weigand, Curfman, Brainerd, Harris & Kaufman, Wichita, 1958-

61; gen. counsel Kans. Corp. Commn., 1961-63; ptnr. McCarter, Frizzel & Wettig, Wichita, 1963-68, McCarter & Badger, Wichita, 1968-73; pvt. practice law St. Louis, 1968-76; ptnr. McCarter & Greenley, St. Louis, 1976-85; mng. ptnr. Gage & Tucker, St. Louis, 1985-87, Husch and Eppenberger, St. Louis, 1987-89; McCarter & Greenley, 1990—; prof. law, assoc. dir. law sch. Nat. Energy Law and Policy Inst. Tulsa U., 1977-79; prof. law, coach nat. moot ct. coll. of law Stetson U. Coll., St. Petersburg, Fla., 1980-84; mem. govtl. adv. coun. Gulf Oil Corp., 1977-81 ; legal com. Interstate Oil Compact Commn. Co-author: Missouri Lawyers Guide; assoc. editor Washburn U. Law Rev., 1952-53; contbr. articles to profl. jours. Chmn. Wichita Human Rels. Devel. Adv. Bd., 1967-68; bd. dirs. Peace Haven Assn. With USNR, 1944-46. Recipient Excellent Prof. award U. Tulsa , 1979; vis. scholar Yale U., 1980. Mem. ABA, Kans. Bar Assn., Mo. Bar Assn., Am. Legion, VFW, Native Sons and Daus. Kans (pres. 1957-58), Kappa Sigma, Delta Theta Phi, Principia Dads Club (bd. dirs.). Republican. Office: One Metropolitan Sq Ste 2160 Saint Louis MO 63102-2751

MC CARTER, JOHN ALEXANDER, biochemistry educator; b. Wareham, Eng., Jan. 25, 1918; emigrated to Can., 1919; s. Alexander and Helen T. (McKellar) McC.; m. Patricia Jocelyn St. John, Dec. 27, 1941; children: David G., Robert M., Patricia L., William A. B.A., U. B.C., 1939, M.A., 1941; Ph.D., U. Toronto, 1945. Research officer NRC Can. Atomic Energy Project, Chalk River, Ont., 1945-48; asso. prof. Dalhousie U., Halifax, Can., 1948-50; prof. Dalhousie U., 1950-65; prof. biochemistry, dir. Cancer Research Lab., U. Western Ont., London, 1965-83; prof. dept. biochemistry and microbiology U. Victoria, B.C., Can., 1980-83; Mem. Med. Research Council Canada, 1961-67; research adv. group Nat. Cancer Inst. Canada, 1967-72. Contbr. articles to profl. jours. Fellow Brit. Empire Cancer Campaign, 1959-60. Fellow Royal Soc. Can.; mem. Can. Biochem. Soc. (pres. 1966-67), Alpha Omega. Research on tumor virology. Home: 3171 Henderson Rd, Victoria, BC Canada V8P 5A3

MC CARTER, JOHN WILBUR, JR., corporation executive; b. Oak Park, Ill., Mar. 2, 1938; s. John Wilbur and Ruth Rebecca McC.; m. Judith Field West, May 1, 1965; children: James Philip, Jeffrey John, Katherine Field. A.B., Princeton U., 1960; postgrad., London Sch. Econs., 1961; M.B.A., Harvard U., 1963. Cons., assoc., v.p. Booz Allen and Hamilton, Inc., Chgo., 1963-69; White House fellow Washington, 1967-68; dir. Bur. Budget and Dept. Fin., State of Ill., Springfield, 1969-73; v.p. DeKalb AgResearch, Ill., 1973-78, dir., 1975-86, exec. v.p., 1978-80, pres., 1981-82; pres., chief exec. officer DeKalb-Pfizer Genetics, 1982-86, chmn., 1986; pres. DeKalb Corp., 1985-86; sr. v.p. Booz Allen & Hamilton Inc., 1987—; bd. dirs. A.M. Castle & Co., W.W. Grainger, Inc. Trustee Chgo. Pub. Television, 1973, chmn., 1989—; trustee Princeton U., 1983-87, U. Chgo., 1993—. Office: Booz Allen & Hamilton Inc 225 W Wacker Dr Chicago IL 60606-1224

MCCARTER, MICHAEL G., insurance company executive; b. 1952; married. MA, Harvard U., 1974. With Cigna Corp., Phila., 1974-77, Reliance Ins. Co., Phila., 1977-85, Cigna Corp., Phila., 1985-86; with Harleysville Group, Inc., Harleysville, Pa., 1986—, now v.p. Office: Harleysville Mutual Insur Co 355 Maple Ave Harleysville PA 19438-2200

MCCARTER, P(ETE) KYLE, JR., Near Eastern studies educator; b. Oxford, Mich., July 9, 1945; s. Pete K. and Mary Ann (Hudson) McC.; children: Robert, David, Mary. B.A. U. Okla., 1967; MDiv, McCormick Theological Seminary, Chgo., 1970; PhD, Harvard U., 1974. Asst. prof. religious studies U. Va., Charlottesville, 1974-79, assoc. prof., 1979-82, prof., 1982-85; William Foxwell Albright prof. of Bibl. and near eastern studies Johns Hopkins U., Balt., 1985—, chmn. near eastern studies, 1991—, assoc. dean sch. arts. and scis., 1987-90; vis. lectr. on bibl. Hebrew Harvard U., Cambridge, Mass., 1978-79; vis. assoc. prof. Dartmouth Coll., Hanover, N.H., 1979; fellow Ctr. for Advanced Studies, U. Va., 1980-82. Author: The Antiquity of the Greek Alphabet and the Early Phoenician Scripts, 1975, I Samuel: A New Translation with Introduction, Notes, and Commentary 1980, II Samuel: A New Translation with Introduction, Notes, and Commentary, 1984, Recovering the Text of the Hebrew Bible: An Introduction fo Textual Criticism, 1986. Mem. Soc. Bibl. Lit., Am. Schs. Oriental Research (pres. 1988-90), Bibl. Colloquium, Colloquium for Bibl. Research. Democrat. Presbyterian. Avocations: squash, fly fishing. Office: Johns Hopkins U 124 Gilman Hall 34th And Charles St Baltimore MD 21218

MCCARTER, ROBERT, banking executive. CEO NBB Bancorp. Office: NBB Bancorp Inc 174 Union St New Bedford MA 02740-6366

MC CARTER, THOMAS N., III, investment counseling company executive; b. N.Y.C., Dec. 16, 1929; s. Thomas N., Jr. and Suzanne M. (Pierson) McC.; student Princeton, 1948-51. Sales exec. Mack Trucks, Inc., N.Y.C., 1952-59; ptnr. Kelly, McCarter, D'Arcy Investment Counsel, N.Y.C., 1959-62; v.p., sec., dir. D'Arcy, McCarter & Chew, N.Y.C., 1962-66; v.p., dir. Trainer, Wortham & Co., Inc., N.Y.C., 1967-71, exec. v.p., 1971-75; chmn. bd., dir. Island Security Bank Ltd., 1976-78; pres. Knottingham Ltd., N.Y.C., 1976-84; gen. ptnr. W.P. Miles Timber Properties, New Orleans; exec. v.p., Yorke McCarter Owen & Bartels, Inc., N.Y.C., 1985-89, also bd. dirs.; fins. cons. Laidlaw Holdings, Inc., 1990-92; pres., bd. dirs., Mentor Mgmt. Group, Inc. N.Y.C., 1986-90; chmn. bd. dirs. Ramapo Land Co., Sloatsburg, N.Y., 1990—; Stillrock Mgmt. Inc., N.Y.C., 1992—; bd. dirs. Parock Group Inc., Covenent Fund; dir. Electronic Retail Corp. Chmn. bd. trustees Christodora Found., Inc., N.Y.C., 1970-93; charter trustee Dalton Sch., N.Y.C., 1968-76, v.p., 1972-76; pres., trustee Civil War Libr. and Mus., Phila., 1985-92; chmn. bd. trustees ASPCA, 1984—; chmn. Loyal Legion Found., N.Y.C.; trustee Children's Aid Soc. N.Y.C., 1973-94, Joffrey Ballet, Found. for Am. Dance, 1973-77; pres., trustee N.Y.C. Marble Cemetery Assn.; mem. Nat. Com. for Preservation of the U.S. Treasury Bldg., 1988-92; trustee Nat. Symphony Orch., Washington, 1990-94. Chartered investment counselor. Mem. Loyal Legion U.S. (comdr. N.Y. State 1964-66, nat. comdr. in chief 1977-81); Racquet and Tennis Club, Brook Club, Links Club, River Club, St. Nicholas Soc., Pilgrims of U.S. (N.Y.C.), Meadow Club (Southampton, N.Y.), Ivy Club (Princeton, N.J.). Republican. Home: 188 East 64th St New York NY 10021 Office: Stillrock Mgmt Inc 18 E 74th St New York NY 10021-2605

MCCARTHY, ABIGAIL QUIGLEY, writer, columnist, educator; b. Wabasha, Minn., Apr. 16, 1915; d. Stephen Michael and Mary Cecelia (O'Leary) Quigley; m. Eugene Joseph McCarthy, June 25, 1945 (separated 1970); children: Ellen Anne, Mary Abigail, Michael Benet, Margaret Alice. BA, Coll. St. Catherine, 1936; MA, U. Minn., 1942; postgrad., U. Chgo., Middlebury Sch. of Eng.; hon. doctorates, Trinity Coll., Cath. U. Am., 9 others. Tchr. Mandan (N.D.) High Sch., 1936-39; asst. prof. Eng. Coll. St. Catherine, St. Paul, 1939-46; columnist Commonweal Mag., N.Y.C., 1974—, RNS, N.Y. Times Syndicate, 1992-94; bd. dirs. Nat. Com. Study of Electorate, Dreyfus Corp., dir. emeritus; pres. Herald Comms., Ltd.; past chmn. bd. Carroll Pub. Co.; Poynter lectr. Ind. U.; Collition lectr. U. Pacific; Audenshaw lectr. Chgo. U.; lectr. Harvard U., Fordham U., Bryn Mawr U., Georgetown U., Hunter U., U. So. Calif., U. Scranton, Boston Coll., Clarke Coll., Stephens U., Trinity U., others. Author: (memoir) Private Faces/Public Places, (novels) Circles, A Washington Story, One Woman Lost; co-author Minnesota Women, At the Edge of Hope, ER: First Lady Without Precedent, Why Catholic?. Founding pres. Clearinghouse Women's Issues; mem. first adv. com. Women's Equity Action League and Women's Polit. Caucus; former mem. Bishops' Com. Edn., Ecumenism; former v.p. Ch. Women United, USA; bd. dirs. Nat. Conf. Interracial Justice. Mem. Wash. Ind. Writers Orgn. (mem. adv. bd.), Phi Beta Kappa. Office: 2126 Connecticut Ave NW Washington DC 20008-1729

MCCARTHY, ALBERT HENRY, human resources executive; b. Worcester, Mass., May 17, 1944; s. Albert H. and Rosemary (Sheehan) McC.; m. Ann F. Arseneault, 1965; children: Erin Marie, Caitlin Ann. BA in Sociology, Coll. Holy Cross, Worcester, Mass., 1968, Cert. Indsl. Rels., 1975; postgrad. Assumption Coll., Worcester, Mass. Recruiter Data Gen. Corp., Southborough, Mass., 1972-73, personnel adminstr., 1973-74, personnel supr., 1974-76; New Eng. dist. personnel mgr. Digitale Equip. Corp., Waltham, Mass., 1976-78; mgr. staffing systems and programs Honeywell Info. Systems, Inc., Waltham, Mass., 1978-80; dir. human resources NEC Info. Systems, Inc., Boxborough, Mass., 1980-84, v.p. human resources, 1984-93; v.p. human resources Simplex Time Recorder Co., Gardner, Mass.,

1993—; speaker, panelist Japan External Trade Orgn./Bus. Wk. Symposium, 1989. author: Personel Journal, 1989, 91, Bureau of Business Practice, Sales Manager's Guide, 1993. Capt. USAF, 1968-71. Recipient Best Practice: Recruitment Category Peronnel Recruitment Program award Human Resource Exec. mag., 1992. Mem. Internat. Assn. Corp. and Profl. Recruiters (co-pres. Boston chpt. 1992-95, bd. dirs. 1994-95), Soc. Human Resource Mgmt. (Yoder Heneman Creative Application award 1990), N.E. Human Resources Assn., Boxborough Bus. Assn. (founding mem.), Human Resource Exec. Forum (founding mem.). Home: 466 Burncoat St Worcester MA 01606-1418 Office: Simplex Time Recorder Co Simplex Plz Gardner MA 01441-0001

MCCARTHY, BEA, state legislator; b. Great Falls, Mont., Apr. 17, 1935; d. Robert Joseph and Rose Mary (Krier) McKenna; m. Edward Joseph McCarthy, June 27, 1959; children: Colleen, Mary, Edward Jr., Patrick, John. BS in Elem Edn., Mont. State U., 1957. Tchr. 1st grade Anaconda, Mont., 1968—; rep. dist. 66 Mont. State Legis., 1994—. Mem. Mont. Bd. Regents, 1983-90, Mont. Bd. Edn., 1983-90. Mem. AAUW, Am. Legion Aux., Ladies Ancient Order Hibernians (past pres.), Phi Beta Phi, Delta Kappa Gamma. Democrat. Roman Catholic. Avocations: needlework, painting, reading. Home: 1906 Ogden Anaconda MT 59711

MCCARTHY, BERNARD WILLIAM, lawyer; b. Bennington, Vt., July 9, 1941; s. Bernard A. and Marion (Toomey) McC.; children: Mark, Kerry, Kara, Megan, Maura. B.A., Siena Coll., 1963; postgrad. So. Ill. U., Carbondale, 1963-64; J.D., Fordham U. 1968. Bar: N.Y. 1969, U.S. Dist. Ct. (so. and ea. dists.) N.Y. 1971, U.S. Ct. Appeals (2d cir.) 1972, U.S. Ct. Appeals (11th cir.) 1982, U.S. Ct. Appeals (6th cir.) 1982, U.S. Supreme Ct. 1975. Assoc. Chadbourne Parke, N.Y.C., 1968-78, ptnr., 1978—. Mem. ABA, N.Y. State Bar Assn. Office: Chadbourne & Parke 30 Rockefeller Plz New York NY 10112

MCCARTHY, BRYANT, accounting firm executive; b. 1939. Student, Hamilton Coll.; MBA, Rutgers U. Ptnr. Ernst & Young, N.Y.C., 1972—, vice-chmn. internat., 1991—. Office: 787 7th Ave New York NY 10019-6018

MCCARTHY, CAROL M., health care association executive, lawyer; b. L.I., N.Y., Oct. 2, 1940; d. Valentine F. and Mary A. (Vozab) Goepfert; m. Michael P. McCarthy, Feb. 1963; children: Claire, Catherine. BA, Trinity Coll., Washington, 1962; MS, SUNY, Stony Brook, 1974; PhD, NYU, 1978, JD, Temple U., 1986. Assoc. dir. Nassau-Suffolk Regional Med. Ctr., Centerreach, N.Y., 1974-76; exec. v.p., chief exec. officer Nassau-Suffolk Hosp. Coun., Melville, N.Y., 1976-78; pres. Delaware Valley Hosp. Coun., Phila., 1978-85, Delaware Valley Health Edn. & Research Found., 1980-85, Mass. Hosp. Assn., Burlington, 1985-86, Am. Hosp. Assn., Chgo., 1986-91; ptnr. Ober, Kaler, Grimes and Shriver, Washington and Balt., 1991—; mem. spl. med. adv. group VA. Office: Ober Kaler Grimes & Shriver 120 E Baltimore St Baltimore MD 21202-1643

MC CARTHY, CHARLES JOSEPH, lawyer, former government official; b. Providence, June 19, 1907; s. John Francis and Mary Elizabeth (Quinn) McC.; m. Gladys Christina McGrail; children: Helen Jacquelyn (Mrs. James F. Hickey), Barbara Ann (Mrs. John J. McCooe), Cormac, William Bernard, Maryellen (Mrs. James A. Jaques III), Dennis Michael. A.B. Providence Coll., 1927; LL.B., Yale U., 1930. Bar: N.Y 1932, R.I 1933, Tenn. 1934, D.C. 1968, U.S. Supreme Ct. 1935. Pvt. practice N.Y.C., 1930-32, Providence, 1932-34; atty. RFC 1934; legal staff TVA, 1934-67, gen. counsel, 1958-67; prin. McCarthy, Sweeney and Harkaway, P.C. (and predecessor firms), Washington, 1968-86; counsel McCarthy, Sweeney and Harkaway, P.C., 1986—; spl. asst. to atty. gen. Dept. Justice, 1938-39. Co-author: A Study of the Electric Power Situation in New England, 1970-1990, Transportation Deregulation, 1986; also articles. Mem. Fed. Bar Assn., D.C. Bar Assn. Home: 3709 S George Mason Dr 306E Falls Church VA 22041 Office: 1750 Pennsylvania Ave NW Washington DC 20006-4502

MCCARTHY, CHARLES RICHARD, lawyer; b. Tully, N.Y., Sept. 22, 1938; s. Charles Richard and Dorothy (Desmond) McC.; m. Susan Esther McCann, Aug. 19, 1961; children: Kelly M., Kevin C., Maura E., Ellen M., Brendan D. BS, LeMoyne Coll., 1960; JD, Georgetown U., 1965. Bar: D.C. Law clk. to Hon. Edward A. Beard Washington, 1964-65; atty. Wyatt, Saltzstein & Moore, Washington, 1965-66; dep. adminstr. criminal justice activities D.C. Superior Ct., Washington, 1966-67; asst. counsel D.C. Office Corp. Counsel, Washington, 1967-68; trial atty. SEC, Washington, 1968-70; atty. Schramm Raddue & Seed, Washington, 1970-75; ptnr. Schramm, Raddue, Seed & McCarthy, Washington, 1977-78; prof. law George Mason Sch. Law., Washington, 1975-77; mng. ptnr. Dunaway, McCarthy & Dye, P.C., Washington, 1978-84; head corp. law dept. Venable, Baetjer, Howard & Civiletti, Washington, 1984-85; mng. ptnr. McCarthy & Durrette, P.C., Washington, 1985-88, McCarthy, Steele & Burek, Washington, 1988—; Blue Sky commnr. for D.C.; 1970; gen. counsel GRC Internat., 1983—, Nat. Assn. Corp. Dirs., 1991—; bd. dirs. Flow General, McLean, Va. Active Hope No. Va., 1970-85, Cath. Charities Arlington, 1985-90, Marymount U., Arlington, 1975-87, chmn. bd. dirs., 1986-87; active Rep. Party Va. Mem. ABA, D.C. Bar Assn., Burning Tree Club, Washington Golf and Country Club, Friendly Sons St. Patrick (Washington), Barristers (Washington), Melrose Club (Hilton Head Island, S.C.). Roman Catholic. Office: 1220 19th St NW Ste 400 Washington DC 20036-2405

MCCARTHY, CORMAC (CHARLES MCCARTHY, JR.), writer; b. Providence, R.I., July 20, 1933; s. Charles Joseph and Gladys (McGrail) McC.; m. Lee Holleman, 1961 (div.); 1 child, Cullen; m. Anne deLisle, 1967 (div.). Author: (novels) The Orchard Keeper, 1965 (William Faulkner Found. award 1965), Outer Dark, 1968, Child of God, 1974, Suttree, 1979, Blood Meridian, or The Evening Redness in the West, 1985, All the Pretty Horses, 1992 (Nat. Book award for fiction 1992, Nat. Book Critics Circle award for fiction 1993), The Crossing, 1994; (teleplays) The Gardner's Son, 1977; (plays) The Stonemason: A Play in Five Acts, 1994. Ingram-Merrill Found. creative writing grantee, 1960, Am. Acad. Arts and Letter traveling fellow, 1965-66, Rockefeller Found. grantee, 1966, Guggenheim fellow, 1976, MacArthur Found. grantee, 1981; recipient Jean Stein award Am. Acad. and Inst. Arts and Letters, 1991. Office: c/o Alfred A. Knopf 201 E 50th St New York NY 10022-7703

MC CARTHY, D. JUSTIN, college president; b. Brockton, Mass.; s. Denis Joseph and Jane Vincent (Dempsey) McC.; m. Rose Mary Hoye; children: Daniel Justin, Rosemary, John Emmet, Vincent Joseph. B.S., Bridgewater State Coll., 1938, Ed.M., 1939; Ed.D., Harvard U., 1955; LL.D. (hon.), Framingham State Coll., 1985. Tchr., prin. Hanover (Mass.) Pub. Schs.; tchr., asst. prin. Belmont (Mass.) Elem. Schs.; dean instrn. U. Maine, Farmington, 1947-48; extension lectr. U. Maine, Orono, 1947-48; supr. student teaching U. Mass. at Amherst, 1948-55; supr. edn., asst. dir. div. state colls. Mass. State Colls., 1955-56, dir. div. state colls., 1956-61; pres. Framingham (Mass.) State Coll., 1961-85; assoc. in edn. Harvard Grad. Sch. Edn., 1980-83; past sr. advisor Nat. Commn. on the Role and Future State Colls. and Univs. Contbr.: articles to profl. jours. including Harvard Educational Review. Chmn. evaluation Nat. Council Accreditation Tchr. Edn., Mass. Bd. Coll. Authority, New Eng. Assn. Colls. and Secondary Schs.; past pres. New Eng. Tchr. Prep. Assn.; mem. 1202 Commn. Higher Edn. Mass. Mem. Assn. Supervision and Curriculum Devel. (past pres.), Phi Delta Kappa, Kappa Delta Pi (hon.). Address: 302 Washington St Box 1209 Duxbury MA 02331

MC CARTHY, DANIEL CHRISTOPHER, JR., manufacturing company executive; b. St. Paul, May 10, 1924; s. Daniel Christopher and Isobel Beatrice (Wilmot) McC.; m. Gail Lloyd Allen, Mar. 9, 1951. B.Mech. Engring. with distinction, Cornell U., 1949. Mgr. profit planning Ford div. Ford Motor Co., 1949-56; dir. mfg. staff Chrysler Corp., 1956-58; controller Chrysler Internat. Geneva, Switzerland, 1958-59; exec. v.p. Pratt & Whitney Co., 1959-61, pres., 1961-64; v.p. bus. equipment group Litton Industries, Orange, N.J., 1964-65; pres. Monroe Internat., Inc. div., 1965-67; founder, v.p., dir. Keene Corp., 1967-74; founder, pres. Gale Corp., 1974-80; founder, chmn. Porta-Feps Corp., 1980-88, Norwood Mfg. Corp., 1980-88; pres., sole proprietor Gale Assocs., cons. and investments, Montclair, N.J., 1982—; founder, dir. Am. Mobile Systems, Inc., 1982-90; cons., dir. JJI Lighting Group Inc., 1980—; M.H. Koomey subs. Maritime Group, AS, 1991-93; gen. ptnr. Fiduciary Capital Mgmt., L.P., 1989—; founder, vice chmn.

Glenco Holdings Inc., 1992-94. Mem. Cornell U. Council. Served with inf. AUS, 1942-46. Mem. ASME, Tau Beta Pi, Phi Kappa Phi, Pi Tau Sigma, Psi Upsilon. Home and Office: Gale Assocs 78 Lloyd Rd Montclair NJ 07042-1729

MCCARTHY, DAVID JEROME, JR., legal educator; b. Hartford, Conn., July 19, 1935; s. David Jerome and Flora Emily (Edmondo) McC.; m. Mary Elizabeth McGlynn, Aug. 13, 1960; children: Emilie Anne, Mary Theresa, Carolyn Elizabeth, Katherine Margaret. AB cum laude, Fairfield (Conn.) U., 1957; LLB, Georgetown U., 1960, LLM, 1962, LLD (hon.), 1983. Bar: Conn. 1960, D.C. 1962. Law clk. U.S. Ct. Appeals D.C. Cir., 1960-61; law clk. to Judge John A. Danaher, 1961-62; atty. Appellate sect. civil div. U.S. Dept. Justice, Washington, 1962-63; dir. D.C. Bail Project, 1963-65; adj. prof. law Georgetown U., 1964-65, assoc. prof., 1965-68, prof., 1968—, asst. dean, 1965-68, assoc. dean, 1968-70, dean, 1975-83, exec. v.p. Law Ctr. Affairs, 1975-83, mem. adv. bd. Health Policy Inst., 1982-88; chmn. exec. com. D.C. Pretrial Services Agy., 1966-87 ; mem. exec. com. Assn. Am. Law Schs., 1981-83, chmn. accreditation com., 1984-86, chmn. accreditation regulations rev. com., 1986-90; mem. Nat. Chamber Found. Task Force on Products Liability, 1978-81; chmn. Nat. Commn. on Taxes and the IRS, 1979-81; mem. Joint Com. on Clin. Legal Edn. Guidelines, Am. Bar Assn.-Am. Assn. Law Schs., 1977-80, Gov.'s Commn. for Modernization of Md. Exec. Br., 1966-67; counsel Md. Gov.'s Fiscal Rev. Com., 1984-86; mem. adv. bd. Nat. Inst. for Citizen Edn. in Law, 1976-86. Author: Local Government Law in a Nutshell, 1975, 3d edit., 1990; co-author: Local Government Law: Cases and Materials, 4sh edit., 1992, supplement, 1995; contbr. articles to profl. jours., chpts. to books. Chmn. bd. dirs. Jesuit Internat. Vols., 1986-89. Recipient Profl. Achievement award Fairfield U. Alumni, 1965, 83. Mem. Am. Law Inst. Democrat. Roman Catholic. Home: 12612 Orchard Brook Ter Potomac MD 20854-2326 Office: Georgetown U Law Ctr 600 New Jersey Ave NW Washington DC 20001-2022

MCCARTHY, DENIS, artist, educator; b. N.Y.C., Feb. 21, 1935; s. Patrick and Carmel (Mulvany) McC. Cert. in fine art, The Cooper Union, 1963; B.F.A., Yale U., 1966, M.F.A., 1966. Instr. in drawing Sch. Visual Art, N.Y.C., 1967-72, NYU, 1976-78; prof. fine art Hunter Coll., N.Y.C., 1971—; vis. lectr. Fordham U., Md. Inst., 1979. One-man shows include: Stable Gallery, N.Y.C., 1970, 55 Mercer Gallery, N.Y.C., 1978, N.Y. State Coll., Old Westbury, 1980; exhibited in group shows: Stable Gallery, 1969, Whitney Mus., N.Y.C., 1969, Reese Palley, N.Y.C., 1970, O.K. Harris, N.Y.C., 1972, Warren Benedek Gallery, N.Y.C., 1973, Whitney Mus., N.Y.C., 1973, Aldrich Mus., Ridgefield, Conn., 1973, Paula Cooper Gallery, N.Y.C., 1974, Michael Wyman Gallery, Chgo., 1974, U. Maine, Portland, 1975, Automation House, N.Y.C., 1976, Hundred Acres Gallery, N.Y.C., 1977, NYU, 1977, N.Y. Acad. Scis., 1983. Home: 147 Spring St New York NY 10012-3860

MC CARTHY, DENIS MICHAEL, investment executive; b. Hartford, Conn., Dec. 4, 1942; s. Charles J. and Mary M. (Moynihan) McC.; m. Linda Horn, Aug. 21, 1965; children: Bryan, Kerry, Kevin. B.S., U. Conn., 1964, M.A., 1965. Asst. sec. Mfrs. Hanover Trust Co., N.Y.C., 1965-68; various positions to exec. v.p., chief fin. officer Triangle Industries, Holmdel, N.J., 1968-81; sr. v.p., chief fin. officer Emery Worldwide, Wilton, Conn., 1981-84; sr. v.p., chief fin. officer Emery Worldwide, 1984-85, exec. v.p., chief oper. officer, 1985-87; pres., chief operating officer Emery Air Freight, 1987-89, also bd. dirs.; sr. v.p. adminstrn., chief fin. officer FMR Corp., 1989—; bd. dirs. Middlesex Mut. Assurance Co., Middletown, Conn. Home: 30 Whiting Rd Wellesley MA 02181-6737 Office: FMR Corp 82 Devonshire St Boston MA 02109-3614

MC CARTHY, EUGENE JOSEPH, writer, former senator; b. Watkins, Minn., Mar. 29, 1916; s. Michael John and Anna (Baden) McC.; m. Abigail Quigley, June 1945; children—Ellen, Mary, Michael, Margaret. A.B., St. John's U., Collegeville, Minn., 1935; A.M., U. of Minn., 1939. Tchr. pub. schs., 1935-40, 45; prof. econ. edn. St. John's U., 1940-42; civilian tech. work with Mil. Intelligence Div., War Dept., 1944; instr. sociology and econs. St. Thomas Coll., St. Paul, 1946-48; mem. 81st-85th Congresses from 4th Minn. dist., 1949-59, mem. ways and means com.; U.S. senator from Minn., 1959-70; mem. senate finance, fgn. relations and govt. ops. coms.; Adlai Stevenson prof. polit. sci. New Sch. for Social Research, 1973-74; syndicated columnist, 1977—; dir. Harcourt Brace Jovanovich, Inc. Author: Frontiers in American Democracy, 1960, Dictionary of American Politics, 1962, A Liberal Answer to the Conservative Challenge, 1964, The Limits of Power, 1967, The Year of the People, 1969, Other Things and The Aardvark, 1970, Up 'Til Now, 1987; also, The Hard Years, 1975, Mr. Raccoon and His Friends, 1977, America Revisited, 1978, Ground Fog and Night, 1979, The Ultimate Tyrany, 1980, Gene McCarthy's Minnesota, 1982, Complexities and Contraries: Essays of Mild Discontent, 1982, The View from Rappahannock, 1984; co-author: A Political Bestiary, 1978, Up 'Til Now, 1987, Required Reading, 1988, 89, The View from Rappahannock II, 1989, Colony of the World, 1993. Roman Catholic. Office: 271 Hawlin Rd Woodville VA 22749

MC CARTHY, FRANCIS F., construction executive. V.p. Mc Carthy Building Co., St. Louis. Office: Mc Carthy Building Co 1341 N Rock Hill Rd Saint Louis MO 63124-1441

MC CARTHY, FRANK MARTIN, surgical sciences educator; b. Olean, N.Y., Aug. 27, 1924; s. Frank Michael and Joan (Quinn) McC.; m. Julia Richmond, Nov. 24, 1949; children: Robert Lee, Joan Lee. B.S., U. Pitts., 1943, D.D.S., 1945, M.D., 1949; M.S. in Oral Surgery, Georgetown U., 1954; Sc.D. (hon.), St. Bonaventure U., 1956. Med. intern Mercy Hosp. Pitts., 1949-50; practice oral surgery L.A., 1954-75; teaching fellow Georgetown U., 1952-53; rsch. fellow NIH, 1953-54; prof. oral surgery U. So. Calif. Sch. Dentistry, 1966-75, prof., chmn. sect. anesthesia and medicine, 1975-90, prof. emeritus, 1990—, chmn. dept. surg. scis., 1979-84, assoc. dean adminstrv. affairs, 1977-79, asst. dean hosp. affairs, 1979-84; dir. anesthesiology U.So. Calif. oral surgery sect. L.A. County Hosp., 1958-89; clin. supr., lectr. dental hygiene program Pasadena City Coll., 1992—; v.p. Am. Dental Bd. Anesthesiology, 1984-89; lectr. in field; mem. adv. panel on dentistry sect. anesthezing agts. Nat. Fire Protection Assn., 1971-79; mem. Am. Nat. Standards Com., 1974-86; cons. in field. Author: Emergencies in Dental Practice, 1967, rev., 1972, 79, Medical Emergencies in Dentistry, 1982, Safe Treatment of the Medically Compromised Patient, 1987, Essentials of Safe Dentistry for the Medically Compromised Patient, 1989; mem. editorial bd.: Calif. Dental Assn. Jour; contbr. articles to profl. publs. Bd. councilors Sch. Dentistry, U. So. Calif., 1972-75. Served as lt., M.C. USNR, 1950-52. Fellow Internat. Assn. Oral Surgeons (founder), Am. Coll. Dentists, Internat. Coll. Dentists; mem. ADA (editorial bd. jour.), Am. Dental Soc. Anesthesiology (Heidbrink award 1977), Am. Assn. Oral-Max Surgeons (chmn. anesthesia com. 1971), So. Calif. Soc. Oral Surgeons (pres. 1974), Calif., Los Angeles County dental assns., Delta Tau Delta, Psi Omega, Phi Rho Sigma, Omicron Kappa Upsilon. Home and Office: 480 S Orange Grove Blvd Apt 11 Pasadena CA 91105-1720

MCCARTHY, G. DANIEL, lawyer; b. Butte, Mont., Mar. 23, 1949; s. George Denis and Mary Agnes (Kiely) McC.; m. Carolyn M. Scully, June 19, 1976; children: Brendan, Katie, Kelly, Sean. BA, U. Dayton, 1971; JD, U. Notre Dame, 1974; AMP, Harvard U., 1994. Bar: Md. 1974, D.C. 1975, U.S. Ct. Appeals (D.C. cir.) 1976, Pa. 1977, N.Y. 1985, U.S. Ct. Appeals (10th cir.) 1985. Assoc. Bilger & Blair, Washington, 1974-77, 79-80; asst. U.S. atty. U.S. Dist. Ct. (ea. dist.) Pa., Phila., 1977-78; atty. Abourezk, Shack & Mendenhall, Washington, 1980-83; atty. AT&T, N.Y.C., 1983-85; sr. v.p., gen. counsel and sec. AT&T Credit Corp., Morristown, N.J., 1985-89; sr. v.p., gen. counsel, sec., chief risk mgmt. officer AT&T Capital Corp., Morristown, 1990—; vis. lectr. Marymount Coll., Arlington, Va., 1979-83; bd. dirs. AT&T Credit Corp., AT&T Capital Ltd., NCR Credit Corp., Eaton Fin. Corp., AT&T Comml. Fin. Corp., AT&T Capital Svcs. Corp., AT&T Systems Leasing Corp., AT&T Capital Holdings Internat. Inc. Mem. ABA, D.C. Bar Assn. Avocation: golf, fly fishing. Home: 82 Van Doren Ave Chatham NJ 07928-2253 Office: AT&T Capital Corp 44 Whippany Rd Morristown NJ 07960-4558

MCCARTHY, GERALD MICHAEL, electronics executive; b. Chgo., June 13, 1941; s. John and Hannah (Naughton) McC.; m. Margaret-Mary O'Neill, June 20, 1964; children: John, Michael, Gerald Jr., Kevin. BS, Loyola U., Chgo., 1963; MBA, U. Chgo., 1976. Order dept. rep. Zenith

Electronics Corp., Chgo., 1965-66, supr. sales plans, 1967-69, asst. mgr. product devel. TV, 1970-71, product mgr. B&W TV, 1971-72, nat. sales tng. mgr., 1972-74, dir. TV product planning, 1974-79, v.p. sales western div., 1979-82, exec. v.p. sales-consumer products, 1982-83; pres. Zenith Sales Co., Chgo., 1983—, Zenith Radio Can., Ltd., 1983—; corp. sr. v.p., mem. office of the pres. Zenith Electronics Corp., Chgo., 1991; corp. exec. v.p. Zenith Electronics Corp., 1993—; also bd. dirs. Zenith Electronics Corp., Glenview, Ill., 1992. Trustee Resurrection Health Care Corp., Chgo., 1983—. Jr. Achievement Chgo., 1983—. Served to 1st lt. U.S. Army, 1963-65. Mem. Electronics Industries Assn. (bd. govs. 1983—). Avocations: fishing, golf. Home: 1745 Dartmouth Ln Deerfield IL 60015-3946 Office: Zenith Electronics Corp 1000 Milwaukee Ave Glenview IL 60025-2423

MC CARTHY, HAROLD CHARLES, retired insurance company executive; b. Madelia, Minn., Dec. 5, 1926; s. Charles and Merle (Humphry) McC.; m. Barbara Kaercher, June 24, 1949; children: David, Susan. B.A., Carleton Coll., Northfield, Minn., 1950; postgrad. With Federated Mut. Ins. Co., Owatonna, Minn., 1950-67; with Meridian Mut. Ins. Co., Indpls., 1967-91; exec. v.p., then exec. v.p., gen. mgr. Meridian Mut. Ins. Co., 1972-75, pres., 1975-90, bd. dirs., past chmn. bd., 1990-91; past pres. North Meridian Bus. Group; past pres., chmn. bd. Meridian Ins. Group, Inc.; chmn. bd., dir. Meridian Life Ins. Co.; past chmn., exec. com., bd. dirs. Ind. Ins. Inst. Former mem. Met. Devel. Commn., Corp. Community Council; bd. dirs. Meth. Health Found., Family Services Assn., Boy Scouts Am.; trustee Butler U. With USNR, 1944-46. Named Sagamore of the Wabash. Mem. Nat. Assn. Ind. Insurers (past chmn. bd. govs.) Indpls. C. of C. (bd. dirs.), Ind. C of C. (bd. dirs.), Skyline Club, Reserve Golf & Tennis Club. Republican. Methodist. Office: 2955 N Meridian St Indianapolis IN 46208-4788

MCCARTHY, J. THOMAS, lawyer, educator; b. Detroit, July 2, 1937; s. John E. and Virginia M. (Hanlon) McC.; m. Nancy Irene Orrell, July 10, 1976. BS, U. Detroit, 1960; JD, U. Mich., 1963. Bar: Calif. 1964. Assoc. Julian Caplan, San Francisco, 1963-66; prof. law U. San Francisco, 1966—; vis. prof. law Univ. Coll., Dublin, summer 1975; vis. prof. law U. Calif., Berkeley, 1976-77, Davis, 1979-80; vis. prof. law Monash U., Melbourne, Australia, 1985; cons. in field; mem. Trademark Rev. Commn., 1986-88. Author: McCarthy on Trademarks and Unfair Competition, 4 vols., 3d edit., 1992; (with Oppenheim and Weston) Federal Antitrust Laws, 1981, McCarthy on Rights of Publicity and Privacy, 1987, McCarthy's Desk Encyclopedia of Intellectual Property, 1991; mem. editorial bd. Trademark Reporter. Recipient Rossman award Patent Office Soc., 1979, Jefferson medal N.J. Intellectual Property Assn., 1994. Mem. Am. Intellectual Property Law Assn. (Watson award 1965), Internat. Assn. for Advancement of Teaching and Rsch. in Intellectual Property, Am. Law Inst. (adv. com. on restatement of law of unfair competition), IEEE.

MCCARTHY, JAMES, sociology researcher, educator. AB in Sociology, Coll. Holy Cross, 1971; MA in Sociology, Ind. U., 1972; PhD in Sociology, Princeton U., 1977. Rsch. assoc. Office Population Rsch. Princeton (N.J.) U., 1977-79; asst. prof. population dynamics and sociology Johns Hopkins U., Balt., 1979-82, assoc. prof., 1982-88, dir. Hopkins Population Ctr., 1984-88; assoc. prof. pub. health Columbia U., N.Y.C., 1988-91, prof. pub. health, 1991—, dir. Ctr. for Population and Family Health, 1988—; cons. UN Fund for Population Activities, 1979, East-West Population Inst., 1979, UN Population Divsn., 1980, World Fertility Survey, 1980, USAID, 1984, 85, NIMH, 1986, NAS, 1987, The World Bank, 1991, U. Mich., 1988-94, Nat. Inst. Child Health and Human Devel., 1991-92, Alan Guttmacher Inst., 1993— Kuwait U., 1993—, others; grant reviewer NIH, 1983, 84, 85, NSF, 1985, Dept. Health and Human Svcs., 1982, 84, Andrew Mellon Found., 1993, Klingenstein Fund, 1993; presenter papers to numerous confs. Manuscript reviewer for numerous jours.; contbr. articles to profl. jours. Mem. APHA, Population Assn. Am. (chair subcom. fertility stats. 1984-85), Internat. Union for Sci. Study of Population. Office: Columbia U Ctr Population & Family Health 60 Haven Ave Level B-3 New York NY 10032

MCCARTHY, JAMES JOSEPH, oceanography educator, museum director; b. Ashland, Oreg., Jan. 25, 1944; m. 1969, 2 children. B.S., Gonzaga U., 1966; Ph.D., Scripps Inst. Oceanography, U. Calif.-San Diego, 1971. Research assoc. biol. oceanography Chesapeake Bay Inst., Johns Hopkins U., 1971-72, assoc. research scientist, 1972-74; asst. prof. Harvard U., 1974-77, assoc. prof., 1977-80, prof. biol. oceanography, 1980—, assoc. dean faculty Arts and Scis., 1986-90; dir. Agassiz Mus. Comparative Zoology, 1982—. Editor: Global Biogeochemical Cycles, 1986-90. Past chmn. Internat. Coun. of Scientific Unions, Scientific Com. Internat. Geosphere-Biosphere Program, 1987—. Fellow AAAS, Am. Acad. Arts and Scis.; mem. Phycol. Soc. Am., Am. Soc. Limnology and Oceanography, Am. Geophys. Union. Office: Mus Comparative Zoology 26 Oxford St Cambridge MA 02138-2902

MCCARTHY, JOHN, computer scientist, educator; b. Boston, Sept. 4, 1927; s. Patrick Joseph and Ida McC.; children: Susan Joanne, Sarah Kathleen, Timothy Talcott. B.S., Calif. Inst. Tech., 1948; Ph.D., Princeton U., 1951. Instr. Princeton U., 1951-53; acting asst. prof. math. Stanford U., 1953-55; asst. prof. Dartmouth Coll., 1955-58; asst. and asso. prof. communications scis. M.I.T., Cambridge, 1958-62; prof. computer sci. Stanford U., 1962—, Charles M. Pigott prof. Sch. Engring., 1987—; dir. Stanford U. Artificial Intelligence Lab., 1965-80. Info. Internat. Inc. Served with AUS, 1945-46. Recipient Kyoto prize, 1988, Nat. medal of Sci. NSF, 1990. Mem. NAS, NAE, Assn. for Computing Machinery (A.M. Turing award 1971), Am. Math. Soc., Am. Assn. Artificial Intelligence (pres. 1983-84). Home: 885 Allardice Way Stanford CA 94305-1050 Office: Stanford U Dept Computer Sci Stanford CA 94305

MCCARTHY, JOHN B., veterinarian, veterinary association executive; b. Mt. Kisco, N.Y., Jan. 14, 1931; m. Ruth J. McCarthy; children: Karen Constantino, Heidi Roy. Student, NYU, 1946-48; DVM, Cornell U., 1952; MBA, L.I. U., 1989. Cert. assn. exec. Owner Animal Hosp., Carmel, N.Y., 1954-62; pres., co-owner County Animal Hosp., Inc., New City, N.Y., 1962-85; exec. assoc. dean Sch. Vet. Med. Ross U., 1985-89; sr. program specialist govtl. rels. divsn. AVMA, Washington, 1990-94; exec. dir. Nat. Academies of Practice, Washington, 1995—; mem. Nat. Conf. on Ecology Surplus Dog and Cat Problem, 1974; co-chair steering com. N.Y. State Workshop on Pet Population, 1975; adj. prof. vet. tech. Mercy Coll., Dobbs Ferry, N.Y., 1984-87; speaker in field. Author: Basic Guide to Veterinary Hospital Management, 1992; editor: Planning Your Veterinary Career, 1988; contbr. articles to profl. jours. Bd. dirs. Rockland County Ctr. for Physically Handicapped, 1975-86, chmn., 1980-82; chmn. bd. Chelsea Landing Land Owners Condominium Assn., 1993—; mem. sch. bd. Carmel. Ctrl. Sch. Dist., 1959-62; bd. dirs. Am. Red Cross, 1963-65; mem. adminstrv. bd. New City United Meth. Ch., 1965-80. 1st lt. vet. svc. USAF, 1952-54. Recipient Merit cert. N.Y. State Humane Assn., 1977. Mem. AVMA (ho. dels. 1984-87), ASAE (legis. summit com. 1993-94), Am. Animal Hosp. Assn. (bd. dirs. 1976-85, pres 1983-84, Appreciation award 1984, 87, 93, 94), Nat. Acad. Practice in Vet. Medicine of Nat. Acads. Practice (founder, disting. practitioner), Am. Soc. Assn. Execs., Am. League Lobbyists, Small Bus. Legis. Coun. (rep.), N.Y. State Vet. Medicine Soc. (pres. 1974, Veterinarian of Yr. award 1980), Westchester Rockalnd Vet. Med. Assn. (pres. 1965), Rotary (Washington chpt., pres. Mahopac-Carmel chpt. 1960-61, New City chpt., 1973-74, hon. mem., Paul Harris fellow 1976), Rotary Internat. (chmn. com. dist. 721, 1984-86, chmn. dist. 7620, 1992-93), Delta Mu Delta. Office: Nat Acad of Prac 1511 K St NW Ste 327 Washington DC 20005-1401

MC CARTHY, JOHN EDWARD, bishop; b. Houston, June 21, 1930; s. George Gaskell and Grace Veronica (O'Brien) McC. Student, St. Mary's Sem., Houston, 1949-56; M.A., St. Thomas U., Houston, 1979. Ordained priest Roman Catholic Ch., 1956; served various Houston Cath. parishes; exec. dir. Nat. Bishops Com. for Spanish speaking, 1966-68; asst. dir. Social Action Office, U.S. Cath. Conf., 1967-69; exec. dir. Tex. Cath. Conf., Houston, 1973-79; ordained aux. bishop Diocese of Galveston-Houston, 1979-86; installed third bishop of Austin, 1986—; bd. dirs. Nat. Center for Urban Ethnic Affairs, Mexican-Am. Cultural Center, Sisters of Charity of the Incarnate Word, Houston, from 1981, St. Thomas U., Houston from 1980. Mem. Cath. Conf. for Urban Ministry. Democrat. Office: PO Box 13327 Austin TX 78711-3327

MCCARTHY, JOHN RUSSELL, photographic company executive; b. Nyack, N.Y., Jan. 28, 1931; s. Russell Chester and Daisy (Lillie) McC.; m.

Joanna Steinkamp, June 20, 1953; children—Laura Ann, Kathy, Molly, Amy, Ellen. B.S., Cornell U., 1953. Mem. employment staff Eastman Kodak Co., Rochester, N.Y., 1953-62, personnel dir., 1962-75, dir. indsl. relations, 1975-82, sr. v.p. corp. relations, 1982—; bd. dirs. Monroe Savs. Bank, Eastman Kodak. Bd. dirs. Monroe Community Coll., Rochester, 1982—; mem. Indsl. Mgmt. Council, Rochester, 1970—; bd. dirs. Family Service of Am., N.Y.C., 1984—, Exec. Service Corp., Rochester, 1985, Rochester Jobs Inc., 1983—. Served to 1st lt. Med. Service Corps., U.S. Army, 1953-55. Republican. Presbyterian. Club: Monroe Golf (Pittsford, N.Y.). Avocations: golf; gardening; reading. Home: 830 Mendon Rd Pittsford NY 14534-9783 Office: Eastman Kodak Co 343 State St Rochester NY 14650-0001

MCCARTHY, JOHN THOMAS, diplomat; b. N.Y.C., Dec. 27, 1939; s. John T. and Elizabeth Rose (Kaffenburger) McC.; m. Barbara Wiest, July 4, 1962 (dec. Oct. 1971); children—John T. III, Elizabeth; m. Marija Pavlovich, July 19, 1975; 1 child, Julia Mara. B.A., Manhattan Coll., 1961; M.P.A., Harvard U., 1973. Econ. counselor U.S. Mission to EEC, Brussels, Belgium, 1976-80; dir. office investment Dept. State, Washington, 1980-83; dep. asst. sec. Dept. State, 1983—; dep. chief of mission Am. Embassy, Islamabad, Pakistan, 1985-88; U.S. ambassador to Lebanon, 1988-91, U.S. ambassador to Tunisia, Tunis, 1991—. Office: Am Embassy Dept of State Washington DC 20521-6360

MCCARTHY, JOSEPH GERALD, plastic surgeon, educator; b. Lowell, Mass., Nov. 28, 1938; s. Joseph H. and Eva (Murphy) McC.; m. Karlan von L. Sloan, June 6, 1964; children: Cara, Stephen. A.B., Harvard U., 1960; M.D., Columbia U., 1964. Diplomate: Am. Bd. Surgery, Am. Bd. Plastic Surgery. Surg. intern and resident Columbia-Presbyn. Med. Ctr.; resident in plastic surgery NYU Med. Ctr., N.Y.C., 1964-73; Lawrence D. Bell prof. plastic surgery NYU Sch. Medicine, N.Y.C., 1981—; dir. NYU Med. Ctr. Inst. Reconstructive Plastic Surgery; attending physician Univ. Hosp.; vis. plastic surgeon Bellevue Hosp.; attending surgeon Manhattan Eye, Ear and Throat Hosp., N.Y.C. VA Hosp. Editor: Symposium on Diagnosis and Treatment of Craniofacial Anomalies, 1979, Plastic Surgery, 1990; assoc. editor Reconstructive Plastic Surgery, 1977, Jour. Plastic and Reconstructive Surgery, Jour. Craniofacial, Genetics and Developmental Biology. Served to lt. comdr. USPHS, 1965-67. Recipient Columbia U. Joseph Garrison Parker prize, 1964, James Barret Brown prize, 1991, 1st prize Plastic Surgery Edn. Found., 1980, Am. Soc. Maxillofacial Surgeons first prize, 1991, 93, 94; named Am. Cancer Soc. fellow Presbyn. Hosp., N.Y.C., 1969-70, prin. investigator NIH, 1974. Fellow ACS; mem. Am. Soc. Plastic and Reconstructive Surgeons, Assn. Acad. Chmns. Plastic Surgery (pres. 1988-89), N.Y. Regional Soc. Plastic and Reconstructive Surgeons (pres. 1984-85), Am. Assn. Plastic Surgeons (historian 1990—), Internat. Assn. Craniomaillofacial Surgeons (pres. 1989-91). Office: NYU Med Ctr Univ Hosp 550 1st Ave New York NY 10016-6402

MCCARTHY, JOSEPH HAROLD, consultant, former retail food company executive; b. Derby, Conn., Dec. 21, 1921; s. Joseph Harold and Kathryn (Feeley) McC.; m. Jean K. Ryan, June 7, 1947; children: Timothy J., Maureen, Barbara, Richard, Joseph Harold. B.S. in Econs., Villanova U., 1944. Sr. v.p. First Nat. Stores Inc., Boston, 1947-76, Grand Union Co., Elmwood Park, N.J., 1976-80; exec. v.p., chief oper. officer Great Atlantic and Pacific Tea Co., Inc., Montvale, N.J., 1980-90, ret., 1990; cons. Great Atlantic and Pacific Tea Co., Inc., North Chatham, Mass., 1990-92. Served to capt. USMC, 1943-46, PTO; served to capt. USMC, 1951-52, Korea. Home: 2030 Imperial Golf C Blvd Naples FL 33942 Office: 38 Captains Walk North Chatham MA 02650-1041

MC CARTHY, JOSEPH MICHAEL, historian, educator; b. Lynn, Mass., Oct. 2, 1940; s. Joseph Donald and Johanna (Downing) Mc C.; AB, St. John's Sem., 1961, postgrad., 1961-63; AM, Boston Coll., 1968, PhD, 1972; m. Kathleen Frances Wright, July 30, 1966; children: Joanna, Kristenmarie, Erika, Joseph Michael. Tchr. Bishop Fenwick H.S., Peabody, Mass., 1964-67; fin. adminstr. Boston Coll., 1967-71; lectr. in edn. Boston Coll., 1971-74, vis. prof., 1990; prof. edn., dir. leadership programs Suffolk U., 1973—; adj. lectr. Merrimack Coll., 1975, Boston U., 1973; prin. Ednl. Mgmt. Svcs., 1976—; gen. editor Garland Pub., 1979-92; bd. dirs. Inst. for Study of Academia, 1992-94. Recipient Hearn scholarship, 1959-61, fellowship, 1961-63. Mem. Am. Hist. Assn., Soc. for Medieval and Renaissance Philosophy, Soc. Romanian Historians, East European Rsch. Inst., Phi Alpha Theta, Phi Delta Kappa. Author: An International List of Articles on the History of Education, 1977; Guinea-Bissau and Cape Verde Islands, 1977; Humanistic Emphases in the Educational Thought of Vincent of Beauvais, 1976; Pierre Teilhard de Chardin, 1981; assoc. editor The Urban and Social Change Rev., 1969-72; asst. editor occasional papers series The Bureaucrat, Inc., 1974-76; contbr. to numerous scholarly jours. Home: 344 West St Duxbury MA 02332-3609 Office: Suffolk U Beacon Hill Boston MA 02114

MCCARTHY, JOSEPH W., motel chain executive. Pres., chief exec. officer Motel 6 G.P., Inc., Dallas.

MCCARTHY, KAREN P., congresswoman, former state representative; b. Mass., Mar. 18, 1947. BS in English, Biology, U. Kans., 1969, MBA, 1985; MEd in English, U. Mo., Kansas City, 1976. Tchr. Shawnee Mission (Kans.) South High Sch., 1969-75, The Sunset Hill (Kans.) Sch., -, 1975-76; mem. Mo. House of Reps., Jefferson City, Mo., 1977-95; cons. govt. affairs Marion Labs., Kansas City, Mo., 1986-93; congresswoman. Mo. 5th Dist. U.S. Congress, Washington, D.C., 1995—; rsch. analyst pub. fin. dept. Stearn Bros. & Co., 1984-85, Kansas City, Mo.; rsch. analyst Midwest Rsch. Inst., econs. and mgmt. scis. dept., Kansas City, 1985-86. Del. Dem. Nat. Conv., 1992, Dem. Nat. Party Conf., 1982, Dem. Nat. Policy Com. Policy Commn., 1985-86; community advisor The Jr. League of Kansas City, 1980-88; spl. adviser Genesis Sch. Recipient Outstanding Young Woman Am. award, 1977, Outstanding Woman Mo. award Phi Chi Theta, Civil Liberties award ACLU of Western Mo., 1983, Woman of Achievement award mid-continent coun. Girl Scouts U.S., 1983, 87, MOVA award, Mo. Victiom Assistance Network, 1988, Annie Baxter award, 1993; named Conservation Legislator of Yr., Conservation Fed. Mo., 1987. Fellow Inst. of Politics; mem. Nat. Conf. on State Legis. (del. on trade and econ. devel. to Fed. Republic of Germany, Bulgaria, Japan, France and Italy, mem. energy com. 1978-84, fed. taxation, trade and econ. devel. com. 1986, chmn. fed. budget and taxation com. 1987, vice chmn. state fed. assembly 1988, pres.-elect 1993), Nat. Dem. Inst. for Internat. Affairs (instr. No. Ireland 1988, Baltic Republics 1992, Hungary 1993). Office: US House Reps 2334 Rayburn House Office Bldg Washington DC 20515-2505

MC CARTHY, KATHRYN A., physicist; b. Lawrence, Mass., Aug. 7, 1924; d. Joseph Augustine and Catherine (Barrett) McCarthy. A.B., Tufts U., 1945, M.S., 1946; Ph.D., Radcliffe Coll., 1957; D.Sc. (hon.), Coll. Holy Cross, 1978; D.H.L. (hon.), Merrimack Coll., 1981. Instr. physics Tufts U., 1946-53, asst. prof., 1953-59, assoc. prof., 1959-62, prof., 1962—; dean Tufts U. (Grad. Sch.), 1969-74, provost, sr. v.p., 1973-79; research fellow in metallurgy Harvard, 1957-59, vis. scholar, 1979-80; research assoc. Baird Assocs., 1947-49, 51, Boston U. Optical Research Lab., summer 1952; assoc. research engr. U. Mich., summer 1957-58; dir. Mass. Electric Co., State Mut. Assurance Co. Trustee Southeastern Mass. U., 1972-74, Merrimack Coll., 1974-83, Coll. Holy Cross, 1980—; corporator Lawrence Meml. Hosp., 1975—, 1978—, chmn., 1991. Fellow Optical Soc., Am. Phys. Soc.; mem. Soc. Women Engrs. (sr.), Phi Beta Kappa, Sigma Xi. Roman Catholic. Home: 1580 Massachusetts Ave Apt 5D Cambridge MA 02138-2926 Office: Tufts U Dept Physics 4 Colby St Medford MA 02155-6013

MCCARTHY, KEVIN JOHN, lawyer; b. N.Y.C., Apr. 8, 1941; s. Vincent Patrick and Mary (H.) McC.; m. Marianne Pitts, Nov. 5, 1966; children: Mary Rita, Kevin, Colin. BS, U. Md., 1963; JD, U. Md. Balt., 1966. Bar: Md. 1966, U.S. Dist. Ct. Md. 1966, U.S. Ct. Appeals (4th cir.) 1966, U.S. Supreme Ct. 1972, D.C. 1976, U.S. Dist. Ct. D.C. 1976, U.S. Ct. Appeals (D.C. cir.) 1976. Law clk. Cir. Ct. for P.G. County, Upper Marlboro, Md., 1964-66; assoc., ptnr. Sasscer, Clagett & Channing, Upper Marlboro, Md., 1966-76; ptnr. O'Malley, Miles & McCarthy, Upper Marlboro, Md., 1976-86, McCarthy, Bacon & Costello, Landover, Md., 1986—; arbitrator Am. Arbitration Assn., Washington, 1972—. Contbg. author: Maryland Civil Patter Jury Instructions, 1975, 2d edit., 1984, 3d edit., 1993. Named The Best Lawyers in Am., Woodward/White. Fellow Am. Bar Found., Md. Bar

Found.; mem. Internat. Assn. Ins. Counsel, Fedn. Ins. and Corp. Counsel, Def. Rsch. Inst., Am. Trial Lawyers Assn., Md. Trial Lawyers Assn., Assn. Def. Trial Attys. Avocations: golf, racquetball, coaching soccer and lacrosse. Office: McCarthy Bacon & Costello 4640 Forbes Blvd Lanham Seabrook MD 20706

MCCARTHY, KEVIN JOSEPH, academic dean, music educator; b. Lakewood, Ohio, July 24, 1938; s. John Joseph and Ruth Hazel (Leary) McC.; m. Maureen Marilyn Spellacy, May 25, 1966; children: Michaela, Mary, Matthew. B in Music Edn., U. Notre Dame, 1960; MusM, Mich. State U., 1961; PhD in Music Edn., Case Western Res. U., 1969. Cert. elem. and secondary tchr., Colo. Dir. music dept. Chanel High Sch., Bedford, Ohio, 1961-62, St. John Coll., Cleve., 1962-66, Roxboro Jr. High Sch. and Cleveland Heights High Sch., Cleve., 1966-67; music dir., prof. Fairmont (W.Va.) State Coll., 1967-69; assoc. prof., assoc. dean music U. Colo., 1969—. Editor Cultural Resource Guide for Colo. Tchrs. (U.S. Dept. Edn.), 1985; contbr. articles on music research to profl. jours. Pres. Boulder (Colo.) Assembly on Arts 1976-79; participator in KGNU-FM Radio weekly classical music show, 1979-80; dir. various ch. choirs. Recipient Disting. Svc. award Nat. Alliance Arts Edn. Kennedy Ctr. Washington, 1985, Van Gogh Arts award Jefferson County, Colo., 1986. Mem. Colo. Alliance Arts Edn. (chmn. 1983-86), Colo. Music Educators Assn. (editor jour. 1970-80, editorial svc. award 1980, pres. 1980-82, Disting. Svc. award 1982).

MCCARTHY, LEO TARCISIUS, state lieutenant governor; b. Auckland, N.Z., Aug. 15, 1930; came to U.S., 1934, naturalized, 1942; s. Daniel and Nora Teresa (Roche) McC.; m. Jacqueline Lee Burke, Dec. 17, 1955; children: Sharon, Conna, Adam, Niall. BS, U. San Francisco, 1955; JD, San Francisco Law Sch., 1961. Bar: Calif. 1963. Supr. Bd. of Supr., San Francisco, 1964-68; assemblyman Calif. State Legislature, Sacramento, 1969-82, assembly speaker, 1974-80; lt. gov. State of Calif., Sacramento, 1983—; Democratic nominee U.S. Senate, 1988. Chmn. Econ. Devel. Commn. of Calif., 1983—; chmn. State Lands Commn., 1989—; regent U. Calif., 1983—; trustee State Coll. and Univ. System, Calif., 1983—; mem. Dem. State Cen. Com., 1969—. With USAF, 1951-52. Roman Catholic. Office: Office of Lt Gov St Capitol Rm 1114 Sacramento CA 95814 *After years of public service, one lesson has become clear all the time: that no one who serves the public, and no institution dedicated to that purpose, is ever bigger than the individuals for whom that service is performed. Any official or governmental body which ceases to care about the plight of the individual citizen no longer fulfills its purpose.*

MCCARTHY, MARK FRANCIS, lawyer; b. Boston, July 8, 1951; s. William Alfred and Martha Louise (Blodgett) McC.; m. Karen Marie Umerley; children: Kevin Francis, Daniel Henry. AB in Theology, Georgetown U., 1973, JD, 1976. Bar: Ohio 1976. Assoc. Sweeney, Mahon, & Vlad, Cleve., 1976-80; ptnr. Arter & Hadden, Cleve., 1980—; atty. asst. to bd. pres. Bd. Cuyahoga County Commrs., Cleve., 1976-80; adj. prof. Case Western Reserve Law Ctr., Cleve., 1986—. Mem. Greater Cleve. Growth Assn. Leadership Cleve., 1979-80; trustee Parmadale, Parma, Ohio. Mem. Ohio Assn. Civil Trial Attys. (chmn. product liability sect. 1989—), Fedn. Ins. & Corp. Counsel, Ct. of Nisi Prius, Rowfant Club, Cleve. Athletic Club. Democrat. Roman Catholic. Avocations: book collecting, fly fishing, upland shooting. Home: 404 Regatta Dr Avon Lake OH 44012 Office: Arter & Hadden 1100 Huntington Bldg 925 Euclid Cleveland OH 44115

MCCARTHY, MARY ANN BARTLEY, electrical engineer; b. Drummond, Okla., Nov. 27, 1923; d. William Clifford and Estella Florence (Williams) Bartley; m. Joseph Manderfield McCarthy, Aug. 23, 1946 (dec. 1983); 1 child, Mary Ann McCarthy Morales. BEE, B of Material Sci., U. Calif., Berkeley, 1976. Aircraft radio technician U.S. Civil Svc., San Antonio and Honolulu, 1942-46; salesperson Sears Roebuck & Co., Enid, Okla., 1954-56; specialist reliability enging. Lockheed Corp., Sunnyvale, Calif., 1977-82, program responsible parts engr., 1986-93 (ret.); rsch. engr. Lockheed Corp., Austin, Tex., 1982-86; presenter 9th Internat. Conf. Women Engrs. and Scientists U. Warwick, Eng., 1991. Contbr. articles to profl. jours. Vol. sci. coord. U. Calif. Berkeley Extension-4H Series Excel, 1991-95, bd. dirs. sci. and youth, 1994—. Fellow Soc. Women Engrs. (sr. life mem., pres. S.W. Tex. chpt. 1984, counsel reps. sec. 1985, pres. Santa Clara Valley chpt. 1986-87, nat. v.p. 1987-88, 88-89, chmn. nat. career guidance 1988-89, coord. 1990-91, counsel sect. rep 1991-92, coord. Resnik Challenger medal 1990-91, 91-92, 92-93); mem. AAUW (life, com. chmn. 1984, co-chmn. literacy com. 1984), Toastmasters (Vanderhoof award 1992, vol. coord. 4-H series, Excel program 1992—), Advanced Toastmaster Silver. Republican. Roman Catholic. Home: 6103 Edenhall Dr San Jose CA 95129-3006

MCCARTHY, MARY LYNN, social work educator; b. Buffalo, Sept. 26, 1950; d. Joseph Timothy and Jean Mary (Weber) McC.; m. David R. Gardam; children: Rachel Lamb, Ethan Gardam. BA, SUNY, Oswego, 1973; MSW, SUNY, Albany, 1982. Cert. social woker. Asst. program dir. Huntington Family Ctr., Syracuse, N.Y., 1973-75; caseworker child protection Onondaga County Dept. Social Svcs., Syracuse, 1975; coord. Community Svc. Alliance, Syracuse, 1976-79; asst. and assoc. human svcs. Profl. Devel. Program - SUNY (Albany, N.Y., 1979-84; intake coord., dir. parent aides St. Catherines Ctr. for Children, Albany, 1983-84; edn. asst. N.Y. State Edn. Dept., Albany, 1984-87; field edn. asst. coord., instr. SUNY Sch. of Social Welfare, Albany, 1987-93, asst. dean student svcs., 1990—, undergrad. field coord., 1993—; chmn. Child Welfare Issues Com., Albany, 1983-88; com. mem. N.Y. State Welfare Adv. Coun., Albany, 1983-84. Recipient Disabled Student Svcs. Achievement award U. Albany, 1993. Mem. NASW (sec. 1983-85, v.p. 1985-88, pres. N.E. divsn. 1988-90, nat. trustee Polit. Action for Candidate Election 1989—, chair 1994-95, N.Y. state trustee 1993—, treas. 1990-94, mem. nat. strategic planning com. 1990-91, Social Worker of Yr. N.E. divsn N.Y. state chpt. 1992), N.Y. State Social Work Edn. Assn. (bd. dirs. 1989), Coun. on Social Work Edn. Avocations: canoeing, camping, gardening. Office: Rockefeller Coll Sch Social Welfare 114 Richardson Hall Albany NY 12222

MCCARTHY, MICHAEL ANDREW, banker, lawyer; b. Northampton, Mass., Mar. 25, 1944; s. Edward George and Florence Vivian (Frechette) M; m. Susan Chan, June 6, 1973; children: Kathleen, Matthew, Thomas. BA, U. Mass., 1968; JD, Harvard U., 1971. Bar: Calif. Assoc. Breed, Abbott & Morgan, N.Y.C., 1971-73; atty. Bank Am., San Francisco, 1973-76; counsel Bank Am., Tokyo, 1976-79; asst. gen. counsel Bank Am., San Francisco, 1979-87; div. gen. counsel Citicorp, San Francisco, 1987—. With USAF, 1962-66. Mem. ABA, Calif. Bar Assn., Bar Assn. San Francisco, Phi Beta Kappa. Republican. Office: Citibank F S B 180 Grand Ave Fl 15 Oakland CA 94612

MCCARTHY, MICHAEL ANTHONY, architecture executive; b. Buffalo, July 15, 1934; s. Joseph William and Mary Genevieve (Pelligrini) McC. BArch, Cornell U., 1957; MArch, Harvard U., 1964. Registered architect, Conn., D.C., Fla., Ga., Mass., Miss., N.Y., N.J., Ohio, Tenn., Vt. With Skidmore Owings & Merrill, N.Y.C., 1964—, designer, 1964-67, participating assoc., 1967-73, ptnr., 1973—; mem. Chase Manhattan Bank Art Com., N.Y.C., 1973—; mem. adv. council Coll. Architecture, Art and Planning Cornell U. Ithaca, N.Y., 1983—. Served to 2d lt. U.S. Army, 1957-59. Fellow AIA; mem. Archtl. League, Mcpl. Arts Soc. Democrat. Roman Catholic. Club: Harvard (N.Y.C.). Avocations: travel, music, art, reading. Home: 309 E 49th St Apt 17A New York NY 10017-1601 Office: Skidmore Owings & Merrill 155 W 15th St # 21 New York NY 10011-6758

MCCARTHY, MICHAEL JOSEPH, communications company executive; b. Davenport, Iowa, Oct. 21, 1944; s. Thomas Patrick and Mary Elizabeth (McCabe) McC.; m. Monica Catherine Martin; children: Michael, Maureen. BA, U. Notre Dame, 1966; MSc, London Sch. Econs., 1968; JD, George Washington U., 1973. Speech writer Office of Telecommunications Policy, Office of Pres. of U.S., Washington, 1972-73; assoc., ptnr. Dow, Lohnes & Albertson, Washington, 1973-85; sr. v.p., sec., gen. counsel A.H. Belo Corp., Dallas, 1985—. Trustee Dallas Bar Found., 1987; bd. dir. N. Tex. Commn. Home: 6138 Oberdeen Ave Dallas TX 75230-4208 Office: A H Belo Corp 400 S Record St Dallas TX 75202-4806

MCCARTHY, MICHAEL SHAWN, health care company executive, lawyer; b. Evergreen Park, Ill., May 16, 1953; s. Martin J. and Margaret Anne (McNeill) McC.; m. Jane F. Alberding, Oct. 28, 1988; children:

Caroline Margaret, Nicholas Michael. BA, Georgetown U., 1975; MS, U. Ill., 1976; JD, Loyola U., 1980. Bar: Ill. 1980, U.S. Dist. Ct. (no. dist.) Ill. 1980. V.p.; sec., gen. counsel Luth. Gen. Health Care System, Park Ridge, Ill., 1980-85, sr. v.p., sec., gen. counsel, 1985-91, sr. v.p. corp. svcs., sec., gen. counsel, 1990-93; chmn., CEO The Parkside Co., Park Ridge, Ill., 1993—; bd. dirs. Cath. Lawyers Guild, Hosps. Organized for Polit. Edn., Juv. Protection Assn. Mem. ABA, Am. Assn. for Preferred Providers Orgn., Ill. Hosp. Assn., Ill. Pub. Health Assn., Ill. State Bar Assn., Chgo. Bar Assn. Roman Catholic. Avocations: golf, travel. Office: The Parkside Co 205 W Touhy Ave Park Ridge IL 60068

MCCARTHY, PATRICK, magazine publishing executive. Joined Women's Wear Daily, 1977; reporter Women's Wear Daily, D.C.; bur. chief Women's Wear Daily, London, Paris; editor Women's Wear Daily, N.Y.C., 1985-88, exec. editor, 1988-92; editor W, N.Y.C., 1985-88, exec. editor, 1988-92; exec. v.p. Fairchild Publs., N.Y.C., 1992—. Recipient Eugenia Sheppard award for fashion journalism CFDA, 1994. Office: Fairchild Publs Seven West 34th St New York NY 10001 also: care Susan Magrino Susan Magrino Agency 167 East 73rd St New York NY 10019*

MCCARTHY, PATRICK A., English educator; b. Charlottesville, Va., July 12, 1945; s. Thomas Blair and Virginia Rose (Feuerstein) McC.; m. Catherine Anne Leatherbury, Aug. 31, 1968; children: Keely, Cailin, Brendan. BA, U. Va., 1967, MA, 1968; PhD, U. Wis., Milw., 1973. Asst. prof., English U. Miami, Coral Gables, Fla., 1976-81, assoc. prof., 1981-84, prof., 1984—; dir. grad. studies Eng. Dept., U. Miami, 1986—; manuscript cons. various univ. presses. Author: The Riddles of Finnegans Wake, 1980, Olaf Stapledon, 1982, Ulysses: Portals of Discovery, 1990, Forests of Symbols: World, Text, and Self in Malcolm Lowry's Fiction, 1994; editor: Critical Essays on Samuel Beckett, 1986, Critical Essays on James Joyce's Finnegans Wake, 1992; co-editor: The Legacy of Olaf Stapledon, 1989. Travel grantee Am. Coun. Learned Socs., 1977; recipient Max Orovitz summer stipend U. Miami, 1980, 82, 85, 90, 92, gen. rsch. support grant, 1990, 92, 93. Mem. MLA, South Atlantic MLA, Internat. James Joyce Found., Am. Coun. Irish Studies. Office: U Miami Dept English Coral Gables FL 33124

MC CARTHY, PATRICK EDWARD, institute president; b. Rumford, Maine, July 23, 1930; s. John W. and Margaret C. (Whalen) McC.; m. Norma Joan Leary, Dec. 2, 1956; children—Sean W., Megan E., Cait S., Hannah R., Patrick E. Student, Dartmouth Coll., 1951-53, U. Maine, 1954-57, Boston U., 1957; M.City and Regional Planning, Harvard U., 1960; H.H.D. (hon.), Stonehill Coll., North Easton, Mass., 1972. Planner San Diego, 1960, City of San Leandro, Calif., 1960-61; urban renewal project dir. Boston Redevel. Authority, 1961-63; exec. dir., sec. Worcester (Mass.) Redevel. Authority, 1963-64; UN chief adviser to Govt. Ireland, 1964-67; dir. adminstrn. Mass. Bd. Higher Edn., 1967-69, dep. chancellor, then chancellor, 1969-75; chancellor U. Maine, 1975-86; pres. MGH Inst. Health Professions, Boston, 1988—; mem. Maine Postsecondary Edn. Commn., 1975-86, Mass. Exec. Com. Ednl. TV, 1973-77, Assn. Am. State Colls. and Univs., 1975-86, Edn. Commn. States, 1975-86, State Higher Edn. Exec. Officers Assn., 1967-86, New Eng. Bd. Higher Edn., 1967-86, Fund for Improvement of Postsecondary Edn., 1979-81; trustee Stonehill Coll., 1972-80, Mellon Participating Mortgage Trust, 1985—; guest lectr., cons. in field. Contbr. profl. publs. Trustee Washingtonian Center Addictions, 1972-76, mem. corp., 1976-78; pres. bd. trustees St. Joseph Hosp., 1980-82. With USMC, 1947-50. Mem. Am. Assn. Higher Edn., Am. Inst. Planners, Acad. Polit. Sci., Christmas Cove Improvement Assn. (v.p. 1972-76, commodore 1973-76, pres. 1979-81), Harvard Club (Boston). Office: MGH Inst Health Professions 101 Merrimac St Boston MA 02114-4719

MCCARTHY, PAUL, lawyer; b. N.Y.C., Jan. 3, 1940. AB, Cornell U., 1961; JD, U. Mich, 1964; MCL, U. Chgo., 1966. Bar: Ill. 1972. Ptnr. Baker & McKenzie, Chgo. Office: Baker & McKenzie 1 Prudential Pla 130 E Randolph Dr Chicago IL 60601-6384

MCCARTHY, PAUL FENTON, aerospace executive, former naval officer; b. Boston, Mar. 3, 1934; s. Paul Fenton and Jane Gertrude (O'Connor) McC.; m. Sandra Williams, June 20, 1959; children: Paul Fenton III, Susan Stacy. B.S. in Marine and Elec. Engring., Mass. Maritime Acad. 1954; M.S. in Mgmt., U.S. Naval Postgrad. Sch., 1964; D of Pub. Adminstrn. (hon.) Mass. Maritime Acad., 1987. Commd. ensign U.S. Navy, 1954, advanced through grades to vice adm., 1985; 7 command tours have included Aircraft Carrier USS Constellation, Carrier & Group One, Task Force Seventy; commdr. U.S. 7th Fleet, 1980-82; dir. R & D USN, Washington, 1980-83; negotiator Naval Air, Incidents at Sea Agreement, Moscow, 1980; ret., 1990; cons. in field Alexandria, Va., 1990-92; pres. McCarthy and McCarthy, Ltd.; v.p., chief engr., dep. gen.mgr. integrated product definition McDonnell Douglas Aerospace, St. Louis, 1992—. Trustee Naval Mus., 1990; bd. visitors Mass. Maritime Acad., 1993. Decorated D.S.M., Legion of Merit, D.F.C., also by govts. of South Vietnam, Korea, Japan. Mem. Mass. Maritime Acad. Alumni Assn., Soc. Exptl. Test Pilots, Naval Inst. Episcopalian. Avocations: research, development and acquisition, aircraft and missile systems, financial management. Home: 16475 Saddle Creek Rd Chesterfield MO 63005

MCCARTHY, PAUL H., library science educator; b. Rochester, N.Y., Oct. 16, 1939. BS in History, St. John Fisher Coll., 1962; MLS, Syracuse U., 1964; cert. archival adminstrn., Am. U., 1966; postgrad., U. Alaska. From asst. to assoc. to prof. libr. sci. U. Alaska, Fairbanks, 1978, contract mgr. libr. addition constrn., 1982-85, archivist, head dept. Alaska and Polar Regions Rasmuson Libr., 1983-87, dir. librs., 1987—; presenter simposia, meetings, confs.; cons. Alaska State Libr., 1969, various other orgns. including Alaska Native Found, Pioneers Alaska; profl. mem. Alaska State Tech. Rev. Bd. Hist. Preservation, 1970-71; grant reviewer Nat. Hist. Pubs. and Records Commn. Contbr. articles to profl. jours., editorial bd. Alaska Jour., 1971-86. Mem. parish coun. steering com. Cath. Ch. Fairbanks, 1970-71, 72-75, v.p., task force diocesan planning, 1984-87; co-founder Marriage Encounter Alaska Corp., 1976, cons. workshop Fairbanks Counseling and Adoption Agy., 1987. Grantee Rasmuson Found., 1972, 82-83, Alaska Hist. Commn., 1974, 84, 85, Alaska Humanities Forum, 1975-76, Rsch. Libr., 1980-81, Alaska State Legis., 1981, 85, Rsch. Libr. Resources, 1983-84, Nat. Hist. Pubs. and Records Commn., 1985, Bentley Libr., 1987-88, NSF, 1989-91, NEH, 1992-93. Fellow Soc. Am. Archivists (com. profl. standards 1988, chair working group long-range planning 1986—, coord. formation Archives Mgmt. Round Table 1986—); mem. ALA, Internat. Coun. Archives, Alaska Libr. Assn. (pres. 1969-71, bd. dirs. 1969-71, various coms.), Alaska Hist. Soc. (pres. 1972-73, chair ann. conf. 1987, various coms. and offices), Polar Librs. Colloguy (co-chmn. program com. 1976), Tanana Yukon Hist. Soc. (bd. dirs., exec. bd. 1974, various coms. and offices). Home: PO Box 80687 Fairbanks AK 99708-0687 Office: U Alaska Fairbanks Rasmuson Libr Fairbanks AK 99775

MCCARTHY, PAUL LOUIS, pediatrics educator; b. Springfield, Mass., Aug. 9, 1941; s. Alfred Lawrence and Minnie Josephine (Vivian) McC.; m. Barbara Jean Burns, Nov. 30, 1963; children: Paul, Scott, Brian. BA, Dartmouth Coll., 1963; MD (cum laude), U., 1969; MA (in privatum), Yale U., 1982. Diplomate Am. Bd. Pediatrics, Am. Bd. Pediatric Rheumatology. Pediat. intern Children's Hosp., Buffalo, 1969-70, pediat. resident, 1970-72; fellow in ambulatory pediatrics Children's Hosp. Med. Ctr., Boston, 1972-74; asst. prof. pediat. Yale U. Sch. Medicine, New Haven, 1974-78, assoc. prof., 1978-82, prof., 1982—, head gen. pediat., 1985—; Morrison lectr. Geisinger Clinic, Danville, Pa., 1990. Author: Evaluation and Management of Febrile Children, 1985; author 4 monographs; contbr. numerous articles to med. jours., chpts. to books. Fellow Am. Acad. Pediatrics; mem. Ambulatory Pediatric Assn. (pres. 1989-90, Armstrong award 1991), Soc. for Pediatric Rsch., Am. Pediatric Soc. Achievements include research in clinical judgment in acute illnesses in children. Avocations: reading, walking. Office: Yale U Sch of Medicine 333 Cedar St New Haven CT 06510

MCCARTHY, ROGER LEE, mechanical engineer. AB in Philosophy with high distinction, U. Mich., 1972, BSME summa cum laude, 1972; MS in Mech. Engring., MIT, 1973, MechE, 1975, PhD in Mech. Engring., 1977. Registered profl. engr., Calif., Ariz. Project engr. machine design and devel. engring. div. Proctor & Gamble, Inc., Cin., 1973-74; program mgr. Spl. Machinery Group Foster-Miller Assocs., Inc., Waltham, Mass., 1976-78; prin. design engr. Failure Analysis Assocs., Inc., Menlo Park, Calif., 1978—;

CEO The Failure Group, Inc., Menlo Park, 1988—. Co-contbr. numerous articles to profl. jours. Mem. Pres.' Commn. on Nat. Medal of Sci., 1992-94; mem. Army Sci. Bd. NSF fellow, 1972-75. Mem. Am. Soc. Metals, ASME, Soc. Automotive Engrs., Am. Welding Soc., Am. Soc. for Testing and Materials, Human Factors Soc., ASHRAE, Nat. Fire Protection Assn., Phi Beta Kappa, Sigma Xi (James B. Angell scholar). Office: Failure Group Inc PO Box 3015 149 Commonwealth Dr Menlo Park CA 94025

MCCARTHY, SEAN MICHAEL, air force pilot; b. Tacoma, Feb. 8, 1971; s. Lawrence Joseph and Mary Ann (Kramer) McC. BS with distinction, USAF Acad., Colorado Springs, 1993. Cadet USAF Acad., Colorado Springs, 1989-93; commd. 2d lt. USAF, 1993; student pilot Undergrad. Pilot Tng., Del Rio, Tex., 1993-94; A-10 pilot USAF, Osan Air Base, Korea, 1995—; summer intern Def. Mapping Agy., Alexandria, Va., 1992. Mem. Nat. Geographic Soc. (Dr. John Oliver LaGorce award 1993). Avocations: weight lifting, cycling, swimming, model building. Home: 1717 Devon Ave Linwood NJ 08221 Office: PSC Box 2675 Laughlin AFB TX 78840*

MC CARTHY, THOMAS PATRICK, magazine publisher; b. Elizabeth, N.J., Mar. 17, 1928; s. Thomas Joseph and Genevieve Elizabeth (Duffy) McC.; m. Joan Ellen Bodet, Jan. 16, 1954; children: Kathleen E., Patricia E., Thomas Patrick. BA, Seton Hall U., East Orange, N.J., 1955. Salesman, Joseph Davis Plastics Co., Kearney, N.J., 1955-57; nat. accounts mgr. ESB Corp., N.Y.C., 1957-65, Bekins Van & Storage Co., N.Y.C., 1965-67; nat. sales mgr. Traffic Mgmt. mag., N.Y.C., 1967-74; pub. Traffic Mgmt. mag., Boston, 1974—; v.p. Traffic Mgmt. mag., 1980-83; pres. Am. Resource Devel. Group, 1983-86, Land-Air-Sea-Transp. Pub. Co., N.Y.C., 1983—; ptnr. PROMATE Energy Systems, Inc., Marshfield, Mass., 1994—; pres. Transp. Mktg. Cons., Marshfield, Mass. Served with AUS, 1950-53. Mem. Bus. Publ. Advt. Assn., Assn. R.R. Advt. Mgrs., Sales & Mktg. Council Am. Trucking Assn. Roman Catholic. Clubs: Lions, K.C. Home: 57 Salt Meadow Waye Marshfield MA 02050-2427 Office: PO Box 1105 Marshfield MA 02050-1105

MCCARTHY, TIMOTHY MICHAEL, career non-commissioned officer; b. Mpls., July 18, 1944; s. Howard Allen and Elonora H. (Joa) McC.; m. Kang Suk Yi, Jan. 7, 1969; 1 child, Sony Srithai. AAS in Gen. Mgmt., El Paso C.C., 1995. With U.S. Army, 1965—; platoon sgt. B Co., 143rd Signal BN, Frankfurt, Germany, 1979-81; discom platoon sgt., 1st sgt. C Co., 143rd Signal BN, Frankfurt, 1981-82; 1st sgt. A Co., 501st Signal BN, Clarksville, Tenn., 1983-84; divsn. chief signal NCO 101st Airborne Divsn., Clarksville, 1984-85; bat. ops. sgt. 102nd Signal Bat., Frankfurt, 1986-87; sgt. maj. 7th Signal Brigade, Mannheim, Germany, 1987-88; command sgt. maj. 72nd Signat Bat., Karlsruhe, Germany, 1988-90, 7th Signal Brigdade, Karlsruhe, 1990-93, Comm.-Electronics Command, Ft. Monmouth, N.J., 1993—. Mem. Noncommissioned Officers Assn. (life, chpt. chmn.), Knights of the Square Table, Assn. of the U.S. Army (life), Armed Forces Comm. Electronics Assn., Signal Corps Regimental Assn. Democrat. Roman Catholic. Avocations: golf, running, skiing. Home: 3534 Biltmore Pl Augusta GA 30906 Office: HQ US Army Comm-Electronics Command Attn AMSEL-CSM Fort Monmouth NJ 07703-5000

MCCARTHY, VINCENT PAUL, lawyer; b. Boston, Sept. 25, 1940; s. John Patrick and Marion Priscilla (Buckley) McC.; children: Vincent, Sybil, Hope. AB, Boston Coll., 1962; JD, Harvard U., 1965. Bar: Mass. 1965. Ptnr. Hale and Dorr, Boston, 1965—, sr. ptnr., 1976—. Bd. dirs., sec. Robert F. Kennedy Action Corps., Inc., Charlesbank Apts.; bd. dirs. Boston Alcohol Detoxifiction Project, Inc., Fund for Boston Neighborhood; active Govs. Adv. Coun. on Alcoholism, Boston, 1984—, Govs. Jud. Nomination Com., 1991—; chmn. Mass. Housing Partnership Fund; former chmn. Boston Ctr. for Arts; adv. coun. Harvard AIDS Inst.; trustee, sec. Franklin Sq. House; past pres. Mass. Assn. for Mental Health; dir., sec.-treas. HRCF Found. Recipient Vols. of Am. Outstanding Svc. award, 1989. Mem. ABA (Pro Bono Publico award 1987), Mass. Bar Assn., Boston Bar Assn. (Pub. Svc. award 1995).

MC CARTHY, WALTER JOHN, JR., retired utility executive; b. N.Y.C. Apr. 20, 1925; s. Walter John and Irene (Trumbl) McC.; m. Linda Lyon, May 6, 1988; children by previous marriage: Walter, David, Sharon, James, William. B.M.E., Cornell U., 1949; grad., Oak Ridge Sch. Reactor Tech., 1952; D.Eng. (hon.), Lawrence Inst. Tech., 1981; D.Sc. (hon.), Eastern Mich. U., 1983; LHD, Wayne State U., 1984; LLD, Alma (Mich.) Coll., 1985. Engr. Public Service Electric & Gas Co., Newark, 1949-56; sect. head Atomic Power Devel. Assos., Detroit, 1956-61; gen. mgr. Power Reactor Devel. Co., Detroit, 1961-68; with Detroit Edison Co., 1968-90, exec. v.p. ops., 1975-77, exec. v.p. divs., 1977-79, pres., chief operating officer, 1979-81, chmn., chief exec. officer, 1981-90, now bd. dirs.; ret., 1990; bd. dirs. Perry Drug Stores, Inc., Comerica Bank Calif., Comerica Bank, Fed. Mogul Corp. Author papers in field. Past chmn., bd. dirs. Inst. Nuclear Power Ops. Fellow Am. Nuclear Soc., Engring. Soc. Detroit; mem. ASME, NAE, Detroit Club. Methodist.

MCCARTHY, WILBERT ALAN, mechanical engineer; b. Wadesboro, N.C., Mar. 22, 1945; s. Wilbert Albert and Myrtle (Greene) McC.; m. Judy Karen Prince, Aug. 19, 1972. Student, Va. Poly. Inst., 1963-66, U. Va. Extension, Falls Church, 1967-70, SUNY, Albany, 1990-91; BS in Mech. Engring., Pacific Western U., 1991, MS in Engring. and Constrn. Mgmt., 1993. Registered profl. engr., Wis., Vt., D.C., N.H., Maine, W.Va. Mech. engring. designer Edward L. Middleton and Assocs., Marlow Heights, Md., 1967-72; mech. engr., project mgr. H.D. Nottingham & Assocs., McLean, Va., 1972-79, sr. mech. engr., project mgr., profl. engr., 1982-83; mech. engr., project mgr., profl. engr. E/A Design Group, Washington, 1979-82; firm assoc., mech. dept. head, sr. mech. engr., profl. engr. Engring. Applications Cons., Burke, Va., 1983-87; firm assoc., dep. ops. mgr., mktg. coord., dir. engring. SAIC Architects, Inc., McLean, 1987-90; pvt. practice Dumfries, Va., 1990-91; project dir., project mgr., mktg. coord., sr. mech. engr. Advanced Cons. Engring., Arlington, Va., 1991-92; program dir., project mgr., mktg. field rep., sr. mech. engr. Engring. Design Group, Washington, 1992—; mechanical sect. head, sr. mechanical engr.; mem. panel arbitrators Am. Arbitration Assn. for disputes in govt., commercial and private constrn. industry. lectr. speaker Inst. for Internat. Rsch., N.Y.C., 1988—; Nat. Energy Mgmt. Inst., N.Y.C., 1988—. Sgt. USAFR, 1966-72. Recipient Award of Excellence for Design of Hynson Bldg. Rehab. Va. Downtown Devel. Assn., 1988, Commendation for Engring. and Mgmt. Proficiency U.S. Dept. Navy, 1987, 88. Mem. ABA (assoc.), Assn. Energy Engrs. (sr.), NSPE, ASHRAE, Am. Soc. Plumbing Engrs., Nat. Coun. Examiners for Engring. and Surveying (cert. profl. engr.). Methodist. Achievements include development of HVAC design projects for American embassies and consulates throughout the world, complete redesign office space expansion Joint Data Systems Support Ctr. Pentagon, mechanical systems design National Fire Academy. Home: HC75 Box 40 LOW Locust Grove VA 22508 Office: Engring Design Group Inc 1825 K St NW Washington DC 20006

MCCARTNEY, CHARLES PRICE, retired obstetrician-gynecologist; b. Barnesville, Ohio, Aug. 18, 1912; s. Jesse Thomas and Carrie (Price) McC.; m. Phyllis Helen Graybill, Sept. 27, 1940; children—Marilyn B., Ann E. B.S., U. Chgo., 1942, M.D., 1943. Diplomate: Am. Bd. Obstetricians and Gynecologists. Intern U. Chgo. Clinics, 1943-44, resident, 1947-50; mem. faculty U. Chgo. Med. Sch., 1950-71, prof. obstetrics and gynecology, 1960-71, Mary Campeau Ryerson prof., 1967-71; clin. prof. obstetrics and gynecology U. Ill., 1971-80, prof. emeritus, 1980—; attending gynecologist and obstetrician Chgo. Lying-In Hosp., 1950—. Mem. Cook County Com. Maternal Welfare, 1965—. Served to maj., M.C. AUS, 1944-46. Fellow Am. Gynecol. Soc.; mem. Am. Gynecol. and Obstetrical Soc., Chgo. Gynecol. Soc. (pres. 1967), Chgo. Med. Soc. (councillor 1960—, pres. 1973, chmn. bd. trustees 1973), Am. Coll. Obstetricians and Gynecologists (chmn. Ill. sect. 1965—), Cen. Assn. Obstetricians and Gynecologists. Home: 916 Thornwood Dr Saint Charles IL 60174

MCCARTNEY, JAMES ROBERT, psychiatrist; b. Elmira, N.Y., Jan. 6, 1932; s. James L. and Edith T. (Tufs) McC; m. Lois McCartney; 4 children. BA, Ohio Wesleyan U., 1952; MD, Columbia U., 1955; MA (Ad Eundem)(hon.), Brown U., 1989. Diplomate Nat. Bd. Med. Examiners, Am. Bd. Psychiatry and Neurology. Intern Boston City Hosp. for Medicine, 1955-56; resident in psychiatry Elizabeth's Hosp., Washington, 1958-59; assoc. attending psychiatrist then attending psychiatrist North Shore U. Hosp.,

1964-80, dir. tng. and edn. dept. psychiatry, 1972-79, chief of liaison svcs., 1973-80, assoc. dir., 1978-80; attending psychiatrist Meadowbrook Hosp., 1961-64; assoc. attending psychiatrist Nassau Hosp., 1964-71; on staff Butler Hosp., 1980—; psychiatrist-in-chief The Miriam Hosp., Providence, 1980—; adv. bd. Mental Health Assn. of Nassau County, 1972-80; cons. impaired physician com. R.I. Med. Soc., 1981—; dir. psychiatry Jewish Home for the Aged, 1985—; physician advisor John Hancock Mutual Life Ins. Co., 1986—; asst. prof. psychiatry Brown U., Providence, 1980-88, assoc. prof., 1988—. Contbr. articles to profl. jours. Capt. U.S. Army, 1956-58. Fellow ACP, Am. Psychiat. Assn., Acad. of Psychosomatic Medicine; mem. AMA, R.I. Med. Soc., Am. Psychosomatic Soc., Assn. for Acad. Psychiatry, Providence Med. Assn., Am. Assn. Gen. Hosp. Psychiatrists, Gerontol. Soc. of Am., Am. Geriatrics Soc. Office: Miriam Hosp 164 Summit Ave Providence RI 02906-2894

MCCARTNEY, N.L., investment banker; b. Jameson, Mo., Oct. 12, 1923; m. Helen M. Walsh, Feb. 11, 1950; children: Patricia, Deborah, Patrick. BS, U. Md., 1956; MBA, Syracuse U., 1959; MPA, George Washington U., 1963. Enlisted U.S. Army, 1944, advanced through grades to col., ret., 1972; dir. S.W. Mo. Health Care Foun., Springfield, 1974-88; pres. Resource Mgmt. Co., Springfield, 1988-90; exec. v.p. Spencer and Assocs., Springfield, 1990-94; instr. Southwest Mo. State U., Springfield, 1972-82. Pres. S.W. Mo. Adv. Coun. Govts., Ozarks Crime Prevention Coun., 1983-93, Vis. Nurse Assn.; mayor of Springfield, 1993-95. Mem. Rotary. Methodist. Home: 1233 E Loren Springfield MO 65804 Office: PO Box 389 Springfield MO 65801

MCCARTNEY, PATRICK KEVIN, newspaper reporter; b. L.A., Sept. 9, 1948; s. Warren Phil and Mildred Pauline (Weiler) McC. BA, U. San Diego, 1970; MA, U. So. Calif., 1983. Statis. analyst L.A. County Probation Dept., Downey, Calif., 1973-79; writer Free Venice (Calif.) Beachhead, 1984-88; editor, reporter Westchester (Calif.) Jour., 1987-88; reporter Blade-Citizen newspaper, Solana Beach, Calif., 1988-89; staff writer Press-Courier, Oxnard, Calif., 1990-91; corr. L.A. Times, Ventura, Calif., 1991—. Contbr. articles to newspapers. Pres. Venice Town Council, 1984-86, Coalition Concerned Communities, L.A., 1986-87; bd. dirs. Not Yet N.Y., L.A., 1986-87; candidate for L.A. City Coun., 1987. Mem. San Diego Press Assn., Venice Hist. Soc. (co-founder, bd. dirs. 1986-88), Encinitas Hist. Soc. (bd. dirs. 1989), Ventura County Press Club (co-founder, bd. dirs. 1991—). Avocations: hiking, outdoor sports, natural science, Calif. history. Home: 930 Tahoe Blvd # 349 Incline Village NV 89451

MCCARTNEY, (JAMES) PAUL, musician; b. Liverpool, Eng., June 18, 1942; s. James and Mary Patricia (Mohin) McC.; m. Linda Eastman, Mar. 12, 1969; 4 children. Hon., Univ. Sussex, Brighton, 1988. With John Lennon and George Harrison in groups Quarrymen, Moondogs, Silver Beatles, 1956-62, also with Ringo Starr in group The Beatles, 1962-70, solo performer and with group, Wings, 1970-80, The Paul McCartney World Tour, 1989; film appearances include: A Hard Day's Night, 1964, Help!, 1965, Let It Be, 1970, Give My Regards to Broad Street, 1984, Get Back, 1991; TV appearances include Magical Mystery Tour, 1967, James Paul McCartney, 1973, Wings Over the World, 1979; producer animated film The Oriental Nightfish, 1978; composer numerous songs including (with John Lennon) Please Please Me, I Want To Hold Your Hand, All My Loving, Can't Buy Me Love, I Saw Her Standing There, Love Me Do, Yesterday, Michelle, She's a Woman, Here, There and Everywhere, Good Day Sunshine, Penny Lane, She's Leaving Home, Fool on the Hill, Back in the USSR, Martha My Dear, Blackbird, Helter Skelter, Hey Jude, Let It Be, The Long and Winding Road, Get Back, (solo) Maybe I'm Amazed, My Love, Live and Let Die, Band on the Run, Silly Love Songs, Another Day, No More Lonely Nights, With a Little Luck; rec. artist: (albums with The Beatles) Meet the Beatles, Introducing the Beatles, Hard Day's Night, Help!, Rubber Soul, Revolver, Sgt. Pepper's Lonely Hearts Club Band, Magical Mystery Tour, The Beatles, Yellow Submarine, Abbey Road, Hey Jude, Let It Be; solo albums include McCartney, 1970, Ram, 1971, Red Rose Speedway, 1973, Band on the Run, 1973, Venus and Mars, 1975, Wings Over America, 1975, Wings at the Speed of Sound, 1976, London Town, 1978, Wings Greatest, 1978, Back to the Egg, 1979, McCartney II, 1980, Tug of War, 1982, Press to Play, 1986, All The Best, 1987, Flowers in the Dirt, 1989, Jet, 1989, Tripping the Live Fantastic,1990, Unplugged/The Official Bootleg, 1991, Off the Ground, 1993, Paul is Live, 1993; composer The Liverpool Oratorio, 1991. Decorated Order of Brit. Empire, 1965; recipient Acad. award (with Beatles) for Best Original Song Score, Let It Be, 1970, 5 Grammy awards with Beatles, 2 solo, 1 with Wings, Ivor Novello award for outstanding services to Brit. music, 1989; named to Rock and Roll Hall of Fame, 1988, Lifetime Achievement award, 1990. *

MC CARTNEY, RALPH FARNHAM, lawyer; b. Charles City, Iowa, Dec. 11, 1924; s. Ralph C. and Helen (Farnham) McC.; JD, U. Mich., 1950; B. Sci., Iowa State U., 1972; m. Rhoda Mae Huxsol, June 30, 1950; children: Ralph, Julia, David. Bar: Iowa 1950. Mem. firm Miller, Hougher & Miller, Des Moines, 1950-52, Frye & McCartney, Charles City, 1952-73, McCartney & Erb, Charles City, 1973-78; judge dist. Ct. Iowa, Charles City, 1978-87; chief judge 2d. Judicial Dist., 1987-92; sr. judge, Ct. Appeals, 1992-94; mem. jud. coordinating com. Iowa Supreme Ct. Chmn. Supreme Ct. Adv. Com. on Adminstrn. of Clks. Offices; mem. Iowa Ho. of Reps., 1967-70, majority floor leader, 1969-70; mem. Iowa Senate, 1973-74. Bd. regents U. Iowa, Iowa State U. U. No. Iowa, Iowa Sch. for Deaf, Iowa Braille and Sight Saving Sch. Served with AUS, 1942-45. Mem. Iowa Bar Assn., Iowa Judges Assn. Home: 1828 Cedar View Dr Charles City IA 50616-9129 Office: Ct Chambers Courthouse Charles City IA 50616

MC CARTNEY, ROBERT CHARLES, lawyer; b. Pitts., May 3, 1934; s. Nathaniel Hugh and Esther Mary (Smith) McC.; m. Janet Carolyn Moore, June 16, 1956; children: Ronald K., Sharon S., Carole J. AB, Princeton U., 1956; JD, Harvard U., 1959. Bar: D.C. 1959, Pa. 1960, U.S. Dist. Ct. (we. dist.) Pa. 1960, U.S. Ct. Appeals (3d dist.) 1960, U.S. Supreme Ct. 1966. Assoc. Eckert, Seamans, Cherin & Mellott, Pitts., 1959-64, ptnr., 1965-93, mem. exec. com., 1991-93, of counsel, 1993—; sec., gen. counsel Ryan Homes, Inc., 1969-93; bd. dirs. United Meth. Found. of Western Pa., 1971—, v.p., 1981-85, chmn. 1985-86; gen. coun. Rimoldi of Am., Inc., 1989—. Solicitor North Pitts. Cmty. Devel. Corp., 1968-76, all. dir. 1985-80; mem. McCandless Indsl. Devel. Authority, 1972—; mem. exec. com. Princeton U. Alumni coun., 1966-70, 76=85, vice chmn., 1981-83, chmn., 1983-85, co-chair Spl. Com. for 250th Anniversary of Princeton U.; trustee Otterbein Coll., 1975-83, Pa. S.W. Assn., 1992—, Pitts. Cultural Trust, 1992—; copr. bd. North Hills Passavant Hosp., 1976—; chmn. conf.-wide endowment program Untied Meth. Conf. Western Pa., 1985-87; bd. dirs. Pitts. Civic Light Opera Assn., 1986—, v.p., 1987-92, pres., 1992—; gen. counsel, dir. The Ireland Inst. Pitts., 1991—; mem. No. Ireland Partnership, 1991—. Princeton fellow Harvard U., 1956-59. Mem. ABA, Pa. Bar Assn., Internat. Bar Assn., Allegheny County Bar Assn., Princeton U. Alumni Assn. West Pa. (pres. 1976-78), Duquesne Club, Princeton Club, Nassau Club. Republican. Home: 9843 Woodland Rd Pittsburgh PA 15237-4362 Office: Eckert Seamans Cherin & Mellott 600 Grant St Fl 42 Pittsburgh PA 15219-2702

MC CARTY, BRUCE, architect; b. South Bend, Ind., Dec. 28, 1920; s. Earl Hauser and Hazel (Beagle) McC.; m. Julia Elizabeth Hayes, Apr. 5, 1945; children: Bruce Hayes, Douglas Hayes, Sarah Elizabeth. B.A., Princeton U., 1944; B.Arch., U. Mich., 1949. Ptnr. Painter, Weeks & McCarty, 1955-65, Bruce McCarty & Assocs., 1965-70; pres. McCarty Bullock Holsaple (Architects, Planners, Engrs., Inc.), Knoxville, Tenn., 1970-84; pres., chmn. McCarty Holsaple McCarty (Architects), Knoxville, Tenn., 1984—; mem. Knox County Met. Planning Commn., 1967-72; master architect planner 1982 World's Fair, 1976-82; prin. architect Knoxville Waterfront Master Plan, 1989. Works include residential, pub. and instnl. architecture. Trustee Dulin Gallery of Art, 1969-74; bd. dirs., co-founder East Tenn. Community Design Ctr., 1970-80; bd. dirs. Knoxville Beautification Bd., 1984-87, 88-91, Knoxville Arts Coun., 1984-87; com. mayor's Waterfron Task Force, 1989; chair Design Tenn., 1992—. 2d lt. USAAF, 1942-45. Recipient AIA EFL 1st honor for Humanities Bldg. U. Tenn.; Prestressed Concrete Inst. award for Mountain View Parking Garages; AIA regional awards for Humanities Bldg. Clarence Brown Theatre, Townview Terrace Housing, U. Tenn., Pedestrian Bridge, Art and Architecture Bldg., St. Johns Luth. Ch.; State of Tenn. Competition winner for U. Tenn. Art and Architecture Bldg..

1975; Mayor's award for Arts, 1975, 82; U. Tenn. Chancellor's assoc.; E. Tenn. chpt. AIA award, 1982; named to Leadership Knoxville, 1994—. Fellow AIA; mem. Tenn. Soc. Architects (pres. 1972), Knoxville C. of C. (dir. 1965-69). Presbyterian (elder). Office: Mc Carty Holsaple Mc Carty Inc Nations Bank Ctr 550 W Main Ave Knoxville TN 37902-2567

MCCARTY, CHESTER EARL, lawyer, retired air force officer; b. Stage Gulch nr. Pendleton, Oreg., Dec. 31, 1905; s. Albert Guy and Nancy Elizabeth (Odom) McC.; m. Julia Caroline Gromoff, July 17, 1926 (dec. Sept. 1989). J.D., Northwestern Coll. of Law, Portland, Oreg., 1929; student, George Washington U., 1952. Bar: Oreg. 1928. Since practiced in Portland; sr. mem. McCarty, Swindells & Nelson and predecessor firms, 1929-77; of counsel Gleason, Scarborough, McNeese, O'Brien & Barnes, P.C., 1977—; legal adviser to Gov. of Oreg., 1931-33; spl. asst. atty. gen. Oreg., 1931-36; chmn. Republican Central Com., Multnomah County, Oreg. 1934-36; elected state senator (declined to serve due to mil. service), 1943; advanced through grades to col. A.C. U.S. Army, 1942-46; commr. Port of Portland (Oreg.), 1950-54; brig. gen. USAF, 1948-52; mem. Res. Forces Policy Bd., 1948-50, maj. gen., 1953; comdr. 305th Air Div. Very Heavy Bombardment, 1948-50, 403d Troop Carrier Wing, 1951-52, 315th Air Div. (combat cargo), also Korean Airlift, 1952-54; Sr. Air Force mem. O'Daniel mission to Indo-China during French occupation, 1952-54 comdr. 18th Air Force, 1954-57; comdr. 12th Air Force, 1957-59, 14th Air Force, 1959-60; asst. chief staff Reserve Forces, USAF, 1960-63; chief staff U.S. Air Forces in Europe, 1963-66, ret. as maj. gen.; former mem. Jud. Conf. 4th and 9th U.S. Circuits. Trustee Lewis and Clark Coll., Air Force Hist. Soc., Northwestern Sch. Law, 1969-87, now life trustee; bd. dirs. Oreg. Trail chpt. ARC, 1966-79. Decorated D.S.M., Legion of Merit with oak leaf cluster, D.F.C., Distinguished Marksman's Medal, Bronze Star, Air Medal with 4 oak leaf clusters; hon. mem. 82d Airborne Div. U.S. Army; hon. pilot French, Thailand and Chinese Air Forces; French Fgn. Legion (hon.); Order of Cloud and Banner China; comdr. Quissam Alouite Cherifien Morocco, Nicham-Iftikhar Tunis; Order of Crown Thailand; Order of Taiguk; Presdl. Citation Korea; Citation and medal for distinguished acts Kingdom of Greece; hon. comdr. of mil. div. Most Excellent Order Brit. Empire; pilot first USAF aircraft flown over South Pole; first pilot to fly same aircraft over both North and South Poles, 1956. Mem. NRA (life), Air Res. Assn. (life, nat. pres. 1947-48), ABA, Fed. Bar Assn. (Oreg. pres. 1977-78), Oreg. State Bar, Res. Officers Assn. (life), Air Force Assn. (life), Izaak Walton League Am. (life), Lang Syne Soc. (pres. 1971), Explorers Club, Am. Rod and Gun Clubs Europe (hon. v.p.), Mil. Order World Wars (life) Am. Legion (life), VFW (life), DAV (life), Order Daedalians (life), Arlington Club, Waverley Country Club, Univ. Club (hon. life), Multnomah Athletic Club, Ends of Earth Club, OX5 Aviation Pioneers, Prince Albert Club (Brussels), Scottish Rite (33 deg. Grand Cross of the Ct. of Honor award 1989), Knights of Red Cross of Constantine, Royal Order Scotland, Masons, Shriners, York Rite Masonic Bodies, Rotary, Delta Theta Phi (life). Presbyterian. Home: 2545 SW Terwilliger Blvd # 926 Portland OR 97201-6310 Office: 5410 SW Macadam Ave Portland OR 97201-6105

MCCARTY, DENNIS L., insurance executive; b. Des Moines, Aug. 27, 1937; s. Francis L. McCarty and Edna V. (Olson) Hall; m. S. Jane Umsted, Sept. 5, 1970; children: Cindy, Adam. BS, Drake U., 1966. CLU, ChFC. Patrolman Des Moines Sheriff's Dept., 1966-69; capt. Johnston (Iowa) Police Dept., 1970-73; sales rep. Travelers Ins. Co., Des Moines, 1973-75, agy. supr., 1975-76; regional mktg. dir. Old Am. Ins. Co., Kansas City, Mo., 1976-79, regional v.p., 1979-87, v.p., 1987—. Sgt. U.S. Army, 1954-62. Mem. Amvets (pub. rels. officer State of Iowa 1964-65), Shriners, Masons, Scottish Rite, Am. Soc. CLU & ChFC. Avocations: golf, boating.

MCCARTY, DONALD JAMES, education educator; b. Ulster, Pa., July 17, 1921; s. James Leonard and Louise (Golden) McC.; m. Mary Elizabeth Donahue, Aug. 23, 1951; children: Mary Louise, Donald James, Kevin, Maureen. B.S. cum laude, Columbia U., 1949; M.A., Tchrs. Coll., Columbia U., 1950; Ph.D., U. Chgo., 1959. Jr. high sch. tchr. Brookings, S.D. 1950-51; sr. high sch. tchr. Toms River, N.J., 1951- 52, Brookings, 1952-53; supt. schs. Colman, S.D., 1953-56; staff assoc. U. Chgo., 1956-59; prof. ednl. adminstrn. Cornell U., Ithaca, N.Y., 1959-66; dean U. Wis. Sch. Edn., Madison, 1966-75; prof. ednl. adminstrn. U. Wis. Sch. Edn., 1975—. Author: (with Charles E. Ramsey) The School Managers: Power and Conflict in American Public Education, 1971, The Dilemma of the Deanship, 1980; also articles. Served to maj. USAAF, 1939-46. Mem. Nat. Coun. Profs. Ednl. Adminstrn. (exec. dir.). Home: 2926 Harvard Dr Madison WI 53705-2206

MCCARTY, FREDERICK BRIGGS, electrical engineer; b. Dilley, Tex., Aug. 11, 1926; s. John Frederick Briggs and Olive Ruth (Snell) Briggs McCarty; m. Doris Mary Cox, May 3, 1950 (div. 1970); children: Mark Frederick, David Lambuth, Jackson Clare; m. Nina Lucile Butman, Aug. 17, 1973. B.S.E.E., U. Tex., 1949. Registered profl. engr. Calif. Design engr. Gen. Electric Co., Schenectady, N.Y., 1949-51; sr. design engr. Convair, Ft. Worth, Tex., 1951-55; sr. engr. Aerojet Gen., Azusa, Calif., 1955-61; sr. engring. specialist Garrett Corp., Torrance, Calif., 1961-91; v.p., founder Patio Pacific, Inc., Torrance, 1973-84; owner, operator Textiger Co. Torrance, 1980-91; cons., 1991—. Author computer software, Textiger word processor, Tiger Tools, Big Mag and Roundrot generator synthesizers. Designer superconducting acyclic motor for U.S. Navy and various high speed elec. machines for aerospace and transp. Patentee in field. Served with USNR, 1944-46, PTO. Mem. IEEE (sr. life), Tau Beta Pi, Eta Kappa Nu. Democrat. Home and Office: 1366 Stonewood Ct San Pedro CA 90732-1550

MCCARTY, HARRY DOWNMAN, tool manufacturing company executive; b. Balt., Aug. 30, 1946; s. H. Downman and Melissa (Dunham) McC.; m. Helen Hilliard, May 13, 1948; children: Cormac Downman, Henning Hilliard. BA, Johns Hopkins U., 1968. Math. instr. Gilman Sch., Balt., 1970-71; sales mgr. Balt. Tool Works Inc., Balt., 1971-79, pres., 1979—; bd. dirs. Tool Ins. Co., Ltd., Hamilton, Bermuda. Co-chmn. Robert Nicolls scholarship fund Friends Sch., Balt., 1986-89. 1st lt. U.S. Army, 1968-70. Recipient Barton Cup winner for campus leadership, Johns Hopkins U., 1968, 1st Team All-Am.-Lacrosse, 1968. Mem. Hand Tools Inst. (bd. dirs. 1985-86, 1990-92), Am. Hardware Mfg. Assn., Am. Supply and Machinery Mfg. Assn., Specialty Tools and Fastener Distbn. Assn., Am. Soc. Metals, Md. Club, L'Hirondelle Club (bd. dirs. 1989-92), ODK Hon. Soc. Republican. Episcopalian. Avocations: tennis, squash, platform tennis, flyfishing. Office: Balt Tool Works Inc 110 W West St Baltimore MD 21230-3725

MCCARTY, MACLYN, medical scientist; b. South Bend, Ind., June 9, 1911; s. Earl Hauser and Hazel Dell (Beagle) McC.; m. Anita Alleyne Davies, June 20, 1934 (div. 1966); children: Maclyn, Richard E., Dale, Colin; m. Marjorie Steiner, Sept. 3, 1966. AB, Stanford U., 1933; MD, Johns Hopkins U., 1937; ScD (hon.), Columbia U., 1976, U. Fla., 1977, Rockefeller U., 1982, Med. Coll. Ohio, 1985, Emory U., 1987, Wittenberg U., 1989; MD (hon.), U. Cologne, Fed. Republic Germany, 1988. House officer, asst. resident physician Johns Hopkins Hosp., 1937-40; assoc. Rockefeller Inst., 1946-48, assoc. mem., 1948-50, mem., 1950—, prof., 1957—, v.p., 1965-78, physician in chief to hosp., 1961-74; research in streptococcal disease and rheumatic fever; Cons. USPHS, NIH. Author: The Transforming Principle: Discovering That Genes are Made of DNA, 1985. Mem. distbn. com. N.Y. Community Trust, 1966-74; chmn. Health Research Council City N.Y., 1972-75; Mem. bd. trustees Helen Hay Whitney Found; chmn. bd. dirs. Pub. Health Research Inst of N.Y., 1985-92. Served with Naval Med. Research Unit, Rockefeller Hosp. USNR, 1942-46. Fellow medicine N.Y. U. Coll. Medicine, 1940-41; NYC fellow med. scis. Rockefeller Inst., 1941-42; Recipient Eli Lilly award in bacteriology and immunology, 1946, 1st Waterford Biomed. Rsch. award, 1977, Wolf Found. prize in medicine, Israel, 1990. Mem. Am. Soc. for Clin. Investigation, Am. Assn. Immunologists, Soc. Am. Bacteriologists, Soc. for Exptl. Biology and Medicine (pres. 1973-75), Harvey Soc. (sec. 1947-50, pres. 1971-72), N.Y. Acad. Medicine, Assn. Am. Physicians (Kober medal 1989), Nat. Acad. Scis. (Kovalenko medal 1988), Am. Acad. Arts and Scis., N.Y. Heart Assn. (1st v.p. 1967, pres. 1969-71), Am. Philos. Soc. Office: Rockefeller U 66th St and York Ave New York NY 10021

MCCARTY, MICHIEL CLEVE, investment banker; b. Russelville, Ark., Aug. 13, 1951; s. Anderson Cleve and Freddie Joan (Campbell) McC.; m. Claire A. Biesterfeldt, July 9, 1977 (div. Dec. 1984); m. Mary Beth Minton,

Feb. 15, 1986; children: Matthew Cleve, Sarah Margaret, Katherine Joan. BA in Physics, Vanderbilt U., 1973; MBA in Fin., Wharton Sch., 1975. Asst. v.p. Citibank NA-Merchant Bank, N.Y.C., 1975-80; sr. v.p. Dillon Read & Co., Inc., N.Y.C., 1980-85, mng. dir., 1985-91; mng. dir. S.G. Warburg & Co. Inc., N.Y.C., 1991—. Clubs: Stanwich, OG Yacht (Greenwich, Ct.). Home: 37 Rock Ridge Ave Greenwich CT 06831-4414 Office: S G Warburg & Co Inc 787 7th Ave New York NY 10019-6018

MCCARTY, RICHARD CHARLES, psychology educator; b. Portsmouth, Va., July 12, 1947; s. Constantine Ambrose and Helen Marie (Householder) McC.; m. Sheila Adair Miltier, July 12, 1965; children: Christopher Charles, Lorraine Marie, Ryan Lester, Patrick James. BS in Biology, Old Dominion U., 1970, MS in Zoology, 1972; PhD in Pathobiology, Johns Hopkins U., 1976. Rsch. assoc. NIMH, Bethesda, Md., 1976-78; asst. prof. U. Va., Charlottesville, 1978-84, assoc. prof., 1984-88, prof., 1988—, chair psychology, 1990—. Co-editor: Stress: Neuroendocrine and Molecular Approaches, 1992; mem. editorial bd. Behavioral and Neural Biology, 1985-90, Physiology and Behavior, 1989—; sec. gen. 6th Symposium on Stress, 1995; contbr. articles to profl. jours. Lt. comdr. USPHS, 1976-78. Recipient Rsch. Scientist Devel. award NIMH, 1985-90; sr. fellow Nat. Heart Lung Blood Inst., NIH, 1984-85. Fellow Soc. Behavioral Medicine, Acad. Behavioral Med. Rsch.; mem. Am. Psychol. Soc., Am. Inst. Stress, Coun. for High Blood Pressure Rsch., AHA. Roman Catholic. Avocations: sports, gardening. Office: U Va Dept Psychology 102 Gilmer Hall Charlottesville VA 22903

MCCARTY, RICHARD EARL, biochemist, biochemistry educator; b. Balt., May 3, 1938; s. Maclyn and Anita (Davies) McC.; m. Kathleen Connolly, June 17, 1961; children—Jennifer A., Richard E., Jr., Gregory P. A.B, Johns Hopkins U., 1960, Ph.D., 1964. Postdoctoral assoc. Pub. Health Research Inst., N.Y.C., 1964-66; asst. prof. Cornell U., Ithaca, N.Y., 1966-72, assoc. prof., 1972-77, prof., 1977-90, prof., 1981-85; dir. biotech. program Cornell U., Ithaca, 1988-90; prof., chmn. Johns Hopkins U., Balt. 1990—; mem. panel NSF, Washington, 1984-86; panel mgr. Photosynthesis and Respiration Program, USDA, Nat. Rsch. Initiative Competitive Grants Program, 1994. Author: (with D. Wharton) Experiments and Methods in Biochemistry, 1972; mem. editorial bd.: Jour. Biol. Chemistry, 1978-88, 95—, assoc. editor, 1981-82; contbr. articles to profl. jours. Recipient Career Devel. award NIH, 1968-73, Charles F. Kettering award for Excellence in Photosynthesis Am. Soc. Plant Physiologists, 1994. Mem. AAAS, Am. Soc. Biochemistry and Molecular Biology, Am. Soc. Plant Physiologists. Home: 2204 Dalewood Rd Lutherville Timonium MD 21093-2701 Office: Johns Hopkins U Dept Biology 3400 N Charles St Baltimore MD 21218

MC CARTY, ROBERT LEE, lawyer; b. New London, Conn., Mar. 1, 1920; s. Robert Patrick and Lyda (Griser) McC.; m. Eileen Joan Noone, Sept. 1, 1945; children: Michael N., Patrick J., Charles Barry. B.S., Bowdoin Coll., 1941; LL.B., Yale U., 1948; LL.M., Georgetown U., 1953. Bar: D.C. 1948, U.S. Supreme Ct 1953, Va. 1976. Assoc. Northcutt Ely, 1948-54; mem. Ely, McCarty & Duncan, 1955-60; ptnr. McCarty and Wheatley, 1961-67, McCarty & Noone, 1968-80, McCarty, Noone & Williams, 1981-87, Heron, Burchette, Ruckert & Rothwell, Washington, 1987-90, Ritts Brickfield & Kaufman, Washington, 1990-92, Brickfield, Burchette & Ritts, Washington, 1993—; mem. Adminstrv. Conf. U.S., 1972-74; mem. adv. appeals bd. U.S. Dept. Edn., 1978-83. Contbr. chpts. to books. Pres. bd. dirs. Belle Haven Citizens Assn., 1959-60. Served with USAAF, 1942-46; Served with USAF, 1951-53; col. Res. Decorated D.F.C (2), Air medal with 3 oak leaf clusters, Army Commendation medal. Fellow Am. Bar Found.; mem. ABA (chmn. sect. adminstrv. law 1967-68), D.C. Bar Assn. (sect. del. to ho. dels. 1968-70), Fed. Bar Assn., D.C.Bar Assn., Va. Bar Assn. Roman Catholic. Clubs: University (Washington), Belle Haven Country (Va.). Home: 2108 Woodmont Rd Alexandria VA 22301-1155 Office: 8th flr West Tower 1025 Thomas Jefferson St NW Washington DC 20007 *If you are to be satisfied with your product, there is no substitute for work.*

MCCARTY, THEODORE FREDERICK, banker; b. Rochester, N.Y., Mar. 6, 1937; s. Theodore Milsom and Elinor (Bauer) McC.; m. Shirley Poll, Aug. 30, 1958 (div. Feb. 1990); children—Lynn A., Jeffrey T.; m. Cynthia Moyer, July 6, 1990. B.B.A., Western Mich. U., 1959; M.B.A., Ind. U., 1960; grad., Stonier Grad. Sch. Banking, Rutgers U., 1973. Sales engr. Gen. Electric Co., Phoenix, 1960-62; pres. AMB Assocs. Constrn. and Devel., Phoenix, 1962-65; bus. developer Am. Nat. Bank & Trust Co. of Mich. (now Old Kent Bank Southwest), Kalamazoo, 1965-66, asst. cashier, 1966, asst. v.p. and comml. loan officer, 1966-69, v.p. and comml. loan officer, 1969-71, v.p., sr. comml. loan officer, head comml. loan dept., 1971-75, sr. v.p., head comml. loan dept., 1975-77, exec. v.p., 1977-80, pres., chief adminstrv. officer, 1980-86, pres., chief exec. officer, 1986—, also bd. dirs, chmn. bd., 1987—, CEO coun., treas., 1991-92. Bd. dirs. Kalamazoo County Econ. Expansion Corp., 1975-85, pres., 1981-83, Western Mich. U. Found., 1987—; dir., vice chmn. Kalamazoo Forum, 1983-85; bd. dirs. Jr. Achievement of Kalamazoo County, Inc., 1974-84, treas., 1975-76, 79-80; trustee Nazareth Coll., Kalamazoo, 1982-91, treas., 1984-85, mem. bus. and exec. com., 1984—, vice chmn., 1986, chmn. 1987-89; bd. dirs. Plaza Arts Circle, Kalamazoo, 1983-87; bd. dirs. steering com. Kalamazoo Energy Office, 1982-84; mem. City of Kalamazoo alternative revenue search com., 1984; mem. Detroit dist. adv. council SBA, 1974-78; bd. dirs. Kalamazoo County Conv. and Visitors' Bur., 1976-77; 1989 Pacesetter chmn. Greater Kalamazoo United Way; adv. bd. Greater Kalamazoo United Way, 1993—. Named Mich. Banker Adv. of Yr., SBA, 1982. Mem. Am. Bankers Assn., Mich. Bankers Assn., Kalamazoo County C. of C. (bd. dirs. 1976-79, 81-83), Am. Inst. Banking, Kalamazoo Country Club, Rotary (treas. 1968-77, v.p. 1976-77, pres. 1977-78). Republican. Presbyterian. Avocations: tennis; golf; cross-country skiing; reading. Home: 9791 Almena Dr Kalamazoo MI 49009-9311 Office: Old Kent Bank Southwest 136 E Michigan Ave Kalamazoo MI 49007-3912

MCCARTY, THOMAS JOSEPH, publishing company executive; b. Waltham, Mass., June 10, 1938; s. Raymond Anthony and Mary Agatha (Riley) McC; m. Colette Ann Koechley, Aug. 3, 1963; children: Matthew Thomas, Brendan James, Sarah Katherine. BA, Holy Cross Coll., 1960; cert., Harvard U., 1961. Various mgmt. positions Oxford U. Press, N.Y.C., 1960-71, mgr. ops., 1971-79, dir. distbn., 1980-81, v.p. distbn., 1982-84, v.p. distbn. and info. systems, 1985-88, sr. v.p., 1988-90; sr. v.p.,gen. mgr. Oxford U. Press, Cary, N.C. ops., 1990—. Trustee N.C. Symphony Found.; mem. adv. bd. U. N.C. Publishing Inst., mem. adv. bd. Sch. Info. and Libr. Sci.; mem. N.C. Mus. Art, English Speaking Union. Mem. Assn. Am. Pubs., Am. Mgmt. Assn., Capital City Club (Raleigh, N.C.), MacGregor Downs Country Club (Cary). Office: Oxford U Press Inc 2001 Evans Rd Cary NC 27513-2009

MCCARTY, W(ILLARD) DUANE, obstetrician-gynecologist, physician executive; b. Alliance, Ohio, Dec. 15, 1930; s. Willard Raymond and Louise L. (Allmon) McC.; m. Frances Ann Rings, Dec. 5, 1959; children: Susan L., James A., Rebecca Ann, Sharon L. BS in Chemistry, Biology, Mt. Union Coll., 1952; MD, Ohio State U., 1956, MMS, 1961. Diplomate Am. Bd. Ob-Gyn. Intern, Univ. Hosps. Ohio State Univ., 1956-57; resident in ob-gyn. Ohio State U. Hosps., Columbus, 1957-61, instr. ob-gyn., 1960-61; assoc. ob-gyn. Lovelace Clinic, Albuquerque, 1963-86; chmn. ob-gyn. Lovelace-Bathan Hosp., Albuquerque, 1967-70; clin. assoc. prof. dept. ob-gyn., Sch. Medicine Univ. New Mex., Albuquerque, 1970-86; v.p., med. dir. Lovelace Health Plan, Albuquerque, 1972-84; clin. dir. Vista Pathways-Vista Sandia Hosp., Albuquerque, 1986-87; field rep., cons. Joint Commn. Accreditation of Hosps.-Ambulatory Care, Chgo., 1975-86; cur. rep. group practice Med. Group Mgmt. Assn., Denver, 1975-80; chmn. cur. quality assurance com. Am. Group Practice Assn., Chgo., 1978-82; v.p. bd. trustees Lovelace Health Plan-Lovelace FDN., Albuquerque, 1980-85; mem. Lovelace Inst. Cmty. Support Group, 1994—, Rsch. Review Bd., 1992. Author, rschr.: Recurrent Abortion, 1963 (MMS award). Founding dir. Profl. Stds. Rev. Orgn.; Albuquerque, 1974; counselor Alcoholics Anonymous, Albuquerque, 1988—; bd. trustees Menaul Sch. Presby. Ch., 1994—. Capt. USAF, 1961-63. Recipient Tchr.-Leader award N.Mex. Ob-Gyn. Soc., 1981. Fellow Am. Coll. Ob-Gyn., Am. Fertility Soc., Am. Coll. Physician Execs.; mem. AMA, Am. Acad. Med. Dirs. (founding trustee 1975—), Am. Soc. Addiction Medicine (cert.), N.Mex. Med. Soc. (continuing edn. com. 1990—; physician aid com. 1984—; sec.-treas. monitor treatment program), S.W. Ob-Gyn. Soc. (pres. 1981-82), Presbyn. Men (John Knox fellow, exec. com., v.p. for mis-

sions 1992-94). Republican. Avocations: barber-shop quartet singing, photography, travel, gardening, Bible study. Home: 610 Graceland Dr SE Albuquerque NM 87108-3335

MCCARTY, WILLIAM BONNER, JR., retail grocery executive; b. Jackson, Miss., Mar. 28, 1921; s. William Bonner Sr. and Elizabeth (Ayers) McC.; m. Isabel Russell; children: William Bonner III, Harrison Russell, Beth Ayers McCarty Harris. BS in Commerce, U. Miss., 1943. With JFM Inc., Jackson, 1946—, chmn. bd., chief exec. officer, 1965—, corp. sec., 1978—; chmn. bd., corp. sec. Sunburst Energy Inc.; pres., bd. dirs. McCarty Corp.; vice chmn. bd., exec. v.p., bd. dirs. Jitney Jungle Stores Am. Inc., So. Jitney Jungle Co. Inc., Interstate Jitney Jungle Stores Inc., Jitney Jungle Wholesale Co. Inc., Jitney Jungle Bakery Inc., Fla. Jitney Jungle Stores Inc., McCarty Holman Co. Inc. Chmn. bd. trustees Dr R.V. Powers and Robert E. Lake Founds., Jackson, 1st Presbyn. Ch. Day Sch., Jackson. Served to lt. inf. U.S. Army, 1943-46. Mem. Nat. Assn. Food Research, Food Merchandisers Edn. Council. Lodge: Kiwanis (pres. Jackson club 1964-65). Avocation: golfing. Home: 4130 Crane Blvd Jackson MS 39216-3405 Office: Jitney-Jungle Stores Am 453 N Mill St Jackson MS 39202-3287

MCCARUS, ERNEST NASSEPH, language educator; b. Charleston, W.Va., Sept. 10, 1922; s. Nasseph Mitchell and Della (Saad) McC.; m. Adele Najib Haddad, Sept. 10, 1955; children: Peter Kevin, Carol Ann. Student, Morris Harvey Coll., 1939-40; A.B., U. Mich., 1945, M.A., 1949, Ph.D., 1956. Translation team capt. Allied Translators and Interpreters' Service, Allied Hqrs., Tokyo, Japan, 1946-47; mem. English Lang. Inst. staff U. Mich., 1948-52, mem. univ. expdn. to Near East, 1951, instr. univ., 1952-56, asst. prof. Arabic, 1956-61; dir. Fgn. Service Inst., Field Sch. Arabic Lang. and Area Study, U.S. Dept. State, Beirut, Lebanon, 1958-60; assoc. prof. dept. Near Eastern studies U. Mich., 1961-67, 1967—, chmn. dept., 1969-77, dir. Center for Arabic Study Abroad, 1974-83, dir. U. Mich. Center for Near Eastern and North African Studies, 1983-92, dir. program for inter-instnl. collaboration in area studies, 1989—. Author: The Development of Arab-American Identity, 1944, Grammar of Kurdish of Sulaimania, Iraq, 1958, (with H. Hoenigswald, R. Noss, J. Yamagiwa) A Survey of Intensive Programs in the Uncommon Languages, 1962, (with A. Yacoub) Elements of Contemporary Arabic, 1962, 3d edn., 1966, (with Raji Rammuny) First Level Arabic: Elementary Literary Arabic for Secondary Schools, 1964, Teacher's Manual to Accompany First Level Arabic, 1964, (with Jamal J. Abdullah) Kurdish Basic Course - Dialect of Sulaimania, Iraq, 1967, Kurdish Readers, Vol. I Newspaper Kurdish, Vol. II. Kurdish Essays, Vol. III Kurdish Short Stories, 1967, A Kurdish-English Dictionary, 1967, (with P. Abboud) Elementary Modern Standard Arabic, 1983, (with R. Rammuny) Word Count of Elementary Modern Literary Arabic Textbooks, 1969, (with P. Abboud, E.T. Abdel-Massih, S. Altoma, W. Erwin, R. Rammuny) Modern Standard Arabic Intermediate Level, 1971, (with R. Rammuny) A Programmed Course in Modern Literary Arabic Phonology and Script, 1974; editor: Language Learning, Vol. VII, 1956-57, Language Learning, Vol. XIII, 1963, An-Nashra, 1967-74, Contemporary Arabic Readers, Vols. I-V, 1962-66, The Development of Arab-American Identity, 1994; contbr. articles to scholastic jours. Served with AUS, 1942-46. Rockefeller fellow, 1951. Mem. Mich. Linguistic Soc. (pres. 1962-63), Am. Assn. Tchrs. Arabic (pres. 1973, exec. coun. 1979-81, 89-92), Middle East Studies Assn. (bd. dirs. 1973-75), Linguistic Soc. Am. Am. Oriental Soc., Linguistic Circle N.Y., Arabic Linguistic Soc. (pres. 1992). Home: 1400 Beechwood Dr Ann Arbor MI 48103-2940

MCCARVER, JAMES TIMOTHY, sportscaster; b. Memphis, Oct. 16, 1941; s. Grover Edward and Alice Levonia (Phelan) McC.; m. Anne McDaniel, Dec. 29, 1964; children: Kathryn Leigh, Kelly Lorraine. Student, Memphis State U., 1963-66. Catcher St. Louis Cardinals, 1959-69, 73, 74, Phila. Phillies 1970-72, 75-79, Sept.-Oct., 1980, Montreal (Can.) Expos., June to Nov., 1972, Boston Red Sox, 1974-75; sportscaster Phila. Phillies, 1980-82, N.Y. Mets, WWOR-TV, 1983—; former sportscaster ABC Sports, N.Y.C., 1984; sportscaster CBS Sports, 1990—. Author: Oh Baby, I Love It, 1987; contbr. articles to sports mags. Chmn. fund raising McGee Rehab. Hosp., Phila., 1988. With U.S. Army, 1962-69. Recipient Emmy awards for local baseball broadcasting, 1986, 87; profl. baseball park named after him by Memphis Chicks, 1977. Mem. AFTRA. Roman Catholic. Avocations: bridge, reading, traveling. Office: care CBS Sports 51 W 52nd St New York NY 10019*

MCCARVILLE, MARK JOHN, food company executive; b. Moorland, Iowa, Sept. 13, 1946; s. Robert A. and Lucille (Hillman) McC.; m. Kathryn Mary Frith, June 3, 1972; children: Megan, Erin, Michael, Patrick. B.A., Loras Coll., 1968; M.B.A., U. Iowa, 1971. Asst. nat. bank examiner U.S. Treasury Dept., Chgo., 1968-72; bus. services officer Am. Nat. Bank, Chgo., 1972-76; sr. v.p. corp. devel. Sara Lee Corp., Chgo., 1976—. Bd. dirs. Inner Commons, 1990—, United Charities, 1991—. Office: Sara Lee Corp 3 First National Plz Chicago IL 60602

MCCASKEY, EDWARD W., professional football team executive; b. Phila., Apr. 27; m. Virginia Halas; 11 children. Student, U. Pa., 1940. Mgr. merchandising Nat. Retail Tea and Coffee Assn., Chgo.; exec. v.p. Mdse. Services, Inc., Chgo.; account exec. E.F. McDonald Co., Chgo.; v.p., treas. Chgo. Bears, 1967-83, chmn. bd. dirs., 1983—. Served to capt, AUS. Office: Chgo Bears 55 E Jackson Blvd Ste 1200 Chicago IL 60604-4105 also: Chicago Bears Halas Hall 250 N Washington Rd Lake Forest IL 60045-2471*

MCCASKEY, MICHAEL B., professional football team executive; b. Lancaster, Pa., Dec. 11, 1943; s. Edward B. and Virginia (Halas) McCaskey; m. Nancy McCaskey; children: John, Kathryn. Grad., Yale U., 1965; PhD, Case Western Res. U. Tchr. UCLA, 1972-75, Harvard U. Sch. Bus., Cambridge, Mass., 1975-82; pres., chief exec. officer Chgo. Bears (NFL), 1983—. Author: The Executive Challenge: Managing Change and Ambiguity. Named Exec. of Yr. Sporting News, 1985. Office: Chgo Bears Halas Hall 250 N Washington Rd Lake Forest IL 60045-2499*

MC CASKEY, RAYMOND F., insurance company executive; b. 1942. With Continental Assurance Co., Chgo., 1963-73; with Health Care Svc. Corp., Chgo., 1976—, now pres., CEO. Office: Health Care Service Corp 233 N Michigan Ave Chicago IL 60601-5655

MCCAUGHAN, JOHN F., chemical company executive; b. Montreal, Can., June 24, 1935. BA, Sir George Williams U., 1957. Chemstr. Betz Labs. Inc., Trevose, Pa. Office: Betz Labs Inc 4636 Somerton Rd Trevose PA 19053-6742*

MCCAUGHEY, ELIZABETH P. (BETSY MCCAUGHEY), state official; b. Oct. 20, 1948; d. Albert Peterkin; m. Thomas McCaughey, 1972 (div. 1994); children: Amanda, Caroline, Diana. BA, Vassar Coll., 1970; MA, Columbia Univ., 1972, PhD, 1976. Public policy expert Manhattan Inst., N.Y.C.; lt. gov. State of N.Y., 1995—; instr. Vassar Coll., 1979, Columbia Univ., 1980-84; chmn. Governor's Medicaid Task Force, 1994. Author: From Loyalist to Founding Father, 1980, Government By Choice, 1987; also articles including an article in The New Republic Nat. Mag. award for Pub. Policy 1995). Recipient Bancroft Dissertation award, Richard B. Morris prize; Woodrow Wilson fellow, Herbert H. Lehman fellow, Honorary Vassar fellow, John Jay fellow, Post Doctoral Rsch. fellow NEH, 1984, John Molin fellow Manhattan Inst., 1993, sr. fellow Ctr. Study of the Presidency. Republican. Office: Office of Lt Governor Executive Chamber State Capitol Rm 326 Albany NY 12224

MCCAULEY, ALFREDA ELLIS, elementary school principal; b. Greensboro, N.C., Sept. 24, 1942; d. David and Elizabeth (Stout) Ellis; m. John McCauley, June 6, 1964; children: Karen Alicia, Sue Lynn. BA, N.C. Cen. U., 1964; MS, N.C. A&T State U., 1976, 82; Dr. U. N.C., Greensboro, 1991. Cert. tchr., counselor, adminstr., N.C.; cert. principal exec. program. Music tchr. Durham (N.C.) County Schs., 1964-66; music tchr. Greensboro Pub. Schs., 1968-76, counselor, 1976-88, prin., 1991—. Active Black Child Devel. Inst., Greensboro, 1988—. mem. ASCD, NEA, Nat. Assn. Elem. Sch. Prins., N.C. Assn. Educators, N.C. Assn. Cupr. and Curriculum Devel. Greensboro Prin.'s Assn., Phi Delta Kappa, Alpha Kappa Alpha. Avocations: playing piano, singing, reading, cooking. Home: 3303 Stonehaven Dr Greensboro NC 27406-5830

MCCAULEY, BRUCE GORDON, financial consultant; b. St. Louis; s. William Maurice and Evylin Adele (Halbert) McC.; m. Barbara Allen Stevens, Mar. 16, 1945 (dec.); children: David S., Sharon; m. Gwen Crumpton Cummings, Nov. 25, 1967. Student, U. Mo., 1939-41, Yale U., 1944; BS in Engring., U. Calif., Berkeley, 1948, MBA, 1949, MS in Indsl. Engring., 1952. Registered profl. engr., N.Y., Calif., Hawaii. Asst. purchasing agt. Curtis Mfg. Co., St. Louis, 1941-43; teaching asst. U. Calif., Berkeley, 1948-49, asst. prof. mech. engring., 1950-56, chmn. indsl. engring. inst., 1954-55; design engr. Standard Oil Co. of Calif., 1949-50; sr. pttar. McCauley & Dunmire, San Francisco, 1952-56; v.p. Shand & Jurs Co., Berkeley, 1956-58, dir., 1957-60, exec. v.p., 1958-60; asst. to pres. Honolulu Star-Bulletin, 1960-62; gen. mgr. Christian Sci. Pub. Soc., Boston, 1962-69; gen. mgr.; sec. N.Y. Daily News Inc., N.Y.C., 1969-74, v.p., 1971-73, sr. v.p., 1973-75, asst. to pres., 1974-75, dir., 1971-75; v.p. Daseke & Co. Inc., Westport, Conn., 1975-77, sr. v.p., 1977-86, mgr. West Coast office, 1978-86; vis. scholar Principia Coll., Elsah, Ill., 1988-91; pres., dir. Rossmoor Mut. 48 Corp., Walnut Creek, 1994—. Bd. dirs. Better Bus. Bur., N.Y.C., 1973-77, N.Y.C. Conv. and Visitors Bur., 1974-77, Albert Baker Found., 1979-90, Asher Found., 1983-93, Sopac Energy Corp., 1986-92. Capt. USAAF, 1943-46, PTO. Mem. ASME, Am. Inst. Indsl. Engrs., Nat. Assn. Accountants, Nat. Soc. Profl. Engrs., U. Calif. Alumni Assn., Principia Alumni Assn., Sigma Xi, Tau Beta Pi, Beta Gamma Sigma, Pi Mu Epsilon. Christian Scientist. Club: Rossmoor Golf (Walnut Creek). Lodges: Masons (32 deg.), Kiwanis. Home: 3266 Ptarmigan Dr Apt 3B Walnut Creek CA 94595-3150

MCCAULEY, CLARK RICHARD, psychology educator; b. Balt., Oct. 13, 1943; s. Clark Richard and Mary Louise (Quinlen) McC.; m. Lisa Marie Beck, Sept. 16, 1989. BS in Biology, Providence Coll., 1965; PhD in Psychology, U. Pa., 1970. Asst. prof. psychology, assoc. prof., prof. Bryn Mawr (Pa.) Coll., 1970—; cons. Harry Frank Guggenheim Found., N.Y.C., 1985—. Mem. AAAS, Internat. Soc. Polit. Psychology, Soc. Personality and Social Psychology, Eastern Psychol. Assn. Roman Catholic. Office: Bryn Mawr Coll Bryn Mawr PA 19010

MCCAULEY, JAMES WEYMANN, ceramics engineer, educator; b. Phila., Mar. 21, 1940; s. Edward Joseph and Emily Marie (Weymann) McC.; m. Mary Ann Malone, June 6, 1964; children: Patrick, Kathleen, Daniel. BS, St. Joseph's Coll., 1961; MS, Pa. State U., 1965, PhD, 1968. Rsch. asst. solid state sci. Pa. State U., University Park, 1966-68; rsch. scientist MATS Tech. Lab. U.S. Army, Watertown, Mass., 1968-74, group leader, 1974-81, div. chief, 1981-90; liaison scientist Far East Rsch. Office U. S. Army, Tokyo, 1988; dean N.Y. State (SUNY) Coll. Ceramics Alfred N.Y U., 1990-94, prof., 1995—; adj. prof. Boston U., 1984-86; bd. dirs. Alfred Tech. Resources Inc.; mem. Army Sci. Bd. Editor books; contbr. articles to sci. and profl. jours.; patentee in field. Vice chmn. Wakefield Cable TV Com., Mass., 1970-80; chmn. Wakefield Conservatin Com., 1980-90. Emeritus fellow Army Rsch. Lab. Fellow Am. Ceramic Soc. (v.p. 1987, trustee 1988-91, 92-95, treas. 1995-96, F.H. Norton award 1987, J.I. Mueller award 1988). Home: HC 64 Box 64L Hillcrest Ext Wellsville NY 14895 Office: Alfred U Coll of Ceramics Alfred NY 14802

MCCAULEY, MICHAEL STEPHEN, lawyer; b. Dubuque, Iowa, Sept. 2, 1947; s. Francis P. and Alberta (Maiers) McC.; m. Patricia Hanna, July 29, 1972; children: Maura, Michael, Meghan. BA, U. Notre Dame, 1969; MPA, Harvard U., 1974; JD, U. Iowa, 1977. Bar: Wis. 1977, U.S. Dist. Ct. (ea. and we. dists.) Wis. 1977, U.S. Ct. Appeals (7th cir.) 1977. Ptnr. Quarles & Brady, Milw.; spkr. in field. Bd. editors Iowa Law Rev., 1976-77; contbr. articles to profl. jours. Dir. Indo-Chinese Refugee Program; chmn. bd. rev. Village of Shorewood, 1980-90; vol. U.S. Peace Corps, 1969-71, Sri Lanka, South Korea. Mem. ABA (vice chmn. environ. quality com. 1990-92, air quality com. 1993-95), Environ. Law Inst., State Bar Wis. (dir. environ. law sect. 1990-93), Wis. Air and Waste Mgmt. Assn. (bd. dirs.), Wis. Environ. Regulatory Corp., Wis. Mfrs. and Commerce Assn., Milw. Bar Assn., Order of Coif. Avocations: golf, running. Office: Quarles & Brady 411 E Wisconsin Ave Milwaukee WI 53202-4409

MC CAULEY, R. PAUL, criminologist, educator; b. Highspire, Pa., Jan. 13, 1943; s. Paul Herbert and Frances Vaden (Harper) McC.; m. Gail Lee Gummo, Jan. 30, 1965; 1 child, Brent Clayton. A.S., Harrisburg Area Community Coll., 1968; B.S., Va. Commonwealth U., 1969; M.S., Eastern Ky. U., 1971; Ph.D. (fellow), Sam Houston U., 1973; certificate Home Office Detective Tng. Course, Eng., 1967. Police officer Highspire Police, 1964-69; adminstr. Burns Internat. Security Services Inc., 1969-71; prof. police sci. and adminstrn., dir. grad. studies in adminstrn. of justice U. Louisville, 1973-82; prof., chmn. dept. criminology Indiana U. of Pa., 1982—; co-founder Sempas Security and Safety Technologies, 1980; advisor Reagan Presdl./Congressional Task Force on Criminal Justice, 1980; mem. staff So. Police Inst., 1973-82, Nat. Crime Prevention Inst., 1973-82; researcher, ptnr. McShan Assocs., 1974-85; cons. U.S. Congress Com. on Emergency Communications, 1967. Co-author: The Criminal Justice System, 1976, 3d edit., 1984; co-founder, editor: Criminal Justice Policy Rev., 1984-86; contbr. chpts. to books, articles to profl. jours.; patents. Active Metro Child Abuse Program, Crime Clinic of Greater Harrisburg, 1965-74; mem. Lower Swatara Twp. Police Civil Service Commn., 1967-69. Served with USMC, 1962-66. Recipient Mayor's Citation, City of Louisville, 1982, Gold medal Educator of the 1980's; honoree Silliman Coll., Yale U., 1984; Fulbright scholar, lectr., Australia, 1987. Mem. Acad. Criminal Justice Scis. (exec. bd. 1980-83, pres. 1985), Navy League (award for disting. community service). Home: 4620 Lucerne Rd Indiana PA 15701-8950 Office: Indiana U of Pa 204 Walsh Hall Indiana PA 15705 *One's philosophy, spirit, and drive contributes more to his relative success than do economic resources, social position, planning, or timing.*

MCCAULEY, RICHARD GRAY, real estate developer, lawyer; b. Balt., June 17, 1940. B.A. cum laude, Williams Coll., 1962; LL.B., U. Va., 1965. Bar: Md. 1965, U.S. Supreme Ct. 1969. Assoc. Piper & Marbury, Balt., 1965-69; asst. atty. gen. State of Md., 1969-71; sr. v.p., gen. counsel, sec. Rouse Co. and subs., Columbia, Md., 1971—; chmn. bd. Md. Deposit Ins. Fund Corp., 1985-86; lectr. Am. Law Inst.; bd. dirs. First Nat. Bank of Atlanta. Bd. dirs. Columbia Park and Recreation Assn. 1972-83, chmn. exec. com., 1972-78, chmn. bd., 1978-83; trustee The Columbia Found., 1984-89, pres., 1987-89; trustee Howard Community Coll. Ednl. Found., 1982-88, vice chair, 1985-88. Mem. ABA, Md. Bar Assn., Balt. City Bar Assn., Am. Judicature Soc., Urban Land Inst., Am. Corp. Counsel Assn., Williams Coll. Alumni Soc. (pres. 1990-92). Office: The Rouse Co 10275 Little Patuxent Pky Columbia MD 21044-3414

MCCAULEY, ROBERT WILLIAM, biologist, educator; b. Toronto, Ont., Can., July 8, 1926; s. Herbert and Mary (Mahaffy) McC.; m. Erika Augusta Hinz, May 19, 1956; children—Eva-Maria, Heidi, Friedrich. BEd, U. Toronto, 1952, B.A., 1955; student, U. Tuebingen, Federal Republic of Germany, 1955; Ph.D., U. Western Ont., 1962. Cert. fisheries biologist. Asst. scientist Fisheries Research Bd. Can., 1956-62; research scientist Ont. Dept. Lands and Forests, Toronto, 1962-65; prof. Wilfrid Laurier U., Waterloo, Ont., 1965-92, prof. emeritus, 1992—; pres. Robert McCauley & Assocs. Aquatic Ecologists, Inc.; cons. Ont. Hydro; Contbr. articles to profl. jours. Mem. Am. Fisheries Soc., Am. Inst. Biol. Scis., Am. Lake Mgmt. Soc., Internat. Assn. for Great Lakes Rsch. Lutheran. Home: 118 Forest Hill Dr, Kitchener, ON Canada N2M 4G3 Office: 75 University Ave, Waterloo, ON Canada

MCCAUSLAND, THOMAS JAMES, JR., brokerage house executive; b. Cleve., Nov. 27, 1934; s. Thomas James and Jean Anna (Hanna) McC.; m. Kathryn Margaret Schacht, Feb. 9, 1957; children: Thomas James III, Andrew John, Theodore Scott. BA in Econs., Beloit (Wis.) Coll., 1956. V.p. A.G. Becker & Co., Inc., Chgo., 1956-74; v.p. The Chgo. Corp., 1974-76, sr. v.p., dir., 1976-83, exec. v.p., 1983-90, vice chmn., 1991—; pres. The Chgo. Corp. Internat., 1990—; also bd. dirs. The Chgo. Corp.; bd. dirs. Chicorp, Inc.; bd. dirs., treas. The LaSalle St. Coun., Chgo. v.p. Hospice the North Shore, Evanston, Ill., 1986-90; bd. dirs. McCormick Theol. Sem., Chgo., 1971-79, Presbyn. Home, Evanston, 1968-74; trustee Beloit Coll., 1987-90. Lt. USN, 1956-59. Mem. Securities Industry Assn. (investment mgmt. com. 1979-82), Union League, United Presbyn. Found. (trustee, vice-chmn. 1980-86), Skokie Country Club (bd. dirs. 1983-85, pres. 1993), Pelican Bay Club (Naples, Fla.). Republican. Avocations: travel, Am. history, golf. Office: The Chgo Corp 208 S La Salle St Chicago IL 60604-1003

MCCAW, CRAIG O., communications executive; b. Centralia, Wash., 1949. Grad., Stanford U., 1971. Pilot; chmn., CEO McCaw Cellular Comm., Inc., 1968-88; chmn. bd. dirs., CEO McCaw Cellular Comm., Inc., Kirkland, Wash., 1982—; chmn., CEO Lin Broadcasting Co., 1990—. Office: McCaw Cellular Comm Inc 5400 Carillon Pt Kirkland WA 98033-7356

MCCAWLEY, AUSTIN, psychiatrist, educator; b. Greenock, Scotland, Jan. 17, 1925; came to U.S., 1954; s. Austin and Anna Theresa (McBride) McC.; m. Gloria Klein, Feb. 15, 1958; children: Joseph, Tessa. MBCHB, U. Glasgow, 1948. Diplomate Am. Bd. Psychiatry and Neurology; DPM Royal Coll. London. Intern Glasgow Royal Infirmary, Scotland, 1948; resident Inst. Living, Harford, Conn., 1954-57, clin. dir., 1960-66; med. dir. Westchestor br. St. Vincent's Hosp., N.Y.C., 1966-72; dir. psychiatry St. Francis Hosp., Hartford, 1972-88; prof. psychiatry U. Conn. Med. Sch., Farmington, 1983-93; pvt. practice, West Hartford, Conn., 1988—. Co-author: The Physician, 1983; contbr. articles to profl. jours. Chmn. Bd. Mental Health, State of Conn., 1981-84, Search Com. for Commr. Mental Health, Conn., 1981; mem. Gov.'s Spl. Task Force on Mental health Policy, Conn., 1982. With RAF, 1948-50. Fellow Am. Psychiat. Assn., Am. Coll. Psychiatry (charter fellow, founder); mem. Conn. Psychiat. Soc. (pres. 1978-79), Hartford Golf Club. Democrat. Roman Catholic. Avocations: music, golf. Home: 128 Westmont St West Hartford CT 06117-2932 Office: 18 N Main St West Hartford CT 06107-1903

MCCAY, THURMAN DWAYNE, university administrator; b. Wynne, Ark., Sept. 2, 1946; s. Thurman Ellis and Vetra Marcella (Jones) McC.; m. Mary Helen Johnston, Oct. 3, 1985; children: Audra Lee, Leesa Marie. BS in Physics, Auburn U., 1968, MS in Engring., 1969, PhD in Engring. and Math., 1974; postgrad. mgmt. sci. program, Air Force Inst. Tech., Wright-Petterson AFB, Ohio, 1985. Rsch. engr. gas diagnostics sect. aerospace projects br. ARO, Inc., Arnold Air Force Station, Tenn., 1973-78; sr. rsch. phys. scientist, plume tech. br. Air Force Rocket Propulsion Lab., Edwards AFB, Calif., 1978-81; sr. aerospace engr., br. chief, chief propulsion divsn. NASA, George G. Marshall Center, Ala., 1981-86; prof. engring. sci. and mechanics adj. prof. engring. U. Tenn. Space Inst., Tullahoma, 1986—, v.p. 1993—; tchr. Auburn U., 1970-72, Calif. State U., Fresno, 1980, U. Ala., Huntsville, 1985, U. Tenn. Space Inst., 1986—; bd. dirs. Tenn. Valley Aerospace Region, U. Tenn. Ctr. for Space Transp. and Applied Rsch.; mem. rev. bd. NASA Lewis Rocket Thruster Rsch. Program, Dept. of Def. Fellowship Program, Indsl. Laser Handbook; mem. nat. adv. bd. NASA Enring. Rsch. Ctr. for Propulsion, Pa. State U., NASA Ctr. for Advanced Space Propulsion, U. Tenn. Space Inst./Calspan. Reviewer Jour. Spacecraft and Rockets, Jour. Propulsion and Power, Jour. Thermophysics and Heat Transfer, Jour. Heat Transfer; contbr. articles to profl. jours.; patentee in field. Maj. U.S. Army, 1972-73. NRC rsch. fellow, 1980-84. Assoc. fellow AIAA (liquid propulsion tech. com. 1984-88, assoc. editor Jour. Propulsion and Power 1988-91); mem. Am. Soc. Metals, Am. Welding Soc., Laser Inst. Am. (chmn. ICALEO 1994), Am. Soc. Engring. Edn. Roman Catholic. Avocation: tennis. Office: Univ Tenn Vice Pres Office UT Space Inst Tullahoma TN 37388 Office: B H Goethert Pky MS-22 Tullahoma TN 37388-8897

MCCHESNEY, ROBERT MICHAEL, SR., political science educator; b. Effingham, Ill., Oct. 5, 1942; s. J.D. and Helen Grace (Russell) McC.; m. Laraine Freeman, Aug. 28, 1965; children: Robert M. Jr., Todd Patrick, Jennifer Laraine, Grant Russell, Brent Steven. BA, U. Southwestern La., 1964; MA, U. Va., 1967, PhD, 1969. Asst. instr. U. Va., Charlottesville, 1967-68; chmn. dept. polit. sci. U. Cen. Ark., Conway, 1971-76, dean coll. scis. and humanities, 1976-82, v.p. for acad. affairs, 1982-89, disting. prof., 1989-90; provost U. Montevallo, Ala., 1990-92; v.p. acad. affairs, 1992—; v.p. Survey Rsch., Inc., Conway, 1989-92; spl. cons. U. Ark. System, Little Rock, 1989. Mem. Carmichael Found., Conway, 1975-79; exec. bd. Quapaw coun. Boy Scouts Am., Little Rock, 1982-88; Birmingham Area Coun., 1995—. Capt. Med. Svc. Corps U.S. Army, 1968-71. Grantee State Justice Inst./Adminstrv. Office of Cts., Ark., 1989. Mem. Ark. Polit. Sci. Assn. (pres. 1975), Ala. Coun. Univ. and Coll. Pres. (chmn. 1993—), Conway C. of C., Montevall C. of C., Rotary (pres. Conway club 1987-88, Paul Harris fellow 1986), Phi Beta Kappa, Phi Kappa Phi. Mormon. Avocations: hunting, fishing, golfing. Home: Flowerhill UM Montevallo AL 35115 Office: U Montevallo Station 6001 Montevallo AL 35115

MC CHESNEY, ROBERT PEARSON, artist; b. Marshall, Mo., Jan. 16, 1913; s. John and Ruby (Pearson) McC.; m. Mary Ellen Fuller, Dec. 17, 1949. Student, Sch. Fine Arts, Washington U., 1931-34, Otis Art Inst., Los Angeles, 1936-37. Represented by Adrianne Fish, San Francisco, Walter Maibaum Fine Arts, N.Y.C., Annex Galleries, Santa Rosa, Calif.; instr. art Calif. Sch. Fine Arts, San Francisco, 1949-51, Santa Rosa Jr. Coll., 1957-58; Trustee San Francisco Art Inst., 1965-67. One-man shows, San Francisco Mus. Modern Art, 1949, 53, San Francisco Art Inst., 1957, Todes Art Gallery, Chgo., 1958, Reed Coll., Portland, Oreg., 1959, Parsons Gallery, Los Angeles, 1960, 61, Bolles Gallery, San Francisco, 1959, 61, 70, 71, N.Y.C., 1962, 20th Century West, N.Y.C., 1965, Both Up Gallery, Berkeley, Calif., 1973, 74, Lincoln Art Center, Santa Rosa, Calif., 1978, U. Calif. Hayward, 1977, Marin County Civic Center, 1980, Gallery Space, San Francisco, 1984, Michaels Gallery, San Francisco, 1985, Adlen Arts, Santa Rosa, Calif., 1986, Calif. Mus. of Art, Luther Burbank Ctr. for the Arts, Santa Rosa, Calif., 1988, Curtis Gallery, San Anselmo, 1989, Carlson Gallery, San Francisco, Calif., 1990, 871 Fine Arts, San Francisco, 1995; retrospective San Francisco Art Commn., 1974, retrospective Wm. Sawyer Art, Reno, 1994; group shows include art Inst. Chgo., 1947, 54, 60, 61, Corcoran Gallery, Washington, 1957, 3d Biennial Sao Paulo, Brazil, 1955, San Francisco Mus. Art Ann., 1945-60, Nordness Gallery, N.Y.C., 1964, Legion of Honor, San Francisco, 1962, 64, Oakland Mus., 1972, 73, Adlen Arts Gallery, Santa Rosa, 1985; represented in permanent collections, Whitney Mus. Am. Art, N.Y.C., Dr. Arnold Come, San Francisco Theol. Sem., San Anselmo, Calif., San Francisco Mus. Art, Oakland Art Mus., Art Inst. Chgo., Legion of Honor, Muskegon (Mich.) Mus. Art, San Francisco Art Commn., Wash. State Arts Commn., Madeline Martin, San Francisco, Harrison Mus. of Art Utah State U., Logan, Laguna Art Mus., Laguna Beach, Calif., Worcester (Mass.) Art Mus., others; mural in, San Francisco Social Services Bldg., 1978. Address: 2955 Sonoma Mountain Rd Petaluma CA 94954 *The desert wilderness, which I truly love to be in as much as possible, has influenced me a great deal. Of course, the artist is no different from anyone else in that he is influenced by everything around him visually and psychologically, but he has the ability to digest this, you might say, and then transform it into art.*

MCCHRISTIAN, JOSEPH ALEXANDER, international business executive; b. Chgo., Oct. 12, 1914; s. Robert Lee and Lillian (Alexander) McC.; BS in Mil. Sci., U.S. Mil. Acad., 1939; grad. Command and Gen. Staff Coll., 1942, Armed Forces Staff Coll., 1951, Army War Coll., 1955, Army Lang. Sch., 1956; m. Dempsie Catherine Van Fleet, Sept. 26, 1940; children: Joseph Alexander, Anne, Lillian. Enlisted U.S. Army, 1933, commnd. 2d lt., 1939, advanced through grades to maj. gen., 1961; various assignments 1933-44; successively armored inf. bn. comdr., asst. chief staff plans and ops., chief staff 10th Armored Div., ETO, 1944-45; asst. chief staff intelligence Hdqrs. U.S. Army, Germany, then dir. intelligence U.S Forces, Austria, 1947-48; comdg. officer 2d Bn., 3d Inf., Ft. McNair, D.C., 1948-49; spl. asst. to chief JUSMAG, Greece, 1949-50; S3 dept. tactics U.S. Mil. Acad., 1951-

53, comdg. officer 1st Regt., U.S. Corp Cadets, 1953-54; U.S. Army attache, Greece, 1956-60; comdg. officer 1st Armored Regt. (tng.), also comdg. officer U.S. Army Tng. Ctr., Armor, Ft. Knox, Ky., 1960-61; chief Western div. Office Asst. Chief Staff-Intelligence, Dept. Army, 1962-63; asst. chief staff intelligence Hdqrs. U.S. Army Pacific, 1963-65; chief Army, Navy, Air Force and Marine Corps Intelligence, Hdqrs. U.S. Mil. Assistance Command, Vietnam, 1965-67; comdg. gen. 2d Armored Div., also III Corps, Ft. Hood, Tex., 1967-68; asst. chief of staff for intelligence Dept. Army, 1968-71; v.p. Overseas Basic Industries, Fla., 1972-74; v.p., gen. Société des Eaux, Athens, Greece, 1974-77, v.p. Ulen Mgmt. Co., Fla., 1972-75, Van Fleet Estates, Inc., Fla., 1970-77. Commr., Town of Jupiter Island (Fla.), 1975-83. Decorated D.S.M. with oak leaf cluster, Silver Star, Legion of Merit, Bronze Star with 3 oak leaf clusters, Air medal, Commendation ribbon, Combat Inf. badge; Croix de Guerre with gold star and bronze star (France); comdr. Royal Order King George 1st, also Disting. Svc. medal (Greece); Nat. Order 5th class and Disting. Svc. Order 1st class (Republic Vietnam); Mil. Merit medal, Chung Mu (Korea). Mem. Mil. Order World Wars, Alumni Assn. U.S. Mil. Acad. Clubs: Army and Navy (Washington); Hobe Sound Yacht, The Island (Hobe Sound, Fla.); Ends of the Earth. Home: 365 South Beach Rd Hobe Sound FL 33455-2428

MCCLAIN, BENJAMIN RICHARD, music educator, educational administrator; b. Highland Park, Mich., May 20, 1931; s. Benjamin Richard and Julia (Hockett) McC.; m. Tahlia Helen Ruth Carter, Feb. 9, 1952 (div.); children: Terrence, Gerald, Sharalyn, Marilyn; m. Shirley Ann Brown, June 16, 1982; stepchildren: Keith, Sheila, Kenneth Hall. BMus, U. Mich., 1959, MusM, 1967, PhD, 1972. Cert. tchr., Mich., Fla., Wash. Jr. high sch. tchr. Inkster (Mich.) Pub. Schs., 1959-62; high sch. tchr. Dearborn Heights (Mich.) Pub. Schs., 1962-67, attendance officer, 1967-68, asst. high sch. prin., 1968-69; high sch. prin. Robichaud High Sch., Dearborn Heights, 1969-72; cons. State Dept. of Edn., Lansing, Mich., 1973-74; prof. Fla. Atlantic U., Boca Raton, 1974-79; academic dean Fla. Meml. Coll., Miami, 1979-80; prof. U. North Fla., Jacksonville, 1980-82, Gonzaga U., Spokane, Wash., 1982-85; with Seattle Pub. Schs., 1985-88; CEO MELT and Assocs., 1985-88; prof. Valdosta (Ga.) State U., 1988—. Editorial bd. The Western Jour. of Black Studies, 1984; contbr. numerous articles to profl. jours. Co-chmn. Athletic Booster Club, Boca Raton, 1977. Recipient Lafayette Allen Sr. Disting. Svc. award, 1973; Mott fellowship U. Mich., 1971-72, Regents Alumni scholarship, 1949-53. Mem. NAACP, Nat. Community Edn. Assn. (human rels. chair), Kiwanis, Phi Delta Kappa, Kappa Alpha Psi. Democrat. Baptist. Avocations: church choir, organist, piano accompanist. Office: Valdosta State Univ EDL Dept Valdosta GA 31698

MCCLAIN, CHARLES JAMES, state educational administrator; b. Ironton, Mo., Sept. 1, 1931; s. John F. and Hazel (Pierce) McC.; children: Anita, Melanie. BEd, S.W. Mo. State U., 1954; MEd, U. Mo., 1957, EdD, 1961; hon. degree, Busan Nat. U., 1992. Mo. Western State Coll., Kirksville Coll. Osteo. Medicine, Cen. Meth. Coll. Pres. Jefferson Coll., Hillsboro, Mo., 1963-70, N.E. Mo. State U., Kirksville, 1970-89; commr. higher edn. State of Mo., Jefferson City, 1989—; panelist, presenter nat. and internat. edn. confs. Contbr. articles to profl. jours. Bd. dirs. United Meth. Found., Mo. Higher Edn. Loan Authority. Recipient Disting. Alumnus award S.W. Mo. State U., 1977, Disting. Svc. award U. Mo. Coll. Edn.; G. Theodore Mitau award, 1983, Alumni award U. Mo.-Columbia, 1989; named Pub. Administr. of Yr. Mo. Inst. Pub. Adminstrn., 1986. Mem. Internat. Assn. Univ. Pres., Am. Assn. State Colls. and Univs., Am. Assn. Higher Edn. (bd. dirs.), Midwestern Higher Edn. Commn., Mo. Coun. Econ. Edn. (exec. com.), Mo. Acad. Sci. Home: PO Box 104503 Jefferson City MO 65110-4503 Office: Higher Edn Coord Bd 3515 Amazonas Dr Jefferson City MO 65109-5717 *One can get a lot done if he/she doesn't care who gets the credit.*

MCCLAIN, CHARLES WILLIAM, JR. (BILL MCCLAIN), army officer; b. Ft. Worth, Aug. 14, 1940; s. Charles William McClain Sr. and Martha Jane (Evans) Gates; children: Michele, Kathleen. BA, Tex. A&M Coll., 1962; MA, Cen. Mich. U., 1981; postgrad., U.S. Army Command and Gen. Staff Coll., Fort Leavenworth, Kans., 1976, U.S Army War Coll., Carlisle Barracks, Pa., 1984. Commd. 2d lt. U.S. Army, 1962, advanced through grades to maj. gen.; 1992; student Air Def. Officer Basic Course Air Def. Sch. U.S. Army, Fort Bliss, Tex., 1962; asst. pub. info. officer Air Def. Ctr. U.S. Army, Fort Bliss, 1962-63, platoon leader Battery B, 6th Missile Bn. (HAWK), 71st Arty., 1963-64, comdr. Battery B, 6th Missile Bn. (HAWK), 71st Arty., 1964-65; asst. ops. officer, 6th Missile Bn. (HAWK), 71st Arty. Fort Bliss, 1965; asst. subsector advisor, later Popular Forces Tng. Ctr. Advisor, Adv. Team 27, U.S. Mil. Assistance Command Vietnam, 1965-66; student Arty. Officer Advanced Course Air Def. Sch. U.S. Army, Fort Bliss, 1966-67; asst. prof. mil sci. Morgan State U., Balt., 1968-71; info. officer 101st Airborne Div. (Airmobile), Vietnam, 1971-72, Ft. Campbell, Ky., 1972-74; exec. officer 1st Bn. 3d Air Def. Arty., 101st Airborne Div. (Airmobile) Ft. Campbell, 1974; asst. air def. officer 1st Bn., 3d Air Def. Arty., 101st Airborne Div. (Airmobile) U.S. Army, Fort Campbell, 1974-75, asst. div. air def. officer, 1st Bn., 3d Air Def. Arty., 101st Airborne Div. (Airmobile), 1976-78; plans and policy officer, later chief plans and policy, Office of Chief Pub. Affairs, Europe U.S. Army, Washington, 1978-79, staff officer, later chief news br., later chief media inquiry br., later chief spl. activities, Office of Chief Pub. Affairs, 1979-83, chief news div., later dir. def. info., Office of the Asst. Sec. Def. (Pub. Affairs), 1983-86; chief Office of Chief Pub. Affairs, Europe U.S. Army, 1986-87; chief Pub. Info. Office, SHAPE, Mons, Belgium, 1987-89; dep. chief pub. affairs Office Sec. Army U.S. Army, Washington, 1989-90, chief pub. affairs Office Sec. Army, 1990—. Decorated Def. Superior Svc. medal with oak leaf cluster, Legion of Merit, Bronze Star, Meritorious Svc. medal with oak leaf cluster, Army Commendation medal with two oak leaf clusters. Office: The Pentagon Chief Pub Affairs Washington DC 20310-1501

MCCLAIN, PAULA DENICE, political scientist; b. Louisville, Jan. 3, 1950; d. Robert Landis and Annette (Williams) McC.; m. Paul C. Jacobson, Jan. 30, 1988; children: Kristina L., Jessica A. BA, Howard U., Washington, 1972; MA, Howard U., 1974, PhD, 1977; postgrad., U. Pa., 1981-82. Asst. prof. dept. polit. sci. U. Wis., Milw., 1977-82; assoc. prof. and prof. pub. affairs Ariz. State U., Tempe, 1982-91; prof. govt. and fgn. affairs U. Va., Charlottesville, 1991—, chair govt. and fgn. affairs, 1994—. Co-author: Race, Place and Risk: Black Homicide in Urban America, 1990, Can We All Get Along? Racial and Ethnic Minorities in American Politics, 1995; editor: Minority Group Influence, 1993; co-editor: Urban Minority Administrators, 1988. Mem. Nat. Conf. Black Polit. Scientists (pres. 1989-90), Am. Polit. Sci. Assn. (mem. coun. 1985-87, v.p. 1993-94), So. Polit. Sci. Assn. (exec. coun. 1992-95). Office: U Va Dept Govt 232 Cabell Hall Charlottesville VA 22901

MCCLAIN, THOMAS E., communications executive; b. East Liverpool, Ohio, July 26, 1950; s. Thomas E. and Helen Marie (Polinski) McC. BA, Case Western Reserve, Cleve., 1972; MA, Kans. State U., 1973. With intergovtl. rels. Ohio EPA, Columbus, 1974-77; legis. liaison Ohio Consumers Counsel, Columbus, 1977-80; dir. Ohio Consumers Counsel, 1980-81; press sec. Ohio Atty. Gen., Columbus, 1982-83; asst. dir. Pub. Utilities Commn., Columbus, 1983; with instnl. rels. dept. Battelle Project Mgmt. Div., Chgo., 1983-84; mgr. instnl. rels. Battelle Project Mgmt. Div., 1984-86; mgr. communications Battelle, Columbus, 1986-88; dir. corp. communications Battelle, 1989—; sec. devel. bd. Children's Hosp., Columbus, 1990—. Vol. Ohio Youth Commn., Columbus, 1975-76; active ARC-Cen. Ohio chpt., 1986-87. Warren Lahr scholar Case Western Reserve U., 1971-72. Mem. Ohio communications program com. 1991-93, bd. dirs. 1994-95). Democrat. Presbyterian. Avocations: basketball, golf, travel. Home: 2689 Camden Rd Columbus OH 43221-3221 Office: Battelle 505 King Ave Columbus OH 43201

MCCLAIN, WILLIAM ANDREW, lawyer; b. Sanford, N.C., Jan. 11, 1913; s. Frank and Blanche (Leslie) McC.; m. Roberta White, Nov. 11, 1944. A.B., Wittenberg U., 1934; J.D., U. Mich., 1937; LL.D. (hon.), Wilberforce U., 1963, U. Cin., 1971; LL.D., Wittenberg U., 1972. Bar: Ohio 1938, U.S. Dist. Ct. (so. dist.) Ohio 1940, U.S. Ct. Appeals (6th cir.) 1946, U.S. Supreme Ct. 1946. Mem. Berry, McClain & White, 1937-58; dep. solicitor, City of Cin., 1957-63, city solicitor, 1963-72; mem. Keating, Muething & Klekamp, Cin., 1972-73; gen. counsel Cin. Br., SBA, 1973-75; judge Hamilton County Common Pleas Ct., 1975-76; judge Mcpl. Ct., 1976-80; of counsel Manley, Burke, Fischer, Lipton & Cook, Cin., 1980—; adj. prof. U.

Cin., 1963-72, Salmon P. Chase Law Sch., 1965-72. Exec. com. ARC, Cin., 1978—; bd. dirs. NCCJ, 1975—. Served to 1st lt. JAGC, U.S. Army, 1943-46. Decorated Army Commendation award; recipient Nat. Layman award, A.M.E. Ch., 1963; Alumni award Wittenberg U., 1966; Nat. Inst. Mcpl. Law Officers award, 1971. Fellow Am. Bar Found.; mem. Am. Judicature Soc., Cin. Bar Assn., Ohio Bar Assn., ABA, Fed. Bar assn., Nat. Bar Assn., Alpha Phi Alpha, Sigma Pi Phi. Republican. Methodist. Clubs: Bankers, Friendly Sons of St. Patrick Lodge: Masons (33 deg.). Home: 2101 Grandin Rd Apt 904 Cincinnati OH 45208-3346

MCCLAIN, WILLIAM THOMAS, lawyer; b. Louisville, June 4, 1926; s. George Lee and Catherine (Spalding) McC.; m. Wanda Barry, Feb. 28, 1949; children: Nina, Catherine, Ann, William, Mary. BS in Metall. Engring., U. Ky., 1948; JD, Loyola U., New Orleans, 1958. Bar: Ill. 1960, D.C. 1988. Engr. Shell Oil Co., Deer Park, Tex., 1948-55; asst. prof. U. Houston, 1951-55; sales engr. Pacific Valves, Inc., New Orleans, 1955-58; assoc. Wier, Greene & Nelson, New Orleans, 1958, Amoco Corp., Chgo., 1959-86, Finnegan, Henderson, Farabow, Garrett & Dunner, Washington, 1987—. With USN, 1944-46. Mem. ABA (chmn. 1987—), Am. Intellectual Property Law Assn. (dir., treas. 1986-90). Republican. Avocations: golf, tennis, reading. Office: Finnegan Henderson Farabow Garrett & Dunner 1300 I St NW Washington DC 20005-3314

MCCLAMROCH, N. HARRIS, aerospace engineering educator, consultant, researcher; b. Houston, Oct. 7, 1942; s. Nathaniel Harris and Dorthy Jean (Orand) McC.; m. Margaret Susan Hobart, Aug. 10, 1963; 1 child, Kristin Jean. B.S., U. Tex., 1963, M.S., 1965, Ph.D., 1967. Prof. dept. elec. engring. and computer sci. U. Mich., Ann Arbor, 1967—, chair dept. aerospace engring., 1992—; research engr. Cambridge U., Eng., 1975, Delft U., Netherlands, 1976, Sandia Labs., Albuquerque, 1977, C.S. Draper Lab., Cambridge, Mass., 1982. Author: State Models of Dynamic Systems, 1980; contbr. numerous articles to profl. jours. Chmn. U. Mich. Faculty Senate, 1987-88, dept. aerospace engring., 1992—. Fellow IEEE (editor Transactions on Automatic Control 1989-92); mem. AAAS. Home: 4056 Thornoaks Dr Ann Arbor MI 48104-4254 Office: U Mich Aerospace Engring Ann Arbor MI 48109

MCCLANAHAN, LARRY DUNCAN, civil engineer, consultant; b. Franklin, Ky., July 30, 1938; s. Ernest William McClanahan and Anne Isabel (Henderson) McClanahan Hodges; m. Betty Jane Marquess, Mar. 16, 1963; children: Michael Curtis, Marta Suzette Stinson, Meredith Angela. BSCE, Tenn. Poly. Inst., 1965; MSCE, Tenn. Tech. U., 1974. Registered profl. engr., Tenn., Ky., Ala. Sr. civil engr. Tenn. Bur. Aero., Nashville, 1965-67; airport planning engr. FAA, Memphis, 1967-68; assoc. R. Dixon Speas & Assocs., Atlanta, 1968-70; prin. Larry D. McClanahan & Assocs., Nashville, 1970—; pres. Agtech-Ky., Inc., Franklin, Ky., 1984-87. Pres. Nannie Perry Sch. PTA, Hendersonville, Tenn., 1975, Woodlands Homeowners Assn., 1992-93; v.p. Jackson Park Cmty. Assn., Nashville, 1985-86, pres., 1986-87, 90-94; chmn. bd. dirs. Hendersonville Mcpl. Airport Authority, 1973-75; geneal. mem. Nashville Met. Pub. Records Commn., 1992—, chmn., 1992—; mem. subarea 4 citizens adv. com. Metro Planning Commn.; alt. chmn. Citizens Postal Adv. Com. for Jere Baxter Sta. of U.S. Post Office. Recipient Sustained Superior Service award FAA, 1968. Mem. SAR (Tenn. soc. state sec., registrar 1985-90, state v.p. 1990-91, pres. 1992-93, founding pres. Sumner chpt. 1990-91, nat. trustee, v.p. gen. so. dist. 1994-95, chmn. nat. Americanism com., DAR liaison, mem. congress planning and nat. nominating coms. 1994—, Disting. Svc. cert. 1986, Meritorious Svc. medal 1987, Florence Kendall medal/award 1991, Liberty medal with 4 oakleaf clusters 1994, Patriot medal 1993), ASCE (chmn. landing area subcom. 1969-71), Soc. Boonesborough, McClanahan Family Assn., Order of Engrs., No. Neck of Va. Hist. Soc., Gen. Soc. Colonial Wars (gov. Tenn. 1994—), Knights Sovereign Mil. Order Temple of Jerusalem, Masons, Freolac Club (Nashville). Republican. Baptist. Avocations: geneology, history, travel, basketball and baseball (amateur coach). Home: 1119 Winding Way Rd Nashville TN 37216-2213 Office: 203A Point East Dr Nashville TN 37216-1403

MCCLANAHAN, LELAND, academic adminstrator; b. Hammond, Ind., Mar. 14, 1931; s. Alonzo Leland and Eva (Hermanson) McC.; m. Lavaughn Adell Meyrer, June 5, 1954; children: Leland, Loren. Diploma, Ctrl. Bible Coll., 1954; PhBB, Nat. Postgrad. Bible Acad., 1969; BA, Southwestern Coll., 1973; MA, Fla. State Christian Coll., 1964, ThD, 1970; PhD, Faith Bible Coll. and Sem., Ft. Lauderdale, Fla. and Marina, Lagos, Nigeria, 1969; MA, Bapt. Christian U., 1988, ThD, 1989, DLitt, 1990, PsyD, 1991, PhD (hon.), 1991, DEd, 1992, D in Bus. Adminstrn., 1993; DD (hon.), Internat. Evangelism Crusades, 1969; PhD, Freedom U., 1989; DD, Trinity Union Coll., 1991; LLD, La. Bapt. U., 1994; StD, PhD, Trinity Internat. U., 1994; PhD, Hawaii U., 1995; HHD, La. Bapt. U., 1995. Diplomate Nat. Bd. Christian Clin. Therapists; ordained pastor, Christian Ch., 1950. Founder, pastor Evangel Temple, Griffith, Ind., 1954-73, Abundant Life Temple, Cocoa, Fla., 1974-77; mgr. ins. divsn. United Agys., Cocoa, Fla., 1979-81; assoc. pastor Merritt Assembly of God, Merritt Island, Fla., 1982-85, Palm Chapel, Merritt Island, 1987-89, 1990-93; chancellor Chapel Christian U., Merritt Island, Fla., 1990—; founder, dir. Griffith Youth Ctr., 1960-70, Todd Nursery Sch., Griffith, 1971-73; founder, chancellor Ind. Bible Coll., Griffith, 1971-73; dir. Chapel Counseling Ctr., Merritt Island, 1990-94. Author: Is Divine Healing For Today?, 1989, Truths From the Gospel of St. John, 1991, An Outline of the Revelation, 1993, Numbers In the Bible, 1994; author 138 coll. courses and books. Recipient Disting. Svc. award U.S. Jaycees, 1966; named Hon. Lt. Col., Gov. Guy Hunt, 1988. Mem. Am. Inst. Clin. Psychotherapists, Am. Assn. Christian Counselors, Nat. Christian Counseling Assn. (assoc., lic.), Internat. Assn. Pastoral Psychologists (lic.), orer of St. John, Knight of Malta (comdr. 1990). Republican. Avocations: reading, walking, watching sports, watching television adventures, weight lifting. Home: 870 Australian St Merritt Island FL 32953-4676 Office: Chapel Christian U 670 N Courtenay Pkwy Ste 15 Merritt Island FL 32953

MC CLANAHAN, RUE (EDDI-RUE MC CLANAHAN), actress; b. Healdton, Okla.; d. William Edwin and Dreda Rheua-Nell (Medaris) McC.; m. 1st, Tom Bish, 1958; 1 child, Mark Thomas Bish; m. 2nd, Norman Hartweg; m. 3rd, Peter DeMaio; m. 4th, Gus Fisher, 1976; m. 5th, Tom Keel, 1984 (div. 1985). B.A. cum laude, U. Tulsa, 1956. Appearances include (theatre) Erie (Pa.) Playhouse, 1957-58; (Broadway) Jimmy Shine, 1968-69, Sticks and Bones, 1972, California Suite, 1977, After-Play, 1995; (TV appearances) L.A., 1959-64, N.Y.C., 1964-73; (TV series) Maude, 1973-78, Apple Pie, 1978, Mama's Family, 1982-84, Golden Girls, 1985-92, Golden Palace, 1992-93; (TV movies) Having Babies III, 1978, Sgt. Matlowch vs the U.S. Air Force, 1978, Rainbow, 1978, Topper, 1979, The Great American Traffic Jam, 1980, Word of Honor, 1981, The Day the Bubble Burst, 1982, The Little Match Girl, 1987, Liberace, 1988, Take My Daughters Please, 1988, Let Me Hear You Whisper, 1988, To the Heroes, 1989, After the Shock, 1990, Children of the Bride, 1990, To My Daughter, 1990, The Dreamer of Oz, 1990, Baby of the Bride, 1991, Mother of the Bride, 1993, Danielle Steele's Message from Nam, 1993, Burning Passion: The Margaret Mitchell Story, 1994; (films) The People Next Door, 1970, They Might Be Giants, 1971, The Pursuit of Happiness, 1971, Modern Love, 1990. Recipient Obie award for leading off-Broadway role in Who's Happy Now, 1970; Emmy award Best Actress in a comedy, 1987; named Woman of Yr., Pasadena Playhouse, 1986; Spl. scholar Pasadena (Calif.) Playhouse, 1959, Phi Beta Gamma scholar, 1955. Mem. Actors Studio, Actors Equity Assn., AFTRA, Screen Actors Guild. Office: Agy for Performing Arts 9000 Sunset Blvd Ste 1200 Los Angeles CA 90069*

MCCLANE, DRAYTON, JR., professional baseball team executive. Owner, chmn. bd. Houston Astros, also chief exec. officer. Office: Houston Astros PO Box 288 Houston TX 77001-0288*

MCCLANE, ROBERT SANFORD, bank holding company executive; b. Kenedy, Tex., May 5, 1939; s. Norris Robert and Ella Addie (Stockton) McC.; m. Sue Nitschke, Mar. 31, 1968; children: Len Stokes, Norris Robert. BS in Bus. Adminstrn., Trinity U., San Antonio, 1961. With Ford Motor Co., Detroit, 1961-62; with Frost Nat. Bank, San Antonio, 1962—, mem. staff, 1962-68, v.p., 1968-78, exec. v.p. Cullen/Frost Bankers, Inc., 1976—, pres., dir., 1985—; bd. dirs. Frost Nat. Bank, San Antonio, C/F Life Ins. Co., San Antonio, Main Plaza Corp., San Antonio, Daltex Gen. Agy., San Antonio. Crusade chmn. Baxar County chpt. Am. Cancer Soc., 1974;

bd. dirs. Bexar County ARC, 1969-72; sr. warden St. Luke's Episopal Ch., San Antonio, 1980; trustee Alamo Pub. Telecomms. Coun., San Antonio, 1981-88, Trinity U., 1990—; chmn. San Antonio Econ. Devel. Found., 1987-89, exec. com. 1985-91. Mem. Bankers Roundtable, Greater San Antonio C. of C. (chmn. leadership San Antonio 1975-76, bd. dirs. exec. com. 1994—), Trinity U. Alumni Assn. (pres. 1968-69, disting. alumnus 1987), San Antonio German Club, Order Alamo, Tex. Cavaliers, Argyle Club, Town Club, Plaza Club (bd. dirs. 1973-92). Episcopalian. Office: Cullen/Frost Bankers Inc 100 W Houston St San Antonio TX 78205-1402

MCCLARAN, GEORGE JOSEPH, SR., retired banker; b. Pitts., July 15, 1924; s. Joseph Fred and Adeline Hester (Barnes) McC.; m. Grace Wilma Hunt, May 6, 1950; children: Lynda Ann, Joanne, George Joseph Jr., Richard Hunt. BA, Ohio Wesleyan U., 1947; postgrad., U. Pitts., 1947-49, Mich. State Normal Coll., 1944. V.p. Pitts. Nat. Bank, 1959-73, sr. v.p., 1973-84, exec. v.p., 1984-85, pres., 1985-88, vice chmn., 1988-89, also bd. dirs., ret.; chmn. bd. dirs. Forbes Health System, Pitts., Western Pa. Devel. Credit Corp., Pitts.;bd. dirs. Forbes Healthmark, Newcomer Products, Latrobe, Pa., Robroy Industries, Inc., Verona, Pa., Forbes Health Found., Pitts., Landmark Ventures, Inc., Pitts. 1st lt. U.S. Army, 1944-45, 50-52. Mem. Duquesne Club, Longue Vue Club (Verona, Pa.) (pres. 1972-74), Bent Tree Country Club (Sarasota), Masons, Shriners. Republican. Clubs: Duquesne; Longue Vue (Verona, Pa.) (pres. 1972-74); Bent Tree Country (Sarasota). Lodges: Masons, Shriners, Royal Order Jesters. Avocations: golf, fishing. Home: 254 Sweet Gum Rd Pittsburgh PA 15238-1348

MCCLARD, JACK EDWARD, lawyer; b. Lafayette, La., May 13, 1946; s. Lee Franklin and Mercedes Cecile (Landry) McC.; m. Marilyn Kay O'Gorman, June 3, 1972; 1 child, Lauren Marion. BA in Hist., Rice U., 1968; JD, U. Tex., 1974. Bar: Va. 1974, U.S. Dist. Ct. (ea. and we. dists.) Va. 1974, D.C. 1981, U.S. Dist. Ct. D.C. 1981, N.Y. 1985, U.S. Dist. Ct. (so. and ea. dists.) N.Y. 1985, U.S. Ct. Appeals (4th cir.) 1978, U.S. Ct. Appeals (D.C. cir.) 1980, U.S. Ct. Appeals (5th cir.) 1993. Assoc. Hunton & Williams, Richmond, Va., 1974-81; ptnr. Hunton & Williams, Richmond, 1981—. Contbr. articles to profl. jours. Served to lt. (j.g.) USN, 1968-71. Mem. ABA, Va. Bar Assn., Richmond Bar Assn., Va. Trial Lawyers Assn., 5th Cir. Bar. Democrat. Episcopalian. Avocations: bridge, gardening. Home: 100 Trowbridge Rd Richmond VA 23233-5724 Office: Hunton & Williams 951 E Byrd St Riverfront Plz E Tower Richmond VA 23219-4074

MC CLARREN, ROBERT ROYCE, librarian; b. Delta, Ohio, Mar. 15, 1921; s. Dresden William Howard and Norma Leona (Whiteman) McC.; m. Margaret Aileen Weed, May 31, 1947; children: Mark Robert, Todd Adams. Student, Antioch Coll., 1938-40; AB, Muskingum Coll., 1942; MA in English, Ohio State U., 1951; MS in L.S., Columbia, 1954; DLitt (hon.), Rosary Coll., 1989. Registration officer VA, Cin., 1946-47; instr. English Gen. Motors Inst., 1949-50; head circulation dept. Oak Park Public Library, Ill., 1954-55; acting head librarian Oak Park Public Library, 1955; head librarian Crawfordsville Public Library, Ind., 1955-58, Huntington Public Library, also Western Counties (W.Va.) Regional Public Library, W.Va., 1958-62; dir. Ind. State Library, 1962-67; system dir. North Suburban Library System, 1967-89; system dir. emeritus, 1990—; cons. libr. Chgo. Pub. Libr. Found., 1990; del. White House Conf. on Librs., 1979; instr. U. Wis., summer 1964, Rosary Coll., 1968-80, U. Tex., summer 1979, 82, No. Ill. U., 1980; pres. W.Va. Libr. Assn., 1960; mem. Gov. Ind. Commn. Arts, 1964-65, Ill. State Libr. Adv. Com., 1972-79, 87-89, chmn., 1975-79, vice chmn., 1988-89; bd. dirs. Ill. Regional Libr. Coun., 1972-82, pres., 1977; chmn. adv. commn. Nat. Periodical System, Nat. Commn. on Librs. and Info. Sci., 1978-81; treas. Ill. Coalition Libr. Advocates, 1982-89. Contbr. articles to profl. jours. Served to 1st lt. AUS, 1942-46, 51-52; maj. Res. Named Ill. Librarian of Yr., 1978. Mem. ALA (councilor 1966-68, 74-78, treas. 1968-72, endowment trustee 1972-78, mem. publ. bd. 1972-75, pres. reference and adv. svc. div. 1975-76, Melville Dewey award 1989), Ill. Libr. Assn. (pres. 1981, Robert R. McClarren Legis. award 1989), Am. Libr. Trustee Assn. (v.p. 1976-77, Assn. Spl. and Coop. Libr. Agys. (pres. 1978-79, Exceptional Achievement award 1982), Ohio Hist. Soc., Am. Philatelic Soc., Sagamore of Wabash (Ind.), Ry. and Locomotive Hist. Soc. Home: 1560 Oakwood Pl Deerfield IL 60015-2014 Office: 200 W Dundee Rd Wheeling IL 60090-4750

MCCLARY, JAMES DALY, retired contractor; b. Boise, Idaho, July 19, 1917; s. Neil Hamaker and Myrtle (Daly) McC.; m. Mary Jane Munger, Feb. 2, 1939; children—Pamela, John. Student, Boise Jr. Coll., 1934-36, A.A., 1957; A.B., Stanford, 1938; LL.D., Gonzaga U., 1976. Laborer to supt. Morrison-Knudsen Co., Inc., Boise, 1932-42, project mgr., asst. dist. mgr., 1942- 47; gen. mgr. Mexican subs. Morrison-Knudsen Co., Inc. 1947-51, asst. to gen. mgr., 1951-53, asst. gen. mgr., 1953-60, dir., 1955-78, v.p., 1956-60, exec. v.p., 1960-72, chmn. bd., 1972-78; mem., vice chmn. Idaho Permanent Bldg. Fund Adv. Council, 1961-64, chmn., 1964-71. Treas. Idaho Rep. Cen. Com., 1964-70; presdl. elector, 1968; trustee Boise Jr. Coll., 1960-83, vice chmn., 1967-73, chmn., 1973-83; bd. dirs. Boise State U. Found., Inc., 1964-91, pres., 1970-81; bd. dirs. AGC Edn. and Rsch. Found., 1974-91, pres., 1974-90; elector Hall of Fame for Great Ams., 1976—; trustee St. Alphonsus Regional Med. Ctr., 1976-82, vice chmn., 1981-82. Recipient George Washington medal of honor Freedoms Found., Valley Forge, Pa., 1977, Disting. Alumnus award Boise State U., 1988; decorated Chevalier and Legion of Honor, Order of DeMolay; named Disting. Alumnus of Yr. Boise State U. Alumni Assn., 1971, Ky. Col. Fellow ASCE, Am. Inst. Constructors; mem. Internat. Road Fedn. (dir. 1972-78, vice chmn. 1977-78), Soc. Am. Mil. Engrs., Assoc. Gen. Contractors Am. (dir. 1958—, exec. com. 1961-78, pres. 1972), Cons. Constructors Council Am., Newcomen Soc., Conf. Bd. (sr. mem.), Idaho Assn. Commerce and Industry (dir., chmn. 1974-77), The Moles (hon., mem. award 1978), Hillcrest Country Club (bd. dirs. 1965-67, 69, pres. 1967), Arid Club (exec. com. 1966), Ariz. Club (Scottsdale), Ariz. Country Club (Phoenix), Univ. Club (Mexico City), Stanford Club (Boise), Capitol Hill Club, Internat. Club (Washington). Episcopalian. Home: 4903 Roberts Rd Boise ID 83705-2805

MCCLARY, SUSAN, musicology educator, writer; b. St. Louis, Oct. 2, 1946. BMus, So. Ill. U., 1968; AM, Harvard, 1971, PhD, 1976. Prof. musicology U. Calif., L.A. Author: (book) Feminine Endings: Music, Gender and Sexuality, 1991; co-editor: (book) Music and Society: The Politics of Composition, Performance and Reception, 1987. MacArthur fellow, 1995. Office: Univ CA Los Angeles Dept Musicology 405 Hilgard Ave Los Angeles CA 90024*

MCCLATCHY, J. D., editor, writer, educator; b. Bryn Mawr, Pa., Aug. 12, 1945; s. J. Donald and Mary Jane (Hayden) McC. BA summa cum laude, Georgetown U., 1967; PhD, Yale U., 1974. Instr. English dept. LaSalle Coll., Phila., 1968-71; asst. prof. English dept. Yale U., New Haven, Conn., 1974-81, lectr. English dept., 1983, 86-87; writer-in-residence CCNY, 1982; writer-in-residence Poetry Ctr. 92d St. YMCA, N.Y.C, 1983-84, workshop leader Poetry Ctr., 1982-91; lectr. Creative Writing program, English dept. Princeton U., 1981-87, 89-93; editor The Yale Rev., New Haven, 1991—; poet-in-residence Southampton Writers Conf., 1988; lectr. MFA Parsons/ New Sch., 1989, English dept. Rutgers U., 1989, writing divsn. Columbia U., 1989, 92; vis. prof. English dept. UCLA, 1990, 92; selection com. Conn. Poetry Cir. Author: (poetry) Scenes from Another Life, 1981, (London 1983), Lantskip, Platan, Creatures Ramp'd, 1983, Stars Principal, 1986, Kilim, 1987, The Rest of the Way, 1990, The Art of Poetry, 1994; librettist: A Question of Taste, 1989, Mario and the Magician, 1994, Orpheus Decending, 1994; editor: The Yale Review, 1991—, (books) Anne Sexton: The Artist and Her Critics, 1978, For James Merrill: A Birthday Tribute, 1986, Recitative: Prose by James Merrill, 1986, Poets on Painters: Essays on the Art of Painting by Twentieth Century Poets, 1988, The Vintage Book of Contemporary American Poetry, 1990, Woman in White: Selected Poems of Emily Dickinson, 1991; assoc. editor Four Quarters, 1968-71; contbg. editor Am. Poetry Review; poetry editor The Yale Review, 1981-91; trans. articles, contbr. poems, stories, articles, reviews to various jours. Bd. dirs. Ingram Merrill Found., 1986—. Recipient gold medal Vergilian Acad., 1967, O. Henry award, 1972, prize Am. Acad. Poets ,1972, Chase Going Woodhouse Poetry prize, 1976, Michener award, 1982, Gordon Barber Meml. award Poetry Soc. Am., 1984, Eunice Tietjens Meml. prize Poetry Mag., 1985, Witter Bynner Poetry prize Am. Acad. and Inst. Arts and Letters, 1985, award in lit., 1991, Oscar Blumenthal prize Poetry Mag., 1988, Levinson prize, 1990, Melville Cane award Poetry Soc. Am., 1991, Literary Lion N.Y. Pub. Libr., 1992; grantee Ingram Merrill Found., 1979, Conn. Commn. Arts,

1981; fellow NEA, 1987, John Simon Guggenheim Meml. Found., 1988; fellow lit. Acad. Am. Poets, 1991; artist resident Djerassi Found., 1988; Woodrow Wilson fellow 1967-68; Yale U. fellow, 1971-72; Ethel Boise Morgan fellow, 1972-74; artist's fellow N.Y. Found. Arts, 1986; artist resident Yaddo, 1991, MacDowell Colony, 1991. Mem. Phi Beta Kappa, Alpha Sigma Nu. Home: 15 Grand St Stonington CT 06378-1340 Office: The Yale Review Yale Univ PO Box 208243 New Haven CT 06520-8243

MCCLATCHY, JAMES B., editor, newspaper publisher; b. Sacramento; s. Carlos K. and Phebe (Briggs) McC.; m. Susan Brewster; children: Carlos F., William B. B.A., Stanford U.; M.S., Columbia U. Reporter Sacramento Bee; reporter, editor Fresno Bee, Calif.; chmn. McClatchy Newspapers, Sacramento.; pres., dir. InterAm. Press Assn.; dir. Calif. Nature Conservancy, Am. Press Inst. Pres., dir. French Am. Bilingual Sch. Served as maj., pilot USAFR, 1945-57. Office: McClatchy Newspapers 21st & Q Sts Sacramento CA 95813

MCCLAUGHERTY, JOHN LEWIS, lawyer; b. Bluefield, W.Va., Feb. 13, 1931; s. William N. and N. Louisa (Shelton) McC.; m. Sallie M. Fredeking, June 27, 1953; children: Martha M. Nepa, John W. BS, Northwestern U., 1953; LLB, W.Va. U., 1956. Bar: W.Va. 1956, U.S. Dist. Ct. (so. dist.) W.Va. 1956, U.S. Ct. Appeals (4th cir.) 1956, U.S. Supreme Ct. 1975, U.S. Ct. Mil. Appeals 1957. Assoc. Jackson & Kelly, Charleston, W.Va., 1959-65, ptnr., 1965—; mem. Nat. Conf. Commrs. on Uniform State Laws, Chgo., 1977—; pres. Ea. Mineral Law Found., Morgantown, W.Va., 1983-84; dir. Wesbanco South Hills, Charleston. Contbr. articles to profl. jours., chpts. to books. Pres. W.Va. Symphony Orch., Charleston, 1982—; trustee Am. Symphony Orch. League, Washington, 1991—, W.Va. Wesleyan Coll., Buckhannon, 1989—; dir. Charleston Renaissance Corp., 1989—. 1st lt. USAF, 1956-59. Named Coal Lawyer of the Yr. Nat. Coal Lawyers Conf., 1983, Mayor's Award for Arts Vol., Fund for the Arts, Charleston, 1990. Fellow Am. Bar Found. (life); mem. ABA, W.Va. Bar Found. (pres. 1992—), Am. Judicature Soc., W.Va. Bar Assn. (pres. 1995—), Kanawha County Bar Assn. (pres. 1980-82), Kiwanis, Masons, Shriners, Order of Coif. Democrat. Methodist. Home: 3 Bendcrest Charleston WV 25314 Office: Jackson & Kelly PO Box 553 1600 Laidley Twr Charleston WV 25322

MCCLAVE, DONALD SILSBEE, association executive; b. Cleve., May 7, 1941; s. Charles Green and Anne Elizabeth (Oakley) McC.; m. Christine Phyllis Mary Tomkins, Feb. 19, 1966; children: Andrew Green, Susan Elizabeth (dec.). BA, Denison U., 1963. Mktg. rsch. officer Bank of Calif., San Francisco, 1968-70; v.p. Cen. Nat. Bank, Chgo., 1970-75; v.p. First Interstate Bank, Portland, Oreg., 1975-77, sr. v.p., 1977-79, exec. v.p., 1979-86; pres., chief exec. officer Portland Met. C. of C. 1987—; instr. Grad. Sch. Mktg. and Strategic Planning, Athens, 1982-84, Pacific Coast Sch. Banking, Seattle, 1976-78. Pres. Oreg. Episc. Sch. Bd., Portland, 1983-84; pres. Assn. Oreg. Industries Found., Salem, 1984-85; pres., co-chmn. Japan-Am. Conf. Mayors and C. of C., Portland, 1985, trustee, 1991—, exec. com., 1992—; trustee YMCA of Columbia-Willamette, 1990-92, Portland Student Svcs. Corp., 1991-93; mem. METRO Urban Growth Mgmt. Adv. Com., 1989-92; mem. adv. com. Downtown Housing Preservation Partnership Adv. Com., 1989-94; mem. City of Portland Mayoral Transition Team, 1992, Mayor's Bus. Roundtable, 1993—; bd. dirs. Oreg. Trail chpt. ARC, 1994-95, Tri-Met, 1994—. Avocations: reading, traveling, model bldg. Office: Portland Met C of C 221 NW 2nd Ave Portland OR 97209-3999

MCCLEAN, GRAHAM J., commercial printing company executive. Formerly pres. Moore Bus. Forms & Systems Div., Inc., Lake Forest, Ill.; now pres., COO Quebecor Printing (USA) Corp., Boston. Office: Quebecor Printing (USA) Corp 125 High St Boston MA 02110

MCCLEARY, BENJAMIN WARD, investment banker; b. Washington, July 9, 1944; s. George William and Nancy (Grim) McC.; m. Dierdre Marsters, May 6, 1967 (div. 1977); children: Benjamin, Katherine; m. Jean Muchmore, Oct. 15, 1984. AB, Princeton U., 1966. With Chemical Bank, N.Y.C., 1969-81; trainee, asst. sec., asst. v.p., v.p. Chemical Bank; sr. v.p. Lehman Bros. Kuhn Loeb, N.Y.C., 1981-83; mng. dir. Shearson Lehman Bros., 1983-87, Shearson Lehman Hutton Internat., London, 1987-88, Shearson Lehman Hutton, Inc., N.Y.C., 1988-89; ptnr. McFarland Dewey & Co., N.Y.C., 1989—; dir. Detrex Corp., Detroit, Harvel Plastics, Easton. Lt. (j.g.) USN, 1966-69. Office: McFarland Dewey & Co 230 Park Ave Ste 1450 New York NY 10169-0004

MCCLEARY, HENRY GLEN, geophysicist; b. Casper, Wyo., June 4, 1922; s. Raymond and Wyoma N. (Posey) McCleary Grieve; m. Beryl Tenney Nowlin, May 28, 1950; children: Gail, Glenn, Neil, Paul. Geol. Engr., Colo. Sch. Mines, 1948. From geophysicist to party chief seismic Amoco, various locations, 1948-53; exploration mgr. Woodson Oil Co., Fort Worth, 1953-60; resident mgr. NAMCO, Tripoli, Libya, 1961-62; chief geophysicist to staff geophys. assoc. Amoco Internat. Oil Co., 1963-86, Cairo, London and Buenos Aires, 1963-71, Chgo., 1971-81, Denver, 1981-84, Houston, 1984-86; internat. geophys. cons., 1986—. Served with USN, 1943-46. Named Hon. Admiral Tex. Navy, 1968. Mem. Soc. Exploration Geophysicists, Soc. Petroleum Engrs., AAAS, Houston Gem and Mineral Soc., Profl. Oil People, Sigma Alpha Epsilon, Theta Tau. Republican. Episcopalian. Clubs: Adventurers, Meml. Forest (Houston). Home: 232 Warrenton Dr Houston TX 77024-6226

MCCLEARY, LLOYD E(VERALD), education educator; b. Bradley, Ill., May 10, 1924; s. Hal and Pearl McC.; m. Iva Dene Carter, June 13, 1971; children: Joan Kay, Victoria Lea, Karen Ann. Student, Kans. U., 1941-42; B.S., U. Ill., 1948, M.S., 1950, D.Ed., 1956; postgrad., Sorbonne, Paris, 1946. Tchr., asst. prin. Portland (Oreg.) Public Schs., 1949-51; asst. prin. Univ. High Sch., Urbana, Ill., 1951-52; prin. Univ. High Sch., 1953-56; asst. supt. Evanston Twp. (Ill.) High Sch., 1956-60; assoc. Roosevelt U., 1957-69; mem. faculty U. Mich., summers, 1958-59; prof. edul. adminstrn. U. Utah, 1969—, chmn. dept., 1969-74; assoc. CFK Ltd. Found., 1971-76; dir. projects in Latin Am. for AID, World Bank, Ford Found., Bolivian Govt.; dir. Nat. Sch. Prin. Study, 1976-79, 86-89, res. project Families in Edn., 1992-94; edn. rep. to Utah People to People Program; Keynoter Asian Conf. Edn., 1985; edn. adviser Office of the Queen, Jordan, 1982-86; advisor Nat. Commn. on Standards in the Principalship; U.S. del. Conf. on Status Children, Senegal, 1992, Yr. of the Family, Malta, 1993; J. Lloyd Trump lectr., New Orleans, 1994. Author: Organizational Analysis X-Change, 1975, Politics and Power in Education, 1976, The Senior High School Principalship, 1980, Educational Administration, Today, 1984, High School Leaders and Their Schools, vols. 1 and 2, 1990; editor: Western Hemisphere Edn. Sch. Orgn., 1989—. Served with inf. AUS, 1941-46. Decorated Bronze Star with oak leaf cluster, Army Commendation medal; S.D. Shankland fellow, 1956; Grantee Ford Found., 1968, 72, AID, 1966, 67, 70, 72, 74, 76, CFK Ltd., 1970-74, Rockefeller Family Found., 1979-80, U.S. Dept. State, 1981, 86-87, U.S. Dept. Def., 1986—; recipient Hatch Prize, 1988-89. Mem. Nat. Assn. Secondary Sch. Prins. (cert. of merit 1978, scholar-in-residence fall 1989, grantee 1969, 77, 86—), Assn. Supervision and Curriculum Devel., Nat. Assn. Elem. Sch. Prins., Phi Delta Kappa, Kappa Delta Pi. Methodist. Home: 1470 Wilton Way Salt Lake City UT 84108-2549 Office: 339 MBH University of Utah Salt Lake City UT 84112

MCCLEARY, PAUL FREDERICK, voluntary agency executive; b. Bradley, Ill., May 2, 1930; s. Hal C. and Pearl (Aeicher) McC.; A.B., Olivet Nazarene U., Kankakee, Ill., 1952; M.Div., Garrett-Evang. Sem., Evanston, Ill., 1956; M.A., Northwestern U., 1972; D.D., MacMurray Coll., Jacksonville, Ill., 1970; m. Rachel Timm, Jan. 26, 1951; children—Leslie Ann, Rachel Mary, John Wesley, Timothy Paul. Ordained to ministry United Methodist Ch., 1956; missionary in Bolivia, 1957-68; exec. sec. structure study commn. United Meth. Ch., 1969-72, asst. gen. sec. to Latin Am. 1972-75; exec. dir. Ch. World Service, N.Y.C., 1975-84; assoc. gen. sec. for research Gen. Council on Ministries, United Meth. Ch., 1984-87; exec. v.p. Save the Children, Westport, Conn., 1987-88; exec. dir. Christian Children's Fund Inc., 1988—; mem., bd. dir. Overseas Devel. Council; mem. adv. com. on economic matters World Council Chs.; mem. com. on Dialogue and Devel., Nat. Leadership Commn. on Health Care, Bretton Woods Com.; pres. NGO com. on UNICEF, CODEL, Christian Century Found. Mem. AAAS, Acad. Polit. Sci., Latin Am. Studies Assn., Masons, Rotary, Alpha Kappa Lambda. Democrat. Author: Global Justice and World Hunger, 1978; co-author: Quality of Life in a Global

Society, 1978; contbr. articles to mags. Home: 300 N Ridge Rd Richmond VA 23229-7459 Office: Christian Childrens Fund Inc 2821 Emerywood Pky Richmond VA 23294

MCCLELLAN, ANNE STARR, environmentalist; b. Detroit, Sept. 27, 1960; d. John Drew and Barbara Ann (Kaumneimer) McC.; m. John Alan Rosett, Aug. 15, 1987. BA in Urban Planning, SUNY. With Neighborhood Open Space Coalition, N.Y.C., 1986-87, program dir., 1987-93, exec. dir., 1993—; program dir. Friends of Gateway, N.Y.C., 1992-93, exec. dir., 1993—; cons. South Bronx Greenway System/Consumer Farmer Found., N.Y.C., 1989-93, Pratt Inst., Bklyn., 1989-93, Village of Lansing, N.Y. Greenway Study/Tompkins County Dept. of Planning, 1992—; mem. environ. com. Atlantic Terminal Urban Renewal Area Coalition, 1986-87, exec. com., 1986-93, chairperson alternative plan, 1988-89; mem. Bronx Borough Pres.'s Office Greenway Steering Com., 1990—, East Coast Greenway Alliance, 1991—, chair N.Y. State com., 1994; mem. Flushing Meadows-Corona Park Redevel. Corp. Environ. Com., 1988-90; chairperson environ. impact statement com., mem. design com. Hudson River Park Conservancy Adv. Bd., 1993—; apptd. N.Y. State Intermodal Surface Transportation Efficiency Act Adv. Bd./Enhancement Funding, 1993—; writer, photographer Met. Course. on Housing, 1985-89; co-chairperson Met. Greenways Coun., 1987—; mem. urban park and natural resources task force Nat. Recreation and Park Assn., Nat. Soc. Park Resources, 1993—; mem. greenways and blueways com. Pub. Space for Pub. Life, 1991-93; co-chair Rockaway/Gateway Greenway Adv. Bd., 1993—; bd. dirs. Transp. Alternatives, 1988-90, mem. adv. bd., 1990—. Author: The Brooklyn/Queens Greenway: A Feasibility Study, 1987, The Brooklyn/Queens Greenway: A Design Study, 1988, Toward a Regional Greenway System--An Urban Greenways Inventory for Metro NY, 1992. Active N.Y.C. Bicycle Adv. Com., 1987—, N.Y. State Bicycle Adv. Coun., 1989—, N.Y.C. Bikeway/Walkway Working Group, 1991—. Regipient Nat. Merit award Am. Soc. Landscape Architects, 1990, Rudy Bruner award for Excellence in the Urban Environment, Rudy Bruner Found., 1991; NEA grantee, 1988. Mem. Am. Planning Assn. (chair N.Y.C. chpt. open space com. 1988—, exec. com. 1992—). Avocations: bicycling, photography, sea kayaking. Office: Neighborhood Open Space Coalition 72 Reade St New York NY 10007-1822

MCCLELLAN, BENNETT EARL, producer; b. Sedalia, Mo., Nov. 20, 1952; s. G. Earl and Ruth E. (McQueen) McC.; m. Gail Jones, Sept. 5, 1981; children: Ian Michael, Elizabeth Gayle. MBA, Harvard U., 1981; MFA in Film and TV, UCLA, 1989. Writer, dir. Old Globe Theater, San Diego, 1973-76; artistic dir. Genesis Theater, San Diego, 1977-79; cons. McKinsey & Co., L.A., 1981-87, Arthur D. Little Media & Entertainment Group, Cambridge, Mass., 1987-89; prodn. exec. Hanna-Barbera Prodns., 1990-91; gen. mgr. L.A. Philharmonic Assn., 1992-94, Nicktoons/Games Animation, Studio City, Calif., 1994—. Producer: (TV series) Good News, Bad News, 1988. Paramount fellow Paramount Pictures, 1989; named Outstanding Grad. Student UCLA Alumni Assn., 1990. Mem. Hollywood Radio and TV Soc. (Internat. Broadcasting award 1989), Acad. TV Arts and Scis. Office: Nickelodeon 4040 Vineland Ave Studio City CA 91604

MC CLELLAN, CATHARINE, anthropologist, educator; b. York, Pa., Mar. 1, 1921; d. William Smith and Josephine (Niles) McClellan; m. John Thayer Hitchcock, June 6, 1974. A.B. magna cum laude in Classical Archaeology, Bryn Mawr Coll., 1942; Ph.D. (Anthropology fellow), U. Calif. at Berkeley, 1950. Vis. asst. prof. U. Mo. at Columbia, 1952; asst. prof. anthropology U. Wash., Seattle, 1952-56; anthrop. cons. USPHS, Arctic Health Research Center, Alaska, 1956; asst. prof. anthropology, chmn. dept. anthropology Barnard Coll., Columbia U., 1956-61; asso. prof. anthropology U. Wis. at Madison, 1961-65, prof., 1965-83, prof. emeritus 1983—, John Bascom prof., 1973; vis. lectr. Bryn Mawr (Pa.) Coll., 1954; vis. prof. U. Alaska, 1973, 87. Assoc. editor: Arctic Anthropology, 1961; editor, 1975-82; assoc. editor: The Western Canadian Jour. of Anthropology, 1970-73. Served to lt. WAVES, 1942-46. Margaret Snell fellow AAUW, 1950-51; Am. Acad. Arts and Scis. grantee, 1963-64; Nat. Mus. Can. grantee, 1948-74. Fellow Am. Anthrop. Assn., Royal Anthrop. Inst. Gt. Britain and Ireland, AAAS, Arctic Inst. N.Am.; mem. Am. Ethnol. Soc. (sec.-treas. 1958-59, v.p. 1964, pres. 1965), Kroeber Anthrop. Soc., Am. Folklore Soc., Am. Soc. Ethnohistory (exec. com. 1968-71), Sigma Xi. Various archaeol. and ethnographic field investigations in Alaska and Yukon Territory in Can.

MCCLELLAN, DAVID LAWRENCE, physician; b. Burlington, Iowa, Feb. 13, 1930; s. Harold L. and LaVon H. McC.; children: David, Steven, Mark, Jeffrey. BA, U. Iowa, 1952, MD, 1955. Intern U.S. Naval Hosp., San Diego, 1955-56; med. officer USS Nereus, 1956-58; pvt. practice Garland Med. Office, Spokane, Wash., 1958-64; pres. DeRe Medical Med. Clinic, Spokane, 1964-93; pvt. practice in family medicine Spokane, 1993—; pres., chmn. bd. North Spokane Profl. Bldg., Inc., 1966-86; pres. Inland Health Assocs., Inc., Spokane, 1984-92; pres., bd. dirs. Bio-Chem Environ. Svcs., Seattle, 1984-90; v.p. Forest Resources, 1978-86; pres. Omnex, 1980-86; chief exec. officer Double N Orchards, 1980-87; gen. ptnr. Double N Investments, 1987—; ptnr. Recovre, Inc.; mem. staff Holy Family Hosp.; fin. cons. Asia-Pacific Timber Co., 1991—. Contbr. articles and papers to med. jours. Lt. USN, 1955-58. Fellow Am. Acad. Family Practice; mem. AMA, Am. Profl. Practice Assn., Wash. State Med. Soc., Spokane County Med. Soc., Inland Empire Acad. Family Practice, Internat. Platform Assn. Republican. Roman Catholic. Avocations: art collecting, antique collecting, boating, miniature sculpting, landscaping. Home: 7151 N Audubon Dr Spokane WA 99208-4516 Office: Northpointe Family Medicine 9631 N Nevada St Spokane WA 99207

MCCLELLAN, EDWIN, language educator; b. Kobe, Japan, Oct. 24, 1925; came to U.S., 1952; s. Andrew and Teru (Yokobori) McC.; m. Rachel Elizabeth Pott, May 28, 1955; children: Andrew Lockwood, Sarah Rose. M.A., U. St. Andrews, Scotland, 1952; Ph.D., U. Chgo., 1957. Instr. English U. Chgo., 1957-59, asst. prof. Japanese lang. and lit., 1959-63, asso. prof., 1963-65, prof., 1965-70, Carl Darling Buck prof., 1970-72, chmn. dept. Far Eastern langs. and civilizations, 1966-72; prof. Japanese lit. Yale U., 1972-79, Sumitomo prof. Japanese studies, 1979—, chmn. dept. East Asian langs. and lits., 1973-82, 88-91, chmn. council humanities, 1975-77, chmn. council East Asian studies, 1979-82; vis. lectr. Far Eastern langs. Harvard U., spring 1965; mem. adv. coun. dept. Oriental studies Princeton U., 1966-71; mem. Com. to Visit East Asian Studies Harvard U., 1982-88; Am. adv. com. Japan Found., 1985-95; mem. bd. Coun. for Internat. Exch. Scholars, 1981-84. Translator: Kokoro (Natsume Soseki), 1957, Grass on the Wayside (Soseki), 1969, A Dark Night's Passing (Naoya Shiga), 1976, Fragments of a Past (Eiji Yoshikawa), 1992; author: Two Japanese Novelists: Soseki and Toson, 1969, Woman in the Crested Kimono, 1985; mem. bd. editors Jour. Japanese Studies, 1986—; contbr. articles to profl. jours. Bd. trustees Society Japanese Studies U. Wash., 1992—; mem. Com. on Emerson-Thoreau Medal and Am. Acad. Award for Humanistic Studies Am. Acad. Arts and Scis., 1995—. Fellow Am. Acad. Arts and Scis.; mem. Assn. for Asian Studies (Kikuchi Kan prize 1994). Home: 641 Ridge Rd Hamden CT 06517-2516

MCCLELLAN, JAMES HAROLD, electrical engineering educator; b. Guam, Oct. 5, 1947; s. Harold James McClellan and Esther Mary (Rosenbach) Matkin; m. Carolyn Frances Monjure, May 31, 1969; children--Amy, Scott. B.S., La. State U., 1969; M.S., Rice U., 1972, Ph.D., 1973. Research staff Lincoln Lab., Lexington, Mass., 1973-75; asst. prof. MIT, Cambridge, 1975-78, assoc. prof., 1978-82; tech. cons. Schlumberger Well Services, Austin, Tex., 1982-87, Ga. Inst. of Tech., 1987—; cons. Lincoln Lab. 1975-82, Lawrence Livermore Nat. Lab., Calif., 1979-82, Schlumberger, 1988-89, MathWorks, Inc., Natick, Mass., 1990—. Author: Number Theory in Digital Signal Processing, 1979, Computer-Based Exercises for Signal Processing, 1994. NSF fellow, 1971-73. Fellow IEEE; mem. Speech and Signal Processing Soc. of IEEE, Tau Beta Pi, Eta Kappa Nu. Home: 5169 Sandlewood Ct Marietta GA 30068-2875 Office: Ga Inst Tech Sch of Elec Engring Atlanta GA 30332-0250

MCCLELLAN, JOHN R., school system administrator; b. Supt. Centennial Sch. Dist. 12, Circle Pines, Minn. State finalist Nat. Supt. of Yr., 1992. Office: Centennial Sch Dist 12 4707 North Rd Circle Pines MN 55014-1898

MCCLELLAN, LARRY ALLEN, minister, writer; b. Buffalo, Nov. 3, 1944; s. Edward Lurelle McClellan and Helen (Denison) Erland; m. Diane Eunice Bonfoey, Aug. 19, 1973; children: Kara E., Seth C. Student, U. Ghana,

1964-65; BA in Psychology, Occidental Coll., 1966; MTh, U. Chgo., 1969, D Ministry, 1970. Ordained to ministry Presbyn. Ch. (U.S.A.), 1970. Prof. of sociology and community studies Govs. State U., University Park, Ill., 1970-86; interim pastor Presbyn. Ch. (U.S.A.), Chgo. area, 1980-86; sr. pastor St Paul Community Ch., Homewood, Ill., 1986—; adj. prof. Govs. State U., University Park, Ill., 1987—; newspaper columnist Star Publs. Chgo., 1993—; trustee Internat. Coun. Community Chs. 1989-91, pres., 1991-93. Author: Local History South of Chicago, 1988; developer social simulation games; contbr. articles to profl. publs. Mayor Village of Park Forest South (name now University Park), Ill., 1975-79; co-organizer S. Region Habitat for Humanity, Chgo. area, 1989; pres. S. Suburban Heritage Assn., Chgo. area, 1988-91. Fellow Layne Found., 1966-70, NEH, 1979. Mem. Urban Affairs Assn., Am. Acad. Religion, Assn. for Sociology of Religion, Am. Assn. State and Local History, Ill. State Hist. Soc. (Spl. Achievement award 1989), Chgo. Hist. Soc., South Suburban Ministerial Assn. (pres. 1989-91). Office: St Paul Community Ch 18200 Dixie Hwy Homewood IL 60430-2219

MCCLELLAN, ROGER ORVILLE, toxicologist; b. Tracy, Minn., Jan. 5, 1937; s. Orville and Gladys (Paulson) McC.; m. Kathleen Mary Dunagan, June 23, 1962; children: Eric John, Elizabeth Christine, Katherine Ruth. DVM with highest honors, Wash. State U., 1960; M of Mgmt, U. N.Mex., 1980. diplomate Am. Bd. Vet. Toxicology, cert. Am. Bd. Toxicology. From biol. scientist to sr. scientist Gen. Electric Co., Richland, Wash., 1957-64; sr. scientist biology dept. Pacific N.W. Labs., Richland, Wash., 1965; scientist med. research br. div. biology and medicine AEC, Washington, 1965-66; asst. dir. research, dir. fission product inhalation program Lovelace Found. Med. Edn. and Research, Albuquerque, 1966-73; v.p., dir. research adminstrn., dir. Lovelace Inhalation Toxicology Research Inst., Albuquerque, 1973-76, pres., dir., 1976-88; chmn. bd. dirs. Lovelace Biomedical and Environ. Research Inst., Albuquerque, 1988—; pres. Chem. Industry Inst. Toxicology Research, Triangle Park, N.C., 1988—; mem. research com. Health Effects Inst., 1981-92; bd. dirs. Toxicology Lab. Accreditation Bd., 1982-90, treas., 1984-90; adj. prof. Wash. State U., 1980—, U. Ark., 1970-88; clin. assoc. U. N.Mex., 1971-85, adj. prof. toxicology, 1985—; adj. prof. toxicology and occupational and environ. medicine Duke U., 1988—; adj. prof. toxicology U. N.C. Chapel Hill, 1989—; adj. prof. toxicology N.C. State Univ., 1991—; mem. dose assessment adv. group U.S. Dept. Energy, 1980-87, mem. health and environ. research adv. com., 1984-85; mem. exec. com. sci. adv. bd. EPA, 1974—, mem. environ. health cons., 1980-83, chmn., 1982-83, chmn. radionuclide emissions rev. com., 1984-85, chmn. Clean Air Sci. Adv. Com., 1987-92, chmn. rsch. strategies adv. com., 1992—; mem. com. on toxicology NAS-NRC, 1979-87, chmn., 1980-87; bd. dirs. Lovelace Anderson Endowment Found.; mem. com. risk assessment methodology for hazardous air pollution NAS-NRC, 1991-94, com. biol. effects of Radon, 1994—; pres. Am. Bd. Vet. Toxicology, 1970-73; mem. adv. council Ctr. for Risk Mgmt., Resources for the Future, 1987—; council mem. Nat. Council for Radiation Protection, 1970—; bd. dirs. NC Assn. Biomedical Rsch., 1989-91, N.C. Vet. Medical Found., 1990—, pres., 1993-94. Contbr. articles to profl. jours. Editorial bd. Jour. Toxicology and Environ. Health, 1980—, assoc. editor, 1982—; editorial bd. Fundamental and Applied Toxicology, 1984-89, assoc. editor, 1987-89; editorial bd. Toxicology and Indsl. Health, 1984—; editor CRC Critical Revs. in Toxicology, 1987—; assoc. editor Inhalation Toxicology Jour., 1987—; mem. edit. bd. Regulatory Toxicology and Pharmacology, 1989—. Recipient Herbert E. Stokinger award Am. Conf. Govtl. Indsl. Hygienists, 1985, Alumni Achievement award Wash. State U., 1987, Disting. Assoc. award Dept. Energy, 1987, 88, Arnold Lehman award Soc. Toxicology, 1992; co-recipient Frank R. Blood award Soc. Toxicology, 1989. Fellow AAAS, Am. Acad. Vet. and Comparative Toxicology, Soc. Risk Analysis; mem. Am. Chem. Soc., Inst. Medicine (elected), NAS, Radiation Research Soc. (sec.-treas. 1982-84, chmn. fin. com. 1979-82), Health Physics Soc. (chmn. program com. 1972, Elda E. Anderson award 1974), Soc. Toxicology (v.p.-elect to pres. 1987-90; inhalation specialty sect. v.p. to pres. 1983-86; bd. publs. 1983-86, chmn. 1983-85), Am. Assn. Aerosol Research (bd. dirs. 1982—, treas. 1986-90, v.p. to pres. 1990-93), Am. Vet. Med. Assn., Gesellschaft fur Aerosolforschung, Sigma Xi, Phi Kappa Phi, Phi Zeta. Republican. Lutheran. Home: 1111 Cuatro Cerros Trl SE Albuquerque NM 87123-4149 also: 2903 Bainbridge Dr Apt Q Durham NC 27713-1448 Office: Chem Industry Inst Toxicology PO Box 12137 Durham NC 27709-2137*

MCCLELLAN, THOMAS JAMES, educator; b. Edsville, Miss., Mar. 14, 1944; s. Albert Lee and Jannie (Pempleton) McC.; m. Glorya Jean Cotten, May 3, 1975 (div. Apr. 1976); children: Kelly Tremayne, Terrie Lynn.; m. Joann Evelyn, June 11, 1978. BS in Biology, Chemistry, Miss. Valley Sttate U., 1969; M of Math., Wayne State U., 1990; postgrad., Garrett Theol. Sem., 1991—. Tchr. Highland Park (Mich.) Pub. Schs., 1979-87; tchr. math., sci. Pontiac (Mich.) Pub. Sch. System, 1988—. Contbr. articles to profl. jours. Democrat. Baptist. Avocations: health, gourmet cooking, reading, tennis, basketball. Home: 43 Florence St Highland Park MI 48203-2765 Office: Pontiac Ctrl High Sch 300 W Huron St Pontiac MI 48341-1420

MC CLELLAN, WILLIAM MONSON, library administrator; b. Groton, Mass., Jan. 7, 1934; s. James Lewis and Ruth Caldwell (Monson) McC.; m. Jane Muir, Sept. 3, 1955; children--Jennifer, Anne, Margaret, Amy. B.A., Colo. Coll., 1956, M.A., 1961; A.M. in L.S, U. Mich., Ann Arbor, 1959. Music librarian U. Colo., Boulder, 1959-65; dir. Music Library, U. Ill., Urbana, 1965—; cons. music library resources and services to colls. and univs.; co-dir. Inst. Music Librarianship, Kent State U., 1969. Editor: Music Library Assn. Notes, 1977-82; Contbr. articles to profl. jours. Council on Library Resources fellow, 1976-77. Mem. Internat. Assn. Music Librs., Music. Libr. Assn. (pres. 1971-73, conf. panelist, chmn. stats. subcom. 1990-93). HOme: 1701 Gentry Sq Ln #108 Champaign IL 61821-5956 Office: Music Bldg University of Illinois Urbana IL 61801 *To commit myself daily to giving and opening myself to others in all professional and other contexts.*

MCCLELLAND, BRAMLETTE, engineering executive, consultant; b. Newnan, Ga., Dec. 16, 1920; s. Chalmer Kirk and Annie (Bramlette) McC.; m. Virginia Jane Cowan, Dec. 9, 1949; children: Darcy, Thomas, Terence, Jeffrey, Martha. B.S.C.E., U. Ark., 1940; M.S.C.E., Purdue U., 1942, D.Eng. (hon.), 1984. Design engr. City of Houston, 1943-46; ptnr. Greer & McClelland, Houston, 1946-55; pres., chmn. McClelland Engrs., Houston, 1955-87; chmn. Fugro-McClelland BV, Leidschendam, The Netherlands, 1987-90; cons., 1990—; chmn. NRC Marine Bd., Washington, 1985-86. Author: Foundations-Handbook of Ocean and Underwater Engineering, 1969; author, editor: Planning and Design of Fixed Offshore Platforms, 1985. Scoutmaster Boy Scouts Am., Houston, 1972-73; bd. dirs. Planned Parenthood, Houston, 1972-79; past pres. bd. trustees Emerson Unitarian Ch., Houston. Named Disting. Alumnus, Purdue U., 1965; named to engring. Hall of Fame, U. Ark., 1972; recipient Engr. of Yr. award Tex. Soc. Profl. Engrs., 1981, Disting. Achievement award Offshore Tech. Conf., 1994. Mem. NAE, ASCE (hon., James Laurie Prize 1959, State of the Art award 1971), Assn. Soil and Found. Engrs. (pres. 1978), Internat. Soc. for Soil Mechanics and Found. Engring. Republican. Home: 11207 Tyne Ct Houston TX 77024-7416

MCCLELLAND, EMMA L., state legislator; b. Springfield, Mo., Feb. 26, 1940; m. Alan McClelland; children: Mike, Karen. BA, U. Mo., 1962. Dir. field office, corp. divsn. Mo. Sec. of State, St. Louis; committeewoman Gravis Township; mem. St. Louis County Rep. Cent. Com., Mo. Rep. State Com.; mem. Mo. State Ho. Rep., 1991—, mem. appropriations com., edn. com. Bd. dirs. Epworth Children's Home, Family Supprot Network; elder Webster Groves Presbyn. Ch. Recipient Silver Svc. award Nat. Soc. Autistic Children, Outstanding Svc. award Am. Assn. Mental Deficiency, Spl. Leadership award for govt. YWCA of St. Louis. Mem. Webster Groves C. of C., Pi Lambda Theta. Republican. Home: 455 Pasadena Webster Grove MO 63119 Office: Mo Ho of Reps State Capitol Jefferson City MO 65101

MC CLELLAND, JAMES CRAIG, lawyer; b. New Alexandria, Pa., Sept. 8, 1901; s. James Craig and Cora Blanche (Banhart) McC.; m. Eleanor May Hamilton, June 15, 1929 (dec. July 1964); children--Louise (Mrs. Gerhard Urban), James Craig Jr.; m. Marjorie Brown Hilkert, Mar. 29, 1969. B.A., Coll. Wooster, 1923; LL.B., Western Res. U., 1926. Bar: Ohio bar 1926. Pvt. practice Cleve., 1926—; mem. firm Boer, Mierke, McClelland & Caldwell (and predecessor firms), 1926-82; of counsel Caldwell & Thornton, 1982—. Counsel Berea City Sch. Dist., Southwest Gen. Hosp. Mem. ABA,

Ohio Bar Assn. (past mem. council of dels.), Cleve. Bar Assn. (past mem. exec. com.), Order of the Coif, Delta Sigma Rho. Home: 38 E Carriage Dr Chagrin Falls OH 44022-2875 Office: Park Bldg 140 Public Sq Cleveland OH 44114-2208

MCCLELLAND, JAMES L., psychology educator, cognitive scientist; b. Cambridge, Mass., Dec. 1, 1948; s. Walter Moore and Frances (Shaffer) McC.; m. Heidi Marsha Feldman, May 6, 1978; children: Mollie S., Heather Ann. BA in Psychology, Columbia U., 1970; PhD in Cognitive Psychology, U. Pa., 1975. Asst. prof. dept. psychology U. California, San Diego, 1974-80, assoc. prof., 1980-84; assoc. prof. Carnegie-Mellon U., Pitts., 1984-85, prof. psychology, 1985—, prof. computer sci., 1987—, acting head psychology, 1989-90; vis. scientist dept. psychology and Ctr. Cognitive Sci., MIT, 1982-84; vis. scholar dept. psychology Harvard U., 1982-84; mem. com. on basic rsch. in behavioral and social scis., NRC, 1985, rev. panel for cognition, emotion and personality NIMH, 1983-87, behavioral scis. rsch. br. assessment panel NIMH, 1987-88; co-organizer NSF workshop on connectionism and cognitive sci., 1986. Author: (with others) Parallel Distributed Processing: Explorations in the Microstructure of Cognition, Vols. I, II, 1986; co-author: A Handbook of Models, Programs, and Exercises, 1988; contbr. numerous articles, reports, book chpts. to profl. publs.; sr. editor Cognitive Sci., 1988-91; mem. editorial bd. Perception and Psychophysics, 1977-82, Jour. of Verbal Learning and Verbal Behavior, 1980-84, Cognitive Sci., 1983-88, Cognitive Neuropsychology, 1983—, (book series) Computational Approaches in Cognitive Sci., 1983—, Cognitive Psychology, 1984—, Jour. Exptl. Psychology: General, 1984-87, Lang. and Cognitive Processes, 1988—, Neural Computation, 1989—. Recipient William W. Cumming prize Columbia U., 1970, Rsch. Scientist Career Devel. award NIMH, 1981-86, 87—; NSF fellow, 1970-73, grantee, 1976-79, 80-84, 86-87, 88—; grantee Office Naval Rsch., 1982-87. Fellow AAAS; mem. Cognitive Sci. Soc. (governing bd. 1988—, chmn. 1991—), Psychonomics Soc., Internat. Assn. for Study Attention and Performance (governing bd. 1986—, lectr. 1986), Soc. Exptl. Psychologists (Warren medal 1993), Phi Beta Kappa. Office: Carnegie Mellon U Dept Psychology Pittsburgh PA 15213-3890

MC CLELLAND, JOHN PETER, winery executive; b. N.Y.C., Aug. 17, 1933; s. Harold Stanley and Helen Lucille (Gardner) McC.; m. Ann Carolyn Campbell, Aug. 27, 1954; children: John, Kristen. Student, UCLA, 1951-53. With Almadén Vineyards, Inc., San Jose, Calif., 1958-83; v.p. sales, then v.p. mktg. Almadén Vineyards, Inc., 1970-76, pres., 1976-83; chmn. bd., chief exec. officer Geyser Peak Winery, 1983—. Served with AUS, 1954-56. Mem. Wine Inst. (chmn. public relations com. 1977—, exec. com. 1979—, chmn. 1986-87), Sonoma County Wine Bd., Internat. Wine and Food Soc., Supreme Knight of the Vine, Chaine Des Rotisseurs. Republican. Presbyterian. Office: Geyser Peak Winery PO Box 25 Geyserville CA 95441-0025

MCCLELLAND, MICHAEL, wholesale distribution executive; b. 1947. BS, Ball State U., 1969; MS, St. Francis Coll., 1971. With Hardware Wholesalers Inc., Fort Wayne, Ind., 1974-77 v.p., pres., 1977-81, v.p. sales, 1981-84, v.p. sales mktg., 1984-87, exec. v.p., 1987-92, pres., CEO, 1992—. Office: Hardware Wholesalers Inc Nelson Rd Fort Wayne IN 46803

MCCLELLAND, NORMAN P., food products executive. Ceo., chmn. Shamrock Foods Co., Phoenix, Ariz., 1994—. Office: Shamrock Foods Co 2228 N Black Canyon Hwy Phoenix AZ 85009-2707

MC CLELLAND, ROBERT NELSON, surgeon, educator; b. Gilmer, Tex., Nov. 20, 1929; s. Robert Hilton and Verna Louise (Nelson) McC.; m. Connie Logan, May 5, 1958; children: Robert Christopher, Alison, Julie. B.A., U. Tex., Austin, 1952; M.D., U. Tex., Galveston, 1954. Diplomate Am. Bd. Surgery. Rotating intern U. Kans. Med. center, 1954-55; resident in gen. surgery Parkland Hosp., Dallas, 1957-59, 60-62; instr. surgery Southwestern Med. Sch., U. Tex., Dallas, 1962-63; asst. prof. Southwestern Med. Sch., U. Tex., 1963-67, asso. prof., 1967-71, prof., 1971—, Alvin Baldwin prof. surgery, 1977—; examiner Nat. Bd. Med. Examiners. Editor Audio Jour. Rev. Gen. Surgery, 1971-82, Selected Readings in Gen. Surgery, 1974—; contbr. numerous articles to profl. jours., chpts. to books. Served to capt. M.C. USAF, 1955-57. Fellow ACS (mem. grad. edn. com.); mem. AMA, Am. Surg. Assn., Western Surg. Assn., Soc. Surgery of Alimentary Tract, Am. Gastroent. Assn., Southwestern Surg. Soc., So. Surg. Assn., Dallas Soc. Gen. Surgeons (pres. 1987-88), Tex. Surg. Soc., Tex. Med. Assn., Dallas Country Med. Soc., Soc. Internatale de Chirugie (bd. dirs. Am. chpt.), Phi Beta Kappa, Alpha Omega Alpha. Republican. Lutheran. Home: 3601 Potomac Ave Dallas TX 75205-2110 Office: 5323 Harry Hines Blvd Dallas TX 75235-7200

MCCLELLAND, TIMOTHY REID, baseball umpire; b. Jackson, Mich., Dec. 12, 1951; s. Reid Nathan and Geraldine Betty (Donaldson) McC.; m. Sandra Ann Seltz; children: Cole, Molly, Maggie. BS, Mich. State U., 1974, MA, 1975. Umpire Fla. State League of Minor League Baseball, Lakeland, 1976-77, So. League of Minor League Baseball, Montgomery, Ala., 1978, P.R. Baseball League, 1979, 80, Am. Assn. Minor League Baseball, Wichita, Kans., 1979-82, Am. League of Profl. Baseball, N.Y.C., 1983—. Mentor Valley H.S., West Des Moines, 1993-94; playing Santa Claus to orgns. Mem. Major League Umpires Assn. Mem. Lutheran Ch. Mo. Synod. Umpire Major League All-Star Game, Houston, 1986, Am. League Championship Series, Boston, Oakland, Calif., 1988, World Series of Profl. Baseball, Toronto, Can., Phila., 1993. Home: 5405 Woodland Ave West Des Moines IA 50266 Office: Am League Profl Baseball 350 Park Ave New York NY 10022

MCCLELLAND, W. CLARK, retail company financial executive; b. Detroit, Feb. 6, 1939; s. Fauvia McClelland; m. Marjorie Mele; children: Michael, Troy, Cory, Deborah. Grad. Elizabethtown Coll. 1965. Acct. Coopers and Lybrand, Phila., 1967-70; treas., chief fin. officer Heilig Meyers Corp., Richmond, Va., 1970-74; dir., chief fin. officer Gas Spring Corp., Montgomeryville, Pa., 1974-75; exec. v.p., CFO Hechinger Co., Landover, Md., 1975—. Mem. AICPA, Nat. Capital Group Fin. Execs. Inst. Office: Hechinger Co 3500 Pennsy Dr Landover MD 20785

MC CLELLAND, W. KENT, food products executive. With Shamrock Foods Co., Phoenix, Ariz., 1975-79, Mercantile Bank, Canada, 1980-84, MB Financial Services Corp., L.A., 1980-84; v.p., dir. Shamrock Foods Co., Phoenix, Ariz., 1984-87, pres., coo, 1987—. Office: Shamrock Foods Co 2228 N Black Canyon Hwy Phoenix AZ 85009

MCCLELLAND, WILLIAM CRAIG, paper company executive; b. Orange, N.J., Apr. 21, 1934; s. William N. and Pauline (Lee) McC.; m. Alice Garrett, Dec. 28, 1956; children: Suzanne, Alice Elizabeth, Heather. BS in Econs., Princeton U., 1956; MBA, Harvard U., 1965. Salesman, branch mgr. PPG Industries, Cleve. and Erie, Pa., 1960-63; pres. Watervliet Paper Co. div. Hammermill Paper Co., Mich., 1969-73; product, mktg. mgr. Hammermill Paper Co., Erie, Pa., 1965-69, v.p., dir., 1980-83, exec. v.p., dir., 1983-85, pres., chief exec. officer, 1985-88, also bd. dirs.; sr. v.p. Internat. Paper Co., 1986-87, exec. v.p., 1987-88, also bd. dirs.; exec. v.p. Union Camp Corp., Wayne, N.J., 1988-89, chmn., pres. chief operating officer, 1989—; bd. dirs. Quaker State Corp., PNC Fin. Corp., Allegheny Ludlum Corp. Mem. Coun. Fellows, Behrend Coll. of Pa. State U., 1980-88; dir. Pitts. Theol. Seminary, 1986—. Lt. (j.g.) USN, 1956-59. Home: 7 Ridge Crest Rd Saddle River NJ 07458-3107

MCCLENDON, CHARLES YOUMANS, nonprofessional sports association executive, coach; b. Lewisville, Ark., Oct. 17, 1923; s. Leigh Alexander and Susie (Robey) McC.; m. Dorothy Faye Smart, Dec. 25, 1947; children: Delores Kay McClendon Alberty, Charles Scott. BA, U. Ky., 1950, MA, 1951. Grad. asst. coach football U. Ky., Lexington, 1950-51; asst. coach Vanderbilt U., Nashville, 1952; asst. coach La. State U., Baton Rouge, 1953-61, head coach, 1962-79; exec. dir. Tangerine Bowl (later Fla. Citrus Bowl), Orlando, 1980-81, Am. Football Coaches Assn., Orlando, 1982—; mem. exec. com. Nat. Assoc. Collegiate Dirs. Athletics, Cleve., 1986-88. Chmn. capital contributions Dr. Phillips YMCA, Orlando, 1983-85. Served with USN, 1943-46. Recipient Amos Alonzo Stagg award Am. Football Coaches Assn., 1992, Coll. Football Hall of Fame award Nat. Football Found., 1986, Hall of Fame award Fla. Citrus Bowl, 1985, Gen. Robert Neyland award

Knoxville (Tenn.) Quarterback Club, 1987, John Young award Orlando C. of C., 1981, Disting. Alumnus award So. Ark. U., 1978, Achievement award U. Ky., 1965, Native Son award City of Lewisville, 1963; named Conf. Coach of Yr. Southeastern Conf., 1969, 70, to La. Sports Hall of Fame, 1982, Texarkana Arkansas Sports Hall of Fame, 1976, Ark. Sports Hall of Fame, 1978. Mem. Am. Football Coaches Assn. (pres. 1979, trustee 1974-79, nat. coach of yr. 1970, 35-yr. mem. award 1987. Democrat. Methodist. Avocations: golf, fishing. Office: Am Football Coaches Assn 5900 Old Mcgregor Rd Waco TX 76712-6166

MCCLENDON, EDWIN JAMES, health science educator; b. Troy, Okla., Dec. 3, 1921; s. Charles Wesley and Mattie (Reed) McC.; m. Ruby Wynona Scott, May 5, 1950; children—Edwin James, Melody Jan, Joy Renee. B.S., Okla. East Central State U., 1946; M.Ed., U. Okla., 1954; Ed.D., Wayne State U., Detroit, 1964. Instr. U. Okla., Norman, 1946-47; head speech dept., tchr. Wewoka High Sch., Okla., 1947-49; assoc. dir. Tb Control, Oklahoma City, 1949-51; dir. sch health project Okla. Dept. Health and Edn., Oklahoma City, 1951-54; assoc. dir. Tb Control, Wayne County, Mich., 1954-56; dir. sch. health Wayne County, Mich., 1956-63; dir. secondary edn. Wayne County Intermediate Sch., Detroit, 1963-67; supt. schs. Highland Park, Mich., 1967-68; v.p. Highland Park Coll., Mich., 1968-69; asst. supt. health Mich. Dept. Edn., Lansing, 1969-71; prof., chmn. health edn. U. Mich., Ann Arbor, 1971-88, prof. health behavior and pub. health, 1971-88, prof. emeritus, 1988—; cons. pub. health care, 1985—; cons. WHO, 1978-89, dir. field study for Western Pacific, 1981; health field study of Arabic states, 1979-80; cons., Papua, New Guinea, Japan, Korea, Philippines, 1983-84, Fiji and Malaysia, 1987-88. Author Drug Education-A Teacher's Guide, 1969, Maxi Minds in Mini Cages, The Gifted, 1972, HEalthful Living for Today and Tomorrow, 1981, Health and Wellness, 1987, Evaluation Study of Growing Healthy, 1993; contbr. 60 articles to profl. publs. Chmn. bd. dirs. Am. Cancer Soc., Detroit, 1977-78, mem. nat. pub. edn. com., 1969-83, hon. life mem., 1980—; mem. adv. coun. alcohol abuse NIH, 1976-80; pres. Plymouth-Canton Sch. Bd., 1974-78, 82-91; Tax Rev. Bd., Plymouth, Mich., 1980-85; chmn. Jr. Red Cross S.E. Mich., 1969-73; chmn., cons. Polio Plus immunization campaign, WHO, Rotary Internat; bd. dirs. ARC S.E. Mich., 1992—, exec. com., 1993—, mem. health, safety, youth and internat. coms. Served with USN, 1942-46. Decorated Bronze Star; recipient Disting. Health Edn. award Cen. Mich. U., 1978; adminstrm. bldg. Plymouth-Canton (Mich.) schs. dedicated E. J. McClendon Edn. Ctr., 1992. Fellow Am. Pub. Health Assn., Am. Sch. Health Assn. (pres. 1970-71, Disting. Service award 1962, William A. Howe award 1976), Am. Cancer Soc. (hon. life mem., bd. dirs.), Royal Soc. Health; mem. NEA, AAUP, Mich. Sch. Health Assn. (hon. life mem., Disting. service award 1967, Golden Anniversary award 1985), Am. Social Health Assn. (dir.), Nat. Assn. Curriculum and Devel., Am. Venereal Disease Assn., Alliance Advancement Health Edn., Soc. Pub. Health Edn., Soc. Sex Educators and Counselors, Nat. Council for Internat. Health, Am. Assn. for WHO, Soc. Native Am. Indians, Rotary (pres. 1989-91), Phi Delta Kappa. Democrat. Methodist. Home and Office: 40742 Crabtree Ln Plymouth MI 48170-2742

MCCLENDON, SARAH NEWCOMB, news service executive, writer; b. Tyler, Tex., July 8, 1910; d. Sidney Smith and Annie Rebecca (Bonner) McClendon; 1 child, Sally Newcomb Mac Donald. Grad., Tyler Jr. Coll., U. Mo. Mem. staff Tyler Courier-Times and Tyler Morning Telegraph, 1931-39; reporter Beaumont (Tex.) Enterprise; Washington corr. Phila. Daily News, 1944; founder McClendon News Svc., Washington, 1946—; talk show host Ind. Broadcasters Network; lectr. Faneuil Hall, Boston, Poor Richard's Club, Phila., Cobo Hall, Detroit, Chautauqua Instn., N.Y., Comstock Club, Sacremento; adv. to Senior Beacon; v.p. Nat. Press Club. Author: My Eight Presidents, 1978 (1st prize); contbr. articles to mags. including Esquire, Penthouse, Diplomat; TV appearances include Merv Griffin Show, Tomorrow, Inside the White House, PBS, NBC Meet the Press, KUP Show, NBC Today Show, C-Span, CNN, Fox Morning News, Late Night with David Letterman, Michael Jackson Show (L.A. radio). Mem. VA Adv. Bd. on Women Vets, def. adv. com. Women in the Svcs.; army advisor, mem. task force Women in the Army Policy Rev.; bd. dir. Sam Rayburn Libr., In Our Own Way, So. Poverty Relief Orgn. Served with WAC. Recipient Woman of Achievement award Tex. Press Women, 1978, 2d prize Nat. Fedn. Press Women, 1979, Headliner award Women in Comm., 1st Pres. award for Journalism in Washington, Nat. Fedn. Press Women, Pub. Rels. award Am. Legion, Bob Considine award, 1990, Am. Woman award Women's Rsch. Edn. Inst., 1991. Mem. DAR (Nat. Constn. award 1990), U. Mo. Alumni Assn. (chpt. pres.), Women in Comm (Margaret Caskey award), Am. Legion (post comdr.), Nat. Woman's Party (v.p.), Nat. Coun., Soc. Profl. Journalists (Hall of Fame Washington chpt.), Nat. Press Club (v.p.), Am. Newspaper Women's Club (pres.), Capitol Hill First Friday Club (pres.). Club: Capitol Hill First Friday (pres.). *After covering eleven presidents, I still feel that I am my own self, honest and owned by no one. I believe that journalism is a public trust and that I must uphold that public trust.*

MC CLENDON, WILLIAM HUTCHINSON, III, lawyer; b. New Orleans, Feb. 19, 1933; s. William H. and Eleanor (Eaton) McC.; m. Eugenia Mills Slaughter, Feb. 6, 1960; children: William Hutchinson, IV, Virginia Morris, Eleanor Eaton, Bryan Slaughter. B.A., Tulane U., 1956, LL.B., 1958. Bar: La. 1958, U.S. Supreme Ct. 1964. Atty. Humble Oil & Refining Co., 1958-60; with firm Taylor, Porter, Brooks & Phillips, Baton Rouge, 1960—; ptnr. Taylor, Porter, Brooks & Phillips, 1966—; instr. comml. law and negotiable instruments Am. Inst. Banking, 1963-74; lectr. immovable Property La. Bar Assn. Bridging the Gap Inst., 1965; lectr. La. State U. Law Sch. and Real Estate Seminar chmn., 1972, 74, 76, 80, 82, 85, 87, La. Soc. of Profl. Surveying, 1989, La. Soc. CPA's, 1991, Banking Seminar, 1995; adj. prof. La. State U., 1983—. Contbr. articles to legal jours. Bd. dirs. Cancer Soc. Baton Rouge, 1968-71; trustee Episcopal High Sch., 1976-78; mem. Dean's council Tulane U. Law Sch., 1984-88. Served to capt. AUS. Mem. ABA, Am. Judicature Soc., La. Bar Assn. (chmn. sect. trust estates, probate and immovable property law 1969-70, Meml. award article 1987), Baton Rouge Bar Assn. (chmn. title standards com. 1968-69), Tulane Alumni Assn. Greater Baton Rouge (pres. 1968-69), Baton Rouge Green (bd. dirs. 1991-93), Hilltop Aboretum (bd. dirs. 1993-95), La. Civil Svc. League (mem. 1992-94), La. Tulane Law Alumni (treas. 2d v.p. 1964-65), Kappa Alpha. Republican. Episcopalian (vestry, sr. warden 1975, 81, 84, diocesan standing com. 1985-89). Clubs: Baton Rouge Assembly (treas. 1983); Toastmasters (Baton Rouge) (pres. 1970), Baton Rouge Country (Baton Rouge), Camelot (Baton Rouge); Pickwick (New Orleans). Lodge: Rotary (bd. dirs. Baton Rouge club 1972). Home: Oakland at Gurley 6165 Highway 963 Ethel LA 70730-3615 Office: 451 Florida St Baton Rouge LA 70801-1700

MC CLENNEN, LOUIS, lawyer, educator; b. Cambridge, Mass., May 29, 1912; s. Edward F. and Mary (Crane) McC.; m. Miriam Jacobs, Apr. 25, 1969; children by previous marriage: Adams, James, Helen, Persis, Crane, Emery. AB cum laude, Harvard U., 1934, JD, 1937. Bar: Mass. 1937, Ind. 1940, Ariz. 1946. Practice in Boston, 1937-39, Indpls., 1940-42, Phoenix, 1946—; now pres. McClennen & Fels, P.C.; adj. prof. law (fed. taxation) Ariz. State U., 1974-80, pres. Law Soc., 1981-83. Author: (with others) Arizona Estate Tax, 1953, (with J.T. Melczer Jr.) Arizona Income Tax Regulations, 1954; contbr. articles to profl. mags. Pres. Ariz. Bd. Edn., 1965-69; trustee No. Ariz. Mus.; past pres., bd. dirs. Maricopa County Legal Aid Soc., Phoenix Symphony Assn.; v.p., bd. dirs. Phoenix United Fund; sec., bd. dirs. Phoenix Country Day Sch.; bd. dirs. Ariz. Acad.; regional dir. Harvard Alumni Assn. Maj. USAAF, 1942-46. Mem. ABA, Ariz. Bar Assn., Maricopa County Bar Assn. (dir., past v.p.), Harvard Law Sch. Assn. (v.p.) Lawyers Club Phoenix (pres.), Phoenix Country Club, Eastward Ho Country Club (Chatham, Mass.). Unitarian. Home and Office: 5311 La Plaza Circle Phoenix AZ 85012

MC CLENNEY, BYRON NELSON, community college administrator; b. San Antonio, Dec. 14, 1939; s. Thomas B. and Lorene Holley McC.; children: Mark Nelson, Don Alan; m. Kay McCullough, May 17, 1966. B.A., U. Tex., 1961, MEd, 1963, EdD, 1969. Asst. dean evening div. San Antonio Coll., 1966-68; dean instrn. McLennan Community Coll., Waco, Tex., 1968-70; dean instrn. Eastfield Coll., Dallas County, Tex., 1970-71, pres. 1971-78; pres. Parkersburg (W.Va.) Community Coll., 1978-81, San Antonio Community Coll. Dist., 1981; chancellor Alamo Community Coll. Dist., 1982-86; pres. Community Coll. Denver, 1986—; cons. Nat. Center for Higher Edn. Mgmt. Systems. Author: Management for Productivity, 1980. NDEA fellow, 1965-66; recipient Disting. Alumni award U. Tex. Coll. Edn., 1982-83, Thomas J. Peters Nat. Leadership award League for Innovation, 1989.

Mem. Am. Assn. Community and Jr. Colls. (chmn. pres.'s acad 1983-84, mem. urban commn. 1987-90). Commn. on Instns. of Higher Edn., N. Central Assn. (past). Presbyterian. Club: Rotary (past dist. gov.). Office: Community Coll Denver PO Box 173363 Denver CO 80217

MCCLENON, JOHN RAYMOND, chemistry educator; b. Grinnell, Iowa, May 1, 1937; s. Raymond Benedict and Erika (Weber) McC.; m. Mary Alice Thornton, June 7, 1959; children: Anne Jeanette, Marca Kay, Maureen. B.A., Grinnell Coll., 1959; Ph.D., UCLA, 1964. Asst. prof. Milton Coll., Wis., 1963-65; asst. prof. chemistry Sweet Briar (Va.) Coll., 1965-72, assoc. prof., 1972-76, prof., 1976-82, Charles A. Dana prof., 1982—; head FBN Microcomputing, Lynchburg, Va., 1980—, Johnny McClenon Big Band, Lynchburg, Va., 1978—. Editor: (newsletter) Macintosh User's Group, Sweet Briar Coll. Chmn. ACLU local chpt., 1966-75; prin. clarinettist Lynchburg Symphony, Va., 1976—. Mem. Am. Chem. Soc., AAUP (chmn. Sweet Briar chpt. 1982-83). Democrat. Unitarian. Home: 712 Riverside Dr Lynchburg VA 24503-1327 Office: Sweet Briar Coll PO Box 73 Sweet Briar VA 24595-0073

MCCLIMON, TIMOTHY JOHN, lawyer; b. Clinton, Iowa, July 17, 1953; s. Leonard James and Celeste Margaret (Borman) McC.; m. Suzanne Berman, Jan. 30, 1994. BA magna cum laude, Luther Coll., 1975; MS, St. Cloud State U., 1976; JD, Georgetown U., 1986. Bar: N.Y. 1987. Asst. dir. student activities St. Cloud (Minn.) State U., 1975-76; performing arts coordinator Western Ill. U., Macomb, 1976-79; program specialist Nat. Endowment for the Arts, Washington, 1979-82, program adminstr., 1982-86, law clk., 1985-86; assoc. Webster and Sheffield, N.Y.C., 1986-88; v.p. AT&T Found., N.Y.C., 1988—; adj. prof. NYU, 1990—; bd. dirs. Am. Coun. for Arts, N.Y.C., Second Stage Theatre, N.Y.C., Theatre Comms. Group, N.Y.C., Field Papers, Inc., N.Y.C., Performance Space 122, N.Y.C.; speaker Confs. on Arts Mgmt., 1979—; mem. NEA, Washington, 1986—; mem. mayor's cultural affairs adv. commn. City of N.Y.C., 1992-94. Author: (textbook chpt.) Audiences and the Arts, 1981; contbr. articles to Jour. of Law and the Arts, 1986, other publs., 1989—. Recipient Eagle Scout award Boy Scouts Am., 1967, Faculty award Blue Key Nat. Honor Frat., 1979. Mem. N.Y.C. Bar Assn. (com. mem. 1987-92), ABA (com. mem. 1986-88), N.Y. State Bar Assn., Vol. Lawyers for the Arts. Avocations: photography, tennis, bicycling, traveling, reading. Home: Penthouse 2-C 222 Riverside Dr New York NY 10025 Office: AT&T Found Ste 3100 1301 Ave of Americas New York NY 10019

MCCLINTIC, HOWARD GRESSON, foundation executive; b. Pitts., Feb. 27, 1951; s. Stewart and Pamela Mary (Gresson) McC.; m. Katherine Davis Foss, Sept. 14, 1948; children: Margaret Grosson, Katherine Davis, Henry Stewart. BA in Polit. Sci./Econs., George Washington U., 1973. Legis. asst. U.S. Sen. Howard H. Baker, Washington, 1973-75; assoc. cons. Energy Decisions, Inc., Washington, 1975-78; energy policy analyst Chem Systems, Inc., N.Y.C., 1978-80; tr. cons. Coal Use Group, Inc., Washington, 1980-83; staff officer Nat. Acad. Scis., Washington, 1983-87; exec. dir. The Jefferson Energy Found., Washington, 1987—; spl. cons. Nat. Acad. Scis., 1973-74, Law Offices of Dudley & Warner, N.Y.C., 1979, Internat. Bus. Counsellors, Washington, 1982, Japan Nat. Oil Co., Washington, 1983. Co-editor: NAS Com. Rpt., Oceans in Year 2000, 1974, staff coord. rpts., 1984, 86; exec. producer energy films: Everything Starts With Energy, Energy Policy On Trial, Future Energy Sources, Double Jeopardy, Access to Public Lands and Waters, Nuclear Waste and the West, What Price Cheap Oil?, The Emerging National Energy Strategy. Co-founder The Decade Soc., Washington, 1979-83; coordinator Washingtonians for Bush, 1983; subcom. chmn. U.S. Dept. Energy, 1988; study participant energy Atlantic Council of U.S., Washington, 1989; assoc. mem. Naval War Coll. Found. Mem. Internat. Assn. Energy Economists, Atlantic Council U.S., Am. Energy Assurance Council (advisor 1988—), Rolling Rock Club, Mid-Ocean Club (Bermuda), Gibson Island Club, Chevy Chase Club, Potomac Boat Club. Republican. Episcopalian. Avocations: skiing, golf, tennis, sailing. Home: 5115 Palisade Ln NW Washington DC 20016-5337 Office: The Jefferson Energy Found 1101 16th St NW Washington DC 20036-4803

MC CLINTOCK, ARCHIE GLENN, lawyer; b. Sheridan, Wyo., Mar. 26, 1911; s. James Porter and Martie E. (Glenn) McC.; m. Ina Jean Robinson, May 27, 1939 (dec. 1974); children: Ellery, Jeffry, Kathleen. B.A., U. Wyo., 1933, LLB with honor, 1935. Bar: Wyo. 1935, Calif. 1982. Pvt. practice law Cheyenne, Wyo., 1935-73, 81-83, 87—; justice Wyo. Supreme Ct., Cheyenne, 1973-81; atty. gen. State of Wyo., 1982-87; semi-ret.; adj. prof. law U. Wyo., 1988, 90-92. Mem. Wyo. Fair Employment Practices Commn., 1965-71. Served with USNR, 1944-45. Mem. Wyo. State Bar (pres. 1950-51), Am. Judicature Soc., Order of Coif (hon. mem.) Sigma Nu. Democrat. Club: Elks. Home: 1211 Richardson Ct Cheyenne WY 82001-2424

MCCLINTOCK, EUGENE JEROME, minister; b. San Diego, Calif., Jan. 25, 1924; s. Alberta Jerome and Gladys Elizabeth (Wilsie) McC.:m. Lena LaVerne Brown, Feb. 16, 1947; children: Nathan-Calvin, Joseph, Mark. Student, Caldwell Seminary, 1942-45; BTh, Pentecostal Bible Inst., 1951. Ordained to ministry United Pentecostal Ch. Pastor United Pentecostal Ch., Twin Falls, Idaho, 1945-47, 1st Pentecostal Ch., Aberdeen, Miss., 1949-60, Dupo (Ill.) Pentecostal Ch., 1960-64, Calvary Apostolic Ch., Mt. Vernon, Ill., 1964-79; gen. sec. Sunday sch. United Pentecostal Ch., St. Louis, 1979-82, gen. dir. Sunday sch., 1982—; part time minstr. Pentecostal Bible Inst., Tupelo, Miss., 1950-60. Author: Achieving Excellence in the Sunday School, Vols. I, II, III, IV, 1992; editor Christian Educator, 1982-94. Active ministerial fellowship, Aberdeen, Miss., 1950-60, Dupo, 1960-64, Mt. Vernon, 1964-79. Avocations: golf, photography, travel, writing. Office: United Pentecostal Ch Internat 8855 Dunn Rd Hazelwood MO 63042

MCCLINTOCK, GEORGE DUNLAP, lawyer; b. Pocatello, Idaho, Nov. 30, 1920; s. George Dunlap and Jessie (McCabe) McC.; m. Aileen McHugh, Sept. 19, 1945; children—Jessie Kelly, Catharine, George, Jane Wyatt, Michael, Anne. A.B. cum laude, Dartmouth Coll., 1942; LL.B., Harvard U., 1948. Bar: Minn. 1948. Ptnr. Faegre & Benson, Mpls., 1948-90; dir. Merchants Bank, Rugby, N.D.; trustee Douglas Rees Trust, 1966—, Paul R. Held Testamentary Trusts, 1980—. Trustee, mayor City of Woodland, Minn., 1970-79; exec. bd., Viking council Boy Scouts Am., Mpls., 1959-74, pres., 1966-67; gen. campaign chmn. United Way of Mpls., 1972, bd. dirs., 1973-81, pres., 1976; trustee Convent of Visitation Sch., St. Paul, 1975-81; trustee North Meml. Med. Ctr., Robbinsdale, Minn., 1959-75; trustee Minn. Med. Found., Mpls., 1982-90. Served to lt. USNR, 1942-46. Recipient Disting. Eagle Scout award Boy Scouts Am., 1982. Mem. Mpls. Club (governing com. 1983-89, pres. 1987), Woodhill Country Club (trustee 1985-94). Republican. Presbyterian. Avocations: golf; waterfowl hunting. Office: care Faegre & Benson 2200 Norwest Ctr 90 S 7th St Minneapolis MN 55402

MCCLINTOCK, JESSICA, fashion designer; b. Frenchville, Maine, June 19, 1930; d. Rene Gagnon and Verna Hedrich; m. Frank Staples (dec. 1964); 1 child Scott. BA, San Jose State U., 1963. Edlen. sch. tchr. Marblehead, Mass., 1966-68, Long Island, N.Y., 1968, Sunnyvale, Calif., 1964-65, 68-69; fashion designer Jessica McClintock, Inc., San Francisco, 1969—. Active donor, AIDS and Homeless programs; scholarship sponsor Fashion Inst. Design and Merchandising. Recipient Merit award Design, 1989, Dallas Fashion award, 1988, Tommy award, 1986, Pres. Appreciation award, 1986, Best Interior Store Design, 1986, Calif. Designer award, 1985, Earnie award, 1981, numerous others. Mem. Coun. Fashion Designers of Am., Fashion Inst. Design & Merchandising (adv. bd. 1979—), San Francisco Fashion Industry (pres. 1976-78, bd. dirs. 1989). Office: Jessica McClintock Inc 1400 16th St San Francisco CA 94103-5181

MCCLINTOCK, KENNETH DAVISON, state legislator; b. London, Jan. 19, 1957; arrived in P.R., 1957; s. George Davison and Nivea M. (Hernandez) McC.; m. María E. Batista, 1994. Student, U.P.R., San Juan, 1974-77; JD, Tulane U., 1980. Staff dir. consumer affairs com. P.R. Ho. of Reps., San Juan, 1977, legis. asst., 1978-80; legis. cons. P.R. Ho. of Reps./Senate, San Juan, 1981-92; city councilman San Juan City Coun., 1991-92; senator P.R. Senate, San Juan, 1993—, chmn. govtl. affairs com., fed. and econ. affairs com., select com. econ. regulation; mem., Pres. Carter appointee Nat. Adv. Com. on Juvenile Justice, Washington, 1977-81. Chmn. Dems. for Statehood, San Juan, 1989-93; exec. dir. P.R. State Dem. Com., San Juan, 1984-88; co-chair, host state com. 1995 Coun. State Govt's. Ann. Mtg.,

1994-95; mem. Nat. Exec. Com. Coun. State Govt's., 1995—; mem. exec. com. Coun. State Govt's. Ea. Regional Conf. Recipient Inst. TV and Radio Ethics award P.R. TV and Radio Inst., 1989, 90; named one of Outstanding Young Men, Jaycees, 1984. Democrat. Episcopalian. Avocations: numismatist, reading, swimming. Home: 1406 Villas del Senorial San Juan PR 00926 Office: PR Senate The Capitol San Juan PR 00901

MCCLINTOCK, WILLIAM THOMAS, health care administrator; b. Pittsfield, Mass., Oct. 23, 1934; s. Ernest William and Helen Elizabeth (Clum) M.; m. Wendolyn Hope Eckerman, June 22, 1963; children: Anne Elizabeth, Carol Jean, Thomas Daniel. BA, St. Lawrence U., Canton, N.Y., 1956; MBA, U. Chgo., 1959, MHA, 1962. Prodn. planner Corning Glass Works, Corning, N.Y., 1959-60; adminstrv. resident Highland Hosp., Oakland, Calif., 1961-62; adminstrv. asst. Univ. Hosps. of Cleve., 1962-65; asst. adminstr. Presbyn. Hosp., Whittier, Calif., 1965-68; regional asst. Kaiser Found. Hosps., Oakland, Calif., 1968-70; assoc. dir., exec. dir. Conn. Hosp. Planning Commn., New Haven, 1970-75; project dir., lectr. sch. health studies U. N.H., Durham, 1975-77; regional mgr. Tex. Med. Found., Austin, 1977-81; adminstr. Schick Shadel Hosp., Fort Worth, 1981-87; mgmt. cons. George S. May Internat. Co., Park Ridge, Ill., 1987-88; mgr. Nat. Ctr. Rsch. Programs Am. Heart Assn., Dallas, 1988-89; adminstr. Ambulatory Svcs. Health Care of Tex., Ft. Worth, 1990-92; CEO Boundary Community Hosp. & Nursing Home, Bonners Ferry, Idaho, 1992—. 1st lt. U.S. Army, 1957. Fellow Am. Coll. Health Care Execs., Am. Coll. Addiction Treatment Adminstrs.; mem. Am. Hosp. Assn. (life), Am. Heart Assn. (mem. bd. dirs. Idaho, Mont. affiliates 1993—), Idaho Hosp. Assn. (bd. dirs. 1995—), Unity Lodge No. 9, F&AM, N.Y. Republican. Presbyterian. Avocations: reading, gardening, photography. Home: County Rd 62C PO Box 1226 Bonners Ferry ID 83805-1226 Office: 6640 Kaniksu St Bonners Ferry ID 83805

MC CLINTON, DONALD G., diversified holding company executive; b. Pitts., June 30, 1933; s. Donald K. and Ethel M. McC.; m. Jane Ann Knoebel, Apr. 12, 1958; children: Catherine, D. Scott. B.S., Miami U., Oxford, Ohio, 1955. Audit mgr. Arthur Andersen & Co., Cleve., 1955-62; mgr. accounting E. Ohio Gas Co., Cleve., 1962-66; exec. v.p. Nat. Industries, Inc., Louisville, 1966-79; pres. Yellow Cab Co., Louisville, 1979-94; owner, chmn. bd. Interlock Industries, Inc., 1982-94; pres. Skylight Thoroughbred Tng. Ctr., Inc., 1994—; bd. dirs. Bank of Louisville, Cartenders Heathcorp; trustee Jewish Hosp. Health Care Systems, Inc., 1983—. Mem. Louisville-Jefferson County Bicentennial Commn., 1976-77; mem. council, treas. Old Kentucky Home coun. Boy Scouts Am., 1976—; mem. Citizens at Large Jefferson County Budget Com., 1978-84; bd. overseers Bellarmine Coll., 1978-84; bd. dirs. Ky. Derby Festival, 1978—, Jewish Hosp., Louisville, 1980-86; trustee Spalding U., 1985-91. Mem. Fin. Execs. Inst. Home: 6205 Deep Creek Dr Prospect KY 40059-9348 Office: Skylight Thoroughbred Tng Ctr Inc PO Box 4 Goshen KY 40026

MCCLINTON, DOROTHY HARDAWAY, former business educator; b. Seguin, Tex., Jan. 4, 1925; d. George Washington and Rosetta (Hodge) Hardaway; m. Marion N. Hopkins Sr., Oct. 27, 1951 (div. Dec. 1982); 1 child, Marion N.; m. Elmer McClinton, Aug. 12, 1986; children: Thomas, Evelyn M., Nathaniel. BS, Huston-Tillotson Coll., 1947; MBEd, Tex. So. U., 1960. Tchr. Ball Elem. Sch., Seguin, Tex., 1947-49, Ball Mid. Sch., Seguin, 1949-54; clk., typist Kelly AFB, San Antonio, 1956-57; tchr. Ball High Sch., Seguin, 1957-64; instr. tchr. dept. chair St. Philips Community Coll., San Antonio, 1964-86, prof. emeritus, 1986—; audio visual tutorial cons. Media Systems Corp. subs. Harcourt Brace Jovanovich, Inc., 1978-86; mem. nat. rsch. rev. panel Ohio State U., 1983-84. Chair telethon Uited Negro Coll. Fund, San Antonio, 1990-92; trustee Huston-Tillotson Coll., 1990—. Recipient Bus. Tchr. of Yr. award Tex. Bus. Edn. Assn., Austin, 1981-82, Acad. Achievement award Huston-Tillotson Coll., 1990-91; Inst. for Ednl. Ledership fellow St. Philip's Coll., San Antonio, 1984-85; named Woman of Yr. St. Paul UMC, 1991; inductee Educators' Hall of Fame, Gamma Tau chpt. Phi Delta Kappa, 1993-94. Mem. Alamo Community Coll. Retirees, Top Ladies of Distinction (sgt.-at-arms 1987-92), Huston-Tillotson Coll. Alumni (pres. 1982-91, pres. 1985-87) Delta Sigma Theta, Inc. (pres. 1972-74). Home: 1639 Lone Oak San Antonio TX 78220

MCCLOSKEY, J(OHN) MICHAEL, association executive; b. Eugene, Oreg., Apr. 26, 1934; s. John Clement and Agnes Margaret (Studer) McC.; m. Maxine Mugg, June 17, 1965; stepchildren: Claire, Laura, James, Rosemary Johnson. BA, Harvard U., 1956; JD, U. Oreg., 1961. N.W. rep. Sierra Club, Eugene, 1961-65; asst. to pres. Sierra Club, San Francisco, 1965-66, conservation dir., 1966-69, exec. dir., 1969-85; chmn. Sierra Club, Washington, 1985—, acting exec. dir., 1986-87; vice-chmn. Commn. on Environ. Law and Policy (Internat. Union for Conservation of Nature), Gland, Switzerland, 1978-88; mem. Pres.'s Commn. on Agenda for 1980's, Washington, 1979-80; co-chmn. OSHA-Environ. Conf., Washington, 1983-87; vice chmn. Am. Com. on Internat. Conservation, 1988-90; mem. adj. faculty Sch. Natural Resources, U. Mich., 1988—. Contbr. articles to profl. jours. Bd. dirs. Nat. Resources Coun. Am., 1988-94, vice chmn., 1989-91, chmn., 1992-93, chmn. advocacy forum 1989-91; bd. dirs. Mineral Policy Ctr., 1988—; mem. steering com. Blueprint for Environ., 1987-88; nominated candidate Oreg. Ho. of Reps., 1962. 1st lt. U.S. Army, 1956-58. Recipient award Calif. Conservation Coun., 1969, John Muir award Sierra Club, 1979, UN Environ. Program Global 500 award, 1992. Mem. Internat. Coun. on Environ. Law, Harvard Club, Explorers Club (N.Y.C.). Democrat. Office: Sierra Club 408 C St NE Washington DC 20002-5818

MC CLOSKEY, PAUL N., JR., lawyer, former congressman; b. San Bernardino, Calif., Sept. 29, 1927; m. Helen Hooper McCloskey (div.); children—Nancy, Peter, John, Kathleen. A.B., Stanford, 1950, LL.B., 1953; J.D., Santa Clara Law Sch., 1974. Bar: Calif. bar 1953. Deputy dist. atty. Alameda County, Calif., 1953-54; mem. firm McCloskey, Wilson, Mosher & Martin, Palo Alto, 1956-67; mem. 90th-94th Congresses from 17th Calif. dist., 95th-97th Congresses from 12th Calif. dist., 1967-83; ptnr. Brobeck Phleger & Harrison, 1983-89; now counsel McClung & Davis, Laguna Hills, Calif.; del. UN Law of Sea Conf.; lectr. in law Stanford Law Sch., 1964-67, Santa Clara Law Sch., 1964-67. Author: Truth and Untruth, 1972. Served with USN, 1945-47, to col. USMC, 1950-52. Decorated Navy Cross, Silver Star, Purple Heart. Mem. ABA, Palo Alto Bar Assn. (pres. 1960-61), Santa Clara County Bar Assn. (trustee 1965-67), State Bar Calif. (pres. conf. barristers 1961-62), Phi Delta Phi. Republican. Office: McClung & Davis 24012 De La Plata Calle Ste 150 Laguna Hills CA 92653

MCCLOSKEY, PETER FRANCIS, trade association executive; b. N.Y.C., Jan. 10, 1935; s. Joseph Michael and Frances Mary (McAllister) McC.; m. Louise C. Collins, Nov. 28, 1959; children—Mary Catherine, Margaret Ann, Elizabeth, Patricia. B.S. in Physics, Holy Cross Coll., 1956; postgrad., Georgetown U., 1959-62, Fordham U., 1963-65. Bar: N.Y. 1965, D.C. 1971, Va. 1972, U.S. Supreme Ct. 1980. Contract adminstr. Melpar Inc., Falls Church, Va., 1959-60; rsch. physicist, programmer, systems analyst, mktg. rep., advanced systems mgr., domestic licensing mgr. IBM, 1960-65; v.p. Farrington Mfg. Co., Washington, 1965, pres., 1968-69, chmn. bd., 1969-70; ptnr. Hughes & McCloskey, 1971-73; pres., chief exec. officer Computer and Bus. Equipment Assn., 1973-77; pres. Electronic Industries Assn., Washington, 1977—; dir. Am. Standards Inst. Mem. Peace Corps Adv. Bd., 1981-83. 1st lt. USMC. Recipient Am. jurisprudence prize Fordham U. Mem. Young Presidents Assn., U.S.C. of C. (bd. dirs. 1992—). Roman Catholic. Clubs: University (Washington); Congressional Country, Regency (McLean, Va.); Burning Tree. Lodge: Knights of Malta. Home: 7625 Burford Dr Mc Lean VA 22102-2135 Office: Electronic Industries Assn 2001 Pennsylvania Ave NW Washington DC 20006-1807

MCCLOSKEY, ROBERT, artist; b. Hamilton, Ohio, Sept. 15, 1914; s. Howard Hill and Mabel (Wismaier) McC.; m. Margaret Durand, Nov. 23, 1940; children: Sarah, Jane. Student, Vesper George Sch., N.Y.C., NAD; Litt.D. (hon.), Miami U., Oxford, Ohio, 1962, Mt. Holyoke Coll., South Hadley, Mass., 1967, U. Maine, 1990; hon. degree, Bowdoin Coll., 1991. Artist, illustrator, host, Am. Songfest, Weston Woods bicentennial film.; Executed bas-reliefs, Hamilton Municipal Bldg., Ohio, 1935; author: Lentil, 1940, Make Way for Ducklings, 1941 (bronze ducklings sculpted by Nancy Schön installed Boston Pub. Garden, 1987, replicas placed in Moscow Park, 1991), Homer Price, 1943, Blueberries for Sal, 1948, Centerburg Tales, 1951, One Morning in Maine, 1952, Time of Wonder, 1957, Bert Dow, Deep Water Man, 1963. Recipient numerous awards including President's award for creative work NAD, 1936; recipient numerous awards including Prix de Rome Am. Acad. in Rome, 1939, Caldecott medal for most disting. picture book for children published in 1941, 1942, Caldecott medal for Time of Wonder, 1958, Regina medal Cath. Library Assn., 1974; hon. by. ALA, 1991. Fellow Am. Acad. Rome; mem. P.E.N., Authors League. Am. Home: Little Deer Isle ME 04650

MC CLOSKEY, ROBERT JAMES, former diplomat; b. Phila., Nov. 25, 1922; s. Thomas and Anna (Wallace) McC.; m. Anne Taylor Phelan, July 8, 1961; children: Lisa Siobhan, André Taylor McCloskey. B.S. in Journalism, Temple U., 1953; postgrad., George Washington U., 1958-59. Engaged in hotel work, 1945-50, newspaper reporter, 1952-55; joined U.S. Fgn. Svc. 1955; assigned Hong Kong, 1955-57; publs. officer State Dept., 1957-58; press officer Office of News, 1958-60; assigned U.S. Mission to UN 15th Gen. Assembly, 1960-62; spl. asst. Bur. Pub. Affairs, State Dept., 1962-63; dep. dir. Office News, 1963-64, dir., 1964-66, dep. asst. sec. of state, 1966-69; dep. asst. sec., spl. asst. to sec. for press rels. Office Press Rels., 1969-73; amb. to Republic of Cyprus, 1973-74; amb.-at-large U.S. State Dept., 1974-75, amb.-at-large, asst. sec. state for congl. rels., 1975-76; amb. to The Netherlands, 1976-78, amb. to Greece, 1978-81; ombudsman Washington Post, 1981-83; sr. v.p. Cath. Relief Svcs., Washington, 1984-89; editor Mediterranean Quar., Washington, 1988-90; bd. dirs. Anatoia Coll., Boston, 1981—. Staff sgt. USMC, 1942-45. Mem. Am. Acad. Diplomacy (bd. dirs.). Home: 111 Hesketh St Chevy Chase MD 20815-4222

MCCLUNG, A(LEXANDER) KEITH, JR., lawyer; b. Gallipolis, Ohio, Sept. 13, 1934; s. Alexander Keith and Florence (Juhling) McC.; m. Sandra B. Foley, Aug. 17, 1957; children: Alexander Keith III, Martha E. AB, W.Va. U., 1956; JD, Harvard U., 1959. Bar: W.Va. 1959, Md. 1970, Mich. 1972. Assoc. Jackson, Kelly, Holt & O'Farrell, Charleston, W.Va., 1959-69; assoc. counsel Comml. Credit Corp., Balt., 1969-70, v.p., counsel, 1973-82, gen. atty., 1982-85; sr. gen. atty. Comml. Credit Co., Balt., 1985-89, sr. v.p., gen. counsel, 1989—; v.p., counsel McCullagh Leasing, Inc., Roseville, Mich., 1970-73; bd. dirs. Travelers Bank; trustee Roland Park Found.; mem. adv. coun. Coll. Arts and Sci., W.Va. U. Lt. U.S. Army, 1961-62. Mem. ABA (subcom. uniform comml. code, com. equipment leasing). Democrat. Home: 214 Ridgewood Rd Baltimore MD 21210-2539 Office: Comml Credit Co 300 St Paul Pl Baltimore MD 21202-2120

MC CLUNG, JIM HILL, light manufacturing company executive; b. Buena Vista, Ga., Nov. 8, 1936; s. Jim Hill and Marjorie (Oxford) McC.; m. Jo Patrick, July 5, 1958; children—Jim Hill, Karen Mareese. B.A., Emory U., 1958; M.B.A., Harvard U., 1964. With Lithonia Lighting div. Nat. Svc. Industries, Inc., Conyers, Ga., 1964—; now pres., assoc. dir. Lithonia Lighting div. Nat. Svc. Industries, Inc. Served with USAF, 1958-62. mem. Illuminating Engring. Soc. N.Am. (vice chmn. lighting rsch. and edn. fund), Nat. Elec. Distbrs. Assn. (mfrs. bd.), Nat. Elec. Mfrs. Assn. (nat. lighting bur., bd. dirs.), Intelligent Bldgs. Inst. (bd. dirs.), Lighting Rsch. Inst. (bd. dirs.), Elec. Mfrs. Club, World Pres.'s Orgn. Methodist. Office: Lithonia Lighting Div PO Box A Conyers GA 30207-0067

MC CLUNG, LELAND SWINT, microbiologist, educator; b. Atlanta, Tex., Aug. 4, 1910; s. Joe Baker and Roxie Buelah (Swint) McC.; m. Ruth Wilhelmien Exner, Dec. 25, 1944. A.B., U. Tex., 1931, A.M., 1932; Ph.D, U. Wis., 1934. Research bacteriologist Am. Can Co., Maywood, Ill., 1934-36; instr. in fruit products and jr. bacteriologist Coll. Agr., U. Calif., 1936-37; instr. research medicine George Williams Hooper Found. for Med. Research, U. Calif., 1937-39; asst. prof. Ind. U., Bloomington, 1944-48, assoc. prof. Ind. U., 1944-48, prof., chmn. dept. bacteriology, 1946-66, prof. microbiology, 1966-81, prof. emeritus, 1981—; asst. dir. div. biol. scis., 1965-68. Author: (with Elizabeth McCoy), 2 vols.) The Anaerobic Bacteria and Their Activities in Nature and Disease: A Subject Bibliography, 1939, supplement, 1941; The Anaerobic Bacteria: Their Activities in Nature and Disease: The Literature for 1940-75 (7 vols.), 1982; contbr. articles to sci. jours. John Simon Guggenheim Meml. Found. fellow, 1939-40; rsch. fellow in bacteriology Harvard Med. Sch., 1939-40. Fellow AAAS, Am. Acad. Microbiology (gov. 1961-67, 76-77), Ind. Acad. Sci.; mem. Am. Soc. Microbiology (hon., archivist 1960-82), Soc. Am. Bacteriologists (editl. bd. Jour. Bacteriology 1953-57, archivist 1953-60, chmn. com on edn. 1958-61, Chas. A. Behrens award Ind. br. 1981, Barnett Cohen award Nat. br. 1984), Am. Inst. Biol. Scis. (gov. bd. 1968-74), Inst. Food Tech., Nat. Assn. Biology Tchrs. (pres. 1965), Soc. Indsl. Microbiology, Sigma Xi, Phi Sigma, Gamma Alpha, Alpha Epsilon Delta. Office: Ind U Dept Biology Jordan Hall 138 Bloomington IN 47405

MCCLUNG, RICHARD GOEHRING, lawyer; b. Butler, Pa., June 26, 1913; s. Frank A. and Mary A. (Goehring) McC.; m. Jean Barrett Coffin, Dec. 1, 1951 (dec.); children: Jean C., Mary G., Priscilla B. A.B., Princeton U., 1935; LL.B., Yale U., 1939; cert., Harvard U. Bus. Sch., 1937. Bar: N.Y. 1940. Pvt. practice N.Y.C., 1940—; with Carter, Ledyard & Milburn, 1946—, ptnr., mem. of counsel, 1983—. Served to comdr. USNR, 1942-46. Home: 101D Lewis St Greenwich CT 06830-6660 Office: 2 Wall St New York NY 10005-2001

MCCLURE, BROOKS, management consultant; b. N.Y.C., Mar. 8, 1919; s. Walter Harsha and Angelica (Mendoza) McC.; m. Olga Beatrice Gallik, Oct. 15, 1949; 1 child, Karen. AB summa cum laude, U. Md.; disting. grad., U.S. Naval War Coll. N.Y. corr. Western Press Ltd., Australia, 1939-42; copy editor Washington Eve. Star, 1946-51; joined U.S. Fgn. Service, 1951; information officer, attache embassy Copenhagen, 1951-53; press attache embassy Vienna, 1953-55; information officer, attache embassy Cairo, 1956-57, Seoul, 1957-60, Bonn, 1960-63; policy officer Europe USIA, 1963-66; pub. affairs officer 1st sec. embassy, Copenhagen, 1967-72; spl. asst. policy plans and nat. security council affairs, internat. security affairs Dept. Def., 1972-76; internat. security adviser USIA, 1976-77; program coordinator Crisis Assessment Staff, Dept. Commerce, 1977-78; dir. ops. Internat. Mgmt. Analysis and Resources Corp., 1978-81, v.p., 1982—; sec. Cross-Continent Assocs. Ltd., 1994—; various spl. assignments, Europe, Middle East, Asia, Africa; lectr. FBI Acad., Fgn. Svc. Inst., Inter-Am. Def. Coll., Army War Coll., Navy War Coll. Contbg. author: Modern Guerrilla Warfare, 1962, Dynamics of Terrorism, 1977, International Terrorism in Contemporary World, 1978, Corporate Vulnerability and How to Assess it: Political Terrorism and Business, 1979, Business and the Middle East, 1981, Political Terrorism and Energy, 1981; Contbr. articles profl. jours.; author report to Senate Judiciary Com. on internat. terrorism and hostage def. measures; testifier on internat. security, hostage behavior, def. of Alaskan pipeline, FBI charter U.S. Senate, 1975-79. With AUS, 1942-46, ETO. Mem. Am. Fgn. Svc. Assn., Assn. for Diplomatic Studies, Nat. Press Club, DACOR, Phi Kappa Phi, Alpha Sigma Lambda. Home: 6204 Rockhurst Rd Bethesda MD 20817-1756 Office: IMAR Corp PO Box 34528 Bethesda MD 20827-4528

MCCLURE, DANIEL M., lawyer; b. Enid, Okla., Feb. 5, 1952; s. Larry M. and Marie Dolores (Sarver) McC.; m. Judy Lynn Pinson, Jan. 3, 1976; children: Andrew Mead, Mark William, Kathleen Claire. BA with highest hons., U. Okla., 1974; JD cum laude, Harvard U., 1978. Bar: Tex. 1978, U.S. Dist. Ct. (so. dist., ea. dist.) Tex. 1979, U.S. Ct. Appeals (5th cir., 11th cir.) 1981. Assoc. Fulbright & Jaworski, Houston, 1978-86, ptnr., 1986—. Fellow Tex. Bar Found.; mem. ABA, Nat. Assn. Railroad Trial Counsel, Tex. Bar Assn., Houston Bar Assn. (cert. civil trial law), Harvard Law Sch. Assn. Avocation: tennis. Home: 2 Long Timbers Ln Houston TX 77024-5445 Office: Fulbright & Jaworski 1301 Mckinney St Houston TX 77010-3049

MC CLURE, DONALD STUART, physical chemist, educator; b. Yonkers, N.Y., Aug. 27, 1920; s. Robert Hirt and Helen (Campbell) McC.; m. Laura Lee Thompson, July 9, 1949; children: Edward, Katharine, Kevin. B.Chemistry, U. Minn., 1942; Ph.D., U. Calif., Berkeley, 1948. With war research div. Columbia U., 1942-46; mem. faculty U. Calif., Berkeley, 1948-55; group leader, mem. profl. staff RCA Labs., 1955-62; prof. chemistry U. Chgo., 1962-67; prof. chemistry Princeton (N.J.) U., 1967-91, prof. emeritus, 1991—; vis. lectr. various univs.; cons. to govt. and industry. Author: Electronic Spectra of Molecules and Ions in Crystals, 1959, Some Aspects of Crystal Field Theory, 1964; also articles. Guggenheim fellow Oxford (Eng.) U., 1972-73; Humboldt fellow, 1980; recipient Irving Langmuir prize, 1979.

Fellow Am. Acad. Arts and Scis., Nat. Acad. Scis.; mem. Am. Chem. Soc., Am. Phys. Soc. Home: 23 Hemlock Cir Princeton NJ 08540-5405

MCCLURE, FREDERICK DONALD, investment banker, lawyer; b. Ft. Worth, Feb. 2, 1954; s. Foster Donald and Mayme Nell (Barnett) McC.; m. Harriet Elizabeth Jackson, Dec. 17, 1977; children: Lauren Elizabeth, Frederick Donald. BS, Tex. A&M U., 1976; JD, Baylor U., 1981. Bar: Tex. 1981, U.S. Dist. Ct. (so. dist.) Tex. 1982, U.S. Ct. Appeals (5th cir.) 1982. Agrl. asst. to U.S. Senator John Tower, Washington, 1977-79, legis. dir., 1983-84; assoc. Reynolds, Allen & Cook, Houston, 1981-83; assoc. dep. atty. gen. Dept. Justice, Washington, 1984-85; spl. asst. to pres. for legis affairs White House, Washington, 1985-86, asst. to pres legis. affairs, 1989-92; bd. regents The Tex. A & M U. Sys., 1995—; bd. dirs. Alex Lee, Inc. Mem. Tex. Real Estate Rsch. Adv. Com., College Station, 1979-92; mem. Adv. Coun. on Tech.-Vocat. Edn., Austin, 1975-77; mem. bd. vis. U.S. Naval Acad., 1992-95, chmn., 1994; bd. dirs. Mcpl. Adv. Coun. Tex., 1993. Named Disting. Alumnus Tex. A&M, 1991; Outstanding Young Alumnus Baylor U., 1991. Mem. State Bar Tex., Former Students Assn. of Tex. A&M (v.p. 1985-89, 93-95), Future Farmers Am. (nat. sec. 1973-74), Tex. Future Farmers Am. (state pres. 1972-73), Phi Alpha Delta, Phi Kappa Phi, Alpha Zeta (dir. 1985-93), Alpha Gamma Rho. Republican. Baptist. Home: 6722 Lakehurst Ave Dallas TX 75230 Office: 10723 Preston Rd Ste 171 Dallas TX 75230

MCCLURE, GROVER BENJAMIN, management consultant; b. Houstonia, Mo., Oct. 15, 1918; s. Grover B. and Sue F. (Cook) McC. B.A., U. Richmond, 1939. Pres. internat. div Richardson-Merrell, N.Y.C., 1954-62; pres. Europe and Africa divs. Paris, 1960-81; exec. v.p. Richardson-Vicks, Inc., Wilton, Conn., 1981-85; cons. New Canaan, Conn., 1985—; bd. dirs. Northrup & Johnson Cannes, France; dir. St. Ives Labs., Inc., 1994. Served to lt. comdr. USNR, 1941-46. Republican. Presbyterian. Clubs: Polo (Paris); Silver Springs (Ridgefield, Conn.). Avocations: tennis, golf, travel, yachting. Home and Office: 236 Sunset Hill Rd New Canaan CT 06840-4005

MCCLURE, JAMES FOCHT, JR., federal judge; b. Danville, Pa., Apr. 6, 1931; s. James Focht and Florence Kathryn (Fowler) McC.; m. Elizabeth Louise Barber, June 14, 1952; children: Holly McClure Kerwin, Kimberly Ann Pacala, Jamee McClure Sealy, Mary Elizabeth Hudec, Margaret McClure Persing. AB, Amherst Coll., 1952; JD, U. Pa., 1957. Bar: D.C. 1957, Pa. 1958, U.S. Dist. Ct. D.C. 1957, U.S. Dist. Ct. (ea. and mid. dist.) Pa. 1958, U.S. Ct. Appeals (3d cir.) 1959. Atty., advisor Dept. State, Washington, 1957-58; assoc. Morgan, Lewis & Bockius, Phila., 1958-61; atty. Merck & Co., Inc., N.Y.C., 1961-65; ptnr. McClure & McClure, Lewisburg, Pa., 1965-77, McClure & Light, Lewisburg, 1978-84; pres., judge Ct. Common Pleas, 17th Jud. Dist. Pa., Lewisburg, 1984-90; dist. judge U.S. Dist. Ct. (mid. dist.) Pa., Williamsport, Pa., 1990—; dist. atty. Union County, Lewisburg, 1974-75. Pres. bd. sch. dirs. Lewisburg Area Sch. Dist., 1969-74. Cpl. U.S. Army, 1952-54. Mem. ABA, Pa. Bar Assn., Union County Bar Assn., Bucknell U. Golf Club, Susquehanna Valley Chorale, Order of Coif, Phi Beta Kappa. Republican. Presbyterian. Office: US Dist Ct Federal Bldg 240 W 3rd St # 1448 Williamsport PA 17703-1448

MC CLURE, JAMES J., JR., lawyer, former municipal executive; b. Oak Park, Ill., Sept. 23, 1920; s. James J. and Ada Leslie (Baker) McC.; m. Margaret Carolyn Phelps, Apr. 9, 1949; children: John Phelps, Julia Jean, Donald Stewart. BA, U. Chgo., 1942, JD, 1949. Bar: Ill. 1950. Ptnr. Gardner, Carton & Douglas, Chgo., 1962-91, of counsel, 1991—; mem. Oak Park Plan Commn., 1966-73; mem. Northeastern Ill. Planning Commn., 1973-77, pres., 1975-77; pres. Village of Oak Park, 1973-81, Oak Park Exch. Congress Inc., 1981—. Pres. United Christian Community Svcs., 1967-69, 71-73, Erie Neighborhood House, 1953-55, Oak Park-River Forest Community Chest, 1967; moderator Presbytery Chgo., 1969; mem. Gov.'s Spl. Com. on MPO, 1978-79; bd. dirs. Leadership Council of Met. Open Communities, 1981—, sec., 1990—; bd. dirs. Met. Planning Coun., 1982-93, honorary dir., 1993—; bd. dirs. Community Renewal Soc., 1982-91, v.p. 1984-88, treas. 1988-91; chmn. Century National, 1981—; bd. trustees McCormick Theol. Sem., 1981—, chmn. bd. 1987-90. hon. trustee, 1990—; mem. ch. vocations unit, 1987-92, vice chair 1990; mem. gen. assembly coun. Presbyn. Ch. U.S.A., 1987-90; bd. dirs. Oak Park Edn. Found., 1991—, Oak Park River Forest Community Found., 1991—; mem. Vision 2000 (Oak Park) Coordinating Com., 1995. With USNR, 1942-46. Recipient Disting. Citizen award Oak Park, 1976; Silver Beaver award; Disting. Eagle Scout award Boy Scouts Am. Mem. ABA, Am. Coll. Trust and Estate Counsel, Ill. Bar Assn., Chgo. Bar Assn., Am. Law Inst., Lambda Alpha. Clubs: Univ. (Chgo.). Home: 200 S Maple Ave Oak Park IL 60302-3026 Office: Gardner Carton & Douglas 321 N Clark St Chicago IL 60610-4714 *Love of God, love of family, awareness of both the uniqueness and the contribution of every other human being, a sense of the wholeness of life with my religious faith, my profession of law, my family and my community service each playing an important part and complimenting each other.*

MCCLURE, JANICE LEE, state legislator, farmer, graphic designer; b. Redwood City, Calif., Jan. 1, 1941; d. D. Kelley and Roberta M. (Powell) McC.; 1 child, Keenan Kyle. BFA in Art, U. N.Mex., 1966; BFA in Design, U. Kans., 1982. Mem. Kans. State Senate, Topeka, 1989—; mem. legis. coms. Agrl., Confirmations, Econ. Devel.; mem. Joint Com. on Art and Cultural Resources, Fed. and State Affairs, Fin. Instns. and Ins.; mem. Agrl. and Internat. Trade Com., State Fed. Assembly, Nat. Conf. State Legislatures. Editor, author: (with others) Haskell County, Kansas, 1989, 100 Years Beneath the Plow. Dem. precinct committeewoman, Haskell County, Kans., 1990. Mem. AAUW, Bus. and Profl. Women, Kans. Authors Club. Avocations: textile designing, photography, horseback riding, piano. Home: HC 1 Box 70 Sublette KS 67877-9745 Office: Kansas Legislature Senate Chamber Statehouse Topeka KS 66612

MCCLURE, LUCRETIA WALKER, medical librarian; b. Denver, Jan. 2, 1925; d. Oscar W. and Rachel E. (Stander) Low; m. Arnold L. McClure, May 26, 1946 (dec. Oct. 1992); children: John N., Paul W. BJ, U. Mo., 1945; MA in Librarianship, U. Denver, 1964. Cataloging/serials libr. Edward G. Miner Libr., U. Rochester, N.Y., 1964-68, readers svcs. libr., 1968-72, assoc. libr., 1972-78, med. libr., assoc. prof. med. bibliography, 1979-93, med. libr. emerita, 1993—; bd. dirs. Friends of Nat. Libr. of Medicine, Bethesda, Md., 1991—. Editor Bull., Edward G. Miner Libr., 1979-93; editor IFLA sect. Biol. and Med. Scis. Librs., 1993—; contbr. articles to profl. jours. Recipient Disting. Svc. award U. Rochester, 1992. Fellow Med. Libr. Assn. (chair Upstate N.Y. and Ont. chpt. 1969, parliamentarian 1993—, pres. 1990-91), bd. dirs., fin. chair 1981-83), Assn. Acad. Health Scis. Libr. Dirs. (pres. 1985-86), Internat. Fedn. Libr. Assns., Acad. Health Info. Profls. (Disting. mem.). Home: 164 Elmore Rd Rochester NY 14618

MCCLURE, MICHAEL CLYDE, corporate executive; b. Cin., Nov. 8, 1940; s. Harold L. and Harriet E. (Hissong) McC.; m. Ilse Eleanor Brall, July 26, 1976; children: Brian H., Christopher M. BS in Physics, Purdue U., 1962, M in Indsl. Administrn., 1966; MS in Physics, U. Toledo, 1965. Physicist Goodyear Atomic Corp., 1962, Toledo Scale Corp., 1963-64; mgmt. cons. Booz-Allen & Hamilton, Chgo., 1966-69; investment banker Lehman Bros., N.Y.C., 1969-71; pres. McRand Internat. Ltd., Lake Forest, Ill., 1971—; mem. bd. U. Slavic Lang. Study in the Soviet Union, 1963. Bd. dirs. Lake Forest Symphony. Mem. Internat. Sporthouse Registry (founder, advisor 1980-84), Collectible and Platemakers Guild (bd. dirs.), Cliff Dwellers Club Chgo., Winter Club of Lake Forest. Avocations: golf, horseback riding. Office: McRand Internat Ltd 1 Westminster Pl Lake Forest IL 60045-2122

MC CLURE, MICHAEL THOMAS, poet, playwright, educator; b. Marysville, Kans., Oct. 20, 1932; s. Thomas and Marian Dixie (Johnston) McC.; 1 child, Katherine Jane. Student, U. Wichita, 1951-53, U. Ariz. 1953-54; BA, San Francisco State Coll., 1955. Assoc. prof. humanities and scis. Calif. Coll. Arts and Crafts, 1962-77, prof., 1977—. Playwright-in-residence A.C.T., 1975 (Guggenheim fellow for poetry 1974, recipient award for Poetry NEA 1974, 75, Magic Theatre award 1974, Playwright award Rockefeller Found. 1975); author: (poetry) Hymns to St. Geryon, 1959, Dark Brown, 1961, The New Book, 1961, Ghost Tantras, 1964, Little Odes, 1967, Star, 1970, Rare Angel, 1974, September Blackberries, 1974, Jaguar Skies, 1975, Selected Poems, 1984, Selected Poems, 1986, Simple Eyes and Other

Poems, 1994, (other works) Meat Science Essays, 1963, Freewheelin Frank Secretary of the Angels: As told to Michael McClure, 1969, The Mad Cub, 1970, 95, The Adept, 1971, Hail Thee Who Play, 1974, The Grabbing of the Fairy, 1978, Fragments of Perseus, 1983, Specks, 1985, Rebel Lions, 1991, Lighting the Corners: On Art, Nature and the Visionary, 1993, Three Poems, 1995; playwright: The Beard (N.Y.C. prodn. received two Obies 1967), The Mammals, Gorf, 1976, General Gorgeous, 1976, Josephine the Mouse Singer, 1980 (Obie award for best play), The Beard and VKTMS, 1985; rec. Love Lion, 1993. Bd. dirs. Dry Lands Inst. Recipient Lifetime Achievement Poetry award Nat. Poetry Soc., 1993. Mem. Sons of Anacreon, AAAS. Office: care New Directions 80 8th Ave New York NY 10011-5126

MCCLURE, ROGER JOHN, lawyer; b. Cleve., Nov. 22, 1943; s. Theron R. and Colene (Irwin) McC. BA, Ohio State U., 1965, JD cum laude, 1972; MA, Northwestern U., 1966. Bar: U.S. Ct. Appeals (D.C. cir.) 1974, U.S. Supreme Ct. 1978, Va. 1983, Md. 1983, Ohio, U.S. Ct. Appeals (4th, 5th & 10th cirs.). Asst. atty. gen. State of Ohio, Columbus, 1972; trial atty. FTC, Washington, 1972-76; sr. assoc. Law Offices of A.D. Berkeley, Washington, 1976-81; sole practice Alexandria, Va., 1981-86; pres. Roger J. McClure & Assocs., P.C., Alexandria, 1987—; del. Va. Gen. Assembly, 1992—; adj. prof. Antioch Sch. Law, Washington, 1982-84; mem. adv. bd. Va. Commerce Bank; host talk show Sta. WRC Radio, 1987-93, Sta. WPGC, 1993—. Co-author: Winning the Syndication Game, 1988; bd. editors Ohio State U. Law Rev., 1970-72; contbr. numerous articles to profl. jours. Served with U.S. Army, 1967-69. Decorated Bronze Star. Mem. ABA, D.C. Bar Assn. (real estate steering com. 1982-84, chmn. antitrust divsn. 1975-76), No. Va. Apt. Assn. (bd. dirs. 1988—, 1st v.p. 1987-88, pres. 1988-89), Nat. Network Estate Planning Attys. Avocation: sailing. Office: 500 N Washington St Alexandria VA 22314-2314

MCCLURE, WILLIAM B., JR., lawyer; b. Birmingham, Ala., June 10, 1946; s. William B. Sr. and Sadie (Rosenthal) McC.; children: William B. III, Carl Scott; m. Myra J. Myers. BA, Samford U., 1968, JD magna cum laude, 1972; LLM in Taxation, Georgetown U., 1975. Sr. atty. office of chief counsel, interpretative divsn. IRS, Washington, 1972-76; shareholder Johnson & Gibbs, P.C., Dallas, 1976-93; ptnr. Gardere & Wynne, Dallas, 1993—; lectr. employee benefits LLM program So. Meth. U., 1978-80. Contbr. articles to profl. jours.; speaker in field; mng. editor law rev. Cumberland Sch. Law. Mem. ABA (coun. mem. taxation sect. 1989, chmn. joint com. employee benefits, 1985-86, chmn. employee benefits com. 1984-86, vice chmn. employee benefits com., chmn. southwest regional subcom., chmn. task force fringe benefits, chmn. task force use separate orgns. to avoid antidiscrimination requirements applicable to employee benefit plans), State Bar Tex. (taxation sect.), Dallas Bar Assn. (taxation sect.), Am. Law Inst. Office: Johnson & Gibbs 900 Jackson St Dallas TX 75202-4404

MCCLURE-BIBBY, MARY ANNE, former state legislator; b. Milbank, S.D., Apr. 21, 1939; d. Charles Cornelius and Mary Lucille (Whittom) Burges; m. D.J. McClure, Nov. 17, 1963 (dec. Apr. 1990); 1 child, Kelly Joanne; m. John E. Bibby, May 1, 1993. BA magna cum laude, U. S.D., 1961; postgrad., U. Manchester, Eng., 1961-62; M of Pub. Adminstrn., Syracuse (N.Y.) U., 1980. Staff asst. U.S. Senator Francis Case, Washington, 1959-61; sec. to U.S. gov. State of S.D., Pierre, 1963, with budget office, 1964; exec. sec. to pres. Frontier Airlines, Denver, 1963-64; tchr. Pub. High Schs., Pierre and Redfield, S.D., 1965-66, 68-70; mem. S.D. State Senate, Pierre, 1975-89, pres. pro tem, 1979-89, vice chmn. coun. of state govts., 1987, chmn. coun. of state govts., 1988; spl. asst. to Pres. Bush for intergovernmental affairs, 1989-92; exec. dir. S.D. Bush-Quayle Campaign, 1992. Vice chmn. sch. bd. Redfield Ind. Sch. Dist., 1970-74. Fulbright scholar, 1961-62, Bush Leadership fellow, 1977-80. Mem. Phi Beta Kappa. Republican. Congregationalist. Home: 817 8th Ave Brookings SD 57006-1315

MCCLURG, JAMES EDWARD, research laboratory executive; b. Bassett, Nebr., Mar. 23, 1945; s. Warren James and Delia Emma (Allyn) McC. B.S., N.E. Wesleyan U., 1967; Ph.D., U. Nebr., 1973. Instr., U. Nebr. Coll. Medicine, Omaha, 1973-76, research instr., 1973-76, asst. prof. Med. Ctr., 1984—; v.p., tech, dir. Harris Labs., Inc., Lincoln, Nebr., 1976-82, exec. v.p., 1982-84, pres., chief exec. officer, 1984—; bd. dirs. Lincoln Mut. Life Ins. Co., Lincoln Gen. Hosp. (chmn.), Unemed Corp., Lincoln, Harris Labs. Ltd, Belfast No. Ireland. Mem. editorial bd. Clin. Rsch. Practices and Drug Regulatory Affairs, 1984. Contbr. articles to profl. jours. Trustee Univ. Nebr. Found.; mem. Commn. on Human Rights, Lincoln, 1982-85; com. mem. Nebr. Citizens for Study Higher Edn., Lincoln, 1984; chmn. U. Nebr. Found. Recipient ann. research award Central Assn. Obstetricans and Gynecologists, 1982. Mem. Am. Assn. Lab. Accreditation (bd. dirs.). Republican. Clubs: Century (pres. Nebr. Wesleyan U. 1983-84), Nebraska (Lincoln). Lodge: Rotary. Avocation: boating. Office: Harris Labs Inc PO Box 80837 Lincoln NE 68501-0837

MCCLUSKEY, EDWARD JOSEPH, engineering educator; b. N.Y.C., Oct. 16, 1929; s. Edward Joseph and Rose (Slavin) McC.; m. Lois Thornhill, Feb. 14, 1981; children by previous marriage—Edward Robert, Rosemary, Therese, Joseph, Kevin, David. AB in Math. and Physics, Bowdoin Coll., Brunswick, Maine, 1953, BS, M.S. in Elec. Engring., 1953; ScD MIT, 1956; doctor honoris causa Inst. Nat. Polytech. de Grenoble, 1994. With Bell Telephone Labs., Whippany, N.J., 1955-59; assoc. prof. elec. engring. Princeton, 1959-63, prof., 1963-66, dir. Computer Center, 1961-66; prof. elec. engring. and computer sci. Stanford (Calif.) U., 1967—, dir. Digital Systems Lab., 1969-78; dir. Center for Reliable Computing, 1976—; tech. advisor High Performance Systems, 1987-90. Author: A Survey of Switching Circuit Theory, 1962; Introduction to the Theory of Switching Circuits, 1965; Design of Digital Computers, 1975; Logic Design Principles with Emphasis on Testable Semicustom Circuits, 1986. Editor: Prentice-Hall Computer Engineering Series, 1988-90; assoc. editor: IRE Transactions on Computers, 1959-65; editorial bd. IEEE Design and Test, 1984-86; assoc. editor, IEEE Trans. Computer Aided Design, 1986-87. Patentee in field. Fellow AAAS, IEEE (pres. computer soc. 1970-71, Centennial medal 1984), Assn. Computing Machinery (assoc. editor jour. 1963-69); mem. IEEE Computer Soc. (Tech. Achievement award 1984, Taylor L. Booth Edn. award 1991), Am. Fedn. Info. Processing Socs. (dir., exec. com.), Internat. Fedn. Info. Processing (charter), Japan Soc. Promotion of Sci. Office: Stanford U Ctr for Reliable Computing ERL-460 Stanford CA 94305-4055

MCCLUSKEY, JEAN LOUISE, civil and consulting engineer; b. Pitts., Jan. 8, 1947; d. Matthew Ralph McCluskey Sr. and Violet (Banas) Fontaine. BS in Civil Engring., Northeastern U., 1969; MA in Urban Affairs, Boston U., 1974; postgrad., MIT, 1984. Registered profl. engr., N.Y., Maine, Mass. Staff engr. Metcalf & Eddy, Inc., Boston, 1969-74, project planner/engr. 1974-75, 76-79; sr. environ. engr. Exxon Co. USA, Pelham, N.Y., 1975-76; environ. engr. Stone and Webster Engring. Corp., Boston, 1979-84, project mgr., 1984-89, v.p., 1989-94, dir. project mgmt., 1991-93; also bd. dirs. Stone & Webster Engring. Corp., Boston; pres. Stone & Webster Civil & Transp. Svcs., Inc., 1993-94; v.p., area mgr. Hull (Mass.) Fin. Com., 1985-88; mem. adv. coun. Hull H.S., 1989—; trustee New Eng. Aquarium, 1993—, South Shore Charter Sch., 1994—; mem. govt. affairs com., chair Am. Cons. Engrs. Coun. New England. Recipient Outstanding Woman award Cambridge (Mass.) YWCA, 1986; fellow MIT, 1984. Mem. Water Environ. Fedn., Greater Boston C. of C. (bd. dirs. 1992-94), Chi Epsilon. Roman Catholic. Office: 120 Boylston St Boston MA 02116

MCCLUSKEY, ROBERT TIMMONS, physician; b. New Haven, Jan. 16, 1923; s. Charles Ayling and Lora (Timmons) McC.; m. Jean Ann White, Dec. 28, 1957; children: Ann, James. AB, Yale U., 1944; MD, NYU, 1947. Intern Kings County Hosp., Bklyn., 1947-49; resident Bellevue Hosp., N.Y.C., 1950-52; assoc. prof. pathology NYU, 1956-62, prof., 1962-68; prof. chmn. dept. pathology SUNY, Buffalo, 1968-71; S. Burt Wolbach prof. pathology Harvard U., 1971-75, Mallinckrodt prof. pathology, 1975-82, Benjamin Castleman prof. pathology, 1982-93, emeritus, 1993—; pathologist in chief Children's Hosp. Med. Ctr., Boston, 1971-74; chief pathology Mass. Gen. Hosp., Boston, 1974-91; mem. allery and immunology study sect. NIH, 1969-72, 72-88, pathology study sect., NIH, 1965-68. Editor: (with H. Fudenberg) Clinical Immunology and Immunopathology Board, 1988-94, (with Stanley Cohen) Series on Basic and Clinical Immunology; mem. editorial bd. Archives of Pathology, 1970-80, Kidney Internat., 1971-75, Am. Jour. Pathology, 1982-93. With AUS 1953-55. Mem. Am. Assn. Immunologists, Am. Assn. Pathologists and Bacteriologists, AMA, Am. Soc.

Exptl. Pathology, Harvey Soc., Alpha Omega Alpha, Internat. Soc. Nephrology, N.Y. Acad. of Sci., Transplantion Soc. Home: 208 Gardner Rd Brookline MA 02146-4560 Office: Mass Gen Hosp Fruit St Boston MA 02114

MC CLYMONT, HAMILTON, entertainment industry executive; b. Montreal, Que., Can., Mar. 20, 1944; s. Hamilton, Jr. and Zoe Annis (Cook) McC.; children from previous marriage: Alexander H., Laura C.; m. Torill Samuelsen, Aug. 25, 1990. BA, Dalhousie U., 1969. Adminstrv. dir. Toronto Arts Prodns., 1971-74; adminstr. Neptune Theatre, Halifax, N.S., 1974-76; music officer, fin. Can. Council, Ottawa, Ont., 1976-78; dir., gen. mgr. Vancouver (B.C.) Opera, 1978-82; producer spl. events Expo 86, 1983-85, v.p. entertainment, 1986; prin. Lamont Mgmt. Inc., 1986—; pres. Alpha Projects Internat. Ltd., 1989-90; gen. mgr. Can. Stage Co. Toronto, Ont., 1990—; chmn. Can. Com. of Opera America, 1980-83; pres. Profl. Opera Cos. of Can., 1980-81. Mem. Can. Owners and Pilots Assn.

MCCLYMONT, KENNETH ROSS, power systems engineer, consultant; b. Toronto, Ont., Can., Nov. 13, 1924; s. Herbert Ross and Catherine Elizabeth (McKenzie) McC.; m. Hilda Jean Pearson, Sept. 3, 1949; children: Carol Jean, Lorie Ann, Robert Ross. B of Applied Sci., U. Toronto, 1947. Test engr. Can. Gen. Electric, Peterborough, Ont., 1947; teaching asst. U. Toronto, Ont., 1948-49; rsch. engr. Ont. Hydro, Toronto, 1949-59, planning engr., 1959-72, mgr. generation and transmission, 1972-79, mgr. group planning, 1979-83, cons., 1985—; cons. Nat. Energy. Bd., Ottawa, Ont., 1985; cons. in field, 1985—; cons. Charles T. Main, Boston, 1985, 87, Utilities Profls. Internat., Toronto, 1985—, Ont. Hydro Internat. projects in Ethiopia, Egypt, Turkey, Syria and Jordan, 1987-95, Can. Exec. Svc. Orgn., Costa Rica, 1991, Ashley Robinson & Brodie, Milton, Ont., 1990-93. Fellow IEEE (Centennial medal 1984); mem. Assn. Profl. Engrs. Ont., Lakeshore Yacht Club. Avocations: sailing, golf, tennis, skiing, computers. Home and Office: 2045 Lakeshore Blvd W Ste 203, Toronto, ON Canada M8V 2Z6

MCCOBB, JOHN BRADFORD, JR., lawyer; b. Orange, N.J., Oct. 14, 1939; s. John Bradford and Dorothea Joyce (Hoffman) M.; m. Maureen Kelly, Oct. 6, 1973; 1 dau., Carrie Elizabeth. A.B., Princeton U. cum laude, 1961; J.D., Stanford U., 1966; LL.M., NYU, 1973. Bar: Calif. 1967. Assoc., IBM, Armonk, N.Y., 1966-1974, gen. counsel, Tokyo, 1974-77, lab. counsel, Endicott, N.Y., 1977-79, sr. atty. White Plains, N.Y., 1979-81, regional counsel, Dallas, 1981-83; counsel, sec. IBM Instruments, Inc., Danbury, Conn., 1983-87; area counsel European Labs, Hursley, England, 1987-90; counsel govtl. programs IBM, Washington, 1990—. Trustee Princeton-in-Asia, Inc., 1970-86 . Princeton-in-Asia-teaching fellow at Chinese Univ. of Hong Kong, 1963-65. Mem. ABA, State Bar of Calif., Phi Beta Kappa. Contbr. articles to profl. jours. Office: IBM 1301 K St NW Washington DC 20005-3317

MCCOID, DONALD JAMES, bishop; b. Wheeling, W.Va., Dec. 31, 1943; s. Roy Conrad and Alberta Virginia (Sturm) McC.; m. Saundra Ernette Piisila, Oct. 20, 1973; children: Kimberly, Elizabeth. AB, West Liberty (W.Va.) State Coll., 1965; MDiv, Luth. Theol. Sem., Phila., 1968; DD (hon.), Thiel Coll., 1983. Ordained to ministry Evang. Luth. Ch. in Am., 1968. Pastor St. Luke's Luth. Ch., Monessen, Pa., 1968-72; assoc. pastor St. John's Luth. Ch. Highland, Pitts., 1972-74; area Luth. coord. Western Pa.—W.Va. synod, Luth. Ch. Am., Clarksburg, W.Va., 1974-77; sr. pastor Trinity Luth. Ch., Latrobe, Pa., 1977-87; bishop Southwestern Pa. synod, Evang. Luth. Ch. in Am., Pitts., 1987—; bd. dirs. Pa. Coun. Chs., Harrisburg. Bd. dirs. Religious Leadership Forum, Pitts., 1988—; mem. exec. com. Christian Assocs. S.W. Pa., Pitts., 1988—; chair Coun. Christian Assocs. SW Pa., 1994—. Office: Evang Luth Ch in Am SW PA Synod 9625 Perry Hwy Pittsburgh PA 15237-5555

MCCOLL, HUGH LEON, JR., banker; b. Bennettsville, S.C., June 18, 1935; s. Hugh Leon and Frances Pratt (Carroll) McC.; m. Jane Bratton Spratt, Oct. 3, 1959; children: Hugh Leon III, John Spratt, Jane Bratton. B.S. in Bus. Adminstrn, U. N.C., 1957. Trainee NCNB Nat. Bank, Charlotte, 1959-61, officer, 1961-65, v.p., 1965-68, sr. v.p., 1968, div. exec., 1969, exec. v.p., 1970-73, vice chmn. bd., 1973-74, pres., 1974-83, also dir.; chmn., CEO NationsBank Corp., Charlotte, 1983—; bd. dirs. Sonoco Products Inc., Hartsville, S.C., CSX Corp., Richmond, Va., Jefferson-Pilot Corp., Greensboro, N.C. Trustee Heineman Found., Charlotte, 1976—; Queens Coll., Charlotte; bd. visitors Grad. Sch. Bus. U. N.C. at Chapel Hill; chmn. Charlotte Uptown Devel. Corp., 1978-81, 85. 1st lt. USMCR, 1957-59. Mem. Bankers Roundtable (mem. trialateral commn.), Am. Bankers Assn., N.C. Bankers Assn. (pres. 1974). Democrat. Presbyterian. Office: NationsBank Corp 1 Nationsbank Plz Charlotte NC 28255

MCCOLL, HUGH LEON, III, investment company executive; b. Charlotte, N.C., May 6, 1960; s. Hugh Leon Jr. and Jane (Spratt) McC.; m. REnee E. George, Nov. 30, 1991; 1 child, Hugh Leon IV. BSBA, U. N.C., 1982; MBA, U. Va., 1987. Asst. sec. Mfrs. Hanover Trust Co., N.Y.C., 1982-85; assoc. dir. Bear, Stearns & Co. Inc., N.Y.C., 1987-91; investment dir. The Shelton Cos., Charlotte, 1991-92; pres. The Shelton Cos., Inc., Charlotte, 1992—; chmn. fin. com. Charlotte Organizing Com., 1992-94. Trustee High Point U.; mem. exec. com. Charlotte Sports Commn. Mem. Charlotte Country Club, Charlotte City Club. Avocations: golf, basketball, hunting, tennis.

MCCOLL, JOHN GRAHAM, plant and soil biology educator; b. Sydney, New South Wales, Australia. B.S., Sydney U., Australia, 1963; M.S., Australian Nat. U., 1965; Ph.D., U. Wash., 1969. Postdoctoral research assoc. Yale U., New Haven, 1970; asst. prof. U. Minn., Mpls., 1970-74; prof. Environ. Sci. U. Calif., Berkeley, 1974—. Contbr. articles to profl. jours. Mem. Soil Sci. Soc. Am. Office: U Cal Dept Environ Sci Policy & Mgmt 108 Hilgard Hall Berkeley CA 94720

MCCOLLAM, WILLIAM, JR., utility company executive; b. New Orleans, Mar. 15, 1925; s. William and Marie (Mason) McC.; m. Hope Flower Jofrion, Apr. 20, 1947; children: Ellendale McCollam Hoffman, William Cage, Stephen Mason. B.S., La. State U., 1943; B.S. in Engring., U.S. Mil. Acad., 1946; M.S. in Civil Engring., MIT, 1954. Registered profl. engr., N.Y. Commd. 2d lt. U.S. Army, 1946; advanced through grades to lt. col. U.S Army; resigned U.S. Army, 1961; with Ark. Power and Light Co., Little Rock, 1961-70, exec. asst., 1961-64; v.p. Ark Power and Light Co., Little Rock, 1964-68; sr. v.p. Ark. Power and Light Co., Little Rock, 1968-70; exec. v.p. New Orleans Pub. Service, 1970-71, pres., 1971-78; pres. Edison Electric Inst., Washington, 1978-90, pres. emeritus, 1990—; cons. energy mgmt. Washington, 1990—; bd. dirs. McDermott Internat., Inc., New Orleans, Burns and Roe Enterprises, Inc., Oradell, N.J.; trustee Thomas Alva Edison Found., Detroit, 1978-89; past chmn. S.W. Power Pool, Little Rock, 1973-74, Nat. Elec. Reliability Coun., Princeton, N.J., 1975-78; bd. dirs., exec. com. U.S. Mem. Com., World Energy Coun., Washington, 1978-94. Past pres. Greater New Orleans area C. of C., 1974-75; former chmn. Loyola U., New Orleans, 1975-78; pres.'s council Tulane U., 1982-86. Named to La. State U. Alumni Hall of Distinction, 1985; recipient U.S. Energy award in recognition of outstanding contbn. to world energy coun., 1991. Mem. La. Soc. Profl. Engrs. (A.B. Paterson award 1975). Republican. Episcopalian. Clubs: Chevy Chase, Metropolitan (Washington); Boston, New Orleans Country. Home: 2411 Tracy Pl NW Washington DC 20008-1628 Office: Edison Electric Inst 701 Pennsylvania Ave NW Washington DC 20004-2696

MCCOLLEY, ROBERT MCNAIR, history educator; b. Salina, Kans., Feb. 2, 1933; s. Grant and Alice Elizabeth (McNair) McC.; m. Diane Laurene Kelsey, Aug. 30, 1958; children: Rebecca, Susanna, Teresa, Margaret, Carolyn, Robert Lauren. B.A., Harvard U., 1954, M.A., 1955; Ph.D., U Calif.-Berkeley, 1960. Instr. to prof. history U. Ill., Urbana, 1960—; mem. Com. for Advanced Placement Test in Am. History, 1987-90, chmn. 1988-90. Author: Slavery and Jeffersonian Virginia, 1964 (Dickerson 1964); editor: Federalists, Republicans and Foreign Entanglements, 1969; co-editor: Refracting America, 1993; mem. editorial bd. Jour. of Early Republic, 1981-85, Va. Magg of History and Biography, 1994—; mem. editorial bd. Ill. Hist. Jour., 1984-93, chair, 1991-93; classical lects. reviewer Fanfare mag., 1989—. Mem. Am Hist. Assns., Soc. Historians of Early Republic (pres. 1982), Orgn. Am. Historians, Va. Hist. Soc., Ill. Hist. Soc. (bd. dirs. 1978-81, 92-95), Chgo. Hist. Soc., Cliff Dwellers. Episcopalian. Home: 503 W Illinois St

Urbana IL 61801-3927 Office: U Ill Dept History 810 S Wright St Urbana IL 61801-3611

MC COLLISTER, JOHN CHARLES, writer, clergyman, educator; b. Pitts., June 1, 1935; s. John Charles and Caroline Jesse (Hall) Mc C.; m. Beverly Ann Chase, Aug. 6, 1960; children: Beth Ann, Amy Susan, Michael John. BA, Capital U., 1957; MDiv, Luth. Theol. Sem., Columbus, Ohio, 1961; PhD, Mich. State U., 1969. Ordained to ministry Luth. Ch., 1961. Pastor Zion Luth. Ch., Freeland, Mich., 1961-65, Bethlehem Luth. Ch., Lansing, Mich., 1965-71; prof. religion and Greek Olivet (Mich.) Coll., 1970-74; prof. religion and philosophy Bethune-Cookman Coll., Daytona Beach, Fla., 1974-76; prof. religion and philosophy Embry-Riddle Aero. U., 1976-82, dir. profl. programs 1979-80, cons. to pres., 1980-82; pres. Wright Advt. Co., Daytona Beach, 1975-76; CEO New Arran Prodns., Inc., Daytona Beach, 1993—, Yongestreet Prodns., Ormond Beach, Fla., 1986; pres., CEO McCollister/Grofe Prodns., Daytona Beach, 1992—; arbitrator Fed. Mediation and Conciliation Svc., 1978; spl. master Fla. Pub. Employees Rels. Commn., 1975—; mgmt. cons. Hoover Ball and Bearing, Charlotte, Mich.; bd. dirs. Am. Writers Inst. Host: Open Phone Forum, radio sta. WROD, Daytona Beach, 1974-76; author: A Philosophy of Flight, 1981, So Help Me, God, 1981, The Christian Book of Why, 1983, Problem Solving for Executives, 1984, The Sky is Home, 1986; co-author: The Sunshine Book, 1979, Day by Day, 1990; editor and compiler: A Child is Born, 1972, Portraits of the Christ, 1974, Writing for Dollars, 1995; . contbr. articles to various mags. Vol. probation officer, Mich., 1961-71, hearing officer, 1970-74; commr. Mich. Dept. Commerce, 1969-72; speaker Nat. Lincoln Day Observance, Washington, 1982; internat. adviser Han Nam U., Taejon, Republic of Korea, 1989. Recipient Outstanding Am. award Daytona Beach Jaycees, 1974. Mem. Am. Arbitration Assn. Home and Office: 26 Lazy Eight Dr Daytona Beach FL 32124-6775

MC COLLOM, KENNETH ALLEN, retired university dean; b. Sentinel, Okla., June 17, 1922; s. Walter William and Irene Pearl (Allen) McC.; m. Katherine Tompkins, Jan. 4, 1944; children: Alan Tompkins, Neal Norman. B.S., Okla. State U., 1948; M.S., U. Ill., 1949; Ph.D., Iowa State U., 1964. Engr. Phillips Petroleum Co., Bartlesville, Okla., 1949-51, 54-57; sect. chief, br. mgr. Phillips Petroleum Co. (Atomic Energy div.), Idaho Falls, Idaho, 1951-54, 57-62; project leader Ames (Iowa) Lab. Research Reactor, 1962-64; prof. elec. engring. Okla. State U., Stillwater, 1964-68; asst. dean engring. Okla. State U., 1968-73, assoc. dean engring., 1973-77, dean engring., architecture and tech., 1977-86; adminstrv. judge, mem. atomic safety and licensing bd. panel Nuclear Regulatory Commn., 1976—; cons. AEC; mem. Okla. State Bd. Registration for Profl. Engrs. and Land Surveyors, 1986-92, chmn. 1991-92; mem. Nat. Council for Examiners of Engring. and Surveying, 1986-92. Patentee in field. Asst. condr. Idaho Falls Civic Symphony Orch., 1958-60; bd. mem., Cub Pack leader, asst. scoutmaster Boy Scouts Am., 1960-72; campaign chmn. Stillwater United Fund, 1971-72. Served with AUS, 1942-46, ETO. Recipient Disting. Alumnus award elec. engring. dept. U. Ill., Profl. Devel. citation in engring. Iowa State U., Disting. Svc. award Nat. Coun. for Examiners of Engring. and Surveying, 1992. Fellow Am. Soc. Engring. Edn. (Chester F. Carlson award 1973, Outstanding Engr. in Okla. 1990); mem. IEEE (life, Centennial Medallion award 1993), Am. Nuclear Soc. (chmn. Okla. sect. 1974-75), Nat. Profl. Engrs. Soc. (nat. dir. 1975-78), Okla. Profl. Engrs. Soc. (adminstrv. v.p. 1974-75, exec. v.p. 1975-76, pres. 1976-77). Pres.'s Disting Scholarship established in his name Okla. State U. Home: 1107 W Knapp Ave Stillwater OK 74075-2712

MCCOLLOW, THOMAS JAMES, communications company executive; b. Hartford, Wis., Mar. 29, 1925; s. Owen Conrad and Zita Ann (Gardien) McC.; m. Yvonne Parent, June 18, 1949; children: Mardi, Mark, John (dec.), Timothy. A.B., Dartmouth Coll., 1946, M.B.A., 1947. Acct. Ernst & Ernst, C.P.A.s, Milw., 1947-51; asst. office mgr. Jour. Communications, Inc., Milw., 1951-60, treas., office mgr., 1961-72, sr. v.p. fin. and corp. planning, 1973-77, pres., 1977-83, chmn. bd., 1983—; chmn. bd. Jour./Sentinel, Inc., 1983—, WTMJ, Inc., 1983—. Bd. dirs. Greater Milw. Com., Milw. Redevel. Corp., Greater Milw. United Way, Med. Coll. Wis.; trustee Marquette U. Served to lt. USNR, 1943-46. Mem. Internat. Newspaper Fin. Execs., Am. Newspaper Pubs. Assn., Phi Beta Kappa. Roman Catholic. Clubs: University, Milwaukee Country. Lodge: Rotary. Office: Jour/Sentinel Inc 333 W State St # 661 Milwaukee WI 53203-1305

MCCOLLUM, BETTY, state legislator; b. July 12, 1954; m. Douglas McCollum; 2 children. BS in Edn., Coll. St. Catherine. Retail store mgr. Minn.; mem. Minn. Ho. Reps., 1992—, mem. edn. com., environ. and natural resources com., mem. gen. legis. com., vet. affairs and elections com., mem. transportation and transit com. Mem. St. Croix Valley Coun. Girl Scouts, Greater East Side Boy Scouts. Democrat. Home: 2668 4th Ave E North Saint Paul MN 55109-3116 Office: Minn Ho of Reps State Capitol Saint Paul MN 55155

MCCOLLUM, CLIFFORD GLENN, college dean emeritus; b. South Gifford, Mo., May 12, 1919; s. William Henry and Aultie V. (Westfall) McC.; m. Alice Elizabeth Erickson, Aug. 18, 1940; children: Eric Edward, Lisa Buren. Student, Central Coll., 1935-37; B.S., U. Mo., 1939, M.A., 1947, Ed.D., 1949. Tchr. pub. schs. Monett, Mo., 1938-39, Poplar Bluff, Mo., 1939-41, Boonville, Mo., 1941-42; asst. prof. sci. U. No. Iowa, 1949-55, assoc. prof., 1956-59, prof., 1959-84, prof. emeritus 1984—, head dept. sci., 1957-68; dean U. No. Iowa (Coll. Natural Scis.), 1968-84, dean emeritus, 1984—; prof. State U. N.Y. at Oneonta, 1955-56; Dir., instl. rep. Central States Univs., Inc.; cons. Coronet Instrnl. Films; cons. on sci. curricula to pub. schs. and colls.; speaker in field. Contbr. articles to profl. jours. Served with USAAF, 1943-46. Fellow AAAS (nat. committeeman 1964-67), Iowa Acad. Sci. (pres. 1979-80); mem. Am. Inst. Biol. Scis., Nat. Assn. Biology Tchrs. (regional dir. 1963-65), Nat. Assn. Research in Sci. Teaching, Nat. Sci. Tchrs. Assn., Sigma Xi, Phi Delta Kappa. Home: 2002 Chapel Hill Rd Columbia MO 65203-1916 *My personal response to the philosophical conditions in which we live today is one of preparing to live rather consistently with crises. It is my conviction that the mood of our time is toward a growing pessimism, and much of this is associated with the concomitants of a galloping technology. Yet we are not willing at this point to give up our human condition to the natural evolution that would result from basic environmental mechanisms. We will still try to condition that destiny.*

MCCOLLUM, GARY WAYNE, federal agency administrator; b. Mineral Wells, Tex., Apr. 14, 1939; s. Buster Len and Edna Sue (Fowler) McC.; m. Sonja Dru Woodham, May 27, 1960 (div. 1973); children: Scott, Greg, Cynthia; m. Barbara Jean Millican, Sept. 16, 1978. BS in Biology, East Tex. State U., 1962, MS in Biology, 1963. Quarantine control officer Lunar Receiving Lab., Apollo Program to Moon, NASA Johnson Space Ctr., Houston, 1969-71; med. surveillance office Apollo Flight Crew Health Stabilization Program, Houston, 1971-72, Skylab Flight Crew Health Stabilization Program, Houston, 1972-74; life scis. ground ops. mgr. NASA Life Sci. Project Div., Houston, 1974-78, discipline mgr., 1978-83; payload integration mgr. NASA Space Shuttle Program Office, Houston, 1983-88; program mgr. NASA Hdqs. Office Sci. & Applications, Washington, 1988-93, NASA Hdqs. Office Life & Microgravity Scis. & Applications, Washington, 1993-95, NASA Hdqs. Space Sta. Rsch. Mgmt. Office, Houston, 1995—; successful completion of STS-40/Spacelab Life Scis.-I mission, 1991, STS-47/Spacelab-J (coop. mission with Japan), 1992, STS-58/Spacelab Life Scis.-2 mission, 1993, STS-65/Internat. Microgravity Lab.-2 mission, 1994, NASA Johnson Space Ctr. Rsch. Mgmt. Office, 1995—. 1st lt. USAF, 1963-66. Mem. Am. Inst. Aero. and Astronautics (sr. mem.), Sr. Exec. Assn., Delta Tau Delta. Avocations: all sports, travel. Office: NASA Hdqs Mail OK Washington DC 20546

MC COLLUM, IRA WILLIAM, JR. (BILL MC COLLUM), congressman; b. Brooksville, Fla., July 12, 1944; s. Ira William and Arline Gray (Lockhart) McC.; m. Ingrid Mary Seebohm, Sept. 25, 1971; children: Douglas Michael, Justin Randolph, Andrew Lockhart. BA, U. Fla., 1965, JD, 1968. Bar: Fla. 1968. Ptnr. Pitts, Eubanks & Ross (P.A.), Orlando, Fla., 1973-80; mem. 97th-102nd Congresses from 5th Dist. Fla., 1981-92, 103rd-104th Congresses from 8th Dist. Fla., 1993—; ranking minority mem., mem. banking and fin. svcs. subcom. on fin. instns. supervision, mem. regulation and deposit ins. com., chmn. judiciary subcom. on crime, mem. select com. on intelligence; vice chair House Rep. Conf. 101st-103d Congresses. Chmn. Rep. Exec.

Com. Seminole County, Fla., 1976-80; county chmn.'s rep. 5th Dist. Fla. State Rep. Exec. Com., 1977-80; co-chmn. rep. platform com., 1992. With USN, 1969-72. Mem. Fla. Bar, Naval Res. Assn., Res. Officers Assn., Orange County Bar Assn. (exec. coun. 1975-79), Am. Legion, Mil. Order World Wars, Fla. Blue Key, Phi Delta Phi, Omicron Delta Kappa, Kiwanis. Episcopalian. Office: 2266 Rayburn HOB Washington DC 20515*

MCCOLLUM, JEAN HUBBLE, medical assistant; b. Peoria, Ill., Oct. 21, 1934; d. Claude Ambrose and Josephine Mildred (Beiter) Hubble; m. Everett Monroe Patton, Sept. 4, 1960 (div. Jan. 1969); 1 child, Linda Joanne; m. James Ward McCollum, Jan. 2, 1971; 1 child, Steven Ward. Grad. high sch., Peoria; student, Bradley U., Ill. Cen. Coll. Stenographer Caterpillar Tractor Co., Peoria, 1952-53, supr. stenographer pool, 1953-55, adminstrv. sec., treas., 1955-60, sec., asst. dept. mgr., 1969-71; med. asst. Proctor Community Hosp., Peoria, 1978-82; med. asst. Drs. Taylor, Fox and Morgan, Peoria, 1982-84; freelance med. asst. Meth. Hosp. and numerous physicians, Peoria, 1984-93; office mgr. Dr. Danehower, McLelland and Stone, Peoria, 1994—. Vol. tutor Northmoor Sch., Peoria, 1974-78; bd. dirs., mem. exec. com., chmn. Planned Parenthood, Peoria, 1990-92. Recipient Outstanding Performance award Proctor Hosp., 1981, also various awards for svc. to schs., ch. and hosps. for mentally ill. Mem. Nat. Wildlife Fedn., Mensa Internat. (publs. officer, editor 1987-89), Mothers League (treas. 1977), Willow Knolls Country Club (social com. 1989-90), Nature Conservancy, World Wildlife Fund, Forest Park Found., Jacques Cousteau Soc., Wilderness Soc. Methodist. Avocations: socializing, reading, travel, theatre, yoga. Home: 2822 W Pine Hill Ln Peoria IL 61614-3256

MCCOLLUM, JOHN MORRIS, tenor; b. Coalinga, Calif., Feb. 21, 1922; s. Fay James and Ingaberd Telette (Mason) McC.; m. Mary Margaret Wilson, Jan. 23, 1944; children: Kristi Elizabeth, Timothy James. Student, Coalinga Coll., 1939-40; B.A. in Journalism, U. Calif. at Berkeley, 1947; student voice and acting, Am. Theatre Wing, 1951-53. Reporter, city editor Coalinga Record, 1947-50; editor agrl. news U. Calif. Coll. Agr., 1950-51; prof. music and chmn. voice faculty U. Mich.; dir. U. Mich. div. Nat. Music Camp; faculty Aspen Music Festival and School, 1963-76. Concert and opera singer, 1951—, soloist, Fifth Ave. Presbyn. Ch., N.Y.C., 1953-56, debut, Town Hall, N.Y.C., 1952, with, Boston Symphony Orchestra, Tanglewood, Mass., summer 1952, engagements with Symphony Orchestras in, N.Y.C., Chgo., Phila., San Francisco, Cleve., Washington, St. Louis, Detroit, New Orleans, Toronto, London, Mexico; with opera companies of, Boston, Washington, Toronto, Ft. Worth, Central City, Colo., also, NBC-TV, music festivals and oratorio societies, European debut, Festival of Two Worlds, Spoleto, Italy, summer 1958, Santa Fe Opera Co., leading tenor, N.Y.C. Opera Co., performing mem., Music Assos. of Aspen. (Recipient award Atwater Kent Auditions 1950, Am. Theatre Wing award 1952). Mem. Republican Central Com., Fresno County, Calif., 1950; pres. Ann Arbor Civic Theatre, 1987-88. Served as aviator USNR, World War II. Mem. U. Calif. Alumni Assn., Nat. Assn. Tchrs. Singing, Am. Acad. Tchrs. Singing, Alpha Tau Omega, Sigma Delta Chi, Pi Kappa Lambda. Episcopalian (lay reader). Clubs: Rotary (pres. 1977, Paul Harris fellow), Ann Arbor Golf and Outing (pres. 1979), The Meadows Country Club (Sarasota, Fla.). Home: 3380 W Chelmsford Close Sarasota FL 34235

MCCOLLUM, ROBERT WAYNE, physician, educator; b. Waco, Tex., Jan. 29, 1925; s. Robert Wayne and Minnie (Brown) McC.; m. Audrey Talmage, Oct. 16, 1954; children: Cynthia, Douglas Scott. A.B., Baylor U., 1945; M.D., Johns Hopkins, 1948; D.P.H., London Sch. Hygiene and Tropical Medicine, 1958. Intern pathology Columbia-Presbyn. Med. Center, N.Y.C., 1948-49; intern internal medicine Vanderbilt Hosp., Nashville, 1949-50; asst. resident internal medicine Yale-New Haven Med. Center, 1950-51; mem. faculty Yale Sch. Medicine, 1951-81, prof. epidemiology, 1965-81, chmn. dept. epidemiology and public health, 1969-81; dean Sch. Medicine Dartmouth Coll., Hanover, N.H., 1982-90, prof. epidemiology, 1982—, dean emeritus, 1990—; assoc. physician Yale-New Haven Hosp. from 1954; v.p. Dartmouth-Hitchcock Med. Ctr., 1983-90; cons. WHO, 1962-79; surgeon gen. U.S. Army, from 1960. Contbr. articles on epidemiology and control infectious diseases to profl. jours. Bd. sci. advisers Merck Inst., 1981-85; trustee Mary Hitchcock Meml. Hosp., Hanover, 1982-90. Capt. M.C. AUS, 1952-54. Mem. Assn. Tchrs. Preventive Medicine, Am. Epidemiological Soc., Internat. Epidemiological Assn., Infectious Diseases Soc. Am., Conn. Acad. Sci. and Engring., Am. Coll. Epidemiology. Office: Dartmouth Coll Med Sch Hanover NH 03755-3861

MCCOMAS, DAVID JOHN, science administrator, space physicist; b. Milw., May 22, 1958; s. Harrold James and Hazelyn (Melconian) McC.; m. Richelle Wolff, May 30, 1981; children: Random A., Kaun I., Orion G. BS in Physics, MIT, 1980; MS in Geophysics and Space Physics, UCLA, 1985, PhD in Geophysics and Space Physics, 1986. Mem. staff Los Alamos (N.Mex.) Nat. Lab. 1980-91, sect. leader space plasma and planetary physics, 1991-92, group leader space and atmospheric scis., 1992—; mem. strategic planning com. earth and space scis. divsn. Los Alamos Nat. Lab, 1986; mem. advanced composition explorer phase A study team NASA, 1988-89, mem. space physics data system steering com., 1990-91, mem. inner magnetosphere imaging study team, 1991-94; mem. com. solar-terrestrial rsch. Nat. Rsch. Coun., 1991-94, mem. com. space sci. tech. planning Aeronautics and Space Engring. Bd./space studies bd., 1992, mem. task group rsch. prioritization future space sci. space studies bd., 1994—. Assoc. editor Jour. Geophysical Rsch. - Space Physics, 1993-94; contbr. over 150 sci. papers to profl. jours. Grad. fellow Inst. Geophysics and Planetary Physics, 1983-84. Fellow Am. Geophysical Union (Macelwane medal 1993). Office: Los Alamos Nat Lab MS-D466 Los Alamos NM 87545

MCCOMAS, MURRAY KNABB, direct mail company executive; b. Warren, Pa., Dec. 3, 1936; s. Donald Emory and Edith Mildred (Knabb) McC.; m. Marie Avanelle Oriole, Nov. 13, 1971; children: Julia Marie, Donald Anthony. BS in Econs., U. Pa., 1958. Asst. exec. sec. Sigma Chi Internat. Frat., Evanston, Ill., 1959-62; advit. prodn. mgr. New Process Co. (name now Blair Corp.), Warren, 1962-75, v.p. advt., 1975-87, pres., chmn. bd. dirs., 1987—; bd. dirs. Marine Bank, Erie, Pa. Bd. dirs. Warren County YMCA, bd. dirs. United Way Warren County, 1988—. Mem. Warren County C. of C. (bd. dirs. 1980-84), Sigma Chi (Order of Constantine 1979, Significant Sig 1989, treas., vice chmn., bd. dirs. 1989—), Conewango Club (bd. dirs., pres. 1975-86), Elks. Republican. Presbyterian. Avocations: skiing, canoeing, travel. Home: 321 Bent Twig Rd Warren PA 16365-1408 Office: Blair Corp 220 Hickory St Warren PA 16366-0001

MC COMBS, G. B., publishing company executive; b. Waxahachie, Tex., Nov. 9, 1909; s. Robert Davis and Minnie (Parks) McC.; m. Mary Louise Matthews, Sept. 7, 1928; children: Robert M., Mary Ann (Mrs. James W. Patterson), Nancy K. Student, Randolph Jr. Coll., Cisco, Tex., Trinity U., San Antonio. Sales exec. Fishburn Motor Co., Dallas, 1928-29, Willys Overland Motor Co., Dallas, 1929-30; with Curtis Circulation Co., Phila., 1930—; v.p., dir. single copy sales Curtis Circulation Co., 1953-62, pres., 1962-73, chmn. chief exec. officer, 1965-69, also dir., now cons.; circulation dir. Curtis Pub. Co. Phila., 1962-66, v.p., 1963, sr. v.p., 1964-68, exec. v.p., 1968, pres., 1969-70; dir. Curtis Distbg. Co. Ltd., Toronto, Can., 1953-74, pres., 1957-66, chmn. 1966-70; v.p. dir. Nat. Mag. Service, Chatham, N.J., 1953-67; dir. Moore-Cottrell Subscription Agys., Inc., 1953-68, chmn. bd., 1964-68; dir. Keystone Readers, 1962-68, chmn. bd., 1965-68; v.p. Cadence Industries Corp., Inc., 1970-74, vice-chmn., mem. exec. com., 1974-85; dir. Bantam Books, 1952-63, mem. exec. com., 1957-63; dir. Transworld Pub. Co., 1957-63. Served to lt. USNR, 1944-45. Mem. Bur. Ind. Pubs. and Distbrs. (past chmn., hon. dir., also past pres., hon. dir. 25 Years Club). Club: Country (Naples, Fla.)(pres. 1981-83). Address: 341 Burning Tree Dr Naples FL 33942-6319

MCCOMBS, HUGH R., JR., lawyer; b. Flint, Mich., July 30, 1946. BA, Yale U., 1968; JD cum laude, Boston U., 1973. Bar: Ill. 1975, U.S. Dist. Ct. (no. dist. trial bar) Ill. 1975, U.S. Ct. Appeals (7th cir.) 1979, U.S. Supreme Ct. 1980. Law clk. to Hon. Herbert F. Murray U.S. Dist Ct. (Md. dist.), 1973-74; ptnr. Mayer, Brown & Platt, Chgo. With U.S. Army, 1968-70, Vietnam. Mem. ABA (litigation sect.), Chgo. Bar Assn. Office: Mayer Brown & Platt 190 S La Salle St Chicago IL 60603-3441

MC COMIC, ROBERT BARRY, real estate development company executive, lawyer; b. Selmer, Tenn., Nov. 6, 1939; s. Richard Donald and Ila

Marie (Prather) McC.; children: Thomas Christopher, Robert Geoffrey. BS, Union U., 1961; LLB, Tulane U., 1964; postgrad. in law, U. Freiburg, W. Ger., 1964-65, Hague (Netherlands) Internat. Acad. Law, 1965. Bar: Tenn. 1964, N.Y. 1966, Calif. 1971. Assoc. Donovan Leisure Newton & Irvine, N.Y.C., 1965-68; assoc. gen. counsel Avco Corp., Greenwich, Conn., 1968-70; exec. v.p., pres., CEO Avco Community Developers, Inc., 1973-82; chmn., CEO R.B. McComic, Inc., 1982-92, McComic Consolidated, Inc., 1992—; bd. dirs. CDC Small Bus. Fin. Corp. Pres. emeritus U. Calif. San Diego Found. Honoree Human Relations Inst. Am. Jewish Com., 1981, Kellog's Celebrity Tribute, 1988. Mem. ABA, Calif. Bar Assn., San Diego County Bar Assn., Assn. of Bar of City of N.Y., San Diego Bldg. Industry Assn., San Diego Yacht Club, Order of Coif, Sigma Alpha Epsilon, Omicron Delta Kappa, Lambda Alpha. Home: 2032 Via Casa Alta La Jolla CA 92037-5732 Office: McComic Consolidated Inc 4920 Carroll Canyon Rd San Diego CA 92121-1725

MCCOMMON, HUBERT, benefits, training and development administrator; b. Saulsbury, Tenn., May 4, 1929; s. LeRoy (Roy) Samuel and Ida Lorene (Mercer) McC.; m. Iva Kathryn Dixon, July 1, 1951; children: Dennis Hugh, Christopher Lee. Student, U. Tenn., Memphis, 1953-56; BBA, Memphis State U., 1961, postgrad., 1963. Lic. ins. agt., Tenn. Asst. storekeeper Memphis Light, Gas and Water Div., 1949-61, supr. funds and ins., 1961-67, dir. risk and ins. mgmt., 1967-78; v.p. risk mgmt. Guardsmark Inc., Memphis, 1978-89; v.p. Guardsmark Ins. Svcs. Inc., Memphis, 1979-89; pres., chief exec. officer McCommon Risk Mgmt. Consulting Svcs., Memphis, 1989—; mgr. benefits, tng. and devel. St. Jude Children Rsch. Hosp., Memphis, 1991—; mem. Memphis and Shelby County Ins. Adv. Com., 1969-73; exec. com. Health Systems Mgmt. Inc., Memphis, 1973-74, bd. dirs.; bd. dirs. Risk Studies Found. Inc., N.Y.C., 1973-75; cons. risk mgmt., 1975-90; speaker in field. Contbr. articles to profl. jours. Treas., exec. com. 1st Founds. Inc., Memphis, 1987-90; chmn. bd. deacons First Bapt. Ch., Memphis, 1982, dir. Laotian dept. 1987—, chmn. midtown com., 1993-94. With U.S. Army, 1951-53. Mem. Risk and Inst. Mgmt. Soc. (exec. com., v.p. legis. 1969-70, Pres.'s award 1975), Mid-South Soc. Ins. Mgmt. (pres. 1967-68), World Safety Orgn. (cert. safety exec. 1986, safety and security profl. 1985), Investment Club of Memphis (v.p. 1985-86, 94-95). Republican. Baptist. Avocations: photography, golf, Christmas tree farming, writing, traveling. Home: 5587 S Ashley Sq Memphis TN 38120-2470 Office: 332 N Lauderdale Memphis TN 38105

MC CONAGHA, GLENN LOWERY, chancellor emeritus; b. New Concord, Ohio, June 2, 1910; s. David Hawthorne and Lida (Taylor) McC.; m. Pearl Esther Hook, Apr. 8, 1939. AB, Muskingum Coll., 1932; AM, Ohio State U., 1934; postgrad., U. Pitts., 1936-37; PhD, Ohio State U., 1941; DHL (hon.), Muskingum U., 1988; LittD (hon.), Muskingum Coll., 1990. Instr. social studies Alquippa (Pa.) High Sch., 1934-38; asst. prof. edn. Muskingum Coll., summers 1935-38; instr. edn. Ohio State U., Columbus, 1939-40; asst. dir. field service, 1941-42; pre-induction classification officer U.S. Army, Huntington, W. Va., 1943; exec. officer U.S. Armed Forces Inst., Madison, Wis., 1944-45; commd. U.S. Army, 1947; comdt., 1945-49, ednl. dir., 1949-50, civilian dir., 1950-53; exec. v.p. Muskingum Coll., 1953-62, pres., 1962-64; dean Blackburn Coll., Carlinville, Ill., 1964-65; pres. Blackburn Coll., 1965-74, chancellor, 1974-77, spl. cons., 1977-79 advancement assoc., chancellor emeritus, 1979—. Author: Blackburn College 1837-1987: An Anecdotal and Analytical History of the Private College; also articles in profl. jours.; contbr. to: Bull. of Nat. Assn. Secondary Sch. Prins; Author: monthly publ. Train of Thought, 1965-72. Former trustee Lincoln Acad. Ill.; former mem. Presbyn. Coll. Union; pres., 1972-73. Decorated Army Commendation ribbon Presdl. Unit Citation.; Hon. mem. Brit. Royal Edn. Corp. Mem. Am. Council Assn., Higher Edn. Assn., Asso. Colls. Ill., Mil. Order World Wars, Am. Ednl. Research Assn., NEA, AAUP, Phi Gamma Mu, Alpha Phi Gamma, Phi Delta Kappa. Club: Mason. Home: 10 Taggert Dr Carlinville IL 62626-1564 Office: Blackburn U 3 College Ave Carlinville IL 62626-1903 Success requires, first of all, complete and total dedication. There must be an acceptance of change and an adherence to the goal that anything we can do we can do better. There must be a consistent philosophy which has as its central guidepost the worth and dignity of each individual. There must be honesty, firmness, and forthrightness in dealing with others. Also required is an abiding but critical confidence in the will of our country to meet adversity and there must be an abiding faith in education properly conceived as a learning process which goes on from the cradle to the grave. We must have an ability to face crossroads situations and to make decisions with the full knowledge that each of us in a democratic society must face the consequences of the decisions we make.

MCCONAHEY, STEPHEN GEORGE, securities company executive; b. Fond du Lac, Wis., Nov. 8, 1943; s. George and Charlotte McC.; m. Kathleen Louise Litten, Aug. 19, 1967; children: Heather, Benjamin. BS, U. Wis., 1966; MBA, Harvard U., 1968. Assoc. McKinsey & Co., Washington, 1968-72; White House fellow Washington, 1972-73; program administr. Dept. Transp., Washington, 1973-75; spl. asst. to Pres. Gerald Ford The White House, 1975-77; underwriter, ptnr. Boettcher & Co., Inc., Denver, 1977-80, mgr. pub. fin., 1980-82, mgr. corp. fin., 1982-84, pres., chief exec. officer, 1984-86, chmn. bd., 1986-87; chmn. bd. Boettcher Investment Corp., Denver, 1987-90; sr. v.p. for corp. and internat. devel. Kemper Corp., Chgo., 1991—; exec. v.p. Kemper Fin. Svcs., Inc., Chgo., 1991—; pres., COO Kemper Securities, Inc., Chgo., 1994—; bd. dirs. Kemper Fin. Cos., Inc., Chgo. Trustee Denver Symphony Assn., 1986; chmn. Greater Denver Corp., 1987; bd. dirs. The Denver Partnership; bd. fellows U. Denver. Served with USAR, 1968-74. Mem. Young Presidents Orgn., Greater Denver C. of C. (bd. dirs.), Denver Club, Colo. Harvard Bus. Sch. Club (Denver), Cherry Hills Country Club (Englewood, Colo.), Castle Pines Country Club (Castle Rock, Colo.), Chgo. Club. Home: 1050 E Green Oaks Dr Littleton CO 80121-1325 Office: Kemper Securities Inc 77 W Wacker Dr Chicago IL 60601-9999

MC CONAHEY, WILLIAM MCCONNELL, JR., physician, educator; b. Pitts., May 7, 1916; s. William McConnell and Charlotte Maude (Hixson) McC.; m. Adrienne Parsons Magness, June 15, 1940; children: William McConnell III, Meredith McConahey Pollak, Peter Magness. A.B., Washington and Jefferson Coll., 1938; M.D., Harvard U., 1942; M.S., U. Minn., 1948. Resident internal medicine Mayo Clinic, 1946-48, asst. to staff, 1949, mem. staff internal medicine and endocrinology, 1949-85, emeritus staff, 1986—; cons. internal medicine St. Mary's, Rochester Methodist hosps., 1949-85; chmn. dept. endocrinology Mayo Clinic, 1967-74; prof. medicine Mayo Grad. Sch. Medicine U. Minn., 1966-73, prof. medicine Mayo Med. Sch., 1973—. Author articles in field. Served with M.C. AUS, 1943-45; now col. Res. (ret.). Decorated Silver Star, Bronze Star; recipient Disting. Alumni Service award Washington and Jefferson Coll., 1978. Fellow ACP; mem. Am. Thyroid Assn. (Disting. Service award 1973, pres. 1976), Endocrine Soc., Am. Diabetes Assn., Am. Fedn. Clin. Investigation, AMA, Central Soc. Clin. Research, Zumbro Valley Med. Soc., Phi Beta Kappa, Sigma Xi. Home: 1122 6th St SW Rochester MN 55902-1950

MCCONKEY, JAMES RODNEY, English educator, writer; b. Lakewood, Ohio, Sept. 2, 1921; s. Clayton Delano and Grace (Baird) McC.; m. Gladys Jean Voorhees, May 6, 1944; children: Lawrence Clark, John Crispin, James Clayton. B.A., Cleve. Coll., 1943; M.A., Western Res. U., 1946; Ph.D., U. Iowa, 1953. Teaching fellow, instr. Cleve. Coll., 1945-46; teaching asst. U. Iowa, Iowa City, 1949-50; asst. prof. Morehead State Coll., Ky., 1950-54, assoc. prof., 1954-56; asst. prof. Cornell U., Ithaca, N.Y., 1956-62, assoc. prof., 1962-67, prof., 1967-87, Goldwin Smith prof. English lit., 1987-92; Goldwin Smith prof. emeritus, 1992—; dir. Morehead Writers Workshop, 1951-56, Antioch Seminar in Writing and Pub., Yellow Springs, Ohio, 1957-59. Author: The Novels of E.M. Forster, 1957, Night Stand, 1965, Crossroads, 1968, Journey to Sahalin, 1971, The Tree House Confessions, 1979, Court of Memory, 1983, To a Distant Island, 1984; editor: The Structure of Prose, 1963, Chekhov and Our Age, 1985, Kayo: The Authentic and Annotated Autobiographical Novel from Outer Space, 1987, Rowan's Progress, 1992, Stories From My Life With the Other Animals, 1993. Served with U.S. Army, 1943-45. Guggenheim fellow, 1970; Eugene Saxton Meml. Trust Fund fellow, 1962; recipient Nat. Endowment of Arts essay award, 1968, Am. Acad. and Inst. Arts and Letters award in lit., 1979. Democrat. Home: 402 Aiken Rd Trumansburg NY 14886-9733 Office: Cornell Univ Goldwin Smith Hall Dept English Ithaca NY 14853

MC CONKIE, GEORGE WILSON, education educator; b. Holden, Utah, July 15, 1937; s. G. Wilson and Mabel (Stephenson) McC.; m. Orlene Carol Johnson, Sept. 6, 1962; children: Lynnette Mooth, Heather Usevitch, April Rhiner, Faline Coffelt, George Wilson, Bryce Johnson, Camille, Elissa, Esther, Bryna, Ruth, Anna May, Cynthia, Thomas Oscar. A.A., Dixie Jr. Coll., 1957; B.S., Brigham Young U., 1960, M.S., 1961; Ph.D., Stanford U., 1966. Asst. prof. edn. Cornell U., 1964-70, asso. prof., 1970-75, prof., 1975-78, chmn. dept. edn., 1977-78; prof. U. Ill., Champaign, 1978—, chmn. dept. ednl. psychology, 1993-94; sr. scientist Ctr. for Study of Reading, 1978—; Beckman Inst., 1989—; rsch. fellow Cath. U. Leuven, Belgium, 1991-92. Contbr. articles to profl. publs. NIMH spl. fellow, 1971-72, Fogarty Sr. Internat. fellow, 1991-92; grantee U.S. Office Edn., 1970-73, Nat. Inst. Edn., 1974-77, NIMH, 1974-84, NICHHD, 1983-89, 91-95, AT&T, 1986-89, NSF, 1989-91, CIA, 1991—. Fellow Am. Psychol. Assn.; mem. Am. Ednl. Research Assn., Psychonomic Soc., Cognitive Sci. Soc. Mem. Ch. of Jesus Christ of Latter-day Saints. Home: 2605 Berniece Dr Champaign IL 61821-7225 Office: Beckman Inst for Advanced Sci and Tech 405 N Mathews Ave Urbana IL 61801-2300

MCCONNAUGHEY, GEORGE CARLTON, JR., lawyer; b. Hillsboro, Ohio, Aug. 9, 1925; s. George Carlton and Nelle (Morse) McC.; m. Carolyn Schlieper, June 16, 1951; children: Elizabeth, Susan, Nancy. B.A., Denison U., 1949; LL.B., Ohio State U., 1951, J.D., 1967. Bar: Ohio 1951. Sole practice Columbus; ptnr. McConnaughey & McConnaughey, 1954-57, McConnaughey, McConnaughey & Stradley, 1957-62, Laylin, McConnaughey & Stradley, 1962-67, George, Greek, King, McMahon & McConnaughey, 1967-79, McConnaughey, Stradley, Mone & Moul, 1979-81, Thompson, Hine & Flory (merger McConnaughey, Stradley, Mone & Moul with Thompson, Hine & Flory), Cleve., Columbus, Cin., Dayton and Washington, 1981-93; ret. ptnr. Thompson, Hine & Flory, Columbus, 1993—; bd. dirs. N.Am. Broadcasting Co. (Sta. WMNI and WBZX Radio); asst. atty. gen. State of Ohio, 1951-54. Pres. Upper Arlington (Ohio) Bd. Edn., 1967-69, Columbus Town Meeting Assn., 1974-76; chmn. Ohio Young Reps., 1956; U.S. presdl. elector, 1956; trustee Buckeye Boys Ranch, Columbus, 1967-73, 75-81, Cen. Ohio Ctr. Econ. Edn., Upper Arlington Edn. Found., 1987-93; elder Covenant Presbyn. Ch., Columbus. With U.S. Army, 1943-45, ETO. Fellow Am. Bar Found., Ohio Bar Found., Columbus Bar Found.; mem. ABA (coun. group pub. utility comm. and transp. law sect.), Ohio Bar Assn., Columbus Bar Assn., Am. Judicature Soc., Scioto Country Club, Athletic Club, Rotary, Masons. Home: 1993 Collingswood Rd Columbus OH 43221 Office: Thompson Hine & Flory One Columbus 10 W Broad St Columbus OH 43215

MCCONNELL, ADDISON MITCHELL, JR. (MITCH MCCONNELL, JR.), senator, lawyer; b. Tuscumbia, AL, Feb. 20, 1942; s. Addison Mitchell and Julia (Shockley) McC.; children: Eleanor Hayes, Claire Redmon, Marion Porter; m. Elaine Chao, Feb. 6, 1993. B.A. with honors, U. Louisville, 1964; J.D., U. Ky., 1967. Bar: Ky. 1967. Chief legis. asst. to Senator Marlow Cook, Washington, 1968-70; sole practice Louisville, 1970-74; dep. asst. U.S. atty. gen. Washington, 1974-75; judge Jefferson County, Louisville, 1978-85; mem. U.S. Senate from Ky., 1985—. Chmn. Jefferson County Republican Com., 1973-74; co-chmn. Nat. Child Tragedies Coalition, 1981; chmn., founder Ky. Task Force on Exploited and Missing Children, 1982; mem. Pres.'s Partnership on Child Safety. Recipient commendation Nat. Trust on Hist. Preservation in U.S., 1982, Conservationist of Yr. award League Ky. Sportsmen, 1983, cert. of appreciation Am. Correctional Assn., 1985. Mem. Ky. Assn. County Judge Execs. (pres. 1982), Nat. Inst. Justice (adv. bd. 1982-84). Republican. Baptist. Avocations: fishing; cooking. Office: SR-120 Russell Office Bldg Washington DC 20510-1702

MCCONNELL, CALVIN DALE, clergyman; b. Monte Vista, Colo., Dec. 3, 1928; s. Roy and Leota Fern (Taylor) McC.; m. Mary Caroline Bamberg, Sept. 2, 1952 (dec. Apr. 1986); children: David William, Mark Andrew; m. Velma Duell, Dec. 17, 1988. B.A., U. Denver, 1951; M.Div., Iliff Sch. Theology, 1954; S.T.M., Andover Newton Theol. Sem., 1967. Ordained to ministry United Meth. Ch.; pastor Meth. Ch., Williams, Calif., 1955-58, 1st United Meth. Ch., Palo Alto, Calif. and Stanford U. Wesley Found., 1958-61; chaplain and asst. prof. religion Willamette U., Salem, Oreg., 1961-67; pastor Christ United Meth. Ch., Denver, 1968-72; pastor 1st United Meth. Ch., Boulder, Colo., 1972-79, Colorado Springs, Colo., 1979-80; bishop United Meth. Ch., Portland Area, 1980-88, Seattle Area, 1988—. Trustee U. Puget Sound, Iliff Sch. Theology; pres. United Meth. Ch. Bd. Higher Edn. and Ministry. Office: 2112 3rd Ave Ste 301 Seattle WA 98121-2310

MCCONNELL, CHARLES WARREN, marketing management executive; b. Los Angeles, Sept. 24, 1939; s. Lemuel John and Madeline B. (Bumcrot) McC.; m. Nancy Hackler, Aug. 19, 1961; 1 dau., Melanie Gwen. Student, U. Exeter, Eng., 1959-60; B.A., DePauw U., 1961; M.B.A., Northwestern U., 1963. Product mgr. Gen. Foods Corp., White Plains, N.Y., 1967-71; mktg. dir. Ideal Toy Corp., N.Y.C., 1971-72; area dir. internat. mktg. Playtex, N.Y.C., 1972-74; v.p. mktg. Hanes Corp., Winston-Salem, 1974-77; sr. v.p. mgmt. dir. D'Arcy Masius Benton & Bowles Advt., N.Y.C., 1977-86; exec. v.p., gen. mgr. Bozell/Poppe Tyson, 1986-87; exec. v.p. bus. devel. WPP (subs. Harvard Group), N.Y.C., 1988-89; corp. v.p. mktg. communications McGraw-Hill, Inc., N.Y.C., 1989-90; sr. v.p. mktg. Warner's Intimate Apparel, Bridgeport, Conn., 1990-91; pres. B.D. Baggies div. Apparel Group, Ltd., N.Y.C., 1992-94; exec. v.p. Apparel Group, Ltd., 1992-94; ptnr. The Watson Group, N.Y.C., 1994—. Served to capt. USAF, 1963-67. Mem. Advt. Club N.Y., Am. Mktg. Assn., Innis Arden Golf Club, Delta Chi. Republican. Congregationalist. Office: 37 W 20th St New York NY 10011

MCCONNELL, DAVID GRAHAM, research biochemist, educator; b. Bronxville, N.Y., Dec. 3, 1926; s. Luther Graham and Helen (Slagle) McC.; m. Patricia Barnes, Sept. 5, 1970; children: Ross, Paul D., Teresa Barnes, Alex, Debora Barnes, Margaret H.K. A.B., Columbia U., 1949, A.M., 1949; Ph.D., Ind. U., 1957. Research assoc. Ohio State U., Columbus, 1956-61; assoc. prof. Ohio State U., 1962-71, prof., 1971-72; prof. biochemistry Mich. State U., East Lansing, 1972—. Author: novel The Destruction of Crown City, 1974. Labor ofcl. NAACP, 1966-72. Served with USNR, 1944-46; Served with USMCR, 1950-52. Mem. Am. Soc. Biochemistry and Molecular Biology, Am. Soc. for Cell Biology, Biophys. Soc., Am. Soc. Neurochemistry. Home: East Lansing MI Office: Mich State U Dept Biochemistry East Lansing MI 48824

MCCONNELL, DAVID M., secondary school principal. Prin. Kennebunk (Maine) High Sch. Recipient Blue Ribbon Sch. award U.S. Dept. Edn. 1990-91. Office: Kennebunk H S 89 Fletcher St Kennebunk ME 04043-1998

MCCONNELL, DAVID MOFFATT, lawyer; b. Chester, S.C., June 12, 1912; s. Harvey Elzaphron and Elizabeth (Simpson) McC.; m. Ona Altman, Dec. 31, 1952; children: David Moffatt, Lynn Torbit, Joseph Moore. B.S. summa cum laude, Davidson Coll., 1933; student, Harvard. Grad. Bus. Sch. 1933-34, Law Sch. 1934-35; J.D., Georgetown U., 1939, LL.M., 1940; LLD (hon.), Mex. Acad. Internat. Law, 1987. Bar: S.C. 1936, D.C. 1945, N.C. 1946, U.S. Supreme Ct 1946. With firm Henry & Henry, Chester, 1936; counsel com. govt. reorgn. U.S. Senate, 1937-38; spl. atty. to chief counsel Internal Revenue Service, 1938-41; practice in Charlotte, N.C., 1946—; v.p., gen. counsel Belk Stores, Charlotte, 1946-76; gen. counsel Leggett Stores, 1946-76; dir. So. Nat. Bank, Lumberton, N.C., also chmn. Charlotte bd., 1970-76; U.S. ambassador to UN, 1968-69; Spl. adviser UN Econ. and Social Council; mem. U.S. delegation Fed. Republic Germany Marshall Plan, 1967. Chmn., sec. N.C. Bd. Elections, 1952-60; mem. Mecklenburg County (N.C.) Democratic Party, 1952-57; mem. nat. platform com. Dem. Party, 1964-72; elector U.S. Electoral Coll., 1948, 52. Donor McConnell Collection Tibetan Art to Baton Rouge Arts Mus., 1965; bd. dirs. emeritus Billy Graham Evangelistic Assn.; bd. visitors Davidson Coll., 1972-76; trustee Erskine Coll., Due West, S.C., 1954-58, bd. advisers, 1968-72; trustee Robert Lee Stowe, Jr. Found., Henderson Belk Found. Served to col. U.S. Army, 1940-46, CBI; brig. gen. N.C. State Militia. Decorated Legion of Merit with oak leaf cluster; Order Cloud with banner (Republic China); knight comdr. Order of the Knights of Malta. Fellow Mexican Acad. Internat. Law; mem. Am. N.C. 26th Jud. Dist. bar assns., St. Andrews Soc., Newcomen Soc., Phi Beta Kappa, Kappa Alpha. Presbyterian. Clubs: Mason (Charlotte) (Shriner), Charlotte Country (Charlotte), City (Charlotte), Quail Hollow Country (Charlotte); University (Washington). Home: 920 Granville Rd Charlotte NC 28207-1832

MCCONNELL, DAVID STUART, insurance agent, retired federal executive; b. Charlotte, Mich., Dec. 5, 1935; s. Russell and Beatrice (Martin) McC.; m. Marchelle Elizabeth Wiltshire, June 10, 1960; children: Marchelle Kern, Martin. BA, Olivet Coll., 1957; grad., Union Theol. Sem., Union Sch. Sacred Music, N.Y.C., 1958, 62. Position classifier U.S. Dept. State, Washington, 1961-62; rsch. specialist U.S. Nat. Interdepartmental Seminar, Washington, 1962-66; head East Asia sect. Am. Specialist Program, 1966-68; asst. to acad. advisor U.S. Bd. Fgn. Scholarships, Washington, 1968-69; desk officer Near East br. Bur. Ednl. and Cultural Affairs, Washington, 1969-72; coord. for multi-regional seminars U.S. Office Internat. Visitors, Washington, 1972-87; head internat. visitor programs for Andean nations U.S. Info. Agy., Washington, 1978-87; agt. Liberty Nat. Life Ins., 1994—. Compiler: Problems of Development and Internal Defense, 1966. Mem. 3 cabinet subcoms. on narcotics, Washington, 1973-78; coord. narcotics U.s. Bur. Ednl. and Cultural Affairs, 1973-78, U.S. Info. Agy., Washington, 1978; mem. Montgomery County Econ. Coun. With U.S. Army, 1958-61. Grantee (9) White House Spl. Action Office for Drug Abuse Prevention, Ford Found., 1973. Mem. Greenwood Leflore County C. of C., Kappa Sigma Alpha (founder). Home and Office: RFD 3 Box 152 Carrollton MS 38917

MCCONNELL, DONALD J., ambassador; b. Massillon, Ohio, Sept. 28, 1939; m. Frances C. BA, John Carroll U.; MA, Stanford U.; Harvard U. Joined Fgn. Svc., 1967; staff asst. to asst. sec. for Near East and South Asian Affairs Dept. State, Washington, 1967-68; officer Dept. State, Asmara, 1969-71; with Office of Pres. Dept. State, Washington, 1972; internat. rels. officer Dept. State, Mbabane, Swaziland, 1972-75; polit. counselor Dept. State, Abidjan, Ivory Coast, 1975-76; politico-mil. officer Office European Security and Polit. Affairs Dept. State, 1977-79; with NATO Dept. State, Brussels, 1980-82; dep. polit. counselor Dept. State, Cairo, 1983-85; exec. sec. U.S. Intermedia-Range Nuc. Forces Del. to Arms Control and Disarmament Agy. Dept. State, 1985-87, exec. asst. to counselor, 1987-88, dep. dir. Office European Security and Polit. Affairs, 1988-89; dep. chief of mission Dept. State, Brussels, 1989-92, charge d'affaires, 1993; amb. to Burkina Faso Dept. State, Ouagadougou, 1993—. Fulbright scholar U. Freiburg, Germany;. Office: Dept State Amb to Burkina Faso Washington DC 20521

MCCONNELL, E. HOY, II, advertising executive; b. Syracuse, N.Y., May 14, 1941; s. E. Hoy and Dorothy R. (Schmitt) McC.; m. Patricia Irwin, June 26, 1965; children: E. Hoy, III, Courtney. B.A. in Am. Studies magna cum laude, Yale U., 1963; M.B.A. in Mktg. Harvard Bus. Sch., 1965. With Foote, Cone & Belding, 1965-76; v.p. account supr. Foote, Cone & Belding, Chgo., 1971-72, 74-76, Phoenix, 1972-74; with D'Arcy-MacManus & Masius, Chgo., 1976-85, sr. v.p., dir. client services, then vice chmn., 1978-80, pres., 1980-84, chmn., 1985-88; mng. dir. D'Arcy Masius Benton & Bowles, Chgo., 1986—, also bd. dirs. Bd. dirs. Evanston (Ill.) United Way, 1980-83, Evanston Youth Hockey Assn., 1980-89, pres., 1981-83; bd. dirs. Off the Street Club, 1980—, Bus. Profl. People for Pub. Interest, 1981-83, v.p., 1984-89, pres., 1990—; bd. dirs. Harvard Bus. Sch. Club, 1990-92; mem. Chgo. com. Chgo. Coun. on Fgn. Rels., 1989—. Officer USNR, 1966. Mem. Am. Assn. Advt. Agys. (gov.-at-large Chgo. coun. 1984, sec. 1986, vice chmn. 1987, chmn. 1988-89), BBB Chgo. (advt. rev. bd.), Tavern Club, Glen View Country Club (bd. dirs. 1992—), Dairymen's Country Club, Chgo. Club. Democrat. Unitarian. Home: 2703 Colfax St Evanston IL 60201-2035 Office: D Arcy Masius Benton & Bowles Inc 200 E Randolph Dr Chicago IL 60601-6401

MC CONNELL, EDWARD BOSWORTH, legal organization administrator, lawyer; b. Greenwich, Conn., Apr. 3, 1920; s. Raymond Arnott and Anna Bell (Lee) McC.; m. Jeanne M. Rotton (dec. 1984); children: Annalee, Marilyn, Edward, Barbara, William; m. Florence M. Leonard, (dec. 1991); stepchildren: Susan L. Little, William R. Leonard, Molly M. Leonard. A.B., U. Nebr., 1941, LL.B., 1947; M.B.A. with distinction, Harvard U., 1943. Bar: Nebr. 1947, N.J. 1950. Mem. faculty Rutgers U. Sch. Bus. Adminstrn., Newark, 1947-53; assoc. firm Toner, Speakman and Crowley, Newark, N.J., 1949-50; adminstrv. asst. and law sec. to Chief Justice of N.J., 1950-53; adminstrv. dir. Cts. of N.J., Trenton, 1953-73; also standing master Supreme Ct., 1953-73; pres. Nat. Center for State Cts., Williamsburg, 1973-90, bd. dirs., 1980-90, pres. emeritus, 1990—, cons. on ct. mgmt., 1990—; mem. U.S. Dept. Justice Coun. on Role of Cts. in Am. Society, 1978-83; mem. adv. com. Dispute Resolution Policy Study, Social Sci. Rsch. Inst., U. So. Calif., 1975-79, Civil Litigation Rsch. Project, U. Wis. and U. So. Calif., 1979-83, nat. jud. edn. program to promote equality for men and women in the courts, 1980—; mem. Nat. Inst. Criminal Justice Task Force, Urban Consortium, 1979-83; participant Access to Justice Colloquium, European Univ. Inst., Florence, Italy, 1979; nat. adv. coun. Ctr. Adminstrn. Justice, Wayne State U., 1973-77; nat. project com. State Jud. Info. Systems Project SEARCH Group, 1973-76; lectr. Inst. of Local and State Govt. Wharton Sch. U. Penn., 1955-65, Appellate Judges Seminar, Inst. Jud. Adminstrn., NYU, 1962-75; vis. expert UN Asia and Far East Inst., Tokyo, 1971; mem. Cts. Task Force Nat. Adv. Commn. Criminal Justice Standards and Goals, 1971-73; nat. adv. com. D.C. Ct. Mgmt. Project, 1966-70; trustee Inst. Ct. Mgmt., 1969-73, 84-86; chmn. Nat. Conf. Ct. Adminstrv. Officers, 1956; mem. nat. task force on gender bias in cts. Nat. Assn. Women Judges, 1985—; mem. adv. bd. Nat. Ctr. for Citizen Participation in Adminstrn. of Justice, 1984—; mem. Nat. Commn. Trial Court Performance Standards, 1991—. Mem. adv. com. on article III Commn. on the Bicentennial of the Constitution, 1989-91; adv. com. Judicary Leadership Council, 1990—. Maj. C.E., AUS, 1943-46. Decorated Bronze Star medal; recipient Warren E. Burger award for greatest contbn. to improvement of ct. adminstrn. Inst. for Ct. Mgmt., 1975, Herbert Lincoln Harley award for efficient adminstrn. justice Am. Judicature Soc., 1973, Glenn R. Winters award for outstanding service in jud. adminstrn. Am. Judges Assn., 1974, Tom C. Clark award for outstanding contbns. to field of ct. adminstrn. Nat. Conf. Met. Cts., 1983, Award of Merit Nat. Assn. Ct. Mgmt., 1987, Spl. award, Nat. Assn. Women Judges, 1989, Paul C. Reardon award for disting. svc. Nat. Ctr. for State Cts., 1991, Alumni Achievement award U. Nebr., 1991. Fellow Nat. Acad. Pub. Adminstrn. (mem. panel on evaluation budget decentralization project of fed. cts. 1989-91, chmn. panel on long range planning in fed. cts. 1991-92); mem. ABA (fellow-at-large, coun. mem. 1960-66, 71-80, house of dels., 1977-80, chmn. com. on oversight and goals 1975-76, chmn. com. on jud. compensation jud. adminstrn. div. 1984-89, chmn. jud. adminstrn. div. 1976-77, sect. of litigation task force on excess litigiousness in Am. 1986-88, task force on reduction of litigation cost and delay, jud. adminstrn. div. 1984-94, chmn. 1991-94, mem. long range planning com. 1989-94), N.J. Bar Assn., Nebr. Bar Assn., Kingsmill (Va.) Golf, Tennis and Yacht Clubs, Order of Coif (hon.), Delta Upsilon, Sigma Delta Phi, Phi Delta Phi.

MCCONNELL, ELLIOTT BONNELL, JR., oil company executive; b. Elizabeth, N.J., June 2, 1928; s. Elliott Bonnell and Mildred A. (Snibbe) McC.; m. Sara Gerber, Aug. 16, 1952; children: Marilyn McConnell Huston, James D. A.B., Duke U., 1951; M.S., Pa. State U., 1953; postgrad. Advanced Mgmt. Program, Harvard U., 1973. Exploration mgr. Mobil Oil Corp., U.S. and Can., 1953-69; v.p. land and exploration Gen. Crude Oil Co., Houston, 1969-79; pres. Pennzoil Internat., Houston, 1979-81; exec. v.p. exploration and prodn. Santa Fe Energy Co. subs. Santa Fe S.P. Corp., Houston, 1981-86, petroleum cons. Chmn. Appraisal Rev. Bd. Aransas County, 1989-92; pres. Kay Allegro Property Owners Assn., 1989-92; chmn. Rockport Redistricting Commn., 1991, Rockport Charter Rev. Commn., 1991; elected county commr. Aransas County, 1992. Republican. Clubs: Rockport Country. Avocation: tennis.

MCCONNELL, HARDEN MARSDEN, biophysical chemistry researcher, chemistry educator; b. Richmond, Va., July 18, 1927; s. Harry Raymond and Frances (Coffee) McC.; m. Sophia Milo Glogovac, Oct. 6, 1956; children: Hunter, Trevor, Jane. BS, George Washington U., 1947; PhD, Calif. Inst. Tech., 1951; DSc (hon.), U. Chgo., 1991, George Washington U., 1993. NRC fellow dept. physics U. Chgo., 1950-52; research chemist Shell Devel. Co., Emeryville, Calif., 1952-56; asst. prof. chemistry Calif. Inst. Tech., 1956-58, prof. chemistry and physics, 1963-64; prof. chemistry Stanford U., Calif., 1964-79, Robert Eckles prof. chemistry, 1979—, chmn. dept., 1989—; founder Molecular Devices Corp., 1983—; cons. in field. Contbr. numerous articles to profl. publs.; patentee (in field). Pres. Found. for Basic Rsch. in Chemistry, 1990—; hon. assoc. Neurosci. Rsch. Program. Recipient Calif. sect. award Am. Chem. Soc., 1961, award in pure chemistry Am. Chem. Soc., 1962, Harrison Howe award, 1968, Irving Langmuir award in chem. physics, 1971, Pauling medal Puget Sound and Oreg. sects., 1987, Peter

Debye award in phys. chemistry, 1990; Am. Achievement award George Washington U., 1971; Disting. Alumni award Calif. Inst. Tech., 1982, Sherman Fairchild Disting. scholar, 1988; Dickson prize for sci. Carnegie-Mellon U., 1982, Wolf prize in chemistry, 1984, ISCO award, 1984; Wheland medal U. Chgo., 1988; Nat. Medal Sci., 1989, Brucker prize, 1995. Fellow AAAS, Am. Phys. Soc.; mem. Nat. Acad. Scis. (award in chem. scis. 1988), Am. Acad. Arts and Scis., Am. Soc. Biol. Chemists, Swedish Biophysical Soc., Internat. Acad. Quantum Molecular Scis., Am. Chem. Soc., Biophysical Soc., Internat. Coun. on Magnetic Resource in Biol. Systems, Brit. Biophysical Soc. Office: Stanford U Dept Chemistry Stanford CA 94305

MCCONNELL, JAMES GUY, lawyer; b. Hinsdale, Ill., Sept. 24, 1947; s. William F. and Virginia (Brown) McC.; m. Linda McConnell; children: Colin, Nicholas, Joanna, Cameron, Gabriel. BS in Journalism, Iowa State U., 1969; JD, Northwestern U., 1973. Bar: Ill. 1973, U.S. Dist. Ct. (no. dist.) Ill. 1973, U.S. Ct. Appeals (7th cir.) 1973, U.S. Supreme Ct. 1977. Assoc. Rooks, Pitts & Poust, Chgo., 1973-80, ptnr., 1980-85; ptnr. Bell, Boyd & Lloyd, Chgo., 1985-88, Freeborn & Peters, Chgo., 1990—; adj. prof. Kent Coll. Law Ill. Inst. Tech., Chgo., 1978-83. Author: Comparative Negligence Defense Tactics, 1985; contbg. editor jour. Hazardous Waste & Toxic Torts Law & Strategy. Mem. Dist. 102 Sch. Bd., LaGrange Park, Ill., 1975-76; mem. Dist. 106 Sch. Bd., Bannockburn, Ill., 1989-92. Mem. ABA, Ill. Bar Assn., Chgo. Bar Assn., Soc. Trial Lawyers. Clubs: Legal of Chgo., Law of Chgo.

MCCONNELL, JAMES MICHAEL, federal official; b. Covington, Ky., Dec. 19, 1947; s. Guy Grant and Martha Lee (Beets) McC; m. Wendy Louise Lipton; children: Kevin Andrew, Meghan Eileen. BSBA, Va. Poly. Inst. and State U., 1970. From mgmt. intern to spl. asst. to dirs. Office of Spl. Target Programs Dept. Labor, Washington, 1970-84; with SEC, Washington, 1984—, exec. dir., 1990. Office: SEC Office of Exec Dir 450 5th St NW Washington DC 20549

MC CONNELL, JOHN DOUGLAS, retail corporation executive, owner; b. Dimboola, Victoria, Australia, May 13, 1932; s. William Thomas and Ada Maud (Gardner) McC.; came to U.S., 1964; BA, Melbourne U., 1954; PhD, Stanford U., 1967; m. Gloria Ann Revak, Oct. 12, 1968; children: Joanne Patricia, Meredith Lorraine. Asst. to mng. dir. Automotive & Gen. Industries Ltd., Melbourne, 1954-59; mgr. Eagle M.R. Svc. Pty. Ltd., Melbourne, 1959-64; dir. mgmt. systems SRI Internat., Washington, 1975-77, dir. mgmt. econs. Europe and Middle East, 1977-78, dir. mgmt. svcs. group, Menlo Park, Calif., 1978-80, dir. Food and Forest Products Ctr., 1980-83; v.p. Sungene Techs. Corp., Palo Alto, 1983-85; dir. fin. svcs. ctr. SRI Internat., 1986-87, prin., 1987-91, Menlo Park; pres., CEO, owner Remnant World Inc., San Jose, 1991—; vis. lectr. U. Bradford (Eng.); lectr. San Francisco State U. Contbr. articles to profl. mags. Life gov. Royal Victorian Inst. Blind, 1957—; mem. exec. bd. Stanford Area Council Boy Scouts Am., 1974-94. Decorated officer The Most Venerable Order of St. John of Jerusalem; recipient Silver Beaver award, 1986; Alfred P. Sloan Fellow, 1964-65; GE fellow, 1966. Fellow Australian Inst. Mgmt., Advt. Inst. Australia; mem. Royal Scottish Country Dance Soc. Presbyterian. Clubs: St. Andrews Soc. San Francisco, The Queen's, Army and Navy. Lodge: Masons. Home: 4174 Oak Hill Ave Palo Alto CA 94306-3720 Office: Remnant World Inc 5158 Stevens Creek Blvd San Jose CA 95129

MCCONNELL, JOHN EDWARD, electrical engineering company executive; b. Minot, N.D., July 28, 1931; s. Lloyd Waldorf and Sarah Gladys (Mathis) McC.; m. Carol Claire Myers, July 4, 1952 (dec. Feb. 1989); children: Kathleen Anne, James Mathis, Amy Lynn; m. Heidi Banziger, Sept. 29, 1990. Registered profl. engr., Pa. B.S. in Mech. Engring., U. Pitts., 1952; M.S., Drexel Inst. Tech., 1958. With mktg. and design depts. for turbomachinery Westinghouse Electric Corp., Lester, Pa., 1954-60, 63-67, Pitts., 1960-63; mgr. power generation equipment activities in U.S., ASEA Inc., White Plains, N.Y., 1967-79; regional mgr. power equipment activities Middle Atlantic and Southeastern U.S. regions, 1967-79, mgr. turbine generator dept., 1980-83, mgr. internat. ops. Power Systems div., 1983-84, mgr. transmission substas. dept., 1984-85; mgr. Eastern U.S. ops. ASEA Power Systems Inc., 1985-86, mgr. eastern ops. measurements div. GEC, 1986-91; mgr. eastern region Protection and Control div. GEC Alsthom T&D Inc., 1991—; adviser on energy matters to U.S. congressman 1968-74; speaker and author on energy and electric power topics. Served to 1st lt., C.E., U.S. Army, 1952-54. Mem. IEEE (sr.; energy com., past chmn. subcom. cogeneration, chmn. membership com., power sys. relay com.), IEEE Power Engring. Soc. (sr.; past chmn. chpts. public affairs subcom.), ASME. Republican. Contbr. numerous articles on energy and electric power to industry publs.; developer analytical techniques for power systems performance characteristics and econs. of cogeneration systems. Home: 173 Remington Rd Ridgefield CT 06877-4324 Office: GEC Alsthom T&D Inc 4 Skyline Dr Hawthorne NY 10532

MCCONNELL, JOHN HENDERSON, metal and plastic products manufacturing executive, professional sports team executive; b. New Manchester, W.Va., May 10, 1923; s. Paul Alexander and Mary Louise (Mayhew) McC.; m. Margaret Jane Rardin, Feb. 8, 1946; children—Margaret Louise, John Porter. B.A. in Bus., Mich. State U., 1949; Dr. Law (hon.), Ohio U., 1981. Sales trainee Weirton Steel Co., W.Va., 1950-52; sales mgmt. Shenango-Steel Co., Farrell, Pa., 1952-54; founder, chmn. bd. Worthington Industries, Inc., Columbus, Ohio, 1955—, also past CEO; bd. dirs. Pitts. Pirates; dir. Alltel Corp., Hudson, Ohio, Anchor Hocking, Lancaster, Ohio, Nat. City Corp., Cleve. Bd. dirs. Children's Hosp., Columbus; trustee Ashland Coll., Ohio. Served with USAR, 1943-46. Recipient Ohio Gov.'s award Gov. State of Ohio, 1980; Horatio Alger award Horatio Alger Assn., 1983; named Outstanding Chief Exec. Officer, Fin. World Mag., 1981. Mem. Columbus Area C of C. (chmn. 1978). Republican. Presbyterian. Clubs: Golf (New Albany, Ohio) (pres. 1983—); Brookside Country (Columbus) (pres. 1964-65). Lodge: Masons. Avocations: flying; golf. Office: Worthington Industries Inc 1205 Dearborn Dr Columbus OH 43085-4769*

MCCONNELL, JOHN MICHAEL, federal agency administrator; b. Greenville, S.C., July 26, 1943; s. Harold Eddie and Dorothy Beatrice (Cassell) Mc.; children from previous marriage: Susan Erin McConnell, Jennifer Michelle McConnell; m. Mary Theresa Wagner, Jan. 29, 1988; children: Mark Richard Sentner, Christine Marie Sentner. BA in Econs., Furman U., 1966; MPA in Govt./Pub. Adminstrn., George Washington U., 1986; grad., Nat. Def. U., 1986; PhD in Strategic Intelligence (hon.), Defense Intelligence Coll., 1992. Asst. engr., damage control officer USS Colleton, Mekong Delta, Vietnam, 1967-68; counterintelligence analyst Naval Investigative Svc., Yokosuka, Japan, 1968-70; analyst and supr. CNO Undersea Warfare Intelligence Watch, Washington, 1971-74; force intelligence officer Commdr. Middle East Force Persian Gulf, Indian Ocean, 1974-76; ops. officer Fleet Ocean Surveillance Info. Facility, Rota, Spain, 1976-79; intelligence analyst CNO Intelligence Staff, Washington, 1979-81; intelligence officer Commdr. in Chief Pacific Fleet, Honolulu, 1981-83; fleet intelligence officer Commdr. Seventh Fleet Western Pacific, 1983-85; asst. dir. Naval Intelligence, Washington, 1985-86; chief naval forces divsn. Nat. Security Agy., Ft. Meade, Md., 1987-88; asst. chief staff/intelligence Commdr. in Chief Pacific Fleet, Honolulu, 1988-90; dir, joint staff intelligence Joint Staff, Washington, 1990-92; dir. Nat. Security Agy., Ft. Meade, 1992—. Vice admiral U.S. Navy, 1992—. Recipient Navy Unit Commendation Svc. Navy, 1968, Presdl. Unit Citation Combat Action ribbon CINCPACFLT, Navy Achievement medal Sec. of the Navy, 1974, Navy Commendation medalw/Combat V, 1968, Navy E ribbon Sec. of the Navy, 1984, Nat. Defense Svc. medal with 1 Bronze star, Vietnam Svc. medal with 2 Bronze Stars, Humanitarian Svc. medal, Sea Svc. Deployment ribbon, Navy & Marine Corps Overseas Svc. ribbon, Rep. Vietnam Meritorious Unit Citation Civil Actions Color, Campaign medal Rep. Vietnam, Meritorious Svc. medal with 2 Gold Stars Sec. Navy, 1981, 85, Legion of Merit with 2 Gold Stars, 1985, 87, 90, Defense Superior Svc. medal, 1988, Defense Dist. Svc. medal, 1992. Avocations: world affairs, foreign policy, reading. Office: Dept of Defense National Security Agy Fort George G Meade MD 20755

MCCONNELL, JOHN THOMAS, newspaper executive, publisher; b. Peoria, Ill., May 1, 1945; s. Golden A. and Margaret (Lyon) McC.; 1 child, Justin. B.A., U. Ariz., 1967. Mgr. Fast Printing Co., Peoria, 1970-71; mgmt. trainee Quad-Cities Times, Davenport, Iowa, 1972-73; asst. gen. mgr., then v.p., gen. mgr. Peoria Jour. Star, 1973-81, pub., 1981—, pres., 1987—.

Bd. dirs. Peoria Downtown Devel. Council, Peoria Devel. Corp.; past trustee Methodist Hosp., Peoria. Served with USAR, 1967-69. Named Young Man of Year Peoria Jaycees, 1979. Mem. Peoria Advt. and Selling Club, Peoria C. of C. Congregationalist. Club: Peoria Country. Office: Peoria Jour Star Inc 1 News Plz Peoria IL 61643-0001

MCCONNELL, JOHN WESLEY, real estate-resort developer, corporate executive; b. Steubenville, Ohio, Dec. 3, 1941; m. Clare Yenchochic; 5 children. BS, U. Steubenville, 1967. Various corp. fin. positions Diamond Shamrock Corp., 1967-76, asst. treas., 1976-81, v.p. fin. and adminstrn. coal co., 1981-83, v.p. fin. and adminstrn., 1983-85, exec. v.p., coo, 1985-86; sr. v.p., cfo, treas. Fairfield Communities, Inc., Little Rock, 1986-90, pres., coo, 1990-91, pres., ceo, 1990-92, also bd. dirs. With U.S. Army, 1962-64. Avocations: golf, tennis. Office: Fairfield Communities Inc 2800 Cantrell Rd Little Rock AR 72202-2014

MC CONNELL, JOHN WILKINSON, labor relations educator, labor arbitrator, former socio-economics educator; b. Phila, Oct. 18, 1907; s. John and Lucy (Wilkinson) McC.; m. Harriet Hawley Barlow, July 29, 1933; children: Janet (Mrs. John Alexander), Kathleen (Mrs. David Mervin), Grace (Mrs. Alfred Clark), Judith Ann (Mrs. Henry Sondheimer), John C. B.A., Dickinson Coll., 1929, D.Sc., 1959; Ph.D., Yale U., 1937; LL.D., U. R.I., 1967, Ricker Coll., 1968, U. N.H., 1971. Instr. Am. U. at Cairo, 1929- 32; instr. Yale U., 1935; research asso. Inst. Human Relations, 1934-37; asst. prof. econs. and sociology Am. U., Washington, 1937-39; prof. sociology N.Y. U., 1939-46; prof. indsl. and labor relations Cornell U., 1946-63, dean grad. sch., 1955-59, dean sch. indsl. and labor relations, 1959-63; dir. research in indsl. retirement, 1959—; pres. U. N.H., 1963-71; counselor to coll. Ithaca (N.Y.) Coll., 1971-75, lectr., 1975; adj. prof. labor econs. Cornell U., 1971—; dir. research Twentieth Century Fund, 1951-54; Fulbright lectr. in India, 1953-54; Pub. mem. region II Nat. War Labor Bd., 1943-46, Nat. WSB, 1950-52; mem. Fgn. Service Grievance Bd., Dept. State, 1974-82; cons. pension and retirement systems, mem. human resources research adv. bd. USAF, 1948-53, Social Security Adminstrn.; mem. adv. council Nat. Inst. Child Health and Human Devel., NIH, 1965-69; mem. labor arbitration panel N.Y. State Mediation Service; mem. Fed. Mediation and Conciliation Service; pub. mem. minimum wage bd., P.R., 1956—, chmn., 1960, 1968; chmn. study group on edn. of fgn. students Land-Grant Coll. Assn., 1961. Author: Evolution of Social Classes, 1942, Basic Teachings of Great Economists, 1943, (with Robert Risley) Economic Security, 1951, (with others) America's Needs and Resources, 1955, (with John Corson) Economic Needs of Older People, 1955, Ideas of the Great Economists, 1980; Contbr. articles to profl. jours. Pres. bd. dirs. Tompkins Community Hosp., 1984-86, v.p., 1986-94. Recipient Outstanding Service medal Army Dept., 1967, with oak leaf cluster, 1971; named to Hall of Fame, U. N.H., 1989. Mem. Nat. Acad. Arbitrators, Am. Arbitration Assn., Indsl. Relations Research Assn. (dir. 1951-54), Phi Beta Kappa, Phi Kappa Phi, Omicron Delta Kappa, Pi Gamma Mu. Methodist. Home: 21 Cayuga St # 636 Trumansburg NY 14886-9184

MCCONNELL, JOHN WILLIAM, JR., lawyer; b. Bessemer, Ala., Apr. 17, 1921; s. John W. and Elizabeth (Sheridan) McC.; m. Margaret B. Snider, Jan. 7, 1944; children—Margaret E. (Mrs. John Evans), Rebecca L. (Mrs. A.D. Braden), Catherine L., John W. III. A.B., U. Ala., 1942, M.A., 1946; LL.B., Yale, 1948. Bar: Ala. 1948, D.C. 1977. Atty. Inge, Twitty, Armbrecht & Jackson, Mobile, Ala., 1948-56, Armbrecht, Jackson, McConnell & DeMouy, 1956-65; dir. U.S. Peace Corps, Nigeria, 1965-68; v.p. legal Sea-Land Service, Inc., Menlo Park, N.J., 1968-76; also dir., of counsel Haight, Gardner, Poor & Havens, Washington, 1977-94; Atty. for Reynolds v. Sims on legislative reapportionment, U.S. Supreme Ct., 1963-64. Mem. Ala. Democratic Exec. Com., 1963-65; chmn. Ala. Dem. Steering Com., 1963-65. Served to capt. AUS, 1943-46, 50-52. Mem. ABA, Ala. Bar Assn., D.C. Bar Assn., Maritime Law Assn. Methodist. Home: 926 Seagull Dr Mount Pleasant SC 29464-4145

MCCONNELL, LORELEI CATHERINE, library director; b. Port Jefferson, N.Y., Dec. 5, 1938; d. Alvin and Mary (McConnell) Philibert; m. Thomas McConnell, Jan. 20, 1962; children: Catherine, Michael. BA, Drew U., 1960; MLS, Rutgers U., 1963. Reference libr. Irvington (N.J.) Pub. Libr., 1963-90, dir., 1990—; founder Irvington Literacy Program, 1986, dir., 1986-90. Mem. ALA, N.J. Libr. Assn. (mem. exec. bd. 1990-93, N.J. Libr. of Yr. 1993-94), Internat. Primal Assn., Beta Phi Mu. Home: 563 Park St Montclair NJ 07043-2027 Office: Irvington Pub Libr Civic Sq Irvington NJ 07111

MCCONNELL, MICHAEL, opera company director; b. Charlotte, N.C., Dec. 25, 1954; s. Jackson McConnell and Patsy Anne (King) White. MusB, Coll. Conservatory of Music, U. Cin., 1976, postgrad., 1979. Adj. lectr. Cin. Coll. Conservatory, 1980-81; resident stage dir. Opera Memphis, 1982-84; exec. dir. Lyric Opera Cleve., 1984-94; dir. opera Cleve. Inst. Music, 1991—; dir. opera workshop Baldwin-Wallace Conservatory, Berea, Ohio, 1987-91; frequent panelist opera-music theater NEA. With prodn. staff Santa Fe Opera, Opera Theatre St. Louis, Edinburgh Festival, Opera Memphis, others; stage dir. Opera Theatre St. Louis, Opera Memphis, Opera Theatre Rochester, Memphis Playhouse on Sq., Cin. Opera, Skylight Opera Theatre, Cleve. Inst. Music, Cin. Coll. Conservatory Music, Cleve. Orch., others; contbr. articles to profl. jours. Mem. OPERA Am. (bd. dirs 1993—), Actor's Equity Assn. Office: The Cleve Inst of Music 11021 East Blvd Cleveland OH 44106

MCCONNELL, MICHAEL ARTHUR, lawyer; b. Ft. Worth, Jan. 15, 1947. BA, Loyola U., New Orleans, 1969; JD, U. Tex., 1975. Bar: Tex. 1976, U.S. Dist. Ct. (no. dist.) Tex. 1976, U.S. Dist. Ct. (ea. dist.) Tex. 1981, U.S. Dist. Ct. (we. dist.) Tex. 1982, U.S. Dist. Ct. (so. dist.) Tex. 1989, U.S. Ct. Appeals (5th cir.) Tex. 1980, U.S. Ct. Appeals (10th cir.) 1987. Briefing atty. U.S. Dist. Ct. Hon. Eldon B. Mahon, Ft. Worth, 1976-77; assoc. atty. Cantey, Hanger, Gooch, Munn and Collins, Ft. Worth, 1977-81, ptnr, 1981-83; judge no. dist. U.S. Bankruptcy Ct., Ft. Worth, 1983-86; ptnr. Kelly, Hart & Hallman, Ft. Worth, 1986-88, Jackson & Walker, Ft. Worth, 1988-95. Sgt. USAF, 1969-73. Mem. Nat. Conf. Bankruptcy Judges, Assn. Former Bankruptcy Judges. Office: McConnell & Assocs PC 303 Main St Ste 220 Fort Worth TX 76102

MC CONNELL, MICHAEL W., law educator; b. 1955. BA, Mich. State U., 1976; JD, U. Chgo., 1979. Bar: D.C. 1981. Law clk. to Hon. J. Skelly Wright U.S. Ct. Appeals (D.C. cir.), 1979-80; law clk. to Hon. William J. Brennan Jr. U.S. Supreme Ct., D.C., 1980-81; asst. gen. counsel U.S. Office of Mgmt. and Budget, D.C., 1981-83; asst. to the sol. gen. U.S. Dept. Justice, D.C., 1983-85; asst. prof. U. Chgo., 1984-89, prof., 1989—; mem. Pres'. Intelligence Oversight Bd., 1988—. Mem. Supreme Ct. Hist. Soc., bd. editors yearbook, 1988—. Mem. Order of the Coif, Phi Beta Kappa, Phi Kappa Phi. Office: U Chgo Law Sch 1111 E 60th St Chicago IL 60637-2702

MC CONNELL, ROBERT CHALMERS, former city official; b. Santa Fe, Aug. 7, 1913; s. Chalmers and Mary (Foree) McC.; m. Colleen Alford, Feb. 3, 1948; 1 dau., Julie. B.A., U. N.Mex., 1935; LL.B., George Washington U., 1939. Bar: N.Mex. bar 1941, U.S. Supreme Ct. bar 1947. Law clk. to U.S. circuit judge, 1939-40; asst. dist. atty. N.Mex., 1940-41, 45-47, adminstrv. asst. to congressman from 1947-57, 57-61; spl. asst. to asst. sec. interior, 1961-62; asst. to sec. for congl. liaison Dept. Interior, Washington, 1962-67; asst. sec. for adminstrn. Dept. Interior, 1967-69; mayor City of Redington Beach, Fla., 1971-72; partner McConnell-Wilroy Cons., St. Petersburg, Fla., 1976-77. Mgr. Madeira Beach (Fla.) Little League Baseball; pres. Gulf Beaches Little League; chmn. bd. govs. Redington Beach Assn., 1977-79; chmn. Chaves County Dem. Com., 1944-48. The Biog. History of N.Mex. Recipient Distinguished Service award U.S. Dept. Interior, 1967. Mem. Sigma Chi. Club: Rotary. Home: 15849 Redington Dr Saint Petersburg FL 33708-1743

MC CONNELL, ROBERT EASTWOOD, architect, educator; b. Spokane, Wash., July 15, 1930; s. Robert Ervie and Alma (Eastwood) Mc C.; m. Beverly Ann Vincent, Sept. 12, 1953; children: Kathleen Ann, Karen Eileen, Terri Lynn. B in Archtl. Engring., Wash. State U., 1952, MArch, Mass. Inst. Tech., 1954. Project architect John W. Maloney (Architect), Seattle, 1956-62; asst. prof. architecture Ariz. State U., Tempe, 1964-66; asso. prof. Ariz. State U., 1966-67; prof. U. Kans., Lawrence, 1967-69; prof., head dept.

art and architecture U. Idaho, Moscow, 1969-71; prof. U. Ariz., Tucson, 1971-92; dean Coll. Architecture U. Ariz., 1971-92; prof. emeritus, dean emeritus U. Ariz., Tucson, 1992—, acting assoc. dean, 1994; partner McConnell & Peterson, Architects, Tempe, 1963-66; pvt. practice architecture, 1962—. Author, project dir.: Land Use Planning for Ariz., Ariz. Acad, 1974; Contbr. articles to profl. jours. Chmn. Idaho Gov.'s Awards Program in Arts and Humanities, 1970; project dir. Rio Salado Conceptual Study, Phoenix, 1966; bd. dirs. Tucson Regional Plan, 1972-79. Served with USAF, 1954-56. Fellow AIA (awards 1969, 76, pres. So. Ariz. chpt. 1975-76, bd. dirs. 1971-77); mem. AAUP, Ariz. Town Hall, Ariz. Soc. Architects (mem. coun. of dels. 1971-77, chmn. honor awards jury 1975), Phi Kappa Phi, Scarab, Tau Beta Pi, Sigma Tau. Home: 7001 N Edgewood Pl Tucson AZ 85704-6924 Office: U Ariz Coll Architecture Tucson AZ 85721

MCCONNELL, WILLIAM THOMPSON, commercial banker; b. Zanesville, Ohio, Aug. 8, 1933; s. William Gerald and Mary Gladys (Watt) McC.; m. Jane Charlotte Cook, Aug. 25, 1956; children—Jennifer Wynne, William Gerald. BA, Denison U., 1955; MBA, Northwestern U., 1959. Pres. Park Nat. Bank, Newark, Ohio, 1979-83, pres., chief exec. officer, 1983-93; chmn., chief exec. officer Park Nat. Bank, Newark, 1993—; also bd. dirs. Park Nat. Bank, Newark, Ohio; pres., chief exec. officer Park Nat. Corp., Newark, 1987-94, chmn., CEO, 1994—; bd. dirs. Freight Svcs., Inc., Newark, Consol. Computer Ctr., Newark. Mem. Newark Area C. of C. (past pres., dir. 1977-83), Ohio Bankers Assn. (pres., chmn. 1981-83). Office: Park Nat Bank PO Box 850 Newark OH 43058-0850

MCCONNER, STANLEY JAY, SR., academic administrator; b. Detroit, Dec. 7, 1929; s. Walter Richard and Norma Louise (Hafford) McC.; m. Peggy Miller, June 1951(div.); children: Michele Jay, Stanley Jay; m. Dorothy Hamilton, Apr. 5, 1974. BS in Spl. Edn., Ea. Mich. U., 1953; MS in Reading, U. Conn., 1956; MS in Psychology, Cen. Conn. State U., 1967; PhD in Adminstrn., U. Sarasota, 1973; PhD in Adminstrn. and Policy Studies, Northwestern U., 1986. Tchr. Hartford (Conn.) Pub. Schs., 1953-67; asst. prof., asst. dir. U. Conn., Storrs, 1967-70; exec. dir. Balt. Pub. Schs., 1970-74; dean arts and scis. Kennedy, King Coll., Chgo., 1974-76; dean continuing edn. Chgo. State U., 1976-77, exec. dir. found., 1977-85; asst. prin. Pritzker-Grinker Sch., Chgo., 1985-86; coord. Body Awareness Resource Network Chgo. Health Info. Ctr., 1986-91; staff devel. specialist, reading specialist African Am. Studies Dept. Tucson Unified Sch. Dist., 1991—. Author: Famous Black Americans, 1972, Senate Bill 730: A Report Card, 1985. Bd. dirs. Girl Scouts U.S., Chgo., 1983, Roseland Community Hosp., Chgo., 1986; mem. Chgo. Urban League, Operation People United to Save Humanity, Chgo., Planned Giving Roundtable, Chgo., 1982-86. Named Community Ambassador-Norway Hartford Conn. Bus. Group, 1958; fellow Nat. Counselor Educator, Washington 1976; recipient achievement award, Nat. Assn. Pub. Continuing Adult Edn., Washington 1978; named to Hall of Fame Ea. Mich. U.,1988. Mem. Nat. Soc. Fundraising Execs., Chgo. 1982-86, Chgo. Urban League, 1988—, Operation PUSH, Chgo. 1988—, Phi Delta Kappa, Storrs, Conn., Am. Ednl. Research Assoc., Kiwanis of Chgo. Democrat. Episcopalian. Avocations: running, reading, cooking.

MCCONOMY, JAMES HERBERT, lawyer; b. Pitts., Mar. 24, 1937; s. Murray Michael and Catherine Elizabeth (Herbert) McC.; m. Jeanne Margaret Cronin, Sept. 3, 1960 (div. Apr. 1989); children: Margaret Jeanne, Michael Murray; m. Roberta L. Cavanaugh, June 30, 1989. AB cum laude, Harvard U., 1959, LLB, 1962. Bar: Pa. 1963, U.S. Ct. Appeals (3d cir.) 1972, U.S. Supreme Ct. 1977. Ptnr. Reed, Smith, Shaw & McClay, Pitts., 1962-92; mng. ptnr. Titus & McConomy, Pitts., 1992—. Fellow Am. Coll. Trial Lawyers; mem. ABA, Pa. Bar Assn. (chmn. comml. litigation sect. 1986—), Allegheny County Acad. Trial Lawyers. Republican. Roman Catholic. Clubs: Duquesne, Harvard-Yale-Princeton (Pitts.). Avocations: photography, travel. Home: 1117 Harvard Pl Pittsburgh PA 15205-1726 Office: Titus & McConomy Four Gateway Ctr 20th Fl Pittsburgh PA 15222

MCCONOMY, THOMAS ARTHUR, chemical company executive; b. Wilmerding, Pa., July 26, 1933; s. Thomas Michael Murray and Catherine Elizabeth (Herbert) McC.; m. Eileen Adele Cerutti, June 22, 1956; children: Thomas E., Robert M., Karen E. McConomy Bugos. BSchemE, Carnegie Mellon U., 1955. Svc. engr. Calgon Corp., Pitts., 1955-60; staff engr. Calgon Carbon Corp., Pitts., 1960-67, nat. accounts mgr., 1967-70, divsn. internat. mgr., 1972-74, environ. bus. dir., 1974-75, divsn. dir., 1975-78, divsn. gen. mgr., 1978-79, v.p., 1979-85, pres., chmn., CEO, 1985-94, chmn., 1985—; mgr. Calgon Inter-Am. Corp., Caracas, Venezuela, 1970-72; bd. dirs. PNC Bank (formerly Pitts. Nat. Bank), Equitable Resources. Contbr. tech. articles and papers on indsl. water treatment. Chmn. Carnegie Mellon U., Pitts., 1988; bd. dirs. Pitts. High Tech. Coun. Mem. Greater Pitts. C. of C. (bd. dirs. 1990), Allegheny Country Club, Edgeworth Club (Sewickley, Pa.), Duquesne Club (Pitts.) (dir.). Avocations: stained glass crafting, gardening. Office: Calgon Carbon Corp PO Box 717 Pittsburgh PA 15230-0717

MCCONVILLE, WILLIAM, academic administrator. Rsch. fellow Divinity Sch. Yale U., until 1989; pres. Siena Coll., Loudonville, N.Y., 1989—. Office: Siena Coll Office of Pres Loudonville NY 12211

MCCOOK, KATHLEEN DE LA PEÑA, university educator; b. Chgo.; d. Frank Eugene and Margaret L. (de la Peña) McEntee; m. Philip G. Heim, Mar. 20, 1972 (div.); 1 child, Margaret Marie; m. William Woodrow Lee McCook, Oct. 12, 1991; stepchildren: Cecilia, Billie Jean, Nicole. B.A., U. Ill.; M.A., Marquette U., U. Chgo.; Ph.D., U. Wis.-Madison. Reference librarian Elmhurst Coll. Library, Ill., 1971-72; dir. pub. services Rosary Coll. Library, River Forest, Ill., 1972-76; lectr. U. Wis., Madison, 1976-78; asst. prof. library sci. U. Ill., Urbana, 1978-83; dean, prof. La. State U. Sch. Library and Info. Sci., Baton Rouge, 1983-90; dean grad. sch. La. State U. 1990-92; dir. Sch. Libr. and Info. Sci. U South Fla., 1993—. Author: (with L. Estabrook) Career Profiles, 1983, (with William E. Moen) Occupational Entry, 1989, Adult Services, 1990, (with Gary O. Rolstad) Developing Readers' Advisory Services, 1993, Toward a Just and Productive Soc., 1994; contbr. essays to books, articles to profl. jours. Chmn. Equal Rights Amendment Task Force, Ill., 1977-79; mem. Eugene McCarthy campaign, U. Ill., Chgo., 1968; mem. La. Gov.'s Commn. for Women, 1985-88; bd. dirs. La. Endowment for Humanities, 1991-92. Recipient Disting. Alumnus award U. Wis., 1991; Bradshaw scholar Tex. Woman's Univ., 1994. Mem. ALA (com. chmn. 1980—, editor RQ jour., 1982-88, Pub. Librs. jour. 1989-90, Equality award 1987, Adult Svc. award 1991), Assn. for Libr. and Info. Sci. Edn. (com. chmn. 1981—, pres. 1987-88), Southeastern Libr. Assn., Fla. Libr. Assn. (treas. 1995—), Tampa Bay Libr. Consortium (bd. dirs. 1994—), Women Libr. Workers, Ill. Libr. Assn. (treas. 1981-83), Beta Phi Mu. Democrat. Roman Catholic. Avocation: reading. Office: U South Fla Sch Libr and Info Sci 4202 Fowler Ave E CIS 1040 Tampa FL 33620-8300

MCCOOK, RICHARD PAUL, grocery chain financial executive; b. Miami, Fla., Mar. 15, 1953; s. Leon Ennis and Ruth Erminor (Davenport) McC.; m. Anne Thackerson, Mar. 22, 1975; children: Ryan Wesley, Kelly Lauren. BS in Acctg., Fla. State U., 1975, M in Accountancy, 1976. CPA, Fla. Sr. audit mgr. Peat, Marwick, Mitchell & Co., Jacksonville, Fla., 1976-84; fin. v.p., chief fin. officer Winn-Dixie Stores, Inc., 1984—. Participant Leadership Jacksonville, 1986-87. Mem. Am. Inst. CPA's, Fla. Inst. CPA's, Fin. Execs. Inst. Democrat. Methodist. Club: River (Jacksonville). Avocations: hunting, fishing, tennis. Office: Winn-Dixie Stores Inc 5050 Edgewood Ct Jacksonville FL 32203-0297

MCCOOMB, LLOYD ALEXANDER, transportation executive; b. Edmonton, Alta., Can., Sept. 22, 1945. BASc, U. Toronto, Ont., Can., 1968, PhD, 1981; SM, MIT, 1970. With mil. engring. bd. Can. Armed Forces, 1964-74; sr. devel. officer Transport Devel. Agy. Transport Can., 1974-83; dir. stats. and forecasts Air Adminstrn., Ottawa, Ont., Can., 1983-86; from dir. gen. mktg. to dir. gen. safety and tech. svcs. Airports Group, Ottawa, 1986; now airport gen. mgr. Toronto-Lester B. Pearson Internat. Airport. Office: Lester B Pearson Intl Airport, Transport Canada PO Box 6003, Toronto, ON Canada L5P 1B5

MCCOPPIN, PETER, symphony orchestra conductor; b. Toronto, Ont., Can.; m. Roswitha McCoppin, 1979. BMus in Performance Levi U. Toronto; studied conducting with, Erich Leinsdorf, Prof. Hans Swarosky, Lovro von Maticic, Seriu Celibidache. Formed chamber choir Toronto,

1970-75; condr. orchestral program, prof. conducting Cleve. Inst. Music, 1975-78; guest condr. Alta. Ballet Co., Nat. Ballet Can., major orchs. Can.; music. advisor, condr. Vancouver (B.C.) Symphony Orch., 1988-89, now guest condr.; music dir. Victoria (B.C.) Symphony Orch., 1989—, Charlotte (N.C.) Symphony Orch., 1993—. Guest condr. Thunder Bay (Ont.) Symphony, Syracuse (N.Y.) Symphony; condr. Shanghai Symphony, Ctrl. Philharmonic, Beijing, Tokyo Symphony, Osaka Philharmonic, Gunma Symphony, Sapporo Symphony, Mex. Symphony Mex., Rochester Philharmonic, Buffalo Philharmonic, Tucson Symphony, most major orchs. in Can.; concerts with KBS Symphony, Korea; host B.C. TV Knowledge Network Classic Theatre, TV spls., radio programs. Office: Victoria Symphony Orch, 846 Broughton St lower level, Victoria, BC Canada V8W 1E4*

MCCORD, ALICE BIRD, association executive; b. Enid, Okla.; d. Glenn and Lottabel (Bird) McC. BS, NYU, 1964; MA, Columbia U., 1974. Tng. dir. Gimbels Dept. Store, N.Y.C., 1965-69; personnel dir. The May Dept. Stores, N.Y.C. and St. Louis, 1972-75; cons. Arthur Young & Co., N.Y.C., 1976-78; v.p. personnel Nat. Retail Mchts. Assn., N.Y.C., 1978-85, sr. v.p., 1986-92; sr. v.p. rsch. and planning Nat. Retail Fedn., Inc., N.Y.C., 1992—; cons., prin. ABM Assocs. (specializing in svcs. to internat. retailers U.S. and abroad), 1992—; assn. and retail cons.; guest on nat. and local TV programs. Author: Training and Development. Mem. Am. Psychol. Assn., Am. Soc. Tng. and Devel., Gifts In Kind (bd. dirs.).

MC CORD, KENNETH ARMSTRONG, consulting engineer; b. Balt., May 4, 1921; s. William Ellermeyer and Bertha (Turnt) McC.; m. Carol Blanton, Oct. 12, 1946; children—Thomas B. Kenneth Armstrong, William C., David M., Jean E. B. Engring., Johns Hopkins U., 1941. Registered profl. engr., Md., Va., N.J., D.C., Del. registered profl. surveyor, Md., Del. registered profl. planner, N.J. Ret. ptnr. Whitman, Requardt and Assocs., Balt.; gen. ptnr. B&H Investments, Manassas, Va. Served with C.E. U.S. Army, 1942-46. Decorated Silver Star, Croix de Guerre France. Fellow ASCE; mem. NSPE, Am. Water Works Assn., Am. Cons. Engrs. Coun., Water Pollution Control Fedn., L'Hirondelle Club. Democrat. Presbyterian. Home: 1010 W Wind Ct Baltimore MD 21204-6738

MC CORD, MARSHAL, civil engineer; b. Balt., July 4, 1917; s. William Ellermeyer and Bertha (Turnt) McC.; m. Ruth Helen Schultz, Apr. 20, 1946; 1 dau., Barbara Lynn. B. Engring., Johns Hopkins U., 1937. Draftsman Modjeski & Masters, Harrisburg, Pa., 1937-40; design and project engr. J.E. Greiner Co., Balt., 1946-57; chief engr., v.p. Century Engring., Inc., Towson, Md., 1957-77; dir. engring. and constrn. State of Md., Balt., 1977-86; mem. Md. State Bd. Registration for Profl. Engrs. and Land Surveyors, 1966-76, chmn., 1971-76. Moderator Presbytery of Balt., 1977—. Served with C.E. U.S. Army, 1941-46. Fellow ASCE; mem. Nat. Soc. Profl. Engrs., Md. Soc. Profl. Engrs. (Meritorious Service award 1971). Club: Johns Hopkins. Home: 11630 Glen Arm Rd Glen Arm MD 21057

MCCORD, WILLIAM CHARLES, retired diversified energy company executive; b. San Antonio, Apr. 1, 1928; s. Sam Byard and Helen (Schoepfer) McC.; div.; children: Kathleen McCord Burnett, Martha McCord Pennington, Billy, Helen McCord Curry, Elizabeth McCord Paschal, Richard, Douglas, James, Quannah, Korrin Li, Minta Ann; m. Kay Moran; stepchildren: Heather Moran, Caitlin Moran, James Moran Jr. B.S. in Mech. Engring, Tex. A & M U., 1949. With Enserch Corp. (formerly Lone Star Gas Co.), 1949—, dir. bldg. mgmt., 1965-67; v.p. Enserch Corp. (Dallas div.), 1967, sr. v.p. operations, 1968-70, pres., prin. exec. officer, 1970-77, chmn., pres., 1977-91, chmn., chief exec. officer, 1991-93; sr. v.p. Nipak, Inc., chem. subsidiary, Dallas, 1991-93; ret., 1993; bd. dirs. Enserch Corp., Pool Energy Svcs. Co., Lone Star Techs., Inc. Past pres., mem. exec. bd. Circle Ten council Boy Scouts Am.; mem. nat. exec. bd. Boy Scouts Am.; bd. dirs., former chmn. Tex. Research League, Dallas Citizens Council, State Fair Tex. Mem. Tau Beta Pi. Baptist. Office: One Energy Sq Ste 1025 4925 Greenville Ave Dallas TX 75206

MCCORISON, MARCUS ALLEN, librarian, cultural organization administrator; b. Lancaster, Wis., July 17, 1926; s. Joseph Lyle and Ruth (Mink) McC.; m. Janet Buckbee Knop, June 10, 1950; children: Marcus Allen II, Judith McC. Gove, Andrew Buckbee, Mary McC. Rosenbloom, James Nice, Peter Gardner. AB, Ripon Coll., 1950; MA, U. Vt., 1951, LittD (hon.), 1992; MS, Columbia U., 1954; LHD (hon.), Assumption Coll. Worcester, Mass., 1987, Coll. of the Holy Cross, 1992; LittD (hon.), Clark U., 1992. Librarian Kellogg-Hubbard Library, Montpelier, Vt., 1954-55; chief of rare books dept. Dartmouth Coll. Library, Hanover, N.H., 1955-59; head spl. collections dept. State U. Iowa Libraries, 1959-60; libr. Am. Antiquarian Soc. Worcester, Mass., 1960-91, editor Procs., 1960-67, dir., 1967-89, pres., 1989-92, pres. emeritus, 1993—; cons. pvt. clients Christie, Manson & Woods, Internat., 1993—; cons. A.W. Mellon Found., 1994-95, Callahan, MacIntyre & Assocs., 1994—; mem. N.Am. steering com. 18th Century Short Title Catalogue, 1977—; mem. Com. for a New Eng. Bibliography, 1968-90, treas., 1970-77; mem. adv. coun. Eleutherian Mills-Hagley Found., 1971-74, 87-89; mem. adv. coun. Princeton U. Libr., 1988-92; bd. govs. Rsch. Librs. Group, 1980-91, chmn. preservation com., 1982-85, mem. governance com., 1989-91, chmn. writings of James Fenimore Cooper, 1991—. Author: Vermont Imprints 1778-1820, 1963, The 1764 Catalogue of the Redwood Library, 1965; contbr.: The Pursuit of Knowledge in the Early American Republic, 1976, Publishing and Readership in Revolutionary France and America, 1993; editor: History of Printing in America by Isaiah Thomas, 1970; mem. editorial bd.: History of the Book in America, 1993—. Trustee Fruitlands Mus., 1978-89, Old Sturbridge Village, 1981-92, Hist. Deerfield, Inc., 1991—; mem. bd. mgrs. Lewis Walpole Libr., Yale U., 1995—. With USNR, 1944-46, U.S. Army, 1951-52. Recipient Samuel Pepys medal Ephemera Soc., London, 1980, Disting. Alumni award Ripon Coll., 1989, Columbia U. Sch. Libr. Svc., 1992. Fellow Pilgrim Soc.; mem. Am. Antiquarian Soc., Mass. Hist. Coc., Coll. and Rsch. Librs. Assn. (chmn. rare books sect. 1965-66), Bibliog. Soc. Am. (pres. 1980-84, del. to Am. Coun. Learned Socs. 1985—), Vt. Hist. Soc. (trustee 1956-66), Worcester Hist. Mus. (exec. com. 1967-80), Ind. Rsch. Librs. Assn. (chmn. 1972-73, 78-80), Ctr. for Rsch. on Vt. (assoc.), N.E. Am. Soc. 18th Century Studies (pres. 1978-79), Colonial Soc. Mass., Odd Volumes Club, Grolier Club (councillor 1979-82, 83-84), Century Assn. Democrat. Congregationalist. Home and Office: 3601 Knightsbridge Close Worcester MA 01609-1161

MCCORKINDALE, DOUGLAS HAMILTON, publishing company executive, corporate lawyer; b. N.Y.C., June 14, 1939; s. William Douglas and Kathleen (Miles) McC.; m. Nancy Walsh, Dec. 24, 1991; children by previous marriage: Laura Ann, Heather Jean. BA, Columbia U., 1961, LLB cum laude (Harlan Fiske Stone scholar), 1964. Bar: N.Y. 1964. Assoc. Thacher Proffitt & Wood, N.Y.C., 1964-70, ptnr., 1970-71; gen. counsel, sec. Gannett Co., Inc., 1971-72, v.p., gen. counsel, sec., 1972-77, sr. v.p. fin. and law, 1977-79, sr. v.p., chief fin. officer, 1979-83, pres. diversified media div., 1980-83, exec. v.p., 1983; vice chmn., CFO Gannett Co. Inc., Arlington, Va., 1984—, chief adminstrv. officer, 1986—; dir. all subsidiaries and joint ventures; bd. dirs. Continental Airlines Inc., Frontier Corp., The Global Govt. Plus Fund Inc., Prudential Global Genesis Fund Inc., Prudential Natural Resources Fund Inc., Prudential Multi-Sector Fund Inc.; trustee Prudential Equity Income Fund, Prudential Allocation Fund, Prudential Mcpl. Bond Fund, Mut. Ins. Co. Ltd. Mem. ABA (chmn. com. Exch. Act of 1934 1971-73), N.Y. State Bar Assn., Newspaper Assn. Am., Nat. Press Club, Oak Hill Country Club, Pine Valley Golf Club, Mid Ocean Club, Burning Tree Club. Office: Gannett Co Inc 1100 Wilson Blvd Arlington VA 22209

MCCORKLE, HORACE JACKSON, physician, educator; b. Center Point, Tex., Feb. 5, 1905; s. Homer Thomas and Helen Hart (Cason) McC.; m. Marion Fisher, June 10, 1939; children—Alan, Donald, Malcolm, Douglas, Jeanette. M.D., U. Calif., 1934. Intern San Francisco City and County Hosp., 1933-34; surgeon U. Calif. Med. Sch., 1938—, prof. surgery, 1953—. Mem. Am., Pan Pacific, Western, Pacific Coast surg. assns., Internat. Surg. Soc., Pan Am. Med. Soc., Soc. Exptl. Biology and Medicine, Soc. Univ. Surgeons, Am. Gastroenterol. Assn., Nu Sigma Nu, Kappa Delta Rho. Home: 35 San Fernando Way San Francisco CA 94127-1503

MCCORKLE, MICHAEL, construction company executive; b. Kansas City, Mo., Feb. 8, 1944; s. Clarence E. and Thelma (Head) McC.; m. Sarapage

Zatezalo, Jan. 22, 1966; 1 child, Heather K. BS, Cen. Mo. State U., 1968. Geologist Woodward-Clyde Co. and Fru-Con Cos., Kansas City and St. Louis, 1968-70, Fruco & Assocs., St. Louis, 1970-74; supt. Fruin-Colnon Corp., St. Louis, 1974-80, project mgr., 1980-83, ops. mgr., 1983-85; v.p. Fru-Con Constrn. Corp., St. Louis, 1984-87, exec. v.p., 1989—; pres. Fru-Con Engring. Co., St. Louis, 1987-89, vice chmn., 1989-91; v.p. Suerdrup Corp., St. Louis, 1991-94; v.p., dir. constrn. bus. segment Suerdrup Facilities, Inc., St. Louis, 1994—; mem. adv. bd. Constrn. Industry Inst., Austin, Tex., 1986—. Contbg. author: Materials Management, 1988. Mem. Engrs. Club (St. Louis). Avocation: fly fishing. Office: Suerdrup Facilities Inc 801 N 11th St Saint Louis MO 63101

MCCORKLE, ROBERT ELLSWORTH, agribusiness educator; b. Salinas, Calif., Apr. 3, 1938; s. Stanley Harold and Mabel Eugenia (Vosti) McC.; m. Mary E. McCorkle, June 26, 1965; children: Bonnie Kathleen, Robyn Krystyna. BSc in Farm Mgmt., Calif. Poly. State U., San Luis Obispo, 1960; MSc in Agrl. Econs., U. Calif., Davis, 1962; postgrad., U. Wis., 1969, Oreg. State U., 1966. Rsch. statistician U. Calif., Davis, 1960-62; asst. prof. agrl. bus. Calif. Poly. State U., San Luis Obispo, 1962-66, dir. internat. edn., 1970-74, asst. prof. agrl. mgmt., 1969-76, prof. agribus., 1976—; chief farm mgmt. officer Ministry Agr., Lusaka, Zambia, 1967-69; dir., owner McCorkle Farms, Inc., Willows, Calif., 1970—; vis. prof. Mich. State U., U.S. AID, Washington, 1984-85; dir., owner McCorkle Trucking, Glenn, Calif., 1988—; agrl. economist U.S. AID-Redso ESA, Nairobi, Kenya, 1984-85. Author: Guide for Farming in Zambia, 1968. Pres. Cabrillo Property Owners Assn., Los Osos, Calif., 1976-78; vol. Atty. Gen.'s Adv. Com., Calif., 1972-74. U.S. Peace Corps strategy grantee, Washington, 1976—. Mem. Am. Agrl. Econs. Assn., Western Agrl. Econs. Assn., Calif. Poly. Farm Mgmt. Club, Calif. Poly. Alumni Assn., Blue Key, Alpha Zeta (sr. advisor Delta chpt., nat. high coun. chronicler, bd. dirs., v.p. found.). Republican. Episcopalian. Avocations: hunting, fishing. Office: Calif Poly State U San Luis Obispo CA 93407

MCCORMAC, BILLY MURRAY, physicist, research institution executive, former army officer; b. Zanesville, Ohio, Sept. 8, 1920; s. Samuel Dennis and Phyllis (Murray) M.; m. Dorothy Boros, 1948; children: Norene Leslie, Candace Elizabeth, Lisbeth Phyllis; m. Diana Root, 1968; children: Billy Murray II, Samuel Dennis Root. B.S., Ohio State U., 1943; M.S., U. Va., 1956, Ph.D. in Nuclear Physics, 1957. Commd. 2d lt. U.S. Army, 1943; advanced through grades to lt. col.; physicist U.S. Army (Office Spl. Weapons Devel.), 1957-60; scientist U.S. Army (Office of Chief of Staff), 1960-61; physicist U.S. Army (Def. Atomic Support Agy.), 1961-62, chief electromagnetic br., 1962-63; ret., 1963; sci. advisor rsch. inst. Ill. Inst. Tech., 1963, dir. div. geophysics rsch. inst., 1963-68; sr. cons. scientist Lockheed Rsch. Labs., Palo Alto, Calif., 1968-69, mgr. Radiation Physics Lab., 1969-74, mgr. Electro-optics Lab., 1974-76, mgr. solar and optics physics, 1976-89, staff exec. physical and electronic scis., 1989-92; Chmn. radiation trapped in earth s magnetic field Adv. Study Inst., Norway, 1965, chmn. aurora and airglow, Eng., 1966, Norway, 1968, Can. 1970, chmn. physics and chemistry of atmospheres, France, 1972, Belgium, 1974, chmn. earth's particles and fields, Germany, 1967, Calif., 1969, Italy, 1971, Eng., 1973, Austria, 1975; chmn. Shuttle Environment and Ops.-I, Washington, 1983, -II, Houston, 1985; chmn. Space Station in 21st Century, Reno, 1986, Space Station I, Washington, 1988. Editor: Jour. Water, Air and Soil Pollution, Geophysics and Astrophysics Monographs; editor-in-chief Natural Sinks CO2, 1992, Quantification of Sinks and Sources, 1993. Fellow AIAA (assoc., mem. publ. com. 1981—, v.p. publs. 1987-91); mem. AAAS, Am. Astron. Soc. (sr.), Am. Phys. Soc., Am. Geophys. Union, Marine Tech. Soc. Home: 696 Village Blvd Unit 9 Incline Village NV 89451

MC CORMAC, JOHN WAVERLY, judge; b. Zanesville, Ohio, Feb. 8, 1926; s. Samuel D. and Phyllis (Murray) McC.; m. Martha Ann Cunningham, June 22, 1952; children: Michael Paul, John Mark, James Samuel. B.S., Muskingum Coll., 1951; J.D., Capital U., 1961. Bar: Ohio 1961. Fire protection engr. Ohio Insp. Bur., 1951-60; pvt. practice Columbus, 1961-65; prof. law Capital U., Columbus, 1965-66, 71-74; dean Law Sch. Capital U., 1966-71; judge 10th Dist. Ct. Appeals, 1975-92; prof. law Ohio State U., Columbus, 1993—; mem., staff cons. rules adv. com. Supreme Ct. Ohio; chmn. adv. bd. Vols. in Probation, 1972-74; chmn. Ohio Jud. Conf., 1982-84; commr. Ohio Dispute Resolution com., 1989-92, chmn., 1993—; chief justice Ohio Ct. Appeals Assn., 1989-91. Author: Ohio Civil Rules Practice, 1970, 2nd edit., 1992, Anderson's Ohio Civil Practice, Vol. 1, 1971, Vol. 2, 1976, Vol. 3, 1977, Wrongful Death in Ohio, 1982. Served with USNR, 1943-46. Fellow Ohio Bar Assn. Found.; mem. League Ohio Law Schs. (pres. 1969-70), ABA, Ohio Bar Assn. (council of dels. 1973-77), Columbus Bar Assn. (bd. govs. 1968-72, sec.-treas. 1973-74, pres. 1975-76), Am. Judicature Soc., Phi Alpha Delta. Republican. Club: Masons (33 deg.). Home: 395 Longfellow Ave Columbus OH 43085-3024

MCCORMACK, DONALD PAUL, newspaper consultant; b. Brockton, Mass., Jan. 15, 1926; s. Everett G. and Esther (Lufkin) McC.; m. Petronella Ruth Seger, Apr. 28, 1951; 1 son, Christopher Paul. B.A., U. Pitts., 1949. Corr. U.P.I., 1949-52; asst. city editor Pitts. Sun-Telegraph, 1952-56; pub. relations exec., 1956-64; copy reader N.Y. News, 1964-67, editorial writer, 1967-72, chief editorial writer, 1972-82; cons., 1982—. With USAAF, 1944-46, Pa. N.G., 1954-57. Home and Office: PO Box 3539 Westport CT 06880-8539

MC CORMACK, FRANCIS XAVIER, lawyer, former oil company executive; b. Bklyn., July 9, 1929; s. Joseph and Blanche V. (Dengel) Mc C.; m. Margaret V. Hynes, Apr. 24, 1954; children: Marguerite, Francis Xavier, Sean Michael, Keith John, Cecelia Blanche, Christopher Thomas. AB cum laude, St. Francis Coll., Bklyn., 1951; LLB, Columbia U., 1954. Bar: N.Y. 1955, Mich. 1963, Calif. 1974, Pa. 1975. Assoc. Cravath, Swaine & Moore, N.Y.C., 1956-62; sr. atty. Ford Motor Co., 1962-64, asst. gen. counsel, 1970-72; v.p., gen. counsel, sec. Philco-Ford Corp., 1964-72; v.p., gen. counsel Atlantic Richfield Co., 1972-73, sr. v.p., gen. counsel, 1973-94. Editor Columbia U. Law Rev., 1954. Decorated commendatore Ordine al Merito (Italy); Stone scholar Columbia U., 1954. Mem. Calif. Club, Chancery Club, City Club, Annandale Golf Club. Home and Office: 975 Singingwood Dr Arcadia CA 91006-1924

MC CORMACK, FRED ALLEN, state social services administrator; b. Bklyn., June 10, 1930; s. Frank J. and Rhea (Del Castro) Mc C.; m. Ellen Anne Lockwood, June 19, 1954 (div.); children: Mary Lee, Lynn Anne, Rosemarie, Fred A., Julie Ellen, Rhea Michelle, Claire Eileen; m. Elin Howe, Jan. 1994. BS, Seton Hall U., 1953; MSW, U. Conn., 1955. Social worker Montrose (N.Y.) VA Hosp., 1955-61; adminstr., dir. Tappan Zee Mental Health Ctr., North Tarrytown, N.Y., 1957-62; supr. social worker Orange County Mental Health Clinic, Goshen, N.Y., 1961-62; dir. Sweetwater Counseling Svc., Rock Springs, Wyo., 1962-65; asst. supt., dir. geriatric program Manteno (Ill.) State Hosp., 1965-68; dir. Tacoma Comprehensive Mental Health Ctr., 1968-69; cons. Dept. Instns. Wash., 1968-69, Laurel Haven Sch., Ballwin, Mo., 1977-78; supt. W.G. Murray Children's Ctr., Centralia, Ill., 1969-71, Elisabeth Ludeman Ctr., Park Forest, Ill., 1971-76; dir. San Luis Valley Mental Health Ctr., Alamosa, Colo., 1976-77, Monroe Devel. Ctr., Rochester, N.Y., 1977-80, Suffolk Devel. Ctr., Melville, N.Y., 1980-85; assoc. commr. N.Y. State Office Mental Retardation and Devel. Disabilities, Albany, 1985-93; ret., 1993; part-time tchr. Western Wyo. Jr. Coll., 1963-65, Prairie State Coll., Chicago Heights, Ill., 1965-68, Green River C.C., 1968-69; instr. Adams State Coll., Alamosa, 1977; cons. Snohomish Community Action Coun., Everett, Wash., 1969. Past mem. citizens adv. bd. Sch. Dist. 162, Matteson, Ill.; chmn. Park Forest Sr. Citizens Commn.; past bd. dirs. Gavin Found., Park Forest; bd. dirs. Jones Community Ctr., Chicago Heights; chmn. State Employees Federated Appeal, United Way Rochester, 1979-80, L.I., 1984-85. Recipient cert. of merit Nat. Assn. Physically Handicapped, Dir. of Yr. award N.Y. State Family Care Providers Assn., 1984. Fellow Am. Assn. Mental Deficiency (pres. Ill. chpt. 1972); mem. NASW, Acad. Cert. Social Workers. Home: 1408 Myers Hollow Prescott AZ 86301

MCCORMACK, JOHN JOSEPH, JR., insurance executive; b. Morristown, N.J., Aug. 22, 1944; s. John Joseph and Marion Loretta (Smith) McC.; m. Judith Gail Harvey, July 20, 1968; children—Brendan, Matthew, Margaret. B.B.A., St. Bonaventure U., 1966. Group underwriter Tchrs. Ins. and Annuity Assn.-Coll. Retirement Equities Fund, N.Y.C., 1966-71, benefit plan counselor, 1971-72, asst. adv. officer, 1972-73, adv. officer, 1973-74,

asst. v.p., 1974-75, 2d v.p., 1975-78, v.p., 1978-80, sr. v.p., 1980-83, exec. v.p., 1983—; trustee Am. Psychol. Assn. Ins. Trust, Washington, 1980-90, chmn., 1985-86, trustee investment com., 1990—; trustee Employee Benefit Research Inst., Washington, 1983—, treas., 1986-90. Mem. pres.'s coun. St. Bonaventure U., 1986—, chmn., 1985-89; bd. visitors Ctr. for Study Future Mgmt., 1987-92; trustee Coll. and Univ. Pers. Assn. Found., 1992-94; bd. govs. Investment Co. Inst., 1994—. Roman Catholic. Office: Tchrs Ins & Annuity Assn Am 730 3rd Ave New York NY 10017-3206

MCCORMACK, PATRICIA SEGER, independent press service editor, journalist; b. Pitts., June 11, 1927; d. Arthur John and Anne Irene (McCaffrey) Seger; m. Donald P. McCormack, Apr. 28, 1951; 1 son, Christopher Paul. B.A., U. Pitts., 1949; certificate, U. Mich. internat. Seminar, 1967. News editor weekly newspapers Mt. Lebanon, Pa., 1950-52; med. editor Pitts. Sun Telegraph, 1952-57; med. sci. editor INS, N.Y.C., 1958-59; columnist, family, health and edn. editor UPI, 1959-84, sr. editor, 1987-90. Mem. Boy of Year selection com. Boys Clubs Am., 1966; mem. Coty Fashion award jury, 1965-72, nat. selection com. Century III Leader Scholarship Competition Nat. Assn. Secondary Sch. Prins., 1986. Recipient Biennial Media award Family Service Assn. Am., 1965, Freedom Found. medal; 1st place Sci. Writing award Am. Dental Assn., 1976; Nat. Media award United Negro Coll. Fund, 1977; John Swett award for disting. educating reporting Calif. Edn. Assn., 1981. Mem. AAAS, Nat. Assn. Sci. Writers (life), Edn. Writers Assn., Women's Forum Inc. (N.Y.C.), Nat. Fedn. Press Women (Comm. Achievement medal 1993), Conn. Press Club (v.p., Communicator of Achievement 1993), Conn. Women's Forum. Home and Office: PO Box 3539 Westport CT 06880-2924

MCCORMACK, RICHARD THOMAS FOX, government official; b. Bradford, Pa., Mar. 6, 1941; s. C.H. and Ruth N. (Fox) McC.; m. Karen L. Hagstrom, Oct. 18, 1980; children: Charlotte Louise, Justin Randall, Elizabeth Caroline. B.A., Georgetown U., 1963; Ph.D., U. Fribourg (Switzerland), 1966. With Peace Corps, 1966-67; sr. staff mem. Pres.' Adv. Council on Exec. Orgn., White House, Washington, 1969-71; with Am. Enterprise Inst., 1975-77; dep. asst. sec. for internat. econ. affairs Dept. Treasury, 1974; mem. staff U.S. Senate, 1979-81; asst. sec. state for econ. and bus. affairs U.S. Dept. State, Washington, 1982-85; ambassador Orgn. Am. States U.S. Dept. State, 1985-89, undersec. of state for econ. affairs, 1989-91; candidate in primary elections for U.S. Congress, 1972, 74; cons. Office Telecommunications Policy, 1971, Coun. on Internat. Econ. Policy, 1972, Office Spl. Trade Rep., 1975, Exec. Office of the Pres., Washington; guest scholar Woodrow Wilson Ctr. Smithsonian Instn., Washington, 1991-92; bus. advisor Am. companies, cons. U.S. Govt. on Internat. Econ. Affairs, 1992—. Author: Asians in Kenya, 1971, Managing Japan's Financial Crisis, 1992. Recipient Superior Honor award Dept. State, 1987, Sec. of State's Disting. Svc. award, 1991; decorated Legion of Honor (France). Republican. Home: 1601 Waldon Dr McLean VA 22101 Office: Ste 800 818 Connecticut Ave NW Washington DC 20006

MCCORMACK, ROBERT CORNELIUS, investment banker; b. N.Y.C., Nov. 7, 1939; m. Mary Lester, Dec. 14, 1963; children: Robert Cornelius Jr., Walter, Scott. BA, U. N.C., 1962; MBA, U. Chgo., 1965. V.p. Dillon Read & Co. Inc., 1968-81; mng. dir. Morgan Stanley & Co., Inc., Chgo., 1981-87; dep. asst sec. def. prodn. support U.S. Dept. Def., Washington, 1987-88, dep. under sec. def. indsl. and internat. programs, 1988-89; acting dep. under sec. of def. acquisition U.S. Dept. Def., 1989-90; asst. sec. Navy fin. mgmt. U.S. Dept. Def., Washington, 1990-93; founding ptnr. Trident Capital Inc., Chgo., 1993—. Served to lt. USNR, 1963-66. Office: Trident Capital Inc 141 W Jackson Blvd Fl 29 Chicago IL 60604-2904

MCCORMACK, THOMAS JOSEPH, publishing company executive; b. Boston, Jan. 5, 1932; s. Thomas Joseph and Lena Carolyn (Allen) McC.; m. Sandra Harriet Danenberg, Aug. 21, 1964; children: Daniel Aaron, Jed Charles (dec.), Jessie Ann. Student, U. Conn., 1950-51; A.B. summa cum laude (James Manning scholar), Brown U., 1954; postgrad. (G.H. Palmer scholar, Woodrow Wilson fellow), Harvard U., 1956. Writer radio news WSTC, Stamford, Conn., 1957-59; editor Doubleday & Co., Inc., N.Y.C., 1959-64, Harper & Row, N.Y.C., 1964-67; edn. editor New Am. Library, N.Y.C., 1967-69; dir. trade dept. St. Martin's Press, N.Y.C., 1969-70; pres. St. Martin's Press, 1970-87, chmn., chief exec. officer, editorial dir.; pres., chmn. bd. St. James Press, Ltd., London, 1973-79; dir. Macmillan Ltd., London, Prudential-Bache Govt. Securities Trust; dir. Prudential-Bache High Yield Mcpls., Inc., Prudential-Bache Tax Free Money Fund, Inc., Prudential-Bache High Yield Fund, Inc.; dir. Chancellor New Decade Growth Fund, Inc.; v.p., treas. Sandra D. McCormack, Inc. (Interior Designer.); dir. Pan Books, London; chmn., chief exec. officer Tor Books, N.Y.C.; Author: Afterwords, Novelists on Their Novels, 1969, The Fiction Editor, the Novel and the Novelist, 1988; (play) American Roulette, 1969. Served with AUS, 1954-56. Mem. Assn. Am. Pubs. (dir. 1973-76), Phi Beta Kappa. Clubs: The Players (N.Y.C.), Century Assn. (N.Y.C.). Home: 50 Central Park W New York NY 10023-6028 Office: St Martin's Press Inc 175 Fifth Ave New York NY 10010-7703

MCCORMACK, WILLIAM ARTHUR, lawyer; b. Rochester, N.Y., Sept. 18, 1951; s. Austin Francis and June Ann (Doyle) McC. AB in Polit. Sci. magna cum laude, St. Louis U., 1973; cert., Sorbonne, Paris, 1974; JD, Georgetown U., 1977. Bar: Tex. 1978, D.C. 1979. Assoc. Crutcher, Hull, et al., Dallas, 1977-82; assoc. Hughes & Luce, Dallas, 1982-83, ptnr., 1983—; mem. mgmt. com., exec. com., sect. head, 1993—; mem. adv. com. Mgmt. Inst. Ctr. for Non-profit Mgmt.; bd. dirs. Engles Capital Corp., McCormack Corp.; speaker and author on legal topics. Contbr. articles to profl. jours. Bd. dirs. Alliance Francaise Found., Dallas, Jesuit Found., Dallas Epilepsy Found., pres., 1992, St. Anthony's Sch.; bd. advisors Jesuit Prep., Dallas, St. Anthony's Sch., Bus. Com. for the Arts, Dallas; coun. mem. leadership and patron campaigns circle ten coun. Boy Scouts Am. Mem. ABA, State Bar Assn. Tex. (chmn. minority com.), Dallas Bar Assn. (chmn. legal ethics com., mem. minority commn.), Pi Sigma Alpha, Alpha Sigma Nu. Roman Catholic. Office: Hughes and Luce 1717 Main St Dallas TX 75201-4605

MCCORMICK, BARNES WARNOCK, aerospace engineering educator; b. Waycross, Ga., July 15, 1926; s. Barnes Warnock and Edwina (Brogdon) McC.; m. Emily Joan Hess, July 18, 1946; 1 dau., Cynthia Joan. B.S. in Aero. Engring, Pa. State U., 1948, M.S., 1949, Ph.D., 1954. Research assoc. Pa. State U., University Park, 1949-54, assoc. prof., 1954-55, prof. aero. engring., 1959-92, Boeing prof. aero. engring., 1985-92, prof. emeritus, cons., 1992—, head dept. aerospace engring., 1969-85; assoc. prof., chmn. aero. dept. Wichita U., 1958-59; chief aerodynamics Vertol Helicopter Co., 1955-58; mem. Congl. Adv. Com. Aeros., 1984-86; U.S. coord. flight mechanics panel Adv. Group for Aerospace R&D, 1988—; cons. to industry. Author: Aerodynamics of V/Stol Flight, 1967, Aerodynamics, Aeronautics and Flight Mechanics, 1979, 2d edit. 1995; contbr. articles to profl. jours. Served with USNR, 1944-46. Recipient joint award for achievement in aerospace edn. Am. Soc. Engring. Edn.-Am. Inst. Aeros. and Astronautics, 1976. Fellow Am. Inst. Aeros. and Astronautics (assoc.); mem. ASEE, Am. Helicopter Soc. (tech. council, hon. fellow), Sigma Xi, Sigma Gamma Tau, Tau Beta Pi. Club: Masons. Patentee in field. Home: 611 Glenn Rd State College PA 16803-3475 Office: Pa State U Coll Engring University Park PA 16802

MCCORMICK, CHARLES PERRY, JR., food products company executive; b. Balt., May 29, 1928; s. Charles P. and Marion (Hinds) McM.; m. Marlene Darby Hicks, July 29, 1950 (div. 1980); children: Charles P. III, William C., Linda M., Gail P.; m. Jimi Helen Faulk, July 1, 1980. Student, Johns Hopkins U., 1946-47, Duke U., 1948-49; D Bus. Administration (hon.), Johnson and Wales U., 1991. V.p. new products McCormick Co., Inc., Hunt Valley, Md., 1964-75, v.p. corp. devel., 1975-81, v.p. packaging group, 1985-87, pres., chief exec. officer, 1987-88, chmn., chief exec. officer, 1988-93, chmn. bd., 1994—; chmn., pres. Setco, Inc., Anaheim, Calif., 1981-87, Tubed Products Inc., Easthampton, Mass., 1985-87. Mem. Annapolis Yacht Club, Hunt Valley Golf Club, Sailfish Point Yacht, Sailfish Point Golf Club. Republican. Avocations: sailing, racing, golf, tennis. Office: McCormick & Co Inc 18 Loveton Cir Sparks MD 21152-9202

MCCORMICK, DONALD BRUCE, biochemist, educator; b. Front Royal, Va., July 15, 1932; s. Jesse Allen and Elizabeth (Hord) McC.; m. Norma

Jean Dunn, June 6, 1955; children: Susan Lynn, Donald Bruce, Michael Allen. B.A., Vanderbilt U., 1953, Ph.D., 1958; postdoctoral fellow, U. Calif., Berkeley, 1958-60. Asst. prof. Cornell U., 1960-63, assoc. prof., 1963-69, prof. nutrition, biochemistry and molecular biology, biol. scis., 1969-79, Liberty Hyde Bailey prof. nutritional biochemistry, 1978-79; chmn. dept. biochemistry Emory U., Atlanta, 1979-94, Fuller E. Callaway prof. biochemistry, 1979—; exec. assoc. dean sci. Emory U. Sch. Medicine, 1985-89; vis. lectr. U. Ill, 1963; Wellcome vis. prof. U. Fla., 1986, Med. Coll. Pa., 1989; Hurley lectr. U. Calif., Davis, 1992; O'Dell lectr. U. Mo., Columbia, 1993; biochem. cons. Interdeptl. Com. on Nutrition for Nat. Def., Spain, 1958; mem. and chmn. nutrition study sect. NIH, 1977-81; mem. diet and health com., dietary guidelines implementation com., vice chmn. food and nutrition bd. NRC, Inst. Medicine, NAS; exec. com., chmn. dept. med. biochemistry, Council Acad. Soc., Am. Assn. Med. Colls., 1984-87. Author: (with others) Spain: Nutrition Survey of the Armed Forces, 1958, Molecular Associations in Biology, 1968, Flavins and Flavin Enzymes, 1968, Flavins and Flavoproteins, 1980, 82, 84, 88, 91, Comprehensive Biochemistry, Vol. 21, 1971, Riboflavin, 1974, Metal Ions in Biological Systems, Vol. 1, 1974, Present Knowledge in Nutrition, 6th edit., 1990, Natural Sulphur Compounds, 1979, Vitamin B6, Metabolism and Role in Growth, 1980, Ann. Rev. of Nutrition, Vol. 1, 1981, Vol. 9, 1989, Mechanisms of Enzymatic Reactions: Stereochemistry, 1986, Chemical and Biological Aspects of Vitamin B6 Catalysis, Part A, 1984, Biochemistry of Vitamin B6, 1987, Textbook of Clinical Chemistry, 1987, 94, Modern Nutrition in Health and Disease, 1988, 94, New Trends in Biological Chemistry, 1990, Chemistry and Biochemistry of Flavins, 1991, Encyclopedia of Human Biology, 1991, Liver, 1994; editor: Vitamins and Hormones, Vitamins and Coenzymes. Recipient award Bausch and Lomb, 1950, award Mead Johnson, 1970, award Osborne and Mendel, 1978, award Ga. Nutrition Coun., 1989; Westinghouse Sci. scholar, 1950; fellow NIH, 1957-58, 58-60; Guggenheim fellow, 1966-67. Fellow AAAS; mem. Am. Soc. Biochemistry and Molecular Biology, Am. Inst. Nutrition (pres. 1991), Soc. Exptl. Biology and Medicine, Am. Chem. Soc., Am. Inst. Biol. Sci., Biophysics Soc., Fedn. Am. Socs. Exptls. Biology (bd. dirs., scientific steering group), Microbiol. Soc., Photobiol. Soc., N.Y. Acad. Sci., Protein Soc., Sigma Xi. Home: 2245 Deer Ridge Dr Stone Mountain GA 30087-1129 Office: Emory U Dept Biochemistry Atlanta GA 30322

MCCORMICK, DONALD E., librarian, archivist; b. Hartford, Conn., 1941. BA, Trinity Coll., 1963; MLS, Columbia U., 1967. Drama libr. N.Y. Pub. Libr., N.Y.C., 1965-72, sound recording libr., 1972-73, asst. chief libr., 1973-85, sound archive curator, 1985—. Mem. Assn. Recorded Sound Colls. (past pres. 1988-90), Assoc. Audio Archives (chmn. 1990-94), Music Libr. Assn. Office: NY Libr for Performing Arts Rodgers & Hammerstein Archives 40 Lincoln Center Plz New York NY 10023-7498

MCCORMICK, DOUGLAS WALTER, cable, broadcast executive; b. N.Y.C., Dec. 15, 1949; s. Howard George and Hazel Frances (Sullivan) McC.; m. Karen J. Lane, Dec. 9, 1980; children: Douglas Jr., Luke Patrick. BA, U. Dayton; MBA, Columbia U., 1990. Rsch analyst TeleRep, Inc., L.A., 1970; account exec. Sta. KCOP-TV, L.A., 1970-71, Petry TV, N.Y.C., 1971-80; composer, staff writer The Entertainment Co., N.Y.C., 1980-82; v.p. ea. sales, mgr. Lifetime Cable TV, N.Y.C., 1982-85; v.p. TV sales The Samuel Goldwyn Co., L.A., 1985-86; sr. v.p. sales Lifetime TV Network, LLA., 1986-90, exec. v.p., 1990-95, pres., CEO, 1995—. Composer popular songs for artists including Paul Anka, Gladys Knight, Dusty Springfield, others. Bd. dirs. Parent Action. Mem. Internat. Radio and TV Soc. (bd. dirs.), Nat. Acad. Cable Programming. Office: Lifetime TV Network 36-12 35th Ave Astoria NY 11106*

MC CORMICK, EDWARD ALLEN, foreign language educator; b. Fairfax County, Va., July 1, 1925; s. Jesse Allen and Elizabeth (Hord) McC.; m. Diana Festa, Mar. 1, 1952 (div. Aug. 1973); children: Allen Sergio, Marco Kevin, Carlo Brian; m. Marie Parrice, Apr. 2, 1974 (div. Apr. 1980); m. Phyllis van Slyck, June 10, 1980 (div. May 1985); 1 son, Andrew Stuart; m. Ping Tsai, Mar. 19, 1993. A.B., Randolph-Macon Coll., 1948; Ph.D., U. Berne, Switzerland, 1951; M.A. (hon.), Dartmouth, 1965. Instr. German Princeton U., 1952, asst. prof. German, 1954-58; instr. German U. Mich., 1952-53, Harvard U., 1953-54; asst. prof. German Brown U., 1958-59; mem. faculty Dartmouth, 1959—; prof. German, German and comparative lit., dir. comparative lt. Queens Coll., CUNY, 1966-70; prof. German and comparative lit. Queens Coll., CUNY (Grad. Ctr.) 1970—, exec. officer comparative lit., 1970-74, exec. officer German, 1980-92; retired, 1992. Author: Whitman's Leaves of Grass in deutscher Übertragung, 1953, (with F.G. Ryder) Lebendige Literatur, 1960, 2d edit., 1974, 3d edit., 1986, Theodor Storm's Novellen, 1964; editor: Lessing's Laokoon, 1962, (J.E. Schlegel) On Imitation, 1965, Germans in America, 1983; also articles in jours., encys. Served with 82d Airborne Div. AUS, 1943-46, ETO. Recipient Princeton Bicentennial Preceptorship, 1954-58; Dartmouth Faculty fellow, 1963. Mem. MLA, Am. Comparative Lit. Assn., Am. Assn. Tchrs. German. Home: 309 Calzada de Bougainvilla Marathon FL 33050

MCCORMICK, EDWARD JAMES, JR., lawyer; b. Toledo, May 11, 1921; s. Edward James and Josephine (Beck) McC.; m. Mary Jane Blank, Jan. 27, 1951; children: Mary McCormick Krueger, Edward James III, Patrick William, Michael J. B.S., John Carroll U., 1943; J.D., Western Res. U., 1948. Bar: Ohio 1948, U.S. Supreme Ct. 1980. Mem. teaching staff St. Vincent Hosp. Sch. Nursing, 1951-67. Pvt. practice 1948—; Trustee Toledo Small Bus. Assn., 1950-75, pres., 1954-55, 56-58, 67-68; trustee Goodwill Industries Toledo, 1961-74, chmn. meml. gifts com., mem. exec. com., 1965-70; trustee Lucas County unit Am. Cancer Soc., 1950-61, sec., 1953, v.p., 1954-56, pres., 1957-58; founder, incorporator, sec., trustee Cancer Cytology Research Fund Toledo, Inc., 1956-79; trustee Ohio Cerebral Palsy Assn., 1963-70; incorporator, sec., trustee N.W. Ohio Clin. Engring. Ctr., 1972-74; trustee Friendly Ctr., 1973-83, Ohio Blind Assn., 1970-79; founder-incorporator, trustee, sec. Western Lake Erie Hist. Soc., 1978-85; mem. Toledo Deanery Diocesan Coun. Cath. Men; asst. gen. counsel U.S. Power and Sail Squadrons; life mem. China, Burma and India Vets. Assn., Inc. 1st lt. U.S. Army, 1942-46, USAR, 1946-52. Named Outstanding Young Man of Yr., Toledo Jr. C. of C., 1951; Man of Nation, Woodmen of World, Omaha, 1952. Fellow Ohio State Assn.; mem. ABA, Ohio Bar Assn. (chmn. Am. citizenship com. 1958-67, mem. pub. rels. com. 1967-72, estate planning, probate and trust law com.), Toledo Bar Assn. (chmn. pub. rels. com. 1979, mem. grievance com. 1974-92, chmn. probate, estate planning and trust law com. 1986-90, Disting. Svc. award in memory Robert A. Kelb, Esq. 1993), Lucas County Bar Assn. (chmn. Am. citizenship com.), Am. Trial Lawyers Am., Am. Judicature Soc., Am. Arbitration Assn., Conf. Pvt. Orgns. (sec.-treas.), Toledo C. of C, Toledo Yacht Club (mem. com. 1970-71), Toledo Torch Club, Blue Gavel, Elks (grand esteemed leading knight 1964-65, mem. grand forum 1965-70), Lions (trustee, legal advisor Ohio Eye Research Found. 1956-70; pres. 1957-58, chmn. permanent membership com. 1961-85, hon. mem. 1984, pres. 1957, A.B. Snyder award 1979), Ky. Col. Office: PO Box 1336 Toledo OH 43603-1336

MCCORMICK, EUGENE F., JR., transportation company executive; b. Chgo., 1942; m. Patricia Landini; children: James, Matthew, Erin. Grad., U.S. Mcht. Marine Acad., 1964; MS, Northwestern U., Evanston, Ill., 1969. From deck officer to chief officer Lykes Bros. Steamship Co., Inc., New Orleans, 1964-68, mgr. mktg. services, 1969-72, dep. dir. traffic and ops. for SEABEE vessel, 1972-74, asst. v.p. div. pricing, 1974-77, asst. v.p. fin., 1977-79, sr. v.p. fin., chief fin. officer, 1979-82, pres., chief operating officer, 1986—, also bd. dirs.; founder Interocean Steamship Corp. parent co., 1982, also bd. dirs.; mem. Transp. Research Forum. Mem. Met. Leadership Forum; bd. dirs. USF&G Golf Classic. Serving as lt. comdr. USNR. Recipient Outstanding Achievement award U.S. Mcht. Marine Acad., 1979. Mem. Fin. Execs. Inst., Council Am.-Flag Ship Operators (chair fin. officers' com.), Navy League, U.S. Mcht. Marine Acad. Alumni Assn. (past pres. New Orleans chpt.). Avocations: golf, coaching baseball. Office: 300 Poydras St New Orleans LA 70130-3200 also: Dept Transp Fed Hwy Adminstrn 400 7th St SW Washington DC 20590-0001

MCCORMICK, FLOYD GUY, JR., agricultural educator, college administrator; b. Center, Colo., July 3, 1927; s. Floyd Guy and Gladys (Weir) McC.; m. Constance P. Slane, Sept. 18, 1965; children: Angela Lynn, Craig Alan, Kim Ann, Robert Guy. BS, Colo. State U., 1950, MEd, 1959; PhD, Ohio State U., 1964. Tchr. vocat. agr. State of Colo., 1956-62; asst. prof. agrl.

edn. Ohio State U., 1964-67; mem. com. agr. edn. com. edn. in agr. and natural resources Nat. Acad. Scis., 1967-69; prof. agrl. edn., head dept. U. Ariz., 1967-89, prof. emeritus, dept. head emeritus, 1990—; cons. in-svc. edn., div. vocat. edn. Ohio Dept. Edn., 1963-64; vis. prof. Colo. State U., 1973, U. Sierra Leone, Njala Univ. Coll., 1989; external examiner U. Sierra Leone, 1984, 85, 87; adv. trustee Am. Inst. Cooperatives, Washington, 1985-88; mem. Nat. Coun. Vocat. and Tech. Edn. in Agr., Washington, 1985-88. Co-author: Teacher Education in Agriculture, 1982, Supervised Occupational Experience Handbook, 1982; author: The Power of Positive Teaching, 1994, also instrl. units, tech. bulls., articles in profl. jours.; spl. editor: Agrl. Edn. mag., 1970-74. Trustee Nat. FFA Found. Served with USNR, 1945-46. Named hon. state farmer Colo., 1958, Ariz., 1968, Am. farmer, 1972; recipient Centennial award Ohio State U., 1970, E.B. Knight award NACTA Jour., 1980, Regional Outstanding Tchr. award Nat. Assn. Coll. Tchrs. Agr., 1989, also fellow, 1988, VIP citation Nat. FFA Assn., 1990, Diamond Anniversary award Nat. Vocat. Agr. Assn., 1992. Mem. Am. Vocat Assn. (mem. policy com. agrl. edn. divsn. 1976-79, v.p. divsn. 1985-88, chmn. membership com. 1980-83, sec. agrl. edn. divsn. 1983-86, pres. 1985-88, outstanding svc. awrd 1989), Nat. Vocat. Agr. Tchrs. Assn. (life, Outstanding Svc. award Region I 1974, 83), Am. Assn. Tchr. Educators in Agr. (disting. lectr. 1984, editor newsletter 1975-76, pres. 1976-77, Disting. Svc. award 1978, 88, Rsch. award western region rsch. 1988), Alpha Zeta, Alpha Tau Alpha (hon.), Gamma Sigma Delta, Phi Delta Kappa, Epsilon Pi Tau. Home: 6933 E Paseo San Andres Tucson AZ 85710-2203

MCCORMICK, HUGH THOMAS, lawyer; b. McAlester, Okla., Nov. 24, 1944; s. Hugh O. and Lois (McGucken) McC.; m. Suzanna G. Weingarten, Dec. 5, 1975; 1 child, John B. BA, U. Mich., 1968; JD, Rutgers U., 1977; LLM in Taxation, Georgetown U., 1980. Bar: N.Y. 1977, D.C. 1979, Maine 1981. Atty. office chief counsel interpretative div. IRS, Washington, 1977-81; assoc. Perkins, Thompson, Hinkley & Keddy, Portland, Maine, 1981-83; assoc. LeBoeuf, Lamb, Leiby & MacRae, N.Y.C., 1983-88, counsel, 1989-91; ptnr. LeBoeuf, Lamb, Greene & MacRae, L.L.P., N.Y.C., 1992—; dir. Ins. Tax. Conf., 1993—. Mem. bd. contbrs. and advisors Jour. of Taxation of Investments; contbr. articles to profl. jours. Bd. dirs. Ins. Tax Conf.; trustee U.S. Team Handball Found., N.J., 1985—. Served to 1st lt. U.S. Army, 1966-69. Fellow Am. Bar Found.; mem. ABA (chmn. com. on taxation of ins. cos. 1989, chmn. subcom. sect. of taxation 1989—, mem. torts and ins. practice sect., sect. on taxation), D.C. Bar Assn., N.Y. State Bar Assn. (tax sect., exec. com. 1986-93, co-chmn. ins. co. com. 1986-87, 89-90, co-chmn. fin. intermediaries com. 1990-93, co-chmn. N.Y. State tax matters com. 1988). Democrat. Home: 555 Pelham Manor Rd Pelham Manor NY 10803-2525 Office: LeBoeuf Lamb Greene MacRae LLP 125 W 55th St New York NY 10019-5369

MC CORMICK, JAMES CHARLES, leasing and financial services company executive; b. Cleve., Jan. 23, 1938; s. Michael Patrick and Agnes Christine (Mortensen) McC.; m. Claire A. Maskaly, Nov. 28, 1963 (div. June 1978); children: Kelly, Shannon.; m. Patricia A. Lelko, May 28, 1982. B.S. in Acctg., Regis Coll., Denver, 1960. C.P.A. Accountant Ernst & Ernst, Allentown, Pa., 1963-73; treas. Fuller Co., Catasauqua, Pa., 1973-82; asst. controller GATX Corp., Chgo., 1982-93, dir. internal audit, 1993—. Vol. Chgo. council Boy Scouts Am. Served with USNR, 1960-63. Mem. AICPA, Fin. Execs. Inst. Home: 835 Arbor Ln Glenview IL 60025-3233

MCCORMICK, JAMES CLARENCE, business consultant; b. Kaufman, Tex., Oct. 5, 1924; s. Clarence Snow and Mabel Ruth (Watkins) McC.; m. Barbara Louise Ostling, Jan. 12, 1947; children: Richard, Sharon, Patricia, Michael, Kelly. B.S., B.B.A., So. Meth. U., 1949. Reporter Dun and Bradstreet, Dallas, 1949-55; with Eppler, Guerin & Turner, Inc., Dallas, 1955-87, vice chmn. bd., 1980-82, gen. dir., 1982-87, mem. exec. com.; pvt. practice bus. cons. Dallas, 1987—; Author: The Stone Bruise. Mem. bd. advisors Southwestern Bapt. Theol. Sem.; past bd. dirs. Dallas Soc. for Crippled Children, Meth. Bd. for Ch. Ext., Tex. Lit. Bd., Dallas Orthopaedic Found., Family Shelter, YMCA, Salvation Army. Lt. USAAF, 1942-46. Named Disting. Alumni So. Meth. U., 1994. Mem. Nat. Fin. Analysts Fedn., Air Force Assn., Alpha Kappa Psi, Beta Gamma Sigma. Home: 14145 Valley Creek Dr Dallas TX 75240-2724

MCCORMICK, JAMES EDWARD, oil company executive; b. Providence, Nov. 5, 1927; s. James Edward and Edna Josephine (Smith) McC.; m. Catherine Sullivan, Aug. 30, 1952. AB in Geology, Boston U., 1952. Engr. trainee Sun Oil Co., Beaumont, Tex., 1953-54; jr. geologist Sun Oil Co., Houston, 1954-67, exploration mgr., 1967-70; regional mgr. geology Sun Oil Co., Dallas, 1970-71, exploration program mgr., 1971-74, div. mgr. strategy planning, 1974-77, v.p. internat. exploration and prodn., 1977-86, pres. exploration and prodn., 1986-88; pres. Oryx Energy, Dallas, 1988-92; bd. dirs. Petrolite Corp., St. Louis, Tex. Commerce Bank, B.J. Svcs. Co., Lone Star Tech., Dallas, Snyder Oil Co., Ft. Worth, Tex. Bd. dirs. United Way Met. Dallas, 1986-92; mem. Dallas Citizens Council, 1986-88. Served as sgt. USAF, 1945-48. Mem. Am. Assn. Petroleum Geologists, N.Y. Acad. Scis., Nat. Ocean Industries Assn. (bd. dirs. 1986-92), Northwood Country Club, Las Colinas Country Club, Energy Club, Dallas Petroleum Club. Roman Catholic. Clubs: Northwood Country, Las Colinas Country. Office: McCormick Enterprises 5949 Sherry Ln # 98 Dallas TX 75225-6532

MCCORMICK, JAMES HAROLD, academic administrator; b. Indiana, Pa., Nov. 11, 1938; s. Harold Clark and Mary Blanche (Truby) McCormick; m. Maryan Kough Garner, June 7, 1963; children: David Harold, Douglas Paul. BS, Indiana U. of Pa., 1959; MEd, U. Pitts., 1961, EdD, 1963, postdoctoral, 1966; postdoctoral, Columbia U., U. Mich., 1966-67, Harvard U., 1982. Tchr. Punxsutawney (Pa.) Area Joint Sch. Dist., 1959-61; adminstr. Baldwin-Whitehall Schs., Pitts., 1961-64; grad. asst. U. Pitts., 1962-63; asst. supt. instrn. Washington (Pa.) City Schs., 1964-65; prof. dept. edn. and psychology, asst. dean acad. affairs, acting dean acad. affairs, acting dean tchr. edn., asst. to pres., v.p. adminstrn. and fin. Shippensburg (Pa.) U., 1965-73; pres. Bloomsburg (Pa.) U., 1973-83, pres. emeritus, 1983—; chancellor Pa. State System Higher Edn., Harrisburg, 1983—; Falk intern in politics, 1959; mem. adv. bd. Pa. Ednl. Policy Seminar, Nat. Ctr. for Study Sport in Soc.; mem. Gov.'s Econ. Devel. Partnership Bd.; mem. higher edn. adv. coun. pa. State Bd. Edn.; past commr. Edn. Commn. of the States. Contbr. articles profl. jours. Named One of 10 Outstanding Young Men of Yr., Pa. Jr. C. of C.; recipient Young Leader in Edn. award Phi Delta Kappa, 1981, Disting. Alumnus award Indiana U. Pa., 1981, Outstanding Alumni award Bloomsburg U., 1984, Outstanding Alumnus award U. Pitts., 1985, Adler award Pa. Sch. Admins., 1992. Mem. Am. Assn. State Colls. and Univs. (Pa. state rep. 1988-93, former chmn. acad. and student pers. com., mem. com. on state rels. and task force on ednl. equity), Am. Coun. on Edn. (commn. on women in higher edn.), Nat. Assn. Sys. Heads, (exec. com., past pres.), Commn. State Colls. and Univs. (mem. and past chmn. govt. rels. and student rels. coms.), Assn. Governing Bds. (adv. coun.), Am. Assn. for Affirmative Action, Am. Assn. Higher Edn., Am. Assn. Sch. Admnstrs., Am. Assn. Univ. Adminstrs. (Tosney Leadership award 1993), Pa. Assn. Colls. and Univs. (bd. dirs.), Pers. Assn., Bloomsburg Area C. of C. (pres. 1983), Rotary (bd. dirs. through 1993), Urban League Harrisburg (bd. dirs. through 1992), Phi Delta Kappa. Presbyterian. Home: PO Box 28 Lemoyne PA 17043-0028 Office: Pa State Sys Higher Edn Dixon Univ Ctr 2986 N 2d St Harrisburg PA 17110

MCCORMICK, JAMES HILLMAN, retired broadcast executive; b. Montgomery, Ala., Sept. 10, 1921; s. James Hillman and Odessa (Garrett) McC.; m. Myra Sage, May 20, 1945; children: James Hillman III, Carol. BA in Cinema, U. So. Calif., 1947; postgrad., So. Meth. U., 1974. Theatre mgr. Malco Theatres, Memphis, 1940-41; prodn. asst. So. Film Svc. U. Ga., Athens, Ga., 1947-48; sales exec. Columbia Pictures, Atlanta, 1948-50, Warner Bros., Atlanta, 1950-54; Memphis mgr., Atlanta mgr., ea. sales mgr. CBS, N.Y., 1954-64; division mgr. CBS, Dallas, 1964-71; v.p. Viacom Internat., Dallas, 1971-86; prin. James H. McCormick Broadcast Counselor, Dallas, 1986-89; bd. dirs. Tex. Enfield, Inc., Victoria, 1989-91; mem. v.p. Colosseum Motion Picture Salesmen, 1953-54; mem. founding group which established Viacom as world leader in comms. and entertainment, 1971-86; prodn. mgr. The School That Learned to Eat; bd. mem. Assn. Broadcasting Execs. Tex., 1967. Author: Smart Selling, 1948. Charter mem. Lowboy Hall of Fame, Western Heritage Ctr., Oklahoma City, 1965—; mem. Dallas Mus. Art, 1967—; mem. Tex. State Hist. Assn. Recipient Lifetime Achievement award TV Program Conf., 1986, Rep. Presdl. Legion of Merit, 1993, U.S.

Documentary Film award Edinburgh Film Festival, 1948. Mem. Acad. TV Arts and Scis., Internat. Radio and TV Soc., Nat. Assn. TV Program Execs. (charter), Tex. Assn. Broadcasters, TV Program Conf. (bd. dirs. 1968-69), Cinema Circulus, Broadcast Pioneers, Northwood Club, Kiwanis Internat., Alpha Delta Sigma, Delta Kappa Alpha, Pi Kappa Alpha. Republican. Presbyterian. Avocations: oil painting, tennis, western art. Home: 7318 Kenshire Ln Dallas TX 75230-2432 Office: PO Box 515987 Dallas TX 75251-5987

MCCORMICK, JAMES MICHAEL, management consultant; b. Arlington, Va., Dec. 12, 1947; s. James J. and Emma H. (Fisher) McC.; m. Marsha E. Durham, 1971; 1 child, James M. McCormick Jr. BS with distinction, Cornell U., 1969, M in Engring. and Ops. Research with distinction, 1970. Mem. tech. staff Bell Telephone Labs., Holmdel, N.J., 1968-73; div. head, planning N.Y. Stock Exchange, N.Y.C., 1973-75; engagement mgr. McKinsey & Co., N.Y.C., 1975-77; v.p. ROI Cons., N.Y.C., 1977-80; pres. First Manhattan Cons. Group, N.Y.C., 1980—; cons. various U.S. banks, investment banks and fin. instns., 1975—; speaker various profl. assn. meetings. Club: Larchmont (N.Y.) Yacht. Avocations: boating, auto racing, photography. Office: First Manhattan Cons Group 90 Park Ave New York NY 10016

MCCORMICK, JOHN OWEN, retired comparative literature educator; b. Thief River Falls, Minn., Sept. 20, 1918; s. Owen Charles and Marie Antoinette Beauchemin (Smith) McC.; m. Helen Manuel, 1942; m. Mairi Clare MacInnes, 1954; children: Jonathan, Peter, Antoinette, Fergus. B.A. magna cum laude, U. Minn., 1941; M.A., Harvard U., 1947, Ph.D., 1951. Dean, lectr. Salzburg Seminar in Am. Studies, 1951-52; lectr., prof. Free U. Berlin, 1952-59; prof. comparative lit. Rutgers U., 1959-87, prof. emeritus, 1987—; vis. prof. Nat. U. Mexico, 1961-62, Hachioji (Tokyo) seminar, 1979; Christian Gauss Seminar lectr. Princeton, 1969; resident fellow Sch. Letters of Ind. U., 1970. Author: The Middle Distance: a Comparative History of American Imaginative Literature, 1919-32, 1971, The Complete Aficionado, 1967, (with Mairi MacInnes McCormick) Versions of Censorship, 1962, Der moderne amerikanische Roman, 1960, Amerikanische Lyrik, 1957, Catastrophe and Imagination, 1957, Fiction as Knowledge, 1975, George Santayana: A Biography, 1987, Wolfe, Malraux, Hesse, 1987. Served with USNR, 1941-46. Recipient prize for non-fiction Longview Found., 1960, Am. Acad. and Inst. Arts and Letters award, 1988; Gugenheim fellow, 1964-65, 79-80, Bruern fellow Leeds (Eng.) U., 1975-76, NEH fellow, 1983-84, hon. fellow U. York, 1992. Mem. Taurino Club, Harvard Club.

MCCORMICK, KATHLEEN ANN KRYM, geriatrics nurse, federal agency administrator; b. Manchester, N.H., June 27, 1947. BSN, Barry Coll., 1969; MSN, Boston U., 1971; MS, U. Wis., 1975, PhD, 1978. Capt. nurse officer USPHS; COSTEP nurse USPHS, Staten Island, N.Y., 1968; staff nurse, instr. USPHS, Brighton, Mass., 1970; staff nurse Mercy Hosp., Miami, 1969, St. Elizabeth's Hosp., Brighton, 1970-71; clin. nurse specialist Boston U. Hosp., 1970-71; clin. nurse specialist, instr. U. Wis., Madison, 1971-72; asst. rsch. to chief nursing clin. ctr., dept. Nursing NIH, Bethesda, 1978-83; tech. nurse, co-dir. inpatient geriatric continence project, lab. Behavioral Scis., Gerontology Rsch. Ctr. Nat. Inst. Aging, Balt., 1983-88, dir. nursing rsch., 1988-91; dir. office forum quality and effectiveness health care Agy. Health Care Policy and Rsch., Rockville, Md., 1991-93; sr. sci. adviser Agy. Health Care Policy and Rsch., 1993—; adj. asst. prof. U. Calif., U. Washington, 1979, 82; faculty assoc. U. Md., Balt., 1979-81; ad hoc reviewer biomed. rsch. grants NIH, 1979-80, divsn. nursing rsch. and tng. HRA, 1979-82; instr. Found. Advanced Edn. in Scis., 1981-82; exec. com. Bat. Inst. Aging Liaison Ctr. Nursing Rsch., 1986-91; Surgeon Gen.'s rep. Sec. Alzheimer's Task Force, 1989—; Surgeon Gen. alternate to Bd. Regents Nat. Libr. Medicine, 1989—; co-chair panel guidelines for urinary incontinence in adult, 1990-91; speaker. Editor: Nursing Outlook, 1988-90; mem. editorial staff Mil. Medicine, 1985-93; assoc. editor: Internat. Jour. Tech. and Aging, 1985-87. Recipient award Jour. Acad. Sci., 1965, travel award NSF, 1973, J.D. Lane Jr. Investigator award USPHS Profl. Assn., 1979, Excellence in Writing award Nat. League Nursing/Humana, 1983, award Spl. Recognition Rsch., U. Pa. Sch. Nursing, 1986, Federal Svc. Nursing award, 1987, Surgeon Gen.'s medallion, 1989; grantee U. Wis. Grad. Sch., 1977, Upjohn Co., 1977; Queen's Vis. scholar Royal Adelaide (Austrailia) Hosp., 1990. Fellow Am. Acad. Nursing, Royal Coll. Nursing, Coll. Am. Med. Informatics, Gerontology Soc. Am. (clin. med. sect., computer program coord. 1985-87, clin. medicine rep. publs. com., Nurse of Yr. 1992), Nat. Acad. Scis. Inst. Medicine; mem. ANA (sec., editor newsletter coun. nurse rschrs., 1980-85, vice chairperson exec. com. coun. computer applications in nursing, 1984-86), Am. Lung Assn./Am. Thoracic Soc. (cert. appreciation mid.-Mc. chpt. 1982, 83, 84, chairperson 1983-84, nominating com. 1989, nat. rsch. review com.), Am. Assn. Critical Care Nursing (strategic planning com. 1987-89, Disting. Rsch. award 1986), Am. News Women's Club, Internat. Medical Informatics Assn. (working group 8, program com. 1984—), Assn. Mil. Surgeons (sustaining mem. award 1982), Commd. Officers Assn., Met. Area Nursing Rsch. Consortium, Md. Lung Assn. (awards and grants subcom. 1978,92, v.p. exec. bd. bd. dirs. 1980-87), Capital Speakers Club (10 M), Lambda Sigma, Sigma Delta Epsilon (Eloise Gerry grant-in-aid fellow 1979-80), Sigma Theta Tau (grantee 1976). Office: US Agy Health Care Policy Rsch 2101 E Jefferson St Rockville MD 20852

MC CORMICK, KENNETH DALE, retired editor; b. Madison, N.J., Feb. 25, 1906; s. John Dale and Ida Pearl (Wenger) McC.; children: Dale, Kevin; m. Anne Hutchens, 1968; 1 son, John Bradley. A.B., Willamette U., 1928. With Doubleday and Co., Inc., 1930-92, successively clk., mgr., bookshop, promotion mgr. pub. house, reader in editorial dept., chief asso. editor, 1938, editor in chief, 1942-71, v.p., 1948-71, sr. cons. editor, 1971-92; lectr. on books. Contbr. to Publishers' Weekly. Democrat. CongList. Clubs: Century Assn, Coffee House, Dutch Treat. Home: 670 W End Ave New York NY 10025-7313

MCCORMICK, LOYD WELDON, lawyer; b. Wilson, Tex., Dec. 4, 1928; s. Loyd Franklin and Clara Edith (Monroe) M.; m. Jeanne Alyce Welch, Jan. 29, 1956; children: David W., Janet W. McCormick Riley, Kenneth W. BA, U. Calif., Berkeley, 1950, JD, 1956. Bar: Calif. 1956, U.S. Dist. Ct. (no. dist.) Calif. 1956, U.S. Ct. Appeals (9th cir.) 1956, U.S. Supreme Ct. 1971. Assoc. McCutchen, Doyle, Brown & Enersen, San Francisco, 1956-65, ptnr., 1965—; chmn. legal and tax coms. Nat. Coun. Farmer Coops., Washington, 1980-81; mem. adv. bd. Ojai (Calif.) Ranch and Investment Co., 1987-89; lawyer del. 9th Cir. Jud. Conf., San Francisco, 1988-92, chair, 1990; mem. Commn. Calif. Agriculture and Higher Edn., 1993-95. Pres. Young Reps. of Lafayette, Calif., 1964; mem. Calif. State Rep. Cen. Com., 1968. Lt. (j.g.) USN, 1950-53, Korea. Fellow Am. Coll. Trial Lawyers; mem. ABA, Calif. State Bar, Bar Assn. San Francisco, Am. Judicature Soc., Conf. Bd., Phi Delta Phi, Boalt Hall Alumni Assn. (bd. dirs. 1983-86), Pacific Union Club, Orinda Country Club, Commonwealth Club. Episcopalian. Avocations: tennis, golf, gardening, reading, politics. Home: 21 Via Callados Orinda CA 94563-1123

MCCORMICK, LYLE BERNARD, JR., management consultant; b. Charleston, W.Va., May 31, 1944; s. Lyle Bernard Sr. and Beatrice Lee (Haynes) McC.; m. Linda Marie Brandt, Dec. 27, 1968; 1 child, Stephen Lyle. Degree in bus. adminstrn., U. Ctrl. Fla., 1972. Cert. mgmt. cons. With GE Co., Daytona Beach, Fla., 1967-76; cons. Ingersoll Mfg. Consts., Rockford, Ill., 1976-78; project ind. engr. Daniel Constrn. Co. Warm Springs, Va., 1978-79; v.p. Emerson Cons., Inc., N.Y.C., 1979-86; pres. Omega Cons., Inc., DeLand, Fla., 1986—. With U.S. Army, 1965-67. Mem. Inst. Mgmt. Cons. Democrat. Baptist. Avocations: fishing, tennis, golf, bicycling. Office: Omega Cons Inc 980 Cedar Ridge Ln Deland FL 32720

MCCORMICK, MARIE CLARE, pediatrician, educator; b. Haverhill, Mass., Jan. 7, 1946; d. Richard Sims and Clare Bernadine (Keleher) McC.; m. Robert Jay Blendon, Dec. 30, 1977. BA magna cum laude, Emmanuel Coll., 1967; MD, Johns Hopkins Medical Sch., 1971; ScD, Johns Hopkins, 1978; MA, Harvard, 1991. Diplomate Am. Bd. Pediatrics. Pediatric resident, fellow Johns Hopkins Hosp., Balt., 1971-75; rsch. fellow Johns Hopkins Hosp., 1972-75; asst. prof. U. Ill. Schs. Medicine & Pub. Health, Chgo., 1975-76; pediatrics instr. Johns Hopkins Medical Sch., Balt., 1976-78; asst. prof. healthcare orgn. Johns Hopkins Sch. Hygiene & Pub. Health, 1978-81; asst. prof. pediatrics U. Pa., Phila., 1981-86, assoc. prof. pediatrics, 1986-87; assoc. prof. pediatrics Harvard Medical Sch., Boston, 1987-91;

prof., chair. maternal & child health Harvard Sch. Pub. Health, 1992—; prof. pediatrics . Harvard Medical Sch., 1992—; adj. assoc. prof. pediatrics U. Pa. 1987-92; active attending physician, Johns Hopkins Hosp., 1976-81, asst. physician Children's Hosp. Phila., 1981-84, assoc. physician, 1984-86, sr. physician, 1986-87, assoc. pediatrician Brigham & Women's Hosp., 1987, 88—; vis. prof. Wash. U., St. Louis, 1993; editorial bds. Health Svcs. Rsch., 1985—, Pediatrics in Review, 1986-91, Pediatrics, 1993—; adv. coun. Ctr. Perinatal & Family Health Brigham & Women's Hosp., 1991—; cons. to numerous coms., orgns. and bds. Contbr. articles to profl. jours. Adv. The David and Lucile Packard Found., 1993—; bd. dirs. Family Planning Coun. S.E. Pa., 1984-87; chair com. child health Mayor's Commn. Phila., 1982-83. Recipient Henry Strong Denison scholarship in med. rsch. award Johns Hopkins Sch. Medicine, 1971, Leonard Davis Inst. Health Econs. U. Pa. fellow, 1984—, Johns Hopkins U. Soc. Scholars, 1995. Fellow Am. Acad. Pediatrics; mem. Ambulatory Pediatrics Assn., Soc. Pediatric Rsch. (sr.), Am. Pediatric Soc., Am. Pub. Health Assn., Internat. Epidemiological Assn. Am. Assn. Advancement Scis., Assn. Health Svcs. Rsch., Eastern Soc. Pediatric Rsch., Soc. Pediatric Epidemiologic Rsch., Assn. Tchrs. Maternal & Child Health, Mass. Medical Soc., Norfolk Dist. Medical Soc., Brigham & Women's Medical Staff, Mass. Pub. Health Assn., Johns Hopkins Medical & Surgical Assn., John Hopkins U. Soc. Scholars (elected, 1995). Office: Harvard Sch Pub Health 677 Huntington Ave Boston MA 02115

MCCORMICK, MICHAEL, history educator; b. Tonawanda, N.Y., Nov. 7, 1951; s. Jerome Anthony and Barbara Anne (Bowman) Mc.; m. Magda Jabbour, May 21, 1988; 1 child, Thomas Kennedy III. Grad., Cath. U. Louvain, Belgium, 1971, diploma in Medieval History, 1972, PhD, 1979. Rsch. assoc. Dictionary Medieval Latin Belgian Nat. Com., Louvain, 1976-79; rsch. assoc. Byzantine studies Dumbarton Oaks, Washington, 1979-87; from asst. prof. to prof. dept. history Johns Hopkins U., Balt., 1979-91; prof. Harvard U., Cambridge, Mass., 1991—. Author: Les Annales du haut Moyen âge, 1975, Index Scriptorum Operumque Latino-Belgicorum Medii aevi, 1977, vol. 2, 1979, Eternal Victory: XIIe siecle. Triumphal Rulership in Late Antiquity Byzantium and the Early Medieval West, 1986, 500 Unknown Glosses from the Palatine Virgil, 1992; editorial bd. Bulletin Codicologique, 1978-91, Am. Jour. Philology, 1982-88; bd. editors Speculum Anniversary Monographs, 1989-91. Guggenheim Meml. Found. fellow, 1985-86; Am. Coun. Learned Socs. grantee, 1987. Mem. Medieval Acad. Am. Roman Catholic. Office: Harvard U Dept History Robinson Hall Cambridge MA 02138

MCCORMICK, MICHAEL D., lawyer; b. Vincennes, Ind., Mar. 18, 1948; m. Margaret A. McCormick; children: Claire E., Brooks R. AB, Duke U., 1970; JD, Ind. U., 1980. V.p. I & S McDaniel Inc., Vincennes, 1970-77; ptnr. Scopelitis & Garvin, Indpls., 1980-83; pres. Wales Transp. Co., Dallas, 1983-85; v.p., gen. counsel Overland Express Inc., Indpls., 1985-87, Bindley Western Industries Inc., Indpls., 1987—. Mem. ABA, Ind. Bar Assn., Indpls. Bar Assn.

MCCORMICK, MICHAEL JERRY, judge; b. Fort Lewis, Wash., Oct. 17, 1945; s. Thaddeus Charles and Geraldine (Fogle) McC.; m. Kathleen Karen Kelley, Sept. 2, 1967; children: Patrick Kelley, Karen Michelle. BA, U. Tex.-Austin, 1967; JD, St. Mary's U., 1970. Bar: Tex. 1970. Briefing atty. Tex. Ct. Criminal Appeals, 1970-71; asst. dist. atty., Travis County, Tex., 1971-72; exec. dir. Tex. Dist. and County Attys. Assn., Austin, 1972-80; judge Tex. Ct. Criminal Appeals, Austin, 1981—, presiding judge 1988—; dir. Tex. Ctr. for Judiciary, 1983; vice-chmn. Tex. Commn. on Sentencing, 1984; mem. Tex. Jud. Budget Bd., 1983. Pres. Joslin P.T.A., 1981-83. Served with U.S. Army, 1966-72. Named Rosewood Gavel Outstanding Jurist, St. Mary's U. Sch. Law, 1984. Mem. State Bar Tex., Tex. Dist. and County Attys. Assn. Episcopalian. Author: Branch's Annotated Penal Code, 3d edit., Criminal Forms and Trial Manual, 10th edit., Texas Justice Court Deskbook. Office: Tex Ct Criminal Appeals PO Box 12308 Austin TX 78711-2308

MCCORMICK, MICHAEL PATRICK, optics scientist, meteorologist; b. Canonsburg, Pa., Nov. 23, 1940; married 1962; 2 children. BA, Washington & Jefferson Coll., 1962; MA, Col William & Mary, 1964, PhD in physics, 1967; DSc, Washington & Jefferson Coll., 1981. Head photoelectronic instrumentation sect., 1967-75; chief aerosol measurements rsch. br. NASA, 1975—. Recipient Luie G. Charney award Am. Meteorol. Assn., 1991, Arthur S. Fleming award, 1980. Mem. Am. Geophys Union. Office: Langley Rsch Ctr M/S 475 Bldg 1250 A NASA Hampton VA 23665*

MCCORMICK, RICHARD ARTHUR, priest, religion educator, writer; b. Toledo, Oct. 3, 1922; s. Edward J. McCormick. BA, Loyola U., Chgo., 1945, MA, 1950, hon. degree, 1989; STD, Gregorian U., Rome, 1957; hon. degree, U. Scranton, 1975, Wheeling Coll., W.Va., 1976, Jesuit Sch. Theology, Berkeley, Calif., 1982, Siena Coll., 1985, U. Louvain, 1986, Coll. Holy Cross, 1986, Seattle U., 1987, Fordham U., 1988, Xavier U., 1988, U. San Francisco, 1989, Georgetown U., 1990, Cath. Theol. Union, 1991. Joined S.J., Roman Cath. Ch., 1940, ordained priest, 1953. Prof. moral theology Jesuit Sch. Theology, Chgo., 1957-73; Rose F. Kennedy prof. Christian ethics Georgetown U., Washington, 1974-86; John A. O'Brien prof. U. Notre Dame, Ind., 1986—; rsch. assoc. Woodstock Theol. Ctr., Washington, 1974-86; past mem. Ethics Adv. Bd., HEW; mem. Cath. Commn. on Intellectual and Cultural Affairs; lectr. in field. Author: Ambiguity in Moral Choice, 1973, Notes on Moral Theology, 1965 through 1980, 1980, Notes on Moral Theology 1981-1984, 1984, Health and Medicine in the Catholic Tradition, 1984, The Critical Calling: Moral Dilemmas Since Vatican II, 1989, Corrective Vision: Explorations in Moral Theology, 1994; co-author: (with Paul Ramsey) Doing Evil to Achieve Good, 1978; contbr. to numerous books, articles to Christianity and Crisis, New Cath. World, other religious jours.; co-editor: (with Charles E. Curran) Readings in Moral Theology I: Moral Norms and Catholic Tradition, 1979, Readings in Moral Theology II: The Distinctiveness of Christian Ethics, 1980, Readings in Moral Theology III: Morality and Authority, 1981, Readings in Moral Theology IV: The Use of Scripture in Moral Theology, 1982, Readings in Moral Theology V: Official Catholic Social Teaching, 1986, Readings in Moral Theology VI: Dissent in the Church, 1988, Readings in Moral Theology VII: The Natural Law, 1990, Readings in Moral Theology VIII: Dialogue about Catholic Sexual Teaching, 1993; former assoc. editor Am. mag.; editorial advisor Theology Digest, Hosp. Progress jours.; mem. editorial bd. Jour. Religious Ethics, Jour. Contemporary Health Law and Policy. Former trustee U. Detroit, Fairfield U. Recipient Henry Knowles Beecher award Hastings Ctr., 1988; Inst. Soc., Ethics and Life Scis. fellow. Mem. Am. Acad. Arts and Scis., Cath. Theol. Soc. Am. (past pres., Cardinal Spellman award 1969), Am. Soc. Christian Ethics (past bd. dirs.), Am. Hosp. Assn. (spl. bioethics com.), Nat. Hospice Orgn. (bioethcis com.), Cath. Health Assn. (bioethics com.), Am. Fertility Soc. (ethics com.). Office: U Notre Dame Dept Theology Notre Dame IN 46556

MCCORMICK, RICHARD DAVID, telecommunications company executive; b. Fort Dodge, Iowa, July 4, 1940; s. Elmo Eugene and Virgilla (Lawler) McC.; m. Mary Patricia Smola, June 29, 1963; children: John Richard, Matthew David, Megan Ann, Katherine Maura. B.S. in Elec. Engring., Iowa State U., 1961. With Bell Telephone Co., 1961-85; N.D. v.p., chief exec. officer Northwestern Bell Telephone Co., Fargo, 1974-77; asst. v.p. human resources AT&T, Basking Ridge, N.J., 1977-78; sr. v.p. Northwestern Bell, Omaha, 1978-82, pres., chief exec. officer, 1982-85; exec. v.p. U.S. West Inc., Englewood, Colo., 1985-86, pres., chief oper. officer, 1986-90, pres., chief exec. officer, 1990-91, chmn., pres., chief exec. officer, 1992—; bd. dirs. Super Valu Stores, Norwest Corp. Mem. Phi Gamma Delta. Office: US West Inc 7800 E Orchard Rd Ste 300 Englewood CO 80111-2533*

MC CORMICK, RICHARD PATRICK, history educator; b. N.Y.C., Dec. 24, 1916; s. Patrick Austin and Anna (Smith) McC.; m. Katheryne Crook Levis, Aug. 25, 1945; children: Richard Levis, Dorothy Irene. BA, Rutgers U., 1938, MA, 1940, LittD (hon.), 1982; PhD, U. Pa., 1948. Historian, Phila. Q.M. Depot, 1942-44; instr. U. Del., 1944-45; mem. faculty Rutgers U., 1945—, univ. historian, 1948—; dean Rutgers Coll., 1974-77, Univ. prof. history, 1977-82, Univ. prof. emeritus, 1982—; research adviser Colonial Williamsburg, 1953-61; Fulbright lectr. Cambridge (Eng.) U., 1961-62; Commonwealth lectr. U. London, 1971; chmn. N.J. Hist. Commn., 1967-70. Author: Experiment in Independence, 1950, History of Voting in N.J. 1953, N.J. From Colony to State, 1964, Second American Party System, 1966,

Rutgers: a Bicentennial History, 1966, The Presidential Game, 1982, The Black Student Protest Movement at Rutgers, 1990; co-author: The Case of the Nazi Professor, 1989. Mem. N.J. Tercentenary Commn., 1958-60, Am. Revolution Bicentennial Commn., 1971-74. Social Sci. Research Council fellow, 1956-57. Mem. Am. Hist. Assn., Soc. Historians of Early American Republic (pres. 1988-89), N.J. Hist. Soc. (pres. 1950-57), Phi Beta Kappa. Home: 938 River Rd Piscataway NJ 08854-5504 Office: Summer 42 Julien Rd Harwich Port MA 02646

MCCORMICK, ROBERT JUNIOR, government official; b. Boone, Iowa, Aug. 1, 1929; s. Ivyl Robert and Darlene Adel (Bowes) McC.; m. Shirley May Zerbe, Dec. 24, 1950; children: Elaine, Kathleen, Michael, Tara McCormick Wieting, Tammy McCormick Kirby. Grad., Flying Sch., Williams Field, Ariz., 1951, Parachute Jump Sch., 1964, Armed Forces Staff Coll., Norfolk, Va., 1966, Def. Systems Mgmt. Coll., Ft. Belvoir, Va., 1975; B.S., Tex. Tech. U., 1963. Served as enlisted man USAF, 1948-51, commd. 2d lt., 1951, advanced through grades to col., 1971; pilot USAF, U.S., Japan, Korea, Europe, Vietnam; exec. officer to Gen. George Brown 7th Air Force, Saigon, Vietnam, 1969-70; mil. asst. to asst. sec. of Air Force for research and devel. USAF, Washington, 1970-74; ret. USAF, 1975; exec. officer NASA, Washington, 1976-80; adminstrv. asst. to sec. of Air Force USAF, Washington, 1980—; mem. U.S. Sr. Exec. Service, 1979—. Decorated Air Force Legion of Merit, Bronze star, Air medal, Meritorious Svc. medal, Air Force Exceptional Civilian Svc. medal, 1985, 88, others; recipient Exceptional Svc. medal NASA, 1980, Presdl. Meritorious Rank, 1989, Dept. Def. Disting. Civilian Svc. award, 1994. Mem. ASME, DAV, Air Force Assn., Am. Def. Preparedness Assn., Order of Daedalians, St. Andrews Soc. Washington, Mil. Order of Carabao, Chevaliers du Testevin. Club: Army-Navy Country (Fairfax, Va.). Office: Office of Sec Air Force 1720 Air Force The Pentagon Washington DC 20330-1720

MCCORMICK, ROBERT MATTHEW, III, newspaper executive; b. N.Y.C., Dec. 31, 1938; s. Robert Matthew Jr. and Rita Patricia (McGuinness) McC.; m. Janet Severin Ahrens, Apr. 27, 1957; children: Susan Anne Heisler, Mary Teresa Berrier, Robert M. IV, Mark P. BA, Georgetown U., 1960; grad. advanced mgmt. program, Harvard U., 1978. Mktg. rep. Gen. Foods, Washington, 1960-62; various sales and mktg. positions The Washington Post, 1962-76, v.p. sales, 1976-82; exec. v.p. Chgo. Sun-Times, 1982-83; sr. v.p., sales and mktg. San Francisco News Agy., 1984-86, pres., CEO, 1987-93; exec. v.p. South Jersey Pub. Co., Atlantic City, 1994—; dir. Met. Sunday Newspapers, N.Y.C., 1987—. Bd. dirs. Conv. and Visitors Bur., San Francisco, 1987-93; mem. exec. com., 1990—; mem. Mayor's Fiscal Adv. Com., San Francisco, 1987-93; sector chair United Way Bay Area, San Francisco, 1989-91. Mem. Newspaper Assn. Am., Burning Tree Club, Atlantic City Country Club. Home: 222 Arlington Ave Linwood NJ 08221

MCCORMICK, STEVEN D., lawyer; b. Waterloo, Iowa, Apr. 24, 1946. AB, U. Notre Dame, 1968; JD, Northwestern U., 1971. Bar: Ill. 1972. Ptnr. Kirkland & Ellis, Chgo. Office: Kirkland & Ellis 200 E Randolph Chicago IL 60601

MCCORMICK, STEVEN THOMAS, insurance company executive; b. Phila., Dec. 18, 1955; s. Howard C. and Ruth Marion (Stahl) McC.; m. Helene Mary Trommler, Nov. 21, 1981; children: Matthew Thomas, Bria Helene. BBA, U. Ky., 1978; gen. ins. cert., Ins. Inst. Am., 1980. Cert. adminstrv. mgr., purchasing mgr., ins. agt., Ky., 1980. Supr. trainee Ky. Farm Bur. Ins. Cos., Louisville, 1978-79, supr. micrographics dept., 1979-83, supr. adminstrv. services, 1983-85, mgr. adminstrv. services, 1985-89; asst. v.p. operation, 1989—; dir. Cascade Gardens Condominium Assn. Big brother Big Brothers Am., Lexington, Ky., 1978; den leader Cub Scouts Boy Scouts Am., Lexington, 1979; fund raiser Leukemia Soc., Louisville, 1983, Am. Heart Assn., Louisville, 1985; dir. Cascade Gardens Condo. Assn. 1981-82. Named to Hon. Order Ky. Cols., Outstanding Employee of Yr., Nat. Assn. of Mutual Ins. Cos., 1986; recipient Cert. of Excellence Jefferson County Bd. End., 1988. Mem. Adminstrv. Mgmt. Soc. (internat. top recruiter 1985, chpt. pres. 1988, internat. dir. area 7 1990-91, internat. v.p. profl. devel. 1992-93), Acad. adminstrv. Mgmt. (bd. regents 1991-92, internat. v.p. 1992-93, internat. pres. 1993-94), Louisville Area Telecomms. Assn., Assn. Records Mgrs. and Adminstrs., Nat. Micrographics Assn., U. Ky. Alumni Assn., Toastmasters, Sigma Nu. Republican. Home: 706 Elsmere Cir Louisville KY 40223-2764 Office: Ky Farm Bur Ins Cos PO Box 20700 Louisville KY 40250-0700

MC CORMICK, THOMAS JULIAN, art history educator; b. Syracuse, N.Y., Nov. 14, 1925; s. Thomas Julian and Doris (Raffery) McC.; m. Margaret Emily Dorkey, Mar. 23, 1957; children: Sarah Elizabeth, Martha Dorcas. AB, Syracuse U., 1948, AM, 1949; MFA, Princeton U., 1953, PhD, 1971. Research asst. Va. Mus. Fine Arts, Richmond, 1953-54; instr. Smith Coll., Northampton, Mass., 1954-56; dir., asst. prof. Robert Hull Fleming Mus., U. Vt., 1956-58; assoc. prof., dir. Art Gallery, Vassar Coll., Poughkeepsie, N.Y., 1958-60; assoc. prof., dir. Art Gallery, Vassar Coll., Poughkeepsie, N.Y., 1960-70; Wright-Shippee prof. Wheaton Coll., Norton, Mass., 1970-79; A. Howard Meneely prof. Wheaton Coll., 1981-82, prof., 1979-91, prof. emeritus, 1991—, chmn. art dept., 1970-79, 90-91; Frederic Lindley Morgan prof. archtl. design U. Louisville, 1991; vis. assoc. prof. Williams Coll., 1969; lectr. Worcester (Mass.) Art Mus., 1978; vis. prof. Sch. Architecture, Canterbury, Eng., 1985-86. Author: Charles-Louis Clérisseau and the Genesis of Neo-Classicism, 1990; contbr. articles to profl. jours., exhbn. catalogs. Bd. dirs. Dutchess County (N.Y.) Landmarks Assn., 1968-70, Olana State Historic Site, 1968-70. With AUS, 1944-46, ETO. Corning Mus. Glass fellow, 1954; Fulbright sr. research fellow Gt. Britain, 1966-67, Yugoslavia, 1976-77. Fellow Soc. Antiquaries (London); mem. Coll. Art Assn., Archeol. Inst. Am., Soc. for Eighteenth Century Studies, Delta Kappa Epsilon. Episcopalian. Clubs: Princeton (N.Y.C.); Club of Odd Vols. (Boston). Home: 18 Still St Brookline MA 02146-3444

MCCORMICK, WILLIAM EDWARD, environmental consultant; b. Potters Mills, Pa., Feb. 9, 1912; s. George H. and Nellie (Mingle) McC.; m. Goldie Stover, June 6, 1935; children: John F. (dec.), Kirk W. B.S., Pa. State U., 1933, M.S., 1934. Tchr., Centre Hall (Pa.) High Sch., 1934-37; chemist Willson Products, Inc., Reading, Pa., 1937-43; indsl. hygienist Ga. Dept. Pub. Health, Atlanta, 1946; mgr. indsl. hygiene and toxicology B.F. Goodrich Co., Akron, Ohio, 1946-70; mgr. environ. control B.F. Goodrich Co., 1970-73; mng. dir. Am. Indsl. Hygiene Assn., Akron, 1973-83; exec. sec. Soc. Toxicology, 1976-83; chmn., treas. Envirotox Mgmt., Inc., 1983-93; mem. exec. com. rubber sect. Nat. Safety Coun., 1955-73, gen. chmn., 1971-72; mem. environ. health com. Chlorine Inst., 1983-93; mem. food, drug and cosmetic chems. com. Mfg. Chemists Assn., 1960-73, chmn., 1967-69, also mem. occupational health com., 1965-73; mem. adv. com. on heat stress U.S. Dept. Labor, 1973; mem. Nat. Adv. Com. Occupational Safety and Health, 1983-85; pres. Am. Indsl. Hygiene Found., 1984, trustee, 1982-89. Contbr. articles to profl. jours. Served to capt. USPHS, 1943-46. Recipient Borden award Am. Indsl. Hygiene Assn., 1993. Mem. AAAS, Am. Chem. Soc., Soc. Toxicology, Am. Indsl. Hygiene Assn. (pres. 1964, charter), Indsl. Hygiene Roundtable (charter), Am. Acad. Indsl. Hygiene (charter), Mason (33 degree), Shriner. Republican. Episcopalian. Home and Office: 419 Dorchester Rd Akron OH 44320-1315

MC CORMICK, WILLIAM MARTIN, broadcast executive; b. Hackensack, N.J., Dec. 15, 1921; s. John and Delia Theresa (Murphy) McC.; m. Joan Theresa Dowling, June 29, 1957; children: Jean Marie, Patricia, Joan, William Martin. Student, NYU, 1939-43, B.S., 1946; student, Harvard U., 1943-45. Account exec. Sta. WOR, N.Y.C., 1946-54; asst. sales mgr. Sta. WOR, 1955, dir. sales, 1956-59, v.p., dir. sales, 1959-60; pres., gen. mgr. Sta. WNAC-AM and FM and WNAC-TV, Boston, 1960-64; v.p.; gen. mgr. Sta. WNAC-TV, 1964-69; area v.p. New Eng. WNAC-TV, 1970-72; pres. McCormick Communications, 1972-85, McCormick Broadcasting Corp., 1986—; trustee Charlestown Savs. Bank., 1968-83. Bd. dirs. Catholic TV Ctr., 1970-83, ARC, 1970—; pres. execs. club Greater Boston C. of C., 1965-66, bd. dirs. 1966-68; bd. dirs. Better Bus. Bur., 1966-70. Served with USN, 1941-46. Recipient award Greater Boston C. of C., 1962, citation of merit NCCJ, 1974. Mem. Nat. Assn. Broadcasters, Nat. Radio Broadcasters Assn., New Eng. Broadcasters Assn. Roman Catholic. Clubs: Weston Golf; Oyster Harbors (Osterville, Mass.); John's Island (Vero Beach, Fla.); Wianno (Mass.).

MCCORMICK, WILLIAM THOMAS, JR., electric and gas company executive; b. Washington, Sept. 12, 1944; s. William Thomas and Lucy Valentine (Offutt) McC.; m. Ann Loretta du Mais, June 13, 1969; children: Christopher, Patrick. B.S., Cornell U., 1966; Ph.D., M.I.T., 1969. Mem. staff Inst. for Def. Analysis, Arlington, Va., 1969-72; mem. staff Office of Sci. and Tech., Exec. office of the Pres., Washington, 1972-73; sr. staff mem. Energy Policy Office, The White House, 1973-74; chief sci. and energy tech. br. Office Mgmt. and Budget, Exec. Office of the Pres., 1974-75; dir. commercialization U.S. Energy Research and Devel. Adminstrn., 1975-76; v.p. policy and govt. relations Am. Gas Assn., 1976-78; v.p., asst. to chmn. Am. Natural Resources Co., Detroit, 1978-80; exec. v.p. Mich. Wis. Pipeline Co., Am. Natural Resources System, Detroit, 1980-82; pres. Am. Natural Resources Co., Detroit, 1982-85; chmn., chief exec. officer Consumers Power Co., Jackson, Mich., 1985-92, chmn., 1992—; chmn., CEO CMS Energy Corp.; bd. dirs. Bancorp. Prin. author, editor: Commercialization of Synthetic Fuels in the U.S, 1975. Bd. dirs. Detroit Symphony, St. John Hosp. Alfred P. Sloan scholar, 1962-66. Mem. Econ. Club Detroit (bd. dirs.), Greater Detroit C. of C. (bd. dirs.), Econ. Alliance Mich. (bd. dirs.). Roman Catholic. Clubs: Cosmos (Washington); Detroit Athletic, Country of Detroit, Detroit. Office: Consumers Power Co 212 W Michigan Ave Jackson MI 49201-2236 also: CMS Energy Corp 1100-330 Town Center Dr Dearborn MI 48126*

MCCOTTER, CHARLES KENNEDY, JR., magistrate judge; b. New Bern, N.C., Oct. 29, 1946; s. Charles Kennedy and Lucy (Dunn) McC.; m. Patricia Byrum, Aug. 3, 1968; children—Virginia Byrum, Patricia Dunn. B.S. in Bus., U. N.C.-Chapel Hill, 1968, J.D. 1971. Bar: N.C. 1971, U.S. Dist. Ct. (ea. dist.) N.C. 1971, U.S.Ct. Appeals (4th cir.) 1973. Law clk. to judge U.S. Dist. Ct. (ea. dist.) N.C. 1971-72; sole practice, New Bern, 1973; ptnr. McCotter and Mayo, New Bern, 1974-79; U.S. magistrate judge U.S. Dist. Ct. (ea. dist.) N.C., 1979—; lectr. in field; permanent del. to 4th Cir. Jud. Conf.; mem. Ea. Dist. N.C. Com. on Arraignment Procedures, 1986, chmn. local rules com. for Revision of Local Admiralty Rules, 1985; jud. rep. to local adv. com. Implementation of Civil Justice Reform Act, 1991-94. Bd. visitors U. N.C. Marine Scis. Inst., mem. law alumni bd.; lic. mt. marine master. Mem. ABA, N.C. Bar Assn., Craven County Bar Assn., N.C. Trial Lawyers Assn., Maritime Law Assn. U.S., Nat. Council U.S., Ea. N.C. Inn of Ct., New Bern. C. of C. Episcopalian. Lodges: Rotary. Office: US Courthouse 413-415 Middle St Rm 203 New Bern NC 28563

MCCOTTER, JAMES RAWSON, lawyer; b. Denver, May 19, 1943; s. Charles R. and Jane M. (Ballantine) McC.; m. Carole Lee Hand, Sept. 5, 1965; children: Heidi M., Sage B. BA, Stanford U., 1965; JD, U. Colo., 1969. Bar: Colo. 1969, D.C. 1970, U.S. Dist. Ct. Colo. 1969, U.S. Ct. Appeals (10th and D.C. cirs.) 1970, U.S. Ct. Appeals (5th cir.) 1972, U.S. Supreme Ct. 1974. Law clk. U.S. Ct. Appeals (10th cir.), Denver, 1969-70; assoc. Covington & Burling, Washington, 1970-75; assoc. Kelly, Stansfield & O'Donnell, Denver, 1975-76, ptnr., 1977-86; assoc. gen. counsel Pub. Svc. Co. Colo., 1986-88; sr. v.p., gen. counsel, corp. sec., 1988-93; of counsel LeBoeuf, Lamb, Greene & MacRae, Denver, 1993-94, v.p. dep. gen. counsel, El Paso Natural Gas Co., Tex., 1994—. Editor in chief U. Colo. Law Rev., 1968-69 (Outstanding Achievement award 1969). Dem. precinct committeeman, Denver, 1983-84; bd. dirs. Sewall Rehab. Ctr., Denver, 1979-84, Opera Colo., 1987—; dir., vice chmn. Denver Civic Ventures, Inc., 1988-94; mem. law alumni bd. U. Colo. 1988-91; bd. dirs. Colo. Coun. on Econ. Edn., Found. for Denver Ctr. for Performing Arts Complex. Recipient Disting. Achievement award U. Colo. Law Sch., 1989; named to Outstanding Young Men Am., U.S. Jaycees, 1971; Storke scholar U. Colo., Boulder, 1967. Mem. ABA, Colo. Bar Assn. (adminstrv. law com. 1979-84), Fed. Energy Bar Assn. (chmn. com. on environment 1982-83), Tex. Bar Assn., Coronado Country Club (El Paso), Univ. Club, Denver Country Club, Order of Coif. Episcopalian. Home: 1036 Broadmoor Dr El Paso TX 79912 Office: El Paso Natural Gas Co PO Box 1492 El Paso TX 79978

MCCOUBREY, R. JAMES, advertising executive; b. Grand Mere, Que., Can., Sept. 1, 1944; s. James Addison and Margaret G. F. (Scarratt) McC.; m. Annette L. Hebert, Sept. 16, 1972; children: James Andrew, Matthew Alexander. B. of Commerce, McGill U., 1966, MA, 1967. With brand mgmt. Procter and Gamble, Toronto, Ont., Can., 1967-69; asst. mgr. Young and Rubicam, Montreal, Que., 1969-72; dir. client svcs. Young and Rubicam, Toronto, 1972-74, mgr., 1974-77, pres., 1977-80; area dir. Americas Young and Rubicam, N.Y.C., Toronto, 1980-82; gen. mgr. Europe Young and Rubicam, London, 1982-83; group and area dir. Young and Rubicam, N.Y.C., 1983-85; chmn. Young and Rubicam, Toronto, 1985-90; exec. v.p. Young and Rubicam, N.Y.C., 1984; area dir. Young and Rubicam, Africa, Australia, New Zealand and Can., 1984-90; pres., chief exec. officer Telemedia Inc., North York, Ont., Can., 1990—; Telemedia Communications USA Inc, Charlotte, Vt., 1991—; chmn. Inst. Can. Advt., Toronto, 1981-82; bd. dirs. Greyhound Lines of Can. Dir. Coun. for Bus. and the Arts in Can.; chmn. regional divsn. McGill Univ. Twenty-First Century Fund. Mem. Can. Assn. Broadcasters (bd. dirs.), Young Pres. Orgn. (past chmn.), Internat. Young Pres. Orgn. (v.p., bd. dirs. Can. area), Mag. Assn. Can. (chmn. 1992-94), Royal Can. Yacht Club, Mt. Royal Club, Anglican. Home: 54 Bernard Ave, Toronto, ON Canada M5R 1R5 Office: Telemedia Communications USA Inc Ferry Rd Charlotte VT 05445

MC COVEY, WILLIE LEE, former professional baseball player; b. Mobile, Ala., Jan. 10, 1938; s. Frank and Ester (Jones) McC. Baseball player, minor league, 1955-59; baseball player, minor league San Francisco Giants, 1959-73, 77-80, active in pub. rels., 1981-86, spl. asst. to the pres., 1986—; baseball player San Diego Padres, 1974-76; coach Oakland Athletics, 1976-81. Named Nat. League Rookie of Year, 1959, Most Valuable Player, 1969; Home Run Champion, 1963, 68, 69; Runs Batted In Leader, 1968, 69; Comeback Player of Year, 1977; 8th on All-Time Major League List of Career Home Runs; All-Time Nat. League leader in grand slam home runs; mem. Nat. League All-Star Team, 1963, 66, 68-71; inducted into Baseball Hall of Fame, 1986. Office: care San Francisco Giants Candlestick Park San Francisco CA 94124-3998*

MC COWAN, ROBERT TAYLOR, oil company executive; b. Carlisle, Ky., July 29, 1928; s. William Ray and Susan (Taylor) McC.; m. Nyle Eleanor Yates, Dec. 6, 1953; children—David Wayne, Susan Jill McCowan Sloneker. B.S., U. Ky., 1951, LL.D. (hon.); postgrad., U. Ill., 1964. With Ashland Oil Inc., 1951-88; salesman Ashland Oil Inc., Cin., 1951-54; div. mgr. Ashland Oil Inc., Chgo., 1954-59; spl. rep. Ashland Oil Inc., Ashland, Ky., 1959-64; asst. mgr. refinery sales Ashland Oil Inc., 1964-65, exec. asst., 1965-67, v.p., 1967-70, adminstrv. v.p., 1968-69, also bd. dirs., vice chmn. bd., ret., 1988, now cons., dir. emeritus; exec. v.p., dir., pres. Ashland Petroleum Co., to 1980; bd. dirs. Pacific Resources Inc. Adv. coun., chmn. devel. coun., fellow U. Ky.; chmn. Ctr. Pub. Issues; dir. Ky. Econ. Devel. Corp.; trustee Midway (Ky.) Coll., Cardinal Hill Hosp., Lexington, Ky.; chmn. bd. First Christian Ch., Ashland; dir. Found. Asbury Theol. Sem. Named to 25 Year Club of Petroleum Industry, 1976. Mem. Am. Petroleum Inst. (hon. dir.), Nat. Petroleum Refiners Assn. (dir., chmn. bd. dirs. 1986-88, past chmn. exec. com.), Ashland C. of C. (dir.), Ky. C. of C., Asphalt Inst. (past dir.), U. Ky. Alumni Assn. (past pres. Boyd County), Ind. Petroleum Assn. Am., Omicron Delta Kappa, Beta Gamma Sigma (Bus. Citizen of Yr. award 1988), Delta Tau Delta. Mem. Christian Ch. Club: Bellefonte (dir.). Lodge: Rotary (dir. Ashland club). Home: 2311 Forest Ave Ashland KY 41101-3730 Office: Ashland Oil Inc PO Box 391 Ashland KY 41105-0391

MCCOWN, GEORGE E., venture banking company executive; b. Portland, Oreg., July 1, 1935; s. Floyd Conly and Ada Elizabeth (Stephens) McC.; m. Karen Stone, Mar. 22, 1986; children: Taryn, Daniel, David; stepchildren: Bryan, Norman, Mark, Amy. BSME, Stanford U., 1957; MBA, Harvard U., 1962. Assoc. Am. Rsch. and Devel. Corp, 1962-63; from asst. to the pres. to sr. v.p. Boise (Idaho) Cascade, 1963-80; pres. Boise Cascade Home & Land Corp., 1970-80; chmn. Sequoia Corp., Boise, 1981-83; co-founder, mng. gen. ptnr. McCown De Leeuw & Co., Menlo Park, Calif., 1984—; chmn. bd. BMC West Corp., VANS, Systems Control, Inc., Thrifty Foods, Inc., Graphic Arts Ctr.; vice chmn. Coast Gas Industries, Specialty Paperboard, Inc.; bd. dirs. Hawaiian Air Lines, DIMAC Corp., Tiara Motorcoach, Nimbus CED Internat. Inc., 24 Hour Fitness Inc. Trustee Stanford U.; chmn. fin. com. and investment policy subcom., 1980-85; mem. task force on Financial Policies, dir. Packard Childrens Hosp., Stanford; trustee Nueva

Learning Ctr., Pacific Crest Outward Bound Sch.; chmn. bd. govs. Wyo. Centennial Everest Expdn.; mem. and past chmn. policy adv. bd. Harvard Joint Ctr. for Housing Studies; Ctr. for Real Estate and Urban Econs, U. Calif. at Berkeley, chmn. World Bus. Acad.; overseer Hoover Inst. War, Revolution and Peace. Capt. USAF, 1957-60. Mem. Harvard Bus. Assn. No. Calif. (chmn), Chief Execs. Orgn., World Pres. Orgn., Explorers Club, World Bus. Coun., Bus. Execs. for Nat. Security. Republican. Avocations: classical piano, mountaineering, adventure travel, aviation, tennis, skiing. Home: 250 Greer Rd Woodside CA 94062 Office: McCown De Leeuw & Co 3000 Sandhill Rd # 3-290 Menlo Park CA 94025-7116

MCCOWN, HALE, retired judge; b. Kansas, Ill., Jan. 19, 1914; s. Ross S. and Pauline (Collins) McC.; m. Helen Lanier, July 15, 1938; children: Robert B., William L., Mary Lynn. AB, Hastings Coll., 1935; LLB, Duke U., 1937. Bar: Oreg. 1937, Nebr. 1942. With firm Carey, Hart, Spencer & McCulloch, Portland, 1937-42; pvt. practice Beatrice, Nebr., 1942-65; ptnr. McCown, Baumfalk & Dalke; justice Supreme Court Nebr., 1965-83. Author articles in legal jours. Served to lt. USNR, 1943-45. Fellow Am. Coll. Trial Lawyers, Am. Coll. Trust and Estate Counsel; mem. ABA (legal ethics com. 1957-62), Nebr. Bar Assn. (chmn. ho. dels. 1955-56, pres. 1960-61), Am. Law Inst. (mem. council 1969—), Am. Judicature Soc. Presbyterian.

MCCOY, ANN, artist; b. Boulder, Colo., July 8, 1946; d. Abram Armstrong McC. and Ruthanna (Eames) Evans. B.F.A., U. Colo., 1969; M.A., UCLA, 1972. Instr. dept. art history Barnard Coll., Columbia U., N.Y.C., 1980-83. Exhibited one-woman exhbns., Fourcade, Droll Inc., N.Y.C., 1974, Wallraf-Richartz Mus. Mus. Ludwig, Cologne, W. Ger., 1977, Brooke Alexander Gallery, N.Y.C., 1978, 79, 81, Met. Mus. Art, N.Y.C., 1982, SUNY-Stony Brook, 1983, Kornfeld Gallery, Bern, Switzerland; group shows, Esther Bear Gallery, Santa Barbara, Calif., 1970, Sidney Janis Gallery, N.Y.C., Pasedena Art Mus., 1972, Cusack Gallery, Houston, U. Pa. Inst. Contemporary Art, Phila., U. Nebr. Meml. Art Gallery, Lincoln, Joslyn Art Mus., Omaha, U. Calif.-Santa Barbara, Los Angeles County Art Mus., Whitney Mus. Am. Art, N.Y.C., 1973, Indpls. Mus. Art, Contemporary Arts Ctr., Cin., U. Art Mus., Berkeley, 1975, Aarhus Kunstmus, Galerie Asbaek, Copenhagen, Cocoran Gallery Art, Washington, Wadsworth Athenaeum, Hartford, Conn., Fogg Art Mus., Cambridge, Mass., 1976, Bklyn. Mus., Brooke Alexander Gallery, Margo Leavin Gallery, Los Angeles, 1978, Venice (Italy) Biennial, 1986, Edinburgh (Scotland) Internat., 1988; represented permanent collections, Indpls. Mus. Art, Art Inst. Chgo., Houston Mus. Fine Arts, Los Angeles County Art Mus., Nat. Gallery Australia, Canberra, Whitney Mus. Am. Art, Mus. Modern Art, N.Y.C., Denver Art Mus. Recipient Contemporary Art Council New Talent award Los Angeles County Mus. Art, 1972; recipient Norman Wait Harris award Art Inst. Chgo. 71st Am. Exhbn., 1974, Berliner Kunstlerprogramm Deutscher Akademischer Austauschdienst, 1977, NEA award, 1976. Mem. Analytical Psychology Club. Office: Barnard Coll Dept Art History 116th St and Broadway New York NY 10027

MCCOY, CHARLES WIRTH, JR., superior court judge; b. Washington, Nov. 3, 1946; s. Charles W., Sr. and Mary Katherine (Hammond) McC.; m. Janet Irene Hodge, June 12, 1971; children: Justin Matthew, Seth Gabriel, Jamie Sara-Cay. BS, Purdue U., 1968; JD with honors, U. Tex., 1975; grad., Calif. Judicial Coll., 1993. Bar: Calif. 1975, U.S. Dist. Ct. (no. and ctrl. dists.) Calif. 1976, U.S. Supreme Ct. 1980. Ptnr. Sheppard, Mullin, Richter & Hampton, L.A., 1975-93; judge criminal divsn. dept. 130 L.A. Superior Ct., 1993-94, judge, 1994—, also mem. exec. com.; head teaching quizmaster Sch. Law., U. Tex., 1974-75, consul, mem. legal rsch. bd. Outstanding Rsch. Project, 1975; chief staff, chief dep. State Bd. Equalization, 1991-92; judge pro tem L.A. Mcpl. Ct., 1980-90, vol. settlement officer 1980-81. Contbg. author: Fundamentals of Legal Research, 1978, Model Criminal Antitrust Jury Instructions, 1984; contbr. articles to profl. jours. Founder One-to-One Program for at risk youth. Capt. USMC, 1968-72. ROTC scholar Purdue U., 1964-68; recipient Navy Commendation medal with Combat V. Mem. ABA (antitrust and litigation sects., forum coms. on entertainment and sports law and health law), Assn. Bus. Trial Lawyers, State Bar Calif. (probation monitor referee ct. 1990—), Calif. Judges Assn., L.A. County Bar Assn. (antitrust sect., Inns. Ct. 1993—), Rotary (West Covina chpt.), South Hills Country Club, Delta Tau Delta, Phi Delta Phi, Omnicron Delta Kappa. Republican. Avocations: golf, writing. Home: 1021 Holiday Dr West Covina CA 91791-3482 Office: LA Superior Ct 400 Civic Center Plz Pomona CA 91766-3201

MC COY, DONALD RICHARD, historian; b. Chgo., Jan. 18, 1928; s. Patrick Emmett and Rose Roma (Hewitt) O'Day; m. Sondra Jo Van Meter, June 29, 1980; children: Patricia, Bernard, William. B.A., U. Denver, 1949; M.A., U. Chgo., 1949; Ph.D., Am. U., 1954. Archivist interior sect. Nat. Archives, 1951-52; faculty dept. social studies State U. Coll., Cortland, N.Y., 1952-57; faculty dept. history U. Kans., Lawrence, 1957—; Univ. distinguished prof. U. Kans., 1974—; Fulbright prof. history U. Bonn, Germany, 1962; Mary Ball Washington prof. history Univ. Coll., Dublin, Ireland, 1976-77; dir. spl. rsch. project Harry S. Truman Libr. Inst., 1967-72; prin. investigator Ctrl. Am. Oral History Project, univs. Costa Rica and Kans., 1970-72; mem. adv. com. for protection archives and record ctrs. U.S. GSA, 1974-76; mem. nat. Archives Adv. Coun., 1976-79, Joint com. Historians and Archivists, 1977-80, chmn., 1979-80, adv. com. on the records of Congress, 1991-94. Author: Angry Voices, Left-of-Center Politics in the New Deal Era, 1958, Landon of Kansas, 1966, Calvin Coolidge, The Quiet President, 1967, (with R.T. Ruetten) Quest and Response: Minority Rights during the Truman Administration, 1973, Coming of Age: The United States during the 1920s and 1930s, 1973, The National Archives: America's Ministry of Documents, 1978, The Presidency of Harry S. Truman, 1984. Editor: (with M.L. Fausold) Student Guide to the American Story, II, 1957, (with R.G. O'Connor) Readings in Twentieth Century American History, 1963, (with R.T. Ruetten and J.R. Fuchs) Conference of Scholars on the Truman Administration and Civil Rights, 1968, (with B.K. Zobrist) Conference of Scholars on the Administration of Occupied Areas, 1943-1955, 1970; Contbr. articles to profl. jours. Alderman, Cortland, 1955-57. Served with Signal Corps U.S. Army, 1945-47. Recipient Byron Caldwell Smith award for distinguished writing, 1970; Waldo Gifford Leland prize Soc. Am. Archivists, 1979; Nat. Endowment for Humanities research grantee, 1968-70, 73-74, 81-82. Fellow Soc. Am. Archivists; mem. Am. Hist. Assn., Orgn. Am. Historians, Kans. Hist. Soc. (pres. 1981-82), Phi Beta Kappa. Home: U Kans Dept History 3213 Saddlehorn Dr Lawrence KS 66049

MCCOY, EDWARD FITZGERALD, social services facility administrator; b. Enid, Okla., July 11, 1938; s. Leonard Edward and Florence Wortman (Fitzgerald) McC.; m. Patricia Jean Semon, Sept. 11, 1970 (div. July 1986); children: Mary Clare, Leonard Edward II, Edward Fitzgerald Jr. BA in Polit. Sci., Park Coll., 1961; MA in Rehab. of Blind, Western Mich. U., 1969; postgrad., U. Md., 1971-74. Sales mgr. St. Joseph (Mo.) Surg. Supply, 1961-63; house master Nebr. Sch. for Blind, Nebraska City, 1963-65; dir. recreation Mo. Sch. for Blind, St. Louis, 1965-68; orientation and mobility specialist Montgomery County Pub. Schs., Rockville, Md., 1969-76; child find specialist Montgomery County Pub. Schs., Rockville, Mo., 1976-77; diagnostic prescriptive resource tchr., 1977-78; exec. dir. Fla. Lions Conklin Ctr. for Multihandicapped Blind, Daytona Beach, Fla., 1978—. Charter mem. Planned Giving Coun. Cen. Fla.; sec. East Cen. Fla. Radio Reading Svc.; mem. bd. counselors Bethune-Cookman Coll.; mem. adv. bd. Daytona Beach YWCA, 1993—; mem. Fla. divsn. Blind Svcs. Statewide Rehab. Adv. Coun., 1993—. Named to Ky. Cols., 1991; Western Mich. U. fellow, 1968-69; acad. leave grantee Montgomery County Pub. Sch., 1973-74. Mem. Fla. Assn. for Edn. and Rehab. of the Blind and Visually Impaired (pres. 1992-94), Nat. Soc. Fund Raising Execs. (cert.), Nat. Coun. Pvt. Agys. for the Blind and Visually Impaired, Nat. Accreditation Coun. for Agys. Serving Blind (team chmn.), Fla. Assn. Agys. Serving Blind (pres. 1985-87, treas. 1994—), Nat. Rehab. Assn., Am. Assn. Workers for Blind (pres. Washington chpt. 1977-78), Daytona Beach C. of C. (leadership coun.), Lions (pres. Daytona Beach Club 1982-83, chmn. sight conservation com. 1985—). Democrat. Roman Catholic. Avocations: camping, cooking, water sports. Home: 640 N Nova Rd Apt 115 Ormond Beach FL 32174-4408 Office: Conklin Ctr Multihandicapped Blind 405 White St Daytona Beach FL 32114-2999

MC COY, FREDERICK JOHN, retired plastic surgeon; b. McPherson, Kans., Jan. 17, 1916; s. Merle D. and Mae (Tennis) McC.; m. Mary Bock,

May 17, 1972; children: Judith, Frederick John, Patricia, Melissa, Steven. B.S., U. Kans., 1938, M.D. 1942. Diplomate: Am. Bd. Plastic Surgery (dir. 1973-79, chmn. 1979). Intern Lucas County Hosp., Toledo, 1942-43; resident in plastic surgery U. Tex. Med. Sch., Galveston, 1946; preceptorship in surgery Grand Rapids, Mich., 1947-50; practice medicine specializing in plastic and reconstructive surgery Kansas City, Mo., 1950-93; staff St. Mary's Hosp., 1950-83, St. Joseph's Hosp., 1950—, N. Kansas City Meml. Hosp., 1955—; mem. staff, chief plastic surgery Kansas City Gen. Hosp. and Med. Center, 1952-72, Children's Mercy Hosp., 1954-93, Research Hosp., 1950—, St. Luke's Hosp., 1951—, Baptist Hosp., 1958—, Menorah Hosp., 1950—; chief div. plastic surgery Truman Med. Ctr., 1972-91; chmn. maxillo-facial surgery U. Kansas City Sch. Dentistry, 1950-57; assoc. prof. surgery U. Mo. Med. Sch., Kansas City, 1964-69; clin. prof. surgery U. Mo. Med. Sch., 1969—; pres. McCoy Enterprises, Kansas City, Mo. Contbr. articles to, profl. jours.; editor: Year Book of Plastic and Reconstructive Surgery, 1971-88. Bd. govs. Kansas City Mus., 1959-93, pres., 1973-74. Served to maj. M.C. U.S. Army, 1943-46. Mem. ACS (pres. Mo. chpt. 1973), AMA, Am. Acad. Pediatrics, Am. Soc. Plastic and Reconstructive Surgeons (sec. 1969-73, dir. 1973-76, pres. 1976, chmn. bd. 1977, Spl. Achievement award 1988), Am. Soc. Pediatric Plastic Surgeons, Pan Pacific Surg. Soc., Singleton Surg. Soc. (v.p. 1965), Am. Assn. Plastic Surgeons (founding mem. plastic surgery rsch. coun.), Internat. Soc. Aesthetic Plastic Surgery, Am. Soc. Aesthetic Plastic Surgery, Jackson County Med. Soc. (pres. 1964-65), Kansas City Southwest Clin. Soc. (pres. 1971), Mo. Med. Assn. (v.p. 1975), Internat. Coll. Surgeons (v.p. 1969), Royal Soc. Medicine (London), Kansas City C. of C., Conservation Fedn. Mo., Natural Sci. Soc. (founder, chmn. 1973), Citizens Assn. Kansas City, Explorer's Club, Mission Hills Country Club, Boone and Crocket Club, Phi Delta Theta, Nu Sigma Nu. Republican. Mem. Christian Ch. Home: 5814 Mission Dr Shawnee Mission KS 66208-1139 Office: 500 Nichols Rd Ste 401 Kansas City MO 64112-2018

MCCOY, GERALD LEO, superintendent of schools; b. Worthington, Minn., Dec. 4, 1936; s. Lawrence Joseph and Mildred Alice (Burns) McC.; m. Louise Marie Budde, Oct. 17, 1959; children: Susan, Peggy, Mary, Paul. BS, Mankato (Minn.) State U., 1960; MEd, U. Ill., 1963; EdD, U. Minn., 1978. Cert. English and speech tchr., prin., supt., Minn. Tchr. English, Springfield (Ill.) Schs., 1960-63; tchr. English, Burnsville (Minn.) Schs., 1964-66, prin., 1967-73, asst. supt., 1974-80; supt. Eden Prairie (Minn.) Schs., 1980—; mem. policy bd. Ctr. for Applied Rsch. and Edn. Improvement, Mpls., 1990-92; bd. dirs. Minn. Coun. for Quality, Mpls., 1989—. Mem. Fairview Ridges Planning Bd., Burnsville, 1977-80; bd. dirs. Eden Prairie Found. 1980-88; trustee Fairview Southdale Hosp., Edina, Minn., 1987—. Recipient Outstanding Svc. award Eden Prairie Found., 1988, community contbns. award Minn. Community Edn. Assn., 1990; fellow Bush Exec. Fellows Program, 1983-84. Mem. ASCD, Am. Assn. Sch. Adminstrs., Minn. Assn. Sch. Adminstrs. (Minn. Supt. of Yr. award 1989), West Metro Assn. Sch. Adminstrs. (past pres.), Eden Prairie C. of C. (pres. 1980-88, Outstanding Svc. award 1987), Rotary, Lions, Optimists (Optimist of Yr. award Eden Prairie 1986), Phi Kappa Phi, Phi Delta Kappa. Avocations: fishing, hunting. Office: Eden Prairie Schs 8100 School Rd Eden Prairie MN 55344-2233

MCCOY, JAMES HENRY, oil company executive; b. Evanston, Ill., July 7, 1947; s. James Henry and Helen (Johnson) McC. BSChemE, Mich. Technol. U., 1968. Registered profl. engr., Ill., Mich. Chief startup engr. process div. UOP, Des Plaines, Ill., 1972-78, project engr., 1978-80; mng. engring. Total Petroleum Inc., Alma, Mich., 1980-85, refinery mgr., 1985-87; v.p. wholesale mktg. and supply Total Petroleum Inc., Denver, 1987-89, v.p. refining, 1989-91, sr. v.p. refining and transp., 1991—. Avocations: skiing, biking. Office: Total Petroleum Inc 999 18th St Denver CO 80202-2440

MCCOY, JAMES M., data processing, computer company executive; b. Cheyenne, Wyo., 1946. Grad., San Jose St. U., 1969. With Internat. Bus. Machines Corp., 1968-73; v.p. mktg. Verbatim Corp., 1973-78; with Shugart Assocs., 1978-80; v.p. Quantum Corp., 1980-81; pres., CEO Maxtor Corp., 1982—, chmn. bd., 1986-94; Bd. dirs. Centigram Corp., Exabyte Corp. Office: Maxtor Corp 211 River Oaks Pky San Jose CA 95134-1913*

MCCOY, JERRY JACK, lawyer; b. Pitts., Aug. 4, 1941; s. Norris and Martha (Jack) McC.; children: Madeleine Rena, Allison Norah, Jonathan Howard. BS, W.Va. U., 1963; LLB, Duke U., 1966; LLM in Taxation, N.Y.U., 1967. Bar: D.C. 1968, N.Y. 1967. Assoc. Silverstein & Mullens, Washington, 1968-72, ptnr., 1973-92; of counsel Reid and Priest, N.Y.C., Washington, 1992—; adj. law faculty George Washington U., Washington, 1977-87, U. Miami, Fla., 1983—. Exec. editor: Tax Mgmt., Estates Gifts and Trusts series, Washington, 1972—; co-editor: Charitable Gift Planning News, Dallas, 1983—; contbr. articles to profl. jours. Mem. Am. Law Inst., Am. Coll. Trust and Estate Counsel, Am. Coll. Tax Counsel, ABA (Washington coord. sect. of real property, probate and trust law). Democrat. Jewish. Home: 7401 Westlake Ter Apt 308 Bethesda MD 20817-6526 Office: Reid and Priest 701 Pennsylvania Ave NW Washington DC 20004-2608

MC COY, JOHN BONNET, banker; b. Columbus, Ohio, June 11, 1943; s. John Gardner and Jeanne Newlove (Bonnet) McC.; m. Jane Deborah Taylor, Apr. 21, 1968; children: Tracy Bonnet, Paige Taylor, John Taylor. B.A., Williams Coll., 1965; M.B.A., Stanford U., 1967; LLD (hon.), Williams Coll., 1991; D of Bus. Adminstrn. (hon.), Ohio State U., 1993; LLD (hon.), Kenyon Coll., 1994. With Banc One Corp., Columbus Na., Columbus, Ohio, 1970—, banking officer, 1970-73, v.p., 1973-77, pres., 1977-83; pres.; chief operating officer Banc One Corp., Columbus, Ohio, 1983-84, pres., chief exec. officer, 1984-87, chmn., chief exec. officer, 1987—, also bd. dirs.; pres., COO Banc One Corp., Columbus, Ohio, 1983-84, pres., CEO, 1984-87, chmn. CEO, 1987—, also bd. dirs.; pres. Bank One Trust Co., 1979-81; bd. dirs. Cardinal Health, Inc., Fed. Nat. Mortgage Assn., Ameritech Corp., Tenneco Inc.; fed. adv. coun. Fed. Res. Sys., 1991-93. Active Boy Scouts Am.; trustee, mem. bd. dirs. Kenyon Coll., 1992-95; trustee Stanford U., Children's Hosp., United Way of Franklin County, Columbus Acad., Battelle Meml. Inst.; pres. Columbus Area Growth Found.; chmn. Capitol South Urban Redevel. Corp. Capt. USAF, 1967-70. Recipient Ernest C. Arbuckle award Stanford U., 1994. Mem. Columbus C. of C. (past chmn., trustee), Am. Bankers Assn., Bankers Roundtable (bd. dirs. 1989-94), Assn. Bank Holding Cos., Young Pres.' Orgn. (chmn. Columbus chpt. 1982-83), Cypress Point Club, Links Club N.Y.C. Episcopalian. Office: Banc One Corp 100 E Broad St Columbus OH 43215-3607

MCCOY, JOHN GARDNER, banker; b. Marietta, Ohio, Jan. 30, 1913; s. John Hall and Florence (Buchanan) McC.; m. Jeanne N. Bonnet, Jan. 4, 1941; children: John Bonnet, Virginia B. Fickle. A.B., Marietta Coll., 1935; M.B.A., Stanford, 1937; LL.D. (hon.), Kenyon Coll., 1970, Marietta Coll., 1981. With City Nat. Bank & Trust Co. (now Bank One of Columbus), Columbus, 1937-84; v.p. City Nat. Bank & Trust Co. (now Bank One of Columbus), 1946-58, pres., chmn., chief exec. officer, 1959-77, dir., 1949—; pres., vice chmn., chief exec. officer Banc One Corp., 1966-84, dir., chmn. exec. com. Trustee Marietta Coll., 1966—. Recipient Ernest C. Arbuckle award Stanford Bus. Sch., 1986. Mem. Assn. Bank Holding Cos. (past pres.) Episcopalian. Clubs: Columbus, Columbus Country, Muirfield Golf, Golf, Wequetonsing (Mich.) Golf, Little Harbor (Harbor Springs, Mich.), Royal Poinciana Golf (Naples, Fla.), Hole In-the-Wall Golf (Naples, Fla.), Naples Yacht (Naples, Fla.). Home: 8 Edge Of Woods New Albany OH 43054 Office: Banc One Corp 100 E Broad St Columbus OH 43271-0261

MCCOY, JOHN J., engineering educator; b. N.Y.C.; s. John J. and Margaret Eleanor (Bolt) McC.; m. Kathleen Donohue, June 16; children: John T., Kathleen Kearney, Andrew J. B in Civil Engring., Cooper Union, 1958; MS, Columbia U., 1959, ScD, 1961. Staff engr. IBM, Endicott, N.Y., 1961-63; prof. U. Pa., Phila., 1963-69; prof. Cath. U. Am., Washington, 1969—, dean, 1989—. Office: Cath U Am 620 Michigan Ave NE Washington DC 20064

MCCOY, JOHN JOSEPH, lawyer; b. Cin., Mar. 15, 1952; s. Raymond F. and Margaret T. (Hohmann) McC. BS in Math. summa cum laude, Xavier U., 1974; JD, U. Chgo., 1977. Bar: Ohio 1977, D.C. 1980. Ptnr. Taft, Stettinius & Hollister, Cin., 1977—; lectr. Chism Cin. C. of C., 1984. Pro bono rep. Jr. Achievement Greater Cin., 1978; fund raiser Dan Beard coun. Boy Scouts Am., 1983; fund raising team leader Cin. Regatta, Cin. Ctr.

Devel. Disorders, 1983; account mgr. United Appeal, Cin., 1984; mem. Green Acres Trust adv. com. Village of Indian Hill, 1994—; trustee Vol. Lawyers for the Poor Found., 1994—. Mem. ABA, Ohio State Bar Assn. (banking, comml. and bankruptcy law com., corp. law com., fed. ct. practice com.), Cin. Bar Assn. (fed. cts., common pleas cts. and negligence law com.), Cin. Inn. of Ct. (barrister 1984-86), Cin. Athletic Club (pres. bd. trustees 1986-89). Home: 6700 Wyman Ln Cincinnati OH 45243

MCCOY, KATHERINE BRADEN, designer, educator; b. Decatur, Ill., Oct. 12, 1945; m. Michael McCoy. B.A., Mich. State U., 1967. Designer Unimark Internat., Detroit, 1967-68; sr. designer Chrysler Corp. Identity Office, Detroit, 1968-69, Omnigraphics, Boston, 1969-70, Designers & Ptnrs., Detroit, 1970-71; ptnr. McCoy & McCoy, Detroit, 1971—; co-chmn. dept. design Cranbrook Acad. Art, Bloomfield Hills, Mich., 1971—; Joyce C. Hall Disting. Prof. Kansas City Art Inst., 1987-88; mem. design arts policy panel NEA, 1984-86, chmn. fellowship panel, 1984-86. Exhibited exhibitions, Am. Inst. Graphic Arts Gallery, N.Y.C., 1972-76, 79, Station 100, Chgo., 1978-81; collections arranged Knoll and Herman Miller: The Development of Contemporary Furniture, Cranbrook Acad. Art, 1975, Design in Mich, 1977, Internat. Graphic Design Edn., Icograda, Chgo., 1978; mem. editorial bd., Indsl. Design Mag., 1976—. Recipient Am. Design Rev. awards Indsl. Design mag., 1972-79; recipient Am. Inst. Graphic awards, 1972, Best of Packaging award, Print Casebooks, 1976-79, Interiors Mag. "I" award, 1980, 86, design arts research grant NEA, 1985-86. Fellow Indsl. Designers Soc. Am. (mem. nat. bd. 1979-80, 85-86, exec. v.p. 1981-83, pres. 1983-85, v.p., 1986—, chmn. bd. 1985-87); mem. Am. Inst. Graphic Arts, Soc. Typographic Arts, Am. Inst. Graphic Arts (v.p. 1986-88), Alliance Graphique Internat. Office: Cranbrook Acad Art Design Dept PO Box 801 Bloomfield Hills MI 48303-0801

MCCOY, MARILYN, university official; b. Providence, Mar. 18, 1948; d. James Francis and Eleanor (Regan) McC.; m. Charles R. Thomas, Jan. 28, 1983. BA in Econs., Smith Coll., 1970; M in Pub. Policy, U. Mich., 1972. Dir. Nat. Assn. for Higher Edn. Mgmt. Systems, Boulder, Colo., 1972-80; dir. planning and policy devel. U. Colo., Boulder, 1981-85; v.p. adminstrn. and planning Northwestern U., Evanston, Ill., 1985—; bd. dirs. First Prairie Mutual Funds; mem. nat. adv. panel Nat. Ctr. for Postsecondary Governance and Fin. Co-author: Financing Higher Education in the Fifty States, 1976, 3d edit., 1982. Bd. dirs. Evanston Hosp., 1988—, United Charities, Chgo., 1988—, Chgo. Met. YMCA, 1989—, Mather Found., 1995—. Mem. Am. Assn. for Higher Edn., Soc. for Coll. and Univ. Planning (pres., v.p., sec., bd. dirs. 1980-), Assn. for Instnl. Rsch. (pres., v.p., exec. com., publs. bd. 1978-87), Chgo. Network (chmn. 1992-93), Chgo. Econ. Club. Home: 1100 N Lake Shore Dr Chicago IL 60611-1053 Office: Northwestern U 633 Clark St Evanston IL 60208-0001

MCCOY, MARY ANN, state official; b. Duluth, Minn., Oct. 13, 1924; d. Homer Burke and Avis (Woodworth) Hursh; B.A., Grinnell Coll., 1946; postgrad. Laval U., 1946, Mankato State U., 1964-65, U. Minn., 1970-73; m. Charles Ramon McCoy, June 11, 1949; children—Jeffrey, Mary, Jeremy. Exec. trainee Younkers Inc., Des Moines, 1946; advt. copywriter Des Moines Register & Tribune, 1947; field dir. Duluth (Minn.) Girl Scout Council, 1947-49; with merchandising dept. Dayton's Inc., Mpls., 1966-75; dir. election and legis. manual div. Office of Sec. of State of Minn., St. Paul, 1975-81; exec. dir. Minn. State Ethical Practices Bd., St. Paul, 1981—. Mem. Minn. Hist. Soc. (life, hon. council), Council on Govt. Ethics Laws (steering com. 1986—, treas. 1987—), exec. council Minn. Hist. Soc., 1972-81, 82—; mem. Minn. Supreme Ct. Bd. for Continuing Legal Edn., 1981-87; sec. State Rev. Bd. for Nominations to Nat. Register, 1976—. Mem. Minn. Assn. Pub. Adminstrs., Am. Judicature Soc., Women Historians of Midwest, Am. Assn. State and Local History. Editor, Minn. Legis. Manual, 1975-81. Office: Ethical Practices Bd 625 Robert St N Saint Paul MN 55101-2516

MCCOY, MICHAEL DALE, designer, educator; b. Eaton Rapids, Mich., Sept. 16, 1944; s. Kenneth K. and Beverlee (Finch) McC.; m. Katherine J. Braden, June 24, 1967; 1 dau., Anne Marie. B.A., Mich State U.; M.A., Wayne State U. Designer Sundberg Ferar, Detroit, 1967-68; ptnr. McCoy & McCoy, Bloomfield Hills, Mich., 1971—, Fahnstrom/McCoy, Chgo., 1984—; co-chmn. design dept. Cranbrook Acad. Art, Bloomfield Hills, 1971—; mem. bd. advisors Design Mich., Bloomfield Hills, 1979—. Author: Problem Solving in the Man Made Environment, 1974; editorial bd.: Indsl. Design mag., N.Y.C., 1978—. Recipient award Interiors mag., 1980, 84; recipient Communication Graphics award Am. Inst. Graphic Design, 1980, award Am. Soc. Interior Designers, 1982. Mem. Indsl. Design Soc. Am. (Design Excellence award 1980, 83, European Ergodesign award 1987, Gold medal 1990, IBD award 1990, Indsl. Design mag. Best of Category award 1990). Home: 1952 Traver Rd Apt 103 Ann Arbor MI 48105-1288 Office: Cranbrook Acad Art Dept Design Bloomfield Hills MI 48303

MCCOY, MILLINGTON F., management recruitment company executive; b. Cape Girardeau, Mo., Jan. 22, 1941; d. Howard Hanscom and Mary Helen (Kinder) Flentge; m. W. David McCoy; 1 child, Daniel Phipps. BA, U. Mo., 1962; Cert. in Bus. Adminstrn. program, Harvard-Radcliffe U., 1963. Field market researcher Procter & Gamble Co., N.Y.C., 1964-65; advt. and market rsch. analyst Gardner Advt. Agy., N.Y.C., 1965-66; v.p. Handy Assocs., N.Y.C., 1966-77; mng. dir. Gould, McCoy & Chadick, Inc., N.Y.C., 1977—; founding mem. Com. of 200; panel of experts Boardroom Reports. Mem. Phi Beta Kappa. Avocations: dressage, gardening, skiing. Office: Gould McCoy & Chadick Inc 300 Park Ave New York NY 10022-7402

MCCOY, NEAL S., lawyer; b. Winfield, Kans., Nov. 22, 1940; s. R. Stewart and Alma Elnora (Fry) McC.; m. Catherine Collins, June 6, 1980. A.B. in Polit. Sci., U. Kans., Lawrence; LL.B., Harvard U., 1965; postgrad., Cambridge U., Eng., 1965-66. Bar: Calif. 1965, D.C. 1978. Mem. br. adminstrv. procs. and investigations, div. corp. fin. SEC, Washington, 1966-69; legal asst. to chmn. SEC, 1969-70, chief counsel div. corp. fin., 1970-74, assoc. dir. (compliance) div. corp. fin., 1974-77; ptnr. firm Skadden, Arps, Slate, Meagher & Flom, Washington, 1977—; mem. adv. coun. George Washington U. Med. Ctr., 1990—, Nat. Commn. on Fin. Instn. Reform, Recovery and Enforcement, 1991-93, ad hoc com. ALT Corp. Governance Project. Mem. ad hoc com. ALI Corp. Governance Project; mem. Nat. Commn. on Fin. Instn. Reform, Recovery and Enforcement, 1991—. Mem. ABA, Fed. Bar Assn. (exec. coun. securities law com. 1988—), Nat. Assn. Securities Dealers (legal adv. bd. 1988-93). Office: Skadden Arps Slate Meagher Flom 1440 New York Ave NW Washington DC 20005-2111

MCCOY, PATRICIA ANN, law educator, lawyer; b. Cortland, N.Y., June 20, 1954; d. Donald Richard and Vivian Alicia (Rogers) McC. BA in Govt., Oberlin Coll., 1976; JD, U. Calif., Berkeley, 1983. Bar D.C. Law clk. to hon. Robert S. Vance U.S. Ct. Appeals (11th cir.), Brimingham, Ala., 1983-84; assoc. Mayer, Brown & Platt, Washington, 1984-90, ptnr., 1991-92; asst. prof. Cleve. State U. Cleveland-Marshall Coll. Law, 1992—; editor-in-chief Indsl. Rels. Law Jour., Berkeley, 1982-83. Deutscher Akademischer Austauschdienst fellow, Munich, Germany, 1976-77. Mem. Washington Coun. Lawyers (dir. 1986-92), Oratorio Soc. Washington. Avocations: choral singing, opera. Office: Mayer Brown & Platt 2000 Pennsylvania Ave NW Washington DC 20006-1882 Office: Cleveland-Marshall Coll Law 1801 Euclid Ave Cleveland OH 44115

MC COY, ROBERT BAKER, publisher; b. Arrowsmith, Ill., Mar. 26, 1916; s. Robert Benton and Charlotte (Miller) McC. B.S., Northwestern U., 1950; M.S., 1951; postgrad., U. Ill. extension. Various positions with branches U.S. Govt., 1939-51; mng. editor book dept. Popular Mechanics Mag. Co., Chgo., 1951-60; mng. editor high sch. textbook div. J.B. Lippincott Co., Chgo., 1960-62; owner, pres., chmn. bd. Rio Grande Press Inc. (pubs. nonfiction Western Americana books), Chgo., 1962—, chmn. bd., pres. Rio Grande Press of N.Mex., Inc. Lectr., author articles on Am. Indian, ornithology, travel. Served with AUS, 1941-45. Office: The Rio Grande Press Inc La Casa Escuela PO Box 33 Glorieta NM 87535

MCCOY, THOMAS RAYMOND, lawyer, educator; b. Cin., Apr. 14, 1943; s. Raymond F. and Margaret T. (Hohmann) McC.; m. Judith A. Huth, July 27, 1968; children—Jennifer A., Ellen M. B.S., Xavier U., Cin., 1964; J.D., U. Cin., 1967; LL.M., Harvard U., 1968. Bar: Ohio 1967. Asst. prof. law Vanderbilt U., Nashville, 1968-71, assoc. prof., assoc. dean for acad. affairs,

1971-75, prof., 1975—; mem. Tenn. Supreme Ct. Commn. on Dispute Resolution, 1992-94. Mem. editorial bd. Soundings jour., 1972-85. Bd. dirs. Opportunity House, Inc., Nashville, 1969-81, pres. bd., 1978-80. Mem. ABA, Am. Assn. Law Schs., Nat. Gov.'s Assn. (adv. com. on federalism 1988). Home: 1502 Lynnhurst Ct Brentwood TN 37027-7218 Office: Vanderbilt U Sch Law 21st Ave S Nashville TN 37240

MC COY, TIDAL WINDHAM, former government official; b. Gainesville, Fla., Apr. 25, 1945. Grad., U.S. Mil. Acad., 1967; M.A. in Bus. Fin, George Washington U., 1975. Officer U.S. Army, 1967-72; mem. long-range planning and net assessment group Office of Sec. Def., Washington, 1972-73; mem. staff Nat. Security Council, 1973; staff asst. and then dep. asst. to Sec. Def., 1973-77; sci. asst. to asst. sec. for research, engring. and systems Dept. Navy, 1977-78; dir. policy research, office of under sec. for policy Dept. Def., 1978-79; asst. for nat. security affairs to Sen. Jake Garn, 1979-81; asst. sec. for manpower, res. affairs and installations Dept. Air Force, Washington, 1981-87; asst. sec. for readiness support USAF, Washington, 1987-88; acting sec. and undersec. USAF, 1981-88; sr. assoc. Hecht, Spencer & Assocs., 1988-89; v.p. govt. rels. Thiokol Corp., 1989—. Recipient DOD Outstanding Civil Svc. medal Sec. Defense.

MCCOY, WESLEY LAWRENCE, musician, conductor, educator; b. Memphis, Jan. 27, 1935; s. Harlan Eftin and Gladys (Coggin) McC.; m. Carolyn June Noble, Aug. 26, 1960; children: Jill Laurene McCoy Kurtz, Scott Edward. B.Music Edn., La. State U., 1957, Ph.D., 1970; M of Music Edn, U. Louisville, 1958; M Sacred Music, So. Bapt. Theol. Sem., 1960. Minister of music Beechmont Bapt. Ch., Louisville, 1959-62; also instr. music So. Bapt. Theol. Sem., Louisville; asst. prof. music, dir. bands Carson Newman Coll., Jefferson City, Tenn., 1962-67; asst. prof. music U. S.C., Columbia, 1969-72; asso. prof. music U. Ark., Little Rock, 1972-77; prof. U. Ark., 1977-80, asst. dean for public service Coll. Fine Arts., 1978-79; condr. Wind Ensemble, River City Community Band, 1972-80, Oklahoma City Youth Symphony, 1985-89; chmn. dept. music Phillips U., Enid, Okla., 1980-82, chmn. fine arts div., 1982-84; minister music 1st United Meth. Ch., Edmond, Okla., 1983—; owner Centre Office, Travel Agts. Internat. French horn player, Knoxville (Tenn.) Symphony Orch., 1962-67, Columbia Philharm. Orch., 1969-72, Ark. Symphony Orch., 1972-80, Enid-Phillips Symphony, 1980-84; contbr. to Ch. Musician, 1974-76, 85-86. Co-chmn. Jefferson County (Tenn.) Com. for Goldwater for Pres., 1962; mem. Pulaski County Republican Com., 1977-81. Mem. S.C. Music Educators Assn. (pres. coll. div. 1971-73), Ark. Music Edn. Assn. (chmn. rsch. 1975-80), Phi Mu Alpha, Pi Kappa Lambda, Phi Delta Kappa, Alpha Tau Omega. Republican. Baptist. Home: 1904 Blue Jay Ct Edmond OK 73034-6105 Office: 1331 W Memorial Rd Oklahoma City OK 73114-1423

MC COY, WILLIAM DANIEL, manufacturing executive; b. N.Y.C., Nov. 27, 1929; s. William Daniel and Anna Marie (Murphy) McC.; m. Joan Gillette, Nov. 26, 1960; children: Kirk, Kim, Karen. B.S., Fordham U., 1951; M.B.A., Hofstra U., 1958. With IBM Corp., White Plains, N.Y., 1953-69; mgr. basic systems mktg. IBM Corp., 1969-72; pres. Am. Polymers, Inc., Paterson, N.J., 1972-85; with Philip Morris Indsl., Inc., Milw., 1972—; pres., chief exec. officer Philip Morris Indsl., Inc., until 1985; chmn., chief exec. officer Koch Label Co., 1985—; dir. Wis. Tissue Mills, Inc., Plainwell Paper Co., Inc., W.A. Krueger Co., Phoenix, Chesapeake, West Point, Va., Krueger-Ringier, Chgo. Bd. dirs. Wis. Found. Ind. Colls.; bd. dirs. United Performing Arts Fund, Milw. Art Mus.; trustee Ripon Coll.; vice chmn. United Way, 1976, Wis. region NCCJ, 1980-81. Served to capt. USMC, 1951-53. Mem. Am. Paper Inst., Am. Mgmt. Assn., Wis. Assn. Mfg. and Commerce, Univ. Club. Home: 579 North St Harrison NY 10528-1014 Office: Koch Label Co 579 North St Harrison NY 10528-1014

MCCOY, WILLIAM O., telecommunications executive; b. Snow Hill, N.C., Oct. 26, 1933; s. Marcus Cicero and Anna Kathleen (Shirley) McC.; m. Sara Jane Hart, Dec. 18, 1955; children—Laura Jo McCoy Foster, Kathleen Sue. BS, U. N.C., 1955; MS, MIT, 1968. Gen. mgr. South Central Bell, New Orleans, 1973-76; v.p. South Central Bell, Nashville, 1978; exec. v.p. South Central Bell, Birmingham, Ala., 1978-82, vice chmn., 1982-83; asst. v.p. Am. Tel & Tel, Basking Ridge, N.J., 1976-78; vice chmn. BellSouth Corp., Atlanta, 1993—; dir. First Am. Corp., Nashville, Liberty Corp., Greenville. Chmn. Middle Tenn. Heart Assn., Nashville, 1971; div. chmn. Greater New Orleans Fedn. of Chs., 1974; gen. vice chmn. New Orleans Symphony Campaign, 1975; co-chmn. Ala. United Way Campaign, Birmingham, 1982; adv. council Coll. Bus. Adminstrn., Ga. State U., 1983—. Served to capt. USMC, 1955-59. Republican. Methodist. Office: BellSouth 675 Peachtree St NE Atlanta GA 30308-1928 also: BellSouth Corp 1155 Peachtree St NE Atlanta GA 30309-3600

MCCRABB, DONALD R., religious ministry director; m. Catherine Olds; 1 child, Andrew Thomas. BA in Religion, BA in Polit. Sci., Wright State U., 1975; MA in Theology, U. Dayton, 1978; grad. program, Jesuit Renewal Ctr., Milford, Ohio, 1984. Cert. catechetical leader, Roman Cath. Ch. Campus min. Newman Ctr., Wright State U., Dayton, Ohio, 1975-76; grad. asst. U. Dayton, 1976-78; pastoral assoc. St. Raphael Cath. Ch., Springfield, Ohio, 1978-82; Cath. campus min. Cen. State U., Wilberforce U., 1982-85; exec. dir. Cath. Campus Ministry Assn., 1985—; mem. planning com. Cath. Edn. Futures Project, 1985-88; bd. dirs., site visitor Commn. on Cert. and Accreditation, U.S. Cath. Conf., 1986—. Home: 1433 Constance Ave Dayton OH 45409-1807 Office: Cath Campus Ministry Assn 3000 College Park Ave Dayton OH 45469-0001

MCCRACKEN, A. MICHAEL, accounting firm executive; b. Deland, Fla., Nov. 10, 1951; s. John L. and Elizabeth (Friedlund) McC.; children: Stephanie R., Jay M., Chris B., J. Blake. BS, Jackson U., 1973. CPA, Fla. N.Y.; cert. mgmt. acct. Sr. mgr. nat. office Ernst & Young, Cleve., 1986-87; ptnr., regional dir. mktg. Ernst & Young, Atlanta, 1987-93; ptnr. Ernst & Young Internat., N.Y.C., 1993—. Mem. Fla. Inst. CPAs (mem. numerous coms., Chmn. of Yr. 1986), Inst. Mgmr. Acctg. Avocations: golf, skiing. Office: Ernst & Young 787 7th Ave New York NY 10019-6018

MCCRACKEN, ALEXANDER WALKER, pathologist; b. Motherwell, Lanarkshire, Scotland, Nov. 24, 1931; came to U.S., 1968; s. William and Mary Snedden (Walker) McC.; m. Theresa Credgington, June 4, 1960; children: Fiona Jane, Claire Louise. MD, U. Glasgow, Scotland, 1956. Resident in surgery Glasgow Royal Inf., 1956-57; resident in pathology Royal Air Force, U.K., 1957-61, pathologist, 1962-68; fellow in pathology Royal Postgrad. Med. Sch., London, 1961-62; assoc. prof. Med. Sch., U. Tex., San Antonio, 1968-72; prof. Med. Sch., U. Tex., Houston, 1972-73; dir. of microbiology Baylor U. Med. Ctr., Dallas, 1973-81; pres. med. staff, dir. of labs. Meth. Hosps. of Dallas, 1982—; pres. med. staff Meth. Med. Ctr., 1994-95; adj. prof. pathology Baylor U. Coll. Dentistry, Dallas, 1982—; clin. prof. U. Tex. Southwestern Med. Sch., Dallas, 1986—. Author: Pathologic Mechanisms of Human Disease, 1985, Oral and Clinical Microbiology, 1986, Pathology, 1990, (play) Mister Gilbert, 1985, 89. With Royal Air Force, 1957-68. Decorated Gen. Svc. medal. Fellow Royal Coll. Pathologists, Coll. Am. Pathologists; mem. AAAS, AMA, Am. Soc. Microbiology, Tex. Med. Assn., Dallas County Med. Soc., Tex. Soc. Infectious Diseases, Tex. Med. Found., Assn. of Clin. Chemists, Masons. Republican. Anglican. Avocations: theater, music, gardening. Home: 607 Kessler Lake Dr Dallas TX 75208-3943 Office: Lab Physicians Assn 221 W Colorado Blvd Dallas TX 75208-2359

MCCRACKEN, CARON FRANCIS, data processing consultant; b. Detroit, Jan. 12, 1951; d. William Joseph and Constance Irene (Kramer) McC. AS, Mott Community Coll., 1971; BS, Cen. Mich U., 1973; MA, U. Mich., 1978; Post Bachelor in Computer Sci., Wayne State U., 1993. Tchr. Elkton, Pigeon, Bayport (Mich.) High Schs., 1973-74, Davison (Mich.) Jr. High Sch., 1974-75; instr. Mott Community Coll., Flint, Mich., 1974-78; postgrad. Flint Police Dept., 1993—; campus coord., programmer Systems & Computer Tech. Corp., Detroit, 1981-82, acad. specialist, 1982-83, mgr. acad. computing systems, 1983-84, mgr. adminstrv. computing systems, 1984-85; communications analyst Fruehauf Corp., Detroit, 1985-86, sr. communications analyst, 1986-87; account cons. US Sprint Communications Co., Detroit, 1987-89; account mgr. US Sprint Communications Corp., Detroit, 1989-90; sr. mgr. Technology Specialists, Inc., Phila., 1990-91; tech. cons. Digital Mgmt. Group, Detroit, 1991-92; sr. assoc. info. tech. practice, tech. delivery svcs. Coopers & Lybrand, Detroit, 1992—; adv. bd. CONTEL Bus.

Networks, Atlanta, 1987. Vol. charitable, homeless orgns. including COTS, Core Cities, Paint the Town; vol. computer project Wayne State U., Detroit, 1993—; vol. tech. adv. Detroit cmty. project. Mem. NAFE, Data Processing Mgmt. Assn., Assn. Computing Machinery, Detroit Inst. Arts, Alumni Assn. U. Mich., Bikecentennial Club (Missoula, Mont.). Avocations: distance bicycling and running, golf, personal research, travel. Home: 100 W Hickory Grove H4 Bloomfield Hills MI 48304 Office: Coopers & Lybrand 400 Renaissance Ctr Detroit MI 48276

MC CRACKEN, DANIEL DELBERT, computer science educator, author; b. Hughsville, Mont., July 23, 1930; s. Albert Ray and Blanche (Spear) McC.; m. Evelyn Edwards, 1952; children: Charles, Judith, Cynthia, Virginia, Rachel, Aliza, Thomas.; m. Helen Blumenthal, 1980; 1 stepson, Michael Cohen. B.A. in Math., Central Wash. U., 1950, B.A. in Chemistry, 1951; student, NYU, 1958-59; M.Div., Union Theol. Sem., N.Y.C., 1970. With Gen. Electric Co., 1951-58, dir. tng., computer dept., 1956-57; with AEC Computing Center, N.Y.U., 1958-59; cons. computer programming, writing and tng., 1958—; prof. computer sci. CCNY, 1981—, dept. chair, 1989-91. Author: Digital Computer Programming, 1957, (with H. Weiss and T.H. Lee) Programming Business Computers, 1959, A Guide to FORTRAN Programming, 1961, A Guide to IBM 1401 Programming, 1962, A Guide to ALGOL Programming, 1962, A Guide to COBOL Programming, 1963, (with U. Garbassi) 2d edit., 1970, (with F.J. Gruenberger) Introduction to Electronic Computers, 1963, (with W.S. Dorn) Numerical Methods and FORTRAN Programming, 1964, A Guide to FORTRAN IV Programming, 1965, 2d edit., 1972, FORTRAN with Engineering Applications, 1967, Public Policy and the Expert, 1971, Numerical Methods with FORTRAN IV Case Studies, 1972, A Simplified Guide to FORTRAN Programming, 1974, A Simplified Guide to Structured Cobol Programming, 1976, (with Donald G. Golden) 2d edit., 1988, A Guide to PL/M Programming for Microcomputer Applications, 1978, A Guide to NOMAD for Applications Development, 1981, Computing for Engineers and Scientists with Fortran 77, 1984, (with William I. Salmon) 2d edit., 1988, A Second Course in Computer Science with Pascal, 1987; (with William I. Salmon) A Second Course in Computer Science with Modula-2, 1987, (with Donald G. Golden) Simplified Structured Cobol with Microsoft/Microfocus Cobol, 1990; editor: (with M. Mead, R.L. Shinn and J.E. Carothers) To Love or To Perish: The Technological Crisis and the Churches, 1972. Pres. bd. edn., Ossining, N.Y., 1965-66. Recipient Norbert Wiener award Computer Profls. for Social Responsibility, 1989. Fellow Assn. Computing Machinery (chmn. com. on computers and pub. policy 1972-76, mem. council 1974-82, v.p. 1976-78, pres. 1978-80, Outstanding Contbns. Computer Sci. Edn. award 1992). Democrat. Address: 160 Cabrini Blvd New York NY 10033-1137

MCCRACKEN, ELLIS W., JR., lawyer, corporation executive; B.A., Lebanon Valley Coll., 1963; LL.B., St. John's U., 1967. Bar: N.Y. 1967, N.J. 1969, Ohio 1972. Primary contract atty. foods div. Borden, Inc., 1970-74; assoc. Milbank, Tweed, Hadley & McCloy, 1967-70; v.p., gen. counsel Campbell Taggart, Inc., Dallas, 1980—. Office: Anheuser-Busch Co Saint Louis MO 63118

MCCRACKEN, JOE C., school system administrator. Supt. Lockwood Schs., Billings, Mont. State finalist Nat. Supt. of Yr., 1993. Office: Lockwood Schs 1932 Us Highway 87 E Billings MT 59101-6651

MCCRACKEN, JOHN HARVEY, painter, sculptor; b. Berkeley, Calif., Dec. 9, 1934; s. John H. and Marjorie (Strain) McC.; m. Gail Barringer, May 4, 1991; children: David Gordon, Patrick Daniel. BFA, Calif. Coll. Arts & Crafts, 1962, postgrad., 1962-65. Tchr.: U. Calif., Irvine, 1965-66, L.A., 1966-68. Santa Barbara, 1974-85, Sch. Visual Arts, N.Y.C., 1968-69, Hunter Coll., N.Y.C., 1970-71, U. Nev., Reno, 1971-72, Las Vegas, 1972-75. One man shows include: Robert Elkon Gallery, N.Y.C., 1966, 67, 68, 72, 73, Galerie Ileana Sonnabend, Paris, 1969, Sonnabend Gallery, N.Y.C., 1970, Ace Gallery, L.A., 1985, PS 1, Long Island City, N.Y., 1986, Newport Harbor Art Mus., Calif., 1987, Contemporary Arts Mus., Houston, 1989, HoffmanBorman Gallery, Santa Monica, Calif., 1988, Konrad Fischer Gallery, Düsseldorf, Fed. Republic Germany, 1989, Lisson Gallery, London, 1990, Galerie Nordenhake, Stockholm, 1990, Fred Hoffman Gallery, L.A., 1990, Galerie Froment & Putman, Paris, 1991, Sonnabend Gallery, N.Y.C., 1992, Louver Gallery, L.A., 1993, 94, Galerie Xavier Hufkens, Brussels, 1993, Galerie Art & Public, Geneva, 1994, Galerie Tanit, Munich, 1995, Hochshule Fur Angwandte Kunst, Vienna, 1995, Kunsthalle Basel, Switzerland, 1995; group exhbns. include: Solomon R. Guggenheim Mus., N.Y.C., 1967, Saatchi Gallery, London, 1985, Venice (Italy) Biennale, 1986, Centro de Arte Reina Sofia, Madrid, 1987, Musee St Pierre Art Contemporain, Lyon, France, 1988, Solomon R. Guggenheim Mus., N.Y.C., 1989-90, Carnegie Internat., Carnegie Mus. Art, Pitts., 1991; represented in mus. collections including: Art Inst. Chgo., Solomon R. Guggenheim Mus., N.Y.C.; Mus. Modern Art, N.Y.C., San Francisco Mus. Art, Whitney Mus. Am. Art, N.Y.C., Mus. Contemporary Art, L.A., L.A. County Mus. Art. Grantee, NEA, 1968.

MC CRACKEN, PAUL WINSTON, economist, business educator; b. Richland, Iowa, Dec. 29, 1915; s. Sumner and Mary (Coffin) McC.; m. Emily Ruth Siler, May 27, 1942; children—Linda Jo, Paula Jeanne. Student, William Penn Coll., 1937; M.A., Harvard, 1942, Ph.D., 1948. Faculty Found. Sch., Berea Coll., Ky., 1937-40; economist Dept. Commerce, Washington, 1942-43; fin. economist, dir. research Fed. Res. Bank of Mpls., 1943-48; assoc. prof. Sch. Bus. Adminstrn., U. Mich., 1948-50, prof., 1950-66, Edmund Ezra Day Univ. prof. bus. adminstrn., 1966-86, prof. emeritus, 1986—; chmn. Nat. Bur. Econ. Rsch.; trustee Earhart Found.; mem. pub. oversight bd. AICPA. Author: monographs Can Capitalism Survive?; articles on financial, econ. subjects. Fellow Am. Statis. Assn.; mem. Am. Econ. Assn., Am. Finance Assn., Royal Econ. Soc., Harvard Grad. Soc. (coun.). Presbyn. Clubs: Cosmos (Washington); Harvard (N.Y.C.). Home: 2564 Hawthorn Rd Ann Arbor MI 48104

MC CRACKEN, PHILIP TRAFTON, sculptor; b. Bellingham, Wash., Nov. 14, 1928; s. William Franklin and Maude (Trafton) McC.; m. Anne MacFetridge, Aug. 14, 1954; children—Timothy, Robert, Daniel. B.A. in Sculpture, U. Wash., 1954. Asst. to Henry Moore Eng., 1954. One-man shows: Willard Gallery, N.Y.C., 1960, 65, 68, 70, Seattle Art Mus., 1961, Wash. State Capitol Mus., Olympia, 1964, Art Gallery of Greater Victoria, B.C., 1964, LaJolla (Calif.) Mus. Art, 1970, Anchorage Hist. and Fine Arts Mus., 1970, Tacoma Art Mus., 1980, Kennedy Galleries, N.Y.C., 1985, Lynn McAllister Gallery, Seattle, 1986, 89, Valley Mus. N.W. Art, La Conner, Wash., 1993, Whatcom Mus. Bellingham, Wash., 1994, others; group shows include: Mus. Art, Ogunquit, Maine, 1957, Chgo. Art Inst., 1958, Detroit Inst. Arts, 1958, Pa. Acad. Fine Arts, 1958, Contemporary Art Gallery, Houston, 1958, DeYoung Meml. Mus., San Francisco, 1960, Los Angeles Mcpl. Art Mus., 1960, Galerie Claude Bernard, Paris, 1960, Phillips Gallery, Washington, 1966, Corcoran Gallery, 1966, Mus. Art, Akron, 1967, Finch Coll., N.Y.C., 1968, Rutgers U., 1968, Whitney Mus. Art, 1978, Portland Art Mus., 1976, Mont. State U., Bozeman, 1979, Brigham Young U., 1980, Bellvue (Wash.) Art Mus., 1986, Lynn McAllister Gallery, 1986, Am. Acad. Arts and Letters, N.Y.C., 1986, Schmidt Bingham Gallery, N.Y.C., 1987, Wash. State Capital Mus., 1987, 89, Cheney-Cowles Mus., Spokane, Wash., 1988, Smithsonian Instn., 1991—, Nat. Mus. Ottawa, Can., 1991-92, Gallery Three-Zero, N.Y.C., 1993, Seattle Art Mus., 1994, others; sculptures represented: Norton Bldg., Seattle, Kankakee (Ill.) State Hosp., Swinomish Indian Tribal Center, LaConner, UN Assn., N.Y.C., King County King Dome, Seattle, City Hall, Everett, Wash., others. (Recipient numerous prizes, awards). Address: 401 Guemes Island Rd # B Anacortes WA 98221-9534

MCCRACKEN, STEVEN CARL, lawyer; b. Artesia, Calif., Oct. 29, 1950; s. Glenn A. and Helen V. (Fears) McCracken; m. Susan Lee Waggener, July 29, 1979; children: Casey James, Scott Kevin. BA magna cum laude, U. Calif., Irvine, 1972; JD, U. Va., 1975. Bar: Calif. 1975, U.S. Dist. Ct. (cen. dist.) Calif. 1975, U.S. Ct. Appeals (9th cir.) 1976, U.S. Dist. Ct. (so. dist.) Calif. 1977, D.C. 1979, U.S. Supreme Ct. 1985, U.S. Dist. Ct. (no. dist.) Calif. 1990. Assoc. Gibson, Dunn & Crutcher, L.A., 1975-82; ptnr. Gibson, Dunn & Crutcher, Irvine, Calif., 1983-94; v.p., sec. and gen. counsel Callaway Golf Co., Carlsbad, Calif., 1994—; lawyer rep. Ninth Cir. Jud. Conf. 1989-91. Editor Va. Law Rev., 1973-75, mng. bd. 1974-75, bd. editors The Computer Lawyer, 1984—. Mem. ABA (antitrust sect.), Orange County Bar Assn. (bd. dirs. 1988-90, chmn. fed. ct. com. 1988-89, chmn. bus. litigation

sect. 1990, sec. 1991, treas. 1992, pres.-elect 1993, pres. 1994). Democrat. Office: Callaway Golf Co 2285 Rutherford Rd Carlsbad CA 92008-8815

MCCRACKEN, THOMAS JAMES, JR., lawyer; b. Chgo., Oct. 27, 1952; s. Thomas J. Sr. and Eileen (Brophy) McC.; m. Peggy A. Jamrok; children: Catherine, Michael, Amanda, Quinn. BA, Marquette U., 1974; JD, Loyola U., 1977. Bar: Ill. 1977, U.S. Dist. Ct. (no. dist.) Ill., U.S. Ct. Appeals (7th cir.) 1984. Asst. state's atty. DuPage County State's Atty.'s Office, Wheaton, Ill., 1977-81; assoc. atty. McCracken & Walsh, Chgo., 1981-84; ptnr. McCracken, Walsh deLaVan & Hetler, Chgo., 1984—; commr. Nat. Conf. of Commns. on Uniform State Laws, 1989—; bd. dirs. Oak Trust and Savs. Bank, Chgo. Contbr. articles to profl. jours. State rep. Ill. Gen. Assembly, Springfield, Ill., 1983-93, state senator, 1993; chmn. Regional Trans. Authority, Chgo., 1993—. Named Top Ten Legislators Chgo. Mag., 1990. Mem. Chgo. Bar Assn., Ill. State Bar Assn. Avocations: skiing, fishing, hunting, coaching children's sports. Office: McCracken Walsh deLaVan & Hetler 134 N La Salle St Ste 600 Chicago IL 60602-1004

MCCRACKIN, WILLIAM K., gas company executive; b. Aug. 27, 1933; s. Samuel Cecil and Jean Elaine (Kester) McC; m. Mary Teresa Campbell, Mar. 5, 1957; children: Kevin, Craig, Brian, Karen. BS, Wayne State U., 1956. Contr. Mich. Consol. Gas Co., Detroit, 1976-78, v.p. rate regulatory affairs, 1978-84, sr. v.p. fin. regulatory affairs, 1984-86, vice chmn., chief fin. officer, 1986—, also bd. dirs.; vice chmn., chief fin. officer MCN, Detroit. Chmn. Detroit Sci. Ctr., 1990; bd. dirs. Jr. Achievement Southeastern Mich. Lt. comdr. USN, 1956-60. Mem. U.S.C. of C. (bd. dirs.), Greater Detroit C. of C. (trustee). Office: MCN Corp 500 Griswold St Detroit MI 48226-3700 Office: Detroit Science Ctr 5020 John R St Detroit MI 48202-4045

MCCRADY, BARBARA SACHS, psychologist, educator; b. Evanston, Ill., May 7, 1949; d. James Frederick and Margaret Maxine (Miller) Sachs; m. Dennis D. McCrady, June 13, 1969; 1 child, Eric Paul. BS, Purdue U., 1969; PhD, U. R.I., 1975. Lic. clin. psychologist. Clin. project evaluator Butler Hosp., Providence, 1974-75, chief psychol. assessment program, 1975-76, chief problem drinkers' project, 1976-83; assoc. prof. psychology Rutgers U., Piscataway, N.J., 1983-89, prof. psychology, 1989—; from instr. to assoc. prof. psychiatry Brown U., Providence, 1975-83; acting dir. Rutgers Ctr. Alcohol Studies, Piscataway, 1990-92; reviewer Nat. Inst. on Alcohol Abuse and Alcholism, Washington, 1979-82, extramural scientific adv. bd., 1989-93; cons. Inst. Medicine, Washington, 1988-89. Author: The Alcoholic Marriage, 1977; editor: Marriage and Marital Therapy, 1978, Directions in Alcohol Aubse Treatment Research, 1985, Research on Alcoholics Anonymous: Opportunities and Alternatives, 1993. Grantee Nat. Inst. on Alcohol Abuse and Alcoholism, 1979-83, 1988—. Fellow Am. Psychol. Assn.; mem. Assn. for Advancement Behavior Therapy. Avocations: horseback riding, skiing, piano. Office: Rutgers U Ctr Alcohol Studies Smithers Hall Busch Campus Piscataway NJ 08855-0969

MCCRADY, JAMES DAVID, veterinarian, educator; b. Beaumont, Tex., June 26, 1930; s. James Homer and Lucyle (Ward) McC.; m. Mary Elizabeth McDougald, Sept. 8, 1951; children—David, Diane, Darla. B.S., Tex. A. and M. Coll., 1952, D.V.M., 1958; Ph.D., Baylor U., 1965. Instr., then asst. prof. Tex. A. and M. Coll., 1958- 62; dir. animal rsch., instr. Baylor U. Coll. Medicine, 1962-64; mem. faculty Tex A&M U., 1964—; prof., head dept. vet. physiology and pharmacology Tex. A. and M. Coll., 1966-90, prof., dir. spl. programs, 1990—; adj. prof. Baylor Coll. Medicine, M.D. Anderson Hosp. and Tumor Inst. Served with USAF, 1952-54. Mem. AVMA, Tex. Acad. Sci., Am. Physiol. Soc., Sigma Xi, Phi Kappa Phi, Phi Zeta. Research on comparative cardiovascular and respiratory physiology. Home: 511 Olive St Bryan TX 77801-3506 Office: Tex A&M U College Station TX 77843

MCCRARY, DOUGLAS L., utility company executive; b. 1929; married. B.Mech. Engring., Auburn U., M.Mech. Engring., 1953. With Ala. Power Co., Birmingham, 1953-77; with Southern Co. Services, Inc., 1977-83; pres., CEO Gulf Power Co., Pensacola, Fla., 1983-94, chmn. bd. dirs., 1994—. Office: Gulf Power Co PO Box 1151 Pensacola FL 32520-0001 also: Gulf Power Co 500 Bayfront Pky Pensacola FL 32501-6102

MCCRAW, JOHN RANDOLPH, JR., assistant principal; b. Lynchburg, Va., Nov. 23, 1942; s. John Randolph and Mabel L. (Bethel) McC.; m. Carolyn Lynn Mason, Aug. 3, 1968. BA, Emory and Henry Coll., 1965; MEd, U. Va., 1971; LLB, LaSalle Extension U., 1977; EdD, Va. Poly. Inst. and State U., 1987; cert., Oxford U., 1992. Cert. tchr., adminstr., Va. Tchr. govt. Martinsville (Va.) City Schs., 1965-89; asst. prin. Martinsville Jr. High Sch., 1989-90, Albert Harris Elem. Sch., Martinsville, 1990-93, Martinsville High Sch., 1993—; dir. Martinsville City Schs. Self Studies, Va. Dept. Edn./ So. Assn. Colls. and Schs., 1988-90. Author: The Legal History of Teacher Certification in the Commonwealth of Virginia, 1987, Hands-On-Learning, 1993. Chmn. Martinsville Henry County Rep. party, state senate Rep. dist.; candidate for Martinsville City Coun. Mem. ASCD, Nat. Assn. Elem. Sch. Prins., Va. Assn. Elem. Sch. Prins., Va. Coaches Assn., Mid-Atlantic Notary Assn., Phi Delta Kappa. Baptist. Avocations: politics, law, current events, reading. Home: 178 Meadowview Ln Martinsville VA 24112-5708 Office: Martinsville City Schs 710 Smith Rd Martinsville VA 24112-2531

MCCRAW, LESLIE G., engineering and construction company executive; b. Sandy Springs, S.C., Nov. 3, 1934; s. Leslie Gladstone and Cornelia (Milam) McC.; m. Mary Earle Brown; children: Leslie Gladstone III, James B., John. BSCE, Clemson U., 1956. Registered profl. engr., Del. Design engr. Gulf Oil Corp., Phila., 1956-57; various engring. and constrn. positions E.I. DuPont Co., Wilmington, Del., 1956-75; v.p., mgr. div. Daniel Constrn. Co. Greenville, S.C., 1975-82, pres., 1982-84; pres., chief exec. officer Daniel Internat., Greenville, 1984-86, Fluor Daniel, Greenville and Irvine, Calif., 1986-88; pres. Fluor Corp., Irvine, 1988-90, vice chmn., chief exec. officer, 1990-91, chief exec. officer, chmn. bd. dirs., 1991. Bd. dirs. Allergan and Multimedia Inc., Orange County Performing Arts Ctr., Calif. Econ. Devel. Corp., U.S.-China Bus. Coun.; trustee Hampden-Sydney Coll., Va.; mem. adv. bd. rsch. found., mem. pres.' adv. coun. Clemson U.; mem. bd. visitors U. Calif. Grad. Sch. Mgmt. Mem. Bus. Roundtable, Constrn. Industry's Pres.'s Forum, Nat. Assn. Mfrs. (bd. dirs.), Calif. Bus. Roundtable Palmetto Bus. Forum. Republican. Presbyterian. Office: Fluor Corp Inc 3333 Michelson Dr Irvine CA 92730-0001

MCCRAW, THOMAS KINCAID, business history educator, editor, author; b. Corinth, Miss., Sept. 11, 1940; s. John Carey and Eugenia Olive (Kincaid) McC.; m. Susan Morehead, Sept. 22, 1962; children: Elizabeth Morehead, Thomas Kincaid Jr. BA, U. Miss., 1962; MA, U. Wis., 1968, Ph.D., 1970; MA (hon.), Harvard U., 1978. Tchg. asst. U. Wis., Madison, 1968-69; asst. prof. U. Tex., Austin, 1970-74, assoc. prof., 1974-78; vis. assoc. prof. Bus. Sch., Harvard U., Boston, 1976-78, prof., 1978-89, Straus prof. bus. history, 1989—; dir. research Bus. Sch., Harvard U., 1985-87, co-chmn. bus. govt. and competition area, 1986—; ednl. cons. to cos., U.S., Japan, 1977—. Author: Morgan versus Lilienthal, 1970, TVA and the Power Fight, 1971, Prophets of Regulation, 1984; co-author: The Coming of Managerial Capitalism, 1995; editor: Regulation in Perspective, 1981, American Versus Japan, 1986, The Essential Alfred Chandler, 1988, Bus. History Rev., 1994—; contbr. numerous articles to various publs., chpts. to books. Trustee Bus. History Conf., 1986—, pres., 1989; mem. coun. Mass. Hist. Soc., 1987-92. Lt. USN, 1962-66. Recipient Lyons Master's Essay award Loyola U., Chgo., 1969, Younger Humanist award NEH, 1975, Pulitzer prize in history Columbia U., 1985, Thomas Newcomen Book award, 1986; Woodrow Wilson fellow, 1966-67; named to Alumni Hall of Fame, U. Miss., 1986; Newcomen fellowship Harvard U., 1973-74. Mem. Orgn. Am. Historians, Econ. Hist. Assn., Am. Econ. Assn. Democrat. Roman Catholic. Office: Harvard U Bus Sch Soldiers Field Boston MA 02163

MCCRAY, CURTIS LEE, university president; b. Wheatland, Ind., Jan. 29, 1938; s. Bert and Susan McCray; m. Mary Joyce Macdonald, Sept. 10, 1960; children: Leslie, Jennifer, Meredith. B.A., Knox Coll., Galesburg, Ill., 1960; postgrad. U. Pa., 1960-61; Ph.D., U. Nebr., 1968. Chmn. dept. English, Saginaw Valley Coll., University Center, Mich., 1972-73, dean arts and scis., 1973-75, v.p. acad. affairs, 1975-77; provost, v.p. acad. affairs Govs. State U., Chgo., 1977-82; pres. U. North Fla., Jacksonville, 1982-88, Calif. State U. Long Beach, 1988-93, Millikin U., Decatur, Ill., 1993—. Bd. dirs., 1982-88, campaign chmn. Jacksonville United Way, 1987; bd. dirs. Sta. WJCT Channel 7 and Stereo 90, Jacksonville, 1982-88, Jacksonville Art Mus., 1983-

88, Meml. Med. Ctr., Jacksonville, 1983-88, Jacksonville Community Council, Inc., 1982-88, Arts Assembly Jacksonville, 1984-88, Jacksonville Urban League, 1985-88; hon. dir. Jacksonville Symphony Assn., 1983; mem. Dame Point Bridge Commn., Jacksonville, 1982; mem. Jacksonville High Tech Task Force, 1982; chmn. SUS High Tech. and Industry Council, 1986-88; mem. state relations and undergrad. edn. com. Am. Assn. State Colls. and Univs., 1985-88. Woodrow Wilson fellow, 1960; Johnson fellow, 1966; George F. Baker scholar, 1956; Ford Found. grantee, 1969; recipient Landee award for excellence in teaching Saginaw State Coll., 1972. Mem. AAUP. Club: Torch. Office: Millikin U 1184 W Main St Decatur IL 62522

MCCRAY, RICHARD ALAN, astrophysicist, educator; b. Los Angeles, Nov. 24, 1937; s. Alan Archer and Ruth Elizabeth (Woodworth) McC.; m. Sandra Broomfield; children—Julia, Carla. B.S., Stanford U., 1959; Ph.D., UCLA, 1967. Research fellow Calif. Inst. Tech, Pasadena, 1967-68; asst. prof. astronomy Harvard U., Cambridge, Mass., 1968-71; assoc. prof. astrophysics U. Colo., Boulder, 1971-75, prof., 1975—, chmn. Joint Inst. Lab. Astrophysics, 1981-84, chmn. Ctr. for Astrophysics and Space Astronomy, 1985-86. Contbr. articles to profl. jours. Guggenheim fellow, 1975-76. Mem. NAS, Am. Astron. Soc. (councilor 1980-83, chmn. high energy astrophysics div. 1986-87, Heineman Prize for Astrophysics, 1990), Internat. Astron. Union. Office: U Colo Joint Inst Lab Astrophysics Boulder CO 80309-0440

MCCREA, PETER, oil company executive; b. San Francisco, Nov. 4, 1939; s. Frederick Hoyt and Eleanor Knox (Wheeler) McC.; m. Willinda McClung, Nov. 14, 1964; children: Frederick Hoyt, Sarah Frances. BS, Dartmouth Coll., 1961, BCE, 1962. Engr. Arabian Am. Oil Co., Dhahran, Saudi Arabia, 1964-69; engr. Chevron Corp., San Francisco, 1969-72, various positions, 1972-79; exec. Chevron Chem. Corp., San Francisco, 1979-89; sr. v.p. Chevron Internat. Oil Co., San Francisco, 1990-92; v.p. Chevron USA Products Co., San Francisco, 1992—; pres. San Francisco Pub. Utilities Commn, 1980-83. Chmn. The Fertilizer Inst., Washington, 1987-88; pres. Stony Hill Vineyard, St. Helena, Calif. Mem. Bohemian Club. Office: Chevron USA Products Co 575 Market St San Francisco CA 94105-2823

MCCREADY, KENNETH FRANK, electric utility executive; b. Edmonton, Alta., Can., Oct. 9, 1939; s. Ralph and Lilian McCready; m. Margaret E. Randall, Sept. 2, 1961; children: John, Janet, Brian. BSc, U. Alta., 1963. Supr. data processing and systems Calgary (Alta.) Power Ltd., 1965-67, supr. rates and contracts, 1967-68, adminstrv. asst. to exec. v.p., 1968-72, asst. mgr. mgmt. cons. div., 1972-75; mgr. mgmt. systems dept., gen. mgr. Montreal Engring. Co., Calgary, 1975-76; v.p. adminstrn. Calgary (Alta.) Power Ltd., 1976-80; sr. v.p. ops. TransAlta Utilities, Calgary, 1980-85, pres., chief operating officer, 1985-89, also bd. dirs., 1988—; pres., CEO TransAlta Utilities, TransAlta Energy, 1989-94; CEO TransAlta Corp., TransAlta Utilities, TransAlta Energy, 1994—; pres., CEO TransAlta Corp., Clagary, 1994—; bd. dirs. PanCan. Petroleum Ltd., Hewlett Packard (Can.) Ltd., Conf. Bd. Can. (vice-chmn.), Marigold Found. Ltd.; mem. environ. adv. coun. Dow Chem. Co.; chmn. bd. Advanced Computing Techs., Inc. Van Horne Inst. Past dep. chmn. bd. govs. So. Alta, Inst. of Tech.; chair Alberta Round Table on Environment and Econ.; co-chair Task Force on Environment; mem. com. on trade and enviroment Govt. Can. Internat. Trade Adv.; past pres. N.W. Electric Light and Power Assoc. Mem. Assn. Profl. Engrs., Geologists and Geophysicists of Alta. Asea Brown Boveri, Bus. Coun. on Nat. Issues, World Bus. Coun. for Sustainable Devel., Can. Exec. Svc. Orgn. (adv. coun.), Conserve. Owners' Assn. Alta (past pres.), Calgary C. of C., Men's Can. Club Calgary (past pres.), Ranchmen's Club. Avocations: computers, cycling, photography. Office: TransAlta Corp, 110 12th Ave SW Box 1900, Calgary, AB Canada T2P 2M1

MCCREADY, WILLIAM FLOYD, venture capitalist, entrepreneur; b. Tillamook, Oreg., Mar. 29, 1944; s. William S. and Eleanor L. (Wildfong) McC. BS in Engring. Physics and Math., Oreg. State U., 1966; MS in Nuclear Engring., USN, 1968. Chief nuclear test engr. Pearl Harbor Naval Shipyard, Honolulu, 1971-73; supt. Mauna Kea Astron. Obs., U. Hawaii, Hilo, 1973-76; gen. ptnr. Venture Planning Assocs., Honolulu, 1976—; bus. cons. UN Devel. Program, Bhutan; prin., bd. dirs. Sanchez Comm. Sta. KQNG-AM-FM, Lihue, Kauai, Hawaii, Studebakers of Australia, Sydney, Group (4) Logistics, Ltd.; prin., cons. Kula Bay Tropical Clothes Co., Honolulu, 1988—; gen. ptnr. Venture Investment Ptnrs., Honolulu, 1992; developer Embassy Centre, Ho Chi Minh City, Vietnam, 1994; keynote spkr. Hawaii Gov.'s Symposium on Software Devel., 1991; co-coord. Hawaii Gov.'s Symposium on High Tech. Devel., 1982. Mem. Gov.'s Hawaii 2000 Commn., Hilo, 1973-76; course marshall Honolulu Marathon, 1986-89; telethon panelist Hawaii Easter Seals Soc. for Handicapped, 1985-92; spl. instr. applied econs. Jr. Achievement, 1988-89; mem. Better Bus. Bur. Hawaii. Officer USN, 1966-71, Vietnam. Mem. Inst. Mgmt. Cons. (cert.), Acad. Profl. Cons. and Advisors (cert. profl. cons.), Hawaii Venture Capital Assn. (co-founder, past pres.), Nat. Fedn. Ind. Bus., Small Bus. Hawaii, Rotary (dir. cmty. svc. Pearl Harbor 1990). Avocations: ocean marathon swimming, golf, tennis. Office: Venture Planning Assocs Inc 1188 Bishop St Ste 1508 Honolulu HI 96813-3306

MCCREARY, DUSTIN CAMPBELL, lawyer, arbitrator; b. Cleve., July 19, 1928; s. Robert G. and Helen (Galvin) McC.; m. Jean Doyle, June 1, 1957 (div. Mar. 1973); m. Rosalie Ogden, Sept. 29, 1973; children: William D., Patricia Helen. BA, Hobart Coll., 1952; LLB, Western Res. U., 1955. Bar: Ohio 1955, Wash. 1958. Assoc. Wilmot Baskin Lausche & Kelley, Cleve., 1955-56; trial atty. Nat. Labor Rels. Bd., Washington and Seattle, 1956-62; assoc. Bogle Bogle & Gates, Seattle, 1962-71; ptnr. Bogle & Gates and precedessor firms, Seattle, 1971-89; mem. Wash. State Publ. Employment Rels. Commn., 1991-95; co-founder Ann. Pacific Coast Labor Law Conf., Seattle; labor arbitrator, 1990—. With U.S. Army, 1946-48. Mem. ABA (co-chmn. various subcoms., labor law sect., employee benefit com. 1977-88), Wash. State Bar Assn. (specialization bd. 1986-87), San Juan County Bar Assn., Am. Inns of Ct., Am. Arbitration Assn., Seattle Yacht Club, Wash. Athletic Club, San Juan Island Yacht Club, Phi Delta Phi, Sigma Phi. Democrat. Home and Office: PO Box 368 Friday Harbor WA 98250-0368

MC CREARY, JAMES FRANKLIN, banker, lawyer; b. Farmington, Mo., June 15, 1942; s. Frank J. and Bernice E. (Dugal) McCreary; m. Martha Jean Tucker, June 30, 1962; children: James Franklin, III, Jason Tucker, Josh Adam. BSBA, U. Evansville, 1964; JD, Nashville Law Sch., 1969; MBA, Vanderbilt U., 1980. Bar: Tenn. 1969. With Old Nat. Bank, Evansville, Ind., 1960-64; with First Am. Corp., Nashville, 1972-80, exec. v.p., corp. sec., gen. counsel, 1974-80; with First Am. Nat. Bank Nashville (N.A.), 1964-72, 80-86, exec. v.p., 1980-86; ptnr. Borod & Huggins Attys., Memphis, 1986-87; ptnr. Gerrish & Mc Creary, Memphis, 1988, of counsel, 1988-92, dir., 1993—; pres. Met. Fed. Bank, 1988-91; vis. prof. bus. law David Lipscomb U., 1975-77; instr. law and banking Am. Inst. Banking, 1969-75. Mem. Beta Gamma Sigma. Mem. Ch. of Christ. Office: Gerrish & Mc Creary PC 222 2nd Ave N Nashville TN 37201-1649

MCCREDIE, JAMES ROBERT, fine arts educator; b. Chgo., Dec. 31, 1935; s. William and Mareta (Black) McC.; m. Marian Lucille Miles, Sept. 3, 1960; children: Miles William, Meredeth Black. AB in History and Literature summa cum laude, Harvard U., 1958, AM, 1961, PhD, 1963; student, Am. Sch. Classical Studies, Athens, Greece, 1958-59, 61-62. Instr. NYU, 1963-64, asst. prof., 1965-66, assoc. prof., 1967-70, prof., 1970, 78-88, Sherman Fairchild Prof. Fine Arts, 1988—, dep. dir. Inst. Fine Arts, 1967-69, acting dir., 1982-83, dir., 1983—, asst. field dir. Excavations in Samothrace, 1962, field dir., 1963-65, dir. excavations, 1966—; dir. Am. Sch. Classical Studies at Athens, Greece, 1969-77, chmn. mng. com., 1980-90, trustee, 1980—; vis. mem. Inst. Advanced Study, Princeton, N.J., 1977-78; mem. vis. com. dept. classical and near eastern Archeology Bryn Mayr Coll. 1982, dept. european paintings Met. Mus. Art, 1983—. Ctr. Old World Archaeology and Art Brown U., Providence, 1985; mem. adv. bd. Alexander S. Onassis Ctr. for Hellenic Studies NYU, 1990—; cons. in field. Author: Fortified Military Camps in Attica, Hesperia, 1966, Samothrace, 7, The Rotunda of Arsinoe, 1992; mem. adv. bd. Am. Jour. Archaeology, 1969-81; contbr. articles to prof. jours.. Bd. dirs. Hellenic-Am. Unions. Athens, 1973-77, vice chmn., 1977-87, U.S. Edni. Found.| Greece, 1969-75; active Pres. Adv. Com. on Cultural Property, 1992-95. Charles Norton fellow, 1961-62; named hon. citizen Community of Samothrace, 1976. Mem. Am. Philos. Soc., Archaeol. Inst. Am. (life, trustee 1972-75, mem. exec. com. 1978-81),

Archaeol. Soc. Athens (hon.), Deutsches archaeologisches Inst. (corr.). Home: 30 Battle Rd Princeton NJ 08540 also summer: Palaiopolis GR-680 02, Samothrace Greece Office: NYU Inst Fine Arts 1 E 78th St New York NY 10021

MCCREE, DONALD HANNA, JR., banker; b. Orange, N.J., Sept. 17, 1936; s. Donald Hanna and Elna (Van Houten) McC.; m. Patricia H. Jones, June 13, 1959; children: Donald, Douglas, David. A.B., Dartmouth Coll., 1958. With Mfrs. Hanover Trust Co., N.Y.C., 1960-90; sr. v.p., mgr. Mfrs. Hanover Trust Co. (London br.), 1976-78; sr. v.p., dep. gen. mgr. Mfrs. Hanover Trust Co., N.Y.C., 1978-79, sector exec. v.p. corp. banking, mem. gen. adminstrv. bd., 1980-90,91—; pres., CEO IBJ Schroder Bank and Trust Co., N.Y.C., 1995—. Served with USNR, 1958-60. Mem. Bankers Roundtable, Am. Bankers Assn. (exec. com. comml. lending div.), United Way of N.Y.C. (bd.of dirs.). Club: Whippoorwill, Loblolly. Office: IBJ Schroder Bank & Trust Co 1 State Ste New York NY 10004

MCCREERY, WILLIAM See RAMSEY, BILL

MCCREIGHT, JOHN A., management consultant; b. Phila., Jan. 29, 1938; s. John A. and Marion R. (Vetter) McC.; m. Kim Amet Healey; children: Laura, Cindy, Brian, Kimberly. BS in Mgmt. Scis., Northeastern U., 1968. Cert. mgmt. cons. Chief systems devel. AVCO Apollo Systems, Boston, 1964-68; sr. mgmt. cons. Touche, Ross & Co., Detroit, 1968-72, ptnr., Detroit and N.Y.C., 1972-80, nat. dir., mem. exec. com., N.Y.C., 1980-83 mng. dir. Hayes Hill, N.Y.C., 1983; pres. McCreight & Co., Inc. New Canaan, Conn. and Phila., 1983-86; mng. dir. Hay Group, Inc., N.Y.C., 1986-91; pres. McCreight & Co., Inc., New Canaan and Wilton, Conn., 1991—; mem. Presdl. Task Force to Reduce Cost and Improve Effectiveness of USN; dir. officer Inst. Mgmt. Cons. Adv. Carnegie Hall Bd. Trustees, NIH, N.Y. Mayor's Office, Salvation Army; past chmn. N.Y. Corp. Fund Raising, NIMH; mem. N.Y. Ireland U.S. Coun.; Served with USNR, 1955-63. Mem. Univ. Club (N.Y.C.). Office: McCreight & Co Inc 487 Danbury Rd Wilton CT 06897

MCCRENSKY, EDWARD, international consultant, former organization executive; b. Boston, June 19, 1912; s. Benjamin and Anna (Miller) McC.; m. Louise C. Marshall, Apr. 16, 1942; children: Myron Wilson, Richard Marshall. B.A., Boston Coll., 1933; M.Ed., Boston Tchrs. Coll., 1935; student, Harvard Grad. Sch. Edn., 1940-41. High sch. tchr. Boston, 1936-41; govt. ofcl. U.S. Civil Service Commn., 1941-46; dir. civilian personnel and service Office Naval Research, Washington, 1946-66; chief personnel adminstrn. dept. social and econ. affairs UN, N.Y.C., 1966-68; inter-regional adviser UN, 1968-77; team leader UN, Bangkok, Thailand, 1977-81; internat. cons., 1981—; prof. George Washington U., 1950-68; guest prof. Royal Coll. Sci. and Tech., Strathclyde U., Glasgow, Scotland, 1961; cons. U.S. and internat. orgns.; lectr. human relations and internat. sci. manpower; Author: Wartime Practices in Recruitment, 1946, Scientific Manpower in Europe, 1959, Strategy and Tactics, Professional Recruitment, 1963; Contbr. articles U.S. fgn. jours. Recipient Rockefeller Pub. Service award and fellowship, 1957; Merit citation Nat. Civil Service League, 1955; Distinguished Civilian Service award Navy Dept., 1966. Mem. Soc. Pers. Adminstrn. (pres. 1955-56), Rotary (bd. dirs. Surfside club 1986-89, Paul Harris fellow). Home: 614 7th Ave N Surfside Beach SC 29575-4104 I have always sought to broaden my experience in work, geographical location and cultural differences by accepting available opportunities for personal growth. I have constantly tried to prepare myself through research, planning, and authorship for improved professional capability.

MCCRERY, JAMES (JIM MCCRERY), congressman; b. Shreveport, LA, Sept. 18, 1949; m. Johnette Hawkins, Aug. 3, 1991; 1 child, Claiborne Scott. BA, La. Tech. U., 1971; JD, La. State U., 1975. Bar: La. 1975. Pvt. practice Leesville, La., 1975-78; asst. city atty. City of Shreveport, 1979-80; mem. staff U.S. Rep. Buddy Roemer, 1981-84; regional mgr. Ga.-Pacific Corp., 1984-88; mem. 100th-103rd Congresses from 4th (now 5th) La. dist., 1988—; mem. ways and means com. Office: US Ho of Reps 225 Cannon Ho Ofc Bldg Washington DC 20515

MC CRIE, ROBERT DELBERT, editor, publisher, educator; b. Sarnia, Ont., Can., Oct. 8, 1938; s. Robert Newton and Evelyn May (Johnston) McC.; m. Fulvia Madia, Dec. 22, 1965; children: Carla Alexandra, Mara Elizabeth. B.A., Ohio Wesleyan U., 1960; M.S., U. Toledo, 1962; postgrad., U. Chgo., 1962-63; MA, Hunter Coll., 1994; MPhil, CUNY, 1994, PhD, 1995. Cert. protection profl. Researcher Connective Tissues Research Lab., Copenhagen, 1963; copywriter numerous advt. agys., 1965-70; owner, editor Security Letter, N.Y.C., 1970—; editor, pub. HBJ Publs., N.Y.C., 1973-76; pres. Mags. for Medicine, Inc., N.Y.C., 1972-81; faculty John Jay Coll. Criminal Justice, 1985—, asst. prof., 1986-91, assoc. prof., 1992—; bd. dirs. numerous cos.; cons. in field; speaker at numerous meetings. Editor: Behavioral Medicine, 1978-81, Security Letter Source Book, 1983—, Security Jour., 1989—; contbr. books and articles on security and urban crime and policing. Mem. AAUP, Am. Hist. Assn., Am. Correctional Assn., Am. Soc. Indsl. Security (pres.'s cert. of merit 1990), Nat. Coun. Investigation and Security Svcs. (Duffy Meml. Achievement award 1992), Internat. Security Mmgt. Assn. (Brennan award 1993), Urban History Assn., Union League Club, Alpha Tau Omega, Delta Sigma Rho, Pi Delta Epsilon. Presbyterian (deacon). Home: 49 E 96th St New York NY 10128-0782 Office: 166 E 96th St New York NY 10128-2565 also: John Jay Coll Criminal Justice 899 10th Ave New York NY 10019

MCCRIMMON, JAMES MCNAB, language educator; b. Renton, Scotland, June 16, 1908; came to U.S., 1929, naturalized, 1939; s. John and Margaret (Patterson) McCrimmon; m. Barbara Smith, June 10, 1939; children: Kevin M., John M. B.A., Northwestern U., 1932, M.A., 1933, Ph.D. 1937. Asst. instr. English, Northwestern U., 1933; instr. English, U. Toledo, 1936-38, asst. prof., 1938-43, assoc. prof., 1943-47; faculty U. Ill., 1947—, chmn. humanities div. Galesburg extension, 1947-49; assoc. prof. humanities U. Ill., Urbana, 1949-55, prof., 1955-65; prof. emeritus U. Ill., 1965—, head div. gen. studies, 1954-62, dir. U. High Sch. English project, 1962—; vis. prof. English Fla. State U., 1967-70, lectr., 1970-78. Author: (with MacMinn and Hainds) Bibliography of the Writings of John Stuart Mill, 1945, Writing with a Purpose, 1950, Open Door to Education, (with Louttit and Habberton), 1951, From Source to Statement, 1968. Mem. Nat. Council Tchrs. English, College Conf. Composition and Communication, Phi Kappa Phi. Home: 1330 W Indianhead Dr Tallahassee FL 32301-4763

MC CRONE, ALISTAIR WILLIAM, university president; b. Regina, Sask., Can., Oct. 7, 1931; came to U.S., 1953, naturalized, 1963; s. Hugh McMillan and Kathleen Maude Tallent (Forth) McCrone; m. Judith Ann Saari, May 8, 1958; children: Bruce, Craig, Mary. B.A., U. Sask., 1953; M.S. (Shell fellow), U. Nebr., 1955; Ph.D., U. Kans., 1961. Instr. geology NYU, 1959-61, asst. prof., 1961-64, assoc. prof., 1964-69, prof., 1969-70; chmn. dept. geology N.Y. U., 1966-69; assoc. dean NYU Grad. Sch. Arts and Scis., 1969-70; acad. v.p. U. of Pacific, Stockton, Calif., 1970-74; prof. geology U. of Pacific, 1970-74; pres., prof. geology Humboldt State U., Arcata, Calif., 1974—; lectr. geology CBS-TV network, 1969-70. Contbr. articles to profl. jours. Trustee Pacific Med. Center, San Francisco, 1971-74; mem. Calif. Council for Humanities, 1978-82. Recipient Erasmus Haworth Honors award U. Kans., 1957; named Danforth Assos. convenor N.Y. U., 1966-68, Outstanding Educator of Am., 1975. Fellow AAAS, Geol. Soc. Am., Calif. Acad. Sci.; mem. Am. Assn. Univ. Adminstrs. (bd. dirs. 1986-89), Am. Auto Assn. (bd. dirs. 1990-93), Calif. State Auto Assn. (bd. dirs. 1988—), Assn. Am. Colls. (bd. dirs. 1989, chair 1991), St. Andrews Soc. of N.Y., Sigma Xi. Lodge: Rotary. Office: Humboldt State U Univ Campus Arcata CA 95521

MCCRONE, WALTER COX, research institute executive; b. Wilmington, Del., June 9, 1916; s. Walter Cox and Bessie Lillian (Cook) McC.; m. Lucy Morris Beman, July 13, 1957. B Chemistry, Cornell U., 1938, PhD, 1942. Microscopist, sr. scientist Armour Research Found., Ill. Inst. Tech., Chgo., 1944-56; chmn. bd. Walter C. McCrone Assos. Inc., Chgo., 1956-81; sr. research advisor Walter C. McCrone Assos. Inc., 1956-78; pres. McCrone Research Inst., Inc., 1961-94, chmn. bd., 1961—; vis. prof. chemistry microscopy Cornell U., 1984—; adj. prof. IIT, 1950—, NYU, 1974—, U. Ill., 1989—. Author: Fusion Methods in Chemical Microscopy, 1957, The Particle Atlas, 1967, Particle Atlas Two, 6 vols., 1973-78, Particle Atlas Three Electronic CD-Rom edit., 1992, Polarized Light Microscopy, 1978, Asbestos Particle

Atlas, 1980, Asbestos Identification, 1987; editor: Microscope Jour., 1962—; contbr. over 350 articles to profl. jours. Chmn. bd. trustees Ada S. McKinley Cmty. Svcs., 1962-95, emeritus pres. 1995—; chmn. bd. trustee 1982-94, pres. emeritus 1994— VanderCook Coll. Music; trustee Campbell Ctr., 1990—. Recipient Benedetti-Pichler award Am. Microchem. Soc., 1970, Anachem award Assn. Analytical Chemists, 1981, cert. of merit Franklin Inst., 1982, Forensic Sci. Found., 1983, Madden Disting. Svc. award VanderCook Coll. Music, 1988, Fortissimo award, 1991, Irving Selikoff award Nat. Asbestos Coun., 1990, Founder's Day award Calif. Assn. Criminalists, 1990, Roger Green award, 1991, Pub. Affairs award Chgo. Pub. Schs., 1993. Mem. Am. Chem. Soc. (Pub. Affairs award 1993, Disting. Svc. award USAF AFTAC Program, Am. Phys. Soc., Am. Acad. Forensic Sci. (Disting. Svc. award criminalistics sect. 1984), Am. Inst. Conservators Art (hon.), Internat. Inst. Conservators Art Australian Micros. Soc., N.Y. Micros. Soc. (Ernst Abbe award 2977), La. Micros. Soc., Can. Micros. Soc., Midwest Micros. Soc., Royal Micros. Soc. (hon.), Ill. Micros. Soc., Quekett Micros. Club, Sigma Xi, Phi Kappa Phi, Phi Lambda Upsilon, Alpha Chi Sigma. Achievements include 3 patents in field of explosives technology; proved the Vinland map to be a modern forgery; proved the Turin Shroud to be a medieval painting; developed the analytical methods for detection and identification of asbestos; instituted in Chicago, 1958, first zoning ordinance based on performance standards. Home: 501 E 32nd St Chicago IL 60616-4053 Office: McCrone Rsch Inst 2820 S Michigan Ave Chicago IL 60616-3292

MCCRORY, COLLEEN, ecologist. With Valhalla Wilderness Soc., New Denver, B.C., Can. Recipient Goldman Environ. prize Goldman Environ. Found., 1992. Office: Valhalla Wilderness Society, 307 Sixth Ave Box 224, New Denver, BC Canada V0G 1S0*

MCCRORY, JOHN BROOKS, retired lawyer; b. St. Cloud, Minn., Oct. 23, 1925; s. John Raymond and Mary Lee (Rutter) McC.; m. Margaret Joan Dickson, Sept. 4, 1954 (dec. Apr. 1957); 1 child, William B.; m. Elizabeth Ann Quick, June 27, 1959; children—John B., Ann Elizabeth. B.A., Swarthmore Coll., 1948; J.D., U. Pa., 1951. Bar: N.Y. 1952, D.C. 1985. Assoc. Donovan, Leisure, Newton, Lumbard & Irvine, N.Y.C., 1951-52; assoc. Nixon, Hargrave, Devans & Doyle, Rochester, N.Y., 1952-62, ptnr., 1963-92; retired, 1992. Author: Constitutional Privilege in Libel Law, 1977-90. Served to lt. comdr. USNR, 1943-47, PTO. Fellow Am. Coll. Trial Lawyers; mem. ABA, Monroe County Bar Assn., N.Y. State Bar Assn., D.C. Bar Assn. Republican. Presbyterian. Home: 210 Whitewood Ln Rochester NY 14618-3226 Office: Nixon Hargrave Devans & Doyle Clinton Sq PO Box 1051 Rochester NY 14603-1051

MCCRORY, ROBERT LEE, physicist, mechanical engineering educator; b. Lawton, Okla., Apr. 30, 1946; s. Robert Lee Sr. and Marjorie Marie (Garrett) McC.; m. Betsey Christine Wahl, June 14, 1969; children: Katherine Anne, John Damon, George Garrett. BSc, MIT, 1968, PhD, 1973. Physicist Los Alamos Nat. Lab., Albuquerque, 1973-76; scientist, coleader Lab. for Laser Energetics, U. Rochester, N.Y., 1976-77, sr. scientist, 1977—, dir. theoretical div. 1979-90; dir. Lab. for Laser Energetics, U. Rochester, 1983—; assoc. prof. of physics and astronomy U. Rochester, 1980, prof. of mech. engring., 1983—. Author: Laser Plasma Interactions, 1989, Computer Applications in Plasma Science and Engineering, 1991; contbr. articles to profl. publs. Alfred P. Simon scholar, 1964-67; AEC fellow, 1985; recipient Edward Teller medal, 1994. Fellow Am. Phys. Soc. (mem. fellowship com., mem. exec. com. div. plasma physics, Excellence in Plasma Physics award). Office: U Rochester Lab Laser Energetics 250 E River Rd Rochester NY 14623-1212

MC CRORY, WALLACE WILLARD, pediatrician, educator; b. Racine, Wis., Jan. 19, 1920; s. Willard L. and Beulah (St. Clair) McC.; m. Sylvia E. Hogben, Feb. 6, 1943; children—Pamela, Michael, Christine. B.S., U. Wis., 1941, M.D., 1944. Diplomate: Am. Bd. Pediatrics. Rotating intern Phila. Gen. Hosp., 1944-45; resident pediatrics Children's Hosp., Phila., 1945-46; chief resident physician Children's Hosp., 1948-49, asso. pediatrician, 1953-55, sr. pediatrician, 1955-58; provisional asst. pediatrician to out-patients, Lewis Cass Ledyard, Jr. fellow pediatrics N.Y. Hosp., 1949-50, pediatrician-in-chief, 1961-80, sr. pediatrician, chief pediatric nephrology, 1980—; chief pediatric service Univ. Hosp., Iowa City, 1958-61; instr. pathology U. Wis. Med. Sch., 1942-43; instr. pediatrics U. Pa. Sch. Medicine, 1948-49, instr., research fellow pediatrics, 1950-53, asst. prof., 1953-55, asso. prof., 1955-58; prof. pediatrics, chmn. dept. State U. Iowa Coll. Medicine, 1958-61; prof. pediatrics Cornell U. Med. Coll., 1961—. Pres. Nat. Kidney Found., 1964-66. Served to capt., M.C. AUS, 1946-48. Fellow N.Y. Acad. Medicine, Royal Soc. Medicine; mem. Am. Pediatric Soc., Am. Acad. Pediatrics, Soc. Pediatric Research, Am. Soc. Nephrology, Am. Soc. Pediatric Nephrology, AAAS, Sigma Xi, Alpha Omega Alpha. Home: 171 Salem Rd Pound Ridge NY 10576-1324 Office: NY Hosp Cornell Med Ctr 525 E 68th St New York NY 10021

MCCROSKEY, WILLIAM JAMES, aeronautical engineer; b. San Angelo, Tex., Mar. 9, 1937; s. J. M. and W. Elizabeth (Adams) McC.; m. Elizabeth W. Wear, Jan. 31, 1960; children: Nancy E., Susan C. BS, U. Tex., 1960; MS, Princeton U., 1962, PhD, 1966. Rsch. assoc. Princeton U., 1966; rsch. engr. U.S. Army Aeromechanics Lab., Moffett Field, Calif., 1966-80; sr. rsch. scientist U.S. Army and NASA Aerophysics Directorate, 1980—; exch. scientist Office Nat. Etudes et Recherches Aérosspatiale, Châtillon, France, 1972-73; mem. fluid dynamics panel NATO Adv. Group for Aerospace R & D, 1976-94, chmn., 1989-91. With U.S. Army, 1966-68. Recipient French Medaille l'Aeronautique, 1994, von Kármán medal, 1995. Fellow AIAA (Outstanding Engr. San Francisco sect. 1975, fluid dynamics tech com. 1984-88, internat. activities com. 1990—); mem. ASME (Freeman scholar award 1976), Am. Helicopter Soc. (Howard Hughes award 1991). Office: Ames Rsch Ctr N258-1 Moffett Field CA 94035

MCCUAN, WILLIAM PATRICK, real estate company executive; b. Muskogee, Okla., Oct. 28, 1941; s. Lee L. and LaRee A. (Beverage) McC.; m. Jill Pamela Thomas, May 5, 1982; children: LaRee, Megan. Student, U. Tulsa, 1961-62; BA in Psychology, Baylor U., 1965; MRE, So. Sem., Louisville, 1967; MS, U. Louisville, 1969; postgrad., U. Md., 1971-73. Prof., asst. dean grad. sch. U. Md., Balt., 1969-73; lobbyist, cons. Washington, 1973-76; chmn. bd. KMS Group, Inc., Columbia, Md., 1976-84; CEO MDG Cos. of Naples, Columbia, Md., 1984—; chmn. bd. Tuscasrora Real Estate Corp., Berkeley Springs, W.Va., 1991—; adj. prof. Community Coll., Balt., 1969-72, U. Md., College Park, 1969-71; lectr. Univ. Coll.-Univ. Md., 1970-71, Howard C.C., Columbia, 1987-88; chmn. Pet Holiday, Inc., Toledo, 1973— CEO Uniglobe Columbia Travel Ctr., 1986—; non-lawyer mem. Atty. Grievance Commn., Md., 1990—. Contbr. to numerous publs. bd. dirs. Concert Soc. Md., 1988—; chmn. United Way, Howard County, Md., 1984, Am. Presdl. Inaugural Com., Md., 1988, Howard County Cmty. Partnerships; fin. chmn. Rep. Cen. Com., Howard County, 1988-92; trustee Columbia Found., Howard County; mem. Pres.'s Commn. on Food, Nutrition and Health, Washington, 1970, Howard County Environ. Affairs Bd., Columbia Archives Com.; mem. bus. adv. coun. Howard C.C.; bd. dirs. Congl. Commn. on Mental Health of Children, Washington, 1973-75, Human Svcs. Inst. for Children & Families. Mem. Nat. Assn. Home Builders (bd. dirs. 1979-87, fed. govt. affairs com.), Md. Builders Assn. (pres. 1981-82), Home Builders Assn. Md. (bd. dirs. 1977-82, Award of Honor 1979, Award of Excellence 1980, Presdl. award 1982), Howard County Home Builders Assn. (pres. 1978-80), Howard County C. of C. (pres. bd. dirs. 1984-86). Avocations: private pilot, rare plane and automobile collector. Home: 11838 Farside Rd Ellicott City MD 21042-1526 Office: MDG Bldg 5550 Sterrett Pl Columbia MD 21044-2611

MCCUBBIN, HAMILTON I., social scientist, educator, researcher; b. Honolulu, July 20, 1941; s. Jonathan Kuihe and Betsy Chisayo (Yamamoto) McC.; m. Marilyn Ann Behrens, Nov. 1, 1963; children: Todd Jonathan, Wendy Ann, Laurie Dawn. BS, U. Wis., 1964, MS, 1966, PhD, 1970; postdoctoral, Yale U., 1970, 71; postdoctoral Jou., U. Minn., 1977, Stanford U. Ctr. for Advanced Studies in Behavioral Scis., 1982. Dir. research U.S. Army Retng. Program, Fort Riley, Kans., 1969-71; dir. drug and alcohol treatment program Presidio of San Francisco, 1971-72; dir. family studies Naval Health Rsch. Ctr., San Diego, 1972-76; assoc. prof. social work Family Study Ctr., U. Minn., 1976-78, prof., head dept. family social sci., 1978-84; dean U. Wis. Madison, 1984—; dir. ctr. for excellence in family studies U. Wis. Sys., Madison, 1990—; dir. family stress, coping and health U. Wis. Sys., Madison, 1979—; dir. inst. for the study of resiliency in families U. Wis. Sys., Madison, 1994—; cons. NIMH, NIH, Nat. Inst. Drug Abuse, Office of Naval Rsch.; exec. com. Ctr. on Aging, Ctr. for Experience in Family Studies; mem. Gov.'s Task Force on Torture Victims, 1984-85, Ctr. on Treatment Torture Victims, 1985—, Gov.'s Task Force on Child Abuse, 1986—; mem. Presdl. Commn. on Children in Hawaii, Task Force on Families in Catastrophy; pres. Nat. Coun. on Family Rels., 1986—; chair Gov.'s Task Force on Women and Family, Task Force on Family Stress; mem. Gov.'s Children's Trust Fund; Margaret Mangel lectr. U. Mo., 1984; Bernice M. Wright lectr. Syracuse U., 1984, 1993; Elizabeth Empey lectr. U. Alta., Edmonton, 1985; Ruth Hoeflin lectr. Kans. State U., 1985, Diane Huber lectr. Miami of Ohio U., Oxford Ohio; bd. dirs. Nat. Rsch. Adv. Com., Boysville of Mich., Ann Arbor, 1986—; bd. advisors, Ctr. for the Study of Trauma, U. Calif., San Francisco 1987—; chairperson, Multiculture Adv. Bd., CASEY Found., Seattle, 1989—, Kuwait Internat. Advisory Com. of Higher Organ. Com. Gov. of Kuwait, 1993—, United Arab Emirates Advisory Bd. Univ. of the United Arab Emirates Al Alain, 1963—, Sci. Review Panel Mil. Family Inst. Marywood Coll. Scranton, Pa., 1994—. Author: Family Separation and Reunion, 1974, Families in the Military System, 1976, Family Stress and Work, Models for Self Reliance, Family Stress Coping and Social Support, Families: What Makes Them Work; Family Stress and Coping, Vol. I, Normative Transitions, Vol. II, Catastrophes, Social Stress and the Family, Marriage and the Family: Relationships in Transition, Family Assessment Inventories for Research and Practice, Family Types and Strengths: A Life Cycle and Ecological Perspective, Rituals and Strengths, Balancing Work and Family Life on Wall Street, Sense of Coherence and Resiliency, 1994, Resiliency in Ethnic Minority Families, vol. I, Native and Immigrant American Families, 1995, Resiliency in Ethnic Minority Families, vol II, African American Families, 1995; assoc. editor Jour. Marriage and the Family, 1977—, Jour. Family Issues, 1980—, Jour. Social Relations, Jour. Wellness Perspectives, 1983—, Jour. Family Systems and Health, 1984—; spl. editor Jour. Family Relations, 1979-80; editor Jour. Marriage and Family Rev.; bd. editors Family Systems Medicine, 1984—; mem. editorial bd. of 14 family jours.; contbr. articles to profl. jours. Bd. dirs. Swimming Assn., La Mesa, Calif., 1975-76, Meriter Hosps., Inc., Madison, 1992—; mem. pers. com., pub. svc. com., rsch. and instl. rev. bd.; bd. dirs. Wis. Coun. on Human Concerns and Svcs., 1992—. Maj. AUS, 1969-76, Res. ret., 1990. Decorated D.S.M. with oak leaf cluster; recipient James T. Moran research award, 1984, 85; U.S. Children's Bur. fellow, 1968-69; grantee Gillette Med. Center, 1979, Navy Dept., 1974, Office Naval Research, 1974, Nat. Inst. Drug Abuse. Mem. Nat. Assn. Social Workers (dir. 1979-81), Am. Home Econs. Assn. (Robert Moran award 1984), Am. Public Health Assn., Am. Sociol. Assn., Nat. Coun. Family Rels., Am. Assn. Correctional Psychologists, Soc. in Child Devel., Am. Edn. Rsch. Assn. Home: 21 Winterfest Cir Madison WI 53717 Office: U Wis Sch Family Resources & Consumer Scis 1300 Linden Dr Madison WI 53706-1575 Scholarship reflected in one's research, writing and teaching is achieved through discipline and knowledge and is developed through meaningful relationships with scholars-mentors committed to superior work. Through such relationships, I gained a view of and appreciation of the past, lenses through which to view the present, and the confidence to look into the future. I have been blessed by unique opportunities to learn and by the touch of men and women scholars who gave me a chance and the encouragement to seek the truth.

MC CUE, CAROLYN MOORE, retired pediatric cardiologist; b. Richmond, Va., June 26, 1916; d. Thomas Justin and Caroline (Willingham) Moore; m. Howard M. McCue, Jr., Apr. 5, 1941; children—Carolyn McCue Osteen, Howard McDowell. Student, Wellesley Coll., 1933-35; A.B., Leland Stanford U., 1937; M.D., Med. Coll. Va., 1941. Intern Wis. Gen. Hosp., Madison, 1941-42; resident in pediatrics Children's Hosp., Phila., 1942-43, Med. Coll. Va., 1946-47; dir. pediatric cardiology Med. Coll. Va., Richmond, 1947-81; prof. pediatrics Med. Coll. Va., 1963-91; clin. dir. pediatric cardiology clinics State of Va., 1958-81. Contbr. articles to profl. jours. Named Va. Laureate, 1982. Fellow Am. Acad. Pediatrics, Am. Coll. Physicians, Am. Coll. Cardiology, A.C.P.; mem. Richmond Acad. Medicine (pres. 1975), Richmond Area Heart Assn. (pres. 1959-60), Phi Beta Kappa, Alpha Omega Alpha. Club: Country of Va. Home: 12 Huntley Rd Richmond VA 23226-3306

MCCUE, GERALD MALLON, architect, educator; b. Woodland, Calif., Dec. 5, 1928; s. Floyd F. and Lenore (Mallon) McC.; m. Barbara Walrond, Sept. 1, 1951; children: Scott, Mark, Kent. BA, U. Calif. at Berkeley, 1951, MA, 1952; MA (hon.), Harvard U., 1977. Ptnr. archtl. firm Milano-McCue, Berkeley, Calif., 1953-54; pres. Gerald M. McCue & Assocs., Berkeley, 1954-70, McCue, Boone, Tomsick, San Francisco, 1970-76; prin. MBT Assocs., San Francisco, 1976-80; faculty U. Calif. at Berkeley, 1954-76; prof. architecture and urban design U. Calif. at Berkeley, 1966-76; chmn. dept. U. Calif. at Berkeley, 1966-71; prof. architecture/urban design, chmn. dept. and assoc. dean Grad. Sch. Design Harvard U., 1976-80, dean, 1980-92; John T. Dunlop prof. housing studies Sch. Design and Kennedy Sch. Govt., Harvard U., 1992—. Planning and design commns. executed for variety pub. and pvt. clients with over 30 nat. regional and local design awards. Fellow AIA, Urban Land Inst. Office: Harvard U Grad Sch Design 48 Quincy St Cambridge MA 02138-3000

MCCUE, HOWARD MCDOWELL, III, lawyer, educator; b. Sumter, S.C., Jan. 4, 1946; s. Howard McDowell and Carolyn Hartwell (Moore) McC.; m. Judith Weiss, Apr. 3, 1972; children—Howard McDowell IV, Leigh. A.B., Princeton U., 1968; J.D., Harvard U. 1971. Bar: Mass. 1971, Ill. 1975, U.S. Tax Ct. 1977. Assoc. Hale and Dorr, Boston, 1971-72; assoc. Mayer, Brown & Platt, Chgo., 1975-77, ptnr., 1977—; adj. prof. law master in tax program Chgo. Kent Coll. Law, 1981—. Author: (with others) Drafting Wills and Trust Agreements, 1979, 82, 85, 87, 90; mem. editorial bd. Trusts and Estates mag., 1981—; contbr. articles to profl. jours. Bd. dirs. Art Inst. Chgo., Lawrence Hall Youth Svcs., Northwestern U. Libr. Coun.; bd. dirs., vice chmn. Ravinia Festival Assn. Lt. USN, 1972-75. Princeton U. scholar, 1965. Mem. ABA, Ill. Bar Assn., Chgo. Bar Assn. (fed. tax com., past chmn., exec. coun.), Chgo. Bar Found. (bd. dirs., pres.), Am. Coll. Tax Counsel, Am. Coll. Trust and Estate Counsel, Harvard Law Soc. Ill., Internat. Acad. Estate and Trust Law, Chgo. Club, Kenilworth Club, Phi Beta Kappa. Office: Mayer Brown & Platt 190 S La Salle St Chicago IL 60603-3410

MCCUE, JUDITH W., lawyer; b. Phila., Apr. 7, 1948; d. Emanuel Leo and Rebecca (Raffel) Weiss; m. Howard M. McCue III, Apr. 3, 1971; children: Howard, Leigh. BA cum laude, U. Pa., 1969; JD, Harvard U., 1972. Bar: Ill. 1972, U.S. Tax Ct. 1984. From assoc. to ptnr. Keck, Mahin & Cate, Chgo., 1972—; dir. Schawk, Inc., Des Plaines, Ill., Chgo. Estate Planning Coun. Governing mem. The Orchestral Assn., 1979—. Fellow Am. Coll. Trust and Estate Counsel (com. chair 1991-94, regent 1993—); mem. Chgo. Bar Assn. (chmn. probate practice com. 1984-85, chmn. fed. estate and gift tax divsn. fed. tax com. 1988-89). Office: Keck Mahin & Cate 77 W Wacker Dr Fl 49 Chicago IL 60601-1629

MCCUEN, JOHN FRANCIS, JR., lawyer; b. N.Y.C., Mar. 11, 1944; s. John Francis Sr. and Elizabeth Agnes (Corbett) McC.; children: Sarah, Mary, John. AB, U. Notre Dame, 1966; JD, U. Detroit, 1969. Bar: Mich. 1970, Fla. 1970, Ohio 1978. Legal counsel Kelsey-Hayes Co., Romulus, Mich., 1970-77; corp. counsel Sheller-Globe Corp., Toledo, 1977-79; v.p., gen. counsel Sheller-Globe Corp., 1979-86, sec., 1982-87, sr. v.p. gen. counsel, 1986-89; ptnr. Marshall & Melhorn, Toledo, 1989-92; pvt. practice Law Offices John F. McCuen, Toledo, 1992-93; counsel Butzel Long, Ann Arbor, Mich., 1994; v.p. legal Kelsey Hayes Co., Livonia, Mich., 1995—; bd. dirs. Preferred Rubber Compounding Corp, Trustee Kidney Found. N.W. Ohio, 1979-88, pres., 1984-86. Mem. ABA, Fla. Bar, Mich. Bar, Inverness Club. Home: 2734 Winter Garden Ct Ann Arbor MI 48105 Office: Kelsey Hayes Co 11878 Hubbard Dr Livonia MI 48150

MCCUEN, JOHN JOACHIM, financial company executive; b. Washington, Mar. 30, 1926; s. Joseph Raymond and Josephine (Joachim) McC.; m. Gloria Joyce Seidel, June 16, 1949; children: John Joachim Jr., Les Seidel. BS, U.S. Mil. Acad., 1948; M of Internatl. Affairs, Columbia U., 1961; grad., U.S. Army War Coll., 1968. Commd. 2d lt. U.S. Army, 1948, advanced through grades to col.; dir. internal def. and devel. U.S. Army War Coll., Carlisle Barracks, Pa., 1969-72; chief U.S. Def. Liaison Group, Jakarta, Indonesia, 1972-74; chief field survey office U.S. Army Tng. and Doctrine Command, Ft. Monroe, Va., 1974-76; ret. U.S. Army, 1976; mgr. tng. Chrysler Def., Center Line, Mich., 1977-82; mgr. modification ctr. Land Systems div. Gen. Dynamics, Sterling Heights, Mich., 1982-83; mgr. field ops. Land Systems div. Gen. Dynamics, Warren, Mich., 1983-94; pres. Mich. Econ. Devel. Corp., Birmingham, Mich., Magicom, Inc., Birmingham, 1994—; owner Am. Travel Svc., Birmingham, 1994—; chmn. bd. Highland Found., 1994—; pres. First Internat. Corp., Birmingham, 1995—; ptnr. East West Connection, Birmingham, Mich.; pres. Energy Resource Mgmt. Systems, Inc., Birmingham; armor advisor 3d Royal Thai Army, Utaradit, 1957-58; U.S. rep. users' com. NATO Missile Firing Installation Crete, Paris, 1964-66; advisor Vietnamese Nat. Def. Coll., Saigon, 1968-69; speaker on terrorism and counter insurgency. Author: The Art of Counter Revolutionary War-The Strategy of Counter Insurgency, Faber 1966, Stackpole, 1967, Circulo Militar, 1967. Pres. Troy (Mich.) Community Concert Assn., 1985—, bd. dirs., 1992; past pres. Mich. Oriental Art Soc., Birmingham; pres. Grander View Found. Sr. Housing and Nursing, Milford, Mich., 1984; past 1st reader First Ch. of Christ Scientist, Birmingham, 1989-92; past chmn. region VI N.E. unit Detroit United Way Campaign. Mem. Soc. Logistics Engrs., Nat. Mgmt. Assn., Assn. U.S. Army, Oriental Art Soc. Republican. Avocation: collecting and selling Oriental antiques, lecturing on terrorism and national security. Home: 32863 Balmoral St Beverly Hills MI 48025-3008 Office: Mich Econ Devel Corp 2100 E Maple Rd Ste 301 Birmingham MI 48009

MCCUEN, WILLIAM JAMES (BILL MCCUEN), state official; b. Fort Smith, Ark., Aug. 19, 1943; s. Garland Grandville and Sara Emma (Early) McC.; 1 child, Sonja Michelle. BSE, Coll. of Ozarks, 1968; MSE, Henderson State U., 1972. Tchr. Pomona Unified Sch. Dist., Calif., 1968-69; tchr. Hot Springs Schs., Ark., 1969-71; prin. Hot Springs Schs., 1971-76; judge Garland County Ct., Hot Springs, Ark., 1976-80; commr. state lands State of Ark., Little Rock, 1980-84; sec. of state State of Ark., 1985—. Alderman Hot Springs City Council, 1972-76. Democrat. Presbyterian. Lodges: Lions, Elks. Office: 256 State Capitol Little Rock AR 72201-1011

MCCUISTION, PEG OREM, hospice administrator; b. Houston, July 28, 1930; d. William Darby and Dorothy Mildred (Beckett) Orem; m. Palmer Day McCuistion, Sept. 4, 1949 (div. 1960); 1 child, Leeanne E. BBA, Southwest Tex. State, 1963; MBA, George Washington U., 1968; EdD, Wayne State U., 1989. Patient care adminstr. Holy Cross Hosp., Silver Spring, Md., 1968-79; exec. dir. Hospice of S.E. Mich., Southfield, 1979-86, Hospice Austin, Tex., 1987-94; CEO EMBI, Inc., Arlington, Tex., 1994—. Bd. dirs. Cmty. Home for the Elderly, Austin, 1989-92. Fellow Am. Coll. Health Care Execs. (membership com.); mem. Internat. Hospice Inst. (assoc.), Nat. Hospice Orgn. (chair standards and accreditation com.), Tex. Hospice Orgn. (pres. 1993-94), exec. com., standards and ethics com., edn. com., chair legis. com.), Mich. Hospice Orgn. (chair edn. com., bd. dirs.). Office: Embi Inc 511 Chaffee Dr Arlington TX 76007

MCCUISTION, ROBERT WILEY, lawyer, hospital administrator, management consultant; b. Wilson, Ark., June 15, 1927; s. Ed Talmadge and Ruth Wiley (Bassett) McC.; m. Martha Virginia Golden, June 11, 1949 (dec. Nov. 1991); children: Beth, Dan, Jed.; m. Sudola M. Getz, Feb. 12, 1994. A.B in History and Polit. Sci, Hendrix Coll., Conway, Ark., 1949; J.D., U. Ark., 1952. Bar: Ark. 1952. Practice in Dermott, Ark., 1952-57; dep. pros. atty. 10th Jud. Dist. Ark., 1953-57; bus. mgr. St. Mary's Hosp., Dermott, 1953-56; asst. adminstr., 1956-57; adminstr. Stuttgart (Ark.) Meml. Hosp., 1957-60, Forrest Meml. Hosp., Forrest City, Ark., 1960-68; assoc. adminstr. St. Edward Mercy Hosp., Ft. Smith, Ark., 1968-70; pres. Meml. Med Center, Corpus Christi, Tex., 1970-79; adminstr. Methodist Hosp., Mitchell, S.D., 1979-85, cons., 1985-86; mgmt. cons., owner Creative Leadership Concepts, Arlington, Tex., 1985—; adminstr. Cen. United Meth. Ch., Fayetteville, 1986-91; sec. Ark. Hosp. Adminstrs. Forum, 1958-59, pres., 1959-60; pres. Ark. Hosp. Assn., 1964-65, Areawide Health Planning, 1970; pres. Ark. Conf. Cath. Hosps., 1970; chmn. Twin City Hosp. Council, 1968; v.p. Ark. Assn. Mental Health, 1966-70. Div. chmn. Forrest City United Community Svcs., 1961, Corpus Christi United Way Community Svcs., 1972, DeSoto coun. Boy Scouts Am., Explorer adviser, 1954-57. With USAAF, World War II. Recipient Eminent Leadership award DeSoto Area council Boy Scouts Am., 1956. Mem. Am. Assn. Hosp. Accountants (pres. Ark. chpt. 1957), S.D. Hosp. Assn. (dist. chmn. 1980-81), Mid-West Hosp. Assn. (trustee 1963-65), Am. Coll. Health Execs. (life). Methodist (vice chmn., sec. ofcl. bd. 1957, lay del. S.D. ann. conf. 1980-85). Lodge: Rotary (pres. Forrest City 1964-65). Home and Office: 1912 S St Andrews Ct Arlington TX 76011

MCCULLAGH, GRANT GIBSON, architect; b. Cleve., Apr. 18, 1951; s. Robert Ernest and Barbara Louise (Grant) McC.; m. Suzanne Dewar Folds, Sept. 13, 1975; children: Charles Weston Folds, Grant Gibson Jr. BArch, U. Ill., 1973; MArch, U. Pa., 1975; MBA, U. Chgo., 1979. Registered architect, Ill. Project designer Perkins & Will, Chgo., 1975-77; dir. mktg. The Austin Co., Chgo., 1977-83, asst. dist. mgr., 1983-84, dist. mgr., 1984-88, v.p., 1987-88; chmn., chief exec. officer McClier Corp., Chgo., 1988—. Contbr. articles to various indsl. publs. Bd. dirs. Friends of Prentice Hosp. Mem. FAIA, Chgo. Architecture Found. (pres. 1988-91, adv. bd. trustee 1994—, dir. Design/Build Inst. Am. 1994—). Econ. Club, Chgo. Club, Casino Club, Univ. Club, Indian Hill Country Club. Republican. Episcopalian. Home: 43 Locust Rd Winnetka IL 60093-3725 Office: McClier Corp 401 E Illinois St Chicago IL 60611-4305

MCCULLAGH, JAMES CHARLES, publishing company executive; b. London, Oct. 22, 1941; s. James Christopher and Violet Anne (Smith) McC.; children: Declan, Deirdre. BS, Ind. U. Pa., 1968; MA, Lehigh U., 1970, PhD, 1974. Tchr. Holidaysburg (Pa.) Area High Sch., 1968; teaching asst. Lehigh U., Bethlehem, Pa., 1968-71, doctoral fellow, 1971-73; vis. poet Pa. Council on Arts Inc., Harrisburg, 1974-78; editor Rodale Press Inc., Emaus, Pa., 1979-83, pub., editor dir., group v.p., 1984—; pub. Novii Fermer, USSR, 1991—; pub. dir. Scuba Diving, 1992; sr. v.p. Internat. Mag. Devel. Author: Bicycle Fitness Book, 1984, Bicycling for Health and Fitness, 1995, Cycling for Health, Fitness and Well-Being, 1995, (poetry) That Kingdom Coming Business, 1984; pub.: Mountain Bike, 1994. Served with USN, 1960-64. Recipient Man of Yr. award Bicycle Mfrs. Assn. Am., Washington, 1983. Mem. Am. Assn. Mag. Editors, Mag. Pubs. Assn., Bicycle Fedn. (bd. dirs. 1980—), Bicycle Inst. Am. (pres. 1993—). Democrat. Roman Catholic. Avocations: cycling, swimming. Home: PO Box 265A Lower Saucon Rd RD # 1 Hellertown PA 18055

MC CULLOCH, ERNEST ARMSTRONG, physician, educator; b. Toronto, Ont., Can., Apr. 27, 1926; s. Albert E. and Letitia (Riddell) McC.; m. Ona Mary Morganty, 1953; children: James A., Michael E., Robert E., Cecelia E., Paul A. M.D. with honors, U. Toronto, 1948. Intern Toronto Gen. Hosp., 1949-50, sr. intern 1951-52; NRC fellow dept. pathology U. Toronto, 1950-51; asst. resident Sunnybrook Hosp., Toronto, 1952-53; pvt. practice specializing in internal medicine Toronto, 1954-67; clin. tchr. dept. medicine U. Toronto, 1954-60, asst. prof. dept. med. biophysics, 1959-64, assoc. prof., 1964-66, prof., 1966, asst. prof. medicine, 1967-68, assoc. prof., 1968-70, prof., 1970—, univ. prof., 1982-91, univ. prof. emeritus, 1991—; mem. grad. faculty U. Toronto (Inst. Med. Sci.), 1968—; dir. Inst. Med. Sci. U. Toronto, 1975-79, asst. dean Sch. Grad. Studies, 1979-82; physician Toronto Gen. Hosp., 1960-67; sr. scientist, sr. physician Ont. Cancer Inst., 1957-91, head divsn. biol. rsch., 1982-89, head divsn. cell and molecular biology, 1989-91, sr. scientist emeritus, 1991-93; vis. prof. U. Tex. Med. Ctr. Anderson Cancer Ctr., Houston, 1992-93, adj. prof., 1993—; cons. Nat. Cancer Plan, 1972—; mem. standing com. on health rsch. and devel. Ont. Coun. Health, 1974-82. Author numerous articles on research in hematology; editorial bd.: Blood, 1969-80, Biomedicine, 1973, Clin. Immunology and Immunopathology, 1982—; assoc. editor: Jour. Cellular Physiology, 1966-68; editor, 1968-91. Trustee Banting Rsch. Found., 1975-84, hon. sec.-treas., 1958-74, v.p., 1977-79. Decorated officer Order of Can., 1988; recipient William Goldie prize U. Toronto, 1964, Ann. Gairdner award Internat. Gairdner Found., 1969, Starr Medallist award Dept. Anatomy U. Toronto, 1957; Thomas W. Eadie Medal, 1991, Royal Soc. Canada, Nat. Cancer Inst. Can. fellow, 1954-57. Fellow Royal Soc. Can. (pres. Acad. Sci. 1987-90, Thomas W. Eadie Medal 1991), Royal Coll. Physicians and Surgeons Can.; mem. Can. Acad. Sci., Am. Soc. Exptl. Pathology, Am. Assn. Cancer Rsch., Can. Soc. Cell Biology, Can. Soc. Clin. Investigation, Am. Internat. socs. hematology, Internat. Soc. Exptl. Hematology, Inst. Acad. Medicine (charter mem.). Clubs: Badminton, Racquet. Home: 480 Summerhill Ave, Toronto, ON Canada M4W 2E4 Office: Ont Cancer Inst, 500 Sherborne St, Toronto, ON Canada M4X 1K9 Research success depends on associating with agreeable and talented people.

MC CULLOCH, FRANK W., lawyer, government official, educator, arbitrator; b. Evanston, Ill., Sept. 30, 1905; s. Frank H. and Catharine (Waugh) McC.; m. Edith F. Leverton, 1937; children: William Holt, Frank H. AB, Williams Coll., 1926; LLB, Harvard U., 1929; LLD, Olivet Coll., 1945, Chgo. Theol. Sem., 1961; LL.D., Williams Coll., 1971. Bar: Ill. Practiced Chgo., 1930-35; indsl. relations sec. Council Social Action Congregational-Christian Ch., 1935-46; exec. dir. Chgo. br. Union for Democratic Action, 1942-46; vis. prof. Pacific Sch. Religion, 1939-40, Chgo. Theol. Sem., 1943-45, McCormick Theol. Sem., 1945; dir. labor edn. div. Roosevelt U., Chgo., 1946-49; asst. to Sen. Paul Douglas, 1949-61; chmn. NLRB, 1961-70; vis. prof. law U. N.C., 1971; prof. law U. Va., Charlottesville, 1971-76; also mem. Center Advanced Studies, U. Va., 1971-74, scholar in residence, 1976—; vis prof. N.Y. State Sch. Indsl. and Labor Relations, Cornell U., 1976; cons. Task Force on Labor Relations, Pres.'s Reorgn. Project, 1977. Author: (with Tim Bornstein) The National Labor Relations Board, 1974. Contbr. articles to legal jours. mem. panel Regional War Labor Bd., World War II; mem. Adminstrv. Conf. U.S., 1968-70; adv. com. on fed. hearing examiners Civil Service Commn., 1962-70; Am. team Anglo-Am. adminstrv. Law Exchange, 1969; mem. roster arbitrators Fed. Mediation and Conciliation Service, 1970-88; pub. rev. bd. UAW, 1971-88, Com. on Pub. Employee Rights, Va., 1972-76, Ill. Employee Labor Relations Council, 1973-82; mem. com. experts on application of convs. and recommendations ILO, Geneva, Switzerland, 1974-85; bd. dirs. Migrant Legal Action Program, Washington, 1973-85; mem. Indsl. Devel. Authority Albemarle County, Va., 1977-87. Mem. ABA, Fed. Bar Assn., Ill. Bar Assn., Chgo. Bar Assn., Am. Arbitration Assn. (panel arbitrators), Phi Beta Kappa. Home: Univ Vill 2401 Old Ivy Rd Unit 2307 Charlottesville VA 22903-4853

MCCULLOCH, JAMES CALLAHAN, manufacturing company executive; b. Pittsfield, Mass. Aug. 20, 1947; s. G. Robert and Marion Elizabeth (Callahan) McC.; m. Patricia A. Greene, Dec. 28, 1970; children: William Brennan, Patrick Callahan, Daniel Daly, Peter Brennan, James Callahan II. BS in Commerce, St. Louis U., 1969, MS in Commerce, 1970. With Ford Motor Co., 1970-72; group contr. Chemetron Corp., 1972-80; corp. contr. Six Flags Corp., L.A., 1980-82; v.p. fin. and planning Indsl. Controls Group Allen-Bradley Co., Milw., 1982-86; v.p., chief fin. officer and treas. Sybron Corp., Saddle Brook, N.J., 1986-87, also bd. dirs.; pres. McCulloch Investments, Madison, N.J., 1987—; bd. dirs. Summit Industries, Chgo. Mem. Fin. Exec. Inst., Morris County Golf Club. Republican. Office: McCulloch Investments 14 Main St Ste 200 Madison NJ 07940-1818

MCCULLOCH, RACHEL, economics researcher, educator; b. Bklyn., June 26, 1942; d. Henry and Rose (Offen) Preiss; m. Gary Edward Chamberlain; children: Laura Meressa, Neil Dudley. BA, U. Pa., 1962; MA in Teaching, U. Chgo., 1965, MA, 1971, PhD, 1973; student, MIT, 1966-67. Economist Cabinet Task Force on Oil Import Control, Washington, 1969; instr., then asst. prof. Grad. Sch. Bus. U. Chgo., 1971-73; asst. prof., then assoc. prof. econs. Harvard U., Cambridge, Mass., 1973-79; assoc. prof., then prof. econs. U. Wis., Madison, 1979-87; prof. Brandeis U., Waltham, Mass., 1987—, Rosen Family prof., 1989—, dir. Lemberg Program in Internat. Econs. and Fin., 1990-91, dir. PhD program Grad. Sch. Internat. Econs. and Fin., 1994—; mem. Pres.'s Commn. on Indsl. Competitiveness, 1983-84; mem. adv. coun. Office Tech. Assessment U.S. Congress, 1979-88; cons. World Bank, Washington, 1984-86; mem. com. on internat. rels. studies with People's Republic of China, 1984-91; rsch. assoc. Nat. Bur. Econ. Rsch., Cambridge, 1985-93; mem. adv. com. Inst. for Internat. Econs., Washington, 1987—; faculty Assoc.ment Mgmt. Network, La Jolla, Calif., 1985-92; mem. com. examiners econs. test Grad. Record Exam. Ednl. Testing Svc., 1990—, chair, 1992—; mem. discipline adv. com. for Fulbright scholar awards in econs. Coun. Internat. Exch. Scholars, 1991-93, chair, 1992-93; cons. Global Economy Project, Edn. Film Ctr., 1993-94. Author: Research and Development as a Determinant of U.S. International Competitiveness, 1978; contbr. articles to profl. jours. and books. Grantee NSF, 1975-79, Hoover Inst., 1984-85, German Marshall Fund of U.S., 1985, Ford Found., 1985-88, U.S. Dept. Edn., 1990-91. Mem. Am. Econ. Assn. (dir. summer program for minority students 1983-84), Internat. Trade and Fin. Assn. (bd. dirs. 1993—), New England Women Economists Assn. Home: 10 Frost Rd Lexington MA 02173-1904 Office: Brandeis U Dept Econs Waltham MA 02254

MC CULLOCH, SAMUEL CLYDE, history educator; b. Ararat, Australia, Sept. 3, 1916; came to U.S., 1936, naturalized, 1944; s. Samuel and Agnes Almond (Clyde) McC.; m. Sara Ellen Rand, Feb. 19, 1944; children: Ellen (Mrs. William Henry Meyer III), David Rand, Malcolm Clyde. A.B. with highest honors in History, UCLA, 1940, M.A. (grad. fellow history), 1942; Ph.D., U. Calif. at Los Angeles, 1944. Asst. U. Calif. at Los Angeles, 1943-44; instr. Oberlin Coll., 1944-45; asst. prof. Amherst Coll., 1945-46; vis. asst. prof. U. Mich., 1946-47; mem. faculty Rutgers U., 1947-60, prof. history, assoc. dean arts and scis., 1958-60; dean coll., prof. history San Francisco State Coll., 1960-63; dean humanities, prof. history U. Calif. at Irvine, 1963-70, prof., 1970-87, prof. emeritus, 1987—; coordinator Edn. Abroad Program, 1975-85, dir. Australian Study Ctr., 1986, 87; vis. summer prof. Oberlin Coll., 1945, 46, U. Calif. at Los Angeles, 1947, U. Del., 1949; Fulbright Research prof. Monash U., Melbourne (Australia) U., 1970; Am. Philos. Soc. grantee, 1970. Author: British Humanitarianism, 1950, George Gipps, 1966, River King: The McCulloch Carrying Company and Echura, 1865-1898, 1986, numerous articles, revs.; assoc. editor: Jour. Brit. Studies, 1960-68; bd. advisers, 1968-70; bd. corrs.: Hist. Studies: Australia and New Zealand, 1949-83. Mem. Calif. Curriculum Commn., 1961-67, Highland Park (N.J.) Bd. Edn., 1959-60. Grantee Am. Philos. Soc., Social Sci. Research Council and Rutgers U. Research Council to Australia, 1951; Fulbright research fellow U. Sydney, Australia, 1954-55; grantee Social Sci. Research Council to Eng., summer 1955. Fellow Royal Hist. Soc.; mem. Am. Hist. Assn., Church, Royal Australian hist. socs., A.A.U.P., Conf. Brit. Studies (exec. sec. 1968-73, pres. 1975-77), English Speaking Union (pres. New Brunswick 1957-59), Phi Beta Kappa, Pi Gamma Mu. Episcopalian (vestry). Home: 2121 Windward Ln Newport Beach CA 92660-3820 Office: Dept of History Univ of California Irvine CA 92717

MCCULLOCH, WILLIAM LEONARD, association executive; b. Providence, Mar. 11, 1921; s. William Fraser and Elsie Cornelia (Westeberg) McC.; m. Dolores Ione Collier, July 26, 1952; children—William Fraser, II, Bruce Collier. B.S., U.S. Naval Acad., 1945; M.A. in Internat. Relations, Georgetown U., 1958. Commd. 2d lt. USMC, 1944, advanced through grades to brig. gen., 1971; service in Okinawa, China, Korea and Vietnam; comdg. gen. (1st Marine Div.), 1974-75; congl. aide, 1975-76; exec. dir. Am. Assn. Orthotists and Prosthetists, Washington, 1976-86; pres. nat. office Orthotics and Prosthetics, 1986-88; pres. Assn. Communications and Mktg. Svcs., Washington, 1988—; bd. dirs. Hanger Orthopedic Group. Decorated Legion of Merit with 2 stars, Bronze Star. Mem. Am. Soc. Assn. Execs., U.S. Naval Acad. Class of 1945 Assn. (pres. 1979-80), U.S. Naval Acad. Athletic Assn., Ret. Officers Assn., Capitol Hill Club (Washington), Army-Navy Country Club (Arlington, Va.), Marine Meml. Club (San Francisco), Army and Navy Club (pres.). Republican. Presbyterian. Home and Office: 528 Ft Williams Pky Alexandria VA 22304-1849

MCCULLOH, JOHN MARSHALL, historian; b. Abilene, Kans., Sept. 13, 1943; s. Marshall S. and Gladys Irene (Mobley) McC.; m. Karen Indall, Dec. 26, 1965; children: John Andrew, Katherine Anna Edith. BA, U. Kans., 1965; MA, U. Calif., Berkeley, 1966, PhD, 1971. Acting asst. prof. U. Calif., San Diego, 1971-72, Los Angeles, 1972-73; asst. prof. Kans. State U., Manhattan, 1973-76, assoc. prof., 1976-86, head history dept., 1984-91; prof. Kans. State U., 1986—. Editor: Book, Rabani Mauri Martyrologium. Fellow Woodrow Wilson Found., Alexander Von Humboldt Found., German Acad. Exch. Svc., German Fulbright Commn. Mem. Am. Hist. Assn., Medieval Acad. Am., Am. Soc. Ch. History. Democrat. Episcopal. Home: 1516 Leavenworth St Manhattan KS 66502-4155 Office: Kans State U Dept History Manhattan KS 66506

MCCULLOH, JUDITH MARIE, editor; b. Spring Valley, Ill., Aug. 16, 1935; d. Henry A. and Edna Mae (Traub) Binkele; m. Leon Royce McCulloh, Aug. 26, 1961. BA, Ohio Wesleyan U., 1956; MA, Ohio State U., 1957; PhD, Ind. U., 1970. Asst. to dir. Archives of Traditional Music, Bloomington, Ind., 1964-65; asst. editor U. Ill. Press, Champaign, 1972-77, assoc. editor, 1977-82, sr. editor, 1982-85, exec. editor, 1985—, dir. devel., 1992—; advisor John Edwards Meml. Forum, Los Angeles, 1973—. Mem. Editorial Bd. Jour. Am. Folklore, Washington, 1986-90; co-editor Stars of Country Music, 1975; editor (LP) Green Fields of Ill., 1963, (LP) Hell-Bound Train, 1964, Ethnic Recordings in America, 1982; gen. editor Music in America Life series. Trustee Am. Folklife Ctr., Library of Congress, Washington, 1986—. Fulbright grantee, 1958-59; NDEA grantee, 1961, 62-63; grantee Nat. Endowment for the Humanities, 1978; Disting. Achievement citation Ohio Wesleyan U. Alumni Assn. Fellow Am. Folklore Soc. (pres. 1986-87), Soc. for Ethnomusicology (treas. 1982-86), Sonneck Soc. (1st v.p. 1989-93), Women in Scholarly Pub.; mem. Am. Anthropological Assn. Democrat. Office: U Ill Press 1325 S Oak St Champaign IL 61820-6903

MCCULLOUGH, BENJAMIN FRANKLIN, transportation researcher, educator; b. Austin, Mar. 25, 1934; s. Benjamin Franklin and Mabel Comelia (Kitteridge) McC.; m. Norma Jean Walsh, Sept. 1, 1956; children: Michael Wayne, Bryan Scott, Steven Todd, Franklin Norman, Melanie Jean. MSCE, U. Tex., 1962; PhD of Civil Engring., U. Calif., Berkeley, 1969. Registered profl. engr., Tex. Testing engr. Covair Aircraft Co., Ft. Worth, 1957; design and rsch. engr. Tex. Hwy. Dept., Austin, 1957-66; rsch. engr. Materials R&D, Inc., Oakland, Calif., 1966-68; from asst. to prof. U. Tex., Austin, 1969—, dir. transp. rsch., 1980—. Contbr. articles to profl. jours. Mem. ASCE (Outstanding Paper award 1987), Transp. Rsch. Bd., Coun. Univ. Transp. Ctrs., Univ. Transp. Ctrs. Program, Am. Concrete Inst. Mem. LDS Ch. Avocations: coaching, sports, golfing, U.S. and Tex. history. Office: U Tex Transp Rsch Ctr 3208 Red River Ste 200 Austin TX 78705

MCCULLOUGH, COLLEEN, author; b. Wellington, N.S.W., Australia, June 1, 1937; m. Ric Robinson, Apr. 13, 1984. Student, U. Sydney, Australia; student Inst. Child Health, London U.; student, Yale U.; LittD (hon.), Macquarie U., Sydney, 1993. Rsch. assoc. Yale U. Sch. Medicine, New Haven, Conn., 1967-76. Author: Tim, 1974, The Thorn Birds, 1977, An Indecent Obsession, 1981, Cooking with Colleen McCullough and Jean Easthope, 1982, A Creed for the Third Millennium, 1985, The Ladies of Missalonghi, 1987, The First Man in Rome, 1990, The Grass Crown, 1991, Fortune's Favorites, 1993. Address: Out Yenna, Norfolk Island 2899 Oceania, Australia

MCCULLOUGH, DAVID, author; b. Pitts., July 7, 1933; s. Christian Hax and Ruth (Rankin) McC.; m. Rosalee Ingram Barnes, Dec. 18, 1954; children: Melissa (Mrs. John E. McDonald, Jr.), David, William Barnes, Geoffrey Barnes, Doreen Kane. BA, Yale U., 1955; HLD, Skidmore Coll., 1983, Rensselaer Poly. Inst., 1983; D of Engring. (hon.), Villanova U., 1984; hon. doctorate, Worcester Poly. Inst., 1984; LittD (hon.), Allegheny Coll., 1984; LHD (hon.), Wesleyan U., Middletown, Conn., 1984, Colo. Coll., 1985; LittD (hon.), Middlebury Coll., 1986, U. Indiana at Pa., 1991, U. S.C., 1993; HLD (hon.), U. N.H., 1991; LittD (hon.), U. Pitts., 1994, Union Coll., 1994, Washington Coll., 1994; LHD (hon.), Chatham Coll., 1994. Writer, editor Time, Inc., N.Y.C., 1956-61, USIA, Washington, 1961-64, Am. Heritage Pub. Co., N.Y.C., 1964-70; sr. contbg. editor Am. Heritage mag.; free-lance author, 1970—; Newman vis. prof. American civilization, Cornell U., fall 1989; mem. Bennington (Vt.) Coll. Writers Workshop, 1978-79; scholar-in-residence U. N. Mex., 1979, Wesleyan U. Writers Conf., 1982, 83; mem. adv. bd. Ctr. for the Book, Library of Congress. Author: The Great Bridge, 1972, The Path Between the Seas, 1977, The Johnstown Flood, 1978, Mornings on Horseback, 1981, Brave Companions, 1991, Truman, 1992 (Pulitzer Prize for biography 1993), host TV series: Smithsonian World, 1984-88, The American Experience, 1988—. Mem. Harry S. Truman Centennial Commn.; trustee Nat. Trust Hist. Preservation, Harry S. Truman Libr. Inst., Hist. Soc. Western Pa., Jefferson Legacy Found.; hon. trustee Carnegie Inst. Recipient N.Y. Diamond Jubilee award, 1973, cert. of merit Mcpl. Art Soc. N.Y., 1973, Nat. Book award for history, 1978, Francis Parkman prize, 1978, 93, Samuel Eliot Morison award, 1978, Cornelius Ryan award, 1978, Civil Engring. History and Heritage award, 1978, L.A. Times prize for biography, 1981, Am. Book award for biography, 1982, Harry S. Truman Pub. Svc. award, 1993, St. Louis Lit. award, 1993, Pa. Gov.'s award for excellence, 1993, Pa. Soc. Gold Medal award, 1994. Fellow Soc. Am. Historians (v.p.); mem. ASCE (hon.), Soc. Am. Historians (pres. 1991—). Office: Janklow & Nesbit Associates 598 Madison Ave New York NY 10022

MC CULLOUGH, DONALD FREDERICK, textile manufacturing executive; b. Montclair, N.J., May 6, 1925; s. Willis Gerald and Viola (Mock) McC.; m. Mary Jane Whipple, Dec. 28, 1951 (div. dec. 1962); children: Gregory, Nina, Tracey, Sally; m. Louise C. Voorhees, July 23, 1963. B.S., Yale U., 1945. With Collins & Aikman Corp., N.Y.C., 1946—, sales mgr. yarn div., 1948-50; asst. sales mgr. automotive fabrics Collins & Aikman Corp., Detroit, 1950-51; asst. v.p. sales Collins & Aikman Corp., N.Y.C., 1953-55, pres., 1961-70, 79-84, chief exec. officer, 1961-88, chmn., pres., chief exec. officer, 1970-88, chmn. emeritus, 1988—; bd. dirs. Wickes Cos. Inc., Santa Monica, Calif., Bankers Trust & Bankers Trust N.Y. Corp., N.Y.C., Melville Corp., Harrison, N.Y., Mass. Mut. Life Ins. Co., Springfield, Am. Textile Mfrs. Inst., Washington, past. pres. Trustee The Taft Sch., Watertown, Conn., Greater N.Y. councouncil Boy Scouts Am., Joint Council Econ. Edn., N.Y.C. Served to lt. USNR, 1943-46, 51-53. Recipient Ann. Textile award N.Y. Bd. Trade; Brotherhood award NCCJ. Republican. Clubs: Union League, N.Y. Yacht (N.Y.C.); Storm Trysail (Larchmont, N.Y.); Riverside (Conn.) Yacht; Lyford Cay (Nassau, Bahamas); Round Hill (Greenwich, Conn.). Avocations: sailing, tennis. Home: Apt 206 1155 Winding Oaks Cir E Vero Beach FL 32963-4021 Office: Collins & Aikman Corp 210 Madison Ave New York NY 10016-3802

MCCULLOUGH, GEORGE BIERCE, oil company executive; b. Chgo., Jan. 24, 1925; s. George Bierce McC. and Willie Pauline (Lynch) Oden; m. Alice Colleen Beacham, Jan. 20, 1951; children: Glen, Greg, Pat, Mike. B.B.A., Tulane U., 1948, M.B.A., 1952. Employee relations mgr. Humble Oil & Refining Co., Houston, 1966-69, Esso Europe, Inc., London, 1969-71; employee relations mgr. Exxon Corp., N.Y.C., 1971-80, v.p. employee relations, 1980-86; sr. fellow Orgn. Resources Counselors Inc., N.Y.C., 1986-88; chmn., bd. dirs. Nat. Energy Group, Inc., Dallas, 1988—. Mem. nat. adv. bd. Salvation Army, 1986—; mem. overseas schs. adv. coun. U.S. Dept. State, chmn. 1982-86. Lt. (j.g.) USN, 1943-46. Mem. Personnel Round Table (chmn. 1982-83). Home: 6510 Pauma Dr Houston TX 77069-1741 Office: Nat Energy Group Inc 1350 One Energy Sq 4925 Greenville Ave Dallas TX 75206-4026

MC CULLOUGH, HELEN CRAIG, Oriental languages educator; b. Hollywood, Calif., Feb. 17, 1918; d. Everett Emerson and Mabel (Bishop) Craig; m. William Hoyt McCullough, July 19, 1952; 1 son, Dundas Craig. A.B., U. Calif., Berkeley, 1939, M.A., 1952, Ph.D. 1955. Lectr. in history, Asian langs. Stanford (Calif.) U., 1964-69; lectr. Oriental langs. U. Calif., Berkeley, 1969-75, prof., 1975-88, emerita, 1988—; vis. prof. Harvard U., 1978-79. Author: Yoshitsune, 1966, Tales of Ise, 1968, Okagami, The Great Mirror, 1980; (with William H. McCullough) A Tale of Flowering Fortunes, 1980; Brocade by Night, 1985, Kokin Wakashu, 1985, The Tale of the Heike, 1988, Classical Japanese Prose: An Anthology, 1990, Genji and Heike, 1994; translator, author research articles in field of classical Japanese lit. Served with WAVES, 1943-46. Fulbright fellow, 1955-56. Mem. Sierra Club. Democrat. Home: 40 Alta Rd Berkeley CA 94708-1204 Office: U Calif Dept East Asian Langs Berkeley CA 94720

MCCULLOUGH, HENRY G(LENN) L(UTHER), nuclear engineer; b. Waukegan, Ill., Aug. 5, 1939; s. Fredrick Douglas and Octavia Idelphi (Anderson) McC.; m. Suman'E D'uan Naro, Nov. 6, 1962; children: Barbra, Jeanine, Michelle, Charles, Edmunds, Caroline, Richard, Larry, Robert, Seng, Lynda. BA in Physics, Grinnell Coll., 1961; postgrad. in Nuclear Engring., U. Ariz., 1962; postgrad. in Physics, No. Ill. U., 1972. Registered profl. engr., Wis., Ill.; cert. quality and reliability engr.; lic. wildlife rehab., Ill. Rsch. assoc. A.U.R.A./Kitt Nat. Peak Obs., Tucson, 1965-66; nuclear engr. Babcock & Wilcox Co., Lynchburg, Va., 1966-68; sr. engr. Hittman Nuclear Devel. Corp., Columbia, Md., 1968-70; nuc. specialist Philco-Ford Corp., 1970-71; sci. instr. pilot program Waukegan unit Waukegan Unit

Dist., 1971-73; nuclear safeguards project engr. Sargent & Lundy Engrs., Chgo., 1974-81, project mgmt. engr., 1981-84, cons. engr., 1984-94; mgr. engring. and quality Crane Valves Nuclear Ops., Joliet, Ill., 1994—; Lectr. various orgns. Co-author: Nuclear Glossary, 1986. Bd. dirs. Coun. on Energy Independence, 1979-82; mem. Immaculate Conception Parish Sch. Bd., Waukegan, Ill., 1980-81; mem. Holy Names Soc. Immaculate Conception Ch., Waukegan, 1976—; commr. N.E. Ill. coun. Boy Scouts Am., 1979-83; minister Eucharist St. Joseph Ch., St. Bartholomew Ch., Waukegan, 1992-94; sr. choir mem., minister of the Eucharist St. Pius The X Parish, Granger, Ind., 1994—. 1st lt. USAF, 1962-65. Recipient Black Achiever award Chgo. Met. YMCA, 1981; grantee NSF, 1972. Mem. Am. Nuclear Soc. (chmn. stds. working group 1080-86, activist), Am. Soc. Quality Control (sr. mem. project 28 stds. subcom. svc. quality 1986—, task group to internat. stds. orgn. 1989—, apptd. to U.S. tech. adv. group Internat. Orgn. on Standardization TC/176 on Quality Assurance & Quality Mgmt.), Soc. Am. Mil. Engrs. Republican. Roman Catholic. Office: Crane Valve Nuclear Ops 104 N Chicago St Joliet IL 60434

MC CULLOUGH, JOHN PRICE, retired oil company executive; b. Dallas, May 10, 1925; s. John A. and Alta (McGee) McC.; m. Mary Ann Calvert, Aug. 5, 1946; children: Sherri, Cathryn, Patricia. Student, U. Denver, 1942-43; B.S. in Chem. Engring. U. Okla., 1945; M.S., Oreg. State U., 1948, Ph.D. in Chemistry, 1949. With U.S. Bur. Mines, Bartlesville, Okla., 1949-63, phys. chemist, 1949-57, chief thermodynamics br., 1958-63; mgr. central research div. Mobil Oil Corp., Princeton, N.J., 1963-69, mgr. applied research and devel., 1969-71; gen. mgr. research and devel. Mobil Chem. Co., 1971-78; v.p. environ. health and safety Mobil Research & Devel. Corp., Princeton, N.J., 1978-89; adj. prof. chemistry Okla. State U., Stillwater, 1961-63; vis. fellow Woodrow Wilson Found., 1991—; dir. Internat. Petroleum Industry Environ. Conservation Assn., 1981-89, chmn., 1985-88; dir. Mobil Found., Inc., 1987-89. Co-author: (with Donald Scott) Experimental Thermodynamics, Volume I: Calorimetry of Non-reacting Systems, 1968; contbr. 90 articles on thermodynamics, molecular structure and energetics, environ. and health policy to profl. jours. Mem. adv. com. Mercer County (N.J.) C.C., 1968-69; bd. dirs. Chem. Industry Inst. Toxicology, 1977-89, chmn., 1986-88; bd. dirs. United Community Fund, Princeton, 1963-69, Middlesex-Somerset-Mercer Regional Study Coun., 1968-69, 86-89, World Environment Ctr., 1986-89; mem. adv. bd. Georgetown U. Inst. Health Policy Analysis, 1986-89; trustee Stony Brook-Millstone Watershed Assn., 1989—, vice chmn., 1991-93; trustee Art Mus. Princeton U., 1994—; elder, pres. corp. Nassau Presbyn. Ch., 1995—. Served to lt. (j.g.) USNR, 1943-50. DuPont fellow, 1947-48; recipient Meritorious Service award U.S. Dept. Interior, 1959, Distinguished Service award, 1962; Am. Chem. Soc. award petroleum chemistry, 1963; Chemtech award, 1977; Huffman award Internat. Calorimetry Conf., 1963. Mem. AAAS, Gordon Rsch. Conf. (trustee, chmn. bd. trustees, mem. coun.), Am. Chem. Soc. (editorial bd. Jour. Chem. and Engring. Data, Jour. Phys. Chemistry, mem. coun. com. on chemistry and pub. affairs 1984-92, chmn. 1987-89), Internat. Calorimetry Conf. (chmn. 1960), Am. Inst. Chemists, Sigma Xi. Home: 30 Boudinot St Princeton NJ 08540-3008

MCCULLOUGH, JOSEPH, college president emeritus; b. Pitts., July 6, 1922; s. Joseph Phillip and Margaret (List) McC.; m. Elizabeth Cramer, Mar. 31, 1945; children—Marjorie Ann, Warren. B.F.A., Yale U., 1949-50, M.F.A., 1951; Diploma, Cleve. Sch. Art, 1948; D.F.A. (hon.), U. Evansville, Ind., 1980. Instr. San Jose State Coll., Calif., 1944-49; asst. instr. Yale U., New Haven, 1949-51; asst. dir. Cleve. Inst. Art, 1952-54, dir., 1954-74, pres., 1974-88. Artist paintings, nat. regional and local exhbns., 1948—. Chmn. Fine Arts Adv. Com., Cleve. Planning Commn., 1963-91; trustee Mpls. Coll. of Art and Design, 1988—, Sculpture Ctr. Cleve., 1990—; trustee, sec. Access to the Arts, Cleve., 1991—; Capt. USAAF, 1943-46, ETO. Recipient Cleve. Arts prize Women's City Club, 1971. Mem. Coll. Art Assn. (past dir.). Clubs: Union. Home: 2637 Wellington Rd Cleveland OH 44118-4120

MCCULLOUGH, M. BRUCE, lawyer; b. Princeton, N.J., July 26, 1944; s. Malcolm S. and Ruth S. (Strandness) McC.; m. Kathleen M. Ryan, Apr. 12, 1985. BA in Polit. Sci. and Econs., Whitworth Coll., 1966; JD, U. Mich., 1969. Bar: Pa., Fla., D.C. Ptnr. Buchanan Ingersoll P.C., Pitts. With USAR, 1969-75. Mem. Am. Land Title Assn. (lenders counsel), Chartiers Country Club, Duquesne Club, Rivers Club, Eagle Trace. Avocations: golf, boating, hunting. Office: Buchanan Ingersoll 5800 USX Tower 600 Grant St Ste 57 Pittsburgh PA 15219

MCCULLOUGH, MICHAEL WILLIAM, JR., minister, educator, researcher, writer, missionary, gospel singer, consultant; b. Chgo., May 5, 1950; s. Albert Charles and Magnolia Salome Jane (Ingraham) Henry; m. Denise Sharon Desvignes, July 23, 1977. AA in Speech and Broadcast Communications, Kennedy-King Coll., 1970; BA in Interpersonal Communications, Trinity Coll., Deerfield, Ill., 1988; MA in Religion cum laude, Trinity Evang. Div. Sch., Deerfield, Ill., 1988; MDiv in Urban Ministry, No. Bapt. Theol. Sem., 1990. Ordained to ministry Christian Ch., 1971; cert. urban pastoral educator; cert. tchr. Ill., tchr. Evang. Tchr. Tng. Assn. Exec. dir. Gospel Crusader Revivals Inc., Chgo., 1971-79; assoc. pastor, youth pastor Southside Tabernacle, Chgo., 1977-78; assoc. min. Hyde Park Fellowship, Chgo., 1978-79; sr. pastor Gospel Crusader Revival Tabernacle, Chgo., 1979-88, Metro-Outreach Fellowship Ch., Chgo., 1988—; substitute tchr. South Suburban Sch. Dists. 133, 147, 149, 167, 171, 172, Chgo., 1989—; tgn. missionary, Mex., Can., Germany, Albania, India, Kenya; domestic missionary S.D., Nebr., Mont.; mem., counselor Ministerial Adv. Coun. Chgo. Voc. High Schs., 1986—; exec. dir. Metro Evang. Svc. Sems. and Global Endeavors, Inc., Chgo., 1988; urban ch. cons. M.E.S.S.A.G.E., Inc., 1988—; v.p., acad. dean, prof. Bible, theology, Christian edn. Urban Inst. in Christian Studies, 1988—; exec. bd. Black Men's Midwest Regional Conf., 1990—; instr. religion and humanities Prairie State Coll., Chicago Heights, Ill, 1991—; co-founder, dir. Washington-Westgate Scholastic Fund, 1991—; bd. dirs. Pan Am. Christian Exchange, 1992—; speaker Esmond Elem. Sch., Chgo.; writer divns. Echols David C. Cook Pub. Ho., 1993—. Author: Prophetic Destiny of Persons of Color, Pursuing the Knowledge of the Holy. Urban scholar Trinity Coll., 1987-88; Urban scholar Sem. Consortium for Urban Pastoral Edn., 1988-89; Faculty scholar No. Bapt. Theol. Sem, 1988-90. Mem. Roseland Clergy Assn., Nat. Assn. Black Seminarians, Nat. Black Evang. Assn., Am. Acad. Religion, N.Am. Soc. for Ch. Growth, Soc. for Bibl. Lit., Soc. for Pentecostal Studies, Trinity Evang. Div. Sch. Alumni Assn., No. Bapt. Theol. Sem. Alumni Assn., Sem. Consortium for Urban Pastoral Edn. Alumni Assn., Pan African Christian Exchange Missions Assn., Amb. Fellowship Missions Soc. Office: MESSAGE Inc PO Box 289050 Chicago IL 60628-9050

MCCULLOUGH, R. MICHAEL, management consultant; b. Springfield, Ohio, Dec. 31, 1938; s. Jerome Edward and Sara Amelia (Fitzsimmons) McC.; m. Frances P. Kelly, Nov. 24, 1962; children: Jeanne M., Michael F., Colleen T., Brian A., Kathleen H., Christopher E., Brendan P. B.S in Elec. Engring., U. Detroit, 1962. Engr. Gen. Electric Co., Washington, 1962-65; engr., rsch. dir. Booz Allen & Hamilton, Bethesda, Md., 1965-71, ptnr., 1971-73, mng. ptnr., 1973-84; chmn., chief exec. officer Booz Allen & Hamilton, New York, N.Y., 1984-91; sr. chmn. Booz Allen & Hamilton, McLean, Va., 1991—; bd. dirs. Profl. Svcs. Coun., Washington, pres., 1983-84; bd. dirs. Interstate Hotels, Caterair Internat. Mem. adv. coun. Stanford U., 1985-91; bd. dirs. Wolf Trap Found., 1989—; trustee U. Detroit Mercy, 1990, U.S. - Panama Bus. Coun., U.S. - Russia Bus. Coun. Club: Columbia Country (Chevy Chase, Md.), Burning Tree Country (Bethesda, Md.); Country of Fla. (West Palm Beach); Robert Trent James Golf Club (Manassas, Va.); Pine Valley (N.J.) Golf Club.

MC CULLOUGH, RALPH CLAYTON, II, lawyer, educator; b. Daytona Beach, Fla., Mar. 28, 1941; s. Ralph C. and Doris (Johnson) McC.; m. Elizabeth Grier Henderson, Apr. 5, 1986; children from previous marriage: Melissa Wells, Clayton Baldwin. B.A., Erskine Coll., 1962; J.D., Tulane U., 1965. Bar: La. 1965, S.C. 1974. Assoc. Baldwin, Haspel, Maloney, Rainold and Meyer, New Orleans, 1965-68; asst. prof. law U. S.C., 1968-71, assoc. prof., 1971-75; prof. U. S.C., 2, 1975—; chair prof. of advocacy U. S.C. 1982—; asst. dean Sch. Law, 1970-75, instr. Med. Sch., 1973-79, adj. prof. law and medicine Med. Sch., 1979—; adj. prof. medicine Med. U. of S.C., 1984—; of counsel Finkel, Goldberg, Sheftman & Altman, 1978—; adj. prof. pathology Med. U. S.C., 1985—; asst. dean U. S.C. Sch. Law 1970-75. Author: (with J.L. Underwood) The Civil Trial Manual, 1974, 7th supple-

ment, 1987, The Civil Trial Manual II, 1984, 87, (with Myers and Felix) New Directions in Legal Education, 1970, (with Finkel) S.C. Torts II, 1986, III, 1990; co-reporter S.C. Criminal Code, 1977, S.C. Study Sentencing, 1977. Trustee S.C. dist. U.S. Bankruptcy Ct., 1979—; exec. dir. S.C. Continuing Legal Edn. Program; bd. visitors Erskine Coll.; reporter S.C. Jury Charge Commn., 1991—. Mem. ABA, La. Bar Assn., S.C. Bar (sec. 1975-76, exec. dir. 1972-76, award of service 1978), New Orleans Bar Assn., Am. Trial Lawyers Assn., Am. Law Inst., Southeastern Assn. Am. Law Schs. (pres.), S.C. Trial Lawyers Assn. (bd. govs. 1984-88), Phi Alpha Delta. Republican. Episcopalian. Club: Forest Lake. Home: PO Box 1799 Columbia SC 29202-1799 Office: U SC Sch Law Columbia SC 29208

MCCULLOUGH, RAY DANIEL, JR., insurance company executive; b. Daytona Beach, Fla., Feb. 28, 1938; s. Ray Daniel and Clarice (Malphurs) McC.; m. Barbara Jean Winchester, Aug. 16, 1963; children—Courtney Ann, Justin Ray. BSBA with honors, U. Fla., 1960. C.P.A., Fla. Accountant Deloitte Haskins & Sells (C.P.A.'s), Jacksonville, Fla., 1960-63; with Gulf Life Ins. Co., Jacksonville, 1963-85; v.p., controller Gulf Life Ins. Co., 1971-85; sr. v.p. fin. Dependable Ins. Group, 1985-88; pvt. practice acctg. Jacksonville, 1988—; mem. bus. adv. council U. Fla., Gainesville, 1979-85. Mem. Am., Fla. insts. C.P.A.'s, Jacksonville Toastmasters Club (pres. 1966), Beta Alpha Psi, Beta Gamma Sigma. Home: 10312 Sylvan Ln W Jacksonville FL 32257-6240 Office: 2700 University Blvd W Ste 1A Jacksonville FL 32217-2120

MCCULLOUGH, RICHARD LAWRENCE, advertising agency executive; b. Chgo., Dec. 1, 1937; s. Francis John and Sadie Beatrice McCullough; m. Julia Louise Kreimer, May 6, 1961; children: Stephen, Jeffery, Julie. BS, Marquette U., 1959. Commd. U.S. Army, 1959, advance through grades to sgt., 1966; account exec. Edward H. Weiss Advt., Chgo., 1960-66; account supr. Doyle Dane Bernbach, N.Y.C., 1966-68; sr. v.p. J. Walter Thompson Co., Chgo., 1969-86; pres. E.H. Brown Advt., Chgo., 1986—. Author: Building Country Radio, 1986, A New Look at Country Music Audiences, 1988, (video) Country Music Marketing, 1989. Bd. dirs. Gateway Found., Chgo., 1976—, chmn., 1988-91; bd. dirs. Catholic Charities, Chgo. Mem. Country Music Assn. (dir. 1979—, pres. 1983-85, Pres.'s award 1987), Nat. Assn. Recording Artists and Scis. (Nashville chpt.), North Shore Country Club (Glenview, Ill.), Tower Club, Dairymen's Country Club (Boulder Junction, Wis.), Quail Creek Country Club (Naples, Fla.). Roman Catholic. Home (summer): 2720 Lincoln St Evanston IL 60201 also (winter): St Simone 5633 Turtle Bay Naples FL 33963 Office: EH Brown Advt 20 N Wacker Dr Chicago IL 60606-2806

MCCULLOUGH, ROBERT WILLIS, former textile executive; b. Monclair, N.J., Sept. 19, 1920; s. Willis G. and Viola (Mock) McC.; m. Margaret Elizabeth Hammons, Aug. 12, 1942; children—Constance Joan, Sandra Margaret, D. Scott, Linda Anne. Student, Phila. Textile Sch.; grad., Brown U., 1943. With Collins & Aikman Corp., N.Y.C., 1946-84; exec. v.p. Collins & Aikman Corp., 1955—, chmn. exec. com., 1961-84; ret.; bd. dirs. parent org. Collins & Aikman; adviser to supt. U.S. Naval Acad. Trustee, past chmn. South Street Seaport Mus.; trustee Brown U., Am. Scottish Found., Textile Research Inst. at Princeton. Served from ensign to lt. comdr. USCGR, 1942-46. Named to Brown U. Hall of Fame. Mem. Am. Arbitration Assn. Clubs: Riverside Yacht, N.Y. Yacht (past commodore; chmn. Am.'s Cup Com.), Storm Trysail, Cruising of Am. Home and Office: 93 Club Rd Riverside CT 06878-2003

MCCULLOUGH, ROY LYNN, chemical engineering educator; b. Hilsboro, Tex., Mar. 20, 1934; s. Roy Lee and Rubye Maye (Ingram) McC.; m. Jamis Carol Petersen, Sept. 5, 1958; children: Catherine Lynne, Amanda Kaye, Roy Lawrence. BS, Baylor U., 1955; PhD, U. N.Mex., 1960. Mem. staff Los Alamos (N.Mex.) Sci. Lab., 1955-60; group leader, sect. head Monsanto Co., Durham, N.C., 1960-69; sr. scientist Boeing Co., Seattle, 1969-71; prof. chem. engring. U. Del., Newark, 1971—, dir.Ctr. for Composite Material, 1990-94. Author: Concepts of Fiber-Resin Composites, 1971; mem. editorial bd. Jour. Composite Sci. and Tech., 1984—; contbr. articles to profl. jours. Mem. Am. Inst. Chem. Engrs., Am. Chem. Soc., Am. Phys. Soc., Am. Soc. Composites. Home: 107 Reynard Dr Landenberg PA 19350-1145 Office: U Del Ctr for Composite Material Newark DE 19716

MCCULLOUGH, SAMUEL ALEXANDER, banker; b. Pitts., Nov. 10, 1938; s. Alexander and Mary Ruth (Brady) McC.; m. Katharine Graham, Sept. 23, 1967; children: Bonnie McCullough Wideman, Elizabeth McCullough White, Rebecca D., Anne D., Mary D. BBA, U. Pitts., 1960; LLD (hon.), Albright Coll., Reading, Pa., 1990. With Mellon Bank, N.A., Pitts., 1956-75, asst. cashier, 1964-68, asst. v.p., 1968-71, v.p., 1971-75; sr. v.p. corp. banking group Am. Bank and Trust Co. of Pa., Reading, 1975, exec. v.p., 1977, pres., chief exec. officer, 1978-82, chmn., chief exec. officer, 1982—; pres., chief exec. officer Meridian Bancorp., Inc., Reading, 1983-88, chmn., chief exec. officer, 1988—, also bd. dirs.; and bd. dirs. to all prin. subs. cos.; former rep. 3d Fed. Res. Dist., bd. mem.; chmn. nominating com., past chmn., bd. dirs., exec. com. Greater Phila. 1st Corp.; exec. com. Pa. Chamber Bus. and Industry; former bd. dirs. Fed. Res. Bank Phila. Bd. dirs. Phila. Orch. Assn., exec. com., chmn. facilities com., chmn. audit com., Commonwealth Found., U. Pitts. Joseph M. Katz Grad Sch. Bus.; bd. dirs., mem. planning com. Reading Hosp. and Med. Ctr.; mem. coun. Pa. Soc.; trustee Albright Coll., exec. com., chmn. nominating com.; mem. coun. Pa. Soc.; Valley Forge coun. Boy Scouts Am.; bd. govs. former chmn. Pennsylvanians for Effective Govt.; mem. steering com. Bus. Leaders Organized for Cath. Schs. Recipient Disting. Pennsylvanian award, 1982, Pagoda award for outstanding contbns. to community Berks County Jr. Achievement, 1985, William H. Doran Meml. award, 1987, Bicentennial medal U. Pitts., 1988, Disting. Citizen award Valley Forge coun. Boy Scouts Am., 1988, Am. Enterprise award Pa. Coun. on Econ. Edn., 1989, Outstanding Vol. Fund Raiser award Greater Northeastern Pa. chpt. Nat. Soc. Fund Raising Execs., 1989; Good Scout award Phila. coun. Boy Scouts Am., 1990, Silver Antelope award, 1991, Torch of Liberty award Ea. Pa.-Del. Region Anti-Defamation League, 1992; named Bus. Person of Yr. Berks County C. of C., 1985, Disting. Alumnus U. Pitts., 1993. Mem. Am. Inst. Banking, Am. Bankers Assn., Pa. Bankers Assn., Berks County Bankers Assn., Bankers Roundtable (govt. rels. com.), Internat. Fin. Conf. (past chmn.), Pa. Bus. Roundtable (bd. dirs.), Allegheny Country Club, Berkshire Country Club. Republican. Presbyterian. Office: Meridian Bancorp Inc 35 N 6th St PO Box 1102 Reading PA 19603

MCCULLY, EMILY ARNOLD, illustrator, writer; b. Galesburg, Ill., 1939; d. Wade E. and Kathryn (Maher) Arnold; m. George E. McCully, 1961 (div. 1975); children: Nathaniel, Tad. BA, Brown U., 1961; MA, Columbia U., 1964. Author: How's Your Vacuum Cleaner Working? O'Henry Collection, 1977, A Craving, 1982, (novel) Picnic, 1984 (Christopher award), First Snow, 1985, (novel) Life Drawing, 1986, The Show Must Go On, 1987, School, 1987, You Lucky Duck!, 1988, New Baby, 1988, The Grandma Mix-up, 1988, The Christmas Gift, 1988, Zaza's Big Break, 1989, Grandma's at the Lake, 1990, The Evil Spell, 1990, Speak Up, Blanche!, 1991, Mirette on the Highwire, 1992 (Caldecott medal 1992), Grandma's at Bat, 1993, The Amazing Felix, 1993, My Real Family, 1994, Crossing The New Bridge, 1994, Little Kit, or: The Industrious Flea Circus Girl, 1995, The Pirate Queen, 1995; illustrator: Sea Beach Express, 1966, The Seventeenth Street Gang, 1966, Rex, 1967, Luigi of the Streets, 1967, That Mean Man, 1968, Gooney, 1968, Journey From Peppermint Street, 1968 (Nat. Book award 1969), The Mouse and the Elephant, 1969, The Fisherman, 1969, Tales from the Rue Brocca, 1969, Here I Am, 1969, Twin Spell, 1969, Hobo Toad and the Motorcycle Gang, 1970, Slip! Slop! Gobble!, 1970, Friday Night is Papa Night, 1970, Maxie, 1970, Steffie and Me, 1970, The Cat and the Parrot, 1970, Gertrude's Pocket, 1970, Go and Hush the Baby, 1971, Finders Keepers, 1971, Ma n Da La, 1971 (Bklyn. Mus. award 1976, N.Y. Pub. Libr. award 1976), Hurray for Captain Jane!, 1971, Michael Is Brave, 1971, Finding Out With Your Senses, 1971, Henry's Pennies, 1972, Jane's Blanket, 1972, Grandpa's Long Red Underwear, 1972, Girls Can Too!, 1972, The Boyhood of Grace Jones, 1972, Black Is Brown Is Tan, 1973, Isabelle the Itch, 1973, When Violet Died, 1973, That New Boy, 1973, How To Eat Fried Worms, 1973, Jenny's Revenge, 1974, Her Majesty, Grace Jones, 1974, Tree House Town, 1974, I Want Mama, 1974, Amanda, the Panda and the Redhead, 1975, The Bed Book, 1976, My Street's A Morning Cool Street, 1976, Professor Coconut and the Thief, 1977, Martha's Mad Dog, 1977, That's Mine, 1977, Where Wild Willie, 1978, No Help At All, 1978,

Partners, 1978, The Twenty-Elephant Restaurant, 1978, What I Did Last Summer, 1978, The Highest Hit, 1978, I and Spraggy, 1978, Edward Troy and the Witch Cat, 1978, My Island Grandma, 1979, Whatever Happened to Beverly Bigler's Birthday?, 1979, Last Look, 1979, Ookie-Spooky, 1979, The Black Dog Who Went Into the Woods, 1980, How I Found Myself at the Fair, 1980, How We Got Our First Cat, 1980, Oliver and Allison's Week, 1980, Pajama Walking, 1981, The April Fool, 1981, I Dance in My Red Pajamas, 1982, The Halloween Candy Mystery, 1982, Go and Mush the Baby, 1982, Mitzi and the Terrible Tyrannosaurus Rex, 1983, Best Friend Insurance, 1983, Mail-Order Wings, 1984, Gertrude's Pocket, 1984, Fifth Grade Magic, 1984, The Ghastly Glasses, 1985, Fourth of July, 1985, The Explorer of Barkham Street, 1985, Wheels, 1986, Lulu and the Witch Baby, 1986, Richard and the Vratch, 1987, Molly, 1987, Molly Goes Hiking, 1987, Jam Day, 1987, The Boston Coffee Party, 1988, The Take-Along Dog, 1989, Selene Goes Home, 1989, The Magic Mean Machine, 1989, It Always Happens to Leona, 1989, The Grandpa Days, 1989, Dinah's Mad, Bad Wishes, 1989, Stepbrother Sabotage, 1990, Lulu Goes to Witch School, 1990, The Evil Spell, 1990, The Day Chubby Became Charles, 1990, The Christmas Present Mystery, 1990, Sky Guys to White Cat, 1991, Meatball, 1991, Leona and Ike, 1991, The Butterfly Birthday, 1991, Yankee Doodle Drumsticks, 1992, One Very Best Valentine's Day, 1992, Meet the Lincoln Lions Band, 1992, Jingle Bells Jam, 1992, In My Tent, 1992, Anne Flies the Birthday Bike, 1993, Amzat and His Brothers, 1993. Office: c/o Putnam Pub Group 200 Madison Ave New York NY 10016-3901

MC CUNE, BARRON PATTERSON, federal judge; b. West Newton, Pa., Feb. 19, 1915; s. James Patterson and Lyda Barron (Hammond) McC.; m. Edna Flannery Markey, Dec. 23, 1943; children—Edward M., James H., Barron Patterson. A.B., Washington and Jefferson Coll., 1935; LL.B., U. Pa., 1938. Bar: Pa. bar 1939. Practiced in Washington, Pa., 1939-64; judge 27th Jud. Dist. Ct. Common Pleas, Washington, Pa., 1964-71; judge U.S. Dist. Ct., Western Dist. Pa., Pitts., 1971—; sr. fed. judge. Trustee emeritus Washington and Jefferson Coll.; dir. emeritus Washington (Pa.) Hosp. Served with USNR, 1942-45. Office: US PO & Courthouse 6th Fl Rm 6 7th & Grant Sts Pittsburgh PA 15219

MCCUNE, DAVID FRANKLIN, publisher; b. Trenton, N.J., Jan. 15, 1954; s. George David and Mary Jane McCune; m. Susan Ruth Watt, Apr. 11, 1981; 1 child, Douglas David. BA summa cum laude, Williams Coll., 1975. Free-lance journalist Malmö, Sweden, 1975-80; editor Time Inc., N.Y.C., 1981-83; pres. The Proteus Group Inc., N.Y.C., 1983-87; mktg. dir. Sage Publs. Inc., Newbury Park, Calif., 1988, pres., 1989—. Mem. Soc. for Scholarly Pub., Assn. for Computing Machinery, Young Pres.'s Orgn. Avocations: sailing, skiing. Office: Sage Publications Inc 2455 Teller Rd Thousand Oaks CA 91320-2218

MCCUNE, ELLIS E., retired university system chief administrator, higher education consultant; b. Houston, July 17, 1921; s. Ellis E. and Ruth (Mason) McC.; m. Hilda May Whiteman, Feb. 8, 1946; 1 son, James Donald. Student, Sam Houston State U., 1940-42; B.A., UCLA, 1948, Ph.D., 1957; LHD, Golden Gate U., 1994. Teaching asst. UCLA, 1949-51; from instr. to assoc. prof. polit. sci. Occidental Coll., Los Angeles, 1951-59; chmn. applied politics and econs. curriculum Occidental Coll., 1951-56; asst. prof. Calif. State U., Northridge, 1959-61, assoc. prof., chmn. dept. polit. sci., 1961-63, prof., 1963, dean letters and sci., 1963; dean acad. planning Calif. State Univs. and Colls., 1963-67; pres. Calif. State U. Hayward, 1967-90, pres. emeritus, 1991—; acting chancellor The Calif. State U. System, 1990-91, ret., 1991; cons. govtl. units and agys.; lectr., panelist; mem. Calif. State Scholarship and Loan Commn., 1964-68, chmn., 1967-68; pres. Govtl. Adminstrn. Group Los Angeles, 1959; chair planning com., mem. exec. com., bd. dirs. Eden Med. Ctr. Found., 1994—, pres.-elect, 1995—. Chmn. univs. and colls. div. United Bay Area Crusade, 1969-70, 73-74; bd. dirs. Oakland (Calif.) Museum Assn., 1974-77, 86-88; vice chmn. higher edn. div., East Bay United Way, 1989-90; mem. arts adv. council, 1986-87, devel. com., 1988-89, Bay Area Urban League, bd. trust Calif. Coun. Econ. Edn. No. sect., Emergency Shelter Program Adv. Coun., Hayward Area Hist. Assn., NAACP Hayward chpt.; trustee Calif. Council Econ. Edn.; sec. bd. dirs. Eden Community Found., 1978-79; rsch. fellow Haynes Found, 1957. With USAAF, 1942-46. Mem. Am. Coun. Edn. (adv. com. 1970-72, inst. coll. & univ. adminstrs. 1973-74, bd. dirs. 1985-86), Western Assn. Schs. and Colls. (accrediting commn. sr. colls. and univs. 1974-78, chmn., 1978-82, pres. 1979-81), N.W. Assn. Schs. and Colls. (commn. colls. 1974-80), Assn. Am. Colls. (bd. dirs. 1972-75, vice chmn. 1975-76), Assn. Western Univs. (bd. dirs.), Coun. Postsecondary Accreditation (bd. dirs. 1977-88, exec. com. 1979-88, chmn. 1985-87, immediate past chmn., 1988-89, chmn. com. recognition 1982-84), Am. Assn. State Colls. and Univs. (chmn. accreditation com. 1983-86, com. acad. pers. and acad. freedom 1987-88, com. on acad. affairs 1988-91), Calif. Coun. Edn. (trustee), Western Polit. Sci. Assn. (exec. coun. 1958-61), Hayward C. of C. (dir. 1968-71, 73-76, 77-80, 82-85, 86-90), Regional Assn. East Bay Colls. and Univs. (exec. com. 1974-90, sec. 1975-76, 87-88, vice chmn. 1976-77, 84-85, chmn. 1977-79, 85-86), Rotary, Phi Beta Kappa, Pi Gamma Mu, Pi Sigma Alpha. Club: Bohemian (San Francisco). Home: 17577 Parker Rd Castro Valley CA 94546-1227 Office: Calif State U Pres Emeritus LI 3167 Hayward CA 94542-3053

MC CUNE, JOHN FRANCIS, III, retired architect; b. New Castle, Pa., Oct. 23, 1921; s. John Francis and Alice (Miles) McC.; m. Jeanne Ramsay, Sept. 28, 1946; children—Morgan R., Martha (Mrs. Dennis L. Maddox), David M., William S. Student, Vanderbilt U., 1938-40; B.S. in Architecture, U. Mich., 1943. Draftsman firm Walter E. Bort (Architect), Clinton, Iowa, 1946-47; firm Pope & Kruse (Architects), Wilmington, Del., 1947-54; assoc. Pope & Kruse (Architects), 1955-60; partner firm Pope, Kruse & McCune (Architects), Wilmington, 1961-72; owner McCune Assos. (Architects), Wilmington, 1972-81; v.p., prin. architect Diamond/McCune (Architects & Engrs.), Wilmington, 1981-88. Projects include Gander Hill Correctional Facility; renovation of Wilmington Public Bldg, all Wilmington; historic preservation projects include Presbyn. Ch, New Castle, Old Court House, New Castle, Barrett's Chapel, Frederica, Del., Old State House, Dover, Del., Loockerman Hall, Dover. Mem. Hist. Area Commn., New Castle, Del., 1974-88. Mem. AIA (pres. Del. chpt. 1970-71, mem. nat. com. historic resources 1975-88, state preservation coordinator Del. 1975-88), Soc. Archtl. Historians, Assn. for Preservation Tech., ASTM (com.), Nat. Trust Hist. Preservation, Del. C. of C., Nat. Fire Protection Assn. (com. libraries, museums and hist. bldgs. 1975-88), Kappa Sigma. Home: 14011 Antelope CT Sun City West AZ 85376

MCCUNE, M. DAVIS, architect. BArch, U. Okla.; postgrad., San Diego State U. Registered arch., Tex. Med. arch. Robert F. Marasco & Assocs., San Diego, 1980-82; with Harwood K. Smith & Ptnrs., Dallas, 1982-84; ptnr., project dir. MPI Archs., Dallas. Prin. works include Cyrix Corp., Richardson, Tex., Gen. Electric Capital Corporate Hdqrs., Dallas, Dallas Rehab. Inst., City of Garland Renovations, No. Telecom., Inc., Richardson, NCR Corp., Ft. Worth, U. Tulsa, Baylor U., Waco, Tex., Humana Womens and Childrens Hosp., San Antonio, Humana Womens Hosp., Lake Charles, La., Humana Womens Hosp., Indpls., and numerous others. Active Dallas Hist. Soc. Mem. AIA, Tex. Soc. Archs., Nat. Fire and Protection Assn. Office: MPI Archs 16479 Dallas Pkwy Ste 240 Dallas TX 75248

MCCUNE, MARY JOAN HUXLEY, microbiology educator; b. Lewistown, Mont., Jan. 14, 1932; d. Thomas Leonard and Anna Dorothy (Hardie) Huxley; m. Ronald William McCune, June 7, 1965; children: Anna Orpha, Heather Jean. BS, Mont. State Coll., 1953; MS, Wash. State U., 1955; PhD, Purdue U., 1965. Rsch. technician VA Hosp., Oakland, Calif., 1956-59; bacteriologist U.S. Naval Radiol. Def. Lab., San Francisco, 1959-61; teaching assoc. Purdue U., West Lafayette, Ind., 1961-65, vis. asst. prof. 1965-66; asst. prof. Occidental Coll., L.A., 1966-69; asst. rsch. bacteriologist II U. Calif., L.A., 1969-70; affiliate asst. prof. Idaho State U., Pocatello, Idaho, 1970-80, from asst. prof. to prof. microbiology, 1980—; instr. U. Calif., Davis, 1964. Contbr. articles to profl. jours. Pres. AK chpt. PEO, Pocatello, 1988-89; chair faculty senate Idaho State U., 1994-95. David Ross fellow Purdue U., 1964. Mem. AAAS, N.Y. Acad. Sci., Idaho Acad. Sci. (trustee 1989-, v.p. 1992-93, pres. 1993-94), Am. Soc. for Microbiology (v.p. Intermountain br. 1988-89, pres. 1989-90), Idaho Edn. Alliance for Sci. (bd. dirs.), Sigma Xi, Sigma Delta Epsilon. Presbyterian. Home: 30 Colgate St Pocatello ID 83201-3459 Office: Idaho State U Dept Biol Scis Pocatello ID 83209

MCCUNE, WILLIAM MINTON, construction company executive; b. L.A., Oct. 13, 1922; s. William Wade and Lola Jewel (Minton) McC.; m. Lorraine R. Juelson, Dec. 4, 1943; 1 child, Carol McCune Mann. Chief estimator Diversified Builders, Paramount, Calif., 1948-56; v.p. Diversified Builders, Paramount, 1956-63, pres., 1963-69; exec. v.p. Zapata Constructors, Paramount, 1969-71, pres., 1971-78; exec. v.p. Zapata Corp., Houston, 1978-81; pres., chief exec. officer Macco Constructors, Inc., Paramount, 1981-90, chief exec. officer, 1990-92, chmn. bd. Pilot U.S. Army Air Corps, 1942-46. Mem. Nat. Assn. Corp. Dirs., L.A. World Affairs Coun., Navy League U.S., Huntington Harbour Anglers, Huntington Harbour Yacht Club, Jonathan Club, Tuna Club Avalon. Republican. Avocation: yachting. Office: Macco Constructors Inc 14409 Paramount Blvd Paramount CA 90723-3436

MCCURDY, CHARLES GRIBBEL, publishing company executive; b. N.Y.C., June 28, 1955; m. Lisa Maddox; 1 child, Henry. BA, Yale U., 1977; MBA, Columbia U., 1983. Fin. assoc. treas.'s dept. Macmillan Inc., N.Y.C., 1983-84, dir. internat. treasury ops., 1984-85, dir. devel. for info. services, 1985-86, v.p. corp. devel., 1986-87, v.p. corp. fin., 1987-89; v.p., treas. Newfield Pubs., Shelton, Conn., 1989—. Office: Newfield Pubs 2 Corporate Dr Shelton CT 06484

MCCURDY, GILBERT GEIER, retired retailer; b. Rochester, N.Y., May 25, 1922; s. Gilbert J.C. and Virginia (Geier) McC.; m. Katherine W. Babcock, Nov. 9, 1946; children—Gilbert Kennedy, Lynda Babcock (Mrs. Hotra). B.A., Williams Coll., 1944. With McCurdy & Co., Inc., Rochester, 1946—; controller, asst. treas. McCurdy & Co., Inc., 1953-55, v.p., 1956-59, exec. v.p., 1959-62, pres., gen. mgr., 1962-80, chief exec. officer, 1969-80, chmn. bd., chief exec. officer, 1980-92, chmn. exec. com. of bd., 1993—; chmn. bd. Frederick Atkins, 1968-70; dir. Chase Lincoln First Bank of Rochester. Bd. dirs. Pathway Houses of Rochester; former mem. bd. dirs. United Way Rochester and Monroe County; trustee U. Rochester. 1st lt. Signal Corps, AUS, 1943-46. Mem. Rochester C. of C. (pres. 1975). Baptist. Home: 1 Whitney Ln Rochester NY 14610-3551 Office: Midtown Plaza Rochester NY 14645

MC CURDY, HAROLD GRIER, psychologist; b. Salisbury, N.C., May 30, 1909; s. McKinnon Grier and Nellie (Curd) McC.; m. Mary Burton Derrickson, Sept. 15, 1937; children: John Derrickson, Ann Lewis. A.B., Duke U., 1930, Ph.D., 1938. Asst. prof. biology High Point Coll., 1931-32; caseworker Fed. Transient Bur., Salisbury, N.C., 1934; prof. psychology Milligan Coll., 1938-41; assoc. prof. to prof. psychology and philosophy Meredith Coll., 1941-48; assoc. prof. to Kenan prof. psychology U. N.C., Chapel Hill, 1948-71; Kenan prof. psychology emeritus U. N.C., 1971—. Author: The Personality of Shakespeare, 1953, reprint, 1973, The Personal World, 1961, Personality and Science, 1965, Barbara, 1966, About Mary, 1989, (poetry) Oblation, 1990, 50 Metaphysical Sonnets for a Rock Age, 1993; contbg. author: Historical Roots of Contemporary Psychology, 1968, Humanistic Psychology, 1981, Foundations of Psychology, 1984; poetry The Chastening of Narcissus, 1970, Novus Ordo Seclorum, 1981, And Then the Sky Turned Blue, 1982, Twenty Four Bagatelles in an Antique Mode, 1989, others. Mem. AAAS, Am. Psychol. Assn., Sigma Xi. Democrat. Methodist. Home: 6 Gooseneck Rd Chapel Hill NC 27514-4600

MCCURDY, HARRY WARD, otolaryngologist; b. Branchton, Pa., Aug. 15, 1918; s. Adam Oscar and Sarah Fern (Hindman) McC.; m. Joan Jacqueline Talty, Dec. 10, 1955; children: Bridget Elizabeth, Peter Adam. A.B., Allegheny Coll., 1940; M.D., U. Pa., 1943. Diplomate: Am. Bd. Otolaryngology. Intern Geisinger Meml. Hosp., Danville, Pa., 1944; resident in otolaryngology Geisinger Meml. Hosp., 1944-45, 48-49; resident in pathology Hamot Hosp., Erie, Pa., 1945-48; mem. staff Geisinger Med. Center, Danville, 1948-50; commd. 2d lt. U.S. Army, 1945, advanced through grades to col., 1962-74; mil. cons. Surgeon Gen., U.S. Army, 1964-74; ret., 1974; exec. v.p. Am. Acad. Otolaryngology-Head and Neck Surgery, Washington, 1974-84; mem. staff Walter Reed Army Hosp.; mem. resources council Gallaudet Coll., 1975-80; mem. nat. adv. council Sertoma Found., 1976-84; chmn. FDA Panel on Otolaryngologic Med. Devices, 1974-78, cons., 1978-84. Mem. ACS, AMA, Royal Soc. Medicine (U.K.), Am. Acad. Otolaryngology, Mil. Surgeons Assn., Am. Soc. Assn. Execs., Soc. Med. Consultants to Armed Forces, AAAS, Am. Soc. Facial Plastic Surgery, Soc. Mil. Otolaryngologists, Am. Acad. Facial Plastic and Reconstructive Surgery, Am. Laryngol., Rhinol. and Otol. Soc., Anglo-Am. Med. Soc., Am. Audiology Soc., Royal Soc. Health, Osler Med. Soc., Acad. Medicine, Soc. Univ. Otolaryngologists, Am. Council Otolaryngology, Pan-Am. Soc. Bronchoesophagology., Internat. Fedn. Otolaryngol. Socs. (sec. gen. 1981—), Soc. Mil. Cons. to Armed Forces (sec. 1993—). Republican. Methodist. Clubs: Army Navy, Press, Mil. Attaches of London, Les Chevaliers du Tastevin. Home and Office: 6006 Dellwood Pl Bethesda MD 20817-3812

MCCURDY, LARRY WAYNE, automotive parts company executive; b. Commerce, Tex., July 1, 1935; s. Weldon Lee and Eula Bell (Quinn) McC.; m. Anna Jean Ogle, June 2, 1956; children: Michael, Kimberly, Laurie. BBA, Tex. A&M U., 1957. Jr. acct. Tenneco Inc., Houston, 1958-60; sr. acct. Tenneco Oil Co., Houston, 1960-64; acctg. supr. Tenneco Chems., Houston, 1964-69; div. controller Tenneco Chems., Saddle Brook, N.J., 1970-72, corp. controller, 1972-74, v.p., fin., 1974-78; sr. v.p. fin. Tenneco Automotive, Deerfield, Ill., 1978-80; pres. Walker Mfg. Co., Racine, Wis., 1980-81; exec. v.p. N.Am. ops. Tenneco Automotive, Deerfield, 1981-82; v.p. fin. Echlin Inc., Branford, Conn., 1983, pres. chief operating officer, 1983-85; pres., chief exec. officer Moog Automotive Inc., St. Louis, 1985-94; exec. v.p. ops. Cooper Industries, Houston, 1994—; bd. dirs. Lear Seating Corp., Mohawk Industries, Inc., Breed Tech., Inc. Trustee Somerset County Coll., Somerville, N.J., 1974-78, Millikin U., Decatur, Ill., 1991—; former mem. bd. dirs. Jr. Achievement, Chgo. Mem. Fin. Execs. Inst., Nat. Assn. Accts., Motor Equipment Mfrs. Assn. (chmn. bd. dirs. 1989). Office: Cooper Industries Ste 4000 1001 Fannin Houston TX 77002

MCCURDY, MICHAEL CHARLES, illustrator, author; b. N.Y.C., Feb. 17, 1942; s. Charles Errett and Beatrice (Beatson) McC.; m. Deborah Lamb, Sept. 7, 1968; children: Heather, Mark. BFA, Tufts U., 1964, MFA, 1971. Dir. Penmaen Press, Lincoln, Mass., 1968-85; instr. Concord (Mass.) Acad., 1972-75, Wellesley (Mass.) Coll., 1976. Illustrator: The Man Who Planted Trees, 1985, American Tall Tales, 1991, American Buffalo, 1992, The Winged Life: The Poetry of Henry David Thoreau, 1992, The Beasts of Bethlehem, 1992, McCurdy's World, 1992, The Way West: Journal of a Pioneer Woman, 1993, Giants in the Land, 1993The Gettysburg Address, 1995; author, illustrator: Hannah's Farm, 1988, The Old Man and the Fiddle, 1992; editor; illustrator: Escape From Slavery: The Boyhood of Frederick Douglas in His Own Words, 1994. Mem. Great Barrington (Mass.) Housing Authority, 1990-93. Small press grantee Nat. Endowment Arts, 1978, Mass. Arts and Humanities, 1978. Fellow Simon Rock of Bar Coll.; mem. Soc. of Printers, St. Botolph Club. Democrat. Episcopalian.

MC CURDY, PATRICK PIERRE, editor, consultant; b. Angers, France, Sept. 14, 1928; s. Joseph Alexander and Constance Yolande (Hillairet de Boisferon) McC.; m. Eiko Yamada, May 30, 1953; children: Alan J., Wendy C., Alec J., Jeffrey R. B.S. in Chem. Engring., Carnegie Inst. Tech., 1949. Chem. engr. tech. service dept. Humble Oil & Refining Co., Baytown, Tex., 1949-50; chem. engr. Callery Chem. Co., 1954-56; sr. chem. engr. U.S. Army Engr. R & D Labs., Ft. Belvoir, Va., 1956-60; asst. editor Chem. & Engring. News, Washington, 1960-61, N.Y.C., 1961-62; bur. head Chem. & Engring. News, Frankfurt, Germany, 1962-64, Tokyo, 1964-67; mng. editor Chem. & Engring. News, Washington, 1967-69; editor Chem. & Engring. News, 1969-73; editor in chief Chemical Week, 1973-80, 84-87, editor-in-chief, assoc. pub., 1987-88; dir. communications Am. Chem. Soc., 1988-91, dir. industry rels., 1991-93, editor Today's Chemist at Work, 1989—; cons. American Chemical Soc., 1993—; pub. issues mgr. Dow Chem. Co., Midland, Mich., 1980-82, dir. tech. communications, 1982-84; bd. dirs. Centcom, Ltd. Served to 1st lt. C.E. AUS, 1950-54. Recipient Jesse H. Neal award, 1979, finalist 1985; recipient Carnegie Mellon Univ. Alumni Merit award, 1988. Mem. AICE, Am. Chem. Soc., Fgn. Corrs. Club Japan, Chemist's Club (suburban v.p.), Societe de Chimie Industrielle (bd. dirs. Am. sect., past pres.), Soc. of Chem. Industry (Am. sect.), Comml. Devel. Assn., Tokyo Am. Club, Tau Beta Pi, Phi Kappa Phi, Theta Tau, Phi Kappa. Home: 11717 Chauncey Ln Mason Neck VA 22079-4140 Office: 1155 16th St NW Washington DC 20036-4800

MCCURDY, RICHARD CLARK, engineering consultant; b. Newton, Iowa, Jan. 2, 1909; s. Ralph Bruce and Florence (Clark) McC.; m. Harriet Edith Sutton, Sept. 11, 1933; children: Gregor, Richard, Carolyn, Robert. A.B., Stanford U., 1931, E.M., 1933. With engring. and prodn. div. Shell Oil Co., 1933-47; with prodn. mgmt. Shell Caribbean Petroleum Co., 1947-50; gen. mgr. Shell Group Companies, Venezuela, 1950-53; pres. Shell Chem. Co., N.Y.C., 1953-65; dir. Shell Oil Co., mem. exec. com., 1959-69, pres., chief exec. officer, 1965-69; assoc. adminstr. orgn. and mgmt. NASA, Washington, 1970-73; cons. NASA, 1974-82. Trustee United Seamans Service, 1954-70, Stanford U., 1965-70; trustee Hood Coll., 1968-86, trustee emeritus, 1986—, hon. trustee, 1987—; trustee Rensselaer Poly. Inst., 1974-86, hon. trustee, 1986—. Recipient Disting. Service medal NASA, 1972. Mem. Mfg. Chemists Assn. (dir. 1955-65, chmn. bd. 1961-62, chmn. exec. com. 1964-65), Am. Inst. Mining, Metall. and Petroleum Engrs., Am. Phys. Soc., Am. Petroleum Inst., N.Y. Yacht Club, Noroton (Conn.) Yacht Club (commodore), Cruising of Am. (commodore 1980-82), Beta Theta Pi. Home: Contentment Island Darien CT 06820

MC CURLEY, ROBERT LEE, JR., lawyer; b. Gadsden, Ala., Sept. 7, 1941; s. Robert Lee and Nellie Ruth McC.; 1 child, Allison Leah. BS, U. Ala., 1963, JD, 1966. Bar: Ala. 1966, D.C. 1973, U.S. Ct. Mil. Appeals 1966, U.S. Supreme Ct. 1970, U.S. Ct. Appeals (5th cir.) 1972, U.S. Ct. Appeals (11th cir.) 1973, U.S. Ct. Appeals (fed. cir.) 1981. Am. Law Inst. asst. to dir. Fed. Savs. & Loan Ins. Corp., Washington, 1966-67; partner firm Rains, Rains, McCurley & Wilson, Gadsden, Ala., 1967-75; city judge Southside, Ala., 1970-75; dir. Ala. Law Inst.; assoc. dir. U. Ala. Center Public Law and Service, 1981-82; asst. dean Sch. Law U. Ala., 1978-81; panelist White House Conf. on Volunteerism; pres. Gadsden Jaycees, 1972; mem. White House Fifty States Project; Henry Toll fellow Coun. State Govt., 1992. Editor: Divorce, Alimony and Child Support Custody, 3d edit., 1993, Land Laws of Alabama, 5th edit., 1990, The Legislative Process, 6th edit., 1995, Alabama Law Office Practice Deskbook, 6th edit., 1992, Federally Mandated State Legislation, 1990, Alabama Legislation, Cases and Statutes, 3d edit., 1992, Alabama Election Handbook, 6th edit., 1994. Pres. Gadsden Boys Club, 1971; mem. Nat. Dem. Charter Commn., 1974. Mem. ABA, Am. Law Inst., Order of Coif, Scribes Farrah Law Soc., Commr. Uniform State Laws, Indian Hills Country Club, Univ. Club, Kiwanis (pres. Tuscaloosa club 1976, gov. Ala. dist. 1984, internat. v.p 1991-92, trustee internat. found. 1994—). Baptist.

MCCURN, NEAL PETERS, federal judge; b. Syracuse, N.Y., Apr. 6, 1926. LL.B., Syracuse U., 1952, J.D., 1960. Bar: N.Y. 1952. Ptnr. Mackenzie Smith Lewis Mitchell & Hughes, Syracuse, 1957-79; judge U.S. Dist. Ct. (no. dist.) N.Y., 1979-88; chief judge U.S. Dist. Ct. (no. dist.), N.Y., 1988-93; sr. judge, 1993—; del. N.Y. State Constl. Conv., 1976; mem. 2d Cir. Jud. Council. Pres. Syracuse Common Coun., 1970-78. Mem. ABA, N.Y. State Bar Assn. (chmn. state constn. com.), Onondaga County Bar Assn. (past pres.), Am. Coll. Trial Lawyers, Am. Judicature Soc. (bd. dirs. 1980-84). Office: US Dist Ct 100 S Clinton St Rm 33 Syracuse NY 13260-0001

MCCURRY, MARGARET IRENE, architect, educator; b. Chgo., Sept. 26, 1942; d. Paul D. and Irene B. (Tipler) McC.; m. Stanley Tigerman, Mar. 17, 1979. BA, Vassar Coll., 1964. Registered architect, Ill., Mass., Mich.; registered interior designer, Ill. Design coord. Quaker Oats Co., Chgo., 1964-66; sr. interior designer Skidmore, Owings & Merrill, Chgo., 1966-77; pvt. practice architect Margaret I, Chgo., 1977-82; ptnr. Tigerman, McCurry, Chgo., 1982—; vis. studio critic Art Inst. Chgo., 1985-86, 88, lectr., 1988, bd. dirs. Archtl. Soc., 1988—; adv. bd. textile dept., 1992—; vis. studio critic U. Ill., Chgo., Miami U., Oxford, Ohio, 1990; juror Internat. furniture awards Progressive Architecture mag., N.Y.C., 1986, archt. awards, 1988; juror design grants Nat. Endowment for Arts, Washington, 1983; NEA Challenge Design Rev., 1992; awards com. Gen. Svcs. Administrn., 1992; juror, Wis., Minn., Calif., Va., Washington, Pitts., Ky., Conn. Soc. Architects, Detroit, N.Y.C., Memphis, Austin, L.A. chpts. AIA, Am. Wood Coun., Am. Inst. Architecture Students Design Competition, 1993. Contbr. Chgo. Archtl. Club Jour.; designer, contbr. archtl. exhibit Art Inst. Chgo., 1983-85, 93, Chgo. Hist. Soc., 1984, Gulbenkian Found., Lisbon, Portugal, 1989, Chgo. Athenaeum, 1990, Gwenda Jay Gallery, 1992, Women of Design Traveling Exhbn., 1992-94; archtl. drawings and models in permanent collection Art Inst. Chgo. and Deutsches Architektur Mus., Frankfurt. Chmn. furniture sect. fund raising auction Sta. WTTW-TV, PBS, Chgo., 1975-76; mem. Chgo. Beautiful Com., 1968-70; mem. alumni coun. Grad. Sch. of Design, Harvard U. Loeb fellow Harvard U., 1986-87; recipient Builders Choice Grand award Builders Mag., 1985, Interior Design award Interiors Mag., 1983, Dean of Architecture award Chgo. Design Source and the Merchandise Mart, 1989; inducted into Interior Design Hall of Fame, Interior Design Mag., 1990. Fellow AIA (v.p., bd. dirs. Chgo. chpt. 1984-89, chair person 1993, nat. design com., lectr. Colo. chpt. 1985, nat. conv. 1988, Monterey Design Conf. 1989, Washington Design Ctr. 1989, Nat. Honor award 1984, Nat. Interior Architecture award 1992, Disting. Bldg. award Chgo. chpt. 1984, 86, 91, 94, Disting. Interior Architecture award 1981, 83, 88, 91, product display Neocon award 1985, 88), Coll. of Fellows AIA, Internat. Interior Design Assn., Chgo. Network, Am. Soc. Interior Designers (Nat. Design award 1992, 94, Ill. chpt. Design award 1994, Ill. chpt. Merit award 1994, v.p. bd. dirs. Ill. chpt.), Chgo. Archtl. Club, Arts Club Chgo., Womens Athletic Club. Episcopalian. Avocations: drawing, travel, tennis, skiing, folk art. Home: 910 N Lake Shore Dr Chicago IL 60611-1540 Office: Tigerman Archs McCurry 444 N Wells St Chicago IL 60610-4522

MCCURRY, MICHAEL DEMAREE, government spokesman, press secretary; b. Charleston, S.C., Oct. 27, 1954; s. William Joseph and Rosemary (Demaree) McC.; m. Debra Lyn Jones, June 16, 1984; children: William Harry, Marjorie Vera. BA, Princeton U., 1976; MA, Georgetown U., 1985. Press sec. Sen. Harrison Williams, Washington, 1976-81, Sen. Daniel P. Moynihan, Washington, 1981-83, Sen. John Glenn, Washington, 1984; pub. affairs dir. ERISA Industry Com., Washington, 1985; press sec. Gov. Bruce Babbitt, Phoenix, 1986-88; dir. comms. Dem. Nat. Com., Washington, 1988-90; sr. v.p. Robinson, Lake, Lerer & Montgomery, Washington, 1990-93; spokesman U.S. Dept. State, Washington, 1993-95; press sec. White House, Washington, 1995—. Trustee Jr. Stateman Found., Redwood City, Calif., 1985—; mem. coun. St. Paul's United Meth. Ch., Kensington, Md., 1992—. Office: Dept of State Bureau of Public Affairs 2201 C St NW Washington DC 20520-0001

MCCUSKER, J. STEPHEN, zoo director; b. Chgo., Apr. 18, 1946; s. Richard Joseph and Hilda Mary (Grudgings) McC.; m. Jonolyn E. Wilson. BS, Mich. State U., 1969; MS, Tex. Christian U., 1976. Curator New Eng. Regional Primate Rsch. Ctr., Southboro, Mass., 1969-70; asst. curator Ft. Worth Zool. Pk., 1970-76; gen. curator Washington Pk. Zoo, Portland, Oreg., 1976-86; dir. Reid Pk. Zoo, Tucson, 1986—; cons. Stanley Pk. Zoo, Vancouver, B.C., 1984-87, Larson Co., Tucson, 1987—. Author 14 published papers, articles or chpts., 1971—. Recipient Winston Churchill Traveling fellowship English Speaking Union, British Isles, 1977, several rsch. grants Tex. Christian U., 1974-75. Fellow Am. Assn. of Zool. Pks. and Aquariums, Am. Soc. Mammalogists; mem. Centurions Club (Tucson). Office: Reid Pk Zoo 1100 S Randolph Way Tucson AZ 85716-5835

MCCUSKER, JOHN, environmental consultant; b. Bklyn., May 28, 1939; s. John Michael and Helen Frances (Sweeney) McC.; BBA, St. John's U., 1961; m. Brenda Ann Caprio, June 27, 1964; children: John Christian, Joseph Andrew, David Douglas. Sr. acct. Haskins & Sells, N.Y.C., 1961-67; asst. dir. fin. planning Colt Industries, Inc., N.Y.C., 1967-69; dir. fin. planning Shearson Hammill & Co., N.Y.C., 1969-70; dir. fin. analysis The Allen Group, Inc., Melville, N.Y., 1971-73; asst. corporate controller Geraghty & Miller, Inc., Plainview, N.Y., 1973-76, v.p., controller, 1976-83, v.p. fin., 1983-86, sr. v.p. fin., 1987—. Bd. dirs. Huntington (N.Y.) Hosp., 1979—, chmn., 1989-92, Family Svc. League Suffolk County, Huntington, N.Y. Served with U.S. Army, 1963. CPA, N.Y. Mem. Am. Inst. CPAs, N.Y. State Soc. CPAs, Fin. Execs. Inst., Nassau-Suffolk Hosp. Assn. (chmn. bd. dirs.). Republican. Roman Catholic. Home: 4 Harbor View Dr Huntington NY 11743-6710 Office: Geraghty & Miller Inc 125 E Bethpage Rd Plainview NY 11803

MCCUSKER, MARY LAURETTA, library science educator; b. Sillery, Que., Can., Jan. 18, 1919; came to U.S., 1938, naturalized, 1942; d. Albert James and Laura (Cleary) McC. B.A., Western Md. Coll., 1942; M.S.L.S., Columbia U., 1952, D.L.S. 1963. Joined Order of Preachers, Roman Catholic Ch., 1961; librarian Annapolis (Md.) High Sch., 1942-44, McDonogh Mil. Sch., 1944-47; asst. prof. Iowa State Tchrs. Coll. (now No. Iowa U.), Cedar Falls, 1948-59; vis. prof. library sci. U. Minn., Mpls., summers, 1958-59; assoc. prof. Sch. Library Sci. Rosary Coll., 1963-67, dir., prof. Grad. Sch., 1967-81, prof. emeritus, rsch. assoc., 1981-94, dean grad. sch., 1969-81, dean emeritus, 1994—. Contbr. articles to profl. jours. Continuing Edn. grantee World Book Ency., 1994. Mem. ALA, Assn. Lib. and Info. Sci. Edn., Nat. Cath. Libr. Assn. (pres. No. Ill. chpt. 1987-89, chair acad. sect. No. Ill. chpt. 1992—, sec./treas. acad. session, v.p., pres.-elect, 1995—, chair 1995, co-chair cert. and standards com. 1995—), Ill. Libr. Assn., Ill. Sch. Libr. Media Assn. (chair awards com. 1990-91, 94—), Chgo. Libr. Club, Sch. Libr. Assn. Office: Rosary Coll Grad Sch Library and Info Sci 7900 Division St River Forest IL 60305-1099

MCCUSKEY, ROBERT SCOTT, anatomy educator, researcher; b. Cleve., Sept. 8, 1938; s. Sidney Wilcox and Jeannette M. (Scott) M.; m. Rebecca Woodworth, July 19, 1958 (div.); children: Geofrey, Gregory, Michael; m. Margaret A. Krasovich, Apr. 17, 1993. A.B., Western Res. U., 1960, Ph.D., 1965. Instr. anatomy U. Cin., 1965-67, asst. prof., 1967-71, assoc. prof., 1971-75, prof., 1975-78; prof., chmn. anatomy W.Va. U., Morgantown, 1978-86; prof., head dept. cell biology and anatomy U. Ariz., Tucson, 1986—, prof. physiology, 1987—; vis. prof. U. Heidelberg, Fed. Republic Germany, 1981-83, 87-88, 93-95; cons. Hoffmann-La Rouche, N.J., 1972-75, Procter & Gamble Co., Cin. 1966-86. Recipient NIH Rsch. Career Devel. award, 1969-74; Humboldt Sr. U.S. Scientist prize, Fed. Republic Germany, 1982, Nishimaru award Japan Microcirculatory Soc., 1987; grantee NIH, NSF, 1966—. Mem. AAAS, Microcirculatory Soc., Am. Assn. Anatomists, Am. Assn. Study Liver Diseases, Rsch. Soc. on Alcoholism, Internat. Soc. Exptl. Hematology. Mem. editorial bd. Microvascular Rsch., 1974-84, Shock, 1993—, Am. Jour. Physiology, 1995—; contbr. numerous articles to profl. jours. Office: Ariz Health Scis Ctr Dept Cell Biology and Anatomy 1501 N Campbell Ave Tucson AZ 85724-0001

MCCUTCHAN, GORDON EUGENE, lawyer, insurance company executive; b. Buffalo, Sept. 30, 1935; s. George Lawrence and Mary Esther (De Puy) McC.; m. Linda Brown; children: Lindsey, Elizabeth. B.A., Cornell U., 1956, M.B.A., 1958, LL.B., 1959. Bar: N.Y. 1959, Ohio 1964. Pvt. practice Rome, N.Y., 1959-61; atty., advisor SEC, Washington, 1961-64; ptnr. McCutchan, Druen, Maynard, Rath & Dietrich, 1964-94; mem. office of gen. counsel Nationwide Mut. Ins. Co., Columbus, Ohio, 1964-94, sr. v.p., gen. counsel, 1982-89; exec. v.p., gen. counsel Employers Ins. Wausau, a Mut. Co., 1989-94; exec. v.p. Law and Corp. Svcs., Nationwide Ins. Enterprise, 1994—. Trustee, bd. govs. Franklin U.; trustee Ohio Tuition Trust Authority. Mem. Columbus Bar Assn., Ohio Bar Assn., Am. Corp. Counsel Assn., Assn. Life Inst. Counsel (bd. govs.), Fedn. Ins. and Corp. Counsel, Am. Coun. Life Ins. (chair legal sect. 1992-93). Home: 2376 Oxford Rd Columbus OH 43221-4011 Office: Nationwide Mut Ins Co 1 Nationwide Plz Columbus OH 43215-2423 also: Employers Ins Wausau 2000 Westwood Dr Wausau WI 54401-7802

MCDADE, JAMES RUSSELL, management consultant; b. Dallas, Jan. 15, 1925; s. Marion W. and Jeannette (Reneau) McD.; m. Elaine Bushey, Sep. 10, 1955. BSEE, So. Meth. U., Dallas, 1947; MBA, Northwestern U., Evanston, Ill., 1950. Asst. to pres. Davidson Corp., Chgo., 1951-52; asst. to pres. Mergenthaler Linotype Co., Bklyn., 1952-53, comml. works mgr., 1953-56; chief indsl. engr. Tex. Instruments, Inc., Dallas, 1956-57, product gen. mgr., 1958-60, v.p., 1961-64; chmn. bd. McDade Properties Co., Aspen (Colo.), Denver, Dallas, 1964—; bd. dirs. Pitkin County Bank, Aspen; chmn. bd. dirs. Harley-Davidson Tex., Westec Security of Aspen, Aspen Security, Inc. Founding mem. Aspen Art Mus., 1980; mem. Ballet Aspen, 1980—; pres. club Aspen Valley Hosp., 1984—. Served to 1st lt. USAF, 1943-46. Mem. Rep. Senatorial Inner Circle, Am. Mgmt. Assn., Presidents Assn. Avocations: skiing, horseback riding, camping, swimming. Home and Office: 1000 Red Mountain Rd PO Box 9090 Aspen CO 81612-9090

MCDADE, JOE BILLY, federal judge; b. 1937. BS, Bradley U., 1959, MA, 1960; JD, U. Mich., 1963. Staff atty. antitrust divsn. U.S. Dept. Justice, 1963-65; exec. trainee First Fed. Savs. and Loan Assn., 1965; exec. dir. Greater Peoria (Ill.) Legal Aid Soc., 1965-69; ptnr. Hafele & McDade, Peoria, Ill., 1968-77; pvt. practice Peoria, 1977-82; assoc. cir. judge State of Ill., 1982-88; cir. judge U.S. Cir. Ct., Ill., 1988-91; fed. judge U.S. Dist. Ct. (ctrl. dist.) Ill., 1991—. Bd. dirs. Peoria (Ill.) Pub. Libr., 1965-77, Peoria YMCA, ARC, SHARE Foods, Inc., Peoria Tri-Centennial, Amateur Mus. Club; fin. chmn. St. Peters Cath. Ch.; active Peoria Civic Ctr. Authority, 1976-82; pres. Ill. Health Systems Agy, 1978-80, bd. dirs., 1975-82. Mem. Ill. State Bar Assn., Peoria County Bar Assn. (bd. dirs. 1980-82). Office: US Dist Ct 100 NE Monroe St Peoria IL 61602-1003

MCDADE, JOSEPH MICHAEL, congressman; b. Scranton, Pa., Sept. 29, 1931; s. John B. and Genevieve (Hayes) McD.; children: Joseph, Aileen, Deborah, Mark; m. Sarah Scripture, May 1988; 1 child, Jared. B.A. in Polit. Sci. with honors, U. Notre Dame, 1953; LL.B., U. Pa., 1956; LL.D. (hon.). St. Thomas Aquinas Coll., 1968, U. Scranton, 1969, Misericordia Coll. and Kings Coll., 1981, Marshall State Coll., 1987; H.H.D., Kings Coll. Bar: Pa. bar 1957. Clk. to fed. judge, 1956-57; pvt. practice law Scranton, 1957—; city solicitor, 1962; mem. 88th-103rd Congresses from 10th Pa. dist., Washington, D.C., 1963—; mem. appropriations com. Mem. Am., Pa., Lackawanna County bar assns., Scranton C. of C. Republican. Roman Catholic. Clubs: K.C; James Wilson Law (Phila.). Office: US Ho of Reps 2170 Rayburn Ho Office Bldg Washington DC 20515-3810

MCDANIEL, BOYCE DAWKINS, physicist, educator; b. Brevard, N.C., June 11, 1917; s. Allen Webster and Grace (Dawkins) McD.; m. Jane Chapman Grennell, Aug. 3, 1941; children: Gail P., James G. B.S., Ohio Wesleyan U., 1938; M.S., Case Inst. Tech., 1940; Ph.D., Cornell U., 1943. Staff mem. radiation lab. Mass. Inst. Tech., 1943; physicist Los Alamos Sci. Lab., 1943-46; mem. faculty Cornell U., Ithaca, N.Y., 1944—, prof., 1956-87, assoc. dir. lab. nuclear studies, 1960-67, dir. lab. nuclear studies, 1967-85, Floyd R. Newman prof. nuclear studies, 1977-87, prof. emeritus, 1987—; head accelerator sect. Nat. Accelerator Lab., Batavia, Ill., 1972; mem. high energy physics adv. panel ERDA, 1975-78. Contbr. articles to profl. jours. Trustee Associated Univs., Inc., 1962-75. Vis. fellow Brookhaven Nat. Lab., 1966; Fulbright Research grantee Australian Nat. U., 1953; Guggenheim and Fulbright grantee U. Rome and Synchrotron Lab., Frascati, Italy, 1959-60. Fellow Am. Phys. Soc.; mem. NAS, Univs. Rsch. Assn. (trustee 1971-77, 83-84, chmn. superconducting super-collider bd. overseers 1984-91, mem. 1991-93). Spl. research neutron spectroscopy, gamma ray spectroscopy, high energy photoprodn. K mesons and hyperons, instrumentation for high energy physics, accelerator design and constrn. Home: 26 Woodcrest Ave Ithaca NY 14850-6243

MCDANIEL, CHARLES-GENE, journalism educator, writer; b. Luxora, Ark., Jan. 11, 1931; s. Charles Waite and Edith Estelle (Kelly) McD. B.S., Northwestern U., 1954, M.S. in Journalism, 1955. Reporter Gazette and Daily, York, Pa., 1955-58; sci. writer Chgo. bur. A.P., 1958-79; assoc. prof. journalism dept. Roosevelt U., Chgo., 1979-83, prof., 1984—, chmn. dept., 1979-93, head faculty of journalism and communication studies, 1993—. Contbg. editor Libido; contbr. to anthologies, poems, Ency. Britannica, World Book Ency.; contbr. articles to profl. jours. Chgo. corr. The Med. Post, Toronto, 1979—. Trustee Roosevelt U., 1985-94; bd. dirs. Internat. Press Ctr., Chgo.; mem. Nat. Gay and Lesbian Task Force. Recipient writing awards Erikson Inst. for Early Edn., 1972, writing award AMA, 1974, writing awards Chgo. Inst. for Psychoanalysis, 1971, 73, writing awards Ill. Med Soc., 1972, 73, writing awards ADA, 1975, Am. Psychol. Assn., 1982. Mem. AAUP, ACLU, Fellowship of Reconciliation, War Resisters League, Art Inst. Chgo. (life), Mus. Contemporary Art (charter), Assn. Edn. in Journalism and Mass Comms., Nat. Assn. Lesbian and Gay Journalists, Ill. Arts Alliance, Handgun Control Inc. Home: 5109 S Cornell Ave Chicago IL 60615-4215 Office: 430 S Michigan Ave Chicago IL 60605-1301 That which we achieve for ourselves is for naught unless we have at the same time contributed to a world in which peace and justice prevail.

MCDANIEL, DOLAN KENNETH, oil exploration service company executive; b. Clarksville, Ark., June 9, 1935; s. Lowell William and Dana Estelle (Kinney) McD.; m. Letha Patricia Craven, Jan. 2, 1957; children: Laurie McDaniel Holgate, David. BS, Kans. State U., 1957. Field ops. Geophys. Service Inc., various locations, 1957-66; mgr. Rocky Mountains region Geophys. Service Inc., Denver, 1966-70; mgr. N. Latin Am. Geophys. Service Inc., Bogota, Colombia, 1970-72; mgr. land data collection Geophys. Service Inc., Dallas, 1973-77, mgr. marine exploration, 1977, pres., 1977-88; cons. geophys. industry, 1989—; v.p. Tex. Instruments, Dallas, 1978-88. Mem. Soc. Exploration Geophysicists, Dallas Geophys. Soc., Internat. Assn. Geophys. Contractors (bd. dirs. 1982-89). Home and Office: 213 Crooked Creek Dr Richardson TX 75080-2024

MC DANIEL, JAMES EDWIN, lawyer; b. Dexter, Mo., Nov. 22, 1931; s. William H. and Gertie M. (Woods) McD.; m. Mary Jane Crawford, Jan. 22, 1955; children: John William, Barbara Anne. AB, Washington U., St. Louis, 1957, JD, 1959. Bar: Mo. 1959. Assoc. firm Walther, Barnard, Cloyd & Timm, 1959-60; assoc. firm McDonald, Barnard, Wright & Timm, 1960-63, ptnr., 1963-65; ptnr. firm Barnard, Timm & McDaniel St. Louis, 1965-73; ptnr. firm Barnard & Baer, St. Louis, 1973-82; ptnr. Lashly & Baer, St. Louis, 1982—; pros. atty. City of Glendale, Mo., 1968—; bd. dirs. Airtherm Mfg. Co., Eden Theol. Sem.; lectr. Latvian U., Riga, Inst. Fgn. Rels., Banking in Am., 1992-93. Leader legal del. Chinese-Am. Comparative Law Study, People's Republic China, 1988, Russian-Am. Comparative Law Study, USSR, 1990; trustee, past chmn., past treas. 1st Congl. Ch. St. Louis. With USAF, 1951-55. Fellow Am. Bar Found. (life), St. Louis Bar Found.; mem. ABA (ho. of dels. 1976-80, 84-92, state del. 1986-92, chmn. lawyers conf., jud. adminstrn. divsn. 1985-86, 8th cir. rep. standing com. on fed. judiciary 1992-95), The Mo. Bar (pres. 1981-82, bd. govs. 1974-83), Mo. Assn. Def. Counsel, Bar Assn. Met. St. Louis (pres. 1972), Internat. Assn. Ins. Counsel, Assn. Def. Counsel St. Louis (past pres.), Phi Delta Phi. Home: 767 Elmwood Ave Saint Louis MO 63122-3216 Office: Lashly & Baer 714 Locust St Saint Louis MO 63101-1603

MCDANIEL, JARREL DAVE, lawyer; b. Clovis, N. Mex., Oct. 17, 1930; s. Raymond Lee and Blanch (Booth) McD.; m. Anne Louise McAllister; children: Jarrel Dave Jr., Julia Anne. A.A., Riverside Coll., 1951; B.A., U. Tex., 1956, LL.B. 1957. Bar: Tex. 1957. Assoc. Vinson & Elkins, L.L.P., Houston, 1957-69; ptnr. Vinson & Elkins, Houston, 1969—; author, lectr. in field. Served with USAF, 1950-54. Mem. ABA, Am. Coll. Bankruptcy, State Bar Tex., Am. Bankruptcy Inst., Tex. Bd. Legal Specialization in Bankruptcy (mem. adv. com. 1976—). Roman Catholic. Clubs: Houston, Houston Ctr. Home: 649 Bunker Hill Rd Houston TX 77024-5118 Office: Vinson & Elkins LLP 2500 First City Tower 1001 Fannin St Houston TX 77002-6706

MCDANIEL, JOHN PERRY, health care company executive; b. Findlay, Ohio, Sept. 4, 1942; s. Oliver Perry and Lorraine (Schraeding) McD.; m. Ellen Rachel Garb, June 18, 1966; children—Celia Lorraine, Michael Perry. BS, Wittenberg U.; MHA, U. Mich.; LHD (hon.), Wittenberg U., 1990. Adminstrv. resident Wilmington Med. Ctr., Del. Hosp., 1965-66, asst. adminstrs., 1966-67; asst. adminstr. Community Hosp., Springfield, Ohio, 1967-68; assoc. adminstr. Md. Gen. Hosp., Balt., 1968-72; pres., chief exec. officer Lutheran Hosp. Md., Inc., Balt., 1972-81, Md. Health Care Systems, Inc., Balt., 1977-81; pres. Washington Hosp. Ctr. and Medlantic Healthcare Group, 1981—, Medlantic Mgmt. Corp., 1983—; cons. Westchester Med. Ctr. Found. Inc., White Plains, N.Y., 1980-81; mem. adv. coun. Nat. Ctr. for Therapeutic Riding, Washington, 1983—. Contbr. articles to profl. jours. Mem., bd. dirs. Vol. Hosps. of Am.-Mid. Atlantic, Greater Washington Bd. Trade; mem. Washington Trustees of Fed. City Coun. Fellow Am. Coll. Hosp. Adminstrs.; mem. Royal Soc. Health, U. Mich. Program in Hosp. Adminstrn. Alumni Assn. (bd. dirs.), Howard County Hist. Soc., Univ. Club (Washington), Econ. Club of Washington. Republican. Avocations: horseback riding and other related sports. Office: Medlantic Healthcare Group 100 Irving St NW Washington DC 20010-2911

MCDANIEL, JOSEPH CHANDLER, lawyer; b. Covington, Va., Mar. 24, 1950; s. Everts Hardin and Betty (Chandler) McD.; m. Sandra Lee Bonds, Dec. 27, 1976; children: Sean Kenneth, Caitlin Bonds. BA in Philosophy, Ariz. State U., 1973, JD, 1980. Bar: Ariz. 1980, U.S. Dist. Ct. Ariz. 1981. Law clk. U.S. Bankruptcy Ct., Phoenix, 1980-82; pvt. practice Phoenix, 1982-84; ptnr. McDaniel and Jaburg, P.C., Phoenix, 1984-89, McDaniel and Lee, Phoenix, 1989-91, McDaniel & Gan, P.C., 1991-93, McDaniel & Kamp, P.C., 1993-94, Lerch, McDaniel & Kamp, P.L.C., 1994—; mem. Scriveners Com. Local Rules of Ct. for Dist. of Ariz. Bankruptcy Cts., Phoenix, 1980. Author: A Guide to Researching Bankruptcy Law, 1980; editor: (with others) Arizona Civil Remedies, 1982. Bd. dirs. St. Patrick's Day Parade, 1988-89, Irish Cultural Assn. Phoenix, 1988-89. Mem. ABA (gen. practice sect. bankruptcy com., chmn., dep. chmn. membership com.pubs. bd.), Ariz. Bar Assn. (lectr., co-chmn. continuing legal edn. com., bankruptcy sect. 1987-88, chmn. 1988-89, co-chmn. jud. rels. com. 1990-92), Maricopa County Bankruptcy Practitioners (chmn.), Ariz. Bankruptcy Coalition (bd. dirs. 1986—), Maricopa County Bar Assn., Am. Bankruptcy Inst. Democrat. Roman Catholic. Avocations: computer tech., chess, hiking. Office: Lerch, McDaniel & Kamp, P.L.C. 3636 N Central Ave Ste 990 Phoenix AZ 85012-1939

MCDANIEL, MICHAEL CONWAY DIXON, bishop, theology educator; b. Mt. Pleasant, N.C., Apr. 8, 1929; s. John Henry and Mildred Juanita (Barrier) McD.; m. Marjorie Ruth Schneiter, Nov. 26, 1953; 1 son, John Robert Michael. B.A., U. N.C., 1951; B.D., Wittenberg U., 1954; M.A., U. Chgo., 1969, Ph.D., 1978; D.D. (hon.), Lenoir-Rhyne Coll., 1983; LL.D., Belmont Abbey Coll., 1984. Ordained to ministry United Lutheran Ch. in America, 1954. Pastor Faith (N.C.) Luth. Ch., 1954-58, Ch. of the Ascension, Savannah, Ga., 1958-60; assoc. dir. evangelism United Luth. Ch. in Am., N.Y.C., 1960-62; sr. pastor Edgebrook Luth. Ch., Chgo., 1962-67; pastor, guest lectr. Wittenberg U., Springfield, Ohio, 1970-71; prof. Lenoir-Rhyne Coll., Hickory, N.C., 1971-82, Raymond Morris Bost disting. prof., 1982, dir., prof. Ctr. for Theology, 1991—; bishop N.C. Luth. Ch. in Am., Salisbury, 1982-87, Evang. Luth. Ch. Am., Salisbury, 1988-91; chmn. humanities div. Lenoir-Rhyne Coll., 1973-82; cons., grant coord. NEH, 1977-79; master tchr. Hickory Humanities Forum, 1981—; chmn. task force on ecumenical and interfaith relationships Commn. Forming a New Luth. Ch., 1983-87; rptr. Luth. Orthodox Dialogue In U.S.A., 1983-89;: chmn., cons. bishops governing coun. Evang. Luth. Ch. Am., 1987-89. Author: Welcome to the Lord's Table, 1972. Mem. Englewood Human Relations Council, N.J., 1959-60; pres., bd. trustees Edgebrook Symphony, Chgo., 1965-67; sec. Chgo. Astron. Soc., 1966-67; pres. Community Concerts Assn., Hickory, N.C., 1977-80. Served to sgt. U.S. Army, 1946-48, Korea. Luth. World Fedn. fellow, 1967-69, Mansfield Coll. fellow U. Oxford, 1989; recipient Disting. Alumnus award Trinity Luth. Sem., 1990. Home: 125 42nd Avenue Cir NE Hickory NC 28601-9012 Office: Lenoir-Rhyne Coll Hickory NC 28603 Since Christian faith is a joyous relationship with God, Christian hope is courageously counting on God's promises, and Christian love a daily adventure. The Christian approaches each aspect of life as An Adventure in Courageous Joy.

MCDANIEL, MYRA ATWELL, lawyer, former state official; b. Phila., Dec. 13, 1932; d. Eva Lucinda (Yores) Atwell; m. Reuben Roosevelt McDaniel Jr., Feb. 20, 1955; children: Diane Lorraine, Reuben Roosevelt III. BA, U. Pa., 1954; JD, U. Tex., 1975; LLD, Huston-Tillotson Coll., 1984, Jarvis Christian Coll., 1986. Bar: Tex. 1975, U.S. Dist. Ct. (we. dist.) Tex. 1977, U.S. Dist. Ct. (so. and no. dists.) Tex. 1978, U.S. Ct. Appeals (5th cir.) 1978, U.S. Supreme Ct. 1978, U.S. Dist. Ct. (ea. dist.) Tex. 1979. Asst atty. gen. State of Tex., Austin, 1975-81, chief taxation div., 1979-81, gen. counsel to gov., 1983-84, sec. of state, 1984-87; asst. gen. counsel Tex. R.R. Commn., Austin, 1981-82; gen. counsel Wilson Cos., San Antonio and Midland, Tex., 1982; assoc. Bickerstaff, Heath & Smiley, Austin, 1984, ptnr., 1987—; mem. asset mgmt. adv. com. State Treasury, Austin, 1984-86; mem. legal affairs com. Criminal Justice Policy Council, Austin, 1984-86; mem. legal affairs com. Inter-State Oil Compact, Oklahoma City, 1984-86; bd. dirs. Austin Cons. Group, 1983-86; lectr. in field. Contbr. articles to profl. jours., chpts. to books. Del. Tex. Conf. on Libraries and Info. Scis., Austin, 1978, White House Conf. on Libraries and Info. Scis., Washington, 1979; mem. Library Services and Constrn. Act Adv. Council, 1980-84, chmn., 1983-84; mem. long range plan task force Brackenridge Hosp., Austin, 1981; clk. vestry bd.

St. James Episcopal Ch., Austin, 1981-83, 88-90; bd. visitors U. Tex. Law Sch., 1983—, vice chmn., 1983-85; bd. dirs. Friends of Ronald McDonald House of Cen. Tex., Women's Advocacy, Inc., Capital Area Rehab. Ctr.; trustee Episcopal Found. Tex., 1986-89, St. Edward's U., Austin, 1986—, chmn. acad. com. 1988—; chmn. div. United Way/Capital area campaign, 1986; active nat. adv. bd. Leadership Am.; trustee Episcopal Sem. of SW, 1990—, Assn. Governing Bds. Univs. and Colls. Recipient Tribute to 28 Black Women award Concepts Unltd., 1983; Focus on women honoree Serwa Yetu chpt. Mt. Olive grand chpt. Order of Eastern Star, 1979, Woman of Yr. Longview Metro C. of C., 1985, Woman of Yr. Austin chpt. Internat. Tng. in Communication, 1985, Citizen of Yr. Epsilon Iona chpt. Omega Psi Phi. Master Inns of Ct.; mem. ABA, Am. Bar Found., Tex. Bar Found. (trustee 1986-89), Travis County Bar Assn., Travis County Women Lawyers' Assn., Austin Black Lawyers Assn., State Bar Tex. (chmn. Profl. Efficiency & Econ. Rsch. subcom. 1976-84), Golden Key Nat. Honor Soc., Longhorn Assocs. for Excellence in Women's Athletes (adv. coun. 1988—), Order of Coif (hon. mem.), Omicron Delta Kappa, Delta Phi Alpha. Democrat. Home: 3910 Knollwood Dr Austin TX 78731-2915 Office: San Jacinto Ctr 98 San Jacinto Blvd Ste 1800 Austin TX 78701-4039

MCDANIEL, RANDALL CORNELL, professional football player; b. Phoenix, Dec. 19, 1964. BPE, Ariz. State U., 1988. Offensive guard Minn. Vikings, 1988—. Named NFL All-Pro Team Guard by Sporting News, 1991-93. Played in Pro Bowl, 1988-93. Office: Minn Vikings 9520 Viking Dr Eden Prairie MN 55344*

MCDANIEL, RODERICK ROGERS, petroleum engineer; b. High River, Alta., Can., 1926; s. Dorsey Patton and Daisy (Rogers) McD.; m. Marilyn Bouck, Oct. 16, 1948; children: Nancy, Leslie. BS, U. Okla., 1947. Petroleum reservoir engr. Creole Petroleum Corp., 1947; petroleum reservoir engr. Imperial Oil Ltd., 1948-52, chief reservoir engr., 1952-55; chmn. McDaniel Cons., Calgary, 1955—, PWA Corp, Calgary, 1974-91, Can. Regional Airlines, Calgary, 1991-92; bd. dirs. Honeywell Can. Ltd., Prudential Steel Ltd. Bd. dirs. Calgary Exhbn. and Stampede, 1979-88, hon. bd. dirs., 1988—; dir. Calgary Stampeder Football Team, 1988, Corp. Commissionaires S.A.B. Mem. Assn. Profl. Engrs. Alta and Sask., Can. C. of C. (bd. dirs. 1973), Calgary C. of C. (past pres.), Calgary Petroleum Club (past pres.), Calgary Highlanders (hon. col.), Ranchmen's Club, Calgary Golf and Country Club, Outrigger Club (Honolulu), Mission Hills Country Club. Mem. Progressive Conservative Party. Home: 11 3231 Rideau Ridge Pl SW, Calgary, AB Canada T2S 2T1 Office: McDaniel & Assoc, 2200-255 5th Ave SW, Calgary, AB Canada T2P 3G6

MCDANIEL, WILLIAM HOWARD TAFT, JR., computer information systems educator; b. Ballinger, Tex., Sept. 28, 1941; s. William Howard Taft and Alta Mae (Broadstreet) McD.; m. Betty Jane Johnson, Aug. 16, 1958; children: William H.T. III, Barry Glenn, Bryan Keith. BS summa cum laude, Miss. State U., 1968, MBA, 1968; postgrad., Nova U., 1986. Cert. computer profl. Commd. 2d lt. U.S. Army, 1962, advanced through grades to maj., 1981, computer specialist, 1962-72; systems mgr. U.S. Army, Alexandria, Va., 1973-83; ret. U.S. Army, 1983; planning dir. Electronic Data Systems, Balt., 1983; assoc. prof. computer infosystems No. Va. C.C., Alexandria, 1983-88, head computer infosystems, 1988—; instr. Angelo State U., San Angelo, Tex., 1972-73; computer cons. various orgns., 1983—; adj. faculty George Mason U., Annandale, Va., 1990—; mem. computer history adv. com. Smithsonian Instn., 1977-78. Del. Tex. Rep. Conv., San Angelo, 1973; election judge, Prince Georges County, Md., 1984-92; v.p. Skyline Citizens Assn., Prince Georges County, 1985. Decorated Legion of Merit. Mem. SAR, Data Processing Mgmt. Assn. (pres. 1978-79), Mensa, Masons, Sons of Rep. of Tex., Toastmasters Internat. (area gov. 1979-80), Phi Kappa Phi, Beta Gamma Sigma, Alpha Kappa Psi. Republican. Methodist. Achievements include development of computer information system curriculum materials. Home: 6100 Skyline Ter Suitland MD 20746-3752 Office: No Va CC 3001 N Beauregard St Alexandria VA 22311-5065

MCDANIEL, WILLIAM J., career military officer; b. Muskogee, Okla., Feb. 26, 1943; s. L.B. Allen and Vera Juanita (Purdom) McD.; m. Judy Siebert, May 30, 1964 (div. Apr. 1967); m. Shirley Blair, Dec. 13, 1969; children: Valerie Park, Natalie Park, Tara. MD, U. Okla., 1968. Commd. ensign USN, advanced through grades to rear adm., 1989; orthopedic resident Oakland Naval Hosp., Calif., 1973-77; chief of orthopedics Naval Hosp., Rota, Spain, 1977-80; orthopedics dept. Naval Acad., Annapolis, Md., 1980-83, Nat. War Coll., Washington, 1983-84; fleet surgeon Seventh Fleet, Yokosuka, Japan, 1984-86; commanding officer Naval Hosp., Oak Harbor, Wash., 1986-88, Charleston, S.C., 1988-90, Portmouth, Va., 1992—. Team Physician U.S. Olympic Team, L.A., 1984, cons., Colorado Springs, Colo., 1981—. Inducted Okla. State U. Alumni Hall of Fame, 1994. Mem. Am. Acad. Orthopedic Surgery. Republican. Avocations: sports, racquetball, Kayak, tennis, jogging. Office: Naval Med Ctr Portsmouth VA 23708

MCDANIELS, B. T., bishop. Bishop Northeastern Nebr. region Ch. of God in Christ, Omaha. Office: Ch of God in Christ 1106 N 31st Ave Omaha NE 68131-1433

MCDANIELS, JOHN LOUIS, mathematics educator; b. Alton, Ill., Oct. 3, 1933; s. John Clarence and Carrie Elizabeth (Kortkamp) McD.; m. Betty Lou Verble, June 20, 1964. BS, U. Mo., Rolla, 1960; MS, So. Ill. U., 1977. Registered profl. engr., Ill., Mo. Engr. McDonnell Douglas Corp., St. Louis, 1960-74; prof. Lewis and Clark Community Coll., Godfrey, Ill., 1975—; dist. TEAMS competition coord. Ill. Jr. Engring. Tech. Soc., Lewis and Clark C.C., 1987—, pre-engring. coord., 1975—, water tech. coord., 1975-92. Bd. dirs. Alton (Ill.) Mus. History and Art, 1984-86. With U.S. Army, 1954-56. Mem. Am. Math. Assn. Two-Yr. Colls., Am. Soc. Engring. Edn., Ill. Math. Assn. Community Colls., Kiwanis (Alton-Godfrey Pres. 1989-90, Disting. Pres. award 1990), Sigma Pi Sigma, Tau Beta Pi, Kappa Delta Pi. Presbyterian. Home: 3208 Greenwood Ln Godfrey IL 62035-1815 Office: Lewis and Clark C C 5800 Godfrey Rd Godfrey IL 62035-2426

MCDANIELS, PEGGY ELLEN, special education educator; b. Pulaski, Va., Jan. 4, 1945; d. James H. and Gladys M. (Hurd) Fisher; m. Robert A. McDaniels, Feb. 17, 1973; children: Dawn Marie, Robert C. A Gen. Studies, Schoolcraft Coll., 1976; BA, Ea. Mich. U., 1980, MA, 1985. Cert. adminstr. Woodcock Johnson Psychoednl. Battery. Payroll sec. Otto's Painting and Drywall, West Bloomfield, Mich., 1964-75; office mgr., closing sec. Bing Constrn. Co., West Bloomfield, 1964-75; substitute tchr. Wayne-Westland Schs., Westland, Mich., 1980-83, Farmington (Mich.) Schs., 1980-83; tchr. spl. edn. Romulus (Mich.) Community Schs., 1983-85, Cros-Lex Schs., Croswell, Mich., 1985-87, Pointe Tremble Elem. Sch., Algonac, Mich., 1987—; organizer, recorder Tchr. Assistance Team, Algonac, 1991—. Mem. Coun. Exceptional Children, Learning Disability Assn. (treas. 1988-90), Mich. Assn. Learning Disability Edn., ASCD. Avocations: camping, bicycling, reading. Home: 2406 Military St # 1 Port Huron MI 48060-6665

MC DANNALD, CLYDE ELLIOTT, JR., management consultation company executive; b. N.Y.C., June 29, 1923; s. Clyde E. and Evelyn (Tunison-Morgan) McD.; m. Virginia Washington, Apr. 25, 1953; children: Leslie Ann, Clyde Elliott III, Bruce Robert, Bonnie Washington, Brian Christopher (dec.), Laura Leigh. Market rsch. analyst J. Walter Thompson Co., N.Y.C., 1948-50; asst. dir. market rsch. Nat. Lead Co., N.Y.C., 1950-51; product rsch. supr., account exec. Foote, Cone & Belding, Inc., N.Y.C., 1951-52; product mgr., asst. advt. mgr. Am. Safety Razor Corp., N.Y.C., 1953-54; account exec. Young & Rubicam, N.Y.C., 1956-58; exec. asst. to v.p. advt. mgr. Brown & Williamson Tobacco Corp. subs. Brit.-Am. Tobacco Co., Ltd., Louisville, 1959-63; dir. advt. and mktg. svcs., dir. mktg. Miller Brewing Co., Milw., 1963-65; div. gen. mgr. v.p. consumer products, corp. v.p. Revere Copper & Brass Inc., N.Y.C., 1966-71; pres. chief oper. officer H.H. Pott Distillers Ltd. U.S. subs. H.H. Pott NFGR, N.Y.C., 1972-80, also bd. dirs.; pres., chief exec. officer Oxbridge Cons., Inc., N.Y.C., 1981—; ptnr. Hilbert, Peers and Young, Inc. N.Y.C., 1984—; bd. dirs. West Indies Distillers, Ltd., Distilled Spirits Inst. Washington, McFrank & Williams Inc. and Cooperating Cons. Corp., N.Y.C.; vis. prof. mktg. Fairfield U. Sch. Bus., 1975-77. Apptd. to staff Col. Ky. Govs. 1959-63, 92—; mem. Ky. Hwy. Commn. 1960-63, N.Y. Gov.'s Indsl. Com. 1967-72; bd. govs. N.Y. Mil. Acad., 1970-76, trustee, 1975-92.

Served from pvt. to capt. Inf. USAAF, 1942-45, ETO. Decorated D.F.C. Air medal with 4 oak leaf clusters; recipient Conspicuous Service Cross State of N.Y. with 5 oak leaf clusters, Valor medal UDC, Knickerbocker Greys City of N.Y., War Cross, Sons of Confederate Vets., Medaille de la France Liberee, Croix de Guerre (Belgium), Roi Leopold III, Battle of Britain, Knight Mil. Order of Malta. Mem. SAR, SR (bd. mgrs. 1988), Alumni Fedn. Columbia U., Am. Mgmt. Assn., NAM (mktg. com.), Audit Bur. Circulation, Navy League, St. Andrews Soc. State of N.Y., Am. Revolution Round Table, Am. Legion, VFW, N.Y. Soc. Mil. and Naval Officers World Wars, Sons of Confederate Vets., Sigma Chi (life), Alpha Chi Sigma. Clubs: Columbia U., Explorers, University. Presbyterian. Democrat. Home: 57 Canterbury Ln Wilton CT 06897-4103

MCDARRAH, FRED WILLIAM, photographer, editor, writer, photography reviewer; b. Bklyn., Nov. 5, 1926; s. Howard Arthur and Elizabeth (Swahn) McD.; m. Gloria Schoffel, Nov. 5, 1960; children: Timothy Swann, Patrick James. BA, NYU, 1954. Mem. staff Village Voice Newspaper, N.Y.C., 1959—, picture editor, 1971—; book reviewer ASMP Infinity Mag., 1972-73, Photo Dist. News, 1985-88, The Picture Profl., 1990—. Exhibited in Soho Photo Gallery, 1973, Whitney Mus., 1974, 76-77, Dallas Mus. Art, 1974, San Francisco Mus. Art, 1975, Wadsworth Atheneum, 1975, Sidney Janis Gallery, 1976, Basel (Switzerland) Art Fair, 1976, Alfred Stieglitz Gallery, 1976, Empire State Mus., Albany, N.Y., 1978, Lightworks Gallery, Syracuse, N.Y., 1981, Cape Cod Gallery, Provincetown Mass., 1982, Galleria di Franca Mancini, Pesaro, Italy, 1983, Musée du Quebec, 1987, Anita Shapolsky Gallery, N.Y.C., 1988, Hartnett Gallery U. Rochester, N.Y., 1989, G. Ray Hawkins Gallery, L.A., 1989, Read Gallery Antioch (Ohio) Coll., 1989, Mus. Art/Sci./Industry, Bridgeport, Conn., 1989, N.Y.C. Gallery Queens Mus., 1989, Ctr. Photography, Woodstock, 1989, Frumkin/Adams Gallery, 1990, Musée d'Art Moderne De La Ville de Paris, 1990, Musée d'Art Contemporain, Montreal, 1990, Pollack-Krasner Mus., East Hampton, N.Y., 1990, Found. Cartier, Paris, 1990, Marty Carey Pictures Gallery, Woodstock, N.Y., 1992, Galerie Gilles Ringuet, Belfort, France, 1992, Galerie Contre Jour, Belfort, France, 1992, Galleria La Pescheria, Cesena, Italy, 1994; exhbns. include Jack Kerouac Visions of the Road, Les Rencontres D'Arles, Arles, France, 1991, Jack Kerouac Travelling Writers, Saint-Malo (France) Internat. Festival, 1991, Images of Greenwich Village N.Y. Camera Club, 1992; author: The Beat Scene, 1960, The Artist's World in Pictures, 1961, rev. edit. 1988, Greenwich Village, 1963, New York, New York, 1964, Sculpture in Environment, 1967, Museums in New York, 1973, French edit., 1979, 5th edit., 1990, Photography Marketplace, 2d edit., 1977, Stock Photo and Assignment Source Book, 1977, 2d edit., 1984, Kerouac and Friends: A Beat Generation Album, 1984, Japanese edit, 1990, Frommer's Atlantic City and Cape May, 4th edit., 1991, 5th edit., 1993; co-author: The New Bohemia, 1967, 2d edit., 1990 Guide for Ecumenical Discussion, 1970, Greenwich Village Guide, 1992, Frommer's Virginia, 1992, 2d edit. 1994, Gay Pride: Photographs from Stonewall to Today, 1994; editor: Saturday Rev. Executive Desk Diary, 1962-64; photographer: Personality Posters, Fotofolio (post cards) (polit. and social figures); contbr. articles, picture features to various publs. including N.Y. Mag., Vanity Fair, Entertainment Weekly, Vogue. With U.S. Army, 1944-47. Recipient numerous photography awards including 1st place spot news photo award N.Y. Press Assn., 1964, 68; recipient 1st place feature photo award N.Y. Press Assn., 1967, 1st place picture story award N.Y. Press Assn., 1969, 2nd place spot news photo award N.Y. Press Assn., 1967, 70, 3d place spot news photo award N.Y. Press Assn., 1965, 3d place feature photo award N.Y. Press Assn., 1965, 3d place picture story award N.Y. Press Assn., 1970, 1st place Best Pictorial Series Nat. Newspaper Assn., 1966, Page One award Newspaper Guild N.Y., 1971, 80; Guggenheim fellow in photography, 1972. Mem. Nat. Press Photographers Assn., N.Y. Press Photographers Assn., Am. Soc. Mag. Photographers, Soc. Photog. Edn., Photog. Hist. Soc. N.Y., Authors Guild, N.Y. Press Club, Am. Soc. Picture Profls., Photog. Soc. Am. Office: 36 Cooper Sq New York NY 10003-7118

MCDARRAH, GLORIA SCHOFFEL, editor, author; b. Bronx, N.Y., June 22, 1932; d. Louis and Rose Schoffel; m. Fred W. McDarrah, Nov. 5, 1960; children: Timothy, Patrick. BA in French, Pa. State U., 1953; MA in French, NYU, 1966. Editorial asst. Crowell-Collier, N.Y.C., 1957-59; exec. asst. to pub. Time Inc., N.Y.C., 1959-61; libr., tchr. N.Y.C. Pub. Schs. and St. Luke's Sch., 1972-76; exec. asst. to pres. Capital Cities Communications Inc., N.Y.C., 1972-76; analyst N.Y.C. Landmarks Preservation Commn., 1976-79; project editor Grosset & Dunlap Inc., N.Y.C., 1979-80; sr. editor Prentice Hall trade div. Simon & Schuster Inc., N.Y.C., 1980-88; pres. McDarrah Media Assocs., N.Y.C., 1988—. Author: Frommer's Guide to Virginia, 1992, 2d edit., 1994-95, Frommer's Atlantic City and Cape May, 1985, 4th edit., 1991, 5th edit., 1993-94, The Artist's World, 2d edit., 1988; co-author: Museums in New York, 5th edit., 1990, Photography Marketplace, 1975 (book rev. sect.); co-editor Exec. Desk Diary Saturday Rev., 1962-64; contbg. editor quar. Dollarwise Traveler; editor book rev. The Picture Profl., 1990—; book columnist Manhattan Spirit, 1989—; book reviewer Pub.'s Weekley, 1994—.

MC DAVID, GEORGE EUGENE (GENE MC DAVID), newspaper executive; b. McComb, Miss., June 30, 1930; s. O.C. and Inez S. McDavid; m. Betty Ernestine Tinsley, Sept. 24, 1949; children: Carol McDavid, Martha Gene Newman. B.B.A. cum laude, U. Houston, 1965. Owner, publisher Wilk Amite Record, Gloster, Miss., 1949-58; with Houston Chronicle, 1958—, prodn. mgr., 1967-74, v.p. ops., 1974-85, v.p., gen. mgr., 1985-90, pres., 1990—; adv. bd. Am. Press Inst.; past pres. bd. dirs. S.W. Sch. Printing Mgmt. Chmn. Greater Houston chpt. ARC, nat. bd. govs.; mem. pres.'s counsel Houston Bapt. U.; vice chmn. Sam Houston Boy Scouts Am., Untied Negro Coll. Fund, Asia Soc., Goodwill Industries, YMCA; bd. dirs. Greater Houston Partnership, Nat. Conf. Christians and Jews, Houston region Am. Cancer Soc.; bd. dirs. pres. Houston Symphony; bd. dirs., v.p. Books of the World; mem. devel. bd. U. Hostoun; spl. deacon Second Bapt. Ch., Houston. Recipient Franklin award U. Houston, 1961, Disting. Alumnus award, 1990; Taggart award Tex. Newspaper, 1992, Man of Yr. award NCCJ, 1993; named Outstanding Ex-Citizen Gloster, 1974. Mem. Am. Newspaper Pubs. Assn. (chmn. newsprint com.), So. Newspaper Pubs. Assn. (pres.-elect), Tex. Daily Newspaper Assn. (pres.), Houston C. of C. (Houston Citizen's Community Svc. award 1993), Phi Kappa Phi, Beta Gamma Sigma. Clubs: Houston, Houstonian, Texas, Pine Forest Country. Home: 403 Hunters Park Ln Houston TX 77024-5438 Office: Houston Chronicle 801 Texas St Houston TX 77002-2996

MCDAVID, J. GARY, lawyer; b. Colorado Springs, Colo., May 13, 1947; s. John Arthur and Dorothy Jean (Collins) McD.; m. Janet Louise Kurzeka, June 9, 1973; 1 child, Matthew Collins. Student, U. Bonn., 1968-69; BA, Ohio State U., 1970; JD, Georgetown U., 1973. U.S. Dist. Ct. (N.D. dist.), D.C. Ct. Appeals 1973, U.S. Ct. Appeals (Fed. and D.C. cirs.), U.S. Tax Ct, U.S. Supreme Ct. Law clk. to chief judge U.S. Ct. Claims, Washington, 1973-75; with Hamel & Park, Washington, 1975-86; ptnr. McDermott, Will & Emery, Washington, 1986—; adj. prof. Georgetown U, Washington, 1982-85; speaker tax and corp. issues, 1982—. Served with USAR, 1970-78. Mem. ABA, U.S. Claims Ct. Bar Assn., Fed. Cir. Bar Assn. (bd. dirs. 1987—), Bar Assn. of D.C. (Cert. of Appreciation 1978). Avocations: golf, tennis, jogging. Office: McDermott Will & Emery 1850 K St NW Ste 500 Washington DC 20006-2296

MCDAVID, JANET LOUISE, lawyer; b. Mpls., Jan. 24, 1950; d. Robert Matthew and Lois May (Bratt) Kurzeka; m. John Gary McDavid, June 9, 1973; 1 child, Matthew Collins McDavid. BA, Northwestern U., 1971; JD, Georgetown U., 1974. Bar: D.C. 1974, U.S. Supreme Ct. 1980, U.S. Ct. Appeals (fed. cir.) 1975, (D.C. cir.) 1976, (5th cir.) 1983, (9th cir.) 1986. Assoc. Hogan & Hartson, Washington, 1974-83, ptnr., 1984—; gen. counsel ERAmerica, 1977-83; mem. antitrust task force Dept. Defense, 1993-94. Contbr. articles to profl. jours. Participant Clinton Administrn. Transition Team FTC. Mem. ABA (antitrust sect., vice chmn. civil practice com. 1986-89, sect. 2 com. 1989-90, chmn. franchising com. 1990-91, coun. mem. 1991-94, program officer 1994—; governing com. of forum on franchising 1991—), ACLU, Washington Coun. Lawyers, D.C. Bar Assn., Fed. Bar Assn., Womens Legal Def. Fund, Antitrust Coun. C. of C. Democrat. Office: Hogan & Hartson 555 13th St NW Washington DC 20004-1109

MCDAVID, WILLIAM HENRY, lawyer; b. N.Y.C., May 10, 1946; s. William H. and Margaret B. (Carmody) McD.; m. Sylvia Noin, Dec. 21,

1984; children: Andrew, Madeline, William, Flora. AB, Columbia Coll., N.Y.C., 1968; JD, Yale U., 1972. Assoc. Debevoise & Plimpton, N.Y.C. 1972-81; asst. gen. counsel Bankers Trust Co., N.Y.C., 1981-83, assoc. gen. counsel, 1983-84, v.p., 1984-85, v.p., counsel, 1986-88; gen. counsel Chem. Banking Corp., N.Y.C., 1988—; spl. counsel Adminstrv. Conf. of U.S., Washington, 1988-91. Mem. Bank Capital Markets Assn. (vice chmn. 1988-89, chmn. lawyers com. 1989-90). Office: Chemical Bank Office Gen Coun 270 Park Ave 8th Fl New York NY 10017

MCDERMOTT, AGNES CHARLENE SENAPE, philosophy educator; b. Hazelton, Pa., Mar. 11, 1937; d. Charles G. and Conjetta (Ranieri) Senape; children: Robert C, Lisa G., Jamie C. BA, U. Pa., 1956, Ph.D., 1964; postgrad., U. Calif.-Berkeley, 1960-61, U. Amsterdam, Netherlands, 1963, U. Wis., 1967-69. Instr. math. Drexel Inst. Tech., Phila., 1962-63; asst. prof. philosophy SUNY-Buffalo, 1964-65, Hampton Inst., Va., 1966-67; asst. prof. U. Wis.-Milw., 1967-70; assoc. prof. philosophy U. N.Mex., Albuquerque, 1970-80, prof., dean grad. studies, 1981-86; dean in residence Council of Grad. Schs., Washington, 1985-86; provost, v.p. acad. affairs CUNY, CUNY, 1986-89; prof. philosophy CUNY, 1986-91; dean for acad. and student affairs, cons. Albuquerque Acad., 1991-93; ind. cons. Corrales, N.Mex., 1993—; vis. assoc. prof. U. Wash., Seattle, 1974, U. Calif.-Berkeley, 1973-74, U. Hawaii, Honolulu, 1975; vis. prof. U. Calif.-Berkeley, 1980; lectr., panelist. Author: An Eleventh Century Buddhist Logic of 'Exists', 1969, Boethius' Treatise on the Modes of Signifying, 1980; compiler, editor anthology: Comparative Philosophy: Selected Essays, 1983; rev. editor Phil. East West, 1986—; contbr. articles to profl. jours. Vol. Albuquerque Care Alliance, 1988—. AAUW postdoctoral fellow, 1965-66; NEH Younger Humanist fellow, 1971-72; faculty rsch. fellow U. N.Mex., 1978, 79, 80; U. Pa. grad. fellow, 1961-62; S. Fels Found. fellow, 1963-64;U. Pa. tuition scholar; Pa. Hist. Soc. scholar. Mem. N.Y. Acad. Scis., Am. Philos. Soc., Am. Philos. Assn. (exec. com. 1977-80), Assn. Asian Studies (exec. com. 1977-80), Am. Oriental Soc., Western Assn. Grad. Schs. (pres. 1986-87), Phi Beta Kappa, Pi Mu Epsilon. Democrat. Avocations: skiing, fly-fishing.

MC DERMOTT, ALBERT LEO, lawyer; b. Lowell, Mass., Jan. 21, 1923; s. John Thomas and Josephine (Rohan) McD. A.B., Boston Coll., 1944; LL.B., Georgetown U., 1949. Bar: Mass. 1950, D.C. 1950, U.S. Supreme Ct. 1972. Practice of law Washington, 1950-54; assoc. Ingoldsby & Coles, 1950-52, partner, 1952-54; spl. asst. to Sec. Labor, 1954-61; ptnr. law firm McDermott & Russell (and predecessor), 1961-92; Washington rep. Am. Hotel and Motel Assn., 1963-88; mem. bd. adv. Maritime Cargo Transp. Conf., Fed. Svc. Impasses Panel, 1972-78; alt. rep. Pres. Nixon's Pay Bd., 1971-73; staff dir. Senate Rules Com., 1975-76. Served as Lt. USNR, World War II. Mem. Nat. Acad. Sci. (mem. research council 1957-60), ABA, Bar Assn. D.C. Clubs: Congl. Country, Capitol Hill (Washington); Tavern (N.Y.C.); Rehoboth Country (Del.). Home: 4813 Van Ness St NW Washington DC 20016-2353 Office: US Senate Washington DC 20510

MCDERMOTT, DONA M., historical park administrator. Supt. Valley Forge Nat. Hist. Park, Valley Forge, Pa. Office: Valley Forge Nat Hist Park PO Box 953 Valley Forge PA 19482-0953

MCDERMOTT, DREW VINCENT, computer science educator; b. Madison, Wis., Dec. 27, 1949; s. James Kenneth and Lucy Lea (Hurt) McD.; m. Judith Claire Rosenbaum, July 22, 1974; children: Noel Timothy, Katherine Anne. SB, SM, MIT, 1972, PhD, 1976. Asst. prof. computer sci. Yale U., New Haven, 1976-83, prof., 1983—, chmn. dept., 1991—; bd. dirs. Ctr. for Theoretical and Applied Neurosci., 1992—. Co-author: Introduction to Artificial Intelligence, 1985, Artificial Intelligence Programming, 1987. Fellow Am. Assn. for Artificial Intelligence; mem. Assn. for Computing Machinery. Roman Catholic. Avocation: philosophy of mind. Office: Yale Univ Dept of Computer Sci PO Box 2158 New Haven CT 06520

MCDERMOTT, EDWARD ALOYSIOUS, lawyer; b. Dubuque, Iowa, June 28, 1920; s. Edward L. and Sarah (Larken) McD.; m. Naola Spellman, Sept. 1, 1945; children: Maureen, Edward Aloysious, Charles Joseph, Daniel John. B.A., Loras Coll., Dubuque, 1939; J.D., State U., Iowa, 1942; J.D. (hon.), Xavier U., 1962, Loras Coll., 1973. Bar: Iowa 1942, D.C. 1942, Nebr. 1942. Mem. legal dept. Travelers Ins. Co., Omaha, 1942-43, Montgomery Ward & Co., Chgo., 1943-46; atty. firm O'Connor, Thomas & O'Connor, Dubuque, 1946-50; chief counsel sub-com. privileges and elections U.S. Senate, 1950-51; partner firm O'Connor, Thomas, McDermott & Wright, Dubuque, 1951-61; prof. bus. law and econs. Loras Coll., also Clarke Coll., Dubuque; dep. dir. Office Civil and Def. Moblzn., 1961-62; dep. dir. Office Emergency Planning, 1961-62, dir., 1962-65; ptnr. firm Hogan & Hartson, Washington, 1965-88; ret., 1989; U.S. rep. to sr. com. and other coms. NATO, 1962-65; chmn. Pres.'s Exec. Stockpile Com., 1962-65; mem. bd. advisers Indsl. Coll. Armed Forces, 1962-65; mem. Nat. Conf. Uniform Commrs. State Laws, 1959-64; chmn. Nat. CD Adv. Coun., 1962-65; mem. Pres.'s Com. Employment Handicapped, 1962-65, Pres.'s Com. Manpower, 1963-65, Pres.'s Com. Econ. Impact Def. and Rearmament, 1963-65, Pres.'s Sr. Adv. Com. on Govt. Reorgn., 1978-79; chmn. Com. on Assumptions for Nonmil. and Devel. Commn., Alaska, 1964-65; bd. dirs. Mercedes-Benz N.A., 1985—, mem. ops. com., 1986—; mem. adv. com. Office Comptr. Gen. of U.S., 1990—. Del. Democratic Nat. Conv., 1952, 56, 60, 64; trustee, sec. Ford's Theatre, Christ Child Soc., Religious Educators Found., Loras Coll.; mem. fin. council Archdiocese of Washington, 1985-89; chmn. emeritus Lombardi Cancer Inst.; regent emeritus Coll. Notre Dame; trustee emeritus Colgate U.; mem. council Hosp. St. John and St. Elizabeth, London, Maynooth Coll., Ireland; regent emeritus U. Santa Clara, Calif; bd. advisers Lynchburg (Va.) Coll., Iowa Law Sch. Found., Up With People; v.p. Flax Trust, No. Ireland. Decorated knight Holy Sepulchre; recipient Amvets Spl. Silver Helmet award, 1963. Mem. ABA; mem. Fed. Bar Assn., Iowa Bar Assn. (bd. govs. 1956-60), D.C. Bar Assn., Am. Judicature Soc., John Carroll Soc. (pres. 1972), Am. Ireland Fund (bd. dirs.), Friendly Sons St. Patrick (pres. 1978-79), Ireland Club Fla., The City Club (bd. dirs.), 1925 F Street Club, Met. Club (Washington), Delray Beach Club (Fla.), Knights of Malta Fed. Assn. (pres. 1979-82). Democrat. Home: Lake House South 875 E Camino Real Boca Raton FL 33432 Office: Columbia Sq 555 13th St NW Washington DC 20004-1109

MCDERMOTT, FRANCIS OWEN, lawyer; b. Denver, Feb. 25, 1933; s. Paul Harkins and Agnes (Clarke) McD.; divorced; children: Diana, Daniel, Christopher, Anthony, Justine; m. Estella Marina Idiaquez, June 6, 1986. JD, Am. U., 1960. Bar: D.C. 1960, US Dist. Ct. D.C., 1960, U.S. Ct. Appeals (D.C. cir.) 1960, u.s. Tax Ct. 1961, U.S. Supreme Ct. 1964. Trial atty. office regional counsel IRS, Washington, 1961-65; mem. profl. staff com. on fin. U.S. Senate, Washington, 1965-68; tax counsel Assn. Am. R.R.s, Washington, 1968-73; assoc. Hopkins & Sutter, Washington, 1973-76, ptnr., 1976—; gen. counsel Inst. III., Washington, 1987—. Mem. ABA, Fed. Bar Assn., Nat. Def. Transp. Assn. (v.p., gen. counsel 1974—). Roman Catholic. Avocation: tennis. Home: 1 S Montague St Arlington VA 22204-1007

MCDERMOTT, JAMES A., congressman, psychiatrist; b. Chicago, Ill., Dec. 28, 1936; children: Katherine, James. BS, Wheaton Coll., 1958; MD, U. Ill., 1963. Intern Buffalo Gen. Hosp., 1963-64; resident in adult psychiatry U. Ill. Hosps., Chgo., 1964-66; resident in child psychiatry U. Wash. Hosps., Seattle, 1966-68; asst. clin. prof. dept. psychiatry U. Wash., Seattle, 1970-83; mem. Wash. Ho. of Reps., 1971-72, Wash. Senate, 1975-87; regional med. officer U.S. Fgn. Svc., 1987-88; mem. 101st-104th Congresses from 7th Wash. dist., 1989—; former chmn. stds. of ofcl. conduct com., mem. ways and means com., ranking minority mem., mem. stds. of ofcl. conduct com.; mem. exec. and edn. com. Nat. Conf. State Legislatures. Mem. Wash. State Arts Commn., Wash. Coun. for Prevention Child Abuse and Neglect; Dem. nominee for gov., 1980. Lt. comdr. MC, USN, 1968-70. Mem. Am. Psychiat. Assn., Wash. State Med. Assn., King County Med. Soc. Democrat. Episcopalian. Office: US Ho of Reps 2349 Rayburn HOB Washington DC 20515*

MCDERMOTT, JAMES ALEXANDER, lawyer; b. Tulsa, May 2, 1938; s. Richard Bertram McDermott and Ruth Lamb; m. Renée Rassler, Jan. 1, 1986; children: Melora, Melissa. AB, Princeton U., 1960; JD, U. Mich., 1963. Bar: Ind. 1963. Assoc. Barnes & Thornburg, Indpls., 1963-71, ptnr., 1971-94, counsel, 1994—. Author: Recommended Law Books, 1987. Founder Penrod Soc., Festival Music Soc. Indpls. 1967; rowing commr. X

Pan Am. Games, Indpls., 1987. Democrat. Home: 1008 W McLary Rd Nashville IN 47448-9176 Office: Barnes & Thornburg 11 S Meridian St 1313 Merchants Bank Bldg Indianapolis IN 46204

MC DERMOTT, JOHN FRANCIS, JR., psychiatrist, physician; b. Hartford, Conn., Dec. 12, 1929; s. John Francis and Camilla R. (Cavanaugh) McD.; m. Sarah N. Schemm, Dec. 27, 1958; children: Elizabeth C., John Francis III. A.B., Cornell U., 1951; M.D., N.Y. Med. Coll., 1955. Diplomate in psychiatry and child psychiatry Am. Bd. Psychiatry and Neurology. Intern Henry Ford Hosp., Detroit, 1955-56; resident psychiatry U. Mich. Med. Center, 1956-58, 60-62; practice medicine, specializing in psychiatry and child and adolescent psychiatry Honolulu, 1969-95; instr., asst. prof., asso. prof. psychiatry U. Mich. Sch. Medicine, 1962-69; prof., chmn. dept. psychiatry U. Hawaii Sch. Medicine, 1969-95, prof. emeritus, 1995—; scholar-in-residence Rockefeller Found. Study Ctr., Bellagio, Italy, 1985, 92; chmn. com. cert. in child psychiatry Am. Bd. Psychiatry and Neurology, 1974-78, bd. dirs., 1983-91, chmn. R&D com., 1985-91; sr. vis. scientist dept. exptl. psychology Oxford (Eng.) U., 1993; vis. prof. numerous univs.; cons. numerous mental health clinics and orgns. Author: Psychiatry for the Pediatrician, 1970, Childhood Psychopathology, 1972, Mental Health Education in New Medical Schools, 1973, Roles and Functions of Child Psychiatrists, 1976, Psychiatric Treatment of the Child, 1977, New Directions in Childhood Psychopathology, vol. I, 1980, vol. II, 1982, Raising Cain (and Abel Too), 1980: People and Cultures of Hawaii, 1980, Culture Mind and Therapy: An Introduction to Cultural Psychiatry, 1982, Japanese edit., 1984, The Complete Book on Sibling Rivalry, 1987, German edit., 1991; editor Jour. Am. Acad. Child and Adolescent Psychiatry, 1987—; contbr. over 150 articles to profl. jours.; mem. editorial bds. numerous psychiat. jours. Served with USN, 1958-60. Named Disting. Alumnus N.Y. Med. Coll., 1976. Fellow Am. Psychiat. Assn. (life), Am. Orthopsychiat. Assn., Am. Acad. Child and Adolescent Psychiatry, Am. Coll. Psychiatrists, World Psychiat. Assn. (chmn. child and adolescent psychiatry 1977-89). Clubs: Oahu Country, Outrigger Canoe, Cosmos. Home: Waikii Ranch Kamuela HI 96822-2004 Office: 1319 Punahou St Honolulu HI 96826-1032

MCDERMOTT, JOHN H(ENRY), lawyer; b. Evanston, Ill., June 23, 1931; s. Edward Henry and Goldie Lucile (Boso) McD.; m. Ann Elizabeth Pickard, Feb. 19, 1966; children: Elizabeth A., Mary L., Edward H. BA, Williams Coll., 1953; JD, U. Mich., 1956. Bar: Mich. 1955, Ill. 1956. Assoc. McDermott, Will & Emery, Chgo., 1958-64, ptnr., 1964—; bd. dirs. Patrick Industries Inc. 1st lt. USAF, 1956-58. Mem. ABA, Ill. Bar Assn., Chgo. Bar Assn. Clubs: Commerical of Chgo., Econ. of Chgo., Legal Chgo. (pres. 1981-82), Law Chgo. (pres. 1986-87). Home: 330 Willow Rd Winnetka IL 60093-4130 Office: McDermott Will & Emery 227 W Monroe St Chicago IL 60606-5096

MC DERMOTT, JOHN JOSEPH, philosophy educator; b. N.Y.C., Jan. 5, 1932; s. John J. and Helen (Kelly) McD.; m. Virginia Picarelli, June 14, 1952 (div. Aug., 1990); children: Marise, Michele, David, Brian, Tara; m. Patricia Anne Garner, Dec. 29, 1990. B.A. cum laude, St. Francis Coll., 1953; M.A., Fordham U., 1954, Ph.D., 1959; LL.D., U. Hartford, 1970. Tchr. Latin Loughlin High Sch., Bklyn., 1953-54; instr. philosophy St. Francis Coll., Bklyn., 1954-57; mem. faculty Queens Coll., Flushing, N.Y., 1956-77; assoc. prof. philosophy Queens Coll., 1965-67, prof., 1968-77; prof., head dept. philosophy and humanities Tex. A. and M. U., 1977-81; disting. prof. philosophy Tex. A&M U., 1981—, prof., head dept. med. humanities Coll. Medicine, 1981-90, Abell Prof. liberal arts, 1986—; vis. prof. Am. lit. SUNY-Stony Brook, 1970. Editor: Writings of William James, 1967, Basic Writing of Josiah Royce, 2 vols, 1969, The Philosophy of John Dewey, 2 vols, 1973, A Cultural Introduction to Philosophy, 1985; author: The Culture of Experience, 1976, Streams of Experience, 1986; adv. editor: Collected Works of William James; gen. editor: Correspondence of William James; editorial bds.: Cross Currents, 1968—, Transactions, Jour. Speculative Philosophy; contbr. articles to profl. jours. Trustee Nat. Faculty for Humanities, Arts, Scis. Postdoctoral fellow Union Theol. Sem., 1964-65; recipient E. Harris Harbison award for gifted teaching, 1969-70. Mem. Am. Philos. Assn. (exec. com., 1979-82, Nat. Bd. Officers, 1989-92), Am. Studies Assn., History of Sci. Soc., Peirce Soc. (editorial bd. Trans.), Soc. for Advancement Am. Philosophy (exec. com. 1973, pres. 1977-80, Herbert W. Schneider award 1993). Home: 701 Dexter Dr S College Station TX 77840-6171

MCDERMOTT, KEVIN J., engineering educator, consultant; b. Teaneck, N.J., Nov. 21, 1935; s. Francis X. and Elizabeth (Casey) McD.; m. Ann McDermott, Aug. 3, 1959; children: Kathleen, Kevin, Donna, Michael. BSEE, N.J. Inst. Tech., 1965; MS Indsl. Engring., Columbia U., 1970; EdD, Fairleigh Dickinson U., 1975. Registered profl. engr., N.J. With Bell Telephone Labs., Murray Hill, N.J., 1960-65, Westinghouse Electic, Newark, 1965-67, Columbia U., NASA, N.Y.C., 1967-70, RCA Corp., N.Y.C., 1970-76, Ramapo (N.J.) Coll., 1976-80; prof. N.J. Inst. Tech., Newark, 1980—; engrng. engr. N.J. Inst. Tech., 1983—; bd. dirs. Computer Aided Design/Computer Aided Manufacture Robotics Consortium. Contbr. more than 50 articles to tech. jours. IBM fellow, 1987. Fellow IEEE, Soc. Mech. Engrs.; mem. Inst. Indsl. Engrs. Achievements include research in industrial robot work cells, manufacturing systems, expert systems, analysis of industrial of Robotics, Flexible Manufacturing Systems, expert and vision systems in computer aided design and manufacturing.

MCDERMOTT, LARRY ARNOLD, newspaper publisher, newspaper editor; b. Parkin, Ark., Apr. 27, 1948; s. John Allen and Ida Mae (Harris) McD.; m. Linda Louis Lancaster, Mar. 20, 1969; children: Marshall, Kelly, Amanda. BS, Ark. State U., 1970. Reporter Jonesboro (Ark.) Sun, 1968-70; reporter AP, Richmond, Va., 1970-71, 72-75, Norfolk, Va., 1975-76; polit. correspondent AP, Lansing, Mich., 1976-78; bur. chief AP, Little Rock, 1978-80, Mpls., 1980-84, Detroit, 1984-87; asst. to the pres. AP, N.Y.C., 1987-88; info. specialist UN Command, Seoul, Republic of Korea, 1971-72; copy editor Korea Times, Seoul, 1971-72; editor, bur. chief Booth Newspapers, Lansing, 1988-90; pub. Bay City (Mich.) Times, 1990-92; exec. editor Springfield Union News, Mass., 1993—; v.p., bd. dirs. Mich. State News, East Lansing, 1990-91. bd. dirs. Bay Area Econ. Growth Alliance, Bay City, 1990-91. With U.S. Army, 1970-72. Presbyterian. Avocations: fly fishing, golf, camping. Home: 26 Tennyson Dr East Longmeadow MA 01106-2334 Office: Bay City Times 311 5th St Bay City MI 48708-5806 also: Union-News 1860 Main St Springfield MA 01103-1000*

MCDERMOTT, RENÉE R(ASSLER), lawyer; b. Danville, Pa., Sept. 26, 1950; d. Carl A. and Rose (Gaupp) Rassler; m. James A. McDermott, Jan. 1, 1986. BA, U. So. Fla., 1970, MA, 1972; JD, Ind. U., 1978. Bar: Ind. 1978, U.S. Dist. Ct. (so. and no. dists.) Ind. 1978, U.S. Dist. Ct. Ariz. 1984, U.S. Ct. Appeals (7th cir.) 1979, U.S. Ct. Appeals (9th cir.) 1985. Law clk. to presiding judge U.S. Dist. Ct. (no. dist.) Ind. Ft. Wayne, 1978-80; assoc. Barnes & Thornburg, Indpls., 1980-84, ptnr., 1985-93; pvt. practice Nashville, Ind., 1994—; county atty. County of Brown, Ind., 1994—. Editor in chief Ind. U. Law Jour., 1977-78. Bd. visitors Ind. U. Law Sch., Bloomington, 1979—; bd. dirs. Environ. Quality Control Inc., Indpls. Named one of Outstanding Young Women Am., 1986. Fellow Ind. Bar Found., Am. Bar Found. (life); mem. ABA (chmn. environ. controls com. 1991—, liaison to standing com. on environ. law bus. law sect.), Ind. State Bar Assn. (chmn. young lawyers sect. 1985-86, chmn. environ. law sect. 1989-91), Bar Assn. 7th Fed. Cir., Ind. Mfrs. Assn. (environ. affairs com.), Order of Coif. Avocations: scuba diving, horseback riding, music, reading, hiking. Home and Office: 1008 W McLary Rd Nashville IN 47448-9702 Address: 1008 W McLary Rd Nashville IN 47448

MCDERMOTT, RICHARD T., lawyer, educator; b. Milw., Jan. 30, 1940; s. Richard A. and Sylvia Carmen (Portuondo) McD.; m. Mary Patricia Scanlon, Aug. 24, 1963; children: Richard B., Christina M. BA, Marquette U., 1962; LLB, Fordham U., 1966. Bar: N.Y. 1967. Assoc. Alexander & Green, N.Y.C., 1966-73, ptnr. 1973-86; ptnr. Walter, Conston, Alexander & Green, N.Y.C., 1987-90, Rogers & Wells, N.Y.C., 1990—; adj. prof. law NYU Sch. Law, N.Y.C., 1981—. Author: Legal Aspects of Corporate Finance, 1985. Fellow Am. Bar Found.; mem. ABA, N.Y. State Bar Assn., Bar Assn. City N.Y., Univ. Club, Woodstock Golf Club (N.Y.). Avocations: foreign relations, golf. Office: Rogers & Wells 200 Park Ave New York NY 10166-0153

MCDERMOTT, ROBERT B., lawyer; b. Washington, June 16, 1927; s. Edward H. and Goldie Lucile (Boso) McD.; m. Julia Wood, Nov. 16, 1950; children: John, Jeanne, Charles; m. Jane McDermott, July 31, 1973. A.B., Princeton U., 1948; LL.B., Harvard U., 1951. Bar: D.C. 1951, Ill. 1955. Atty. Office Gen. Counsel, Navy Dept., Washington, 1951-52; assoc McDermott, Will & Emery, Chgo., 1954-60, ptnr., 1961-92, chmn., 1986-91, of counsel, 1992—; bd. dirs. The Cherry Corp., Waukegan, Ill., Furst-McNess Co., Freeport, Ill., Maynard Oil Co., Dallas. Trustee Ill. Inst. Tech., Chgo., 1985—, The Mather Found., Evanston, Ill., 1988—; bd. dirs. Ct. Theatre, Alliance Francaise de Chgo. Lt. USNR, 1945-46, 52-54. Mem. Chgo. Bar Assn. Clubs: Chicago, Economic, University (Chgo.). Home: 990 N Lake Shore Dr Chicago IL 60611-1353 Office: 227 W Monroe St Chicago IL 60606-5016

MC DERMOTT, ROBERT FRANCIS, insurance company executive; b. Boston, July 31, 1920. BS, U.S. Mil. Acad., 1943; MBA, Harvard U., 1950. Commd. USAF, 1943, advanced through grades to brig. gen.; faculty dean USAF Acad., 1956-68, ret.; with United Svcs. Auto. Assn., San Antonio, Tex., 1968—, now chmn., CEO, atty.-in-fact; CEO, pres. La Cantera Devel. Co., La Cantera Hospitality, Inc., Fiesta Tex. Showpark, Inc., HTO, Inc. Author articles in field. Office: United Svcs Automobile Assn 9800 Fredericksburg Rd San Antonio TX 78288-0001*

MCDERMOTT, ROBERT FRANCIS, JR., lawyer; b. Cambridge, Mass., Nov. 3, 1945; s. Robert F. and Alice McD.; children: Robert F. III, Peter M. BA, Harvard U., 1967; LLB, Yale U., 1970. Bar: Ga. 1973, Va. 1976, U.S. Dist. Ct. D.C. 1980, U.S. Ct. Appeals 1980, U.S. Dist. Ct. (ea. dist.) Va. 1976, U.S. Supreme Ct. 1982. Staff asst. to the pres. White House, Washington, 1970-72; staff asst. to dep. atty. gen. and assoc. dep. atty. gen. Dept. of Justice, Washington, 1974-75; asst. U.S. atty. U.S. Dist. Ct. (ea. dist.) Va., 1975-79; atty. Jones, Day, Reavis & Pogue, Washington, 1979—. Office: Jones Day Reavis & Pogue 1450 G St NW Washington DC 20005-2088

MCDERMOTT, THOMAS CURTIS, health care and consumer products company executive; b. Somerville, Mass., June 25, 1936; s. Thomas Curtis and Kathryn (Vinicomb) McD.; m. Gloria Newmark, June 7, 1958; children—Thomas, Mark, James, Andrew. B.S., Providence Coll. Mgr. corp. security Bristol Myers, N.Y.C., 1965-70; dir. personnel, indsl. relations E.R. Squibb & Son, Princeton, N.J., 1971-78; v.p. human resources Bausch & Lomb, Rochester, N.Y., 1978-80, sr. v.p. human resources, 1981-82, group pres., 1982-85, exec. v.p., pres. U.S. ops., 1985—, pres., chief operating officer, 1986—; v.p. human resources Gen. Cinema, Chestnut Hill, Mass., 1980-81; bd. dirs. Bausch & Lomb, Rochester, Chase Lincoln First Regional Bank, A.T. Cross Co., Lincoln, R.I., Goulds Pumps, Seneca Falls, N.Y. Trustee Rochester Inst. Tech. Served to 1st lt. U.S. Army, 1958-62. Mem. Soc. Former FBI Agts., Rochester C. of C. (bd. dirs.). Roman Catholic. Clubs: Genessee Valley (Rochester), Oak Hill Country, Country Club of Rochester. Avocations: tennis; golf; skiing. Home: PO Box 541 East Orleans MA 02643-0541

MCDERMOTT, THOMAS JOHN, JR., lawyer; b. Santa Monica, Calif., Mar. 23, 1931; s. Thomas J. Sr. and Etha Irene (Cook) McD.; m. Yolanda; children: Jodi Friedman, Kimberly E., Kish S. BA, UCLA, 1953, JD, 1958. Bar: Calif. 1959. Ptnr., Gray, Binkley and Pfaelzer, Los Angeles, 1964-67, Kadison, Pfaelzer, Woodward, Quinn and Rossi, Los Angeles, 1967-87, Rogers & Wells, 1987-93, Bryan Cave, 1993-95, Manatt, Phelps & Phillips, 1995—. Served with U.S. Army, 1953-56, Korea. Fellow Am. Coll. Trial Lawyers; mem. ABA, UCLA Law Alumni Assn. (pres. 1961-62), Assn. of Bus. Trial Lawyers (pres. 1980-81, mem. exec. com. 9th cir. jud. conf. 1993—), State Bar Calif. (chair litigation sect. 1993-94), Order of Coif. Office: Manatt Phelps & Phillips 11355 West Olympic Blvd Los Angeles CA 90064-1614

MC DERMOTT, WILLIAM VINCENT, JR., physician, educator; b. Salem, Mass., Mar. 7, 1917; s. William Vincent and Mary A. (Feenan) McD.; m. Blanche O'Riorden, May 15, 1943 (dec. July 1969); children: Blanche Anne, William Shaw, Jane Travers Hoch; m. Mary Boit Bingham, June 1, 1976 (dec. 1984); m. Frances Weld Gardiner, June 16, 1989 (dec. 1993). A.B., Harvard U., 1938, M.D., 1942. Diplomate: Nat. Bd. Med. Examiners (chmn. surgery test com.), Am. Bd. Surgery. Intern Mass. Gen. Hosp., Boston, 1942; asst. resident surgeon Mass. Gen. Hosp., 1946-49, chief resident surgeon, 1950; practice medicine specializing in surgery Boston, 1951—; mem. staff Mass. Gen. Hosp., 1951—, New Eng. Deaconess Hosp., 1963—; mem. corp. vis. com., 1968—; USPHS fellow dept. biochemistry Sch. Medicine, Yale U., 1949-50; from instr. to prof. surgery Med. Sch. Harvard U., 1951-69, Cheever prof. surgery, 1969-87, prof. surgery emeritus, 1987—, sec. Faculty of Medicine, 1985-87; vis. prof. prof. nem Kings Coll. Hosp. Med. Sch., London, 1960; dir. Harvard surg. unit, Sears surg. labs. Boston City Hosp., 1963-73; dir. Harvard Surg. Service and Cancer Research Inst., 1973-80; chmn. dept. surgery New Eng. Deaconess Hosp., 1980-85, mem. corporation, 1988—. Author three books, over 200 sci. papers; contbr. 12 chpts. to books; mem. editorial bd. Jour. Surg. Research, 1960-73, Jour. Surg. Oncology, 1970—. Pres. Med. Found. Boston, 1968-70, trustee, 1970-87, hon. trustee, 1987—. Maj. M.C. AUS, 1943-46, ETO. Decorated Bronze Star, oak leaf cluster, 5 battle stars; recipient Disting. Alumnus award Harvard U., 1992. Mem. ACS (bd. govs. 1984-90, pres. Mass. chpt. 1980), Soc. Univ. Surgeons, Am. Surg. Assn., Am. Acad. Arts and Scis., New Eng. Surg. Soc. (pres. 1985-86), Boston Surg. Soc. (pres. 1971), Harvard Med. Alumni Assn. (treas. 1965-68, pres. 1975-76, dir. alumni rels. 1987-93, bd. dirs. 1993—), Société de Chirurgie Internationale, Am. Acad. Surgery, Soc. Surgery of Alimentary Tract, Aesculapian Club (pres. 1971), Harvard Club of Boston (bd. govs. 1971-77), Tavern, Country Club. Home: 570 Bridge St Dedham MA 02026-4131 Office: New Eng Deaconess Hosp Boston MA 02215

MCDEVITT, BRIAN PETER, educational consultant; b. Jersey City, Dec. 29, 1944; s. Bernard Aloysius and Veronica Sabina (Bender) McD.; m. Dorothy Helen Gilligan, Oct. 19, 1968; children: Peter David, Timothy Bernard. BS, Seton Hall U., 1966; MA, Columbia U., 1971. Tchr. history St. Patrick's High Sch., Elizabeth, N.J., 1966-68, Vail Deane High Sch., Elizabeth, N.J., 1968-70; fed. grant writer Alexian Bros. Hosp., Elizabeth, N.J., 1970-72, Union County Coll., Cranford, N.J., 1972-76; prin., owner Ednl. Svcs., Westfield, N.J., 1976—; adj. prof. history Union County Coll., Cranford, N.J., 1976—; adj. prof. classics Montclair (N.J.) State Coll., 1990—. Author: The Irish Librists, 1988, The Irish Librists and the Scrolls of Aristotle, 1993, A Historian's Thematic Study of Western Civilization, 1994, Evidence of an Ancient Greek Navigation System, 1995; (video) The Minoans According to Sir Arthur Evans; contbr. articles to profl. jours. N.J. Dept. Higher Edn. grantee. Mem. Trireme Trust U.S.A. (internat. rowing team 1990), Friends of Trireme (London), Soc. Naval Architects and Marine Engrs., Assn. Ancient Historians, Soc. Ancient Greek Philosophy, Assn. Muslim Social Scientists, Westfield United Fund, Westfield P.A.L., Westfield Basketball Assn., Westfield Baseball Assn., Boy Scouts Am. Roman Catholic. Avocations: golfing, rowing, basketball, playing piano, stamp collecting. Home: 607 S Chestnut St Westfield NJ 07090

MCDEVITT, CHARLES FRANCIS, state supreme court justice; b. Pocatello, Idaho, Jan. 5, 1932; s. Bernard A. and Margaret (Hermann) McD.; m. Virginia L. Heller, Aug. 14, 1954; children: Eileen A., Kathryn A., Brian A., Sheila A., Terrence A., Neil A., Kendal A. LLB, U. Idaho, 1956. Bar: 1956. Ptnr. Richards, Haga & Eberle, Boise, 1956-62; gen. counsel, asst. sec. Boise Cascade Corp., 1962-65; mem. Idaho State Legislature, 1963-66; sec., gen. counsel Boise Cascade Corp., 1965-67, v.p. sec., 1967-68; v.p. Beck Industries, 1968-70; group v.p. Singer Co., N.Y.C., 1970-72, exec. v.p., 1973-76; pub. defender Ada County, Boise, 1976-78; co-founder Givens, McDevitt, Pursley & Webb, Boise, 1978-89; justice Idaho Supreme Ct., Boise, 1989—; chief justice, 1993—; served on Gov.'s Select Com. on Taxation, Boise, 1988-89. Home: 4940 Boise River Ln Boise ID 83706-5706 Office: Idaho Supreme Ct 451 W State St Boise ID 83702-6006

MCDEVITT, DANIEL BERNARD, communications, computer and control systems application engineer; b. Pocatello, Idaho, Apr. 14, 1927; s. Bernard Aloysius and Margaret Helen (Hermann) McD.; m. MaryAnn Bohrer, June 14, 1952. BSEE, U. Idaho, 1950. Registered profl. engr.: Tex., Ark., Okla. Quality control and value engr. GE, Erie, Phila., 1950-53; sales engr. GE, Cleve., 1954-56, regional mgr., 1956-59; v.p. mktg. Nelson Elec. Mfg. Co.,

Tulsa, 1959-62; owner Dan B. McDevitt & Assoc., Tulsa, 1962—; pres. Progress Engring., Tulsa, 1965—, RADIUS Rsch. and Devel. Inst. of the U.S., Tulsa, 1963—; gen. mgr. Manhattan-McDevitt-Progress Engring. & Wallace Ltd., Tulsa, 1975—; mem. Okla. Coun. Reorganization-State Exec. Br., Oklahoma City, 1971-73; advisor Saudi Arabia Air Force Acad., Riyad, 1974-77; chmn. Okla. State Communications Coun., 1972-74; mem. adv. counsel U.S. SBA. Author: Controlling the Uncontrollable-Mgmt. Retail, 1969, (pamphlet) A Strategy for U.S.A. Economic Preeminence, 1985-87; contbr. over 20 articles to Oil & Gas Jour., Am. Engr., Datamation Network World, Systems. Advisor Okla. State Gov., Oklahoma City, 1970-74; chmn. Okla. Coun. on Environment, Oklahoma City, 1970—, Latah County Dem. Orgn., Moscow, Idaho, 1948-50. Officer candidate USMCR, 1944-51, South Pacific, Republic of Korea. Recipient Meritorious Achievement award Okla. State Gov., 1974, Appreciation medallion Saudi Arabia Air Force Acad., 1975. Mem. IEEE, NSPE. Democrat. Roman Catholic. Achievements include development of retail software systems, computer models. Office: Progress Engring PO Box 700270 Tulsa OK 74170-0270

MCDEVITT, HUGH O'NEILL, immunology educator, physician; b. Cin., 1930. M.D., Harvard U., 1955. Diplomate: Am. Bd. Internal Medicine. Intern Peter Bent Brigham Hosp., Boston, 1955-56, sr. asst. resident in medicine, 1961-62; asst. resident Bell Hosp., 1956-57; research fellow dept. bacteriology and immunology Harvard U., 1959-61; USPHS spl. fellow Nat. Inst. Med. Research, Mill Hill, London, 1962-64; physician Stanford U. Hosp., Calif., 1966—; assoc. prof. Stanford U. Sch. Medicine, Calif., 1969-72, prof. med. immunology, 1972—, prof. med. microbiology, 1980—, Burt and Marian Avery Prof. Immunology, 1990—; cons. physician VA Hosp., Palo Alto, Calif., 1968—. Served as capt. M.C., AUS, 1957-59. Mem. NAS, AAAS, Am. Fedn. Clin. Rsch., Am. Soc. Clin. Investigation, Am. Assn. Immunologists, Transplantation Soc., Inst. Medicine, Royal Soc. (fgn.). Office: Stanford U Dept Microbiology Stanford CA 94305

MC DEVITT, JOSEPH BRYAN, retired university administrator, retired naval officer; b. McGehee, Ark., Dec. 22, 1918; s. John and Mary Ann (Zimmer) McD.; m. Kathleen Rita Vaughan, 1943 (dec. 1961), m. Catherine Irene Beatty, Jan. 30, 1965 (dec. 1980); m. Ernestine Moody Minshew, Oct. 9, 1982; children: Jeffrey Bryan, Paul Killian, Rodney Peter, Rita Elizabeth, John Stephen, David Andrew, Joseph Bryan, Richard Vincent, Eugena Rose, Edward Francis, Gerald Christopher, Lisa Ernestine. Student, So. Ill. U., 1936-38; B.A., U. Ill., 1940, J.D., 1942. Bar: Ill. 1952. Commd. ensign U.S. Navy, 1943, advanced through grades to rear adm., 1968; boat group comdr. U.S.S. Leon, 1944-46; with legal office 8th Naval Dist. New Orleans, 1950; legal officer to comdr. Amphibious Force, Atlantic Fleet, 1952, mem. mil. justice div. Office Judge Adv. Gen., 1954, naval liaison officer to U.S. Senate, 1956; staff legal officer Marine Corps. Schs. Quantico, Va., 1958; student Naval War Coll., 1958-59, assigned Joint Chiefs Staff, 1959-61, dir. internat. law div. Office Judge Adv. Gen., 1962-65, legal affairs officer to comdr. in chief Pacific, 1965-68, judge adv. gen. of navy, 1968-72, ret., 1972; chief exec. officer People to People Programs Inc., Washington, 1972-73; v.p. exec. affairs, univ. counsel, sec. bd. trustees Clemson U., S.C., 1973-85, ret., 1985. Decorated Purple Heart, Legion of Merit, D.S.M. Mem. Am. Ill., Fed. Inter-Am. bar assns., Judge Advs. Assn., Am. Soc. Internat. Law. Catholic. Home: Stiles Point Plantatio Charleston SC 29412

MCDEVITT, SHEILA MARIE, lawyer, energy company executive; b. St. Petersburg, Fla., Jan. 15, 1947; d. Frank Davis and Marie (Barfield) McD. AA, St. Petersburg Jr. Coll., 1966; BA in Govt., Fla. State U., 1968, JD, 1978. Bar: Fla. 1978. Research asst. Fla. Legis. Reference Bur., Tallahassee, 1968-69; adminstr., research assoc. Constitution Revision Commn. Ga. Gen. Assembly, Atlanta, 1969-70; adminstrv. asst., analyst Fla. State Sen., Tallahassee, Tampa, 1970-79; assoc. McLain, Walkley & Stuart, P.A., Tampa, Seminole, Fla., 1979-81; govtl. affairs counsel Tampa Electric Co., 1981-82, corp. counsel, 1982-86; sr. corp. counsel Teco Energy, Inc., Tampa, 1986-89, asst. v.p., 1989-92; v.p., asst. gen. counsel, 1992—; mem. Worker's Compensation Adv. Council Fla. Dept. Labor, Tallahassee, 1984-86. Bd. dirs. Vol. Ctr. Hillsborough County, Tampa, 1984-85; chmn., trustee Tampa Lowry Park Zoo Soc., 1986-94, also legal advisor; bd. dirs. Hillsborough County Easter Seal Soc., 1994—; mem. Fla. State Rep. Exec. Com., Tallahassee, 1974-75, Hillsborough County Reps. Exec. Com., 1974-75; transition team Fla. Gov. Bob Martinez, 1986-87; apptd. by Sen. Connic Mack to Fed. Jud. Adv. Commn., 1989—. Mem. ABA, Fed. Energy Bar Assn., Fla. Bar (vice-chmn. then chmn. energy law com. 1984-87, jud. nominating procedures com. 1986-91, jud. adminstrn. selection and tenure com. 1991-93), Hillsborough County Bar Assn. (chmn. law week com. 1990, chmn. corp. counsel com. 1986-87, chmn. internat. law com. 1994—), Am. Corp. Counsel Assn. (bd. dirs. Ctrl. Fla. chpt. 1986-87), Tampa Club, Tiger Bay Club, Tampa Yacht and Country Club. Republican. Roman Catholic. Avocations: photography, bicycling, reading, boating. Home: 3211 W Swann Ave Apt 201 Tampa FL 33609-4651 Office: TECO Energy Inc PO Box 111 702 N Franklin St Tampa FL 33601

MCDIARMID, LUCY, English educator; b. Louisville, Mar. 29, 1947; m. Harris B. Savin, Oct. 13, 1984; children: Emily Clare, Katharine Eliza. BA, Swarthmore (Pa.) Coll., 1968; MA, Harvard U., 1969, PhD, 1972. Asst. prof. Boston U., 1972-74; from asst. prof. to assoc. prof. Swarthmore Coll., 1974-81; asst. prof. U. Md. Balt. County, Catonsville, 1982-84; prof. Villanova (Pa.) U., 1984—; vis. prof. English Princeton U., 1995; mem. exec. com. Am. Conf. for Irish Studies, 1987-91, v.p., 1995—. Author: Saving Civilization: Yeats, Eliot and Auden Between the Wars, 1984, Auden's Apologies for Poetry, 1990; co-editor: Selected Writings of Lady Gregory, 1995, High and Low Moderns: Literature and Culture, 1889-1939, 1995; contbr. articles to profl. jours. NEH fellow, 1981-82; ACLS grantee, 1976, Bunting Inst. fellow, 1981-82, Guggenheim fellow, 1993-94; vis. fellow N.Y. Inst. Humanities, 1993-95. Mem. Internat. Assn. for Study Anglo-Irish Lit. (Am. sec.-treas. 1994—), Phi Beta Kappa. Home: 1931 Panama St Philadelphia PA 19103-6609 Office: Villanova U Dept Of English Villanova PA 19085

MCDILL, THOMAS ALLISON, minister; b. Cicero, Ill., June 4, 1926; s. Samuel and Agnes (Lindsay) McD.; m. Ruth Catherine Starr, June 4, 1949; children: Karen Joyce, Jane Alison, Steven Thomas. Th.B., No. Baptist Sem., Oakbrook, Ill., 1951; B.A., Trinity Coll., 1954; M.Div., Trinity Evang. Div. Sch., 1955, DD, 1989; D.Ministries, Bethel Theol. Sem., 1975. Ordained to ministry Evang. Free Ch. Am., 1949. Pastor Community Bible Ch., Berwyn, Ill., 1947-51, Grace Evang. Free Ch., Chgo., 1951-58, Liberty Bible Ch., Valparaiso, Ind., 1959-67, Crystal Evang. Free Ch., Mpls., 1967-76; v.p. moderator Evang. Free Ch. of Am., 1973-74, chmn. home missions bd., 1968-72, chmn. exec. bd., 1973-90, pres., 1976-90, ret., 1990; min. at large Evang. Free Ch. Am., 1991—. Contbr. articles to publs. Chmn. bd. Trinity Coll., Deerfield, Ill., 1974-76; bd. govs. Trinity Western Coll.; bd. dirs. Trinity Evang. Divinity Sch. Mem. Evang. Free Ch. Ministerial Assn., Evang. Ministers Assn., Nat. Assn. Evangelicals (bd. adminstrn. 1976—, mem. exec. com. 1981-88), Greater Mpls. Assn. Evangelicals (bd. dirs., sec. bd. 1969-73). Home: 4246 Goldenrod Ln N Minneapolis MN 55441-1241 Office: 901 E 78th St Bloomington MN 55420-1334

MC DONAGH, EDWARD CHARLES, sociologist, university administrator; b. Edmonton, Alta., Can., Jan. 23, 1915; came to U.S., 1922, naturalized, 1936; s. Henry Fry and Aletta (Bowles) McD.; m. Louise Lucille Lorenzi, Aug. 14, 1940 (dec.); children: Eileen, Patricia. A.B., U. So. Calif., 1937, A.M., 1938, Ph.D., 1942. Asst. prof. So. Ill. U., Carbondale, 1940-46, asst. to pres., 1942-44; asst. prof. U. Okla., Norman, 1946-47; asst. prof. U. So. Calif., L.A., 1947-49, assoc. prof., 1949-56, prof., 1956-69, head dept., 1958-62, assoc. dean divsn. social scis. and comms., 1960-63, chmn. univ. acad. affairs com., 1963; head dept. sociology U. Ala., 1969-71; chmn. dept. sociology Ohio State U., Columbus, 1971-74, acting dean Coll. Social and Behavioral Scis., 1974-75, dean Coll. Social and Behavioral Scis., 1975-78, chmn. coordinating coun. deans Colls. Arts and Scis., 1977-78, prof. emeritus Colls. Arts and Scis., 1981—; Smith-Mundt prof., Sweden, 1956-57; vis. prof. U. Hawaii, 1965; cons. Los Angeles and related sch. dists.; mem. Region XV Woodrow Wilson Selection Com., 1961-62. Author: (with E.S. Richards) Ethnic Relations in the U.S, 1953, (with J.E. Nordskog, M.J. Vincent) Analyzing Social Problems, 1956, (with Jon Simpson) Social Problems: Persistent Challenges, 1965, rev., 1969; assoc. editor: Sociology and Social Research, 1947-69; editorial cons.: Sociometry, 1962-65; Contbr. articles to profl. publs. Served with AUS, 1944-46. Fellow Am. Sociol. Assn. (co-

chmn. nat. conf. com. 1963, budget and exec. office com. 1975-78); mem. AAUP, AAAS, Am. Assn. Pub. Opinion Rsch., Alpha Kappa Delta (pres. united chtps. 1965-66), Phi Beta Kappa (chpt. pres. 1959-60), Blue Key, Skull and Dagger. Democrat. Home: 1 Spencer Dr Apt 201 Amherst MA 01002-3364

MCDONAGH, THOMAS JOSEPH, physician; b. N.Y.C., Feb. 29, 1932; s. John and Delia (Lee) McD.; m. Helen Marie Drury, May 18, 1957; children: Kevin T., Eileen D., Thomas J., Brian P., Patricia M. B.S., CCNY; M.D., Columbia U. Diplomate Am. Bd. Internal Medicine, Am. Bd. Preventive Medicine-Occupational Medicine. Intern Bronx Mcpl. Hosp., N.Y., 1957-58, resident, 1958-60; fellow in medicine, trainee in gastroenterology Albert Einstein Coll. Medicine, Bronx, 1960-62; pvt. practice internal medicine Coatesville, Pa., 1962-64; sr. physician Exxon Corp., N.Y.C., 1964-69, asst. med. dir., 1969-79; dir. medicine and environ. health Exxon Chem. Co., Darien, Conn., 1979-80, dir. medicine and environ. affairs, 1980-81; v.p. medicine and occupational health Exxon Corp., Dallas, 1981—; dir. medicine and environ. health Exxon Co. Internat., Florham Park, N.J., 1986—; bd. dirs. Nat. Assn. Drug Abuse Problems, N.Y.C., 1981-92; bd. dirs. Nat. Fund. Med. Edn., San Francisco, 1983—. Contbr. articles in field to med. jours. Chmn. bd. appeals Inc. Village of Bellerose, N.Y., 1977-84, trustee, 1965-77, dep. mayor, 1975-77. Fellow ACP, Am. Coll. Occupational and Environ. Medicine (bd. dirs. 1989-92), Am. Coll. Preventive Medicine; mem. AMA, N.Y. Acad. Scis., N.Y. Acad Medicine. Roman Catholic. Office: Exxon Co Internat 200 Park Ave Florham Park NJ 07932-1002

MCDONALD, ALAN ANGUS, federal judge; b. Harrah, Wash., Dec. 13, 1927; s. Angus and Nell (Britt) McD.; m. Ruby K., Aug. 22, 1949; children: Janelle Jo, Saralee Sue, Stacy. BS, U. Wash., 1950, LLB, 1952. Dep. pros. atty. Yakima County, Wash., 1952-54; assoc. Halverson & Applegate, Yakima, 1954-56; ptnr. Halverson, Applegate & McDonald, Yakima, 1956-85; judge U.S. Dist. Ct. (ea. dist.) Wash., Yakima, 1985—. Fellow Am. Coll. Trial Lawyers; Yakima C. of C. (bd. dirs.). Clubs: Yakima Country, Royal Duck (Yakima). Office: US Dist Ct PO Box 2706 Yakima WA 98907

MCDONALD, ALICE COIG, state education official; b. Chalmette, La., Sept. 26, 1940; d. Olas Casimere and Genevieve Louise (Heck) Coig; m. Glenn McDonald, July 16, 1967; 1 child, Michel. B.S., Loyola U., New Orleans, 1962; M.Ed., Loyola U., 1966; cert. rank I sch. adminstrn., Spalding Coll., 1975. Tchr. St. Bernard Pub. Schs., Chalmette, La., 1962-67; counselor, instructional coordinator Jefferson County Schs., Louisville, 1967-77; ednl. adviser Jefferson County Govt., Louisville, 1977-78; chief exec. asst. Office of Mayor, Louisville, 1978-80; dep. supt. pub. instrn. Ky. Dept. Edn., Frankfort, 1980-83, supt. pub. instrn., 1984—; bd. dirs., com. mem. Ky. Council on Higher Edn., 1984—, Ky. Juvenile Justice Com., 1984—, Ky. Ednl. TV Authority, 1984—, So. Regional Council Ednl. Improvement, 1984—. Mem. Pres.'s Adv. Com. on Women, 1978-80; active Democratic Nat. Convs., 1972, 76, 80, 84; pres. Dem. Woman's Club Ky., 1974-76 Ky. mem. Nat. Dem. Com., 1976-79, mem. exec. com. 1977—. Mem. Council Chief State Sch. Officers, Women in Sch. Adminstrn., NEA, Ky. Edn. Assn., River City Bus. and Profl. Women. Home: 6501 Gunpowder Ln Prospect KY 40059-9334 Office: Ky Dept Edn Capital Plaza Towers Fl 1 Frankfort KY 40601

MCDONALD, ALONZO LOWRY, JR., manufacturing executive; b. Atlanta, Aug. 5, 1928; s. Alonzo Lowry Sr. and Lois (Burrell) McD.; m. Suzanne Moffitt, May 9, 1959; four children. AB in Journalism, Emory U., 1948; MBA with distinction, Harvard U., 1956. Asst. to sales mgr. air conditioning div. Westinghouse Electric Corp., Staunton, Va., 1956-57; Western zone mgr. Westinghouse Electric Corp., St. Louis, 1957-60; assoc. N.Y. office McKinsey & Co., Inc., 1960-64, prin. London office, 1964-66, mng. prin. Zurich Office, 1966-68, mng. dir. Paris Office, 1968-73; mng. dir., chief exec. officer of firm worldwide, 1973-76; dir. N.Y. Office, 1976-77; dep. spl. trade rep., also ambassador in charge U.S. del. Tokyo round of Multilateral Trade Negotiations, 1977-79; acting spl. trade rep. Washington, 1979; asst. to Pres. U.S., White House staff dir., 1979-81; mem. faculty Harvard U. Grad. Sch. Bus. Adminstrn., Boston, 1981; pres. The Bendix Corp., Southfield, Mich., 1981-83; chmn., chief exec. officer Avenir Group, Inc., Bloomfield Hills, Mich., 1983—. Mem. vestry Am. Cathedral in Paris, 1970-73; vestry, warden St. Joseph of Arimathea Episcopal Ch., Elmsford, N.Y., 1974-77; trustee CED, 1975—; chmn. Williamsburg Charter Found., Washington, 1986-90; mem. dean's adv. coun. Harvard U. Div. Sch., Boston, 1989—; trustee Emory U., 1992—. With USMCR, 1950-52. Mem. Coun. Fgn. Rels., Trinity Forum (chmn., trustee). Office: 5505 Corporate Dr Suite 400 Troy MI 48098

MC DONALD, ANDREW J., bishop; b. Savannah, Ga., Oct. 24, 1923; s. James Bernard and Theresa (McGrael) McD. AB, St. Mary's Sem., Balt., 1945, STL, 1948; JCB, Cath. U. Am., 1949; JCD, Lateran U., Rome, 1951. Ordained priest Roman Cath. Ch., 1948. Consecrated bishop, 1972; curate Port Wentworth, Ga., 1952-57; chancellor Diocese of Savannah, 1952-68; vicar gen., from 1968, vice oficialis, 1952-57, oficialis, 1957; pastor Blessed Sacrament Ch., 1963; named papal chamberlain, 1956, domestic prelate, 1959; bishop Diocese of Little Rock, 1972—. Office: Diocese of Little Rock PO Box 7239 2415 N Tyler St Little Rock AR 72207-3740

MC DONALD, ANDREW JEWETT, securities firm executive; b. Cin., Sept. 7, 1929; s. Matthew Arnold and Jane (Jewett) Mc D. Grad., Hotchkiss Sch., 1947, Yale U., 1951. With Paine, Webber, Jackson & Curtis Inc., Boston, 1955—; dir. Paine, Webber, Jackson & Curtis Inc. (New Eng. region), 1972-73; sr. v.p. dir. Paine, Webber, Jackson & Curtis Inc. (Eastern div.), 1973—; dir. F. W. Paine Found., 1973—; allied mem. N.Y. Stock Exchange, 1971—. Mem. Flight Safety Found., 1971—. Served with USAF, 1951-55. Mem. Am. Farmland Trust (life), Am. Aviation Hist. Soc. Clubs: Aero of New Eng. (Boston), Fed. (Boston), Down Town (Boston), Yale (Boston). Home: 5 Stonehill Dr Stoneham MA 02180-3945

MCDONALD, ANGUS WHEELER, farmer; b. Washington, Apr. 21, 1927; s. John Yates and Dorothy Helen (Bosworth) McD.; m. Mary Joan Montgomery, May 8, 1952 (div. Sept. 1958); children: Mary Ann Hetzer, Paul Yates. BA, Columbia Union Coll., 1974. Farmer, owner Pleasant View Farm, Charles Town, W.Va., 1953—. Presdl. candidate Democratic Party, 1987-88, 92. With U.S. Army, 1946-47. Mem. AARP, Jefferson County Farm Bur., W.Va. State Hort. Soc., No. W.Va. Automobile Club, Am. Legion, The Moose. Avocations: photography, travel, attending historical events. Home and Office: Pleasant View Farm RR 3 Box 142 Charles Town WV 25414-9413

MCDONALD, ARTHUR BRUCE, physics educator; b. Sydney, N.S., Canada, Aug. 29, 1943; s. A. Bruce and Valerie M. (DeRoche) McD.; m. Janet Catherine MacDonald, July 16, 1966; children: Bruce, Heather, Ross, Fraser. BSc in Physics, Dalhousie U., 1964, MSc in Physics, 1965; PhD, Calif. Inst. Tech., 1969. Post doctoral fellow Chalk River (Ont., Can.) Nuclear Labs., 1969-70, research scientist, 1970-82; prof. physics Princeton (N.J.) U., 1982-89; prof. physics Queen's U., Kingston, Ont., Can., 1989—; dir. Sudbury Neutrino Obs., 1989—; mem. adv. com. nuclear sci. divsn. Lawrence Berkeley Lab., 1992—; mem. nuclear sci. adv. com. Dept. Energy/ NSF, 1987-89; adv. com. Triumf Experiment, 1987-89; mem. subatomic physics rev. com. Natural Sci. and Engring. Rsch. Coun. Can., 1987-89. Fellow Am. Physical Soc.; mem. Can. Assn. Physicists (bd. dirs. 1978-80). Avocation: skiing. Office: Queens U Stirling Hall, Dept Physics, Kingston, ON Canada K7L 3N6

MCDONALD, AUDRA ANN, actress. BFA, Juilliard Sch., 1993. Stage appearances include (regional) Man of La Mancha, Evita, The Wiz, A Chorus Line, Grease, Anything Goes (Broadway) The Secret Garden, Carousel (Antoinette Perry award for featured actress in a musical 1994), Master Class. Office: Peter Strain & Assocs 1501 Broadway 2900 New York NY 10036

MCDONALD, BARBARA ANN, marketing educator; b. Chatham, Ill., Oct. 21, 1938; d. Marshall Earl McDonald and Florence A. (Carter) Hollis; m. Jack McAge, July 22, 1977 (div. 1979). MBA, U. Ill., 1988. Staff mgr. AT&T, Chgo., 1984-85; sales mgr. AT&T, Champaign, Ill., 1985-88; instr., developer Nat. Sales Sch. AT&T, Cin., 1988-89; mgr. mktg. AT&T Info.

Systems, Carmel, Ind., 1989; prin. McDonald's Bus. Svcs., Grand Junction, Colo., 1991—; owner, mgr. Once Again-Collectibles, Mahomet, 1991-93; adj. prof., com. dir. MBA program U. Ill., Champaign, 1990-93; cons. AT&T Profl. Sales Affiliates, Chgo., others; presented owrkshops on mgmt. and sales skills, wrote sales course AT&T sales assocs./agts., 1994; contractual work of Univ. Wis.-Parkside; faculty Mesa State Coll., 1995—. Author: After Market Account Executive, 1988; contbr. articles to jours., newspapers. Treas. Spring Lake Assn., Mahomet, 1990, v.p., pres., 1991-93; bd. dirs. Sta. WPGU, Daily Illini, U. Ill., Champaign-Urbana, 1993-94. Mem. Am. Mktg. Assn. (campus adviser 1991-92), Kiwanis. Republican. Avocations: cooking, gardening, writing. Home: 2420 Wintergreen Dr Grand Junction CO 81506

MCDONALD, BERNARD ROBERT, federal agency administrator; b. Kansas City, Kans., Nov. 17, 1940; s. Bernard Luther and Mabel McD.; m. Jean Graves, June 7, 1963; children: Aaron Michael, Elizabeth Kathleen. BA, Park Coll., Parkville, Mo., 1962; MA, Kans. State U., 1964; PhD, Mich. State U., 1968. Prof. math. U. Okla., Norman, 1968-83, chmn. math. dept., 1981-83; program dir. div. math. scis. NSF, Washington, 1983-86, program dir. spl. projects, 1986-88, dep. dir. div. math. scis., head office of spl. projects, 1988—. Author: R-linear Endomorphism, 1983, Geometric Algebra, 1976, Finite Rings, 1974, Ring Theory III, 1980. Mem. Am. Math. Soc., Math. Assn. Am., Soc. Ind. and Applied Math., Assn. Women Math., Sigma Xi. Home: 4001 9th St N Apt 721 Arlington VA 22203-1961 Office: NSF Div Math Scis Rm 1025 4201 Wilson Blvd Arlington VA 22230

MCDONALD, C. W., mining executive; b. 1940. BA in Mining Engring., U. Ala., 1965. With Consolidated Coal Co., Pitts., 1966—, now exec. v.p. Office: Consolidation Coal Co Consol Plz Pittsburgh PA 15241

MCDONALD, CAPERS WALTER, biomedical engineer, corporate executive; b. Georgetown, S.C., Nov. 29, 1951; s. WalBern and Cecilia (Lockwood) McD.; m. Marion E. Kiper, Aug. 23, 1975; child, Adam Capers. BS in Engring. magna cum laude, Duke U., 1974; MS in Mech. Engring., MIT, 1976; MBA, Harvard U., 1983. Registered profl. engr., N.C. Dir. mktg. dept. Becton Dickinson Co., Sunnyvale, Calif., 1978-81; cons. Booz, Allen & Hamilton, San Francisco, 1982-84; v.p. HP Genenchem, S. San Francisco, Calif., 1984-87; bio-analytic systems mgr. Hewlett-Packard Corp., Palo Alto, Calif., 1987; v.p. Orion Instruments, Inc., Redwood City, Calif., 1987-88; v.p. Spectroscopy Imaging Systems, Fremont, Calif., 1988-90, pres., 1990-92; pres., ceo Microbiological Assoc., Inc., Rockville, Md., 1992—; pres., CEO MAGENTA Corp., Rockville, 1993—; chmn., dir. MAGENTA Svcs., Ltd., Stirling, Scotland, 1994—, Microbiol. Assn., Inc.; guest lectr. Weizmann Inst., Rehovot, Israel, 1977, All-Union Cardiology Ctr., Moscow, 1978, Inst. Hematology Munich, 1978, Christ Church (New Zealand) Clin. Sch., 1980, U. Edinburgh, Scotland, 1981. Author: chpt. Flow Cytometry and Sorting, 1979; patentee flow microfluorometer; contbr. articles to profl. jours. Asst. scout master Boy Scouts Am., Georgetown, 1965-66. Duke U. scholar, 1970-74, MIT scholar, 1974-76; NSF fellow, 1974. Mem. N.C. Acad. Scis., Harvard U. Alumni Assn., Duke U. Alumni Assn., MIT Alumni Assn., Rotary, Sigma Xi, Tau Beta Pi, Phi Eta Sigma, Pi Mus Epsilon. Republican. Methodist. Avocations: fresh and salt water fishing, travel. Home: 12221 Lake Potomac Terr Potomac MD 20854 Office: 9900 Blackwell Rd Rockville MD 20850

MCDONALD, CHARLES EUGENE, lawyer; b. Canyon, Tex., Feb. 21, 1927; s. Bryan Eugene and Mary Pickett (Davidson) McD.; m. Edna Gail Chapman, July 5, 1947; children: Mary Conner, Charles E. McDonald Jr., Wesley Monroe McDonald, Patrick Sean McDonald. BS, West Tex. State Tchr.'s Coll., Canyon, 1948; JD, U. Tex., 1953. Bar: Tex. 1953. Coach Idalou (Tex.) ISD, 1947-48; tchr. Midland (tex.) ISD, 1948-50; pvt. practice Midland, 1953-65, Alpine, Tex., 1965-67, Bangs, Tex., 1967—. Midland county sch. supt., 1954-58; pres. Bangs Lions Club, 1983. Mem. State Bar Tex., Brown County Bar Assn. (pres. 1991-93). Methodist. Avocations: golf, watching horse racing. Office: 101 S 1st St Bangs TX 76823

MC DONALD, CHARLES J., physician, educator; b. Tampa, Fla., Dec. 6, 1931; s. George B. and Bertha C. (Harbin) Mc D.; m. Maureen McDonald; children—Marc S., Norman D., Eric S. B.S. magna cum laude, A&T Coll. N.C., 1951; M.S., U. Mich., 1952; M.D. with highest honors, Howard U., 1960. Diplomate: Am. Bd. Dermatology. Rotating intern Hosp. St. Raphael, New Haven, 1960-61; asst. resident in medicine Hosp. St. Raphael, 1961-63; asst. resident in dermatology Yale U., 1963-65, spl. USPHS research fellow, chief resident in dermatology, 1965-66, instr. in medicine and pharmacology, 1966-67, asst. prof. medicine and pharmacology, 1967-68; asst. prof. med. sci. Brown U., 1968-69, assoc. prof., 1969-74, prof., 1974—, dir. dermatology program, 1970-74, head subsect. dermatology, 1974-82, dir. dermatology, 1982—; dir. dermatology Roger Williams Gen. Hosp., 1968—; physician-in-charge dermatology R.I. Hosp., 1989—; mem. com. and task force, chmn. task force on minority affairs Am. Acad. Dermatology, 1975-80; mem. dermatology adv. panel FDA, until 1978, cons., 1978—; mem. pharm. scis. rev. commn. NIH, 1979-83, adv. com. Arthritis, Muscular/Skeletal and Skin Disease Inst., 1993—; chmn. com. pub. edn., dir., v.p. R.I. divsn. Am. Cancer Soc., 1978-80, pres., 1980-83, bd. dirs. nat. soc., 1983—, nat. dir. at large, 1990—, mem. nat. exec. com., 1991—; residency rev. com. dermatology ACGME, 1992—. Dermatology editor Postgrad. Medicine; contbr. numerous articles to med. publs. Trustee Howard U., 1993—; bd. dirs. Providence Health Care Found. (chmn. med. adv. com. 1976-87), Providence Fund for Edn., Providence Pub. Libr., 1987—, sec., 1991; mem. R.I. State Bd. Edn., 1970-72. Served to maj. USAF, 1952-56. Recipient Disting. Service award Hosp. Assn. R.I., 1971, Disting. Alumni award Howard U. Coll. Medicine, 1983, St. George medal nat. divsn. Am. Cancer Soc., 1992. Mem. Am., New Eng. (v.p. 1983-84, pres. 1984-85) R.I., Noah Worcester (bd. dirs. 1983-86) dermatol. assns., Soc. Investigative Dermatology, Am. Fedn. Clin. Research, Am. Acad. Dermatology (bd. dirs. 1987-91, Nat. Med. Assn. (chmn. sect. dermatology 1973-75), AAAS, Am. Soc. Clin. Oncology, Dermatology Found. (chmn. sci. com. 1972-76), Assn. Profs. Dermatology (bd. dirs. 1991—), Sigma Xi, Alpha Omega Alpha, Alpha Kappa Mu, Beta Kappa Chi. Democrat. Office: 825 Chalkstone Ave Providence RI 02908-4728

MCDONALD, DAVID J., food products company executive; b. 1928; married. BA, U. Pacific, 1951. Dir. planning Schlitz Brewing Co., 1961-68; with Lucca Packing Co. of Calif., 1968-81; with Curtice-Burns Foods, Inc., 1981—, pres., chief exec. officer, dir., 1985—. Served with U.S. Army, 1946-48. Office: Curtice-Burns Foods Inc 90 Linden Pl Rochester NY 14625-2830

MC DONALD, DAVID WILLIAM, chemist, educator; b. Shreveport, La., Aug. 4, 1923; s. Maxwell Wood and Mary Estelle (Weber) McD.; m. Nell Cullen Welch, July 31, 1948; children: Mason, Thomas, Daniel, David. BS, U. Southwestern La., 1943; PhD, U. Tex., 1951. Chemist Humble Oil & Refining Co., Baytown, Tex., 1943-44, 46-47; rsch. chemist, group leader Monsanto Co., Texas City, Tex., 1951-59; rsch. sect. leader, mgr. Monsanto Co., 1959-67; product adminstr. Monsanto Co., St. Louis, 1967-69, dir. research plastics div., 1969-74; dir. tech. plastics div. Monsanto Co., 1974-80, dir. tech. plans, corp. rsch. and devel. staff, 1980-82; sr. assoc. Pugh-Roberts Assocs., Inc., Cambridge, Mass., 1983-93; mng. cons. PA Consulting Group, Santa Rosa, Calif., 1993—; affiliate prof. tech. mgmt. Washington U., St. Louis, 1983-88; cons. in field, 1982—; vis. lectr., scholar Stanford U., 1989. Served with USNR, 1944-46. Mem. Am. Chem. Soc., Soc. Plastics Engrs., AAAS, Sigma Xi. Episcopalian. Patentee in field. Home and Office: 423 Pythian Rd Santa Rosa CA 95409-6324

MCDONALD, FORREST, historian, educator; b. Orange, Tex., Jan. 7, 1927; s. John Forrest and Myra (McGill) McD.; m. Ellen Shapiro, Aug. 1, 1963; children from previous marriage: Kathy, Forrest Howard, Marcy Ann, Stephen, Kevin. BA, MA, U. Tex., 1949, PhD, 1955; MA (hon.), Brown U., 1962; LHD (hon.), SUNY, Geneseo, 1989. Exec. sec. Am. History Research Ctr., Madison, Wis., 1953-58; assoc. prof. history Brown U., Providence, 1959-63, prof., 1963-67; prof. Wayne State U., Detroit, 1967-76; prof. U. Ala., Tuscaloosa, 1976-87, disting. univ. research prof., 1987—; James Pinckney Harrison prof. Coll. of William and Mary, Williamsburg, Va., 1986-87; presdl. appointee Bd. Fgn. Scholarships, Washington, 1985-87; advisor Ctr. Jud. Studies, Cumberland, Va., 1985-92; mem. fellowship selection com. Richard M. Weaver Fellowships, Bryn Mawr, Pa., 1980—. Author: We The People, 1958, Insull, 1962, E Pluribus Unum, 1965, Alex-

ander Hamilton, 1979 (Frances Tavern Book award 1980), Novus Ordo Seclorum, 1985, Requiem, 1988, The American Presidency: An Intellectual History, 1994. Trustee Phila. Soc., North Adams, Mich., 1983-86, 87-90, pres. 1988-90; co-chmn. New Eng. for Goldwater, 1964. Served with USN, 1945-46. Recipient George Washington medal Freedom's Found., Valley Forge, Pa., 1980, Best Book award Am. Revolution Round Table, N.Y., 1986, Richard M. Weaver award Ingersoll Found., 1990, First Salvatori award Heritage Found., 1992, Salavatori Book award Intercollegiate Studio Inst., 1994; Guggenheim fellow, N.Y., 1962-63; Jefferson lectr. NEH, 1987. Republican. Avocations: horticulture, tennis. Office: U Alabama PO Box 870212 Tuscaloosa AL 35487-0212

MCDONALD, FRANK ALBERT, JR., personnel director; b. Waycross, Ga., June 29, 1932; s. Frank Albert Sr. and Mertice (Chancey) McD.; m. Jane Donnelly Wallace, Feb. 7, 1959; children: Frank A. III, Christopher W., P. Keith, Matthew O. BSBA, U. Fla., 1958. Mgmt. trainee State Farm Ins., Jacksonville, Fla., 1958-59; with Gen. Telephone Co., Tampa, Fla., 1959-67; indsl. rels. administr. Sperry Rand Corp., Charlottesville, Va., 1967-69; dir. pres. Richmond Newspapers, Inc., Richmond, Va., 1969—. Vestryman Temple Terrace-St. Matthews Episc. Ch.; pres. Carver Elem. Sch. PTA; founding bd. mem., chmn. Consumer Credit Counseling Svc. Va., St. John's Hosp. for Alcohol and Drug Abuse; mem. adv. bd. sch. social work Va. Commonwealth U.; mem. bus. adv. bd. J. Sargeant Reynolds Community Coll.; chmn. tech. adv. bd. T.A.C. Richmond Area Manpower Planning. With USN, 1951-58. Mem. Soc. for Human Resources Mgmt. (v.p. region IV), Bay Vista Civic Assn., Cen. Fla. Am. Soc. Tng. Dirs., Richmond Chpt. Pers. Adminstrs., Tuckahoe Recreation Assn. (1st v.p.), St. Petersburg C. of C., Jacksonville Jr. C. of C. Temple Terrose, Fla., Lions Club (pres.), Lions Club Charlottesville, Va., Kiwanis. Republican. Avocations: racquet ball, community service. Home: 11415 Homestead Ln Richmond VA 23233-4617 Office: Richmond Newspapers Inc 333 E Grace St Richmond VA 23293-1000

MC DONALD, FRANK BETHUNE, physicist; b. Columbus, Ga., May 28, 1925; s. Frank B. and Lucy (Kyle) McD.; m. Virginia Ballew, June 15, 1951 (dec. 1977); children: Kyle Louise McDonald Jossi, Robert Kyle, Douglas Frank; m. Irene Negosh Kelejian, Nov. 7, 1987. BS, Duke U., 1948; MS, U. Minn., 1951, PhD (AEC fellow), 1955. Rsch. assoc. State U. Iowa, Iowa City, 1953-56, asst. prof. physics, 1956-59; chief lab. for high energy astrophysics Goddard Space Flight Ctr. NASA, Greenbelt, Md., 1959-82; mem. phys. scis. com. space program adv. coun. NASA, 1974-76; the NASA chief scientist, 1982-87; assoc. dir., chief scientist Goddard Space Flight Ctr. NASA, 1987-89; sr. policy analyst Office Sci. and Tech. Policy, Exec. Office of Pres., Washington, 1982; sr. rsch. scientist Inst. for Phys. Sci. and Tech. U. Md., College Park, 1989—; part-time prof. U. Md., College Park, 1963-82; mem. Geophysics Rsch. Forum, 1985-88; Internat. Union Pure and Applied Physics mem. Internat. Commn. on Cosmic Rays, 1981-84, sec. to commn., 1984-87, chmn., 1987-90; NASA rep. to NASA Adv. Coun., 1984-89. Editor: High Energy Particles and Quanta in Astrophysics, 1974; assoc. editor: Jour. Geophys. Research, 1964-67; mem. editorial bd.: Space Sci. Revs.; Research in cosmic ray physics. With USNR, 1942-45. Recipient Exceptional Sci. Achievement award NASA, 1964, 78, 86, Outstanding Leadership medal, 1981; Presdl. Mgmt. Improvement cert., 1971; Presdl. rank of meritorious exec. Sr. Exec. Service, 1980, 89, W. Randolph Lovelace II award Am. Astronautical Soc., 1986. Fellow Am. Phys. Soc. (chmn. div. cosmic physics 1973-74, mem. council 1982—, mem. exec. com. 1983); mem. Am. Inst. Physics (council, governing bd. 1983-86), Am. Geophys. Union, Washington Philos. Soc., Am. Astronom. Soc., Nat. Acad. Sci., Sigma Xi, Phi Beta Kappa. Office: U Md IPST Rm 3245 Computer Sci Space Bui College Park MD 20742

MCDONALD, GAIL CLEMENTS, government official; b. Ft. Worth, Tex., Mar. 9, 1944; d. Eugene and Cornelia (Nagle) Clements; m. William C. Scott, Aug. 26, 1967 (div. 1976); 1 child, Jill Miriah Scott; m. Danny Lee McDonald, Aug. 6, 1982. BA, Tex. Christian U., Ft. Worth, 1966, MA, 1967. Instr. social sci. Cooke County Jr. Coll., Gainesville, Tex., 1967-69, Langston (Okla.) U., 1969, Tulsa Jr. Coll., 1977-79; instr. humanities Okla. State U., Stillwater, 1971-74; adminstrv. asst. bd. ednl. and cultural affairs Gov. David L. Boren, Oklahoma City, 1975-78; legis. aide Sen. David L. Boren, Tulsa, 1979; state assoc. Inst. for Ednl. Leadership, George Washington U., Washington, 1979-81; exec. asst. Commr. Norma H. Eagleton, Okla. Corp. Commr., Oklahoma City, 1979-81; commr. ICC, Washington, 1990—, vice chmn., 1993, chmn. 1993-95. Bd. dirs. Okla. Sci. & Arts Found., 1975-83; exec. com. Frontiers of Sci. Found., 1976-80; fundraiser Washington chpt. Spl. Olympics. Named Woman of Yr., Women's Transp. Seminar, 1991. Mem. Nat. Assn. Regulatory Commrs. (transp. com.), Exec. Women in Govt., Conservation Round Table (chmn. 1990), Transp. Table Washington, Toastmasters (pres. 1988), Phi Alpha Theta. Democrat. Episcopalian. Avocations: gardening, bird watching. Office: ICC Rm 4211 12th and Constitution Ave NW Washington DC 20423-0001

MCDONALD, GAIL JACOLEV, lawyer; b. Port Arthur, Tex., Nov. 18, 1945; d. Leon and Ruth Jacolev. BA cum laude, Mount Holyoke Coll., 1967; MA, Columbia U., 1968; JD with high honors, U. Tex., 1974. Bar: Tex. 1974. Mgmt. intern U.S. Office of Edn., Washington, 1968-70; planning cons. Tex. Edn. Agy., Austin, 1970-71; student devel. specialist U. Tex., Austin, 1971-72; assoc. Butler & Binion, L.L.P., Houston, 1974-81; ptnr. Butler & Binion, Houston, 1981—; bd. dirs. A.I.M. Inc., Houston; sec. Shippers Stevedoring Co., Seaport Terminals, Inc., 1989—. Trustee Escape Ctr., 1992—. Mem. ABA, Tex. State Bar Assn., Houston Bar Assn., Order Coif, Chancellors. Home: 3715 Darcus St Houston TX 77005-3703 Office: Butler & Binion LLP 1600 1st Interstate Bank Plz Houston TX 77002

MCDONALD, GAIL MARGARET, human resources, government relations and communications executive; b. Pittsfield, Mass., Feb. 14, 1948; d. James Mitchell and Hazel Rita (Braud) McD.; m. Jeffrey John Murphy, Mar. 12, 1977; children: Lindsey Palmer, Jaime Christine. BA, Duke U., 1970; MS in Indsl. and Labor Rels., Cornell U., 1973. Pers. specialist Xerox Corp., Rochester, N.Y., 1972-74; human resources cons. Met. Life, N.Y.C., 1974-76; asst. treas. Bankers Trust Co., N.Y.C., 1976-77; mgr. pers. devel. Ryder System, Inc., Miami, Fla., 1977-79; dir., then group dir. compensation Ryder System, Inc., Miami, 1979-86, v.p. human resources devel., 1986-87, v.p. human resources devel. Vehicle Leasing & Svc. div., 1988-89, sr. v.p. human resources, 1989-91, sr. v.p. fed. govt. rels. and communications, 1991-94; pres. The McDonald Group Inc., Dallas, 1994—. Bd. dirs. Miami Children's Hosp., 1989-94, chairperson quality assurance, 1992-94; bd. dirs., exec. com. Beacon Coun., Miami, 1989-94, treas., chairperson fin. and compensation com., 1991-94; mem. adv. bd. Ctr. for Advanced Human Resource Studies-Indsl. and Labor Rels., Cornell U., Ithaca, N.Y., 1991-94. Mem. NAM (bd. dirs. 1991-94), Human Resources Planning Soc., Soc. of Human Resources Mgmt. Roman Catholic. Office: McDonald Group Inc 3421 Purdue Dallas TX 75225-7638

MCDONALD, GREGORY CHRISTOPHER, author; b. Shrewsbury, Mass., Feb. 15, 1937; s. Irving Thomas and Mae (Haggerty) M.; m. Susan Aiken, Jan. 12, 1963 (div. Oct. 1990); children: Christopher Gregory, Douglas Gregory. BA, Harvard U., 1958. bd. dirs. Camaldon Corp. Novelist, critic Boston Globe, 1966-73; author: (novels) Running Scared, 1964, Fletch, 1974, Confess, Fletch, 1976, Flynn, 1977, Love Among the Mashed Potatoes, 1978, Fletch's Fortune, 1978, Fletch Forever, 1978, Who Took Toby Rinaldi?, 1980, Fletch and the Widow Bradley, 1981, The Buck Passes Flynn, 1981, Fletch's Moxie, 1982, Fletch and the Man Who, 1983, Carioca Fletch, Flynn's In, 1984, Fletch Won, Safekeeping, 1985, Fletch, Too, 1986; (non-fiction) The Education of Gregory Mcdonald, 1985, Fletch Chronicle, Vol. 1, Bull's Eye (drama), 1986, A World Too Wide, 1987, Fletch Chronicle, Vol. 2, 1987, Exits and Entrances, 1988, Fletch Chronicle, Vol. 3, 1988, Merely Players, 1988, The Brave, 1991, Son of Fletch, 1993, Fletch Reflected, 1994, Skylar, 1995; editor: Last Laughs, 1986, Bach Cantata Singers, 1973-80. Mem. vis. com. Boston Mus. Fine Arts, 1970-73, 85—; mem. Lincoln Recreation Com., 1977, 78; mem. Winthrop House Sr. Commons Harvard Coll. 1982—. Recipient Humanitarian of Yr. award Tenn. Assn. Fed. Execs., 1989, Citizen of Yr. award Nat. Assn. Social Workers, 1990, Roger William Straus award NCCJ, 1990, Alex Haley award, 1992. Mem. Authors Guild, Dramatists Guild, Mystery Writers Am. (dir. 1977—, pres. 1985-86, Poe award 1975, 77), Crime Writers Eng., Writers Guild Am., Mass. Chiefs Police Assn., Giles Countians United. Clubs:

Harvard (Boston); Overseas Press (N.Y.C.); Hillcrest Country (Pulaski, Tenn.). Office: care Arthur Greene Esq 101 Park Ave New York NY 10178-0002

MC DONALD, HENRY STANTON, electrical engineer; b. Carlisle, Pa., Oct. 28, 1927; s. Robert Clarence and Olive Elizabeth (Berry) McD.; children: H. Stanton, Pattie Elizabeth. B.E.E., Catholic U. Am. 1950; D.Eng., Johns Hopkins U., 1955. Instr. elec. engring. Johns Hopkins U., 1952-55; head gov. systems research dept. AT&T Bell Labs., Whippany, N.J., 1955-91; cons. Dept. Def., 1976—. Contbr. chpts. to books, articles to profl. jours. Served with U.S. Navy, 1945-46. Fellow IEEE, AT&T Bell Labs.; mem. Assn. Computing Machinery, AAAS, Sigma Xi. Republican. Unitarian. Patentee in field. Home: 810 Skyline Dr San Luis Obispo CA 93405-1054

MCDONALD, JAMES L., accounting firm executive; b. 1943. Former ptnr. in charge internat. tax svcs. West Coast region Price Waterhouse, co-chmn., 1993—. Office: Price Waterhouse 1251 Avenue Of The Americas New York NY 10020-1104*

MC DONALD, JAMES MICHAEL, JR., research institute consultant; b. Chgo., Jan. 19, 1924; s. James Michael and Gertrude Isabel (Dame) McD.; m. Helen Elizabeth Sharp, Feb. 3, 1948; children: Megan, Melissa, Rebecca. AB cum laude, Syracuse U., 1949; MA, Sch. Advanced Internat. Studies, 1950; postgrad., Bologna Ctr, 1956-57; grad., Nat. War Coll., 1969. Joined U.S. Fgn. Service, 1950; assigned Germany, 1951-56, Italy, 1956-57, France, 1957-58, Washington, 1958-61, Nicaragua, 1961-65, Dominican Republic, 1969-71; dep. pub affairs officer Rome, 1971-74; chief resource and ops. analysis USIA, Washington, 1974-75; dir. seminar and studies program Battelle Meml. Inst., 1975-83, internat. programs mgr., corp. edn. and tng. advisor, 1983-85, cons., 1985—. Trustee, v.p., past pres. Seattle Opera. With USAAF, 1943-47. Recipient Superior Honor award USIA, 1975. Mem. Rainier Club. Address: 1278 NW Blakely Ct Seattle WA 98177

MCDONALD, JEANNE GRAY (MRS. JOHN B. MCDONALD), television producer; b. Seattle, Sept. 10, 1917; d. George Patrick and Mary Edna (Gray) Murphy; m. John B. Mc Donald, June 30, 1951; children: Gregory Roland Stoner, Jeanne Eve. Student, Columbia U., 1940, Art Students League, 1940-43, Nat. Acad. Dramatic Art, 1945. Radio producer, commentator The Woman's Voice Sta. KMPC, L.A., 1947-50; TV producer, commentator, writer The Woman's Voice Sta. KTTV-CBS, L.A., 1950-51; TV producer, commentator The Jeanne Gray Show Sta. KNXT-TV CBS, L.A., 1951-53; West Coast editor Home Show NBC, L.A., 1955-56; TV film producer documentaries and travelogues Virgonian Prodns., L.A., 1953—. Author: The Power of Belonging, 1978. Women's chmn. Los Angeles Beautiful, 1971; mem. Women's Aux. St. John's Hosp.; trustee Freedoms Found. at Valley Forge, 1966—, founder, pres. women's chpt., Los Angeles County chpt., 1965-66, Western dir. women's chpt., 1967-68, nat. chmn. 1968-71, nat. chmn. women vols., 1973-75, hon life mem. Recipient Francis Holmes Outstanding Achievement award, 1949, Silver Mike award, 1948, Emmy award Acad. TV Arts and Scis., 1951, Lulu award Los Angeles Advt. Women, 1952, Genii award Radio and TV Women, 1956, George Washington Honor award Freedoms Found. Valley Forge, 1967, honor cert., 1972, Morale award Christians and Jews for Law and Morality, 1968, Exceptional Service award Freedoms Found., 1975, Liberty Belle award Rep. Women's Club, 1975, Leadership award Los Angeles City Schs., 1976, Theodore Roosevelt award USN League, 1986. Mem. Am. Women in Radio and TV, Radio and TV Women So. Calif. (hon., life, founder, 1st pres. 1952), Footlighters (v.p. 1958-59), Los Angeles C. of C. (bd. dirs. women's div. 1948-54, exec. bd., women's div. 1954-66, pres. women's div. 1963-64, hon. past pres. women's div. 1979), L.A. Orphanage Guild, DAR, Les Dames de Champagne, Bel Air Garden Club, Calif. Yacht Club. Home: 910 Stradella Rd Bel Air CA 90077

MCDONALD, JOHN C., telecommunications company executive; b. San Bernardino, Calif., 1936. BSEE, Stanford U., 1957, MS, 1959. Engr. GTE Sylvania, 1958-63; v.p. Vidar Corp., 1963-75, TRW Inc., 1975-81; pres. MBX Inc., 1981-82; formerly v.p., now exec. v.p. Contel Corp., Atlanta, 1982—. Office: Contel Corp 245 Perimeter Ctr Pkwy Atlanta GA 30348

MCDONALD, JOHN CECIL, lawyer; b. Lorimor, Iowa, Feb. 19, 1924; s. Cecil F. and Mary Elsie (Fletcher) McD.; m. Barbara Joan Berry, May 8, 1943; children: Mary Elisabeth (Mrs. Dell Richard), Joan Frances (Mrs. Andrew Ackerman), Jean Maurine. Student, Simpson Coll., 1942, So. Ill. U., 1943; J.D., Drake U., 1948. Bar: Iowa 1948, U.S. Ct. Mil. Appeals 1956, U.S. Supreme Ct. 1956. Practiced in Dallas Center, Iowa, 1948—; sr. ptnr. McDonald, Brown & Fagen and predecessor firms, 1971—; county atty. Dallas County, 1958-62; asst. county atty., 1963-69; city atty. Dallas Center, 1956-80. Mem. Simpson Coll. Alumni Council, pres., 1977-80; legal adviser Dallas Community Bd. Edn., 1953-69, pres., mem., 1968-76; nat. adv. com. Cen. Coll.; alt. del. Iowa Coordinating Council for Post-High Sch. Edn.; finance chmn. Dallas County Rep.Cen. Com., 1954-63, chmn., 1963-68; chmn. Iowa 7th Congl. Dist. Rep. Cen. Com., 1968-69, Iowa Rep. Cen. Com., 1969-75; mem. Rep. Nat. Com., 1969-88, mem. exec. com., 1973—; mem. Rule 29 com., com. on reform; mem. Gov. Iowa's inaugural com., 1969, 71, 73, 75, 79; del. Rep. Nat. Conv., 1964, 72, 76, 80, 84, chmn. com. on contests, 1976, 80, 84, 88, chmn. com. on credentials, 1976, 80, 88, mem. com. on arrangements and exec. com. of com. on arrangements, 1976, 80, 84, mem. rules rev. com., 1977-84; chmn. Midwest Rep. State Chairmen's Assn., 1973-75, Nat. Rep. State Chairmen's Adv. Com., 1973-75; hon. co-chmn. Vice Pres.'s Inaugural, 1981; trustee Dallas County Hosp., Perry, Iowa; bd. visitors U.S. Air Force Acad., 1975-78, chmn., 1977-78; trustee Simpson Coll., 1978—; bd. Iowa Student Loan Liquidity Corp., 1987—; mem. Iowa Coll. Aid Commn., 1989—; mem. Iowa Bd. Regents, 1981-87, pres., 1985-87; bd. dirs. Iowa Public Broadcasting Network, 1981-85; U.S. commr. Am. Battle Monuments Commn., 1982—. Served with USAAF, 1942-46; Col. USAF, 1951-52, ret. Recipient Alumni Achievement award Simpson Coll., 1974; Disting. Service award Drake U., 1978. Mem. ABA, Iowa Bar Assn. (past chmn. spl. com. on mil. affairs, mem. mil. affairs com.), Dallas County Bar Assn. (past pres.), Am. Legion, Farm Bur., Blackhawks, Drake U. Law Sch. Alumni Assn. (class officer), Comml. Club (past pres.) (Dallas Ctr.), Hillcrest Country Club (past pres.) (Adel, Iowa), Des Moines Club, Masons (32 degree), Shriners, Rotary (past pres. Dallas Ctr.), Alpha Tau Omega, Delta Theta Phi, Alpha Psi Omega. Presbyn. Clubs: Commercial (past pres.) (Dallas Center); Hillcrest Country (past pres.) (Adel, Iowa); Des Moines, Lincoln, Embassy (Des Moines). Lodges: Masons (32 deg.) Shriners, Rotary (past pres. Dallas Center). Home: PO Box 250 Dallas Center IA 50063-0250 Office: McDonald Brown & Fagen PO Box 250 Dallas Center IA 50063-0250

MCDONALD, JOHN CLIFTON, surgeon; b. Baldwyn, Miss., July 25, 1930; s. Edgar Hone and Ethel (Knight) McD.; m. Martha Dennis, Sept. 9, 1956; children: Melissa Lee, Karen Ann, Martha Knight. B.S., Miss. Coll., 1951; M.D., Tulane U., 1955. Diplomate: Am. Bd. Surgery. Intern Confederate Meml. Med. Ctr., Shreveport, La., 1955-56; asst. resident Meyer Meml. Hosp., Buffalo, 1958-62, resident, 1962-63, from asst. attending surgeon to attending surgeon, 1963-68, assoc. dir. surg. research lab., 1965-68; from asst. attending surgeon to attending surgeon Deaconess Hosp., Buffalo, 1965-69, head sect. transplantation, 1966-68; dir. transplantation Charity Hosp. of La., New Orleans, 1969-77, vis. surgeon, 1969-77; clin. asst. surgeon Touro Infirmary, New Orleans, 1969-77; mem. med. staff So. Bapt. Hosp., New Orleans, 1969-77; assoc. mem. dept. surgery Hotel Dieu Hosp., 1969-77; surgeon in chief La. State U. Med. Ctr., Shreveport, 1977—, prof., chmn. dept. surgery, 1977—; asst. prof. surgery SUNY-Buffalo, 1965-68; cons. surgeon various La. Hosps., 1969-77; dir. La. Organ Procurement Program, 1971-77; cons. N.W. La. Emergency Med. Services, 1977—; Buswell research fellow in immunology SUNY-Buffalo, 1963-65, instr. surgery, 1963-65, assoc. prof., 1965-68; assoc. prof. surgery Tulane U. Sch. Medicine, 1969-72, prof., 1972-77; assoc. prof. microbiology and immunology, 1969-77, dir. surg. research labs., 1969-77, dir. transplantation labs., 1969-77, dir. Med. Ctr. Histocompatability Testing Lab., 1969-77. Contbr. articles to med. jours. Served to capt. USAF, 1956-58. Recipient Owl Club award for outstanding teaching Tulane U., 1977; grantee Kidney Found., 1966-67, NIH, 1969—, Schlieder Found., 1970-73, Cancer Assn. Greater New Orleans, 1971-72, La. Regional Med. Program, 1971-73. Mem. AMA, ACS, Am. Assn. Clin. Histocompatability Testing (founding), Am. Assn. Immunologists, Am. Soc. for Artificial Internal Organs, Am. Soc. Transplant Surgeons (founding, pres. 1987), Buffalo Surg. Soc. (sec. 1968), So. Surg. Assn. (Arthur H. Shipley award 1972, treas. 1988-91, sec. 1991-3, pres. 1993-94), Surg. Assn. La. (dir. 1977—; pres. 1983), Am. Assn. for Surgery of Trauma, Transplantation Soc., Southeastern Surg. Congress, Am. Surg. Assn., Halsted Soc. (pres. 1991), Soc. U. Surgeons, La. Med. Soc., Shreveport Med. Soc., United Network for Organ Sharing (pres. 1986-88). Office: Dept Surgery Sch of Medicine La State U Shreveport LA 71130

MCDONALD, JOHN FRANCIS PATRICK, electrical engineering educator; b. Narberth, Pa., Jan. 14, 1942; s. Frank Patrick and Lulu Ann (Hegedus) McD.; m. Karen Marie Knapp, May 26, 1979. BSEE, MIT, 1963; MS in Engring., Yale U., 1965, PhD, 1969. Instr. Yale U., New Haven, 1968-69, asst. prof., 1969-74; assoc. prof. Rensselaer Poly. Inst., Troy, N.Y., 1974-86, prof., 1986—; founder Rensselaer Ctr. for Integrated Electronics, 1980—. Contbr. articles to 185 profl. publs. Patentee in field. Recipient numerous grants, 1974—. Mem. ACM, IEEE, Optical Soc., Acoustical Soc., Vacuum Soc., Materials Rsch. Soc. Office: Rensselaer Poly Inst Ctr for Integrated Electronics Troy NY 12181

MCDONALD, JOHN GREGORY, financial investment educator; b. Stockton, Calif., 1937; m. Melody McDonald. BS, Stanford U., 1960, MBA, 1962, PhD, 1967. Mem. faculty Grad. Sch. Bus. Stanford U., Calif., 1968—; now The IBJ prof. fin. Grad. Sch. Bus. Stanford U.; vis. prof. U. Paris, 1972, Columbia Bus. Sch., 1975, Harvard Bus. Sch. 1986; vice chmn., bd. govs. NASD/NASDAQ Stock Market, 1989-90; mem. adv. bd. InterWest Venture Capital; dir. Investment Co. of Am., New Perspective Fund, Inc., Scholastic Corp., Varian, EuroPacific Growth Fund. Contbr. articles to profl. jours. Bd. overseers vis. com. Harvard U. Bus. Sch., Cambridge, Mass., 1994—. Fulbright scholar, Paris, 1967-68. Office: Stanford U Grad Sch Bus Stanford CA 94305

MC DONALD, JOHN JOSEPH, electronics executive; b. N.Y.C., Apr. 18, 1930; s. John J. and Margaret (Shanley) McD.; m. Tessa de R. Greenfield, Aug. 22, 1956; children: Kathryn, Elizabeth, Andrew. B.A., Bklyn. Coll., 1951. With Sperry Rand Corp., Blue Bell, Pa., 1954-75; v.p. Sperry Rand Corp., 1972-75; mng. dir. Casio Electronics Ltd., London, 1975-78; pres. Casio Europe Casio Electronics Ltd., 1975-78; pres., chief exec. officer Casio, Inc., Fairfield, N.J., 1978—, also bd. dirs.; chmn. Casio Can. Ltd., 1988-90, pres., chief exec. officer, 1990—; bd. dirs. Casio Mfg. Corp., Casio de Mex. S.A. Served with U.S. Army, 1952-54. Mem. Brit. Inst. Mktg., Am. Mgmt. Assn., Electronic Industries Assn. (bd. govs.), Electronic Industries Found. (trustee 1987—), Consumer Electronics Group (bd. dirs.). Home: PO Box 322 Hope NJ 07844-0322 Office: 570 Mt Pleasant Ave Dover NJ 07801-1600

MC DONALD, JOHN RICHARD, lawyer; b. Connersville, Ind., Aug. 8, 1933; s. Vernon Louis and Thelma (Venham) McD.; m. Mary Alice Boyd, Aug. 17, 1957; children: Anne Elizabeth, John Richard, Colleen Lynn. B.A., U. Ariz., 1957, LL.B., 1960. Bar: Ariz. 1960. Since practiced in Tucson; assoc. Richard N. Roylston, 1961-62; pvt. practice, 1963-65; ptnr. McDonald & Rykken, 1965-68, DeConcini & McDonald (now DeConcini, McDonald, Brammer, Yetwin, Lacy, P.C.), 1968—; mem. adv. bd. Dependable Nurses, Inc., 1994—. Mem. Ariz. Law Rev. Pres., bd. dirs. Comstock Children's Hosp. Found.; v.p. Ariz. Sch. Bds. Assn., 1979, pres., 1981; v.p. All Ariz. Sch. Bd., 1981; v.p. bd. dirs. Tucson Assn. for Blind; trustee Catalina Foothills Sch. Dist., 1976-82; mem. Tucson Com. on Fgn. Rels., 1989—;bd. dirs. Tucson Unified Sch. Dist. Ednl. Enrichment Found., Ariz. Acad., 1981—. Mem. Ariz. Bar Assn., Ariz. Law Rev. Assn. (pres. 1994), Pima County Bar Assn. (dir. 1978-86, pres. 1984-85), Nat. Coun. Sch. Attys. (dir. 1992—), Delta Chi. Republican. Presbyn. Home: 6151 N Camino Almonte Tucson AZ 85718-3729 Office: 2525 E Broadway Blvd Tucson AZ 85716-5303

MC DONALD, JOHN WARLICK, diplomat, global strategist; b. Coblenz, Germany, Feb. 18, 1922; s. John Warlick and Ethel Mae (Raynor) McD.; m. Barbara Jane Stewart, Oct. 23, 1943 (div.); children: Marilyn Ruth, James Stewart, Kathleen Ethel, Laura Ellen; m. Christel Meyer, Oct. 24, 1970. A.B. U. Ill., 1943, JD, 1946; D (hon.), Mt. Mercy Coll., 1989, Teikyo Marycrest U., 1991, Salisbury State U., 1993. Bar: Ill. 1946, U.S. Supreme Ct. 1951. With legal div. Office Mil Govt., Berlin, 1947; asst. dist. atty. U.S. Mil. Govt. Cts., Frankfort, Germany, 1947-50; with Allied High Commn., Bonn, Germany, 1950-52; U.S. mission to NATO and OEEC, Paris, 1952-54; fgn. affairs officer Dept. State, Washington, 1954-55; exec. sec. to dir. ICA, Washington, 1955-59; U.S. econ. coord. for CENTO affairs Ankara, Turkey, 1959-63; chief econ. and comml. sect. Am. Embassy, Cairo, 1963-66; student Nat. War Coll., Washington, 1966-67; dep. dir. office econ. and social affairs Bur. Internat. Orgn. Affairs, Dept. State, 1967-68, dir., 1968-71; coord. UN Multilateral Devel. Programs, Dept. State, 1971-74, acting dep. asst. sec. econ. and social affairs, 1971, 73; dep. dir. gen. ILO, Geneva, 1974-78; pres. INTELSAT Conf. Privileges and Immunities, 1978; U.S. coord. Tech. Coop. among Developing Countries, 1978; rep. with rank of amb. to UN Conf., 1978—; sec. gen. 27th Colombo Plan Ministerial Meeting, 1978; U.S. coord. UN Decade on Drinking Water and Sanitation, 1979; U.S. coord., ambassador Third World Conf. on Indsl. Devel., 1979, World Assembly on Aging, 1980-82; chmn. fed. inter-agy. com. Internat. Yr. of Disabled Persons, 1980-81; U.S. rep. Internat. Youth Yr., 1981-83; coord. multilateral affairs Ctr. Study of Fgn. Affairs, 1983-87; profl. lectr. in law George Washington U. Nat. Law Ctr., 1987-88, lectr. in conflict resolution, multilateral diplomacy and art of negotiation; pres. Iowa Peace Inst., Grinnell, 1988-92; prof. polit. sci. Grinnell Coll., 1989-92; Disting. vis. prof. George Mason U., Fairfax, Va., 1992-93; chmn. Inst. for Multi-Track Diplomacy, Washington, 1992—; mem. Fgn. Affairs Res. Corps., 1993—. Author: The North-South Dialogue and the UN, 1982, How to Be A Delegate, 1984; co-editor: Itnernational Negotiation, 1985, Perspectives on Negotiation, 1986, Conflict Resolution: Track Two Diplomacy, 1987, U.S. Soviet Summitry, 1987, US Bases Overseas; Negotiations with Spain, Greece and The Philippines, 1990, Multi-Track Diplomacy, 1991, revised, 1993, Defining A U.S. Negotiating Style, 1995; contbr. articles on aging, terrorism, water conflict resolution. Bd. dirs. Global Water, 1982—; Touchstone Theatre, 1982-88, World Com.-UN Decade of Disabled Persons, 1987—; Countdown 2001, 1987-93, People-to-People Com. for Handicapped, 1987—; bd. dirs. Am. Impact Found., 1987-89, chmn. bd., 1988-89; dir. Am. Assn. Internat. Aging, 1983—; chmn., 1983—; v.p. nat. capital area UN Assn., 1993—, mem., 1978—. Recipient Superior Honor award, 1972, Presdl. Meritorious Service award, 1984; named Patriot of Yr., Kansas City, 1987. Mem. ABA, Am. Fgn. Svc. Assn., U.S. Assn. for Club of Rome, UN Assn. (v.p. nat. capitol area 1978—), Soc. Profls. in Dispute Resolution, Consortium of Peace Rsch., Edn. and Devel., Delta Kappa Upsilon, Phi Delta Phi, Cosmos Club. Office: IMTD 1819 H St NW Ste 1200 Washington DC 20006

MCDONALD, JOSEPH LEE, insurance broker; b. Bremerton, Wash., Aug. 15, 1931; s. Joseph Okane and Ida Elizabeth (Finholm) McD.; m. Glorietta Maness, Jan. 22, 1954 (dec. 1984); children: Holly Ann Chaffin, Andrew Lee McDonald; m. Beverly Mae Falkner, June 22, 1986. BS, U. Wash., 1954. Various mgmt. positions AT&T, 1956-62; broker, ptnr. McDonald & McGarry Co., Seattle, 1982-84; ptnr., exec. McDonald Ins. Group, Kirkland, Wash., 1984—; v.p. bd. dirs. Chimayo Inc., Seattle, 1990—, Santa Fe Food Corp., Seattle, 1991—. City councilman City of Bellevue, 1971-75; commr. Water Dist. #97, Bellevue, 1967-71, Lake Hills Sewer Dist., Bellevue, 1965-71; pres. Wash. State Assn. of Sewer Dists., Seattle, 1969. With U.S. Army, 1954-56. Mem. Coll. Club of Seattle, Overlake Golf and Country Club, Western Assn. of Ins. Brokers, Ind. Ins. Agts. Assn., Seattle Master Builders Assn., Apt. Assn. of Seattle and King County, Roche Harbor Yacht Club. Avocations: skiing, sailing, tennis. Home: 7235 91st Pl SE Mercer Island WA 98040 Office: McDonald Ins Group 416-6th St South Kirkland WA 98033

MC DONALD, JOSEPH VALENTINE, neurosurgeon; b. N.Y.C., June 7, 1925; s. Benedict and Catherine Eleanor (Chadney) McD.; m. Carolyn Alice Patricia Petersen, Apr. 30 1955; children: Judith Katherine McDonald Aquadro, Elizabeth Ann McDonald Iwanicki, Catherine Eleanor McDonald Schneider, Joseph Bede, David Randolph. A.B., Coll. Holy Cross, 1945; M.D., U. Pitts., 1949. Intern St. Vincent's Hosp., N.Y.C., 1949-50; rsch. fellow neuroanatomy Vanderbilt U., 1950-51; gen. surgery asst. resident Cushing VA Hosp., Boston, 1951-52; neurology extern Lenox Hill Hosp., 1952; asst. resident neurosurgery Johns Hopkins Hosp., 1953-55, resident

neurosurgeon, 1955-56; practice medicine specializing in neurol. surgery Rochester, N.Y., 1956—; emeritus prof. neurosurgery and neurology U. Rochester Med. Sch. Mem. Soc. Neurol. Surgeons, A.C.S., Am. Assn. Neurol. Surgeons, Congress Neurosurgeons. Home: 800 Allens Creek Rd Rochester NY 14618-3412 Office: Strong Meml Hosp Div Neurosurgery Rochester NY 14642

MCDONALD, KENNETH WILLIAM, principal; b. Kalamazoo, Apr. 24, 1945; s. Kenneth Earl and Elizabeth (Nash) McD. BS, Western Mich. U., 1972, MA with honors, 1978. Tchr. Nashville Pub. Schs., Nashville, 1973-76; from tchr. to asst. prin. Kalamazoo Pub. Schs., 1976-86; prin. Edison Sch., Kalamazoo, 1986—; adv. Kalamazoo County 4-H, 1991—. With USMCR. Graduate fellow Western Mich. U., 1976, George Peabody-Vanderbilt U., 1976. Mem. ASCD, Phi Delta Kappa. Avocations: gardening, fishing, woodworking, travel, reading. Home: 1440 S Crooked Lake Dr Kalamazoo MI 49009 Office: Edison Sch 924 Russell Kalamazoo MI 49001

MCDONALD, LESLIE, art director, production designer. Prodn. designer: (films) The Grifters, 1990, (with Dennis Gassner) Hero, 1992; art dir.: (films) Bugsy, 1991 (Academy award nomination best art direction 1991), (with Jim Teergarden) Forrest Gump, 1994 (Academy award nomination best art direction 1994). Office: care Art Directors Guild 11365 Ventura Blvd #315 Studio City CA 91604*

MCDONALD, MALCOLM GIDEON, education educator; b. Boise, Idaho, Mar. 22, 1932; s. Gideon L. and Annette (Connell) McD.; m. Glenda S. Yarbrough, Nov. 23, 1962; children: Ronald, Steven, Michael. AA, Boise Jr. Coll., 1951; BA, Wash. State U., 1954, MA, 1972, EdD, U. Idaho, 1991. Prof. North Idaho Coll., Coeur d'Alene, Idaho, 1977-78; exec. dir. Spokane Higher Edn. Office, 1978-84; dir. CAREERS, Eastern Wash. U., 1984-86; dir. continuing edn. Eastern Wash. U., Cheney, Wash., 1986-89, asst. prof. dept. comm. studies 1989-94. Ret. lt. col. U.S. Army. Recipient Legion of Merit award, Bronze stars (2), Air medals (11), Meritorious Svc. medal, Commendation medal (5), Vietnam medal of Gallantry, 1954-76. Presbyterian. Avocation: sports. Home: 2841 Spalding Dr Las Vegas NV 89134

MCDONALD, MARIANNE, classicist; b. Chgo., Jan. 2, 1937; d. Eugene Francis and Inez (Riddle) McD.; children: Eugene, Conrad, Bryan, Bridget, Kirstie (dec.), Hiroshi. BA magna cum laude, Bryn Mawr Coll., 1958; MA, U. Chgo., 1960; PhD, U. Calif., Irvine, 1975, doctorate (hon.) Am. Coll. Greece, 1988, hon. diploma Am. Archaeological Assn. Teaching asst. classics U. Calif., Irvine, 1974, D Litt (hon.) U. Athens, Greece, 1994, U. Dublin, 1994. instr. Greek, Latin and English, mythology, modern cinema, 1975-79, founder, rsch. fellow Thesaurus Linguae Graecae Project, 1975—; bd. dir. Centrum. Bd. dirs. Am. Coll. of Greece, 1981—, Scripps Hosp., 1981; Am. Sch. Classical Studies, 1986—; mem. bd. overseers U. Calif. San Diego, 1985—; nat. bd. advisors Am. Biog. Inst., 1982—; founder Hajime Mori Chair for Japanese Studies, U. Calif., San Diego, 1985, McDonald Ctr. for Alcohol and Substance Abuse, 1984, Thesaurus Linguarum Hibernicae, 1991—; vis. prof. U. Dublin, 1990—; adj. prof. theatre U. Calif., San Diego, 1990, prof. theatre and classics, 1994; prof. U. Dublin, 1990—, U. Calif., San Diego, 1994. Recipient Ellen Browning Scripps Humanitarian award, 1975; Disting. Svc. award U. Calif-Irvine, 1982, Irvine medal, 1987, 3rd Prize Midwest Poetry Ctr. Contest, 1987; named one of the Community Leaders Am., 1979-80, Philanthropist of Yr., 1985, Headliner San Diego Press Club, 1985, Philanthropist of Yr. Honorary Nat. Conf. Christians and Jews, 1986, Woman of Distinction Salvation Army, 1986, Eleventh Woman Living Legacy, 1986, Woman of Yr. AHEPA, 1988, San Diego Woman of Distinction, 1990, Woman of Yr. AXIOS, 1991; recipient Bravissimo gold medal San Diego Opera, 1990, Gold Medal Soc. Internationalization of Greek Lang., 1990, Athens medal, 1991, Piraeus medal, 1991, award Desmoi, 1992, award Hellenic Assn of Univ. Women, 1992, Academy of Achievement award AHEPA, 1992, Woman of Delphi award European Cultural Ctr. Delphi, 1992, Civis Universitatis award U. Calif. San Diego, 1993, Hypatia award Hellenic U. Women, 1993, Am.-Ireland Fund Heritage award, 1994, Contribution to Greek Letters award Aristotle U. Thessaloniki, 1994, Order of the Phoenix, Greece, 1994. Vol. Decade Women's International Ctr., 1994. Mem. MLA, AAUP, Am. Philol. Assn., Soc. for the Preservation of the Greek Heritage (pres.), Libr. of Am., Am. Classical League, Philol. Assn. Pacific Coast, Am. Comparative Lit. Assn., Modern and Classical Lang. Assn. So. Calif., Hellenic Soc., Calif. Fgn. Lang. Tchrs. Assn., Internat. Platform Assn., Greek Language Found. (pres.), Royal Irish Acad., Greece's Order of the Phoenix (commdr. 1994), Olbos Enterprises (pres.), KPBS Producers Club, Hellenic Univ. Club (bd. dir.). Author: Terms for Happiness in Euripides, 1978, Semilemmatized Concordances to Euripides' Alcestis, 1977, Cyclops, Andromache, Medea, 1978, Heraclidae, Hippolytus, 1979, Hecuba, 1984, Hercules Furens, 1984, Electra, 1984, Ion, 1985, Trojan Women, 1988, Iphigenia in Taurus, 1988, Euripides in Cinema: The Heart Made Visible, 1983; translator: The Cost of Kindness and Other Fabulous Tales (Shinichi Hoshi), 1986, (chpt.) Views of Clytemnestra, Ancient and Modern, 1990, Classics and Cinema, 1990, Modern Critical Theory and Classical Literature, 1994, A Challenge to Democracy, 1994, Ancient Sun/ Modern Light: Greek Drama on the Modern Stage, 1990; contbr. numerous articles to profl. jours. Avocations: karate, harp (medieval), skiing, diving. Home: PO Box 929 Rancho Santa Fe CA 92067-0929 Office: U Calif at San Diego Dept Theatre La Jolla CA 92093

MCDONALD, MARY M., lawyer; b. 1944. BA, D'Youville Coll., 1966; JD, Fordham U., 1969. Bar: N.Y. 1969. Counsel corp. staff Merck & Co., v.p., gen. counsel, 1991—. Office: Merck & Co PO Box 2000 126 E Lincoln Ave Rahway NJ 07065*

MCDONALD, MICHAEL LEE, career naval officer; b. Salt Lake City, Oct. 23, 1949; s. Jack Alex and Dorothy Elsie (Mantle) McD.; m. Celia McKean Smoot, June 23, 1975; children: Sarah Lynn, Michelle Elise, AnnMarie, Jeffrey Michael, Matthew David, Emily Jane. BA, U. Utah, 1973; MA, U. Iowa, 1977. Commd. ensign USN, 1975; advanced through grades to comdr., 1991; patient adminstr. Naval Hosp., Great Lakes, Ill., 1977-80, Oakland, Calif., 1980-82; med. recruiter Navy Recruiting Dist., San Francisco, 1982-84; adminstr. Navy Environ. and Preventative Medicine Unit # 7, Naples, Italy, 1984-87; staff officer Navy Med. Commd. Europe, London, 1987-89; healthcare advisor U.S. Naval Forces Europe, London, 1989-91; exec. officer Naval Med. Clinic, Seattle, 1991-93, commdg. officer, 1993-94; officer in charge Branch Med. Clinic, Everett, Pa., 1994—. Coach Northshore Little League, Bothell, Wash., 1992, 93; scoutmaster Boy Scouts Am., Dublin, Calif., 1981-85, instl. sponsor, Naples, Italy, 1985-87. Fellow Am. Coll. Healthcare Execs. Mem. LDS Ch. Avocations: golf, basketball, English literature, cycling. Home and Office: 19225 4th Dr SE Bothell WA 98012-7013

Campbell County Hist. Soc., 1989—, pres. bd., 1991—. Served to col. U.S. Army, 1942-46, 50-53. Decorated Presdl. award for Outstanding Meritorious Svc.; decorated numerous other medals; recipient Superior Performance award AEC, 1960, cert. recognition IRS, 1966, medal Sec. Army, 1971, Cert. svc. Dept. Commerce, 1972, Presdl. Achievement award Rep. Nat. Com., 1982, Tenn. Gov.'s Outstanding Achievement award, 1992, Merit award Tenn. Hist. Commn., 1993, Proclamation Tenn. Ho. of Reps., 1993, Tenn. Libr. Assn. award of Merit, 1994. Mem Inst. Applied Behavioral Sci., NEA, Am. Soc. Tng. and Devel., Adult Edn. Assn., Libr. of Congress Assocs. (charter), Am. Legion, Clan Donald U.S.A., Rotary, Masons. Methodist. Home and Office: 109 Crestview Dr La Follette TN 37766-4822 *Society has lost much because of failure to persist. To be sure you are right and go ahead is the thing. Many of life's goals have been lost simply because one has given up too soon. To have the steadfastness to persist in the face of great odds has largely accounted for what measure of success I have achieved.*

MCDONALD, PARKER LEE, state supreme court justice; b. Sebring, Fla., May 23, 1924; s. Monroe R. and Mattie (Etheredge) McD.; m. Velma Ruth McDonald, Dec. 17, 1949; children: Martha Rebecca, Bruce Lee, Robert Reid, Ruth Ann. B.S., B.A., LL.B., U. Fla., 1950. Pvt. practice Sebring, Fla., 1950-51, Orlando, Fla., 1951-61; judge Fla. Cir. Ct., 9th Judicial Dist. Orlando, 1961-79; justice Fla. Supreme Ct., Tallahassee, 1979, 86—, chief justice, 1986-88. Methodist. Office: Fla Supreme Ct Supreme Ct Bldg Tallahassee FL 32399

MC DONALD, PATRICK ALLEN, lawyer, arbitrator, educator; b. Detroit, May 11, 1936; s. Lawrence John and Estelle (Maks) Mc D.; m. Margaret Mercier, Aug. 10, 1963; children: Michael Lawrence, Colleen Marie, Patrick Joseph, Timothy, Margaret, Thomas, Maureen. PhB cum laude, U. Detroit, 1958, JD magna cum laude, 1961; LLM (E. Barrett Prettyman Trial scholar, Hugh J. Fegan fellow), Georgetown U., 1962. Bar: D.C. 1961, Mich. 1961, Colo. 1993. Case worker Dept. Pub. Welfare, Detroit, 1958; field examiner NLRB, Detroit, 1961; practiced in Washington, 1961-62; trial cons. NIH, Bethesda, Md., 1962; staff judge adv. USAF, France, 1962-65; ptnr. Monagham, LoPrete, Mc Donald, Yakima & Grenke, Detroit, 1965—; bd. dirs., chmn. Delta Dental Plan of Mich.; vice-chmn. Delta Dental Plan of Ohio; bd. dirs., v.p. Guest House, Lake Orion, Mich., Rochester, Minn., Detroit Athletic Club, Brighton Hosp.; instr. polit. sci. and law U. Md., 1963-65, U. Detroit Law Sch., adj. prof., 1965—. Co-author: Law and Tactics in Federal Criminal Cases, 1963. Mem. Detroit Bd. Edn., 1966-76, pres.; sec., trustee Mt. Elliott Cemetary Assn.; mem. U. Detroit Sports Hall of Fame; mem. adv. bd. Providence Hosp., Southfield, Mich.; exec. bd. U. Detroit Pres.'s Cabinet. Named one of Five Outstanding Young Men of Mich., Outstanding Young Man of Detroit. Mem. ABA, Detroit Bar Assn., State Bar Mich. (commr.), U. Detroit Alumni Assn. (bd. dirs.), Nmesa, Blue Key, Alpha Phi Omega (pres. Eta Pi chpt. 1955), Alpha Sigma Nu (v.p. 1960). Home: 5165 Lashbrook Ln E Brighton MI 48116-9002 Office: 1700 N Woodward Ave Bloomfield Hills MI 48304-2249 *In the field of law, as an attorney, professor and arbitrator, I have prayed and attempted to be able in argument, accurate in analysis, correct in conclusion, candid with clients, honest with adversaries, and responsible for obligations assigned to me. I have advocated moderation in all things with the exception of my love for Him who created me.*

MCDONALD, ROBERT BOND, chemical company executive; b. Seattle, Oct. 31, 1936; s. Theodore Day and Elizabeth Wood (Robbins) McD.; m. Eleanore Mary Beca, June 27, 1959; children: James Arthur, Kylie Robbins. BE, Yale U., 1958; MS, U. Wash., 1960. Mng. dir. Great Lakes Chem. Corp., Lancaster, Eng., 1977-79; asst. to pres. Great Lakes Chem. Corp., West Lafayette, Ind., 1979-81, v.p., 1981-87, sr. v.p., 1987-94, exec. v.p., COO, pres., CEO, 1994—; bd. dirs. Huntsman Chem. Corp., Kao-Quaker, Japan, Tetrabrom Tech., Ltd., Israel, QO Chems., Assoc. Octel, U.K.; v.p. COB Octel Am., Inc. Mem. Ind. Soc. Chgo., Newcomen Soc., Tippecanoe County Hist. Assn., Greater Lafayette Mus. Art, Greater Lafayette C of C. (bd. dirs. 1987-90). Republican. Episcopalian. Office: Gt Lakes Chem Corp 1 Great Lakes Blvd PO Box 2200 West Lafayette IN 47906

MCDONALD, ROBERT DELOS, manufacturing company executive; b. Dubuque, Iowa, Jan. 30, 1931; s. Delos Lyon and Virginia (Kolck) McD.; m. Jane M. Locher, Jan. 16, 1960 (div. Jan. 1970); children: Jean, Patricia, Maria, Sharon, Rob; m. Marilyn I. Miller, July 4, 1978. BA in Econs., U. Iowa, 1953. With A.Y. McDonald Mfg. Co., Dubuque, 1956—, salesman, 1956-60, sales mgr., 1961-64, mgr. Dubuque wholesale br., 1965-72, v.p. 1971-72, corp. sec., 1972-83, sr. v.p., corp. sec., 1983-85, pres., 1985-95, chmn. bd., chief exec. officer, 1987—, also bd. dirs., 1964—; bd. dirs. Brock-McVey Co., Lexington, Ky., 1964—, A.Y. McDonald Supply Co., Inc., Dubuque, 1984—; sr. v.p., bd. dirs. A.Y. McDonald Industries, Inc., Dubuque, 1983—; chmn. bd., pres., chief exec. officer, bd. dirs. A.Y.M. Inc. Albia, Iowa, 1988—. Trustee, bd. dirs. A.Y. McDonald Mfg. Co. Charitable Found., 1978—, pres., 1982—; bd. dirs. Stonehill Care Ctr., Dubuque, 1984-92, chmn. bd., 1991-92; bd. dirs. Dubuque Boys Club, 1989—, Dubuque Bank & Trust Co., 1994—; trustee United Way Svcs., Inc., Dubuque, 1989—; chmn. Stonehill Benevolent Found., Dubuque, 1989-92; mem. adv. coun. region VII SBA, Cedar Rapids, Iowa, 1984—: mem. adv. bd. Jr. Achievement Tri-States, Inc., 1991—; mem. adv. bd. Iowa State Fair Blue Ribbon Found., 1993—. Lt. USNR, 1953-56. Mem. Am. Mgmt. Assn., Am. Supply Assn., Am. Water Works Assn., Dubuque Area C. of C., Am. Legion, Dubuque Shooting Soc., Dubuque Golf and Country Club, Sigma Alpha Epsilon. Republican. Roman Catholic. Home: Fountain Hill 3399 Eagle Point Dr Dubuque IA 52001 Office: AY McDonald Mfg Co PO Box 508 Dubuque IA 52004-0508

MC DONALD, ROBERT EMMETT, company executive; b. Red Wing, Minn., Apr. 29, 1915; s. Mitchell W. and Olivia (Carlson) McD.; m. Marion L. Wigley, Sept. 14, 1946; children: Patricia L., Barbara C. B.B.A., B.E.E., U. Minn., 1940; postgrad., U. Chgo., 1942. Employment interviewer Commonwealth Edison Co., Chgo., 1940-43; supr. accessory maintenance Northwest Airlines, St. Paul, 1946-51; dir. maintenance No. region Braniff Airways, Mpls., 1951-53; mgr. ops., then v.p., mgr. def. div. Univac, St. Paul, 1953-64; pres. Univac div. Sperry Rand Corp., Blue Bell, Pa., 1966-71; exec. v.p. parent co. Univac div. Sperry Rand Corp., 1966-72; pres., COO Sperry Rand Corp., N.Y.C., 1972-79; vice chmn. bd. Sperry Rand Corp., 1979-80; dir. CertainTeed Corp., Valley Forge, Pa., SKF Industries, Phila., 1979-85, Glenmede Corp., Phila.; mgmt. cons. Trustee U. Minn. Found., 1975-85. Served to lt. USNR, 1943-46. Mem. Tau Beta Pi, Eta Kappa Nu, Acacia. Clubs: Phila. Country, Union League (Phila.). Home: 1125 Robin Rd Gladwyne PA 19035-1007

MCDONALD, STANFORD LAUREL, clinical psychologist; b. Lincoln, Nebr., Mar. 14, 1929; s. Laurel C. and Irene Virginia (Frey) McD.; m. Shirley P. Peterson, Apr. 26, 1964; children: Stacia E. V., Jeffrey J.S., Kathleen S., Patricia M. AB, Nebr. Wesleyan U., 1956; MA, U. Nebr., 1959, postgrad., 1958-60; PhD, Fielding Inst., 1974. Licensed clin. psychologist, Ill. Intern Nebr. Psychiat. Inst., Omaha, 1957-58; staff psychologist Presbyn. St. Lukes Hosp., Chgo., 1960-61; sch. psychologist Chgo. Bd. Edn., 1961-65; chief psychologist SPEED Devel. Ctr., Chicago Heights, Ill., 1965-79; pvt. practice psychology Park Forest, Ill., 1980—; comty. prof. Gov.'s State U., University Park, Ill., 1974—; clin. dir. Behavioral Health Assocs., Park Forest, 1980. Contbr. papers for profl. convs. With USMC, 1950-52, Korea. Fellow Am. Orthopsychiat. Assn.; mem. Am. Psychol. Assn., Biofeedback Soc. Ill. (past. pres.), N.Y. Acad. Scis., Midwestern Psychological Assn., 1st Marine Divsn. Assn., Zeta Psi, Psi Chi. Avocations: personal computers, sports fans. Home: 255 Rich Rd Park Forest IL 60466-1629 Office: Ste 4 24 Centre Park Forest IL 60466-2058

MC DONALD, STEPHEN LEE, economics educator; b. Arkadelphia, Ark., Aug. 8, 1924; s. Claud Bethel and Ruth Jane (Gresham) McD.; m. Elizabeth Gene Brewer, Aug. 14, 1945; children: Martha Elizabeth Mc Donald Worchel, Kathryn Ann Mc Donald McGlothlin. B.A., La. Poly. Inst., 1947; M.A., U. Tex., 1948, Ph.D., 1951. Asst. prof. U. Tex., Austin, 1950-56, prof. econs., 1961—, Josey prof. in energy studies, 1983-85, Duncan prof. econs., 1985—; chmn. dept. U. Tex., 1972-76, 78-79, 88-89; sr. fellow Bur. Bus. Rsch., 1990—; economist Humble Oil & Refining Co., 1956-57; assoc. prof., prof., chmn. dept. La. State U., 1957-61; mem. faculty Stonier

Grad. Sch. Banking; staff assoc., Brookings Instn., 1961-63; mem. econs. adv. panel NSF, 1962-64; cons. to govt. and industry, 1957—. Author: Federal Tax Treatment of Income from Oil and Gas, 1963, Petroleum Conservation in the United States, 1971, The Leasing of Federal Lands for Fossil Fuels Production, 1979; mem. editorial bds.: So. Econ. Journal, 1961-64, Energy Jour., 1979-86; contbr. articles to profl. jours. Served with USNR, 1943-46. Recipient Citation for Excellence Am. Bankers Assn.; Ford Found. grantee, 1964; Resources for Future grantee, 1967, 76; Pres. Assocs. award teaching excellence, 1982. Mem. Am. Econ. Assn., So. Econ. Assn. (v.p. 1969-70), Southwestern Econ. Assn. (pres. 1964-65), Internat. Assn. Energy Econs., Gamma Epsilon, Phi Kappa Phi. Democrat. Methodist. Home: 4002 Sierra Dr Austin TX 78731-3914

MCDONALD, THOMAS ALEXANDER, lawyer; b. Chgo., Aug. 20, 1942; s. Owen Gerard and Lois (Gray) McD.; m. Sharon Diane Hirk, Nov. 25, 1967; children: Cristin, Katie, Courtney, Thomas Jr. AB, Georgetown U., 1965; JD, Loyola U., Chgo., 1968. Bar: Ill. 1969, U.S. Dist. Ct. (no. dist.) Ill. 1969. Ptnr. Clausen Miller, PC, Chgo., 1969—. Mem. ABA, Ill. Bar Assn., Chgo. Bar Assn. Office: Clausen Miller PC 10 S La Salle St Chicago IL 60603-1002

MCDONALD, TIM, professional football player; b. Fresno, Calif., Jan. 6, 1965. Student, U. So. Calif. With St. Louis Cardinals, 1987; safety Phoenix Cardinals (formerly St. Louis Cardinals), 1988-92; with S.F. 49ers, 1993—. Named defense back The Sporting News All-America team, 1985. Played in Pro Bowl, 1989, 1991, 92, 93. Office: San Francisco 49ers 4949 Centennial Blvd Santa Clara CA 95054-1229*

MCDONALD, WARREN GEORGE, accountant, former savings and loan executive; b. Oakland, Calif., Feb. 14, 1939; s. George Daniel and Barbara (Sainsot) McD.; m. Roberta Anne Peterson, Apr. 27, 1968; children: Edward Bruce, Deborah Lynn. B.A., San Francisco State Coll., 1962. CPA, Calif. Ptnr. Main Lafrentz & Co., CPAs, San Francisco, 1969-74; v.p., treas. Imperial Corp. Am., San Diego, 1975-80; v.p. fin. No. Calif. Savs. & Loan, Palo Alto, 1980-82; sr. v.p. fin. Unified Mortgage Co., Santa Clara, Calif., 1982-85; pres. Saratoga Savs., 1985-89; pvt. practice cons. San Francisco, 1989—. Co-author: Power Above The Law, 1990. Served to capt. USCGR. Mem. AICPA, Calif. Soc. CPAs, Inst. Mgmt. Accts., Res. Officers Assn. Home: 1430 Wendy Way Menlo Park CA 94025-6022

MCDONALD, WILLIAM ANDREW, classics educator; b. Warkworth, Ont., Can., Apr. 26, 1913; came to U.S., 1936, naturalized, 1943; s. William Douglas and Jean (Lane) McD.; m. Elizabeth Jackson Anderson, June 28, 1941; children: Susan, Elizabeth. B.A., U. Toronto, 1935, M.A., 1936; Ph.D., Johns Hopkins, 1940. Asst. prof. classics Lehigh U., 1939-43; tech. writer Consol. Vultee Aircraft Co., 1943-45; asso. prof. classics U. Tex., Austin, 1945-46; prof. classics, chmn. dept. Moravian Coll., Bethlehem, Pa., 1946-48; prof. classics U. Minn., 1948-80, Regents' prof. classical studies, 1973-80; dir. honors div. U. Minn. (Coll. Liberal Arts), 1964-67; dir. Minn. Messenia expdn. in S.W. Greece, 1961-92, dir. grad. center for ancient studies, 1973-78, 85-86; Research prof. Am. Sch. Classical Studies, Athens, 1978-79; excavation staff Johns Hopkins U. at Olynthus, 1938, U. Cin. at Pylos, 1939, 53; dir. Nichoria excavation, 1969-75. Author: Political Meeting Places of Greeks, 1943, Progress into the Past, 1967, (with C.C. Thomas) 2d edit., 1990, (with D. J. Georgacas) Place Names of Southwest Peloponnesus, 1969, (with G. Rapp Jr.) Minnesota Messenia Expedition: Reconstructing A Bronze Age Regional Environment, 1972, (with W.D.E. Coulson and John Rosser) Excavations at Nichoria in Southwest Greece: Dark Age and Byzantine Occupation, 1983, (with N.C. Wilkie) Bronze Age Occupation, 1992. Vogeler Meml. fellow Johns Hopkins, 1936-38; Royal Soc. Can. fellow Am. Sch. Classical Studies, Athens, 1938-39; Guggenheim fellow, 1958-59, 67-68. Mem. Archaeol. Inst. Am. (exec. com. Gold medal for Disting. Archaeol. Achievement 1981), Am. Philol. Assn., Assn. for Field Archaeology (v.p.), Soc. Prof. Archaeologists (dir.). Home: 1666 Coffman St # 333 Saint Paul MN 55108-1326 Office: Univ Minn 331 Folwell Hall Minneapolis MN 55455

MCDONALD, WILLIAM HENRY, financial executive; b. Ottawa, Ont., Can., Sept. 8, 1924; s. Joseph and Constance Mary (Gordon) McD.; m. D. Gwen Selkirk, July 8, 1950; 1 child, Barbara Elaine. Grad. high sch. Credit and operating mgr. B.F. Goodrich Co., Winnipeg, Man., Can., 1945-49; fin. adminstrn. officer Govt. Can., Ottawa, 1949-55; asst. gen. mgr. mortgages Bank of N.S., 1955-66; mng. dir. Boyd Stott & McDonald Ltd., Toronto, Ont., 1966-79; exec. v.p., dir. Morguard Trust Co., 1966-74; chmn. bd. Can. Comml. Bank, Toronto, 1976-81, chmn. exec. com., 1981-84; chmn. bd. Can. Comml. Bank Mortgage Investment Corp., 1983-84; pres., CEO, dir. Boyd Stott and McDonald Techs., Ltd., 1984—; pres. Thornton McDonald Assocs., Inc. Chmn. bd. govs. J. Douglas Ferguson Hist. Research Found., 1971—. Served with RCNVR, 1943-45. Mem. Can. Paper Money Soc. (hon. pres.), Internat. Bank Note Soc. (life), Can. Credit Inst., Classical & Medieval Numismatic Soc. (exec. sec.). Conservative. Anglican. Office: PO Box 956 Sta B, Willowdale, ON Canada M2K 2T6

MCDONALD, WILLIAM HENRY, lawyer; b. Niangua, Mo., Feb. 27, 1946; s. Milburn and Fannie M. McDonald; m. Janice E. Robinson, July 13, 1968; children: Melissa L., Meghan M. BS in Pub. Adminstrn., Southwest Mo. State U., 1968; JD, U. Mo., 1971. Bar: Mo. 1971, U.S. Dist. Ct. (we. dist.) Mo. 1973, U.S. Supreme Ct. 1978, U.S. Ct. Appeals (8th cir.) 1982. Pres. Woolsey, Fisher, Whiteaker & McDonald, A.C., Springfield, Mo., 1973—. Chmn. blue ribbon task force on Delivery of Mental Health Services to Southwest Mo., Mo. Commn. Continuing Legal Edn.; pres. Tan Oaks Homeowners Assn.; mem. fin. com. Child Adv. Council, Rep. Nat. Com., Mo. Rep. Com., Greene County Nat. Com.; active various Southwest Mo. State U. Clubs; bd. dirs. Greene County div. Am. Heart Assn., Ozarks regional Am. Athletic Union Jr. Olympics; pres., bd. dirs. Springfield Little Theatre. Served to capt. U.S. Army, 1971-73. Named one of Outstanding Young Men Am., 1978, 81, Outstanding Young Men Springfield, 1980. Fellow ABA (litigation and torts and ins. sects., fellow young lawyers sect.); mem. Mo. Bar Assn. (chmn. spl. com. on mandatory continuing edn., various coms., recipient pres. award 1986), Greene County Bar Assn. (bd. dirs., chmn. pub. edn. speakers bur.), Met. Bar Assn. St. Louis, Assn. Trial Lawyers Am., Def. Rsch. Inst., Am. Judicature Soc., Am. Bd. Trial Advs., Nat. Bd. Trial Advs., 31st Jud. Cir. Bar Com. (chmn.), Supreme Ct. Hist. Soc., U. Mo.-Kansas City Sch. Law Found., Springfield Area C.of C. (v.p.), Beta Omega Tau, Kappa Epsilon. Presbyterian. Home: 4857 E Royal Dr Springfield MO 65809-2425 Office: Woolsey Fisher Whiteaker & McDonald 300 S Jefferson Ave Ste 600 Springfield MO 65806-2221

MCDONALD, WILLIS, IV, lawyer; b. N.Y.C., Aug. 25, 1926; s. Willis McDonald III and Elizabeth Beaumont (Pfaff) McD.; m. Mary Lou H. Bellows, May 12, 1967; stepchildren: Randall F. Bellows Jr., Lisa L. Acker. B.S., Yale U., 1949; LL.B., U. Va., 1953. Bar: Va. 1952, N.Y. 1955. Assoc. White & Case, N.Y.C., 1953-63, ptnr., 1963—. Lay leader, trustee First Ch. of Round Hill, Greenwich, Conn., chmn. bd. trustees, 1990—; pres. Mesa Ranch Inc., Cody, Wyo.; trustee Buffalo Bill Hist. Ctr., Cody. Fellow Am. Bar Found., Am. Coll. Investment Counsel (pres. 1981-82, trustee); mem. ABA, Va. Bar Assn., N.Y. State Bar Assn., Assn. of Bar of City of N.Y., N.Y. County Lawyers Assn. Republican. Episcopalian. Clubs: N.Y. Yacht, Yale, Down Town Assn. (N.Y.C.); Indian Harbor Yacht, Stanwich (Greenwich); Wigwam Country (Litchfield Park, Ariz.). Office: White & Case 1155 Ave Of The Americas New York NY 10036-2711

MCDONELL, HORACE GEORGE, JR., instrument company executive; b. N.Y.C., Sept. 23, 1928; s. Horace Gustave and Anabel (Armstrong) McD.; m. Eileen Romar, Sept. 6, 1952; children: Victoria (dec.), Diane, Horace. A.B., Adelphi Coll., 1952; postgrad., Harvard U., 1962. Engr. Sperry Gyroscope Co., N.Y.C., 1952; with Perkin-Elmer Corp., Norwalk, Conn., 1963—; mgr. instrument group Perkin-Elmer Corp., 1967-77, v.p., 1966-69, sr. v.p., 1969-77, exec. v.p. 1977-80, pres., 1980-85, chmn., 1985-90, ret., 1990; bd. dirs. Perkin Elmer, Ltd. U.K. UniRoyal, Inc., Perkin Elmer Internat., Inc., Harvey Hubbell, Inc., Ethan Allen Inc.; Mem. adv. task force on export controls U.S. Def. Sci. Bd., 1975—; chmn. instrumentation subcom., 1975—. Mem. Bd. Edn., Ridgefield, Conn., 1969; Bd. dirs. Conn. Sci. Fair.; Trustee. bd. dirs. Danbury (Conn.) Hosp.; trustee Adelphi U.; bd. dirs. Danbury Health Svcs. With AUS, 1946-48. Mem. Sci. Apparatus Maker Assn. (dir., chmn. analytical instrument sect.), Am. Inst. Physics, AAAS,

Instrument Soc. Am., Am. Electronics Assn. (bd. dirs. 1984-89, chmn. 1987). Home: Powder Horn Dr Ridgefield CT 06877 Office: Perkin-Elmer Corp 761 Main Ave Norwalk CT 06859-0003

MCDONELL, KATHERINE MANDUSIC, association executive; b. Mansfield, Ohio, Nov. 8, 1954; d. Sam and Ann Julia (Konves) Mandusic; m. Edwin D. McDonell, Aug. 18, 1979 (div. Dec. 1994). BA, Ohio Wesleyan U.; MA in History and Mus. Studies, Case Western Res.; MBA, Ind. U. Rschr. Conner Prairie Mus., Fishers, Ind., 1978-82; exec. dir./rsch. historian Ind. Med. History Mus./Ind. Hist. Soc., Indpls., 1982-91; asst. dir. for comm. and mktg. Ind. U. Ctr. on Philanthropy, 1991-93; exec. dir. Roller Skating Assn., Indpls., 1993—. Author: The Journals of William A. Lindsay, 1989; contbg. editor The Encyclopedia of Indianapolis, 1994; contbr. articles to profl. jours. Pres. Altrusa Internat. of Indpls., 1995—; bd. dirs. Nat. Mus. of Roller Skating, Lincoln, 1994—; rec. sec. Crown Hill Soc., Indpls., 1993-95. Mem. Am. Soc. of Assn. Execs., Nat. Soc. of Fund Raising Execs. (cert.), Columbia club, Am. Mktg. Assn., Beta Gamma Sigma, Sigma Iota Epsilon, Phi Beta Kappa. Avocations: reading, walking, gourmet cooking, traveling. Office: Roller Skating Assn Ste 123 7301 Georgetown Rd Indianapolis IN 46268

MCDONELL, ROBERT TERRY, magazine editor, novelist; b. Norfolk, Va., Aug. 1, 1944; s. Robert Meinard and Irma Sophronia (Nelson) McD.; m. Joan Raffeld Hitzig, June 15, 1981; Robert Nicholas Campbell, Thomas Hunter Campbell. Student, U. Calif., Berkeley, 1962-63, San Jose State U., 1963-64; BA in Art, U. Calif., Irvine, 1967. With AP, N.Y.C., 1970-72; reporter Los Angeles Weekly, 1972-73; asso. editor San Francisco mag. 1974-76, City mag., San Francisco, 1976-77; sr. editor San Francisco mag., 1977, Outside mag., San Francisco, 1978-79; founding editor Rocky Mountain mag., Denver, 1979-80; mng. editor Rolling Stone mag., N.Y.C., 1980-83; asst. mng. editor Newsweek Mag., N.Y.C., 1983-86; founder Smart mag., N.Y.C., 1986-90; editor-in-chief Esquire mag., N.Y.C., 1990-93; editor-in-chief, pub. Sports Afield Mag., N.Y.C., 1994—. Author: California Bloodstock, 1980, paperback edit., 1989; screenwriter: Miami Vice, China Beach. Office: Sports Afield 250 W 55th St New York NY 10019-1412

MCDONNELL, ARCHIE JOSEPH, environmental engineer; b. N.Y.C., June 3, 1936; s. Patrick and Margaret (O'Reilly) McD.; m. Nancy Carol Schaeffer, June 18, 1966; children: Patrick, Sean. BS in Civil Engring., Manhattan Coll., 1958; MS in Civil Engring., Pa. State U., 1960, PhD in Civil Engring., 1963. Prof. Pa. State U., University Park, 1963-93; asst. dir. Water Resources Rsch. Ctr., Pa. State U., 1969-82; dir. Inst. for Rsch. on Land and Water Resources, Pa. State U., 1982-86, Environ. Resources Rsch. Inst., Pa. State U., 1986—; bd. dirs. Pa. Environ. Coun., 1989—, Nat. Assn. State Univs. & Land Grant Colls., 1990-92, chmn. water resources com., 1985-91; mem. rsch. & modeling subcom. EPA Chesapeake Bay Program, 1984-86, sci. & tech. adv. com., 1984—, exec. com., 1988-92; U.S. rep. Internat. Joint Commn., 1976-79, 87-89; mem. Pa. State Conservation Com., 1988-89, water resources policy adv. com. Pa. Dept. Environ. Resources, 1979-82, air & water quality tech. adv. com., 1983—, chmn. water quality subcom., 1986-88; chmn. Northeast Water Inst. Dirs., 1973-74; mem. exec. com. Nat. Assn. Water Inst. Dirs., 1975-78. Contbr. articles to profl. jours. Fellow U.S. Pub. Health Svc., 1961-62; recipient Commendation cert. Internat. Joint Commn., Conservationist of Yr. award Chesapeake Bay Found., Washington, 1986, Outstanding Rsch. award Pa. State U. Engring. Soc., 1988, Outstanding Profl. Rsch. award Water Pollution Control Assn. Pa., 1990, Karl M. Mason medal Pa. Assn. Environ. Profls., 1991, Gabriel Narutowicz medal Ministry Environ. Protection and Natural Resources, Poland, 1991. Mem. ASCE (chmn. 1972-73, exec. com. 1976-80, J. James R. Croes Rsch. medal 1976, Outstanding Svc. award 1981), Water Environ. Fedn. (co-chmn. 1991—), Fed. Water Pollution Control Fedn., Internat. Assn. Water Pollution Rsch., Am. Soc. Limnology and Oceanography, Chi Epsilon, Sigma Xi, Phi Kappa Phi. Achievements include demonstration of low cost treatment method for renovation of acidmine waters. Office: Pa State U 100 Land Water Research Bldg University Park PA 16802

MCDONNELL, DENNIS J., securities industry executive; b. Chgo., May 20, 1942; s. Lawrence J. and Eleanor (Lama) McD.; m. Kate A. McDonnell, Sept. 13, 1986. B.S. in Econs., Loyola U., Chgo., 1965; M.A. in Econs., UCLA, 1969. Vice pres. Continental Bank, Chgo., 1969-83; pres., dir. Van Kampen Merritt Investment Adv Corp. (formerly Van Kampen Merritt), Lisle, Ill., 1983—; dir. Van Kempen Merritt Capital Investment Adv. Corp., Naperville, Ill., 1983—; dir. McCarthy, Crisanti & Maffei, Inc., N.Y.C. Lt. USN, 1965-68. Mem. Soc. Mcpl. Analysts (pres. 1978-79), Nat. Fedn. Mcpl. Analysts, Mcpl. Bond Club Chgo., Columbia Yacht Club. Roman Catholic. Avocation: yacht racing. Office: Van Kampen Merritt Am Capital Investment Adv Corp 1 Parkview Plz Villa Park IL 60181-4400

MC DONNELL, EDWARD FRANCIS, distillery executive; b. Boston, July 27, 1935; s. John and Margaret (O'Neill) McD.; m. Catherine McNamara, July 18, 1959; children: Edward, Paul, Elizabeth. B.S., Suffolk U., 1959. With Raytheon Co., 1960-64, bus. mgr. radio and TV tube op., 1965-66; with Gen. Foods Corp., 1966-75; fin. ops. mgr. Gen. Foods Internat., 1966-67, asst. to pres., 1968; pres., chief exec. officer Gen. Foods Internat. (Kibin S.P. subs.), Brazil, 1969-75; with Pillsbury Co., Mpls., 1975-81; corp. exec. v.p., pres. Pillsbury Internat., 1978-81; v.p. Pillsbury Internat., Europe, 1977-81; pres. internat. group Seagram's & Sons, N.Y.C., 1981—; now exec. v.p. internat. Joseph E. Seagram and Sons Inc., N.Y.C. Office: Seagram & Son 375 Park Ave New York NY 10152-0002

MCDONNELL, JAMES, English educator; b. London, Eng., May 2, 1937; came to U.S., 1965; s. Patrick and Mary (Brennan) McD.; m. Jane Rutherford Taylor, Aug., 1968; children: Paul A., Katherine R. BA in English, Cambridge (Eng.) U., 1965, MA in English, 1967; PhD, Washington U., 1974. Instr. Carleton Coll., Northfield, Minn., 1969-74, asst. prof., 1974-77, assoc. prof., 1977-84, prof., 1984—; vis. lectr. in English, Trinity Coll., Dublin, Ireland, 1986; chair dept. English, Carleton Coll., 1989-92; external evaluator English dept. Furman U., Greenville, S.C., 1992; external reviewer English dept. Samford U., Birmingham, Ala., 1992. Contbr. articles to profl. jours. Cons., panelist and lectr. Guthrie Theatre, Minn., 1985, 88, 90. Mem. MLA, AAUP, Nat. Coun. Tchrs. of English, English Inst., Assn. Depts. English, Cambridge Union. Avocation: acting. Home: 309 Washington St Northfield MN 55057 Office: Carleton Coll 100 S College St Northfield MN 55057

MCDONNELL, JOHN FINNEY, aerospace and aircraft manufacturing executive; b. Mar. 18, 1938; s. James Smith and Mary Elizabeth (Finney) McD.; m. Anne Marbury, June 16, 1961. BS in Aero. Engring., Princeton U., 1960, MS in Aero. Engring., 1962; postgrad. in bus. adminstrn., Washington U., St. Louis, 1962-66. Strength engr. McDonnell Aircraft Co. (subs. McDonnell Douglas Corp.), St. Louis, 1962, corp. analyst, 1963-65, contract coord., adminstr., 1965-68; asst. to v.p. fin. Douglas Aircraft Co. (subs. McDonnell Douglas Corp.), 1968; v.p. McDonnell Douglas Fin. Corp. (subs. McDonnell Douglas Corp.), 1968-71; staff v.p. fiscal McDonnell Douglas Corp., 1971-75, corp. v.p. fin. and devel., 1975-77, corp. exec. v.p., 1977-80, pres., 1980—, mem. exec. com., 1975—, chmn., 1988—, past CEO, also bd. dirs.; bd. dirs. Ralston Purina Co. Bd. commrs. St. Louis Sci. Ctr.; trustee KETC, Washington U.; also chmn. nat. coun. faculty arts and scis. com. Office: McDonnell Douglas Corp PO Box 516 Saint Louis MO 63166-0516*

MCDONNELL, MARY, actress; b. Wilkes-Barre, Pa., 1952; m. Randle Mell; 1 child, Olivia. Appearances include (theatre) Buried Child, 1978-79, Letters Home, 1979, Still Life, 1981 (Obie award 1981), The Death of a Miner, 1981-82, A Weekend Near Madison, 1982-83, Red River, 1982-83, Black Angel, 1982-83, All Night Long, 1984, The Three Sisters, 1984-85, Savage in Limbo, 1985, Stitchers and Starlight Tailors, 1985-86, Execution of Justice, 1986, A Doll's House, 1986-87, Three Ways Home, 1988, The Heidi Chronicles, 1990, (TV series) E/R, 1984-85, (TV movies) Money on the Side, 1982, Courage, 1986, O, Pioneers!, 1991, The American Clock, 1993, Blue Chips, 1993, (films) Garbo Talks, 1984, Matewan, 1987, Tiger Warsaw, 1988, Dances with Wolves, 1990 (Golden Globe award nomination 1990, Acad. Award nomination 1990), Grand Canyon, 1991, Sneakers, 1992, Passion Fish, 1992 (Acad. Award nomination 1993), Blue Chips, 1994. Office: William Morris Agy 151 S El Camino Dr Beverly Hills CA 90212-2704*

MCDONNELL, SANFORD NOYES, aircraft company executive; b. Little Rock, Oct. 12, 1922; s. William Archie and Carolyn (Cherry) McD.; m. Priscilla Robb, Sept. 3, 1946; children: Robbin McDonnell MacVittie, William Randall. BA in Econs., Princeton U., 1945; BS in Mech. Engring., U. Colo., 1948; MS in Applied Mechanics, Washington U., St. Louis, 1954. With McDonnell Douglas Corp. (formerly McDonnell Aircraft Corp.), St. Louis, 1948—, v.p., 1959-66, pres. McDonnell Aircraft div., 1966-71, corp. exec. v.p., 1971, corp. pres., from 1971, chief exec. officer, from 1972, chmn., 1980-88, chmn. emeritus, 1988—, also bd. dirs. Active St. Louis United Way; mem. exec. bd. St. Louis and nat. councils Boy Scouts Am.; trustee, elder Presbyn. Ch. Fellow AIAA; mem. Navy League U.S. (life), Tau Beta Pi. Office: McDonnell Douglas Corp PO Box 516 Saint Louis MO 63166-0516

MCDONNELL, SUE KARTIN, lawyer; b. Phila., Mar. 15, 1948; d. William and Ruth F. (Swyer) Kartin; m. John Joseph McDonnell III, June 14, 1970; 1 child, Liam Kartin. BA, Barnard Coll., 1970; JD, Columbia U., 1973. Bar: N.Y. 1974, Calif. 1979, Ohio, 1988, U.S. Dist. Ct. (so. dist.) N.Y., U.S. Dist. Ct. (cen. dist.) Calif., U.S. Dist. Ct. (so. dist.) Ohio, U.S. Ct. Appeals (2d, 4th and 9th cirs.), U.S. Supreme Ct. Assoc. Donovan Leisure Newton & Irvine, N.Y.C. and L.A., 1973-82; ptnr. Donovan Leisure Newton & Irvine, L.A., 1982-87; shareholder Smith & Schnacke, Dayton, Ohio, 1988-89; ptnr. Thompson, Hine and Flory, Dayton, Ohio, 1989—. Bd. dirs. Legal Aid Soc. Dayton, Inc. Mem. ABA (antitrust, litigation, patent, trademark and copyright sects.), Calif. State Bar Assn., Dayton Bar Assn., Am. Inns of Ct. (Master of the Bench, Carl Kessler Inn), Phi Beta Kappa. Office: Thompson Hine and Flory 2000 Courthouse Pla NE Dayton OH 45401

MC DONOUGH, GEORGE FRANCIS, JR., aerospace engineer; b. Chgo., July 3, 1928; s. George Francis and Minnie L. (Bartoli) McD.; m. Louise Guthrie, June 4, 1955; children: Michael Neil (dec.), Kathleen Louise, Thomas Charles, Daniel George. B.S., Marquette U., Milw., 1953; M.S., U. Ill., 1956, Ph.D., 1959. Asst. prof. U. Ill., 1959-60; assoc. prof. San Jose (Calif.) State Coll., 1960-61; sr. engr. E.H. Plesset Assos., Los Angeles, 1961-63; sr. scientist United Aircraft Corp., Los Angeles, 1963; with George C. Marshall Space Flight Center, NASA, Huntsville, Ala., 1963—, dep. dir. data systems lab., 1974-78, dep. assoc. dir. engring., 1978-81, dir. systems dynamics lab., 1981-86, dir. structures and dynamics lab., 1986-88, dep. dir. for space systems, sci. and engring., 1988-89, dir. sci. and engr., 1989—; chmn. NASA Engring. Mgmt. Coun., 1993—; lectr. U. Ala., Huntsville, 1965—. Co-author: Wind Effects on Launch Vehicles, 1970. Chmn. Westbury Civic Assn., 1965-67; mem. Huntsville Air Pollution Control Bd., 1977—, vice-chmn., 1978-80, 87—, chmn., 1980-82, 85-87; mem. adv. coun. Coll. Engring., Marquette U., 1991—; mem. bd. visitors U. Ala., Birmingham, 1993—. With USNR, 1945-47, 51-52. Recipient Superior Performance award NASA, 1964, Superior Achievement award, 1966, Exceptional Svc. medal, 1973, Outstanding Leadership medal, 1982, 88, Group Achievement award, 1982, 84, 87-88, 92, Outstanding Performance rating, 1987-91, Profl. Achievement award Coll. Engring., Marquette U., 1991, Disting. Engring. Alumnus award Marquette U., 1994; named Presdl. Meritorious Exec., 1988, Presdl. Disting. Exec., 1992; dir.'s commendation George C. Marshall Space Flight Ctr., 1973. Mem. ASCE, AIAA, Whitesburg Yacht Club (chaplain 1988-90, fleet capt. 1990-94), Sigma Xi (pres. Huntsville 1972-74). Democrat. Roman Catholic. Home: 1902 Fairmont Rd SE Huntsville AL 35801-1443 Office: George C Marshall Space Flight Ctr Code Ea01 Huntsville AL 35812

MCDONOUGH, JAMES FRANCIS, civil engineer, educator; b. Boston, June 7, 1939; s. John Joseph and Blanche Cecelia (Murphy) McD.; m. Kathryn Ann Hilvert, Mar. 9, 1985; children by previous marriage: John, James, Jennifer. BS in Civil Engring., Northeastern U., 1962, MS in Civil Engring., 1964; PhD, U. Cin., 1968, MBA, 1981. Registered profl. engr., Ohio. Project engr. Fay, Spofford & Thorndike, Boston, 1962; teaching asst. Northeastern U., 1962-64; teaching asst. U. Cin., 1965, instr. civil engring., 1965-68, asst. prof., 1968-74, assoc. prof., 1974-78, William Thoms prof. civil engring., chmn. dept. civil and environ. engring., 1978-86, assoc. dean acad. affairs, 1986—; vis. prof. faculty engring. Kabul U., Afghanistan, 1969-71; vis. prof. N.C. State U., 1971. Contbr. articles to profl. jours. Pres. Greenhills Winton Sports Assn., 1981-83, treas., 1977-81. Recipient Teaching Excellence award U. Cin., 1973-75; Dow Chem. Outstanding Young Faculty award Am. Soc. for Engring. Edn., 1975; Outstanding Engring. Educator award Am. Soc. Engring. Edn.-Western Electric, 1977; Profl. Accomplishment award Acad.-Tech. and Sci. Council Cin., 1979. Fellow Am. Soc. Engring. Edn. (v.p. 1984-86, chmn. sect. 1982-83, v.p. membership affairs 1992—); mem. ASCE (zone sec. 1983, sect. pres. 1982), NSPE (chmn. Ohio state bd. registration for engrs. and surveyors 1987-90), Ohio Soc. Profl. Engrs., Tech. Socs. Coun. Cin. (Disting. Engr. of Yr. award 1993), ASEE (Centennial medal 1993, George Wadlin Dsiting. Svc. award 1993), NCEES (Profl. Accomplishment award 1993), Sigma Xi, Tau Beta Pi, Chi Epsilon, Beta Gamma Sigma. Roman Catholic. Home: 342 W Conference Dr Boca Raton FL 33486-3155 Office: U Cin Mail Location # 18 Cincinnati OH 45221

MCDONOUGH, JOHN MICHAEL, lawyer; b. Evanston, Ill., Dec. 30, 1944; s. John Justin and Anne Elizabeth (O'Brien) McD.; m. Susan J. Moran, Sept. 19, 1982; 1 child, John E. M. A.B., Princeton U., 1966; LL.B., Yale U., 1969. Bar: Ill. 1969, Fla. 1991. Assoc. Sidley & Austin, Chgo., 1969-75, ptnr., 1975—. Bd. dirs. Met. Planning Coun., 1978—, pres. 1982-84; bd. dirs. Ctr. Am. Archeology, 1980-85, chmn. 1982-84; bd. dirs. Leadership Greater Chgo., 1984-90, sec.-treas., 1987-90; bd. dirs., sec.-treas. Lakefront Gardens, Inc.; bd. dirs. Brain Rsch. Found., pres. 1989-94. With JAGC, USAR, 1969-75. Mem. ABA, Ill. Bar Assn., Chgo. Bar Assn., Chgo. Club, Racquet Club, Commonwealth Club, Econ. Club, Phi Beta Kappa. Democrat. Episcopalian. Home: 1209 N Astor St Chicago IL 60610-2300 Office: Sidley & Austin 1 First Nat Plz Ste 4400 Chicago IL 60603

MC DONOUGH, JOHN RICHARD, lawyer; b. St. Paul, May 16, 1919; s. John Richard and Gena (Olson) McD.; m. Margaret Poot, Sept. 10, 1944; children—Jana Margaret, John Jacobus. Student, U. Wash., 1937-40; LL.B., Columbia U., 1946. Bar: Calif. 1949. Asst. prof. law Stanford U., 1946-49, prof., 1952-69; assoc. firm Brobeck, Phleger & Harrison, San Francisco, 1949-52; asst. dep. atty. gen. U.S. Dept. Justice, Washington, 1967-68; asso. dep. atty. gen. U.S. Dept. Justice, 1968-69; of counsel and ptnr. firm Keatinge & Sterling, L.A., 1969-70; ptnr. Ball, Hunt, Hart, Brown and Baerwitz, 1970-90, Carlsmith Ball Wichman Murray Case & Ichiki, L.A., 1990—; exec. sec. Calif. Law Revision Commn., 1954-59, mem. commn., 1959-67, vice chmn. 1960-64, chmn., 1964-65; participant various continuing edn. programs. Served with U.S. Army, 1942-46. Mem. ABA, State Bar Calif., Los Angeles County Bar Assn., Am. Coll. Trial Lawyers. Democrat. Office: Carlsmith Ball Wichman Murray Case & Ichiki 555 S Flower St Fl 25 Los Angeles CA 90071-2300

MCDONOUGH, JOSEPH CORBETT, former army officer, aviation consultant; b. N.Y.C., Sept. 30, 1924; s. Joseph Walter and Catherine Loretta (Corbett) McD.; m. Mary Patricia Aaron, June 10, 1945; children—Joseph Corbett, Thomas Michael, Robert Timothy. B.S., U.S. Mil. Acad., West Point, N.Y., 1945; M.A., Georgetown U., Washington, 1957; grad., U.S. Command and Gen. Staff Coll., 1954, Brit. Staff Coll., Camberly, 1958, U.S. Army War Coll., 1965. Commd. 2d lt. U.S. Army, 1945, advanced through grades to maj. gen., 1973, served in Philippine Scouts, 1945-47, served with 82d Airborne Div., 1948-51; served with 40th Inf. Div. U.S. Army, Korea, 1952-53; instr. U.S. Naval Acad., 1954-57; staff and command U.S. Army, Europe, 1958-61; with Office Personnel Mgmt., Dept. Army, Washington, 1961-64; mem. staff Office Under Sec. Army, Washington, 1965-67; bn. and brigade comdr. 1st Calvary Div. U.S. Army, Vietnam, 1967-68; with Joint Chiefs of Staff, Washington, 1968-71; brigade and asst. div. comdr. Vietnam, 1971-72; chief of staff CENTO, Turkey, 1972-73; comdg. gen. 8th Inf. Div. U.S. Army, Germany, 1973-75; U.S. Comdr. Berlin, 1975-78; ret. U.S. Army, 1978; cons. numerous govt. agys., 1978-79; v.p., gen. mgr. Butler Aviation, BWI Airport, Md., 1980-83; v.p. ops. Butler Aviation Internat., 1983-86; cons., 1986-88; pres. Butler Aviation Internat., 1988-90; cons., 1990—. Decorated D.S.M. with oak leaf cluster, Silver Star, Legion of Merit with oak leaf cluster, D.F.C., Bronze Star, Air medal with 32 oak leaf clusters, Army Commendation medal with 2 oak leaf clusters. Mem. Assn. U.S. Army, Army Aviation Assn. Address: 219 Greenbury Ct Annapolis MD 21401

MCDONOUGH, PATRICK DENNIS, university executive; b. Virginia, Minn., Jan. 30, 1942; s. James Morris and Vivian S. (Knudtson) McD.; children: Jeffrey, Anne; m. Karen Howe, June 27, 1981. BA cum laude, Moorhead State U., 1964; MA, U. Kans., 1969; PhD, U. Minn., 1972. Asst. prof. theatre Emporia (Kans.) State U., 1966-70; dir. sales, mktg. Guthrie Theater, Mpls., 1971, 72; asst. prof. speech, dir. of forensics Moorhead (Minn.) State U., 1972-73; assoc. prof., mng. dir., chair Marshall Performing Arts Ctr. U. Minn., Duluth, 1973-76; dean fine arts, prof. U. Evansville (Ind.), 1976-81; vice chancellor, prof. U. Wis., Stevens Point, 1981-84; program dir. (edn. and leadership) W.K. Kellogg Found., Battle Creek, Mich., 1984-89; 15th pres., prof. theatre and mgmt. Marietta (Ohio) Coll., 1989-95, exec. dir. McDonough Ctr. for Leadership and Bus.; assoc. vice chancellor planning and analysis Calif. State U. Sys., Long Beach, 1995—; pres. Emporia chpt. AAUP, 1969; cons. Lexington (Ky.) Children's Theatre, 1979; festival evaluator Am. Coll. Theatre Festival, 4 states, 1975, 76; mem. theatre panel Ind. Arts Commn., Indpls., 1977-79; mem. arts orgn. panel Mich. Arts Bd., Detroit, 1985-89; presenter workshops, conv. programs. Producer, dir. 100 plays and musicals, 1964-84; contbr. articles to profl. publs. Bd. visitors U. Wis., Stevens Point, 1988-90; dist. organizer Eugene McCarthy Presdl. Campaign, Emporia, 1968; mem. leadership commn. Am. Coun. Edn., 1989-94; mem. exec. com. Campus Compact, 1990-95; bd. dirs. numerous civic and arts orgns., 1973-90; chmn. govs. adv. com. on vol. svc., Ohio, 1990-93; mem. leadership studies project U. Md., 1994—. Recipient Disting. Alumnus award Moorhead State U., 1989; grantee Minn. Arts Bd., 1974-76, Ind. Arts Commn., 1976-79. Mem. Am. Assn. Higher Edn., Univ. and Coll. Theatre Assn. (v.p. 1982-83), Marietta Country Club, Stevens Point Country Club, Athletic Club of Columbus. Democrat. Episcopalian. Avocations: travel, international relations, arts. Office: Calif State U Sys 400 Golden Shore Long Beach CA 90802-4275

MCDONOUGH, PATRICK JOSEPH, lawyer; b. Los Angeles, Oct. 11, 1943; s. Thomas John and Cecilia Veronica (Roach) McD.; m. Susan Ann Singletary, Dec. 30, 1967; 1 child, Colleen Marie. BA, Calif. State U., Northridge, 1967; JD, Loyola U., Los Angeles, 1971. Bar: Calif. 1971, U.S. Dist. Ct. (cen. dist.) Calif. 1971. Assoc. counsel. Auto Club So. Calif., Los Angeles, 1971-77, sec., assoc. counsel, 1977-86; sr. v.p., gen. counsel Johnson & Higgens Calif., Los Angeles, 1986—. Active United Wat Koko Challenge, 1993—. Mem. ABA, Calif. State Bar Assn. (ins. law com. 1993—), Los Angeles Bar Assn. (chmn. corp. law sect. 1987-88, Outstanding Corp. Coun. 1992), Inst. Corp Counsel (chmn. 1986-87), Am. Corp. Counsel Assn. Southern Calif. (bd. dirs. 1985-87), Assn. Calif. Tort Reform (bd. dirs. 1986—), L.A. Bar Found. (bd. dirs. 1993—)Town Hall Calif. Roman Catholic. Avocations: boating, sailing, fishing. Office: Johnson & Higgins Calif 2029 Century Park E Fl 24 Los Angeles CA 90067-2901

MCDONOUGH, PATRICK JOSEPH, JR., lawyer; b. Paterson, N.J., Sept. 13, 1941; s. Patrick Joseph and Margaret Mary (Bohan) McD.; m. Joanne Catherine Hansen, Dec. 26, 1966; children: Patrick Joseph III, Katherine Ann. BS, St. Joseph's U., Phila., 1964; AM, NYU, 1969; JD, Seton Hall Law Sch., Newark, 1976. Bar: N.J. 1978. Tchr. N.J. high schs., Elizabeth, N.J., 1964-69; dist. mgr. AT&T Hdqrs., N.Y.C., 1969-79, Morristown, N.J., 1981-90; mng. dir. internat. div. AT&T Hdqrs., East Brunswick, N.J., 1991—; legis. asst. U.S. Senate, Washington, 1980-81; speaker in field. Author: Are Your Electronic Files Secure?, 1989; co-author: Guide to Prosecution of Telecommunication Fraud by the Use of Computer Crime Statutes, 1989. advancement chair Watchung (N.J.) Area Boy Scouts Am., 1985—; chair Utility Adv. Bd., Cranford, N.J., 1976-79; mem. Zoning Bd. Adjustment, Cranford, 1978-79; mem. Union County (N.J.) Com., 1977-79; pres. Cranford (N.J.) Rep. Club, 1977-78. Recipient grant NSF, 1968. Mem. ABA (chmn., computer crime com. 1986—, contbr. to publ. guide 1989, Trial Mag. 1989), N.J. Bar Assn., Summit (N.J.) Bar Assn., Communications Fraud Control Assn. Home: 93 Pine Grove Ave Summit NJ 07901-2436 Office: AT&T 21-101 100th Naricon Pl East Brunswick NJ 08816

MCDONOUGH, REGINALD MILTON, religious organization executive; b. Mt. Vernon, Tex., Aug. 16, 1936; s. J.C. McDonough and Gladys (White) Branch; m. Joan Bird, Aug. 28, 1956; children: Michael Keith, Teri Royce. BS, East Tex. Bapt. U., 1957; MRE, New Orleans Bapt. Theol. Sem., 1960, DEd, 1967; DD, U. Richmond, 1988. Ordained to ministry Bapt. Ch. Minister Bapt. Ch., Arcadia, La., 1959-60; instr. East Tex. Bapt. U., Marshall, 1960-61; minister edn. North End Bapt. Ch., Beaumont, Tex., 1961-64; cons. ch. adminstrn. Bapt. Sun. Sch. Bd., Nashville, 1964-65, supr. ch. adminstrn., 1965-78, dept. dir., 1978-80; exec. v.p. exec. com. So. Bapt. Conv., Nashville, 1981-86; exec. dir. Bapt. Gen. Assn. Va., Richmond, 1987—. Author: Working with Volunteer Leaders in the Church, 1976, Keys to Effective Motivation, 1979, A Church on Mission, 1980; editor monthly mag. Bapt. Program, 1981-86. Recipient Eagle Scout award Boy Scouts Am., 1951, Disting. Alumnus award, New Orleans Bapt. Theol. Sem., 1979, Disting. Achievement award East Tex. Bapt. U. Alumni Assn., 1984. Mem. Soc. Religious Orgns. Mgrs. Avocations: flying, skiing, golfing. Home: 12800 Knightcross Rd Midlothian VA 23113-9608 Office: Va Bapt Gen Bd PO Box 8568 Richmond VA 23226-0568

MC DONOUGH, RICHARD DOYLE, retired paper company executive; b. St. Stephen, N.B., Can., May 8, 1931; s. Kenneth Paul and Mary (Doyle) McD.; m. Caroline Wilkins, July 7, 1956; children: Elizabeth Wilkins, Richard David, Philip Bradford. AB, Dartmouth Coll., 1952. Mgmt. trainee Gen. Electric Co., Lynn, Mass., 1953-56; various fin. positions lamp div. Gen. Electric Co., Monterrey, Mex., 1956-59; controller Mexican subs. Gen. Electric Co., Mexico City, 1959-63; cost supr. Singer Co., N.Y.C., 1964; fin. dir. Singer Co., Clydebank, Scotland, 1965-66; controller Eur. div. Singer Co., London, 1967-69; v.p. ops. Home Furnishings Group, 1969; v.p., corp. contr. Singer Co., N.Y.C., 1970-73; corp. v.p., pres. mail order div. Singer Co., Hanau, Fed. Republic of Germany, 1973-76; v.p. Singer Co., London, 1976-79; sr. v.p., CFO, dir. Bowater Inc., Darien, Conn., 1979-92, vice chmn., CFO, 1992-93, vice chmn., 1993-94, ret., 1994; dir. GEO Internat., Xylem Investments, Compensation Resources Group. Mem. Am. Forest and Paper Assn. (fin. com. 1980-94, steering com. 1987-94, vice chmn. 1989-91, chmn. 1991-93), Fin. Execs. Inst., Greenwich Country Club. Republican. Episcopalian. Avocations: scuba, opera. Home: Barons Mead E Point Ln Old Greenwich CT 06870-2403 Office: 25 East Point Ln Old Greenwich CT 06870-2403

MCDONOUGH, RUSSELL CHARLES, retired state supreme court justice; b. Glendive, Mont., Dec. 7, 1924; s. Roy James and Elsie Marie (Johnson) McD.; m. Dora Jean Bidwell, Mar. 17, 1946; children: Ann Remmich, Michael, Kay Jensen, Kevin, Daniel, Mary Garfield. JD, George Washington U., 1949. Bar: Mont. 1950. Pvt. practice Glendive, Mont., 1950-83; judge Gen. Jurisdiction State of Montana, Glendive, 1983-87; justice Mont. Supreme Ct., Helena, 1987-93, ret., 1993. City atty. City of Glendive, 1953-57; county atty. Dawson County, Mon., 1957-63; mem. Mont. Constl. Conv., Helena, 1972. 1st lt. AC, U.S. Army, 1943-45, ETO. Decorated DFC. Mem. Mont. Bar Assn. Roman Catholic. Home: 1805 Joslyn # 131 Helena MT 59601

MC DONOUGH, WILLIAM, corporate lawyer; b. 1943. Sr. v.p., gen. counsel Federal Reserve Bank of Boston, Mass. Office: Federal Reserve Bnk of Boston 600 Atlantic Ave Boston MA 02210

MCDONOUGH, WILLIAM J., banker; b. Chgo., 1934; married. B.S., Coll. of Holy Cross, 1956; M.A., Georgetown U., 1962. Spl. asst. to amb. Am. Embassy, Uruguay, 1961-67; st. economist Inter-Am. affairs to amb., 1961-67; with 1st Nat. Bank of Chgo., 1967-89, asst. v.p. internat. banking dept., 1967-70; v.p., gen. mgr. 1st Nat. Bank of Chgo., Paris, 1970-72; area head, Europe, Middle East and Africa 1st Nat. Bank of Chgo., 1972-73, sr. v.p., head internat. banking dept., 1973-75, exec. v.p., 1975-89; CFO 1st Nat. Bank of Chgo., 1982-89; chmn. asset and liability mgmt. com. 1st Nat. Bank of Chgo., until 1989; vice chmn. 1st Chgo. Corp. and 1st Nat Bank Chgo., 1986-89; exec. v.p., head bank fin. markets group Fed. Res. Bank of N.Y., 1992-93, pres. 1992-93, pres., CEO, 1993—. Served U. USN, 1956-61. Office: Fed Res Bank of NY 33 Liberty St New York NY 10045

MCDORMAND, FRANCES, actress; b. Ill. 1957. Student, Yale U. Sch. Drama. Stage appearances include Awake and Sing!, N.Y.C., 1984, Painting Churches, N.Y.C., 1984, The Three Sisters, Mpls., 1985, N.J., 1991, All My

Sons, New Haven, 1986, A Streetcar Named Desire, N.Y.C., 1988, Moon for the Misbegotten, 1992, Sisters Rosensweig, N.Y.C., 1993, The Swan, N.Y.C., 1993; TV appearances include The Twilight Zone, The Equalizer, Spencer: For Hire, Hill Street Blues, (series) Legwork, 1986-87, (TV movies) Scandal Sheet, 1985, Vengeance: The Story of Tony Cimo, 1986, Crazy In Love, 1992; film appearances include Blood Simple, 1984, Crime Wave, 1986, Raising Arizona, 1987, Mississippi Burning, 1988, Chattahoochee, 1990, Darkman, 1990, Miller's Crossing, 1990, Hidden Agenda, 1990, The Butcher's Wife, 1991, Passed Away, 1992, Short Cuts, 1993, Beyond Rangoon, 1995. Office: William Morris Agy 1350 Avenue Of The Americas New York NY 10019-4701*

MCDOUGAL, ALFRED LEROY, publisher; b. Evanston, Ill., Feb. 12, 1931; s. Alfred L. and Mary (Gillett) McD.; m. Gudrun Fenger, May 7, 1960 (div. 1982); children: Thomas, Stephen; m. Nancy A. Lauter, Mar. 1, 1986. BA, Yale U., 1953; MBA, Harvard U., 1957. Asst. to pres. Rand McNally & Co., Skokie, Ill., 1962-65, mgr. sch. dept., 1965-69; pres. McDougal, Littell & Co., Evanston, Ill., 1969-91, chmn., chief exec. officer, 1991-94; dir. Houghton Mifflin Co., Boston, 1994—; chmn. McDougal Family Found. Trustee Hadley Sch. for Blind, Winnetka, Ill., 1980-83; chmn. budget com. Evanston United Fund, 1974-76, bd. dirs.; bd. dirs. Evanston YMCA, 1988-94, Youth Job Ctr., 1987—, chmn. 1989-91, Opportunity Internat., 1994—, Literacy Chgo., 1992—, treas., 1994—. With U.S. Army, 1953-55. Mem. Assn. Am. Pubs. (exec. com. sch. divsn. 1981—, chmn. 1988-89, 92-94, dir. 1987-89), No. Ill. Assn. (1st v.p. 1984, chmn. 1985). Office: ALM Corp 401 N Michigan Ave 27th Fl Chicago IL 60611

MCDOUGAL, LUTHER LOVE, III, law educator; b. Paris, Tex., Oct. 19, 1938; s. Luther Love and Dorothy Harriet (Atkinson) McD.; m. Mary Anne McDougal, Apr. 12, 1959; children—Luther IV, Katherine, Kim, Mark, Myres. Student, Vanderbilt U., 1956-58; B.A., U. Miss., 1959, LL.B, 1962; LL.M., Yale U., 1966. Assoc. Blair & Anderson, Tupelo, Miss., 1962; ptnr. Riley & McDougal, Tupelo, 1963-64; prof. law U. Miss., Oxford, 1964-70, U. Ariz., Tucson, 1970-74; W. R. Irby prof. law Tulane U., New Orleans, 1974—; chmn. bd. N. Miss. Rural Legal Services, Oxford, 1967-70, Ctr. for Legal Studies of Intergovtl. Relations, New Orleans, 1982-86. Author: Property, Wealth, Land: Allocation, Planning and Development, 1981, Cases on American Conflicts Law, 1982, 2d edit., 1989, American Conflicts Law, 1986, Louisiana Oil and Gas Law, 1988; contbr. articles to profl. jours. Mem. Am. Law Inst. Democrat. Office: Tulane U Law Sch 6329 Freret St New Orleans LA 70118-5670

MCDOUGAL, STUART YEATMAN, comparative literature educator; author; b. L.A., Apr. 10, 1942; s. Murray and Marian (Yeatman) McD.; m. Menakka Weerasinghe, Apr. 29, 1967 (div. 1977); children—Dyanthe Rose, Gavin Rohan; m. Nora Gunneng, Aug. 4, 1979; children—Angus Gunneng, Tobias Yeatman. B.A., Haverford Coll., 1964; M.A., U. Pa., 1965, Ph.D., 1970. Lectr. U. Lausanne, Switzerland, 1965-66; asst. prof. Mich. State U., East Lansing, 1970-72; from asst. prof. to prof. English, comparative lit. and film /video U. Mich., Ann Arbor, 1972-85; dir. program in comparative lit. U. Mich., Ann Arbor, 1981—. Author: Ezra Pound and the Troubadour Tradition, 1972 (Bredvold prize 1973), 2d edit. 1991; Made into Movies: From Literature to Film, 1985, 5th edit. 1994. Editor: Dante Among the Moderns, 1985. Contbr. articles to profl. jours. Am. Council of Learned Socs. fellow, 1974-75; U. Mich. Rackham Research grantee, 1975-76; Fulbright Assn. sr. lectr., Italy, 1978; recipient Faculty Recognition award, U. Mich., 1987. Mem. MLA, Am. Comparative Lit. Assn. (sec.-treas. 1983-89, v.p. 1989-91, pres. 1991-93), Internat. Comparative Lit. Assn., Soc. Cinema Studies. Democrat. Office: U Mich Program in Comparative Lit 411 Mason Hall Ann Arbor MI 48109

MCDOUGAL, WILLIAM SCOTT, urology educator; b. Grand Rapids, Mich., 1942; s. William Julian and Verna Wilma (Pasma) McD.; m. Mary Stuart Logan, Sept. 19, 1992; 1 child, Molly Katherine. AB, Dartmouth Coll., 1964; MD, Cornell U., 1968. Intern in surgery U. Hosps., Cleve., 1968-69, resident in surgery, 1969-75, attending urologist, 1977-80; postdoctoral fellow in physiology Yale U., New Haven, 1971-72; postdoctoral fellow in surgery Case-Western Res. U., Cleve., 1972-75; chief burn study div. Inst. Surg. Rsch. Brook Army Med. Ctr., Ft. Sam Houston, 1975-77; instr. surgery U. Tex., San Antonio, 1975-77; asst. prof. urology Case Western Res. U., Cleve., 1977-78, assoc. prof. 1978-80; assoc. prof. Dartmouth Coll., Hanover, N.H., 1980-84, chmn. dept. urology, 1982-84; prof., chmn. dept. urology Vanderbilt U., Nashville, 1984-90; prof. surgery Harvard Med. Sch., 1991—; chief urology Mass. Gen. Hosp., Boston, 1991—. Office: Mass Gen Hosp Dept Urology Fruit St Boston MA 02114

MCDOUGALL, DONALD BLAKE, retired government official, librarian; b. Moose Jaw, Sask., Can., Mar. 6, 1938; s. Daniel Albert and Donela (McRae) McD.; m. Norma Rose Peacock, May 19, 1962. B.A., U. Sask., 1966, B.Ed., 1966; M.L.S., U. Toronto, 1969, M.L.S., U. Alta., 1983. Classroom tchr., Regina Bd. Edn., Sask., 1960-63, vice prin., 1963-68; asst. chief libr. Stratford Pub. Library, Ont., Can., 1969, chief libr., 1970-72; supr. info. svcs. Edmonton Pub. Library, Alta., Can., 1972, head pub. svcs., 1973-74; legislature libr. Province of Alta. , Edmonton, 1974-87; asst. dep. min., legis. libr. Legis. Assembly Alta., 1987-93, ret., 1993. Editor microfilm: Alberta Scrapbook Hansard, 1906-1964, 1976, editor Book: A History of the Legislature Library, 1979, Princess Louise Carline Alberta 1988, Lieutenant-Governors of the Northwest Territories and Alberta, 1876-1991, 1991, Premiers of the Northwest Territories and Alberta, 1887-1991, 1991. Govt. Sask. scholar, 1965; recipient Queen's Silver Jubilee medal Govt. Can., 1977; named Hon. Clk.-At-The-Table, Legis. Assembly Alberta, 1987. Mem. Alta. Govt. Libraries Council (chmn. 1975), Assn. Parliamentary Librarians in Can. (pres. 1980-82), Edmonton Library Assn., Hist. Soc. Alta. (v.p. Edmonton chpt. 1987), Library Assn. Alta., Can. Library Assn., Inst. Pub. Adminstrn. Can., Beta Phi Mu. Presbyterian. Clubs: Edmonton Jaguar Drivers, Edmonton Scottish Soc. Home: 209 Rhatigan Rd W, Edmonton, AB Canada T6R 1A2

MC DOUGAL, DUGALD STEWART, retired lawyer; b. Indpls., May 15, 1916; s. George and Effie (Barclay) McD.; m. Carol Brueggeman, Aug. 1938; children: George, Duncan, Walter, Robert; m. Judith Stephen, Dec. 1967. A.B., U. Chgo., 1935, J.D., 1937. Bar: Ill. 1937. Since practiced in Chgo.; sr. ptnr. McDougall, Hersh & Scott, 1961-87; sec., dir. Aladdin Industries, Inc. Served with USNR, 1942-46. Fellow Am. Coll. Trial Lawyers; mem. ABA, Am. Patent Law Assn., Patent Law Assn. Chgo., Law Club Chgo. Clubs: Union League (Chgo.); Olympia Fields (Ill.) Country. Office: Theodore R Scott 77 W Wacker Dr Chicago IL 60601-1629

MCDOUGALL, IAIN ROSS, nuclear medicine educator; b. Glasgow, Scotland, Dec. 18, 1943; came to U.S., 1976; s. Archibald McDougall and Jean Cairns; m. Elizabeth Wilson, Sept. 6, 1968; children: Shona, Stewart. MB, ChB, U. Glasgow, 1967, PhD, 1973. Diplomate Am. Bd. Nuclear Medicine (chmn. 1985-87), Am. Bd. Internal Medicine (gov. 1984-86). Lectr. in medicine U. Glasgow, 1969-76; fellow Harkness-Stanford Med. Ctr., 1972-74; assoc. prof. radiology and medicine Stanford (Calif.) U., 1976-84, prof. radiology and medicine, 1985—. Contbr. numerous articles to sci. jours. Fellow Royal Coll. Physicians (Glasgow), Am. Coll. Physicians; mem. Am. Thyroid Assn., Soc. Nuclear Medicine, Western Assn. for Clin. Research. Office: Stanford U Med Ctr Divsn Nuclear Medicine Stanford CA 94305

MCDOUGALL, JOHN ROLAND, civil engineer; b. Edmonton, Alta., Can., Apr. 4, 1945; s. John Frederick and Phyllis Eirene (Sladden) McD.; m. Susan Carley, July 2, 1971 (div. 1995); children: John Christopher, Jordan Page, Michael Tait. BSCE, U. Alta., Edmonton, 1967. Registered profl. engr., Alta. Engr. Imperial Oil Ltd., Calgary, Alta., 1967-69; sr. engr. Imperial Oil Ltd., Edmonton, Alta., 1969-75; treas. McDougall & Secord, Edmonton, 1969-85; v.p. McDougall & Secord, Ltd., 1975-90, pres., 1990—; pres., chief exec. officer Dalcor Cos., Edmonton, 1975-91; chmn. Trade Innoventures, Inc., 1992—; chair engring. mgmt. U. Alta., Edmonton, 1991—; chmn. D.B. Robinson & Assocs., Edmonton; bd. dirs. Edmonton Northlands; chmn. World Trade Centre, Edmonton, 1994—; mem. adv. bd. Royal Trust Corp., 1984-94. Chmn. Edmonton Civic Govt. Assn., 1975-77; mem. Premiers Coun. on Sci. and Tech., 1990. Fellow Can. Acad. Engrs. (bd. dirs. 1992—); mem. Can. Coun. Profl. Engrs. (pres. 1990-91), Assn. Profl. Engrs. Alta. (hon. life, pres. 1980-81), Can. Engring. Manpower Bd. (chmn. 1985-

88), Edmonton C. of C. (pres. 1989), Loyal Edmonton Regiment (hon.), Edmonton Club (pres. 1983-84). Anglican. Avocations: skiing, travel, cycling, philately, railroad modeling. Office: U Alta Faculty Engring, Edmonton, AB Canada T6G 2G8

MCDOUGALL, RONALD ALEXANDER, restaurant executive; b. Chgo., Aug. 12, 1942; s. John A. and Doris E. (Sengstock) McD.; m. Dale O. Ryser, Feb. 1, 1964 (div. July 1969); children: Timothy, Jonathan; m. Carolyn Kay Conley, Aug. 9, 1979; 1 child, Matthew. BBA, U. Wis., 1964, MBA, 1965. With Procter & Gamble, Cin., 1967-68, Sara Lee, Deerfield, Ill., 1969-72, The Pillsbury Co., Mpls., 1972-74, S&A Restaurant Corp., Dallas, 1974-82, Burger King, Miami, Fla., 1982-83; pres., COO Brinker Internat., Dallas, 1983—. Bd. dirs. Susan G. Komen Found., U. Wis. 1st lt. U.S. Army, 1965-67. Mem. Nat. Restaurant Assn., Am. Mgmt. Assn., Bent Tree Country Club, Aerobics Activity Ctr., Employment Policies Inst. Republican. Presbyterian. Avocations: tennis, running, baseball, cycling, golf. Office: Brinker Internat 6820 LBJ Fwy Dallas TX 75240-6515

MCDOUGALL, WALTER ALLAN, history educator; b. Washington, Dec. 3, 1946; s. Dugald Stewart and Carol Alberta (Brueggeman) McD.; m. Jonna Van Zanten, Aug. 6, 1988. BA, Amherst Coll., 1968; MA, U. Chgo., 1971, PhD, 1974. Asst. prof. U. Calif., Berkeley, 1975-83, assoc. prof. history, 1983-87, prof., 1987—; now Alloy-Ansin prof. internat. rels., prof. history U. Pa.; vis. scholar Hoover Inst., Stanford, Calif., 1986; mem. adv. panel Office Tech. Assessment, U.S. Congress, 1982-84, Harvard/Carnegie Study on Prevention of Nuclear War, 1985-86; witness House Sci. Tech. Com., U.S. Congress, 1985. Author: France's Rhineland Diplomacy, 1914-24: The Last Bid for a Balance of Power in Europe, 1978, The Grenada Papers, 1984, The Heavens and the Earth: A Political History of the Space Age, 1985 (Pulitzer prize 1986), Let the Sea Make a Noise...: A History of the North Pacific from Magellan to MacArthur, 1993; contbr. numerous articles to profl. and scholarly jours. Vestryman St. Peter's Episcopal Ch., Oakland, Calif, 1984—. Served as sgt. U.S. Army, 1968-70, Vietnam. Recipient Men and Women Under 40 Who are Changing Am. award Esquire Mag., 1984, Dexter Prize award for History of Tech., 1986; resident fellow Wilson Ctr. Smithsonian, 1981-82, Nat. Air and Space Mus., 1982. Mem. Hoover Instn., Delta Kappa Epsilon. Avocations: baseball, all selections music. Office: U Pennsylvania Dept History Philadelphia PA 19104-6379

MC DOW, JOHN JETT, agricultural engineering educator; b. Covington, Tenn., Jan. 6, 1925; s. Robert Simpson and Lucy Ann (Cocke) McD.; m. Dorothy Virginia Glass, Dec. 22, 1946; children: Ronald Allan, Jane Virginia. Student, Franklin and Marshall Coll. 1944-45; B.S., U. Tenn., 1948; M.S., Mich. State U., 1949, Ph.D., 1957. Registered profl. engr., Tenn., La. Instr. Mich. State U., 1949; instr. Okla. State U., 1949-51, asst. prof. agrl. engring., 1951; assoc. prof. La. Poly. U., 1951-57, prof., 1957-62, head agrl. engring. dept., 1953-62; prof., head dept. agrl. engring. U. Tenn., Knoxville, 1962-73; dean admissions and records U. Tenn., 1973-83, prof. agrl. engring., 1983-92, prof. emeritus, 1992—; cons./collaborator Agrl. Research Service, U.S. Dept. Agr., 1970-76; leader Rotary Internat. Found. Group Study Exchange Team to Philippines, 1984; mem. scholarship selection com. N.Am. Philips Corp., 1976-88. Contbr. articles to profl. jours. Mem. La. Engring. Council, 1955-56; bd. dirs. Tenn.-Venezuela-Amazonas Partners, 1977-80. Comdr. USNR, World War II, ret. So. Fellowship grantee, 1957. Mem. Am. Soc. Agrl. Engring. (dir. 1973-75), Am. Soc. Engring. Edn. (sec. agrl. engring. div 1971-72, vice chmn. 1972-73, chmn. 1973-74), Sigma Xi, Tau Beta Pi, Pi Mu Epsilon, Omicron Delta Kappa, Gamma Sigma Delta, Phi Kappa Phi (v.p. 1971-77, nat. pres. elect 1977-80, pres. 1980-83, pres. found. 1974-78). Lodge: Rotary (pres. 1989-90, chmn. dist. scholarship selection com. 1982-87, 88-91). Home: 2008 Walnut Hills Dr Knoxville TN 37920-2946

MC DOWALL, RODDY, actor; b. London, Sept. 28, 1928; s. Thomas Andrew and Winifred Mc D. Educated, St. Joseph's Sch., London. Actor, films include: Scavenger Hunt, Man Hunt, 1941, How Green Was My Valley, 1941, Confirm or Deny, 1941, Son of Fury, 1942, On the Sunny Side, 1942, The Pied Piper, 1942, My Friend Flicka, 1943, Lassie Come Home, 1943, White Cliffs of Dover, 1944, Macbeth, 1948, Kidnapped, 1948, Tuna Clipper, 1949, Black Midnight, 1949, Killer Shark, 1950, Steel Fist, 1952, The Subterraneans, 1960, Midnight Lace, 1960, The Longest Day, 1962, Cleopatra, 1963, The Greatest Story Ever Told, 1965, That Darn Cat, 1965, The Loved One, 1965, The Third Day, 1965, Inside Daisy Clover, 1965, It, 1966, Lord Love a Duck, 1966, The Defector, 1966, Bullwhip Griffin, 1967, The Cool Ones, 1967, Planet of the Apes, 1968, The Poseidon Adventure, 1972, Funny Lady, 1975, Charlie Chan and the Curse of the Dragon Queen, 1981, Evil Under the Sun, 1982, Class of 84, 1984, Fright Night, 1985, Dead of Winter, 1986, Overboard, 1987, The Big Picture, 1989, Destroyer, 1989, Fright Night Part 2, 1988, Cutting Class, 1989, Shakma, 1990; debut as dir. in The Devil's Widow, 1971; Broadway appearances include: Misalliance, Mean Johnny Barrows, Escapade, Doctor's Dilemma, No Time for Sergeants, Good as Gold, Compulsion, Handful of Fire, Look after Lulu, The Fighting Cock, 1959-60, Camelot, 1960-61, The Astrakhan Coat, 1966; numerous TV appearances on Macmillan & Wife; regular on TV series Planet of the Apes, 1974, Bridges to Cross, 1986; TV films include: Miracle on 34th Street, The Elevator, 1974, Hart to Hart, 1979, The Martian Chronicles, 1980, The Memory of Eva Ryker, 1980, Mae West, 1982, This Girl for Hire, 1983, The Zany Adventures of Robin Hood, 1984; author: Double Exposure: Take Two, 1989. Recipient Emmy award for Best Supporting Actor, 1960; Tony award for Best Supporting Actor. Office: Innovative Artists Talent & Lit Agy 1999 Ave Of The Stars Los Angeles CA 90067*

MC DOWELL, CHARLES EAGER, lawyer, retired military officer; b. Manchester, N.H., Sept. 9, 1923; s. Joseph Curry and Mildred (Eager) McD.; m. Carolyn A. Gibbons, June 21, 1947; children—Robin, Patricia. A.B., Dartmouth Coll., 1947; J.D., U. Va., 1950. Bar: Tex. 1950, Va. 1981, D.C. 1981. With land div. Shell Oil Co., Houston, 1950; commd. lt. (j.g.) USN, 1951, advanced through grades to rear adm., 1976; staff legal officer Comdr. Service Force, U.S. Pacific Fleet; staff judge adv., head internat. law div. Naval War Coll., 1963-66; staff legal officer, comdr. 7th Fleet, 1966-68; sr. Navy mem. ad hoc com., dep. asst. judge adv. gen. Office Judge Adv. Gen. Dept. Def., Washington, 1968-72; staff judge adv. on staff comdr. in chief U.S. Naval Forces, Europe, London, 1972-75; comdg. officer Naval Justice Sch., Newport, R.I., 1975-76; dep. judge adv. gen. Navy Dept., Washington, 1976-78, judge adv. gen., 1978-80; pvt. practice Dumfries, Va., 1981—. Served to 2d lt. AUS, 1943-46. Decorated D.S.M., Bronze Star, Joint Service Commendation medal, Navy Commendation medal with Combat V, Purple Heart, Combat Inf. badge. Mem. Fed. Bar Assn., Tex. Bar Assn., Va. Bar Assn., D.C. Bar Assn., Judge Advs. Assn., Order of Coif, Chi Phi. Methodist. Club: Square Dancer. Home: 1106 Croton Dr Alexandria VA 22308-2008 Office: The Law Bldg 201 Waters Ln Dumfries VA 22026-2209

MCDOWELL, CHARLES R., columnist, news analyst, lecturer; b. Danville, Ky., June 24, 1926; m. Ann Webb, Apr. 26, 1952. BA, Washington & Lee U., 1948; MS in Journalism, Columbia U., 1949; LHD (hon.), Washington & Lee U., 1975; hon. degree, Centre Coll. With Richmond (Va.) Times-Dispatch, 1949-65, Washington corr., columnist, 1965—; panelist PBS Washington Week in Review, 1977—. Author: One Thing After Another, 1960, What Did You Have in Mind?, 1963, Campaign Fever, 1965; author: (with others) Beyond Reagan, 1986; writer, narrator (documentary) Summer of Judgment, 1983, 84; voices (TV series) The Civil War, 1990, Baseball, 1994; commentator weekly TV series The Lawmakers; contbr. articles to profl. jours. Past chmn. Standing Com. Corrs. Recipient Nat. Headliner award, 1960, George Mason award Richmond chpt. Sigma Delta Chi, 1983, Burkett Miller Presdl. award White-Burkett Miller Ctr. Pub. Affairs at U. Va., 1984. Mem. Gridiron Club (past pres.). Office: 1214 National Press Bldg Washington DC 20045

MCDOWELL, DAVID E., pharmaceutical executive; b. 1942. AA, Orange Coast Jr. Coll., 1962; MS, Stanford U., 1978. V.p., gen. mgr. quality control Internat. Bus. Machines, Armonk, N.Y., 1991—, pres., COO McKesson Corp., 1991—. Office: McKesson Corp 1 Post St San Francisco CA 94104-5201

MCDOWELL, DONALD L., hospital administrator; b. Indpls., June 9, 1934; married; 5 children. BS Acctg., Ohio State U., 1956; grad. Edn.

Adminstrn., U. Fla. Acctg. tng. program Chevrolet divsn. Gen. Motors Corp., Toledo, Ohio, 1956-58, acctg. asst. supr. Chevrolet divsn., 1958-59; acctg. supr. Chevrolet divsn. Gen. Motors Corp., Atlanta, 1959-61; controller U. Fla., Gainesville, 1961-67; dir. mgmt. info. systems Fla. Bd. Regents, Tallahassee, 1967-68; v.p. adminstrv. affairs Fla. Internat. U., Miami, 1969-74; exec. dir. ops. Vanderbilt U., 1974-76, v.p. bus. affairs, 1976-80; exec. v.p., treas. Maine Med. Ctr., 1980-91, interim pres., 1990-91, pres., 1991—; bd. dirs. Maine Bank and Trust; com. mem. So. Assn. Colls. and Schs., program classification com. Nat. Ctr. Higher Edn. Mgmt. Systems; educator Fla. Internat. U.; city mgrs. adv. com. Portland. Mem. Bldg. com. YWCA Portland; chmn. Hosp. adv. com. Maine Health Care Fin. Commn.; at-large mem. House Dels. Am. Hosp. Assn.; Pres'. coun. visitors U. So. Maine; bd. dirs. ARC, Greater Portland United Way, Park Danforth Home for the Aged, Portland C. of C. (pres. 1990-91), Community Health Svcs., Portland Stage Co., Maine Hosp. Assn., Portland Symphony Orchstras, Voluntary Hosps. Am., New England (treas.), Regional C. of C. (chmn.), Maine Devel. Found., Ptnrs. for Progress, New England Healthcare Assembly. Office: Maine Med Ctr 22 Bramhall St Portland ME 04102

MCDOWELL, EDWARD R. H., chemical engineer; b. Cleve., Aug. 13, 1932; s. Blake and Lois (Held) McD.; m. Joyce Patricia Dudley, June 18, 1955; children: Edward R. H. Jr., James D. BSChemE, Cornell U., 1955; MS, Calif. Inst. Tech., 1960, PhD, 1964. Registered prof. chem. engr., Calif. Instr. Cornell U. Ithaca, N.Y., 1955; assoc. rsch. engr. Calif. Rsch. Corp., El Segundo, 1955-59; instr. Calif. Inst. Tech., Pasadena, 1959-63; rsch. engr. Chevron Rsch. Corp., La Habra, Calif., 1963-66, sr. rsch. engr., 1966-68; sr. engring. assoc. Chevron Oil Field Rsch. Co., La Habra, 1968-74, mgr., 1974-86; gen. ptnr. C. Blake McDowell Ltd. Partnership, Akron, Ohio, 1986—. NSF fellow Calif. Inst. Tech., 1961-63; recipient Engring. Merit award Orange County Engring. Coun., 1985. Fellow Am. Inst. Chem. Engrs. (pres. 1989, v.p. 1988, dir. 1982-84, Civic Achievement award 1983, F.J. & Dorothy Van Anwepen award 1992), Inst. for Advancement of Engring.; mem. Soc. Petroleum Engrs., Am. Assn. Engring. Socs. (bd. govs.), King Harbor Yacht Club (commodore 1990, vice commodore 1989, rear commodore 1988), St. Francis Yacht Club (San Francisco), Transpacific Yacht Club (Long Beach, Calif.), Assn. Santa Monica Bay Yacht Clubs (commodore 1989, vice commodore 1988, rear commodore 1987), Nawiliwili Yacht Club (Lihue, Hawaii), Magic Castle Club, Manhattan Country Club, The Cornell Club (N.Y.C.). Avocations: offshore sailboat racing (winner ULDB70 Season Sailing Championship 1990, 92), magic. Home: 2510 The Strand Hermosa Beach CA 90254-2553

MCDOWELL, ELIZABETH MARY, pathology educator; b. Kew Gardens, Surrey, Eng., Mar. 30, 1940; came to U.S., 1971; d. Arthur and Peggy (Bryant) McD. B Vet. Medicine, Royal Vet. Coll., London, 1963; BA, Cambridge U., 1968, PhD, 1971. Gen. practice vet. medicine, 1964-66; Nuffield Found. tng. scholar Cambridge (Eng.) U., 1966-71; instr. dept. pathology U. Md., Balt., 1971-73, asst. prof., 1973-76, assoc. prof., 1976-80, prof., 1980—. Co-author: Biopsy Pathology of the Bronchi, 1987; editor: Lung Carcinomas, 1987; contbr. over 120 articles to sci. jours., chpts. to books. Rsch. grantee NIH, 1979-92. Fellow Royal Coll. Vet. Surgeons Gt. Britain and Ireland. Avocations: conservation education, gardening, swimming. Home: 606 W 37th St Baltimore MD 21211-2230 Office: U Md 10 S Pine St Baltimore MD 21201-1192

MCDOWELL, EUGENE CHARLES, systems analyst; b. Washington, Jan. 13, 1940; s. Charles Jacob and Voilet Marie (Brown) McD.; m. Jill Perry Huntley, May 4, 1986 (dec. 1989); m. Hendrika Maria Ram, Mar. 21, 1992; step-daughter, Deepa Maria Long. BA, Am. U., 1962; MA, U. Chgo., 1966, 76; adv. cert. in Pub. Adminstrn., U.S. Dept. of Agr. Grad. Sch., 1973; grad. cert., Mastery U., 1995. Rsch. asst. ops. rsch. office Johns Hopkins U., Bethesda, Md., 1958-61; rsch. asst. Rsch. Analysis Corp., McLean, Va., 1961-66, ops. rsch. analyst, 1966-71; ops. rsch. analyst Nat. Bur. Standards, Gaithersburg, Md., 1971-80, program. analyst, 1980-82; ops. rsch. analyst Nat. Oceanic and Atmospheric Adminstrn., Rockville, Md., 1982-87, computer systems analyst, 1987—. Pres. Hemlock Soc. Nat. Capital Area, Washington, 1991-94, mem. bd. dirs. 1990—, Nuclear Free Am., Balt., 1991-94, mem. bd. dirs. 1989—, Garrett Park (Md.) Citizens Assn., 1982-84; originator nuclear-free zones in U.S., Garrett Park, Md., 1982; auditor North Bethesda Congress of Citizens Assn., 1982-84; active U. Chgo. Profl. Achievement Award Com., Washington, 1977—, chmn., 1982-84. Mem. Hemlock Soc. USA (life), AAAS (life), Philos. Soc. Washington (life), Azalea Soc. Am., Metropolitan Washington Bioethics Network, Standards Engring. Soc. (chmn. bd. govs. 1983-84, sr. 1982). Democrat. Unitarian. Avocations: gardening, reading. Home: PO Box 92 Garrett Park MD 20896-0092

MCDOWELL, FLETCHER HUGHES, physician, educator; b. Denver, Aug. 5, 1923; married. BA, Dartmouth Coll., 1943; MD, Cornell U., 1947. From instr. to assoc. prof. medicine Cornell U. Med. Coll., N.Y.C., 1968—, assoc. dean Med. Coll., from 1970, Winifred Masterson Burke prof. rehab. medicine; med. dir. Burke Rehab. Hosp., White Plains, N.Y., from 1973. Mem. Am. Acad. Neurology, Am. Neurol. Assn., Am. Fedn. Clin. Research. Office: Burke Rehab Ctr 785 Mamaroneck Ave White Plains NY 10605-2523

MCDOWELL, JACK BURNS, professional baseball player; b. Van Nuys, Calif., Jan. 16, 1966. Grad. Stanford U. Baseball player Chgo. White Sox, 1987-88, 90-94, N.Y. Yankees, 1994—. mem. Am. League All-Star Team, 1991-93; Sporting News All-Star Team, 1992, 93; Am. League Complete Games Leader, 1991-92; recipient Cy Young award Baseball Writers Assn. Am., 1993; named Sporting News Pitcher of Yr., 1993. Office: NY Yankees Yankee Stadium E 161st St & River Ave Bronx NY 10451*

MC DOWELL, JACK SHERMAN, political consultant; b. Alameda, Calif., Feb. 23, 1914; s. John Sherman and Myra Lorraine (Frierson) McD.; m. Jeanette California Ofelth, June 18, 1938; children: Nancy Lynn (Mrs. Henry A. Swanson, Jr.), Peggy Joanne (Mrs. G.P. Cramer), Judy Carolina. Student, San Jose State Coll., 1931-32. With Alameda Times-Star, 1926-31, San Jose Evening News, 1932; owner, operator with brother Turlock Daily Jour., 1933-40, Eugene (Oreg.) Daily News, 1941-42; staff writer San Francisco Call-Bull. (now Examiner), 1942-50, war corr. Pacific, 1944, daily columnist, 1946-50, city editor, 1950-56, polit. editor, columnist, 1956-69; specialist in ballot measures Woodward & McDowell (polit. campaign mgmt. advt. and pub. relations), 1969—; News dir. Gov. Ronald Reagan campaign, 1970, Senator S.I. Hayakawa campaign, 1976. Co-author: (with Chaplain Howell M. Forgy) And Pass the Ammunition, 1944; Contbr. articles to mags. Recipient best news photo award Calif. Newspaper Pub. Assn., 1939, Pulitzer prize for distinguished reporting, 1944. Mem. Am. Assn. Polit. Cons. Club: Press (San Francisco). Home: 97 Normandy Ln Atherton CA 94027-3816 Office: 111 Anza Blvd Burlingame CA 94010-1932

MCDOWELL, JAMES W., JR., milk products company executive; b. 1942; married. BS, U. Ky., 1965. Field supr. Kyana Milk Producers Assn., until 1965; chief oper. officer, sr. v.p. sales engring. purchasing Dairymen, Inc., Louisville, 1965, now chief exec. officer and exec. v.p., exec. v.p. Flav-O-Rich, Inc., Louisville. Office: Flav-O-Rich Inc 10140 Linn Station Rd Louisville KY 40223-3813

MCDOWELL, JAY HORTENSTINE, lawyer; b. New Orleans, July 10, 1936; s. Jacob Leonidas Hortenstine and Martha (Grace) Babcock; m. Kari Keyser, Oct. 24, 1959; children: Paul H., Sean C., Kari K. Student, Eastbourne Coll., Sussex, Eng., 1954-55; BA, Yale U., 1959; LLB, U. Va., 1963. Bar: N.Y. 1964. Assoc. Cadwalader, Wickersham & Taft, N.Y.C., 1963-71, ptnr., 1972—; trustee Issac H. Tuttle Fund, N.Y.C., 1968—, pres., 1985—. V.p., bd. dirs. St. Mary's Hosp. for Children, Bayside, N.Y., 1972—. Mem. ABA, Assn. Bar of City of N.Y. Clubs: Union (N.Y.), Shelter Island Yacht (N.Y.). Office: Cadwalader Wickersham & Taft 100 Maiden Ln New York NY 10038-4818

MCDOWELL, JENNIFER, sociologist, composer, playwright, publisher; b. Albuquerque; d. Willard A. and Margaret Frances (Garrison) McD.; m. Milton Lowenthal, July 2, 1973. BA, U. Calif., 1957; MA, San Diego State U., 1958; postgrad., Sorbonne, Paris, 1959; MLS, U. Calif., 1963; PhD, U. Oreg., 1973. Tchr. English Abraham Lincoln High Sch., San Jose, Calif. 1960-61; free-lance editor Soviet field, Berkeley, Calif., 1961-63; rsch. asst. sociology U. Oreg., Eugene, 1964-66; editor, pub. Merlin Papers, San Jose,

1969—, Merlin Press, San Jose, 1973—; rsch. cons. sociology San Jose, 1973—; music pub. Lipstick and Toy Balloons Pub. Co., San Jose, 1978—; composer Paramount Pictures, 1982-88; tchr. writing workshops; poetry readings, 1969-73; co-producer radio show lit. and culture Sta. KALX, Berkeley, 1971-72. Author: (with Milton Lowenthal) Black Politics: A Study and Annotated Bibliography of the Mississippi Freedom Democratic Party, 1971 (featured at Smithsonian Instn. spl. event 1992), Contemporary Women Poets: An Anthology of California Poets, 1977, Ronnie Goose Rhymes for Grown-ups, 1984; co-author: (plays off-off Broadway) Betsy and Phyllis, 1986, Mack the Knife Your Friendly Dentist, 1986, The Estrogen Party To End War, 1986, The Oatmeal Party Comes to Order, 1986, Plays) Betsy Meets the Wacky Iraqi, 1991, Bella and Phyllis, 1994; contbr. poems, plays, essays, articles, sport stories, and book revs. to lit. mags., news mags. and anthologies; rschr. women's autobiog. writings, contemporary writing in poetry, Soviet studies, civil rights movement, and George Orwell, 1962—; writer: (songs) Money Makes a Woman Free, 1976, 3 songs featured in Parade of Am. Music; co-creator mus. comedy Russia's Secret Plot To Take Back Alaska, 1988. Recipient 8 awards Am. Song Festival, 1976-79, Bill Casey Award in Letters, 1980; doctoral fellow AAUW, 1971-73; grantee Calif. Arts Coun., 1976-77. Mem. Am. Sociol. Assn., Soc. Sci. Study of Religion, Poetry Orgn. for Women, Dramatists Guild, Phi Beta Kappa, Sigma Alpha Iota, Beta Phi Mu, Kappa Kappa Gamma. Democrat. Office: care Merlin Press PO Box 5602 San Jose CA 95150-5602

MC DOWELL, JOHN B., bishop; b. New Castle, Pa., July 17, 1921; s. Bernard A. and Louise M. (Hannon) McD. B.A., St. Vincent Coll., 1942, M.A., 1944; M.A., Catholic U. Am., 1950, Ph.D., 1952; Litt.D. (hon.), Duquesne U., 1962; grad., St. Vincent Sem., Latrobe, Pa. Ordained priest Roman Catholic Ch., 1945, consecrated as titular bishop of Tamazuca and aux. bishop of Pitts., 1966—; asst. pastor St. Irenaeus Ch., Oakmont, 1945-49; asst. supt. schs. Diocese of Pitts., 1952-55, supt. schs., 1955-70, vicar for edn., from 1970; now vicar gen.; pastor Epiphany Parish, Pitts., 1969—; papal chamberlain to Pope Pius XII, 1956, to Pope John XXIII, 1958; domestic prelate to Pope Paul VI, 1964; chmn. ad hoc com. on moral values in our soc. Nat. Conf. Cath. Bishops, from 1973, Bishops Com. for Pastoral on Moral Values, from 1976; mem. Internat. Council for Catechesis, from 1975. Co-author elem. sch. religions series, jr. high sch. lit. series, elem. sci. series and elem. reading series; contbr. ednl. articles to various publs.; former editor: Cath. Educator Mag. Bd. dirs. Allegheny County Community Coll.; bd. dirs. Western Pa. Safety Council, Duquesne U. Named Man of Yr. in Religion Pitts., 1970, 93, Educator of Yr., United Pvt. Acad. Schs. Assn., 1978, Man of Yr., Pitts. chpt. KC, 1989. Mem. Nat. Cath. Ednl. Assn., Cath. Ednl. Assn. Pa., Omicron Delta Kappa Gamma Circle (hon.). Office: Epiphany Ch 1018 Centre Ave Pittsburgh PA 15219-3596 also: Chancery Office 111 Blvd Of The Allies Pittsburgh PA 15222-1618*

MCDOWELL, JOHN EUGENE, lawyer; b. Toledo, Nov. 22, 1927; s. Glenn Hugh and Evelyn (Millspaugh) McD.; m. Jean Ann Hepler, June 18, 1950; children: Jane Lynn McDowell Thummel, Sheila Lorraine McDowell Laing. BS, Miami U., Oxford, Ohio, 1949; JD, U. Mich., 1952. Bar: Ohio 1952. Assoc. Dinsmore & Shohl, Cin., 1952-59, ptnr., 1959—; bd. dirs. Structural Dynamics Rsch. Corp., Milford, Ohio. Mem. solicitation coms. United Appeal, Cin., NCCJ, Cin., Boy Scouts Am., Cin. Mem. ABA, Ohio Bar Assn., Cin. Bar Assn., Cin. Country Club, Queen City Club, Order of Coif. Democrat. Episcopalian. Office: Dinsmore & Shohl 1900 Chemed Ctr 255 E 5th St Cincinnati OH 45202-4700

MCDOWELL, JOHN HOLMES, folklore educator, institute director; b. Washington, Sept. 24, 1946; s. Joseph Edward and Margaret (Holmes) McD.; children from previous marriage, Juan, Sofia; m. Patricia A. Glushko, Sept. 4, 1987; 1 child, Michael. BA in Music, Swarthmore Coll., 1969; PhD in Anthropology, U. Tex., 1975. Prof., chair Folklore Inst. Ind. U., Bloomington. Author: Children's Riddling, 1979 (Chgo. Folklore prize U. Chgo. 1979), Sayings of the Ancestors: The Spiritual Life of the Sibundoy Indians, 1989, So Wise Were Our Elders: Mythic Narratives of the Kamsá, 1994; editor: Andean Musics, 1987, Andean Cosmologies through Time: Persistence and Emergence, 1992; editor Jour. Folklore Rsch., 1986-92, Spl. Publs. of Folklore Inst., 1990—; author video prodns.; contbr. articles to profl. jours. John Simon Guggenheim fellow, 1994. Mem. Hoosier Folklore Soc. (pres. 1994). Avocations: soccer, L.Am. music. Home: 516 W 3d St Bloomington IN 47403 Office: Ind U Folklore Inst 504 N Fess Bloomington IN 47401

MCDOWELL, MALCOLM, actor; b. Leeds, Eng., June 13, 1943; m. Mary Steenburgen, 1980 (div.); 2 children. Began career with Royal Shakespeare Co., Stratford, Eng., 1965-66; early TV appearances include: role of Dixon of Dock Green in Z Cars, British TV; other TV appearances: Little Red Riding Hood, Faerie Tale Theatre, Showtime TV, 1983, Gulag, HBO, 1985; stage appearance: In Celebration, N.Y.C., 1984; films include: Poor Cow, 1967, If..., 1969, Figures in a Landscape, 1970, The Raging Moon, 1971, A Clockwork Orange, 1971, O Lucky Man, 1973, Royal Flash, 1975, Aces High, 1976, Voyage of the Damned, 1977, Caligula, 1977, The Passage, 1978, Time After Time, 1979, Cat People, 1981, Britannia Hospital, 1984, Blue Thunder, 1983, Get Crazy, 1983, Cross Creek, 1983, Sunset, 1987, Buy and Cell, 1989, Class of 1999, 1989, Bopha!, 1993, Milk Money, 1994, The Caller, Star Trek: Generations, 1994, Tank Girl, 1995. *

MCDOWELL, MICHAEL DAVID, lawyer, utility executive; b. Lewisburg, Pa., May 10, 1948; s. David Leonard and Mary Ellen (Scallan) McD.; m. Martha LaMantia, Aug. 4, 1973; 1 child, Daniel Joseph. B.S. in Bus. Mgmt., U. Dayton, 1970; J.D., U. Pitts., 1973. Bar: Pa. 1973, U.S. Dist. Ct. (mid. dist.) Pa. 1973, U.S. Tax Ct. 1974, U.S. Ct. Appeals (3d cir.) 1974, U.S. Dist. Ct. (we. dist.) Pa. 1975, U.S. Supreme Ct. 1977, U.S. Ct. Internat. Trade 1981, U.S. Ct. Appeals (fed. cir.) 1982. Assoc. U.S. atty. Dept. Justice, Lewisburg, Pa., 1973-75; assoc. Hirsch, Weise & Tillman, Pitts., 1975-76, Plowman & Spiegel, Pitts., 1976-80; counsel Dravo Corp., Pitts., 1980-86, sr. counsel, 1987; atty. West Penn Power Co., Greensburg, Pa., 1987—; mem. panel of arbitrators Am. Arbitration Assn., 1978—; Pa. Bur. Mediation, 1983—, Pa. Labor Relations Bd., 1985—. Contbr. articles to profl. jours. Mem. Union County Child Welfare adv. com., 1974-75; account exec. Southwestern Pa. United Way, Pitts., 1983; bd. govs. Pine Run Homeowners Assn., 1986-87; mem. nat. panel consumer arbitrators Better Bus. Bur., 1986—; sr. arbitrator, 1989—; mem. supervisory com. ALCOBAR Credit Union, 1986-87. Recipient Dravo Corp. Editorial Achievement awards, 1982, 83, 85, 86; nominated as one of Outstanding Young Men. Am., 1983,84. Fellow Am. Bar Found., Pa. Bar Found.; mem. ABA (Ho. of Dels. 1985-91, exec. coun. sect. labor and employment law 1983-85, exec. council young lawyers div. 1982-84, chmn. YLD Labor Law Com. 1981-83, fellow, 1985—), Pa. Bar Assn. (Ho. of Dels. 1980-94, chmn. special rules subcom. Disciplinary Bd. Study Com. 1983-93, com. on legal ethics and profl. responsibility, 1983—, arbitrator lawyer dispute resolution program 1987—, house com. on rules and calendar 1991-94, Outstanding Young Lawyer award 1984, Spl. Achievement award 1986,), Allegheny County Bar Assn. (profl. ethics com. 1980—, bd. govs. 1979, 85-91, asst. sec.-treas. 1979, chmn. young lawyers sect. 1978, council professionalism 1988-90, by-laws com. 1980—, award for outstanding leadership and valuable contbns. to bar 1979), Nat. Constructors Assn. (gen. counsels com. 1983-87), Am. Corp. Counsel Assn., McCandless Swimming Club (Pitts., bd. govs. 1982-85), Phi Alpha Delta (justice 1972-73, cert. Outstanding Service 1973). Republican. Roman Catholic. Office: West Penn Power Co 800 Cabin Hill Dr Greensburg PA 15601-1650

MCDOWELL, ROBERT, farmer; b. Iowa, Sept. 11, 1924; s. Gerald J. and Vera Grace (Hagist) McD.; m. Elnora Miner, Apr. 3, 1927; children: Gina Lorraine McDowell Bennett, Robert Gerald. BA, Iowa Wesleyan Coll., 1948. Vice chmn. Farmland Industries, Inc., Kansas City, Mo., 1981—; pres. Hog Corp., 1981, Ke-Wash R.R., F&M Inc., Keota Farms, Inc., M&W, Inc., Iowa Turkey Fedn., Des Moines. Chmn. Keota Devel., 1950-75, Keota Sch. Bd., 1975-87, Keota Coop. Bd., 1960-80; elder United Presbyn. Ch., Keota, 1950; leader Boy Scouts Am., Cub Scouts Am. Named Outstanding Man Yr., Keota Jaycees, 1950, Outstanding Farmer, Future Farmers Am., 1970. Democrat. Avocations: golfing, fishing, boating, reading. Home: RR 1 Box 113 Keota IA 52248-9419 Office: Farmland Industries Inc 3315 N Oak Trafficway Kansas City MO 64116

MCDOWELL, ROBERT NEIL, accounting company executive; b. Oakland, Calif., Sept. 20, 1945; s. Kenneth Eugene and Edythe (Bowman) McD.; m. Ruth Edith Bartleson, July 6, 1968; children: Scott, Amy. BA, Juniata Coll., 1967; MA, U. Md., 1974. Mgr. pers. and rehab. Goodwill Industries, Balt., 1967-69; assoc. dir. career planning U. Md., College Park, 1969-74; mgr. pers. Coopers & Lybrand, Chgo., 1974-77; office dir. pers. and adminstrn. Coopers & Lybrand, Phoenix, 1977-80; staff dir. to vice chmn. Coopers & Lybrand, Phila., 1980-83; assoc. nat. dir. pers. Coopers & Lybrand, N.Y.C., 1983-87, staff dir. to chmn. and dep. chmn., 1987-88, nat. dir. personnel, 1988—. Mem. Human Resource Planning Soc., Am. Acctg. Assn., Am. Soc. for Tng. and Devel., Madison Golf Club. Office: Coopers & Lybrand 1251 Ave Of The Americas New York NY 10020-1104

MCDOWELL, ROBIN SCOTT, physical chemist; b. Greenwich, Conn., Nov. 14, 1934; s. James Duffil and Aimee Marguerite (Lavers) McD.; m. Arlene R. Egertsen, Nov. 23, 1963; children: Jennifer Ellen, Allison Elizabeth. BA, Haverford Coll., 1956; PhD, MIT, 1960. Mem. staff Los Alamos (N.Mex.) Nat. Lab., 1960-81, asst. group leader, 1981-82, fellow, 1983-91; sr. chief scientist in chem. structure and dynamics program Battelle Pacific N.W. Labs, Richland, Wash., 1991—. Contbr. articles to profl. jours. and encyclopaedias. Chmn. Los Alamos County Libr. Bd., 1981-82; mem. bd. Mid-Columbia Symphony, 1994—. Mem. AAAS, Am. Chem. Soc., Optical Soc. Am., Coblentz Soc. Inc. (pres. 1987-89), Soc. Applied Spectroscopy, Sigma Xi. Achievements include pioneering in infrared laser spectroscopy of inorganic molecules. Office: Battelle Pacific NW Labs Richland WA 99352

MCDOWELL, THEODORE NOYES, public relations consultant; b. Washington, Oct. 20, 1925; s. Ralph Walker McDowell and Ruth Noyes Sheldon; m. Mildred Bowen, Mar. 5, 1945; children: Patricia B., Janet Ruth Curtis, Theodora McDowell Herskovitz, Theodore Noyes Jr. BA, Duke U., 1947. Reporter Washington Star Newspaper, 1947-51, asst. promotion mgr., 1951-53; account exec. Evening Star Broadcasting Co., Washington, 1953-55, TV program mgr., 1955-62, gen. mgr. news and pub. affairs and sec., 1962-70; dir. office of pub. affairs U.S. Dept. Transp., Washington, 1970-71; regional rep. of the sec. U.S. Dept. Transp., Atlanta, 1971-76; self-employed media cons. Hilton Head Island, S.C., 1976—. Former mem. and vice chmn. governing bd. Nat. Cathedral Sch., Washington; former bd. dirs. Children's Hosp., Washington, chmn. Pres.'s Cup Regatta, 1960-61; elder Presbyn. Ch. With USN, 1943-46. Recipient Meritorious Achievement award Sec. Transp., 1971, Sec.'s award, 1973, Nat. Def. Transp. Assn. award, 1972-73. Mem. Radio TV News Dirs. Assn. (former bd. dirs.), AP Radio/TV Assn. (bd. dirs., past pres.), Soc. Profl. Journalists, Broadcast Pioneers, Toastmasters. Presbyterian (elder). Home and Office: 29 Ruddy Turnstone Rd Hilton Head Island SC 29928-5704

MCDOWELL, WILLIAM S., lawyer; b. Chgo., Mar. 16, 1941. BBA, U. Mich., 1963, JD with distinction, 1966. Bar: Ill. 1966. Ptnr. Baker & McKenzie, Chgo. Office: Baker & McKenzie 1 Prudential Plz 130 E Randolph Dr Chicago IL 60601

MCDUFFIE, FREDERIC CLEMENT, physician; b. Lawrence, Mass., Apr. 27, 1924; m. Isabel Simpson Wiggin, May 31, 1952; children: Elisabeth Wiggin, Joan Selden, Deborah Howard, Charles Dennett. Grad., Harvard U., M.D. cum laude, 1951. Diplomate Am. Bd. Internal Medicine and Subbd. Rheumatology. Intern Peter Bent Brigham Hosp., Boston, 1951-52; resident Peter Bent Brigham Hosp., 1952-53, 56-57; tng. in phys. chemistry Harvard U., 1953-54; in immunology Columbia Coll. Physicians and Surgeons, 1954-56; asst. prof. internal medicine U. Miss., Jackson, 1957-62; asst. prof. microbiology U. Miss., 1957-64, assoc. prof., 1964-65; cons. medicine and microbiology Mayo Clinic and Mayo Found., Rochester, Minn., 1965; asst. prof. internal medicine and microbiology Mayo Grad. Sch. Medicine, 1965-69, asso. prof., 1969-73; asso. prof. Mayo Med. Sch., 1973, prof. internal medicine and immunology, 1974-79; prof. medicine Emory U., Atlanta, 1979—; vis. investigator Center for Disease Control, Atlanta, 1979-88; sr. v.p. med. affairs Arthritis Found., Atlanta, 1979-87; dir. Piedmont Hosp. Arthritis Ctr., 1988—; pres. Miss. chpt. Arthritis Found., 1962-63; bd. dirs., mem. exec. com. Miss. chpt. Arthritis Found. (Minn. chpt.), 1974-79, chmn. med. and sci. com., 1973-74; nat. trustee, 1978-79, chmn. nat. research com., 1978-79; trustee Nat. Health Coun., 1984—. Editorial bd. Arthritis and Rheumatism, 1976-81, Jour. Rheumatology, 1974—; editor Jour. Lab. and Clin. Medicine, 1977-79; contbr. articles to profl. jours. Served with U.S. Army, 1943-45. Mem. Am. Assn. Immunologists, Am. Rheumatism Assn., Central Rheumatism Assn. (pres. 1973-74), Central Soc. Clin. Research (council 1977-79), Soc. Exptl. Biology and Medicine, Am. Fedn. Clin. Research, A.C.P., Alpha Omega Alpha. Home: 3155 Arden Rd NW Atlanta GA 30305-1916 Office: Piedmont Hosp 2001 Peachtree Rd NE Ste 200 Atlanta GA 30309-1476

MCDUFFIE, KEITH A., literature educator, magazine director; b. Spokane, Wash., Feb. 12, 1932; s. Clair L. and Helen Marie (Yaeger) McDuffie; m. Helen E. Ferry, June 5, 1965 (div. Sept. 1992); children: Anne Leslie, Andrew Keith; m. Pamela Philips Bacarisse, Aug. 14, 1995. BA in English, Gonzaga U., Spokane, 1954; MA in Spanish, Middlebury (Vt.) Coll., 1960, Univ. Complutense, Madrid, Spain, 1960; PhD in Hispanic Lit., U. Pitts., 1969. Prof. U. Mont., 1969-74; Mellon postdoctoral fellow U. Pitts., 1974, prof., chair dept. Hispanic Lit., 1975-92, prof. Hispanic Lit., 1992—; editor Revista Iberoamericana, Pitts., 1991—. Co-author: Co-Textes: Cesar Vallejo, 1987; co-editor: Texto y Contexto-Actas 19 Congreso del IILI, 1980, En Este Aire de America: Homenaje a Alfredo Roggiano, 1990. With U.S. Army Security Agy., 1954-56. Mellon Predoctoral fellow U. Pitts., 1965, Title VI fellow U.S. Govt., 1966; Spanish Govt. scholar Spanish Govt., 1959-60. Contbg. mem. Instituto Internacional de Literatura Iberoamericana (bd. dirs. 1991—, exec. dir. 1991—). Democrat. Home: Apt 1001 220 N Dithridge Pittsburgh PA 15213

MC DUFFIE, MALCOLM, oil company executive; b. San Francisco, Nov. 14, 1915; s. William Chester and Mary (Skaife) McD.; m. Mary Sutherland de Surville, Dec. 8, 1951; children: Cynthia de Surville, Duncan de Surville. A.B. in Econs. Stanford U., 1940. With O.C. Field Gasoline Corp., 1940-41, Wilmington Gasoline Corp., 1941-42; with Mohawk Petroleum Corp., 1945-80, pres., dir., 1969-80; dir. Res. Oil & Gas Co., 1973-80, ex v.p., 1977-80; sp. asst. to pres. Getty Oil Co., Los Angeles, 1980-82. Bd. overseers Huntington Library, Art Gallery and Bot. Gardens, 1972—; bd. dirs. Calif. Inst. Tech. Assocs., 1976-82. Mem. Nat. Petroleum Refiners Assn. (Dir. 1970-80), Ind. Refiners Assn. Calif. (pres. 1967-69, 77-78, dir. 1950-80), Rancheros Visitadores. Republican. Episcopalian. Clubs: California (Los Angeles); Bohemian (San Francisco); Valley Hunt (Pasadena, Calif.), Annandale Golf (Pasadena, Calif.); Birnam Wood (Santa Barbara, Calif.), Valley (Montecito, Calif.). Office: 180 S Lake Ave Ste 315 Pasadena CA 91101-2619

MCDUFFIE, MARCIA JENSEN, pediatrics educator, researcher; b. Phila., Apr. 10, 1949; d. John Calvin and Agnes Margaret (Jakob) J.; children: Kathryn Steere, Joanna Steere, Michael. Student, Duke U., 1967-69; BA cum laude with honors in Biochemistry, U. Pa., 1971; MD with honors, U. N.C., 1981. Diplomate Am. Bd. Pediat. Pediat. intern U. Colo. Health Scis. Ctr., Denver, 1981-82, resident in pediat., 1982-84, asst. prof., 1987-93, rsch. mem. Barbara Davis Ctr. for Childhood Diabetes, 1989-93; postdoctoral fellow div. basic immunology dept. medicine Nat. Jewish Ctr. for Immunology and Respiratory Medicine, Denver, 1984-87; assoc. prof. U. Va. Health Scis. Ctr., Charlottesville, 1993—; reviewer Sci., Diabetes, Jour. Clin. Investigation, European Jour. Pediat., Lab. Investigation. Assoc. editor Jour. Immunology, 1992-94; contbr. articles to profl. jours. Recipient career devel. award Juvenile Diabetes Found., 1992-95; rsch. grantee Juvenile Diabetes Found., 1991-95, Am. Diabetes Assn., 1994-96. Mem. Soc. for Pediatric Rsch., Am. Assn. Immunologists. Office: U Va Health Scis Ctr MR-4 Rm 5116 Charlottesville VA 22908

MCEACHEN, RICHARD EDWARD, banker, lawyer; b. Omaha, Sept. 24, 1933; s. Howard D. and Ada Carolyn Helen (Baumann) McE.; m. Judith Ann Gray, June 28, 1969; children: Mark E., Neil H. BS, U. Kans., Lawrence, 1955; JD, U. Mich., 1961. Bar: Mo. 1961, Kans. 1962. Assoc. Hillix, Hall, Hasburgh, Brown & Hoffhaus, Kansas City, Mo., 1961-62; sr. v.p. First Nat. Bank, Kansas City, Mo., 1962-75; exec. v.p. Commerce Bank Kansas City, Mo., 1975-85, Centerre Bank of Kansas City N.A., 1985-87,

Security Bank Kansas City, Kans., 1987-88; exec. v.p., trust officer UMB Overland Park Bank, 1988-93; atty. Ferree, Bunn & O'Grady Chartered, Overland Park, 1994—. Gov. Am. Royal Assn., Kansas City, Mo., 1970—, amb., 1980—; bd. dirs. Harry S. Truman Med. Ctr., Kansas City, 1974-86, mem. fin. com., 1975-86, treas., 1979-84, bd. govs., 1986—, mem. bldg. and grounds com., 1993—; trustee Clearinghouse for Midcontinent Founds., 1980-87; bd. dirs. Greater Kansas City Mental Health Found., 1963-69, treas., 1964-69, v.p. 1967-69; adv. bd. urban svcs. YMCA, Kansas City, 1976-83; cubmaster Kanza dist. Boy Scouts Am., 1982-83, dist. vice-chmn., 1982-83, troop com., 1983-90, treas., 1986-88; bd. dirs. Scout Booster Club, Inc., 1989-94; mem. planned gift com. William Rockhill Nelson Gallery Art, Children's Mercy Hosp. Planned Gift Coun., 1991; mem. adv. com. Legal Assistance Program Avila Coll., 1978-80, adv. coun. Future Farmers Am., 1972-82; mgr. Oppenstein Bros. Found., 1979-85, George & Dollie LaRue Found., 1981-85; trustee Village Presbyn. Ch., 1987-90, chmn., 1989-90, elder, 1994—; bd. dir. Village Presbyn. Ch. Found., 1987-89, 94—; bd. dirs. Estate Planning Coun., 1984-86, Shawnee Mission Med. Ctr. Found., 1988—, fin. com., 1989-92. Mem. Nat. Assn. Securities Dealers Inc. (bd. arbitrators), Am. Arbitration Assn. (panel arbitrators), Estate Planning Soc. Kansas City, Mo. Bar Assn., Kans. Bar Assn., Johnson County Bar Assn., Kansas City Met. Bar Assn., Estate Planning Assn. (pres. 1974-75), Kansas City Jr. C. of C. (v.p. 1964-66), Lawyers Assn. Kansas City, Ea. Kans. Estate Planning Coun., Indian Hills Club, Delta Tau Delta Alumni (v.p. Kansas City chpt. 1978-80). Republican. Home: 9100 El Monte St Shawnee Mission KS 66207-2627 Office: One Glenwood Pl Ste 300 PO Box 12570 Shawnee Mission KS 66212

MCEACHERN, ALLAN, Canadian justice; b. Vancouver, B.C., Can., May 20, 1926; s. John A. and Blanche L. (Roadhouse) McE.; m. Gloria, July 17, 1953; children: Jean Williams, Joanne Evans. BA, U. B.C., Vancouver, 1949; LLB, U. B.C., 1950. Assoc., sr. ptnr., barrister, solicitor Messrs. Russell & DuMoulin, Vancouver, B.C., 1950-78; chief justice Supreme Ct. B.C., Vancouver, 1979-88, Ct. Appeals B.C., Vancouver, 1988—. Pres. Kats Rugby Club, Vancouver, 1953-64, B.C. Lions Football Club, Vancouver, 1967, 68, 69, We. Football Conf., 1964, Can. Football League, 1967-68, commr. 1967-68. Mem. Can. Bar Assn. (bd. dirs.), Vancouver Bar Assn. (bd. dirs.), Legal Aid Soc. (pres. 1977-78), Law Soc. B.C. (bencher 1971-79). Avocations: sailing, gardening, walking, summer cottage. Home: 1414 W King Edward Ave, Vancouver, BC Canada V6H 2A2 Office: Law Cts, 800 Smithe St, Vancouver, BC Canada V6Z 2E1

MCEACHRAN, ANGUS, newspaper editor; b. Memphis, Aug. 24, 1939; s. Angus G. and Maxine (Taylor) McE.; m. Ann Blackwell; children: Angus G. 111, Amanda Simmons. Student, George Washington U., 1958-59, Memphis State U., 1959-61. Reporter The Comml. Appeal, Memphis, 1960-63, asst. city editor, 1963-65, metro editor, 1965-69, asst. mng. editor, 1969-77; exec. editor Birmingham (Ala.) Post-Herald, 1977-78, editor, 1978-82; exec. editor The Pitts. Press., 1982-83, editor, 1983-92; editor The Commercial Appeal, Memphis, Tenn., 1993-94, editor, pres., 1994—; corr. N.Y. Times, Wall St. Jour., Newsweek, The Nat. Observer. Mem. Am. Soc. Newspaper Editors, Pa. Soc. Newspaper Editors (bd. dirs.), Sigma Delta. Roman Catholic. Avocations: fishing, hiking, reading, racquetball. Home: 872 River Park Dr Memphis TN 38103 Office: Commercial Appeal 495 Union Ave Memphis TN 38103

MCELHANEY, JAMES HARRY, biomedical engineer; b. Phila., Oct. 27, 1933; s. James H. and Olga M. (Lazuk) McE.; m. Eileen M. Esbensen, Nov. 17, 1954; children—Kathy, Amy, Liza. B.S., Villanova U., 1955; M.S., U. Pa., 1960; Ph.D., W.Va. U., 1964. Registered profl. engr., Pa. Mech. engr. Philco Corp., Phila., 1955-59; asst. prof. mech. engring. Villanova (Pa.) U., 1959-62; prof. theoretical and applied mechanics W.Va. U., Morgantown, 1962-69; asso. prof. mech. engring., head biomechanics dept. Hwy. Safety Research Inst., U. Mich., 1969-74; prof. biomechanics, chmn. biomed. engr-ing. dept. Duke U., Durham, N.C., 1974—; prof. exptl. orthopaedics Duke U. Med Ctr., 1986—; dir. grad. studies, Duke U., 1974-75; cons. Ford Motor Co., Am. Motors Co., Chrysler Corp., Westinghouse Corp., NIH, others; chmn. com. on indsl. head protection Am. Nat. Standards Inst. Editor: mech. engring. sect. Jour. of Bioengring, 1977—; mem. editorial adv. bd.: mech. engring. sect. Jour. of Biomechanics, 1967—; Contbr. articles on bi-omechanics to profl. jours. Served with U.S. Army Res., 1955-63. NIH grantee, 1967—. Mem. Am. Soc. Engring. Edn., ASME (chmn. bioengring. div. 1975—, asso. editor Trans. on Biomech. Engring.), Soc. for Exptl. Stress Analysis, Soc. Automotive Engrs. (chmn. anthropometric dummy study com.), Southeastern Neurol. Soc. (pres. elect), Biomedical Engring. Soc., Am. Acad. Mechanics, Sigma Xi, Pi Tau Sigma. Club: Duke Men's. Home: 3411 Cambridge Dr Durham NC 27707-4507 Office: Biomedical Engring Dept Duke U Durham NC 27707

MC ELHANEY, JAMES WILSON, lawyer, educator; b. N.Y.C., Dec. 10, 1937; s. Lewis Keck and Sara Jane (Hess) McE.; m. Maxine Dennis Jones, Aug. 17, 1961; children: David, Benjamin. A.B., Duke U., 1960; LL.B. 1962. Bar: Wis. 1962. Assoc. firm Wickham, Borgelt, Skogstad & Powell, 1966; asst. prof. U. Md. Law Sch., 1966-69, assoc. prof., 1969-72; vis. prof. So. Meth. U. Sch. of Law, Dallas, 1973-74; prof. So. Meth. U. Sch. of Law, 1974-76; Joseph C. Hostetler prof. trial practice and advocacy Case Western Res. U. Sch. of Law, Cleve., 1976—; mem. faculty Nat. Inst. Trial Advocacy, Boulder, Colo., 1975—; vis. prof. U. Tulsa Coll. Law, summer 1977, 79, Ind. U. Law Sch., summer 1980; cons. to U.S. Atty. Gen. on Justice Dept. Advocacy Tng. Programs, 1979—; lectr. in field. Author: Effective Litiga-tion: Trials, Problems and Materials, 1974, Trial Notebook on Tape: The Basics, 1989, McElhaney's Trial Notebook on Tape: Advanced Techniques, 1991, McElhaney's Trial Notebook on Tape: Evidence, Foundations and Objections, 1992, McElhaney's Trial Notebook on Tape: Winning Tactics, 1994; editor in chief Litigation mag., 1984-86, sr. editor., 1986—; contbr. columns to Trial Notebook, Litigation, to profl. jours. Recipient Out-standing Prof. award So. Meth. U., 1976, Disting. Tchr. of Yr. award Sch. Law, Case Western Res. U., 1989. Mem. ABA (council on litigation 1987—, author jour. column Litigation), Assn. Am. Law Schs. (chmn. sect. trial advocacy 1974-76, chmn. sect. evidence 1978). Office: Case Western Res U 11075 E Boulevard Cleveland OH 44106 *The lamp of doctrine is a flickering and unsteady guide; we are led more by facts than obtuse theory.*

MC ELHANEY, JOHN HINES, lawyer; b. Milw., Apr. 16, 1934; s. Lewis Keck and Sara Jane (Hess) McE.; m. Jacquelyn Masur, Aug. 4, 1962; chil-dren—Scott, Victoria. B.B.A., So. Meth. U., 1956, J.D., 1958. Bar: Tex. bar 1958. Pvt. practice law Dallas, 1958—; shareholder Locke Purnell Rain Harrell, 1976—; lectr. law So. Meth. U., 1967-76. Contbr. articles to legal jours. Trustee St. Mark's Sch. Tex., 1980-86. Fellow Am. Coll. Trial Lawyers; mem. Am. Bd. Trial Advs., ABA, Tex. Bar Assn., So. Meth. U. Law Alumni Assn. (pres. 1972-73, dir. 1970-73), Town and Gown Club (pres. 1981-82). Presbyterian. Home: 5340 Tanbark Dr Dallas TX 75229-5555 Office: Locke Purnell Rain Harrell 2200 Ross Ave Ste 2200 Dallas TX 75201-6766

MCELHINNY, HAROLD JOHN, lawyer; b. San Francisco, Jan. 5, 1947; s. Harold James and Margaret I. (Mahoney) McE.; m. Mary Ellen McElhinny, June 22, 1968; children: Hannah, Jennifer, William. BA in Polit. Sci., U. Santa Clara, 1970; JD, U. Calif., Berkeley, 1975. Bar: Calif. 1976, U.S. Supreme Ct. 1983. Vol. Peace Corps, Tripoli, Libya, 1968-69; juvenile counselor Santa Clara County (Calif.) Juvenile Hall, 1969-72; law clk. U.S. Dist. Ct., Hartford, Conn., 1975-76; ptnr. Morrison & Foerster, San Francisco, 1976—. Mem. ABA, Calif. State Bar Assn., State Bar Calif. (rev. dept. 1986-89, chair 1988), San Francisco Bar Assn., Am. Intellectual Property Law Assn., Assn. Bus. Trial Lawyers (bd. govs. 1992—). Democrat. Roman Catholic. Office: Morrison & Foerster 345 California St San Francisco CA 94104

MCELHINNY, WILSON DUNBAR, banker; b. Detroit, July 27, 1929; s. William Dunbar and Elizabeth (Wilson) McE.; m. Barbara Cheney Watkins, June 6, 1952 (dec.); children: David Ashton, Ward Cheney, Edward Wilson, William Dunbar; m. Lisa Lesher, Mar., 1993. BA, Yale U., 1953. With Union and New Haven Trust Co., 1952-63; with Reading Trust Co., Pa., 1963-68, pres., 1968-70; pres. Nat. Central Bank (formerly Reading Trust Co.), Pa., 1970-79, chief exec. officer, 1975-79; chmn. bd. dirs., pres., chief exec. officer Hamilton Bank (formerly Nat. Central Bank), Lancaster, Pa., 1979-81, chmn. bd. dirs., chief exec. officer, 1981-83, chmn. bd. dirs., 1981-

90; pres. CoreStates Fin. Corp., Phila., 1983-86, vice chmn., 1986-90; pres., chmn. Hamilton Bank, Lancaster, Pa., 1988-90, also dir.; bd. dirs. Hunt Mfg. Co., Phila., Educators Mut. Life Ins. Co., Reading Eagle Co., Wohlsen Constrn. Co.; chmn. bd. Irex Corp. Bd. dirs. Lancaster Gen. Hosp. Found. Mem. Pa. C. of C. (chmn. 1990-92), Hamilton Club (Lancaster), Lancaster Country Club. Home and Office: 198 Pinetown Rd Leola PA 17540

MCELIECE, ROBERT JAMES, electrical engineering educator, author, consultant; b. Washington, May 21, 1942; s. Richard Frederick and Norma Frances (Ferris) McE.; m. Constance Jeannette Holst, June 20, 1964 (div. Oct. 1987); children: Angela, Karen, Elizabeth; m. Laif Swanson, Mar. 19, 1988; 1 child, David. BS, Calif. Inst. Tech., 1964, PhD, 1967. Mem. tech. staff, group supr. Jet Propulsion Lab., Pasadena, Calif., 1963-78, cons., 1978—; prof. math, rsch. prof., coordinator sci. lab. U. Ill., Urbana, 1978-82; prof. elec. engring. Calif. Inst. Tech., Pasadena, 1982—; cons. Cyclotomics, Inc., Berkeley, Calif., 1978—. Author: Theory of Information and Coding, 1977, Finite Fields, 1986, Introduction to Discrete Mathematics, 1989; contbr. articles to profl. jours. Fellow IEEE ; mem. Info. Theory Group IEEE (pres. 1984), Am. Math. Soc. Avocation: running. Office: Calif Inst Tech Dept Elec Engring # 116-81 Pasadena CA 91125

MCELLIGOTT, JAMES PATRICK, JR., lawyer; b. Chgo., Jan. 11, 1948; s. James Patrick and Helen Cecelia (Hogan) McE.; children: Michael Sean, Andrew David; m. Trina Reff, Aug. 25, 1985. BA, U. Ill., Urbana, 1970; JD, Harvard U., 1973. Bar: Va. 1974, U.S. Dist. Ct. (ea. and we. dists.) Va. 1974, U.S. Ct. Appeals (4th cir.) 1974, U.S. Supreme Ct. 1979. Research asst. U. Ill., 1970; assoc. McGuire, Woods & Battle, Richmond, 1973-79; ptnr. McGuire, Woods, Battle & Boothe, Richmond, 1979—. Mem. exec. com. Va. Home for Boys, Richmond, 1976—, pres. bd. govs., 1981-83; mem. Leadership Metro Richmond-Met. C. of C., 1984-85; bd. dirs. ARC Greater Richmond Chpt., 1990—, chmn., 1994—. Mem. ABA, Va. Bar Assn. (exec. com., chmn. pub. rels. com. 1978-82, producer pub. svc. message 1973, Hot Spot award 1973), Richmond Bar Assn., Fed. Bar Assn. (pres. Richmond chpt. 1986), Nat. Sch. Bds. Assn., Coun. of Sch. Attys., Phi Beta Kappa, Phi Kappa Phi, Omicron Delta Epsilon. Home: 203 Cyril Ln Richmond VA 23229-7740 Office: McGuire Woods Battle & Boothe One James Ctr Richmond VA 23219-3229

MC ELRATH, RICHARD ELSWORTH, insurance company executive; b. Thompsontown, Pa., Oct. 11, 1932; s. Clayton Ellsworth and Jane Elizabeth (Shoop) McE.; m. Donna Gail Booher, Aug. 18, 1952; children—Leslie Jo, Jennifer Jo, Josie Arlene Elizabeth, Rebekah Clare. B.S. cum laude, Elizabethtown (Pa.) Coll., 1955; M.B.A. cum laude, Harvard U., 1961. Research asst. Harvard U., 1961-62; asst. to pres. Callaway Mills Co., LaGrange, Ga., 1963-65; with Irving Trust Co., N.Y.C., 1965-73; v.p. Irving Trust Co., 1969-73; treas. Travelers Ins. Annuity Assn. and Coll. Retirement Equities Fund, 1973-81; v.p. Met. Life Ins. Co., 1982—; pres., dir. MetLife Funding, Inc., MetLife Credit, Inc., 1984—. Author articles, case studies. Trustee Elizabethtown Coll.; mem. Society Valley Hosp., Ridgewood, N.J.; mem. Boston Rep. Com., 1961-63, Troup County (Ga.) Rep. Com., 1964-65; bd. dirs. Family Counseling Svc., Ridgewood, 1986-92. Lt. comdr. USNR, 1956-59. Mem. Assn. Gov. Bds. Univs. and Colls. Methodist. Club: Harvard (N.Y.C.). Home: 17 Cedar St Glen Rock NJ 07452-1608 Office: 1 Madison Ave New York NY 10010

MC ELROY, BOBBIE, furniture manufacturing executive; b. Little Rock, Apr. 2, 1936; d. Johnnie Robert and Lela Ruth (Vining) Custer; m. Warren Lawrence McElroy, Nov. 6, 1953; children: Lawrence Lee, Ronald Alan. Sec. Antioch Baptist Ch., Little Rock, 1962-74; sec., treas. Rock City Furniture, Inc., North Little Rock, 1974—. Home: 22 Colony Rd Little Rock AR 72207 Office: Rock City Furniture Inc PO Box 9046 North Little Rock AR 72119

MCELROY, CHARLOTTE ANN, principal; b. Dimmitt, Tex., Oct. 24, 1939; d. William Robert and Mary Ilene (Cooper) McE. BA, West Tex. State U., 1962, MEd, 1964; postgrad., Calif. State U., Santa Barbara, 1966-68. Tchr. Amarillo (Tex.) Schs., 1962-65; 1st and 2d grade tchr. Ventura (Calif.) Schs., 1965-66, 4th, 5th and 6th grade tchr., 1966-74, elem. coun-selor, 1974-76, spl. edn. tchr., 1976-77, counselor, phys. edn. tchr., 1977-78; asst. prin. Cabrillo Jr. High Sch., Ventura Unified Schs., 1978-80; prin. E. P. Foster Elem. Sch., Ventura Unified Schs., 1980-84, Anacapa Middle Sch., Ventura Unified Schs., 1984—; presenter in field. Recipient Nat. Blue Ribbon Sch. award Nat. Edn. Dept., 1990-91, Calif. Disting. Sch. award, 1989-90; named one of Outstanding Principals, State Calif., 1992-93. Mem. Ventura Adminstrs. Assn., Calif. League Middle Schs., Assn. Calif. Sch. Adminstrs., Kappa Kappa Gamma. Democrat. Avocations: skiing, reading, music, gardening. Home: 2250 Los Encinos Rd Ojai CA 93023-9709 Office: Anacapa Middle Sch 100 S Mills Rd Ventura CA 93003-3487

MCELROY, EDMUND G., JR., financial executive; b. N.Y.C., June 26, 1941; s. Edmund G. and Elizabeth (Arnold) McE.; m. Marcy Leanne Ham, June 13, 1964; children: Scott E., Elizabeth M., Todd C., Peter J. BA in Econs., Lafayette Coll., 1964; MBA, NYU, 1971. Asst. v.p. Irving Trust Co., N.Y., 1964-71; dir. cash and banking Avon Products, Inc., N.Y.C., 1971-81; asst. treas. Nabisco Brands, East Hanover, N.J., 1981-85; treas. Dyson-Kissner-Moran Corp., N.Y.C., 1985-93; asst. treas. and dir. of corp. treasury Gateway 2000, Inc., North Sioux City, S.D., 1994—. Councilman Borough of Ho-ho-kus, N.J., 1984-94; active Bergen County United Way, Paramus, N.J., 1983-86. Mem. Internat. Fin. Group, N.Y. Treas. Group, Nat. Assn. Corp. Treas., Midwest Treasury Mgmt. Assn. Republican. Episcopalian. Avocations: skiing, running, tennis, hiking. Office: Gateway 2000 Inc 610 Gateway Dr North Sioux City SD 57049

MCELROY, EDWARD J., union officer; b. Providence, Mar. 17, 1941; s. Edward J. Sr. and Clara (Angelone) McE.; m. Edwina Barbara Ricci, Apr. 20, 1963; children: Kathleen, Mary, Stephen, Elizabeth. AB, Providence Coll., 1962. Cert. tchr. Tchr. Lockwood Jr. High Sch., Warwick, R.I., 1962-72; pres. Warwick Tchrs. Union, Warwick, R.I., 1967-69, R.I. Fed. Tchrs., Am. Fed. Tchrs., Providence, 1971-92; v.p. Am. Fed. Tchrs., AFLCIO, Providence, 1974-92; sec. treas. Am. Fed. Tchrs., AFLCIO, Washington, 1992—; pres. R.I. AFLCIO, Providence, 1977-92. Exec. com. mem. R.I. Democratic State Com., Providence, 1976-92; sec. exec. com. United Way So. New England, Providence, 1978-92; devel. commn. R.I. State, 1984-85, mem. Workforce 2000, 1987-92. Recipient Quirk Inst. award Providence Coll., 1980. Mem. Aurora Civic Assn. Democrat. Roman Catholic. Avocations: golf, photography, reading. Office: Am. Fed Tchrs AFL CIO 555 New Jersey Ave NW Washington DC 20001-2029

MCELROY, FREDERICK WILLIAM, economics educator, consultant; b. Dublin, Ireland, May 18, 1939; came to U.S., 1963; s. Herbert John and Annie Maureen (McDowell) McE.; m. Kathleen Child, Sept. 8, 1964; chil-dren: Dominique, Hugh. BA, Nat. U. of Ireland, Dublin, 1960; MA, U. Coll. Dublin, 1961; PhD, Georgetown U., 1967. Asst. prof. econs. SUNY, Buffalo, 1967-68; asst. prof. econs. Georgetown U., Washington, 1968-71, assoc. prof. econs., 1971-77, prof. econs., 1977—; chair econs. dept., 1994—; cons. in antitrust cases; cons. Grocery Mfrs. of Am., Washington, 1976—. Contbr. articles to profl. jours. Trustee, treas. Help the Aged, Washington, 1982-86; bd. dirs. Oxfam-Am., Boston, 1976-79. Mem. Am. Econs. Assn., Phi Beta Kappa, Alpha Sigma Nu. Democrat. Roman Catholic. Avoca-tions: tennis, golf. Home: 5013 Brookdale Rd Bethesda MD 20816-1709 Office: Georgetown U Dept Econs Washington DC 20057

MC ELROY, JOHN HARLEY, electrical engineering educator; b. Marion, Ohio, June 27, 1936; s. Francis and Alice Marie McElroy; m. Eleonore Hildegard Schmidt, Mar. 18, 1957. B.S. in Elec. Engring. U. Tex., Austin, 1966; M.E.E., Cath. U. Am., 1973, Ph.D., 1978. Instr. guided missiles Air Defense Sch. U.S. Army, 1957-63; rsch. asst. Quantum Electronics rsch. Lab U. Texas, Austin, 1963-66; staff Goddard Flight Center, Greenbelt, Md., 1966-79, 80-82; chief communications tech. div. Goddard Flight Center, 1978-79, dep. dir. center, 1980-82; dir. communications programs NASA Hdqrs., Washington, 1979-80; asst. adminstr. NOAA, Washington, 1982-85; dir. spl. projects Hughes Aircraft Co., Los Angeles, 1985-86; v.p. tech. Hughes Communications, Inc., 1986-87; dean coll. engring., prof. elec. engr-ing. U. Tex., Arlington, 1987—; cons. satellite communications and earth observations. Contbr. articles to profl. jours. Served with AUS, 1954-63. Recipient Apollo Achievement award NASA, 1969, Applications Tech.

Satellite award, 1975, Earth Resources Satellite award, 1973; named Wernher von Braun Meml. Lectr. Smithsonian Instn. Fellow AIAA, Washington Acad. Scis., IEEE. Home: PO Box 1122 Arlington TX 76004-1122 Office: U Tex Arlington PO Box 19019 Arlington TX 76019

MCELROY, JOHN LEE, JR., brokerage house executive; b. Richmond, Va., Feb. 28, 1931; s. John Lee and Margaret (Williams) McE.; m. Aminta Sorrel Mackall, Oct. 12, 1957; children: John Lee III, Mary Earle McElroy Robertson, Sorrel M., Margaret W. B, U. Va., 1953, postgrad., 1964. Securities analyst State Planters Bank, Richmond, 1955-58; stockbroker Wheat, 1st Securities, Inc., Richmond, 1958-63, mgr., ptnr., 1963-86, chmn., chief exec. officer, 1986—, also bd. dirs.; vice chmn., chief exec. officer WFS Fin. Corp., 1986—; also bd. dirs. Piper, Jaffray & Hopwood, Mpls. Pres. Va. Hist. Soc., Richmond, Children's Home Soc., Richmond; bd. dirs. Cen. Richmond Assn., Ch. Schs. of Diocese Va., St. Catherine's Sch., St. Timothy's Sch., Vestry St. Paul's Ch.; trustee St. Paul's Episcopal Ch. Home. Lt. (j.g.) USCG, 1953-55. Republican. Episcopalian. Avocations: golf, sailing, hunting. Home: 13 River Rd Richmond VA 23226-3310 Office: Wheat First Securities Inc 707 E Main St Richmond VA 23219-2814

MCELROY, SISTER MAUREEN, secondary school principal. Prin. St. Mary Acad.-Bay View, Riverside, R.I. Recipient Blue Ribbon Sch. award U.S. Dept. Edn., 1990-91. Office: St Mary Acad-Bay View 3070 Pawtucket Ave Riverside RI 02915-5105

MCELROY, MICHAEL, physicist, researcher; b. Shercock, County Cavan, Ireland, May 18, 1939; married, 1963. B.A., Queen's U., Belfast, Ireland, 1960; Ph.D. in Math., Belfast, Ireland, 1962. Project assoc. Theoretical Chemistry Inst., U. Wis., 1962-63; from asst. physicist to physicist Kitt Peak Nat. Obs., 1963-71; physicist Ctr. Earth and Planetary Physics Harvard U., Cambridge, Mass., 1971—, now Abbott Lawrence Rotch prof. atmospheric sci.; chmn. Dept. Earth and Planetary Scis. Harvard U., 1986—; mem. Mars panel Lunar and Planetary Missions Bd., NASA, 1968-69, Stratospheric Research Adv. Com., Space and Terrestrial Applied Adv. Com. Atmospheric Sci., Nat. Acad. Sci. Space Sci. Bd.; chmn. Com. Planetary and Lunar Exploration. Recipient James B. Macelwane award Am. Geophys. Union, 1968; recipient Newcomb Cleve. prize AAAS, 1977, Pub. Service medal NASA, 1978. Office: Harvard U Dept Earth and Planetary scis 20 Oxford St Cambridge MA 02138

MC ELROY, WILLIAM DAVID, biochemist, educator; b. Rogers, Tex., Jan. 22, 1917; s. William D. and Ora (Shipley) McE.; m. Nella Winch, Dec. 23, 1940 (div.); children—Mary Elizabeth, Ann Reed, Thomas Shipley, Wil-liam David; m. Marlene A. DeLuca, Aug. 28, 1967; 1 son, Eric Gene. B.A., Stanford, 1939; M.A., Reed Coll., 1941; Ph.D., Princeton U., 1943; D.Sc., U. Buffalo, 1962, Mich. State U., 1970, Loyola U., Chgo., 1970, U. Notre Dame, 1975, Calif. Sch. Profl. Psychology, 1978; D.Pub. Service, Providence Coll., 1970; LL.D., U. Pitts., 1971, Johns Hopkins U., 1977. War research, com. med. research OSRD, Princeton, 1942-45; NRC fellow Stanford, 1945-46; instr. biology dept. Johns Hopkins, 1946, successively asst. and asso. prof., prof. biology, 1951-69, chmn. biology dept., 1956-69; also dir. McCollum-Pratt Inst., 1949-64; dir. NSF, Washington, 1969-71; chancellor U. Calif., San Diego, 1972-80, prof., from 1980, now prof. emeritus. Author textbook.; Editor: (with Bentley Glass) Copper Metabolism, 1950, Phosphorus Metabolism, 2 vols, 1951, 52, Mechanism of Enzyme Action, The Chemical Basis of Development, 1959, Light and Life, 1961, Cellular Physiology and Biochemistry, 1961, (with C.P. Swanson) Foundations of Modern Biology series, 1961-64. Mem. Sch. Bd. Baltimore City, 1958-68. Recipient Barnett Cohen award in bacteriology, 1958; Rumford prize Am. Acad. Arts and Scis., 1964. Mem. AAAS (pres. 1976, chmn. 1977), Am. Inst. Biol. Scis. (pres. 1968), Am. Chem. Soc., Nat. Acad. Sci., Am. Soc. Biol. Chemists (pres. 1963-64), Soc. Gen. Physiology (pres. 1960-61), Soc. Naturalists, Soc. Zoologists, Am. Acad. Arts and Scis., Am. Soc. Bacteri-ologists, Am. Philos. Soc.,Sigma Xi, Kappa Sigma. Office: U Calif at San Diego La Jolla CA 92093

MC ELROY, WILLIAM THEODORE, lawyer; b. Newark, Jan. 20, 1925; s. William J. and Matilda (Hamilton) McE.; m. Emilie Hoinowski, Jan. 18, 1947; children: Karen L., William J., Ruth P. LL.B. cum laude, Rutgers U., 1950. Bar: N.J. bar 1949. Assoc. Duggan, Shaw & Hughes, Newark, 1949-50; with McElroy, Connell, Foley & Geiser (and predecessor firms), Newark, 1950-78; ptnr. McElroy, Connell, Foley & Geiser (and predecessor firms), 1956-78; judge Superior Ct. N.J., Morristown, 1978-80; Appellate Div. Superior Ct. N.J., 1980-85; ptnr. McElroy, Deutsch & Mulvaney, Morris-town, N.J., 1985—. Served with USNR, 1942-45. Fellow Am. Coll. Trial Lawyers; mem. ABA, N.J. Bar Assn. (chmn. civil procedure sect. 1973-74), Essex County Bar Assn., Morris County Bar Assn., Trial Attys. N.J. (Dist-ing. Svc. in cause of justice award 1986).d. Home: 80 Old Farm Rd Basking Ridge NJ 07920-9721 Office: 1300 Mt Kemble Ave PO Box 2075 Morris-town NJ 07960

MCELVAIN, DAVID PLOWMAN, manufacturing company financial ex-ecutive; b. Chgo., Oct. 16, 1937; s. Carl R. and Ruth P. (Plowman) McE.; B.B.A., U. Ariz., 1961, M.B.A., 1962; m. Mary Rosalind Hysong, Dec. 20, 1961; children—Jana, Jodi. Consolidation accountant, exec. div. Dresser Industries, Inc., Dallas, 1962-67, corporate fin. controller, 1973-76, dir. fin. services, 1976-78, staff v.p. fin. service and risk mgmt., 1978-82, exec. v.p. fin. services group, 1982-83, pres. fin. services group, 1984-86, v.p. fin., chief fin. officer, 1987—; controller crane, hoist & tower div., Muskegon, Mich., 1967-73. Cert. mgmt. acct. Mem. Nat. Assn. Accts., Beta Gamma Sigma, Phi Delta Theta. Episcopalian. Home: 3806 Beverly Dr Dallas TX 75205-2808 Office: Dresser Industries Inc 1600 Pacific Bldg PO Box 718 Dallas TX 75221-0718

MCELVEEN, JUNIUS CARLISLE, JR., lawyer; b. Rogersville, Tenn., Feb. 17, 1947; s. Junius Carlisle and Martha Kathleen (Harrison) McE.; m. Mary Wallace Pyles, Sept. 22, 1973; children: Kathryn Carlisle, Sarah Elizabeth. BA cum laude, U. Va., 1969, JD, 1972. Bar: Va. 1972, Calif. 1975, U.S. Dist. Ct. (ea. dist.) Va. 1976, D.C. 1978, U.S. Ct. Appeals (4th cir.) 1978, U.S. Ct. Appeals (Fed. cir.) 1986, U.S. Ct. Appeals (11th cir.) 1990. Rsch. assoc. Atlantic Richfield, Washington, 1972; assoc. Pender & Coward, Norfolk, Va., 1976-77; assoc. Seyfarth, Shaw, Washington, 1977-80, ptnr., 1981-83, Jones, Day, Reavis & Pogue, Washington, 1983—; mem. adv. com., reproductive hazards in the workplace Office of Tech. Assessment, Wash-ington, 1984-86; mem. adv. council Ctr. Environ. Health, U. Conn., 1986—; mem. editorial bd. The Occupational and Environ. Medicine Report, 1986—; contbr. articles to legal jours. Elder Kirkwood Presbyn. Ch., Springfield, Va., 1984-86. Served as lt. USN, 1972-75. Mem. ABA, Va. State Bar, State Bar Calif., Phi Beta Kappa, Phi Delta Phi (sec. local chpt. 1971-72, Outstanding Grad. award 1972). Home: 10113 Homar Pond Dr Fairfax VA 22039-1650 Office: Jones Day Reavis & Pogue 1450 G St NW Ste 600 Washington DC 20005-2088

MCELVEEN, WILLIAM HENRY, minister; b. Winston-Salem, N.C., June 7, 1932; s. Adam Ezra and Selma Anita (Adams) McE.; m. Carol Lee Sloan, Aug. 25, 1955; children: Miriam Lee Story, Gregory William, David Wil-liam. BA, Davidson Coll., 1954; MDiv, Moravian Theol. Sem., 1958, DD (hon.), 1994; MA, Wake Forest U., 1971. Assoc. pastor Home Moravian Ch., Winston-Salem, N.C., 1958-61; pastor Messiah Moravian Ch., Winston-Salem, 1961-70; exec. dir. bd. Christian edn. So. Province Moravian Ch. of Am., Winston-Salem, 1970-80, v.p., asst. to pres., 1993—; founding pastor Unity Moravian Ch., Lewisville, N.C., 1980-93; exec. dir. Bd. Christian Edn. and Evangelism. Contbr. articles to profl. jours. Chair Model Cities Com., Winston-Salem, 1970s. Democrat. Avocations: carpentry, electrical wiring, gardening, walking, bicycling. Office: Moravian Church in Am Drawer O, Salem Sta Winston Salem NC 27108

MCELVEEN, WILLIAM LINDSAY, broadcasting executive, lecturer; b. Columbia, S.C., Sept. 20, 1950; s. Henry Moody and Dorothy Butler (Sligh) McE.; m. Laurie Wells Boyle, Sept. 8, 1969 (div. 1976); 1 child, Earle Sligh; m. Catharine Elizabeth McCaslin, Aug. 13, 1992; 1 child, Kerry Elizabeth McCaslin. BA in English, Univ. of South, 1972. Acct. exec. Sta. WNOK-FM, Columbia, S.C., 1972-73; mng. dir. Sta. WNOK-FM, Columbia, 1973-79; v.p., gen. mgr. Stas. WNOK-AM-FM, Columbia, 1979-84; pres. Audubon Broadcasting Co., Columbia, 1984-89, Radio South Carolina,

Columbia, 1989—; lectr. Internat. Media Fund, Washington, 1993—. Chmn. bd. dirs. Columbia Urban League, 1983-85; bd. dirs. Crimestoppers of Midlands, 1984-88, S.C. Law Inst., Columbia, 1985-88, Helpline of Midlands, 1986-90; gen. campaign chair United Negro Coll. Fund, Columbia, 1985-86; mem. exec. com. United Way of Midlands, Columbia, 1987-88. Mem. Nat. Assn. Broadcasters (bd. dirs. 1988-92), S.C. Broadcasters Assn. (mem. exec. com., bd. dirs. 1980-87, pres. 1988-92), Columbia Advt. Fedn. (pres. 1980-81), Media Club of Columbia (bd. dirs., pres. 1983-84). Presbyterian. Avocations: golf, tennis, travelling. Home: 263 Tombee Ln Columbia SC 29209 Office: Radio SC 1801 Charleston Hwy Cayce SC 29033

MCELWAIN, FRANKLIN ROY, educational administrator; b. Caribou, Maine, Oct. 22, 1954; s. Ralph Bearce and Adrina (Roy) McE.; m. Joan Aucoin, June 17, 1978; children: Diana, Lauren, Spencer. BS in Agrl. Mechanization, U. Maine, 1977, MPA, 1988. Farmer Red Wagon Farms, Caribou, 1977-85; rsch. asst. U. Maine Agrl. Experiment Sta., Presque Isle, summers 1982-85; tchr. Limestone (Maine) Jr./Sr. High Sch., 1985-93; asst. prin. Caribou (Maine) High Sch., 1993—; advisor Future Farmers Am., Limestone High Sch., 1985—; assoc. supr. Cen. Aroostook Soil and Water, Presque Isle, 1990—; text reviewer Delmar Pubs., Albany, N.Y., 1990-92; academic team leader Limestone High Sch., 1991-92. Sec. Caribou PTA, 1982; mem. Caribou Bd. of Edn. review com., 1991-92; mem. Parish Coun., Caribou, 1988-90; advisor Cath. Youth Orgn., Caribou, 1979-81. Named Maine Tchr. Yr., 1992, Agriscience Tchr. Yr., 1986; recipient Excellence in Edn. award U. Maine, 1992. Mem. Nat. Tchrs. Assn., Nat. Vocat. Agr. Tchrs. Assn., Maine Assn. Agr. Tchrs., Maine Resource Bank, Maine Edn. Talent Pool, Limestone Future Farmers Am. Alumni Assn. (sec. 1986—), Maine Dirigo Found., Maine Plant Food Edni. Soc. Republican. Roman Catholic. Avocations: running, basketball, cross-country skiing, woodworking. Home: Sweden Rd Box 551 Caribou ME 04736

MC ELWAIN, JOSEPH ARTHUR, retired power company executive; b. Deer Lodge, Mont., Nov. 13, 1919; s. Lee Chaffee and Johanna (Petersen) McE.; m. Mary Cleaver Witt, Mar. 8, 1945 (dec. June 1992); children—Lee William and Lori Louise (twins). B.A., U. Mont., 1943, LL.B., 1947. Bar: Mont. 1947. Individual practice law Deer Lodge, 1947-63; Washington legis. counsel Mont. Power Co., Butte, 1954-63, counsel, 1963-65, asst. to pres., 1965-67, v.p., 1967-70, exec. v.p., dir., 1970, then chmn., chief exec. officer, now ret.; dir. Mont. Power Co., First Bank System 1975-84, Devel. Credit Corp. Mont.; MHD Devel. Corp. 1986—; mem. U.S. nat. com. World Energy Conf.; Mont. dir. for U.S. Savs. Bonds, 1980-81; cons. in field. Mem. Mont. Pub. Land Law Rev. Adv. Com. City atty. Deer Lodge, 1950-57, 60-63; mem. Mont. Ho. of Reps., 1949-55, majority floor leader, 1951; mem. Mont. State Senate, 1962-64; state chmn. Republican Central Com., Mont., 1952-54; mem. adv. com. Edison Electric Inst., U. Mont. Found., Missoula, Rocky Mountain Coll., Billings; bd. dirs. Mont. Internat. Trade Commn. Served with AUS, World War II and Korea. Recipient Justdin Miller award, 1947. Mem. Mont., Am. bar assns. Episcopalian. Clubs: Masons, Shriners, Kiwanis. Home: 1500 Carolina Ave Butte MT 59701-5557 Office: 40 E Broadway St Butte MT 59701-9394

MCELWEE, ANDREW ALLISON, finance executive, lawyer; b. Dover, N.J., Apr. 10, 1955; s. Andrew Allison and Grace Lloyd (Lloyd) M.; m. Connie Chapman, May 24, 1980; children: Alexandra Chapman, Andrew Allison III. BA, Davidson Coll., 1977; JD, U. Va., 1980. Bar: N.Y. 1981, N.J. 1981, U.S. Dist. Ct. (ea. and so. dists.) N.Y. Assoc. Dewey, Ballantine, Bushby, Palmer & Wood, N.Y.C., 1980-83, Morgan Stanky & Co. Inc., N.Y.C., 1984-85; v.p. fin. Bellemead Devel. Corp., Roseland, N.J., 1985—; bd. dirs. Lamont Fin. Services, Inc., Essex Falls, N.J. Bd. dirs. World Impact, Inc., Newark, 1986—; elder First Presbyn. Ch., Caldwell, N.J., 1983-87. Mem. ABA, N.J. Bar Assn., N.Y. Bar Assn. Home: 4 Stone House Rd Mendham NJ 07945-3125 Office: Bellemead Devel Corp 4 Becker Farm Rd Roseland NJ 07068-1734

MC ELWEE, JOHN GERARD, retired life insurance company executive; b. Port Bannatyne, Scotland, Dec. 19, 1921; came to U.S., 1925; s. James and Margaret (Fitzgerald) McE.; m. Barbara Sullivan, Mar. 31, 1951; children: Neal, Janet, Sheila, Brian. Attended, Boston Coll., 1939-42, LLB, 1950, LLD (hon.), 1987; grad. advanced mgmt. program, Harvard U., 1960; LLD (hon.), Bentley Coll., 1986. With John Hancock Mut. Life Ins. Co., Boston, 1945-93, asst. sec., 1957-61, 2d v.p., 1961-65, v.p., 1965-71, sr. v.p., sec., 1972-74, exec. v.p., sec., 1974-79, pres., 1979-81, chmn., 1982-86, also bd. dirs., 1976-93; bd. dirs. Data Gen. Corp. Trustee, assoc. Boston Coll.; life trustee Boston Mus. Sci. With USN, 1941-45. Mem. Weston Golf Club, Comml. Club, Knights of Malta. Roman Catholic. Home: 139 Buckskin Dr Weston MA 02193-1131

MCENIRY, ROBERT FRANCIS, education educator; b. Milw., Feb. 22, 1918; s. Frank Michael and Mary (Brown) McE. BA, St. Louis U., 1941, MA, 1944, PhL, ThL cum laude, 1953; PhD, Ohio State U., 1972. Instr. classics St. Louis U. High Sch., 1944-47, Creighton Prep. Sch., Omaha, 1947-48; asst. prof., chmn. classics Rockhurst Coll., Kansas City, Mo., 1953-58; retreat dir. White House Retreat, St. Louis, 1958-68; assoc. research prof. Creighton U., Omaha, 1972-89; dir., facilitator Growth for Couples, 1975-89; lectr. Creighton Natural Family Planning Ctr.; facilitator groups Adult Children of Alcoholism and Dysfunctional Families, 1989-93; vis. lectr. San Francisco Sch. Theology, San Anselmo, Calif., 1985; presenter over 700 lectrs., seminars and workshops in 43 states and 12 fgn. countries on value decisions during high anxiety and stress; exec. dir. Studies Adult Survivors of Abuse, 1993—; tchr., counselor in marriage and family issues. Editor and pub. Interaction Review, 1982-89; editor Scholar and Educator, 1974-76; mem. editorial bd. Counseling and Values, 1976-82; editor (book) Pastoral Counseling, 1977, Premarriage Counseling, 1978; contbr. over 180 articles to profl. jours.; literary agent, 1992—. Mem. Bd. of Pastoral Ministry, Omaha, 1972-78. Research grantee Council for Theol. Reflection, 1975-77; recipient Research award Creighton U., 1977. Fellow Nat. Acad. Counselors and Family Therapists (editor book rev. 1979-91); mem. APA, Am. Assn. for Religious Values in Counseling (editor newsletter 1982-89, Outstanding Svc. award 1985, Meritorious Svc. award 1989), Phi Delta Kappa (exec. com. 1977-83, del. 1981-83). Avocations: photography, Civil War sites, yoga. Home: 3016 Paddock Rd apt 12B Omaha NE 68124-2942 Office: Creighton Univ Dept Edn Omaha NE 68178

MCENROE, CAROLINE ANN, legal assistant; b. Bronx, N.Y., Jan. 21, 1935; d. Patrick David and Annie Marie (Donohue) Fay; m. William T. McEnroe, Apr. 16, 1955; children: Colleen, Patrick, Kieran, Peggyanne. Grad., Krissler Bus. Inst., Poughkeepsie, N.Y., 1953. Cert. legal asst., N.Y. Superior ct. clk. County Ct. Dutchess County, Poughkeepsie, N.Y., 1978-79; legal adminstrv. asst. to pub. defender County of Dutchess, Poughkeepsie, 1979—; bd. dirs. N.Y. State Magistrates Assn., 1974; pres. Dutchess County Magistrates Assn., 1973. Town justice Town of Amenia, N.Y., 1968-76, coun. woman, 1981-85; vol. March of Dimes Dutchess County, Heart Fund Dutchess County; active Ch. Bldg. Fund Campaign, Amenia; tchr. Confraternity of Christian Doctrine classes, 1976-88; eucharistic minister Sharon (Conn.) Hosp. Mem. State Magistrates' Assn., Dutchess County Magistrates' Assn. Republican. Roman Catholic. Home: RR 1 Box 370A Amenia NY 12501-0486 Office: Pub Defender Dutchess County 22 Market St Poughkeepsie NY 12601-3222

MCENROE, JOHN PATRICK, lawyer; b. N.Y.C., Mar. 25, 1935; s. John Joseph and Kathleen C. (Kellaghan) McE.; m. Katherine Callender Tresham, Dec. 7, 1957; children: John, Mark T., Patrick W. BA, Cath. U. Am., 1955; JD, Fordham U., 1964. Bar: N.Y. 1965, U.S. Dist. Ct. (so. dist.) 1966, D.C. 1982. Assoc. Kelley, Drye, Newhall, Maginess & Warren, N.Y.C., 1964-67; assoc. Paul, Weiss, Rifkind, Wharton & Garrison, N.Y.C., 1967-74, ptnr., 1974—. Served to 1st lt. USAF, 1955-59. Mem. ABA, Assn. of Bar of City of N.Y. Office: Paul Weiss Rifkind Wharton & Garrison 1285 Ave Of The Americas New York NY 10019-6028

MCENROE, JOHN PATRICK, JR., professional tennis player; b. Wiesbaden, Fed. Republic Germany, Feb. 16, 1959; s. John Patrick and Katy McEnroe; m. Tatum O'Neal, Aug. 1, 1986; children: Kevin Jack, Sean. Grad., Trinity Sch., N.Y.C., 1977; student, Stanford U. Winner numerous U.S. jr. singles and doubles titles; winner jr. titles French Mixed Doubles, 1977, French Jr. Singles, 1977, Italian Indoor Doubles, 1978; winner Nat.

Coll. Athletic Assn. Intercollegiate U.S. Men's Singles title, 1978; professional tennis player, 1978-93; played on victorious U.S. Davis Cup Team, 1978, 79, 81, 82, 92; winner Stockholm Open, 1978, Benson and Hedges Tournament, 1978, Grand Prix Masters singles and doubles, Wembley, 1978, Grand Prix Masters Tournament, N.Y.C., 1979, New Orleans Grand Prix, 1979, WCT Milan Internat., Italy, 1979, Stella Artois Tournament, London, 1979, U.S. Open Men's Singles Championship, 1979, 80, 81, 84, World Championship Tennis Championship, 1979, 83, Australian Indoor Singles Championship, 1980-83, U.S. Indoor Singles Championship, 1980-83, Wimbledon Singles, 1981, 83, 84, Tournament of Champions, 1981, 83, AT & T Challenge, 1987, Japan Open, 1988, U.S. Hard Court Singles, 1989, Wimbledon Doubles, 1992; tennis sportscaster USA Network, 1993; mem. Men's Seniors' Tour Circuit, 1994. Office: care John P McEnroe Sr Paul Weiss Rifkind Wharton & Garrison 1285 Ave the Americas New York NY 10019-6028*

MCENROE, PATRICK, professional tennis player; b. Manhasset, N.Y., July 1, 1966; s. John Patrick Sr. and Katy McEnroe. Student, U. Stanford. Ranked 12th U.S. Tennis Assn., 1991. Mem. U.S. Davis Cup Team, 1993, 94. Office: care US Tennis Assn 1212 Ave of the Americas New York NY 10036*

MCENROE, PAUL, reporter. Gen. assignment reporter, National writer Mpls. Star Tribune, Mpls. Office: Star Tribune 425 Portland Ave Minneapolis MN 55488-0001

MCENTEE, GERALD W., labor union official; b. Phila., Jan. 11, 1935; four children. B in Econs., LaSalle Coll., 1956; postgrad., Temple U., Harvard U. With Am. Fedn. State County and Mcpl. Employees, 1973—; former leader Dist Coun. 13, Harrisburg, Penn.; union internat. v.p., mem. exec. bd., since 1974; internat. pres. Washington, 1981—. Office: AFSCME 1625 L St NW Washington DC 20036-5687

MCENTEE, ROBERT EDWARD, management consultant; b. Franklin, N.J., Mar. 22, 1932; s. William J. and Marie C. (Gorman) McE.; m. Ruth M. Kathalynas, Sept. 29, 1956; children—Kathleen, Susan, Jane, Robert, Christopher. B.S., Villanova U., 1953. C.P.A., N.J. With Price Waterhouse, 1955-63; sr. fin., adminstrv. exec. Beecham Inc., West Paterson, N.J., 1963-88; pres. fin. div. Beecham Inc., 1974-88; pres., chief oper. officer Russ Berrie & Co., Inc., Oakland, N.J., 1988-90; pvt. practice cons., 1990—; bd. dirs. Valley Nat. Bancorp, Wayne, N.J. Mem. bd. govs. Cathedral Healthcare System, Archdiocese of Newark, also mem. archdiocese pension bd. Served with U.S. Army, 1953-55. Mem. Am. Inst. C.P.A.s, N.J. Soc. C.P.A.s, Fin. Exec. Inst. Roman Catholic. Home: 2225 First Ave Spring Lake NJ 07762

MCENTIRE, REBA N., country singer; b. McAlester, Okla., Mar. 28, 1955; d. Clark Vincent and Jacqueline (Smith) McE.; m. Narvel Blackstock, 1989; 1 child, Shelby Steven McEntire Blackstock. Student elem. edn., music, Southeastern State U., Durant, Okla., 1976. Rec. artist Mercury Records, 1978-83, MCA Records, 1984—. Albums include Whoever's in New England (Gold award), 1986, What Am I Gonna Do About You (Gold award), 1987, Greatest Hits (Gold award, Platinum award, U.S., Can.), 1987, Merry Christmas To You, 1987, The Last One To Know (Gold award), 1988, Reba (Gold award 1988), Sweet 16 (Gold award 1989, U.S.), Rumor Has It (Gold award 1991, Platinum award 1992, Double Platinum 1992), Reba Live (Gold award 1990, Gold award 1991, Platinum award 1991), For My Broken Heart, 1991, Forever in Your Eyes, 1992, It's Your Call, 1992, Read My Mind, 1994, Reba compilation video (Gold award, Platinum award 1992); author: (with Tom Carter) Reba: My Story, 1994; actress: (miniseries) Buffalo Girls, 1995. Spokesperson Middle Tenn. United Way, 1988, Nat. and State 4-H Alumni, Bob Hope's Hope for a Drug Free Am.; Nat. spokesperson Am. Lung Assn., 1990-91. Recipient numerous awards in Country music including Disting. Alumni award Southeastern State U., Female vocalist award Country Music Assn., 1984, 85, 86, 87, Grammy award for Best Country Vocal Performance, 1987, 2 Grammy nominations, 1994, Grammy award, Best Country Vocal Collaboration for "Does He Love You" with Linda Davis, 1994, Entertainer of Yr. award Country Radio Awards, 1994, Female Vocalist award, 1994; named Entertainer of Yr., Country Music Assn., 1986, Female Vocalist of Yr. Acad. Country Music, 1984, 85, 86, 87, 92, Top Female Vocalist, 1991, Am. Music award favorite female country singer, 1988, 90, 91, 92, 93, Am. Music award, 1989, 90, 91, 92, Best Album, 1991, Favorite Female Vocalist, 1994, Favorite Female Vocalist, Peoples Choice Award, 1992, Favorite Female Country Vocalist, 1992, 93, Favorite Female Vocalist, TNN Viewer's Choice Awards, 1993, Favorite Female Country Artist, Billboard, 1994. Mem. Country Music Assn., Acad. County Music, Nat. Acad. Rec. Arts and Scis., Grand Ol' Opry, AFTRA, Nashville Songwriters Assn. Inc. Avocations: golf, shopping, being with Narvel and Shelby, horse racing, raising horses.

MCERLANE, JOSEPH JAMES, insurance company executive; b. Phila., Mar. 5, 1948; s. Joseph Leo and Theophila Mary (Szymanski) McE.; m. Florence Mary Myhasuk; children: Joan Reardon, Rebecca Ann, Megan Diane, Erin Moira, Joseph James Jr. BA, Villanova U., 1970. CLU; cert. employee benefit specialist. Group sales asst. Metro. Life Ins. Co., Phila., 1970-72; mgr. group bus. svcs. Investors Diversified Svcs., Valley Forge, Pa., 1972-74; from mgr. to dir. to v.p. and divisional mgr. group ins. sales Investors Diversified Svcs., Mpls., 1974-84; pres. Nat. Benefit Resources Group Svcs., Inc., Mpls., 1984—. Mem. bd. Annunciation Sch., Mpls., 1984-87, chmn., 1986-87. Mem. Mass. Mktg. Inst., Self-Insured Inst. Am. (bd. dirs. 1993—), Sertoma (Mpls. Sertoman of Yr. 1982). Office: Nat Benefit Resources Group Svcs Inc 5353 Gamble Dr Minneapolis MN 55416-1509

MCEVILLY, JAMES PATRICK, JR., lawyer; b. Phila., July 30, 1943; s. James P. and Virginia Frances (Madden) McE.; m. Joan Elizabeth O'Connor; children: James III, Christopher, Sara, Michael. BS, St. Joseph's U., 1965; JD, Temple U., 1971. Bar: Pa. 1971, U.S. Dist. Ct. (ea. dist.) Pa. 1972, U.S. Ct. Appeals (3d cir) 1975, U.S. Supreme Ct. 1982. Law clk. to president judge Phila. Mcpl. Ct., 1971-73; assoc. Galfand, Berger, Lurie & March, Phila., 1973-76; asst. dist. atty. Phila. Dist. Atty., 1976-79; prin. McEvilly & Assocs., Feasterville, Pa., 1979—; assoc. prof. Temple U. Law Profl. Commons, Southampton, 1983-86. Editor Temple U. Law Rev., 1971. Mem. Pa. Trial Lawyers Assn., Bucks County Bar Assn., Phila. Bar Assn., Trial Lawyers Am. Home: 1401 Silo Rd Yardley PA 19067-4240 Office: McEvilly & Assocs 1200 Bustleton Pike Ste 1B Feasterville PA 19053-4118

MC EVILLY, THOMAS VINCENT, seismologist; b. East Saint Louis, Ill., Sept. 2, 1934; s. Robert John and Frances Nathalie (Earnshaw) Mc E.; m. Dorothy K. Hopfinger, Oct. 23, 1970; children: Mary, Susan, Ann, Steven, Joseph, Adrian. BS, St. Louis U., 1956, PhD, 1964. Geophysicist California Co., New Orleans, 1957-60; engring. v.p. Sprengnether Instrument Co., St. Louis, 1962-67; asst. prof. seismology U. Calif., Berkeley, 1964-68, assoc. prof., 1968-74, prof., 1974—, chmn. dept. geology and geophysics, 1976-80, asst. dir. seismographic sta., 1960-94; dir. earth sci. div. Lawrence Berkeley Lab., 1982-93; chmn. bd. dirs. Inc. Research Instns. for Seismology, 1984-86; cons. numerous govt. agys., geotech. cos. Contbr. numerous articles to profl. jours. Mem. Am. Geophys. Union, Royal Astron. Soc., Seismol. Soc. Am. (editor bull. 1976-85), Soc. Exploration Geophysicists, AAAS, Phi Beta Kappa. Office: Univ Calif Dept Geology and Geophysics Berkeley CA 94720

MCEVILY, DANIEL VINCENT SEAN, lawyer, author; b. N.Y.C., June 25, 1944; s. Patrick Vincent and Margaret Dolores (Hawley) McE.; m. Adele Carroll Daly, Sept. 1, 1973 (div. Nov. 1986); 1 child, Kathleen Kerry. BS in Fgn. Svc., Georgetown U., 1966; JD, Cath. U., 1972. Bar: D.C. 1973, Tex. 1994, U.S. Supreme Ct. 1976. Assoc., ptnr. Hamilton and Hamilton, Washington, 1973-81; ptnr. Foley & McEvily, Washington, 1981-89; Alexander & McEvily, Houston, 1989—. Author: Anthem for No Nation, 1989, A Tangled Woven Web, 1990. Capt. USMC, 1966-69, Viet Nam. Decorated 13 personal and unit decorations USMC, 1967. Mem. Am. Legion (post #1 Paris, counsel 1991—). Roman Catholic. Avocations: sculling, rugby, fox hunting. Office: Alexander & McEvily 24th Fl 5 Post Oak Park Fl 24 Houston TX 77027-3413

MCEVOY, JAMES F., lawyer; b. N.Y.C., Nov. 8, 1931; s. James and Ellen (Murphy) McE.; m. Patricia Ann Collin, July 29, 1961; children: Mary P., James B., Bernadette M., Michael J., Sarah E. BA, St. John's U., N.Y.C., 1953, JD, 1959. Bar: N.Y. 1960, Ga. 1983, U.S. Dist. Ct. (no. dist.) Ga. 1983. Atty. legal dept. Met. Life Ins. Co., N.Y.C., 1960-72; asst. gen. counsel Met. Life Ins. Co., Atlanta, 1972-78, assoc. gen counsel, 1978-88; ptnr. Hansell & Post, Atlanta, 1988-89, Jones, Day, Reavis & Pogue, Atlanta, 1989—. With U.S. Army, 1953-55. Mem. Am. Coll. Real Estate Lawyers, Am. Land Title Assn. (assoc. lender's counsel group), Assn. Life Ins. Counsel, Ga. Bar Assn., Commerce Club. Roman Catholic. Office: Jones Day Reavis & Pogue 3500 One Peachtree Ctr 303 Peachtree St NE Atlanta GA 30308-3201

MCEVOY, NAN TUCKER, publishing company executive; b. San Mateo, Calif., July 15, 1919; s. Nion R. and Phyllis (de Young) Tucker; m. Dennis McEvoy, 1948 (div.); 1 child, Nion Tucker McEvoy. Student, Georgetown U., 1975. Newspaper reporter San Francisco Chronicle, 1944-46, N.Y. Herald Tribune, N.Y.C., 1946-47, Washington Post, 1947-48; rep. in pub. rels. John Homes, Inc., Washington, 1959-60; spl. asst. to dir. U.S. Peace Corps, Washington, 1961-64; mem. U.S. delegation UNESCO, Washington, 1964-65; dir. Population Coun., Washington, 1965-70; co-founder, dep. dir. Preterm, Inc., Washington, 1970-74; chmn. bd. Chronicle Pub. Co., San Francisco, 1975—. Mem. nat. bd. dirs. Smithsonian Instn., Washington, 1994—; mem. Brookings coun. Brookings Instn., Washington, 1994—; commr. Nat. Mus. Art, Washington; mem. U. Calif. San Francisco Found., 1993—; formerly arbitrator Am. Arbitration Assn., Washington. Named Woman of Yr., Washingtonian Mag., 1973. Mem. Am. Art Forum, Burlingame Country Club, The River Club, Commonwealth Club of Calif., World Affairs Coun., Villa Taverna. Avocation: overseeing California olive grove ranch in anticipation of producing fine olive oil. Office: The Chronicle Pub Co 655 Montgomery St Ste 1430 San Francisco CA 94111

MC EWAN, LEONARD, former judge; b. Great Falls, Mont., Feb. 17, 1925; s. Leonard Wellington and Olga (Trinastich) McE.; m. Cameon Wolfe, Sept. 2, 1953 (dec. 1977); m. Mary Hurst Amschel, Feb. 20, 1988. B.S. U. Wyo., 1955, J.D.; 1957. Bar: Wyo. bar 1957. Practice in Sheridan, 1957-69; municipal judge City Sheridan, 1958-69; justice Wyo. Supreme Ct., Cheyenne, 1969-75; chief justice Wyo. Supreme Ct., 1975; dist. judge Sheridan, Wyo., 1975-85. Trustee Sheridan Coll., 1963-69, Sheridan County YMCA, 1963-68, All-American Indian Days, 1959-63, N. Am. Indian Found., 1960-67. Served with USAAF, 1943-46. Recipient Distinguished Service award Jr. C. of C., 1960. Mem. Wyo. State Bar, Am. Bar Assn., Am. Legion, U. Wyo. Alumni Assn. (bd. dirs. 1962-66), Sigma Alpha Epsilon. Episcopalian. Lodges: Elks, Eagles, Masons, Rotary, Quarterback. Address: PO Box 460 Story WY 82842

MCEWAN, WILLARD WINFIELD, JR., lawyer, judge; b. Evanston, Ill., Dec. 26, 1934; s. Willard Winfield Sr. and Esther (Sprenger) McE; children: Michael, Elizabeth, Allison. BS, Claremont Men's Coll., 1956; JD, U. Calif., San Francisco, 1960. Bar: Calif. 1960, U.S. Dist. Ct. (no. and so. dists.) Calif. 1960, U.S. Supreme Ct. 1974. Commd. U.S. Army, 1956, advanced through grades to capt., 1965, resigned, 1968; dep. legis. counsel City of Sacramento, Calif., 1960-61; asst. city atty. City of Santa Barbara, Calif., 1961-62; pvt. practice atty. Santa Barbara, 1962—; judge U.S. Magistrate Ct., Santa Barbara County, 1973—; atty. Goleta Water Dist., 1986-87; lectr. Santa Barbara Adult Edn. Program. Founder, bd. dirs., officer, gen legal coun. Santa Barbara Coun. for Retarded, 1962-72; active WORK Workshop for Handicapped, Assn. Retarded Citizens, Santa Barbara City Landmarks Adv. Com., 1967-73; v.p. Santa Barbara Harbor Pageants and Exhibits Com., 1964; chmn. Citizens Save our Shoreline Com., 1964, Citizens Community Master Plan Com., 1964, YMCA Membership Drive, 1964, Citizens Adv. Com. on Sch. Dist. Tax Needs, 1965; commr. Santa Barbara City Water Commn., 1965, City of Santa Barbara Recreation Commn., 1970-73. Recipient Disting. Svc. award Jr. C. of C., 1965; named Santa Barbara's Young Man of Yr. 1965. Mem. Am. Heart Assn. (pres. Santa Barbara County chpt. 1981-82), Santa Barbara Heart Assn. (bd. dirs., pres. bd. dirs. 1981-82, chmn. Heart Sunday 1973, 75), Santa Barbara Malacological Soc., Santa Barbara Kiwanis (pres. 1967), C. of C. (com. on local govt., state legislation com., bd. dirs., past v.p. bd. dirs., pres. bd. dirs. 1981-82, chmn. several coms.). Republican. Roman Catholic. Avocations: golf, skiing. Office: US Courthouse 8 E Figueroa St Ste 210 Santa Barbara CA 93101-2720

MCEWEN, ALEXANDER CAMPBELL, cadastral studies educator, former Canadian government official, surveying consultant; b. Ryde, Isle of Wight, Eng., Aug. 22, 1926; emigrated to Can., 1949; s. Walter Scott and Florence Lilian (Goodall) McE.; m. Patricia Stuart Richards, July 27, 1956 (div. 1988); m. Sherry Lee Wilson, June 13, 1993; children: Ann Florence, Sheila Jean, Laura Susan. LL.B., U. London, 1966, Ph.D., 1979; LL.M., U. East Africa, 1970. Sr. surveyor H. Wheeler Assocs., Toronto, Ont., Can., 1961-62; sec. treas. Assn. Ont. Land Surveyors, Toronto, 1963-64; prin. Survey Tng. Centre, Dar es Salaam, Tanzania, 1964-70; survey cons. Ottawa, Ont., Can., 1970-72; dir. lands and surveys Govt. Nfld., St. John's, 1972-76; commr. Internat. Boundary Commn., Ottawa, Ont., 1976-90; survey adviser Govt. Can., Jesselton, North Borneo, 1954-56, Lagos, Nigeria, 1989-90; tech. expert UN, Victoria, Seychelles, 1958-61; survey cons. Can. Exec. Service Orgn., Kingston, Jamaica, 1981, Quito, Ecuador, 1986; prof. cadastral studies, dept. geomatics engring. U. Calgary, Alta., Can., 1991—. Author: International Boundaries of East Africa, 1971 In Search of the Highlands, 1988; contbr. articles to profl. jours. Served with Royal Armoured Corp. Mem. Can. Inst. Geomatics (mem. coun. 1977-81, Jim Jones award 1967, 83, 90, Presdl. citation 1981), Western Can. Bd. Examiners for Land Surveyors (registrar, bd. dirs. 1991—), Assn. Ont. Land Surveyors (sec.-treas. 1963-64), Assn. Nfld. Land Surveyors (bd. examiners 1975-76), PEN, Writer's Union Can. Home: 2129 2d Ave NW, Calgary, AB Canada T2N OG8 Office: U Calgary, Dept Geomatics Engring, 2500 University Dr NW, Calgary, AB Canada T2N 1N4

MCEWEN, ALFRED SHERMAN, planetary geologist; b. Lawrence, Kans., July 22, 1954; s. William Edwin and Miriam (Sherman) McE.; m. Eileen Hany; 1 child, Ian. B.S., SUNY-Syracuse, 1975; B.S. No. Ariz. U., 1981, M.S., 1983; PhD Ariz. State U., 1988. Vol. Peace Corps, Guatemala, Central Am., 1975-77; soil conservationist Soil Conservation Service, USDA, Windsor, Conn., 1978-80; geologist U.S. Geol. Survey, Flagstaff, Ariz., 1981—. Mem. Galileo and Cassini Spacecraft Sci. Teams. Contbr. articles, image processing-color images to profl. jours. Mem. Am. Geophys. Union, Am. Astron. Soc., Geol. Soc. Am. Home: 3890 N Paradise Rd Flagstaff AZ 86004-1613 Office: US Geol Survey 2255 N Gemini Dr Flagstaff AZ 86001-1637

MCEWEN, JAMES, publishing executive. Pub. Family Cir., N.Y.C. Office: Gruner & Jahr USA Pub Family Cir 110 Fifth Ave New York NY 10011*

MCEWEN, JEAN, painter; b. Montreal, Que., Can., Dec. 14, 1923; s. William and Elaine (Renaud) McE.; m. Indra Kagis, Sept. 18, 1976; children: Jean Sabin, Marianne Jérémie; children by previous marriage: Isabelle, Domenique. Grad., U. Montreal, 1947. Tchr. U. Concordia, Montreal. One-man exhbns. include, Gallery Godart-Lefort, Montreal, 1962-69, Gallery Montreal, 1963, Gallery Moos, Toronto, 1963-69, Gallery Martha Jackson, N.Y.C., 1963, Mayer Gallery, Paris, 1964, group exhbns. include, Dunn Internat. Exhbn., Tate Gallery, London, 1963; rep. permanent collections, Mus. Modern Art, N.Y.C., Walker Art Center, Mpls., Albright-Knox Art Gallery, Buffalo, Hirshhorn Mus., Smithsonian Instn., Ottawa Mus., Toronto Mus.; commd. for stained glass window, Sir George Williams U., 1966, murals for, Toronto Airport, Plase Arts, Montreal. (Winner Quebec Art competition 1962, recipient Jessie Dow award Montreal Spring Exhbn. 1964), large mural Bank Scotia, Montreal, head office, 1991; major retrospect Mont. Mus. Fine Arts. 1987—. grantee Can. Council, 1977-78. Academician Royal Can. Acad. Arts. Roman Catholic. Address: 3908 Parc Lafontaine Rue, Montreal, PQ Canada H2L 3M6

MCEWEN, JOSEPH, JR., distributing company executive; b. Rahway, N.J., June 20, 1921; s. Joseph and Thora (Thompson) McE.; m. Aila; children: Joseph, Jacqueline, Anne, Susan. Student in engring., Temple U. Test engr. Wright Aero. Co., 1941, Lawrence Engring. Co., 1941-43; sales engr.

Rapistan of Pa., 1946-55; v.p. Modern Handling Equipment Co., Bristol, Pa., 1955-79, pres., 1960-79, pres. modern group, 1979—. Bd. dirs. Distbn., Research and Edn. Found., World Affairs Council, Phila. Served to 2d lt. U.S. Army 1943-45. Mem. Internat. Material Handling Soc., Nat. Assn. Wholesalers and Distbrs. (presl 1976), Material Handling Distbrs. Assn. (pres. 1966), Pa. C. of C. (bd. dirs.). Clubs: Mfrs. Golf and Country, St. Petersburg Yacht. Home: 2230 Huntingdon Rd Huntingdon Valley PA 19006-4308 Office: Modern Group Ltd 2501 Durham Rd Bristol PA 19007-6923

MCEWEN, LARRY BURDETTE, retired English and theater arts educator, author; b. Clay Center, Nebr., Aug. 4, 1934; s. Gerald E. and Marie L. (Pennington) McE.; m. Charlotte E. Alloway, Feb. 14, 1978; children: Diana J. Stiles, Sheila J. Lacy. AB, Augustana Coll., Rock Island, Ill., 1962; MS, Ill. State U., 1968. Cert. tchr., Nebr. Prof. theatre arts Blackburn Coll., Carlinville, Ill., 1969-75; counselor div. vocat. rehab. Nebr. Dept. Edn., Lincoln, 1976-82; tchr. English Hastings (Nebr.) Sr. High Sch., 1983-92; vis. lectr. Mt. Senario Coll., Ladysmith, Wis., 1971, Knox Coll., Galesburg, Ill. 1974. Author: Much Ado About Shakespeare, 1992, Goose and Fables, 1993; author Apple Software; dir. 62 theatrical prodns.; contbr. numerous articles to profl. publs. With USAF, 1951-52. Grad. fellow Ind. U., 1968-69; Quad-City Music Guild scholar, 1961-62. Mem. NEA, Nebr. State Edn. Assn., Acad. Computers English, Apple Programmers Developers Assn., Nat. Apple Users Group, Nat. Coun. Tchrs. English, Alpha Psi Omega, Alpha Phi Omega. Home and Office: 603 E 5th St Hastings NE 68901-5336

MCFADDEN, BRUCE ALDEN, biochemistry educator; b. La Grande, Oreg., Sept. 23, 1930; s. Eugene Field and Mary Elizabeth (McMaster) McF.; m. Roberta Ray Wilson, June 14, 1958; children: Paul, David, John. AB in Chemistry with honors, Whitman Coll., 1952, DSc (hon.), 1978; PhD in Biochemistry, UCLA, 1956. From instr. to prof. chemistry Wash. State U., Pullman, 1956-66, prof. biochemistry, 1974—, dir. sci. devel., 1974-78, chmn. dept. biochemistry, 1978-84; vis. prof. U. Leicester, Eng., 1972-73, U. Florence, Italy, 1980, Tech. U., Munich, 1980-81; vis. scientist Minority Instns. (FASEB), 1988; mem. study sect. NIH, Bethesda, Md., 1978-79, 82; panelist rsch. grants U.D. Dept. Energy, 1983, 91; panelist Frasch grants Am. Chem. Soc., 1982-87; cons. to numerous jours. and agys., Pullman, 1966—. Editor Archives Microbiology, 1977-83; contbr. articles to profl. jours.; patentee in field. Pres. Sunnyside Sch. PTA, Pullman, 1972; chmn 1984 and Beyond Citizens' com., Pullman Sch. Bd., 1983-84. Recipient Disting. Sr. U.S. Scientist award Humboldt Found. Tech. U. Munich, 1980-81; fellow Guggenheim Found., 1972-73, NIH, 1954-56, 63-69, 73; grantee in field. Fellow AAAS; mem. Am. Chem. Soc. (pres. Wash.-Idaho Border sect. 1963-64), Am. Soc. Biol. Chem. & Molecular Biol., Am. Soc. Microbiologists, Pacific Slope Biochem. Soc. (pres. 1973-74), Am. Soc. Plant Physiologists, Sigma Xi, Phi Kappa Phi, Phi Lambda Upsilon (pres. 1955). Democrat. Home: 1465 SW Wadleigh Dr Pullman WA 99163-2048 Office: Wash State U Biochemistry Dept Pullman WA 99164

MCFADDEN, DANIEL LITTLE, economics educator; b. Raleigh, N.C., July 29, 1937; s. Robert S. and Alice (Little) McF.; m. Beverlee Tito Simboli, Dec. 15, 1962; children: Nina, Robert, Raymond. BS, U. Minn., 1957, PhD, 1962; LLD, U. Chgo., 1992. Mellon fellow U. Pitts., Pa., 1962-63; asst. prof. U. Calif., Berkeley, 1963-65, assoc. prof., 1965-67, prof., 1967-77; research prof. Yale U., New Haven, 1977-78; prof. MIT, Cambridge, Mass.; now prof. dept. econs. U. Calif., Berkeley; mem. econs. adv. panel NSF, 1969-71, Universities Nat. Bur., 1974-77, rev. com. Calif. Energy Com. Forecasts, 1979, Sloan Found. Book Com., 1977-79, NAS Com. on Basic Research in Social Scis., 1982—, NAS Com. on Energy Demand Modeling, 1983-84; chmn. AEA Awards Com., 1981-84, NSF-NBER Conf. on the Econs. of Uncertainty, 1970—; bd. dirs. Nat. Bur. Econ. Research, 1976-77, 1980-83; dir. Econometrics Lab. U. Calif. Berkeley, 1991—; mem. NAS Commn. Behavioral and Social Scis. and Edn., 1989—. Editor: Jour. Statis. Physics, 1968-70, Econometric Soc. monographs, 1980-83; bd. editors: Am. Econ. Rev., 1971-74, Jour. Math. Econs., 1973-77, Transp. Research, 1978-80; assoc. editor: Jour. Econometrics, 1977-78. Mem. adv. com. Transp. Models Project, Met. Transp. Commn., 1975, City of Berkeley Coordinated Transit Project, 1975-76; exec. com. Transp. Research Bd., 1975-78. Recipient John Bates Clark medal, 1975, Outstanding Teacher award MIT Econ. Dept., 1981, Frisch medal, 1986. Mem. Am. Acad. Arts and Scis., Nat. Acad. Sci., Am. Econ. Assn. (exec. com. 1985-87, v.p. 1994), Econometric Soc. (exec. com. 1983-86, v.p. 1984, pres. 1985), Am. Statis. Assn., Math. Assn. Am., Transp. Rsch. Bd. Democrat. Avocations: biking, tennis, squash, sailing, skiing. Home: 1370 Trancas St # 152 Napa CA 94558-2912 Office: U Calif Econs Dept 549 Evans Hall # 3880 Berkeley CA 94720-3880

MCFADDEN, DAVID REVERE, museum curator, director; b. Devils Lake, N.D., Aug. 28, 1947; B.A. U. Minn., 1972, MA, 1978. Assoc. curator Mpls. Inst. Arts, 1976-78, curator, 1978; asst. dir. collections and rsch., curator decorative arts Cooper-Hewitt, Nat. Mus. of Design, N.Y.C., 1978—; adj. prof. art Cooper-Hewitt-Parsons M.A. program, N.Y.C., 1983—; Gov. Decorative Arts Trust; pres. applied arts com. Internat. Coun. Mus., 1993—; mem. exhbn. com. Am. Fedn. Arts. Author: Scandinavian Modern Design (Wittenborn award 1984), 1983, L'Art de Vivre: Decorative Arts and Design in France 1789-1989, 1989. Decorated knight 1st class Order of the Lion (Finland), 1984; knight commdr. Order of No. Star (Sweden); chevalier des l'Ordre des Arts et des Letrres (France). Recipient Awards of Merit Smithsonian Instn., 1981, 88, 89, Presdl. Design award, 1994; fellow Kress Found., 1973-74. Mem. Worshipful Co. Goldsmiths London. Office: The Smithsonian Instn Cooper-Hewitt Mus 2 E 91st St New York NY 10128-0669

MCFADDEN, DENNIS, experimental psychology educator; b. Oct. 2, 1940; s. Samuel John and Evelyn (Dinnerson) McF.; m. Nancy L. Wilson, Dec. 28, 1960; children: Tracie Ann, Devin James. BA, Sacramento State Coll., Calif., 1962; PhD, Ind U., 1967. Assoc. prof. U. Tex., Austin, 1967-72, assoc. prof., 1972-77, prof., 1977—. Contbr. articles to profl. jours. Recipient Jacob K. Javits Neurosci. Investigator award, 1984-89, Claude D. Pepper award, 1989-91; named Piper Prof., Minnie Stevens Piper Found., 1987. Fellow AAAS, Acoustical Soc. Am.; mem. Assn. for Rsch. Otolaryngology, CHABA (NAS-NRC com. on hearing, bioacoustics and biomechanics). Office: U Tex Dept Psychology Mezes Hall # 330 Austin TX 78712

MCFADDEN, EDWARD REGIS, JR., pulmonary educator; b. Pitts., Aug. 2, 1936. BA, St. Vincent Coll., 1958; MD, U. Pitts., 1963. Assoc. prof. medicine U. Tex. Med. Br., Galveston, 1972-73; asst. prof. Harvard U., Boston, 1973-77, assoc. prof., 1977-81, 81-84; assoc. prof. MIT div. health sci., Boston, 1979-84; prof. medicine Case Western Res. U., Cleve., 1984—; dir. Airway Disease Ctr. Univ. Hosp., Cleve., 1984—; respiratory therapy, 1985—, Clin. Research Ctr., 1986—. Editor-in-chief Airway Diseases, N.Y.C., 1985—; contbr. articles to profl. jours. Recipient George W. Thorn Teaching award Peter Bent Brigham Hosp., Boston, 1980. Fellow ACP; mem. Am. Fedn. Clin. Research, Am. Thoracic Soc., So. Soc. Clin. Investigation, Am. Physiol. Soc., Am. Acad. Allergy and Immunology, Am. Soc. Clin. Investigation, Assn. Am. Physicians. Office: 2706 Landon Rd Cleveland OH 44122-2008 Office: Univ Hosps Cleve 2074 Abington Rd Cleveland OH 44106-2602

MCFADDEN, FRANK HAMPTON, lawyer, business executive, former judge; b. Oxford, Miss., Nov. 20, 1925; s. John Angus and Ruby (Roy) McF.; m. Jane Porter Nabers, Sept. 30, 1960; children—Frank Hampton, Angus Nabers, Jane Porter. B.A., U. Miss., 1950; LL.B., Yale U., 1955. Bar: N.Y. 1956, Ala. 1959. Assoc. firm Lord, Day & Lord, N.Y.C., 1955-58; assoc. firm Bradley, Arant, Rose & White, Birmingham, Ala., 1958-63, partner, 1963-69; judge U.S. Dist. Ct. No. Dist. Ala., Birmingham, 1969-73; chief judge U.S. Dist. Ct. No. Dist. Ala., 1973-81; sr. v.p., gen. counsel Blount, Inc., Montgomery, Ala., 1982-91, exec. v.p. adminstrn. and govt. affairs, 1991, exec. v.p. legal affairs, 1991-93, exec. v.p., gen. counsel, 1993-; chmn. Blount Energy Resource Corp., Montgomery, 1983-88. Mem. jud. panel Ctr. for Pub. Resources, 1985—. Served from ensign to lt. USNR, 1944-49, 51-53. Fellow Am. Coll. Constrn. Lawyers; mem. Am. Corp. Counsel Assn. (bd. dirs. 1984-93, chmn. 1989). Office: Blount Inc PO Box 949 4520 Executive Park Dr Montgomery AL 36116-1602

MC FADDEN, G. BRUCE, hospital administrator; b. Winchester, Va., Feb. 19, 1934; s. S. Donald and Ruth D. McF.; m. Lois F. Richardson, Aug. 22, 1964; children—Christopher, Amy. BS, Va. Poly. Inst., 1953; MHA, Med.

Coll. Va. (Va. Commonwealth U.), 1961. Asst. administr. Meml. Hosp. at Easton, Md., Inc., 1963-70; v.p. Pa. Hosp., Phila., 1970-75; dir. U. Md. Hosp., Balt., 1975-82; pres. Robert Wood Johnson, University Hosp., 1982-88; exec. dir. N.Y. Health Career Ctr., N.Y.C., 1989-91, N.Y. Regional Transplant Program, N.Y.C., 1991—; cons. Hosp. Joint Practice Demonstration Project, Nat. Joint Practice Commn. of AMA, ANA; preceptor for programs in health care adminstrn. Med. Coll. Va., Columbia U., N.Y. U., U. Pa., Temple U.; bd. dirs., mem. recognition com. Am. Blood Commn.; bd. dirs., mem. exec. com. Central Md. Health Systems Agy.; chmn. Accreditation Council on Grad. Med. Edn.; chmn. Cen. Jersey Health Care Corp., New Brunswick; bd. dirs. New Brunswick Savs. Bank;. Bd. dirs. Vis. Nurse Soc., Phila., George St. Playhouse, New Brunswick, N.J., Westfield YMCA, N.J.; bd. dirs., vice chmn. Community Nursing Svcs. of Phila.; pres. Robert Wood; mem. Bd. of Edn., Westfield, N.J. Fellow Am. Coll. Hosp. Adminstrs.; mem. Am. Hosp. Assn. (chmn. coun. on human resources, chmn. spl. coms. on mandatory continuing edn., gen. coun.). Home: 248 Sylvania Pl Westfield NJ 07090-3124 Office: NY Regional Transplant Program Ste 1244 475 Riverside Dr New York NY 10115

MC FADDEN, GEORGE LINUS, retired army officer; b. Sharon, Pa., Oct. 16, 1927; s. George Linus and Frances Jane (Byrne) McF.; m. Floretta Theresa McFadden, Nov. 20, 1948; children: Kenneth William, Mark Edward, Mary Kathleen, Robert Bernard, George Linus, William. B.E., U. Omaha, 1961; M.S., George Washington U., 1967; grad., Advanced Mgmt. Program, Harvard U., 1971. Pvt. U.S. Army, 1946, advanced through grades to maj. gen., 1976; comdg. officer (7th inf. div. arty.), Korea, 1969-70; dep. comdg. gen. U.S. Army Security Agy., Arlington, Va., 1972-74; dep. dir. for field mgmt. and evaluation, dep. chief central security service Fort George G. Meade, Md., 1975-78; dep. dir. ops. Nat. Security Agy., 1978-79; comdg. gen. U.S. Army So. European Task Force, Vicenza, Italy, 1979-82; corp. v.p. CompuDyne Corp., 1986-89; sr. v.p. The Abbott Group, Inc., Annapolis, Md., 1989—; dir. Washington Studies and Analysis Group McDonnell Douglas Corp., 1985-86; dir. security affairs Dept. Energy, 1991—. Pres., chmn. bd. dirs. Met. Washington chpt. Arthritis Found., 1986—. Decorated D.F.C., D.S.M., Silver Star, Bronze Star, Purple Heart, others. Mem. Armed Forces Communications and Electronics Assn. Roman Catholic.

MC FADDEN, JAMES PATRICK, publisher; b. Youngstown, Ohio, Sept. 25, 1930; s. Francis Jerome and Recelba Katherine (Onorato) McF.; m. Faith Abbott, Apr. 18, 1959; children—Robert Arthur, Maria James, Patrick Abbott, Regina Laudis, Christina Luke. B.A., Youngstown Coll., 1953. Reporter Youngstown Vindicator, 1952-54; with Nat. Rev. mag., N.Y.C. 1956-89; assoc. pub. Nat. Rev. mag., 1971-83, cons. to editor, 1983-89; pres. Communications Distbn., N.Y.C., 1968—; v.p. Ultra Arts, Inc., N.Y.C., 1960-80; pres. Ultra Arts, Inc., 1980—; chmn. The Ad Hoc Com in Def. of Life, Inc., N.Y.C., 1973—. Editor Human Life Rev., 1975—, Lifeletter, 1973—, Cath. Eye, 1983—. Pres. Human Life Found., 1974—; chmn. Nat. Com. Cath. Laymen, 1977—. Served with CIC AUS, 1954-56. Roman Catholic. Home: 1050 Park Ave New York NY 10028-1031 Office: 150 E 35th St New York NY 10016-4178

MC FADDEN, JOHN VOLNEY, retired manufacturing company executive; b. N.Y.C., Oct. 3, 1931; s. Volney and Mary Lucile (McConkie) McF.; m. Marie Linstead, June 27, 1953; children—Deborah, John Scott, David. B.S. in Commerce and Fin, Bucknell U., 1953; J.D., Detroit Coll. Law, 1960. Pres., vice-chmn. MTD Products, Inc., Cleve., 1960-92, with, 1960-92; pres. MTD Products Inc., Cleve., 1980-91, vice chmn., 1990-92; bd. dris. Nat. Machinery Inc., Fusion Inc., Star Bank, Flambeau Corp.; chmn. bd. dirs. Guarantee Specialties Inc.; chmn. financing adv. bd. State of Ohio Devel.; past pres. Cleve. World Trade Assn. Trustee, chmn. Health Cleve. Lt. Supply Corps USN. Mem. Greater Cleve. Growth Assn. (bd. dirs.), Cleve. Yachting Club. Office: Camelot Ptnrs 20160 Parkside Dr Cleveland OH 44116-1347

MC FADDEN, JOSEPH MICHAEL, university president; b. Joliet, Ill., Feb. 12, 1932; s. Francis Joseph and Lucille (Adler) McF.; m. Norma Cardwell, Oct. 10, 1958; children: Timothy Joseph, Mary Colleen, Jonathan Andrew. B.A., Lewis Coll., 1954; M.A., U. Chgo., 1961; Ph.D., No. Ill. U., 1968. Tchr. history Joliet Cath. High Sch., 1957-60; mem. faculty history dept. Lewis Coll., Lockport, Ill., 1960-70, assoc. prof., 1967-70, v.p. acad. affairs, 1968-70; prof. history, dean sch. Nat. and Social Sci., Kearney (Nebr.) State Coll., 1970-74; prof. history, dean Sch. Social and Behavioral Scis., Slippery Rock (Pa.) State Coll., 1974-77; pres. No. State Coll., Aberdeen, S.D., 1977-82, U. S.D., Vermillion, 1982-88, U. St. Thomas, Houston, 1988—. Served with USNR, 1954-56. Roman Catholic. Office: U St Thomas Office of Pres 3812 Montrose Blvd Houston TX 77006-4626

MCFADDEN, JOSEPH PATRICK, insurance company executive; b. Norristown, Pa., Jan. 1, 1939; s. Joseph Patrick and Anna (Brennan) McF.; m. Patricia Ann Burke, Jan. 28, 1961; children: Mary Ann, Linda, Patricia, Joseph, Nancy, Meghan. BA, LaSalle U., 1961. Claim adjuster Allstate Ins. Co., Valley Forge, Pa., 1963-66; various mgmt. positions Valley Forge and Harrison, N.Y., 1966-74; regional claim mgr. Rochester, N.Y., 1974-76, Murray Hill, N.J., 1976-79; zone claim mgr. Bannockburn, Ill., 1979-81; asst. regional mgr. Skokie, Ill., 1981-83; asst. v.p. Northbrook, Ill., 1983-84; regional v.p. Santa Ana, Calif., 1984-86; claim v.p. Northbrook, 1986-91; territorial v.p. 1991—. Served to 1st lt. U.S. Army, 1961-63. Mem. Nat. Auto Theft Bur. (bd. govs. 1986), Nat. Assn. Ind. Insurers (claims com. 1986), Ins. Crime Prevention Inst., Ins. Info. Inst. (adv. panel on legal issues). Roman Catholic. Home: 1005 Ashley Ln Libertyville IL 60048-3813 Office: Allstate Ins Co 2775 Sanders Rd Ste F6B Northbrook IL 60062-6127

MCFADDEN, LEON LAMBERT, artist, inventor; b. St. Paul, Apr. 19, 1920; s. Frank Grover and Irene Manilla Lambert McF.; m. Karyn Flannery, Nov. 6, 1986. Student, several colls., univs., art insts. Prin. McFadden Commercial Studios, 1946-50; with McFadden-Kaump Art Service, 1952-54; pres. McFadden Advt. (merger with Sundial Services), 1954-70; mktg. dir. Kinelogic Corp., Mountain View, Calif., 1965-70; dir. rsch. and devel. proprietary patents Sundial Svcs., Inc., 1968-70; art instr. various Calif. community colls., 1972-74; minority bus. cons. VISTA/ACTION, 1974-75; pres., CEO Prometheus Project, Inc., Yreka, Calif., 1975—. Inventor, patentee 18 mechanical tools and devices; prin. artistic works include large assemblage painting of liberty, found image works (represented in White House spl. collection). Served with USN, 1942-46, PTO. Mem. AAAS, Mensa, Artists Equity Assn. Inc., Artists Equity Assn. N.Y., Siskiyou Artists Assn., Sierra Club. Home: 551 N Main St Yreka CA 96097 Studio: Liberty Painting Corp 6725 Old Hwy 99 Yreka CA 96097-9725

MCFADDEN, MARY JOSEPHINE, fashion industry executive; b. N.Y.C., Oct. 1, 1938; d. Alexander Bloomfield and Mary Josephine (Cutting) McF.; m. Philip Harari; 1 child, Justine. Ed., Sorbonne, Paris, France, Traphagen Sch. Design, 1957, Columbia, 1959-62; DFA, Internat. Fine Arts Coll., 1984. Pub. relations dir. Christian Dior, N.Y.C., 1962-64; merchandising editor Vogue South Africa, 1964-65, editor, 1965-69; polit. and travel columnist Rand (South Africa) Daily Mail, 1965-68; founder sculptural workshop Vukutu, Rhodesia, 1968-70; spl. projects editor Vogue U.S.A., 1973; pres. Mary McFadden, Inc., N.Y.C., 1976—; ptnr. MMcF Collection by Mary McFadden, 1991—; bd. dirs., advisor Sch. Design and Merchandising Kent State U., Eugene O'Neill Meml. Theatre Ctr.; mem. profl. com. Cooper-Hewitt Mus., Smithsonian Inst., Nat. Mus. of Design. Fashion and jewelry designer, 1973—. Advisor Nat. Endowment for Arts. Recipient Am. Fashion Critics award-Coty award, 1976, 78, 79, Audemars Piguet Fashion award, 1976, Rex award, 1977, award More Coll. Art, 1977, Pa. Gov.'s award, 1977, Roscoe award, 1978, Pres.'s Fellows award RISD, 1979, Neiman-Marcus award of excellence, 1979, Design Excellence award Pratt Inst., 1993, award N.Y. Landmarks Conservancy, 1994; named to Fashion Hall of Fame, 1979; fellow RISD. Mem. Fashion Group, Coun. Fashion Designers Am. (pres., past bd. dirs.). Office: Mary McFadden Inc 240 W 35th St Fl 17 New York NY 10001-2506

MCFADDEN, PETER WILLIAM, mechanical engineering educator; b. Stamford, Conn., Aug. 2, 1932; s. Kenneth E. and Marie (Gleason) McF.; children: Peter, Kathleen, Mary. B.S. in Mech. Engring. U. Conn., 1954, M.S. 1956; Ph.D., Purdue U., 1959. Registered profl. engr., Ind. Asst.

instr. U. Conn., 1954-56, prof. mech. engring., 1971—, dean Sch. Engring., 1971-85, dir. devel., 1985-88, provost, v.p., 1988, exec. asst. to pres.; exec. sec. to bd. trustees, 1989—; mem. faculty Purdue U., 1956-71; prof. mech. engring., head Purdue U. (Sch. Mech. Engring.), 1965-71; postdoctoral research Swiss Fed. Inst., Zurich, 1960-61; cons. to industry, 1959—. Mem. ASME, Am. Soc. Engring. Edn. Research in cryogenics, heat transfer, mass transfer. Office: U Conn Gulley Hall U-48 352 Mansfield Rd Storrs Mansfield CT 06268

MC FADDEN, ROBERT DENNIS, reporter; b. Milw., Feb. 11, 1937; s. Francis Joseph and Violet (Charleston) McF.; student U. Wis., Eau Claire, 1955-57; B.S. cum laude, U. Wis., Madison, 1960; m. Judith Marian Silverman, June 20, 1971; 1 son, Nolan Seth. Reporter Wisconsin Rapids (Wis.) Daily Tribune, 1957-58, Wis. State Jour., Madison, 1958-59, Cin. Enquirer, 1960-61; sr. writer, reporter N.Y. Times, 1961—. Co-author: No Hiding Place, 1981; Outrage: The Story Behind the Tawana Brawley Hoax, 1990. Served with U.S. Army, 1960-61, Res., 1961-68. Recipient Byline award N.Y. Press Club, 1973, 74, 80, 87, 89, 92, Page One award Newspaper Guild N.Y., 1978, Spot News award Uniformed Firemen's Assn., 1967, Spot News award L.I. Press Club, 1984, Chancellor's award for Disting. Svc. U. Wis., 1987, Excellence in Local Reporting award N.Y. Newspaper Publ. Assn., 1988, Spot News award N.Y. State Associated Press, 1989, In Depth Reporting award, 1989, 91, Ochs Prize in Journalism, 1989, Best News/ Feature Story award Internat. Assn. Fire Fighters, 1991; mem. N.Y. Times team winner Pulitzer Prize for Spot News Reporting, 1994. Mem. N.Y. Soc. Silurians (Spot News Story award 1977, Peter Kihss award 1987, Investigative reporting award 1989, Excellence in Journalism award 1994, gov. 1988—). Office: NY Times 229 West 43rd St New York NY 10036

MCFADDEN, THOMAS, academic administrator; b. N.Y.C., Nov. 12, 1935; m. Monica A. Dowdall; children—Monica, David. B.A., Cathedral Coll., 1957; S.T.L., Gregorian U., 1961; S.T.D., Cath. U., 1963. Asst. prof. St. Joseph's Coll., Bklyn., 1963-66, chmn. theology dept. Cathedral Coll., Douglaston, N.Y., 1966-68; asst. prof. Loyola Coll., Balt., 1968-69; prof. St. Joseph's U., Phila., 1970-82, dean Coll. Arts and Scis., 1982-87; acad. v.p. St. John Fisher Coll., Rochester, N.Y., 1987-92; pres. Marymount Coll., Calif., 1992—; vis. prof. Cath. U., Washington, 1967-68, LaSalle U., Phila., summer 1974-79. Author: editor: New Cath. Ency., 1974, 79. Editor, Dictionary of Religion, 3 vols., 1979; editor: Liberation, Revolution and Freedom, 1975, America in Theological Perspective, 1976. Recipient Disting. Teaching award Lindback, 1978, N.Y. State Excelsior award Bd. Examiners, 1991; HEW grantee, 1972; CAPHE grantee, 1985. Mem. AAUP, Coll. Theology Soc. (chmn. pubs. com. 1973-77). Democrat. Roman Catholic. Office: Marymount Coll 30800 Palos Verdes Dr E Rancho Palos Verdes CA 90275-6299

MCFALL, CATHERINE GARDNER, poet, critic, educator; b. Jacksonville, Fla., July 10, 1952; d. Albert Dodge and Joan (Livingston) McF.; m. Peter Forbes Olberg, Oct. 21, 1978; 1 child, Amanda Olberg. Baccalaureat, U. Paris, 1973; A.B. magna cum laude, Wheaton Coll., Norton, Mass., 1974; M.A., Johns Hopkins U., 1975; PhD, NYU, 1990. Editorial asst., short story editor Ladies' Home Jour., N.Y.C., 1975-77; adminstrv. dir. Poetry Soc. Am., N.Y.C., 1981-83; instr. writing NYU, N.Y.C., 1983-87, asst. dir. Poetics Inst., 1984-86; asst. prof. humanities Cooper Union, N.Y.C., 1990—. Author: Jonathan's Clou, 1986, Discovery (Nation award) 1989, Naming the Animals, 1994; contbr. poetry and revs. to mags. including Paris Rev., New Yorker, N.Y. Times, others. MacDowell Colony fellow, 1980, 86, Yaddo fellow, 1981, 84, 91, 93, Nat. Arts Club Poetry scholar Bread Loaf Writers Conf., 1983. Mem. Poets and Writers, Poetry Soc. Am., Assoc. Writing Programs, MLA, Nat. Book Critics Circle.

MCFALLS, JOSEPH A., JR., sociologist, demographer, educator; b. Phila., July 11, 1945; BS, St. Joseph's Coll., Phila., 1967; MBA, Harvard U., 1969; MA in Demography, U. Pa., 1971, PhD, 1977; m. Marguerite Harvey, 1971. Mem. faculty Temple U., Phila., 1978-86, assoc. prof. sociology, 1978-86; prof. faculty Villanova (Pa.) U., 1986—; research assoc. Population Studies Ctr., U. Pa., Phila., 1974—; Inst. Continuous Study of Man, Ea. Pa. Psychiat. Inst., Phila., 1974; demographic and bus. cons.; manuscript reviewer; guest on radio and TV shows. Mem. Internat. Union Sci. Study of Population, Population Assn. Am., Soc. Study of Social Biology. Author: Psychopathology and Subfecundity, 1979, Frustrated Fertility: A Population Paradox, 1979; Disease and Fertility, 1984, Social Problems, 1988, Population, 1991, Sociology, 1995; also articles. Office: Villanova U. Sociology Dept Villanova PA 19085

MCFARLAN, FRANKLIN WARREN, business administration educator; b. Boston, Oct. 18, 1937; s. Ronald Lyman and Ethel Warren (White) McF.; m. Margaret Karen Nelson, Dec. 17, 1971; children: Andrew, Clarissa, Elizabeth. A.B., Harvard Coll., 1959, M.B.A., 1961, D.B.A., 1965. Asst. prof. Harvard Bus. Sch., Boston, 1964-68, assoc. prof., 1968-73, prof. bus. adminstrn., 1973—; sr. assoc. dean, dir. rsch., 1991—; dir. Providian Corp., Louisville, Pioneer Hy-Bred Corp., Des Moines, Computer Sci. Corp., L.A. Author: (with Richard Nolan) Information Systems Administration, 1973, (with James L. McKenney and James Cash) Corporate Information Management, 1987, 3d edit., 1992; editor: (with Richard Nolan) Information Systems Handbook, 1973, Information Systems Research Challenge, 1984; sr. editor MIS Quar., 1986-88. Bd. dirs., pres. Belmont (Mass.) Day Sch., 1982-86; bd. dirs. Dana Hall Sch., Wellesley, Mass., 1982-94, chmn. bd., 1990-93; trustee Mt. Auburn Hosp., 1991—, chmn. bd., 1995—; trustee Winsor Sch., 1994—. 1st lt. U.S. Army, 1962-67. Republican. Episcopalian. Club: The Country (Brookline, Mass.). Home: 37 Beatrice Cir Belmont MA 02178-2657 Office: Harvard Bus Sch Soldiers Field Rd Boston MA 02163

MCFARLAND, CLAUDETTE, real estate executive, lawyer, social worker, pastor, consultant; b. St. Louis, Dec. 8, 1935; B.A., Roosevelt U., 1958; LL.B., N.C. Central U., 1965, J.D., 1970; M.S.W., U. Ill., 1969, M.A. in Bus. Adminstrn., 1972, Ph.D. in Sociology, 1977; m. Vernon A. Winstead, Sr., 1964; children: Vernon, Claudette. Pres. McFarland Enterprises, Inc., Chgo., 1961—; v.p. V.A.W. Industries, Chgo., 1972—; mem. adv. bd. Shore Nat. Bank, 1978—; cons. City of Chgo. Dept. Housing, 1979—. Founder, organizer South Shore Sr. Citizens Center, 1974—, St. Philip Neri Troup 859, Girl Scouts Am., 1975, Troup 1358, 1978, mem. exec. bd. dirs., 1975-78; pub. relations dir., mem. exec. bd. League of Women Voters, 1970-71; exec. dir. South Shore Commn., 1985—; v.p. South Shore Econ. Devel. Commn., 1987—; co-pastor/founder Holy Family United in God First Ch. and Soc.; mem. consumer adv. bd. Chgo. Defender newspaper, 1976-78; editor, pub. Chgo. South Shore Scene Newspaper, 1983—; chmn. Jack and Jill of Am. Chgo. Found., 1976—; mem. exec. bd. Chgo. South Shore Commn., 1968-78, 88—, women's aux. bd. Provident Hosp., 1975-78, Chgo. Beautiful Com., 1975-88, Friends of the Park, 1975-75-88, Friends of the Park, 1976-ark, 1976-782 Mayor's Commn. for African-Amer. Affairs; trustee Du Sable Mus., 1976-78. Recipient numerous awards including Outstanding Women of Yr. Girl Scouts Am., 1975, Gamma Phi Delta, 1975, Outstanding Community Service award Afro-Am. Patrolman's League, 1975, Outstanding Humanitarian Service award Peoples Ch., 1975, Pres.'s Leadership Trophy Chgo. and No. Dist. Assn. Women and Girls Clubs, 1976, Plaque Nat. Negro Labor Relations League, 1978. Mem. Women's Internat. League for Peace and Freedom, Chgo. Council Fgn. Relations, Internat. Visitors Center, Chgo. Assn. Commerce and Industry, Nat. Council Negro Women (pres. Chgo. chpt. 1974-78, Ill. chpt. 1974-78), Am. Assn. Catholic Women, Church Women United, Nat. Assn. Univ. Women, Nat. Bar Assn, AAUW (exec. dir., CEO 1988—, chmn. pub.info.and pub. policy com. 1990-91), N.C. Central Alumni Assn., League of Black Women, Ill. Women's Soc., Nat. Council Jewish Women (life), Chgo. and No. Dist. Assn. Girls Clubs, The Links, Inc. (former mem. exec. bd. Chgo.; del. internat. convention), PUSH, NOW, NAACP, Urban League, Alpha Kappa Alpha (life) (chmn. nat. com. 1976-77, internat. grantsmanship com. 1991—, delegate 1992, treas. Xi Nu Omega chpt. 1991), Tau Gamma Delta (life). Address: 7433 S Constance Ave Chicago IL 60649-3609

MCFARLAND, DAVID E., university official; b. Enid, Okla., Sept. 25, 1938; s. Eugene James McF. and Lydia May (Catlin) Lawson; m. Marcia Ruth Lake, Nov. 3, 1957 (div. 1978); children: Jennifer, Jeffrey, Jon, Julie; m. Susan Kaye Siler, Mar. 3, 1979 (div. 1994); 1 child, Matthew Chapple; m. Barbara Ambrogro, Oct. 1994. BS, Wichita State U., 1961, MS, 1964; PhD, U. Kans., 1967. Stress analysis engr. Boeing Co., Wichita, Kans., 1957-

64; instr. U. Kans., Lawrence, 1964-67; asst. v.p., dean Wichita State U., 1967-81; dean. sch. tech., Pittsburgh State U., Kans., 1981-85; provost, v.p. acad. affairs Cen. Mo. State U., 1985-88; pres. Kutztown U. of Pa., 1988—. Author: Mechanics of Materials, 1977; Analysis of Plates, 1972. Contbr. articles to tech. jours. Office: Kutztown U of Pa Office of Pres Kutztown PA 19530

MC FARLAND, FRANK EUGENE, university official; b. Ft. Towson, Okla., Sept. 8, 1918; s. Thomas Edward and Sadie Margaret (Gayer) McF.; m. Trudy Hudson Lively, Dec. 20, 1947 (dec.); children—Marsha Lane, Martha Lynne McFarland Cox. B.A. cum laude, Baylor U., 1950; M.A. Columbia U., 1953, Ed.D., 1959; postgrad., U. Tex., 1956, Tex. A. and M. U., 1956. Lic. psychologist, Okla. Counselor Tex. A&M U., College Station, 1950-51; acting dir. counseling Tex. A&M U., 1951, personal and vocat. counselor, 1951-55, instr., 1951-53, asst. prof. psychology, 1953-55, acting dir. testing and research basic div., asst. prof. psychology, 1955-56, dir. testing and research, basic div., assoc. prof., 1956-69; dir. student personnel Coll. Arts and Scis., assoc. prof. Okla. State U., Stillwater, 1959-61; dean student affairs, prof. psychology Okla. State U., 1961-68, prof. edn. Coll. Edn., 1968-73, dir. student services, prof. applied behavioral studies, 1973-84, dir. student svcs., prof. applied behavioral studies emeritus, 1984—; treas., adminstrv. sec. Okla. State U. Emeriti Assn., 1990—. Author: Compilation of Research Studies from 1953-59, 1959, Student Attitudes Toward the Basic Division, 1958; contbr. articles to profl. jours. First v.p. United Fund Stillwater, Inc., 1963-64, pres., 1964-65; cabinet adviser Will Rogers council Boy Scouts Am., 1961-63; mem. Mayor's Com. on Hosp. Adv. Bd., 1963-66; mem. devel. council Baylor U., 1983—; treas., bd. dirs. YMCA Found.; treas. Stillwater YMCA Found., Inc., 1986—. Served with AUS, 1941-45. Decorated Purple Heart with oak leaf cluster, Bronze Star; recipient Okla. State U. Student Senate award of recognition, 1968; Columbia U. faculty fellow, 1952-53. Mem. Am. Psychol. Assn., Okla. Psychol. Assn. (assoc.), Am. Personnel and Guidance Assn., Southwestern Assn. Student Personnel Adminstrs., Okla. Personnel, Guidance and Counseling Assn., Okla. Deans and Counselors Assn., Okla. Edn. Assn. (pres. 1972-73), Omicron Delta Kappa (achievement award for outstanding contbn. to Okla. State U. 1968), Phi Delta Kappa, Kappa Delta Pi, Alpha Chi, Psi, Chi, Sigma Epsilon Sigma, Phi Kappa Phi, Omicron Delta Kappa (coll. rep.). Lodge: Rotary. Home: 1224 N Lincoln St Stillwater OK 74075-2749

MCFARLAND, GERTRUDE KAY, health scientist administrator; b. Grosshöchstetten, Switzerland, Aug. 1, 1941; d. John and Emma (Blatter) Ramseier; m. Alvin L. McFarland, July 1968. BSN, U. Cin., 1964; MS, U. Calif., San Francisco, 1966, postgrad., 1967; D of Nursing Sci., Cath. U. Am., 1977. Chief nursing edn. St. Elizabeth, NIMH, USPHS, Washington, 1979-80, team leader nursing edn., 1978-79; nurse cons. div. of nursing USPHS, Rockville, Md., 1980-87; health scientist adminstr. nursing rsch. study sect. NIH, USPHS, Bethesda, Md., 1987—; del. leader People to People Delegation, Peoples Rep. of China, 1986, Rep. of Korea, 1989, Ea. Europe, 1990. Author: (with M.D. Thomas) Psychiatric Mental Health Nursing, 1991 (Book of Yr. award Am. Jour. Nursing 1990), (with McFarlane) Nursing Diagnoses and Intervention, 1993, (with Wasli and Gerety) Nursing Diagnoses and Process in Psychiatric Mental Health Nursing, 1992), (with J. Thompson and Others) Mosby's Clinical Nursing, 1993 (Classic Book award Am. Jour. Nursing 1987), (with M. Kim and A. McLane) Pocket Guide to Nursing Diagnoses, 1995 (Book of Yr. award Am. Jour. Nursing 1984). Recipient Disting. Alumnus award U. Cin., 1985, NIH Award of Merit, 1990, N. Am. NDX Assoc. Unique Contbn. award, 1992. Mem. N.Am. Nursing Diagnosis Assn. (bd. dirs. 1983-89), Am. Acad. Nursing.

MC FARLAND, H. RICHARD, food company executive; b. Hoopeston, Ill., Aug. 19, 1930; s. Arthur Bryan and Jennie (Wilkey) McF.; m. Sarah Forney, Dec. 30, 1967. B.S. U. Ill., 1952. With Campbell Soup Co., Camden, N.J., 1957-67; mgr. purchasing Campbell Soup Co., 1961-67; dir. procurement Keebler Co., Elmhurst, Ill., 1967-69; v.p. purchasing and distbn. Ky. Fried Chicken Corp., Louisville, 1969-74; v.p. food svcs., sales and distbn. Ky. Fried Chicken Corp., 1974-75; pres., dir. Mid-Continent Carton Co., Louisville, 1974-75, Ky. Fried Chicken Mfg. Corp., Nashville, 1974-75; owner, pres., dir. McFarland Foods Corp., Indpls., 1975—; bd. dirs. Fountain Trust Co., Ind., Covington Svc. Corp., Ind.; pres., bd. dirs. Ky. Fried Chicken Advt., Inc., Ind., 1975-87, exec. coun., 1988-91; mem. exec. coun., nat. franchise coun. Ky. Fried Chicken, 1979-85; bd. dirs. Ky. fried Chicken Nat. Purchasing Coop., 1981-85, chmn. ins. com., 1982-84; chmn. processed foods com. World's Poultry Congress, 1974; dir. nat. advt. coun. Ky. Fried Chicken, 1985-91, exec. com., 1988-90, chmn., 1989-90; mem. devel. com. U. Ill., 1989—. Mem. U. Ill. Found., 1992—; bd. dirs., 1993—; chmn. U. Ill. Nat. Advocates, 1994—; life pres. U. Ill. Sr. Class of '52; bd. dirs. Ind. Fedn. Children and Youth, 1983-84; chmn. campaign Ind. Ky. Fried Chicken March of Dimes, 1977-88; nat. trustee McCormick Theol. Sem., 1993—. 1st lt. USAF, 1952-54, Korea. Recipient Award of Merit U. Ill. Coll. Agr., 1988; hon. chief police Louisville, 1970. Mem. Ky. Restaurant Assns. (bd. dirs. 1970-75), Nat. Broiler Coun. (bd. dirs. 1971-74), Ind. Restaurant Assn., Am. Shorthorn Breeders Assn., Great Lakes Ky. Fried Chicken Franchise Assn. (bd. dirs. 1975-91, 1st v.p. 1978-79, pres. 1979-80), Delta Upsilon. Presbyterian. Clubs: Main Line Ski (Phila.) (pres. 1964); Hillcrest Country. Home: 6361 Avalon Ln Indianapolis IN 46220-5009 Office: 6284 Rucker Rd Ste M Indianapolis IN 46220-4851

MCFARLAND, JAMES W., academic administrator. Dean bus. adminstrn. U. Houston, University Park, until 1988; dean Freeman Sch. Bus. Tulane U., New Orleans, 1988—. Office: Dean School of Business Tulane University New Orleans LA 70118

MCFARLAND, JANE ELIZABETH, librarian; b. Athens, Tenn., June 22, 1937; d. John Homer and Martha Virginia (Large) McFarland. AB, Smith Coll., 1959; M in Divinity, Yale U., 1963; MS in LS, U. N.C., 1971. Tchr. hist. and religion Northfield Schs., Mass., 1961-62; head librarian reference and circulation Yale Divinity Library, New Haven, Conn., 1963-71; head librarian Bradford (Mass.) Coll., 1972-77; reference librarian U. Tenn., Chattanooga, Tenn., 1977-80; head librarian reference dept Chattanooga-Hamilton County Bicentennial Library, Tenn., 1980-86, acting dir., 1986, dir., 1986—. Mem. Chattanooga Library Assn., Tenn. Library Assn., Southeastern Library Assn., Am. Library Assn., Phi Beta Kappa (treas. 1987, 88). Democrat. Roman Catholic. Avocations: reading, travel, needlework. Home: 1701 Estrellita Cir Chattanooga TN 37421-5754 Office: Chattanooga-Hamilton County Libr 1001 Broad St Chattanooga TN 37402-2620

MCFARLAND, JON WELDON, county commissioner; b. Wenatchee, Wash., Aug. 23, 1938; s. Charles Edward and Maud Elizabeth (Brennan) McF.; m. Kay Annette Erbes, Apr. 5, 1956; children: Colleen, Michael, Heather. BS in Edn., Eastern Wash. State U., 1961; MS in Personnel Adminstrn., George Washington U., 1966; Grad., Command and Gen. Staff Coll., Fort Leavenworth, Kans., 1970, U.S. Army War Coll., Carlisle Barracks, Pa., 1980. Commd. U.S. Army, 1961, advanced through grades to col., 1981, retired, 1988; ops. officer European Hdqtrs., U.S. Army, Heidelberg, Fed. Republic Germany, 1980-83; commdr. 16th mil. police brigade U.S. Army, Fort Bragg, N.C., 1983-85, provost marshal 18th Airborne Corps, 1983-85; asst. commandant, commdr. of troops U.S. Army Mil. Police Sch., Fort McClellan, Ala., 1985-88; county commr. Columbia County, Wash., 1989—; dir., owner Mr. Mc's Direct Mktg. Svcs., 1992—; owner, dir. Spectro-Optics of Ea. Wash., Dayton, 1994—; vice chmn. Southeastern Emergency Med. and Trauma Coun., Wash., 1990-94, chmn., 1995—; chmn. Columbia County Bd. Commrs., 1990, 93; bd. dirs. Emergency Mgmt. Svcs., Columbia County. Author: History of Civil Disturbance 1960-68, 1969. Bd. dirs. Columbia County Pub. Health Dist., Dayton, 1989—, chmn., 1995—; bd. dirs. Project Timothy Pub. Svcs., Columbia County Health Found., 1989—; vice chmn. Palouse Econ. Devel. Corp., 1990-92, chmn., 1993-95. Decorated Legion of Merit, Bronze Star, numerous others. Mem. Assn. U.S. Army, Wash. State Assn. Counties, U.S. Army War Coll. Found., Kiwanis (bd. dirs. Dayton 1990—). Democrat. Roman Catholic. Avocations: woodworking, pottery, fishing, hunting, travel. Home: RR 3 Box 248 Dayton WA 99328-9792 Office: Columbia County 341 E Main Dayton WA 99328

MCFARLAND, KAY ELEANOR, state supreme court justice; b. Coffeyville, Kans., July 20, 1935; d. Kenneth W. and Margaret E. (Thrall) McF. BA magna cum laude, Washburn U., Topeka, 1957, JD, 1964. Bar: Kans. 1964. Sole practice Topeka, 1964-71; probate and juvenile judge Shawnee County, Topeka, 1971-73; dist. judge Topeka, 1973-77; assoc. justice Kans. Supreme Ct., 1977—. Mem. Kans. Bar Assn., Irish Wolfhound Clubs of Eng., Ireland and Am. Office: Kans Supreme Ct Kans Jud Ctr 301 W 10th St Topeka KS 66612

MCFARLAND, KAY FLOWERS, medical educator; b. Daytona Beach, Fla., Jan. 27, 1942; d. Ernest Clyde and Sarah Elizabeth (Holder) Flowers; m. Dee Edward McFarland, Aug. 18, 1963; children: Grace, Joy, Eric, Sarah. BS, Wake Forest Coll., 1963; MD, Bowman Gray Sch. Medicine. 1966. Diplomate Am. Bd. Internal Medicine, Am. Bd. Endocrinology. Intern N.C. Bapt. Hosp., Winston-Salem; resident medicine Cleve. Clinic; fellow endocrinology Med. Coll. Ga., Augusta, from instr. to asst. prof. medicine, 1971-77; assoc. prof. to prof. ob-gyn. Sch. Medicine U. S.C., Columbia, 1977-86, prof. medicine Sch. Medicine, 1986—, assoc. dean continuing edn. Sch. Medicine, 1986-91. contbr. chpts. to books and articles to profl. jours. Fellow ACP; mem. Am. Diabetes Assn. (past pres. Augusta chpt., Profl. award 1975). Avocations: music, writing. Office: Univ S C Sch Medicine 2 Richland Medical Park Ste 506 Columbia SC 29203

MCFARLAND, LAWRENCE D., photographer, educator; b. Wichita, Kans., Sept. 1, 1942. BFA, Kansas City Art Inst., 1973; MFA, U. Nebr., 1976. Asst. prof. photography Colo. Mountain Coll., Vail and Leadville, 1976-77, 78-79; artist-in-residence, staff instr. Aperion Workshops, Inc., Millerton, N.Y., 1977-78; co-dir. Etherton Edits., Tuscon, 1983—; instr. Divsn. Continuing Edn. U. Ariz., Tuscon, 1984; asst. prof. photography Kansas City Art Inst., 1984; assoc. prof. photography U. Tex., Austin, 1985—; artist-in-residence U. Vt., 1978, Syracuse (N.Y.) U., 1981, Ariz. Western Coll., Yuma, 1985-86, Hajiinei/Place of Emergence, Ariz., 1986-87; vis. artist U. Tex., Austin, 1981, Nexus Gallery for Photography, Atlanta, 1983, Ariz. Western Coll. Art Symposium, 1984, SRO Gallery, Tex. Tech U., Lubbock, 1988; lectr. in field. Solo exhbns. include Sheldon Meml. Art Gallery, Lincoln, Nebr., 1977, U. Vt., Burlington, 1979, Internat. Mus. Photography, Rochester, N.Y., 1980, Photocollect, N.Y.C., 1982, Etherton Gallery, Tuscon, 1982, 85, Lone Star Gallery, Austin, Tex., 1983, Nexus Gallery for Photography, Atlanta, 1983, Wall Works, Yuma, Tex., 1986, SRO Gallery, Lubbock, Tex., 1988, Trans Avant-Gard Gallery, Austin, 1990; group exhbns. include Portlant (Maine) Mus. Art, 1979, Hayden Gallery-MIT, Cambridge, Mass., 1977, Creative Photography Gallery-MIT, Cambridge, 1979, Santa Barbara (Calif.) Mus. Art, 1979, Photography Southwest Gallery, Scottsdale, Ariz., 1981, Internat. Mus. Photography, Rochester, 1982, Nagasi Gallery, Tokyo, 1982, Phoenix Art Mus., 1982, Art Inst. Chgo., 1983, Hudson River Mus., Yonkers, N.Y., 1984, Spiva Art Ctr., Joplin, Mo., 1984, Burden Gallery, N.Y.C., 1985, The Baker Gallery, Kansas City, 1985, Hood Mus. Art-Dartmouth Coll., 1986, Mexic-Arte, Austin, 1986, Gallery 1107, Carbondale, Ill., 1986, Amon Carter Mus., Ft. Worth, 1986, 89, Photocollect Gallery, 1986, Mus. Photog. Arts, San Diego, 1987, Mus. Fine Arts, Santa Fe, 1987, San Francisco Mus. Modern Art, 1987, Chgo. Art Inst., 1987, Laguna Gloria Art Mus., Austin, 1987, 89, Abilene Fine Arts Mus., 1987, Fotofest Internat., Houston, 1988, Mus. Fine Arts, Houston, 1991, 92; permanent collections include The Libr. of Congress, Mus. Modern Art, N.Y.C., High Mus. Art, Atlanta, Mpls. Art Inst., Internat. Mus. Art, Rochester, Art Inst. Chgo., Mus. N.Mex., Madison (Wis.) Art Ctr., New Orleans Mus. Art, Can. Mus. Architecture, Mus. Photog. Arts, San Diego, Houston Mus. Fine Arts. Visual Artists Fellowship grantee NEA, 1978-79, 84-85, 90-91, Ferguson grantee Friends of Photography, 1982, Ariz. Commn. Arts/U. Ariz. grantee Ctr. Creative Photography, 1984-85. Home: 1702 Ravey St Austin TX 78704 Office: U Tex Dept Art Austin TX 78712

MCFARLAND, MARY A., elementary/secondary school educator/administrator; b. St. Louis, Nov. 12, 1937; d. Allen and Maryann (Crawford) Mabry; m. Gerald McFarland, May 30, 1959. BS in Elem. Edn., S.E. Mo. State U., 1959; MA in Secondary Edn., Washington U., St. Louis, 1965; PhD in Curriculum and Instrn., St. Louis U., 1977. Cert. tchr. elem., secondary, supt., Mo. Elem. tchr. Berkeley Sch. Dist., St. Louis, 1959-64; secondary tchr. Parkway Sch. Dist., St. Louis, 1965-75, social studies coord. K-12, 1975—, dir. staff devel., 1984—; adj. prof. Maryville U., St. Louis, 1990—; cons. pvt. practice, Chesterfield, Mo. Co-author: (text series) The World Around Us, 1990, 3d rev. edit., 1995; contbr. articles to profl. jours. Nat. faculty Nat. Issues Forum, Dayton, Ohio; mem. ABA Spl. Com. on Youth Edn., Chgo. Mem. ASCD, Social Sci. Edn. Consortium, Nat. Coun. for Social Studies (pres. 1989-90), Mo. Coun. for Social Studies (pres. 1980-81). Democrat. Methodist. Avocations: music, sailing. Office: Parkway Schs Dist Instrnl Svcs 12657 Fee Fee Rd Saint Louis MO 63146

MC FARLAND, NORMAN FRANCIS, bishop; b. Martinez, Calif., Feb. 21, 1922; student St. Patrick's Sem., Menlo Park, Calif.; J.C.D., Cath. U. Am. Ordained priest Roman Catholic Ch., 1946, consecrated bishop, 1970; titular bishop of Bida and aux. bishop of San Francisco, 1970-74; apostolic adminstr. Diocese of Reno, 1974-76; bishop Diocese of Reno-Las Vegas, 1976-87, Diocese of Orange, Calif., 1987—. Office: Marywook Ctr 2811 E Villa Real Dr Orange CA 92667-1999

MCFARLAND, RICHARD M., executive recruiting consultant; b. Portland, Maine, Sept. 10, 1923; s. George Fiske and Phyllys C. (Macomber) McF.; BChemE, Rensselaer Poly. Inst., 1944; postgrad. U. Mich., 1946-47; m. Virginia Fitz-Randolph Ripley, Dec. 6, 1947; children: Richard Macomber, Kirk, Jane. Prodn. supr. E. I. duPont, 1947-51; mgr. agrl. chem. market research Brea Chem. (Calif.) subs. Union Oil Co., 1953-55; product mgr. chem. div. FMC Corp., N.Y.C., 1955-59; mgr. mktg. devel. Tex. Butadiene & Chem., N.Y.C., 1959-60; pres. Cumberland Chem. Corp., N.Y.C., 1960-67; gen. mgr. inorganic div. Wyandotte Chem. Co. (Mich.), 1967-69; assoc. Heidrick & Struggles, Inc., N.Y.C., 1969-72, v.p., 1972-81; founder, pres. Brissenden, McFarland, Wagoner & Fuccella, Inc. and predecessors, Stamford, Conn., 1981—. Ensign USNR, 1943-46, lt. comdr., 1951-53. Mem. Am. Chem. Soc., Lambda Chi Alpha. Clubs: Landmark, Cedar Point Yacht, Nutmeg Curling. Patentee in field. Home: 16 Clover Ln Westport CT 06880-2626 Office: Brissenden McFarland Fuccella & Reynolds Inc 721 Us Highway 202/206 Bridgewater NJ 08807-1760

MCFARLAND, RICHARD MACKLIN, retired journalist; b. Blockton, Iowa, Mar. 27, 1922; s. William Harold McFarland and Elsie (Sisson) McFarland Chavannes; m. Jacquelyn Jean Folske, Mar. 22, 1955; children: Marcy Ann, Scott Macklin, Elizabeth Ann McFarland Heyda, Kathryn Belle. BA, U. Iowa, 1944. Newsman UPI, Des Moines, 1944-45, Chgo. 1945, 46-47; bur. mgr. UPI, Bismarck, N.D., 1944-45, Herrin, Ill., 1945, Sioux Falls, S.D., 1947-49, Milw., 1949-51; legis. reporter UPI, Des Moines, 1947, Pierre, S.D., 1949; Iowa mgr. UPI, Des Moines, 1951-54; NW mgr. UPI, Mpls., 1954-55; Wis. mgr. UPI, Milw., 1956-57, regional exec. sales, 1958-59; bur. mgr. UPI, Chgo., 1960-61; Minn. mgr. UPI, Mpls., 1961-69; Mich. editor UPI, Detroit, 1969-71; Minn. editor UPI, Mpls., 1971-84; bur. mgr.-capitol reporter UPI, St. Paul, 1985-89; bd. dirs. Minn. Press Club, 1981-84. Former deacon, Advent Luth. Ch., Roseville, Minn., 8 yrs. Served with USN, 1943-44. Avocations: reading, music, fishing, backpacking, golf. Home: 7312 5th Ave NW Bradenton FL 34209-1522

MC FARLAND, ROBERT HAROLD, physicist, educator; b. Severy, Kans., Jan. 10, 1918; s. Robert Eugene and Georgia (Simpson) McF.; m. Twilah Mae Seefeld, Aug. 28, 1940; children: Robert Alan, Rodney Jon. B.S. and B.A., Kans. State Tchrs. Coll., Emporia, 1940; Ph.M. (Mendenhall fellow), U. Wis., 1943, Ph.D., 1947. Sci. instr., coach high sch. Chase, Kans., 1940-41; instr. navy radio sch. U. Wis., Madison, 1943-44; sr. engr. Sylvania Elec. Corp., 1944-46; faculty Kans. State U., 1947-60, prof. physics, 1954-60, dir. nuclear lab., 1958-60; physicist U. Calif. Lawrence Radiation Lab., 1960-69; dean Grad. Sch., U. Mo., Rolla, 1969-79, dir. instnl. analysis and planning, 1979-82; prof. physics U. Mo., Rolla, 1969-84, prof. emeritus physics dept., 1985—; v.p. acad. affairs U. Mo. System, 1974-75; intergovtl. Personnel Act appointee Dept. Energy, Washington, 1982-84; vis. prof. U. Calif., Berkeley, 1980-81; mem. Grad. Record Exams. Bd., 1971-75, chmn. steering com., 1972-73; cons. Well Surveys Inc., Tulsa, 1953-54, Argonne Nat. Lab., Chgo., 1955-59, Kans. Dept. Pub. Health, 1956-57, cons. in residence Lawrence Radiation Lab., U. Calif., 1957, 58, 59, med. physics U. Okla. Med. Sch., 1971, grad. schs., PhD physics program, Utah State U., 1972; physicist, regional counselor Office Ordnance Research, Durham, N.C., 1955. Contbr. articles to profl. jours. Active Boy Scouts Am., 1952—, mem. exec. bd. San Francisco Bay Area council, 1964-68, Ozark Council, 1986—; chmn. Livermore (Calif.) Library Bond drive, 1964. Mem. Kans. N.G., 1936-40. Recipient Silver Beaver award Boy Scouts Am., 1968, Community Service award C. of C., 1965, Disting. Alumnus award Kans. State Tchrs. Coll., 1969; named Disting. Lt. Gov., Kiwanis, 1985. Fellow Kiwanis Internat., 1992, fellow AAAS, Am. Phys. Soc.; mem. AAUP (chpt. pres. 1956-57), Am. Assn. Physics Tchrs., Mo. Acad. Sci., Mo. Assn. Phys. Sci. Tchrs., Am. Soc. Engring. Edn., Kiwanis (lt. gov. Mo.-Ark. dist. 1984-85, internat. accredited rep. 1985-92), Sigma Xi, Lambda Delta Lambda, Xi Phi, Kappa Mu Epsilon, Kappa Delta Pi, Pi Mu Epsilon, Gamma Sigma Delta, Phi Kappa Phi. Patentee in field of light prodn., vacuum prodn., controlled thermonuclear reactions. Home: 309 Christy Dr Rolla MO 65401-4073 Office: U Mo Physics Dept Rolla MO 65401 *Continuation of the last hundred years of major progress in the quality of life for the human race will not only require the best of our educational systems and technological talents but a sincere interest in all of us to contribute positively toward our collective well-being.*

MC FARLAND, THOMAS L., book publishing executive; m. Dianne L. McFarland; 2 children. BA in English and Journalism, Westminster Coll.; MA in History of Ideas, Johns Hopkins U. Reporter Intelligencer Jour., Lancaster, Pa., 1957; editor-in-chief Stanwix House, Inc., Pitts., 1958-63; mktg. mgr. Johns Hopkins U. Press, Balt., 1963-67, asst. dir. ops. and mktg., 1967-73; part-time jours. mgr. & acquisitions editor, asst. dir. ops. and mktg. U. Calif. Press, Berkeley, 1973-79; dir., editor Univ. Press New Eng., Hanover, N.H., 1979—; dep. chmn., dir. European mktg. office several Am. univ. presses, Trevor Brown Assocs., Ltd., London, 1970—; invited speaker Translation Ctr. Columbia U., Buenos Aires, 1989; met with scholarly pubs. univs. sponsored USIA, China, 1985; mem. adv. bd. NAS Press, 1980-89; cons. U. Calgary Press, U. Alta. Press, 1991, U. Tenn. Press, 1989, U. Minn. Press, 1988, U. Colo. Office of Pres., 1987, Duke U. Press Office of Provost, 1978, others; judge New Eng. Book Show, 1990, Sara Josepha Hale Award, 1989—; student, lectr. Graphic Arts Ctr., Dartmouth Coll., Hanover; faculty mem. pub. seminar. Bd. dirs. Opera North, 1992—; pres. Congregl. Ch. Dartmouth Coll., 1985-88, bd. elders, 1985-88; mem. book and author event com. Friends of Hopkins Ctr./Hood Mus. Art, Dartmouth Coll., 1984—; bd. dirs., 1987-89. Mem. AAUP (del. univ. press pub. meeting Soviet Union 1989, pres. 1989-90, bd. dirs. 1975-78, 88-91, chair govt. and found. rels. com. 1989—, chair exec. dir. search com. 1990, chair membership and standards com. 1985, chair annual meeting program com. 1984, numerous panels, workshops). Avocations: community chorus, piano, house and garden projects. Home: 23 Valley Rd Hanover NH 03755-2230 Office: Univ Press Of NE 23 S Main St Hanover NH 03755-2048

MCFARLAND, VICTOR ALAN, toxicologist; b. Crescent City, Calif., Oct. 10, 1937; s. Victor Marion McFarland and Anna Jean (Endert) Castanos; m. Dwilette Gambrell; children: Frederick Marshall, Daniel Leonard McFarland. BS in Psychology, St. Mary's Coll., 1959; BS in Pharmacy, Oreg. State U., 1964; PhD in Pharmacology/Toxicology, N.E. La. U., 1994. Cert. environ. profl. Rsch. assoc. U. Calif., Bodega Marine Lab., 1972-78; rsch. biologist, prin. investigator, rsch. team leader USAE Waterways Experiment Sta., Vicksburg, Miss., 1978—; mem. U.S. EPA/U.S. Army C.E. Joint Tech. coms. on dioxin, sediment quality criteria, bioaccumulation, 1992—; tech. reviewer of programs, proposals and reports. Editor sediment toxicology sect. Quintessence, 1994—. Recipient R&D Tech. Achievement award Dept. Army, 1988. Mem. Soc. of Environ. Toxicology and Chemistry (Miss. state councilman South Ctrl. chpt. 1986, ad hoc founding com. 1986-87, tech. reviewer 1987—), Nat. Assn. of Environ. Profls., Sigma Xi, Rho Chi. Avocations: sailing, fishing, travel, music.

MCFARLANE, BETH LUCETTA TROESTER, former mayor; b. Osterdock, Iowa, Mar. 9, 1918; d. Francis Charles and Ella Carrie (Moser) Troester; M. George Evert McFarlane, June 20, 1943 (dec. May 1972); children: Douglas, Steven (dec.), Susan, George. BA in Edn., U. No. Iowa, 1962, MA in Edn., 1971. Cert. tchr. Tchr. rural and elem. schs., Iowa, 1936-50, 55-56; elem. tchr. Oelwein Community Schs., Iowa, 1964-64, jr. high reading tchr., 1964-71, reading specialist, 1971-83; mayor of Oelwein, 1982-89; evaluator North Cen. Accreditation Assn. for Ednl. Programs; mem. planning team for confs. for Iowa Cities, N.E. Iowa, 1985; v.p. N.E. Iowa Regional Council for Econ. Devel., 1986-89; mem. Area Econ. Devel. Com. N.E. Iowa, 1985, Legis. Interim Study Com. on Rural Econ. Devel., 1987-88; mem. policy com. Iowa League Municipalities, 1987-88; bd. dirs. Oelwein Indsl. Devel. Corp., 1982-91, Oelwein Betterment Corp., 1982-94. V.p. Fayette County Tourism Council, 1987-88; Iowa State Steering Com. on Road Use Tax Financing, 1988-89; chmn. bd. govs. Oelwein Community Ctr, 1990-94; chmn. Reorganized LDS Ch. Bldg. and Fin. Com., 1980—, Dist. Ch. Fin. Com., 1992—, Dist. Ch. Revolving Loan Com., 1982—. Named Iowa Reading Tchr. of Yr., Internat. Reading Assn. Iowa, 1978; recipient Outstanding Contbrn. to Reading Council Activities award Internat. Reading Assn. N.E. Iowa, 1978, State of Iowa's Gov.s' Leadership award, 1988. Mem. N.E. Iowa Reading Council (pres. 1975-77), MacDowell Music and Arts Orgn. (pres. 1978-80), Oelwein Bus. and Profl. Women (Woman of Yr. 1983), Oelwein Area Ret. Sch. Pers. (pres. 1994—), Oelwein Area C. of C. (bd. dirs. 1986-89, Humanitarian award 1987), Delta Kappa Gamma (pres. 1980-82). Republican. Mem. Reorganized Ch. of Jesus Christ of Latter Day Saints. Avocations: hiking, refinishing antiques, gardening, jogging, creative sewing. Home: 512 7th Ave NE Oelwein IA 50662-1326

MC FARLANE, KAREN ELIZABETH, concert artists manager; b. St. Louis, Jan. 2, 1942; d. Nicholas and Bonita Margaret (Fults) Walz; m. Ralph Leo McFarlane, Nov. 30, 1968 (div.); children: Sarah Louise.; m. Walter Holtkamp, June 19, 1982. B.Mus.Ed. (Presser Music Found. scholar), Lindenwood Coll., 1964. Public sch. music St. Louis County, 1964-66; music asst. Riverside Ch., N.Y.C., 1966-70; dir. music St. Mark's Episc. Ch., San Marcos, Tex., 1971-73, Park Ave. Christian Ch., N.Y.C., 1974-81; also pres. Murtagh/McFarlane Artists, Inc., Cleve., 1976-88; pres. Karen McFarlane Artists, Cleve., 1989—. Mem. Am. Guild Organists, Nat. Assn. Performing Arts Mgrs. and Agts., Inc., Internat. Soc. Performing Arts Adminstrn. Republican. Presbyterian. Office: 12429 Cedar Rd Cleveland OH 44106-3172

MCFARLANE, NEIL, church administrator. Children's dir. The Missionary Church, Fort Wayne, Ind. Office: The Missionary Ch PO Box 9127 3811 Vanguard Dr Fort Wayne IN 46809-3304

MCFARLANE, WILLIAM F., wholesale nut company executive. Vice chmn., dir. Calif. Almond Growers Exchange, Sacramento. Office: Calif Almond Growers Exch 1802 C St Sacramento CA 95814-1010

MCFARLIN, DIANE H., newspaper editor; b. Lake Wales, Fla., July 10, 1954; d. Ruffie Denton Hooten and Anna Loraine (Peeples) Huff; m. Henry Briggs McFarlin, Aug. 28, 1976 (div. 1993). BS, U. Fla., 1976. Reporter Sarasota (Fla.) Jour., 1976-77, asst. news editor, 1977-78, city editor, 1978-82; asst. mng. editor Sarasota (Fla.) Herald Tribune, 1983-84, mng. editor, 1985-87; exec. editor Gainesville (Fla.) Sun, 1987-90, Sarasota Herald-Tribune, 1990—; mem. adv. bd. U. Fla. Coll. Journalism and Comm., 1987—. Mem. accrediting coun. Edn. in Journalism and Mass Comms., 1994—. Mem. Am. Soc. Newspaper Editors (com. chair 1992, 94, bd. dirs. 1994—), Fla. Soc. Newspaper Editors (sec.-treas. 1993, v.p. 1994, pres. 1995). Office: Sarasota Herald-Tribune 801 S Tamiami Trail Sarasota FL 34230

MCFARLIN, RICHARD FRANCIS, industrial chemist, researcher; b. Oklahoma City, Oct. 12, 1929; s. Loy Lester and Julie Mae (Collins) McF.; m. Clare Jane Burroughs, Apr. 4, 1953; children: Robin Sue McFarlin Godwin, Richard Prescott, Rebecca Lynn McFarlin Bray, Roger Whitsitt. BS, Va. Mil. Inst., 1951; MS, Purdue U., 1953, PhD, 1956. Rsch. chemist Monsanto Chem. Co., St. Louis, 1956-60; supr. inorganic rsch. Internat. Minerals and Chems., Mulberry, Fla., 1961; mgr. Agr. Rsch. Ctr. Armour Agrl. Chem. Co., Atlanta, 1962; v.p. rsch., ops., devel. & adminstrn. div. agri-chems. U.S. Steel, Atlanta, 1986; tech. dir. Lester Labs. Inc. Atlanta, 1986-88; exec. dir. Fla. Inst. Phosphate Rsch., Bartow, 1988—; mem. bd. advisors engring. coun. U. South Fla., Lakeland, 1990—, U. Fla., Gainesville, 1991—; mem. bd. advisors Inst. Recyclable Materials La. State

U., Baton Rouge, 1990—. Capt. USAR, 1951-61. M. M. Cohn Found. scholar, 1947, L. D. Wall scholar, 1949, O. M. Baldinger scholar, 1950. Presbyterian. Achievements include eight U.S. and foreign patents for selective organic reducing agents, fertilizer processes and selective biocides. Home: 6611 Sweetbriar Ln Lakeland FL 33813-3598 Office: Fla Inst Phosphate Rsch 1855 W Main St Bartow FL 33830-7718

MCFARLIN, ROBERT PAUL, former army officer, consultant; b. L.A., Dec. 6, 1942; s. Paul Combs and Marion Esther (Fair) McF.; m. Barbara Jean Hinson, Sept. 6, 1962; children: Douglas Paul, Erin Elizabeth McFarlin Wheeler. BA, Trinity U., 1964; MS, Fla. Inst. Tech., 1978. Commd. 2d lt. U.S. Army, 1964, advanced through grades to brig. gen., 1989; student U.S. Army Command and Gen. Staff Coll., Ft. Leavenworth, Kans., 1975-76; logistics staff officer Hdqrs. Dept. Army, Arlington, Va., 1978-80; bn. comdr. 705th Maintenance Bn., Ft. Polk, La., 1980-82; student U.S. Army War Coll., Carlisle, Pa., 1982-83; dir. materiel mgmt. U.S. Army Armament, Munitions and Chem. Command, Rock Island, Ill., 1983-84, chief of staff, 1984; comdr. support command 5th Inf. Div., Ft. Polk, 1984-87; asst. comdt. U.S. Army Ordnance Ctr. and Sch., Aberdeen Proving Ground, Md., 1987-89; comdg. gen. 2d Corps Support Command, Nellingen, Germany and Saudi Arabia, 1989-91; 200th Theater Army Materiel Mgmt. Ctr. Zweibruecken, Germany, 1991-92; exec. dir. distbn. Def. Logistics Agy., Washington, 1992—. Decorated D.S.M., Legion of Merit; recipient Keys to City award Mayor of Natchitoches, La., 1986, Ehrenkreuz der Bundeswehr award German Govt., 1991, Ehrenurkunde award Flak Rgt. 25, 1991. Mem. Assn. U.S. Army, U.S. Army Ordnance Assn., Coun. of Logistics Mgmt., Warehouse Edn. and Rsch. Presbyterian (elder). Avocations: golf, skiing, history, languages. Address: 6210 Roudsby Ln Alexandria VA 22315

MCFATE, KENNETH LEVERNE, association administrator; b. LeClaire, Iowa, Feb. 5, 1924; s. Samuel Albert and Margaret (Spear) McF.; m. Imogene Grace Kness, Jan. 27, 1951; children: Daniel Elliott, Kathryn Margaret, Sharon Ann. BS in Agrl. Engring., Iowa State U., 1950; MS in Agrl. Engring., U. Mo., 1959. Registered profl. engr., Mo. Agrl. sales engr. Ill. No. Utility Co., Aledo, 1950-51; extension agrl. engr. Iowa State U., Ames, 1951-53, rsch. agrl. engr., 1953-56; prof. agrl. engr. U. Mo., Columbia, 1956-86, prof. emeritus, 1986; dir. Mo. Farm Electric Coun., Columbia, 1956-75; exec. mgr. Nat. Farm Electric Coun., Columbia, 1975-86; pres., exec. mgr. Nat. Food & Energy Coun., Columbia, 1986-91; pres. emeritus, 1991; mgr. Electrotechnology Rsch., 1991-93; bd. dirs. Internat. Com. Agrl. Engrs., Brussels, 1989-94. Editor, author: (with others) Handbook for Elsevier Science, 1984-89; editor: Electrical Energy in Agriculture, 1989; mem. editorial bd. Energy in Agriculture for Elsevier Sci., Amsterdam, The Netherlands, 1981-88. Mem. Kiwanis Club Aledo, 1951, Lions Club, Gilbert, Iowa, 1955. 2d lt. USAAF, 1943-45. Fellow Am. Soc. Agrl. Engrs. (George Kable Elec. award 1974); mem. Future Farmers of Am. (hon. Am. Farmer degree 1991), Alpha Epsilon, Gamma Sigma Delta. Republican. Presbyterian. Avocations: technical writing, gardening, old car restoration, woodworking. Home: 9450 E Highway HH Hallsville MO 65255-9724

MC FATE, PATRICIA ANN, scientist, education, foundation executive; b. Detroit, Mar. 19, 1936; d. John Earle and Mary Louise (Bliss) McF.; m. Sidney Norman Graybeal, Sept. 10, 1988. B.A. (Alumni scholar), Mich. State U., 1954; M.A., Northwestern U., 1956, Ph.D., 1965; M.A. (hon.), U. Pa., 1977. Assoc. prof. English, asst. dean liberal arts and scis. U. Ill., Chgo., 1967-74; assoc. prof. English, assoc. vice chancellor acad. affairs U. Ill., 1974-75; assoc. prof. folklore Faculty Arts and Scis., U. Pa., Phila., 1975-81; prof. tech. and soc. Coll. Engring. and Applied Sci., 1975-81, vice provost, 1975-78; dep. chmn. Nat. Endowment for Humanities, Washington, 1978-81; exec. v.p. Am.-Scandinavian Found., N.Y.C., 1981-82, pres., 1982-88; sr. scientist Sci. Applications Internat. Corp., Mc Lean, Va., 1988—; program dir. Ctr. for Nat. Security Negotiations, 1988—; cons. US. Univ. versmt., 1989—; vis. assoc. prof. dept. medicine Rush U., Chgo., 1970-85; bd. dirs. CoreStates Bank, N.A., CoreStates Fin. Corp., Raoul Wallenberg Com. of U.S. Author: The Writings of James Stephens, 1979, Uncollected Prose of James Stephens, 1983; exec. producer Northern Stars, 1985, Diego Rivera: I Paint What I See, 1989; contbr. articles in fields of sci. policy and lit. to various jours. Bd. dirs. Inst. Cancer Rsch., Swedish Coun. Am. Decorated officer Order of Leopold II Belgium, comdr. Order Icelandic Falcon, comdr. Royal Order of Polar Star (Sweden), comdr. Order of Lion (Finland), comdr. Royal Norwegian Order Merit, Knight 1st class Royal Order Dannebrog (Denmark); U. Ill. Grad. Coll. faculty fellow, 1968; Swedish Bicentennial Fund grantee, 1981. Fellow N.Y. Acad. Scis.; mem. AAAS (chmn. com. on sci., engring. and pub. policy 1984-87, com. on sci. and internat. security 1976-79, 88-93), Coun. on Fgn. Rels., Acad. Scis. Phila. (founding mem., corr. sec. 1977-79), N.Y. Sci. Policy Assn., Am. Women for Internat. Understanding, Cosmplitan Club (Phila.), Theta Alpha Phi, Omega Beta Pi, Delta Delta Delta. Office: Sci Applications Internat Corp 1710 Goodridge Dr Mc Lean VA 22102-3701

MC FEATTERS, DALE STITT, retired electric company executive; b. Avella, Pa., Aug. 20, 1911; s. James Dale and Alice Mabel (Stitt) McF.; m. Tirzah McHenry Bigham, Sept. 29, 1938; children: Dale Bigham, Ann Carol McFeatters Koepke, Susan Love. Student, Art Inst. Pitts., U. Pitts. Reporter, feature writer, news commentator, fin. editor Pitts. Press., 1931-45; with Westinghouse Electric Corp., Pitts., 1945-73; dir. employee info., dir. info. services, v.p. Westinghouse Electric Corp., 1945-73. Creator: nationally syndicated cartoon Strictly Business. Mem. Nat. Cartoonists Soc. Republican. Episcopalian. Clubs: Duquesne (Pitts.), Chartiers Country (Pitts.); Rolling Rock (Ligonier, Pa.); Nat. Press (Washington). Lodge: Masons. Home: 1461 Navahoe Dr Pittsburgh PA 15228-1617

MC FEDRIES, ROBERT, JR., power industry executive, chemical engineer; b. Chgo., Nov. 11, 1930; s. Robert and Elizabeth (Sharp) McF.; m. Beverly Elaine Carlson, Oct. 25, 1952; children: Randall Robert, Victoria Elaine. BSChemE, Purdue U., 1952, MSChemE, 1956. Devel. engr. Dow Chem. Co., Midland, Mich., 1955-64, research dir., 1964-73, v.p. Dow Chem. Investment and Fin., 1973-75, rsch. dir., 1975-83, dir. mergers and acquisitions, 1983-87, v.p., 1987-90; chmn. Destec Energy, Inc., Houston, 1990—. Patentee multi layer film, 1965. Served to 1st lt. USAF, 1952-54. Mem. AIChE, Am. Chem. Soc., Fiddlesticks Country Club. Republican. Presbyterian. Avocations: golf, tennis, cross country skiing. Home: 15590 Queensferry Dr Fort Meyers FL 33912-4003 Office: Destec Energy Inc PO Box 4411 Houston TX 77210-4411

MC FEE, ARTHUR STORER, physician; b. Portland, Maine, May 1, 1932; s. Arthur Stewart and Helen Knight (Dresser) McF.; m. Iris Goeschel, May 13, 1967. B.A. cum laude, Harvard U., 1953, M.D., 1957; M.S., U. Minn., 1966, Ph.D., 1967. Diplomate: Am. Bd. Surgery. Intern U. Minn. Hosp., 1957-58, resident in surgery, 1958-65; asst. prof. surgery U. Tex. Med. Sch., San Antonio, 1967-70; assoc. prof. U. Tex. Med. Sch., 1970-74, prof., 1974—; co-dir. surg. ICU Med. Ctr. Hosp., San Antonio, 1968—; spl. cons. on emergency med. care text to AAOS. Contbr. articles to profl. jours. Served with USNR, 1965-67. Fellow ACS; mem. AMA, Am. Assn. History of Medicine, Assn. Acad. Surgery, Tex. Med. Assn., Bexar County Med. Soc., Tex. Surg. Soc., Western Surg. Assn., San Antonio Surg. Soc., Soc. Surgery Alimentary Tract, So. Med. Assn., N.Y. Acad. Scis., Royal Soc. Medicine, So. Surg. Assn., Internat. Surg. Soc., Halsted Soc., J. Bradley Aust Surg. Soc. Home: 131 Brittany Dr San Antonio TX 78212-1721 Office: 7703 Floyd Curl Dr San Antonio TX 78284-7842 *Most of my life has been spent in training surgeons. It has been an informative experience.*

MCFEE, RICHARD, electrical engineer, physicist; b. Pitts., Jan. 24, 1925; s. William and Beatrice (Allender) McF.; m. Anne Stauffer, June 26, 1947 (div. 1960); m. 2d., Joanellen Lewis, Dec. 31, 1974. BEE, Yale U., 1947; MS in Physics, Syracuse U., 1949; PhDEE, U. Mich., 1955. Rsch. asstt. Syracuse U. Med. Sch., 1947-48; instr. Syracuse U. elec. engring. dept., 1948-49; rsch. assoc. U. Mich. Med. Sch., 1949-51; engr. Electro-Mech. Rsch. Inc., Ridgefield, Conn., 1951-52; mem. tech. staff Bell Telephone Labs., Whippany, N.J., 1952-57; prof. elec. engring. Syracuse U., 1957-82; ind. researcher Union Springs, N.Y., 1982-86, Hawi, Hawaii, 1986—; cons. Arthur D. Little Inc., Cambridge, Mass., 1960-61, cardiovascular study sect. NIH, GE Inc., Crouse Hinds Inc., Syracuse, N.Y., 1970, Stanford U. physics dept., 1974-75. Author numerous articles on electronics, electrocardiography, magneto-cardiography, superconductivity, circuit theory, thermodynamics, inertial

navigation, elec. measurements, energy conservation, rehab. equipment; patentee in field. Sgt. U.S. Army, 1943-46. Sci. Faculty fellowship NSF, Stanford U., 1970. Fellow IEEE; mem. AAAS, Sigma Xi. Home and Office: PO Box 989 Kapaau HI 96755-0989

MC FEE, THOMAS STUART, government agency administrator; b. Delafield, Wis., Nov. 19, 1930; s. Leon Worrick and Marguerette Ella (Morris) McFee; m. Mary Virginia Butler, June 7, 1952; children: Richard Stuart, John Worrick, Charles Paxton. BS, U. Md., 1953, postgrad., 1956-60. Mathematician math. computation divsn. David Taylor Model Basin, Navy Dept., Washington, 1956-58; dir. sys. analysis br. ops. rsch. divsn. David Taylor Model Basin, Navy Dept., 1958-62; project leader weapons sys. evaluation group U.S. Dept. Def., 1962-65; tech. asst. to dir. Sci. and Tech. Office, Exec. Office of Pres., White House, 1965-66; dir. sys. devel. HEW, 1967-69, dep. asst. sec. for program sys., planning and evaluation, 1969-71, dep. asst. sec. for mgmt. planning and tech., 1971-77, dep. asst. sec. for mgmt., 1977-78; asst. sec. for pers. adminstrn. HHS, 1978—. With USAF, 1954-56. Mem. Am. Soc. Pub. Adminstrn., Am. Consortium for Internat. Pub. Adminstrn., Nat. Acad. Pub. Adminstrn. (elected). Office: HHS Office of Personnel Adminstrn 200 Independence Ave SW Washington DC 20201

MCFEE, WILLIAM WARREN, soil scientist; b. Concord, Tenn., Jan. 8, 1935; s. Fred Thomas and Ellen Belle (Russell) McF.; m. Barbara Anella Steelman, June 23, 1957; children—Sabra Anne, Patricia Lynn, Thomas Hallie. B.S., U. Tenn., 1957; M.S., Cornell U., 1963, Ph.D., 1966. Mem. faculty Purdue U., 1965—, prof. soil sci., 1973—; dir. natural resources and environ. sci. program, 1975-91, head dept. agronomy, 1991—; vis. prof. U. Fla., 1986-87; cons. U.S. Forest Svc., Desert Rsch. Inst. Author articles in field, chpts. in books. Served with USAR, 1958-61. Alpha Zeta scholar, 1957; named Outstanding Agr. Tchr. Purdue U., 1972; recipient Am. Educator award Soil Sci. Soc., 1987. Fellow Am. Soc. Agronomy (resident edn. award 1989), Soil Sci. Soc. Am. (pres. 1991-92); mem. Internat. Soil Sci. Soc., Soc. Am. Foresters, Sigma Xi. Presbyterian. Home: 708 Mccormick Rd West Lafayette IN 47906-4915 Office: Purdue U Agronomy Dept LILY West Lafayette IN 47907

MCFEELEY, MARK B., federal judge; b. Orlando, Fla., May 5, 1944; s. William Joseph and Belle (Levy) M.; m. Patricia Anne Josephson, June 10, 1972; children—Matthew Randolph, Morgan Diana. B.S., U.S. Mcht. Marine Acad., 1966; J.D. cum laude, U. N.Mex., 1972. Bar: N.Mex. 1972, U.S. Dist. Ct. N.Mex. 1972, U.S. Ct. Appeals (10th cir.) 1972. Law clk. presiding judge U.S. Ct. Appeals, 10th Cir., 1972-73; ptnr. Felker & McFeeley, 1974-77, officer, dir. Felker, McFeeley & Ish, 1977-83; judge U.S. Bankruptcy Ct. Dist. N.Mex., Albuquerque, 1981-83, 83—. Mem. editorial bd. N.Mex. Law Rev., 1971-72. Contbr. articles to profl. jours. Served with USNR, 1966-78. Mem. ABA, Nat. Conf. Bankruptcy Judges, Comml. Law League Am., N.Mex. Bar Assn., Albuquerque Bar Assn. Office: US Dist Ct PO Box 546 Albuquerque NM 87103-0546

MCFEELY, WILLIAM DRAKE, publishing company executive; b. Port Chester, N.Y., July 15, 1954; s. William Shield and Mary (Drake) McF.; m. Karen Gail Eliason, Aug. 12, 1978; children: Matthew Benson, Eric Daniel, Laura Mae. BA cum laude, Amherst Coll., 1976. Coll. traveler W.W. Norton & Co., Inc., N.Y.C., 1976-80, asst. sales mgr., 1980-82, editor, 1982—, v.p. 1990-94, bd. dirs., 1990—, pres., 1994—; pres., bd. dirs. Liveright Pub. Corp., N.Y.C., 1994—, Nat. Book Co., Scranton, Pa., 1994—. Mem. Seven Bridges Field Club (pres. 1989). Home: 106 Seven Bridges Rd Chappaqua NY 10514 Office: W.W. Norton & Co 500 Fifth Ave New York NY 10514

MC FEELY, WILLIAM SHIELD, historian, writer; b. N.Y.C., Sept. 25, 1930; s. William C. and Marguerite (Shield) Mc F.; m. Mary Drake, Sept. 13, 1952; children: William Drake, Eliza, Jennifer. B.A., Amherst Coll., 1952, L.H.D., 1982; M.A., Yale U., 1962, Ph.D., 1966; LD, Washington Coll., 1986. Asst. prof. history and Am. studies Yale U., 1966-69, assoc. prof., 1969-70; dean faculty Mount Holyoke Coll., 1970-73, prof. history, 1970-80, Rodman prof. history, 1980-82, Andrew W. Mellon prof. in the humanities, 1982-86; Richard B. Russell prof. Am. history U. Ga., Athens, 1986-94, Abraham Baldwin prof. of Humanities, 1994—; tchr. Yale-Harvard-Columbia intensive summer studies program, 1967-69; vis. prof. history Univ. Coll. London, 1978-79, Amherst Coll., 1980-81, U. Mass., 1984-85, John J. McCloy prof., 1988-89 ; cons. to com. on judiciary U.S. Ho. of Reps., 1974. Author: Yankee Stepfather: Gen. O.O. Howard and the Freedmen, 1968, Grant: A Biography, 1981, Frederick Douglass, 1991, Sapelo's People, 1994. Recipient Pulitzer Prize in biography, 1982, Francis Parkman prize, 1982, Lincoln prize, 1992, Avery O. Craven award, 1992; Morse fellow, 1968-69, fellow Am. Coun. Learned Socs., 1974-75, Huntington Library, 1976, 83, Guggenheim fellow, 1982-83, assoc. fellow Charles Warren Ctr., 1991-91, vis. scholar W.E.B. Du Bois Inst., Harvard U., 1992—; NEH grantee, 1986-87. Mem. Am. Hist. Assn., So. Hist. Assn., Assn. Study Afro-Am. Life and History, Orgn. Am. Historians, PEN Ctr., Century Assn., Authors Guild. Home: 445 Franklin St # 25 Athens GA 30606 Office: U Ga 301 LeConte Hall Athens GA 30602

MC FERON, DEAN EARL, mechanical engineer; b. Portland, Oreg., Dec. 24, 1923; s. Wallace Suitor and Ruth Carolyn (Fessler) McF.; m. Phyllis Grace Ehlers, Nov. 10, 1945; children: David Brooks, Phyllis Ann, Douglas Dean, Donald Brooks. Student, Oreg. State Coll., 1942-43; BSME with spl. honors, U. Colo., 1945, MSME, 1948; PhD, U. Ill., 1956. Instr. U. Colo., Boulder, 1946-48; assoc. prof. U. Ill., 1948-58; rsch. assoc. Argonne (Ill.) Nat. Lab., 1957-58; prof. mech. engring., assoc. dean U. Wash., Seattle, 1958-82; prof. emeritus U. Wash., 1983—; cons. to industry, 1959-80. Served with USNR, 1942-46, to comdr. Res., 1946-72. Co-recipient Outstanding Tech. Applications Paper award ASHRAE, 1974; Edul. Achievement award Soc. Mfg. Engrs., 1970; NSF faculty fellow, 1967-68. Mem. ASME, Am. Soc. Engring. Edn., U.S. Naval Inst. (life), Sigma Xi (nat. dir. 1972-80, nat. pres. 1978), Tau Beta Pi, Sigma Tau, Pi Tau Sigma. Home: 4008 NE 40th St Seattle WA 98105-5422 Office: U Wash Dept Mech Engring Seattle WA 98195 *What matters most in life is what you can do for others.*

MCFERRIN, BOBBY, singer, musician, composer and conductor. Creative chair St. Paul Chamber Orch. Albums: Bobby McFerrin, 1982, The Voice, 1984, Spontaneous Inventions, 1986, Simple Pleasure, 1988, Medicine Music, 1990, (with Chick Corea) Play, 1992, (with Yo Yo Ma) Hush, 1992, (with St. Paul Chamber Orch.) Paper Music, 1995. Recipient 10 Grammy awards, Emmy award, ACE award. Office: c/o Original Artists 853 Broadway Ste 1901 New York NY 10003

MCFERSON, D. RICHARD, insurance company executive; b. 1952. With New Eng. Life, until 1978; sr. v.p. fin., then exec. v.p. Nationwide Mut. Ins. Co., 1978-88, pres., dir., 1988—; also pres. Nationwide Mut. Fire Ins., Nationwide Gen. Ins. Co.; sr. v.p. fin., dir. Nationwide Fin. Svcs. Inc.; sr. v.p. Nationwide Devel. Co. Office: Nationwide Mut Ins Co 1 Nationwide Plz Columbus OH 43216

MCGAFFEY, JERE D., lawyer; b. Lincoln, Nebr., Oct. 6, 1935; s. Don Larsen and Doris (Lanning) McG.; m. Ruth S. Michelsen, Aug. 19, 1956; children: Beth, Karen. B.A., B.Sc. with high distinction, U. Nebr., 1957; LL.B. magna cum laude, Harvard U., 1961. Bar: Wis. 1961. Mem. firm Foley & Lardner, Milw., 1961—, ptnr., 1968—; dir. Wis. Gas Co., Smith Investment Co., WICOR. Author works in field. Chmn. bd. dirs. Helen Bader Found.; former chmn. bd. dirs. Aurora Health Care; vice chmn. legis. Milw. Met. Assn. Commerce; former chmn. Wis. Taxpayers Alliance, sec., treas., 1994—; chmn. bd. visitors U. Wis. Med. Sch., Madison; chmn. bd. advisors U. Wis. Nursing Sch., Milw. Mem. ABA (chmn. tax sect. 1990-91), AICPA, Wis. Bar Assn., Milw. Bar Assn., Wis. Inst. CPA's, Am. Coll. Tax Counsel (vice chmn. regent), Am. Coll. Trust and Estate Counsel (chmn. bus. planning com.), Am. Law Inst., Univ. Club, Milw. Club, Milw. Country Club, Harvard Club N.Y.C., Univ. Club Washington, Phi Beta Kappa, Beta Gamma Sigma, Delta Sigma Rho. Home: 12852 NW Shoreland Dr Thiensville WI 53097-2304 Office: Foley & Lardner 777 E Wisconsin Ave Ste 3600 Milwaukee WI 53202-5302

MCGAGH, WILLIAM GILBERT, financial consultant; b. Boston, May 29, 1929; s. Thomas A. and Mary M. (McDonough) McG.; m. Sarah Ann McQuigg, Sept. 23, 1961; children: Margaret Ellen, Sarah Elizabeth. BSBA, Boston Coll., 1950; MBA, Harvard U., 1952; MS, MIT, 1965. Fin. analyst Ford Motor Co., Dearborn, Mich., 1953-55; mem. staff treas. office Chrysler Corp., Detroit, 1955-64; compt., treas. Canadian div. Chrysler Corp., Windsor, 1965-67; staff exec-fin. Latin Am. ops. Chrysler Corp., Detroit, 1967-68, asst. treas., 1968-75, treas., 1975-76, v.p., treas., 1976-80; sr. v.p. fin. Northrop Corp., Los Angeles, 1980-88; owner McGagh Assocs., Beverly Hills, Calif., 1988—; bd. dirs. Pacific Am. Income Shares, Inc., Western Asset Trust, Inc., Chrysalis. Board dirs. Greater L.A. Zoo Assn., John Tracy Clinic (pres. 1994—), Mt. St. Mary's Coll. With USAF, 1952-53. Sloan fellow MIT, 1965. Mem. fin. Execs. Inst. (pres. Detroit chpt. 1979-80), Harvard Bus. Sch. Assn. So. Calif. (bd. dirs.). Clubs: Orchard Lake Country; Harvard (N.Y.C. and Boston); Beach (Santa Monica, Calif.); Los Angeles Country, California (Los Angeles), Eastward Ho Country. (Chatham, Mass.). Home: 2189 Century Hl Los Angeles CA 90067-3516 Office: McGagh Assocs 9601 Wilshire Blvd Ste 623 Beverly Hills CA 90210-5278

MCGAHA, MICHAEL DENNIS, Spanish educator; b. Dallas, Tex., Dec. 31, 1941; s. William N. and Helen Charlotte (Fields) McG.; m. Agnes Anne Mycue, Aug. 7, 1964; children: Joseph P., John M. BA, U. Dallas, 1965; PhD, U. Tex., 1970. Prof. of Spanish Pomona Coll., Claremont, Calif., 1970—. Editor: Cervantes and the Renaissance, 1980, Approaches to Theater, 1982, Lope's Fábula de Perseo, 1985; translator: Acting Is Believing, 1986. Fulbright Found. grantee, 1965-66; NEH fellow, 1980-81. Mem. MLA (assembly del. 1990-92), Soc. for Spanish and Portuguese Hist. Studies (assoc. editor Hispania 1986-92), Cervantes Soc. Am. (editor Cervantes 1987-92). Democrat. Jewish. Office: Pomona Coll 333 College Way Claremont CA 91711 Home: 424 W Harrison Ave Claremont CA 91711-4631

MCGANN, BARBARA ELIZABETH, military officer; b. Newport, R.I., Sept. 27, 1946; d. John Henry and Rose Elizabeth (Hein) McG. BA in English, Coll. of Our Lady of Elms, 1969; MS in Mgmt., Salve Regina U., 1983; MA in Nat. Security Affairs, Georgetown U., 1987. Commd. officer USN, 1970, advanced through grades to rear admiral select, 1993; pub. affairs officer Tng. Air Wing ONE, Meridian, Miss., 1970-72; manpower analyst Navy Recruiting Dist., Navy Recruiting Command, L.A., 1972-1974; surface warfare assignment officer Naval Mil. Pers. Command, Washington; manpower analyst Plans and Policy Directorate Joint Chiefs of Staff, Washington; exec. officer Navy Recruiting Dist. N.J.; manpower analyst Sec. of the Navy, Washington, 1983-85; staff of the comdr., sr. gen. unrestricted line officer Mil. Pers. Command, 1985-87; comdr. Naval Support Activity, Holy Loch, Scotland, 1987-89; staff, watch capt. Middle East crisis Office of Dep. Chief Naval Ops., 1989-90; exec. asst. to the commdr. Navey Recruiting Command, 1990-91; assumed command Navey Recruiting Area Eight, 1991-93; with strategic studies group Chief of Naval Ops., Naval War Coll., Newport, R.I., 1993—. Roman Catholic. Avocations: jogging, theatre. Office: Naval War Coll SSG Naval Base Newport RI 02841

MCGANN, JEROME JOHN, English language educator; b. N.Y.C., July 22, 1937; s. John Joseph and Marie Violet (Lecouffe) McG.; m. Anne Patricia Lanni, July 26, 1938; children: Geoffrey, Christopher, Jennifer. BS, Le Moyne Coll., 1959; MA, Syracuse U., 1962; PhD, Yale U., 1966. From asst. prof. to prof. U. Chgo., 1966-75; prof. Johns Hopkins U., Balt., 1975-80; Dreyfuss prof. humanities Calif. Inst. Tech., Pasadena, 1980-86; John Stewart Bryan prof. English U. Va., Charlottesville, 1987—. Author: Swinburne: An Experiment in Criticism, 1972 (Melville Cane award 1972), The Romantic Ideology, 1983, The Beauty of Inflections, 1985, Social Values and Poetic Acts, 1987, Towards a Literature of Knowledge, 1989, The Textual Condition, 1991, Black Riders: The Visible Language of Modernism, 1993; editor: The New Oxford Book of Verse of the Romantic Period, 1993, Sentimental Poetics: A Revolution in Literary Style, 1995, Byron: Complete Poetical Works, 7 vols., 1980-93; author, editor 22 scholarly books and 3 poetry books. Fulbright fellow, Fels Found. fellow, Eng., 1965-66; Guggenheim fellow, Eng., 1970-71, 74-75; NEH fellow, Eng. and Europe, 1975-76, 87-88. Fellow Am. Acad. Arts and Scis.; mem. MLA. Office: U Va Dept English Charlottesville VA 22903

MCGANN, JOHN RAYMOND, bishop; b. Bklyn., Dec. 2, 1924; s. Thomas Joseph and Mary (Ryan) McG. Student, Cathedral Coll. Immaculate Conception, 1944, Sem. Immaculate Conception, Huntington, 1950; LL.D., St. Johns U., 1971; L.H.D., Molloy Coll., 1977, Niagara U., 1983, St. Joseph's Coll., 1983, Adelphi U., 1985. Ordained priest Roman Cath. Ch., 1950, ordained bishop, 1971. Asst. priest St. Anne's, Brentwood, 1950-57; asst. chaplain St. Joseph Convent, Brentwood, 1950-54; tchr. religion St. Joseph Acad., 1950-54; assoc. Cath. chaplain Pilgrim State Hosp., 1950-57; asst. chancellor Diocese of Rockville Centre, 1957-67, vice chancellor, 1967-71; sec. to Bishop Kellenberg, 1957-59; elevated to papal chamberlain, 1959; sec. to Bishop Kellenberg, 1959-70; apptd. titular bishop of Morosbisdus and aux. bishop Diocese of Rockville Centre, 1970-76, bishop, 1976—; Del. Sacred Congregation for Religious to Marianists, 1973-76; theol. cons. Nat. Conf. Cath. Bishops, Rome, 1974, treas. 1984-87; mem. adminstrv. com., 1977-79; Anglican/Roman Cath. task force on pastoral ministry of bishops, 1978-81, nat. adv. com. U.S. Cath. Conf., 1969-70, 81-83, treas. 1984-87; mem. health affairs com., 1972-75, adminstrv. bd., 1976-79, sem. admissions bd. Diocese Rockville Centre, 1971-76, diocesan boundary commn., 1971-76, Tri-Conf. Religious Retirement Project, 1985-88; mem. Papal visit, 1986-87. Bd. Diocesan Svcs., Inc., 1971-76; com. that established Consultation Svcs. for Religious, 1972-74; vicar gen. Diocese Rockville Centre, 1971-76, Episc. vicar, Suffolk County, 1971-76; mem. N.Y. State Cath. Conf. Com. on Prison Apostolate, 1971-74, U.S. Bishops' Com. for Apostolate to Laity, 1972-76, Rockville Centre Diocesan Bd. Consultors, 1969-76; Episc. mem. N.Y. State Cath. Com., 1974-78; chmn. N.Y. State Bishops' Com. on Elective Process, 1974—, Com. Religious Studies in Pub. Edn., 1975-79; mem. com. on edul. concerns, com. on priests senates and couns. N.Y. State Cath. Conf.; bd. dirs. Good Samaritan Hosp., West Islip, N.Y., 1972-76, chmn., 1976—; trustee Cath. Charities Diocese of Rockville Centre, 1971-76; trustee St. Charles Hosp., Port Jefferson, N.Y., 1972-76, chmn., 1976—; pres. Mercy Hosp., St. Francis Hosp., 1976—; chmn. Consolation Residence, 1976—; bd. advisers Sem. Immaculate Conception, 1975—; treas. Nat. Conf. Cath. Bishops U.S. Cath. Conf., 1984-87, ad hoc com. on stewardship, 1988—, tri-conf. commnn. on religious life and ministry, 1988-91; mem. Papal Visit, 1986-87, Tri-conf. Religious Retirement Project, 1985-88; chmn. Nat. Conf. Cath. Bishops/U.S. Cath. Conf. Telecommunications Network Am., 1990-93; mem. adminstrv. bd. Nat. Conf. Cath. Bishops, 1991-93. Office: 50 N Park Ave Rockville Centre NY 11570-4184*

MCGANNEY, THOMAS, lawyer; b. San Mateo, Calif., Mar. 12, 1938; s. Daniel James and Mary Irene (Ewen) McG.; m. Mildred Kalik; children—Jennifer, Abigail, Melanie, Juliana. B.A., Stanford U., 1959; LL.B., Harvard U., 1962. Bar: N.Y. 1963, U.S. Dist. Ct. (so. and ea. dists.) N.Y. 1965, U.S. Ct. Appeals (2d cir.) 1966, (3d cir.) 1969, (10th cir.) 1970, U.S. Supreme Ct. 1971. Law clk. U.S. Dist. Ct., So. Dist. N.Y., 1962-64; assoc. White & Case, N.Y.C., 1964-72, ptnr., 1973—; adj. prof. NYU Law Sch., 1984-86. Mem. Am. Coll. Trial Lawyers, N.Y. State Bar Assn., ABA, Fed. Bar Council, Assn. Bar City N.Y. Office: White & Case 1155 Ave Of The Americas New York NY 10036-2711

MCGAREY MADKOUR, MARY ELAINE BLISS, state legislator; b. Swanton, Vt., Apr. 12, 1927; d. Robert Porter Sr. and Edith Louise (Tuscany) Bliss; m. Walter Allen McGarey, Aug. 26, 1950 (dec. Aug. 1964); children: Pamela McGarey Murphy, Patricia McGarey Berard, Michael James; m. Joseph Louis Madkour, Dec. 29, 1966; 1 child, Carrie Madkour Major. Clk. typist Ctrl. Vt. Ry., St. Albans, Vt., 1945-46, 48-50; psychiat. aide Inst. Living, Hartford, Conn., 1946-47, 50—; asst. mgr. Jesse Welden Inn, St. Albans, 1964; real estate agt. Hoisington Realty, Bennington, Vt., 1985-92; mem. Vt. Ho. of Reps., Montpelier, 1992—. Bd. dirs. Vt. Assn. for Blind and Visually Handicapped, Vt. affiliate Am. Diabetes Assn., Burlington, 1982-88; town chmn. Vt. Green Up Day, Bennington, 1989; trustee Bennington Mus., 1975—; chmn. Bloodmobile canteen ARC, Bennington, 1980-86; mem. Southwestern Vt. Hosp. Aux., 1980—. Named Red Oak Homemaker, Red Oak (Iowa) C. of C., 1961. Mem. Southwestern Vt. Realtors Assn., Plain Dirt Gardeners (past pres.), Women's Fellowship (past pres.), Park McCullough Assn., Garden Club Am. (trustee, Pres. award 1992). Republican. Congregationalist. Avocations: tennis, golf, crafts, gardening, knitting. Home: 401 Jefferson Heights Bennington VT 05201 Office: Vt State Legislature State House State St Montpelier VT 05602

MCGARR, FRANK JAMES, retired federal judge, dispute resolution consultant; b. 1921. A.B., Loyola U., Chgo., 1942; J.D., Loyola U., 1950. Bar: Ill. 1950. Assoc. firm Dallstream Schiff Stern & Hardin, Chgo., 1952-54; asst. U.S. atty. No. dist. of Ill., 1954-55, first asst. U.S. atty., 1955-58; ptnr. firm McKay Solum & McGarr, Chgo., 1958-69; first asst. atty. gen. State of Ill., 1969-70; judge U.S. Dist. Ct. for No. Ill., 1970-88, chief judge, 1980-86, sr. judge, 1986-88; of counsel Phelan Pope Cahill & Devine Ltd., Chgo., 1988—. Served with USN, 1942-45. Mem. Am. Coll. Trial Lawyers, 7th Cir. Bar Assn., Chgo. Bar Assn. Home: 4146 Venard Rd Downers Grove IL 60515 Office: Phelan Pope Cahill & Devine 311 S Wacker Dr # 4200 Chicago IL 60606-6618

MC GARRAH, ROBERT EYNON, business administration educator; b. Scranton, Pa., July 16, 1921; s. Henry Stanley and Jane May (Eynon) McG.; m. Barbara Anne Moore, Oct. 20, 1943; children—Robert Eynon, Anne Louise, Douglas Moore. B.S., Lafayette Coll., 1943; M.S., Princeton, 1948; Ph.D., Cornell U., 1951. Instr. Princeton, 1946-48; from instr. to asso. prof. indsl. engring. Cornell U., 1948-58; asso. prof. bus. adminstrn. Harvard Grad. Sch. Bus. Adminstrs., 1958-63; prof. Imede Mgmt. Devel. Inst., U. Lausanne, Switzerland, 1963-65; asst. dir. def. research and engring., internat. programs Office Sec. of Def., 1966-68; v.p. Logistics Mgmt. Inst., 1965-66; dir. Center Bus. and Econ. Research, 1968-72; prof. mgmt. Sch. Bus. Adminstrn., U. Mass., Amherst, 1968—; cons. in field, 1948—; Faculty fellow U.S. Gen. Acctg. Office, Washington, 1974-75; expert in mgmt. edn. UN-Internat. Labor Orgn. Project on Mgmt. Devel., Nigeria, West Africa, 1978; cons. programs indsl. devel. State of Mass., 1983-85. Author: Production and Logistics Management, 1963, Four Volume Production Casebook Series, 1964, Productivity Management, 1982, Defense-industrial Policies, 1982, Manufacturing for the Security of the United States, 1990; also papers. Trustee Moses Brown Preparatory Sch. Served with USNR, 1943-46, 51-53; mem. Am. com. on U.S.-Soviet Relations, 1983—. Fellow New Eng. Bd. Higher Edn., 1974-78, 80. Mem. Inst. Mgmt. Scis., AAUP, Am. Inst. Indsl. Engrs., Phi Kappa Phi. Home: 17 Elm St Amherst MA 01002

MCGARRELL, JAMES, artist, educator; b. Indpls., Feb. 22, 1930; s. James and Gretchen (Heermann) McG.; m. Anna Harris, June 24, 1955; children: Andrew Rider, Flora Raven. B.A., Ind. U., 1953; M.A., UCLA, 1955. Artist-in-residence Reed Coll., Portland, Oreg., 1956-59; prof. fine arts, dir. grad. painting Ind. U., Bloomington, 1959-80; prof. fine arts Washington U., St. Louis, 1981-93, prof. emeritus, 1993—; artist in residence Dartmouth Coll., 1992. One man exhbns. include Frumkin/Adams Gallery, N.Y.C., 1961, 64, 66, 68, 71, 73, 77, 80, 84, 86, 88, 89, 90, 91, 93, Galerie Claude Bernard, Paris, 1967, 70, 74, Galleria Il Fante de Spade, Rome and Milan, 1967, 71, 72, 74, 76, 79, Galeria Gian Ferrari, Milan, 1981, 83, Galerie Simonne Stern, New Orleans, 1989, 91, 94, 95, Struve Gallery, Chgo., 1988, 90, More Gallery, Phila., 1987, 89, Utah Mus. Art, Salt Lake City, 1972, Art Mus. U. N.Mex., Albuquerque, 1982, St. Louis Art Mus., 1985, Art Mus. U. Ariz., Tucson; represented in permanent collections at Mus. Modern Art, Met. Mus. Art, Whitney Mus. Am. Art, Pa. Acad., Phila., Santa Barbara Mus. Art, San Francisco Art Mus., Art Inst. Chgo., Joseph Hirshhorn Mus., Washington, St. Louis Art Mus., Hamburg (Germany) Mus. Art, Centre Georges Pompidou, Paris. Bd. govs. Skowhegan Sch. Painting and Sculpture. Recipient Am. Acad. Arts and Letters Lifetime Achievement award, 1995; Fulbright fellow, 1955-56; Guggenheim Found. fellow, 1965; Nat. Endowment for Arts grantee, 1967, 85. Mem. Nat. Acad. Art Assn. (bd. dirs. 1969-73), Academie des Beaux Arts de L'Institut de France, Nat. Acad. Design. Home: PO Box 39 Newbury VT 05051-0039

MCGARRY, EUGENE L., university official; b. West Chicago, Ill., June 9, 1930; s. Joseph C. and Rose (Gorgal) McG.; m. Jetta F. Grubbs, June 11, 1955; 1 son, Michael. B.A., Cornell Coll., 1952; M.A., Northwestern U. 1956; Ph.D., U. Iowa, 1961. Asst. prof. social scis. U. Minn., Mpls., 1960-62; asst. prof., advisement coordinator, asso. prof. and asso. dean edn., prof. and dean edn. Calif. State U., Fullerton, 1962-71; asso. v.p. acad. adminstrn. Calif. State U., 1971-77, dir. Univ. Learning Ctr., 1977-92, chmn. tchr. edn., 1983-84; ret., 1992. Served with AUS, 1952-54. Home: 403 S Paseo Serena Anaheim CA 92807-4214

MCGARRY, FREDERICK JEROME, civil engineering educator; b. Rutland, Vt., Aug. 22, 1927; s. William John and Ellen (Dunn) McG.; m. Alice M. Reilly, Oct. 7, 1950 (dec. Jan. 1971); children: Martha Ellen, Alice Catherine, Joan Louise, Carol Elizabeth, Susan Elizabeth, Janet Marian. A.B., Middlebury (Vt.) Coll., 1950; S.B., Mass. Inst. Tech., 1950, S.M., 1953. Faculty MIT, 1950—, prof. civil engring., 1965—, prof. materials sci. and engring., 1974—, head materials div., 1964—, dir. materials research lab., 1964—, assoc. dir. inter-Am. program civil engring., 1961—, dir. summer session, 1983—. Contbr. numerous articles to profl. jours. Recipient Best Paper award Soc. Plastics Industry, 1968, 91. Mem. AAAS, ASTM, Soc. Rheology, Soc. Plastics Engrs., Am. Soc. Metals, Sigma Xi. Home: 90 Bakers Hill Rd Weston MA 02193-1774 Office: Mass Inst Tech 77 Massachusetts Ave Cambridge MA 02139-4307

MCGARRY, J. MICHAEL, III, lawyer; b. Sacramento, Calif., July 30, 1943. BS, U. Pa., 1965; LLB, U. Va., 1969. Bar: D.C. 1969, Md. 1972. Law clk. to Hon. Matthew F. McGuire U.S. Dist. Ct. (D.C. dist.), Wash., 1969-70; asst. U.S. atty. U.S. Attys. Office, 1970-73; ptnr. Winston & Strawn, Washington. Office: Winston & Strawn 1400 L St NW Washington DC 20005-3509

MCGARRY, JOHN EVERETT, lawyer; b. Madison, Wis., May 11, 1939; s. Daniel E. and Margaret A. (Haas) McG.; m. Kate Wilkinson, Aug. 26, 1961; children: John Eric, Andrew Lawrence. BA, Lehigh U., 1961, BS in Metall. Engring., 1962; LLB, Georgetown U., 1966. Bar: Okla. 1966, Mich. 1968. Atty. Phillips Petroleum Co., Bartlesville, Okla., 1966-67, Price, Heneveld, Huizenga & Cooper, Grand Rapids, Mich., 1967-70; pvt. practice, Grand Rapids, 1970-72; ptnr. McGarry & Waters, Grand Rapids, 1973-78, Varnum Riddering Wierengo & Christenson, Grand Rapids, 1979-84, Varnum Riddering Schmidt & Howlett, Grand Rapids, 1984—. Mem. Opera Grand Rapids, 1984-92, pres., 1991. Mem. Am. Intellectual Property Law Assn. (chair harmonization com. 1993—). Office: Varnum Riddering Schmidt & Howlett PO Box 352 Bridgewater Pl Grand Rapids MI 49501-0352

MCGARRY, JOHN PATRICK, JR., advertising agency executive; b. Elizabeth, N.J., Nov. 22, 1939; s. John Patrick and Elizabeth (Weber) McG.; m. Gilda R. Spurio, Oct. 24, 1964; children: Victoria Elizabeth, John Patrick, III. BS in Mktg. Econs, Villanova U., 1961. Salesman Exxon Corp., Elizabeth, 1961-64; advt. exec. Young and Rubicam N.Y.C., 1965-69, sr. v.p., mgmt. supr., 1969-87, pres., mem. ops. com., advt. exec. com., 1987—; vice chmn. Young and Rubicam Advt. Worldwide, N.Y.C., 1990—; chmn. Client Svcs. Worldwide, N.Y.C., 1987—; pres., CEO Young and Rubicam N.Am., N.Y.C., 1992-94; chmn., CEO Young and Rubicam Advt., Worldwide, N.Y.C., 1994—; bd. dirs. Caramoor; mem. corp. exec.'s com. Young and Rubicam, 1992. Bd. dirs. New Youth Performing Theatre, Bedford, N.Y., Regional Rev. League, Westchester, 4 A's, Louisville Opera Assn., 1981-83, Dominican Coll., Drop-out Prevention Fund, United Negro Coll. Fund, 1994—; bd. dirs. N.Y. coun. Boy Scouts Am., 1992; head parents fund St. Lawrence U. Mem. Internat. Advt. Assn. (pres. U.S. and Can.), Proprietary Assn. (bd. dirs.), Bedford Club, Golf and Tennis Club, N.Y. Athletic Club, The Roundabout Theater (adv. bd. 1994—). Democrat. Roman Catholic. Home: 465 Cantitoe Rd Bedford NY 10506 Office: Young & Rubicam Inc 285 Madison Ave New York NY 10017-6486

MCGARRY, JOHN WARREN, government official. Grad. cum laude, Holy Cross Coll., Georgetown U. Law Ctr. Asst. atty gen. State of Mass., practicing atty.; chief counsel House Spl. Com to Investigate Campaign Expenditures; mem. spl. counsel on Elections Com. on House Adminstrn. 1973-78; appointed to Fed. Election Commn., 1978—, chmn., 1981, 85, 91. Office: Fed Election Commn 999 E St NW Washington DC 20463-0002

MCGARRY, ROBERT GEORGE, safety engineer; b. Mpls., Jan. 4, 1917; s. Emmett Frank and Ethel Florence (Bryant) McG.; m. Janalee Judy, Sept. 22, 1986; children from previous marriage: Mary Kathleen, Nancy Margaret, Susan Elaine, Kevin Robert. BS in Indsl. Engring., U. Minn., 1939; MS in Safety Engring., Ga. Inst. Tech., 1947. Registered profl. engr., Calif.; cert. safety profl. Sr. safety engr. U.S. Fidelity & Guaranty Co., Atlanta, Mpls., 1950-63; Bechtel Corp., San Francisco, 1963-77; corp. safety engr. Burns & McDonnell Engrs., Cons., Kansas City, Mo., 1977-82; con. safety engr., Lee's Summit, Mo., 1982—. With USN, 1942-46. Recipient Minn. Gov.'s Outstanding Safety Achievement award, 1969; scholar Advanced Inst. Nuclear Studies. Mem. NSPE, Am. Soc. Safety Engrs. (chmn. engring. com.), Vets. of Safety Internat. (dir.-at-large), NSPE, Mo. Soc. Profl. Engrs., Profl. Engrs. in Pvt. Practice, Am. arbitration Assn. (arbitrator), Masons, Shriners. Home and Office: PO Box 9914 Kansas City MO 64134-0914

MCGARRY, WILLIAM ANDREW, JR., career counselor; b. Roswell, N.Mex., Sept. 8, 1954; s. William Andrew and Margaret Mary (Padberg) McG. BSEE, U. New Orleans, 1976, MEd in Counseling, 1989. Cert. engr.-in-tng., La., cert. rehabilitation counselor. Engr. Amoco Prodn. Co., New Orleans, 1972; quality control engr. Tex. Instruments, Dallas, 1977, Digicon Exploration Corp., Houston, 1973; quality assurance engr. Petro-Marine Engring., New Orleans, 1978-82; adminstr. U. New Orleans, 1986-88; peer counselor Ind. Living Ctr., New Orleans, 1987-89; counselor Austin Community Coll., 1990; career guidance counselor Tex. Commn. for the Blind, Austin, 1990—. U. New Orleans scholar, 1987. Mem. Am. Counseling Assn., Assn. Handicap Student Svc. Programs in Postsecondary Edn. (svc. cert. 1988), La. Cons. Engrs., Nat. Fedn. Blind La. (treas. 1982-86, scholar 1987), Alpha Theta Epsilon, Omicron Delta Kappa (v.p.). Office: Tex Commn For The Blin Austin TX 78756

MCGARY, BETTY WINSTEAD, minister, counselor, individual, marriage, and family therapist; b. Louisville, June 21, 1936; d. Philip Miller and Mary Jo (Winstead) McG.; married, 1960 (div. 1979); children: Thomas Edward, Mary Alyson, Andrew Philip Pearce. BS, Samford U., 1958; MA, So. Bapt. Theol. Sem., 1961; EdD, U. Louisville, 1988. Ordained to ministry Bapt. Ch., 1986; cert. secondary tchr., Ky., Ga.; lic. profl. counselor, marriage and family therapist, Tex. Min. to youth Broadway Bapt. Ch., Louisville, 1958-60; learning disability and behavior disorders specialist Jefferson County Schs., Muscogee Schs., Cobb County Schs. Louisville, Columbus, Ga., Atlanta, 1964-88; min. to adults South Main Bapt. Ch., Houston, 1986-90; assoc. pastor Calder Bapt. Ch., Beaumont, Tex., 1991—; marriage enrichment cons. Pastoral Inst., Columbus, 1973-76; co-founder and coord. Ctr. for Women in Ministry, Louisville, 1983-86, exec. bd. dirs., 1983-90; cons. Tex. Christian Life Commn., Ft. Worth, 1989-93; co-therapist pvt. practice, Houston, 1989—; mem. Leadership Coun., Triangle Interfaith Project, Beaumont, 1995—. Author: (with others) The New Has Come, 1988, A Costly Obedience: Sermons by Women of Steadfast Spirit, 1994; co-editor nat. newsletter Folio: A Newsletter for Southern Bapt. Women in Ministry, 1983-86. Vice-chairperson exec. bd. dirs. handicapped Boy Scouts Am., Houston, 1986-90; mem. leadership coun. Triangle Interfaith Project, Beaumont, 1995—. Recipient citation for Disting. Svc. So. Bapt. Theol. Sem., 1984, Dean's citation Outstanding Achievement U. Louisville, 1988. Mem. The Alliance of Bapts. (exec. bd. dirs. 1988-90, v.p. 1990-91), So. Bapt. Women in Minstry (pres. 1988-90), Bapt. Gen. Conv. of Tex. (exec. bd. dirs.), Leadership Beaumont. Avocations: gardening, interior design, travel. Home: 2107 Bartlett St Houston TX 77098-5305 Office: Calder Bapt Ch 1005 N 11th St Beaumont TX 77702-1204 *All around us there are new opportunities for creating, ordering, liberating and healing our world. It is our calling and our challenge to be God's partners in these holy purposes.*

MC GAUGH, JAMES LAFAYETTE, psychobiologist; b. Long Beach, Calif., Dec. 17, 1931; s. William Rufus and Daphne (Hermes) McG.; m. Carol J. Becker, Mar. 15, 1952; children: Douglas, Janice, Linda. BA, San Jose State U., 1953; PhD (Abraham Rosenberg fellow), U. Calif. - Berkeley, 1959; sr. postdoctoral fellow, NAS-NRC, Istituto Superiore di Sanità, Rome, 1961-62; DSc (hon.), So. Ill. U., 1991. Asst. prof., assoc. prof. psychology San Jose State U., 1957-61; assoc. prof. psychology U. Oreg., 1961-64; assoc. prof. U. Calif., Irvine, 1964-66, founding chmn. dept. psychobiology, 1964-67, 71-74, 86-89, prof., 1966-94; rsch. prof., 1994—; dean Sch. Biol. Sci. U. Calif., Irvine, 1967-70, vice chancellor acad. affairs, 1975-77, exec. vice chancellor, 1978-82, founding dir. Ctr. Neurobiology of Learning and Memory, 1983—; Mem. adv. coms. NIMH, 1965-78, Mental Health Coun. NIMH, 1992—. Author: (with J.B. Cooper) Integrating Principles of Social Psychology, 1963, (with H.F. Harlow, R.F. Thompson) Psychology, 1971, (with M.J. Herz) Memory Consolidation, 1972, Learning and Memory: An Introduction, 1973, (with R.F. Thompson and T. Nelson) Psychology 1, 1977, (with C. Cotman) Behavioral Neuroscience, 1980; editor: (with N.M. Weinberger, R.E. Whalen) Psychobiology, 1966, Psychobiology-Behavior from a Biological Perspective, 1971, The Chemistry of Mood, Motivation and Memory, 1972, (with M. Fink, S.S. Kety, T.A. Williams) Psychobiology of Convulsive Therapy, 1974, (with L.F. Petrinovich) Knowing, Thinking, and Believing, 1976, (with R.R. Drucker-Colin) Neurobiology of Sleep and Memory, 1977, (with S.B. Kiesler) Aging, Biology and Behavior, 1981, (with G. Lynch and N.M. Weinberger) Neurobiology of Learning and Memory, 1984, (with N.M. Weinberger and G. Lynch) Memory Systems of the Brain, 1985, Contemporary Psychology, 1985, (with C.D. Woody and D.L. Alkon) Cellular Mechanisms of Conditioning and Behavioral Plasticity, 1988, (with N.M. Weinberger and G. Lynch) Brain Organization and Memory: Cells, Systems and Circuits, 1990, (with R.C.A. Frederickson and D.L. Felten) Peripheral Signaling of the Brain, 1991, (with L. Squire, G. Lynch and N.M. Weinberger) Memory: Organization and Locus of Change, 1991; author over 350 sci. papers; founding editor Behavioral Biology, 1972-78, Behavioral and Neural Biology, 1979—. Recipient medal U. Calif., Irvine, 1992. Fellow AAAS, Am. Acad. Arts and Scis., Soc. Exptl. Psychologists, Am. Psychol. Soc. (William James fellow 1989, pres. 1989-91), Western Psychol. Assn. (pres. 1992-93); mem. NAS (chmn. psychol. sect. 1992-95), APA (chief sci. advisor 1986-88, Sci. Contbn. award 1981), Internat. Brain Rsch. Orgn., Soc. Neurosci., Am. Coll. Neuropsychopharmacology, CINP, Psychonomic Soc., European Behavioral Pharmacology Soc., Phi Beta Kappa, Sigma Xi. Office: U Calif School Med Dept Psychiatry Irvine CA 92717-0002

MC GAUGHAN, ALEXANDER STANLEY, architect; b. Phila., May 18, 1912; s. Henry T. and Mable (Colgan) McG.; m. Virginia Storm, July 11, 1936 (dec. Sept. 1989); 1 son, Alexander Stanley; m. Maria R. Drayer, Oct. 27, 1990. BArch, U. Mich., 1934. Draftsman, designer Pontiac, Mich., 1934-36; architect Resettlement Adminstrn. and Farm Security Adminstrn., 1936-44; labor economist, planner WPB, Washington, 1944-45; housing economist, prodn. engr. Nat. Housing Agcy., Washington, 1945-47; indsl. designer Cairns Corp., N.Y.C., also Hugh Johnson Assos., Washington, 1947-50; partner McGaughan & Johnson, Washington, 1950-80; asst. dir. design and constrn. Gallaudet U., Environ. Design Center for the Deaf, 1980-84; univ. architect Am. U., Washington, 1984-87; archtl. cons., 1988—; spl. cons. Nat. Security Resources Bd., Def. Prodn. Adminstrn., HHFA, HUD, Dept. Def.; mem. D.C. Bd. Examiners and Registrars Architects, 1966-73, pres., 1969-72; dir. Mid. Atlantic region Nat. Coun. Archtl. Registration Bds., 1966-73, chmn., 1970-71, chmn. exam. com. on design and site planning, 1972-73. Prin. works include Charred Oak Estates, Md., doctor's residence D.C. Gen. Hosp., housing, Carlisle Barracks, Pa., housing for USAF and U.S. Army C.E., ea. U.S., shopping ctrs., McLean, Va., Greenbelt, Md., Fairfax County, Va., Prince Georges County, Md., Washington pub. schs., Andrew Radar Clinic, Ft. Myer, Va., D.C. Police Acad., 2d, 4th and 5th dist. police hdqrs., Washington; patentee aluminum bldg. systems. Bd. govs. Washington Bldg. Congress, 1968-71, bd. dirs., 1973-76; mem. President's Com. on Employment People with Disabilities, 1974-93; bd. dirs. Nat. Ctr. for Barrier Free Environ., 1974-79. Recipient 1st award for contemporary architecture and land planning Md. Homebuilders, 1962; disting. urban landscape award U.S. Army C.E., 1968; disting. archtl. award, 1969; nat. archtl. award of excellence mm. Inst. Steel Constrn., 1973. Fellow AIA (pres. Washington met. chpt. 1963, chmmn. nat. com. archtl. competitions 1966-67, mem. permanent brier free task force 1974-77, rep. to Am. Nat. Standards Inst. A 117.1 com. 1977-88); mem. Nat. Trust for Hist. Preservation, Am. Arbitration Assn. (nat. panel arbitrators), Cosmos Club (bd. mgmt. 1979-80. Home and Office: 2028 Hillyer Pl NW Washington DC 20009-1006

MCGAUGHEY, EMMETT CONNELL, advertising agency executive; b. St. Paul, May 20, 1911; s. Emmett Walter and Frances (Connell) McG.; m. Mary Etta Freese, Oct. 27, 1939; children: Terrence, Dennis, Mark, Mary

Frances. B.S., U. Wash., 1934. Sales promotion Gen. Motors Corp., 1934-41; spl. agt. FBI, 1941-49; So. Calif. mgr. Cappel, MacDonald & Co., 1950-51; exec. v.p. Erwin Wasey, Ruthrauff & Ryan, Inc., Los Angeles and N.Y.C., 1951-63; sr. v.p. Hixson & Jorgenson, Inc., Los Angeles, 1964-65; exec. v.p. Hixson & Jorgenson, Inc., 1965-68; chmn. Dailey & Assos., Los Angeles, 1968—, Dailey Internat. Group, 1981—; mem. adv. bd. Calif. Pacific Nat. Bank. Past officer-or-dir. Los Angeles chpt. ARC, So. Calif. chpt. Arthritis and Rheumatism Found. (Nat. Distinguished Service award 1963), Calif. chpt. Multiple Sclerosis Soc., Los Angeles County Heart Assn. Am. Cancer Soc.; chmn. Los Angeles-Auckland Sister City Com., Comn. to Secure a Mayors Residence; mem. Los Angeles Police Commn., 1952-61, 66-73, v.p., 1954-55, 57-58, 69-70, pres., 1955-56, 58-59, 70-71, sr. mem., 1959-61; mem. assos Calif. Inst. Tech.; mem. commerce assos. U. So. Calif.; bd. dirs. So. Calif. Symphony, Hollywood Bowl Assn.; mem. bd. airport commrs. City of Los Angeles, 1979-85, v.p., 1981-82, pres., 1982-83; chmn. bd. trustees Orthopedic Hosp.; envoy to New Zealand and Tonga Summer Olympics, 1984; trustee Ireland's Children, Inc., mem. com. on internat. trade, City of Los Angeles; pres. Southern Calif. chpt. Am. Irish Found., 1985; 1st v.p. Greater Los Angeles Vis. & Conv. Bur., 1985-87, pres., 1988. Recipient award merit Blind Children's Center, 1971. Mem. Nat. Outdoor Advt. Bur., Soc. Former Spl. Agts. FBI (nat. pres. 1964), Los Angeles C. of C. (dir.), Air Force Assn., Aerospace Council, U. Wash. Alumni Assn. (trustee), Chi Psi (Distinguished Service award 1966), Alpha Delta Sigma. Clubs: Masons, Shriners, Rotary (pres. Los Angeles 1978, dir.); Capitol Hill (Washington); California (Los Angeles), 100 (Los Angeles); Lake Arrowhead Country, Los Angeles Athletic. Office: 3055 Wilshire Blvd Los Angeles CA 90010-1108

MC GAUGHY, JOHN BELL, civil engineer; b. Norfolk, Va., Nov. 5, 1914; s. John Bell and Frances Vivian (Coleman) McG.; m. Charlotte Edna Schwartz, Jan. 20, 1940 (dec. Dec. 1978); 1 child, John Bell; m. Page Cook Axson, Sept. 26, 1981. Student, U. Va., 1933-35; B.S. in Civil Engring., Duke U., 1938. Asst. to project engr. U.S. Dept. Agr., Farmville, Va., 1936-37; tech. asst. civil engring. sect. U.S. Coast Guard, Portsmouth, Va., 1938-39; civil engr. constrn. q.m. U.S. Army, Albrook Field, C.Z., 1939-41; chief mil. design sect. U.S. Engrs. Office, Norfolk, 1941-44; sr. partner McGaughy, Marshall & McMillan (architects and cons. engrs.)(formerly Lublin, McGaughy & Assocs), Norfolk, 1945-65; pres. MMM Design Group (formerly McGaughy, Marshall & McMillan), Norfolk, Washington, Dublin, Ireland, Frankfurt, Fed. Republic Germany, 1965-81, chmn. bd., chief exec. officer, 1981—; spl. cons. Office Coal Research U.S. Dept. Interior; mem. Va. Gov.'s Met. Areas Study Commn.; chmn. faculty Norfolk extension U. Va., 1943-46. Named Va. Engr. of Yr., 1970. Fellow ASCE; mem. Am. Concrete Inst., ASTM, Am. Road Bldg. Assn. (bd. dirs. engring. div. 1966-68), Nat. Soc. Profl. Engrs. (v.p. 1957-59), Va. C. of C., Norfolk C. of C. (bd. dirs. 1960-63), Va. Soc. Profl. Engrs. (past pres.), Engrs. Club Hampton Roads (past pres.), Soc. Am. Mil. Engrs., Va. Engring. Found. (bd. dirs. 1970-72, 90—), Phi Delta Theta, Thelta Tau. Clubs: Cedar Point Golf (Suffolk); Harbor, Norfolk Yacht and Country (Norfolk); Princess Anne Country (Virginia Beach, Va.). Home: 5905 Studeley Ave Norfolk VA 23508-1030 Office: 229 W Bute St PO Box 269 Norfolk VA 23501

MCGAURAN, MICHAEL, manufacturing executive, light. Treas. Sonopress, Inc., Weaverville, N.C. Office: Sonopress Inc 108 Monticello Rd Weaverville NC 28787*

MCGAVIN, DARREN, actor, director, producer; b. Spokane, Wash., May 7, 1922; s. Reid Delano Richardson and Grace (Bogart) McG.; m. Kathie Browne, Dec. 31, 1969; children: York, Megan, Bridget, Bogart. Student, U. of Pacific, 1 year, Neighborhood Playhouse, 6 months, Actors Studio. pres., chief exec. Taurean Films (S.A.), Tympanum Corp. Films include Fear, 1946, Queen for a Day, 1951, Summer Madness, 1955, The Court Martial of Billy Mitchell, 1955, The Man with the Golden Arm, 1956, The Delicate Delinquent, 1957, Beau James, 1957, The Case Against Brooklyn, 1958, Bullet for a Badman, 1964, The Great Sioux Massacre, 1963, Mrs. Pollifax, Spy, 1970, The Petty Story, 1972, B Must Die, 1972, The Poetry Story, 1974, No Deposit, No Return, 1975, Mission Mars, Airport '77, 1977, Hot Lead and Cold Feet, 1978, Repo, 1980, Zero to Sixty, 1980, Hangar 18, 1980, Firebird, 1981, A Christmas Story, 1984, The Natural, 1984, Raw Deal, 1985, From the Hip, 1986, Captain America, 1988, Blood and Concrete, 1990, Billy Madison, 1994; plays include Captain Brassbound's Conversion, The Rainmaker, Tunnel of Love, My Three Angels, Dinner at Eight, The Innkeepers, The King and I (revival, Lincoln Ctr., N.Y.C.); TV series Mike Hammer, 1958-59, Riverboat, 1960-61, The Outsider, 1968-69, The Night Stalker, 1974-75; TV films The Challenge, 1970, Tribes, 1970, Something Evil, 1972, Law and Order, 1976, Brink's, 1976, The Night Stalker, 1977, The Night Strangler, 1978, Child of the Night, 1990, Perfect Harmony, 1990, Greetings, 1993-94; TV series Kolchak: The Night Stalker, 1978-79, Murphy Brown, 1990 (Emmy award); directorial debut with film Happy Mother's Day . . . Love, George, 1973. Mem. Screen Actors Guild, Actors Equity Assn., Dirs. Guild Am., Writers Guild Am., AFTRA. Office: PO Box 2939 Beverly Hills CA 90213-2939 *Do nothing you will be ashamed of, honor all commitments, and hope for the best.*

MCGAVRAN, FREDERICK JAEGER, lawyer; b. Columbus, Ohio, Apr. 24, 1943; s. James Holt and Marion (Jaeger) McG.; m. Elizabeth Dowling, Jan. 5, 1980; children: Sarah Ann, Marian Katherine. BA, Kenyon Coll., 1965; JD, Harvard U., 1972. Bar: Ohio 1972, U.S. Supreme Ct. 1984, Ky. 1992. Assoc. Kyte, Conlan, Wulsin & Vogeler, Cin., 1972-78, Frost & Jacobs, Cin., 1978—. Editor: Sixth Circuit Federal Practice Manual, 1993. Lt. USN, 1965-69. Mem. Fed. Bar Assn. (Cin. chpt. 1984-85, mem. exec. com. Cin. chpt. 1985—), Ohio State Bar Assn. (chmn. com. on fed. cts. 1982-85), Univ. Club of Cin. Home: 2560 Perkins Ln Cincinnati OH 45208-2723 Office: Frost & Jacobs 2500 Pnc Ctr Cincinnati OH 45202

MCGAW, KENNETH ROY, wholesale distribution executive; b. Parry Sound, Ont., Can., Aug. 25, 1926; s. Dalton Earnest and Grace (Crockford) McG. Student, Denison U., 1946-48; B.A., Western Res. U., 1949. With Bigelow Carpets, N.Y. and Ohio, 1949-53; representing Frederick Cooper Lamps, Inc., Chgo., 1953—; home furnishing salesman Gates Mills, Ohio, 1958-74, Fort Lauderdale, 1974-77, Dallas, 1978-79; pres. Ken McGaw, Inc., Dallas, 1979—; factory rep. for maj. furniture and furniture accessory mfrs. Bd. dirs. Big Bros. Cleve., 1963-65, Dallas Opera Co., 1981-92; v.p. Nat. Council on Alcoholism, Cleve., 1972-74; chmn. fundraising drive Wholesale div. Dallas Industry for Dallas Opera, 1982-83; ruling elder 1st Presbyterian Ch., Dallas., 1981—. Served to 2d lt. U.S. Army, 1944-46. Mem. Greater Dallas Home Furnishings Assn. (bd. dirs. 1985-86), S.W. Homefurnishings Assn., S.W. Roadrunners Assn., Internat. Homefurnishings Reps. Assn. Lodge: Rotary. Home: 8360 E San Bernardo Dr Scottsdale AZ 85258-2430

MCGEADY, SISTER MARY ROSE, religious organization administrator, psychologist; b. Hazelton, Pa., June 28, 1928; d. Joseph James and Catherine Cecilia (Mundie) McG. BA in Sociology, Emmanuel Coll., 1955; MA in Clin. Psychology, Fordham U., 1961; DHL (hon.), St. John's U., Queens, N.Y., 1982, Coll. New Rochelle, N.Y., 1991, Fordham U., 1991, Niagara U., 1991, Coll. St. Rose, Albany, N.Y., 1991, DePaul U., 1991. Joined Daus. of Charity St. Vincent De Paul, Roman Cath. Ch., 1946. Dir. Astor Home Clinics, Rhinebeck, N.Y., 1961-66; exec. dir. Nazareth Child Care Ctr., Boston, 1966-71; dir. mental health Cath. Charities Bklyn., 1971-79, assoc. exec. dir., 1987-90; dir. Kennedy Child Study Ctr., N.Y.C., 1979-81; provincial supr. Daus. of Charity St. Vincent DePaul, Albany, 1981-87; pres., chief exec. officer Covenant House, N.Y.C., 1990—; bd. dirs. Cardinal Cooke Health Care Ctr., N.Y.C., Meninger Found., Kans., St. Michael's Coll., Vt., Ctr. for Human Devel., Washington. Author: Catholic Special Education, 1979. Mem. N.Y. State Mental Health Svcs. Couns., Albany, 1983-90, N.Y. State Mental Health Planning Coun., Albany, 1986-91, Cath. Charities USA, 1966—. Recipient svc. award N.Y.C. Dept. Mental Health, 1988, Encouragement award Cath. U. Am., 1991. Home: 75 Lewis Ave Brooklyn NY 11206-7097 Office: Covenant House 346 W 17th St New York NY 10011-5002

MCGEE, DOROTHY HORTON, writer, historian; b. West Point, N.Y., Nov. 30, 1913; d. Hugh Henry and Dorothy (Brown) McG.; ed. Sch. of St. Mary, 1920-21, Green Vale Sch., 1921-28, Brearley Sch., 1928-29, Fermata Sch., 1929-31. Asst. historian Inc. Village of Roslyn (N.Y.), 1950-58; historian Inc. Village of Matinecock, 1966—. Author: Skipper Sandra, 1950;

Sally Townsend, Patriot, 1952; The Boarding School Mystery, 1953; Famous Signers of the Declaration, 1955; Alexander Hamilton-New Yorker, 1957; Herbert Hoover: Engineer, Humanitarian, Statesman, 1959, rev. edit., 1965; The Pearl Pendant Mystery, 1960; Framers of the Constitution, 1968; author booklets, articles hist. and sailing subjects. Chmn., Oyster Bay Am. Bicentennial Revolution Commn., 1971—; historian Town of Oyster Bay, 1982—; mem. Nassau County Am. Revolution Bicentennial Commn.; hon. dir. The Friends of Raynham Hall, Inc.; treas. Family Welfare Assn. Nassau County, Inc., 1956-58; dir. Family Service Assn. Nassau County, 1958-69. Recipient Cert. of award for outstanding contbn. children's lit. N.Y. State Assn. Elem. Sch. Prins., 1959; award Nat. Soc. Children of Am. Revolution, 1960; award N.Y. Assn. Supervision and Curriculum Devel. 1961; hist. award Town of Oyster Bay, 1963; Cert. Theodore Roosevelt Assn., 1976. Fellow Soc. Am. Historians; mem. Soc. Preservation L.I. Antiquities (hon. dir.), Nat. Trust Hist. Preservation, N.Y. Geneal. and Biol. Soc. (dir., trustee), Oyster Bay Hist. Soc. (pres. 1971-75, chmn. 1975-79, trustee), Theodore Roosevelt Assn. (trustee), Townsend Soc. Am. (trustee). Republican. Address: Box 142 Locust Valley NY 11560

MCGEE, GARY CALVIN, lawyer; b. Washington, May 14, 1940; s. Guy C. and Juanita (Byrnes) McG.; m. Nancy Rucker. Aug. 20, 1966; children: Christopher N., William Todd. BS, Coll. of William and Mary, 1962; LLB, U. Va., 1965. Bar: Va. 1965. Law clk. to presiding justice U.S. Dist. Ct., Alexandria, Va., 1965-66; assoc. McGuire, Woods, Battle & Boothe, Charlottesville, Va., 1966-72; ptnr. McGuire, Woods, Battle & Boothe, Charlottesville, 1972—; trustee and sec. Perry Found. Pres. Charlottesville Albemarle Chamber, 1987; pres. Thomas Jefferson Area United Way, Charlotte, Va., 1984, campaign chmn.; 1980; pres. Charlothesville-Albemarle Assn. for Retarded Citizens, 1970-72. Recipient Community Builders award Masons, 1990. Mem. Va. State Bar (bd. govs. real property sect. 1989-94), Va. Bar Assn., Charlottesville Bar Assn., Omicron Delta Kappa. Republican. Methodist. Office: PO Box 1288 Charlottesville VA 22902-1288

MCGEE, HALL THOMAS, JR., newspaper, radio and television executive; b. Charleston, S.C., Aug. 7, 1913; s. Hall Thomas and Gertrude Wyman (Frampton) McG.; m. Margaret Anne Pringle, June 29, 1939; children—Margaret Anne McGee McManes, Hall Thomas, III. B.S., Coll. Charleston, 1935; postgrad., Harvard U. Bus. Sch., 1936. With Eve. Post Pub. Co. and News and Courier Co., Charleston, 1936-87; treas. Eve. Post Pub. Co. and News and Courier Co., 1945-81, v.p., gen. mgr., 1969-84, pres., 1984-87, also dir., 1945—; trustee retirement plan, 1955—; treas., dir. Rochelle Corp., Beaufort, S.C., 1962-75, Aiken Cablevision, Inc., S.C., 1965-83, Banner Corp., Cambridge, Md., 1965-86, Aiken Communications, Inc., 1968-87 , Georgetown Communications, Inc., S.C., 1973-87 , Waynesboro Pub. Co., Va., 1974-82; treas., dir. Portal Communications, Inc., El Paso, Tex., 1974-86, Sangre de Cristo Communications, Inc., Pueblo, Colo., Editors Press Service Inc., N.Y.C., Buenos Aires (Argentina) Herald, Mardel Communications, Inc., Salisbury, Md., 1980-86. Bd. dirs. Charleston YMCA; treas. Charleston Indsl. Assn., 1964-80; pres., trustee Grant Home, Charleston, 1975-86; trustee Coll. Charleston, 1952-68, Magnolia Cemetery, Charleston, 1970-86, Roper Found., 1988—; elder Second Presbyn. Ch., 1958—. Mem. Am. Newspaper Pubs. Assn. (chmn. taxation com.), So. Newspaper Pubs. Assn. (dir.), S.C. Press Assn. (past pres.), St. Cecilia Soc., S.C. Soc., St. Andrews Soc., Agrl. Soc. S.C., Huguenot Soc. S.C., Rotary (dir. Charleston chpt.), Carolina Yacht Club, Supper Club. Home: 200 Wentworth St Charleston SC 29401-1233 Office: Executive Suites 171 Church St Ste 300 Charleston SC 29401-3165

MCGEE, HAROLD JOHNSTON, university president; b. Portsmouth, Va., Apr. 13, 1937; s. Harold Valentine McGee and Clara Mae (Johnston) Weber; m. Mary Frances Eure, Mar. 22, 1959; children: Harold Johnston, Mary Margaret, Matthew Hayden; m. Linda Gayle Stevens, Apr. 3, 1976; 1 child, Andrew Meade. BS, Old Dominion U., 1959; MEd, U. Va., 1962, EdD, 1968. Tchr. Falls Church (Va.) City Schs., 1959-62; asst. dean, then dean of admissions Old Dominion U., Norfolk, Va., 1962-65; field rep., program officer, sr. program officer U.S. Office Edn. Bur. Higher Edn., Charlottesville, 1965-70; provost Tidewater Community Coll., Portsmouth, 1970-71; founding pres. Piedmont Va. Community Coll., Charlottesville, 1971-75; various offices including dean grad. sch., asst. to pres., v.p. student affairs, v.p. adminstrv. affairs, sec. bd. visitors James Madison U., Harrisonburg, Va., 1975-86; pres. Jacksonville (Ala.) State U., 1986—; bd. dirs. Marine Environ. Scis. Consortium, Dauphin Island, Ala., Gulf South Conf., chmn., 1990-92; bd. dirs. Birmingham, Calhoun County C. of C., vice chmn., 1988-90; chmn. Ala. Coun. Univ. Pres.'s, 1991-93; mem. Gov.'s Tax Reform Task Force, 1991-92. Author: Impact of Federal Support, 1968, The Virginia Project, 1976. Mem. United Way of Calhoun County, Ala., Knox Concert Series Adv. Bd., Anniston, Ala., Leadership Ala., Anniston Mus. of Natural History Found. Bd. Mem. NCAA (coun. 1991—), Soc. Coll. and Univ. Planning Am. Assn. Higher Edn., Am. Counseling Assn., Phi Delta Kappa. Episcopalian. Club: Capital City (Montgomery, Ala.). Lodge: Rotary. Office: Jacksonville State U Office of Pres Jacksonville AL 36265

MCGEE, HENRY ALEXANDER, JR., university official; b. Atlanta, Sept. 12, 1929; s. Henry Alexander and Arrie Mae (Mallory) McG.; m. Betty Rose Herndon, July 29, 1951; children: Henry Alexander, Charles Nelson, Kathy Nan. B.Chem. Engring., Ga. Inst. Tech., 1951, Ph.D., 1955; postgrad., U. Wis., 1955-56. Research scientist Army Rocket and Guided Missile Agy. and NASA, Huntsville, Ala., 1956-59; from assoc. prof. to prof. chem. engring. Ga. Inst. Tech., Atlanta, 1959-71; prof. Va. Poly. Inst. and State U., Blacksburg, 1971-94, head dept. chem. engring., 1971-82; assoc. provost for engring. Va. Commonwealth U., Richmond, 1994—; vis. prof. Calif. Inst. Tech., 1964; dir. chem. and thermal sys. div. NSF, Washington, 1990-93; cons. in field. Author: Molecular Engineering, 1991; editorial adv. bd.: Chemical Abstracts; contbr. numerous articles to profl. publs. Danforth Assoc.; recipient various rsch. grants NSF, NASA, Air Force Office Sci. Rsch.; named one of five Outstanding Young Men of Yr. Atlanta, 1964, Acad. Disting. Engring. Alumni, Ga. Tech., 1994. Fellow Am. Inst. Chem. Engrs. (chmn. nat. program com., editorial bd. Jour.), Am. Chem. Soc., AAAS (chmn. sect. on engring. 1985-86); mem. Sigma Xi. Republican. Home: 2924 W Stony Hill Ct #1A Richmond VA 23235 Office: Va Commonwealth U Richmond VA 23284

MCGEE, HENRY W., JR., legal educator, lawyer; b. 1932; BS in Journalism, Northwestern U., 1954; JD, DePaul U. 1957; LLM, Columbia U., 1970. Bar: Ill. 1957, Calif. 1975. Asst. state's atty. Cook County (Ill.) 1958-61; assoc. Jesmer & Harris, Chgo., 1962-66; regional dir. OEO Legal Svc. Program, Gt. Lakes Region, 1966-67; legal dir. Juvenile Delinquency Rsch. Project, Ctr. for Studies in Criminal Justice, U. Chgo., 1967-68; acting prof. UCLA Law Sch., 1969-72, prof., 1972—; vis. fellow Wolfson Coll., Oxford (Eng.) U., 1973; vis. prof. U. Florence Inst. Comparative Law and Proc., 1976, Fed. U. Rio de Janeiro Planning Rsch. Inst., 1987, Nat. Autonomous U. Mex. Legal Rsch. Inst., 1988; Fulbright rsch. prof. and vis. prof. law U. Madrid, 1982; mem. ABA-Am. Assn. Law Schs. Clin. Guidelines Com., 1977—. Mem. Blue Key. Co-author: Housing and Community Development, 1981. Office: UCLA Law Sch 405 Hilgard Ave Los Angeles CA 90024-1476

MCGEE, JAMES GLADNEY, JR., diversified products company executive; b. Honea Path, S.C., Oct. 2, 1932; s. James Gladney and Elizabeth (Williams) McG.; m. Claire Redman; children: Renee Foster, Claire Howle, James G. III. BS, Clemson U., 1953; exec. devel. program, U. S.C., High Point Coll. With Sonoco Products Co., Hartsville, S.C., 1959—; v.p. gen. products div., 1973-79, corp. v.p. indsl. packaging group, 1979-86, corp. group v.p., 1986—, pres. Sonoco Internat., 1986—; Mem. Gov.'s Export Adv. Com., State of S.C., 1987; mem. adv. bd. Clemson (S.C.) U. Coll. Commerce and Industry, 1983—; mem. Lang. and Internat. Trade Adv. Com., Clemson U. Served to 1st It. U.S. Army, 1953-55. Mem. Am. Textile Mfg. Inst. Episcopalian. Avocations: read, art, golf, hunting, salt water fishing. Home: 1319 Greenbriar Rd Hartsville SC 29550-6107 Office: Sonoco Products Co N 2nd St Hartsville SC 29550-4302

MCGEE, JAMES SEARS, historian; b. Houston, July 12, 1942; s. William Sears and Mary Elizabeth (Peterson) McG.; m. Mary Arnall Broach, Aug. 20, 1966; children: Elizabeth, Claude. BA, Rice U., 1964; MA, Yale U., 1966, M in Philosophy, 1968, PhD, 1970. Asst. prof. Ga. So. Coll., Statesboro, 1969-71; asst. prof. history U. Calif., Santa Barbara, 1971-78, assoc.

prof., 1978-84, prof., 1984—, chmn. dept., 1990-95. Author: The Godly Man in Stuart England, 1976; editor: The Miscellaneous Works of John Bunyan, Vol. 3, 1987. Named Disting. Tchr. in Soc. Scis., U. Calif., Santa Barbara, 1989; fellow Abraham Found., 1962-63; Woodrow Wilson fellow, 1964-65; recipient summer stipend NEH, 1975. Mem. Am. Soc. Ch. History, Am. Hist. Assn. N.Am. Conf. on Brit. Studies. Democrat. Episcopalian. Avocation: gardening. Office: U Calif Dept History Santa Barbara CA 93106

MC GEE, JOHN FRAMPTON, communications company executive; b. Charleston, S.C., Jan. 9, 1923; s. Hall Thomas and Gertrude (Frampton) McG.; m. Ruth Bouknight Smedley, June 19, 1971; children: Beverly C. McGee Kinder, Catharine F. McGee Mebane, Charles V. Smedley. BS in Bus. and Polit. Sci., Davidson Coll., 1943. With Charleston (S.C.) Post-News and Courier, 1946-62; asst. gen. mgr. State-Record Newspapers, Columbia, S.C., 1962-64, gen. mgr., pres., co-pub., 1964-69; gen. exec. Knight Newspaper, Inc., Miami, Fla., 1969-70; pres., associated pub. Charleston (W.Va.) Daily Mail, 1970-87, pub., 1987-90; pres. Clay Communications, Inc. parent co. Charleston Daily Mail, Raleigh Register, Post-Herald, Beckley (W.Va.), Enquirer-Jour., Monroe, N.C., Shelby (N.C.) Daily Star, Sta. WWAY-TV, N.C., Sta. KFDX-TV, Tex., Sta. KJAC-TV, Tex., Sta. WAPT-TV, Miss., 1970-87; gen. ptnr. McGee Enterprises, Charleston, 1987—; bd. dirs., mem. exec. com. AP, N.Y.C.; bd. dirs. Thomson Newspapers, Inc., N.Y.C. and Toronto, Can., United Nat. Bank, Charleston, W.Va.; mem. adv. bd. Sch. Journalism, W.Va. U.; vis. prof. Grad Sch. Journalism. U. Nairobi, Kenya, 1992, 93, Harare Zimbabwe, 1993, 94; vis. lectr. media matters USIS Wind Hook Namibia, 1994. Vice chmn. Charleston Area Med. Ctr., U. Charleston; chmn. bd. visitors Davidson (N.C.) Coll., trustee; mem. gen. exec. bd. Presbyn. Ch., U.S.A., 1974-76; mem. S.C. Commn. for Higher Edn., 1966-69. Capt. inf. U.S. Army, 1943-45. Decorated Purple Heart with one oak leaf cluster, Bronze Star with three oak leaf clusters, Combat Infantry badge, Croix de Guerre with palm (France and Belgium), Presdl. Merit citation. Mem. So. Newspaper Pubs. Assn. (bd. dirs. 1967-69), Internat. Press Inst. (bd. dirs. Am. com., mem. Internat. Press Inst.-UNESCO commn. for free press during South African elections 1994), W.Va. Press Assn. (pres. 1977-78), New Eng. Soc. S.C. Clubs: Cosmos (Charleston, W.Va.), Edgewood Country of W.Va. Office: McGee Enterprises Bank One Ctr Ste 812 Charleston WV 25301

MC GEE, JOSEPH JOHN, JR., former insurance company executive; b. Kansas City, Mo., Dec. 2, 1919; s. Joseph J. and Margaret (Cronin) McG.; m. Anne Cunningham, Apr. 30, 1949; children: Sally, Peter, Mary, John, David, Julie, Simon. Attended, Rockhurst Coll., Kansas City, Georgetown U. Asst. sec. Old Am. Ins. Co., Kansas City, Mo., 1939-45; v.p. Old Am. Ins. Co., 1946-51, exec. v.p. 1952-55, pres., 1956-87; ins. cons. Kansas City, Mo., 1987-91. Bd. dirs. Truman Med. Ctr., Truman Libr. Inst. for Nat. and Internat. Affairs; trustee emeritus Rockhurst Coll.; pres. McGee Found. Office: 4900 Main St Ste 717 Kansas City MO 64112-2644

MCGEE, REECE JEROME, sociology educator, researcher; b. St. Paul, Oct. 19, 1929; s. Reece John and Vivian Jeanette (McFarland) McG.; m. Betty Ann Enns, June 10, 1950 (div. 1978); children: Kaelin Christine, Reece Jon, Shanna Beth; m. Sharron Ann Onken, Dec. 2, 1978. BA, U. Minn., 1952, MA, 1953, PhD, 1956. Asst. prof. Humboldt State Coll., Arcata, Calif., 1956; rsch. assoc. U. Minn., Mpls., 1957; asst. prof. U. Tex., Austin, 1957-61, assoc. prof., 1961-64; vis. assoc. prof. Macalester Coll., St. Paul, 1964-65, prof., 1965-67; prof., master tchr. Purdue U., West Lafayette, Ind., 1967-94, prof. emeritus, 1994—, head. dept. sociology and anthropology, 1987-92. Co-author: The Academic Marketplace, 1958; author: Academic Janus, 1971; co-editor: Teaching Sociology: The Quest for Excellence, 1984; editor: Teaching the Mass Class, 1986, 2nd edit., 1991. Sgt. U.S. Army, 1950-51. Mem. Am. Sociol. Assn. (Teaching award sect. on undergrad. edn. 1982, Teaching award 1994), North Cen. Sociol. Assn. (Teaching award 1987), AAUP, Phi Beta Kappa. Democrat. Episcopalian. Avocations: sailing, motorcycles. Office: Purdue U Stone Hall 1365 Dept Sociology & Anthropol West Lafayette IN 47907-1365

MCGEE, ROBERT MERRILL, oil company executive; b. Laramie, Wyo., Dec. 15, 1946; s. Gale William and Loraine (Baker) McG.; m. Mary Louise Lehman, July 26, 1969; children: Kirk Lehman, Scott Baker. BA in Polit. Sci., Allegheny Coll., 1969. Bus. assoc. B.F. Goodrich Co., Akron, Ohio, 1969-70; dir. of info. Nat. Petroleum Coun., Washington, 1970-73; asst. dir. pub. rels. Occidental Internat. Corp., Washington, 1973-74, exec. asst. to pres., 1974-76, v.p., 1976-78, exec. v.p., 1978-82, sr. exec. v.p., 1982-91, pres., 1991—; v.p. Occidental Petroleum Corp., 1994—. Pres. Pan Am. Devel. Found., Washington, 1985; bd. govs. Ford's Theatre, Washington, 1991—; trustee Bus. Coun. for Internat. Understanding, N.Y.C., 1991—; Karl Landegger program in internat. bus. diplomacy, Sch. Fgn. Svc., Georgetown U., Washington, 1991—; mem. The President's Commn. on White House Fellowships, 1993—; bd. dirs. Inst. for Environment and Nat. Resources Rsch. & Policy, U. Wyo., 1994—; Meridian Internat. Ctr., 1994—. Mem. The Econ. Club of Wash., Internat. Club of Wash., Nat. Press Club, Robert Trent Jones Golf Club. Office: Occidental Internat Corp Ste 375 1747 Pennsylvania Ave NW Washington DC 20006-4604

MCGEE, WILLIAM G., air transportation company executive. Chmn., COO, CEO Braniff, Inc., Orlando, Fla. Office: Braniff Inc PO Box 628099 255 S Orange Ave Ste 875 Orlando FL 32801-3452

MCGEE, WILLIAM HOWARD JOHN, library system coordinator; b. Rochester, N.Y., May 15, 1942; s. William Peter and Cecilia Matilda (Kuhn) McG.; m. Sheila Anne Drumm, Sept. 4, 1965; children: Kathleen Moira, Margaret Frances. BA with honors, U. Toronto, Ont., Can., 1965; MEd, U. Toronto, 1973; MLS, U. Western Ont., London, 1980. Tchr. Mimico (Ont.) High Sch., 1966-67; tchr., libr. Applewood Secondary Sch., Mississauga, Ont., 1967-71; libr. Crestwood Secondary Sch., Peterborough, Ont., 1971-74; libr. cons. Cayman Islands Edn. Dept., Grand Cayman, B.W.I., 1975-79; adminstrv. asst. Lake Erie Regional Libr., London, Ont., 1980-83; chief libr. Ft. Erie (Ont.) Pub. Libr., 1983-86; asst. dir. McAllen (Tex.) Pub. Libr., 1986-89; coord. Hidalgo County Libr. System, McAllen, 1989—; cons. Grand Ct. Libr., Grand Cayman, 1974-79; mem. Tex. State Libr. Task Force, Austin, Tex., 1991-93; adv. coun. Libr. Svcs. Consultation Act, Austin, 1993—. Editor InTraLogue jour., 1980-83; assoc. editor Can. Jour. Info. Sci., 1980. Mem. ALA, Ont. Libr. Assn., Tex. Libr. Assn. (chmn. dist. # 4 1994—), Bibliothecaires Francophones Internat. Roman Catholic. Avocations: gourmet cooking, music, travel, reading. Office: Hidalgo County Libr Sys 4305 N 10th St Ste E Mcallen TX 78504-3009

MCGEE, WILLIAM TOBIN, intensivist; b. Port Chester, N.Y., May 23, 1957; s. James R. and Mary (Delzotto) McG.; m. Sarah McGrath; children: Erin, Kelly, Mary. BA in Physics, Dartmouth Coll., 1979; MD, N.Y. Med. Coll., 1983. Diplomate Am. Bd. Internal Medicine with spl. qualifications in Critical Care. Resident in internal medicine Baystate Med. Ctr., Springfield, Mass., 1983-86, intensivist, acting dir. surg. ICU, 1990—; fellow in critical care St. Louis U./St. John's Mercy Med. Ctr., St. Louis, 1986-88. DeWitt Wallace fellow rehab. medicine Rusk Inst. NYU Med. Ctr. Fellow Coll. Chest Physicians; mem. AMA, Soc. Critical Care Medicine, Am. Soc. Parenteral and Enteral Nutrition. Roman Catholic. Avocations: skiing, biking, hiking, sailing, windsurfing. Office: Baystate Med Ctr 759 Chestnut St Springfield MA 01199-1001

MCGEEIN, MARY MARTHA, health care organization executive; b. Toledo, Oct. 26, 1938; d. Andrew John and Gertrude Ceceil (Doyle) McG.; m. Thomas Dale Winkeljohn, Nov. 26, 1959 (div. 1977); children: Ellen T., Mary Beth, Joseph J., Katherine M.; m. Ronald Allan Schnepper, May 21, 1980. RN, Mercy Sch. of Nursing, Toledo, 1959; BSN, Marymount U., 1983; MBA, U. Pa., 1992. Cert. in-patient ob/gyn care/RNC. Nurse Luth. Hosp., Fort Wayne, Ind., 1959-60, Mercy Hosp., Toledo, 1960-62, Holy Cross Hosp., Silver Spring, Md. 1967-83; spl. asst. to pres. for pub. liaison and dir. pub. liaison The White House, Washington, 1983-88; assoc. dir. Nat. Coun. Community Hosps., Washington, 1988-92, v.p., 1992—; bd. dirs. Indigo Inst., Washington; vis. prof. Wharton Sch. U. Pa., Phila., 1992—; grants reviewer Dept. H.H.H./U.S., Washington, 1991—; expert work group mem. U.S. Dept. H.H.S., Washington, 1991—; bd. dirs. Health Care Liability Alliance, Washington, 1993—. Fundraiser Am. Diabetes Assn., Washington, 1988—; vol. mentor No. Va. Women's Ctr., Arlington, Va.,

1987—; vol. health care provider Tutwiler (Miss.) Rural Clinic, 1989—; task force mem. Nat. Policy Forum, Washington, 1994—. Mem. Internat. Childbirth Educators, Assn. Women's Health Obstet. and Neonatal Nurses, Sigma Theta Tau. Office: Nat Coun Comm Hosps 1700 K St NW Washington DC 20006-3800

MCGEENEY, JOHN STEPHEN, lawyer; b. Manhasset, N.Y., Dec. 22, 1934; s. John Joseph and Marion Alice (Morse) McG.; m. Diane Tyler; children: Michael Morse, Luke Stephen. AB, Amherst Coll., 1956; JD, Harvard U., 1959. Bar: Conn., U.S. Dist. Ct. Conn. 1961, U.S. Supreme Ct. 1965, U.S. Dist Ct. (ea. dist.) Va. 1967, U.S. Ct. Appeals (2d cir.) 1969, U.S. Ct. Appeals (4th cir.) 1971, U.S. Dist. Ct. (so. dist.) N.Y. 1980, U.S. Dist. Ct. Mont. 1987. Assoc. Cummings & Lockwood, Stamford, Conn., 1959-68, ptnr., 1968-89; ptnr. Paul, Hastings, Janofsky & Walker, Stamford, 1989—; bd. dirs. Dorr-Oliver Inc., Milford, 1989—. Fellow Am. Coll. Trial Lawyers; mem. ABA, Fed. Bar Coun., Conn. Bar Assn. (Fed. Practice com.). Office: Paul Hastings Janofsky & Walker 1055 Washington Blvd Stamford CT 06901-2217

MCGEER, EDITH GRAEF, neurological science educator emerita; b. N.Y.C., Nov. 18, 1923; d. Charles and Charlotte Annie (Ruhl) Graef; m. Patrick L. McGeer, Apr. 15, 1954; children: Patrick Charles, Brian Theodore, Victoria Lynn. BA, Swarthmore Coll., 1944; PhD, U. Va., 1946; DSc (hon.), U. Victoria, 1987. Research chemist E.I. DuPont de Nemours & Co., Wilmington, Va., 1946-54; research assoc. div. neurological sci. U. B.C., Vancouver, Can., 1954-74; assoc. prof. U. B.C., Vancouver, 1974-76, prof., acting head, 1976-83, prof., head., 1983-89, prof. emerita, 1989—. Author: (with others) Molecular Neurobiology of the Mammalian Brain, 1978, 2d. edit.; 1987; editor: (with others) Kainic Acid as a Tool in Neurobiology, 1978, Glutamine, Glutamate, and GABA, 1983; contbr. articles to profl. jours. Decorated officer Order of Can.; recipient Citation Am. Chem. Soc., 1958, Rsch. Prize in Psychiatry Clarke Inst., 1992. Fellow Can. Coll. Neuropsychopharmacology; mem. Can. Biochemical Soc., Internat. Brain Research Orgn., Internat. Soc. Neurochemistry, Soc. Neuroscience, Am. Neurochemical Soc. (councilor 1979-83), North Pacific Soc. Neurology and Psychiatry (hon. fellow), Lychnos Soc., Sigma Xi, Phi Beta Kappa. Office: U BC Div Neurol Scis, 2255 Wesbrook Mall, Vancouver, BC Canada V6T 1Z3

MCGEER, JAMES PETER, research executive, consultant; b. Vancouver, B.C., Can., May 14, 1922; s. James Arthur and Ada Alice (Schwenger) McG.; m. Catherine Pearson Deas, June 22, 1948; children: Mary, Allison, James, Thomas. BA, U. B.C., 1944, MA, 1946; MA, Princeton U., 1948, PhD, 1949. Researcher Alcan R & D, Arvida, Que., Can., 1949-52, group leader, 1952-59, pilot plant dir., 1960-67; dept. head Alcan Smelters, Arvida, Que., Can., 1968-71, asst. div. head, 1972-73; mgr. tech. transfer Alcan Smelter Svcs., Montreal, Que., 1973-77; dir. rsch. Alcan Internat. Ltd., Kingston, Ont., Can., 1978-82, dir. lab., 1983-87; mng. dir. Ont. Ctr. Materials, Kingston, 1988—; chmn. bd. Can. Rsch. Mgmt. Assn., Toronto, Ont., 1990-91, Welding Inst. Can., Mississauga, Ont., 1988-90, Can. U. Ind. Coun. Advanced Ceramics, Ottawa, Ont., 1986-88; dir. Metall. Soc., Pitts., 1987-89; Can. Coun. lectr. Am. Soc. Metals, 1985-86; disting. lectr. Can. Inst. Mining Metallurgy, 1987. Contbr. articles to profl. jours. Chmn. bd. Que. Assn. Protestant Sch. Bds., Montreal, 1968-70. Recipient Airey award Can. Inst. for Mining and Metallurgy, 1993, Forum award Xerox Can., 1994. Mem. Anglican Ch. Office: Ontario Ctr Materials Rsch, PO Box 1146, Kingston, ON Canada K7L 4Y5

MCGEHEE, FRANK SUTTON, paper company executive; b. Aug. 15, 1928; s. Clifford G. and Ray (Sutton) McGehee; m. Ann Whitehurst, Mar. 18, 1949; children: Frank Sutton, David Searcy, Ann Lynwood Riley. BA in Econs., U. Ala., 1950. Co-founder, co-chmn. bd. Jacksonville Paper Co. (now UNIJAX), 1950-64; dir. Flagship Banks of Jacksonville; co-founder, co-chmn. bd. Mac Paper Converters, Inc., now chmn. bd., CEO. Trustee, mem. exec. com. Bolles Sch.; past pres., dir. Wolfson Childrens Hosp.; past pres., pres. bd. Ga. Christian Sch. and Home, North Fla. Coun. Boy Scouts Am.; past chmn. Weyerhaeuser Mcht. Coun., Kimberly Clark Mcht. Coun.; active San Jose Ch. of Christ. Mem. Nat. Paper Trade Assn. (dir.), Jacksonville Businessmen Club (sec., dir.), Tournament Players Club (founder), River Club, San Jose Country Club, Sawgrass Country Club, Plantation Country Club. Home: 6750 Epping Forest Way N Jacksonville FL 32217-2688 Office: MAC Papers Inc 3300 Phillipps Hwy PO Box 5369 Jacksonville FL 32247*

MC GEHEE, H(ARRY) COLEMAN, JR., bishop; b. Richmond, Va., July 7, 1923; s. Harry Coleman and Ann Lee (Cheatwood) McG.; m. June Stewart, Feb. 1, 1946; children: Lesley, Alexander, Harry III, Donald, Cary. BS, Va. Poly. Inst.; 1947; JD, U. Richmond, 1949; MDiv, Va. Theol. Sem., 1957, DD, 1973. Bar: Va. 1949, U.S. Supreme Ct. 1954; ordained to ministry Episcopal Ch., 1957. Spl. counsel dept. hwys. State of Va., 1949-51, gen. counsel employment svc., 1951, asst. atty. gen., 1951-54; rector Immanuel Ch.-on-the-Hill, Va. Sem., 1960-71; bishop Diocese of Mich., Detroit, 1971-90; adv. bd. Nicaraguan Network, Ctr. for Peace and Conflict Studies, Wayne State U.; bd. dirs. Mich. Religious Coalition for Abortion Rights, 1976-84; trustee Va. Theol. Sem., 1978-93; pres. Episc. Ch. Pub. Co., 1978-85. Columnist: Detroit News, 1979-85; weekly commentator pub. radio sta. WDET-AM, Detroit, 1984-90. Mem. Gov.'s Commn. on Status of Women, 1965-66, Mayor's Civic Com., Alexandria, 1967-68; sponsor Nat. Assn. for ERA, 1977-85; pres. Alexandria Legal Aid Soc., 1969-71; bd. dirs. No. Va. Fairhousing Corp., 1963-67; pres. Mich. Coalition for Human Rights, 1980-89; chmn. Citizens' Com. for Justice in Mich., 1983-84; sponsor Farm Labor Orgn. for Children, 1983-85; bd. dirs. Pub. Benefit Corp., Detroit, 1988-90, Mich. Citizens for Personal Freedom, 1989-92, Poverty and Social Reform Inst., Detroit, 1989—, Bread for the World, 1990-94, Ams. United for Separation of Ch. and State, 1990, ACLU Oakland County, Mich., 1991-94; co-chair Lesbian-Gay Found. Mich., 1991—. 1st It. C.E., U.S. Army, 1943-46. Named Feminist of Yr. Detroit NOW, 1978; recipient Humanitarian award Detroit ACLU, 1984, Phillip Hart medal Mich. Women's Studies Assn., 1984, Sayre award for justice and peace Episc. Peace Fellowship, 1988, Spirit of Detroit award, 1989, Archbishop Romero award Mich. Labor Com., 1990, Brotherhood award AME Ch., Detroit, 1993, Ira Jayne award Detroit br. NAACP, 1993, Martin Luther King, Jr. award United Ch. of Christ, 1995. Mem. Detroit Econ. Club (bd. dirs.). Home: 1496 Ashover Dr Bloomfield Hills MI 48304-1215 Office: Diocese of Mich 4800 Woodward Ave Detroit MI 48201-1310

MC GEHEE, LARRY THOMAS, university administrator; b. Paris, Tenn., May 18, 1936; s. George Eugene and Margaret Elizabeth (Thomas) McG.; m. Elizabeth Hathhorn Boden, Aug. 26, 1961; children: Elizabeth Hathhorn, Margaret Thomas. BA, Transylvania Coll., 1958; BD, Yale U., 1963, MA, 1964, PhD, 1969. Dir., asst. v.p. for univ. relations U. Ala., 1966-68, exec. asst. to pres., 1968-69, exec. v.p. 1969-71; lectr., assoc. prof. dept. Am. studies, 1969-71, acad. v.p.; 1971; chancellor U. Tenn., Martin, 1971-79; spl. asst. to pres. U. Tenn., Knoxville, 1979-82; v.p. coll., prof. religion Wofford Coll., Spartanburg, S.C., 1982—. Danforth fellow Yale U., 1960-66. Home: 1047 Woodburn Rd Spartanburg SC 29302-2867 Office: Wofford Coll 429 N Church St Spartanburg SC 29303-3663

MCGEHEE, RICHARD PAUL, mathematics educator; b. San Diego, Sept. 20, 1943; s. Maurice S. and Edith M. (Adamson) McG.; m. Tamara Stovall, Feb. 27, 1981; children: Lindsey M., Cordelia D. BS, Calif. Inst. Tech., 1964; MS, U. Wis., 1965, PhD, 1969. Vis. mem. Courant Inst. Math. Sci., N.Y.C., 1969-70; asst. prof. then assoc. prof. math. U. Minn., Mpls., 1970-79, prof., 1979—, head dept. math., 1986-90; vis. Ulam prof. U. Colo., Boulder, 1990-91. dir. Geometry Ctr., 1994—. Mem. Am. Math. Soc.

MCGEHEE, THOMAS RIVES, paper company executive; b. Jacksonville, Fla., July 12, 1924; s. Clifford Graham and Ray (Sutton) McG. Student Davidson Coll., 1942-43, BS in Chemistry, U. Ala. 1948; m. Delia Houser, Nov. 3, 1950; children: Delia McGehee II, Thomas R. Jr. V.p. Jacksonville Paper Co., 1948-56, pres., 1956-64, Mac Papers, Inc., Jacksonville, 1964-79, co-founder, chief exec. officer, chmn. bd., 1979—; co-chmn, chief exec. officer Mac Papers Converters, Inc., 1965—, pres., North Fla. TV-47, Inc., 1979-90; pres. Higley Pub. Co., 1968-90; bd. dirs. Barnett Bank of Jacksonville, 1951-89; chmn. exec. com. Sta. WTLV-TV 12, 1972-78 numerous real estate interests. Chmn. and founder Greater Jacksonville Community Found., 1964-84, trustee, 1964-89; trustee Jacksonville U., 1959—, vice chmn., 1962-65, chmn., 1991-92; mem. U. Fla. Pres.' Coun., U. Fla. Health & Sci. Ctr.; mem. post secondary edn. planning commn. State of Fla., 1987-90; bd. dirs. Dreams Come True, pres. and founder 1984-88; bd. dirs. Bapt. Hosp. Found., 1986-90; vice chmn. Every Home For Christ, 1987—; past mem., officer numerous other community orgs. Served with U.S. Army, 1943-46, ETO. Recipient 3 Battle Stars, Fla. Gov.'s award, 1962. Mem. NAM (dir. 1964-66), Assn. Industries Fla. (dir. 1961-63), Nat. Paper Trade Assn., So. Paper Trade Assn., Nat. Assn. Broadcasters, Fla. State C. of C., Phi Gamma Delta (pres. 1948). Republican. Episcopalian. Clubs: River (dir. 1980-83), Fla. Yacht, Timuquana Country, Ponte Vedra, Plantation Country, Blowing Rock Country (bd. dirs. 1991-94). Home: Park Plz Condominiums 505 Lancaster St 6B Jacksonville FL 32204 Office: MAC Papers Inc 3300 Phillips Hwy PO Box 5369 Jacksonville FL 32247

MCGEORGE, RONALD KENNETH, hospital executive; b. Fredericton, N.B., Can., June 7, 1944; s. Hubert Oswald and Ruth Johanna (Kolding) McG.; m. Gail F. Mitchell, July 17, 1970; children: Ronald Millard, Scott, Dacia Gail. B.S., Houghton Coll., 1966; diploma in hosp. adminstrn., U. Toronto, 1969. Adminstrv. counsellor N.S. Hosp. Ins. Commn., Halifax, 1969-70; asst. exec. dir. Izaak Walton Killam Hosp. for Children, Halifax, 1970-72; v.p. Greater Niagara Gen. Hosp., Niagara Falls, Ont., 1972-74; chmn. Council Teaching Hosps.; exec. dir. Halifax Infirmary, 1974-79, Kingston Gen. Hosp., Ont., 1980-90; CEO Dr. Everett Chalmers Hosp., 1990-92; pres., chief exec. officer Region 3 Hosp. Corp., Fredericton, N.B., Can., 1992—; preceptor hosp. adminstrn. U. Ottawa, U. Toronto; chmn. Ont. Council Adminstrn. Teaching Hosps.; cons. in field. Contbr. articles to profl. jours. Chmn., pres. Wesleyan Men, 1st Wesleyan Ch. Named Bus. Alumnus of Yr., Houghton Coll., 1987. Mem. Can. Coll. Health Services Execs. (pres. 1979-80), Assn. Hosp. Adminstrs. N.S. (pres.-elect 1972), N.S. Assn. Health Orgns. (dir.), Ont. Council Adminstrs. of Teaching Hosps. (pres.), Ont. Hosp. Assn. (mem. exec. com., chmn. exec. com. 1989-90), Alumni Assn. of Bethany Bible Coll. (pres.). Home: 182 Springwater Ln, Fredericton, NB Canada E3C 1J1 Office: 565 Priestman St, Fredericton, NB Canada E3B 5N5

MCGERVEY, JOHN DONALD, physics educator, researcher; b. Pitts., Aug. 9, 1931; s. Daniel Donald and Eleanor (Rogerson) McG.; m. Nancy Ruth Maher, July 6, 1957; children: Anne, Donald, Joan. BS in Math., U. Pitts., 1952; postgrad., U. Chgo., 1952-53; MS in Physics, Carnegie Inst. Tech., 1955, PhD in Physics, 1960. Instr. math. Carnegie Inst. Tech., Pitts., 1957-60; asst. prof. physics Case Western Res. U., Cleve., 1960-65, assoc. prof., 1965-78, prof. physics, 1978—; vis. scientist Kernforschungsanlage, Julich, Fed. Republic Germany, 1972-73, U. der Bundeswehr München, Fed. Republic Germany, 1988, U. Göttingen, Germany, 1994; Sci. Resch. Coun. vis. fellow U. East Anglia, Norwich, Eng., 1978-79; resident rsch. assoc. Argonne (Ill.) Nat. Lab., 1985; faculty participant Oak Ridge Assoc. Univs., 1974-90; cons. WQED-TV, Pitts., 1994, Glencoe-Merrill Pub., 1992—. Author: Introduction to Modern Physics, 1971, Spanish lang. edit., 1975, 2d edit., 1983, Probabilities in Everyday Life, 1986, paperback edit., 1989, Quantum Mechanics: Concepts and Applications, 1995. Pres. Cath. Interracial Coun. of Cleve., 1969-72; bd. dirs. Commn. on Cath. Cmty. Action, Cleve., 1969-78; pres. Project Equality of Ohio, Columbus, 1970-72; mem. Physicians for Social Responsibility, Cleve., 1982—; mem. speakers bur. Union Concerned Scientists, 1992—. NSF fellow, 1952; grantee AEC, 1963-66, NSF, 1969-72, 74-81, 85, 87, 90—, NASA, 1981-85, Army Rsch. Office, 1986—. Mem. AAAS, AAUP (mem. chpt. 1983-84), Am. Phys. Soc., Am. Assn. Physics Tchrs., Cleve. Astron. Soc., ACLU, Sierra Club, Cleve. Philosophical Club, Cleveland Heights Tennis Club, Sigma Xi. Democrat. Roman Catholic. Home: 1819 Wilton Rd Cleveland OH 44118-1628 Office: Case Western Reserve U Dept Physics Cleveland OH 44106

MCGETTIGAN, CHARLES CARROLL, JR., investment banker; b. San Francisco, Mar. 28, 1945; s. Charles Carroll McGettigan and Molly (Fay) McGettigan Pedley; m. Katharine Havard King, Nov. 1, 1975 (div. 1981); m. Meriwether Lewis Stovall, Aug. 6, 1983; 1 child, Meriwether Lewis Fay. AB in Govt., Georgetown U., 1966; MBA in Fin., U. Pa., 1969. Assoc., asst. v.p., v.p. Blyth Eastman Dillon, N.Y.C., 1970-75, 1st v.p., 1975-78, sr. v.p., San Francisco, 1978-80; sr. v.p. Dillon, Read & Co., San Francisco, 1980-83; gen. ptnr. Woodman Kirkpatrick & Gilbreath, San Francisco, 1983-84; prin. corp. fin. Hambrecht & Quist, Inc., San Francisco, 1984-88, mng. dir. founder McGettigan, Wick & Co., Inc., San Francisco, 1988—; gen. ptnr., founder Proactive Ptnrs. L.P., San Francisco, 1990—, Proactive Investment Mgrs., L.P., 1991—; gen. ptnr. Fremont Proactive Ptnrs., L.P., 1991—; bd. dirs. PMR Corp., San Diego, I.-Flow Corp., Irvine, Calif., Sonex Rsch., Inc., Annapolis, Md., Modtech, Inc., Perris, Calif.; chmn. Onsite Energy Corp., Carlsbad, Calif.; adv. dir. Chesapeake Ventures, Balt., 1984-94. Trustee St. Francis Meml. Hosp., San Francisco, 1980-86; mem. United San Francisco Rep. fin. com., 1983—, steering com., 1986—; adv. bd. dirs. Leavey Sch. Bus. Adminstrn., Santa Clara U., Calif., 1984-1990. With USN, 1966. Named Confrerie des Chevaliers du Tastevin, 1991. Mem. The Brook, Racquet and Tennis Club (N.Y.), The Pacific Union Club, Bohemian Club (San Francisco), San Francisco Golf Club, Burlingame Country Club (Hillsborough, Calif.), Calif. Club (L.A.), Boston Club (New Orleans), Piping Rock Club (Locust Valley, N.Y.). Republican. Roman Catholic. Home: 3375 Clay St San Francisco CA 94118-2006 Office: McGettigan Wick & Co Inc 50 Osgood Pl San Francisco CA 94133

MCGHEE, GEORGE CREWS, petroleum producer, former government official; b. Waco, Tex., Mar. 10, 1912; s. George Summers and Magnolia (Spruce) McG.; m. Cecilia Jeanne De Golyer, Nov. 24, 1938; children: Marcia Spruce, George DeGolyer, Dorothy Hart, Michael Anthony, Cecilia Goodrich, Valerie Foster. Student, So. Meth. U., 1928, DCL, 1953; BS, U. Okla., 1933; DPhil (Oxon), (Rhodes scholar), Oxford U., 1937; postgrad., U. London, 1937; LL.D., Tulane U., 1957, U. Md., 1965; D.Sc., U. Tampa, 1969. Registered profl. engr., Tex. Geologist Atlantic Refining Co., 1930-31; geophysicist Continental Oil Co., 1933-34, Compagnie Generale de Geophysique, Morocco, 1935; v.p. Nat. Geophys. Co., 1937-40; partner DeGolyer, MacNaughton & McGhee, Dallas, 1940-41; ind. explorer, producer oil, 1940—; sole owner McGhee Prodn. Co.; chmn. bd. Saturday Rev., 1973-77; Coordinator for aid to Greece and Turkey Dept. State, 1947-49, spl. asst. to sec. state, 1949; asst. sec. for Dept. State (Near Eastern, South Asian, African affairs), 1949-51; mem. various adv. groups to pvt., govtl. orgns., 1940—; U.S. ambassador, chief Am. Mission for Aid to Turkey, 1951-53; sr. adviser N. Atlantic Treaty Council, Ottawa, Can., 1951; mem. bd. Middle East Inst., 1953-58; cons. Nat. Security Council, 1958-59; mem. Pres.'s Com. to study U.S. Mil. Assistance program, 1958-59; chmn. policy planning council, counselor Dept. State, 1961; under-sec. state for polit. affairs, 1961-63; ambassador Fed. Republic of Germany, 1963-68; ambassador-at-large, 1968-69; spl. rep. to chmn. Urban Coalition, 1969-70; chmn. bd. Bus. Council for Internat. Understanding, 1969-73; mem. bd. Fed. City Council, Washington, 1958-61, 1970-74; pres. Fed. City Council, 1970-74; vice chmn. Japan-U.S. Internat. Adv. Council, 1970-74; chmn. adv. com. on housing and urban devel. Nat. Acad. Scis., 1970-74; bd. dirs. Procter & Gamble Co., Am. Security Bank, Washington, TransWorld Corp., Transworld Airlines.; mem. Am. Council on Germany, 1969—, Fed. City Housing Corp., 1972—; hon. fellow Queen's Coll., Oxford, 1968; guest lectr. Nat., Air, Naval War Colls., Salzburg Seminar, Austria, 1960. Author: Envoy to the Middle World, 1983, At the Creation of a New Germany, 1989, The U.S.-Turkish-NATO Middle East Connection, 1990, Dance of the Billions, 1990, International Community: A Goal for a New World Order, 1992, Life in Alanya: Turkish Delight, 1992; editor: Diplomacy for the Future, 1987, National Interest and Global Goals, 1989; contbr. to profl. publs.; patentee in field. Trustee Thessalonica (Greece) Agrl. and Indsl. Inst. (Am. Farm Sch.), 1949-61; mem. bd. devel. So. Meth. U., 1949-61; bd. dirs. Near East Found., 1956-61, Aspen Inst. Humanistic Studies, 1958—, Atlantic Council, Atlantic Inst. for Internat. Affairs, Resources for Future; vice chmn. bd. dirs. Inst. for Study of Diplomacy, Georgetown U., Washington; trustee or bd. dirs. Com. for Econ. Devel., 1957—, Fgn. Service Edn. Found. and Sch. Advanced Internat. Studies, Johns Hopkins, 1947—. Nat. Civil Service League, 1969-73, Population Crisis Com., 1992—. Population Crisis Found. Tex., 1969-70, Nat. Trust for Historic Preservation, 1971-75, Duke U., 1962—, Vassar Coll., 1959-61, Am. U., 1980—. Asia Found., 1973—, Va. Outdoors Found.; adv. council Renewable Natural Resources Found., 1973-74; bd. dirs., treas. Piedmont Environmental Council; internat. com. YMCA, 1949-61; adv. council dept. Oriental langs. and lits. Princeton, 1949-61; vis. com. Middle Eastern Studies and Summer Sch., Harvard, 1954-61; sponsor Atlantic Inst., 1954-60; chmn. nat. adv. com. Ctr. for Book, Library of

Congress, 1980-82; mem. Folger Library Council, 1983-85, Inst. Turkish Studies, 1983-85, Carnegie Coun.; mem. vis. com. Arthur M. Sackler Gallery, Smithsonian Instn.; trustee Am. U., 1981—; mem. German Am. Cultural Fund, 1992—, Circle Nat. Gallery Art, 1991, Carnegie Coun., 1990—, CED subcom. Global Econ. Strategy for U.S., 1991—; bd. dirs. adv. bd. Am.-Turkish Friendship Coun., Nat. Tree Trust, 1992—. Served with USNR, 1943-45; lt. col. USAF Res., 1945-72. Decorated Legion of Merit with 3 battle stars; Order of Cherifien Empire Morocco; recipient Distinguished Service award U.S. Jr. C. of C., 1949, Distinguished Service citation U. Okla., 1952, So. Meth. U. Distinguished Alumnus award, 1955; Andrew Wellington Cordier fellow Columbia U.; named Hon. citizen Ankara, Turkey, 1954. Mem. NAS (pres.'s circle), Am. Assn. Petroleum Geologists, Soc. Exploration Geophysicists (Spl. Commendation award 1992), m. Inst. Mining, Metall. and Petroleum Engrs., English SPeaking Union (chmn. bd. 1970-74), Am. Philos. Soc., Coun. Am. Mbs., Smithsonian Nat. Assocs. (chmn. 1975-78), Sigma Si Phi Beta Kappa, Cosmos Club, Metro. Club, Washington. Episcopalian. Home and Office: Farmers Delight 36276 Mountville Rd Middleburg VA 22117 also: Turkish Delight, Alanya Turkey

MC GIBBON, PAULINE MILLS, former Canadian government official, former university chancellor; b. Sarnia, Ont., Can., Oct. 20, 1910; d. Alfred William and Ethel (French) Mills; m. Donald Walker McGibbon, Jan. 26, 1935. B.A., U. Toronto, 1933, LL.D. (hon.), 1975, D.L.S., 1979; LL.D. (hon.), U. Alta., 1967, Queen's U., 1974, U. Western Ont., 1974; D.U., U. Ottawa, 1972, Laval U., 1976, McMaster U., 1981, Carlton U., 1981; B.A.A. (hon.), Ryerson Poly. Inst., 1974; L.H.D. (hon.), St. Lawrence U., 1977; LLD, Windsor U., 1988. Dir. IBM Can. Ltd., 1972-74, Imasco, 1973-74, George Weston Ltd., 1980-95; chancellor U. Toronto, 1971-74; lt. gov. Province of Ont., Toronto, 1974-80; chancellor U. Guelph, 1977-83. Chmn. bd. trustees Nat. Arts Centre, Ottawa, 1980-84; v.p. Massey Hall-Roy Thompson Hall, 1980-91; pres. Dominion Drama Festival, 1957-59, Can. Conf. Arts, 1972-73; mem. Can. Council, 1968-71, U. Toronto Senate, 1952-61; chmn. bd. dirs. duMaurier Arts Ltd., 1979—; chmn. bd. govs. Nat. Theatre Sch. Can., 1966-69; bd. govs. Womens Coll. Hosp. 1960-76, chmn. bd. govs., 1970-74; bd. govs. Upper Can. Coll., 1971-74; chmn. selection com. Ont. Rhodes Scholarships, 1984-90. Decorated officer Order of Can., 1967, companion, 1988; dame Order St. Lazarus; dame of grace Order St. John Jerusalem; Grand Prior Can.; recipient Can. drama award, 1957; Centennial medal, 1967; civic award of merit City of Toronto, 1966; Centennial medal, 1967; award of merit Canadian Pub. Relations Soc., 1972; named hon. col. Toronto Service Bn., 1975. Fellow Heraldry Soc. Can. (hon.), Royal Coll. Physicians and Surgeons Can. (hon.); mem. Imperial Order Daus. of Empire (pres. nat. chpt. 1963-65, hon. v.p. nat. chpt., hon. pres. Mcpl. chpt. Toronto), Royal Can. Mil. Inst., Royal Can. Legion (1st woman mem. Ft. York br.), Order of Ont., Canadian Club, Ladies Club. Home: 20 Avoca Ave Apt 2004, Toronto, ON Canada M4T 2B8

MC GIBBON, WILLIAM, landscape architect; b. 1941. With Mc Kay Nursery, Madison, Wis., 1963-65, Hugh A Dega Assocs., Madison, Wis., 1965-67; with Johnson, Johnson & Roy, Inc., Ann Arbor, Mich., 1967—, now pres. Office: Johnson Johnson & Roy Inc 110 Miller Ave Ann Arbor MI 48104

MCGIBBON, WILLIAM ALEXANDER, rancher, photographer; b. Evanston, Ill.; s. Edmund L. and Catherine (Klink) M.; m. Nancy Hornaday, Aug. 27, 1966; children: Heather M., Andrew W. BA, U. Pa., 1966; postgrad., U. Ariz., 1970-71. Pres., chief exec. officer Santa Rita Ranch, Inc., Green Valley, Ariz., 1970—; adv. com. Coll. Agr., U. Ariz., Tucson. Photographer: photographs pub. in numerous agrl. and livestock publs., 1980—. Mem. Continental Sch. Bd. Green Valley, 1976-84, pres., 1978-84; mem. Ariz. Bd. Pesticide Control, Phoenix, 1983-86; bd. dirs. Green Valley Community Fund, 1988—. Mem. Ariz. Cattlemen's Assn. (bd. dirs.), Nat. Cattlemen's Assn., Green Valley Rotary Club (pres. 1986, v.p. Green Valley Rotary Club Found. 1988—), So. Ariz. Cattlemen's Assn. (pres.), Cattle Growers Assn. (v.p., pres.-elect), Freelance Photographers Orgn. Republican. Avocations: cattle ranching. Home and Office: Santa Rita Ranch Inc 8200 E Box Canyon Rd PO Box 647 Green Valley AZ 85622-0647

MCGIFF, JOHN C(HARLES), pharmacologist; b. N.Y.C., Aug. 6, 1927; s. John Francis and Rose (Rieger) McG.; m. Sara Leighton Babb, Feb. 8, 1958 (dec.); children: John, Katharine, Sara, Jeremiah, Elizabeth. B.S., Georgetown U., 1947; M.D., Columbia U., 1951; Doctorate Honoris Causa, Copernicus Acad. Medicine, Cracow, Poland, 1987. Diplomate: Am. Bd. Internal Medicine. Intern U. Cin., 1951-52; resident in medicine U. Va. Med. Center, 1952-53; tng. in physiology and pharmacology Columbia Presbyn. Hosp., N.Y.C., 1957-58; mem. faculty U. Pa. Med. Sch., 1961-66; dir. cardiovascular sect. St. Louis U. Med. Sch., 1966-71; dir. clin. pharmacology Med. Coll. Wis., Milw., 1971-75; prof., chmn. dept. pharmacology U. Tenn. Center Health Scis., 1975-79, N.Y. Med. Coll., Valhalla, 1979—; vis. scientist Wellcome Rsch. Labs., Beckenham, Eng., 1975-76; adv. bd. Am. Heart Assn., Kidney Found.; mem. nat. vis. coun. for health sci. faculties Columbia U. Coll. Physicians and Surgeons, 1987; mam. arteriosclerosis hypertension and lipid adv. com. NIH, 1987; cons. in field; chmn. cardiovascular renal study sect. Nat. Heart, Lung and Blood Inst. NIH, 1994. Author articles in books; contbr. articles to profl. jours. Pres. sch. bd. St. Louis Cathedral Sch., 1970. Served as flight surgeon M.C. USMCR, 1955-57, Korea. Recipient Medal of Achievement Copernicus Acad. Medicine, Cracow, Poland, 1984; Terence Cardinal Cooke medal for Disting. Service in Health Care, 1985; CIBA award Am. Heart Assn., 1986, Merit award Nat. Heart, Lung, and Blood Inst. of NIH; Burroughs Wellcome Fund scholar, 1971-74. Mem. Am. Physiol. Soc., Am. Soc. Pharmacology and Exptl. Therapeutics, Council High Blood Pressure Research (med. adv. bd. 1968), Am. Soc. Clin. Investigation, Brit. Pharmacology Soc. Roman Catholic. Home: 5 Bay Rd East Patchogue NY 11772 Office: NY Med Coll Dept Pharmacology Valhalla NY 10595

MC GIFFERT, DAVID ELIOT, lawyer, former government official; b. Boston, June 27, 1926; s. Arthur Cushman and Elizabeth (Eliot) McG.; m. Enud De Kibedi-Varga, Jan. 21, 1966; children: Laura, Carola.; m. Nelse Greenway, Apr. 9, 1983. Student, U. Calif.-Berkeley, 1944; B.A., Harvard U., 1949, LL.B., 1953; postgrad., Cambridge (Eng.) U., 1950. Bar: D.C. 1954. With firm Covington & Burling, Washington, 1953-55, 57-61; ptnr. Covington & Burling, 1969-77, 81—; lectr. law U. Wis., 1956; asst. to sec. def. for legis. affairs Dept. Def., 1962-65, undersec. army, 1965-69, asst. sec. for internat. security affairs, 1977-81. Served with USNR, 1944-46. Mem. Am. Bar Assn., Council Fgn. Relations, Alpha Delta Phi. Club: Metropolitan (Washington). Home: 3819 Veazey St NW Washington DC 20016 Office: Covington & Burling 1201 Pennsylvania Ave NW PO Box 7566 Washington DC 20044

MC GIFFERT, JOHN RUTHERFORD, retired cultural institute director, retired army officer; b. Jefferson Barracks, Mo., Aug. 5, 1926; s. Stephen Yates and Louise Brockenbrough (Jones) McG.; m. Patricia Ann Clipp, May 2, 1946; children: William Christian, Katherine Louise, Elizabeth Ann, Mary Margaret. Student, Va. Mil. Inst., 1944; B.S., U. Md., 1967; M.S., George Washington U., 1968. Joined U.S. Army as pvt., 1945, advanced through grades to lt. gen., 1977; assignments in Germany, Iceland, Vietnam; dir. of Army Staff Office Chief of Staff Hdqrs. Dept. of Army Washington, 1977-80; comdg. gen. 5th U.S. Army Ft. Sam Houston, Tex., 1980-83; ret. U.S. Army, 1983; adminstr. U. Tex. Inst. Texan Cultures, San Antonio, 1983-85; dir. U. Tex. Inst. Texan Cultures, 1985-91; v.p. downtown ops. U. Tex., San Antonio, 1989-91. Decorated D.S.M., Silver Star, D.F.C., Legion of Merit, Bronze Star, Air medal, others. Mem. Assn. U.S. Army, Field Arty. Assn. Episcopalian. Home: 8926 Willmon Way San Antonio TX 78239-1947

MCGIFFERT, MICHAEL, history educator, editor; b. Chgo., Oct. 5, 1928; s. Arthur Cushman and Elisabeth (Eliot) McG.; m. Genevieve White Mischel, Aug. 13, 1960; m. Elizabeth Eastman, June 19, 1949 (div. 1960). B.A., Harvard Coll., 1949; B.D., Yale U., 1952, Ph.D., 1958; postgrad., Union Theol. Sem., N.Y.C. 1949-50. Instr. history Colgate U., Hamilton, N.Y., 1954-55, 56-60, U. Md. College Park, 1955-56; asst. prof. history U. Denver, 1960-64, assoc. prof., 1964-69, prof. history, 1969-74; editor William and Mary Quar., Inst. Early Am. History and Culture, prof. history, Coll. William and Mary, Williamsburg, Va., 1972—. Author: The Higher learning in Colorado, 1964; editor: The Character of Americans, 1964

(rev. edit.), 1969, Puritanism and the American Experience, 1969, (with Robert A. Skotheim) American Social Thought, 1972, God's Plot: The Paradoxes of Puritan Piety, 1972, God's Plot: Puritan Spirituality in Thomas Shepard's Cambridge, 1994. Faculty rsch. grantee U. Denver, 1970, Coll. William and Mary, 1981-82, 89; rsch. fellow NEH, 1977-78. Mem. Am. Hist. Assn., Orgn. Am. Historians, Confr. of Hist. Jours. (pres.1987-89). Home: 102 Old Glory Ct Williamsburg VA 23185-4914 Office: Inst Early Am History & Culture PO Box 8781 Williamsburg VA 23187-8781

MCGILBERRY, JOE HERMAN, food service executive; b. Mobile, Ala., Aug. 6, 1943; s. Thomas Henry and Yvonne (Jorden) McG.; m. Betty Sue Reynolds, Dec. 20, 1964; children: Joe H. Jr., Michele, Brent. BS, Auburn U., 1965; MS, U. Tenn., 1972; PhD, TEx. A&M U., 1978. Gen. plant asst. Gen. Telephone Fla., Tampa, 1966; systems analyst E.I. DuPont de Nemours & Co., Old Hickory, Tenn., 1966-68; research asst. U. Tenn., Knoxville, 1968-69; advanced materials engr. Union Carbide Corp., Texas City, TX, 1969-70; asst. prof. Tenn. Tech. U., Cookeville, 1970-72, 73-75, 76-77; mgr. prodn. support Fleetguard div. Cummins Engine, Cookeville, 1972-73; assoc. research engr. Tex. A&M U., College Station, 1975-76; mgr. food and fiber ctr. Miss. State Coop. Extension Program, 1978-94, state program leader, enterprise and cmty. resource devel. coop. ext.. svc., 1991—; cons. Dunlap Industries, U. Tenn. at Nashville, Norwalk Furniture Corp., Teledyne-Stillman, Genco Stamping, Inc., Riley Enterprises; lectr. various seminars and presentations, 1978—. Author numerous articles in field. Mem. Inst. Indsl. Engrs. (sr.), Miss. Indsl. Devel. Council, Order Engrs., Nat. Assn. County Agrl. Agts., Miss. Assn. County Agrl. Agts., Alpha Phi Mu. Office: Box 9642 201 Bost Extension Bldg Mississippi State MS 39762-9600

MC GILL, ARCHIE JOSEPH, venture capital and business speaker; b. Winona, Minn., May 29, 1931; s. Archibald Joseph and Anne (Lettner) McG.; m. Jeanne Sullivan, Mar. 17, 1974; children: Archibald Joseph, III, Mark E., Gregory P., Debora, Karen, Susan, Brian. B.A. in Econs, St. Mary's Coll., Winona, 1956. With IBM Corp., 1956-69; v.p. market ops. IBM Corp., White Plains, N.Y., 1956-69; founder, pres. McGill Assocs., White Plains, 1970-73; dir. market mgmt. AT&T Co., 1973-78, v.p. bus. mktg., 1978-83; pres. Advanced Info. Systems Am. Bell, Inc., 1983; pres., chief exec. officer Rothschild Ventures, Inc., 1983; now pres. Chardonnay, Inc.; dir. numerous cos.; dir. Guarantee Bank, Moscow. Bd. dirs. Steadman/Hawkins Found., Jimmy Huegga Found. With USAF, 1951-54. Named Mktg. Statesman of Year Sales Execs. Club, 1978.

MCGILL, DAN MAYS, insurance business educator; b. Greenback, Tenn., Sept. 27, 1919; s. John Burton and Jane (Mays) McG.; m. Elaine Kem, June 22, 1952; children: Douglas Russell, Melanie Mays. BA, Maryville Coll., 1940, LLD (hon.), 1982; MA, Vanderbilt U., 1941; PhD, U. Pa., 1947. Assoc. prof. fin. U. Tenn., Knoxville, 1947-48; Julian Price assoc. prof. ins. U. N.C., Chapel Hill, 1948-51; assoc. prof. ins. U. Pa., Phila., 1952-56, Frederick H. Ecker prof. life ins., 1959-90; trustee N.W. Mut. Life Ins. Co., Milw., 1978-90; bd. dirs. NRG Life Reassurance Corp., Phila., 1984-94, Phila. Reins. Corp., 1990-94; exec. dir. S.S. Huebner Found., 1954-75, 78-86, chmn., 1965-94; dir. rsch. Pension Rsch. Coun., 1952-90; chmn., mem. governing bd. Leonard Davis Inst. Health Econs., 1967-90; 1st chmn. adv. commn. Pension Benefit Guaranty Corp., 1975-78, mem 1978-81. Author: An Analysis of Government Life Insurance, 1949, The Fundamentals of Private Pensions, 6th edit., 1989, Legal Aspects of Life Insurance, 1959, Fulfilling Pension Expectations, 1962, Life Insurance, 1967, Preservation of Pension Benefit Rights, 1972, others; editor: (with others) World Insurance Trends, 1959, others. Chmn. bd. pensions Presbyn. Ch. U.S., 1977-88; trustee Presbyn. Med. Ctr., U. Pa., 1987—, chmn. Boettner Inst. Fin. Gerontology, 1993—; mem. retirement bd. Mass. Bay Transp. Authority, 1980—. Maj. USAAF, 1942-46, 51-52. Recipient Disting. Alumni award Maryville Coll., 1962, Huebner Gold medal award Am. Coll., 1977, Gold medal Internat. Ins. Soc., 1987. Mem. Am. Risk and Ins. Assn. (pres. 1959, Elizur Wright award 1955, 81). Republican. Presbyterian. Clubs: Union League, Pyramid. Avocations: music, travel, sports. Home: 50 Belmont Ave Bala Cynwyd PA 19004-2437 Office: 2 Bala Plaza Ste 300 Bala Cynwyd PA 19004

MCGILL, ESBY CLIFTON, former college official; b. Omaha, Ark., Jan. 12, 1914; s. James Preston and Celia (Stafford) McG.; m. Ruth Evelyn Jones, Oct. 22, 1932 (dec.); children: Barbara (Mrs. Forrest E. Nelson), Marilyn (Mrs. Joel Pahk); m. Mary Elizabeth Beardsley, July 5, 1978. BS, S.W. Mo. State U., 1940; MS, Okla. State U., 1941; EdD, NYU, 1955. Tchr. public schs. Mo., 1932-33, 35-39; head bus. dept. High Sch. Stillwater, Okla., 1941-42; assoc. prof. in charge of U.S. Naval Radio Sch., Tex. A&M U., College Station, 1942-44; chmn. div. bus. Emporia State U, Kans., 1945-59; chmn. bus. edn. dept. Utah State U., Logan, 1959-60; dean faculties, dir. acad. planning, dir. summer sessions So. Oreg. State Coll., Ashland, 1960-77; dir. summer sessions So. Oreg. State Coll., 1976-79, dir. continuing edn., 1976-78, dir. non-traditional programs, 1978-79; comml. loan officer for Jackson-Josephine Counties Coos, Curry, Douglas Bus. Devel. Corp., Medford, Oreg., 1990-91; cons. curriculum for schs. in cen. states, 1950-69; mem. regional adv. bd. So. Oreg. State Coll., 1st term, 1987-89, 2d term, 1989-91, 3d term, 1991-93, 4th term, 1994—. Author: Communications Typing, 1944, Production Typing, 1955, Business Principles, Organization and Management, 1958, rev., 1963, Briefhand, 1957, manuals in field; also contbr. over 100 articles to profl. jours.; spl. editor: Bus. Edn. Quar, 1951-55; mem. editorial bd.: Bus. Edn. Forum, 1956-59, Nat. Assn. Bus. Tchr. Tng. Instns. Bull, 1951-55. Chmn. Downtown Redevel. Com., Ashland, Oreg., 1967-71; bd. dirs. Peter Britt Music and Arts Festival Assn., Jacksonville, Oreg., 1966-69, Ashland Rotary Found., Jackson-Josephine Counties, Oreg. Comprehensive Health Planning Unit. Recipient Founder's Day award NYU, 1956, Man of Yr. award Ashland C. of C., 1965. Mem. NEA, Oreg. Edn. Assn., Nat. Assn. Bus. Tchr. Edn. Instns. (past pres., bd. dirs.), United Bus. Edn. Assn. (past pres., bd. dirs.), Mountain Plains Bus. Edn. Assn. (past pres., bd. dirs.), North Central Assn. Conf. Summer Schs. and Future Bus. Leaders Am. (past bd. dirs. both), Nat. Office Mgmt. Assn. (hon.), Ashland C. of C. (pres., bd. dirs.), Am. Assn. Colls. Tchr. Edn. (liaison officer for Oreg. 1970-73), Svc. Corp. Ret. Execs. (chmn. chpt. 269 1985-86, 86-87, 87-88, 88-89), SCORE (alternate dist. rep. Portland dist. 1988-89, dist. rep. Portland dist. 1990-91, asst. regional dir. region 10 1991-92, dir. region 10 States of Alaska, Idaho, Oreg. and Wash. 1993—, nat. treas. 1994—), Phi Delta Kappa, Kappa Delta Pi, Delta Pi Epsilon, Pi Omega Pi, Pi Gamma Mu, Sigma Tau Gamma. Clubs: Mason, Rotary (past sec., pres. bd. Ashland, gov. internat. dist. 5110, 1983-84, materials chmn. pres. elect tng. program 9 dists. U.S. Can. S.W. 1990-94, mem. chmn. 1991—, rep. Rotary Internat. Coun. Legislation dist. 5110 1992, 95, Paul Harris fellow). Home: 1785 Zemke Rd Talent OR 97540-9718

MCGILL, HENRY COLEMAN, JR., physician, educator, researcher; b. Nashville, Oct. 1, 1921; s. Henry Coleman and Thursa (Lowry) McG.; m. Cloace Laurite Ferguson, Sept. 12, 1945; children—Margaret Ann, Laurilynn, Elizabeth Gail. B.A., Vanderbilt U., 1943, M.D., 1946. Intern Vanderbilt Hosp., Nashville, 1946-47; asst. prof. La. State U. Med. Ctr., New Orleans, 1950-55, assoc. prof., 1955-61, prof., chmn. pathology, 1961-66, U. Tex. Health Sci. Ctr., San Antonio, 1966-72 prof., 1972-91; sci. dir. S.W. Found. for Biomed. Rsch. San Antonio, 1979—. Served to capt. U.S. Army, 1948-50. Mem. Phi Beta Kappa, Sigma Xi, Alpha Omega Alpha. Contbr. numerous articles to profl. jours. Home: 4102 Fawnridge Dr San Antonio TX 78229-4212 Office: PO Box 21847 San Antonio TX 78228-0009

MCGILL, JAY, magazine publisher. Pub. Country Living, N.Y.C. Office: Country Living Hearst Mags 224 West 57th St New York NY 10019-5201*

MCGILL, JENNIFER HOUSER, non-profit association administrator; b. Abingdon, Va., Mar. 3, 1957; d. Mason L. and Margaret Jane (Powers) H.; m. James B. McGill, July 15, 1978; children: Melissa Diane, Mark James. AA, Va. Highlands Community Coll., Abingdon, 1978, BA, U. S.C., 1980. Reporter, editor Sumter (S.C.) Daily ITEM, 1980-81; assoc. editor Sandlapper Mag., Columbia, S.C., 1981-82; membership editor Assn. for Edn. in Journalism/Mass Comm., Columbia, 1982-83, adminstrv. asst., 1984-85, exec. dir., 1985—; mem. nat. steering com. Journalist-in-Career Project, Columbia, 1985-86. Home: 4102 Fawnridge Dr San Antonio TX 78229-4212 Home: 4102 Fawnridge Dr. Mem. Lioness Club (3d v.p. 1990-91, 2d v.p. 1991-92). Avocations: reading, cooking, biking. Office: Assn Schs Journalism & Mass Comm 1621 College St Columbia SC 29208

MCGILL, MAURICE LEON, financial executive; b. Malden, Mo., Aug. 22, 1936; s. William Howard and Iris (Phillips) McG.; m. Wanda Coral Wirt, Feb. 2, 1957; children—Melany, Melinda, William Shannon. B.S., U. Mo. 1958, M.A., 1959. C.P.A., Mo., Iowa, Ariz. Mgr. Touche, Ross, Bailey & Smart, Kansas City, Mo., 1959-64; fin. v.p., treas. Iowa Beef Packers, Inc., Dakota City, Nebr., 1964-69; exec. v.p., treas. Spencer Foods, Inc., Iowa, 1969-71, also dir.; sr. v.p. Diamond Reo Trucks, Inc., Lansing, Mich., 1971-72; fin. v.p. Ariz. Colo. Land & Cattle Co., Phoenix, 1972-75; ptnr. Touche Ross & Co., Phoenix, 1975-81; exec. v.p. fin. and adminstrn., treas., bd. dirs. IBP, Inc., Dakota City, Nebr., 1981-89; pres., bd. dirs. Wirmac Corp., Garland, Tex., 1989—; bd. dirs. Bluebonnet Savs. Bank, Dallas. Mem. AICPA, Iowa Soc. CPAs, Ea. Hills Country Club. Home: 1414 Seminary Rdg Garland TX 75043-1241

MCGILL, ROBERT ERNEST, III, retired manufacturing company executive; b. San Francisco, Apr. 30, 1931; s. Robert Ernest and Madeleine Melanie (Ignace) McG.; m. Daphne Urquhart Driver, Apr. 26, 1958; children: Robert Ernest, Meredith Louise, Christina Elizabeth, James Alexander. B.A., Williams Coll., 1954; M.B.A., Harvard U., 1956. With Morgan Stanley & Co. (investment bankers), N.Y.C., 1956-63; mem. fin. staff Air Products & Chems., Inc., Allentown, Pa., 1963-64; dir. corp. planning and devel. Air Products & Chems., Inc., 1964-68; v.p. Gen. Interiors Corp., N.Y.C., 1968-70; exec. v.p. Gen. Interiors Corp., 1970-73; v.p. fin. Ethan Allen, Inc., Danbury, Conn., 1973-75; v.p. fin., sec. Dexter Corp., Windsor Locks, Conn., 1975-83, sr. v.p. fin. and adminstrn., dir., 1983-89, exec. v.p., 1989-94; pres. Kettlebrook Ins. Co. Ltd., 1983-93, chmn., 1993-94; pres. Dexter Credit Corp., 1982-88; bd. dirs. Analytical Tech., Inc., The Conn. Surety Corp.; bd. mgrs. Travelers Funds for Variable Annuities; trustee Travelers Mut. Fund. Trustee Colt Bequest, Inc.; mem. exec. com. Greater Hartford Arts Coun., 1989-94; bd. overseers U. Conn. Sch. Bus., 1991-95; bd. dirs. Conn. Pub. Expenditures Coun., 1980-95. Mem. N.Y. Soc. Security Analysts, Fin. Execs. Inst. (pres. Hartford chpt. 1984-85), Inroads (bd. dirs. Hartford chpt. 1990-95). Home: 295 Hancock Rd Williamstown MA 01267-3005

MCGILL, SAM PEYTON, state senator, automobile dealer, farmer; b. Lincoln County, Ga., Aug. 30, 1914; s. Adolphus Cecil and Lillian Inez (Norman) McG.; student S. Ga. State Coll.; m. Florence Clary, Sept. 22, 1935; children—Sam Clary, Kathryn McGill Lamar. Owner service sta., 1936-38; owner, pres. McGill Truck & Tractor (inc. into McGill's Inc. 1975), 1939—; owner Wilkes County Stockyard, Washington, Ga., 1950—; owner, S.P. McGill Farms, 1942—; dir. Washington Loan & Banking Co. Mem. Washington City Council, 1952-58; mem. Ga. State Senate, chmn. agr. com. Named Wilkes County Citizen of Yr., 1977; recipient Ga. County Agts. award, 1974; Disting. Service award U. Ga. Vet. Sch.; Hon. State FFA Farmer degree. Mem. Ga. Farm Equipment Assn., Ga. Stockyard Assn., Nat. Livestock Mktg. Assn. Democrat. Baptist. Clubs: Lions, Wilkes Country, Atlanta City, Atlanta Athletic. Office: 402 N Bypass E Washington GA 30673-5340

MCGILL, THOMAS CONLEY, physics educator; b. Port Arthur, Tex., Mar. 20, 1942; s. Thomas Conley and Susie Elizabeth (Collins) McG.; m. Toby Elizabeth Cone, Dec. 27, 1966; children: Angela Elizabeth, Sara Elizabeth. BS in Math., Lamar State Coll., 1963, BEE, 1964; MEE, Calif. Inst. Tech., 1965, PHD, 1969. NATO postdoctoral fellow U. Bristol, Eng., 1969-70; NRC postdoctoral fellow Princeton (N.J.) U., 1970-71; from asst. to assoc. prof. applied physics Calif. Inst. Tech., Pasadena, 1971-77, prof., 1977-85, Fletcher Jones prof. applied physics, 1985—; cons. Hughes Research Labs., Malibu, Calif., 1967—, Def. Advance Projects Agy./Materials Research Council, Arlington, Va., 1979—, Xerox Palo Alto (Calif.) Research Corp., 1984—. Alfred P. Sloan Found. fellow, 1974. Fellow Am. Physical Soc.; mem. AAAS, IEEE, Am. Vacuum Soc., Sigma Xi. Office: Calif Inst of Tech Mail Code 128 # 95 Pasadena CA 91125

MCGILL, THOMAS EMERSON, psychology educator; b. Sharon, Pa., Sept. 26, 1930; s. Emerson Dickson and Margaret Hughes (McCallen) McG.; m. Nancy C. Welch, June 14, 1955; children: Michael Howard, Steven Emerson. BA, Youngstown State U., 1954; MA, Princeton U., 1957, PhD, 1958. Instr. psychology Williams Coll., Williamstown, Mass., 1958-59, asst. prof., 1960-64, assoc. prof., 1965-69, prof., 1969-91, chmn. dept. psychology, 1976-82, 85-86, Hales prof., 1970-91, prof. emeritus, 1991—; postdoctoral fellow U. Calif., Berkeley, 1959-60; sr. postdoctoral fellow U. Edinburgh, 1964-65, vis. research fellow, 1969-70. Editor: Readings in Animal Behavior, 3d edit, 1977, (with Dewsbury and Sachs) Sex and Behavior, 1977. USPHS grantee, 1960-82; sr. postdoctoral fellow Nat. Acad. Sci., 1964-65. Fellow AAAS; mem. Newfoundland Club N.Am. (dir. 1980-94, pres. 1990-92), Newfoundland Club New Eng. (pres. 1980-82), Sigma Xi. Home: 137 Laura Ln Tiverton RI 02878 Office: Williams Coll Dept Of Psychology Williamstown MA 01267

MCGILL, WARREN EVERETT, lawyer, consultant; b. Brazil, Ind., Sept. 10, 1923; s. Ira and Joyce S. (Wenning) McG.; m. Irene Marie Kish, Aug. 31, 1946; children: Cecelia, Daniel, Nancy, Mary Beth, Mark. BS, Ind. U., 1944, JD with honors, 1945. Bar: Ind. 1945. Assoc. Oare, Thornburg, McGill & Deahl, South Bend, Ind., 1945-60; ptnr. Thornburg, McGill, Deahl, Harman, Carey & Murray, South Bend, 1960-83; ptnr. Barnes & Thornburg, South Bend, 1983-89, of counsel, 1989—; chmn. Probate Code Study Commn., Ind., 1972-90. Editor, co-author: Indiana Land Trust Practice, 1980, Trust Litigation, 1981; asst. editor, co-author: Probate Code 1975 Reform, 1975; author: Special Comment on Indiana Probate Code, 1982. Sec., dir. Michiana Arts and Scis. coun., Inc., South Bend, 1965—; pres. Com. of 100, South Bend, Mishawaka, Ind., 1960-64; community adv. bd. Channel 34 Pub. TV, No. Ind., So. Mich., 1982-86. Recipient Community Achievement Citation, City of South Bend, 1985. Fellow Ind. Acad. Law Alumni; mem. ABA, St. Joseph County Bar Assn., Am. Coll. Trust and Estate Counsel (chmn. membership com. 1972-90), Ind. State Bar Assn. (chmn. ho. dels. 1982-83, Presdl. citation 1985), Ind. Bar Found. (pres. 1984-86, bd. dirs. 1984-89), Ind. Continuing Legal Edn. Forum (bd. dirs. 1984-90), Morris Park Country Club (pres. 1978), Summit Club. Avocations: golf, history, travel. Home: 2831 Caroline St South Bend IN 46614-1543 Office: Barnes & Thornburg 600 1st Source Bank Ctr 100 N Michigan St South Bend IN 46601-1630

MCGILL, WILLIAM JAMES, JR., academic administrator; b. St. Louis, Mo., Mar. 25, 1936; s. William James Sr. and Ethel (Williams) McG.; m. Ellen Buck, June 18, 1960; children: Sara Louise, Susan Elizabeth, Alison Marcia. BA, Trinity Coll., 1957; MA, Harvard U., 1958, PhD, 1961, grad. Inst. Edml. Mgmt., 1989. Instr. history Western Md. Coll., Westminster, 1960-62; asst. prof. history Alma (Mich.) Coll., 1962-68, assoc. prof., 1968-72; dean of coll. Washington & Jefferson Coll., Washington, Pa., 1972-75; prof. history, 1972-84; asst. dir., div. edn. programs NEH, Washington, 1984-86; v.p., dean faculty Lebanon Valley Coll., Annville, Pa., 1986—, acting pres., 1987-88. Author: Maria Theresa, 1972; contbr. 53 articles to profl. jours., 43 book revs., numerous poems; poetry editor Spitball Mag., 1993—. Assoc. to rector St. Luke's Episc. Ch., Lebanon, Pa., 1986—; priest-in-charge St. George's Episc. Ch., Waynesburg, Pa., 1974-83; actor Washington Theater Wing, Washington, 1984-86, Gretna Playhouse, Mt. Gretna, Pa., 1987-90; bd. dirs. Lebanon County United Way, 1987—, Gretna Prodns., Mt. Gretna, 1986-90, 91-92; trustee Penn Sch. Art and Design, 1992—. Mem. Am. Assn. Higher Edn., Phi Beta Kappa. Avocations: sailing, writing, acting. Home: PO Box 682 Cornwall PA 17016-0682 Office: Lebanon Valley Coll Office Academic Affairs Annville PA 17003

MC GILLEM, CLARE DUANE, electrical engineering educator; b. Clinton, Mich., Oct. 9, 1923; s. Virgil and Starlie (Weaver) McG.; m. Frances Ann Wilson, Nov. 29, 1947; 1 child, Mary Ann. BSEE, U. Mich., 1947; MSE, Purdue U., 1949, PhD, 1955. Rsch. engr. Diamond Chain Co. Inc., Indpls., 1947-51; head functional design U.S. Naval Avionics Ctr., Indpls., 1951-56; head mil. and elec. engring. AC Spark Plug, GM, Flint, Mich., 1956-58; dir. elec. and applied rsch. AC Spark Plug, GM, Milw., 1958-59; program mgr. def. rsch. div. GM, Santa Barbara, Calif., 1959-62; prof. elec. engring. Purdue U., West Lafayette, Ind., 1963-92, assoc. dean engring., 1968-72, prof. emeritus of elec. engring., 1992—; dir. engring. expt. sta. Purdue U., West Lafayette, Ind., 1968-72; bd. dirs. VETRONICS In., West Lafayette, pres., 1984—; pres. Tech. Assocs. Inc., West Lafayette, 1977—. Co-author: Probabilistic Methods of Signal and System Analysis, 1971, Continuous and Discrete Signal and System Analysis, 1974, Modern Communications and Spread Spectrum, 1986. Lt. (j.g.) USN, 1943-46, PTO. Recipient Meritorious Civilian Svc. award USN, 1955. Fellow IEEE (Centennial award 1984, J. Fred Peoples award 1988). Avocation: duplicate bridge, amateur radio. Office: Sch Elec Engring Purdue U West Lafayette IN 47907

MCGILLEY, SISTER MARY JANET, nun, educator, writer, academic administrator; b. Kansas City, Mo., Dec. 4, 1924; d. James P. and Peg (Ryan) McG. B.A., St. Mary Coll., 1945; M.A., Boston Coll., 1951; Ph.D., Fordham U., 1956; postgrad., U. Notre Dame, 1960, Columbia U., 1964. Social worker Kansas City, 1945-46; joined Sisters of Charity of Leavenworth, 1946; tchr. English Hayden High Sch., Topeka, 1948-50, Billings (Mont.) Central High Sch., 1951-53; faculty dept. English St. Mary Coll., Leavenworth, Kans., 1956-64; pres. St. Mary Coll., 1964-89, Disting. prof. English and Liberal Studies, 1990—. Contbr. articles, fiction and poetry to various jours. Bd. dirs. United Way of Leavenworth, 1966-85; mem. Mayor's Adv. Coun., 1967-72; bd. dirs. Kans. Ind. Coll. Fund, 1964-89, exec. com., 1985-86, vice chmn., 1984-85, chmn., 1985-86. Recipient Alumnae award St. Mary Coll., 1969; Disting. Service award Baker U., 1981, Leavenworth Bus. Woman of Yr. Athena award, 1986. Mem. Nat. Coun. Tchrs. of English, Nat. Assn. Ind. Colls. and Univs. (bd. dirs. 1982-85), Kans. Ind. Coll. Assn. (bd. dirs. 1964-89, treas. 1982-84, v.p. 1984-85, chmn. exec. com. 1985-86), Am. Coun. Edn. (com. on women in higher edn. 1980-85), Am. Assn. Higher Edn., Kansas City Regional Coun. for Higher Edn. (bd. dirs. 1965-89, treas. 1984-85, v.p. 1986-88), Ind. Coll. Funds Am. (exec. com. 1974-77, trustee-at-large 1975-76), North Cen. Assn. Colls. and Schs. (exec. commr. Com. on Insts. Higher Edn. 1980-88, vice chair 1985-86, chair 1987-88), Leavenworth C. of C. (bd. dirs. 1964-89), Assn. Am. Colls. (commn. liberal learning 1970-73, com. on curriculum and faculty devel. 1979-82) St. Mary Alumni Assn. (hon. pres. 1964-89), Delta Epsilon Sigma. Democrat. Office: St Mary Coll 4100 S 4th St Leavenworth KS 66048-5082

MC GILLICUDDY, JOHN FRANCIS, retired banker; b. Harrison, N.Y., Dec. 30, 1930; s. Michael J. and Anna (Munro) McG.; m. Constance Burtis, Sept. 9, 1954; children: Michael Sean, Faith Burtis Benoit, Constance Erin Mc Gillicuddy Mills, Brian Munro, John Walsh. A.B., Princeton, 1952; LL.B., Harvard, 1955. With Mfrs. Hanover Trust Co. subs. Mfrs. Hanover Corp., N.Y.C., 1958-91, v.p., 1962-66, sr. v.p., 1966-69, exec. v.p., asst. to chmn., 1969-70, vice chmn., dir., 1970, pres., 1971-91, chmn., chief exec. officer, 1979-91; chmn. bd., chief exec. officer Chem. Banking Corp., N.Y.C., 1992-93, ret., 1994; bd. dirs. USX Corp., Chem. Banking Corp., Continental Copr., Empire Blue Cross and Blue Shield, UAL Corp. Bd. dirs. Nat. Multiple Sclerosis Soc.; trustee, chmn. N.Y. Hosp., N.Y. Pub. Libr.; trustee emeritus Princeton U.; pres. Boy Scouts Am., Greater N.Y. Couns. Lt. (j.g.) USNR, 1955-58. Mem. Bus. Coun., Westchester Country Club (Rye, N.Y.), Blind Brook Club (Port Chester, N.Y.), Princeton Club (N.Y.C.), Augusta Nat. Golf Club (Ga.), Pine Valley Golf Club (N.J.), Laurel Valley Golf Club (Ligonier, Pa.), Seminole Golf Club (north Palm Beach, Fla.), Links Club (N.Y.C.), Sky Club (N.Y.C.). Roman Catholic. Office: Chem Banking Corp 270 Park Ave New York NY 10017-2014

MCGILLIS, KELLY, actress; b. Newport, Calif., July 9, 1957; m. Fred Tillman, Dec. 31, 1988; 3 children. Student, Pacific Conservatory of Performing Arts, Juilliard Sch. Music. Actress: (feature films) Reuben, Reuben, 1983, Witness, 1985, Top Gun, 1986, Made in Heaven, 1987, Promised Land, 1988, The House on Carroll Street, 1988, The Accused, 1988, Winter People, 1989, The Babe, 1992, North, 1994; (TV films) Sweet Revenge, 1984, Private Sessions, 1985, Grand Isle (also prod.), 1991, Bonds of Love, 1993, In the Best of Families: Marriage, Pride and Madness, 1994; (stage) Hedda Gabler, Roundabout Theatre Company, 1994. •

MCGILLIVRAY, DONALD DEAN, seed company executive, agronomist; b. Muscatine, Iowa, Aug. 28, 1928; s. Walter C. and Pearl E. (Potter) M.; m. Betty J. Anderson, June 24, 1951; children—Ann E., Jean M. B.S. in Agronomy, Iowa State U., 1950. Asst. mgr. Iowa, Minn., Wis. sect. Funk Seeds Internat., Belle Plaine, Iowa, 1965-69, mgr., 1969-70, mgr. hybrid corn ops., Bloomington, Ill., 1970-75, v.p. ops., 1976-82, pres., 1982-88; assoc. Smart Seeds, Inc., 1989—; dir. U.S. Feed Grains Coun., Washington, D.C., 1984-87. Bd. dirs. Ill. Agrl. Leadership Found., Macomb, Ill., 1985—, chmn. bd. 1990—, Ill. Wesleyan Assocs., 1986-89; adv. bd. Bro-Menn Hosp., pres., 1989-90. Sgt. U.S. Army, 1951-53. Mem. Am. Seed Trade Assn. (bd. dirs. 1978—, chmn. 1978-79, 2d v.p. 1986-87, 1st v.p. 1987-88, pres. 1988-89), Am. Seed Rsch. Found. (bd. dirs. 1982—, pres. 1984-87), Masons.

MCGILLIVRAY, KAREN, elementary school educator; b. Richland, Oreg., Aug. 24, 1936; d. Kenneth Melton and Catharina (Sass) McG. BS in Edn. cum laude, Ea. Oreg. State Coll., 1958; MRE, Pacific Sch. Religion, 1963. Cert. tchr., Oreg. 4th grade tchr. Salem (Oreg.)-Keizer Pub. Schs.; ret., 1995. Contbr. articles, stories to ednl. mags. U.S. Govt. grantee. Mem. NEAR, Oreg. Edn. Assn. (rep. assembly), Oreg. Retired Educators Assn., Salem Edn. Assn. (officer), Oreg. Ret. Tchrs. Assn., Phi Delta Kappa (officer), Delta Kappa Gamma (officer). Methodist. Home: 325 Cedarwood Ave Mcminnville OR 97128

MC GIMPSEY, RONALD ALAN, oil company executive; b. Cleve., June 7, 1944; s. John E. and Muriel N. McGimpsey; m. Linda V. Tiffany, Apr. 20, 1974. BS, Case Inst. Tech., 1966; MS, Case Western Res. U., 1974; grad. exec. program, Stanford U., 1987. With BP Am. Inc. (formerly Standard Oil Co.), Ohio, 1966—; treas. BP Am. Inc. (formerly Standard Oil Co.), 1977-81, v.p. fin., 1981-82, sr. v.p. crude trading and transp., 1982-86; sr. v.p. petroleum products and refining BP Am. Inc. (formerly Standard Oil Co.), Cleve., 1986-89; group contr. BP-London, 1989-91; regional sr. v.p., CFO BP America, Cleve., 1991-92, sr. v.p., fin. officer, 1992-93; CEO BP Australia, Melbourne, 1994—. Chmn. bd. trustees Marymount Hosp., Cleve., 1986-88; adv. bd. Case Inst. Tech. Mem. Bus. Coun. Australia, Australia Inst. of Petroleum (chmn. 1995—). Office: BP Australia, 360 Elizabeth St, Melbourne 3000, Australia

MC GIMSEY, CHARLES ROBERT, III, anthropologist; b. Dallas, June 18, 1925; s. Charles Robert, Jr. and Ellen Randolph (Parks) McG.; m. Mary Elizabeth Conger, Dec. 20, 1949; children—Charles Robert, Brian Keith, Mark Douglass. Student, Vanderbilt U., 1942-43, U. of South, 1943-44; B.A., U. N.Mex., 1949; M.A., Harvard U., 1954, Ph.D., 1958. Instr. U. Ark., Fayetteville, 1957; asst. prof. U. Ark., 1958-62, assoc. prof., 1962-67, prof. anthropology, 1967-90, prof. emeritus, 1990—, chmn. dept., 1969-72; asst. curator U. Ark. Mus., 1957-59, dir., 1959-83; dir. Ark. Archeol. Survey, 1967-90, dir. emeritus, 1990—; cons. archeology U.S. GAO, 1979-87, U.S./Internat. Com. on Monuments and Sites; Rep. to Internat. Com. on Archeol. Heritage Mgmt., 1988—. Author: (with G.R. Willey) Monagrillo Culture of Panama, 1954, Mariana Mesa, 1980, Indians of Arkansas, 1969, Public Archeology, 1972, Archeology and Archeological Resources, 1973, (with H.A. Davis) The Management of Archeological Resources, 1977; assoc. editor Am. Antiquity, 1972-87; Co-editor (with H. A. Davis) Southeastern Museums Conf., 1964-73; Contbr. articles to profl. jours. Mem. Ark. Rev. Com., Historic Preservation Program, 1968-76; collaborator Nat. Park Service, 1971-74, adviser, 1974-77; mem. Com. on Recovery Archeol. Remains, 1971-78; mem. adv. bd. dirs. Red River Mus., 1975-76; mem. adv. bd. Am. Indian Archeol. Inst., 1975-80, Ark. Natural and Cultural Heritage Dept., 1976-90. Served to lt. (j.g.) USNR, 1943-47. Recipient Cert. Recognition State of Ark., 1990; rsch. grantee Am. Philos. Soc., Am. Acad. Arts and Scis., Andean Rsch. Inst., Nat. Park Service, NSF, Smithsonian Instn. Wenner-Gren Found.; rsch. fellow dept. archaeology U. Cambridge, 1985-86, assoc. mem. Darwin Coll., 1985—. Fellow Am. Anthrop. Assn.; mem. Soc. for Am. Archaeology (pres. 1974-75, Disting. Svc. award 1975), Ark. Archeol. Soc. (editor 1960-83, Preservationist award 1989), Southeastern Museums Conf. (council 1962-71, editor 1964-71), Am. Soc. for Conservation Archeology (founding mem. 1974, award for outstanding contbn. 1980), Soc. Profl. Archeologists (founder 1976, dir. 1976-79, pres. 1983-84, Seiberling award 1989), Am. Assn. Museums, Am. Assn. for State and Local History (award of merit 1985). Home: 435 Hawthorne St Fayetteville AR 72701-1935 Office: Ark Archeol Survey PO Box 1249 Fayetteville AR 72702-1249

MCGINLEY, EDWARD STILLMAN, II, naval officer; b. Allentown, Pa., June 9, 1939; s. Edward Stillman and Dorothy Mae (Kandle) McG.; m. Connie Lee Mayo, July 1, 1962; children: Amanda Lee, Edward Stillman III. BS, U.S. Naval Acad., 1961; advanced degree in naval architecture,

MIT, 1970; MSA, George Washington U., 1972; cert. exec. program, U. Va., 1981. Commd. ensign USN, 1961, advanced through grades to rear adm. 1990, various positions in submarine engring., 1962-76; repair officer USN, Rota (Spain) and Charleston, S.C., 1976-83; ops. mgr. Mare Island Naval Shipyard, Vallejo, Calif., 1983-87; comdr. Norfolk Naval Shipyard, Portsmouth, Va., 1987-90; maintenance officer U.S. Pacific Fleet, Honolulu, 1990-93; comdr. Naval Surface Warfare Ctr., Washington, 1993-94; vice-comdr. Naval Sea Sys. Command, Washington, 1994—. Contbr. articles to profl. jours. Recipient Environ. award Sec. of Navy, 1987, Productivity Improvement award Inst. Indsl. Engrs., 1988, Quality Improvement award Office Mgmt. and Budget, 1989, Productivity award U.S. Senate, 1990. Mem. Am. Soc. Naval Engrs. (nat. counselor), Soc. Naval Arch. and Marine Engrs., U.S. Naval Inst., Am. Soc. for Quality Control, Rotary, Sigma Xi, Tau Beta Pi. Republican. mem. United Church of Christ. Avocations: art, running. Home: Qtrs M-1 Washington Navy Yard Washington DC 20374 Office: Naval Sea Sys Command SEA 09 2531 Jeff Davis Hwy Arlington VA 22242-5160

MCGINLEY, JOSEPH PATRICK, brokerage house executive; b. Phila., Mar. 17, 1947; s. Joseph Robert and Kathaleen (Brennan) McG.; m. Linda L. Irvin, May 15, 1970 (div. 1981); children: Lisa C., Andrew S.; m. Sharon A. Malloy, Sept. 7, 1984; 1 child, Christopher J. BSBA, Villanova U., 1965-69. Sr. v.p. Dean Witter, Phila., 1974—; bd. dirs. Tara Investments Ltd., Phila., Orion Assoc., Phila., Florence Ave. Corp., Phila. Co-founder A Better Chance of Lower Merion. Mem. Union League Yacht Club (vice commodore), Union League of Phila., Cynwyd Club, Corinthian Yacht Club (Phila.). Republican. Roman Catholic. Avocation: yachting. Office: Dean Witter Reynolds 2 Logan Sq Philadelphia PA 19103-2707

MCGINLEY, MORGAN, newspaper editor; b. New London, Conn., Mar. 1, 1942; s. Morgan Sr. and Elizabeth (Zuccardy) McG.; m. Mary Elizabeth Dowd, Sept. 11, 1971; children: John, Carolyn, Brendan. BA, Colby Coll., 1964. Reporter Providence Jour., 1965; reporter The Day, New London, 1965-75, asst. city editor, 1975-78, night city editor, 1978-81, asst. editorial page editor, 1981-82, editorial page editor, 1982—; writer in residence Emerson Coll., Boston, 1992. Bd. dirs. Salvation Army, New London, 1976—, Found. Open Govt., Conn., 1993—; chmn. Conn. Coun. on Freedom of Info.; mem. Task Force on Minorities in the Newspaper Bus.; panelist Conn. Pub. TV Fourth Estate Show, 1987—. With U.S. Army, 1965; cpl. Army NG, 1965-70. Fellow Washington Journalism Ctr., 1969, Knight Ctr. Specialized Journalism U. Md., 1991; recipient 1st Place Edtl. Writing award New Eng. AP News Execs. Assn., 1st Place award for Edtl. Writing New Eng. Press Assn., 1st Place awards Soc. Profl. Journalists. Mem. Nat. Conf. Edtl. Writers (chmn. minorities com. 1988—, bd. dirs. 1989-90, 92-93, chair membership 1993-94, mem. editl. mgmt. and ops. com., sec. 1995), New Eng. Soc. Newspaper Editors (bd. dirs. 1987—, minority affairs com., pres. 1992, past v.p., treas. and sec.), New Eng. Newspaper Assn. (mem. minority affairs com.), Trout United. Bd. dirs. Thames Valley chpt. 1972—). Episcopalian. Avocations: fly fishing, fly tying. Home: 119 Glenwood Ave New London CT 06320-4302 Office: The Day Pub Co 47 Eugene Oneill Dr New London CT 06320-6306

MCGINLEY, RONALD JAMES, entomologist, researcher; b. Palo Alto, Calif., Sept. 30, 1950. AS, Monterey Peninsula Coll., 1970; BS, U. Calif., Davis, 1972; PhD, U. Calif., Berkeley, 1978. Asst. prof. biology, asst. curator Mus. Comparative Zoology Harvard U., Cambridge, Mass., 1979-83; rsch. entomologist dept. entomology Nat. Mus. Natural Hist., Smithsonian Instn., Washington, 1983-87, chmn. dept. entomology, 1987-92; rsch. entomologist, 1992—. Author: Systematics of the Colletidae Based on Mature Larvae with Phenetic Analysis on Apoid Larvae, 1981. Office: Nat Mus Natural History Dept Entomology NHB 105 Smithsonian Instn Washington DC 20560-0001•

MCGINN, BERNARD JOHN, religious educator; b. Yonkers, N.Y., Aug. 19, 1937; s. Bernard John and Catherine Ann (Faulds) McG.; m. Patricia Ann Ferris, July 10, 1971; children: Daniel, John. BA, St. Joseph's Sem., Yonkers, N.Y., 1959; Licentiate in Sacred Theology, Gregorian U., Rome, 1963; PhD, Brandeis U., 1970. Diocesan priest Archdiocese N.Y., N.Y.C., 1963-71; prof. U. Chgo., 1969—, Naomi Shenstone Donnelly Prof., 1992—; program coord. Inst. for Advanced Study of Religion, Divinity Sch., U. Chgo., 1980-92. Author: The Calabrian Abbott, 1985, Meister Eckhart, 1986, Growth of Mysticism, 1994, Antichrist, 1994; editor: (series) Classics of Western Spirituality, 1978, (book) God and Creation, 1990, Foundations of Mysticism, 1991. Fellow Medieval Acad. Am. Home: 5701 S Kenwood Ave Chicago IL 60637-1718 Office: U Chgo Divinity Sch 1025 E 58th St Chicago IL 60637-1509

MCGINN, SUSAN FRANCES, musician; b. Detroit, May 26, 1961; d. Michael Thomas and Bernice Frances (DePollo) McG. MusB, U. Mich., 1983; MusM, U. Ill., 1985; postgrad., Ind. U., 1985-89. Co-prin. flute L.A. Philharm. Inst., 1985, Nat. Repertory Orch., Keystone, Colo., 1987, Nat. Orchestral Inst., College Park, Md., 1989, Schleswig-Holstein Musik Festival, Salzau, Germany, 1988, 89; prin. flute, flutist wind quintet Canton (Ohio) Symphony Orch., 1989-90, Honolulu Symphony Orch., 1990—; grad. teaching asst. U. Ill., Urbana, 1983-85; assoc. instr. Ind. U., Bloomington, 1986-89; flutist spring wind quinted Chamber Music Hawaii, Honolulu, 1990-92. Scholar U. Ill., 1983-85; fellow Ind. U., 1985-86, scholar, 1986-89. Avocations: mask collecting, making decorative art. Office: Hawaii Symphony Orch Ste V-IB 444 Hobron Ln Honolulu HI 96815

MC GINNES, EDGAR ALLEN, JR., forestry educator; b. Chestown, Md., Feb. 15, 1926; s. Edgar Allen and Emily Frances (Howard) McG.; m. Jean Marie Heidemann, June 23, 1951; children—Jeffrey, Christine, Karen. B.S., Pa. State U., 1950, M.F., 1951; Ph.D., N.Y. State Coll. Forestry, 1955. Research chemist Am. Viscose Corp., 1951-52, research scientist, 1955-60; prof. forestry U. Mo., Columbia, 1960-88; cons. abnormal wood formation. Contbr. articles to profl. jours. Served with AUS, 1944-46. Fellow AAAS (coun. 1970-74), Am. Inst. Chemists, Soc. Am. Foresters, Mo. Acad. Scis. (pres. 1981-82); mem. Am. Chemists Soc., TAPPI, Forest Products Rsch. Soc. (chmn. midwest sect. 1986-87), Internat. Assn. Wood Anatomists, Soc. Wood Sci. and Tech. (pres. 1986-87), Kappa Sigma. Club: Cosmopolitan Internat. (Columbia) (pres. 1971-72). Home: 900 Bourn Ave Columbia MO 65203-1457

MCGINNES, PAUL R., environmental chemist; b. Detroit, Mar. 23, 1946; s. Harold P. and Elizabeth J. (Stubbs) McG.; m. Marilyn Thomas, Dec. 27, 1966 (div. Aug. 1979); children: Christen, John; m. Diane E. Johnson, July 14, 1990. BS, Wheaton (Ill.) Coll., 1968; MS, U. Ill., 1971, PhD, 1974. Registered profl. engr., Fla. Pres. McGinnes Labs., Inc., West Palm Beach, Fla., 1974—. Supr. Soil and Water Conservation Bd., Palm Beach County, Fla., 1990. Mem. Am. Chem. Soc., Fla. Engring. Soc. (Engr. of Yr. 1988). Achievements include patents in therapeutic methods and substances. Office: McGinnes Labs Inc 4168 Westroads Dr West Palm Beach FL 33407-1241

MC GINNESS, WILLIAM GEORGE, III, manufacturing company executive; b. Lock Haven, Pa., Apr. 9, 1948; s. William George and Ruby Jean (Cooper) McG.; children: Scott Robert, Patrick Robert. B.Chemistry, Lock Haven State U., 1970. Prodn. mgr. Am. Color & Chem. Corp., Lock Haven, Pa., 1969-75; lab. mgr. Novamont/Montedison, Florence, Ky., 1976-79; prodn. mgr. Sun Chem., Cin., 1979-80; v.p. tech. services Natmar, Inc., Cin., 1980-83; pres., chief exec. officer Angstrom Techs., Florence, Ky., 1983—; dir. Natmar, Inc., Sperti Drug Products, Inc., Antex Corp. Mem. Am. Chem. Soc., Soc. Profl. Engrs., Am. Assn. Textile Chemists and Colorists, Soc. Mfg. Engrs., Machine Vision Assn., Robotics Internat., AAAS. Republican. Lutheran. Clubs: Bankers (Cin.), Chemists (N.Y.C.). Home: 5323 Country Club Ln Burlington KY 41005-9779 Office: Angstrom Techs Inc Ste 208 1895 Airport Exchange Blvd ste 110 Covington KY 41018-3174

MCGINNIES, ELLIOTT MORSE, psychologist, educator; b. Buffalo, Sept. 19, 1921; s. Elliott Morse and Mabel Christina (Hussong) McG.; m. Bessie Yeh, Jan. 27, 1967; children: Michelle, Lisa, Amy. BA, SUNY-Buffalo, 1943; MA, Brown U., 1944; PhD, Harvard U., 1948. Teaching fellow Harvard U., 1944-47; asst. prof. U. Ala. 1947-52; assoc. prof., then prof. U. Md., 1952-70; prof. emeritus, 1987—; vis. scholar U. Calif., Berkeley 1987-88; Fulbright prof. Nat. Taiwan U. With AUS, 1943. Fellow Am. Psychol. Assn.; mem. Eastern

Psychol. Assn., Psychonomic Soc., Sigma Xi. Author: Social Behavior: A Functional Analysis, 1970, The Reinforcement of Social Behavior, 1971, Attitudes, Conflict and Social Change, 1972, Perspectives on Social Behavior, 1994. Office: The Am Univ Dept of Psychology 4400 Massachusetts Ave NW Washington DC 20016-8001

MC GINNIS, ARTHUR JOSEPH, publisher; b. Paterson, N.J., Apr. 5, 1911; s. Arthur L. and Rose (Seyer) McG.; m. Roselind P. Diskon, May 17, 1939; children: Roselind P. (Mrs. Joseph W. Mullen, Jr.), Carolyn M., Kathleen M. (Mrs. A.A. Stein III), Patricia A., Arthur J. B.A., Fordham U., 1932; M.B.A., Harvard, 1934. Traveling auditor, 1934-35; staff statistician Western Union Telegraph Co., 1935-40; assoc. editor Ry. Age, 1940-44, fin. editor, 1944-46; asst. treas. Simmons-Boardman Pub. Corp., 1946-50; mem. White House press corps, Washington, 1950-58; treas., dir. Simmons-Boardman Pub. Corp., 1950-54, exec. v.p., treas., 1954-58, pres., treas., 1958-72, chmn. exec. com., treas., chief exec. officer, 1972—; pub. Am. Builder mag., 1955-61. Trustee Monmouth Med. Center, Long Branch, N.J., 1956—; chmn. devel. com. Roman Catholic. Clubs: N.Y. Athletic (N.Y.C.), Harvard Business (N.Y.C.), Nat. Arts (N.Y.C.); Deal (N.J.) Golf and Country (pres.), Allenhurst (N.J.) Bathing. Home & Office: 345 Hudson St New York NY 10014-4502

MCGINNIS, ARTHUR JOSEPH, JR., public relations executive; b. Jersey City, N.J., Mar. 12, 1952; s. Arthur Joseph and Roselind (Diskon) McG.; m. Kim Elizabeth Midgarden; children: Kirsten Elizabeth, Ashley Alexandra. BS, Siena Coll., 1975. Mgr. trainee Lebhar-Friedman, N.Y.C., 1975-76; regional sales mgr. Simmons-Boardman Pub. Corp., Chgo., 1976-77; pub. Plant Location Mag., Simmons-Boardman, N.Y.C., 1977-89; v.p. mktg. Railway Div., Simmons-Boardman, N.Y.C., 1978-88; exec. v.p., sec. Simmons-Boardman Pub. Co., N.Y.C., 1987-88; chmn. bd., Simmons-Boardman Pub. Co. N.Y.C., 1991—; pres., pub. Simmons-Boardman Pub. Corp., N.Y.C., 1988—; pres. Simmons-Boardman Books, Omaha, 1989—; chmn. bd., 1992—; bd. dirs. Am. Bus. Press. Home: 35 Chestow Ct Belle Mead NJ 08502 Office: Simmons Boardman Pub Corp 345 Hudson St New York NY 10014-4502

MCGINNIS, CHARLES IRVING, civil engineer; b. Kansas City, Mo., Jan. 31, 1928; s. Paul Sherman and Sidney (Bacon) McG.; m. Shirley Ann Meyer, Nov. 5, 1955; children: Gail B., Ann K., James P. BS, Tex. A&M., 1949; M.Engring., Tex. A & M Coll., 1950; grad., Army Engring. Sch., 1955, Command and Gen. Staff Coll., 1959, Armed Forces Staff Coll., 1962, Army War Coll., 1969. Registered profl. engr., Tex., Mo. Enlisted as pvt. U.S. Army, 1945, advanced through grades to maj. gen., 1976; area engr. Ethiopia and Somali Republic, 1962-65; dist. engr. St. Paul, 1969-71; dir. engring. and constrn. bur. Panama Canal Co., 1971-72, v.p., 1972-74; lt. gov. C.Z., 1972-74; div. engr. southwestern div. C.E., Dallas, 1974-77; dir. civil works Office Chief of Engrs. U.S. Army, Washington, 1977-79; civil engr., 1979—; exec. v.p. Fru-con Corp.; pres. Fruco Engrs., Inc., 1981-87; assoc. dir. Constrn. Industry Inst. U.S. Tex., 1987-93; sr. lectr. civil engring. dept. U. Tex., Austin, 1992—; mem. vis. com., dept. civil engring. M.I.T., 1978-81; mem. Mississippi River Commn., 1975-77, Bd. Engrs. for Rivers and Harbors, 1975-77. Chmn. Combined Fedn. Campaign coordinating com., C.Z., 1972-74; pres. C.Z. coun. Boy Scouts Am., 1973-74; mem. exec. bd. St. Louis area coun., 1983-87, Capitol area coun., 1987-90; mem. com. mgmt. Balboa YMCA, 1973-74; trustee C.Z. United Way, 1972-74. Decorated D.S.M., Legion of Merit with oak leaf cluster, Joint Svcs. Commendation medal, U.S. Army Commendation with oak leaf cluster, Chuong My medal 1st class Vietnam. Fellow ASCE, Soc. Am. Mil. Engrs. (past pres. Twin Cities post and Panama post); mem. NSPE (nmn. water policy task force 1979-81), Assn. U.S. Army, Mil. Order of the World Wars, Tau Beta Pi, Chi Epsilon. Episcopalian. Address: 10006 Sausalito Dr Austin TX 78759-6106 The simple four-part philosophy which has well served three generations of my family requires an uncompromising commitment to honesty in all things, industry, concentration on the job and on personal objectives, and economy of all resources, both natural and man-made.

MC GINNIS, JAMES MICHAEL, physician; b. Columbia, Mo., July 12, 1944; s. Leland Glenn and Lillian Ruth (Mackler) McG.; m. Patricia Anne Gwaltney, Aug. 4, 1978; children—Brian, Katherine. A.B., U. Calif., Berkeley, 1966; M.A., M.D., UCLA, 1971; M.P.P., Harvard U., 1977. House officer in internal medicine Boston City Hosp., 1971-72; internat. med. officer HEW, 1972-74; dir. Office for Asia and Western Pacific, 1974-75; state coordinator smallpox eradication program WHO, India, 1974-75; fellow Harvard Center for Community Health and Med. Care, Boston, 1976-77; cons. to sec. HEW, Washington, 1977; dep. asst. sec. for health and dir. office of disease prevention and health promotion HEW, 1977—; asst. surgeon gen., 1980—; acting dir. office of rsch. integrity, 1992-93; instr. medicine George Washington U. Med. Sch., 1973-75; adj. prof. health policy Duke U., 1979—; chair, sec. task force on smoking and health; chair exec. com. HHS Environ. Health Policy Com.; mem. U.S. Japan Leadership program. Mem. editl. bd. Jour. Med. Edn., 1975-78, Jour. Preventive Medicine, 1987—, Jour. Health Promotion, 1992—; editor-in-chief: Healthy People 2000, Surgeon General's Report on Nutrition and Health, Determining Risks to Health. Served with USPHS, 1972-75, 77—. Recipient Arthur S. Flemming Pub. Svc. award, 1979, USPHS Disting. Svc. medal, 1989, Surgeon Gen.'s Exemplary Svc. medal, 1988, Fed. Profile in Leadership award 1989. Fellow Am. Coll. Epidemiology, Am. Coll. Preventive Medicine. Office: 330 C St SW Washington DC 20201-0001

MCGINNIS, JAMES WESLEY, petroleum company executive; b. Caney, Kans., Oct. 8, 1943; s. James Riley and Reta (Clark) McG.; A.A., Coffeyville Coll., 1963; B.S., Pittsburg U., 1968; children—James Randall, Russell Brent. Analyst/programmer Phillips Petroleum Co., Bartlesville, Okla., 1968-74, mgmt. services cons., 1975-77, dir. projects. info. mgmt. div., exploration and production group, 1978—; tchr. Tulsa Vo-Tech Sch., 1981-82. Mem. Assn. Systems Mgmt. Republican. Clubs: Musicians Assn., Frank Phillips Mens. Lodge: Elks. Home: 4516 SE Barlow Dr Bartlesville OK 74006-6701 Office: 1 MW Bldg Bartlesville OK 74004

MCGINNIS, JOAN ADELL, secondary school educator; b. Erie, Pa., Jan. 20, 1932; d. Roy Hamilton and Sara Zelma (Gorman) Sjöberg; m. Richard H. Edwards, Aug. 6, 1954 (div. 1965); m. George William McGinnis, Dec. 29, 1966 (dec. Apr. 1994). BA, St. Lawrence U., Canton, N.Y., 1953. Cert. tchr., Calif. Spl. proxies Sun Life Assurance Co., Montreal, 1952-53; pvt. sec. Detroit Trust, 1953-54; sec. Meth. Ch., Lancaster, Calif., 1964—; tchr. Sunny Hills High Sch., Fullerton, Calif., 1966—; contr. Mission Viejo (Calif.) Sheet Metal, 1980-81; dept. sec. Fgn. Lang. Dept. Sunny Hills High Sch., 1966-80, dept. chair, 1987-89; internat. baccalaureate examiner in Spanish, 1991—, French, 1992—; advanced placement examiner in Spanish, 1990—. Mem. Am. Assn. Tchrs. Spanish and Portuguese, Modern Classical Lang. Assn. Calif., Fgn. Lang. Assn. Orange County (Exptl. Tchr. of Orange County award 1994), Am. Women's Orgn. Republican. Avocations: languages, music, drama. Home: 26382 Estanciero Dr Mission Viejo CA 92691 Office: Sunny Hills High Sch 1801 W Warburton Way Fullerton CA 92633-2299

MCGINNIS, JOHN OLDHAM, lawyer, educator; b. N.Y.C., Mar. 21, 1957; s. John Patrick and Pauline Ruth (Oldham) McG. BA magna cum laude, Harvard U., 1978, JD magna cum laude, 1983; MA, Oxford U., Eng., 1980. Bar: N.Y. 1984. Law clk. to judge U.S. Ct. Appeals (D.C. cir.), Washington, 1983-84; assoc. Sullivan & Cromwell, N.Y.C., 1984-85; atty./advisor Office Legal Counsel, Dept. Justice, Washington, 1985-87, dep. asst. atty. gen., 1987-91; prof. Benjamin N. Cardozo Sch. Law, N.Y.C., 1991—. Contbr. articles to profl. jours.; editor Harvard Law Rev., 1982-83. Home: 21 E 22nd St New York NY 10010-5332 Office: Cardozo Law Sch 55 5th Ave New York NY 10003-4301

MCGINNIS, MARCY ANN, television news executive producer; b. Long Branch, N.J., Apr. 9, 1950; d. Joseph Arthur and Ruth (Thomas) McG. AAS, Marymount U., 1970. Exec. sec. news Sta. CBS News, N.Y.C., 1970-71; adminstrv. asst. Sta. CBS TV, N.Y.C., 1971-73, asst. producer, 1973-76, assoc. producer, 1976-82, producer, 1982-85, sr. producer, 1985-89, exec. producer, 1989-92; dep. bur. chief London der. CBS NEWSNET Europe, 1992-95, TV news exec. prodr., v.p. and London bur. chief, 1995—. Mem. NATAS, NAFE, TV and Radio Working Press Assn. Roman

Catholic. Home: 14 Southwell Gardens # 6, London SW7 4RL, England Office: CBS News, 68 Knightsbridge, London SW1X 7LL, England

MCGINNIS, ROBERT CAMPBELL, lawyer; b. Dallas, Jan. 1, 1918; s. Edward Karl and Helen Louise (Campbell) McG.; m. Ethel Clift, May 14, 1945; children: Mary, Campbell, John, Robert, Michael. AB, U. Tex., 1938; LLB, Yale U., 1941. Bar: Tex. 1941, Ohio 1942, U.S. Dist. Ct. (no. dist.) Tex. 1948, U.S. Dist. Ct. (we. dist.) Tex. 1950. Assoc. Squires, Sanders & Dempsey, Cleve., 1941-42, Carrington, Gowan, Dallas, 1946-49; ptnr. McGinnis, Lochridge & Kilgore and predecessor firm Powell, Wirtz & Rauhut, Austin, Tex., 1950-95; chmn. Tex. Com. Jud. Ethics, 1972-78; bd. dirs. Republic Bank, Austin. Served to lt. USNR, 1942-46, PTO. Fellow Am. Bar Found.; mem. ABA, Tex. Bar Assn., U.S. Lawn Tennis Assn. (hon. life). Presbyterian. Home: 2708 Scenic Dr Austin TX 78703-1039 Office: McGinnis Lochridge & Kilgore 919 Congress Ave Austin TX 78701-2421 Died Feb. 22, 1995.

MCGINNIS, ROBERT E., lawyer; b. Caldwell, Ohio, May 1, 1931; s. Earl Peregoy and Mary Ethel (Richner) McG.; m. Jane Ann Lindenmeyer, Sept. 12, 1953; children: Sharon Ann, David E. BA, Ohio Wesleyan U., 1952; JD, Ohio State U., 1954. Bar: Ohio 1954, Calif. 1956. Asst. judge advocate USAF, 1954-56; sr. ptnr. Luce, Forward, Hamilton & Scripps, San Diego, 1956—. Trustee Wesley Meth. Ch., San Diego, Fine Arts Soc., First Meth. Ch., La Mesa, Calif.; counsel Kensington Community Ch.; dir. San Diego Opera Assn., corp. sec., v.p. Republican. Mem. United Ch. Christ. Office: Luce Forward Hamilton & Scripps 600 W Broadway Ste 2600 San Diego CA 92101-3711

MCGINNIS, W. PATRICK, diversified company executive. V.p. Ralston Purina Co., St. Louis, pres. branded foods group. Office: Ralston Purina Co Checkerboard Sq Saint Louis MO 63164

MC GINNISS, JOE, writer; b. N.Y.C., Dec. 9, 1942; s. Joseph Aloysius and Mary (Leonard) McG.; m. Christine Cook, Sept. 25, 1965 (div.); children: Christine, Suzanne, Joe; m. Nancy Doherty, Nov. 20, 1976; children: Matthew, James. BS, Holy Cross Coll., 1964. Reporter Port Chester (N.Y.) Daily Item, 1964, Worcester (Mass.) Telegram, 1965, Phila. Bull., 1966, Phila. Inquirer, 1967-68. Author: The Selling of the President, 1968, The Dream Team, 1972, Heroes, 1976, Going to Extremes, 1980, Fatal Vision, 1983, Blind Faith, 1989, Cruel Doubt, 1991, The Last Brother, 1993. Office: care Morton L Janklow Assocs 598 Madison Ave New York NY 10022-1614

MCGINNITY, MAUREEN ANNELL, lawyer; b. Monroe, Wis., Apr. 6, 1956; d. James Arthur and Marie Beatrice (Novak) McG.; m. Richard W. Ziervogel, July 17, 1982; 1 child, Brigitte Kathleen. BS, U. Wis., Milw., 1977; JD, U. Wis., 1982. Bar: Wis. 1982, U.S. Dist. Ct. (ea. and we. dists.) Wis. 1982, U.S. Ct. Appeals (7th cir.) 1989, U.S. Supreme Ct. 1991, U.S. Ct. Appeals (1st cir.) 1991. Assoc. Foley & Lardner, Milw., 1982-91, ptnr., 1991—; mem. Wis. Supreme Ct. Planning and Policy Adv. Com., Madison, 1991-94; adv. bd. Domestic Violence Legal Clinic, Milw., 1991—. Treas. Waukesha (Wis.) County Emergency Food Pantry, 1988-94; trustee Boys & Girls Club Greater Milw., 1991—; bd. dirs. Task Force on Battered Women & Children, Inc., 1994—. Recipient Outstanding Svc. award Legal Action Wis., Milw., 1984, 93 Outstanding Fundraising awards Boys & Girls Club Greater Milw., 1987-92, Cert. Recognition, Common Coun. Task Force on Sexual Assault & Domestic Violence, Milw., 1991, Cert. Appreciation, Wis. Equal Justice Task Force, Madison, 1991. Mem. ABA, State Bar Wis. (bd. govs. 1992—, Pro Bono award 1990, chair 1993-94), Assn. for Women Lawyers (various offices, pres. 1992-93), Milw. Young Lawyers Assn. (bd. dirs. 1987-92, pres. 1990-91, Pres.' award 1991), Profl. Dimensions. Office: Foley & Lardner 777 E Wisconsin Ave Milwaukee WI 53202-5302

MCGINTY, JOHN, marketing consultant; b. Neosho, Mo., Dec. 5, 1911; s. Abner Crawford and Blanche (Hale) McG.; m. Glenella Florence Davison, July 15, 1934; children: Marilyn McGinty Stewart, Marjorie McGinty Kilpatrick, Maureen, John Edward, Melanie McGinty Tate, Melinda. BCS, Drake U., 1932; LLB, City Coll. Law, St. Louis, 1936; DHL (hon.), Drury Coll., 1988. Bar: Mo. bar 1936. Mgr. closing div. Fed. Land Bank of St. Louis, 1933-44; with Ralston Purina Co., St. Louis, 1944-73; editor sales publs., mgr. publs., sales promotion mgr. Ralston Purina Co., 1944-59, v.p. and dir. sales promotion, 1959-63, v.p., dir. advt. and sales promotion, 1963-69, v.p., dir. mktg. services, 1969-73; meeting cons. for firms including Ralston Purina, DeLaval Separator Co., Monsanto Co., Babcock Industries Inc., Mktg. Intercontinental, Hudson Foods, Inc., 1973—; chmn. bd. Christian Bd. Publs., St. Louis, 1955-84. Author: How to Raise the Level of Giving in Your Church, 1978. Trustee Disciples Div. House, U. Chgo., Drake U., 1966-74; chmn. bd. trustees Drury Coll., 1970-73, life trustee. Home: 12 Country Club Ter Saint Louis MO 63122-4673

MCGINTY, JOHN B., orthopaedic surgeon, educator; b. Boston, Nov. 19, 1930; s. Katherine V. Daley; m. Beth A. Dignan, June 6, 1956 (div. June 1984); children: Kathleen C., Ellen B., John B. Jr.; m. Rosemarie M. Morwessel, Nov. 23, 1985; 1 child, Ryan D. AB, Harvard U., 1952; MD, Tufts U., 1956. Diplomate Am. Bd. Orthopaedic Surgery. Surg. resident Yale-New Haven Hosp., 1956-58; orthopaedic resident Harvard Program, Boston, 1958-62; orthopaedic surgeon U.S. Army Hosp., Frankfurt, Fed. Republic Germany, 1962-64; chief of orthopaedics U.S. Army Hosp., Valley Forge, Pa., 1964-66; pvt. practice Newton, Mass., 1966-84; chief/orthopaedic surgery Newton Wellesley Hosp., 1975-84; prof., chmn. dept. orthopaedic surgery Med. U. S.C., Charleston, 1984—; lectr. orthopaedic surgery Harvard U., Boston, 1966-84; clin. prof. orthopaedic surgery Tufts U., Boston, 1974-84. Editor: Arthroscopic Surg. Update, 1986, Operative Arthroscopy, 1991; contbr. articles to profl. jours. Fellow Am. Acad. Orthopaedic Surgeons; mem. Am. Orthopaedic Assn., Assn. of Bone and Joint Surgeons, Internat. Soc. Orthopaedic Surgery & Traumatology, Can. Orthopaedic Assn., Country Club of Charleston, Alpha Omega Alpha. Avocations: golf, boating, fishing.

MC GINTY, JOHN MILTON, architect; b. Houston, Apr. 24, 1935; s. Milton Bowles and Ruth Louise (Dreaper) McG.; m. Juanita Jones, May 4, 1957; children: Christopher Harold, Jacqueline Ruth McGinty Carlson. B.S., Rice U., 1957; M.F.A., Princeton U., 1961. With archtl. firm Barnes, Landes & Goodman, Austin, Tex., 1957-58, Ingram & Harris, Beaumont, Tex., 1958-59; prin. McGinty Partnership, Architects, Inc., Houston, 1961-89, City Assos., Inc., 1979-91, Bovay-McGinty, Inc., engrs. & architects, Houston, 1989-91; co-owner Am. Constrn. Investigations Inc., Houston, 1991—; instr. archtl. design U. Houston, 1965-67; White House fellow, asst. to Sec. of Interior, 1967-68; vis. prof. architecture Rice U., 1969-70. Named Disting. Alumni, Rice U., 1986. Fellow AIA (mem. U.S. delegation to USSR 1972, pres. Houston chpt. 1973, nat. pres. 1977). Home: 3614 Montrose Blvd 607 Parc IV Houston TX 77006 Office: Am Constrn Investigations Inc 602 Sawyer St Fl 2 Houston TX 77007-7513

MCGINTY, MICHAEL DENNIS, air force officer; b. Waukegan, Ill., Sept. 20, 1942; s. Roy Leonard and Betty Jane (Anderson) McG.; m. Karen Lee Dibble, July 2, 1965; children: Shannon, Timothy. BA in Math., U. Minn., 1964; MA in Pub. Adminstrn., Shippensburg U., 1983. Commd. 2d lt. USAF, 1965, advanced through grades to maj. gen., 1992; chief of standarization and evaluation 3d Tactical Fighter Wing, Clark Air Base, The Philippines, 1975-76; ops. officer 9th Tactical Fighter Squadron, Holloman AFB, N.Mex., 1976-78; grad. student Air Command and Staff Coll., Maxwell AFB, Ala., 1979; chief of officer assignments Hdqrs. Tactical Air Command, Langley AFB, Va., 1979-82; grad. student U.S. Army War Coll., Carlisle, Pa., 1983; dep. comdr. for ops. 355th Tactical Tng. Wing, Davis-Monthan AFB, Ariz., 1983-85; chief cols. group Air Force Mil. Pers. Ctr., Randolph AFB, Tex., 1985-87; vice comdr. 10th Tactical Fighter Wing, RAF Alconbury, U.K., 1987-88, comdr., 1988-90; dep. chief of staff for plans and requirements Air Tng. Command, Randolph AFB, 1990; vice comdr. Air Force Mil. Pers. Ctr., Randolph AFB, 1990-92, comdr., 1992-94; dir. pers. programs, edn. and tng. USAF The Pentagon, Washington, 1994—. Author: Low Altitude Training for F-4 Aircrews, 1979, Theory Z Management: Can It Be Used Effectively in the Air Force, 1983. Decorated Disting. Svc. medal, Legion of Merit (2), DFC (2), Meritorious Svc. medal (4), Air medal (10). Mem. Air Force Assn., Ret. Officers' Assn., Order of Daedalians (flight capt. Tucson club 1984-85), Pi Sigma Alpha. Republican. Roman Catholic. Avocations: running, hiking, camping, out-

door activities. Home: 75 Westover Ave SW Washington DC 20336-5409 Office: Hg USAF/DPP 1040 Air Force Pentagon Washington DC 20030

MCGINTY, MILTON BRADFORD, architect, real estate development executive; b. Houston, July 6, 1946; s. Milton Bowles and Ruth Louise (Dreaper) McG.; m. Margaret Louise O'Donnel, Dec. 11, 1967; 1 child, Daniel Milton. B.A., William Marsh Rice U., Houston, 1970, B.Arch., 1973; M.B.A., Fla. Atlantic U., 1980. Registered architect, Tex.; lic. real estate broker, Tex. Draftsman Carden L. Jenkins, Engr., Houston, 1967-70; job capt. Welton Becket & Assocs., Houston, 1970-74; project architect The McGinty Partnership Architects, Inc., Houston, 1974-76, v.p., 1976-81, dir., 1976-90; pres., founder City Assocs., Inc., Houston, 1981, also bd. dirs.; chmn., CEO, bd. dirs. McGinty Corp. Group, Houston; vis. seminar lectr. Am. Inst. Landscapes Architects, 1981. Archtl. works include: Hyatt-Regency Hotel, New Orleans, 1972, Meml. Central, Houston, 1979, 5300 Meml. Bldg., Houston, 1982. Bd. dirs. Rice Design Alliance, Houston, 1979-81. Mem. AIA, Nat. Assn. Realtors, Tex. Soc. Architects, Tex. Soc. Realtors, Houston Philos. Soc. (exec. com. 1986-87, 89-90), Kiwanis (sec. Houston 1983-85, sec. div. 3 Tex.-Okla. dist. 1985, bd. dirs. 1985-89, Disting. Club sec. 1983-85), Shriners, Masons. Episcopalian. Avocation: photography. Office: City Assocs Inc Ste 200 602 Sawyer St Houston TX 77007-7510

MCGINTY, THOMAS EDWARD, management consultant; b. Holyoke, Mass., Aug. 20, 1929; s. Patrick John and Alice May (Hill) McG.; m. June Theresa Coutu, Jan. 27, 1951; children: Thomas, Michael, Matthew. B.S. in Econs. and Commerce, U. Vt., 1951; M.B.A., NYU, 1957. Chartered fin. analyst. Sr. fin. analyst Moody's Investor Service, 1955-59, Model, Roland and Stone, N.Y.C., 1959-62; with Cleve.-Cliffs Iron Co., 1962-83, v.p. fin., 1971-75, sr. v.p., 1975-83; pres. Belvoir Cons., Inc., 1983—; chmn. bd. Ormet Corp., 1986-89; bd. dirs. Horsburgh & Scott Co., Park Ohio Industries. Author: Project Organization and Finance, 1981. Bd. advisers Notre Dame Coll. Served with U.S. Army, 1951-55, Korea. Decorated Bronze Star. Mem. Assn. Investment Mgmt. and Rsch., Cleve. Skating Club, Wilderness Country Club (Naples, Fla.). Roman Catholic. Home: 2705 Belvoir Blvd Cleveland OH 44122-1925 Office: Belvoir Cons 23200 Chagrin Blvd Ste 325 Cleveland OH 44122

MCGIRR, DAVID WILLIAM JOHN, investment banker; b. Glasgow, Scotland, May 19, 1954; came to U.S., 1991; s. Edward McCombie and Diane Curzon (Woods) McG.; m. Margaret Joslin Richardson, May 9, 1981; children: William David, Katherine Joslin, Lucy Ann, Elizabeth Margaret. BSc with honors, U. Glasgow, 1976; MBA, U. Pa., 1978. Assoc. S.G. Warburg & Co. Ltd., London, 1978-80, exec. dir., 1981-86; mng. dir. S.G. Warburg & Co. Inc., N.Y.C., 1991—, CFO, 1992—; assoc. Warburg Paribas Becker Inc., N.Y.C., 1980-81; exec. dir. S.G. Warburg Securities, London, 1986-87; CEO S.G. Warburg Securities (Can.) Ltd., Toronto, Ont., Can., 1987-89; COO, CFO Bunting Warburg Inc., Toronto, 1989-91; mem. selection com. Thouron Scholarship. Thouron scholar, 1976-78. Mem. Nat. Club (Can.). Avocations: collecting cars, motor racing, family. Office: S G Warburg & Co Inc 277 Park Ave New York NY 10172

MCGIVERIN, ARTHUR A., state supreme court justice; b. Iowa City, Iowa, Nov. 10, 1928; s. Joseph J. and Mary B. McG.; m. Mary Joan McGiverin, Apr. 20, 1951; children: Teresa, Thomas, Bruce, Nancy. BSC with high honors, U. Iowa, 1951, JD, 1956. Bar: Iowa 1956. Pvt. practice law Ottumwa, Iowa, 1956; alt. mcpl. judge Ottumwa, 1960-65; judge Iowa Dist. Ct. 8th Jud. Dist., 1965-78; assoc. justice Iowa Supreme Ct., Des Moines, 1978-87, chief justice, 1987—. Mem. Iowa Supreme Ct. Commn. on Continuing Legal Edn., 1975. Served to 1st lt. U.S. Army, 1946-48, 51-53. Mem. Iowa State Bar Assn., Am. Law Inst. Roman Catholic. Avocation: golf. Office: Iowa Supreme Ct State Capital Bldg Des Moines IA 50319

MCGIVERIN, DONALD SCOTT, retail company executive; b. Calgary, Alta., Can., Apr. 4, 1924; s. Alfred Chester and Ella (Scott) McG.; m. Margaret-Ann Weld, Sept. 9, 1950 (dec. Nov. 1968); children—Mary Edith, Richard Weld (dec.). B.Comm., U. Man., 1945; M.B.A., Ohio State U., 1946. Mng. dir. retail stores Hudson's Bay Co., Winnipeg, Man., Can., 1969-72, pres., dir., 1972-85, gov., dir., 1982—; bd. dirs. Mfrs. Life Ins. Co., Mfrs. Capital Corp., DuPont Can. Ltd., Noranda Inc. Bd. govs. Wellesley Hosp. Mem. Rosedale Golf Club, Granite Club, York Club, Toronto Club, LyFord Cay Club (Naussau, Bahamas), Loxahatchee Club (Jupiter, Fla.), Phi Kappa Pi, Beta Gamma Sigma. Home: 44 Charles St W, Toronto, ON Canada M4Y 1R8 Office: Hudsons Bay Co, 401 Bay St, Toronto, ON Canada M5H 2Y4

MCGIVERN, ARTHUR J., corporate lawyer, food products company executive; b. Chgo., 1947. BS, Northwestern U., 1969, JD, 1974. Now v.p., assoc. gen. counsel, sec. Beatrice Cos., Inc., Chgo.; bd. dirs. Mathers Fund, Inc. Office: Kemper Securities Holdings 31 Flr 77 W Wacker Dr Fl 31 Chicago IL 60601-1629

MC GLAMERY, MARSHAL DEAN, agronomy, weed science educator; b. Mooreland, Okla., July 29, 1932; s. Walter Gaiford and Bernice (Gardner) McG.; m. Marilyn Hudson, June 2, 1957; children—Paul, Steve. B.S., Okla. State U., 1956, M.S., 1958; Ph.D., U. Ill., 1965. Instr. Panhandle A. and M. Coll., 1958-60; agronomist Agribus. Co., Lawrence, Kans., 1960-61; teaching asst. U. Ill., 1961-63, research fellow, 1963-65, asst. prof. weed sci., 1965-70, asso. prof., 1970-76, prof., 1976—; extension agronomist, 1965—. Served with U.S. Army, 1953-55. NSF fellow, 1963. Mem. Am. Soc. Agronomy, Weed Sci. Soc. Am., Council Agr. and Tech. Baptist. Home: 35 Lange Ave Savoy IL 61874-9705 Office: 1102 S Goodwin Ave Urbana IL 61801-4709

MCGLAMERY, THORNTON PATRICK, map librarian; b. Washington, Nov. 7, 1947; s. Thornton Blair and Mary Crawford (Duty) McG.; m. Lenore Grunko, Aug. 17, 1974; children: Zoë, John Gabriel. BA in Anthropology, U. Maine, 1974; MLS, Cath. U. Am., 1980. Libr. technician Libr. of Congress, Washington, 1975-80; map libr. Homer Babbidge Libr. U. Conn., Storrs, 1980—. With U.S. Army, 1967-70, Vietnam. Mem. ALA (chair map and geography roundtable 1992-93), Libr. and Tech. Info. Assn. (co-chair 1993-94), N.E. Map Orgn. (chair 1988-89). Home: 95 Hanks Hills Rd Storrs CT 06268 Office: U Conn Map Libr Homer Babbidge Libr Storrs CT 06269-1005

MCGLAMRY, MAX REGINALD, lawyer; b. Wilcox County, Ga., Sept. 12, 1928; s. Edgar Lee and Allie Bea (Faircloth) McG.; m. Jean Louise Hilyer, Dec. 28, 1950; children: Sharon Kay McGlamry Hendrix, Michael Lee. BS, Auburn U., 1948; LLB cum laude, Mercer U., 1952, JD cum laude, 1952. Bar: Ga. 1953, U.S. Dist. Ct. (mid. dist.) Ga. 1954, U.S. Dist. Ct. (no. dist.) Calif. 1988, U.S. Dist. Ct. (no. dist.) Ga. 1989, U.S. Ct. Appeals (5th cir.) 1964, U.S. Ct. Appeals (11th cir.) 1981, U.S. Ct. Appeals (4th cir.) 1985, U.S. Supreme Ct. 1972. Pvt. practice Columbus, Ga., 1953-64; from ptnr. to officer Swift, Pease, Davidson & Chapman (name changed to Page, Scrantom, Harris, McGlamry, & Chapman, P.C.), Columbus, 1964-85; ptnr. Pope, Kellogg, McGlamry, Kilpatrick & Morrison, Columbus, 1985-90, Pope, McGlamry, Kilpatrick & Morrison, Columbus, 1990—. Mem. exec. com. Muscogee County Dem. Orgn., Columbus, 1956-60; bd. dirs. Columbus Jr. C. of C. With USN, 1948-49. Am. Coll. Trust & Estate Counsel fellow, 1973, Ga. Bar Found. Inc. fellow, 1983. Mem. ABA, ATLA, State Bar Ga., Ga. Trial Lawyers Assn., Columbus Lawyers Club (pres. 1964-65), Lions (Columbus chpt. pres. 1967-68), Chattahoochee River Club, Green Island Country Club, Phi Kappa Phi, Alpha Epsilon Delta, Phi Alpha Delta, Pi Kappa Alpha. Democrat. Methodist. Avocations: golf, fishing. Home: 2937 Lynda Ln Columbus GA 31906 Office: Pope McGlamry Kilpatrick & Morrison PO Box 2128 318 11th St 2nd Fl Columbus GA 31902

MCGLASSON, JAMES DEAN, publishing executive; b. Roswell, N.Mex., Mar. 22, 1944; s. Dean A. and Nadean (McPherson) McG.; m. Christine Gail Dawson, Feb. 17, 1966 (div. Jan. 1980); m. Linda Renee Horn, Sept. 1, 1981; children: Kimberly Ann, Patrick Dean. Student, Mira Costa Coll. Dir. advt. Daily Tribune, Greeley, Colo., 1977-81; v.p. sales and mktg. Tahoe Tribune, South Lake Tahoe, Calif., 1981-82; v.p., pub. Press-Courier Pub. Co., Vista, Calif., 1982-85; v.p., gen. mgr. Newhall (Calif.) Signal, 1985—; pres. Newhall (Calif.) Printing, 1985—. Bd. dirs. Boys Club of Vista, 1983—; bd. dirs. YMCA, Vista, 1984-85. Served with USN, 1966-68.

Mem. Calif. Newspaper Advt. Execs. Assn., Calif. Newspaper Pubs. Assn. Club: Civitan (Vista). Lodges: Rotary, Masons. Home: PO Box 4815 Las Vegas NV 89127-0815 Office: Newhall Signal/Newhall Printing 24000 Creekside Rd PO Box 877 Valencia CA 91355

MCGLAUCHLIN, TOM, artist; b. Turtle, Wis., Sept. 14, 1934; s. Charles Orion and Frances Lenore (Cadman) McG.; m. Patricia Ann Smith, Aug. 5, 1961; children: Christopher, Jennifer (dec.), Patrick (dec.). BS in Art, U. Wis., 1959, MS in Art, 1960; studied pottery with James McKinnell, 1962. Instr. dept. art and art edn. U. Wis., Madison, 1960-61; instr. art dept. Cornell Coll., Mt. Vernon, Iowa, 1961-64, asst. prof. art dept., 1964-68; assoc. prof., chmn. art dept Cornell Coll., Mt. Vernon, N.Y., 1968-71; instr. Toledo Mus. Art, 1971-82, prof., dir. glass program, 1982-84. One-man exhbns. include Habatat Gallery, Dearborn, Mich., 1979, Glass Art Gallery, Toronto, 1981, 85, Glass Gallery, Bethesda, Md., 1981, 85, 87, 91, Heller Gallery, N.Y.C., 1983, B.Z. Wagman Gallery, St. Louis, 1983, Running Ridge Gallery, Santa Fe, 1990; selected group exhbns. include Toledo Mus. Art, 1972, 88, Glasmuseum Frauenau, Franenau, Germany, 1977, Habatat Gallery, 1980, 84, The Hand and the Spirit Gallery, Scottsdale, Ariz., 1980, Gallery of Contemporary Crafts, Detroit, 1980, The Naples (Fla.) Art Gallery, 1981, The Craftsman's Gallery, Scarsdale, N.Y., 1981, 84, The Nat. Mus. Modern Art, Kyoto and Tokyo, 1981, Perception Gallery, Houston, 1985, The AirLoft Gallery, Honolulu, 1986, The Corning (N.Y.) Mus. Glass, 1987; selected competitive exhbns. include Everson Mus. Art, Syracuse, N.Y., 1961, 62, Mus. Contemporary Crafts, N.Y.C., 1962, Corning Glass Mus., Met. Mus. Art, N.Y.C., Victoria and Albert Mus., London, Musee Ars Decoratif, Paris; public collections include Toledo Mus. Art, The Smithsonian Collection, Washington, Portland (Oreg.) Art Mus., New Orleans Mus. Art, Mus. Contemporary Crafts, Musee des arts decoratifs de la Ville de Lausanne, Switzerland, Minn. Mus. Art, St. Paul, Kunstmuseum, Dusseldorf, Germany, Corning Glass Mus. Grantee Associated Colls. Midwest, 1966-67; recipient First Jury award Toledo Glass Nat. II, 1968. Mem. Am. Crafts Coun., Internat. Sculpture Soc., Ohio Designer-Craftsmen, Glass Art Soc. Office: The Glass Studio 1940 W Central Ave Toledo OH 43606-3944

MCGLAUGHLIN, THOMAS HOWARD, publisher, retired naval officer; b. Cin., Jan. 12, 1928; s. George Godden and Cordelia (Herrlinger) McG.; m. Moana Maharam-Stone, Jan. 4, 1984. BS in Elec. Engring., U.S. Naval Acad., 1950. Lic. master mariner. Commd. ensign U.S. Navy, 1950, advanced through grades to capt., 1970; White House aide to Pres. John F. Kennedy, Washington, 1960-63; exec. officer USS Prichett, Long Beach, Calif., 1963-65; comdg. officer USS Maddox, Long Beach, 1965-67; exec. officer USS Boston, Boston, 1967-70; chief naval ops. Comdr.-in-Chief, Pacific, Honolulu, 1970-74; chief of staff Mil. Sealift Command, N.Y.C., 1974-79; ret. U.S. Navy, 1979; pres. Falmouth Press, Honolulu, 1983—; marine surveyor R.W. Dickieson Internat., Inc., Honolulu, 1982—; master M.V. Rella Mae, Honolulu, 1981-90, Royal Taipan, Cebu, Philippines, 1990. Hon. police chief Boston Police Dept., 1969. Decorated Bronze Star; recipient medal for Outstanding Svc., Am. Legion, Pitts., 1942. Mem. Nat. Def. Transp. Assn., VFW (life), U.S. Naval Acad. Alumni Assn. (life), The Retired Officers Assn. Republican. Presbyterian. Avocations: flying, scuba diving. Home: 581 Kamoku St The Royal Iolani # 1702 Honolulu HI 96826 Office: RW Dickieson Internat Inc 46-208 Kahuhipa St Kaneohe HI 96744-3944

MCGLINCHEY, ALEXANDER HERBERT, federal judge; b. Ft. Worth, Aug. 11, 1930; s. Alexander H. and Hilda (Cornelison) McG.; m. Nelda L. Anderson, Dec. 28, 1961; children: Alexander Harold, Finlay Parnell, Zan Edward, Patrick Jonathan Andrew. BA, Tex. Christian U., 1951; postgrad, Georgetown U., 1951-52; JD, So. Meth. U., 1954, LLM, 1965. Bar: Tex. 1954, U.S. Supreme Ct. 1975, U.S. Dist. Ct. (no. dist.) Tex. Trust administr. 1st Nat. Bank, Ft. Worth, 1958-60; ptnr. Pepper, Markward & McGlinchey, Ft. Worth, 1961-65; pvt. practice Ft. Worth, 1965-66; asst. U.S. Atty., criminal chief U.S. Atty.'s Office, Ft. Worth, 1966-75; judge U.S. Magistrate, Ft. Worth, 1975—. Lt. (j.g.) USNR, 1954-57. Mem. State Bar Tex., Tarrant County Bar Assn. Office: US Dist Ct 520 US Courthouse 501 W 10th St Fort Worth TX 76102-3637

MCGLINCHEY, JOSEPH DENNIS, retail corporation executive; b. Lowell, Mass., Mar. 14, 1938; s. Patrick Joseph and Grace E. (Copley) McG.; m. Joan Fitzgerald, Sept. 12, 1964; children: Joseph II, Mark, Christopher, David. BA in Acctg., Bentley Coll., 1965; MBA, Babson Coll., 1971. Internal auditor The Stop and Shop Cos., Inc., Boston, 1962-65, dir. fin. planning and control, 1973-74, corp. controller, 1974-77, v.p., corp. controller, 1977-83, v.p. fin., chief acctg. officer, 1983-86, sr. v.p., chief fin. officer, 1986—; controller Gilchrist Co., Boston, 1969-72; mem. adv. bd. New Eng. region Arkwright Mus. Ins. Co., Norwalk, Conn., 1988-92. Bd. overseers, mem. fin. com. Harvard Community Health Plan, Brookline, Mass., 1985-91; treas. St. Mary's Parish, Randolph, Mass.; mem. gen. bd. Greater Boston YMCA, 1993—. With U.S. Army. Roman Catholic. Home: 360 Beacon St Boston MA 02116 Office: Stop & Shop Cos Inc 1 Quincy Center Plz Quincy MA 02169

MCGLINN, FRANK CRESSON POTTS, lawyer; b. Phila., Nov. 19, 1914; s. John Alexander and Emma Frances (Potts) McG.; m. Louise Cabeen Lea, Sept. 9, 1942; children: Marion McGlinn Lockwood, Louise McGlinn Preston, Alice McGlinn Fetter, Ann. AB, U. N.C., 1937; JD, U. Pa., 1940; LLD (hon.), Villanova U., 1970. Assoc. Pepper, Hamilton & Scheetz, Phila., 1945-53; dir. Rep. Fin. Com. of Pa., Phila., 1945-53; v.p., asst. to pres. Al Paul Lefton Co. Advt., Phila., 1953-57; exec. v.p. Fidelity Bank, Phila., 1957-78; sr. v.p. Western Savs. Bank, Phila., 1978-82; exec. v.p. Barra Found., Wyndmoor, Pa., 1982-83; pres. McGlinn Assocs., Haverford, Pa., 1983—; dir. Rittenhouse Trust Co., Phila., 1984—; cons. William Penn Found., 1978-82, Barra Found., 1983-85. Trustee, bd. dirs. Free Library Phila., 1948-89; trustee Temple U., Phila., 1955-73, Hist. Soc. Pa., 1978-85; mem. Pa. Coun. on the Arts, 1964-71, 79-87; mem. coun. mgrs. Archdiocese of Phila., 1970-89; drive chmn. ARC, 1949; chmn. Cancer Crusade, 1954, Cath. Charities Appeal, 1966; chmn. Young Rep. Club Pa., 1949-51, vice chmn., 1951; chmn. Rep. Nat. Fin. Com., 1963-65, mem. exec. com., 1965-77; alt. del. Rep. Nat. Conv., 1940, 52, del., 1964, 68, 72, 76; chmn. NCCJ, Phila., 1961-66, hon. chmn., 1966-95; chmn. World Affairs Coun., Phila., 1966-68, mem. adv. bd., 1968—; trustee William Penn Found., Phila., 1971-78; bd. dirs. Walnut St. Theatre, Phila., 1969—, pres., 1977-81; bd. dirs. Maritime Mus., Phila., 1985-90, Actors Fund Am., 1987—; chmn. adv. bd. Peoples Light and Theatre Co.; mem. adv. bd. Goodspeed Opera Co. Lt. USNR, 1942-46. Decorated Purple Heart; knight comdr. Equestrian Order of St. Gregory the Great; recipient Humanitarian award NCCJ, 1967. Mem. Phila. Bar Assn., Merion Cricket Club, Knights of Malta. Republican. Roman Catholic. Avocations: theater, fishing. Home: 729 Millbrook Ln Haverford PA 19041-1210 *Peace-understanding-tolerance in the world can only be achieved through complete freedom of expression and the opportunity to freely question all such expressions. To work toward such a goal is the first step toward one's own success and a better world.*

MC GLOTHLIN, JAMES HARRISON, lawyer; b. Louisville, May 31, 1910; s. William Joseph and May Belle (Williams) McG.; m. Patricia Charlotte Dowd, Dec. 31, 1944; children: Susan Louise Detchon, Patricia Anne Stewart, Kathryn Holly. B.A. summa cum laude, Furman U., 1929; M.A., U. Va., 1930; J.D. magna cum laude, Harvard, 1936. Bar: D.C. 1937, N.Y. 1939, U.S. Supreme Ct. 1946. Tchr. Tech. High Sch., Atlanta, 1930-33; law clk. Judge H.M. Stephens, 1936-37; practice in Washington, 1940—; assoc. Cravath, Swaine & Moore, N.Y.C., 1937-40; assoc. Covington & Burling, 1940-50, partner, 1950-78, sr. ptnr., 1979—; prof. Cath. U. Law Sch., 1947-49; v.p. law So. Ry. Co., 1967-70, exec. v.p. law and fin., 1970-75, cons. to CEO, 1975-79; mem. financial adv. panel Nat. Rail Passenger Transp. Corp., 1971-76. Contbr. articles to legal jours. Mem. adv. council Furman U. Served with AUS, 1941-42; to lt. comdr. USNR, 1942-46. Mem. ABA (anti-trust com., P.U. sect.), D.C. Bar Assn., Am. Arbitration Assn., Met. Club, Chevy Chase (Md.) Club, Sea Island Golf Club (Ga.), Madison Beach Club (Conn.), Phi Gamma Delta. Democrat. Baptist. Home: 247 W 27th St Sea Island GA 31561 also: 14 Cambridge Dr Madison CT 06443-3016 Office: 1201 Pennsylvania Ave PO Box 7566 NW Washington DC 20044

MCGLOTHLIN, RAY, JR., petroleum company executive. Chmn. E-Z Serve Inc., Abilene, Tex., also bd. dirs. Office: E-Z Serve Inc Drawer 612007 Dallas TX 75261-2007

MCGLOTTEN, ROBERT MILLER, labor union official; b. Phila., Apr. 12, 1938; s. Samuel and Sadie (Gray) McGlotten; m. Cheryl Goode McGlotten; children: Karen, Robin, Darlene. BS in Indsl. Relations, St. Joseph's U., 1961; grad., U. Pa., 1965. With AFL-CIO, Washington, 1967-73, 1974—; staff rep. Dept. Civil Rights, 1967-70, dir. Human Resources Devel. Inst., 1970-72, legis. rep. Dept. Legislation, 1974-80, asst. dir. dept., 1980-86, dir. dept., 1986—; asst. to sec. U.S. Dept. Labor, Washington, 1973-74; v.p. Negro Trade Union Council, Phila., 1962-68; pres. Am. League of Lobbyists, Washington, 1984; bd. dirs. Ctr. for Ambulatory Surgery Inc., 1981—. Bd. dirs. A.P. Randolph Inst., 1976—, Joint Ctr. Polit. and Econ. Studies, 1992; former trustee Benedict Coll., 1988. Served to sgt. U.S. Army, 1957-59. Recipient William Dawson award Congl. Black Caucus, Washington, 1981, A. Philip Randolph Achievement award, San Francisco, 1987. Office: AFL-CIO Dept Legis 815 16th St NW Rm 309 Washington DC 20006-4104

MCGLYNN, JOSEPH LEO, JR., federal judge; b. Phila., Feb. 13, 1925; s. Joseph Leo and Margaret Loretta (Ryan) McG.; m. Jocelyn M. Gates, Aug. 26, 1950; children: Jocelyn, Leo, Timothy, Suzanne, Alisa, Deirdre, Caroline, Elizabeth, Meghan, Brendan. B.S., Mt. St. Mary's Coll., 1948; LL.B., U. Pa., 1951. Bar: Pa. 1952. Asst. U.S. atty. Phila., 1953-60; assoc., then ptnr. Blank Rudenko Klaus & Rome, Phila., 1960-65; judge County Ct. of Phila., 1965-68, Ct. of Common Pleas, 1st Jud. Dist. of Pa., 1968-74, U.S. Dist. Ct. (ea. dist.) Pa., Phila., 1974—. Served with USN, 1943-46, PTO. Mem. Phila. Bar Assn. Office: US Dist Ct 16614 Us Courthouse Philadelphia PA 19106

MCGLYNN, MICHAEL JAMES, bakery company executive; b. Mpls., June 10, 1950; s. Burton James and Patricia (Jones) M.; m. Elizabeth Cravens, July 8, 1972 (div. 1983); children: Elizabeth Ann, Emily Katherine; m. Julie Bean, Sept. 23, 1983; stepchildren: Jennifer Leslie, Elissa Hill. BS, U. Colo., 1972. V.p. McGlynn Bakeries Co., Mpls., 1972-80, pres., 1981—. Dir. Minn. Family Bus. Council, Mpls., 1979; contact exec. United Way, 1981-87. Mem. Minn. Bakers Assn., Retail Bakers Am., Am. Bakers Assn. Republican. Roman Catholic. Clubs: Interlachen, Country (Edina, Minn.), Mpls. Home: 5025 Schaefer Rd Edina MN 55436-1142 Office: McGlynn Bakeries Inc 7350 Commerce Ln Minneapolis MN 55432

MCGLYNN, RICHARD BRUCE, lawyer; b. Kearny, N.J., Dec. 16, 1938; s. William Edward and Irene Louise (Mohr) M.; m. Victoria Sargent Bell, June 15, 1963; children: Margaret, Mary Elizabeth, Melissa. AB, Princeton U., 1960; LLB, Rutgers U., 1963. Bar: N.J. 1963, U.S. Dist. Ct. N.J. 1963, U.S. Supreme Ct. 1976, U.S. Ct. Appeals (3d cir.) 1984. Asst. prosecutor Essex County, Newark, N.J., 1965-67; dep. atty. gen. State of N.J., Trenton, 1970-73; judge Essex County Dist. Ct., Newark, 1974-76; commr. Bd. Pub. Utilities, State of N.J., Newark, 1976-80; ptnr. Stryker Tams & Dill, Newark, 1980-92, LeBoeuf, Lamb, Greene & MacRae, Newark, 1992-94; v.p., gen. counsel United Water Resources, Harrington Park, N.J., 1994—; bd. dirs. Atlantic Energy Inc., Pleasantville, N.J. Candidate Rep. Gubernatorial primary, N.J., 1981; chmn. N.J. Shakespeare Festival, N.J., 1989-92, dir., 1994—; dir. Ctr. for the Analysis of Pub. Issues, N.J., 1983—. Mem. ABA, N.J. Bar Assn. (Young Lawyer of Yr. young lawyers sect. 1975), Am. Law Inst., Am. Judicature Soc., Nassau Club, Short Hills Club, Univ. Glee Club N.Y.C. Episcopalian. Avocations: small group singing, tennis, paddle tennis. Home: 30 Hurlingham Club Rd Far Hills NJ 07931 Office: United Water Resources 200 Old Hook Rd Harrington Park NJ 07640

MC GLYNN, SEAN PATRICK, physical chemist, educator; b. Dungloe, Ireland, Mar. 8, 1931; came to U.S., 1952, naturalized, 1957; s. Daniel and Catherine (Brennan) McG.; m. Helen Magdalena Salacz-von Dohnanyi, 4Apr. 11, 1955; children: Sean Ernst, Daniel Julian, Brian Charles, Sheila Ann, Alan Patrick. B.S., Nat. U. Ireland, 1951, M.S., 1952; Ph.D., Fla. State U., 1956. Fellow Fla. State U., 1956, U. Wash., 1956-57; mem. faculty La. State U., 1957—, prof. chemistry, 1964—, Boyd prof. chemistry, 1967—, dean Grad. Sch., 1981-82, vice chancellor for research, 1981-91; asso. prof. biophysics Yale U., 1961; Humboldt prof. physics U. Bonn, W.Ger., 1979-80; cons. to pvt. cos. Author: (with others) Molecular Spectroscopy of the Triplet State, 1969, Introduction to Applied Quantum Chemistry, 1971, Photophysics and Photochemistry in the Vacuum Ultraviolet, 1985, The Geometry of Genetics, 1988; editor Wiley-Interscience Monographs in Chem. Physics; contbr. over 400 articles and chpts. to profl. pubs. Fellow Research Corp., 1960-63; Sloan fellow, 1964-68; recipient award Baton Rouge Council Engring. and Sci. Socs., 1962-63; Sr. Scientist award Alexander von Humboldt Found., 1979; Disting. Research medal U. Bologna, Italy, 1979. Mem. Am. Chem. Soc. (S.W. regional award 1967, Fla. sect. award 1970, Coates award 1977), AAAS, Am. Phys. Soc. Research molecular electronic spectroscopy, electronic structure, energy transfer, molecular genetics, bioenergetics, mathematical biology, optoacoustics, optogalvanics. Home: 1056 E Lakeview Dr Baton Rouge LA 70810-4621

MC GOLDRICK, JOHN GARDINER, lawyer; b. Grand View-on-Hudson, N.Y., July 25, 1932; s. Francis Michael and Elizabeth Theresa (Leitner) McG.; m. Cathleen Elinor Cloney, June 5, 1965; children: John Francis, Ann Cathleen. Student, Coll. of Holy Cross, Worcester, Mass., 1950-51; seminarian, S.J., 1951-58; AB, Fordham U., 1957; JD, Georgetown U., 1961. Bar: N.Y. 1962, U.S. Dist. Ct. (so. and ea. dists.) N.Y. 1975, U.S. Ct. Appeals (2d cir.) 1975, U.S. Supreme Ct. 1975. Assoc. Lowenstein, Pitcher, Hotchkiss, Amann & Parr, N.Y.C., 1961-66, Kaye, Scholer, Fierman, Hays & Handler, N.Y.C., 1966-69; ptnr. Schulte & McGoldrick, N.Y.C., 1969-81; counsel to Gov. Hugh L. Carey, N.Y., 1981-82; ptnr. Schulte Roth & Zabel, 1983—; commr. Port Authority N.Y. and N.J., 1982-93, chair audit com., 1985-93; bd. dirs. Com. on Modern Cts., Inc., 1983-94; mem. N.Y.C. Mayor's Com. on Judiciary, 1990-93. Bd. dirs., mem. exec. com. Georgetown U., 1973-79, vice chmn. bd., 1975-79. Fellow Am. Bar Found.; Am. Law Inst., N.Y. State Bar Assn. (com. on state constitution 1985-93, chmn. 1987-90, mem. ho. of dels. 1985-91, spl. com. lawyers in pub. svc. 1986-88, com. on fin. 1990—), Assn. of Bar of City of N.Y. (com. on profl. responsibilities 1974-76, com. on grievances 1976-79, com. profl. discipline 1980, com. 2d century 1982-88, treas., mem. exec. com. 1984-87, com. on govt. ethics 1988-93), Univ. Club. Home: 111 E 80th St New York NY 10021-0334 Office: Schulte Roth & Zabel 900 3rd Ave New York NY 10022-4728

MCGOLDRICK, MARGARET MARY, hospital administrator; b. Phila., Dec. 17, 1952; d. Owen Francis McGoldrick and Helen Merrick (Welsh) Pancoast; m. Richard William Owens, Aug. 10, 1984; 1 child, Sarah Katelin. BA, Temple U., 1973, MBA, 1976. Lic. nursing home adminstr., Pa. Vice pres. Am. Med. Ctrs., Spring House, Pa., 1976-80; asst. exec. dir. Hahnemann U. Hosp., Spring House, 1980-81, assoc. exec. dir., 1982—. Contbr. articles to profl. jours. Vice pres. Phoenixville (Pa.) YMCA, 1982, Delaware Valley Hosp. Laundry, Phila., 1985—; bd. dirs. Keystone Kidney Ctr., Willow Grove, Pa., 1987—. Mem. Am. Coll. Health Care Execs., Hosp. Assn. Pa., Delaware Valley Hosp. Coun., Temple U. Health Adminstrn. Alumni Assn. (pres. 1979-80). Avocations: jogging, cross country skiing, golf, bicycling, orienteering. Home: 1030 W King Rd Malvern PA 19355-3120 Office: Allegheny United Hosps 100 W Laurel Ave Cheltenham PA 19012

MCGONIGAL, PEARL, former lieutenant governor; b. Melville, Sask., Can., June 10, 1929; d. Fred and Kathryne Kuhlman; m. Marvin A. McGonigal, Nov. 3, 1948; 1 child, Kimberly Jane. Ed. Melville, Sask.; LLD (hon.), U. Man. Formerly engaged in banking, mdse. rep.; mem. St. James-Assiniboia (Man.) City Council, 1969-71; mem. Greater Winnipeg (Man.) City Council, 1971-81, chmn. com. on recreation and social services, 1977-79, dep. mayor and chmn. exec. policy com., 1979-81; lt. gov. Man., 1981-86; mem. adv. bd. Royal Trust Co., 1987—; trustee First Can. Mortgage Fund; bd. dirs. Mediacom Inc., Can. Imperial Bank of Commerce; commr. Man. Law Reform Commn. Author: Frankly Feminine Cookbook, 1975, Bringing It All Together. Cookbook, 1990; weekly columnist: Reliance Press Ltd. Newspapers, 1970-81. Bd. dirs. Winnipeg Conv. Centre, 1975-77, Red River Exhbn., 1975-81, Rainbow Stage, 1976-81, Man. Blue Cross; ex-officio mem. Man. Theatre Centre, 1977-81; mem. Winnipeg Conv. and Visitors Bur., 1973-75, Man. Environ. Concil, 1974-76, Man. Aviation Council, 1974-77; mem. selection com. Faculty Dental Hygiene, U. Man., 1977-80; bd. mgmt. Winnipeg Home Improvement Program, 1979-81; chmn. adv. com. Sch. Nursing, Grace Gen. Hosp., 1972-93; past chmn. St. James-Assiniboia Inter-faith Immigration Council; former mem. vestry St. Andrew's Anglican Ch.; former vol. Lions Manor, Sherbrook Day Centre; chmn. bd. mgmt. Grace Gen. Hosp., 1987-93; chmn. bd. reference Catherine Booth Bible Coll., 1987; commr. Man. Law Reform Commn.; campaign chmn. United Way of Winnipeg, 1990; vice chair Grey Cup Festival, '91; hon. col. 402 City of Winnipeg Squadron, 1992. Decorated dame Order of St. John; recipient award dist. 64 Toastmasters, 1974, award Elks, Winnipeg, 1975, Nat. B'nai B'rith Humanitarian award, 1984, Citizen of Yr. award KC, 1987, Order of Disting. Aux. Svc., Salvation Army, 1991, Hadassah-Wizo Woman of Yr. award, 1994; named hon. col. 735th Comm. Regt. Mem. Order of Can., Beta Sigma Phi (1st Lady of Yr. 1986). Liberal. Club: Winnipeg Winter. Lodge: KC (Citizen of Yr. 1987). Home: 51-361 Westwood Dr, Winnipeg, MB Canada R3K 1G4

MCGONIGAL, RICHARD M., lawyer; b. Cleve., May 4, 1940; s. Richard C. and Claudia (Nesmith) McG.; m. Marilyn S. Marsh, June 2, 1962 (div. May 1992); children: Jennifer S., Michael J., Katherine A., Kevin M.; m. Ellen E. Hausler, June 12, 1992. BA, Harvard U., 1962; JD, Columbia U., 1965. Bar: Ohio 1965, Fla. 1978, D.C. 1980, N.Y. 1990. Assoc. Squire, Sanders & Dempsey, Cleve., 1965-74, ptnr., 1975-78; sr. corp. ptnr. Morgan, Lewis & Bockius, Miami, Fla., 1978-89, N.Y.C., 1990—. Editor-in-chief Jurimetrics Jour. of Law, Sci. and Tech., 1975-77. Capt. US Army, 1967-69, Vietnam. Decorated Purple Heart, Bronze Star. Mem. ABA (chmn. coun. sci. tech. sect. Chgo. 1984-85), Computer Law Assn. (bd. dirs. 1978-82), Harvard Club (N.Y.C.). Democrat. Episcopalian. Avocations: squash, tennis, hiking, photography. Office: Morgan Lewis & Bockius 101 Park Ave New York NY 10178-0060

MCGONIGLE, JAMES GREGORY, training consultant; b. Bklyn., Nov. 17, 1945; s. William John and Helen Bernadette (Dennin) McG.; m. Francine Anne Falango, May 27, 1972; children: MarieElena, Lauren Anne. AAS in Acctg., CUNY, 1972; BS in Fin. summa cum laude, L.I. U., 1980. Cert. fin. planner Internat. Bd. Cert. Fin. Planners. Account exec. Coburn Credit Corp., Rockville Centre, N.Y., 1965-66; asst. credit mgr. UNI-CARD, Greatneck, N.Y., 1966-68; accounts receivable mgr. Granite Leasing Corp., Garden City, N.Y., 1968-73; v.p. Citicorp., N.Y.C., 1973-88; cons. O/E Learning, Inc., Detroit, 1988-90; regional dir. Ednl. Techs., Inc., Troy, Mich., 1989—; adj. faculty Coll. for Fin. Planning, Denver. Vol. Family Svc. Assn., Nassau, N.Y., 1981-84, Better Bus. Bur., Farmingdale, N.Y., 1987—; vol., career advisor L.I. U., Brookville, N.Y., 1990—; treas. W. Tresper Clarke Friends of Arts, 1988-89. Mem. ABA (assoc.), Fin. Mgmt. Assn., Internat. Assn. Fin. Planning, Adelphi Soc. Cert. Fin. Planners, Internat. Assn. Registered Fin. Planners (speaker's bur.), Nat. Assn. Life Underwriters, Nat. Panel Consumer Arbitrators, Nat. Ctr. for Fin. Edn., Inst. Cert. Fin. Planners (bd. dirs. L.I. 1989-92), N.Y. State Assn. Cert. Fin. Planners, Delta Mu Delta. Republican. Roman Catholic. Avocations: bicycling, public speaking, traveling, writing, gardening. Home: 2167 Plum Tree Rd N Westbury NY 11590-6029 Office: 33 Willis Ave Mineola NY 11501-4411

MCGOOHAN, PATRICK JOSEPH, actor; b. Astoria L.I., N.Y., Mar. 19, 1928; s. Thomas and Rose McG.; m. Joan Drummond, 1951; children: Ann, Frances, Catherine. Worked with Sheffield (Eng.) Repertory Co., Bristol (Eng.) Old Vic. Co. Stage debut in London in The Brontes, St. James Theatre, 1948; appeared: stage prodns. Serious Charge, London, 1955, Moby Dick, London, 1955, Pack of Lies, 1985; acted in films including: Passage Home, 1955, High Tide at Noon, 1956, Hell Drivers, 1957, The Quare Fellow, 1962, Life for Ruth, 1962, Ice Station Zebra, 1968, Mary Queen of Scots, 1972, The Genius, 1975, Silver Streak, 1976, Brass Target, 1978, Scanners, 1981, Baby...Secret of the Lost Legend, 1985, Braveheart, 1995; TV series includes: Danger Man, 1961 (in U.S. as "Secret Agent" 1965-66), The Prisoner, 1968-69, Rafferty, 1977; TV movies include: The Man in the Iron Mask, 1978, Koroshi, 1978, 3 Sovereigns for Sarah, 1985, Jamaica Inn, 1985; wrote, directed and appeared in various episodes in Columbo series. Recipient Brit. award for best TV actor of yr. 1963, Brit. award for best stage actor of yr. in play Brand, 1959, Emmy award Nat. Acad. TV Arts and Scis., 1975. Office: care Jack Fields and Assocs 9255 W Sunset Blvd Ste 1105 Los Angeles CA 90069-3308 also: DGA 7920 W Sunset Blvd Los Angeles CA 90046-3300*

MC GOON, DWIGHT CHARLES, retired surgeon, educator; b. Marengo, Iowa, Mar. 24, 1925; s. Charles Douglas and Ada Belle (Buhlman) McG.; m. Betty Lou Hall, Apr. 2, 1948; children: Michael, Susan, Betsy, Sarah. Student, Iowa State U. 1942-43, St. Ambrose Coll., Davenport, Iowa, 1943-44; M.D., Johns Hopkins U., 1948. Intern Johns Hopkins Hosp., 1948-49, resident in surgery, 1949-54; cons. in surgery Mayo Clinic, Rochester, Minn., 1957—; Stuart W. Harrington prof. surgery Mayo Med. Sch., 1975-79. Editor-in-chief Jour. Thoracic and Cardiovascular Surgery, 1977-87; editorial bd.: Circulation, 1970-76, Surgery, 1971-77, Am. Jour. Cardiology, 1969-77, Am. Heart Jour, 1969-76; contbr. numerous articles to profl. jours. Served with USN, 1943-45; with M.C. USAF, 1954-56. Fellow ACS; mem. Am. Assn. Thoracic Surgery (pres. 1983-84), Am. Coll. Cardiology (trustee 1979-83), Am. Surg. Assn., Soc. Clin. Surgery, Soc. Univ. Surgeons, Johns Hopkins Soc. Scholars, Phi Beta Kappa, Alpha Omega Alpha. Presbyterian. Home: 706 12th Ave SW Rochester MN 55902-2028 Office: Mayo Clinic 200 1st St SW Rochester MN 55905-0001

MCGOUGH, DUANE THEODORE, economist, government official; b. Rice Lake, Wis., Aug. 3, 1932; s. James Patrick and Josephine Margaret (Huerth) McG.; m. Donna Mae Jones, June 13, 1959. Student, Wis. State Coll., Eau Claire, 1950-52, U. Wis., 1952-54, 56-60; B.S. in Light Constrn. Industry, U. Wis., 1959, M.B.A. in Urban Land Econs., 1962; postgrad., U. So. Calif., 1968-69. Housing mgmt. officer Pub. Housing Adminstrn. Atlanta, 1960-62; program planning analyst Pub. Housing Adminstrn. Phila., 1962-67; program analyst HUD, Washington, 1967-68, 69-70; industry economist HUD, 1970-73, supervisory economist, 1973-77, dir. housing and demographic analysis, 1977—, govt. tech. rep. ann. housing survey, 1977-83; govt. tech. rep. Am. Housing Survey, 1984—; acting dep. asst. sec. for econ. affairs (chief economist) HUD, Washington, 1977, 82, 84-85; U.S. rep housing spetcum. UN Econ. Commn. for Europe, Geneva, 1976, 79, 82; HUD rep. Interagy. Com. on Population Rsch., 1978—, Interagy. Forum on Aging-Related Stats., 1986—; mem. policy com. Year 2000Census. Editor: President's Report on Housing Goals, 1974-78, Nat. Housing Prodn. Report, 1980, 82; sec. Quarterly U.S. Housing Market Conditions Report, 1994—. With U.S. Army, 1954-56; saxophonist 7th Army Band. Fellow NAt. Inst. Pub. Affairs, 1969; recipient Outstanding Performance award Pub. Housing Adminstrn., Phila., 1966, HUD, 1984, 92, Career Edn. award Nat. Inst. Pub. Affairs, 1968-69, Cert. Spl. Achievement, HUD, 1978, 83, 84, Cert. Superior Svc., HUD, 1988, Cert. Appreciation, Bur. Census, 1990. Mem. Am. Econ. Assn., Am. Real Estate and Urban Econ. Assn., Nat. Economists Club, Lambda Alpha Internat. (v.p. programs 1987-89, chmn. real estate and fin. com. George Washington chpt. 1990-92, dir.-at-large 1992-93). Avocations: music, gardening, rockhounding. Office: HUD Office Econ Affairs 7th and D Sts SW Washington DC 20410

MCGOUGH, JOHN PAUL, conveyor and power transmission company executive; b. Pitts., June 14, 1935; s. Patrick J. and Adelean R. (Skillen) McG.; m. Alice M. Gase, Feb. 15, 1958 (div. Dec. 1974); children: Mary G., Paul, Daniel J., Timothy F.X. Student, St. Vincent Coll., Latrobe, Pa., 1953-57; BA, DePaul U., Chgo., 1966; MA, Montclair State Coll., 1973. Sales rep. Shields Rubber Corp., Pitts., 1957-62; dist. mgr. Fabreeka Products Co., Skokie, Ill., 1962-67; regional mgr. Fabreeka Products Co., Wayne, N.J., 1967-75, Continental Rubber Works, Erie, Pa., 1975-76; dir. mktg. Daneline Inc., Kenilworth, N.J., 1976-80; exec. v.p., chief exec. officer Volta Internat., Livingston, N.J., 1980-83; pres., chief exec. officer J. E. Rhoads & Sons Inc., Newark, Del., 1983-90, vice chmn., 1990—. Mem. county com. Wayne Dem. Orgn., 1968-72; vice chmn. Wayne Dem. Club, 1969-70. With U.S. Army, 1957-62. Mem. Pitts. Athletic Club. Unitarian.

MCGOUGH, PETER MYLES, physician; b. Culver City, Calif., Mar. 27, 1952; s. Myles Douglas and Cecelia Marie (McVay) McG.; m. Colleen Ann Dolan, May 30, 1987; children: Cara, Conor. BA in Biology with hons., U.

Calif.-San Diego, 1974; MD, U. So. Calif., 1979. Intern then resident Providence Med. Ctr., Seattle, 1979-82, practice medicine specializing in family practice, 1982—; rsch. assoc. S. M. Grundy VA Hosp., San Diego, 1973-75; asst. clin. prof. U. Wash. Sch. Medicine, 1987—. Contbr. articles to profl. jours. Pres. Physcians for Social Responsibility, Seattle, 1987-90. George Gerber scholar, 1976-79; Calif. State scholar, 1971-74. Fellow Am. Acad. Family Physicians; mem. Am. Coll. Physician Execs., Wash. State Med. Soc. (chmn. legis. com. 1989—, v.p. 1992-93, pres.-elect 1993-94, pres. 1994-95), Wash. Acad. Family Physicians (chmn. legis. com. 1986-92). Democrat. Avocations: skiing, sailing. Office: 3400 California Ave SW Seattle WA 98116-3358

MCGOUGH, WALTER THOMAS, lawyer; b. Steubenville, Ohio, June 4, 1919; s. Frank C. and Nellie C. (Curran) McG.; m. Jane Fitzpatrick, Nov. 24, 1949; children: Jane Ellen, W. Thomas Jr., Hugh F., Marita. Student, Duquesne U., 1936-41; LL.B., U. Pitts., 1948. Bar: U.S. Dist. Ct. Pa. 1948. Assoc. Reed Smith Shaw & McClay, Pitts., 1948-58, ptnr., 1958—, head litigation dept., 1965-79. Case editor U. Pitts. Law Rev. Served to capt. USAAF, 1941-46. Mem. ABA, Am. Law Inst., Pa. Bar Assn., Allegheny County Bar Assn., Am. Judicature Soc. (dir. 1981-88), Acad. Trial Lawyers Allegheny County, 3d Cir. Jud. Conf., Order of Coif. Republican. Roman Catholic. Clubs: Duquesne, Press, Ross Mountain, Pitts. Athletic. Home: 825D Morewood Ave Pittsburgh PA 15213-2911 Office: Reed Smith Shaw & McClay James H Reed Bldg 435 6th Ave Pittsburgh PA 15219-1886

MCGOUGH, WALTER THOMAS, JR., lawyer; b. Pitts., Nov. 7, 1953; s. Walter Thomas and Jane (Fitzpatrick) McG.; m. Rebecca Gai Frazier, June 24, 1978; children: Emily Ann, Walter Thomas III. BA, Princeton U., 1975; JD, U. Va., 1978. Bar: Pa., D.C., U.S. Dist. Ct. (we. dist.) Pa. 1980, U.S. Ct. Appeals (3d cir.) 1983, U.S. Ct. Appeals (6th cir.) 1984, Pa. Supreme Ct. 1978, U.S. Supreme Ct. 1983. Law clk. to judge U.S. Ct. Appeals 3d Cir., Wilmington, Del., 1978-79; law clk. to Hon. William H. Rehnquist U.S. Supreme Ct., Washington, 1979-80; asst. U.S. atty. We. Dist. Pa., 1980-82; assoc. Reed, Smith, Shaw & McClay, Pitts., 1982-86, ptnr., 1987—; assoc. counsel Sen. Select Com. on Secret Mil. Asst. to Iran and the Nicaraguan Opposition, Washington, 1987; mem. lawyers adv. com. U.S. Ct. Appeals (3d cir.), 1987-89, chmn., 1989; atty. Fed. Criminal Justice Def. Panel West Dist. Pa., 1983—. Contbr. articles to profl. jours. Mem. Allegheny County (Pa.) Bd. Assistance, 1986-90, chmn., 1989-90; bd. visitors H. John Heinz III Pub. Policy and Mgmt., Carnegie-Mellon U., Pitts., 1987—; mem. 3d Cir. Task Force on Rule 11, 1987-89. Mem. Allegheny County Bar Assn. (ethics com. 1983-86, bd. gov.'s 1994—), Allegheny County Acad. Trial Lawyers, Duquesne Club, Ross Mountain Club, World Affairs Coun. Office: Reed Smith Shaw & McClay 435 6th Ave Pittsburgh PA 15219-1809

MCGOVERN, A. LANE, lawyer; b. Boston, Aug. 29, 1924; s. James J. and Marion (Stritzinger) McG.; m. Ann Felice Williamson, Nov. 26, 1952; children—Susan Ann, Sara Williamson, Lisa Stevenson, Laura Stritzinger. A.B., Harvard U., 1948, LL.B., 1951. Bar: Mass. 1953, U.S. Supreme Ct. 1957. Assoc. Cahill, Gordon, Zachry & Reindel, N.Y.C., 1951-52; assoc. Ropes & Gray, Boston, 1952-65, ptnr., 1965—; instr. trial practice Harvard U. Law Sch., 1971-72; dir. Winchester Savs. Bank, Mass., Winchester Hosp. Chmn. Winchester Zoning Bd. Appeals, 1961-70; mem. Sch. Com. Winchester, 1970-73; chmn. Boston Better Bus. Bur., 1973-74. Served with U.S. Army, 1943-46. Fellow Am. Coll. Trial Lawyers; mem. Mass. Bar Assn., Boston Bar Assn., Monday Club (Winchester), Phi Beta Kappa. Republican. Episcopalian. Avocations: tennis; surf swimming. Home: 12 Dartmouth St Winchester MA 01890-2355 Office: Ropes & Gray 1 International Pl Boston MA 02110-2624

MC GOVERN, GEORGE STANLEY, former senator; b. Avon, S.D., July 19, 1922; s. Joseph C. and Frances (McLean) McG.; m. Eleanor Stegeberg, Oct. 31, 1943; children: Ann, Susan, Teresa, Steven, Mary. BA, Dakota Wesleyan U., 1945; MA, Northwestern U., 1949, PhD, 1953. Prof. history and polit. sci. Dakota Wesleyan U., 1949-53; exec. sec. S.D. Dem. Party, 1953-55; mem. 85th-86th Congresses, 1st Dist. S.D.; spl. asst. to Pres., dir. Food for Peace, 1961-62; U.S. senator from S.D., 1963-81, chmn. senate select com. on nutrition and human needs; pres. Middle East Policy Coun.; chmn. Ams. for Common Sense, Washington, 1981-82; guest lectr. Northwestern U., Evanston, Ill., Duke U., Columbia U., Cornell U., Munich, Berlin, and numerous others in U.S. and Europe, from 1981. Author: The Colorado Coal Strike, 1913-14, 1953, War Against Want, 1964, Agricultural Thought in the Twentieth Century, 1967, A Time of War, A Time of Peace, 1968, (with Leonard Guttridge) The Great Coalfield War, 1972, An American Journey, 1974, Grassroots, 1978. Democratic candidate for Pres. U.S., 1972; candidate for presdl. nomination Dem. Party, 1984. Served as pilot USAAF, World War II. Decorated D.F.C. Mem. Am. Hist. Assn. Methodist. Clubs: Mason (33 deg., Shriner), Elk, Kiwanian. *

MCGOVERN, JOHN FRANCIS, financial executive; b. Port Chester, N.Y., June 4, 1946; s. Charles William and Jeanette Mary (Farrell) McG.; m. Gertrude Anne Mills, June 21, 1969; children—Robert Francis, Sarah Mills. B.S. in Econs., Fordham U., 1968. Asst. treas. Chase Manhattan Bank, N.Y.C., 1973-74, 2d v.p., 1974-76, v.p., 1976-80, v.p. div. treas. forest products, 1980-81; v.p. project fin Ga.-Pacific Corp., Portland, Oreg., 1981-83, v.p., 1983—. Fund raiser Am. Heart Assn., Atlanta, 1985—; adviser Atlanta Ballet, 1985. Served with U.S. Army, 1968-70. Mem. Fin. Execs. Inst. Republican. Roman Catholic. Club: Atlanta Country. Avocations: golf; tennis; skiing; jogging. Office: Ga-Pacific Corp 133 Peachtree St NE Atlanta GA 30303-1808

MCGOVERN, JOHN HUGH, urologist, educator; b. Bayonne, N.J., Dec. 18, 1924; s. Patrick and Mary (McGovern) McG.; m. Mary Alice Cavazos, Aug. 2, 1980; children by previous marriage: John Hugh, Robert, Ward, Raymond. BS, Columbia U., 1947; MD, SUNY, Bklyn., 1952. Diplomate Am. Bd. Urology. Rotating intern Bklyn. Hosp., 1952-53; asst. resident in surgery Bklyn. VA Hosp., 1953-54; with urology N.Y. Hosp., 1954-56; exchange surg. registrar West London Hosp., Eng., 1956-57; resident in urol. surgery N.Y. Hosp., 1957-58, rsch. asst. pediatric urology, 1958-59, asst. attending surgeon James Buchanan Brady Found., 1959-61, assoc. attending surgeon, 1961-66, attending surgeon, 1966—; asst. in surgery Med. Coll. Cornell U., 1957-59, asst. prof. clin. surgery, 1959-64, assoc. prof., 1964-72, prof., 1972—; attending staff in urology Lenox Hill Hosp., 1969—, in-charge urology, 1969-83; cons. urology Rockefeller Inst., St. Vincent's Hosp., Mercy Hosp., Phelps Meml. Hosp.; chmn. coun. on urology Nat. Kidney Found., 1982. Contbr. articles to profl. jours., chpts. to books. Lt. M.C., U.S. Army, 1942-45. Recipient Conatvoy mos medal Chile, 1975, Tree of Life award Nat. Kidney Found., 1990; named Huesped de Honor, Mimunicipalidad de Guayaquil (Ecuador), 1976; award in urology Kidney Found. N.Y., 1977, Sir Peter Freyer medal, Galway, Ireland, 1980. Fellow N.Y. Acad. Medicine (exec. com. urol. sect. 1968-72, chmn. 1972), ACS (credentials com. 1991—), Am. Acad. Pediatrics (urological); mem. AMA (diagnostic and therapeutic tech. assessment bd. 1991—, diagnostic and therepautic tech. assessment program panel 1991, DATTA panel 1991—), Am. Assn. G.U. Surgeons, N.Y. State Med. Soc. (chmn. urol. sect. 1975), Med. Soc. County N.Y., Am. Urol. Assn. (hon. mem. 1994—, pres.-elect 1988-89, pres. 1989-90, pres. N.Y. sect. 1979-80, N.Y. rep. exec. com. 1982-87, socioecons. com. 1987, chmn. fiscal affairs rev. com. 1987, chmn. awards com. 1990, time and place com. 1989-90), N.Y. State Urol. Soc. (exec. com. 1982—), Pan Pacific Surg. Assn., Am. Assn. Clin. Urologists (pres.-elect 1987-88, pres. 1988-89, bd. dirs. 1984—, mem. interpersonal rels. com. 1975—, govt. rels. com. 1989-90, program com. 1989-90, nominating com. 1989-90), Assn. Am. Physicians and Surgeons, Pan Am. Med. Assn. (diplomate 1981—), Urol. Investigators Forum, Soc. Pediatric Urology (pres.-elect 1979-80, pres. 1980-81), Am. Trauma Soc., Kidney Found. (med. adv. bd. N.Y. sect., trustee, 1979) Société Internationale d'Urologie (exec. com. U.S. sect.); hon. mem. Sociedad Peruana de Urologia, Sociedad Guatemale de Urologia, Sociedad Ecuadoriana de Urologia, Royal Coll. Surgeons (London). Home and Office: 53 E 70th St New York NY 10021

MCGOVERN, JOHN JOSEPH, former air pollution control association executive, consultant; b. Pitts., June 21, 1920; s. John F. and Philomene (Henigin) McG.; m. Doris I. Judy, Sept. 25, 1947 (dec. 1986); children: John Joseph, Joseph Edgar, Daniel Paul, Michael James, William Patrick, Edward Vernon; m. Patricia E. Carothers, Apr. 1987. B.S., Carnegie Inst. Tech., 1942, M.S., 1944, Sc.D., 1946. Fellow, then sr. fellow Mellon Inst., Pitts.,

1945-50; head research services Mellon Inst., 1958-71; dir. ednl. and research services Carnegie-Mellon U., 1971-73, asst. dir. div. sponsored research, 1973; asst. dir. Carnegie-Mellon Inst. Research, 1974-76; info. scientist U. Pitts., 1976—; asst. services mgr. Air Pollution Control Assn., 1979-83, mem. services mgr.; 1983-87; asst. chief chemist, then chief chemist Koppers Co., Inc., 1950-58. Editor: The Crucible, 1970-76. Mem. Spectroscopy Soc. Pitts. (chmn. 1951), Am. Chem. Soc. (sec. Pitts. 1960, chmn. sect. 1964, dir.), PITTCON (pres. 1951). Club: Chemists (pres. Pitts. 1968-69). Home and Office: 1606 Parkline Dr # 4 Pittsburgh PA 15227-1645

MCGOVERN, MICHAEL BARBOT, lawyer; b. N.Y.C., Mar. 6, 1947; s. Michael Malachy and Annette (Barbot) McG.; m. Christine Anne Beaudet, Sept. 2, 1972; children: Kathleen, Ellen, Maura. AB, Georgetown U., 1969, JD, 1972; LLM (Taxation), George Washington U., 1987. From assoc. to ptnr. Wilkes & Artis, Washington, 1973-79; sole practice Washington, 1980; ptnr. Lambert, Griffin & McGovern, Washington, 1981-84; sole practice Washington, 1984-87; ptnr. Venable, Baetjer, Howard & Civiletti, Washington, 1987-93; counsel Montedoninco, Hamilton & Altman, D.C., 1994—. Bd. dirs. Hist. Soc. Washington, 1984-93; co-founder, vice-chair, bd. dirs. Greater Bethesda-Chevy Chase Coalition Inc., 1986—; pres. Westmoreland Citizens Assn. Inc., 1988-90; mem. Leadership Washington, 1987—. Capt. USAFR, 1969-82. Recipient Distinguished Service award Fed. Bar Assn., 1978. Mem. ABA, Fed. Bar Assn., D.C. Bar Assn., Md. State Bar Assn., Columbia Country Club (Chevy Chase), Met. Club (Washington), Barristers, John Carroll Soc. Republican. Catholic. Home: 5414 Albemarle St Bethesda MD 20816-1825 Office: Montedonico Hamilton & Altman 5301 Wisconsin Ave NW Ste 400 Washington DC 20015

MCGOVERN, PATRICIA, state senator. Mem. Mass. State Senate from Dist. 2. Mem. Mass. State Democratic Com. Office: Mass State Senate State Capital Boston MA 02133

MCGOVERN, PATRICK J., communications executive. BA in Physics, M.I.T. With Internat. Data Corp., Framingham, Mass., 1964—, chmn., 1976—; with IDG Comm. Inc., Framingham, 1987—. Office: Internat Data CorpConsulting 5 Speen St Framingham MA 01701-9015

MCGOVERN, RICHARD GORDON, food company executive; b. Norristown, Pa., Oct. 22, 1926; s. James Joseph and Marion (Stritzinger) McG.; m. Julia Merrow, June 4, 1955; children: Lucinda, Jennifer, Martha, Douglas. Student, Williams Coll., 1944-45, Coll. Holy Cross, 1945-46; AB, Brown U., 1948; MBA, Harvard U., 1950. With Pepperidge Farm, Inc., 1956-80, pres., 1968-80; dir., v.p. Campbell Soup Co., 1976-80, exec. v.p., 1980, pres., 1980-89, ret., 1989; bd. dirs. N.Am. Life Assurance Co., Toronto, Ont., Can., Merrow Machine Co., Newington, Conn., George Weston, Ltd., Toronto. Lt. USNR, 1944-46, 52-54. Mem. Am. Mktg. Assn., Am. Soc. Bakery Engrs., Grocery Mfrs. Assn. (past. bd. dirs.), Phi Beta Kappa, Sigma Xi, Delta Upsilon. Home: 182 Lounsbury Rd Ridgefield CT 06877-4725

MCGOVERN, THOMAS AQUINAS, utility executive; b. N.Y.C., Mar. 2, 1933; s. Thomas Aquinas and Helen Frances (Carroll) McG.; m. Miriam Anne Howley, July 16, 1955; children: Cecilia, Louise, Pamela. BS in History, Coll. of the Holy Cross, 1954; MA in Econs., L.I. U., 1965. Dep. asst. Consol. Edison Co. of N.Y., N.Y.C., 1958-61, supts. asst., 1961-66, asst. supt., 1967-68, supt., 1968-69, staff dir., 1969-70, asst. to exec. v.p., 1970-72, exec. dir., 1972-82, asst. v.p., 1982-89, v.p., 1989—; mem. Edison Elec. Inst. Sec. Commn., Washington, 1976-90, Mailers' Tech. Adv. Com., Washington, 1990-91; vice-chmn. Nat. Postal Coun., Washington, 1982—; pres. D.C.K. Mgmt. Corp., N.Y.C., 1982—; mem. Real Estate Bd. N.Y., N.Y.C., 1988—. Mem. N.Y.C. (N.Y.) Health and Hosps. Security Adv. Com., 1985; pres. Westchester County Police Meml., White Plains, N.Y., 1987—. With U.S. Army, 1954-56. Recipient Svcs. to Nation and FBI award FBI, N.Y.C., 1984, Svc. to Law Enforcement Community award N.Y. State Chiefs of Police, Albany, N.Y., 1989, Appreciation for Svc. award N.Y. State Fedn. of Police, Briarcliff Manor, N.Y., 1989, Svc. to Orgns. award FBI Marine Corps Assn., Cresskill, N.J., 1989, Svc. to Orgns. award N.Y.C. Honor Legion, Richmond Hill, N.Y. Mem. KC, Am. Legion, Assn. of the U.S. Army, U.S. Naval Inst., FBI Marine Corps Assn., Pi Gamma Mu. Roman Catholic. Avocations: U.S. mil. history, post card collecting, toy soldier collecting, Royal Doulton china collecting. Office: Consol Edison Co NY Inc 4 Irving Pl New York NY 10003-3502

MC GOVERN, WALTER T., federal judge; b. Seattle, May 24, 1922; s. C. Arthur and Anne Marie (Thies) McG.; m. Rita Marie Olsen, June 29, 1946; children: Katrina M., Shawn E., A. Renee. B.A., U. Wash., 1949, LL.B., 1950. Bar: Wash. 1950. Practiced law in Seattle, 1950-59; mem. firm Kerr, McCord, Greenleaf & Moen; judge Municipal Ct., Seattle, 1959-65, Superior Ct., Wash., 1965-68, Wash. Supreme Ct., 1968-71, U.S. Dist. Ct. (we. dist.) Wash., 1971—; chief judge, 1975-87; mem. subcom. on supporting personnel Jud. Conf. U.S., 1981-87, chmn. subcom., 1983, mem. adminstrn. com., 1983-87, chmn. jud. resources com., 1987-91. Mem. Am. Judicature Soc., Wash. State Superior Ct. Judges Assn., Seattle King County Bar Assn. (treas.), Phi Delta Phi. Club: Seattle Tennis (pres. 1968). Office: US Dist Ct US Courthouse 5th Fl 1010 5th Ave Seattle WA 98104-1130

MC GOVERN, WILLIAM MONTGOMERY, JR., law educator; b. Evanston, Ill., July 9, 1934; s. William Montgomery and Margaret (Montgomery) McG.; m. Katharine Watts, Sept. 20, 1958; children: William Montgomery III, Elizabeth Lee, Katharine Margaret. A.B., Princeton U., 1955; LL.B., Harvard U., 1958. Bar: Ill. 1959. Assoc. Sidley, Austin, Burgess & Smith, Chgo., 1959-63; asst. prof. law Northwestern U. Sch. of Law, Chgo., 1963-66; assoc. prof. Northwestern U. Sch. of Law, 1966-68, prof., 1968-72; prof. law Sch. Law, UCLA, 1972—; vis. prof. U. Minn. Law Sch., 1979-80, U. Va. Law Sch., 1983. Author: Wills, Trusts and Future Interests: An Introduction to Estate Planning, 1983; (with Lary Lawrence) Cases and Problems on Contracts and Sales, 1986; (with Sheldon Kurtz and Jan Rein) Wills, Trusts and Estates, 1988; bd. editors: Harvard Law Rev, 1956-58; Contbr. articles profl. jours. Served with U.S. Army, 1958-59. Home: 17319 Magnolia Blvd Encino CA 91316-2542 Office: UCLA Sch Law 405 Hilgard Ave Los Angeles CA 90024-1722

MCGOWAN, GEORGE VINCENT, public utility executive; b. Balt., Jan. 30, 1928; s. Joseph H. and Ethna M. (Prahl) McG.; m. Carol Murray, Aug. 6, 1977; children by a previous marriage: Gregg Blair, Bradford Kirby. BS in M.E., U. Md., 1951; LHD (hon.), Villa Julie Coll., 1991, Loyola Coll., Md., 1992. Registered profl. engr., Md. Project engr. nuclear power plant Balt. Gas & Electric Co., 1967-72, chief nuclear engr., 1972-74, pres., chief operating officer, 1980-87, chmn. bd. dirs., CEO, 1988-92, chmn. exec. com., 1993—, mgr. corp. staff services, 1974-78, v.p. mgmt. and staff services, 1978-79; bd. dirs. Balt. Life Ins. Co., McCormick & Co., Life of Md., Inc., UNC Inc., Orgn. Resources Counselors, Inc., NationsBank, N.A., Hartland & Co. Bd. dirs. U. Md. Med. Sys., United Way Ctrl. Md., Coll.Bound Found., Md. Pride of Balt.; chmn. bd. regents U. Md. Sys., Balt. Symphony Orch. Recipient Disting. Alumnus award U. Md. Coll. Engring., 1980, U. Md., 1987, Disting. Marylander award Advt. and Profl. Club Balt., 1992, Disting. Citizen award U. md., 1991, Disting. Citizen of Yr. award Balt. coun. Boy Scouts Am., 1991, Disting. Alumnus award Md. Poly. Inst., 1992, Nat. Multiple Sclerosis Soc. Corp. Honoree, Md. chpt., 1993, Outstanding Vol. Fund Raiser award Nat. Soc. Fund Raising Execs., 1993, Pub. Affairs award Md. Bus. Coun., 1994. Mem. ASME (James N. Landis medal 1992), Am. Nuclear Soc., U.S. Energy Assn. of the World Energy Conf., Engring. Soc. Balt. (Founders Day award 1988), Caves Valley Golf Club, The Ctr. Club (pres. bd. govs.), U. Md. M. Club, Talbot Country Club, Annapolis Yacht Club, Md. Club. Presbyterian. Office: Balt Gas & Electric Co PO Box 1475 Baltimore MD 21203-1475

MCGOWAN, HAROLD, real estate developer, investor, scientist, author, philanthropist; b. Weehawken, N.J., June 23, 1909; s. Sylvester and Grace (Kalbfleish) McG.; m. Anne Cecelia McTiernan, Jan. 15, 1938; children—Linda Anne, Harold Charles, Janice Marie. Ed., Bklyn. Poly. Inst., Pratt Inst., N.Y. U.; student, N.Y. Tech.; eds., Hubbard (Eng.) U.; D.Sc., Coll. Fla. Chmn. bd. Atomic Rsch. Inst.; pres. Harold McGowan Builders; owner, developer Central Islip Shopping Center, Central Islip Indsl. Center; developer, builder Brinsley Gardens, Rolling Green, Slater Park, Clover Green, Maple Acres, Wheeler Acres; owner-donor Little League Baseball

Pks. Sculptures include: Bless Them; Victory, Eternity, Love and Hate, Triumph; author: Green Flight, (originator) The Thoughtron Theory of Life and Matter, Race with Death across the Sahara, The Incorrigibles, The Frigid Trap, The Shah's Swiss Secret, Another World for Christmas, The Spirit of Christmas in Words and Sculpture, The Making of a Universalist, The Journeyman, $800,000 for Love, Beyond the Visible, Shock after Shock, Christmas Stories, Short Stories, Born Again, You Are Forever, Black Shroud Over Bagdad, The Gold Mine; mural Back to Creation; holder U.S. patent to form one-piece plywood corner units, U.S. patent apparatus for forming one-piece plywood corner units. Hwy. commr., Suffolk County; chmn. Recreation & Parks-Islip; past dir. Suffolk County Girl Scouts; land donor St. John of God R.C. Ch., The Episcopal Ch. of the Messiah, Ctrl. Islip Sch. Dist. Recipient Winston Churchill Medal of Wisdom, 1986, Wisdom Hall of Fame, Beverly Hills, Calif., 1970; Churchill fellow, 1989. Mem. AAAS, IEEE, Explorers Club, Mensa Internat. Avocations: sculpture, art, philanthropy. Address: 28 2d Ave Central Islip NY 11722 *To become a really whole and successful person, one should recognize the efforts and good will of those living and dead who developed the culture, the fruits of which he enjoys, and repay his benefactors by contributing more to that society than he takes and also by doing good deeds to make the society better than he found it. He must also strive to understand the world and his relationship to it and know that the universe is neither capricious nor mysterious, that miracles do not happen. Everything and every action can only occur within the bounds of the laws of physics, chemistry, and biology. He must further realize that he is eternal and the basic purpose of human life is to become aware of and to live by these universal laws. The acme of a person's accomplishments would be his comprehension of the structure of the physical universe, the processes of life, the nature of his mind and his own being and intelligence.*

MCGOWAN, HUGH BARRY, insurance agency executive; b. Indpls., Apr. 11, 1944; s. William Kohling and Martha Elizabeth (Barry) McG.; m. Jeanmarie Fillenwarth, Nov. 2, 1968; children: Hugh, Michael, Mary Ellen. BBA in Fin., U. Notre Dame, 1966. CPCU. With McGowan & Brosnan, Inc. (now McGowan & Stanley, Inc.), Indpls., 1969—; pres. McGowan & Brosnan, Inc. (now McGowan Ins. Group, Inc.), Indpls., 1977—; mem. adv. coun. Ind. Ins. Co., 1986-89, Ind. Office, Aetna Casualty & Surety Co., 1988-91; mem. adv. coun. Ind. Office, Gen. Accident Ins. Co., 1987-90, chmn., 1989. Trustee Cathedral High Sch.; bd. dirs. Cath. Social Svcs.; past pres. bd. dirs. Cath. Youth Orgn.; past mem. fund drive Indpls. Mus. Art; assoc. mem., mem. parade and memberships coms. 500 Festival Com.; mem. Commn. for Downtown, Indpls. Recipient Albert Busald award Cath. Youth Orgn., 1986, St. John Bosco award, 1989. Mem. Soc. CPCU's (bd. dirs. Ind. chpt. 1978-86, v.p. 1982-83, pres. 1984-85, budget and fin. nat. com. 1986-92, bd. dirs. East Cen. region 1990-93, bd. regional v.p. 1993—), Ind. Ins. Agts. Indpls. (bd. dirs. 1983—, v.p. 1988-89, pres. 1990-91, chmn. commol. lines com. 1988-89, bd. dirs. dist. 8, 1988-92, Agt. of Yr. award 1984, State Public Image award 1993), Ind. Ins. Agents Ind. (v.p. 1994-95), Indpls. C. of C., Notre Dame Alumni Club Indpls. (past pres., past chmn. scholarship com., award of yr. 1987), Econs. Club Indpls. Office: 10 W Market St Ste 1850 Indianapolis IN 46204-2972

MC GOWAN, JAMES ATKINSON, business executive, financial consultant; b. De Soto, Mo., Nov. 10, 1914; s. James Electra and Dora Mercer (Atkinson) McG.; m. Barbara Louise Bevan, Apr. 5, 1941; m. Margaret Mercier Johns, Dec. 21, 1974; children: James Michael, John Barrie, Susan Alexandra, Jean Christine. AA, Little Rock Jr. Coll., 1934; BSChemE, Iowa State U., 1936. With Aluminum Co. Am., 1936-79; dist. sales mgr. Aluminum Co. Am., Cleve., 1959-60; gen. mgr. indsl. sales Aluminum Co. Am., Pitts., 1962-67, v.p., 1967-75; exec. v.p. Aluminum Co. Am., 1975-79; v.p. Amcan Trading Co. subs. Am. Can Corp., Pitts., 1980-81; fin. cons.; arbitrator Better Bus. Bus. Mem. AICE, Chem. Mfg. Assn. (dir.), Aluminum Assn., Nat. Assn. Corrosion Engrs., Sigma Chi. Republican. Episcopalian. Clubs: Duquesne, Fox Chapel Golf, Rolling Rock.

MCGOWAN, JOHN EDWARD, JR., clinical microbiology educator, epidemiologist, infectious diseases specialist; b. Poughkeepsie, N.Y., June 30, 1942; s. John Edward and Doris Robinson (Wearne) McG.; m. Linda Kay Hudson, May 28, 1967; 1 child, Angela Kay. B.M.S., Dartmouth Coll., 1965; M.D., Harvard U., 1967. Diplomate Am. Bd. Internal Medicine, Am. Bd. Infectious Diseases, Am. Bd. Pathology in Med. Microbiology. Intern, resident Harvard Service, Boston City Hosp., 1967-69; research fellowship Thorndike Lab. Harvard Med. Sch., 1971-72; instr. Harvard Med. Sch., Boston, 1972-73; asst. prof. Emory Med. Sch., Atlanta, 1973-76, assoc. prof., 1977-81, prof. pathology and medicine, 1982—; prof. epidemiology Emory Sch. Pub. Health, 1992—; dir. microbiology Grady Meml. Hosp., Atlanta, 1982—, asst. dir. clin. labs., 1985—. Assoc. editor, Infection Control and Hosp. Epidemiology jour., 1980-92; contbr. 200 sci. articles to profl. jours. Governing bd. Young Singers of Callanwolde, Decatur, Ga., 1981-86; treas. Leafmore Creek-Park Club, Decatur, 1982-84; mem. panel on microbial devices FDA, 1985-89, cons., 1989-91, chmn., 1992-94. Served to sr. surgeon with USPHS, 1969-71. Fellow Infectious Diseases Soc. Am. (antimicrobial agts. com. 1980-93, tuberculosis com. 1993—, governing bd. 1995—). So. Soc. for Clin. Investigation, Coll. of Am. Pathologists (coun. 1993—), Am. Coll. of Epidemiology; mem. Am. Soc. for Microbiology (div. chmn. 1982-84, governing bd. 1984-87), Soc. Hosp. Epidemiologists of Am. (pres. 1981), Am. Hosp. Assn. (panel on infections in hosps. 1989—). Office: Emory U Sch Medicine 69 Butler St SE Atlanta GA 30303-3056

MCGOWAN, JOSEPH ANTHONY, JR., news executive; b. Sheridan, Wyo., May 16, 1931; s. Joseph Anthony and Eda B. (Harris) McG.; m. Patricia Donnette Mitchell, June 7, 1958 (div. 1980); children—Joseph Howard, Colleen Diane; m. Catherine Doris Netick, June 12, 1982. B.S., U. Wyo. Newsman AP, Miami, Fla., 1960-64; bur. chief AP, New Delhi, India, 1965-68, Lima, Peru, 1968-70, Indpls., 1970-75, Boston, 1975-78, Denver, 1978—; lectr. U. Denver, 1978—, Colo. U., Boulder, 1978—, Northeastern U., Boston, 1975-78. Scoutmaster Boy Scouts Am., Sudbury, Mass., 1977-78. Served with USNR, 1953-55. Named Disting. Alumnus, U. Wyo., 1992; Knight Internat. Press fellow to Pakistan, 1995. Mem. Denver Press Club (bd. dirs. 1989-92), Press Club Boston, Colo. Assn. Commerce and Industry (communications council 1986-89), Sigma Delta Chi (Big Hat award 1983). Republican. Avocations: bird hunting; cross country skiing; fishing, cross country bicycling. Office: AP 1444 Wazee St Ste 130 Denver CO 80202-1395

MCGOWAN, MICHAEL BENEDICT, investment banker; b. Wilkes-Barre, Pa., Jan. 21, 1950; s. John W. and Catherine (Hore) McG.; m. Nancy King, May 24, 1980; children: Nicholas King, Grace Caroline. BArch, U. Ark., 1977; MBA, U. Va., 1981. Architect Cromwell Firm, Little Rock, 1976-79; v.p. Oliver Carr Co., Washington, 1981-85; sr. v.p. Stephens Inc., Little Rock, 1985—. Mem. econ. cluster team Clinton-Gore Transition Team, Washington, 1992. Home: PO Box 542 Turner Mountain Rd Ivy VA 22945 Office: Stephens Inc 111 Center St PO Box 3507 Little Rock AR 72201

MCGOWAN, PATRICK FRANCIS, lawyer; b. N.Y.C., July 23, 1940; s. Francis Patrick and Sonia Veronica (Koslow) M.; m. Patricia Neil, June 6, 1964; children: Susan Claire, Kathleen Anne. BA, Rice U., 1962; JD, U. Tex.-Austin, 1965. Bar: Tex. 1965, U.S. Tax Ct., 1972, U.S. Ct. Appeals (5th cir.) 1969, U.S. Ct. Appeals (fed. cir.) 1993, U.S. Supreme Ct. 1970. Briefing atty. Tex. Supreme Ct., Austin, Tex., 1965-66; ptnr. Strasburger & Price, Dallas, 1966—; pres., chmn. bd. Tex Lex, Inc. Contbr. numerous articles on trademark, copyright and franchise law. Bd. advisors Dallas Ft. Worth Sch. Law. Mem. ABA (forum com. on franchising, trademark and unfair competition com., patent, trademark and copyright law sect.), State Bar Tex. (intellectual property sect., com. continuing legal edn.), Coll. State Bar Tex. faculty Franchising inst., 1987—, Intellectual Property Inst., 1992—, S.W. Legal Found. Patent Law Inst., 1992—, Dallas Bar Assn., Internat. Anti Counterfeiting Assn., Tex. Law Review Editors Assn., Phi Delta Phi. Office: Strasburger & Price 4300 NationsBank Plz 901 Main St Dallas TX 75202-3707

MC GOWIN, WILLIAM EDWARD, artist; b. Hattiesburg, Miss., June 2, 1938; s. William Edward and Emily (Ratliff) McG.; m. Claudia DeMonte, May 28, 1977; children: Leah, Jill. B.S., U. So. Miss., 1961; M.A., U. Ala., 1964. prof. art SUNY, Old Westbury, 1978—, Coll. Old Westbury; mem. faculty Corcoran Gallery Art, 1966-77, head sculpture dept., 1967-74; lectr. in field. One-man shows include Corcoran Gallery Art, Washington, 1962,

71, 75, Martha Jackson Gallery N.Y.C., 1968, Am. Cultural Ctr., Paris, 1974, Mus. Modern Art, Paris, 1978, Brooks Jackson Gallery, Iolas, N.Y.C., 1978-80, Fendrick Gallery, Washington, 1977-80, U. Colo., New Orleans Contemporary Art Ctr., 1982, Project Studios 1, L.I., N.Y., Cranbrook Acad., Bloomfield Hills, Mich., 1983, Art Park, Lewiston, N.Y., 1984, Gracie Mansion Gallery, N.Y.C., 1985, 86, 89, Mus. Fine Arts, Miami, Jones, Troyer Gallery, Washington, 1987, 89, 91, Boca Raton (Fla.) Mus., 1991, Margulis-Taplin Gallery, Miami, Fla., 1993, Paris-New York-Bangkok Gallery, Bangkok, Thailand, 1994; group shows include Contemporary Mus., Houston, Miss. Mus. Art, Whitney Mus., N.Y.C., Detroit Inst. Art, Guggenheim Mus., Speed Mus., Ky., Cologne (Germany) Art Fair, Zurich (Switzerland) Art Fair; represented in permanent collections Phillips Collection, Washington, Indpls. Mus. Art, Addison Mus. Art, Andover, Mass., Corcoran Gallery Art, Nat. Collection Fine Arts, Washington, New Orleans Mus. Art, Whitney Mus. Am. Art, N.Y.C. Guggenheim Mus. N.Y.C., Hirshhorn Gallery and Sculpture Garden; commd. Staet of Va., 1985, Percent for Art, N.Y.C., 1992, City of Jubail, Saudi Arabia, 1993, Dallas Rapid Transit Authority, 1994; works reviewed in numeuors newspapers, jours., and books. Recipient Oscar for painting, 1977, Painting prize 9th Internat. Painting Festival, prize Cagnes-sur-Mer, France, 1977, Miss. Arts and Letters award for visual arts, 1980; Nat. Endowment for Arts grantee, 1967-68, 79-80, GSA grantee, 1978-79, Pub. Outdoor Sculpture grantee Nat. Endowment, 1977, 79, Cassandra Found. grantee. Home and Office: 96 Grand St New York NY 10013

MCGOWN, WAYNE, academic administrator; b. Stevens Point, Wis., Feb. 28, 1929; s. Homer Ernest and Amy Irene (Winkler) McG.; m. Hildy Grevstad, July 1, 1961; children: Carolyn, Ronald, Daniel. BBA, U. Wis., 1950, MS, 1958. State budget dir. State of Wis., Madison, 1963-67, dep. sec. then sec. Dept. Adminstrn., 1967-75, dep. sec. Dept. Transp., 1975-77, dep. sec. Dept. Industry, Labor and Human Rels., 1977-79; spl. asst. to chancellor U. Wis., Madison, 1979-90, dir. univ. rsch. park, 1984—, exec. asst. to chancellor, 1990-94; spl. asst. for health scis., 1994—; cons. UN Tech. Svcs., Ankara, Turkey, 1979, Coun. State Govts., Lexington, Ky., 1960-68. Bd. dirs. Hist. Sites Found., Baraboo, Wis., 1986—: V.p. State of Wis. Boy Scouts Am., Madison, 1990—, bd. dirs., 1988—. With U.S. Army, 1951-53. Fellow Nat. Acad. Pub. Adminstrn. (Adminstr. of Yr. 1987); mem. Nat. Assn. State Budget Dirs (life, past pres.). Avocations: camping, travel, cross-country skiing. Home: 106 Nautilus Dr Madison WI 53705-4330 Office: U Wis 161 Bascom Hall 1265 Warf Bldg 610 Walnut St Madison WI 53705-2336

MCGRADY, CLYDE A., secondary school principal. Prin. A. S. Staley Mid. Sch., Americus, Ga. Recipient Elem. Sch. Recognition award U.S. Dept. Edn., 1989-90. Office: A S Staley Middle Sch 915 N Lee St Americus GA 31709-3047

MCGRADY, DONALD LEE, Spanish language educator; b. Greenhurst, Md., Jan. 17, 1935; s. Francis Guy and Lida Amelia (Ewing) McG.; m. Marina Ignacia Pedroza, Sept. 6, 1958; children: Martha, Sandra, Daniel, Arthur. BA, Swarthmore Coll., 1957; AM, Harvard, 1958; PhD, Indiana Univ., 1961. Instr. U. Tex., Austin, 1961-63, asst. prof., 1963-64; asst. prof. U. Calif., Santa Barbara, 1964-67, assoc. prof., 1967-69; assoc. prof. U. Va., Charlottesville, 1969-71, prof., 1971-94; prof. emeritus, 1994—; vis. assoc. prof. U. Calif., Berkeley, 1969. Author: La Novela Historica en Colombia, 1877-1959, 1962, Mateo Aleman, 1968, Critical edition of Jorge Isaacs Maria, 1970, Bibliografia sobre Jorge Isaacs, 1971, Jorge Isaacs, 1972, Critical edition of Cristobal de Tamariz Novelas en verso, 1974, Critical edition of Lope de Vega's La francesilla, 1981, Edition of Lope de Vega's La bella malmaridada, 1986, Critical edition of Jorge Isaacs Maria, 1986., Critical edition of Lope de Vega, Fuente Ovejuna, 1993, Edition of Lope de Vega's Prosas, 2 vols., 1995. Guggenheim fellow Guggenheim Found., N.Y., 1972-73, NEH fellow NEH, Washington, 1976-77. Mem. Asociacion Internacional de Hispanistas, Asociacion Internacional Siglo de Oro, Comediantes. Home: 530 North First St Charlottesville VA 22902

MCGRATH, DENNIS BRITTON, public relations executive; b. Mpls., Mar. 11, 1937; s. James William and Rosalia Clara (Britton) McG.; m. Susan J. Smith, Apr. 15, 1961 (div. 1972); children: Daniel Scott, Amy Susan; m. Elizabeth Ann Buckley, Sept. 15, 1983; 1 stepson, Felix Buckley Jones. BA in Journalism, U. Minn., 1963. Publs. editor Mut. Service Ins. Co., St. Paul, 1963-65; pub. relations account exec. Kerker, Peterson Advt., Mpls., 1965-69; dir. advt. and pub. relations Dain, Kalman & Quail, Mpls., 1969-70; v.p., dir. pub. relations Carmichael Lynch Advt., Mpls., 1970-75; editor Corp. Report Goldletter Dorn Communications, Mpls., 1975; sr. account supr. Kerker & Assocs., Mpls., 1975-77; v.p. Padilla & Speer Inc., Mpls., 1977-79; v.p. communications Gelco Corp., Mpls., 1979-81; v.p., regional mgr. Doremus & Co., Mpls., 1981-83; pres. Mona Meyer McGrath & Gavin, Mpls., 1983-93, chief exec. officer, 1993—. Bi-monthly columnist corp. report mag. Communications, 1974-88. Bd. dirs. Cricket Theatre Mpls., 1985-89, Women's Econ. Devel. Corp., St. Paul, 1986-88, Project Pride in Living, Mpls., 1994—. Minn. Hearing Soc., 1990, The Mpls. Youth Trust, 1991-94, De LaSalle H.S., 1991-94, Mpls. Aquatennial, 1992—, pres., 1993, Greater Mpls. Visitor and Conv. Assn., 1991—. Mem. Pub. Rels. Soc. Am. (accredited, bd. dirs. 1988-90), Nat. Investor Rels. Inst. (pres. Twin Cities chpt. 1984), Pub. Rels. Soc. Counselors Acad. (exec. com. 1994—), Minn. Press Club (chmn., pres. 1980, 81, bd. dirs. 1979-80), Mpls. Club, Mpls. Athletic Club. Democrat. Roman Catholic. Avocations: squash, biking, fishing, reading. Home: 284 Pelham Blvd Saint Paul MN 55104-4935 Office: Mona Meyer McGrath and Gavin Ste 500 8400 Normandale Lake Blvd Bloomington MN 55437

MCGRATH, DON JOHN, banker; b. Springfield, Ill., June 15, 1948; s. Donald John and Wilma P. (Beck) McG.; m. Patricia Ratti, May 7, 1983. B.S. in Mktg., U. Ill., 1970; M.B.A., Boston U., 1973. Investment officer Banque Nationale de Paris, San Francisco, 1975-76, treas., San Francisco and Los Angeles, 1976-78, v.p. and treas., 1978-80; v.p., treas. Bank of the West, San Francisco, 1980, v.p., chief fin. officer, 1980-81, sr. v.p., chief fin. officer, 1981-84, sr. exec. v.p., chief fin. officer, 1984-87, sr. exec. v.p., chief oper. officer, 1987-91, pres., chief oper. officer, 1991—. Bd. dirs. Commonwealth Club Calif., Nature Conservancy Calif. Mem. Calif. Bankers Assn. (bd. dirs.), Univ. Club, St. Francis Yacht Club (San Francisco), Silicon Valley Capital Club (San Jose, Calif.), Diablo (Calif.) Country Club. Office: Bank of the West 1450 Treat Blvd Walnut Creek CA 94596-2168

MCGRATH, EDWARD A., electrical equipment company executive; b. 1930; married. BS, Fordham U., 1952. With Graybar Electric Co., Inc., St. Louis, from 1955, v.p., 1979-89, pres., CEO, 1989—, also bd. dirs. Lt. USN, 1952-55. Office: Graybar Electric Co Inc PO Box 7231 Saint Louis MO 63177-1231 also: Graybar Electric Co 34 N Meramec Ave Saint Louis MO 63105-3874

MCGRATH, EUGENE R., utility company executive; b. New York City, 1942. BSME, Manhattan Coll., 1963; MBA, Iona Coll., 1980. With Consol. Edison Co. N.Y., N.Y.C., 1963—, from v.p. to pres. and chief oper. officer, 1978-89, now chmn., pres., chief exec. officer, also bd. dirs. Office: Consol Edison Co NY Inc 4 Irving Pl Rm 1610 New York NY 10003-3502

MCGRATH, JAMES ALOYSIUS, Canadian provincial official; b. Buchans, Nfld., Can., Nov. 1, 1932; s. Patrick and Mary (Cole) McG.; m. Margaret Smart, Sept. 4, 1960; children: Kathleen, Caroline, Margaret-Moira, Joanna, Sean, Shelagh. LLD (hon.), St. Francis Xavier U., 1979, Meml. U. Nfld., 1992. Provincial sec. Prog. Conservative Party, St. John's, Nfld., 1955-57, pres., 1965-68; m.p. from St. John's East Ho. of Commons, 1957-61, 68-86, parliamentary sec. to minister mines and tech. surveys, 1962, exec. asst. leader opposition, 1963-65, ofcl. opposition spokesman on consumer and corp. affairs, regional and econ. expansion, labour, consumer affairs, housing and urban affairs, 1968-79, mem. Queen's privy council, minister fisheries and oceans, 1979-80, ofcl. spokesman opposition health and welfare, housing, employment and immigration, mem. joint senate and house com. Can. constitution, 1980-84, chmn. spl. com. reform ho. commons, mem. trilateral commn., internat. council parliamentarians global action, 1984-86; lt. gov. Nfld., 1986-91; with Nat. Transp. Agy. Can., Ottawa, 1992—; speaker in field. Served with RCAF, 1950-55. Recipient Queen's Jubilee medal, Humanitarian award Boys and Girls Clubs Can.; named Knight Order of St. John, Officer of Red Cross (hon., life). Mem. Commonwealth Parliamentary Assn., Knights of Malta (hon. life). Lodges: Knights of Malta. Office: 15 Eddy St, Ottawa, ON Canada K1A 0N9

MCGRATH, JAMES CHARLES, III, financial services company executive, lawyer, consultant; b. Davenport, Iowa, May 25, 1942; s. James Charles and Genevieve (Clarke) McG.; m. Sherburne Everett, Apr. 11, 1970. BA, U. Notre Dame, 1964; JD, U. Iowa, 1967. Bar: Iowa 1967, U.S. Ct. 1971, U.S. Ct. Mil. Appeals 1974, U.S. Ct. Appeals (D.C. cir.) 1971, U.S. Supreme Ct. 1970. Spl. agt. FBI, Balt., N.Y.C., 1967-71; trial atty. Dept. Justice, Washinton, 1971-75; dir. investigations Am. Express Co., N.Y.C., 1975-77, v.p. corp. security, 1978-82, sr. v.p. security, 1982-89; pres. McGrath Internat., Inc., 1989—; mem. overseas security adv. coun. U.S. State Dept., 1985-88; bd. dirs. Barringer Techs. Inc., New Providence, N.J. Mem. Soc. Former Spl. Agts. FBI, Am. Soc. Indsl. Security (chmn. white collar crime com. 1985-88), Internat. Assn. Credit Card Investigators (exec. adv. bd. 1985-88), Iowa State Bar Assn., D.C. Bar Assn., U.S.C. of C. (white collar crime adv. panel 1979—), Debordieu Club (Georgetown, S.C.), Phi Delta Phi. Office: McGrath Internat Inc PO Box 1384 Georgetown SC 29442

MCGRATH, JAMES EDWARD, chemistry educator; b. Easton, N.Y., July 11, 1934; s. Thomas Augustine and Marguerite Monica (Hiland) McG.; m. Marlene Mary Potter, May 9, 1959; children: Colleen McGrath Kraft, Patricia McGrath Hoover, Matthew, Barbara, Elizabeth McGrath Throckmorton, Joseph. BS in Chemistry, St. Bernadine of Siena Coll., 1956; MS in Chemistry, U. Akron, 1964, PhD in Polymer Sci., 1967. Rsch. chemist rsch. divsn. Rayonier, Inc., Whippany, N.J., 1956-59, Goodyear Tire & Rubber Co., Akron, Ohio, 1959-65; mem. staff Inst. Polymer Sci., U. Akron, 1965-67; sr. rsch. chemist Union Carbide Corp., Bound Brook, N.J., 1967-69, project scientist, 1969-72, rsch. scientist, 1972-74, rsch. scientist, group leader, 1974-75; asst. prof. chemistry Va. Poly. Inst. and State U., Blacksburg, 1975-76, assoc. prof. chemistry, 1976-79, prof. chemistry, 1980-87; dir. Materials Inst. Va. Tech., 1987-89, prof. dept. chem., co-dir. polymer materials and interface lab., 1979—, ethyl chaired prof. chem., 1986—, dir. NSF sci. and tech. ctr., 1989—; bd. dirs. ChemFab Inc., N.H.; mem. fire safety report com. NAS/NRC; mem. external adv. com. High Performance Polymers and Ceramics Ctr., Clark Atlanta U. Author, editor: Polyimides: Materials, Chemistry and Characterization, 1989; co-author (with Noshay): Block Copolymers: Overview and Critical Survey, 1977; mem. editl. bd. Jour. Polymer Sci., 1987—, Polymer, 1990—, High Performance Polymeric Polymers, 1990—; adv. bd. Jour. Polymer Sci., 1989—, Advances in Polymeric Sci. Capt. U.S. Army, 1957. Mem. NAS (mem. nat. materials bd. 1992—), NAE, Soc. Plastics Engrs. (Internat. Rsch. award 1987, Outstanding Achievement award 1992). Republican. Roman Catholic. Avocations: music, tennis, travel. Office: NSF Sci & Tech Ctr Va Inst Tech 2108 Hahn Hall Blacksburg VA 24061

MCGRATH, JAMES THOMAS, real estate investment company executive; b. N.Y., Nov. 10, 1942; s. Thomas James and Mary Ita (Finnegan) McG.; m. Paulette L. Franck, Aug. 16, 1980; 1 child, Tara (dec.). BS in Acctg., Providence Coll., 1964. CPA, N.Y. Sr. auditor Coopers & Lybrand, N.Y.C., 1968-72, mgmt. cons., 1972-74; group controller IU Internat. Corp., Phila., 1974-77; v.p. fin. Taylor Engring. Corp. subs. IU Internat., Detroit, 1977-78; controller Pool Co. subs. Enserch Corp., Houston, 1978-85; sr. v.p. fin., treas. Lone Star Gas Co. subs. Ensench Corp., Dallas, 1985-91; pres. McGrath & Assocs., Inc., Dallas, 1991—. Bd. dirs. ARC, Dallas chpt., 1990-93. Lt. USN, 1964-68. Mem. AICPA, Dallas Athletic Club, St. Vincent de Paul Soc. Republican. Roman Catholic. Avocations: golf, cooking, skiing, sailing. Home and Office: 2838 Colleen Dr Garland TX 75043-1215

MCGRATH, JOHN FRANCIS, utility executive; b. Freeport, N.Y., May 4, 1925; s. John Francis and Catherine Frances (Maune) McG.; m. Catherine Elizabeth Zainor, June 22, 1946; children—Joseph R., Susan M., Martha J., Thomas J. B.S., U.S. Mcht. Marine Acad., 1944; A.B., Muhlenberg Coll., Allentown, Pa., 1948; J.D., St. John's U., Bklyn., 1952; grad. bus. exec. program, U. Minn. Grad. Sch., 1973. Bar: N.Y. bar 1952, Minn. bar 1958. Atty. firm Casey, Lane & Mittendorf, N.Y.C., 1953-58; jud. inquiry asst. counsel N.Y. State Supreme Ct., 1957-58; atty. U.S. Steel Corp., Duluth, Minn., 1958-64; with Minn. Power & Light Co., Duluth, 1964-83; sr. v.p. Minn. Power & Light Co., 1978-83, gen. counsel, 1975-83, sec., 1979-88; adj. prof., gen. counsel Coll. St. Scholastica, Duluth; vol. atty. Bay Area Legal Svcs., Tampa, Fla. Bd. dirs. emeritus Duluth Cathedral H.S., 1972, St. Anne's Residence, Duluth, 1963-83; commr. Seaway Port Authority, Duluth, 1966-76, pres., 1970, 75; bd. dirs., sec. Good Samaritan Fund Greater Sun City Center, Fla.; mem. Hillsborough County Bd. Zoning Adjustment, 1992-94. With U.S. Mcht. Marine, 1943-46. Mem. Minn. Bar Assn., St. Louis County Bar Assn., Golf Club of Cypress Creek, K.C. (4th degree). Democrat. Roman Catholic. Home: 2036 Hampstead Cir Sun City Center FL 33573-7350

MC GRATH, JOHN JOSEPH, retired management consultant; b. Hartford, Conn., Sept. 26, 1910; s. John William and Mary Ellen (Sayers) McG.; m. Virginia L. Bonenfant, May 23, 1938; children: John P., Teresa L. (Mrs. John B. Winfield), Marygay C. (dec.), Timothy S., Richard P. A.B., U. Conn., 1933; postgrad., N.Y. U., 1936-37; postgrad. Carnegie fellow, Yale, 1937-38. Dir. Bur. Adult Edn., Hartford, 1938-41; lectr. NYU Sch. Retailing, 1947-55; mgr. tng. dept. Macy's, N.Y.C., 1946-55; mgr. edn. dept. J.C. Penney Co., 1955-59; v.p. orgn. Allied Stores Corp., 1959-75. Past bd. dirs. Allied Stores Found.; Past mem. Cardinal's Com. of Laity N.Y.C.; former mem. univ. council St. John's U.; past adv. bd. Molloy Coll.; past bd. dirs., sec., treas. B. Earl Puckett Fund for Retail Edn.; former chmn. bd. Orgn. Devel. Council.; mem. Nat. Com. for Community Service, from 1963. Served to lt. col. AUS, 1941-45; col. Res. ret. Recipient Disting. Service medal Molloy Coll. Mem. Nat. Retail Mchts. Assn. (past v.p.), Distributive Edn. Clubs Am. (past v.p.), N.Y. Marine Corps Fathers Assn. (past v.p.). Roman Catholic. Home: 23 Lincoln Ct Rockville Centre NY 11570-5744

MCGRATH, JUDITH, broadcast executive; b. Scranton, PA, 1952. Former fashion copywriter Mademoiselle; now pres. MTV Networks, Inc., New York, NY. Office: MTV Networks 1515 Broadway New York NY 10036-1903*

MCGRATH, KATHRYN BRADLEY, lawyer; b. Norfolk, Va., Sept. 2, 1944; d. James Pierce and Kathryn (Hoyle) Bradley; m. John J. McGrath Jr., June 8, 1968; children: Ian M., James D. AB, Mt. Holyoke Coll., 1966; JD, Georgetown U., 1969. Ptnr. Gardner, Carton & Douglas, Washington, 1979-83; dir. div. investment mgmt. SEC, Washington, 1983-90; ptnr. Morgan, Lewis & Bockius, Washington, 1990—. Named Disting. Exec. Pres. Reagan, 1987. Mem. Fed. Bar Assn. (exec. council securities law com.). Office: Morgan Lewis & Bockius 1800 M St NW Washington DC 20036-5869

MC GRATH, LEE PARR, author, public relations executive; b. Robstown, Tex.; d. James Carl and Margaret Marden (Russ) Parr; m. Richard J. McGrath, Nov. 5, 1955 (div. 1975); children: John Parr, Margaret Lee, Maureen Alison; m. Robert Lansing Phipps, Jan. 1, 1989. B.A., So. Methodist U., 1955. Book reviewer Dallas Morning News, 1953, New Orleans Times-Picayune, 1956; guest editor Mademoiselle mag., 1952; chmn. bd. McGrath/Power Assocs., N.Y.C., 1973-93; chmn. bd. dirs. McGrath/ Crossen Assocs., Richmond, Va., chmn., 1993—; pub. rels. cons. Waldenbooks, Campbell Soup Co., Reebok, N.Y. Times Mag. Group, Citibank. Author: Creative Careers For Women, 1968, Do-It-All-Yourself Needlepoint, 1971, What is a Father?, 1969, What Is a Mother?, 1969, What Is a Grandmother?, 1970, What Is a Grandfather?, 1970, What Is a Brother?, 1971, What Is a Sister?, 1971, What Is a Friend?, 1971, What Is a Pet?, 1971, Celebrity Needlepoint, 1972, Housekeeping With Antiques, 1971. Recipient Prix de Paris Vogue, 1954. Mem. Pub. Rels. Soc. Am., Am. Soc. Journalists and Authors, Cousteau Soc. (bd. dirs.), Cosmopolitan Club, Phi Beta Kappa. Home: Bolan Hall Plantation Ridgeland SC 29936 Office: McGrath/Power Assocs 5805 River Rd Richmond VA 23226

MCGRATH, MARY HELENA, plastic surgeon, educator; b. N.Y.C., Apr. 12, 1945; d. Vincent J. and Mary M. (Manning) McG.; m. Richard H. Simon, Apr. 11, 1970; children: Margaret E. Simon, Richard M. Simon. BA, Coll. New Rochelle, 1966; MD, St. Louis U. 1970; MPH, George Washington U., 1994. Lic. surgeon, D.C. Resident in surg.

pathology U. Colo. Med. Ctr., Denver, 1970-71, intern in gen. surgery, 1971-72, resident in gen. surgery, 1971-75, chief resident in gen. surgery, 1975-76; resident in plastic and reconstructive surgery Yale U. Sch. Medicine, New Haven, Conn., 1976-77; chief resident plastic and reconstructive surgery Yale U. Sch. Medicine, New Haven, 1977-78; fellow in hand surgery U. Conn.-Yale U., New Haven, 1978; instr. in surgery divsn. plastic and reconstructive surgery Yale U. Sch. Medicine, New Haven, 1977-78, asst. prof. plastic surgery, 1978-80; attending in plastic and reconstructive surgery Yale-New Haven Hosp., 1978-80, Columbia-Presbyn. Hosp., N.Y.C., 1980-84, George Washington U. Med. Ctr., Washington, 1984—, Children's Nat. Med. Ctr., Washington, 1985—; asst. prof. plastic surgery Columbia U., N.Y.C., 1980-84; assoc. prof. plastic surgery Sch. Medicine, George Washington U., Washington, 1984-87, prof. plastic surgery, 1987—; attending physician VA Hosp., West Haven, Conn., 1978-80; attending in surgery Hopital Albert Schweitzer, Deschapelles, Haiti, 1980; co-investigator Charles W. Ohse Fund, Yale U. Sch. Medicine, 1979; prin. investigator various rsch. grants, 1979-89; historian, bd. dirs. Am. Bd. Plastic Surgery, 1991-95; guest examiner certifying exam., 1986-88; specialist site visitor Residency Rev. Com. for Plastic Surgery, 1985, 87, 91, 94; presenter in field; cons. in field. Co-editor: (with M.L. Turner) Dermatology for Plastic Surgeons, 1993; assoc. editor: The Jour. of Hand Surgery, 1984-89, Plastic and Reconstructive Surgery, 1989-95, chmn. nominating com., 1994—; contbr. book chpts.: Problems in General Surgery, 1985, Human and Ethical Issues in the Surgical Care of Patients with Life-Threatening Disease, 1986, Problems in Aesthetic Surgery, Biological Causes and Clinical Solutions, 1986; guest reviewer numerous jours.; contbr. articles, abstracts to profl. jours. Fellow ACS (1st prize resident papers Conn. chpt. 1977); mem. AAAS, AMA, Am. Assn. Hand Surgery (exec. sec. 1988-90, rsch. grants com. 1983-86, chmn. edn. com. 1983-88, 1st prize am. resident contest 1978, and numerous other coms.; D.C. chpt. program ann. meeting chmn. 1992, v.p. 1993-94, pres. 1994—), Am. Assn. Plastic Surgeons (pub. info. com. 1988-89, James Barrrett Brown com. 1990-92, rsch. and edn. com. 1992-95), Am. Burn Assn., Am. Soc. for Aesthetic Plastic Surgery (FDA implant task force 1990—, pub. edn. com. 1991-92, sci. rsch. com. 1990—), Am. Soc. Maxillofacial Surgeons, Am. Soc. Plastic and Reconstructive Surgery (chmn. ethics com. 1985-87, chmn device/tech. evaluation com. 1993-94, bd. dirs. 1994—; mem. edn. found. bd. dirs. 1985-88, treas. 1989-92, v.p. 1992-93, pres.-elect 1993-94, pres. 1994-95, numerous other coms.), Am. Soc. Reconstructive Microsurgery (mem. edn. com. 1992-94), Am. Soc. Surgery of Hand (chmn. 1987 ann. residents' and fellows conf. 1986-87, mem. rsch. com. 1988-90, and others), Assn. Acad. Chmn. Plastic Surgery (mem. prerequisite tng. com. 1990-92, mem. com. aesthetic surgery tng. 1992—), Assn. Acad. Surgery, D.C. Met. Area Soc. Plastic and Reconstructive Surgeons, Internat. Soc. Reconstructive Surgery, Met. D.C. Soc. Surgery Hand, N.Y. Surg. Soc., Northeastern Soc. Plastic Surgeons (chmn. sci. program com. 1991, chmn. fin. com. 1992-93, treas. 1993—, others), Plastic Surgery Rsch. Coun. (chmn.-elect 1989, chmn. 1990), Soc. Ancient Medicine, Surg. Biology Club III, The Wound Healing Soc., Washington Acad. Surgery, Washington Med. and Surg. Soc. Office: George Washington U # 6B-422 2150 Penn Ave NW Washington DC 20037

MCGRATH, MICHAEL ALAN, state government officer; b. Trenton, N.J., Oct. 27, 1942; s. Lyman Levitt and Ada Frances (Hofreiter) McG.; m. Marsha Louise Palmer, Aug. 6, 1966; children: David Patrick, Stephen Gregory, Christopher Andrew. AA, Daytona Beach Jr. Coll., 1967; BA, Stetson U., 1969. Supr. 1st Trust Co., St. Paul, 1969-72; v.p. Internat. Dairy Queen, Inc., Bloomington, Minn., 1972-84; dir. ops. WISCECO, Inc., Bloomington, 1984; bus. mgr. McGraw-Hill, Inc., Edina, Minn., 1985; pres. Policy Advisors, Inc., Bloomington, 1986; treas. State of Minn., St. Paul, 1987—; mem. State Bd. Investment, State Exec. Coun., 1987—; bd. dirs. Minn. State Retirement Systems, St. Paul; Minn. rep. Pub. Fin. Network, 1989—. Mem. editorial bd. Pension Fund News, 1988-90. Chmn. bd. dirs. Urban Concerns Workshop, Inc., St. Paul, 1984-86; sec. League Minn. Human Rights Commn., Mpls., 1985-86; chmn. sen. dist. 41 Dem. Farm Labor Party, 1984-86, treas. 3d congl. dist., New Hope, Minn., 1986, pres. Dem. Farm Labor Club, Bloomington, 1982-84. Served with USAF, 1962-66. Mem. Nat. Assn. State Treas. (midwest v.p. 1988-89, sec.-treas. 1990-94, sr. v.p. 1994-95, coun. of state govts., fin. com. 1993-94, long range planning com. 1995—), Govt. Fin. Officers Assn., Nat. Assn. State Auditors, Comptrs. and Treas. Office: Office of Treasury State Minn 50 Sherburne Ave Ste 303 Saint Paul MN 55155-1470

MCGRATH, RICHARD PAUL, lawyer; b. Chgo., Aug. 10, 1929; s. John Francis and Helen Leone (Hoyer) M.; m. Luisa Sacco y Artze, Aug. 12, 1956; children: Lisa, Deborah, Holly. BA magna cum laude, Georgetown U., 1951; JD cum laude, Harvard U., 1954. Bar: D.C. 1954, N.Y. 1955, Mass. 1957, Conn. 1960, U.S. Supreme Ct. 1965. Assoc. Hughes, Hubbard, Blair and Reed, 1954-57; corp. counsel Raytheon Co., 1957-60; assoc. Cummings & Lockwood, Stamford, Conn., 1960-63, ptnr., 1963—; bd. dirs. Stamford Partnership, Landmark Club; gen. counsel, corp. sec. Internat. Exec. Svc. Corps, 1990—, mem. coun., 1990—. Editorial bd. Harvard Law Rev., 1952-54; contbr. articles to profl. jours.; panelist law seminars. Past pres. Fairfield County Coun. Boy Scouts Am. Mem. ABA, Conn. Bar Assn. (chmn. corp. law com. 1984-86, fee disputes arbitration com. 1980-84), Pi Gamma Mu, Eta Sigma Phi, Gold Key Soc., Stamford Rotary Club (past pres.), Woodway Country Club (Darien, Conn., bd. govs., sec. 1983-91). Avocations: golf, trap, chess. Office: Cummings & Lockwood 4 Stamford Plz Stamford CT 06901-3215

MCGRATH, THOMAS J., lawyer, writer, film producer; b. N.Y.C., Oct. 8, 1932; m. Mary Lee McGrath, Aug. 4, 1956 (dec.); children: Maura Lee, J. Connell; m. Diahn Williams, Sept. 28, 1974; 1 child, Courtney C. B.A., NYU, 1956, J.D., 1960. Bar: N.Y. 1960. Assoc. Milbank, Tweed, Hadley & McCloy, N.Y.C., 1960-69; ptnr. Simpson, Thacher & Bartlett, N.Y.C., 1970—; lectr., writer Practicing Law Inst., 1976—, Am. Law Inst. ABA, 1976-81. Author: Carryover Basis Under Tax Reform Act, 1977; contbg. author: Estate and Gift Tax After ERTA, 1982; producer: feature film Deadly Hero, 1977. Bd. dirs. N.Y. Philharm.; trustee Am. Austrian Found., Tanzania Wildlife Fund. With U.S. Army, 1953-54, Korea. Fellow Am. Coll. Probate Counsel; mem. N.Y. State Bar Assn., ABA, Assn. Bar City N.Y. Home: 988 5th Ave New York NY 10021-0143 Office: Simpson Thacher & Bartlett 425 Lexington Ave New York NY 10017-3903

MCGRATH, WILLIAM JOSEPH, lawyer; b. Cleve., July 6, 1943; s. William Peter and Marie Agnes (Wolf) McG.; m. Mary Ann Ostrenga; children: William Peter, Geoffrey Walton, Megan Joy. AB, John Carroll U., 1965; MA, Loyola U., 1967; JD, Harvard U., 1970. Bar: Ill. 1970. Assoc. McDermott, Will & Emery, Chgo., 1970-75, ptnr., 1976—; bd. dirs. Tomy Am., inc., Brea, Calif. Trustee Boys and Girls Club Found., 1983. Mem. ABA. Democrat. Roman Catholic. Clubs: Evanston Golf; Union League (Chgo.). Home: 943 Edgemere Ct Evanston IL 60202-1428 Office: McDermott Will & Emery 227 W Monroe St Chicago IL 60606-5016

MC GRATH, WILLIAM RESTORE, transportation planner, traffic engineer; b. Stratford, Conn., Oct. 4, 1922; s. Thomas Christopher and Alpha Retta (Perry) McG.; m. Lillian Joyce DeAngelis, Mar. 9, 1945; children: Brian, David, Raymond, Harold, Vincent, Mary, Kevin, Rita, Beverly, Nora, Margaret. B.C.E., Rensselaer Poly. Inst., 1930; diploma, Yale Bur. Hwy. Traffic, 1951. Registered profl. engr. Calif., Conn., Mass., N.J., N.Y., Fla., Maine, N.H. Mem. faculty Yale Bur. Hwy. Traffic, New Haven, 1951-55; dir. traffic and parking City of New Haven, 1955-63; transp. coordinator Boston Redevel. Authority, 1963-68; commr. dept. traffic and parking City of Boston, 1968-70; v.p. Raymond Parish Pine & Weiner, Tarrytown, N.Y., 1970-79; mgr. traffic and parking Daniel, Mann, Johnson & Mendenhall, 1980-83; ptnr. McGrath, O'Rourke & Assocs., 1983-85; owner/mgr. McGrath Engring., Cape Coral, Fla., 1985-87; transp. planner Lee County Dept. Transp. & Engring., 1987-94; cons. AID, Madras, India, 1963, Dublin, Ireland, 1965; Cons. World Trade Center, Moscow, USSR, 1974. Mem. exec. com. Met. Area Planning Council, Boston, 1965-70, Gov.'s Council on Transp., 1968-70; mem. urban ecology adv. council Inst. Ecology, 1973—. Served with USNR, 1943-45. Mem. NSPE, Inst. Transp. Engrs. (hon., nat. pres. 1973, chmn. equal opportunity com., chmn. U.S. legis. com.), Transp. Rsch. Bd., Fla. Engring. Soc., Sigma Xi, Tau Beta Pi, Chi Epsilon. Roman Catholic. Home: 215 SE 14th Ct Cape Coral FL 33990-1738 Office: 4906 Victoria Dr Unit 104 Cape Coral FL 33904

MC GRAW, DARRELL VIVIAN, JR., attorney general; b. Mullens, W.Va., Nov. 8, 1936; s. Darrell Vivian and Julia (ZeKany) McG.; m. Jorea Marple; children: Elizabeth, Sarah, Darrell, Elliott. AB, W.Va. U., 1961, JD, 1964, MA, 1977. Bar: W.Va. 1964. Gen. atty. Fgn. Claims Settlement Commn., U.S. Dept. State, 1964; counsel to gov. State of W.Va., 1965-68; pvt. practice Charleston, Shepherdstown and Morgantown, 1968-76; judge W.Va. Supreme Ct. Appeals, Charleston, 1977-88, chief justice, 1982-93; atty. gen. State of W.Va., Charleston, 1993—. Served with U.S. Army, 1954-57. Fellow W.Va. U., NCEP/Ford Found. Fellow Am. Polit. Sci. Assn. Democrat. Office: State Capitol 26 East Charleston WV 25305

MCGRAW, DONALD JESSE, biologist, historian of science, writer; b. Altadena, Calif., Oct. 27, 1943; s. Jesse E. and Mary L. (Hajostek) McG.; m. Laura Lee Hansen, July 13, 1968; children: Adrienne, Holly, Rachel. BS in Biol. Scis., Calif. State Poly. Coll., 1965; MS, Utah State U., 1967; PhD, Oreg. State U., 1976. Registered microbiologist Am. Acad. Microbiology. Research asst. microbiology Utah State U., 1965-66, teaching asst. food and aquatic microbiology, 1966-67; grad. teaching asst. gen. biology Oreg. State U., 1970-72, instr., 1972-73; tchr. phys. and biol. scis. U.S. Bur. Indian Affairs Boarding Sch., Shonto, Ariz., 1974-75; asst. prof. biology Franklin Coll., Ind., 1975-78; adj. asst. prof. biology Ind. Central U., Indpls., 1977-78; adj. asst. prof. Ind. U.-Purdue U., Columbus, 1978; mem. faculty Yavapai Community Coll., Prescott, Ariz., 1978-79; assoc. dir. Ute Research Lab., Ft. Duchesne, Utah, 1980-81, dir., 1981-82; vis. prof. biology Bard Coll., N.Y., Spring 1984, Coll. St. Thomas, Minn., 1985-87; adj. asst. prof. biology, assoc. provost U. San Diego, 1988—; ranger-naturalist U.S. Nat. Park Svc., summers, 1970-79, 83-86, vol., 1989—; writer, 1968—; adj. faculty Southwestern Coll., 1989-92. Contbr. numerous articles on history of microbiology and history of antibiotics to sci. publs. Commr. San Diego County Columbian Quincentenary Commn., 1990-93, chmn. edn. com., 1990-93; mem. pres.'s adv. com. San Diego Zool. Soc., 1995—. Recipient Disting. Alumnus award, Calif. State Poly. U., 1991, Monrovia High Sch., 1991; Eli Lilly doctoral grantee Oreg. State U., 1973-74. Mem. AAAS, History of Sci. Soc., Cabrillo Hist. Assn. (bd. dirs. 1989-94, vice chair 1992, chair 1993, 94), Alpha Scholastic Honor Soc. of Franklin Coll. (pres. 1976-78), Sigma Xi, Beta Beta Beta. Office: U San Diego Office of Provost 5998 Alcala Park San Diego CA 92110-2492

MCGRAW, HAROLD WHITTLESEY, JR., publisher; b. Bklyn., Jan. 10, 1918; s. Harold Whittlesey and Louise (Higgins) McG.; m. Anne PerLee, Nov. 30, 1940; children: Suzanne, Harold Whittlesey III, Thomas Per-Lee, Robert Pearse. Grad., Lawrenceville (N.J.) Sch., 1936; A.B., Princeton U., 1940. With G.M. Basford (advt. agy.), N.Y.C., 1940-41, Brentano's Bookstores, Inc., 1946; with McGraw-Hill Book Co., Inc., N.Y.C., 1947—, successively promotion mgr., dir. co. advt. and trade sales, 1947-55, dir., v.p. charge trade book, indsl. and bus. book depts., co. advt., 1955-61, sr. v.p., 1961-68, pres., chief exec. officer, 1968-74; pres., chief exec. officer McGraw-Hill, Inc., 1974-83, chairman, 1976-88; chairman emeritus, 1988—; bd. dirs. McGraw Hill, Inc., 1954-88. Founder, pres., bd. dirs. Bus. Council Effective Literacy and Bus. Press Edn. Found. Served as capt. USAAF, 1941-45. Clubs: Bent Pine (Vero Beach); Blind Brook (Purchase, N.Y.); Wee Burn (Darien, Conn.). Home: Watch Tower Rd Darien CT 06820 Office: McGraw-Hill Inc 1221 Ave Of The Americas New York NY 10020-1001

MCGRAW, JACK WILSON, government official; b. Balt., May 19, 1943; s. P.W. and Nina (Gwinn) McG.; m. Nancy F. Foster, Aug. 31, 1974; children—David, Mark. B.A., Morris Harvey Coll., 1964; B.Div., Tex. Christian U., 1967. Ordained minister Christian Ch. (Disciples of Christ). Dir. temporary housing HUD, Washington, 1979-82; asst. assoc. dir. Fed. Emergency Mgmt. Agy., Washington, 1982, dir., 1982-83; dep. asst. adminstr. EPA Office Solid Waste and Emergency Response, Washington, 1983-88, acting asst. adminstr.; dep. regional adminstr. EPA Regional Office, Denver, 1988—. Nominee William H. Jump award HUD, 1972, Presdl. Rank award for sr. exec. service. Presbyterian. Avocation: skiing. Home: 8074 S Oneida St Englewood CO 80112-3128 Office: EPA Regional Office 999 18th St Denver CO 80202-2440

MCGRAW, JAMES L., retired ophthalmologist, educator; b. Syracuse, N.Y., Sept. 7, 1917; s. John J. and Elizabeth B. (Hemmer) M. A.B., Syracuse U., 1938, M.D., 1941; D.M.S., Columbia U., 1946. Diplomate Am. Bd. Ophthalmology. Intern, Grad. Hosp. U. Pa., 1941-42; resident Inst. Ophthalmology of Presbyn. Hosp., N.Y.C., 1942-46; teaching and research fellow Inst. Ophthalmology, Columbia U. Coll. Physicians and Surgeons, N.Y.C., 1945-46, instr. ophthalmology, 1945-46; clin. instr. ophthalmology SUNYHealth Sci. Ctr. Hosp., Syracuse, N.Y., 1947-54, clin. assoc. prof., 1954-57, prof., dept. chmn., 1957-84, prof. emeritus, 1984—; attending ophthalmologist Crouse-Irving Meml. Hosp.; Univ. Hosp. SUNY; cons. VA Hosp. Contbr. articles to profl. jours, papers to profl. orgns. Served to maj. M.C., U.S. Army, 1950-52. Mem. Onondaga County Med. Soc., N.Y. State Med. Soc., AMA, Am. Acad. Ophthalmology (Honor award 1963), Nat. Soc. for Prevention Blindness, Nat. Med. Found. for Eye Care, Am. Bd. Ophthalmology, N.Y. Ophthal. Soc., Inst. Ophthalmology Alumni Assn., N.Y. Eye Bank, Alpha Omega Alpha. Roman Catholic. Club: Skaneateles Country. Home: 3069 E Lake Rd Skaneateles NY 13152-9002 Office: Eye Cons of Syracuse 224 Harrison St Syracuse NY 13202-3052

MCGRAW, JAMES MICHAEL, manufacturing company executive; b. Detroit, Mar. 26, 1945; s. Sheldon William and Rose Mary (Leszczynski) McG.; 1 child, Christie. BS in Acctg., U. Detroit, 1967; MBA, U. Mich., 1968. CPA, Mich. Audit sr. Touche Ross & Co., Detroit, 1968-75; mgr. fin. analysis Fruehauf Corp., Detroit, 1975-77; v.p. fin. Fruehauf Internat. Ltd., Detroit, 1977-87, exec. v.p. Fruehauf Internat., Ltd., 1988-93; v.p. sales, mktg. and internat. ops. Morgan Corp., 1993—; adj. lectr. Walsh Coll., Troy, Mich., 1975-77. Dir. S.E. Mich. Jr. Achievement. With U.S. Army, 1969-71. Mem. AICPA, Mich. Assn. CPAs, Internat. Bus. Forum, World Trade Club, Alpha Sigma Nu. Roman Catholic. Home: 20 Vincent Dr Honey Brook PA 19344 Office: Morgan Corp 1 Morgan Way Morgantown PA 19543

MCGRAW, ROBERT PIERCE, publishing executive; b. Bronxville, N.Y., June 13, 1954; s. Harold W. Jr. and Anne (Per-Lee) McG.; m. Dawn A. Watson, Sept. 15, 1979; children: Avery Christine, Dale Per-Lee. AB, Princeton U., 1976. Sales rep. McGraw Hill Book Co., Chgo., 1976-79; editor McGraw-Hill Inc., N.Y.C., 1979-82, editorial dir., 1982-83, gen. mgr., 1983-85, group v.p., 1985-87, exec. v.p., 1987—; dep. dir. Med. China. Ltd., Hong Kong, 1986—. Republican. Presbyterian. Office: McGraw-Hill Inc 1221 Ave Of The Americas New York NY 10020-1001

MCGRAW, WARREN RANDOLPH, II, state legislator, lawyer; b. Pineville, W.Va., June 13, 1963; s. Warren R. and Peggy (Shufflebarger) McG. BS in Edn., East Tenn. State U., 1985; JD, John Marshall Law Sch., 1988. Asst. atty. gen., 1988-89; mem. W.Va. Ho. of Dels., 1992—. Vol. Boys Club of Am., Spl. Olympics; mem. Raleigh County YMCA; bd. dirs. Tri-County Baseball Assn.; chmn. bd. dirs. Beckley Tri-County Baseball Assn.; past mem. 9th Senatorial Dist. Dem. Exec. Com., 4th Congl. Dist.; active NAACP. Mem. NFL Players Assn., W.Va. State Bar Assn., Ga. State Bar Assn., Raleigh Bar Assn., Wyo. Bar Assn., AFL-CIO, Beckley Rotary Club. Democrat. Methodist. Avocation: former professional football player.

MCGREAL, JOSEPH A., JR., publishing company executive; b. Bklyn., Mar. 6, 1935; s. Joseph A. and Aresta (Noon) McG.; m. Margaret A. Molloy, June 6, 1959; children—Patrick, Pegeen, Joseph. B.B.A., St. Francis Coll., 1962. Pub. Romaine Pierson Programs Inc., Port Washington, N.Y. Served with U.S. Army, 1955-57. Home: 52 Rockywood Rd Manhasset NY 11030-2513 Office: Romaine Pierson Pubs Inc 80 Shore Rd Port Washington NY 11050-2215

MC GREGOR, DONALD THORNTON, newspaper editor, journalist; b. McLennan County, Tex., Mar. 20, 1924; s. Marshall Thornton and Flora Elvira (Welch) McG.; m. Alice Carlene Barnhill, Dec. 21, 1946; children: Alice Diane McGregor Tyrone, Robert Thornton, Donald Wayne. B.A., Baylor U., Waco, Tex., 1947; postgrad., Southwestern Baptist Theol. Sem., Ft. Worth, 1951-52. Agr. reporter Midland (Tex.) Reporter-Telegram, 1948-49; continuity dir. Sta. KCRS, Midland, 1949-50; editorial asso. Bapt. Standard, Dallas, 1952-55; real estate editor Dallas Times Herald, 1959; pub.

relations exec. Union Bankers Ins. Co., Dallas, 1955-58; asso. editor Bapt. Standard, 1959-71; editor Calif. So. Bapt., Fresno, 1971-73; publisher Kemp (Tex.) News, Ferris (Tex.) Wheel, also Dawson (Tex.) Herald, 1973-74; asso. editor Bapt. Record, Jackson, Miss., 1974-76, editor, 1976-90; ret., 1990. Chmn. public rels. adv. com. So. Bapt. Conv., 1979-80. Served with AUS, 1943-45; prisoner of war, Germany, 1944-45. Decorated Purple Heart; recipient Distinguished Service award So. Bapt. Conv., 1973. Mem. So. Bapt. Press Assn. (sec.-treas. 1964-68, pres. 1981, chmn. Bapt. press liaison com. 1988-90), Associated Bapt. Press (co-founder and bd. dirs., exec. dir. 1994—). Home: PO Box 850547 Mesquite TX 75185

MCGREGOR, JACK EDWIN, natural resource company executive; b. Kittanning, Pa., Sept. 22, 1934; s. Russell Alexander and Leah Rachel (Hampton) McG.; m. Carol Dangerfield, Nov. 23, 1955 (div. Mar. 1992); children: Nancy, Douglas, Elisabeth, Heather; m. Mary-Jane Foster, Jan. 2, 1993. BS, Yale U., 1956; LLB, U. Pitts., 1962. Bar: Pa. 1963, D.C. 1971, U.S. Supreme Ct. 1971. Pres. Pitts. Penguins Hockey Club, 1966-70; assoc. Reed Smith Shaw & McClay, Pitts., 1962-68, 70; gen. counsel U.S. Pay Bd., Washington, 1971-72; asst. legal adviser econ. affairs Dept. State, Washington, 1971; v.p., gen. counsel Potomac Electric Power Corp., Washington, 1972-74; exec. v.p., chief ops. officer Carey Energy Corp., N.Y.C., 1974-79; pres., chief exec. officer Hampton-Douglas Corp., Bedford, N.Y., and Washington, 1979-85; exec. v.p. Aquarion Co., Bridgeport, 1985-88, pres., dir., 1988—, CEO, 1990—; dir. People's Bank, Physicians Health Svcs., Inc., Bay State Gas Co.; pres. Nat. Assn. Water Cos. Mem. Pa. Senate, 1962-70; del., asst. floor mgr. Republican Nat. Conv., 1964; co-chair Conn. Gov.-elect John Roland's Transition Team, 1994-95; bd. dirs. Fairfield U., Barnum Mus. Found., Mystic Marinelife Aquarium, Conn. Gov.'s Greenways Com., Conn. Com. Regional Plan Assn. Capt. USMC, 1956-59. Mem. ABA, D.C. Bar Assn., Pa. Bar Assn., Country Club of Fairfield, Chevy Chase (Md.) Club, Conn. Golf Club. Presbyterian. Home: 74 Freeborn Rd Easton CT 06612 Office: Aquarion Co 835 Main St Bridgeport CT 06601-2353

MCGREGOR, MARTIN LUTHER, JR., lawyer; b. Rossville, Ga., Mar. 25, 1940; s. Martin Luther and Ora Louise (Stanley) McG.; m. Linda Joyce Buehler, June 31, 1978; children: Martin Luther III, James Franklin. BS in Chemistry, U. Ga., 1962; PhD, U. S.C., 1969; JD, Okla. U., 1978. Bar: Tex. 1979, U.S. Patent Office 1978, U.S. Supreme Ct. 1985. Various teaching positions Ga. and S.C., 1966-70; rsch. assoc. Okla. State U., Stillwater, 1971-76; rsch. chemist FMC Corp., Middleport, N.Y., 1976-77; assoc. atty. Baker & Botts, Houston, 1978-85; atty. Norvell & Assocs., Houston, 1985-86; mng. ptnr. Jamison McGregor & Harris, Houston, 1986-89; sr. biotech. specialist Baker & Botts, Houston, 1989-94; head biotech. Gardere & Wynn, Dallas, 1994—; adj. prof. chemistry U. Tex., Arlington, 1995—. Mem. editorial bd. Biotech. Law Reports; contbr. articles to profl. jours. Mem. steering com. BioInternat. '93 Found. for the Future, Houston, 1992—, Andrews Campaign, Houston, 1992; bd. dirs. Mangum Manor Civic Assn., Houston, 1986. 2d lt. USAR, 1962-65. Named to Order of the Coif, Okla. U., 1978. Mem. AAAS, Houston Intellectual Property Law Assn., Am. Chem. Soc., Am. Arbitration Assn. (panel of patent arbitrators), Biotech. Ind. Orgn. (co-chair law 1993—), Assn. Biotech. Cos. (chair tech. transfer 1992-93, co-chair regulatory and patents 1991-92, gen. counsel s.w. chpt.). Unitarian Universalist. Avocations: camping, soccer coaching, chess. Office: Gardere & Wynne 1601 Elm St Ste 3000 Dallas TX 75201

MC GREGOR, MAURICE, cardiologist, medical educator; b. South Africa, Mar. 24, 1920; s. Frank and Eleanor (Roechling) McG.; m. Margaret Rigsby Becklake, Mar. 20, 1948; children—James Andrew, Margaret Jane. M.B., B.Ch., U. Witwatersrand, Johannesburg, South Africa, 1942, M.D., 1947. Lectr. U. Witwatersrand, 1950-57; assoc. prof. medicine McGill U., Montreal, Que., Can., 1958-66, prof. medicine, 1966—, prof. emeritus, 1987—; dean medicine, 1967-72, vice prin. health care, 1972-74; physician-in-chief Royal Victoria Hosp., 1974-79, sr. physician, 1980—; dean medicine U. Witwatersrand, Republic of South Africa, 1984-86; chmn. Council for the Evaluation of Health Tech., Que., 1988-94. Contbr. numerous articles to tech. jours. Fellow Royal Coll. Physicians (London, Eng.), Royal Coll. Physicians and Surgeons Can. Research in physiology, physiopathology of coronary circulation in health and disease, health tech., health policy. Home: 532 Pine Ave W, Montreal, PQ Canada H2W 1S6 Office: M4 76 Royal Victoria Hospital, 687 Pine Ave W, Montreal, PQ Canada H3A 1A1

MCGREGOR, WALTER, medical products company designer, inventor, consultant, educator; b. Kiew, Ukraine, Nov. 2, 1937; came to U.S., 1957; s. William and Lydia (Aplass) McG.; m. Helen McGregor, July 18, 1965; children: Roxanne, Walter. BS, Fairleigh Dickinson U., 1973, MBA, 1975. Sect. leader Ethicon Inc., Somerville, N.J., 1965-68, supr., 1968-76, mgr., 1976-83, dir. surg. products devel. and materials engring., 1983-92, dir. of tech., 1992-94; pres., CEO Biomark Tech. Inc., Flemington, N.J., 1994—; sr. v.p. Global Med. Countertrade Corp., 1994—; pres. Global Med. Countertrade Svcs., Inc., 1994—; guest cons. Wilmer Inst., Johns Hopkins Hosp. Rsch. Lab., Balt., 1965-70; guest lectr. dept. plastic surgery U. Va. Med. Sch., Charlottesville, 1986—. Contbr. articles to profl. jours. Patentee surg. instruments. Life mem. Rep. Presdl. Task Force, Washington, 1994—; mem. Rep. Nat. Com., 1991. Fellow Soc. for Advancement of Med. Instrumentation; mem. Am. Med. Informatics Assn. (founding), Am. Mktg. Assn. (profl.), Med. Mktg. Assn. Avocations: stamp collecting, fishing, reading in surgical developments. Home: 104 Hoffman Rd Flemington NJ 08822-7023 Office: Biomark Tech Inc 104 Hoffman Rd Flemington NJ 08822

MCGREW, JEAN B., superintendent. Supt. Northfield Twp. High Sch. Dist. 225, Glenview, Ill. Recipient State Finalist for Nat. Supt. of Yr. award, 1992. Office: Northfield Twp HS Dist 225 1835 Landwehr Rd Glenview IL 60025-1241

MCGRIFF, DEBORAH, school system administrator. Supt. Detroit public schs. Office: Detroit SD 5057 Woodward Ave Detroit MI 48202-4049

MCGRIFF, FRED (FREDERICK STANLEY MCGRIFF), baseball player; b. Tampa, Oct. 31, 1963. Grad. high sch., Tampa. Baseball player N.Y. Yankees, 1981-82, Toronto Blue Jays, 1982-90, San Diego Padres, 1990-93, Atlanta Braves, 1993—. Named to Sporting News All-Star team, 1989, 92, 93; recipient Silver Slugger award, 1989, 92, 93; mem. Nat. League All-Star Team, 1992, 94; Am. League Home Run Leader, 1989; Nat. League Home Run Leader, 1992. Office: Atlanta Braves PO Box 4064 Atlanta GA 30302

MCGROARTY, BRUCE JAMES, building products manufacturing executive; b. Montreal, Que., Can., Sept. 1, 1942; came to U.S., 1980; s. Herbert Thomas and Margaret Ann (Langon) McG.; m. Bernice Dianne MacArthur, May 15, 1965; children: Shannon, Tracey, Brent, Leigh, Ryan. BBA, Ryerson U., Toronto, Ont., Can., 1968, BBM, 1975; MBA, McMaster U., Hamilton, Ont., Can., 1977. Rep. maj. accts. Abitibi-Price, Inc., Toronto, 1972-75, corp. planner, 1975-80; mgr. mktg. services Abitibi-Price Corp., Troy, Mich., 1980-83; plant mgr. Abitibi-Price Corp., Toledo, 1983-84; exec. v.p. Abitibi-Price Corp., Troy, 1984-85; pres. Abitibi-Price Corp. subs. Abitibi-Price, Inc., Troy, 1985—; chmn. bd., chief exec. officer, dir. Azerty, Inc., Orchard Park, N.Y. Avocations: skiing, squash, hockey, boating, education. Home: 20435 Ronsdale Dr Franklin MI 48025-3865 Office: Azerty Inc 13 Centre Dr Orchard Park NY 14127*

MC GRODDY, JAMES CLEARY, computer company executive; b. N.Y.C., Apr. 6, 1937; s. Charles B. and Helen F. (Cleary) McG.; children: Kathleen, Sheila, Christine, James. B.S. St. Joseph's U., 1958; Ph.D., U. Md., 1964. With IBM, 1965—; v.p. devel. and mfg. gen. tech. officer IBM, White Plains, N.Y., 1977—; prof. Tech. U. Denmark, 1970-71. Contbr. articles to profl. jours.; patentee in field. Fellow IEEE, Am. Phys. Soc. (George E. Pake prize 1995). Office: IBM Science and Tech Old Orchard Rd Armonk NY 10504-1709

MC GRORY, MARY, columnist; b. Boston, 1918; d. Edward Patrick and Mary (Jacobs) McGrory. A.B., Emmanuel Coll. Reporter Boston Herald Traveler, 1942-47; book reviewer Washington Star, 1947-54, feature writer for nat. staff, 1954-81; now syndicated columnist The Washington Post, Universal Press Syndicate. Recipient George Polk Meml. award; Pulitzer prize for commentary, 1975. Office: Washington Post 1150 15th St NW Washington DC 20071

MCGRORY, MARY KATHLEEN, university official; b. N.Y.C., Mar. 22, 1933; d. Patrick Joseph and Mary Kate (Gilvary) McG. BA, Pace U., 1957; MA, U. Notre Dame, 1962; PhD, Columbia U., 1969; DHL, Albertus Magnus Coll., 1984; LLD, Briarwood Coll., 1990; DHL, Trinity Coll., 1991. Prof. English Western Conn. State U., Danbury, 1969-78; dean of arts and scis. Eastern Conn. State U., Willimantic, 1978-80, v.p. for acad. affairs, 1981-85; pres. Hartford Coll. for Women, Conn., 1985-91; sr. fellow U. Va. Commonwealth Ctr., Charlottesville, 1991-92; exec. dir. Soc. Values in Higher Edn./Georgetown U., Washington, 1992—; pres. MKM Assocs., Holland, Ma., 1983—. Author: Yeats, Joyce & Beckett, 1975. Bd. dirs. Hartford Hosp., 1985-93; chmn. bd. govs. Greater Hartford Consortium Higher Edn., 1989-90. Fels Found. fellow, 1966-67, NEH summer fellow, 1975; Ludwig Vogelstein Found. travel grantee, 1973. Mem. New Eng. Jr. Community and Tech. Coll. Coun. (v.p. 1988-91), Am. Assn. Higher Edn., Med. Acad. of Am., Greater Hartford C. of C. (bd. dirs. 1989-91), Hartford Club (bd. dirs. 1988-91). Avocations: writing, swimming, piano. Home: 1727 Massachusetts Ave NW Washington DC 20036 Office: Georgetown U Soc For Values Higher Washington DC 20057

MCGRUDER, ROBERT, newspaper publishing executive. Mng. editor Detroit Free Press. Office: 321 W Lafayette Blvd Detroit MI 48226-2703*

MC GRUDER, STEPHEN JONES, portfolio manager; b. Louisville, Nov. 14, 1943; s. Clement W. and Elizabeth Boyer (Short) McG.; m. Angeline W. Goreau, Mar. 19, 1983; 1 child, Keaton A. BS in Chemistry, Stanford U., 1966; BA in Econs, Claremont Men's Coll., 1966. Chartered fin. analyst. V.p. Surveyor Fund, N.Y.C., 1978-86, The Portfolio Group, N.Y.C., 1986-88, Wafra Investment Adv. Group, N.Y.C., 1988-95, Lord Abbett, N.Y.C., 1995—. Mem. Fin. Analysts Fedn., Univ. Club. Republican. Presbyterian. Office: Wafra Investment Adv Group 1 W 54th St # 22 New York NY 10019-5404

MCGUANE, THOMAS FRANCIS, III, author, screenwriter; b. Wyandotte, Mich., Dec. 11, 1939; s. Thomas Francis and Alice Rita (Torphy) McG.; m. Portia Crockett, Sept. 8, 1962 (div. 1975); 1 child, Thomas Francis; m. Margot Kidder, 1976 (div. 1977); 1 child, Maggie; m. Laurie Buffett, Sept. 19, 1977; 1 child, Anne Buffett; 1 stepchild, Heather. BA, Mich. State U., 1962; MFA, Yale U., 1965; Wallace Stegner fellow, Stanford U., 1966; PhD (hon.), Mont. State U., 1993. Author: The Sporting Club, 1969, The Bushwacked Piano, 1971 (Richard and Hinda Rosenthal Found. award for fiction 1971), Ninety-Two in the Shade, 1973 (Nat. Book award nomination 1974), Panama, 1977, An Outside Chance: Essays on Sport, 1980, Nobody's Angel, 1982, Something to be Desired, 1984, In the Crazies: Book and Portfolio, 1984, To Skin a Cat, 1986, Keep the Change, 1989, An Outside Chance: Classic and New Essays on Sport, 1990, Nothing But Blue Skies, 1992, Sons, 1993; screenwriter: (films) Rancho Deluxe, 1975, Missouri Breaks, 1976, Tom Horn, 1980, Cold Feet, 1989; screenwriter, dir.: (films) Ninety-Two in the Shade, 1975; editor: Best American Sports Writing, 1992; contbr. to Sports Illustrated mag., 1969-73. Wallace Stegner fellow Stanford Univ., 1966-67; recipient Mont. Gov.'s award 1988, N.W. Bookseller's award 1992, Golden Plate award Am. Acad. Achievement, 1993. Mem. Tale Club of N.Y. Address: PO Box 25 Mc Leod MT 59052-0025*

MCGUE, CHRISTIE, federal official; b. Colombus, Ohio, Feb. 1, 1949; m. Robert Calt, Nov. 13, 1992. Sr. mgmt. analyst Nuclear Regulatory Comm., Washington, 1973-76; asst. dir. Office of Elec. Power Regulations, asst. dir. Office of Hydropower Licensing Fed. Energy Regulatory Comm., Washington, 1977-85; with Dept. Interior, Washington, 1986-88; dep. exec. dir. Fed. Energy Regulatory Commn., Washington, 1990-93, exec. dir., CFO, 1994—. Office: Fed Energy Regulatory Commn 825 N Capitol St NE Rm 9106 Washington DC 20426

MCGUFF, JOE, newspaper editor. V.p., editor Kansas City Star. Office: Kansas City Star 1729 Grand Ave Kansas City MO 64108-1413

MCGUIGAN, CHARLES JAMES, rehabilitation therapist; b. Maple Shade, N.J., May 8, 1944; s. Charles J. and Frances G. (Abbott) McG.; divorced; 1 child, Richard Holmes. AA, Atlantic C.C., 1977; student, Montclair State Coll., 1977-78, Glassboro State Coll., 1981-83, 88; BA in Social Sci. and History, Thomas A. Edison Coll., 1983. Cert. elem. tchr. N.J., computer specialist Fla., CPR, first aid, team tng., rehab. therapist. Tchr. 4th and 5th grades, track coach St. Nicholas Sch., Atlantic City, 1978-84; tchr. 5th grade, track coach St. Michaels Sch., Atlantic City, 1984-88; security guard Securex, Inc., Tampa, Fla., 1988; resident tng. instr. Upper Pinellas Assn. for Retarded Citizens, Clearwater, Fla., 1988-89; rehab. therapist Gulf Coast Ctr., Ft. Myers, Fla., 1989—; track coach Camden (N.J.) Diocese Office, 1983-88. Author poetry; contbr. to anthologies. Singer with barbershop quartet, musical shows; tchr. creative writing Unity Ch., Ft. Myers, Fla. Recipient Outstanding Citizen award Equal Opportunity Fund, 1975, Liberty Bell award City of Phila., 1976, Outstanding Counselor award Atlantic Human Resource, 1984; named Golden Poet of Yr. World of Poetry, 1991; 95 Presidential Poetry award Iliad Press. Mem. Kappa Delta Pi. Republican. Roman Catholic. Avocations: creative writing, travel, reading, computers, raising chows. Home: 53 Granite St Rockland ME 04841

MC GUIGAN, FRANK JOSEPH, psychologist, educator; b. Oklahoma City, Dec. 7, 1924. BA, UCLA, 1945, MA, 1949; PhD, U. So. Calif., 1950. Instr. Pepperdine Coll., 1949-50; asst. prof. U. Nev., 1950-51; rsch. assoc. Psychol. Corp., 1950-51; rsch. scientist, sr. rsch. scientist, acting dir. rsch. Human Resources Rsch. Office, George Washington U., 1951-55; prof. psychology (Hollins Coll.), Roanoke, Va., 1955-76; chmn. dept. (Hollins Coll.), 1955-76; rsch. prof. (Grad. Sch.); prof. dept. psychology, dep. psychiatry and behavioral scis. (Sch. Medicine); dir. Performance Rsch. Lab., Inst. Advanced Study, U. Louisville, 1976-83; prof. psychology, dir. Inst. Stress Mgmt. U.S. Internat. U., San Diego, 1983—; adj. prof. psychiatry and behavioral scis. U. Louisville Sch. Medicine, 1986—; adj. rsch. prof. N.C. State U., 1970-72; vis. prof. U. Hawaii, summer 1965, U. Calif., Santa Barbara, 1966, Hiroshima Shudo U., 1984; Nat. Acad. Scis. vis. scientist, Hungary, 1975, Bulgaria, 1987; sr. rsch. fellow Naval Health Rsch. Ctr., summer 1991. Author: numerous books in field including The Biological Basis of Behavior, 1963, Contemporary Studies in Psychology, 1972, Cognitive Psychophysiology - Principles of Covert Behavior, 1978, Experimental Psychology: Methods of Research, 6th edit., 1993, Psychophysiological Measurement of Covert Behavior—A Guide for the Laboratory, 1979, Calm Down—A Guide for Stress and Tension Control, 2d edit., 1992, Stress and Tension Control: Procs. of Internat., Interdisciplinary Conf. on Stress and Tension Control, 1980, vol. 2, 1984, vol. 3, 1989; (with Edmund Jacobson) cassettes Self-Directed Progressive Relaxation Training Instructions, 1981, Critical Issues in Psychology, Psychiatry and Physiology, 1986, Biological Psychology--A Cybernetic Science, 1994; editor numerous works in field.; editor, Internat. Jour. Stress Mgmt.; contbr. articles to profl. jours.; mem. editorial bd. Archiv fur Arzneitherapie, Biofeedback and Self-regulation, Activitas Nervosae Superioris. Served with USNR, 1942-46. Recipient award for outstanding contbns. to edn. in psychology Am. Psychol. Found., 1973, Blue medal of honor Union Scientists Bulgaria, 1980, medal of Sechenov USSR Acad. Med. Scis., 1983, medal of Anohkin, 1984, Pres.'s medal U. Hiroshima-Shudo, 1982, medal Okayama U., 1987, medal Tbilisi (USSR) Inst. Physiology, 1989, Edmund Jacobson award for stress mgmt., 1995, Gold medal award for lifetime achievement in application of psychology Am. Psychol. Found., 1995. Fellow APA, Internat. Soc. Rsch. on Aggression; mem. Am. Assn. Advancement of Tension Control (now Internat. Stress Mgmt. Assn.) (exec. dir. 1973-82, pres. 1985-89, exec. dir. 1992—, chmn. bd. dirs.), Pavlovian Soc. (mem. exec. bd. 1973—, pres. 1975-86, editor, chmn. publ. bd. Pavlovian Jour. Biol. Sci.), Am. Physiol. Soc., Biofeedback Soc. Am., Internam. Soc. Psychology, Internat. Congress of Applied Psychology, Psychonomic Soc., Soc. Psychophysiol. Rsch., Bulgarian Soc. for Psychiatry (hon.), Sigma Xi. Office: US Internat U Inst for Stress Mgmt 10455 Pomerado Rd San Diego CA 92131-1717

MC GUIGAN, JAMES EDWARD, physician, scientist, educator; b. Paterson, N.J., Aug. 20, 1931; s. Harold Taylor and Marie (Lloyd) McG.; m. Nancy Baron; children: Sheila, Maura, John. Student, Coll. Holy Cross, 1949-50; BS, Seattle U., 1952; MD, St. Louis U., 1956; PhD (hon.), Uppsala U., Sweden, 1989. Diplomate Am. Bd. Internal Medicine, Am. Bd. Gastroenterology. Intern Pa. Hosp., 1956-57; asst. resident in medicine U.

Wash. Sch. Medicine, Seattle, 1960-62; fellow in gastroenterology U. Wash. Sch. Medicine, 1962-64; spl. fellow in immunology Washington U. Sch. Medicine, St. Louis, 1964-66; asst. prof. medicine Washington U. Sch. Medicine, 1966-69; chief div. gastroenterology U. Fla. Coll. Medicine, Gainesville, 1969-78; prof. U. Fla. Coll. Medicine, 1969—, chmn. dept. medicine, 1976—; Mem. program projects com. Nat. Inst. Arthritis, Metabolic and Digestive Diseases, NIH, 1971-73, mem. gen. medicine A study sect., 1974-76, chmn., 1976-78. Served to capt. USAF, 1957-60. Research fellow in gastroenterology; Spl. fellow in immunology; Career Devel. award; research grantee NIH; research grantee Am. Heart Assn.; research grantee Am. Cancer Soc. Mem. Am. Assn. Immunologists, Am. Gastroent. Assn. (Disting. Achievement award 1974), Am. Soc. Clin. Investigation, Assn. Am. Physicians, Assn. Profs. of Medicine, Fla. Clin. Practice Assn. (pres. 1985-91), Alachua County Med. Soc. (pres. 1985-86), Sigma Xi. Research and publs. in gastroenterology and immunology.

MCGUIGAN, JOHN V., lawyer; b. Sydney, Australia, July 11, 1949; s. Douglas and Majorie (Long) McG.; m. Rondel Clare McGregor, May 14, 1971; children: Fiona, Andrew, James, Stephanie. BEc, Sydney U., 1968, LLB, 1973. Bar: Supreme Ct. New South Wales, Australia, 1975, Supreme Ct. Victoria, Australia, 1982, Supreme Ct. Eng. and Wales, 1985, Supreme Ct. Hong Kong, 1985; CPA, Australia. With Price Waterhouse, 1969-73, Baker & McKenzie, Sydney, Australia, 1973-85; ptnr. Baker & McKenzie, Hong Kong, 1985-91, Chgo., 1992—. Chmn. Kellet Sch., Hong Kong, 1986-91. Mem. Coun. Ams., Econ. Club Chgo., Univ. Club, Hong Kong Club, Exec. Club Chgo. Avocations: skiing, jogging, tennis. Office: Baker & McKenzie Ste 2500 130 E Randolph Chicago IL 60601

MCGUIGAN, THOMAS J., engineering company executive; b. Toronto, Ont., Can., Jan. 3, 1942; s. Thomas F. and Priscilla M (Robitaille) McG.; m. Ileana Petrie, Aug. 3, 1968; children: Andrea, Mark. BSc., U. Toronto, Can., 1963. Project engr. Litton Systems Can. Ltd., Etobicoke, Ont., 1963-71, dir. advance programs, 1971-81, v.p. mktg., 1981-86, pres., 1986—; v.p. Litton Industries, L.A., 1988—. Office: Litton Systems Can Ltd, 25 City View Dr, Etobicoke, ON Canada M9W 5A7

MCGUINN, MARTIN GREGORY, banker, lawyer; b. Phila., Sept. 9, 1942; s. Martin G. and Rita (Horgan) McG.; m. Ann M. Muldoon, Sept. 17, 1977; children: Patrick J., Christopher M. A.B., Villanova U., 1964, J.D., 1967. Bar: Pa. bar 1967, N.Y. bar 1970. Assoc. Sullivan & Cromwell, N.Y.C., 1970-77; mng. counsel The Singer Co., Stamford, Conn., 1977-80; vice chmn. Mellon Bank, Pitts., 1981—; bd. consultors Villanova Law Sch., 1972—, chmn. 1985-87. Editor in chief Villanova Law Rev., Vol. 12, 1966-67. Bd. dirs. U. Pitts. Med. Ctr., Carnegie Inst., Carnegie Mus. Art; mem. Carnegie 100, World Affairs Coun. Pitts. Mem. ABA, N.Y. State Bar Assn., Pa. Bar Assn., Allegheny County Bar Assn., Bankers Roundtable, Am. Law Inst., Am. Soc. Corp. Secs. (chmn. 1990-91), Pa. Chamber of Bus. and Industry (bd. dirs.). Home: 714 Amberson Ave Pittsburgh PA 15232-1446 Office: Mellon Bank Corp 1 Mellon Bank Ctr Pittsburgh PA 15258-0001

MCGUINN, MICHAEL EDWARD, III, retired army officer; b. Spartanburg, S.C., Feb. 22, 1925; s. Michael Edward Jr. and Margaret Cordelia (Shackleford) McG.; m. Betty Gay Corn, 1948 (div. 1951); m. Phyllis Fryer, Oct. 7, 1952; childen: Michael Edward IV, Carol Ann McGuinn Branch. Student, Clemson U., 1941-43, 46, Coll. William and Mary, 1962-63. Served with U.S. Navy, PTO, 1943-46; commd. 2d lt. U.S. Army, 1949, advanced through grades to col., 1971; served on U.S. Dept. Army Gen. Staff, Washington, 1966-68; comdr. 10th Transp. Bn. U.S. Army, Vietnam, 1968-69; chief transp. div. U.S. Readiness Command, MacDill AFB, Fla., 1969-72; ret. U.S. Army, 1972; state govt. svc. various locations, 1972-82; chief of staff Ga. State Def. Force, an Agy. of the State of Ga., Atlanta, 1987—. Decorated Legion of Merit (2), Army Commendation medal (2), Naval Commendation medal. Mem. U.S. Army Transp. Mus., The Old Guard of the Gate City Guard. Avocations: military history, photography, home workshop. Home: 6420 Tanacrest Ct NW Atlanta GA 30328 Office: Ga State Def Force PO Box 17965 Atlanta GA 30316-0965

MC GUIRE, ALFRED JAMES, former basketball coach, sports equipment company executive, basketball commentator; b. N.Y.C., Sept. 7, 1931; s. John and Winifred (Sullivan) McG.; m. Patricia Sharkey, Aug. 22, 1953; children: Alfred J., Noreen, Robert. B.A., St. John's Coll., Bklyn., 1952. Coach Dartmouth Coll., Hanover, N.H., 1955-57, Belmont Abbey Coll., Belmont, N.C., 1957-64; athletic dir., head basketball coach Marquette U., Milw., 1964-77; v.p., dir. sports edn. publs. Medalist Industries, Milw., 1970-78, also bd. dirs.; basketball commentator NBC, 1978-95; profl. basketball player, N.Y., 1951-52, Balt., 1954; pres. Hall of Fame Basketball Camps, 1967—. Trustee Milw. County Stadium Recreation Commn., 1972—. Named Sports Figure of Year Wis. C. of C., 1974; Coach of Year AP, UPI, Sporting News, U.S. Basketball Writers Assn., 1971, 74. Mem. Nat. Assn. Basketball Coaches. Club: Westmoor Country. Office: care NBC Sports 30 Rockefeller Plz New York NY 10112-0001*

MCGUIRE, BERYL EDWARD, retired federal judge; b. Oakfield, N.Y., May 25, 1935; s. Harold E. and Pearl E. (Ralyea) McG.; m. Prudence Ann Wester, Oct. 17, 1959. B.S. in Bus. Adminstrn., U. Buffalo, 1958, J.D., 1959. Bar: N.Y. 1960, U.S. Dist. Ct. (we. dist.) N.Y. Law clk. U.S. Dist. Ct. (we. dist.) N.Y., 1960-62; referee in bankruptcy U.S. Dist. Ct. (we. dist.) N.Y., 1968—; bankruptcy judge, 1973-79, U.S. bankruptcy judge, 1979-93; ret. 1993. Office: US Bankruptcy Ct 310 US Courthouse 68 Court St Buffalo NY 14202-3405

MCGUIRE, CHARLES CARROLL, JR., banking executive; b. Balt., Jan. 28, 1932; s. Charles Carroll and Mary Catherine (Gunning) McG.; m. Mary Ballman, June 27, 1953; children: Charles, III, Mark T., James M., David M. BS in Acctg., U. Balt., 1955. CPA, Md. Mgt. Ernst & Whinney, Balt., 1957-73; sr. v.p., treas. Mercantile Bankshares Corp., Balt., 1973—; pres., dir. MBC Agy., Inc., Balt., 1979—, Mercantile Life Ins. Co., Balt., 1979—. Contbr. articles to profl. jours. Bd. dirs. YMCA, Catonsville, Md., 1984-85. Served with U.S. Army, 1955-57. Mem. Fin. Execs. Inst., Am. Inst. CPAs, Md. Assn. CPAs, Md. Pub. Fin. Officers Assn. (sec. 1960-70). Democrat. Roman Catholic. Avocations: boating, fishing, reading. Office: Merc Bankshares Corp Two Hopkins Pla PO Box 1477 Baltimore MD 21203-1477

MC GUIRE, DOROTHY HACKETT, actress; b. Omaha, June 14, 1916; d. Thomas Johnston and Isabel (Flaherty) McG.; m. John Swope, July 18, 1943 (dec.); children: Topo Swope, Mark Swope. Student, Pine Manor Jr. Coll., 1936-38. Stage debut in A Kiss for Cinderella, Omaha, 1933; played stock in Deertrees, Maine; N.Y.C. debut as understudy in Stop-Over, 1938; played role of Emily in Our town, on Broadway, 1938; toured with My Dear Children, 1939; starred in Claudia, 1941; toured in USO prodn. Dear Ruth, Europe, 1945, USO prodn. Tonight at 8:30, 1947, Summer and Smoke, 1950; appeared in Broadway prodn. Legend of Lovers, 1951, Joan at the Stake, 1954, Winesburg, Ohio, 1958, The Night of the Iguana, 1976, Cause Celebre, 1979; film appearances include: Claudia, 1943, A Tree Grows in Brooklyn, 1945, The Enchanted Cottage, 1945, Claudia and David, 1946, The Spiral Staircase, 1946, Gentlemen's Agreement, 1947, Mr. 880, Invitation, 1952, Make Haste to Live, 1954, Three Coins in the Fountain, 1954, Trial, 1955, Friendly Persuasion, 1956, Old Yeller, 1957, This Earth is Mine, 1959, A Summer Place, 1959, The Remarkable Mr. Penny Pincher, The Swiss Family Robinson, 1960, The Dark at the Top of the Stairs, 1960, Susan Slade, 1961, Summer Magic, 1962, The Greatest Story Ever Told, 1965, Flight of the Doves, 1971; film appearances include (voice only) Jonathan Livingston Seagull, 1973; appeared in: TV movie She Waits, 1971, TV prodn Am. Playhouse: I Never Sang For My Father, 1988; radio serial Big Sister, 1937; Juliette in: Romeo and Juliette; Ophelia in Hamlet, 1951; TV appearances include U.S. Steel Hour, 1954, Lux Video Theatre, 1954, Climax, 1954, 56, Play House 90, Another Part of the Forest, 1972, The Runaways, 1975, The Philadelphia Story, 1954, Rich Man Poor Man, 1970, Little Women, 1978, The Incredible Journey of Doctor Meg Laurel, Ghost Dancing, 1983, Love Boat, 1984. Recipient N.Y. Drama Critics Circle award, 1941; named Best Actress by Nat. Bd. Rev., 1955. Mem. Screen Actors Guild, Actors Equity Assn., AFTRA. Office: Raymond J Gertz Acctg Corp 10351 Santa Monica Blvd Los Angeles CA 90025-6912

MCGUIRE, ELAINE C., nursing administrator; b. Cin., Nov. 12, 1944; d. Robert J. and Virginia (Wessner) Holloway; m. Kenneth W. Brewer July 20, 1968 (dec. Dec. 1976); children: Kelli Anne , Kevin Robert; m. Frank O. McGuire, Dec. 3, 1982. Diploma, Good Samaritan Hosp., Cin., 1966; BSN, Coll. Mt. St. Joseph, Cin., 1980; MSN, U. Cin., 1989, MBA, 1993. Cert. nurse advanced adminstrn. Staff nurse Good Samaritan Hosp., Cin., 1977-79, asst. head nurse, 1979-81, head nurse, 1981-85, sr. nursing mgr., 1985-90, adminstrv. dir., 1990—. Mem. Am. Orgn. Nurse Execs. (past pres. greater Cin. cun. nurse mgr. affiliates), Ohio Orgn. Nurse Execs., Greater Cin. Orgn. Nurse Execs. (past sec., treas.), Sigma Theta Tau. Home: 848 Genenbill Dr Cincinnati OH 45238-4715 Office: Good Samaritan Hosp 375 Dixmyth Ave Cincinnati OH 45220-2489

MCGUIRE, JAMES CHARLES, aircraft company executive; b. St. Louis, Aug. 8, 1917; s. John Patrick and Anna Beulah (Erbar) McG.; A.B., Washington U., St. Louis, 1949, M.A. (Univ. fellow), 1953, Ph.D., 1954; m. Eunice Leota Sloop, Mar. 21, 1942 (div. June 1948); 1 child: Judith Lynn; m. Ingrid Elisabeth Getreu, Sept. 16, 1954. Research assoc. Ohio State U., 1953-56; rsch. psychologist Aeromed. Lab., Wright-Patterson AFB, Ohio, 1956-59; group supr. Boeing Airplane Co., Seattle, 1959-61; dept. mgr. Internat. Electric Corp., Paramus, N.J., 1961-62; sr. human factors scientist System Devel. Corp., Santa Monica, Calif., 1962-67; v.p. Booz-Allen Applied Rsch., Saigon, Vietnam, 1967-72; v.p. Assoc. Cons. Internat., Saigon, 1972-75, Bethesda, Md., 1975-78; br. chief Human Factors, System Tech. Devel., 1978-82; prin. staff engr. tech. modernization methodology Douglas Aircraft Co., Long Beach, Calif., 1982-85; program mgr. cockpit automation tech. program, Northrop Aircraft div., Hawthorne, Calif., 1985-87; sect. mgr. aircraft programs human factors engring. dept. Douglas Aircraft Co., Long Beach, 1987—, sr. staff engr. Crew Systems Tech., 1990-93; prin. engr. tech. McDonnell Douglas Aerospace Transport Aircraft, 1993-94; prin. engr.-scientist, crew sys. tech., advanced transport aircraft devel., McDonnell Douglas Aerospace, 1995—; lectr. Nat. Def. Coll., Vietnamese Armed Forces, Saigon, 1971. Served with AUS, 1940-46. Decorated Bronze Star medal with oak leaf cluster; recipient Tech. Svc. First Class medal Republic South Vietnam Armed Forces, 1968. Mem. Am. Psychol. Assn., IEEE, Computer Soc. of IEEE, Human Factors Soc., Am. Assn. Artificial Intelligence, Phi Beta Kappa, Sigma Xi. Republican. Home: 23201 Mindanao Circle Monarch Beach CA 92629-3625 Office: McDonnell Douglas Aerospace Advanced Transport Aircraft Devel 1510 Hughes Way Mail Code 71-11 Long Beach CA 90810-1870

MCGUIRE, JOHN MURRAY, chemist, researcher; b. New Bedford, Mass., May 15, 1929; s. Thomas C., Jr. and Mary W. (Murray) McG.; m. Harriet S. Drake, Aug. 5, 1954; children: Joseph P., John M. Jr., Thomas C., D. Vincent, James E., M. Catherine. BS in Chemistry, U. Miami, Coral Gables, Fla., 1948, MS in Phys. Chemistry, 1951; PhD in Phys. Chemistry, U. Fla., Gainesville, 1955. Product chemist GE, Waterford, N.Y., 1955-57; sr. rsch. chemist W. R. Grace R & D, Clarksville, Md., 1957-60; sr. chemist, supr. GE, Syracuse, N.Y., 1960-70; engr. advanced materials GE, Decatur, Ill., 1970-71; rsch. chemist EPA, Athens, Ga., 1971-73, supervisory rsch. chemist, 1973—. Editorial advisor Biomedical Mass Spectrometry jour., 1974-83; contbr. articles to tech. pubs. Decorated knight and knight commdr. of Holy Sepulchre of Jerusalem. Mem. Am. Chem. Soc. (sect. chmn. 1986), Am. Soc. Mass Spectrometry (chmn. environ. com. 1973-75), KC (grand knight Athens 1973-79, state dep. Ga. 1986-87, Ga. master 4th degree 1988-92). Republican. Roman Catholic. Avocations: reading, church work. Office: EPA College Sta Athens GA 30613-0801

MC GUIRE, JOSEPH WILLIAM, business educator; b. Milw., Mar. 14, 1925; s. William B. and Marion (Dunn) McG.; m. Margaret Drewek, Aug. 20, 1946; children: Laurence, Karen, Eileen, Kevin. Ph.B., Marquette U., 1948, D.B.A. (hon.), 1981; M.B.A., Columbia U., 1950, Ph.D., 1956; LL.D. (hon.), St. Benedict's Coll., 1968. Asst. prof. U. Wash. Coll. Bus. Adminstrn., Seattle, 1954-56; assoc. prof. U. Wash. Coll. Bus. Adminstrn., 1956-61, prof., 1961-63; prof., dean U. Kans. Sch. Bus., 1963-68; dean Coll. Commerce and Bus. Adminstrn., prof. U. Ill., Urbana, 1968-71; v.p. planning U. Calif., Berkeley, 1971-74; prof. adminstrn. U. Calif., Irvine, 1973—, assoc. dean exec. degree programs, 1990-94; vis. prof. Netherlands Coll. Econs., Rotterdam, 1957-58; dept. econs. U. Hawaii, 1962-63; Michael Smrfit Grad. Sch. of Bus. Univ. Coll., Dublin, Ireland, 1993, Am. U. of Armenia, 1993; Ford. vi. rsch. prof. Carnegie-Mellon U. Grad. Sch. Indsl. adminstrn., 1987-88; cons. editor Wadsworth Pub. Co., 1964-70, Goodyear Pub. Co., 1973-81, Scott Foresman & Co., 1981-90. Author: Business and Society, 1963, Theories of Business Behavior, 1964, Factors Affecting the Growth of Manufacturing Firms, 1963, Inequality; The Poor and the Rich in America, 1968; Editor, contbr.: Interdisciplinary Studies in Business Behavior, 1962, Contemporary Management: Issues and Viewpoints, 1973. Served with USAAF, 1943-45. Recipient McKenzie awards, 1963, 65. Fellow Am. Acad. Mgmt. (bd. govs. 1967-70), Internat. Acad. Mgmt.; mem. Am. Assn. Collegiate Schs. Bus. (dir. 1970-71), Am. Econ. Assn., AAUP, Am. Inst. Decision Scis., Western Econs. Assn., Western Tax Assn. (dir. 1977-80), Assn. Social Econs. (exec. council 1970-75, pres. 1973-74), Western Acad. Mgmt. (dir. 1975-81, pres. 1980-81), Phi Beta Kappa, Beta Gamma Sigma. Home: 5566 B Via Portora Laguna Hills CA 92653

MCGUIRE, MARY JO, state legislator; b. 1956. BA in Bus. Adminstrn., Coll. of St. Catherine; JD, Hamline U.; postgrad., Harvard U., 1995—. Mem. Minn. Ho. of Reps., 1988-94, mem. judiciary com., judiciary fin. divsn., vice chair local govt. and met. affairs; mem. labor and mgmt. rels. com. Democrat. Home: 1529 Iowa Ave W Saint Paul MN 55108-2128 Office: Minn Ho of Reps State Ho Office Bldg Saint Paul MN 55155

MCGUIRE, MAVIS LOUISE, professional society administrator; b. Sioux Falls, S.D., Oct. 6, 1948; d. Francis and Beverly Beatrice McG.; m. Kenneth Chatzinoff, May 22, 1983. BSN, U. Iowa, 1974, MA in Nursing, 1976. Cert. pediatric nurse practitioner. Pediatric nurse practitioner Children & Youth Project, Davenport, Iowa, 1976-77; dir. pediatric nurse practitioner program Gwynedd Mercy Coll., Gwynedd Valley, Pa., 1977-84; exec. dir. Nat. Assn. Pediatric Nurse Assocs. & Practitioners, Cherry Hill, N.J., 1981—; bd. dirs. Pa. Nurses Assn. Dist. Level, 1978-80; cons. in field. Mem. edit. bd. Jour Pediatric Health Care, 1986—. Fellow Nat. Assn. Pediatric Assocs. and Practitioners; mem. NAFE, Nat. Assn. Assn. Execs., Sigma Theta Tau. Avocation: music. Home: 2 Greenbriar Ln Riverton NJ 08077-3876 Office: Nat Assn Pediatric Nurse Assocs and Practitioners 1101 Kings Hwy N # 206 Cherry Hill NJ 08034-1912

MCGUIRE, MICHAEL FRANCIS, plastic and reconstructive surgeon; b. St. Louis, Oct. 4, 1946; s. Arthur Patrick and Virginia Claribel (Gannon) McG. BA, Columbia U., 1968, D of Medicine, 1972. Diplomate Am. Bd. Surgery, Am. Bd. Plastic Surgery. Intern UCLA, 1972-73, resident in gen. surgery, 1973-77, resident in plastic surgery, 1978-80; fellow in plastic surgery rsch. Stanford (Calif.) U., 1977-78; traveling fellow in plastic surgery Gt. Britain, 1980; chief plastic surgery L.A. County-Olive View Med. Ctr., Sylmar, Calif., 1980-85; pvt. practice Santa Monica, Calif., 1980—; bd. dirs. Calif. Med. Rev., Inc.; pres. Pacific Coast Plastic Surgery Ctr., Inc., Santa Monica, 1987—; asst. clin. prof. surgery UCLA, 1980—, mem. exec. com., 1993—; vice chmn. plastic surgery St. John's Hosp., Santa Monica, 1987-91, chmn. plastic surgery, 1992—; dir. cleft palate team L.A. County-Olive View Med. Ctr., 1986—; mem. ops. com. Med. Profl. Group, 1995. Charter patron L.A. Music Ctr. Opera, 1983—, sponsoring patron L.A. County Art Mus., 1986—, patron Colleague Helpers in Philanthropic Svc., Bel Air, Calif., 1987, 93, 95. Fellow ACS, Royal Soc. Medicine; mem. Am. Soc. Plastic and Reconstructive Surgeons, Inc., Am. Soc. Aesthetic Plastic Surgery, L.A. County Med. Assn., Calif. Soc. Plastic Surgery (exec. com., auditor 1988-89, program chmn. 1994), recer. coun. 1991-94, treas. 1994—), Calif. Med. Assn. (del. 1992, 93, 94, 95), Am. Assn. Accreditation of Ambulatory Surgery (facilities ops. com. 1995—), Alpha Omega Alpha. Democrat. Episcopalian. Avocations: golf, travel, collecting antique Irish glass, opera, modern art. Office: 1301 20th St Ste 460 Santa Monica CA 90404-2054

MCGUIRE, PATRICIA A., lawyer, academic administrator; b. Phila., Nov. 13, 1952; d. Edward J. and Mary R. McGuire. BA cum laude, Trinity Coll., 1974; JD, Georgetown U., 1977. Bar: Pa. 1977, D.C. Ct. Appeals 1979. Program dir. Georgetown U. St. Law Clinic, Washington, 1977-82; asst. dean for devel. and external affairs Georgetown U. Law Ctr., Washington, 1982-89; pres. Trinity Coll., Washington, 1989—; adj. prof. law Georgetown U., 1977-82, Georgetown Law Ctr., 1987—; commr. Mid. States Commn. on Higher Edn., 1991—; bd. dirs. Acacia Group. Editor: Street Law Mock Trial Manual, 1984; contbr. articles to profl. jours. Trustee Trinity Coll. 1986—; bd. dirs. Assn. Cath. Colls. and Univs., 1991—, Eugene and Agnes Meyer Found.; mem. adv. bd. Merion Mercy Acad. and Sisters of Mercy, 1990—; bd. dirs. Nat. Assn. Ind. Colls. and Univs.; mem. commn. govt. rels. Am. Coun. Edn. Recipient Daytime Emmy, TV Acad., N.Y.C., 1979-80. Mem. ABA, Assn. Am. Law Schs. (instl. advancement 1985—), Coun. for the Advancement and Support of Edn., Trinity Coll. Alumnae Assn. (pres. 1986-89). Democrat. Roman Catholic. Office: Trinity Coll Office of the President 125 Michigan Ave NE Washington DC 20017-1094

MCGUIRE, RAYMOND L., telecommunications company executive. Exec. v.p. govt. affairs Bell South Corp., Atlanta. Office: BellSouth Corp 1155 Peachtree St NE Atlanta GA 30367

MCGUIRE, ROGER ALAN, foreign service officer; b. Troy, Ohio, July 1, 1943; s. Charles M. and Mary L. (Coppock) McG.; m. Harriet H. Cooke, July 12, 1969; children: Sara, Casey. BA, Beloit Coll., 1965; MA, U. Wis., 1967. Country desk officer Dept. State, Washington, 1974-78; dep. chief of mission Am. Embassy, Maputo, Mozambique, 1978-80; congl. fellow Am. Polit. Sci. Assn., Washington, 1980-81; polit. officer Am. Embassy, Asuncion, Paraguay, 1981-83, Lusaka, Zambia, 1983-86; dep. dir. Office of West African Affairs Dept. of State, Washington, 1986-88; chief of mission Am. Embassy, Windhoek, Namibia, 1988-90; consul Am. Consulate, Porto Alegre, Brazil, 1990-92; U.S. amb. to Guinea-Bissau, 1992—. Recipient Superior Honor award U.S. Agy. for Internat. Devel., 1969. Mem. Rotary Internat., Phi Beta Kappa. Home and Office: Am Embassy-Bissau Dept Of State Washington DC 20521

MCGUIRE, TIMOTHY JAMES, newspaper editor, lawyer; b. Mount Pleasant, Mich., Mar. 24, 1949; s. James Edward and Anita Matilda (Starr) McG.; m. T. Jean Fannin, May 10, 1975; children: Tracy, Jason, Jeffrey. Ba, Aquinas Coll., Grand Rapids, Mich., 1971; JD cum laude, William Mitchell Coll. Law, St. Paul, 1987. Bar: Minn. 1987. Mng. editor Ypsilanti Press, Mich., 1973-75, Corpus Christi Caller, Tex., 1975-77, Lakeland Ledger, Fla., 1977-79, Mpls. Star, 1979-82; mng. editor features and sports Mpls. Star and Tribune, 1982-84, mng. editor, 1984-91, exec. editor, 1991-93; editor, gen. mgr. reader customer unit, 1993—; Pulitzer Prize juror, 1988-89, 95. Bd. dirs. Minn. Meeting. Mem. Am. Soc. Newspaper Editors (bd. dirs. 1992—, chmn. change com. 1994-95), Minn. State Bar Assn. Roman Catholic. Avocation: sports. Home: 3645 Rosewood Ln N Minneapolis MN 55441-1127 Office: Star Tribune 425 Portland Ave Minneapolis MN 55488-0001

MCGUIRE, TIMOTHY WILLIAM, economics and management educator, dean; b. Englewood, N.J., Nov. 30, 1938; s. Charles James and Marie (McCarthy) McG.; children: Timothy William Jr., Gretchen Elizabeth, Michael Joseph; m. Nancy Paule Melone, 1991. BS in Indsl. Mgmt., Carnegie Inst. Tech., 1960, MS in Econs., 1961; PhD in Econs., Stanford U., 1968. Staff mem. Coun. Econ. Advisors, 1963-64; rsch. assoc. in econs. Grad. Sch. Indsl. Adminstrn., Carnegie Mellon U., Pitts., 1964-66, asst. prof. econs., 1966-69, assoc. prof., 1969-75, prof., 1975-79, prof. mgmt. and econs., 1982—, dep. dean, 1983-90; prof. social scis. and econs. Dept. Social Scis. Carnegie Mellon U., Pitts., 1981-82; prof. econs., chmn. dept. U. Iowa, Iowa City, 1979-80; dean, Harry B. Miller prof. bus. Charles H. Lundquist Coll. Bus., U. Oreg., Eugene, 1994—; sr. visitor U. Cambridge, Eng., summer, 1970; vice chmn. bd. dirs. Mgmt. Sci. Assocs., Inc., Pitts. Contbr. articles to profl. jours. Woodrow Wilson Nat. Hon. fellow Carnegie Inst. Tech., 1960-61; Stanford U. fellow, 1961-62; fellow Ford Found., 1962-63, 70-71. Mem. Internat. Soc. Bayesian Analysis, Am. Econ. Assn., Am. Mktg. Assn., Inst. Mgmt. Scis., Ops. Rsch. Soc. Am., Soc. Judgment and Decision Making, Am. Statis. Assn., Tau Beta Pi, Omicron Delta Kappa. Home: 3302 Stoney Ridge Dr Eugene OR 97405 Office: Charles Lundquist Coll Bus 1208 U Oreg Eugene OR 97403-1208

MC GUIRE, WILLIAM, civil engineer, educator; b. S.I., N.Y., Dec. 17, 1920; s. Edward Joseph and Phoebe (Gamble) McG.; m. Barbara Weld, Feb. 5, 1944; children—Robert Weld, Thomas Rhodes. B.S. in Civil Engring., Bucknell U., 1942; M.Civil Engring., Cornell U., 1947. Structural designer Jackson & Moreland (engrs.), Boston, 1947-49; faculty Cornell U., Ithaca, 1949—; prof. civil engring. Cornell U., 1960-90, prof. emeritus of civil engring., 1990—; dir. Cornell U. (Sch. Civil Engring.), 1966-68; vis. prof. civil engring. Asian Inst. Tech., Bangkok, Thailand, 1968-70; vis. research engr. Nat. Bur. Standards, 1972; Gledden vis. sr. fellow U. Western Australia, 1973; cons. structural engr., 1951—; vis. prof. U. Tokyo, 1979, U. Strathclyde, 1986. Author: Steel Structures, 1967, (with R.H. Gallagher) Matrix Structural Analysis, 1979. Served to lt. USNR, 1942-45. Recipient Naval Letter of Commendation, award for Outstanding Achievement, Bucknell U., 1987, T.R. Higgins Lectureship award Am. Inst. Steel Constrs., 1992. Fellow ASCE (pres. Ithaca 1964, Norman medal 1962, 94, Hardesty award 1992, honorary mem. 1994); mem. Internat. Assn. Bridge and Structural Engring., Nat. Acad. Engring., Sigma Xi, Chi Epsilon, Kappa Delta Rho. Congregationalist. Home: 121 Simsbury Dr Ithaca NY 14850-1728

MCGUIRE, WILLIAM B(ENEDICT), lawyer; b. Newark, Feb. 14, 1929; m. Joan Glinane, June 3, 1968; children: Joan Ellen, Ralph R., James C., Keith P., Grant W. BS, Fordham U., 1950; JD, Seton Hall U., 1958; LLM in Taxation, NYU, 1963. Bar: N.J. 1958, U.S. Dist. Ct. N.J. 1958, U.S. Supreme Ct. 1971, U.S.C. Ct. Appeals (3rd cir.) 1980, N.Y. 1982. Chief acct. Hanover Fire Ins. Co., N.Y.C., 1950-58; sr. ptnr. Lum, Biunno & Tompkins, Newark, 1958-83, Tompkins, Mc Guire & Wachenfeld, 1984—; asst. prosecutor Essex County, N.J., 1964-65; bd. dirs. Ind. Coll. Fund of N.J., St. Peter's Coll., Delbarton Sch.; trustee St. Barnabas Hosp.; mem. Essex County Ethics Com., 1974-77; mem. com. to review State Commn. of Investigation, 1982. Fellow Am. Coll. Trial Lawyers, Am. Bar Found., Am. Bd. Trial Advocates, Internat. Acad. Trial Lawyers, Internat. Soc. Barristers; mem. ABA, N.J. State Bar Assn. (trustee 1982-89, sec. 1989-90, treas. 1990-91, 2nd v.p. 1991-92, 1st v.p. 1992-93, pres. elect 1993-94, pres. 1994—), N.J. State Bar Found. (pres. 1988-89), Essex County Bar Assn. (pres. 1975-76), Internat. Assn. Ins. Counsel, Fedn. Ins. Counsel, Def. Research Inst., Maritime Law Assn. U.S., Am. Arbitration Assn., Trial Attys. N.J., Assn. Fed. Bar N.J. (pres. 1985-88). Roman Catholic. Club: Essex County Country (pres. 1983), Newark. Office: 4 Gateway Ctr 100 Mulberry St Newark NJ 07102-4004

MCGUIRE, WILLIAM DENNIS, health care system executive; b. Glen Ridge, N.J., Sept. 24, 1943; s. John William and Kathleen Mary (Sexton) McG.; B.A., U. Notre Dame, 1965; M.H.A., U. Mich., 1968; m. Nancy Katherine Hoyne, Aug. 13, 1966; children: Kathleen Anne, Colleen Dempsey. Asst. adminstr. U. Wis. Hosps., Madison, 1971-74; adminstr. Children's Med. Ctr., Dayton, Ohio, 1974-79; sr. v.p. Mercy Cath. Med. Ctr., Phila., 1979-80; chief exec. officer Wills Eye Hosp., Phila., 1980-85; pres., chief exec. officer Mercy Health Care System, Scranton, Pa., 1985-89; pres., chief exec. officer Mt. Carmel Health, Columbus, Ohio, 1989-92; pres., chief exec. officer Incarnate Word Health Services, San Antonio, 1992—; adj. faculty dept. health care Trinity U., 1992—; asst. prof. Ohio State U., 1990-92; asst. clin. prof. Wright State U. Sch. Medicine, Dayton, Ohio, 1978-79; instr. U. Wis., Madison, 1972-73; mem. Wilkes Coll. Health Adminstrn. Adv. Com., 1988-89, Coll. Misericordia Health Care Task Force, 1988-89. Trustee Community Blood Ctr., 1977-79, Cath. Social Svcs., 1976-79, pres., 1978-79; bd. dirs. Coop. Purchasing Corp., 1974-79; mem. Dayton Pub. Schs. Lay Adv. Com. on Vocat. Edn., 1974-79; pres. Dayton Area Young Adminstrs. Group, 1977; pres. elect Greater Dayton Area Hosp. Assn., 1979; mem. allied health technologies adv. com. Sinclair Community Coll., 1974-79; bd. dirs. Covenant Health System, 1992—, Consolidated Cath. Casualty Risk Retention Group, 1992—; active United Way, ARC. Mem. Am. Coll. Healthcare Execs., Acad. for Cath. Health Care Leadership, Mercy Leadership Group, Nat. Commn. Cath. Health Care Ministry-Resource Devel. Com., 1988-89, Maj. Cath. Hosp. Alliance, 1989—, chmn.- elect, 1995—, sec. 1990-95, Health Care Fin. Mgmt. Assn., Am. Acad. Univ. Profs. Ophthalmology, Am. Soc. Law and Medicine, Am. Hosp. Assn., Am. Assn. Eye and Ear Hosps. (pres.-elect 1984-85), Health Mgmt. Edn. Assn. (pres. 1987-88), Tex. Hosp. Assn., Ohio Hosp. Assn., Hosp. Assn. Pa., Cath. Health Assn. Am. Pub. Health Assn., Pa. Pub. Health Assn., Del. Valley Hosp. Council, Pa. Emergency Health Svcs. Coun., Del. County Emergency Health Svcs. Coun., Nat. Union Hosp. and Health Care Employees (plan trustee), Pa. Hosps. Ins. Co. Adv. Coun., 1988-89, C. of C., U. Notre Dame Alumni Assn., U. Mich.

Alumni Assn., U. Wis. Med. Sch. Alumni Assn., Wills Eye Soc., Sorin Soc., Notre Dame Club (pres. 1971, v.p. 1983-84), Plaza Club, Dominion Country Club. Republican. Roman Catholic. Home: 23 Carriage Hls San Antonio TX 78257-1206 Office: Incarnate Word Health Svcs 9311 San Pedro Ave Ste 1250 San Antonio TX 78216-4469

MC GUIRE, WILLIAM JAMES, social psychology educator; b. N.Y.C., Feb. 17, 1925; s. James William and Anne M. (Mitchell) McG.; m. Claire Vernick, Dec. 29, 1954; children—James William, Anne Maureen, Steven Thomas. BA, Fordham U., 1949, MA, 1950; PhD, Yale U., 1954; PhD (hon.), Eötvös U., Budapest, Hungary, 1990. Postdoctoral fellow U. Minn., 1954-55; assoc. prof. psychology U. Ill., 1958-61; prof. Columbia U., 1961-67, U. Calif., San Diego, 1967-70; vis. prof. London Sch. Econs., 1970-71; asst. prof. Yale U., New Haven, 1955-58, prof., 1971—, chmn. dept. psychology, 1971-73; Mem. adv. panel for sociology and social psychology NSF, 1963-65; mem. review panel for social scis. NIMH, 1968-72, cons., 1974-85. Author: Content and Processes in the Experience of Self, 1988, A Perspectivist Approach to Strategic Planning, 1989, Structure of Attitudes and Attitude Systems, 1989, The Content, Structure, and Operation of Thought Systems, 1991; contbr. to Ency. Brit.; editor Jour. Personality and Social Psychology, 1967-70; cons. editor European Jour. Social Psychology, 1978—, Jour. Applied Social Psychology, 1983—, Jour. Exptl. Social Psychology, 1994—, Pub. Opinion Quar., 1990—. With AUS, 1943-46. Recipient Ann. Social Psychology award AAAS, 1964, Gen. Electric Found. awards, 1963, 64, 66, Disting. Scientist award Soc. Exptl. Social Psychology, 1992; grantee NSF, 1960-79, NIH, 1979—; Fulbright fellow Louvain (Belgium) U., 1950-51, Ctr. for Advanced Study in Behavioral Scis. fellow, 1965-66, Guggenheim fellow, 1970-71, William James fellow Am. Psychol. Soc., 1989—. Fellow APA (pres. divsn. personality and social psychology 1973-74, Disting. Sci. Contbn. award 1988); mem. Am. Sociol. Assn., Am. Assn. Pub. Opinion Rsch., Sigma Xi. Home: 225 St Ronan St New Haven CT 06511 Office: Yale U Dept Psychology Box 208205 New Haven CT 06520-8205

MC GUIRE, WILLIAM W., health maintenance organization executive; b. Troy, N.Y., 1948. Grad., U. Tex., 1970, U. Tex., 1974. Chmn., CEO, pres., dir. United Healthcare Corp.; dir. SciMed Life Ins. Co., Systems, Inc., Mpls. Office: United Healthcare Corp 300 Opus Ctr 9900 Bren Rd E Minnetonka MN 55343*

MCGUIRK, RONALD CHARLES, banker; b. Balt., Dec. 9, 1938; s. Charles F. and Grace E. (Delcher) McG.; m. Katherine Sauer, Oct. 1, 1960; children: Frank D., Ann E. Student St. John's Coll., Annapolis, Md., 1956-59. Sr. data processing officer 1st Nat. Bank, Balt., 1966-72, v.p. data processing, 1972-76, v.p. mktg., 1976-80, sr. v.p. mktg., 1980-90, sr. v.p. corp. plan, chief of staff to CEO, 1990-94; sr. v.p., corporate sec. First Md. Bancorp, Balt., 1995—. Bd. dirs. North Arundel Hosp., Glen Burnie, Md, 1974—, Internet, Inc., 1990—, Glen Burnie Urban Renewal Com., 1995—, Annapolis Symphony, 1991-92; mem. adv. bd. Hist. Annapolis, 1982-85, dir., 1985-90; chmn. Annapolis Boundary Commn., 1983-84; mem. Anne Arundel County Coun., 1974-82, Anne Arundel County Libr. Bd., 1974-84; pres. Anne Arundel County Scholarship for Scholars/Bd. Edn., 1983-85, treas., 1985-88; mem. Anne Arundel County Charter Rev. Commn., 1986, Anne Arundel County Govt. Salary Commn., 1985, 89; chmn. Anne Arundel County Impact Fee Study Task Force, 1987; pres. Anne Arundel County YMCA, 1987-89, bd. dirs. 1982-87, 89-90; mem. Commn. for Ednl. Excellence, 1988-90; vice chmn. Ft. Meade Coordinating Coun., 1989-91; active Exec. Commn. Md. Bus.-Industry PAC 1991—, Anne Arundel County Charter and Orgn. Transition Group, 1991; corp. ptnr. Sch. bus. and Mgmt. Morgan State U., 1991-92. Mem. Ctr. Studies. Democrat. Roman Catholic. Office: 1st Nat Bank Md PO Box 1596 Baltimore MD 21203

MCGUIRK, TERRENCE, former broadcasting company executive; b. Bklyn., Apr. 2, 1925; s. William Edward and Loretta Beatrice (Lanigan) McG.; m. Gloria Helen Geoghan, June 17, 1950; children: Terence F., Sara McGuirk Duncan, Susan McGuirk Blank, Kathleen McGuirk Magee, Melissa McGuirk Bowman, Bryan, Michelle McGuirk O'Connor. B.S., Fordham U., 1950. Nat. sales mgr. St. WAGA-TV, Atlanta, 1966-68; mgr. Sta. WAGA-TV, Atlanta, 1970-75; eastern sales mgr. Storer TV Sales, N.Y.C., 1968-70; pres., gen. mgr. Sta. WTEN-TV, Albany, N.Y., 1976-82; pres. Knight-Ridder Broadcasting, Inc., 1982-85; ret. Assoc. trustee Siena Coll., Loudonville, N.Y., 1979-83; trustee Meml. Hosp. Found., 1980-83; dir. Albany chpt. ARC, 1987-91. Served with U.S. Army, 1943-46. Mem. Mariner Sands Country Club, Schuyler Meadows Club (dir. 1979-84), Babylon Yacht Club (hon.).

MCGUIRL, MARLENE DANA CALLIS, law librarian, educator; b. Hammond, Ind., Mar. 22, 1938; d. Daniel David and Helen Elizabeth (Baludis) Callis; m. James Franklin McGuirl, Apr. 24, 1965. A.B., Ind. U., 1959; J.D., DePaul U., 1963; M.A.L.S., Rosary Coll., 1965; LL.M., George Washington U., 1978, postgrad. Harvard U., 1985. Bar: Ill. 1963, Ind. 1964, D.C. 1972. Asst. DePaul Coll. of Law Library, 1961-62, asst. law librarian, 1962-65; ref. law librarian Boston Coll. Sch. Law, 1965-66; library dir. D.C. Bar Library, 1966-70; asst. chief Am.-Brit. Law Div. Libr. of Congress, Washington, 1970, chief, 1970-90, environ. cons., 1990—; counsel Cooter & Gell, 1992-93; adminstr. Washington Met. Transit Authority, 1994—; lectr. cons. Nat. Clearinghouse on Poverty Law, OEO, Washington, 1967-69, Northwestern U. Nat. Inst. Edn. in Law and Poverty, 1969, D.C. Office of Corp. Counsel, 1969-70; instr. law librarianship Grad. Sch. of U.S. Dept. of Agr., 1968-72; lectr. legal lit. Cath. U., 1972; adj. asst. prof., 1973-91; lectr. environ. law George Washington U., 1979—; judge Nat. and Internat. Law Moot Ct. Competition, 1976-78, 90—; pres. Hamburger Heaven, Inc., Palm Beach, Fla., 1981-91, L'Image de Marlene Ltd., 1986-92, Clinique de Beauté Inc., 1987-92, Heads & Hands Inc., 1987-92, Horizon Design & Mfg. Co., Inc., 1987—; dir. Stoneridge Farm Inc., Gt. Falls, Va., 1984—. Contbr. articles to profl. jours. Mem. Georgetown Citizens Assn.; trustee D.C. Law Students in Ct.; del. Ind. Democratic Conv., 1964. Recipient Meritorious Service award Library of Congress, 1974, letter of commendation Dir. of Personnel, 1976, cert. of appreciation, 1981-84. Mem. ABA (facilities law library Congress mem. 1976-89), Fed. Bar Assn. (chpt. council 1972-76), Ill. Bar Assn., Women's Bar Assn. (pres. 1972-73, exec. bd. 1977-77, Outstanding Contbn. to Human Rights award 1975), D.C. Bar Assn., Am. Bar Found., Nat. Assn. Women Lawyers, Am. Assn. Law Libraries, (exec. bd. 1973-77), Law Librarians Soc. of Washington (pres. 1971-73), Exec. Women in Govt. Home: 3416 P St NW Washington DC 20007-2705

MC GUIRT, WAYNE ROBERT, publishing company executive; b. Englewood, N.J., May 19, 1943; s. Wayne Paul and Helen Elaine (Rinaldi) McG.; B.A., Fordham U., 1965; M.B.A. in Fin., Columbia U., 1972; M.B.A. in Mktg., N.Y. U., 1981; m. Lisa Berger, Sept. 12, 1975. Computer ops. mgr. CIT Fin. Co., N.Y.C., 1966-68; fin. leasing specialist Efficient Leasing Corp., Ft. Lee, N.J., 1968-71; comptrollers asst. Time Inc., N.Y.C., 1972-73 ; asst. bus. mgr. Sports Illustrated, N.Y.C., 1973-75; bus. mgr. U.S. edit. Time Mag., N.Y.C., 1975-77; dir. planning Dow Jones & Co., Inc., N.Y.C., 1978-81; v.p. devel. Richard D. Irwin, Subs. Dow Jones, Homewood, Ill., 1981-84; chmn., CEO Probus Pub. Co., Chgo., 1984—. Mem. unit bd. Boys & Girls Clubs, Chgo. Bank of N.Y. fellow, 1971-72. Mem. Beta Gamma Sigma. Republican. Roman Catholic. Clubs: Tower, East Bank. Office: Probus Pub Co 1925 N Clybourn Ave Chicago IL 60614-4946

MCGUNIGLE, BRIAN EDWARD, lawyer; b. Boston, Nov. 2, 1947; s. Daniel H. and Mona (Tyldesley) McG.; m. Mary Ann Caven, Aug. 9, 1974. BA, Harvard U., 1968; MA, Nat. Univ. of Ireland, 1969; JD, Harvard U., 1973; LLM, U. London, 1974. Bar: N.Y. 1975. Assoc. Coudert Bros., N.Y.C., 1974-80, ptnr., 1981—. Fulbright scholar Ireland, 1968-69; Knox fellow, Eng., 1973-74. Office: Coudert Bros 1114 Avenue Of The Americas New York NY 10036-7701

MC GURN, BARRETT, communications executive, writer; b. N.Y.C., Aug. 6, 1914; s. William Barrett and Alice (Schneider) McG.; m. Mary Elizabeth Johnson, May 30, 1942 (dec. Feb. 1960); children: William Barrett III, Elizabeth (Mrs. John J. Hehn), Andrew; m. Janice Ann McLaughlin, June 19, 1962; children: Summers, Martin Barrett, Mark Barrett. AB, Fordham U., 1935, LittD, 1958. Editor Fordham Ram, 1934-35; with N.Y. Herald Tribune, 1935-66; asst. corr. N.Y. Herald Tribune, Rome, 1939, bur. chief, 1946-52, 55-62; reporting staff N.Y. Herald Tribune, 1935-42, 62-66; bur.

chief N.Y. Herald Tribune, Paris, 1952-55; acting chief bur. N.Y. Herald Tribune, Moscow, 1958; with, assignments in Morocco, Algeria, Tunisia, Hungary (1956 revolution), Egypt, Greece, Yugoslavia, Poland, Cen. Africa, Gaza Strip. N.Y. Herald Tribune, 1946-62; press attache Am. Embassy, Rome, 1966-68; counselor for press affairs Am. Embassy, Vietnam, 1968-69; U.S. consular officer, sec. appointed by Pres., 1969; dir. U.S. Govt. Press Ctr., Vietnam, 1968-69; White House and Pentagon liaison for State Dept. spokesman Washington, 1969-72; World Affairs commentator USIA, 1972-73; dir. pub. info. U.S. Supreme Ct., Washington, 1973-82; dir. communications Cath. Archdiocese of Washington, 1984-87; pres. Carroll Pub. Co. pub. Cath. Standard and El Pregonero, 1987-91; dir. Our Sunday Vistor Pub. Co., 1988—; mem. Italian-Am. com. to select Italian fellowship winners for study in U.S., 1950-52; mem. U.S. Nat. Cath. Com. on Comm. Policy, 1970-74, White House Com. on Drug Control Info., 1970-72; mem. interdept. com. on U.S. govt. press info. policy, 1970, interdept. U.S. govt. task force to rescue 100 Ams. kidnapped in Jordan, 1970, one-man U.S. Presdl. mission to Cambodia on media news problems, 1970; archivist John Carroll Soc., Washington, 1990—. Author: Decade in Europe, 1959, A Reporter Looks at the Vatican, 1962, A Reporter Looks at American Catholicism, 1967; contbg. author: The Best from Yank, 1945, Yank, the GI Story of the War, 1946, Combat, 1950, Highlights from Yank, 1953, Overseas Press Club Cook Book, 1962, I Can Tell it Now, 1964, U.S. Book of Facts, Statistics and Information, 1966, New Catholic Treasury of Wit and Humor, 1967, How I Got that Story, 1967, Heroes for Our Times, 1968, Newsbreak, 1975, Saints for all Seasons, 1978, Informing the People, 1981, The Courage to Grow Old, 1989, Am. Peoples Encyclopedia Yearbook, Close To Glory: Yank Correspondents Untold Stories of World War II, 1992; contbr. articles to profl. jours. Trustee Corrs. Fund, 1965-68; mem. bd. Anglo-Am. Charity Fund in Italy, 1967-68; v.p. Citizens Assn., Westmoreland Hills, Md., 1984-86. Sgt. AUS, 1942-45. Decorated Purple Heart; grand knight Italian Order of Merit; Vietnam Psychol. Warfare medal 1st class; recipient Polk award for outstanding fgn. reporting L.I. U., 1956; named best press corr. abroad Overseas Press Club, 1957; recipient N.Y.C. Fire Dept. Essay Silver Medal, 1924, N.Y. Times Oratorical Contest Bronze Medal, 1930; Christopher award for one of ten most inspiring books of year, 1959; named Man of Year Cath. Inst. Press, 1962, Fordham U. Alumnus of Year in communications, 1963; co-winner ann. Golden Typewriter award N.Y. Newspaper Reporters Assn., 1965, nominated by N.Y. Herald Tribune for Journalism Pulitzer Prize, 1965; outstanding pub. service award N.Y. chpt. Sigma Delta Chi, 1965; recipient Page One award N.Y. Newspaper Guild, 1966, Silurians award, 1966, award N.Y. Newspaper Reporters Assn., 1966, Citation for pub. service N.Y.C. Citizens Budget Commn., 1966, Meritorious Honor award Dept. State, 1972; Ann. Achievement award Fordham U. Club, Washington, 1986. Mem. Fgn. Press Assn. Italy (v.p. 1951-52, pres. 1961-62), SHAPE Corrs. Assn. Italy (treas. 1955), Authors Guild, Am. Fgn. Svc. Assn., Pax Romana Soc. for Cath. Intellectuals (Washington chmn. 1986—, dir. 1994—), Overseas Press Club (pres. 1963-65), Nat. Press Club, Kenwood Club, Cosmos Club, Fordham U. Club Washington (bd.s 1990—). Roman Catholic. Home: 5229 Duvall Dr Bethesda MD 20816-1875 Providing information to our democratic public has been the work of my life both as a foreign correspondent, as a government spokesman, and as a lecturer. The newsman and the person who speaks for government share the same objective of explaining government policy. The spokesman has an added responsibility—to help government policy succeed. The reporter and the spokesman sometimes are at war with one another, but it is a war in behalf of the same beneficiary: the people.

MCGURN, WILLIAM BARRETT, III, lawyer; b. N.Y.C., Apr. 3, 1943; s. Barrett and Mary Elizabeth (Johnson) McG.; m. Catherine Roche, June 17, 1972; children Mary Anne, Edward Johnson. BA, Yale U., 1965; JD, Harvard U., 1972. Bar: D.C. 1973, Paris 1992. Assoc.t Cleary, Gottlieb, Steen & Hamilton, Paris and Washington, 1972-80, ptnr., 1981—. Chmn. Dem. Abroad, France, 1987-89, mem. exec. com., 1989—; gov. Am. Hosp. Paris, 1991—, sec., 1992—. Lt. USNR, 1967-69. Mem. ABA, Am. Club Paris. Democrat. Home: 29 Ave Bosquet, 75007 Paris France Office: Cleary Gottlieb Steen & Hamilton, 41 Ave Friedland, 75008 Paris France

MCGWIRE, MARK DAVID, professional baseball player; b. Pomona, Calif., Oct. 1, 1963; s. John and Ginger McGwire; m. Kathy McGwire; 1 child, Matthew. Student, U. So. Calif. With Oakland Athletics, 1984—; player World Series, 1988, 89, 90. Named Am. League Rookie of Yr. Baseball Writers' Assn. Am., 1987, Sporting News, 1987; recipient Gold Glove award, 1990; named to All-Star team, 1987-92; recipient Silver Slugger Award, 1992; Am. League Home Run Leader, 1987; mem. U.S. Olympic Baseball Team, 1984. Office: Oakland Athletics Oakland-Alameda County Coliseum 7000 Coliseum Way Oakland CA 94621-1945*

MCHALE, EDWARD ROBERTSON, retired lawyer; b. Chgo., Jan. 24, 1921; s. Edward F. and Martha (Robertson) McH.; m. Helen Louise Lindgren, Aug. 28, 1953; children: Nancy Ellen McHale Kaufman, Sally Jane McHale Cutler, John Robertson. B.S.S., Northwestern U., 1942; LL.B., Harvard U., 1948. Bar: Calif. 1949. Asst. U.S. atty. U.S. atty. So. Dist. Calif., 1949-61, chief tax div., 1954-61; assoc. Mitchell, Silberberg & Knupp, Los Angeles, 1961-64; partner Mitchell, Silberberg & Knupp, 1965-86, mgr. litigation dept, 1978-82; pres. Edward R. McHale, P.C., 1979—; lectr. U. So. Calif. Law Center, 1958-61. Co-author: Handling Federal Tax Litigation, 1961. Served to lt. USNR, 1943-46. Mem. Fed. Bar Assn. (past pres. Los Angeles chpt., past nat. v.p. for 9th Circuit), Assn. Bus. Trial Lawyers (bd. govs. 1981-83), State Bar Calif., Delta Sigma Rho. Democrat. Lutheran. Clubs: South Hills Country (West Covina); Clan Donnachaidh Soc. Home: 1116 S Serena Dr West Covina CA 91791-3754

MCHALE, KEVIN EDWARD, former professional basketball player; b. Hibbing, Minn., Dec. 19, 1957; m. Lynn McHale; children: Kristyn, Michael. Student, U. Minn., 1976-80. Basketball player Boston Celtics, 1980-93; v.p. Minn. Timberwolves. Named to NBA All Rookie Team, 1981, NBA All-Defensive First Team, 1986-88, All-NBA First Team, 1987, NBA All-Star Game, 1984, 86-91; recipient NBA Sixth Man award, 1984, 85. Played on NBA Championship Team, 1981, 84, 86. Office: Minn Timberwolves Target Ctr 600 First Ave N Minneapolis MN 55403*

MCHALE, MAGDA CORDELL, academic administrator, trend analyst; b. June 24, 1921; widow. Sr. research assoc. Ctr. for Integrative Studies, SUNY-Binghamton, 1968-76; sr. research assoc. Ctr. for Integrative Studies, U. Houston, 1977-79; dir. Ctr. for Integrative Studies, SUNY-Buffalo, 1980—. Contbr. articles, papers, reports in field; mem. editorial bd. profl. publications. Grantee UN Environ. Programme, Ctr. for Econ. and Social Studies of Third World, Intergovernmental Bur. for Informatics, Hubert H. Humphrey Inst. Pub. Affairs, Aspen Inst., Population Reference Bur. Fellow World Acad. of Art and Sci., Royal Soc. Arts; mem. N.Y. Acad. Scis., U.S. Assn. for Club of Rome, World Future Soc., Assn. Internationale Futuribles (hon.), World Futures Studies Fedn. (v.p.). Office: SUNY-Ctr for Integrative Studies Sch of Architecture and Planning 333 Hayes Hall Buffalo NY 14214

MCHALE, PAUL, congressman, lawyer; b. Bethlehem, Pa., July 26, 1950; m. Katherine McHale; children: Matthew, Mary, Luke. BA in Govt. sigma cum laude, Lehigh U., 1972; JD, Georgetown U. Law Sch. 1977. Atty. Bethlehem, 1977-82; mem. Pa. Ho. of Reps., 1983-92, 103rd-104th Congresses from 15th Pa. dist., 1993—; mem. nat. security com., mem. sci. com. Infantry officer USMC, Okinawa, Philippines, 1972-74; Maj. USMCR Persian Gulf, 1990-92. Decorated Navy Commendation medal. Mem. Phi Beta Kappa. Democrat. *

MCHALE, ROBERT MICHAEL, lawyer; b. Youngstown, Ohio, Oct. 14, 1932; s. John F. and Elizabeth (Prendergast) M.; children: John F. II, Rachel Anne, Robert M. Jr. Student, St. Mary's Coll., Moraga, Calif., 1950-53; JD, Tulane U., 1956. Bar: La. 1956, U.S. Dist. Ct. (we. dist.) La. 1958, U.S. Ct Mil. Appeals 1959, U.S. Supreme Ct. 1959, U.S. Ct. Appeals (5th cir.) 1960, U.S. Dist. Ct. (ea. dist.) La. 1963. Ptnr. Rogers, McHale & St. Romain, Lake Charles, La., 1960-70; prin. McHale, Bufkin & Dees, Lake Charles, 1970-94, McHale, Schwartzberg & Willis, Lake Charles, 1995—; bd. dirs. Cameron (La.) State Bank; chair mineral bd. State of La., 1992-94, chair legal and title controversy commn., 1994—. Democrat. Roman Catholic. Avocations: horse racing, railroads. Office: 1901 Oak Park Blvd Lake Charles LA 70601-8915

MCHALE, THOMAS ANTHONY, sales and marketing consultant; b. Wilkes Barre, Pa., Dec. 15, 1914; s. Joseph Aloysius and Grace Ann (Dougherty) McH.; m. Ruth B. Gilligan, Apr. 29, 1939. B.B.A. in Mgmt, St. John's U., Jamaica, N.Y., 1953. With Am. Photo Corp., Washington, 1941-45; auditor Arthur Young & Co. (C.P.A.'s), 1946-50, Dale Carnegie Inc., 1950-53; with Drake Bakeries (subs. Borden, Inc.), Wayne, N.J., 1953-78, pres., 1971-78; pres. TAM of Chatham, W. Chatham, Mass., 1979—, cons. sales and mktg. to food industry, 1979—. Recipient various certs. appreciation. Mem. Am. Bakers Assn., Am. Soc. Bakery Engrs., Delta Mu Delta. Republican. Roman Catholic. Address: 17 Geranium Dr PO Box 664 West Chatham MA 02669-0664

MCHALE, VINCENT EDWARD, political science educator; b. Jenkins Twp., Pa., Apr. 17, 1939; m. Ann Barbara Cotner, Nov. 8, 1963; 1 child, Patrick James. A.B., Wilkes Coll., 1964; M.A., Pa. State U., 1966, Ph.D. in Polit. Sci., 1969. Asst. prof. polit. sci. U. Pa., Phila., 1969-75, dir. grad. studies, 1971-73; assoc. prof. Case Western Res. U., Cleve., 1975-84, prof., 1984—, chmn. dept. polit. sci., 1978—; vis. lectr. John Carroll U., summer 1980, Beaver Coll., spring 1975. Author: (with A.P. Frognier and D. Paranzino) Vote, Clivages Socio-politiques et Developpement Regional en Belgique, 1974. Co-editor; contbr.: Evaluating Transnational Programs in Government and Business, 1980; Political Parties of Europe, 1983; edtl. adv. bd. Worldmark Ency. of Nations, 1994—. Contbr. chpts. to books, articles to profl. jours. Project cons. Council Econ Opportunity in Greater Cleve., 1978-81; mem. Morris Abrams Award Com., 1977—. Recipient Outstanding Prof. award Lux chpt. Mortar Bd., 1989, 90; named one of Most Interesting People of 1988, Cleve. Mag.; NSF grantee, 1971-72; HEW grantee, 1976-78; Woodrow Wilson fellow, 1968, Ruth Young Boucke fellow, 1967-68; All-Univ. fellow, 1967-68. Mem. Phi Kappa Phi. Home: 3070 Coleridge Rd Cleveland OH 44118-3556 Office: Case Western Res U Cleveland OH 44106

MCHARG, IAN LENNOX, landscape architect, regional planner, educator; b. Clydebank, Scotland, Nov. 20, 1920; came to U.S., 1946, naturalized, 1960; s. John Lennox and Harriet (Bain) McH.; m. Pauline Crena de Iongh, Aug. 30, 1947 (dec. 1974); children: Alistair Craig, Malcolm Lennox, Ian William, Andrew Maxwell; m. Carol Ann Smyser, May 28, 1977. B.Landscape Architecture, Harvard U., 1949, M.Landscape Architecture, 1950, M.City Planning, 1951; L.H.D. (hon.), Amherst Coll., 1970, Bates Coll., 1978; H.H.D. (hon.), Lewis and Clark Coll., 1970; D.L. (hon.), Heriot-Watt U., Edinburgh, Scotland. Planner Dept. Health, Scotland, 1950-54; prof. dept. landscape architecture and regional planning U. Pa., Phila., 1954-86; disting. sci. lectr. Brookhaven Nat. Lab., 1968; Horace Albright Meml. lectr. U. Calif., Berkeley, 1969; Danz lectr. U. Wash., Seattle, 1971; Brown and Haley lectr. U. Puget Sound, 1971; Found. prof. U. Auckland, 1986; sr. vis. prof. U. Calif., Berkeley, 1986-87; vis. prof. Pa. State U., Harvard U., 1994; Bruce Gott prof. architecture Okla. U., 1994. Prin. works include: Ecol. Study for Mpls.-St. Paul Met. Area, San Francisco Met. Area, plan for New Town, Ponchartrain, New Orleans, plan for New Town, Woodlands, Tex., Environ. Park for Tehran, Iran, Amelia Island, Medford, Sanibel, EMAP, Nat. Ecol. Inventory; author: Design With Nature, 1969. Mem. White House Conf. on Conservation, Recreation and Natural Beauty, Children and Youth, Energy and Environ., 1970, Task Force on Potomac, 1968. Maj. Brit. Army, 1939-46, World War II. Recipient B.Y. Morrison medal N.Am. Wildlife Mgmt. Assn., 1971, Creative Arts award Brandeis U., 1972, Phila. Art Alliance award, 1975, Rene du Bos award, 1986, Alfred La Gasse award, 1987, Nat. Medal of Art, 1990, Richard Neutra medal, 1992, CELA Outstanding Educator award, 1992, Outstanding Achievement award Harvard U., 1992, Thomas Jefferson medal U. Va., 1995. Fellow Royal Soc. Art, Am. Soc. Landscape Architects (Bradford Williams medal 1968, 76, ASLA medal 1984), Inst. Landscape Architects, Royal Inst. Brit. Architects; mem. NAS (com. on sci. in nat. pks. 1991-92), AIA (hon., Allied Professions medal 1972). Office: U Pa Dept Landscape Architecture & Regional Planning Philadelphia PA 19104

MC HARGUE, CARL JACK, research laboratory administrator; b. Corbin, Ky., Jan. 30, 1926; s. John David and Virginia (Thomas) McH. B.S. in Metall. Engring., U. Ky., 1949, M.S., 1951, Ph.D., 1953; m. Edith Trovillion, Aug. 28, 1948; children: Anne Odell McHargue Diegel, Carol Virginia, Margaret Katherine McHargue Behrendt; m. Betty Ford, Sept. 30, 1960. Instr. U. Ky., Lexington, 1949-53; with Oak Ridge Nat. Lab., 1953-90, sect. head, 1960-80, program mgr. for materials scis., 1961-88, sr. rsch. staff 1980-90; prof. metall. engring. U. Tenn., Knoxville, 1963—, dir. ctr. materials processing, 1991—; vis. prof. U. Newcastle upon Tyne, Eng., 1987; adj. prof. Vanderfilt U., 1988—. With AUS, 1944-46. Fellow Metall. Soc. AIME, Am. Soc. for Metals; mem. Am. Nuclear Soc., Materials Rsch. Soc., Sigma Xi, Tau Beta Pi. Republican. Presbyterian. Contbr. numerous articles in field to profl. jours. Home: 7201 Sheffield Dr Knoxville TN 37909-2414 Office: U Tenn 102 Estabrook Hall Knoxville TN 37996-2350

MCHENRY, BARNABAS, lawyer; b. Harrisburg, Pa., Oct. 30, 1929; s. William Cecil and Louise (Perkins) McH.; m. Marie Bannon Jones, Dec. 13, 1952; children: Thomas J.P., W.H. Davis, John W.H. A.B., Princeton U., 1952; LL.B., Columbia U., 1957. Bar: N.Y. 1957. Assoc. Lord, Day, & Lord, N.Y.C., 1957-62; gen. counsel The Reader's Digest Assn., Inc. N.Y.C., 1962-85; exec. dir. Wallace Funds, N.Y.C., 1985-86; now chmn. 2 N.Y. state orgns. Trustee Boscobel Restoration, Inc., 1964, Am. Conservation Assn., 1977, Supreme Ct. Hist. Soc., 1980, Hudson River Found. for Sci. and Environ. Rsch., Inc., Saratoga Performing Arts Ctr., 1984, Aperture Found., 1986; trustee emeritus Met. Mus. Art, 1980; mem. N.Y. State Commn. on Restoration of Capitol, 1979; coun. mem. Villa I Tatti, Harvard Sch. Renaissance Studies, 1982; chmn. Empire State Plz. Art Commn., 1984; regent emeritus Smithsonian Instn., 1985; commr. Palisades Interstate Park Commn., 1987, chmn. Hudson River Valley Greenway Coun., 1989, adv. coun. hist. preservation, 1992. Home: 164 E 72nd St New York NY 10021-4363

MC HENRY, DEAN EUGENE, academic administrator emeritus; b. nr. Lompoc, Calif., Oct. 18, 1910; s. William Thomas and Virgie (Hilton) McH.; m. Jane Snyder, Feb. 23, 1935; children—Sally (Mrs. Kenneth Mackenzie), Dean Eugene, Nancy (Mrs. L.S. Fletcher), Henry. A.B., U. Calif. at Los Angeles, 1932; M.A., Stanford U., 1933; Ph.D., U. Calif. at Berkeley, 1936; Litt.D., U. Western Australia, 1963; LL.D., U. Nev., 1966, Grinnell Coll., 1967. Instr. govt. Williams Coll., 1936-37; asst. prof. polit. sci. Pa. State Coll., 1937-39; asst. prof. polit. sci. U. Calif. at Los Angeles, 1939-45, assoc. prof., 1945-50, prof. polit. sci., 1950-63, coordinator Navy tng. program, 1943-46, dean div. social scis., 1947-50, chmn. dept. polit. sci., 1950-52; Fulbright vis. prof. U. Western Australia, 1954; acad. asst. to pres. U. Calif. (statewide), 1958-60, dean of acad. planning, 1960-61; prof. comparative govt., chancellor U. Calif., Santa Cruz, 1961-74; chancellor emeritus U. Calif., 1974—; prof. McHenry Vineyard, 1979—; cons. S.Am. univs. Ford Found., 1961; mem. Coll. Entrance Exam. Bd., 1964-67; dir. State Nev. U. Survey, 1955-57, Survey of Higher Edn. in Kansas City Area, 1957; mem. Master Plan Survey of Higher Edn. in Cal., 1959- 60; mem. adv. bd. U.S. Naval Postgrad. Sch., 1970-74. Author: The Labor Party in Transition, 1931-38, 1938, California Government: Politics and Administration, (with W.W. Crouch), 1945, The American Federal Government, (with J.H. Ferguson), 1947, 14th edit., 1981, The American System of Government, (with J.H. Ferguson), 1947, 14th edit., 1981, The Third Force in Canada, 1950, Elements of American Government, (with J.H. Ferguson), 1950, 9th edit., 1970, American Government Today, (with E.B. Fincher and J.H. Ferguson), 1951, State and Local Government in California, (with W.W. Crouch and others), 1952, California Government and Politics, 1956, 4th edit., 1967, Academic Departments: Problems, Variations and Alternatives, 1977. Candidate for mayor, City Los Angeles, 1950; for rep. to congress 22d Dist., 1952. Carnegie fellow in New Zealand, 1946-47; Fulbright lectr. in Australia, 1954. Office: McHenry Libr U Calif Santa Cruz CA 95064

MCHENRY, DONALD F., former diplomat, international affairs consultant, educator; b. St. Louis, Oct. 13, 1936; s. Limas and Dora Lee (Brooks) McH.; m. Mary Elizabeth Williamson (div. 1978); children: Michael Stephen, Christina Ann, Elizabeth Ann. B.S., Ill. State U., 1957; M.S., So. Ill. U., 1959. Instr. Howard U., 1959-62; with Dept. State, 1963-73, internat. affairs officer, 1963-66, officer-in-charge dependent area affairs, 1966-68, asst. to sec., 1968-69, spl. asst. to counselor, 1969-71; internat. affairs fellow Council Fgn. Relations, guest scholar Brookings Instn., 1971-73; project dir. Carnegie Endowment Internat. Peace, 1973-77; lectr. Am. U., 1975; U.S.

dep. rep. UN Security Council, 1977-79; ambassador to UN, 1979-81; lectr. Georgetown U., 1973-74; Univ. research prof. diplomacy and internat. relations Georgetown U, 1981—; pres. IRC Group; bd. dirs. AT&T, Internat. Paper Co., Coca-Cola Co., Bank of Boston Corp., Smith Kline Beecham plc; former bd. govs. Am. Stock Exchange, 1981-87. Author: Micronesia: Trust Betrayed, 1975; mem. editorial bd.: Fgn. Policy mag; contbr. articles to profl. jours. Trustee Brookings Instn., Mayo Found., Johnson Found., Columbia U.; bd. dirs. Inst. for Internat. Econs., Am. Dirchley Found.; chmn. of bd. Africare; bd. givs. UN Assn. of U.S., Mid. East Inst. Recipient Superior Service award Dept. State, 1966; Family of Man award N.Y. Council Chs., 1980. Fellow Am. Acad. Arts and Scis. Office: Georgetown U Sch Fgn Svc ICC 301 Washington DC 20057-1052

MCHENRY, HENRY MALCOLM, anthropologist, educator; b. Los Angeles, May 19, 1944; s. Dean Eugene and Emma Jane (Snyder) McH.; m. Linda Jean Conway, June 25, 1966; children: Lindsay Jean, Annalisa Jane. BA, U. Calif., Davis, 1966, MA, 1967; PhD, Harvard U., 1972. Asst. prof. anthropology U. Calif., Davis, 1971-76, assoc. prof. anthropology, 1976-81, prof. anthropology, 1981—, chmn. dept. anthropology, 1984-88. Fellow Am. Anthrop. Assn., Calif. Acad. Sci.; mem. Am. Assn. Phys. Anthropologists (exec. com. 1981-85), Soc. Study Evolution, Soc. Vertebrate Paleontology, Phi Beta Kappa, Phi Kappa Phi. Democrat. Buddhist. Avocation: winemaker. Home: 330 11th St Davis CA 95616-2010 Office: U of Calif Davis Dept Of Anthropology Davis CA 95616

MC HENRY, MARTIN CHRISTOPHER, physician, educator; b. San Francisco, Feb. 9, 1932; s. Merl and Marcella (Bricca) McH.; m. Patricia Grace Hughes, Apr. 27, 1957; children: Michael, Christopher, Timothy, Mary Ann, Jeffrey, Paul, Kevin, William, Monica, Martin Christopher. Student, U. Santa Clara, 1950-53; MD, U. Cin., 1957; MS in Medicine, U. Minn., 1966. Intern, Highland Alameda County (Calif.) Hosp., Oakland, 1957-58; resident, internal medicine fellow Mayo Clinic, Rochester, Minn., 1958-61, spl. appointee in infectious diseases, 1963-64; staff physician infectious diseases Henry Ford Hosp., Detroit, 1964-67; staff physician Cleve. Clinic, 1967-72, chmn. dept. infectious diseases, 1972-92; sr. physician infectious diseases, 1992—. Asst. clin. prof. Case Western Res. U., 1970-77, assoc. clin. prof. medicine, 1977-91, clin. prof. medicine, 1991—; assoc. vis. physician Cleve. Met. Gen. Hosp., 1970—; cons. VA Hosp., Cleve., 1973—. Chmn. manpower com. Swine Influenza Program, Cleve., 1976. Served with USNR, 1961-63. Named Disting. Tchr. in Medicine Cleve. Clinic, 1972, 90; recipient 1st ann. Bruce Hubbard Stewart award Cleve. Clinic Found. for Humanities in Medicine, 1985, Nightingale Physician Collaboration award Cleve. Clinic Found. Divsn. Nursing, 1995. Diplomate Am. Bd. Internal Medicine. Fellow ACP, Infectious Diseases Soc. Am., Am. Coll. Chest Physicians (chmn. com. cardiopulmonary infections 1975-77, 81-83), Royal Soc. Medicine of Great Britain; mem. Am. Soc. Clin. Pharmacology and Therapeutics (chmn. sect. infectious diseases and antimicrobial agts., 1970-77, 80-85, dir.), Am. Thoracic Soc., Am. Soc. Clin. Pathologists, Am. Fedn. Clin. Rsch., Am. Soc. Tropical Medicine and Hygiene, Am. Soc. Microbiology, N.Y. Acad. Scis. Contbr. numerous articles to profl. jours., also chpts. to books. Home: 2779 Belgrave Rd Pepper Pike OH 44124 Office: 9500 Euclid Ave Cleveland OH 44195-0001

MC HENRY, POWELL, lawyer; b. Cinn., May 14, 1926; s. L. Lee McHenry and Marguerite L. (Powell) Heinz; m. Venna Mae Guerrea, Aug. 27, 1948; children: Scott, Marshall, Jody Lee, Gale Lynn. AB, U. Cinn., 1949; LLB, Harvard U., 1951, JD, 1969. Bar: Ohio 1951, U.S. Ct. Appeals (6th cir.) 1964, U.S. Supreme Ct. 1966. Assoc. Dinsmore, Shohl, Sawyer & Dinsmore, Cinn., 1951-58; ptnr. Dinsmore, Shohl, Coates & Deupree (and predecessors), Cinn., 1958-75; gen. counsel Federated Dept. Stores, Inc., 1971-75; assoc. gen. counsel Procter & Gamble Co., 1975-76, v.p., gen. counsel, 1976-83, v. v.p., gen. counsel, 1983-91; counsel Dinsmore & Shohl, Cin., 1991—; bd. dirs. Eagle Picher Industries, Inc., 1991—. Mem. com. Hamilton County Pub. Defender, Cinn. With USNR, 1944-46. Recipient award of merit Ohio Legal Center Inst., 1969. Mem. ABA, Ohio Bar Assn., Cin. Bar Assn. (pres. 1979-80, exec. com. 1975-81), Harvard U. Law Sch. Assn. Cin. (pres. 1960-61), Am. Law Inst., Assn. Gen. Counsel (pres. 1986-88), Harvard Club, Western Hill Country Club (bd. dirs. 1964-70, sec. 1966-69, 87-89, treas. 1969-70, 89-90), Queen City Club, Commonwealth Club. Republican. Methodist. Office: Dinsmore & Shohl 1900 Chemed Ctr 255 E 5th St Cincinnati OH 45202-4700

MCHENRY, ROBERT (DALE), editor; b. St. Louis, Apr. 30, 1945; s. Robert Dale and Pearl Lenna (Nalley) McH.; m. Carolyn F. Amundson, Oct. 2, 1971; children: Curran, Zachary. BA in English Lit., Northwestern U., 1966; MA in English Lit., U. Mich., 1967; MBA in Mgmt. Northwestern U., 1987. Proofreader, prodn. editor Ency. Britannica, Inc., Chgo., 1967-69, editor, 1974-75, dir. yearbooks, 1985-86, mng. editor, 1986-90, gen. editor, v.p., 1990—; editor San Francisco Prodns., Inc., Chgo., 1969-74; sr. editor Merriam-Webster, Inc., Springfield, Mass., 1975-82. Editor: Documentary History of Conservation in America, 1972, Webster's American Military Biographies, 1978, Liberty's Women, 1980, Webster's New Biographical Dictionary, 1983. Mem. United Ch. of Christ.

MCHUGH, EARL STEPHEN, dentist; b. Colorado Springs, Colo., Feb. 27, 1936; s. Earl Clifton and Margaret Mary (Higgins) M.; m. Joan Bleckwell, Aug. 24, 1957; children: Kevin, Stacey, Julie. BA, Cornell U., 1958; DDS, U. Mo., 1962. Pvt. practice, Kansas City, Mo., 1964—; lectr. U. Mo. Dental Sch., Kansas City, 1988, clin. staff, 1989, 90, 91, 92, 93, 94, 95, ethics seminar faculty staff, addiction in dentistry faculty, 1995; cons. Hallmark, Inc., Kansas City, 1988. Contbr. articles to profl. jours. Deacon Presbyn. Ch. Prairie Village, Kans., 1982-84; vol. Shawnee Mission Hosp. Kans., 1985-88; lectr. Drug Recovery Program, Kansas City, Kans., 1988-89, 92, 93, 94. Capt. Dental Corp, U.S. Army, 1962-64. Mem. Valley Hope Assn. (bd. dirs. 1989-90), Audubon Soc. Ornithologist of Yr. Kansas City chpt. 1990), Kans. Ornithol. Soc. (v.p. 1989-90, pres. 1990-91), Internat. Coun. Bird Preservation (Kans. del. 1990, coord. Kans. Breeding Bird Atlas 1992, 93, 94, 95, chmn. Kans. bird records com.), Omicron Kappa Upsilon, Chi Psi.

MCHUGH, EDWARD FRANCIS, JR., lawyer; b. Cambridge, Mass., Sept. 6, 1932; s. Edward Francis and Eleanor (Whelton) McH.; m. Mary Judith Murchison, Sept. 15, 1962; children: Mary, Alexandra, Edward III, Michael. AB, Georgetown U., 1953, LLB, 1958. Bar: Mass., 1958, U.S. Dist. Ct. Mass. 1958, D.C. 1958, U.S. Ct. Appeals (D.C. cir.) 1958. Law clk. U.S. Ct. Appeals (D.C. cir.), Washington, 1958-59; assoc., jr. ptnr, then ptnr. Nutter, McClennen & Fish, Boston, 1959—; gen. counsel Two/Ten Found., Watertown, Mass., 1975—; counsel, sec. New Eng. Aquarium Corp., Boston, 1987—; gen. counsel and clk. South Shore Health and Ednl. Corp. and South Shore Hosp., 1991—. Editor in chief Georgetown Law Journal, 1958; contbr. to profl. publs. Trustee Notre Dame Acad.; Hingham, Mass., 1975-85, Harold Brooks Found., Quincy, Mass., 1987-88; chmn. bd. trustees South Shore Hosp. and South Shore Health and Ednl. Corp., Weymouth, Mass., 1986-88. 1st lt. USAF, 1953-55. Mem. Boston Bar Assn. (mem. coun. 1984-87), Knights of Malta, Hatherly Country Club (pres. 1978-79, bd. dirs.), Clover Club. Roman Catholic. Office: Nutter McClennen & Fish 1 International Pl Boston MA 02110-2699

MCHUGH, HEATHER, poet; b. Calif., Aug. 20, 1948. BA, Radcliffe Coll., 1970; MA, U. Denver, 1972. Assoc. prof. English SUNY, Binghamton, 1976-82; prof. English, Milliman writer-in-residence U. Wash. Seattle, 1983—; vis. prof. Columbia U., 1987; Holloway lectr. U. Calif. Berkeley, 1987; judge Nat. Poetry Series book award, 1986, Poetry Soc. Am. book award, 1987. Author: (poetry) Dangers, 1977, A World of Difference, 1981, To the Quick, 1987, Shades, 1988, Broken English: Poetry and Partiality, 1993, Hinge and Sign: Poems, 1968-1993, 1994 (Nat. Book award nomination 1994); editor: The Matter with Stairs, 1986; translator: D'Apres Tout: Poems by Jean Follain, 1981, Because the Sea Is Black: Poems by Blaga Dimitrova, 1989. Cummington Community for the Arts fellow, 1970; Provinceton Fine Arts Work Ctr. fellow, 1972; MacDowell Colony fellow, 1973, 74, 76; Nat. Endowment for Arts grantee, 1974, 81; Yaddo Colony fellow, 1980; Bellagio grantee Rockefeller Found., 1986; recipient Acad. Am. Poets prize, 1972. Office: Univ of Washington Dept of English GN 30 Seattle WA 98195*

MCHUGH, HELEN FRANCES, university dean, home economist; b. Tucson, Aug. 19, 1931; d. James Patrick and Mary Catherine (Hochstatter) McH.; m. Herbert J. Brauer, Mar. 26, 1982. B.S. with distinction, U. Mo.-, Columbia, 1958, M.S., 1959; Ph.D., Iowa State U., 1965. Instr. U. Tex., Austin, 1961-63; asst. prof. U. Tex., 1963-66, assoc. prof., 1966-67; asso. prof. Ind. State U., Terre Haute, 1967-69; asso. prof., dept. head Oreg. State U., Corvallis, 1969-73; prof., dean Coll. Home Econs., U. Del., Newark, 1973-75; prof. consumer econs., dean Coll. Human Resource Scis. assoc. dir. Colo. Experiment Sta., Colo. State U., Ft. Collins, 1976—; cons. in field. Chmn. policy bd.: Jour. Consumer Research, 1978-80. Recipient Disting. Service award U. Mo. Alumni Assn., 1975. Mem. Am. Econ. Assn., Am. Agrl. Econs. Assn., Am. Home Econs. Assn. (bd. dirs. 1973-75), Assn. Adminstrs. Home Econs. (pres. 1978-79), Sigma Xi, Gamma Sigma Delta, Phi Kappa Phi. Roman Catholic. Office: Colorado State U Agricultural Experimen Fort Collins CO 80523

MCHUGH, JAMES JOSEPH, retired associate dean; b. Phila., Aug. 12, 1930; s. James Joseph and Patience Mary (McGowan) McH.; m. Rita Marie Huber, May 21, 1960; children: Margaret Marie, James Joseph IV. B.A. (with honors), U. Pa., 1951, LL.B., 1954; M.S. in Internat. Relations, George Washington U., 1972. Bar: Pa. 1955. Commd. ensign U.S. Navy, 1955, advanced through grades to rear adm., 1980; legal officer Naval Air Station, Point Mugu, Calif., 1955-58; staff officer Office Judge Adv. Gen., Washington, 1959-63; staff instr. U.S. Naval Justice Sch., Newport, R.I., 1963-65; counsel Bur. Naval Personnel, Washington, 1965-68; asst. fleet judge adv. to comdr. in chief U.S. Pacific Fleet, 1968-71; spl. counsel to chief naval ops. Washington, 1972-76; officer in charge Naval Legal Service Office, San Francisco, 1976-78; asst. judge adv. gen. Washington, 1978-80; dep. judge adv. gen. Alexandria, Va., 1980-82, judge adv. gen., 1982-84; asst. dean McGeorge Sch. Law, Sacramento, 1984-86, assoc. dean, 1987-93. Decorated D.S.M., Legion of Merit (2), Meritorious Svc. medal (2), Navy Commendation medal. Mem. ABA, Order of Coif (hon.), Phi Beta Kappa. Republican. Roman Catholic. Home: 4704 Olive Oak Way Carmichael CA 95608-5663

MCHUGH, JAMES LENAHAN, JR., lawyer; b. Pitts., June 28, 1937; s. James Lenahan and Annette (Dalton) McH.; m. Mary-Ann Curto, Feb. 16, 1963 (div. 1988); children: Angela Dalton Sherrill, Hillary Lenahan Clagett; m. Rosa Lamoreaux, Sept. 8, 1991. BA, Duquesne U., 1959; LLB, Villanova U., 1962. Bar: D.C. 1963. Law clk. U.S. Dist. Ct. (ea. dist.) Pa., Phila., 1962-63; law clk. to Assoc. Justice Tom C. Clark, U.S. Supreme Ct., Washington, 1963-64; assoc. Steptoe & Johnson, Washington, 1967-70, ptnr., 1970-94; gen. counsel APA, Washington, 1994—; mem. bd. consultors Law Sch., Villanova (Pa.) U., 1973—; dir. Higher Achievement Program, Washington, 1984-87; coord. Washington Lawyers' Project, Robert F. Kennedy Meml. Found., Washington, 1972-75. Editor-in-chief Villanova Law Rev., Vol. VII, 1961-62; chmn. editorial adv. bd. Fed. Comm. Law Jour., 1981-84. Bd. dirs. Columbia Hosp. for Women's Found., Washington, 1985—, Children's Radio Theatre, Washington, 1983-86; chmn. exec. giving Archbishop's Appeal, Archdiocese of Washington, 1982-84; mem. bd. visitors Ctr. for Study of Orgns. and Mgmt., U. Md. Univ. Coll., 1987-92; bd. dirs. Human Resources Rsch. Orgn., Inc., 1978—; chmn. bd. dirs., 1991—; mem. advisors Inst. for Conflict Analysis and Resolution, George Mason U., 1990-94. Capt. U.S. Army, 1964-67. Mem. ABA (forum com. health law), Nat. Health Lawyers Assn., D.C. Bar Assn., Choral Arts Soc., Order of Coif. Home: 4112 Fessenden St NW Washington DC 20016-4227 Office: APA 750 1st St NE Washington DC 20002-4242

MCHUGH, JAMES T., bishop; b. Orange, N.J., Jan. 3, 1932. Educated at Seton Hall Univ., Immaculate Conception Sem. (Darlington, N.J.), Fordham Univ., Catholic Univ., Angelicum (Rome). Ordained priest, 1957; consecrated bishop, 1988. Asst. dir. Family Life Div., U.S. Cath. Conf. 1965-67, dir., 1967-75; dir. Office for Pro-Life Activities, Nat. Conf. Cath. Bishops, 1972-78; aux. bishop Newark, 1987-89; bishop Diocese of Camden, N.J., 1989—. Home: Marywood PO Box 577 Blackwood NJ 08012 Office: The Chancery PO Box 709 1845 Haddon Ave Camden NJ 08101

MCHUGH, JOHN JAMES, consultant; b. Greenwich, Conn., May 14, 1931; s. John and Marie J. (Brady) McH.; m. Clara Louise Canals, Jan. 26, 1939; children: Aletha, John, Edward, Kathleen. B.S., Georgetown U., 1953; LL.B., Fordham U., 1958. Bar: N.Y. 1958. Assoc. firm Cravath, Swaine & Moore, N.Y.C., 1958-62; asst. gen. counsel, asst. sec. Rheem Mfg. Co., N.Y.C., 1962-68; sec. City Investing Co., N.Y.C., 1968-85, v.p. 1974-85; v.p. adminstrn., sec. Home Group, Inc, N.Y.C., 1985-88; cons. in field N.Y.C. and Greenwich, 1988—. Articles editor: Fordham Law Rev., 1957-58. Active fund raising for various orgns. Served to lt. (j.g.) USN, 1953-55. Kennedy scholar, 1957-58. Mem. Am. Soc. Corp. Secs., ABA (assoc.). Republican. Roman Catholic.

MC HUGH, JOHN LAURENCE, marine biologist, educator; b. Vancouver, B.C., Can., Nov. 24, 1911; came to U.S., 1946, naturalized, 1958; s. John and Annie Margaret (Woodward) McH.; m. Sophie Kehan, Mar. 30, 1979; children by previous marriage—Peter Chadwick, Heather, Jan Margaret. B.A., U. B.C., 1936, M.A., 1938; Ph.D. U. Calif. at Los Angeles, 1950. Summer sci. asst. Fisheries Research Bd. Can., 1929-37, fishery biologist, 1938-41; research asso. Scripps Instn. Oceanography, 1948-51; dir. Va. Fisheries Lab., Gloucester Point, 1951-59; prof. marine biology Coll. William and Mary, 1951-59; chmn. sci. com. Atlantic States Marine Fisheries Commn., 1956-58; chief div. biol. research Bur. Comml. Fisheries, Dept. Interior, 1959-63, asst. dir. for biol. research, 1963-66, dep. dir. bur., 1966-70; acting dir. Office Marine Resources, 1968-70; head NSF Office for Internat. Decade Ocean Exploration, 1970; prof. marine resources SUNY-Stony Brook, 1970-82, prof. emeritus, 1982—; U.S. commr. Inter-Am. Tropical Tuna Commn., 1960-70, sec. commn., 1960-61, 67-68, sec. U.S. sect., 1961-67, head U.S. del., 1967-70; dep. U.S. commr. Internat. Whaling Commn., 1961-67, commr., 1967-73, vice chmn., 1968-71, chmn., 1971-72; mem. U.S. nat. com. Internat. Biol. Program, 1968-70; adv. com. marine resources research to dir.-gen. FAO, 1967-71; mem. U.S. dels. to internat. sci., fishery meetings, 1959-72, NRC, 1963-69; mem. com. on internat. marine sci. affairs policy, ocean affairs bd. Nat. Acad. Scis.-Nat. Acad. Engring., 1971-74, com. on aquatic food resources, food and nutrition bd., 1973-74, vice chmn., 1973; mem. blue ribbon panel to rev. fed. programs on continental shelf. Office Sci. and Tech., Exec. Office Pres., 1971; chmn. select com. to rev. Eastern Pacific Oceanic Conf., Scripps Instn. Oceanography, 1972; mem. steering com., chmn. panel on fisheries, chmn. working group on information needs for effective mgmt. Coastal Zone workshop Woods Hole Oceanographic Instn., 1971-72; hon. mem. Whaling Mus. Soc., Cold Spring Harbor, N.Y., 1972-76; sec. Internat. Marine Archives, Nantucket, Mass., 1973-78; cons. to Nat. Council Marine Resources and Engring. Devel., 1970-71, Smithsonian Instn., 1970-72, Nat. Oceanic and Atmospheric Adminstrn., 1971-73, Riverside Research Inst., N.Y.C., 1971-72, Town of Islip, N.Y., 1974-78; mem. Mid-Atlantic Regional Fishery Mgmt. Council, 1976-79, mem. sci. and statis. com., 1980-84; mem. steering com. Nat. Acad. Sci.-NRC Panel to Review Fishery Research, 1975-76. Author: Fishery Management; contbr. numerous sci. papers, book chpts., articles to profl. lit. Served to capt. Canadian Army, 1941-45. Recipient Disting. Teaching award Marine Scis. Rsch. Ctr. Assocs., 1977, cert. for meritorious svc. Marine Scis. Rsch. Ctr./U. Stony Brook, 1994; fellow Internat. Oceanographic Found., 1955-74; trustee emeritus, 1974—; fellow Woodrow Wilson Internat. Ctr. for Scholars Smithsonian Instn., summer 1971. Mem. AAAS (selection com., Rosensteil award 1976), Am. Fisheries Soc. (Bronze medal, award of excellence 1984), Nat. Shellfisheries Assn. (citation 1984, hon. mem.), Va. Acad. Scis. (past chmn. biology sect.), Atlantic Estuarine Research Soc. (hon., past pres.), Am. Inst. Fishery Research Biologists, Nat. Shellfisheries Assn. (hon. member.), Estuarine Research Fedn. (hon. member.), Sigma Xi, Beta Theta Pi. Home: Vinson Hall Apt 170 6251 Old Dominion Dr Mc Lean VA 22101

MCHUGH, JOHN MICHAEL, congressman, former state senator; b. Watertown, N.Y., Sept. 29, 1948; s. Donald and Jane (O'Neill) McH. BA in Polit. Sci., Syracuse U., 1970; MPA, Nelson A. Rockefeller Grad. Sch. Pub. Affairs, 1977. Asst. city mngr. Watertown, 1968-73; confidential asst. Watertown City Mgrs. Office, 1971-76; chief of research, liaison with local govts. Office of N.Y. State Senator H.D. Barclay, 1976-84; U.S. senator from 46th N.Y. dist., chmn. joint legis. comm. on dairy industry devel., 1987-92; mem. 103rd-104th Congresses from 24th N.Y. dist., 1993—; chmn. govt. reform and oversight subcom. on postal svc., mem. nat. sucurity com.

Mem. Legis. Commn. on Modernization of the Tax Code, Nat. Conf. State Legis., Commerce & Econ. Devel. Com., Commerce, Labor and Regulation Com. of the State Fed. Assembly, Coun. State Govt. Eastern Regional Conf. Com. on Fiscal Affairs. Recipient 40 Outstanding Alumni awards Syracuse U., Individual Achievement award N.Y. State Dept. Econ. Devel.; named to Hon. First Citizen, City of Watertown, 1976. Mem. Legis. on State Legislators (nat. conf. state legislators), Nat. Conf. State Legislators (vice chmn. agrl. and internat. trade com. State-Fed. Assembly), Am. Soc. Young Polit. Leaders. Republican. Roman Catholic. Avocations: boating, snow skiing, music. Office: US Ho of Reps 416 Cannon HOB Washington DC 20515-3224*

MC HUGH, PAUL R., psychiatrist, neurologist, educator; b. Lawrence, Mass., May 21, 1931; s. Francis Paul and Mary Dorothea (Herlihy) McH.; m. Jean Barlow, Dec. 27, 1959; children: Clare Mary, Patrick Daniel, Denis Timothy. AB, Harvard U., 1952, MD, 1956. Diplomate: Am. Bd. Psychiatry and Neurology. Intern Peter Bent Brigham Hosp., Boston, 1956-57; resident in neurology Mass. Gen. Hosp., 1957-60, fellow in neuropathology, 1958-59; teaching fellow in neurology and neuropathology Harvard, 1957-60; clin. asst. psychiatry Maudsley Hosp., London, Eng., 1960-61; mem. neuropsychiatry div. Walter Reed Army Inst. Research, Washington, 1961-64; asst. prof. psychiatry and neurology Cornell U., N.Y.C., 1964-68; assoc. prof. Cornell U., 1968-71, prof., 1971; dir. electroencephalography N.Y. Hosp., 1964-68; founder, dir. N.Y. Hosp. Bourne Behavioral Rsch. Lab., 1967-68, clin. dir., supr. psychiat. edn., founder, dir. Weschester divsn. dept. psychiatry, 1968-73; prof., chmn. dept. psychiatry U. Oreg. Health Sci. Center, Portland, 1973-75; Henry Phipps prof. psychiatry Johns Hopkins, Balt., 1975—; chmn. dept. psychiatry Johns Hopkins, 1975—, prof. dept. mental hygiene, 1976—; psychiatrist-in-chief Johns Hopkins Hosp., 1975—; dir. Blades Ctr. for Clin. Practice and Rsch. in Alcoholism Johns Hopkins Med. Inst., 1992—; chmn. med. staff Johns Hopkins Hosp., 1983-89, trustee, 1983—; vis. prof. Guys Hosp., London, Eng., 1976; chmn. bio-psychology Study sect. NIH, 1986-89. Author: The Perspectives of Psychiatry, 1983 (with Phillip R. Slavney) Psychiatric Polarities, 1987, Genes, Brain and Behavior, 1990; contbg. author: Cecil-Loeb Textbook of Medicine; mem. editorial bd. Am. Jour. Physiology, Jour. Nervous and Mental Disease, Comprehensive Psychiatry, Medicine, Psychol. Medicine, 1976—, Am. Scholar; contbr. articles to profl. jours. Mem. Md. Gov.'s Adv. Com., 1977-80. Grantee NIH, 1964-68, 67-70, 70-74, 75—; recipient William C. Menninger award ACP, 1987. Fellow Royal Coll. Psychiatry, Am. Psychiat. Assn.; mem. NAS, Am. Neurol. Assn., Am. Physiol. Soc., Harvey Soc., Am. Coll. Neuropsychopharmacology, Am. Psychopath. Assn., Pavlovian Soc., Inst. Medicine. Club: W Hamilton St. Home: 3707 St Paul St Baltimore MD 21218-2403 Office: Johns Hopkins Med Insts 600 N Wolfe St Baltimore MD 21287-7413

MCHUGH, RICHARD WALKER, lawyer; b. Sullivan, Ind., Dec. 9, 1952; s. Richard Harrison and Virginia Ann (Robinson) McH.; m. Marsha J. Marshall, May 24, 1975; children: Walker, Cora. BA, Wabash Coll., 1975; JD, U. Mich., 1978. Bar: Mich. 1984, Ky. 1979, U.S. Supreme Ct. 1987. Assoc. Youngdahl Law Firm, Little Rock, 1978-79; staff atty. Legal Aid Soc., Louisville, 1979-84; assoc. gen. counsel Internat. Union UAW, Detroit, 1984-95; pvt. atty. Ann Arbor, Mich., 1995—; dir. Mich. Legal Svcs., Detroit, 1986-91. Mem. Nat. Acad. Social Inst., ABA (com. on unemployment ins. law 1985—). Democrat. Avocations: fishing, backpacking. Office: UAW Legal Dept 8000 E Jefferson Ave Detroit MI 48214-2699

MCHUGH, THOMAS EDWARD, state supreme court justice; b. Charleston, W.Va., Mar. 26, 1936; s. Paul and Melba McHugh; m. Judith McHugh, Mar. 14, 1959; children: Karen, Cindy, James, John. AB, W.Va. U., 1958, LLB, 1964. Bar: W.Va. 1964. Pvt. practice law Charleston, 1964-66, 69-74; law clk. to presiding judge Harlan Calhoun W.Va. Supreme Ct. of Appeals, 1966-68; chief judge Cir. Ct. (13th cir.) W.Va., Charleston, 1974-80; assoc. justice W.Va. Supreme Ct., Charleston, 1980—; chief justice W. Va Supreme Ct, Charleston, WV, 1984, 88, 92—. Served to 1st lt. U.S. Army, 1958-61. Mem. W.Va. Jud. Assn., W.Va. Bar Assn., Order of the Coif. Democrat. Roman Catholic. Office: WVa Supreme Ct 317 State Capitol Charleston WV 25305-0001

MCHUGH, WILLIAM DENNIS, dental educator, researcher; b. Berwick, Northumberland, U.K., May 8, 1929; came to U.S., 1970, naturalized, 1977; s. Gerald D. and Jeanne (Stewart) McH.; m. Susan Mary Cort, Feb. 22, 1958; children: Moira A. McHugh Douglas, Alan N.C. B of Dental Surgery cum laude, St. Andrews (U.K.) Univ., 1954, DDS, 1959. House surgeon in oral surgery Dundee (Scotland) Dental Sch., 1950, sr. house surgeon in orthodontics, 1952-53; instr. dept. operative dentistry Royal Dental Sch. Malmö, Sweden, 1954-55; lectr. in periodontology and pathology Royal Dental Hosp., London, 1956-58; lectr. periodontology and preventive dentistry St. Andrews U. Dental Sch., 1959-62, sr. lectr., head dept., 1962-65, prof., chmn. dept., 1965-70; prof. clin. dentistry and dental rsch., assoc. dean for dental affairs Sch. Medicine and Dentistry, U. Rochester, N.Y., 1970—; dir. Eastman Dental Ctr., Rochester, 1970—; cons. Scottish Ea. Regional Hosp. Bd., 1962-65, Genesee (N.Y.) Hosp., 1971—; cons. planning and projects various schs. dentistry including U. Conn., 1984, U. Riyadh, Saudi Arabia, 1984, U. Pa., 1985-90, Columbia U., 1986—, W.Va. U., 1986-87; cons. Nat. Inst. Dental Health, NIH, Bethesda, Md., 1975—; mem. Nat. Adv. Dental Rsch. Coun., 1987-91; dentist-in-chief Strong Meml. Hosp., 1971-75, dentist, 1975—; mem. ambulatory care com. Finger Lakes Health Systems Agy., 1976-78; med. adv. com. Monroe Community Hosp., 1971-83. Editor: Dental Plaque, 1970; co-editor: Systematized Prevention of Oral Disease, 1987; assoc. editor Jour. Periodontal Rsch., 1966-71, Jour. Am. Coll. Dentists, 1987—; mem. editorial bd. Community Dentistry and Oral Epidemiology, 1972-74, Preventive Dentistry, 1973-81, J. Clin. Periodontology, 1989—; editor Proc. Brit. Soc. Periodontology, 1960-62; contbr. numerous articles to profl. jours. Mem. archtl. rev. bd. Town of Brighton, 1982-89. Flight lt. RAF, 1951-53. Rsch. fellow and Nuffield Found. fellow Royal Dental Coll., Sweden, 1954-56, rshc. fellow oral pathology U. Birmingham, 1959; NIH grantee, 1970-87, 78-81, 80—, Eastman Kodak Co., grantee 1982-88. Fellow Am. Coll. Dentists, Internat. Coll. Dentists, AAAS; mem. Am. Assn. Dental Rsch. (pres. 1983-84), Internat. Assn. Dental Rsch. (pres. 1988-89), Am. Assn. Dental Schs. (v.p advanced edn. and fed. dental svcs 1980-83), ADA (cons. Coun. Dental Therapeutics 1985), Brit. Soc. Periodontology (pres. 1969-70), Brit. Dental Assn. (pres. N. of Scotland br. 1967-68), Monroe County Dental Soc. (community svcs., hosps. profl. conduct com. 1985-86), Dental Soc. State N.Y., Rochester Dental Study Club, Royal Coll. Surgeons of Edinburgh, Internat. Coll. Dentists, Genesee Valley Club (Rochester, gov. 1987-93), Rotary. Avocations: gardening, tennis, squash. Office: Eastman Dental Ctr 625 Elmwood Ave Rochester NY 14620-2913

MC ILHENNY, JAMES HARRISON, association executive; b. Cleve., Nov. 9, 1927; s. Edward Lott and Noreen Isobel (Spence) McI.; m. Dorothy Dean Johnson, Aug. 11, 1951 (div.); 1 child, Claire B.; m. Candace Von Salzen, Sept. 14, 1990. Student, USCG Acad., 1945-47; B.A. in Econs, U. Mich., 1950. Pres. I. Miller & Sons, Inc., 1962-65; dir., v.p. Hickok Mfg. Co., Rochester, N.Y., 1965-68; sr. v.p. Macmillan, Inc., N.Y.C., 1968-72; exec. v.p. Macmillan, Inc., 1972-80, U.S. News & World Report, Washington, 1980-81; pres. U.S. News & World Report, 1981-85, chief exec. officer, 1981-85; pres. Diversified Printing, Atglen, Pa., 1985-87; pres., CEO Coun. Better Bus. Burs., 1987—; bd. dirs. Manhattan Life Ins. Corp. Served with USCG, 1945-47. Mem. Sigma Nu. Home: 410 Pommander Walk Alexandria VA 22314-3846 Office: Coun Better Bus Burs 4200 Wilson Blvd Ste 800 Arlington VA 22203-1800

MCILVAINE, JOSEPH PETER, professional baseball team executive; b. Bryn Mawr, Pa., Jan. 18, 1948; s. Joseph Francis and Mary Margaret (Wack) McI.; m. Martha Anne Marmer, Nov. 24, 1973; children: Timothy, Susan, Patrick. BA, St. Charles Borromeo Sem., Phila., 1969. Tchr. Our Mother of Good Counsel, Bryn Mawr, Pa., 1969-72; deliveryman United Parcel Svc., West Chester, Pa., 1972-73; profl. baseball player Detroit Tigers, 1969-73; major league baseball scout Balt. Orioles, 1974-76, Calif. Angels, Anaheim, 1977-78, Milw. Brewers, 1979-80; dir. scouting N.Y. Mets, Flushing, 1980-85, v.p. dir. baseball ops., 1986-90; exec. v.p., gen. mgr. San Diego Padres, 1990-93; former gen. mgr. N.Y. Mets, now exec. v.p. baseball ops.; cons. Athletes for Life, Washington, 1988—; bd. dirs. Major League Scouting Bur., Newport Beach, Calif., Returning Baseball to Inner Cities,

L.A. Recipient World Series ring Major League Baseball, Flushing, 1986. Mem. Fla. Diamond Club (pres. 1980-81, Exec. of Yr. award 1984). Avocation: golf. *

MCILVAINE, WILLIAM L., secondary school educator; b. Knoxville, Tenn., Apr. 24, 1935; s. Victor Caryl and Eleanor (Dickinson) McI.; m. Ruby Christine Smith, June 11, 1960; children: Ruby Celeste McIlvaine Davis, Joanna Noelle McIlvaine. Student, Mars Hill Coll., 1957-59; B Music Edn., N.E. La. State U., 1962; MCM in Conducting, New Orleans Bapt. Theol. Sem., 1968; M in Microcomputers with high honors, Nat. Radio Inst., 1987; MS in Edn. Adminstrn., N.C. Agrl. and Tech. State U., 1991. Cert. tchr., La., Ala., N.C.; cert. ednl. adminstr., supervision in curriculum, computers on grad. level, 1987. Band dir. Jefferson County Schs., Birmingham, Ala., 1962-63; dir. music, edn. and youth programs Front St. Bapt. Ch., Statesville, N.C., 1963-66; assoc. pastor, dir. music and youth programs Sugar Creek Bapt. Ch., Charlotte, N.C., 1968-70; band dir. Charlotte Mecklenburg Schs., 1970-73, Randolph County Schs., Asheboro, N.C., 1973-90; tchr. East Montgomery H.S., Biscoe, N.C., 1990—; chmn. computer curriculum devel. com., Troy, N.C., 1991-92. Music dir. Calvary United Meth., Asheboro, 1989-92, West Bend United Meth., Asheboro, 1992-94; dir. adult divsn. Sunday Sch. 1st Bapt. Ch., 1995—. With U.S. Army, 1954-57, Greenland. Mem. ASCD, NEA, N.C. Assn. Educators. Republican. Avocations: research, woodwork. Home: 3234 Meredith Country Rd Asheboro NC 27203 Office: East Montgomery H S PO Box 768 Biscoe NC 27209

MCILVANE, EDWARD JAMES, artist, instructor, designer; b. N.Y.C., July 5, 1947; s. Edward James Sr. and Irene (Logue) McI.; m. Rose F. Aloisi, 1970 (div. 1985); children: Jessica, Blake. BS in Edn. and Art Edn., St. John's U., N.Y.C., 1975; MFA, R.I. Sch. Design, 1978. Stained glass craftsman Claude Gaches Studio, L.I., 1969-71, The Lamb Studio, N.J., 1971-72, Greenland Studio, N.Y.C., 1972-75, Helmut-Schardt Studio, Northport, N.Y., 1975-78; freelance artist and designer Providence, 1978—; guest artist Summrvail Workshop for Art, Vail, Colo. 1980, N.Y. Exptl. Glass Workshop, N.Y.C., 1980; program coord. Pilchuck Sch., Stanwood, Wash., 1979; instr. Haystack Mt. Sch. Crafts, Deer Isle, Maine, 1977. Prin. works include Johnson's Wax Co., Rancine, Wis., Temple Beth-El, Prov., R.I., Providence Coll., Bank of Boston, Joseph W. Martin, Jr. Inst. for Law and Soc. Stonehill Coll., North Easton, Mass., Licht residence, Little Compton, R.I., Vinyl Tech. Sch., Middletown, Conn., Presbyn. World Hdqs., Louisville. R.I. State Coun. on the Arts fellow, 1980, 86, Nat. Endowment for the Arts fellow, 1983. Mem. Glass Art Soc. Avocations: Tai Chi, angling. Home: 8 Table Rock Rd Lincoln RI 02865-3928 Office: Studio 21 Holden St Providence RI 02908-5754

MCILVEEN, EDWARD E., electrical engineer, association executive; b. Passaic, N.J., Aug. 3, 1911; s. Bert Henry and Rachel (Shephard) McI.; m. Virginia Griffith, Apr. 7, 1934 (div. 1944); 1 dau., Elizabeth Maude; m. Linda Jane Sparnon, July 2, 1944; children: Richard H., Lynne R., Nancy P. B.M.E. cum laude, Poly. Univ. Bklyn., 1943. Engring. asst. Western Union Telegraph, N.Y.C., 1932-41; research engr. The Okonite Co., Passaic, N.J., 1941-54, asst. mgr. engring., 1954-63, mgr. cable devel., 1963-68; v.p. engring. The Okonite Co., Ramsey, N.J., 1968-78; sec.-treas. Insulated Cable Engrs. Assn., South Yarmouth, Mass., 1978—. Fellow IEEE (insulated conductors com.); mem. Montclair Soc. Engrs. (pres. 1960-61), Bass River Yacht Club (South Yarmouth), Kappa Sigma, Sigma Xi. Home: 33 Crosby St South Yarmouth MA 02664 Office: Insulated Cable Engrs Assn Inc PO Box 440 South Yarmouth MA 02664

MCILWAIN, CARL EDWIN, physicist; b. Houston, Mar. 26, 1931; s. Glenn William and Alma Ora (Miller) McI.; m. Mary Louise Hocker, Dec. 30, 1952; children—Janet Louise, Craig Ian. B.A., N. Tex. State Coll., Denton, 1953; M.S., State U. Iowa, 1956, Ph.D., 1960. Asst. prof. State U. Iowa, 1960-62; assoc. prof. physics U. Calif.-, San Diego, 1962-66; prof. U. Calif., 1966—; mem. space scis. steering com., fields and particles subcom. NASA, 1962-66; mem. potential contamination and interference from space expts. Space Sci. Bd., Nat. Acad. Scis.-NRC, 1964-71; mem. advisory com. for radiation hazards in supersonic transports FAA, 1967-71; mem. Fachbeirat Inst. Extraterrestrial Physics, Max Planck Inst., Garching, Fed. Republic Germany, 1977-83. Space Sci. Bd., NRC, 1983-86. Author. Guggenheim fellow, 1968, 72; recipient Space Sci. award Am. Inst. Aeros. and Astronautics, 1970; Computer Art award U.S. Users Automatic Info. Display Equipment, 1971; Sr. U.S. Scientist award Alexander von Humboldt Found., Ger., 1976. Fellow Am. Geophys. Union (John A. Fleming award 1975); mem. Am. Phys. Soc., Am. Astron. Soc. Patentee in field. Home: 6662 Avenida Manana La Jolla CA 92037-6228 Office: Cass, 0111 Univ Calif San Diego La Jolla CA 92093-0111

MCILWAIN, THOMAS DAVID, fishery administrator, marine biologist, educator; b. Pascagoula, Miss., Nov. 15, 1940; s. Julius Coleman and Kathleen (Folsom) McI.; m. Janet Ellen Chapman, Dec. 29, 1962; 1 child, Stacey Lee. BS in Biology and Psychology, U. So. Miss., 1964, MS in Biology, 1966, PhD in Zoology, 1978. Lab. aid U.S. Bur. Comml. Fisheries, Pascagoula, summer 1958; instr. biology U. So. Miss., Hattiesburg, 1964-66; tchr. sci. St. Martin (Miss.) High Sch., 1965-66; rsch. biologist Gulf Coast Rsch. Lab., Ocean Springs, Miss., 1966-67, sect. leader, 1967-78, asst. dir. fisheries, 1978-83, dir., 1989-94; legis. assoc. U.S. Congressman Trent Lott, Washington, 1983-84; fishery adminstr. Nat. Marine Fisheries Svc., Pascagoula, Miss., 1994—; prof. U. So. Miss., 1989—; fishery cons. Gulf and South Atlantic Fishery Devel. Found., Tampa, 1984-86, Republic of Honduras, 1990; pres. bd. dirs. Miss.-Ala. Sea Grant Consortium, Ocean Springs, 1991—. Contbr. numerous articles to profl. jours. Chmn. Harbor Commn., Ocean Springs, 1980—; bd. dirs. Jackson County United Way, Pascagoula, 1991—. Fellow Am. Inst. Fish Rsch. Scientists (regional dir. 1980); mem. Am. Fisheries Soc. (cert. fishery scientist), World Mariculture Soc., Miss. Acad. Scis. (bd. dirs. 1981), U.S. of C (chmn. environ. com. 1990—), So. Assn. Marine Labs. (pres. 1991-94). Presbyterian. Avocations: sailing, scuba diving, fishing. Office: Nat Marine Fisheries Svc Pascagoula Lab PO Drawer 1207 Pascagoula MS 39568-1207

MC ILWAIN, WILLIAM FRANKLIN, newspaper editor, writer; b. Lancaster, S.C., Dec. 15, 1925; s. William Franklin and Docia (Higgins) McI.; m. Anne Dalton, Nov. 28, 1952 (div. 1973); children: Nancy, William Franklin III; m. K. L. Brelsford, June 5, 1978 (div. 1983). B.A., Wake Forest Coll., 1949; postgrad., Harvard, 1957-58. Various positions with Wilmington (N.C.) Star, 1943, Charlotte (N.C.) Observer, 1945, Jacksonville (Fla.) Jour., 1945, Winston-Salem (N.C.) Jour.-Sentinel, 1949-52, Richmond (Va.) Times-Dispatch, 1952-54; chief copy editor Newsday, Garden City, N.Y., 1954-57; day news editor Newsday, 1957-60, city editor, 1960-64, mng. editor, 1964-66, editor, 1967-70; writer-in-residence Wake Forest U., 1970-71; dorm leader Alcoholic Rehab. Ctr., Butner, N.C., 1971; dep. mng. editor Toronto Star, 1971-73; mng. editor The Record, Hackensack, N.J., 1973-77; editor Boston Herald Am., 1977-79; dep. editor Washington Star, 1979-81, exec. mng. editor, 1981; editor Ark. Gazette, 1981-82; founding editor N.Y. Newsday, 1982-84; exec. editor Sarasota (Fla.) Herald-Tribune, 1984-90; sr. editor N.Y. Times Regional Newspaper Group, 1991-92; chmn. Bill Mc Ilwain, Inc., 1993—; Stone Ridge lectr., 1978. Author: The Glass Rooster, 1960, (with Walter Friedenberg) Legends of Baptist Hollow, 1949; collaborator: (with Newsday staff) Naked Came The Stranger, 1969, A Farewell to Alcohol, 1973; contbr. to: Reader's Digest, Harper's, Esquire, Atlantic Monthly. Mem. Pres. Johnson's Commn. on Civil Rights. With USMC, 1944. Mem. Am. Soc. Newspaper Editors, Soc. Nieman Fellows. Home and Office: 305 N Channel Dr Wrightsville NC 28480-2723 As Fats Waller said, "One never knows, do one?".

MC INDOE, DARRELL BRUCE, SR., communications executive; b. San Antonio, Mar. 28, 1957; s. Darrell Winfred and Carole Jean (McClain) McI.; m. Deborah Louise Clarkson, Aug. 4, 1982; children: Darrell Bruce Jr., Garrett Adam. BS in Physics, Allegheny Coll., 1979; MS in Computer Sci., Johns Hopkins U., 1984. Mem. tech. staff Computer Scis. Corp., Silver Spring, Md., 1979-82; pres. CSSI, Columbia, Md., 1982—. Mem. IEEE, Assn. Computing Machinery, Wash. Tech.'s Fast 50 Club, Assn. Old Crows. Office: CSSI 10260 Old Columbia Rd Columbia MD 21046

MC INDOE, DARRELL WINFRED, nuclear medicine physician, former air force officer; b. Wilkinsburg, Pa., Sept. 28, 1930; s. Clarence Wilbert and Dorothy Josephine (Morrow) McI.; m. Carole Jean McClain, Aug. 23, 1952; children: Sherri L., Wendy L., Darrell B., Ronald S., Holly B. B.S., Allegheny Coll., 1952; M.D., Temple U., 1956, M.S., 1960. Commd. 2d lt. M.C. U.S. Air Force, 1956, advanced through grades to col., 1971; intern Brooke Army Med. Ctr., San Antonio, 1956-57; resident in medicine Temple U. Med. Ctr., Phila., 1957-60; chief internal medicine and hosp. svcs. Norton AFB, 1960-64; chief internal medicine and hosp. services 7520 U.S. Air Force Hosp., U.K., 1964-68; vis. rsch. fellow Royal Post Grad. Med. Sch., London, 1968-69; chief endocrinology svcs., chmn. dept. nuclear medicine USAF Med. Center, Keesler AFB, Miss., 1969-75; dep. dir. Armed Forces Radiobiology Rsch. Inst., Def. Nuclear Agy., Bethesda, Md., 1975-77; dir. Armed Forces Radiobiology Rsch. Inst., Def. Nuclear Agy., 1977-79; staff physician nuclear medicine br., dept. radiology Nat. Naval Med. Center, Bethesda, 1979-82; sr. lectr. mil. medicine Uniformed U. of Health Scis., Bethesda, 1975-80; asst. prof. radiology/nuclear medicine and rsch. program coord. Uniformed U. of Health Scis., 1980-82; assoc. div. nuclear medicine St. Joseph Hosp., Towson, Md., 1982-91, dir. div. nuclear medicine, 1992—; med. advisor Nev. ops. office Dept. Energy, Las Vegas; cons. in field. Fellow Royal Soc. Medicine, Am. Coll. Nuclear Physicians (regent Ea. USA); mem. Am. Coll. Nuclear Physicians, Air Force Soc. Physicians (bd. govs. 1973-77), Uniformed Services Nuclear Medicine Assn. (pres. 1975), Soc. Nuclear Medicine (pres. Mideastern chpt.), Md. Soc. Nuclear Medicine (pres.-elect), AMA, Health Physics Soc. (dir. Balt., Washington chpt.), Assn. Mil. Surgeons U.S., Soc. Med. Cons.'s to Armed Forces, Alexander Graham Bell Soc. Home: 12405 Borges Ave Silver Spring MD 20904-2940 Office: St Joseph Hosp Towson MD 21204

MC INERNEY, DENIS, lawyer; b. N.Y.C., May 31, 1925; s. Denis and Anne (Keane) McI.; m. Mary Irene Murphy, Nov. 14, 1953; children: Kathleen Mc Inerney O'Hare, Denis J., Maura Mc Inerney Romano. BSS, Fordham U., 1948, JD cum laude, 1951; bar: N.Y. 1951, D.C. 1961. Instr. philosophy Fordham U., 1948-51; assoc. Cahill Gordon & Reindel, N.Y.C., 1951-61, ptnr., 1961-90, sr. counsel, 1991—; vice chmn. Com. Character and Fitness Admission State Bar N.Y., 1st Jud. Dept., 1979—; lectr. in field. Co-author: Practitioners Handbook for Appeals to the Appellate Divisions of the State of New York, 1979, Practitioners Handbook for Appeals to the Court of Appeals of the State of New York, 1981. Bd. dirs. Vols. of Legal Svc., Inc., 1985—, Cath. Youth Orgn., 1975—; mem. bd. visitors Fordham Law Sch., 1989—; trustee Fordham U., 1988-94. Sgt. 82d Airborne Divsn. U.S. Army, 1943-46, ETO. Decorated Knight of Malta, Knight of the Holy Sepulcher; recipient Achievement in Law award Fordham U., 1977. Fellow Am. Coll. Trial Lawyers (state chmn. 1980-82); mem. ABA, N.Y. State Bar Assn., New York County Lawyers Assn. (pres. 1982-84), Fordham U. Law Alumni Assn. (pres. 1968-72, medal of achievement 1975). Roman Catholic. Clubs: Westchester Country, Univ. Office: Cahill Gordon & Reindel 80 Pine St New York NY 10005-1701

MCINERNEY, JAMES EUGENE, JR., association executive; b. Springfield, Mass., Aug. 3, 1930; s. James Eugene and Rose Elizabeth (Adikes) McI.; m. Mary Catherine Hill, July 17, 1963; children: Anne Elizabeth, James Eugene, III. B.S., U.S. Mil. Acad., 1952; M.S. in Engring. Princeton U., 1960; postgrad., Royal Air Force Staff Coll., 1964; M.S. in Internat. Affairs, George Washington U., 1970. Commd. 2d lt. USAF, 1952, advanced through grades to maj. gen., 1976; fighter pilot Korea, Japan and Ger.; comdr. tactical fighter squadron Thailand, 1967; tactical fighter wing Ger., 1971; sr. U.S. adviser Turkish Air Force, 1973; dir. mil. assistance and sales Hdqrs. USAF, 1975-78; comdt. Indsl. Coll. Armed Forces, 1978-79; dir. programs Hdqrs. USAF, 1979-80, asst. dep. chief of staff for programs and evaluation, 1980; dir. legis. liaison McDonnell Douglas Corp., Washington, 1980-83, dir. internat. affairs, 1983-86; v.p. Am. League for Exports and Security Assistance, 1986-89, exec. v.p., 1989-92; v.p. Am. Def. Preparedness Assn., 1992—. Decorated Air Force Cross, D.S.M. (2), Silver Star (3), D.F.C. (7), Bronze Star, Meritorious Service medal (2), Air medal (18), Air Force Commendation medal; Vietnamese Crosses of Gallantry with palm and star; Republic of Korea Cheongsu medal. Mem. Air Force Assn. (citation of honor 1968). Roman Catholic. Home: 1031 Delf Dr Mc Lean VA 22101-2009

MCINERNEY, JAY, author; b. Hartford, Conn., Jan. 13, 1955; s. John Barrett and Marilyn Jean (Murphy) McI.; m. Merry Reymond, June 2, 1984 (dec.); m. Helen Bransford, Dec. 27, 1991. BA, Williams Coll., 1976; postgrad., Syracuse U. Reporter Hunterdon County Democrat, Flemington, N.J., 1977; textbook editor Time Life Pubs., Osaka, Japan, 1978-79; fact checker New Yorker, N.Y.C., 1980; reader Random House Pubs., N.Y.C., 1980-81; instr. English Syracuse U., 1983; writer, 1983—. Author: (novels) Bright Lights, Big City, 1984, Ransom, 1985, Story of My Life, 1988, Brightness Falls, 1992; screenwriter: (films) Bright Lights, Big City, 1988; contbr. articles to profl. jours. Princeton in Asia fellow, 1977. Mem. Authors Guild, PEN, Writers Guild. Address: 1572 Old Hillsboro Rd Franklin TN 37064 Office: care Amanda Urban Intl Creative Mgt 40 W 57th St New York NY 10019*

MCINERNEY, JOSEPH ALOYSIUS, hotel executive; b. Oak Park, Ill., Sept. 2, 1939; s. Joseph Aloysius and Helene (Mustari) McI.; m. Ruth McClelland, Aug. 29, 1969; children—Joseph A., Susan B. Student, Loyola U., Chgo., 1959-61; B.A. cum laude, Boston Coll., 1974. With Sheraton-Chgo. Hotel, 1961-65, regional dir. franchise ops., 1966-67, dir. franchise devel., 1968-69; gen. mgr. Sheraton-Winston, Salem, 1969-70; v.p., asst. to pres. Sheraton Corp., 1970-73, sr. v.p., dir. franchise ops., 1973-79; sr. v.p. Sheraton Corp., pres. Sheraton Corp. (Franchise div.), 1979-86; pres. Hawthorn Suites, 1986-91; pres., chief exec. officer Travelodge Internat., 1991-92; pres., CEO Forte Hotels, Inc., 1992—; guest lectr. Cornell Hotel Sch., Boston U. Hotel Sch., U. N.H. Hotel Sch., Mich. State U., San Diego State U. Former mem. industry sector adv. com. U.S. Dept. Commerce, also U.S. trade rep.; mem. adv. bd. Master Sci. degree program in hospitality industry studies at NYU; mem. hospitality adv. bd. N.Mex. State, Calif. Poly. Mach.; former trustee Boston U. Med. Ctr., Bethune-Cookman Coll.; bd. trustees St. Vincent de Paul Village; exec. com. San Diego Roundtable. Mem. Am. Hotel & Motel Assn. (govtl. affairs com.), Am. Hotel & Motel Ednl. Inst. (chmn.). Office: Forte Hotels Inc 1973 Friendship Dr El Cajon CA 92020-1140

MCINERNEY, JOSEPH JOHN, biomedical engineer, educator; b. Boston, Aug. 13, 1932; s. John Joseph and Anne (Berry) McI.; m. Suzanne Finke, Oct. 20, 1970; children by previous marriage: Joseph, Lynn, Maureen; children by present marriage: Kathleen, John. B.S. in Mech. Engring., Northeastern U., 1960; M.S. in Nuclear Engring., Pa. State U., 1962, Ph.D. in Theoretical Physics, 1964, M.S. in Human Physiology, 1980. Nuclear physicist Knolls Atomic Lab., Schenectady, 1964-76; postdoctoral fellow Sch. Medicine, Pa. State U., Hershey, 1976-79, staff rsch. scientist, 1979—; asst. prof. depts. biomed. engring. and medicine, Pa. State U., State College, 1984-90, assoc. prof., 1990—; referee Am. Nuclear Soc., Hinsdale, Ill., 1966—, Med. Biol. Engring., 1986—; cons. Whitaker Found., Harrisburg, Pa., 1981—, NIH; mem. standard com. Am. Nuclear Soc., Hinsdale, 1966—. Patentee in field. Contbr. articles to profl. jours. Served with USN, 1951-55. NIH fellow, 1976-79; Whitaker Found. grantee, 1979-81; Am. Heart Assn. grantee, 1979-80; NIH grantee, 1976-84, 84—, Pa. Rsch. Corp. grantee, 1983-84, Applied Rsch. Labs. grantee, 1985—. Mem. Am. Nuclear Soc., Am. Heart Assn., AAAS, Am. Physiol. Soc., Am. Fedn. Clin. Rsch., Am. Assn. Physicists in Medicine, IEEE (referee 1986—), Sigma Xi, Pi Tau Sigma. Democrat. Home: 260 Quarry Rd Hummelstown PA 17036-8902 Office: Pa State U Milton S Hershey Med Ctr PO Box 850 Hershey PA 17033-0850

MCINERNEY, THOMAS EDWARD, financial executive; b. Brampton, Ont., Can., Dec. 26, 1960; s. Edward Harold and Magdelene Andree (Dulfault) McI.; m. Anna Maria Spada, July 31, 1982; childredn: Anthony Edward, Tara Mary Andree. Grad. high sch. Bookkeeper, fin. planner Farm Bus. Cons., London, Ont., 1981-84; adv. fin. planner Investors Syndicate Ltd., London 1984-86; div. mgr. Investors Syndicate Ltd., Winnipeg, Man., 1986—. Author mo. column, London, 1987—. Mem. Canadian Assn. Fin. Planners. Office: Investors Syndicate Ltd, 200-401 Clarence St, London, ON Canada N6A3M6

MCINERNY, RALPH MATTHEW, philosophy educator, author; b. Mpls., Feb. 24, 1929; s. Austin Clifford and Vivian Gertrude (Rush) McI.; m. Constance Terrill Kunert, Jan. 3, 2953; children: Cathleen, Mary, Anne, David, Elizabeth, Daniel. BA, St. Paul Sem., 1951; MA, U. Minn., 1952; PhD summa cum laude, Lval U., 1954. Instr. Creighton U., 1954-55; prof. U. Notre Dame, Ind., 1955—, Michael P. Grace prof. medieval studies, 1988—, dir. dept., 1978-85; vis. prof. Cornell U., 1988, Cath. U., 1971, Louvain, 1983; founder Internat. Catholic Univ. (philos. works) The Logic of Analogy, 1961, History of Western Philosophy, vol. 1, 1963, vol. 2, 1968, Thomism in an Age of Renewal, 1966, Studies in Analogy, 1967, New Themes in Christian Philosophy, 1967, St. Thomas Aquinas, 1976, Ethica Thomistica, 1982, History of the Ambrosiana, 1983, Being and Predication, 1986, Miracles, 1986, Art and Prudence, 1988, A First Glance at St. Thomas: Handbook for Peeping Thomists, 1989, Boethius and Aquinas, 1989, Aquinas on Human Action, 1991, The Question of Christian Ethics, 1993, Aquinas Against the Averroists, 1993; (novels) Jolly Rogerson, 1967, A Narrow Time, 1969, The Priest, 1973, Gate of Heaven, 1975, Rogerson at Bay, 1976, Her Death of Cold, 1977, The Seventh Station, 1977, Romanesque, 1977, Spinnaker, 1977, Quick as a Dodo, 1978, Bishop as Pawn, 1978, La Cavalcade Romaine, 1979, Lying Three, 1979, Abecedary, 1979, Second Vespers, 1980, Rhyme and Reason, 1981, Thicker than Water, 1981, A Loss of Patients, 1982, The Grass Widow, 1983, Connolly's Life, 1983, Getting Away with Murder, 1984, And Then There Were Nun, 1984, The Noonday Devil, 1985, Sine Qua Nun, 1986, Leave of Absence, 1986, Rest in Pieces, 1985, Cause and Effect, 1987, The Basket Case, 1987, Veil of Ignorance, 1988, Abracadaver, 1989, Body and Soil, 1989, Four on the Floor, 1989, Frigor Mortis, 1989, Savings and Loan, 1990, The Search Committee, 1991, The Nominative Case, 1991, Sister Hood, 1991, Judas Priest, 1991, Easeful Death, 1991, Infra Dig, 1992, Desert Sinner, 1992, Seed of Doubt, 1993, The Basket Case, 1993, Nun Plussed, 1993, Mom and Dead, 1994, The Cardinal Offense; editor The New Scholasticism, 1967-89; editor, pub. Crisis, 1982—; pub. Catholic Dossier. Exec. dir. Wethersfield Inst., 1989-92; bd. govs. Thomas Aquinas Coll., Santa Paula, Calif., 1992—. With USMCR, 1946-47. Fulbright rsch. fellow, Belgium, 1959-60, NEH fellow, 1977-78, NEA fellow, 1983, Fulbright scholar, Argentina, 1986, 87. Fellow Pontifical Roman Acad. St. Thomas Aquinas; mem. Am. Philos. Assn., Am. Cath. Philos. Assn. (past pres., recipient medals), Am. Metaphys. Soc. (pres. 1992), Internat. Soc. for Study Medieval Philosophy, Medieval Acad., Mystery Writers Am., Authors Guild, Fellowship Cath. Scholars (pres. 1992—), Cath. Acad. Scis. Home: 2158 Portage Ave South Bend IN 46616-2035 Office: U of Notre Dame Dept of Philosophy 336 Oshaugnessy Hall Notre Dame IN 46556-5939

MCINNES, HAROLD A., manufacturing company executive; b. Groton, Conn., 1927. B.S.M.E., MIT, 1949. With Delco Appliance div. Gen. Motors Corp., 1949-55, Tracerlab, Inc., 1955-60, Reed Rolled Thread Die Co., 1960-62, Dresser Industries, Inc., 1962-65, AMP, Inc., Harrisburg, Pa., 1965—; mfg. mgr. packaging components AMP, Inc., 1966-70, mgr. automach div., 1970-73, group dir. gen. products, 1973-78, v.p. mfg. resources planning, 1978-79, corp. v.p. engring. and tech. resources, 1979-81, pres., 1981-86, vice chmn., bd. dirs. 1986-90, chmn., chief exec. officer, 1990-93, chmn. exec. com., 1993—; bd. dirs. PPG Industries, Pitts. Mem. Elec. Mfrs. Club. Office: AMP Inc 470 Friendship Rd Harrisburg PA 17111-1203*

MC INNES, ROBERT MALCOLM, lawyer, business consultant; b. Pictou, N.S., Can., July 17, 1930; naturalized U.S. citizen, 1964; s. John Logan and Jenny MacKay (Malcolm) McI.; m. June Hughena O'Brien, Apr. 19, 1952; children: Donald, Elizabeth, Susan. B.A., Dalhousie U., Halifax, N.S., 1951, LL.B., 1953; postgrad., Harvard U. Bus. Sch., 1968. Assoc. firm Duquet, MacKay, Weldon & Tetreault, Montreal, Que., Can., 1953-57; with Pickands Mather & Co., Cleve., 1957-69, 71-87; v.p. Pickands Mather & Co., 1971-73, exec. v.p., 1973-83, pres., chief exec. officer, 1983-87; gen. counsel, treas. Diamond Shamrock Corp., 1969-71; group exec. v.p. Cleve. Cliffs Inc., 1987-88; of counsel Arter and Hadden, Cleve., 1988-94; bd. dirs. Brush Wellman Inc., Cliffs Drilling Co. Mem. Cleve. Bar Assn., Mayfield Country Club, Union Club. Republican. Methodist. Home: 32300 Meadow Lark Way Pepper Pike OH 44124-5510

MC INNES, WILLIAM CHARLES, priest, campus ministry director; b. Boston, Jan. 20, 1923; s. William Charles and Mary (Byrne) McI. B.S., Boston Coll., 1946, A.B., 1950, M.A., 1951; S.T.L., Weston Coll., 1958; Ph.D., N.Y. U., 1955. Joined Soc. of Jesus, 1946; ordained priest Roman Cath. Ch., 1957; prof. mktg. and bus. ethics Boston Coll. Sch. Bus. Adminstrn., 1959-63, assoc. dean, 1961-63, dir. honors program, 1963-64, mem. citizens seminar planning com., 1959-63; pres. Fairfield (Conn.) U., 1964-73, prof. urban problems, 1969-72; pres. U. San Francisco, 1972-77, Assn. Jesuit Colls. and Univs., 1977-89; campus min. U. Conn., Storrs, 1990—; vis. fellow Woodstock Theol. Ctr., 1990-91. Past chmn. bd. ABCD (cmty. action agys.); pres. Conn. Assn. for Cmty. Action Programs; founder Fairfield County Cmty. forum, Conn. Charter Oak Coll.; life mem. United Cerebral Palsy Assn. Fairfield County; bd. dirs., vice chmn. Nat. Better Bus. Bur. Found.; mem. adv. com. Conn. Dept. Social Svcs., 1993—. Served to capt. USAAF, 1942-46, CBI. Mem. Beta Gamma Sigma, Alpha Sigma Nu, Delta Sigma Pi, Phi Kappa Theta, Alpha Epsilon Delta. Home: 46 N Eagleville Rd Storrs CT 06268

MCINNIS, HELEN LOUISE, publishing company executive; b. Fall River, Mass.; d. Hugh Michael and Louise Patricia (Waldron) McI. B.A., Merrimack Coll., 1967; M.A., Duquesne U., 1969. Asst. editor Holt, Rinehart & Winston, N.Y.C., 1971-73; editor D. Van Nostrand Co., N.Y.C., 1972-75; sr. v.p., dir. coll. dept. Scribner Book Co., Inc., N.Y.C., 1976-91; asst. v.p., exec. editor Macmillan Pub. Co., 1985-91; v.p., exec. editor Humanities and Social Scis., Oxford U. Press, N.Y.C., 1991—. Editor, author: Viewpoints: American Cities, 1972. Mem. Assn. Am. Pubs. (chmn. com. higher edn. div. 1980-82, exec. bd. 1982-84). Democrat. Roman Catholic. Home: 253 W 72d St Apt 1505 New York NY 10023 Office: Oxford U Press 200 Madison Ave New York NY 10016

MCINNIS, SCOTT STEVE, congressman, lawyer; b. Glenwood Springs, Colo., May 9, 1953; s. Kohler McInnis and Carol Kreir; m. Lori McInnis; children: Daxon, Tessa, Andrea. BA, Ft. Lewis Coll., 1975; JD, St. Mary's Law Sch., 1980. Atty. Delaney & Balcomb P.C., Glenwood Springs, Colo., 1981—; mem. Colo. Ho. of Reps., 1984-93; majority leader, 1990—; mem. 103d-104th Congresses from 3d Colo. Dist., 1993—; chmn. agrl. livestock and natural resources com., 1986-90, mem. rules com. Recipient Florence Sabin award, 1984, Guardian of Small Bus. award Nat. Fed. Ind. Bus., 1990, Lee Atwater Leadership award, 1991, and various awards from United Vets. Commn.; named Legislator of Decade and Legislator of Yr by Colo. Ski Country and Colo. Wildlife Found. Mem. Elks, Rotary, Phi Delta Phi. Republican. Roman Catholic. Office: US Ho of Reps 215 Cannon HOB Washington DC 20515-0603*

MCINTIRE, JERALD GENE, investment executive, former municipal official; b. Abilene, Tex., Mar. 16, 1938; s. Andrew Noble and Viola (Richey) McI.; m. Linda Carole Sanders, Aug. 28, 1964 (div. Mar. 1976); children: Christian Tilghman, Ross Andrew, John Patrick Morgan. AA, N.Mex. Mil. Inst., 1958; BA, Ea. N.Mex. U., 1964. Ptnr., officer Ruffino Prodns., Dallas, 1960-64; tchr., drama dir. Roswell (N.Mex.) Pub. Schs., 1966-70; tchr. curriculum Thiokol Chem., Roswell, 1970-74; pvt. bus. mgr. Dallas, 1974-77; career coordinator Soc. Ednl. Reconstrn./Jobs for Progress, Dallas, 1977-82; council asst. City of Dallas, 1982-83, asst. to mayor pro tem, 1983-87, asst. to mayor, 1987-89; pres., chief exec. officer Multinational Investments, Multinational Offshore Venture, M'N'M Antiquities, Grand Caymen, Bahamas, 1990—; ptnr., officer Multi-Nat. Investments, Inc., Dallas, 1980. Con., v.p. Chrysalis Home & Health Care, Dallas, 1985-87; devel. dir., mem. sch. bd. Immaculate Conception Sch., Grand Prairie, Tex., 1983-85. Mem. Nat. Assn. Council Assts. Democrat. Jewish. Avocations: gardening, travel, writing, music, riding. Office: Multinational Investments, Multinational Offshore Venture, Grand Cayman Bahamas

MCINTIRE, LARRY VERN, chemical engineering educator; b. St. Paul, June 28, 1943; s. James Lawrence and Lenore Vineal (Converse) McI.; m. Mary Beth McEnery, July 5, 1969. BChemE, MS, Cornell U., 1966; MA, Princeton U., 1968, PhD, 1970. Registered profl. engr., Tex. Asst. prof. Rice U., Houston, 1970-74, assoc. prof., 1974-78, prof. chem. engring.,

1978—, E.D. Butcher prof., 1983—, chmn. dept., 1981-91, chmn. Bioscis. and Bioengring. Inst., 1991—, chmn. rsch. coun., 1988-91, dir. Biomed. Engring. Lab., 1980—; speaker faculty coun., 1994-95; adj. prof. medicine Baylor Coll. Medicine, Houston, 1982—; U. Tex. Med. Sch., Houston, 1982—; chmn. blood/materials working group NIH, Bethesda, Md., 1982-85; mem. surgery and bioengring. study sect. NIH, 1984-88; mem. com. on bioprocessing NRC, 1991—; chmn. rheology subcom. Internat. Coun. on Thrombosis and Hemostasis, 1985-89. Contbr. more than 160 articles to profl. jours. Recipient Merit award NIH, 1989; NSF fellow Cornell U., Princeton U., 1965-69, NATO-NSF postdoctoral fellow Imperial Coll., London, 1976-77. Fellow Am. Inst. Med. Biol. Engring. (sec., treas. 1993—), ASCE (officer lical sect. 1980-81, 86, Food Pharm. and Bioengring. divsn. award 1992); mem. AAAS, Biomed. Engring. Soc. (bd. dirs. 1992—, pres. 1995—, Disting. lectr. 1992), N.Am. Soc. Biorheology (v.p. 1992-94, pres. 1994—), N.Y. Acad. Scis., Am. Heart Assn. (coun. on thrombosis, exec. com. 1994—), Faculty Club Rice U. (bd. dirs., chmn. 1982-84), Sigma Xi (nat. lectr. 1993—). Presbyterian. Avocations: tennis, squash, classical music, hiking. Office: Rice U Inst Biomed Engring and Bioengring John W Cox Lab Biomed Engring Houston TX 77251-1892

MCINTOSH, CAROLYN MEADE, retired educational administrator; b. Waynesburg, Ky., Oct. 21, 1928; d. Clarence Hobert and Sarah Letitia (Bentley) Meade; m. Edgar G. McIntosh, Aug. 21, 1948; children: Wayne, Jeanne, Penny, Jimmi, Carol. BS, Miami U., Oxford, Ohio, 1962; MEd, Xavier U., Cin., 1966. Elem. tchr. Ohio, 1961-79; prin. New Richmond (Ohio) Sch. Dist., 1980-91; ret., 1991; tchr. Clermont County Adult Edn. Program, 1970-95, Clermont County dir.of Headstrart 1971-72, Clearmont County Rep. to Ohio elem. adminstr., 1985-87, Pres. Clermont and Brown County adminstr., 1988-89. Editor Ret. Tchrs. Newsletter. Pres. New Richmond Bd. Edn.; v.p. U.S. Grant Vocat. Sch. Bd. Edn.; mem. Clermont County Excellence in Edn. Com.; mem. edn. adv. com. Clermont Coll.; mem. adv. bd. Bethany Children's Home; mem. Clermont 2001 Com.; mem. Rep. Ctrl. Com. of Clermont County. Recipient New Richmond Adminstr. of the Yr. award City of New Richmond, 1989. Mem. AAUW, ASCD, NAESP, Nat. Sch. Bd. Assn., Ohio Sch. Bd. Assn., Ohio Assn. Elem. Sch. Adminstrs. (all county legis. liaison), Ohio County Ret. Tchrs. Assn., Clermont County Ret. Tchrs. Assn. (v.p.), Order Eastern Star, Phi Delta Kappa, Delta Kappa Gamma (pres. chpt.). Baptist.

MCINTOSH, DAVID M., congressman; b. June 8, 1958; m. Ruthie McIntosh. Grad., Yale Coll., 1980, U. Chgo., 1983. Bar: Ind., U.S. Supreme Ct. Spl. asst. domestic affairs to Pres. Reagan; spl. asst. to Atty. Gen. Meese; liaison Pres.'s Commn. on Privatization; spl. asst. to V.P. Quayle, dep. legal counsel to; exec. dir. Pres.'s Coun. on Competitiveness; sr. fellow Citizens for a Sound Economy; founder Federalist Soc. for Law & Pub. Policy, now co-chmn.; mem. U.S. Ho. of Reps., 104 Congress, Washington, 1995—, mem. Govt. Reform & Oversight Com., chmn. panel's Econ. Growth, Natural Resources and Regulatory Affairs Subcom. Mem. State Bar of Ind. Republican. Office: US House Reps 2217 Rayburn House Office Bldg Washington DC 20515-1402*

MCINTOSH, DECOURCY EYRE, museum director; b. Balt., Dec. 1, 1942; s. David Gregg and Grace (Wright) McI.; m. Susan Reed Bell, Nov. 11, 1967; children: Madeline Eyre, David Gregg. AB, Harvard U., 1965. Program officer Richard King Mellon Found., Pitts., 1969-74; exec. dir. Hist. Savannah (Ga.) Found., 1974-77; mng. dir. Minn. Landmarks, St. Paul, 1977-79; v.p. Mpls. Soc. Fine Arts, 1979-84; exec. dir. Helen Clay Frick Found., Pitts., 1984—, Frick Art & Hist. Ctr., Pitts., 1990—. Editor: (exhbn. catalogues) 19th Century French Drawings from Lyon, 1992, Renaissance & Baroque Bronzes in The Frick Art Museum, 1993, Florentine Drawings of the 17th & 18th Centuries from Lille, 1994. Pres. Heritage Health Found., Pitts., 1992—; trustee Pitts. History & Landmarks, 1984—, Art Svcs. Internat., Alexandria, 1990—; bd. dirs. Pitts. Parks & Playgrounds Fund, 1986—, Preservation Pa., 1991—. Mem. Am. Assn. Mus., Century Assn., Pitts. Golf Club, Walpole Soc. Office: The Frick Art & Hist Ctr 7227 Reynolds St Pittsburgh PA 15208

MC INTOSH, DOUGLAS J., insurance company executive. With Blue Cross Blue Shield of R.I., Providence, 1966-77, pres., 1977—. Office: Blue Cross Blue Shield of RI 444 Westminster St Providence RI 02903-3279

MCINTOSH, ELAINE VIRGINIA, nutrition educator; b. Webster, S.D., Jan. 30, 1924; d. Louis James and Cora Boletta (Bakke) Nelson; m. Thomas Henry McIntosh, Aug. 28, 1955; children: James George, Ronald Thomas, Charles Nelson. BA magna cum laude, Augustana Coll., Sioux Falls, S.D., 1945; MA, U. S.D., 1949; PhD, Iowa State U., 1954. Registered dietitian. Instr., asst. prof. Sioux Falls Coll., 1945-48; instr. Iowa State U., Ames, 1949-53, rsch. assoc., 1955-62; postdoctoral rsch. assoc. U. Ill., Urbana, 1954-55; asst. prof. human biology U. Wis., Green Bay, 1968-72, assoc. prof., 1972-85, prof., 1985-90, emeritus prof., 1990—, writer, cons., 1990—, chmn. human biology dept., 1975-80, asst. to vice chancellor, asst. to chancellor, 1974-76. Contbr. numerous articles on bacterial metabolism, meat biochemistry and nutrition edn. to profl. jours. Fellow USPHS, 1948-49; grantee U. Wis. System, 1972. Mem. Am. Dietetic Assn., Inst. Food Technologists, Wis. Dietetics Assn., Wis. Nutrition Coun. (pres. 1974-75), Sigma Xi. Republican. Avocations: writing, travel. Office: U Wis 2420 Nicolet Dr Green Bay WI 54311-7001

MCINTOSH, HENRY DEANE, cardiologist; b. Gainesville, Fla., July 19, 1921; s. Thomas Irvin and Nelle Deane (Calwell) McI.; m. Harriet Owens, Nov. 6, 1945; children: Thomas Irvin, James Owens, Willa Elizabeth. BS, Davidson Coll., 1943; MD, U. Pa., 1950; DSc (hon.), U Francisco Martinique, Guatemala de la Asuncion, 1987. Diplomate Am. Bd. Internal Medicine, subspecialty bd. cardiovascular disease. Intern medicine Duke U., 1950-51, fellow cardiology, 1952-54, instr. medicine Sch. Medicine, 1954-55, assoc., 1955-57, from asst. prof. to assoc. prof., 1957-62, prof., 1962-70, chief cardiology divsn., 1966-70; asst. resident medicine Lawson VA Hosp., Atlanta, 1951-52; chief resident medicine VA Hosp., Durham, N.C., 1954-55, asst. chief cardiovascular-renal sect., 1955-56; prof., chmn. dept. medicine Baylor Coll. Medicine, Houston, 1970-77, chief sect. cardiology, 1977, adj. prof. medicine, 1977—; chief med. svc. The Meth. Hosp., Houston, 1970-77; clin. prof. medicine U. Fla. Sch. Medicine, Gainesville, 1977—, U. South Fla. Sch. Medicine, Tampa, 1993—; cons. VA Hosps., Durham, 1956-70, Watts Hosp., Durham, 1956-79, Womack U.S. Army Hosp., Ft. Bragg, N.C., 1957-70, Portsmouth (Va.) Naval Hosp., 1957-70, VA Hosp., Houston, 1970-77, Harris County Dist. Hosps., Houston, 1970-77, St. Luke's Episcopal Hosp., Houston, 1970-77, Hermann Hosp., Houston, 1970-77, Lakeland Regional Med. Ctr., 1977-92, St. Joseph's Hosp., Tampa, 1992—; med. dir. prevention and rehab. ctr. St. Joseph's Heart Inst., Tampa, 1992—. Editorial bd. Circulation, Heart and Lung, Am. Jour. Cardiology, Am. Jour. Geriatric Cardiology; asst. editor Modern Concepts in Cardiovascular Disease, 1967; editor Baylor Cardiology Series, 1975-87; contbr. 240 articles to profl. jours. Found., dir. Heartbeat Internat., Lakeland, Fla., 1983-84, Tampa, Fla., 1992—pres., 1993—. Capt. U.S. Army, 1943-45. Decorated Silver Star; decorated Croix de Guerre with two bronze and one silver star; recipient Disting. Alumni award Duke U. Med. Ctr., 1972, Rotary Internat. Hon. Fellowship, 1985, Paul Harris Fellow, 1986, U.S. Presdl. Citation from Ronald Reagan, Heartbeat Internat., 1986, Disting. Kennedy Lectureship, Univ. Assn. Emergency Medicine, 1986, Disting. Alumni award Davidson Coll., 1988. Fellow Am. Coll. Cardiology (disting. mem. 1974-75, govt. rels. com. 1986-93, prevention com. 1986-90, chair 1987-90, rep. to pub. health svc. objectives for the yr. 2000, 1988—); mem. AMA, ACP, NASPE (continuing med. edn. coun. 1988-91, bldg. com. 1992—), Disting. Svc. award 1991), Am. Fedn. Clin. Rsch., Soc. Soc. Clin. Investigation (Founders award 1984), Assn. Univ. Cardiologists, Am. Clin. and Climatol. Soc., Am. Soc. Internal Medicine, Am. Heart Assn. (v.p. 1977-78, rsch. com. 1986-90, chair sci. sessions com. 1971-73, coun. clin. cardiology 1975-76, disting. achievement award coun. clin. cardiology 1986), Coun. Geriatric Cardiology (membership com. 1986—, pres. 1991-92). Presbyterian. Avocations: jogging, fostering international good will, public education. Home: PO Box 1788 Lakeland FL 33802-1788 Office: St. Joseph's Heart Inst PO Box 4227 3003 Dr Martin Luther King Blvd Tampa FL 33677-4227

MC INTOSH, JAMES EUGENE, JR., interior designer; b. Dadeville, Ala., Nov. 13, 1938; s. James Eugene and Jessie (Latimer) McI. B.Interior Design, Auburn (Ala.) U., 1961. Designer contract div. Rich's Dept. Store,

Atlanta, 1961-64; assoc. William Trapnell & Assocs., Atlanta, 1964-70; dir. Interior Concepts, Inc., Atlanta, 1970-72; dir. design comml. design div. Rich's Dept. Store, 1972-80; v.p. Comml. Interior Designs, Inc., 1980-82; exec. staff Rollins Inc., 1982-85; owner Gene Mc Intosh & Assocs., 1985—. Fellow Am. Soc. Interior Designers (Presdl. citation 1974); mem. Nat. Trust Hist. Preservation, Ala. Hist. Soc., High Mus. Art. Soc. Archtl. Historians. Home and Office: Gene McIntosh & Assocs PO Box 53253 Atlanta GA 30355-1253

MC INTOSH, J(OHN) RICHARD, biologist, educator; b. N.Y.C., Sept. 25, 1939; s. Rustin and Millicent Margaret (Carey) McI.; m. Marjorie Rogers Keniston, Aug. 30, 1961; children—Robert K., Elspeth R., Craig T. B.A. in Physics, Harvard U., 1961, Ph.D. in Biophysics, 1968. Instr. in math. and physics Cambridge Sch., Weston, Mass., 1961-63; asst. prof. biology Harvard U., 1968-70; asst. prof. U. Colo., Boulder, 1970-72; assoc. prof. U. Colo., 1972-76, prof., 1977—, chmn. dept. molecular, cellular and devel. biology, 1977-78, dir. Lab for High Voltage Electron Microscopy, 1986—. Contbr. numerous articles to profl. jours.; mem. editorial bd. Jour. Cell Biology, 1978-82, 86-90, Cell Motility, 1986-87. Recipient Teaching Recognition award U. Colo., 1974, Scholar award Am. Cancer Soc., 1976, 90; Am. Cancer Soc. grantee, 1971-90, NSF grantee, 1970-82, NIH grantee, 1973-78, 80—; Eleanor Roosevelt Internat. Cancer fellow, 1984; Guggenheim fellow, 1990-91. Mem. Am. Soc. Cell Biology (coun. 1977-80, 86-89, pres. 1993-94), Am. Cancer Soc. (cell biology panel 1983-87, rsch. prof. 1994—), NIH (molecular cytology study sect. 1988-92). Home: 870 Willowbrook Rd Boulder CO 80302-7439 Office: Dept Molecular Devel and Devel Biology U Colo Boulder CO 80309-0347

MCINTOSH, JOSEPH WILLIAM, health administration consultant; b. Marion, Ind., July 1, 1936; s. Joseph Dawson and Maxine A. (Coffel) McI.; children: Mark Joseph, Marchelle Dawn. AB, U. Indpls., 1958; MS in Pub. Health, U. N.C., 1959; D of Health Sci., Ind. U., 1970; MS, Troy (Ala.) State U., 1983. Cert. health edn. specialist. Director Pub. Health/ Health and Hosp. Corp., Indpls., 1959-70; pub.health cons. Inst. Community and Area Devel., U. Ga., Athens, 1970-73; asst. prof. health edn. U. Ga., Athens, 1970-73; chair dept. allied health Columbus (Ga.) Coll., 1973—, dir. Regional Health Professions Edn. Ctr., 1970. Author project report and monograph. Bd. dirs. Wagon Wheel Gun Club, Geneva, Ga., 1975-85, Columbus Symphony, 1983-90; ombudsman West Ctrl. Ga. Coun. on Aging, Columbus, 1983-85. Named to Outstanding Young Men of Am., 1968. Mem. Natural Resource Def. Fund, Nat. Environ. Health Assn., Ind. Environ. Health Assn. Avocations: antiques, coins, golf, shooting sports. Office: Wellness Assocs 2850 Hamilton Rd Columbus GA 31904

MCINTOSH, L(ORNE) WILLIAM, marketing executive; b. Kingston, Ont., Can., May 1, 1945; s. Jack Lorne and Lillian (Oaks) McI.; m. Delthyn Lee Johnson, Mar. 11, 1965. BSBA, Lehigh U., 1967, MBA, 1968. Asst. prof. Union Coll., Cranford, N.J., 1968-72; sr. market rsch. analyst Merck, Sharp & Dohme, West Point, Pa., 1972-75, advt. copywriter, 1975-77, product mgr., 1977-80, assoc. dir. advt., 1980-82, dir. licensing and acquisitions, 1982, sr. dir. mktg., 1983-86; exec. v.p. mktg. Medco Containment Svcs., Inc., Fair Lawn, N.J., 1987-88; v.p. mktg. and bus. devel. Boehringer Mannheim Pharms., Rockville, Md., 1988-92; chmn. bd., chief exec. officer Target Mktg. Systems, Inc., Blue Bell, Pa., 1992-93; sr. v.p., bus. devel. & com. ops. Zynaxis, Inc., Malvern, Pa., 1993—. Mem. Am. Econ. Assn., Am. Mktg. Assn., Lic. Execs. Soc., Antique Automobile Club Am., Model A Ford Club Am., Vintage Chevrolet Club Am., Beta Gamma Sigma. Avocations: antique automobiles, woodworking, antique furniture restoration, boating, music. Home: 161 Polo Dr North Wales PA 19454-4273 Office: 371 Phoenixville Pike Malvern PA 19355-9603

MCINTOSH, PAUL EUGENE, county government official; b. Wabash, Ind., June 23, 1951; s. Jay Morton and Catherine Louise (Parsley) McI.; m. Susan Marie Hegedus, Sept. 5, 1981; children: Erin, Ian. B Pub. Affairs, Ind. U., 1978, MPA, 1980. Intern HEW, Washington, 1979; legis. analyst Ind. Legislature, Indpls., 1980-81; mgmt. cons. Hughes, Heiss and Assocs., San Mateo, Calif., 1981-82; adminstrv. analyst County of Solano, Fairfield, Calif., 1982-86; dep. county adminstr. County of Solano, 1986-88; chief adminstrv. officer County of El Dorado, Placerville, Calif., 1988—; project mgr., Solano County Justice Ctr., Fairfield, 1984-88. With USN, 1970-74, Vietnam. Mem. Am. Correctional Assn., Pi Alpha Alpha. Avocations: backpacking, golf. Office: El Dorado County Adminstr 330 Fair Ln Placerville CA 95667-4103

MCINTOSH, ROBERT EDWARD, JR., electrical engineering educator, consultant, electronics executive; b. Hartford, Conn., Jan. 19, 1940; s. Robert Edward and Natalie Rose (Glynn) McI.; m. Anne Marie Potvin, July 7, 1962; children—Robert Edward III, Edgar J., Michael T., William P., Matthew P. B.S.E.E., Worcester Poly. Inst., 1962; S.M. in Applied Physics, Harvard U., 1964; Ph.D. in Elec. Engring., U. Iowa, 1967. Mem. tech. staff Bell Telephone Labs, North Andover, Mass., 1962-65; asst. prof. elec. engring. U. Mass., Amherst, 1967-70, assoc. prof., 1970-73, prof., 1973—, coord. microwave electronics group, 1980-87, dir. microwave remote sensing lab., 1981—, acting head dept. elec. and computer engring., 1983-84; treas. Quadrant Engring., Inc., Amherst, 1982-84, 88-91, pres. 1984-87, 91—; mem. adv. bd. ECE Dept. Worcester Poly. Inst., 1992—. Assoc. editor Radio Sci., 1987-89; contbr. articles to profl. jours. Recipient sr. faculty scholarship award Alumni Coll. Engring., U. Mass., 1984, dept. of ECE Faculty award, 1987, 90, 92, GE Teaching award, 1988, Univ. Disting. Lectr. award, 1992, Hobart Newell award WPI, 1993; rsch. grantee NSF, NASA, Dept. Energy, Air Force Office Sci. Rsch., Army Rsch. Office, Office Naval Rsch., numerous electronics cos., 1967—. Fellow IEEE (Centennial medal 1984, tech. activities bd. 1984-85, fellows com. 1986-89); mem. Antennas Propagation Soc. (sec.-treas. 1980-83, v.p. 1984, pres. 1985, editor newsletter 1979-81, assoc. editor Trans. 1984-87, editor 1989-92), Geosci. Remote Sensing Soc. (sec.-treas. 1980-83, pres. 1984), Internat. Radio Sci. Union (U.S. nat. com. 1984-92), Am. Phys. Soc. Democrat. Roman Catholic. Avocations: athletics, music, theatre. Office: U Mass Dept Elec Computer Eng Amherst MA 01003

MCINTOSH, SUSAN KEECH, anthropology educator; b. Dunkirk, N.Y., Feb. 2, 1951; d. S. Elwin and Lucille M. (Stone) Keech; m. Roderick J. McIntosh, June 28, 1976; children: David Alexander, Annick Michele. Student, Wellesley Coll., 1969-71; BA in Anthropology summa cum laude, U. Pa., 1973; MA in Archaeology, Cambridge U., Eng., 1975; MA in Anthropology, U. Calif., Santa Barbara, 1976, PhD in Anthropology, 1979. Teaching asst. U. Calif., 1975-77; instr. Santa Barbara C.C., 1976; vis. asst. prof. Washington U., St. Louis, 1978-80; from adj. asst. prof. to assoc. prof. anthropology Rice U., Houston, 1980-88, prof., 1988—; master Baker coll. Rice U., 1989-88, treas. com. masters, 1986-89, chair com. campus climate women, pres.'s commn. women, 1988-89, mem. faculty coun., 1993—; mem. archaeology panel NSF, 1988-90; co-dir. various excavations and surveys. Author: (with R.J. McIntosh) Prehistoric Investigations in the Region of Jenne, Mali, 1980, Excavations at Jenne-jeno: the 1981 season, 1995; contbr. articles to profl. jours.; assoc. editor for archaeology Current Anthropology, 1985-87; mem. editorial bd. Jour. World Prehistory, 1987—, Jour. African History, 1989-94, Antiquity, 1993—, African Archaeol. Rev., 1995—; contbg. editor Jour. Archeol. Rsch., 1992—. Fulbright-Hayes grantee, 1973, patent fund grantee U. Calif., 1976, grantee NSF, 1977—, Nat. Geog. Soc., 1983-92; Thouron Brit.-Am. Exch. fellow, 1973-75, fellow Stanford U., 1989-90. Mem. Am. Anthrop. Assn., Soc. Am. Archaeology, Am. Assn. Phys. Anthropologists, Soc. Africanist Archaeologists Am., Prehistoric Soc., West African Archeol. Assn., Société des Africanistes, Panafrican Congress Prehistory, Mande Studies Assn., Phi Beta Kappa. Avocations: classical music, tennis, skiing. Office: Rice University Anthropology Dept PO Box 1892 Dept Houston TX 77251-1892

MCINTOSH, TERRIE TUCKETT, lawyer; b. Ft. Lewis, Wash., July 20, 1944; d. Robert LeRoy and Elda (Perry) Tuckett; m. Clifton Dennis McIntosh, Oct. 13, 1969; children: Alison, John. BA, U. Utah, 1967; MA, U. Ill., 1970; JD, Harvard U., 1978. Bar: NY 1979, Utah 1980. Assoc. Hughes, Hubbard & Reed, N.Y.C., 1978-79; assoc. Fabian & Clendenin, Salt Lake City, 1979-84, shareholder, 1984-86; staff atty. Questar Corp., Salt Lake City, 1986-88, sr. atty., 1988-92, sr. corp. counsel, 1992—; instr. philosophy Douglass Coll. Rutgers U., New Brunswick, N.J., 1971-72; mem. adv. com. civil procedure Utah Supreme Ct., Salt Lake City, 1987—; mem.

jud. nominating com. 5th Cir. Ct., Salt Lake City, 1986-88. Mem. Utah State Bar (ethics and discipline screening panel 1989—, co-chair law related edn. com. 1985-86), Women Lawyers of Utah (chair exec. com. 1986-87), Harvard Alumni Assn. Utah (bd. dirs. 1987—), Phi Beta Kappa, Phi Kappa Phi. Office: Questar Corp PO Box 45433 180 E 1st South St Salt Lake City UT 84147

MCINTYRE, BRUCE HERBERT, publishing company executive; b. Takoma Park, Md., Jan. 24, 1930; s. Orrin Raymond and Leila Hazel (Olmsted) McI.; m. Natalie Ann Wolff, Oct. 10, 1953; children: Douglas A., Elizabeth W., Emily O., Catherine N., Jane A. Student, Gannon Coll., 1954-57, U. Akron, 1958-61. Reporter, city editor Erie (Pa.) Times and News, 1949-57; reporter, city editor, asst. to exec. editor Akron (Ohio) Beacon Jour., 1958-67; with Battle Creek (Mich.) Enquirer & News, 1967-71, asst. mng. editor, 1967-68, mng. editor, 1968-71; exec. v.p., editor Oakland Press, Pontiac, Mich., 1971-77; pub. Oakland Press, 1977-95; v.p., pub. div. Capital Cities/ABC Inc., 1987—; chmn. Great Lakes Media Inc., Birmingham, Mich., 1995—; lectr. Am. Press Inst., 1968—; journalism juror Pulitzer Prizes, 1972—. Served with AUS, 1951-53; lt. col. Res. ret. Mem. Soc. Profl. Journalists. Episcopalian. Club: Pine Lake Country (Bloomfield, Mich.). Office: Great Lakes Media Inc 700 E Maple St Ste 303 Birmingham MI 48009

MCINTYRE, DEBORAH, psychotherapist, author; b. Pensacola, Fla., Sept. 11, 1955; d. John Joseph and Mary Cecelia (Campbell) McI.; m. Denis Miller Donovan, Sept. 6, 1985. BA in Psychology, George Mason U., 1976; MA Counseling Psychology, U. West Fla., 1980; AA in Nursing, Pensacola Jr. Coll., 1981. Diplomate Am. Bd. Med. Psychotherapists; RN, Va., Fla. Child psychotherapist Holly Hall Sch. for Exceptional Children, Vienna, Va., 1975-77; area rep. Youth For Understanding, Vienna, 1976-78; vol. child psychotherapist Children's Resource Ctr. of N.W. Fla., Pensacola, Fla., 1979-80; staff/charge nurse med. surgery Va. Beach Gen. Hosp., 1981-83; intake coord., child and family psychotherapist Psychiatric Inst., Norfolk, Va., 1982-83; head nurse, program coord., child and family therapist Children's Service, Horizon Hosp., Clearwater, Fla., 1983; child and adolescent psychotherapist The Children's Ctr. for Devel. Psychiatry, St. Petersburg, Fla., 1983—; cons., trainer Project Playpen, Juvenile Welfare Bd., St. Petersburg, 1985-87; cons. Early Childhood coun. of Pinellas County; participant in workshops and seminars for mental health care. Author: (with Denis M. Donovan) Healing the Hurt Child: A Developmental-Contextual Approach, 1990, Strategic Parenting, 1995; contbr. articles to profl. jours., chpts. to books. Fellow Am. Psychol. Soc.; mem. Am. Orthopsychiat. Assn. Roman Catholic. Office: Childrens Ctr Devel Psychiatry 6675 13th Ave N Ste 1 Saint Petersburg FL 33710-5401

MCINTYRE, DONALD CONROY, opera singer, baritone; b. Auckland, New Zealand, Oct. 22, 1934; s. George D. and Hermyn McI.; m. Jill Redington, 1961; 3 children. Student, Auckland Tchrs. Tng. Coll.; Guildhall Sch. Music, London; MusD, Auckland U., 1992. Prin. bass Sadler's Wells Opera, London, 1960-67, Royal Opera House-Covent Garden, London, from 1967. Appeared at Bayreuth Festival, 1967-81, 87, 88; frequent internat. guest appearances maj. opera houses including Metropolitan, N.Y.C., La Scala, Milan, Vienna, Paris, Munich, Berlin, Hamburg, Zurich, Chgo., Savonlinna Festival, Sydney, Buenos Aires; roles include: Wotan and Wanderer, Der Ring, Dutchman, Der Fliegende Hollander, Telramund, Lohengrin, Barak, Die Frau ohne Schatten, Pizzaro, Fidelio, Golaud, Pelleas et Melisande, Kurwenal, Tristan and Isold, Gurnemanz, Klingsor and Amfortas, Parsifal, Heyst, Victory, Jochanaan, Salome, Macbeth, Scarpia, Tosca, The Count, Marriage of Figaro, Nick Shadow, The Rake's Progress, Hans Sachs, Die Meistersinger, The Doctor, Woyzeck, Cardillac, Cardillac Hindemith, Kasper, Der Frieshutz, Rocco, Fidelio, Prospero, Un Re Un Ascolta (Brit. premier), Balstrode, Peter Grimes, Shakloviti, Khovanshina, Sarastro Zauberflöte, Hans Sachs die Meistersinger recs. include Pelleas et Melisande, Oedipus Rex, Il Torvatore, Parsifal, The Ring Damnation of Faust, Messiah Beethoven's 9th, Boris, Lady Macbeth of Mtsensk. Decorated comdr. Order of Brit. Empire; created knight, 1992; recipient Worldwide Fidelio medal Assn. Internat. Dirs. of Opera, 1989, New Zealand Commemoration award, 1990. Home: Foxhill Farm, Jackass Ln, Keston, Bromley, Kent BR2 6AN, England Office: care Ingpen & Williams, 14 Kensington Ct, London W8 5DN, England also: Org Interntional Opera et Concert, 19, rue Vignon, F-7 rue Vignon Paris France

MCINTYRE, DOUGLAS ALEXANDER, magazine publisher; b. Erie, Pa., Mar. 16, 1955; s. Bruce Herbert and Natalie Ann (Wolff) McI.; children: Garrett Wolff, Hunter Garrahan; m. Patricia Yarberry Allen, Apr. 20, 1995. B.A. magna cum laude, Harvard U., 1977. Strategic planner Time Inc., N.Y.C., 1977-81; asst. to pres. Penthouse Internat., N.Y.C., 1981-82; assoc. Veronis, Suhler and Assocs., N.Y.C., 1982-83; gen. mgr. Fin. World, N.Y.C., 1983-84, pres., pub., 1984—; pres. Harvard Advocate Trustees Inc., 1983—. Mem. Harvard Club. Episcopalian. Office: Fin World Mag 1328 Broadway New York NY 10001-2116

MCINTYRE, ELIZABETH GEARY, Olympic athlete; b. Hanover, N.H., 1965. AB, Dartmouth Coll., 1988. Silver medalist, women's moguls final freestyle skiing Olympic Games, Lillehammer, Norway, 1994. Office: US Olympic Com 1750 E Boulder St Colorado Springs CO 80909*

MCINTYRE, GUY MAURICE, professional football player; b. Thomasville, Ga., Feb. 17, 1961. Student, U. Ga. Offensive guard San Francisco 49ers, 1984-94; played in Super Bowl XIX, 1984, XXIII, 1988, XXIV, 1989. Played in Pro Bowl, 1989-93. *

MC INTYRE, HENRY LANGENBERG, former business executive, lawyer; b. St. Louis, Sept. 30, 1912; s. Joseph Shelby and Ida (Langenberg) McI.; m. Winifred Wheeler, Dec. 21, 1934; children: Robert W., Shelby H., Virginia H., Penelope T. A.B., Princeton U., 1933; J.D., Northwestern U., 1936. Bar: Ill. 1936. Practiced in Chgo., 1936-41; sec.-treas. Hiller Helicopters, 1946-52; partner McIntyre & Parker (real estate, mfr. devels.), 1952-58; pres. Pacific Industries, San Francisco, 1958-64; dir. Pacific Intermountain Express, 1960-64; partner McIntyre & Gage, 1965-70; sec.-treas. Bangert & Co., San Francisco, 1971-75. Mem. Palo Alto Planning Commn., 1953-56; chmn. Children's Health Coun., 1954-56; founder Population Resource Center, Princeton, N.J., 1976—; bd. dirs. Palo-Stanford Hosp., 1955-57, Planned Parenthood Fedn. Am., 1958-63, Internat. Planned Parenthood Fedn. 1962-70, Alzheimer's Disease and Related Disorders Assn., Chgo., 1987-92. Served as maj. F.A. AUS, 1942-45. Mem. Phi Beta Kappa, Phi Delta Phi, Order of Coif. Republican. Episcopalian. Clubs: Cottage (Princeton); Cypress Point, Burlingame (Calif.) Country; Eldorado Country (Calif.). Home: 55 Serrano Dr Atherton CA 94027-3961

MC INTYRE, JAMES A., diversified financial services executive; b. 1932. BS, U. So. Calif., 1954. With Ernst & Ernst, L.A., 1958-63; pres. Fremont Indemnity Co., 1963-80; pres., CEO Fremont Gen. Corp., Santa Monica, Calif., 1980—. Office: Fremont Gen Corp 2020 Santa Monica Blvd Santa Monica CA 90404-2023

MCINTYRE, JOEL FRANKLYN, lawyer; b. Fairbury, Nebr., Sept. 19, 1938; s. Frank Otto and Maxine Olive (Ward) McI.; m. Suzanne Jane Sahl, June 22, 1958; children: Joel Franklyn, Jr., David William, Jeffrey Bayne, Erin Suzanne, Matthew Kay, Karyn Suzanne, Kathleen Suzanne, Michael Joel. B.A., Stanford U., 1960; J.D., UCLA, 1963. Bar: Calif. 1963. Assoc. Paul, Hastings, Janofsky & Walker, Los Angeles, 1963-70, ptnr., 1970-93; sr. ptnr. McIntyre & Lubeck, Costa Mesa, Calif., 1993—; dir. Internat. Aluminum Corp., Crown City Plating Co. Mem. Phi Delta Phi. Republican. Club: San Garbriel Country. Home: 60 W Arthur Ave Arcadia CA 91007-8201 Office: McIntyre & Lubeck 3070 Bristol St Ste 450 Costa Mesa CA 92626

MCINTYRE, JOHN ARMIN, physics educator; b. Seattle, June 2, 1920; s. Harry Iron and Florence (Armin) McI.; m. Madeleine Forseman, June 15, 1947; 1 son, John Forsman. B.S., U. Wash., 1943; M.A., Princeton U., 1948, Ph.D., 1950. Mem. faculty elec. engring. Carnegie Inst. Tech., Pitts., 1943; radio engr. Westinghouse Elec. Co., Balt., 1944; research asso. Stanford, 1950-57; mem. faculty Yale, 1957-63, asso. prof., 1960-63; prof. physics Tex. A&M U., College Station, 1963—; asso. dir. Cyclotron Inst.,

1965-70; Mem. council Oak Ridge Asso. Univs., 1964-71. Fellow Am. Phys. Soc., Am. Sci. Affiliation (exec. council 1968-73); mem. AAAS. Presbyn. Research and publs. on scintillation counters for gamma ray spectroscopy; determination of nuclear charge distbns. by electron scattering; study of nuclear structure by neutron transfer reactions; devel. variable energy gamma ray beams, gamma ray cameras. Home: 2316 Bristol St Bryan TX 77802-2405 Office: Tex A&M U Dept Physics College Station TX 77843

MCINTYRE, JOHN DUNCAN, health care executive; b. Dinapore, India, Jan. 7, 1938. Certs. in Chemistry, Slough Coll., Eng., 1959; external degree in Chemistry, London U., 1961. With Eli Lilly Internat., 1966-74; with Johnson and Johnson, 1974-85, regional v.p. pharm. bus. Europe; v.p. Europe Abbott Internat., Ltd., 1985-90, pres., 1990—; sr. v.p. Abbott Labs., Abbott Pk., Ill., 1990—. Mem. Royal Inst. Chemistry (assoc.), Inst. Dirs. Office: Abbott Labs Abbott Park IL 60064

MCINTYRE, JOHN GEORGE WALLACE, real estate development and management consultant; b. Toronto, Ont., Can., July 26, 1920; s. George Crerar and Gwendolyn Alberta (Wallace) McI.; m. Ruth Elizabeth Wilson, July 26, 1945 (dec.); children: Angus, Heather, Robert, Anne. B of Commerce, U. Toronto, 1941; MBA, Harvard U., 1947. Budget acct. Abitibi Paper Co., Toronto, 1947-51; budget mgr., asst. gen. mgr. Ford of Can., Windsor, Ont., 1951-58, gen. mgr. mfg. ops., 1963-65; asst. mng. dir., mng. dir. Ford of Australia, Melbourne, 1958-63; exec. v.p., pres. Columbia Cellulose Ltd., Vancouver, B.C., Can., 1965-67; v.p. retail devel. and distbn. Hudson's Bay Co., Toronto, 1967-84; pres. Rupert's Land Tng. Co., Hudson's Bay Co. Devels. Ltd.; trustee Internat. Council of Shopping Ctrs., 1970-84; v.p., gen. mgr. Broadcast Tor. Devel. Project Can. Broadcasting Corp., 1984-88; cons., 1988—. Served to capt. Royal Can. Ordnance Corps., 1942-45, ETO. Address: 53 Widdicombe Hill Blvd Ste 401E, Weston, ON Canada M9R 1Y3

MCINTYRE, JOHN WILLIAM, banker; b. Valdosta, Ga., Sept. 14, 1930; s. James A. and Julia (Norton) McI.; m. Joan Pruitt, Oct. 8, 1955; children: Anna, John William, Martha, Michael. B.B.A., Emory U., 1951; grad. exec. mgmt. program, Stanford U., 1966. With Citizens & So. Nat. Bank, 1951—; gen. v.p. Citizens & So. Nat. Bank, Atlanta, 1977-79; pres. Citizens & So. Nat. Bank, 1979—, chmn., chief exec. officer, 1990—, also bd. dirs.; chmn., chief exec. officer Citizens and So. Ga. Corp., 1980—, also bd. dirs. (chmn. bd. dirs. Citizens and So. Corp. (parent co.), 1986; bd. dirs. Master Card Internat., Inc., Kaiser Found. Health Plan Ga. Trustee Emory U.; bd. sponsors Atlanta Symphony; trustee Lovett Sch., Atlanta; bd. dirs. City of Atlanta, Fulton County Recreation Authority, Atlanta Exec. Svc. Corps, Bus. Coun. Ga. With USAR, 1952-54. Mem. Assn. Res. City Banks, Ga. C. of C. (dir.). Baptist. Clubs: Piedmont Driving, Cherokee Town and Country, Commerce. Office: Citizens & So Corp 35 Broad St NW Atlanta GA 30303-2302

MCINTYRE, JUDITH WATLAND, ornithologist, biology educator; b. Kansas City, Mo., Aug. 19, 1930; d. Clarence and Pearl (Tyrholm) Watland; m. John Patrick McIntyre, Sept. 14, 1957; children: Perry, Richard, Anthony. BA, Carleton Coll., 1952; MA, U. Minn., 1970, PhD, 1975. Asst. prof. biology Syracuse (N.Y.) U., 1977-80; asst. prof. biology Utica (N.Y.) Coll., Syracuse U., 1979-81, assoc. prof., 1981-86; prof. biology Utica (N.Y.) Coll. Syracuse U., 1986—; coord./chair biology dept. Utica Coll., 1983-84, 90; sci. cons. Survival Anglia, London, 1989—. Author: Common Loon: Spirit of Northern Lakes, 1988; contbr. articles to profl. jours.; author/producer (slide/tape program) Hello, I'm a Loon!, 1985. Mem. bd. dirs. budget panel United Way, Utica, 1982-86; pres. Kirkland Bird Club, Clinton, N.Y., 1987-89; trustee The Nature Conservancy, CNY chpt., 1983—; trustee emeritus N.Am. Loon Fund, Meredith, N.H., 1994—; dir. Oikos Rsch. Found., Utica, 1976—, Wilson Ornithological Soc. (coun. Ann Arbor 1989-91). Recipient Harold T. Clark award for excellence in rsch.; rsch. grantee NSF, 1968-71, 81-82, Nat. Geog., 1980, 89, Mercer Industries, 1986-91, Exxon, 1989-90, N.Am. Loon Fund, 1981, 83, 87, 89. Fellow Am. Ornithologists' Union, Cooper Ornithol. Soc., Assn. Field Ornithologists, AAAS, Animal Behavior Soc., Minn. Ornithologists' Union, Fedn. N.Y. State Bird Clubs, Sigma Xi. Office: Utica Coll Syracuse U Burrstone Rd Utica NY 13502

MCINTYRE, KATHRYN JOAN, publisher, editorial director; b. Pitts., Jan. 7, 1952; d. William E. and Marianne (Schroth) McI.; m. Toby Roberts, May 13, 1974 (div. Nov. 1982); m. Ronald Jacks, Dec. 31, 1983. BA, Syracuse U., 1974. Reporter Lake Placid (N.Y.) News, 1974-76; freelance writer, 1976-77; assoc. editor Bus. Ins., Chgo., 1977-78, news editor, 1978-79, mng. editor, 1979-80, editor, 1980-92, assoc. pub., 1987-92, pub.; editorial dir. 1992—; v.p. Crain Comm., Inc., 1993—. Recipient Inst. award Ins. Inst. Am., 1979, Goodell award Risk and Ins. Mgmt. Soc., 1989, award for editorial N.Y. State Bus. Press Editors, 1989, 91. Mem. Am. Soc. Bus. Press Editors (award for editorial 1984, 86), Soc. Profl. Journalists, Women in Communication, Assn. Profl. Ins. Women (Ins. Woman of Yr. award 1989), The Chgo. Network, Internat. Alliance, Union League Club, Phi Beta Kappa. Democrat. Episcopalian. Avocations: photography, sailing, horseback riding. Home: 232 E Walton St Chicago IL 60611-1535 Office: Business Ins 740 N Rush St Chicago IL 60611-2525

MCINTYRE, NORMAN F., petroleum industry executive; b. Pangman, Sask., Can., Oct. 21, 1945; s. Donald and Jean (Cruickshank) McI.; m. Lana Jean, June 10, 1967; children: Jason Lee, Spencer James. BSc in Petroleum Engring., U. Wyo., 1971; MS in Mgmt., MIT, 1991. Various positions with Mobil Oil, U.S., Can., to 1982; group mgr. engring. offshore divsn. Petro-Can., 1982-83, gen. mgr. frontier devel. offshore divsn., 1983, v.p. frontier devel., 1983-86, v.p. prodn. devel., 1986-89; sr. v.p. western region Petro-Can. Products, 1989-90; pres. Petro-Can. Resources, Calgary, Alta., Can., 1990—; dir. Panarctic Oils Ltd., Petroleum Transmission Co. Office: Petro-Canada, 150-6th Ave SW PO Box 2844, Calgary, AB Canada T2P 3E3

MCINTYRE, OSWALD ROSS, physician; b. Chgo., Feb. 13, 1932; m. Jean Geary, June 5, 1957; children—Margaret Jean, Archibald Ross, Elizabeth Geary. A.B. cum laude, Dartmouth Coll., 1953, postgrad, 1953-55; M.D., Harvard U., 1957. Intern U. Pa. Hosp., 1957-58; resident in medicine Dartmouth Med. Sch. Affiliated Hosps., 1958-60; instr. medicine Dartmouth Coll., 1964-66, asst. prof. medicine, 1966-69, assoc. prof. medicine, 1969-75, prof., 1976—; James J. Carroll prof. oncology, 1980-95, dir. Norris Cotton Cancer Center, 1975-92, prof. emeritus, 1995—; attending physician VA Hosp., White River Junction, Vt., 1964; cons. in hematology and oncology; acting chmn. dept. medicine Dartmouth-Hitchcock Med. Ctr., 1987-89; chmn. Cancer and Leukemia Group B., 1990-95. With USPHS, 1961-63. Served with USPHS, 1961-63. Fellow AAAS; mem. Am. Fedn. Clin. Rsch., Am. Soc. Hematology, Internat. Assn. Study Lung Cancer, Am. Assn. Cancer Rsch., Am. Soc. Clin. Oncology, Assn. Cancer Inst. (pres. 1988-89), New Eng. Cancer Soc. (pres. 1989-90). Home: 155A River Rd Lyme NH 03768-5003

MCINTYRE, PETER MASTIN, physicist, educator; b. Clewiston, Fla., Sept. 26, 1947; s. Peter Mastin and Ruby Eugenia (Richaud) McI.; m. Rebecca Biek, June 29, 1968; children: Peter B., Colin H., Jana M., Robert J. BS, U. Chgo., 1967, MS, 1968, PhD, 1973. Asst. prof. Harvard U., Cambridge, Mass., 1975-80; group leader Fermilab, Batavia, Ill., 1978-80; assoc. prof. Tex. A&M U., College Station, 1980-84, prof. physics, 1985—, assoc. dean Coll. of Sci., 1990-92; pres. Accelerator Tech. Corp., College Station, 1986—; dir. Tex. Accelerator Ctr., The Woodlands, 1991-93. Prin. author Tex. SSC Site Proposal, 1988; patentee in field. Sloan Found. fellow, 1976-78; recipient IR-100 award Indsl. Rsch. Mag., 1980. Mem. AAAS, Am. Phys. Soc. (pres. Tex. sect. 1990-91). Achievements include research in Proton-Antiporton Colliding Beams, Continuous Unitized Tunneling System, Gigatron High Power Microwave Amplifier, Gas Microstrip Chamber for X-rays and Charged Particles, Electronic and X-ray Disinfestation of Foods, X-ray Cameras for Mammography, Porous Silicon Substrate for Electronic Sequencing of DNA. Home: 611 Montclair Ave College Station TX 77840-2868 Office: Tex A&M U Dept Physics College Station TX 77843

MCINTYRE, RITA ANN, nursing consultant; b. Lansford, Pa., Feb. 25, 1938; d. Tobias M. and Mary Rose (Uher) Krajcirik; children: Richard James, Tobias Michael, Gerard David. RN, Sacred Heart Hosp. Sch. Nurses, Allentown, Pa., 1958; BS, Wilkes Coll., 1971; MBA, Xavier U., 1972. Dir. of nursing Allentown Osteopathic Hosp., Grandview Hosp.,

Dayton, Ohio; v.p. Good Samaritan Hosp., Cin.; nursing cons. Creative Nursing Mgmt., Mpls. Mem. ANA. Home: Apt 1112 2625 N Meridian St Indianapolis IN 46208-7710

MC INTYRE, ROBERT ALLEN, JR., business turnaround executive; b. Gettysburg, Pa., Jan. 6, 1940; s. Robert A. and Leona Hazel (Stoner) McInTyre Baughman; m. Rosemary Holland, Mar. 25, 1967; children: Nicole, Brian. Student, U. Portland, 1962-63, U. Md., 1963-64; BA, York Coll., 1971; MS, U. Wis., 1974; PhD, Southwestern U., 1982. Field salesman L.E. Smith, Inc., Gettysburg, Pa., 1958-61; tool and die maker apprentice Black & Decker Mfg. Co., Hampstead, Md., 1965-69; mfg. mgmt. trainee Black & Decker Mfg. Co., 1965-69, prodn. supr., 1970-71; mfg. engr., 1971; sr. mfg. engr. Wis. Knife Works, subs. Black & Decker Mfg. Co., Beloit, 1971-73, mfg. engr. mgr., 1973, mfg. engring. and quality control mgr., 1973-74, engring. and customer svc. mgr., 1974-75; engring. dir. Davenport Machine Tool, subs. Dover Corp., Rochester, N.Y., 1975-76; v.p. mfg. Bernard Welding, subs. Dover Corp., Beecher, Ill., 1976-77; v.p. mfg. and engring., 1977-78; gen. mgr., v.p. Marvel Lighting Corp., subs. Swingline, Inc., Mullins, S.C., 1978, exec. v.p., 1979, pres., 1979-80, dir., 1981-84; exec. v.p. Swingline Inc., subs. American Brands Inc. Long Island City, N.Y., 1980; pres., chief exec. officer, dir. MCM Products, Inc. subs. American Brands, N.Y.C., 1981-84; chmn., dir. W.R. Case & Sons Cutlery Co., Bradford, Pa., 1981-84; pres., dir. Marson Corp. of P.R., 1981-84, Marson Sales Inc., Chelsea, Mass., 1981-84; chmn., pres., CEO, dir. P.C.F.E., Inc., Ridgefield, N.J., 1984—; pres., CEO PCF Enterprises Inc., Mechanicsburg, Pa., 1987—, Positive Cash Flow Enterprises, Inc., Mechanicsburg, Pa., 1992—; dir. Master Lock Co., Milw., 1983-84; trustee C & L Realty Trust, Chelsea, 1981-84. Served with USAF, 1961-65, Vietnam.

MCINTYRE, ROBERT MALCOLM, utility company executive; b. Portland, Oreg., Dec. 18, 1923; s. Daniel A. and Bessie W. (Earsley) McI.; m. Marilyn Westcott, Aug. 27, 1949; 1 child, Julie. BA, UCLA, 1950; postgrad., UCLA, U. Soc Calif., Columbia U. With So. Calif. Gas Co. (subs. Pacific Enterprises), L.A., 1952-67, gen. sales mgr., 1967-70, v.p., 1970-74, sr. v.p., 1974-80, pres., 1980-85, chmn., chief exec. officer, 1985-88; also bd. dirs. So. Calif. Gas Co. (subs. Pacific Enterprises); regent's prof. U. Calif., Irvine. Mem. Korean Am. Centennial Commn., Huntington Libr. Soc. Fellows, L.A. Olympic Citizens Adv. Commn.; mem. bus. coun. Newport Harbor Art Mus.; mem. steering com. Orange County Bus. Com. for Arts; mem. ad hoc com. on city fin., L.A.; bd. dirs. NCCJ, Calif. Coun. Environ. and Econ. Balance, Calif. Found. Environment and Economy, L.A. United Way, Hoag Meml. Hosp.; trustee UCLA Found., L.A. Orthopaedic Hosp., mem. exec. com.; pres. Hoag Hosp. Found., L.A. Chamber Assocs. Lt. USN, 1942-46. Decorated Order of the Rising Sun with Gold Rays and Ribbon (Japan); recipient Outstanding Svc. award Mex. Am. Legal Def. Fund, 1981, Humanitarian award NCCJ, Roy Wilkins award L.A. chpt. NAACP, others. Mem. Pacific Coast Gas Assn. (past dir., 49er Club award 1979), Am. Gas Assn., Inst. Gas Tech. (trustee), U.S.-Mex. C. of C., L.A. C. of C. (past chmn. Medici award), Calif. Club, 100 Club, Big Canyon Country Club, Center Club, Pacific Club, The Lakes Country Club, Phi Kappa Psi. Republican. Presbyterian. Avocations: swimming, fishing, golf. Office: So Calif Gas Co 555 W 5th St Los Angeles CA 90013-1010

MCINTYRE, ROBERT WALTER, church official; b. Bethlehem, Pa., June 20, 1922; s. Simon Jesse and Ruth (Young) McI.; m. Edith Jones, Sept. 1, 1944 (dec. Jan. 1953); m. Elizabeth Norman, Nov. 6, 1953; children: Judith McIntyre Keilholtz, Joy McIntyre McCallum, John, James, June McIntyre Brannon. Student, Miltonvale Wesleyan Coll., 1939-43; B.Religion, Marion Coll., 1944, LittD (hon.), 1980, B.A., 1959; postgrad., Ball State U., 1960-61; D.D. (hon.), Ea. Pilgram Coll., 1969; LLD (hon.), Houghton Coll., 1976; DHL (hon.), Ctrl. Wesleyan Coll., 1988. Ordained to ministry The Wesleyan Ch., 1945. Pastor Marengo, Ohio 1944-47, Columbus, Ohio 1947-52, Coshocton, Ohio, 1952-55; exec. sec. dept. youth The Wesleyan Ch., Marion, Ind., 1955-68; editor The Wesleyan Youth, Marion, 1955-68; gen. editor The Wesleyan Ch., editor The Wesleyan Adv., Marion, 1968-73; assoc. editor The Preacher's Mag., Marion, 1973-88; gen. supt. The Wesleyan Ch., Marion, 1973-88; mem. gen. bd. adminstrn. The Wesleyan Ch., 1955-88, mem. Commn. Christian Edn., 1959-73, 76-80, chmn. Commn. Christian Edn., 1976-80, mem. exec. bd., 1968-88; chmn. Commn. on World Missions, 1973-76, Commn. on Publs., 1980-84, Commn. on Extension and Evangelism, 1984-88; spl. asst. to the pres. Ind. Wesleyan U., Marion, 1988-93; denominational rep., bd. adminstrn. Nat. Assn. Evangelicals, 1973-83, exec. com., 1978-80, 81-87, 2d v.p., 1981-82, 1st v.p., 1982-84, pres., 1984-86, mem., 1973—; denominational rep. The Lord's Day Alliance, 1973-76; trustee Marion Coll., Asbury Theol. Sem., 1976—. Author: Ten Commandments for Teen-Agers, 1965; editor: Program Pathways for Young Adults, 1964, Mandate for Mission; 1970; contbr. articles to religious jours. Mem. Christian Holiness Assn. (chmn. social action commn. 1971-73, sec. 1973-76), Wesleyan Toehol. Soc., Best Years Fellowship (gen. dir. 1992—). Home: 4613 S Star Dr Marion IN 46953-7303

MCINTYRE, RONALD LLEWELLYN, electric utility executive; b. Detroit, May 12, 1934; s. Nathaniel Francis McIntyre and Cheaber (Hudson) Farmer; m. Amalia Rosario Leon, June 17, 1961; children: Carmen Maria, Norman Lawrence, Maritza Cheaber, Yvonne Amalia, Carlos Leonel. BSEE, Wayne State U., 1962, MSEE, 1968. Registered profl. engr., Mich. Rsch. engr. Detroit Edison Co., 1963-68, instr., control systems engr., 1968-71, reactor systems engr., 1971-72, assoc. project engr., 1972-74, supr. power supply planning, 1974-80, corp. strategic planning, 1980-81, bus. mgr. dist. heating, 1981-86, dir. engring. rsch., 1986-90, gen. dir. tech. and engring. svcs., 1990-91; supt. River Rouge Power Plant, 1991-94, dir. environ. initiatives, 1994—; v.p. Utility Tech. Svcs., Detroit, 1984—; adv. bd. Wayne State U. 1987—; bd. vis. Oakland U., Rochester, Mich., 1988—; exec. com. and bd. dirs. Metro Ctr. High Tech., Detroit, 1988—. Contbr. articles to profl. jours. Bd. dirs. Detroit Sci. Ctr., 1988—; active Mich. Emergency Preparedness Adv. Coun., Lansing, 1985—; deacon Archdiocese Detroit, 1986—. Mem. IEEE, Engring. Soc. Detroit, Edison Boat Club, Etta Kappa Nu. Roman Catholic. Avocations: golfing, sailing, photography, reading, biking. Office: Detroit Edison Co 2000 2nd Ave Detroit MI 48226-1279

MCINTYRE, THOMAS, recording industry executive; b. 1948. Treas. Bertelsmann Music Group, N.Y.C., 1985—. Office: Bertelsmann Music Group 1540 Broadway New York NY 10036*

MCINTYRE, VALENE SMITH, anthropology educator; b. Spokane, Wash., Feb. 14, 1926; d. Ernst Frank and Lucy (Blachly) S.; m. Edwin Chesteen Golay, June 7, 1970 (dec. June 1980; m. Stanley George McIntyre, Nov. 26, 1983. BA in Geography, U. Calif., 1946, MA in Geography, 1950; PhD in Anthropology, U. Utah, 1966. Prof. earth sci. L.A. City Coll., 1947-67; prof. anthropology Calif. State U., Chico, 1967—; cons. World Tourism Orgn., Madrid, 1987. Editor: Hosts and Guests: The Anthrop, 1989, Tourism Alternatives: Potentials and Problems in the Development of Tourism, 1992. Mem. Internat. Acad. for Study Tourism, Anthrop. Soc. Wash., Cent. Travel Counselors, Am. Anthrop. Assn., AAUW, Butte Creek Country Club, Soroptimists. Republican. Avocations: traveling, aviation, photography. Office: U Calif Dept Anthropology Chico CA 95929

MC ISAAC, GEORGE SCOTT, business policy educator, past business executive; b. Auburn, N.Y., July 25, 1930; s. Robert Scott and Agnes Congalton (Aitchison) McI.; m. Betsy Clark, Sept. 11, 1954; children: Ian Scott, Christopher Clark. B.S., Yale U., 1952; M.S., U. Rochester, 1961. In mfg. mgmt. Eastman Kodak Co., Rochester, N.Y., 1954-62; prin., dir. McKinsey & Co. (Mgmt. Consultants), N.Y.C., Dusseldorf, Ger., Washington, 1962-78; asst. sec. of energy for resource applications U.S. Dept. Energy, Washington, 1978-80; sr. v.p. Schlegel Corp., Rochester, 1980-85; AT&T resident mgmt. fellow; exec. prof. bus. and pub. policy William E. Simon Grad. Sch. Bus. Adminstrn., U. Rochester, 1985—; cons. Dept. Def., U.S. Postal Service, HUD, German Agrl. Ministry, Govt. of Tanzania, various pvt. clients. Contbr. articles to bus. jours. Bd. dirs. Rochester Hosp. Corp.; trustee Internat. Mus. Photography, George Eastman House. Lt. USMC, 1952-54. Clubs: Met. (Washington), Genesee Valley (Rochester). Office: Dewey Hall Grad Sch Mgmt U Rochester Rochester NY 14627

MCISAAC, PAUL ROWLEY, electrical engineer, educator; b. Port Washington, N.Y., Apr. 20, 1926; s. Robert Milton and June Zatella (Barrus) McI.; m. Mary Lou Heldenbrand, Sept. 10, 1949; children—Wendy Lee,

Karen Jo, Hugh Paul, Kathleen Anne. B.E.E., Cornell U., 1949; M.S.E., U. Mich., 1950, Ph.D., 1954. Research engr. Microwave Tube div. Sperry Gyroscope Co., Great Neck, N.Y., 1954-59; assoc. prof. elec. engring. Cornell U., 1959-65, prof., 1965—, assoc. dean engring., 1975-80. Served with USN, 1944-46. Rotary Found. fellow, 1951-52. Mem. IEEE, AAAS, Sigma Xi. Office: Cornell University 306 Phillips Hall Ithaca NY 14853-5401

MCIVOR, DONALD KENNETH, retired petroleum company executive, university administrator; b. Winnipeg, Man., Can., Apr. 12, 1928; s. Kenneth MacIver and Nellie Beatrice (Rutherford) McI.; m. Avonia Isabel Forbes, 1953; children: Gordon, Deborah, Donald, Daniel. B.S. with honors in Geology, U. Man., 1950; postgrad. Nat. Def. Coll., 1973. Geophysical trainee seismic crew Imperial Oil Ltd., Alta., 1950, various operational and rsch. positions in exploration, 1950-58; held various positions including asst. to exploration mgr., suprv. exploration planning, mgr. exploration rsch. Imperial Oil Ltd., Calgary, 1958-68; with Jersey Prodn. Rsch. Co. Imperial Oil Ltd., Angola, France and Tulsa, Okla.; asst. mgr., mgr. corp. planning Toronto HO, 1968-69, mgr. exploration, 1970-72, sr. v.p., dir., 1973, exec. v.p., 1975; v.p. oil and gas exploration and prodn. Exxon Corp., 1977-81; dep. chmn., dir. Imperial Oil Ltd., 1981, chmn., chief exec. officer, 1982-85; dir., sr. v.p. Exxon Corp., Dallas, 1985-92; exec.-in-residence Queen's U. Bus. Sch., Nat. Coun. on Econ. Edn.; exec. v.p. Internat. Exec. Svc. Corps. Mem. Can. Soc. Petroleum Geologists, Am. Petroleum Inst. Home: 111 Hemlock Hill Rd New Canaan CT 06840-3004

MCKAGAN, DUFF (MICHAEL MCKAGAN), bassist; b. Feb. 5, 1964. Bassist Guns n' Roses, 1985—. Albums with Guns n' Roses include Live Like a Suicide, 1986, Appetite for Destruction, 1987, Guns n' Roses Lies, 1988, Use Your Illusion 1, 1991, Use Your Illusion II, 1991, The Spaghetti Incident?, 1993; solo album: Believe in Me, 1993. Office: care Geffen Records 9130 W Sunset Blvd West Hollywood CA 90069-3110*

MCKANE, DAVID BENNETT, business executive; b. Salem, Mass., July 10, 1945; s. Vernon Wilson and Barbara Inez (Bennett) McK.; m. Wilson Lineburgh Baldwin, Apr. 16, 1977; adopted daughters, Taylor A., Lee and Paige Baldwin. BA, Dartmouth Coll., 1967; MBA, Amos Tuck Sch., 1969. Product mgr. Church & Dwight Co. Inc. (Arm and Hammer Products), N.Y.C., 1969-72; v.p. NTA Inc. N.Y.C., Nanuet, N.Y., 1972-75; v.p., exec. asst. to chmn. Schick Inc., Westport, Conn., 1975-77, sr. v.p., 1977-79, COO, exec. v.p., 1979-84, treas., 1980-84, also bd. dirs.; chmn., CEO A.I. Friedman, Inc., N.Y.C., 1985-87; chmn. McKane Robbins & Co. Inc., N.Y.C. and Westport, 1986—; bd. dirs. Oakhurst Dairy, Portland, Maine. Mem. bd. trustees Greens Farms (Conn.) Acad., 1991—; vice chmn. Associated Schs., Dartmouth Coll. Capital Campaign, 1991—. Mem. New England Soc. in City of N.Y., Mass. Mayflower Soc., Union Club (N.Y.C.), Fairfield County Hunt Club, Country Club of Fairfield. Episcopalian. Home: 48 Owenoke Park Westport CT 06880-6833

MC KAUGHAN, HOWARD PAUL, linguistics educator; b. Canoga Park, Calif., July 5, 1922; s. Paul and Edith (Barton) McK.; m. Barbara Jean Budroe, Dec. 25, 1943; children: Edith (Mrs. Daniel Skene Santoro), Charlotte (Ms. Charlotte Barnhart), Patricia (Mrs. Stephen B. Pike), Barbara (Mrs. Ronald Chester Bell), Judith (Mrs. Frank L. Achilles III). AB, UCLA, 1945, MTh, Dallas Theol. Sem., 1946; MA, Cornell U., 1952, PhD 1957. Mem. linguistic research team Summer Inst. Linguistics, Mexico, 1946-52; asso. dir. Summer Inst. Linguistics, Philippines, also assoc. dir. summer sessions U. N.D., 1952-57, dir. Philippine br., 1957-61; research asst. prof. anthropology U. Wash., 1961-62; research assoc. prof., 1962-63; assoc. prof. linguistics U. Hawaii, 1963-64, prof. linguistics, 1964-88, prof. emeritus, 1988—, chmn. dept., 1963-66, dir. Pacific and Asian Linguistics Inst., 1964, 1966-69, assoc. dean grad. div., 1965-72, dean grad. div., dir. research, 1972-79, acting chancellor, 1979, interim vice chancellor acad. affairs, 1981-82, acting dir research, 1982-84, acting dean grad. div., 1982-83, dean, 1984-87, dir. research relations, 1987-88; lectr. linguistics U. Philippines, summers, 1954, 60; Fulbright vis. prof. Philippine Normal Coll.-Ateneo De La Salle Consortium, Philippines, 1977, De La Salle U., Philippines, 1992; vis. prof. linguistics Bukidnon State Coll., Malaybalay, Philippines, 1993, 94; prin. Wycliffe Sch. Linguistics, summers 1953, 61; vis. prof. Australian Nat. U., Canberra, 1970; adj. prof. linguistics U. Okla., summers 1984, 85, 86; vis. prof., head dept. linguistics Payap U., Chiang Mai, Thailand, 1989-90. Sr. scholar East-West Ctr., Honolulu, 1964; NDEA Maranao-Philippines research grantee, 1963-65; Office of Edn. Hawaii English grantee, 1965-66; NSF Jeh Language of South Vietnam grantee, 1969-70, Maranao Linguistic Studies, 1971-72, numerous other research grants. Mem. linguistic socs. Am., Philippines, Western Assn. Grad. Schs. (pres. 1978), Hawaii, Linguistic Circle N.Y., Philippine Assn. Lang. Tchrs., Hawaii Govt. Employees Assn., Phi Beta Kappa, Phi Kappa Phi. Author (with B. McKaughan): Chatino Dictionary, 1951; (with J. Forster) Ilocano: An Intensive Language Course, 1952; The Inflection and Syntax of Maranao Verbs, 1959; (with B. Macaraya): A Maranao Dictionary, 1967. Editor: Pali Language Texts: Philippines, 21 vols., 1971; The Languages of the Eastern Family of the East New Guinea Highlands Stock, 1973, Maranao Stories, 1995, Stories from the Darangen, 1994; contbr. articles, chpts. to books, sci. jours. Home: 420 S Hill Rd Mcminnville OR 97128

MC KAY, ALEXANDER GORDON, classics educator; b. Toronto, Can., Dec. 24, 1924; s. Alexander Lynn and Marjory Maude Redfern (Nicoll) McKay; m. Helen Jean Zulauf, Dec. 24, 1964; stepchildren: Julie Anne Stephanie Brott, Danae Helen Fraser. BA, U. Toronto, 1946; MA, Yale U., 1947, Princeton U., 1948; PhD, Princeton U., 1950; LLD (hon.), U. Man., 1986, Brock U., 1990, Queen's U., 1991; DLitt (hon.), McMaster U., 1992, U. Waterloo, 1993. Mem. faculty classics Wells Coll., 1949-50, U. Pa., 1950-51, U. Man., 1951-52, 55-57, Mt. Allison U., 1952-53, Waterloo Coll., 1953-55; mem. faculty McMaster U., 1957-90, prof., chmn. dept. classics, 1962-68, 76-79, dean humanities, 1968-73, mem. faculty senate, 1968-73, 85-87, prof. emeritus, 1990—; Disting. vis. prof. classics U. Colo., 1978; prof. in charge Intercollegiate Center for Classical Studies, Rome, 1975; vis. mem. Inst. Advanced Study, Princeton, 1979, 81; vis. scholar U. Tex., Austin, 1987, Hardt, Vandoeuvres, Geneva, 1988; vis. fellow Trinity Coll., Cambridge, 1988; adj. prof. Miami U., Oxford, Ohio, 1989, 92, 93, 94; adj. prof. humanities York U., 1990—; Disting. vis. lectr. Concordia U., Montreal, Que., 1992-93, Rockefeller Study and Conf. Ctr., Bellagio (Como) Italy, 1993. Author: Naples and Campania: Texts and Illustrations, 1962, Roman Lyric Poetry: Catullus and Horace, 2d edit, 1974, Vergil's Italy, 1970, Cumae and the Phlegraean Fields, 1972, Naples and Coastal Campania, 1972, Houses, Villas and Palaces in the Roman World, 1975, Roman Satire, 1976, Vitruvius, Architect and Engineer, 1978, 2d edit., 1985, Römische Häuser, Villen und Paläste, 1980, Roma Antiqua: Latium and Etruria, 1986; co-author: Selections from Vergil, Aeneid II, IV and VI (Dido and Aeneas), 1988, The Two Worlds of the Poet: New Perspectives on Vergil, 1992, Tragedy, Love, and Change: Roman Poetic Themes and Variations, 1994. Pres., bd. govs. Hamilton Philharm. Orch., 1967—; Hamilton Chamber Music Soc., 1965-67, Hamilton br. Archtl. Conservancy Ont., 1965-67, Hamilton and Region Arts Coun., 1971-72; bd. dirs. Can. Fedn. Humanities, 1980-82; v.p., dir. Internat. Acad. Union, 1978-90; trustee Hamilton Found., 1972-75; bd. govs. St. George MacMillan String Ensemble, 1988-90; mem. adv. bd. Inst. for the Classical Tradition, Boston U., 1987-88; v.p., dir. Bach-Elgar Choral Soc., Hamilton, 1992-95. Decorated knight comdr. Order St. John of Jerusalem; officer Order of Can.; recipient Silver Jubilee medal Queen Elizabeth II, 1977, 125th Anniversary medal Can. Confedn.; Woodrow Wilson fellow, 1947-48, Can. Coun. fellow, 1973-74, Killam rsch. fellow, 1979-80, fellow Vanier Coll., York U., 1991—. Fellow Royal Soc. Can. (hon. editor 1970-83, pres. 1984-87, past pres. 1987-89, Centennial medal 1982); mem. Vergilian Soc. (pres. 1972-74, Hon. Pres. for Life 1988—, chmn. 1972-75), Classical Assn. Mid. West and South (pres. 1972-73, award of merit 1978, chmn. award of merit com. 1989-91), Classical Assn. Can. (v.p. 1970-72, 76-78, pres. 1978-80), Ont. Classical Assn. (hon. pres. 1994—), Societas Cumana (trustee 1993—), The Campanian Soc., Inc. (dir. 1994—), Yale Club (N.Y.C.), Univ. Club (Pitts.), Tamahaac Club (Ancaster), Arts and Letters Club (Toronto), X Club (Toronto), Pres.'s Club, Faculty Club (McMaster). Home: 1 Turner Ave, Hamilton, ON Canada L8P 3K4 Office: McMaster U, Dept of Classics, Hamilton, ON Canada L8S 4M2

MCKAY, CAROL RUTH, photographic editor; b. Des Moines, Dec. 4, 1948; d. Gordon William and Topaz (Riles) Bird; m. Richard Donn McKay, Oct. 12, 1985; children: Alexandra Elizabeth, Nicholas Gordon. B.A. in Photojournalism and News Editorial, U. Iowa, 1971; postgrad., Ind. U., 1979. Milw. Bur. staff UPI, Milw., 1971; photog. editor Milw. Sentinel, 1972-77, Louisville Courier-Jour., 1977, Milw. Jour., 1977-78; teaching asst. Ind. U., Bloomington, 1978-79; photog. editor and dir. photography Kansas City Star, 1979-81; photog. editor The White House, 1981-89, US News & World Report, Washington, 1989—. Recipient Disting. Alumni award U. Iowa, 1984. Mem. Nat. Press Photographers Assn. (recipient special citation, 1993), Alpha Phi. Home: 9713 Bunchberry Pl Vienna VA 22181-5428

MCKAY, CRAIG, film editor. Editor: (films) Scarecrow, 1973, Thieves, 1977, Melvin and Howard, 1980, (with Dede Allen) Reds, 1981 (Academy award nomination best film editing 1981), Swing Shift, 1984, Something Wild, 1986, (with Alan Miller) Crack in the Mirror, 1987, Married to the Mob, 1988, She-Devil, 1989, Miami Blues, 1990, The Silence of the Lambs, 1991 (Academy award nomination best film editing 1991), Shining Through, 1992, (with Elena Maganini) Mad Dog and Glory, 1993, Philadelphia, 1993, (TV movies) Private Sessions, 1985. Address: 345 W 58th St New York NY 10019*

MC KAY, DEAN RAYMOND, computer company executive; b. Seattle, Nov. 13, 1921; s. Joseph and Nora (MacDermitt) McK.; m. Jean Davis, Dec. 26, 1942; children: Dean Brian, Bruce Thompson, Robert Joseph. BA, U. Wash., 1944; postgrad., Harvard U., 1955. With IBM Corp., Armonk, N.Y., 1946-82, from br. mgr. to dir. pers. div. data processing, 1957-61, v.p. communications, 1961-69, v.p. corp. ops. and services staff, 1969, mem. mgmt. com., 1970, sr. v.p., 1971, sr. v.p., group exec. data processing mktg., 1972—, sr. v.p. corp. ops. and services staffs, mem. corp. mgmt. com., bd. dir., 1978-82, mem. adv. bd., 1982—; bd. dirs. Marsh & McLennan Cos. Inc., N.Y.C., MCI Communications Corp., Washington, MARCAM, Newton, Mass., Du Pont, Wilmington, Del. Served to lt. (s.g.) Intelligence Corps USNR, 1942-46. Mem. Phi Beta Kappa. Clubs: Ekwanok (Manchester, Vt.); Gulf Stream (Delray Beach, Fla.), Blind Brook (Purchase, N.Y.).

MC KAY, EMILY GANTZ, civil rights professional; b. Columbus, Ohio, Mar. 13, 1945; d. Harry S. and Edwina (Bookwalter) Gantz; BA, Stanford U., 1966, MA, 1967; m. Jack Alexander McKay, July 3, 1965. Pub. info. specialist Community Action Pitts., 1967-68, exec. asst. to manpower dir., 1968-69, rsch. assoc., 1969-70; free-lance cons., 1969-70; pub. rels. and materials specialist Metropolitan Cleve. JOBS Council, 1971-72; rsch. and mgmt. cons. BLK Group, Inc., Washington, 1970-73; dir. tech. products Am. Tech. Assistance Corp., McLean, Va., 1973-74; rsch. and mgmt. cons. CONSAD Rsch. Corp., Pitts., 1974-76, v.p. 1976-78; spl. asst. to Pres. for planning and eval. Nat. Coun. La Raza, Washington, 1978-82, v.p. rsch., advocacy and legislation, 1981-88, exec. v.p., 1983-88, cons. to the pres., 1988-90, v.p. for instl. devel., 1991-93, sr. v.p. instl. devel., 1993-94; pres. MOSAICA Ctr. for Nonprofit Devel. and Pluralism, 1994—; mem. adv. merit selection panel Superior Ct. D.C., 1987-90; cons. resource devel. New Israel Fund, 1989-91; cons. City of Cleve., Nat. Assn. Community Devel. Nat. Coun. La Raza, 1975-78, Ford Found., 1989, Nat. AIDS Network, 1988-89, Am. Cultural Ctr., Israel, 1990, Nat. Hispana Leadership Inst., 1993; vol. orgnl. cons. SHATIL, Jerusalem and community based groups in Israel, 1987—; guest faculty Union Grad. Sch.; adj. faculty Am. U., Washington, 1995—. Author: numerous tng. nonprofit orgn. devel. materials. Cochmn. Citizens Adv. Com. to D.C. Bar, 1986-87; mem. Mayor's Commn. Coop. Econ. Devel., 1981-83; non-lawyer mem. bd. govs. D.C. Bar, 1982-85; exec. com., bd. dirs Indochina Resource Action Ctr., 1982-92; bd. dirs Southeast Asia Resource Action Ctr., 1993—; co-chmn. Citizens Commn. Adminstrn. Justice, 1982-84; mem. exec. com. Coalition on Human Needs, 1981-88; mem. Washington area steering com. New Israel Fund, 1989-91; co-chmn. adv. com. to Washington dist. office dir. Immigration and Naturalization Svc., 1984-88; chair Refugee Women in Devel., 1987-90, vice chair, 1990-94; mem. nat. adv. bd. Project Blueprint United Way Am., 1992-94, mem. diversity com., 1994—; vice chair Fund for the Future of Our Children, 1994—; bd. advisors Internat. Ctr. for Residential Edn., 1994—; treas. bd. dir. Mary's Ctr. for Maternal and Child Care, 1995—. Ford Found. nat. honors fellow, 1966-67; recipient I. Pat Rios award Guadalupe Ctr., 1988; mem. working group Memorandum of Understanding between HHS and Israeli Ministry of Labour and Social Welfare, 1990-94, chairperson subcom. Youth at Risk, 1992-94. Mem. NAACP, Women in Communications, Phi Beta Kappa. Democrat. Home: 3200 19th St NW Washington DC 20010-1006 Office: 1735 I St NW Ste 501 Washington DC 20006-2400

MCKAY, EUGENE HENRY, JR., food company executive; b. Battle Creek, Mich., June 25, 1929; s. Eugene Henry and Ella Florence (Everest) McK.; m. Beverly June Blakeman, Nov. 6, 1951 (div. 1981); children: Eugene, John Blakeman, Heather Melinda, Henry III; m. Janice Lee Rook, 1989. BA, Mich. State U., 1951. Prodn. mgr. Battle Creek Food Co., 1955-60; franchise mgr. Archway Cookies, Inc., 1960-65, v.p., 1965-75, exec. v.p., 1975-85, pres., ptnr., 1985—. Maj. U.S. Army, 1951-54. Republican. Presbyterian. Office: Archway Cookies Inc 5451 W Dickman Rd Battle Creek MI 49015-1080

MCKAY, JACK ALEXANDER, electronics engineer, physicist; b. Alhambra, Calif., Apr. 3, 1942; s. Gordon Alexander and Helen Leona (Lappin) McK.; m. Emily Gantz, July 3, 1965. BS in Physics, Stanford U., 1964, MSEE, 1967; MS in Physics, Carnegie-Mellon U., 1969, PhD in Physics, 1974. Rsch. physicist Naval Rsch. Lab., Washington, 1974-84; rsch. scientist Phys. Scis. Inc., Alexandria, Va., 1984-91; scientist Rsch. Support Instruments, Hunt Valley, Md., 1991—. Home: 3200 19th St NW Washington DC 20010-1006 Office: Rsch Support Instruments 318 Clubhouse Lane Hunt Valley MD 21031

MC KAY, JIM, television sports commentator; b. Phila., Sept. 24, 1921; s. Joseph F. and Florence (Gallagher) McManus; m. Margaret Dempsey, Oct. 2, 1948; children: Mary Edwina, Sean Joseph. A.B., Loyola Coll., Balt., 1943, HLD (hon.), 1981. Reporter Balt. Evening Sun, 1946-47; news and sports commentator sta. WMAR- TV, Balt., 1947-50; sports commentator CBS Network, 1950-61; host This is New York, 1958-59; sports commentator for Winter and Summer Olympics, 1960-88; host ABC Wide World of Sports, from 1961; now commentator ABC Sports; chmn. "Maryland Million" Horse Racing Program, 1986—. Author: My Wide World, 1973. Served to lt. USNR, 1943-46. Decorated Officer's Cross Order of Merit (Fed. Republic Germany), 1974; recipient 12 Emmy awards, George Polk Meml. award, 1973, Olympic medal Austria, 1977, Engelhard award Thoroughbred Breeders of Ky., 1978, 90, Humphrey S. Finney award Md. Racing Writers, 1985, Nat. Turf Writers award, 1987, Peabody Award, 1989; named to Sportscasters Hall of Fame, 1987, U.S. Olympic Hall of Fame, 1989. Clubs: Jockey, Balt. Country, Md. Club, Hamilton St., Pinetree (Fla.) Golf Club. Avocations: raising and breeding race horses. Office: ABC Sports 47 W 66th St New York NY 10023

MCKAY, JOHN, lawyer; b. Seattle, June 19, 1956; s. John Larkin and Kathleen (Tierney) M. BA, U. Wash., 1978; JD, Creighton U., 1982. Bar: Wash. 1982, U.S. Dist. Ct. (we. dist.) Wash. 1982, U.S. Supreme Ct. 1990, U.S. Ct. Appeals (9th cir.) 1990. Ptnr. Lane Powell Spears Lubersky, Seattle, 1982-92, Cairncross & Hempelmann, Seattle, 1992—. White House fellow, Washington, 1989-90. Mem. ABA (bd. govs. 1991-94), Wash. State Bar Assn. (pres. young lawyers divsn. 1988-89). Republican. Roman Catholic. Avocations: soccer, golf. Office: Cairncross & Hempelmann 701 5th Ave Ste 7000 Seattle WA 98104-7009

MCKAY, JOHN A., mining equipment manufacturing executive; b. New Castle, Pa., Nov. 10, 1933; s. Archie G. and Gladys M. (Slater) McK.; m. Sara K. Mikels; children: Mark, Jeffrey, Patricia. BSBA, Youngstown U., 1956; grad., Kent State U.; postgrad., Stanford U., 1977. With B.F. Goodrich Co., Akron, Ohio, 1956-80, pres. engring. systems div., 1976-78, sr. v.p. engineered products group, 1978-80, v.p., 1978-80; exec. v.p. McNeil Corp., Akron, 1980-86, also bd. dirs.; pres. Beloit (Wis.) Corp., 1986-92, CEO, 1992—; pres. Harnischfeger Ind., Brookfield, Wis., 1992—; bd. dirs Beloit Corp., 1st Nat. Bank & Trust Co., Beloit, Sandusky Foundry, Ohio. Bd. dirs. U. Maine, Pulp and Paper Found., 1988—. Mem. Paper Industry Mgmt. Assn., TAPPI, Coated and Processed Paper Assn. Republican.

Avocations: golf, fishing. Office: Harnischfeger Ind 13400 Bishops Ln Brookfield WI 53005

MCKAY, KENNETH GARDINER, physicist, electronics company executive; b. Montreal, Que., Can., Apr. 8, 1917; came to U.S., 1946, naturalized, 1954; s. James Gardiner and Margaret (Nicholas) McK.; m. Irene C. Smith, July 25, 1942; children—Margaret Craig, Kenneth Gardiner. B.Sc., McGill U., 1938, M.Sc., 1939; Sc.D, MIT, 1941; D.Eng. (hon.), Stevens Inst. Tech., 1980. Research engr. Nat. Research Council Can., 1941-46; with Bell Telephone Labs., 1946-66, 73-80, dir. solid state device devel., 1957-59, v.p. systems engring., 1959-62, exec. v.p. systems engring., 1962-66, exec. v.p., 1973-80; v.p. engring AT&T, 1966-73; chmn. bd. Bellcomm Inc., 1966-73, Charles Stark Draper Lab., 1982-87; advisor Ministry of Transp. and Comms., Republic of China, 1982—. Trustee Stevens Inst. Tech., 1974-87; bd. govs. McGill U., 1972-77, N.Y. Coll. Osteo. Medicine, 1980-89; mem. vis. com. for engring. Stanford U., 1974-87; mem. sci. and acad. adv. com. U. Calif., 1980-88; mem. Sci. and Tech. Adv. Group, Republic of China, 1982—. Fellow IEEE, Am. Phys. Soc., N.Y. Acad. Scis.; mem. NAS, NAE (councillor 1970-73), Century Assn. Home and Office: 5 Carolina Meadows # 206 Chapel Hill NC 27514-8522

MCKAY, LAURA L., banker, consultant; b. Watonga, Okla., Mar. 3, 1947; d. Frank Bradford and Elizabeth Jane (Smith) Drew; m. Cecil O. McKay, Sept. 20, 1969; 1 child, Leslie. BSBA, Oreg. State U., 1969. New br. research U.S. Bank, Portland, Oreg., 1969-80; cash mgmt. officer U.S. Bank, Portland, 1980-82, asst. v.p., 1982-87, v.p., 1987-94; founder, cons. LLM Cons., Milw., 1994—. Chmn. Budget Com., North Clackamas Sch. Dist., 1982-84. Mem. Nat. Cash Mgrs. Assn., Nat. Assn. Bank Women (chmn. Oreg. group 1979-80), Portland Cash Mgrs. Assn., Portland C. of C. Republican. Office: LLM Cons 5686 SE Viewcrest Milwaukie OR 97267

MCKAY, MICHAEL DENNIS, lawyer; b. Omaha, May 12, 1951; s. John Larkin and Kathleen (Tierney) McK.; m. Christy Ann Cordwin, Apr. 22, 1978; children: Kevin Tierney, Kathleen Lindsay, John Larkin. BA in Polit. Sci. with distinction, U. Wash., 1973; JD, Creighton U., 1976. Bar: Wash. 1976, U.S. Dist. Ct. (we. dist.) Wash. 1978, U.S. Dist. Ct. (ea. dist.) Wash. 1982, U.S. Ct. Appeals (9th cir.) 1982, U.S. Supreme Ct. 1993. Sr. dep. pros. atty. King County, Seattle, 1976-81; ptnr. McKay & Gaitan, Seattle, 1981-89; U.S. atty. we. dist. Wash. Seattle, 1989-93; ptnr. Lane Powell Spears Lubersky, Seattle, 1993-95, McKay, Chadwell & Matthews PLLC, Seattle, 1995—. Bd. dirs. Mental Health North, Seattle, 1982-85, St. Joseph Sch. Bd., 1984-87, Our Lady of Fatima Sch. Commn., 1994—, Creighton U., 1988-90; mem. stadium adv. bd. Seattle Kingdome, 1987-89; state vice chmn. George Bush for Pres., 1988; mem. U.S. Atty. Gen. Adv. Com., 1991-93, vice chmn., 1992. Mem. Creighton U. Alumni Assn. (pres. 1988-90, nat. alumni bd. 1988-92), Wash. Athletic Club, Columbia Tower Club. Republican. Roman Catholic. Avocations: tennis, running, swimming. Office: McKay Chadwell & Matthews 7201 Columbia Ctr Seattle WA 98104

MCKAY, MONROE GUNN, federal judge; b. Huntsville, Utah, May 30, 1928; s. James Gunn and Elizabeth (Peterson) McK.; m. Lucile A. Kinnison, Aug. 6, 1954; children: Michele, Valanne, Margaret, James, Melanie, Nathan, Bruce, Lisa, Monroe. B.S., Brigham Young U., 1957; J.D., U. Chgo., 1960. Bar: Ariz. 1961. Law clk. Ariz. Supreme Ct., 1960-61; assoc. firm Lewis & Roca, Phoenix, 1961-66; ptnr. Lewis & Roca, 1968-74; assoc. prof. Brigham Young U., 1974-76, prof., 1976-77; judge U.S. Ct. of Appeals (10th cir.), Denver, 1977—, chief judge, 1991—. Mem. Phoenix Community Council Juvenile Problems, 1968-74; pres. Ariz. Assn. for Health and Welfare, 1970-72; dir. Peace Corps, Malawi, Africa, 1966-68; bd. dirs., pres. Maricopa county Legal Aid Soc., 1972-74. Served with USMCR, 1946-48. Mem. ABA, Ariz. Bar Assn., Maricopa County Bar Assn., Am. Law Inst., Am. Judicature Soc., Order of Coif, Blue Key, Phi Kappa Phi. Mem. Ch. Jesus Christ of Latter-day Saints. Office: US Ct Appeals 6012 Fed Bldg 125 S State St Salt Lake City UT 84138-1102*

MC KAY, NEIL, banker; b. East Tawas, Mich., Aug. 9, 1917; s. Lloyd G. and Rose (McDonald) McK.; m. Olive D. Baird, Nov. 11, 1950; children: Julia B., Lynn B., Hunter L. A.B., U. Mich., 1939, J.D. with distinction, 1946. Bar: Mich. 1946, Ill. 1947. With firm Winston & Strawn, Chgo., 1946-63; partner Winston & Strawn, 1964-64, mem. mgmt. com., 1958-63; with First Nat. Bank of Chgo., 1963-83, from v.p. charge heavy industry lending div., gen. mgr. London br., to exec. v.p., cashier, 1970-75, vice chmn. bd., 1976-83, also dir.; exec. v.p., sec. First Chgo. Corp., 1970-75, vice chmn. bd., 1976-83; also bd. dirs.; bd. dirs. Baird & Warner, Inc., Chgo.; founding dir. Student Loan Mktg. Assn. Mem.: U. Mich. Law Rev; assoc. editor-in-chief: U. Mich. Law Rev., 1942, sr. editor, 1946. Trustee Morton Arboretum; former trustee Kalamazoo Coll. and Ill. Inst. Tech. Served with USNR, 1942-46. Mem. ABA, Ill. Bar Assn., Chgo. Bar Assn., Order of Coif, Dunham Woods Riding Club, CHgo. Hort. Soc. (sec., bd. dirs.) Clubs: Chicago (Chgo.), Mid-Day (Chgo.); Geneva Golf. Office: One First Nat Plz First National Plz Rm 2538 Chicago IL 60603

MC KAY, ROBERT JAMES, JR., pediatrician, educator; b. N.Y.C., Oct. 8, 1917; s. Robert James and Mary (Montgomery) McK.; m. Elizabeth Stewardson Foote, May 30, 1943; children: Robert James III, David Montgomery, Daniel Graham, Timothy Foote. Grad., Lawrenceville (N.J.) Sch., 1934; A.B., Princeton U., 1939; M.D., Harvard U., 1943. Intern Columbia-Presbyn. Med. Center, N.Y.C., 1943; asst. resident Columbia-Presbyn. Med. Center, 1947; chief resident Childrens Hosp. Med. Center, Boston, 1948; Milton fellow pharmacology Harvard Med. Sch., 1949; asst. prof. dept. pediatrics U. Vt. Coll. of Medicine, 1950-52, asso. prof., 1952-55, prof., 1955-87, prof. emeritus, 1987—, chmn. dept. 1950-83; Fulbright lectr. U. Groningen, Netherlands, 1960. Contbr. articles to profl. jours. Served from 1st lt. to capt. M.C. AUS, 1944-46. Decorated Bronze Star medal; recipient Jaycee Distinguished Service award, 1953; John and Mary Markle Found. scholar in med. sci., 1950-55. Mem. AMA, Am. Acad. Pediatrics (pres. 1971), Soc. for Pediatric Research, Am. Soc. Human Genetics, Am. Pediatric Soc., New Eng. Pediatric Soc. (pres. 1966), Can. Pediatric Soc., Ambulatory Pediatric Assn., Soc. Behavioral Pediatrics, Sigma Xi, Alpha Omega Alpha. Home: 99 Sunset Hill Rd Williston VT 05495-9614

MC KAY, SAMUEL LEROY, clergyman; b. Charlotte, N.C., Oct. 15, 1913; s. Elmer Ranson and Arlena (Benfield) McK.; A.B. cum laude, Erskine Coll., 1937; B.D. cum laude, Erskine Theol. Sem., 1939; postgrad. U. Ga., 1941-42, Union Theol. Sem., 1957; m. Martha Elizabeth Caldwell, Apr. 29, 1939; children: Samuel LeRoy, Mary Louise, William Ranson. Ordained to ministry of Presbyn. Ch., 1940; pastor Prosperity Assoc. Ref. Ch., Fayetteville, Tenn., 1942-46, Bethel Assoc. Ref. Ch., Oak Hill, Ala., 1946-50, 1st Asso. Ref. Ch., Salisbury, N.C., 1950-53, 1st Ch. U.S., Dallas, N.C., 1953-60, First Ch., Kernersville, N.C., 1960-66, Cooleemee (N.C.) Presbyn. Ch., 1966-69, Broadway (N.C.) Presbyn. Ch., 1969-80; Cape Fear Presbyn. Ch., 1983-91, Sardis Presbyn. Ch., 1984-86; stated clk. Gen. Synod Assoc. Ref. Presbyn. Ch., 1950-53; commr. Gen. Assembly Presbyn. Ch. U.S., 1960, 69; permanent clk. Winston-Salem Presbytery, 1961-69, chmn. leadership edn. com., 1964-69, chmn. Christian edn. com., 1967-68; chmn. nominations com. Fayetteville Presbytery, 1977-79; mem. hunger task force Fayetteville Presbytery, 1984-88, chmn. com. on Bangladesh, 1985-87; supr. chaplaincy program Davie County Hosp., 1968-69. Pres. Dallas PTA, 1955-56; bd. mgrs. Kernersville YMCA, 1962-66, chmn. membership com., 1963, treas., 1964, pres., 1965-66; bd. dirs. Winston-Salem-Forsyth County YMCA, 1965-66. Mem. Kernersville Area Ministers Assn. (pres. 1963-64), N.C. Poetry Soc. (dir. 1971—, chmn. poetry contests 1970-72, 83-88, editor ann. book Award-Winning Poems 1970-90; pres. 1971-74), Clan MacKay Soc. N.Am. (pres. 1971-75, chaplain 1976-90—; coun. 1983-90, honored guest, prin. speaker 1985 internat. gathering Glasgow, Scotland 1985, speaker at Clan Mackay Soc. Centenary Celebration, Edinburgh, Scotland, 1988, elected hon. mem. 1988, keynote speaker at meeting, Atlanta 1994). Lodge: Lions. Author: (poems) Harbinger, 1992; contbr. articles and sermons to periodicals and publs. Perhaps the first thing to mark one's breeding is respect for the person of others and courtesy in matters of disagreement.

MC KAY, THOMAS, JR., lawyer; b. Kearny, N.J., Sept. 26, 1920; s. Thomas and Mary (Paterson) McK.; m. Rosemary T. LaMarra, Oct. 5, 1946; children—Thomas III, Barbara Anne, Robert Michael. A.B., Rutgers U., 1941; LL.B., N.Y. U., 1944. Bar: N.J. 1945, Ill. 1967. Assoc. to Arthur T. Vanderbilt, 1944-47; assoc. firm Toner, Speakman & Crowley, Newark,

1947-50; with McGraw-Edison Co. (and predecessor), 1950-80, sec., gen. counsel, 1967-80, v.p., 1973-80; v.p., gen. counsel, sec. Swift Ind. Corp., Chgo., 1980-84; of counsel Boodell Sears Giambalvo & Crowley, Chgo., 1984-87; securities industry arbitrator pub., 1988—. Vol. legal aid atty. Prairie State Legal Svcs., Inc., St. Charles, Ill., 1987—. Mem. Am. Arbitration Assn. (comml. and securities law arbitrator). Home: 1435 Hampton Crse Saint Charles IL 60174-1319

MC KAYLE, DONALD COHEN, choreographer, director, writer, dance educator; b. N.Y.C., July 6, 1930; s. Philip Augustus and Eva Wilhelmina (Cohen) McK.; m. Esta Beck, 1954; m. Leah Levin, 1965; children—Gabrielle, Liane, Guy Eylon. Student, CCNY. mem. faculty Bennington Coll., Sarah Lawrence Coll., Conn. Coll., Bard Coll., Neighborhood Playhouse, Juilliard Sch., Martha Graham Sch., Am. Dance Festival; artistic dir., dean Calif. Inst. Arts Sch. of Dance; prof. dance, artistic dir. U. Calif., Irvine. Dancing debut, 1948; dir., 1964—; choreographer, 1950—, for cos. including, Alvin Ailey Am. Dance Theater, Batsheva Dance Co. Israel, Repertory Dance Theater, San Francisco Ballet, Cleve. San Jose Ballet, Dayton Comtemporary Dance Co., Cleo Parker Robinson Dance Ensemble; dir., choreographer stage prodns.: Free and Easy, 1961, Trumpets of the Lord, 1963 (Tony award nominee for best dir. and best choreographer 1975), Raisin, 1974 (Tony award nominee for best choreographer 1974), Dr. Jazz, 1975 (Tony award nominee for best choreographer 1975), The Last Minstrel Show, 1978, Evolution of the Blues, 1978-79, My Heart Belongs to Daddy, 1979, Sophisticated Ladies, 1981 (Best Choreographer award Outer Critics Cir. 1981, Tony award nominee for best choreographer 1981); choreographer stage prodns.: The Tempest, 1963-64, Anthony and Cleopatra, 1963-64, As You Like It, 1963-64, Golden Boy, 1964 (Tony award nominee for Best Choreographer, 1965), A Time for Singing, 1966, The Four Musketeers, 1967, I'm Solomon, 1968, Mass., 1972; choreographer films: The Great White Hope, 1968, Bed Knobs and Broomsticks, 1970, Charlie and the Angel, 1972, The Jazz Singer, 1980; T.V. works include: Baseball Ballet, 1963, Amahl and the Night Visitors, 1963, Fan Fare, 1965, Jazz Dance, U.S.A., 1965, The Strolling Twenties, 1965, Ten Blocks of the Camino Real, 1966, The Ed Sullivan Show, 1966-67, The Bill Cosby Special, 1967, Soul, 1968, Soul, 1968, TCB, 1968, The Second Bill Cosby Special, 1968, The Sounds of Summer, 1969, The Leslie Uggams Show, 1969, Dick Van Dyke and the Other, 1969, And Beautiful, 1969, Yesterday, Today and Tomorrow, 1970, The Super Comedy Bowl, 1971, A Funny Thing Happened on the Way to a Special, 1972, The New Bill Cosby Show, 1972-73, Angelitos Negros, 1973, Free to Be You and Me, 1974, Good Times, 1974-78, The Minstrel Man, 1977 (Emmy nominee 1977), The Richard Pryor Special, 1977, Cindy, 1978; choreographer concert works: Games, 1951, Nocturne, 1952, Rainbow Round My Shoulder, 1959, Dist. Storyville, 1962, They Called Her Moses, Incantation, 1968, Migrations, 1972, Album Leaves, 1976, Blood Memories, 1976, and numerous others, (staged club acts and TV specials for Diana Ross, Ann-Margret, Harry Belafonte, Mary Tyler Moore and others. Recipient Drama League Critics award Evolution of the Blues, Samuel H. Scripps Am. Dance Festival award, 1992, Capezio award, 1963, Lauds and Laurels profl. achievement award U. Calif. Irvine Alumni Assn., 1992, Life-time Achievement award Am. Dance Guild, 1994, Living Legend award Nat. Black Arts Festival, 1994.

MCKEACHIE, WILBERT JAMES, psychologist, educator; b. Clarkston, Mich., Aug. 24, 1921; s. Bert A. and Edith E. (Welberry) McK.; m. Virginia Mae Mack, Oct. 30, 1942; children: Linda, Karen. BA, Mich. State Normal Coll., 1942; MA, U. Mich., 1946, PhD, 1949; LLD, Ea. Mich. U., 1957, U. Cin.; ScD, Northwestern U., 1973, Denison U., 1975, Nat. Acad. Edn., 1977; DLitt (hon.), Hope Coll., 1985; LHD (hon.), Shawnee State U., 1994. Faculty U. Mich., 1946—, prof. psychology, 1961—, chmn. dept., 1961-71, dir. Center for Research in Learning and Teaching, 1975-83; mem. nat. adv. mental health council NIMH, 1976-80; mem. spl. med. adv. group VA, 1967-72. Author: (with J.E. Milholland) Undergraduate Curricula in Psychology, 1961, (with Charlotte Doyle and Mary Margaret Moffett) Psychology, 1966, 3d edit., 1977 (also Spanish edit. and instr.'s manual), Teaching Tips, 9th edit., 1994. Trustee Kalamazoo Coll., 1964-77; trustee-at-large Am. Psychol. Found., 1974-84, 92—, pres., 1979-82. Officer USNR, 1943-45. Recipient Outstanding Tchr. award U. Mich. Alumni Assn., Am. Coll. Testing-Am. Ednl. Rsch. Assn. award for outstanding rsch. on coll. students, 1973, career contbns. award, 1990, award for disting. teaching in psychology Am. Psychol. Found., 1985. Mem. Am. Psychol. Assn. (sec., dir., pres. 1976-77, Disting. Career Contbn. to Edn. and Tng. in Psychology award 1987, E.L. Thorndike award for outstanding rsch., 1988), Internat. Assn. Applied Psychology (pres. div. ednl. instrn. and sch. psychology 1982-86), Am. Assn. Higher Edn. (dir. 1974-80, pres. 1978), AAUP (pres. U. Mich. chpt. 1970-71), AAAS (chmn. sect. on psychology 1976-77), Sigma Xi. Baptist. Home: 4660 Joy Rd Dexter MI 48130 Office: U Mich Dept Psychology 525 E University Ann Arbor MI 48109-1346

MCKEAGUE, DAVID WILLIAM, district judge; b. Pitts., Nov. 5, 1946; s. Herbert William and Phyllis (Forsyth) McK.; m. Nancy L. Palmer, May 20, 1989; children: Mike, Melissa, Sarah, Laura, Elizabeth, Adam. BA, U. Mich., 1968, JD, 1971. Bar: Mich. 1971, U.S. Dist. Ct. (we. dist.) Mich. 1972, U.S. Dist. Ct. (ea. dist.) 1978, U.S. Ct. Appeals (6th cir.) 1988. Assoc. Foster, Swift, Collins & Smith, Lansing, Mich., 1971-76, ptnr., 1976-92; sec.-treas. Foster, Swift, Collins & Smith, 1990-92; judge U.S. Dist. Ct., Western Dist. Mich., Lansing, 1992—. Mem. nat. com. U. Mich. Law Sch. Fund; 1980-92; bd. dirs. Impression 5 Mus., 1985-92; gen. counsel Mich. Rep. State Com., 1989-92. Mem. Mich. Bar Assn., Ingham County Bar Assn., Fed. Bar Assn. (Western Mich. chpt., bd. dirs. 1991—), Lansing County Club (dir. 1988-92). Roman Catholic. Office: US Dist Ct 315 W Allegan St Lansing MI 48933

MCKEAN, HENRY P., mathematics institute administrator; b. Wenham, Mass., Dec. 14, 1930. AB, Dartmouth Coll., 1952; PhD, Princeton U., 1955. Instr. Princeton (N.J.) U., 1955-57; instr. MIT, Cambridge, 1958-63, prof., 1964-66; prof. Rockefeller U., N.Y.C., 1966-70, dep. dir., chmn. dept. math., 1984-88; prof. Courant Inst. Math. Scis. NYU, 1970—, dir., 1988—; vis. prof. Kyoto U., 1957-58, Rockefeller U., 1963-64; George Eastman prof. Balliol Coll., Oxford U., 1979-80. Contbr. numerous articles to profl. jours. Mem. NAS, Am. Acad. Arts and Scis. Office: NYU Courant Inst Math Scis 251 Mercer St New York NY 10012-1185

MC KEAN, HUGH FERGUSON, college president, painter, writer; b. Beaver Falls, Pa., July 28, 1908; s. Arthur and Eleanor (Ferguson) McK.; m. Jeannette Genius, June 28, 1945. A.B., Rollins Coll., 1930; M.A., Williams Coll., 1940; Dr. Space Edn., Fla. Inst. Tech., 1963; L.H.D., Stetson U. Coll. Law, 1961; L.L.D., U. Tampa, 1970; D.F.A., Rollins Coll., 1972. Instr. art Rollins Coll., Winter Park, Fla., 1932-35; asst. prof. Rollins Coll., 1935-37, asst. prof., asst. to dir. dept. art, 1937-41, assoc. prof., 1941-45, prof. art, dir. Charles Hosmer Morse Mus. Am. Art, 1942—, acting pres., 1951-52, pres., 1952-69, now pres. emeritus, chancellor, 1969-73; chmn. bd. pres. Charles Hosmer Morse Found., 1976—; mem. Fla. Fine Arts Coun., 1970-74; pres. Winter Park Land Co. Author: The 'Lost' Treasures of Louis Comfort Tiffany, 1980; works exhibited, Second Nat. Exhbn. Am. Painting, N.Y., Soc. The Four Arts, Palm Beach, Fla., 1948, Allied Artists Am. Ann Exhbn., 1949, 4th Southeastern Ann., Atlanta, 1949, numerous ann. exhbns., Fla. Fedn. Art, collections, Tol. Mus. Art U. Va. Trustee Louis Comfort Tiffany Found., 1959—; charter pres. Channel 24 ETV, Orlando, Fla.; bd. visitors Def. Intelligence Sch., 1968-78. Lt. comdr. USNR, 1942-45. Recipient Decoration Honor Rollins Coll., 1942; Cervantes medal Hispanic Inst. in Fla., 1952; John Young award Orlando Area C. of C., 1967; best work in show Fla. Fedn. Art Ann. Exhbn., 1931, 49; best Fla. landscape, 1949. Mem. Am. Soc. Order St. John, Nat. Soccer Coaches Am., Omicron Delta Kappa. Clubs: X, Century Assn. (N.Y.C.); Orlando (Fla.) Country; University (N.Y.C.); University (Winter Park). Home: 930 Genius Dr Winter Park FL 32789-5120

MC KEAN, JOHN ROSSEEL OVERTON, university dean; b. Cortland, N.Y., July 31, 1928; s. Norman Dodge and Janet (Passage) McK.; m. Ruth MacDonald, July 2, 1955; children: Janet, Annalise. B.A., Coll. William and Mary, 1951; M.Ed., Cornell U., 1956, Ed.D., 1961. Tchr. Landon Sch. for Boys, Washington, 1952-53; tchr. Central Sch., Homer, N.Y., 1953-55; asst. prof. history, dean students Allegheny Coll., 1957-67; headmaster Kingswood Sch. for Girls, Cranbrook, Bloomfield Hills, Mich., 1967-68; dean Hobart Coll., 1968-73; v.p. Coll. Kenyon Coll., Gambier, Ohio, 1973-77;

dean arts and scis. State U. N.Y. at Canton, 1977-92. Mem. SUNY Council Deans Arts and Scis., Nat. Assn. Student Personnel Adminstrs. (pres. Pa. 1958-59), SUNY Council Two-Yr. Bus. Adminstrs., Nat. Assn. Student Personnel Adminstrs. (dir. 1959-61), Am. Assn. Higher Edn., Community Coll. Gen. Edn. Assn., Middle States Assn. Colls. and Secondary Schs., Direct Descs. Signers Declaration Independence (v.p. Va.), St. Lawrence County Hist. Soc., Geneva Concerts Assn. (dir. 1969-72), Am. Hist. Assn., Round Table, English-Speaking Union, Phi Delta Kappa, Kappa Sigma. Club: Rotarian. Home: 1184 Jamestown Rd Unit 46 Williamstown VA 23185

MC KEAN, KEITH FERGUSON, former education educator; b. Beaver Falls, Pa., Aug. 18, 1915; s. Arthur and Eleanor (Ferguson) McK.; m. Catherine Stevenson, Oct. 31, 1942 (div. 1965); children—Kevin, Bruce; m. Joan Sanford Canter, Sept. 26, 1969. AB, Williams Coll., 1938; MA, U. Chgo., 1940; Ph.D. (Rackham fellow), U. Mich., 1950. Instr. U. Toledo, 1940-42; prof. N.C. State U., 1949-62, Elmira Coll., 1961-68; prof. U. No. Iowa, Cedar Falls, 1968-80, prof. emeritus, 1980—; lectr. Morse Mus. Am. Art, 1981—. Author: Cross Currents in the South, 1960, The Moral Measure of Literature, 1961, Critical Approaches to Fiction, 1968, Informative and Persuasive Prose, 1971. bd. dirs. Winter Pk. Libr., 1982-86, Friends of Orlando Libr., 1987-90, Winter Park Hist. Assn., 1993-95; mem. evaluation com. Orlando Human Svcs. Coun., 1989-91. 1st lt. USAAF, 1942-46. Ford Faculty fellow for postdoctoral study, 1954-55. Mem. AAUP, Univ. Club of Winter Park, Delta Kappa Epsilon. Home: 1010 Bonita Dr Winter Park FL 32789-2724 *I am deeply impressed with the part that plain chance plays in one's success or failure. Everything I have achieved that is really desirable was, in large measure, an accident of such things as time or place. Indeed, I might have accomplished far less than I actually have or far more—depending on factors over which I had no control. We are all created equal, in one sense, because all men are created equally dependent on blind chance, and a full realization of this fact can temper foolish pride and guard against excessive self-abasement.*

MC KEAN, MICHAEL, actor; b. N.Y.C., Oct. 17, 1947; s. Gilbert and Ruth McKean; m. Susan McKean; children: Colin Russell, Fletcher. Student, Carnegie Inst. Tech., NYU. Toured with satirical comedy group The Credibility Gap; TV appearances include The Goodtime Girls, More Than Friends, American Bandstand, The TV Show ; regular on ABC-TV series Laverne and Shirley, 1976-83, Grand, 1989, Dream On, 1990—, Sessions, 1991, Spinal Tap Anniversary Spl., 1992, Saturday Night Live, 1994—; actor: (films) 1941, 1979, Used Cars, 1980, Young Doctors in Love, 1982, This is Spinal Tap, 1984, Clue, 1985, D.A.R.Y.L., 1985, Jumpin Jack Flash, 1986, Light of Day, 1987, Planes, Trains, & Automobiles, 1987, Short Circuit II, 1988, Earth Girls Are Easy, 1989, Flashback, 1989, The Big Picture, 1989, Book of Love, 1991, True Identity, 1991, Memoirs of an Invisible Man, 1992, Man Trouble, 1992, Mojo Flats, 1993, Coneheads, 1993, Airheads, 1994, Radioland Murders, 1994, The Brady Bunch Movie, 1995; (Broadway) Accomplice, 1989, (TV movies) More Than Friends, 1978, Classified Love, 1986, Murder in High Places, 1991; rec. artist: (with David Lander) Lenny and the Squiggtones, This is Spinal Tap. Office: care William Morris Agy 151 El Camino Beverly Hills CA 90211

MCKEAN, ROBERT JACKSON, JR., retired lawyer; b. N.Y.C., Dec. 21, 1925; s. Robert Jackson and Isabel (Murphy) McK.; m. Sally H. Ament; children from previous marriage: Katherine, Douglas, Lauren, Andrew. B.A., Amherst Coll., 1950; LL.B., Harvard U., 1953. Bar: N.Y. 1954. Assoc. Simpson Thacher & Bartlett, N.Y.C., 1953-62, ptnr., 1962-85; pres. Nat. Bldg. Mus., Washington, 1986. Trustee Amherst Coll., Mass., Folger Shakespeare Library, Washington. Served with U.S. Army, 1944-46, ETO. Recipient medal for eminent service Amherst Coll., 1968. Mem. Phi Beta Kappa. Democrat.

MCKEAN, THOMAS WAYNE, dentist, retired naval officer; b. Adams County, Ind., May 18, 1928; s. Gorman F. and Elmira B. (Staley) McK.; m. Marilyn Kimberlin, Aug. 9, 1952; children: Thomas Wayne, Randall K., Dana K. D.D.S., Ind. U., 1953; grad., Naval Dental Sch., 1963. Diplomate: Am. Bd. Oral Surgery. Commd. ensign Dental Corps USN, 1949, advanced through grades to rear adm., 1980; stationed at Naval Tng. Ctr., Great Lakes, Ill., 1953; dental officer U.S.S. Randall, 1953-56; head dental svc., asst. dental officer U.S. Naval Acad./Naval Hosp., Annapolis, Md., 1956-59; dental officer FASRON III; asst. dental officer U.S. Naval Sta., Bermuda, 1959-63; postgrad. student Naval Dental Sch., Bethesda, Md., 1963-64; resident oral and maxillofacial surgery Naval Hosp., Great Lakes, Ill., 1964-66; dental officer U.S.S America, 1966-68; chief oral surgery Naval Hosp., Orlando, Fla., 1968-70; dir. oral surgery and gen. practice residency tng. programs Naval Regional Med. Ctr., Great Lakes, 1970-74, chmn. dept. dentistry, 1970-74; cons., lectr. U.S. Army, Fort Sheridan, Ill., 1970-74; dir. oral surgery and gen. practice residency tng. programs Naval Regional Med. Ctr., Oakland, Calif., 1974-78; chmn., dept. dentistry Naval Regional Med. Ctr., 1974-78; lectr. oral surgery Letterman Army Med. Ctr., San Francisco, 1974-78; clin. lectr. dept. oral surgery U. of Pacific Sch. Dentistry, San Francisco, 1974-78; comdg. officer Naval Regional Dental Ctr., Pensacola, Fla., 1978-80; lectr. oral surgery Pensacola (Fla.) Jr. Coll., 1978-80; cons., lectr. Dwight D. Eisenhower Army Regional Med. Ctr., Augusta, Ga., 1978-80; insp. gen. dental Bur. Medicine and Surgery, Dept. of Navy, Washington, 1980-81; comdg. officer Naval Regional Dental Ctr., San Diego, 1981-82; insp. gen. Naval Med. Command, Washington, 1983-85; ret. USN, 1985. Contbr. articles to profl. jours. Chmn. bd. trustees UMC, Winter Park, 1992; bd. dirs. Circle of Friends Fla. Hosp. Found., 1989-91, Fla. Hosp. Found., 1991—, chmn. bd., 1993-94. Decorated Humanitarian Service medal, Legion of Merit with Gold Star, Meritorious Service medal, Nat. Def. Service medal with star, Vietnam Service medal, Republic of Vietnam Campaign medal with device, others; recipient Alumnus of Yr. award Ind. U. Sch.of Dentistry Alumnus Assn., 1988. Fellow Am. Dental Soc. of Anesthesiology, Internat. Coll. Dentists, Am. Coll. Dentists, Internat. Assn. Oral Surgeons; mem. Am. Assn. Oral and Maxillofacial Surgeons, ADA, Western Soc. Oral Surgeons, Assn. Mil. Surgeons U.S. (medal), Fla. Soc. Oral Surgeons, Delta Sigma Delta, Sigma Chi (Significant Sig award 1983). Home: 1309 Temple Grove Ct Winter Park FL 32789-2716

MCKEE, ALAN REEL, foreign service officer; b. Des Moines, May 23, 1943; s. T. Bonar and Lois Ellen (Reel) McK.; m. Martha Berry, July 16, 1966; children: Alexander, Amanda. BA, Dartmouth Coll., 1964; MA, Tufts U., 1968, MA in Law and Diplomacy, 1969. Country officer for Nigeria Dept. of State, 1972-73, mem. secretariat staff, 1974-75, country officer Norway & Denmark Office No. European Affairs, 1983-85, dep. dir. Office So. African Affairs, 1989-91, dir. Office West African Anglophone & Lusophone Affairs, 1991-93; chief polit.-econ. sect. Am. Embassy, Dakar, Senegal, 1975-78; polit. officer Am. Embassy, Ottawa, Can., 1978-82; congl. fellow Office of Senator Edward M. Kennedy, 1982-83; polit. counselor U.S. Embassy, The Hague, The Netherlands, 1985-89; U.S. consul gen. Johannesburg, South Africa, 1993—; rsch. intern U.S. AID, Accra, Ghana, 1968. Participant Operation Crossroads Africa, Zimbabwe, 1962. Capt. U.S. Army, 1964-67, Vietnam. Decorated Bronze Star. Mem. Am. Fgn. Svc. Assn., Johannesburg South Rotary (hon.). Home: 6611 River Rd, Bethesda. South Africa Office: US Consulate Gen, PO Box 2155, Johannesburg 2000, South Africa

MCKEE, CHRISTOPHER FULTON, astrophysics and astronomy educator; b. Washington, Sept. 6, 1942; m. Suzanne P. McKee; 3 children. AB in Physics summa cum laude, Harvard U., 1963; PhD in Physics, U. Calif., Berkeley, 1970. Physicist Lawrence Livermore (Calif.) Labs., 1969-70, cons., 1970—; rsch. fellow in astrophysics Calif. Inst. Tech., Pasadena, 1970-71; asst. prof. astronomy Harvard U., Cambridge, 1971-74; asst. prof. physics and astronomy U. Calif., Berkeley, 1974-77, assoc. prof., 1977-78, prof., 1978—, Miller Rsch. prof., 1984-85; assoc. dir. Space Scis. Lab. Berkeley, 1978-83, acting dir., 1983-84, dir., 1985—; dir. Theoretical Astrophysics Ctr. Berkeley, 1985. Fannie and John Hertz Found. fellow, 1963-69; Sherman Fairchild Disting. scholar, 1981, Nat. Acad. Scis., 1992. Fellow Am. Phys. Soc. (exec. com. astrophysics div. 1986-88); mem. Am. Astron. Soc. (councillor 1981-84), Internat. Astron. Union, Phi Beta Kappa. Office: U Calif Dept Physics Space Sciences Lab Berkeley CA 94720

MCKEE, CHRISTOPHER FULTON, librarian, naval historian, educator; b. Bklyn., June 14, 1935; s. William Ralph and Frances (Manning) M.; m. Ann Adamczyk, 1993; children: Sharon, David. B. AB, U. St. Thomas,

Houston, 1957; AMLS, U. Mich., 1960. Catalogue libr. Washington and Lee U., Lexington, Va., 1958-62; social sci. libr. So. Ill. U., Edwardsville, 1962-66; book selection officer So. Ill. U., 1967-69, asst. dir., 1969-72; libr. of coll. Grinnell Coll., Iowa, 1972—; Samuel R. and Marie-Louise Rosenthal prof.; Sec. of Navy rsch. chair in naval history Naval Hist. Ctr., Washington, 1990-91; trustee Bibliog. Ctr. Rsch., Denver, 1984-88. Author: Edward Preble, 1972, A Gentlemanly and Honorable Profession: The Creation of the U.S. Naval Officer Corps, 1794-1815, 1991. NEH-Newberry Libr. fellow, 1978-79; recipient U.S. Naval History prize for best pub. article, 1985, John Lyman book award N.Am. Soc. Oceanic History, 1991, Samuel Eliot Morison Disting. Svc. award USS Constitution Mus., Boston, 1992. Mem. Am. Hist. Assn., Navy Records Soc., Soc. for Mil. History, Orgn. Am. Historians. Soc. Historians of Early Republic, U.S. Naval Inst. Home: PO Box 272 Grinnell IA 50112-0272 Office: Grinnell Coll Burling Libr PO Box 805 Grinnell IA 50112-0811

MC KEE, FRAN, retired naval officer; b. Florence, Ala., Sept. 13, 1926; d. Thomas W. and Geneva (Lumpkins) McK. BS, U. Ala., 1950; postgrad., Gen. Line Sch., Postgrad. Sch. USN, Monterey, Calif., 1957; MS in Internat. Affairs, George Washington U., 1970, Naval War Coll., 1970; D. in Pub.Adminstrn. (hon.), Mass. Maritime Acad., 1978. Commd. ensign USN, 1950, advanced through grades to rear adm., 1976; service in various U.S. locations and in Morocco and Spain; dep. asst. chief for human goals (Bur. Naval Personnel), 1972-73; comdg. officer Naval Security Group Activity Ft. Meade, Md., 1973-76; dir. naval enlist. devel. Staff of Chief Naval Edn. and Tng. Naval Air Sta., Pensacola, Fla., 1976-78; dir. human resource mgmt. div. Office Chief of Naval Ops., Navy Dept. Washington, 1978-81; ret., 1981. Mem. Nat. Com. Armed Svcs. YMCA of U.S.A., 1981-83; VA Women's Adv. Com. for Vets.' Affairs, 1988-91; mem. Nat. Adv. Com. for Women in Mil. Svc. Meml. Found., 1988—. Decorated Legion of Merit with gold star, Meritorious Svc. medal; recipient DAR Medal of Honor, 1982, Nat. Vets. award, 1993; elected to Ala. Acad. Honor, 1979; first woman line officer in USN promoted to flag rank, 1976, first woman naval officer promoted to rear adm. Episcopalian. Home: 7420 Adams Park Ct Annandale VA 22003-5722

MC KEE, GEORGE MOFFITT, JR., civil engineer, consultant; b. Valparaiso, Nebr., Mar. 27, 1924; s. George Moffitt and Iva (Santrock) McK.; student Kans. State Coll. Agr. and Applied Sci., 1942-43, Bowling Green State U., 1943; B.S. in Civil Engring., U. Mich., 1947; m. Mary Lee Taylor, Aug. 11, 1945; children—Michael Craig, Thomas Lee, Mary Kathleen, Marsha Coleen, Charlotte Anne. Draftsman, Jackson Constrn. Co., Colby, Kans., 1945-46; asst. engr. Thomas County, Colby, 1946; engr. Sherman County, Goodland, Kans., 1947-51; salesman Oehlert Tractor & Equipment Co., Colby, 1951-52; owner, operator George M. McKee, Jr., cons. engrs., Colby, 1952-72; sr. v.p. engring. Contract Surety Consultants, Wichita, Kans., 1974—. Adv. rep. Kans. State U., Manhattan, 1957-62; mem. adv. com. N.W. Kans. Area Vocat. Tech. Sch., Goodland, 1967-71. Served with USMCR, 1942-45. Registered profl. civil engr., Kans., Okla., registered land Surveyor, Kans. Mem. Kans. Engring. Soc. (pres. N.W. profl. engrs. chpt. 1962-63, treas. cons. engrs. sect. 1961-63), Kansas County Engr's. Assn. (dist.-v.p. 1950-51), N.W. Kans. Hwy. Ofcls. Assn. (sec. 1948-49), Nat. Soc. Profl. Engrs., Kans. State U. Alumni Assn. (pres. Thomas County 1956-57), Am. Legion (Goodland 1st vice comdr. 1948-49), The Alumni Assn. U. Mich. (life), Colby C. of C. (v.p. 1963-64), Goodland Jr. C. of C. (pres. 1951-52). Methodist (chmn. ofcl. bd. 1966-67). Mason (32 deg., Shriner); Order Eastern Star. Home: 8930 Suncrest St # 502 Wichita KS 67212-4069 Office: 6500 W Kellogg Dr Wichita KS 67209-2212

MC KEE, JAMES, JR., retired banker; b. Utica, N.Y., Aug. 29, 1918; s. James and Marie Roze (Tuller) McK.; m. Doris Elsie Nafis, June 28, 1947; children: James III, Nancy C. (dec.), Peter C., David R., John S. BS., Syracuse U., 1940. Exec. v.p.; cashier First Nat. Bank, Richfield Springs, N.Y., 1940-56; with State Bank of Albany, N.Y., 1956-83; v.p., cashier State Bank of Albany, 1969-83, sr. v.p., cashier, 1982-83. Co-chmn. United Fund, Clinton County, 1969; treas. Ea. Adirondack Econ. Devel. Commn., 1967-69; treas., bd. mgrs. Parsons Child and Family Center, 1971-78, assoc. mem. bd., 1979—; mem. Plattsburgh Coll. Found., mem. Planned Giving Commn.; bd. dirs. Champlain Devel. Corp., 1989, New Industries for Clinton County, 1969; trustee Albany Rotary Found., Inc., 1983-85, v.p. 1986-88; trustee Champlain Valley Physicians Hosp., 1969. Served to maj. C.E., AUS, 1942-46, ETO. Decorated Bronze Star; Paul Harris fellow Rotary, 1980. Mem. Norstar Bank Quarter Century Club (pres. 1974-75), Elks, Rotary (treas. dist. 719 1983-89, asst. treas. dist. 704 1989-90, treas. dist. 704 1990-91, pres. Albany 1974-75, Rotarian of Yr. 1988, hon. mem. Albany, mem. Plattsburgh bd. dirs. 1990-94), Ft. Orange Club, Alpha Kappa Psi, Delta Kappa Epsilon, Phi Kappa Phi, Beta Gamma Sigma, Beta Alpha Psi. Home: 30 Tanglewood Dr Port Kent NY 12975

MCKEE, JOSEPH FULTON, engineering and construction executive; b. Placerville, Calif., Apr. 28, 1921; s. Joseph Fulton and Pearl Margarite (Varroza) McK.; m. Eva Deane Adcock, Mar. 15, 1949 (dec.); m. Sharon Lucille Ricketts Adamson, Jan. 23, 1982; children—Robert Deane, Reneé E. Hackbarth. B.C.E., U. Santa Clara, 1947. Constrn. engr. Western Contracting Corp., 1947-50; supt., project engr., gen. supt. constrn. Morrison-Knudsen Co., Western U.S., 1950-54; project engr., constrn. mgr. Morrison-Knudsen Co., Western U.S., Morocco, 1954-57; constrn. mgr. Morrison-Knudsen Co., Western U.S., Iran, 1957-60, worldwide, 1960-65; area mgr. Morrison-Knudsen Co., Western U.S., Australia, 1965-73; v.p. Morrison-Knudsen Co., Western U.S., Europe, Africa, Mid-East, 1973-77; sr. v.p. Morrison-Knudsen Co., Western U.S., Tehran, 1977-80, Boise, Idaho, 1981-81; project dir. Cerrejon Coal Project, Colombia, 1981-85; exec. v.p internat. Morrison-Knudsen Engrs., San Francisco, 1985-86, ret., 1986. Served to lt. C.E., USN, 1943-46. Mem. ASCE, Chi Epsilon, Tau Beta Pi. Republican. Roman Catholic. Office: 4781 River Pl Boise ID 83703-1952

MCKEE, KATHRYN DIAN GRANT, banker; b. L.A., Sept. 12, 1937; d. Clifford William and Amelia Rosalia (Shacher) G.; m. Paul Eugene McKee, June 17, 1961; children: Scott Alexander, Grant Christopher. BA, U. Calif., Santa Barbara, 1959; grad. Sch. Mgmt. Exec. Program, UCLA, 1979. Cert. compensation and benefits. Mgr. Mattel, Inc., Hawthorne, Calif., 1963-74; dir. Twentieth Century Fox Film Corp., L.A., 1975-80; sr. v.p. 1st Interstate Bank, Ltd., L.A., 1980-93; sr. v.p. and human resources dir. Am.'s Standard Chartered Bank, 1993—; dir. Accordia benefits of Southern Calif., 1991—, mem. exec. com. H.R. div. of Am. Bankers Assn., 1991-93; bd. dirs. Bank Certification Inst. Am. Bankers Assn., 1992-94; treas. Pers. Accreditation Inst., 1983-86, pres., 1986. Contbr. articles to profl. jours. Pres. GEM Theatre Guild, Garden Grove, Calif., 1984-86; bd. dirs. Vis. Nurses Assn., L.A., 1984-88; bd. dirs. SHRM, 1986-92, treas., 1989, vice-chmn., 1990, chmn., 1991, pres. SHRM Found., 1994, 95. Recipient Sr. Honor Key award U. Calif., Santa Barbara, 1959, named Outstanding Sr. Woman, 1959; recipient William Winter award Am. Compensation Assn., 1986, Excellence award L.A. Pers. Indsl. Rels. Assn., 1990, Profl. Excellence award SHRM, 1994. Mem. Internat. Assn. Pers. Women (various offices, past nat. pres., Mem. of Yr. 1986), Orgn. Women Execs., L.A. Athletic Club. Office: Standard Chartered Bank 707 Wilshire Blvd Los Angeles CA 90017-3501

MCKEE, KEITH EARL, manufacturing technology executive; b. Chgo., Sept. 9, 1928; s. Charles Richard and Maude Alice (Hamlin) McK.; m. Lorraine Marie Celichowski, Oct. 26, 1951; children: Pamela Ann Houser, Paul Earl. BS, Ill. Inst. Tech., 1950, MS, 1956, PhD, 1962. Engr. Swift & Co., Chgo., 1953-54; rsch. engr. Armour Rsch. Found., Chgo., 1954-62; dir. design and product assurance Andrew Corp., Orland Park, Ill., 1962-67; dir. engring. Rsch. Ctr. Ill. Inst. Tech., Chgo., 1967-80, dir. mfg. prodn. ctr., 1977—; adj. prof. Ill. Inst. Tech., Chgo., 1979—; coord. Nat. Conf. on Fluid Power, Chgo., 1983-88; mem. com. on materials and processing Dept. Def., Washington, 1986—. Author: Productivity and Technology, 1988; editor: Automated Inspection and Process Control, 1987; co-editor: Manufacturing High Technology Handbook, 1987; mng. editor: Manufacturing Competitiveness Frontier, 1977—. Capt. USMC, 1950-54. Recipient outstanding presentation award Am. Soc. of Quality Control, Milw., 1983. Fellow World Acad. Productivity Scis.; mem. ASCE, Am. Def. Preparedness Assn. (pres. Chgo. chpt. 1972—), Am. Assn. Engring. Soc. (Washington) (coor. com. on productivity 1978-88), Inst. of Indsl. Engrs., Soc. Mfg. Engrs. (Gold medal 1991), Am. Assn. for Artificial Intelligence, Robotic Industry Assn. (bd. dir. 1978-81), Assn. for Mfg. Excellence, Soc. for Computer Simulation.

Democrat. Roman Catholic. Home: 18519 Clyde Rd Homewood IL 60430-3015 Office: Illinois Inst Tech Mfg Productivity Ctr 3350 S Federal St Chicago IL 60616-3732

MC KEE, KINNAIRD ROWE, retired naval officer; b. Louisville, Ky., Aug. 14, 1929; s. James H. and Kathleen (Sutton) McK.; m. Betty Ann Harris, June 23, 1953; children: James Henry III, Anne Arnold. BS, U.S. Naval Acad., 1951; grad., Nuclear Power Tng., 1958. Commd. ensign U.S. Navy, 1951, advanced through grades to adm., 1982; served in (Pacific fleet destroyer Marshall), Korean War; served in div. naval reactors (AEC), 1964-66; comdg. officer nuclear attack submarine (DACE), 1966-69; asst. to dir. program planning (Office Chief of Naval Ops.), Washington, 1969-70; exec. dir. (Chief Naval Ops. Exec. Panel), 1970-73; comdr. (U.S. and NATO submarine forces), 1973-75; supt. (U.S. Naval Acad.), Annapolis, 1975-78; comdr. U.S. Third Fleet, 1978-79; dir. naval warfare (Chief of Naval Ops.), Washington, 1979-82; dir. naval nuclear propulsion Washington, 1982-88, ret.; bd. dirs. Peco Energy Corp., Entergy Corp., Entergy Ops., Inc. Mem. U.S. Naval Inst. Home: 214 Morris St Oxford MD 21654-0610

MCKEE, MARGARET JEAN, federal agency executive; b. New Haven, June 20, 1929; d. Waldo McCutcheon and Elizabeth (Thayer) McKee; A.B., Vassar Coll., 1951. Staff asst. United Rep. Fin. Com., N.Y.C., 1952; staff asst. N.Y. Rep. State Com., N.Y.C., 1953-55; staff asst. Crusade for Freedom (name later changed to Radio Free Europe Fund), N.Y.C., 1955-57; researcher Stricker & Henning Research Assocs., Inc., N.Y.C., 1957-59; exec. sec. New Yorkers for Nixon (name later changed to N.Y. State Ind. Citizens for Nixon Lodge), N.Y.C., 1959-60; asst. to Raymond Moley, polit. columnist, N.Y.C., 1961; asst. campaign com. Louis J. Lefkowitz for Mayor, N.Y.C., 1961; research programmer, treas. Consensus, Inc., N.Y.C., 1962-67; spl. asst. to U.S. Senator Jacob K. Javits, N.Y., 1967-73, adminstrv. asst., 1973-75; dep. adminstr. Am. Revolution Bicentennial Adminstrn., 1976, acting adminstr., 1976-77; chief of staff Perry B. Duryea (minority leader) N.Y. State Assembly, 1978; public affairs cons., 1978-80; dir. govt. relations Gen. Mills Restaurant Group, Inc., 1980-83; exec. dir. Fed. Mediation and Conciliation Service, 1983-86; mem. Fed. Labor Rels. Authority, 1986-89, chmn., 1989-94; mem. Nat. Partnership Coun., 1993-94; bd. dirs. Interam. Life Ins. Co., 1979-86. Mem. N.Y. State Bingo Control Commn., 1965-72, U.S. Adv. Commn. on Public Diplomacy, 1979-82; mem. Nat. Partnership Coun., 1993—; pres. Bklyn. Heights Slope Young Rep. Club, 1955-56; co-chmn. Bklyn. Citizens for Eisenhower-Nixon, 1956; chmn. 2d Jud. Dist. Assn. N.Y. State Young Rep. Clubs, Inc., 1957-58, vice-chmn., mem. bd. govs., 1958-60, v.p., 1960-62; pres., 1962-64; mem. exec. com. Fedn. Women's Rep. Clubs N.Y. State, Inc., 1960-64, mem. council, 1964-70; mem. exec. com. N.Y. Rep. State Com. 1962-64; co-chmn. spl. assts. Rockefeller for Pres. Nat. Campaign com., N.Y.C., 1964; co-dir. N.Y. Rep. State Campaign Com., 1964; asst. campaign mgr. Kenneth B. Keating for Judge Ct. Appeals, N.Y., 1965; dir. scheduling Gov. Rockefeller campaign, 1966, Sen. Charles E. Goodell campaign, 1970; dir. scheduling and speakers' bur. N.Y. Com. to Re-elect the Pres., 1972; dir. planning and strategy, Conn. Reagan-Bush campaign, Hartford, 1980; mem. annual fund adv. com. Vassar Coll., 1992—. Mem. bd. govs. Women's Nat. Rep. Club, N.Y.C., 1963-66. Mem. Jr. League of Bklyn. (past dir.), Exec. Women in Govt. (chmn. 1986), Nat. Women's Edn. Fund (mem. bd.), Am. Newspaper Women's Club, Nat. Soc. Colonial Dames Am. Episcopalian. Club: Vassar (past dir., Bklyn.). Home: 532 S Brooksvale Rd Cheshire CT 06410

MCKEE, MARY ELIZABETH, producer; b. Syracuse, N.Y., Feb. 14, 1949; d. Anthony Henry and Mary (Robards) Krystosik; m. Peter S. Fama, June 27, 1970 (div. Mar. 1973); 1 child, Kiralie Fama; m. Michael R. McKee, Feb. 15, 1975 (Oct. 1978); 1 child, Quinn. BFA, Fla. Internat. U., Miami, 1974; MFA, Memphis State U., 1977. Copywriter announcer Sta. WREC/WZXR Radio, Memphis, 1978-79; creative dir. Cit Neifert & Assoc. Advt., Memphis, 1979-82; promotion dir. Sta. WGNX-TV, Atlanta, 1982-86; program mgr. Sta. WVEU-TV, Atlanta, 1986-90; v.p. sta. mgr. Sta. WHSP-TV, Vineland, N.J., 1990—; adj. prof. Glassboro State U., 1990—. Actor in field (Top 10 Memphis Mag. 1979). Vol. Com. to Feed the Hungry, Atlanta, 1988, Tenn. Talking Libr., Memphis, 1982; mem. Greenpeace, 1987—; mem. adv. coun. SES, Easter Seal Soc. N.J. Recipient Merit award Tenn. Talking Libr., 1982; named Best TV Comml. Memphis Advt. Club, 1982; Hair scholar Fla. Internat. U., 1973. Mem. AFTRA, Nat. Assn. Broadcasters, Am. Women in Radio and TV (publicity chmn. 1985-86), Nat. Assn. TV Program Execs., Internat. Platform Soc., Broadcast Cable Fin. Mgmt. Assn., Rotary. Democrat. Roman Catholic. Avocations: writing journals, published poet, running and video production bus., bicycling. Home: 55 S Dover Ave Atlantic City NJ 08401-5912 Office: Sta WHSP-TV 4449 Delsea Dr Newfield NJ 08344-9609

MCKEE, PENELOPE MELNA, library director; b. New Liskeard, Ont., Can., Dec. 31, 1938; d. Melvin Hugh and Violet Mary (Hooton) Olimer; m. Arthur Donald McKee, Mar. 5, 1960 (div. 1985); children: Suzanne, Carolyn, Stephen. BA with honors, U. Toronto, Can., 1960, BLS, 1961, MLS, 1980; diploma, Coll. Applied Arts and Tech., 1976. Cert. mcpl. mgr. Ont. Mcpl. Mgmt. Devel. Bd. Fine arts libr. North York Pub. Libr., Ont., Can., 1961-63, reference libr., 1969-74; reference libr. Toronto Montessori Schs., Thornhill, Ont., 1974-76; cons. Grolier Pub., Toronto, 1976; libr. supr. Toronto Pub. Libr., 1977-80; dir. Aurora Pub. Libr., Ont., Can., 1980-86, Peterborough Pub. Libr., Ont., Can., 1986-90, Edmonton Pub. Libr., Alta., Can., 1990—; adj. assoc. prof. U. Alta., Edmonton, 1992—; cons. Edmonton Cath. Sch. Bd., 1992. Contbr. articles to profl. jours. Vice chmn. Project Hostel, Aurora, 1986-89; bd. dirs. Friends of Trent Severn Waterway, Peterborough, 1990; active Edmonton Centennial Celebrations Com., 1992. Russell scholar U. Toronto, 1956. Mem. Canadian Libr. Assn., Ontario Libr. Assn. (pres.), Libr. Assn. Alta., Alta. Pub. Libr. Dirs. Coun. (chair), Rotary Club of Downtown Edmonton (pub. rels. chmn.). Avocations: reading, music, curling, canoeing. Office: Edmonton Public Libr, 7 Sir Winston Churchill Sq, Edmonton, AB Canada T5J 2V4

MCKEE, RAE ELLEN, special education educator. Tchr. remedial reading Slanesville (W.Va.) Elem. Sch. Recipient Nat. Remedial Reading Tchr. of Yr. award, 1991. Office: Slanesville Elem Sch RR 29 Slanesville WV 25444

MCKEE, RICHARD MILES, animal studies educator; b. Cottonwood Falls, Kans., Oct. 8, 1929; m. Marjorie Fisk, June 22, 1952; children: Dave, Richard, Annell, John. BS in Agriculture, Kans. State Coll. Agriculture and Applied Sci., 1951; MS in Animal Husbandry, Kans. State U., 1963; PhD in Animal Science, U. Ky., 1968. Herdsman Moxley Hall Hereford Ranch, Coun. Grove, Kans., 1951-52, 54-55, Luckhardt Farms, Tarkio, Mo., 1955-58; asst. mgr. L&J Crusoe Ranch, Cheboygan, Mich., 1958-59; asst. instr., cattle herdsman Kans. State U., Manhattan, 1959-65, from asst. prof. to assoc. prof., 1959-65, prof., departmental teaching coord., 1976—; program participant and/or official judge numerous shows, field days including Kans. Jr. Hereford Field Day, Kans. Jr. Shorthorn Field Day, Better Livestock Day, Kans. Jr. Livestock Assn., Am. Jr. Hereford Assn. Field Day, Cheyenne, Wyo., 1973, Kans. Jr. Polled Hereford Field Day, Am. Jr. Shorthorn Assn., Kans. City, Mo., 1965, Am. Internat. Jr. Charolais Assn. Show, Lincoln, Nebr., 1976, Am. Royal 4-H Livestock Judging Contest, Kans. City, 1975, Jr. Livestock Activities various cattle breed assns. nationwide, 1977-81; served on many breed assn. coms.; judge County Fairs; official judge 14 different Nat. Beef Breed Shows U.S. and Can.; conducted 60 livestock judging and showmanship schs. at county level. Contbr. articles to profl. jours. Deacon 1st Presbyn. Ch., Manhattan, 1969-75, Sunday Sch. tchr., Chancel choir, elder; project leader com. mem. 4-H; foster parent Kans. State U. Football Program. Lt. USMC, 1952-54, Korea. Named Hon. State Farmer of Kans.; Hall of Merit Honoree for Edn. by Am. Polled Hereford Assn., 1985; NDEA scholar U. Ky., 1966-67; Miles McKee Student Enrichment Fund established at Kans. State U. Mem. Am. Soc. Animal Sci., Kans. Livestock Assn. (beef cattle improvement com. 1970-78, cow-calf clinic com. 1973, 74, 75, 76, 77, 78), Nat. Assn. Colls. and Tchrs. Agriculture, Block and Bridle Club, Am. Jr. Hereford Assn. (hon.), FarmHouse, Sigma Xi, Phi Kappa Phi, Alpha Zeta, Gamma Sigma Delta, Alpha Tau Alpha (hon.). Home: 901 Juniper Dr Manhattan KS 66502-3148 Office: Dept of Animal Scis & Industry Kansas State U Manhattan KS 66506

MCKEE, ROGER CURTIS, federal magistrate judge; b. Waterloo, Iowa, Feb. 11, 1931; s. James A. and Leonace (Burrell) McK.; m. Roberta Jeanne

Orvis, Sept. 3, 1954; children: Andrea Jane, Brian Curtis, Paul Robert. BA, State Coll. of Iowa, 1955; MA, U. Ill., 1960; JD, U. San Diego 1959. Bar: Calif. 1970, U.S. Dist. Ct. (so. dist.) Calif. 1969, U.S. Ct. Appeals (9th cir.) 1971. Telegrapher, agt. Ill. Cen. R.R., 1950-55; tng. asst. No. Ill. Gas Co., Aurora, 1959-60; with indsl. rels. dept. Convair div. Gen. Dynamics Corp., San Diego, 1960-68; contract adminstr. and supr. Datagraphix div. Gen. Dynamics Corp., San Diego, 1968-69, asst. counsel, 1969-70; ptnr. Powell & McKee, San Diego, 1970-75, Millsberg, Dickstein & McKee, San Diego, 1975-83; magistrate judge U.S. Dist. Ct. for So. Dist. Calif., San Diego, 1983—; presiding magistrate judge, 1993—. Bd. trustees So. Calif. Presbyn. Homes, L.A., 1979-81; moderator Presbytery of San Diego, 1980. Capt. USNR, 1949-85. Mem. Calif. Bar Assn., Fed. Magistrate Judges Assn., Navy League U.S., Naval Res. Officers Assn., Res. Officers Assn., Dixieland Jazz Soc. (bd. dirs. San Diego chpt. 1984—). Republican. Office: US Cts Bldg 940 Front St San Diego CA 92189-0010

MCKEE, THEODORE A., federal judge; b. 1947. B.A., SUNY, Cortland, 1969; J.D. magna cum laude, Syracuse U. Coll. of Law, 1975. Dir. of minority recruitment & admissions SUNY, Binghamton, 1969-72; atty. Wolf, Block, Schorr & Solis-Cohen, Phila., 1975-77; asst. U.S. atty., Eastern Dist. PA, 1977-80, asst. U.S. atty., Eastern Dist. Gen. Crimes Unit, Narcotics and Firearms Unit, then Polit. Corruption Unit; lecturer Rutgers U. Coll. of Law, 1980-91; dep. city solicitor Law Dept., Phila., 1980-83; gen. counsel Phila. Parking Auth., 1983; judge Ct. of Common Pleas, 1st Jud. Dist, PA, 1984-94, judge major felony program, 1986, judge orphans' ct. divsn., 1992; circuit judge Third Circuit, Phila., 1994—; mem. ABA: 1975-77, 1990-93; Nat. Bar Assn.; Barristers' Assn. of Phila.; Temple Inn of Court; bd. of dirs.: Crime Prevention Assn., Diagnostic & Rehabilitation Ctr. of Phila. mem. World Affairs Council, Urban League of Amer.; bd. of dirs., New Directions for Women, Inc. Office: Rm 20614 601 Market St Philadelphia PA 19106*

MCKEE, THOMAS FREDERICK, lawyer; b. Cleve., Oct. 27, 1948; s. Harry Wilbert and Virginia (Light) McK. BA with high distinction, U. Mich., 1970; JD, Case Western Rs. U., 1975. Bar: Ohio 1975, U.S. Dist. Ct. (no. dist.) Ohio 1975, U.S. Supreme Ct. 1979. Assoc. firm Calfee, Halter & Griswold, Cleve., 1975-81, ptnr., 1982—; also mem. exec. com., chmn. operating com.; sec. McDonald & Co. Investments, Inc., Chart Industries, Inc.; bd. dirs. Mr. Coffee, Inc. Contbg. editor Going Public, 1985. Mem. ABA (com. fed. regulation securities law sect.), Bar Assn. Greater Cleve., Order of Coif., Union Club, Tavern Club, Country Club, Hillbrook Club. Home: 210 Pheasant Run Dr Chagrin Falls OH 44022-2968 Office: Calfee Halter & Griswold Ste 1400 McDonald Investment Ctr 800 Superior Ave E Cleveland OH 44114

MCKEE, THOMAS J., lawyer; b. Lorain, Ohio, Nov. 17, 1930; s. James Anthony and Winifred Agnes (Martin) McK.; m. Nancy R. Romero, Jan. 24, 1959; children: Andrew, Thomas, Peter, Nancy, Kerry, Joseph. BA, St. Mary's U., 1954; STB, Gregorian U., 1956; JD, Georgetown U., 1961. Assoc. Hirschberg, Pettengill & Strong, Greenwich, Conn., 1961-68, ptnr., 1968-77; ptnr. Whitman & Ransom, Greenwich, 1978-93, Whitman Breed Abbott & Morgan, Greenwich, 1993—. Fellow Am. Coll. Trust and Estate Counsel; mem. Conn. Bar Assn., Greenwich Bar Assn. Club: Stamford (Conn.) Yacht. Avocations: photography, computer programming. Home: 321 Stamford Ave Stamford CT 06902-8203 Office: Whitman Breed Abbott & Morgan PO Box 2250 Greenwich CT 06836-2250

MCKEE, WILLIAM DAVID, lawyer; b. N.Y.C., Aug. 11, 1926; s. H. Harper and Mabel (Hughes) McK.; m. Eleanor Lyn Messenkopf, Sept. 13, 1947; children: Rebecca Inez, Harper Charles, Joshua Monte. BSME, Duke U., 1946; LLB, Columbia U., 1949. Bar: Calif. 1950. Rsch. assoc. Am. Law Inst., Berkeley, Calif., 1949-50; assoc. Orrick, Herrington & Sutcliffe, San Francisco, 1950-57, ptnr., 1958-88, chmn., chief exec. officer, 1983-86; bd. dirs. Golden West Fin. Corp., Oakland, Calif., World Savs. & Loan Assn. Served as ensign USNR, 1943-46. Mem. Calif. Bar Assn. Democrat. Home: 1271 Redwood Ln Lafayette CA 94549-2429 Office: Orrick Herrington & Sutcliffe Old Federal Reserve Bank Bldg 400 Sansome St San Francisco CA 94111

MCKEEN, ALEXANDER C., engineering consulting company owner; b. Albion, Mich., Oct. 10, 1927; s. John Nisbet and Janet (Callander) McK.; m. Evelyn Mae Feldkamp, Aug. 18, 1951; Jeffrey, Brian, Andrew. BSME, U. Mich., 1950; MBA, Mich. State U., 1968. Registered profl. engr., Mich. Asst. supt. maintenance Cadillac Motor Car div. GM, Detroit, 1961-65, plant engr., 1965-67, supt. final assembly, 1967-69, asst. dir. reliability, 1969-72; exec. engr. Product Assurance GM, Warren, Mich., 1972-75, asst. dir. Engring. Analysis, 1975-77, dir. Engring Analysis, 1977-87; pres., owner Engring. Analysis Assocs., Inc., Birmingham, Mich., 1987—. Pres. Dells of Bloomfield Home Owners Assn., Bloomfield Hills, Mich., 1987-88; trustee Kirk in Hills, Bloomfield Hills, 1990-93. Capt. USAR, 1950-62. Mem. Soc. Auto. Engrs., Am. Soc. Quality Control, Engring. Soc. Detroit, Detroit Athletic Club, Stonycroft Hills Golf Club, Beta Gamma Sigma. Avocations: tennis, golf, photography, travel, gardening. Home: 5286 Kellen Ln Bloomfield Hills MI 48302-2738 Office: Engring Analysis Assocs Inc 30600 Telegraph Rd Ste 2370 Bingham Farms MI 48025-4532

MC KEEN, CHESTER M., JR., business executive; b. Shelby, Ohio, Mar. 18, 1923; s. Chester Mancil and Nettie Augusta (Fox) McK.; m. Alma Virginia Pierce, Mar. 1946; children: David Richard, Karin, Thomas Kevin. BS in Mil. Sci., U. Md., 1962; MBA, Babson Coll., Wellesley, Mass., 1962. Advanced through grades to maj. gen. U.S. Army, 1942-77; dir. logistics Bell Helicopter Internat., Tehran, Iran, 1977-79; v.p. procurement Bell Helicopter Textron, Ft. Worth, 1979-82; v.p. materiel Bell Helicopter Textron, 1982-89; pres. Logistics Svcs. Internat., Arlington, Tex.; chmn. bd. dirs. ISES Inc.; bd. dirs. Exec. Svc. Corps Tarrant County, chmn. Decorated D.S.M., Legion of Merit (3), Commendation medal (3). Mem. Am. Mgmt. Assn., Am. Def. Preparedness Assn. (v.p. S.W. region), Assn. U.S. Army, Ridglea Country Club, Rotary, Masons (33 degree), Shriners, Sigma Pi. Home: 2310 Woodsong Trl Arlington TX 76016-1037 Office: ISES Inc 328 Pipeline Rd Hurst TX 76053

MCKEEVER, JEFFREY D., computer company executive; b. Marion, Ind., 1942. Grad., U. Ariz., Tucson, 1965; MBA, U. Ariz., 1973. Co-founder, dir. Microage Inc., Tempe. Office: Microage Inc 2308 S 55th St Tempe AZ 85282-1824

MCKEEVER, JOHN EUGENE, lawyer; b. Phila., Oct. 24, 1947; s. John James and Marie Julia (Supper) McK.; children: John Joseph, Jeannine Marie. BA magna cum laude with distinction, U. Pa., 1969, JD magna cum laude, 1972. Bar: Pa. 1972, U.S. Dist. Ct. (ea. dist.) Pa. 1972, U.S. Dist. Ct. (mid. dist.) Pa. 1977, U.S. Ct. Appeals (3rd cir.) 1979, U.S. Ct. Appeals (D.C. cir.) 1981, U.S. Supreme Ct. 1981. Assoc. Schnader, Harrison, Segal & Lewis, Phila., 1972-80, ptnr., 1980—. Mem. Pres. Coun. Allentown Coll. St. Francis De Sales, Center Valley, Pa., 1980—; Bus. Leadership Organized for Cath. Schs., Phila., 1984—, adv. com. De Sales Sch. Theology, Washington, trustee, 1988-91; capt. spl. gifts com. Cath. Charities Appeal, Phila., 1986-91; bd. dirs. Jr. Achievement, Phila., 1986—. Mem. Pa. Bar Assn., Phila. Bar Assn., Pro-Life Lawyers' Guild (bd. dirs. 1983-84, chancellor 1984-86), St. Thomas More Soc. (gov. 1979-91, pres. 1981-82), Order of Coif, Phi Beta Kappa, Pi Gamma Mu. Republican. Roman Catholic. Office: Schnader Harrison Segal & Lewis Ste 3600 1600 Market St Philadelphia PA 19103-4247

MCKEITHEN, WALTER FOX, secretary of state; b. Columbia, La., Sept. 8, 1946; s. John Jesse and Marjorie (Funderburk) McK.; m. Yvonne May; children: Marjorie, Marianne, Rebecca, John Jesse. B in History and Social Studies, La. Tech. U., 1972. Owner, operator Apparel Mart Dept. Store, Columbia, 1974-83, McKeithen Chem. & Cementing, Columbia, 1979-88; mem. appropriation, natural resources and joint budged coms. La. Ho. of Reps., Baton Rouge, 1983-87; sec. of state State of La., Baton Rouge, 1987—; tchr., coach Caldwell Parish High Sch., Grayson, La., 1975-78; past mem. La. Assn. Educators. Past v.p. Caldwell Parish Jaycees; trustee La. Sch. Employees' Retirement System; mem. La. Tourist Devel. Commn.; second injury bd. La. Workmen's Compensation; mem. State Bd. Election Supervisors and State Bond Commn., La. Farm Bur., Am. Petroleum Inst.; administrv. bd. Broadmoor Meth. Ch. Recipient Outstanding Legislator award La. Assn. Educators, 1985, Golden Apple award La. Fedn. Tchrs.,

1986. Republican. Methodist. Office: Dept of State State Capitol 20th Fl PO Box 94125 Baton Rouge LA 70804-9125

MCKELDIN, WILLIAM EVANS, management consultant; b. Richmond, Va., Aug. 14, 1927; s. Robert A.W. and Mary E. (Burke) McK.; BS in Bus. Adminstrn., Temple U. 1951, postgrad., 1951-53; postgrad. U. Pitts., 1953-54; m. Phyllis Shellhase, Jan. 23, 1982; children by previous marriage: William Evans, Roberts E. Various employee relations and mgmt. positions with Westinghouse Corp., Pitts., 1950-62, Farrel Corp., Rochester, N.Y., 1963-66, Gen. Signal Corp., Norwalk, Conn. and Watertown, N.Y., 1966-71, Copperweld Steel Co. Warren, Ohio, 1971-75, Tenn. Forging Steel, Knoxville, 1975-77, Val Bradley Assocs., West Chester, Pa., 1977-79; pres. and owner McKeldin Assocs., West Chester, 1979—. Bd. dirs. United Fund, YMCA, ARC, Rochester Inst. Tech., Jefferson Community Coll., Kent State U. Served with USAAF, 1945-47. Mem. Inst. Mgmt. Cons., Am. Soc. Safety Engrs., Am. Soc. Personnel Adminstrn., C. of C. (dir.) Republican. Presbyterian. Clubs: Masons, Rotary. Contbr. articles to trade jours. Office: McKeldin Assocs 125 Willowbrook Ln West Chester PA 19382

MCKELL, CYRUS M., college dean, plant physiologist, consultant; b. Payson, Utah, Mar. 19, 1926; s. Robert D. and Mary C. (Ellsworth) McK.; m. Betty Johnson; children: Meredith Sue, Brian Marcus, John Cyrus. BS, U. Utah, 1949, MS, 1950; PhD, Oreg. State U., 1956; postgrad., U. Calif., Davis, 1957. Instr. botany Oreg. State U., Corvallis, 1955-56; range rsch. plant physiologist U. Calif. USDA-Agri. Research Service, Davis, 1956-60; prof., dept. chmn. U. Calif., Riverside, 1960-69; prof. dept. head., dir. Utah State U., Logan, 1969-80; v.p. research NPI, Salt Lake City, 1980-88; dean Coll. of Sci. Weber State U., Ogden, Utah, 1988-94; v.p. rsch. Applied Ecol. Svcs. Inc., Salt Lake City, 1995—; cons. Ford Found. 1968-72, Rockefeller Found., 1964-70, 89, UN, 1978, 90, NAS, 1980, 89, 91, 92, 93, USAID, 1972, UN Devel. Program, 1989. Editor: Grass Biology and Utilization, 1971, Useful Wildland Shrubs, 1972, Rehabilitation of Western Wildlife Habitat, 1978, Paradoxes of Western Energy Development, 1984, Resource Inventory and Baseline Study Methods for Developing Countries, 1983, Shrub Biology and Utilization, 1989, Wilderness Issues, Arid Lands of the Western United States, 1992; contbr. over 230 articles to profl. jours. Chmn. Cache County Planning Commn., Logan, 1974-79; mem. Utah Energy Conservation and Devel. Coun., 1976-79, Gov.'s Sci. Adv. Coun., 1988—, chmn. 1990-91; active Commn. of the Californias, Riverside, 1965-68. 1st lt. USAF, 1951-53. Recipient Utah Gov.'s Sci. and Tech. medal, 1990; Fulbright scholar Spain, 1967-68; World Travel grantee Rockefeller Found., 1964. Fellow AAAS (com. chmn. 1979-89, sci. exchange to China grantee 1984-85, 89, sci. panel U.S.-Chile 1987); mem. Am. Soc. Agronomy, Soc. Range Mgmt. (pres. Calif. sect. 1965, pres. Utah sect 1982). Mem. LDS Ch. Avocations: travel, photography. Home: 2248 E 4000 S Salt Lake City UT 84124-1864

MCKELLAR, ANDREW ROBERT, physicist, researcher; b. Ottawa, Ont., Can., Mar. 28, 1945; s. Andrew and Mary (Crouch) McK.; m. Barbara Irene Merriam, Oct. 5, 1974; children: Ian, Ann. BSc, U. Victoria, B.C., Can., 1966; MSc, U. Toronto, Ont., 1968, PhD, 1970. Rsch. officer Nat. Rsch. Coun. Can., Ottawa, 1973—. Fellow Royal Soc. Can.; mem. Can. Assn. Physicists (Herzberg medal 1982), Optical Soc. Am., Am. Astron. Soc. Office: Nat Rsch Coun Can, 100 Sussex Dr, Ottawa, ON Canada K1A 0R6

MCKELLAR, C. H., grocery chain executive; b. 1937. With Winn-Dixie Stores, Inc., 1957—; supt. retail ops. Jacksonville (Fla.) div. 1978-80, corp. v.p., mgr., 1980-81; v.p., mgr. Montgomery div., 1981-83; sr. v.p., regional dir. Jacksonville, from 1986, now exec. v.p., dir. Office: Winn-Dixie Stores Inc PO Box B Jacksonville FL 32203-0297

MCKELLEN, IAN, actor; b. Burnley, Eng., May 25, 1939; s. Denis Murray and Margery (Sutcliffe) McK.; ed. St. Catharine's Coll., Cambridge, Eng. Prof. Oxford U., 1990-91. First stage appearance as Roper in A Man for All Seasons, Belgrade Theatre, Coventry, Eng., 1961; numerous other parts include title roles in Henry V, Luther, Ipswich, 1962-63, Aufidius in Coriolanus, Arthur Seaton in Saturday Night and Sunday Morning, title role in Sir Thomas More, Nottingham Playhouse, 1963-64; London debut as Godfrey in A Scent of Flowers, 1964, Claudio in Much Ado About Nothing, Andrew Cobham in Their Very Own and Golden City, 1966; title part in O'Flaherty, V.C. and Bonapart in The Man of Destiny, 1966, (Broadway debut) Leonidik in The Promise, London, 1966-67, Richard II, Edward II, Hamlet, Prospect Theatre Co., 1968-71; Capt. Plume in The Recruiting Officer; founder-mem. Actors' Co., Edinburgh Festival, 1972 and touring as Giovanni in Tis Pity She's A Whore, Page-Boy in Ruling the Roost, title role Wood Demon; debut with R.S.C. as Dr. Faustus, Edinburgh Festival, 1974; title role in The Marquis of Keith, Philip the Bastard in King John, 1974-75, Young Vic Colin in Ashes, 1975; Royal Shakespeare Co.: Burglar in Too True to be Good, Romeo, Macbeth, Leontes in The Winter's Tale, Face in The Alchemist, Bernick in Pillars of the Community, Langevin in Days of the Commune, 1976-78, Ivanov in Every Good Boy Deserves Favour, Toby Belch in Twelfth Night, Andrei in The Three Sisters, Max in Bent, 1979, Amadeus, N.Y.C., 1980, Iago in Othello, The Other Place, Stratford, 1989; European tour of one-man show Acting Shakespeare, 1983, also Los Angeles, N.Y.C., 1984, one-man show A Knight Out at the Lyceum (devised especially for Gay Games IV), 1994; assoc. dir. Nat. Theatre, London, 1984-86, plays include: Venice Preserved, Wild Honey, Coriolanus, Duchess of Malfi, The Cherry Orchard, King Lear, Richard m. Napoli Milionaria, Uncle Vanya, others; dir. first prodn. The Prime of Miss Jean Brodie, Liverpool Playhouse, 1969, A Private Matter, 1973, The Clandestine Marriage, 1975; films include: Alfred the Great, 1969, The Promise, 1969, A Touch of Love, 1969, The Keep, 1982, Plenty, Zina, 1985, Scandal, 1988, The Ballad of Little Jo, 1992, I'll Do Anything, 1992, Last Action Hero, 1993, Six Degrees of Separation, 1993, The Shadow, 1994, Jack and Sarah, 1994, Restoration, 1994; TV appearances include: David Copperfield, 1965, Ross, 1969, Richard II, Edward II and Hamlet, 1970, Hedda Gabler, 1974, Macbeth, Every Good Boy Deserves Favour, Dying Day, 1979, Acting Shakespeare, 1981, The Scarlet Pimpernel, 1982, And the Band Played On, 1993 (Emmy nomination, Supporting Actor - Special, 1994). Recipient Clarence Derwent award, 1964; Variety and Plays and Players awards, 1966; Actor of Year, Plays and Players, 1976; award Soc. of West End Theatres for Best Actor in Revival, 1977, for Best Comedy Performance, 1978, for Best Actor in a New Play, 1979, Tony Award for Best Actor, Drama Desk Award, Outer Critics' Circle Award, N.Y. Drama League Award, 1981; Performer of Yr. award Royal TV soc., 1983. Decorated comdr. Order Brit. Empire, knight Bachelor. Mem. Brit. Actors' Equity (coun. 1970-71). Office: ICM Oxford House, 76 Oxford St, London W1N 0AX, England

MCKELVEY, ANDREW J., advertising executive. Chmn. bd., pres. TMP Worldwide, Inc., N.Y.C. Office: TMP Worldwide Inc 1633 Broadway 33rd Fl New York NY 10019

MCKELVEY, DON RICHARD, finance company executive; b. Morganton, N.C., Feb. 13, 1944; s. Vincent Paul and Velma (Robinson) Game; m. Mary Ann DeDio, May 7, 1967; children: Shawn, Don. BA, Murray U., Ky., 1966. Sales NCR, Dayton, Ohio, 1966-70; nat. acct. mgr. Data 100 Co., Mpls., 1970-77; v.p. sales TEC, Inc., Tuscon, 1977-81; chmn., pres. Telco Tech., Emerson, N.J., 1981-88; chmn. Donaldson Capital, Harrington, N.J., 1988—; dir. Eastern Micro, Marlboro, Mass., 1982-92. Office: Telco Tech PO Box 68 Harrington Park NJ 07640-0068

MCKELVEY, JACK M., bishop; b. Wilmington, Del., Dec. 8, 1941; m. Linda Boardman; children: Heather, Glen, Drew, Marissa. B in Psychology, U. del.; MDiv, Va. Theol. Seminary. ordained to deaconate Episc. Ch., 1966, to priesthood, 1967. Vicar St. John the Baptist Ch., Milton, Del., 1965-70, Holy Trinity Ch., Wilmington, 1970-79; rector St. Paul's Ch., Englewood, N.J., 1979—; elected Suffragan Bishop Diocese of Newark, 1990—; mem. faculty Inter-Met Seminary, Washington, 1976; former mem. diocesan coun. Del., commns. on ministry and standing coms.; pres. standing com. diocese of Newark; co-founder Van Ost Family Inst. Co-author: Inter-Met Seminary: Bold Experiment in Theological Education. Office: 24 Rector St Newark NJ 07102-4512

MCKELVEY, JAMES MORGAN, chemical engineering educator; b. St. Louis, Aug. 22, 1925; s. James Grey and Muriel (Morgan) McK.; m. Edith Rothbauer, Dec. 28, 1957; children: James, Robert; m. Judith Hood

Forgotson, Sept. 4, 1992. B.S., U. Mo.-Rolla, 1945; M.S., Washington U., St. Louis, 1947, Ph.D., 1950. Research engr. E.I. DuPont de Nemours & Co., Inc., 1950-54; asst. prof. chem. engring. Johns Hopkins U., Balt., 1954-57; mem. faculty Washington U., St. Louis, 1957—; dean Sch. Engring. and Applied Sci., 1964-91, prof. chem. engring., 1991—. Recipient Disting. Educator award Soc. Plastics Engrs., 1979. Home: 9861 Copper Hill Rd Saint Louis MO 63124

MC KELVEY, JEAN TREPP, industrial relations educator; b. St. Louis, Feb. 9, 1908; d. Samuel and Blanche (Goodman) Trepp; m. Blake McKelvey, June 29, 1934. AB, Wellesley Coll., 1929; MA, Radcliffe Coll., 1931, PhD, 1933. Mem. faculty Sarah Lawrence Coll., 1932-45, N.Y. State Sch. Indsl. and Labor Rels., Cornell U. Ithaca, N.Y., 1946—; from asst. prof. to assoc. prof. indsl. rels. N.Y. State Sch. Indsl. and Labor Rels., Cornell U., 1946-49, prof., 1949—; vis. prof. Sch. Law Cornell U., 1977-78; mem. pub. panel, hearing officer, arbitrator Nat. War Labor Bd. 1944-45; mem. inquiry into Rochester Transit dispute N.Y. State Bd., 1952; mem. pub. adv. com. to sec. of labor, 1953; mem. N.Y. State Bd. Mediation, 1956-66; mem. presdl. emergency bd. on ry. shopcrafts dispute, 1964, ry. signalmen dispute, 1971; mem. Fed. Svc. Impasses Panel, 1970-90. Author: The Uses of Field Work in Teaching Economics, 1939, AFL Attitudes Toward Production, 1952, Dock Labor Disputes in Great Britain, 1953, Fact Finding in Public Employment Disputes, 1969, Sex and the Single Arbitrator, 1971. Editor: The Duty of Fair Representation, 1977; The Changing Law of Fair Representation, 1985, Cleared For Takeoff: Airline Labor Relations Under Deregulation, 1988; also several vols. on arbitration. Alumnae trustee Wellesley Coll. 1946-53. Mem. Nat. Acad. Arbitrators (past pres.), Am. Fedn. Tchrs. (mem. pub. rev. bd. 1969-73), Am. Arbitration Assn. (mem. nat. panel, mem. UAW pub. rev. bd. 1957—), Indsl. Rels. Rsch. Assn., Phi Beta Kappa. Home: 53 Aberthaw Rd Rochester NY 14610-2905 Office: Cornell U NYSSILR 16 Main St W Rochester NY 14614-1601

MC KELVEY, JOHN CLIFFORD, research institute executive; b. Decatur, Ill., Jan. 25, 1934; s. Clifford Venice and Pauline Lytton (Runkel) McK.; m. Carolyn Tenney, May 23, 1980; children: Sean, Kerry, Tara, Evelyn, Aaron. B.A., Stanford U., 1956, M.B.A., 1958. Research analyst Stanford Research Inst., Palo Alto, Calif., 1959-60; indsl. economist Stanford Research Inst., 1960-64; with Midwest Research Inst., Kansas City, Mo., 1964—; v.p. econs. and mgmt. sci. Midwest Research Inst., 1970-73, exec. v.p., 1973-75, pres., chief exec. officer, 1975—; chmn. Menninger Found. Bd., 1994. Trustee Rockhurst Coll., 1993; mem. Civic Coun. of Greater Kansas City; bd. regents Rockhurst Coll., Kansas City, Mo., 1977; bd. dirs. Yellow Corp., North Star Found., 1981, Mid-Am. Mfg. Tech. Ctr., 1991; trustee The Menninger Found., 1975. Clubs: Carriage, Mission Hills, Hallbrook Country. Home: 912 W 121st Ter Kansas City MO 64145-1015 Office: Midwest Rsch Inst 425 Volker Blvd Kansas City MO 64110-2299

MC KELVEY, JOHN JAY, JR., retired foundation executive; b. Albany, N.Y., July 16, 1917; s. John Jay and Louise E. (Brunning) McK.; m. Josephine G. Faulkner, June 28, 1941; children: John Jay III, Richard Drummond, Edward Faulkner, Laurence Brunning. A.B., Oberlin Coll., 1939; M.S., Va. Poly. Inst., 1941; Ph.D., Cornell U., 1945. Investigator N.Y. State Agrl. Sta., 1942-45; with Rockefeller Found., 1945-83, dep. dir. agrl. sci., 1966-68, assoc. dir. agrl. scis., 1968-83; cons. in field, 1959—; Mem. survey team natural resources No. Region Nigeria FAO-ICA, 1960; cons. UN spl. fund project agrl. research, Thailand, 1964; study com. manpower needs and ednl. capabilities in Africa Edn. and World Affairs, 1964-65; rev. commn. higher edn. Botswana, Lesotho and Swaziland Overseas Devel. Ministry U.K., 1966; overseas liaison com. study team higher edn., Sierra Leone, 1968; mem. agrl. edn. mission to U.S. Pacific, Overseas Devel. Ministry of U.K., 1970; mem. Africa sci. bd. Nat. Acad. Scis., 1961-68, vice chmn., 1964-68, mem. sci. orgn. devel. bd., 1966-68, mem. bd. sci. and tech. internat. devel., also chmn. Africa sci. panel, 1968—, chmn. adv. panel on arid lands of, sub-Saharan Africa, 1974; chmn. com. African agrl. research capabilities Nat. Acad. Scis./Agrl. Bd., 1971-74; mem. vis. com. for biology and related research facilities Harvard Coll., 1975-81; mem. area adv. com. for Africa Council for Internat. Exchange of Scholars, 1976-80; mem. Chappaqua Internat. Exchange, 1976-78; chmn. USAID/IBAR Task Force, 1978-79. Author: Man Against Tse-tse, 1973; editor: (with R.L. Metcalf) The Future for Insecticides, 1976, (with H.H. Shorey) Chemical Control of Insect Behavior, 1977, (with Louis H. Miller and John A. Pino), Immunity to Blood Parasites of Animals and Man, 1977, (with Bruce F. Eldridge and Karl Maramorosch) Vectors of Disease Agents, 1980, (with K. Maramarosch) Subviral Pathogens of Plants and Animals, 1985; contbr. articles to profl. jours., chpts. to books. Trustee Internat. Inst. Tropical Agr., Ibadan, Nigeria, 1971-87, chmn., 1983-87; vice chmn. governing coun. Internat. Trypanotolerance Ctr., The Gambia, 1981-89, chmn., 1988-89; pres. Internat. Fund for Agrl. Rsch., 1985-87, bd. dirs. 1988, chmn., 1989-93; bd. govs. Inst. for Agrl. Rsch., Ahmadu Bello U., Zaria, Nigeria, 1971-74; moderator Federated Ch. West Winfield, 1995—. Mem. AAAS, Entomol. Soc. Am., Assn. for Advancement Agrl. Sci. in Africa (founding). Home: Richfield Springs NY 13439

MCKELVEY, JUDITH GRANT, lawyer, educator, university dean; b. Milw., July 19, 1935; d. Lionel Alexander and Bernadine R. (Verdun) Grant. B.S. in Philosophy, U. Wis., 1957, J.D., 1959. Bar: Wis. 1959, Calif. 1968. Atty. FCC, Washington, 1959-62; adj. prof. U. Md., Europe, 1965; prof. law Golden Gate U. Sch. Law, San Francisco, 1968—; dean Golden Gate U. Sch. Law (Sch. Law), 1974-81. Contbr. to: Damages Book, 1975, 76. Bd. dirs. San Francisco Neighborhood Legal Assistance Found. Fellow Am. Bar Found.; mem. ABA, Wis. Bar Assn., Calif. Bar Assn., San Francisco Bar Assn. (dir. 1975-77, chmn. legis. com., sec.-treas., pres.-elect 1980-83, pres. 1984), Calif. Women Lawyers (1st pres.), Law in a Free Soc. (exec. com.), Continuing Edn. of Bar (chmn. real estate subcom., mem. joint adv. com.), legal services to children, Inc. (pres. 1987-89), San Francisco Neighborhood Legal Assistance Found. (dir. and exec. com. 1985-87), Lawyers Com. for Urban Affairs (dir. and exec. com. 1985-87, co-chairperson 1988-90). Office: Golden Gate U Sch Law 536 Mission St San Francisco CA 94105-2967

MCKELVIE, RODERICK R., federal judge; b. 1946. BA, Harvard U., 1968; ME, Roosevelt U., 1970; JD, U. Pa., 1973. Law clk. to Hon. Caleb Layton U.S. Dist. Ct., Wilmington, Del., 1973-74; assoc. Richards, Layton & Finger, Wilmington, 1974-79; ptnr. Ashby, McKelvie & Geddes, Wilmington, 1979-92; fed. judge U.S. Dist. Ct. (Del. dist.), Wilmington, 1992—. Active World Affairs Coun., 1988—, United Way Govt. Rels. Commn. Mem. ABA, Del. State Bar, Richard S. Rodney Inn of Ct. (mem. exec. com., pres. 1992-93). Office: US Dist Ct 844 N King St # 10 Wilmington DE 19801

MCKELVY, NICOLE ANDRÉE, librarian; b. Paris, France, Mar. 5, 1932; came to U.S., 1960; d. André François and Marie Léonie (Bihr) Burdeyron; m. Raymond E. Hortness, July, 1958 (div. Jan. 1971); children: Estelle, Raymond Jr., André, Roy, Jeannette. Dawid; m. William T. Sean McKelvy, Dec., 1981. Baccalaureat, Coll. de Jeunes Filles, Chateauroux, France, 1949; student, Pan Am. U., 1972-81. Cert. tchr., Tex. Chief operator, interpreter U.S. Forces in France, Chateauroux, 1952-60; tchr.'s aide Pharr, San Juan, Alamo (Tex.) Ind. Sch. Dist., 1968-69; income tax preparer, tchr. H&R Block, McAllen, Tex., 1969-83; clk. acquisitions and periodicals Pan Am. U., Edinburg, Tex., 1971-72, sr. clk. acquisitions, 1972-80; adminstrv. supr. interlibr. loan office U. Tex.-Pan Am. U., Edinburg, 1980-93; dir. Alamo Pub. Libr., 1988—; mem. OCLC panel on Interlibr. Loan, ALA Midwinter Conf., San Antonio, Tex. 1992. Pres. Am. Legion Aux., Pharr/Alamo, 1975—; counselor, vol. Juv. Ct. Coun., Alamo, 1989—. Mem. Tex. Libr. Assn., Valley Libr. Assn. (v.p., pres.). Avocations: knitting, embroidering, camping, music, collecting unicorns. Home: Box 2302 Alamo TX 78516 Office: Lalo Arcaute Pub Libr Box 2501 Alamo TX 78516

MCKELWAY, ALEXANDER JEFFREY, religion studies educator; b. Durham, N.C., Dec. 8, 1932; s. Alexander Jeffrey and Alice (Gibbon) McK.; m. Adelaide Bullard, Sept. 17, 1960; children: Alexander J., Daniel, Matthew Phillip. AB, Davidson Coll., 1954; BD, Princeton Theol. Sem., 1954-57; ThD, U. Basil, 1963. Minister Vienna (Austria) Community Ch., 1958-60; asst. prof. Dartmouth Coll., Hanover, N.H., 1963-65; Paul B. Freeland prof. religion Davidson (N.C.) Coll., 1965—, faculty chair, 1991-94; vis. prof. Princeton (N.J.) Theol. Sem., 1973, 86, 87; active The Fulbright Commn.,

Vienna, Austria, 1958-60. Author: The Systematic Theology of Paul Tillich, 1964, The Freedom of God and Human Liberation, 1991; editor: The Context of Contemporary Theology, 1974. Chair jud. com. Synod of N.C., 1975; moderator Charlotte (N.C.) Presbytery, 1985, active, 1972—; active Kincaid for Congress com., Charlotte, N.C., 1980, Ex. Com. Dem. Party, Davidson, 1975-77. Grad. fellow in theology Princeton Sem., 1957, Younger Scholars fellow NEH, 1969. Mem. Am. Acad. Religion, Calvin Studies Soc., Duodecim Soc., Am. Theol. Soc. Office: Davidson Coll Dept Religion Davidson NC 28036

MCKENNA, ALVIN JAMES, lawyer; b. New Orleans, Aug. 17, 1943; s. Dixon N. Sr. and Mabel (Duplantier) McK.; m. Carol Jean Windheim, 1963; children: Sara, Alvin James Jr., Martha, Andrea, Erin, Rebecca. AB, Canisius Coll., 1963; JD, Notre Dame U., 1966. Bar: N.Y. 1966, Ohio 1967, U.S. Dist. Ct. (so. dist.) Ohio 1968, U.S. Dist. Ct. (no. dist.) Ohio 1978, U.S. Ct. Appeals (6th cir.) 1969, U.S. Supreme Ct. 1977. Law clk. to presiding justice U.S. Dist. Ct. (so. dist.), Columbus, Ohio, 1966-68; asst. U.S. atty., 1968-70; ptnr. Porter, Wright, Morris & Arthur, 1970—. Mem. Gahanna (Ohio) City Council, 1972-80, 82-84; chmn. Gahanna Charter Rev. Commn., 1981; v.p. Community Urban Redevel. Corp., Gahanna, 1984—. Named one of Ten Outstanding Young Persons in Columbus, Jaycees, 1974. Mem. ABA, Ohio Bar Assn., Fed. Bar Assn. (pres. Columbus chpt. 1973-74), Columbus Bar Assn. (chair fed. cts. com. 1972-74). Home: 202 Academy Ct Columbus OH 43230-2104 Office: Porter Wright Morris & Arthur 41 S High St Columbus OH 43215-6101

MCKENNA, ANDREW JAMES, paper distribution and printing company executive, baseball club executive; b. Chgo., Sept. 17, 1929; s. Andrew James and Anita (Fruin) McK.; m. Mary Joan Pickett, June 20, 1953; children: Suzanne, Karen, Andrew, William, Joan, Kathleen, Margaret. B.S., U. Notre Dame, 1951; JD., DePaul U., 1954. Bar: Ill. Chmn., pres., CEO Schwarz Paper Co., Morton Grove, Ill., 1964—; dir. Chgo. Nat. League Ball Club Inc., Chgo. Bears.; bd. dirs. Dean Foods Co., First Nat. Bank Chgo., First Chgo. Corp., Skyline Corp., Tribune Co., AON Corp., McDonald's Corp.; bd. govs. Chgo. Stock Exch. Chmn. bd. trustees U. Notre Dame; bd. dirs. Cath. Charities of Chgo., Children's Meml. Med. Ctr. Chgo., Mus. Sci. & Industry, Chgo. Mem. Chgo. Athletic Assn., Econs. Club, Lyric Opera (bd. dirs.), Chgo. Club, Comml. Club, Econs. Club, Glen View Golf Club, Old Elm Club, Merit Club, Casino Club, The Island Club. Home: 60 Locust Rd Winnetka IL 60093-3751 Office: Schwarz Paper Co 8338 Austin Ave Morton Grove IL 60053-3288

MCKENNA, DAVID LOREN, seminary president, clergyman; b. Detroit, May 5, 1929; s. William Loren and Ilme E. (Matson) McK.; m. Jean Voorheis, June 9, 1950; children: David Douglas, Debra Lynn, Suzanne Marie, Robert Bruce. AA, Spring Arbor Jr. Coll., 1949; BA magna cum laude in History, Western Mich. U., 1951; MDiv, Asbury Theol. Sem., 1953; MA, U. Mich., 1955, PhD (Clifford Woody scholar), 1958; LLD, Houghton Coll., 1974, Spring Arbor Coll., 1976, Lewis and Clark Coll., 1978, Seattle U., 1982, Marion Coll., 1983; LHD, Roberts Wesleyan Coll., 1986. Ordained to ministry Free Methodist Ch. N.Am., 1950; dean of men Spring Arbor Jr. Coll., 1953-55, instr. psychology, 1955-60, acad. dean, 1955-57, v.p., 1958-60, pres., 1961-68; lectr. higher edn. U. Mich., 1958-60; asst. prof., coord. Ctr. for the Study of Higher Edn., Ohio State U., Columbus, 1960-61; pres. Seattle Pacific U., 1968-82, Asbury Theol. Sem., 1982-94; del. World Meth. Coun., London, 1966, Nairobi, Kenya, 1987, Singapore, 1991, v.p. N.Am. sect., 1987—; chmn. Mich. Commn. Coll. Accrediting, 1966-68; bd. dirs. Council Advancement Small Colls., 1964-67; pres. Assn. Free Meth. Colls., 1968-70; chmn. Christian Coll. Consortium, 1970-74; participant Internat. Congress World Evangelization, 1974, Consultation on World Evangelization, Pattaya, Thailand, 1980, Lausanne II, Manila, 1989; mem. bd. adminstrn., exec. com. Nat. Assn. Evangelicals, 2d v.p., 1975-81; bd. reference Black Evangelistic Enterprise, Evangelicals for Social Action, Ugandan Relief, Youth for Christ Internat. Author: The Jesus Model, 1976, Awake, My Conscience!, 1977, The Communicator's Commentary: Mark, 1982, The Communicator's Commentary: Job, 1986, Renewing Our Ministry, 1986, Mega Truth, 1986, The Whisper of His Grace, 1987, Discovering Job, 1988, Power to Follow, Grace to Lead, 1989, Love Your Work, 1990, The Coming Great Awakening, 1990, Communicator's Commentary on Isaiah, vol. I, 1993, vol. II, 1994, When Our Parents Need Us Most, 1994; exec. editor: The Urban Crisis, 1969, Minister's Personal Library, 1987-89, Religious Book Club, 1989—; nat. radio commentator: This is Our World, 1983—; contbr. articles to profl. jours. Pres. United Community Services, Jackson, Mich., 1968, Wash. Coll. Assn., 1970, 76; trustee United Way, Pacific Sci. Ctr., Seattle Found., Spring Arbor Coll., 1983—; bd. dirs. Bread for the World, 1980-86, Jr. Achievement, 1966-68, Land O'Lakes council Boy Scouts Am., 1965-68; mem. Wash. State Council Postsecondary Edn. 1969-74, Pacific Sci. Ctr., 1969-82, Seattle Found., 1975-82; v.p. Bluegrass Tomorrow, 1989—; chmn. R & D com. United Way Bluegrass, 1984-89, bd. dirs., 1987—; sec. Nat. Religious Partnership Environment, 1993—. Named One of Outstanding Young Men of Yr., Jr. C. of C., Seattle and Puget Sound, 1965, Outstanding Citizen of Yr., 1976, Outstanding Educator, Religious Heritage of Am., 1993; recipient Others award Salvation Army, 1994; Named in his honor McKenna Hall, Seattle Pacific U., 1983, David L. and Janet McKenna Chapel, Asbury Theol. Sem., 1994. Mem. Assn. Am. Colls. (dir. 1974-77), Ind. Colls. Wash. (pres. 1969-71, co-chmn. 1968-70, 79-80), Wash. State Council Econ. Edn. (dir. 1980), Am. Council Edn. (interassn. pres.'s com. on accreditation 1979-80), N.W. Assn. Schs. and Colls. (commr. 1975-79), N. Central Assn. Colls. and Schs. (chmn., dir. 1966-68), Nat. Assn. Ind. Colls. and Univs. (dir. 1976-80, sec. 1978), Council Postsecondary Accreditation (dir. 1979—), Seattle C. of C., Wash. Friends of Higher Edn., Wash. Athletic Club (bd. govs.), Rainier Club (Seattle), The Diet Club, Lafayette (Ky.) Club, Lexington Tennis Club, Rotary (pres. Jackson chpt. 1966-67, Paul Harris fellow 1982), Phi Kappa Phi. Office: Asbury Theol Sem Office of Pres Wilmore KY 40390

MCKENNA, FRANK JOSEPH, Canadian politician, lawyer; b. Apohaqui, N.B., Can., Jan. 19, 1948; s. Durward and Olive (Moody) McK.; m. Julie Friel; children: Tobias John, Christine Alice, James Durward. BA with honors, St. Francis Xavier U., 1970; postgrad., Queen's U., 1970-71; LLB, U. N.B., 1974; DSc (hon.), Université de Moncton, Can., 1988; LLD (hon.), University of N.B., Can., 1988, Mt. Allison U., Can., 1991. Spl. asst. to pres. Privy Council, 1971; rsch. asst. Constl. Law Unit, 1973-74; v.p. U. N.B. Faculty of Law Liberal Assn., Fredericton, 1974; ptnr. Martin, Lordon, McKenna & Bowes, Chatham, 1974-87; mem. N.B. Liberal Party, 1982, leader, 1985; premier Province of N.B., Fredericton, 1987—. Recipient Vanier award, 1988, Distinction award Can. Advanced Tech. Assn., 1994; named Econ. Developer of Yr., Econ. Developers' Assn. Can., 1993, Chair, Can. Quality Month, 1994. Mem. Can. Bar Assn., N.B. Bar Assn. Liberal. Avocations: jogging, baseball, hockey. Office: PO Box 6000, Fredericton, NB Canada E3B 5H1

MCKENNA, GEORGE LAVERNE, art museum curator; b. Detroit, Dec. 7, 1924; s. John LaVerne and Carolyn Georgia (Schwab) McK.; m. Janice Ballinger, July 22, 1966. Student, U. Oreg., 1943-44, U. Calif., Berkeley, 1948-49, U. Chgo., 1950; AB, Wayne State U., 1948, MA, 1951. Curator prints, drawings and photographs Nelson-Atkins Mus. Art, Kansas City, Mo., 1952—; cons. Hallmark Cards, Inc., Kansas City, 1974-76. Curator, author exhbn. and coll. catalogues. With U.S. Army, 1943-46. Mem. Am. Assn. Mus., Print Coun. Am. Office: Nelson-Atkins Mus Art 4525 Oak St Kansas City MO 64111-1818

MCKENNA, J. FRANK, III, lawyer; b. Pitts., Nov. 9, 1948; s. J. Frank Jr. and Antoinette (Schlafly) McK.; m. Colleen Shaughnessy, Mar. 25, 1972; children: Collette M., J. Frank IV, Laura J., Stephen J. BA, Williams Coll., 1970; JD, U. Pitts., 1973. Bar: Pa. 1973. Assoc. Thorp, Reed & Armstrong, Pitts., 1973-82, ptnr., 1982-88; ptnr. Babst, Calland, Clements & Zomnir, Pitts., 1988—. Served to lt. USAFR, 1973-74. Named one of Outstanding Young Men In Am., 1982. Mem. ABA, Pa. Bar Assn., Allegheny County Bar Assn. (chmn. young lawyers sect. 1980, v.p. 1987, bd. govs. 1988-89, pres.-elect 1991, pres. 1992), Am. Law Inst., Am. Judicature Soc., Pitts. Field Club, Pitts. Athletic Club. Avocations: hunting, fishing. Home: 101 Fox Ridge Farms Dr Pittsburgh PA 15215-1142 Office: Babst Calland Clements & Zonmir 2 Gateway Ctr Pittsburgh PA 15222-1402

MC KENNA, JAMES ALOYSIUS, broadcasting executive, former lawyer; b. Poughkeepsie, N.Y., July 1, 1918; s. James Aloysius and Eleanor Frances (Mahoney) McK.; m. Rebekah Ann Rial, Sept. 1, 1941; children: Michelle M., James A., Dennis M., Matthew M., Marc W., Aileen M. Student, Manhattan Coll., 1934-35; B.S., Cath. U., 1938; LL.B., Georgetown U., 1942. Bar: D.C. 1941, U.S. Supreme Ct. 1947. Counsel Civil Aeronautics Bd., 1941-42; asst. to gen. counsel Office Alien Property Custodian, 1942-44; practicing lawyer Washington, 1946-87; ptnr. McKenna, Wilkinson & Kittner, 1952-87. Lt. (j.g.) USNR; active duty 1944-46. Named Outstanding Alumni Cath. U. Am., 1978; recipient DuBois medal Mt. St. Mary's Coll., 1966. Mem. FCC Bar Assn., Inst. Radio Engrs., Georgetown U. Alumni Assn., Delta Theta Phi. Home: 5219 Oakland Rd Bethesda MD 20815-6640

MCKENNA, JOHN DENNIS, environmental testing engineer; b. N.Y.C., Apr. 1, 1940; s. Hubert Guy and Elizabeth Ann (Record) McK.; BSChemE, Manhattan Coll., 1961; MSChemE, Newark Coll. Engring., 1968; MBA, Rider Coll., 1974, PhD, Walden U., 1991; m. Christel Klages, Dec. 26, 1964; children: Marc, Michelle. Tech. asst. to pres. Eldib Engring. & Rsch. Co., Newark, 1964-67; project mgr. Princeton Chem. Rsch., Inc. (N.J.), 1967-68; projects dir. Rsch. Cottrell Environ. Systems, Bound Brook, N.J., 1968-72; v.p., then pres. Enviro-Systems & Rsch., Inc., Roanoke, Va., 1973-79; pres. ETS, Inc., Roanoke, 1979-91, ETS Internat. Inc., 1991—; chmn. air pollution adv. bd. State of Va.; workshop lectr. and sci reviewer publs. EPA, 1978-79. Author chpts. to books; contbr. articles to profl. jours. Recipient Outstanding Engring. Grad. Manhattan Coll. Centennial award, 1992. Mem. AIChE (treas. Ctrl. Va. chpt.), Air Pollution Control Assn., Air and Waste Mgmt. Assn. (divsn. chmn. tech. coun., Pitts.), Tau Beta Pi (N.Y. Xi chpt.). Roman Catholic. Home: RR 1 PO Box 1925 Rocky Mount VA 24151-9607 Office: ETS Inc 1401 Municipal Rd NW Roanoke VA 24012-1309

MCKENNA, LAWRENCE M., federal judge; b. 1933. AB, Fordham Coll., 1956; LLB, Columbia U., 1959. With Simpson Thacher & Bartlett, N.Y.C., 1959-69, Wormser, Kiely, Alessandroni, Hyde & McCann, N.Y.C., 1969-90; judge U.S. Dist. Ct. (so. dist.), N.Y., 1990—. Mem. N.Y. State Bar Assn., Copyright Soc. USA. Office: US Dist Ct US Courthouse Foley Sq New York NY 10007-1501

MC KENNA, MALCOLM CARNEGIE, vertebrate paleontologist, curator, educator; b. Pomona, Calif., July 21, 1930; s. Donald Carnegie and Bernice Caroline (Waller) McK.; m. Priscilla Coffey, June 17, 1952; children: Douglas M. Katharine L., Andrew M., Bruce C. B.A., U. Calif., Berkeley, 1954, Ph.D., 1958. Instr. dept. paleontology U. Calif., Berkeley, 1958-59; asst. curator dept. vertebrate paleontology Am. Mus. Natural History, N.Y.C., 1960-64; assoc. curator Am. Mus. Natural History, 1964-65; Frick assoc. curator, chmn. Frick Lab., 1965-68, Frick curator, 1968—; asst. prof. geology Columbia U., N.Y.C., 1960-64, assoc. prof., 1964-72, prof. geol. scis., 1972—; research assoc. U. Colo. Mus., Boulder, 1962—. Contbr. articles on fossil mammals and their evolution, the dating of Mesozoic and Tertiary sedimentary rocks, and paleogeography and plate tectonics to profl. jours. Bd. dirs. Bergen Community (N.J.) Mus., 1964-67, pres., 1965-66; trustee Flat Rock Brook Nature Assn., N.J., 1979-93, Raymond Alf Mus., Webb Sch. of Calif., 1980—, Dwight-Englewood Sch., Englewood, N.J., 1968-80; bd. dirs. Flat Rock Brook Nature Assn., N.J., 1979-84; trustee Claremont McKenna Coll., Calif., 1983-91; Planned Parenthood Bergen County, N.J., 1979-88, Mus. No. Ariz., 1978-85, 87-93. Nat. Acad. Scis. exchange fellow USSR, 1965. Fellow AAAS, Explorers Club, Geol. Soc. Am.; mem. Grand Canyon Natural History Assn. (bd. dirs. 1972-76), Soc. Systematic Zoology (coun. 1974-77), Soc. Vertebrate Paleontology (v.p. 1975, pres. 1976), Am. Geophys. Union, Am. Soc. Mammalogists, Paleontol. Soc. (award 1992), Soc. for Study Evolution, Polish Acad. Scis. (fgn.), Sigma Xi. Office: Am Mus Nat History Vertebrate Paleontology Central Park St W New York NY 10026-4355 also: Columbia Univ 420 Lewisohn Hall Broadway 116th St New York NY 10027

MCKENNA, MARGARET ANNE, college president; b. R.I., June 3, 1945; d. Joseph John and Mary (Burns) McK.; children: Michael Aaron McKenna Miller, David Christopher McKenna Miller. BA in Sociology, Emmanuel Coll., 1967; postgrad., Boston Coll. Law Sch., 1968; JD, So. Meth. U., 1971; LLD (hon.), U. Upsala, N.J., 1978, Fitchburg (Mass.) State Coll., 1979, Regis Coll., 1982; D Commnunity Affairs, U. R.I., 1979. Bar: Tex. 1971, D.C. 1973. Atty. Dept. Justice, Washington, 1971-73; exec. dir. Internat. Assn. Ofcl. Human Rights Agys., Washington, 1973-74; mgmt. cons. Dept. Treasury, Washington, 1975-76; dep. council to Pres. White House, Washington, 1976-79; dep. undersec. Dept. Edn., Washington, 1979-81; dir. Mary Ingraham Bunting Inst., Radcliffe Coll., Cambridge, Mass., 1981-85; v.p. program planning Radcliffe Coll., Cambridge, 1982-85; pres. Lesley Coll., Cambridge, 1985—; bd. dirs. Stride Rite Corp., Cambridge, Best Products Co., Inc., Richmond, Va., Consolidated Natural Gas Co., Pitts., Coun. of Ind. Colls., Washington. Chair higher edn. task force Clinton Transition, 1992-93; chair edn. task force Mayor Thomas Marino Transition Com., 1994. Recipient Outstanding Contribution award Civil Rights Leadership Conf., 1978; named Woman of Yr. Women's Equity Action League, 1979, Outstanding Woman of Yr. Big Sister Assn., 1986. Democrat. Office: Lesley Coll Office of the President 29 Everett St Cambridge MA 02138-2790

MCKENNA, MARIANNE, architect; b. Montreal, Que., Can., Sept. 25, 1950; d. Richard D. and Anna M. (Lohr) McK.; m. Ian C.; children: Cameron Lohr, Portia McKinley. Attended, The Study Montreal, 1969; BA, Swarthmore Coll., 1972; MArch, Yale U., 1976. Asst. architect Bobrow & Fieldman, Montreal, Can., 1976-78; architect Denys Lasdun, Redhouse & Softley, London, 1978-79; architect Barton Myers Assocs., 1980-87, assoc., 1981—; founding ptnr. Kuwabara Payne McKenna Blumberg Archs., Toronto, 1987—; assoc. prof. architecture U. Toronto, 1994—; guest critic, U. Toronto, U. Waterloo, McGill U., Yale U., 1975-87; exec. dir. Ont. Coll. of Art. Selected projects include Union Libr., Toronto, Hasbro Toy Co. N.Y.C.; selected projects present firm York U. Ctr. Fine Arts 3, Tudhope Assocs. Design Studios Toronto, 35 E Wacker Addition Corp., Kitchener City Hall, Royal Conservatory of Music Master Plan, Facility for Federally Sentenced Women, Kitchener. Recipient Gov. Gen.'s award for Architecture, Royal Archtl. Inst. Can., 1994. Mem. Ont. Assn. Architects, Ordre des architectes de Québec, Royal Architecture Inst. Can. Office: Kuwabara Payne McKenna Blumberg Archs, 322 King St W 3rd Fl, Toronto, ON Canada M5V 1J2

MCKENNA, MATTHEW MORGAN, lawyer; b. Washington, Apr. 29, 1950; s. James Aloysius and Rebecca (Rial) McK.; m. Nancy Fitzpatrick, Sept. 11, 1976; children: Matthew, James, Christine, Connor. BA, Hamilton Coll., 1972; JD, Georgetown U., 1975, LLM, 1978. Bar: N.Y. 1977. Clk. to Hon. Fred B. Ugast, Superior Ct., Washington, 1975-76; assoc. Olwine, Connelly, N.Y.C., 1976-79; assoc. Winthrop, Stimson, Putnam & Roberts, N.Y.C., 1979-83, ptnr., 1984-93; v.p. taxes PepsiCo, Purchase, N.Y., 1993—; adj. prof. Sch. Law, Fordham U., N.Y.C., 1983-94. Trustee Merrill Lynch Found., 1986-95, Mt. St. Mary's Coll., Emmitsburg, Md., 1994—. Mem. ABA (tax sect.), N.Y. State Bar Assn. (chmn. com. on fgn. activities of U.S. taxpayers), Assn. Bar City N.Y. (com. internat. taxation). Home: 35 Valley Rd Bronxville NY 10708-2226 Office: PepsiCo 700 Anderson Hill Rd Purchase NY 10577

MCKENNA, MICHAEL JOSEPH, manufacturing company executive; b. Phila., Feb. 18, 1935; s. Michael J. and Stella Marie (Gramigna) McK.; B.S., LaSalle Coll., 1962; m. Letitia Ward, Feb. 9, 1957; children—Letitia, Carol, Suzanne, Kathleen Jane, Margaret. With Crown Cork & Seal Co., Phila., 1957—, sales rep., 1969, dist. sales mgr., Phila., 1970, regional sales mgr., 1974, v.p. sales and mktg., 1979-86, former sr. v.p., also bd. dirs., now exec. v.p., pres. N.Am. Divsn., Crown Cork & Seal Co., Inc. Founding bd. dirs. Northampton Twp. Library, 1967-71; pres. Churchville PTA, 1969-70. Served with U.S. Army, 1955-57. Mem. Can. Mfrs. Inst. (standing com. 1980—). Republican. Roman Catholic. Club: Old Guard Soc. Home: 247 Magnolia Dr Southampton PA 18966-1456 Office: Crown Cork & Seal Co Inc 9300 Ashton Rd Philadelphia PA 19136*

MCKENNA, QUENTIN CARNEGIE, tool company executive; b. Claremont, Calif., Sept. 2, 1926; s. George Alexander and Lillian Frances (Street) McK.; m. Barbara Louise Williamson, Sept. 12, 1948 (div. 1984);

children: Candace, Megan, Carl, Erin; m. Barbara K. Somogye, Mar. 18, 1989. B.A. cum laude, Pomona Coll., 1948; postgrad., Stanford U. (Hewlett Packard fellow), 1948-50, U. So. Calif., 1951-53, UCLA, 1968-69. Mem. tech. staff guided missile div. Hughes Aircraft Co., 1950-52; with Indsl. Electronics, 1952-55; with Hughes Aircraft Co., 1955-78, asst. group exec. missile systems group, 1977-78; with Kennametal, Inc., Latrobe, Pa., 1978—, CEO, 1974-91, chmn. bd. dirs.; bd. dirs. Interlake Corp.; adj. prof. indsl. adminstrn. Grad. Sch. Indsl. Adminstrn., Carnegie-Mellon U., 1990—. Patentee in field. Trustee St. Vincent Coll., 1981-89; mem. com. bd. trustees Carnegie Sci. Ctr., Carnegie Inst., 1989. Recipient Eli Whitney Meml. award, Soc. Mfg. Engrs., 1983. Mem. Phi Beta Kappa, Sigma Xi. Episcopalian. *

MCKENNA, RICHARD HENRY, hospital consultant; b. Covington, Ky., Dec. 19, 1927; s. Charles Joseph and Mary Florence (Wieck) McK.; m. Patricia Mary Macdonald, Jan. 6, 1979; children: Linda Ann, Theresa K., Joan Marie; stepchildren: Stuart J Goodman, Ann Elizabeth Goodman. BS in Commerce, U. Cin., 1959, MBA, Xavier U., 1963. CPA, Ohio, Ky. Acct., Andrew Jergens Co., Cin., 1947-55; treas., dir. Ramsey Bus. Equipment, Inc., Cin., 1955-59; asst. to pres. Oakley Die and Mfg. Co., Cin.,1959-60, Electro-Jet Tool Co., Inc., Cin., 1959-60; pvt. practice acctg., No. Ky. and Cin., 1960-62; bus. mgr. St. Joseph Hosp., Lexington, Ky., 1962-66; asst. adminstr. fin. U. Ky. Hosp., Lexington, 1966-70; v.p., CFO St. Lawrence Hosp., Lansing, Mich., 1970-87; adj. faculty Aquinas Coll., Grand Rapids, Mich., 1980-89, asst. prof.; chmn. bd. McKenna & McKenna Assocs., Cons., Inc., 1983—; chmn. bd. North Grand River Coop. Laundry, 1986-87; v.p., CFO, asst. sec. and treas. St. Joseph's Hosp., Inc., Savannah, Ga., 1987-95, St. Joseph's Health Ctr., Inc., 1987-90. Former mem. adv. com. to commr. of fin. State of Ky.; chmn. cath. divsn. Oak Hills Bus. Com.; mem. speakers com. Oak Hill Sch. Dist.; bd. dirs. Savannah YMCA, 1992—. Served with U.S. Mcht. Marine, 1945-47, U.S. Army, 1948-51. Mem. Healthcare Fin. Mgmt. Assn. (Follmer award, past dir. Ky. chpt.), Am. Mgmt. Assn., Am. Inst. CPAs, Ky. Soc. CPAs, Mich. Hosp. Assn. (former mem. com. on reimbursement), Ga. Hosp. Assn. (com. on fin. and mgmt.), Delta Mu Delta, Alpha Sigma Lambda.

MCKENNA, ROBERT J., car rental company executive. BA, Iona Coll. With Hertz Corp., 1960-82, successively sales exec., v.p., gen. mgr. truck div., pres. Hertz Equipment Rental Corp.; sr. v.p. ops. Holland Am. Line; pres. Holland Am. Cruise; sr. v.p., gen. mgr. Avis Rent-a-Car; now exec. v.p. Nat. Car Rental System, Inc., Mpls. Office: Nat Car Rental System Inc 7700 France Ave S Minneapolis MN 55435-5296

MC KENNA, SIDNEY F., technical company executive; b. Detroit, Nov. 27, 1922; s. Michael James and Elizabeth Josephine McK.; m. Helen Mary Spiroff, Sept. 20, 1944; children—Lynne Marie McKenna Hoss, Dennis Michael, Patrick Conlon, Mary Elizabeth McKenna Raimondi, Maureen T. McKenna Anderson, Christopher John. A.B., U. Mich., Ann Arbor, 1947; M.A., Wayne State U., 1948. With Ward Baking Co., Detroit, 1939-41; prodn. worker Cadillac Motor Car. (div. Gen. Motors Corp.), Detroit, 1941-42; mem. indsl. relations staff Ford Motor Co., Dearborn, Mich., 1942-79, v.p., 1974-79; sr. v.p. human resources United Techs. Corp., Hartford, Conn., 1980-86, sr. v.p. employee and external relations, 1986-87, sr. v.p. pub. affairs, 1987-90; ret., 1990; bd. dirs. Schwartz Velue Fund. Chmn. adv. bd. Providence Hosp., Detroit, 1972-80; bd. dirs. Brighton (Mich.) Hosp., 1976-80, Mercy Coll., Detroit, 1976-80, United Found., 1976-80, St. Francis Hosp., Hartford, Conn., 1983-89, St. Joseph's Coll., 1988-89. Served with USN, 1942-46. Decorated knight St. Gregory. Mem. Labor Policy Assn. (chmn.), Bus. Roundtable, Orgn. Resources Counselors, Nat. Assn. Mfrs. (bd. dirs. 1988-89), Bloomfield Hills Country Club, Birmingham Athletic Club, Mariner Sands Golf Club, K.C. Roman Catholic. Home: 5680 SE Winged Foot Dr Stuart FL 34997-8642

MCKENNA, TERENCE PATRICK, insurance company executive; b. Oldham, Lancashire, Eng., Sept. 3, 1928; came to U.S., 1929, naturalized, 1939; s. Patrick A. and Mary F. McK.; m. Patricia Buckley, Sept. 22, 1973. Student: St. Thomas Coll., Bloomfield, Conn., 1946-48. With John Hancock Mut. Life Ins. Co., 1951-87; gen. agt. John Hancock Mut. Life Ins. Co., Cherry Hill, N.J., 1963-67; field v.p. gen. agy. dept. John Hancock Mut. Life Ins. Co., Atlanta, 1967-69; field v.p. dist. agy. dept. John Hancock Mut. Life Ins. Co., Boston, 1969-73, 2d v.p. mktg. ops. dept., 1973-74, v.p. dept., 1974-76, sr. v.p. dept., 1976-83, sr. v.p. gen. agy. sales dept., 1983-87; ret. 1987; v.p., also bd. dirs. John Hancock Variable Life Ins. Co.; chmn. bd. mgrs. I.V.A.; bd. dirs. John Hancock Distbrs. Inc., John Hancock Property and Casualty Ins. Co. Served with USMC, 1952-54. Mem. Am. Coll. Life Underwriters, Am. Soc. CLU's, Palm Beach Gardens, Ballen Isles C. C., Univ. Club (Boston), Woods Hole Golf Club (Falmouth, Mass.). Clubs: Univ. (Boston).

MC KENNA, THOMAS JOSEPH, advertising executive; b. Chgo., Oct. 20, 1929; s. Robert Emmet and Helen Elizabeth (Norton) McK.; m. Geraldine M. Bednarz, May 23, 1953 (div. June 1976); children—Terence Patrick, Kathleen Mary, Thomas Joseph Jr. B.A., Northwestern U., 1952. Advt. mgr. farm div. Montgomery Ward, Chgo., 1952-56; mgr. sales promotion Ency. Brit., Chgo., 1956-58, dir. advt. and sales promotion, 1958-61; v.p. Marketways, Inc., Chgo., 1962-63; exec. v.p. Hefter-McKenna Advt., Oak Park, Ill., 1963-69; sr. v.p. creative Douglas Dunhill, Inc., Chgo., 1969-81; pres. McKenna & Erdos, Ltd., Chgo., 1981-91; chmn. McKenna Assocs., Chgo., 1991—. With USAF, 1951-52. Recipient 29 creative awards Chgo. Assn. Direct Mktg., 1973-84. Mem. Direct Mktg. Assn. (Silver Mailbox award 1975). Office: Mc Kenna Assocs 6007 Sheridan Rd Chicago IL 60660-3039

MCKENNA, THOMAS MORRISON, JR., social services organization executive; b. Chgo., July 19, 1937; s. Thomas Morrison and Martha (Stanley) McK.; m. Kay Mary O'Connor, Sept. 10, 1960; children: Mark, Lisa. BA, De Pauw U., 1959; MSW, Columbia U., 1961. Group worker Hamilton-Madison House, N.Y.C., 1961-63, exec. dir., 1967-71; assoc. exec. dir. Bronx (N.Y.) River Neighborhood House, 1963-67; exec. dir. United Neighborhood Houses, N.Y.C., 1971-76, State Communities Aid Assn., N.Y.C. and Albany, N.Y., 1976-85; nat. exec. dir. Big Bros./Big Sisters Am., Phila., 1985—; asst. prof. NYU Sch. Social Work, 1974-82; mem. bd. overseers U. Pa. Sch. Social Work, 1991—. Mem. bd. local sch. dist. 8, Bronx, 1964-67; coun. against poverty N.Y.C. Antipoverty Bd., 1971-76; adv. bd. Columbia U. Sch. Social Work, 1980-84; chmn. adv. bd. N.Y.C. Dept. Social Svcs., 1977-85. Mem. NASW (pres. N.Y.C. chpt. 1983-85), One to One Found. Avocations: sailing, tennis. Home: 1307 E Susquehanna Ave Philadelphia PA 19125-2823 Office: Big Bros/Big Sisters Am 230 N 13th St Philadelphia PA 19107-1538

MCKENNA, VIRGIL VINCENT, psychology educator, researcher; b. Mineola, N.Y., Apr. 20, 1935; s. Virgil Vincent McKenna and Mary (Winifred) Quinn; m. Willafay Cardwell Hopkins, Aug. 24, 1957; children—Quinn Hopkins, Elizabeth Conroy. A.B., Coll. William and Mary, 1957; M.A., Swarthmore Coll., 1959; Ph.D., Princeton U., 1967. Research asst. Swarthmore Coll., Pa., 1957-59; instr. psychology Carleton Coll., Northfield, Minn., 1959-60; asst. instr. USPHS fellow Princeton U., N.J., 1960-62; prof. psychology Coll. William and Mary, Williamsburg, Va., 1962—; research asst. Ednl. Testing Service, Princeton, N.J., 1962-63. Author: Stylistic Factors in Learning and Retention, 1968; co-editor: Introductory Psychology: Readings for Discussion, 1982; contbr. articles to profl. jours. NSF fellow, 1960; grantee NASA contract 1975, Ctr. for Population Rsch. contract 1976, NEH summer seminar, 1988. Mem. Eastern Psychol. Assn., Soc. Personology, So. Soc. Philosophy and Psychology (R.M. Griffith award 1965), Sigma Xi. Democrat. Avocations: wire fox terriers; poetry. Home: 126 Shirley Ave PO Box 1931 Williamsburg VA 23187 Office: Coll William and Mary Dept Psychology Williamsburg VA 23185

MC KENNA, WILLIAM EDWARD, entrepreneur; b. Boston, Aug. 9, 1919; s. Alfred W. and Mary E.C. (Quigley) McK.; children: William P., Kathleen M., Daniel J., Eileen F., Paul V., Mary Ellen; m. Mary N. Smith, Oct. 3, 1968. A.B., Holy Cross Coll., 1947; M.B.A., Harvard, 1949. Diplomate: C.P.A., N.Y., Calif. Staff accountant Touche, Niven, Bailey & Smart, N.Y.C., 1949-52; v.p., controller Monroe Calculating Machine Co., Orange, N.J., 1952-60; also dir.; v.p., treas., controller Litton Industries,

Beverly Hills, Calif., 1960-63; sr. v.p. Litton Industries Bus. Equipment Group, Beverly Hills, 1964-67; also dir.; chmn., chief exec., dir. Hunt Foods & Industries, Inc., Fullerton, Calif., 1967-68; chmn., chief exec., dir. Norton Simon, Inc., Fullerton, 1968-69; bus. cons., 1969-70; chmn., dir. Technicolor, Inc., Hollywood, Calif., 1970-76; chmn. bd. Sambo's Restaurants Inc., Santa Barbara, Calif., 1979-81, Vencap, Inc., Irvine, Calif., 1977-79; now gen. ptnr. MCK Investment Co., Beverly Hills, Calif.; bd. dirs. Calif. Amplifier, Inc., Safeguard Health Enterprises, Inc., Calprop Corp., WMS Industries, Inc., Williams Hospitality Group, Drexler Tech., Inc.. Mem. pres.'s council, regent, assoc. trustee Coll. Holy Cross; trustee St. John's Hosp. Found.; regent St. Mary's Coll., Calif. Mem. Am. Inst. C.P.A.s, Nat. Assn. Accts., Fin. Execs. Inst., Calif. Soc. C.P.A.s, N.Y. Soc. C.P.A.s, N.J. Soc. C.P.A.s, Tailhook Assn., Delta Epsilon, Alpha Sigma Nu. Home and Office: 912 Oxford Way Beverly Hills CA 90210-2841

MCKENNA, WILLIAM JOHN, textile products executive; b. N.Y.C., Oct. 11, 1926; s. William T. and Florence (Valis) McK.; m. Jean T. McNulty, Aug. 27, 1949 (dec. Nov. 1984); children: Kevin, Marybeth, Peter, Dawn; m. Karen Lynne Hilgert, Aug. 6, 1988; children: Katherine Lynne, William John IV. BBA, Iona Coll., 1949; M.S. (Univ. Store Service scholar), NYU, 1950. V.p. Hat Corp. Am., N.Y.C., 1961-63, v.p. mktg., 1961-63, exec. v.p., 1963-67; pres. Manhattan Shirt Co. N.Y.C., 1967-74, Lee Co., Inc., Shawnee Mission, Kans., 1974-82, also dir.; pres., dir. Kellwood Co., St. Louis, 1982—, chief exec. officer, 1984—, also bd. dirs., chmn., pres., chief exec. officer, 1991—; dir. Genovese Drug Stores, Melville, N.Y., United Mo. Bancshares, Kansas City, Mo., United Mo. Bank of St. Louis. Trustee St. Louis U., Boys Hope; permanent deacon Archdiocese St. Louis. With USN, 1944-46, PTO. Mem. Sovereign Mil. Order Malta, St. Louis Club, Bellerive Country Club. Roman Catholic. Office: Kellwood Co PO Box 14734 Saint Louis MO 63178-4374

MCKENNA, WILLIAM STUART, sales and marketing executive; b. New Rochelle, N.Y., Apr. 10, 1943; s. William Howard and Genevieve Margaret (Connacher) McK.; m. Linda Ann Gilbert, Apr. 13, 1973; children: Keri Lynn, Kimberly Marie. BA, U. Mass., 1966. Asst. mgr. pers. Welch Candy divsn. Nabisco, Inc., Mansfield, Mass., 1966-68, salesman Welch Candy divsn., 1968-71; salesman Fuji X-Ray Film, Hartford, Conn., 1971-73; territory sales mgr. Sweetheart Cup, Somerville, Mass., 1973-74, mgr. instl. markets, 1976-82; mgr. regional sales Sweetheart Cup, Balt., 1982-86; mgr. divsnl. sales Ft. Howard/Sweetheart, Balt., 1986-87; v.p. nat. accounts Ziff Co., West Boylston, Mass., 1988-89, v.p. sales, 1989-90, exec. v.p., 1990—. Co-chair Shrewsbury Sch. Bldg. Assn., Mass., 1992; coach Odyssey of the Mind, College Park, Md., 1993. Mem. Nat. restaurant Assn., New England Wholesale Food Distbn. Assn., Mass. Restaurant Assn., Mass. Fodd Assn., ISSA. Avocations: building and home improvement, reading, swimming, golf. Office: Ziff Co Inc 180 Shrewsbury St West Boylston MA 01583-2106

MC KENNEY, WALTER GIBBS, JR., lawyer, publishing company executive; b. Jacobsville, Md., Apr. 22, 1913; s. Walter Gibbs and Mary (Starkey) McK.; m. Florence Roberta Rea, July 17, 1939. Student, Dickinson Sem., 1935-37; Ph.B. Dickinson Coll., 1939; J.D., U. Va., 1942; LL.D. Dickinson Sch. Law, 1964; D.H.L., Lycoming Coll., 1984. Bar: Md. 1942. Practiced in Balt., 1942—; partner McKenney, Thomsen & Burke; partner, gen. mgr., editor Taxes & Estates Pub. Co., Balt., 1946—; chmn. trust com. Equitable Bank, N.A., Balt., 1970-84; dir. Equitable Bancorp., 1960-84; lectr. Southwestern Grad. Sch. Banking, 1966-76. Editor Taxes and Estates, 1946—, Minimizing Taxes, 1946-84, The Educator, 1965—, The Patron, 1968-84. Pres. Kelso Home for Girls; mem. bd. child care Balt. Conf. Meth. Ch., pres., 1961-64; pres. Balt. Estate Planning Council, 1963-64; trustee Goucher Coll., 1968-84, Dickinson Coll., Lycoming Coll., Wesley Theol. Sem., Loyola Coll. at Balt., 1975-83, Franklin Sq. Hosp., Franklin Square Found., Franklin Square Health System, Helix Health System. Served to lt. USNR, 1942-45. Mem. ABA, Md., Balt. bar assns. Republican. Methodist. Home: 105 Brightwood Club Dr Lutherville MD 21093-3628 Office: One N Charles St Ste 400 Baltimore MD 21201

MCKENNON, KEITH ROBERT, chemical company executive; b. Condon, Oreg., Dec. 25, 1933; s. Russel M. and Lois E. (Edgerton) McK.; m. Patricia Dragon, Sept. 30, 1961; children: Brian, Marc, Kevin. B.S., Oreg. State U., 1955. Rsch. chemist Dow Chem. Co., Pittsburg, Calif., 1955-67; sales mgr. Dow Chem. Co., Houston, 1967; research mgr. Dow Chem. Co., Midland, Mich., 1968-69, bus. mgr., 1969-80, v.p., 1980-83, group v.p., 1983-87, exec. v.p., 1987-92, also bd. dirs.; pres. Dow USA, 1987-89; chmn., chief exec. officer Dow Corning Corp., 1992-94, also bd. dirs.; chmn. PacifiCorp, Portland, Oreg., 1994—; bd. dirs. PacifiCorp, Tektronix, Marion Merrill Dow. Patentee. Republican. Presbyterian. Home: PO Box 5542 Stateline NV 89449-5542 Office: PacifiCorp # 1600 700 NE Multnomah Portland OR 97202

MCKENNY, COLLIN GRAD, banker; b. Seattle, July 29, 1944; d. Edward Paul and Betty B. (Collins) Grad; m. Jon W. McKenny, June 15, 1975 (div. June 1982); m. Spencer Frank Ison, Dec. 31, 1985. BA, U. Wash., Seattle, 1966; MBA, Seattle U., 1969; grad., Pacific Coast Banking Sch., 1979. From mgmt. trainee to v.p. Peoples Nat. Bank, Seattle, 1966-85; sr. v.p. Barclays Bank of Calif., San Francisco, 1985-88, Star Banc Corp., Cin., 1988—. Treas. Salvation Army, Federal Way, Wash., 1981-83; bd. dirs. Boys & Girls Clubs, Seattle, 1982-85. Mem. Am. Bankers Assn. (bd. dirs. bancard exec. com., chmn. ann. conf. 1989—, chmn. bankcard schools 1990-94), Cin. Bus. Incubator (chmn.), Bankers Club, Chi Omega. Office: Star Banc Corp 425 Walnut St Cincinnati OH 45202-3912

MCKENNY, JERE WESLEY, energy firm executive; b. Okmulgee, Okla., Feb. 14, 1929; s. Jere Claus and Juanita (Hunter) McK.; m. Anne Ross Stewart, May 4, 1957; children: Jere James, Robert Stewart. BS in Geol. Engring. U. Okla., 1951, MS in Geol. Engring. 1952. With Kerr-McGee Corp., Oklahoma City, 1953—, mgr. oil and gas exploration, 1968-69, v.p. oil and gas exploration, 1969-74, v.p. exploration, 1974-77, vice chmn., 1977-83, pres., 1983-84, pres., chief operating officer, 1984—; Mem. adv. bd. Sch. Geology and Geophysics U. Okla. Served with U.S. Army, 1953-55. Mem. Am. Assn. Petroleum Geologists, Am. Petroleum Inst. (bd. dirs.), Ind. petroleum Assn. Am. (bd. dirs.), Houston Geol. Soc., Oklahoma City Geol. Soc., Oklahoma City U. C. of C., Oklahoma City Allied Arts Found., Okla. Heritage Found., Sigma Xi, Sigma Gamma Epsilon. Episcopalian. Office: Kerr-McGee Corp PO Box 25861 Oklahoma City OK 73125-0861

MC KENZIE, HAROLD CANTRELL, JR., retired manufacturing executive; b. Carrollton, Ga., Dec. 25, 1931; s. Harold Cantrell and Sue (Tanner) McK.; m. Katherine Branch, Apr. 11, 1958; children—Ansley, Katherine, Harold Cantrell, III. B.Indsl. Engring., Ga. Inst. Tech., 1953; J.D., Emory U., 1955; A.M.P., Harvard Bus. Sch. Bar: Ga. 1955. Law clk. to judge U.S. Dist. Ct., Atlanta, 1956; ptnr. firm Troutman, Sams, Schroder & Lockerman, Atlanta, 1957-67; with Ga. Power Co., 1967-81; dir. Internet Corp., 1971—; pres. So. Electric Internat., Inc., 1981-85; chmn., chief exec. officer Machine Techs., Inc. (doing bus. as MacTech Inc.), Martinsville, Va., 1986-89; sr. adv. facilities Atlanta Project of Carter Presdl. Ctr., 1992—. Mem. State Bar Ga., Capital City (Atlanta), Piedmont Driving Club. Episcopalian. Office: 172 Huntington Rd Atlanta GA 30309-1504

MCKENZIE, HERBERT A(LONZA), pharmaceutical company executive; b. Savannah, Ga., Dec. 23, 1934; s. Herbert A. and Marie L. (Lytjen) McK.; m. Joan B. Baggs, Dec. 19, 1959; children: Catherine B. McKenzie Bowman, Gregory M., Susan M. McKenzie Carson. BS, Clemson U., 1956; grad. exec. program, Stanford U., 1986. Sales mgmt. positions Am. Cyanamid, Wayne, N.J., 1956-71, mktg. mgr., 1971-73, gen. mgr., 1973-80; pres. Hilton Davis Chem. Co. div. Sterling Drug, Inc.; corp. v.p. Sterling Drug, Inc., 1980-81; pres. Sterling Chem. Group, 1982-85, Sterling Japan, Can., Australasia and Pacific Rim Group, Sterling Chem. Group, 1985-88, Sterling Internat.; corp. v.p. Sterling Drug, Inc. subs. Eastman Kodak, 1988-90, corp. exec. v.p.; pres. Sterling Consumer Health Group, N.Y.C., 1991-92; advisor Synthetic Organic Chem. Mfrs. Assn., 1976-78, Industry Sector. Adv. Com., 1977-80, Office Spl. Trade Negotiations, Dept. Commerce, 1977-80, Romanoff Internat., Inc., Charlotte, N.C., 1990-91. Patentee in field. Bd. dirs. Coop. Ireland, 1988-92, Coun. Better Bus. Bur., 1991-92. With USN, 1959. Mem. Dry Colors Mfg. (pres. 1976-78).

MCKENZIE, JAMES MILTON, excavating company executive; b. Fairbury, Nebr., Mar. 10, 1945; s. Donald Eugene and Elizabeth June (Green) McK.; m. Alice Jay Unrath, July 31, 1971; children: Matthew James, Sabrina Alice. Student, Colo. State U., Ft. Collins, 1965-66. Heavy equipment operator Valley Excavating, Inc., Boulder, Colo., 1968-73, owner, pres., 1973—; cons. bldg. trades dept. Boulder Valley Dist. Vocat. Tech. Sch., 1985—. Adviser Boulder area Boy Scouts Am., 1983—. Sgt. U.S. Army, 1966-68, Vietnam. Mem. Boulder Co. of C. (Small Bus. of Yr. 1991), Am. Legion, Elks. Republican. Presbyterian. Avocations: woodworking, metal working, landscaping, skiing, fishing. Office: Valley Excavating Inc 1726 N 63d St Boulder CO 80301

MC KENZIE, JEREMY ALEC, food service and baking company executive; b. Stamford, Conn., Sept. 27, 1941; s. George Kenneth and Barbara (Mitchell) McK.; m. Susan Hallaran, Mar. 30, 1963; children—Scott G., Kristin W., Jennifer K., Timothy M. B.S., N.Y. U., 1965; M.B.A. with distinction, Harvard U., 1967. Adminstrv. asst. to sales mgr. Owens Corning Fiberglas Corp., N.Y.C., 1962-65; dir. corp. planning Squibb Corp., N.Y.C., 1967-71; v.p. restaurant div. Dobbs Houses Inc., Memphis, 1971-75; exec. v.p. terminal and restaurant div. Dobbs Houses Inc., 1975-77; v.p. restaurant group W.R. Grace & Co., Costa Mesa, Calif., 1978-81; v.p., dir. New Am. Restaurant Corp., Costa Mesa, 1980-81; pres. Franklin Corp. and Steak 'n Shake, both Indpls., 1981-85; pres., chief exec. officer, bd. dirs. Storione U.S.A., Storione and Andre's, Las Vegas, 1985-88, Andre's French Bakery, Las Vegas, Las Vegas French Bakery, 1988—; dir. McKenzie Mgmt. and Research Co., N.Y.C.; chmn., founder Nev. chpt. YPO, 1985-87, membership chmn. 1987-88; advisor Am. Forces Info. Service; advisor stars and stripes adv. task force U.S. Dept. of Def. Served with USCGR, 1961-62. Clubs: Met., Harvard, Can. (N.Y.C.). Home: 9316 Valencia Canyon Dr Las Vegas NV 89117-7128 Office: Hughes Airport Ctr 871 Grier Dr Ste 2B Las Vegas NV 89119-3717

MC KENZIE, JOHN MAXWELL, physician; b. Glasgow, Scotland, Nov. 13, 1927; came to U.S., 1980; s. Thomas Wilson and Isabell Connor (Spencer) McK.; m. Vieno Laine Kangas, June 29, 1957; children—Ann, Ian, Lesley, Gordon. M.B., Ch.B. U. St. Andrews, Scotland, 1950, M.D., 1958. Intern U. St. Andrews, 1950-51, resident, 1953-55, fellow, 1955-56, 57-58; research trainee, fellow Tufts U., 1956-57, 58-59; clin. asst. medicine McGill U., Montreal, Que., Can., 1959-61; asst., then assoc. prof. McGill U., 1961-68, prof., 1968-80; prof. U. Miami, 1980—, chmn. dept. medicine, 1980-94. Contbr. numerous articles to profl. jours. Served with Royal Army Med. Corps, 1951-53. Recipient Killam award Can. Coun., 1980. Mem. Am. Thyroid Assn. (Parke-Davis disting. lectr. 1981, pres. 1983-84), Am. Soc. Clin. Investigation, Endocrine Soc. (Ayerst award 1961, Rorer Pharm. Clin. Investigator award 1990), Am. Physiol. Soc., Assn. Am. Physicians, Am. Fedn. Clin. Rsch., AAAS, Internat. Soc. Neuroendocrinology, European Thyroid Assn. (corr.). Home: 12505 SW 63rd Ave Miami FL 33156 Office: U Miami Jackson Meml Med Ctr 1611 NW 12th Ave Miami FL 33136-1005

MCKENZIE, KENNETH, retail grocery executive. Chmn. Grocery Supply Cos., Inc., Sulphur Springs, Tex., also bd. dirs. Office: Grocery Supply Cos Inc PO Box 638 130 Hillcrest Dr Sulphur Springs TX 75483-0638

MCKENZIE, KEVIN PATRICK, ballet dancer; b. Burlington, Vt., Apr. 29, 1954; s. Raymond James and Ruth (Davison) McK. Grad. high sch., Washington. Mem. corps de ballet Nat. Ballet of Washington, 1972-74; prin. Joffrey Ballet, N.Y.C., 1974-78, Am. Ballet Theatre, N.Y.C., 1979-91; artistic assoc. Washington Ballet, 1991-92; artistic dir. Am. Ballet Theatre, N.Y.C., 1992—; pres. bd. dirs. Am. Ballet Theatre Dancers Fund, Inc., 1982-89; assoc. dir. New Amsterdam Ballet, N.Y.C., 1984—. Appeared in film Unicorn, Gorgon and Monticore, Sta. WETA-TV, Washington, 1971; guest dancer Houston Ballet, 1978, Spoleto Festival, 1980, 84, Theatre des Champs Elysees, Paris, 1981, Sadler's Wells Theatre, London, 1981, Asami Maki Ballet Co., Tokyo, 1983, Aspen Festival, 1982; producer, dir. The Party of the Year, 1982; choreographer Groupo Zambaria Ballet, 1984, Liszt Etudes, 1991, Lucy and the Count, 1992; created roles in Adrienne Dellos' The Blind Man's Daughter, Seoul, Korea, 1986, Amnon V'Tamar, S.P.E.B.S.Q.S.A.; appeared with Martine Van Hamel in Swan Lake, Nat. Ballet of Cuba, Havanna, 1986, Merrill Ashley in Tchaikowsky Pas de Deux, Bolshoi Theater, Moscow, 1986; repertoire as dancer includes La Bayadere, Carmen, Cinderella, Coppelia, Dim Lustre, Don Quixote, Giselle, The Garden of Villandry, Jardin aux lilas, The Leaves Are Fading, Pillar of Fire, Raymonda, Requiem, Rodeo, Romeo and Juliet, The Sleeping Beauty, Swan Lake, La Sylphide; other dances include Paquita, Sylvia Pas de Deux, Theme and Variations. Recipient Silver medal Varna (Bulgaria) Internat. Ballet Competitions, 1972, Artistic Achievement medal Dept. State, U.S. Govt., 1972, Artistic Achievement medal Mayor of Burlington, Vt., 1984, Performing Arts award, Am. Ireland Fund, 1994; Kevin McKenzie Day proclaimed by City of Burlington, 1985. Office: Am Ballet Theatre 890 Broadway New York NY 10003-1211

MC KENZIE, LIONEL WILFRED, economist, educator; b. Montezuma, Ga., Jan. 26, 1919; s. Lionel Wilfred and Lida (Rushin) McK.; m. Blanche Veron, Jan. 2, 1943; children—Lionel Wilfred, Gwendolyn Veron, David Rushin. AB, Duke U., 1939; MA, Princeton U., 1946, PhD, 1956; BLitt, Oxford (Eng.) U., 1949; postgrad., U. Chgo., 1950-51, LLD (hon.), 1991. Asst. economist WPB, 1942; instr. Mass. Inst. Tech., 1946; asst. prof., then asso. prof. Duke, 1948-57; prof. econs. U. Rochester, 1957-64, John Munro prof. econs., 1964-67, Wilson prof. econs., 1967-89, Wilson prof. emeritus, 1989—, chmn. dept., 1957-66; Taussig research prof. Harvard U., 1980-81; Mem. math. div. NRC, 1960-63, mem. behavioral scis. div., 1964-70; mem. math., social scis. bd. Center Advanced Study in Behavioral Scis., Palo Alto, Calif., 1964-70, chmn., 1969-70. Assoc. editor Internat. Econs. Rev., 1964—, Jour. Econ. theory, 1970-73, Jour. Internat. Econs., 1970-84, Econ. Theory, 1991—; contbr. articles to profl. jours. Served to lt. (s.g.) USNR, 1943-45. Rhodes scholar Oriel Coll. Oxford U., 1939; Guggenheim fellow, 1973-74; fellow Center for Advanced Study in Behavioral Scis., 1973-74. Fellow Econometric Soc. (coun. 1973-78, pres. 1977), Am. Acad. Arts and Scis., Am. Econ. Assn.; mem. NAS, Royal Econ. Soc., Am. Math. Soc., Am. Econ. Assn. (Disting. Fellow 1993), Phi Beta Kappa (chpt. v.p. 1968-70, chpt. pres. 1972-73). Home: 225 Dorchester Rd Rochester NY 14610-1322

MCKENZIE, MARY BETH, artist; b. Cleve.; d. William Jennings and Mary Elizabeth (McCray) McK.; m. Tony Mysak, May 8, 1974; children: Zsuzsa McKenzie Mysak, Maria McKenzie Mysak. Student, Mus. Fine Arts, Boston, 1964-65, Cooper Sch. Art, Cleve., 1965-67; diploma, Nat. Acad. Design, N.Y.C., 1974. Painting instr. Nat. Acad. Design, N.Y.C., 1981—. Author: A Painterly Approach, 1987; contbr. articles to profl. jours.; one-woman shows include Nat. Arts Club, N.Y.C., 1976, FAR Gallery, N.Y.C., 1980, Perin and Sharpe Gallery, New Canaan, Conn., 1981, Frank Caro Gallery, N.Y.C., 1988-89, Joseph Keiffer Gallery, N.Y.C., 1991; exhibited in group shows at Sindin Gallery, N.Y.C., 1985-86; permanent collections include Met. Mus. Art, N.Y.C., The Butler Mus. Am. Art, Mus. City of N.Y., NAD, Art Student's League of N.Y. Recipient Nat. Scholastic award Mus. Fine Arts, Boston, numerous awards including Thomas B. Clark prize and the Isaac N. Maynard prize Nat. Acad. Design, Greenshields Found. grantee, Stacey Found. grantee. Mem. Nat. Acad. Design, Pastel Soc. Am. (Best In Show, Award of Exceptional Merit, Exhbn. Com. award), Allied Artists Am. (Gold medal, The Jane Peterson award, Grumbacher Cash award, Silver medal), Audubon Artists (Pastel Soc. Am. award). Home: 525 W 54th St New York NY 10036-3405

MCKENZIE, MICHAEL K., wholesale executive. Past pres., CEO G.S.C. Enterprises, Inc., Sulphur Springs, Tex., now chmn. bd., CEO, also bd. dirs. Office: GSC Enterprises Inc 130 Hillcrest Dr Sulphur Springs TX 75482

MC KENZIE, RAY, anesthesiologist, educator; b. Turua, N.Z., July 9, 1927; s. Robert Keith and Edith Harfield (Collingwood) McK.; m. Barbara Mavis Snelling, Dec. 11, 1954; children: Robyn Kay, William Brett, Melvern Craig, Glenn Carrick. Student, Hauraki Plains Coll., 1939-45; M.B. Ch.B., U. Otago, 1952. Intern Auckland (N.Z.) Hosp., 1953, resident, 1954-56, cons. anesthetist, 1961-66; dir. anesthesia Mowasat Hosp., Kuwait, 1967-69; asst. prof. U. Pitts., 1969-71, assoc. prof., 1971-77, prof., 1977—; dir. surg. anesthesia Magee-Women's Hosp., Pitts., 1971-73, dir. anesthesia, 1973-92, prof. rsch., 1992—. Mem. Bro.'s Bro. Found., 1971—. Served with Royal N.Z. Air Force, 1957-59. Fellow Faculty Anesthetists Royal Coll. Surgeons

(Eng.); mem. Internat. Research Soc., Pa. Med. Soc., Am., Pa., Western Pa. socs. anesthesiologists. Home: 325 Richland Ln Pittsburgh PA 15208-2730 Office: Magee Womens Hosp Halket And Forbes St Pittsburgh PA 15213 *There is no electric elevator to success. Step up the stairs. Don't stare up the steps.*

MCKENZIE, ROBERT E., lawyer; b. Cheboygan, Mich., Dec. 7, 1947; s. Alexander Orlando and Edna Jean (Burt) McK.; m. Theresia Wolf, Apr. 26, 1975; 1 child, Robert A. BA in Personnel Adminstrn., Mich. State U., 1970; JD with high honors, Ill. Inst. Tech., 1979. Bar: Ill. 1979, U.S. Dist. Ct. (no. dist.) Ill. 1979, U.S. Tax Ct. 1979, U.S. Ct. Appeals (7th cir.) 1979, U.S. Supreme Ct. 1984; lic. pvt. pilot. Revenue officer IRS, Chgo., 1972-78; ptnr. McKenzie & McKenzie, Chgo., 1979—; lectr. Tax Seminars Inst., Chgo., 1984—. Author: Representation Before the Collection Divison of the IRS, 1989; co-author: Representing the Audited Taxpayer Before the IRS, 1990; contbr. articles to profl. jours. Mem. vocat. adv. bd. Ridgewood High, Norridge, Ill., 1981-86; Lake Briarwood Bd. dirs., Arlington Heights, 1985-86; coordinator John Anderson for Pres., 1980; del. Rep. Nat. Conv., Detroit, 1980, Ill. State Rep. Conv., Peoria, 1980. Served with U.S. Army, 1970. Recipient scholarship Mich. State U., 1966-70, State of Mich., 1966-70, Silas Strawn scholarship ITT, 1977. Mem. ABA (tax sect., chmn. employment tax com. 1992-94), Chgo. Bar Assn. (sec. exec. tax com 1993-95, vice-chair 1995), N.W. Suburban Bar Assn. (chmn. econs. of law com. 1986-87), Fed. Bar Assn. (tax com.), Rotary (pres. Norridge club 1985-86). Avocation: flying, genealogy. Office: 5450 N Cumberland Chicago IL 60656-3652

MCKENZIE, RUTH BATES HARRIS, diversity human relations consultant, writer; d. Harry B. Delaney and Florence (Phillips) Graham; m. Alfred U. McKenzie, Aug. 25, 1987. B.S., Fla. A&M U.; M.B.A., NYU, 1957. Exec. dir. D.C. Human Relations Commn.; also equal opportunity officer, D.C., 1960-69; dir. human relations dept. Montgomery County (Md.) Pub. Schs., 1969-71; dep. asst. adminstr. NASA, 1971-76; human relations dir. Office Sec. Interior, Washington, 1978-88, ret., 1988; lectr., author, 1988—. Author: Handbooks for Careerists, 1965, Personal Power Words, 1986, Trigger Words, 1987, (autobiography) Harlem Princess, 1991. Recipient over 100 awards including those from Omega Psi Phi, Sigma Gamma Rho, Alpha Phi Alpha, Nat. Bus. League, 1974, 75, 94, space div. Rockwell Internat., 1975, Cosmopolitan Bus. and Profl. Women's Club, 1978; recipient Sojourner Truth award Nat. Assn. Negro Bus. and Profl. Womens' Clubs, 1966, Martin Luther King award D.C. chpt. NAACP, 1969, Disting. Svc. award Federally Employed Women, 1976, keys to cities of Cocoa Beach and Jacksonville, Fla., 1980, Woman of Distinction award Washingtonian mag., 1986, Nat. Disting. Black Woman award Black Women in Sisterhood for Action, 1986, Meritorious Svc. award Dept. Interior, 1987, Sally Ride Disting. Am. Woman award Air Force Assn., 1987, Pioneer award Tuskegee Airmen, 1989, Black Women's Polit. Caucus award, 1991, Women of Distinction Nat. award Delta Sigma Theta, 1994, 25th Anniversary Civil Rights award NASA, 1994, Superior Leadership award Greater Washington Urban League Guild, 1994; named Nat. Black Woman of Distinction, Dollars and Cents mag., 1986; featured in Black History Month, 1992; featured in exhibit Balt. Washington Nat. Airport, 1992, Black History Living Legend award (history/journalism) U of D.C., 1993. Mem. Cosmopolitan Bus. and Profl. Women's Club (founder), Delta Sigma Theta (founder Alcorn U. chpt.), Iota Phi Lambda (hon.). Home: 311 Bonhill Dr Fort Washington MD 20744-5333 *I hope I never rise so high that I lose sight of the people who helped put me up there. True happiness is the reward we receive when we make others happy without reminding them.*

MCKEON, GEORGE A., lawyer; b. Orangeburg, N.Y., Jan. 22, 1937; s. Thomas Patrick and Elizabeth Anna McKeon; m. Ellen Ann Connors, June 27, 1959 (dec. Aug. 1977); children: John, Alice, Thomas; m. Fay L. Akins, Aug. 28, 1981. BA, Fairleigh Dickinson U., 1959; LLB, Fordham U., 1963. Bar: N.Y., 1964, Conn., 1967, U.S. Dist. Ct., Conn., 1971. With contracts negotiation Bendix Corp., Teterboro, N.J., 1958-65; div. asst. counsel United Technologies, Windsor Locks, Conn., 1965-69; asst. counsel Travelers Ins. Co., Hartford, Conn., 1969-73, assoc. counsel, 1973-76, counsel, 1976-81; assoc. gen. counsel Travelers Ins. Co., Hartford, 1981-84; gen. counsel Travelers Ins. Co., Hartford, Conn., 1984—; mem. faculty U. Conn. Referee Vol. Pub. Defender Program, Conn. Mem. ABA (chmn. corp. counsel com. tort and ins. practice sect. 1985-87, mem. commn. on Mass. torts 1987-88), N.Y. Bar Assn., Conn. Bar Assn., Hartford County Bar Assn. Roman Catholic. Home: 36 Bradley Brook Dr North Granby CT 06060-1521 Office: Travelers Corp 1 Tower Sq Hartford CT 06183-1050

MCKEON, HOWARD P. (BUCK MCKEON), congressman, former mayor; b. Los Angeles; m. Patricia; 6 children. BS, Brigham Young U. Mem. Coun. City of Santa Clarita, Calif., 1987-92, mayor, 1987-88; mem. 103rd Congress from 25th Calif. dist., 1993—; founding dir., chmn. Valencia Nat. Bank; co-owner Howard & Phil's Western Wear, Inc. Hon. chmn. Leukemia Soc. Celebrity program, 1990, Red Cross Community Support Campaign, 1992; active Dist. Com. Boy Scouts Am.; chmn., trustee William S. Hart Sch. dist., 1979-87; chmn., dir. Henry Mayo Newhall Meml. Hosp., 1983-88; mem. Calif. Rep. State Ctrl. Com., 1988-92; bd. dirs. Santa Clarita Valley Sml. Bus. Devel. Ctr., 1990-92, Canyon Country C. of C., 1988-92. Office: US Ho of Reps 307 Cannon Ho Ofc Bldg Washington DC 20515

MCKEON, KATHRYN LOTHSCHUETZ, nursing administrator; b. Washington, Nov. 18, 1951; d. John Malcolm and Mary Elizabeth (Goedde) Lothschuetz; 1 child, Heather Ann. BSN, Barry U., 1973; MSN, Cath. U. Am., 1979; PhD candidate, U. Md., 1988—. CNAA. Staff nurse Cedars of Lebanon Med. Ctr., Miami, Fla., 1973; head nurse South Fla. State Hosp., Hollywood, 1973-74; dir. nursing edn. Fla. State Hosp., Hollywood, 1974-76; clin. instr. Sibley Meml. Hosp., Washington, 1976-77, clin. nursing supr., 1977-79; chief mental health NIH Clin. Ctr., Bethesda, Md., 1979-89, acting chief cancer, 1982-83, 85-86, chief neuro and aging, 1988-89, assoc. dir. clin. ctr., DON, 1989—; cons. adv. bd. Humana Hosp., Indpls., 1987-89, Indian Health Svc., Shiprock, N.Mex., 1988-89; pres. Friends of the Clin. Cen., Bethesda, 1988-91; first disting. lectr. Robert Wood Johnson U., N.J., 1990. Mem. editorial bd. Applied Nursing Rsch., N.Y., 1990—; contbr. articles to profl. jours. Admiral USPHS, 1979—. Mem. ANA, Am. Orgn. Nurse Execs., Commd. Officers Assn., Soc. for Edn. and Rsch. Psychiat. Nursing, Sigma Theta Tau. Avocations: horseback riding, swimming. Home: 1721 Vesper St Vienna VA 22182 Office: NIH Clin Ctr 9000 Rockville Pike Bethesda MD 20892

MCKEON, ROBERT B., textiles executive. Co. chmn. Collins & Aikman Group, Charlotte, N.C., 1988—; managing dir. Wasserstein Parella & Co Inc., 1988—. Office: Collins & Aikman Group Inc 8320 University Exec Park Charlotte NC 28262

MCKEON, ROBERT B., retail chain stores executive; b. 1954. Co-chmn. bd. Wickes Cos. Inc., Santa Monica, Calif.; mng. dir. Wasserstein Perella, N.Y.C. Office: Wickes Cos Inc Ste 102 8320 University Exec Park Dr Charlotte NC 28262-3369

MCKEOUGH, WILLIAM DARCY, investment company exceitive; b. Chatham, Ont., Can., Jan. 31, 1933; s. George Grant and Florence Sewell (Woodward) McK.; m. Margaret Joyce Walker, June 18, 1965; children: Walker Stewart, James Grant. BA, U. Western Ont., 1954; LLD (hon.), Wilfred Laurier U., 1980, L.L.D. (hon.), 1980. Chmn. McKeough Investments Ltd.; bd. dirs. Can. Imperial Bank Commerce, Can. Gen. Tower Ltd., Global Stone Corp., Intertan Inc., Medicom Inc., Numac Energy Ltd., Moranda Mines Ltds., Ranger Forest Products Inc., St. Mary's Cement Ltd., Sunquest Tours Ltd., Varity Corp. Inc. Former mem. exec. com. Anglican Diocese of Huron; former mem. Gen. Synod, Anglican Ch. Can.; mem. Chatham City Council, 1960-63; also mem. Planning Bd. and Lower Thames Valley Conservation Authority; former mem. Chatham-Kent adv. bd. Can. Nat. Inst. of the Blind; former bd. dirs. Chatham YMCA, Chatham Little Theatre; former chmn. and pres. bd. govs. pres. Ridley Coll.; former bd. govs. Stratford Shakespearian Festival, Wilfrid Laurier U.; former mem. Can. group Trilateral Commn.; mem. Ont. Legislature, 1963-78, minister without portfolio, 1966, minister mcpl. affairs, 1967; treas. and minister of econs., also chmn. Treasury Bd., 1971-72, minister mcpl. affairs, 1972, treas. and minister of econs. and intergovtl. affairs, 1972, parliamentary asst. to premier Ont., 1973, minister of energy, 1973-75, treas. and minister econs. and intergovtl. affairs, 1975-78. Decorated officer of Order of Can. Home and Office: PO Box 940, Chatham, ON Canada N7M 5L3

MCKEOWN, JAMES CHARLES, accounting educator, consultant; b. Cleve., Nov. 3, 1945; s. Charles Joseph and Dara Ferrol (Prew) McK.; m. Mary Alinda Park, Jan. 2, 1965 (div. May 1980); children—Jeffrey Charles, Pamela Lynn; m. 2d, Nancy Ann Stratton, Jan. 3, 1981. B.S. in Math. with high honors, Mich. State U., 1966, Ph.D. in Bus. Adminstrn., 1969. Asst. prof. accountancy U. Ill., Urbana-Champaign, 1968-73, assoc. prof., 1973-76, prof., 1976-80, Weldon Powell prof. accountancy, 1980-83, A.C. Littleton prof. accountancy, 1983-89; disting. prof. acctg. Pa. State U., University Park, 1989-92, Ernst & Young prof. acctg., 1992—; cons. research, computers; expert witness. Editor: Inflation and Current Value Accounting, 1979; author computer-delivered acctg. course PLATO for Elementary Accounting, 1978; contbr. numerous articles to acad. jours. Recipient Instructional award U. Ill., Urbana-Champaign, 1970, Weldon Powell award, 1973; Fred Roedgers Research award U. Ill., 1978; Ford Found. fellow, 1967-68. Mem. Am. Acctg. Assn. (Manuscript award 1970), Am. Statis. Assn., Decision Scis. Inst., Inst. Mgmt. Accts. Republican. Office: Pa State U 210 Beam Bus Adminstrn Bldg University Park PA 16802

MCKEOWN, MARY MARGARET, lawyer; b. Casper, Wyo., May 11, 1951; d. Robert Mark and Evelyn Margaret (Lipsack) McK.; m. Peter Francis Cowhey, June 29, 1985; 1 child, Megan Margaret. BA in Internat. Affairs, U. Wyo., 1972; JD, Georgetown U., 1975. Bar: Wash. 1975, D.C. 1982. Assoc. Perkins Coie, Seattle, 1975-79, Washington, 1979-80; White House fellow U.S. Dept. Interior and White House, Washington, 1980-81; ptnr., mem. exec. com. Perkins Coie, Seattle, 1981—; mng. dir. strategic planning and client rels., 1990—; trustee The Pub. Defender, Seattle, 1982-85; rep. 9th Cir. Judicial Conf., San Francisco, 1985-89, mem. gender bias task force, 1992-93. Author: Girl Scout's Guide to New York, 1990; contbr. chpt. to book and articles to profl. jours. Nat. bd. dirs. Girl Scouts Am., N.Y.C., 1976-87; bd. dirs. Family Svcs., Seattle, 1982-84, Corp. coun. for the Arts, Seattle, 1988—; bd. gen. counsel Downtown Seattle Assn., 1986-89; mem. exec. com. Wash. Coun. Internat. Trade, 1994—. Recipient Rising Stars of the 80's award Legal Times Washington, 1983, 100 Young Women of Promise, Good Housekeeping, 1985; named Washington's Winningest Trial Lawyers Washington Journal, 1992; Japan leadership fellow, 1992-93. Fellow ABA (ho. of dels. 1990—); mem. ACLU (chmn. legal com. 1982-85), Fed. Bar Assn. (trustee western dist. Wash. 1980-90), Wash. Bar Assn. (chmn. jud. recommendations 1989-90), Seattle-King County Bar Assn. (trustee, sec. 1984-85, Outstanding Lawyer award 1992), Legal Found. Wash. (trustee, pres. 1989-90), Washington Women Lawyers (bd. dirs., pres. 1978-79), Nat. Assn. Iolta Programs (bd. dirs. 1989-91), Fed. Ct. Pro Bono Civil Rights Panel. Avocations: travel, classical piano, hiking, gourmet cooking, tennis. Home: 1522 40th Ave Seattle WA 98122-3510 Office: Perkins Coie 1201 3rd Ave Seattle WA 98101-3099

MC KEOWN, WILLIAM TAYLOR, magazine editor, author; b. Ft. Collins, Colo., July 4, 1921; s. Stuart Ellison and Eunice Harris (Akin) Mc K.; m. Lorraine Laredo; children: Elizabeth Ellison, Katherine, Suzanne. AB, Bowdoin Coll., 1942; student, Columbia U. Grad. Sch., 1948. Editor Fawcett Library Series, 1953-56; founding editor True's Boating Yearbook, 1955-56; founding editor Popular Boating mag., 1956, editor-in-chief, 1956-62; CEO The Mc Keown Co., N.Y.C., 1993—; editl. dir. Computer Travel Info., 1994—; travel editor Davis Publs.; outdoor/boating/travel editor Popular Mechanics, 1971-82; sr. editor Outdoor Life, 1983-93. Author weekly NEA syndicated newspaper column American Afloat, 1959-65; contbr. fiction, non-fiction to nat. mags., 1947—; author: Boating Handbook, 1956, Boating in America, 1960. Pilot USAAF, WW II, ETO. Mem. Am. Power Boat Assn., U.S. Power Squadrons, 357 FIghter Group Assn., N.Y. Yacht Club, Overseas Press Club, Royal Danish Yacht Club (Copenhagen), Turtles Internat. Avocation: international competitor in power and sail racing events. Office: The Mc Keown Co 420 Lexington Ave New York NY 10170

MCKERNAN, JOHN JOSEPH, English language educator; b. Omaha, May 11, 1942; s. John Joseph and Monica Louise (Nagengast) McK.; m. Llewellyn Teresa McKinnie, Aug. 3, 1967; 1 child, Kathleen Claire. BA in English, U. Omaha, 1965; MA in English, U. Ark., 1967; MFA in Writing, Columbia U., N.Y.C., 1971; PhD in English, Boston U., 1981. Instr. English U. Omaha, 1966-67; prof. St. Marys (Md.) Coll., 1989-91; instr. Marshall U., Huntington, W.Va., 1967-72, asst. prof., 1972-80, assoc. prof., 1980-81, prof. English, 1981—; dir. writing Marshall U., 1984-89, St. Marys Coll., 1989-91; founding dir. Marshall Writing Project, 1986-89. Author: (books of poems) Walking Along the Missouri River, 1977, Erasing the Blackboard, 1978, Multitudes, 1992, The Book of I, 1993; (books) The Writers Workbook, 1988, The Writers Handbook, 1988, 2d edit., 1991; compiler: Academic Almanac, 1981; editor The Little Rev., Huntington, 1967—. Boston U. fellow, 1975-77, NEH rsch. fellow, 1973, Lyceum fellow W.Va. Humanities Coun., 1984; recipient Disting. Creative award Marshall Rsch. Bd., 1979. Roman Catholic. Avocations: stamp collecting, bird watching, gardening. Office: Marshall University 3rd Ave & Hal Greer Blvd Huntington WV 25701

MCKERNAN, LEO JOSEPH, manufacturing company executive; b. Phila., Feb. 17, 1938; s. Leo Joseph and Mary (Dever) McK. Student, Iona Coll., 1956-59, NYU, 1961-62, U. Bridgeport, 1962-64. With Eaton Corp., Carol Stream, Ill., 1959-74, mgr. mfg. Controls div., 1974; v.p., gen. mgr. Axle div. Clark Equipment Co., Buchanan, Mich., 1974-77, group v.p., 1977-83, sr. v.p., then exec. v.p., then chief oper. officer, 1983-86; pres., chief exec. officer Clark Equipment Co., South Bend, Ind., 1986—, chmn., 1988—, also bd. dirs.; mem. supervisory bd. VME Group N.V.; bd. dirs. 1st Source Corp., Lincoln Nat. Corp., Nat. Assn. Mfrs. Bd. dirs. St. Joseph Community Found., Ind.; mem. U. Notre Dame Engring. Adv. Coun., 1985—; corp. grants com. 1988—. Office: Clark Equipment Co PO Box 7008 100 N Michigan St South Bend IN 46601-1630

MCKERNS, CHARLES JOSEPH, lawyer; b. Shenandoah, Pa., July 17, 1935; s. Charles Francis and Bridgett Ann (Barrett) McK.; m. Helen Patricia Nott, Feb. 13, 1960; children: Charles J. Jr., Michael H., Patricia B. BS, Georgetown U., 1957, JD, 1960. Bar: D.C. 1960, U.S. Ct. Appeals (D.C. cir.) 1961, U.S. Supreme Ct. 1971, Va. 1992. Law clk. to assoc. judge U.S. Ct. Appeals (D.C. cir), Washington, 1960-61; assoc. Dow, Lohnes & Albertson, Washington, 1961-65, ptnr., 1965-91, of counsel, 1991—; ptnr. McKerns and McKerns, Heathsville, Va., 1991—; bd. dirs. Palmer Communications Inc. 1st lt. U.S. Army, 1957-59. Mem. ABA, University Club, Belle Haven Country Club (Alexandria, Va.), Indian Creek Yacht and Country Club (Kilmarnock, Va.). Republican. Roman Catholic. Avocations: reading, swimming. Home: Windy Blue Ophelia VA 22550 Office: McKerns & McKerns PO Box 188 McKerns Bldg Heathsville VA 22473-0188 also: Dow Lohnes & Albertson 1255 23rd St NW Washington DC 20037

MCKERROW, AMANDA, ballet dancer; b. Albuquerque; d. Alan and Constance McKerrow; m. John Gardner. Student, Met. Acad. Ballet, Bethesda, Md., Washington Sch. Ballet. With Washington Ballet Co., 1980-82; with Am. Ballet Theatre, N.Y.C., 1982—, soloist, from 1983, prin. dancer, 1987—. Toured Europe with Washington Ballet; danced in Margot Fonteyn Gala at Metropolitan Opera House; featured in Pavlova Tribute film, also many guest appearances; leading roles in Ballet Imperial, La Bayadere, Manon, Birthday Offering, Dim Lustre, Donizetti Variations, Giselle, Graduation Ball, The Leaves Are Fading, Nine Sinatra Songs, The Nutcracker, Pillar of Fire, Requiem, Romeo and Juliet, The Sleeping Beauty, Les Sylphides, Push Comes to Shove, Symphony Concertante, Symphonic Variations, Theme and Variations, Stravinsky Violin Concerto, Swan Lake, Triad, Duets, Etudes, Coppelia, Voluntaries and Rodeo; created leading role in Bruch Violin Concerto No. 1, Some Assembly Required and Agnus De Mille's The Other. Recipient N.Y. Woman award for dance, 1991; co-winner gold prize for women Moscow Internat. Ballet Competition, 1981. Office: Am Ballet Theatre 890 Broadway New York NY 10003-1211

MCKESSON, JOHN ALEXANDER, III, international relations educator; b. N.Y.C., Mar. 29, 1922; s. John Alexander and Mildred Fleming (Warner) McK.; m. Erna Jensson, Jan. 4, 1950 (dec. May 1971); 1 child, John A. IV. AB, Columbia U., 1941, MA in Internat. Rels., 1942, MA in Art

History, 1982; LLD (hon.), Ea. Mich. U., 1972. Fgn. svc. officer Dept. of State, Washington and abroad, 1947-75; Am. amb. Libreville, Gabon, 1971-75; v.p. Etudes Travaux et Gestion, Paris, 1975-78; editor-in-chief UN Plaza Mag., N.Y.C., 1980-81; prof. NYU, N.Y.C., 1983—. Contbr. articles to profl. jours. Lt. USN, 1942-46. Decorated Commdr. Order of Equatorial Star of Gabon, 1975, Nat. Order of Senegal, 1967. Mem. Fgn. Svc. Assn., Met. Club Washington, Regency Club. Episcopalian. Avocation: bridge. Home: 880 Fifth Ave New York NY 10021

MCKESSY, STEPHEN W., accounting firm executive; b. 1937. Vice chmn. Coopers & Lybrand, N.Y.C. Office: Coopers & Lybrand 1251 Ave of the Americas New York NY 10020-1104

MC KETTA, JOHN J., JR., chemical engineering educator; b. Wyano, Pa., Oct. 17, 1915; s. John J. and Mary (Gelet) McK.; m. Helen Elisabeth Smith, Oct. 17, 1943; children: Charles William, John J. III, Robert Andrew, Mary Anne. B.S., Tri-State Coll., Angola, Ind., 1937; B.S.E., U. Mich., 1943, M.S., 1944, Ph.D., 1946; D.Eng. (hon.), Tri-State Coll., 1965, Drexel U., 1977; Sc.D., U. Toledo, 1973. Diplomate: registered profl. engr., Tex., Mich. Group leader tech. dept. Wyandotte Chem. Corp., Mich., 1937-40; asst. supt. caustic soda div. Wyandotte Chem. Corp., 1940-41; teaching fellow U. Mich., 1942-44, instr. chem. engring., 1944-45; faculty U. Tex., Austin, 1946—; successively asst. prof. chem. engring., assoc. prof., then prof. chem. engring. U. Tex., 1951-52, 54—, E.P. Schoch prof. chem. engring., 1970-81, Joe C. Walter chair, 1981—; asst. dir. Tex. petroleum research com., 1951-52, 54-56, exec. vice chancellor acad. affairs U. Tex. System, 1969-70; J.C. Walter in Chem. Engring. U. Tex., 1970—; editorial dir. Petroleum Refiner, 1952-54; pres. Chemdal Cons., 1957-73; dir. Gulf Pub. Co., Howell Corp., Houston, Tesoro Petroleum Co., San Antonio; Chmn. Tex. AEC, So. Interstate Nuclear Bd., 1963-70; mem. Tex. Radiation Adv. Bd., 1978-84; chmn. Nat. Energy Policy Com., 1970-72, Nat. Air Quality Control Com., 1972-85; mem. adv. bd. Carnegie-Mellon Inst. Research, 1978-84; pres. Reagans's rep. on U.S. Acid Precipitation Task Force, 1982-88; apptd. mem. Nuclear Waste Tech. Rev. Bd., 1992—. Author: series Advances in Petroleum Chemistry and Refining; Chmn. editorial com.: series Petroleum Refiner; mem. adv. bd.: series Internat. Chem. Engring. mag; editorial bd.: series Ency. of Chem. Tech; exec. editor: series Ency. of Chem. Processing and Design (65 vols.). Bd. regents Tri-State U., 1957—. Recipient Bronze plaque Am. Inst. Chem. Engrs., 1952, Charles Schwab award Am. Steel Inst., 1973, Lamme award as outstanding U.S. educator, 1976, Joe J. King Profl. Engring. Achievement award U. Tex., 1976, Gen. Dynamics Teaching Excellence award, 1979, Triple E award for contbns. to nat. issues on energy, environment and econs Nat. Environ. Devel. Assn., 1976, Boris Pregal Sci. and Tech. award NAS, 1978, Internat. Chem. Engring. award, Italy, 1984, Pres. Herbert Hoover award for advancing well-being of humanity and developing richer and more enduring civilization Joint Engring. Socs., 1989, Centennial award exceptional contbn. Am. Soc. Engring. Edn., 1993; named Disting. Alumnus U. Mich. Coll. Engring., 1953, Tri-State Coll., 1956; fellow Allied Chem. & Dye, 1945-46; named Disting. fellow Carnegie-Mellon U., 1978. Mem. Am. Chem. Soc. (chmn. Central Tex. sect. 1950), Am. Inst. Chem. Engrs. (chmn. nat. membership com. 1955, regional exec. com., nat. dir., nat. v.p. 1961, pres. 1962, service to soc. award 1975), Am. Soc. Engring. Edn., Chem. Markets Research Assn., Am. Gas Assn. (adv. bd. chems. from gas 1954), Houston C. of C. (chmn. refining div. 1954, vice chmn. research and statistics com. 1954), Engrs. Joint Council (dir.), Engrs. Joint Countil Profl. Devel. (dir. 1963-85), Nat. Acad. Engring., Sigma Xi, Chi Epsilon, Alpha Psi Omega, Tau Omega, Phi Lambda Upsilon, Phi Kappa Phi, Iota Alpha, Omega Chi Epsilon, Tau Beta Pi, Omicron Delta Kappa. Home: 5227 Tortuga Trl Austin TX 78731-4501

MCKEY, THOMAS J., lawyer; b. Detroit, Jan. 9, 1934; s. Thomas J. and Pauline H. (Feys) McK.; m. Lila W. Webber, Sept. 3, 1960; children: Tim, Christopher, Heather, Brenda. BS, USCG Acad., 1955; JD, U. Mich., 1962; MA in Psychology, Antioch U., 1995. Bar: Wash. 1962. Mediator, arbitrator Bogle & Gates, Seattle, 1962—, ptnr., 1970—; former chmn. N.W. Admiralty Law Inst., Seattle; mem. permanent adv. bd. Tulane Admiralty Law Inst., New Orleans, 1981—. Former bd. dirs. Bellvue (Wash.) Area Self-Improvement Coun., N.W. Seaport, Seattle, Coast Guard Mus. N.W., Seattle, Friends of Youth, Seattle; bd. dirs. Resource Inst., Seattle. Comdr. USCGR. Mem. Maritime Law Assn. U.S. (exec. com. 1979-82), Seattle C. of C. (former chmn. maritime steering com.). Office: Bogle & Gates 2 Union Sq Seattle WA 98101-2322

MCKHANN, GUY MEAD, physician, educator; b. Boston, Mar. 20, 1932; s. Charles Fremont and Amelia (Priest) McK.; m. Katherine E. Henderson, Nov. 30, 1957 (div. 1983); children: Ian, James, Emily, Guy, Charles. Student, Harvard U., 1948-51; M.D. Yale U., 1955. Intern New York Hosp., 1955-56; asst. resident pediatrics Johns Hopkins Hosp., Balt., 1956-57; clin. asso. NIH, Bethesda, Md., 1957-60; resident neurology Mass. Gen. Hosp., Boston, 1960-63; asst. and asso. prof. pediatrics and neurology Stanford (Calif.) U., 1963-69; prof. neurology Johns Hopkins, Balt., 1969—, Kennedy prof. neurology, head neurology dept., 1969-88, prof. neurology, dir. Zanuyl Krieger Mind Brain Inst., 1988—; cons. NIH, 1969—. Served with USPHS, 1957-60. Markle scholar, 1964-69; Joseph P. Kennedy Jr. scholar, 1963-69. Fellow AAAS; mem. Am. Acad. Neurology, Am. Neurol. Assn., Am. Neurochem. Soc., Soc. Neuroscis., Inst. Medicine, Alpha Omega Alpha. Research on normal and abnormal human nervous system. Home: 6526 Montrose Ave Baltimore MD 21212-1023 Office: Zanvyl Krieger Mind Inst Johns Hopkins Hosp 338 Krieger Hall Baltimore MD 21218

MCKIBBEN, HOWARD D., federal judge; b. Apr. 1, 1940; s. James D. and Bernice McKibben; m. Mary Ann McKibben, July 2, 1966; children: Mark, Susan. B.S., Bradley U., 1962; M.P.A., U. Pitts., 1964; J.D., U. Mich., 1967. Assoc. George W. Abbott Law Office, 1967-71; dep. dist. atty. Douglas County, Nev., 1969-71, dist. atty., 1971-77; dist. ct. judge State of Nev., 1977-84; judge U.S. Dist. Ct. Nev., Reno, 1984—. Mem. ABA, Nev. Bar Assn., Am. Inns of Ct. (pres. Nev. chpt. 1986-88). Methodist. Avocations: tennis, golf, racquetball. Home: PO Box 588 Verdi NV 89439-0588 Office: US Dist Ct 300 Booth St Rm 5137 Reno NV 89509-1356

MCKIBBEN, RYAN TIMOTHY, newspaper executive; b. Watertown, S.D., June 25, 1958; s. Bernard Dean and Patricia Martha (Loehr) McK.; m. Mary Elizabeth O'Donnell, Oct. 3, 1981; children: Sean Robert, Michael Patrick. Grad. high sch., Jamesville, Wis. Classified advt. exec. Green Bay (Wis.) Press Gazette, 1977-79; display advt. exec. Racine (Wis.) Jour. Times, 1979-80; advt. dir. Oshkosh (Wis.) Northwestern, 1980-82, dir. sales/mktg., 1982-84; advt. dir. Reno Gazette-Jour., 1984-85, Madison (Wis.) Newspapers Inc., 1985-88; v.p., gen. mgr., dir., sr. v.p. advt. and mktg. Denver Post, 1988-90, exec. v.p., gen. mgr., 1990-93, pub., 1993—; bd. dirs. Newspapers First, N.Y.C. Mem. mktg. com. Metro Area Boys Clubs, Denver, 1988—; bd. dirs. Nat. Jewish Ctr. for Immunology and Respiratory Medicine, Denver, Denver Metro Conv. Bur., Denver Ctr. for Performing Arts, Colo. Symphony, Colo. Forum, Colo. Concer, Castle Pines Golf Club. Mem. Am. Press Inst., Newspaper Advt. Coop. Network (bd. dirs. 1989—), Internat. Newspaper Advt./Mktg. Execs., (com. mem 1989—), Denver Advt. Fedn., Boys and Girls Club, Columbine Country Club. Republican. Roman Catholic. Home: 5350 S Race Ct Littleton CO 80121 Office: Denver Post 1560 Broadway Denver CO 80202-5133

MCKIBBIN, JOHN MEEK, III, aluminum company executive; b. Pitts., May 30, 1931; s. John M. Jr. and Eleanor (Kennedy) McK.; m. Katherine Ellison; children: Mary Jane, John, Suzanne, Kelly, Stanton, Margaret, James. BS in Econs., U. Va., 1956. Salesman Alcoa, N.Y.C., 1952-62; asst. mgr. industry Pitts., 1962-66, mgr. industry div., 1966-68, mgr. industry, 1968-70; v.p. sales and mktg. Rolling div. Nat. Aluminum Corp., Danbury, Conn., 1971-79, sr. v.p., 1979-81, pres., 1981-84; exec. v.p. Nat. Aluminum Corp., Pitts., 1984-85, pres., 1985—. Inventor packaging box, 1975. Bd. dirs. Sewickley Valley Hosp., 1989—. Served as sgt. U.S. Army, 1953-55. Mem. Aluminum Assn. (chmn. packaging 1968-69, div. 1984-86; exec. com. 1986—, bd. dirs. 1986—). Republican. Episcopalian. Clubs: Allegheny Country (Sewickley, Pa.), Edgeworth. Avocation: golf. Home: Fair Acres Dr Sewickley PA 15143-9368 Office: Nat Aluminum Corp 2 Robinson Pla Ste 300 Pittsburgh PA 15205

MCKIE, FRANCIS PAUL, journalist; b. Jarrow-upon-Tyne, England, Dec. 18, 1958; arrived in Can., 1963; s. Francis David and Sonia (Marley) McK.; m. Ellen Frances Robinson, May 26, 1984; 1 child, Sean David. BA, U. Toronto, 1982. Free-lance film critic Winnipeg (Man., Can.) Free Press, 1985-87, staff film critic, 1988-92, features writer, 1992-94; news reporter, features writer, columnist Winnipeg (Man., Can.) Free Press, $, 1994—. Mem. Winnipeg Press Club (pres. 1990, house chair/treas. 1989). Avocations: movies, Trekkies, Blue Jays. Office: Winnipeg Free Press, 1355 Mountain Ave, Winnipeg, MB Canada R2X 3B6

MC KIE, TODD STODDARD, artist; b. Boston, Apr. 25, 1944; s. Roy Albert and Lois E. (Barwood) McK.; m. Judy Anne Kensley, Apr. 10, 1967; 1 son, Jesse Simon. BFA, RISD, 1966. Vis. artist RISD, 1977, Mass. Coll. Art, 1977-78, Sch. Mus. Fine Arts, Boston, 1979; lectr. schs. and museums. Exhibited in one-man shows Harcus Krakow Gallery, Boston, 1977, 79, 83, Aquavella Gallery, N.Y.C., 1978, 79, 81, Hokin-Kaufman Gallery, Chgo., 1983, Helander Gallery, N.Y.C., 1990, 92, Toale Gallery, Boston, 1994; exhibited in group shows including, Whitney Museum Am. Art, N.Y.C., 1975, Harcus Krakow Gallery, 1975, 78, Mus. Fine Arts, Boston, 1975, 77, 81, Acquavella Gallery, 1976, 78, 79, 81, Inst. Contemporary Art, Boston, 1979, Addison Gallery Am. Art, 1981; represented in permanent collections including Fogg Art Mus., Cambridge, Mass., M.I.T., Cambridge, Brockton (Mass.) Mus., Mus. Fine Arts, Boston, DeCordova Mus., Lincoln, Mass., Rose Art Mus. Brandeis U.; also numerous pvt. collections. Recipient Blanch E. Colman award Colman Found., 1974; Artists Found. fellow Boston, 1975, 89. Home and Office: 117R Magazine St Cambridge MA 02139-3955

MCKIE, W. GILMORE, human resources executive; b. Marquette, Mich., Aug. 25, 1927; s. Walter G. and Amy Gertrude (Larson) McK.; m. Elenore R. MacNally, Sept. 9, 1950 (div. Nov. 1962); 1 child, Janet; m. Mary Simmons, Mar. 21, 1964 (dec. Aug. 1970) 1 child, Gwen DeBuck; m. Eunice Winifred Curtis, July 10, 1971; children: Ellen Sheive, Norrine Halvorsen. BS in Econs., U. Rochester, 1951. Employment interviewer Taylor Instruments Cos', Rochester, N.Y., 1951-60; employment mgr. Graflex, Inc., Rochester, 1960-62, Gen. Railway Signal Co., Rochester, 1962-67; dir. human resources The Singer Co., Rochester, Binghamton,, N.Y.C., 1967-77, Norwich-Eaton Pharms., Norwich, N.Y., 1977-80; personnel mgr. Ness Automatic Machine Products, Rochester, 1980-84; v.p. human resources Marine Midland Bank, N.A., Rochester, 1984-89; pres. HRM Cons., Inc., Rochester, 1989-93; founder, pres. adr Support Svcs., Rochester, N.Y., 1993—; mgmt. adv. bd. Cornell U. Extension div., Rochester, 1984-90; mem. job svc. employer com. N.Y. State Dept. Labor, 1993—. Adv. bd. Salvation Army, Rochester 1986—; vice chair N.Y. State divsn. Human Rights, Rochester, 1987—; bd. dirs. Ralph Bunche Scholarship Fund, Rochester, 1990—, Youth at Risk, Rochester, 1988—; bd. govs. N.Y. State Fingerlakes Regional Edn. Ctr. for Econ. Devel., Rochester, 1984—; exec. com. United Negro Coll. Fund, Rochester, 1986—; adv. bd. chair Coll. Continuing Edn. Rochester Inst. Tech., 1985-90; chair Lothus C. Carson Human Rights Awards Luncheon, Rochester, 1991. Mem. Soc. for Human Resource Mgmt. (dist. dir N.Y. state 1985-89, pers. rsch. com 1989—, pres. Genesee Valley chpt. 1982-84, chmn. bd. 1984-87, founder 1982), Industrial Mgmt. Coun. Rochester (mem. human resource adv. com. 1988-90, chmn. industrial pers. group 1983-84, vice chmn. bank pers. group 1985-90), Rochester Assn. Automatic Machining (pres. 1982-83), Rochester Profl. Cons. Network, Pers. Testing Coun. Upstate N.Y., Broome County C. of C. (pres. Industrial Rels. Com. 1977), Chenango C. of C. (dir. 1978), Chenango-Deleware Bus. Edn. Ctr. (past v.p. 1977-78). Republican. Lutheran. Avocations: golf, trap and skeet shooting, woodworking. Office: HRM Support Svcs 2854 St Paul Blvd Rochester NY 14617-3740

MCKIERNAN, JOHN WILLIAM, mechanical engineer; b. Hannibal, Mo., Jan. 12, 1923; s. Charles and Anna Laura (Turner) McK.; m. Jeannette Dorothy Hagen, Aug. 26, 1945; children—Kathleen J., Linda J., John E. B.S., U. Mo., 1947; M.S., Iowa State Coll., 1950. With E.I. duPont de Nemours & Co., Inc., Richmond, Va., 1947-48; faculty Iowa State Coll., 1948-51; mech. engr. Sandia Nat. Lab., Albuquerque, 1951-85. Served with USAAF, 1943-45. Decorated D.F.C., Air medal. Fellow ASME (v.p., bd. govs.). Mem. Christian Ch. Home: 1709 Cardenas Dr NE Albuquerque NM 87110-6629

MCKILLOP, DANIEL JAMES, insurance company real estate executive; b. N.Y.C., June 18, 1948; s. Daniel James and Martha (Laux) McK.; m. Irene M. Flood, June 22, 1974. BA in History, Siena Coll., 1969; MBA in Fin., St. John's U., 1975. Cert. property mgr. V.p. real estate N.Y. Life Ins. Co., 1969—. Roman Catholic. Avocations: hunting, fishing. Home: Box 332 Port Monmouth NJ 07758 Office: New York Life Insurance CO 51 Madison Ave Rm 904 New York NY 10010

MCKILLOP, WILLIAM LAWIE, forest economics educator; b. Aberdeen, Scotland, June 3, 1933; came to U.S., 1961; s. William L.M. and Isabella (Morrison) McK.; m. Kathleen Jessie Smith, Feb. 15, 1958; children: Lesley, Robin, Aileen, Valerie. BS, U. Aberdeen, 1954; MS, U. N.B., Can., 1959; MA, PhD, U. Calif., Berkeley, 1965. Forest economist Can. Forestry Service, Ottawa, Ont., 1958-61; mem. faculty U. Calif., Berkeley, 1964-75, prof. forest econs., 1975—. Contbr. articles to profl. jours. Served to lt. C.E., Brit. Army, 1954-56. Mem. Soc. Am. Foresters, Am. Econ. Assn. Home: 40 Sleepy Hollow Ln Orinda CA 94563-1321 Office: Univ of Calif Dept Forestry & Resource Mgmt Berkeley CA 94720

MCKIM, PAUL ARTHUR, management consultant, retired petroleum executive; b. Milford, Conn., Feb. 1, 1923; s. Arthur Wheatley and Helen Agnes (Brennan) McK.; m. Daisy Flora Brown, June 18, 1945; 1 dau., Meredith Ann. Student, Lamar Inst. Tech., 1940-42; BS in Chem. Engring., La. State U., 1943, MS, 1947, PhD, 1949; grad. Advanced Mgmt. Program, Harvard, 1959; grad. Aspen Inst. Humanistic Studies Exec. Program, 1970. With Ethyl Corp., 1949-62, asst. gen. mgr. research and devel. operations, 1958-62; v.p., gen. mgr. rsch. and devel. Atlantic Refining Co., Phila., 1962-66; v.p. Atlantic Richfield Co., 1966-78; v.p. comml. devel. Arco Chem. Co., 1966-69, v.p. nuclear operations and comml. devel., 1969-73; exec. v.p. Sinclair Koppers Co., 1973; pres. Arco Polymers, Inc., 1974-78; asst. to pres. Tex. Eastern Corp., 1978-80, v.p., 1980-84, sr. v.p., 1985-88; Chmn. US Organizing com. for 12th World Petroleum Congress, Houston, 1987. Past bd. mgrs. Franklin Inst. Research Labs; past vice chmn. bd. mgrs. Spring Garden Coll., Phila. Coll. Art.; past vice chmn. World Affairs Council of Phila. Served to lt. (j.g.) USNR, 1944-46. Mem. Am. Inst. Chem. Engrs., Am. Petroleum Inst., Alpha Chi Sigma, Omicron Delta Kappa, Tau Beta Pi, Phi Lambda Upsilon, Phi Kappa Phi, Delta Kappa Epsilon. Clubs: Union League, Merion (Pa.) Cricket, Merion Golf, Houston, Lakewood Yacht, Shreveport (La.) Country. Home: 5405 Holly Springs Dr Houston TX 77056-2021

MCKIM, SAMUEL JOHN, III, lawyer; b. Pitts., Dec. 31, 1938; s. Samuel John and Harriet Frieda (Roehl) McK.; children: David Hunt, Andrew John; m. Eugenia A. Leverich. AA cum laude, Port Huron Jr. Coll., 1959; BA cum laude, U. Mich., 1961, JD cum laude, U. Mich., 1964. Bar: Mich. 1965, U.S. Dist. Ct. (so. dist.) Mich. 1965, U.S. Ct. Appeals (6th cir.) 1969, U.S. Supreme Ct., 1994. Assoc. Miller, Canfield, Paddock and Stone, Detroit, Bloomfield Hills, Kalamazoo, Lansing, Monroe, Traverse City and Grand Rapids, Mich., Washington, Boca Raton, Fla., Gdansk, Poland, 1964-71, sr. ptnr., 1971—; head state and local tax sect., 1985—, chmn. tax dept., 1989-94, mng. ptnr., 1979-85, chmn., mng. ptnr., 1984-85; mem. tax coun. State Bar Mich., 1981-84, chmn. state and local tax com. real property sect., 1982-90; profl. law sch. Wayne State U., 1993—. Bd. dirs., past chmn. Goodwill Industries of Greater Detroit, 1970—; dir. Goodwill Industries Found., 1982-95; elder Presbyn. ch.; coun. mem. at large Detroit area coun. Boy Scouts Am., 1987—. Mem. ABA, Mich. Bar Assn., Detroit Bar Assn., Detroit Club, Barrister's Soc., Ostego Ski Club, Order of Coif, Phi Delta Phi. Assoc. editor Mich. Law Rev. Home: 32778 Friar Tuck Ln Franklin MI 48025-2500 Office: Miller Canfield Paddock & Stone 150 W Jefferson Ave Detroit MI 48226-4429

MCKINLAY, DONALD CARL, lawyer; b. Chgo., June 3, 1916; s. Donald Sinclair and Frances (Wielenberg) McK.; m. Helen Stevenson Moore, Oct. 14, 1967; children by previous marriage: Susan Harried, David, Thomas. B.A., Dartmouth Coll., 1937, A.M., 1974; J.D., U. Chgo., 1940.

Bar: Ill. 1940, Colo. bar 1946. With firm Taylor, Miller, Busch & Boyden, Chgo., 1940-42; atty. in gen. practice Denver, 1946-51; asst. atty. gen. State of Colo., 1948-50; partner firm Holme Roberts & Owen, Denver, 1951-81; sr. partner Denver office firm Mayer, Brown & Platt, Chgo., Washington, N.Y.C., London, Houston, Los Angeles, Tokyo, 1981-88; ret. Denver office firm Mayer, Brown & Platt, Chgo.; gen. counsel, sec., trustee Aspen Inst. for Humanistic Studies, 1963-88. Trustee Dartmouth Coll., 1974-84; mem. Colo. Commn. on Higher Edn., 1966-75, chmn., 1968-72. Served to lt. U.S. Navy, 1942-46, PTO. Fellow Am. Coll. Trial Lawyers. Democrat. Presbyterian.

MCKINLESS, KATHY JEAN, accountant; b. Augusta, Ga., June 15, 1954; d. Jack M. and Jean K. (Norby) VanderWood; m. Darryl P. Calderon, Mar. 17, 1979 (dec. June 1988); children: Christopher, Jackie; m. Richard T. McKinless, July 1, 1989; children: Ashley, Thomas. BS in Acctg., U. S.C., 1975, MBA, 1978. CPA, D.C. Acct. Clarkson, Harden & Gantt, Columbia, 1975-79; sr. acct. KPMG Peat Marwick, Washington, 1979-80, mgr., 1980-86, ptnr., 1986—; spkr. Mortgage Bankers Assn., Fin. Mgrs. Soc., Nat. Assn. Coll. and Univ. Bus. Officers, Fed. Fin. Insts. Exam. Coun. Mem. Governance com., treas., bd. dirs. Coun. of Nation's Capital Girl Scouts U.S., 1985—. Office: KPMG Peat Marwick 2001 M St NW Washington DC 20036-3310

MCKINLEY, BRUNSON, diplomat; b. Miami, Fla., Feb. 8, 1943; s. Kenneth William and Lois Rebecca (Hiestand) McK.; m. Nancy Padlon, Sept. 11, 1971; children: Harley Joseph, Sarah Elizabeth. BA, U. Chgo., 1962; MA, Harvard U., 1964. Third sec. U.S. Embassy, Rome, 1971-72; spl. asst. U.S. Liaison Office, Peking, China, 1973-74; dep. prin. officer U.S. Consulate Gen., Danang, Republic of Vietnam, 1975; staff officer Dept. State, Washington, 1975-76, officer-in-charge Italian affairs, 1976-78; first sec. Am. Embassy, London, 1978-81; dep. polit. advisor U.S. Mission, Berlin, 1981-83; dep. exec. sec. Dept. State, Washington, 1983-86; U.S. ambassador Am. Embassy, Port-Au-Prince, Haiti, 1986-89; deputy for policy bur. european affairs U.S. Dept. State, Washington, 1990-91, dep. asst. sec. state for refugee programs, 1991-93, sr. dep. asst. sec. state for population, refugees and migration, 1993—. Contbr. various publs. in field of migration. Served to capt. U.S. Army, 1965-71, Vietnam. Decorated Bronze Star, Award for Valor, Suprior Hon. award. Mem. Army and Navy Club, Bath Club (London), Phi Beta Kappa. Avocations: walking, running, ice skating, languages. Home: 7064 31st St NW Washington DC 20015-1402 Office: Bur of Population Refugees & Migration US Dept State Washington DC 20520-5824

MCKINLEY, JOHN HENRY, sales executive; b. Harlan, Ky., Feb. 28, 1939; s. John Henry and Nina (Howard) McK.; m. W. Ruth Young, Aug. 15, 1964; 1 child, Mary Hayes. BS in Textile Chemistry, Ga. Tex. Tech U., 1962; postgrad., U. Tenn., 1965, 66, Naval War Coll., 1980, Nat. Def. U., 1982, Army War Coll., 1991. Chemist Eastman Chem. Co., Kingsport, Tenn., 1963-67; lab. mgr. Eastman Chem. Co., Lodi, N.J. 1967-70; sales rep. Eastman Chem. Co., Greensboro, N.C., 1970-73; sr. sales rep. in charge Eastman Chem. Co., L.A., 1974-81; dist. mgr. Eastman Chem. Co., Houston, 1982-86; bus. team analysis Eastman Chem. Co., Kingsport, 1986-88, mgr. nat. distbrs., 1988-89; dir. sales N.Am. Eastman Fine Chems. Bus. Orgn., Kingsport, 1990-91, dir. sales Ams., 1992-93, dir. sales worldwide, 1994—. Bd. dirs. Kingsport (Tenn.) Symphony, 1986-91. Rear admiral USNR, 1961—. Decorate Legion of Merit, Meritorious Svc. medals Pres. of the U.S., 1986, 89, Navy Commendation medals Sec. of Def., 1990. Mem. Am. Assn. Textile Colorists and Chemists (chmn. Pacific chpt. 1975-76), Res. Officers Assn. (v.p. Navy Tenn. 1994—), Naval Inst., Naval Res. Assn. Kingsport C. of C., Kiwanis Club (Kingsport, com. chmn. 1986, 88, 89). Episcopalian. Home: 4 Longview Ln Kingsport TN 37660-4518 Office: Eastman Fine Chems PO Box 451 Kingsport TN 37662-0451

MC KINLEY, JOHN KEY, retired oil company executive; b. Tuscaloosa, Ala., Mar. 24, 1920; s. Virgil Parks and Mary Emma (Key) McK.; m. Helen Grace Heare, July 19, 1946; children: John Key Jr., Mark Charles. BS in Chem. Engring, U. Ala., 1940, M.S. in Organic Chemistry, 1941, LL.D. (hon.), 1972; grad., Advanced Mgmt. Program, Harvard U., 1962; LL.D. (hon.), Troy State U., 1974. Registered profl. engr., Tex. With Texaco Inc., 1941-86; asst. dir. research Texaco Inc., Beacon, N.Y., 1957-59; asst. to v.p. Texaco Inc., 1959-60, mgr. comml. devel., 1960; gen. mgr. petrochem dept. Texaco Inc., N.Y.C., 1960-67; v.p. petrochem. dept., v.p. in charge supply and distbn Texaco Inc., 1967-71, sr. v.p. worldwide refining, petrochems., also supply and distbn., 1971, pres., dir., 1971-80, pres., chief operating officer, chmn. exec. com., 1980, chmn. bd., pres., chief exec. officer, 1980-83, chmn. bd., chief exec. officer, 1983-86, ret., 1986, bd. dirs. emeritus; bd. dirs. Federated Dept. Stores, Inc. Patentee for chem. processing. Hon. bd. dirs. Met. Opera Assocs.; nat. chmn. Met. Opera Centennial Fund, 1980; bd. dirs. The Ams. Soc.; mem. Bus. Coun. Maj. AUS, 1941-45, ETO. Decorated Bronze Star; recipient George Washington Honor medal Freedoms Found., 1972; Andrew Wellington Cordier fellow Columbia U.; named to Ala. Bus. Hall of Fame, 1982, Ala. Acad. Honor, 1983, State of Ala. Engring. Hall of Fame, 1992. Fellow Am. Inst. Chem. Engrs.; mem. Am. Petroleum Inst. (hon. dir.), Wee Burn Country Club, Links Club, Brook Club, Augusta Nat. Golf Club, Blind Brook County Club, North River Yacht, Sigma Xi, Tau Beta Pi, Gamma Sigma Epsilon, Kappa Sigma. Office: One Canterbury Green Stamford CT 06901

MCKINLEY, LOREN DHUE, museum director; b. Tillamook, Oreg., Feb. 1, 1920; s. Henry Raymond and Flora (Phillips) McK.; m. Mary Eileen Sessions, May 22, 1942; children: Candace Eileen, Scott Dhu, Kevin Loren, Laurie Lee, Maris Colleen. Student, Oreg. State U., U. Oreg.; D.Sc., U. Portland, 1973. Advt. mgr. Headlight Herald, Tillamook, 1946; partner Kenwood Press, Tillamook, 1949; dir. Oreg. Mus. Sci. and Industry, Portland, 1966-78; chief exec. officer Oreg. Mus. Sci. and Industry, 1978—; bd. dirs. Fred Hutchinson Cancer Rsch. Ctr. Found.; Portland ops. mgr. Office of Devel. Oreg. State U. Mayor of Tillamook, 1954-60; pres. Leukemia Assn. Oreg. Inc., 1983—; bd. dirs. St. Mary's Acad., 1993—; mem. Oreg. State U Found. Served with AUS, World War II, ETO, MTO. Decorated Bronze Star with oak leaf cluster; named 1st Citizen of Oreg., 1951; recipient award Oreg. Mus. Sci. and Industry, 1965, Elsie M.B. Naumberg award as outstanding sci. mus. dir., 1968, citation for outstanding svc. Oreg. Acad. Sci., 1971, Aubrey Watzek award Lewis and Clark Coll., 1973. Mem. Assn. Sci. and Tech. Ctrs. Am. (pres. 1973—), League Oreg. Cities (past pres.), Kappa Sigma. Republican. Home and Office: 11925 SW Belvidere Pl Portland OR 97225-5805

MCKINLEY, (JENNIFER CAROLYN) ROBIN, writer; b. Warren, Ohio, Nov. 16, 1952; d. William and Jeanne Carolyn (Turrell) McK; m. Peter Dickinson, Jan. 3, 1992. Student, Dickinson Coll., 1970-72; BA, Bowdoin Coll., 1975, PhD (hon.), 1986. Editor, transcriber Ward and Paul, Washington, 1972-73; rsch. asst. Rsch. Assocs., Brunswick, Maine, 1976-77; tchr., counselor pvt. secondary sch., Natick, Maine, 1978; edit. asst. Little, Brown & Co., Boston, 1979-81; barn mgr. horse farm Holliston, Mass., 1981-82; clerk Books of Wonder, N.Y.C., 1983—; freelance reader, copy and line editor, 1983—. Author: Beauty: A Retelling of the Story of Beauty and the Beast, 1978 (Horn book Honor list citation 1978), The Door in the Hedge, 1981, The Blue Sword, 1982 (Best Young adult books citation ALA 1982, Newbery Honor citation 1983), The Hero and the Crown, 1984 (Horn book honor list citation 1985, ALA Newbery medal 1985), The Outlaws of Sherwood, 1988, Rowan, 1992, My Father is in the Navy, 1992, Deerskin, 1993 (Best Young Adult Books citation ALA 1993, Best Adult Books for Young Adults citation ALA 1993), A Knot in the Grain and Other Stories, 1994; contbr.: Elsewhere Vol. II, 1982, Vol. III, 1984, Faery, 1985, Writers for Children, 1988; editor, contbr.: Imaginary Lands, 1985 (World Fantasy award Best Anthology 1986); adapter: Jungle Book Tales, 1985, Black Beauty, 1986, The Light Princess, 1988. Office: Merrilee Heifetz Writers House 21 W 26th St New York NY 10010-1003

MCKINLEY, VICKY LYNN, biology educator; b. Dayton, Ohio, Feb. 13, 1957; d. Dale and Kathryn (Andrick) McK. BS, Wright State U., 1979; MS, U. Cin., 1981, PhD, 1985. Teaching asst. Wright State U., Dayton, 1978-79; chemist Nat. Distillers & Chem. Co., Cin., 1979-80; grad. asst. U. Cin., 1980-83, pre-doctoral rsch. fellow, 1984-85; postdoctoral rsch. fellow U. Calgary, Alta., Can., 1985-86; asst. prof. biology Roosevelt U., Chgo., 1987-92, assoc. prof., 1992—; exam writer Am. Coll. Testing; cons. John Wiley & Sons, Inc.,

MCAT. Contbr. articles to profl. jours. Recipient Acad. Scholarship award Wright State U., 1975-76, Summer fellowship U. Cin. Rsch. Coun., 1983, Univ. Dean's Disting. Dissertation fellowship, 1984-85, Postdoctoral fellowship Alta. Oil Sands Tech. and Rsch. Authority, 1985—; named All-Star Prof., Chgo. Tribune, 1993. Mem. AAAS, Nat. Assn. Biology Tchrs., Am. Soc. Microbiology (N. Paul Hudson commendation Ohio branch 1981), Ill. Soc. Microbiology, Chgo. Herpetological Soc., Soc. Coll. Sci. Tchrs., Sigma Xi. Avocations: photography, backpacking, antique restoration. Office: Roosevelt U Dept Biology 430 S Michigan Ave Chicago IL 60605-1301

MCKINLEY, WILLIAM A., educator, physicist; b. Dallas, Aug. 23, 1917; s. William A. and Nora (Richards) McK.; m. Georgia MacKinnon, Nov. 16, 1940 (div. 1969); children—William A. III, Kathryn; m. Hedi Faludi 1969. B.A., U. Tex., 1939; Ph.D., Mass. Inst. Tech., 1947. Fellow Inst. Neurology, Northwestern U. Med. Sch., 1940-42; staff mem. Radiation Lab. Mass. Inst. Tech., 1943-45; mem. faculty Rensselaer Poly. Inst., 1947—; prof. physics, 1955-84, emeritus prof. physics, 1985—. Mem. AAAS, Am. Phys. Soc., Am. Assn. Physics Tchrs., Phi Beta Kappa, Sigma Xi. Spl. research quantum scattering theory, quantum field theory, electrophysiology central nervous system. Home: PO Box 411 Altamont NY 12009-0411 Office: Rensselaer Poly Inst Troy NY 12180

MCKINLEY, WILLIAM THOMAS, composer, performer, educator; b. New Kensington, Pa., Dec. 9, 1938; s. Daniel Edward and Ellen Lee (Henson) M.; m. Marlene Marie Mildner, Apr. 11, 1956; children: Thomas Jr., Derrick, Jory, Sean, Elliott. BFA, Carnegie-Mellon U., 1960; MM, Yale U., 1966, DMA, 1969. Mem. music faculty SUNY-Albany, 1968-69; prof. music U. Chgo., 1969-73; prof. composition and jazz studies New Eng. Conservatory Music, Boston, 1973—. Composer numerous works for orch., chamber ensembles, choral works, oratorio, also solo works; commns. include works for Koussevitzky Music Found., 1982, Lincoln Ctr. Chamber Music Soc., 1985, Boston Symphony Pops, 1986, Concert Artist Guild, 1988, Stan Getz, 1988, Am. Symphony, 1988, (2) Fromm Found., John Williams, 1989, NEA Consortium, Rheinische Philharmonie, Fed. Republic Germany, 1990, Queensland Youth Orch., Australia, 1990, Bolshoi Ballet Theatre Orch. USSR, 1990, Pitts. New Music Ensemble, 1991, Quintet Ams., 1992, Md. Bach Aria Group, 1992, Berlin Saxophone Quartet, 1992, 93, Richard Stolzman, 1993, Seattle Symphony, 1993, Absolut Vodka, 1994; performance recs. with Berlin Radio Symphony and Richard Stolzman, Rheinische Philharm., Warsaw Philharm., St. Petersburg Philharm., Slovak Radio Symphony, Seattle Symphony, Krakow Philharm., Silesian Philharm., Prague Radio Symphony, Solati Trio, Manhattan Sinfonia, Cleve. Quartet. Recipient Naumberg prize Naumberg Found., 1975; Nat. Endowment Arts composer fellow, 1975-83; Am. Acad. Music award, Am. Acad. and Inst. Arts and Letters, 1983; Guggenheim fellow, 1985; 3 Mass Council fellowships. Mem. Am. Composers Alliance, Am. Music Ctr. Home: 240 West St Reading MA 01867-2847

MCKINNELL, NOEL MICHAEL, architect, educator; b. Salford, Eng., Dec. 25, 1935; came to U.S., 1959; s. Ronald Johnston and Elizabeth McK.; m. Jane Beardmore D'Esopo, Sept. 16, 1961; children: Caitlin Elizabeth, Phoebe Berrien. B.A., Manchester U., Eng., 1958; M.S., Columbia U., 1960; M.A. hon., Harvard U., 1978. Registered arch., Mass., Minn., Mo., N.H., N.J., N.Y., Ct., Gt. Brit.; cert. Nat. Coun. Archtl. Registration Bds. Cofounder, prin. Kallmann & McKinnell, Boston, 1962-78; prin. Kallmann, McKinnell & Wood, Inc,, Boston, 1978—; asst. prof. Grad. Sch. Design Harvard U., Cambridge, Mass., 1963-66, assoc. prof., 1966-71, prof., 1971-83, Nelson Robinson Jr. prof., 1983-87. Archtl. works Boston City Hall, Am. Acad. Arts and Scis., Becton Dickinson Corp. Hdqrs., Hynes Conv. Ctr., Bass Ctr.-Yale U., Shad Hall-Harvard Bus. Sch., Hauser Hall-Harvard Law Sch., Marx Hall-Princeton, others. Recipient Silver medal Royal Manchester Inst., 1960, Arnold W. Brunner prize Nat. Inst. Arts & Letters, 1969, Honor award Boston Soc. Archs., 1994; William Hale Kendall fellow Columbia U., 1960. Fellow AIA; mem. Am. Acad. Arts and Scis. Home: 121 Beacon St Boston MA 02115-1515 Office: Kallmann McKinnell Wood Arch 939 Boylston St Boston MA 02115-3104

MCKINNELL, ROBERT GILMORE, zoology, genetics and cell biology educator; b. Springfield, Mo., Aug. 9, 1926; s. William Parks and Mary Catherine (Gilmore) McK.; m. Beverly Walton Kerr, Jan. 24, 1964; children: Nancy Elizabeth, Robert Gilmore, Susan Kerr. AB, U. Mo., 1948; BS, Drury Coll., 1949, DSc (hon.), 1993; PhD, U. Minn., 1959. Research assoc. Inst. Cancer Research, Phila., 1958-61; asst. prof. biology Tulane U., New Orleans, 1961-65; assoc. prof. Tulane U., 1965-69, prof., 1969-70; prof. zoology U. Minn., Mpls., 1970—; prof. genetics and cell biology U. Minn. St. Paul, 1976—; vis. scientist Dow Chem. Co., Freeport, Tex., 1976; guest dept. zoology U. Calif., Berkeley, 1979; Royal Soc. guest rsch. fellow Nuffield dept. pathology John Radcliffe Hosp., Oxford U., 1981-82; NATO vis. scientist Akademisch Ziekenhuis, Ghent, Belgium, 1984; faculty rsch. assoc. Naval Med. Rsch. Inst., Bethesda, Md., 1988; secretariat Third Internat. Conf. Differentiation, 1978; mem. amphibian com. Inst. Lab. Animal Resources, NRC, 1970-73, mem. adv. coun., 1974; mem. panel genetic and cellular resources program NIH, 1981-82, spl. study sect., Bethesda, 1990. Author: Cloning: Amphibian Nuclear Transplantation, 1978, Cloning, A Biologist Reports, 1979; sr. editor: Differentiation and Neoplasia, 1980, Cloning: Leben aus der Retorte, 1981, Cloning, of Frogs, Mice, and other Animals, 1985; mem. editorial bd. Differentiation, 1973—; assoc. editor Gamete Research, 1980-86; contbr. articles to profl. jours. Served to lt. USNR, 1944-47, 51-53. Recipient Outstanding Teaching award Newcomb Coll., Tulane U., 1970; Disting. Alumni award Drury Coll., 1979, Morse Alumni Teaching award U. Minn., 1992; Research fellow Nat. Cancer Inst., 1957-58; Sr. Sci. fellow NATO, 1974. Fellow AAAS, Linnean Soc. (London); mem. Am. Assn.Cancer Rsch., Am. Assn. for Cancer Edn. Metastasis Soc., Am. Inst. Biol. Scis., Soc. for Devel. Biology, Internat. Soc. for Study of Comparative Oncology, Inc., Internat. Soc. Differentiation (exec. com., sec.-treas. 1975-92, pres. elect 1992-94, pres. 1994—), Gown-in-Town Club, Sigma Xi. Home: 2124 Hoyt Ave W Saint Paul MN 55108-1315 Office: U Minn Dept Genetics Cell Bio Saint Paul MN 55108

MCKINNEY, ALEXANDER STUART, neurologist; b. N.Y.C., Feb. 3, 1933; s. John McDowell and Katherine Elizabeth (Morse) McK.; m. Carolyn Clifton Braman, Aug. 15, 1958 (div. July 1985); children: James, David, Mark; m. Susan Jennifer Lowe, July 30, 1985; children: Josephine, Mary, Jennifer. AB, Princeton U., 1955; MD, Columbia U., 1959. Diplomate Am. Bd. Neurology. Intern St. Luke's Hosp., N.Y.C., 1959-60; resident N.Y. Neurological Inst., 1960-63; prof. neurology Emory U., Atlanta, 1965-85; pvt. practice Mountain Med. Assocs., Clyde, N.C., 1985-95; chief of staff Haywood County Hosp., Clyde, N.C., 1989-90. Contbr. articles to profl. jours. Served to lt. comdr. USNR, 1963-65. Fellow Am. Acad. Neurology, Royal Soc. Medicine; mem. N.C. Med. Soc. (vice councillor 1991-94), N.C. Neurol. Soc. (pres. 1992). Avocations: travel, gardening. Home: 5 Holston Village Rd Waynesville NC 28786

MC KINNEY, ALEXIS, public relations consultant; b. Cin., Mar. 13, 1907; s. John Austin and Gertrude (Kofler) McK.; m. Esther Ryker Simmons, Aug. 27, 1930 (dec. 1985); 1 dau., Eunice Christine; m. Margaret Jane Miles, Sept. 14, 1986 (dec. 1990); m. Irene Vogel Stevenson, Apr. 6, 1991. Ed. pub. schs., Colo., and Tex. Enlisted in U.S. Navy, 1923, served aboard U.S.S. New Mexico, 1923-27; circulation agt. Pueblo (Colo.) Star-Jour., 1928; reporter Pueblo Chieftain, 1929, state editor, 1930, city editor, 1931-32; co-pub. and editor Rocky Ford Tribune, 1933-34; news editor Alamosa (Colo.) Daily Courier, 1934-42; statehouse reporter Denver Post, 1942-45; information officer U.S. Bur. Reclamation, Denver, 1945-46; asst. city editor Denver Post, 1946, city editor, 1946-47, mng. editor, 1947-49, asst. pub., 1949-63; project dir. Rio Grande-land, Durango, Colo., 1973; dir. pub. relations Denver & Rio Grande Western R.R. Co., 1965-73; pub. relations cons. Rio Grande Industries, Inc., 1973—. Trustee Colo. R.R. Hist. Found. and Mus. Mem. all-Navy championship rifle team, 1927. Mem. Pub. Relations Soc. Am., R.R. Pub. Relations Assn., Sigma Delta Chi. Conglist. Address: 3131 E Alameda Ave #505 Denver CO 80209-3411

MCKINNEY, CHARLES CECIL, investment company executive; b. Newdale, N.C., Nov. 30, 1931; s. Sherbert Day and Florence Van (Hall) McK.; children—Emry Lynn, Robin Ashley, Marc Jason; m. Suzanne Reeves, Apr. 3, 1988. B.S.B.A., U. N.C.-Chapel Hill, 1957; student, U. Tenn., 1950-52. V.p., creative dir. J.T. Howard Advt., 1957-68; chmn. bd.,

chief exec. officer McKinney & Silver, Raleigh, N.C., 1968-90; chmn., pres., chief exec. officer Onyx Corp., 1991—. Trustee N.C. Symphony, Raleigh, 1983-87; bd. visitors U. N.C., Chapel Hill, 1989-91; bd. vis. Kenan Flagler Sch. Bus., 1985-94. Recipient profl. awards. Mem. N.C. Mus. Art, Sphinx Club (Raleigh), Figure Eight Yacht Club (N.C.), Cardinal Club (Raleigh). Republican. Home: 1021 Cowper Dr Raleigh NC 27608-2228

MCKINNEY, CYNTHIA ANN, congresswoman; b. Mar. 17, 1955; d. Billy and Leola McKinney; 1 child, Coy Grandison, Jr. B, U. So. Calif.; postgrad., Ga. State U., U. Wis.; Tufts U. Former instr. Clark Atlanta U., Atlanta Met. Coll.; former mem. Ga. Ho. of Reps.; mem. 103rd Congress from 11th Ga. dist., 1993—; instr. Agnes Scott Coll. Diplomatic fellow Spellman Coll. Home: 765 Shorter Ter NW Atlanta GA 30318-7140 Office: US Ho of Reps Office Of House Mems Washington DC 20515

MC KINNEY, DAVID E(WING), information processing products company executive; b. Harriman, Tenn., Nov. 28, 1934; s. David Lloyd and Mattie (Ewing) McK.; m. Mary, John, James, Mark; m. Nancy Coates Hale, Aug. 29, 1991. Student (Founders scholar), Vanderbilt U., 1952-53; B.S. in Mktg. (Gen. Electric scholar), U. Tenn., 1956. With IBM, 1956—; br. mgr. IBM, New Orleans, 1966-68; exec. asst. to chmn. bd. IBM, Armonk, N.Y., 1971-73; pres. info. records div. IBM, Princeton, N.J., 1975-76; v.p. office products div. IBM, Franklin Lakes, N.J., 1976-77; v.p. personnel IBM, Armonk, 1979-80; asst. group exec. IBM Gen. Bus. Group, White Plains, N.Y., 1980—; v.p., asst. group exec. IBM Info. Systems Group, Rye, 1982—; pres. IBM World Trade, Americas/Far East Corp., 1986—, v.p. communications, sr. v.p. corp. ops. staff, mgmt. com., corp. mgmt. bd., 1987-89; pres., dir. gen. IBM Europe, Paris, 1989-91; sr. v.p. IBM Corp., Armonk, N.Y., 1991-92; bd. dirs. Gen. Re. Corp., Paxar Corp. Mem. adv. bd. T. J. Watson Found.; Providence; bd. dirs., corp. mem. Brown U.; bd. dirs. Internat. Exec. Svc. Corps, N.Y. Philharmonic; trustee Am. U., Paris; elder 1st Presbyn. Ch., New Canaan, Conn. Served to lt. U.S. Army, 1957-58. Clubs: Country of New Canaan;.

MCKINNEY, DONALD, art gallery director, art dealer; b. N.Y.C., May 2, 1931. Student, Columbia U., 1954-57, London U., 1960-62. Pres. Marlborough Gallery, N.Y.C., 1974-78; dir. Hirschl & Adler Modern Galleries, N.Y.C., 1981-93; pres. Andre Emmerich Gallery, N.Y.C., 1993—. Co-author: Mark Rothko, 1971; contbr. Jackson Pollack Catalogue Raisonne, 1978. Mem. The Century Club.

MCKINNEY, DONALD LEE, magazine editor; b. Evanston, Ill., July 12, 1923; s. Guy Doane and Cora Redfield (Brenton) McK.; m. Mary Frances Joyce, Dec. 14, 1958; children—Jennifer Joyce, Douglas Guy. A.B., U. N.C., 1948. Salesman textbooks John Wiley & Sons, N.Y.C., 1949-52; freelance writer mostly comic books with some short articles and fiction, 1952-54; asst. mng. editor True mag., N.Y.C., 1955-62; editor articles Saturday Evening Post, 1962-69; spl. features editor N.Y. Daily News, 1969-70; mng. editor McCalls mag., N.Y.C., 1969-86; Gonzales prof. journalism U. S.C., Beaufort, 1986-90, prof. emeritus, 1990—. Author: Writing Magazine Articles That Sell, 1994; reporter, book reviewer. Served with USNR, 1943-46. Democrat. Home: 9 Spanish Moss Rd Hilton Head Island SC 29928 *I learned early that it is important to speak up if you think you are being treated unfairly; sometimes it's true, and nobody else will complain if you don't. I also learned that in my business, and probably in most others, it is best to always say what you think. Truth is usually more helpful than any assortment of euphemisms, and it also saves a lot of worry over who you have lied to and just what you've said. Truth is not only the best policy—by all odds it's the easiest to keep track of.*

MCKINNEY, E. KIRK, JR., retired insurance company executive; b. Indpls., Mar. 27, 1923; s. E. Kirk and Irene M. (Hurley) McK.; m. Alice Hollenbeck Greene, June 18, 1949; children: Kirk Ashley, Alan Brooks, Nora Claire McKinney Hiatt, Margot Knight. A.B., U. Mich., 1948. Asst. treas. Jefferson Nat. Life Ins. Co., Indpls., 1949-52, asst. to pres., asst. treas., 1952-53, treas., asst. to pres., 1953-55, v.p., treas., 1955-59, pres., 1959-90, chmn. bd., 1970-90, ret., 1990; vice chmn. bd. Somerset Group Inc., 1986-89, ret., 1990; bd. dirs. Zimmer Paper Products, Inc. Corp. relations com. U. Mich.; former pres., former chief exec. officer, bd. govs. Indpls. Mus. Art, now treas.; bd. dirs., mem. exec. com., past bd. dirs. (hon.) Greater Indpls. Progress Com.; former vice chmn. Indpls.-Marion County Bd. Ethics; former dir. Park Tudor Sch., Community Svc. Coun. Indpls., Hosp. Devel. Corp., Ind. Repertory Theater; past adv. com. Indpls. Retirement Home; former bd. dirs., and pres. Episcopal Community Services, Inc.; former vice chmn., life trustee Nature Conservancy; mem. adv. bd. Ind. U., Purdue U.; active Indpls. Symphony Orch.; former bd. dirs. Ind. Pub. Broadcasting Soc. Capt. Q.M.C., AUS, 1942-46. Mem. Life Office Mgmt. Assn. (bd. dirs. 1981-83), Am. Council Life Ins. (state v.p 1973-75, dir., exec. com. 1976-79), Assn. Ind. Life Ins. Cos. (pres. 1969-71), Indpls. C. of C., Sigma Chi. Democrat. Club: Economic of Indpls. (bd. dirs.). Home: 250 W 77th St Indianapolis IN 46260-3608 Office: 1330 W 38th St Indianapolis IN 46208-4103

MC KINNEY, GEORGE WESLEY, JR., banking educator; b. Amigo, W.Va., May 27, 1922; s. George W. and Charlotte (Ashworth) McK.; m. Lucille Christian, Sept. 5, 1941; children: George Wesley III, Mary, Ruth. A.B., Berea Coll., 1942; M.A., U. Va., 1947, Ph.D., 1949; postgrad. Stonier Grad. Sch. Banking, 1958. With Fed. Res. Bank Richmond, Va., 1948-60; asst. v.p. Fed. Res. Bank Richmond, 1958-60; with Irving Trust Co., N.Y.C., 1960-82; sr. v.p. Irving Trust Co., 1968-82, head econ. research and planning div., 1968-78, chmn. econ. adv. com., 1978-82; U. Va. Bankers prof. bank mgmt. McIntire Sch. Commerce U. Va., 1982-88, prof. emeritus, 1988—. Author: Federal Taxing and Spending in Virginia, 1949, Federal Reserve Discount Window, 1960, Management of Commercial Bank Funds, 1974, rev. edit., 1980; Contbr. to books. Bd. visitors Nat. Def. U., 1979-82. Served to capt. AUS, 1942-45. Fellow Nat. Assn. Bus. Economists (pres. 1965-66); mem. Phi Kappa Phi. Office: University of Virginia McIntire School of Commerce Charlottesville VA 22903

MCKINNEY, JAMES CARROLL, baritone, educator; b. Minden, La., Jan. 11, 1921; s. William C. and Carolyn (Hilman) McK.; m. Elizabeth Richmond, Aug. 28, 1949; children: James Carroll, Timothy Richmond, John Kevin. Student, La. Poly. Inst., 1938-41; student, Stanford U., 1943-44; MusB, La. State U., 1949, MusM, 1950; D.Mus. Arts, U. So. Calif., 1969; student in, London, 1979-80, 86. Grad. asst. La. State U., 1949-50; asst. prof. music theory Southwestern Baptist Theol. Sem., Ft. Worth, 1950-54; chmn. dept. music theory, composition Southwestern Baptist Theol. Sem., 1954-56, dean Sch. Ch. Music, disting. prof. of voice, 1956-94, emeritus dean and disting. prof., 1994—; baritone soloist First Presbyn. Ch., Hollywood, Calif., 1957-58, First Methodist Ch., Ft. Worth, 1963-67; guest tchr. U. So. Calif., 1958; vis. evaluator Nat. Assn. Schs. Music; vis. lectr. Hong Kong Bapt. Coll., Hong Kong Bapt. Theol. Sem., 1971-72; participant Internat. Congress Voice Tchrs., Strasbourg, France, 1987; faculty mem. Symposium on Care of the Profl. Voice, N.Y.C., 1988, Phila., 1989-95; master tchr. in NATS intern program. Presented solo recitals; appeared TV and choral prodns., Bangkok, Thailand, Hong Kong, Israel, Jordan, 1971-72; Author: The Beginning Music Reader, 1958, The Progressing Music Reader, 1959, You Can Read Music, 1960, The Advanced Music Reader, 1961, Mastering Music Reading, 1964, Study Guide for Fundamentals of Music, 1964, Vocal Fundamentals Kit, 1976, Vocal Development Kit, 1977, The Diagnosis and Correction of Vocal Faults, 1982, 2nd edit., 1994, Five Practical Lessons in Singing, 1982 (trans. into Korean, Portuguese, and Spanish). Bd. dirs. Ft. Worth Symphony Orch. Assn., Ft. Worth Civic Music Assn., Van Cliburn Internat., Piano Competition, Ft. Worth Opera, 1987-94. Mem. Music Tchrs. Nat. Assn. (pres. Ft. Worth chpt.), Music Educators Nat. Conf., Nat. Assn. Tchrs. Singing (lt. gov., regional gov. jour. 1987—), Am. Acad. Tchrs. Singing, Am. Choral Dirs. Assn., Tex. Assn. Music Schs. (pres.), Ft. Worth Voice Tchrs. Forum (pres.), Phi Mu Alpha Sinfonia, Omicron Delta Kappa, Phi Kappa Phi, Pi Kappa Lambda. Baptist. Office: Southwestern Bapt Theol Sem PO Box 22000 1809 W Broadus Ave Fort Worth TX 76115-2137 *The longer I live, the more certain I become that the basic value systems passed on to me by my parents are valid. Inherent in all their systems were personal integrity and abiding respect for the rights of others. My chief hope is that I may be as effective as they in transmitting these values to my own children and to the students with whom I come in contact.*

MCKINNEY, JAMES CLAYTON, electronics executive, electrical engineer; b. Charleston, W.Va., June 3, 1940; s. George Clayton and Leona (Adams) McK. B.S.E.E., W.Va. Inst. Tech., 1963. Mem. staff Sta. WMON, Montgomery, W.Va., 1961-63; stringer AP, Charleston, W.Va., 1961-63; with FCC, Washington, 1963-87, chief ops. br., 1969-73, chief monitoring div., 1973, chief enforcement div., 1974, dep. chief Field Ops. Bur., 1974-80, chief Field Ops. Bur., 1980-81, chief Pvt. Radio Bur., 1981-83; chief Mass Media Bur. FCC, 1983-87; dep. asst. to Pres., dir. White House Mil. Office Washington, 1987-89; chmn. Advanced TV Systems Com., Washington, 1989—; chmn. U.S. del. UN Conf. on Radio, Geneva, 1986.; mem. U.S. Dels., Geneva, 1978-79, Can., 1984, Italy, 1985, Mexico, 1986, S.Am., 1986, Fed. Republic Germany, 1990; mem. presdl. dels., NATO, UN, Mexico, USSR, Can., Eng., Finland, Econ. Summit, 1987-88; U.S. Spokesman High Definition TV Conf., Geneva, 1989. Author: (with Eliot Maxwell) Future of Electronic Information Handling at the FCC—Blue Print for the 80's, 1980; (with G.A. Fehlner) Direct Broadcast Satellites in the United States, 1985; New Look at AM Radio, 1986, HDTV Approaches the End Game, 1991. Vice chmn. Montreux Medal Award Com., 1990-95; chmn. High Definition TV World Conf., 1990-93; chmn. strategic planning group for Internat. Consultative Com. for Radio, Dept. State, 1990-91; bd. dirs. Bowler Found., 1990—. Recipient Outstanding Fed. Exec. award FCC, 1979, 80, 82, 83, 85, 86; Presdl. Rank award for disting. exec. service, 1985, Gold medal for disting. fed. service, 1987, TV Engring. Achievement award, 1992. Fellow Radio Club Am., Soc. Broadcast Engrs. (sr.), Broadcast Pioneers, Soc. Motion Picture and TV Engrs. (presdl. proclamation 1991); mem. Fed. Exec. Assn., Cosmos Club of Washington. Episcopalian. Home: 6514 Gretna Green Way Alexandria VA 22312-3114 Office: Advanced TV Systems Com 1750 K St NW Washington DC 20006-2356

MCKINNEY, JOHN ADAMS, JR., lawyer; b. Washington, Mar. 10, 1948; s. John A. and Cleo G. (Turner) McK., m. Carol A. Cowen, Dec. 22, 1970; children: John III, Thomas. BA, Principia Coll., 1970; JD, Coll. William and Mary, 1973. Bar: N.J. 1973. Assoc. Mason, Griffin & Pierson, Princeton, N.J., 1973-77; gen. atty. Nabisco, Inc., East Hanover, N.J., 1977-79; asst. counsel Republic Steel Corp., Cleve., 1979-84; sr. atty. AT&T, Berkeley Heights, N.J., 1984-90; mem. McCarter & English, 1990—. Mem. ABA (vice chair sect. natural resources energy and environ. law solid and hazardous waste com. 1990—, chair, teleconf. programs 1994—), N.J. Bar Assn. (dir. environ. law sect. 1992—). Office: McCarter & English 4 Gateway Ctr 100 Mulberry St Newark NJ 07102-4004

MCKINNEY, JOHN BENJAMIN, steel company executive; b. St. Louis, Nov. 12, 1932; s. Clifford Paul and Mary Adeline (Myers) McK.; m. Margaret Stickney Stark, Oct. 31, 1953; children: Jeffrey Stark, Susan Mary, John Benjamin. BA, U. Va., 1954. With Laclede Steel Co., St. Louis, 1956—, salesman and asst. to rpodn. sales mgrs., 1957-63, St. Louis dist. mgr., 1963-67, mgr. sales indsl. products, 1967-75, gen. sales mgr., 1975-76, v.p. sales, 1976-81, exec. v.p., 1981, pres., chief exec. officer, 1982—, dir.; bd. dirs. Boatmen's Trust. Co. Bd. dirs. Whitfield Sch., John Allen Love Charitable Fund, Webster U. 1st lt. U.S. Army, 1954-56. Mem. Am. Iron and Steel Inst. (bd. dirs.), Steel Mfrs. Assn. Clubs: St. Louis Country Club, Noonday Club, Stadium Club, Log Cabin Club, Automobile Club Mo. (bd. dirs.). Republican. Roman Catholic. Home: 19 Picardy Ln Saint Louis MO 63124-1606 Office: 1 Metropolitan Sq Saint Louis MO 63102-2733

MCKINNEY, JOSEPH F., diversified manufacturing holding company executive; b. Phila., 1931. BS, St. Joseph's Coll., 1952; MBA, Harvard U., 1957. Dir. rsch. Warner, Jennings, Mandel & Longstreth, 1957-60; founder, pres. Electro-Sci. Investors, Inc., Richardson, Tex., 1960-63; v.p. Brown, Allen & Co., 1963-64; dir. corp. fin. Ling & Co., 1964-65, Goodbody & Co., 1965-66; pres Tyler Corp., Dallas, Tex., 1966-83, 1987-94, chmn., chief exec. officer, 1972—, also bd. dirs. Office: Tyler Corp 2121 San Jacinto St Dallas TX 75201

MCKINNEY, JUDSON THAD, broadcast executive; b. Sacramento, Aug. 21, 1941; s. Judson Bartlet and Mildred Eoline (Taylor) McK. Student, Sacramento State U., 1959-61, Western Bapt. Bible Coll., 1961-62, Am. River Coll., 1962-63. Prodn. dir. Sta. KEBR, Sacramento, 1962-65; sta. mgr. Sta. KAMB, Merced, Calif., 1965-68, Sta. KEAR, San Francisco, 1975-78, 79-88, WFME, Newark, 1978; western regional mgr. Family Stas. Inc., 1988—. Chmn. bd. 1st Bapt. Ch. of San Francisco, 1985-91. Mem. Nat. Religious Broadcasters., Nat. Assn. Evangelicals. Republican. Lodge: Gideons. Office: Family Stations inc 290 Hegenberger Rd Oakland CA 94621-1436

MCKINNEY, LARRY J., federal judge; b. South Bend, Ind., July 4, 1944; s. Lawrence E. and Helen (Byers) McK.; m. Carole Jean Marie Lyon, Aug. 19, 1966; children: Joshua E., Andrew G. BA, MacMurray Coll., Jacksonville, Ill., 1966; JD, Ind. U., 1969. Bar: Ind. 1970, U.S. Dist. Ct. (so. dist.) Ind. 1970. Law clk. to atty. gen. State of Ind., Indpls., 1969-70, dep. atty. gen., 1970-71; ptnr. Rodgers and McKinney, Edinburgh, Ind. 1971-75, James F.T. Sargent, Greenwood, Ind., 1975-79; judge Johnson County Cir. Ct., Franklin, Ind., 1979-87, U.S. Dist. Ct. (so. dist.) in Indpls., 1987—. Presbyterian. Avocations: reading, jogging. Office: US Dist Ct 330 US Courthouse 46 E Ohio St Indianapolis IN 46204-1903

MC KINNEY, MONTGOMERY NELSON, advertising executive; b. Chgo., June 20, 1910; s. William Ayer and Roberta (Montgomery) McK.; m. Virginia Dickey, Nov. 2, 1957; children by previous marriage: Jane McKinney McDonald, William; children: Beth McKinney, Robert. BA, Oberlin Coll., 1934, HHD (hon.), 1989. Treas., with sales, advt. and sales promotion depts. Kitchen Art Foods, Inc., Chgo., 1934-40; v.p. Earle Ludgin & Co., Chgo., 1940-55; account supr. Leo Burnett Co., Inc., Chgo., 1956; v.p. Doyle Dane Bernbach, Inc., Los Angeles, 1957-69, sr. v.p. client services, 1969-75; exec. v.p., dir. client services Chiat/Day, Inc., Los Angeles, 1975-76, chmn. bd., 1976-83; chmn. Doyle Dane Bernbach/West, Los Angeles, 1983-86, DDB Needham West (merger Doyle Dane Bernbach and Needham, Harper and Steers), Los Angeles, 1986-87; vice chmn. Kresser, Craig, 1988—; mem. faculty Inst. Advanced Advt. Studies, 1964-68. Chmn. campaign Winnetka (Ill.) Community Chest, 1950, pres., 1952; trustee John Thomas Dye Sch., Bel Air, Calif., 1966-75, pres., 1973-75; trustee Oberlin Coll., 1971-85, emeritus trustee, 1986— ; trustee, chmn. fin. com. Winnetka Congregational Ch., 1950-56. Served to lt. USNR, 1944-46. Recipient silver medal Am. Advt. Fedn., 1983. Mem. Am. Assn. Advt. Agys. (gov. So. Calif. council 1972-76, sec.-treas. 1972, vice chmn. 1973, chmn. 1974-75, nat. dir. 1981-83), West States Assn. Advt. Agys. (dir. 1978-83, Advt. Leader of Yr. 1980), Los Angeles Advt. Club. Methodist (trustee 1970-74, vice chmn. 1973-74). Clubs: Riviera Country (Pacific Palisades, Calif.); Los Angeles Athletic. Home: 140 Ocean Park Blvd Apt 625 Santa Monica CA 90405-3579 Office: Kresser Craig 2501 Colorado Ave Santa Monica CA 90404-3550

MCKINNEY, RICHARD ISHMAEL, philosophy educator; b. Live Oak, Fla., Aug. 20, 1906; s. George Patterson and Sallie Richard (Ellis) McK.; m. Phyllis Vivian Kimbrough, June 27, 1933 (dec. May 1965); children: George Kimbrough, Phyllis Zanaida McKinney Bynum; m. Lena Roberta Martin, Aug. 5, 1967. BA, Morehouse Coll., 1931; BD, Andover Newton Theol. Sch., 1934, STM, 1937; PhD, Yale U., 1942; DD, St. Paul's Coll., Lawrenceville, Va., 1978. Pastor Pond St. Bapt. Ch., Providence, 1933-35; asst. prof. philosophy and religion Va. Union U., Richmond, Va., 1935-42, dean Sch. of Religion, 1942-44, acting v.p., 1978-79; pres Storer Coll., Harpers Ferry, W.Va., 1944-50; chmn. dept. philosophy Morgan State U., Balt., 1951-76, acting dean Coll. Arts and Scis., 1977-78; disting. scholar in philos. theology Coppin State Coll., Balt., 1983; vis. prof. U. Pa., Phila., spring 1972, U. Ife, Ife-Ife, Nigeria, spring 1974. Author: Religion in Higher Education Among Negroes, 1945, History of First Baptist Church of Charlottesville, 1863-1980, 1981, History of the Black Baptists of Florida, 1850-1985, 1987; contbr. articles to profl. jours. Bd. dirs. Balt. Urban League, 1958-59, Luth. Hosp., Balt., 1963-65, Am. Cancer Soc., Balt., 1965-70, Enoch Pratt Libr., Balt., 1991—. Mem. AAUP, NEA, Am. Philos. Assn., Soc. for Values in Higher Edn., Soc. for Existential Philosophy and Phenomenology, Phi Beta Kappa, Omega Psi Phi, Sigma Pi Phi (nat. pres. 1986-88), Phi Sigma Tau (nat. pres. 1959-62). Democrat. Avocation: cabinet maker. Home: 2408 Overland Ave Baltimore MD 21214 Office: Coppin State Coll 2500 W North Ave Baltimore MD 21216

MC KINNEY, ROBERT MOODY, newspaper editor and publisher; b. Shattuck, Okla., Aug. 28, 1910; s. Edwin S. and Eva (Moody) McK.; married, 1943; 1 child, Mrs. Meade Martin; m. Marie-Louise de Montmollin, May 7, 1970. AB, U. Okla., 1932; LLD, U. N.Mex., 1964. Investment analyst Standard Stats. Co., Inc. (now Standard and Poor's Co.), 1932-34; ptnr. Young-Kolbe & Co., 1934-38, Robert R. Young & Co., 1938-42; exec. v.p., treas. Pathe Film Co., 1934-39, Allegheny Corp., 1936-42, Pittston Corp. and subs., 1936-42; v.p. Fremkir Corp., 1937-50, Allan Corp., 1937-50; exec. v.p., treas. Mo. Pacific R.R., 1938-42; ptnr. Scheffmeyer, McKinney & Co., 1945-50; editor, pub. Santa Fe New Mexican, 1949—; chmn. bd. The New Mexican, Inc., 1949—; profl. corp. dir. 10 N.Y.S.E. cos., 1934-86; chmn. Robert Moody Found.; chmn. N.Mex. Econ. Devel. Commn. and Water Resources Devel. Bd., 1949-51; asst. sec. U.S. Dept. Interior, 1951-52; chmn. panel to report to Congress on impact of Peaceful Uses of Atomic Energy, 1955-56; permanent U.S. rep. to Internat. Atomic Energy Agy., Vienna, 1957-58; U.S. rep. Internat. Conf. Peaceful Uses Atomic Energy, Geneva, 1958; U.S. ambassador to, Switzerland, 1961-63; exec. officer Presdl. Task Force on Internat. Investments, 1963-64; chmn. Presdl. Commn. on Travel, 1968; chmn. bd. visitors U. Okla., 1968-72; U.S. rep. Internat. Centre Settlement Investment Disputes, Washington, 1967-74. Author: Hymn to Wreckage: A Picaresque Interpretation of History, 1947, The Scientific Foundation for European Integration, 1959, On Increasing Effectiveness of Western Science and Technology, 1959, The Red Challenge to Technological Renewal, 1960, Review of the International Atomic Policies and Programs of the United States, 1960, The Toad and the Water Witch, 1985, Variations on a Marxist Interpretation of Culture, 1986. Served from lt. (j.g.) to lt. USNR, 1942-45. Recipient Disting. Service medal U.S. Dept. Treasury, 1968, Disting. Service medal U. Okla., 1972. Mem. Am. Soc. Newspaper Editors, Coun. Fgn. Rels., Newspaper Assn. of Am., Phi Beta Kappa, Phi Gamma Delta. Democrat. Episcopalian. Clubs: Chevy Chase (Md.); F Street, Metropolitan (Washington); University, Brook, Century, Links, Knickerbocker, River (N.Y.C.). Home: Wind Fields 39850 Snickersville Tpke Middleburg VA 22117-9411 Office: PO Box 1705 Santa Fe NM 87504-1705

MC KINNEY, ROSS ERWIN, civil engineering educator; b. San Antonio, Aug. 2, 1926; s. Roy Earl and Beatrice (Saylor) McK.; m. Margaret McKinney Curtis, June 21, 1952; children: Ross Erwin, Margaret E., William S., Susanne C. B.A., So. Meth. U., 1948, B.S. in Civil Engring, 1948; S.M., MIT, 1949, Sc.D., 1951. San. scientist S.W. Found. for Research and Edn., San Antonio, 1951-53; asst. prof. MIT, 1953-58, assoc. prof., 1958-60; prof. U. Kans., 1960-63, chmn. dept. civil engring., 1963-66, Parker prof. civil engring., 1966-76, N.T. Veatch prof. environ. engring., 1976-93, prof. emeritus, 1993—; adv. prof. Tongji U., Shanghai, Peoples Rep. China, 1985; v.p. Rolf Eliassen Assocs., Winchester, Mass., 1954-60; pres. Environ. Pollution Control Services, Lawrence, Kans., 1969-73. Author: Microbiology for Sanitary Engineers, 1962; Editor: Nat. Conf. on Solid Waste Research, 1964, 2d Internat. Symposium for Waste Treatment Lagoons, 1970. Mem. Cambridge (Mass.) Water Bd., 1953-59, Lawrence-Douglas County Health Bd., 1969-76, Kans. Water Quality Adv. Council, 1965-76, Kans. Solid Waste Adv. Council, 1970-76, Kans. Environ. Adv. Bd., 1976-85. Served with USNR, 1943-46. Recipient Harrison P. Eddy award, 1962, Water Pollution Control Fedn. Rudolph Hering award, 1964, U.S. Presdl. Commendation, 1971, Environ. Quality award EPA Region VII, 1979, Chancellors Teaching award U. Kans., 1986. Mem. ASCE (hon.), Am. Water Works Assn. (Thomas R. Camp medal 1982), Am. Pub. Works Assn., Am. Chem. Soc., Am. Soc. Microbiologists, AAAS, Internat. Assn. Water Pollution Rsch., Am. Acad. Environ. Engrs., Kans. Water Pollution Control Assn. (hon. mem., Gordon M. Fair medal 1991), NAE, Sigma Xi, Sigma Tau, Kappa Mu Epsilon, Chi Epsilon, Tau Beta Pi. Achievements include patent for water treatment process. Home: 2617 Oxford Rd Lawrence KS 66049-2822

MCKINNEY, SALLY VITKUS, realty company executive, business owner; b. Muncie, Ind., Aug. 6, 1944; d. Robert Brookins and Mary (Mann) Gooden; m. Alan George Vitkus (div. Jan. 1979); m. James Larry McKinney, Feb. 1, 1986. AA, William Woods Coll., 1964; BSBA, U. Ariz., 1966; postgrad., U. Nev., Las Vegas, 1966-68. Tchr. Las Vegas Day Sch., 1972-76; salesperson Globe Realty, Las Vegas, 1976-79; owner, pres. Realty West, Las Vegas, 1979—. Rec. sec. Clark County Rep. Cen. Com., Las Vegas, 1982, 1st vice chmn., 1985; vice chmn. Nev. Rep. com., 1986, chmn., 1987-88; mem. Assistance League Las Vegas. Recipient award Nat. Assn. Home Builders, 1981, 82, 83. Mem. Nat. Assn. Realtors, Las Vegas Bd. Realtors, Greater Las Vegas C. of C., Gen. Fedn. Womens Clubs (Outstanding Young Woman Am. 1979, exec. bd. 1980-82), Jr. League Las Vegas, Mesquite Club (chmn. pub. affairs com. 1986-87, past pres.). Presbyterian. Avocations: tennis, boating. Home: 132 Ultra Dr Henderson NV 89014-8306 Office: Realty West 3340 Topaz St Ste 40B Las Vegas NV 89121-3903

MCKINNEY, VENORA WARE, librarian; b. Meridian, Okla., June 16, 1937. BA, Langston U., 1959; MLS, U. Ill., 1965. Librarian Milw. Pub. Library, 1962-68, br. librarian, 1979-83, dep. city librarian, 1983—; librarian Peoria Pub. Schs., Ill., 1969, Milw. Pub. Schs., 1972-79; adj. faculty U. Wis., Milw.; mem. Wis. Govs. Coun. on Libr. Devel., 1983-92; bd. dirs. V.E. Carter Child Devel. Group. Bd. dirs. Milw. Repertory Theatre; coun. adv. Sch. Libr. and Info. Sci., U. Wis., Madison, 1992—. Nat. Forum for Black Pub. Adminstrs. fellow Exec. Leadership Inst., George Mason U. Mem. ALA Black Caucus, Wis. Libr. Assn. (v.p. 1994, pres. 1995—), Wis. Black Libres. Network, Pub. Libr. Assn., Links Inc., Delta Sigma Theta. Baptist. Office: Milw Pub Libr 814 W Wisconsin Ave Milwaukee WI 53233-2309

MCKINNEY, WILLIAM T., psychiatrist, educator; b. Rome, Ga., Sept. 20, 1937. BA cum laude, Baylor U., 1959; MD, Vanderbilt U., 1963. Diplomate Nat. Bd. Med. Examiners (mem. psychiatry test com. 1982-87, chmn. 1984-87); cert. Am. Bd. Psychiatry and Neurology (sr. examiner 1979-90, bd. dirs. 1991—, mem. rsch. com., co-chair part I test com., chair added qualifications in geriatric psychiatry test com., mem. part II audio visual com., mem. disability accomodations com., rep. to residency rev. com.). Intern in medicine Bowman Gray Sch. Medicine, Wake Forest U., Winston-Salem, N.C., 1963-64; resident dept. psychiatry Sch. Medicine, U. N.C., Chapel Hill., 1964-66, Sch. Medicine, Stanford (Calif.) U., 1966-67; clin. assoc. psychosomatic sect. adult psychiatry br., tng. specialist, asst. br. chief NIMH, Bethesda, Md., 1967-69; asst. prof. psychiatry dept. psychiatry Sch. Medicine, U. Wis., Madison, 1969-72, assoc. prof. psychiatry, 1972-74, prof. psychiatry, 1974-93; Asher prof. of psychiatry dept. psychiatry and behavioral scis., dir. Asher Ctr. for Study and Treatment of Depressive Disorders Med. Sch., Northwestern U., Chgo., 1993—; part-time clin. pvt. practice, Bethesda, 1967-69; NIMH rsch. career investigator Sch. Medicine, U. Wis., Madison, 1970-75, rsch. administration Primate Lab., 1974-93, affiliate sci. Wis. Regional Primate Rsch. Ctr., 1974-93, affiliate prof. psychology dept. psychology, 1974-93, chmn. dept. psychiatry, 1975-80, dir. Wis. Psychiat. Rsch. Inst. Ctr. Health Scis., 1975-80; sr. staff psychiatrist William S. Middleton Meml. VA Hosp., Madison, Wis., 1974-93; rschr. sub dept. animal behaviour U. Cambridge, Eng., 1974; mem. rsch. com. VA Behavioral Scis., 1976-79; Abbott Sigma XI Club lectr., 1976; Milw. Psychiat. Hosp. lectr., 1977; mem. program adv. com. and workshop chmn. Dahlem Found. Internat. Conf. on Depression, Berlin, 1982; U. Minn. lectr. at Festshrift, 1982; cons. grad. sch. U. Minn., 1982; fellow Ctr. Advanced Study in Behavioral Scis., Stanford, Calif., 1983-84; mem. external adv. bd. Clin. Rsch. Ctr. Dept. Psychiatry U. N.C., Chapel Hill, 1984—, cons., bd. advisors clin. rsch. fellow tng. program dept. psychology, 1988—; William F. Orr lectr. Vanderbilt U., 1985; vis. prof. dept. psychiatry U. Tex. Health Scis. Ctr., Dallas, 1986, U. Utah Sch. Medicine, Salt Lake City, 1987, U. Minn. Sch. Medicine, Mpls., 1988; cons. biol. scis. tng. br. divsn. manpower and tng. programs NIMH, 1975-76, mem. psychiatry spl. tng. com. 1983, plenary lectr., Clearwater, Fla., 1987, co-chairperson Workshop on Non-Human Primate Models of Psychopathology, 1987, mem. biol. psychopathology spl. rev. com., 1992—; mem. sci. core group MacArthur Found. Mental Health Rsch. Network I: The Psychobiology of Depression and Other Affective Disorders, 1988-93; vis. spkr. So. Calif. Psychiat. Soc., L.A., 1988; plenary lectr. Soc. Biol. Psychiatry ann. meeting, Montreal, 1988; vis. prof. Dalhousie U. Sch. Medicine, N.S., 1989, HCA Riveredge Hosp., Chgo., 1989, U. Pa., Phila., 1991, U. N.Mex., Albuquerque, 1992, Northwestern U., Chgo., 1992; invited spkr. Animal Models in Psychopharmacology Symposium, Duphar, Amsterdam, 1990; vis. spkr., cons. CIBA-GEIGY, Basel, Switzerland, 1990; mem. minority instns. rsch. devel. rev. com. Alcohol, Drug Abuse and Mental Health Adminstrn., 1990;

guest spkr. Inst. Pa. Hosp., Phila., 1991; reviewer Human Frontier Sci. Program, 1992—; external cons. dept. psychiatry Mental Health Clin. Rsch. Ctr. U. Tex. Southwestern Med. Ctr., Dallas, 1992—; presenter in field. Author: Animal Models of Mental Disorders: A New Comparative Psychiatry, 1988; co-author: Mood Disorders: Towards a New Psychobiology, 1984; mem. editl. bd. Archives of Psychiatry and Neurol. Scis., Contemporary Psychiatry, 1981-82, Ethology and Sociobiology, Experientia, 1982-89, Trends in Neurosciences, 1982-86, Neuropsychopharmacology, 1987-90; manuscript and book reviewer numerous sci. jours.; contbr. articles to profl. jours. USHPS fellow in biostats.bilt U., 1962; recipient Beauchamp award Vanderbilt U. Med. Sch., 1963, Rsch. Career Devel. award NIMH, 1975, Rsch. Leave award U. Wis., 1983-84, Am. Acad. Pediats. award, 1991. Fellow Am. Psychiat. Assn. (cons. psychiat. edn. consultation svc. 1983—), Am. Coll. Psychiatrists, Am. Coll. Neuropsychopharmacology (mem. constn. and rules com. 1985-87, mem. ethics com. 1987-89, mem. fin. com. 1990-92, panel chair San Juan, P.R. 1992, panel presenter 1992); mem. Am. Soc. Primatologists, Am. Psychosomatic Soc. (mem. program com. 1975-76), Internat. Primatology Soc., Internat. Coll. Neurobiology, Biol. Psychiatry and Psychopharmacology (lectr. Zurich 1985), Internat. Soc. Devel. Psychobiology, Internat. Soc. Ethological and Behavioral Pharmacology (bd. advisors 1983—), Collegium Internat. Neuro-Psychopharmacologicum, Psychiat. Rsch. Soc., Soc. Neuroscience, Wis. Psychiat. Assn. (chmn. program com. 1972, co-chairperson task force on sexual misconduct and membership edn. 1986-88, pres.-elect 1989-91, pres. 1991-93). Office: Northwestern U Med Sch Dept Psychiatry and Behavioral Scis 303 E Chicago Ave Ward Bldg 9-176 Chicago IL 60611

MCKINNEY-KELLER, MARGARET FRANCES, retired special education educator; b. Houston, Mo., Nov. 25, 1929; d. George Weimer and Thelma May (Davis) Van Pelt; m. Roy Calvin McKinney Sr., Nov. 11, 1947 (dec. Feb. 1990); children: Deanna Kay Little, Roy Calvin Jr.; m. Clarence Emree Keller, June 8, 1991; 1 child, Dennis Lee Keller. BS with honors, Bradley U., 1963, MA in Counselor Edn., 1968, postgrad., 1992; postgrad., U. Ill., 1993—, Aurora Coll., Ill. Ctrl. Coll. In real estate Peoria, Ill., 1951-57; tchr. Oak Ridge Sch., Willow Springs, Mo., 1947-48, pvt. kindergarten, Washington, Ill., 1957-59, Dist. 50 Schs., Washington, Ill., 1959-67; tchr. socially maladjusted Washington Twp. Spl. Edn. Coop., 1967-70; tchr. behavior disordered Tazewell-Mason Counties Spl. Edn., Washington, Ill., 1970-78; resource tchr. Dist. 50 Schs., Washington, 1978-94; ret., 1994; cons. moderator Active Parenting Group, Washington, 1972—; vol. Proctor Hosp. Aux. Group, 1994—. Vol. Proctor Hosp., 1994—; com. mem. to establish Tazewell County Health Dept., 1960s; pres. gov. bd. Faith Luth. Day Care Ctr., Washington, 1970—, Washington Sr. Citizens, 1982-91; coach Spl. Olympics, Washington, 1970—; pres. Faith Luth. Ch. Coun., Washington, 1985-86; laity v.p. No. Conf. Evang. Luth. Ch. Am., Ctrl. Ill., 1986-92. Mem. AAUW, Washington Bus. and Profl. Women (pres. 1979-80, 88-89), Am. Legion Aux., German-Am. Soc., Alpha Delta Kappa (state office). Avocations: travel, cooking, oil painting, crocheting. Home: 603 Sherwood Park Rd Washington IL 61571

MCKINNIS, MICHAEL B., lawyer; b. Mo., 1946. BS, Drake U., 1967; JD, U. Mo., 1970. Bar: Mo. 1970. Ptnr. Bryan Cave, St. Louis. Mem. ABA, Order of Coif, Phi Delta Phi. Office: Bryan Cave 1 Met Sq 211 N Broadway Saint Louis MO 63102

MC KINNON, ALAN LEO, banker; b. Boston, Feb. 13, 1928; s. Frederic W. and Helen L. (Cunningham) McK.; m. Eleanor Hannigan, Aug. 13, 1955; children—Alan Leo, Brian, Ian. B.S. in Bus. Adminstrn, Boston U., 1950; student, Bentley Coll., Columbia Grad. Bus. Sch. CPA, Mass. Pub. accountant Alexander, Grant & Co. (formerly Patterson, Teele & Dennis), Boston, 1953-61; tax and ins. mgr. United-Carr, Inc., Boston, 1961-69; exec. v.p. 1st Nat. Bank Boston, 1973-80, 1980—; exec. v.p., chief fin. officer 1st Nat. Boston Corp., 1972-86; bd. dirs. Bank of Boston Internat., Miami, N.Y.C., Boston Overseas Fin. Corp., Bank of Boston Internat., L. A., Mortgage Corp. of the South, FNBC Acceptance Corp., Birmingham, Ala., Caribbean Am. Svc. Investment and Finance Co. Ltd. Bd. dirs. Milton Hosp.; mem. Town Meeting, Milton, 1971—. Served with USNR, 1946-47. Mem. Fin. Execs. Inst., Tax Execs. Inst., Mass. Soc. CPA's, Fed. Club, Milton-Hoosic Club, Milton Town Club, Treasurers Club. Home: 12 Longwood Rd Chestnut Hill MA 02167-1707 Office: 1st Nat Bank Boston 100 Federal St Boston MA 02110-1802

MCKINNON, ARNOLD BORDEN, transportation company executive; b. Goldsboro, N.C., Aug. 13, 1927; s. Henry Alexander and Margaret (Borden) McK.; m. Oriana McArthur, July 19, 1950; children: Arnold Borden Jr., Colin McArthur, Henry Alexander. AB, Duke U., 1950, LLB, 1951; grad. Advanced Mgmt. Program, Harvard U., 1972. Bar: D.C. 1951, N.C. 1966. With Norfolk So. Corp. (formerly So. Ry. System), Norfolk, Va., 1951—, v.p. law, 1971-75, sr. v.p. law and acctg., 1975-77, exec. v.p. law and acctg., 1977-81, exec. v.p. law and fin., 1981-82, exec. v.p. mktg., 1982-86, vice chmn., 1986-87, chmn., pres., CEO, 1987-91; chmn., 1991-92, chmn. exec. com., 1992—, also bd. dirs. Va. Port Authority, Nat. Maritime Ctr. Found., Global Transpark Found.; active Coal Industry Adv. Bd., Mil. Civilian Liaison Group, CADRE Found.; chmn. bus. adv. com. Northwestern U. Transp. Ctr.; trustee Med. Coll. Hampton Rds. Found., Va. Union Theol. Sem.; vice-chmn. Va. Gov.'s Econ. Adv. Coun.; commr. Norfolk Redevel. and Housing Authority. With U.S. Army, 1946-47. Mem. ABA, N.C. Bar Assn., D.C. Bar Assn., Am. Soc. Corp. Execs., Norfolk Yacht and Country Club, The Harbor Club, Chevy Chase Club, Metropolitan Club (Washington), Laurel Valley Golf Club, Norfolk Rotary, India House (N.Y.C.), Cedar Point Club (Suffolk, Va.). Presbyterian. Home: 552 Mowbray Arch Norfolk VA 23507-2130 Office: Norfolk So Corp 3 Commercial Pl Norfolk VA 23510-2191

MC KINNON, CLINTON D., editor, former congressman; b. Dallas, Feb. 5, 1906; s. John C. and Tennie Clifdell (Hawkins) McK.; m. Lucille Virginia McVey, Oct. 15, 1932; children—Clinton Dan, Michael, Connie. A.B., U. Redlands, Calif., 1930, L.H.D. (hon.), 1967; postgrad., U. Geneva, Switzerland, 1930. Reporter, editor, advt. mgr. on various So. Calif. newspapers, 1931-35; pres., gen. mgr. Valley News Corp., North Hollywood, Calif., 1935-43; established San Fernando Valley Times, 1935, Los Angeles Aircraft Times, 1940, Long Beach Shipyard Times, 1941; established San Diego Daily Jour., 1944, editor, pub. and owner, 1944-48; co-owner Coronado Jour., 1953-72; owner Radio Sta. KSDJ (Columbia affiliate), San Diego, 1945-48; pres., editor and pub. Los Angeles Daily News, 1954; pres., gen. mgr. Alvarado Television Co., Inc., KVOA-TV, Tucson and KOAT-TV, Albuquerque, 1955-63; chmn. San Diego North Shores Pub. Co., San Diego, 1953-72, Sentinel Savs. and Loan Assn., 1963-69, San Diego Transit Co., 1966-71; sec. South Tex. Telecasting Co. Inc., 1963-79; Chmn. Indsl. Devel. Commn., San Diego, 1964-66, Econ. Devel. Corp., San Diego County, 1966-67, San Diego Urban Coalition, 1967-69; mem. Gov.'s Bus. Adv. Council, Calif. Bd. dirs. U. Calif., San Diego Sch. Medicine, 1979—; bd. dirs. Cancer Center Research Bd., U. Calif., San Diego, 1981—; Mem. 81st-82d Congresses from Calif.; vice chmn. Democratic State Central Com. of Calif., 1952-54. Recipient San Diego Golden Man and Boy award, 1968; San Diego Mayor's award of merit, 1971; named to San Diego Transit Hall of Fame, 1987. Clubs: Rotarian, San Diego Yacht. Home: 1125 Pacific Beach Dr Apt 401 San Diego CA 92109-5155 Office: 945 Hornblend St San Diego CA 92109-4057

MC KINNON, CLINTON DAN, aerospace transportation executive; b. San Bernardino, Calif., Jan. 27, 1934; s. Clinton Dotson and Lucille V. (McVey) McK.; m. Janice Bernard; children: Holly Jean, Sherri Lynn, Clinton Scott, Lisa Caroline. B.A., U. Mo., 1956; honorary doctorate, Nat. U., 1987. Page U.S. Ho. of Reps., 1950-52; reporter, photographer, advt. salesman Sentinel Newspaper, San Diego, 1960-62; owner, pres. KSON Radio, San Diego, 1962-85, KSON-FM, San Diego, 1964-85; pub. La Jolla (Calif.) Light Jour., 1969-73; owner House of Hits (book and music pub.), San Diego, 1972—; co-owner KIll-TV, Corpus Christi, Tex., 1964—, KBMT-TV, Beaumont, Tex., 1976—, KUSI-TV, San Diego, 1992—; chmn. CAB, Washington, 1981-84; with spl. projects CIA, 1985-86; chmn., pres. North Am. Airlines, Jamaica, N.Y., 1989—. Author: The Good Life, 1974, Bullseye—One Reactor (aka Bullseye Iraq), 1986, Everything You Need to Know Before You're Hijacked, 1986, The Ten Second Message, 1994, Rescue Pilot, 1994, Words of Honor, 1995. Chmn. exec. com. Greater San Diego Billy Graham Crusade. Served as aviator USNR, 1956-60. Recipient Advt. Man of Year award San Diego Advt. and Sales Club, 1971; Radio Sta. Mgr. of Year award Billboard Mag., 1973; Internat. Pres.'s award Youth for Christ, 1975; Man of Distinction award Mexican-Am. Found., 1976; George Washington Honor medal Freedoms Found., 1976; Headliner of Yr. (govt.), San Diego Press Club, 1985. Mem. Country Music Assn. (pres. 1977, recipient pres. award 1980), C. of C. (dir.), Nat. Assn. Broadcasters (bd. dirs. 1970-74), Calif. Broadcasters Assn. (dir.), Navy League (Media Man of Yr. 1980). Club: Rotary (San Diego). Set Navy helicopter peacetime rescue record of 62 air/sea rescues, 1958; 1st person to close down fed. govt. regulatory agy., CAB, 1984. Office: N Am Airlines JFK International Ste 250 Jamaica NY 11430

MCKINNON, DANIEL WAYNE, JR., naval officer; b. St. Joseph, Mo., Apr. 26, 1934; s. Daniel Wayne and Amber Ruth (McClanahan) McK.; m. Rae Lynne Hopper, Apr. 21, 1957; 1 child, Daniel W. III. BSBA, U. Mo., 1956; MBA with distinction, U. Mich., 1966; grad. (disting.), Indsl. Coll. Armed Forces, Washington, 1975. Commd. ensign USN, 1956, advanced through grades to rear adm., 1983; exec. asst. to comdr. Naval Supply Systems Command, Washington, 1970-74, dir. supply corps pers., 1982-83, dep. comdr. for inventory and systems integrity, 1983-84, vice comdr., 1984-86, comdr., 1988—; ship supply readiness officer, supply systems ops. officer Naval Logistic Command, Pacific Fleet, Pearl Harbor, Hawaii, 1975-78; dir. shipbuilding contracts div. Naval Sea Systems Command, Washington, 1978-80; comdg. officer Naval Supply Depot, Subic Bay, The Philippines, 1980-82; dep. dir. for acquisition mgmt. Def. Logistics Agy., Cameron Station, Va., 1986-88; chief Navy supply corps, comdr. Naval Supply Systems, 1988-91; ret. USN, 1991—; pres., CEO NISH (formerly Nat. Industries for Severly Handicapped), Vienna, Va., 1992—. Chmn. Annandale (Va.) Cen. Bus. Dist. Planning Com., 1986-91, Pres.'s Com. for Purchase from the Blind and Other Severely Handicapped, Washington, 1986—; mem. strategic devel. bd. U. Mo.; bd. dirs. Va. Industries for Blind, 1991—, Project Handclasp, 1994—. Decorated D.S.M., Legion of Merit. Recipient Disting. Svc. award Nat. Industries for Severely Handicapped, 1991; Capstone fellow Nat. Def. U., 1986. Mem. Navy Supply Corps Assn. (pres. Ga. chpt. 1988-91), Nat. Contract Mgmt. Assn. (bd. advisors 1986—), Navy Fed. Credit Union (vice chmn. 1986-92), Navy Mut. Aid Assn. (bd. dirs. 1982-91), Comprehensive Tech. Internat. (bd. dirs. 1992—), Army and Navy Club, Beta Theta Pi, Beta Gamma Sigma, Phi Kappa Phi.

MCKINNON, FLOYD WINGFIELD, textile executive; b. Columbus, Ga., Dec. 1, 1942; s. Malcolm Angus and Sarah C. (Bullock) McK.; m. Barbara Evans Roles, June 18, 1966; children: James Wingfield, Sarah Elizabeth, Robert Kent. A.B., Washington and Lee U., 1964. Lic. airplane pilot. V.p. Cotswold Industries, Inc., N.Y.C., 1966—, also bd. dirs.; v.p., corp. sec. Cen. Textiles, Inc., S.C., 1984—, also bd. dirs.; arbitrator Am. Arbitration Assn. 1983—. Pres. Berkley-in-Scarsdale Assn., 1980; admissions rep. Washington and Lee U., 1979-89, 93—. Mem. Aircraft Owner's and Pilot's Assn., St. Andrews Soc. N.Y., Ch. Club N.Y. Republican. Episcopalian. Clubs: Union League (bd. govs. 1974-77, 88-91, sec. 1981-83, vice chmn. admissions com. 1995) (N.Y.C.); Scarsdale Golf (bd. govs. 1983—, pres. 1990-91) (Hartsdale, N.Y.); Bras Coupe (exec. com. 1980—) (Maniwaki, Can.). Home: 26 Taunton Rd Scarsdale NY 10583-5610 Office: Cotswold Industries 10 E 40th St New York NY 10016

MC KINNON, F(RANCIS) (ARTHUR) RICHARD, utility executive; b. Delburne, Alta., Can., Mar. 5, 1933; s. John Donald and Ruth Rebecca (Sundberg) McK.; m. Elma Lorraine Lebsack, June 1, 1957; children: Kenneth Richard, Stephen David, Karen Diane. B. Commerce, U. Alta., 1954; postgrad., Stanford Exec. Program, Stanford U., 1982. With Alta. Gas Trunk Line Co. Ltd., Calgary, 1960-75, treas., 1971-75; dir. fin. TransAlta Utilities Corp. (formerly Calgary Power Ltd.), 1975—, treas., 1976-81, v.p. fin., 1981—; v.p. fin. Trans Alta Energy Corp., Trans Alta Corp.; bd. dirs. AEC Power Ltd. Past bd. dirs. Foothills Gen. Hosp., Calgary. Fellow Inst. Chartered Accts. of Alta.; mem. Can. Inst. Chartered Accts., Fin. Execs. Inst. Can. (past chmn., past pres., bd. dirs. Calgary chpt., v.p.), Fin. Execs. Inst. (bd. dirs.). Clubs: Calgary Petroleum, Canyon Meadows Golf and Country. Home: 1412 Windsor St, Calgary, AB Canada T2N 3X3 Office: TransAlta Utilities Corp, 110 12th Ave SW, Calgary, AB Canada T2P 2M1

MCKINNON, ISAIAH, police chief; b. Montgomery, Ala., June 21, 1943; s. Cota and Lula (Jones) McK.; m. Patrice Anne McKinnon; children: Jeffrey Christopher, Jason Patrick. BA in History/Law Enforcement, Mercy Coll. of Detroit, 1975; MA in Criminal Justice, U. Detroit, 1978; PhD in Adminstrn. and Higher Edn., Mich. State U., 1981; grad., FBI Nat. Acad., 1977. Police officer Detroit Police Dept., 1965-71, sgt., 1971-74, lt., 1974-77, inspector, 1977-84, chief of police, 1994—; dir. pub. safety U. Detroit, 1984-89; dir. security Renaissance Ctr., Detroit, 1989-93; lectr. Detroit Met. Police Acad., Mich. State Police Acad., Mich. Assn. Police; trainer in field; presenter Nat. Bapt. Ministers Conv., Ala. State U.; mem. Leadership and Mgmt. Adv. Bd.; adj. prof. criminal justice U. Detroit, 1984, Wayne State U., 1985-86, Wayne County C.C., 1988—; asst. prof. criminal justice Mercy Coll. of Detroit, 1978-86; security cons. Limbach Co., Detroit, Marathon Petroleum Co., Detroit, State of Mich. Workers Disability Compensation Bldg., Detroit, Rubloff Mgmt. Co., Chgo. Author: Police and the Nurse, 1984, Police and Child Abuse, 1992; contbr. articles to newspapers; guest columnist Mich. Chronicle. Trustee Grosse Point Acad.; past mem., bd. dirs. Ronald McDonald House, Children's Ctr. Wayne County; past mem. youth devel. com. Detroit Urban League; mem. Dad's Club U. Detroit Jesuit H.S.; bd. dirs. U. Detroit, 1974—, Wayne County C.C., Detroit, 1975—. With USAF, 1961-65. Recipient Spirit of Detroit award, numerous citations, commendations. Mem. F.B.I. Nat. Acad. Grads. Office: Police Dept 1300 Beaubien St Detroit MI 48226-2308

MCKINNON, JAMES BUCKNER, real estate sales executive, writer, researcher; b. Tacoma, Dec. 5, 1916; s. James Mitchell and Rochelle Lenore (Buckner) McK.; m. Mary C. Corbitt, Dec. 1961 (div. June 1963); 1 child, James H.C.; m. Marylyn Adelle Coote, Mar. 12, 1967 (div. May 1977); 1 child, Michelyn; m. Martha Sackmann, June 12, 1977. BA in Internat. Studies, U. Wash., 1983, H.M. Jackson Sch. Police detective Los Angeles Police Dept., 1946-50; bn. security officer 1st med. bn. 1st Marine div. Fleet Marine Force, 1950-53; owner, operator, mgr., dir. promotional sales The Saucy Dog Drive-In, Venice, Calif., 1953-63; salesman new car sales and leasing Burien Mercury, Seattle, 1963-66; real estate salesman and appraiser various firms Seattle, 1966—; instr., lectr. U.S. Naval Support Activity, Sandpoint, Wash., 1964-74; mem., lectr. NRC 11-8, Naval Postgrad. Sch., Monterey, Calif., 1975-76; Burien Mercury announcer KOMO TV. Author: (poetry) On the Threshold of a Dream, Vol. III, 1992, Best Poems of the 90's, 1992; contbr. to anthologies: Where Words Haven't Spoken, 1993, Fire From Within, 1994; contbr. articles to various newspapers and mil. jours. Mem. br. adv. com. Wash. State YMCA, Seattle, 1994—, treas., 1986-94, mem. so. dist. fin. bd., 1989-93, 94, 95-96. With USN, 1939-53, PTO, Korea. Recipient Wilmer Culver Meml. award Culver Alumni Fictioneers, Seattle, 1979, Silver Poet award World of Poetry Press, 1986, Golden Poet award, 1987-92, Best Poet of the 90's Nat. Libr. of Poetry, 1992; Occidental Coll. scholar, 1935; named to Honorable Order Ky. Cols., 1976; named One of Best New Poets, Am. Poetry Assn. Anthology, 1988. Mem. Internat. Soc. Authors and Artists, Internat. Platform Assn., U.S. Naval Inst. (life), Internat. Soc. Poets (life), N.W. Writers Conf., Ret. Officers Assn. (life), Mensa, Acad. Am. Poets, KP, Masons. Republican. Home: 2312 41st Ave SW Seattle WA 98116-2060 Personal philosophy: To realize one's greatest potential pursue goals that hold the greatest potential meaning in life.

MCKINNON, MICHAEL DEE, broadcast executive; b. Los Angeles, June 12, 1939; s. Cinton D. and Lucille (McVey) M.; m. Camille, Mar. 10, 1964 (div. Oct. 1970);m. Sandra E.; children: Don, Gaylynn, Mike, Mark. Student, U. Redlands, 1957-59, Harvard. Owner, pres. Sta. KIII-TV, Corpus Christi, Tex., Sta. KBMT-TV, Beaumont, Tex.; part owner Sta. KUSI-TV, San Diego; co-owner Sta. KBVO-TV, Austin, Tex.; owner McKinnon Leasing Co., Corpus Christi. Bd. dirs. First City Bank, Corpus Christi, bd. govs. Redlands U., Calif., exec. com. bd. dirs. Art Mus. of S. Tex., Corpus Christi; mem. Texas State Senate, 1972-76 (chmn. Nominations Com.), worked on Pres. Reagan's campaign, bd. dirs. adv. council, Sch. Communications, U. Tex., Salvation Army Adv. Bd., chmn. S. Tex. Planned Parenthood League, Urban Coalition Com., Tex. affiliate Am. Heart Assn., fund raising com., TV and Radio Political Action Com. Named Boss of Year, Nat. Secs. Internat. Assn., 1970, Outstanding Young Man of Year, Jr.

C. of C., 1971, awarded Pres. Citation. Mem. Tex. Assn. Broadcasters (dir. 1965-72, pres., 1971), Nat. Assn. Broadcasters (small market com. 1972-73), Broadcast Promotion Assn, Assn. Broadcast Execs.Tex., Corpus Christ Ad Club, TV Bur. Advt. Home: 3302 Ocean Dr Corpus Christi TX 78411-1407 Office: PO Box 6669 Corpus Christi TX 78466-6669

MCKINNON, RICHARD ANTHONY, airline executive; b. Edison, Ga., Apr. 11, 1940; s. William Ralph and Sara Agnes (DeWolfe) McK.; m. Gale Shaw, Sept. 12, 1964; children: Malia, Kirk. BS, U.S. Mil. Acad., 1963; JD, Emory U., 1970. Bar: Ga., 1970. Atty. Powell Goldstein Fraser & Murphy, Atlanta, 1970-72; v.p. traffic and mktg. devel. Delta Airlines, Atlanta, 1972-84; exec. v.p., chief operating officer Cert. Tours, Ft. Lauderdale, Fla., 1985-86; exec. v.p. mktg. and planning Pan Am., N.Y.C., 1986-87; v.p. advt. and mktg. programs Am. Airlines, Dallas/Ft. Worth, 1987—; Trustee Inst. Cert. Travel Agts., Wellesley, Mass., 1980-87. Head Atlanta div. United Way, 1985; bd. dirs. Atlanta chpt. Am. Cancer Soc., 1985; mem. world bd. govs. USO, Washington, 1984-87; mem. French nat. adv. bd. N.Am., N.Y.C., 1985-87; treas. Michael Bowers for Atty. Gen. campaign, Atlanta, 1982. Mem. ABA, Ga. Bar Assn., Atlanta Bar Assn. Baptist. Clubs: Sky (N.Y.C.), Cherokee Country (Atlanta). Avocation: golf.

MCKINSEY, ELIZABETH, college dean; b. Columbia, Mo., Aug. 10, 1947; d. J. Wendell and A. Ruhamah (Peret) McK.; m. Thomas N. Clough, June 18, 1977; children: Emily, Peter. BA, Radcliffe Coll., 1970; PhD, Harvard U., 1976. From instr. to asst. prof. English Bryn Mawr (Pa.) Coll., 1975-77; from asst. to assoc. prof. English Harvard U., Cambridge, Mass., 1977-85; dir. Bunting Inst. Radcliffe Coll., Cambridge, 1985-89; dean Carleton Coll., Northfield, Minn., 1989—. Author: Niagara Falls: Icon of the American Sublime, 1985; contbr. articles and revs. to profl. jours. and lit. mags. NEH fellow, 1980. Mem. MLA, Am. Conf. Acad. Deans (bd. dirs.), Nat. Coun. for Rsch. on Women (assoc.), Am. Studies Assn., Nat. Assn. Women in Edn., Phi Beta Kappa (pres. Iota of Mass. chpt. 1986-89). Home: 815 2nd St E Northfield MN 55057-2308 Office: Carleton Coll 1 N College St Northfield MN 55057

MCKINSTRY, GREGORY JOHN DUNCAN, retail executive; b. Vancouver, B.C., Can., Sept. 6, 1947; s. F. John B. and Margaret L. McKinstry; m. Nancy M. Crane, June 22, 1974. B of Commerce, U. B.C., 1970, MBA, 1985. Research mgr. Eaton's, Toronto, Can., 1970-72; co-service mgr. Eaton's, Vancouver, 1972-74; sr. mktg. rep. IBM Can. Ltd., Vancouver, 1974-79; research mgr. Woodward's Ltd., Vancouver, 1979-82, co-accounting mgr., 1982-85, treas., 1985-87; sr. v.p. fin., 1987-89; sr. v.p., chief fin. officer Bear Creek Corp., Medford, Oreg., 1990—. Bd. dirs. Vancouver Kidney Found., 1985-86; mem. Vancouver Bd. Trade; bd. dirs. P.A. Woodward Found.; bd. dirs., treas. Schneider Mus. Art. Mem. Fin. Exec. Inst., Vancouver Club. Avocations: photography, swimming, golf. Office: Bear Creek Corp 2818 S Pacific Hwy Medford OR 97501-8752

MCKIRAHAN, RICHARD DUNCAN, JR., classics and philosophy educator; b. Berkeley, Calif., July 27, 1945; s. Richard Duncan and Helen Marion (Hixson) McK.; m. Voula Tsouna, June 3, 1961; 1 child, Helen Hamilton. AB, U. Calif., Berkeley, 1966; BA, U. Oxford, Eng., 1969; MA, Oxford U., Eng., 1979; PhD, Harvard U., 1973. Teaching fellow, tutor Harvard U., Cambridge, Mass., 1971-73; asst. prof. classics and philosophy Pomona Coll., Claremont, Calif., 1973-79, assoc. prof., 1979-87, E.C. Norton prof. classics and philosophy, 1987—, chair dept. classics, 1992—. Author: Socrates and Plato, A Comprehensive Bibliography, 1958-73, 1978, Plato's Meno, 1986, Principles and Proofs: Aristotle's Theory of Demonstrative Science, 1992, Philosophy Before Socrates, 1994; also articles on Greek philosophy, math. and scis. Marshall Aid Commemoration Commn. scholar, U. Oxford, 1966-69; Woodrow Wilson Found. fellow, 1966-67; NEH grantee, 1975, 85, 90. Mem. Am. Philol. Assn., Soc. Ancient Greek Philosophy, Phi Beta Kappa. Office: Pomona Coll Dept Classics 140 W 6th St Claremont CA 91711

MCKISSACK, PATRICIA CARWELL, children's book author; b. Nashville, Sept. 9, 1944; d. Robert and Erma Carwell; m. Frederick L. McKissack, Dec. 12, 1965; children: Fredrick L. Jr., Robert, John. BA, Tenn. State U., 1964; MA, Webster U., 1975. Jr. high sch. tchr. Kirkland, Mo., 1968-75; children's book editor Concordia Pub. House, 1976-81, Inst. Children's Lit., 1984—; part-time English instr. Forest Park Coll., St. Louis, 1975—; instr. U. Mo., St. Louis, 1978—. Author: Good Shepard Prayer, 1978, God Gives New Life, 1979, Ask the Kids, 1979, Who is Who?, 1983, Martin Luther King, Jr.: A Man to Remember, 1984, Paul Laurence Dunbar: A Poet to Remember, 1984, Michael Jackson, Superstar, 1984, Lights Out, Christopher, 1984, It's the Truth, Christopher, 1984 (C.S. Lewis Silver Medal award Christian Sch. Mag. 1984), The Apache, 1984, Mary McLeod Bethune: A Great American Educator, 1985, Aztec Indians, 1985, The Inca, 1985, The Maya, 1985, Flossie and the Fox, 1986, Our Martin Luther King Book, 1986, Who is Coming?, 1986, Give It with Love, Christopher: Christopher Learns about Gifts and Giving, 1988, Speak Up, Christopher: Christopher Learns the Difference Between Right and Wrong, 1988, A Troll in a Hole, 1988, Nettie Jo's Friends, 1988 (Parent's Choice award 1990), Mirandy and Brother Wind, 1988, Monkey-Monkey's Trick: Based on an African Folk-Tale, 1989, Jesse Jackson: A Biography, 1989, (with Ruthilde Kronberg) A Piece of Wind and Other Stories to Tell, 1990, No Need for Alarm, 1990, A Million Fish-More or Less, 1992, The Dark Thirty: Southern Tales of the Supernatural, 1992, Christmas in the Big House-Christmas in the Quarters, 1992, Sojourner Truth: "Ain't I a Woman?", 1992 (Boston Globe/Horn Book award 1993, NAACP Image award for children's literature 1994); (with Frederick L. McKissack) Look What You've Done Now, Moses, 1984, Abram, Abram, Where Are We Going?, 1984 (C.S. Lewis Silver Medal award Christian Sch. Mag. 1984), Cinderella, 1985, Country Mouse and City Mouse, 1985, The Little Red Hen, 1985, The Three Bears, 1985, The Ugly Little Duck, 1986, When Do You Talk to God? Prayers for Small Children, 1986, King Midas and His Gold, 1986, Frederick Douglass: The Black Lion, 1987, A Real Winner, 1987, The King's New Clothes, 1987, Tall Phil and Small Bill, 1987, Three Billy Goats Gruff, 1987, My Bible ABC Book, 1987, The Civil Rights Movement in America from 1865 to the Present, 1987, All Paths Lead to Bethlehem, 1987, Messy Bessey, 1987, The Big Bug Book of Counting, 1987, The Big Bug Book of Opposites, 1987, The Big Bug Book of Places to Go, 1987, The Big Bug Book of the Alphabet, 1987, The Big Bug Book of Things to Do, 1987, Bugs!, 1988, The Children's ABC Christmas, 1988, Constance Stumbles, 1988, Oh, Happy, Happy Day! A Child's Easter in Story, Song and Prayer, 1989, God Made Something Wonderful, 1989, Messy Bessey's Closet, 1989, James Weldon Johnson: "Lift Every Voice and Sing", 1990, A Long Hard Journey: The Story of the Pullman Porter, 1990 (Coretta Scott King award 1990, Jane Addams Peace award 1990), Taking a Stand Against Racism and Racial Discrimination, 1990, W.E.B. DuBois, 1990, The Story of Booker T. Washington, 1991, Messy Bessey's Garden, 1991, African Americans, 1991, From Heaven Above: The Story of Christmas Proclaimed by the Angels, 1992, Tennessee Trailblazers, 1993, Black Diamond: The Story of the Negro Baseball League, 1994, African-American Scientists, 1994, African American Inventors, 1994, The Royal Kingdoms of Ghana, Mali, and Songhay: Life in Medieval Africa, 1994; (Great African American series with Frederick McKissack) Carter G. Woodson: The Father of Black History, 1991, Frederick Douglass: Leader Against Slavery, 1991, George Washington Carver: The Peanut Scientist, 1991, Ida B. Wells-Barnett: A Voice Against Violence, 1991, Louis Armstrong: Jazz Musician, 1991, Marian Anderson: A Great Singer, 1991, Martin Luther King, Jr.: Man of Peace, 1991, Mary Church Terrell: Leader for Equality, 1991, Mary McLeod Bethune: A Greatacher, 1991, Ralph J. Bunche: Peacemaker, 1991, Jesse Owens: Olympic Star, 1992, Langston Hughes: Great American Poet, 1992, Soujourner Truth: A Voice for Freedom, 1992, Zora Neale Hurston: Writer and Storyteller, 1992, Satchel Page: The Best Arm in Baseball, 1992, Paul Robeson: A Voice to Remember, 1992, Madam C.J. Walker: Self-Made Millionaire, 1992, Booker T. Washington: Leader and Educator, 1992, Lorraine Hansberry: Dramatist and Activist, 1994; (with others) The World in 1492, 1992; (with Ron Berry and Bartholomew) Scrappy the Squabbler, 1993, Moogie the Messy Beastie, 1993, Hogger the Hoarding Beastie, 1993, Glumby the Grumbler, 1993, Fritter the Wasteful Beastie, 1993, Crassy the Crude Beastie, 1993. Recipient Helen Keating Ott award Nat. Ch. and Synagogue Librs. Assn., 1980. Office: 5900 Pershing Ave Saint Louis MO 63112-1514*

MCKISSOCK, PAUL KENDRICK, plastic surgeon; b. Lakeland, Fla., Oct. 27, 1925; s. Percival Kendrick and Helen Williams (Morse) McK.; m. Joan McShane, 1951; children—Ellen, John, Scott. B.A. in Zoology, UCLA, 1950; M.D. (James A. Gibson Anat. award 1953), U. Buffalo, 1956. Diplomate: Am. Bd. Plastic Surgery. Intern Los Angeles County Gen. Hosp., 1956-57; resident VA Hosp., Los Angeles, UCLA, 1957-63; fellow in plastic surgery Queen Victoria Hosp., East Grinstead, Eng., 1963; practice medicine specializing in plastic and reconstructive surgery Torrance, Calif., 1963—; pres. Paul K. McKissock M.D. Inc., 1968—; mem. staff Torrance Meml. Hosp., Little Company of Mary Hosp.; clin. prof. UCLA Med. Sch. Contbr. articles med. publs. Served with USNR, 1943-46. Mem. Am. Soc. Plastic and Reconstructive Surgeons, Am. Soc. Aesthetic Plastic Surgeons, Am. Assn. Plastic Surgeons, Calif. Soc. Plastic Surgeons. Republican. Presbyterian. Home: 75-280 Inverness Dr Indian Wells CA 92210 Office: D-513 44489 Town Center Way Palm Desert CA 92260-2729

MC KITRICK, ERIC LOUIS, historian, educator; b. Battle Creek, Mich., July 5, 1919; s. Fred Louis and Colleen (Hodges) McK.; m. Edyth Carol Stevenson, Dec. 26, 1946; children—Frederick Louis II, Enid Lael, Charles Keith, Mary Caroline. B.S., Columbia, 1949, M.A., 1951, Ph.D., 1959. Asst. prof. history U. Chgo., 1955-59; asst. prof. history Douglass Coll., Rutgers U., 1955-60; asso. prof. history Columbia, 1960-65, prof., 1965—; Pitt prof. Am. history and instns. Cambridge (Eng.) U., 1973-74; Harmsworth prof. Am. history Oxford (Eng.) U., 1979-80. Author: Andrew Johnson and Reconstruction, 1960, Slavery Defended: Views of the Old South, 1963, Andrew Johnson: A Profile, 1969, The Hofstadter Aegis: A Memorial, 1974, (with Stanley Elkins) The Age of Federalism, 1993. Served with AUS, 1941-45. Recipient Dunning prize Am. Hist. Assn., 1960, Order of the Cincinnati, 1995; Ford Found. fellow, 1957-58; Rockefeller Found. fellow, 1962-63; Nat. Endowment for Humanities fellow, 1967-68; Guggenheim Found. fellow, 1970-71, 76-77. Fellow Am. Philos. Soc., Am. Council Learned Socs. Club: Century (N.Y.C.). Office: Dept of History Columbia University New York NY 10027

MCKITRICK, JAMES THOMAS, retail executive; b. Cin., Sept. 14, 1945; s. Harry J. and L. May (Buck) McK.; m. Margaret J. Haynes, Sept. 6, 1975; children: Angela, Greg, Randal, Paul, Sheri, Richard, Mike. Student, Salem Coll., 1963-64. Dir. mdse. K Mart Corp., Troy, Mich., 1965-84; exec. v.p., gen. mgr. T.G. & Y. Stores, Oklahoma City, 1984-86, exec. v.p. merchandising and mktg., 1986; pres., chief exec. officer Warehouse Club, Skokie, Ill., 1986-87; pres., chief operating officer G.C. Murphy Co. subs. Ames, Rocky Hill, Conn., 1987—; chmn. Zayre Discount, Rocky Hill, 1988—. Republican. Methodist. Home: 57 Hillsdale Dr Newport Beach CA 92660-4235 Office: Central Tractor Farm Family Ctr 3915 Delaware Ave Des Moines IA 50313

MCKITTRICK, WILLIAM WOOD, lawyer; b. Mt. Carmel, Ill., July 11, 1915; s. Lafe E. and Mary Lynn (Wood) McK.; m. Carolyn Lenne Davis, Dec. 19, 1942; children—Lynn McKittrick Pond, Bruce W. A.B., DePauw U., 1936; J.D., Northwestern U., 1939. Bar: Ill. Assoc. Pope & Ballard, Chgo., 1939-48, ptnr., 1948-52; atty. Office Gen. Counsel, Panama C.Z., 1942; ptnr. Vedder, Price, Kaufman & Kammholz, Chgo., 1952-95; lectr. on labor law Northwestern U. Sch. Law, Chgo., 1961-62. Case note editor, mem. editorial bd. Ill. Law Rev., 1938-39. Life trustee Orchestral Assn. of Chgo. Symphony Orch., 1980—, Chgo. Symphony Musicians Pension Trust, 1987—; bd. dirs. Am. Symphony Orch. League, 1986-93, mem. exec. com., 1988-91; trustee Newberry Libr., Chgo., 1984—, mem. exec. com., 1989—; vice chmn. exec. bd. Libr. Coun., Northwestern U., 1984—; chmn. Friends of Ryerson & Burnham Librs., Art Inst. Chgo., 1988-90, mem. com. on librs., 1982—. Served to lt. USNR, 1943-45, PTO. Recipient Service award Northwestern U., 1968. Mem. ABA, Ill. Bar Assn., Chgo. Bar Assn. (lectr. various programs 1940-70, bd. mgrs. 1961-63), Legal Club of Chgo., Univ. Club (Chgo.), Michigan Shores Club, Skokie Country Club, Caxton Club of Chgo. (v.p. 1982-83, pres. 1983-85). Home: 232 Essex Rd Kenilworth IL 60043-1122

MCKNEW, LINDA ALEXANDER, health facility administrator; b. Omaha, July 18, 1949; d. Robert and Josephine (Urek) Alexander; m. Thomas McKnew, 1983; children: Karen, Tommy, Jeffrey, Sara. BSN, U. Fla., 1972, MSN, 1982. RN, Fla. Head nurse in ICU Desota Meml. Hosp., Arcadia, Fla.; asst. DON Alachua Gen. Hosp., Gainesville, Fla., DON, asst. administr. Johnson and Johnson fellow, 1987, Mellen fellow. Mem. Fla. Orgn of Nurse Execs., Internat. Rotary. Home: 5008 NW 13th Ave Gainesville FL 32605-4543

MCKNEW, ROBERT DAVID, banker; b. Washington, Dec. 8, 1947; s. Raymond George and Violet May (Karchem) McK.; m. Doris Ann Hagerty, Aug. 29, 1970; 1 child, Anne Elizabeth. B.A. Dickinson Coll., 1969; M.B.A., Amos Tuck Sch., Dartmouth Coll. 1971. Sr. v.p., treas. Continental Ill. Corp., Chgo., 1982-85; exec. v.p., treas. 1st City Bancorp. of Tex., Houston, 1985-87; sr. v.p., dept. exec. Bank of Boston, from 1987; now with Chem. Bank, N.Y.C.; sect. leader Prochnow Sch. Banking, Madison, Wis., 1976-85. Bd. dirs. Chgo. council Girl Scouts U.S., 1983-85. Mem. Dealer Bank Assn. (bd. dirs. 1981-85, pres. 1984-85), Bond Club Chgo. (trustee 1980-82), Mcpl. Bond Club Chgo. Episcopalian. Clubs: Indian Hill (Winnetka, Ill.); Union League (Chgo.). Home: 1 Amberwood Ln Boxford MA 01921-2124 Office: Chem Bank 277 Park Ave New York NY 10172-0002

MCKNIGHT, CHARLES NOEL, lawyer; b. Darby, Pa., Dec. 25, 1944; s. John Agustine and Mildred (Collins) McK.; div.; children: Charles Sean, Carolyn Noel, Jennifer Lauren. BSc, Spring Hill Coll., 1971; JD, U. Ala., 1974. Bar: U.S. Dist. Ct. (so. dist.) Ala. 1976, U.S. Ct. Appeals (5th cir.) 1976, U.S. Ct. Appeals (11th cir.) 1981. Law clk. to judge U.S. Dist. Ct. (so. dist.) Ala., Mobile, 1974-76; pvt. practice Mobile, 1976-81, 88—; ptnr. Bryant and McKnight, Mobile, 1981-85, McKnight and Seidel, Mobile, 1986-88; bd. dirs. Ala. Aviation Hall of Fame, Birmingham, 1990-91; judge Town of Dauphin Island, Ala., 1989—; dep. judge City of Mobile, 1990—; spl. probate judte, spl. dist. judge County of Mobile, 1992—. STaff sgt. USAF, 1964-68. Mem. Assn. Trial Lawyers Am., Ala. Trial Lawyers Assn., Mobile Bar Assn., Ala. Bar Assn. Democrat. Roman Catholic. Avocations: boating, fishing, flying. Home: 11301 Getchell Dr Theodore AL 36582 Office: 250 Congress St Mobile AL 36602

MCKNIGHT, EDGAR VERNON, religion educator; b. Wilson, S.C., Nov. 21, 1931; s. William G. and Carrie B. (DeMars) McK.; m. Shirley Robinson, June 4, 1955; children: Deborah Lynn, Edgar Vernon Jr. BS, Coll. Charleston, 1953; MDiv, So. Bapt. Theol. Sem., 1956, PhD, 1960. From asst. prof. to assoc. dean for academic affairs Furman U., Greenville, S.C., 1963-73; prof. Furman U., Greenville, 1974—. Author: Opening the Bible, 1967, What is Form Criticism, 1969, Meaning in Texts, 1978, The Bible and the Reader, 1985, Postmodern Use of the Bible, 1988. Pres. Torch Club, Greenville, 1992. Fulbright prof. U. Tuebingen, 1981-82, U. Muenster, 1995-96, William R. Kenan Jr. prof. Furman U., 1982—; bye fellow Robinson Coll. Cambridge U., Eng., 1988-89. Mem. AAUP, Am. Acad. Religion, Soc. Bibl. Lit. (coun. mem. 1976-81), Soc. N.T. Studies, Phi Beta Kappa. Home: 201 Alpine Way Greenville SC 29609-5058 Office: Furman U Greenville SC 29613

MCKNIGHT, FREDERICK L., lawyer; b. Kansas City, Mo., Nov. 28, 1947; s. Harry A. and Donna Ruth (Breining) McK.; m. Linda Jean McKnight, June 20, 1970; children: Justin Teague, Cristin Ruth. AB honors, Princeton U., 1969; JD, U. Calif., Berkeley, 1972. Bar: Calif. 1973, N.Y. 1973. adv. com. Jones, Day, Reavis & Pogue, Cleve., 1991—. Bd. dirs. Econ. Devel. Corp., L.A., 1992—. Mem. ABA (health care sect.), Assn. Bus. Trial Lawyers. Office: Jones Day Reavis & Pogue 555 W 5th St Ste 4600 Los Angeles CA 90013-1025

MC KNIGHT, JOHN LACY, physics educator; b. Monroe, Mich., Sept. 13, 1931; s. Joseph Daniel and Esther (Lacy) McK.; m. Joyce Nunn, May 30, 1964; 1 son, Andrew. A.B., U. Mich., 1953; M.S., Yale, 1954, Ph.D., 1957. Mem. Faculty Coll. William and Mary, 1957—, prof. physics, 1966—; cons. to Colonial Williamsburg Found. on 17th and 18th century sci. instruments. Mem. editorial bd. Eighteenth Century Life. Pres. Va. Wilderness Com., 1969-70; bd. dirs. Conservation Coun. Va., 1969-71; trustee Va. chpt. Nature Conservancy, 1971-78, chmn. bd., 1975-77. Mem. Am. Phys. Soc., AAAS,

Philosophy of Sci. Assn., History of Sci. Soc., Soc. History of Tech., Phi Beta Kappa, Sigma Xi, Phi Kappa Phi. Home: 701 College Ter Williamsburg VA 23185-3532

MCKNIGHT, JOSEPH WEBB, law educator, historian; b. San Angelo, Tex., Feb. 17, 1925; s. John Banning and Helen Katherine (Webb) McK.; m. Julia Ann Dyer, July 19, 1957; children—John Banton, Joseph Adair; m. Mildred Katherine Virginia Payne, Aug. 9, 1975. B.A., U. Tex., 1947, Oxford U., Eng., 1949; B.C.L., Oxford U., Eng., 1950, M.A., 1954; LL.M., Columbia U., 1959. Bar: Tex. 1951, U.S. Ct. Appeals (5th cir.) 1982. Assoc. Cravath, Swaine & Moore, N.Y.C., 1951-55; asst. prof. So Meth. U., Dallas, 1955-57, assoc. prof., 1957-63, prof. law, 1963—, acad. dean, 1977-80, Larry and Jane Harlan faculty fellow, 1991—; vis. prof. various univs. Gen. editor Creditors' Rights in Texas, 1963; author: (with William A. Reppy, Jr.) Texas Matrimonial Property Law, 1983; contbr. articles to profl. jours. Pres., Tex. Old Missions and Forts Restoration Assn., 1977-79; bd. dirs. San Jacinto Mus. History Assn., 1976—; mem. exec. coun. Tex. State Hist. Assn., 1988-91. Served to lt. USNR, 1942-47. Rhodes scholar, 1947-50; James Kent fellow, 1958-59; Academico, Acad. Mexicana de Derecho Internat., 1988. Mem. ABA, State Bar Tex., Dallas Bar Assn., Tex. Bar Found. (v.p. 1959), Nat. Legal Aid and Defenders Assn. (bd. dirs. 1963-66), Selden Soc., Am. Soc. Legal History (v.p. 1967-68, bd. dirs. 1967-75), Inst. Texan Cultures (exec. bd. 1990—), Sigma Chi. Democrat. Episcopalian. Office: So Meth U Law School Dallas TX 75275-0116

MC KNIGHT, PAUL JAMES, JR., hospital corporate executive; b. Nashville, Dec. 22, 1935; s. Paul James and Elizabeth Mayo (Cate) McK.; B.A. in Bus. Adminstrn., Emory U., 1957; cert. in hosp. adminstrn. St. Louis U., 1974; m. Ruth Evelyn McBryde, Jan. 26, 1963; children—Paul James, Margaret, Mary Ann. Corp. personnel dir. Hosp. Corp. Am., Nashville, 1969-70, v.p., 1980-87, sr. v.p., pres. Fla. group, 1987—; adminstr. Epperson Hosp., 1971-72, North Fla. Regional Hosp., 1972-80; preceptor U. Fla. Sch. Health and Hosp. Adminstrn.; mem. Statewide Health Planning Council, 1982-86. Bd. dirs. Athens (Tenn.) C. of C., Gainesville C. of C., Civitan Regional Blood Bank of North Fla. Served with USN, 1957-61. Paul Harris fellow, 1981. Mem. Am. Coll. Hosp. Adminstrs., Fla. League Hosps. (pres. 1976), Fla. C. of C. (dir. 1984-88), Fedn. Am. Hosps. (dir.). Republican. Methodist. Club: Rotary. Home: 2356 N Arendell Way Tallahassee FL 32308-6006 Office: Hosp Corp Am 1830 Buford Ct Tallahassee FL 32308-4456

MCKNIGHT, STEVEN LANIER, molecular biologist; b. El Paso, Tex., Aug. 27, 1949; s. Frank Gillespie and Sara Elise (Stevens) McK.; m. Jacquelynn Ann Zimmer, Sept. 16, 1978; children: Nell, Grace, Frances, John Stevens. BA, U. Tex., 1974; PhD, U.Va., 1977. Postdoctoral fellow Carnegie Instn. Washington, Balt., 1977-79, staff assoc., 1979-81, mem. staff, 1984-92; co-founder, dir. rsch. Tularik Inc., 1991—. Contbr. articles to jours. in field. With U.S. Army, 1969-71, Vietnam. Decorated ARCOM medal; recipient Eli Lilly prize Am. Soc. Microbiology, 1987, Newcomb-Cleveland prize Sci. mag., 1989, NAS Molecular Biology award Nat. Acad. Sci., 1991. Fellow Carnegie Inst. (Washington, hon.); mem. Nat. Acad. Scis., Am. Acad. Arts and Scis., Am. Soc. for Biochemistry and Molecular Biology, Am. Soc. for Cell Biology, Japanese Biochem. Soc. Democrat. Home: 530 Roehampton Rd Hillsborough CA 94010-6854 Office: Tularik Inc 270 Grand View Ave San Francisco CA 94114-3152

MCKNIGHT, WILLIAM BALDWIN, physics educator; b. Macon, Ga., July 4, 1923; s. Gilbert Franklin and Exie (Baldwin) McK.; m. Helen Mabel Bowling, Oct. 1, 1955; children: Tandy Ringoringo, Linda McKnight Way. BS, Purdue U., 1950; PhD, Oxford U., 1968. Physicist Underwater Sound Reference Lab., Orlando, Fla., 1952-53, U.S. Army Missile Command, Redstone Arsenal, Ala., 1953-61; supervisory research physicist Army Missile Command, Redstone Arsenal, 1961-74; cons. Ballistic Missile Def. Advanced Tech. Ctr., 1975; research prof. physics U. Ala., Huntsville, 1974—; pres. Tech. Research Assocs. Inc., 1984—. Contbr. articles to profl. jours. Vice pres. Cotaco Communities League, Somerville, Ala., 1964-65; mem. Madison County Rep. Exec. Com.; mgr. Gordo Area C. of C., 1993—; chmn. Pickens County Health Coun., 1994—. With USAAF, 1943-45. Decorated D.F.C., Air medal with three oak leaf clusters; recipient Research and Devel. award U.S. Army, 1961, 64; Sec. of Army fellow, 1966-67. Fellow Optical Soc. Am.; mem. IEEE (sr.), Am. Phys. Soc., Sigma Xi, Sigma Pi Sigma. Mem. Ch. of Christ. Clubs: United Oxford, Cambridge Univ. Home: RR 1 Box 141A Gordo AL 35466-9801 Office: PO Box 1247 Huntsville AL 35899-0001

MCKNIGHT, WILLIAM EDWIN, minister; b. Grenada, Miss., Mar. 21, 1938; s. Leslie Spurgeon and Lucy Jennings (Sistrunk) McK.; m Sue Belle Roberts, Aug. 5, 1960; children: Susan Michele, William Roberts. BA, Millsaps Coll., 1960; BD, Lexington (Ky.) Theol. Sem., 1963. Ordained to ministry, 1964. Chaplain intern Grady Hosp., Atlanta, 1963-64; pastor First Christian Ch., Cleveland, Miss., 1964-67, Inverness, Miss., 1964-67; assoc. pastor First Christian Ch., Jackson, Miss., 1967-70; regional minister Christian Ch. (Disciples of Christ) in Miss., Jackson, 1971—; bd. dirs. Nat. City Christian Ch., Washington, Christian Brotherhood Homes, Jackson, So. Christian Svcs., Macon, Ga.; mem. Gen. Bd. the Christian Ch., Indpls., 1969—, bd. dirs. fin. coun., 1979-82; mem. bd. higher edn., St. Louis, 1979-80. Named one of Outstanding Young Men Am. U.S. Jaycees, 1976. Mem. Miss. Religious Leadership Conf. (pres. 1984-85), Conf. Regional Ministers and Moderators (pres. 1985-86). Office: Christian Ch in Miss 1619 N West St Jackson MS 39202-1418

MC KNIGHT, WILLIAM WARREN, JR., publisher; b. Normal, Ill., June 9, 1913; s. William Warren and Isabel Alida (Travis) McK.; m. Alice McGuire, Oct. 30, 1937; children: William Warren, III, Michael Joe, John James. B.S. in Bus. Adminstrn., Northwestern U., 1938. With McKnight Pub. Co., Bloomington, Ill., 1938-83; sec.-treas. McKnight Pub. Co., 1949-56, pres., 1956-67, chmn. bd., 1968-79; bd. dirs. Gen. Telephone Co. Ill. Champion Fed. Savs. & Loan Assn., chmn. bd. Pres. Bloomington Rotary Club, 1952, Bloomington C. of C., 1954; mem. Ill. Commn. Higher Edn., 1956-60; chmn. Bloomington-Normal Airport Authority, 1965-70, CETA Pvt. Industry Council Ill. Balance of State, 1979-81. Served with USNR, 1942-46. Recipient Disting. Service award Bloomington Kiwanis Club, 1963, Disting. Service award Normal C. of C., 1973; Good Govt. award Bloomington Jaycees, 1970; Edn. Constrn. award Edn. Council Graphic Arts Industry, 1974; Disting. Alumni award Ill. State U., 1978; Disting. Service award Spirit of McLean County, 1982; Disting. Service citation Epsilon Pi Tau, 1983; award of Merit Am. Vocat. Assn., 1990; disting. assoc. award Coun. on Tech. Tchr. Edn., 1995. Mem. Graphic Arts Edn. Assn., Internat. Tech. Edn. Assn., Nat. Assn. Indsl. and Tech. Tchrs. Educators, Ill. C. of C. (dir. 1964-69), Ill. Mfrs. Assn. (dir. 1954-62). Republican. Presbyterian. Clubs: Coll. Alumni, Bloomington Country. Home: 401 W Vernon Normal IL 61761 Home (winter): 7788 Stallion Rd Scottsdale AZ 85258

MC KOY, BASIL VINCENT CHARLES, theoretical chemist, educator; b. Trinidad, W.I., Mar. 25, 1938; came to U.S., 1960, naturalized, 1973. s. Allan Cecil and Doris Augusta McK.; m. Anne Ellen Shannon, Mar. 18, 1967; 1 son, Christopher Allan. B.Chem. Eng., N.S. Tech. U., 1960; Ph.D. in Chemistry (Univ. fellow), Yale U., 1964. Instr. chemistry Calif. Inst. Tech., 1964-66, asst. prof. chemistry, 1966-69, asso. prof., 1975-79, prof. theoretical chemistry, 1975—, chmn. of faculty, 1985-87; cons. Lawrence Livermore Lab, U. Calif., Livermore, 1994—; Inst. Def. Analysis, 1984—; vis. prof. Max Planck Inst., Munich, Ger., 1976—, U. Paris, 1968—, U. Campinas, Brazil, 1996—; lectr. Nobel Symposium, Goteborg, Sweden, 1979. Contbr. articles to Jour. Physics, London, chem. Physics Letters, Phys. Rev., Jour. Chem. Physics; bd. editors; Chem. Physics Jour., 1977-79; mem. adv. editoral bd., 1992—; co-editor: Electron-Molecule and Photon-Molecule Collisions, 1979, 83, Swarm Studies and Inelastic Electron-Molecuale Collisions, 1986; co-author: Electron-Molecule Collisions and Photoionization Processes, 1982. Recipient medal Gov.-Gen. Can., 1960; Alfred P. Sloan Found. fellow, 1969-73; Guggenheim fellow, 1973-74. Fellow Am. Phys. Soc. Home: 3855 Keswick Rd La Canada Flintridge CA 91011-3945 Office: Calif Inst Tech Div Chemistry Pasadena CA 91125

MC KUEN, ROD, poet, composer, author; b. Oakland, Calif., Apr. 29, 1933; s. Clarice Woolever. Pres. Stanyan Records, Discus Records, New Gramaphone Soc., Mr. Kelly Prodns., Montcalm Prodns., Stanyan Books, Cheval Books, Biplane Books, Rod McKuen Enterprises; v.p. Tamarack Books; poetry columnist Cosmopolitan, 1970-71. Appeared in numerous films, TV, concerts; composer motion picture scores, background music for TV, modern classical music; film scores include Joanna, 1968, The Prime of Miss Jean Brodie, 1969 (Academy award nomination best musical score 1969), Me, Natalie, 1969, Travels With Charlie, 1969, The Loner, 1969, Say Goodbye, 1970 (Emmy award best musical score 1970), A Boy Named Charlie Brown, 1970 (Academy award nomination best musical score 1970), Come to Your Senses, 1971, Scandalous John, 1971, Wildflowers, 1971, The Seagull, 1972, Lisa, Bright and Dark, 1973, Big Mo, 1973, The Borrowers, 1973, Hello Again, 1974 (Emmy award best musical score 1977), Emily, 1975, The Unknown War, 1979, Man to Himself, 1980, Portrait of Rod McKuen, 1982, Death Rides this Trial, 1983, The Living End, 1983; record prodr. for Frank Sinatra, Sylvia Syms, Kingston Trio, Petula Clark; author: And Autumn Came, 1954, Stanyan Street and Other Sorrows, 1966, Listen to the Warm, 1967, Twelve Years of Christmas, 1968, Lonesome Cities, 1968, The World of Rod McKuen, 1968, Sea Cycle, 1969, In Someone's Shadow, 1969, Frank Sinatra: A Man Alone, 1969, With Love..., 1970, Caught in the Quiet, 1970, Rod McKuen at Carnegie Hall, 1970, Moment to Moment, 1971, The Carols of Christmas, 1971, So My Sheep Can Safely Graze, 1971, Pastorale: A Collection of Lyrics, 1971, And to Each Season, 1972, Grand Tour, 1972, Beyond the Boardwalk, 1972, Fields of Wonder, 1972, Rod McKuen Calendar and Datebook 1973, 1972, Come to Me in Silence, 1973, Seasons in the Sun, 1974, Celebrations of the Heart, 1975, The Rod McKuen Omnibus, 1975, Hand in Hand, 1976, Finding My Father: One Man's Search for Identity, 1976, The Sea Around Me, 1977, Coming Close to the Earth, 1978, We Touch the Sky, 1979, Love's Been Good to Me, 1979, The Power Bright and Shining: Images of My Country, 1980, Looking for a Friend, 1980, An Outstretched Hand: Poems, Prayers, and Meditations, 1980, The Beautiful Strangers, 1981, Too Many Midnights, 1981, Rod McKuen's Book of Days and a Month of Sundays, 1981, Watch for the Wind, 1983, The Sound of Solitude, 1983, Suspension Bridge, 1984, Valentines, 1986, Intervals, 1986; editor: Henry David Thoreau, The Wind That Blows Is All That Anybody Knows, 1970, The Will to Win, 1971; music collections include New Ballads, 1970, Seasons in the Sun, 1982; songs include Jean, If You Go Away, Seasons in the Sun, I'm Not Afraid, The Lovers, Love's Been Good to Me; compositions include Concerto Number Three for Piano and Orchestra, 1972, The Hains of My Country, 1972, Suite for Narrator and Orchestra: The City, 1973 (Pulitzer Prize nomination for classical music 1973), Ballad of Distances, 1973, Bicentennial Ballet, 1975, Symphony Number Three, 1975; spoken word albums include Lonesome Cities, 1969 (Grammy award best spoken album 1969). Mem. adv. bd. Market Theatre, Johannesburg, S. Africa, Fund for Animals, Internat. Edn.; mem. bd. dirs. Am. Nat. Theatre of Ballet, Am. Dance Ensemble, Calif. Music Theater, Animal Concern; bd. govs. Nat. Acad. Rec. Arts and Scis.; trustee AGVA Welfare Trust Fund, Freedoms Found., U. Nebr.; pres. Nat. Com. for Prevention of Child Abuse. Recipient Grand Prix du Disc (Paris), 1966, 74, 75, 82, Golden Globe award, 1969, Motion Picture Daily award, 1969, Freedoms Found. medal of honor, 1975, Horatio Alger award, 1975, Humanitarian award First Amendment Soc., 1977, Outstanding Poet award Carl Sandburg Soc., 1978, Literary Trust award Brandeis U., 1981, Sylvester Pat Weaver award for pub. svc. broadcasting, 1981, Freedoms Found. Patriot medal, 1981, Community Svc. award Myasthenia Gravis Found., 1986; named Entertainer of Yr. Shriners Club L.A., 1975, Man of Yr. U. Detroit, 1978, Man of Yr. Salvation Army, 1982. Mem. Modern Poetry Assn., ASCAP, Writers Guild, Am. Guild Authors and Composers (dir.), Internat. Platform Assn., AFTRA, AGVA (pres.). Office: PO Box 2783 Los Angeles CA 90028 also: Am Guild Variety Artists 1984 5th Ave New York NY 10010*

MCKUNE, ELIZABETH D., diplomat; b. Detroit, Nov. 15, 1947; d. Clarence M. and Yolande B. Davenport; m. Kenneth R. McKune, June 5, 1974. BA, Carleton Coll., 1970; M Internat. Rels., Johns Hopkins U., 1972. Mgmt. intern US Dept. Commerce, Washington, 1972-73, fgn. svc. officer, 1973—. Recipient Meritorious Honor award U.S. Info. Agcy., 1988, Meritorious Honor award U.S. State Dept., 1980. Office: Am Embassy Muscat c/o Dept of State Washington DC 20521-6220

MCKUSICK, VINCENT LEE, former state supreme judicial court chief justice, lawyer; b. Parkman, Maine, Oct. 21, 1921; s. Carroll Lee and Ethel (Buzzell) McK.; m. Nancy Elizabeth Green, June 23, 1951; children: Barbara Jane McKusick Liscord, James Emory, Katherine McKusick Ralston, Anne Elizabeth. A.B., Bates Coll., 1943; S.B., S.M., MIT, 1947; LL.B., Harvard U., 1950; LL.D., Colby Coll., 1976, Nasson Coll., 1978, Bates Coll., 1979, Bowdoin Coll., 1979, Suffolk U., 1983; L.H.D., U. So. Maine, 1978, Thomas Coll., 1981. Bar: Maine 1952. Law clk. to Chief Judge Learned Hand, 1950-51; to Justice Felix Frankfurter, 1951-52; partner Pierce, Atwood, Scribner, Allen & McKusick and predecessors, Portland, Maine, 1953-77; chief justice Maine Supreme Jud. Ct., 1977-92; of counsel to Pierce, Atwood, Scribner, Allen, Smith & Lancaster, Portland, Maine, 1992—; mem. adv. coun. rules of civil procedure Maine Supreme Jud. Ct., 1957-59, chmn. 1966-75; commr. on uniform state laws, 1968-76, sec. nat. conf. 1975-77; mem. Conf. of Chief Justices, 1977-92, bd. dirs. 1980-82, 91-92, pres.-elect 1989-90, pres. 1990-91; dir. Nat. Ctr. for State Ctrs., 1988-89, chmn.-elect 1989-90, chmn. 1990-91; spl. master U.S. Supreme Ct. Conn. v. N.H., 1992-93, La. v. Miss., 1994; leader Am. Judges del. to China, 1983, USSR., 1988; leader U.S. State Dept. Rule of Law Del. to Republic of Ga., 1992; mem. permanent com. Oliver Wendell Holmes Devise, 1993—. Author: Patrict Policy of Educational Institutions, 1947, (with Richard H. Field) Maine Civil Practice, 1959, supplements, 1962, 67, (with Richard H. Field and L. Kinvin Wroth) 2d edit., 1970, supplements, 1972, 74, 77; also articles in legal pubs. Trustee emeritus Bates Coll.; mem. adv. com. on pvt. internat. law U.S. State Dept., 1980-85, Fed.-State Jurisdiction com., Jud. Conf. of U.S., 1987-89. With AUS, 1943-46. Recipient The Maine prize, U. Maine System, 1993, Benjamin E. Mays award, Bates Coll., 1994. Fellow Am. Bar Found. (bd. dirs. 1977-87), Am. Philos. Soc. (coun. 1990—); mem. ABA (chmn. fed. rules com. 1966-71, bd. editors jour. 1971-80, chmn. 1976-77, mem. study group to China 1978, hodels. 1983-87), Maine Bar Assn., Cumberland County Bar Assn., Am. Arbitration Assn. (bd. dirs. 1994—), Am. Judicature Soc. (bd. 1976-78, 92—), Am. Law Inst. (coun. 1969—), Maine Jud. Coun. (chmn. 1977-92), Inst. Jud. Adminstrn., Supreme Ct. Hist. Soc. (trustee 1994—), Rotary Club (hon., past pres.), Portland Yacht Club, Downeast Yacht Club, Phi Beta Kappa, Sigma Xi, Tau Beta Pi. Republican. Unitarian. Home: 1152 Shore Rd Cape Eliz ME 04107-2115 Office: 1 Monument Sq Portland ME 04101-4033

MCLACHLIN, BEVERLEY, supreme court judge; b. Pincher Creek, Alta., Can., Sept. 7, 1943; m. Roderick McLachlin (dec. 1988); 1 child, Angus; m. Frank E. McArdle, 1992. B.A., U. Alta., MA in Philosophy, LLB, LLD, 1990; LLD, U.B.C., 1990. Bar: Alta. 1969, B.C. 1971. Assoc. Wood, Moir, Hyde and Ross, Edmonton, Alta., Can., 1969-71, Thomas, Herdy, Mitchell & Co., Fort St. John, B.C., Can., 1971-72, Bull, Housser and Tupper, Vancouver, B.C., 1972-75; lectr., assoc. prof., prof. with tenure U. B.C., 1974-81; appointed to County Ct., Vancouver, 1981; justice Supreme Ct. of B.C., 1981-85, B.C. Ct. of Appeal, 1985-88; chief justice Supreme Ct. of B.C., 1988; justice Supreme Ct. Can., Ottawa, Ont., 1989—. Co-author: B.C. Supreme Court Practice, B.C. Court Forums, Canadian Law of Arch. and Engring.; mem. editorial adv. bd. Family Law Restatement Project, 1987-88, Civil Jury Instruction, 1988; contbr. numerous articles to profl. jours. Office: Supreme Ct Bldg, Wellington St, Ottawa, ON Canada K1A 0J1

MCLAFFERTY, FRED WARREN, chemist, educator; b. Evanston, Ill., May 11, 1923; s. Joel E. and Margaret E. (Keifer) McL.; m. Elizabeth E. Curley, Feb. 5, 1948; children: Sara L., Joel E., Martha A., Samuel A., Ann E. B.S., U. Nebr., 1943, D.Sc. (hon.), 1983, M.S., 1947; Ph.D., Cornell U., 1950; D.Sc. (hon.), U. Liege, Belgium, 1987; DSc (hon.), Purdue U., 1995. Postdoctoral fellow U. Iowa, 1949-50; research chemist, div. leader Dow Chem. Co., 1950-56; dir. Eastern Research Lab., 1956-64; prof. chemistry Purdue U., 1964-68, Cornell U., 1968—; mem. chem. sci. and tech. bd., numerical data adv. bd., bd. Army sci. tech., bd. radioactive waste mgmt. NRC; chem. co-chmn. World Bank's Chinese Univ. Devel. Project. Author: Mass Spectrometry of Organic Ions, 1963, Mass Spectral Correlations, 2d edit., 1981, Interpretation of Mass Spectra, 4th edit., 1993, Tandem Mass Spectrometry, 1983, Advances in Analytical Chemistry and Instrumentation, (with C.N. Reilley), Vols. 4-7, 1967-70, Index and Bibliography of Mass Spectrometry, (with J. Pinzelik), 1967, Atlas of Mass Spectral Data; (with E. Stenhagen and S. Abrahamsson), 1969, Registry of Mass Spectral Data, 1974; (with D.B. Stauffer) Wiley/NBS Registry of Mass Spectral Data, 1989,
Important Peak Index of Mass Spectral Data, 1991; editor: Accounts of Chemical Research, 1986-94; co-editor: (with E. Stenhagen and S. Abrahamsson) Archives of Mass Spectral Data, 1969-72. Served with AUS, 1942-45, ETO. Decorated Purple Heart, Combat Inf. badge, Bronze Star with 4 oak leaf clusters; recipient Pitts. Spectroscopy award Spectroscopy Soc. Pitts., 1975, Gold medal U. Naples, 1989; John Simon Guggenheim fellow, 1972, Overseas fellow Churchill Coll., Cambridge U., Eng., 1979; W.L. Evans award Ohio State U., 1987, Robert Boyle Medal in Analytical Chemistry, 1992, Royal Soc. of Chemistry. Fellow NAS, AAAS, N.Y. Acad. Scis., Am. Acad. Arts and Scis.; mem. Soc. Analytical Chemists (Pitts. Analytical Chemist award 1987, Pioneer Analytical Instrumentation award 1994), Am. Chem. Soc. (chmn. analytical chem. div. 1969, chmn. Midland sect. 1956, Northeastern sect. 1964, award chem. instrumentation 1971, award analytical chemistry 1981, Nichols medal N.Y. sect. 1984, Oesper award Cin. sect. 1985, Lind award Ea. Tenn. sect. 1986, award mass spectrometry 1989), Internat. Spectrometry Orgn. (Sir J.J. Thomson medal 1985), Assn. Analytical Chemists (Anachem award 1985), Am. Soc. Mass Spectrometry (founder, sec. 1957-58), Royal Soc. Chemistry London (Robert Boyle medal 1992), Sigma Xi, Phi Lambda Upsilon, Alpha Chi Sigma. Home: 103 Needham Pl Ithaca NY 14850-2120

MCLAIN, JOHN LOWELL, resource specialist, consultant; b. Havre, Mont., Jan. 23, 1942; s. Woodrow B. and Ann Teresa (Bolta) McL.; m. Carolyn Louise Peterson, June 27, 1964; children: Nicole Rachelle, Tanya Lynn. BS in Range Mgmt., Mont. State U., 1969. Cert. range mgmt. cons.; cert. soil erosion & sediment control specialist. Soil conservationist USDA Soil Conservation Svc., Miles City, Mont., 1969-71; range conservationist USDA Soil Conservation Svc., Glendive, Mont., 1971-74; area range conservationist USDA Soil Conservation Svc., Minden, Nev., 1974-76, dist. conservationist, 1976-78; prin. resource specialist Resource Concepts Inc., Carson City, Nev., 1978—; bd. dirs. Range Mag., Carson City. Mem. citizens adv. bd. U. Nev.-Reno, 1981-92; Nev. del. Coun. for Agrl. Rsch. Ext. & Teaching, Washington, 1983—. Recipient Outstanding Achievement award Carson Valley Conservation Dist., 1978; named Man of 1980s Carson City Appeal newspaper, 1988. Mem. Soc. for Range Mgmt. (pres. Nev. sect. 1980, Rangeman of Yr. Nev. sect. 1981), Soil Conservation Soc. (pres. Nev. sect. 1980), Soc. Range Mgmt (dir. 1993—), Resource Restoration Internat. (mem. adv. com. 1992—). Roman Catholic. Avocations: fishing, guitar/singing, horseback riding, skiing, hunting. Home: 2424 Manhattan Dr Carson City NV 89703-5416 Office: Resource Concepts Inc 340 N Minnesota St Carson City NV 89703-4152

MCLAIN, MAURICE CLAYTON, lawyer, real estate executive; b. Hillsboro, Tex., Sept. 22, 1929; s. Otis Ogen and Rachel Elizabeth (Estes) McL.; m. Martha Orlana Gould, Sept. 25, 1953; 1 child, William Gould. Student, Hillsboro Jr. Coll., 1945-46, Tex. A&M Coll., 1946-47; BA in Math, North Tex. State U., 1950; JD, So. Meth. U., 1962. Bar: Tex. 1962, U.S. Supreme Ct. 1976, U.S. Ct. Appeals (4th, 5th, 9th, 11th cirs.). Coord. engring. contracts Vought Aerospace div. LTV Corp., Dallas, 1961-64; assoc. firm Abney & Burleson, Dallas, 1964-66; counsel Fed. Nat. Mortgage Assn., Dallas, 1966-69; sr. v.p., gen. counsel USLIFE Real Estate Svcs. Corp., Dallas, 1970-84; of counsel Clark, Thomas, Winters & Newton, Austin, Tex., 1984-86; atty. Fed. Deposit Ins. Corp., Dallas, 1987-91, Baker, Glast & Middleton, Dallas, 1991; chmn. real estate specialization adv. comm. Tex. Bd. Legal Specialization, Dallas, 1987-91; shareholder Youngblood & Youngblood, Dallas, 1991—. Mem. ABA, Dallas Bar Assn., State Bar Tex., Am. Coll. Real Estate Attys., Assn. Life Ins. Counsel, Mortgage Bankers Assn. Am., SAR, Dallas Scottish Soc., English Speaking Union, Phi Delta Phi, Sigma Phi Epsilon. Republican. Episcopalian. Home: 3908 Royal Ln Dallas TX 75229-4047

MC LANATHAN, RICHARD (BARTON KENNEDY), author, consultant; b. Methuen, Mass., Mar. 12, 1916; s. Frank Watson and Helen (Kennedy) McL.; m. Jane Fuller, Jan. 2, 1942. Grad., Choate Sch., 1934; A.B., Harvard U., 1938, Ph.D., 1951. Instr. English and history Allen-Stevenson Sch., N.Y.C., 1938-43; asst. curator paintings Mus. Fine Arts, Boston, 1946-48; asst. curator decorative arts Mus. Fine Arts, 1949-54, sec. of museum, 1949-56, editor museum pubs., 1952-57, asso. curator decorative arts, 1954, curator decorative arts, 1954-57; dir. Mus. Art, Munson-Williams-Proctor Inst., Utica, N.Y., 1957-61; exec. dir. Am. Assn. Museums, Washington, 1976-78; trustee, mem. exec. com. Boston Arts Festival, 1954-59; curator Am. Nat. art exhbn., Moscow, 1959, Am. specialist to W. Ger., Poland and Denmark, 1959, Yugoslavia, 1961; mem. U.S. Nat. Commn. for UNESCO, 1976-79, Corcoran Biennial Jury, 1960, N.Y. State Council Arts, 1960-64; bd. advisers Albany (N.Y.) Inst. History and Art, 1958-70; cons. in field, 1961-75, 79—. Author: Images of the Universe: Leonardo da Vinci, The Artist as Scientist, 1966, The Pageant of Medieval Art, 1966, The American Tradition in the Arts, 1968, A Guide to Civilisation: The Kenneth Clark Films on the Cultural Life of Western Man, 1970, The Brandywine Heritage, 1971, Art in America, 1973, The Art of Marguerite Stix, 1977, National Gallery of Art, East Building: A Profile, 1978, Romantic America; catalogue of the inaugural exhbn. of Tampa Museum, 1979, World Art in American Museums, A Personal Guide, 1983, Gilbert Stuart, 1986, Leonardo da Vinci, 1990, fgn. lang. edits., 1991, Michelangelo, 1993, Rubens, 1995; co-author: M. and M. Karolik Collection of American Paintings, 1815-1855, 1949; editor: Catalogue of Classical Coins, 1955; cons. editor: Art and Man, Nat. Gallery Art, 1969-76; adv. editor: The Great Contemporary Issues: The Arts, 1978; decorative arts editor: Webster's Unabridged Dictionary, 1955; contbr.: Am. Foundation Philanthropy, 1967. Bd. advisers Boys Clubs Boston, 1950-57; trustee Boys' Club Utica, 1959-61, Brandywine River Mus., 1970-75, Maine Maritime Mus., 1984-89; bd. dirs. St. Luke's Meml. Hosp. Center, Utica, 1957-61. Sr. fellow Am. Acad. Rome, 1948-49; recipient Distinguished Service award USIA, 1959; Prix de Rome, 1948; Rockefeller sr. fellow Met. Mus., 1975-76. Mem. Am. Assn. Museums, Harvard Soc. Fellows. Home: The Stone School House Phippsburg ME 04562

MCLANE, DAVID GLENN, lawyer; b. Dallas, Jan. 17, 1943; s. Alfred Ervin and Dixie Marie (Martin) McL.; m. Sally Ruth Payne, Apr. 5, 1963; children: Cynthia Lynn, Kathleen Michelle, Michael Scott; m. Beverly Anne Bledsoe, Feb. 5, 1983; children: Morgan Elizabeth, Nicholas Martin, Elizabeth Clark. BA, So. Meth. U., 1963, LLB, 1966. Bar: Tex. 1966, U.S. Supreme Ct. 1971. Briefing atty. Supreme Ct. Tex., 1966-67; assoc., then ptnr. Gardere & Wynne and predecessors, Dallas, 1967—; mem. faculty So. Meth. U.; lectr. in field. Bd. dirs. Urban Services br. Dallas YMCA, 1977-84, Dallas Symphony Assn., 1980-93; mem. Dallas County AIDS Planning Commn. Task Force, 1988; pres. coun. Dallas Theol. Sem., 1994—. Mem. ABA, Tex. Bar Assn., Dallas Bar Assn., S.W. Benefits Assn. (bd. dirs. 1975-80, pres 1978-79), So. Meth. U. Law Alumni Assn. (sec., bd. dirs. 1981-85, Vol. of Yr. award 1984), So. Meth. U. Alumni Assn. (bd. dirs. 1972-77). Presbyterian. Contbg. author: Texas Corporations—Law and Practice, 1984; editor: Incorporation Planning in Texas, 1977. Office: 3000 Thanksgiving Tower Dallas TX 75201

MCLANE, FREDERICK BERG, lawyer; b. Long Beach, Calif., July 24, 1941; s. Adrian B. and Arlie K. (Burrell) McL.; m. Lois C. Roberts, Jan. 28, 1967; children: Willard, Anita. BA, Stanford U., 1963; LLB, Yale U., 1966. Bar: Calif. 1967, U.S. Dist. Ct. (cen. dist.) Calif. 1967. Assoc. prof. law U. Miss., Oxford, 1966-68; assoc. O'Melveny & Myers, L.A., 1968-74, ptnr., 1975—; com. of counsel HUD, Los Angeles, 1979-84; lectr. in field. Pres., bd. dirs. Legal Aid Found., L.A., 1974-83; deacon Congl. Ch., Sherman Oaks, Calif., 1979-83; vice-chair LA Music Ctr., Unified Fund, 1992-94; bd. dirs. Calif. Mus. Found., 1991—. Mem. ABA (banking com.), Calif. Bar Assn. (fin. insts. com., uniform comml. codes), L.A. Bar Assn., Order of Coif, Calif. Club (L.A.), L.A. Country Club, Lakeside Golf Club (L.A.), Lake Arrowhead Country Club (Calif.). Democrat. Avocations: golf, skiing, walking, reading. Office: O'Melveny & Myers 400 S Hope St Los Angeles CA 90071

MCLANE, HENRY EARL, JR., philosophy educator; b. Statesboro, Ga., Aug. 18, 1932; s. Henry Earl and Lillie Ora (Beasley) McL.; m. Barbara Helen Gardner, Nov. 7, 1934; children—Debra Lynn, Shawn Creg. B.A., George Washington U., 1955; postgrad., Johns Hopkins U., 1955-56; M.A., Yale U., 1958, Ph.D., 1961. Instr. philosophy Washburn U. of Topeka, Kans., 1960-61; asst. prof. Washburn U. of Topeka, 1961-64, assoc. prof., 1964-65; vis. assoc. prof. Coll. of William and Mary, Williamsburg, Va., 1965-66; assoc. prof. Coll. of William and Mary, 1967-77, prof. philosophy,

1978—; diving coach Coll. of William and Mary, 1976-87. Contbr. articles to profl. publs. Danforth Found. fellow, 1955-60. Mem. Am. Philos. Assn. Democrat. Baptist. Avocations: playing violin; music. Home: 116 Dogwood Dr Williamsburg VA 23185-3743 Office: Coll of William and Mary Dept Philosophy PO Box 8795 Williamsburg VA 23187-8795

MCLANE, JAMES WOODS, insurance executive; b. New Canaan, Conn., Jan. 27, 1939; s. William Lawrence and Elizabeth Fish (Benjamin) McL.; m. Fay Sargent, Apr. 27, 1963 (div. 1980); children—James Woods, Benjamin Sargent; m. Nancy Coe, May 5, 1984; 1 child, Joshua Coe. B.A., Yale U., 1961; M.B.A., Harvard U., 1967. Cons. Booz, Allen & Hamilton, N.Y.C., 1967-69; exec. asst. to sec. HEW, Washington, 1969-70; staff asst. to Pres. U.S., White House, 1971-72; dep. dir. Cost of Living Council, Washington, 1972-74; v.p. mcht. banking group Citibank N.A., N.Y.C., 1974-79; sr. v.p. and head corp. fin. div. Citibank N.A., 1980-83; sr. v.p., mng. dir. Citicorp Internat. Bank Ltd., 1983-84; head Europe, Middle East, Africa div (Global Investment Bank), London, 1983-84; pres., chief exec. officer Citicorp Ins. Group Inc., 1984-91; div. exec. Citibank Global Ins. Div., 1984-91, Capital Investments Div., 1988-90; chief exec. officer Aetna Health Plans, Hartford, Conn., 1991—; group exec. Aetna Life & Casualty, 1992-93, exec. v.p., 1993—; chmn. AMBAC, Inc., AMBAC Indemnity, Capital Markets Assurance Corp., Citicorp Ins. (U.S.A.) Inc., Citicorp Ins. (Bermuda) Ltd.; bd. dirs. Citicorp Ins. Brokers Ltd., Citibank (N.Y. state), Family Guardian Life Ins. Co. Chmn. bd. Outward Bound U.S.A.; trustee Wadsworth Atheneum, Old State House Assn.; campaign mgr. Mass. Gov. Sargent's Reelection Campaign, 1970; mem. hon. degrees com. Yale U., 1973-74; bd. dirs., 1st v.p., campaign chmn. Greenwich (Conn.) Health Assn.; trustee St. George's Sch., 1981-85; elder Brick Ch., N.Y.C., 1988-91. With USN, 1961-65, Vietnam. Mem. Yale Club of N.Y., Twin Lakes Beach Club, Hartford Golf Club. Republican. Office: Aetna Health Plans 151 Farmington Ave MB66 Hartford CT 06156-0001

MC LANE, JOHN ROY, JR., lawyer; b. Manchester, N.H., Feb. 19, 1916; s. John R. and Elisabeth (Bancroft) Mc L.; m. Blanche Marshall, Feb. 15, 1935; children: John Roy III, Andrew M. (dec.), Lyn, Blanche M., Angus; m. 2d, Elisabeth Deane, Dec. 30, 1960; children: Towner D., Virginia W., Kathryn E., Duncan C. Bar: N.H. 1941. Practiced in Manchester, since 1941; dir. firm McLane, Graf, Raulerson & Middleton, P.A., 1941-42, 45—. Alderman, Manchester, 1952-53; trustee Spaulding-Potter Charitable Trusts, 1958-72, N.H. State Hosp., 1949-62, Hurricane Island Outward Bound Sch., 1972-79; chmn. N.H. Adv. Commn. on Health and Welfare, 1965-68; trustee, sec. Norwin S. and Elizabeth N. Bean Found., 1967-94; trustee, clk. St. Paul's Sch., 1952-83; distbg. dir. N.H. Charitable Fund, 1962-69; bd. dirs. Coun. on Founds, 1968-74, chmn., 1970-72; bd. dirs. Child and Family Svcs. N.H., 1946-71, pres., 1963-71; bd. dirs. Palace Theatre Trust, 1974—. Lt. USNR, 1942-45. Mem. ABA, N.H. Bar Assn., Manchester Bar Assn. Republican. Episcopalian (vestry 1963, 68). Home: 1595 River Rd Manchester NH 03104-1628 Office: 900 Elm St Manchester NH 03101-2007

MCLANE, ROBERT DRAYTON, JR., food products company executive; b. Cameron, Tex., July 22, 1936; s. Robert Drayton and Gladys (Blaylock) McL.; m. Mary Elizabeth Cockrell, Feb. 2, 1972; children: Robert Drayton III, Denton. BBA, Baylor U., 1958; MS, Mich. State U., 1959. With McLane Co., Inc., Temple, Tex., 1957—, v.p., 1964-74, exec. v.p., sec.-treas., 1974-78, chief exec. officer, pres., 1978—, also bd. dirs.; bd. dirs. First Nat. Bank, Temple, Tex. Pres. United Way Campaign, Temple, 1985—; mem. Tex. State Bd. Mental Health and Mental Retardation, 1985—, exec. bd. Heart O'Tex. Council Boy Scouts Am., 1968—; bd. dirs. Scott and White Meml. Hosp., Temple, 1985—. Recipient Mgmt. Excellence and Achievement award Coll. Bus. Mgmt. U. Ga., 1986; named Entrepreneur of Yr. Arthur Young/Venture Dallas, 1987. Mem. Nat. Am. Wholesale Grocers Assn. (chmn. 1986-88), Nat. Assn. Convenience Stores, Grocery Mfrs. Am., Tex. Food Industry Assn. Baptist. Avocation: tennis. Office: McLane High Plains Inc 4747 McLane Pky Temple TX 76504

MCLAREN, DIGBY JOHNS, geologist, educator; b. Carrickfergus, Northern Ireland, Dec. 11, 1919; m. Phyllis Mary Matkin, Mar. 25, 1942; children: Ian, Patrick, Alison. Student, Queen's Coll., Cambridge U., 1938-40; BA, Cambridge U., 1941, MA (Harkness scholar), 1948; PhD, Mich. U., 1951; DSc (hon.), U. Ottawa, 1980, Carleton U., 1993, U. Waterloo, 1995. Geologist Geol. Survey Can., Ottawa, Ont., 1948-80; dir. gen. Geol. Survey Can., 1973-80; sr. sci. advisor Can. Dept. Energy, Mines and Resources, Ottawa, 1981-84; vis. prof. U. Ottawa, 1981-90; 1st dir. Inst. Sedimentary and Petroleum Geology, Calgary, Alta., Can., 1967-73; pres. Commn. on Stratigraphy, Internat. Union Geol. Scis., 1972-76; apptd. 14th dir. Geol. Survey Can., 1973; chmn. bd. Internat. Geol. Correlation Program, UNESCO, 1976-80. Contbr. memoirs, bulls., papers, geol. maps, sci. articles in field of Devonian geology and paleontology of Western and Arctic Canada, internat. correlation and boundary definition, global extinctions and asteroid impacts, and global change. Served to capt. Royal Arty. Brit. Army, 1940-46. Decorated officer Order of Can.; recipient Gold medal (sci.) Profl. Inst. Pub. Service of Can., 1979, Hollis D. Hedberg Energy award So. Meth. U., 1994. Fellow Royal Soc. Can. (pres. 1987-90), Royal Soc. London, European Union of Geoscis. (hon.), U.S. Nat. Acad. Scis. (fgn. assoc.), Geol. Soc. France (hon.), Geol. Soc. London (hon., Coke medal 1986), Am. Philos. Soc. (fgn. mem.); mem. Geol. Soc. Germany (hon., Leopold von Buch medal 1983), Geol. Soc. Am. (pres. 1982), Paleontol. Soc. (pres. 1969), Geol. Assn. Can. (Logan medal 1987), Can. Soc. Petroleum Geologists (pres. 1971, hon.). Home: 248 Marilyn Ave, Ottawa, ON Canada K1V 7E5

MCLAREN, FRED B., supermarket chain executive; b. 1934. With Hughes Mkts. Inc., L.A., 1959—, formerly dir. ops., pres., 1974—, also bd. dirs. Office: Hughes Markets Inc 2716 N San Fernando Rd Los Angeles CA 90065-1383

MCLAREN, JAMES CLARK, French educator; b. Halifax, N.S., Can., June 19, 1925; came to U.S., 1947, naturalized, 1952; s. Philip Doane and Margaret (MacGregor/Clark) McL.; m. Helen Elizabeth Oestreich, Jan. 25, 1957; children: Susan Atwell, James Philip. B.A., Dalhousie U., 1945, M.A., 1946; diplôme d'études, Sorbonne, Paris, 1947; Ph.D., Columbia U., 1951. Lectr. French Columbia U., N.Y.C., 1947-48; instr. Johns Hopkins U., Balt., 1948-52, asst. prof., 1952-56; assoc. prof., then chmn. Chatham Coll., Pitts., 1956-65, chmn. dept. modern langs., 1957-65; prof. French U. Del., Newark, 1965-85, prof. emeritus, 1985—, chmn. grad. program French, 1966-81; vis. lectr. French lit. U. Pitts., 1957-63. Author: The Theatre of André Gide, 1953; essayist in field, reviewer; writer poetry. Recipient Buhl Humanities award Chatham Coll., 1964; French Govt. scholar, Sorbonne, 1946-47; Grad. residence scholar Columbia U., 1948-49; Todd scholar Columbia U., 1948-49. Mem. MLA, Am. Assn. Tchrs. of French. Home: 802 S Chapel St Newark DE 19713-3718 Office: U Del Newark DE 19716 My goal as a teacher and writer has been to try to view the relativity and inter-relationship of ideas and themes: to attempt a critical synthesis out of any specific analysis of a text or author. However specialized the topic, it loses its relevance if isolated from the broader contexts within which it evolves or contrasts. This, I think, is the real meaning of the Humanities.

MC LAREN, JOHN ALEXANDER, retired physician; b. Vancouver, B.C., Can., Mar. 21, 1919; came to U.S., 1948, naturalized, 1952; s. Henry Moncrieff and Elizabeth Jean (Dingwall) McL.; m. Valerie Jean Adams, June 24, 1944; children: John Alexander, Jeannie McLaren Martz, Duncan R., Laurie McLaren Gates. B.A., U. B.C., 1939; M.D., C.M., McGill U., Montreal, 1943. Diplomate: Am. Bd. Internal Medicine. Intern and resident Montreal Gen. Hosp.; resident Toronto Gen. Hosp., 1946-48; gen. practice internal medicine Wilmette and Evanston, Ill., 1948-68; v.p. patient care services Evanston (Ill.) Hosp., 1968-74, v.p. mktg., 1976-80; v.p. orgn., planning and staffing Glenbrook Hosp., Glenview, Ill., 1974-76; physician Northcare Med. Group, 1980-84; asst. prof. medicine Northwestern U. Med. Sch.; mem. Nat. Bd. Med. Examiners, 1975-78; long-term care council Joint Commn. Accreditation Hosps., 1971-78. Served with M.C. Can. Army, 1943-46. Mem. Chgo. Med. Soc., AMA. Club: Mission Hills Country (Northbrook). Home: 3741 Mission Hills Rd #201 Northbrook IL 60625-7470

MC LAREN, MALCOLM GRANT, IV, ceramic engineering educator; b. Denver, July 22, 1928; s. George W. and Evelyn (Hodgson) McL.; m. Barbara Stephen, Sept. 23, 1950; children: Malcolm Grant, George, Thomas, Michael. B.S., Rutgers U., 1950, M.S., 1951, Ph.D., 1962. Research asst. Rutgers U., New Brunswick, N.J., 1950-54, mem. faculty, 1962—, prof. ceramics, chmn. dept. ceramics, 1969-94, dir. Inst. for Engineered Materials, 1987—; chief ceramist Paper Makers Importing Co., Easton, Pa., 1954-55; v.p., dir. Paper Makers Importing Co., 1957-62; hon. life prof. Tsing Hua U., Beijing, China, 1992. Author articles in field. Served to 1st lt. USAF, 1955-57. Recipient Gardner award Rutgers U., 1970; Man of Yr. award Associação Brasiliana de Cerâmica, 1978; Dr. Harvey Wiley medal FDA, 1984; Ann. award Ceramic Assn. N.J.; Outstanding Engr. award Rutgers U., 1989. Fellow Am. Ceramic Soc. (Disting. life, v.p. 1974, pres. 1979-80, Albert Victor Bleininger award 1979, Founders award Phila. sect. 1983), Brit. Inst. Ceramics; mem. Am. Soc. Engring. Edn., Ceramic Ednl. Coun. (pres.), Internat. Ceramic Fedn. (pres. 1989-90), The Acad. Ceramics (pres., bd. trustees 1993-96), Associação Brasiliana de Cerâmica (hon. life), Cap and Skull Rutgers U., Sigma Xi, Phi Lambda Upsilon, Phi Gamma Delta, Tau Beta Pi, Keramos. Home: 297 Spring Mills Rd Milford NJ 08848-1945 Office: Rutgers U Ceramics Dept New Brunswick NJ 08903

MCLARNAN, DONALD EDWARD, banker, corporation executive; b. Nashua, Iowa, Dec. 19, 1906; s. Samuel and Grace (Prudhon) McL.; m. Virginia Rickard, May 5, 1939; children: Marilyn, Marcia, Roxane. A.B., U. So. Calif., 1930; grad., Southwestern U. Law Sch., 1933; postgrad., Cambridge U. Trust appraiser, property mgr. Security-Pacific Nat. Bank, Los Angeles, 1935-54; regional dir. SBA for, So. Calif., Ariz., Nev., 1954-61; area adminstr. SBA for, Alaska, Western U.S., Hawaii, Guam, Samoa, U.S. Trust Terr., 1969-73; pres. Am. MARC, Inc. (offshore oil drillers and mfr. diesel engines), 1961-63, Terminal Drilling & Prodn. Co., Haney & Williams Drilling Co., Western Offshore, 1961-63; v.p., dir. Edgemar Dairy, Santa Monica Dairy Co., 1954-70; founder, pres., chmn. bd. Mission Nat. Bank, 1963-67; pres. Demco Trading Co., Mut. Trading Co.; dir. Coast Fed. Savs. & Loan; cons. numerous corps.; guest lectr. various univs. Contbr. articles on mgmt. and fin. to profl. jours. Chmn. fed. agys. div. Community Chest, 1956; nat. pres. Teachers Day, 1956; bd. councillors U. So. Calif.; founder, chmn., pres. Soc. Care and Protection Injured Innocent; adv. bd. Los Angeles City Coll.; bd. dirs. Calif. Easter Seal Soc.; nat. chmn. U. So. Calif. Drug Abuse Program. Recipient Los Angeles City and County Civic Leadership award, 1959. Mem. Nat. Assn. People with Disabilities (pres.); Mem. Skull and Dagger, Delta Chi. Clubs: Mason (Los Angeles) (K.T., Shriner), Los Angeles (Los Angeles), Jonathan (Los Angeles). Home: 135 S Norton Ave Los Angeles CA 90004-3916 Office: 1111 Crenshaw Blvd Los Angeles CA 90019-3112

MCLARNEY, CHARLES PATRICK, lawyer; b. Hemple, Mo., Mar. 28, 1942; s. Charles Joseph and Owatonna Mary (Sayles) McL.; m. Martina Borkowski, Aug. 28, 1965; children: Ellen, Megan, Michael. BS, St. Benedict's Coll., 1964; JD, U. Mo., 1968. Bar: Mo. 1968, U.S. Dist. Ct. (we. dist.) Mo. 1968, U.S. Ct. Appeals (8th cir.), U.S. Supreme Ct. 1968. Assoc. Shook, Hardy & Bacon, Kansas City, Mo., 1972—, ptnr., 1972-93; mng. ptnr Shook, Hardy & Bacon P.C., 1985-88, 91—, shareholder, pres., 1993—. Active Friends of Art, Kans. City, 1980—. Fellow Internat. Soc. Barristers (bd. dirs. 1989-94), Am. Coll. Trial Lawyers; mem. Kansas City Met. Bar (Inn of Ct. Master 1980-92) Lawyers Assn. Kansas City (pres. 1987-88), Mo Bar (bd. govs. 1991-94), Kansas City Soc. Fellows, Eight Twenty-Two Club, Kansas City Club, Plaza Bus. Breakfast Club (pres. 1983-84). Democrat. Roman Catholic. Avocations: tennis, golf, skiing. Office: Shook Hardy & Bacon PC Ste 2200 1200 Main St Kansas City MO 64105-2118

MCLARNON, MARY FRANCES, neurologist; b. Montreal, Que., Canada, May 13, 1944; came to U.S., 1969; d. John Francis and Patricia Jessica (Dore) McL.; m. Malcolm Weiner, Dec. 21, 1975; m. Lawrence Zingesser, Oct. 12, 1982; children: Andrea, Eliza. BS, McGill U., 1965, MD, 1969. Intern St. Vincent's Hosp., N.Y.C., 1969-70; fellow seizure unit Boston Children's Hosp., 1970-71; resident in neurology Albert Einstein Coll. Medicine, Bronx, N.Y., 1971-73; resident in radiology N.Y. Hosp.-Cornell Med. Ctr., N.Y.C., 1973-76; pvt. practice.

MCLARTY, THOMAS F., III (MACK MCLARTY), federal official; b. Hope, Ark., June 14, 1946; s. Thomas Franklin and Helen (Hesterly) McL.; m. Donna Kay Cochran, June 14, 1969; children: Mark Cochran, Franklin Hesterly. BA, U. Arkansas, Fayetteville, 1968. Founder, pres. McLarty Leasing System Inc., Little Rock, 1969-79; pres. McLarty Cos., 1979-83; with Arkla Inc., Shreveport, from 1983, pres., CEO Arkla Gas divsn., 1983; pres., COO Arkla Gas divsn. Arkla, Inc., Shreveport, 1984, chmn. bd., pres., CEO, from 1985; chief of staff The White House, Washington, 1993-94, sr. adviser to President Clinton, 1994—; chmn. Arkla Energy Mktg. Co., Shreveport, La., Arkla Chem. Corp., Shreveport, AER-Ark. Gas Transit Co., Shreveport; chmn., chief exec. officer, Miss. River Transmission Corp., St. Louis, MRT Energy Mktg. Co., St. Louis, Ark. La. Fin. Corp., Shreveport. Mem. Ark. Ho. of Reps., 1970-72; chmn. Ark. Dem. Com.; mem. Dem. Nat. Com., 1974-76; treas. David Pryor Gubernatorial Campaign, 1974, Gov. Bill Clinton campaign, 1978; bd. dirs. Hendrix Coll., Conway, Ark.; bd. visitors U. Ark., Little Rock; former chmn. United Negro Coll. Fund Campaign, fund-raising campaign Ark. Symphony. Mem. Greater Little Rock C. of C. (pres. 1983). Office: The White House 1600 Pennsylvania Ave NW Washington DC 20500-0001

MCLAUGHLIN, ANN, educational administrator, former federal official, lecturer, advisor; b. Newark, Nov. 16, 1941; d. Edward Joseph and Marie (Koellhoffer) Lauenstein. B.A., Marymount Coll. Supr. network comml. schedule ABC, N.Y.C., 1963-66; dir. alumnae relations Marymount Coll., Tarrytown, N.Y., 1966-69; account exec. Myers-Infoplan Internat. Inc., N.Y.C., 1969-71; dir. communications Presdl. Election Com., Washington, 1971-72; asst. to chmn. and press sec. Presdl. Inaugural Com., Washington, 1972-73; dir. Office of Pub. Affairs, EPA, Washington, 1973-74; govt. relations and communications exec. Union Carbide Corp., N.Y.C. and Washington, 1974-77; pub. affairs, issues mgmt. counseling McLaughlin & Co., 1977-81; asst. sec. for pub. affairs Dept. Treasury, Washington, 1981-84; under sec. Dept. of Interior, Washington, 1984-87; cons. Ctr. Strategic and Internat. Studies, Washington, 1987; sec. of labor Dept. of Labor, Washington, 1987-89; vis. fellow The Urban Inst., 1989-92; pres., CEO New Am. Schs. Devel. Corp., 1992-93; vis. fellow The Urban Inst., 1989-92; chmn. Pres.'s Commn. Aviation Security and Terrorism, 1989-90; mem. Am. Coun. on Capital Formation, 1976-78; mem. environ. edn. task force HEW, 1976-77; mem. Def. Adv. Com. of Women in the Svcs., 1973-74; bd. dirs. GM, Union Camp Corp., Kellogg Co., Nordstrom Co., Host Marriott Corp., Vulcan Materials Co., AMR Corp., Fannie Mae, Potomac Electric Power Co., Pub. Agenda Found.; vice chmn., trustee Aspen Inst.; pres. Fed. City Coun., 1990—. Mem. bd. overseers Wharton Sch. U. Pa.; bd. dirs. Ctr. Strategic and Internat. Studies, The Conservation Fund; trustee Urban Inst., 1989—. Mem. Cosmos Club, Met. Club, Econ. Club, F St. Club. Republican. Roman Catholic.

MCLAUGHLIN, ANNE ELIZABETH, secondary education educator; b. Springfield, Mass., Sept. 16, 1942; d. Terrence John and Sara Anne (Hartford) McTiernan. BA, Elms Coll., 1966; MEd, U. Lowell, 1976; M in Edn. Administrn., Salem State U., 1988; postgrad., Harvard U., 1995. Cert. reading specialist Mass., N.H.; cert. adminstr. Mass., N.H. Tchr. reading John Duggan Middle Sch., Springfield, Mass., 1967-72, Andover (Mass.) High Sch., 1972-74; with Middlesex Ho. Corrections, Bellrica, Mass., 1974-76; clinician, cons. Northeastern U., Boston, 1976-77; reading specialist Exeter Area Jr. High, N.H., 1977—; evaluator New England Assn. Schs. and Colls., 1987; instr. Elms Coll., Chicopee, Mass., 1991—; chairperson Sch. Adminstr. Unit # 16 staff devel. com., Exeter Area Jr. High. Sch. improvement com.; co-pres. Seacoast Reading Coun.; founder Libr. Card Program for Am. Libr. Week. Fellow Nat. Endowment for Arts, 1979; recipient commendation Internat. Reading Assn., 1992. Mem. NEA (legis. com.), Exeter Edn. Assn. (rep. to Congress), Peace and Justice for Children Caucus, Granite State Reading Coun., Assn. for Supervision and Curriculum Devel., Nat. Coun. Tchrs of English. Avocations: skiing, boating, world traveling. Home: 2 Elbow Ln - B Newburyport MA 01950 Office: Sch Adminstr Unit # 16 Front St Exeter NH 03833

MCLAUGHLIN, CALVIN STURGIS, biochemistry educator; b. St. Joseph, Mo., May 29, 1936; s. Calvin Sturgis and Agnes Jane McLaughlin; m. Chin Helen Moy, Sept. 7, 1960; children—Heather Chin Chu, Christine Leng Oy,

Andrew Calvin Moy. BS, King Coll., 1958; postgrad. Yale U., 1958-59; PhD, MIT, 1964. Postdoctoral fellow Institut de Biologie Physico-Chimique, Paris, 1964-66; prof. biochemistry U. Calif., Irvine, 1966—, dir. Cancer Research Inst., 1981-83; vis. prof. Sch. Botany Oxford U., Eng., 1976, 80; mem. peer rev. panels Am. Cancer Soc., NSF, NIH, VA. Contbr. numerous articles to profl. jours.; mem. editorial bds. Jour. Bacteriology, 1975-80, Exptl. Mycology, 1980-86; reviewer profl. jours. Bd. dirs. Am. Cancer Soc., Orange County, 1980-89; mem. Traffic Affairs Com., Newport Beach, Calif., 1972-78. Named Outstanding Tchr. U. Calif.-Irvine, 1978, Gabriel Lester Meml. Lectr. Reed Coll., 1979; fellow Rockefeller Found., 1958-59, Upjohn Found., 1959-60, Nutrition Found., 1960-61, NIH, 1961-64, Am. Cancer Soc., 1964-66. Mem. Genetics Soc. Am., Am. Soc. Biol. Chemistry, Am. Soc. Microbiology, Am. Soc. Mycology, Am. Soc. for Cell Biology, Yeast Genetics and Molecular Biology Soc. Am. (co-chair 1986-88). Presbyterian. Office: U Calif-Irvine Dept Biol Chemistry Irvine CA 92717

MCLAUGHLIN, DAVID J., management consultant; b. Boston, Apr. 3, 1936; s. John H. and Katherine C. (Mc Mahon) M.; m. P. Bradley C. McLaughlin, Nov. 14, 1986; 1 child, Devon Leigh; children from previous marriage: Lori McLaughlin Najuchi, John Randall McLaughlin. BA, Holy Cross Coll., 1958; MA, Fordham U., 1959. Mgr., human resources mgr. Am. Airlines, N.Y.C., Buffalo, N.Y., 1960-61; asst. dir. personnel Luria Brackers Inc., N.Y.C., 1961-63; assoc., mgr. McKinsey & Co. Inc., N.Y.C., 1963-66; prin. McKinsey & Co. Inc., N.Y.C., L.A., 1969-78; v.p. employee rels. Eastern Airlines Inc., N.Y.C., 1966-69; pres. Pentacle Group Inc., San Francisco, 1978-81; gen. ptnr. Hay Group Inc., Phila., 1981-84; pres. McLaughlin One Co. Inc., N.Y.C., Essex, Conn., 1985—; bd. dirs. Sci. Atlanta Inc., Exide Electronics Group Inc., Smart & Final Inc. Author: The Executive Money Map, 1975. Mem. Assn. Mgmt. Orgn. Design (exec. com., bd. dirs., v.p. 1992-93). Avocations: gardening, tennis, photography. Office: McLaughlin and Company Inc 19 N Main St Essex CT 06426-1019

MCLAUGHLIN, DAVID JORDAN, botanist; b. Providence, Oct. 19, 1940; s. Walter Joseph and Abby Christina (Kilmartin) McL.; m. Esther Tuckerman Gaw, Feb. 1, 1964; children: Abigail Gaw, Elise Manning. AB, Brown U., 1962; postgrad., McGill U., Montreal, 1962-63; PhD, U. Calif, Berkeley, 1968. Postdoctoral fellow U. Copenhagen, Denmark, 1968-69; asst. prof. U. Minn., Mpls., 1969-73, assoc. prof., 1973-80, prof., 1980—; vis. assoc. prof. U. Colo., Boulder, 1975-76; vis. scientist U. Bristol, Eng., 1983-84. Author: (with others) An Atlas of Fungal Ultrastructure, 1974; contbr. articles to profl. jours. NSF grantee. Fellow Linnean Soc. London; mem. AAAS, Am. Inst. Biol. Scis., Mycol. Soc. Am. (editorial bd. 1982-90, editor in chief Mycologia 1990—), Bot. Soc. Am., British Mycol. Soc., Minn. Native Plant Soc. (bd. dirs. 1987, pres. 1988-90), Sigma Xi. Office: U Minn Dept Of Plant Biology Saint Paul MN 55108

MC LAUGHLIN, DAVID THOMAS, academic administrator, business executive; b. Grand Rapids, Mich., Mar. 16, 1932; s. Wilfred P. and Arlene (Sunderlin) McL.; m. Judith Ann Landauer, Mar. 26, 1955; children: William, Wendy, Susan, C. Jay. B.A., Dartmouth Coll., 1954, M.B.A., 1955. With Champion Internat. Co., 1957-70; v.p., gen. mgr. Champion Internat. Co. (Champion packages div.), 1957-70; pres., chief exec. officer Toro Co., Bloomington, Minn., 1970-77; chmn., chief exec. officer Toro Co., Mpls., 1977-81; pres. Dartmouth Coll., Hanover, N.H., 1981-87; chmn. The Aspen Inst., Aspen, Colo., 1987-88, Queenstown, Md., 1987-94; pres., CEO The Aspen Inst., Aspen, Colo., Queenstown, Md., 1994—; chmn., CEO The Aspen Inst., Washington; bd. dirs. Westinghouse Elec. Corp., Pitts., Chase Manhattan Bank, Chase Manhattan Corp., N.Y., Arco, L.A.; chair Std. Fusee Corp., Easton, Md. Served with USAF, 1955-57. Office: The Aspen Inst PO Box 222 Carmichael Rd Queenstown MD 21658-0222

MCLAUGHLIN, DONA HOUGEN, library director; b. Berea, Ky., Aug. 6, 1943; d. Richard Torger and Mary (Groser) Hougen; m. Peter Jay Marshall, Sept. 1, 1964 (div. 1977); children: Christina, Cary Hougen; m. Paul Victor McLaughlin, June 23, 1979. AB in Fine Arts, Coll. William & Mary, 1965. Libr. West Point (Va.) High Sch., 1965; tchr. art, English and French York Acad., Shackelfords, Va., 1966; tchr. English, French Eli Whitney Sch., Westboro, Mass., 1967; continuity dir. WBLG Radio, Lexington, Ky., 1968; owner Cookie People, Westboro, 1969-78; editor of publs. Thom McAn Shoe Co., Worcester, Mass., 1978-79; substitute libr. Starr Libr., Rhinebeck, N.Y., 1980-89, 1989—. Bd. trustees, v.p., pres. Friends of Starr Libr. Mem. Mid-Hudson Libr. Sys. Dirs. Assn. (mem. interlibr. loan adv. com.), Dutchess County Pub. Libr. Dirs. Assn. Home: 39 Lorraine Dr Rhinebeck NY 12572 Office: Starr Libr 66 W Market St Rhinebeck NY 12572

MCLAUGHLIN, EDWARD, chemical engineering educator, dean; b. Ballymena, Antrim, Ireland, Oct. 16, 1928; came to U.S., 1970; s. Patrick Joseph and Helena Mary (Leonard) McL.; m. Aine Friel, Apr. 3, 1956; children: Fiona, Declan, Donagh, Bronagh. PhD, Diploma Imperial Coll., U. London, 1956, DSc, 1974. Registered profl. engr., La. Lectr. Imperial Coll. 1956-61, sr. lectr., 1962-66; reader U. London, 1966-70; prof. chem. engring. La. State U., Baton Rouge, 1970—, chmn. dept., 1979-87, dean Coll. Engring., 1987—; asst. to dir. Salter's Inst., London, 1960-70. Contbr. 90 articles to profl. jours. NSF sr. fgn. scientist, 1967-68. Mem. Am. Inst. Chem. Engrs. (chmn. Baton Rouge chpt. 1979-80), La. Engring. Soc., Sigma Xi. Republican. Roman Catholic. Avocations: farming and forestry, collecting old scientific instruments. Home: 12571 E Millburn Ave Baton Rouge LA 70815-6845 Office: La State Univ Coll Engring 3304 Ceba Baton Rouge LA 70803

MC LAUGHLIN, HARRY ROLL, architect; b. Indpls., Nov. 29, 1922; s. William T. and Ruth E. (Roll) McL.; m. Linda Hamilton, Oct. 23, 1954; 1 child Harry Roll Jr. Grad., Wabash Coll., 1983. Registered architect, Ind., Ohio Ill., Nat. Coun. Archtl. Registration Bds.; lic. real estate broker, Ind. Past pres. James Assocs. Inc., Indpls.; specializing in restoration of historic bldgs. and domestic architecture. Restorations include Old State Bank State Meml, Vincennes, Andrew Wylie House, Bloomington, Old Opera House State Meml, New Harmony, Old Morris-Butler House, Indpls. (Merit award 1972), Market St. Restoration and Maria Creek Baptist Ch., Vincennes, Ind., Benjamin Harrison House, Old James Ball Residence, Lafayette, Ind. (1st Design award 1972), Lockerbie Sq. Master Plan Park Sch., Indpls., Knox County Ct. House, Vincennes, Ind., J.K. Lilly House, Indpls., 1972, Waiting Station and Chapel, Crown Hill Cemetery, Indpls., 1972, Blackford-Condit House Ind. State U., Terre Haute, Ind. several Indian houses Angel Mounds. Archaeol. Site and Interpretative Center, nr. Evansville, Ind.; architect: Glenn A. Black Mus. Archaeology, Ind. U., Bloomington; Restoration Morgan County Ct. House, Indpls. City Market, Hist. Schofield House, Madison, Ind., Ernie Pyle Birthplace, Dana, Ind., Phi Kappa Psi Nat. Hdqrs, Indpls., 1980 (Design award), East Coll. Bldg, DePauw U., Greencastle, Ind., Pres.'s House Restoration, DePauw U., 1992; contbr. articles to profl. jours.; Illustrator: Harmonist Construction. Past chmn. bd., past pres., now chmn. emeritus Historic Landmarks Found.; bd. dirs., archtl. adviser, bd. advisers Historic Madison, Inc.; mem. adv. council Historic Am. Bldgs. survey Nat. Park Service, 1967-73; past mem. Ind. Profl. Rev. Com. for Nat. Register Nominations, 1967-81; past adv. bd. Conner Prairie Mus., Patrick Henry Sullivan Found.; past adviser Indpls. Historic Preservation Commn.; past mem. preservation com. Ind. U.; architect mem. Meridian St. Preservation Commn.; hon. mem. Ind. Bicentennial Commn.; bd. dirs. Park-Tudor Sch., 1972-85; past nat. bd. dirs. Preservation Action; trustee Masonic Heritage Found.; bd. dirs. Masonic Home, 1984-91; bd. dirs. Indpls. Pub. Library Found., 1986—, treas. 1988, v.p., 1989, pres. 1990; bd. dirs. Hist. New Harmony Found., 1987—; trustee Eiteljorg Mus. Western Art; past mem. Hamilton County Tourism Commn., 1989-91. Served with USNR, 1943-45. Recipient numerous award including gov.'s citation State of Ind., 1967, Sagamore of Wabash award, 1967, 80, 82; Mayor's citation for svcs. in preservation archtl. heritage City of Indpls., sec.'s citation U.S. Dept. Interior, design and environ. citation for work in preservation, 1975. Fellow AIA (mem. nat. com. historic bldgs., chmn. historic resources com. 1970); mem. Ind. Soc. Architects (state preservation coordinator 1960—; Biennial award 1972, Design award 1978), Nat. Trust Hist. Preservation (past trustee, bd. advisers), Soc. Archtl. Historians (Wilbur D. Peat award Ctrl. Ind. chpt. outstanding contbns. to understanding and appreciation of archtl. heritage 1993, past bd. dirs.), Ind. Com. for Presevation of Archtl. Records, Indpls. Mus. Art (corres. chmn. bldgs. com., bd. govs. 1986—), Assn. Preservation Tech., Zionsville C. of C. (hon. bd. dirs.), U.S. Capitol (hon. trustee), Ind. Hist. Soc. (trustee, bldg. com.),

Marion County Hist. Soc. (past v.p., bd. dirs.), Zionsville Hist. Soc. (hon. life), Navy League U.S. (life), Ind. State Mus. Soc. (charter), English Speaking Union (bd. dirs Indpls.), Newcomen Soc. of U.S., Hamilton County Hist. Soc. (life), Woodstock Club (bd. dirs. 1982-86, pres. 1985, ex-officio 1986), Literary Club, Amateur Movie Club, Skyline Club (life mem.), Packard Club, Masons (33 deg.). Home and Office: 950 W 116th St Carmel IN 46032-8864

MC LAUGHLIN, HERBERT E., architect; b. Chgo., June 15, 1934; s. Herbert and Corinne (Brewer) McL.; m. Eve Pell, Apr. 1960 (div. June 1970); children—Daniel, Peter, John. B.Arch., Yale U., 1956, M.Arch., 1958. Architect, Skidmore Owings Merrill, 1961-62; ptnr. Ellis Kaplan, San Francisco, 1962-63; ptnr.-in-charge of design Kaplan/McLaughlin/Diaz, San Francisco, 1963—; vis. lectr. various univs.; speaker. Contbr. articles to profl. jours. Bd. dirs. Soc. San Francisco Planning and Urban Renewal, Soc. Archtl. Heritage; mem. ad hoc adv. com. architecture U.S. Dept. Justice. Served to 1st lt. USAF, 1958-61. Recipient numerous awards, including Honor award Napa chpt. AIA for Cronan House, 1966; award of recognition Am. Hosp. Assn., 1968; Honor award for Martin Luther King Sq., San Francisco, AIA, 1972; Honors award No. Calif. chpt. AIA for Tomales Bay Housing, Calif., 1974, Martin Luther King Sq., San Francisco, 1974 (also Nat. Honors award); Record Houses Award, 1976; ACA/AIA Merit award for Contra Costa Detention Facility, 1978; Record Houses award, 1979; Pacific Coast Builders Gold Nugget award (2), 1979, 83; spl. citation S.W. Wash. chpt. AIA for St. Peter Hosp., Olympia, 1980; Outstanding Project award Nat. Concrete Masonry Assn., 1982; cert. of nat. recognition HUD, 1983; Merit award Calif. Hist. Preservation Conf., 1983; Merit award Builder's Choice, 1983, Grand award, 1983; Merit award No. Calif. chpt. Am. Concrete Inst., 1983. Mem. AIA (chmn. nat. task force). Home: 2315 Broadway St San Francisco CA 94115-1233 Office: Kaplan/McLaughlin/Diaz 222 Vallejo St San Francisco CA 94111-1522

MC LAUGHLIN, JEROME MICHAEL, lawyer, shipping company executive; b. St. Louis, Jan. 11, 1929; s. John Thomas and Mary Adelaide (White) McL.; m. Delphine M. McClellan, June 15, 1957; children—Margaret D., Mary Martha, Elizabeth O., Jerome Michael, John T. A.B., St. Louis U., 1950, J.D., 1954. Bar: Mo. 1954, U.S. Supreme Ct. 1972. V.p. internat. Indemnity, St. Louis, 1955-56; asst. circuit atty. City of St. Louis, 1957-58; partner firm Willson, Cunningham & McClellan, St. Louis, 1958-78; v.p., gen. counsel Alexander & Baldwin, Inc., Honolulu, 1978-79; sr. v.p. Philippines, Micronesia & Orient Navigation Co., San Francisco, 1979-87, exec. v.p., 1987—; instr. philosophy St. Louis U., 1955-60. Served to capt. USMC, 1951-53, Korea. Mem. Mo. Bar Assn., Maritime Law Assn. U.S., Soc. Maritime Arbitrators San Francisco (past pres.). Republican. Roman Catholic. Home: 1225 Hillview Dr Menlo Park CA 94025-5510 Office: 353 Sacramento St San Francisco CA 94111-3620

MC LAUGHLIN, JOHN FRANCIS, civil engineer, educator; b. N.Y.C., Sept. 21, 1927; s. William Francis and Anna (Goodwin) McL.; m. Eleanor Thomas Tretheway, Nov. 22, 1950; children: Susan, Donald, Cynthia, Kevin. B.C.E., Syracuse U., 1950; M.S. in Civil Engring., Purdue U., 1953, Ph.D., 1957. Mem. faculty Purdue U., 1950—, prof. civil engring., 1963—, head Sch. Civil Engring., 1968-78, asst. dean engring. Sch. Civil Engring. 1977-80, assoc. dean engring., 1980-94, interim dean engring., 1994—; cons. in field. Served with USAAF, 1945-47. Fellow ASCE, Hwy. Research Bd.; mem. ASTM (bd. dirs. 1984-86), Am. Concrete Inst. (hon. mem., bd. dirs., v.p. 1977-79, pres. 1979), Am. Nat. Studies Inst. (bd. dirs. 1992—), Sigma Xi, Tau Beta Pi, Chi Epsilon, Theta Tau. Home: 112 Sumac Dr West Lafayette IN 47906-2157 Office: Purdue U Civil Engring Dept DOE/ENAD Lafayette IN 47907

MCLAUGHLIN, JOHN JOSEPH, broadcast executive, television producer, political commentator, journalist; b. Providence, Mar. 29, 1927; s. Augustus Hugh and Eva Philomena (Turcotte) McL.; m. Ann Lauenstein, Aug. 23, 1975 (div. 1992). AB, Boston Coll., 1951, MA in Philosophy, 1952, BDiv, 1959, MA in English, 1961; PhD, Columbia U., 1967. Ordained priest Roman Catholic ch., 1960. Mem. Jesuit Order, N.E., N.Y. and Washington; resigned order and priesthood, 1975; tchr., dir. communications Fairfield (Conn.) Univ. and Preparatory Sch., 1960-64; assoc. editor America Mag., N.Y.C., 1967-70; spl. asst. to Pres. Richard Nixon and Gerald Ford, Washington, 1971-74; pres. McLaughlin and Co. Pub. Policy Cons., Washington, 1975-79; radio talk-show host Sta. WRC-AM, Washington, 1979-82; pres., chmn. bd. dirs. Oliver Prodns., Inc., Washington, 1983—; lectr. numerous univs., corps. and orgns. nationwide, 1963—; host TV series, Sta. WJAR-TV, Providence, 1962-63, Sta. WNHC-TV, New Haven, 1963, Sta. WTIC-TV, Hartford, 1963, Sta. WOR-TV, N.Y.C., 1964; host, exec. producer Biafra Today report ABC-TV Network, 1969; radio commentator Sta. WSTC, Stamford, Conn., 1964, CBS Network Radio, N.Y.C., 1964, Nat. Pub. Radio All Things Considered, Washington, 1981-85; dir. film insts. Yale U., Holy Cross Coll., Manhattanville Coll.; juror Am. Film Festival, 1969; congressional testimony pub. broadcasting and TV license renewal, Washington, 1967, 69. Author: Love Before Marriage, 1970; editor National Review, Washington, 1981-89, columnist From Washington Straight, 1982-89; TV host and exec. producer The McLaughlin Group NBC and PBS TV stas., 1982—, John McLaughlin's One on One, 1984—, McLaughlin CNBC cable system, 1989-94; host spl. episode (TV show) Cheers, 1990. Rep. candidate U.S. Senate, R.I., 1970. Recipient Excellence in Journalism award Cath. Press Assn., 1969, News Media award VFW, 1984; nominee Nat. Acad. Cable Programming ACE award, 1989, 90, 91, 94; The McLaughlin Group named Best Polit. Talk Show, Washingtonian mag., 1987-93. Mem. NATAS (Emmy award 1984), Am. Fedn. TV and Radio Artists, Screen Actors Guild. Office: Oliver Prodns Inc 1211 Connecticut Ave NW Ste 810 Washington DC 20036-2701

MCLAUGHLIN, JOHN MICHAEL, JR., engineer, engineering company executive; b. Chgo., Apr. 14, 1936; s. John Michael Sr. and Helen M. (Walsh) McL.; m. Jeannine Marie Mannos, Jan. 25, 1958; children: Anne, John, Kathryn, Colleen, Michael, Erin. BS, Ill. Inst. Tech., 1958, MS, 1970. Structural engr. Austin Co., Chgo., 1962-64; ptnr. Sargent & Lundy, Chgo., 1964—. Contbr. articles to profl. jours. Pres. Home Sch. Assn., LaGrange, Ill., 1978; chmn. Bldg. Bd. Appeals, LaGrange, 1983-86. Served to 1st lt. USAF, 1958-62. Fellow Am. Concrete Inst.; mem. ASCE, Am. Inst. Steel Constrn., Earthquake Engring. Research Inst., Bldg. Officials and Code Adminstrs. Internat., Inc., Post-Tensioning Inst., Structural Stability Research Council. Structural Engrs. Assn. Ill., Seismological Soc. Am. Office: Sargent & Lundy 55 E Monroe St Chicago IL 60603-5702

MCLAUGHLIN, JOHN SHERMAN, lawyer; b. Pitts., Apr. 1, 1932; s. John H. and Dorothy I. (Schrecongost) McL.; m. Suzanne Shaver, June 5, 1971; children—Dorothy, Sarah, Martha. A.B., Harvard U., 1954, LL.B., 1957. Bar: Pa. 1958, U.S. Supreme Ct. 1967. Assoc. Reed, Smith, Shaw & McClay, Pitts., 1957-71; ptnr. Reed, Smith, Shaw & McClay, 1971—. Trustee Harmarville Rehab. Ctr., Inc., 1980-87, Western Pa. Sch. for the Deaf, 1985—; pres. Pa. NG Assn., 1976-78; justice of peace Borough of Edgewood, 1963-73; dir. Pitts. Symphony soc., 1987-94, Winchester Thurston Sch., 1985—; life trustee Carnegie Libr. of Pitts. and Carnegie Inst., 1994—. Lt. col. Air NG, 1957-79. Mem. Am. Law Inst., Am. Coll. Trust and Estate Counsel, Soc. Hosp. Attys., Allegheny County Bar Assn., Duquesne Club, Rolling Rock Club (Ligonier, Pa.). Office: Reed Smith Shaw & McClay 435 6th Ave Pittsburgh PA 15219-1809

MCLAUGHLIN, JOSEPH, lawyer; b. Newark, Aug. 1, 1941; s. Joseph Nicholas and Genevieve Veronica (Landiere) McL.; m. Elisabeth Lippold, July 31, 1965; children: Elisabeth, Jessica, Emilie. AB, Columbia U., 1962, LLB, 1965. With Sullivan & Cromwell, N.Y.C., 1968-76; v.p., gen. counsel Goldman, Sachs & Co., 1976-88, cons., 1988-90; ptnr. Brown & Wood, N.Y.C., 1993—; adj. prof. law NYU Sch. Law, 1988—; speaker, presenter in field. Contbr. articles to profl. jours. Trustee Greenwich (Conn.) Acad., 1988—; treas. Presbyn. Ch. Old Greenwich, 1988-91; bd. dirs. United Way, Greenwich, 1993—; mem. Rep. Town com., Greenwich, 1993—. Jervey fellow Parker Sch. Fgn. Comparative Law, Columbia Law Sch., U. Munich, 1966-68. Mem. ABA (sect. bus. law, fed. regulation securities com., subcom. broker-dealermarkets 1985—, subcom. civil litigation and SEC enforcement matters 1989—, task force rule 10b-6 1992—, co-chair task force sellers' due diligence and similar defenses under fed. securities laws 1989-92), Am. Law Inst., Assn. of Bar of City of N.Y. (internat. law com. 1979-84, chair 1981-

84, civil rights com. 1984-87, internat. arms control and security affairs com. 1988-90), N.Y. Stock Exch. (legal adv. com. to bd. govs. 1985-88, subcom. corp. governance, subcom. internat. issues 1988—), Securities Industry Assn. (fed. regulations com. 1978-88, chair 1982-84), Nat. Assn. Securities Dealers, Inc. (corp. financing com. 1983-86), Am. Arbitration Assn. (dir. 1986-90). Republican. Congregationalist. Office: Brown & Wood 1 World Trade Ctr New York NY 10048-0001

MC LAUGHLIN, JOSEPH MAILEY, lawyer; b. Los Angeles, July 10, 1928; s. James Aloysius and Cecilia Ann (Mailey) McL.; m. Beverly Jane Walker, July 24, 1949; children: Stephen Joseph, Lawrence James, Suzanne Carol, Eileen Louise. J.D., Loyola U., Los Angeles, 1955. Bar: Calif. 1955, U.S. Supreme Ct. 1959. Mem. firm McLaughlin and Irvin, L.A., 1955—, San Francisco, 1969—; lectr. labor relations Loyola U., Los Angeles, 1958-60, mem. bd. visitors law sch., 1987—; pres. Food Employers Council, Inc., 1984-89. Contbg. author: Labor Law for General Practitioners, 1960. Served to 1st lt. USAF, 1951-53. Mem. San Francisco, Long Beach, Los Angeles County, Fed., Am., Internat., Inter-Am. bar assns., State Bar Calif., Am. Judicature Soc., Assn. Bus. Trial Lawyers, Am. Soc. Internat. Law. Clubs: California, Los Angeles Stock Exchange (pres. 1972). Office: 333 S Grand Ave Fl 33 Los Angeles CA 90071-1504

MCLAUGHLIN, JOSEPH MICHAEL, federal judge, law educator; b. Brooklyn, N.Y., Mar. 20, 1933; s. Joseph Michael and Mary Catherine (Flanagan) McL.; m. Frances Elizabeth Lynch, Oct. 10, 1959; children: Joseph, Mary Jo, Matthew, Andrew. A.B., Fordham Coll., 1954, LL.B., 1959; LL.M., NYU, 1964; LL.D., Mercy Coll., White Plains, N.Y., 1981. Bar: N.Y. 1959. Assoc. Cahill, Gordon, N.Y.C., 1959-61; prof. law Fordham U., N.Y.C., 1961-71, dean Sch. of Law, 1971-81, adj. prof., 1981—; judge U.S. Dist. Ct. Eastern Dist. N.Y., Bklyn., 1981-90, U.S. Ct. Appeals (2nd Cir.), N.Y.C., 1990—; adj. prof. St. John's Law Sch., N.Y.C., 1982—; chmn. N.Y. Law Revision Commn., Albany, 1975-82. Author: (with Peterfreund) New York Practice, 1964, Evidence, 1979; also articles. Served to capt. U.S. Army, 1955-57, Korea. Mem. ABA, Assn. of Bar of City of N.Y., N.Y. State Bar Assn. Roman Catholic. Club: Lotos. Office: US Courthouse US Ct Appeals 40 Foley Square New York NY 10007*

MCLAUGHLIN, JOSEPH THOMAS, lawyer; b. Boston, Mar. 30, 1944; s. James Francis and Madeline Louise (Hickman) McL.; m. Christine E. Mullen, Sept. 2, 1967; children: Amy Melissa, Caitlin Christine, Ian Michael. BA magna cum laude, Boston Coll., 1965, JD, Cornell U., 1968. Bar: Mass. 1969, N.Y. State 1968, U.S. Supreme Ct. 1974. Research asst. Brit. Council of Archaeology, Winchester, Eng., 1964; site supr. Brit. Council of Archaeology, 1966; legis. asst. Rep. Thomas P. O'Neill, Washington, 1967; research asst. Cornell U., 1967-68; law clk. to chief justice Mass. Superior Ct., 1968-69; assoc. Shearman & Sterling, N.Y.C., 1969-76, ptnr., 1976—; adj. prof. Fordham Law Sch., 1981—. Author: Federal Class Action Digests, 1974, 1976; contbr. articles to profl. jours. Exec. dir. Brooklyn Heights Draft Counseling Service, 1970-74, Presbyn. Task Force for Justice Counseling Service, 1973-75; v.p., bd. dirs Brooklyn Heights Assn., 1973-77; bd. dirs. Willoughby Settlement House, Inc., Ingersoll-Willoughby Community Ctr., Inc., 1970-75, United Neighborhood Houses, 1976-78, Good Shepherd Residences, Resources for Children with Spl. Needs Inc. Mem. ABA, Assn. of Bar of City of N.Y. (mem. com. on profl. discord 1986—), N.Y. State Bar Assn. (chmn. com. on marijuana and drug abuse 1972-75), Am. Law Inst., Am. Arbitration Assn., N.Y. Lawyers for Pub. Interest (chmn. bd. dirs.) ABAC (com. on promoting settlements), World Arbitration Assn., Heights Casino Club. Home: 174 State St Brooklyn NY 11201-5610 Office: Shearman & Sterling 153 E 53rd St New York NY 10022

MCLAUGHLIN, KEVIN MICHAEL, sheriff; b. Burlington, Vt., July 4, 1952. Student, Champlain Coll., Burlington, 1972, 83. Dep. sheriff Chittenden County Sheriffs Office, Burlington, 1973-77, chief dep., 1977-86, sheriff, 1987—; advisor Champlain Coll. Law Enforcement Adv. Bd., Burlington, 1975—. Mem. Chittenden County Dem. Com., Burlington. Mem. Nat. FBI Assocs., Nat. Sheriffs Assn. (staff drug prevention and edn. com. 1987—), Vt. Police Assn., Vt. Sheriffs Assn., Law Enforcement Coordinating Com. State of Vt. Democrat. Roman Catholic. Office: Chittenden County Sheriff PO Box 1426 Burlington VT 05402-1426

MC LAUGHLIN, LEIGHTON BATES, II, journalism educator, former newspaperman; b. Evanston, Ill., Apr. 10, 1930; s. Leighton Bates and Gwendolyn I. (Markle) McL.; m. Beverly Jean Jeske, May 5, 1962; children: Leighton Bates III, Jeffrey, Steven, Patrick. Student English lit., Kenyon Coll., Gambier, Ohio, 1948-50, Northwestern U., 1951; BA in English lit., UCLA, 1983; MA in communications, Calif. State U., Fullerton, 1990. Copyboy, reporter, rewriteman City News Bur., Chgo., 1957-58; reporter, rewriteman Chgo. Sun-Times, 1958-62; rewriteman, asst. city editor Ariz. Jour., Phoenix, 1962; reporter Miami (Fla.) Herald, 1962-64; successively rewriteman, night city editor, 1st asst. city editor, telegraph editor Chgo. Sun-Times, 1964-74; dir. Chgo. Daily News/Sun-Times News Service, 1974-79; editorial coord. electronics newspaper div. Field Enterprises, 1975-79; adminstr. reference libr. and communications ctr. Field Newspapers, 1976-79; editor News Am. Syndicate, Irvine, Calif., 1979-85; mng. editor San Gabriel Valley Daily Tribune, 1986; assoc. prof. journalism Riverside (Calif.) Community Coll., 1987—, chmn. performing arts and media dept., 1993—; lectr. in journalism Calif. State U.-Fullerton, 1984—; fill-in editor The Press-Enterprise, Riverside, Calif., 1988—; lectr., condr. seminars in field. Author articles in field. Served to 1st lt. USMC, 1951-54. Recipient Stick-o-Type award for best feature story Chgo. Newspaper Guild, 1961, Best News story award Ill. AP and UPI, 1967. Mem. Soc. Profl. Journalists, Verban Soc., Psi Upsilon. Office: Riverside Community Coll 4800 Magnolia Ave Riverside CA 92506-1242 *Reporting the news is like any other intellectual activity in that it involves research, verification, organization, and clarity of presentation. But news reporting is unique in that all this is done on a dead run, in time for the day's editions.*

MCLAUGHLIN, MARGUERITE P., state senator, logging company executive; b. Matchwood, Mich., Oct. 15, 1928; d. Harvey Martin and Luella Margaret (Livingston) Miller; m. George Bruce McLaughlin, 1947; children: Pamela, Bruce Jr., Cynthia. Owner, operator contract logging firm, Orofino, Idaho; mem. Idaho Ho. of Reps., 1978-80; mem. Idaho Senate, 6th term., asst. Dem. leader, 1990, 91, 92, 93; chair Democrat Caucus, 1995—. mem. Senate Fin. Com., 1987—, Gov.'s Adv. Coun. Workers Compensation, 1990—, State of Idaho Endowment Fund Investment Bd., 1991—, legis. coun., 1989-94, State of Idaho Job Tng. Coun., 1989—. Trustee Joint Sch. Dist. 171, 1976-80; pres. Orofino Celebration, Inc. Democrat. Roman Catholic. Office: Idaho State Senate State Capital Boise ID 83702

MCLAUGHLIN, MARY RITTLING, magazine editor; b. Buffalo; d. Joseph and Irene (Meyer) Rittling; m. Charles Edward McLaughlin, June 21, 1962 (div. May 1981) children—Daniel (dec.), Maud Rosie. BA, Manhattanville Coll., 1956. Reporter Buffalo Evening News, 1956-58; copywriter Harper's Bazaar, N.Y.C., 1959-61; editor McCall's Mag., N.Y.C., 1973-79; mng. editor Working Mother Mag., N.Y.C., 1979-85; exec. editor Working Mother Mag., 1985—. Mem. Am. Soc. Mag. Editors, Women's Media Group. Office: Working Mother Mag 230 Park Ave New York NY 10169-0005

MCLAUGHLIN, MAUREEN A., federal agency administrator. BA in Econs., Boston Coll., 1977; MA in Pub. Policy, U. Pa., 1979. Asst. assoc. and prin. analyst U.S. Congressional Budget Office, 1979-88; dir. post secondary edn. divsn., Planning and Evaluation Svc. U.S. Dept. Edn., 1988—, acting asst. sec. for postsecondary edn., 1993, acting dep. asst. sec. for higher edn. programs, student fin. assistance programs, 1993-94, sr. policy advisor to the asst. sec. for post secondary edn., 1994—. Chair adv. com. mem. Fiscal Affairs 1990-92; mem. Bd. dirs. Arlington Symphony, 1990-93, sec. 1992-93, v. chair Arlington Adv. Com. on Arts and Humanities, 1987-88, mem. Commn. on Arlington's Future, 1986, chair task force on housing and neighborhoods. Office: Post Secondary Edn Office US Dept Edn 7th & D St SW Washington DC 20202

MCLAUGHLIN, MICHAEL JOHN, financial executive; b. Bklyn., Apr. 13, 1951; s. Michael John and Dorothy May (Reposky) McL.; m. Patricia Ann Concannon, June 24, 1978; children: Michael, Matthew, Brian. BS, Manhattan Coll., 1972; MBA, St. John's U., Queens, N.Y., 1978; JD, Pace

U., 1984. Bar: N.Y. 1985; CPA, N.Y. Auditor Arthur Young & Co., N.Y.C., 1972-75; asst. controller Montrex Corp., N.Y.C., 1975-78; mgr. corp. acctg. Gen. Housewares Corp., Stamford, Conn., 1977-79, asst. controller, 1979-81, controller, 1981-86; v.p.-controller Preway Inc., Stamford and Wisconsin Rapids, Wis., 1986-87, v.p.-controller, sec., treas., 1987-88, v.p. fin., treas., sec., 1988-89; v.p. fin. and adminstrn. Hayden Roofing Co., Inc., West Nyack, N.Y., 1989-91; v.p. fin., chief fin. officer Celadon Group, Inc., 1991-93; v.p. fin. and adminstrn. A.T. Clayton & Co. Inc., Greenwich, Conn., 1993—. Mem. ABA, N.Y. State Bar Assn., Am. Inst. CPA's, N.Y. State Soc. CPA's. Republican. Roman Catholic. Office: A T Clayton & Co Inc 600 Steamboat Rd Greenwich CT 06830-7167

MCLAUGHLIN, MICHAEL JOHN, insurance company executive; b. Cambridge, Mass., Feb. 14, 1944; s. Michael John and Evelyn Katherine (Quinn) McL. A.B., Boston Coll., 1965; J.D., N.Y. U., 1968. Bar: N.Y., Mass. With N.Y. Life Ins. Co., 1968—, sr. v.p. info. systems and services dept., 1982-88, sr. v.p., 1988-91, sr. v.p., dep. gen. counsel, 1991—. Mem. ABA, N.Y. State Bar Assn. Office: NY Life Ins Co 51 Madison Ave New York NY 10010-1603

MCLAUGHLIN, PATRICK MICHAEL, lawyer; b. Monahans, Tex., July 23, 1946; s. Patrick John and Ann (Donnelly) M.; m. Christine Manos, Aug. 21, 1970; children—Brian Patrick, Christopher Michael, Conor Andrew. B.Gen. Studies, Ohio U., 1972; J.D., Case Western Res. U., 1976. Bar: Ohio 1976, U.S. Dist. Ct. (no. dist.) Ohio 1978, U.S. Ct. Appeals (6th cir.) 1979, U.S. Supreme Ct. 1980; U.S. Dist. Ct. (so. dist.) Ohio 1989, U.S. Ct. Appeals (5th cir.). Dir. vets. edn. project. Am. Assn. Community and Jr. Colls., Washington, 1972-73; law clk. Common Pleas Ct., Cleve., 1976-77; law clk. to judge 8th Jud. Dist. Ct. of Appeals, Cleve., 1977-78; asst. U.S. atty. No. Dist. Ohio, Cleve., 1978-82; chief civil div. No. Dist. Ohio, 1982-84; U.S. atty. No. Dist. Ohio, Cleve., 1984-88; ptnr. Janik & McLaughlin, Cleve., 1988-89, Mansour, Gavin, Gerlack & Manos Co., L.P.A., Cleve., 1989—; cons. Nat. League of Cities, U.S. Conf. Mayors, 1971-72; co-creator Opportunity Fair for Veterans Concept, 1971. Editor-in-chief Case Western Res. Jour. Internat. Law, 1975-76. Chmn. North Ohio Drug Abuse Task Force, 1986-88; chmn. Law Enforcement Coordinating Commn., North Ohio, 1985-88; chmn. civil issues subcom. Atty. Gen.'s Adv. Com., 1986-88; exec. v.p. Greater Cleve. Vets. Meml., Inc., 1993, pres., 1994-96. Decorated Silver Star, Bronze Star, Purple Heart, Army Commendation medal, Vietnamese Cross of Gallantry with Silver and Bronze Stars. Mem. ABA, FBA, Ohio Bar Assn., Cleve. Bar Assn., Nat. Assn. Former U.S. Attys., Soc. 1st Divsn., Order of Ahepa, Vietnam Vets. Am., Nat. Vietnam Vets. Network (Disting. Vietnam Vet. award 1985), Nat. Assn. Concerned Vets. (nat. v.p. external affairs 1971-72, exec. dir. 1972-73), Cuyahoga County Vets. (award 1985), Nat. Soc. SAR (law enforcement commendation medal 1989). Republican. Roman Catholic. Office: Mansour Gavin Gerlack & Manos 2150 Illuminating Bldg 55 Public Sq Cleveland OH 44113-1913

MCLAUGHLIN, PHILIP VANDOREN, JR., mechanical engineering educator, researcher, consultant; b. Elizabeth, N.J., Nov. 10, 1939; s. Philip VanDoren and Ruth Evans (Landis) McL.; m. Phoebe Ann Feeney, Aug. 19, 1961; children: Philip VanDoren III, Patrick Evans, Christi Duff. BSCE, U. Pa., 1961, MS in Engring. Mechanics, 1964, PhD in Engring. Mechanics, 1969. Assoc. engr. Boeing-Vertol, Morton, Pa., 1962-63, engr. II, 1963; rsch. engr. Scott Paper Co., Phila., 1963-65, rsch. project engr., 1965-69, sr. rsch. project engr. 1969; asst. prof. theoretical and applied mechanics U. Ill., Urbana, 1969-73, assoc. mem. engring. 1971-72; project mgr. Materials Scis. Corp., Blue Bell, Pa., 1973-76; assoc. prof. mech. engring. Villanova (Pa.) U., 1976-81, prof., 1981—; judge Cons. Engrs.'s Coun. Ill. 1st Ann. Engring. Excellence Awards Competition, 1972; cons. Naval Air Engring. Ctr., Lakehurst, N.J., 1977-79, U.S. Steel Corp., Trenton, N.J., 1980-82, RCA Corp., Moorestown, N.J., 1986, Coal Tech Corp., Merion Station, Pa., 1986, Air Products and Chems., Inc., Allentown, Pa., 1986; vis. prof. dept. engring. U. Cambridge, Eng., 1990-91. Reviewer Prentice Hall, 1980—, Jour. Engring. Mechanics, 1973-83, AIAA Jour., 1970-87, Materials Evaluation, 1988, Jour. Composite Materials, 1988—, Composites Sci. and Tech., 1990—, others; contbr. articles to Jour. Applied Mechanics, Internat. Jour. Solids and Structures, Jour. Engring. Materials and Tech., NDT Internat., others. Rsch. grantee NSF, 1970-72, Naval Air Engring. Ctr., 1978-84, Lawrence Livermore Nat. Lab., 1979-81, Naval Air Warfare Ctr., 1985-86, RCA Corp., 1986-87; sr. rsch. assoc. Nat. Rsch. Coun., Washington, 1983-84; USN-Am. Soc. Engring. Edn. sr. faculty fellow, 1995. Sr. faculty fellow USN-Am. Soc. Engring. Edn.; mem. ASCE (chmn. engring. mechanics div. com. on inelastic behavior 1977-79, assoc. editor Jour. Engring. Mechanics Div. 1977-79, mem. aerospace div. com. on structures and materials 1986—), ASME (chmn. aplied mechanics div. Phila. sect. 1981-83, mem. materials div. com. on composites 1992—), Am. Acad. Mechanics, Am. Soc. for Engring. Edn., Am. Soc. Composites, Sigma Xi. Achievements include research and consulting on composite materials and structures, structural analysis and design and inelastic behavior. Office: Villanova U Dept Mech Engring 800 Lancaster Ave Villanova PA 19085

MCLAUGHLIN, RICHARD WARREN, retired insurance company executive; b. Boston, Nov. 25, 1930; m. Marilyn Slye, 1956; children: Kathleen, Richard Warren Jr., Thomas, Judy. B.S., Boston Coll., 1952; grad. Advanced Mgmt. Program, Harvard U., 1979. Trainee Travelers Ins. Co., Hartford, Conn., 1956, asst. sec., 1966-69, sec., 1969-70, 2d. v.p., 1970-73, v.p., 1973-81, sr. v.p., 1981-85; exec. v.p. Travelers Corp., Hartford, Conn., 1985-91; pres. Travelers Ins. Co., Hartford, Conn., 1991—; chmn. Travelers Indemnity Co., Hartford, 1991—. Corporator St. Francis Hosp. Capt. USAF, 1952-56, Korea. Mem. Eastward Ho Club (Chatham, Mass.), Hawks Nest Club (Vero Beach, Fla.). Home: PO Box 947 Eastham MA 02642-0947

MCLAUGHLIN, T. MARK, lawyer; b. Salem, Mass., Apr. 20, 1953; s. Terrence E. and Mary E. (Donlon) McL.; m. Sandra L. Roman, Oct. 16, 1982; children: Daniel, Kathleen, Eileen. BA in Econs., U. Notre Dame, 1975, JD, 1978. Bar: Ill. 1978, U.S. Dist. Ct. (no. dist.) Ill. 1978, U.S. Ct. Appeals (7th & 11th cirs.) 1982, U.S. Dist. Ct. (ctrl. dist.) Ill. 1992, U.S. Dist. Ct. (ea. dist.) Wis. 1992. Assoc. Mayer, Brown & Platt, Chgo., 1978-84, ptnr., 1985—; adj. faculty law Loyola U., Chgo., 1983, 86-90. Bd. dirs. no. Ill. affiliate Am. Diabetes Assn., Chgo., 1985-94. Mem. ABA (franchising forum com. antitrust law sect.), Phi Beta Kappa. Office: Mayer Brown & Platt 190 S La Salle St Chicago IL 60603-3410

MCLAUGHLIN, TED JOHN, speech educator; b. Elkhart, Ind., Dec. 23, 1921; s. Frederick L. and Agnes (McBride) McL.; m. Helen F. Myers, Aug. 24, 1946. B.A., Manchester Coll., 1947; M.A., U. Wis., 1948, Ph.D., 1952. Instr. speech U. Wis., Milw., 1949-53; asst. prof. U. Wis., 1953-56, asso. prof., 1957-65, prof., 1965-67, prof. communication, 1967-87, prof. emeritus, 1987—, sec. faculty, 1956-59, asso. dean humanities and communication, 1962-65, 67-69, asso. dean Grad. Sch., 1971-76. Author: (with others) Communication, 1964, Cases and Projects in Communication, 1965. Bd. dirs. U. Faculty Assn. Served with AUS, 1943-47. Mem. AAAS, Friends of Art, Milw. Art Center, Central States Speech Assn., AAUP, Internat. Communication Assn., Speech Communication Assn., Wis. Acad. Scis., Arts and Letters (past v.p., sec.). Home: 2809 Plaza Amarilla Santa Fe NM 87505-6507

MCLAUGHLIN, WILLIAM IRVING, space technical manager; b. Oak Park, Ill., Mar. 6, 1935; s. William Lahey and Eileen (Irving) McL.; student Calif. Inst. Tech. 1953-57; B.S., U. Calif.-Berkeley, 1963, M.A., 1966, Ph.D., 1968; m. Karen Bjorneby, Aug. 20, 1960; children—William, Margot, Walter, Eileen. Mem. tech. staff Bellcomm, Inc., 1968-71; mem. tech. staff Jet Propulsion Lab., Pasadena, Calif., 1971—; supr. terrestrial planets mission design group, 1981-83, mission design mgr. for Infrared Astron. Satellite, 1982-83, mgr. flight engring. office for Voyager/Uranus project, 1983-86; mgr. mission profile and sequencing sect., 1986—. Served with USMC, 1957-60. Recipient Apollo Achievement award, 1969, Exceptional Service medal NASA, 1984, Outstanding Leadership medal NASA, 1986. Fellow Brit. Interplanetary Soc.; mem. Internat. Acad. Astros., Phi Beta Kappa, Sigma Xi. Monthly columnist Spaceflight mag., 1982—. Home: 4626 Janvier Way La Crescenta CA 91214-3126 Office: Jet Propulsion Lab 4800 Oak Grove Dr Pasadena CA 91109

MCLAURIN, RONALD DE, political analyst, consultant, author, journalist; b. Oakland, Calif., Oct. 8, 1944; s. Lauchlin De and Marie Annette

(Friedman) McL.; m. Joan Adcock, June 11, 1966; children: Leila, Cara. B.A., U. So. Calif., 1965; student, U. Tunis, Tunisia, 1964-65; A.M., Tufts U., 1966, M.A.L.D, 1967, Ph.D., 1973. Instr. Merrimack Coll., North Andover, Mass., 1966-67; mgmt. asst. Office Sec. Def., Washington, 65-68; asst. for Africa Office Asst. Sec. Def. for Internat. Security Affairs, 1968-69; rsch. scientist Am. Inst. Rsch., Washington, 1969-75; sr. assoc. Abbott Assocs., Inc., Springfield, Va., 1975-94; sec.-treas. Abbott Assocs., Inc., 1985-86, pres., 1986-94; exec. dir. Pacific Century Inst., 1989-91; columnist Diyar newspaper, 1991; internat. rsch. assoc. Inha U., Korea, 1985—; fellow Ctr. Internat. Devel. U. Md., 1983-86, ptnr. Aurora Ltd., 1986-87; dir. Lau-Mar Ltd., Honolulu, 1981-86, also chmn.; cons. Allen Wayne, Ltd., 1985-86, Am. Insts. Rsch., 1975-76, Analytical Assessments Corp. 1977-79, BDM Corp., 1985-90, Booz Allen & Hamilton, 1989, Bus. Coun. Internat. Understanding, 1984-87, 92—, CBOL Corp., 1988—, C&O Resources, 1993—, Ctr. Advanced Internat. Studies, U. Miami, 1973, Ctr. Advanced Rsch. Inc., 1977-82, Ctr. Strategic and Internat. Studies, Georgetown U., 1981, 84, Grolier, 1990—, Gulf Cons. Group, 1982-83, Armitage Assocs., 1994—, Human Resources Rsch. Orgn., 1989, Internat. Cultural Found., 1981, Office Pres. Lebanon, 1984-85, 87, Ministry Def. Lebanon, 1984-85, Washington Embassy Lebanon, 1983-88, Office Crown Prince Jordan, 1982-85, Maison du Futur, 1989-91, Mid. East Assessments Group, 1982-89, Manly, Inc., 1989, Nat. Def. U., 1990-91, Profs. World Peace Acad., 1981, RBI, Inc., 1991, Royal Sci. Soc. (Jordan), 1982-83, Synergy Cons. Ltd., 1990—, TRW, 1987, Trans Devel. Corp., 1986-87, Univ. Ky. Rsch. Found., 1992-93, Sci. Applications Internat. Corp., 1994—; Joint Econ. Com. U.S. Congress, 1977-78, Libr. Congress, 1977-78, Office of Asst. Sec. U.S. Dept. Def., 1973, A.R. Wagner and Co., 1976-77; with U. Ky. Rsch. Found., 1992-93. Author: The Middle East in Soviet Policy, 1975, The Art and Science of Psychological Operations, 2 vols., 1976, Foreign Policy Making in the Middle East, 1977, The Political Role of Minority Groups in the Middle East, 1979, Beyond Camp David, 1981, Military Propaganda, 1982, Middle East Foreign Policy: Issues and Processes, 1982, Lebanon and the World in the 1980s, 1983, The Emergence of a New Lebanon: Fantasy or Reality?, 1984, Jordan: The Impact of Social Change on the Tribes, 1984, U.S. Defense Posture in the Pacific, 1987, Alliance Under Tension: Critical Issues in U.S.-Korean Relations, 1988, The Dilemma of Third World Defense Industries: Supplier Controls and Recipient Autonomy, 1989, The U.S. and the Defense of the Pacific, 1989; contbg. editor Mid. East Insight, 1991—; mem. editorial bd. Exec. Internat. Insight, 1992—; cons. editor Asia-Pacific Def. Forum, 1976-84; contbr. articles to profl. jours. Mem. Internat. Studies Assn., Inter-Univ. Seminar Armed Forces and Soc., Middle East Inst., Fgn. Policy Research Inst. Psychol. Ops. Soc. Home: 8600 Powder Horn Rd Springfield VA 22152-2721 Office: Abbott Assocs Inc PO Box 2124 Springfield VA 22152-0124

MC LEAN, DON, singer, instrumentalist, composer; b. New Rochelle, N.Y., Oct. 2, 1945; s. Donald and Elizabeth (Bucci) McL.; m. Patrisha Shnier, Mar., 1987. Student, Villanova U., 1964; BBA, Iona Coll., 1968. Pres., owner The Benny Bird Co., Inc., Fairfield, Conn.; recorded for United Artists, Arista Records, EMI Records; star BBC-TV spls., 1973, 78. Albums include Tapestry, 1972, American Pie, 1972, Don McLean, 1972, Playin' Favourites, 1973, Homeless Brother, 1974, Solo, 1976, Prime Time, 1987, Chain Lightning, 1979, Very Best of, 1980, Believers, 1982, Dominion, 1983, The Best of Don McLean, 1987, Don McLean's Greatest Hits Then & Now, 1987, Love Tracks, 1988, For the Memories, 1989, Don McLean's Greatest Hits Live, 1990, Headroom, 1991, Classics, 1992; singles include American Pie, 1971, Vincent, 1971, Crying, 1980; wrote Perry Como hit And I Love You So, 1973. Mem. bd. Hudson River Sloop Restoration, World Hunger Yr., Advs. for Arts; fund raiser Scenic Hudson, Hudson River Fisherman's Assn. Recipient more than 30 gold and platinum records worldwide, 5 grammy award nominations and others; Israel Cultural award, 1981. Mem. Coffee House Club. Office: Benny Bird Co 1838 Black Rock Tpke Fairfield CT 06430-3505*

MC LEAN, DONALD MILLIS, microbiology, pathology educator, physician; b. Melbourne, Australia, July 26, 1926; s. Donald and Nellie (Millis) McL.; married. B.Sc., U. Melbourne, 1947, M.B., 1950, M.D., 1954. Fellow Rockefeller Found., N.Y.C. and Hamilton, Mont., 1955; vis. instr. bacteriology U. Minn., Mpls., 1957; med. officer Commonwealth Serum Labs., Melbourne, 1957; virologist Research Inst., Hosp. for Sick Children, Toronto, Ont., Can., 1958-67; assoc. prof. microbiology, assoc. in pediatrics U. Toronto Med. Sch., 1962-67; prof. microbiology U. B.C. Med. Sch., Vancouver, Can., 1967-91, prof. emeritus Pathology, 1991—. Author: Virology in Health Care, 1980, Immunological Investigation of Human Virus Disease, 1982, Same-Day Virus Diagnosis, 1984, Virological Infections, 1988, Medical Microbiology Synopsis, 1991, Acute Viral Infections, 1991; contbr. articles to profl. jours. Fellow Royal Coll. Physicians (Can.), Royal Coll. Pathologists; mem. Am. Epidemiological Soc., Am. Soc. Tropical Medicine, Can. Med. Assn., Am. Soc. Microbiology, Am. Soc. Virology. Home: 6-5885 Yew Street, Vancouver, BC Canada V6M 3Y5

MCLEAN, EDWARD PETER, executive search consultant; b. N.Y.C., Apr. 9, 1941; s. John James and Patricia (Stanton) McL.; m. Janet Hotger, Feb. 6, 1970 (dec. Feb. 20, 1980); children: Edward Stanton, Brent Peter. BS, Manhattan Coll., 1963; MBA, Columbia U., 1965. Mktg. rep. N.Y. Stock Exchange, 1968-69; gen. mgr. Am. Thread Co./Totals Ltd., Stamford, Conn., 1969-77; sr. v.p., dir. Billington, Fox & Ellis, Inc., N.Y.C., 1977-82; ptnr., sr. dir. Spencer Stuart, N.Y.C., Phila., 1983—. Trustee Am. Symphony Orch., N.Y.C., 1987; dir. Columbia Bus. Sch. Alumni, N.Y.C., 1988—. Capt. U.S. Army, 1965-68. Mem. Met. Club, Econ. Club of N.Y., N.Y. Athletic Club, Sons of the American Revolution. Home: 715 St Rd Solebury PA 18963 Office: SpencerStuart 55 E 52nd St New York NY 10055-0002

MC LEAN, GEORGE FRANCIS, philosophy of religion educator, clergyman; b. Lowell, Mass., June 29, 1929; s. Arthur and Agnes (McHugh) McL. Ph.L., Gregorian U., Rome, 1952, S.T.L., 1956; Ph.D., Cath. U. Am., 1958. Joined Order Oblates of Mary Immaculate, 1949; ordained priest Roman Catholic Ch., 1955; prof. metaphysics, philosophy of religion Cath U. Am., Washington, 1958—; rsch. scholar U. Madras, 1969, 77-78, 85, U. Paris, 1970, Ctr. for Oriental Rsch., Cairo, 1991; adv. prof. Fudan U., Shanghai, 1994—. Author: Man's Knowledge of God According to Paul Tillich, 1958, Perspectives on Reality, 1966, An Annotated Bibliography of Philosophy in Catholic Thought, 1966, A Bibliography of Christian Philosophy and Contemporary Issues, 1966, Readings in Ancient Western Philosophy, 1970, Ancient Western Philosophy, 1971, Plenitude and Participation, 1978, Tradition and Contemporary Life: Hermeneutics of Perennial Wisdom and Social Change, 1986; editor: numerous books including Philosophy and the Integration of Contemporary Catholic Education, 1962, Philosophy in a Technological Culture, 1964, Christian Philosophy and Religions Renewal, 1966, Philosophy and Contemporary Man, 1968, Religion in Contemporary Thought, 1973, Traces of God in a Secular Culture, 1973, The Impact of Belief, 1974, The Role of Reason in Belief, 1974, New Dynamics in Ethical Thinking, 1974, Philosophy and Civil Law, 1975, Freedom, 1976, Ethical Wisdom East and/or West, 1977, Act and Agent: Philosophical Foundations of Moral Education and Character Development, 1986, 92, Psychological Foundations of Moral Education and Character Development, 1986, 92, Character Development in Schools and Beyond, 1987, 92, Person and Nature, 1988, Person and Society, 1988, Person and God, 1988, The Nature of Metaphysical Knowledge, 1988, The Social Context and Values: Perspectives of the Americas, 1989, Culture Human Rights and Peace in Central America, 1989, On Reading the Philosophers for the 21st Century, 1989, Research on Culture and Values, 1989, Man and Nature: The Chinese Tradition and The Future, 1989, Relations Between Cultures, 1991, Urbanization and Values, 1991, Place of the Person in Social Life, 1991, Chinese Foundations for Moral Education and Character Development, 1991, Morality, Metaphysics and Chinese Culture, 1992, The Foundations of Social Life, 1992, Person and Community, 1992, Tradition, Harmony and Trancendence, 1993, Islam and the Political Order, 1993, Psychology, Phenomenology and Chinese Philosophy, 1994, Values in Philippine Culture and Education, 1994, The Filipino Mind, 1994, The Philosophy of Person: Solidarity and Cultural Creativity, 1994, Private and Public Social Inventions in Modern Societies, 1994, Traditions and Present Problems of Czech Political Culture, 1994, Czech Philosophy in the XXth Century, 1994, Language, Values and the Slovak Nation, 1994, Morality, Public Life in a Time for Change, 1994, National Identity as an Issue of Knowledge and Morality, 1994, Personal Freedom and National Resurgence,

1994; area editor: New Cath. Ency. Mem. Am. Cath. Philos. Assn. (nat. sec. 1965-80), World Union Cath. Philos. Socs. (sec. gen. 1973—), InterUniv. Com. Research and Policy Studies (sec. 1975-77), Internat. Soc. Metaphysics (gen. sec. 1974—), Council Research in Values and Philosophy (sec. 1980—), Internat. Fedn. Philos. Socs. (dir. 1978-88), Cath. Learned Socs. and Scholars (sec. 1975-77). Home: 391 Michigan Ave NE Washington DC 20017-1586 Office: Cath U Am Washington DC 20064

MC LEAN, JACKIE, jazz saxophonist, educator, composer, community activist; b. N.Y.C., May 17, 1932. Bandmaster, counselor N.Y. State Correction Dept.; chmn., prof. Hartt Sch. Music, Hartford, Conn., from 1968; founder Artist Collective, Inc., Hartford, 1970; founder African Am. music program (jazz degree) Hartt sch. music U. Hartford. With Art Blakey's Jazz Messengers, performed with Charles Mingus; actor: film The Connection; albums include Monuments, New York Calling, Antiquity, Live at Montmarte, Ode To Super, A Ghetto Lullaby, Lights Out, Dr. Jackle, The Meeting, Jack Knife, New and Old Gospel, Let Freedom Ring, Destination Out, One Step Beyond, Grachan Moncur III, (with Jackie McLean Quintet) Dynasty, 1990, Rites of Passage, 1991, Triloka: Rhythm of the Earth, 1992, Jackie MacAttack, 1993, Rhythm of the Earth, 1993; guest artist album by Jazz Messengers Midnight Session, 1993; led McLean Jazz Dynasty tour with son Rene in 6 countries in Southern Africa, 1993. Decorated officer of the Arts (France); recipient Bent award U. Hartford; named #1 in Downbeat Mag. Critics Poll, 1994, #1 in Jazz Tunes Mag. Readers' Poll. Office: care Artists Collective Inc 35 Clark St Hartford CT 06120-2000

MCLEAN, JAMES ALBERT, artist, educator; b. Gibsland, La., Nov. 25, 1928; s. Charles Edward and Lucille (Bowdon) McL.; m. Ocelia Jo Perkins, Nov. 27, 1954; 1 child: Gregory Scott. BA, Southwestern La. Inst., 1950; BD, So. Meth. U., 1953; MFA, Tulane U., 1961. Meth. student dir. Centenary Coll., Shreveport, La., 1957-59; head art dept. LaGrange (Ga.) Coll., 1964-66; assoc. prof. art Ga. State U., Atlanta, 1967-68, prof. art, 1968-95; ret., 1995. Exhibited in numerous group shows including Brooklyn Mus., 1976-77, Positive/Negative Exhbn., 1988, Sigraph Exhbn. 1988, 89, Clemson U. Nat. Print and Drawing Exhbn., 1989, Purdue U. Small Print Exhbn., 1990. Mem. Sigraph. Avocations: animation, puppetry. Home: 1256 Dunwoody Knolls Dr Atlanta GA 30338-3219

MCLEAN, KIRK, professional hockey player; b. Willowdale, Ont., Can., June 26, 1966. Goalie Vancouver (Can.) Canucks. Named to NHL All-Star 2nd Team, 1991-92. Office: Vancouver Canucks, 100 N Renfrew St, Vancouver, BC Canada V5K 3N7*

MCLEAN, ROBERT DAVID, lawyer; b. Mar. 1, 1945; s. Edward D. McLean; m. Rosemary P. McLean; children: Ann P., Robert P.; m. Leslie Taft Breed; children: Edward B., Katherine T. BA, Northwestern U.; JD, Yale U. Law clk. to Justice Thurgood Marshall U.S. Supreme Ct.; ptnr. Sidley & Austin, Chgo., 1975—, also exec. com. chrmn., 1993—. Note and comment editor Yale U. Law Rev. Office: Sidley & Austin 1 First Nat Plz Chicago IL 60603

MCLEAN, (ANDREW) STUART, educator, journalist; b. Montreal, Que., Can., Apr. 19, 1948; s. Andrew Thompson and Margret Patricia (Godkin) McL.; m. Linda Read, July 10, 1982; children: Andrew, Robert, Christopher Trowbridge. Adminstr. Dawson Coll., Montreal, 1971-74; exec. prodr. Sunday Morning CBC Radio, 1981-83; dir. broadcast journalism Ryerson Poly. Inst., Toronto, Ont., Can., 1984—, prof., 1987—. Co-writer (film) Looking for Miracles; author: The Morningside World of Stuart McLean, 1989, Welcome Home: Travels in Small Town Canada, 1992 (Best Nonfiction award Can. Authors Assn. 1993), Stories from the Vinyl Cafe, 1995; contbr.: The New Morningside Papers, 1987, The Latest Morningside Papers, 1989. Recipient Best Documentary award ACTRA, 1979, Human Rights Broadcast Journalism award B'nai Brith, 1985; Rooke fellow for tchg. and writing Trent U., 1994. Office: care Ryerson Polytechnic U, 350 Victoria St, Toronto, ON Canada M5B 2K3

MC LEAN, THOMAS EDWIN, retired manufacturing company executive; b. St. Petersburg, Fla., Feb. 14, 1925; s. Annis and Grace (Bell) McL.; m. Virginia Starr, Feb. 20, 1948; children: Brent Starr, Thomas Edwin, Lynn Elizabeth. B.S. in Bus. Adminstrn, U. Fla., 1950; grad., Ind. U. Sch. Savs. and Loan, 1967, also Am. Savs. and Loan Inst. Partner firm Gassner and McLean (C.P.A.'s), St. Petersburg, 1953-65; sr. v.p., sec. First Fed. Savs. & Loan Assn., St. Petersburg, 1965-69; exec. v.p. St. Petersburg Fed. Savs. & Loan Assn., 1969-71, pres., 1971-75; also dir.; pres. Manufactured Housing Products Co., 1978-86; pres. Abilities, Inc. of Fla., 1968-70; dir. Southwestern Suppliers Inc. Pres. Jr. Achievement Pinellas County, 1968-71, St. Petersburg Relocation Assistance Corp., 1971-75; mem. bishop's finance com. Episcopal Diocese S.W. Fla.; chmn. Bishop's Com. on State of Ch., 1973-75; mem. Com. of 100, chmn., 1970; mem. Pinellas County Budget Commn., 1954-56, Pinellas County Tourist Devel. Commn., 1978—; Chmn. bd. dirs. Anclote Psychiat. Center, 1973—; bd. dirs. St. Petersburg Speech and Hearing Clinic, pres., 1968-69, Pinellas Assn. Retarded Children, 1969-72, Police Athletic League, 1971-74, Community Alliance, 1972-74, Sunny Shores Villas, 1964-68, Suncoast Manor, 1969-75, Pinellas Horizon Mental Health Center and Hosp., 1977-79. Served with AUS, 1943-45. Decorated Purple Heart; named Sertoman of Yr., 1957-58; Liberty Bell award St. Petersburg Bar Assn., 1975. Mem. Nat. League Insured Savs. Assns. (chmn. finance com. 1973, mem. exec. com. 1972-74), U.S. Savs. and Loan Leagues, Fla. Savs. and Loan Leagues (chmn. advt. and pub. relations com. 1970-72), Sales and Mktg. Club (pres. 1968-69), St. Petersburg Area C. of C. (dir., pres. 1975-76), Suncoast C. of C. (dir.). Republican. Episcopalian (treas., sr. warden). Clubs: Rotary, Yacht (St. Petersburg), Dragon (dir.), Tiger Bay (pres.), Suncoasters, Golden Triangle. Home: 1339 43rd Ave N Saint Petersburg FL 33703

MCLEAN, THOMAS NEIL, editor; b. Blythewood, S.C., July 30, 1938; s. Hudnalle Bridges and Helen (Allen) McL.; m. Margaret Ann McMurray, Mar. 3, 1962; children: Thomas Neil, Melanie Ann, Patrick David. B.A., U. S.C., 1960; postgrad., Boston U., 1962. With Columbia (S.C.) Newspapers Inc., 1964—; asst. mng. editor The State, 1972-73; editor The Columbia Record, 1973-80; exec. editor The State and The Columbia Record, 1980-90, editorial page editor, v.p., 1990—. Mem. S.C. Consumer Affairs Commn.; trustee United Way, Columbia, mem. City of Columbia Bicentennial Commn.; chmn. Crime Stoppers; bd. dirs. Providence Hosp. Served with USAF, 1961-64. Mem. Am. Soc. Newspaper Editors, AP Mng. Editors Assn., S.C. AP News Council (pres.), Assn. U.S. Army (mem. chpt.), Sigma Delta Chi. Clubs: Summit, Capital City, Kiwanis (dir. local club). Home: 5 Myrtle Ct Columbia SC 29205-3025 Office: The State PO Box 1333 Columbia SC 29202-1333

MCLEAN, VINCENT RONALD, former manufacturing company financial executive; b. Detroit, June 1, 1931; s. Frederick Ronald and Bernice Mary (Vincent) McL.; m. Joyce Adrienne Koch, July 23, 1960; children—Judith Adrienne, Bruce Ronald. B.B.A., U. Mich., 1954, M.B.A., 1955. Fin. analyst Ford Motor Co., Detroit, 1954-55, Mobil Oil Corp., N.Y.C., 1958-69; treas. Mobil Chem. Co., N.Y.C., 1966-69; v.p. fin., treas. NL Industries, N.Y.C., 1969-76, exec. v.p. fin. and planning, dir., 1976-82; exec. v.p., chief fin. officer, dir. Sperry Corp., N.Y.C., 1982-86; sr. advisor Wertheim Schroder & Co., N.Y.C., 1988-89; bd. dirs. Alexander and Alexander Svcs., Inc., Legal and Gen. Am., Inc., William Penn Life Ins. Co. N.Y., Banner Life Ins. Co., Md. Served with U.S. Army, 1955-57. Mem. N.Y. Soc. Security Analysts, Econ. Club N.Y. Home: 702 Shackamaxon Dr Westfield NJ 07090-3408

MCLEAN, WALTER FRANKLIN, international consultant, pastor, former Canadian government official; b. Leamington, Ont., Can., Apr. 26, 1936; s. J.L.W. McL.; m. Barbara Muriel Scott, Aug. 19, 1961; children: Scott, Chima, Ian, Duncan. BA, Victoria Coll., U. B.C., 1957; M.Div., Knox Coll., U. Toronto, 1960; PhD (hon.), Wilfred Laurier U., 1995. Ordained to ministry, Presbyterian Ch. Minister Knox Presby. Ch., Waterloo, 1971-79; mem. House of Commons, Ottawa, Ont., Can., 1979-93; Sec. of State of Can., 1984-85, min. of immigration, 1985-86; min. resp. for status of women Govt. of Can., 1984-86; pres. Franklin Consulting, Ltd., Waterloo, Ontario, Canada, 1994; CUSO, Nigeria coordinator, 1962-67; chaplain U. Nigeria, 1962-67; dep. dir. Internat. Program Canadian Centennial, 1967; exec. dir. Man. Assn. for World Devel., 1970; past chmn. World Concerns Commn.

Canadian Council Chs.; Can. del. Gen. Assemblies UN, 1986-93; apptd. spl. rep. Commonwealth and South African affairs, 1989-93; Can. rep. So. Africa Devel. Coordination Conf., 1987-93; del. Commonwealth Fgn. Mins. Against Apartheid, 1987-93, African Devel. Bank, 1990-91, Assn. West European Parliamentarians Against Apartheid, 1988-89; leader fact finding mission to Mozambique, 1987, Can. delegation UN Conf. on Women, Nairobi, 1985; led Parliamentary del. to observe the pre-election process and attended Namibian Independence, Mar. 21, 1990; chmn. parliamentary Com. on Devel. and Human Rights; Commonwealth observer South African and Sri Lanka elections1994. Alderman City of Waterloo, Ont., 1976-79; co-founder UN based Parliamentarians Global Action. Chaplain 404 wing RCAF. Recipient award Can. U. Svcs. Overseas, 1990. Mem. Can. Bur. Internat. Edn., Waterloo Rotary. Progressive Conservative.

MC LEAN, WILLIAM L., III, publisher; b. Phila., Oct. 4, 1927; s. William L., Jr. and Eleanor Ray (Bushnell) McL.; m. Elizabeth D. Peterson, Sept. 4, 1954; children: Elizabeth, William L. IV, Helen Brooke Katzenbach, Sandra, Warden. BA, Princeton U., 1949. With The Bull., Phila., 1949-80; v.p. The Bull., 1969-74, sr. v.p., 1974-75, editor, pub., 1975-80; pres. Ind. Publs., Inc., Bryn Mawr, Pa., 1976—; chmn. bd. Ind. Publs., Inc., 1980—. Trustee Acad. Natural Scis.; trustee, treas. Pa. chpt. Nature Conservancy. Mem. Pa. Newspapers Pubs. Assn. (pres. 1964, trustee Pa. Newpaper Pubs. Found.), Blooming Grove Club, Hunting and Fishing Club, Franklin Inn Club. Episcopalian. Home: 139 Cherry Ln Wynnewood PA 19096-1208 Office: Ind Publs Inc 945 Haverford Rd Bryn Mawr PA 19010-3814

MCLEARN, MICHAEL BAYLIS, lawyer; b. N.Y.C., Dec. 3, 1936; s. Frank Cecil and Mildred (Adams) McL.; m. Katherine Barnhart Grant, Feb. 25, 1967; children: Elizabeth Baylis, Douglas Grant, Victoria Schoo. B.A., Northwestern U., 1958; J.D., U. Mich., 1961. Bar: N.Y. 1961, Conn. 1970. Assoc. Kramer, Marx, Greelee & Backus, N.Y.C., 1961-68, ptnr., 1969-72; asst. gen. counsel UniDynamics Corp., N.Y.C., 1972-78; sr. v.p. adminstrn., gen. counsel UniDynamics Corp., Stamford, Conn., 1981-85; v.p., gen. counsel Dyneer Corp., Westport, Conn., 1978-81; v.p., gen. counsel, sec. Crystal Brands, Inc., N.Y.C., 1985—. Mem. ABA, N.Y. State Bar Assn., Conn. Bar Assn., Assn. of Bar of City of N.Y. Club: Greenwich Country. Office: Crystal Brands Inc 404 5th Ave New York NY 10018

MCLEISH, DAVID JAMES DOW, employee benefits consulting executive, actuary; b. Blairlogie, Scotland, Feb. 3, 1936; came to U.S., 1988; From student to asst. actuary Scottish Mut. Assurance Soc., Glasgow, 1953-68; dir., chmn., mng. dir. Godwins Ltd., Farnborough, Eng., 1969-87; chmn., chief exec. officer Godwins Internat. Holdings Inc., Briarcliff Manor, N.Y., 1988—; pres. Soc. Pension Cons. (U.K.), 1982-84; mem. Occupational Pension Bd., U.K., 1984-87. Contbr. numerous articles to profl. pubs. Fellow Faculty of Actuaries in Scotland, Pension Mgmt. Inst., Royal Soc. for Encouragment of Arts, Mfrs. and Commerce; mem. Soc. Actuaries (U.S. assoc.), Acad. Actuaries (U.S.). Office: Godwins Internat Holdings Inc 549 Pleasantville Rd, N Bldg Briarcliff Manor NY 10510-1952*

MCLELLAN, A. ANNE, Canadian government official; b. Hants County, N.S., Can., Aug. 31, 1950; d. Howard Gilmore and Joan Mary (Pullan) McL. BA, Dalhousie U., LLB, 1974; LLM, King's Coll., U. London, 1974. Bar: N.S., 1976. Asst. prof. law U. N.B., Can., 1976-80; assoc. prof. law U. Alta., Edmonton, Can., 1980-89, assoc. dean faculty of law, 1985-87, prof. law, 1989-93, acting dean, 1991-92; M.P. for Edmonton Northwest Ho. of Commons, Can., 1993—; minister natural resources Office of Minister Energy, Mines and Resources, Ottawa, Ont., Can., 1993—; commentator on Can. Charter of Rights and Freedoms and on human rights issues. Contbr. articles to profl. publs. Past bd. dirs. Can. Civil Liberties Assn., Alta. Legal Aid; past v.p. U. Alta. Faculty Assn. Office: House of Commons, Rm 323 West Block, Ottawa, ON Canada K1A 0A6

MCLELLAN, HAROLD LINDEN, health care company executive; b. Bowling Green, KY., Oct. 7, 1937; s. Norman and Vernelle (Flanagan) McL.; m. Betty A. Nash, July 12, 1974; children by previous marriage: Pam, Jeff, Wendy. B.S., Western Ky. U., 1959. Note teller Bowling Green Bank & Trust Co., 1960; spl. agt. U.S. Dept. Treasury, 1961-67; v.p. constrn. Humana Inc., Louisville, 1967-79, sr. v.p. facility mgmt., 1979—. Mem. corp. council Western Ky. U., 1985—; bd. dirs. Ky. Ctr. for Spl. Children, 1985—, Presbyn. Homes and Services Ky., Louisville, 1986—. Mem. Main St. Assn. (bd. dirs. 1986—). Club: Hunting Creek Country (Goshen, Ky.) (bd. dirs. 1979-86, pres. 1982-85). Office: Humana Inc PO Box 1438 Louisville KY 40201-1438

MCLELLAN, JOSEPH DUNCAN, critic, journalist; b. Quincy, Mass., Mar. 27, 1929; s. Malcolm and Elsie May (Turner) McL.; m. Estelle Marie Cajolet, Feb. 3, 1951; children—Joseph, Laura, Andree, Sandra. B.A., Boston Coll., 1951, M.A., 1953. Reporter, columnist The Pilot, Boston, 1953-67; editor fgn. news Religious News Service, N.Y.C., 1967-70; editor mag. AD 1970, S. Bend, Ind., 1970; dir. spl. projects N.C. News Service, D.C., 1970-72; writer, editor The Washington Post, D.C., 1972-82, music critic, 1982-95; music critic emeritus, 1995—. Mem. Music Critics Assn., Book Critics Circle, Assn. U.S. Chess Journalists. Club: Mensa (D.C.). Avocations: chess; computers; video equipment and software; poetry translation. Home: 1224 Fairmont St NW Washington DC 20009-5322 Office: Washington Post 1150 15th St NW Washington DC 20071-0002

MCLELLAN, RICHARD DOUGLAS, lawyer; b. Peoria, Ill., May 21, 1942; s. Charles Douglas and Catherine Mary (McCuaig) McL. B.A. with honors, Mich. State U., 1964; J.D., U. Mich., 1967. Bar: Mich. 1968. Pvt. practice Lansing, Mich., 1968-69; adminstrv. asst. to Gov. William G. Milliken State of Mich., 1969-73; ptnr. McLellan, Schlaybaugh & Whitbeck, Lansing, 1973-82; mem.-in-charge govt. policy group Dykema Gossett PLLC, Lansing, 1982—; transition dir. Office Gov.-Elect, State of Mich., 1990; adj. prof. internat. studies Mich. State U., 1993—. Dir. Mich. C. of C., 1983—, chmn., 1993-94; bd. dirs. Mackinac Ctr., treas., 1983-84, sec. 1990—; treas. Cornerstone Found., 1967—; pres. Mich. chpt. Arthritis Found., 1984-86, Nat. Ho. of Dels.; pres. Library of Mich. Found., 1986—; trustee Oxford Found.; chmn. Mich. Law Rev. Commn., 1985—; nat. pres., trustee, Delta Sigma Phi Found., 1989-91; mem. bd. govs. Cranbrook Inst. Sci.; vice chair, trustee Mich. Japan Found.; ich., 1990; mem. nat. adv. food and drug com. HEW, 1975-77; dir. Internat.U.S. Presdl. observer to Bulgarian elections, 1990; dir. Okemos Coun. Boy Scouts Am.; chmn. Mich. Corrections Commn., 1991; sec., mem. Mich. Internat. Trade Authority, 1991—. Named Small Bus. Adv. of Yr. SBA, 1983. Mem. ABA, Internat. Bar Assn., Mich. Bar Assn., Ingham County Bar Assn., Asia-Pacific Lawyers Assn., Rep. Nat. Lawyers Assn., Am. Soc. Assn. Execs., Am. Counsel Assn., Am. Soc. for Neurosci., Mich. Soc. Assn. Execs., Am. C. of C. of Italy (hon. rep.), Capitol Hill Club (Washington), Lansing City Club (pres. 1986-87), Econ. Club Detroit, Renaissance Club, Rotary. Home: 1191 Carriageway N East Lansing MI 48823 Office: 800 Michigan Nat Towers Lansing MI 48933

MCLELLAND, JOSEPH CUMMING, philosophy educator, former university dean; b. Scotland, Sept. 10, 1925; s. David and Jessie (Cumming) McL.; m. Audrey Brunton, Aug. 23, 1947; children—Jonathan, Peter, Andrew, Margaret. B.A., McMaster U., Hamilton, Ont., Can., 1946; M.A., U. Toronto, 1949; B.D., Knox Coll., Toronto, 1951; Ph.D., New Coll. U. Edinburgh, Scotland, 1953; D.D., Montreal Diocesan Theol. Coll., 1973, Knox Coll., Toronto, 1976. Ordained to ministry Presbyn. Ch., 1949; minister in Val D'Or, Que., 1949-53, Bolton, Ont., 1953-57; Robert prof. philosophy of religion and ethics Presbyn. Coll., Montreal, 1957-64; McConnell prof. philosophy religion McGill U., 1964-91, prof. emeritus, 1992—, dean faculty religious studies, 1975-85. Author: Visible Words of God, 1957, The Clown and the Crocodile, 1970, God the Anonymous, 1976, Prometheus Rebound: Irony of Atheism, 1988; assoc. editor: Studies in Religion, 1970-73, editor, 1973-75; mem. editl. bd. Theology Today, 1960-80; gen. editor: Peter Martyr Library, 1993—. Co-chmn. Orthodox and Reformed Chs. Consulation N. Am., 1968-72. Can. Council grantee, 1968, 80-81, 85-86, 92—. Mem. Canadian Theol. Soc. (past pres.), Canadian Soc. Study Religion. Office: 3520 University St, Montreal, PQ Canada H3A 2A7

MCLEMORE, DAVID EUGENE, editor, writer; b. Longview, Tex., July 7, 1946; s. Eugene Bass and Lee (Campbell) McL.; m. Virginia Nell Messec, Apr. 21, 1979; children: Gabriel, Samuel. BA, Okla. State U., 1968; postgrad., U. Tex., San Antonio, 1975-76. Cmty. info. Bexar County Hosp.

Dist., San Antonio, 1972-75; reporter San Antonio Express, 1975-81; bur. chief Dallas Morning News, 1981—. Author: (pictorial history) A Place in Time, 1979. With U.S. Army, 1969-71. Methodist. Office: Dallas Morning News 314 E Commerce #401 San Antonio TX 78205

MC LEMORE, ROBERT HENRY, petroleum engineer, consultant; b. Dallas, Feb. 28, 1910; s. Edward Eugene and Margaret (Butler) Mc L.; m. Ethel Ruth Ward, June 30, 1935. B.S., Tex. A & M Coll., 1933. Div. engr. Sun Oil Co., Dallas, 1933-41; exec. v.p., gen. mgr. Welex Jet Services, Ft. Worth, 1946-53; cons. engr., 1953-55; v.p., gen. mgr. Turbo Drill div. Dresser Industries, Dallas, 1955-57; pres., dir. Otis Engring. Corp., 1957-75; dir. Halliburton Co., 1968-75; councilor Tex. A & M U. Research Found. Served from lt. to col. USAAF, 1941-45. Mem. Soc. Petroleum Engrs. (treas. 1960-63, pres. 1970, dir. 1969-72, DeGolyer Disting. Service medal 1976), Mid Continent Oil and Gas Assn., Am. Petroleum Inst., Independent Producers Assn. Am., AIME (hon. mem.; dir. 1969-72, v.p. 1971, Roger McConnell Engring. Achievement award 1975). Clubs: Petroleum; Engrs. (Dallas); Northwood Country. Home: 8600 Skyline Dr # 1107 Dallas TX 75243-4158

MCLENDON, GEORGE LELAND, chemistry educator, researcher; b. Ft. Worth, June 6, 1952; s. George and Beata (Shaw) McL.; m. Donna Turner, Aug. 20, 1973; children: Heather, Audrey. BS, U. Tex., El Paso, 1972; PhD, Tex. A&M U., 1976. Assot. prof. chemistry U. Rochester (N.Y.), 1976-80, assoc. prof., 1980-84, prof., 1984—, Tracy Harris prof., 1990-94; R.W. Moore prof. Princeton (N.J.) U., 1994—; cons., mem. vis. bd. Solar Energy Rsch. Inst., 1986-89; adv. com. NSF, 1988-91. Contbr. 150 articles and revs. to profl. jours. Recipient Dreyfus Tchr. Scholar award, 1979-84; A.P. Sloan fellow, 1980-85; Guggenheim Found. and Worcester Coll. fellow, Oxford, Eng., 1989. Mem. Am. Chem. Soc. (Pure Chemistry award 1987, Eli Lilly award 1990, Akron sect. award 1992), Am. Phys. Soc., Materials Rsch. Soc. Episcopalian.

MC LENDON, HEATH BRIAN, securities investment company executive; b. San Francisco, May 24, 1933; s. Jesse Heath and Clara Martha (Nelson) McL.; m. Judith Nelson Locke, May 30, 1959; children: Laurie, Eric, Brian and Michael (twins). BA, Stanford U., 1955; MBA, Harvard U., 1959. With Shearson Lehman Brothers, N.Y.C., 1960-93; mng. dir. Smith Barney, 1993—; chmn. Strategy Advisors, N.Y.C., 1971—; bd. dirs. East N.Y. Savs. Bank; chmn. The Italy Fund, Inc., 1986—; Zenix Income Fund; adv. dir. First Empire State Corp. Pres. bd. trustees N.J. Shakespeare Festival, 1975-76; trustee Drew U., 1975—, chmn. bd., 1992. Served to 1st lt. AUS, 1955-57. Mem. N.Y. Soc. Security Analysts, N.Y. Assn. Bus. Economists, Money Marketeers. Presbyterian. Clubs: Baltusrol, Bay Head Yacht. Home: 70 Hillcrest Ave Summit NJ 07901-2023 Office: Smith Barney 388 Greenwich St New York NY 10013

MCLENNAN, BARBARA NANCY, trade association executive, lawyer; b. N.Y.C., Mar. 25, 1940; d. Sol and Gertrude (Rochkind) Miller; m. Kenneth McLennan, Aug. 14, 1962; children: Gordon, Laura. BA magna cum laude, CCNY, 1961; MS, U. Wis., 1962, PhD, 1965; JD, Georgetown U., 1983. Bar: D.C. 1983, Va. 1991, U.S. Ct. Internat. Trade 1988, U.S. Ct. Appeals (D.C. cir.) 1988, U.S. Supreme Ct. 1988. From asst. prof. to assoc. prof. Temple U., Phila., 1965-78; budget analyst Com. on Budget, U.S. Ho. of Reps., Washington, 1978-81; legis. asst. fin. and budget Sen. Dan Quayle, Washington, 1981-84; internat. tax specialist IRS, U.S. Dept. Treasury, Washington, 1984-89; dep. asst. sec. trade, info. and analysis U.S. Dept. Commerce, Washington, 1989-91; prin., atty.-at-law Bitonti and Wilhelm, PC., McLean, Va., 1991-93; staff v.p. govt.-legal affairs consumer electronics group Electronic Industries Assn., Washington, 1993-94, staff v.p. tech. policy, consumer electronics group, 1994—; sr. polit. scientist SRI-Internat., Arlington, Va., 1971-74; vis. prof. Am. Coll., Paris, 1975-76; cons. UNESCO, Paris, 1977-78. Author: Comparative Political Systems, 1975; contbr. numerous articles to profl. jours. Mem. parents adv. coun. Randolph-Macon Coll., Ashland, Va., 1989-92. NDEA fellow, 1962-65. Mem. ABA, Am. Soc. Assn. Execs., D.C. Bar Assn., Fed. Bar Assn., Phi Beta Kappa. Home: 6950 Duncraig Ct Mc Lean VA 22101 Office: Electronic Industries Assn 2001 Pennsylvania Ave NW Washington DC 20006-1813 Office: Electronic Industries Assn 2500 Wilson Blvd Arlington VA 22201-3834

MCLENNAN, BERNICE CLAIRE, human resources professional; b. Malden, Mass., Dec. 26, 1936; d. Ralph Cyril Worth and Alice Seaman (Hunter) Worth Barrett; m. Hubert Earle McLennan, Oct. 28, 1961; 1 child, Cynthia Alice. Student, Moody Bible Inst., 1958, Salem State Coll., 1988, Bentley Coll., 1989. Youth dir. Faith Evangelical Ch., Melrose, Mass., 1971-77; adminstrv. asst. Boston (Mass.) Redevel. Authority, 1977-85, adminstrt. coord., 1985-87, asst. sec. to the authority, 1981—, dir. human resources, 1988—; moderator Faith Evangelical Ch., Melrose, 1985-88, Christian edn. chair, 1973-76. Sec. Melrose (Mass.) Sch. Com., 1983-85; vol. Boston (Mass.) Youth Campaign, 1989, 90. Mem. Internat. Pers. Mgmt. Assn., Assn. Affirmative Action Profls. Avocations: Christian edn., women's issues, drug/alcohol edn. Home: 31 Botolph St Melrose MA 02176-1126 Office: Boston Redevel Authority City Hall One City Hall Sq Boston MA 02201

MCLEOD, E. DOUGLAS, real estate developer, lawyer; b. Galveston, Tex., Aug. 6, 1941; s. Vaughn Watkins McL. and Dorothy (Milroy) Burton; m. Sarah Jackson Helms, Mar. 20, 1965 (div. 1979); children: Chanse, Alexandra, Lindsey; m. Joan Margaret Williams, Dec. 26, 1979; 1 child, Joanie; stepchildren: Meg, Libbie. BBA, U. North Tex., 1965; postgrad., So. Meth. U., 1965-66; JD, South Tex. Coll. Law, 1990; LLM, U. Houston, 1993. Lic. real estate broker. Pres., owner McLeod Properties & co., Galveston, Tex., 1967—; tchr. Galveston Ind. Sch. Dist., 1967-69; banker W.L. Moody & Co., Galveston, 1969-72; developer, broker McLeod Properties/Builders, Galveston, 1972-82; developer Moody Found., Galveston, 1982—; bd. dirs. Am. Nat. Ins. Co., Galveston, Nat. Western Life Ins. Co., Austin, Anrem Corp., Galveston, Moody Gardens Inc., Galveston, , chmn., 1984—; bd. dirs. Colonel Inc., Galveston, v.p., 1985—; bd. dirs. Ctr. Transp. & Commerce, Glaveston. Pres., trustee Galveston Ind. Sch. Dist., 1969-73; mayor pro-tem, mem. city coun. City of Galveston, 1973-76; state legislator Tex. Ho. of Reps., Austin, 1976-83; bd. visitors So. Tex. Coll. Law, 1990—; mem. adv. bd. U. Houston, 1986—; bd. dirs. Ronald McDonald House, 1986-93, Trinity Episcopal Sch., 1990—. With USMC, 1961-67. South Tex. Coll. Law fellow, 1990-95. Mem. Tex. Trial Lawyers Assn. (mem. legis. com. 1991—), Granaderos De Galvez, Marine Corps League. Democrat. Episcopalian. Avocations: physical fitness advocate, legal history collector, family archivist. Home: 53 Cedar Lawn Cir Galveston TX 77551-4631 Office: The Moody Found 2302 Post Office St Ste 704 Galveston TX 77550

MCLEOD, JACK MYRON, communications educator; b. Chgo., Aug. 30, 1930; s. William Theodore and Ellen Victoria (Hanson) McL.; divorced May 1983; children: Douglas Malcolm, Katherine Laurie. B.S. in Journalism, U. Wis., 1952, M.S. in Journalism, 1953; M.A. in Sociology, U. Mich., 1957, Ph.D. in Social Psychology, 1962. Asst. study dir. Survey Research Ctr. Inst. Social Research, U. Mich., Ann Arbor, 1957-62; asst. prof., then prof. Sch. Journalism and Mass Communications, U. Wis., Madison, 1962—; chmn. Mass Communications Research Ctr. U. Wis., Madison, 1967—; Maier-Bascom prof. journalism and mass communications U. Wis., Madison, 1981—. Served with AUS, 1953-55. U. Mich. Gen. Electric Corp. fellow, 1959-60; U. Leeds (Eng.) sr. vis. research fellow, 1973; NSF, NIMH, Markle Found. prin. investigator. Mem. Am. Sociol. Assn., Assn. Edn. Journalism and Mass Communication, Internat. Communication Assn., AAUP. Office: Mass Communications Research Ctr U Wis 5174 Vilas Hall Madison WI 53706-1497

MCLEOD, JOHN WISHART, architect; b. Edinburgh, Scotland, Mar. 24, 1908; s. Thomas and Catherine (Wishart) McL.; m. Helen G. Rath, July 11, 1936; children: Ian Wishart, Cathie Ann. Student, Columbia U., N.Y. Beaux-Arts Inst. Design, Columbia Tchrs. Coll. Archtl. tng. in N.Y., N.J. area, 1930-36; prin. McLeod, Ferrara & Ensign and predecessor firms, Elizabeth, N.J., 1936-41, Washington, 1946-80; with WPB, 1941-46; mem. Bd. Examiners and Registrars Architects of D.C., 1959-66; mem. U.S. del. UNESCO-IBE Conf. Sch. Bldg., Geneva, 1957; mem. vice chmn. U.S. del. UNESCO-U.N. Conf. Sch. Bldg., London, 1962; mem., co-chmn. constrn. adv. com. fallout shelters Dept. Def., 1962-76; planning cons. Found. Barre De La Maja, La Corunna, Spain, 1976. Prin. works include ednl. facilities,

author: Urban Schools in Europe, 1968; co-author: Planning America's School Buildings, 1960. Fellow AIA (chmn. nat. com. ednl. facilities 1950-63, pres. Washington-Met. chpt. 1961); mem. Coun. Ednl. Facility Planners Internat. (Planner of Yr. award 1975), Palm Beach Watercolor Soc. (spl. award 8th ann. exhbn. 1991). Home: 404 NW 72nd St Boca Raton FL 33487

MCLEOD, NORMAN CARL, librarian; b. Sackville, New Brunswick, Can., Nov. 11, 1943; s. Carl Victor and Marjorie Pauline (Hicks) McL.; m. Marie-Reine Marguerite Yolande Dubois, July 8, 1972; 1 child, Isabelle. BA, Mt. Allison U., Sackville, 1965; BLS, U. Toronto, Ont., Can., 1967; MLS, McGill U., Montreal, Que., Can., 1975; diploma in pub. adminstrn., U. Western Ont., 1987. Librarian Kitchener (Ont.) Pub. Library, 1967-69, Bishop's U., Lennoxville, Quebec, Can., 1969-75; chief librarian Sources Pub./Bibliotheque Municipaledes Sources, Roxboro, Quebec, Can., 1975-77, Guelph (Ont.) Pub. Library, 1977—. Mem. Rotary. Avocations: reading, music. Office: Guelph Pub Library, 100 Norfolk St, Guelph, ON Canada N1H 4J6

MCLEOD, PHILIP R., publishing executive; b. Winnipeg, Manitoba, Canada, May 4, 1943; s. Donald G. and Phyllis (Brown) McL.; m. Cheryl Amy Stewart, Sept. 25, 1965 (div. 1992); children: Shawn Robert, Erin Dawn; m. Virginia Mary Corner, Nov. 6, 1992. Journalist Bowes Pub., Grande Prairie, Alta Truro, N.S., 1962-76; journalist, dep. mng. editor Toronto (Ont.) Star, 1976-87; editor-in-chief London (Ont.) Free Press, 1987—; dir. The Can. Press, Toronto, 1974-76. Southam fellow Southam Newspapers, 1970. Mem. The London Club. Avocations: canoeing, skiing. Office: The London Free Press, 369 York St, London, ON Canada N6A 4G1

MCLEOD, ROBERT MACFARLAN, lawyer, arbitrator; b. Toronto, Ont., Can., Oct. 13, 1925; s. William Green and Eliza Vest (Macfarlan) McL.; m. Siddney Anne Mercer, June 21, 1950; children—Ann Payne, William Mercer, Elizabeth Macfarlan. B.S., U. Wis.-Madison, 1950; J.D., U. Wis., 1952. Bar: Calif. 1953, Va. 1952. Assoc. faculty U. Calif. Law Sch., Berkeley, 1952-53; assoc., then ptnr. Thelen Marrin Johnson & Bridges, San Francisco, 1953-86, of counsel, 1986—; real estate broker Hill & Co., San Francisco, 1986-92; vis. lectr. U. Calif. Law Sch., Berkeley, 1965-86; arbitrator Calif. State Constrn. Arbitration Panel, 1978-90; arbitrator constrn. industry panel Am. Arbitration Assn., 1982—; judge pro tem San Francisco Mcpl. Ct., 1980-81; mem. Calif. Pub. Contract Code Com., 1980-83. Contbr. chpts. to books, articles to profl. jours; bd. editors Va. Law Rev., 1951-52. Sustaining mem. Mus. Soc., San Francisco, 1974—; mem. Nat. Trust, London, 1982—, Forum for Architecture, N.Y.C., 1984-86, Found. for San Francisco's Archtl. Heritage, 1987-93, Nat. Trust for Hist. Preservation, 1987—. With inf. U.S. Army, 1943-46, ETO. Decorated Bronze Star medal. Mem. Bar Assn. San Francisco, State Bar Calif., The Guardsmen, San Francisco Gold Club, Order of Coif, Phi Alpha Delta, Delta Kappa Epsilon. Republican. Avocations: travel; golf. Office: Thelen MarrinJohnson & Bridges 2 Embarcadero Ctr San Francisco CA 94111-3995

MCLEOD, RONALD, educational administrator. Supt. of schs. El Paso, Tex. Office: PO Box 20100 El Paso TX 79998-0100

MCLEOD, WILLIAM LASATER, JR., judge, former state legislator; b. Marks, Miss., Feb. 27, 1931; s. William Lasater and Sara Louise (Macaulay) McL.; m. Marilyn Qualls, June 16, 1962; children: Sara Nelson Judson, Martha Ellen, Ruth Elizabeth. AB, Princeton U., 1953; JD, La. State U., 1958. Bar: La. 1958, U.S. Supreme Ct. 1980. Sole practice, Lake Charles, La., 1958-62; ptnr. McLeod & Little, Lake Charles, 1976-90; dist. judge Calcasieu Parish, 1991—; mem. La. Ho. of Reps., 1968-76; mem. La. Senate, 1976-90. Chmn. Lake Charles Salvation Army Adv. Bd., 1965-66; pres. Calcasieu Area Coun. Boy Scouts Am., 1978; elder Presbyn. Ch. Served with U.S. Army, 1953-55. Recipient Disting. Service award Lake Charles Jaycees, 1963, Civic Service award S.W. La. C. of C., 1986. Mem. ABA, La. Bar Assn., S.W. La. Bar Assn. (pres. 1980). Democrat. Lodge: Masons. Office: Calcasieu Parish Courthouse 1000 Ryan St Lake Charles LA 70601

MCLEOD, WILSON CHURCHILL, lawyer; b. Hamilton, Ont., Can., Aug. 25, 1938; s. Wilson Churchill and Christine Carol (Ard) McL.; m. Lynn Ann Winston, Nov. 6, 1962 (div. 1977); children: Wilson Churchill, Alexandra Lynn; m. Mary Alwina Van Ogtrop, Aug. 15, 1978 (separated). BA, McMaster U., Can., 1960; LLB cum laude, Harvard U., 1963. Bar: Mass. 1969; solicitor Eng., 1975. Asst. trust officer The Nat. Shawmut Bank Boston, 1963-67; cons. Crane & Hawkins, London, 1967-82; ptnr. Bryan Cave, London, 1982-92, Brown & Wood, London, 1992—; mem. internat. adv. bd. Boston Private Bank & Trust Co. Home: Longholt, Hall Ln, Ingatestone, Essex CM4 9NN, England Office: Brown & Wood, Blackwell House Guildhall Yard, London EC2V 5AB, England

MC LERAN, JAMES HERBERT, university dean, oral surgeon; b. Audubon, Iowa, Apr. 9, 1931; s. Louis D. and Alma K. (Christensen) McL.; m. Hermine Weinert Hayden, July 15, 1979; 1 children, Stephen Andrew; step children: John Wilson Hayden, Charles Matthew Hayden. BS, Simpson Coll., 1953; DDS, U. Iowa, 1957, MS, 1962. Diplomate: Am. Bd. Oral and Maxillofacial Surgery. Instr. U. Iowa, 1959-60, asst. prof., 1963-67, assoc. prof., 1967-69, prof. oral surgery, 1972—, assoc. dean Coll. Dentistry, 1972-74, dean, 1974—; prof. and chmn. dept. oral surgery U. N.C., Chapel Hill, 1969-72. Served with Dental Corps USN, 1957-59. Recipient Finkbine Leadership award U. Iowa, 1957; named Instr. of Yr. Jr. ADA, 1964, Outstanding Instr. award, 1965. Mem. ADA, Am. Assn. Oral and Maxillofacial Surgeons, Iowa Assn. Oral and Maxillofacial Surgeons, Internat. Assn. Dental Rsch., Midwestern Assn. Oral and Maxillofacial Surgeons, N.C. Soc. Dental Surgeons, N.C. Dental Soc., Iowa Dental Assn. (Disting. Svc. award 1992), Univ. Dist. Dental Soc., Johnson County Dental Soc., Am. Coll. Dentists, Internat. Coll. Dentists, Fedn. Dentaire Internat., Am. Assn. Dental Schs. (pres. 1978-79), Psi Omega. Lodge: Rotary. Office: U Iowa Coll Dentistry Iowa City IA 52242

MCLESKEY, CHARLES HAMILTON, anesthesiology educator; b. Phila., Nov. 8, 1946; s. W. Hamilton and Marion A. (Butts) McL.; m. Nanci S. Simmons, June 3, 1972; children: Travis, Heather. BA, Susquehanna U., 1968; MD, Wake Forest U., 1972. Diplomate Am. Bd. Anesthesiology. Intern Maine Med. Ctr., Portland, 1972-73; resident in anesthesiology U. Wash. Sch. Medicine, Seattle, 1973-76, NIH rsch. trainee, 1974-75; clin. teaching assoc. dept. anesthesiology U. Calif., San Francisco, 1976-78; asst. prof. anesthesiology Wake Forest U. Bowman Gray Sch. Medicine, Winston-Salem, N.C., 1978-83, assoc. prof., 1983-84; assoc. prof. U. Tex. Med. Br., Galveston, 1985-87; assoc. prof. U. Colo. Health Sci. Ctr., Denver, 1987-91, prof., 1991-93, dir. acad. affairs, 1987-93; prof., chmn. dept. anesthesiology Tex. A&M U., 1993—; chmn. dept. anesthesiology Scott and White Clin. and Meml. Hosp. Temple, Tex., 1993—; cons., lectr. Janssen Pharmaceutica, Piscataway, N.J., 1980—; Alza Corp., Palo Alto, Calif., 1986—; cons. Glaxo-Wellcome Co., Research Triangle Park, N.C., Abbott Labs., Chgo., Marion Merrill Dow, Kansas City, Kans.; lectr. to over 500 nat. and state med. orgns., 1982—; examiner Am. Bd. Anesthesiology. Assoc. editor Anesthesiology Rev.; editor Geriatric Anesthesiology, 1989; contbr. numerous articles to med. jours. Mem. choir Friendswood (Tex.) Meth. Ch., 1985-87; mem. Friendswood Fine Arts Commn., 1985-87. Lt. comdr. M.C., USN, 1976-78. Woodruff-Fisher scholar, 1964-68. Mem. Internat. Platform Assn., Assn. U. Anesthetists, Am. Soc. Anesthesiologists (del. 1983-85, 88—), Soc. for Edn. in Anesthesia (v.p.), Colo. Soc. Anesthesiologists (pres.), Oenophile Soc., Nat. Speakers Assn., Evergreen Newcomers, Alpha Omega Alpha. Republican. Presbyterian. Avocations: running, fishing, racquetball, squash. Office: PO Box 3160 Temple TX 76505

MCLIN, RHINE LANA, state legislator, funeral service executive, educator; b. Dayton, Ohio, Oct. 3, 1948; d. C. Josef, Jr. and Bernice (Cottman) McL. B.A. in Sociology, Parsons Coll., 1969; M.Ed., Xavier U., Cin., 1972; postgrad. in law U. Dayton, 1974-76, AA in Mortuary Sci., Cin. Coll., 1988. Lic. funeral dir.; cert. tchr., Ohio. Tchr. Dayton Bd. Edn., 1970-72; divorce counselor Domestic Relations Ct., Dayton, 1972-73; law clk. Montgomery Common Pleas Ct., Dayton, 1973-74; v.p., dir., embalmer McLin Funeral Homes, Dayton, 1972—; instr. Central State U., Wilberforce, Ohio, 1982—; mem. Ohio Ho. of Reps., 1988-94; state senator Ohio State Senate, 1994—; com: mem. Human Svcs. and Aging Com., Agrl. Com., Hwys. and Transp.

Com., Energy, Natural Resources and Environ. Com. Mem. Democratic Voters League, Dayton. Mem. Nat. Funeral Dirs. Assn., Ohio Funeral Dirs. Assn., Montgomery County Funeral Dirs. Assn., NAACP (life), Nat. Council Negro Women (life), Delta Sigma Theta. Home: 1130 Germantown St Dayton OH 45408-1465 Office: Ohio State Senate State House Columbus OH 43215

MCLIN, STEPHEN T., investment banker; b. St. Louis, Nov. 11, 1946; s. Leonard Dale and Hazel (Goodlett) McL.; m. Rebecca Missen, 1965 (div. 1975); children: Cynthia Jeanne, Stephen Dale; m. Catherine Anne Crespi, 1981; children: Scott Thomas, Stephanie Therese. BSChemE, U. Ill.-Urbana, 1968; MSME, Stanford U., 1970, MBA, 1972. Rch. engr. Atlantic Richfield Corp., Anaheim, Calif., 1968-69; staff officer First Chgo. Corp., 1972-74; asst. v.p. Bank of Am., San Francisco, 1974-75, v.p., 1975-81, sr. v.p., 1981-86, exec. v.p., 1986-87; pres., CEO Am. First Fin. Corp., San Francisco, 1987—, AF Eureka Holdings, Inc., San Francisco, 1993—; chmn., dir. Eureka Bank, Foster City, Calif., 1988—; adj. prof. Golden Gate U., San Francisco, 1976-82; bd. dirs. Charles Schwab & Co., San Francisco. Bd. regents John F. Kennedy U., Orinda, Calif., 1982-85; mem. citizens stamp adv. com. U.S. Postal Svcs., 1990—. Recipient Disting. Svc. award Golden Gate U., 1982. Mem. San Francisco Golf Club, Pacific Union Club, Bankers Club, Contra Costa Country Club, San Francisco Bay Club. Office: Am First Fin Corp 555 California St Ste 4490 San Francisco CA 94104-1709

MCLIN, WILLIAM MERRIMAN, foundation administrator; b. Attleboro, Mass., Feb. 22, 1945; s. William Hellen and Helen Francis (Orr) McL. B.A., George Washington U., 1967; M.Ed., U. Md., 1974. Exec. dir. Prince Georges County (Md.) chpt. Am. Cancer Soc., 1968-70; dir. programs Am. Cancer Soc. (Md. div.), 1970-72; dir. youth programs nat. office Am. Cancer Soc., N.Y.C., 1972-76; dep. exec. dir. Epilepsy Found. Am., Washington, 1976-79; exec. v.p. Epilepsy Found. Am., 1979—; pres. Nat. Health Coun., N.Y.C., 1989-91; pres. Internat. Bur. for Epilepsy, 1989-93. Mem. Am. Public Health Assn., Am. Soc. Assn. Execs. Office: Epilepsy Foundation of America 4351 Garden City Dr Hyattsville MD 20785-2223

MCLINDON, GERALD JOSEPH, planning and environmental design consultant, university dean emeritus; b. Bathgate, Scotland, Aug. 27, 1923; s. Patrick J. and Anne (Sloan) MacL.; m. Agnes Helena Cooke, July 12, 1951; children: Michael, Christopher, Maureen, Ann, Andrew, John, Duncan. Student, Liverpool Coll. Tech. City and Guilds of London Structural Engring., 1948; B.Arch. with Honors; Dipl.C.D., U. Liverpool, Eng., 1949, 51; M.L.A., Harvard U., 1954. Asst. prof. U. Mass., Amherst, 1951-55; dir. Metroplan, Little Rock, 1955-58; planning dir. Cloverdale Corp., Little Rock, 1958-60; owner Gerald J. McLindon (planning consultants), Little Rock, 1960-63; dir. Market St. Devel. Project, San Francisco, 1963-66; dir. state planning State of La., 1968-70; dean La. State U. Coll. Design, Baton Rouge, 1966-80; prin. Gerald J. McLindon & Assos. (planning cons.), 1960—; cons. to several U.S. Army Corps of Engrs. divs. and dists., Oak Ridge Nat. Lab., Tenn., U.S. Army Engr. Inst. for Water Resources; mem. Am. Council for Constrn. Edn., 1974—, mem. accreditation com., 1974, chmn. guidance com., 1975, sr. v.p., 1977-78, pres., 1978-80, trustee, 1980-85, mem. profl. recognition com., 1985-87; mem. La. Gov.'s Com. on Waste Mgmt., also chmn. subcom. on recycling and waste reduction, 1976-78; planning cons. to mayor pres. of East Baton Rouge; adj. prof. coll. design La. State U., 1993; cons. Amite RIver Basin Commn., La., 1993. Contbr. articles to profl. publs. Mem. La. Domed Stadium Adv. Bd., 1966-72, La. Health Planning Council, 1968-74, La. Health Planning Exec. Com., 1969-74, La. Mississippi River Crossing Adv. Com., 1971-72, Gov.'s Citizens Adv. Com. Transp. New Orleans, 1972-78; La. Trails Adv. Council mem. nat. air pollution manpower adv. com. EPA, 1971-76; commr. Offshore La. Deep Draft Harbor and Terminal Authority, 1972—; mem. standards com. Found. for Interior Design Edn. Research, 1972-77, mem. accreditation com., 1977-85; mem. transp. com. La. Goals Program; mem. environ. adv. bd. chief engrs. Corps Engrs., Washington, 1977, chmn., 1978-83; mem. codes com. NRC, 1980-81; mem. com. on hwys. and AOC Nat. Acad. Scis., 1982-83; mem. com. on abandoned mine land rsch. priorities NRC, 1987-88; mem. Permanent Internat. Assn. Nav. Congresses, 1980-85; chmn. East Baton Rouge Stormwater Mgmt. Adv. Bd., 1989; chmn. Gov.'s Interagy. Task Force on Flood Prevention and Mitigation, 1990, mem. State Mineral Bd., 1989-91; leader People to People Internat. Program. Served with Brit. Army, 1942-45. Recipient spl. citation, cert. of appreciation U.S. Army, Commdrs. award for pub. svc. U.S. Army C.E., 1990, Nasville dist. Environ. Design award, 1990, Govs. award, La., 1990, Baton Rouge Green award for Profl. Achievement, 1994; Fulbright scholar, 1950-51, Uriel M. Crocker scholar, 1950. Fellow Am. Inst. (Constructors) com. on goals and objectives); mem. ASME (com. for safety and pollution prevention equipment used in offshore gas ops., subcom. on cert. and accrediation 1976-78), Am. Inst. Landscape Architects (hon.), Royal Inst. Brit. Archs., Am. Inst. Interior Designers (hon.), Am. Soc. Landscape Archs. (spl. award for outstanding contbns. to better environ., merit award for profl. excellence in comm. 1986), Royal Agrl. Soc. Engrs., Ariz. Sr. Acad., Baton Rouge C. of C. (transp. com.), Sigma Lambda Alpha. Home: 635 Riveroaks Pl Baton Rouge LA 70815-4070 *It is natural that our accomplishments are a contemporary measure of success. But the greater measure and one which will stand the test of time is how much we have done for others.*

MCLOONE, EUGENE P., education educator; b. Phila., Nov. 11, 1929; married. BA, LaSalle Coll., 1951; MS, U. Denver, 1952; PhD, U. Ill., 1961. Rsch. dir. Nat. Ctr. for Edn. Stats./U.S. Dept. Edn., Washington, 1979-81; prof. edn. dept. edn. policy, planning, adminstrn. Coll. of Edn./U. Md., 1975—, assoc. prof., 1967-75, assoc. prof. dept. econs., 1967—; assoc. dir. Rsch. Divsn. NEA, Washington, 1968-69, staff contact, 1968-70; atty. gen. State of N.J., 1981-83, State of W.Va., 1981; cons. Addison-Wesley Pubs., 1992-93, Bur. of Spl. Edn., Dept. Edn., 1992, Jour. Econs. and Edn., 1989-90, Jour. Edn. Fin., 1989-93, Nat. Tax Assn., 1989, office Edn. Rsch. and Improvement, 1989, others; lectr. in field; mem. various rsch. couns.; panel mem. Statis. for Supply and Demand of Pre-Collegiate Sci. and Math Tchrs., Nat. Rsch. Coun., Nat. Acad. Scis., 1986-90, others. Author: Pre-College Science and Mathematics Teachers: Monitoring Supply, Demand, and Quality, 1990, Report of Panel, Toward Understanding Teacher Supply and Demand: Priorities for Research and Development Interim Report, Profiles in School Support, 1969-70; others; co-author: Public School Finance: Profiles of the State, 1979, Documentation and Analysis of Maryland Special Services Information System, 1977, others; contbr. articles to profl. jours.; editor books in field. Grantee Bur. of the Handicapped, U.S.O.E., 1977, Nat. Ctr. for Edn. Stats., 1971, 73, others; recipient numerous awards in field. Mem. Am. Econ. Assn., Am. Assn. Sch. Adminstrs., NEA, Phi Delta Kappa.

MCLOUGHLIN, PHILIP ROBERT, insurance company executive; b. Hartford, Conn., Oct. 23, 1946; s. Elmore Irving and Marie Concetta (Montano) McL.; m. Rose Marie Demeo, Oct. 19, 1974; children: Johanna, Hadley. BA, Middlebury Coll., 1968; JD, U. Chgo., 1971. Bar: Conn. 1971, Mass. 1978. Pres. Phoenix Equity Planning Corp., Hartford, 1982-83, 90—; v.p. Phoenix Mut. Life Ins. Co., Hartford, 1983-84, gen. counsel, 1983-88, sr. v.p., 1984-87, exec. v.p., 1987-89; exec. v.p. investments, 1989—; pres. Big Edge Series Fund, Phoenix Series Fund, Phoenix Total Return Fund, Phoenix Multi-Portfolio Fund. Bd. dirs. United Way of Capital Area, Hartford, mem. exec. com.; trustee Conn. Pub. Expenditure Coun., Hartford. Mem. ABA. Office: Phoenix Mut Life Ins Co One American Row Hartford CT 06115

MC LUCAS, JOHN LUTHER, aerospace company executive; b. Fayetteville, N.C., Aug. 22, 1920; s. John Luther and Viola (Conley) McL.; m. Patricia Knapp, July 27, 1946 (div. 1981); children: Pamela McLucas Byers, Susan, John C., Roderick M.; m. Harriet D. Black, Sept. 25, 1981. B.S., Davidson Coll., 1941; M.S., Tulane U., 1943; Ph.D., Pa. State U., 1950, D.Sc., 1974. V.p., tech. dir. Haller, Raymond & Brown, Inc., State College, Pa., 1950-57; pres. HRB-Singer, Inc., State College, 1958-62; dep. dir. rsch. and engring. Dept. Def., 1962-64; asst. sec.-gen. for sci. affairs NATO, Paris, France, 1964-66; pres., chief exec. officer Mitre Corp., Bedford, Mass., 1966-69; undersec. of Air Force, 1969-73, sec. of Air Force, 1973-75; adminstr. FAA, 1975-77; pres. Comsat Gen. Corp., Washington, 1977-79; exec. v.p. COMSAT, 1979-80, pres. world systems div., 1980-83, exec. v.p., chief strategic officer, 1983-85; chmn. bd. dirs. External Tanks Inc.; bd. dirs. Dulles Access Rapid Transit, Inc., Orbital Scis. Corp.; mem. USAF Sci.

Adv. Bd., 1967-69, 77-84, Def. Sci. Bd., 1968-69; chmn. USAF SDAG, 1979-83; chmn. bd. dirs. Internat. Space U., 1987-93, active, 1987—. Author: Space Commerce, 1991; contbr. articles to tech. lit. Chmn. bd. Wolf Trap Found., 1986-88; chmn. bd. Arthur C. Clarke Found. of U.S.; chmn. bd. dirs. ISY Internat. Space Yr. Assn. U.S., 1987-93; chmn. NASA adv. council, 1988-91. Served with USNR, 1943-46. Recipient Disting. Service award Dept. Def., 1964, 1st bronze palm, 1973, silver palm, 1975. Fellow IEEE, AAAS, AIAA (hon., pres.); mem. NAE (coun. 1988-93), Nat. Rsch. Coun. (chmn. Air Force studies bd. 1987-91), Tower Club, Belle Haven Club, Sigma Xi, Sigma Pi Sigma. Patentee and author in field. Home and Office: 1213 Villamay Blvd Alexandria VA 22307-2051

MCLUCAS, WILLIAM ROBERT, federal agency director; b. Altoona, Pa., Aug. 12, 1950; s. James Daniel and Ruth Virginia (Sweeney) McL. BA in Polit. Sci. with distinction, Pa. State U., 1972; JD, Temple U., 1975. Bar: Pa. 1975. Atty. Fed. Home Loan Bank Bd., 1975-77; successively atty., br. chief, asst. dir., assoc. dir., dir. div. enforcement SEC, Washington, 1977—. Rsch. editor Temple Law Quar., 1972-75; contbr. articles to profl. jours. Mem. Phi Beta Kappa. Office: SEC Div of Enforcement 450 5th St NW Washington DC 20549

MC LURE, CHARLES E., JR., economist; b. Sierra Blanca, Tex., Apr. 14, 1940; s. Charles E. and Dessie (Evans) McL.; m. Patsy Nell Carroll, Sept. 17, 1962. B.A., U. Kans., 1962; M.A., Princeton U., 1964, Ph.D., 1966. Asst. prof. econs. Rice U., Houston, 1965-69, assoc. prof., 1969-72, prof., 1972-79, Allyn R. and Gladys M. Cline prof. econs., 1973-79; exec. dir. for research Nat. Bur. Econ. Research, Cambridge, Mass., 1977-78, v.p., 1978-81; sr. fellow Hoover Instn., Stanford U., 1981—; dep. asst. sec. Dept. Treasury, 1983-85; sr. staff economist Coun. Econ. Advisers, Washington, 1969-70; vis. lectr. U. Wyo., 1972; vis. prof. Stanford U., 1973; cons. U.S. Treasury Dept., Labor Dept., World Bank, UN, OAS, Tax Found., Com. Econ. Devel., IMF, govts. Can., Colombia, Malaysia, Panama, Jamaica, Bolivia, Indonesia, New Zealand, Trinidad and Tobago, Venezuela, Guatemala, Peoples Republic China, Egypt, Malawi, Mex., Bulgaria, Brazil, Russia, Ukraine, Kazakhstan, South Africa. Author: Fiscal Failure: Lessons of the Sixties, 1972, (with N. Ture) Value Added Tax: Two Views, 1972, (with M. Gillis) La Reforma Tributaria Colombiana de 1974, 1977, Must Corporate Income Be Taxed Twice?, 1979, Economic Perperspectives on State Taxation of Multijurisdictional Corporations, 1986, The Value Added Tax: Key to Deficit Reduction, 1987; co-author: Taxation of Income from Business and Capital in Colombia, 1989; also numerous articles on econs. and public finance. Ford Found. faculty research fellow, 1967-68. Mem. Am. Econ. Assn., Nat. Tax Assn., Beta Theta Pi. Home: 250 Yerba Santa Ave Los Altos CA 94022-1609 Office: Stanford U Hoover Instn Stanford CA 94305-6010

MCMACKIN, JOHN WILLIAM, lawyer; b. Effingham, Ill., July 9, 1930; s. John Thomas and Eilene (Wilson) McM.; m. Martha Baldridge, Dec. 3, 1960; children: Patricia Marie, John Thomas II. LLB, U. Ill., 1953. Bar: U.S. Dist. Ct. (no. dist.) Tex. 1958. Assoc. Decker, Jones, McMackin, McClane, Hall & Bates and predecessor firms, Ft. Worth, 1955-60, ptnr., 1960—; chmn. bd. Blessings Corp., Newport News, Va., 1990—; bd. dirs. Williamson-Dickie Mfg. Co., Ft. Worth, NLS Industries Inc., Ft. Worth, Lewis & Lambert Metal Contractors Inc., Ft. Worth. Bd. dirs. N. Tex. Pub. TV, Dallas, 1988-94. 1st lt. USAF, 1953-55. Mem. ABA, Tex. Bar Assn., Tarrant County Bar Assn., River Crest Country Club (bd. dirs. 1978-81). Episcopalian. Office: Decker Jones McMackin McClane Hall & Bates 301 Commerce St Ste 2400 Fort Worth TX 76102-4124

MCMAHAN, JESSE THOMAS, aerospace consulting firm executive; b. Jefferson City, Mo., Feb. 9, 1944; s. Jesse T. and Dorothy Virginia (Stadler) McM.; m. Priscilla Julia Leyne, Nov. 16, 1969. BSEE, U. Mo., Rolla, 1966, MS of Engring. Mgmt., 1973. Commd. 2d lt. USAF, 1968, advanced through grades to col., 1985; engr. U.S. Naval Ordnance Lab., Silver Spring, Md., 1966-68; dir. avionics control Aero. Sys. Divsn. USAF, Dayton, 1986-88; dir. spl. projects Air Force Sys. Command USAF, Andrews AFB, Md., 1988-90; dir. electronic & spl. programs hdqs. USAF, Pentagon, Washington, 1990-93; co-pres. Modern Tech. Solutions, Inc., Alexandria, Va., 1993—. Republican. Episcopalian. Avocations: sailing, running, biking, astronomy, ham radio. Home: 5149 Heritage Ln Alexandria VA 22311 Office: Modern Tech Solutions Inc Ste 206 2121 Eisenhower Ave Alexandria VA 22314

MC MAHAN, JOHN WILLIAM, real estate investment advisor; b. San Antonio, Aug. 4, 1937; s. John William and Lena Margaret (Coleman) McM.; A.B., U. So. Calif., 1959; M.B.A., Harvard U., 1961; m. Jacqueline Mary Cardozo, Sept. 22, 1973; children—Cathy, Jason by previous marriage; children—Justin, Vanessa. Dir. feasibility studies Charles Luckman Assos., 1961-63; founder, prin. Devel. Research Assos., Los Angeles, 1963-70; v.p. real estate services Booz, Allen & Hamilton, N.Y.C., 1970-73; mem. faculty Stanford U. Grad. Sch. Bus., 1974—; founder, prin. John McMahan Real Estate Advisors, Inc., San Francisco, 1976-90; pres., chief exec. officer Mellan/McMahan Reed Estate Advisors, Inc., 1990—. Mem. Soc. Real Estate Counsellors, Urban Land Inst., Am. Econ. Assn., Am. Inst. Planners, Lambda Alpha, Royal Town Planning Inst. U.K. Clubs: Bankers, Jonathan. Author: Property Development: Effective Decision Making in Uncertain Times, 1989; McGraw Hill Real Estate Pocket Guide, 1979; editor: Ency. of Urban Planning, 1973. Office: 201 California St San Francisco CA 94111-5001

MC MAHAN, ROBERT CHANDLER, savings and loan association executive; b. Sevierville, Tenn., June 17, 1940; s. Homer Wright and Cathryn Alexander (Murphy) McM.; m. Judith Ann Raymer, Dec. 23, 1963; children: Kellie Elizabeth, Alice Marie. BBA, Ga. State U., 1972; grad., Sch. Savs. and Loan, U. Ind., 1977. Mgr. Creditthrift Fin. Corp., Tenn., La., Tex. and Ga., 1961-69; with Decatur Fed. Savs. and Loan Assn., Ga., 1969—; sr. v.p., mgr. loan dept. Decatur Fed. Savs. and Loan Assn., 1974-75, exec. v.p., chief operating officer, 1975-84, pres., chief operating officer, 1984—, also dir.; pres., dir. DFS Services, Inc.; dir., sec. Ga. Interchange Network, 1984-86, treas., 1986-87, pres. 1987-88. Bd. dirs. Decatur-DeKalb YMCA, 1974-76, 79-81, sec., 1976; bd. dirs., treas. Goals for DeKalb, 1977-80; mem. Leadership Atlanta, 1976-77, Leadership Ga., 1980; chmn. bd. Med. Assistance for State of Ga., 1982-84; mem. adv. bd. Salvation Army, 1985-87; bd. dirs. Wesley Homes, 1986—, Cotton States Ins. Co., 1987—; bd. dirs. Ga. League of Savs. Insts., 1987—, vice-chmn., 1987—. Served with AUS, 1962-63. Mem. Home Builders Assn. Met. Atlanta (dir.), Ga. League Saving Insts. (vice-chmn. 1987—), Bus. Council Ga. (bd. dirs. 1986-88), DeKalb Bd. Realtors, DeKalb Developers Assn., Citizens for Better Govt., DeKalb C. of C. (v.p., pres. 1981-82), Sigma Phi Omega. Mem. Ch. of Christ. Lodges: Rotary, Masons. Home: 1691 Grove Park Way Decatur GA 30033-1312 Office: Dfsoutheastern Inc 250 E Ponce De Leon Ave Decatur GA 30030-3404

MCMAHON, CATHERINE DRISCOLL, lawyer; b. Mineola, N.Y., Apr. 28, 1950; d. Matthew Joseph and Elizabeth (Driscoll) McM.; m. Gregory Arthur McGrath, Sept. 10, 1977 (div. 1991); children: Elizabeth Driscoll, Kerry Margaret, Michael Riley. BA, Simmons Coll., 1972; JD, Boston Coll., 1975; postgrad., Suffolk U., 1972-73; LL.M., NYU, 1980. Bar: N.Y. 1976, D.C. 1979, U.S. Supreme Ct. 1980, U.S. Tax Ct., 1991. Tax atty. asst. Exxon Corp., N.Y.C., 1975-76, asst. tax atty., 1976-77, sr. tax atty., 1979-81; tax atty. Exxon Internat. Co., N.Y.C., 1977-79, sr. tax counsel, Florham Park, N.J., 1990-92; sr. tax counsel Exxon Co., U.S.A., Houston, 1992—; tax mgr. Exxon Rsch. & Engring. Co., Florham Park, 1981-90. Bd. dirs. S.E. Morris chpt. ARC, Madison, N.J., 1983. Recipient TWIN award YMCA, Plainfield/Westfield, N.J., 1983. Mem. ABA, N.Y. State Bar Assn., D.C. Bar Assn. Roman Catholic. Office: Exxon Co USA 800 Bell Houston TX 77001

MC MAHON, CHARLES JOSEPH, JR., materials science educator; b. Phila., July 10, 1933; s. Charles Joseph and Alice (Schu) McM.; m. Helen June O'Brien, Jan. 31, 1959; children: Christine, Charles, Elise, Robert, David. B.S., U. Pa., 1955; Sc.D., MIT, 1963. Instr. metallurgy MIT, 1958-62, research asst., 1962-63; postdoctoral fellow U. Pa., 1963-64; asst. prof. dept. materials sci. and engring., 1964-68, assoc. prof., 1968-74, prof., 1974—; cons. in field. Editor: Microplasticity, 1968; contbr. articles to profl. jours. Served with USN, 1955-58. Churchill Overseas fellow Churchill Coll., Cambridge U., Eng., 1973-74; recipient Alexander von Humboldt Sr.

U.S. Scientist award, U. Göttingen, 1983-84. Fellow AIME, Am. Soc. Metals, Nat. Acad. Engring., Inst. Metals U.K.; mem. AAAS, U.S. Rowing Assn., Vesper Boat Club (Phila.). Democrat. Roman Catholic. Home: 7103 Sherman St Philadelphia PA 19119-3306 Office: U Pa Philadelphia PA 19104

MCMAHON, COLLEEN, lawyer; b. Columbus, Ohio, July 18, 1951; d. John Patrick and Patricia Paterson (McDanel) McM.; m. Frank V. Sica, May 16, 1981; children: Moira Catherine, Patrick McMahon, Brian Vincent. BA summa cum laude, Ohio State U., 1973; JD cum laude, Harvard U., 1976. Bar: N.Y. 1977, U.S. Dist. Ct. (so. and ea. dists.) N.Y. 1977, U.S. Ct. Appeals (2d cir.) 1978, U.S. Supreme Ct. 1980, U.S. Ct. Appeals (5th cir.) 1985, D.C. 1985. Spl. asst. U.S. mission to the UN, N.Y.C., 1979-80; assoc. Paul, Weiss, Rifkind, Wharton & Garrison, N.Y.C., 1976-79, 80-84, ptnr., 1984—; bd. dirs., gen. counsel Danceworks, Inc., N.Y.C., 1977-83; mem. Coun. N.Y. Law Assocs., 1977-81; chair The Jury Project, N.Y. Office Ct. Adminstrn., 1993—. Bd. dirs. Vol. Lawyers for the Arts, N.Y.C., 1979-83, Dance Theater Workshop, 1978-83; vice chancellor Episcopal Diocese of N.Y. Mem. ABA, Assn. of Bar of City of N.Y. (mem. coun. on jud. adminstrn. 1983-89, chmn. com. on state cts. of superior jurisdiction 1983-86, com. on women profession 1989—, chmn. 1992—), Am. Law Inst., Am. Judicature Soc., Westchester County Bar Assn., N.Y. State Bar Assn. (mem. ho. of dels. 1986-89), Fed. Bar Coun. Republican. Episcopalian. Office: Paul Weiss Rifkind Wharton & Garrison 1285 Avenue Of The Americas New York NY 10019-6028

MCMAHON, DONALD AYLWARD, investor, corporate director; b. N.Y.C., Feb. 20, 1931; s. William F. and Anne (Aylward) McM.; m. Nancy Lantz, Apr. 12, 1953; children: Gail, Brian, Lisa, Glenn, Ann, Carol, William, Douglas. M.B.A., Emory U., 1982. With Dime Savs. Bank, Bklyn., 1952; salesman Monroe Calculating Machine Co., Bklyn., 1952-55; asst. br. mgr. Monroe Calculating Machine Co., Pitts., 1955-56; br. mgr. Monroe Calculating Machine Co., Phila., 1956-63; asst. gen. sales mgr. Monroe Calculating Machine Co., Orange, N.J., 1963-64; Eastern regional gen. sales mgr. Monroe Calculating Machine Co., 1964-65, v.p. mktg., 1965-66; pres. Monroe Calculator Co. div. Litton Industries, Inc., Orange, 1966-70; v.p. Litton Industries, 1967-70; pres., chief operating officer, dir. Baker Industries, Inc., Parsippany, N.J., 1970-74; pres., chief exec. officer, dir. Royal Crown Cos., Inc., Atlanta, 1975-85; bd. dirs. Intelligent Systems Corp., Atlanta, Norrell Corp., Atlanta. Bd. dirs. Boys Clubs Metro Atlanta. Mem. Sovereign Order of Knights of Malta. Home: 1665 Winterthur Close NW Atlanta GA 30328-4688

MC MAHON, ED, television personality; b. Detroit, Mar. 6, 1923; children: Claudia, Michael, Linda, Jeffrey, Katherine Mary, Alexis. Ed., Boston Coll.; B.A., Cath. U. Am. TV announcer: Tonight Show, 1962-92; appeared in films The Incident, 1967, Fun with Dick and Jane, 1975, Butterfly; host TV series The Kraft Music Hall, 1968, Whodunnit?, 1979, TV's Bloopers and Practical Jokes, Ed McMahon's Star Search; host TV specials: Thanksgiving Day Parade, (co-host) Jerry Lewis Labor Day Telethon; numerous other TV appearances; appeared on Broadway in The Impossible Years. Active Muscular Dystrophy Assn. With USMC, PTO; col. res., ret. Address: care Walt Disney World Co 1675 Buena Vista Dr Ste 410 Lake Buena Vista FL 32830*

MCMAHON, EDWARD FRANCIS, oil industry executive, consultant; b. N.Y.C., Dec. 13, 1930; s. Edward Francis and Ellen (Tully) McM.; m. Rosemary Freda McMahon, Feb. 5, 1955; children: Ned, Mary Ellen, Tracey Ann, Thomas, Mark. BCE, Villanova U., 1954; MBA, CUNY, 1957; postgrad., Stanford U., 1970. Gen. mgr. polymers group Shell Chem. Co., Houston, 1975-81; gen. mgr. comm. sales Shell Refining & Mktg., Houston, 1981-83, v.p. supplies and transp., 1983-85; exec. v.p. Atlantic Refining and Mktg., King of Prussia, Pa., 1985-87; v.p. Solomon Assocs., Dallas, 1987-90; pres. McMahon Assocs., Houston, 1992-93, 94—, Kerr-McGee Refining Corp., Houston, 1991-94; adj. prof. So. Meth. U., Dallas, 1989. Lt. USN, 1954-57. Stanford/Sloan fellow, 1969-70. Mem. Am. Mgmt. Assn., Am. Petroleum Inst., Sugar Creek Country Club, Houston City Club. Roman Catholic. Avocation: reading. Home: 211 Laurel Springs Ct Sugar Land TX 77478

MCMAHON, EDWARD PETER, systems engineer, consultant; b. Jersey City, May 30, 1940; s. Edward Patrick and Blanche Elizabeth (Verbout) McM.; m. Barbara Ann Reedy, May 7, 1966; children: Joseph, James. AB, BEE, Cath. U. Am., 1963; SMEE, MIT, 1964; PhD, Poly. Inst. Bklyn., 1969. Engr. GE, King of Prussia, Pa., 1964-70; systems engr. GE, Washington, 1970-71; dir. optics system dept. Gen. Rsch. Corp., Arlington, Va., 1971-74; mem. staff CIA, Washington, 1974-81; mem. tech. staff MRJ, Inc., Oakton, Va., 1981-86, v.p., 1986-87, pres., 1987—. Dir. Perkin-Elmer Advanced Devel. Ctr., 1986; cubmaster, asst. scoutmaster Nat. Capitol Area coun. Boy Scouts Am., 1977-86; chmn. edn. com N.Va.Tech. Coun., 1992—; mem. supts. bus. and industry adv. com. Fairfax Pub. Schs., 1992—. Mem. IEEE, Ops. Rsch. Soc. Am., Phi Beta Kappa, Sigma Xi (assoc.), Tau Beta Pi. Republican. Roman Catholic. Avocations: fine art photography, woodworking, hiking, cross-country skiing, model making. Home: 8224 Inverness Hollow Ter Rockville MD 20854-2726

MCMAHON, ELEANOR MARIE, education educator; b. Pawtucket, R.I., Oct. 25, 1929; d. William Frank and Anne Angela (Cunningham) Hess; m. Richard P. McMahon, Feb. 14, 1927. B.S. summa cum laude, Coll. of St. Elizabeth, Convent Station, N.J., 1950, H.H.D. (hon.), 1975; M.A., Brown U., 1954; Ed.D., Harvard U., 1967; D.Pedagogy (hon.), Mt. St. Josph Coll., Wakefield, R.I., 1974; Sem. of Our Lady of Providence, 1975; Hum.D. (hon.), Providence Coll., 1976; LLD, Regis Coll., 1985, EdD (hon.) Roger Williams Coll., 1986; D in Pub. Svc. (hon.) R.I. Coll., 1988. Dir. lab. experiences R.I. Coll., Providence, 1968-70, assoc. dean ednl. studies, 1970-71, dean ednl. studies, 1971-77, acting exec. dir. coll. advancement and support, 1977-78, provost, v.p. acad. affairs, 1978-82; commr. higher edn. State of R.I., Providence, 1982-89; fellow Brown U., 1988—; regent Seton Hall U., S. Orange, N.J., 1992—; Disting. vis. prof. Alfred Taubman Ctr., Brown U., 1989—; vis. prof. dept. govt. Georgetown U., 1990-94; sec.-treas., exec. com. New Eng. Assn. Schs. and Colls., 1982, pres., 1988-89; vice chmn. coun. on acad. affairs. mem. coll. bd., 1984-87; mem. Edn. Commn. of States, Denver, 1983-89, New Eng. Bd. Higher Edn., Boston, 1984—, chair-elect, 1985-86; active Nat. Com. on Higher Edn. Governance, 1995—. Contbr. articles to profl. publs. Mem. R.I. Strategic Devel. Commn., 1982-84; mem. gov.'s vis. com. to U. Maine, 1984-86; chmn. R.I. Commn. EC 1992, 1989-92, Gov. Econ. Strategy Task Force, 1991-92; mem. Rockefeller Brothers Fund Minority Fellowship Program, 1990-94; mem. steering com. R.I. Project on Rethinking Govt., 1992—; mem. Providence Blueprint for Edn. Commn., 1991-93; mem. corp., mem. exec. com. Providence Coll., 1974-82, Pres. Coun., 1982—; trustee Coll. of St. Elizabeth, 1967-72, Providence Country Day Sch., East Providence, R.I., 1975-81, 90-92; alumnae trustee Brown U., 1985-88. Named to R.I. Hall of Fame, 1986; recipient Outstanding Community Service award Blackstone Valley Jr. Women's Club, 1976, Outstanding Woman award R.I. chpt. Internat. Fedn. Catholic Alumnae, 1977, Disting. Svc. award R.I. Bd. Govs., 1989, Disting. Pub. Svc. award R.I. ASPA, 1989, Disting. Svc. award, R.I. Pub. Expenditure Coun., 1987, Brotherhood award NCCJ, 1992. Roman Catholic. Avocations: travel, reading. Office: Alfred Taubman Ctr Pub Policy & Am Instns Brown U Providence RI 02912

MCMAHON, GARY FRANCIS, accountant; b. Flandreau, S.D., Aug. 31, 1937; s. James Merohan and Eleanora B. (Lemon) McM. Johnson; m. Shirley J. Hahn, Sept. 6, 1958; children—Callae, Michele, Michael. B.S., U. S.D., 1959; M.B.A., U. Wis., 1960. C.P.A., Colo. Acct. Deloitte Haskins & Sells, Denver, 1961-71, ptnr., 1971-77, ptnr.-in-charge, 1977-83, regional mng. ptnr., 1983—. Bd. dirs., treas. Colo. Outward Bound Sch., Denver, 1978-82, trustee, 1982-88; bd. dirs. Boys Clubs Denver, 1980-85, Colo. Council on Econ. Edn., Boulder, 1979-88. Served as lt. U.S. Army, 1960. Named Alumnus of Yr., U. S.D., 1973. Mem. AICPA, Colo. Soc. CPAs, Nat. Assn. Accts. Republican. Roman Catholic. Clubs: Denver (pres. 1982-83), Denver Country. Lodge: Rotary (bd. dirs. Denver 1978-83, pres. 1983-84). Home: 1603 Dowling Dr Irving TX 75038-5947 Office: Deloitte & Touche 1400 Lincoln Pla Lb # 4 Dallas TX 75201

MC MAHON, GEORGE JOSEPH, academic administrator; b. N.Y.C., June 20, 1923; s. Martin Joseph and Mary (O'Connor) McM. A.B., Woodstock Coll., 1946, Ph.L., 1947, M.A., 1948, S.T.L., 1954; M.A., Fordham U.,

---

1951; Ph.D., Laval U., 1959. Joined Soc. of Jesus, 1940; ordained priest Roman Catholic Ch., 1953; instr. physics and Latin Regis High Sch., N.Y.C., 1947-49; instr. philosophy St. Peter's Coll., Jersey City, 1958-60; asst. dean. dir. St. Peter's Coll. (Sch. Bus. Adminstrn.), 1961-62; instr. philosophy Loyola Sem., Shrub Oak, N.Y., 1960-61; dean Fordham Coll., Fordham U., Bronx, N.Y., 1962-74, v.p. adminstrn. Fordham U., 1974-87, v.p. Lincoln Ctr. campus, 1987-94, chaplain, 1994—. Author: The Order of Procedure in the Philosophy of Nature, 1958, The Proemium to the Physics of Aristotle, 1957. Vice pres. Friends of U. Laval, Que., Can.; trustee Marymount Sch. N.Y., Wheeling (W.Va.) Coll., Xavier High Sch., N.Y.C.

MCMAHON, JOHN ALEXANDER, lawyer, educator; b. Monongahela, Pa., July 31, 1921; s. John Hamilton and Jean (Alexander) McM.; m. Betty Wagner, Sept. 14, 1947 (div. Mar. 1977); children: Alexander Talpey, Sarah Francis, Elizabeth Wagner, Ann Wallace; m. Anne Fountain Willets, May 1, 1977. A.B. magna cum laude, Duke U., 1942; student, Harvard U. Bus. Sch., 1942-43; J.D., Law Sch., 1948; LL.D., Wake Forest U., 1978; D.Sc. (hon.), Georgetown U. Sch. Medicine, 1985. Bar: N.C. 1950. Prof. pub. law and govt., asst. dir. Inst. Govt. U. N.C., 1948-59; gen. counsel, sec.-treas. N.C. Assn. County Commrs., Chapel Hill, 1959-65; v.p. spl. devel. Hosp. Saving Assn., Chapel Hill, N.C., 1965-67; pres. N.C. Blue Cross and Blue Shield, Inc., Chapel Hill, 1968-72, Am. Hosp. Assn., Chgo., 1972-86; chmn. dept. health adminstrn. Duke U., Durham, N.C., 1986-92, exec.-in-residence Fuqua Sch. Bus., 1992—; mem. Chapel Hill bd. N.C. Nat. Bank, 1967-72; bd. govs. Blue Cross Assn., 1969-72; mem. Orange County Welfare Bd., 1956-63; chmn. N.C. Comprehensive Health Planning Coun., 1968-72, Health Planning Coun. of Central N.C., 1963-69; mem. President's Com. on Health Edn., 1971-72; mem. com. health services industry and health industry adv. com. Econ. Stablzn. Program, 1971-74; mem. adv. coun. Kate Bitting Reynolds Health Care Trust, 1971—; mem. adv. coun. Northwestern U., 1973-86; mem. med. adv. com. VA, 1975-85; bd. dirs. Community Health Care Found. Inc., San Francisco, Eason, Earl and Assocs., Greenville, S.C., The Forest at Duke, Durham, N.C. Author: North Carolina County Government, 1959, The North Carolina Local Government Commission, 1960; editor: N.C. County Yearbook, 1959-64, Proceedings of the Annual National Forum on Hospital and Health Affairs, 1993—. Mem. Orange County Dem. Exec. Com., also chmn. Kings Mill Precinct, 1964-68; chmn. bd. trustees Duke U., 1971-83, chmn. emeritus, 1983—; bd. dirs. Rsch. Triangle Found., 1971-83, 92—, Nat. Ctr. for Health Edn., 1974-86; bd. mgrs., mem. exec. com. Internat. Hosp. Fedn., London, 1975-85, pres., 1981-83. With USAAF, 1942-46, col. Res., ret. Mem. N.C. State Bar, Inst. Medicine of NAS, N.C. Citizens Assn. (bd. dirs. 1972), Duke Alumni Assn. (pres. 1968-70), Hope Valley Country Club (Durham), Dunes Golf and Beach Club (Myrtle Beach). Presbyterian. Home: 181 Winterthur Dr Durham NC 27707-3929 Office: Duke U Fuqua Sch Bus Durham NC 27708-0120

MCMAHON, JOHN PATRICK, lawyer; b. Monroeville, Ohio, Feb. 8, 1919; s. George James and Eleanor Helene (Ruffing) McM.; m. Patricia Patterson McDanel, May 6, 1950 (dec. July 1983); children: Colleen, Kevin, Patricia, Brian, Barry, Michael; m. Mary Echard, Mar. 7, 1987. B.A. cum laude, Ohio State U., 1940, J.D. summa cum laude, 1942. Bar: Ohio 1942, U.S. Supreme Ct. 1949, U.S. Dist. Ct. Ohio 1949, U.S. Ct. Appeals (6th cir.) 1959, U.S. Ct. Appeals (D.C. cir.) 1975. Ptnr. George, Greek, King, McMahon, Columbus, Ohio, 1954-79, Baker & Hostetler, Columbus, 1979-85; with nat. coun. Ohio State U. Coll. Law, 1980—. Trustee Columbus Cancer Clinic, 1982. Served to capt. USAAF, 1943-46, PTO. Mem. ABA, Ohio Bar Assn., Columbus Bar Assn., Transp. Lawyers Assn., Univ. Club (Columbus), Maennerchor (Columbus), Pres.' Club of Ohio State U. (Columbus). Clubs: University (Columbus), Faculty (Columbus), Pres.' of Ohio State U. (Columbus). Home: 2580 Halstead Rd Columbus OH 43221-2916 Office: Baker & Hostetler 65 E State St Columbus OH 43215-4213

MCMAHON, JOSEPH EINAR, lawyer, consultant; b. Chgo., Aug. 26, 1940; s. Reynold Bernard and Dorothy Marie (Oftedahl) McM. B.A. cum laude, Denison U., 1962; J.D., U. Mich., 1965. Bar: Mass. 1968, D.C. 1980. Asst. to Atty. Gen. and Senator Edward Brooke, Boston and Washington, 1965-67; exec. asst. Lt. Gov. Sargent of Mass., Boston, 1967-69; v.p. BedStuy D&S Corp. Restoration, Bklyn., 1969-74; dir. govt. regulations Westinghouse Electric Corp., Washington, 1974-78; v.p. corp. affairs Federated Dept. Stores, Cin., 1978-80; atty., cons. McMahon and Assocs., Washington, 1980—; exec. dir. (part time), bd. dirs. The Get Ahead Found./USA, 1991—. Trustee Denison U.; visitor U. Mich. Law Sch.; 1st v.p. Boston Rep. Com., 1968-69; presdl. appointee Nat. Coun. Econ. Opportunity, 1975-76; exec. dir. Nat. Bus. for Reagan-Bush Com., 1980; dir. Luther Inst., Washington, Fgn. Students Svc. Coun., Rodale Inst., Emmaus, Pa.; trustee Gettysburg Luth. Sem.; dir. Luth. Lesbian and Gay Min., San Francisco. Mem. Phi Delta Phi, Pi Sigma Alpha, Omicron Delta Kappa. Lutheran. Clubs: Nat. Press, University, Capitol Hill (Washington). Office: McMahon & Assocs 1924 N St NW Washington DC 20036-1604

MCMAHON, MAEVE, principal. Prin. St. Leo the Great Elem. Sch., New Orleans. Recipient DOE Elem. Sch. Recognition Program award, 1989-90. Office: St Leo the Great Elem Sch 1501 Abundance St New Orleans LA 70119

MCMAHON, MARIBETH LOVETTE, physicist; b. Bradford, Pa., June 8, 1949; d. James Harry and Josephine Rose (Sylvester) Lovette; m. Frank Joseph MaMahon, Nov. 19, 1976. B.S. in Math., Pa. State U., 1971, B.S. in Physics, 1971, M.S. in Physics, 1974; Ph.D. in Physics, 1976. Research asst. Pa. State U., 1971-76; advanced research and devel. engr. GTE Sylvania, Danvers, Mass., 1976-78; sr. physicist 3M Co., St. Paul, 1978-79, market devel. supr., 1979-83; market devel. mgr. Galileo Electro-Optics Corp., Sturbridge, Mass., 1983-84; product mgr. Varian Assocs., Lexington, Mass., 1984-85; mktg. dir. Bowmar, Acton, Mass., 1985-86; pres. Kilduff Inc., Sturbridge, Mass., 1986—. Recipient Cert. in Appreciation of Service Pa. State U., 1971. Mem. Optical Soc. Am., Assn. Women in Sci., Assn. Physicists in Medicine, Sigma Pi Sigma, Sigma Xi. Home: 160 Brookfield Rd Fiskdale MA 01518-1136 Office: Kilduff Inc Sturbridge MA 01566

MCMAHON, PAUL FRANCIS, international management consultant; b. Malone, N.Y., Apr. 28, 1945; s. Philip Francis and Shirley (Roy) M.; m. Sheila Ann Lester, Nov. 30, 1963; children—Michael, Marsha. B.S., Syracuse U., 1968. CPA, N.Y.; cert. mgmt. acct., cert. mgmt. cons. Various staff positions Ernst & Young, Syracuse, N.Y., 1968-73, mgr., 1975-79; ptnr. in charge of mgmt. cons. in Europe Ernst & Young, Brussels, 1979-84; vice chmn. Ernst & Young, Cleve., 1984-87; exec. ptnr. Ernst & Young Internat., N.Y., 1987-93; chmn. Ernst & Young Ea. Europe, 1990-93; regional dir. Asia/Pacific Ernst & Young Internat., Singapore, 1994—; controller Coop. Mktg. Agy., Syracuse, 1973-75. Treas. Bus. Coun. for Internat. Understanding. Mem. AICPA, N.Y. Soc. CPA's, Inst. Mgmt. Acctg., Assn. Mgmt. Cons. Firms (dir.), Coun. Cons. Orgns. (past chmn.). Democrat. Roman Catholic. Avocations: photography, natural history, travel, gardening, biographies. Home: 239 Arcadia Rd 02-03 Arcadia Gdn, Singapore 1128, Singapore Office: Ernst & Young Internat, PO Box 384, Singapore 9007, Singapore

MCMAHON, TERRENCE JOHN, foreign service officer; b. Rockford, Ill., Aug. 7, 1936; s. Hugh Raymond McMahon and Lucille Isabelle (Hayes) Driscoll; m. Phyllis Ruth Anderson, Dec. 2, 1967; children: Kevin, Michael, Kathleen, Marianne. BS in Accountancy, U. Ill., 1958; M Internat. Pub. Policy, Johns Hopkins U., 1983. CPA, Ill. Audit supr. Coopers and Lybrand, Rockford, Ill., 1958-68; fin. analyst U.S. AID, Washington, 1968-70; dep. contr. U.S. AID, Rio de Janeiro, 1970-73; contr. U.S. AID, Kabul, Afghanistan, 1973-77, Amman, Jordan, 1977-79; dep. contr. U.S. AID, Washington, 1979-83; contr. U.S. AID, Cairo, 1983-86; dir. Office of Procurement U.S. AID, Washington 1986-92; dir. U.S. AID, Kiev, Ukraine, 1993-95. Recipient Presdl. Meritorious Svc. award for fgn. svc. Pres. of U.S., 1985, 92. Mem. AICPA. Roman Catholic. Avocations: fishing, boating, travel. Home: 10 Bay View St Sequim WA 98382

MCMAHON, THOMAS ARTHUR, biology and applied mechanics educator; b. Dayton, Ohio, Apr. 21, 1943; s. Howard Oldford and Lucille (Nelson) McM.; m. Carol Ehlers, June 20, 1965; children: James Robert, Elizabeth Kirsten. B.S., Cornell U., 1965; S.M., MIT, 1967, Ph.D., 1970. Postdoctoral fellow Harvard U., Cambridge, Mass., 1969-70, lectr. bioengring., 1970-71, asst. prof., 1971-74, assoc. prof., 1974-77, prof. applied mechanics and biology, 1977—; cons. numerous industries, legal firms. Author: (novels), Principles of American Nuclear Chemistry, 1970, McKay's Bees, 1979, Loving Little Egypt, 1987; (non-Fiction) Muscles, Reflexes and Locomotion, 1984; (with others) On Size and Life, 1983. Grantee NIH; System Devel. Found., Sloan Found.; recipient Richard and Hinde Rosenthal award Am. Acad. and Inst. Arts and Letters, 1988. Mem. Biomed. Engring. Soc., Am. Physiol. Soc., N.Y. Acad. Scis., PEN. Home: 65 Crest Rd Wellesley MA 02181-4620 Office: Harvard U Dept Applied Scis Pierce Hall Cambridge MA 02138

MCMAHON, THOMAS MICHAEL, lawyer; b. Evanston, Ill., May 11, 1941; s. Robert C. and Kathryn D. (Dwyer) McM.; m. M. Ann Kaufman, July 11, 1964; children—Michael, Patrick. Student: U. Notre Dame, 1959-61; B.A., Marquette U., 1963; J.D. magna cum laude, Northwestern U., 1970. Bar: Ill. 1970. Mgr. legal adv. sect. Ill. EPA, Springfield, 1970-72; assoc. firm Sidley & Austin, Chgo., 1972-75, ptnr., founder nat. environ. group, 1975—; lectr. environ. law Euromoney, Centaur and Inst. for Internat. Rsch. confs., London, Japanese EPA Conf., Tokyo; mem. City of Evanston Environ. Control Bd., 1981-83. Author: The Superfund Handbook, 1989, International Environmental Law and Regulation, 1992, Legal Guide to Working with Environmental Consultants, 1992, The Environmental Manual, 1992. Served to lt. USN, 1963-67. Decorated Republic of Vietnam Campaign medal. Mem. ABA (vice chmn. environ. quality com. and environ. aspects of bus. trans. com., vice chmn. internat. environ. law com., lectr. confs., teleconfs. and satellite seminars), U.K. Environ. Law Assn., Order of Coif. Office: Sidley & Austin 1 First Nat Plz Chicago IL 60603

MCMAINS, MELVIN L(EE), controller; b. Oskaloosa, Iowa, Aug. 1, 1941; m. Kathryn Elaine Murphy; children: Kimberly, Lindsay. BA, U. Northern Iowa, 1966, MA, 1968. CPA, Iowa; CMA. Corp. contr., chief acctg. officer HON Industries, Inc., Muscatine, Iowa, 1979—. Mem. AICPA, Fin. Execs. Inst., Iowa Soc. CPA's, Inst. Mgmt. Accts., Geneva Golf and Country Club. Office: HON Industries PO Box 1109 Muscatine IA 52761-7109

MCMANIGAL, SHIRLEY ANN, university dean; b. Deering, Mo., May 4, 1938; d. Jadie C. and Willie B. (Groves) Naile. BS, Ark. State U., 1971; MS, U. Okla., 1976, PhD, 1979. Lic. med. technologist, clin. lab. dir. Med. technologist, 1958-75; chair dept. med. tech. U. So. Miss., Hattiesburg, 1979-83; chair dept. med. tech. Tex. Tech U. Health Scis. Ctr., Lubbock, 1983-87, dean Sch. Allied Health, 1987—; gov.'s appointee to statewide health coord. coun., 1994—. Leadership Tex., 1992; Lt. Alumnae Regl. dir., 1994—. Recipient Citation, State of Tex., 1988; named Woman of Yr., AAUW, Tex. div., 1990, Woman of Excellence in Edn. YWCA, Lubbock, 1990. Mem. AAUW (bd. dirs. Tex. 1990-94), Am. Coun. on Edn./Nat. Identification Program (steering com. for Tex.), Clin. Lab. Mgmt. Assn. (chair edn. com. 1989, 91), Am. Soc. Med. Tech., Nat. Assn. Women in Edn., So. Assn. Allied Health Deans at Acad. Health Ctrs., S.W. Assn. Clin. Microbiology, Tex. Soc. Allied Health Professions (pres. 1990-91), Tex. Soc. Med. Tech. (Educator of Yr. 1990), Alpha Eta, Phi Beta Delta (gov. appointee to statewide health coord. coun. 1994—). Home: 5003 94th St Lubbock TX 79424-4813 Office: Tex Tech U Health Scis Ctr Sch Allied Health Lubbock TX 79430

MCMANMON, THOMAS ARTHUR, JR., oil industry executive; b. Boston, Sept. 10, 1943; s. T. Arthur and Maura (Sullivan) M.; m. Suzanne Cole, Nov. 17, 1973; children: Katherine, Suzanne, Thomas III. BA in History, U. Notre Dame, 1966; MBA, Dartmouth Coll., 1968. V.p. N.E. Merchants Bank, Boston, 1968-77; sr. v.p. Entwistle Corp., Hudson, Mass., 1977-78, Global Petroleum Corp., Waltham, Mass., 1978—; dir. Griffith Consumers Corp., Cheverly, Md., 1985—, Atlantic Petroleum Corp., Chelsea, Mass., 1989, Montello Oil Corp., Waltham, Mass., 1980, Carl King, Dover,Del., 1985, Nimrod Nat. Gas, Tulsa. Dir. New England Fuel Inst., Watertown, Mass., 1980—. Mem. Marion-Beverly Yacht Club, Sippican Tennis Club, Boston Algonquin Club, Brookline Country Club. Office: Global Petroleum Corp 800 South St Waltham MA 02154-1439

MCMANUS, CHARLES E., school system administrator. Supt. schs. Diocese of Worcester, Mass. Office: Sch Dept 49 Elm St Worcester MA 01609-2514

MCMANUS, DECLAN PATRICK See COSTELLO, ELVIS

MCMANUS, EDWARD HUBBARD, government official; b. Roxbury, Mass., Jan. 11, 1939; s. Paul Carter and Dorothy (Shaw) McM.; m. Sharon Pickett, Feb. 10, 1968; children: Kevin, Keith, Michael. B.A., U. Mass., 1960; M.A., U. Wis., 1970. Mgmt. analyst Bur. Internat. Commerce, Dept. Commerce, Washington, 1965-66; asst. to adminstrv. officer NIMH, NIH, Bethesda, Md., 1966-68; adminstrv. officer div. research resources NIH, Bethesda, 1968-69; asst. exec. officer div. research resources NIH, Bethesda, Md., 1970-71; fin. mgmt. officer Nat. Library Medicine, Bethesda, 1971-73; exec. officer Nat. Eye Inst., Bethesda, 1973-81, dep. dir., 1981—. Served to lt. (j.g.) USN, 1961-64. Mem. Am. Mgmt. Assn., Am. Soc. Pub. Adminstrv., Internat. Agy. for Prevention of Blindness (exec. bd.). Office: Nat Eye Inst 31/6A05 31 Center Dr MSC 2510 Bethesda MD 20892

MC MANUS, EDWARD JOSEPH, federal judge; b. Keokuk, Iowa, Feb. 9, 1920; s. Edward W. and Kathleen (O'Connor) McM.; m. Sally A. Hassett, June 30, 1948 (dec.); children: David P., Edward W., John N., Thomas J., Dennis Q.; m. Esther Y. Kanealy, Sept. 15, 1987. Student, St. Ambrose Coll., 1936-38; B.A., U. Iowa, 1940, J.D., 1942. Bar: Iowa 1942. Gen. practice of law Keokuk, 1946-62, city atty., 1946-55; mem. Iowa Senate, 1955-59; lt. gov. Iowa, 1959-61; chief U.S. judge No. Dist. Iowa, 1962-85, sr. U.S. judge, 1985—. Del Democratic Nat. Conv., 1956, 60. Served as lt. AC USNR, 1942-46. Office: US Dist Ct 329 US Courthouse 101 1st St SE Cedar Rapids IA 52407-4825

MCMANUS, HUGH F., principal. Prin. John T. Hoggard High Sch., Wilmington, N.C. Recipient Blue Ribbon Sch. award, 1990-91. Office: John T Hoggard High Sch 4305 Shipyard Blvd Wilmington NC 28403

MCMANUS, JAMES WILLIAM, lawyer; b. Kansas City, Mo., Aug. 1, 1945; s. Gerald B. and Mary M. (Hagan) McM.; m. Julie C. Waters, Feb. 17, 1973. BA, Rockhurst Coll., 1967; JD, St. Louis U., 1971. Bar: Mo. 1971, U.S. Dist. Ct. (we. dist.) Mo. 1972, U.S. Ct. Appeals (8th cir.) 1974, U.S. Supreme Ct. 1979. Law clk. to presiding justice U.S. Dist. Ct. (we. dist.) Mo., 1971-73; assoc. Shughart, Thomson & Kilroy, P.C., Kansas City, 1973-76, dir., 1977-94; counsel Dysart, Taylor, Penner, Lay & Lewandowski, P.C., Kansas City, 1994—; course lectr. med. jurisprudence U. Health Scis., Coll. Osteo. Medicine, Kansas City, 1994. Mem. adv. coun. St. Joseph Health Ctr., 1989—. Mem. ABA, Mo. Bar Assn., Kansas City Lawyers Assn., Kansas City Met. Bar Assn. (vice chmn. alt. dispute resolution com. 1994-95, chmn. med. malpractice com. 1989), Mo. Orgn. Def. Lawyers, St. Louis Alumni Assn. (pres. 1984-92), St. Louis U Law Sch. Alumni Assns. Home: 6824 Valley Rd Kansas City MO 64113-1929 Office: Dysart Taylor Penner Lay & Lewandowski PC 4420 Madison Ave Kansas City MO 64111-1917

MCMANUS, JAMES WILLIAM, chemist, researcher; b. Atlanta, Oct. 7, 1944; s. Claude William and Sara Louise (Cook) McM.; m. Ruth Krieger, Apr. 10, 1971; children: Angela Ruth, Meagan Joy. BS in Chemistry, Auburn U., 1971. Mgr. Cook's Grocery Co., Atlanta, 1970-73; analytical chemist North Chem. Co., Atlanta, 1973-74; staff chemist, 1975-76, sr. staff chemist, 1976-78, sr. chemist, 1978-89, rsch. fellow, 1989—; bd. dirs. M. Taylor, Inc., Albany, 1988—, rsch. fellow, 1989-94, chmn. chemistry sect., 1994—. Mem. editorial bd. Process Control and Quality, 1990—; inventor, patentee in field. Mem. Am. Chem. Soc. (cert.). Republican. Baptist. Office: Merck and Co Inc 3517 Radium Springs Rd Albany GA 31705-9596

MCMANUS, JASON DONALD, editor; b. Mission, Kans., Mar. 3, 1934; s. John Alan and Stella Frances (Gosney) McM.; m. Patricia Ann Paulson, Oct. 18, 1958 (div. Feb. 1966); 1 child, John Alan; m. Deborah Hall Murphy, Dec. 2, 1973; children: Sophie Eleanor, Mage Caroline. B.A., Davidson Coll., 1956, Litt.D. (hon.), 1979; M.P.A., Princeton U., 1958;

postgrad., Oxford U., 1958-59; LittD (hon.), Monmouth Coll., 1988, U. N.C., 1991, Loyola U., Balt., 1992. Common Market bur. chief Time Mag., Paris, 1962-64; assoc. editor Time Mag., N.Y.C., 1964-68, sr. editor, 1968-75, asst. mng. editor, 1975-78, exec. editor, 1978-83, mng. editor, 1985-87; corp. editor Time Inc., N.Y.C., 1983-85; editor-in-chief Time Warner Inc., N.Y.C., 1987-95. Author: short stories Introduction, 1960. Mem. presdl. adv. commn. Internat. Edn. Exchange, 1982-83. Rhodes scholar, 1958-59. Club: Century Assn. (N.Y.C.). Office: Time & Life Bldg New York NY 10020

MCMANUS, JOHN FRANCIS, association executive, writer; b. Bklyn., Jan. 24, 1935; s. V. Paul and Dorothy F. (Devenport) McM.; m. Mary Helen O'Reilly, Oct. 19, 1957; children: John G., Margaret A., Paul J., Mary Anne Power. BS in Physics, Holy Cross Coll., 1957. Elec. engr. Transitron Corp., Wakefield, Mass., 1960-66; field coord. The John Birch Soc., Belmont, Mass., 1966-68, projects mgr., 1968-73, dir. pub. rels., 1973-91; pres. The John Birch Soc., Appleton, Wis., 1991—. Author: An Overview of Our World, 1971, The Insiders: Architects of the New World Order, 1992, 4th edit., 1995, Financial Terrorism: Hijacking America Under the Threat of Bankruptcy, 1993, Changing Commands: The Betrayal of America's Military, 1995; author weekly column, 1973—. Lt. USMC, 1957-60, capt., USMCR, 1960-68. Avocations: reading, golf, family. Home: PO Box 3076 Wakefield MA 01880-0772 Office: John Birch Society PO Box 8040 Appleton WI 54913-8040

MCMANUS, JOHN FRANCIS, III, advertising executive; b. Bklyn., Mar. 8, 1919; s. John Francis and Helen Jane (Cleary) McM.; m. Regina Delores Smith, Feb. 12, 1942 (div. June 1950); m. Sara Grace Scerra, Mar. 8, 1951 (dec. Aug. 1970); children: John Francis IV, Jane Frances, Stephan George, Kathleen Elizabeth; m. Jane Caroline Lewis, Apr. 25, 1974. BFA, Cooper Union Inst. Art, N.Y.C., 1941; student, Silvermine Guild Art Ctr., Norwalk, Conn., 1987, 88, 89; BA, NYU, 1947. Advt. dir. Thayer, Inc., Gardner, Mass., 1948-52; account supr. and copy chief Zimmer, Keller, Calvert, Detroit, 1952-57; account mgmt. McCann-Erickson, Inc., N.Y.C., 1957-58; v.p., mgmt. supr. Doyle, Dane, Bernbach, Inc., N.Y.C., 1958-69; sr. v.p., mgmt. Super-Smith/Greenland, Inc., N.Y.C., 1969-70; pres., creative dir. The McManusCo., Westport, Conn., 1970—; bd. dirs. Stamford Art Assn., Homes Conn., Holiday Cruise Lines; official artist USCG, 1988—. Writer series on Am. Way of Life, mag., 1949 (Freedom Found. gold medals 1949, 50); mgmt. supr. Avis, We Try Harder campaign, 1964, Mobil Detergent Campaign, 1968, Rheingold Would You Have the Guts? campaign, 1971 (Clio, Effie awards 1971). Capt. USAAF, 1942-46. Recipient Le Premier Prix Festival Internat., DU Film Publicitaire, Venice, France, 1960, Freedoms Found. Gold medals, Freedoms Found. Inc., Valley Forge, Pa., 1969-70, Effie, Am. Mktg. Assn., N.Y.C., 1972, Archie award, Nat. Assn. Indsl. Advts., N.Y.C., 1984. Mem. Am. Watercolor Soc., Am. Soc. Marine Artists, Westport Arts Council, Fairfield County Bus. Execs. Republican. Roman Catholic. Avocations: painting marine and seascapes, writing, photography, travel. Office: The McManus Co PO Box 446 Greens Farms CT 06436-0446

MCMANUS, MARTIN JOSEPH, lawyer, priest; b. Toledo, Mar. 24, 1919; s. Martin Joseph and Elizabeth Marie (McDermott) McM. AB, John Carroll U., 1939; LLB, Georgetown U., 1942; LLM, U. So. Calif., 1946; D in Juridical Sci., NYU, 1961; B in Canon Law, Cath. U. Am., 1964; Licentiate in Canon Law, D in Canon Law, The Pontifical Univ. Lateran, 1965; Licentiate in Sacred Theology, The Pontifical Univ. Urbanianum, 1966; D in Sacred Theology, The Pontifical Univ. Angelicum, 1967. Bar: Calif. 1947, U.S. Supreme Ct. 1960; ordained priest Roman Cath. Ch., 1959. Pvt. practice L.A., 1947-54; prof. law Southwestern U., L.A., 1947-57; prof. law U. San Diego, 1959-63, dean Law Sch., 1960-63; atty.-advisor U.S. Govt., Washington, 1977-82; counsel to bishop 2d Vatican Coun., Rome, 1962-65; advisor, cons. Republican Nat. Com., Washington, 1965-77; adminstrv. law judge HHS, Southfield, Mich., 1982—. Office: HHS SSA Office Hearings-Aps 29500 Greenfield Rd Oak Park MI 48237

MCMANUS, PATRICK FRANCIS, educator, writer; b. Sandpoint, Idaho, Aug. 25, 1933; s. Francis Edward McManus and Mabel Delana (Klaus) DeMers; m. Darlene Madge Keough, Feb. 3, 1954; children: Kelly C., Shannon M., Peggy F., Erin B. BA in English, Wash. State U., 1956, MA in English, 1962, postgrad., 1965-67. News reporter Daily Olympian, Olympia, Wash., 1956; editor Wash. State U., Pullman, 1956-59; with Ea. Wash. U., Cheney, 1959—; ret., 1983; news reporter Sta. KREM-TV, 1960-62; assoc. prof. Ea. Wash. U., Cheney, 1971-74, prof., 1974-83, prof. emeritus, 1983—. Author: A Fine and Pleasant Misery, 1978, Kid Camping from Aaaaiii! to Zip, 1979, They Shoot Canoes, Don't They?, 1981, Never Sniff a Gift Fish, 1983, The Grasshopper Trap, 1985, Rubber Legs & White Tail-Hairs, 1987, The Night The Bear Ate Goombaw, 1989, Whatchagot Stew, 1989, Real Ponies Don't Go Oink!, 1991, The Good Samaritan Strikes Again, 1992, How I Got This Way, 1994, (stage play) A Fine and Pleasant: The Humor of Patrick F. McManus, 1994; assoc. editor Field & Stream mag., 1977-81; editor-at-large Outdoor Life, 1981—. Recipient Booksellers award P.N.W. Booksellers, 1983, Trustees medal EWU, 1984, Gov.'s award Wash. State Libr., 1985, Excellence in Craft award OWAA, 1986, Disting. Achievement award WSU, 1994, Founder's Day award EWU, 1994. Mem. Authors Guild, Outdoor Writers Am. (bd. dirs. 1981-84, Excellence award 1986). Roman Catholic. Avocations: outdoor sports, woodworking, traveling. Office: PO Box 28216 Spokane WA 99228-8216

MCMANUS, RICHARD PHILIP, lawyer; b. Keokuk, Iowa, Oct. 20, 1929; s. Edward William and Kathleen (O'Connor) M.; m. Marjorie Theresa Mullaney, Nov. 5, 1955; children: Michael L., Mark J., Matthew A. BA, St. Ambrose U., Davenport, Iowa, 1949; JD, U. Mich., 1952; MBA, Roosevelt U., Chgo., 1965. Bar: Calif. 1982, Ill. 1958, Iowa 1952. Ptnr. McManus & McManus, Keokuk, 1953-63; div. counsel USN Facility Engring. Command, Great Lakes, Ill., 1963-66; v.p., dir. bus. law Household Fin. Corp., Chgo., 1966-81; exec. v.p., sec. Security Pacific Fin. Svcs., Inc., San Diego, 1981-92; pres., bd. dirs. Mosamac Co., Inc., 1992—; bd. dirs. Security Pacific Fin. Systems and subs., San Diego; mem. gen. com. Conf. Consumer Fin. Law, Chgo., 1975-92. Contbr. articles to profl. jours. Bd. dirs., treas., atty. Tijuana/San Diego Habitat for Humanity, Inc., 1992-95. Mem. ABA, Calif. Bar Assn., Ill. Bar Assn., San Diego Bar Assn., Calif. Fin. Svcs. Assn. (chmn. law com. 1981-92), Am. Fin. Svcs. Assn. (chmn. law forum 1980-81, Disting. Svc. award 1990), Lions, Elks, KC, Beta Gamma Sigma. Democrat. Roman Catholic. Avocations: golf, flying, sailing, woodworking. Home: 17305 Campillo Dr San Diego CA 92128-2149

MC MANUS, SAMUEL PLYLER, chemist, academic administrator; b. Edgemoor, S.C., Oct. 29, 1938; s. Henry Plyler and Louise (Sanders) McM.; m. Nancy Fincher, Mar. 26, 1959; children—Samuel Plyler, Robert Adair. B.S. in Chemistry, The Citadel, 1960; M.S., Clemson U., 1962, Ph.D. in Chemistry, 1964. Research chemist Du Pont, Phila., 1964; asst. prof. chemistry U. Ala., Huntsville, 1966-68; assoc. prof. U. Ala., 1968-73, prof., 1973—, chmn. dept. chemistry 1970-72, 77-78, dir. materials sci. program 1988-89, grad. dean, 1989-94, assoc. v.p. acad. affairs, 1990-91, assoc. provost, 1991-93, interim provost, 1993-94, provost, v.p. acad. affairs, 1994—; vis. faculty mem. U. S.C., 1974-75; mem. Ala. Coun. Grad. Deans, 1989-94, (chmn. 1992-93), Conf. So. Grad. Schs. (com. Issues and Planning, 1993-94), Cons. to govt. and industry. Author: Neighboring Group Participation; Editor: Organic Reactive Intermediates, Nucleophilicity; Contbr. articles on chemistry to sci. jours. Committeeman Tenn Valley council Boy Scouts Am., 1973-75. Served to capt. U.S. Army, 1964-66. Named Outstanding Educator U. Ala., Huntsville, 1971, 74; Sigma Xi Researcher of Yr., 1978; Alumni fellow Clemson U., 1961; Petroleum Research Fund grantee, 1968-87 ; NASA-Am. Soc. Engring. Edn. fellow, 1981, 82. Mem. Am. Chem. Soc. (councillor 1970-74, 78-80, 83-93, bd. dirs. 1966-74, 78-80, 83-93, nat. awards com. 1987-89), Ala. Acad. Sci. (v.p. 1973-74, exec. com. 1967, 73-74), AAAS, Am. Assn. State Colls. and Univs. (com. sci. and tech. 1978), Ala. Coun. Chief Acad. Officers (chmn 1994—), Sigma Xi (chpt. sect. 1967-69, pres. 1970-71, exec. com. 1967-72), Phi Kappa Phi (chpt. v.p. 1988-89, pres. 1989-90). Clubs: Rotary Internat., Lake Guntersville Yacht (treas. 1975, gov. 1974-83, 88-90, 93—), commodore 1977, chmn. bd. govs. 1978, chmn. exec. com. 1978-79, 1993—), Yacht Club Assn. Ala. (pres., chmn. bd. commodores 1977). Office: Office of the Provost U Ala Huntsville AL 35899
At the beginning of my academic career I was fortunate to have realized that opportunity always exists. Success requires that one seize even the fleeting opportunity and to be creative with the available resources.

MCMANUS, WALTER LEONARD, investment executive; b. N.Y.C., Apr. 27, 1918; s. Charles E. and Eva M. (Olt) McM.; m. Lillian Ziegler, June 6, 1941; children: Walter Leonard, Peter David, Susan. Student, Harvard Bus. Sch.; BS in Fin. Sci., Georgetown U., 1940. With Crown Cork & Seal Co., Inc., Balt., 1940-60; became sec. Crown Cork & Seal Co., Inc., 1945, v.p., 1949, sec.-treas., 1958-60; pres., dir. Cem Securities Corp.; assoc. Castlewood Realty Co.; dir. Hospice of Martin County, Fla. Mem. Halifax River Yacht Club, Lighthouse Point Yacht Club, Cocoanut Point Yacht Club, Internat. Order of Blue Gavel. Home: 1766 NW Harbor Pl North River Shores Stuart FL 34994 Office: E Joppa Rd Ste 204 Baltimore MD 21268

MCMARTIN, JOHN, actor; b. Warsaw, Ind.; children: Kathleen Alice, Susan Helen. Actor Broadway prodns. including Artist Descending a Staircase, 1989, The Conquering Hero, Blood, Sweat and Stanley Poole, Children From Their Games, A Rainy Day in Newark, Sweet Charity, Follies, The Great God, Brown, Don Juan, The Visit, Chemin de Fer, Love For Love, Rules of the Game, Happy New Year, A Little Family Business, Show Boat, 1994-95 (Tony nominee - Lead Actor in a Musical, 1995); Off-Broadway prodns. Little Mary Sunshine, The Misanthrope, Too Much Johnson, Henry IV, Julius Caesar; films: Sweet Charity, All The President's Men, Pennies From Heaven, Brubaker, Legal Eagles. Recipient Theatre World award, 1959; nominee 2 Tony awards, 1967, 74; recipient 2 Drama Desk awards, 1974. Club: The Players (N.Y.C.). Office: The Artists Agy 1000 Santa Monica Blvd North Hollywood CA 91601*

MCMASTER, BELLE MILLER, religious organization administrator; b. Atlanta, May 24, 1932; d. Patrick Dwight and Lila (Bonner) Miller; m. George R. McMaster June 19, 1953; children: Lisa McMaster Stork, George Neel, Patrick Miller. BA, Agnes Scott Coll., 1953; MA, U. Louisville, 1970, PhD, 1974. Assoc. corp. witness Presbyn. Ch. USA, Atlanta, 1974-77, dir. corp. witness, 1977-81, dir. div. corp. and social mission, 1981-87; dir. social justice and peacemaking unit Presbyn. Ch. USA, Louisville, Ky., 1987-93; acting dir. program women in theology and ministry Candler Sch. Theology Emory U., 1993—; dir. advanced studies Candler Sch. Theology Emory U., 1995—; vice moderator chs. commn. internat. affairs World Coun. Chs. 1984-91; chair commn. internat. affairs Nat. Coun. Chs., N.Y.C., 1986-89, v.p., 1990—, chair ch. world svc. and witness unit com., 1990—; bd. dirs. Ecumenical Devel. Corp. U.S.A., 1992—. Author: Witnessing to the Kingdom, 1982; contbr. articles to profl. jours. Pres. League of Women Voters, Greenville, S.C., 1963-64; bd. dirs. Interfaith Housing, Atlanta, 1975-81. Danforth fellow, 1969-74. Mem. MLA, Acad. Am. Religion, Soc. for Values in Higher Edn., Phi Beta Kappa. Office: Emory U Candler Sch Theology Atlanta GA 30322

MCMASTER, BRIAN JOHN, artistic director; With internat. artists dept. EMI, 1968-73; controller opera planning English Nat. Opera, 1973-76; mng. dir. Welsh Nat. Opera, Cardiff, 1976-91; dir. Edinburgh (Scotland) Internat. Festival, 1991—; artistic dir. Vancouver Opera (B.C., Can.), 1983-89. Office: Edinburgh Festival, 21 Market St, Edinburgh EH1 1BW, Scotland

MCMASTER, HAROLD ASHLEY, inventor, retired manufacturing company executive; b. Deshler, Ohio, July 20, 1916; s. George and Laura (Butler) McM.; m. Helen Elizabeth Clark, Apr. 30, 1937; children: Ronald, Jeanine McMaster Sandwich, Nancy McMaster Cobie, Alan. BA, Ohio State U., 1938, MS, 1939; D Applied Sci. (hon.), Bowling Green (Ohio) State U., 1983; DSc (hon.), Defiance Coll., 1985, U. Toledo, 1987, Med. Coll. Ohio, 1991; LHD (hon.), Sienna Heights Coll., 1988. Rsch. physicist Libbey-Owens-Ford, Toledo, Ohio, 1940-42, mgr. optical glass lab., 1942-48; founder Permaglass, Inc., Milbury, Ohio, 1948-71; chmn., co-founder Glasstech, Inc., Perrysburg, Ohio, 1971-93; former chmn. bd. Huntington Nat. Bank, Woodville, Ohio. Holder 98 patents. Bd. dirs., trustee Defiance (Ohio) Coll., 1991—; bd. dirs. Bowling Green State U. Found., 1991—, U. Toledo Found., 1991—; trustee Toledo Mus. Art, 1991—; mem. steering com. Toledo Symphony, 1991—. Recipient Disting. Citizen award Med. Coll. Ohio, 1988, Outstanding Cmty. Svc. award Nat. Glass Assn., 1989, Nat. Medallion award Beta Gamma Sigma, 1990; inducted into Hall of Excellence, Ohio Found. for Ind. Colls., 1989, Ohio Sci. and Tech. Hall of Fame, 1991. Fellow Am. Ceramic Soc.; mem. Rotary, Sigma Xi. Republican. Avocations: astronomy, travel.

MCMASTER, JAMES HENRY, orthopaedic surgeon; b. Pitts., Feb. 14, 1939; s. James J. and Clara (Ketter) McM.; m. Judith L. Ryan, June 30; children: Laurie R. McMaster Southorn, Amy L., Kristin R. (dec.). BA, Washington and Jefferson U., 1960; MD, Temple U., 1964. Diplomate Am. Bd. Orthopaedic Surgeons; lic. physician, Pa. Rotating intern Harrisburg (Pa.) Polyclinic Hosp., 1964-65, gen. surgery resident, 1965-66; orthopaedic surgery resident U. Pitts. Sch. Medicine, 1966-69, asst. prof. dept. orthopaedic surgery, 1971-75, dir. Orthopaedic Rsch. Lab., 1971-76, assoc. prof. dept. orthopaedic surgery, 1975-79, assoc. clin. prof., 1979-82, clin. prof., 1982—; prof. surgery orthopaedics dept. surgery Med. Coll. Pa., Phila., 1988—; mem. attending staff Children's Orthopaedic Clinic, Jackson Meml. Hosp., Miami, 1969-71; chmn. dept. orthopaedic surgery Allegheny Gen. Hosp., Pitts., 1976; exec. v.p. clin. affairs Allegheny Health Svcs., Inc., Pitts., 1988—; pres., COO Allegheny-Singer Rsch. Inst., Pitts. 1988-89, pres., CEO, 1990—; orthopaedic cons. Princess Margaret Hosp., Nassau, Bahamas, 1972—; bd. dirs. Allegheny Health Svcs., Inc., Allegheny Gen. Hosp., Allegheny Health Found., Allegheny Health Svcs. Providers Ins. Co. Contbr. articles to profl. jours., chpts. to books. Mem. Pres. Circle, Pitts. Symphony Soc. Maj. USAF, 1969-71. Kappa Scholar award Washington and Jefferson Coll., Disting. Alm. award Pitts. chpt. Nat. Football Found., 1984; grantee The Robert and Mary Weisbrod Found., 1986-90. Mem. AMA, Am. Acad. Orthopaedic Surgeons, Am. Fedn. Clin. Rsch., Ea. Orthopaedic Assn., Orthopaedic Rsch. Soc., Am. Coll. Sports Medicine, Pa. Med. Soc., Allegheny County Med. Soc., Pa. Med. Soc., Am. Orthopaedic Soc. Sports Medicine, Am. Orthopaedic Assn., Pa. Orthopaedic Soc., Musculoskeletal Tumor Soc., Assn. Arthritic Hip and Knee Surgery, Alexis deTocqueville Soc. Republican. Avocations: golf, jogging, reading. Office: Allegheny-Singer Rsch Inst 1 Allegheny Sq Ste 880 Pittsburgh PA 15212-5346

MCMASTER, JULIET SYLVIA, English language educator; b. Kisumu, Kenya, Aug. 2, 1937; emigrated to Can., 1961, naturalized, 1976; d. Sydney Herbert and Sylvia (Hook) Fazan; m. Rowland McMaster, May 10, 1968; children: Rawdon, Lindsey. B.A. with honors, Oxford U., 1959; M.A., U. Alta., 1963, Ph.D., 1965. Asst. prof. English U. Alta., Edmonton, Can., 1965-70; assoc. prof. U. Alta., 1970-76, prof. English, 1976-86, Univ. prof., 1986—. Author: Thackeray: The Major Novels, 1971; editor: Jane Austen's Achievement, 1976, Jane Austen on Love, 1978, Trollope's Palliser Novels, 1978, (with R.D. McMaster), The Novel from Sterne to James, 1981, Dickens the Designer, 1987, Jane Austen the Novelist, 1995; gen. editor Juvenilia Press, 1993—; illustrator/editor children's picture book: (by Jane Austen) The Beautiful Cassandra, 1993; contbr. articles to profl. jours. Fellow Can. Coun., 1969-70, Guggenheim Found., 1976-77, Killam Found., 1987-89; recipient Molson prize in Humanities for Outstanding Contbn. to Canadian Culture, 1994. Fellow Royal Soc. Can.; mem. Victorian Studies Assn. Western Can. (founding pres. 1972), Assn. Can. Univ. Tchrs. English (pres. 1976-78), MLA, Jane Austen Soc. N.Am. (dir. 1980-91). Office: U Alta, Dept English, Edmonton, AB Canada T6G 2E5

MCMASTER, ROBERT RAYMOND, accountant; b. Cleve., June 14, 1948; s. William G. and Elizabeth (Smith) McM.; m. Jane M. Pepple, June 27, 1970; children: William R., Sarah J. BS in Acctg., Miami U., Oxford, Ohio, 1970. CPA, Ohio, N.Y. Mem. audit staff Sta. KPMG, Columbus, Ohio, 1970-75; mgr. Sta. KPMG, N.Y.C., 1975-78; sr. mgr. Peat Marwick Main & Co., Columbus, 1977-81, ptnr., 1981, mng. ptnr., 1988—; area mng. ptnr., 1992. Pres. Planned Parenthood Ctrl. Ohio, Columbus, 1988, 89; bd. dirs. Riverside Meth. Hosp. Found., Columbus, 1988-91, Unverferth Hosp. Found., 1990-92, Children's Hosp. Found., 1990—, Children's Hosp., chmn., 1993—; mem. fin. com. Columbus Mus. Art. Mem. AICPA, Ohio Soc. CPAs (pres. Columbus chpt. 1983-84), Columbus Bar Assn. (ethics com. 1989-91), Scioto Country Club, Muirfield Village Golf Club. Avocations: golf, tennis, skiing, basketball. Office: KPMG Peat Marwick 2 Nationwide Pla Columbus OH 43215

MCMASTERS, PAUL KENNETH, foundation executive; b. Dade County, Mo., Jan. 18, 1942; s. James Harvey and Evelyn Gail (Carmack) McM.; m. Priscilla Jean Thomas, Feb. 19, 1967; 1 child, Amy Elaine. BA, SW Mo.

State U., 1965, MA, 1973. From gen. assignment reporter to asst. mng. editor The Daily News, Springfield, Mo., 1970-79; mng. editor Coffeyville (Kans.) Jour., 1979-82; states editor USA Today, Arlington, Va., 1982-83, editorial editor, then ops. dir. editorial dept., 1983-87, dep. editorial dir., 1987-91, assoc editorial editorial page, 1991-92; v.p. The Freedom Forum, Arlington, 1992—; exec. dir. The Freedom Forum 1st Amendment Ctr. Nashville, 1992—; speaker in field. Mem. editorial bd.: Newspaper Rsch. Jour.; contbr. articles to profl. jours. Bd. dirs. Student Law Press Ctr. Recipient Inglehart First Amendment award Coll. Media Advisors, 1992, Human Rights Leadership award Freedom Mag., 1993. Mem. Soc. Profl. Journalists (pres. 1993-94, past chmn. freedom of info., past sec.-treas., also bd. dirs., Wells Meml. Key award 1990), Am. Soc. Newspaper Editors (mem. FOI com.), Assn. Educators in Journalism and Mass Comm. (newspaper divsn. exec. com.). Office: The Freedom Forum 1st Amendment Ctr 1207 18th Ave S Nashville TN 37212

MCMEEKIN, DOROTHY, botany, plant pathology educator; b. Boston, Feb. 24, 1932; d. Thomas LeRoy and Vera (Crockatt) McM. BA, Wilson Coll., 1953; MA, Wellesley Coll., 1955; PhD, Cornell U., 1959. Asst. prof. Upsala Coll., East Orange, N.J., 1959-64, Bowling Green State U., Ohio, 1964-66; prof. natural sci. Mich. State U., East Lansing, 1966-89, prof. botany, plant pathology, 1989—. Author: Diego Rivera: Science and Creativity, 1985; contbr. articles to profl. jours. Mem. Am. Phytopath. Soc., Mycol. Soc. Am., Soc. Econ. Bot., Mich. Bot. Soc. (bd. dirs. 1985—), Mich. Women's Studies Assn., Sigma Xi, Phi Kappa Phi. Avocations: gardening, sewing, travel, drawing. Home: 1055 Marigold Ave East Lansing MI 48823-5128 Office: Mich State U Dept Botany-Plant Pathology 335 N Kedzie East Lansing MI 48824-0001

MC MEEL, JOHN PAUL, newspaper syndicate and publishing executive; b. South Bend, Ind., Jan. 26, 1936; s. James E. and Naomi R. (Reilly) McM.; m. Susan S. Sykes, Apr. 16, 1966; children: Maureen, Suzanne, Bridget. BS, U. Notre Dame, 1957. Sales dir. Hall Syndicate, 1960-67; asst. gen. mgr., sales dir. Publishers-Hall Syndicate, 1968-70; co-founder Universal Press Syndicate, Kansas City, Mo., 1970; pres. Universal Press Syndicate, 1970—; bd. dirs. Newspaper Features Coun., Universal/Belo Prodns.; chmn. bd. Andrews & McMeel Inc., 1973—; chmn. bd. dirs. Nat. Cath. Reporter; mem. adv. coun. Inst. for Ch. Life, U. Notre Dame; bd. dirs. Am. City Bus. Jours., Christmas in April U.S.A. Co-founder Christmas in October, Kansas City, 1984—, James F. Andrews fellowship program U. Notre Dame, 1981. Mem. Fed. Assn. USA, Sovereign Mil. Order Malta, Internat. Press Inst. (bd. dirs. Am. com.). Home: Three Sunset Pl 5300 Sunset Dr Kansas City MO 64112-2358 Office: Universal Press Syndicate 4900 Main St Fl 9 Kansas City MO 64112-2644

MCMEEN, ALBERT RALPH, III, writer, lecturer; b. Lewistown, Pa., Oct. 4, 1942; s. Albert Ralph and Margaret McDowell (Parker) McM.; BA in Econs., Williams Coll., 1964; MBA in Fin. (Columbia Internat. Fellows scholar 1964), Columbia U., 1966; m. A. Mary Kelley, June 6, 1965 (div.); children: Albert Ralph, Christopher Benjamin. Asst. v.p. Chem. Bank, N.Y.C., 1966-75; v.p. mktg. Irving Leasing Co. subs. Irving Trust Co., N.Y.C., 1975-80; v.p. regional ops. USI Capital and Leasing affiliate U.S. Industries, Inc., N.Y.C., 1980-83; pres. Tng. Assocs., Inc., 1983—; assoc. adj. prof. NYU, 1979—; asst. prof. L.I. U. 1986-93; lectr. Am. Mgmt. Assn., 1986—, cons. N.Y. Life Ins., 1989-91, Am. Bankers Assn., 1992-94. Mem. legis. com. Citizens' Union, 1968-75; bd. dirs. Columbia U. Alumni Assn., 1970-75; sec. Gay Fathers Inc. Recipient Columbia Bus. Sch. service award, 1966. Mem. ASTD, Fin. Ind. Tng. Assn. (exec. dir. 1994—). Democrat. Author: Treasurers and Controllers New Equipment Leasing Guide, 1984, Equipment Leasing Guide for Lessees, 1990, Debt Repayment Capacity, 1992, Financial Statement Analysis, 1993, Statement Analysis Series, 1994, Guide to Consumer Lending Computer Based Training, 1995. Home: 333 W 88th St New York NY 10024-2219

MCMEEN, ELMER ELLSWORTH, III, lawyer, guitarist; b. Lewistown, Pa., June 3, 1947; s. Elmer Ellsworth II and Frances Josephine McM.; m. Sheila Ann Taenzler, July 31, 1971; children—Jonathan Ellsworth, Daniel Biddle, James Cunningham and Mary Josephine (twins). A.B. cum laude, Harvard U., 1969; J.D. cum laude, U. Pa., 1972. Bar: 1973, U.S. Ct. Appeals (2d cir.) 1973, U.S. Dist. Ct. (so. and ea. dists.) N.Y. 1973. Assoc. Cravath, Swaine & Moore, N.Y.C., 1972-75; assoc. LeBoeuf, Lamb, Greene & MacRae L.L.P., N.Y.C., 1975-78, ptnr., 1979—; lectr. Editor U. Pa. Law Rev., 1970-72. Contbr. articles to profl. jours; solo guitar serenade Piney Ridge Music; solo guitar recs. Of Soul and Spirit, Irish Guitar Encores by Shanachie Records, solo guitar instructional audio and video lessons Stefan Grossman's Guitar Workshop. Chmn. N.Y.C. regional com. for U. Pa. Law Sch., 1984-86; class sec. Mt. Hermon Sch. Class of 1965, Mass., 1984-91. Fellow Am. Coll. Investment Counsel; mem. ABA, N.Y. State Bar Assn. (mem. corp. law com.), Rockaway River Country Club, Harvard Club (N.Y.C.). Office: LeBoeuf Lamb Greene & MacRae LLP 125 W 55th St New York NY 10019-5369

MCMENAMIN, JOAN STITT, headmistress; b. N.Y.C., May 7, 1925; d. William Britton and Josephene Lloyd (White) Stitt; m. Edward B. McMenamin, Jan. 24, 1953. BA in Econs., Smith Coll., 1946. With Econ. Cooperation Adminstrn., Paris, 1949-50; office mgr. Ford Found., N.Y.C., 1951-52; history tchr. Nightingale-Bamford Sch., N.Y.C., 1962-63, asst. to headmistress, 1963-65, asst. headmistress, 1965-71, headmistress, 1971—; mem. adv. council for nonpub. schs. N.Y. State Commr. of Edn., 1985-87; pres. Guild Ind. Schs. N.Y., 1983-85; mem. admissions com. Nat. Assn. Ind. Schs., 1977-79. Former vice chmn. English-Speaking Union Exchange Scholarship Program; former spl. advisor Parents League N.Y.; bd. dirs. Council for Religion in Ind. Schs., 1976-79, Ind. Sch. Orchs., Inc., 1980-84; trustee A Better Chance, Inc., 1977-83, The Town Sch., 1975-77, Ind. Ednl. Svcs., 1985-89, The Laurenceville School, 1989, Buckley Sch., 1977—, Council for Basic Edn., Washington, 1978—, Clark Found., 1979—, Robert Coll. of Istanbul, Turkey, 1979—, WICAT Founds., 1976—. Mem. Nat. Assn. Prins. of Girls' Schs. (pres. 1983-85), N.Y. State Assn. Ind. Schs. (chmn. 1985-87), Headmasters Assn., Country Day Sch. Headmasters Assn. (vice pres. 1987—, exec. com. 1987-90), Headmistresses Assn. of East. Democrat. Presbyterian. Club: Cosmopolitan (N.Y.C.); Bridgehampton (N.Y.). Avocation: reading. Home: 14 E 90th St New York NY 10128-0671 Office: Nightingale-Bamford Sch 20 E 92nd St New York NY 10128-0660

MCMENAMIN, JOHN ROBERT, lawyer; b. Evanston, Ill., Sept. 30, 1946. BA, U. Notre Dame, 1968, JD, 1971. Bar: Ill. 1971. Law clk. to presiding judge U.S. Ct. Appeals (7th cir.), 1971-72; ptnr. Mayer, Brown & Platt, Chgo., 1978-89, McDermott, Will & Emery, Chgo., 1989—. Chmn. adv. bd. Holy Trinity High Sch., Chgo., 1986-88. Mem. ABA, Mid-Am. Com. Roman Catholic. Clubs: Law, Legal, University (Chgo.), Econ. (Chgo.). Office: McDermott Will & Emery 227 W Monroe St Chicago IL 60606-5016

MCMENAMIN, RICHARD F., lawyer; b. Nov. 23, 1946. BA, St. Joseph's Coll., 1968; MA, Boston U., 1971; JD, Temple U., 1977. Bar: Pa. 1977. Ptnr. Morgan, Lewis & Bockius, Phila. Office: Morgan Lewis & Bockius 2000 One Logan Sq Philadelphia PA 19103

MCMENAMY, KRISTEN, model; b. Easton, Pa.; d. Charles and Eileen McM. Modelling contracts with Gianni Versace, Calvin Klein, Karl Lagerfeld. Named Harper's Bazaar Model of Yr., 1993. Office: Elite Model Mgmt Corp 111 E 22nd St 2d Fl New York NY 10010

MC MENNAMIN, GEORGE BARRY, advertising agency executive; b. N.Y.C., May 23, 1922; s. Harold G. and Hazel F. (Stanbridge) McM.; m. Marilynn L. Simon, Sept. 9, 1946; children: Marilynn Breeze, Karen Foster. BS, Harvard U., 1945. With Doremus & Co., N.Y.C., 1946-88, exec. v.p., 1967-73, pres., 1973-84, vice chmn., 1984-88, also mem. exec. com.; pub. Worldpaper, Boston, 1988. Served to lt. (j.g.) USNR, 1944-46. Mem. Fin. Advt. and Mktg. Assn. Met. N.Y. (pres. 1967), Down Town Assn., Hasty Pudding Inst. 1770, Harvard Club. Speakers Club, Harvard Club, New Canaan Country Club, Pilgrims Club of U.S. Republican. Episcopalian. Home: 28 Cross Ridge Rd New Canaan CT 06840-2311

MCMENNAMY, ROGER NEAL, community development company executive; b. Amarillo, Tex., Oct. 9, 1942; s. Wilson Foch and Mildred Evelyn (Freudiger) McM.; m. Marilyn Kay Gibbons, Jan. 1, 1967; children: Timothy Neal, Traci Nicole. Student Abilene Christian U., 1961-62; BBA in Mgmt. cum laude, U. Tex., Arlington, 1970; MBA in Fin., U. Tex., Austin, 1971. CPA, Tex. Contr., treas. E.N. Wolcott Corp., Houston, 1971-73; mem. corp. staff ELPAC, Inc., Houston, 1973-74; gen. mgr. BS&B Mfg., Houston, 1974-75; gen. mgr. adminstrn. Gulf Interstate Co., Houston, 1975-77; exec. v.p., chief fin. officer NWS Supply Group, Houston, 1977-83; v.p., chief fin. officer Newpark Resources, Inc., Lafayette, La., 1983-86; sr. v.p., chief fin. officer Gemcraft, Inc., 1986-88; exec. v.p., chief fin. officer Cooper Communities, Inc., Bella Vista, Ark., 1988-90, pres., chief exec. officer, 1990—, also bd. dirs.; bd. dirs. Boatmen's Bank of N.W. Ark., Fayetteville. Mem. N.W. Ark. Coun., Fayetteville; bd. dirs. Walton Arts Ctr., Fayetteville, 1994—. Mem. AICPA, Am. Resort Devel. Assn. (bd. dirs. 1991—), Ark. State C. of C. (bd. dirs.). Avocations: skiing, travel, golf, waterfowl hunting. Office: Cooper Communities Inc 1801 Forest Hills Blvd Bella Vista AR 72714-2395

MCMICHAEL, FRANCIS CLAY, civil engineering educator, environmental engineering consultant; b. Phila., Aug. 8, 1937; s. Francis and Estella Marie (Walker) McM.; m. Catherine Patricia Barati, Aug. 16, 1969; children: Jessica Elizabeth, Laureen Marie. B.S., Lehigh U., 1958; M.S., Calif. Inst. Tech., 1959, Ph.D., 1963. Asst. prof. Princeton U., 1965-67; sr. fellow Mellon Inst., Pitts., 1967-72; assoc. prof. Carnegie-Mellon U., Pitts., 1972-75, prof., 1975—; The Walter J. Blenko Sr. prof. environ. engring. Carnegie-Mellon U., 1981—, dept. head civil engring., 1975-80; sr. tech. advisor ERT Inc., Pitts., 1979-81. Mem. editorial bd. Waste Mgmt. and Rsch. Jour. Served with USPHS, 1962-65. Mem. ASCE, Water Pollution Control Fedn., Am. Inst. Chem. Engrs., Am. Geophys. Union, Soc. for Risk Analysis, Internat. Solid Wastes Assn. Presbyterian. Home: 7001 Penn Ave Pittsburgh PA 15208-2407 Office: Carnegie-Mellon U Pittsburgh PA 15213

MCMICHAEL, GUY H., III, federal official; b. South Bend, Ind., Dec. 26, 1939; m. Nancy Moore. AB, Harvard U., 1962; JD, U. Mich., 1967. Pvt. practice, 1967-71; dept. prosecuting atty. State of Ind., 1967-71; gen. counsel com. vet. affairs U.S. Senate, Washington, 1971-77; gen. coun. Dept. Vet. Affairs (formerly VA), Washington, 1977-81; adminstrv. judge bd. contract appeals Dept. Vet. Affairs, Washington, 1981-90, chmn., chief adminstrv. judge, 1990—. With U.S. Army, 1962-64. Mem. ABA, Bd. Contract Appeals Judges Assn. (pres. 1989-90), Ind. Bar Assn., D.C. Bar Assn. Office: Dept Vet Affairs Bd Contract Appeals 1800 G St NW Rm 545 Washington DC 20006

MCMICHAEL, RONALD L., superintendent. Supt. Longview (Tex.) ISD. Named state finalist Nat. Supt. of Yr. award, 1992. Office: Longview ISD PO Box 3268 Longview TX 75606-3268

MC MILLAN, BROCKWAY, former communications executive; b. Mpls., Mar. 30, 1915; s. Franklin and Luvena (Brockway) McM.; m. Audrey Wishard, Sept. 2, 1942; children—Sarah Linn McMillan Taylor, Douglas Wishard, Gordon Brockway. Student, Armour Inst. Tech., 1932-34; B.S., Mass. Inst. Tech., 1936, Ph.D., 1939. Procter fellow Princeton, 1939-40, H.B. Fine instr., 1940-41; with Bell Telephone Labs., 1946-61, dir. mil. research, 1959-61; asst. sec. research and devel. U.S. Air Force, 1961-63, under-sec., 1963-65; exec. dir. mil. research Bell Telephone Labs., Whippany, N.J., 1965-69; v.p. mil. devel. Bell Telephone Labs., 1969-79. Mem. Bd. Edn. Summit, N.J., 1958-61. Served with USNR, 1942-45. Fellow IEEE; mem. Soc. Indsl. and Applied Math. (pres. 1959-60), Am. Math. Soc., Math. Assn. Am., Inst. Math. Stats., AAAS, Nat. Acad. Engring. Home: Carter Point Rd Sedgwick ME 04676

MCMILLAN, C. STEVEN, manufacturing company executive; b. Tyler, Tex., Dec. 10, 1945; s. Charles and Faye (Mills) McM.; m. Kelly McMillan, Jan. 16, 1988; children: Mandy, Megan. BS, Auburn U., 1968; MBA, Harvard U., 1973. Mgmt. cons. McKinsey & Co., Chgo., 1973-76; pres. Aqualux Water Processing Co., Ft. Lauderdale, Fla., 1976-79, Electrolux Corp., Toronto, Ont., Can., 1979-82; chmn. chief exec. officer, dir. Electrolux Corp., Stamford, Conn., 1982-86; sr. v.p. strategy devel. Sara Lee Corp., Chgo., 1986-90; sr. v.p., chief exec. officer SaraLee Bakery-Worldwide, Chgo., 1990—; chmn. bd. dirs. Electrolux Corp., 1990—. Mem. Harvard Bus. Sch. Club of Chgo. (v.p.). Office: Sara Lee Corp 3 First National Plz Chicago IL 60602

MCMILLAN, CAMPBELL WHITE, pediatric hematologist; b. Soochow, China, Jan. 10, 1927; s. Henry Hudson and Leila McNeill (Memory) McM.; m. Florence Jean MacKenzie, June 11, 1955; children: Ian Johnson, Sally Hudson, Donna Jean, Andrew Duncan, Bridget White, Wendy McNeill. B.S. summa cum laude, Wake Forest Coll., 1948; M.D., Bowman Gray Sch. Medicine, 1952. Diplomate Am. Bd. Pediatrics, Pediatric Hematology-Oncology. Intern Harvard Med. Service, Boston City Hosp., 1952-53; resident in pediatrics Children's Hosp. Med. Center, Boston, 1953-55; registrar in pediatrics St. Mary's Hosp., London, 1955; pediatrician Nemazee Hosp., Shiraz, Iran, 1956-58; fellow in pediatric hematology Harvard U., 1958-60; instr. pediatrics, 1960-61; gen. practice pediatrics Laurinburg, N.C., 1961-63; asst. prof. pediatrics U. N.C., Chapel Hill, 1963-68; asso. prof. U. N.C., 1968-72, prof., 1972-92, chief div. pediatric hematology, 1963-83, prof. emeritus, 1992—; Asso. dir. Clin. Research Center, U. N.C., 1966-78. Assoc. editor: Blood Diseases of Infancy and Childhood, 1978, 84; contbr. articles profl. jours., chpts. in books. Served with USNR, 1945-46. Recipient Lederle Med. Faculty award, 1964, Disting. Alumnus award Bowman Gray Sch. Medicine, 1972. Fellow Am. Acad. Pediatrics; mem. Soc. Pediatric Rsch., Am. Pediatric Soc., Phi Beta Kappa, Alpha Omega Alpha. Democrat. Episcopalian. Home: 408 Ridgecrest Dr Chapel Hill NC 27514-2103 *It was my extremely good fortune to live and to work in a time of the most explosive growth medical knowledge has ever undergone.*

MCMILLAN, CHARLES WILLIAM, consulting company executive; b. Ft. Collins, Colo., Feb. 9, 1926; s. Charles and Margaret (Jennings) McM.; m. Jardell Hollier, Feb. 12, 1951; children: Brett W., Kurt C., Scott P. B.S., Colo. State U., 1948. Asst. 4-H agt. Denver, 1948; county agrl. agt. LaJara, Colo., 1949-50, Julesburg, 1950-53; faculty Colo. State U., 1954; div. head, agrl. research dept. Swift & Co., Chgo., 1954-59; exec. v.p. Am. Nat. Cattlemen's Assn., 1959-77; v.p. Nat. Cattlemen's Assn., 1977-81; asst. sec. for mktg. and inspection services USDA, Washington, 1981-85; pres. McMillan and Farrell Assocs., inc., Washington, 1985-94, C.W. McMillan Co., Alexandria, Va., 1994—; bd. dirs. RTI Inc.; vice chmn. Western Assocs. Inc. Served to lt. (j.g.) USNR, World War II. Mem. Inst. for Sci. in Soc. (bd. dirs.), Newcomen Soc. N.Am., Sigma Alpha Epsilon. Club: Capitol Hill. Home: 4003 Pine Brook Rd Alexandria VA 22310-2144 Office: PO Box 10009 Alexandria VA 22310-0009

MCMILLAN, DONALD EDGAR, pharmacologist; b. Butler, Pa., Sept. 23, 1937; s. Chandler Burdell and Ruth Elizabeth (Beach) McM.; m. Marjorie Ann Leavitt, Feb. 4, 1963; children: David Craig, Pamela Jean. B.S., Grove City Coll., 1959; M.S., U. Pitts., 1962, Ph.D., 1965. Postdoctoral fellow Harvard U. Med. Sch., 1965-66; instr. in pharmacology SUNY Downstate Med. Ctr., N.Y.C., 1967-68, asst. prof., 1968-69; asst. prof. pharmacology U. N.C., 1969-72, asso. prof., 1972-76, prof., 1976-78; asso. prof. pharmacology U. Ark. for Med. Scis., 1978-80, prof., chmn. dept. pharmacology and toxicology, 1980—, prof. psychiatry, 1985—, Wilbur D. Mills prof. alcoholism and drug abuse prevention, 1991—; vis. lectr. U. Ctrl. Caracas, Venezuela, 1974; mem. neurobiology rev. panel NSF, 1979-80; IRG mem. Nat. Inst. Drug Abuse, 1982-88, SRC mem., chair 1994—, SRC research, 1988—; bd. dirs. Chapel Hill (N.C.) Drug Action Com., 1977-78; cons. Health Effects Inst., 1985-86; cons. sci. adv. bd. EPA, 1985-89; spl. merit rev. bd. Armed Forces Radiobiology Rsch. Inst., 1982; mem. com. toxicity data elements NRC, 1980-83. Author: Central Nervous System Pharmacology—A Self Instruction Text, 1974, 2d, rev. edit., 1979; research, numerous publs. in behavioral pharmacology and drug abuse; bd. editors Jour. Pharmacology and Exptl. Therapeutics, 1972—, Psychopharmacology, 1973-81, Neurotoxicology, 1979-82, Toxicology and Applied Pharmacology, 1982-89, Neurobehavioral/Toxicology and Teratology, 1982-90, Behavioral Pharmacology, 1989—. Grantee NIMH, 1971-74, Nat. Inst. Environ. Health Scis., 1976-80, N.C. Alcoholism Rsch. Authority, 1975-77, EPA,

1982-85, Kellogg Found., 1987-92, U.S. Dept. Edn., 1989-91, Nat. Inst. Drug Abuse, 1976—. Mem. AAAS, Behavioral Pharmacology Soc. (pres. 1982-84), Behavioral Toxicology Soc. (pres. 1988-90), Am. Soc. Pharmacology and Exptl. Therapeutics, Internat. Narcotics Rsch. European Behavioral Pharmacology Soc., Club, Soc. Toxicologists (pres. So. Cen. chpt. 1985-86), Com. on Problems of Drug Dependence, N.Y. Acad. Sci., Sigma Xi. Home: 100 Longway Dr Little Rock AR 72211-9531 Office: U Ark Med Scis Sch Medicine Dept Pharmacology & Toxicol 4301 W Markham Little Rock AR 72205

MCMILLAN, DONALD ERNEST, internal medicine educator, state program director; b. San Francisco, Dec. 13, 1931; s. George Ernest and Agnes Josephine (McGaffigan) McM.; m. Marilyn Marshal, June 23, 1956; children: David, Mark, Kathleen, Robert, Bruce, Rhannon. AB with distinction, Stanford U., 1953, MD, 1957. Diplomate Am. Bd. of Internal Medicine, Am. Bd. of Endocrinology and Metabolism. Intern USPHS Hosp., San Francisco, 1957-58; resident USPHS Hosp., New Orleans, San Francisco, 1959-63, dir. metabolic service, 1965-68, assoc chief of medicine, endocrinology, 1968-82; chief endocrine and diabetes clinics Santa Barbara (Calif.) Gen. Hosp., 1968-82; lab. dir. Sansum Med. Rsch. Found., Santa Barbara, 1972-82; dir. research Hal B. Wallis Research Facility, Rancho Mirage, Calif., 1982-87; prof. internal medicine U. So. Fla., 1987—; co-dir. diabetes ctr. State Fla. Sch. Medicine, 1987—; staff physician James A. Haley Vets. Hosp., 1987—; spl. reviewer NIH Spl. Study Sect., 1980-81; clin. prof. of medicine, U. So. Calif., 1980-88; cons. numerous agys. and founds. Reviewer numerous sci. jours.; contbr. articles to profl. jours. Recipient USPHS Clin. Soc. Research Prize, 1963, Mary Jane Kugel award Juvenile Diabetes Found., 1982; fellow U. Calif. Med. Ctr., San Francisco, 1963-65, mem. AAAS, Am. Diabetes Assn. (pres. So. Calif. Affiliate 1982-83, bd. dirs. 1984-87), Am. Fedn. for Clinical Research, AMA, Am. Physiological Soc., Biorheology Soc., Endocrine Soc., Glycoconjugate Soc., Microcirculatory Soc., Sigma Xi, Phi Beta Kappa. Republican. Roman Catholic. Avocations: wind surfing, back packing, camping. Home: 2409 W Watrous Ave Tampa FL 33629-5342 Office: U South Fla 12901 Bruce B Downs Blvd Tampa FL 33612-4742

MC MILLAN, GEORGE DUNCAN HASTIE, JR., lawyer, former state official; b. Greenville, Ala., Oct. 11, 1943; s. George Duncan Hastie and Jean (Autrey) McM.; m. Ann Louise Dial, Nov. 20, 1971; children: George Duncan Hastie, III, Ann Dial. B.A. magna cum laude, Auburn U., 1966; LL.B. (Southeastern Regional scholar) U. Va., 1969. Bar: Ala. bar 1969. Research asst. dept. agronomy Auburn U., summers 1963-65; law clk. firm Lange, Simpson, Robinson & Somerville, Birmingham, Ala., summers 1967-68; law clk. to judge U.S. Dist. Ct. No. Dist. Ala., 1969-70; instr. U. Ala. Law Sch., 1969-70; individual practice law Birmingham, 1970-71; ptnr. firm McMillan & Spratling, Birmingham, 1971-86; of counsel Haskell, Slaughter, Young and Lewis, 1986; ptnr. McMillan, Jones and Assocs., 1987-90; pres. McMillan & Assocs., 1990—; mem. Ala. Ho. of Reps., 1973, Ala. Senate, 1974-78; lt. gov. Ala., 1979-83; vice-chmn. Nat. Conf. Lt. Govs., 1980-82; mem. Permanent Study Commn. on Ala.'s Jud. System, 1975-79. Chmn. Ala. Film Commn., 1976-83; mem. Arts Task Force, Nat. Conf. State Legislatures, 1978-80, Multi-State Transp. Adv. Bd., 1974-79; mem. exec. com. So. Growth Policies Bd., 1974-83, vice chmn., 1981-83; bd. dirs. Campfire, Inc., 1975-82, Met. YMCA, Birmingham, Boys and Girls Ranches, Ala., Positive Maturity, 1987—; chmn. bd., pres. Birmingham Cultural and Heritage Found., 1988—; pres., bd. dirs. Birmingham Repertory Theatre, 1989—; exec. producer City Stages; Served to lt. USAR, 1969. Recipient award Ala. Nurses Assn., 1975; named Legislator of Yr. Ala. Forestry Assn., 1978; Hardest Working Senator Capitol Press Corps, 1976; 1 of 4 Outstanding Young Men Ala. Jaycees, 1977; 1 of 10 Most Outstanding State Legislators Assn. Govtl. Employees, 1978; award Birmingham Emancipation Assn., 1977; award Ala. Hist. Commn., 1978; James Tingle award, 1979, Citizen of Yr. award City of Birmingham, 1990. Mem. Birmingham Bar Assn., Ala. Bar Assn., Am. Bar Assn., Birmingham Jaycees, Ala. Jaycees (dir. 1970-72), Birmingham Urban League, United Negro Coll. Fund. Democrat. Mem. Ch. of Christ. Club: Rotary (Birmingham). Office: PO Box 11311 Birmingham AL 35202-1311

MCMILLAN, HOWARD LAMAR, JR., banker; b. Jackson, Miss., Aug. 29, 1939; s. Howard Lamar and Mary Frances (Byars) McM.; m. Mary Eliza Love, July 5, 1964; children: Eliza Love McMillan Garraway, Howard Lamar III. BA in Banking & Finance, U. Miss., Oxford, 1960; postgrad., La. State U., 1966, Harvard U., 1979. With Deposit Guaranty Nat. Bank, Jackson, 1960, v.p., 1972-73, sr. v.p., 1973-77, exec. v.p. corp. div., 1977-81, exec. v.p. state bank div., 1981-84, pres., dir., 1987—; pres., dir. Deposit Guaranty Corp., Jackson, 1984—. Gen. chmn. United Way, Jackson, 1989—. Mem. Am. Bankers Assn. (bd. dirs. 1988—), Miss. Bankers Assn. (chmn. fed. legis. com.), Jackson C. of C. (bd. dirs. 1989—), Univ. Miss. Alumni Assn. (pres. 1988), 100 Club (Jackson). Avocations: golfing, snow skiing, reading. Office: Deposit Guaranty Nat Bank PO Box 1200 Jackson MS 39215

MC MILLAN, JAMES, manufacturing executive; b. Grosse Pointe Farms, Mich.; s. James Thayer and Anne Davenport (Russel) McM.; m. Virginia Cutting, Jan. 4, 1935; children: Francis Wetmore (Sandy), Virginia. A.B., Yale, 1934. With Detroit & Cleve. Nav. Co., supt., asst. gen. mgr., gen. mgr., pres., chmn. bd., 1934-48; pres. McMillan Packard, Inc., pres., dir. Great Lakes-Oceanic Line, Inc.; security-ins. broker Multivest Financial Corp., Inc.; dir. Detroit Bank & Trust Co., Packard Motor Car Co., Studebaker Corp., Detroit Bank, Detroit Trust Co., Ferry-Morse Seed Co., Detroit & Cleve. Nav. Co., Am. Presidents Life Ins. Co., Grand Rapids, Mich.; v.p., dir., treas. Boyer-Campbell Co.; adminstrv. exec. asst. Am. Nat. Gas Service Co.; cons. Glover Assos., Inc., N.Y.C., Ordnance Tank Automotive Center, U.S. Army; mgmt. cons. Glover Assos. (Can.) Ltd. Exec. asst. United Found., 1964—; Bd. dirs. ARC; trustee Grosse Pointe War Meml. Assn., Detroit Hist. Assn., Mich. State Appellate Defender Commn., Grace Hosp., Grosse Pointe Country Day Sch., Detroit U., Sch. Corp., Estate James T. McMillan, Katherine K. Brookfield Trust.; Village commr., police commr. Grosse Pointe Park. Mem. Nat. Assn. Security Dealers, Detroit Bd. Commerce (dir. 1938-43), Mich. Hort. Soc. (trustee, treas.), Newcomen Soc. N.Am., Mason Club, St. Clair Flats Shooting Club, Yondotega Club, Detroit Country Club, Grosse Pointe Club (pres. 1953), Detroit Club (pres. 1962), Sakonnet Golf Club (Little Compton, R.I.). Republican. Presbyn. (elder, trustee). Home: 46 Sunningdale Dr Grosse Pointe MI 48236-1664 Office: Free Press Bldg Detroit MI 48226

MCMILLAN, JAMES BRYAN, federal judge, retired; b. Goldsboro, N.C., Dec. 19, 1916; s. Robert Hunter and Louise (Outlaw) McM.; m. Margaret Blair Miles, Feb. 27, 1944 (dec. Mar. 1985); children: James Bryan, Marjorie Miles Rodell; m. Holly Smith Neaves, Aug. 23, 1987. Grad., Presbyn. Jr. Coll., 1934; AB, U. N.C. 1937; JD, Harvard U., 1940; LLD (hon.), Belmont Abbey Coll., 1982, Davidson Coll., 1984, Johnson C. Smith Coll., 1985, U. N.C., 1988, St. Andrews Presbyn. Coll., 1989, U. N.C., Charlotte, 1990, LHD (hon.), Queens Coll., 1991. Bar: N.C. 1941. Mem. staff N.C. atty.-gen., 1940-42; ptnr. Helms, Mulliss, McMillan & Johnston, Charlotte, 1946-77; judge U.S. Dist. Ct. (we. dist.) N.C., Charlotte, 1968-93, retired, 1993, judge pro tem Charlotte City Ct., 1947-51; mem. faculty Nat. Inst. Trial Advocacy, Boulder, Colo., 1973-81; instr. trial advocacy course Harvard Law Sch., 1975-93 , U. N.C. Law Sch., 1976-78, U. Fla Law Sch., 1980-82; mem. N.C. Cts. Commn., 1963-71. Pres. Travelers Aid Soc., 1957-59; bd. visitors Davidson Coll. Lt. USNR, 1942-46, ETO. Recipient Algernon Sydney Sullivan award St. Andrews Presbyn. Coll. Fellow Internat. Acad. Trial Lawyers; mem. ABA, 26th Dist. Bar Assn. (pres. 1957-58), N.C. Bar Assn. (pres. 1960-61), Am. Judicature Soc. (dir. 1984—). United World Federalists, Newcomen Soc., St. Andrews Coll. Alumni Assn. (pres. 1965-66), Order of Coif, Golden Fleece, Omicron Delta Kappa. Democrat. Presbyterian. Home: 1930 Mecklenburg Ave Charlotte NC 28205-2451

MCMILLAN, JAMES THOMAS, aerospace company executive; b. Alhambra, Calif., Aug. 5, 1925; s. James and Mary W. (O'Hurley) McM.; m. Jean Grunland, June 27, 1953; children: Suzanne, Brian, David, Kathryn, Mary. B in Engring., U. So. Calif., 1951; JD, UCLA, 1964. Engr. freeway system design Calif. State Div. Hwys., Los Angeles, 1951-52; engr. hydraulic studies Calif. State Div. Water Resources, Los Angeles, 1953-54; patent engr. Douglas Aircraft Co., 1954-56, asst. patent counsel, 1956-59, asst. gen. counsel, 1959-67, v.p. fin., 1967-68; pres. McDonnell Douglas Fin. Corp.,

1968—, chmn., 1988—, also bd. dirs.; corp. v.p. McDonnell Douglas Corp., 1967-88, sr. v.p.-group exec., 1988—; pres. MCD Realty Co., 1974-78; chmn. bd. dirs. McDonnell Douglas Travel Co., 1986—, McDonnell Douglas Realty Co., 1988—, McDonnell Douglas Truck Services Inc., 1983—; Irish Aerospace Ltd., 1984—; chmn., chief exec. officer McDonnell Douglas Fin. Corp. Ltd., 1981—, also bd. dirs.; pres. McDonnell Douglas-West Personnel Community Service Inc., 1987—, also bd. dirs.; bd. dirs. Pvt. Export Funding Corp., 1988—. Bd. regents Loyola Marymount U., mem. assocs.; past trustee UCLA. Served with USNR, 1943-46. Mem. ABA, Calif. Bar Assns., Los Angeles County Bar Assn., Los Angeles C. of C., Nat. Def. Transp. Assn., Los Angeles World Affairs Council, Order of Coif, Chi Epsilon, Tau Beta Pi. Clubs: Bel-Air Country, California, Los Angeles. Avocations: jogging, running, handball, racquetball. Office: McDonnell Douglas Fin Corp 340 Golden Shore St Long Beach CA 90802-4249

MCMILLAN, JOHN A., retail executive; b. 1931. BA, U. Wash., 1957. With Nordstrom Inc., Seattle, 1957—, exec. v.p., 1975—, pres., 1989—, co-chmn., 1991—. Office: Nordstrom Inc 1501 5th Ave Seattle WA 98101-1603*

MCMILLAN, LEE RICHARDS, II, lawyer; b. New Orleans, Aug. 26, 1947; s. John H. and Phoebe (Skillman) McM.; m. Lynne Clark Pottharst, June 27, 1970; children: Leslie Clark, Hillary Anne, Lee Richards III. BS in Commerce, Washington and Lee U., 1969; JD, Tulane U., 1972; LLM in Taxation, NYU, 1976. Bar: La. 1972. Assoc. Jones, Walker, Waechter, Poitevent, Carrere & Denegre, New Orleans, 1976-79, ptnr., 1979—; sect. head, corp. and securities sect., 1987-90, 94—, exec. com., 1990-94, chmn. exec. com., 1991-94; bd. dirs. Mech. Equipment Co., Inc., New Orleans, 1977—, vice-chmn., 1980-86, chmn. bd., 1986—, pres., 1989—. Bd. trustees New Orleans Mus. Art, 1989—; bd. dirs. Bur. Govt. Rsch. New Orleans, 1987-93, Louise S. McGehee Sch., New Orleans, 1982-88, co-chmn. capital fund dr., 1984-86, pres. bd. dirs., 1986-88; bd. govs. Isidore Newman Sch., New Orleans, 1991—. Lt. JAGC USNR, 1972-75. Mem. ABA (com. on negotiated acquisitions 1986-94), La. State Bar Assn. (chmn. corp. and bus. law sect. 1985-86, mem. com. on bar admissions 1986-87), Young Pres. Orgn. Republican. Episcopalian. Avocation: sailing. Office: Jones Walker Waechter Poitevent Carrere & Denegre 201 Saint Charles Ave New Orleans LA 70170-1000

MCMILLAN, M. SEAN, lawyer. Diploma U. Munich, 1963; cert. Internat. Sch., Copenhagen, Denmark, 1962; SB, U. So. Calif., 1967; JD, Harvard U., 1970. Bar: Calif. 1971. Spl. projects dir. Mass. Gen. Hosp., Boston, 1967-70; ptnr. Keatinge, Libbott, Bates & Loo, Los Angeles, 1970-74, Loo, Merideth & McMillan, Los Angeles, 1974-85, Bryan/Cave, Los Angeles/Santa Monica, 1986—. Mem. Assn. Computing Machinery, ABA, Am. Soc. Internat. Law, Phi Beta Kappa, Phi Kappa Phi. Editor: Harvard Internat. Law Jour., 1968-70. Office: Bryan Cave 120 Broadway Ste 500 Santa Monica CA 90401

MCMILLAN, MARY BIGELOW, retired minister, volunteer; b. St. Paul, July 30, 1919; d. Charles Henry and Allison (McKibbin) Bigelow; m. Richard McMillan, June 26, 1943; children: Richard Jr., Charles B., Douglas D., M. Allison, Anne E. BA, Vassar Coll., 1941; MDiv, United Theol. Sem. Twin Cities, 1978, DDiv (hon.), 1989. Ordained to ministry Presbyn. Ch., 1978. Asst. min. House of Hope Presbyn. Ch., St. Paul, 1978-82; interim pres. United Theol. Sem. Twin Cities, New Brighton, Minn., 1982-83, ret., 1987. Contbr. author: The Good Steward, 1983. Trustee Minn. Ch. Found., Mpls., 1984—, United Theol. Sem. Twin Cities, 1977-89, also chmn. bd. trustees; bd. dirs. Inst. for Ecumenical and Cultural Rsch., Collegeville, Minn., 1982—; regional dir. Assn. Jr. Leagues, N.Y.C., 1959-61, pres. St. Paul chpt., 1957-59; vice chair Ramsey County Welfare Bd., St. Paul, 1962-66, St. Paul Health and Welfare Planning Coun., 1964-70, F.R. Bigelow Found., St. Paul, 1988-95, also 1st vice chair; trustee Wilder Found., 1973-89, also 1st vice chair. Recipient award for community planning United Way, 1965, also for yr. round leadership, 1973, Leadership in Community Svc. award YWCA, 1980, Sisterhood award NCCJ, Mpls., 1989; named Disting Alumna award St. Paul Acad. and Summit Sch., 1988. Mem. New Century Club. Avocations: golf, knitting, reading. Home: 2532 Manitou Is Saint Paul MN 55110-3901

MCMILLAN, ROBERT ALLAN, chemical company executive; b. Santa Barbara, Calif., Dec. 18, 1942; s. Edward and Thelma (Zuercher) McM.; m. Peggy Sue Damron, Oct. 17, 1964; children: Donald James, Jeffrey Scott; m. Christine Collins, June 17, 1983; children: Michelle Diane Ball, Suzanne Mary Ball. BS in Econs., U. Calif., Santa Barbara, 1968; PhD in Econs., U. Calif., Berkeley, 1972. Cons., economist Bank of Am., San Francisco, 1968-71; economist FRS, Cleve., 1971-74; economist BF Goodrich Co., Akron, Ohio, 1974-75, dir. econ. research, 1975-77, dir. analysis and control, 1977-78, dir. investor relations, 1978-82, exec. dir. planning and devel., 1982-86, v.p., treas., 1986—. Chmn. Akron Area Joint Econ. Council, 1985. Named Seer of Yr., Harvard U., 1977, 84. Mem. Fin. Execs. Inst., Conf. Bus. Economists, Nat. Assn. Corp. Treas. Office: B F Goodrich Co 3925 Embassy Pky Akron OH 44333-1763

MC MILLAN, R(OBERT) BRUCE, museum executive, anthropologist; b. Springfield, Mo., Dec. 3, 1937; s. George Glassey and Winnie Mae (Booth) McM.; m. Virginia Kay Moore, Sept. 30, 1961; children: Robert Gregory, Michael David, Lynn Kathryn. B.S. in Edn, S.W. Mo. State U., 1960; M.A. in Anthropology, U. Mo., Columbia, 1963; Ph.D. in Anthropology (NSF fellow), U. Colo., Boulder, 1971. Rsch. assoc. in archaeology U. Mo., 1963-65, 68-69; assoc. curator anthropology Ill. State Mus., Springfield, 1969-72; curator anthropology Ill. State Mus., 1972-73, asst. mus. dir., 1973-76, mus. dir., 1977—; exec. sec. Ill. State Mus. Soc., 1977—; lectr. in anthropology Northwestern U., 1973; bd. dirs. Found. Ill. Archaeology, 1978-83. Editor: (with W. Raymond Wood) Prehistoric Man and His Environments, 1976. Mem. Ill. Spl. Events Commn., 1977-79; program chmn., 1977-78; commr. Ill. and Mich. Canal Nat. Heritage Corridor Commn., 1988—. NSF grantee, 1971, 72, 80; Nat. Endowment for Humanities grantee, 1978. Fellow AAAS, Am. Anthrop. Assn.; mem. Am. Assn. Mus. (council 1982-86), Midwest Mus. Conf. (pres.), Soc. Am. Archaeology, Current Anthropology (asso.), Am. Quaternary Assn., Sigma Xi. Office: Ill State Mus Spring and Edwards Sts Springfield IL 62706 also: Dickson Mounds Museum Lewistown IL 61542

MCMILLAN, ROBERT RALPH, lawyer; b. N.Y.C., May 21, 1932; s. Harry and Vivian (Beatty) McM.; m. Jane Gail Arbo, June 7, 1958; children: Robin, Karen, Kenneth. Student, Adelphi U., 1951-52, 55-56; JD, Bklyn. Law Sch., 1960. Bar: N.Y. 1960. Spl. asst. staff of Richard M. Nixon, N.Y., Washington, 1960, 64-65; counsel Senator Kenneth B. Keating, Washington, 1960-62; govt. rels. advisor Mobil Oil Co., N.Y.C., 1962-63, 65-68; v.p. Avon Products, N.Y.C., 1973-78, 79-85; sr. v.p. A&S Dept. Stores, N.Y.C., 1978-79; counsel Rivkin, Radler, Bayh, Hart & Kremer, Uniondale, N.Y., 1986-91; ptnr. McMillan, Rather, Bennett & Rigano, P.C., Melville, N.Y., 1991—; bd. dirs. Lumex, Inc., Bayshore, N.Y., Key Bank N.Y., Empire Blue Cross Blue Shield, Panama Canal Commn., 1989-94, chmn., 1993-94. News commentator Sta. WLIW-TV, 1993—. Trustee Adelphi U., 1984-89; bd. dirs. L.I. (N.Y.) Assn.; chmn. L.I. Housing Parntership, 1988—. 1st lt. U.S. Army, 1952-54. Decorated Bronze Star. Mem. Nassau County Bar Assn., Suffolk County Bar Assn. Republican. Avocations: golf, swimming. Office: McMillan Rather Bennett & Rigano 395 N Service Rd Melville NY 11747-3139

MCMILLAN, TERRY L., writer, educator; b. Port Huron, Mich., Oct. 18, 1951; d. Edward McMillan and Madeline Washington Tillman; 1 child, Solomon Welch. BS in Journalism, U. Calif., Berkeley, 1979; MFA, Columbia Univ., N.Y.C., 1979. Instr. U. Wyoming, Laramie, 1987-90; prof. U. Ariz., Tucson, 1990-92. Author: Mama, 1987, Disappearing Acts, 1989, Waiting to Exhale, 1992; (with Nawal El Saadawi) Ergo! the Bumbershoot Literary Magazine (vol. 8 no. 1), 1993; editor: Breaking Ice: An Anthology of Contemporary African-American Fiction, 1990. Recipient National Endowment for the Arts fellowship, 1988. Office: care Free at Last PO Box 2408 Danville CA 94526 also: care Molly Friedrich Aaron Priest Literary Agency 122 East 42nd St Ste 3902 New York NY 10168*

MCMILLEN, DONALD F., chemist. BS in Chemistry, U. Notre Dame, 1963; PhD in Organic Chemistry, Stanford U., 1967. Sr. staff scientist

molecular physics lab Stanford Rsch. Inst., Menlo Park, Calif. Recipient Henry H. Storch award in Fuel Chemistry Am. Chem. Soc., 1995. Office: Stanford Rsch Inst Molecular Physics Lab Menlo Park CA 94025*

MCMILLEN, JAMES THOMAS, lawyer; b. Murfreesboro, Tenn., Mar. 4, 1942; s. James Clyde and Mable Bell (Waldron) McM.; m. Janice Elaine Ligon, June 29, 1974; children: Rachel Leeanne, Shayne Brandon. BS in Math., Middle Tenn. State U., 1968; JD, Nashville Sch. Law, 1975. Bar: Tenn. 1975, Tex. 1985, U.S. Dist. Ct. (mid. dist.) Tenn. 1976, U.S. Dist. Ct. (so. dist.) Tex. 1985, U.S. Dist. Ct. (we. and no. dists.) Tex. 1989, U.S. Ct. Appeals (6th cir.) 1977, U.S. Ct. Appeals (5th cir.) 1985, U.S. Supreme Ct. 1978; cert. bus. and consumer bankruptcy law Tex. Bd. Legal Specialization. Programmer Baird-Ward Printing Co., Nashville, 1968-69; project mgr. Norvel Systems, Inc., Memphis, 1969-70; computer technician Concept Data Svc., Memphis, 1970; programmer, analyst Baird-Ward Printing Co., Nashville, 1970-75; atty., pvt. practice Nashville, 1975-78, Murfreesboro, 1978-83; atty. disaster loan program SBA, Nashville, 1983-84; br. counsel atty. SBA, Corpus Christi, Tex., 1984-85; sr. assoc. atty. Kleberg, Dyer, Redford & Weil, Corpus Christi, Tex., 1985-87; atty., pvt. practice Corpus Christi, Tex., 1987—; speaker on ethics ann. conv. Nat. Assn. Consumer Bankruptcy Attys., San Francisco, 1994, chmn. 1995 conv. site. Com. chmn. Troop 220 Gulf Coast Coun. Boy Scouts Am., 1993. Recipient Cert. of Appreciation, State of Tenn., 1972; named Boss of Yr., Murfreesboro Legal Secs. Assn., 1981. Mem. ABA, Am. Bankruptcy Inst. (cert. bus. and consumer bankruptcy law), Tex. Bar Assn., Coastal Bend Bankruptcy Assn. (pres. 1991-92, bd. dirs. 191—), Am. Arbitration Assn., Coll. of State Bar, Cooper's Inn Honor Soc., Alpha Psi Omega. Democrat. Episcopalian. Avocations: travel, RVing. Office: 1420 American Bank Plz 711 N Carancahua Corpus Christi TX 78475

MCMILLEN, LOUIS ALBERT, architect; b. St. Louis, Oct. 24, 1916; s. Drury A. and Eleanor (Stockstrom) McM.; m. Persis White, Aug. 26, 1949; children: Michael Albert, Louis Stockstrom, Leander A.C. Grad., St. George's Sch., Newport, R.I., 1935; B.F.A., Yale U., 1940; M.Arch., Harvard U., 1947. Vice pres., dir. Architects Collaborative Inc., Cambridge, Mass., 1947-70; pres. Architects Collaborative Inc., 1970-80; pres. Architects Collaborative Internat. Ltd., Vaduz, 1959—; Architect in residence Am. Acad. Rome, 1968, 69; Mem. planning bd., Concord, Mass., 1958-60. Prin. works include master planning air bases in U.S., ednl. facilities in, New Eng.; commd. to do: U. Bagdad, Iraq, 1959, U. Mosul, Iraq, 1965, W.Va. State Parks, Hawks Nest, Canaan Valley, Pipestem/Bluestone and Twin Falls; office bldg., Kuwait Fund for Arab Econ. Devel., 1968, total tourist facilities, Porto Carras, Sithonia, Greece, 1969. Served to lt. USNR, 1942-46. Fellow AIA; mem. Boston Soc. Architects, Soc. Fellows Am. Acad. in Rome, Zeta Psi. Clubs: Naval and Military (London); Old North Bridge Hounds (joint master); Somerset (Boston). Home: PO Box 490 Essex MA 01929-0009

MCMILLEN, ROBERT STEWART, lawyer; b. Yonkers, N.Y., Feb. 25, 1943; s. David Harry and Blodwyn Elizabeth (Evans) McM.; m. Dorothea Anne Murray, July 2, 1966; children: Elissa London, Tara Evans. BS, U. Rochester, 1964; JD cum laude, Albany Law Sch. Union U., 1969. Bar: N.Y. 1969, U.S. Dist. Ct. (no. dist.) N.Y. 1969. Assoc. Clark, Bartlett & Caffry, Glens Falls, N.Y., 1969-73; ptnr. Caffry, Pontiff, Stewart, Rhodes & Judge, Glens Falls, 1974-80; prin. Bartlett, Pontiff, Stewart & Rhodes, P.C., Glens Falls, 1981—; sr. law examiner N.Y. State Bd. Law Examiners, Albany, 1980—; pres., bd. dirs. Community Title Agy., Inc., Glens Falls, 1984—. Editor-in-chief Albany Law Rev., 1968-69. Bd. dirs., officer Voluntary Action Ctr. of Glens Falls Area, Inc., 1970—; bd. dirs., treas. Arts and Crafts Ctr. of Warren County, Inc., Glens Falls, 1984-94; mem. Warren County Rep. Com., Queensbury, N.Y., 1979—; alternate or del. Rep. Jud. Nominating Com., 4th Jud. Dist. N.Y., 1977-95. Recipient Disting. Svc. award Voluntary Action Ctr. of Glens Falls Area, Inc., 1990. Mem. ABA, N.Y. State Bar Assn. (mem. com. profl. ethics 1990—), Warren County Bar Assn. (bd. dirs. 1979-82). Avocations: family activities, downhill skiing, boating, hockey. Home: 27 Moorwood Dr Queensbury NY 12804-1010 Office: 1 Washington St Glens Falls NY 12801-2963

MCMILLEN, (CHARLES) THOMAS, federal official; b. Elmira, N.Y., May 26, 1952. BS, U. Md., 1974; BA, MA, Oxford U., 1978. Profl. basketball player Buffalo Braves, 1975-77, N.Y. Knicks, 1977, Atlanta Hawks, 1977-83, Washington Bullets, 1983-86; mem. 100th-102nd Congresses from 4th Md. dist., Washington, 1987-92. Author: (with Paul Coggins) Out of Bounds; How the American Sports Establishment is Being Driven by Greed and Hypocrisy-and What Needs to be Done About It, 1992. Co-chmn. Pres.' Coun. Phys. Fitness and Sports, 1993—. Rhodes scholar; named to U.S. Olympic Team, 1972. Office: Pres Coun Phys Fitness and Sports 701 Pennsylvania Ave NW Ste 250 Washington DC 20004-3608

MC MILLEN, THOMAS ROBERTS, lawyer, arbitrator, mediator, retired judge; b. Decatur, Ill., June 8, 1916; s. Rolla C. and Ruth (Roberts) Mc M.; m. Anne Ford, Aug. 16, 1946; children: Margot F., Patricia R., Anne C. Scheyer. AB, Princeton U., 1938; LLB, Harvard U., 1941. Bar: Ill. 1941, U.S. Supreme Ct. 1948. Mem. firm Bell, Boyd, Lloyd, Haddad & Burns, Chgo., 1946-66; judge Cook County Cir. Ct., Cook County, Ill., 1966-71, U.S. Dist. Ct. (no. dist.) Ill., Chgo., 1971-85, ret.; pvt. practice Chgo., 1985—. Mem. arbitration panels Am. Arbitration Assn., Fed. Med. and Conciliation Svc., Chgo. Bd. Options Exch., Ill. State Bd. Edn., Judicate. Maj. CIC, AUS, 1941-45. Decorated Bronze Star medal, European Battle Stars (4), Croix de Guerre. Mem. Chgo. Bar Assn. (mem. bd. mgrs. 1964-66), 7th Cir. Bar Assn., Counter Intelligence Corps Assn., Chgo. Farmers (bd. dirs. 1989), Assn. Am. Rhodes Scholars, Indian Hill Country Club, Univ. Club Chgo., Phi Beta Kappa. Home and Office: 231 Forest St Winnetka IL 60093-3856

MCMILLER, ANITA WILLIAMS, army officer, transportation professional, educator; b. Chgo., Dec. 23, 1946; d. Chester Leon and Marion Claudette (Martin) Williams; m. Robert Melvin McMiller, July 29, 1967 (div. 1980). BS in Edn., No. Ill. U., 1968; MBA, Fla. Inst. Tech., 1979; M of Mil. Arts and Sci., U.S. Army Command & Gen. Staff Coll., 1990; postgrad., US Army War Coll., Carlisle, Pa., 1993-94. Social worker County of Cook, Chgo., 1968-69; recruiter analyst, dir. personnel State of Ill., Chgo., 1969-75; commd. 1st lt. U.S. Army, 1975, advanced through grades to lt. col., 1991; platoon leader, motor officer, exec. officer 155th Transp. Co., Ft. Eustis, Va. and Okinawa, Japan, 1976-78; S-1 pers. and adminstrn. officer 38th Transp. Bn., Ft. Eustis, 1978-79; installation transp. officer, fin. mgr. 3d Armor Div., Hanau, Germany, 1979-82, transp. co. comdr., 1982-83; transp. plans officer Mil. Traffic Mgmt. Command, Falls Church, Va., 1983-85; tour with Sea Land Corp., Menlo Park, N.J., 1985-86; dep. comdr., ops. officer Bremerhaven (Germany) Terminal, 1986-89; logistics staff officer The Pentagon, Washington, 1990-91; comdr. 1320th Port Battalion Mil. Traffic Mgmt. Command, U.K. Terminal, Felixstowe, Great Britain, 1991-93; staff officer Office Joint Chiefs of Staff, The Pentagon, Washington, 1994—; instr. Cen. Tex. Coll., Hanau, Fed. Republic Germany, 1981-83, Phillips Bus. Coll., Alexandria, Va., 1983-84, City Colls. Chgo., 1987-89. Contbr. articles to profl. jours. Child advocate, foster mother Army Community Service, Hanau, 1980-83; tutor Parent-Tchr. Club Hanau Schs., 1981-83; vol. Vis. Nurses Assn. No. Va., 1983-85; coordinator, English tutor Adopt-a-Sch. Project, Washington, 1983-85; treas. Bremerhaven Girl Scouts Coun., 1987-89, mem. Red Cross. Mem. Nat. Def. Transp. Assn., Assn. U.S. Army, Fedn. Bus. Profl. Women, Rocks, Inc., Am. Legion, British Legion, Alpha Kappa Alpha. Avocations: skiing, golf, running, hist. rsch. Home: PO Box 46344 Washington DC 20050-6344 Office: J7/EAD 7000 Joint Staff The Pentagon Washington DC 20318-7000

MCMILLIAN, THEODORE, federal judge; b. St. Louis, Jan. 28, 1919; m. Minnie E. Foster, Dec. 8, 1941. BS, Lincoln U., 1941, HHD (hon.), 1981; LLD, St. Louis U., 1949; HHD (hon.), U. Mo., St. Louis, 1978. Mem. firm Lynch & McMillian, St. Louis, 1949-53; asst. circuit atty. City of St. Louis, 1953-56; judge U.S. Ct. Appeals (8th cir.) 1978—; judge Circuit Ct. for City St. Louis, 1956-72, Mo. Ct. Appeals eastern div., 1972-78; asso. prof. adminstrn. justice U. Mo., St. Louis, 1970—; asso. prof. Webster Coll. Grad. Program, 1977; mem. faculty Nat. Coll. Juvenile Justice, U. Nev., 1972—. Served to 1st lt. Signal Corps U.S. Army, 1942-46. Recipient Alumni Merit award St. Louis U., 1965. Mem. Lawyers Assn., Mo., Mound City bar assns., Am. Judicature Soc., Phi Beta Kappa, Alpha Sigma Nu. Office: US

Ct Appeals 8th Circuit 526 US Ct & Custom House 1114 Market St Saint Louis MO 63101-2043*

MCMILLIN, DAVID ROBERT, chemistry educator; b. E. St. Louis, Jan. 1, 1948; s. Robert Cecil and Clara Rose (Thereon) McM.; m. Nicole Wilson, Nov. 3, 1974; children: Robert Stephen, Andrew Wilson. BA, Knox Coll., 1969; PhD, U. Ill., 1973. Postdoctoral fellow Calif. Inst. Tech., Pasadena, 1974; asst. prof. chemistry Purdue U., West Lafayette, Ind., 1975-80, assoc. prof., 1980-85, prof., 1985—. Contbr. articles to profl. jours. Recipient F.D. Martin Teaching award Purdue U., 1975. Mem. Am. Chem. Soc., Inter-Am. Photochem. Soc. (sec. 1986-90, v.p. 1994—), Phi Beta Kappa, Sigma Xi. Presbyterian. Avocations: sports, reading. Office: Purdue U Dept Chemistry West Lafayette IN 47907-1393

MCMILLIN, JEANIE BYRD, biochemist, medical educator; b. Spartanburg, S.C., Sept. 26, 1939; d. Walter Louis and Frances Elizabeth (Austell) McM.; m. Wallace Barry VanWinkle, 1987; children: Elizabeth, David Emerson. BA, Converse Coll., 1961; Ph.D. in Biochemistry, U. N.C., 1967; D.Sc. (hon.), Converse Coll., 1988. Research assoc., instr. U. N.C., Chapel Hill, N.C., 1967-68; research assoc. Cornell Med. Coll., N.Y.C., 1968-69; instr. Baylor Coll. Medicine, Houston, 1969-72, asst. prof., 1972-80, assoc. prof. medicine, biochemistry and pediatrics, 1980-85, prof., 1985-86; prof. medicine and cell biology, dir. cardiac biochemistry U. Ala.-Birmingham, 1986-89; prof. pathology U. Tex. Health Sci. Ctr., Houston, 1989—, dir. grad. studies, 1992—; cons. NIH, 1979—, mem. cardiovascular pulmonary study sect., 1982-86; ad hoc cons. bd. sci. counselors Nat. Inst. on Aging, 1987; mem. can. research rev. com. Am. Heart Assn., 1981-86, Ala. affiliate, 1986-89, Tex. affiliate, 1990—, mem. exec. bd., program and nominating coms. Coun. on Basic Sci.; cardiol. adv. com. Nat. Heart, Lung and Blood Inst., 1987-91, chair basic sci. subcom., 1989-91. Fulbright fellow in chemistry, 1961-62; NASA fellow, 1962-66; USPHS fellow, 1966-67; grantee Am. Heart Assn., 1978-81, Muscular Dystrophy Assn., 1980-83, NIH, 1977—. Mem. Internat. Study Group for Research in Cardiac Metabolism, Biophys. Soc., Cardiac Muscle Soc., Am. Soc. Biol. Chemists, Am. Physiol. Soc. (fellow cardiovascular sect.), Sigma Xi (treas. U. Ala-Birmingham chpt.). Editorial bd. Am. Jour. Physiology, 1980-93, Circulation, 1986-88, 93—, Jour. Molecular Cell Cardiology, 1986—; contbr. articles to various publs. Office: Dept Pathology U Tex Health Sci Ctr 6431 Fannin St Houston TX 77030-1501

MC MILLION, JOHN MACON, retired newspaper publisher; b. Coffeyville, Kans., Dec. 25, 1929; s. John Dibrell and Mattie Anna (Macon) McM.; m. Melanie Ann McMillion; children: John Thomas, Johanna, Jennifer, Amanda. Student, Vanderbilt U., 1947-49; B.S. in Journalism, U. Kans., 1956. Police reporter Amarillo (Tex.) Globe-News, 1956; sports editor, telegraph editor Grand Junction (Colo.) Daily Sentinel, 1956-58; mng. editor Alliance (Nebr.) Times-Herald, 1958-59, Clovis (N.Mex.) Jour., 1959-62; gen. mgr. Pasadena (Tex.) Citizen, 1962; bur. mgr. UPI, 1962-66; exec. editor Albuquerque Jour., 1966-69; bus. mgr. Albuquerque Pub. Co., 1971-75; pub. Herald and News-Tribune, Duluth, Minn., 1975-86, Akron (Ohio) Beacon Jour., 1986-90, ret.; campaign mgr. gubernatorial campaign, 1969-71. Served with USN, 1950-54. Address: 12404 Royal Oak Ct NE Albuquerque NM 87111-6237

MCMINDES, ROY JAMES, aggregate company executive; b. Essex, Md., July 12, 1923; s. Roy Preston and Edith S. (Sh) McM.; m. Prudence Atsinger, June 8, 1946; children: Gail Karen, Joan Susan, James Lee. B.S., U. Md., 1948. Pres., Sheridan Corp., Lebanon, Pa., 1951—, Grays Ferry Brick Co., Lebanon, 1971—, Waylite Co., Lebanon, 1976-88; chmn. bd. Peoples Nat. Bank, Lebanon, 1984-92, dir., 1965-92. Bd. dirs. Lebanon YMCA, 1968-86, Good Samaritan Hosp., Lebanon, 1970-93. With A.C., USN, 1943-46, mem. USNR, 1946-52. Recipient Founders Day award Lebanon Valley Coll., 1987. Mem. Lebanon Valley C. of C. (pres. 1973), Lebanon Country Club, Shriners, Jesters. Republican. Presbyterian. Office: 1212 W Maple St Lebanon PA 17042-0009

MCMINN, WILLIAM A., chemicals company executive; b. 1931. With FMC Corp., Chgo., 1967-85, Cain Chemical Co., Kearney, N.J., 1987-88; chmn., dir. Arcadian Corp., Memphis, 1989—; dir. Sterling Chems., Houston. Office: Arcadian Corp 6750 Poplar Ave Ste 600 Memphis TN 38138-7424

MCMORROW, RICHARD MARK, research company executive; b. Boston, Aug. 8, 1941; s. J. Edward and Marie L. (Martine) McM.; m. Ursula M. Rodgers, Apr. 24, 1965; children: Ethan Rodgers, Juliet Marie. Student, Northeastern U., 1959-61, Bentley Coll., Waltham, Mass., 1962-65; J.D., New Eng. Sch. Law, Boston, 1968. Bar: Mass. bar 1971. With Commonwealth Energy Co., Cambridge, Mass., 1969-76; sec. Commonwealth Energy Co., 1973-76, Columbus So. Power Co., Columbus, 1976-79; v.p. law and risk mgmt. Columbus So. Power Co., 1979—; asst. v.p. Am. Electric Power, 1983-94; pres. CoconaRsch. Corp., Columbus, 1994—; bd. dirs. Elford Inc., System Sports Inc. Trustee Columbus Zoo, Ctr. Sci. and Industry., Columbus, Ballet Met., Columbus, Columbus Assn. for Performing Arts; chmn. bd. trustees Grant Med. Ctr. Found., Nat. Safety Coun., Columbus. With USCGR, 1963-68. Mem. ABA, Ohio Bar Assn., Mass. Bar Assn., Columbus C. of C., Rotary. Office: One Riverside Pla 2234 Summit St Columbus OH 43201

MCMULKIN, FRANCIS JOHN, steel company executive; b. Sault Ste. Marie, Ont., Can., Dec. 7, 1915; s. George Alexander and Leanor Augusta (Zryd) McM.; m. Margaret Lilian Winch, Sept. 21, 1946; children: John Bruce, Mary Diane. B.S. in Metallurgy, Mich. Coll. Mining and Tech., 1937; M.E., Mich. Tech. U., 1945, D.Engring. (hon.), 1972. Formerly metallurgist Algoma Steel Corp., Sault Ste. Marie; then research fellow Ont. Research Found., Mississauga, 1942-47; research and devel. engr. Dominion Foundries & Steel Ltd., Hamilton, Ont., Can., from 1947, then dir. research Dominion Foundries & Steel Ltd., until 1964, v.p. research, 1964-85; Howe Meml. lectr., 1973. Contbr. articles to profl. publs. Recipient Disting. Alumnus award Mich. Tech. U., 1976. Fellow Am. Soc. Metals (life mem., William Hunt Eisenman award 1968), Engring. Inst. Can. (life mem., John Galbraith prize 1945), mem. Can. Inst. Mining nd Metallurgy (H.T. Airey Meml. Ann. Conf. Lecture award), AIME (Basic Oxygen Steel award 1963, charter disting. mem. Iron and Steel Soc. 1976), Iron and Steel Inst., U.K., Royal Over-Seas League (London), Hamilton Club, Hamilton Golf and Country Club, Mid Ocean Club (Bermuda). Mem. United Ch. of Canada. Home: 270 Roseland Crescent, Burlington, ON Canada L7N 1S3 Office: PO Box 2460, Hamilton, ON Canada L8N 3J5

MC MULLAN, DOROTHY, nurse educator; b. Bloomfield, N.J., June 19, 1911; d. Samuel H. and Anne (Gardiner) McM.; m. Bernard J. Pisani, July 10, 1982. Diploma, Cornell U.-N.Y. Hosp. Sch. Nursing, 1935; B.S. N.Y., 1948, M.A., 1950, Ed.D., 1962. Pub. health nurse Henry St. Vis. Nurse Service, N.Y.C., 1935-39; pvt. duty nurse N.Y.C., 1939-41; instr. N.Y. Hosp.-Cornell U. Sch. Nursing, 1947-55; supr. N.Y. Hosp.-Cornell Med. Center, 1947-50, asst. dept. head 1950-53, adminstrv. asst. nursing services for methods improvements, 1953-55; instr. N.Y. Hosp.-Cornell Med. Center (Sch. Nursing); dir., prof. nursing Russell Sage Coll., 1955-61; dean, prof. Ind. State U. Sch. Nursing, Terre Haute, 1962-71; dir. div. nursing Nat. League for Nursing, N.Y., 1971-77; chmn. dept. baccalaureate and higher edn. N.Y. League, 1960-62; mem. Nat. Commn. on Allied Health Edn., 1977-80; cons. on nurse edn., 1977-80; cons. Council on Postsecondary Accreditation, 1977-78; v.p. N.Y. Nurses Assn., 1960-61; pres. Vigo County Coordinating Council, 1968-69; mem. adv. bd. Ind. Regional Med. Planning, 1966-71; sec. exec. com. Ind. Comprehensive Health Council, 1967-71; mem. adv. com. on women in services U.S. Dept. Def., 1971-73; mem. nursing adv. com. Am. Cancer Soc., 1975-77; mem. com. on health manpower Nat. Health Council, 1975-79. Author: (with Hayt, Groeschel) Law of Hospital and Nurse, 1958, The Role of the Nurse as Employee: A Case of Mutual Responsibilities, 1976, Preparation of the Nurse Specialist, 1977. Bd. dirs. Vigo County cancer Soc., Vigo County cerebral Palsy Assn., Goodwill Industries Terre Haute, Cmty. Found. Wabash Valley, 1964-71; mem. Heritage Found.; mem. coun. Citizens Against Govt. Waste. Recipient Ann. award of Vigo County Ind. Bus. and Profl. Women's Orgn., 1967, Army Nurse Corps Spl. award, 1973, Dept. of Def. cert., N.Y. Founders Day cert., 1963, Pres.'s award Ind. State U., 1988, Disting. Alumnus award Cornell U./N.Y. Hosp. Sch. Nursing Alumni Assn., 1990; recognized for disting. and devoted svc. as pres. Ind. League for Nursing, 1966-71; named in People of Progress in Terre Haute, 1967. Mem. APHA, Cornell U.-N.Y. Hosp. Sch. Nursing Alumnae Assn. (pres. 1950-52), Ind. League for Nursing (pres. 1966-71), So. N.Y. League for Nursing (pres. 1980-82, exec. sec. 1982-88, award 1987, Dorothy McMullan Pisani ann. award 1987), League Nursing (mem. exec. com., chmn. Gt. Lakes Regional Assembly 1969-71), Nat. League Nursing (bd. dirs. 1981-83), Assn. Higher Edn., Inst. Biomed. Edn. (bd. dirs. 1984-89), Am. Assn. for World Health (exec. com. 1980-90, exec. 1984-89), N.Y. County Med. Soc. Auxiliary (v.p. 1984-90), Kappa Delta Pi. Republican. Episcopalian. Home: 209 Sunset Ave Englewood NJ 07631-4413

MCMULLAN, WILLIAM PATRICK, JR., banker; b. Lake, Miss., Nov. 20, 1925; s. William Patrick and Mary Lucy (Pace) McM.; m. Rosemary Lyons, Nov. 22, 1950; children: Julie, William Patrick III, Michael L., Mary Charlotte, Robert J.; m. Deborah Sutton; 1 child, Wilson M. B.B.A., U. Miss., 1948; M.B.A., Wharton Sch. Fin., U. Pa., 1949; D.B.A. (hon.), William Carey Coll., 1981. Pres. Newton County Bank, Newton, Miss., 1950-57, vice chmn., 1970—; state banking commr. State of Miss., Jackson, 1957-60; exec. v.p. Deposit Guaranty Nat. Bank, Jackson, 1960-68, vice chmn., 1968-73, pres., 1973-75; chmn. The Mississippi Bank, Jackson, 1975-83, First Miss. Nat. Corp., 1983-84; dir Mobile Communications Corp. Am., Jackson; dir. Cal-Maine Foods, Jackson, Magna Corp., Jackson. Chmn. Jackson Mcpl. Airport Authority, 1965-85; trustee Miss. Bapt. Med. Ctr., Jackson, 1970-86; mem. exec. com. Dem. Nat. Fin. Coun., 1976-84; state fin. chmn. Jimmy Carter for Pres. Campaign, 1976-80. With USAF, 1943-45. Mem. Met. Club (N.Y.C.), Country Club of Jackson, Capital City Club (Jackson, Miss.), Palm Bay Bankers Club (Miami), Boca Grande Club, Ponte Vedra Club. Episcopalian. Home: 101 Terebra Ct Ponte Vedra Beach FL 32082-2450

MCMULLAN, WILLIAM PATRICK, III, investment banker; b. Newton, Miss., Dec. 29, 1952; s. William Patrick Jr. and Rosemary (Lyons) McM.; m. Rachel Smiley McPherson, Oct. 16, 1982. BA, Vanderbilt U., 1974; MBA, U. Pa., 1976. V.p. Lehman Bros. Kuhn Loeb, N.Y.C., 1976-82; assoc. dir. Prudential-Bache Securities, N.Y.C., 1982-85; mng. dir. Donaldson, Lufkin & Jenrette Securities Corp., N.Y.C., 1985—. Mem. Metropolitan Club, Mashomack Fish and Game Club, Lawrence Beach Club. Home: 607 6th St Brooklyn NY 11215-3701 Office: Donaldson Lufkin & Jenrette Securities Corp 140 Broadway New York NY 10005-1101

MC MULLEN, EDWIN WALLACE, JR., English language educator; b. Quincy, Fla., Dec. 8, 1915; s. Edwin Wallace and Sara Della (Moore) McM.; m. Marian Elizabeth Hoper, June 9, 1946; children: William Wallace, Charles Edwin. B.A., U. Fla., 1936; M.A., Columbia U., 1939, Ph.D., 1950. Instr. English Pa. State U., 1946-48, State U. Iowa, 1950-52; spl. instr. in report writing U.S. Dept. Def., Washington, 1953; sr. reporter U.S. Dept. Def., 1952-57; asst. editor Merriam Webster Dictionary Co., 1957; asst. prof. English Lehigh U., 1957-61, Fairleigh Dickinson U., Madison, N.J., 1961-62; assoc. prof. Fairleigh Dickinson U., 1962-72, prof., 1973-82, chmn. dept. lang. and lit., 1962-65, emeritus, 1982; founder, dir. Names Inst., 1962-86; chmn. publs. subcom. Morris County Tercentenary Com., N.J., 1962-63. Author: English Topographic Terms in Florida, 1563-1874, 1953; contbr. articles to profl. publs.; editor: Names, 1962-65; editor, contbr.: Pubs, Place-Names and Patronymics: Selected Papers of the Names Institute, 1980; editor, contbr. Names New and Old: Papers of the Names Inst., 1993. Served with Signal Corps, U.S. Army, 1942-46. Mem. MLA, Am. Name Soc. (pres. 1976), Internat. Congress on Onomastic Scis., Internat. Linguistic Assn., Am. Dialect Soc., English Place-Name Soc., Morris County Hist. Soc., Old Guard of Summit (N.J.), Nat. Coun. Tchrs. English, Meth. Friendship Club (past co-pres.). Democrat. Methodist. Home: 15 Rosewood Dr Madison NJ 07940-1120 Office: Fairleigh Dickinson U English Dept Madison NJ 07940 *Chaucer sums up my philosophy in his description of the Clerk: "And gladly wolde he lerne and gladly teche.".*

MCMULLEN, JOHN J., professional hockey team executive; m. Jacqueline McMullen; children: Peter, Catharine, John Jr. BSEE, U.S. Naval Acad., 1940; DMechE, Swiss Fed. Tech. Inst.; M in Naval Architecture and Marine Engring., MIT. Commd. ensign USN, 1940, advanced through grades to comdr., resigned, 1954; chief ship constrn. and repair U.S. Maritime Adminstrn. Office, Washington, 1954-57; chmn. John J. McMullen Assocs., Inc., 1957—; ltd. ptnr. N.Y. Yankees Baseball Team, 1974; chmn. Houston Astros Baseball Team, 1979-92, N.J. Devils Hockey Team, East Rutherford, N.J., 1981—. Office: NJ Devils PO Box 504 East Rutherford NJ 07073-0504*

MC MULLEN, THOMAS HENRY, retired air force officer; b. Dayton, Ohio, July 4, 1929; s. Clements and Adelaide Palmer (Lewis) McM.; m. Clara Faye Kirkwood, Mar. 28, 1956; children—Susan Marie, Thomas Clements, John Kirkwood. Student, St. Mary's U. Tex., 1945-47; B.S. in Mil. Engring, U.S. Mil. Acad., 1951; M.S. in Astronautics, Air Force Inst. Tech., 1964; M.S. in Adminstrn, George Washington U., 1971; student, Indsl. Coll. Armed Forces, Ft. McNair, Washington, 1970-71. Commd. 2d lt. U.S. Air Force, 1951, advanced through grades to lt. gen.; 1980; flight trainee Hondo AB, Tex., Bryan AFB, Tex. and Nellis AFB, Nev., 1951-52; fighter pilot/flight comdr. (K-13 AB), Suwon, Korea, 1952-53; flight test maintenance officer Kelly AFB, Tex., 1953-59; Air Force flight acceptance test pilot at (Gen. Dynamics Inc.), Ft. Worth, 1959-62; project officer, Gemini Launch Vehicle Program, officer (Space Systems Div.), Los Angeles, 1964-66; air liaison officer 25th Inf. Div. Cu Chi, South Vietnam, 1967-68; asst. mission dir. Apollo Program Hdqrs. NASA Washington, 1968-70; B-1 dep. system program dir. Wright Patterson AFB, Ohio, 1971-73; A-10 System program dir., 1973-74; vice comdr. Tactical Air Warfare Center Eglin AFB, Fla., 1974-75; comdr. (Tactical Air Warfare Center), 1975-76; dep. chief of staff/requirements Hdqrs. Tactical Air Command Langley AFB, Va., 1976-79; dep. chief of staff/systems Hdqrs. Air Force Systems Command Andrews AFB, Md., 1979-80; vice comdr. Tactical Air Command, 1980-82; comdr. Aero. Systems Div. Wright-Patterson AFB, Ohio, 1982-86; ret. USAF, 1986; cons. in aerospace Washington, 1986—. Decorated D.S.M. with two oak leaf clusters, Silver Star, Legion of Merit, D.F.C. with oak leaf cluster, Bronze Star, Meritorious Service medal with oak leaf cluster, Air Force Commendation medal with oak leaf cluster, Air medal with 18 oak leaf clusters, Purple Heart; Cross of Gallantry with palm Vietnam; recipient Exceptional Service medal NASA, 1969, Group Achievement award, 1969, 71. Fellow AIAA (asso.); mem. Air Force Assn., Order Daedalians, Tau Beta Pi. Presbyterian. Home and Office: 6301 Chaucer View Cir Alexandria VA 22304-3548 *The key to success is a combination of fortunate circumstance, hard work, and a willingness to accept responsibility. Few people get ahead without some combination of all three.*

MC MULLIAN, AMOS RYALS, food company executive; b. Jackson County, Fla., Aug. 28, 1937; s. Andrew Jackson and Willie Ross (Ryals) McM.; m. Jackie Williams, Aug. 27, 1960; children: Amos Ryals, Britton Jackelyn. BS, Fla. State U., 1962. Successively asst. controller, data processing coordinator, adminstrv. asst. to gen. mgr., asst. plant mgr., plant mgr. Flowers Baking Co., Thomasville, Ga., 1963-70, pres. Atlanta Baking Co. div., 1970-72, regional v.p. parent co., 1972-74, pres., chief operating officer bakery div., 1974-76, chief operating officer industry, 1976-81, pres., 1976-83, dir., 1981—, chief exec. officer, 1983—, co-chmn. exec. com., 1983—, vice chmn. industry and chmn. exec. com., 1984-85, chmn. bd., 1985—. Mem. adv. bd. President's Club, Fla. State U.; trustee Southeastern Legal Found.; vestryman, sr. warden Episcopal Ch.; bd. govs. Ga. Pub. Policy Found. With USMC, 1958-61. Named Outstanding Bus. Alumnus, Fla. State U. Mem. NAM (bd. dirs.), Thomasville Landmarks Soc., Atlanta Bakers Club (past pres.), Atlanta Commerce Club, Gridiron Soc. (U. Ga.) Office: Flowers Industries Inc US Hwy 19 S Thomasville GA 31799-1338

MCMULLIN, CARLETON EUGENE, automotive business executive; b. Hutchinson, Kans., Feb. 17, 1932; s. Cloys E. and Beatrice (Jennings) McM.; m. Beth Becker; children: Lucinda Lou, Charis Ann. B.A., U. Okla., 1954; M.P.A., U. Kans., 1958. Asst. city mgr. City of Corpus Christi, Tex., 1957-58; city mgr. City of McAlester, Okla., 1958-62, City of Oak Ridge, Tenn., 1962-73, City of Little Rock, 1973-80; pres. NPT, Inc., 1994; pres. Keystone Enterprises Inc., Cemac Corp., Exceltune Corp., Pinnacle Investments, Inc., 1992; v.p., treas. Devonian Corp.; sec. Precision Tune Franchise Adv. Council, 1979-80; chmn. Assn. Precision Tune Area Sub-Franchisors, 1979-

80, sec. 1991; cons. in field; mem. intergovtl. sci. engring. tech. adv. panel U.S. Office Sci. and Tech. Policy, 1977-79; mem. NSF Adv. Council, 1977-79; chmn. Urban Tech. System Adv. Bd., 1979. Commr. Little Rock Housing Authority, 1987-92. Served with Signal Corps U.S. Army, 1954-56. Mem. Internat. City Mgmt. Assn., Rotary. Episcopalian. Home: 12821 Ridgehaven Rd Little Rock AR 72211-2207

MC MULLIN, ERNAN VINCENT, philosophy educator; b. Donegal, Ireland, Oct. 13, 1924; came to U.S., 1954; s. Vincent Paul and Carmel (Farrell) McM. BSc, Maynooth (Ireland) Coll., 1945, BD, 1948; postgrad. theoretical physics, Dublin Inst. Advanced Studies, 1949-50; BPh, U. Louvain, Belgium, 1951, LPh, 1953, PhD, 1954; DLitt (hon.), Loyola U., Chgo., 1969, Nat. U. Ireland, 1990. Ordained priest Roman Catholic Ch., 1949; faculty U. Notre Dame, 1954-57, 59—, assoc. prof. philosophy, 1964, prof. philosophy, 1966-94, prof. emeritus, 1994—, chmn. dept., 1965-72, O'Hara prof. philosophy, 1984-94; postdoctoral fellow Yale U., 1957-59; vis. prof. U. Minn., 1964-65, U. Cape Town, summers 1972-73, UCLA, 1977, Princeton U., 1991, Yale U., 1992; Cardinal Mercier lectr. U. Louvain, Belgium, 1995; mem. exec. bd. Coun. Philos. Studies, 1970-75; chmn. philosophy of sci. div. Internat. Congress Philosophy, 1968, 73; chmn. U.S. Nat. Com. for History and Philosophy of Sci., 1982-84, 86-87. Author: Newton on Matter and Activity, 1978, The Inference That Makes Science, 1992; editor: The Concept of Matter, 1963, Galileo, Man of Science, 1967, The Concept of Matter in Modern Philosophy, 1978, Death and Decision, 1978, Issues in Computer Diagnosis, 1983, Evolution and Creation, 1985, Construction and Constraint: The Shaping of Scientific Rationality; co-editor: (with J.T. Cushing) The Philosophical Consequences of Quantum Theory, 1989, The Social Dimensions of Science, 1992; cons. editor Jour. Medicine and Philosophy, 1977-93 , Studies History and Philosophy of Science, 1970-75, 1983—, Brit. Jour. Philos. Sci., 1988—, Perspectives on Science, 1992—. Romanell-Phi Beta Kappa Prof. of Philosophy, 1993-94; NSF rsch. grantee Cambridge U., 1968-69; vis. rsch. fellow, 1973-74, 83, 87, U. Pitts., 1979. Fellow AAAS (chmn. sect. L 1977-78), Am. Acad. Arts and Scis., Internat. Acad. History Sci.; mem. Am. Cath. Philos. Assn. (pres. 1966-67, Aquinas medal 1981), Philosophy of Sci. Assn. (governing bd. 1969-73, pres. 1980-82), Metaphys. Assn. Am. (exec. coun. 1968-72, pres. 1973-74), Am. Philos. Assn. (exec. coun. 1977-81, pres. western divsn. 1983-84), History of Sci. Soc. (exec. coun. 1988-92), Sigma Xi. Address: PO Box 1066 Notre Dame IN 46556-1066

MCMULLIN, RUTH RONEY, publishing company executive, management fellow; b. N.Y.C., Feb. 9, 1942; d. Richard Thomas and Virginia (Goodwin) Roney; m. Thomas Ryan McMullin, Apr. 27, 1968; 1 child, David Patrick. BA, Conn. Coll., 1963; MS in Pub. and Pvt. Mgmt., Yale U., 1979. Market researcher Aviation Week Mag. McGraw- Hill Co., N.Y.C., 1962-64; assoc. editor, bus. mgr. Doubleday & Co., N.Y.C., 1964-66; mgr. Natural History Press, 1967-70; v.p., treas. Weston (Conn.) Woods, Inc., 1970-71; staff assoc. Gen. Electric, Fairfield, Conn., 1979-82; mng. fin. analyst GECC Transp., Stamford, Conn., 1982-84; credit analyst corp. fin. dept. GECC, Stamford, 1984-85; sr. v.p. GECC Capital Markets Group, Inc., N.Y.C., 1985-87; exec. v.p., chief operating officer John Wiley & Sons, N.Y.C., 1987-89, pres., CEO, 1989-90; pres., CEO Harvard Bus. Sch. Pub. Corp., Boston, 1991-94; mgmt. fellow Yale Sch. of Mgmt., 1994—; mem. chmn.'s com., acting CEO UNR Industries Inc., Chgo., 1991-92; mgmt. fellow Sch. Mgmt. Yale U., New Haven, Conn., 1994—; bd. dirs. Bausch & Lomb, Rochester, N.Y., UNR Industries Inc., Chgo., Middlesex (Conn.) Mut. Assurance, Fleet Fin., Providence; vis. prof. Sch. Mgmt., Yale U., New Haven, Conn., 1994—. Mem. dean's adv. bd. Sch. Mgmt. Yale U.; bd. dirs. Yale U. Alumni Fund, Yale U. Press, Math. Scis. Edn. Bd. Mem. N.Y. Yacht Club, Stamford Yacht Club. Avocations: sailing, skiing. Home: 274 Beacon St Boston MA 02116 Office: Yale U Sch Mgmt Box 208200 New Haven CT 06520-8200

MCMUNN, RICHARD EARL, editor, writer; b. Peoria, Ill., Apr. 2, 1949; s. Earl A. and Doris L. (Vollmer) McM.; m. Diane Marie Corrigan, Dec. 16, 1972; children: Shannon Marie Margaret, Erin Maureen (dec.), Meaghan Bridget Colleen. BS, Bradley U., 1971. Intern Peoria Jour. Star, 1969-70; news editor The Cath. Post, Peoria, 1970-74; asst. editor So. Cross, San Diego, 1974-77; editor Our Sunday Visitor, Huntington, Ind., 1977-84; dir. publs. Cath. League for Religious and Civil Rights, Milw., 1985-88; editor Columbia mag., KC, New Haven, 1988—; with print sales Con P. Curran, St. Louis, 1984. Editor: Religion in Politics, 1985, Quest for Religious Freedom II, 1986, Pius XII's Defense of Jews and Others, 1987. Bd. dirs. Sacred Heart Sch., New Haven, 1989—. Recipient Outstanding Journalism Grad. award Sigma Delta Chi, 1971, numerous awards Cath. Press Assn., 1971—. Mem. KC (grand knight 1990—), Sacred Heart Acad. Father's Club (treas. 1991—). Roman Catholic. Home: 28 Canterbury Rd Hamden CT 06514-2014 Office: Knights of Columbus 1 Columbus Plz New Haven CT 06510-3325

MCMURRAY, JOSEPH PATRICK BRENDAN, financial consultant; b. Bronx, N.Y., Mar. 1912; s. Bartholemew A. and Katherine A. (O'Connell) McM.; m. Isabelle C. Kenny, Nov. 21, 1940 (dec. 1960); children: Gerald, Joseph Patrick Brendan, Kathleen (Mrs. Jeffrey Nelson), Isabelle (Mrs. George M. Pullis), Kevin, Brien; m. Rose-Marie Mooney Barker, Aug. 26, 1961; stepchildren: Walter Barker, Diane (Mrs. Patrick Crehan), Robert Barker (dec.). A.B., Bklyn. Coll., 1936; postgrad., New Sch. Social Research, 1937-40; LL.D., Iona Coll., 1959, Holy Cross Coll., 1962, Loyola U., 1969; Litt.D., U. Tampa, 1961; L.H.D., Am. Internat. Coll., 1964. Dir. U.S. Senate Edn. Labor Com., 1944-47; adminstrv. asst. Senator Wagner, 1947-48; cons. staff dir. banking and currency com. U.S. Senate, 1948-54; exec. dir. N.Y.C. Housing Authority, 1955-57; exec. housing N.Y. State, 1955-59; pres. Queensborough Community Coll., Bayside, N.Y., 1959-61; chmn. bd. FHLB, 1961-65; pres. Queens Coll., Flushing, N.Y., 1965-71, Coll. New Rochelle, N.Y., 1971-73; spl. asst. to speaker U.S. Ho. of Reps., Washington, 1974-76; cons. 1st Pennco Securities Inc., N.Y.C., 1977-80, Ameribond Securities Assocs., N.Y.C., 1980-83; adj. prof. L.I. U., 1957-58; trustee Bowery Savs. Bank, 1966-85. Author: Ways and Means of Providing Housing for Families Unable to Afford Rentals or Mortgage Payments Necessary to Adequate Private Housing, 1960; contbr. numerous studies and surveys of housing throughout the world, articles in sociology, econs., bus. jours. Mem. Mayor's Rent Guidelines Bd., N.Y.C., 1969-75; chmn. Pres.-Elect Kennedy Task Force on Housing and Urban Devel., 1960. Decorated Knight of Holy Sepulchre N.Y. Roman Cath. Archdiocese; decorated knight office Order of Merit Italian Republic; recipient award of merit Bklyn. Coll., 1952, Alumnus of Yr., 1959, Presdl. medal 50th Ann. Commencement, 1986. Mem. Am. Econs. Assn., Nat. Housing Ofcls. Assn., Internat. Catholic Peace Assn., Nat. Council Catholic Men, Am. Acad. of Sr. Profls. at Eckerd Coll., Phi Beta Kappa, Pi Gamma Mu, Kappa Delta Pi, Alpha Phi Omega. Roman Catholic. Clubs: Lotus (N.Y.C.), University (N.Y.C.); Congl. County (Md.). Lodge: KC. Home: College Harbor 4650 54th Ave S Saint Petersburg FL 33711-4665

MCMURRAY, WILLIAM, consultant, retired electrical engineer; b. Los Angeles, Aug. 15, 1929; s. William Arthur and Genevieve Leona (Arnold) McM.; m. Marion Elizabeth Schnipp, Oct. 22, 1955; children: William B., Shirley A., Robert C., Barbara C. BSc in Engring. with first class honors, Battersea Poly., London, 1950; MS, Union Coll., 1956; LLD (hon.), Concordia U., Montreal, Que., Can., 1986. Test engr. Gen. Electric, Pittsfield, Mass., 1950-51; elec. engr. corp. rsch. and devel. Gen. Electric, Schenectady, N.Y., 1953-88; cons., 1989—. Author: Theory and Design of Cycloconverters, 1972; contbg. author: Principles of Inverter Circuits, 1964; patentee in field; contbr. 28 articles to profl. jours. Chmn. troop 31 Boy Scouts Am., Schenectady, 1973. Served as pvt. U.S. Army, 1951-53. Recipient William Newell award Power Electronics Specialists Conf., 1978. Fellow IEEE (Magnetics Soc., chmn. static power converter com. Industry Applications Soc. 1982-83, Centennial medal 1984, Lamme medal 1984), Instn. Elec. Engrs. (assoc.). Republican. Avocations: canoeing, archaeology. Office: Cons Engr PO Box 741 Schenectady NY 12301-0741

MC MURRIN, LEE RAY, educational administrator; b. Ind., June 29, 1930; s. Albert R. and Myrtle E. (Brickley) McM.; m. Frances, Aug. 19, 1956; children: Michelle, Marianne, Marshall. BS in Secondary Edn, Olivet Coll., Kankakee, Ill., 1952; M.Ed., U. Cin., 1955; postgrad. Miami U., Oxford, Ohio, 1955, Kent State U., 1957, Ohio State U., 1958-65; Ph.D., U. Toledo, 1971. Elem. tchr. Sharonville (Ohio) Schs., 1952-55; prin., elem. supr. Leetonia (Ohio) Schs., 1955-58; asst. supt. Dover City (Ohio) Schs.,

1958-60, South-Western City Schs., Grove City, Ohio, 1960-65; asst. supt. Toledo Pub. Schs., 1965-71, dep. supt., 1971-75; supt. schs. Milw. Pub. Schs., 1975-87; supt. Beachwood (Ohio) City Schs., 1987—; past pres., mem. Coun. Gt. City Schs.; mem. partnership coordinating com. Univ. Coun. on Ednl. Adminstrn.; bd. dirs. Wis. State Coun. Econ. Edn., Joint Coun. Econ. Edn. Mem. coun. bd. Milw. Children's Hosp., Milw. Symphony Orch.; bd. dirs. NCCJ, Milw., Jr. Achievement Southeastern Wis. Served with inf. U.S. Army, 1953-55. Mem. Am. Assn. Sch. Adminstrs., Bucheye Assn. of Sch. Adminstrs., ASCD, Large City Supts. Group, Greater Cleve. Sch. Supts. Assn. (pres. 1993-94), Nat. Sch. Bds. Assn., NAACP, Rotary (bd. dirs. 1976-87), Phi Delta Kappa. Methodist. Home: 16608 Aldersyde Dr Cleveland OH 44120-2514 Office: Beachwood City Sch Dist 24601 Fairmount Blvd Cleveland OH 44122-2239

MC MURRIN, STERLING MOSS, philosophy educator; b. Woods Cross, Utah, Jan. 12, 1914; s. Joseph W. and Gertrude (Moss) McM.; m. Natalie Barbara Cotterel, June 8, 1938; children: Gertrude Ann, Joseph Cotterel, Sterling James, Natalie Laurie, Melanie. A.B., U. Utah, 1936, M.A., 1937, LL.D., 1961; Ph.D., U. So. Calif., 1946, LL.D.; LL.D., Clark U., Del. State Coll., 1962, Pepperdine Coll., 1967; D.Litt., U. Puget Sound, 1963; D. Hum. Litt., Westminster Coll., 1985. Asst. prof. philosophy U. So. Calif., 1946-48; prof. philosophy U. Utah, Salt Lake City, 1948-64; dean Coll. Letters and Sci. U. Utah, 1954-60, acad. v.p., 1960-61, Ericksen disting. prof., 1964-87, E.E. Erichson Disting. prof. emeritus, 1987—; provost, 1965-66, U. Marshall dean Grad. Sch., 1966-78, prof. philosophy edn., 1968-83, prof. history, 1970—, adj. prof. philosophy, 1979—; vis. scholar Columbia U., 1952-53, Union Theol. Sem., 1952-53; Ford fellow Princeton U., 1952-53; U.S. commr. edn., 1961-62; cons. to Am. Tel. & Tel. Co., IBM Corp., Com. for Econ. Devel., Fund Advancement Edn., D.C. Commn. Licensure, Office Sci. and Tech. Exec. Office Pres. Author: (with James L. Jarrett) Contemporary Philosophy, 1954 (with B.A.G. Fuller) A History of Philosophy, 2 vols., 1955, Religion, Reason, and Truth, 1983; co-author: Toward Understanding the New Testament, 1990, History of the Tanner Lectures on Human Values, 1994, The Crisis of Western Culture, 1994 (with Jackson Newell) Conversations with Sterling McMurrin, 1995; editor: The Schools and the Challenge of Innovation, 1969, Functional Education for Disadvantaged Youth, 1971, The Conditions for Educational Equality, 1971, Resources for Urban Schools: Better Use and Balance, 1971, On the Meaning of the University, 1976, The Tanner Lectures on Human Values, Vol. I, 1980, Vol. II, 1981, Vol. III, 1982, Vol. IV, 1983, Vol. V, 1984, Vol. VI, 1985, Vol. VII, 1986, Vol. VIII, 1988, Values at War, 1983, Liberty, Equality and Law, 1987; contbr. monographs, articles, revs. on philosophy, religion and edn. to profl. jours. Mem. U.S. Commn. UNESCO, 1961-62; mem. Bd. Fgn. Scholarships, 1961-62; exec. bd. Nat. Cultural Center; chmn. Fed. Commn. on Instructional Tech.; adviser, chancellor U. Teheran, 1958-59; v.p. 25th Internat. Congress on Edn., Geneva, Switzerland, 1962; mem. U.S. dels. on edn. and cultural affairs to, Washington, Chile, Japan, 1962; chmn. Mountain States and Midcontinent manpower adv. coms. U.S. Dept. Labor, 1965-68; mem. higher commn. Northwest Assn. Secondary and Higher Schs., 1964-73; sr. commr. Western Assn. Schs. and Colls., 1974-77; mem. Grad. Record Exam. Bd., 1974-79; Bd. dirs. Agy. for Instrnl. Television, 1974-78; trustee Carnegie Found. Advancement Teaching, Am. U. of Rome; adv. com. for philosophy Princeton U.; mem. bd. nat. humanities ctr. Yale U., mem. nat. bd. fellowships and associateships NRC, 1974-77; trustee Tanner Lecture Trust, 1977-89, Westminster Coll., 1986-91; dir. Tanner Lectures on Human Values, 1978-87; bd. dirs. Utah Humanities Endowment, 1977-83. Recipient Coll. of Humanities award U. Utah, 1992. Mem. Am. Philos. Assn. (v.p.), Mountain Plains Philos. Assn. (pres.), Nat. Assn. State Univs. and Land-Grant Colls. (com. on fed. legislation), Phi Beta Kappa, Phi Kappa Phi (Rosenblatt prize 1984, 1st Gov.'s Award in Humanities 1988). Home: 2969 Devonshire Cir Salt Lake City UT 84108-2526

MCMURRY, IDANELLE SAM, educational consultant; b. Morganfield, Ky., Dec. 6, 1924; d. Sam Anderson and Aurelia Marie (Robertson) McM. B.A., Vanderbilt U., 1945, M.A., 1946. Tchr. English Abbot Acad., Andover, Mass., 1946-50, Hockaday Sch., Dallas, 1951-54, San Jacinto High Sch., Houston, 1954-55; dean of girls Kinkaid Sch., Houston, 1955-63; headmistress Harpeth Hall Sch., Nashville, 1963-79, Hockaday Sch., Dallas, 1979-89, ret.; now pvt. sch. cons. The Edn. Group, Dallas; Bd. dirs. Ednl. Records Bur., 1979-85, trustee, 1980-85. Bd. dirs. Tex. council Girl Scouts U.S., 1980-82, Town North YMCA; trustee Winston Sch., 1979-85, Spl. Care Sch., 1979-81, Asheville Sch., Manzano Day Sch. Mem. Nat. Study Sch. Evaluation (bd. dirs. 1979-83), Headmasters Assn., Nat. Assn. Ind. Schs. (bd. dirs. 1974-84, acad. com. 1974-79, sec. 1978-80, chmn. 1980-84), So. Assn. Ind. Schs. (pres. 1974-75), Tenn. Assn. Ind. Schs. (pres. 1967-68), Mid-South Assn. Ind. Schs. (pres. 1972-73), Ind. Schs. Assn. S.W. (v.p. 1967—), Nat. Assn. Prins. Schs. for Girls (sec. 1970-72, pres. 1975-77, coun. 1970-79), Nat. Assn. Secondary Sch. Prins., Country Day Sch. Headmasters Assn. (exe. com. 1984-87, v.p. 1988-89), So. Assn. Colls. and Schs. (adminstrv. coun. 1974-77, ctrl. reviewing com. 1972-77, vice chmn. secondary commn. 1975-76, chmn. 1976-77, bd. dirs. 1976-81), Ladies Hermitage Assn., Vanderbilt Aid Soc. (sec. 1971-73, pres. 1994-96), Ind. Edn. Svcs. (trustee 1980-88, chmn. 1986-88), Susan Komen Found. (adv. bd.), Belle Meade Club, Centennial Club, Phi Beta Kappa, Pi Beta Phi. Republican. Presbyterian. Office: 5 Strawberry Hill Nashville TN 37215-4118

MCMURRY, JOHN EDWARD, chemistry educator; b. N.Y.C., July 27, 1942; s. Edward and Marguerite Ann (Hotchkiss) McM.; m. Susan Elizabeth Sobuta, Sept. 4, 1964; children—Peter Michael, David Andrew, Paul Matthew. B.A., Harvard U., 1964; M.A., Columbia U., 1965, Ph.D., 1967. Prof. chemistry U. Calif., Santa Cruz, 1967-80, Cornell U., Ithaca, N.Y., 1980—. Author: Organic Chemistry, 1984, Chemistry, 1995 and other textbooks. Assoc. editor Accounts of Chem. Research, 1975-95. Recipient Humboldt Sr. Sci. award, 1987; Sloan Found. fellow, 1969-71; Career awardee NIH, 1975-80. Fellow AAAS; mem. Am. Chem. Soc. Home: 625 Highland Rd Ithaca NY 14850-2326 Office: Cornell Univ Dept Chemistry Baker Lab Ithaca NY 14853

MCMURRY, PETER HOWARD, mechanical engineering educator; b. Palmerton, Pa., July 5, 1947; s. Howard V. and Margaret A. (Gifford) McM.; m. Pamela S. Schain, May 10, 1969; children—Timothy, Nathaniel. B.A. in Physics, U. Pa., 1969; M.S. in Environ. Engring Sci., Calif. Inst. Tech., 1973, Ph.D. in Environ. Engring Sci., 1977. Asst. prof. Univ. Minn., Mpls., 1977-83, assoc. prof. mech. engring., 1983—. Contbr. articles to profl. jours. Mem. Am. Assn. Aerosol Research, Am. Chem. Soc., AAAS, Air Waste Mgmt. Assn., ASME, Sigma Xi. Office: Univ Minn Dept Mech Engring 111 Church St SE Minneapolis MN 55455

MCMURTRY, BURTON JOHN, venture capital investor, electrical engineer; b. Houston, Mar. 26, 1935; s. James G. and Alberta Elizabeth (Matteson) McM.; m. Ann Kathryn Meck, June 9, 1956; children—Cathryn Ann, John Eric. BA, Rice U., 1956, BSEE, 1957, MSEE, Stanford U., 1959, Ph.D. in Elec. Engring. (Raytheon fellow), 1962. Engr. Microwave Tube div. Sylvania, Mountain View, Calif., 1957-62; rsch. asst. Stanford U., 1960-62; head lab. rsch. and devel. in electro-optics GTE, Sylvania, Mountain View, 1962-66; mgr. Equipment Engring. Labs., 1967-68; dir., gen. mgr. electro-optics orgn. Sylvania Electronic Systems, 1968-69; assoc. Jack L. Melchor (personal venture capital investment bus.), Los Altos, Calif., 1969-70; pres. Palo Alto Investment Co., Calif., 1970-73; gen. partner Dennis, Jamieson & McMurtry, Menlo Park, Calif., 1973—, TVI Mgmt., TVI Mgmt.-2, TVI Mgmt.-3, Menlo Park, 1980—; bd. dirs. Veri-Fone, Aradigm, Edify, E.O Networks, Intnit, Spectralink. Contbr. articles, chpts. to electronics publs., mainly on microwave tubes, lasers, optical detectors. Bd. dirs. El Camino Hosp. Found.; elder Menlo Park Presbyn. Ch.; mem. major gifts com. Stanford U.; trustee Rice U. Recipient Alfred Noble prize, 1964. Fellow IEEE; mem. Nat. Venture Capital Assn. (pres. 1986-87, chmn. 1987-88), Western Assn. Venture Capitalists (pres. 1972-73), Am. Phys. Soc., Optical Soc. Am., Sigma Xi (sr. award 1957), Sigma Tau, Tau Beta Pi. Home: 7 Coal Mine Vw Menlo Park CA 94028-8016 Office: Tech Venture Investors 3000 Sandhill Rd Menlo Park CA 94025-7116

MC MURTRY, JAMES GILMER, III, neurosurgeon; b. Houston, June 11, 1932; s. James Gilmer and Alberta Elizabeth (Matteson) McM.; student Rice U., Houston, 1950-53; M.D. cum laude, Baylor U., Houston, 1957. Intern, Hosp. U. Pa., Phila., 1957-58; resident gen. surgery Baylor U. Affiliated Hosps., Houston, 1958-59; asst. neurol. surgery Coll. Physicians and

Surgeons, Columbia U., N.Y.C., 1959-60; asst. resident neurol. surgery and neurology Neurol. Inst. N.Y., Columbia Presbyn. Med. Center, N.Y.C., 1960-62, chief resident neurol. surgery, 1962-63; Nat. Inst. Neurol. Disease and Blindness spl. fellow neurol. surgery Coll. Physicians and Surgeons, Columbia U., N.Y.C., 1963-64; instr. neurol. surgery, 1963-65, assoc., 1965-68, asst. prof. clin. neurol. surgery, 1968-73, assoc. prof., 1973-89, prof., 1989—; asst. attending neurol. surgeon Neurol. Inst. N.Y., N.Y.C., 1964-73, assoc. attending neurol. surgeon, 1973-89, attending neurol. surgeon, 1989—; chief neurol. surgery clinic Vanderbilt Clinic, Columbia Presbyn. Med. Center, N.Y.C., 1964-68; attending-in-charge neurosurgery Lenox Hill Hosp., N.Y.C., 1970-91; assoc. cons. neurol. surgery Englewood (N.J.) Hosp., 1964—; asst. cons. neurol. surgery Harlem Hosp., N.Y.C., 1964—; cons. neurol. surgery Bronx (N.Y.) VA Hosp., 1964-65; mem. NIH Parkinson Research Group, Columbia U., 1965—; mem. med. adv. bd. N.Y. State Athletic Commn. Jesse H. Jones scholar Baylor U. Coll. Medicine, 1953-57, Allen fellow dept. neurol. surgery Columbia U., 1964-65. Diplomate Am. Bd. Neurol. Surgery. Fellow ACS, Linnean Soc. (London); trustee Glimmerglass Opera, Morris-Jumel, Opera Manhattan. Mem. AAUP, AAAS, AMA, Am. Assn. Neurol. Surgeons, European Congress Pediatric Neurosurgery, Am. Soc. Stereotaxic Surgeons, Pan Am. Med. Assn., N.Y. State Soc. Surgeons, N.Y. State Neurosurgery Soc., N.Y. Acad. Sci., N.Y. Neurosurg. Soc., Med. Soc. State N.Y., N.Y. County Med. Soc., Osler Soc., Baylor U. Coll. Medicine Alumni Assn., Med. Strollers, The Med. Soc. of London, The Harveian Soc., Alpha Omega Alpha. Presbyn. Clubs: The Union (N.Y.C.), The Garrick (London), The Atheneum (London), The Met. Opera (N.Y.C.), The Norfolk Yacht and Country. Author: Medical Examination Review Book-Neurological Surgery, 1970, rev. edit., 1975; Neurological Surgery Case Histories, 1975; contbr. articles to profl. jours. Home: 1 Cobb Ln Tarrytown NY 10591-3003 Office: 710 W 168th St New York NY 10032-2603

MCMURTRY, LARRY JEFF, author; b. Wichita Falls, Tex., June 3, 1936; s. William Jefferson and Hazel Ruth (McIver) McM.; m. Josephine Ballard, July 15, 1959 (div. 1966); 1 child, James. BA, N.Tex. State Coll., 1958; MA, Rice U., 1960. Instr. Tex. Christian U., Ft. Worth, 1961-62; lectr. in English and creative writing Rice U., Houston, 1963-69; co-owner Booked Up Book Store, Washington, from 1970; vis. prof. George Mason Coll., 1970, Am. Univ., 1970-71. Author: (novels) Horseman, Pass By, 1961 (Jesse H. Jones award Texas Inst. of Letters 1962), Leaving Cheyenne, 1963, The Last Picture Show, 1966, Moving On, 1970, All My Friends Are Going to be Strangers, 1972, Terms of Endearment, 1975, Somebody's Darling, 1978, Cadillac Jack, 1982, The Desert Rose, 1983, Lonesome Dove, 1985 (Pulitzer prize for fiction 1986), Texasville, 1987, Anything for Billy, 1988, Some Can Whistle, 1989, Buffalo Girls, 1990, The Evening Star, 1992, Streets of Laredo, 1993, (with Diana Ossana) Pretty Boy Floyd, 1994, The Late Child, 1995, (essays) In a Narrow Grave: Essays on Texas, 1968, It's Always We Rambled: An Essay on Rodeo, 1974, Film Flam: Essays on Hollywood, 1987; screenwriter: (with Peter Bogdanovich) The Last Picture Show, 1971 (Academy award nomination best adapted screenplay 1971), Texasville, 1990, Montana, 1990, Falling From Grace, 1992, (with Cybill Shepard) Memphis, 1992; also articles, essays, book revs. in N.Y. Times, Saturday Rev., Washington Post, Am. Film, others. Wallace Stegner fellow, 1960, Guggenheim fellow, 1964; recipient Barbara McCombs/Lon Tinkle award Texas Inst. of Letters, 1986. Mem. Tex. Inst. Letters (Jesse H. Jones award 1962). Office: Simon & Schuster 1230 6th Ave New York NY 10020-1513 also: c/o Jerry Katzman Pres William Morris Agy 151 El Camino Dr Beverly Hills CA 90212*

MCMURTRY, R. ROY, chief justice; b. Toronto, Ont., Can., May 31, 1932; s. Roland Roy and Doris Elizabeth (Belcher) McM.; m. Ria Jean Macrae, Apr. 18, 1957; children: Janet, James, Harry, Jeannie, Erin, Michael. BA with honors, U. Toronto, 1954; LLB, Osgoode Hall Law Sch., 1958; LLD (hon.), U. Ottawa, 1983, Leeds U., U.K., 1988, York U., 1991. Bar: Called to bar 1958, created Queen's counsel 1970. Partner firm Benson, McMurtry, Percival and Brown; mem. Provincial Parliament for Eglinton, 1975-85; atty. gen. for Ont., 1975-85, solicitor gen. for Ont., 1978-82, high commnr. for Can. to Gt. Brit. and No. Ireland, 1985-88; ptnr. Blaney, McMurtry Stapells, Toronto, 1988-91; chmn. Can. Football League, 1989-91; assoc. chief justice Ont. Ct. Justice, Toronto, 1991-94, chief justice, 1994—; freeman of City of London, 1986. Mem. United Ch. of Can. Office: Ont Ct Gen Div, 130 Queen St W, Toronto, ON Canada M5H 2N5

MC NAB, MAXWELL DOUGLAS, professional sports executive; b. Watson, Sask., Can., June 21, 1924; came to U.S., 1966; s. Peter McIntyre and Dorcas Delilah (Thompson) McN.; m. June Cleone Ness, June 23, 1951; children: Peter Maxwell, Michael Ian, David Martin. Student, U. Sask., 1942-43, 45-46. Profl. hockey player Omaha Knights, 1946-48, Detroit Redwings, 1948-52, New Westminster (B.C.) Royals, 1952-59; coach San Francisco Seals, 1961-62; gen. mgr.-coach Vancouver (B.C.) Canucks, 1962-66; v.p., gen. mgr. San Diego Gulls, 1966-74; pres. Central Hockey League, 1974-75; gen. mgr. Washington Capitals, 1975-81; v.p. hockey ops. N.J. Devils, Nat. Hockey League, 1982—, gen. mgr., 1983—. Mem. Parks and Recreation Bd., New Westminster, 1960-61; mem. New Westminster Library Bd., 1963-65. Served with Royal Can. Air Force and Can. Army, 1943-45. Named Most Valuable Player, Western Hockey League, 1958; recipient Outstanding Contribution award Breitbard Athletic Found., San Diego, 1974. Club: Tantallon Golf and Country. Office: NJ Devils PO Box 504 East Rutherford NJ 07073-0504

MCNABB, FRANK WILLIAM, consumer products company executive; b. Cleve., Apr. 10, 1936; s. Frank L. and Bonita McNabb; m. L. Kay Dixon, Sept. 10, 1959; children: Tom, Mark, Kathy. BME, Ohio State U., 1960; MBA, U. Vt., 1971. Project engr. Union Carbide Corp., Red Oak, Iowa, 1960-64; plant engr. Union Carbide Corp., Charlotte, N.C., 1964-65; gen. foreman prodn. Union Carbide Corp., Bennington, Vt., 1965-66; asst. plant mgr. Union Carbide Corp., St. Albans, Vt., 1966-70; plant mgr. Union Carbide Corp., Wayne, N.J., 1970-76; dir. automotive mfg. Union Carbide Corp., Wayne, 1976-79, dir. home mfg., 1979-80; gen. mgr. prodn. Union Carbide Corp., East Hartford, Conn., 1980-86; v.p. ops. mgr. ops. 1st Brands Corp., Danbury, Conn., 1986-89; exec. v.p. ops. and tech. First Brands Corp., 1990—. Roman Catholic. Avocations: skiing, running, tennis. Office: First Brands Corp 83 Wooster Heights Rd Box 1911 Danbury CT 06813-1911

MCNAIR, CARL HERBERT, JR., army officer, aeronautical engineer; b. Pensacola, Fla., Sept. 22, 1933; s. Carl Herbert and Hallie Rebecca (Edwards) McN.; m. Jo Ann Wilson, Oct. 26, 1957; children: Cynthia Leigh, Carl Herbert III, Courtney Ann. B.S., U.S. Mil. Acad., 1955; B.Aero. Engring., Ga. Inst. Tech., 1963, M.S. in Aero. Engring., 1963; M.S. in Pub. Adminstrn., Shippinsburg State Coll., 1971. Commd. 2d lt. U.S. Army, 1955, advanced through grades to maj. gen., 1987; comdr. troop brigade U.S. Army Aviation Ctr., Fort Rucker, Ala., 1974-75; dep. for aviation to asst. sec. of Army Office Sec. of Army, U.S. Army, Washington, 1975-77, exec. to dep. chief of staff for research, devel. and acquisition, 1977-78; dep. dir. requirements and aviation officer Office of Dep. Chief of Staff for Ops. and Plans, 1978-79; dep. comdg. gen. U.S. Army Aviation Ctr., Fort Rucker, Ala., 1979-80, comdg. gen., 1980-83; dep. chief staff combat devels. U.S. Army Tng. and Doctrine Command, Fort Monroe, Va., 1983-84, chief of staff, 1985-87; ret. U.S. Army, 1987; v.p. Burdeshaw Assocs., Ltd., Bethesda, Md., 1988-90; pres. Dyncorp Support Svcs. Div., Reston, Va., 1990-94, Dyncorp Enterprise Mgmt., Reston, 1994—; corp. v.p. Dyncorp, Reston, 1994—. Contbr. articles to profl. jours. Pres. Uniformed Svcs. Benefit Assn., Kansas City, Mo., 1980-82, Assn. of U.S. Army, Washington, 1988-92 (Washington chpt., exec. v.p. 2d region 1992—); v.p. Army Aviation Assn. Am., 1990-93, sec.-treas. 1993—), Westport, Conn.; v.p. Ala.-Fla. coun. Boy Scouts Am., Dothan, Ala., 1979-83; mem. nat. bd. dirs. Mil. Community Youth Ministries, 1988-93; pres. West Point Soc., Washington, 1992—; mem. bd. dirs. Army Aviation Mus. Found. Decorated D.S.M. with oak leaf cluster, Legion of Merit with two leaf clusters, D.F.C. with three oak leaf clusters, Bronze Star medal with V devices with oak leaf cluster, Air medal with V devices and 51 oak leaf clusters, Disting. Service medal State of Ala.; named Disting. Grad. Sch. Aerospace Engring. Ga. Inst. Tech., Sigma Gamma Tau, 1963; recipient Silver Beaver Achievement Boy Scouts Am., 1981; recipient Crosses of Military Svc., Korean Conflict, Vietnam, Jeff Davis award United Daus. of the Confederacy, 1977, 88; numerous flight awards Korea, Vietnam, France, Republic of China. Mem. Assn. U.S. Army (mil. adviser 1979-87), Army Aviation Assn. Am. (v.p. 1979-83, 85-87, 90-

93, sec.-treas. 1993—), Am. Def. Preparedness Assn. (bd. dirs. Washington chpt. 1993—), Order of Daedalians, Am. Helicopter Soc., Air Force Assn., Navy League, Masons. Methodist. Home: 7821 Friars Ct Alexandria VA 22306-2717 *The military service, perhaps more than any other profession, provides us with a unique opportunity to serve both our fellow man and our God -in preserving the Peace and the Freedom cherished by mankind. It is within such a framework that I have charted the course of my life, remembering always Duty-Honor-Country.*

MCNAIR, JOHN FRANKLIN, III, banker; b. Laurinburg, N.C., Apr. 12, 1927; s. John Franklin and Martha (Fairley) McN.; m. Martha Fowler, June 16, 1951; children: John Franklin IV, Elizabeth Fowler. BS, Davidson Coll., 1949; postgrad., U. N.C., 1954-56. Pres. McNair Automotive Co., Inc., Laurinburg, 1949-66, The State Bank, Laurinburg, 1966-68; sr. v.p. Wachovia Bank & Trust, Laurinburg, 1968-70, Raleigh, N.C., 1970-72; exec. v.p. Wachovia Bank & Trust, Winston-Salem, N.C., 1972-77, vice chmn. 1977-85; vice chmn. The Wachovia Corp., Winston-Salem, N.C., 1977-87, pres., chief exec. officer, 1987-90; pres., chief exec. officer Wachovia Bank & Trust Co, 1987-90, also dir.; pres. 1st First Wachovia Corp., 1986-90; bd. dirs. Piedmont Natural Gas Co., Park Comm. Inc., N.C. Enterprise Corp., 1990-93; bd. dirs., pres. N.C. Railroad Co., 1993—. Mem. N.C. State Hwy. Commn., Raleigh, 1965-69, Commn. on Future N.C., Raleigh, 1981-83; chmn. N.C. Bd. Econ. Devel., 1979-85, N.C. Coun. Econ. Edn., Greensboro, 1980-82, Ind. Coll. Fund N.C., 1989-91, N.C. Citizens for Bus. and Industry, 1988-89; trustee Peace Coll., Raleigh, 1980-89, Davidson Coll., 1985-93; trustee Winston-Salem Found., 1983-91, chmn., 1989-91; co-chmn. gov.'s adv. com. Superconducting Supercollider Project, 1988; trustee, mem. exec. com. Rsch. Triangle Found., 1986—, vice chmn., 1990-93, chmn., 1992—; trustee exec. com. Winston-Salem Bus., Inc., 1986—, chmn., 1990-95; mem. govt. performance com. State of N.C., 1991-93; bd. dirs. N.C. Enterprise Corp., 1988-93; chmn. Qual Choice of N.C., Inc., 1994—. With USN, 1945-46. Recipient Young Man of Yr. award Laurinburg Jaycees, 1962; recipient Silver Beaver award Boy Scouts Am., 1967. Mem. Am. Bankers Assn. (state v.p. 1980-81), Res. City Bankers Assn., N.C. Bankers Assn. (pres. 1976-77), Cape Fear County Club (Wilmington, N.C.), Old Town Club, Piedmont Club, St. Andrews Soc., Rotary. Democrat. Presbyterian. Home: 234 NW Pine Valley Rd Winston-Salem NC 27104-1808 Office: Wachovia Bank NC PO Box 3099 Winston-Salem NC 27102-3099

MCNAIR, JOHN WILLIAM, JR., civil engineer; b. Asheville, N.C., June 17, 1926; s. John William and Annie (Woody) McN.; m. June Clemens Kratz; children—Jeffry, Marsha, Cathy. B.S. in Forestry, Pa. State U., 1950; B.S.C.E., Va. Poly. Inst. State U., 1955; postgrad. in engring. U. Va., 1957-58. Registered profl. engr., Va. and other states. Forester U.S. Forest Service, Flagstaff, Ariz., 1950, U.S. Gypsum Co., Buena Vista, VA., 1951; mem. engring. faculty U. Va., Charlottesville, 1955-58; prin. John McNair & Assocs., Waynesboro, VA., 1958—; owner Brucheum Group, Waynesboro, 1983—; with Va. Bd. Architects, Profl. Engrs. and Land Surveyors, 1969-79, v.p.; 1977-78, pres., 1978-79. Author numerous engring. and land mgmt. study reports. Mem. Waynesboro City Council, 1968-72, vice mayor, 1970-72; chmn. Waynesboro INdsl. devel. Authority, 1984—. Served to capt. AUS, 1944-46, 51-53; France, Okinawa. Recipient Disting. Service cert. Va. Soc. Profl. Engrs., 1971. Fellow ASCE; mem. Acad. Environ. Engrs. (diplomate). Republican. Presbyterian. Lodge: Rotary. Office: John McNair and Assocs Wayne Ave LB & B Bldg Waynesboro VA 22980

MCNAIR, RUSSELL ARTHUR, JR., lawyer; b. Detroit, Dec. 2, 1934; s. Russell Arthur and Virla (Standish) McN.; m. Rosemary M. Chesbrough, Apr. 6, 1957; children: Julie McNair Schwerin, Russell Arthur III, Douglas S. AB in Econs. cum laude, Princeton U., 1956; JD with distinction, U. Mich., 1960. Bar: Mich. 1960. Assoc. Dickinson, Wright, Moon, Van Dusen & Freeman, Detroit, 1960-67, ptnr., 1968—, chmn., 1994—; adj. prof. U. Detroit Sch. Law, 1968-72; mem. adv. bd. Fin. Transactions Inst. 1984—; adj. prof. Wayne State U. Law Sch., 1994—; spkr. in field. Trustee Children's Home, Detroit, 1975-85, pres., 1986-87; dir. Civic Searchlight, Inc., 1994—; mem. adv. bd. United Way, 1994—. Mem. ABA, Mich. Bar Assn., Detroit Bar Assn., Am. Law Inst., Am. Coll. Real Estate Lawyers. Republican. Presbyterian. Avocations: golf, tennis, platform tennis. Home: 308 Touraine Rd Grosse Pointe MI 48236-3311 Office: Dickinson Wright Moon et al 1 Detroit Ctr 500 Woodward Ave Ste 4000 Detroit MI 48226-3423

MCNALL, BRUCE, professional sports executive, numismatist; m. Jane Cody; children: Katie, Bruce. Student, UCLA. Founder, chmn. bd. Numismatic Fine Arts, Inc., L.A.; owner, chmn. bd. Summa Stable, Inc.; chmn. bd. Gladden Entertainment Corp.; former ptnr. Dallas Mavericks NBA; co-owner L.A. Kings, 1986-87, sole owner, 1988-94, co-owner, 1994—; owner Toronto Argonauts, 1991—. Office: LA Kings 3900 W Manchester Blvd Inglewood CA 90305-2200*

MCNALLY, ANDREW, III, printer, publisher; b. Chgo., Aug. 17, 1909; s. Andrew and Eleanor (Vilas) McN.; m. Margaret Clark MacMillin, Nov. 20, 1936 (dec.); children: Betty Jane, Andrew, Edward Clark. AB, Yale U., 1931; LHD (hon.), St. Lawrence U., 1986. With Rand McNally & Co., Chgo., 1931, N.Y. sales office v.p., dir., 1933, pres., 1948-74; chmn. bd. Rand McNally & Co., 1974-93, chmn. emeritus, 1993—. Life trustee Art Inst. Chgo.; trustee Washington Crossing Found., Antique Boat Mus.; past pres., bd. dirs. Girl's Latin Sch., Infant Welfare Soc., Graphic Arts Tech. Found.; internat. adv. bd. Frederic Remington Art Mus.; mem. Northwestern U. Libr. Coun.; governing mem. Orchestral Assn.; past pres., trustee Chgo. Hist. Soc. Capt. C.E., U.S. Army Map Svc., 1942-45. Fellow Royal Geog. Soc.; mem. Geog. Soc. Chgo. (past pres.), Newberry Library (hon. trustee). Office: Rand McNally & Co 8255 Central Park Ave Skokie IL 60076-2908 Office: PO Box 7600 Chicago IL 60680-7600

MCNALLY, ANDREW, IV, publishing executive; b. Chgo., Nov. 11, 1939; s. Andrew and Margaret C. (MacMillin) McN.; m. Jeanine Sanchez, July 3, 1966; children: Andrew, Carrie, Ward. BA, U. N.C., 1963; MBA, U. Chgo., 1969. Bus. mgr. edn. divsn. Rand McNally & Co., Chgo., 1967-70, exec. v.p., sec., 1970-74, pres., 1974—, CEO, 1978—, also chmn. bd. dirs., 1993—; bd. dirs. Mercury Fin. Inc., Hubbell Inc., Walter Foster Publs., Latin Am. Discovery Fund, Morgan Stanley Asia Pacific Fund, Zenith Electronics Corp., Allendale Ins.; mem. vis. com. Bus. Sch. U. N.C. Trustee Newberry Libr.; bd. dirs. Children's Meml. Hosp.; active vis. com. of libr. U. Chgo. With Air Force N.G., 1963-69. Mem. Chgo. Map. Soc., Chgo. Club, Saddle and Cycle Club, Commonwealth Club, Glen View Golf Club, Links (N.Y.C.). Office: Rand McNally & Co 8255 Central Park Ave Skokie IL 60076-2908

MCNALLY, JAMES HENRY, physicist, defense consultant; b. Orange, N.J., Dec. 18, 1936; s. James Osborne and Edith Maude (Jones) McN.; m. Nancy Lee Eudaley, July 4, 1976. B. in Engring. Physics, Cornell U., 1959; PhD in Physics, Calif. Inst. Tech., 1966. Staff mem. program mgr. Los Alamos (N.Mex.) Nat. Lab., 1965-74; asst. dir for laser and isotope separation tech. AEC/ERDA, Washington, 1974-75; assoc. div. leader, dep. for inertial fusion, asst. for nat. sec. issues Los Alamos Nat. Lab., 1975-86; dep. asst. dir. Arms Control and Disarmament Agy., Washington, 1986-88; dir. office staff Los Alamos Nat. Lab., 1988-90, Washington Inst., 1990—; cons., 1990—; U.S. del. Geneva Conf. on Disarmament, 1969, 73, 74, Threshold Test Ban Treaty, Moscow, 1974, Nuclear Testing Talks, Geneva, 1986-88. Bd. dirs. Wilson Mesa Met. Water Dist., 1976-88; v.p. Mountain Canine Corps, 1994—. Mem. AAAS, Am. Phys. Soc., Internat. Inst. Strategic Studies. Home and Office: 550 Rim Rd Los Alamos NM 87544-2931

MCNALLY, JOHN JOSEPH, lawyer; b. N.Y.C., July 1, 1927; s. Edward E. and Virginia L. (O'Brien) McN.; m. Sally Vose Greeley, Jan. 25, 1958; children: Martha, Sarah, Elizabeth, Julie, Thomas. A.B., Coll. Holy Cross, 1950; LL.B., Harvard U., 1953. Bar: N.Y. 1953. Assoc. White & Case, N.Y.C., 1953-63, ptnr., 1964—; bd. dirs. Mohawk Paper Mills, Inc., Cohoes, N.Y.; panelist in field. Trustee Caedmon Sch., N.Y.C., 1968—; bd. dirs. Community Fund of Bronxville-Eastchester-Tuckahoe, Inc., 1986—, All Hallows High Sch., N.Y.C., 1991—; mem. bd. gov's. Lawrence Hosp., Bronxville, N.Y., 1990—. Fellow Am. Bar Found.; mem. N.Y. State Bar Assn., N.Y. County Lawyers Assn., Bar Assn. City N.Y. Home: 58 Avon Rd Bronxville NY 10708-1723 Office: White & Case 1155 Ave Of The Americas New York NY 10036-2711

MCNALLY, TERRENCE, playwright; b. St. Petersburg, Fla., Nov. 3, 1939; s. Hubert Arthur and Dorothy Katharine (Rapp) McN. B.A., Columbia U., 1960. Stage mgr. Actors Studio, N.Y.C., 1961, tutor, 1961-62; film critic The Seventh Art., 1963-65; asst. editor Columbia Coll. Today, N.Y.C., 1965-66. Author: (plays) The Lady of the Camellias, 1963, And Things That Go Bump in the Night, 1964, Apple Pie and Last Gasps, 1966, Sweet Eros, 1968, Witness, 1968, Tour, 1968, Cuba Si!, 1968, Noon, 1968, Next, 1969, Where Has Tommy Flowers Gone?, 1971, Bad Habits, 1971 (Obie award 1971), Botticelli, 1971, Bringing It All Back Home, 1971, Whiskey, 1973, The Tubs, 1974, The Ritz, 1975 (Obie award best play 1974), The Golden Age, 1975, Broadway, Broadway, 1979, The Five Forty-Eight, 1974, The Lisbon Traviata, 1979, It's Only a Play, 1982, The Rink, 1984, Frankie and Johnny in the Clair de Lune, 1988, The Lisbon Traviata, 1989, Up in Saratoga, 1990, Kiss of the Spider Woman, 1990 (Tony award best book of a musical 1993), Andre's Mother, 1990 (Emmy award), Preludes, Fuges & Rifts, 1991, Lips Together, Teeth Apart, 1991, (screenplay) Frankie and Johnny, 1991, A Perfect Ganesh, 1993 (Pulitzer prize for drama nomination 1994), Love! Valour! Compassion!, 1994 (Outer Critics' Circle award best Broadway play 1995), Master Class, 1994. Recipient Dramatists Guild Hull-Warriner award, 1973, 88, 90; Guggenheim fellow, 1966, 69. Mem. Am. Acad. Arts and Letters, Dramatists Guild (v.p. 1981—). Office: care Gilbert Parker William Morris Agy 1350 Ave Of The Americas New York NY 10019-4701*

MCNALLY, THOMAS CHARLES, III, lawyer; b. San Francisco, Dec. 5, 1938; s. Thomas Charles and Claire Marie (Egan) McN.; m. Paula Ann Berger, Sept. 3, 1960; children: Megan, Martin, J. Tevis. B.S., U. San Francisco, 1960; J.D., Hastings Coll. Law, U. Cal. at San Francisco, 1963. Bar: Calif. bar 1964. Dep. atty. gen. State Calif., 1964; assoc. firm Bohnert, Flowers & McCarthy, San Francisco, 1965-68; asst. sec., counsel DiGiorgio Corp., San Francisco, 1968-73; sec., counsel DiGiorgio Corp., 1974-75; sec., gen. counsel Consol. Fibres, Inc., San Francisco, 1975-88, v.p., 1981-88; also dir. Consol. Fibres, Inc.; of counsel McInerney & Dillon, P.C., Oakland, Calif., 1989-91; pvt. practice San Francisco, 1991—; lectr. McGeorge Bar Rev., 1964-65, Continuing Edn. of Bar, U. Calif., 1975-76; judge moot ct. U. San Francisco, 1974-84; arbitrator Am. Arbitration Assn., NASD, 1988—. Co-chmn. Mill Valley Citizens Adv. Com., 1974-76; mem. pub. affairs com. San Francisco Assn. Mental Health, 1965-69; commr. Mill Valley Park and Recreation Commn., 1988-93, chmn., 1990. Mem. ABA, State Bar Calif., San Francisco Bar Assn. Republican. Roman Catholic (lector). Clubs: Olympic, Scott Valley Tennis (founder, dir. 1971-76, pres., dir. 1980-82), World Trade. Home: 3 Midhill Dr Mill Valley CA 94941-1490 Office: 455 Market St Fl 19 San Francisco CA 94105-2420

MC NAMAR, RICHARD TIMOTHY, merchant banker; b. Olney, Ill., Apr. 21, 1939; s. Charles A. and Mary Louise (Diver) McN.; m. Mary Ann Lyons, Aug. 10, 1963 (div.); children: Brendan, Lindsay; m. Karen K. Kwiatt, Dec. 14, 1985. A.B., Villanova U., 1961; J.D., U. Mich., 1963; M.B.A., Dartmouth Coll., 1965. Legal and fin. counselor Standard Oil Co. of Calif., 1965-66; mgmt. cons. McKinsey & Co., Inc., San Francisco, N.Y.C. and Amsterdam, 1966-71; dir. Case Mgmt. and Analysis Bd., 1972; mgmt. cons. Cost of Living Council, Washington, 1973; exec. dir. FTC, Washington, 1973-77; exec. v.p. Beneficial Standard Corp., Los Angeles, 1977-81; dep. sec. Treasury Dept. Treasury, Washington, 1981-85; mem. pvt. investment partnership, 1985-87; mng. dir. Conover & McNamar Inc., Los Angeles, 1987-90; vice chmn. Bank of New Eng. Corp., Boston, 1990-91; mng. dir. Oppenheimer & Co., Inc., L.A., 1991-94; chmn. Finance, Inc., 1994—; dir. NACRE, Inc. Trustee Boston Ballet Co. Mem. ABA, Calif. State Bar Assn., Fin. Execs. Inst., Bretton Woods Comte (bd. dirs.). Republican. Office: Ste 2300 10880 Wilshire Blvd Los Angeles CA 90024-3913

MCNAMARA, A. J., federal judge; b. 1936. BS, La. State U., 1959; JD, Loyola U., New Orleans, 1968. Bailiff, law clk. U.S. Dist. Ct., New Orleans, 1966-68, sole practice, 1968-72; ptnr. Monton, Roy, Carmouche, Hailey, Bivens & McNamara, New Orleans, 1972-78, Hailey, McNamara, McNamara & Hall, 1978-82; judge U.S. Dist. Ct. (ea. dist.) La., New Orleans, 1982—. Mem. La. Ho. of Reps., 1976-80. Office: US Dist Ct C-316 US Courthouse 500 Camp St New Orleans LA 70130-3313

MCNAMARA, ANNE H., lawyer, corporate executive; b. Shanghai, Republic of China, Oct. 18, 1947; came to U.S. 1949; d. John M. and Marion P. (Murphy) H.; m. Martin B. McNamara, Jan. 15, 1977. AB, Vassar Coll., 1969; JD, Cornell U., 1973. Bar: N.Y. 1973, Tex. 1981. Assoc. Shea, Gould, Climenko & Casey, N.Y.C., 1972-76; from asst. corp. sec. to corp. sec. Am. Airlines, Inc., Dallas, 1976-88, v.p. pers. resources, 1988; sr. v.p., gen. counsel Am. Airlines (AMR Corp.), Dallas, 1988—; bd. dirs. Louisville Gas & Electric Co., LG&E Energy Corp. Office: Am Airlines Inc Mail Drop 5675 PO Box 619616 Dallas TX 75261-9616

MCNAMARA, BRENDA NORMA, secondary education educator; b. Blackpool, Lancashire, Eng., Aug. 8, 1945; came to U.S. 1946; d. Milford Hampson and Nola (Welsby) Jones; m. Michael James McNamara, July 19, 1969. BA in History, Calif. State U., Long Beach, 1967; postgrad., Calif. State U., various campuses, 1967—. Cert. secondary tchr. and lang. devel. specialist, Calif. Tchr. history West High Sch., Torrance, Calif., 1968—; dept. chair, 1989—; cons. in field. Co-author: World History, 1984. Western Internat. Studies Consortium grantee, 1988. Mem. Calif. Tchrs. Assn., Calif. Coun. for Social Studies, Torrance Tchrs. Assn. (bd. dirs. 1992—), South Bay Coun. for Social Studies, Nat. Tchrs. Assn., Nat. Coun. for Social Studies. Avocations: travel, theater, myster reading, gourmet cooking. Office: West High Sch 20401 Victor St Torrance CA 90503-2297

MCNAMARA, E. MICHAEL, cosmetics executive. V.p. mktg. Noxele Corp., Hunt Vanley, Md. Office: DEP Corp 2101 E Via Arado Compton CA 90220

MCNAMARA, EDWARD HOWARD, county official, former mayor; b. Detroit, Sept. 21, 1926; s. Andrew Kursina and Ellen Gertrude (Bennett) McN.; m. Lucille Yvonne Martin, June 26, 1948; children—Colleen, Michael, Nancy, Kevin, Terence. Ph.B., U. Detroit, 1959; Ph.D. (hon.), Madonna Coll., 1982. Mgr. Mich. Bell Telephone Co., Detroit, 1948-70; mayor City of Livonia, Mich., 1970-86; county exec. Wayne County, Detroit, 1987—. Served with USN, 1944-46. Democrat. Roman Catholic. Home: 16501 Park St Livonia MI 48154-2203 Office: Office of the County Exec 350 Wayne County Bldg 600 Randolph St Detroit MI 48226

MCNAMARA, FRANCIS JOHN, writer; b. Bklyn., Nov. 19, 1915; s. Sylvester John and Adelia Ferris (French) McN.; m. Katherine Elizabeth Foley, Nov. 20, 1945; children: Jane Marie, Ellen Elizabeth. BA, St. John's U., 1938; MA, Niagara U., 1939. Assoc. reg. sales mgr. UN Relief & Rehab. Adminstrn., Jehol & Hupeh Provinces, China, 1946-47; editor Counterattack, N.Y.C., 1950-54; dir. nat. security program VFW, Washington, 1954-58; research analyst and cons. House Com. on Un-Am. Activities, Washington, 1958-61; dir research House Com. on Un-Am. Activities, 1961-62, staff dir., 1962-69; exec. sec. Subversive Activities Control Bd., Washington, 1970-73; exec. dir. The Hale Found., Washington, 1981; vice chmn. Security and Intelligence Found., Arlington, Va., 1987-90; sr. fellow Ctr. for Intelligence Studies, Arlington, 1990-93; bd. dirs. Coun. for Def. of Freedom, Washington, 1952-94; bd. advisors Nathan Hale Inst., Washington, 1983—. Author: U.S. Counterintelligence Today, 1985, Patterns of Communist Espionage, 1959; contbr. articles to profl. jours. Served to maj. U.S. Army, 1941-46. Mem. Assn. Former Intelligence Officers. Republican. Roman Catholic. Avocations: gardening, photography. Address: 8040 Cindy Ln Bethesda MD 20817-6913

MC NAMARA, FRANCIS JOSEPH, JR., foundation executive, lawyer; b. Boston, Nov. 30, 1927; s. Francis Joseph and Louise (English) McN.; m. Noreen E. O'Connor, June 18, 1953 (dec. Feb. 1984); children: Francis Joseph III, Moira Patricia (Mrs. Lance F. James), John Allen, Kathleen Louise (Mrs. Robert J. Hugin), Martha Jeanne (Mrs. JAmes R. Bordewick), Mark Jeffrey; m. Lois L. Magner, Jan. 17, 1986. A.B., Georgetown U., 1949, LL.B., 1951; LL.D. (hon.), Fairfield U., 1983. Bar: Conn. 1952. Assoc. firm Pullman, Comley, Bradley & Reeves, 1953; asst. U.S. Atty., dist. Conn., 1953-57; assoc. firm Cummings & Lockwood, Stamford, Conn., 1957-59; ptnr. Cummings & Lockwood, 1959-91; guest lectr. Salzburg (Austria)

Seminar, 1981; chmn. grievance com. U.S. Dist. Ct. Conn., 1983-89. Trustee Fairfield (Conn.) U., 1968-80, trustee emeritus, 1980—; trustee Charles E. Culpeper Trust; chmn. bd. Charles E. Culpeper Found., 1968-91, pres., 1991—. Served with USNR, 1946, 51-53. Fellow Am. Bar Found., Am. Coll. Trial Lawyers (state com. 1989-91, state chmn. 1989-90); mem. U.S. Supreme Ct. Hist. Soc. (Conn. state chmn. 1989-91, trustee 1992), Navy League U.S., Knight of Holy Sepulchre, Knight of Malta, Knight of St. Gregory the Great, Wee Burn Country Club (Darien, Conn.), Turf and Field Club (N.Y.). Republican. Roman Catholic. Home: 75 Bank St New Canaan CT 06840 also: 10 Lost Beach Ln Vero Beach FL 32960 Office: Charles E. Culpeper Found 695 E Main St Ste 404 Stamford CT 06901-2138

MCNAMARA, FRANCIS T., ambassador; b. Troy, N.Y., Nov. 2, 1927; married; 7 children. BA, Russell Sage Coll., 1953; MS, George Washington U., 1972; student, Armed Forces Staff Coll., 1967, Naval War Coll., 1971-72. Vice-consul, econ. officer Am. Consulate Gen., Salisbury, Rhodesia, 1957-59; consul-polit. officer Am. Consulate Gen., Lubumbashi, Zaire, 1961-63; polit. and econ. officer Am. Consulate Gen., Dar-Es Salaam, Tanzania, 1964-66; dep. chief mission Am. Consulate Gen., Lusaka, Zambia, 1967; provincial advisor Vinh Long and Quang Tri provinces Am. Embassy, Viet Nam, 1967-69; consul gen. Am. Consulate Gen., Danang, Vietnam, 1969-71; chargé d'affaires, dep. chief mission Am. Embassy, Cotonou, Benin, Viet Nam, 1972-74; consul gen. Am. Consulate Gen., Can Tho, Vietnam, 1974-75, Québec, Can., 1975-79; dep. asst. sec. of state for pub. affairs Dept. of State, Washington, 1979-81; amb. to Republic of Gabon and Republic of Sao Tome and Principe Am. Embassy, 1981-84; chargé d'affaires, dep. chief of mission Am. Embassy, Beirut, 1985-87; amb. to Republic of Cape Verde Am. Embassy, 1989—; fgn. affairs fellow Hoover Instn. Stanford (Calif.) U., 1984-85; sr. rsch. fellow Nat. Def. U., 1987-89. Author: France in Black Africa, 1989. With USN, 1944-46, 50-51. Office: Am Embassy, Rua Hojl Ya Yenna 81, Praia Cape Verde Home: 102 Gresham Pl Falls Church VA 22046-3440

MC NAMARA, J(OHN) DONALD, lawyer, business executive; b. Bridgeport, Conn., Feb. 28, 1924; s. John T. and Agnes (Keating) McN.; m. Shirley Addison Holdridge, Nov. 5, 1960. B.A., Dartmouth Coll., 1945; M.A. in Govt., Harvard U., 1947, LL.B., 1950. Bar: N.Y. 1951, Conn. 1951. Assoc. Hall, Haywood, Patterson & Taylor, N.Y.C., 1951-53, 55-56; asst. U.S. atty. So. Dist. N.Y., 1953-55; asso. firm Wickes, Riddell, Bloomer, Jacobi & McGuire, N.Y.C., 1956-57; asso., then partner firm Nottingham & McEniry (and successor), N.Y.C., 1957-59; sec., gen. counsel Interpub. Group of Companies, Inc., N.Y.C., 1960-79; dir. Interpub. Group of Companies, Inc., 1965-85, sr. v.p., 1966-73, exec. v.p., 1973-79, pres., 1980-85, mem. exec. com., 1967-85, mem. fin. com., 1980-85. Chmn. U.S. Nat. Tennis Championships, 1965. Served to lt. (j.g.) USNR, 1943-46. Mem. River Club, Univ. Club, Met. Opera Club, Ekwanok Country Club (bd. govs. Manchester, Vt. 1991—), Dorset (Vt.) Field Club, West Side Tennis Club pres. Forest Hills, N.Y. 1964-66, 79-80). Home: 350 E 57th St New York NY 10022-2953 also: River Rd Manchester VT 05254

MCNAMARA, JOHN F., health services company executive; b. 1935. V.p., gen. mgr. McKesson Drug Co., L.A., 1974-78, pres. Value Rite div., 1978-81; with Alco Health Svcs. Corp. Inc., Valley Forge, Pa., 1981—, pres. Kauffman-Lettimer div., 1981-83, v.p., 1983-84, exec. v.p., 1984-85, chief operating officer, exec. v.p., 1985-87, pres., chief operating officer, 1987-88, chmn., pres., chief exec. officer, 1988—, also bd. dirs. Office: Ameri Source Corp PO Box 959 Valley Forge PA 19482

MCNAMARA, JOHN JEFFREY, advertising executive; b. N.Y., Jan. 31, 1937; s. John Joseph and Alexandra (Salem) M. BA, N.Y. Law Sch., 1963. Asst. v.p. Albert Frank Guenther Law Inc., N.Y., 1959-66; acct. supr., v.p. Doremus and Co., N.Y., 1966-74; v.p., exec. v.p. Wiley Kiernan Inc Charles Barker Ayer, N.Y., 1974-76; v.p. acct. supr. Tinker Campbell Ewald, N.Y., 1976-78; pres., chmn. John McNamara Advt. Inc., N.Y., 1978—; corr. cons. Hamilton College Alumni, Clinton, N.Y., 1978-88. Republican. Presbyterian. Avocations: boating, golf, restoring old cars, houses. Home: 420 Majors Path Southampton NY 11968-2402 Office: 27 Whitehall St New York NY 10004-2210

MC NAMARA, JOHN J(OSEPH), advertising executive, writer; b. Yonkers, N.Y., Mar. 7, 1934; m. Patricia A. Widmann, Sept. 14, 1963; children: Mary, John. B.S., Yale U., 1956; M.B.A., NYU, 1963. Exec. v.p., eastern regional dir. Young & Rubicam, N.Y.C., 1979; pres. Young & Rubicam U.S.A., from 1982; later pres. McCann Erickson Worldwide, ret., 1988; writer, cons., bd. dirs. in field. Author: Advertising Agency Management, 1989. Pres. Pelham United Way, N.Y.; mem. Pelham Manor Zoning Bd.; chmn. Pelham Manor Planning Bd.; trustee City of Pelham Manor, mayor, 1989-90. Served to 1st lt. USMC, 1956-58. Clubs: Pelham Country (pres.), Winged Foot. Office: PO Box 8092 Vero Beach FL 32963-3450

MCNAMARA, JOHN STEPHEN, artist, educator; b. Cambridge, Mass., Feb. 16, 1950; s. John Stephen and Mary (Adams) McN. BFA in Painting, Mass. Coll. Art, Boston, 1971, MFA in Painting, 1977. Tchr. Mus. Fine Arts Sch., Boston, 1983; undergrad. and grad. painting tchr. Mass. Coll. Art, Boston, 1988; undergrad. painting tchr. Boston Archtl. Ctr., Boston, 1977; color fundamentals tchr. Mass. Coll. Art, Boston, 1987, undergrad. drawing, 1975-88; vis. lectr. San Francisco Art Inst., 1992, 93, U. Calif., Berkeley, 1993, 94, 95. One-man shows include Starvaridis Gallery, Boston, 1985, Bess Cutler Gallery, 1986, Mass. Coll. Art, 1986, Honolulu Acad. Fine Art, 1987, Nielson Gallery, 1990, 92, Miller Block Gallery, Boston, 1995; exhibited in group shows at Boston Collects, Mus. Fine Arts, Stavaridis Gallery, 1986, Bess Cutler Gallery, N.Y.C., 1987, Am. Painters and Sculptors, Met. Mus. Art, N.Y.C., 1988, Resonant Abstraciton, Fuller Mus. Art, Brockton, Mass., 1989-90. Mass. Art and Humanities grantee, 1980, 83, 86, 89, Award in the Visual Arts grantee, 1982, Nat. Endowment Arts grantee, 1981. Home: 1150 Sanchez St San Francisco CA 94114-3857

MC NAMARA, JOSEPH DONALD, researcher, retired police chief, novelist; b. N.Y.C., Dec. 16, 1934; s. Michael and Eleanor (Shepherd) McN.; divorced; children: Donald, Laura, Karen. BS, John Jay Coll., 1968; fellow, Harvard Law Sch., 1970; DPA (Littauer fellow), Harvard U., 1973. Served to dep. insp. Police Dept., N.Y.C., 1956-73; police chief Kansas City, Mo., 1973-76, San Jose, Calif., 1976-91; rsch. fellow Hoover Instn., Stanford U., 1991—; adj. instr. Northeastern U., 1972, John Jay Coll., 1973, Rockhurst Coll., 1975-76, San Jose State U., 1980; cons. U.S. Civil Rights Commn., 1978; lectr., appearances on nat. TV; apptd. nat. adv. bd. U.S. Bur. Justice Stats., 1980, U.S. Drug Control Policy Office, 1993; commentator Pub. Broadcasting Radio. Author: (non-fiction) Safe and Sane, 1984, (novel) The First Directive Crown, 1985, Fatal Command, 1987, The Blue Mirage, 1990; contbr. articles to profl. publs. Bd. dirs. Drug Policy Found., Washington; active NCCJ. Served with U.S. Army, 1958-60. Named one of 200 Young Am. Leaders Time mag., 1975; recipient disting. alumni award John Jay Coll., 1979, Pres.'s award Western Soc. Criminology1979, Morrison Gitchoff award Western Soc. Criminology, 1992, H.B. Spear award Drug Policy Found., 1992; Kansas City police named Best in Country by Nat. Newspaper Enterprises, 1974, San Jose Police Dept. named Nat. Model U.S. Civil Rights Commn., 1980; named Law Enforcement Officer of Yr., Calif. Trial Lawyers Assn., 1991. Mem. Internat. Assn. Chiefs of Police, Calif. Police Chiefs Assn., Calif. Peace Officers Assn., Major Cities Police Chiefs Assn., Police Exec. Research Forum (dir.). Office: Hoover Instn Stanford CA 94305 *In our country, social mobility is possible for people from even the most humble backgrounds. Despite problems, our nation has provided more liberty and dignity for the common individual than any other civilization in history. Continuation of our free society depends upon how successful we are in teaching each new generation an appreciation of our precious freedoms and the patience to achieve progress within our democratic process.*

MC NAMARA, LAWRENCE J., bishop; b. Chgo., Aug. 5, 1928; s. Lawrence and Margaret (Knusman) McN. B.A., St. Paul Sem., 1949, S.T.L., Catholic U. Am., 1953. Ordained priest Roman Catholic Ch., 1953; parish priest, tchr. Kansas City-St. Joseph Diocese, 1953-57; dir. diocesan Refugee Resettlement, 1957-60; chaplain Jackson County Jail, 1957-64; exec. dir. Campaign for Human Devel., 1973-77; bishop of Grand Island Nebr., 1978—. Recipient award Cath. Relief Services. Office: Chancery Office 311 W 17th St PO Box 996 Grand Island NE 68801-3521

MCNAMARA, LAWRENCE JOHN, lawyer; b. Evergreen Park, Ill., Aug. 10, 1950; s. William Francis and Florence M. (Nicholson) McN.; m. Martha Ann Sanchez, Jan. 7, 1992. BA, Ill. Coll.; JD, Vanderbilt U. Bar: Tex. 1976, D.C. 1988, U.S. Dist. Ct. (so. dist.) Tex. 1977, U.S. Dist. Ct. (ea. dist.) Tex. 1978, U.S. Dist. Ct. (no. dist.) Tex. 1985, U.S. Dist. Ct. (we. dist.) Tex. 1991, U.S. Ct. Appeals (5th cir.) 1976, U.S. Ct. Appeals (11th cir.) 1981, U.S. Ct. Appeals (7th cir.) 1989, U.S. Ct. Appeals (9th cir.) 1991, U.S. Ct. Appeals (8th cir.) 1994, U.S. Supreme Ct. 1979. Assoc. Baker & Botts, Houston, 1976-85; ptnr. Baker, Smith & Mills, Dallas, 1985-87; ptnr., shareholder Johnson & Wortley, Dallas, 1987-95; ptnr. Liddell, Sapp, Dallas, 1995—. Mem. ABA, Tex. Bd. Legal Specialization (cert.), Phi Beta Kappa. Roman Catholic. Avocation: golf, running. Office: Liddell Sapp 2200 Ross Ave Ste 900 Dallas TX 75201-2774

MCNAMARA, MARTIN BURR, lawyer, oil and gas company executive; b. Danbury, Conn., Sept. 10, 1947; s. William Joseph and Geraldine Margaret (Young) McN.; m. Anne Rose Hogan, Jan. 15, 1977. BA in English, Providence Coll., 1969; JD, Yale U., 1972. Bar: N.Y. 1973, U.S. Dist. Ct. (so. and ea. dists.) N.Y. 1973, (no. dist.) Tex. 1993, U.S. Ct. Appeals (2d cir.) 1973, Tex. 1980, U.S. Ct. Appeals (5th and 11th cirs.) 1980. Assoc. Shea & Gould, N.Y.C., 1972-76; asst. U.S. atty. (so. dist.) N.Y., N.Y.C., 1976-79; v.p., gen. counsel, sec. Tex. Oil & Gas Corp., Dallas, 1979-91; gen. counsel, sr. v.p. adminstrn. Delhi Gas Pipeline Corp., Dallas, 1979-91; mng. ptnr. Gibson, Dunn & Crutcher, Dallas, 1991—; lectr. State Bar of Tex., Dallas Bar Assn., U. Tex. Corp. Coun. Inst., Okla. Bar Assn. bd. dirs. Sonat Offshore Drilling, Inc.; lectr. State Bar of Tex., Dallas Bar ASsn., U. Tex. Corp. Counsel Inst., Okla. Bar Assn. Mem. exec. com. Yale Law Sch. Assn., 1983-86. Mem. State Bar of Tex. (vice chmn. corp. counsel sect. 1984-86, chmn.-elect 1987-88, chmn. 1988-89), Bar Assn. Fifth Fed. Cir., Assn. Bar City of N.Y., N.Y. State Bar Assn., Fed. Energy Bar Assn. Republican. Roman Catholic. Club: Petroleum. Office: Gibson Dunn & Crutcher 5500 Bank One Ctr 1717 Main Dallas TX 75201

MC NAMARA, RIEMAN, JR., retired banker; b. Richmond, Va., July 25, 1928; s. Rieman and Selina (Heyward) McN.; m. Merrily Brooks, Aug. 2, 1958; children: Brooks, Daniel Heyward. BS, Va. Poly. Inst. and State U., 1948; Chartered Fin. Analyst, U. Va., 1966. Field rep. Burroughs Corp., 1950-52; asst. trust officer Central Nat. Bank, Richmond, 1952-58; v.p., trust officer So. Bank & Trust Co., Richmond, 1958-65; sr. v.p. So. Bank & Trust Co., 1965-68, exec. v.p., 1968, exec. v.p., dir., 1969, pres., 1972-77, vice chmn., 1977-85; exec. v.p. Jefferson Nat. Bank (merged 1985), 1985-93; ret. Trustee Grace and Holy Trinity Endowment Fund, Inc., Va. Commonwealth U. Found., Westminster Canterbury Found. 2d lt. inf. AUS, 1948-50. Mem. Richmond Soc. Fin. Analysts (past pres.), Bond Club Va. (past pres.), SR, Descs. Signers Declaration Independence (past pres. gen.). Episcopalian. Clubs: Va. Creepers (Richmond), Focus (Richmond), Commonwealth, Country of Va. (Richmond). Office: Jefferson Nat Bank 2nd and Grace Sts Richmond VA 23219

MC NAMARA, ROBERT STRANGE, former banking executive, cabinet member; b. San Francisco, June 9, 1916; s. Robert James and Clara Nell (Strange) McN.; m. Margaret Craig, Aug. 13, 1940 (dec.); children: Margaret Elizabeth, Kathleen, Robert Craig. AB, U. Calif., 1937; MBA, Harvard U., 1939; LLD (hon.), U. Calif., U. Mich., Columbia U., Harvard U., George Washington U., Princeton U., Amherst Coll., Williams Coll., U. Ala., Ohio State U., NYU, U. Notre Dame, U. Pa., U. St. Andrews, U. Philippines, Aberdeen U., Oxford U., U. S.C. Asst. prof. bus. adminstrn. Harvard U., 1940-43; exec. Ford Motor Co., 1946-61, pres. co., 1960-61, co. dir., 1957-61; sec. U.S. Dept. Def., 1961-68; pres. World Bank, 1968-81; mem. , trustee pub. and pvt. instns. including Overseas Devel. Coun., Urban Inst., Enterprise Found., Brookings Inst.; spl. cons. War Dept., 1942. Author: The Essence of Security, 1968, One Hundred Countries-Two Billion People, 1973, The McNamara Years at the World Bank, 1981, Blundering Into Disaster, 1986, Out of the Cold, 1989, In Retrospect, 1995. Served as lt. col. USAAF, 1943-46. Decorated Legion of Merit, D.S.M.; recipient Presdl. Medal of Freedom with distinction, Christian A. Herter Meml. award, Albert Pick Jr. award U. Chgo., 1979, Franklin D. Roosevelt Freedom from Want medal, 1983, Onassis Athinai prize, 1988. Mem. Phi Beta Kappa. Office: 1455 Pennsylvania Ave NW Washington DC 20004-1008

MCNAMARA, THOMAS EDMUND, diplomat; b. New Haven, Sept. 16, 1940; s. Joseph Michael and Anne Marie (Meehan) McN.; m. Emma Julia Fonseca, June 11, 1966; children: David Fonseca, Michelle Anne. BA, Manhattan Coll., 1962; MA, Notre Dame U., 1964. Joined fgn. svc. State Dept., 1965; 2nd sec. Am. Embassy, Paris, 1967-69; BENELUX desk officer european bur. State Dept., 1969-71; consul Am. Consulate, Lubumbashi, Zaire, 1971-72, Bukavu, Zaire, 1972-73; with Armed Forces Staff Coll., Norfolk, Va., 1973-74; internat. affairs officer Arms Control & Disarmament Agy., 1974-75; chief external divsn., polit. sect. Am. Embassy, Moscow, 1976-78; office dir., polit.-mil. bur. State Dept., Washington, 1978-80; dep. chief of mission Am. Embassy, Kinshasa, Zaire, 1980-83; dept. asst. sec., bur. polit.-mil. affairs State Dept., Washington, 1983-86; sr. seminar Fgn. Svc. Inst., Washington, 1986-87; dir. counterterrorism and narcotics Nat. Security Coun., 1987-88; ambassador to Colombia, 1988-91; special asst. to the pres. White House, Washington, 1991-92; coord. for counterterrorism State Dept., Washington, 1992-93, prin. dep. asst. sec., bur. polit.-mil. affairs, 1993—. Contbr. articles to profl. jours. Recipient Superior Honor award Dept. State, 1980, 84, 86. Mem. Am. Fgn. Service Assn., Army-Navy Club. Office: Pol Mil Affairs Bur 2201 C St NW Washington DC 20520-0001

MCNAMARA, THOMAS NEAL, lawyer; b. Washington, Dec. 1, 1930; s. Philip Joseph and Louise Loretta (Ryan) McN.; children: John Michael, George Denison, Mary Louise; m. Deana Hollingsworth, Dec. 21, 1986; stepchildren: John W. Hollingsworth, Christopher M. Hollingsworth, Kim R. Hollingsworth. B.A., Duke U., 1952; J.D. with honors, George Washington U., 1959. Bar: Va. 1959, Calif. 1960. Assoc. Pillsbury, Madison & Sutro, San Francisco, 1959-66, ptnr., 1967-86; mng. ptnr. L.A., 1986-89, chmn., 1990-95. Contbr. articles to profl. jours. Trustee Dixie Sch. Dist., San Rafael, Calif., 1964-76; dir. San Francisco Home Health Svc., 1975-82, Hospice of Marin (Calif.), 1988-91, Bay Area Coun., 1990-95; mem. bd. advisors Nat. Law Ctr., George Washington U. Law Sch., 1991—. Served to Lt. comdr. USNR, 1952-56, Korea. Fellow Am. Bar Found. (life), Am. Coll. Tax Counsel; mem. ABA, Calif. Bar Assn., San Francisco Bar Assn., Va. Bar Assn., Internat. Game Fish Assn. (Calif. rep. 1983—), Order of Coif, Pacific-Union Club, The Family Club, Presidio Golf Club. Republican. Roman Catholic. Office: Pillsbury Madison & Sutro PO Box 7880 San Francisco CA 94120-7880

MCNAMARA, TOM, newspaper editor. Managing editor-news USA Today, Arlington, Va. Office: USA Today 1000 Wilson Blvd Arlington VA 22209-3991*

MCNAMEE, BERNARD JOSEPH, lawyer; b. Yeadon, Pa., Sept. 8, 1935; s. Bernard L. and Mary E. (Maher) McN.; m. Barbara McGowan, June 20, 1964; children: Bernard L., Lynne M. BA, St. Mary's U., 1957; STB, Cath. U. Am., 1959; JD, U. Va., 1962; MBA, Mich. State U., 1969. Bar: Pa. 1963, Ind. 1967, N.Y. 1975, Va. 1976, Texas 1979, Calif. 1986. Trainee bur. competition FTC, D.C., 1961; assoc. Clark Ladner Fortenbaugh & Young, Phila., 1962-66; from atty. to asst. counsel Miles Labs., Inc., Elkhart, Ind., 1966-74; gen. counsel Hooker Chem. & Plastics Corp., Niagara Falls, N.Y., 1974-78; assoc. gen. counsel Hooker Chem. Co., Houston, 1978-82; sr. counsel Gulf Oil Corp., Houston, 1982-85; assoc. gen. counsel Chevron Chem. Co., San Ramon, Calif., 1985-89; v.p., gen. counsel Ferro Corp., Cleve., 1989—; tchr., lectr. U. Notre Dame, 1972. Contbr. articles to profl. jours. Mem. ABA, Niagara Frontier Corp. Counsel Assn. (founder, pres. 1977-78). Office: Ferro Corp 1000 Lakeside Ave E Cleveland OH 44114-1147

MCNAMEE, SISTER CATHERINE, educational association executive; b. Troy, N.Y., Nov. 13, 1931; d. Thomas Ignatius McNamee and Kathryn McNamee Marois. B.A., Coll. of St. Rose, 1953, D.H.L. (hon.), 1975; M.Ed., Boston Coll. 1955, M.A., 1958; Ph.D., U. Madrid, 1967. Grad. asst. Boston Coll., 1954-55; asst. registrar Boston Coll. (Grad. Sch.), 1955-57; acad. v.p. Coll. St. Rose, Albany, N.Y., 1968-75; dir. liberal arts Thomas Edison Coll., Trenton, 1975-76; pres. Trinity Coll. Burlington, Vt., 1976-79, Coll. St. Catherine, St. Paul, 1979-84; dean Dexter Hanley Coll., U.

MCNAMEE, DANIEL VINCENT, III, management consultant; b. N.Y.C., Sept. 21, 1944; s. Daniel Vincent McNamee Jr. and Barbara Burroughs (Cooley) Dudley; m. Susan Anderson Thompson, Oct. 21, 1978. BA, Yale U., 1967; post grad. Balliol Coll. Oxford, England. Assoc. pub. MORE mag., N.Y.C., 1973-74; v.p. circulation Downe Communications, Inc., N.Y.C., 1974-77; dir. planning Chartcom, Inc., N.Y.C., 1977-78; v.p. consumer mktg. Charter Pub., N.Y.C., 1978-79; pres. The McNamee Cons. Co., N.Y.C., 1979—; ptnr. The Electronic Pub. Consulting Group; bd. dirs. First Albany (N.Y.) Corp., Silver Eagle Pubs., N.Y.C., Multi-Local Media Corp., Merrick, N.Y. Trustee Assocs. Coun. Oxford Centre for Mgmt. Studies, 1984—, Ocean Liner Mus., N.Y.C., 1985—, E.N. Huyck Preserve Inc. With U.S. Army, 1969-71. Mem. Yale Club (N.Y.C.), Manursing Island Club (Rye, N.Y.). Democrat. Presbyterian. Avocations: reading, skiing, tennis, theater, sailing. Home: 42 Orchard Ln Rye NY 10580-3638 Office: The McNamee Cons Group 535 Fifth Ave New York NY 10017-3610

MCNAMEE, LOUISE, advertising agency executive; m. Tom M. Attended, Mary Baldwin Coll., Va. With rsch. dept. Kelly Nason; exec. v.p., dir. mktg. and rsch. Della Femina, Travisano & Ptnrs., Inc. (now Della Famina McNamee, Inc.), N.Y.C., 1979-84, ptnr., 1982—, acting pres., from 1984, past pres., chief operating officer, chief exec. officer, 1992-93; now ptnr., pres. Messner, Vetere, Berger, McNamee, Schmetterer, Euro RSCG, N.Y.C., 1993—. Named Advt. Woman of Yr. Advt. Women of N.Y., 1988. Office: Della Femina McNamee Inc 350 Hudson St New York NY 10014

MCNAMEE, STEPHEN M., federal judge; b. 1942. B.A., U. Cinn., 1964; M.A., J.D., U. Ariz., 1969. U.S. atty. Dist. of Ariz., Phoenix, 1985-90; judge U.S. Dist. Ct. Ariz., Phoenix, 1990—. Office: 1400 US Courthouse 230 N 1st Ave Phoenix AZ 85025-0230

MCNAUGHTON, JOHN D., director. Films include Henry: Portrait of a Serial Killer, 1989, The Borrower, 1991, Sex, Drugs, Rock & Roll, 1991, Mad Dog and Glory, 1993, Girls in Prison, 1994. Office: ICM 8942 Wilshire Blvd Beverly Hills CA 90211-1908 also: 1370 N Milwaukee Ave Chicago IL 60622-2149*

MCNAUGHTON, ROBERT FORBES, JR., computer science educator; b. Bklyn., Mar. 13, 1924; s. Robert Forbes and Helen (Brown) McN.; m. Ann Gerardo, Dec. 20, 1948 (div. 1957); children: Nicholas F., Sarah E. McNaughton Deppa; m. Vivien Leonard, June 23, 1974. Student, Bklyn. Coll., 1942-43, 46; BA, Columbia U., 1948; PhD, Harvard U., 1951. Tchr. philosophy Ohio State U., 1951-52, U. Mich., 1953-54, Stanford U., 1954-57; tchr. computer sci. and elec. engring. Moore Sch. Elec. Engring., U. Pa., 1957-64, MIT, 1964-66; prof. computer sci., math. Rensselaer Poly. Inst., Troy, N.Y., 1966-89, prof. emeritus, 1989—; vis. prof. dept. computer sci. SUNY at Albany, 1989-90; researcher Office Naval Rsch., 1952-53, RCA, Moorestown, summer 1960, Princeton, summer 1963. Served with AUS, 1943-46. Recipient Levy medal Franklin Inst., 1956. Mem. Assn. Symbolic Logic, Assn. Computing Machinery, Am. Math. Soc., Math. Assn. Am., Phi Beta Kappa. Home: 2511 15th St Troy NY 12180-1704

MCNAUGHTON, SAMUEL JOSEPH, ecology educator; b. Takoma Park, Md., Aug. 10, 1939; s. Frank and Ruth Ellen (Flanders) McNaughton Francis; m. Margaret Mae Smith, Sept. 7, 1959; children: Robert Sean, Erin Michelle. BS, N.W. Mo. State Coll., 1961; PhD, U. Tex., 1964. Asst. prof. Portland State Coll., Oreg., 1964-65; asst. prof. Syracuse (N.Y.) U., 1966-69, assoc. prof., 1969-73, prof., 1973—; William R. Kenan Jr. prof. of sci., 1992—. Author (with others) General Ecology, 1979; contbr. articles to profl. jours. Fellow AAAS, Explorers Club; mem. Ecol. Soc. Am., Sigma Xi. Avocation: model railroading. Home: 306 Hurlburt Rd Syracuse NY 13224-1823 Office: Syracuse U 130 College Pl Syracuse NY 13210-2819

MCNEAL, ANN P. WOODHULL, physiology professor; b. Orange, N.J., Oct. 20, 1942; d. James D. W. and Hazel V. Mc.; m. Albert S. Woodhull, May 1, 1965 (div. 1986); 1 child, Gordon. BA, Swarthmore Coll., 1964; PhD, U. Wash., Seattle, 1972. From asst. prof. to prof. Hampshire Coll., Amherst, Mass., 1972—; program dir. divsn. undergrad. edn. NSF, 1993-94. Contbr. articles to profl. jours. Mem. Peace Activists East West (sec. 1985-89), Amherst, Mass., Pelham Athletic Club (pres. 1986-89), Pelham, Mass. Mem. Am. Coll. Sports Medicine. Avocations: hiking, feminism, ecology, politics. Office: Hampshire Coll Natural Sci Amherst MA 01002

MCNEAL, DALE WILLIAM, JR., biological sciences educator; b. Kansas City, Kans., Nov. 23, 1939; s. Dale William and Geraldine Estelle (Reed) McN.; m. Arlene Joyce Purvis, Feb. 26, 1966. B.A., Colo. Coll., 1962; M.S., SUNY Coll. Environ. Sci. and Forestry, Syracuse, 1964; Ph.D., Wash. State U., 1969. Asst. prof. dept. biol. scis. U. Pacific, Stockton, Calif., 1969-74, assoc. prof., 1974-79, prof., 1979—, chmn. dept., 1978-84. Contbr. articles to profl. jours. Served with U.S. Army, 1964-66. Mem. Am. Bot. Soc., Calif. Bot. Soc. (pres. 1987-88), Am. Soc. Plant Taxonomists, Internat. Soc. Plant Taxonomy, Calif. Acad. Scis., Sigma Xi. Republican. Episcopalian. Office: U Pacific Dept Biol Scis Stockton CA 95211

MCNEALEY, J. JEFFREY, lawyer, corporate executive; b. Cin., Feb. 8, 1944; s. J. Lawrence and Louise McNealey; m. Sara Wilson, Sept. 24, 1988; children: Anne Elizabeth, John Alexander. BA, Cornell U., 1966; JD, Ohio State U., 1969. Ptnr. Porter, Wright, Morris & Arthur, Columbus, Ohio, 1969—; bd. dirs. TRC Cos., Windsor, Conn., 1985—; sec., bd. dirs. The Smoot Corp., Columbus, 1972—. Trustee Columbus Cancer Clinic, 1972—; past pres.; trustee German Village Soc., Columbus, 1986—; past pres.; bd. dirs. Columbus chpt. ARC, 1983-86, Columbus Urban League, 1984-90; active Union League Chgo., 1982—. Mem. ABA, Ohio State Bar Assn. (past chmn. environ. com. 1978-84), Columbus Bar Assn., Columbus Country Club, Capital Club of Columbus, Cornell Club of Ctrl. Ohio (trustee 1978—, past pres.). Episcopalian. Avocations: flying, racquet sports, wood working, flyfishing. Office: Porter Wright Morris & Arthur 41 S High St Fl 30 Columbus OH 43215-6101

MC NEALY, SCOTT, computer company executive; b. 1954. BA, Harvard U., 1976; MBA, Stanford U., 1980. Chmn., pres., chief exec. officer Sun Microsystems Inc., Mountain View, Calif.; with Rockwell Internat. Corp., Troy, Mich., 1976-78, sales engr.; staff engr. FMC Corp., Chgo., 1980-81; dir. ops. Onyx Systems, San Jose, Calif., 1981-82; with Sun Microsystems Inc., Mountain View, Calif., 1982—, now chmn. bd., pres., chief exec. officer, also dir. Office: Sun Microsystems Inc 2550 Garcia Ave Mountain View CA 94043-1100*

MCNEAR, BARBARA BAXTER, financial communications executive, consultant; b. Chgo., Oct. 9, 1939; d. Carl Henden and Alice Gertrude (Parrish) Baxter; m. Robert Erskine McNear, Apr. 13, 1968 (div. 1981); 1 child, Amanda Baxter; m. Glenn Philip Eisen, June 7, 1987. B.S. in Journalism, Northwestern U., 1961. Editorial asst. Scott Foresman & Co., Chgo., 1961; pub. rels. dir. Market Facts Inc., Chgo., 1961-63; account supr. Philip Lesly Co., Chgo., 1963-68, 69; account exec. Burson-Marsteller, Chgo., 1968; dir. communications CNA Fin. Corp., Chgo., 1969-74; pub. rels. Gould Inc., Chgo., 1974; v.p. Harris Bank, Chgo., 1974-80, Fireman's Fund Ins. Co., San Francisco, 1980-83; sr. v.p. First Chgo. Corp., 1983-86; v.p. communications Xerox Fin. Svcs., Inc., Stamford, Conn., 1987-93; mgr. shareholder comm. Xerox Corp. Stamford, 1993—. Bd. dirs. Seneca, Inc., Basking Ridge, N.J., Fairfield County Pub. Rels. Assn. Mem. Pub. Relations Soc. Am., Nat. Investor Rels. Inst. (pres. Chgo. chpt. 1974-75, bd. dirs. Chgo. chpt.). Episcopalian. Club: Cliffdwellers, Princeton. Home: 23 Telva Rd Wilton CT 06897-3733 Office: Xerox Corp 800 Long Ridge Rd Stamford CT 06904

MCNEARY, JOSEPH ALLEN, apparel executive; b. N.Y.C., Jan. 17, 1948; s. John Joseph and Catherine (Lemon) McN.; m. Mary Ellen Franck, 1969 (div. May 1982); 1 child, David Lionel; m. Priscilla Ann Campbell, Apr. 11, 1987. BA, Georgetown U., 1969. Buyer Lord & Taylor, N.Y.C., 1972-75; div. v.p. Saks Fifth Ave., N.Y.C., 1976-85; div. pres. Levi Strauss, N.Y.C., 1985-86; div. pres. dresses dept., sr. v.p. Liz Claiborne Inc., N.Y.C., 1986—; mem. policy com., found. com. Liz Claiborne Inc., 1989—; pres. Liz Claiborne Retail Group, 1990—. Mem. bd. Clearport Sch. Mem. Heights Casino Club (Bklyn.). Democrat. Office: Liz Claiborne Inc 119 W 40th St New York NY 10018-2500

MCNEEL, VAN LOUIS, chemical company executive; b. Laurel, Miss., July 4, 1925; s. George Louis and Pauline (Webb) McN.; m. Betty Tarwater, July 6, 1959 (div. 1966); 1 child, Clayton Webb; m. Diane Kidd, Dec. 30, 1971; 1 child, Ian Edward. Student, Sanford U. (formerly Howard Coll.); LLB, U. Ala., 1949. Project mgr. Reynolds Metals, N.Y.C. and Jacksonville, Fla., 1949-51; div. mgr. Olin Mathieson Chem. Corp., Atlanta, 1951-60, dir. internat. ops., 1960-63; pres. Polymer Internat. Corp., N.Y.C., 1963-64; chmn., chief exec. officer Polymer Internat. Corp., Tampa, Fla., 1964—; pres. Internat. Container Systems, Tampa, 1985—, also bd. dirs.; chmn. Security Tag Systems, St. Petersburg, Fla., 1981—, also bd. dirs.; bd. dirs. SouthTrust Bank of Tampa (formerly Gulf Bay Bank). Trustee U. Tampa, 1955—; bd. dirs. Tampa chpt. ARC.; mem. Golden Triangle Civic Assn., Tampa Bay Area Trade Council Fgn. Relations. Mem. Am. Mgmt. Assn., Soc. Plastic Engrs. Clubs: Palma Ceia Golf and Country, Tampa Yacht and Country, Ctr. Club, University (Tampa). Office: Polymer Internat Corp 5401 W Kennedy Blvd Tampa FL 33609-2433

MCNEELEY, DONALD ROBERT, steel company executive; b. Chgo., July 31, 1954; s. Donald Robert and Alma Theresa (Gray) McN.; m. Elizabeth Dianne Smith, Aug. 23, 1975; children: Kelly Dianne, Meghan Maureen. BA, U. Wis., 1979; MBA summa cum laude, George Williams Coll., 1985; PhD cum laude, Columbia Pacific U., 1986; MS in Mgmt. and Organizational Behavior, Ill. Benedictine Coll., 1991. With Chgo. Tube and Iron Co., 1972-77, ops. mgr., 1977-79, corp. mgr. employee relations, 1979-82, v.p. ops., 1982-84, exec. v.p., 1984-91, pres., chief oper. officer, 1991—, also bd. dirs.; trustee Plumbing and Heating Wholesalers Retirement Income Plan, Chgo., 1987—, negotiator labor com., 1982—; adj. prof. mgmt. De Paul U., Chgo., 1992—; mem. bus. adv. coun. Editor: Employment in Illinois, 1983; contbr. articles to profl. jours. Trustee, 1st v.p. Found. for Continuing Edn., Steel Svc. Ctr. Inst., Cleve., 1981—; chmn. Tubular Products Coun., Steel Svc. Ctr. Inst., 1994—; dir. Com. for Monetary Rsch. and Edn., Greenwich, Conn., 1988—. Mem. Steel Service Ctr. Inst. Republican. Roman Catholic. Club: La Grange (Ill.) Country. Avocations: golf, reading, investing.

MCNEELY, JOHN J., lawyer; b. Mpls., Oct. 8, 1931; s. John J. Sr. and Mae (Carlin) McN.; children: Mary Ann, John J., Michael F., Patricia C., David C. BS, Georgetown U., 1955, JD, 1958. Bar: Minn. 1958. Law clk. Minn. Supreme Ct., St. Paul, 1958-59; ptnr. Briggs & Morgan, St. Paul, 1959—. Sgt. USMC, 1950-52. Fellow Am. Coll. Trust and Estate Counsel; mem. ABA, Minn. State Bar Assn., Ramsey County Bar Assn., Pool and Yacht Club, Wedgewood Country Club. Home: 1183 Ivy Hills Dr Saint Paul MN 55118 Office: Briggs & Morgan 2200 1st Nat Bank Bldg Saint Paul MN 55101

MCNEELY, MARK HALL, advertising executive; b. Evanston, Ill., Apr. 19, 1950; s. E.L. and Alice (Hall) McN.; m. Corinne Burge, Aug. 3, 1985. BA, U. So. Calif., L.A., 1972; MBA, Harvard U., 1976. Prin. Competitive Strategies Inc., N.Y.C., 1980-84; mgr. advt. strategy Ford Motor Co., Detroit, 1984-86; dir. strategic planning Ogilvy and Mather, N.Y.C., 1986-88; chmn. Cole & Weber Inc., Seattle, 1988—. Office: Cole & Weber Inc 308 Occidental Ave S Seattle WA 98104

MCNEELY, STEPHEN ALLEN, outdoor advertising company executive; b. Mayfield, Ky., Sept. 28, 1948; s. Albert Thomas and Katherine (Green) McN.; m. Linda Benson (div. 1986); children: Jennifer Leigh, Todd Allen; m. Susan Hartfelder, Dec. 31, 1987; children: Morgan Elizabeth, Rachel Katherine. BS, U. Ky., 1968, MBA, 1973; postgrad., Wharton Sch., 1980. Mgr. retail bus. Exxon Corp., N.Y.C.; dir. internat. sales Gilbarco/Div. of Exxon, Greensboro, N.C., 1984-85, gen. mgr., pres., 1985-86; pres. Chase Capital, Dallas, 1988-87; chief oper. officer Tenneco Auto Retail Svcs., Chgo., 1987-89; pres., chief exec. officer GE Capital Auto Resale Svcs., Chgo., 1989-91, Patrick Media Group/GE Capital, Chgo., 1991—; bd. dirs. Advt. Coun., N.Y.C., Outdoor Advt. Assn. Am., Washington, Traffic Audit Bur., N.Y.C., Chgo. Advt. Fedn., Fla. Raceplex. Lt. USAF. Mem. Nat. Assn. for Prevention Child Abuse, Nat. Children's Found. (chmn. 1978-84). Avocations: skiing, golf, auto racing. Office: Patrick Media Group 737 N Michigan Ave Ste 1300 Chicago IL 60611

MCNEESE, JACK MARVIN, communications executive; b. Seattle, Jan. 9, 1929; s. William Joseph and Mary Elizabeth (Fritz) McN.; m. Dolores May Winkler, Apr. 20, 1940 (div. 1953); 1 child John Martin; m. Natoma June Young. Grad. high sch., Seattle. Telephone installer Pacific N.W. Bell, Seattle, 1948-60; with telephone mktg. dept. Pacific N.W. Bell, Tacoma, 1960-67; communications cons. Communication Mgmt. Concepts, Seattle, 1967-73; pres., founder, communications cons. Telcom Mgmt. Concepts, Federal Way, Wash., 1973—. With U.S. Army, 1955-59. Mem. Soc. Telecommunications Consultants, Twinlakes Golf and Country Club. Masons. Republican. Avocation: skiing. Home: 2618 SW 323rd St Federal Way WA 98023-2521 Office: Telcom Mgmt Concepts Inc 2025 S 341st Pl Federal Way WA 98003-6861

MC NEICE, JOHN AMBROSE, JR., investment company executive; b. Quincy, Mass., Sept. 28, 1932; s. John Ambrose and Gladys Lydia (Starratt) McN.; m. Margarete Emma aust, Apr. 2, 1956; children: Gabriele S., Margarete Anne. B.A. magna cum laude, Boston Coll., 1954; M.B.A., Northeastern U., Boston, 1960. Chartered fin. analyst. With Colonial Mgmt. Assos., Inc. (subsidiary of TCG, Inc.), Boston, 1956—, v.p., 1968-73, dir. investment rsch., 1973, exec. v.p., 1974, pres., chief exec. officer, 1975-83, chmn., 1983—; chmn., chief exec. officer The Colonial Group, Inc., 1985—; bd. dirs., Am. Ireland Fund. Trustee Boston Coll., Boston Coll. High Sch., St. John's Sem.; chmn. bd. trustees Cath. Charities-Archdiocese of Boston, Nativity Preparatory Sch.; mem. Carney Hosp. Found., Corp. Wentworth Inst. Tech.; bd. visitors Peter F. Drucker Ctr., Claremont U.; bd. dirs. Peter F. Drucker Found.; bd. dirs., exec. com. United Way of Massachusetts Bay; bd. overseers Northeastern U.; trustee, pres. Third Century Found., Archdioces of Boston; dir. Pope John XXIII Med.-Moral Rsch. and Edn. Ctr., Fin. coun., Archdiocese of Boston; mem. Bd. of Overseers, Facing History and Ourselves Nat. Found., Inc.; pres., bd. trustee Better Opportunities Scholarship Foundation, Inc.; exec. com., CEO Fundamental Change in Edn. With AUS, 1954-56. Mem. Knights of Malta, Union Club, Wollaston Golf Club. Roman Catholic. Home: 47 Green St Canton MA 02021-1023 Office: The Colonial Group Inc 1 Financial Ctr Boston MA 02111-2621

MCNEIL, BARBARA JOYCE, radiologist; b. Cambridge, Mass., Feb. 11, 1941; d. Archibald Pius and Katherine (Joyce) McN. A.B., Emmanuel Coll., 1962; M.D., Harvard U., 1966, Ph.D., 1972. Diplomate: Am. Bd. Nuclear Medicine. Intern Mass. Gen. Hosp., Boston, 1966-67, resident in nuclear medicine, 1971-73; prof. radiology and clin. epidemiology Harvard Med. Sch. and Brigham & Women's Hosp., Boston, 1983—, dir. ctr. for cost effective care, 1980-93; chmn. dept., Ridley Watts prof. health care policy Harvard Med. Sch., 1988—; chmn. Blue Cross-Mass. Hosp. Assn. Fund for Coop. Innovation, 1981-87; mem. Prospective Payment Assessment Commn., 1983-91; mem. nat. adv. coun. Agy. for Health Care Policy, Rsch. and Evaluation, 1991—. Editor: Critical Issues in Medical Technology, 1982; contbr. articles to profl. jours. Fellow AAAS, Am. Coll. Nuclear Physicians; mem. Am. Acad. Arts and Scis., Inst. Medicine (coun. 1991—), Fleischner Soc., Nat. Coun. on Radiation Protection, Am. Coll. Radiology, Soc. Nuclear Medicine. Office: Harvard Med Sch 25 Shattuck St Boston MA 02115-6092

MC NEIL, DONALD LEWIS, retired multiple association management company executive; b. Milw., Dec. 20, 1926; s. Robert Lewis and Elizabeth Barbara (Bloesius) McN.; m. Mildred M. Hancock, Sept. 2, 1950. PhB, Marquette U., 1950. Editor Pewaukee (Wis.) Post, 1948-50; advt. copywriter Sears Roebuck, Milw., 1952-53; press. dir. United Way of Greater Milw., 1953-57; mgr. adminstrv. services Med. Soc. Milwaukee County, 1957-62;

v.p. Exec. Dir., Inc., Milw., 1962-67; pres. Exec. Dir., Inc., 1967-94; ret., 1994; organizer, dir. Hartland Nat. Bank (Wis.). Pub. Am. Christmas Tree Jour., 1966-92. Pres. Hartland United Way, 1949-58; active Republican politics. With USN, 1944-46, 50-52. Mem. Am. Soc. Assn. Execs., VFW, Am. Legion, Urgan League, Lac LaBelle Golf Club, St. Charles Ch. Men's Club. Republican. Roman Catholic. Home: 432 E Capitol Dr Hartland WI 53029-2202

MCNEIL, HEIDI LORETTA, lawyer; b. Preston, Iowa, Apr. 7, 1959; d. Archie Hugo and Heidi (Waltert) McN.; m. L. William Staudenmaier III. BA in Journalism and Broadcasting with distinction, U. Iowa, 1981, JD with distinction, 1985. Bar: Ariz. 1985, U.S. Dist. Ct. Ariz. 1985, U.S. Ct. Appeals (9th cir.) 1985, U.S. Ct. Appeals (10th cir.) 1990. Sports journalist The Daily Iowan, Iowa City, 1977-81, Quad City Times, Davenport, Iowa, 1981-82; ptnr. Snell & Wilmer, Phoenix, 1985—; judge pro tem Maricopa County. Mem. ABA (chair young lawyers corp. counsel issues com. 1992-93, dir. 1993-94, spl. projects coord. 1994-95, commn. on domestic violence 1995—), Ariz. Bar Assn. (Indian law sect. exec. coun. and officer 1993—, young lawyers exec. coun. 1991-94), Maricopa County Bar Assn. (bd. dirs. 1991—, young lawyers exec. bd. dirs. and officer 1987-93, pres. 1991-92), Internat. Assn. Gaming Attys., Native Am. Bar Assn., Ariz. Women's Lawyers, Phoenix Assn. Def. Counsel, Phi Beta Kappa, Phi Eta Sigma. Lutheran. Avocations: running, golf, skiing, hiking, bicycling.

MCNEIL, JOHN D., insurance company executive; b. Southampton, Eng., Feb. 17, 1934; came to Can., 1956; s. Spencer Ewart and Janet McNeil; m. Isobel Esther Spence, Dec. 24, 1956; children: Spencer, Claire, John, Alison, David. MA with honors, U. Edinburgh, 1956. With Sun Life Assurance Co. of Can., Montreal, Que., 1955-56, with investment dept., 1956, asst. treas., 1962-66, v.p. securities and investments, 1979, sr. v.p., gen. mgr. U.S. div., 1982-85, exec. v.p., 1985-87, dep. chmn., dir., 1987—; chmn., CEO Sun Life Assurance Co. of Can.; with Mut. Funds Mgmt. Corp., Ltd., 1966-73, Morrison, Krembil, Ltd., 1974-75; adminstrt. Morrison, Krembil Ltd., 1974-75; bd. dirs., chmn., pres., trustee numerous affiliated Sun Life cos. Mem. Inst. Chartered Fin. Analysts, Toronto Soc. Fin. Analysts. Club: Canadian (bd. dirs.). Home: 10 McKenzie Ave, Toronto, ON Canada M4W 1J9 Office: Sun Life Assurance Co Can, PO Box 4250 Sta A, Toronto, ON Canada M5W 2C9 also: Sun Life Ins & Annuity Co NY 80 Broad St # 25 New York NY 10004-2209

MCNEIL, JOSEPH MALCOLM, advertising executive; b. Detroit, Oct. 27, 1937; s. Joseph Edgar and Dorothy (Karick) McN.; m. Carol Jean Nave; children: Joseph Paul, Sean Michael, Jennifer Marie. BA in Advt. and English, Mich. State U., 1960. Copywriter D.P. Brother & Co., Detroit, 1962-64; copy group supr. BBD&O, Inc., Detroit, 1964-66; v.p., creative dir. BBD&O, Inc., N.Y.C., 1967-76; group supr. Campbell-Ewald Co., Detroit, 1966-67; exec. v.p., dir. creative svcs. N.W. Ayer, Seattle, 1976-79; sr. v.p., group creative dir. N.W. Ayer, N.Y.C., 1979-80; sr. v.p., creative dir. Campbell-Mithun, Mpls., 1980-83; exec. v.p., exec. creative dir. Creamer, Inc., N.Y.C., 1983-84; sr. v.p., creative dir. McCann-Erickson Inc., N.Y.C., 1984-86, The John Bergin Group/McCann-Erickson Inc., N.Y.C., 1986-87; exec. v.p., exec. creative dir., mem. mgmt. com., bd. dirs. Ross Roy Communications, Bloomfield Hills, Mich., 1987—. Pfc. U.S. Army. Recipient Gold and Bronze Lions Cannes Film Festival, Spike awards (3) Internat. Broadcasting Assn., Clio awards (8), Effie awards (4), Addy awards (2), Best in the West, Internat. Film Festival awards (3); honored in Smithsonian Instn. Living History sect.; named to Internat. Broadcasting Awards Hall of Fame. Mem. NATAS (Detroit chpt.), Adcraft Club Detroit. Republican. Roman Catholic. Avocations: writing, music, golf, water skiing. Office: Ross Roy Communications 100 Bloomfield Hills Pky Bloomfield Hills MI 48304-2906

MCNEIL, STEVEN ARTHUR, food company executive; b. Ft. Thomas, Ky., May 6, 1942; s. Arthur James and Ruby Marie (Lindell) McN.; m. Kathryn Louise Knapp, Aug. 27, 1966; children: Andrew James, Kathryn Marie. BA, Ohio Wesleyan U., 1964; MBA, Dartmouth U., 1966. Mgr. mktg. and devel. Gen. Foods Corp., 1966-80; mgr. mktg. and devel. Campbell Soup Co., Camden, N.J., 1980-81; mgr. Swanson bus. unit, 1981-83, gen. mgr., 1983-84, group gen. mgr., 1984-85, corp. v.p., 1985—; pres. Mrs. Paul's, 1988-90; sr. v.p., gen. mgr. N.Am., The Haagen-Dazs Co., Inc., Teaneck, N.J., 1990-91; pres., chief oper. officer Bumble Bee SeaFoods, Inc., San Diego, 1992-93; dean Rowan Sch. of Bus. Rowan Coll. N.J., 1994—; bd. dirs. South Jersey Industries Inc., Folsom, N.J.; chmn., mem. exec. com. Frozen Food Inst., McLean, Va. Trustee West Jersey Health and Hosp. Found., Camden, sec., 1989-91; co-founder The Friends of tne Nyacks, Nyack, N.Y., 1972. Mem. South Jersey C. of C. (bd. dirs. 1994—), La Costa Country Club.

MCNEILL, ALFRED THOMAS, JR., construction executive; b. Elizabeth, N.J., Dec. 21, 1936; s. Alfred T. and Mary Ellen (Byrne) McN.; m. Dorothy J. Keidat, Oct. 4, 1981; children: Mary McNeill Ivanoski, Gabrielle McNeill Hensley, Matthew, Christopher, Peter, Bartholomew, Elizabeth McNeill Downes, Catherine, Gwyneth Elizabeth. BSCE, Lehigh U., 1958. Registered profl. engr., Ohio, N.Y. With Turner Constrn. Co., 1958—; field engr. Turner Constrn. Co., N.Y.C., 1958; supt. Turner Constrn. Co., Cin., 1961, gen. supt., 1969; corp. v.p. ops. Turner Constrn. Co., N.Y.C., 1973; v.p., gen. mgr. Turner Constrn. Co., Phila., 1975, regional sr. v.p., 1981; pres., chief exec. officer Turner Constrn. Co., N.Y.C., 1985; pres. The Turner Corp., N.Y.C., 1986-89, chmn. bd., chief exec. officer, 1989—, also dir.; chmn. State of Ohio Apprenticeship Coun., Cin., 1970-73; mem. nat. collective bargaining com. Associated Gen. Contractors, 1970-75; mem. labor policy com. Gen. Bldg. Contractors Assn., 1975-80, bd. dirs., 1978-84; bd. dirs. Tchrs. Properties, Inc., Rouse-Tchrs. Properties; adv. bd. Liberty Mut. Ins. Co.; mem. Constrn. Industry Pres.'s Forum; mem. civil engring. adv. bd. Lehigh U. Co-author: Construction Management for the General Contractor, 1974. Mem. chmn.'s circle USA-ROC Econ. Coun., N.Y.C. Partnership, NYU Real Estate Inst. Adv. Bd. 2d lt. U.S. Army, 1959, capt. Res. Recipient award Nat. Associated Gen. Contrators, 1974, De La Salle medal Manhattan Coll., 1991. Mem. Am. Inst. Constructors (constructor), Regional Plan Assn. (bd. dirs. 1985-87), Econ. Club N.Y., Aronimink Country Club (Newtown Square, Pa.), The Sky Club (N.Y.C. v.p., bd. govs.), Blind Brook Club (Purchase, N.Y.), Ocean Reef Club (Key Largo, Fla.). Roman Catholic. Avocation: golf. Office: The Turner Corp 375 Hudson St New York NY 10014*

MC NEILL, CHARLES JAMES, publishing executive; b. Newton, Kans., Dec. 1, 1912; s. Hugh Andrew and Elizabeth (Sheehan) McN.; m. Mary Elizabeth O'Neill, Nov. 6, 1935; 1 dau., Mary Sharon McGlynn. A.B., St. Benedict's Coll., 1933, L.H.D., 1956; postgrad., U. Denver, 1934-36; B.J., Register Coll. Journalism, Denver, 1935, M.J., 1937, D.Journalism, 1939. Librarian Sacred Heart Jr. Coll., 1933; exec. sec. Cath. Action Com. of Men, Wichita, Kans., 1933-34; staff Cath. Advance, Wichita, 1934; asso. editor Register Sisters of Cath. Newspapers, 1934-43; staff Geo. A. Pflaum, Pub., Inc., Dayton, Ohio, 1946-49, asst. to pres., 1949-51, gen. mgr., 1951-57; asst. European dir. Radio Free Europe, Munich, Germany, 1957-61; treas. Internat. Television Devel. Corp., N.Y.C., 1961-63, Inter Tel N.V., Amsterdam, 1961-63; v.p. Kane, McNeill, Inc., N.Y.C., 1963-72, Cath. Lists, Inc., Mt. Vernon, N.Y., 1965-72; pres. Cath. Lists, Inc., 1972-86; dir. Intertel (Prodns.) S.A., Brussels, 1961-63; Ofcl. del. Internat. Union Cath. Press ECOSOC, 1952-56; nat. council USO, 1956; bd. advisers Nat. Fund Raising Conf., 1968-69; bd. dirs. Our Sunday Visitor, Inc., 1968-86. Author: The Sacramentals, 1938, Prayers, 1939, Catholic Church in Colorado, 1943, (with Gregory Smith) Divine Love Story, 1941. Served with AUS, 1943-46. Recipient Disting. Service award Nat. Cath. Devel. Conf., 1984. Mem. Classroom Periodical Pubs. Assn. (chmn. 1950-57), Cath. Press Assn. (pres. 1954-56, St. Francis de Sales award 1987), Cath. Assn. Internat. Peace (v.p. 1953-59), Nat. Cath. Edn. Assn., C of C. Democrat. Home: 860 Grand Concourse Bronx NY 10451-2814 Office: 22 W 1st St Ste 511 Mount Vernon NY 10550-2600

MCNEILL, CORBIN ASAHEL, JR., utility executive; b. Santa Fe, July 6, 1939; s. Corbin Asahel and Madeline (Thielen) McN.; m. Dorice Schiller, June 16, 1962; children: Michele, Corbin IV, Kevin, Alicia, Timothy. BS in Marine Engring., U.S. Naval Acad., 1962; postgrad., Naval Nuclear Power Sch., Mare Island, Md., 1962-63, U. Calif., Berkeley, 1975-76, Syracuse U., 1983-84. Commd. ensign USN, 1962, advanced through grades to comdr.,

1981, ret., 1981; sr. v.p. nuclear generation N.Y. Power Authority, White Plains, 1981-85, Pub. Service Electric & Gas Co., Hancocks Bridge, N.J., 1985-88; exec. v.p. nuclear div. PECO Energy Co., 1988-90; pres., chief operating officer Phila. Electric Co., 1990—; pres. Adwin Equipment Co., Phila., 1990—. Trustee The Meml. Hosp. of Salem County (N.J.) Inc., 1986; chmn. TeamWalk March of Dimes, Salem, 1986; bd. dirs. Oswego (N.Y.) C. of C., 1982-83. Mem. Am. Nuclear Soc., Nuclear Utility Mgmt. and Resources Com. Avocation: skiing, reading. Office: PECO Energy Co PO Box 8699 Philadelphia PA 19101-8699*

MCNEILL, DANIEL RICHARD, writer; b. San Francisco, June 1, 1947; s. Daniel Harry and Maureen Evangeline (Sherriff) McN.; m. Rosalind Deborah Gold, Dec. 20, 1984. AB, U. Calif., Berkeley, 1975; JD, Harvard U., 1982. Author: Fuzzy Logic, 1993 (L.A. Times Book prize 1993). Mem. Authors Guild. Avocations: hiking, swimming. Home and Office: # 2 9905 Farragut Culver City CA 90232

MCNEILL, G. DAVID, psychologist, educator; b. Santa Rosa, Calif., Dec. 21, 1931; s. Glenn H. and Ethel G. (Little) McN.; m. Nobuko Baba, Dec. 17, 1957; children: Cheryl, Randall Baba. A.B., U. Calif. at Berkeley, 1953, Ph.D., 1962. Research fellow Harvard U., 1962-65; asst. prof. psychology U. Mich., 1965-66, assoc. prof., 1966-68; prof. psychology and linguistics U. Chgo., 1969—, chmn. dept. psychology, 1991—; mem. Inst. Advanced Study, Princeton, 1973-75; fellow Netherlands Inst. for Advanced Studies, 1983-84. Author: The Acquisition of Language, 1970, The Conceptual Basis of Language, 1979, Psycholinguistics: A New Approach, 1987, Gengo Shinrigaku, 1991 and Hand and Mind: What Gestures Reveal about Thought, 1992. Recipient Faculty achievement award Burlington No., 1991, ann. awards for excellence in pub. Assn. of Am. Pubs. for Hand and Mind, 1992, Gordon J. Laing award U. Chgo. Press, 1995; Guggenheim fellow, 1973-74; grantee NSF, 1983-89, Spencer Found., 1979-82, 89-92, NIDCD, 1992—; Fellow AAAS, Am. Psychol. Soc.; mem. Cognitive Sci. Soc., Linguistic Soc. Am., Violoncello Soc., Phi Beta Kappa, Sigma Xi. Office: U Chgo Dept Psychology 5848 S University Ave Chicago IL 60637-1515

MCNEILL, JOHN, museum administrator; b. Edinburgh, Scotland, U.K., Sept. 15, 1933; s. Thomas and Helen Lawrie (Eagle) McN.; m. Bridget Mariel Winterton, July 29, 1961 (div. 1990); children: Andrew Thomas, Douglas Paul; m. Marilyn Lois James, Apr. 6, 1990. BSc with honors, U. Edinburgh, 1955, PhD, 1960. Asst. lectr. dept. agrl. botany U. Reading, Eng., 1957-60, lectr. agrl. botany, 1960-61; lectr. dept. botany U. Liverpool, Eng., 1961-69; rsch. scientist Plant Rsch. Inst. Agriculture, Ottawa, Can., 1969-77; sr. rsch. scientist Biosystematics Rsch. Inst. Agr., Ottawa, Can., 1977-81; prof. dept. biology U. Ottawa, Can., 1981-87; regius keeper Royal Botanic Garden, Edinburgh, Scotland, 1987-89; assoc. dir. Royal Ont. Mus., Toronto, Can., 1989-90, acting dir., 1990-91, dir., 1991—; prof. dept. botany U. Toronto, Can., 1990—; curator herbarium U. Liverpool, 1964-69; dep. sr. tutor faculty sci., 1967-69; vis. assoc. prof. dept botany U. Wash., Seattle, 1969; acting assoc. prof. dept. population and environ. biology U. Calif., Irvine, 1969; chief taxonomy and econ. botany sect. Plant Rsch. Inst. Agriculture, Ottawa, Can., 1969-73; sessional lectr. dept. biology U. Ottawa, 1977, chmn. dept. biology, 1981-87, mem. faculty sci. teaching com., 1987, mem. univ. rsch. com., 1986-87, mem. univ. adv. com. on computing, 1984-87, mem. sch. grad. studies, adj. prof., 1987-91; vis. prof. dept. botany U. Toronto, 1978; adj. prof. dept. biology Carleton U., 1973-79; hon. prof. dept. botany U. Edinburgh, 1989, hon. fellow faculty sci., 1988-89; dir. George R. Gardiner Mus. Ceramic Art, Toronto, 1991—; pres. Royal Ont. Mus. Found., 1992—; contbr. to numerous sci. meetings throughout U.S., Can. Europe. Author: (with others) Grasses on Ontario, 1980, The Genus Atriplex (Chenopodiaceae) in Canada, 1983, Preliminary Inventory of Canadian Weeds, 1988; author book chpts.; editor: (with others) Phenetic and Phylogenetic Classification, 1964, International Code of Botanical Nomenclature, 1983, 88, 94, French edit., 1988, German edit., 1989, 95, Japanese edit., 1992; mem. editl. com. Flora of N.Am., 1985—; nomenclature advisor, 1987—; contbr. articles to profl. jours. NSERC Operating grantee, 1982-85, 1985-88, 1989-92. Fellow Linnean Soc. London; mem. Am. Soc. Naturalists, Am. Soc. Plant Taxonomists, Biol. Coun. Can. (v.p. 1984-85, v.p. and pres.-elect 1985-86, pres. 1986-87), Can. Coun. Univ. Biology Chmn. (v.p. 1983-84, pres. 1984-85, past pres. 1985-86), Botanical Soc. Brit. Isles, Botanical Soc. Edinburgh (v.p. 1987-89), Can. Botanical Assn. (chmn. systematics and phytogeography sect. 1981-83), Natural Scis. and Engring. Rsch. Coun. Can. (mem. population biology grant selection com. 1981-84), Classification Soc., Hennig Soc., Hunt Inst. Botanical Documentation, Internat. Union Biol. Scis. (voting mem. exec. 1985-88, alt. mem. exec. 1991—), Internat. Assn. Botanical and Mycological Socs. (sec. 1986-93, chmn. 1993—), Internat. Assn. Plant Taxonomy (coun. mem. 1981-87, 93—, adminstr. fin. 1987-93), Internat. Congress Systematic and Evolutionary Biology (mem. internat. com. 1980-90), Internat. Orgn. Plant Biosystematists (mem. coun. 1989-92), Annales Botanici Fennici (mem. adv. bd.), Acta Botanica Fennica, Internat. Assn. Botanical Gardens, Internat. Weed Sci. Soc., Orgn. for Phyto-Taxonomic Investigation of Mediterranean Area (dir. 1989—). Royal Caledonian Hort. Soc., Royal Hort. Soc., Soc. Systematic Biology, Systematics Assn. (mem. coun. 1959-62, 64-66, gen. sec. 1966-69), Ottawa Field Naturalists Club, Scottish Rock Garden Club. Office: Royal Ontario Museum, 100 Queen's Park, Toronto, ON Canada M5S 2C6

MCNEILL, JOHN HENDERSON, government official, lawyer; b. Phila., Jan. 31, 1941; s. John Henderson and Cecilia Marie (Murphy) McN.; m. Helen Elizabeth Foley, June 18, 1966; children: John Henderson IV, Bronwin Jane Foley, Andrew Patrick Joseph. BA, U. Notre Dame, 1962; JD, Villanova U., 1965; LLM, London Sch. Econs., 1971, PhD, 1974; diploma Hague Acad. Internat. Law, 1973. Bar: Pa. 1966, U.S. Supreme Ct. 1970, D.C. 1981. Assoc. Sheer & Mazzocone, Phila., 1966; asst. defender Defender Assn. Phila., 1966-67; law clk. to Hon. Wm. W. Vogel, Judge, Ct. Common Pleas, Montgomery County, Pa., 1969-70; internat. rels. officer ACDA, 1974-75, atty. adv., 1975-78, asst. gen. counsel, 1979-83; asst. gen. counsel internat. affairs and intelligence, U.S. Dept. Def., 1983-92, dep. gen. counsel internat. affairs and intelligence, 1992-93, acting gen. counsel, 1993, sr. dep. gen. counsel internat. affairs and intelligence, 1993—; legal adv. U.S. del. SALT, 1977-79, Intermediate Range Nuclear Forces Negotiations with USSR, 1981-82, Strategic Arms Reduction Talks with USSR, 1983, Dept. Def. rep. Maritime Boundary Talks with USSR, 1984-90; chmn. Dept. Def. Task Force on Law of the Sea Conv., 1994—; cons. Amnesty Internat., London, 1971-73, IAEA, Vienna, 1976, Ford Found., 1990; lectr. U. Notre Dame London Centre Legal Studies, 1973-74, Paul H. Nitze Sch. Advanced Internat. Studies Johns Hopkins U., Washington, 1994—; adj. prof. law Georgetown U., 1987—; Charles H. Stockton prof. internat. law U.S. Naval War Coll., 1990-91. Mem. editorial adv. bd. Internat. Legal Materials, 1992—; contbr. articles to profl. jours., including Am. Jour. Internat. Law. Bd. dirs. Crusade D.C. div. Am. Cancer Soc., 1976-77; bd. consultors Villanova U. Law Sch., 1978—; mem. internat. adv. com. John D. and Catherine T. MacArthur Found. Project on Governing Rules of Internat. Law, 1990-93. 2d lt. USAF, 1967-68. Career mem. U.S. Sr. Exec. Service, 1983—. Recipient Meritorious Honor award ACDA, 1979, Leadership Honor award Nat. Capital Area Combined Fed. Campaign, 1982; awarded rank of meritorious exec., U.S. Pres., 1987, 92; Centre Studies and Rsch. in Internat. Law and Internat. Rels., Hague Acad. Internat. Law scholar, 1974; London Sch. Econs. Internat. Law scholar, 1973. Mem. Am. Soc. Internat. Law. (exec. coun. 1986-89, exec. com. 1988-89), Coun. Fgn. Rels., Internat. Inst. Strategic Studies, Fed. Bar Assn., Inter-Am. Bar Assn., Internat. Law Assn., Cosmos Club (bd. mgmt. 1994—). Roman Catholic. Office: Pentagon Rm 3e963 Washington DC 20301

MCNEILL, JOHN HUGH, university dean; b. Chgo., July 5, 1938; s. John and Agnes Margaret (McLean) McN.; m. Sharon Keneffly, July 27, 1963; children: Sandra, Laurie. BS, U. Alta., Can., 1960, MS, 1962; PhD, U. Mich., 1967. Lectr. pharmacy Dalhousie U., 1962-63, U. Alta., 1963; research assoc. U. Mich., Ann Arbor, 1963-65, teaching fellow, 1965-66; asst. instr. Mich. State U., East Lansing, 1966-67, asst. prof., 1967-71; assoc. prof. U. B.C., 1971-72, assoc. prof. chmn. div. pharmacology and toxicology, 1972-75, dir. research and grad. studies Faculty Pharm. Scis., 1977-78, asst. dean, 1978-81, research dir. Med. Research Council, 1981-82, prof., assoc. dean research and grad. studies, 1982-84, dean Faculty Pharm. Scis., 1985—. Contbr. over 400 tech. articles to profl. jours. Mem. Pharm. Soc. Can. (various coms. 1974-88, council 1977-83, v.p. 1979, pres. 1980-81), Am. Soc. for Pharm. and Therapeutics (J.J. Abel award com. 1981, Upjohn award com., 1978-80, chmn. mem. com. 1983-86), Western Pharm. Soc. (council

1977-81, pres. 1979-80, past pres. 1980-81), N.Y. Acad. Scis., Internat. Soc. for Heart Research (council 1986—), AAAS, B.C. Coll. Pharms. (council 1985—), Internat. Union Pharmacologists (Can. rep. 1982-88), Am. Pharm. Assn., Can. Cardiovascular Soc. Office: The Univ of BC, The Faculty of Pharm Scis, 2146 East Mall, Vancouver, BC Canada V6T IZ3

MCNEILL, K(ENNETH) G(ORDON), medical physicist; b. Cheshire, Eng., Dec. 21, 1926; s. Ferguson and Elizabeth (Stevenson) McN.; m. J. Ruth S. Robertson, Nov. 6, 1959; 1 dau., Diane E.S. B.A., Oxford (Eng.) U., 1947, M.A., 1950, D.Phil. (Harmsworth Sr. scholar), 1950. Sir John Dill Meml. fellow Yale U., 1950-51; Nuffield research fellow Glasgow (Scotland) U., 1951-52, lectr., 1952-57; mem. faculty U. Toronto, Ont., Can., Can., 1957-92; prof. physics U. Toronto, Ont., Can., 1963-92, prof. medicine, 1969-92; spl. staff mem. Toronto Gen. Hosp., 1974-92; fellow Trinity Coll., Toronto, 1963-92, prof. emeritus, 1992—; mem. adv. com. radiation protection to Ministry Nat. Health and Welfare, 1964-68; mem. nuclear accident contingency planning bd. Govt. of Ont., 1974—; hon. prof. Monash U., Melbourne, 1988; pres. Kishmul Resources Inc. Author: (with J. Maclachlan, P.T. Spencer, J. Bell) Matter and Energy, 1963, 3d edit., 1987, French edit., 1981; contbr. numerous articles to profl. jours. Mem. governing coun. U. Toronto, 1980-86, 89-92. Fellow Instn. Nuclear Engrs. (U.K.); mem. Can. Assn. Physicists, Can. Radiation Protection Assn. Research on low energy nuclear physics and med. physics. Home: 70 Rathnelly Ave, Toronto, ON Canada M4V 2M6

MCNEILL, ROBERT PATRICK, investment counselor; b. Chgo., Mar. 17, 1941; s. Donald Thomas and Katherine (Bennett) McN.; m. Martha Stephan, Sept. 12, 1964; children—Jennifer, Donald, Victoria, Stephan, Elizabeth. B.A. summa cum laude (valedictorian), U. Notre Dame, 1963; M.Letters, Oxford (Eng.) U., 1967. Chartered investment counselor. Assoc. Stein Roe & Farnham, Chgo., 1967-72, gen. ptnr., 1972-77, sr. ptnr., 1977-86, exec. v.p., 1986-89; pres., mng. dir. Stein Roe Internat., Chgo., 1989—; underwriting mem. Lloyds of London, 1980—; dir. Comml. Chgo. Corp.; vice chmn. bd. Hill Internat. Prodn. Co., Houston, 1982—; dir., adv. bd. Touche Remnant Investment Counselors, London, 1983—; dir. TR Worldwide Strategy Fund, Luxembourg, Konrad Adenauer Fund for European Policy Studies, Fed. Republic Germany. Voting mem., sec Ill. Rhodes Scholarship Selection Com.; voting mem. Ill. rep. Great Lakes Dist. Rhodes Scholarship Selection Com.; bd. dirs. Kennedy Sch. for Retarded Children, Palos Park, Ill., 1972—, Winnetka United Way, Ill., 1984—, division St. YMCA, Chgo., 1972—; assoc. Rush-Presbyterian-St. Lukes Med. Ctr., Chgo., 1975—; mem. leadership com. Rush Alzheimer's Disease Ctr. Rhodes scholar, 1963. Fellow Fin. Analysts Fedn.; mem. Chgo. Council on Fgn. Relations (bd. dirs., treas. 1975—), Inst. European Studies (bd. govs., vice-chmn. 1981—), Investment Analysts Soc. Chgo. (chgo. com., com. on fgn. affairs, com. on internat. and domestic issues), Assn. for Investment Mgmt. and Rsch., Chgo. Soc. Clubs, Econ. Club of Chgo, Sunset Ridge Country (bd. dirs. Northfield, Ill. 1989—). Avocations: coin collecting; bridge; golf; skiing; art. Office: 1 S Wacker Dr Chicago IL 60606-4614

MCNEILL, THOMAS B., lawyer; b. Chgo., Oct. 28, 1934; s. Donald T. and Katherine M. (Bennett) McN.; m. Ingrid Sieder, May 11, 1963; children: Christine, Thomas, Stephanie. B.A., U. Notre Dame, 1956, J.D., 1958. Ptnr. Mayer, Brown & Platt, Chgo., 1962—; dir. Deltona Corp., Miami, Fla. Served to capt. JAGC USAF, 1959-62. Mem. Chgo. Bar Assn., Chgo. Council Lawyers, Law Club Chgo., Legal Club Chgo. Club: Indian Hill (Winnetka, Ill.). Home: 930 Fisher Ln Winnetka IL 60093-1563 Office: Mayer Brown & Platt 190 S La Salle St Chicago IL 60603-3410

MCNEILL, THOMAS RAY, lawyer; b. Pitts., June 2, 1952; s. Thomas William McNeill and Mary (Shively) Hiss; m. Patsy Lynch, June 25, 1977; children: Elizabeth, Kathleen, Thomas. BSBA, U. Fla., 1974; JD, Emory U., 1977. Bar: Ga. 1977, U.S. Dist. Ct. (no. dist.) Ga. 1977. Assoc. Powell, Goldstein, Frazer & Murphy, Atlanta, 1977-84, ptnr., 1984—, mgr. corp. dept., 1993—. Mem. Ga. Bar Assn., Emory U. Alumni Assn. (pres. exec. com. Atlanta chpt. 1988-89, co-chmn. barristers com. Atlanta chpt.), Beta Gamma Sigma. Office: Powell Goldstein Frazer & Murphy Ste 1600 191 Peachtree St Atlanta GA 30303-1741

MCNEILL, WILLIAM, environmental scientist; b. Evanston, Ill., Jan. 1, 1930; s. John and Ebba Katrina (Hansen) McN.; m. Caryl Mook, June 15, 1951 (dec. 1969); children: Elizabeth Marie, Charles Craig, Margaret Ruth; m. Caecilia Cinquanto, Oct. 10, 1970. BA, Colgate U., 1951; MA, Temple U., 1955, PhD, 1961. Chief phys. chemistry br. Frankford Arsenal U.S. Army, Phila., 1955-70, dir. applied sci., 1970-75; chief scientist, environ. mgr. Rocky Mountain Arsenal U.S. Army, Denver, 1975-80, dir. tech. ops., 1980-85; gen. mgr. Battelle Denver Ops., 1985-88; sr. tech. adviser Sci. Applications Internat. Corp., Golden, Colo., 1989-92; dir. tech. devel. Sci. Applications Internat. Corp., Oak Ridge, Tenn., 1992—; mem. materials adv. bd. ceramics Nat. Acad. Sci./Nat. Rsch. Coun., Washington, 1966; mem. Gov.'s Task Group on Rocky Mountain Arsenal, 1976, Colo. Pollution Prevention Adv. Bd., Denver, 1991—. Contbr. articles to Jour. Che. Physics, Applied Physics Letters, other profl. publs. Mem. Am. Chem. Soc.,Hazardous Material Control Rsch. Inst., Air and Waste Mgmt. Assn. Achievements include 10 patents for electrochemical processes, inorganic materials sythesis, electro-optical devices; demonstration and use of narrow-band optical absorbers for laser protection; leader in development of Army environmental programs. Home: 319 Cliffrose Ct Lafayette CO 80026

MC NEILL, WILLIAM HARDY, retired history educator, writer; b. Vancouver, B.C., Can., Oct. 31, 1917; s. John Thomas and Netta (Hardy) McN.; m. Elizabeth Darbishire, Sept. 7, 1946; children: Ruth Netta, Deborah Joan, John Robert, Andrew Duncan. B.A., U. Chgo., 1938, M.A., 1939; Ph.D., Cornell U., 1947; 18 hon. degrees. Faculty U. Chgo., 1947-87, prof. history, 1957-87, Robert A. Millikan Disting. Svc. prof., 1969-87, prof. emeritus, 1987—, chmn. dept., 1961-67; pres. Demos Found., 1980-86, chmn. bd., 1980-86; George Eastman vis. prof. Oxford (Eng.) U., 1980-81. Author: Greek Dilemma, War and Aftermath, 1947, Report on the Greeks, 1948, History Handbook of Western Civilization, 1948, rev. and enlarged 6th edit., 1986, America, Britain and Russia, Their Cooperation and Conflict, 1941-46, 1953, Past and Future, 1954, Greece: American Aid in Action, 1947-56, 1957, Rise of the West: A History of the Human Community, 1963, 9th edit., 1991 (Nat. Book award, Gordon J. Laing prize), Europe's Steppe Frontier, 1500-1800, 1964, A World History, 1967, 3d edit., 1979, The Contemporary World, 1967, 2d edit., 1975, The Ecumene: Story of Humanity, 1973, Venice, the Hinge of Europe, 1081-1797, 1974, The Shape of European History, 1974, Plagues and Peoples, 1976, Metamorphosis of Greece since World War II, 1978, The Human Condition, An Ecological and Historical View, 1980, Pursuit of Power, 1982, The Great Frontier, 1983, Mythistory and other Essays, 1986, A History of the Human Community, 1986, Polyethnicity and National Unity in World History, 1987, Arnold J. Toynbee: A Life, 1989, Population and Politics Since 1750, 1990, Hutchins' University: A Memoir of the University of Chicago 1929-50, 1991, The Global Tradition: Conquerors, Catastrophies and Community, 1992, Keeping Together in Time: Dance & Drill in Human History, 1995; editor: Lord Acton, Essays in the Liberal Interpretation of History, 1967, (with others) Readings in World History, Vols. I-X, 1968-73, Human Migration, 1978, Jour. Modern History, 1971-79, Jour. Modern Greek Studies, 1983-85; bd. editors Ency. Brit., 1981—; contbr. numerous articles and reviews to profl. jours., chpts. to books. Trustee Athens Coll., 1970-88; vice chmn. Christopher Columbus Quincentenary Jubilee Commn., 1985-93; co-chair curriculum task force Nat. Commn. on Social Studies, 1987-89; mem. Bradley Commn. on the Teaching of History, 1986-89; vice chmn. Nat. Coun. for History Edn., 1990-94, Nat. Coun. for History Standards, 1992-94. Fulbright Research scholar Royal Inst. Internat. Affairs, Eng., 1950-51; Rockefeller grantee, 1951-52; Ford Faculty fellow, 1954-55; Carnegie grantee, 1957-62, 63-64; Guggenheim fellow, 1971-72, 86-87; Josiah H. Macy grantee, 1973-74; Rockefeller grantee, 1976. Fellow Am. Philos. Soc., Am. Acad. Arts and Scis., Brit. Acad. Arts and Scis. (corr.), Royal Hist. Soc. (corr.); mem. Am. Hist. Assn. (council, del. Am. Council Learned Socs., pres. 1985). Office: PO Box 45 Colebrook CT 06021-0045

MCNELLY, JOHN TAYLOR, journalist, educator; b. Lancaster, Wis., Oct. 2, 1923; s. Stephen Sumner and Caroline Hurd (Taylor) McN.; m. Pamela Edith Thompson, Dec. 20, 1952; children: Barbara, Duncan. B.A., U. Wis., 1946, M.A., 1957; Ph.D., Mich. State U., 1961. Reporter AP, Milw., 1948-

52, Reuters, London, 1952-53; news editor U. Wis. News Service, Madison, 1957; instr., then assoc. prof. Mich. State U., East Lansing, 1957-66; assoc. prof., then prof. U. Wis., Madison, 1966-82, Evjue-Bascom prof., 1982-88, prof. emeritus, 1988—; asst. dir. Inter-Am. Mass Communications Program, San Jose, Costa Rica, 1961-62; vis. prof. Berlin Inst. Mass. Communication in Developing Nations, W.Ger., 1965, Agrarian U., Lima, Peru, 1968-69; communication cons. UNESCO, Latin Am., 1970-75; lectr. USIA, Latin Am., 1968, 74, 80. Co-author: Communication and Social Change in Latin America, 1968; assoc. editor: Journalism Quar., 1975-77; contbr. monographs and articles to communication publs. Served with USAF, 1942-43. Fulbright-Hays Faculty fellow Lima, Peru, 1968-69. Home: 134 Larkin St Madison WI 53705-5116

MCNEMAR, DONALD WILLIAM, consultant, headmaster; b. Wilmington, Ohio, June 1, 1943; s. Robert Arthur and Kathryn (Hunt) McN.; m. Britta Schein, Aug. 18, 1968; children—Heather Osborn, Galen Rebecca. B.A., Earlham Coll., Richmond, Ind., 1965; Ph.D., Princeton U., 1971. Asst. prof., then asso. prof. govt. Dartmouth Coll., 1970-81, assoc. dean faculty social scis., 1978-81; headmaster Phillips Acad., Andover, Mass. 1981-94; cons. Conflict Mgmt. Group, Cambridge, Mass., 1994—. Mem. exec. com. N.H. Council World Affairs, 1975-81; com. mem. Quaker office UN, 1978-82; trustee School Year Abroad, 1981-94, Prep for Prep, 1988-94, Earlham Coll., 1990—, Northfield Mt. Hermon Sch., 1994—. Danforth fellow, 1965-69. Regional adv. bd. BayBank, 1981-94. Home: 65 Bay State Rd Apt 5 Boston MA 02215-1808 Office: Phillips Acad Andover MA 01810

MC NERNEY, WALTER JAMES, health policy educator, consultant; b. New Haven, June 8, 1925; s. Robert Francis and Anna Gertrude (Shanley) McN.; m. Shirley Ann Hamilton, June 26, 1948; children: Walter James, Peter Hamilton, Jennifer Allison, Daniel Martin, Richard Hamilton. B.S., Yale U., 1947; M.H.A., U. Minn., 1950. Research asst. Labor-Mgmt. Center, Yale U., 1947; instr. advanced math. Hopkins Prep. Sch., New Haven, 1947-48; adminstrv. resident R.I. Hosp., Providence, 1949-50; asst. to coordinator Hosp. and Clinics of Med. Center, U. Pitts., 1950-53; also instr., then asst. prof. hosp. adminstrn. at univ. Grad. Sch. Pub. Health, U. Pitts., 1953-55; assoc. prof., dir. program hosp. adminstrn. Sch. Bus. Adminstrn., U. Mich., 1955-58; prof., dir. Bur. Hosp. Adminstrn., 1958-61; pres. Blue Cross Assn., Chgo., 1961-77; pres., chief exec. officer Blue Cross and Blue Shield Assns., Chgo., 1977-81; Herman Smith prof. health policy Grad. Sch. Mgmt., Northwestern U., 1982—; cons. in field, 1982—; mem. Nat. Coun. on Health Planning and Devel., HEW, 1976-82; mem. bd. dirs. Nat. Health Coun., 1963-77, pres., 1972-73; mem. nat. commn. on cost of med. care AMA, 1977, mem. com. on pvt. philanthropy, 1977-78; past pres. Internat. Fedn. Vol. Health Svc. Funds; mem. devel. com. Yale U.; trustee Nat. Exec. Svc. Corps; chmn. task force on Medicaid and related programs HEW, 1969-70; charter mem. Inst. Medicine-NAS, chmn. bd. on health care svcs., chmn. bd. on spl. initiatives; mem. physician payment rev. commn. U.S. Congress, Dept. Vets.' Affairs; mem. Commn. on the Future Structure of Vets. Health Care; mem. coal commn. U.S. Dept. Labor; mem. nat. adv. coun. for health care policy, rsch. and evaluation HHS; bd dirs. Stanley Works, Medicus, Value Health Inc., Nellcor Inc., Osteo Tech., Ventritex, Inc., Hanger Orthopedics Group Inc.; chmn. bd. McNerney Heintz, Inc., Am. Health Properties Inc.; adv. coun. to dean Yale U.Med. Sch.; vis. com. U. Mich. Med. Ctr., adv. coun. chmn. Agency for Health Care Policy and Rsch., chmn. bd. trustees Med. Outcomes Trust. Author: Hospital and Medical Economics, 1962, Regionalization and Rural Health Care, 1962; contbr. articles to profl. jours. Mem. Pres.' Com. on Health Edn., 1972-73; trustee Hosp. Research and Ednl. Trust. Inst. for Future; vis. com. Harvard Med. and Dental Schs. Served to lt. (j.g.) USNR, 1943-46. Named 1 of 100 most important young men and women in U.S. by Life Mag., 1962; recipient Justin Ford Kimball award Am. Hosp. Assn., 1967; Outstanding Achievement award U. Minn., 1970; sec.'s unit citation HEW, 1970; recipient Yale medal, 1979, award for meritorious service AMA, 1981, award of honor Am. Hosp. Assn., 1982; Nuffield Provincial Hosps. Trust-Kings Fund (Eng.) fellow, 1970. Fellow Am. Pub. Health Assn., Am. Coll. Hosp. Adminstrs. (Silver medal 1978); mem. Am. Mgmt. Assn. (dir., trustee), Royal Soc. Health, Sigma Xi, Delta Sigma Pi. Clubs: Commonwealth, Yale (N.Y.C.). Office: Northwestern U Grad Sch Mgmt 2001 Sheridan Rd Evanston IL 60208-0814

MC NEW, BENNIE BANKS, economics and finance educator; b. Greenbrier, Ark., Nov. 12, 1931; s. Roland H. and Stella (Avery) McN.; m. Bonnie Lou Stone, Mar. 31, 1956; children—Bonnie Banks, Mary Kathleen, William Michael. B.S., Ark. State Tchrs. Coll., 1953; M.B.A., U. Ark., 1954; Ph.D., U. Tex., 1961. Asst. nat. bank examiner, 1954-56; indsl. specialist U. Ark. Indsl. Research and Extension Center, 1956-59; lectr. finance U. Tex., 1959-61; prof. banking U. Miss., University, 1961-65; dean U. Miss. (Sch. Bus. Adminstrn.), 1965-79, Sch. Bus., Middle Tenn. State U., Murfreesboro, 1980-88; prof. econs. and fin. U. Cen. Ark., Conway, 1988—; asst. dir., v.p Grad. Sch. Banking of South, La. State U., 1966—. Author: (with Charles L. Prather) Fraud Control for Commercial Banks, 1962; contbg. author: Money and Banking Casebook, 1966, The Bankers Handbook, 1966, A History of Mississippi, 1973. Served with AUS, 1950-51. Mem. Southwestern Fin. Assn., So. Fin. Assn., Fin. Execs. Inst., Beta Gamma Sigma, Delta Pi Epsilon, Delta Sigma Pi, Omicron Delta Kappa, Phi Kappa Phi, Lions (pres. Oxford, Miss. 1964-65). Home: 12 Bainbridge Dr Conway AR 72032-7217 Office: Univ Central Arkansas PO Box 5025 Conway AR 72035

MCNICHOLAS, DAVID PAUL, automobile rental company executive; b. Youngstown, Ohio, Mar. 1, 1941; s. Paul James and Mary Frances (Dignan) McN.; m. Patricia Marie McAtee; children: Paula, John, Catherine, Tim, Dan. BBA, Youngstown State U., 1962. With Youngstown Sheet and Tube Co. (now subs. LTV), 1964-78, from trainee to dir. data processing; with Avis Inc., N.Y.C., 1978—, sr. v.p., 1985-90, exec. v.p., 1990—, also bd. dirs.; bd. dirs. Ohio Franchise Operater, Inc., Cilva Holding Ltd. Office: Avis Inc 900 Old Country Rd Garden City NY 11530-2128

MCNICHOLAS, KATHLEEN WINIFRED, cardiac surgeon; b. Phila., May 5, 1948; d. Edward M. and Josephine (Nalazek) McN. BS with honors, Chestnut Hill Coll., 1969; MD magna cum laude, Thomas Jefferson U., 1973. Diplomate Am. Bd. Surgery, Am. Bd. Thoracic Surgery. Intern Presbyn. Hosp., N.Y.C., 1973-74, resident in gen. surgery, 1974-78, resident and chief resident thoracic and cardiovascular surgery, 1978-80; surg. ho. officer Hosp. for Sick Children, London, 1976, sr. registrar thoracic unit, 1980; attending physician United Hosp. Med. Ctr., 1981; attending physician Deborah Heart and Lung Ctr., Brown Mills, N.J., 1981-85, dir. dept. pediats. thoracic and cardiovascular surgery, 1983-85, dir. pediat. ICU, 1983-85; attending physician dept. surgery sect. cardiovascular surgery Christiana Hosp., Newark, Del., 1986—, dir. pediat. cardiac surgery, 1987—; clin. asst. prof. Rutgers Med. Sch., Piscataway, N.J., 1984—; clin. assoc. prof. Med. Coll. Pa., Phila., 1987—; attending physician dept. surgery sect. cardiovascular surgery Grad. Hosp., Phila., 1985—, A.I. duPont Inst., Wilmington, Del., 1986—; presenter in field. Contbr. articles to profl. jours. Montgomery County Med. Soc. scholar, 1969-73. Fellow ACS, Am. Coll. Cardiology, Am. Coll. Chest Physicians, Am. Coll. Angiology (mem. sci. coun.); mem. AMA, Am. Heart Assn. (mem. coun. cardiovascular surgery), Pa. Assn. Thoracic Surgery, Pa. Acad. Cardiology, Pa. Acad. Cardiovascular Perfusion, Pa. Med. Soc., Del. Acad. Pediats., Del. Med. Soc., N.J. Soc. Thoracic Surgeons, Burlington Med. Soc., Assn. Women Surgeons, Acad. Medicine N.J., Colls. Phila. County Med. Soc., Hobart A. Hare Honor Med. Soc., John H. Gibbon Jr. Surg. Soc., Soc. Heart Transplantation, Soc. Thoracic Surgery. Roman Catholic. Avocations: sports, reading. Home: 4 Rockland Mills Rockland DE 19732 Office: Med Arts Pavilion 4745 Stanton-Ogletown Rd Ste 2 Newark DE 19713-2070

MCNICHOLS, GERALD ROBERT, consulting company executive; b. Cleve., Nov. 21, 1943; s. Charles Wellington and June Beatrice (Kalal) McN.; m. Paula Kay Austin, Dec. 26, 1964; children: G. Robert Jr., Kay Lynn, Melissa Sue. BS with honors, Case-Western Res. U., 1965; MS, U. Pa., 1966; ScD, George Washington U., 1976. Cert. cost estimator/analyst. Sr. ops. analyst Office of Sec., Dept. of Def., Washington, 1966-70; v.p. GenTech, Inc., Bethesda, Md., 1976-77, J. Watson Noah, Inc., Falls Church, Va., 1977-78; pres., chief exec. officer Mgmt. Cons. and Rsch., Inc., Falls Church, 1978—. Co-author: Operations Research for Decision Making, 1975; editor Cost Analysis, 1984; contbr. articles to profl. jours. Pres. Rondelay Civic Assn., Fairfax Sta., Va., 1985-87. Capt. USAF, 1966-70.

Mem. Inst. Cost Analysis (pres. 1985-88), Internat. Soc. Parametric Analysts (bd. dirs. 1982-84), Ops. Rsch. Soc. Am. (chmn. mil. applications sect.), Mil. Ops. Rsch. Soc. (sec., treas. 1986-87, v.p adminstrn. 1987-88, bd. dirs. 1985-88, 92—), Soc. Cost Estimating and Analysis (bd. dirs. 1990-93). Home: 8133 Rondelay Ln Fairfax VA 22039-2305 Office: Mgmt Cons & Rsch Inc 5113 Leesburg Pike Ste 509 Falls Church VA 22041-3204

MCNICOL, DAVID LEON, federal official; b. South Gate, Calif., May 18, 1944; s. Charles D. and Mary W. (Heisel) McN.; m. Lore Anne Long, Mar. 25, 1967; children: Katharine Anne, Elizabeth Mary. BA magna cum laude, Harvard U., 1966; MS, MIT, 1968, PhD, 1973. Asst. prof. econs. U. Pa., Phila., 1971-75; sr. staff economist Pres.'s Coun. of Econ. Advisors, Washington, 1976; vis. assoc. prof. econs. Calif. Inst. Tech., Pasadena, 1976-77; sr. economist Office of the Sec., U.S. Dept. of Treasury, Washington, 1977-79; dir. Office of Econ. Analysis U.S. Dept. Energy, Washington, 1980-81, dep. asst. adminstr. Office of Applied Analysis, 1981-82; dir. Econ. Analysis and Resource Planning Div. Office of Sec. of Def., Office of Program Analysis and Evaluation, Washington, 1982-88, dep. asst. sec., dep. dir., 1988—, chmn. cost analysis improvement group, 1988—. Author over 20 publs. on commodity markets, regulatory econs., energy issues and econ. aspects of the U.S. def. program. Recipient Spl. Svc. award Dept. Energy, 1981, Presdl. Rank award U.S. Govt., 1988, 93, Disting Civilian Svc. medal Dept. Def., 1988, 91, 93. Mem. Am. Econ. Assn., Harvard Club of Washington. Home: 6901 Pineway Univ Park MD 20782-1163 Office: Dept Def OSD: PA&E The Pentagon Washington DC 20301

MC NICOL, DONALD EDWARD, lawyer; b. Kew Gardens, N.Y., Aug. 11, 1921; s. William J. and Margaret (McGirr) McN.; m. Carmen Gallego, July 10, 1988; children: Elaine McNicol Postley, Janet McNicol Barton, Donald Edward, Paul Mansfield, Andrea Gallego. AB, Harvard U., 1942, LLB, 1948. Bar: N.Y. 1949. Asso. Davis, Polk, Wardwell, Sunderland & Kiendl. N.Y.C. 1948-54; assoc. Hall, Haywood, Patterson & Taylor, N.Y.C., 1954-56; ptnr. Hall, McNicol, Hamilton & Clark, 1956-92; of counsel Keck, Mahin & Cate, N.Y.C., 1992—; bd. dirs. Thomas Pub. Co., Bank of Westbury. Trustee Boys and Girls Club Am. Served with AUS, 1942-46. Mem. Assn. Bar City N.Y., Harvard Club (bd. mgrs. N.Y.C. 1967-69). Home: 461 Berry Hill Rd Syosset NY 11791-1117 Office: Keck Mahin & Cate 220 E 42nd St New York NY 10017-5806

MC NITT, WILLARD CHARLES, business executive; b. Chgo., June 6, 1920; s. Willard C. and Louise (Richardson) McN.; m. Charlotte D. Boyd, Sept. 14, 1946; children: Willard Charles, James D., Peter B. McNitt. B.A., Amherst Coll., 1942; A.M., Harvard Grad. Sch. Bus. Adminstrn., 1942; student, Northwestern Grad. Sch. Bus. Adminstrn., U. Chgo. Sch. Bus. Adminstrn., 1947. Asst. market planning and research Foote, Cone & Belding Co., Chgo., 1946-47; asst. sales promotion and advt. Bell & Gosset Co., Morton Grove, Ill., 1947-48; v.p. sales and mktg. Bowes Industries, Inc., Chgo., 1948-54; gen. mgr. sales and mktg. Clayton Mark & Co., Evanston, Ill., 1954-58; pres., dir. Bowey's. Inc., Chgo., 1958-62; pres., dir. mem. exec. com. H.M. Byllesby Co., Chgo., 1962-63; group v.p., dir. Consol. Foods Corp., Chgo., 1963-67; exec. v.p. consumer products group W.R. Grace & Co., N.Y.C., 1967-72; exec. v.p., dir., mem. exec. com. Ward Foods, Inc., Wilmette, Ill., 1972-73; chief operating officer, pres., dir., mem. exec. com. Ward Foods, Inc., 1973-76; pres., chief exec. officer, dir. Westgate-Calif. Corp., and Sun Harbor Industries, San Diego, 1977-80; pres., chief exec. officer Nalley's Fine Foods, Tacoma, 1980-83; chmn., dir. Joseph Magnin Inc., 1982-85; chmn. Blue Moon Cheese Co., Thorpe, Wis., 1983—; operating ptnr. Wallner & Co., La Jolla, Calif.; vice chmn., pres., chief exec. officer, dir., mem. exec. com. Foremost Dairies, Inc., San Francisco, 1983-85; chmn. Epcom; bd. dirs. ATI, NCIC, Blue Moon Cheese, Del. Lightweight. Troop head local Boy Scouts Am., 1957-67. Served to lt. (s.g.) USNR, 1942-46. Mem. Executives Club (Chgo.), Amherst Club, Harvard Bus. Sch. Club (Chgo., N.Y.C.), Indian Hill Country Club (Winnetka), Dairymen's Club (Boulder Junction, Wis.), Rancho Santa Fe Country Club, Fairbanks Ranch Country Club (Rancho Santa Fe), Rio Mar Country Club (Vero Beach, Fla.), Chi Psi. Republican. Congregationalist. Address: Victoria 1630 Sheridan Rd Apt 2C Wilmette IL 60091-1888

MCNULTY, CARRELL STEWART, JR., manufacturing company executive, architect; b. Newark, Dec. 4, 1924; s. Carrell Stewart and Marjorie (Yaegerlehner) McN.; m. Barbara Brokaw, June 21, 1952; children: Peter Carrell, Susan Abigail. Student, Emory U., 1941-43, U. N.C., 1943-44; BArch, Columbia U., 1950, MS in Urban Planning, 1963. Registered architect, Pa. Assoc. SMS Architects, Stamford, Conn., 1950-58, gen. ptnr., 1958-73; pvt. practice architecture Weston, Conn., 1973-76; pres. CMW Co., Weston, 1975-77, NB Products, Inc., Horsham, Pa., 1976-94, NB Instruments, Inc., Horsham, 1993-93, Environ. Svcs. and Products, Inc., Horsham, 1994—; mem. Conn. Soc. Architects, 1963-73, sec., 1964-67, pres., 1969-70. Chairperson S.W. Regional Planning Agy., Norwalk, Conn., 1967-71; mem. Gov.'s Com. on Environ., New Haven, 1970, chairperson Gov.'s Task Force on Housing, Norwalk, 1972; bd. dirs. sec. Habitat for Humanity of Greater Bucks, Doylestown, Pa., 1990—. Lt. (j.g.) USNR, 1943-46; PTO. Recipient citation Am. Assn. Sch. Adminstrs., 1960, 6th Biennial Design award HUD, 1973; grantee HUD, Housing Rsch., 1970. Fellow AIA (mem. urban design com. 1963-73, chmn. 1971); mem. Water Pollution Control Fedn., Bucks County Choral Soc., Sigma Nu. Democrat. Mem. United Ch. of Christ (deacon 1965-71, elder 1989-92). Avocations: computers, model building, choral music. Home: Century House # 234 303 W State St Doylestown PA 18901-3559 Office: Environ Svcs and Products Inc 903 Sheehy Dr Horsham PA 19044-1231

MCNULTY, CHESTER HOWARD, bank holding company executive; b. Melbourne, Fla., Dec. 12, 1935; s. Chester H. and Jennie (Lassan) McN.; m. Sylvia Maxwell, July 20, 1957; children—Thad, Laurie, Paul, Shannon. B.S. in Bus. Adminstrn, U. Fla., 1957, J.D, 1964. Bar: Fla. bar 1965. Vice pres. Fla. State Bank of Sanford, 1957-60, pres., 1966-74; pres. 1st State Bank of Ft. Meade, Fla., 1960-62; asso. firm Bentley, Miller, Sinder, Carr, Chiles & Ellsworth, Lakeland, Fla., 1965; pres. Flagship Banks, Inc., Miami Beach, Fla., 1974-76, vice chmn., 1976-77, exec. v.p., 1977-84; vice chmn. Sun Bank N.A., 1984-86; pres., chief exec. officer The Enterprise Bank N.A., Winter Park, Fla., 1986-93; retired. Home: 530 E Central Blvd Apt 1902 Orlando FL 32801-4306

MCNULTY, DERMOT, public relations executive; b. Dublin, Ireland, Mar. 11, 1949; s. William J. and Margaret M. (Reigh) McN.; m. Paula Ann Gaber, 1977. BA in Journalism, Marquette U., 1971. Sr. v.p. Burson Marsteller, Hong Kong, 1985-87, Cohn & Wolfe, N.Y.C., 1987-88; exec. v.p. Burson Marsteller, N.Y.C., 1988-89, Shandwick N.Am., N.Y.C., 1989-90; dir. internat. mktg. Shandwick plc, London, 1990-91, COO, 1991-94, CEO, 1994—, also bd. dirs. Avocations: arts, golf, tennis. Office: 61 Grosvenor St, London W1X 9DA, England

MCNULTY, HENRY BRYANT, journalist; b. Hartford, Conn., May 6, 1947; s. J. Bard and Marjorie (Grant) McN.; m. Anne Margaret Schneider, Sept. 7, 1985; 1 child, Frederick Gardiner Bard McNulty. B.A. in English, Cornell U., 1969. Op-Ed editor Hartford Courant, Conn., 1976-78, features editor, 1978-84, assoc. editor, 1984-95, town editorials editor, 1995—. Contbg. author: The British Invasion, 1982. Mem. Orgn. News Ombudsmen (bd. dirs., v.p., pres.), Soc. Decendents of Founders of Hartford, Cornell Club (N.Y.).

MCNULTY, JOHN KENT, lawyer, educator; b. Buffalo, Oct. 13, 1934; s. Robert William and Margaret Ellen (Duthie) McN.; m. Linda Conner, Aug. 20, 1955 (div. Feb. 1977); children: Martha Jane, Jennifer, John K. Jr.; m. Babette B. Barton, Mar. 23, 1978 (div. May 1988). A.B. with high honors, Swarthmore Coll., 1956; LL.B., Yale U., 1959. Bar: Ohio 1961, U.S. Supreme Ct. 1964. Law clk. Justice Hugo L. Black, U.S. Supreme Ct., Washington, 1959-60; vis. prof. Sch. Law U. Tex., summer 1960, Yale U., fall 1990; assoc. Jones, Day, Cockley & Reavis, Cleve., 1960-64; prof. law U. Calif., Berkeley, 1964-91, Roger J. Traynor prof. law, 1991—; of counsel Baker and McKenzie, San Francisco, 1974-75; acad. visitor London Sch. Econs., 1985, Cambridge U., 1994, U. Edinburgh, 1994; vis. fellow Wolfson Coll., Cambridge, 1994; lectr. univs. Cologne, Hamburg, Kansei, Kyoto, London, Munich, Seoul, Tokyo, Tilburg, Amsterdam, Rotterdam, Vienna, Tohoku, Tübingen, others; mem. adv. bd. Carolina Acad. Press and Tax Mgmt. Author: Federal Income Taxation of Individuals, 5th edit., 1995,

Federal Estate and Gift Taxation, 5th edit., 1994, Federal Income Taxation of S Corporations, 1992. Guggenheim fellow, 1977. Mem. Am. Bar Assn., Am. Law Inst., Internat. Fiscal Assn. (council U.S. br.), Internat. Tax and Bus. Lawyer (mem. bd. overseers), Order of Coif, Phi Beta Kappa. Home: 1176 Grizzly Peak Blvd Berkeley CA 94708-1741 Office: U Calif Sch Law 389 Boalt Hall Berkeley CA 94720

MCNULTY, JOHN WILLIAM, retired public relations executive, automobile company executive; b. N.Y.C., June 29, 1927; s. Christopher and Margaret (Kennedy) McN.; m. Margaret Rose Cooney, Nov. 11, 1950 (dec. Aug. 1978); children: Suellen McNulty Kinna, Jean McNulty Crocker, John, Peter, Jodi Wyatt Phelan, Russell Wyatt; m. Jean Fayette Winslow, Sept. 6, 1980. BS, Fordham U., 1949. Dir. pub. relations Lincoln Ctr., N.Y.C., 1958-63; assoc. John D. Rockefeller 3rd, N.Y.C., 1963-66; asst. to Pres. Lyndon B. Johnson, Washington, 1966-68; exec. asst. to vice chmn., 1974-76, pub. affairs coord., 1976-77, dir. corp. comm., 1977-79, v.p. pub. rels., 1979-90, ret., 1990. Trustee Nat. Racing Mus., Saratoga. Served with USN, 1945-46, PTO. Recipient Communications Achievement award Fordham U., 1977. Mem. Kenwood Club, Orchard Lake Country Club. Democrat. Home: 1071 Celestial St Cincinnati OH 45202

MCNULTY, MATTHEW FRANCIS, JR., health sciences and health services administrator, educator, university administrator, consultant, horse and cattle breeder; b. Elizabeth, N.J., Nov. 26, 1914; s. Matthew Francis and Abby Helen (Dwyer) McN.; m. Mary Nell Johnson, May 4, 1946; children: Matthew Francis III, Mary Lauren. BS, St. Peter's Coll., 1938, DHL (hon.), 1978; postgrad., Rutgers U. Law Sch., 1939-41; grad., Officer Candidate Sch., U.S. Army, 1941, U.S. Army Staff and Command Sch., Ft. Leavenworth, 1945; MHA, Northwestern U., 1949; MPH, U. N.C., 1952; ScD (hon.), U. Ala., 1969, Georgetown U., 1986. Contract writer, mgmt. trainee acturial div. Prudential Life Ins. Co., Newark, N.J., 1938-46; dir. med. adminstrn. VA, Chgo. and Washington, 1946-49; project officer to take over and operate new VA Teaching Hosps. VA, Little Rock, Birmingham, Ala. and Chgo., 1949-54; adminstr. U. Ala. Jefferson-Hillman Hosp., Birmingham, 1954-60; founding gen. dir. U. Ala. Hosps. and Clinics, 1960-66; founding prof. hosp. adminstrn. U. Ala. Grad. Sch., 1954-69, vis. prof., 1969—, founding dir. grad. program health adminstrn., 1964-69; prof. epidemiology and preventive medicine Sch. Medicine U. Ala., 1960-69; founding dean Sch. Health Administrn. (now Sch. Health Related Profls.), 1965-69; pres. Matthew F. McNulty, Jr. & Assocs., Inc., 1954-91; founding dir. Coun. Teaching Hosps. and assoc. dir. Assn. Am. Med. Colls., 1966-69; prof. community medicine and internat. health Georgetown U., 1969-89, prof. emeritus 1989—, v.p. med. ctr. affairs, 1969-72, exec. v.p., med. ctr. affairs, 1972-74; chancellor, dir. Georgetown U. Med. Ctr., 1974-86; chancellor emeritus Georgetown U., 1986—; chmn. acad. affairs com., trustee Hahnemann U., Phila, 1987—; trustee Fla. Found. for Active Aging, 1989—; cons. VA Adv. Com. on Geriatrics & Gerontology, 1991—; founding chmn. bd. Univ. D.C. Affiliated Health Plan, Inc., 1974-78; founding chmn. bd. trustees Georgetown U. Community Health Plan, Inc., 1972-80; vis. prof. Cen. U., Caracas, Venezuela, 1957-61; hosp. cons. 1953—; bd. dirs. Kaiser-Georgetown Community Health Plan, Inc., Washington, 1980-85, bd. dirs. Kaiser Health Plans and Hosps., Oakland, Calif., 1980-85, emeritus, 1985—; mem. Statutory VA Spl. Med. Adv. Group, 1978-89, Higher Edn. Com. on Dental Schs. Curriculum, 1978-79; preceptor hosp. adminstrn. Northwestern U., Washington U., U. Iowa, U. Minn., 1953-69; mem. nat. adv. com. health research projects Ga. Inst. Tech., 1959-65, 73-85; nat. adv. com. health rsch. projects U. Pitts., 1956-60; adv. com. W.K. Kellogg Found., 1960-65; vis. cons., lectr. Venezuelan Ministry Health and Social Welfare, 1967-69; dir. Blue Cross-Blue Shield Ala., 1960-61, 65-68; trustee, mem. exec. com. Blue Cross and Blue Shield Nat. Capital Area, 1973-89, Washington Bd. Trade, 1972-86; mem. feasability study P.R. VA Med. Care, 1949, feasability study Ariz. Med. Edn., 1956. Bd. dirs. Greater Birmingham United Appeal, 1960-66; trustee, chmn. Jefferson County (Ala.) Tb Sanatorium, 1958-64; mem. health services research study sect. NIH, 1963-67; cons. USPHS, 1959-63; mem. White House Conf. on Health, 1965, on Medicare Implementation, 1966, NIH, USPHS and DHEW Commns., 1967-86, others; trustee Nat. Council Internat. Health, 1975-86; pres. Nat. League Nursing, 1979-81. Served to maj. USAAF, 1942-46, lt. col. USAFR, 1946-55. Recipient Disting. Alumnus award Northwestern U., 1973, Disting. Alumnus award U. N.C., John Benjamin Nichol award Med. Soc. D.C., Mayor and D.C. Coun., Matthew F. McNulty, Jr. Unanimous Recognition Resolution of 1986, Centennial award Georgetown U. Alumni Assn. award, 1982, Patrick Healy Disting. Svc. award, 1985, Alumni Life Senator Election award, 1986; named to Hon. Order Ky Cols., 1984. Fellow Am. Pub. Health Assn., Am. Coll. Healthcare Execs. (life, bd. regents and council of regents 1961-67, Disting. Health Sci. Exec. award 1976); mem AAAS, Am. Hosp. Assn. (life, Disting. Service award 1984), Ala. Hosp. Assn. (past pres.), Nat. Lr Nursing (past pres.), D.C. League Nursing (past dir.), Nat. Forum Health Planning (past pres., Disting. award, 1987), Council Med. Adminstrn., Internat. Hosp. Fedn., Jefferson County Ala. Vis. Nursing Assn. (past pres., Disting. Service award), Ala. Pub. Health Assn. (past chmn. med. care sect.), Southeastern Hosp. Conf. (past dir.), Birmingham Hosp. Council (past pres.), Hosp. Council Nat. Capital Area (pres. 1985-89, exec. com. 1989—, past pres. 1989-93, treas. 1993—), Assn. Univ. Programs in Hosp. Adminstrn. (Disting. award 1971), Greater Birmingham Area C. of C. (Merit award), Washington Acad. of Medicine, Am. Assn. Med. Colls. (founding chmn. teaching hosp. council 1964-69, Disting. Service Mem.), Royal Soc. Health, Am. Systems Mgmt. Soc. (Disting. award), Orgn. Univ. Health Ctr. Adminstrs., Santa Gertrudis Breeders Internat., Bashkir Curley Horse Breeders Assn., Med. Soc. of D.C. (John Benjamin Nichols award 1982), Univ. Club Ala., Cosmos Club, City Tavern Club, KC (3d degree, coun. 10499 Ocean Springs, 4th degree Francis Deignan Assembly), Knights of Malta, Omicron Kappa Upsilon. Home and Office: Teoc Pentref 3100 Phil Davis Rd Ocean Springs MS 39564-9076

MCNULTY, MICHAEL FRANCIS, lawyer; b. Tucson, Apr. 29, 1951; s. James Francis and Jacquelyn (Boevers) McN.; m. Linda Cataldo, Mar. 25, 1984; 1 child, Clare. BA, Yale U., 1973; JD, U. Ariz., 1977. Bar: Ariz. 1977, D.C. 1978. Miner Phelps-Dodge Copper Co., Bisbee, Ariz., 1971; journalist Ariz. Trial Lawyers Assn., Tucson, 1975-76; staff atty. subcom. on energy and environ. Ho. of Reps., Washington, 1977-78; polit. liaison, bd. dirs. Office of Tech. Assessment U.S. Congress, Washington, 1978; adminstrv. asst. Rep. Morris Udall Ho. of Reps., Washington, 1980; dir. Tucson Office of the Ariz. Dept. Water Resources, 1981-84; ptnr. Streich Lang PA, Tucson, 1984-90, Brown & Bain PA, Tucson, 1990—; guest lectr. Coll. Law U. Ariz., Tucson, 1985-90. Trustee Tucson Pub. Libr., 1988-85, bd. dirs. Sam Hughes Neighborhood Assn., Tucson, 1987-91, Native Seeds/ SEARCH, Tucson, 1988—, Ctr. for Software Excellence, 1993—. Recipient 3d Pl. award Clover Internat. Collection of Poetry, 1972. Mem. ABA (sect. on sci. and tech., sect. on intellectual property). Avocations: composing, poetry, equestrian competition, surfing the "Web". Office: Brown & Bain PA 1 S Church Ave Ste 1900 Tucson AZ 85701-1621

MCNULTY, MICHAEL ROBERT, congressman; b. Troy, N.Y., Sept. 16, 1947; s. John J. and Madelon McN; m. Nancy Ann Lazzaro; children: Michele, Angela, Nancy, Maria. Grad., St. Joseph's Inst., Barrytown, N.Y., 1965, Loyola U. Rome Ctr., 1968, Hill Sch. Ins., N.Y.C., 1970; B.A. in Polit. Sci., Coll. Holy Cross, 1969; LHD honoris causa, Coll. St. Rose, 1991; LLD honoris causa, Siena Coll., 1993. Town supr. Town of Green Island, N.Y., 1969-77, mayor, 1977-82; mem. N.Y. State Assembly, 1982-88, chmn. subcom. on town and village elections, mem. legis. commn. on rural resources, 1983-88, asst. dir. adminstrv. regulations rev. commn., 1977-82, mem. adminstrv. regulations rev. com., 1983-88; past chmn. planning com. Capital Dist. Transp. Com.; mem. 101st-102nd Congresses from 23rd N.Y. dist., 1989-92, 103d-104th Congresses from 21st N.Y. dist., 1993—; mem. internat. rels. com.; past chmn. task force for constrn. Troy-Green Island Bridge; chmn. United Way campaign, 1982. Mem. staff com. on edn. N.Y. State Constl. Conv., 1967; del. Dem. Nat. Conv., 1972, 92; campaign mgr. John J. McNulty Jr. for Sheriff of Albany County, N.Y., 1973; participant 1974 polit. campaign mgmt. inst. Kent State U., Ohio; past mem. Albany County Dem. Com.; past chmn. Green Island Dem. Com.; past mem. N.Y. State Dem. Com. Office: US Ho of Reps 2442 Rayburn HOB Washington DC 20510-3221*

MCNULTY, ROBERT HOLMES, civic association executive; b. Oakland, Calif., June 20, 1940; s. Frederick James and Ruth (Holmes) McN.; m.

Penelope Cuff, Dec. 27, 1964; children: Maria, Abigail. BS in Bus. Administrn., U. Calif., Berkeley, 1962, JD, 1965. Property acquisition planner Safeway Stores, Internat., Oakland, 1962; archeol. asst. Colonial Williamsburg, Va., 1968; rsch. asst. Nat. Mus. of History and Tech. The Smithsonian Instn., Washington, 1968-69, asst. to the dir., 1969-70; environ. advisor GSA, Washington, 1970-71; asst. dir. architecture and environ. arts program NEA, Washington, 1971-78; acting dir. grad. program in hist. preservation Sch. Architecture Columbia U., N.Y.C., 1978-79; pres. Ptnrs. for Livable Places, Washington, 1979—; cons. Task Force on Land Use and Urban Growth, 1972, German Marshall Fund, Washington, 1978; bd. visitors U. Ind. Sch. Pub. Adminstrn., 1991—. Author: Neighborhood Conservation: A Handbook of Methods and Techniques, 1976, Economics of Amenity, 1985, Entrepreneurial American City, 1985, Return of the Livable City, 1986; editor: (report) State of the American Community, 1994. Served to capt. U.S. Army, 1966-68. Smithsonian Inst. grantee, 1972, 73, Graham Found. grantee 1978; Loeb fellow Harvard U., 1973-74; Pierson Coll. guest fellow, Yale U., 1985. Mem. Calif. Bar Assn., Nat. Press Club. Home: 4006 62nd St Bethesda MD 20816-2622 Office: Ptnrs for Livable Places 1429 21st St NW Washington DC 20036-5902

MCNULTY, ROBERTA JO, educational administrator; b. Cin., July 17, 1945; d. Edward Norman and Ruth Marcella (Glass) Stuebing; children: Meredith Corinne, Brian Edward, Stephen Barrett. BS in Edn., U. Cin., 1967; MA in Edn., Coll. of Mount St. Joseph, 1989; PhD in Ednl. Adminstrn. and Supervision, Bowling Green State U., 1993. Elem. tchr. St. Mary Sch., Urbana, Ohio, 1968; elem. tchr. Urbana (Ohio) City Schs., 1968-70, middle sch. tchr., 1970-71; off-campus liaison Mt. St. Joseph Coll., 1987-89; adj. faculty Bowling Green State U., 1990—; gen. edn. supr., testing coord. curriculum devel. and implementation Fulton County Office of Edn., Wauseon, Ohio, 1992—; Lamaza instr. Scioto Meml. Illustrated Lamaze Edn., Portsmouth, Ohio, 1983-84, Tiffin (Ohio) Childbirth Edn. Assn., 1984-87; mem. Project Discovery; proficiency test review com. Ohio Dept. Edn., 1993-94. Grad. editor Am. Secondary Edn., 1989-94. Sch. bd. mem. St. Mary Sch., Urbana, Ohio, 1971-75; parent adv. com. Wheelersburg (Ohio) Local Schs., 1978-84; parents coun. U. Evansville, 1990-93; exec. dir. Am. Cancer Soc., Tiffin, Ohio, 1985; treas. Parents' Boosters Club, Portsmouth YMCA, 1979-84; Y-Wives com. chairperson Tiffin-Cmty. YMCA, 1984-87. Recipient Doctoral fellowship Bowling Green State U., 1989-92, Svc. Appreciation award Cub Scouts, 1990-92. Mem. ASCD, Ednl. Leadership Assn., N.W. Ohio Assn. for Supervision and Curriculum Devel., Ohio Sch. Suprs. Assn., Ohio Coun. Tchrs. English Language Arts, Assn. Tchr. Educators, Ohio Assn. Tchr. Educators (nat. del.), Phi Delta Kappa. Avocations: tennis, desk-top publishing, travel, interior design, bicycling, camping. Office: Fulton County Office of Edn 602 S Shoop Ave Wauseon OH 43567-0338

MCNULTY-MAJORS, SUSAN ROSE, special education administrator; b. Fargo, N.D., Oct. 5, 1944; d. Leo G. McNulty and Jane Lyon (McDonald) McNulty-Schmallen; d Herbert G. Schmallen (stepfather); m. B. Joseph Majors II, Aug. 23, 1975. BS, N.D. State U., 1966; MA, U. Mich., 1969. Lic. tchr., Mass., Minn.; lic. ind. clin. social worker; cert. chem. dependency practitioner. Tchr. sci. Incarnation Sch., Mpls., 1966-67; tchr. English George Daly Jr. High Sch., Flint, Mich., 1967-68; tchr. New Boston (Mich.) Elem. Sch., 1969-70; tchr. home econs. Newton (Mass.) Jr. High Sch., 1970-73; program adminstr. Bell Hill Recovery Ctr., Wadena, Minn., 1973-80, exec. dir., 1980-85; coord. emotionally and behavior disordered edn. Wadena Pub. Schs. TOW Spl. Edn. Coop., 1985-94; dir. spl. edn. PAWN Spl. Edn. Coop., Park Rapids, Minn., 1994—; mem. Wadena Tech. Adv. Bd., 1978—. Mem. adv. bd. Todd-Wadena Community Corrections, Long Prairie, Minn., 1975—; mem. Woodview adv. bd., 1990—. Fresh Air Camp fellow U. Mich., 1968; recipient Ashland Oil Golden Apple Achievement award. Roman Catholic. Avocations: sailing, biking, reading. Home: 843 SW 7th St Wadena MN 56482 Office: PAWN Spl Edn Coop Box 193 Park Rapids MN 56470

MCNUTT, CHARLIE FULLER, JR., bishop; b. Charleston, W.Va., Feb. 27, 1931; s. Charlie Fuller and Mary (Ford) McN.; m. Alice Turnbull, Mar. 3, 1962; children: Thomas Ford, Charlie Fuller III, Alison Turnbull. AB, Washington and Lee U., 1953; MDiv, Va. Theol. Sem., 1956, DD (hon.), 1981; MS, Fla. State U., 1970. Ordained to ministry Episcopal Ch., 1956. Vicar, Christ Ch., Williamston, W.Va., 1956-60; asst. rector St. John's Episc. Ch., Tallahassee, Fla., 1960-62; rector St. Luke's Episc. Ch., Jacksonville, Fla., 1962-68; planning dir. Diocese of Fla., 1968-74; archdeacon of Jacksonville Diocese of Fla., 1970-74; rector Trinity Episc. Ch., Martinsburg, W.Va., 1974-80; consecrated bishop Episc. Diocese Cen. Pa., Harrisburg, 1980—; bd. dirs. Pa. Coun. Chs., Harrisburg, chmn. dept. social ministry, 1982-86, pres. 1991-94. Bd. dirs. Appalachian People's Svc. Orgn., pres., 1985-87; bd. dirs. Boy Scouts Am., Harrisburg, 1981-86; mem. exec. coun. Nat. Ch., 1984-94; mem. standing com. on program, budget and fin. Nat. Episcopal Ch., 1983-90; co-chmn. Pa. Conf. Interch. Cooperation. Mem. Phi Beta Kappa. Democrat. Home: 2428 Lincoln St Camp Hill PA 17011-3637 Office: Episcopal Diocese Ctrl Pa PO Box 11937 221 N Front St Ste 201 Harrisburg PA 17108-1937

MCNUTT, JACK WRAY, oil company executive; b. Norphlet, Ark., Sept. 7, 1934; s. Fay D. and Mattie E. (Garner) McN.; m. Jordine Chesshir, Aug. 19, 1955; 1 child, Marsha. BS, Harding Coll., 1956; MS, Columbia U., 1957. Acct. Murphy Oil Corp., El Dorado, Ark., 1957-68, exec. mgmt asst., 1968-69, exec. v.p., 1981-88, chief operating officer, 1986-88, pres., chief exec. officer, 1988—, also bd. dirs.; v.p. planning Murphy Ea. Oil Co., London, 1969-72, pres., 1972-81; bd. dirs. Ocean Drilling & Exploration Co., New Orleans, First Nat. Bank El Dorado, Ark., Murphy Oil Co. Ltd., Calgary, Alta., Can. Mem. Am. Petroleum Inst., Am. Econ. Assn., Nat. Assn. Bus. Economists, 25 Yr. Club of Petroleum Industry, Nat. Petroleum Council. Home: 1705 W Cedar St El Dorado AR 71730-5309 Office: Murphy Oil Corp 200 E Peach St El Dorado AR 71730-5850

MCNUTT, KRISTEN WALLWORK, consumer affairs executive; b. Nashville, Nov. 17, 1941; d. Gerald M. and Lee Wallwork; m. David McNutt, Sept. 13, 1969. BA in Chemistry, Duke U., 1963; MS in Nutrition, Columbia U., 1965; PhD in Biochemistry, Vanderbilt U., 1970; JD, DePaul U., 1984. Bar: N.Y. 1984, D.C. 1984. Exec. dir. Nat. Nutrition Consortium, Washington, 1979-81; asst. prof. pub. health U. Ill., Chgo., 1981-83; assoc. dir. Good Housekeeping Inst., N.Y.C., 1982-85; v.p. consumer affairs Kraft Inc., Glenview, Ill., 1985-87; pres. Consumer Choices Unltd. Inc., Evanston, 1988—. Author: Nutrition and Food Choices, 1979; editor: Sugars in Nutrition, 1975, Consumer Mags. Digest, 1989—. Bd. dirs. Better Bus. Bur., Chgo. and No. Ill., 1986-88; FDA Food Adv. Com., 1992-94. Mem. N.Y. Bar Assn., D.C. Bar Assn., Fedn. Am. Socs. Exptl. Biology (Congl. Sci. fellow), Soc. for Nutrition Edn. (pres. 1983-84), Am. Inst. Nutrition, Am. Dietetics Assn., Am. Coun. on Consumer Interests. Home and Office: Consumer Choices Inc 2272 Woodview Dr Ste 401 Ypsilanti MI 48198-6818

MCNUTT, MARCIA KEMPER, geophysicist; b. Mpls., Minn., Feb. 19, 1952; widowed, 1988; 3 children. BA, Colorado Coll., 1973; PhD, Scripps Inst. Oceanography, 1978. Geophysicist US Geol. Survey, 1979-82; asst. prof. geophysics MIT, 1982-86, assoc. prof., 1986-89, prof., 1989—, Griswold prof., 1991—; pres. tectonophysics sect. AGU, 1994—; mem. com. on criteria for fed. support of rsch. & devel., 1995—. Mem. Am. Geophys. Union (Macelavane award 1988). Office: MIT Dept of Earth Atmospheric& Planetary Sci 77 Massachusetts Ave Cambridge MA 02139-3594

MCNUTT, SUZZANNE MARIE, lawyer; b. Walla Walla, Wash., June 3, 1962; d. John Richard and Janette Elaine (Egg) Heathman; m. Robert Mark McNutt, Oct. 26, 1985. BA cum laude, Wash. State U., 1985; JD, U. Idaho, 1994. Fin. analyst Dean Witter Reynolds, Boise, Idaho, 1985-86, account exec., 1986-88; sr. legal asst. Boise Cascade Corp., 1988-91; law clk. Idaho State Ct. Appeals, 1992; intern IRS, 1993, Idaho State Dept. Fin., 1993; law clk. Idaho State Ct. Appeals, 1992, 94—; instr. Basic Investing for the Boise Community Ednl. System, 1986-87; bd. dirs. The Courthouse; guest lectr. Boise High Sch., 1987—. Staff mem. U. Idaho Law Rev., 1992-93. Co-chmn. fund drive United Way, 1988; fundraiser, vol. Discovery Ctr. Idaho, Paint the Town, Hays Shelter Home, 1988—; mem. mktg. and future planning com. Jr. League Boise, 1988-91; vol. steering com. Boise Cascade Corp., 1989-91; program dir. Idaho Hugh O'Brian Youth Leadership Found., 1989-91. Mem. ABA, Idaho State Bar (pres. student divsn. Idaho state corp. and

securities sect. 1992-94), Boise Area C. of C. (membership rels. com. 1987-90, chmn. 1989, chmn. leadership program 1988-90). Republican. Roman Catholic. Avocation: sports.

MCNUTT, WILLIAM JAMES, consulting engineer; b. Phila., Aug. 31, 1927; s. Thomas T. and Mary V. McNutt; m. Eleanor M. McGonigal, Aug. 19, 1950. BSEE, Tufts Coll., 1950; MSEE, Ill. Inst. Tech., 1952. Design and devel. engr. large transformer dept. GE, Pittsfield, Mass., 1952-66, mgr. advance devel. engring., large transformer dept., 1966-86; pres. Berkshire Transformer Cons., Pittsfield, 1987—; U.S. rep. transformers study com. Conf. Internat. des Grands Reseaux Electriques, 1977-88; expert advisor on transformers U.S. Nat. Com. of Internat. Electrotech. Commn., 1987—. Editor: (with others) Standard Handbook for Electrical Engineers, 1987; contbr. articles to IEEE Trans., 1958— (prize papers 1974, 83-84, 90). Treas. South Congl. Ch., Pittsfield, 1988-91. Power Systems Engring. fellow Westinghouse Electric Corp., 1950-52. Fellow IEEE (chmn. transformers com. 1981-82). Avocations: golf, tennis, bridge.

MCPARTLAND, JAMES MICHAEL, university official; b. N.Y.C., Sept. 26, 1939; s. James J. and Helen M. (Leddy) McP. BS, Cornell U., 1961, MS, 1963; PhD, Johns Hopkins U., 1968. Rschr. U.S. Office Edn., Washington, 1965-67, U.S. Commn. Civil Rights, Washington, 1967-68; asst. dir. Ctr. Social Orgn. Schs., Johns Hopkins U., Balt., 1968-75, co-dir., 1976-94; dir., 1994—. Co-author: Equality of Educational Opportunity, 1966; author: (with others) Encyclopedia of Educational Research, 1992, Review of Research in Education, 1993; co-editor: Violence in Schools, 1977. Mem. Am. Ednl. Rsch. Assn., Am. Sociol. Assn., Am. Statis. Assn. Democrat. Roman Catholic. Avocation: music. Home: 1102 S Streeper St Baltimore MD 21224-4873 Office: Johns Hopkins U CSOS 3505 N Charles St Baltimore MD 21218-2404

MCPEAK, MERRILL ANTHONY, business executive, consultant, retired officer; b. Santa Rosa, Calif., Jan. 9, 1936; s. Merrill Addison McPeak and Winifred Alice (Stewart) McPeak Bendall; m. Elynor Fay Moskowitz, Nov. 10, 1956; children—Mark Allen, Brian David. A.B. San Diego State Coll., Calif., 1957; M.S., George Washington U., Washington, 1974. Commd. 2d lt. USAF, 1957, advanced through grades to gen., 1988; demonstration pilot USAF Thunderbirds, Nellis AFB, Nev., 1966-68; comdr. Misty Forward Air Controllers, Phu Cat, Republic of Vietnam, 1969, 20th Tactical Fighter Wing, RAF, Upper Heyford, Eng., 1980-81; dep. chief staff plans Tactical Air Command, Langley AFB, Va., 1982-85; dep. chief staff programs and resources Hdqrs. U.S. Air Force, Washington, 1985-87; comdr. 12th Air Force, Bergstrom AFB, Tex., 1987-88; comdr.-in-chief Pacific Air Forces, Hickam AFB, Hawaii, 1988-90; chief of staff USAF, Washington, 1990-94; businessman, cons., 1994—. Officer USAF, retired. Decorated DSM, Silver Star, Legion of Merit, DFC. Mem. Internat. Inst. Strategic Studies, Air Force Assn., Coun. Fgn. Rels., Daedalians, Sigma Chi. Home: Air House 2333 S Rolfe Arlington VA 22202 Office: USAF Office Chief of Staff Hq USAF Washington DC 20330-2000

MC PHAIL, ANDREW TENNENT, chemist, educator; b. Glasgow, Scotland, Sept. 23, 1937; s. Archibald Donaldson and Mary (Tennent) McP.; m. Annette Carson Paton, Aug. 4, 1961; children: Neil Andrew, Donald Robert. B.S. with honors, U. Glasgow, 1959, Ph.D, 1963. Asst. lectr. chemistry U. Glasgow, 1961-64; research assoc. dept. chemistry U. Ill., 1964-66; lectr. chemistry U. Sussex, Eng., 1966-68; assoc. prof. chemistry Duke U., 1968-73, prof., 1973—, dir. X-ray Structure Ctr., 1984—; adj. prof. Sch. Pharmacy U. N.C.-Chapel Hill, 1983—; cons. Schering Research Corp., Burroughs Wellcome Co., Research Triangle Inst. Contbr. articles to profl. jours. Fellow Am. Crystallographic Assn.; mem. Royal Soc. Chemistry (London), Am. Chem. Soc., Sigma Xi, Phi Lambda Upsilon. Co-inventor pharmacologically active amine-carboxyboranes and related compounds. Home: 331 Smith Dr Durham NC 27712-1627 Office: Paul M Gross Chemical Lab Duke U Durham NC 27706

MCPHAIL, JOANN WINSTEAD, writer, art dealer, small business owner; b. Trenton, Fla., Feb. 17, 1941; d. William Emerson and Donna Mae (Crawford) Winstead; m. James Michael McPhail, June 15, 1963; children: Angela C. McPhail Morris, Dana Denise, Whitney Gold McPhail Casso. Student, Fla. So. Coll., 1959-60, St. John's River Jr. Coll., Palatka, Fla., 1960-61, Houston (Tex.) C.C. With Jim Walter Corp., Houston, 1961-62; receptionist Oil and Gas Property Mgmt. Inc., Houston, 1962-63; sec. to mng. atty. State Farm Ins. Co., Houston, 1963-64; saleswoman, decorator Oneil-Anderson, Houston, 1973; sec. Law Offices of Ed Christensen, Houston, 1980-82; advt. mgr. Egalitarian Houston (Tex.) C.C. Systems, 1981; entrepreneur, writer, art agent Golden Galleries, Houston, 1990—; fashion display artist, 1985-86; property mgr., 1994—; property mgr., 1994—. Freelance writer, photographer: Elegance of Needlepoint, 1970, S.W. Art Mag., A Touch of Greatness, 1973, Sweet 70's Anthology, The Budding of Tomorrow, 1974; columnist Egalitarian: The Name Game, Design Your Own Wall Covering, Student Profile, 1981, National Library of Poetry, Fireworks, 1995; contbr. poetry to various publs.; playwright, 1993—. Vol. PTO bd. Sharptown Middle Sch.; assoc. mem. Houston C. of C., Galleria; active ch. leadership activities. Republican. Methodist. Home: 2608 Stanford Houston TX 77006

MCPHEDRAN, NORMAN TAIT, surgeon, educator; b. Saskatoon, Sask., Can., Feb. 12, 1924; s. Norman Neil and Olive Mabel (Tait) McP.; m. Jean Anne Young, June 19, 1950; children—Norman, Peter, Duncan, Bruce, James. M.D., U. Toronto, 1950. Lectr., then asst. prof. U. Toronto, 1958-69; prof. surgery U. Calgary Med. Sch., 1969-81, former head prof. surgery, head dept. developing med. sch., 1981-89; prof. emeritus, 1989—. Author: Canadian Medical Schools - Two Hundred Years of Medical History, 1822-1992; contbr. articles to profl. jours.; chpts. in books. Served with Can. Army, 1942-45. Recipient George Armstrong Peter prize U. Toronto, 1960, McLaughlin fellow, 1957-58. Fellow Royal Coll. Surgeons Can.; mem. Can. Med. Assn., Am. Surg. Assn., Cen. Surg. Assn., ACS (regent 1985-93). Mem. United Ch. Christ. Club: Earl Gray Golf.

MCPHEE, SISTER GLENN ANNE, school system administrator. Supt. Cath. schs. Archdiocese of San Francisco. Office: Office of Supt Cath Schs 443 Church St San Francisco CA 94114-1720

MC PHEE, HENRY ROEMER, lawyer; b. Ames, Iowa, Jan. 11, 1925; s. Harry Roemer and Mary (Ziegler) McP.; m. Joanne Lambert, May 19, 1956 (div. Dec. 1991); children: Henry Roemer III, Joanne, Larkin, Charles. AB cum laude, Princeton U., 1947; LLB, Harvard U., 1950. Bar: N.J. 1951, Ill. 1961, D.C. 1966. Exec. asst. to gov. State of N.J., Trenton, 1950-52; assoc. R.E. & A.D. Watson, New Brunswick, N.J., 1952-54; asst. to gen. counsel FTC, Washington, 1954; exec. asst. White House, Washington, 1954-57; asst. spl. counsel Pres. U.S., Washington, 1957-58, assoc. spl. counsel, pres., 1958-61; ptnr. Hamel & Park, Washington, 1961-88; mem. mgmt. com. Hamel & Park, 1975-85, mng. ptnr., 1980-83; prtnr. Hopkins & Sutter, 1988-93, of counsel, 1994—; sec. N.J. Commn. on Interstate Cooperation, 1952-54; gen. counsel Rep. Nat. Fin. Com., 1968-73; Rep. Nat. Com., Washington, 1968. Chmn. bldg. com. Potomac (Md.) Presbyn. Ch., 1965-67; v.p. Rep. Club, Princeton, 1952-54; bd. dirs. Eisenhower World Affairs Inst., 1983—, treas., 1991-93. Mem. ABA, D.C. Bar Assn., N.J. Bar Assn., Lincoln's Inn Soc. Harvard Law Sch. Republican. Presbyterian. Clubs: Tower (Princeton U.); Princeton (Washington) (pres. 1970-72), Metropolitan (Washington), Capitol Hill (Washington). Avocation: tennis. Home: 11615 Partridge Run Ln Potomac MD 20854 Office: Hopkins & Sutter 888 16th St NW Washington DC 20006-4103

MC PHEE, JOHN ANGUS, writer; b. Princeton, N.J., Mar. 8, 1931; s. Harry Roemer and Mary (Ziegler) McP.; m. Pryde Brown, Mar. 16, 1957; children: Laura, Sarah, Jenny, Martha; m. Yolanda Whitman, Mar. 8, 1972; stepchildren: Cole Harrop, Andrew Harrop, Katherine Ryan, Vanessa Speir. AB, Princeton U., 1953; postgrad., Magdalene Coll., Cambridge (Eng.) U., 1953-54; LittD (hon.), Bates Coll., 1978, Colby Coll., 1978, Williams Coll., 1979, U. Alaska, 1980, Coll. William and Mary, 1988, Rutgers U., 1988; ScD, Maine Maritime Acad., 1992. TV playwright for Robert Montgomery Presents, N.Y.C., 1955-56; contbg. editor, assoc. editor Time mag., 1957-64; staff writer The New Yorker mag., 1965—; Ferris prof. journalism Princeton U., 1975—. Author: A Sense of Where You Are, 1965, The Headmaster, 1966, Oranges, 1967, The Pine Barrens, 1968, A Roomful of Hovings, 1968, Levels of the Game, 1969, The Crofter and the Laird, 1970, Encounters with the Archdruid, 1971, The Deltoid Pumpkin Seed, 1973, The Curve of Binding Energy, 1974, Pieces of the Frame, 1975, The Survival of the Bark Canoe, 1975, Coming into the Country, 1977, Giving Good Weight, 1979, Basin and Range, 1981, In Suspect Terrain, 1983, La Place de la Concorde Suisse, 1984, Table of Contents, 1985, Rising from the Plains, 1986, The Control of Nature, 1989, Looking for a Ship, 1990, Assembling California, 1993, The Ransom of Russian Art, 1994. Recipient award in lit. Am. Acad. and Inst. Arts and Letters, 1977, Woodrow Wilson award Princeton U., 1982, John Wesley Powell award U.S. Geol. Survey, 1988, John Burroughs medal, 1990, Walter Sullivan award Am. Geophys. Union, 1993. Fellow Geol. Soc. Am.; mem. Am. Acad. Arts and Letters.

MCPHEE, JONATHAN, music director, conductor. LRAM, Royal Acad. Music; BM, MM, Juilliard Sch. Music dir., prin. condr. Boston Ballet, 1988—. Condr. dance cos. including The Joffrey Ballet, The Martha Graham Dance Co., The Dance Theatre of Harlem, Am. Ballet Theatre, N.Y.C. Ballet, The Royal Ballet, Covent Garden, Nat. Ballet of Can., orchs. including Buffalo Philharm., Joffrey Ballet Orch., Rochester Philharm., N.Y.C. Opera Orch., BBC Scottish Symphony, Hague Philharm., Boston Pops, Syracuse Symphony, San Diego Symphony, San Francisco Symphony, Orchestre Colonne, Paris, The Nat. Philharm. Orch., London, Danish Radio Symphony Orch.; recs. for filming of Martha Graham works, Cave of the Heart, Errand Into the Maze, El Penintent, Michael Gandolfi's Caution to the Wind; author rev. version Stravinsky's Rite of Spring; composer, arranger for ballets. Office: Boston Ballet 19 Clarendon St Boston MA 02116-6107

MCPHEE, RICHARD S., church administrator. Exec. dir. American Baptist Men of the American Baptist Church, Valley Forge, Pa. Office: Am Baptist Church PO Box 851 Valley Forge PA 19482

MC PHEETERS, EDWIN KEITH, architect, educator; b. Stillwater, Okla., Mar. 26, 1924; s. William Henry and Eva Winona (Mitchell) McP.; m. Patricia Ann Foster, Jan. 29, 1950 (div. 1981); children: Marc Foster, Kevin Mitchell, Michael Hunter; m. Mary Louise Marvin, July 21, 1984. B.Arch., Okla. State U., 1949; M.F.A., Princeton U., 1956. Instr. architecture U. Fla., 1949-51; asst. prof. Ala. Poly. Inst., Auburn U., 1951-54; fellow Princeton U., 1955, 81; from asst. prof. to prof. U. Ark., 1956-66; prof. Renssealer Poly. Inst., 1966-69, dean, 1966-69; prof. Auburn (Ala.) U., 1969-89, dean Sch. Architecture and Fine Arts,, 1969-88, dean, prof. emeritus, 1989—; adj. prof. Frank Lloyd Wright Sch. of Architecture, 1992—; mem. Ala. Bd. Registration for Architects, 1978-87; profl. adviser South Ctrl. Bell Telephone Co., 1977-79, So. Co., 1979-81, Ala. Power Co., 1979-81, Okla. State U., 1983, Ala. Sch. Fine Arts, 1985-86; cons. Taliesin Architects, 1988-92. Served to 2d lt. USAAC, 1943-45; capt. USAFR 1945-57. Fellow AIA (pres. Ala. coun. 1978, Merit award 1976, East Ala. Design awards 1986, 87, 90, 92); mem. Assn. Collegiate Schs. Arch. (bd. dirs. 1970-77, Disting. Prof. 1989), Blue Key, Kappa Sigma, Omicron Delta Kappa, Kappa Kappa Psi, Tau Sigma Delta, Rotary. Episcopalian.

MC PHERSON, ALICE RUTH, ophthalmologist; b. Regina, Sask., Can., June 30, 1926; came to U.S., 1938, naturalized, 1958; d. Gordon and Viola (Hoover) McP. BS, U. Wis., 1948, MD, 1951. Diplomate Am. Bd. Ophthalmology. Intern Santa Barbara (Calif.) Cottage Hosp., 1951-52; resident anesthesiology Hartford (Conn.) Hosp., 1952; resident ophthalmology Chgo. Eye, Ear, Nose and Throat Hosp., 1953, U. Wis. Hosps., 1953-55; ophthalmologist Davis and Duehr Eye Clinic, Madison, Wis., 1956-57; clin. instr. U. Wis., 1956-57; fellow retina service Mass. Eye and Ear Infirmary, 1957-58; ophthalmologist Scott and White Clinic, Temple, Tex., 1958-60; practice medicine specializing in ophthalmology and retinal diseases Houston, 1960—; mem. staff Methodist, St. Luke's, Tex. Children's hosps., Houston; clin. asst. prof. Baylor Coll. Medicine, Houston, 1959-61, asst. prof. ophthalmology, 1961-69, clin. asst. prof., 1969-75, clin. prof., 1975—; cons. retinal diseases VA Hosp., Houston, 1960—, Ben Taub Hosp., Houston, 1960—; mem. adv. com. for active staff appointment sect. of ophthalmology Meth. Hosp., 1986-91, equipment com., 1993, vol. clin. faculity appointments and promotions com., 1993—. Editor: New and Controversial Aspects of Retinal Detachment, 1968, New and Controversial Aspects of Vitreoretinal Surgery, 1977, Retinopathy of Prematurity: Current Concepts and Controversies, 1986. Ambassador Houston Ballet, mem. Houston Ballet Found.; mem. pres.'s council Houston Grand Opera, mem.; mem. conductors circle Houston Symphony, mem. Houston Symphony Soc.; mem. campaign for 80s Baylor Coll. Medicine; mem. Assn. for Community TV, Better Bus. Bur., Physicians' Benevolent Fund, South Tex. Diabetes Assn. Inc., Jr. League Houston. Recipient Honor award Am. Acad. Ophthalmology, 1976, Award of Appreciation, Knights Templar Eye Found., 1978, Woodlands Medal for Outstanding Contbn. to the Econ. Devel. of Community, 1988; Alice R. Mc Pherson Lab for Retina Rsch. dedicated Baylor Ctr. for Biotech., 1988,; Alice R. Mc Pherson Day proclaimed in her honor Mayor of City of Houston, Mar. 12, 1988. Fellow Am. Acad. Ophthalmology (2d v.p. 1979, com. for pub. and profl. rels., vice chmn. program devel. found. bd. trustees, sr. honor award 1986), ACS (credentials and Tex. credentials com., com. on applications); mem. Vitreous Soc., AMA, Tex. Med. Assn., Pan-Am. Med. Assn., Internat. Coll. Surgeons (vice regent 1991—), Am. Med. Women's Assn., Retina Soc. (v.p. 1976-77, pres. 1978-79, credentials com.), Internat. Coll. Ocular Surgeons (vice regent 1991), Am. Soc. Contemporary Ophthalmology (Charles Schepens Hon. award), Am. Bd. Laser Surgery, Internat. Assn. Ocular Surgeons, Harris County Med. Soc., Houston Acad. Medicine, Houston Ophthalmol. Soc. (credentials com., pres. 1990-91), Internat. Soc. Eye Research (cred. com. 1992—), Macula Soc. (credentialing com. 1992—), 9th Dist. Med. Soc., Pan Am. Assn. Ophthalmology (bd. dirs., membership com., bd. dirs. Pan Am. ednl. fund, v.p. 1991-92, AJO letter 1993, pres.-elect 1992—), Research to Prevent Blindness, So. Med. Soc., Tex. Med. Assn., Vitreous Soc., Tex. Ophthal. Assn., Soc. Eye Surgeons, Harris County Med. Soc., Assn. Research Surgeons, U. Wis. Ophthal. Alumni Assn. (founding pres. 1990-93, founded Alice R. McPherson lectureship 1994), French Ophthal. Soc., Internat. Med. Assembly S.W. Tex., Schepens Internat. Soc. (sec. 1986-93, v.p. 1993—), Jules Gonin Club. Research in vision and ophthalmology. Office: Tex Med Ctr 6560 Fannin St Ste 2200 Houston TX 77030-2727

MCPHERSON, DONALD J., metallurgist; married; children: Marjorie, Linda. B.S., M.S., Ph.D., Ohio State U., D.Sc. (hon.), 1975. Assoc. metallurgist Argonne Nat. Lab., to 1950; research metallurgist, asst. div. mgr., div. mgr., v.p. IIT Research Inst., 1950-69; v.p., dir. tech. Kaiser Aluminum and Chem. Corp., Oakland, Calif., 1969-82; Mem. numerous govt. coms. on devel. titanium for def. applications.; chmn. nat. materials adv. bd. NRC, 1982-84. Contbr. numerous articles on titanium and its alloys to profl. jours. Bd. dirs. Research Found. Ohio State U., Jr. Achievement of Bay Area, 1980-82. Recipient Outstanding Young Men award Chgo. Jr. Assn. Commerce and Industry, 1956; Distinguished Alumnus and Centennial Achievement awards Ohio State U. Fellow Am. Soc. Metals (trustee, Campbell Meml. lectr. 1974), hon. mem.; mem. AIME (chmn. titanium com.; chmn. Inst. of Metals div.; bd. dirs. Metall. Soc.), Am. Ceramic Soc. Home: 9369 E Via Montoya Scottsdale AZ 85255-5013

MCPHERSON, DONALD PAXTON, III, lawyer; b. Balt., Aug. 9, 1941; s. Donald Paxton Jr. and Janet Lewis Russell McPherson; children: Donald Russell, Cynthia Quandt. AB, Princeton U., 1963; LLB, Columbia U., 1966. Bar: Md. 1966, U.S. Dist. Ct. Md. 1967, U.S. Ct. Appeals (4th cir.) 1967. Assoc. Piper & Marbury, Balt., 1966-74, prtnr., 1974—, head real estate dept., 1980-94. Mem. ABA, Md. Bar Assn. Democrat. Presbyterian. Avocations: swimming, bicycling, hiking. Office: Piper & Marbury 36 S Charles St Baltimore MD 21201

MC PHERSON, FRANK ALFRED, manufacturing corporate executive; b. Stilwell, Okla., Apr. 29, 1933; s. Younce B. and Maurine Francis (Strauss) McP.; m. Nadine Wall, Sept. 10, 1955; 4 children. BS, Okla. State U., 1957. With Kerr-McGeeCorp., 1957—; gen. mgr. Gulf Coast Oil and gas ops., Morgan City, La., 1969-73; pres. Kerr-McGee Coal, 1973-76, Kerr-McGee Nuclear, 1976-77; vice chmn. Kerr-McGee Corp., 1977-80, pres., 1980—, chmn., CEO, 1983—; bd. dirs. Kimberly-Clark Corp. Patentee in field. Bd. dirs. Okla. chpt. Nature Conservancy, U.S. Olympic Com. for Okla., Bapt. Med. Ctr. Okla., Okla. Med. Rsch. Found., Okla. State U. Found., Okla. State Fair; mem. Task Force 2000; trustee Oklahoma City Community Found.; mem. bd. govs. Kirkpatrick Ctr.; active Okla. Found.

Excellence, Okla. Acad. for State Goals, Bus. Roundtable; mem. adv. com. U. Okla. Coll. Medicine; chmn. Oklahoma City Pub. Schs. Found. Capt. USAF, 1957-60. Mem. Conf. Bd., So. Mining Engrs. Am., Am. Petroleum Inst. (dir.). Nat. Petroleum Council, 25-Yr. Club of Petroleum Industry Oklahoma City C. of C. (dir.), Okla. State C. of C. Republican. Baptist. Office: Kerr-McGee Corp PO Box 25861 Oklahoma City OK 73125-0861*

MCPHERSON, GARY LEE, lawyer, state representative; b. Auburn, Wash., Dec. 4, 1962; s. Percy Ivan and Vicki Mae (Voyles) McP.; children: Christina, Elizabeth, Ashley. BS in Bus. Adminstrn., Union Coll., 1985; JD, U. Nebr., 1988. Bar: Colo. 1989, Nebr. 1989, U.S. Dist. Ct. Colo. 1989, U.S. Ct. Appeals (10th cir.) 1989. Legal/legis. aide Knudsen, Berkheimer & Richardson, Lincoln, Nebr., 1981-85; law clk. Crosby, Guenzel & Davis, Lincoln, 1986; law clk. ethics com. Nebr. State Bar Assn., Lincoln, 1987; assoc. Hall & Evans, Denver, 1987-89; Elrod, Katz, Preeo & Look, P.C., Denver, 1989-90, Fortune & Lawritson, P.C., Denver, 1990-93; pvt. practice McPherson & Hull, Aurora, Colo., 1993—; state rep. State of Colo., Denver, 1994—. Author: Handbook on Professional Malpractice, 1987, rev. edit., 1988; contbr. articles to profl. jours. Bd. dirs. Arapahoe Park & Recreation Bd., Aurora, 1991-95; dist. capt. Arapahoe County Rep. Dist. 8, Aurora, 1992-95; vice chmn. House Dist. 40, Aurora, 1993; chmn. Senate Dist. 28, Aurora, 1993. Recipient Internat. Acad. Trial Lawyers award, 1987, 88, Aurora Pub. Schs. Supts. award, 1992. Mem. ABA (bd. dirs. litigation com. 1992-93, young lawyers divsn. prelaw counseling com. 1992-93), Colo. Bar Assn. (sec., treas. young lawyers divsn. 1991-93, chair-elect 1993, chmn. 1994-95), Arapahoe County Bar Assn., Aurora Rep. Forum, Arapahoe County Rep. Mens Club. Republican. Avocations: aviation, scuba, politics, backpacking, snow skiing. Home: 5410 S Cathay Way Aurora CO 80015-4822 Office: 14291 E 4th Ave Ste 206 Aurora CO 80011-8724

MC PHERSON, HARRY CUMMINGS, JR., lawyer; b. Tyler, Tex., Aug. 22, 1929; s. Harry Cummings and Nan (Hight) McP.; m. Clayton Read, Aug. 30, 1952 (div.); children: Courtenay, Peter B.; m. Mary Patricia DeGroot, Oct. 17, 1981; 1 child, Sam B. B.A., U. South, 1949, D.C.L. (hon.), 1965; student, Columbia U., 1949-50; LL.B., U. Tex., 1956. Bar: Tex. 1955. Asst. gen. counsel Democratic policy com. U.S. Senate, 1956-59, asso. counsel, 1959-61, gen. counsel, 1961-63; dep. under sec. internat. affairs Dept. Army, 1963-64; asst. sec. ednl. and cultural affairs Dept. State, 1964-65; spl. asst. and counsel to Pres. Johnson, 1965-66, spl. counsel, 1966-69; pvt. practice law Washington, 1969—; chmn. task force on domestic policy Dem. Adv. Coun. Elected Ofcls., 1974-76; mem. Pres.'s Commn. on Accident at Three Mile Island, 1979; vice chmn. John F. Kennedy Ctr. for Performing Arts, 1969-76, gen. counsel, 1977-91; bd. dirs. Woodrow Wilson Internat. Ctr. for Scholars, 1969-74; pres. Fed. City Coun., 1983-88; apptd. vice chmn. U.S. Internat. Cultural and Trade Ctr. Commn., 1988-93. Author: A Political Education, 1972, 95. Mem. U.S. Base Closure and Realignment Commn., 1993. 2d lt. USAF, 1950-53. Recipient Disting. Civilian Svc. award Dept. Army, 1964, Arthur S. Flemming award, 1968, Judge Learned Hand Human Rels. award Am. Jewish Com., 1994. Mem. D.C. Bar Assn., N.Y. Council on Fgn. Relations (dir. 1974-77), Econ. Club. of Washington (pres. 1992—). Democrat. Episcopalian. Home: 10213 Montgomery Ave Kensington MD 20895-3325 Office: 901 15th St NW Washington DC 20005-2327

MCPHERSON, JAMES ALAN, writer, educator; b. Savannah, Ga., Sept. 16, 1943; s. James and Mable (Smalls) McP.; 1 dau., Rachel Alice. BA, Morris Brown Coll., 1965; LLB, Harvard, 1968; MFA, U. Iowa, 1971. Asst. prof. lit. U. Calif., Santa Cruz, 1969-71, Morgan State U., 1975-76; assoc. prof. English U. Va., Charlottesville, 1976-81; prof. English U. Iowa, 1981—; mem. lit. panel Nat. Endowment for Arts, 1977-80; lectr., Japan, 1989-90; vis. scholar Yale Law Sch., 1978-79. Author: Hue and Cry, 1969, Railroad, 1976, Elbow Room, 1977 (Pulitzer prize 1978), A World Unsuspected, 1987, The Prevailing South, 1988, Confronting Racial Differences, 1990, Lure and Loathing, 1993, Crossings, 1993; editor: Double Take Mag., 1995—; contbr. editor Atlantic Monthly, Boston, 1969. Recipient award in lit. Nat. Inst. Arts and Letters, 1970, MacArthur Found. award, 1981, Excellence in Teaching award U. Iowa, 1991, Green Eyeshades award Soc. So. Journalists, 1994; stories selected for O'Henry Collection and Best American Short Stories, 1969, 73, best Am. Essays, 1990, 94; Guggenheim fellow, 1972-73; Atlantic grantee, 1968. Mem. ACLU, NAACP, P.E.N., Am. Acad. Arts and Scis. (elected mem. 1995), Authors League.

MC PHERSON, JAMES MUNRO, history educator; b. Valley City, N.D., Oct. 11, 1936; s. James Munro and Miriam (Osborn) McP.; m. Patricia Rasche, Dec. 28, 1957; 1 dau., Joanna Erika. B.A., Gustavus Adolphus Coll., 1958; Ph.D., Johns Hopkins U., 1963. Mem. faculty Princeton U., 1962—, prof. history, 1972—, Edwards prof. Am. history, 1982, George Henry Davis '86 prof. Am. history, 1991. Author: Struggle for Equality, 1964 (Ainsfield-Wolf award race rels. 1965), The Negro's Civil War, 1965, Marching Toward Freedom: The Negro in the Civil War, 1968, Blacks in America: Bibliographical Essays, 1971, The Abolitionist LEgacy: From Reconstruction to the NAACP, 1975, Ordeal by Dire: The Civil War and Reconstruction, 1981, 2d edit., 1992, Battle Cry of Freedom: The Civil War Era, 1988 (Pulitzer prize for history 1989), Abraham Lincoln and the Second American Revulotion, 1991, Images of the Civil War, 1992, Gettysburg, 1993, What They Fought For, 1861-1865, 1994, The Atlas of the Civil War, 1994. Danforth fellow, 1958-62, Guggenheim fellow, 1967-68, Huntington-Nat. Endowment for Humanities fellow, 1977-78, fellow Behavioral Scis. Ctr., Stanford U., 1982-83, Huntington-Seaver Inst. fellow, 1987-88. Mem. Am. Philos. Soc., Am., So. hist. assns., Orgn. Am. Historians, Phi Beta Kappa. Home: 15 Randall Rd Princeton NJ 08540-3609

MCPHERSON, JOHN BARKLEY, aerospace consultant, retired military officer; b. Virginia, Minn., Oct. 4, 1917; s. Barkley John and Anna (Holmgren) McP.; m. Leota Irene Wilson, July 16, 1940; children—Kenneth, Sue McPherson Cain, Shirley McPherson Curs, Robin McPherson Rohrback. B.C.E., U. Ariz., 1940. Commd. 2d lt., cav. U.S. Army, 1940; advanced through grades to lt. gen. USAF, 1968; assigned (B-29s, World War II, PTO); comdr. Walker AFB, Roswell, N.Mex., 1950-52; dir. faculty (Air War Coll.), 1955-56; dep. comdr. (5th Air Div. Morocco), 1956-58; comdr. (379th Bomb Wing), Homestead AFB, Fla., 1958-59, (823d Air Div.), Homestead AFB, 1959-62, (810th Air Div.), Minot AFB, N.D., 1962-64; vice dir. ops., joint staff (Joint Chiefs Staff), 1964-67, vice dir. joint staff, 1967-68, asst. to chmn., 1968-70; comdt. (Nat. War Coll.), 1970-73; ret., 1973; cons. Martin Marietta Aerospace, 1973-85; mem. Sr. Govt. Rev. Panel, 1985-91. Decorated D.S.M. with two oak leaf clusters, Legion of Merit, Bronze Star; recipient Gen. H.S. Vandenberg Aerospace Edn. award, 1984; Centennial medallion award U. Ariz., 1989, Disting. Citizen award, 1995; named Outstanding Young Man of Yr., Roswell, 1951. Mem. Air Force Hist. Found. (pres. 1974-83), Air Force Assn., Nat. Space Club, Order of Daedalians, Theta Tau, Kappa Sigma. Home: 3881 Rust Hill Pl Fairfax VA 22030-3919

MCPHERSON, LARRY E(UGENE), photographer, educator; b. Newark, Ohio, May 1, 1943; s. Eugene Edward and Ethel Grace (Lehman) McP. BA, MA; B.A., Columbia Coll., Chgo., 1976; M.A., No. Ill. U., 1978. Instr. Columbia Coll., 1971-76; assoc. prof. photography U. Memphis, 1978—; instr. Sch. of Art Inst. Chgo., spring 1972; workshop instr. Ohio State U., Columbus, summer 1980, VSW Summer Inst., Rochester, N.Y., summer 1988. One-man shows include Art Inst. Chgo., 1969, 78, 81, Dayton Art Inst., 1992; exhibited in group shows at Mus. Modern Art, N.Y.C., 1978, Corcoran Gallery Art, Washington, 1982, George Eastman House, Rochester, N.Y., 1982, New Orleans Mus. Art, 1992; represented in permanent collections Mus. Modern Art, Art Inst. Chgo., George Eastman House, New Orleans Mus. Art, Mus. Fine Arts, Houston, Memphis Brooks Mus. Art. Faculty Devel. grantee Memphis State U., springs 1983, 92; grantee-fellow Nat. Endowment for Arts, 1975, 79; Guggenheim fellow, 1980. Mem. Soc. Photog. Edn. Home: 3293 Southern Ave Apt 5 Memphis TN 38111-8321 Office: U Memphis Dept Art Memphis TN 38152

MCPHERSON, MARY PATTERSON, academic administrator; b. Abington, Pa., May 14, 1935; d. John B. and Marjorie Hoffman (Higgins) McP. A.B., Smith Coll., 1957, LL.D., 1981; M.A., U. Del., 1960; Ph.D., Bryn Mawr Coll., 1969; LL.D. (hon.), Juniata Coll., 1975, Smith Coll., 1981, Princeton U., 1984, U. Rochester, 1984, U. Pa., 1985; Litt.D. (hon.), Haverford Coll., 1980; L.H.D. (hon.), Lafayette Coll., 1982, U. Pa., 1985;

LHD (hon.), Med. Coll. Pa., 1985. Instr. philosophy U. Del., 1959-61; asst. fellow and lectr. dept. philosophy Bryn Mawr Coll., 1961-63, asst. dean, 1964-69, assoc. dean, 1969-70; dean Bryn Mawr Coll. (Undergrad. Coll.), 1970-78, assoc. prof., from 1970; acting pres. Bryn Mawr Coll., 1976-77, pres., 1978—; bd. dirs. Provident Nat. Bank of Phila., Bell Telephone Co. Pa., Dayton Hudson Corp.; mem. commn. on women in higher edn. Am. Council on Edn., bd. dirs., 1979-82. Bd. dirs. Agnes Irwin Sch. 1971—; bd. dirs. Shipley Sch., 1972—; Phillips Exeter Acad., 1973-76, Wilson Coll., 1976-79, Greater Phila. Movement, 1973-77, Internat. House of Phila., 1974-76, Josiah Macy, Jr. Found., 1977—, Carnegie Found. for Advancement Teaching, 1978-86, Univ. Mus., Phila., 1977-79, University City Sci. Center, 1979-85, Brookings Inst., 1984—, Phila. Contributionship, 1985—, Carnegie Corp. N.Y., 1985—, Nat. Humanities Ctr., 1986—, Amherst Coll., 1986—. Mem. Soc. for Ancient Greek Philosophy, Am. Philos. Soc. Clubs: Fullerton, Cosmopolitan. Office: Bryn Mawr Coll Office of the President Merion Ave Bryn Mawr PA 19010*

MCPHERSON, MILTON MONROE, history educator; b. Beatrice, Ala., Oct. 19, 1928; s. Laurence Milton and Annie Mae (Bell) McP.; m. Carolyn Elizabeth Coley, Dec. 16, 1955; children: Milton Jr., Herbert L., Gretchen M. BA, U. Ala., 1950, MA, 1959, PhD in Am. History, 1970. Asst. prof. history Miss. Coll., Clinton, 1959-60, Mercer U., Macon, Ga., 1960-61, Ala. Coll., Montevallo, 1961-62, Pensacola (Fla.) Jr. Coll., 1962-68; assoc. prof. history Troy (Ala.) State U., 1968-87, prof. history, 1987-89; prof. history emeritus, 1989—. Editor: Memories That Lingered: The Life and Times of Laurence Milton McPherson, 1993. 1st lt. U.S. Army, 1950-53. Mem. NEA, Ala. Hist. Assn., So. Hist. Assn. Avocations: writing, reading, photography, walking, traveling. Home: 206 Sherwood Ave Troy AL 36081

MC PHERSON, PAUL FRANCIS, publishing and investment banking executive; b. Boston, Apr. 30, 1931; s. William Andrew and Margaret Frances (Rice) McP.; m. Mary Loretta Sanders, June 10, 1953; children: Paul, Kevin, Gary, Scott. BSBA, Boston Coll., 1952; MBA, Babson Coll., 1955. With McGraw Hill, Inc., N.Y.C., 1955-89; advt. sales mgr. McGraw-Hill Pub. Co., 1963-66, group v.p., 1973-76, exec. v.p., 1976-79; pres. McGraw-Hill Info. Systems Co., 1979-80; pres. McGraw-Hill Pub. Co., 1980-83, exec. v.p., 1983-89; pres., chief exec. officer FM Bus. Pubs. Inc., N.Y.C., 1988-92; sr. advisor AdMedia Corp. Advisors, N.Y.C., 1992-93, mng. dir., 1993—. Served with U.S. Army, 1952-54. Mem. Am. Bus. Press (bd. dirs., past chmn.), Mag. Pubs. Am. (bd. dirs., past chmn.), Advt. Coun. (dir., past vice chmn.), Audit Bur. Circulations (dir., past vice chmn.), Woodway Country Club. Home: 10 Drum Hill Ln Stamford CT 06902-1406 Office: AdMedia Corp Advisors Inc 866 3rd Ave New York NY 10022-6221

MC PHERSON, ROBERT DONALD, retired lawyer; b. Madison, Wis., Dec. 21, 1936; s. Clifford James and Alice Irene (Peterson) McP.; m. Nancy Joann Buenzli, Aug. 17, 1957; children—Searl Kelly, Eileen Patricia, Maureen Teresa, Cathleen Marie. B.A., U. Tex., El Paso, 1960; J.D., North Tex. Coll. Law, Houston, 1969. Bar: Tex. 1969. Tchr. English various schs., El Paso, Tex. and Menomonie, Wis., 1960-62; claims rep. Employers Casualty Co. Tex., 1962-66, staff claims rep., 1966-68; ptnr. Bousquet & McPherson, Houston, 1969-76; pvt. practice Houston, 1976-80; ptnr. McPherson & McPherson, Houston, 1980-87, McPherson & Ruman, Houston, 1987-89; pvt. practice Houston, 1989-90; ptnr. Mc Pherson & Mahar, Houston, 1990-91; instr. history and govt. South Tex. Jr. Coll., 1969-71; adj. prof. law South Tex. Coll. Law, 1972-78. Served with AUS, 1953-56. Mem. State Bar Tex., Order of Lytae.

MC PHERSON, ROLF KENNEDY, clergyman, church official; b. Providence, Mar. 23, 1913; s. Harold S. and Aimee (Semple) McP.; m. Lorna De Smith, July 21, 1931 (dec.); children—Marlene (dec.), Kay. Grad., So. Cal. Radio Inst., 1933; D.D. (hon.), L.I.F.E. Bible Coll., 1944; LLD (hon.), L.I.F.E. Bible Coll., Los Angeles, 1988. Ordained to ministry Internat. Ch. Foursquare Gospel, 1940. Pres. Internat. Ch. Foursquare Gospel, L.A., 1944-88, dir., 1944-92; dir. emeritus, 1992—; pres., dir. L.I.F.E. Bible Coll., Inc., L.A., 1944-88. Mem. Echo Park Evangelistic Assn. (pres. 1944—). Office: Internat Ch Foursquare Gospel 1910 W Sunset Blvd Ste 200 Los Angeles CA 90026-0176

MCPHERSON, SANDRA JEAN, poet, educator; b. San Jose, Calif., Aug. 2, 1943; d. John Emmet and Joyce (Turney) Todd; adopted d. Walter James and Frances K. (Gibson) McP.; m. Henry D. Carlile, 1966 (div. 1985); 1 child, Phoebe; m. Walter D. Pavlich, 1995. BA in English, San Jose (Calif.) State U., 1965; postgrad., U. Wash., 1965-66. Vis. lectr. U Iowa Writers Workshop, 1974-76, 78-80; Holloway lectr. U. Calif., Berkeley, 1981; tchr. poetry workshop Oreg. Writers Workshop, Portland, 1981-85; prof. English U. Calif., Davis, 1985—. Author: (poetry) Elegies for the Hot Season, 1970, Radiation, 1973, The Year of Our Birth, 1978, Patron Happiness, 1983, Streamers, 1988, The God of Indeterminacy, 1993. Recipient Nat. Endowment for the Arts awards; award in lit. Am. Acad. and Inst. Arts and Letters, 1987; Ingram Merrill Found. fellow; grantee Guggenheim Found., 1976, Oreg. Arts Commn., 1984-85. Democrat. Avocation: collector and exhibitor of African-American quilts. Office: U Calif Dept English Davis CA 95616

MCPHERSON, VANZETTA PENN, federal judge; b. Montgomery, Ala., May 26, 1947; d. Luther Lincoln and Sadie Lee (Gardner) P.; m. Winston D. Durant, Aug. 17, 1968 (div. Apr. 1979); 1 child, Raegan Winston; m. Thomas McPherson Jr., Nov. 16, 1985. BS in Speech Pathology, Howard U., Washington, 1969; MA in Speech Pathology, Columbia U., 1971, JD, 1974. Bar: N.Y. 1975, Ala. 1976, U.S. Dist. Ct. (so. dist.) N.Y. 1975, U.S. Dist. Ct. (mid. dist.) Ala. 1980, U.S. Ct. Appeals (2d cir.) 1975, U.S. Ct. Appeals (11th cir.) 1981, U.S. Supreme Ct. Assoc. Hughes, Hubbard & Reed, N.Y.C. 1974-75; asst. atty. gen. Ala. Atty. Gen. Office, Montgomery, 1975-78; pvt. practice Montgomery, 1978-92; magistrate judge U.S. Dist. Ct. (mid. dist.) Ala., Montgomery, 1992—; co-owner Roots & Wings, A Cultural Bookplace, Montgomery, 1989—. Dir. Ala. Shakespeare Festival, Montgomery, 1987—; chmn. trustees Dexter Ave. King Meml. Bapt. Ch., Montgomery, 1988; chmn. Leadership Montgomery; bd. mem. Lighthouse Counseling Ctr., Montgomery, 1981-84, Montgomery County Pub. Libr., 1989-90; v.p. Lanier High Sch. Parent Tchr. Student Assn., Montgomery, 1990-91. Recipient cert. Ala. Jud. Coll.; named Woman of Achievement Montgomery Advertiser, 1989, Boss of Yr. Montgomery Assn. Legal Secs., 1992, Woman of Yr. Gamma Phi Delta, Montgomery, 1992, Citizen of Yr. Delta Sigma Theta, Montgomery, 1992. Mem. ABA (law office design award 1985), Nat. Bar Assn., Ala. State Bar Assn. (chmn. family law sect. 1989-90), N.Y. State Bar Assn., Montgomery Inn of Cts. (master bencher 1992—), Ala. Black Lawyers Assn. (pres. 1979-80). Office: US Dist Ct Mid Dist Ala PO Box 1629 15 Lee St Montgomery AL 36102

MCQUADE, CHARLES BRIAN, data processing executive; b. N.Y.C., May 1, 1941; s. Charles P. and Cecelia M. (Doyle) McQ.; m. Mary M. McGuiness, Oct. 14, 1967; children: Brian, Tarajean, Laura, James, Maggie. BS, Fordham U., 1962; postgrad., CUNY, Baruch, 1967-71. Exec. Am. Stock Exchange, N.Y.C., 1966-72; pres., chief exec. officer Securities Industry Automation Corp., N.Y.C., 1972—; also bd. dirs. Mem. fin. adv. bd. United Way N.Y., N.Y.C., 1987—; mem. system adv. bd. CUNY, N.Y.C., 1987. Served to lt. USNR, 1962-65. Roman Catholic. Avocations: tennis, skiing, gardening. Home: PO Box 7045 Ardsley On Hudson NY 10503-0045 Office: Securities Industry Corp 2 Metrotech Ctr New York NY 10167-0002

MC QUADE, HENRY FORD, state justice; b. Pocatello, Idaho, Oct. 11, 1915; s. M. Joseph and Mary E. (Farnan) McQ.; m. Mary E. Downing, Apr. 11, 1942; children—Sharon McQuade Grisham, Michael, Frances McQuade Munning, Robert, Joseph, Peter, William. A.B., U. Idaho, 1940, LL.B., 1943. Bar: Idaho 1946. Practice in Pocatello, 1946-51; pros. atty. Bannock County, Idaho, 1946-50; judge 5th Jud. Dist., Idaho, 1951-56; justice Idaho Supreme Ct., 1957-76, chief justice, 1972-75; dep. administr. Law Enforcement Assistance Adminstrn., U.S. Dept. Justice, Washington, 1976; adminstrv. law judge Occupational Safety and Health Rev. Commn., Washington, 1976-81; mem. Nat. Commn. on Criminal Justice Standards and Goals, 1971-73, Nat. Commn. Hwy. Traffic Safety, 1971-74. Chmn. Idaho Gov.'s Com. Traffic Safety, 1958-59, Idaho YMCA Youth Legislature, 1958-69, Boise chpt. ARC, 1970-71. Mem. Am. Bar Assn., Am. Judicature Soc., Idaho State Bar. Home: 1002 Ranch Rd Boise ID 83702-1440

MC QUADE, LAWRENCE CARROLL, lawyer, corporate executive; b. Yonkers, N.Y., Aug. 12, 1927; s. Edward A. and Thelma (Keefe) McQ.; m. de Rosset Parker Morrissey, Aug. 3, 1968 (dec. Oct. 1978); 1 child, Andrew Parker; m. Margaret Osmer, Mar. 15, 1980. BA with distinction, Yale U., 1950; BA, Oxford (Eng.) U., 1952, MA, 1956; LLB cum laude, Harvard U., 1954; MA (hon.), Colby Coll., 1981. Bar: N.Y. 1955, D.C. 1968. Assoc. Sullivan & Cromwell, N.Y.C., 1954-60; spl. asst. to asst. sec. for internat. security affairs U.S. Dept. Def., Washington, 1961-63; dep. asst. sec. U.S. Dept. Commerce, Washington, 1963-64, asst. to sec., 1965-67, asst. sec., 1967-69; pres. Procon Inc., Des Plaines, Ill., 1969-75; CEO, dir. Procon Inc., 1969-75; v.p. Universal Oil Products Co., 1972-75; v.p. W.R. Grace & Co., N.Y.C., 1975-78, sr. v.p., 1978-83, exec. v.p., 1983-87, also bd. dirs.; vice chmn. Prudential Mut. Fund Mgmt., N.Y.C., 1988-95; mng. dir. Prudential Securities Inc., 1988-92; chmn., CEO Universal Money Ctrs., 1987-88; expert advisor commn. on transnat. corps. UN, 1989-93; bd. dirs. Bunzl, Quixote Corp., Oxford Analytica. Author: (with others) The Ghana Report, 1959; contbr. (with others) articles to profl. jours. Bd. dirs. Fgn. Bondholders Protective Coun., N.Y.C., 1978—, The Am. Forum, 1985—, Am. Coun. on Germany, 1985-94; trustee Colby Coll. 1981-89, trustee emeritus, 1989—; dir., vice chmn. Czech and Slovak Am. Enterprise Funds, 1994—; mem. Bretton Woods Com. Rhodes scholar Oxford U., 1952. Mem. Coun. Fgn. Rels. N.Y., Chgo. Coun. Fgn. Rels. (bd. dirs. 1969-75), Nat. Fgn. Trade Coun. (bd. dirs. 1979-87), Atlantic Coun. U.S. (bd. dirs. 1969—), Mgmt. and Devel. Inst. (bd. dirs. 1970—), Overseas Devel. Coun. (bd. dirs. 1974-87), Pres.'s Cir. of NAS, Harvard Club, Century Club, Pilgrims Club, Met. Club (Washington), Phi Beta Kappa.

MC QUADE, WALTER, author; b. Port Washington, N.Y., May 1, 1922; s. Walter P. and Thomase (Dwyer) McQ.; m. Ann Aikman, Nov. 25, 1950; children—Molly Elizabeth, Benjamin Barr, Kate Maud. B.Arch., Cornell U., 1947. Writer Archtl. Forum mag., 1947-64; architecture and design critic The Nation, 1959-65, Life mag., 1970-74; bd. editors Fortune mag., 1964-85; contbg. editor Connoisseur Mag., 1985-91; vis. critic Yale U. Sch. Architecture, 1962; mem. N.Y.C. Planning Commn., 1967-72. Author: Schoolhouse, 1958, Cities Fit To Live In, 1971, Stress, 1975, The Longevity Factor, 1979, Architecture in the Real World, 1985. Served with AUS, 1942-46. Ford Found. fellow, 1960; co-recipient Grand prize Milan Trennale, 1960; recipient Howard Blakeslee award Am. Heart Assn., 1972; Penney award U. Mo., 1972. Fellow AIA (Architecture Critics' medal 1974). Roman Catholic. Home: 3 Grosvenor Pl Great Neck NY 11021-4534

MCQUAID, J. DENNIS, lawyer; b. San Diego, Apr. 19, 1939. AB, St. Patrick's Coll., 1961; JD, U. San Francisco 1970. Bar: Calif. 1970. Ptnr. Keck, Mahin & Cate, San Francisco. Mem. planning commn. City of Novato, Calif., 1977-78, mayor of city, 1985, mem. city coun., 1983-87. Mem. State Bar Calif. Office: Keck Mahin & Cate 1 Maritime Plz 23rd Fl San Francisco CA 94111-2496

MCQUAID, JOHN G., lawyer; b. N.Y.C., Jan. 4, 1918; s. Paul Augustine and Louise (Gaffney) McQ.; m. Betty Frances Seay, May 27, 1989; children from previous marriage: John G. Jr., Catherine M., Elizabeth L. BA, Yale Coll., 1940, LLB, 1947. Bar: N.Y. 1948, U.S. Supreme Ct. 1954. Assoc. Townley Updike Carter & Rodgers, N.Y.C., 1947-52; with Nat. Prodn. Auth., Washington, 1952-54; pvt. practice White Plains, N.Y., 1954-60; ptnr. Fingar & McQuaid, White Plains, 1960-65, McCarthy, Fingar, Donovan, Drazen & Smith, White Plains, 1965—; dir., asst. sec. Dewey Electronics Corp., Oakland, N.J., 1955—. Co-author/editor: New York Wills and Trusts, 2d edit., 1961, 3d edit., 1990; co-editor: West's Trust and Wills Document Assembly, 1993, New York Will Manual. 2d lt. U.S. Army, 1942-46. Fellow Am. Coll. Trusts and Estates Counsel; mem. N.Y. State Bar Assn. (chmn. trusts and estates law sect. 1981), White Plains Bar Assn. (pres. 1961), Ardsley Country Club. Home: Hudson House PO Box 7011 Ardsley-On-Hudson NY 10503-7011 Office: McCarthy Fingar Donovan Drazen & Smith 11 Martine Ave White Plains NY 10606-1934

MCQUAID, JOSEPH WOODBURY, newspaper executive; b. Manchester, N.H., Feb. 12, 1949; s. Bernard John and Margaret (Griffin) McQ.; m. Signe Karin Anderson, Nov. 2, 1975; children—Katharine, Brendan. Student, U. N.H., 1967-69. Reporter Union Leader, Manchester, N.H., 1969-71; Sunday editor N.H. Sunday News, Manchester, N.H., 1971-76; mng. editor Union Leader-Sunday News, Manchester, N.H., 1976-82, editor-in-chief, 1982—; v.p., 1986—; gen. mgr., 1992—; dir. Union Leader Corp., Manchester. Sec. Manchester Indsl. Council, 1974-84. Roman Catholic. Home: 256 N Bay St Manchester NH 03104-2324 Office: Union Leader Corp 100 William Loeb Dr Manchester NH 03109-5309

MCQUARRIE, BRUCE CALE, mathematics educator; b. Easton, Pa., Jan. 6, 1929; s. William Craven Hurd and Florence Mabel (Cale) McQ.; m. Betty Ann Palmer, Dec. 25, 1948 (div. 1983) children—Nancy, Laura, Amy. A.B. Lafayette Coll., 1951; M.A., U. N.H., 1956; Ph.D., Boston U., 1971. Instr. Tucson Indian Sch., Ariz., 1951-52; instr. Wasatch Acad., Mt. Pleasant, Utah, 1956-60; instr. math., asst. prof., assoc. prof. Worcester Poly. Inst., Mass., 1960—, prof. math., dept. head math. scis., 1983-86, prof. emeritus, 1990—. Mem. Democratic Town Com., Auburn, Mass., 1970-90. With U.S. Army, 1952-54. Home: 10 Eames Dr Auburn MA 01501-1308 Office: Worcester Poly Inst 100 Institute Rd Worcester MA 01609-2247

MCQUARRIE, CLAUDE MONROE, III, lawyer; b. Ft. Benning, Ga., Oct. 15, 1950; s. Claude Monroe Jr. and Rosanne (Sprinkle) McQ.; m. Patricia Elaine Swanson, Dec. 23, 1977; children: Kevin Andrew, Ryan Christopher, Erin Elizabeth. BS, U.S. Mil. Acad., 1972; JD with distinction, St. Mary's U., San Antonio, 1978. Bar: Tex. 1978, U.S. Dist. Ct. (so. dist.) Tex. 1982, U.S. Ct. Mil. Appeals 1979. Commd. 2d lt. U.S. Army, 1972, advanced through grades to capt., 1976, resigned, 1982; assoc. Fulbright & Jaworski, Houston, 1982-89, ptnr., 1989—. Editor Law Rev., 1977-78. Mem. ABA, Houston Bar Assn., John M. Harlan Soc., Phi Delta Phi. Avocations: golf, skiing. Home: 2802 Eagle Creek Dr Humble TX 77345-1311 Office: Fulbright & Jaworski 1301 Mckinney St Houston TX 77010-3049

MCQUARRIE, DONALD GRAY, surgeon, educator; b. Richfield, Utah, Apr. 17, 1931; s. John Gray and LoRetta (Smith) McQ.; m. Dolores Jean Dietrich, July 16, 1956; children—William Gray, Michelle Dolores Colton. B.S., U. Utah, 1952, M.D., 1956; Ph.D., U. Minn., 1964. Diplomate Am. Bd. Surgery, Am. Bd. Thoracic and Cardiovascular Surgery. Intern U. Minn. Hosps., 1956-57; resident in surgery U. Minn. Mpls., 1957-59, resident, 1961-65, asst. prof. surgery, 1964-68, assoc. prof. surgery, 1968-72, prof. surgery, 1972—, vice chmn. dept. surgery, 1993—; mem. surg. staff Mpls. VA Hosp., 1964—; chief surgical svc., 1993—, resident in thoracic surgery, 1965-66, dir. surg. research lab., 1964-78; vis. prof. U. Tex.-San Antonio, 1974, U. Ind. and Indpls. VA, 1977, affiliated program U. Ariz., Phoenix, 1982, Case Western Res. U., 1986. Editor, contbg. author: Head and Neck Cancer, 1986, Reoperations in General Surgery, 1991; contbr. articles on surg. and basic med. scis. to profl. publs., 1955—. Served to lt. M.C., USN, 1959-61. USPHS postdoctoral fellow, 1962-65. Fellow ACS (commn. on cancer 1980-89, exec. council commn. on operating room environ. 1985-91, pres. Minn. chpt. 1983-84, liaison to Assn. Oper. Rm. Nurses 1985—, gov. 1990—); mem. Minn. Surg. Soc. (pres. 1980-81), Assn. Acad. Surgery, Mpls. Surg. Soc. (pres. 1978-79), Soc. Head and Neck Surgeons, Central Surg. Assn., Soc. Univ. Surgeons, Société Internationale de Chirurgie, Am. Surg. Assn., Assn. VA Surgeons (pres. 1987), Soc. Surg. Oncology, Hennepin County Med. Soc., Minn. Med. Assn., Am. Soc. Clin. Oncology, Phi Beta Kappa, Phi Kappa Phi. Clubs: Minneapolis, Interlachen Country (Mpls.). Avocations: computer applications to medicine; jewelry design; lapidary work. Home: 6625 Mohawk Trl Minneapolis MN 55439-1029 Office: Mpls VA Med Ctr Dept Surgery 1 Veterans Dr Minneapolis MN 55417-2300

MCQUEEN, JUSTICE ELLIS (L. Q. JONES), actor, director; b. Beaumont, Tex., Aug. 19, 1927; s. Justice Ellis and Pat (Stephens) McQ.; m. Sue Helen Lewis, Oct. 10, 1950 (dec.); children: Marlin Randolph, Marilyn Helen, Steven Lewis. Student, Lamar Jr. Coll., 1944, Lon Morris Coll., 1949, U. Tex., 1950-51. Actor numerous motion picture films, TV shows, dir.: motion picture films including A Boy and His Dog, 1975 (recipient Hugo award, Sci. Fiction achievement award for dramatic presentation); producer The Big Thickett, Come In, Children, The Witchmaker; author: The Brotherhood of Satan, 1971. Served with USNR, 1945-46. Mem.

Screen Actors Guild. Republican. Methodist. Home and Office: 2144 N Cahuenga Blvd Los Angeles CA 90068-2708

MC QUEEN, ROBERT CHARLES, retired insurance executive; b. Santiago, Chile, Jan. 23, 1921; s. Charles Alfred and Grace Juanita (Abrecht) McQ.; m. Donna Marie Ikeler, Oct. 6, 1945; children: Scott, Jerry, Monte, Donald. A.B., Dartmouth Coll., 1942. Mathematician, Equitable Life Assurance Soc., N.Y.C., 1945-49; group actuary Union Central Life Ins. Co., Cin., 1949-57; with Mut. Benefit Life Ins. Co., Newark, 1957-85; exec. v.p. Mut. Benefit Life Ins. Co., 1969-71, sr. exec. v.p., chief adminstrv. officer, 1971-85, dir., 1978-85; bd. dirs. St. Barnabas Corp. (formerly Trimark Corp.). Pres. Millburn Twp. (N.J.) Bd. Edn., 1969-71, Naples (Fla.) Bridge Ctr., 1994—; chmn. BBB Met. N.Y., 1978-80; chmn. bd. trustees St. Barnabas Hosp., Livingston, N.J., 1983-91, trustee, 1991—. With OSS, 1943-45. Fellow Soc. Actuaries; mem. Am. Acad. Actuaries, Internat. Actuarial Assn., Canoe Brook Country Club, Quail Creek Club. Republican. Episcopalian. Home: 12988 Bald Cypress Ln Naples FL 33999-8526

MCQUEEN, SCOTT ROBERT, broadcasting company executive; b. Peekskill, N.Y., June 30, 1946; s. Robert Charles and Donna Marie (Ikeler) McQ.; m. Loretta A. Dybala, May 17, 1980; children: Geoffrey Scott, Mallory Morgan, Brian Daniel; 1 child, by previous marriage, Tasha Lea. B.A., Dartmouth Coll., 1968. Founder Sconnix Radio Ent., Inc., Laconia, N.H., 1968; Founder Sconnix Radio Ent., Inc. (became Sconnix Group Broadcasting, Inc.), 1971, pres., 1971—. Chmn. Magic Childrens Fund, 1991—; bd. advisors Pincrest Sch., Boca Raton, Fla. With N.H.N.G., 1968-69. Mem. Nat. Assn. Broadcasters, Nat. Radio Broadcsters Assn., Lakes Region C. of C. (dir. 1977-81), Rotary, Royal Palm Yacht and Country Club, Ocean Reef Club (Key Largo, Fla.). Home: 431 Coconut Palm Rd Boca Raton FL 33432-7915 Office: 3000 N 28th Ter Hollywood FL 33020-1302 also: Village West Gilford NH 03246

MCQUEEN, SHERMAN JOHN, JR., entertainment company executive; b. Monrovia, Calif., May 29, 1928; s. Sherman John, Sr. and Ethel (Morrison) McQ.; m. Irene Cecelia Anderson, June 21, 1957 (div. 1965); children: Amy Lynn, Susan Marie; m. Margaret Ann Ross, Dec. 31, 1967. B.A., Occidental Coll., 1949. Sports dir. Sta. KREM, Spokane, Wash., 1948-50; newscaster Sta. WIND, Chgo., 1950-52; mgr. sta. rels. Mut. Broadcasting, L.A., 1952-54; mgr. bus. affairs CBS, L.A., 1954-57; v.p., account supr. D'Arcy Advt., L.A., 1957-60; sr. v.p. broadcasting Foote, Cone and Belding, L.A., 1960-79; pres. FCB Entertainment, Burbank, Calif., 1979—; chmn. Old Mill. Adv. Bd., San Marino, Calif. 1974-82, Telecom. Group, City San Marino, 1994—; mem. com. Pasadena (Calif.) Tounament Roses, 1974-94. Prodr. (TV program series) Hallmark Hall of Fame, 1960-83 (Emmy award 1982), Sportslook, 1981-90 (Ace award 1987); editor FCB Network News, 1994. Recipient Silver award Am. Advt. Fedn., 1968. Mem. TV Acad. (chair com. 1990-91), Pacific Pioneer Broadcasters (bd. dirs. 1994—), So. Calif. Sportscasters (bd. dirs. 1982-83), Hollywood Ad Club (pres. 1965, Silver award 1966), Hollywood Radio and TV Soc. (pres. 1966-67, Ollie award 1967-68), San Marino Rotary (bd. dirs. 1978). Republican. Presbyterian. Avocations: book and document collecting, travel, golf, gardening. Office: FCB Entertainment 3601 W Olive Ave Burbank CA 91505-4603

MCQUEEN, THOMAS K., lawyer; b. Washington, Sept. 26, 1949. BA, Colo. State U., 1971; JD, DePaul U., 1974. Bar: Ill. 1974, U.S. Dist. Ct. (no. dist.) 1974, U.S. Ct. Appeals (7th cir.) 1975. Asst. U.S. atty. U.S. Attys. Office, 1974-79, dep. chief criminal litigation divsn., 1977-79; cons., asst. to spl. counsel Subcom. to Investigate Activities of Individuals Representing Interests of Fgn. Govts., U.S. Senate, Washington, 1980; ptnr. Jenner & Block, Chgo.; adj. prof. law Northwestern U., 1984—. Mem. ABA (mem. criminal justice sect., com. internat. criminal law), Fed. Bar Assn. (dir. Chgo. chpt. 1987—), Ill. State Bar Assn., Fed. Trial Bar, Nat. Assn. Criminal Def. Lawyers. Office: Jenner & Block 1 IBM Plz Chicago IL 60611

MC QUEENEY, HENRY MARTIN, SR., publisher; b. N.Y.C., Oct. 29, 1938; s. John Henry and Catherine Mary (Quigg) McQ.; m. Elizabeth Bernino, May 14, 1960; children: Mary E., Henry M. Jr., John P., Matthew S. B.B.A., St. Johns U., 1960; postgrad., U. Rochester, 1965-67. City sales rep. Curtis Circulation div. Curtis Pub. Co., 1960-62; asst. mgr. Curtis Circulation div. Curtis Pub. Co., N.Y.C., 1962-63; field mgr. Curtis Circulation div. Curtis Pub. Co., Rochester, N.Y., 1964-67; dept. mgr., account exec. Curtis Circulation div. Curtis Pub. Co., Phila., 1968-74; v.p. sales, exec. v.p. mktg. Manor Books, Inc., N.Y.C., 1974-76; pres. Manor Books, Inc. 1976-79, Wood Hill Press, Inc., 1979-89, Scott Mag. Dist. Corp., N.Y.C., 1989-93, Kearny Pub., Inc., 1993—; chmn. bd. Oui mag., 1981-82; pres., CEO, J.Q. Adams Prodns., Inc., 1983-94; rep. Western N.Y. Pubs.; cons. Bipad Ednl. Program. Pres. parish bd. Roman Catholic Ch., 1965, editor newspaper, Spencerport, N.Y., 1965, diocesan leader, mem. lay bd., Rochester, 1964-67; certified as tchr. Confraternity Christian Doctrine, Diocese of Rochester, 1964. Served with USAFR, 1956-64. Mem. Am. Legion. Home: 12 Blenheim Ln Centerport NY 11721-1704 Office: Kearny Pub Inc 28 W 25th St New York NY 10010-2705

MCQUEENEY, THOMAS A., publisher; b. N.Y.C., Aug. 21, 1937; s. Henry J. and Jeannette A. (Beaton) McQ.; m. Ellyn M. Carney, Oct. 11, 1970; children: Kicha Lee, Miya Lyn, Jana Mai. BBA, Northeastern U., 1964. Market analyst Gillette Co., Boston, 1964-65; research analyst Chase Manhattan Bank, N.Y.C., 1965-68; portfolio mgr. Portfolio Planning, Inc., N.Y.C., 1968-71; pub., pres. Money Market Directories, Inc., Charlottesville, Va., 1971—. Editor: Real Estate Investing by Pension Fund Adminstrs., 1975. Mem. Indsl. Devel. Bd. Authority, Albemarle County, 1980—. Bd. advisors U. Calif.-Berkeley Grad. Sch. Journalism, 1991—, U. Calif.-Riverside Grad. Sch. Mgmt., 1994—. Recipient Journalism award Calif. State Bar Assn., 1967, Sweepstakes award Twin Counties Press Club, Riverside and San Bernardino, 1972. Mem. Am. Soc. Newspaper Editors (bd. dirs. 1992—), Calif. Soc. Newspaper Editors (bd. dirs. 1988-95), Calif. Newspaper Pubs. Assn. (bd. dirs. 1992—), Soc. Profl. Journalists, U. Calif.-Santa Barbara Alumni Assn. (bd. dirs. 1983-89). Home: 5717 Bedford Dr Riverside CA 92506-3404 Office: Press-Enterprise Co 3512 14th St Riverside CA 92501-3878

MCQUILKIN, JOHN ROBERTSON, religion educator, academic administrator, writer; b. Columbia, S.C., Sept. 7, 1927; s. Robert C. and Marguerite (Lambie) McQ.; m. Muriel Elaine Webendorfer, Aug. 24, 1948; children: Helen Marguerite, Robert Paul (dec.), David John, Virginia Anne, Amy Lambie, Douglas Kent. BA, Columbia Internat. U., 1947; M.Div., Fuller Theol. Sem., 1950; postgrad., No. Bapt. Theol. Sem., 1947-48. Prof. Greek, religious edn. and theology Columbia (S.C.) Internat. U., 1950-52; pres. Internat. U., 1968-90; chancellor Columbia (S.C.) Bible Coll. and Sem., 1990-93; headmaster Ben Lippen Sch., Asheville, N.C., 1952-55; missionary The Evang. Alliance Mission, Japan, 1956-68; acting pres. Tokyo Christian U., 1963-65. Author: Measuring the Church Growth Movement, 1974, Understanding and Applying the Bible, 1992, The Great Omission, 1984, An Introduction to Biblical Ethics, 1995; contbr. articles to religious jours. Mem. Evangel. Missiological Soc. (gen. dir. 1994—).

MC QUILLAN, JOSEPH MICHAEL, finance company executive; b. Meridian, Miss., Aug. 9, 1931; s. John Vincent and Florence (Hoban) McQ.; divorced; children: Joseph Michael, James Vincent, Ann Marie, Tom Charles, Mary Clare, Tim Sean; m. Barbara Crawford, Nov. 25, 1983. B.S., Creighton U., Omaha, 1956. Mgr. Arthur Andersen & Co. (CPAs), Omaha

and L.A., 1956-63; comptr. Cudahy Co., Phoenix, 1963-66; exec. v.p., comptr. Assoc. Corp. N.Am., 1969—; sr. exec. v.p. Assoc. Corp. N.Am., South Bend, Ind., 1988—; vice chmn. Assoc. Corp. N.Am., 1991; pres. Assocs. Fin. Svcs. Co. Inc., Dallas, 1991; pres. Ford Consumer Fin. Co., Dallas, 1990. Served with USAF, 1951-55. Mem. Nat. Assn. CPAs, Beta Alpha Pi. Home: 4417 Windsor Ridge Dr Irving TX 75038-6303 Office: Assoc Corp N Am PO Box 660237 250 Carpenter Frwy Dallas TX 75062-2789

MCQUILLAN, WILLIAM HUGH, building company executive; b. Newtown, Conn., Apr. 6, 1935; s. Alexander Jerome and Madeleine (McLaughlin) McQ.; m. Eileen Mary Craig, Aug. 29, 1959; children—Madeleine, William, Maureen, Patrick. B.B.A., Fairfield U., 1959. Asst. v.p. Fairfield Homes Inc., Conn., 1959-64; v.p. Am. Gen. Contrn. Co., Botsford, 1964-68; various mgmt. positions ITT Levitt and Sons, Lake Success, N.Y., 1968-74; sr. v.p. Gen. Devel. Corp., Miami, 1974-91; pres The McQuillan Corp., Stuart, Fla., 1991-94; v.p. Nat. Guardian Securities, Inc., Greenwich, Conn., 1994—. Served with U.S. Army, 1959-63. Mem. Nat. Assn. Homebuilders. Roman Catholic. Address: 76 S River Rd Stuart FL 34996

MCQUILLEN, HARRY A., publishing company executive. Formerly with Prentice-Hall; former dir. mktg. services Coll. div. McGraw-Hill; former editor-in-chief Coll. div. CBS Pub., pres. Ednl. and Profl. Pub. div., 1983-87; group v.p. Gen. Pub. Group Macmillan Inc., N.Y.C., 1987-88, v.p.; 1988; pres. Macmillan Pub. Co., 1988-91; pres., CEO K-III Mag Corp., N.Y.C. 1991—; pres. K-III Media Group, N.Y.C., 1994—. Office: K-III Mags 10th Fl 717 5th Ave Fl 10 New York NY 10022-8101

MC QUILLEN, MICHAEL PAUL, physician; b. N.Y.C., Sept. 9, 1932; s. Paul and Dorothy Marian (Moore) McQ.; m. Louise Devlin; children: Daniel, Thomas, Patrick, Kathleen. B.A. cum laude, Georgetown U., 1953, M.D., 1957; MA, U. Va., 1994. Diplomate Am. Bd. Psychiatry and Neurology (bd. dirs. 1991-95, exec. com. 1995). Rotating intern Royal Victoria Hosp., Montreal, Que., Can., 1957-58; resident in neurology Georgetown U. Med. Center, 1958-60; fellow in physiology Johns Hopkins U. Med. Sch. and Hosp., 1960-62, instr. medicine, 1962-65; mem. faculty U. Ky. Med. Center, 1965-74, prof. neurology, 1972-74, prof., chmn. neurology, 1987-93; prof. neurology, chmn. dept. Med. Coll. Wis., Milw., 1974-87; clin. faculty mem. dept. neurology U. Va. Health Sci. Ctr., Charlottesville, 1993-94; prof. neurology U. Rochester St. Mary's Hosp., N.Y., 1995—; vis. sci. Inst. Neurophysiology U. Copenhagen, 1971-72; vis. prof. U. Ky. Med. Ctr., 1978, Royal Coll. Surgeons, Ireland, 1983. Author articles, papers in field. Mem. Cath. Commn. on Intellectual Affairs. Recipient Neurology medal Georgetown U. Med. Sch., 1957; Clin. Teaching award Med. Coll. Wis., 1976; Disting. Service award N.Y. Med. Coll., 1983; named to Johns Hopkins Soc. Scholars, 1981. Fellow Am. Acad. Neurology; mem. Royal Acad. Medicine Ireland, Nat. Myasthenia Gravis Found. (chmn. 1981-83), Am. Neurol. Assn., N.Y. Acad. Scis., Assn. U. Profs. Neurology, Am. Assn. Electromyography and Electrodiagnosis, AMA, Wis. Neurol. Assn. (pres. 81-82), Milw. Acad. Medicine, Alpha Omega Alpha. Home: 4 Bragdon Dr Rochester NY 14618 Office: St Mary's Hosp Rochester NY 14613

MCQUINN, MICHAEL RAND, lawyer; b. Butler, Mo., July 4, 1946; s. Verdun M. and Helen Ruane (Sanderson) McQ.; m. Laura M. McQuinn, June 30, 1973; children: Matthew, Thomas. AB, Stanford U., 1969, JD, 1972. Bar: Calif. 1972, D.C. 1981, U.S. Supreme Ct., U.S. Dist. Ct. D.C., U.S. Ct. of Appeals D.C. Teaching fellow law Stanford (Calif.) U., 1972-73; atty. Calif. Law Revision Com., Stanford, 1973-74; trial atty. antitrust div. U.S. Dept. Justice, Washington, 1974-76, asst. chief evaluation, 1976-79; assoc. prof. law U. Houston, 1979-80; assoc. Cahill, Gordon & Reindel, Washington, 1980-84, ptnr., 1984—. Mem. ABA (antitrust sect.), Order of the Coif, Fairfax (Va.) Country Club. Avocation: golf. Home: 4828 Fox Chapel Rd Fairfax VA 22030-4509 Office: Cahill Gordon & Reindel 1990 K St NW Washington DC 20006-1103

MC QUINN, WILLIAM P., corporation executive; b. Waterbury, Conn., May 2, 1936; s. William and Bridget (Flynn) McQ.; m. Lorese Hucks, Apr. 17, 1964; children: Kathryn, Norah, Linda, Jennifer. B.S., Bryant Coll., 1956. C.P.A., Conn. Mgmt. auditor NASA, Washington, 1962-64; asst. controller Scovill Mfg. Co., Waterbury, 1964-67; controller C F & I Steel Co., Pueblo, Colo., 1967-71; v.p. financial services Loews Corp., N.Y.C., 1971-73; chief exec. officer Williams Hudson Am. subs. Williams Hudson Group Ltd., Eng., 1973-75; pres. Pegasus Design Group (formerly Williams Hudson Am.), 1975-78; v.p. M.W. Houck, Inc., Rye, N.Y., 1979-82; chief operating officer Cusinarts Inc, Greenwich, CT, 1982-88; exec. v.p. CHC of Conn., Inc., 1988-94; chmn., CEO Fin. Svcs. Inc., Old Greenwich, Conn. 1994—. Served with U.S. Army, 1959. Mem. Am. Inst. C.P.A.s, Fin. Execs. Inst. Home: 8 Vista Ave Old Greenwich CT 06870-2135

MCQUISTON, ROBERT EARL, lawyer; b. Pitts., Feb. 4, 1936; s. Theodore O. and Bertha L. (Kegley) McQ.; m. Mary Hope Missimer, June 30, 1962; children: Mary Hope, Elizabeth Ann. BA magna cum laude, Yale U., 1958; JD cum laude, Harvard U., 1961. Bar: Pa. 1962. Assoc. Ballard, Spahr, Andrews & Ingersoll, Phila., Balt., Denver, Washington, Salt Lake City, 1962-69, ptnr., 1969—; mem. nat. adv. group to Commr. IRS, Washington, 1985-87; lectr. in law Temple U., 1968-69, also various tax insts.; bd. dirs. Macromedia Inc., Hackensack, N.J., Gateway Communications, Inc., Binghamton, N.Y. Contbr. articles to profl. jours. Mem. Rep. Fin. Com., Harrisburg, Pa., 1983-86; trustee Am. Soc. Hypertension, 1992—. Mem. ABA (active numerous coms. sect. taxation 1969—, including coun. mem. 1979-85, vice chmn., sect. taxation 1982-85), Phila. Bar Assn. (bd. govs. 1978-80, mem. coun. 1986—, sec. treas sect. on taxation 1973-75, vice chmn. 1976-78, chmn. 1978-80), Am. Coll. Tax Counsel (charter, regent 1990—, vice chmn. 1993-94, chmn. 1994—), Nat. Conf. Lawyers and CPAs, Pyramid Club. Episcopalian. Home: 111 Ridgewood Rd Wayne PA 19087-2810 Office: Ballard Spahr Andrews et al 1735 Market St Fl 51 Philadelphia PA 19103-7599

MCQUOWN, JUDITH HERSHKOWITZ, author, financial advisor; b. N.Y.C., Apr. 8, 1941; d. Frederick Ephraim and Pearl (Rosenberg) H.; m. Michael L. McQuown, Jan. 13, 1969 (div. 1980); m. Harrison Roth, Dec. 7, 1985 (div. 1995). AB, Hunter Coll., 1963; postgrad., N.Y. Inst. Fin., N.Y.C., 1965. Chief underwriting div. mcpl. securities City of N.Y., 1972-73; chief exec. officer Judith H. McQuown & Co., Inc., N.Y.C., 1973—. Author: Inc. Yourself: How to Profit by Setting Up Your Own Corporation, 8th edit., 1995, Tax Shelters That Work for Everyone, 1979, The Fashion Survival Manual, 1981, Playing the Takeover Market, 1982, How to Profit After You Inc. Yourself, 1985, Keep One Suitcase Empty: The Bargain Shopper's Guide to the Finest Factory Outlets in the British Isles, 1987, Keep One Suitcase Empty: The Bargain Shopper's Guide to the Finest Factory Outlets in Europe, 1988, Use Your Own Corporation to Get Rich, 1991; contbg. editor Boardroom Reports, Physician's Fin. News, Physician's Guide to Money Mgmt.; seminars The Learning Annex, The Discovery Ctr., Boston Ctr. for Adult Edn. Mem. Am. Soc. Journalists and Authors, Nat. Arts Club. Home and Office: 315 E 72nd St New York NY 10021-4626

MCRAE, DAVID CARROLL, hospital administrator; b. Winston-Salem, N.C., Apr. 15, 1946; married. B. U. N.C., 1968, MHA, 1975; M, East Carolina U., 1985. Adminstr. Medictr. of Am., Raleigh, N.C., 1971-72, Hillhaven Convalescent Ctr., Raleigh, 1972-76; v.p. Univ. Med. Ctr. Pitt County Meml. Hosp., Greenville, N.C., 1976-84, sr. v.p., 1985-86, sr. v.p., chief oper. officer, 1986-89, pres., chief exec. officer, 1989—. Home: 303 Williamsburg Dr Greenville NC 27858-6329 Office: Pitt County Meml Hosp-Univ Med Ctr Ea Carolina-Pitt County PO Box 6028 Greenville NC 27835-6028

MCRAE, HAMILTON EUGENE, III, lawyer; b. Midland, Tex., Oct. 29, 1937; s. Hamilton Eugene and Adrian (Hagaman) McR.; m. Betty Hawkins, Aug. 27, 1960; children: Elizabeth Ann, Stephanie Adrian, Scott Hawkins. BSEE, U. Ariz., 1961; student, USAF Electronics Sch. 1961-62; postgrad., U. Redlands, Calif., 1962-63; JD with honors and distinction, U. Ariz., 1967; LHD (hon.), Sterling Coll., 1992; vis. fellow, Darwin Coll. Cambridge (Eng.) U. Bar: Ariz. 1967, U.S. Supreme Ct. 1979; cert. real estate specialist, Ariz. Elec. engr. Salt River Project, Phoenix, 1967; assoc. Jennings, Strouss & Salmon, Phoenix, 1967-71, ptnr., 1971-85, chmn. real estate dept., 1980-85, mem. policy com., 1982-85, mem. fin. com., 1981-85, chmn. bus. devel. com., 1982-85; ptnr. and co-founder Stuckey & McRae, Phoenix, 1985—; co-founder, chmn. bd. Republic Cos., Phoenix, 1985—; magistrate Paradise Valley, Ariz., 1983-85; juvenile referee Superior Ct., 1983-85; pres., dir. Phoenix Realty & Trust Co., 1970—; officer Indsl. Devel. Corp. Maricopa County, 1972-86; instr. and lectr. in real estate; officer, bd. dirs. other corps.; adj. prof. Frank Lloyd Wright Sch. Architecture, Scottsdale, Ariz., 1989—; instr. Ariz. State U. Coll. Architecture and Environ. Design; lead instr. ten-state-bar seminar on Advanced Real Estate Transactions, 1992; evaluation com. for cert. real estate specialist Ariz. Bar, 1994—. Contbr. articles to profl. jours. Elder Valley Presbyn. Ch., Scottsdale, Ariz., 1973-75, 82-85, chair evangelism com. 1973-74, corp. pres., 1974-75, 84-85, trustee, 1973-75, 82-85, chmn. exec. com., 1984, mem. mission com. 1993—; trustee Upward Found., Phoenix, 1977-80, Valley Presbyn. Found., 1982-83, Ariz. Acad., 1971—; trustee, mem. exec. com. Phi Gamma Delta Ednl. Found., Washington, 1974-84; trustee Phi Gamma Delta Internat., 1984-86; bd. dirs. Archon, 1986-87; founder, trustee, pres. McRae Found., 1980—; bd. dirs. Food for Hungry Inc. (Internat. Relief), 1985-95, exec.-treas. com. 1986—, chmn. bd. dirs. 1987-92; chmn. bd. dirs. Food for Hungry Internat. 1993-95; pres. adv. coun., 1995—; trustee, mem. exec. com. Ariz. Mus. Sci. and Tech., 1984—, 1st v.p., 1985-86, pres., 1986-88, chmn. bd. dirs., 1988-90; Lambda Alpha Internat. Hon. Land Econs. Soc, 1988—; sec.-treas. Ariz. State U. Coun. for Design Excellence, 1989-90, bd. dirs. 1988—, pres. 1990-91; mem. Crisis Nursery Office of the Chair, 1988-89, Maricopa Community Colls. Found., 1988—, sec. 1990-91, 2d v.p 1993-94, 1st v.p. and pres. elect 1994-95, pres. 1995—, Phoenix Cmty. Alliance, 1988-90, Interchurch Ctr. Corp., 1987-90, Western Art Assocs., bd. dirs., 1989-91, Phoenix Com. on Fgn. Rels., 1988—, U. Ariz. Pres.'s Club, 1984—, chmn., 1991-92; bd. dirs. Econ. Club of Phoenix, 1987—, Ctrl. Ariz. Shelter Svcs. 1995—, sec.-treas., 1991-92, v.p., 1992-93, pres. 1993-94; mem. adv. bd. Help Wanted USA, 1990-92; vol. fund raiser YMCA, Salvation Army, others; bd. dirs. Frank Lloyd Wright Found., 1992—; mem. Taliesin Coun., 1985—; founding mem. Frank Lloyd Wright Soc., 1993—; mem. fin. com. Kyl for Congress, 1985-92, bd. dir. campaign bd. Kyl for U.S. Senate, 1993-94; Senator Kyl Coun., 1995—; campaign com. Symington for Gov. '90, 1989—, mem. gubernatorial adv. bd., 1990-91; mem. Gov.'s Selection Com. for State Revenue Dir., 1993; mem. bond com. City of Phoenix, 1987-88; mem. Ariz. State U. Coun. of 100, 1985-89, investment com., 1985-89; bd. govs. Twelve Who Care Hon Kachina, 1991; mem. adv. coun. Maricopa County Sports Authority, 1989-93; mem. Ariz. Coalition for Tomorrow, 1990-92; founding mem., bd. dirs. Waste Not Inc., 1992-94, pres., 1990-92, chmn., 1992-94. 1st lt. USAF, 1961-64,. Recipient various mil. award. Mem. ABA, AIEE, AIME, Ariz. Bar Assn., Maricopa County Bar Assn., U. Ariz. Alumni Assn., Nat. Soc. Fund Raising Execs, Bar com. for selecting real estate specialists, Clan McRae Soc. N.Am, Phoenix Exec. Club, Jackson Hole Racquet Club, Teton Pines Country Club, Tau Beta Pi. Republican. Home: 810 AZ 85253-2907 Office: Republic Cos 2425 E Camelback Rd Ste 900 Phoenix AZ 85016-4215

MCRAE, JOHN MALCOLM, college dean, architect; b. Vicksburg, Miss., Sept. 4, 1942; s. John L. and Thelma L. (Nabors) McR.; m. Sharon Koscak, July 23, 1971; children: Shane, Kelley, Ryan. BArch, U. Tex., 1966; MArch, Rice U., 1967. Registered architect, Fla. Instr. dept. architecture U. Fla. Gainesville, 1967-70, asst. prof., 1970-75, assoc. prof., 1975-80, prof., 1980-87, asst. dean Coll. Architecture, 1977-79, assoc. dean, 1979-87, dir. instrn., 1979, acting chmn. dept. architecture, 1981-85, chmn., 1983-87, acting chmn. dept. interior design, 1984-86; dean Sch. Architecture Miss. State U., Starkville, 1987—; pvt. cons., 1971—; advisor Miss. Bd. Licensing Activities, 1987—; assoc. Ctr. Gerontol. Studies U. Fla., 1976—; adv. bd. Pinellas County Fine Arts Coun., Clearwater, Fla., 1979; adv. coun. nat. program Architects-in-School sponsored by Nat. Endowment for Arts, 1978-79; mem. steering com. environments and aging program Gerontol. Soc. Am., 1978-79; chmn. Fla. legis. com. on housing for elderly, 1986-87; awards juror Jacksonville Arts Coun., Fla., 1982; juror archtl. achievements Orlando Mag., 1986; others. Major archtl. projects and consultations include Hist. Am. Bldgs. Survey, Nat. Pk. Svc., Washington, Community Evang. Free Ch., Gainesville, Fla., 1976-79, Bethel Bapt. Ch., Marion Oaks, Fla., 1978-79, Found. for Aging Rsch., Clearwater, 1982, Sunrise Retirement Community, Carrbora, N.C., 1979, 1981, Advent Christian Village, 1986-87, So. Coll. Tech., Atlanta, 1988; employed by John Gifford) Sparks Ave. Shopping Ctr., Comml. Bldg. Federal St., Wannacomet Bldg. Complex, Harbor House Hotel Complex, others, also pvt. residencies, Nantucket, Mass., 1971-73; cons. various archtl. firms including Myrl Hanes and Assocs., Zeisel Rsch. Group; author jour. articles, tchr.'s guides, workbooks, teaching modules, reports. Bd. dirs. Miss. Downtown Devel. Assocs., 1987—. Grantee Nat. Endowment for Arts, 1970-71, 77-79, rsch. grantee U. Fla., 1974, 76-77, Gerontol. Soc. grantee, 1976-77, Fla. Ednl. Rsch. and Devel., 1976-77, State of Fla., 1986, 87, Miss. State U., Rsch. Initiation grant, 1987-88. Fellow AIA (alternate state dir. Fla. chpt. 1979-80, chpt. 1981-82, chm. coms. on design and collegiate rels. 1982-84, corr. mem. com. on health 1986, nat. vice chair designate architects in edn. com. 1992—, nat. archtl. accrediting bd. taks force 1991, juror Sarasota chpt. ann. awards program 1985, Mid-Fla. chpt. design awards 1986, chmn. state awards jury S.C. chpt. 1988, mem. landscape archtl. teams various univs. 1981—). Office: Miss State U Sch Architecture PO Drawer AQ Mississippi State MS 39762

MCRAE, KAREN K., state legislator; b. Detroit, Feb. 19, 1944; m. Gossett W. McRae; 2 children. BSL, Georgetown U., 1965. Mem. N.H. Ho. of Reps.; vice chmn. sci., tech. and energy com. Active Goffstown Conservation Com., 1972—, chmn., 1975-79. Mem. Georgetown U. Alumni Assn. (class mem. 1975—). Avocations: skiing, gardening, gourmet cooking, baking, reading. Home: 469 Black Brook Rd Goffstown NH 03045 Office: NH Ho of Reps State Capitol Concord NH 03301

MC RAE, KENNETH DOUGLAS, political scientist, educator; b. Toronto, Ont., Can., Jan. 20, 1925; s. Douglas Archibald and Margaret Constance McR.; m. Dorothea Annette Simon, Aug. 4, 1950; children: Patricia, Sandra, Karen, Susan. BA, U. Toronto, 1946; AM, Harvard U., 1947, PhD, 1954; postgrad., Oxford (Eng.) U., 1948-50, postdoctoral research, 1953-55. Lectr. in polit. sci. U. Toronto, 1950-52; asst. prof. polit. sci. Carleton U., Ottawa, Ont., 1955-57, assoc. prof., 1957-64, prof., 1964—; research supr. Royal Commn. on Bilingualism and Biculturalism, 1964-69. Author: (with Louis Hartz and others) The Founding of New Societies: Studies in the History of the United States, Latin America, South Africa, Canada and Australia, 1964, Switzerland: Example of Cultural Coexistence, 1964, Conflict and Compromise in Multilingual Societies, Vol. 1, Switzerland, 1983, Vol. 2, Belgium, 1986; editor: The Six Bookes of a Commonwealte (Jean Bodin), 1962; editor and project dir.: The Federal Capital: Governmental Institutions, 1969; editor, contbg. author: Consociational Democracy: Political Accommodation in Segmented Societies, 1974; contbg. author: Conflict and Peacemaking in Multiethnic Societies, 1990. Fellow Royal Soc. Can. (hon. sec. 1980-83); mem. Can. Polit. Sci. Assn. (pres. 1978-79), Soc. Scientiarum Fennica (fgn. mem.), Renaissance Soc. Am. Office: Carleton U, Dept Polit Sci, Ottawa, ON Canada K1S 5B6

MCRAE, PAUL ANTHONY, symphony orchestra conductor; b. Liverpool, England, Dec. 4, 1945; came to U.S. 1946; s. Thomas and Florence (Gordon) McR.; m. Sherry Louise Williams, Nov. 23, 1979; children: Blaine, Ashley, Tyler. Student, Juilliard Sch., 1962-63; MusB, Eastman Sch. Music, 1963-67; master classes in conducting, Aspen (Colo.) Music Festival, 1964, 69, 79, 82; diploma, Accademia Musicale Chigiana, Siena, Italy, 1984. Cert. musical conductor. Asst. conductor Hochstein Sinfonia, Rochester, N.Y., 1965-67; 2d and assoc. prin. trumpet player Rochester (N.Y.) Philharm. Orch., 1966-74; music dir., condr. Boca Raton (Fla.) Symphony Orch., 1982-84; guest condr. Philharmonia Hungarica, Recklinghausen, German Dem. Republic, 1984, Russe Symphony Orch., Bulgaria, 1984, London Symphony Orch., 1984, 85, 87, 88; resident condr. Philharm. Orch. Fla. Ft. Lauderdale, 1985-87; guest condr. English Chamber Orch., 1985, Royal Philharm. Orch., London, 1986-87, 88, Pitts. Symphony Orch., 1986, Anchorage (Alaska) Symphony Orch., 1986, Lake Forest (Ill.) Symphony Orch., 1986-87; music dir. Lake Forest Symphony Orch., 1987—; Greensboro (N.C.) Symphony Orch., 1987—, New Orch. of Ill., 1988—; Dir. music Ballet Fla., West Palm Beach, 1983-84. Albums include Dvorak Symphony #8 performed by Philharmonia Hungarica, 1984, Mozart Symphony #31 and #34 Overture to Der Schauspieldirektor performed by English Chamber Orch., 1984, Stravinsky Pulcinella Suite Respighi Gli Uccelli performed English Chamber Orch., 1984; music ednl. videocassettes, "The Listener", "The Thrill of the Orchestra", 1987, DIscovering the Orch. (Critic's Choice award Nat. Libr.

Assn., 1988). Avocations: boating, fishing, tennis. Office: Greensboro Symphony Orch 712 Summit Ave Greensboro NC 27405-7832 also: Lake Forest Symphony Orch 700 E Westleigh Rd Lake Forest IL 60045

MCRAE, ROBERT MALCOLM, JR., federal judge; b. Memphis, Dec. 31, 1921; s. Robert Malcolm and Irene (Pontius) McR.; m. Louise Howry, July 31, 1943; children: Susan Campbell, Robert Malcolm III, Duncan Farquhar, Thomas Alexander Todd. BA, Vanderbilt U., 1943; LLB, U. Va., 1948. Bar: Tenn. 1948. Practice in Memphis, 1948-64; judge Tenn. Circuit Ct., 1964-66; judge U.S. Dist. Ct. (we. dist.) Tenn., Memphis, 1966-94, chief judge, 1979-86, sr. judge, 1987-94; mem. Jud. Council 6th Cir., 1982-85, Jud. Conf. Commn. Adminstrn. Criminal Law, 1979-86, Jud. Conf. U.S., 1984-87. Pres. Episcopal Ch. men of Tenn., 1964-65. Mem. Dist. Judges Assn. 6th Circuit (pres.). Home: 220 Baronne Pl Memphis TN 38117

MCRAE, THOMAS KENNETH, retired investment company executive; b. Richmond, Va., July 7, 1906; s. Christopher Duncan and Sarah Alice (Lawrence) McR.; m. Marion Lanier White, Sept. 11, 1937; children: Thomas Kenneth Jr., John Daniel. B.A., U. Richmond, 1927; postgrad. Sch. Banking, Rutgers U., 1936-38. Asst. cashier First Mchts. Nat. Bank, Richmond, 1940-46, asst. v.p., 1946-49, v.p., 1949-63, sr. v.p., 1963-71; v.p. Davenport and Co., Richmond, 1971-85, sr. investment officer, 1985-90. Trustee Va. Supplemental Retirement System, 1964-71; active Va. Mus. Fine Arts. Mem. Richmond Soc. Fin. Analysts. Republican. Baptist. Clubs: Country of Va., Downtown, Bd. of Va. Lodges: Masons, Rotary. Avocations: golf; stamp collecting.

MCRAITH, JOHN JEREMIAH, bishop; b. Hutchinson, Minn., Dec. 6, 1934; s. Arthur Luke and Marie (Hanley) McR. B.A., Loras Coll., Dubuque, Iowa, 1956. Ordained priest, Roman Cath. Ch. 1960. Assoc. pastor St. Mary's Ch., Sleepy Eye, Minn., 1960-64, assoc. pastor, 1968-71; pastor St. Michael's Ch., Mickoy, Minn., 1964-67, St. Leo's Ch., St. Leo, Minn., 1967-68; dir. Nat. Cath. Rural Life, Des Moines, 1971-78; vicar gen. Diocese of New Ulm, Minn., 1978-82; bishop Owensboro, Ky., 1982—. Home: 501 W 5th St Owensboro KY 42301-0765 Office: 600 Locust St Owensboro KY 42301-2130

MCRARY, JOHN WALTER, III, defense contract research and development company executive; b. Asheville, N.C., July 16, 1939; s. John Walter Jr. and Margaret Gladys (Johnson) McR.; m. Carolyn Celeste Clapp, Dec. 27, 1960. B.S. in Physics, N.C. State U., 1961, M.S. in Physics, 1963, Ph.D. in Physics, 1964. Mem. tech. staff aerospace service div. Pan Am. Worldways, Cocoa Beach, Fla., 1964-70; exec. v.p. Sci. Applications Internat. Corp., Huntsville, Ala., 1971—, vice chmn. bd. dirs., mgr. software policy, 1987—, mem. exec. and ops., chmn. exec. com., mgr. corp. bus. devel., 1988—, chmn. corp. risk com., chmn. fixed price rev. bd., also bd. dirs.; chmn. Sci. Applications Internat. Corp. subs. comsystems, 1977-78, JRB Assocs., 1977; bd. dirs. Saudi SAIC, SAIC-Comml.; adj. asst. prof. physics Fla. Inst. Tech., Melbourne, 1964-65; adj. asst. prof. math. U. Fla.-Cape Caneveral, 1967-69. Author profl. reports, papers; also articles. Adviser U. Ala. Sci. and Tech. Panel, Huntsville, 1984—. Nat. Merit scholar, 1957-61; AEC fellow, 1961-62; NSF fellow, 1963-64. Mem. Heritage Club. Republican. Methodist. Avocations: running, swimming. Office: Science Applications Inter Corp 6725 Odyssey Dr NW Huntsville AL 35806-3300

MCREE, EDWARD BARXDALE, hospital administrator; b. Pauls Valley, Okla., Oct. 20, 1931; s. Henry Barxdale and Mary (Shumate) McR.; B.A. Okla. City U., 1953; student U. Okla., 1953; student Central State Coll. 1954-55; m. Jan Bryant, Aug. 23, 1953; children—Scott, Kent, Chad. Adminstr. Eaton Rapids (Mich.) Community Hosp., 1957-61; pres. Ingham Med. Center, Lansing, Mich., 1961—; dir. Grad. Med. Edn., Inc., 1970—, treas., 1978-79, pres., 1979-81; pres. Mid-Mich. Emergency Services Council, 1978-81; dir. Kent Bank & Trust, Lansing, N.A., Olo Kent Bank of Lansing; bd. dirs. Blue Cross/Blue Shield of Mich. Mem. Eaton Rapids (Mich.) Bd. Edn., 1964-71, treas., 1968-71. Pres., Tri-County Emergency Med. Services Council, 1974—, also mem. bd. dirs.; bd. dirs. Blue Cross Mich., 1974-75, 1986; bd. dirs. Hosp. Purchasing Service Mich., 1973—, pres., 1976-77, chmn., 1987; bd. dirs. Mid-Mich. chpt. ARC, 1979—, treas., 1980—, chmn., 1981-83; bd. dirs. Lansing Symphony Assn., 1984—. Served with AUS, 1955-57. Mem. Mich. (v.p. 1965-68), Southwestern Mich. (pres. 1968) hosp. assns., Am. Hosp. Assn. (regent 1987—), Am. Hosp. Assn., Univ. Club Mich. State U. (bd. dirs. 1985—), Lambda Chi Alpha. Beta Beta Beta. Methodist (mem. West Mich. Conf. Bd. Finance 1972—). Lodge: Rotary (bd. dirs. Lansing club 1985—). Club: Rotary. Contbr. articles to profl. jours. Home: 123 N East St Eaton Rapids MI 48827-1314 Office: Mich Affiliated Health System System, Ingram Med Ctr 401 W Greenlawn Ave Lansing MI 48910-2819

MCREYNOLDS, NEIL LAWRENCE, consultant; b. Seattle, July 27, 1934; s. Dorr E. and Margaret (Gillies) McR.; m. Nancy Joyce Drew, June 21, 1957; children: Christopher, Bonnie. BA in Journalism, U. Wash., 1956. Assoc. editor Bellevue (Wash.) Am., 1956-60, editor, 1960-67; press sec. to Gov. Dan Evans State of Wash., Olympia, 1967-73; N.W. regional mgr. for pub. rels. and pub. affairs ITT Corp., Seattle, 1973-80; v.p. corp. rels. Puget Sound Power & Light, Bellevue, 1980-87, sr. v.p., 1987-95; prin. McReynolds & Assocs., Seattle, 1995—; bd. dirs. Continental Savs. Bank, Seattle, 1986—, chmn. com. adv. com., rsch. adv. coun. Electric Power Rsch. Inst., 1989-90. Bd. dirs. Seattle Symphony, 1981-89, Ind. Colls. of Wash., 1984-95, Corp. Coun. for Arts, 1985-94; chmn., bd. dirs. Fred Hutchinson Cancer Rsch. Ctr., 1993-95; chmn., bd., Leadership Tomorrow, Seattle, 1987; pres. Seattle Ctr. Found., 1979-80, Electric Info. Coun., 1988; chmn. bd. trustees Bellevue C.C., 1976-77; chmn. bd. dirs. Seattle-King County Econ. Devel. Coun., 1994; state chmn. Nature Conservancy, 1988-90; mem. Wash. State Commn. on Trial Cts., 1990; chmn. King County 2000, 1988-90. Named Citizen of Yr., Bellevue, One of Wash. State's Three Outstanding Young Men; recipient Pres. medal Pacific Luth. U. Mem. Pub. Rels. Soc. Am. (accredited), N.W. Elec. Light and Power Assn. (pres. 1992-93), Greater Seattle C. of C. (bd. dirs. 1979—), Rainier Club (trustee 1995—), Overlake Gold and Country Club (trustee 1993—), Bellevue Athletic Club, Rotary (pres. Downtown Seattle Club 1991-92), Sigma Delta Chi. Republican. Episcopalian. Avocations: golf, hiking, skiing, photography. Home: 14312 SE 45 St Bellevue WA 98006 Office: 2000 Two Union Square 601 Union St Seattle WA 98101-2326

MCROBERTS, JOYCE, state legislator; b. Salmon, Idaho, July 31, 1941; m. Darrel S. McRoberts; children: Walter, Angela, Douglas. Ed., Twin Falls Bus. Coll. Senate maj. leader Idaho State Senate. Republican. Home: PO Box 2016 Twin Falls ID 83303-3855

MCRORIE, WILLIAM EDWARD, life insurance company executive; b. Rutherfordton, N.C., Apr. 8, 1940; s. Cyrus Brown and Rosalie (Thompson) McR.; m. Hope Evangeline Foster, Sept. 9, 1962; children: Mark Edward, Jennifer Lynn. LLB, U. N.C., 1964. CLU; Bar: N.C. State mgr. Sturdivant Life Ins. Co., Lynchburg, Va., 1965-68; sr. v.p. First Colony, Lynchburg, 1969—; sec. Jamestown Life Ins. Co., Lynchburg, 1981—. Vice mayor City of Lynchburg. Mem. ABA, N.C. Bar Assn., Va. Bar Assn., Assn. Life Ins. Counsel, Christian Legal Soc., John Lynch Soc. (sec. 1970—). Home: 2600 Link Rd Lynchburg VA 24503-3012 Office: First Colony Life Ins Co PO Box 1280 Lynchburg VA 24505-1280

MC ROSTIE, CLAIR NEIL, economics educator; b. Owatonna, Minn., Dec. 16, 1930; s. Neil Hale and Myrtle Julia (Peterson) McR.; m. Ursula Anne Schwieger, Aug. 29, 1968. BSBA cum laude, Gustavus Adolphus Coll., 1952; MA in Mktg., Mich. State U., 1953; Ph.D. in Fin., U. Wis., 1963; postgrad., U. Minn., 1971-72, Am. Grad. Sch. Internat. Mgmt., 1980-81; cert., Coll. for Fin. Planning, 1990. Cert. fin. planner. Faculty Gustavus Adolphus Coll., St. Peter, Minn., 1958—; chmn. dept. econs. and bus. Gustavus Adolphus Coll., 1967-83, chmn., mem. various coms., 1971—; teaching asst. Sch. Commerce, U. Wis., 1960-62; lectr. European div. U. Md., 1966-67; vis. prof. Am. Grad. Sch. Internat. Mgmt., 1980-81; pres. World Trade Week, Inc., 1987. Editor: Global Resources: Perspectives and Alternatives, 1978, The Future of the Market Economy, 1979. Congregation pres. First Luth. Ch., St. Peter, Minn., 1972-73, 93, chmn. pastoral call com., 1968-69, chmn. staffing com., 1975, mem. ch. council, 1968-74, 89-93; chmn. social ministry com. Minn. Synod, Luth. Ch. Am., 1975; chmn. Rep. council arts professions, scis., Minn., 1968-70, co-chmn. state task force on Vietnam,

1968; mem. adv. commn. Minn. Dept. Manpower Services, 1967-71; mem. North Central Regional Manpower Adv. Com.; Bd. dirs. Midwest China Resource Study Center; del. White House Conf. Aging, 1971. Served with U.S. Army, 1954-56. Recipient Leavey Found. award Freedoms Found., Valley Forge, Pa.; Research fellow Fed. Res. Bank of Chgo., 1962-63. Mem. Fin. Execs. Inst., Inst. Cert. Fin. Planners, Fin. Profls. Assn., Soc. Coll. and Univ. Planning, Minn. Econs. Assn. (bd. dirs. 1974-75, 79-80), Sierra Club (exec. com. North Star chpt., Midwest regional conservation com.; 4th officer nat. coun. 1972-78), Alpha Kappa Psi, Iota Delta Gamma, Sigma Epsilon. Republican. Lutheran. Avocations: bird watching, backpacking, fitness and health. Home: Rural Rt 1 Box 198 Saint Peter MN 56082 Office: Gustavus Adolphus Coll Saint Peter MN 56082

MCRUER, DUANE TORRANCE, aerospace engineering executive; b. Bakersfield, Calif., Oct. 25, 1925; s. John Torrance and Ruth Inez (Bartlett) McR.; m. Betty June Mechura, Oct. 5, 1955; 1 child, Lara McRuer Case; 1 stepson, Stephen Harsey. BS in Engring., Calif. Inst. Tech., 1945, MEE, 1948. Registered profl. engr., Calif. Tech. chief, flight controls Northrop Aircraft Inc., Hawthorne, Calif., 1948-54; pres. Controls Specialists Inc., Inglewood, Calif., 1954-57; pres., tech. dir. Systems Tech. Inc., Hawthorne, Calif., 1957—; Regents' lectr. U. Calif., Santa Barbara, 1976; Mem. NRC Aero. and Space Engring Bd., Washington, 1988—, NASA Aero. Adv. Com., Washington, 1978-88, Am. Automatic Control Coun. (pres. 1969-73); bd. dirs. Ear Internat., Los Angeles. Author: Analysis of Nonlinear Control Systems, 1961, Aircraft Dynamics and Automatic Control, 1974; author more than 100 tech. papers, 1948—; patentee in field. Lt. (j.g.) USNR, 1943-53. Recipient Louis Levy medal Franklin Inst., Phila., 1960, Disting. Alumnus award Calif. Inst. Tech., 1983. Fellow AIAA (Mechanics and Control of Flight award, 1970), Soc. Automotive Engrs., IEEE, Human Factors Soc. (A.W. Williams award 1976), AAAS, Caltech Assocs. (Pasadena), Am. Alpine Club (N.Y.C.), Sierra Club. Episcopalian. Avocation: mountaineering. Office: Systems Tech Inc 13766 Hawthorne Blvd Hawthorne CA 90250-7083

MCSHAN, CLYDE GRIFFIN, II, financial executive; b. New Orleans, Feb. 8, 1945; s. Clyde G. and Ursula C. (Mumme) McS.; m. Deborah A. Lark, Oct. 16, 1971; children: Madylin, Kristy, Suzanne. BA, Southeastern La. U., 1966. Cert. internal auditor, cert. govt. fin. mgr., cert. office automation profl. Auditor Office of the Inspector Gen., New Orleans, 1965-72; audit br. chief Cen. Voucher Payment Ctr., New Orleans, 1972-73; evaluation staff chief Nat. Fin. Ctr., New Orleans, 1973-74, processing br. chief, 1974, ops. div. chief, 1974-78, acctg. div. chief, 1978-79, ops. div. chief, 1979-80, dep. dir., 1980-81, dir., 1981-93; dep. chief fin. officer, dir. fin. mgmt. U.S. Dept. Commerce, 1993—. Contbr. articles to profl. jours. Chmn. CASU Tenant Bd. Dirs., New Orleans, 1989-93, policy com. Fed. Exec. Bd., New Orleans, 1990-93, chmn., 1989-90, 92-93; chmn. unit I United Way of Greater New Orleans, 1991, vice chmn. community resources divsn. 1991, chair 1992-93, bd. trustees, 1990-94, chmn. unit VII, 1990, chmn. unit V, 1991, 1992-93. VIII-93; treas. Tulane U. pub. adv. com. for computer info. sys., 1987-93; acctg. dept. advt. bd. U. New Orleans, 1991; pres. acctg. bd. U. New Orleans, 1992-93. VIII-93. Army, 1965-71. Named Outstanding 1990 Campaign Vol. of Yr. United Way, 1991, Leadership award 1989; recipient Communication and Leadership award Toastmasters, 1991, award New Orleans chpt. Federally Employed Women, 1990, 91, Presdl. Meritorious Rank award, 1988, New Orleans Fed. Exec. Bd. award for outstanding leadership, 1989, Spl. award Office of the Comptroller Gen., 1989, Disting. Exec. Svc. award Sr. Exec. Assn. USDA, 1989; named as Federal 100 info. systems mgr. by Fed. Computer Wk., 1990, Elmer Staats Disting. Leadership award, 1993, Donald L. Scantledvry Meml. award for Disting. Leadership in Fin. Mgmt., 1995. Mem. Assn. Govt. Accts. (New Orleans chpt. pres. 1972-73, dir. 1970-71, 73-74, 74-75, 76-77, S.W. region v.p. 1975-76, South Ctrl. region v.p. 1981-82, mem. nat. exec. com. 1983-84, 93—, chmn. fin. mgmt. enhancement bd. 1988-89, chmn. emerging issues 1990-91, chmn. tech. program com. 1991—, nat. pres.-elect 1993-94, nat. pres. 1994-95), Inst. Internal Auditors, Sr. Exec. Asn., Fed. Exec. Inst. Alumni Assn. Republican. Roman Catholic. Avocation: gardening. Home: 5624 Camphor St Metairie LA 70003-2210

MCSHANE, JOSEPH M., priest, dean, theology educator; b. N.Y.C., June 19, 1949; s. Owen Patrick and Catherine Veronica (Shelley) McS. AB, Boston Coll., 1972, AM, 1972; MDiv, STM, Jesuit Sch. Theology, Berkeley, Calif., 1977; PhD, U. Chgo., 1981. Ordained priest Roman Cath. Ch. English tchr. Canisius H.S., Buffalo, 1972-74; asst. prof. religious studies LeMoyne Coll., Syracuse, N.Y., 1982-87, assoc. prof. religious studies, 1987-91, prof., 1991-92, chairperson, 1991-92; dean Fordham Coll., Bronx, N.Y., 1992—, prof. theology, 1992—; vis. prof. history Loyola House, Berkley, Mich., 1986-87; bd. trustees U. Scranton, Pa., 1993—, Fordham Prep. Sch., Bronx, N.Y., 1993—, Regis H.S., N.Y.C., 1993—, Canisius Coll., Buffalo, 1994—. Author chpt. to book; creator video: The Pilgrimage of the People of God: An Introduction to the Study of Church History, 1991; contbr. articles to profl. jours. Recipient Prize Cath. Press Assn., 1992. Mem. Am. Cath. Hist. Assn., Am. Soc. Ch. History, Phi Beta Kappa. Democrat. Home: 441 E Fordham Rd Bronx NY 10458 Office: Fordham U Bronx NY 10458

MCSHEFFERTY, JOHN, research company executive; b. Akron, Ohio, Mar. 14, 1929; s. John and Jean (Conway) McS.; m. Glenna Gloria Childs, Apr. 18, 1959; children: John III, Amy Childs. BSc, U. Glasgow, 1953, PhD, 1957. Various rsch. positions Sterling Winthrop Rsch. Inst., Rensselaer, N.Y., 1957-62; dir. pharm. devel. Ortho Pharm. Corp. div. Johnson and Johnson, Raritan, N.J., 1962-75; dir. rsch. Janssen R & D, Inc., Piscataway, N.J., 1975-77; v.p. R & D family products Internat. Playtex, Paramus, N.J., 1977-79; pres. Gillette Rsch. Inst., Gaithersburg, Md., 1979—. Fellow Royal Pharm. Soc. of Great Britain; mem. Indsl. Rsch. Inst. (bd. dirs. 1994—), Am. Chem. Soc., Am. Pharm. Assn., Soc. Cosmetic Chemists, Dirs. Indsl. Rsch. Assn. Rsch. Dirs., Sigma Xi. Office: Gillette Rsch Inst 401 Professional Dr Gaithersburg MD 20879-3429

MC SHEFFREY, GERALD RAINEY, architect, educator, city planner; b. Belfast, Ireland, Aug. 13, 1931; s. Hugh and Jane (Piggot) McS.; m. Norma Isabella Lowry, June 4, 1956; children: Laurence, Niall, Aidan. Student, Belfast Coll. Tech., 1950-56; Diploma in Architecture, Univ. Coll., U. London, 1959; Diploma in Civic Design, U. Edinburgh, Scotland, 1963. Archtl. asst. various archtl. firms Belfast, 1950-57; design architect Munce and Kennedy, Belfast, 1957-62; architect/planner Liverpool (Eng.) City Planning Dept. and Livingston New Town, 1963-65; asso. partner James Munce Partnership, Belfast, 1965-68; prin. planning officer (design) Belfast City Planning Dept., 1968-71; prof. architecture U. Kans., 1971-73, dir. archtl. studies, 1976-79; Belfast regional architect, dir. devel. No. Ireland Housing, 1973-76; prof. architecture, dean Coll. Architecture, Planning and Design, Ill. Inst. Tech., 1979-82; dean Coll. Architecture and Environ. Design Ariz. State U., Tempe, 1982-86, prof. architecture, 1988—; v.p. Ariz. State U. West Campus, Phoenix, 1985-88; vis. fellow Princeton (N.J.) U., 1989; external examiner in urban design and landscape studies U. Edinburgh, 1973-76. Author: (with James Munce Partnership) Londonderry Area Plan, 1968. Fulbright award, 1965. Fellow Royal Inst. Brit. Architects, Royal Town Planning Inst.; mem. AIA. Episcopalian. Office: Ariz State U Coll Architecture & Environ Design Tempe AZ 85287-1605

MCSHIRLEY, MARJORIE STONE, art director. Art dir.: (films) Pee-Wee's Big Adventure, 1985, Back to the Future II, 1989, Three Fugitives, 1989, Back to the Future III, 1990, The Addams Family, 1991. Office: care Art Directors Guild 11365 Ventura Blvd #315 Studio City CA 91604*

MCSORLEY, CISCO, lawyer; b. Albuquerque, July 8, 1950; s. Frank N. and Virginia E. (Norton) McS. BA, U. N.Mex., 1974, JD, 1979; postdoctoral sch. govt. Harvard U., 1986. Bar: N.Mex. 1980, U.S. Dist. Ct. N.Mex. 1980. Tchr. Academia Cotopaxi, Quito, Ecuador, S. Am., 1973-76; sole practice Albuquerque, 1980—. State rep. N.Mex. Ho. Reps., Albuquerque, 1984—. Mem. ABA, N. Mex. Bar Assn., N. Mex. Trial Lawyers Assn., Assn. Trial Lawyers Am. Democrat. Mem. Soc. of Friends. Avocations: basketball.

MCSPADDEN, PETER FORD, retired advertising agency executive; b. Montclair, N.J., Oct. 2, 1930; s. Chester F. and Janet (Chase) McS.; m.

Barbara Dodds, June 30, 1956; children—Douglas Dodds, David Ford, Peter Chase. A.B., Dartmouth, 1952. Account exec. McCann-Erickson, Inc., N.Y.C., 1956-59; with Dancer-Fitzgerald-Sample, Inc., N.Y.C., from 1959, v.p., account supr., 1965-68, sr. v.p., mangt. supr., 1968-72, exec. v.p., 1972-74, pres., chief operating officer, from 1974; chmn. bd., chief operating officer Saatchi & Saatchi DFS Inc., N.Y.C., 1986-88, also bd. dirs., ret., 1988; pres., bd. dirs. DFS/Dorland Worldwide; bd. dirs. Am. Advt. Fedn., Am. Assn. Advt. Agys., TriState U.; mem. Nat. Advt. Rev. Bd.; bd. trustees Bradford Coll; vice chmn. Broadstreet TV Inc, 1989—. Chmn. bd. visitors Rockefeller Ctr., Dartmouth Coll.; pres. Greenwich (Conn.) Young Republican Club, 1966-67; bd. dirs. United Way of Tri-State, 1995 Spl. Olympic Games; campaign mgr. Congressman Lowell P. Weicker, 1968, Senator Weicker, 1970, 76, 82, 88; mem. Rep. Town Com., Greenwich, 1965-68; trustee Greenwich Hosp. Served to lt. (j.g.) USNR, 1952-55. Mem. Am. Assn. Advt. Agys. (dir.). Clubs: Riverside (Conn.) Yacht, Greenwich Country, Megunticook Golf. Home: 46 Carriglea Dr Riverside CT 06878-2402

MCSPARRAN, ROBERT B., food products executive. Pres. Inter-State Milk Producers Coop, Southhampton, Pa. Office: Inter-State Milk Producers Coop 1225 Industrial Blvd Southampton PA 18966-4010

MCSTEEN, MARTHA ABERNATHY, organization executive; b. Iowa Park, Tex., May 25, 1923; d. King Peyton and Iva Mae (Dawson) Abernathy; m. George Steven McSteen, Oct. 13, 1943 (dec. Jan. 1945); m. Marshall Parks, Apr. 6, 1991. BA, Rice U., 1944; MA, U. Okla., 1972; JD (hon.), Austin Coll., 1985. Claims rep., supr. and dist. mgr. Social Security Adminstrn., Dallas, 1947-65, regional commr., 1976-83; acting commr. Social Security Adminstrn., Washington, 1983-86; regional adminstr. Medicare, Denver and Dallas, 1965-76; cons. Nat. Com. To Preserve Social Security and Medicare, Dallas, 1987-89, pres., 1989—; U.S. rep. to Internat. Social Security Assn., 1985, 86. Bd. dirs. Buck Found., San Francisco, 1991—; Setting Priorities for Retirement Yrs. Found., Washington, 1991—; Prevention of Blindness Found., Washington, 1993—; Claude and Mildred Pepper Found. Recipient Commr.'s citation Social Security Adminstrn., 1961, 66, 71, Disting. Svc. award HEW, 1979, Presdl. Meritorious Exec. award, 1980, Nat. Pub. Svc. award Am. Soc. for Pub. Adminstrn., 1986, Presdl. Disting. Exec. award, 1987; fellow Social Security Adminstrn., 1968-69. Office: Nat Com Preserve Social Security & Medicare 2000 K St NW # 800 Washington DC 20006-1873

MCSWAIN, RICHARD HORACE, materials engineer, consultant; b. Greenville, Ala., Sept. 27, 1949; s. Howard Horace and La Belle (Henderson) McS.; m. Wanda Lynn Hare, June 9, 1972; children: Rachel Lynn, John Angus, Daniel Richard. BS in Materials Engring., Auburn U., 1972, MS in Materials Engring., 1974; PhD in Materials Engring., U. Fla., 1985. Teaching and rsch. asst. Auburn (Ala.) U., 1972-73; metallurgist Sv. Rsch. Inst., Birmingham, Ala., 1973-76; materials engr. Naval Aviation Depot, Pensacola, Fla., 1977-88, head metallic materials engring., 1988-90; pres. McSwain Engring., Inc., 1991—; cons. materials engr., Pensacola, 1982-90; presenter in field. Contbr. articles to tech. jours. Mem. ASTM, SAE Internat., ASM Internat. (chpt. edn. chmn. 1975-76), Am. Welding Soc., Nat. Assn. Corrosion Engrs., Electron Microscopy Soc., Internat. Soc. Air Safety Investigators. Presbyterian. Avocations: boating, fishing, running. Home: 1405 Kings Rd Cantonment FL 32533-8951 Office: McSwain Engring Inc PO Box 10847 Pensacola FL 32524-0847

MCSWEENEY, FRANCES KAYE, psychology educator; b. Rochester, N.Y., Feb. 6, 1948; d. Edward William and Elsie Winifred (Kingston) McS. BA, Smith Coll., 1969; MA, Harvard U., 1972, PhD, 1974. Lectr. McMaster U., Hamilton, Ont., Can., 1973-74; asst. prof. Wash. State U., Pullman, 1974-79, assoc. prof., 1979-83, prof. psychology, 1983—, chmn. dept. psychology, 1986-94; cons. in field. Contbr. articles to profl. jours. Woodrow Wilson fellow, Sloan Fellow, 1968-69; NSF fellow, 1970-72; NIMH fellow, 1973. Fellow Am. Psychol. Assn., Am. Psychol. Soc.; mem. Western Psychol. Assn., Psychonomic Soc., Assn. Behavior Analysis, Phi Kappa Phi, Phi Beta Kappa, Sigma Xi. Home: SW 860 Alcora Pullman WA 99163 Office: Wash State U Dept Psychology Pullman WA 99164-4820

MCSWEENEY, MAURICE J. (MARC), lawyer; b. Chgo., July 3, 1938; s. Thomas J. and Margaret F. (Ahern) McS.; m. Sandra A. Panosh, Sept. 30, 1967; children: Erin, Sean. BS, DePaul U., 1960; JD, U. Chgo., 1963. Ptnr. Foley and Lardner, Milw., 1963—. Bd. dirs. Milw. Pub. Schs., 1973-79, Milw. chpt. ARC, 1979-83, Alverno Coll., Milw., 1984—, Health Edn. Ctr. of Wis., 1987—. Fellow Am. Coll. Trial Lawyers; mem. ABA, Wis. Bar Assn., Milw. Bar Assn., Am. Judicature Soc. (bd. dirs. 1988-93), Rotary (bd. dirs. Milw. 1986-88). Avocations: skiing, tennis, karate. Office: Foley & Lardner 777 E Wisconsin Ave Milwaukee WI 53202-5302

MCSWEENEY, MICHAEL TERRENCE, manufacturing executive; b. Rockford, Ill., Jan. 28, 1937; s. John Carpenter and Julia Elizabeth (McCann) McS.; m. Louise Antionette Walters, Aug. 20, 1960; children—David, Mark. B.S.E., No. Ill. U., 1961. Indsl. engr. MicroSwitch div. Honeywell Inc., Freeport, Ill., 1960-63; sr. v.p. Metromail div. Metromedia, Inc., N.Y.C., 1963-80; v.p., gen. mgr. Harlequin Reader Service, Toronto, Ont., Can., 1980-82; exec. v.p. Harlequin Enterprises, Ltd. Toronto, Ont., Can., 1982-85; pres., chief exec. officer Bear Creek Corp., Medford, Oreg., 1985-88; pres., chief exec. officer, dir. DIMAC Corp., St. Louis, 1988—; mem. mktg./direct mktg. adv bd. U. Mo., Kansas City, 1992—; instr. Am. Mgmt. Assn., N.Y.C., 1976-77, Dale Carnegie Mgmt. Instrn., Iowa, Ill., 1968-71; mem., past chmn. mailers tech. adv. com. to postmaster gen., Washington, 1978—; bd. dirs. So. Oreg. State Coll. Regional Adv. Bd., 1986-88; trustee Peter Britt Music & Arts Assn., Medford, 1986-88, Rogue Valley Community Health Ctr., 1987-88. Contbr. articles to profl. jours. County campaign chmn. U.S. senatorial candidate, Henry County, Iowa, 1966, 68; trustee St. Elizabeth Hosp., Lincoln, Nebr., 1973-75; bd. dirs. Regional Airport Authority, Burlington, Iowa, 1976-79. Served as tech. sgt. USAF, 1954-58. Recipient Leadership award Boy Scouts Am., 1968, Career Counseling commendation Iowa Wesleyan Coll., 1976, Leadership commendation U.S. Post Office, 1982. Mem. Direct Mktg. Assn. (ethics com. 1970-72, bd. dirs. 1987—, chmn. govt. affairs com. 1987—, fin. com. 1987-88), Mail Advt. Svc. Assn. (bd. dirs. 1979-80, Commendation award 1980), Can. Direct Mktg. Assn., Direct Mktg. Assn. Toronto, VFW, Phi Kappa Theta (trustee 1979-83, 90—). Republican. Roman Catholic. Lodges: Kiwanis, K.C. Avocations: flying; swimming; golf. Home: 12818 Topping Manor Dr Saint Louis MO 63131-1815 Office: DIMAC Corp 1 Corporate Woods Dr Bridgeton MO 63044-3807

MCSWEENEY, WILLIAM LINCOLN, JR., publishing executive; b. Boston, Nov. 9, 1930; s. William Lincoln and Ruth Patricia (Desmond) McS.; B.S., Boston Coll., 1953; M.L.A., So. Meth. U., 1980; m. Anne Cornelia Bulman, Aug. 18, 1956; children: Anne C., William L., Siobhan White, Arthur J., Sean B. Tchr. English, Killingly (Conn.) High Sch., 1956-57; with Hallmark Cards, Inc., Kansas City, Mo., 1957-86, area pers. mgr., 1968, sales tng. mgr., 1969-86, dir. corp. tng. and devel., 1970-86; pub. Nat. Catholic Reporter Co., 1986—. Bd. dirs. Cath. Social Services, Kansas City Archdiocese, 1975-88, pres., 1980-84; bd. dirs. United Community Services Kansas City, 1978-84, mem. exec. com., 1978-84; bd. dirs. Kansas City Amigos De Las Americas, 1977-80, pres., 1979; bd. dirs. Johnson County YMCA, 1978-79, Jesuit Vol. Corps, Midwest, 1989-95, Mexican Am. Cultural Ctr., San Antonio, 1990—; bd. dirs. Pan Ednl. Inst., 1979-83, pres., 1980-81; mem. Boston Coll. Alumni Admissions Council, 1976—; mem. chancellor's adv. bd. Met. Community Colls., 1979-80; mem. Dem. Com., Johnson County, Kans., 1980-86; bd. advisors Sch. Social Welfare, U. Kans., 1983—, chair, 1983-91, 93—, Avila Coll. 1991—, Ctrl. City Parochial Sch. Bd.; chair Mayor's UN Day Dinner, Kansas City, Mo., 1990; trustee NCCJ, 1991—. Served with U.S. Army, 1953-56. Mem. Internat. Rels. Coun. of Kansas City (bd. dirs. 1989—), Cath. Press Assn., Assoc. Ch. Press, Internat. Press Inst., UN Assn., Inter-Am. Press Inst., Kans. City Press Inst., Boston Coll. Alumni Assn. (past bd. dirs.), Boston Coll. Club (Kansas City), Bus. Execs. Nat. Security. Roman Catholic. Office: 115 E Armour Blvd PO Box 419281 Kansas City MO 64141

MCSWEENY, JOHN EDWARD, defense industry executive; b. San Mateo, Calif., July 19, 1936; s. Edward Joseph and Alice (Barrett) McS.; m. Aug. 26, 1967; children: Sean Edward, Patrick Michael, Erin Marie, Kevin Joseph. BSEE, Loyola U., L.A., 1959; MSEE, U. Colo., 1961. Registered

profl. engr., Calif. Electronics engr. Gen. Dynamics Pomona (Calif.) Div., 1961-66, design specialist, 1966-69, sect. head, 1969-70, sr. project engr., 1970-72, dir. phalanx program, 1972-76, v.p., program dir. Navy moderate range tactical weapons, 1976-80, v.p., dep. gen. mgr. programs, 1980-81, v.p., dep. gen mgr. fin. and adminstrn., 1981-82; v.p., gen. mgr. Gen. Dynamics Convair Div., San Diego, 1982—. Mem. Am. Def. Preparedness Assn., Navy League. Roman Catholic. Avocations: boating, golf. Office: Gen Dynamics/Convair Div PO Box 85357 San Diego CA 92186-5357

MCSWEENY, WILLIAM FRANCIS, petroleum company executive, author; b. Haverhill, Mass., Mar. 31, 1929; s. William Francis and Mary Florence (Doyle) McS.; m. Dorothy Pierce, Jan. 20, 1969; children: William Francis III, Cathy Ann, Ethan Madden Maverick, Terrell Pierce. Reporter, columnist, fgn. corr. Hearst Newspapers, 1943-67; dep. chmn., dir. pub. affairs Occidental Internat. Corp., 1967-68; spl. asst. to White House Chief of Staff, 1968-69; sr. exec. v.p., bd. dirs. Occidental Internat. Corp., Washington, 1969—, pres., 1976-91; exec. v.p. Occidental Petroleum Corp., 1984-91; cons. to chmn. Occidental Petroleum Corp., Washington, 1991—; dir. Fin. Gen. Bankshares Co., Washington, 1978-82, Chevy Chase Savs. and Loan, 1985—; mem. Lloyd's of London; pres.'s rep. to USSR, 1979; mem. Pres.'s Inaugural Com., 1980, 84, 92; Presdl. spl. rep. to Oman, 1980, Bolivia, 1982; Pres.'s com. Korean War Meml., 1987; Pres.'s commr. Exec. Exch., 1976-81; mem. N.E. White Ho. Fellows Bd.; mem. U.S. Com. UNESCO; spl. counsel speaker of Ho. of Reps., 1971-72. Author: Go Up for Glory, 1965, Violence Every Sunday, 1966, The Impossible Dream, 1967; also articles. Bd. visitors Fletcher Sch. Law and Diplomacy, Tufts U.; bd. advisors Karl F. Landegger Program Internat. Bus. Diplomacy, Sch. Fgn. Svc., Georgetown U.; trustee, pres. Holton Arms; chmn. Washington Episc. Sch.; chmn. Meridian House Internat., life trustee; World Affairs Coun.; bd. dirs. The Atlantic Coun., Overseer Exec. Coun. Fgn. Diplomats, Dept. of State, The Brookings Instn. Coun, 1991—; vice chmn. Sec. of State Fine Arts Commn., Kennedy Ctr. Community Bd.; chmn. Ford's Theatre, 1988—; bd. dirs. Very Spl. Arts, Arena Stage, Corcoran Gallery Art, Africare, Fed. City Coun., Washington Opera, Folger Shakespeare Theater, Cities in Schs. Nat. Learning Ctr, USO, Arms Control Assn., Nat. Assn. So. Poor, Duke Ellington Sch., Washington Ednl. TV, 1989—; v.p. Ct. of Mary Rose, Portsmouth, Eng.; pres. Commn. to Preserve U.S. Cultural Heritage Abroad, Ams. Internat. Fedn. Insts. for Advanced Studies; co-chair State dept. diplomatic rooms endowment; chmn. Lombardi Cancer Ctr. Coun., Georgetown U. Med. Ctr.; pres. Americas Internat. Instutes for Advanced Studies; vice chmn. Kennedy Ctr.; trustee V.P. Residence Found. Served to maj., inf. AUS, 1950-53. Recipient Outstanding Young Man award Boston Jaycees, 1961, U.S. Disting. Svc. award, 1968, Outstanding Svc. Spl. award, 1969, D.C. Disting. Citizen award, 1981, Paul Hill award Kennedy Ctr., 1983, D.C. Cultural award, 1983, Armenian Earthquake Hero medal, 1989, Lincoln medal, 1991, Helen Hayes award, 1991, numerous awards for domestic reporting, awards for reporting from Vietnam and Middle East, including Best U.S. Reporting award, 1964. Mem. Smithsonian Inst. (mem. nat. adv. com. Kellogg Project), Alfalfa Club, Cosmos Club, 1925 F St. Club (trustee, Washington), Internat. Club (trustee). Office: Occidental Petroleum Corp 10889 Wilshire Blvd Los Angeles CA 90024-4200

MCSWINEY, CHARLES RONALD, lawyer; b. Nashville, Apr. 23, 1943; s. James W. and Jewell (Bellar) Mc.; m. Jane Detrick McSwiney, Jan. 2, 1970. BA, Kenyon Coll., Gambier, Ohio, 1965; JD, U. Cin., 1968. Assoc. Smith & Schnacke, Dayton, Ohio, 1968-72, ptnr., 1972-89, pres. and mng. ptnr., 1984-89; sr. v.p., gen. counsel The Danis Cos., Dayton, 1989-92; vice chmn. Carillon Capital, Inc., Dayton, 1992—; pres. interchange exec. Presdl. Commn. on Personnel Interchange Washington, 1972-73. Chmn., pres. bd. trustees Dayton Ballet Assn., 1985-88; trustee Columbus (Ohio) Symphony Orch., 1981-84; chmn. Dayton Performing Arts Fund, 1989-92, Dayton Devel. Coun., 1987-90, Wright State U. Found., Dayton, 1988-94, Miami Valley Sch., Dayton, 1988-94, Arts Ctr. Found., 1986—; mem. bd. advisors Wright State U. Coll. Bus. Adminstrn., 1988—; bd. vis. U. Cin. Coll. Law, 1987-89. Recipient Bronze Medal for Performance U.S. EPA, 1973. Mem. ABA, Ohio Bar Assn., Dayton Bar Assn., Dayton Area C. of C. (trustee 1987-90). Republican. Presbyterian. Home: 3780 Ridgeleigh Rd Dayton OH 45429-1253 Office: Carillon Capital Inc Kettering Tower Ste 1480 Dayton OH 45423-1480

MC SWINEY, JAMES WILMER, retired pulp and paper manufacturing company executive; b. McEwen, Tenn., Nov. 13, 1915; s. James S. and Delia (Conroy) McS.; m. Jewel Bellar, 1940; children: Charles Ronald, Margaret Ann. Grad., Harvard Advanced Mgmt. Program, 1954. Lab. technician, shipping clk. Nashville div. The Mead Corp., 1934-39; asst. office mgr. Harriman div., 1939; plant mgr. Rockport, Ind., 1940; asst. office mgr. Kingsport (Tenn.) div.), 1941-44; exec. asst. to pres. Dayton, Ohio, 1954-57; v.p. devel., 1957-59; adminstrv v.p. Harriman div. (Kingsport (Tenn.) div.), 1959; group v.p., gen. mgr. Mead Bd. div., 1961-63, exec. v.p. corp., 1963-67, pres., chief exec. officer, 1968-71, chmn. bd., chief exec. officer, 1971-78, chmn. bd., 1978-82, also dir.; acct., office mgr., asst. sec.-treas. Brunswick Pulp & Paper Co., Ga., 1944-45; bd. dirs. Ultra-Met, Cryste Co., Energy Innovations Inc., Gosiger, Inc., Sea Island Co., Miami Valley Rsch. Trustee Com. for Econ. Devel.; chmn. bd. dirs. Air Force Found. Inst. of Tech. Aviation cadet USAAF, 1942-44. Home: PO Box 30604 Sea Island GA 31561 Office: Mead World HQs Dayton OH 45463

MCTAGGART-COWAN, IAN, retired university chancellor; b. Edinburgh, Scotland, June 25, 1910; s. Garry McTaggart and Laura (Mackenzie) McTaggart-Cowan; m. Joyce Stewart Racey, Apr. 21, 1936; children—Garry Ian McTaggart, Ann McTaggart (Mrs. Mikkel Schau). B.A., U. B.C., 1932, D.Sc., 1977; Ph.D., U. Calif.-Berkeley, 1935; LL.D., U. Alta., 1971, Simon Fraser U., 1981; D.Environ. Sci., Waterloo U., 1976; D.Sc., U. Victoria, 1985. Head teaching fellow U. Calif.-Berkeley, 1932-35; asst. biologist B.C. Provincial Mus., Victoria, 1935-38; asst. dir. B.C. Provincial Mus., 1938-40; with U. B.C., Vancouver, 1940-76; asst. prof. zoology U. B.C., 1940-45, prof. zoology, 1945-53, prof., head zoology dept., 1953-64, dean faculty grad. studies, 1964-75, dean emeritus, 1975—, mem. senate, 1952-75; mem. acad. bd. Province B.C., 1964-78, chmn., 1969-75, chmn. acad. council, 1978-84; chancellor U. Victoria, 1979-85. Mem. Environ. Coun. Can., 1971-74, chmn., 1974-82; bd. govs. Arctic Inst., 1950-56, 1985-89, Nature Trust, 1978—; mem. select com. nat. parks U.S. Sec. Interior, 1966-67; chmn. Can. Com. on Whales and Whaling, 1976-93, Habital Enhancement Com., B.C., 1980—. Decorated officer Order of Can., 1981; Order of B.C., 1991; recipient Leopold medal, 1970, Can. Centennial medal, 1964, Fry medal, 1976, Queen Elizabeth Jubilee medal, 1977, 125th Ann. Confederate medal, 1993. Fellow AAAS, Royal Soc. Can., Calif. Acad. Sci., Pacific Sci. Assn. (hon. life), Wildlife Soc. (hon. life), Alta., B.C. soc. profl. biology (hon. life). Home: 3919 Woodhaven Terr, Victoria, BC Canada V8N 1S7

MCTAGUE, JOHN PAUL, automobile manufacturing company executive, chemist; b. Jersey City, Nov. 28, 1938; s. James Aloysius and Teresa Eugenia (Hanley) McT.; m. Carole Frances Reilly, Dec. 30, 1961; children: Kevin W., Catherine E., Margaret A., Maureen E. BS in Chemistry, Georgetown U., 1960; PhD, Brown U., 1965. Mem. tech. staff N.Am. Rockwell Sci. Ctr. Thousand Oaks, Calif., 1964-70; prof. chemistry, mem. Inst. Geophysics and Planetary Physics UCLA, 1970-82; chmn. nat. synchrotron light source dept. Brookhaven Nat. Lab., Upton, N.Y., 1982-83; dep. dir. Office Sci. and Tech. Policy, Exec. Office of Pres., Washington, 1983-86, acting sci. advisor to Pres. Reagan, 1986; v.p. rsch. Ford Motor Co., Dearborn, Mich., 1986-90; v.p. tech. affairs Ford Motor Co., 1990—; bd. dirs. Raychem Corp.; adj. prof. chemistry Columbia, U., 1982-83. Mem. Pres.'s Coun. Advisors on Sci. and Tech., 1990-93; mem. adv.bd. Sec. Energy, 1990—. Alfred P. Sloan Research fellow, 1971-73; NATO sr. fellow, 1973; John Simon Guggenheim Meml. fellow, 1975-76. Fellow AAAS, Am. Phys. Soc.; mem. Am. Chem. Soc. (Calif. sect. award 1975), Soc. Automotive Engrs., Engring. Soc. Detroit, Barton Hills Country Club, Sigma Xi. Office: Ford Motor Co The American Rd Dearborn MI 48121

MCTARNAGHAN, ROY E., acadamic administrator. Vice chancellor acad. programs State U. System Fla., Tallahassee, 1975—, exec. vice chancellor, 1989—; interim pres. U. North Fla., Jacksonville, 1988-89. Office: State U System Fla 325 W Gaines St Tallahassee FL 32399-1950

MCTEER, ROBERT D., JR., bank executive. Pres. ceo Federal Reserve Bank of Dallas, Tex. Office: Fed Res Bank 2200 N Pearl St Dallas TX 75201

MCTIER, CHARLES HARVEY, foundation administrator; b. Columbus, Ga., Jan. 28, 1939; s. Roy and Julia (Harvey) McT.; m. Margaret Lucy Ruyl, Aug. 23, 1962; children: Margaret Marie, Charles Harvey Jr. BBA, Emory U., 1961. Administrv. asst. hosp. Emory U., Atlanta, 1961-63, bus. mgr. dept. psychiat. Sch. Med., 1963-66, assoc. dir. personnel, 1966-69, asst. to pres., bd. trustees, 1969-71; sec. Robert W. Woodruff Found., Joseph B. Whitehead Found., Lettie Pate Evans Found., Inc., Lettie Pate Whitehead Found., Inc., Atlanta, 1971-77, sec., treas., 1977-87, v.p., sec., treas., 1987-88, pres., 1988—; chmn. Atlanta Founds. Forum, 1985-86; treas. Coun. on Founds., Washington, 1992—, chmn. audit and fin. com., 1990—; mgmt. com., 1987—, nominating com., 1987-88, program com., 1985-87; chmn. Found. Ctr. N.Y.C., 1994—, trustee, 1991—, exec. com., 1992—, fin. and audit com., 1991—, chmn. nominating com., 1992, chmn. program and fund devel. adv. com., 1993—; chmn. bd. trustees Southeastern Coun. Founds., Atlanta, 1989-92, trustee, 1985-92, chmn. program com., 1989, chmn. membership com., 1986-89; pub. mem. Joint Commn. on Accreditation of Health Care Orgns., 1994—; dir. Trust Co. Bank and Trust Co. of Ga. Trustee, North Ga. United Meth. Found., 1985-92; trustee, treas. Meth. Found. Ret. Mins., 1980; chmn. new ch. devel. com. North Ga. United Meth. Conf., 1980-85; trustee North Ga. United Meth. Found., 1985-92; mem. bd. vis. Emory U., 1985-87. Mem. Assn. Emory Alumni (bd. govs. 1987-91), Pres.'s Cir. of Nat. Acad. Scis./Inst. of Medicine, Commerce Club (bd. dirs.), Druid Hills Golf Club. Avocations: golf, travel. Office: Joseph B Whitehead Found 50 Hurt Plz SE Ste 1200 Atlanta GA 30303-2916

MC TIERNAN, JOHN, film director; b. Albany, N.Y., Jan. 8, 1951. Dir., screenwriter Nomads, 1985; dir. Predator, 1987, Die Hard, 1988, The Hunt For Red October, 1990, Medicine Man, 1992, The Last Action Hero, 1993, Die Hard With a Vengeance, 1995. Office: CAA 9830 Wilshire Blvd Beverly Hills CA 90212-1804*

MCVAY, JOHN EDWARD, professional football club executive; b. Bellaire, Ohio, Jan. 5, 1931; s. John A. and Helen (Andrews) McV.; m. Eva Lee; children: John R., James P., Timothy G. B.S. in Edn., Miami U., Oxford, Ohio, 1953; M.A. in Sch. Adminstrn., Kent (Ohio) State U., 1963. Asst. football coach, instr. phys. edn. Mich. State U., 1962-65; head coach, dir. athletics U. Dayton, Ohio, 1965-74; head coach, gen. mgr. Memphis in World Football League, 1974-76; head football coach New York Giants, Nat. Football League, 1976-78; dir. player personnel San Francisco 49ers, Nat. Football League, 1979-80, dir. football ops. 1980-81, v.p. adminstrn., 1981-83, gen. mgr., v.p., 1983-89; v.p. FB ops., 1990—. Exec. dir. Catholic Youth Council, Canton, Ohio, 1959-62. Named to Miami U. Athletic Hall of Fame, named NFL exec. of the year, 1989. Mem. Sigma Chi (Significant Sig award), Phi Epsilon Kappa, Phi Delta Kappa. Won five Super Bowl Championships 1981, 1984, 88, 89, 94. Office: care San Francisco 49ers 4949 Centennial Blvd Santa Clara CA 95054-1254

MCVERRY, THOMAS LEO, manufacturing company executive; b. Pitts., Aug. 2, 1938; m. Jean L. Smith, Apr. 29, 1961; children: Thomas, Michael, Amy. BA, U. Pitts., 1960, MBA, 1962. CPA, N.Y.; CFP. Sr. acct. Deloitte & Touche, N.Y.C., 1962-66; contr., treas. Church & Dwight Co., Inc., N.Y.C., 1966-73; v.p. fin., resources Rexham Corp., Charlotte, N.C., 1973-90, also bd. dirs.; pres. McVerry & Assocs., Charlotte, 1990—; trustee 1st Union Funds, Evergreen Funds; vice chmn. bd. Carolina Coop. Fed. Credit Union. Chmn. bd. edn. Charlotte Cath. High Sch., 1977-84, fin. com. St. Gabriel's Parish, Charlotte, 1976-82; v.p. Waldwick (N.J.) Bd. Edn., 1970-73. Mem. Am. Mgmt. Assn. (bd. dirs.), Assn., fin. Execs. Inst. (bd. mem. S.C. chpt.). Home and Office: 4419 N Parview Dr Charlotte NC 28226-3433

MCVEY, EUGENE STEVEN, electrical engineering educator, consultant; b. Wayne, W.Va., Dec. 6, 1927; s. Eugene S. and Mary E. (Atkins) McV.; m. Lexie Ann Bard, Aug. 14, 1949; children: Mary Beth, Rebecca Sue, Lexie Ann, Eugene Steven, Mark Andrew. B.S.E.E., U. Louisville, 1950; M.S. in Engring., Purdue U., 1955, Ph.D., 1960. With Naval Ordnance Plant, Indpls., 1950-56; group leader ITT Fransworth, Ft. Wayne, Ind., 1956-57; asst. prof., instr. Purdue U., Lafayette, Ind., 1957-61; prof. elec. engring. U. Va., Charlottesville, 1961-94, prof. emeritus, 1994; cons. to industry and govt. Served with USN, 1945-47. Fellow IEEE (Eugene Mittlement Achievement award 1982); mem. Sigma Xi, Eta Kappa Nu. Office: U Va Dept of Elec Engring Thornton Hall Charlottesville VA 22901

MCVEY, GEORGE JENNINGS, headmaster; b. Richmond, Va., Feb. 8, 1939; s. Henry Hanna and Eva Lawson (Jennings) McV.; m. Nancy Harrison McLaughlin, Dec. 22, 1962; children—George Jennings Jr., James Harrison, Henry Hanna. Diploma St. Christopher's Sch., Richmond, Va., 1957; BS magna cum laude, Hampden-Sydney, Coll., Va., 1961, BA magna cum laude, 1961, LLD, 1976; MA, Va. Commonwealth Coll., 1973. Instr. math. and English St. Christopher's Sch., Richmond, 1961-65; asst. prin. Middle Sch., 1965-66, prin., thesis dir. studies, 1969, asst. headmaster, 1971-72, acting headmaster, 1972-73, headmaster, 1973—; counselor and head counselor Camp Maxwelton, 1956-63; dir. Camp Briar Hills, 1964-68; bd. dirs. Johnston Willis Hosp., 1984—; former adv. bd. mem. River Rd. Br. Colonial Savings & Loan; bd. dirs. New Va. Review, Buford Acad. 1980, New Cmty. Sch.; commr. Gov. Commn. on Champion Sch. Former bd. dirs. Blue Cross-Blue Shield of Va., Richmond ARC, English Speaking Union, Aylett Country Day Sch., Friends of Richmond Pub. Libr., Va. Adv. Com. on Tchr. Edn.; active Grace & Holy Trinity Ch., Richmond. Mem. Nat. Assn. Ind. Schs. (bd. dirs., treas.), Va. Assn. Ind. Schs. (mem. exec. com., past pres.), Va. Coun. Ptrl.Edn. (pres.), Country Day Headmaster's Assn., Phi Beta Kappa, Chi Phi (past pres.), Omicron Delta Kappa, Eta Sigma Phi. Clubs: Country Club of Va., The Forum, The Richmond Hundred. Office: St Christopher's Sch 711 St Christophers Rd Richmond VA 23226-2750

MCVEY, HENRY HANNA, III, lawyer; b. Richmond, Va., Aug. 12, 1935; s. Henry Hanna Jr. and Eva Lawson (Jennings) McV.; m. Reba Jean Robinson, Dec. 12, 1964; children: Margaret Anne McVey Singleton, Lewis Lawson, Ian Douglas. BS, BA magna cum laude, Hampden-Sydney Coll., 1957; LLB, U. Va., 1960. Bar: Va., 1960, U.S. Dist. Ct. (ea. dist.) Va. 1960, U.S. Ct. Appeals (4th cir.) 1965, U.S. Supreme Ct. 1970. Assoc. Battle, Neal, Harris, Minor & Williams, Richmond, 1960-66; ptnr. McGuire, Woods, Battle & Boothe (and predecessor firm), Richmond, 1966—; mem. adv. group under Civil Justice Reform Act of 1990, U.S. Dist. Ct. (ea. dist.) Va. Bd. dirs. Richmond Symphony, 1977-78, 87—, v.p., 1979-81, exec. v.p., 1981-83, pres., 1983-85, chmn. bd. dirs., 1985-87; bd. dirs. Carpenter Ctr. for Performing Arts, 1982-89; trustee Hampden-Sydney Coll., 1989-94, 95—; mem. Commn. on Archtl. Rev., City of Richmond, 1985—. Fellow Am. Coll. Trial Lawyers; mem. ABA, Va. Assn. Def. Attys. (v.p. 1981-83, treas. 1983-84, pres.-elect 1984-85, pres. 1985-86), Def. Research and Trial Lawyers Assn. (past state chmn., regional v.p. 1985-87, bd. dirs. 1987-90), Am. Bd. Trial Advocacy (adv.), Fedn. Ins. and Corp. Counsel, Bar Assn. City of Richmond, Va. Bar Assn., Country Club of Va., Bull and Bear Club, Capital Club. Presbyterian. Home: PO Box 43 Schley VA 23154 Office: McGuire Woods Battle & Boothe One James Ctr Richmond VA 23219

MCVICKER, JESSE JAY, artist, educator; b. Vici, Okla., Oct. 18, 1911; s. Jesse Allen and Clara Mae (Hendrick) McV.; m. Laura Beth Paul, Aug. 20, 1938. B.A., Okla. State U., 1940, M.A., 1941. Faculty Okla. State U. Stillwater, 1941—; prof. art Okla. State U., 1959-77, prof. emeritus, 1977—, head dept., 1959-77. Exhbns. include Med. Mus. Art, Mus. Non-Objective Painting, Chgo. Art Inst., N.A.D., Library of Congress, San Francisco Mus. Art, Denver Art Mus., Pa. Acad. Fine Arts, Carnegie Inst., Print Club Phila., Salon Des Realities Nouvelles, Paris, France, Dallas, Mus. Fine Arts, Galleria Origine, Rome, Italy, Whitney Mus. Am. Art; represented in permanent collections Library of Congress, Seattle Art Mus., Dallas Mus. Fine Arts, Met. Mus. Art, Joslyn Meml. Art Mus.; bibliography Graphic Works by J. Jay McVicker, 1986. Served with USNR, 1943-46. Mem. Soc. Am. Graphic Artists, Audubon Artists (John Taylor Arms award 1990), Print Club Phila., Pi Kappa Alpha.

MC VIE, CHRISTINE PERFECT, musician; b. Eng., July 12, 1943; m. John McVie (div.); m. Eddy Quintela. Student art sch., pvt. student sculpture. Singer, keyboardist, Fleetwood Mac, from 1970; albums with Fleetwood Mac include: Fleetwood Mac, 1968, Fleetwood Mac in Chicago, 1969, Then Play On, 1969, English Rose, 1969, Kiln House, 1970, Future Games, 1971, Bare Trees, 1972, Penguin, Mystery To Me, Heroes Are Hard to Find, 1975, Fleetwood Mac, 1976, Rumours, 1977, Tusk, 1979, Fleetwood Mac Live, 1980, Mirage, 1982, Jumping at Shadows, 1985, Tango in the Night, 1987, Greatest Hits, 1988, Behind the Mask, 1990; solo albums include Christine Perfect, 1969, Christine McVie, 1984; composer: songs including Spare Me a Little of Your Love, Don't Stop, You Make Loving Fun, Over and Over, Hold Me, Songbird, Got a Hold on Me, Heroes Are Hard to Find, Little Lies, As Long as You Follow, Save Me., Skies the Limit. Office: care Warner Bros Records 3300 Warner Blvd Burbank CA 91505-4632*

MCVISK, WILLIAM KILBURN, lawyer; b. Chgo., Oct. 8, 1953; s. Felix Kilburn and June (DePear) Visk; m. Marlaine Joyce McDonough, June 20, 1975. BA, U. Ill, 1974; JD, Northwestern U., 1977. Bar: Ill. 1977, U.S. Dist. Ct. (no. dist.) Ill. 1977, U.S. Ct. Appeals (7th cir.) 1978. Assoc. Jerome H. Torshen, Ltd., Chgo., 1977-80, Silets & Martin, Chgo., 1980-81; assoc. Peterson & Ross, Chgo., 1981-85, ptnr., 1985—. Contbr. articles to profl. jours. Mem. ABA, Chgo. Bar Assn., Def. Research Inst., Am. Assn. Hosp. Attys., Ill. Assn. Hosp. Attys., Ill. Assn. Def. Trial Lawyers. Office: Peterson & Ross 200 E Randolph Dr Chicago IL 60601-6401

MCVOY, KIRK WARREN, physicist, educator; b. Mpls., Feb. 22, 1928; s. Kirk Warren and Phyllis (Farmer) McV.; m. Hilda A. Van Der Laan, Aug. 15, 1953; children—Christopher, Lawrence, Annelies. B.A., Carleton Coll., 1950; B.A. (Rhodes scholar), Oxford U., Eng., 1952; Dipl., U. Gottingen, Germany, 1953; Ph.D., Cornell U, 1956. Research asso. Brookhaven Nat. Lab., Upton, N.Y., 1956-58; asst. prof. Brandeis U., 1958-62; asso. prof. U. Wis., 1963-67, prof. physics, 1967—; vis. distinguished prof. physics Bklyn. Coll., 1970-71; vis. prof. Ind. U., 1971-72. Fulbright research grantee U. Utrecht, Netherlands, 1960-61; sr. scientist awardee A. von Humboldt Found., Max-Planck-Institut für Kernphysik, Heidelberg, W. Ger., 1980-81. Fellow Am. Phys. Soc. Achievements include rsch. and publs. on nuclear reaction theory. Office: U Wis Dept Physics 1150 University Ave Madison WI 53706

MCWALTERS, PETER, state agency administrator; b. Oct. 8, 1946; m. Alice Bond McWalters; children: Jennifer, Molly, Katherine. BA in History and Philosophy, Boston Coll., 1968; MS in Pub. Adminstrn., SUNY Brockport, 1979, cert. advanced study ednl. adminstrn., 1981. Permanent N.Y. State Teaching Cert social studies 7-12, Sch. Adminstrn., Sch. Dist. Adminstrn. Tchr.-trainer Eng. for speakers other langs. U.S. Peace Corps., Rep. Philippines; tchr. Eng. for speakers other langs. City Sch. Dist., Rochester, N.Y., 1970-71; tchr. social studies Interim Jr. High Sch., Rochester, 1971-78; Magnet Sch. planning specialist City Sch. Dist., Rochester, 1978-81, coord. Mgmt. Inst., 1980-81, supervising dir. planning and budgeting, 1981-85, supt. schs., 1985-91; commr. elem. and secondary edn. State of R.I., 1992—; bd. dirs. Nat. Ctr. Edn. and Economy, mem. new standards project; bd. dirs. Ctr. Ednl. Devel., Rochester; mem. Edn. Commn. of States, Coun. Chief State Schs. Officers, Coun. Great Cities Schs., 21st Century Edn. Commm. Bd. dirs. Urban League, Rochester; mem. United Way Task Force, Rochester; gov. bd., exec. com. Rochester New Futures Initiative, Inc.; mem. Goals for Greater Rochester, Inc. Mem. Am. Assn. Sch. Adminstrs., Assn. Supervision and Curriculum Devel., Phi Delta Kappa. Home: 26 Diman Pl Providence RI 02906-2104 Office: Elem and Sec Office 22 Hayes St Providence RI 02908-5025

MCWETHY, JOHN FLEETWOOD, journalist; b. Aurora, Ill., Feb. 28, 1947; s. John Adams and Mary Helen (Bell) McW.; m. Laurie Duncan, June 25, 1971; children: Adam Duncan, James Ian. B.A., DePauw U., 1969; M.S., Columbia U., 1970. Def. writer Congl. Quar., Washington, 1970-72; sci. editor U.S. News & World Report, Washington, 1972-77, chief White House corr., 1977-79; chief Pentagon corr. ABC News, Washington, 1979-84; chief corr. ABC News Nat. Security and Sr. State Dept., Washington, 1984—. Contbg. author: Power of the Pentagon, 1972. Recipient DuPont award Columbia U. Sch. Journalism, 1984; 3 Emmy awards, 1984, 91, 92, Overseas Press Club award for Inside the Other Side, 1987. Home: 5028 30th St N Arlington VA 22207-2717

MCWETHY, PATRICIA JOAN, educational association administrator; b. Chgo., Feb. 27, 1946; d. Frank E. and Emma (Kuehne) McW.; m. H. Frank Eden; children: Kristin Beth, Justin Nicholas. BA, Northwestern U., 1968; MA, U. Minn., 1970; MBA, George Washington U., 1981. Geog. analyst CIA, McLean, Va., 1970-71; research asst. NSF, Washington, 1972-74, spl. asst. to dir., 1975; assoc. program dir. human geography and regional sci. program NSF, 1976-79; exec. dir. Assn. Am. Geographers, Washington, 1979-84, Nat. Assn. Biology Tchrs., Reston, Va., 1984-95; pres., exec. dir. Nat. Sci. Edn. Leadership Assn., Arlington, Va., 1995—; prin. investigator NSF grant on biotechnology equip. ednl. resource partnership, 1989-93, NSF funded internat. symposium on "Basic Biol. Concepts: What Should the World's Children Know?", 1992-94; chmn. adv. com. Nat. Com. Sci. Standards & Assessment, 1992—; mem. Commn. for Biology Edn., Internt. Union Biol. Sci., 1988—; mem. exec. com. Alliance for Environ. Edn., 1987-90, chmn. program com. 1990; conductor seminars in field; lectr. in field. Author monograph and papers in field; editor handbook. Recipient Outstanding Performance award, NSF, 1973; NSF fellow, 1968-69. Mem. Am. Soc. Assn. Execs., Phi Beta Kappa. Office: PO Box 5556 Arlington VA 22205

MCWHINEY, GRADY, history educator; b. Sherveport, La., July 15, 1928; s. Henry Grady and Mayme (Holland) McW.; m. Sue B. Baca, Nov. 20, 1947. B.S., Centenary Coll. of La., 1950; M.A., La. State U., 1951; Ph.D., Columbia U., 1960. Asst. prof. Troy State U., Ala., 1952-54, Millsaps Coll., Jackson, Miss., 1956-59, Northwestern U., Evanston, Ill., 1960-65; assoc. prof. to prof. U.B. C., Vancouver, Can., 1965-70; vis. prof. U. Calif.- Berkeley, 1959-60, 67-68; prof. Wayne State U., Detroit, 1970-75; vis. prof. Tulane U., New Orleans, summer 1970, U. Mich., Ann Arbor, 1972-73; prof. history, dir. and disting. sr. fellow ctr. for study of so. history and culture U. Ala. University, 1975-83; Lyndon Baines Johnson prof. Am. history Tex. Christian U., Ft. Worth, 1983—; mem. NEH Selection Com., 1973, Jefferson Davis Award Com., 1970-72, 75-77; rsch. fellow Mosher Inst. for Def. Studies, 1988—; James Murfin Meml. lectr., 1990, Marian Alexander Blake lectr., 1991; Conf. Meml. speaker, 1991. Author: Braxton Bragg and Confederate Defeat, Vol. 1, 1969, 2d edit., 1991, Southerners and Other Americans, 1973, (with Perry D. Jamieson) Attack and Die: Civil War Military Tactics of the Southern Heritage, 1982, Cracker Culture: Celtic Ways in the Old South, 1988, (with J.L. Hallock) Braxton Bragg 2 vols., 1991, An American Civil War Primer, 1992, Battle in the Wilderness: Grant Meets Lee, 1994; editor: (with Sue McWhiney) To Mexico with Taylor and Scott, 1845-1847, 1969, Grant, Lee, Lincoln and the Radicals, 1964, (with Robert Weibe) Historical Vistas, 2 vols., 1963-64, Reconstruction and the Freedmen, 1963, (with Douglas Southall Freeman) Robert E. Lee's Dispatches to Jefferson Davis, 1957, 94. Served with USMC, 1945-47. Recipient Frank E. Vandiver award Houston Civil War Round Table, 1993, Charles L. "Pie" Dufour award New Orleans Civil War Round Table, 1994, Outstanding Scholar award U. Ala., 1980, Gallant Service award Chgo. Civil War Round Table, 1979, Harry S. Truman award, 1970, Pacific Br. award Am. Hist. Assn., 1969; Huntington Library fellow, 1984; recipient Jefferson Davis medal United Daughters of the Confederacy, 1992, Honor award Sons Confederate Vets Tex. Divsn., 1993; rsch. fellow Mosher Inst. Defense Studies, 1988—. Fellow St. George Tucker Soc.; mem. Ala. Hist. Assn. (pres. 1978-79), So. Hist. Assn. (exec. council 1976-79), Phila. Soc., St. Louis Civil War Round Table (hon.), Civil War Round Table U.K. (hon.), Main St. Com., Phi Beta Kappa. Home: 3245 S University Dr Fort Worth TX 76109-2239 Office: Tex Christian U Dept History Fort Worth TX 76129

MC WHINNEY, EDWARD WATSON, Canadian government legislator; b. Sydney, Australia, May 19, 1924; s. Matthew and Evelyn Annie (Watson) McW.; m. Emily Ingalore Sabatzky, June 27, 1951. LLB, U. Sydney, 1949; LLM, Yale U., 1951, D Juridical Sci., 1953; diploma, Acad. de Droit Internat., The Hague, 1950. Bar: Called to Australian bar 1949, apptd. Queen's counsel, Can 1967. Crown prosecutor Sydney, 1949-50; lectr., then asst. prof. Law Sch. and Grad. Sch., Yale U., 1951-55; prof. law, mem. Centre Russian Studies, U. Toronto, Ont., Can., 1955-66; prof. law, dir. Inst. Air and Space Law, McGill U., Montreal, Que., Can., 1966-71; prof. law, dir. internat. and comparative legal studies U. Ind., Indpls., 1971-74; disting.

prof. Simon Fraser U., Burnaby, B.C., 1974-93; mem. Permanent Ct. Arbitration, The Hague, 1985-91; Paul Martin prof. U. Windsor, Can., 1986; prof. emeritus, 1992; M.P. Ho. of Commons, Ottawa, Ont., Can., 1993—; vis. prof. Ecole Libre des Hautes Etudes, 1952, Heidelberg and Max-Planck-Inst., 1960-61, 90, NYU, 1954, Faculté Internat. de Droit Comparé, Luxembourg, 1959-60, U. San Antonio, 1963, U. Laval, Que., 1967, U. Paris, 1968, U. Madrid, 1968, U. Aix-Marseille, 1969, U. Nacional Autónoma de México, 1965, Inst. Univ. Luxembourg, 1972, 74, 76, Acad. Internat. Law, The Hague, 1973, 90, Aristotelian U., Thessaloniki, Greece, 1974, 78, 85, U. Nice, 1976-77, Jagellonian U., Cracow, Poland, 1976, U. Paris I (Sorbonne), 1982, 85, Coll. de France, Paris, 1983, Meiji U., Tokyo, 1987, Inst. Internat. Relations, Bejing, 1987, 92; legal cons. UN, 1953-54; cons. Japanese Commn. Constn., mem. prime minister Ont. Adv. Com. Confedn., 1964-71; cons. U.S. Naval War Coll., 1961-68; legal cons. Ministère de la Justice, Que., 1969-70; 74-75; constl. adviser to prime minister of Que., 1974-75; royal commr. Commn. Lang. Rights. Que., 1968-72; cons. U.S. Senate select com. presdl. campaign activities, 1973; spl. commr. inquiry Legislature B.C., 1974-75; chief adv. Fed. Govt.'s Task Force on Nat. Unity, 1978; commr. of enquiry, City of Vancouver, 1979; constl. adv. Fedn. Can. Municipalities, 1978-82; spl. advisor Can. del. UN Gen. Assembly, ann. sessions, 1981, 82, 83; constl. adviser Indian Nations (Treaties 6-9), Can., 1980-82; mem. Assoc. de l'Inst. de Droit Internat., 1967, membre titulaire, 1975; mem. Assoc. de l'Acad. Internat. de Droit Comparé, Paris, 1986, mem. Deutsche Gesellschaft für Völkerrecht, 1992. Author: Judical Review, 4th edit, 1969, Canadian Jurisprudence, 1958, Föderalismus und Bundesverfassungsrecht, 1961, Constitutionalism in Germany, 1962, Comparative Federalism, 2d edit, 1965, Peaceful Coexistence and Soviet-Western International Law, 1964, Law Foreign Policy and the East-West Détente, 1964, Federal Constitution-Making for a Multi-National World, 1966, International Law and World Revolution, 1967, Conflit idéologique et ordre public mondial, 1970, (with M.A. Bradley) The Freedom of the Air, 1968, New Frontiers in Space Law, 1969, The International Law of Communications, 1970, Aerial Piracy and International Law, 1971, (with Pierre Pescatore) Federalism and Supreme Courts and the Integration of Legal Systems, 1973, Parliament and Parliamentary Power Today, 1976, The Executive and Executive Power Today, 1977, (with J-D Gendron and others) La situation de la langue françaisé au Québec (3 vols.), 1973, The Illegal Diversion of Aircraft and International Law, 1974, Parliamentary Privilege and the Broadcasting of Parliamentary Debates, 1975, The International Law of Detente, 1978, The World Court and the Contemporary International Law-making Process, 1979, Quebec and the Constitution, 1979, Municipal Government in a New Canadian Federal System, 1980, Conflict and Compromise: International Law and World Order in a Revolutionary Age, 1981, Constitution-Making: Principles, Process, Practice, 1981, Canada and the Constitution, 1982, United Nations Law Making, 1984, Supreme Courts and Judicial Law-Making, 1986, Les Nations-Unies et la Formation du Droit, 1986, Aerial Piracy and International Terorism, 1987, The International Court of Justice and the Western Tradition of International Law, 1987, (with Nagendra Singh) Nuclear Weapons and Contemporary International Law, 1988, Judicial Settlement of International Disputes, 1990, (with G.I. Tunkin and V.S. Vereshechetin) From Coexistence to Cooperation: International Law and Organisation in the Post-Cold War Era, 1991, (with J. Zaslove and W. Wolf) Federalism-in-the-Making, Contemporary Canadian and German Constitutionalism, National and Trans-national, 1992, Judge Shigeru Oda and the Progressive Development of International Law, 1992, Judge Manfred Lachs and Judicial Law-Making, 1994; bd. editors Australian Quar., 1949-50, Can. Yearbook of Internat. Law, 1963—, Jour. Media Law and Practice, 1980-85, Annuaire International de Justice Constitutionnelle, 1987—; editorial adv. com. Ency. Britannica, 1985—; contbr. to Ency. Brit. Served as officer Australian Air Force, 1943-45. Fellow Carnegie Endowment, 1951; Fulbright fellow, 1950-51; Sterling fellow Yale, 1950-51; Rockefeller fellow, 1960-61, 66-68; Can. Council fellow, 1960-61; fellow Am. Soc. Internat. Law, 1962-63. Mem. Australian Inst. Polit. Sci. (dir.), Internat. Law Assn. (pres. Toronto br. 1964-66, pres. Montreal br. 1970-71, chmn. exec. com. Canadian br. 1972-75), Canadian Bar Assn. (council Ont. 1956-58), Yale Law Sch. Assn. (pres. Can. 1964-69), Canadian Civil Liberties Assn. (v.p. 1965-67), Am. Soc. Internat. Law (council 1965-68), Am. Fgn. Law Assn., Inst. interamericano de Estudios Juridicos Internacionales (dir. 1965—), Inst. Grand-Ducal de Luxembourg, Internat. Commn. Jurists (mem. coun. Can. br. 1988—), Knights of Mark Twain (U.S.) (hon.). Home: 1949 Beach Ave, Vancouver, BC Canada V6G 1Z2 Office: House of Commons 555d Ctr Block, Parliament of Can, Ottawa, ON Canada K1A 0A6

MCWHINNEY, IAN RENWICK, physician, medical educator; b. Burnley, Eng., Oct. 11, 1926; emigrated to Can., 1968, naturalized, 1981; s. Archibald Renwick and Mary (Freeland) McW.; m. Betty Heap, Apr. 30; children: Heather, Julie. MB, BCh, Cambridge (Eng.) U., 1949; MD, Cambridge (Eng.) U., Eng.; MD (hon.), U. Oslo, 1991. Intern St. Bartholomews Hosp., London, 1949-50; resident (Warwick), Eng., 1953-54; pvt. practice medicine Stratford-on-Avon, Eng., 1954-68; prof. family medicine U. Western Ont., London, Can., 1968-92; prof. emeritus U. Western Ont., London, 1992—; med. dir. palliative care unit Parkwood Hosp., 1986-91. Author: The Early Signs of Illness, 1964, Introduction to Family Medicine, 1981, A Textbook of Family Medicine, 1989. Capt. Royal Army M.C., 1951-53. Recipient Excellence cert. Soc. Tchrs. Family Medicine, 1979, Curtis G. Hames Rsch. award, 1989. Fellow Coll. Family Physicians (Victor Johnston orator 1980), Royal Coll. Gen. Practitioners, Royal Coll. Physicians; mem. Inst. Medicine-Nat. Acad. Scis. (fgn. assoc.). Office: U Western Ont, Dept Family Medicine, London, ON Canada N6A 5C1

MCWHINNEY, MADELINE H. (MRS. JOHN DENNY DALE), economist; b. Denver, Mar. 11, 1922; d. Leroy and Alice (Houston) McW.; BA, Smith Coll., 1943; MBA, NYU, 1947; m. John D. Dale, June 23, 1961; 1 child, Thomas Denny. Economist, Fed. Res. Bank N.Y., 1943-73, chief fin. and trade statis. div., 1955-59, mgr. market stats. dept., 1960-65, asst. v.p., 1965-73; pres. First Women's Bank, N.Y.C., 1974-76; trustee Retirement System Fed. Res. Bank, 1955-58; vis. lectr. N.Y.U. Grad. Sch. Bus., 1976-77; pres. Dale, Elliott & Co., Inc., Red Bank, N.J., 1977—; mem. N.J. Casino Control Commn., 1980-82, Women's Econ. Round Table, 1978-89, chmn. 1987-88; bd. govs. Am. Stock Exch., 1977-81. Trustee, Carnegie Corp. N.Y., 1974-82, Central Savs. Bank of N.Y., 1980-82, Charles F. Kettering Found., 1975-93, chmn. 1987-91, Inst. Internat. Edn., 1975—, Investor Responsibility Rsch. Ctr., Inc., 1974-81; asst. dir. Whitney Mus. Am. Art, 1983-86; dir. Atlantic Energy Co., 1983-93; trustee The Mgrs. Funds, 1983—; mem. adv. com. prof. ethics N.J. Supreme Ct., 1983—. Recipient Smith Coll. medal, 1971, Alumni Achievement award N.Y.U. Grad. Sch. Bus. Adminstrn. Alumni Assn., 1971; N.Y.U. Crystal award, 1982. Mem. Am. Fin. Assn. (past dir.), Money Marketeers (v.p. 1960, pres. 1961-62), Alumni Assn. Grad. Sch. Bus. Adminstrn. NYU (dir. 1951-63, pres. 1957-59), Am. Econ. Assn., Soc. Meml. Ctr., N.J. Com. for Humanities, Phi Beta Kappa Assocs. (v.p. 1979-87). Home: 24 Blossom Cove Rd Red Bank NJ 07701-6302 Office: PO Box 458 Red Bank NJ 07701-0458

MCWHIRTER, BRUCE J., lawyer; b. Chgo., Sept. 11, 1931; s. Sydney and Martha McW.; m. Judith Hallett, Apr. 14, 1960; children—Cameron, Andrew. B.S., Northwestern U., 1952; LL.B., Harvard U., 1955. Bar: D.C. 1955, Ill. 1955, U.S. Ct. Appeals (7th cir.) 1963, U.S. Supreme Ct. Assoc. Lord, Bissell & Brook, Chgo., 1958-62; assoc., then ptnr. Ross & Hardies, Chgo., 1962—; now sr. ptnr. Editor: Donnelley SEC Handbook, 1972-87; contbr. articles to profl. publs. Served with U.S. Army, 1955-57, Japan. Mem. ABA, Chgo. Bar Assn., Law Club Chgo., Harvard Law Soc. Ill. (bd. dirs. 1984), Harvard Club (N.Y.C.), Phi Beta Kappa. Democrat. Home: 111 Sheridan Rd Winnetka IL 60093-4223 Office: Ross & Hardies 150 N Michigan Ave Ste 2500 Chicago IL 60601-7567

MCWHIRTER, GLENNA SUZANNE (NICKIE MCWHIRTER), newspaper columnist; b. Peoria, Ill., June 28, 1929; d. Alfred Leon and Garnet Lorene (Short) Sotier; m. Edward Ford McWhirter (div.); children: Suzanne McWhirter Orlicki, Charles Edward, James Richard. BS in English Lang. and Lit., U. Mich., postgrad., 1960-63. Editl. asst. McGraw-Hill Pub. Co., Detroit, 1951-54; staff writer Detroit Free Press, Inc., Detroit, 1963-88; columnist Detroit News Inc., Detroit, 1988—; adv. copy writer Campbell-Ewald Co., Detroit, 1967-68. Author: Pea Soup, 1984. Winner 1st Place Commentary award UPI, Mich., 1979; 1st Place Columns AP, Mich., 1978, 81; 1st Place Columns Detroit Press Club Found., Mich., 1978; Disting. Service award State of Mich., 1985. Mem. Women in Comm. (Headliner

award 1978), Alpha Gamma Delta. Avocations: flower gardening; tennis. Home: 88 Meadow Ln Grosse Pointe MI 48236-3803

MCWHIRTER, JAMES HERMAN, consulting engineering business executive, financial planner; b. Mercer, Pa., July 4, 1924; s. John Herman and Blanche Rebecca (Anderson) McW.; m. Suzanne Kibler, July 5, 1952; children: Kathleen, Meg Allyn, John Richard, Thomas Charles, Robert Brian. BS, Columbia U., 1945; MS, Carnegie Inst. Tech., 1947. Registered profl. engr., Pa; cert. fin. planner. Devel. engr. Westinghouse Electric Corp., Sharon, Pa., 1948-65; rsch. engr. Westinghouse Rsch. Labs., Pitts., 1965-89; registered rep. Allegheny Investments, Ltd., Pitts., 1987—; pres. Optimization, Ltd., Murrysville, Pa., 1989—. Contbr. articles on engring. and fin. planning to profl. jours.; spkr. on fin. planning. Lt. (j.g.) USNR, 1945-58. Fellow IEEE. Republican. Presbyterian. Home and Office: 3660 Forbes Trail Dr Murrysville PA 15668-1054

MCWHIRTER, JOHN RUBEN, chemical engineering educator; b. East St. Louis, Ill., Dec. 29, 1937; s. Walter and Mildred (Johnson) McW.; m. Gail Balthrope, June 28, 1958 (div. Aug. 1978); children: John Winfield, Andrew James, Mark Steven, Brian Michael; m. Anne Burlingham, Mar. 31, 1979 (div. Dec. 1990); m. Jeanette D. Heiser, Mar. 21, 1992. BS in Chem. Engring., U. Ill., 1959; MS in Chem. Engring., Pa. State U., 1961, PhD in Chem. Engring., 1962; postgrad. exec. program, Stanford U., 1971. Research engr. E.I. Du Pont de Nemours & Co., Wilmington, Del., 1962-63; mgr. research and devel. Mixing Equipment Co., Rochester, N.Y., 1963-66; section engr. engring. devel. lab. Linde div. Union Carbide Corp., Tonawanda, N.Y., 1966-67, div. engr. engring. devel. lab., 1967-68, mgr. chem. engring. div. and special projects, 1968-69, product mgr., 1969-70; mgr. wastewater treatment systems Linde div. Union Carbide Corp., N.Y.C., 1970-72, gen. mgr. environ. systems dept., 1973-76, v.p., gen. mgr. environ. systems dept., 1977-78; v.p., gen. mgr. insecticides and intermediates agrl. products div. Union Carbide, N.Y.C., 1978-83, v.p., gen. mgr. agrl. chems., 1983-86; prof. chem. engring. Pa. State U., State College, Pa., 1986—. Author: The Use of High Purity Oxygen in the Activated Sludge Process, 1978; contbr. articles to profl. jours.; presented numerous papers at profl. confs.; patentee in field. Recipient Best Paper Presentation award Nat. Am. Inst. Chem. Engrs., 1963, Outstanding Personal Achievement award Chem. Engring. Mag., 1970, Kirkpatrick award, 1971, Outstanding Engring. Alumnus award Pa. State U., 1984, Arthur Dehan Little award Am. Inst. Chem. Engrs., 1991. Mem. Am. Inst. Chem. Engrs., Am. Mgmt. Assn., Am. Chem. Soc., Am. Assn. for the Advancement of Sci., N.Y. Acad. Scis., Water Pollution Control Fedn., Tau Beta Pi, Phi Lambda Upsilon, Sigma Tau, Alhpa Chi Sigma, Delta Tau Delta. Republican. Home: 505 Outer Dr State College PA 16801-7936 Office: Pa State U 122 Fenske Lab University Park PA 16802-4400

MCWHORTER, ALAN LOUIS, electronics researcher, engineering educator; b. Crowley, La., Aug. 25, 1930; s. Arthur Walton and Andree (Genet) McW. Student, Tulane U., 1947-48; BEE, U. Ill., 1951; ScD, MIT, 1955. Staff mem. Lincoln Lab., MIT, Lexington, 1955-59, asst. head. solid state div., 1962-63, assoc. head, 1963-65, head, 1965-94; fellow, 1994—; from asst. to assoc. prof. elec. engring. MIT, Cambridge, 1959-66, prof. elec. engring., 1966—; mem. elec. engring. adv. coun. U. Pa., 1987-93; cons. mem. adv. group on electron devices Office of the Under Sec. of Def., Acquisition and Tech., 1991—. Contbr. articles to profl. jours. Fellow IEEE (assoc. editor Transaction on Electron Devices 1959-64, edit. bd. Proc. 1966-69, 74-76, David Sarnoff award 1971), Am. Physical Soc. (exec. com. div. solid state physics 1968-70); mem. Nat. Acad. Engring. Office: MIT Lincoln Lab PO Box 73 Lexington MA 02173-9108

MCWHORTER, DONALD LEE, bank executive; b. 1935. BBA, U. Ky., 1958; grad., Wis. Grad. Sch. Banking. Various officer positions Bank One Milford, NA (now Bank One Cin., NA), 1960-83, pres., CEO, 1972-83; pres. Bank One Columbus, 1983-88; chmn. bd., CEO Banc One Svcs. Corp., 1988-89; chmn. bd., CEO, dir. Banc One Ohio Corp., 1989-92; pres. Banc One Corp., Columbus, Ohio, 1992—; bd. dirs. VISA USA, VISA Internat., Wharton Fin. Instns. Ctr. Trustee Ohio Dominican Coll., 1984—; mem. dean's adv. coun. Ind. U. Sch. Bus., 1994—. Office: Banc One Corp 100 E Broad St Columbus OH 43271-0261

MCWHORTER, HOBART AMORY, JR., lawyer; b. Birmingham, Ala., Dec. 24, 1931; s. Hobart Amory and Marjorie (Westgate) McW.; divorced; children: Margaret G., Marjorie W. BA, Yale U., 1953; LLB, U. Va., 1958. Bar: Ala. 1958. Ptnr. Bradley Arant Rose & White, Birmingham, 1958—. 1st lt. U.S. Army, 1953-55. Fellow Am. Coll. Trial Lawyers; mem. Internat. Assn. Ins. Counsel, Nat. Assn. R.R. Counsel, Products Liability Def. Coun. Republican. Presbyterian. Office: Bradley Arant Rose & White 1400 Park Pl Tower 2001 Park Pl Birmingham AL 35203-2735

MCWHORTER, KATHLEEN, orthodontist; b. Houston, May 29, 1953; d. Archer and Lucile (Taft) McW. BA summa cum laude, U. Houston, 1986; DDS with honors, Baylor Coll., 1990. Mgr. Am. Internat. Rent-A-Car, Houston, 1979-87; mktg. researcher Concoco Oil Co., Houston, 1979-83; orthodontist Baylor Coll. Dentistry, Dallas, 1990—; presenter Am. Assn. Dental Rsch., Montreal, Que., Can., 1988, Cin., 1990; rsch. fellow Baylor Coll. Dentistry, Dallas, 1987, 88, 89. Contbr. articles to profl. jours. Mem. ADA, Am. Assn. Orthodontists, Am. Assn. Women Dentists, Am. Assn. Dentistry for Children, Internat. Assn. Dental Rsch., Am. Assn. Dental Rsch., Tex. Dental Assn., Dallas County Dental Soc., The Crescent Club. Avocations: tennis, walking, music, water skiing. Office: Baylor U Coll Dentistry Dept Orthodontics 3302 Gaston Ave Dallas TX 75246-2013

MCWHORTER, RALPH CLAYTON, health care company executive; b. Chattanooga, Sept. 27, 1933; s. Ralph C. McWhorter and Gladys (Dover) Franks; children: Jodie, Stuart. Student, U. Tenn., 1951-52; BS, Samford U., 1955. Asst. administr. Phoebe Putney Meml. Hosp., 1956-65; administr. Americus-Sumter Regional Hosp., 1965-67, West Ga. Med. Ctr., 1967-70; administr. Palmyra Park Hosp. Hosp. Corp. Am., Nashville, 1970-73, div. v.p., 1973-76, sr. v.p. domestic ops., 1976-80, exec. v.p., 1980-85, pres., chief oper. officer, 1985-87, also bd. dirs.; chmn., chief exec. officer Health-Trust, Inc., Nashville, 1987—. Co-author: Management Dimensions, 1988. Campaign chair United Way Mid. Tenn., 1991. Fellow Am. Coll. Healthcare Execs.; mem. Am. Hosp. Assn. (bd. dirs.), Fedn. Am. Health Systems (pres. 1990, chmn. 1991). Methodist. Avocations: water sports, boating. Office: HealthTrust Inc 4525 Harding Rd Nashville TN 37205-2119*

MCWILLIAM, JOANNE ELIZABETH, religion educator; b. Toronto, Ont., Can., Dec. 10, 1928; d. Cecil Edward and Edna Viola (Archer) McW.; children, Leslie Mary Giroday, Elizabeth McEwen, Sean Dewart, Colin Dewart; m. C Peter Slater, June 6, 1987. BA, U. Toronto, 1951, MA, 1953; MA, U. St. Michael's, Toronto, 1966, PhD, 1968. Asst. prof. religious studies U. Toronto, 1968-74, assoc. prof., 1974-87, prof., 1987, chairperson dept. religious studies, 1990-92, 93-94; Mary Crooke Hoffman prof. of Dogmatic Theology The Gen. Theol. Sem., N.Y.C. 1994—. Author: The Theology of Grace of Theodore of Mopsuestia, 1971, Death and Resurrection in the Fathers, 1986; editor: Augustine: Rhetor to Theologian, 1991, Toronto Jour. Theology. Mem. Can. Soc. for Patristic Studies (pres. 1987—), Conf. Anglican Theologians (pres. 1990—), Can. Soc. for the Study of Religion, Can. Theol. Soc., Am. Theol. Soc., Am. Acad. Religion. Anglican. Home: 59 Duggan Ave, Toronto, ON Canada M4V 1Y1 Office: The Gen Theol Sem 175 9th Ave New York NY 10011-4972

MCWILLIAMS, BETTY JANE, science administrator, communication disorders educator, researcher; d. Harry J. and Martha (McClure) McW. B.S., Ohio State U., 1949; M.S., U. Pitts., 1950, Ph.D., 1953. Speech pathologist Ohio County Easter Seal Soc., Wheeling, W.Va., 1950-51; instr. U. Pitts., 1951-54, asst. prof., 1954-59, assoc. prof., 1959-67, prof., 1967-91, prof. emeritus, 1991—, dir. cleft palate craniofacial ctr., 1969-91, dir. emeritus, 1993—; vis. prof. U. N.C., Chapel Hill, 1955, Howard U., Washington, 1977-78; cons. Western Pa. Hosp., Pitts. 1972-91, Montefiore Hosp., N.Y.C., 1975-87, Walter Reed Army Hosp., Washington, 1984-87; mem. Pa. Acad. Com. on Tech. Devel., Harrisburg, Pa., 1984-87; mem. standards and peer rev. com. Pa. Fedn. of Cleft Palate Clinics, 1985-87. Sr. author: Cleft Palate Speech, 1984, revised edit., 1990; contbr. articles to profl. jours. Recipient Herbert Cooper Meml. award Cooper Clinic, 1979, award of recognition Pa. Acad. Dentistry for Children, 1989, award of recognition Pa. Dental Soc., 1991. Fellow Am. Speech, Lang. and Hearing Assn. (cert. clin.

competence), Am. Coll. Dentists; mem. APA, Am. Cleft Palate Craniofacial Assn. (pres. 1965, asst. sec. gen. 1st internat. congress 1969, editor 1975-81, pres. Found. 1982-83, svc. award 1975, Honors of Assn. 1987), Pa. Fedn. Cleft Palate Clinics (pres. 1980-82, 89-90, legis. com. 1991—). Avocations: antiques; needlework; cooking; reading. Home and Office: 512 Bigham Rd Pittsburgh PA 15211-1412

MCWILLIAMS, BRUCE WAYNE, marketing professional; b. Vancouver, B.C., Canada, Sept. 23, 1932; came to U.S., 1975; s. Lloyd and Mamie (Bateman) McW.; m. Heather Oxland, Nov. 15, 1957 (div.); children: Sandra, Roderic; m. Sheila Albin, June 23, 1990. Student, U. B.C., Vancouver, 1950-54. Account exec. asst. Brit. Petroleum Co., London, 1957-62; asst. dir. B.C. Govt. Travel Bur., 1962-64; mng. dir. HCF-Ergon Advt., Athens, Greece, 1964-67; dir. HCF-Internat., London, 1967-70; dir. pub. relations Occidental Internat. Oil Inc., Paris and London, 1970-75; dir. pub. affairs Occidental Petroleum Corp., Los Angeles, 1975-80; dir. pub. relations and advt. Comark, Newport Beach, Calif., 1980-81; ptnr. Chester Burger & Co. Inc., N.Y.C., 1981-83; sr. v.p. Ogilvy & Mather PR, Chgo., 1983-85; sr. corp. relations officer Internat. Fin. Corp., 1985-88; pres. The McWilliams Co., 1988-90; mktg. dir. Nixon, Hargrave, Devans & Doyle, Rochester, N.Y., 1990-92, Powell, Goldstein, Frazer & Murphy, Washington, 1993—. Mem. Pub. Relations Soc. Am. Club: Naval and Mil. (London).

MCWILLIAMS, C. PAUL, JR., engineering executive; b. Louisville, June 4, 1931; s. Cleo Paul and Audrey Dora (Hale) McW.; m. Barbara Ann Sparks, Feb. 22, 1950 (div. 1962); children: Bruce Kevin, Craig Tinsley; m. Barbara Ann Heintz, Apr. 25, 1980; 1 stepchild, Kimberly Jean Moorhouse Swigert. B Chem. Engring., U. Louisville, 1954, M Engring., 1972. Lic. profl. engr., N.Y., N.C. Sr. process devel. engr. Olin Mathieson Chem. Corp., Brandenburg, Ky., 1958-66, Rochester, N.Y., 1958-66; sr. chem. engr. GTE Sylvania, Seneca Falls, N.Y., 1966-74, Eastman Kodak Co., Rochester, 1974-81; prin., treas. Flint & Sherburne Assocs., P.C., Rochester, 1981-89; project engr. Roy F. Weston, Inc., Rochester, 1989-92; engring. mgr. ECCO Inc. (Environ. Cons. Co., Inc.), Buffalo, 1992-94; pres. ECCO Engring., Buffalo, 1993-94; staff engr. Environ. Products & Svcs., Inc., Rochester, N.Y., 1994—; cons. water tech. Water Tech. Corp., Tonawanda, N.Y., 1973-76; product rsch. panel Chem. Engring. Mag., 1982-83. Author: Waste Disposal Manual, 1976. Life mem. Rep. Presdl. Task Force, Webster, N.Y., 1986—; mem. Rep. Nat. Com., Webster, 1991-92. 1st lt. USAF, 1954-58, ret. lt. col. USAF Res., 1982. Decorated Meritorious Svc. medal. Mem. NSPE, AIChE, Soc. Am. Mil. Engrs., Res. Officers Assn. (life), Monroe Profl. Engrs. Soc. (environ. com. 1972-75, chmn. 1973-75, bd. dirs. 1982-84, program chmn. 1984), Cons. Engrs. Coun. N.Y. State (program chmn. Rochester chpt. 1986-87, sec. 1987-88, treas. 1989). Episcopalian. Achievements include replacing boiler feedwater regulators, related instrumentation and control systems and blowdown at a N.Y. State U. facility; system design for dry fabric dust collectors to remove fly ash from coal-fired boilers' flue gas. Home: 1132 Woodbridge Ln Webster NY 14580-8709 Office: Environ Products & Svcs Inc 230 McKee Rd Rochester NY 14611

MCWILLIAMS, CHRIS PATER ELISSA, elementary school educator; b. Cin., Oct. 23, 1937; d. Ray C. and Mary Loretta (Collins) Pater; m. Nabeel David Elissa, Aug. 15, 1964 (dec. Aug. 1975); children: Sue Renea, Ramsey Nabeel; m. Jim Bill McWilliams, Apr. 14, 1977 (dec. Sept. 1993). BA, Our Lady of Cin. Coll., 1959; MEd, Xavier U., 1965. Cert. tchr. elem., social studies, Tex. Elem. tchr. Cin. Parochial Schs., 1960-64, Champaign County Schs., Urbana, Ohio, 1968; tchr. social studies St. Mary's Elem. Sch., Urbana, 1968-73; tchr. Granbury (Tex.) Ind. Sch. Dist., 1981—; instr. Tarleton State U., Stephenville, Tex., 1989-90. Contbr. (text) Texas: Yesterday, Today and Tomorrow, 1988; music editor (newspaper) Jerusalem Star, 1966. Me. Hood Gen. Hosp. Aux., 1978—; chmn. Hood County Blood Drive, Granbury, 1978-82. Recipient scholarship Our Lady of Cin. Coll., 1955, Betty Crocker Homemaker award, Gen. Mills, 1955. Mem. Nat. Coun. Social Studies, Tex. Alliance for Geog. Edn., Phi Delta Kappa, Delta Kappa Gamma (pres. Lambda Pi chpt. 1988-90). Roman Catholic. Avocations: piano, reading, needlework, cooking, walking. Home: 249 Northwood Ter Granbury TX 76049

MCWILLIAMS, DENNIS MICHAEL, lawyer; b. Chgo., Jan. 15, 1941; s. Thomas F. and Dorothy A. (Dorney) McW.; divorced; children: Colleen P., Sean D. BA, U. Notre Dame, 1962, BSME, 1969; JD, Loyola U., Chgo., 1968. Bar: Ill. 1968, U.S. Dist. Ct. (no. dist.) Ill. 1968, U.S. Ct. Appeals (7th cir.) 1968, U.S. Ct. Appeals (fed. cir.) 1985. Patent atty. Borg-Warner Corp., Chgo., 1966-72; assoc. Mann Brown & McWilliams, Chgo., 1972-76; ptnr. Mann, McWilliams, Zummer & Sweeney, Chgo., 1976-89, Lee, Mann, Smith, McWilliams, Sweeney & Ohlson, Chgo., 1989—; instr. John Marshall Law Sch., Chgo., 1986—. Mem. ABA (chmn. com. 1980-), Patent Law Assn. Chgo., Union League Club. Avocations: owning race horses, tennis. Office: Lee Mann Smith McWilliams Sweeney & Ohlson 209 S LaSalle Ste 410 Chicago IL 60604

MCWILLIAMS, EDWIN JOSEPH, banker; b. Spokane, Washington, Aug. 11, 1919; s. Frank S. and Alice (Conlan) McW.; m. Betty J. Galbreath, Aug. 15, 1944; children: Lawrence, Barbara Anne, Marijoan, Peter. Student, U. Notre Dame, 1937-38, Marquette U., 1938-40; B.S. in Bus. Adminstrn, Gonzaga U., 1943. With Fidelity Mutual Savings Bank, Spokane, 1940-82; exec. v.p. Fidelity Mutual Savings Bank, 1955-58, pres., 1958-82; pres. Fidelity Service Corp., 1983-87; mem. adv. council Wash. State Dept. Commerce and Econ. Devel., 1977-80; U.S. del. Internat. Savs. Bank Inst., 1975, 76, 79. Pres. United Crusade Spokane County, 1966; past pres., mem. exec. bd. Inland Empire coun., region 11 exec. com Boy Scouts Am.; past pres. Spokane Unltd.; mem. adv. coun. Sch. Bus., Gonzaga U.; bd. dirs., mem. exec. com. Expo '74 World's Fair; past mem. bd. regents Ft. Wright Coll., Spokane; past bd. dirs. Sacred Heart Med. Ctr.; past bd. regents Wash. State U.; bd. dirs. Fairmont Meml. Assn. Served to lt. (j.g.) USNR, 1943-45. Mem. Nat. Assn. Mut. Savs. Banks (chmn. 1976-77), Mut. Savs. Banks Assn. State of Wash. (pres. 1980), Am. Savs. and Loan Inst. (past gov. dist. XI), Spokane C. of C. (pres. 1974-75). Roman Catholic. Clubs: Rotary of Spokane, K.C. Home: 1717 S Upper Terrace Rd Spokane WA 99203-3558

MCWILLIAMS, JOHN LAWRENCE, III, lawyer; b. Phila., Dec. 21, 1943; s. John Lawrence Jr. and Elizabeth Dolores (Chevalier) McW.; m. Paula Ann Root, July 19, 1969 (dec.); children: John Lawrence, IV, Robert Root, Anne Elizabeth, David Stanford, Peter Farrell; m. Kathleen Nolan Pradella, Apr. 3, 1993. BS, St. Joseph's U., 1965; JD, Seton Hall U., 1969. Bar: N.J. 1969, N.Y. 1975, U.S. Supreme Ct. 1975, Fla. 1977. Trial atty. regional office SEC, N.Y.C., 1969-72; assoc. Mudge Rose Guthrie & Alexander, N.Y.C., 1972-77; mem. Freeman, Richardson, Watson & Kelly, P.A., Jacksonville, Fla., 1977-89, chmn., pres., 1984-89, ptnr. Squire, Sanders & Dempsey, 1989—; apptd. spl. asst. to U.S. atty. Dist. of N.J., 1971. Trustee Mcpl. Service Dist. Ponte Vedra Beach, 1981-85, chmn. bd. trustees, 1984-85; treas. Ponte Vedra Cmty. Assn., 1980-82; mem. Leadership Jacksonville, 1981, mem. steering com., 1982; dir. Jacksonville Country Day Sch., 1985-87; pres. Jacksonville Beaches Ponte Vedra Unit Am. Cancer Soc., 1988-90. Mem. ABA, Nat. Assn. Bond Lawyers, Fla. Bar, Jacksonville C. of C. Republican. Roman Catholic. Clubs: Ponte Vedra, Sawgrass, River. Home: 3040 Timberlake Pt Ponte Vedra Beach FL 32082-3726 Office: Squire Sanders & Dempsey One Enterprise Ctr 225 Water St Ste 2100 Jacksonville FL 32202-4424

MCWILLIAMS, JOHN MICHAEL, lawyer; b. Annapolis, Md., Aug. 17, 1939; s. William J. and Helen (Disharon) McW.; m. Frances Edelen McCabe, May 30, 1970; children: M. Edelen, J. Michael, James McC. B.S., Georgetown U., 1964; LL.B., U. Md., 1967; LLD (hon.), U. Balt., 1993. Bar: Md. 1967, U.S. Supreme Ct. 1970, U.S. Ct. Internat. Trade 1991, U.S. Ct. Mil. Appeals 1992. Law clk. Chief Judge Roszel C. Thomsen, U.S. Dist. Ct. Md., 1967-68; assoc. Piper and Marbury, Balt., 1968-69; asst. atty. gen. State of Md., 1969-76; gen. counsel Md. Dept. Transp., 1971-76; sr. ptnr. Tydings and Rosenberg, Balt., 1977—; permanent mem. 4th Circuit Jud. Conf. Asst. editor Law Rev., U. Md., 1967. Chmn. Md. adv. council to Nat. Legal Services Corp., 1975-78; commr. Gov.'s Com. to Revise Annotated Code of Md., 1973-78; transition dir. Md. Gov.-Elect Harry Hughes, 1978-79, com. sen. adv. coun. to Clinton-Gore Presidential Com.; mem. Md. Indsl. Devel. Financing Authority, 1980, Greater Balt. Com., 1979—; mem. exec. com. Econ. Devel. Council Greater Balt., 1979-83; vice chmn. bd. Washington/ Balt. Regional Assn., 1980-83; mem. Md. Econ. and Community Devel. Adv. Commn., 1983-87; chmn. bd. Md. Econ. Devel. Corp., 1984-89. Served

to 1st lt. U.S. Army, 1958-60. Fellow Am. Bar Found. (bd. dirs. 1986-88, 91-93), Md. Bar Found. (dir. 1980-82); mem. ABA (pres. 1992-93, mem. ho. of dels. 1976—, chmn. 1986-88; chmn. Md. del. 1976-86, bd. editors jour. 1986-88, 91-93), Md. Bar Assn. (pres. 1981-82), Nat. Conf. Bar Pres. (exec. council 1982-85), Bar Assn. Balt. City, Am. Law Inst., Am. Judicature Soc. (dir. 1974-81, exec. com. 1975-77), Am. Acad. Jud. Edn. (dir. 1977), Am. Arbitration Assn. (various panels), Md. Law Rev. (trustee 1980-83), Md. Inst. Continuing Edn. Lawyers (trustee 1980-83), Inst. Internat. Bus. Law and Practice (corr.), Center Club, Md. Club, Rule Day Club. Democrat. Roman Catholic. Home: 3 Merryman Ct Baltimore MD 21210-2815 Office: 26th Fl 100 E Pratt St Baltimore MD 21202-1009

MCWILLIAMS, MARGARET ANN, home economics educator; author; b. Osage, Iowa, May 26, 1929; d. Alvin Randall and Mildred Irene (Lane) Edgar; children: Roger, Kathleen. BS, Iowa State U., 1951, MS, 1953; PhD, Oreg. State U., 1968. Registered dietitian. Asst. prof. home econs. Calif. State U., L.A., 1961-66, assoc. prof., 1966-68, prof., 1968-92, prof. emeritus, 1992—, chmn. dept., 1968-76; pres. Plycon Press, 1978—. Author: Food Fundamentals, 1966, 6th edit., 1995, Nutrition for the Growing Years, 1967, 5th edit., 1993, Experimental Foods Laboratory Manual, 1977, 4th edit., 1994, (with L. Kotschevar) Understanding Food, 1969, Illustrated Guide to Food Preparation, 1970, 7th edit., 1995, (with L. Davis) Food for You, 1971, 2d edit., 1976, The Meatless Cookbook, 1973, (with F. Stare) Living Nutrition, 1973, 4th edit., 1984, Nutrition for Good Health, 1974, 2d edit., 1982 (with H. Paine), Modern Food Preservation, Fundamentals of Meal Management, 1978, 2d edit., 1993, Foods: Experimental Perspectives, 1989, 2d edit., 1993. Chmn. bd. Beach Cities Symphony, 1991-94. Recipient Alumni Centennial award Iowa State U., 1971, Profl. Achievement award, 1977; Phi Upsilon Omicron Nat. Founders fellow, 1964; Home Economist in Bus. Nat. Found. fellow, 1967; Outstanding Prof. award Calif. State U., 1976. Mem. Am. Dietetic Assn., Inst. Food Technologists, Phi Kappa Phi, Phi Upsilon Omicron, Omicron Nu, Iota Sigma Pi, Sigma Delta Epsilon, Sigma Alpha Iota. Home: PO Box 220 Redondo Beach CA 90277-0220

MCWILLIAMS, MICHAEL G., writer, television critic; b. Detroit, Aug. 28, 1952; s. Henry and Mary (Toarmina) McW. BA, Wayne State U., 1975; MFA, Columbia U., 1978. Free-lance writer Detroit News, Monthly Detroit mag., 1979-82, Village Voice, Rolling Stone, TV Guide, Advt. Age, N.Y. Daily News, L.A. Herald Examiner, N.Y.C., 1982-87; TV critic The Detroit News, 1988—. Author: TV Sirens, 1987, (with others) The Premiere Guide to Movies on Video, 1991. Recipient Assn. of Sunday and Feature Editors award, 1st pl. Arts Criticism, 1992. Mem. Phi Beta Kappa. Avocations: TV, movies, theater, music. Office: Detroit News 615 W Lafayette Blvd Detroit MI 48226-3197

MCWILLIAMS, MIKE C., lawyer; b. Dallas, Nov. 10, 1948; s. Earl Dewitt and Mary Louise (Campbell) McW.; m. Sally Swatzell, Sept. 1, 1973; children: Michael, Matthew. BBA in Fin., U. Tex., 1969, JD, 1973. Bar: Tex. 1973. Assoc. Elliott, Meer, Vetter, Denton & Bates, Dallas, 1973-78; ptnr. Denton & Generis, Dallas, 1978-80, Moore & Peterson, P.C., Dallas, 1980-89, Winstead, Sechrest & Minick, Dallas, 1989—. Editor: Texas International Law Journal, 1972-73. Mem. ABA, Tex. State Bar Assn., Dallas Bar Assn., Phi Delta Phi, Beta Gamma Sigma. Office: Winstead Sechrest & Minick 5400 Renaissance Tower 1201 Elm St Dallas TX 75270-2016

MCWILLIAMS, PETER, poet; b. Detroit, Aug. 5, 1949; s. Henry G. and Mary (Toarmina) McW. Student, Ea. Mich. U., Maharishi Internat. U. Tchr. transcendental meditation Internat. Meditation Soc., L.A.; poet laureate Maharishi Internat. U.; co-founder Three Rivers Pr.; pub. Versemonger Pr., Lion Pr.; owner Leo Pr. Author: (with Denise Denniston) The TM Book: How to Enjoy the Rest of Your Life, 1975, (with Melba Colgrove and Harold Bloomfield) How to Survive the Loss of a Love: 58 Things to Do When There Is Nothing to Be Done, 1976, You Can't Afford the Luxury of a Negative Thought: A Book for People with Any Life-Threatening Illness-Including Life, 1988, (with Colgrove and Bloomfield) Surviving, Healing, and Growing: The How to Survive the Loss of a Love Workbook, 1991, LIFE 101: Everything We Wish We Had Learned About Life in School - But Didn't, 1991, Focus on the Positive: The You Can't Afford the Luxury of a Negative Thought Workbook, 1991, The Portable LIFE 101: 179 Essential Lessons, 1992, DO IT! Let's Get Off Our Butts, 1992, Portraits: A Book of Photographs by Peter McWilliams, 1992, WEALTH 101: Wealth Is Much More Than Money, 1993, We Give To Love: Giving Is Such a Selfish Thing, 1993, The Portable DO IT!: 172 Essential Excerpts Plus 190 Quotations, 1993, Ain't Nobody's Business If You Do: The Absurdity of Consensual Crimes in a Free Society, 1993, LIFE 102: What to Do When Your Guru Sues You, 1994, (with Bloomfield) How to Heal Depression, 1994, What Jesus and the Bible Really Said about Drugs, Sex, Gays, Gambling, Prostitution, Alternative Healing, Assisted Suicide and Other Consensual "Sins", 1994, That Book About Drugs, 1995, LOVE 101: To Love Oneself Is the Beginning of a Lifelong Romance, 1995; (poetry) Come Love with Me and Be My Life, 1967, I Have Loved, 1968, For Lovers and No Others, 1968, I Love Therefore I am, 1969, The Hard Stuff: Love, 1969, Evolving at the Speed of Love, 1971, Surviving the Loss of a Love, 1971, Love: An Experience Of, 1972, Love and All the Other Verbs of Life, 1973, Love Is Yes, 1973, This Longing May Shorten My Life, 1974, Catch Me With Your Smile, 1976, I Marry You Because, 1993. Office: Prelude Press 8159 Santa Monica Blvd Los Angeles CA 90046*

MCWILLIAMS, ROBERT HUGH, federal judge; b. Salina, Kans., Apr. 27, 1916; s. Robert Hugh and Laura (Nicholson) McW.; m. Catherine Ann Cooper, Nov. 4, 1942 (dec.); 1 son, Edward Cooper; m. Joan Harcourt, Mar. 8, 1986. A.B., U. Denver, 1938, LL.B., 1941. Bar: Colo. bar 1941. Colo. dist. judge Denver, 1952-60; justice Colo. Supreme Ct., 1961-68, chief justice, 1969-70; judge U.S. Ct. Appeals (10th cir.), Denver, 1970—. Served with AUS, World War II. Mem. Phi Beta Kappa, Omicron Delta Kappa, Phi Delta Phi, Kappa Sigma. Republican. Episcopalian. Home: 137 Jersey St Denver CO 00220 Office: Byon White/US Courthouse 1823 Stout St Denver CO 80257

MCWILLIAMS, ROGER DEAN, physicist, educator; b. Ames, Iowa, Aug. 18, 1954; s. Donald Arthur and Margaret Ann (Edgar) McW.; m. Carol Lee Carter, Sept. 7, 1985; 1 child, Alice Louise. BA, U. Calif., Irvine, 1975; PhD, Princeton U., 1980. Rsch. asst. Princeton (N.J.) U., 1975-80; asst. prof. in physics U. Calif., Irvine, 1980-87, assoc. prof., 1987-91, prof., 1991—, cons., expert witness for physics and law, 1983—, cons., expert witness for physics in sports, 1988—. Mem. Am. Phys. Soc., Am. Geophys. Union, Phi Beta Kappa. Office: U Calif Physics Irvine CA 92717

MEACHAM, CHARLES HARDING, government official; b. Newman, Calif., Sept. 21, 1925; s. Vernon A. and Sara (Paulsen) M.; m. June Lorraine Yunker, June 22, 1946; children—Charles Paulsen, Bruce Herbert. B.S., Utah State U., 1950. Biologist Calif. Dept. Fish and Game, 1950-56, Alaska Dept. Fisheries, 1956-59; regional supr. regions II and III Alaska Dept. Fish and Game, 1959-68; dir. internat. fisheries Office Gov. Alaska, 1968-69; commr. U.S. Fish and Wildlife Service, Dept. Interior, 1969-70, dep. asst. sec. for fish and wildlife, pks. and marine resources, commr. Internat. North Pacific Fisheries Commn. and Gt. Lakes Fishery Commn., 1969-70, commr. Internat. Pacific Salmon Fisheries Commn., 1969-70, commr. Great Lakes Fishery Commn., 1969-70; asst. to area dir. U.S. Fish and Wildlife Service, Dept. Interior, Alaska, 1971-74; dir. internat. affairs Office of Gov., Juneau, Alaska, 1975-80; pres. Meacham & Assocs., Anchorage, 1980—; dep. commr. U.S. North Pacific Fur Seal Commn.; mem. Pacific and North Pacific Fisheries Mgmt. Councils, 1976-81; internat. nat. park system adv. bd. U.S. Dept. Interior. Bd. dir. Resource Devel. Coun. for Alaska. With USMCR, 1943-46. Mem. Am. Fisheries Soc., Wildlife Soc., Pacific Fisheries Biologists, Internat. Assn. Game, Fish and Conservation Commrs., Ducks Unlimited, Alaska Miners Assn., Am. Legion. Club: Elks. Address: PO Box 428 Sequim WA 98382-0428

MEACHAM, CHARLES P., president, capital consulting; b. Susanville, Calif., Apr. 29, 1947; m. Charlene D. Heriot, 1969; 3 children. BS, Humboldt State U., 1969, MS in Fisheries, 1971. Comml. fisherman Bristol Bay, Alaska, 1963-64; with Bumble Bee Seafoods, Bristol Bay, S.E. Alaska, 1967-69; fisheries cons. Winzler & Kelly Engring., Eureka, Calif., 1969-71; seafood insp. U.S. Army Med. Dept., Ft. Richardson, Alaska, 1971-74; staff biologist Alaska Dept. of Fish and Game, Juneau, Alaska, 1974-75; rsch.

biologist Artic Char investigations Alaska Dept. of Fish and Game, Dillingham, Alaska, 1975-77; Bristol Bay rsch. project leader Alaska Dept. of Fish and Game, Anchorage, 1978-81, regional rsch. supr., 1981-89, mgr. fishery program divsn. of oil spill impact assessment and restoration, 1990-91; dep. commr. Alaska Dept. of Fish and Game, Juneau, 1991-95; pres. Capital Consulting, 1995—; affiliate faculty U. Alaska, 1983-87; mem. Bering Sea/Aleutians plan team N. Pacific Fisheries Mgmt. Council, 1989, Alaska Regional Marine Rsch. Bd., 1992—, Pacific Fisheries Mgmt. Coun., 1991—; commr. Pacific States Marine Fisheries Commn., 1991—; presidential appointment as commr. for Pacific Salmon Commn., 1991—. Mem. Mayor's Task Force on Fisheries, Anchorage, 1988-89, Alaska Tourism Coordinating Commn., 1992—; mem. review team Alaska Sci. & Tech. Found., 1989; alt. mem. Exxon Valdez Oil Spill Trustee Coun., 1992—. Mem. NAS, OSB (fisheries com., 1992, 95), Am. Fisheries Soc. (life, v.p. Alaska chpt. 1975, pres. elect 1977, pres. 1978), Am. Inst. of Fishery Rsch. Biologists. Home: 533 Main St Juneau AK 99801-1153

MEACHAM, STANDISH, historian, educator; b. Cin., Mar. 12, 1932; s. Standish and Eleanor (Rapp) M.; m. Sarah Shartle, Aug. 24, 1957 (div. 1993); children: Edith, Louisa, Samuel. B.A., Yale U., 1954; Ph.D., Harvard U., 1961. Asst. prof. history Harvard U., 1962-67; mem. faculty U. Tex., Austin, 1967—; prof. history U. Tex., 1970—, chmn. dept. history, 1969-72, 84-89, dean Coll. Liberal Arts, 1989-92. Author: Henry Thornton of Clapham, 1964, Lord Bishop: The Life of Samuel Wilberforce, 1970, A Life Apart, 1977, (with R. Flukinger and Larry Schaaf) Paul Martin, Victorian Photographer, 1977, (with E. M. Burns and Robert Lerner) Western Civilizations, 12th edit., 1993, Toynbee Hall and Social Reform, 1987; editor: (Edward Bulwer) England and the English, 1970. Trustee Brooks Sch., North Andover, Mass., 1983—; dir. Live Oak Fund for Change, 1992, Planned Parenthood of Austin, 1993—. Am. Council Learned Socs. fellow, 1965-66, 79-80; Guggenheim Found. fellow, 1972-73. Office: U Tex Garrison Hall 101 Austin TX 78712-1163

MEACHAM, WILLIAM FELAND, neurological surgeon, educator; b. Washington, Dec. 12, 1913; s. Marion H. and Mamie (Henderson) M.; m. Alice Marie Mathews, June 14, 1944; children: William Feland, Patrick, Barbara, Robert. B.S., Western Ky. State Coll., 1936; M.D., Vanderbilt U., 1940. Diplomate: Am. Bd. Surgery, Am. Bd. Neurol. Surgery. Intern surgery Vanderbilt U. Hosp., Nashville, 1940-41; asst. resident surgery Vanderbilt U. Hosp., 1941-43, resident surgeon, 1943-44, asst. vis. surgeon, 1944; asso. vis. surgeon Out-Patient Service, 1944; asst. in surgery Vanderbilt U. Sch. Medicine, 1941-43, instr. surgery, 1943-44, William Henry Howe fellow in neurol. surgery, 1945-47, asst. clin. prof. surgery, 1947-50, assoc. clin. prof. surgery, 1950-53, assoc. prof. neurol. surgery, 1953-54, prof. neurol. surgery, 1954-59, clin. prof. neurol. surgery, 1959-85, prof. emeritus clin. neurosurgery, 1985—; vol. asst. Montreal Neurol. Inst., 1947; asst. clin. prof. neurol. surgery Meharry Med. Sch., 1947-50, clin. prof., 1950—; attending neurosurgeon Nashville Gen., St. Thomas, Mid-State Bapt. hosps., Riverside and Madison Sanitaria; cons. in neurosurgery Thayer Vets. Hosp., Murfreesboro (Tenn.) Vets. Hosp., Jr. League Home for Crippled Children.; Chmn. Study Commn. on Stroke, Tenn. Mid South Regional Med. Program, 1968. Mem. Am. Acad. Neurol. Surgery, ACS (chmn. adv. council for neurol. surgery 1959-63, bd. govs. 1964- 66, bd. regents 1966-75, 2d v.p. 1982-83), AMA, Nashville Acad. Medicine (past pres., chmn. bd. dirs.), Nashville Surg. Soc. (past pres.), Am. Surg. Assn., Neurosurg. Soc. Am. (past pres., mem. exec. council), Neurosurg. Travel Club, Soc. Neurol. Surgeons (pres. 1971), Soc. Univ. Surgeons, Southeastern Surg. Congress, So. Med. Assn., So. Neurosurg. Soc. (past pres.), Tenn. Med. Assn., Am. Assn. Neurol. Surgeons (dir., past sec., past treas., pres. 1972), Am. Cancer Soc. (dir.), Sigma Xi, Alpha Omega Alpha. Methodist. Home: 3513 Woodmont Blvd Nashville TN 37215-1427 Office: 709 St Thomas Med Pla 4230 Harding Rd Nashville TN 37205-2013

MEACHIN, DAVID JAMES PERCY, investment banker, import-export executive; b. Teignmouth, Devon, Eng., Jan. 1, 1941; came to U.S., 1969; s. James Alfred and Ena Annie Meachin; m. Barbara Marshall Maxwell, Sept. 25, 1971; children: Jonathan J.M., Philip D.M. BS in Physical Sci., U. Natal, Republic South Africa, 1960; BSchemE, U. Cape Town, Republic South Africa, 1963; MS in Petroleum Engring., French Petroleum Inst., Paris, 1965; diploma in Indsl. Mgmt., Cambridge (Eng.) U., 1966; MBA with distinction, Harvard U., 1971. Project engr. Humphreys and Glasgow Ltd., London, 1966-69; 2d v.p. investment banking Smith Barney and Co. Inc., N.Y.C. and Tokyo, 1971-75; v.p., gen. mgr. internat. corp. fin. Salomon Bros., N.Y.C. and London, 1975-81; mng. dir. investment banking Merrill Lynch Capital Markets, N.Y.C., 1981-91; chmn., chief exec. officer Cross Border Enterprises Inc., 1991—; gen. ptnr. Meachin, Rath & Co., 1991—; bd. dirs. Ground Round Restaurants. Dir. Spartek Emerging Opportunities of India Fund; dir., past chmn. British Am. Edhl. Found.; elder Brick Presbyn. Ch., N.Y.C., 1988—; bd. dirs., vice-chmn. U. Cape Town Found., N.Y.C., 1985—; mem. UN Assn. Coun. of Fellows. Mem. Misquamicut Club (bd. govs.), Watch Hill Yacht Club, Hurlingham Club, United Oxford and Cambridge Club, Jupiter Island Club, Harvard Club, Union Club, Sky Club. Avocations: sailing, golf, tennis, squash. Home: 1105 Park Ave New York NY 10128-1200 Office: Cross Border Enterprises Inc 441 Lexington Ave New York NY 10017-3910

MEAD, BEVERLEY TUPPER, physician, educator; b. New Orleans, Jan. 22, 1923; s. Harold Tupper and Helen Edith (Hunt) M.; m. Thelma Ruth Cottingham, June 8, 1947. B.S., U. S.C., 1943; M.D., Med. Coll. S.C., 1947; M.S., U. Utah, 1958. Intern Detroit Receiving Hosp., 1947-48, resident, 1948-51; asst. prof. U. Utah, 1954-61; assoc. prof. U. Ky., 1961-65; prof. psychiatry and behavioral sci. Creighton U. Sch. Medicine, Omaha, 1965—; chmn. dept. Creighton U. Sch. Medicine, 1965-77, assoc. dean for acad. and faculty affairs, 1980-88. *The approval of others does not concern me as much as my approval of myself.*

MEAD, BEVERLY MIRIUM ANDERSON, writer, educator; b. St. Paul, May 29, 1927; d. Martin and Anna Mae (Oshanyk) Anderson; m. Jerome Morton Nemiro, Feb. 10, 1951 (div. May 1975); children: Guy Samuel, Lee Anna, Dee Martin; m. William Isaac Mead, Aug. 8, 1992. Student Reed Coll., 1943-44; BA, U. Colo., 1947; postgrad., U. Denver. Tchr. Seattle Pub. Schs., 1945-46; fashion coordinator, dir. Denver Dry Goods Co., 1948-51; fashion model, Denver, 1951-58, 78—; fashion dir. Denver Market Week Assn., 1952-53; free-lance writer, Denver, 1958—; moderator TV program Your Preschool Child, Denver, 1955-56; instr. writing and communications U. Colo. Denver Ctr., 1970—, U. Calif., San Diego, 1976-78, Met. State Coll., 1985; dir. pub. relations Fairmont Hotel, Denver, 1979-80; free lance fashion and TV model; author, co-author: The Complete Book of High Altitude Baking, 1961, Colorado a la Carte, 1963, Colorado a la Carte, Series II, 1966, (with Donna Hamilton) The High Altitude Cookbook, 1969, The Busy People's Cookbook, 1971 (Better Homes and Gardens Book Club selection 1971), Where to Eat in Colorado, 1967, Lunch Box Cookbook, 1965, Complete Book of High Altitude Baking, 1961, (under name Beverly Anderson) Single After 50, 1978, The New High Altitude Cookbook, 1980. Co-founder, pres. Jr. Symphony Guild, Denver, 1959-60; active Friends of Denver Libr., Opera Colo. Recipient Top Hand award Colo. Authors' League, 1969, 72, 79-82, 100 Best Best Books of Yr. award N.Y. Times, 1969, 71; named one of Colo.'s Women of Yr., Denver Post, 1964. Mem. Am. Soc. Journalists and Authors, Colo. Authors League (dir. 1969-79), Authors Guild, Authors League Am., Friends Denver Library, Rotary, Sigma Delta Chi, Kappa Alpha Theta. Address: 23 Polo Club Dr Denver CO 80209

MEAD, CARVER ANDRESS, computer science educator; b. Bakersfield, Calif., May 1, 1934. B.S., Calif. Inst. Tech., 1956, M.S., 1957, Ph.D., 1960; hon. doctorate. U. of Lund, 1987, U. So. Calif., 1991. Prof. Calif. Inst. Tech., Pasadena, 1957—, Gordon and Betty Moore prof. engring. and applied sci., 1980—; bd. dirs. Synaptics Inc., San Jose, Aptix Corp., San Jose. Author: Introduction to VLSI Systems, 1979 (Electronic Achievements award 1981, Harold Pender award 1984, John Price Wetherhill award 1985), Analog VLSI and Neural Systems, 1989. Recipient T.D. Callinan award Electrochem. Soc., 1971, Centennial medal IEEE, 1984, Harry Goode Meml. award Am. Fedn. Info. Processing Socs., Inc., 1985, award for Outstanding Rsch., INNS, 1992, Robert Dexter Conrad award USN, 1994. Fellow IEEE, Am. Phys. Soc., Franklin Inst. (life), Am. Acad. Arts and Scis.; mem. NAE, NAS, Royal Swedish Acad. Engring. Sci. (fgn.), Sigma Xi. Office:

Calif Inst Tech Physics Computation MS 139-74 1201 E California Blvd Pasadena CA 91125-0001

MEAD, DANA GEORGE, diversified industrial manufacturing company executive; b. Cresco, Iowa, Feb. 22, 1936; s. George Francis and Evelyn Grace (Derr) M.; m. Nancy L. Cooper, Apr. 12, 1958; children: Dana George, Mark Cooper. B.S. (Disting. Cadet), U.S. Mil. Acad., 1957; Ph.D., M.I.T., 1967. Commd. 2d lt. U.S. Army, 1957, advanced through grades to col., 1974; service in W. Ger. and Vietnam; White House fellow, 1970-71; staff asst. to Pres. Nixon, 1970-72; assoc. dir., then dep. dir. Domestic Council, White House, 1972-74; permanent prof. social sci. dept., dep. head U.S. Mil. Acad., 1974-78; ret., 1978; v.p. human resources Internat. Paper Co., N.Y.C., 1978-81, v.p., group exec., 1981-87; sr. v.p. Internat. Paper Co., Purchase, 1987-89, exec. v.p., dir, 1989-92; COO Tenneco Inc., Houston, 1992-93, pres., chmn., CEO, 1994—, also bd. dirs.; CEO, chmn. J.I. Case, Racine, Wis., 1992-94, chmn., 1995—; bd. dirs. Nat. Westminster Bancorp, Cummins Engine Co., Alco Standard, Baker Hughes Corp., Logistics Mgmt. Inst., Washington. Author articles on nat. security and domestic policy, business and manufacturing planning. Mem. Pres.'s Commn. on White House Fellowships, West Point Soc., N.Y., 1980—, White House Fellows Assn. and Found., 1981-82; bd. dirs. White House Fellows Found., 1978-83; mem. MIT Vis. Com. Polit. Scis. Decorated Legion of Merit with oak leaf cluster, Bronze Star with oak leaf cluster, Meritorious Service medal, Air medal with 3 oak leaf clusters, Army Commendation medal, Presdl. Service badge, Combat Inf. badge; Vietnam Cross Gallantry with palm, silver and bronze stars. Mem. Nat. Assn. Mfg. (vice chmn. 1995—), Coun. Fgn. Rels., Assn. Grads. West Point (trustee), Univ. Club, Met. Club (N.Y.), Houston Racquet Club, Houstonian Club. Republican. Home: 145 Radney Rd Houston TX 77024-7334 Office: Tenneco Inc PO Box 2511 Houston TX 77252-2511

MEAD, EDWARD MATHEWS, newpaper executive; b. Erie, Pa., Oct. 13, 1926; s. John James and Grace (Finerty) M.; m. Allene Steimer, Feb. 16, 1957; children: John James, Edward Mathews, Daniel Patrick. Student, U. N.C., 1945-46; B.A. in History, Princeton U., 1949. Trainee Trenton Times, 1949-50; night editor Erie Times, 1950-54, Sunday editor, 1954-56, asst. to pub., 1956-64, asst. pub., 1964-73, pres., 1973—, also co-pub, also treas., columnist, editor. Mem. Erie Com. on Community Devel., 1971—, sec., 1980; bd. dirs. St. Vincent Hosp., from 1974, pres., 1980; bd. dirs. Villa Maria Coll., from 1977, pres., 1979. Served with USMC, 1945-46. Mem. Pa. Asso. Press (pres. 1977), Pa. Newspaper Pubs. Assn. (dir. from 1977). Roman Catholic. Office: Time Publishing Co. Times Sq W 12th & Sassafras Sts Erie PA 16534*

MEAD, GEORGE WILSON, II, paper company executive; b. Milw., Oct. 11, 1927; s. Stanton W. and Dorothy (Williams) M.; m. Helen Patricia Anderson, Sept. 3, 1949 (div. Feb. 1990); children: Deborah, David, Leslie; m. Susan A. Feith, Aug. 25, 1990. B.S., Yale U., 1950; M.S., Inst. Paper Chemistry, Wis., 1952. With Consol. Papers, Inc., Wisconsin Rapids, Wis., 1952—, v.p. ops., 1962-66, pres., chief exec. officer, 1966-71, chmn. bd., CEO, 1971-93; chmn. bd., 1993—; also bd. dirs. Consol. Papers, Inc., Wisconsin Rapids, Wis.; chmn., dir. Consol. Water Power Co.; bd. dirs. Snap-On Tools Corp., Firstar Corp. Co-chmn. bldg. fund drive Riverview Hosp., Wisconsin Rapids, 1963-64, mem. bd., 1961-77; dirs. Consol's Civic Found.; bd. dirs. Nat. Coun. for Air and Stream Improvement; trustee Lawrence U.; chmn. bd. trustees Inst. Paper Sci. and Tech., 1988-90. Mem. TAPPI (bd. dirs. 1969-72), Am. Paper Inst. (bd. dirs. 1967-69, 80—), Chgo. Club, Elks (exalted ruler 1958), Rotary. Office: Consol Papers Inc PO Box 8050 Wisconsin Rapids WI 54495-8050

MEAD, GILBERT D(UNBAR), geophysicist, lawyer; b. Madison, Wis., May 31, 1930; s. Stanton Witter and Dorothy Elizabeth (Williams) M.; m. Jaylee Montague, Nov. 18, 1968; children: Elizabeth, Diana, Stanton, Robert. BS, Yale U., 1952; PhD in Physics, U. Calif., Berkeley, 1962; JD, U. Md., 1991. Tchr. sci. San Benito High Sch., Hollister, Calif., 1953-55; rsch. asst. Lawrence Radiation Lab., Berkeley, 1957-62; physicist theoretical div. NASA Goddard Space Flight Ctr., Greenbelt, Md., 1962-74; head geophysics br. NASA Goddard Space Flight Ctr., 1974-79; geophysicist crustal dynamics project, 1979-87; bd. dirs., chmn. audit com., mem. nominating com. Consolidated Papers, Inc., Wisconsin Rapids, Wis., 1974—. Editor: (with W. Hess) Introduction to Space Science, 1968; contbr. numerous articles to profl. jours. Trustee Beloit Coll., 1976-87, Arena Stage, Washington, 1991—. Recipient Outstanding Svc. award Goddard Space Flight Ctr., 1978. Mem. Md. State Bar Assn., D.C. Bar Assn., Am. Geophys. Union (chmn. ann. meeting com. 1971-73). Home: 2700 Virginia Ave NW Apt 701 Washington DC 20037-1908

MEAD, JAMES MATTHEW, insurance company executive; b. Erie, Pa., June 10, 1945; s. James Leonard and Olga (Richter) M.; m. Rhoda Ginsberg, Sept. 2, 1967 (div. 1971); m. Elaine Margaret Lytle, Mar. 8, 1975. BS, Pa. State U., 1967, MA, 1970. Instr. bus. Pa. State U., Middletown, 1968-71; asst. to ins. commr. Commonwealth of Pa., Harrisburg, 1971-74; asst. to pres. Capital Blue Cross, Harrisburg, 1974-78, sr. v.p., 1978-84, pres., chief exec.officer, 1984—; bd. dirs. Blue Cross & Blue Shield Assn., Chgo., BCS Fin., Chgo., Fed. Res. Bank Phila., chmn. 1994-95. Contbr. articles on health care to profl. publs. Mem. bd. advisors Pa. State U., 1985-93; chmn. savs. bond campaign for Ctrl. Pa., U.S. Treasury Dept., Harrisburg, 1986-87; bd. dirs. United Way Capital Region, pres. 1994. Paul Harris fellow Rotary Internat., 1988. Mem. Capital Region C. of C. (bd. dirs., treas. 1987-90), Country Club of Harrisburg. Avocation: tennis. Home: 201 Hearth Rd Camp Hill PA 17011-8455 Office: Capital Blue Cross 2500 Elmerton Ave Harrisburg PA 17177-0001

MEAD, JOHN MILTON, banker; b. Schenectady, Oct. 26, 1924; s. Milton Samuel and Jane (Drake) M.; m. Marguerite Ann Stone, Jan. 3, 1948; children: Ann Elizabeth, Jane Stone, Mary Ames. B.S., U. Mo., 1950; postgrad., U. Wis., 1963-65. Auditor Schenectady Trust Co., 1950-51; v.p. auditor First Trust & Deposit Co., Syracuse, N.Y., 1955-77; v.p.; compliance officer Key Corp., Albany, N.Y., 1977-86, ret., 1986. Served with USAAF, 1943-46; Served with USAF, 1951-55. Mem. Inst. Internal Auditors (past pres. Central N.Y. chpt.), Am. Legion (past post comdr.). Republican. Presbyterian. Clubs: Marcellus Optimist (past pres.), Glens Falls Country. Home: 27 Yorkshire Dr Queensbury NY 12804

MEAD, JOHN STANLEY, university administrator; b. Indpls., Dec. 9, 1953; s. Judson and Jane (Stanley) M.; m. Virginia Potter, Aug. 11, 1979; children: Christopher, Carolyn. BA, Ind. U., 1976; JD, U. Ill., 1979. Bar: Ill. Staff atty. Ill. Energy Resources Commn., Springfield, 1979-82, staff dir., 1982-85; mgr. coal rsch. Ill. Dept. Energy Natural Resources, Springfield, 1985-87, dir. office of coal devel. and mktg., 1987-89; dir. coal rsch. ctr. So. Ill. U., Carbondale, 1989—; b. dirs. Mid-West Univ. Energy Consortium Inc., Chgo.; mem., past chair Ill. Clean Coal Inst., 1986—, adv. com. Carbondale Bus. Devel. Corp., 1994. Recipient gold medal Tech. Univ. Ostrava, Czech Republic, 1992. Mem. Am. Radio Relay League, Ill. State Bar Assn., Ill. Vehicle Preservation Assn., Carbondale Rotary. Lutheran. Home: RR 4 Box 340 Carbondale IL 62901 Office: So Ill U Coal Rsch Ctr Mail Code 4623 Carbondale IL 62901

MEAD, LAWRENCE MYERS, JR., retired aerospace executive; b. Plainfield, N.J., May 11, 1918; s. Lawrence Myers and Eleanor Whitman (Machado) M.; m. Janet Chase, Feb. 21, 1942; children—Lawrence Myers, Kirtland Chase, Jonathan Taylor, Bradford Machado. B.S.E., Princeton U., 1940, C.E., 1941; postgrad. mgmt., Harvard Bus. Sch., 1964. With Grumman Corp., Bethpage, N.Y., 1941-93; v.p. tech. ops. Grumman Aerospace Corp., Bethpage, N.Y., 1972-75, sr. v.p. tech. ops., 1975-81, sr. v.p tech. ops., 1981-83; sr. mgmt. cons., 1983-93. Trustee, police commr., dep. mayor Village of Huntington Bay, N.Y., 1975-80; trustee N.Y.C. Hall of Sci. Fellow Poly. U., 1981. Fellow AIAA; mem. NAE, L.I. Forum on Tech. (bd. dirs., past chmn. bd.), Soc. Logistic Engrs., Soc. Advancement Materials and Process Engring., Princeton U. Alumni Assn., Am. Model Yacht Assn., Huntington Country Club. Democrat. Patentee in field; designer A6A Intruder Navy All Weather Bomber, Gulfstream III Exec. Jet Transport. Home: 88 Notch Hill Rd # 253 North Branford CT 06471

MEAD, LOREN BENJAMIN, writer, consultant; b. Florence, S.C., Feb. 17, 1930; s. Walter Russell and Dorothy (Nauss) M.; m. Polly A. Mellette,

Aug. 25, 1951; children: Walter Russell, Christopher Allen, Barbara Holladay Mead Wise, Philip Sidney. BA, U. of the South, 1951, DD (hon.), 1982; MA, U. S.C., 1951; MDiv, Va. Sem., Alexandria, 1955, DD (hon.), 1984; DD (hon.), Berkeley Div. Sch., New Haven, 1986. Ordained priest Episcopal Ch., 1956. Rector Trinity Episcopal Ch., Pinopolis, S.C., 1955-57, Ch. of the Holy Family, Chapel Hill, N.C., 1957-69; exec. dir. Project Test Pattern, Washington, 1969-74; founder, pres. Alban Inst., Washington, 1974-94. Author: New Hope for Congregations, 1972, Critical Moment, 1988, The Once and Future Church, 1991, More Than Numbers, 1993, Transforming Congregations For The Future, 1994. Recipient Spl. Achievement award Interim Pastor Network, 1990. Mem. Acad. Parish Clergy (bd. dirs. 1973-75), Soc. for Advancement of Continuing Edn. for Ministry. Democrat. Office: Alban Inst 4550 Montgomery Ave Ste 433N Bethesda MD 20814-3341

MEAD, PHILIP BARTLETT, healthcare administrator, physician; b. Poughkeepsie, N.Y., June 23, 1937; s. Ralph Allen and Altina (Gervin) M.; m. Ann Elaine Smith, June 27, 1964; children: Ralph Allen II, David Smith. BA, Hamilton Coll., 1959; MD, Cornell U., 1963. Diplomate Nat. Bd. Med. Examiners, Am. Bd. Ob-Gyn. Intern in medicine Bellevue Hosp., N.Y.C., 1963-64; resident in ob-gyn. N.Y. Hosp./Cornell Med. Ctr., N.Y.C., 1964-69; asst. prof. U. Vt. Coll. Medicine, Burlington, 1971-76, assoc. prof., 1976-81, prof., 1981—; hosp. epidemiologist Med. Ctr. Hosp. of Vt., Burlington, 1984-93; dir. clin. sys. Vt. Acad. Med. Ctr., Burlington, 1993-95; sr. v.p., med. dir. Fletcher Allen Health Care, Burlington, 1995—. Lt. comdr. M.C., USN, 1969-71. Fellow ACOG, Infectious Disease Soc. Am.; mem. Infectious Disease Soc. Ob-Gyn. (pres. 1987-88), Soc. Hosp. Epidemiologists, Phi Beta Kappa, Alpha Omega Alpha. Republican. Methodist. Home: 10 Pinehurst Dr Shelburne VT 05482-7240 Office: Fletcher Allen Health Care Burlington VA 05401

MEAD, PRISCILLA, state legislator; m. John L. Mead; children: John, Willian, Neel, Sarah. Student, Ohio State U. Councilwoman Upper Arlington, Ohio, 1982-90, mayor, 1986-90; mem. Ohio Ho. of Reps. Mem. Franklin County Child Abuse and Neglect Found., Coun. for Ethics and Econs. Recipient Svc. award Northwest Kiwanis, Woman of Yr. award Upper Arlington Rotary, Citizen of Yr. award U.S.C. of C. Mem. LWV, Upper Arlington Edn. Found., Jr. League Columbus, Upper Arlington C. of C., Delta Gamma. Republican. Home: 2281 Brixton Rd Columbus OH 43221-3117 Office: Ohio Ho of Reps State House Columbus OH 43215

MEAD, ROBERT NORMAN, accountant; b. Englewood, N.J., Mar. 17, 1948; s. Robert Mead; m. Sandy Mead (div.); children: Kristen, Amanda. BS, Ind. State U., 1972. CPA, Ind., Ky. Acct Arthur Young, Louisville, 1978-84, 1988-88; treas. City of Prospect, Ky., 1983, 84; state treas. Commonwealth of Ky., Frankfort, 1988-92; bd. dirs. Ky. Lottery Corp., Tchrs. Retirement, Ky. Grain Ins. Bd.; vice chmn. Ky. Investment Commn. Bd. dirs. Jr. Achievement, Cen. Ky. Kidney Found. Mem. AICPA, Ky. Soc. CPAs. Democrat.

MEAD, TRAY C., museum administrator; b. Mesa, Ariz., Apr. 1, 1950; s. Norman Wesley and Peggy Lee (Barrows) M.; m. Barbara Celaya, Feb. 9, 1981; children: Michael Adam, Kristiana Nicole. BA in Edn., Ariz. State U., 1973. Cert. tchr., Ariz. Publisher Ariz. Northland Mag., Flagstaff, 1973-77; mus. dir. Mesa Southwest Mus., 1977—; founding dir. Ariz. Fed. Credit Union, Phoenix, 1980-85. Author: Mesa, Beneath the Superstitions, 1988, Sirrine House Story, 1992; editor: Mesa Grande, 1979, Capturing the Canyon, 1987; field editor Ariz. White Mountain Mag., 1965—; contbg. editor Tonto Trails Mag., 1970—. Founding dir. Mesa Conv. and Tourism Bureau, 1999—; founding chmn. S.W. Svc. Corp., Phoenix, 1981-85; bd. dirs., founding pres. Arts in Mesa, 1980—. Recipient Excellence award Centennial Com., 1978, Golden Quill award Caligraphic Soc. Ariz., 1987, Native Am. Heritage award U.S.M.C. Netherlands, 1991; named Hon. Medicine Man, Ft. Apache Tribe, 1971. Hon. chmn. Mesa Parade, Mayor City of Mesa, 1980. Mem. Nat. Trust Hist. Preservation, Am. Assn. State and Local Histories, Am. Assn. Mus., Mus. Assn. Ariz. (founding mem., v.p. 1982—), Ctrl. Ariz. Mus. Assn. (founding pres. 1978—), Mesa C. of C. (com. chmn. 1979-89). Avocations: sculpting, painting, hiking, reading. Home: 370 E Pinon Way Gilbert AZ 85234-4573 Office: Mesa Southwest Museum 53 N Macdonald Mesa AZ 85201-7325

MEAD, WAYLAND MCCON, lawyer; b. Roxbury, N.Y., Nov. 25, 1931; s. Irvin John and Dorothy (Seablom) M.; m. Barbara Jean Wales, Aug. 24, 1958; children: Michael John, David Scott, Deborah Ellen. B.S., Cornell U., 1953, J.D., 1958. Bar: N.Y. 1958. Assoc. Sage, Gray, Todd & Sims, N.Y.C., 1958-59; atty. Mut. Ins. Rating Bur., N.Y.C., 1959-62, Continental Ins. Co., N.Y.C., 1962-65; atty., then sec., counsel Am. Home Assurance Co., N.Y.C., 1965-75; sec., counsel Nat. Union Fire Ins. Co., N.Y.C., 1968-75; asst. v.p., counsel Am. Internat. Group, Inc., N.Y.C., 1969-75; v.p., gen. counsel Am. Internat. Group, Inc., 1975-82, sr. v.p., gen. counsel, 1982—; now acting gen. counsel; dir. Transatlantic Reins. Co., N.Y.C., Am. Home Assurance Co., N.Y.C., Commerce and Industry Ins. Co., N.Y.C., AIU Ins. Co., United Guaranty Corp., United Guaranty NC; chmn. ad hoc com. property and casualty ins. industry, N.Y.C., 1976. Bd. dirs. New Alternatives for Children, 1987—. 2nd Lt. U.S. Army, 1953-55. Mem. ABA. Home: 22 Lucille Ct Massapequa NY 11758-6503 Office: Am Internat Group Inc 70 Pine St New York NY 10270-0001*

MEADE, DALE MICHAEL, laboratory director; b. Lodi, Wis., Aug. 7, 1939; s. Merlin Jones and Valborg (Olson) M.; m. Helen Eva Flentje, Oct. 26, 1959 (div. Dec. 1979); children: Loretta, Carla Fleming. BS with high honors in Elec. Engring., U. Wis., 1961, MS in Physics, 1962, PhD in Physics, 1965. Asst. prof. physics U. Wis., Madison, 1967-69, assoc. prof., 1969-72, prof., 1972-74; head FM-1 Princeton (N.J.) Plasma Physics Lab, 1973, head PDX Ops., 1975-80, head exptl. divsn. rsch. dept., head TFTR rsch. program, 1980-82, head exptl. divsn., head TFTR rsch. ops. divsn., 1982-86, head exptl. physics rsch. dept., head TFTR project, 1986-91, dep. dir., 1991—. Recipient Disting. Svc. Citation U. Wis. Coll. Engring., Madison, 1990, Disting. Assoc. award U.S. Dept. Energy, Washington, 1994. Fellow Am. Phys. Soc.; mem. AAAS. Office: Princeton Plasma Physics Lab US Rt #1 N PO Box 451 Princeton NJ 08543

MEADE, EVERARD KIDDER, JR., retired broadcasting and publishing executive; b. Tappahannock, Va., Oct. 3, 1919; s. Everard Kidder and Della (Wright) M.; m. Alice Amory Winslow, Sept. 1944; children: Mary Devereux, Everard Kidder III, Susanna Fitzhugh. B.S., U.S. Mil. Acad., 1943. Mem. Hoover Commn., U.S. Depts. Def. and State, 1946-53; v.p. Colonial Williamsburg, Inc., 1953-55; assoc. Earl Newsom & Co., 1955-57; v.p. CBS Inc., 1957-82. Served from 2d lt. to lt. col. U.S. Army, 1939-46. Mem. SAR, VFW, Fgn. Policy Assn., Century Assn. (N.Y.C.), Army and Navy Club, Sailfish Club of Fla., Soc. Colonial Wars, Bar Harbor (Maine) Yacht Club, Bath and Tennis Club (Fla.), Rockaway (N.Y.) Hunting Club. Episcopalian.

MEADE, JAMES EDWARD, economist; b. Dorset, Eng., June 23, 1907; s. Charles Hippisley and Kathleen (Cotton-Stapleton) M.; m. Elizabeth Margaret Wilson, Mar. 14, 1933; children—Thomas Wilson, Charlotte Elizabeth Meade Lewis, Bridget Ariane Meade Dommen, Carol Margaret Meade Dasgupta. Student, Oriel Coll., Oxford U., 1926-30, Trinity Coll., Cambridge U., 1930-31; MA, Oxford U., Cambridge U.; Dr. (hon.), U. Basel, U. Hull, U. Bath, U. Oxford; student, U. Glasgow, U. Essex, U. Athens. Fellow, lectr. econs. Hertford Coll., Oxford U., 1930-37; hon. fellow London Sch. Econs.; editor World Econ. Survey, League of Nations, Geneva, 1937-40; mem. econ. sect. Cabinet Secretariat, London, 1940-45, dir., 1945-47; prof. commerce London Sch. Econs., 1947-57; prof. polit. economy Cambridge U., 1957-69, sr. research fellow Christ's Coll., 1969-74; vis. prof. Australian Nat. U., 1956; chmn. Econ. Survey Mission to Mauritius, 1960; chmn. Com. on Structure and Reform of Direct Taxation, 1974-77; gov. Nat. Inst. Econ. and Social Research, 1947—, LSE, 1960-74, Malvern Coll., 1972—. Author: The Rate of Interest in a Progressive State, 1933; Economic Analysis and Policy, 1936; Consumers Credits and Unemployment, 1937; League of Nations World Economic Surveys, 1938 and 1939; Economic Basis of a Durable Peace, 1940; Planning and the Price Mechanism, 1948; The Balance of Payments, 1951; Trade and Welfare, 1955; A Geometry of International Trade, 1952; Problems of Economic Union, 1953; The Theory of Customs Unions, 1955; Control of Inflation, 1958; Neo-Classical Theory of

Economic Growth, 1960; Efficiency, Equality and the Ownership of Property, 1964; The Sationary Economy, 1965; The Theory of Indicative Planning, 1967; The Growing Economy, 1968; The Controlled Economy, 1971; The Theory of Economic Externalities, 1973; The Intelligent Radical's Guide to Economic Policy, 1975; The Just Economy, 1976; Stagflation, Vol. I: Wage-Fixing, 1982, Vol. II, Demand Management, 1983, Alternate Systems of Business Organization and of Workers' Remuneration, 1986; Collected Papers: Vols. 1, 2, and 3, 1988, Vol. 4, 1989; Macroeconomic Policy: Inflation, Wealth and the Exchange Rate (jointly), 1989; Agathotopia: The Economics of Partnership, 1989, Liberty, Equality and Efficiency, 1993. Decorated companion Order of Bath; recipient Nobel prize in econs., 1977. Fellow Brit. Acad.; mem. Royal Econ. Soc. (past pres.), Brit. Assn. (past sect. pres.), Nat. Acad. Scis. (U.S.) (fgn. asso.), Eugenics Soc. (past mem. council), Am. Acad. Arts and Scis. (fgn. hon.), Academia Europaea (emeritus mem.). Office: Dept Applied Econs, U Cambridge, Cambridge England

MEADE, KENNETH ALBERT, minister; b. Sweet Valley, Pa., June 14, 1935; s. Delbert H. and Dorothea I. (Myers) M.; m. Jeanette H. Quigley, Dec. 18, 1954 ; children: Jane M. Meade Ulm, Mark K. Ministerial cert., Ea. Christian Inst., East Orange, N.J., 1955; DD (hon.), Milligan Coll., Tenn., 1986, Ea. Christian Coll., Bel Air, Md., 1986. Ordained to ministry Ch. of Christ, 1955. Student min. Ch. of Christ, Bklyn. and Greenpoint, N.Y., 1952-53; mem. Meade-Bennett Evangelistic Team, East Orange, 1953-55; sr. min. Ch. of Christ at Manor Woods, Rockville, Md., 1956—; pres. N.Am. Christian Conv., Cin., 1986, Ea. Christian Conv., Rockville, 1969, 74, 82. Contbr. numerous articles to religion mags. Trustee Milligan Coll. Recipient Award of Honor, Am. Legion, 1952, Highest Comml. award Lehman High Sch. Alumni Assn., 1952. Office: Ch of Christ at Manor Woods 5300 Norbeck Rd Rockville MD 20853-2303

MEADER, JOHN DANIEL, state agency administrator, judge; b. Ballston Spa, N.Y., Oct. 22, 1931; s. Jerome Clement and Doris Luella (Conner) M.; m. Joyce Margaret Cowin, Mar. 2, 1963; children: John Daniel Jr., Julia Rae, Keith Alan. BA, Yale U., 1954; JD, Cornell U., 1962. Bar: N.Y. 1963, U.S. Dist. Ct. (no. dist.) N.Y. 1963, U.S. Ct. Appeals (2d cir.) 1966, U.S. Supreme Ct. 1967, U.S. Ct. Mil. Appeals 1973, Ohio 1978, U.S. Dist. Ct. (no. dist.) Ohio 1979, Fla. 1983, U.S. Ct. Appeals (4th cir.) 1992, U.S. Ct. Appeals (fed. cir.) 1993. Sales engr. Albany (N.Y.) Internat. Corp., 1954-59; asst. track coach Cornell U., 1959-62; asst. sec., asst. to pres. Albany Internat. Corp., 1962-65; asst. atty. gen. State of N.Y., Albany, 1965-68; ops. counsel, attesting sec. GE, Schenectady, 1968-77; gen. counsel, asst. sec. Glidden div. SCM Corp., Cleve., 1977-81; chmn. bd., pres. Applied Power Tech. Co., Fernandina Beach, Fla., 1981-84; pres. Applied Energy, Inc., Ballston Spa, 1984-88; judge N.Y. State Workers Compensation Bd., Albany, 1988—; dir. Saratoga Mut. Fire Ins. Co. Author: Labor Law Manual, 1972, Contract Law Manual, 1974, Patent Law Manual, 1978. Candidate U.S. Ho. of Reps., 29th Dist. N.Y., 1964, N.Y. Supreme Ct., 1975, 87, 93. Col. JAGC, USAR, 1968—, dep. staff judge adv. 3d U.S. Army & Cen. Command, 1984. Nat. AAU High Sch. 1000 Yard Indoor Track Champion, 1949, Nat. AAU Prep. Sch. 440 and 880 Yard Indoor Track Champion, 1950, Nat. AAU Outstanding Performer award, Melrose Games Assn., 1950, Heptagonal Track 880-Yard Champion 1954. Mem. ABA, N.Y. State Bar Assn., Fla. Bar, Amelia Island Plantation Club, Cyprus Temple Club, Yale Club Jacksonville (pres.), Masons. Republican. Presbyterian. Home: 271 Round Lake Rd Ballston Lake NY 12019-1714 Office: NY State Workers Compensation Bd 100 Broadway Albany NY 12241-0001

MEADER, RALPH GIBSON, medical administrator; b. Eaton Rapids, Mich., Sept. 6, 1904; s. Robert Eugene and Jennie Editha (Gibson) M.; m. Olive Myrle Root, June 16, 1928; 1 child, Mary Batcheller. A.B., Ohio Wesleyan U., 1925; student, U. Mich., summers 1926, 27, 28; A.M., Hamilton Coll., 1927; Ph.D., Yale U., 1932; LL.D., Phila. Coll. Osteopathy, 1956; Sc.D., Ohio Wesleyan U., 1958. Instr. biology Hamilton Coll., 1925-27; part-time instr. biology Wesleyan U., 1928-29; asst. prof. biology Hamilton Coll., 1927-28; fellow in neuroanatomy Blossom Fund, Yale U. Sch. Medicine, 1929-31; instr. anatomy Yale U. Sch. Medicine, 1931-37, asst. prof., 1937-45, assoc. prof. anatomy, 1945-48; asst. dir. bd. sci. advisors Jane Coffin Childs Meml. Fund for Med. Research, 1942-48; spl. cons. USPHS; as sci. dir. cancer research grants br. Nat. Cancer Inst., 1947-48, chief of br., 1948-60, asso. dir. grants and tng., 1960-65; exec. sec. Nat. Adv. Cancer Council, 1947-65; dep. dir. for research adminstrn. and exec. sec. com. on research Mass. Gen. Hosp., Boston, 1965-76; cons. as asst. to assoc. gen. dir. Mass. Gen. Hosp., 1976-78, cons. grants and contracts, 1977—, also mem. Com. on Research; spl. cons. Nat. Cancer Inst., 1965—; biologist N.Y. State Biol. Survey, 1929-30; mem. biomed. library rev. com. Nat. Library Medicine, 1974-76, chmn., 1975-76, cons., 1976—; cons. Lovelace Med. Found., Albuquerque, 1980-82; Rockefeller Found. fellow in neurology U. Amsterdam, Netherlands, 1938-39. Incorporator Eunice Kennedy Shriver Ctr. for Mental Retardation, Waltham, Mass., 1969—, trustee, 1969-83, pres. bd. trustees, 1977-83; incorporator Spaulding Youth Ctr., Tilton, N.H., 1967—, trustee, 1967-85, pres. bd. trustees, 1972-75, trustee emeritus, 1985—; mem. com. to revise town master plan Town of Sanbornton, N.H. Recipient Superior Service award HEW, 1959; Alumni Disting. Achievement Citation award Ohio Wesleyan U., 1984, (with wife) Goodyear Conservation award of merit, 1988; named (with wife) Conservation Cooperator of Yr., Belknap County, N.H. Conservation Dist., 1988, (with wife) Outstanding Cooperator of Yr., N.H. Assn. Conservation Dists., 1988. Fellow AAAS; mem. Am. Assn. Anatomists, Am. Assn. Cancer Research, Soc. Study of Devel. and Growth, Corp. of Bermuda Biol. Sta. for Research, Inc., N.H. Hist. Soc., Durham Hist. Assn. (N.H.), Nantucket Hist. Soc. (Mass.), Sanbornton Hist. Soc. (v.p., chmn. program com. 1983-85), Phi Beta Kappa, Sigma Xi. Home: Calef Farm 207 Calef Hill Rd Sanbornton NH 03269-2005

MEADERS, NOBUKO YOSHIZAWA, therapist, psychoanalyst; b. Kobe, Hyogo-ken, Japan, Mar. 2, 1942; d. Shigenobu and Ayako (Takahashi) Tsuchiya; m. Wilson E. Meaders, Apr. 2, 1976 (div. Apr. 1985); m. Takeshi Yoshizawa, June 15, 1989. AA, Seiwa Coll., Nishinomiya, Japan, 1965, Warren Wilson Coll., Swannanoa, N.C., 1967; BA, So. Meth. U., Dallas, 1969; MS in Social Work, U. Tex., Arlington, 1971; cert. psychotherapy-psychoanalysis, Postgrad. Ctr. Mental Health, N.Y.C., 1977, cert. in supervision psychotherapeutic processes, 1979. Cert. social worker, N.Y.; diplomate Am. Bd. Examiners in Clin. Social Work. Psychiat. social worker Killgore Children's Psychiat. Hosp., Amarillo, Tex., 1971-73, Jewish Child Care Assn., Childville div., N.Y.C., 1973-74; supr. social work, social work dept. Bellevue Hosp., N.Y.C., 1974-76; asst. dir. tng. Postgrad. Ctr. Mental Health, N.Y.C., 1979-82, assoc. supr., 1979-82, supr., 1982-85, sr. supr., 1985—, tng. analyst, 1989—; pvt. practice psychotherapy and psychoanalysis N.Y.C., 1976—; clin. cons. Pace U. Personal Devel. Ctr., N.Y.C., 1987—; mem. adv. bd. Japanese-Am. Cons. Ctr., N.Y.C., 1983—. Fellow N.Y. Soc. Clin. Social Work Psychotherapists; mem. NASW, Acad. Cert. Social Workers. Avocations: sculpting, drawing, gardening, writing.

MEADERS, PAUL LE SOURD, lawyer; b. Amarillo, Tex., Feb. 1, 1930; s. Paul Le Sourd and Lorna Irene (Pumroy) M.; m. Patricia Rockefeller, Mar. 21, 1953 (dec.); m. Jane W. Dickely, Apr. 2, 1966; children: Phyllis P., Paul Le Sourd III. BA, U. Va., 1952; LLB, U. Tex., 1957; LLM, NYU, 1961. Bar: Tex. 1956, N.Y. 1959. Atty. office chief counsel IRS, 1957-59; asst. U.S. atty. So. Dist. N.Y., 1951-61; assoc. Breed Abbott & Morgan, N.Y.C., 1961-63, Reid & Priest, N.Y.C., 1963-67; ptnr. Morris & McVeigh, N.Y.C., 1967-77, McKenzie, Meaders & Ives, N.Y.C., 1977-90, Meaders, Duckworth & Moore, 1990—. 1st lt. U.S. Army, 1952-54. Mem. ABA (estate tax com. tax sect.) N.Y. State Bar Assn., Tex. Bar Assn., Seldon Soc., Brit. Inst. Internat. and Comparative Law, Internat. Bar Assn., Vets. Corps Arty. (life), U. Va. Alumni Assn. (pres. N.Y.C. chpt. 1982-84), Friendly Sons of St. Patrick (life), Ch. Club, Pilgrims of U.S. Club, Bronxville Field Club, Carlton Club (London). Episcopalian. Office: 551 Fifth Ave Ste 1704 New York NY 10176-0037

MEADLOCK, JAMES W., computer graphics company executive; b. 1933; married. BSEE, N.C. State U., 1956. Dept. mgr. IBM, 1956-69; pres. Intergraph Corp., Huntsville, Ala., 1969—; also chmn. bd. dirs. Intergraph Corp., Huntsville; chief exec. officer Intergraph Corp., 1989—. Office: Intergraph Corp Huntsville AL 35894-0001

MEADLOCK, NANCY B., computer graphics company executive; b. 1938; married. BSMA, Athens Coll., 1969. With Intergraph Corp., 1969—, v.p. for adminstrn., now exec. v.p., dir. Office: Intergraph Corp 1 Madison Industrial Park Huntsville AL 35894-0001*

MEADOR, DANIEL JOHN, lawyer, educator; b. Selma, Ala., Dec. 7, 1926; s. Daniel John and Mabel (Kirkpatrick) M.; m. Janet Caroline Heilmann, Nov. 19, 1955; children: Janet Barrie, Anna Kirkpatrick, Daniel John. B.S., Auburn U., 1949; J.D., U. Ala., 1951; LL.M., Harvard U., 1954. Bar: Ala. 1951, Va. 1961. Law clk. to U.S. Supreme Ct. Justice Hugo L. Black, 1954-55; assoc. firm Lange, Simpson, Robinson & Somerville, Birmingham, 1955-57; faculty U. Va. Law Sch., 1957-66, prof. law, 1961-66; prof., dean U. Ala. Law Sch., 1966-70; James Monroe prof. law U. Va., Charlottesville, 1970-94, prof. emeritus, 1994—; asst. atty. gen. U.S., 1977-79, dir. grad. program for judges, 1979-95; Fulbright lectr., U.K., 1965-66; vis. prof. U.S. Mil. Acad., 1984; Chmn. Southeastern Conf. Assn. Am. Law Schs., 1964-65; chmn. Cts. Task Force Nat. Adv. Commn. on Criminal Justice, 1971-72; dir. appellate justice project Nat. Center for State Cts., 1972-74; mem. Adv. Council on Appellate Justice, 1971-75, Council on Role of Cts., 1978-84; bd. dirs. State Justice Inst., 1986-92. Author: Preludes to Gideon, 1967, Criminal Appeals-Practices and American Reforms, 1973, Mr. Justice Black and His Books, 1974, Appellate Courts: Staff and Process in the Crisis of Volume, 1974, (with Carrington and Rosenberg) Justice on Appeal, 1976, Impressions of Law in East Germany, 1986, American Courts, 1991, (with J. Bernstein) Appellate Courts in the United States, 1994, His Father's House, 1994, (with Rosenberg and Carrington) Appellate Courts: Structures, Functions, Processes, and Personnel, 1994; also articles in legal periodicals; editor: Va. Bar News, 1962-65. Served to 1st lt. AUS, 1951-53. Decorated Bronze Star.; IREX fellow German Dem. Republic, 1983. Mem. ABA (chmn. standing com. on fed. judl. improvements 1987-90), Ala. Bar Assn., Va. Bar Assn. (exec. com. 1983-86), Am. Law Inst., Am. Judicature Soc. (bd. dirs. 1975-77, 80-83), Soc. Pub. Tchrs. Law, Am. Soc. Legal History (bd. dirs. 1968-71), Order of Coif, Raven Soc., Phi Delta Phi, Omicron Delta Kappa, Kappa Alpha. Presbyn. Office: U Va Sch Law Charlottesville VA 22903

MEADOR, JOHN MILWARD, JR., university dean; b. Louisville, Nov. 4, 1946; s. John Milward and Ruth Inez (Miller) M.; m. Judith Ann Hay, Dec. 22, 1969; children: John Milward III, Elise Kathleen. BA, U. Louisville, 1968; MA, U. Tex., 1972, MLS, 1973; cert. in pub. adminstrn., U. Utah, 1982. Cert. tchr., Ky., Tex. Stacks supr. U. Louisville Librs., 1965-68; English bibliographer M.D. Anderson Libr. U. Houston, 1973-74, head reference dept. social scis. and humanities, 1974-77, head gen. reference dept., 1977-80; asst. dir. pub. svcs. Marriott Libr. U. Utah, Salt Lake City, 1980-84; dean libr. svcs. S.W. Mo. State U., Springfield, 1984-93; dean librs. U. Miss., University, 1993—; bd. dirs. Mo. Libr. Network Corp., 1984-90, St. Louis, S.W. Mo. Libr. Network, Springfield, 1984-86; chmn. Mo. Northwestern Online Total Integrated Systems (NOTIS) Users Group, 1988-89. Co-author: The Robinson Jeffers Collection at the University of Houston, 1975; contbr. articles to profl. jours. Sponsor Community Alternative Svc. Program, Springfield and St. Louis, 1985-93; mem. governing bd. Mo. Rsch. and Edn. Network, MOREnet, 1991-93; With U.S. Army, 1969-71, Vietnam. Recipient Nat. Essay award Propeller Club of U.S., 1964; named to Honorable Order of Ky. Colonels, Gov. Ky., 1978; summer scholar English-Speaking Union, Edinburgh, Scotland, 1968; Apple Computer's Higher Edn. Acad. Devel. Donation Program grantee, 1990. Mem. ALA, Am. Assn. for Higher Edn., Assn. Coll. Rsch. Librs., Bibliog. Soc. Am., Libr. Adminstrn. and Mgmt. Assn., other profl. orgns., English-Speaking Union Club, Rotary (chmn. students guests com. Springfield chpt. 1986-89, chmn. scholarships com. 1989-90, bd. dirs. 1990-91, bd. dirs. Oxford chpt. 1995—). Avocations: raising pure bred airedale terriers, fishing, book collecting. Home: PO Box 787 University MS 38677-0787 Office: U Miss J D Williams Libr University MS 38677

MEADOR, ROBERT LYMAN, dentist; b. Portland, Oreg., Jan. 20, 1934; m. Sharon Lynn Caillouet, Apr. 10, 1967 (div. June 1978); m. Charlotte Ann Dodson, Sept. 14, 1985. BS, U. Oreg., 1957; DMD, U. Oreg., Portland, 1959. Lic. dentist, Calif., N.Mex., Oreg. Chief, attending dental staff Orange (Calif.) County Med. Ctr., 1966-67, chief, restorative dental service, 1971-77; assoc. dentistry Loma Linda (Calif.) U., 1969-70; clin. assoc. prof. diagnostic scis., oral diagnosis and emergency clinic. U. So. Calif., Los Angeles, 1981-83, clin. assoc. prof.; dir., gen. practice residency and clin. restorative service U. Calif., Irving, 1974-77; chief, attending dental staff Fullerton (Calif.) Community Hosp., 1982-83. Contbr. articles to profl. jours. Mem. Am. Heart Assn. (bd. dirs. Orange County chpts. 1981—, active dental CPR program 1975—, chmn. emergency services com. 1975—, co-chmn. hypertension control com. 1975-78); active Allied Health Profls., Yorba Linda City Planning Commn.; pres. Richard M. Nixon Birthplace Found., 1982-86. Served to Capt. USAF, 1959-62. Named one of Outstanding Young Men Am., 1966, Outstanding State Dir., Calif. Jaycees, 1965; Paul Harris fellow, Yorba Linda Rotary club, 1980. Mem. Acad. Gen. Dentistry (mastership 1984), Am. Assn. Hosp. Denstists (Calif. vice-chmn. 1974-80), Am. Dental Assn. and Local Components, Am. Dental Soc. of Anesthesiology, Am. Edodontic Soc., Calif. Soc. Anesthesiology (pres.-elect 1983-84, pres. 1984-85), Orange County Dental Soc. (chmn. continuing edn. com. 1973-74, chmn. children's dental clinic com 1970-71), Yorba Linda C of C. (pres. 1971-72), North Orange County Jaycees (dist. gov. state of Calif., 1968-69, outstanding dist. chmn. 1966), Yorba Linda Jaycees (pres. 1966-67, disting. service award 1967, Kay Man award 1967).

MEADOR, RON, newspaper editor, writer; b. Buffalo, N.Y., Nov. 24, 1952; s. Meril E. and Evelyn (Lyons) M.; divorced; 1 child, Benjamin Brian. BA, Ind. U., 1975. Copy editor The Courier-Journal, Louisville, 1975-78, The New York Times, 1978-80; reporter, state editor, city editor Star Tribune, Mpls., Minn., 1980—; asst. mng. editor for spl. projects and nat. news Star Tribune, Mpls. Mem. Investigative Reporters and Editors, Inc. Office: Star Tribune 425 Portland Ave Minneapolis MN 55488-0001*

MEADORS, ALLEN COATS, health administrator, educator; b. Van Buren, Ark., May 17, 1947; s. Hal Barron and Allene Coats (Means) M. AA, Saddleback Coll., 1967; BBA, U. Cen. Ark., 1969; MBA, U. No. Colo., 1974; M. in Pub. Administrn., U. Kans., 1975; MA in Psychology, Webster U., 1979; MA in Health Svcs. Mgmt., 1980, PhD in Administrn, So. Ill. U., 1981. Assoc. adminstr. Forbes Hosp., Topeka, 1971-73; asst. dir. health svcs. devel. Blue Cross Blue Shield of Kans., Topeka, 1973-76; asst. dir. Kansas City Health Dept. (Mo.), 1976-77; program dir., asst. prof. So. Ill. U., Carbondale, and Webster U., St. Louis, 1978-82; assoc. prof., dir. div. health adminstrn. U. Tex., Galveston, 1982-84; exec. dir. N.W. Ark. Radiation Therapy Inst., Springdale, Ark., 1984-87; prof., chmn. dept. health adminstrn. U. Okla., Oklahoma City, interim dean Coll. Public Health, 1989-90; mem. faculty Calif. State U., Long Beach, 1977-81; grad. faculty U. Ark. Sch. Bus. Adminstrn., Fayetteville, 1984-87; prof., chmn. dept. health administrn. U. Okla.; 1987-90; dean Coll. Health, Social and Pub. Svcs. Ea. Wash. U., Cheney, 1990-94; CEO Pa. State U., Altoona, 1994—; cons. Surgeon Gen. Office and Air Force System Command. Bd. dirs. Martin Luther King Hosp., Health Care Svcs. Adv. Bd. Served with Med. Service Corps, USAF, 1969-73. Fellow Am. Coll. Healthcare Execs., Ark. Hosp. Assn.; mem. Am. Hosp. Assn., Am. Pub. Health Assn. Contbr. articles to profl. jours. Home: PO Box 9 Altoona PA 16603-0009 Office: Pa State U 3000 Ivyside Park Altoona PA 16601-3760

MEADORS, HOWARD CLARENCE, JR., electrical engineer; b. Chgo., July 31, 1938; s. Howard Clarence and Eileen May (Baker) M.; m. Phyllis Anne Rennebaum, July 18, 1964; children: Henry Charles, William Howard, Laura Phyllis, Pamela Susan. SB, MIT, 1960, SM, 1962, Profl. Degree in Elec. Engring., 1964; PhD, Poly. Inst. NY., 1976. Mem. tech. staff Bell Tel. Labs., Inc., Holmdel, N.J., 1966-82; disting. mem. tech. staff AT&T Info. Systems Labs., Holmdel, 1983-85, supr. product devel., 1985-86; supr. adv. data communications AT&T Bell Labs., Middletown, N.J., 1986-91; Disting. mem. tech. staff AT&T Bus. Communications Systems, Holmdel, N.J., 1991-94; disting. mem. tech. staff AT&T Network Systems, Holmdel, N.J., 1994—; ednl. counselor MIT, 1973—, regional vice chmn., 1983—. Inventor in field. With Signal Corps, U.S. Army, 1964-66. Mem. IEEE (sr. mem. 1987), Sigma Xi, Eta Kappa Nu. Office: AT&T Bell Labs Crawfords Corner Rd Holmdel NJ 07733

MEADOW, LYNNE (CAROLYN MEADOW), theatrical producer and director; b. New Haven, Nov. 12, 1946; d. Frank and Virginia R. Meadow. BA cum laude, Bryn Mawr Coll., 1968; postgrad., Yale U., 1968-70. Dir. Theatre Communications Group, 1978-80; adj. prof. SUNY, Stony Brook, 1975-76, Yale U., Circle in the Sq., 1977-78, 89-91, NYU, 1977-80; theatre and music/theatre panelist Nat. Endowment for Arts, 1977-88; artistic advisor Fund for New Am. Plays, 1988-90. Artistic dir. Manhattan Theatre Club, N.Y.C., 1972—; guest dir. Nat. Playwrights Conf., Eugene O'Neill Theatre Ctr., 1975-77, Phoenix Theatre, 1976; dir. Ashes for Manhattan Theatre Club and N.Y. Shakespeare Festival, 1977; prodr. off-Broadway shows Ain't Misbehavin', 1978, Crimes of the Heart, 1981, Miss Firecracker Contest, 1984, Frankie and Johnny, 1987, Eastern Standard, 1988, Lisbon Traviata, 1989, Lips Together, Teeth Apart, 1991, Four Dogs and a Bone, 1993, Love! Valour! Compassion!, 1994; dir. Principia Scritoriae, 1986, Woman in Mind, 1988 (Drama Desk award), Eleemosynary, 1989, Absent Friends, 1991; dir. Broadway prodn. A Small Family Business, 1992, The Loman Family Picnic, 1993; co-prodr. off-Broadway and Broadway show Mass Appeal, 1981. Recipient Citation of Merit Nat. Coun. Women, 1976, Outer Circle Critics award 1977, Drama Desk award, 1977, Obie award for Ashes, 1977, Margo Jones award for Continued Encouragement New Playwrights, 1981, Critics Circle award Outstanding Revival on or off Broadway for Loot, 1986, Lucille Lortel award for Outstanding Achievement, 1987, Spl. Drama Desk award, 1989, N.Y. Drama Critics Circle award Best Fgn. Play for Aristocrats, 1989, Torch of Hope award, 1989, Manhattan Mag. award, 1994, Lee Reynolds award League Profl. Theatre Women, 1994; named Northwood Inst. Disting. Woman of Yr., 1990, Person of Yr., Nat. Theatre Conf., 1992. Office: Manhattan Theatre Club 453 W 16th St 2nd Fl New York NY 10011-5896

MEADOWS, DONALD FREDERICK, librarian; b. Regina, Sask., Can., Jan. 13, 1937; s. Frederick John and Doris Eileen (Willock) M.; m. Ruth Susan Cochran, June 10, 1960; children—Scott Frederick, George Edward. B.A., U. Sask., 1962; B.L.S., U. B.C., 1968. Library cons. Sask. Provincial Library, Regina, 1968-69; asst. provincial librarian Sask. Provincial Library, 1969-70, provincial librarian, province of Sask., 1970-81; dir. Met. Toronto Library, 1981-86; dir. Vancouver Island Regional Library, Nanaimo, B.C., Can., 1986—, also bd. dirs. Mem. Canadian Library Assn., ALA, B.C. Library Assn. Mem. United. Ch. Can. Office: Vancouver Island Regional Library, PO Box 3333, Nanaimo, BC Canada V9R 5N3

MEADOWS, DONELLA, environmentalist. Adjunct prof. environ. sci. Dartmouth Coll., Hanover, N.H. Recipient MacArthur Fellowship MacArthur Found., 1994. Office: Dartmouth College Dept Envir Sci Hanover NH 03755*

MEADOWS, JENNIFER ELIZABETH, retired editor, tattoo artist; b. Texarkana, Tex., Jan. 20, 1947; d. Walter Edward and Martha Elizabeth (McCoy) Willis; m. Joe R. Matthews (div.); 1 child, Chris; m. Rich Meadows. AA, Cottey Coll., 1965; BS, U. Tex., Arlington, 1978. Actuarial asst. S.W. Life Ins. Co., Dallas; proofreader Royal Bus. Forms, Arlington, Tex.; substitute tchr. Arlington (Tex.) Ind. Sch. Dist.; reporter The Dallas Morning News, 1980-83, asst. editor, 1983-86, editor, 1986-94; columnist The Dallas Morning News, 1980-94. Vol. The Dallas Opera; tng. coord. Kairos Found., 1990—. Avocations: calligraphy, massage, svc. to the community. Office: 904 W Pioneer Pky Arlington TX 76013-6330

MEADOWS, JUDITH ADAMS, law librarian, educator; b. Spartanburg, S.C., June 5, 1945; d. Thomas Taylor and Virginia (Dayton) Adams; m. Bruce R. Meadows; children: Beth Ann Blackwood, Ted Adams Meadows. BA, Am. U., 1967; MLS, U. Md., 1979. Law libr. Aspen Sys. Corp., Gaithersburg, Md., 1979-81; dir. Fairfax (Va.) Law Libr., 1981-84, State Law Libr., Helena, Mont., 1984—; vis. prof. U. Wash., Seattle, 1994; adj. prof. Coll. Great Falls, Mont., 1989—; presiding ofcl. Gov.'s Conf. on Libr. Info. Svc., Helena, Mont., 1991. Author: (book chpts.) From Yellow Pads to Computers, 1991, Law Librarianship, 1994; contbr. articles to profl. jours. Bd. dirs. Helena Presents, 1986-92. Recipient Disting. Svc. award State Bar of Mont., 1991. Mem. Am. Assn. Law Librs. (treas. 1992-95), N.W. Consortium of Law Librs. (pres.), Mont. Libr. Assn. (sec. 1986-88). Avocations: gourmet cooking, cross-country skiing, reading, gardening. Office: State Law Libr Mont Justice Bldg 215 N Sanders Helena MT 59620-3004

MEADS, DONALD EDWARD, management services company executive; b. Salem, Mass., Sept. 23, 1920; s. Laurence G. and Gertrude F. M.; m. Jane Lightner, June 15, 1943; children: Edward G., Robert C., Laurence G., Judith C. Antrim, Suzanne M. O'Neil, Clifford L., Nancy Chapin. A.B. in Pre-Law, Dartmouth Coll., 1942; M.B.A. in Fin., Harvard U., 1947. Vice-pres., vice-chmn. investment com. N.Y. Life Ins. Co., N.Y.C., 1947-61; v.p. fin., chmn. investment com. Investors Diversified Services Inc., Mpls., 1961-65; pres., chief exec. officer Internat. Basic Economy Corp., N.Y.C., 1965-67, chmn., chief exec. officer, 1967-71; exec. v.p., dir., chief fin. officer, chmn. investment com. INA Corp., Phila., 1971-74; chmn. bd., chief exec. officer CertainTeed Corp., Valley Forge, Pa., 1974-78, dir., 1973-78; chmn. Mateer-Burt Co., Inc., Plymouth Meeting, Pa., 1984-87; chmn. Phila. First Group Inc., 1982-90; chmn. Carver Assocs., Inc., Plymouth Meeting, 1978—; dir. Perdue Farms, Inc., Salisbury, Md.; hon. life trustee Valley Forge Mil. Acad. & Coll., Wayne Pa., trustee emeritus Thomas Jefferson U., Phila.; bd. dirs. Independence Hall Assn., Phila.; hon. dir. Marine Corps Scholarship Found., Princeton, N.J.; mem. Phila. Com. on Fgn. Relations; bd. dirs. World Affairs Council Phila. Served to capt. USMC, 1942-45. Decorated D.F.C., Air medals (6). Mem. Harvard Club of N.Y.C., Sunday Breakfast Club, Union League (Phila.), Rockefeller Ctr. Club (N.Y.C.). *Andrew Jackson imparted much wisdom when he said: "One man with courage makes a majority".*

MEADS, WALTER FREDERICK, executive recruitment consultant; b. Ft. Wayne, Ind., Mar. 11, 1923; s. Frederick C. and Minnie E. (Stephenson) M.; m. Mary E. Smith, Mar. 21, 1975; children by previous marriage: Kenneth W., Catherine L. B.S., Kent State U., 1948; M.A., Fairfield U. With Norman Malone & Assos., Akron, Ohio, 1946-48, Griswold-Eshleman Co., Cleve., 1949-53, Fuller, Smith & Ross, Cleve., 1953-55; sr. v.p., head of creative svc., mem. mgmt. com., vice chmn. plans and rev. bds. J. Walter Thompson Co., N.Y.C., 1955-72; pres. Meads & Assocs., 1972—. With USAAF, 1943-45. Recipient numerous nat. and local advt. industry awards. Home: 4420 Orangewood Loop E Lakeland FL 33813 Office: 6700 S Florida Ave Ste 4 Lakeland FL 33813 *Creative freedom is probably the core concept at the heart of my life—not only for myself but for others. Life is never static; it either deteriorates or grows. All growth, to me, springs from the creative doers of the world. The rest of humanity goes along for the ride. And creative growth, in any field or endeavor, demands an attitude of freedom to shake off the shackles of habit and find new and better ways of doing things.*

MEAGHER, GEORGE VINCENT, mechanical engineer; b. Halifax, N.S., Can., Apr. 23, 1919; s. John Nicholas and Blanche Margaret (Seals) M.; m. Evelyn Margaret Hamm, June 2, 1945; children: Maureen, Lindsey, Lise Shelagh. BSc, Dalhousie U., Halifax, 1940; B of Engring., McGill U., 1942. Engring. and mgmt. positions in industry, 1942-56; with Dilworth, Secord, Meagher & Assocs. Ltd., Toronto, 1957-92; chmn. Dilworth, Secord, Meagher & Assocs. Ltd., 1988-92; pres. DSMA-Tata Ltd, 1985—; vice chmn. Tata-DSMA, Bombay, India; dir. State Bank India, Can. Ltd., Toronto, 1984-94; dir. and past chmn. Can.-India Bus. Coun.; pres. George V. Meagher Inc. Fellow Engring. Inst. Can.; mem. Assn. Profl. Engrs. Ont., Nat. Club (Toronto). Home: # 1402, 500 Avenue Rd, Toronto, ON Canada M4V 2J6

MEAGHER, JAMES FRANCIS, atmospheric research executive; b. Sydney, Can., Oct. 23, 1946; came to U.S., 1967; s. James Marcellus and Margaret Evelyn (MacDougall) M.; m. Elizabeth Strapp; children: Jeffrey James, Elizabeth Kathleen. BSc, St. Francis Xavier, 1967; PhD, Cath. U. of Am., 1971. Rsch. fellow U. Wash., Seattle, 1971-73, Pa. State U., 1973-76; dir. atmospheric rsch. Tenn. Valley Authority, Muscle Shoals, Ala., 1976—; sci. adv. com. Nat. Acid Precipitation Assessment Program, Washington, 1987-93; mgr. Atmospheric Scis. TVA, Eviron. Rsch Ctr., 1993—. Contbr. chpt. to book, articles to profl. jours. Mem. Am. Chem. Soc., Am. Geophys. Union, Sigma Xi. Avocations: sailing, youth soccer. Home: 204 Seminole Ct Florence AL 35630 Office: USG TUA 212 Ceb Muscle Shoals AL 35660

MEAGHER, MARK JOSEPH, publishing company executive; b. Balt., July 9, 1932; s. Harry Royce and Maria Paula (Demarco) M.; m. Gabriela Sierra, Dec. 24, 1983. Student, U. Notre Dame, 1950-51; B.S., U. Md., 1954. C.P.A. Accountant Price Waterhouse & Co., Balt., 1954-57; systems analyst IBM, Balt., 1957-58; mgmt. cons. McKinsey Co., Washington, 1958-61; exec. v.p. McGraw Hill Book Co., N.Y.C., 1961-70; v.p. fin. and adminstrn. Washington Post Co., N.Y.C., 1970-74; exec. v.p., gen. mgr. Washington Post Co., 1974-76, pres. newspaper div., 1976-77, pres., chief operating officer co., 1977-80, dir., 1977-80; pres., chief operating officer, dir. Penthouse Internat. Ltd., 1981; ptnr. Holding Capital Group, N.Y.C., 1982—; gen. ptnr., chmn. Fin. World Ptnrs., N.Y.C., 1983—; dir. Maple Press. V.p. Urban League New Brunswick, N.J., 1967-69; chmn. housing com. Metuchen/Edison (N.J.) unit NAACP, 1968; bd. dirs. World Affairs Coun.; vice chmn., trustee U. Md. Found., 1978-88. Mem. Hon. Accounting Soc., Am. Inst. CPA's (Eisenhower fellow 1980). Republican. Roman Catholic. Office: Financial World Ptnrs 1328 Broadway New York NY 10001-2121

MEAGHER, MICHAEL, radiologist; b. New Rochelle, N.Y., Oct. 24, 1942; s. Joseph Aloysius and Elizabeth (Ahern) M.; m. Martha Batten Mitchell, 1968; children: Kelly, Courtney. Student, Rensselaer Poly. Inst., 1960-62; AB with distinction, U. Rochester, 1964; MD, Stanford U., 1969. Diplomate Am. Bd. Radiology, Nat. Bd. Med. Examiners. Intern in medicine Cornell U., N.Y. Hosp., 1969-70; jr. asst. resident in diagnostic radiology U. Wash., Seattle, 1970-71, sr. asst. resident diagnostic radiology, 1973-74, resident diagnostic radiology, 1974-75; active staff mem. dept. radiology Queen's Med. Ctr., Honolulu, 1975—, Leahi Hosp., Honolulu, 1981—, Kahuku (Hawaii) Hosp., 1988—; pres. Radiology Assocs., Inc., 1978, 81-84, 90; chmn. dept. radiology Queen's Med. Ctr., 1979-80, 82-86, 88-90, dir. dept. radiology, 1985-91; dir. magnetic resonance imaging, 1991—, chmn. cancer com., 1980-82; mem. med. staff Hawaii Health Tech. Magnetic Resonance Imaging Facility, Honolulu, 1986—, chief of staff, 1978; clin. instr. dept. radiology U. Hawaii Sch. Medicine, 1983-89, clin. assoc. prof., 1989-93, clin. prof., 1993—, clin. assoc. prof. dept. radiology Cancer Rsch. Ctr. Hawaii, 1989—; clin. asst. prof. dept. radiology U. Wash. Sch. Medicine, 1980-88; presenter in fld. Contbr. articles to profl. publs. Chmn. high tech. adv. com. State Health Planning and Devel. Agy., 1983—; bd. dirs. Friends of Hawaii Pub. TV, 1979-81; pres., CEO Queen's Health Care Plan, Honolulu, 1985-89, chmn. bd. dirs. 1983-91; bd. dirs. Managed Care Mgmt., Inc., Honolulu, 1990; v.p. bd. dirs. Hawaii Opera Theatre, 1990-91, treas., 1991—. Lt. comdr. USN, 1971-73. NIH fellow, 1966; Kaiser Found. grantee, 1967. Fellow Am. Coll. Radiology; mem. AMA, Hawaii State Radiol. Soc. (sec.-treas. 1978-79, v.p. 1979-80, pres. 1980-81), Radiol. Soc. N.Am., Soc. Computer Applications in Radiology (charter), Am. Roentgen Ray Soc. Home: 1234 Maunawili Rd Kailua HI 96734 Office: Queen's Med Ctr Dept Radiology Honolulu HI 96813

MEAGHER, THOMAS FRANCIS VINCENT, research and development company executive; b. Ellensburg, Wash., Aug. 9, 1935; s. Martin C. and Agnes C. (Heraty) M.; m. Alberta Frances Hatzenbeler, June 9, 1956; children: Michael, Brian, Kathy, Scott, Chris, Keri, Tim. BSEE, U. Wash., 1960; MS in Applied Sci., U. Calif., Davis, 1966. Staff mem. Sandia Nat. Labs., Livermore, Calif., 1960-67; program mgr. Kaman Scis. Corp., Colorado Springs, Colo., 1967-79; pvt. practice, Colorado Springs, 1979-80; chmn., pres., chief exec. officer, founder Aptek, Inc., Colorado Springs, 1980—. With U.S. Army, 1953-56. Mem. AIAA, Am. Def. Preparedness Assn., U.S. Space Found., Colorado Springs C. of C. Republican. Roman Catholic. Avocations: skiing, sailing, fishing, archery. Office: Aptek Inc 1257 Lake Plaza Dr Colorado Springs CO 80906-3578

MEAKER, MARIJANE AGNES, author; b. Auburn, N.Y., May 27, 1927; d. Ellis R. and Ida T. M. B.A., U. Mo., 1949. Author: novels (under own name) Sudden Endings, 1965, Hometown, 1967, Game of Survival, 1969, Don't Rely on Gemini, 1971, Shockproof Sydney Skate, 1972, 2d edit., 1990; (under pseudonym M.E. Kerr), Dinky Hocker Shoots Smack, 1972, Gentlehands, 1978, If I Love You, Am I Trapped Forever, 1973, I'll Love You When You're More Like Me, 1977, Is That You, Miss Blue?, 1975, Love is a Missing Person, 1975, The Son of Someone Famous, 1975, Little Little, 1981 (Soc. Children's Books Writers award 1982), What I Really Think of You, 1982, Me Me Me Me Me: Not a Novel (Best Books for Young Adults ALA), 1983, Him She Loves?, 1984, I Stay Near You (Best Books for Young Adults ALA), 1985, Night Kites, 1986, Fell, 1987, Fell Back, 1989, Fell Down, 1990; (under pseudonym Mary James) Shoebag, 1990, The Shuteyes, 1993, Frankenlouse, 1994, (M.E. Kerr) Linger, 1993, Deliver Us from Evie, 1994. Recipient Notable Children's Book award ALA, 1972, Book of Yr. award Sch. Library Jour., 1972, 77, 78, Christopher award, 1978, Night Kites award ALA, 1986, Margaret A. Edwards award ALA, 1993.

MEAL, LARIE, chemistry educator, consultant; b. Cin., June 15, 1939; d. George Lawrence Meal and Dorothy Louise (Heileman) Fitzpatrick. BS in Chemistry, U. Cin., 1961, PhD in Chemistry, 1966. Rsch. chemist U.S. Indsl. Chems., Cin., 1966-67; instr. chemistry U. Cin., 1968-69, asst. prof., 1969-75, assoc. prof., 1975-90, prof., 1990—, researcher, 1980—; cons. in field. Contbr. articles to sci. jours. Mem. AAAS, N.Y. Acad. Scis., Am. Chem. Soc., Internat. assn. Arson Investigators, NOW, Planned Parenthood, Iota Sigma Pi. Democrat. Avocations: gardening, yard work. Home: 2231 Slane Ave Norwood OH 45212-3615 Office: U Cin 2220 Victory Pky Cincinnati OH 45206-2822

MEALEY, GEORGE ALLAN, mining executive; b. Astoria, Oreg., Aug. 14, 1933; s. George Asher Mealey and Edna (Sloop) Hubert; m. Jean Rosemary Younger, Mar. 1, 1958; children: Ruth, Mary, Allen, Bruce. BS in Mining Engring., Mont. Sch. Mines, 1956; MBA in Mgmt., Coll. Notre Dame, Belmont, Calif., 1975. Jr. mining engr. Hecla Mining Co., Moab, Utah, 1956; mining engr. U.S. Ops. Mission, Korea, 1958-61, Am. Gilsomite Co., Bonanza, Utah, 1961-63; with Braden Copper Co., Sewell, Chile, 1963-70; chief engr. Denison Mines, Elliot Lake, Ont., Can., 1970-73; engr. mgr. Fluor Utah, San Mateo, Calif., 1973-75; with Freeport McMoRan, New Orleans, 1975—; exec. v.p. Freeport Indonesia, New Orleans, 1981—; sr. v.p. Freeport Gold Co., 1984—; bd. dirs. Freeport Indonesia, Inc.; Freeport McMoRan Resource Ptnrs., Freeport Minerals Co. Served with U.S. Army, 1956-58. Mem. Am. Inst. Mining Engring., Mining and Metallurgical Soc. Am. (v.p. 1980). Republican. Roman Catholic. Clubs: City (New Orleans); Mining (N.Y.C.). Home: 6215 Hurst St New Orleans LA 70118-6160

MEALMAN, GLENN, corporate marketing executive; b. Prescott, Kans., June 10, 1934; s. Edgar R. and Mary E. (Holstein) M.; m. Gloria Gail Proch, June 12, 1955; children: Michael Edward, Cathy Gail. BS in Bus., Kans. State Coll., Emporia, 1957; postgrad., Harvard U., 1970. With Fleming Cos., Topeka, 1957—, sr. v.p. mktg., 1981-82, exec. v.p. mktg., 1982-86, exec. v.p. Mid-Am. region, 1986-93, exec. v.p. nat. accts., 1994—; dir. PBI-Gordon Co., KCCI. Pres. bd. Topeka YMCA, 1981; trustee Ottawa U., Kans., 1980. Served with USNR, 1954-56. Mem. Kans. State C. of C. and Industry (bd. dirs. 1991—), Blue Hills Country Club, Rotary. Baptist. Office: Fleming Cos Inc Ste 850 7101 College Blvd Overland Park KS 66210-9999 also: Fleming Cos Inc 6301 Waterford Blvd Oklahoma City OK 73118-1124

MEALOR, WILLIAM THEODORE, JR., geography educator, university administrator, consultant; b. Atlanta, Apr. 20, 1940; s. William Theodore and Doris (Pittman) M.; m. Jennifer Joyce Hancock, Dec. 28, 1968; children—Stephen Theodore, Augusta Everett, William Griggs. B.A., U. Fla., 1962; M.A., U. Ga., 1964, Ph.D., 1972. Instr. dept. geography U. Ga., Athens, 1970-71; asst. prof. dept. geography and area devel. U. So. Miss., Hattiesburg, 1971-75, assoc. prof., 1975-78; asst. dean Coll. Liberal Arts, 1977-78; prof., chmn. dept. geography Memphis State U., 1978-83, prof., chmn. dept. geography and planning, 1983-86, interim dean Coll. Arts and Scis., 1987-88, assoc. v.p. for acad. affairs, 1994, chmn. dept. geography and planning 1989-90, dir. instnl. self study, 1992-94, interim vice provost Acad. Affairs, 1992-94, prof. geography and planning, 1994—; cons. real estate devel. and land use analysis. Contbr. articles to profl. jours. Active Memphis Job Conf. Served to 1st lt. U.S. Army, 1964-66; Vietnam. Recipient Miss. Marine Resources Coun. award, 1974-75, U.S. Dept. Transp. award, 1974-76, 79-80, Miss. R&D Ctr. award, 1976-77, Carnegie Corp. award, 1988-89, NSF award, 1981, 89-91, 94—, Nat. Ctr. Acad. Achievement and Transfer award, 1991-94; NASA Remote Sensing grantee, 1972-75.

Mem. Assn. Am. Geographers, Am. Geog. Soc., Nat. Council Geog. Edn., Tenn. Geog. Soc. (pres. 1984-86), Sigma Xi, Phi Kappa Phi, Pi Gamma Mu, Gamma Theta Upsilon, Pi Tau Chi, Sigma Chi, Omicron Delta Kappa. Presbyterian. Office: Dept Geography Memphis State U Memphis TN 38152

MEANEY, MICHAEL JOSEPH, lawyer; b. Washington, Nov. 16, 1952; s. Thomas F. and Mary R. (McCallum) M.; m. Eva A. Czikk, Sept. 6, 1980; children: Timothy, Emily, Evan. AB, Georgetown U., 1974; JD, Ohio State U., 1977. Bar: Ohio 1977. Assoc. Burke, Haber & Berick, Cleve., 1977-86; ptnr. Berick, Pearlman & Mills, Cleve., 1986-89, Benesch, Friedlander, Coplan & Aronoff, Cleve., 1989—. Mem. Ohio State Bar Assn., Cleve. Bar Assn. Office: Benesch Friedlander Coplan & Aronoff 2300 BP America Bldg 200 Public Square Cleveland OH 44114

MEANS, FRED ERNEST, dean; b. Pacolet, S.C.; s. Fred Sr. and Lemor E. (Tucker) M.; m. Helen Pryor; children: Vincent, Marc, Chad. BS, NYU, 1959; MA, Trenton State Coll., 1963; MEd, Rutgers U., 1973, EdD, 1975. Cert. tchr., N.Y., N.J. Tchr. PS 621, N.Y.C., 1959-60, Dayton Elem. Sch., Newark, 1960-65; tchr., title coord. South Side High Sch., Newark, 1965-70; lectr., program dir. Rutgers U., New Brunswick, N.J., 1970-71, dir., 1970-75; dir. Jersey City State Coll., 1975-78, dir., asst. dean, 1978-85, dean, 1985—; prin. Cleveland Head Start, Newark, summers 1968, 69, 70; bd. dirs. Newark Bd. Edn., 1973-76, Rsch. for Better Schs., 1983—. Chmn. Newark-Essex Congress Racial Equality, 1964-65; bd. dirs. United Community Corp. Newark Anti-Poverty Agy., 1966, Bus. Indsl. Coord. Coun., Newark, 1967-69, Action for Sickle Cell, Hudson County, N.J., 1982-89; pres. Orgn. Negro Edn., Newark, 1967-70; com. chair Nat. Alliance Black Sch. Edn., 1974-75. With U.S. Army, 1953-56. Mem. ASCD, N.J. Assn. Black Educators (Outstanding Black Educator 1987), Nat. Alliance Black Sch. Educators (com. chair 1974-75), N.J. Coun. Edn. (bd. dirs. 1991), Assn. Tchr. Educators (presenter 1991), Am. Assn. Colls. for Tchr. Educators (presenter 1990, 92, 93, 94), Am. Edn. Rsch. Assn. (presenter 1980), Alpha Phi Alpha, Phi Delta Kappa. Democrat. Baptist. Avocations: boating, swimming, scuba, walking, tennis. Office: Jersey City State Coll 2039 John F Kennedy Blvd Jersey City NJ 07305-1527

MEANS, GEORGE ROBERT, organization executive; b. Bloomington, Ill., July 5, 1907; s. Arthur John and Alice (Johnson) M.; m. Martha Cowart, Aug. 5, 1950. B.Ed., Ill. State U., 1930; A.M., Clark U., 1932; H.H.D. (hon.), Rikkyo U., Tokyo, Ill. Wesleyan U.; Ill. State U.; H.H.D. (hon.), Ky. Wesleyan Coll. Cartographer, map editor, 1932-35; with Rotary Internat., 1935—; beginning as conv. mgr., successively head Middle Asia office Rotary Internat., Bombay, India; asst. gen. sec. Rotary Internat., 1948-52, gen. sec., 1953-72; sec. Rotary Found., 1953-72; hon. dir. Washington Nat. Corp.; dir. Hertzberg-New Method, Inc., Ind. State Retirement Home Guaranty Fund. Author: Rotary's Return to Japan, also numerous articles. Mem.-at-large nat. council Boy Scouts Am. Served as comdr. USNR, 1942-46. Decorated Legion of Honor France; Chilean Order of Merit; Japanese Order of Rising Sun; Italian Order of Merit; recipient Disting. Service award Geog. Soc. Chgo., 1972; Paul Harris fellow The Rotary Found. Fellow Am. Geog. Soc.; mem. Rotary Club (Evanston, Bloomington, Ill., Sydney, Australia, Kyoto, Osaka and Tokyo, Japan, Seoul, Korea, Cape Town, South Africa, Ituzaingo, Saavedra, Argentina, Greenwood, Ind.), Gamma Theta Upsilon. Home: 1067 Smock Dr Greenwood IN 46143-2426

MEANS, JOHN BARKLEY, foreign language educator, association executive; b. Cin., Jan. 2, 1939; s. Walker Wilson and Rosetta Miller (Barkley) M. BA, U. Ill., 1960, MA, 1963; PhD, U. Ill. at Urbana, 1968. U.S. Govt. rsch. analyst on Latin Am. Washington, 1962-64; assoc. prof. Spanish and Portugese Temple U., Phila., 1972-82, prof. critical langs., 1982—, co-chmn. dept. Spanish and Portuguese, 1971-75, dir. Center for Critical Langs., 1975—, dir. Inst. for Langs. and Internat. Studies, 1987—, chmn. dept. Germanic and Slavic Langs., 1992-94; cons. on Brazilian-Portuguese and second lang. acquisition and self-instrnl. programs for less commonly taught langs., 1968—; cons. to founds., pubs., univs. and govt. agys. Editor: Essays on Brazilian Literature, 1971; author: (with others) Language in Education: Theory and Practice, 1988—; contbr. numerous articles to profl. jours. Trustee Bristol (Pa.) Riverside Theatre, 1991—; mng. trustee Means Charitable Trust, 1991—. 1st lt. U.S. Army, 1960-62. NDEA fellow, 1962, 64; grantee U.S. Dept. Edn., 1979-81, Japan Found., 1980, 82, 89-91, ARCO Found., 1991-92. Mem. MLA, S.R., Nat. Coun. on Langs. and Internat. Studies (bd. dirs.), Joint Nat. Com. for Langs. (bd. dirs.), Nat. Assn. Self-Instrnl. Lang. Programs (exec. dir. 1977—, editor jour. 1978-94), Am. Coun. on Teaching Fgn. Lang., Nat. Coun. Orgns. Less Commonly Taught Langs. (sec.-treas.), Nat. Assn. State Univs. and Land-Grant Colls., Pi Kappa Phi, Phi Lambda Beta, Sigma Delta Pi. Home: PO Box 565 Yardley PA 19067-8565 Office: Temple U Anderson Hall 022-38 Ctr for Critical Langs Philadelphia PA 19122

MEANS, MARIANNE, political columnist; b. Sioux City, Iowa, June 13, 1934; d. Ernest Maynard and Else Marie Johanne (Andersen) Hansen; m. Warren Weaver, Jr. B.A., U. Nebr., 1956; J.D., George Washington U., 1977. Copy editor Lincoln (Nebr.) Jour., 1955-57; woman's editor No. Va. Sun, Arlington, 1957-59; Washington bur. corr. Hearst Newspapers, 1959-61, White House corr., 1961-65; polit. columnist King Features Syndicate, 1965—, N.Y. Times News, 1994—; commentator Spectrum CBS radio, Mut. Broadcasting Network, Voice of Am., U.S.I.A. World Network, Post Newsweek Stas., Nat. Pub. Radio. Author: The Woman in the White House, 1963. Recipient Front Page award N.Y. Newspaper Women, 1962; Tex. Headliners award, 1976, Hall of Fame-Sigma Delta Chi, 1988. Mem. White House Corrs. Assn., Nat. Press Found. (chmn.), Internat. Women's Media Found. (bd. dirs.), Gridiron Club, Cosmos Club, Nat. Press Club, Phi Beta Kappa, Delta Delta Delta, Sigma Delta Chi (Hall of Fame). Home: 1521 31st St NW Washington DC 20007-3075 Office: 1701 Pennsylvania Ave NW Washington DC 20006-5801

MEANS, MICHAEL DAVID, hospital administrator; b. Lakeland, Fla., Jan. 19, 1950; married. B, U. Fla., 1971, MHA, 1974. Adminstrv. resident Manatee Meml. Hosp., Bradenton, Fla., 1974, adminstrv. asst., 1974-78; asst. dir. Orlando (Fla.) Regional Med. Ctr., 1978-80, assoc. exec. dir., 1980-81, exec. v.p., chief oper. officer, 1981-88; pres., chief exec. officer Holmes Regional Healthcare System, Melbourne, Fla., 1988—. Mem. Fla. Hosp. Assn. Home: 1848 River Shore Dr Indialantic FL 32903-4514 Office: Holmes Regional Med Ctr 1350 S Hickory St Melbourne FL 32901-3276

MEANS, TERRY ROBERT, federal judge; b. Roswell, N.Mex., July 3, 1948; s. Lewis Prude and Doris Emaree (Hightower) M.; m. JoAnn Huffman Harris, June 2, 1973; children: Robert, MaryAnn, Emily. BA, So. Meth. U., Dallas, 1971; JD, So. Meth. U., 1974. Bar: Tex. 1974, U.S. Dist. Ct. (no. dist.) Tex. 1976, U.S. Ct. Appeals (5th cir.) 1978, U.S. Dist. Ct. (we. dist., ea. dist.) Tex. 1991. Ptnr. Means & Means, Corsicana, Tex., 1974-89; justice 10th Ct. Appeals, Waco, Tex., 1989-90; judge U.S. Dist. Ct. for Northern Dist. Tex., Ft. Worth, 1991—. Chmn Navarro County Rep. party, Corsicana, 1976-88; pres. YMCA, Corsicana, 1984. Mem. State Bar Tex., Tarrant County Bar Assn., McLennan County Bar Assn. Baptist. Avocations: coaching soccer, racquetball. Office: 201 US Courthouse 501 W 10th St Fort Worth TX 76102-3637

MEANS, THOMAS CORNELL, lawyer; b. Charleston, S.C., Oct. 3, 1947; s. Thomas Lucas and Dean (Cornell) M.; m. Judith Faye Perlmutter, Sept. 10, 1977; children: Benjamin Thomas, Samuel Thomas. AB, Dartmouth Coll., 1969; postgrad., Princeton Theol. Sem., 1970-71; M of Pub. Adminstrv., U. Colo., 1975; JD, George Washington U., 1978. Bar: D.C. 1978, U.S. Dist. Ct. (D.C. dist.) 1979, U.S. Ct. Appeals (4th and D.C. cirs.) 1979, U.S. Ct. Appeals (10th cir.) 1983, U.S. Ct. Appeals (6th and 11th cirs.) 1989, U.S. Ct. Appeals (9th cir.) 1992, U.S. Ct. Appeals (8th cir.) 1993. Social worker Vinyard Childcare, Ann Arbor, Mich., 1969-70; rsch. analyst, registered lobbyist Colo. Counties, Inc., Denver, 1972-75; assoc. Jones, Day, Reavis and Pogue, Washington, 1978-79; assoc. then ptnr. Crowell & Moring, Washington, 1979—; mem. state adv. coun. on pub. Pers. Mgmt., Colo. State Govt., Denver, 1974-75; lectr. mining law; chmn. coal com. Ea. Mineral Law Found., 1989-89, chmn. spl. insts., asst. sec., 1989-91, sec., 1991-92, v.p., 1992-93, pres. 1993-94; bd. advisors Nat. Law Ctr., 1993-94. Contbr. articles to profl. jours. Trustee Ea. Mineral Law Found., 1989—; mem. adv. bd. editors, 1994—. Mem. George Washington Law Alumni

Assn. (bd. dirs. 1986—, treas. 1987-88, sec. 1988-90, pres. 1992-94), Order of Coif, Cosmos Club (Washington), Phi Beta Kappa. Home: 6411 Dahlonega Rd Bethesda MD 20816-2101 Office: Crowell & Moring 1001 Pennsylvania Ave NW Washington DC 20004-2505

MEANY, JOHN JOSEPH, newspaper publisher; b. Port Jervis, N.Y., Nov. 7, 1939; s. John J. Sr. and Dorothy E. (Simmons) M.; m. Kathleen J. Wukich, June 15, 1978; children: Stephen, Patrick, Matthew, Mary Beth. BS, East Stroudsburg (Pa.) U., 1961; MS, SUNY, New Paltz, 1976. Tchr. Port Jervis High Sch., 1961-77; circulation mgr. Gazette-Jour., Reno, Nev., 1978-82; circulation dir. Tribune Star, Terra Haute, Ind., 1982-85, gen. mgr., 1985-89, pub., 1990—; pub. Times, Leavenworth, Kans., 1989-90. Dir. United Way, Terre Haute, 1985—, Boy Scouts, Terre Haute, 1991-92; bd. assocs. Rose Hulman Coll., Terre Haute, 1990—. Mem. Inland Press Assn., Terre Haute C. of C. (dir. 1990—). Roman Catholic. Avocations: reading, travel. Office: Tribune Star 721 Wabash Ave Terre Haute IN 47807-3203*

MEARA, ANNE, actress, playwright, writer; b. Bklyn., Sept. 20; d. Edward Joseph and Mary (Dempsey) M.; m. Gerald Stiller, Sept. 14, 1954; children: Amy, Benjamin. Student, Herbert Berghoff Studio, 1953-54. Apprentice in summer stock, Southold, L.I. and Woodstock, N.Y., 1950-53; off-Broadway appearances include A Month in the Country, 1954, Maedchen in Uniform, 1955 (Show Bus. off-Broadway award), Ulysses in Nightown, 1958, The House of Blue Leaves, 1970, Spookhouse, 1983, Bosoms and Neglect, 1986, also with Shakespeare Co., Two Gentlemen of Verona, Cen. Park, N.Y.C., 1957, Romeo and Juliet, 1988, Eastern Standard, 1989, Anna Christie, 1993 (Tony nomination Best Supporting Actress), After-Play, 1995; film appearances include The Out-of-Towners, 1968, Lovers and Other Strangers, 1969, The Boys From Brazil, 1978, Fame, 1979, Nasty Habits (with husband Jerry Stiller), 1976, An Open Window, 1990, Mia, 1990, Awakenings, 1991, Reality Bites, 1994; comedy act, 1963—; appearances Happy Medium and Medium Rare, Chgo., 1960-61, Village Gate, Phase Two and Blue Angel, N.Y.C., 1963, The Establishment, London, 1963; syndicated TV series Take Five With Stiller and Meara, 1977-78; numerous appearances on TV game and talk shows, also spls. and variety shows; rec. numerous commls. for TV and radio (co-recipient Vocie of Imagery award Advt. Bur. N.Y.); star TV series Kate McShane, 1975; other TV appearances Archie Bunker's Place, 1979, The Sunset Gang, The Detective, 1990, Avenue Z Afternoon, 1991, Alf, 1986; writer, actress TV movie The Other Woman, 1983 (co-recipient Writer's Guild Outstanding Achievement award 1983), Alf, To Make Up to Break Up, The Stiller and Meara Pilot; author: (play) After-Play, 1994.

MEARS, GARY H., career military officer; b. Boone, Iowa, May 23, 1936; s. Ora Jackson and Theda Blanche (Wiltse) M.; m. Jacqueline Sue Olson, Sept. 2, 1956; children: Gregory, Kimberly Mears Allen, Tracie Mears Wells. BS in Commerce, U. Iowa, 1958; MS in Pers. Counseling, Troy State U., 1978. Commd. 2d lt. USAF, advanced through grades to lt. gen., 1991; dep. comdr. 62d Mil. Airlift Wing, McChord AFB, Washington, 1981-82, vice comdr., 1982-83; comdr. 1606th Air Base Wing, Kirtland AFB, N.M., 1982-83, 834th Airlift Divsn., Hickam AFB, Hawaii, 1983-85; vice comdr. Warner Robins Air Logistics Ctr., Robins AFB, Ga., 1985-86; dep. chief staff logistics Mil. Airlift Command, Scott AFB, Ill., 1986-89; vice dir. for logistics The Joint Staff/J4, Washington, 1989-91, dir. for logistics, 1991—. Mem. NDTA, Masons, Order Ea. Star, Delta Chi. Avocation: golf. Home: #183 15555 Huntington Village Ln Huntington Beach CA 92647 Office: McDonnell Douglas Transport Rm 2E828 1510 Hughes Way Long Beach CA 90810-1870

MEARS, PATRICK EDWARD, lawyer; b. Flint, Mich., Oct. 3, 1951; s. Edward Patrick and Estelle Veronica (Mislik) M.; m. Geraldine O'Connor, July 18, 1981. BA, U. Mich., 1973, JD, 1976. Bar: N.Y. 1977, U.S. Dist. Ct. (so. and ea. dists.) N.Y. 1977, Mich. 1980, U.S. Dist. Ct. (we. and ea. dists.) Mich. 1980, U.S. Ct. Appeals (6th cir.) 1983. Assoc. firm Milbank, Tweed, Hadley & McCloy, N.Y.C., 1976-79; ptnr. Warner, Norcross & Judd, Grand Rapids, Mich., 1980-91; mem. Dykema Gossett PLLC, Grand Rapids, 1991—; adj. prof. Grand Valley State U., Allendale, Mich., 1981-84. Author: Michigan Collection Law, 1981, 2d edit., 1983, Basic Bankruptcy Law, 1986, Bankruptcy Law and Practice in Michigan, 1987; contbr. articles to profl jours. Chairperson legis. com. East Grand Rapids Parent-Tchr. Assn., 1992-94; dir. Children's Law Ctr., 1994, Grand Rapids Ballet, 1994—, East Grand Rapids Pub. Sch. Found., 1994—. Fellow Am. Coll. Bankruptcy; mem. ABA (chairperson assignment of rents and leases subcom., workouts enforcement of creditors rights and bankruptcy com. ABA real property sect. 1993—), Mich. State Bar Assn. (mem. coun. real property sect. 1993—), Am. Bankruptcy Inst., Fed. Bar Assn. (chairperson bankruptcy sect. We. Mich. chpt. 1992-94), Comml. Law League Am., Peninsular Club (Grand Rapids), East Hills Athletic Club. Office: Dykema Gossett 200 Old Town Riverfront Bu Grand Rapids MI 49503

MEARS, RONA ROBBINS, lawyer; b. Stillwater, Minn., Oct. 3, 1938; d. Glaydon Donaldson and Lois Lorane (Hoehne) Robbins; m. John Ashley Mears, Aug. 20, 1960; children: John LaMonte, Matthew Von. BS, U. Minn., 1960; MBA, JD, So. Meth. U., 1982. Bar: Tex. 1992. Bus. adminstr. 1st Unitarian Ch., Dallas, 1973-77; assoc. atty. Haynes and Boone, Dallas, 1982-89, ptnr., internat. sect., 1989—. Co-editor: International Loan Workouts and Bankruptcies, 1989; contbr. articles to profl. jours. Mem. U.S. Delegation, NAFTA Adv. Com. on Pvt. Comml. Disputes, 1994—. Rsch. fellow Southwestern Legal Found., Dallas, 1986—; recipient 1st prize INSOL Internat. Article Competition, 1989. Mem. ABA (sec. internat. sect. 1994—), Tex. Bar Found., State Bar Tex. (chmn. internat. sect. 1993-94), Tex.-Mex. Bar Assn. (co-vice chair 1994—), Dallas Bar Assn. (chmn. internat. sect. 1984-86), Internat. Bar Assn. (mem. com. on creditors rights, coord. internat. insolvency coop. project 1988-91), U.S.-Mex. C. of C. (bd. dirs. S.W. chpt. 1987—). Democrat. Office: Haynes and Boone LLP 3100 Nations Bank Plz 901 Main St Dallas TX 75202-3707

MEARS, WALTER ROBERT, journalist; b. Lynn, Mass., Jan. 11, 1935; s. Edward Lewis and Edythe Emily (Campbell) M.; m. Sally Danton, Dec. 28, 1956 (dec. Dec. 1962); children: Pamela (dec.), Walter Robert Jr. (dec.); m. Joyce Marie Lund, Aug. 4, 1963 (div. 1983); children: Stephanie Joy, Susan Marie; m. Carroll Ann Rambo, Mar. 1, 1986 (div. 1995). B.A., Middlebury Coll., 1956, Litt.D. (hon.), 1977. Newsman AP, Boston, 1956; corr. AP, Montpelier, Vt., 1956-60; state house corr. AP, Boston, 1960-61; newsman AP, Washington, 1961-69; chief polit. writer AP, 1969-72, asst. chief Washington bur., 1973-74, spl. corr., 1975, chief, 1977-83, v.p., 1978—; exec. editor, 1984-88, v.p., columnist, 1989—. Author: (with John Chancellor) The News Business, 1983. Trustee Middlebury Coll., 1980-84. Recipient ann. award AP Mng. Editors Assn., 1973; Pulitzer prize for Nat. Reporting, 1977. Mem. Phi Beta Kappa, Delta Kappa Epsilon. Clubs: Gridiron, Burning Tree. Office: Associated Press 2021 K St NW # 600 Washington DC 20006-1082

MEASELLE, RICHARD L., accountant; b. Detroit, Sept. 29, 1938; s. Leland Stanford and Jean Therese (Saydak) M.; m. Susan Stauft, Dec. 30, 1961; children: Jeffrey, Laura, Susana, Millicent, Stephen. BS in Bus., Miami U., Oxford, Ohio, 1961. Office mng. ptnr. Arthur Andersen, Barcelona, Spain, 1970-72, Detroit, 1975-87; mng. ptnr. acctg. and audit worldwide Arthur Andersen, 1987-89, mng. ptnr., audit and bus. adv., tax and consulting worldwide, 1989—; area mng. ptnr. Arthur Andersen, Mich., Ohio, Ky. and Wis., 1985-87; mem., bd. ptnrs., mem. exec. com. Arthur Andersen Worldwide Orgn. Co-author: Helping Public Schools Succeed, 1989. Chmn. bd. trustees U. Detroit, 1985; trustee Detroit Econ. Growth Corp., 1975-87; chmn. United Negro Coll. Fund, Detroit, 1982; spanish consul Hon. Spanish Consul, Mich. chpt., 1972-88; mem. Detroit Consular Corps.; mem. vis. com. U. Mich. Sch. of Bus. Adminstrv., 1990; mem. USSR Global Partnership Coun., 1990, Tax Found.'s Policy Coun., 1990; mem. com. Chgo. Coun. Fgn. Rels., 1991. With USMC, 1958-64, res. Named Hon. Alumnus of Yr. U. Detroit, 1984, Acct. of Yr. Beta Alpha Psi-Miami U., 1989; recipient Pres.'s Cabinet award U. Detroit, 1989. Mem. AICPA, The Econ. Club of N.Y. Avocations: skiing, tennis. Office: Arthur Andersen & Co 69 W Washington St Ste 3500 Chicago IL 60602-3004

MEAT LOAF (MARVIN LEE ADAY), popular musician, actor; b. Dallas, Sept. 27, 1951; m. Leslie Aday (Edmonds), 1975; children: Pearl, Amanda. Albums include Featuring Stoney and Meat Loaf, 1970, Free For All, 1976, Bat OutOf Hell, 1977, DeadRinger, 1982, Midnight at The Lost

and Found, 1983, Bad Attitude, 1984, Hits Out Of Hell, 1985, Blind Before I Stop, 1986, Meat Loaf Live, 1987, Bat Out Of Hell II: Back Into Hell, 1993; appeared in plays Hair, The RockyHorror Show, National Lampoon Show, More Than You Deserve, Rockabye Hamlet, BillyThe Kid & Jean Harlow, As You Like It, Othello; appeared in films The Rocky Horror Picture Show, 1975, Americathon, 1979, Scavenger Hunt, 1979, Roadie, 1980,Dead Ringer, 1981, The Squeeze, 1986, Out of Bounds, 1986, Motorama, 1990, Gun & Betty Lou's Handbag, 1991, Wayne's World, 1992, Leap of Faith, 1992. Received Grammy for Best Rock Vocal Solo Performance, 1993. Office: c/o MCA Records 70 Universal Terrace Pky Universal City CA 91608*

MEBANE, GEORGE ALLEN, corporate executive, rancher; b. Greensboro, N.C., Sept. 28, 1929; s. George Allen III and Elizabeth (Armstrong) M.; m. Pat Pannill, Aug. 23, 1950 (dec.); children: George Allen IV, William Michael, Lucy Mebane Webster; m. Marianne Cheek, June 28, 1987. BS, Phila. Coll. Textile and Sci., 1950, D Textiles (hon.), 1986. Supr. Sale Knitting Co., Martinsville, Va., 1950-52; salesman Am. & Efird Mills, Mt. Holly, N.C., 1954-56, Burlington, Ind., Greensboro, 1956-64; pres., chief exec. officer Throwing Corp. Am., Swepsonville, N.C., 1964-67, Universal Textured Yarns, Inc., Mebane, N.C., 1967-71; pres., chief exec. officer Unifi, Inc., Greensboro, 1971-78, chmn., chief exec. officer, 1978-85, chmn., 1985—. Sgt. U.S. Army, 1952-54; Korea. Mem. Am. Synthetic Yarns Assn. (bd. dirs. 1977-80), Am. Textile Mfg. Inst. (bd. dirs. 1986-89), N.C. Textile Assn. (bd. dirs. 1988-90). Democrat. Presbyterian. Office: Unifi Inc PO Box 19109 Greensboro NC 27419-9109

MEBANE, WILLIAM BLACK, controller, financial consultant; b. Vernon, Tex., Dec. 15, 1927; s. David Mitchell and Ida Virginia (Black) M.; m. Joan Hebbard Dumper, Nov. 24, 1956; children—David Alexander, Virginia Ann. B.B.A., Tex. A&M U., 1952; M.B.A., Harvard U., 1954. Mem. treas.'s office staff Gen. Motors Corp., N.Y.C., 1954-70; sec.-treas. Alfred P. Sloan Found., N.Y.C., 1971-78; dir. fin. and adminstrn. Am. Diabetes Assn., N.Y.C., 1979-80; dir. planning Am. Diabetes Assn., 1981; v.p., comptroller NCCJ, Inc., N.Y.C., 1981-86, v.p. for fiscal affairs, 1987-88; fin. cons. Internat. House, N.Y.C., 1989-90; ind. fin. cons., 1990-91; contr. Better Bus. Bur., N.Y.C., 1991—. Vol. Essex Council Boy Scouts Am., 1967—. Served with USAAF, 1946-49. Recipient Silver Beaver award Boy Scouts Am., 1982. Republican. Presbyterian. Clubs: Harvard Bus. Sch. (N.Y.C.); Short Hills (N.J.). Home: 36 Haddonfield Rd Short Hills NJ 07078-3402

MEBANE, WILLIAM DEBERNIERE, newspaper publisher; b. Durham, N.C., Jan. 14, 1949; s. John Gilmer and Harriet deBerniere (Elmore) M.; m. Catharine Frampton McGee, May 30, 1970; children—William deBerniere, Harriet Bacot, Jane Bacot, Catharine Frampton, John McGee, Beverly Canby. B.A., U. N.C., 1971, cert. in exec. program, 1981. V.p. Greenville News-Piedmont, S.C., 1976-82, bus. mgr., 1976-78, gen. mgr., 1978-81, co-pub., 1981-84, pres., 1982—, pub., 1984-92; v.p Multimedia Newspaper Co., Greenville, 1984-92, pres., 1989—; v.p. Multimedia Inc., 1989—. Commr. S.C. Mental Retardation Commn., 1983-89, vice chmn., 1988; past pres. Greenville Symphony Assn.; campaign chmn. United Way Greenville County, 1984, v.p. resource devel., 1985, v.p. mktg. and commns., 1986, 1st v.p., 1987, pres., 1988; treas. Goodwill Industries of Upper S.C., 1980-81; past pres. Greenville Assn. Retarded Children; mem. First Amendment Congress Bd., 1987-88, N.C. Soc. of the Cin., Corp. Coalition on Infant Mortality, 1988; bd. dirs. Greenville Hosp. System, 1993—. Mem. AP (com. 1985—, nominating com. 1991—, chmn. 1992—), Am. Newspaper Pubs. Assn. (com. 1982—), So. Newspaper Pubs. Assn. (treas. 1990, chmn. com. 1983-84, pres. 1992, chmn. 1993), So. Govs. Assn., S.C. Press Assn. (treas. 1984-85, v.p. dailies 1986, pres. 1987), Young Pres.'s Orgn., Huguenot Soc., Greenville C. of C. (bd. dirs., v.p. 1981-82, bd. dirs. 1987-88), Poinsett Club, Delta Kappa Epsilon. Avocation: outdoorsman. Home: 119 Crescent Ave Greenville SC 29605-2812 Office: Multimedia Newspaper Co 305 S Main St PO Box 1688 Greenville SC 29602-1688

MEBUS, CHARLES ALBERT, veterinarian; b. Paterson, N.J., Sept. 10, 1932; s. Charles Albert and Mary (Ponstingel) M.; m. Sept. 10, 1955; children: Jane C., Patricia A., Charles A. DVM, N.Y. State Vet. Coll., 1956; MS, Kans. State U., 1962, PhD, 1965. Diplomate Am. Coll. Vet. Pathologists. Gen. practice Dover, Del., 1958-60; NDEA staff asst. Kans. State U., Manhattan, 1960-63, assoc. prof., 1963-65; prof. U. Nebr., Lincoln, 1965-77; rsch. leder Agrl. Rsch. Svc. USDA, Greenport, N.Y., 1977-88; chief Animal and Plant Health Inspection Svc. USDA Foreign Animal Disease Diagnostic Lab., Greenport, N.Y., 1988-95. Vestry Holy Trinity Ch., Greenport. 1st lt. U.S. Army, 1956-68. Mem. AVMA, U.S. Animal Health Assn., Am. Assn. Vet. Diagnosticians. Episcopalian. Office: 2145 Wells Ave Southold NY 11944

MEBUS, ROBERT GWYNNE, lawyer; b. Ft. Worth, Aug. 28, 1940; s. Robert Lee and Lucille (Cooke) M.; children: Elizabeth, Mary Ellen. BBA, So. Meth. U., 1962, LLB, 1965. Bar: Tex. 1965, U.S. Dist. Ct. (no. and ea. dists.) 1966, U.S. Ct. Appeals (5th cir.) 1965, U.S. Supreme Ct. 1969. Assoc. Malone, Seay & Gwinn, Dallas, 1965-67; ptnr. Seay, Gwinn, Crawford, Dallas, 1967-69, Seay, Gwinn, Crawford, Mebus, Dallas, 1969-82, Haynes and Boone, Dallas, 1982—; Mem. Tex. State Bar (chmn. labor law sect. 1982-83, chmn. labor law adv. commn. 1982-83), Tex. Bd. Legal Specialization. Contbg. editor: (book) Developing Labor Law, 1967, 2d edit., 1987. Mem. ABA (labor law sect.), Tex. Bar Found. Avocations: tennis, photography, gardening. Office: Haynes and Boone 3100 NationsBank Plz 901 Main St Dallas TX 75202-3707

MEBUST, WINSTON KEITH, surgeon, educator; b. Malta, Mont., July 2, 1933; s. Hans G. and Anna C. (Leiseth) M.; m. Lora June Peterson, Sept. 15, 1955; children—Leanne, Kevin, Kreg, Kari. Student, U. Wash., 1951-54, M.D., 1958. Diplomate: Am. Bd. Urology (trustee 1983-89, pres. 1988-89). Intern King County Hosp., Seattle, 1958-59; resident Virginia Mason Hosp., Seattle, 1959-63, Kans. U. Med. Center, 1963-66; practice medicine, specializing in urology, 1966—; instr. surgery and urology U. Kans. Med. Center, Kansas City, 1966-69; asst. prof. U. Kans. Med. Center, 1969-72, asso. prof., 1972-76, chmn. urology sect., 1974—, prof., 1977—; chief urology service VA Hosp., Kansas City, Mo., 1966-75. Contbr. articles, chpts. to med. jours. and texts. Served with U.S. Army, 1961-63. Mem. ACS, Am. Cancer Soc., Am. Bd. Surgery, Kansas City Urol. Assn., Assn. for Acad. Surgery, Am. Urol. Assn. (pres South Cen. sect. 1983, exec. com. 1992—), Wyandotte Med. Soc., Kans. Med. Assn., Soc. Univ. Urologists, Am. Assn. Genitourinary Surgeons, Sigma Xi, Alpha Omega Alpha. Republican. Home: 292 Seneca Trl W Kansas City KS 66106-9689 Office: 39th and Rainbow Blvd Kansas City MO 66103

MECCA, JOSEPH NICHOLAS, logistics and manufacturing company executive; b. Passaic, N.J., May 8, 1947; s. Dante Virgilio and Theresa Ann (Digangi) M.; m. Margaret Diane Cooper, Jan. 7, 1969; children: Joseph Jr., Anthony, Margaret. BS in Ops. Mgmt., Thomas Edison State Coll., 1981, BS in Human Resouce Mgmt., 1981. Dept. mgr. W.T. Grant, Paterson, N.J., 1964; dept. supr. Popular Svcs. Club, Passaic, 1970-71; gen. mgr. K-Mart Apparel Corp., North Bergen, N.J., 1971-82; v.p. ops. Fortunoff, Wayne, N.J., 1982-84, Commodore Bus. Machines, Inc., West Chester, Pa., 1984-93; v.p. worldwide transp. and internat. trade adminstrn. GM US Ops., Mfg.; v.p., logistics integration, configuration and mfg. ops. Intelligent Electronics, Exton, Pa., 1994—. With USN, 1965-70, Vietnam, commdr. USNR. Recipient Commendation and Achievement medals, USN Seabees, Vietnam Service medals. Mem. Am. Mgmt. Assn., Mgmt. Assn. Del Valley, Soc. Am. Mil. Engrs., Naval Res. Assn., Am. Soc. Transp. and Logistics, VFW, Am. Legion. Republican. Avocations: bowling, shooter, baseball. Home: 807 Nathan Hale Dr West Chester PA 19382-7053 Office: 507 Nathan Hale Dr West Chester PA 19382

MECH, TERRENCE FRANCIS, library director; b. Birdorup Park, Wiltshire, Eng., Feb. 24, 1953; s. Emil Paul and Madelyn (Tremmel) M. BS, U. Wis. Stevens Point, 1975; MS, Ill. State U., 1978; MLS, Clarion U., 1979; EdD, Pa. State U., 1990. Pub. svcs. libr. Tusculum Coll., Greenville, Tenn., 1979-80; info. libr. U. of the Ozarks, Clarksville, Ark., 1980-82; libr. dir. King's Coll., Wilkes-Barre, Pa., 1982-94, v.p. for info. and instrnl. techs., dir. libr., 1994—; bd. dirs. Northeastern Pa. Bibliographic Ctr. 1982—; mem. officer Coun. Pa. Libr. Networks, 1984-89, chair, 1987-89. Contbr. chpts. to books and articles to profl. jours. Mem. ALA, Pa. Libr. Assn. (bd. dirs.

1986-87, various coms. 1985—). Office: Kings Coll 14 W Jackson St Wilkes Barre PA 18701-2010

MECH, WILLIAM PAUL, mathematics educator, director honors program; b. La Crosse, Wis., Mar. 10, 1942; s. Stephen John and Eunice (Sampson) M.; m. Mary Ethel Bayne, Feb. 2, 1964 (div. Dec. 1980); children: Elizabeth Ann, Kathryn Marie, Stephen Glen; m. Victoria Craig Hunt, Aug. 4, 1983. BA, Wash. State U., 1964; MS, U. Ill., 1965, PhD, 1970. Instr. maths. U. Ill., Urbana, 1967-69; asst. prof. Boise (Idaho) State U., 1970-73, assoc. prof., 1973-77, prof., 1977—, chmn. dept. math., 1975-80, dir. honors program, 1971—; cons. Hanford Engring. Devel. Labs., Richland, Wash., 1976, Capital Computer Corp., Boise, 1982. Contbr. articles on honors programs to profl. jours. Vol. coord. ptnrs. in edn. Boise schs., 1985-89; active Coun. on Fgn. Rels., Boise, 1974—. Grantee NSF, 1980. Mem. AAAS, Math. Assn. Am., Nat. Collegiate Honors Coun. (pres. 1981-82, exec. sec.-treas. 1988—), Sigma Xi, Phi Beta Kappa, Phi Kappa Phi (chpt. pres. 1973-75). Home: 325 Mcguffin Ln Boise ID 83712-8345 Office: Boise State U Honors Program 1910 University Dr Boise ID 83725-0001

MECHAM, GLENN JEFFERSON, lawyer, mayor; b. Logan, Utah, Dec. 11, 1935; s. Everett H. and Lillie (Dunford) M.; m. Mae Parson, June 5, 1957; children: Jeff B., Scott R., Marcia, Suzanne. BS, Utah State U., 1957; JD, U. Utah, 1961; grad. Air Command and Staff Coll., Air War Coll., 1984. Bar: Utah 1961, Supreme Ct. U.S., U.S. Ct. Appeals (10th Cir.), U.S. Dist. Ct. Utah, U.S. Ct. Claims. Gen. practice law, 1961-65; atty. Duchesne County, Utah, 1962, City of Duchesne, 1962; city judge Roy City, Utah, 1963-66; judge City of Ogden, Utah, 1966-69, mayor, 1991-92; lectr. law and govt. Stevens-Henager Coll., Ogden, 1963-75; asst. U.S. dist. atty. State of Utah, 1969-72; ptnr. Mecham & Richards, Ogden, Utah, 1972-82; pres. Penn Mountain Mining Co., South Pacific Internat. Bank, Ltd.; mem. Bur. Justice Stats. Adv. Bd., U.S. Dept. Justice, U.S. Conf. Mayors. Chmn. Ogden City Housing Authority; chmn. bd. trustees Utah State U., Space Dynamics Lab. Utah State U.; mem. adv. coun. Fed. Home Loan Bank; pres. Utah League Cities and Towns, 1981-82. Col. USAF, 1957. Mem. ABA, Weber County Bar Assn. (pres. 1966-68), Utah Bar Assn., Am. Judicature Soc., Weber County Bar Legal Svcs. (chmn. bd. trustees 1966-69), Utah Assn. Mcpl. Judges (sec.), Sigma Chi, Phi Alpha Delta. Home: 1715 Darling St Ogden UT 84403-0556 Office: City of Ogden 2484 Washington Blvd # 300 Ogden UT 84401

MECHAM, STEVEN RAY, school system administrator; b. Salt Lake City, Oct. 10, 1938; s. Milton Claudius and Marjorie (White) M.; m. Donna Jean Johnson, Jan. 22, 1943; children: Brian Paul, Allan LeRoy. AS, Weber State Coll., 1958; BS, U. Utah, 1963; MA, Tchrs. Coll., Columbia U., 1965; postgrad. McGill U.; PhD U. Santa Barbara, Calif., 1981. Prin., Montreal (Que.) Oral Sch., 1966-70; state dir. hearing impaired Conn. Dept. Edn., 1970-71; dir. guidance Lexington Sch. for the Deaf, N.Y.C., 1971-72; supt. Exton Elem., Ana Frank Jr. & Sr. High Sch., Mexico City, 1972-77; coord. spl. edn. Weber Sch. Dist., Ogden, Utah, 1977-78; prin. Roosevelt Elem. Sch., Ogden, 1978-82; asst. supt. Weber County Schs., Ogden, 1982-87, Utah Schs., 1990—; supt. Weber Sch. Dist., 1993—; instr. U. Utah, 1965-66, St. Joseph Coll., Hartford, Conn., 1970-71; pres. Finnish Mission-LDS Russia and Baltic States, 1987-90; adj. prof. McGill U.; instr. Tchrs. Coll., Columbia U., 1968-70; acting chmn. dept. edn. U. Americas, Mexico City, 1976-77; cons. Far West Labs., San Francisco. Bd. dirs. Instituto Mexicano Norte Americano de Relaciones Culturales, Mexico City, 1975-76; bishop Ch. Jesus Christ of Latter-day Saints, chmn. Cancer Crusade; pres. Finnish Mission Ch. Jesus Christ of Latter-day Saints; bd. dirs. Am. Cancer Soc. Weber County. Mem. Am. Orgn. Educators of Hearing Impaired (pres.), Can. Hearing Soc. (dir.) Utah Assn. Elem. Sch. Prins., Nat. Assn. Elem. Sch. Prins., Internat. Reading Assn., Am. Assn. Sch. Adminstrs., Alexander Graham Bell Assn. Club: Rotary. Contbr. articles to profl. jours. Home: 2163 Jennifer Dr Ogden UT 84403-4965 Office: 5320 Adams Ave Ogden UT 84405

MECHANIC, DAVID, social sciences educator; b. N.Y.C., Feb. 21, 1936; s. Louis and Tillie (Penn) M.; m. Kathleen Mars Wiltshire; children: Robert Edmund, Michael Alexander. B.A., CCNY, 1956; M.A., Stanford U., 1957, Ph.D., 1959. Faculty U. Wis., Madison, 1960-79; prof. sociology U. Wis., 1965-73, John Bascom prof., 1973-79; dir. U. Wis. (Center for Med. Sociology and Health Services Research), 1971-79, chmn. dept. sociology, 1968-70; prof. social work and sociology Rutgers U., New Brunswick, N.J., 1979—; acting dean faculty arts and scis. Rutgers U., 1980-81, Univ. prof., dean faculty arts and scis., 1981-84, Univ. prof. and Rene Dubos prof. behavioral scis., 1984—; dir. Inst. for Health, Health Care Policy and Aging Research, 1985—; mem. panel on health svcs. rsch. Pres.'s Sci. Adv. Com., 1971-72; mem. treatment com. on reduction of cancer mortality Nat. Cancer Inst., 1984; vice-chmn. com. pain, disability and chronic illness behavior Inst. Medicine-Nat. Acad. Scis., 1985-86, mem. panel on prevention of disability, 1989-90; mem. Com. on Prevention of Mental Disorder, 1992-94; coordinator panel Pres.'s Commn. Mental Health, 1977-78; mem. Nat. Adv. Council Aging, NIH, 1982-86; expert adv. panel on mental health, WHO, 1984-89; mem. health adv. bd. GAO, 1987—; mem. panel on tech., ins. and health care system Office of Tech. U.S. Congress, 1992—; mem. nat. com. on vital and health statistics HHS, 1988-92; mem. commn. on behavioral and social scis. and edn. NRC, 1989—, commn. on med. edn. Robert Wood Johnson Found., 1990-92; mem. com. Picker/Commonwealth Scholar's Program, 1992—; nat. adv. com. Robert Wood Johnson Scholars in Health Policy Rsch. Program, 1992—; panel on Rethinking Disability Policy, Nat. Acad. Social Ins., 1993—; vis. scholar Kings Fund Inst., London, 1994—. Author: Students Under Stress, 1962, 2d edit., 1978, Medical Sociology, 1968, rev. edit., 1978, Mental Health and Social Policy, 1969, rev. edit., 1980, 89, Public Expectations and Health Care, 1972, Politics, Medicine and Social Science, 1974, (with Charles E. Lewis and Rashi Fein) A Right to Health, 1976, Growth of Bureaucratic Medicine, 1976, Future Problems in Health Care, 1979, From Advocacy to Allocation: The Evolving American Health Care System, 1986, Painful Choices: Research and Essays on Health Care, 1989, Inescapable Decisions: The Imperatives of Health Reform, 1994; author, editor: Symptoms, Illness Behavior and Help-Seeking; editor: Handbook of Health, Health Care and the Health Professions, 1983, Improving Mental Health Services: What the Social Sciences Can Tell Us, 1987; Co-editor: (with Robert Houser, Archibald Haller and Tess Hauser) Social Structure and Personality, 1982, (with Linda Aiken) Applications of Social Science to Clinical Medicine and Social Policy, 1986; Paying for Services: Promises and Pitfalls of Capitation, 1989; (with Marian Osterweis and Arthur Kleinman) Pain and Disability: Clinical Behavior and Public Policy Perspectives, 1987, (with Carl Taube and Ann Hohmann) The Future of Mental Health Services Research, 1989. Fellow Ctr. for Advanced Study in Behavioral Scis., 1974-75, NIMH rsch. fellow, 1965-66, Ford Behavioral Sci. fellow, 1956-57, Guggenheim fellow, 1977-78; recipient Ward medal CCNY, 1956, Med. Sociologist award Am. Sociol. Assn., 1983, Carl Taube award Am. Pub. Health Assn., 1990, Disting. Investigator award Assn. for Health Svcs. Rsch., 1991, Disting. Contbn. award mental health sect. Soc. for Study of Social Problems, 1991, Emily Mumford medal Columbia U., 1991. Fellow AAAS (chmn. sect. social, econ. and polit. scis. 1985); mem. Am. Sociol. Assn. (governing coun. 1977-78, chmn. med. sociol. sect. 1969-70, chmn. publs. com. 1989-91, chmn. mental health sect. 1992-93), Sociol. Rsch. Assn. (pres. 1991-92), Inst. Medicine-Nat. Acad. Scis. (governing coun. 1972-74), Nat. Acad. Scis., Am. Acad. Arts and Scis., Hogg Found. Mental Health (nat. adv. coun. 1987), Phi Beta Kappa. Office: Rutgers U Inst Health Care Policd Aging Rsch 30 College Ave New Brunswick NJ 08903 Home: 14 Cameron St Princeton NJ 08540

MECHANIC, WILLIAM M., television and motion picture industry executive; b. Detroit. BA in English, Mich. State U.; PhD in Film, U. So. Calif. Dir. programming SelecTV, 1978-80, v.p. programming 1980-82; v.p. pay TV Paramount Pictures Corp., 1982-84; v.p. pay TV sales Walt Disney Pictures and TV, 1984-85, sr. v.p. video, 1985-87, pres. internat. theatrical distbn. and worldwide video, 1987-93; pres. 20th Century Fox, 1993—. Office: 20th Century Fox PO Box 900 Beverly Hills CA 90213*

MECHEM, CHARLES STANLEY, JR., former broadcasting executive, golf association executive; b. Nelsonville, Ohio, Sept. 12, 1930; s. Charles Stanley and Helen (Hall) M.; m. Marilyn Brown, Aug. 31, 1952; children: Melissa, Daniel, Allison. A.B., Miami U., Oxford, Ohio, 1952; LL.B., Yale U., 1955. Bar: Ohio 1955. Practice in Cin., 1955-67; partner Taft, Stettinius

& Hollister, 1965-67; chmn. bd. Taft Broadcasting Co. (now named Gt. American Broadcasting Co.), Cin., 1967-90; now commr. LPGA, Daytona, Fla.; dir. Star Bank N.A. Cin., Deutz-Allis Corp., Myers Y. Cooper Co., Eagle Picher Industries. Mead Corp., Ohio Nat. Life Ins. Co., U.S. Shoe Corp., J.M. Smucker Co. Cin. Bus. Com. Served to 1st lt., Judge Adv. Gen. Corps U.S. Army, 1956-59. Mem. Cin. C. of C. (pres. 1977). Club: Commercial (Cin.). Office: LPGA Ste B 2570 W International Speedway Daytona Beach FL 32114*

MECHEM, EDWIN LEARD, judge; b. Alamogordo, N.Mex., July 2, 1912; s. Edwin and Eunice (Leard) M.; Dorothy Heller, Dec. 30, 1932 (dec. 1972); children: Martha M. Vigil, John H., Jesse (dec. 1968), Walter M.; m. Josephine Donavan, May 28, 1976. L.L.B., U. Ark., 1939; L.L.D. (hon.), N.Mex. State U., 1975. Bar: N.Mex. 1939, U.S. Dist. Ct. N.Mex. 1939. Lawyer Las Cruces and Albuquerque, 1939-70; now judge U.S. Dist. Ct. N.Mex., Albuquerque; spl. agt. FBI Dept. Justice, various locations, 1942-45; mem. legislature State of N.Mex., 1947-48, gov., 1951-54, 57-58, 61-62; senator U.S. Govt., Washington, 1963-64. Mem. ABA, N.Mex. Bar Assn., Am. Law Inst. Republican. Methodist. Avocation: travel. Office: US Dist Ct PO Box 97 Albuquerque NM 87103-0097

MECHETTI, FABIO, orchestra conductor; b. Sao Paulo, Brazil, Aug. 27, 1957; came to U.S., 1981; s. Marcello Nicola and Vilma (Correa) M.; m. Aida MAria Itibere Ribeiro da Silva. BA, Sao Paulo U., 1981; MusM, Julliard Sch., 1985. Asst. condr. Sao Paulo Opera Theatre, 1979-81, Spokane (Wash.) Symphony Orch., 1984-85; assoc. condr. Nat. Symphony Orch., Washington, 1985—; resident condr. San Diego Symphony Orch., 1987-88; assoc. condr. Syracuse Symphony Orch., 1989-93, music dir., 1993—; music dir. Spokane Symphony, 1993—. Translator: (into Portuguese) The Classical Style, 1989. Decorated Knight of Sao Paulo, 1987; recipient Key to City of San Diego, 1988, Exxon Arts Endowment award Affiliate Artists, 1985-88, 1st place Nicolai Malko Internat. Competition for Young Conductors, 1989. Avocations: reading, writing, stamp collecting. Office: Spokane Symphony Orchestra 621 W Mallon Ste 203 Spokane WA 99201 Office: care Michael Schmidt Artists International 59 E 54th St/Ste 83 New York NY 10022*

MECHLIN, GEORGE FRANCIS, electrical manufacturing company executive; b. Pitts., July 23, 1923; s. George Francis and Ruth (Butler) M.; m. Mary Louise Megaffin, June 25, 1949; children—Thomas Walker, Ann Louise. B.S. in Physics, U. Pitts., 1944, M.S. in Physics, 1949, Ph.D. in Physics, 1951. With Westinghouse Electric Corp., 1949-87; gen. mgr. astronuclear/oceanic div. Westinghouse Electric Corp., Balt., 1971-72, v.p. astronuclear lab., oceanic and marine divs., 1972-73; v.p. R & D Westinghouse Electric Corp., Pitts., 1973-87; pub. svc. cons., 1990—. Past bd. dirs. Buhl Planatarium. Recipient Meritorious Public Service award U.S. Navy, 1961, John J. Montgomery award Nat. Soc. Aerospace Profls. and San Diego Aerospace Mus., 1961; Order of Merit award Westinghouse Electric Corp., 1961. Mem. Am. Phys. Soc., AIAA, Nat. Acad. Engring., Sigma Xi. Home: 960 Via Malibu Aptos CA 95003-5617

MECIMORE, CHARLES DOUGLAS, accounting educator; b. Belmont, N.C., Aug. 20, 1934; s. John Edgar and Hattie (Bolick) M.; m. Barbara Jean Chiddie, June 7, 1959; children: Laura Jean, Charles D. Jr., John Amos. BS, Pfeiffer Coll., 1958; MS, U. N.C., 1962; PhD, U. Ala., 1966. CPA, N.C.; CMA. Asst. prof. U. Ala., Tuscaloosa, 1966-67; assoc. prof. U. Ga., Athens, 1967-71; prof. U. Cin., 1971-79; prof. acctg. Sch. Bus. and Econs., U. N.C., Greensboro, 1980—; head dept. Sch. Bus. and Econs., U. N.C., 1980-89. Served with USAF, 1951-55. Univ. scholar, 1963-66; Haskins and Sells fellow, 1962-64; Beyer bronze medal, 1974. Mem. AICPAs, N.C. Assn. CPAs (Outstanding Educator 1985), Am. Acctg. Assn., Inst. Mgmt. Acctg. Home: 1532 Westridge Rd Greensboro NC 27410-2940 Office: Sch Bus and Econs U NC Greensboro NC 27412

MECKE, THEODORE HART MCCALLA, JR., management consultant; b. Phila., Mar. 6, 1923; s. Theodore Hart McCalla and Genevieve (Loughney) M.; m. Mary E. Flaherty, July 14, 1956; children: William Moyn, Theodore Hart III, John Chetwood, Stephen Campbell. Student, LaSalle U., Phila., 1941, LL.D. (hon.), 1964; D Mgmt. (hon.), Lawrence Technol. U., 1983. Mng. editor Germantown (Pa.) Courier, 1942-43, 46-49; with Ford Motor Co., Dearborn, Mich., 1949-80; gen. pub. rels. mgr. Ford Motor Co., 1957-63, v.p. pub. rels., 1963-69, v.p. pub. affairs group, 1969-80; pres. Econ. Club Detroit, 1980-84, Hartwood Assocs., Detroit, 1984-93; trustee Henry Ford Health Sys., Detroit. Served with AUS, 1943-45. Mem. Mil. Order Loyal Legion, Am. Legion. Roman Catholic. Clubs: Country of Detroit, Detroit, Yondotega. Home: 400 Chalfonte Ave Grosse Pointe MI 48236-2943

MECKEL, PETER TIMOTHY, arts administrator, educator; b. Yankton, S.D., Nov. 28, 1941; s. Myron Eugene and Cynthia Ann (Turnblom) M.; m. Louise Gloria Mudge, Sept. 8, 1962; children: Christina Louise, Christopher Mark; m. Adrienne Dawn Maravich, Dec. 30, 1972; children: Moya Anne, Jon-Peter. Ed. Rockford Coll., Occidental Coll. Founder, gen. dir. Hidden Valley Music Seminars, Carmel Valley, Calif., 1963—, dir. Hidden Valley Opera Ensemble, Masters Festival of Chamber Music, Master Class Series; cons. in field. Mem. Music Educators Nat. Conf. Congregationalist. Office: Hidden Valley Opera Ensemble PO Box 116 Carmel Valley CA 93924-0116

MECKLENBURG, GARY ALAN, hospital executive; m. Lynn Kraemer; children: John, Sarah. BA, Northwestern U., 1968; MBA, U. Chgo., 1970. Adminstrv. resident Presbyn.-St. Luke's Hosp., Chgo., 1969-70, adminstrv. asst., 1970-71, asst. supt., 1971-76, assoc. supt., 1976-77; assoc. supt. U. Wis. Hosps., Madison, 1977-80; adminstr. Stanford U. Hosp. Clinics, Calif.; pres. chief exec. officer St. Joseph's Hosp., Milw., 1980-85; pres., dir. Franciscan Health Care Inc., Milw., 1985; pres., chief exec. officer Northwestern Meml. Hosp., Northwestern Meml. Corp., Chgo., 1985—; preceptor, guest lectr., mem. adv. bd. Kellogg Sch. Mgmt., chgo., 1986—; pres., chief exec. officer, dir. Northwestern Healthcare Network, 1990-92. Recipient Harold M. Coon, M.D. Merit award Wis. Hosp. Assn., 1974. Mem. Am. Hosp. Assn. (sect. met. hosps. 1984-92, chmn. 1991, regional policy bd. #5 1984-85, 87-94, 95—, ho. dels. 1984, 87—, com. med. edn. 1987-90), Ill Hosp. Assn. (bd. dirs. 1988—, chmn. 1994, steering com. coun. teaching hosps. 1985—), U. Chgo. Hosp. Adminstrn. Alumni Assn. (pres. 1985-86), Econ. Club Chgo., Comml. Club Chgo. Office: Northwestern Meml Hosp Superior St & Fairbanks Ct Chicago IL 60611

MECKLER, ALAN MARSHALL, publisher, author; b. N.Y.C., July 25, 1945; s. Herman Louis and Lillian (Brodsky) M.; m. Ellen Laurie Finkelstein, Sept. 10, 1969; children—Naomi, Kate, Caroline, John. B.A., Columbia Coll., 1967; M.A., Columbia U., 1968, Ph.D., 1980. Pres., chmn., CEO Mecklermedia Corp., Westport, Conn., 1970—. Author: The Draft and Its Enemies, 1973; Micropublishing: A History of Scholarly Micropublishing in America, 1938-80, 1982; Complete Guide to Winning Lotteries by Mail, 1985. Served with USAR, 1969-75. Office: 20 Ketchum St Westport CT 06880-5808

MECREDY, JAMES R., management consultant; b. Roanoke, Va., Sept. 24, 1918; s. James Roderick and Rosalie Digges (Miller) M.; m. Alice Chatfield, April 8, 1944; children: Robert Clark, Thomas Randolph, Russell Edwards. BSME, Purdue U., 1941; attended, Case Inst. Tech., 1946-48, Alexander Hamilton Inst., 1941-43. Student engr. Gen. Motors Corp., Anderson, Ind., 1941-43; foundry foreman Delco-Remy-G.M., Bedford, Ind., 1943-45; foundry engr., trouble shooter Nat. Bronze and Aluminum Foundry Co., Cleve., 1945-46; machine designer Motch & Merryweather Machinery Co., Cleve., 1946-47; engr. Cleve. Range Co., 1947-54, chief engr., 1954-71, v.p. ops., 1971-74; mgmt. cons., 1974-75; tchr. shop, math. Delco-Remy Foundary, Bedford, Ind., 1943-44, blue print reading, 1943-44. Author: (manual) Instrn. and Maintenance Manual, 1973, District Boy Scouts, 1959; patentee. Dir., coach swimming Anderson YMCA, 1941-42; coach Little League Baseball, Lakewood, Ohio, 1950; precinct committeeman Rep. Com., 1945-46; chmn. dist. fund raising Boy Scouts Am., 1975, scoutmaster, 1955-77, chmn. protestant com., 1974-94. Recipient Scouting Wood badge, 1964, Silver Beaver award Boy Scouts Am., 1968, Nat. Hornaday award N.Y. Zool. Body, 1977, St. Georges award Cleve. Cath. Diocese, 1982, God and Svc. award Presbyn. Western Res., 1991, Nat. Eagle Scout Scoutmaster award, 1990. Mem. Nat. Assn. Presbyn. Scouters (trustee, deacon 1957-66, regional v.p. 1992—), Kiwanis (pres. 1982-83). Avocations: photography,

travel, camping, canoeing, wood carving. Home: 13425 Cliff Dr Cleveland OH 44107-1401

MEDAK, PETER, film director; b. Budapest, Hungary; arrived in Eng., 1956; came to U.S., 1979; s. Gyula and Elisabeth (Diamonstein) M.; m. Julia Migenes, July 31, 1989; children: Christopher, Karen, Joshua, Cornelia, Martina, Jessica. Dir. (films) Negatives, 1968, A Day in the Death of Joe Egg, 1970, The Ruling Class, 1971, Ghost in a Nonnday's Sun, 1973, The Odd Job, 1977, The Changling, 1979, Zorro the Gay Blade, 1980, The Men's Club, 1986, The Krays, 1989, La Voix Humane, 1990, Let Him Have It, 1991, Romeo is Bleeding, 1992, Pontiac Moon, 1994, (stage) Miss Julie, 1977 (opera) Salome, 1988, La Voix Humane, and others. Mem. Dir.'s Guild of Am., Dir.'s Guild of U.K., Assn. of Cinematographers, Allied Technicians, Dir.'s Guild of Can. Jewish. Office: Fred Actman & Co 9255 W Sunset Blvd Ste 901 Los Angeles CA 90069-3306

MEDALIE, RICHARD JAMES, lawyer; b. Duluth, Minn., July 21, 1929; s. William Louis and Mona (Kolad) M.; m. Susan Diane Abrams, June 5, 1960; children: Samuel David, Daniel Alexander. B.A. summa cum laude, U. Minn., 1952; cert., U. London, 1953; A.M., Harvard U., 1955, J.D. cum laude, 1958. Bar: D.C. 1958, N.Y. 1963. Law clk. to Hon. George T. Washington U.S. Ct. Appeals, Washington, 1958-59; asst. solicitor gen. U.S., 1960-62; assoc. Kaye, Scholer, Fierman, Hays & Handler, N.Y.C., 1962-65; dep. dir. Ford Found. Inst. Criminal Law and Procedure, Georgetown U. Law Ctr., 1965-68; ptnr. Friedman & Medalie and Predecessors, Washington, 1968-88, 94—, Medalie & Ferry, Washington, 1988-94; exec. dir. The Appleseed Found., Washington, 1993-94, chmn. bd., 1993—; adj. prof. adminstrv. and criminal law Georgetown U. Law Center, 1967-70; Mem. D.C. Law Revision Commn., 1975-87, chmn. Criminal Law Task Force, mem. exec. com., 1978-82; panel comml. arbitrators Am. Arbitration Assn., 1964—; vice chmn. Harvard Law Sch. Fund, 1981-84, chmn. nat. maj. gifts, 1984-86, dep. chmn., 1986-87, chmn. 1987-89. Author: From Escobedo to Miranda: The Anatomy of a Supreme Court Decision, 1966; co-author: Federal Consumer Safety Legislation, 1970; co-author, editor: Commercial Arbitration for the 1990s, 1991; co-editor: Crime: A Community Responds, 1967; staff: Harvard Law Rev., 1956-58; case editor, 1957-58; contbr. articles to legal jours. Bd. dirs. alumni assn. Expt. in Internat. Living, Brattleboro, Vt., 1961-64, pres., 1962-63. Fulbright scholar, 1952-53; Ford fellow, 1954-55. Mem. ABA (program chair 1984, 90, chair legis. subcom. 1986-89, ADR/arbitration com., vice chair 1991-94, arbitration com. litigation sect.), D.C. Unified Bar, Assn. Bar City N.Y., Am. Law Inst., Harvard Law Sch. Assn. D.C. (pres. 1976-77, nat. v.p 1977-78), Harvard Alumni Assn. (law sch. del. 1991-95), Harvard Club of D.C. (v.p. 1979-82), Cosmos Club, Harvard Club of N.Y.C., Phi Beta Kappa, Phi Alpha Theta. Home: 3113 Macomb St NW Washington DC 20008-3325 Office: 1901 Pennsylvania Ave NW Washington DC 20006-3405

MEDANI, CHARLES RICHARD, pediatric nephrology educator; b. Jersey City, Feb. 11, 1949; s. Renato Eugene and Helen (Peterson) M.; m. Helen E. Walker; children: Jessica, Daniel. BS with honors, U. Md., 1971, MD, 1975; MBA, U. Balt., 1990. Diplomate Am. Bd. Pediatrics, Am. Bd. Pediatric Nephrology. Resident in pediatrics U. Conn., Farmington, 1975-77; fellow in pediatric nephrology Georgetown U., Washington, 1977-79; asst. prof. pediatrics, dir. pediatric nephrology U. Md. Sch. Medicine, Balt., 1979-90; dir. pediatric nephrology, assoc. chmn. pediatrics Sinai Hosp., Balt., 1990—; team physician for men's and women's judo world championships, 1987; judo color commentator Goodwill Games Moscow, 1986. Contbr. articles on nephrology to profl. jours. Chmn. Nat. Masters Judo Program, 1981-94. Named Nat. men's throwing Kata champion, 1988-90, 93. Mem. Internat. Soc. Nephrology, Internat. Paediatric Nephrology Soc., Am. Soc. Pediatric Nephrology, Am. Soc. Nephrology, Md. Judo (pres. 1980-86), Sigma Iota Epsilon, Beta Gamma Sigma. Office: Sinai Hosp Belvedere Ave Baltimore MD 21215-5202

MEDAVOY, MIKE, motion picture company executive; b. Shanghai, China, Jan. 21, 1941; came to U.S., 1957, naturalized, 1962; s. Michael and Dora Medavoy; 1 child, Brian. B.A., UCLA, 1963. With Casting dept. Universal Studios, 1963; agt. Bill Robinson Assos., Los Angeles, 1963-64; v.p. motion picture dept. GAC/CMA Co., 1965-71, IFA Co., 1971-74; sr. v.p. United Artists Corp., 1974-78; one of founders, exec. v.p. Orion Pictures Co., Burbank, Calif., 1978-82; exec. v.p. Orion Pictures Corp. (formerly Orion Pictures Co.), Burbank, Calif., 1982-90; chmn. Tri-Star Pictures, Inc., Burbank, 1990—; bd. dirs. Sony Pictures Corp. Mem. vis. com. Boston Museum Fine Arts.; chmn. Ctr. Internat. Strategic Affairs , UCLA, Com. to Cure Cancer through Immunization UCLA; co-chmn. Olympic Sports Fedn. Com., Music Ctr. Unified Fund Campaign; bd. govs. Sundance Inst., 1980-86; bd. dirs. Calif. Mus. Sci. and Industry, 1984-87. Recipient Academy award for One Flew Over the Cuckoo's Nest, Rocky, Annie Hall, Amadeus, Platoon, Dances With Wolves, Silence of the Lamb. Mem. Acad. Motion Picture Arts and Scis. (gov. 1977-81), UCLA Found., UCLA Chancellors Assocs.

MEDDLETON, DANIEL JOSEPH, health facility administrator; b. July 11, 1936. AA in Bus. Adminstrn., Broome Tech. Community Coll., Binghamton, N.Y., 1959; BSBA, Mich. Technol. U., 1964; M in Health Care Adminstrn., Univ. Minn., 1966. Asst. adminstr. Univ. Cin. Med. Ctr., 1968-70; assoc. adminstr. Providence Hosp., Anchorage, Alaska, 1970-76; exec. v.p. Benedictine Hosp., Kingston, N.Y., 1976-82; dir. Div. Planning, Policy and Prog. Evaluation State of Alaska/Dept. Health and Social Svcs., 1983-84; owner Kits Cameras, Juneau, Alaska, 1984-90; adminstr. Juneau Pioneers' Home, 1988-93, Alaska Psychiat. Hosp., 1993—. Bd. dirs. Alaska Econ. Devel. Adv. Coun.; steering coun. Southeast Alaska Regional Econ. Devel. Inst., 1987; bd. dirs. Big Bros./Big Sisters, others. Fellow Am. Coll. Health Care Execs.; mem. No. N.Y. Met. Hosp. Assn. (past bd. dirs.), Mid Hudson Health Systems Agy. (past bd. dirs.), Rotary, others. Avocations: outdoor sports, photography, camping, backpacking, sailing, flying. Home: 3820 Resurrection Dr Anchorage AK 99504

MEDEARIS, DONALD NORMAN, JR., physician, educator; b. Kansas City, Kans., Aug. 22, 1927; s. Donald Norman and Gladys (Sandford) M.; m. Mary Ellen Marble, Aug. 25, 1956; children: Donald Harrison, Ellen Sandford, John Norman, Jennifer Marble. A.B., U. Kans., 1950; M.D., Harvard U., 1953. Diplomate: Am. Bd. Pediatrics. Intern internal medicine Barnes Hosp., St. Louis, 1953-54; resident pediatrics Children's Hosp., Cin., 1954-56; rsch. fellow pediatrics Harvard U. rsch. div. infectious diseases Children's Med. Ctr., Boston, 1956-58; from asst. to assoc. prof. pediatrics and microbiology Johns Hopkins Sch. Medicine, Balt., 1959-65; Joseph P. Kennedy Jr. Meml. Found. Sr. Rsch. Scholar in Mental Retardation, 1960-65; prof. pediatrics U. Pitts. Sch. Medicine, 1965-74, chmn. dept., 1965-69, dean, 1969-74; med. dir. Children's Hosp., Pitts., 1965-69; prof. pediatrics Case Western Res. U., Cleve., 1974-77; dir. pediatrics Cleve. Met. Gen. Hosp., 1974-77; Charles Wilder prof. pediatrics Harvard U. Med. Sch., 1977—; chief Children's Svc. Mass. Gen. Hosp., Boston, 1977—; mem. Pres.'s Commn. on Study Ethical Problems in Medicine and Biomed. and Behavioral Rsch., 1979-82. Contbr. articles to profl. jours., texts. Vestry Trinity Ch., Boston, 1983-87. Served with USNR, 1945-46. Mem. Am. Acad. Pediatrics, Am. Pediatric Soc., Infectious Disease Soc. Am., Inst. Medicine/Nat. Acad. Scis., Alpha Omega Alpha. Office: Massachusetts Gen Hosp Fruit St Boston MA 02114

MEDEARIS, KENNETH GORDON, research consultant, educator; b. Peoria, Ill., Aug. 5, 1930; s. Harold Oscar and Ferol Mae (Rowlett) M.; m. Mary Genevieve Barlow, June 28, 1953; children—Mark Allen, Mary Lynne, Terry Gordon. B.S., U. Ill., 1952, M.S., 1953; Ph.D., Stanford U., 1962. Registered profl. engr., Calif., Colo., N.Mex., Pa. Stress analyst Sandia Corp., Albuquerque, 1957-58; asst. prof. civil engring., U. N.Mex., 1958-62; assoc. prof. engring Ariz. State U., 1962-63; engr., computer cons., Sunnyvale, Calif., 1963-66; dir. Computer Ctr., prof. civil engring. Colo. State U., Ft. Collins, 1966-69, adj. prof. civil and mech. engring., 1969—; lectr. N.Mex. State U., 1982—; cons. Kenneth Medearis Assoc., Ft. Collins, 1969—; research and vibration engring. cons., Ft. Collins, 1969—; evaluation cons. UN. Author: Numerical-Computer Methods for Engineers and Physical Scientists, 1974. Contbr. articles to profl. jours. Mem. Stanford Regional Cabinet. Served to 1st lt. USAF, 1953-56. Recipient Outstanding Engring. Achievement award No. Colo. Profl. Engrs., 1974, Outstanding Engring. Achievement award Profl. Engrs. Colo., 1974, Disting. Engring. Alumnus award U. Ill., 1988. Mem. Colo. Earthquake Research Soc. (v.p.),

Univs. Council for Earthquake Engring., Internat. Orgn. for Standardization, UN Tech. Evaluation Team, ASCE, Seismol. Soc. Am., Larimer County Computer Soc. (chmn. 1974—), Aircraft Owners and Pilots Assn., Sigma Xi, Phi Sigma Kappa, Chi Epsilon, Sigma Tau, Tau Beta Pi. Methodist. Lodge: Rotary. Home: 1901 Seminole Dr Fort Collins CO 80525-1537 Office: 1413 S College Ave Fort Collins CO 80524-4115

MEDEARIS, ROGER NORMAN, artist; b. Fayette, Mo., Mar. 6, 1920; s. Thomas Whittier and Mara (Miller) M.; m. Elizabeth Burrall Sterling, Jan. 16, 1976; 1 son, Thomas Whittier, III. Pupil of, Thomas Hart Benton, 1938-41. One-man exhbns. include Kende Galleries, N.Y.C., 1949, 50, Capricorn Galleries, Bethesda, Md., 1971, 78, 81, 84, 94; group exhbns. include AAA Galleries, Met. Mus. Art, NAD, N.Y.C., Carnegie Mellon U., Pitts., Butler Inst. Am. Art, Youngstown, Ohio, Albrecht-Kemper Mus. Art, St. Joseph, Mo., Spencer Mus. Art, Lawrence, Kans., many others; represented in numerous pvt. and public collections, including, D.C. Mcpl. Ct., Nat. Mus. Am. Art, Washington, Nelson-Atkins Mus. Art, Kansas City, Butler Inst. Am. Art, Hunt Inst., Pitts., Albrecht-Kemper Art Mus., St. Joseph, Mo.; commd. by Nat. Recreation & Park Assn., 1982, Print Club Albany, 1994; work reviewed in various articles, monographs; subject of various art books. With USN Dept., 1942-45, AUS, 1945-46. Address: 2270 Melville Dr San Marino CA 91108

MEDENICA, GORDON, corporate planner; b. Darmstadt, Fed. Republic Germany, Oct. 26, 1951; came to U.S., 1952; s. Walter Vojislav and Heidi Hedwig (Knoerzer) M.; m. Ann Margaret Connolly, Jan. 2, 1982; children: Madeline, Candice. AB, Harvard U., 1973, MBA, 1979. Staff acct. Meahl, McNamara & Co., Boston, 1973-74; exec. dir. BMW Car Club Am., Cambridge, Mass., 1974-77; analyst corp. planning Marriott Corp., Washington, 1979-80, sr. analyst hotel planning, 1981-82; sr. analyst strategic planning N.Y. Times Co., N.Y.C., 1982-83; project mgr. strategic planning, 1984, mgr. strategic planning and corp. devel., 1984-86, dir. planning, 1986-90; v.p. corp. planning, 1990-93, v.p. ops. and planning, 1993—. Office: The New York Times Co 229 W 43rd St New York NY 10036-3913

MEDERO, JOANNE TRIMBLE, lawyer; b. Plainfield, N.J., July 14, 1954; d. David Wills and Gail (Woodhull) Trimble; m. Frederick R. Medero, Jan. 2, 1988. BA magna cum laude, St. Lawrence U., 1975; JD with honors, George Washington U., 1978. Bar: D.C. 1978. Assoc. Hamel and Park, Washington, 1978-81; asst. gen. counsel Student Loan Mktg. Assn., Washington, 1981-83; assoc. ptnr. Phillips, King, Smith, Wright and Levi, Washington, 1983-86; from dep. assoc. dir. to assoc. dir. presdl. personnel The White House, Washington, 1986-89; gen. counsel Commodity Futures Trading Commn., Washington, 1989—; co=founder Fin. Innovation Study Com., Washington, 1991—. Mem. Federalist Soc., Fed. Bar Assn. (chair gen. counsels com. 1991-92), Rep. Nat. Lawyers Assn., Am. Assn. Fin. Engrs., Phi Beta Kappa. Republican. Protestant. Office: Commodity Futures Trading Commn 2033 K St NW Washington DC 20581-0002

MEDEROS, CAROLINA LUISA, transportation policy consultant; b. Rochester, Minn., July 1, 1947; d. Luis O. and Carolina (del Valle) M. BA, Vanderbilt U., 1969; MA, U. Chgo., 1971. Adminstrv. asst. Lt. Gov. of Ill., Chgo., 1972; sr. research assoc. U. Chgo., 1972; project mgr., cons. Urban Dynamics, Inner City Fund and Community Programs Inc., Chgo., 1972-73; legis. asst. to Senate pres. Ill. State Senate, Chgo. and Springfield, 1973-76; program analyst Dept. Transp., Washington, 1976-79, chief, trans. assistance programs div., 1979-81, dir. programs and evaluation, 1981-84, chairwoman, sec.'s safety rev. task force, 1985-88; deputy asst. sec. for safety Dept. Transp., 1988-89; cons. Patton Boggs LLP, Washington, 1990—. Recipient award for Meritorious Achievement, Sec. Transp. 1980, Superior Achievement award U.S. Dept. Transp., 1981, Sec.'s Gold Medal Award for Outstanding Achievement, 1986, Presdl. Rank award, 1987. Mem. Womens Transp. Seminar, Coun. for Excellence in Govt. Home: 2723 O St NW Washington DC 20007-3128 Office: Patton Boggs LLP 2550 M St NW Washington DC 20037-1301

MEDFORD, DALE LEON, industrial company executive; b. Dayton, Ohio, May 24, 1950; s. Forest L. and Gertrude M. (Rismiller) M.; m. Karen L. Blair, June 12, 1971; children: Bethany, Kristina. BS in Acctg., Miami U., Oxford, Ohio, 1972. Treas. Reyna Fin. Corp., Dayton, 1981-86, pres., chief exec. officer, 1983-86; treas., asst. sec. The Reynolds and Reynolds Co., Dayton, 1979-81, v.p., treas., 1981-85, v.p. corp. fin., treas., 1985-86, v.p. corp. fin., chief fin. officer, 1986—. Pres. Dayton Opera Assn., 1986-88, trustee, 1986—; trustee Dayton Performing Arts Fund, 1986-88; bd. dirs. Dayton da Vinci, 1987—. Mem. AICPA, Fin. Execs. Inst. (pres., dir. Dayton chpt. 1988—, officer, bd. dirs. 1984—). Lutheran. Avocations: boating, golf. Office: Reynolds & Reynolds Co 115 S Ludlow St Dayton OH 45402-1812

MEDFORD-ROSOW, TRACI, lawyer; b. Alexandria, Va., June 6, 1955; d. Charles Eugene and Jean (Tully) M.; m. Joel Rosow, Aug. 12, 1978; children: Chad, Kyra. BS, Va. Poly. Inst. and State U., 1977; JD, Bklyn. Law Sch., 1980; LLM, NYU, 1984. Bar: N.Y. 1981, D.C. 1981. Atty. Pfizer Inc., N.Y.C., 1980-81, mgr. health care, 1981-84, corp. counsel Europe, 1984-86; corp. counsel Internat. Patent Litigation, N.Y.C., 1987—. Named to People to Watch list Fortune Mag., N.Y.C., 1986. Mem. ABA, N.Y. Bar Assn., D.C. Bar Assn., Phi Beta Kappa. Episcopalian. Avocation: chess. Home: 2 Candlewood Ct Scarsdale NY 10583-3228 Office: Pfizer Inc 235 E 42d St New York NY 10017

MEDICUS, HEINRICH ADOLF, physicist, educator; b. Zurich, Switzerland, Dec. 24, 1918; came to U.S., 1950; s. Friedrich Georg and Clara Anna (Frey) M.; m. Hildegard Julie Schmelz, June 15, 1961. Dipl. Naturwiss., Swiss Fed. Inst. Tech., Zurich, 1943, Dr.sc.nat., 1949. Research assoc. Swiss Fed. Inst. Tech., 1943-50; visitor Lawrence Berkeley Lab., Calif., 1950-51, MIT, Cambridge, 1951-52; instr., then vis. asst. prof. MIT, 1952-55; assoc. prof. Rensselaer Poly. Inst., Troy, N.Y., 1955-72, prof., 1972-86, prof. emeritus, 1987—; vis. scientist Atomic Energy Research Establishment Harwell, Eng., 1967-68, Swiss Inst. Nuclear Research, Villigen, 1974-75. Co-author: Fields and Particles, 1973; contbr. articles on physics, history of physics and enology. Pres. Hudson-Mohawk Swiss Soc., Albany, N.Y., 1974—. Served to lt. arty. Swiss Army, 1937-50. Fellow, Swiss Found., 1950-52. Mem. Am. Phys. Soc., Swiss Phys. Soc., Hist. of Sci. Soc., Swiss Am. Hist.Soc., Soc. Wine Educators, Société des Vignerons, Delta Tau Delta (pres. house corp. of Upsilon chpt. 1984-91, faculty advisor 1991-95). Presbyterian. Club: Swiss Alpine (Zurich). Avocations: wine education, internat. student exchange programs. Home: 1 The Knoll East Acres Troy NY 12180 Office: Rensselaer Poly Inst Dept Physics Troy NY 12180

MEDIN, A. LOUIS, computer company executive; b. Balt., Oct. 2, 1925; s. Nathan and Bessie (Zell) M.; B.E. in Chem. Engring., Johns Hopkins U., 1948; Ph.D. in Chem. Engring., Ohio State U., 1951; m. Julia A. Levin, Dec. 24, 1950; children—Douglas, David, Thomas, Linda. Registered profl. engr., Md. Chem. engr. AEC, Wilmington, Del., 1951-53; research engr. Ford Motor Co., Dearborn, Mich., 1953-55; chief chem. nuclear reactor tech. ALCO Products, Schenectady, 1955-58; head nuclear research engr. U.S. Steel, Monroeville, Pa., 1958-63; project mgr. missile design AVCO Corp., Wilmington, Mass., 1963-65; mgr. sci. applications IBM, Manassas, Va., 1965-72, mgr. advanced applications, 1975-87; exec. dir. Inst. for Simulation and Tng., Orlando, Fla., 1987—; chmn. symposia on def. research and devel.; asst. dir. environment and life scis. Dept. Def., 1972-74; lectr. in field. Contbr. articles to profl. and tech. jours. Mem. Monroeville Parks and Recreation Commn., 1960; chmn. Monroeville Mental Health Assn., 1961; mem. Monroeville Zoning and Planning Commn., 1961; dep. precinct chmn. Montgomery County Rep. Com., 1982. Served with USN, 1944-46, PTO. Recipient award Am. Chem. Soc., 1957. Fellow Am. Inst. Chemists; mem. Nat. Security Indsl. Assn., Am. Inst. Chem. Engrs., Am. Def. Preparedness Assn. (chmn. sci. and engring. tech. div. 1981-90, editorial advisor Def. Jour., Am. Def. award 1984, Gold medal 1990), Am. Metall. Soc., Johns Hopkins's U. Alumni Assn., Ohio State U. Alumni Assn. Home: 714 Bear Creek Cir Casselberry FL 32708-3857

MEDIN, JULIA ADELE, mathematics educator, researcher; b. Dayton, Ohio, Jan. 16, 1929; d. Caroline (Feinberg) Levitt; m. A. Louis Medin, Dec. 24, 1950; children: Douglas, David, Thomas, Linda. BS in Maths. Edn., Ohio State U., 1951; MA in Higher Edn., George Washington U., 1977; PhD

in Counseling and Edn., Am. U., 1985. Cert. tchr., Fla., Md. Rsch. engr. Sun Oil Co., Marcus Hook, Pa., 1951-53; tchr. maths. Montgomery County Pub. Schs., Rockville, Md., 1973-88; asst. prof. maths. U. Ctrl. Fla., Orlando, 1988-90, sr. ednl. technologist Inst. for Simulation and Tng., 1990—; mem. adv. steering com. U.S. Dept. Edn. Title II, Washington, 1985-89; sr. math. educator, rschr. Inst. for Simulation & Tng., Orlando, 1988—. Author: Loc. of Cont. & Test Anxiety of Mar. Math. Studies, 1985; contbg. author: Math for 14 & 17 Yr. Olds, 1987; contbr. articles to profl. jours. Dem. committeewoman Town of Monroeville, Pa., 1962; religious sch. dir. Beth Tikva Religious Sch., Rockville, 1971; cons. Monroeville Mental Health, 1960. Mem. Nat. Coun. Tchrs. of Math., Maths. Assn. Am. (task force on minorities in math.), Women and Maths. in Edn., Sch. Sci. and Maths. Assn., Assn. Tchr. Educators, Phi Delta Kappa, Kappa Delta Pi, NCTM, PME. Home: 714 Bear Creek Cir Casselberry FL 32708-3857 Office: U Ctrl Fla Inst for Simulation and Tng 3280 Progress Dr Orlando FL 32826-0544

MEDIN, LOWELL ANSGARD, security company executive; b. Shafer Twp., Minn., Aug. 28, 1932; s. Ansgaard Phillip Magnus and Adelaide Marie Christine (Grandstrand) M.; m. Frances Irene Knutson, Sept. 13, 1958; children: Kimberly June, James Lowell. AS in Liberal Arts, U. Minn., 1957, BBA, 1959. Dairy farmer Medin Farm, Franconia Twp., 1951-53; silo builder Lindstrom Silo, 1956-58; employment mgr. John Wood Co., St. Paul, 1959; salesperson Diversey Co., LaCrosse, Wis., 1959-60; rebuyer, inventory mgr. Montgomery Ward, St. Paul, 1960-67; rebuyer, rebuyer mgr. Montgomery Ward, Chgo., 1967-85; with sales dept. J.T. Gen. Store, Palatine, Ill., 1986; rebuying mgr. Sportsmen's Guide, Golden Valley, Minn., 1987; inventory mgr. Donald Bruce and Co., Chgo., 1988-91; supr. Pinkerton Security Ops., 1992. Author: (with others) Shafer Swamp to Chisago City, 1989, The Pioneers of Chisago County 1838-1870, 1992, The Knutson/Stavenau Family Roots, 1994. Candidate for polit. office, Mpls., 1967; del. Minn. State Dem.-Farm Labor Conv., 1956, 58; chmn. cancer drive Village of Palatine, 1968, mem. dist. 6 adv. coun., 1989—; mem. Homeowners Coun., Palatine, 1976-77; mem. coun. Christ Luth. Ch., Palatine, 1981-86; officer Chicago County DFL Party, 1956-60; del. Chicago County DFL Conv., 1956, 58; pres. Palonis Park Homeowners assn., Palatine, 1976-82. Cpl. U.S. Army, 1953-55, ETO. Mem. Nat. Ill. Civil War Roundtable (chartered officer 1983-86, trustee, sec., 2d v.p.), VFW (life, post 981, Arlington Hts.), Am. Legion (life, post 690, Palatine), Alpha Phi Omega. Republican. Lutheran. Avocations: genealogy, gardening, Am. history, Civil War period. Home: 121 S Linden Ave Palatine IL 60067-6342

MEDIN, MYRON JAMES, JR., city manager; b. Ladysmith, Wis., July 8, 1931; s. Myron James and Mildred Clara (Johnson) M.; m. Alice Louise Moholt, May 14, 1955; children: John, Karen, Anne. BA, St. Olaf Coll., 1954; MPA, U. Mich., 1959. Adminstrv. asst. to city mgr. City of Fond du Lac, Wis., 1959-64, city mgr., 1967-83; city mgr. City of New Ulm, Minn., 1964-67; city adminstr. City of Kansas City, 1983-85; pres., gen. mgr. Bella Vista Village Property Owners Assn., Ark., 1986-92; mem. com. human devel. Nat. League of Cities, Washington, 1974-80, com. on govtl. relations, 1971-73; chmn. City Plan Commn., Fond du Lac, Wis., 1967-83. Bd. dirs. United Way, Kansas City, Kans., 1984-85, YMCA, 1984-85, Kansas City Community Coll. Found., Kansas City, 1984-85; mem. Gov.'s Regionalism Task Force Adv. Com., Madison, Wis., 1968-70; trustee Phillips Pro-Celebrity Golf Tennis Charity Classic, 1991-92. Lt. USAF, 1955-57. Recipient Community Service award Fond du Lac Assn. of Commerce, 1978. Mem. Internat. City Mgmt. Assn., Wis. City Mgmt. Assn. (pres. 1975-76), Wis. League of Municipalities (bd. dirs. 1978-80), Wis. Alliance of Cities (v.p. 1972-73), Am. Soc. Pub. Adminstrn. (bd. dirs. 1984-85, Pub. Adminstr. of Yr. award 1985), Bella Vista-Bentonville C. of C. (bd. dirs. 1987-91), Nat. Trust for Hist. Preservation. Lutheran. Avocations: swimming, reading, tennis, gardening, genealogy. Home: 1 Audley Cir Bella Vista AR 72714-5645

MEDINA, JOSE ENRIQUE, dentist, educator; b. Santurce, P.R., May 1, 1926; s. Jose Wilfredo and Genoveva (de la Baume) M.; m. Betty Lee Mansfield, June 5, 1948 (dec. Feb. 1975); children—Elizabeth Lee, Jose Enrique, Virginia Genoveva; m. Patricia Fay Pachler, Dec. 26, 1975. Student, Johns Hopkins, 1942-44; D.D.S., U. Md., 1948. Instr. Berlitz Sch. Langs., 1944-48; instr. operative dentistry dept. U. Md. Sch. Dentistry, 1948-50, asst. prof., 1950-52, asso. prof., 1952-57, prof., head, 1957-66, asst. dean, 1964-67; prof. clin. dentistry, assoc. dean Coll. Dentistry, U. Fla., Gainesville, 1967-69; prof. clin. dentistry Coll. Dentistry, U. Fla., 1969—, dean, 1969-74, dir. health center planning and utilization, 1974-76; v.p. for facilities planning and ops. J. Hillis Miller Health Center, 1976-86; Cons. USPHS, U.S. Naval Dental Sch., Bethesda, VA Hosp., Gainesville, Miami; Pres. So. Conf. Dental Deans and Examiners, 1973; mem. nat. adv. dental research council Nat. Inst. Dental Research, NIH, 1973-76; charter mem. Am. Bd. Operative Dentistry, pres., 1980-87; mentor George M. Hollenback Operative Dentistry Sem. Group, 1961—, N.H. Gold Foil Study Group, 1987—. Pres. Sunnybrook (Md.) Community Assn., 1963-65. Served with USNR, 1944-46. Decorated Knight Comdr., Order of Bernardo O'Higgins (Chile), 1991; recipient Disting. Alumnus award R.I. Alumni Assn. U. Md., 1965, U. Md. Sch. Dentistry Alumni Assn., 1985, Disting. Faculty award U. Fla. Blue Key, 1986, Tchr. of Yr. award U. Fla., 1987, Outstanding Clinician of Yr. award, 1987, 92, Andres Cendan Dentist of Yr. award Dade Dental Study Group, 1990; named to Hall of Fame, U. Md. Alumni Assn. , 1990, hon. prof. U. De San Carlos, Guatemala, 1960—. Fellow Internat. Coll. Dentists (trustee found. 1993—, dep. regent Fla. sect. 1988-91, regent dist 5 USA sect. 1992—), AADS, Acad. Gen. Dentistry (hon.), Acad. Dentistry Internat.; mem. ADA, Fla. Dental Assn. (Disting. Svc. award 1978), Am. Acad. Gold Foil Operators (editor 1958-63, pres. 1965, Disting. Mem. award 1986), Am. Coll. Dentists (Disting. Faculty award 1989, chmn. Fla. sect. 1992-93, William J. Gies award 1990), Internat. Assn. Dental Rsch., Acad. Operative Dentistry (charter, George Hollenback meml. prize 1985, trustee Acad. Found., 1986—, v.p. 1989, pres. elect 1990, pres. 1991), Am. Acad. Restorative Dentistry, Health Edn. Media Assn. (dir.), Royal Soc. Health, N.Y. Acad. Sci., Am. Acad. Oral Medicine (hon.), Fla. Acad. Dental Practice Adminstrn. (hon.), Guatemala Dental Soc. (hon.), Chile Dental Assn. (hon.), Optimists Club (Md.), Masons, Kiwanis, Omicron Kappa Upsilon. Home: 5002 NW 18th Pl Gainesville FL 32605-3430

MEDINA, KATHRYN BACH, book editor; b. Plainfield, N.J.; d. F. Earl and Elizabeth E. Bach; m. Standish F. Medina Jr.; 1 child, Nathaniel Forde. B.A., Smith Coll. Various editorial positions Doubleday Pub. Co., Inc., N.Y.C., 1965-85; exec. editor, v.p. Random House, N.Y.C., 1985—; assoc. fellow Jonathan Edwards Coll., Yale U., New Haven, 1982—. Editor books by James Atlas, Peter Benchley, Anita Brookner, Ethan Canin, Agnes deMille, Mary Gordon, James A. Michener, Anna Quindlen, Nancy Reagan, James Reston, William Safire, Maggie Scarf, Hedrick Smith, Daniel Yergin, others.

MEDINA, STANDISH FORDE, JR., lawyer; b. Orange, N.J., June 16, 1940; s. Standish F. and Hope Tyler (Kiesewetter) M.; m. Kathryn L. Bach, Apr. 20, 1968; 1 child, Nathaniel Forde. A.B. cum laude, Princeton U., 1962; LL.B. magna cum laude, Columbia U., 1965. LL.M., 1966. Bar: N.Y. 1965, U.S. Supreme Ct. 1970, U.S. Dist. Ct. (so. dist., ea. dist.) N.Y., U.S. Ct. Appeals (2d, 3d, 4th, 5th, 7th, 11th, D.C. cirs.). Assoc. in law Columbia Law Sch., 1965-66; lectr. Columbia Law Sch., N.Y.C., 1992; instr. law orientation program in Am. law Princeton U., summer 1991; assoc. Debevoise & Plimpton, N.Y.C., 1966-72, ptnr., 1973—. Author: Reflections Below, 1991. Trustee The Hill Sch., Pottstown, Pa., 1976-91, St. Bernard's Sch., N.Y.C., 1992—, Episc. Sch., N.Y.C., 1988-93. Fellow Am. Coll. of Trial Lawyers; mem. ABA (vice-chmn. com. on fed. cts., litigation sect. 1981-82, co-chmn. com. pleadings motions and pretrial 1986-87), Fed. Bar Coun., N.Y. State Bar Assn., Assn. of Bar of City of N.Y. (mem. exec. com. 1982-86, chmn. membership com. 1986-90, chmn. com. fed. cts. 1978-81, mem. judiciary com. 1978-81, mem. nominating com. 1986-87, mem. com. on ct. requirements 1978-81, mem. fed. legis. com. 1971-75), Am. Law Inst., 2d Cir. Com. on Improvement Civil Litigation (chmn. 1986-90), Legal Aid Soc. (chmn. assoc. and young lawyers com. 1972). Office: Debevoise & Plimpton 875 3rd Ave New York NY 10022-6225

MEDITCH, JAMES STEPHEN, electrical engineering educator; b. Indpls., July 30, 1934; s. Vladimir Stephen and Alexandra (Gogeff) M.; m. Theresa Claire Scott, Apr. 4, 1964; children: James Stephen Jr., Sandra Anne. BSEE,

Purdue U., 1956, PhD, 1961; SM, MIT, 1957. Staff engr. Aerospace Corp., Los Angeles, 1961-65; assoc. prof. elec. engring. Northwestern U., 1965-67; mem. tech. staff Boeing Sci. Research Labs., Seattle, 1967-70; prof. U. Calif., Irvine, 1970-77; prof. U. Wash., Seattle, 1977—, chmn. dept. elec. engring., 1977-85, assoc. dean engring., 1987-90. Author: Stochastic Optimal Linear Estimation and Control, 1969; co-editor: Computer Communication Networks, 1984. Fellow IEEE (Disting. mem. control systems soc., 1983, editor Proceedings 1983-85, Centennial medal 1984). Office: U Wash Dept Elec Engring Ft # 10 Seattle WA 98195

MEDITZ, WALTER JOSEPH, engineering consultant; b. Bklyn., June 4, 1917; s. Joseph and Marie (Gaspar) M.; m. Elizabeth M. Cagney, Jan. 9, 1944; children—Jeannette Jordan, Mary Beth Banks. B.C.E., Bklyn Poly. Inst., 1939, M.M.E., 1941; M.Indsl. Engring., Ga. Inst. Tech., 1951. Research engr., lab. instr. Bklyn. Poly. Inst., 1939-40; civil engr., supt. Spencer, White & Prentice, 1940-41; asst. to design and prodn. mgr. Frederick R. Harris, 1941-43; chief indsl. engr. Naval Aircraft, Norfolk, Va., 1943-46; asst. chief engr. Boyle-Midway, N.Y.C., 1946-47; plant mgr. Boyle-Midway, Atlanta, 1947-51; asst. to pres. Boyle-Midway, N.Y.C., 1951-55, Standard Packaging Corp., N.Y.C., 1955-57; v.p. for mfg. Standard Packaging Corp., 1957-67; mgr. facilities to divisional v.p. Doubleday & Co., Inc., Garden City, N.Y., 1967-83; pres. Meditz Engring. Assocs., 1984—. Served from ensign to lt. (s.g.) USNR, 1943-46. J. Waldo Smith fellow ASCE, 1939; Bklyn. Poly. Inst. fellow, 1939. Mem. Soc. for Advancement Mgmt., Highland Park Club (bd. dirs.), Lake Wales Country Club, Alpha Pi Mu. Home: PO Box 404 Buck Hill Falls PA 18323-0404

MEDLAND, WILLIAM JAMES, college president; b. Logansport, Ind., Jan. 1, 1941; s. Thomas Gallagher and Mary Elizabeth (Hassett) M.; m. Donna Lee Bahnaman, Mar. 12, 1977; 1 child, Mark David. BA, U. Notre Dame, 1966; student, St. Louis U., 1972-74; MA in History, Ball State U., 1967, MA in Edn., 1979, PhD in History, 1980; postgrad., Inst. for Mgmt. Lifelong Edn., Harvard U., 1985, Ctr. Internat. Cooperation and Security Studies, U. Wis., 1988, Ctr. Internat. Studies, MIT, 1989, Freie Universitat, Berlin, 1991. Instr. history and philosophy Donnelly coll., Kansas City, Kans., 1967-70; curricular advisor Ball State U., Muncie, Ind., 1970-71, teaching fellow, 1977-80; asst. dean St. Louis (Mo.) U., 1971-75; employee supr. Wilson, Inc., Logansport, 1975-76; ops. mgr. Watson-Jenkins, Inc., Indpls., 1976-77; dean of coll., asst. prof. history Springfield (Ill.) Coll., 1980-81; acad. dean, assoc. prof. history and edn. Marymount Coll., Salina, Kans., 1981-86; exec. v.p., provost, prof. history St. Mary's Coll., Winona, Minn., 1986-91; pres., prof. history Viterbo Coll., LaCrosse, Wis., 1991—; edn. cons. Am. Inst. Banking, Springfield, 1980-81; advisor Adv. Com. to Sch. Bd., Salina, 1984, Salina Diocesan Bd. Edn., 1981-83; evaluator North Cen. Assn., Chgo., 1987—; mem. steering com. for proposed U. Volga, Dubna, Russia. Author: Cuban Missile Crisis of 1962-Needless or Necessary?, 1988, reprint, 1990, A Guide to Writing College Research Papers, 1989, The Catholic School: A Bibliographical Resource Guide, 1990; editor: Ind. Acad. Social Scis. jour., 1979, Perspectives: A Liberal Arts Exchange (faculty jour.), 1988. Coll. solicitor United Way, St. Louis, 1973; coord. Coll./Comty. Artist Series, Salina, 1981-84; bd. dirs. Immaculate Heart of Mary Sem., Winona, 1987-91; mem. Am. Heart Assn., 1992-93. Fellow Ctr. Internat. Studies, MIT/Harvard U., 1989. Mem. Am. Assn. Higher Edn., Orgn. Am. Historians, Am. Assn. Coll. Press., Am. Assn. Ind. Coll. Press. Wis. Assn. Ind. Colls. and Univs. (bd. dirs.), Wis. Found. for Ind. Colls. (bd. dirs.), Am. Hist. Assn., La Crosse Med. Health Sci. Consortium (bd. dirs.), La Crosse D of C. (co-chair Adm. 2000 com.), K.C., Rotary, Phi Alpha Theta (rsch. award Ball State U. 1979), Phi Delta Kappa. Democrat. Roman Catholic. Avocations: reading, research, hiking, cross-country skiing. Home: 414 29th St S La Crosse WI 54601-6013 Office: Viterbo Coll Office of Pres 815 9th St S La Crosse WI 54601-8802

MEDLEY, ALEX ROY, executive minister; b. Columbus, Ga., Aug. 4, 1948; s. Howard and Clois Mildred (Chumney) M.; m. Patricia Stauffer, May 10, 1975; children: James Ethan, Christopher Jordan. BA magna cum laude, U. Chattanooga, 1970; cert., Grad. Sch. Ecumenical Studies, Celigny, Switzerland, 1973; MDiv, Princeton Sem., 1974. Ordained to ministry Bapt. Ch., 1975. Assoc. pastor First Bapt. Ch. Trenton, N.J., 1974-77; adminstrv. intern Nat. Ministries Am. Bapt. Chs. U.S.A., Valley Forge, Pa., 1977, nat. dir. Christian ctr., 1978-85; min. of world mission support, area min. Am. Bapt. Chs. N.J., East Orange, 1986-92, exec. min., 1992—; intern World Coun. Chs., Geneva, Switzerland, 1973; rep. North American Bapt. Fellowship, Washington, 1975-77; mem. domestic hunger/poverty working group Nat. Coun. Chs. of Christ, 1978-85; conf. speaker Am. Bapt. Chs., 1979. Editor (newsletter) Social Edn. for Action Newsletter, 1978-79. Bd. dirs. Ch. World Svc./CROP, N.J., 1975-77, Occupational Tng. Ctr., Burlington, N.J., 1992; sec. Key Inmate Edn. Project, Trenton, 1986. Mem. Am. Bapt. Regional Exec. Mins. Coun. Avocations: reading, fishing, hiking. Home: 12 Courtland Ln Willingboro NJ 08046-3406 Office: Am Bapt Chs in NJ 161 Freeway Dr E East Orange NJ 07018-4042

MEDLEY, DONALD MATTHIAS, education educator, consultant; b. Faulkton, S.D., Feb. 18, 1917; s. Thomas Arnot and Cecilia Agnes (Kellen) M.; m. Betty Ann Robertsen, Aug. 23, 1948; 1 child, Timothy Laurence. B.S., Coll. St. Thomas, St. Paul, 1938; M.A., U. Minn., 1950, Ph.D., 1954. Tchr., Am. Sch. Guadalajara, Mex., 1941-42, Floodwood Pub. Schs., Minn., 1946-48; instr. English, Coll. St. Thomas, 1948-50; asst. prof. CUNY, 1954-59, assoc. prof., 1959-64, prof., 1964-65; sr. research psychologist Ednl. Testing Service, Princeton, N.J., 1965-70; disting. prof. U. Va., Charlottesville, 1970-87, prof. emeritus, 1987—; mem. exec. bd. Consortium for the Improvement of Tchr. Evaluation, Atlanta, 1985-87. Author: Measurement-Based Evaluation of Teacher Performance, 1984; author: (with others) Handbook of Research on Teaching, 1963, The Teacher's Handbook, 1971, Research on Teaching: Concepts, Findings, and Implications, 1979, Encyclopedia of Educational Research, 5th edit., 1982, 6th edit., 1992, Developing Skills for Instructional Supervision, 1984, Advances in Teacher Education, 1984, International Encyclopedia of Education: Research and Studies, 1984, 2d edit., 1994, Assessment of Teaching: Purposes, Practices, and Implications for the Profession, 1990; contbr. articles to profl. jours. Served as staff sgt. U.S. Army, 1942-46. Fellow Am. Psychol. Assn.; mem. Am. Ednl. Research Assn. (div. sec. 1962), Nat. Council on Measurement in Edn., Assn. Tchr. Educators. Democrat. Roman Catholic. Avocations: conjuring, travel.

MEDLEY, STEVEN PAUL, association executive; b. Palo Alto, Calif., July 11, 1949; s. Robert William and Hermie May (Palmer) M.; m. Jane Rowley, Mar. 12, 1976; children: Charles, Joseph, Andrew. Student, Brown U., 1967-69; BA, Stanford U., 1971; MLS, U. Oreg., 1975; JD, U. Calif., Davis, 1981. Bar: Oreg. 1981. Park ranger, then libr., curator Nat. Park Svc., Yosemite Nat. Park, Calif., 1971-78; pres. Schultz, Salisbury, Cauble and Medley, Grants Pass, Oreg., 1981-85; pres. Yosemite Assn., Yosemite Nat. Park, 1985—. Author: Complete Guidebook to Yosemite National Park, 1990; co-author: Legends of the Yosemite Miwok, 1993. Office: Yosemite Assn PO Box 230 El Portal CA 95318-0230

MEDLIN, JOHN GRIMES, JR., banker; b. Benson, N.C., Nov. 23, 1933; s. John Grimes and Mabel (Stephenson) M. BS in Bus. Adminstrn., U. N.C., 1956; grad. The Exec. Program, U. Va., 1965. With Wachovia Bank & Trust Co., Winston-Salem, N.C., 1959—, pres., 1974, pres., CEO Wachovia Bank and Wachovia Corp., Winston-Salem, N.C., 1977-93; chmn. bd. Wachovia Corp., Winston-Salem, N.C., 1987—; bd. dirs. US Air Group, Inc., RJR Nabisco, Inc., Wachovia Corp., BellSouth Corp., Nat. Svc. Industries, Inc., Burlington Industries Inc., Media Gen. Inc. Trustee Nat. Humanities Ctr., Wake Forest U., Kenan Inst. Pvt. Enterprise, Kenan Inst. Arts; active numerous civic and svc. orgns. With USNR, 1956-59. Mem. Phi Delta Theta. Office: Wachovia Corp 301 N Main St PO Box 3099 Winston Salem NC 27150

MEDLOCK, ANN, non-profit organization executive, writer, speaker; b. Portsmouth, Va., May 6, 1933; d. Frank Wesley and Olive Edna (Litz) Medlock; m. Thomas Proctor Crawford, Mar. 5, 1955 (div.); 1 child, Philip Courtney; m. John Peasley Miraglia, June 22, 1966 (div.); children: Cynthia Medlock, David Medlock; m. John A. Graham, June 13, 1982. BA magna cum laude, U. Md., 1964. Free-lance writer N.Y.C., Princeton (N.J.) and Saigon, Republic of Vietnam, 1959-85; editor Vietnam Presse, Saigon, 1959-61, Macmillan Pub. Inc., N.Y.C., 1966-69; founder Medlock & Co. Pub.

Rels., 1972-82; speechwriter the Aga Khan, N.Y.C., 1979-80; editor-in-chief Children's Express, N.Y.C., 1978-79; founder, pres. The Giraffe Project, N.Y.C. and Whidbey Island, Wash., 1983—; judge Creative Altruism Awards, Sausalito, Calif., 1988-92. Eddie Bauer Heroes for the Earth Award, 1990-93. Editor: The Giraffe Gazette, 1983-92. Mem. planning bd. City of Langley, Wash., 1986-88; co-founder Citizens for Sensible Devel., Whidbey Island, 1988; bd. advisors Cmty. Action Network, 1986—, Windstar Found., Snowmass, Colo., 1984-92, U.S.-Soviet Ptnrs. Project, Seattle, 1989-92; bd. dirs. Hedgebrook Writers' Colony. Recipient Pub. Svc. award Am. Values, 1989, 1st Pl. award Wash. Press Assn., 1991. Avocations: painting, poetry, designing. Office: The Giraffe Project 197 Second St PO Box 759 Langley WA 98260

MEDLOCK, DONALD LARSON, lawyer; b. Port Chester, N.Y., Mar. 8, 1927; s. J. Harold and Emma Adelaide (MacLennan) M.; m. Katharine Smedes Nicholson, May 21, 1955; children: Katharine Baird, Margaret MacLennan, William Nicholson. BA with honors, Yale U., 1947, LLB, 1950. Bar: N.Y. 1950, U.S. Dist. Ct. (so. dist.) N.Y. 1951, U.S. Dist. Ct. (ea. dist.) N.Y. 1952, U.S. Tax Ct. 1952, U.S. Ct. Custom and Patent Appeals, U.S. Ct. Appeals (2d cir.) 1951. Assoc. Putnam & Roberts, N.Y.C., 1950-56, ptnr., 1957-94, sr. counsel, 1995—; bd. dirs. Bancard Sys. of N.Y. Inc., Port Washington. Editor Yale Law Jour., New Haven, 1948-50. Sec., bd. dirs. Port Washington Community Chest, 1959-61; bd. dirs. Port Washington Estates Assn., 1958-61; mem. ann. fund parents com. Taft Sch., 1979-81; bd. mgrs., exec. com. William Sloane Ho. YMCA of Greater N.Y., 1979-84; chmn. univ. coun. com. on Law Sch. Yale U., 1979-86; chmn. Yale Alumni Fund, 1984-86, bd. dirs., 1955—, exec. com., 1980-88; chmn. Yale Law Sch. Fund, 1974-76; mem. devel. bd. Yale U., 1984-88, exec. com., 1984-86; exec. com. Yale Law Sch., 1975-79, hon., 1979—; bd. dirs. Assn. Yale Alumni, 1984-86, rep.-at-large, 1979-82, com. on undergrad. admisssions, 1979-82, com. on Yale medal, 1981; exec. com. Assn. Families U. Denver, 1982-84. Recipient citation Yale Law Sch., 1977, Yale Alumni Fund Chmn.'s award, 1979, 87, Yale medal, 1994. Mem. ABA, Fed. Power Bar Assn., Assn. of Bar of City of N.Y. (com. on profl. ethics 1958-61), Corbey Ct. Yale Law Sch., Tuscarora Club (Margaretville, N.Y., bd. dirs. 1963-95, sec. 1970-86, v.p. 1984-86), Landfall Club, Manhasset Bay Yacht Club, Mory's Assn., India House, Scroll and Key Soc., Yale Club N.Y.C., Phi Beta Kappa, Phi Delta Phi. Avocations: trout fishing, tennis, reading, crossword puzzles.

MEDLOCK, THOMAS TRAVIS, lawyer; b. Joanna, SC, Aug. 28, 1934; s. Melvin Kelly and Mayme (DuBose) M.; m. Laura Virginia Orr, Oct. 11, 1969; children: Tom, Glenn. AB, Wofford Coll., 1956, LLD (hon.), 1985; LLB, U. S.C., 1959; HHD (hon.) Francis Marion Coll., 1987; LHD (hon.), U. Charleston, 1992. Bar: S.C. 1960, U.S. Supreme Ct. 1976. Asst. atty. gen. S.C. Atty. Gen.'s Office, Columbia, 1961-62; mem. S.C. Ho. of Reps., 1965-72, S.C. Senate, 1973-76; atty gen. S.C., 1983-95; chmn. Gov. sub.-com. on econ. devel. for S.C., 1975-76; legis. com. S.C. State Bar Assn., 1979-80. Mem. S.C. Stat Tri-Centennial Commn., 1967-71; chmn. U.S. Pres.'s Com. on Children and Youth, S.C., 1971; mem. Wofford Coll. Alumni Bd., Spartanburg, S.C., 1972; bd. visitors Winthrop Coll., Rock Hill, S.C., 1975. Capt. USAR, 1957. Mem. ABA, S.C. Bar Assn., Richland County Bar Assn., Assn. Trial Lawyers Am., Phi Beta Kappa, Phi Alpha Delta, Blue Key, Phi Gamma Mu, Kappa Sigma. Democrat. Methodist.

MEDNICK, MURRAY, playwright; b. Bklyn., Aug. 24, 1939; s. Sol Joseph and Betty (Greenstein) M. Student, Bklyn. Coll., 1957-60. Author: The Hawk, 1968, The Hunter, 1969, The Shadow Ripens, 1969, The Deer Kill, 1971, Are You Lookin?, 1973, Black Hole in Space, 1975, Taxes, 1975, The Coyote Cycle, 1978-84, Iowa and Blessings for Public Broadcasting System, 1977, 78, Scar, 1985, Heads, 1987, Shatter 'n Wade, 1990, Fedunn, 1992, Joe & Betty, 1994; also pub. in West Coast Plays; poems in Transatlantic Rev; others.; 1st prodn. at Theatre Genesis, N.Y.C., 1966; v.p., N.Y. Theatre Strategy, 1972, artistic dir.; Padua Hills Playwrights' Workshop, 1978-94. Grantee Rockefeller Found., 1968, 72, Guggenheim Found., 1973; recipient Poetry award Nat. Coun. Arts, 1968, Creative Artists Pub. Svc. award, 1973, Obie award for The Deer Kill, 1970, Ovation lifetime achievement award L.A. Theater League., 1992. Mem. Writers Guild, New Dramatists.

MEDNICK, ROBERT, accountant; b. Chgo., Apr. 1, 1940; s. Harry and Nettie (Brenner) M.; m. Susan Lee Levinson, Oct. 28, 1962; children: Michael Jon, Julie Eden, Adam Charles. BSBA, Roosevelt U., Chgo., 1962. CPA, Ill. Staff asst. Arthur Andersen & Co., Chgo., 1962-63, sr. acct., 1963-66, mgr., 1966-71, ptnr., 1971—; mng. dir. SEC policies, 1973-76, mng. dir. auditing procedures, 1976-79, mng. ptnr. profl. and regulatory matters, 1993—; vice chmn. com. on profl. standards Arthur Andersen & Co., 1979-82, chmn. com., 1982—. Contbr. articles to profl. jours. Bd. dirs. Roosevelt U., Chgo., 1980—, vice chmn., 1986—, sr. vice chmn., 1994—; bd. dirs. Auditorium Theatre Coun., 1990—, Lake Shore Dr. Synagogue, 1992—; co-chmn. adv. coun. Chgo. Action for Soviet Jewry, Highland Park, Ill., 1983-87; bd. dirs., exec. com. Am. Judicature Soc., 1990, vice chmn., 1993—; bd. overseers Rand Corp. Inst. Civil Justice, 1994—. Sgt. USAFR, 1965-69. Recipient Silver medal Ill. CPA Soc., 1962; named One of Ten Outstanding Young Men in Chgo., Chgo. Jr. C. of C., 1973-74; recipient Rolf A. Weil Disting. Service award, Roosevelt U., Chgo., 1983; Max Block award N.Y. State C.P.A. Soc., 1984; Am. Literary award Jour. Acctg., 1986, 88. Mem. AICPA (bd. dirs. 1986-87, 92-94, numerous coms., Elijah Watt Sells award 1962), Am. Acctg. Assn., Ill. CPA Soc. (acctg. prins. com. 1973, legal liability com. 1986—, mgmt. of acctg. practice com. 1991—), Mid-Day Club, Standard Club, Sandburg Tennis Club. Jewish. Avocations: tennis, collecting art.

MEDOFF, JAMES LAWRENCE, economics educator; b. Providence, May 13, 1947; s. Edward Bernard and Syvia (Darman) M.; m. Leslie Miller, Sept. 19, 1970; children: Justin, Susanna. BA in Econs., Brown U., 1969; MA in Econs., Harvard U., 1973, PhD in Econs., 1975. Prof. dept. econs. Harvard U., Cambridge, Mass., 1976—. Office: Harvard U Dept Econs Cambridge MA 02138

MEDOFF, MARK HOWARD, playwright, screenwriter, novelist; b. Mt. Carmel, Ill., Mar. 18, 1940; s. Lawrence Ray and Thelma Irene (Butt) M.; m. Stephanie Thorne, June 24, 1972; children: Debra, Rachel, Jessica. B.A., U. Miami, Fla., 1962; M.A., Stanford U., 1966; D.H.L., Gallaudet Coll., 1981. Instr. English and drama N.Mex. State U., 1966-79, dramatist in residence, 1974—, head dept. drama, 1978-87, prof. drama, 1979-93, artistic dir., 1982-87; artistic dir. Am. S.W. Theatre Co., 1984-87. Author: (plays) When You Comin' Back, Red Ryder?, 1974, The Wager, 1975, The Kramer, 1975, The Halloween Bandit, 1978, The Conversion of Aaron Weiss, 1978, Firekeeper, 1978, The Last Chance Saloon, 1979, Children of a Lesser God, 1980 (Soc. West Theatres best play award 1982), The Majestic Kid, 1981, The Hands of Its Enemy, 1984, Kringle's Window, 1985, The Heart Outright, 1986 (novel) Dreams of Long Lasting; (films) When You Comin' Back, Red Ryder?, 1979, Off Beat, 1986, Apology, 1986, Children of a Lesser God, 1986, Good Guys Wear Black, 1978, Clara's Heart, 1988, The Majestic Kid, 1988, City of Joy, 1992, Homage, 1995; workers appear in Best Plays, 1973-74, 74-75, 79-80, Best Short Plays, 1975, The Homage that Follows, 1987; plays Stumps, 1989, Stefanie Hero, 1990. Guggenheim fellow, 1974-75; recipient Obie award, Drama Desk award, Outer Critics Circle award, Media award Pres.'s Com. Employment Handicapped, Tony award; Oscar award nominee for Best Screenplay for Children of a Lesser God, 1987. Mem. Dramatists Guild, Writers Guild Am., Actors Equity Assn., Screen Actors Guild Pen. Office: PO Box 3072 Las Cruces NM 88003-3072

MEDONIS, ROBERT XAVIER, lawyer; b. Pitts., May 31, 1931; s. Vincent X. and Anastasia T. (Puida) M.; m. M. Kathleen Castor, Dec. 29, 1962; children: Meg Toomey, Robert Xavier, Mark D. BEd, Duquesne U., 1953, MA, 1985; JD, U. Pitts., 1958. Bar: Pa. 1959, U.S. Supreme Ct. 1966, U.S. Ct. Appeals (3d cir.) 1976. Trial atty. criminal div. Legal Aid Soc., Pitts., 1960-61; trial atty. Allegheny County Dist. Atty.'s Office, Pitts., 1964-71; assoc. Cleland, Hurt & Bowman, Pitts., 1961-63; pvt. practice, 1958-60, 63-64, 71-93; assoc. Karlowitz and Cromer, Pitts., 1993—. Bd. dirs. World Trade Ctr., Pitts. Capt. U.S. Army, 1953-55. Mem. ABA, Pa. Bar Assn., Allegheny County Bar Assn., Internat. Bar Assn., Pa. Trial Lawyers Assn., We. Pa. Trial Lawyers Assn., Lithuanian Am. Bar Assn., Am. Ins. of Ct., China-Am. Trade Soc. (founder, pres.). Home: 737 Shady Ln Pittsburgh PA 15228-2450 Office: 800 USX Towers Pittsburgh PA 15219

MEDVECKY, ROBERT STEPHEN, lawyer; b. Bridgeport, Conn., Feb. 12, 1931; s. Stephen and Elizabeth (Petro) M.; m. Ellen R. Munt, Nov. 11, 1966; children—Allison L., Beth A., Craig R. A.B., Dartmouth, 1952; J.D. Harvard, 1955. Bar: Ill. bar 1955, Conn. bar 1958, D.C. bar 1972, Fla. bar 1989. Asso. firm Lord, Bissell & Brook, Chgo., 1955-57; gen. atty. So. New Eng. Telephone Co., New Haven, 1957-71; v.p., gen. counsel, sec. Amtrak, Washington, 1971-75; partner firm Lord, Bissell & Brook, Washington, 1975-78, Reid & Priest, N.Y.C., 1978-87. Clubs: Harvard (N.Y.C.), Fiddlesticks Country (Ft. Meyers, Fla.), Saphire Valley Country (Cashlers, N.C.). Home: 15491 Kilbirnie Dr Fort Myers FL 33912-2424 Home (summer): 29 Pine Ridge Trl Sapphire NC 28774-9625

MEDVED, MICHAEL, film critic, author; b. Phila., Oct. 3, 1948; s. David Bernard and Renate Rosa (Hirsch) M.; m. Nancy Harris Herman, Aug. 5, 1972 (div. 1983); m. Diane Elvenstar, Jan. 27, 1985; children: Sarah Julia, Shayna Elana, Daniel Joshua. BA, Yale U., 1969; MFA, Calif. State U., San Francisco, 1974. Speech writer, polit. cons. various campaigns and politicians, Conn., Calif., D.C., 1970-73; advt. creative dir. Anrick Inc., Oakland, Calif., 1973-74; freelance writer Los Angeles, 1974—; on-air film critic People Now, Cable News Network, Los Angeles, 1980-83; on-air film critic, co-host Sneak Previews PBS, 1985—; chief film critic N.Y. Post, 1993—; Hollywood corr. The Sunday Times of London. Author: What Really Happened to the Class of '65?, 1976, The Shadow Presidents, 1979, Hospital, 1983, Hollywood vs. America, 1992, (with Harry Medved) The 50 Worst Films of All Time, 1978, The Golden Turkey Awards, 1980, The Hollywood Hall of Shame, 1984, Son of Golden Turkey Awards, 1986, Hollywood vs. America, 1992. Co-founder, pres. Pacific Jewish Ctr., Venice, Calif., 1977—; pres. Emanuel Streisand Sch., Venice, 1980-85. Mem. Writers Guild Am., AFTRA. Avocation: classical music. Office: Sta WTTW-TV 5400 N St Louis Ave Chicago IL 60625-4698

MEDVED, PAUL STANLEY, lawyer; b. Milw., May 6, 1956; s. Frank F. and Evelyn F. (Poplawski) M.; m. Danita C. Cole, Aug. 27, 1988. BA with Honors, Marquette U., 1978; JD, Columbia U., 1981. Bar: Wis. 1981, US Dist. Ct. (ea. dist.) Wis. 1981, U.S. Dist. Ct. (we. dist.) Wis. 1984, U.S. Ct. Appeals (7th cir.) 1984. Assoc. Michael, Best & Friedrich, Milw., 1981-88, ptnr., 1988—. Office: Michael Best & Friedrich 100 E Wisconsin Ave Milwaukee WI 53202-4107

MEDVIN, HARVEY NORMAN, financial executive, treasurer; b. Chgo., Sept. 6, 1936; s. Benjamin and Clara (Edelstein) M.; m. Sheila S. Spitzner, July 5, 1965; children: Arla Risa, Steven Merrill. BS in Acctg., U. Ill., 1958. CPA, Ill. Mem. audit staff Coopers & Lybrand, 1958-63; treas., v.p. The Martin Brower Co., Des Plaines, Ill., 1963-73, Ryan Ins. Group, Inc., Chgo., 1983—; sr. v.p., chief fin. officer Combined Internat. Corp. Chgo., Chgo., 1983—; exec. v.p., chief fin. officer, treas. Aon Corp., Chgo., 1987—; also bd. dirs. all subs.; bd. dirs. Schwarz Paper Co., Morton Grove, Ill., La Salle Bank Corp., La Salle Nat. Bank Chgo. Bd. dirs. Highland Park (Ill.) Hosp.; bd. govs. Chgo. Lighthouse for Blind; trustee Ravina Festival Highland Park, Ill., La Salla Nat. Bank, La Salle Nat. Corp., Chgo. With U.S. Army, 1958-59. Mem. AICPA. Office: Aon Corp 123 N Wacker Dr Chicago IL 60606

MEDWICK, CRAIG STEVEN, lawyer; b. Bronx, N.Y., Oct. 7, 1953; s. Leonard and Esther (Samberg) M.; m. Rosalie Maimone, Aug. 11, 1974; children: Jennifer, James, Julia, John. BA, SUNY, Binghamton, 1974; JD, NYU, 1977. Bar: N.Y. 1978. Assoc. Singer, Hutner, Levine & Seeman, N.Y.C., 1977-82; assoc., then ptnr. Demov, Morris & Hammerling, N.Y.C., 1982-87; ptnr. Rogers & Wells, N.Y.C., 1987—, vice chmn. adminstrn. corp. dept., 1992—. Contbg. author: McGraw-Hill M&A Handbook, 1993. Pres. bd. dirs. Nassau-Suffolk Svcs. for Autistic, Inc., Plainview, N.Y., 1992—. Mem. ABA, N.Y. State Bar Assn., Phi Beta Kappa. Office: Rogers & Wells 200 Park Ave Ste 5200 New York NY 10166-0153

MEDZIHRADSKY, FEDOR, biochemist, educator; b. Kikinda, Yugoslavia, Feb. 4, 1932; came to U.S., 1966; s. Miklos and Melanie (Gettmann) M.; m. Mechthild Westmeyer, Sept. 13, 1967; children: Sofia, Oliver. MS in Chemistry, Technische Hochschule Munich, Fed. Republic Germany, 1961; PhD in Biochemistry, 1965. Instr. biochemistry U. Munich, 1965-66; postdoctoral assoc. U. Wis.-Madison and Washington U., St. Louis, 1966-69; asst. prof. biochemistry U. Mich., Ann Arbor, 1969-73, assoc. prof. biochemistry, 1973-81, assoc. prof. pharmacology, 1975-81, prof. biochemistry and pharmacology, 1981—, dir. biochemistry lab., Upjohn Ctr. Clin. Pharmacology, 1969-76; dir. and co-dir. biochemistry core lab. Mich. Diabetes Rsch. and Tng. Ctr., U. Mich. Med. Ctr. 1977-91; vis. assoc. prof. Stanford U., 1975-76; vis. prof. U. Calif., San Diego, 1983-84, U. Utrecht and U. Wageningen, The Netherlands, 1992-93; invited lectr. nat. and internat. meetings. Contbr. over 200 articles to profl. jours. and chpts. to books; mem. editorial bd. Drug Metabolism and Disposition, 1982-94. Recipient Nat. Rsch. Svc. award USPHS, 1975-76, Kaiser Permanente award for excellence in teaching U. Mich., 1983; USPHS grantee, 1971—; Fogarty Senior Internat. fellowship, 1992-93. Mem. AAAS, Am. Soc. Neurochemistry, Am. Soc. Biochemistry and Molecular Biology, Am. Soc. Pharmacology and Exptl. Therapeutics, Soc. Biol. Chemistry (Germany), Sigma Xi. Achievements include research in neurochemistry, molecular pharmacology, membrane biochemistry.

MEE, CHARLES L., JR., playwright, historian, editor; b. Evanston, Ill., Sept. 15, 1938; s. Charles L. and Sarah (Lowe) M.; m. Suzi Baker (div.); children: Erin, Charles; m. Kathleen Tolan; children: Sarah, Alice. BA, Harvard U., 1960. Editor-in-chief Horizon mag., 1971-79. Author: Meeting at Potsdam, 1976, A Visit to Haldeman, 1978, The End of Order, 1980, The Marshall Plan, 1982, The Ohio Gang, 1983, Vienna: Lusthaus, 1986, The Investigation of the Murder in El Salvador, 1986, The Genius of the People, 1987, The Constitutional Convention, The Sequel, 1988, Rembrant's Portrait, 1988, The Imperialists at the Club Cave Canem, 1988, Another Person Is A Foreign Country, 1991, Orestes, 1992, The Bacchae, 1993, Playing God, 1993, Agamemnon, 1994, The Trojan Women A Love Story, 1995. Mem. Urban Inst. (bd. dirs.), En Garde Arts (bd. dirs.). Office: care Lois Wallace 177 E 70th St New York NY 10021-5109

MEE, HERB, JR., natural resource/environmental services executive; b. Oklahoma City, June 16, 1928; s. Herbert Martin and Margaret Adair (Lackey) M.; m. Marlene W., Sept. 8, 1978; children from previous marriage: Christopher W., Michael M. (twins). BA cum laude, Harvard U., 1950; advanced transp. mgmt. program, Northwestern U., 1965. Ptnr. in fire and casualty ins. agy. Oklahoma City, 1950-53, ind. oil and gas lease broker, 1953-54; with land dept. Woods Corp., Oklahoma City, 1956-72, v.p., then. exec. v.p., pres., chief exec. officer, 1968-72; pres. Beard Co., Oklahoma City, 1974—; bd. dirs. Alladin Plastics Inc., Liberty Bancorp, Inc., chmn. investment com.; bd. dirs., Liberty Bank and Trust Co. of Okla. City, N.A. and Liberty Bank and Trust Co. of Tulsa, N.A., E.F. Craven Co. Chmn. fin. com. Community Ch. of the Redeemer. Served with U.S. Army, 1955-56. Mem. Chief Execs. Orgn., Oklahoma City Golf and Country Club (pres. 1982-84). Republican. Avocations: golf, backgammon. Office: The Beard Co 5600 N May Ave Oklahoma City OK 73112-4275

MEECH, KAREN JEAN, astronomer; b. Denver, July 9, 1959; d. Lloyd Augustus and Patricia Ann (Marshall) M. BA cum laude in Physics, Rice U., 1981; PhD in Planetary Astronomy, MIT, 1987. Rsch. asst. Maria Mitchell Obs., Nantucket, Mass., 1978, Am. Assn. Variable Star Observers, 1979; rsch. asst. archaeoastronomy EARTHWATCH, Cusco, Peru, 1980; univ. lab. asst. molecular physics Rice U., Houston, 1980-81, quantum physics grader, 1980-81; rsch. asst. Am. Assn. Variable Star Observers, 1981-82; rsch. specialist MIT, Cambridge, 1981-82, grad. teaching asst., 1982-86, grad. rsch. asst., 1986-87; asst. astronomer Inst. for Astronomy, Honolulu, 1987-91, assoc. astronomer, 1992—; mem. IFA Computer Adv. Com., 1991-93, IFA Endowment Com., 1991, U. Rsch. Coun., 1990-93, NASA Planetary Astronomy Com. II, 1993-94, NASA Planetary Sci. Data Steering Group, 1993-95, IFA Admissions Com., 1992-93, NASA Planetary Astronomy Rev. Panel, 1990-91, Cerro Tololo Interamerican Obs. User's Com., 1991-95, USIA Internat. Teleconf., 1991; chair IFA Scholarship Com., 1991; interviewer Rice U. Alumni, 1989—; reviewer. Contbr. articles to Astron. Jour., Science, Icarus, Nature, Astrophysi.Jour., Bull. Am. Astronomy Soc., Info. Bull. Variable Stars, Minor Planet Circular, IAU Circular. Safety diver U. Hawaii Scuba class, 1988-90; vol. Honolulu Zool. Soc. Zoo Fun Run,

1991-92; active Dept. Edn. H.S. Student Career Program, Honolulu, 1988; organizer H.S. Tchr.-Student Asst. Workshops, 1993-95; local organizing chair Divsn. Planetary Astronomy meeting, Kona, Hawaii, 1995; faculty senate U. Hi., 1995—; ccom. Annie Jump Cannon award, 1995—; judge Hi. State Sci. Fair, 1992—; bd. dirs. Kilolokahi, 1995—. Scholar Bd. of Govs., 1980, Grad. Student Rschrs. fellow NASA, 1986-87; recipient Annie Jump Cannon award in Astronomy, 1988, Harold C. Urey prize in Astronomy Am. Astron. Soc., Heaps prize in Physics, 1981. Mem. Am. Astron. Soc. (divsn. planetary scis., 1995), Internat. Astron. Union-Commn. 15, Am. Assn. Variable Star Observers. Achievements include co-discovery of the outburst of Halley's comet at the longest distance from the sun for a recorded outburst; discovery of cometary activity on object 2060 Chiron.Pioneer in observations of outer solar system comets. Office: Inst for Astronomy 2680 Woodlawn Dr Honolulu HI 96822-1839

MEECHAM, WILLIAM CORVELL, engineering educator; b. Detroit; s. William Edward and Mabel Catherine (Wilcox) M.; m. Barbara Jane Brown, Sept. 4, 1948 (dec.); children: Janice Lynn, William James; m. Della Fern Carson., BS, U. Mich., 1948, MS, 1948, PhD in Physics, 1954. Head acoustics lab. Willow Run Labs., Ann Arbor, Mich., 1959-60; asst. prof. U. Mich., Ann Arbor, 1958-60; prof. U. Minn., Mpls., 1960-67; prof. fluid mechanics and acoustics UCLA, 1967—, chmn. dept. mechanics and structures, 1972-73; cons. Aerospace Corp., El Segundo, Calif., 1975-80, Rand Corp., Santa Monica, Calif., 1964-74, Bolt, Beranek and Newman, Cambridge, Mass., 1968-73, Arete Assocs., Encino, Calif., 1976—, CRT Corp., Chatsworth, Calif., 1985—. Author: (with R. Lutomirski) Lasar Systems, 1973; author 120 papers on fluid mechanics and acoustics. Treas. Unitarian Ch., Ann Arbor, Mich., 1958-60; advisor U.S. Congress Com. on Pub. Works, Congl. Record Report N.J., 1972; mem. Calif. Space and Def. Council, U.S. Congress, 1982—. Served with U.S. Army, 1944-46. Mich. Alumni scholar 1942-44, Donovan scholar U. Mich., 1944-45; UCLA senate rsch. grantee, 1968—, NASA rsch. grantee, 1971—; Office Naval Rsch. grantee, 1977-85; recipient Disting. Svc. award UCLA Army. Fellow Acoustical Soc. Am. (gen. chmn. meeting 1973), AIAA (assoc. fellow); mem. com. aeroacoustics 1972-75); mem. Am. Phys. Soc. (fluid dynamics div.), Inst. Noise Control Engring., Sigma Xi, Tau Beta Pi. Home: 927 Glenhaven Dr Pacific Palisades CA 90272-2202 Office: UCLA Sch Engring & Applied Sci Los Angeles CA 90024

MEEGAN, SISTER ELIZABETH, school system administrator. Supt. Cath. schs. Diocese of Phoenix. Office: Office of Schs Supt 111 Blvd of the Allies Pittsburgh PA 15222

MEEHAN, DAVID HOWARD, insurance company executive; b. New Castle, Pa., Nov. 11, 1928; s. Howard Platt and Cienwen (Lewis) M.; m. Nancy M. Kiebort, Sept. 5, 1953; children: Mary Beth, Molly, Martha, David, John. B.A. in Econs., Allegheny Coll., 1950. Supt. USF&G, Pitts., 1953-61; supt. USF&G, Balt., 1961-66, asst. v.p., 1966-72, v.p., 1972-80, sr. v.p., 1980-82, exec. v.p., 1982—; advisor Balt. Local Initiative Support Corp., 1982—. Bd. dirs. Hood Coll., 1981-86. Served with U.S. Army, 1950-52. Office: US Fidelity & Guaranty Co 100 Light St PO Box 1138 Baltimore MD 21202

MEEHAN, GERRY, professional hockey team executive; b. Toronto, Ont., Can.; m. Mirella Meehan; children: Danny, Adam, Katie. Grad., Canisius Coll.; JD, U. Buffalo, 1982. Professional hockey player Toronto Maple Leafs, 1968, Phila. Flyers, 1969; professional hockey player Buffalo Sabres, 1970-74, asst. gen. mgr., 1984-86, former gen. mgr.; player Vancouver (Can.) Canucks, 1975, Atlanta Flames (now Calgary Flames), 1975, Washington Capitals, 1976-79; atty. Cohen Swados Wright Hanifin Bradford Brett, Buffalo, 1984; exec. v.p. for sports operations Buffalo Sabres. Office: Buffalo Sabres Meml Auditorium 140 Main St Buffalo NY 14202*

MEEHAN, JOHN, artistic director; b. Brisbane, Australia. Studied with, Patricia MacDonald; student, Australian Ballet Sch., Melbourne. Mem. Australian Ballet, 1970-72, soloist, 1972-74, prin. dancer, 1974; artistic dir. Royal Winnipeg Ballet, 1990-93; guest artist, prin. dancer Am. Ballet Theatre, 1977. Leading roles include The Sleeping Beauty, Romeo and Juliet, Giselle, Onegin, Fokine's Firebird, Les Sylphides, George Balanchie's Theme and Variations, Teltley's Sphinx, Pierrot Lunaire and Voluntaries, Anthony Tudor's The Leaves are Fading, Lilac Garden, Baryshnikov's Don Quixote; created leading role in Gemini; Can. debut The Merry Widow with the Nat. Ballet of Can. 1986; danced at Kennedy Centre, Washington; co-starred with Karen Kain TV prodn. The Merry Widow, 1987; created two original pas de deux for ABT, Le ReTour, Adagio for Stings; choreographer Echoes for the Washington Ballet; singer, dancer feature role mus. rev. Noel; mus. debut in Song and Dance; dance premiere Dim Lustre, ABT, 1985; dancer Jacob's Pillow Dance Festival, 1985; guest appearances with the N.Y.C. Ballet; with Merrill Ashley in The Nutcracker, Divertimento No. 15, Swan Lake, Gounod Symphony, Piano Concerto No. 2. Scholar Australian Ballet Sch. Office: Canada's Royal Winnipeg Ballet, 380 Graham Ave, Winnipeg, MB Canada R3C 4K2

MEEHAN, JOHN J., mortgage company executive. Sr. v.p. fin., treas. Fed. Nat. Mortgage Assn., Washington. Office: Fed Nat Mortgage Assn 3900 Wisconsin Ave NW Washington DC 20016-2892

MEEHAN, JOHN JOSEPH, brokerage house executive; b. Bklyn., Mar. 18, 1945; s. John Joseph and Marie Kathleen (McGuinness) M.; m. Mary Lou Muniz, June 20, 1970 (div. 1976); 1 child, Michael; m. Janice Anne Napoli, Dec. 5, 1980; children: Matthew, Martin. A.A.S., St. John's U., Jamaica, N.Y., 1965. Asst. treas. for trading Chase Manhattan Bank, N.Y.C., 1968-72; sr. trader agys. Goldman, Sachs & Co., N.Y.C., 1972-75; sr. v.p.fin. treas. Fed. Nat. Mortgage Assn., N.Y.C., Washington, 1975-85; sr. v.p., mgr. govt. bond dept. Dean Witter Reynolds Inc., N.Y.C., 1985-88; sr. v.p., dir., mng. dir., dep. chief exec. officer Deutsch Bank Govt. Securities, Inc., N.Y.C., 1988-93; mng. dir. Deutsch Bank Securities Corp., N.Y.C., 1993—. Served to sgt. USMC, 1966-68, Vietnam. Roman Catholic. Avocations: golf; tennis; coaching boys' football; baseball. Home: 5 Lincoln Pl Port Washington NY 11050-3220 Office: Deutsche Bank Securities 31 W 52nd St New York NY 10019-6118

MEEHAN, JOHN JOSEPH, JR., hospital administrator; b. Boston, Jan. 29, 1946; s. John Joseph and Marjorie Louise (Hill) M.; m. Pamela Marshall, Mar. 25, 1973; children—Seth, Andrew, Sean. B.A., Dartmouth Coll., Hanover, N.H., 1968; M.H.A., U. Minn., Mpls., 1974. Unit mgr. Boston Hosp. Women, 1971-72; adminstrv. resident Hennepin County Gen. Hosp., Mpls., 1973-74; v.p. Putnam Meml. Hosp., Bennington, Vt., 1974-79; asst. dir. Hartford Hosp., Conn., 1979-81, assoc. exec. dir., 1981-85, exec. v.p., 1985-87, pres., chief operating officer, 1987-89; pres., chief exec. officer, 1989—; faculty Hartford Grad. Ctr., 1979-81; preceptor U. Minn., 1981—, Yale U., New Haven, 1981—; mem. New Eng. Health Care Assembly, 1975—, officer, 1982-92. Active Bennington Lion's Club, 1975-79, Conn. Hosp. Assn. Urban League Greater Hartford, 1979—, Greater Hartford C. of C., 1979—, also bd. dirs., 1994—; chmn. ARC, Bennington, 1978-79; bd. dirs. St. Joseph Coll., ConnectiCare IPA/HMO, Mech. Savs. Bank, 1993—; corporator St. Francis Hosp., 1988—, Inst. Living, 1993—; fellow Am. Leadership Forum, 1993—. Served to lt. (j.g.) USNR, 1968-70. Decorated Naval medals and ribbons, 1968-70; recipient Disting. Naval Grad. award, 1968, Stuart Thompson M.D. award U. Minn., 1974. Mem. Am. Hosp. Assn., Conn. Hosp. Assn. (bd. dirs.), Capital Area Health Consortium.

MEEHAN, MARTIN THOMAS, congressman, lawyer; b. Dec. 30, 1956; s. Martin T. and Alice (Britton) M. BA in Polit. Sci., Edn. cum laude, U. Mass., Lowell, 1978; MPA, Suffolk U., 1981, JD, 1986; student, Harvard U., 1987-88. Adminstrv. asst. to mayor City of Lowell, Mass., 1978-79; press asst. Congressman James M. Shannon, Mass., 1979-81; del. Dem. Nat. Conv., 1980, 84, 88; head rsch. analyst Joint Com. on Elec. Laws Mass. State Senate, 1981-84; dir. pub. affairs Govt. of Mass., 1985-86, dep. sec. state, 1986-90; 1st asst. dist. atty. Middlesex County, Mass., 1991-92; mem. 103rd-104th Congresses from 5th Mass. Dist., 1993—; mem. nat. security com., ranking minority mem., mem. small bus. subcom. on tax and fin.; former teacher, adj. instr. U. Lowell, Mass.; lawyer 1986—. Named Student of Yr. Lowell Exchange Club, 1975. Mem. ABA, Mass. Bar Assn., U. Lowell Alumni Assn., The Newspaper Guild, Internat. Fedn. Journalists.

Democrat. Roman Catholic. Office: US Ho of Reps 318 Cannon HOB Washington DC 20515-2105*

MEEHL, PAUL EVERETT, psychologist, educator; b. Mpls., Jan. 3, 1920; s. Otto John and Blanche Edna (Duncan) Swedal; m. Alyce M. Roworth, Sept. 6, 1941 (dec. 1972); children: Karen, Erik; m. Leslie Jane Yonce, Nov. 17, 1973. A.B., U. Minn., 1941, Ph.D., 1945; Sc.D., Adelphi U., 1984. Diplomate Am. Bd. Profl. Psychology (dir. psychology, bd. dirs.1957-62, Disting. Svc. and Outstanding Contbns. award 1989). Instr., asst., assoc. prof., chmn. dept. psychology U. Minn., 1951-57, prof., prof. dept. psychiatry Med. Sch., 1952-90, regents' prof. psychology, 1968-89, Hathaway-Meehl prof. psychology, 1990-93, regent's prof. psychology emeritus, 1993—; prof. Minn. Ctr. for Philosophy of Sci., 1953-56, 69—, prof. philosophy, 1971—; acting chief clin. psychology VA Hosp., Mpls., 1947-49; participant Dartmouth Conf. on Behavior Theory, 1950; mem. panel on criminal deterrence Nat. Acad. Sci., 1975-77; practice psychotherapy, 1951-94; staff Nicollet Clinic, 1970-80. Author: (with S.R. Hathaway) Atlas for Clinical Use of MMPI, 1951, (with others) Modern Learning Theory, 1954, Clinical Versus Statistical Prediction, 1954, What, Then, Is Man?, 1958, Psychodiagnosis, 1973, Selected Philosophical and Methodological Papers, 1991; contbr. articles to profl. legal and philos. jours. Recipient Ednl. Testing Svc. award for contbns. to measurement, 1994, Clin. Psychology Centennial prize for lifetime achievement APA, Bruno Klopfer disting. contbn. award, 1979, Gold medal for life achievement application of psychology Am. Psychol. Found., 1989, Disting. Svc. award Am. Bd. Profl. Psychologists, 1989, Joseph Zubin prize lifetime contbns. to psychopathology, 1989; William James fellow Am. Psychol. Soc., 1989. Fellow Inst. for Advanced Study in Rational Psychotherapy; mem. Am. Psychol. Assn. (pres. 1961-62, Disting. Contbr. award clin. div. 1967, Disting. Sci. Contbr. award 1958, Disting. Scientist award 1976, Disting. Contbn. to Knowledge award 1993), Am. Acad. of Arts and Scis., Nat. Acad. of Sci., Philosophy Sci. Assn., Sigma Xi, Phi Beta Kappa, Psi Chi. Home: 1544 E River Ter Minneapolis MN 55414-3646 Office: U Minn N218 Elliott Hall 75 E River Rd Minneapolis MN 55455-0280

MEEK, CARRIE P., congresswoman; 3 children. BS, Fla. A&M U., 1946, MS, U. Mich., 1948. Mem. Fla. Senate from Dist. 36, 1982-1992. Mem. 103rd-104th Congress from 17th Fla. dist., 1993—. Democrat. Office: US Ho of Reps 404 Cannon House Office Bldg Washington DC 20515*

MEEK, GERRY, library director. Dir. Calgary (Alta.) Pub. Libr., Can. Office: Calgary Pub Libr, 616 Macleod Trail SE, Calgary, AB Canada T2G 2M2

MEEK, PAUL DERALD, oil and chemical company executive; b. McAllen, Tex., Aug. 15, 1930; s. William Van and Martha Mary (Sharp) M.; m. Betty Catherine Robertson, Apr. 18, 1954; children: Paula Marie Meek Burford, Kathy Diane Meek Hasemann, Carol Ann Meek Miller, Linda Rae Meek. B.S. in Chem. Engring, U. Tex., Austin, 1953. Mem. tech. dept. Humble Oil & Refining Co., Baytown, Tex., 1953-55; with Cosden Oil & Chem. Co., 1955-76, pres., 1968-76; dir. Fina, Inc. (formerly Am. Petrofina, Inc.), Dallas, 1968—, v.p. parent co. 1968-76, pres., chief operating officer, 1976-83, pres., chief exec. officer, 1983-86, chmn. bd., pres., chief exec. officer, 1984-86, chmn. bd., 1986—; apptd. by Gov. Wm. P. Clements, Jr. chmn. Pub. Utilites Commn. of Tex., 1989-92. Contbg. author: Advances in Petroleum Chemistry and Refining, 1957. Chmn. chem. engring. vis. com. U. Tex., 1975-76; mem. adv. coun. Coll. Engring. Found., U. Tex., Austin, 1979—, U. Tex. Longhorn Found., 1989—, Coll. of NaturalScis. Found., 1989—; bd. visitors McDonald Observatory dept. astronomy, U. Tex.; cochmn. indsl. div. United Way of Met. Dallas, 1981-83. Named Disting. Engring. Grad. U. Tex., Austin, 1969. Mem. Am. Petroleum Inst. (bd. dirs.), 25 Yr. Club of the Petroleum Industry, Founders Club of the Petrochem. Industry, Dallas Wildcat Com. (chmn. exec. com. 1987-88). Office: Fina Inc 8350 N Central Expwy PO Box 2159 Dallas TX 75221*

MEEK, PHILLIP JOSEPH, communications executive; b. Los Angeles, Nov. 17, 1937; s. Joseph Alcinus and Clara Amy (Phillips) M.; m. Nancy Jean LaPorte, June 25, 1960; children: Katherine Amy, Brian Joseph, Laurie Noel. B.A. cum laude, Ohio Wesleyan U., 1959; M.B.A., Harvard U., 1961. Fin. analyst Ford Motor Co., 1961-63, supr. capacity planning, 1963-66, supr. domestic scheduling, 1966, controller mktg. services, 1966-68; on loan as pres. Econ. Devel. Corp. Greater Detroit, 1968-70; pres., pub. Oakland Press Co., Pontiac, Mich., 1970-77; exec. v.p., gen. mgr. Ft. Worth Star-Telegram, 1977-79, pres., editorial chmn. 1980-82, pres., pub., 1982-86; sr. v.p., pres. pub. group Capital Cities/ABC Inc., N.Y.C., 1986—. Past mem. Pontiac Stadium Bldg. Authority; pres. United Way Pontiac-North Oakland, 1977; pres. Tarrant County United Way, 1982-83, chmn., 1983-84; bd. dirs. Arts Council of Ft. Worth and Tarrant County; chmn. North Tex. Commn., 1983-84; bd. dirs. Tex. Ind. Coll. Fund; trustee Ohio Wesleyan U., 1984—. Mem. Am. Newspaper Pubs. Assn., So. Newspaper Pubs. Assn., Tex. Daily Newspaper Assn. (pres. 1984), Ft. Worth C. of C. (dir. 1980-83); Mem. Phi Beta Kappa, Omicron Delta Kappa, Sigma Delta Chi, Pi Delta Epsilon, Phi Gamma Delta. Methodist. Clubs: Stanwich (Conn.); Crystal Downs (Mich.). Office: Capital Cities/ABC Inc 77 W 66th St New York NY 10023-6201

MEEK, VIOLET IMHOF, dean; b. Geneva, Ill., June 12, 1939; d. John and Violet (Krepel) Imhof; m. Devon W. Meek, Aug. 21, 1965 (dec. 1988); children: Brian, Karen; m. Don M. Dell, Jan. 4, 1992. BA summa cum laude, St. Olaf Coll., 1960; MS, U. Ill., 1962, PhD in Chemistry, 1964. Instr. chemistry Mount Holyoke Coll., South Hadley, Mass., 1964-65; asst. prof. to prof. Ohio Wesleyan U., Delaware, Ohio, 1965-84, dean for ednl. svcs., 1980-84; dir. annual programs Coun. Ind. Colls., Washington, 1984-86; assoc. dir. sponsored programs devel. Rsch. Found. Ohio State U., Columbus, 1986-91; dean, dir. Ohio State U., Lima, 1992—; vis. dean U. Calif., Berkeley, 1982, Stanford U., Palo Alto, Calif., 1982; reviewer GTE Sci. and Tech. Program, Princeton, N.J., 1986-92, Goldwater Nat. Fellowships, Princeton, 1990-95. Co-author: Experimental General Chemistry, 1984; contbr. articles to profl. jours. Bd. dirs. Luth. Campus Ministries, Columbia, 1988-91, Lutheran Social Svcs., 1988-91, Americom Bank, Lima, 1992—, Lima Symphony Orch., 1993—, Art Space, Lima, 1993—, Allen Lima Leadership, 1993—, Am. House, 1992—, Lima Vets. Meml. Civic Ctr. Found., 1992—; chmn. synodical coms. Evangelical Luth. Ch. in Am. Columbbus, 1982, Allen County C. of C., 1995—. Recipient Woodrow Wilson Fellowship, 1960. Mem. Nat. Coun. Rsch. Adminstrs. (named Outstanding New Profl. midwest region 1990), Am. Assn. Higher Edn., Phi Beta Kappa. Avocations: music, skiing, woodworking, Civil War history, travel. Home: 209 W Beechwold Blvd Columbus OH 43214-2012 Office: Ohio State U 4240 Campus Dr Lima OH 45804

MEEKER, GUY BENTLEY, banker; b. Calcutta, India, Nov. 4, 1945; (parents Am. citizens); s. Lincoln Voght and Fortune Helen (Bentley) M.; m. Lavenia Yale Nelson, Apr. 27, 1967 (div. 1979); children: G. Bentley Jr., Melissa Anne; m. Marcia Lee Zink, Nov. 4, 1984. BSBA, Georgetown U., 1967; MBA, George Washington U., 1970. Cons. OAS, Washington, 1971-73; v.p. The Deltec Banking Corp., Nassau, Bahamas & N.Y.C., 1973-78, Comml. Credit Internat. Banking Corp., Balt., 1978-82; sr. v.p., gen. mgr. Union Planters Internat. Bank, N.Y.C., 1982-84; exec. v.p., gen. mgr. Worthen Bank Internat., N.Y.C., 1984-86; exec. v.p. and chief exec. officer N.Am. Bank Cen. Asia, N.Y.C., 1984-93; supervisory dir. BCA Bank Europe N.V., Amsterdam, The Netherlands, 1993—. Contbr. articles, monographs in field. Mem. Bankers Assn. Fgn. Trade (internat. adv. coun., 1992—, vice chmn. IAC, 1994—), Inst. Internat. Bankers (legis. and regulatory com. 1992-94, bd. trustees 1994-97), Asia Soc. (corp. coun. 1987—), River Club, Coffee House Club, Dutch Treat Club, melrose Club (S.C.). Roman Catholic.

MEEKER, ROBERT ELDON, retired manufacturing company executive; b. Moline, Ill., Sept. 6, 1930; s. Paul Edwin and Esther (Carlson) M.; m. Dorothy Elaine Nelson, Dec. 23, 1951; children—Julie Lynn, Laurie Allison Meeker Gamel, Bradford Nelson. B.S. in Chemistry, Ill. Wesleyan U., 1952; Ph.D in Phys. Chemistry, Northwestern U., 1955. Chemist, supr. Shell Devel. Co., Emeryville, Calif., 1955-64; mgr.-dir. synthetic rubber tech. ctr. Shell Chem. Co., Torrance, Calif., 1964-66; mgr. new projects Shell Chem. Co., N.Y.C., 1966-69; dir. exploratory sci., exploration and prodn. rsch. ctr. Shell Devel. Co., Houston, 1969-71; gen. mgr., head new enterprises div. Royal Dutch-Shell Co., London, 1971-72; v.p. comml., gen. mgr. Billiton

aluminum B.V. Billiton Internat. Metals subs. Shell Co., The Hague, The Netherlands, 1972-74; pres. Roxana Shale Oil Co. subs. Shell Co., Houston, 1974-76; v.p., gen. mgr. energy systems mgmt. div. TRW, Inc., Redondo Beach, Calif., 1976-80; v.p., gen. mgr. maj. programs TRW, Inc., 1980-86; pvt. practice cons., real estate developer Tucson, 1986-94. Patentee in field. Trustee Ill. Wesleyan U., Bloomington, 1982—; v.p., bd. dirs. Cobblestone Homeowners Assn., 1991-92, pres., bd. dirs., 1992-94, sec., security chmn., 1994—. Recipient Disting. Alumnus award Ill. Wesleyan U., 1981. Mem. Mercedes Benz Club Am. (pres. Chaparral sect. 1992-94). Republican. Lutheran. Avocations: photography; swimming; travel. Home and Office: 7240 N Star Fury Pl Tucson AZ 85718-1345

MEEKS, CAROL JEAN, educator; b. Columbus, Ohio, Mar. 9, 1946; d. Clarence Eugene and Clara Johanna (Schwartz) B.; m. Joseph Meeks, Aug. 17, 1968 (div. 1981); 1 child: Catherine Rachael. BS, Ohio State U., Mex., 1968; MS, Ohio State U., 1969, PhD, 1972. Rsch. asst., assoc. Ohio State U., Columbus, 1968-71; internship Columbus Area C. of C., Ohio, 1970; lectr. Ohio State U., Columbus, 1970, 72; asst. prof. U. Mass., Amherst, 1972-74; asst. prof. Cornell U., Ithaca, N.Y., 1974-78, assoc. prof., 1978-80; legis. fellow Senate Com. Banking, 1984; supr. economist, head housing section USDA, Washington, 1980-85; assoc. prof. housing and consumer econs. U. Ga., Athens, 1985-90, prof., 1990—, head housing and consumer econs., 1992—; rsch. fellow Nat. Inst. for Consumer Rsch., Oslo, Norway, 1982; cons. Yale U., 1976-77, HUD, Cambridge, Mass., 1978, MIT Ctr. for Real Estate Devel. Ford Found. Project on Housing Policy; del. N.E. Ctr. for Rural Devel. Housing Policy Conf. Reviewer Home Econ. Rsch. Jour., 1987—, ACCI conf., 1987—; contbr. articles to profl. mags. Mem. panel town of Amherst Landlord Tenant Bd.; bd. dirs. Am. Coun. Consumer Interests; mem. adv. coun. HUD Nat. Mfg. Housing, 1978-80, 91-93; chair Housing Mfg. Inst. Consensus Commn. on Fed. Standards. Recipient Young Profl. award Ohio State U., 1979; named one of Outstanding Young Women of Am., 1979; Columbus Womens Chpt. Am. Real Estate Bds. scholar, Gen. Foods fellow 1971-72, HEW grantee, 1978, travel grantee NSF bldg. rsch. bd. , AID grantee. Mem. Soc. Govt. Economists (bd. dirs. 1984-85, co-chmn. 1985), Am. Assn. Housing Educators (newsletter editor 1976-79, pres. 1983-84), Nat. Inst. Bldg. Sci. (bd. sec. 1984, 85, 89—, bd. dirs. 1981-83, 85, 87-93, features commn.), Am. Real Estate and Urban Econs. Assn., Internat. Assn. Housing Sci., Com. on Status of Women in Econs., Nat. Assn. Home Builders (Smart House contract 1989), Epsilon Sigma Phi, Omicron Nu, Kappa Omicron Nu (v.p. of programs 1995-96), others. Office: U Ga 215 Dawson Hall Athens GA 30602-3622

MEEKS, HERBERT LESSIG, III, pastor, former school system administrator; b. National City, Calif., May 12, 1946; s. Herbert Lessig Jr. and Hazel Evelyn (Howard) M.; m. Ardena Lorraine Bice, June 30, 1971; children: Herbert Lessig IV, Laura Dawn, Misty Danae. Grad. in Theology, Bapt. Bible Coll., 1972; BS in Interdisciplinary Studies, Liberty U., Lynchburg, Va., 1989; MS in Edn., Tenn. Temple U., 1989; MA in Religion, Liberty U., 1990. Tchr. Mt. Vernon Christian Sch., Stockbridge, Ga., 1975-82; prin. Mt. Zion Christian Acad., Jonesboro, Ga., 1982-90; elem. prin. Des Moines Christian Sch., 1990-93; prin. N.W. Acad., Houston, 1993-94; sr. pastor 1st Bapt. Ch. Genoa, Houston, 1994—. Instr. ARC, Atlanta; candidate Ga. Ho. of Reps., Atlanta, 1980; bd. dirs Concerned Christian for Good Govt., Atlanta, 1980-82; notary pub. Clayton County, Ga., 1983-90. Served to sgt. USAF, 1966-69. Mem. Assn. Christian Schs. Internat. (conv. planning com. 1985-90, accreditation/cons. chmn., Behind the Scenes award 1986), Nat. Rifle Assn. (life), Am. Pistol and Rifle Assn. Republican. Avocations: flying, hunting, politics, econs. Home: 12102 Palmcroft Houston TX 77034 Office: 1st Bapt Ch Genoa 12717 Almeda-Genoa Houston TX 77034

MEEKS, PATRICIA LOWE, secondary school educator; b. Enid, Okla., Oct. 21, 1928; d. Henry Preston and Veda Gay (Combs) Lowe; m. James Donald Meeks, Feb. 28, 1953 (div. Aug. 1975); children: Mary Gay, Ann Lowe, James Robert David. BA, Phillips U., 1951; MA in English, U. Colo., 1973. Cert. tchr., Colo., Okla. Tchr. English Garber (Okla.) High Sch., 1952-53; tchr. English and journalism Hillcrest High Sch., Dallas, 1955-57; teaching asst. U. Colo., Boulder, 1965-66; tchr. English Cherry Creek High Sch., Englewood, Colo., 1966-91; supr. grades K-12 English Oklahoma City Pub. Schs., 1991—; cons. Coll. Bd. Rocky Mt. Region, Denver, 1973-91; advanced placement reader, table leader, 1989-94, table leader, 1994—. Mem. alumni bd. Phillips U. Fulbright exch. tchr. U.S. Dept. Edn., 1980-81; grantee NEH, 1986, English-Speaking Union, 1987. Mem. ASCD, NEA, AAUW, Nat. Fulbright Assn., Okla. Coun. Tchrs. English, Nat. Coun. Tchrs. English, Nature Conservancy, Alumni Bd. Phillips U. Republican. Episcopalian. Avocations: art history, bird watching, jazz, reading. Home: 5806 N Pennsylvania Ave Oklahoma City OK 73112 Office: Oklahoma City Pub Schs 900 N Klein Oklahoma City OK 73106

MEEKS, WAYNE A., religious studies educator; b. Aliceville, Ala., Jan. 8, 1932; s. Benjamin L. and Winnie (Gavin) M.; m. Martha Evelina Fowler, June 10, 1954; children—Suzanne, Edith, Ellen. BS, U. Ala.-Tuscaloosa, 1953; BD, Austin Presbyn. Theol. Sem., 1956; MA, Yale U., 1964, PhD, 1965; Doctor Theologiae honoris causa, U. Uppsala, Sweden, 1990. Instr. religion Dartmouth Coll., Hanover, N.H., 1964-65; asst. prof. religious studies Ind. U., Bloomington, 1966-68, assoc. prof., 1968-69; assoc. prof. religious studies Yale U., New Haven, 1969-73, prof. religious studies, 1973-84, Woolsey prof. Bibl. studies, 1984—; dir. divsn. of Humanities, 1988-91. Author: Go From Your Father's House, 1964; The Prophet-King, 1967; First Urban Christians, 1983; Moral World of the First Christians, 1986, Origins of Christian Morality, 1993. Contbr. articles to profl. jours. Fulbright fellow, 1956-57; Kent fellow, 1962-64; NEH fellow, 1975-76; Guggenheim fellow, 1979-80. Fellow British Acad.; mem. Soc. Bibl. Lit. (pres. 1985), Am. Acad. Religion (bd. dirs. 1974-77), Studiorum Novi Testamenti Societas (editorial bd. 1979-82). Democrat. Presbyterian. Avocations: cabinet-making; hiking. Office: Yale U Dept Religious Studies PO Box 208287 Yale Station New Haven CT 06520-8287

MEELIA, RICHARD J., healthcare products executive. Pres. Kendall Co., Mansfield, Mass. Office: Kendall Company 15 Hampshire St Mansfield MA 02048-1139*

MEEM, JAMES LAWRENCE, JR., nuclear scientist; b. N.Y., Dec. 24, 1915; s. James Lawrence and Phyllis (Deaderick) M.; m. Buena Vista Speake, Sept. 5, 1940; children: James, John. B.S., U.S. Mil. Inst., 1939; M.S., Ind. U., 1947, Ph.D., 1949. Aero. research sci. NACA, 1940-46; dir. bulk shielding reactor Oak Ridge Nat. Lab., 1950-53, in charge nuclear operation aircraft reactor expt., 1954-55; chief reactor sci. Alco Products, Inc., 1955-57; in charge startup and initial testing Army Package Power Reactor, 1957; prof. nuclear engring. U. Va., Charlottesville, 1957-81; prof. emeritus, 1981—; cons. U.S. Army Fgn. Sci. and Tech. Ctr., 1981-90; vis. cons. nuclear fuel cycle programs Sandia Labs., Albuquerque, 1977-78; vis. staff mem. Los Alamos Sci. Lab., 1967-68; mem. U.S.-Japan Seminar Optimization of Nuclear Engring. Edn., Tokai-mura, 1973. Author: Two Group Reactor Theory, 1964. Fellow Am. Nuclear Soc. (sec. reactor ops. div. 1966-68, vice chmn. 1968-70, chmn. 1970-71, Exceptional Service award 1980); mem. Am. Phys. Soc., Am. Soc. Engring. Edn., SAR. Home: University Village # 1201 2401 Old Ivy Rd Charlottesville VA 22903-4853

MEENAN, JAMES JOSEPH, communications executive; b. Mpls., Nov. 10, 1943; s. Leonard Louis and Mary (Brennan) M.; m. Clare Hunnewinkel, July 16, 1966; children: Daniel, Marcy, Mark. BSBA, St. Mary's Coll., 1965; M in Mgmt. Sci., Stevens Inst. Tech., 1978. Mgmt. trainee AT&T Teletype Corp., 1966, various positions, 1966-80; asst. contr. ops. Western Electric, 1980-82, corporate contr., 1982-84; v.p.fin. AT&T Network Sys., 1984-85; CFO AT&T Info. Sys., 1985-87; corporate v.p. AT&T Fin. Ops. and Sys., 1987-89; v.p., CFO AT&T Comm. Svcs. Group, Basking Ridge, N.J., 1989-95; pres., CEO AT&T Canada Inc., Toronto, 1995—; bd. dirs. Unitel Comm., Inc., Toronto. Past pres. Fathers and Friends Delbarton Sch., Morristown, N.J., 1986-89; bd. trustees Tri-County Scholarship Fund, Paterson, N.J., 1990—, Coll. of St. Elizabeth, Convent Station, N.J., 1990—. Mem. Fin. Execs. Inst. Office: AT&T Canada Inc, 320 Front Street West, Toronto, ON Canada M5V 3C4

MEENAN, PATRICK HENRY, state legislator; b. Casper, Wyo., Sept. 24, 1927; s. Hugh Martin and Margaret (Kelly) M.; BS cum laude, U. Notre Dame, 1949; m. Shirley Louise Byron, Dec. 30, 1950; children: Maurya Ann, Kevin Patrick, Michael James, Patricia Kelly. CPA Raab, Roush & Gaymon, Casper, 1949-53, ptnr. 1960-68; asst. treas. Williston Oil & Gas Co., 1953-55; ptnr. Meenan & Higgins, Casper, 1955-60; pres. KATI-AM & FM, Casper, 1963-81, KAWY Stero Radio, 1967-81; ptnr. Meenan, Miracle & Sherrill, CPAs, 1975-76; sec. dir. Bank of Casper, 1980-87; pres. PM Enterprises, Inc., 1981—; Erin Corp. Councilman City of Casper, 1956-65, v.p., 1961, mayor, 1962, 65; mem. Wyo. Ho. of Reps., 1969-89, majority floor leader, 1983-85, Speaker Pro Tem, 1985-87, Speaker of the House, 1987-89, chmn. house-rules com., chmn. mgmt. council, 1987-89; mem. exec. com. Western Legis. Conf. Coun. of State Govts., 1983-89; chmn. Nat. Conf. State Legis. Energy and Environ. Com., 1985. Named Young Man of Year, Jr. C. of C., Casper, 1962; Boss of Year, 1965; Distinguished Pub. Servant award City of Casper. Mem. AICPA, Casper Country Club, Notre Dame Alumni (nat. dir. 1972-75), Wyo. So. CPAs, Nat., Wyo. assns. broadcasters. Elk, K.C. Republican. Roman Catholic. Home: 3070 E 4th St Casper WY 82609-2104 Office: PM Enterprises Inc 300 Country Club Rd Ste 211 Hilltop Nat Tower PO Box 9727 Casper WY 82609

MEENDSEN, FRED CHARLES, food company executive; b. Garden City, N.Y., Oct. 28, 1933; s. Frederick Herman and Charlotte Mabel (Reiss) M.; B.A., Colgate U., 1954; M.B.A., Harvard U., 1956; m. Nancy Lou Gross, Nov. 16, 1957; children: Fred Charles, Martha Anne. Mem. mktg. and sales mgmt. dept. Velsicol Chem. Corp., Chgo., 1957-63; with CPC Internat., Inc., Englewood Cliffs, N.J., 1963—, pres. subs. Peterson/Puritan, Inc., Danville, Ill., 1977-83, pres. subs. Can. Starch Co., 1983-84, v.p. parent co., 1983—, pres. N.Am. region Corn Wet Milling div., 1984-88, v.p. corp. affairs, 1988-93, v.p. govt. affairs, 1994—; dir. Can. Starch Co., 1983-88; chmn. Casco Co.; mem. U.S. C. of C. Can. Rels. Com., 1986—, Food and Agr. Com., 1988—; sec. Agr. Adv. Comm. on Trade, 1987-92; pres., Colgate U. Alumni Corp., 1991-93, bd. dirs. 1988—; trustee Colgate U., 1993—. Served to 1st lt. U.S. Army, 1956-59. Author: Atomic Energy and Business Strategy, 1956. Home: 24472 Trice Field Ct Saint Michaels MD 21663-2618 Office: CPC Internat Inc Internat Plz Englewood Cliffs NJ 07632

MEERS, HENRY W., investment banker; b. Joliet, Ill., July 12, 1908; s. Robert and Mary (Cullen) M.; m. Evelyn Huckins; children: Henry Weber, Albert Huckins, Robert. A.B., U. Ill., 1930. With Halsey, Stuart & Co., Chgo., 1930-35, Harriman, Ripley & Co., 1936-42; resident partner White, Weld & Co., 1946-72, vice chmn., 1972-78; mng. dir. Merrill Lynch & Co. Investment Banking Group, Chgo., 1978—, Merrill Lynch Trust Co., Chgo., 1992—; dir. DuKane Corp.; chmn. bd. govs. Assn. Stock Exchange Firms, 1968-69; bd. govs. Midwest Stock Exchange, 1957-60, N.Y. Stock Exchange, 1970-71. Del. Nat. Rep. Conv., 1984, alternate del., 1988; bd. dirs. Nat. Recreation Park Assn.; mem. Chgo. Crime Commn.; chmn. Modern Cts. Ill., 1970, Met. Crusade Mercy, 1967-68; life trustee U. Chgo., Ch. Internat. House; life trustee, chair Chgo. Ednl. TV Sta.-WTTW, PBS, 1978-89; life trustee Lake Forest Acad.; trustee Lake Forest Coll., 1968-76; bd. dirs. Children's Meml. Hosp., chmn., 1970-75; pres. bd. trustees Latin Sch. Chgo., 1956-58; bd. dirs. U. Ill. Found.; mem. citizens bd. Loyola U.; chmn. Chgo. coun. Boy Scouts Am., 1952-56; mem. Ill. Compensation Rev. Bd.; chair Internat. House, U. Chgo. Comdr. USNR, 1942-46. Recipient Man of Yr. award NCCJ, 1969, Founders award, 1992. Mem. Investment Analysts Soc., Ducks Unltd. (nat. trustee 1980-90), Chgo. Club, Chgo. Univ. Club, Comml. Club Chgo., Links Club (N.Y.C.), Onwentsia Club, Old Elm Club, Seminole Golf Club, Shore Acres Club, Bohemian Club (San Francisco), The Island Club (Hobe Sound, Fla.), Phi Beta Kappa. Home: 550 N Green Bay Rd Lake Forest IL 60045-2146 Office: Merrill Lynch 5500 Sears Towers Chicago IL 60606

MEEUSE, BASTIAAN JACOB DIRK, biologist, educator, researcher; b. Sukabumi, Indonesia, May 9, 1916; came to U.S., 1947; s. Adrianus Dirkszoon and Jannigje (Kruithof) M.; m. Johanne Roberta ten Have, Aug. 28, 1942; children: Karen Barbara, Peter Nicholas. BSc in Biology, U. Leiden, The Netherlands, 1936, M, 1939; D in Tech. Sci., U. Delft, The Netherlands, 1943. Tchr. Hort. Inst., Boskoop, The Netherlands, 1939-42; asst. lectr. U. Delft, 1942-46, chief asst. lectr., 1946-49, lectr., 1949-52; asst. prof. U. Wash., Seattle, 1952-55, assoc. prof., 1955-60, prof. botany, 1960-86, prof. emeritus, 1986—; corr. Royal Dutch Acad. Scis., Amsterdam, The Netherlands, 1965—; vis. prof. U. Nijmegen, The Netherlands, 1985; cons. Shell Devel. Co., Modesto, Calif., 1986-87. Author: The Story of Pollination, 1961, The Sex Life of Flowers, 1984; contbr. articles to profl. jours. Fellow NSF, 1962-63, Rockefeller Found., 1947-49. Mem. Royal Dutch Bot. Soc., Am. Soc. Plant Physiologists, Am. Bot. Soc., Native Plant Soc., Sigma Xi. Club: Holland-America (Seattle). Avocations: photography, hiking, showing films, lecturing. Office: U Wash Botany Dept KB-15 Seattle WA 98195

MEEZAN, ELIAS, pharmacologist, educator; b. N.Y.C., Mar. 5, 1942; s. Maurice and Rachel (Epstein) M.; m. Elisabeth Gascard, May 14, 1967; children: David, Nathan, Joshua. BS in Chemistry, CCNY, 1962; PhD in Biochemistry, Duke U., 1966. Asst. prof. physiology and pharmacology Duke U., Durham, N.C., 1969-70; asst. prof. pharmacology U. Ariz., Tucson, 1970-75; assoc. prof. U. Ariz., 1975-79; prof., chmn. dept. pharmacology U. Ala., Birmingham, 1979-89, prof., dir. Metabolic Diseases Rsch. Lab., 1989-93, prof. dept. pharmacology, 1993—. Asso. editor: Life Sci, 1973-79. Helen Hay Whitney postdoctoral fellow, 1966-69; recipient NIH Research Career Devel. award, 1977-79. Mem. Am. Soc. Pharmacology and Exptl. Therapeutics, Am. Soc. Biol. Chemistry, AAUP, AAAS, N.Y. Acad. Sci., Assn. Med. Sch.Pharmacology. Democrat. Jewish. Isolated retinal microvasculature; developer method for isolating ultrastructurally and chemically intact basement membranes. Home: 1202 Cheval Ln Birmingham AL 35216-2037 Office: U Ala Dept Pharmacology Birmingham AL 35294

MEGAN, THOMAS IGNATIUS, judge; b. Chgo., Dec. 24, 1913; s. Charles P. and May M. (Magan) M.; m. Lucyanne Flaherty, Apr. 17, 1948; children: Anne, Thomas, Jane, Sarah, William, Molly. A.B., U. Ill., 1935; J.D., U. Chgo., 1938. Bar: Ill. 1939, N.Y. 1941. Mem. firm Pruitt & Grealis, Chgo., 1939-40, Pruitt, Hale & MacIntyre, N.Y.C., 1941; atty. U.S. Ordnance Dept., Chgo., 1941-42, Chgo., Rock Island and Pacific R.R. Co., Chgo., 1945-70; v.p., gen. counsel Chgo., Rock Island and Pacific R.R. Co., 1970-74, v.p. law, 1974-75; adminstrv. law judge ICC, Washington, 1975-81, HHS, Washington, 1981, FERC, Washington, 1981—. Served to maj. AUS, 1942-45. Mem. ABA, Soc. Trial Lawyers Chgo., Chgo. Law Club, Phi Kappa Tau, Phi Delta Phi. Club: Union League (Chgo.). Home: 11108 Waycroft Way Rockville MD 20852-3217 Office: 810 First St NE Washington DC 20426

MEGAW, ROBERT NEILL ELLISON, English educator; b. Ottawa, Can., Oct. 7, 1920; came to U.S., 1925, naturalized, 1936; s. John Wesley and Eileen (Ellison) M.; m. Ann Barber, Dec. 20, 1947; children—Peter Kenneth McNeill, Margaret McNeill, Laura McNeill. Student, Duke U., 1937-40; M.A., U. Chgo., 1947, Ph.D., 1950. Mem. faculty Williams Colls., 1950-69, prof. English, 1965; Carnegie intern Harvard U., 1955-56; prof. English U. Tex., Austin, 1969-85; chmn. dept. U. Tex., 1969-72, prof. emeritus, 1985—; cons. acad. planning, 1962—; mem. nat. bd. cons. NEH, 1974—. Contbr. poetry to Hellas, Sequoia, Negative Capability, The Spectator, The Lyric, others. Served to 1st lt. USAAF, 1942-45. Nat. Humanities Faculty, 1969—. Mem. MLA, Am. Ednl. Theatre Assn., AAUP (chmn. research and publ. 1965-71, pres. Tex. conf. 1976-78, chmn. assembly state confs. 1978-81), Tex. Assn. Coll. Tchrs., Tex. Faculty Assn., Nat., Fed., State poetry socs., Poetry Soc. Am., Acad. Am. Poets, Common Cause, ACLU, NAACP, Phi Beta Kappa (speaker, panelist 1980—). Democrat. Home: 2805 Bowman Ave Austin TX 78703-1608 Office: U Tex Dept English Parlin Hall Austin TX 78712

MEGGERS, BETTY J(ANE), anthropologist; b. Washington, Dec. 5, 1921; d. William Frederick and Edith (Raddant) M.; m. Clifford Evans, Sept. 13, 1946. AB, U. Pa., 1943; MA, U. Mich., 1944; PhD, Columbia U., 1952; D (hon.), U. de Guayaquil, Ecuador, 1987, U. Fed. Rio de Janeiro, Brazil, 1994. Instr. anthropology Am. U., Washington, 1950-51; rsch. assoc. Smithsonian Instn., 1954—, expert, 1981—; founder, pres. Taraxacum Inc., 1977—; hon. prof. U. de Azuay, Ecuador, 1991. Author: Environmental Limitation on the Development of Culture, 1954, Ecuador, 1966, Amazonia,

1971, Prehistoric America, 1972, (with Clifford Evans) Archaeological Investigations at the Mouth of the Amazon, 1957, Archaeological Investigations in British Guiana, 1960, (with Clifford Evans and Emilio Estrada) Early Formative Period of Coastal Ecuador, 1965, (with Clifford Evans) Archaeological Investigations on the Rio Napo, Eastern Ecuador, 1968; editor: Prehistoria Sudamericana, 1992. Recipient award for sci. achievement Washington Acad. Sci., 1956; gold medal 37th Internat. Congress of Americanists, 1966; Order Al Merito Govt. Ecuador, 1966; Order Bernardo O'Higgins Govt. Chile, 1985; Sec.'s Gold medal for exceptional service Smithsonian Instn., 1986; Order Andres Bello Govt. Venezuela, 1988; Order Al Mérito por Servicios Distinguidos Govt. Peru, 1989. Hon. fellow Assn. Tropical Biology (councilor 1976-78, pres.-elect 1982, pres. 1983); fellow AAAS; mem. Soc. Am. Archeology (exec. bd. 1962-64), Am. Anthrop. Assn. (exec. sec. 1959-61), Am. Ethnol. Soc., Anthrop. Soc. Wash. (treas. 1955-60, v.p. 1965-66, pres. 1966-68), Academia Nacional Historia, Ecuador (corr.), Phi Beta Kappa, Sigma Xi. Home: 7121 Highway 162 Hollywood SC 29449 Office: Post and Courier 134 Columbus St Charleston SC 29403

MEGGETT, LINDA LINETTE, reporter; b. Charleston, S.C.; d. James Lee and Arabell (Cohen) M. BA in Journalism, Marshall U., 1985. Reporter Herald Dispatch, Huntington, W.Va., 1985-88, Desert Sun, Palm Springs, Calif., 1988-90; reporter govt. Santa Barbara (Calif.) News-Press, 1990-92; reporter higher edn. Post and Courier, Charleston, S.C., 1992—. Author: Black Issues in Higher Education, 1994. Planning com. mem. YWCA, Charleston, 1994—. Mem. Nat. Assn. Black Journalists, S.C. Coastal Assn. Black Journalists (treas. 1993-95), Sigma Gamma Rho (rec. sec. Delta Iota Sigma chpt.). Methodist. Avocations: travel, reading, exercise. Home: 7121 Highway 162 Hollywood SC 29449 Office: Post and Courier 134 Columbus St Charleston SC 29403

MEGHREBLIAN, ROBERT VARTAN, manufacturing executive, physicist; b. Cairo, Sept. 6, 1922; came to U.S., 1923, naturalized, 1946; s. Vahan V. and Mary (Kurkjian) M.; m. Margaret M. Gordon, 1987; children: David V., Susan L. B.Engring. (Gotshall-Powell scholar), Rensselaer Poly. Inst., 1943; M.S. (Guggenheim fellow), Calif. Inst. Tech., 1950, Ph.D. (Guggenheim fellow), 1953. Lectr. Oak Ridge Nat. Lab., 1952-55, asso. project mgr., 1955-58; chief sect. Physics Jet Propulsion Lab., Calif. Inst. Tech., 1958-60, mgr. space scis. div., 1960-68, dep. asst. lab dir., 1968-71, assoc. prof. applied mechanics, 1960-61; v.p. research and engring. Cabot Corp., Boston, 1971-79, v.p., 1971-87; pres. Distrigas Corp., 1979-85; gen. mgr. Cabot Crystals Bus. Unit, 1985-86, dir. corp. planning and devel., 1986-87. Author: Reactor Analysis, 1960. Served to lt. (j.g.) USN, 1941-46, PTO, ATO. Fellow AIAA (assoc.), Am. Nuclear Soc.; mem. Tennis Club Santa Barbara, Santa Barbara Club, Montecito Assn. (bd. dirs., v.p. 1994, pres. 1995, chair archtl. rev. com. 1993-95), Sigma Xi. Home: 440 Woodley Rd Montecito CA 93108-2006

MEGILL, ALLAN D., historian; b. Regina, Sask., Can., Apr. 20, 1947; came to U.S., 1980; s. Ralph Peter and Jean Tudhope (Dickson) M.; divorced; children: Jason Robert, Jessica Susan, Jonathan David. BA, U. Sask., 1969; MA, U. Toronto, 1970; PhD, Columbia U., 1975. From instr. to prof. history U. Iowa, Iowa City, 1974-90; prof. history U. Va., Charlottesville, 1990—; rsch. fellow in history of ideas Australian Nat. U., Canberra, ACT, 1977-79, temp. lectr. modern European studies, 1979; chair Page-Barbour and Richard lectrs. com., U. Va., 1994—. Author: Prophets of Extremity, 1985; editor: Rethinking Objectivity, 1994; co-editor: The Rhetoric of the Human Sciences, 1987; consulting editor: Jour. of the History of Ideas, 1986-89, mem. editl. bd., 1990—; mem. editl. bd. Social Epistemology, 1986—, U. Press of Va., 1991-94; contbr. articles to profl. jours. Mem. Am. Hist. Assn. Office: University of Virginia Corcoran Dept of History Randall Hall # 221 Charlottesville VA 22903-3284

MEGILL, ROBERT EDGAR, retired oil company executive, consultant; b. Lawrence, Kans., Nov. 26, 1923; s. David Lucian and Margaret (Caskey) M.; m. Margaret Ann Webb, Feb. 24, 1945; children: Gregory Alan, Jana Lynn Green. B.S. in Geol. Engring., U. Tulsa, 1948. Various positions Exxon Co., U.S.A., Houston, 1941-84, div. planning mgr., Houston and Corpus Christi, Tex., 1965-73, coordinator planning, Houston, 1973-76, coordinator econ. evaluation, 1976-84; cons. advisor to petroleum industry. Author: An Introduction to Exploration Economics, 3d edit., 1988; How to be a More Productive Employee, 2d edit., 1980; May I Touch Your Life (poems), 1979; An Introduction to Risk Analysis, 2d edit., 1984; Life in the Corporate Orbit, 1981; Long Range Exploration Planning, 1985; contbr. articles to profl. jours. Served with USN, 1942-45, PTO. Mem. Am. Assn. Petroleum Geologists (assoc. editor 1983—, columnist Explorer Mag. 1984—). Republican. Methodist. Lodge: Masons. Avocations: golf; reading; writing. Home: 4314 Valley Branch Dr Humble TX 77339-1867

MEGIVERN, KATHLEEN, association director, lawyer; b. Apalachin, N.Y., Apr. 16, 1950; d. John David and Katherine Augusta (Gibbons) M.; m. James Albert Mecklenburger, Jan. 5, 1986. BA, SUNY, Oneonta, 1972; JD, Cath. U., 1979. Bar: D.C. 1979. Adminstrv. asst. Am. Coun. of the Blind, Washington, 1973-79, staff lawyer, 1979-81; exec. dir. Assn. for Edn. and Rehab. of the Blind, Alexandria, Va., 1981—. Contbg. editor Braille Forum, 1987-90. Bd. dirs. Nat. Accreditation Coun., N.Y.C., 1982-86; treas. Affiliated Leadership League of and for the Blind, L.A., 1986—; mem. Human Rights Commn., Alexandria, 1990—; vice chair Commn. on Disabled, Alexandria, 1989—. Recipient Outstanding Article of Yr. award Am. Coun. Blind, 1979, spl. award Task Force on Rights and Empowerment Ams. with Disabilities, 1991. Mem. Am. Blind Lawyers Assn. (hon.), D.C. Bar Assn., Womens Bar Assn. Avocations: movies, folk music, good books. Office: Assn for Edn & Rehab of the Blind 206 N Washington St Alexandria VA 22314-2528

MEGNA, JEROME FRANCIS, academic administrator, educator; b. Bklyn., Mar. 11, 1939; s. James G. and Irene (Bodkin) M.; m. Doreen Ann Filippi, Dec. 23, 1973; 1 child, Donna Marie. BA, St. Francis Coll., 1966; MA, NYU, 1968, PhD, Ball State U., 1972. Tchr. English Franciscan Bros., Bklyn., 1959-69; instr. English Ball State U., Muncie, Ind., 1969-71; prof. edn. CUNY, Bklyn., 1971-88; dean of edn. Rider Coll., Lawrenceville, N.J., 1988—. Author: Study Guide on Italian Americans, 1978; contbr. articles to profl. jours. Democrat. Roman Catholic. Avocations: reading, music, swimming. Office: Rider Coll 2083 Lawrenceville Rd Trenton NJ 08648-3099

MEHAFFY, THOMAS N., retired tire company executive; b. Rushden, Northamptonshire, Eng., Sept. 23, 1932; came to U.S., 1977; s. James Edward and Sarah (Moloney) M.; m. Catherine Mary Ryle, Mar. 23, 1963; children: Catherine A., Siobhan M., Deirdre E., Brendan R. BSc in Econs., London Sch. Econs., U. London, 1956. Mgr. econ. studies Dunlop Rubber Co., London, 1959-66; mgr. econs. Ford of Britain, Warley, Essex, Eng., 1966-67; mgr. bus. studies Ford of Europe, Warley, 1967-73; dir. profit analysis Brit. Steel Corp., London, 1973-77; dir. corp. planning and market research Dunlop Tire Corp., Buffalo, 1977-91; bus. advisor Dunlop Tire Corp., 1991-93, Trico Products Corp., Buffalo, N.Y., 1993-94. Served with Brit. Arty., 1951-53. Home and Office: 5129 Willowbrook Dr Clarence NY 14031-1476

MEHLFELDT, HORST K., tire manufacturing company; b. 1939; married. Grad., Hamburg U., Germany, 1964. With Enka AG, Upper Wppertal, Germany, 1964-76, Digital Equipment Corp., Maynard, Mass., 1976-85, Temptronic Corp., Newton, Mass., 1985-89; sr. v.p. Gen. Tire Co., Akron, Ohio, 1989—.

MEHLINGER, HOWARD DEAN, education educator; b. Hillsboro, Kans., Aug. 22, 1931; s. Alex and Alice Hilda (Skibbee) M.; m. Carolee Ann Case, Dec. 28, 1952; children: Bradley Case, Barbara Ann, Susan Kay. BA, McPherson (Kans.) Coll., 1953; MS in Edn, U. Kans., 1959, PhD, 1964. Co-dir. social studies project Pitts. pub. schs., 1963-64; asst. dir. fgn. relations project North Central Assn. Schs. and Colls., Chgo., 1964-65; mem. faculty Ind. U., Bloomington, 1965—, prof. history and edn., 1974—, dean Sch. Edn., 1981-90, dir. Ctr. for Excellence in Edn., 1990—; social studies adviser Houghton Mifflin Pub. Co.; cons. U.S. Office Edn. Co-author: American Political Behavior, 2d edit, 1977, Count Witte and The Tsarist Government in the 1905 Revolution, 1972, Toward Effective Instruction in the Social Studies, 1974; editorial bd. Education and Society, history tchr;

editor: UNESCO Handbook on the Teaching of Social Studies, 1981; co-editor: Yearbook on the Social Studies, 1981. STAG grantee Dept. State, 1975. Mem. NEA, Nat. Council Social Studies, Am. Edn. Research Assn., Am. Hist. Assn., Am. Assn. for Advancement Slavic Studies, Phi Beta Kappa, Phi Alpha Theta, Pi Sigma Alpha, Phi Delta Kappa. Home: 3271 Ramble Rd E Bloomington IN 47408-1094 Office: Ind Univ Ctr Excellence Edn 230 N Rose St Bloomington IN 47405-1004

MEHLMAN, EDWIN STEPHEN, endodontist; b. Hartford, Conn., Nov. 30, 1935; s. Sol Abraham and Rose (Slitt) M.; m. Lesley Judith Lunin, June 13, 1959; children: Jeffrey Cole, Brian Scott, Erik Van. BA, Wesleyan U., 1957; DDS, U. Pa., 1961; cert. endodontics, Boston U., 1965. Diplomate Am. Bd. Endodontists. Instr. oral medicine Sch. Dental Medicine Harvard U., Boston, 1965-67; clin. instr. endodontics Sch. Dental Medicine Tufts U., Boston, 1968-70; lectr. endodontics Sch. Dental Medicine Harvard U., Boston, 1970-72, asst. clin. prof. endodontics Sch. Dental Medicine, 1972—; staff assoc. Forsyth Dental Ctr., Boston, 1965—; pvt. practice Providence, 1965—; vis. lectr. dental hygiene U. R.I., Kingston, 1965-71, Community Coll. R.I., Lincoln, 1990—; cons. com. on accreditation of Dentists and Dental Aux. Edn. Programs, 1974-78. Contbr. articles to profl. jours. Pres. Temple Habonim, Barrington, R.I., 1968-70, Bur. Jewish Edn. of R.I., 1980-84; area v.p. Jewish Fedn. R.I., 1975-78; mem. R.I. Legis. Commn. to Study Malpractice Crisis, 1985-86; chmn. R.I. Dental Polit. Action Com., 1987-90. Capt. USAF, 1961-63. Fellow Am. Coll. Dentists, Internat. Coll. Dentists, Pierre Fauchard Acad. (Award of Merit); mem. ADA (coun. on govt. affairs and fed. dental svcs. 1988-92, vice chmn. 1991-92, 1st v.p. 1994-95), Am. Assn. Endodontists (dir. 1988-91), R.I. Dental Assn. (pres. 1986-87). Jewish. Avocations: tennis, reading, civic activities. Home: 6 Ridgeland Rd Barrington RI 02806-4028 Office: 130 Waterman St Providence RI 02906-2010 also: 1090 New London Ave Cranston RI 02920

MEHLMAN, MARK FRANKLIN, lawyer; b. L.A., Dec. 18, 1947; s. Jack and Elaine Pearl (Lopater) M.; m. Barbara Ann Novak, Aug. 20, 1972; children: David, Jennifer, Ilyse. BA, U. Mich., 1969; LLB, U. Mich., 1973. Bar: Ill. 1973; U.S. Dist. Ct. (no. dist.) Ill. 1973. Assoc. Sonnenschein, Nath & Rosenthal, Chgo., 1973-80, ptnr., 1980—. Trustee Groveland Health Svcs., Highland Park (Ill.) Hosp. 1991—; treas. and mem. exec. com. Bd. of Trustees Spertus Inst. Jewish Studies, Chgo., 1992—; vice chmn. regional bd. Anti Defamation League, 1987-89, hon. life mem. nat. commn., 1993—. Mem. Am. Coll. Real Estate Lawyers, ABA (chmn. mortgages and other debt financing subcoms. 1991—, subcom. on loan participation agreements 1988-89, collateralized mortgage obligations subcom. 1987-88). Office: Sonnenschein Nath & Rosenthal 233 S Wacker Dr Ste 8000 Chicago IL 60606-6404

MEHLMAN, MAXWELL JONATHAN, law educator; b. Washington, Nov. 4, 1948; s. Jacob and Betty (Hoffman) M.; m. Cheryl A. Stone, Sept. 15, 1979; children: Aurora, Gabriel. BA, Reed Coll., 1970, Oxford U., England, 1972; JD, Yale U., 1975. Bar: D.C. 1976, Ohio 1988. Assoc. Arnold & Porter, Washington, 1975-84; asst. of counsel Case Western Res. U., Cleve., 1984-87, assoc. prof. 1987-90, prof. law, 1990—, also dir. Law Medicine Ctr. Sch. Law, 1986—; spl. counsel N.Y. State Bar, N.Y.C., 1988-94, Nat. Kidney Found., 1991; cons. Am. Assn. Ret. Persons, Washington, 1992. Editor: High Tech Home Care, 1991; contbr. articles to profl. jours. Active steering com. AIDS Commn. Greater Cleve., 1986-90. Rhodes scholar, 1970; rsch. grantee NIH, 1992-94. Mem. Am. Assn. Law Schs. (chmn. sect. on law, medicine and health care 1990), Phi Beta Kappa. Avocation: skiing. Office: Case Western Reserve U Sch Law-Law Medcine Ctr Gund Hall 11075 E Blvd Cleveland OH 44106

MEHRA, JAGDISH, physicist; b. Meerut, India, Apr. 8, 1937; came to U.S., 1957; s. Bhagwan Das and Shanti Devi (Kakkar) M.; m. Marlis Helene Lehn, Apr. 27, 1959; 1 child Anil. MS, UCLA, 1960; PhD, U. Neuchatel, 1963. Sr. lectr. U. Neuchatel (Switzerland), 1963-64; asst. prof. physics Purdue U., Hammond, Ind., 1964-65; assoc. prof. U. Mass., North Dartmouth, 1965-67; program dir. Sci. Rsch. Assocs. (IBM), Chgo., 1967-69; spl. rsch. assoc. U. Tex., Austin, Tex., 1969-73; prof. Inst. Solvay Inst., Brussels, 1973-88; Sir Julian Huxley prof. UNESCO, Paris, 1989-93; disting. prof. physics The Citadel, Charleston, S.C., 1993—; mem. edit. bd. Founds. of Physics, Denver, 1988—. Author: The Quantum Principle, 1974, Einstein, Hilbert and Theory of Gravitation, 1974, The Solvay Conferences on Physics, 1975, The Historical Development of Quantum Theory, 1982, 87, The Beat of a Different Drum: The Life and Science of Richard Feynman, 1993; editor: The Physicist's Conception of Nature, 1973. Rsch. grantee Krupp Found., 1978-80, J.D. and C.T. MacArthur Found., 1982-85, Minna-James-Heineman Found., 1985-87; recipient Humboldt prize, 1976. Mem. Am. Phys. Soc., Swiss Phys. Soc., History Sci. Soc., Sherlock Holmes Soc. London. Home: 7830 Candle Ln Houston TX 77071

MEHRA, RAJNISH, finance educator; b. New Delhi, Jan. 15, 1950; came to U.S., 1972; s. Bhagwan Das and Raj-Mohini (Vadera) M.; m. Neeru Narula, Jan. 4, 1977; 1 child, Chaitanya. BS in Math. honors, St. Stephen's Coll., U. Delhi, 1966-67; BTech in Elec. Engring., Indian Inst. Tech., Kanpur, 1972; MS in Computer Sci., Rice U., 1974; MS in Indsl. Adminstrn., Carnegie-Mellon U., 1975, PhD, 1978. Instr. adminstrn. and mgmt. sci. Carnegie-Mellon U., Pitts., 1974-76; asst. prof. Queens U., Kingston, Ont., Can., 1976-77; asst. prof., then prof. fin. U. Calif., Santa Barbara, 1985—, dir. Masters of Bus. Econs. program, 1992—; dir. joint econ.-engring. program, 1994—; vis. asst. prof. UCLA, 1980; vis. prof. fin. U. Lausanne, Swizerland, 1981, Sloan Sch. Mgmt., MIT, 1987-89; vis. scholar U. Chgo., 1979, Norwegian Sch. Econs. and Bus. Adminstrn., 1982, Stockholm Sch. Econs., 1988, Wharton Sch., U. Pa., 1990; vis. assoc. Oxford U., 1986; cons. Internat. Monetary Fund, 1989—. Assoc. editor Jour. Econ. Dynamics and Control; contbr. Growth Theory, Vol. 10, Internat. Library of Critical Writings in Economics, 1991, Encyclopedia of Business Cycles, Panics and Depressions, 1995; contbr. articles to profl. jours.; referee mag. jours. in field. William Larimer Mellon fellow, 1974-76; NSF grantee, 1980—. Mem. IEEE (sr.), Am. Econ. Assn., Am. Fin. Assn., Econometric Soc., Tau Beta Pi. Home: 938 W Campus Ln Santa Barbara CA 93117-4344 Office: U Calif Santa Barbara CA 93106

MEHRA, RAMAN KUMAR, data processing executive, automation and control engineering researcher; b. Lahore, Punjab, India, Feb. 10, 1943; came to U.S., 1964; s. Madan Mohan and Vidya Vati (Khanna) M.; m. Anjoo Talwar; children: Archana, Mandira, Kunal. BEE, Punjab Engring. Coll., 1964; MS in Engring., Harvard U., 1965, PhD, 1968. Assoc. prof. Harvard U., Cambridge, Mass., 1972-76; pres., chief exec. officer Sci. Systems Co., Inc., Woburn, Mass., 1976—. Author: System Identification, 1976; also tech. papers on model algorithmic control (Best Paper award Internat. Fedn. Automatic Control, 1983). Recipient Eckman award Am. Automatic Control Coun., St. Louis, 1971. Fellow IEEE. Avocations: hiking, skiing, tennis. Home: 5 Angier Rd Lexington MA 02173-1608 Office: Sci Systems Co Inc 500 W Cummings Park Woburn MA 01801-6506

MEHRABIAN, ROBERT, academic administrator; b. Tehran, Iran. Former prof. MIT, U. Ill., Urbana; dean Coll. of Engring. U. Calif., Santa Barbara, until 1990; past dir. Ctr. Materials Sci. Nat. Bur. of Standards; pres. Carnegie-Mellon U., Pitts., 1990—. Office: Carnegie-Mellon U Office of the Pres 5000 Forbes Ave Pittsburgh PA 15213-3815

MEHRING, CLINTON WARREN, engineering executive; b. New Haven, Ind., Feb. 14, 1924; s. Fred Emmett and Florence Edith (Hutson) M.; m. Carol Jane Adams, Mar. 9, 1946; children—James Warren, Charles David, John Steven (dec.), Martha Jane. B.S., Case Inst. Tech., 1950; M.S., U. Colo., 1956. Registered profl. engr., Wyo., Colo., Nev. Design engr. U.S. Bur. Reclamation, Denver, 1950-56; design engr. Tipton & Kalmbach, Denver, 1956-58; asst. resident engr. Tipton & Kalmbach, Quito, Ecuador, 1959-61; asst. chief design engr. Tipton & Kalmbach, Lahor, Pakistan, 1962-65; v.p. Tipton & Kalmbach, Denver, 1966-73, exec. v.p., 1973-79, pres., 1979—, also bd. dirs. Served with AUS, 1943-45. Recipient Theta Tau award as outstanding grad. Case Inst. Tech., 1950. Fellow ASCE (life); mem. Am. Cons. Engrs. Coun., U.S. Com. on Large Dams, Am. Concrete Inst., U.S. Com. Irrigation and Drainage (life), Sigma Xi, Tau Beta Pi, Theta Tau, Sigma Chi, Blue Key. Methodist. Club: Denver Athletic. Home: 1821

Mt Zion Dr Golden CO 80401-1733 Office: 1331 17th St Denver CO 80202-1566

MEHROTRA, SUDHIR C., engineering company executive; b. 1946. BS, India Inst. Tech., Kampur, India, 1968; PhD (hon.), U. Kan., 1979. Instr., prof. U. Kan., 1968-79; pres., treas. Vigyan, Inc., Hampton, Va., 1979—. Office: Vigyan Inc 30 Research Dr Hampton VA 23666*

MEHTA, A. SONNY, publishing company executive; b. India, 1943. Student, Cambridge U. Worked in paperback publishing U.K.; formerly with Pan and Picador pubs., U.K.; pub., pres. Alfred A. Knopf div. of Random House, N.Y.C., 1987—, now pres., editor-in-chief; pres. Knopf Pub. Group, N.Y.C. Office: Alfred A Knopf Inc 201 E 50th St New York NY 10022-7703

MEHTA, JAY, financial executive; b. Varanasi, India, Aug. 16, 1943; came to U.S., 1970; m. Vineeta Mehta, Feb. 20, 1969; children: Nina, Vineet. MBA in Fin., Rutgers U., 1974; MBA in Taxation, Fairleigh Dickenson U., 1983. CPA, N.J.; cert. mgmt. acct. Contract estimator NE region Otis Elevator Co. Subs. United Techs. Inc., Montvale, N.J., 1970-73, sr. contract estimator NE region, 1974-75; corp. staff acct. Otis Elevator Co. Subs. United Techs. Inc., N.Y.C., 1976-77, sr. corp. acct., 1978; div. contr. OKI Electric Overseas Corp., Hackensack, N.J., 1979-84; corp. contr. OKI Am. Inc., Hackensack, 1984—, sr. dir. fin., treas., 1990, v.p. fin., treas., 1994—; trustee OKI Am. Savs. Plan, 1981—; ofcl. grader Inst. Mgmt. Acctg., Montvale, N.J., 1986—. Mem. Am. Mgmt. Assn., N.J. Soc. CPA's. Republican. Avocations: reading, golf, computers. Office: OKI Am Inc Three University Pla Hackensack NJ 07601

MEHTA, NARINDER KUMAR, marketing executive; b. Lahore, Punjab, India, Feb. 18, 1938; came to U.S., 1959; s. Puran Chand and Raj Rani Mehta; m. Narayanaswamy Sampath; children: Kiren, Ravi. B of Commerce, U. Delhi, India, 1958; MA, U. Minn., 1961. Program dir. All India Mgmt. Assn., New Delhi, India, 1963-67; with Am. Express Co., Chgo., 1968-82; nat. sales dir. Am. Express Co., N.Y.C., 1975-80, v.p. sales, 1980-82; sr. v.p. Shearson Lehman/Am. Express, Boston, 1982-85, Capital Credit Corp., Fairfield, N.J., 1985—; sr. v.p. Temporary Investment Funds, 1982-85, Trust for Short Term Fed. Securities, 1982-85, Mcpl. Fund for Calif. Investors, 1983-85; conducted seminars for profl. assns., colls. and univs. Contbr. articles to profl. jours. Nat. v.p. Muscular Dystrophy Assn., N.Y.C., 1984-86; student body pres. U. Delhi, India, 1958-59. Recipient 1st prize inter-coll. debate, 1958. Mem. Am. Mgmt. Assn., Tau Kappa Epsilon. Avocations: running, swimming, traveling, reading. Office: Capital Credit Corp 492 Route 46 Fairfield NJ 07004

MEHTA, SHAILESH J., banker; b. Bombay, Maharashtra, India, Apr. 22, 1949; came to U.S., 1971; s. Jayantilal B. and Manjula J. Mehta; m. Kalpa S. Doshi, Dec. 19, 1973; children: Sameet, Sheetal. B.S. in Mech. Engring., Indian Inst. Tech., 1971; M.S. in Ops. Research, Case Western Res. U., 1973, Ph.D. in Ops. Research and Computer Sci., 1975. Sr. ops. analyst Cleve. Trust Co., 1973-75, ops. officer, 1975-76, asst. v.p. card ops., 1976-77, v.p. corp. ops. adminstrn., 1979, v.p. advanced systems planning, 1977-78, v.p. info. systems, 1979-82; exec. v.p. banking services AmeriTrust, Cleve., 1974-86; exec. v.p., COO First Deposit Corp., San Francisco, 1986-88, pres., CEO, 1988—; chmn. bd. First Deposit Nat. Bank, Tilton, N.H., 1986—; pres., chief exec. officer, chmn. bd. First Deposit Savs. Bank, Redding, Calif., 1986-90; CEO, chmn. bd. First Deposit Nat. Credit Card Bank, Concord, N.H., 1990—; pres., dir. A.T. Venture Capital Group, Cleve., 1982-86. Mem. community adv. coun. U. Calif., Berkeley, 1991—. Mem. Am. Bankers Assn. (telecommunications group 1984—), Ohio Venture Assn., Calif. Commn. for Econ. Devel's. Adv. Coun. on Asia. Office: First Deposit Corp 88 Kearny St San Francisco CA 94108-5530

MEHTA, VED (PARKASH), writer, literature and history educator; b. Lahore, Punjab, India, Mar. 21, 1934; came to U.S., 1949; s. Amolak Ram and Shanti Devi (Mehra) M.; m. Linn Fenimore Cooper Cary, Dec. 17, 1983; children: Alexandra Sage, Natasha Cary. BA, Pomona Coll., 1956, DLitt (hon.), 1972; BA, Oxford U., Eng., 1959; MA, Harvard U., 1961, Oxford U., Eng., 1962; DLitt (hon.), Bard Coll., 1982, Williams Coll., 1986, Bowdoin Coll., 1995; DUniv. (hon.), Stirling U., Scotland, 1988. Staff writer New Yorker mag., 1961-94; Rosenkranz chair in writing Yale U., New Haven, 1990-93, assoc. fellow Berkeley Coll., 1988—, residential fellow Berkeley Coll., 1990-93, lectr. in English, 1991-93, lectr. in History, 1990-93; Randolph Vis. Disting. prof. English and history Vassar Coll., N.Y., 1994—; Arnold Bernhard prof. English and History Williams Coll., Mass., 1994; vis. fellow lit. Balliol Coll., Oxford U., 1988-89; vis. scholar Case Western Res. U., 1974; vis. prof. lit. Bard Coll., 1985, 86; Noble Found. vis. prof. art and cultural history Sarah Lawrence Coll., 1988; vis. prof. English NYU, 1989-90. Author: Face to Face, 1957 (Secondary Edn. Ann. Book award 1958), Walking the Indian Streets, 1960, rev. edit., 1971, Fly and Fly-Bottle, 1963, 2d edit., 1983, The New Theologian, 1966, Delinquent Chacha, 1967, Portrait of India, 1970, 2d edit., 1993, John is Easy to Please, 1971, Mahatma Gandhi and His Apostles, 1977, 2d edit., 1993, The New India, 1978, The Photographs of Chachaji, 1980, A Family Affair: India Under Three Prime Ministers, 1982, Three Stories if the Raj, 1986, Rajiv Gandhi and Rama's Kingdom, 1995; (autobiog. series) Continents of Exile: Daddyji, 1972, Mamaji, 1979, Vedi, 1982, The Kedge Between the Streams, 1984, Sound-Shadows of the New World, 1986, The Stolen Light, 1989, Up at Oxford, 1993; also articles; writer, narrator TV film Chachji, My Poor Relation, 1978 (DuPont Columbia award). mem. usage panel Am. Heritage Dictionary, 1982. Recipient award Assn. Indians in Am., 1978, Signet medal, 1983, Disting. Svc. award Asian/Pacific ALA, 1986, Liberty medal Mayor of N.Y.C., 1986, Centenary Barrows award Pomona Coll., 1987, Lion medal N.Y. Pub. Libr., 1990, Asian-Am. Heritage Month award N.Y. State, 1991; Hazen fellow, 1956-59, Harvard Prize fellow, 1959-60, Residential fellow Eliot House, 1959-61, Guggenheim fellow, 1971-72, 77-78, MacArthur Prize fellow, 1982-87, N.Y. Inst. for Humanities fellow, 1988-92; Ford Found. grantee, 1971-76, grantee Pub. Policy, 1979-82. Mem. Coun. on Fgn. Rels., Century Assn. (trustee 1973-75). Avocations: Indian and Western music, cycling. Home: 139 E 79th St New York NY 10021-0324

MEHTA, ZARIN, symphony administrator; b. Bombay, India, Oct. 28, 1938; came to Can., 1962, naturalized, 1969; s. Mehli and Tehmina Mehta; m. Carmen Lasky, July 1, 1966; children—Rohanna, Rustom. Chartered acct., London, 1957. Acct. Frederic B. Smart & Co., London, 1957-62; Coopers & Lybrand, Montreal, Que., Can., 1962-81; mng. dir. Orchestre Symphonique de Montreal, 1981-90, dir.; exec. dir., chief oper. officer Chgo. Ravinia Festival, 1990—. Fellow Inst. Chartered Accts. in Eng. and Wales; mem. Ordre des Comptables Agrees du Que. Office: Ravinia Festival 400 Iris Lane Highland Park IL 60035-3662

MEHTA, ZUBIN, conductor, musician; b. Bombay, India, Apr. 29, 1936; came to U.S., 1961; s. Mehli Nowrowji and Tehmina (Daruvala) M.; m. Nancy Diane Kovack; children: Zarina, Merwan. Student, St. Xavier's Coll., Bombay, 1951-53. State Acad. Music, Vienna, Austria, 1954-60; LL.D., Sir George Williams U., Montreal, 1965; D.Mus. (hon.), Occidental Coll.; hon. doctorate, Colgate U., Brooklyn Coll., Westminster Choir Coll., Juilliard Sch., Weizmann Inst. Sci. (Israel). Music dir. Montreal (Can.) Symphony Orch., 1961-67, Los Angeles Philharmonic Orch., 1962-78; mus. dir.: Israel Philharmonic, from 1969, appointed dir. for life, 1981; music dir. N.Y. Philharmonic, 1978-91, guest condr. Met. Opera, Salzburg (Austria) Festival, Vienna Philharmonic, Berlin Philharmonic, La Scala, Milan, Italy, music dir., Maggio Musicale Florence, Italy, rec. artist for. Decca, CBS, RCA, New World Records, (recipient 1st prize Liverpool (Eng.) Condrs. Competition 1958). Decorated Padma Bhushan India, 1967, commendatore of Italy. Office: Israel Philharm Orch, 1 Huberman St Box 11292, 61112 Tel Aviv Israel also: Orch Maggio Musicale, Teatro, Comunale Via Solferino 15, I-50123 Florence Italy

MEHURON, WILLIAM OTTO, electronics company executive; b. Hammond, Ind., Nov. 20, 1937; s. Arthur and Margaret Irene (Soroka) M.; m. Charlotte Anne Nyheim, Aug. 26, 1982; children Kimberly Anne, Kristine Lynn. BSEE, Purdue U., 1959; MSEE, U. Pa., 1962, PhD, 1966. Tech. staff RCA, Moorestown, N.J., 1954-69, GE, Phila., 1966-68; group leader Mitre Corp., McLean, Va., 1969-74; tech. dir. naval intelligence Dept. Navy, Washington, 1974-81; dir. rsch. and engring. Nat. Security Agy., Ft. Meade,

Md., 1981-85; v.p., gen. mgr. data systems div. Ampex Corp. subs. Allied-Signal Co., Redwood City, Calif., 1985-86; sr. v.p. product ops. Daisy Systems Corp., Mountain View, Calif., 1986-88; v.p., gen. mgr. Networks and Info. Security div. Security div. Unisys Def. Systems, McLean, Va., 1988-91; pres. Mehuron Assocs. Inc., 1991—. Mem. IEEE, AAAS, Armed Forces Communication and Electronics Assn., Security Affairs Support Assn., Air Force Assn. Avocations: amateur radio (W4XM), running, tennis, cooking, antiques. Home: 8107 Birnam Wood Dr Mc Lean VA 22102-2712

MEI, KENNETH K., electrical engineering and computer sciences educator; b. Shanghai, China, May 19, 1932; came to U.S., 1956; m. Chiu Huei-Chum, May 16, 1989; children: Cynthia, Audrey, An-kai. PhD, U. Wis., 1962. Prof. U. Calif., Berkeley, 1962—. Contbr. over 100 papers to profl. jours. Recipient Best Paper award Antennas & Propagation Soc. of IEEE, 1967. Fellow IEEE; mem. Union Radio Sci. Internat. Office: Eecs U Calif Berkeley CA 94720

MEIBURG, CHARLES OWEN, business administration educator; b. Seneca, S.C., Dec. 17, 1931; s. Albert and Gladys Katherine (Burley) M.; m. Elizabeth Rhodes Glenn, June 11, 1955; children: Charles O. Jr., Howard Glenn, Elizabeth Rhodes. BS in Arts and Scis., Clemson U., 1953; MA in Econs., U. Va., 1958, PhD in Econs., 1960. Assoc. prof. U. Va., Charlottesville, 1964-69, prof., 1969-82, J. Harvie Wilkinson, Jr. prof. bus. adminstrn., 1982—; dir. Taylor Murphy Inst. U. Va., 1967-83; assoc. dean Darden Sch. U. Va., 1983-89. Co-author: Cases on Financial Institutions, 1979, Cases in Bank Management, 1986; editor (with others) Loan Officers Handbook, 1986. 1st lt. U.S. Army, 1953-55. Mem. Am. Econ. Assn., Fin. Mgmt. Assn., Assn. for U. Bus. and Econ. Rsch. (pres. 1971). Home: 3345 Kirkwood Ct Keswick VA 22947 Office: U Va Darden Sch PO Box 6550 Charlottesville VA 22906-6550

MEIDER, ELMER CHARLES, JR., publishing company executive; b. Buffalo, Feb. 7, 1946; s. Elmer Charles and Marie (Gress) M.; m. Teri René Mertz; children: Lisa Marie, Elmer Charles III, Tracy L., Anna Simms. B.B.A., Cleve. State U., 1971. Advt. research analyst Meldrum & Fewsmith (advt.), Cleve., 1967-69; sales promotion supr. ESB Inc., Cleve., 1969-72; sr. market research analyst, consumer products group Miles Labs., Elkhart, Ind., 1972-74; v.p., dir. mktg. World Book-Childcraft Internat. Inc., Chgo., 1974-83; v.p., gen. mgr. Tandy Home Edn. Systems (div. Radio Shack), 1983-86; pres. Highlights for Children Inc., 1986—; cons. mktg. research and mktg.; bd. dirs. Fifth-Third Bank, Columbus, Ohio. Bd. dirs. Ctrl. Ohio, Vols. Am. Mem. Am. Mktg. Assn., Direct Selling Assn. Republican. Episcopalian. Home: 559 Cardinal Hill Ln Powell OH 43065-9358 Office: Highlights for Children 2300 W 5th Ave Columbus OH 43272

MEIER, AUGUST, historian, educator; b. N.Y.C., Apr. 30, 1923; s. Frank A. and Clara (Cohen) M. AB, Oberlin Coll., 1945; AM, Columbia U., 1949, PhD, 1957; LittD, Rutgers U., 1994. Asst. prof. history Tougaloo (Miss.) Coll., 1945-49; research asst. to pres. Fisk U., 1953, asst. prof. history, 1953-56; asst., assoc. prof. history Morgan State Coll., Balt., 1957-64; prof. history Roosevelt U., Chgo., 1964-67; prof. history Kent (Ohio) State U., 1967-69, univ. prof., 1969-93; prof. emeritus, 1993—. Author: Negro Thought in America, 1880-1915, 1963, (with Elliott Rudwick) From Plantation to Ghetto, 1966, 3d edit., 1976, (with Elliott Rudwick) Black Detroit and the Rise of the UAW, 1979, (with Elliott Rudwick) CORE: A Study In The Civil Rights Movement, 1942-68, 1973, (with Elliott Rudwick) Along the Color Line: Explorations in the Black Experience, 1976, (with Elliott Rudwick) Black History and the Historical Profession, 1986; editor: (with Francis Broderick) Negro Protest Thought in the Twentieth Century, 1966, (with Francis Broderick and Elliott Rudwick) rev. edit. renamed Black Protest Thought in The Twentieth Century, 1971, (with Elliott Rudwick) The Making of Black America, 1969, (with Elliott Rudwick and John H. Bracey, Jr.), Black Nationalism in America, 1970, (with John Hope Franklin) Black Leaders of the Twentieth Century, 1982, (with Leon Litwack) Black Leaders of the Nineteenth Century, 1988, A White Scholar And The Black Community 1945-1965, 1993; gen. editor: Atheneum Negro in Am. Life Series, 1966-74, University of Illinois Press Blacks in the New World Series, 1972—, (with Elliott Rudwick and John Bracey) University Publications of America Black Studies Research Sources on Microfilm, 1980—; mem. editorial adv. bd.: Booker T. Washington Papers, 1967-85, Civil War History, 1970—, Jour. Am. History, 1974-77. Sec. Newark br. NAACP, 1951-52, 56-57; chmn. Balt. chpt. Ams. for Democratic Action, 1960-61, mem. nat. bd., exec. com., 1960-61; active Newark chpt. CORE, 1963-64, Balt. chpt. SNCC, 1960-63. Advanced grad. fellow Am. Council Learned Socs., 1952; Guggenheim fellow, 1971-72; Nat. Endowment for Humanities fellow, 1975-77; Center for Advanced Study in Behavioral Scis. fellow, 1976-77. Mem. Am. Hist. Assn., So. Hist. Assn. (v.p. 1991, pres. 1992), Assn. Study Negro Life and History, Orgn. Am. Historians (del. to Am. Coun. Learned Socs. 1979-83, chmn. program com. 1990). Unitarian. Home: 305 W End Ave # 701 New York NY 10023-8102

MEIER, GEORGE KARL, III, pastor, lawyer; b. Glen Ridge, N.J., Jan. 13, 1944; s. George Karl and Mary Claire (Myers) M.; children: G.K., Leslie; m. Therese DesCamp, Oct. 10, 1992. BS, Washington and Lee U., 1966; JD, Dickinson Sch. Law, 1969; MDiv, Pacific Sch. of Religion, 1992. Bar: N.J. 1969, Oreg. 1970, U.S. Dist. Ct. N.J. 1969, U.S. Dist. Ct. Oreg. 1970, U.S. Ct. Appeals (9th cir.) 1971, U.S. Ct. Appeals (fed. cir.) 1987, U.S. Supreme Ct. 1973. Law clk. NJ Superior Court Appellate Div., 1969-70; assoc. Stoel, Rives, Boley, Jones & Grey, Portland, Oreg., 1970-75, ptnr., 1976-89; spl. dep. atty. gen. State of Idaho, 1988-89; spl. asst. to pres. Pacific Sch. Religion, Berkeley, Calif., 1992; pastor Pioneer Congl. Ch., Sacramento, Calif., 1992—. Co-founder Ctrl. City Concern, 1978, SW Youth Svc. Ctr., Portland; chmn. ctrl. adv. bd. Dept. Human Resources; pres. consistory Hillside Community Ch., Portland, 1984-85; mem. acad. com. Pacific Sch. of Religion, 1989-91; interim dir. youth programs Epworth Meth. Ch., 1992; bd. dirs. No. Calif. New. Conf. of the United Ch. of Christ, 1993—, Francis House, 1992—, Cathedral Pioneer Ch. Homes, Inc., 1992—. Recipient Outstanding Svc. award Cen. City Concern 1976-89. Mem. Oreg. State Bar Assn. Mem. United Ch. of Christ. Office: Pioneer Congregational Ch 2700 L St Sacramento CA 95816-5614

MEIER, GERALD M., economics educator; b. Tacoma, Wash., Feb. 9, 1923; s. Max and Bessie (Nagel) M.; m. Gretl Slote, Oct. 23, 1954; children: David, Daniel, Jeremy, Andrew. BA in Econs., Reed Coll., 1947; BLitt in Econs., Oxford (Eng.) U., 1952; PhD, Harvard U., 1953; MA (hon.), Wesleyan U., Middletown, Conn., 1959. Instr. Williams Coll., Williamstown, Pa., 1952-54; asst. prof. Wesleyan U., 1954-59, prof. econs., 1959-63; prof. econs. Stanford (Calif.) U., 1963—; research assoc. Oxford U., 1957-58; vis. lectr. Yale U., New Haven, 1955-56, vis. assoc. prof., 1956-59, vis. prof., 1959-61; vis. prof. Stanford U., 1962; cons. Asia Soc., Bank Am., East-West Ctr., Food and Agrl. Orgn., Goodyear Internat., NSF, others; internat. lectr. in field. Author: International Trade anbd Development, 1963, Leading Issues in Development Economics, 1964, The International Economics of Development, 1968, 2d edit., 1978, Leading Issues in Economic Development: Studies in International Poverty, 4th edit., 1984; (with R.E. Baldwin) Economic Development, 1957; gen. editor: Econ. Devel. Series, Econ. Theory and the Underdevel. Countries, Human Resources as the Wealth of Nations, 1973, Fin. Deepening in Econ. Devel., 1975, Agrl. and Structural Transformation, 1975, Gen. X-Efficiency Theory of Econ. Devel., 1978; editor: International Economic Reform: Collected Papers of Emile Despres, 1973, Problems of Trade Policy, 1973, Problems of a World Monetary Order, 1982, Problemsod Cooperation for Development, 1977, Toward a New International Development, 1982, La Nueva Era de Desarollo, 1978, Internat. Econs. of Development, International Economics: Theory of Policy, 1982, New International Development POlicy, 1982, Pricing Policy for Development Management, 1983, Pioneers in Development, 1985, Emerging from Poverty: The Economics that Really Matters, 1984, Financing Asian Development, 1986, Pioneers in Development, 1987, Asian Development: Economic Success and Policy Lessons; author numerous chpts. to books and articles to profl. jours. Rhodes scholar, 1948-52, Rockefeller Found. Study Ctr. resident scholar, 1981; Guggenheim fellow, 1957-58, Brookings Nat. Research fellow, 1961-62, Russel Sage Found. resident fellow, 1976-77; Social Sci. Research Council Faculty research grantee, 1968, Internat. Legal Ctr. research grantee, 1970, Rockefeller Found. research grantee, 1974-75. Mem. Am. Econ. Assn. Rhodes Scholars, Am. Econ. Assn., Royal Econ. Soc., Am. Soc. Internat. Law, Phi Beta Kappa. Home: 774 Santa Ynez St Palo Alto

CA 94305-8441 Office: Stanford U Grad Sch of Bus Stanford CA 94305-5015

MEIER, GUSTAV, symphony conductor. Conductor Lansing (Mich.) Symphony.

MEIER, HENRY GEORGE, architect; b. Indpls., July 14, 1929; s. Virgil and Elizabeth (Whiteside) M.; m. Peggy Nelson, June 28, 1953; children: Scott J., Bruce W., Paul T., Thomas A. BArch, U. Cin., 1953. Lic. architect Ind., Mich., Ky., Ill., Iowa, Fla., Ohio; lic. landscape architect Ind. Pvt. practice architecture Indpls., 1964-90; sr. architect Ball State U., Muncie, Ind., 1990—. Contbr. Indiana Architect mag. Bd. dirs. Am. Bapt. Chs./U.S.A., Valley Forge, Pa., 1970-77, Bd. Bldg. Appeals, Indpls. 1979-85. Served to 1st lt. USMC, 1953-55. Fellow AIA (bd. dirs. 1981-85); mem. Ind. Soc. Architects (pres. 1975, Edward D. Pierre award 1979), Constrn. Specifications Inst., Interfaith Forum on Religion Art and Architecture (v.p. 1981). Republican. Lodges: Masons, Shriners.

MEIER, LOUIS LEONARD, JR., lawyer; b. Hawthorne, Calif., Oct. 12, 1918; s. Louis Leonard and Celestine Helen (Gabriel) M.; m. Donna Eleonora Tomacelli-Filomarino, June 5, 1954; children: Renée, Sharon Clark, Catherine, Marina. B.S., U.S. Naval Acad., 1942; LL.B., Georgetown U., 1951; grad., U.S. Naval War Coll., 1963. Bar: Va. 1951, U.S. Supreme Ct. 1970, D.C. 1973. Legal and legis. asst. to Chmn. Joint Chiefs of Staff, Washington, 1965-67; comdr. Guided Missile Destroyer Squadron 18, Atlantic Fleet, U.S. Navy, 1967-69; mem policy planning staff Office Sec. State, Washington, 1969-72; Washington counsel ASCE, 1972-82, exec. dir., 1982-83; sole practice Washington, 1983—. Served to capt. USN, 1941-72. Decorated Legion Merit; recipient U.S.S. Gherardi Battle Efficiency award, 1951, U.S.S. John S. McCain Battle Efficiency award, 1954. Mem. ABA, Nat. Inst. Bldg. Scis., Conf. Fedn. Environ. Engrs., Met. Club, Chevy Chase Country Club, N.Y. Yacht Club, Spouting Rock Beach Assn. Republican. Roman Catholic. Home and Office: 5132 Baltan Rd Bethesda MD 20816-2350

MEIER, MARK F., research scientist, glaciologist, educator; b. Iowa City, Dec. 19, 1925; s. Norman C. and Clea (Grimes) M.; m. Barbara McKinley, Sept. 16, 1955; children: Lauren G., Mark S., Gretchen A. BSEE, U. Iowa, 1949, MS in Geology, 1951; PhD in Geology and Applied Mechanics, Calif. Inst. Tech., 1957. Instr. Occidental Coll., L.A., 1952-55; chief glaciology project office U.S. Geol. Survey, Tacoma, 1956-85; dir. Inst. Arctic & Alpine Rsch. U. Colo., Boulder, 1985-94; vis. prof. Dartmouth Coll., Hanover, N.H., 1964; rsch. prof. U. Wash., Seattle, 1964-86; profl. geol. scis. U. Colo., 1985—; pres. Internat. Comn. on Snow and Ice, 1967-71; pres. Internat. Assn. Hydrol. Scis., 1979-83; Mendenhall lectr. U.S. Geol. Survey, 1982, Walter Orr Roberts Disting. lectr. Aspen Global Change Inst., 1992. Contbr. articles to profl. jours. With USN, 1945-46. Recipient 3 medals Acad. Scis. Moscow, USSR, 1970-85, Disting. Svc. award (Gold medal) U.S. Dept. of the Interior, 1968; Meier Valley, Antarctica named in his honor U.S. and U.K. Bd. Geographic Names. Fellow AAAS (John Wesley Powell Meml. lectr. 1994), Am. Geophys. Union (com. chmn.), Geol. Soc. Am., (com. mem.), Internat. Glaciological Soc. (v.p., coun., Seligman Crystal 1985), Arctic Inst. N.Am. (gov. 1987-93). Office: U Colo Inst Arctic and Alpine Rsch 1560 30th St Boulder CO 80309-0450

MEIER, MATTHIAS S(EBASTIAN), historian; b. Covington, Ky., June 4, 1917; s. Matthias J. and Mary (Berberich) M.; married; 5 children. B.A., U. Miami, 1948; M.A., Mexico City Coll., 1949; Ph.D. in Latin Am. History, U. Calif.-Berkeley, 1954. Lectr. U.S. history San Francisco State Coll., summers 1953-55; lectr. U.S. And Latin Am. history Bakersfield Coll., 1955-63; asst. prof. Fresno State Coll., summer 1956, fall 1962; asst. prof. Latin Am. history Santa Clara U., 1963-66, assoc. prof., 1966-72, prof., 1972-89, Patrick A. Donohoe prof. history, 1983-89, emeritus; Fulbright lectr. Nat. U. Tucuman and Inst. Nacional de Profesorado Secundario, Buenos Aires, Argentina, 1958-59; lectr. U. Ibero-Am., summer 1965; vis. prof. San Jose State Coll., spring 1968. Author: (with Feliciano Rivera) The Chicanos: A History of Mexican Americans, 1972, A Bibliography for Chicano History, 1972; editor: (with Feliciano Rivera) Readings on La Raza: Twentieth Century, 1973, Dictionary of Mexican American History, 1981, Bibliography of Mexican American History, 1984, Mexican American Biographies, 1988, update of Carey McWilliams's North From Mexico (publ. 1949), 1990, revision, update The Chicanos (new title Mexiacn Americans/American Mexicans), 1993. Served with Signal Corps U.S. Army, 1942-46. Mem. Pacific Coast Council Latin Am. Studies (pres. 1964-65, 76-77), Latin Am. Studies Assn., Conf. Latin Am. Historians, Assn. Borderlands Scholars, Nat. Assn. for Chicano Studies. Office: Dept History Santa Clara U Santa Clara CA 95053

MEIER, PAUL, statistician, mathematics educator; b. N.Y.C., July 24, 1924; m. Louise Goldstone; children: Diane, Karen, Joan. B.S. in Physics, Math., Oberlin Coll., 1945; postgrad. program in applied math., Brown U., 1945; M.A. in Math., Princeton U., 1947, Ph.D., 1951. Asst. prof. math. Lehigh U., 1948-49; research sec. Phila. Tb and Health Assn., 1949-51; research assoc. analytical research group, Forrestal Research Ctr. Princeton U., 1951-52; research assoc. dept. biostats. Sch. of Hygiene and Pub. Health, Johns Hopkins U., 1952-57, asst. prof., 1953-55, assoc. prof., 1955-57; assoc. prof. dept. stats. div. biol. scis. U. Chgo., 1957-62, prof. stats., 1962—, chmn. dept. stats., 1962-92, dir. Biomed. Computation Facilities, 1962-69, prof. theoretical biology, 1968-74, acting chmn. dept. stats., 1970-71, chmn. dept. stats., 1973-74, 83-86, Ralph and Mary Otis Isham Disting. Service Prof. Stats. and the Pharm. and Physiol. Scis., 1975-84; spl. fellow NIH U. London Sch. of Hygiene and Tropical Medicine and Imperial Coll., 1966-67; Howard Levene Prof. Stats. Columbia U., N.Y.C., 1992—, chmn. dept. stats., 1992—, head divsn. biostats. Sch. of Pub. Health, 1992—; mem. com. on lung cancer Am. Cancer Soc., 1959-62; mem. spl. study sect. biomath. and stats. Nat. Inst. Gen. Med. Scis. NIH, 1965-70, mem. therapeutic evaluation com., Nat. Heart Inst. 1967-71; mem. adv. bd. Environ. Health Resource Ctr. State of Ill. Inst. Environ. Quality, 1971-75; mem. Task Force on Health Considerations of Nat. Energy Policy Am. Pub. Health Assn., 1972-74; mem. adv. bd. VA Coop. Study of the Pathogenic Effects of Sickle Cell Trait, 1973-78; mem. adv. council dept. stats. Princeton U., 1974-76; mem. Computer and Biomath. Scis. Study Sect. NIH, 1974-77; vis. prof. dept. stats. and ctr. analysis of health practices Harvard Sch. Pub. Health, 1975-76; dir. Data Quality Control Ctr. for Persantine-Aspirin Reinfarction Study, 1975-81; mem. Policy Adv. Bd. Multiple Risk Factor Intervention Trial, 1976-78; mem. Com. on Nat. Stats., 1977-81; mem. Clin. Trials Rev. Com., Nat. Heart, Lung and Blood Inst., NIH, 1978-81; dir. Data Audit Ctr. for Internat. Mexiletine and Placebo Antiarrhythmic Coronary Trial (IMPACT), 1979-85; vis. prof. stats. Columbia U., N.Y.C., 1991-92; mem. adv. com. anti-viral drugs FDA, 1990-93. Fellow John Simon Guggenheim Meml. Found., Ctr. for Advanced Study in Behavioral Scis., Stanford U., 1982-83. Fellow AAAS, Am. Statis. Assn. (bd. dirs., v.p. 1965-67, chmn. com. on computers in stats. 1967, chmn. sect. on tng. 1974), Royal Statis. Soc., Am. Pub. Health Assn., Am. Thoracic Soc., Inst. Math Stats. (chmn. com. on fellows 1979), Am. Heart Assn. (coun. on epidemiology, com. on fellows 1978) Am. Acad. Arts and Scis., mem. Biometric Soc. (exec. com. Ea. N.Am. Region, pres. Ea. N.Am. Region, 1967), Soc. Clin. Trials (pres. 1991-92), Am. Math. Soc., Math Assn. Am., Assn. for Symbolic Logic, Soc. for Indsl./Applied Math, Sigma Xi, Phi Beta Kappa. Office: Columbia Univ Dept Stats 618 Mathematics New York NY 10027

MEIER, RICHARD ALAN, architect; b. Newark, Oct. 12, 1934; s. Jerome and Carolyn (Kalenbacher) M.; m. Katherine Gormley, Jan. 21, 1978; children: Joseph Max, Ana Moss. BArch, Cornell U., 1957; hon. doctorate, U. Naples, Italy, 1991. Registered profl. architect, N.Y., N.J., Conn., Mich., Va., Fla., Ind., Ga., Calif. Architect Frank Grad & Sons, N.J., 1957, Davis, Brody & Wisniewski, N.Y.C., 1958-59, Skidmore, Owings & Merrill, 1959-60, Marcel Breuer & Assocs., 1960-63; architect, prin. Richard Meier & Assocs., N.Y.C., 1963-80, Richard Meier & Ptnrs., 1980—; resident architect Am. Acad. in Rome, 1973-74; vis. critic Pratt. Inst., 1960-62, 65, Princeton, 1963, Syracuse U., 1964; William Henry Bishop vis. prof. architecture Yale U., 1975, 77, vis. critic, 1967, 72, 73, 77; vis. prof. Harvard U., 1977, Eliot Noyes vis. critic in architecture 1980-81; Harvey S. Perloff vis. prof. Architecture, UCLA, 1987; vis. prof. UCLA, 1988; mem. adv. coun. Cornell U. Coll. Art, Architecture and Planning; mem. Jerusalem Com. Exhbns., XV Triennale, Milan, Italy, 1973, Mus. Modern Art, N.Y.C., 1975, Princeton U.,

Biennale, Venice, Italy, 1976, Cooper-Hewitt Mus., N.Y.C., 1976-77, Leo Castelli Gallery, N.Y.C., 1977, Rosa Esman Gallery, N.Y.C., 1978, 80, N.J. State Mus., 1978, Modernism Gallery, San Francisco, Wadsworth Atheneum, Hartford, Conn., High Mus. Art, Atlanta Harvard U., Max Protetch Gallery, 1980, Syracuse U., Mus. Modern Art., N.Y.C., 1981, Whitney Mus. Art, N.Y.C., 1982, Knoll Internat., Tokyo, Japan, 1988, October Gallery, London, 1990, Royal Palace, Naples, Italy, 1991; adj. prof. archtecture Cooper Union, 1963-73. Prin. works include Westbeth Artists Housing, N.Y.C., Bronx (N.Y.) Devel. Ctr., Smith House, Darien, Conn.; house in Old Westbury, N.Y.; Douglas House, Harbor Springs, Mich., Twin Parks NE Housing, N.Y.C., Atheneum, New Harmony, Ind., N.Y. ; house in Palm Beach, Fla., Pound Ridge, N.Y.; Hoffman and Saltzman houses, East Hampton, N.Y., Shamberg house, Mt. Kisco, N.Y., Hartford (Conn.) Sem., Mus. für Kunsthandwerk, Frankfurt, Germany, Des Moines Art Ctr., Iowa; house in Pitts.; High Mus. Art, Atlanta ; Bridgeport Ctr., Conn., Office and Lab. Complex, Germany, 1989, Nat. Investment Bank, City Hall and Cen. Libr., The Hague, The Netherlands, Cornell U. Alumni and Admissions Ctr., Ithaca, N.Y., Canal Headquarters, Paris, Mus. Contemporary Art, Barcelona, Spain, Arp Mus., Rolandswerth, Germany, Swiss Volksbank, Basel, Singapore, The Getty Ctr., L.A., SwissAir Hdqs, Melville, N.Y., Fed. Courthouse, Islip, N.Y., others; author: Richard Meier Architect, Rizzoli, 1984, Richard Meier Architect 2, Rizzoli, 1991, The Getty Ctr. Design Process, J. Paul Getty Trust, 1991; contbr. articles to profl. jours. Decorated officer de l'Ordre des Arts et des Lettres (France), 1984; recipient Arnold Brunner Meml. prize Am. Acad. Arts and Letters, 1972, Albert S. Bard Civic award City Club N.Y., 1973, 1st honor award for excellence in architecture and urban design, 1977, R.S. Reynolds Meml. award, 1977, Archtl. Record award of excellence for design, 1964, 68, 69, 70, 77, Am. Inst. Steel Constrn. award, 1978, 79, design award 1st prize Kunsthandwerk Competition, Frankfurt am Main, Fed. Republic Germany, 1980, Pritzker Prize for Architecture, 1984. Fellow AIA (medal of honor N.Y. chpt. 1980, nat. design com. 1972-74, 12 AIA nat. awards 1968-1993, 31 chpt. awards, N.Y., 1965-93, Chgo. Architecture award, 4 Progressive Architecture awards, 1979, 89, 90, 91 ; mem. NAD, Internat. Inst. Architects, Royal Inst. Brit. Architects (Royal gold medal 1988), Belgian Royal Acad. Art (Lifetime achievement award Guild Hall, 1991, commander de l'Ordre des Arts et Lettres, French republic, 1992). Address: 475 10th Ave New York NY 10018-1120

MEIER, RICHARD LOUIS, futurist, planner, behavioral scientist; b. Kendallville, Ind., May 16, 1920; s. Walter A. and Mary (Lottman) M.; m. Gitta Unger, May 20, 1944 (dec.); children: Karen Reeds, Andrea Meier Whitmore, Alan; m. Robin Standish, Apr. 21, 1992. Student, No. Ill. State Tchrs. Coll., 1936-39; BS, U. Ill., 1940; MA, UCLA, 1942, PhD, 1944. With Calif. Research Corp., 1943-47; exec. sec. Fedn. Am. Scis., 1947-48; with Petrocarbon, Ltd., 1949-50; Fulbright scholar Manchester U. Eng., 1949-50; asst. prof. program of edn. and research in planning U. Chgo., 1950-56; research social scientist Mental Health Research Inst., U. Mich., Ann Arbor, 1957—; asso. prof. conservation Mental Health Research Inst., U. Mich., 1960-65, prof., 1965-67; prof. environ. design U. Calif., Berkeley, 1967-90; prof. emeritus U. Calif., 1990—; vis. lectr. Harvard U., 1959-60; vis. prof. Grad. Sch. Ekistics, Athens, 1962, U. Calif., Berkeley, 1966; cons. on social planning and resources planning Joint Ctr. for Urban Studies, MIT and Harvard U., in Venezuela, 1963-65; developer program for using inter-active media for edn. of illiterates for econ. devel. and population planning in Africa and Asia. Author: Science and Economic Development, 1956, Modern Science and the Human Fertility Problem, 1959, A Communications Theory of Urban Growth, 1962, Developmental Planning, 1965, Resource-Conserving Urbanism for South Asia, 1968, Planning for an Urban World, 1974, Urban Futures Observed: In the Asian Third World, 1980, Ecological Planning and Design, 1993; contbr. numerous articles to profl. jours. Mem. AAAS, Am. Planning Assn., Am. Chem. Soc., Am. Sociol. Assn., Soc. for Gen. Sys. Rsch., Fedn. Am. Scis., Holis-Soc. for Sustainable Future, Internat. Solar Energy Soc. Home: 636 Colusa Berkeley CA 94707

MEIER, THOMAS JOSEPH, geologist, consultant, engineering firm executive; b. Superior, Nebr., June 16, 1948; s. Hugh Milton and Stella Bella (Dugas) M.; student U. Kans., 1966-69, U.S. Army Engr. Sch., 1969, Met. State Coll., 1976-78; BA in Geology, U. Colo., 1980; m. Jo Ann Weeks, June 4, 1968; 1 child, Nicole Victoria. Office mgr. Testing & Engring. Services, Inc., Colorado Springs, Colo., 1972-74; v.p. Thomas E. Summerlee & Assocs., Inc., Vail, Colo., 1974-76; mktg. exec. Fox & Assocs., Inc., Phoenix, Denver, 1976-84, v.p. mktg. corp. hdqrs., Denver, 1984—, dir., 1982—; tech. services rep., geologist, Phoenix, 1981-84; dir. Thomas E. Summerlee & Assos., 1975-76. Rep. Dist. Committeeman, Jefferson County, Colo., 1980. Served with C.E., U.S. Army, 1969-72. Decorated Bronze Star; recipient Meritorious Service award Lai Kae Orphanage, Lai Kae, S.Vietnam, 1970. Mem. Soc. Mktg. Profl. Services, Denver Info. Network, Industries for Jeffco, Soc. Am. Mil. Engrs. (past pres. Phoenix), Am. Mgmt. Assn., U. Kans. Alumni Assn., U. Colo. Alumni Assn., Denver C. of C., Colo. Assn. Commerce and Industry, Metro North C. of C., Nat. Assn. Indsl. and Office Parks, Colo. Mining Assn., Cons. Engrs. Council. Roman Catholic. Contbr. articles to profl. publs. Author: Environmental Geology Digest, 2 vols. Home: 7535 S Jasmine Ct Englewood CO 80112-2464 Office: 4765 Independence St Wheat Ridge CO 80033-2937

MEIER, THOMAS KEITH, college president, English educator; b. Houston, Apr. 12, 1940; s. Herbert H. and Madeleine (Keith) M.; m. Mila Hillard, June 30, 1962; children: John Hillard, Keith Reilly. BA, U. Tex., 1962; AM, Columbia U., 1963; MBA, Harvard U., 1967; PhD, Columbia U., 1969. Fin. mgr., employee rels. mgr. Exxon Co., U.S.A. and Exxon Rsch. Engring. Co., Houston, Florham Park, N.J., 1969-79; pres. Castleton (Vt.) State Coll., 1979-87, Elmira (N.Y.) Coll., 1987—; regent Lee Coll., Baytown, Tex., 1972-73; pres. Vt. Higher Edn. Coun., 1981-82; mem. Johnson Found. (Troutbeck) Leadership Seminar, 1991—; bd. dirs. Chemung Canal Trust Co., Coll. Consortium Finger Lakes, N.Y. Author: Defoe and the Defense of Commerce, 1987; contbr. articles to profl. jours. Bd. dirs. Union County Urban League, Elizabeth, N.J., 1973-76, Rutland Region C. of C., 1982-86, Arnot Art Mus., 1987—, So. Tier Econ. Growth, 1987—, N.E.-Midwest Congl. Leadership Coun., 1988—; bd. dirs. Chemung County United Way, 1990-93, chmn 1992-93; corp. bd. dirs. Rutland Hosp., 1980-87. Lt. U.S. Army, 1963-65. Recipient Outstanding Periodical Essay award Tex. Books Rev., 1979, medal of merit Elmira Coll. Alumni Assn., 1991; Weaver fellow, 1968. Mem. Pico Ski Club, Elmira Country Club, Elmira City Club, Harvard Club of N.Y.C., Phi Beta Kappa, Phi Eta Sigma, Phi Alpha Theta, Theta Xi. Episcopalian. Home: The President's Home 855 College Ave Elmira NY 14901-2001 Office: Elmira Coll Office of Pres Elmira NY 14901

MEIER, WILBUR LEROY, JR., industrial engineer, educator, former university chancellor; b. Elgin, Tex., Jan. 3, 1939; s. Wilbur Leroy and Ruby (Hall) M.; m. Judy Lee Longbotham, Aug. 30, 1958; children: Melynn, Marla, Melissa. BS, U. Tex., 1962, MS, 1964, PhD, 1967. Planning engr. Tex. Water Devel. Bd., Austin, 1962-66, cons., 1967-72; research engr. U. Tex., Austin, 1966; asst. prof. indsl. engring. Tex. A&M U., College Station, 1967-68; assoc prof Tex. A&M U., 1968-70, prof., 1970-73, asst. head dept. indsl. engring., 1972-73; prof., chmn. dept. indsl. engring. Iowa State U., Ames, 1973-74; prof., head sch. of indsl. engring. Purdue U., West Lafayette, Ind., 1974-81; dean Coll. Engring., Pa. State U., University Park, 1981-87; chancellor U. Houston System, 1987-89; prof. indsl. engring. Pa. State U. University Park, 1989-91; dir. div. engring. infrastructure renewal NSF, Washington, 1989-91; dean Coll. Engring. N.C. State U., 1991-93, prof. indsl. engring., 1991—; mem. bd. visitors Air Force Inst. Technology; cons. Ohio Bd. Regents, 1990, U. Arizona, 1989, Indsl. Rsch. Inst., St. Louis, 1979, Environments for Tomorrow, Inc., Washington, 1970-81, Water Resources Engrs., Inc., Walnut Creek, Calif., 1969-70, Computer Graphics, Inc., Bryan, Tex., 1969-70, Kaiser Engrs., Oakland, Calif., 1971, Tracor, Inc., Austin, 1966-68, div. planning coordination Tex. Gov.'s Office, 1969, Office of Tech. Assessment, 1982-86, Southeast Ctr. for Elec. Engring. Edn., 1978—; mem. rev. team Naval Rsch. Adv. Com. Editor: Marcel Dekker Pub. Co., 1978—; Contbr. articles to profl. jours. Recipient Bliss medal Soc. Am. Mil. Engrs., 1986, Am. Spirit award USAF, 1984; named Outstanding Young Engr. of Yr. Tex. Soc. Profl. Engrs., 1966, Disting. Grad. Coll. Engring., U. Tex. at Austin, 1987; USPHS fellow, 1966. Fellow AAAS, Am. Soc. Engring. Edn. (chmn. indsl. engring. divsn. 1978-83), Inst. Indsl. Engrs. (dir. ops. research div. 1975, pres. Ind. chpt. 1976, program chmn. 1973-75, editorial bd. Trans., publ. chmn., newsletter editor engring. economy div. 1972-73, v.p. region VIII 1977-79, exec. v.p. chpt. ops. 1981-83, pres. 1985-86); mem. Ops.

Research Soc. Am., Inst. Mgmt. Scis. (v.p. S.W. chpt. 1971-72), ASCE (sec.-treas. Austin br. 1965-66, chmn. research com., tech. council water resources planning and mgmt. 1972-74), Am. Assn. Engring. Socs. (bd. govs. 1984-86), Nat. Assn. State Univ. and Land Grant Colls. (mem. engring. legis. task force 1983-87), Assn. Engring. Colls. Pa. (pres. 1985-86, treas. 1981-87), Air Force Assn. (advisor sci. and tech. com. 1984-87), Nat. Soc. Profl. Engrs., Profl. Engrs. in Edn. (vice chmn. N.E. region 1985-87, bd. govs. 1983-85), Sigma Xi, Tau Beta Pi, Alpha Pi Mu (asso. editor Cogwheel 1970-75, regional dir. 1976-77, exec. v.p. 1977-80, pres. 1980-82), Phi Kappa Phi, Chi Epsilon. Lodge: Rotary. Home: 7504 Grist Mill Rd Raleigh NC 27615-5411

MEIERING, MARK C., lawyer; b. Roswell, N.Mex., Sept. 28, 1944; m. Gail Marino. BBA, U. Notre Dame, 1966; JD, NYU, 1969. Bar: N.Mex. 1970, U.S. Dist. Ct. N.Mex. 1970, U.S. Ct. Appeals (10th cir.) 1971, U.S. Supreme Ct. 1977; bd. cert. in civil litigation Nat. Bd. Trial Advocacy. Law clk. Hon. D.C. Hill, U.S. Ct. Appeals, Wichita, Kans., 1969-71; asst. U.S. atty. Dist. of N.Mex., Albuquerque, 1971-76; assoc. Rodey Law Firm, Albuquerque, 1976—; asst. staff judge advocate USAR, Albuquerque, 1971-76. Chmn. bd. dirs. Sandia Prep. Sch., Albuquerque, 1991-92. Mem. Am. Bd. Trial Advocates (assoc.), Greater Albuquerque C. of C. Office: Rodey Law Firm PO Box 1888 Albuquerque NM 87103-1888

MEIGHAN, STUART SPENCE, hospital consultant, internist, writer; b. Glasgow, Scotland, Jan. 30, 1923; came to U.S., 1962; s. Stuart Spence and Annie Louise (Brown) M; m. Anne Stewart Henderson, Nov. 4, 1952 (div. 1968); children: Jane Spence, Stuart Spence; m. Louise Rhys McGregor, July 7, 1985. MB, U. Glasgow, 1945. Registrar, sr. registrar Nat. Health Svc., U.K., 1948-57; sr. staff mem. Allan Blair Meml. Clinic, Regina, Sask., Can. 1957-62; internist Cleland Clinic, Oregon City, Oreg., 1962-64; dir. med. affairs Good Samaritan Hosp., Portland, Oreg., 1964-78; pres. Spence Meighan and Assocs., Portland, 1978—; cons. several hosps. and orgns. Contbr. over 100 articles to profl. jours. Lt. Royal Navy, 1944-48. Recipient Disting. Svc. award Am. Soc. Internal Medicine. Fellow Am. Coll. Physicians, Royal Coll. Physicians. Avocations: sailing, tennis, theater, rugby football, music. Home and Office: 408 NW Rainier Ter Portland OR 97210-3347

MEIGHER, S. CHRISTOPHER, III, communications and media investor; b. N.Y.C., Sept. 23, 1946; s. Stephen Christopher and Denise (Connor) Todd; m. Grace Tebbutt, Aug. 8, 1970; children: Elizabeth, Amanda. A.B. Dartmouth Coll., 1968; P.M.D., Harvard U., 1974. Dir. circulation Fortune mag., N.Y.C., 1972-74, Sports Illustrated mag., N.Y.C., 1974-76, Time mag. N.Y.C., 1976-79; v.p. circulation Time, Inc., N.Y.C., 1981-83; pres. Time Distbn. Services, N.Y.C., 1979-81; pub. People mag., N.Y.C., 1983-85, exec. v.p., group pub., 1985-90; pres. Time Inc. Mags. N.Y., N.Y.C., 1990-92; bd. dirs. Book of the Month Club, N.Y.C., Asiaweek Ltd., Hong Kong, Sunset Pub. Co., Southern Progress (Birmingham), Advt. Council, Inc., Mag. Publishers Assn., America Online, Washington. Trustee Boys Club, N.Y.C., South St. Seaport, N.Y.; bd. dirs. Meml. Sloan Kettering Dream Team, Am. Ballet Theatre, N.Y. Recipient Disting. Service award Brandeis U., 1983. Mem. River Club, Brook Club, Racquet & Tennis (N.Y.), N.Y. Yacht Club (trustee), Am. Yacht Club, Lake George Club, Clove Valley Rod and Gun Club. Home: 164 E 72nd St New York NY 10021-4363 Office: Meigher Comm. LP 100 Ave of Americans New York NY 10013

MEIGS, JOHN FORSYTH, lawyer; b. Boston, Dec. 4, 1941; s. Charles H. and Florence S. (Truitt) M; m. Faith C. Watson; children: Amy, Perry, John. BA, Yale U., 1964; LLB, U. Pa., 1969. Bar: Pa. 1969, U.S. Supreme Ct. 1977. Assoc. Saul, Ewing, Remick & Saul, Phila., 1969-76, ptnr., 1976—. Trustee Phila. Maritime Mus., 1978—; mem. Com. of 70, 1976—; trustee Woodmere Art Mus., 1987—. Contbr. articles to profl. jours. Mem. ABA, Pa. Bar Assn., Phila. Bar Assn. Episcopalian. Home: 6 Norman Ln Philadelphia PA 19118-3617 Office: Saul Ewing Remick & Saul 3800 Centre Sq W Philadelphia PA 19102

MEIGS, JOSEPH CARL, JR., retired English language educator; b. New London, N.C., Aug. 29, 1930; s. Joseph Carl and Lola Vann (Eddins) M; m. Elizabeth Eleanor Stevenson, Sept. 12, 1953; children: Geoffrey Montgomery, Jonathan Hervey, Edward Stevenson. BA, Wake Forest U., 1952; MA, Tulane U., 1957. English and French tchr. Aquadale (N.C.) High Sch., 1952-53; tchr. Metairie (La.) Park Country Day Sch., 1954-55; instr. in English Salem Coll., Winston-Salem, N.C., 1957-62, Tulane U., New Orleans, 1962-64, Marquette U., Milw., 1964-67; asst. prof., then assoc. prof. English Ea. Conn. State U., Willimantic, 1967-93, chmn. dept. English, 1972-74, 87-88, 1990-93; ret., 1993; vis. prof. U. Hawaii, Hilo, 1988-89, 94-95. Grantee Carnegie Inst., 1953, Danforth Found., 1960. Mem. Linguistic Soc. Am., Soc. for Pidgin and Creole Studies, Phi Beta Kappa, Omicron Delta Kappa. Democrat. Avocations: photography, gardening, cooking, hiking. Home: PO Box 852 Brooklyn CT 06234-0852

MEIGS, MONTGOMERY CUNNINGHAM, JR., military officer; b. Anapolis, Md., Jan. 11, 1945; s. Montgomery Cunningham and Elizabeth Shoemaker (Griggs) M; m. Mary Ann Mellenbruch, July 6, 1968; children: William Bradford, Matthew Montgomery. BS, U.S. Mil. Acad., West Point, N.Y., 1967; MA in History, U. Wis., 1977, PhD in History, 1982. Commd. 2d lt. U.S. Army, 1967, advanced through grades to brig. gen.; internat. affairs fellow Coun. Fgn. Rels., N.Y.C., 1981-82; exec. officer 2d Armored Cavalry Regiment, Nurnberg, Germany, 1982-84; comdr. 1st Squadron, 1st Cavalry, 1st AD, Schwabach, Germany, 1984-86; rsch. fellow Nat. Def. U., Washington, 1986-87; chief strategic applications br. J-5 Joint Staff, Washington, 1987-90; comdr. 2d Bn., 1st Armored Divsn., Erlangen, Germany, 1990-91; comdg. gen. 7th Army Tng. Command, Grafenwoehr, Germany, 1991-93; chief of staff V U.S. Corps, Frankfurt, Germany, 1993-94; dep. chief of staff ops. HQ USAREUR & 7th Army, Heidelberg, Germany, 1994—. Author: Slide Rules and Submarines, 1990; contbr. articles to profl. jours. Decorated Purple Heart, Def. Superior Svc. Medal, Legion of Merit with oak leaf cluster, Bronze Star medal with V device and 2 oak leaf clusters. Avocation: hunting. Home: Box 3 HQ USAREUR CMR 420 APO AE 09063 Office: USAREUR & 7th Army DCSOPS APO AE 09014

MEIJER, DOUGLAS, retail company executive; b. 1954. With Meijer Inc., 1967—, co-chmn., dir., 1990—. Office: Meijer Inc 2929 Walker Ave NW Grand Rapids MI 49504

MEIJER, FREDERIK, retail company executive; b. 1919. married. Former pres. Meijer, Inc., then chmn. bd., chief exec. officer, 1975-90, chmn. exec. com., chief exec. officer, 1990—, also bd. dirs. Office: Meijer Inc 2929 Walker Ave NW Grand Rapids MI 49504-9428

MEIJER, HENDRIK, retail company executive; b. 1952. With Meijer Inc., Grand Rapids, Mich., 1963—, co-chmn., 1990—. Office: Meijer Inc 2929 Walker Ave NW Grand Rapids MI 49504-9428

MEIJER, MARK, retail executive. With Bud's Ambulance Service, Grand Rapids, Mich., 1977-79; pres. EMS Inc., Grand Rapids, Mich., 1979—, Meijer Companies LTD, Grand Rapids, Mich. Office: Meijer Companies LTD 2929 Walker Ave NW Grand Rapids MI 49504

MEIJER, PAUL HERMAN ERNST, educator, physicist; b. The Hague, Netherlands, Nov. 14, 1921; came to U.S., 1953, naturalized, 1959; s. Herman Willem and Elisabet (Kossmann) M; m. Marianne Schwarz, Feb. 17, 1949; children: Onko Frans (dec.), Miriam, Daniel, Mark, Corinne. Ph.D., U. Leiden, Netherlands, 1951. Research assoc. U. Leiden, 1952-53, Duke U., 1954-55; vis. lectr. Case Inst. Tech., 1953-54; asst. prof. U. Del., 1955-56; asso. prof. Cath. U., Washington, 1956-60; prof. physics Cath. U., 1960-92, prof. emeritus, 1992—, chmn. dept., 1980-83; vis. prof. U. Paris, 1964-65, 72, 78, U. Nancy, 1984, 88; part-time appointment Nat. Bur. Standards; short time appointments at Naval Ordnance Lab., Livermore Radiation Lab., Naval Research Lab., Night Vision Lab., Ft. Belvoir. Author: (with E. Bauer) Group Theory, 1962; editor: Group Theory and Solid State Physics, 1964. Fulbright grantee, 1953-55, 77-78; Guggenheim grantee, 1964-65; Fulbright sr. fellow, 1978. Fellow Am. Phys. Socs.; mem. European Phys. Soc., Phys. Soc. Netherlands, Fedn. Am. Scientists, Fulbright Alumni Assn., Sigma Xi. Research, publs. statis. mechanics solids

and liquids, group theory and other fields. Home: 1438 Geranium St NW Washington DC 20012-1518 Office: Physics Dept Hannan Hall Cath U Am Washington DC 20064 also: Thermo Physics div Nat Inst Stds and Tech Gaithersburg MD 20899

MEIKLE, PHILIP G., government agency executive; b. Glendale, W.Va., Dec. 5, 1937; s. Philip and Caroline Elizabeth (Stephens) M; m. Linda Kay Price, July 14, 1961 (div. Aug. 1976); children—Philip Kevin, Melissa Kay. B.S. in Mining Engring., W.Va. U., 1961, M.S. in Mining Engring., 1965; M.Engring. Adminstrn., George Washington U., 1980. Registered profl. engr. Mining engr. Duquesne Light Co., Pitts., 1961-63; research engr. W.Va. U., Morgantown, 1963-66; materials engr. Mobay Chem. Co., New Martinsville, W.Va., 1966-68; asst. dir. Nat. Ash Assn., Washington, 1968-72; staff mining engr. U.S. Bur. Mines, Washington, 1972-82, div. chief, 1982—; mem. U.S. Nat. Com. for Tunneling Tech.; Nat. Acad. Scis., Washington, 1985-90, chmn., 1988-89; lectr. in field. Contbr. articles to profl. jours., chpts. to books. Recipient Superior Svc. award Dept. Interior, 1980, Meritorious Svc. award, 1986, Disting. Svc. award, 1991, Presdl. Rank award, 1991. Mem. AIME, Fed. Exec. Inst. Alumni Assn., Sigma Xi (life), Tau Beta Pi (life). Republican. Baptist. Lodge: Masons. Avocations: racquetball; tennis; golf. Office: Bur of Mines 810 7th St NW Washington DC 20241

MEIKLE, THOMAS HARRY, JR., foundation administrator, neuroscientist, educator; b. Troy, Pa., Mar. 24, 1929; s. Thomas H. and Elizabeth (MacMorran) M; m. Jane T. Germer, Aug. 26, 1966 (div. 1983); children: David Andrew, Sarah Elizabeth; m. Jacqueline Winterkorn, Sept. 27, 1986. A.B., Cornell U., 1951, M.D., 1954. Intern Jefferson Hosp., Phila., 1954-55; clin. fellow Inst. Neurology, London, Eng., 1957-58; research fellow Inst. Neurol. Scis., U. Pa., Phila., 1958-61; instr., asst. prof., assoc. prof., prof. anatomy Cornell U. Med. Coll., N.Y.C., 1961-87, acting dean medicine, 1976-77, dep. dean, 1977-79, dean, provost, 1980-87; dean Cornell U. Grad. Sch. Med. Scis., 1969-76; v.p. Josiah Macy, Jr. Found., N.Y.C., 1980, pres., 1987—; career scientist Health Research Council, N.Y.C., 1969-71. Served to capt. M.C. AUS, 1955-57, Korea. Markle Found. scholar in acad. medicine, 1963-68. Home and Office: Josiah Macy Jr Found 44 E 64th St New York NY 10021-7306

MEIKLEJOHN, ALVIN J., JR., state senator, lawyer, accountant.; b. Omaha, June 18, 1923; B.S., J.D., U. Denver, 1951; m. Lorraine J. Meiklejohn; children: Pamela Ann, Shelley Lou, Bruce Ian, Scott Alvin. Mem. Colo. Senate from 19th dist., 1976—, chmn. com. edn.; mem. Edn. Commn. of States, 1981—, chmn. Colo. Commn. on Ach. in Edn., 1995; chmn., 1993—. Mem. Jefferson Sch. Dist. No. R-1 Bd. Edn., 1971-77, pres., 1973-77; commnr. Commn. on Uniform State Laws, 1988—. Served to capt. U.S. Army, 1940-46; to maj. USAF, 1947-51. Mem. Colo. Soc. CPA's, Arvada C. of C. Republican. Clubs: Masons, Shriners. Home: 7540 Kline Dr Arvada CO 80005-3732 Office: Jones & Keller PC 1625 Broadway Ste 1600 Denver CO 80202-4730

MEIKLEJOHN, DONALD, philosophy educator; b. Providence, June 1, 1909; s. Alexander and Nannine (LaVilla) M; m. Betty Moore, Aug. 25, 1941; children: Alexander M., Douglas, Elizabeth, Donald Stuart. AB, U. Wis., 1930; PhD, Harvard, 1936. Instr. philosophy Dartmouth, 1936-38; assoc. prof. philosophy Coll. William and Mary, 1938-46; assoc. prof. U. Chgo., 1946-59, prof., 1959-63; chmn. Coll. Social Sci. Group, 1958-61; prof. philosophy and social sci. Syracuse U., 1963—, dir. pub. affairs and citizenship Maxwell Sch., 1963-75, emeritus, 1975—, adj. prof. pub. affairs, 1989-94; vis. prof. Coll. of the Atlantic, Bar Harbor, Maine, 1979-83, faculty, 1983—. Author: Freedom and the Public, 1965; co-author: Participation in Government, 1988; articles in field. Served from pvt. to 1st lt. AUS, 1942-46. Mem. ACLU (dir. Ill.), Am. Phi Beta Kappa. Club: Hyde Park Neighborhood (dir.). Home: RR 1 Box 309 East Calais VT 05650-9704 *A life-long career as a teacher in American colleges has been tremendously rewarding in terms both of intellectual stimulus and personal association. The chance such a career offers to follow, however inadequately, the example of Socrates in questioning the fundamental values and concepts effective in American public life is as much, I believe, as any teacher may fairly expect. For this I am deeply grateful.*

MEIKSIN, ZVI H., electrical engineering educator; b. 1926. BSEE, Israel Inst. Tech., Haifa, 1950, Dipl. Ing., 1951; MSEE, Carnegie Mellon U., 1953; PhDEE, U. Pitts., 1959. Registered profl. engr. Pa. Design engr. McGraw Edison, Cannonsburg, Pa., 1953-54; sr. project engr. Westinghouse Electric Corp., Pitts., 1956-59; prof. dept. elec. engring. U. Pitts., 1959-91; prof. emeritus, 1991—; pres. Transcom. Co., Pitts., 1989—; cons. entr. 33 orgns. in U.S., Europe, 1959—. Author: Thin & Thick Films, 1976, Active Filter Design, 1990; co-author: Electronic Design, 1980, 84, Microprocessor Based Design, 1986; jour. referee profl. publs., 1970—; contbr. articles to profl. jours.; inventor, holder 6 patents in field. Fellow IEEE (award coms.); mem. Eta Kappa Nu, Sigma Xi. Office: Transcom Co PO Box 8113 Pittsburgh PA 15217-0113

MEILAN, CELIA, food products executive; b. Bklyn., Jan. 21, 1920; d. Ventura Lorenzo and Susana (Prego) M. Student, CCNY, 1943-46. Codes and ciphers translator security divsn. U.S. Censorship Office, N.Y.C., 1942-46; sec., treas. Albumina Supply Co., N.Y.C., 1946-55; co-founder, co-owner, sec., treas., fin. officer Internat. Proteins Corp., Fairfield, N.J., 1955-86, exec. v.p., 1986-93; pres. Internat. Proteins Corp., Fairfield, 1993; also bd. dirs. Internat. Proteins Corp., Fairfield, N.J.; bd. dirs. Pesquera Taboquilla, Panama City, Republic of Panama, 1969—, Inversiones Pesqueras S.A., Brit. V.I.; v.p., bd. dirs. Atlantic Shippers of Tex. Inc., Port Arthur, 1989, Atlantic Shippers Inc., Morehead City, N.C., Empacadora Nacional S.A., Panama City, Republic of Panama; exec. v.p., bd. dirs. Fairfield Fishing Co., Liberia, Internat. Proteins Chile S.A., Santiago. Named One of Top 50 Women Bus. Owners, Working Woman mag. and Nat. Found. Women Bus. Owners, 1994, 95. Mem. Nat. Found. Women Bus. Owners, Spanish Benevolent Soc. (bd. dirs. 1955-62). Avocations: travel, hand crafts, backgammon, puzzles. Office: 204 Passaic Ave Fairfield NJ 07004-3407

MEILGAARD, MORTEN CHRISTIAN, food products executive, international consultant; b. Vigerslev, Denmark, Nov. 11, 1928; s. Anton Christian Meilgaard and Ane Maria Elisa Larsen; m. Manon Meadows, Oct. 29, 1962; children: Stephen Paul, Justin Christian. MSChemE, Tech. U. Denmark, 1952, DS in Food Sci., 1982. Rsch. chemist Carlsberg Breweries, Copenhagen, Denmark, 1947-57; dir. and co-owner Alfred Jorgensen Lab. for Fermentation, Copenhagen, 1957-67; dir. rsch. and devel. Cerveceria Cuauhtemoc, Monterrey, Mex., 1967-73; v.p. rsch. Stroh Brewery Co., Detroit, 1973-89, pres. Strohtech Inc. div., 1986-91; cons., 1991—; vis. prof. Agrl. U. Denmark, 1994—. Author: Sensory Evaluation Techniques, 1987, 2d edit., 1991; contbr. articles to profl. jours. Recipient Schwarz award, 1974. Fellow Inst. Technologists; mem. Internat. Med. Advisory Group, European Chemoreception Rsch. Orgn., Assn. Chemoreception Scis., Inst. Food Technologists, Am. Chem. Soc., Dansk Ingeniorforening, Am. Wine Soc., Air Pollution Control Assn., Master Brewers Assn. Am. (chmn. various coms., award of merit 1990), Am. Soc. Brewing Chemists (chmn. various coms.), ASTM (chmn. various coms., award of merit 1992), U.S. Hop Rsch. Coun. (pres. 1978-80, 1982-84, founder). Avocations: theatre, music, sailing, skiing. Home: 2938 Moon Lake Dr West Bloomfield MI 48323-1841 Office: Stroh Brewery Co 100 River Place Dr Detroit MI 48207-4291

MEILING, GEORGE ROBERT LUCAS, bank holding company executive; b. Columbus, Ohio, Nov. 28, 1942; s. Richard Lewis and Ann Elizabeth (Lucas) M. BA, Yale U., 1964; MBA, Harvard U., 1966. With Chem. Bank, N.Y.C., 1966; contr. Bank One Columbus, Ohio, 1971-73; asst. treas. Banc One Corp., Columbus, 1973-77, treas., 1977—. Mem. alumni bd. Columbus Acad., 1974-78; bd. dirs. Greater Columbus Arts Coun., 1986-87, Pro Musica, 1987-90, AmeriFlora '92, Columbus Light Opera Co., 1990-92; treas., bd. dirs. Am. Rose Soc., 1987-91. Capt. USAF, 1966-69. Mem. Nat. Investor Rels. Inst., Bank Investors Rels. Assn., Assn. Yale Alumni (dir. 1978-80), Green Lawn Cemetary Assn. (dir. 1988—), Army and Navy Club, Yale Club, Columbus Club (dir. 1994—), Yale Cen. Ohio Club (pres. 1976-78), Columbus Country Club. Anglican. Home: 91 N Columbia Ave Columbus OH 43209-1414 Office: Banc One Corp 100 E Broad St Columbus OH 43271-0251

MEILING, GERALD STEWART, materials scientist; b. Provo, Utah, Sept. 12, 1936; s. Harry Louis and Iona (Falker) M.; m. Jane Olive Sprunt, July 20, 1962; children—John Scott, William David, Marcine Elizabeth. B.S., U. Utah, 1958; M.S., MIT, 1959, Sc.D., 1966. Sr. scientist Corning, Inc., N.Y., 1966-69, devel. assoc., 1971-76, devel. mgr., 1976-82, dir. devel., 1982-86, dir. rsch., 1986—, v.p., sr. v.p., 1994—; sr. rsch. scientist Signetics, Sunnyvale, Calif., 1969-71; bd. dirs. Samsung Corning, Seoul, Korea; mem. earth scis. adv. bd. Stanford U., 1985—; mem. materials sci. adv. bd. U. Calif. Santa Barbara, Cornell U. Patentee in photochromics. Fellow Am. Ceramic Soc.; mem. IEEE, N.Y. Acad. Scis., Indsl. Rsch. Inst., Sigma Xi. Republican. Mem. LDS Ch. Office: Corning Inc R&D Labs Sullivan Park Corning NY 14830

MEILMAN, EDWARD, physician; b. Boston, Apr. 6, 1915; s. Harry and Jennie (Sholofsky) M.; m. Rhoeda Berman, Mar. 6, 1946. A.B., Harvard U., 1936, M.D., 1940. Intern Mt. Sinai Hosp., N.Y.C., 1940-42; resident Beth Israel Hosp., Boston, 1946-48; assoc. in med. and med. research Beth Israel Hosp., 1948-53; chmn. dept. medicine L.I. Jewish-Hillside Med. Center, New Hyde Park, N.Y., 1953-82, chmn. emeritus dept. medicine, 1982—; prof. medicine SUNY, Stony Brook, 1971—. Contbr. articles to profl. jours. Served with USAAF, 1942-46. Fellow N.Y. Acad. Medicine, N.Y. Acad. Scis.; mem. Am. Heart Assn. (fellow council clin. cardiology, council arteriosclerosis), Am. Fedn. Clin. Research, Harvey Soc., Am. Rheumatism Assn., Phi Beta Kappa, Alpha Omega Alpha. Democrat. Jewish. Club: Harvard (N.Y.C.); Harvard (L.I.).

MEIMA, RALPH CHESTER, JR., corporate execuitve, former foreign service officer; b. Chgo., Mar. 29, 1927; s. Ralph Chester and Grace Georgine (Larson) M.; children: Ralph Chester III, Stephen H.; m. Elizabeth B. Frazier, 1994. B.A., U. Americas, Mexico City, 1952; M.B.A., Am. U., 1964. With Carborundum Co., Perth Amboy, N.J., 1952-53, Johns-Manville Corp., N.Y.C., 1953-58, Security Storage Co., Washington, 1958-61, Dept. Commerce, 1961-68; joined U.S. Fgn. Service, 1968; consul gen. Marseille, France, 1977-80; on loan as export devel. cons. State of Md., 1980-82; pres. Atlantic Eastern Corp., 1982-87, Phoenix Internat. Mktg. Corp., 1987-89; pres., chief exec. officer FTI Inc., Annapolis, Md., 1989—. Served with USN, 1945-46. Office: FTI Inc 1812 Margaret Ave Annapolis MD 21401-4108

MEINDL, JAMES DONALD, electrical engineering educator, administrator; b. Pitts., Apr. 20, 1933; s. Louis M. and Elizabeth F. (Steinhauser) M.; m. Frederica Ziegler, May 21, 1961; children: Peter James, Candace Ann. B.S., Carnegie Mellon U., 1955, M.S., 1956, PhD, 1958. Engr. Autonetics Co., Downey, Calif., 1957, Westinghouse Co., Pitts., 1958-59; head sect. microelectronics U.S. Army Electronics Command, Ft. Monmouth, N.J., 1959-62; chief br. semicondr. and microelectronics U.S. Army Electronics Command, 1962-65, dir. div. integrated electronics, 1965-67; assoc. prof. elec. engring. Stanford U., 1967-70, prof., 1970-84, John M. Fluke prof. elec. engring., 1984-86, assoc. dean research, 1984-86, dir. integrated circuits lab., 1969-84; co-founder Telesensory Systems Inc., 1971-84; dir. Electronics Labs., Stanford U., 1972-86, dir. Ctr. Integrated Systems, 1981-86; v.p. acad. affairs, provost Rensselaer Poly. Inst., Troy, N.Y., 1986-88, prof. sci. and engring., 1986-93, sr. v.p. acad. affairs, provost, 1988-93; Joseph M. Pettit Chair prof. microelectronics Ga. Inst. Tech., Atlanta, 1993—; cons. to govt., industry. Author: Micropower Circuits, 1969; editor: Brief Lessons in High Technology, 1989; patentee integrated cir. field; contbr. numerous articles to profl. publs. Served to 1st lt. AUS, 1959-61. Recipient Arthur S. Flemming Commn. award Washington Jr. C. of C., 1967; J.J. Ebers award IEEE Electron Devices Soc., 1980. Fellow IEEE (Solid State Circuits Coun. editor jour. 1966-71, Internat. Outstanding Paper ann. awards 1970, 75-78, Beatrice K. Winner award Internat. conf. 1988, solid State Circuits medal, 1989, Edn. medal 1990), AAAS, Am. Acad. Arts and Scis.; mem. AAUP, NAE, Am. Soc. Engr. Edn. (Benjamin Garver Lamme edal 1991), Electrochem. Soc., Biomed. Engring. Soc. (co-editor Annals of Biomed. Engring. 1976-80), Sigma Xi, Tau Beta Pi, Eta Kappa Nu, Phi Kappa Phi. *

MEINDL, ROBERT JAMES, English language educator; b. Wausau, Wis., Sept. 17, 1936; s. George Martin and Adeline Emilie (Goetsch) M.; m. Victoria Lynn Chavez; children: Karin Rose, George Andrew, Damian Kurt, Erika Wittmer, Christopher Smith, Gabrielle Remelia. BS, U. Wis., 1958; MA, U. Conn., 1960; PhD, Tulane U., 1965. Teaching asst. U. Conn., Storrs, 1958-60; teaching fellow Tulane U., 1960-62; lectr. U. Wis., Green Bay, 1963-65; from asst. to full prof. English Calif. State U., Sacramento, 1965—. Translator: Studies in John Gower, 1981; book rev. editor: Studia Mystica Jour., 1984-89; contbr. numerous articles to profl. jours. With USNR, 1953-61, 79—, PTO, ETO. Mem. Medieval Acad. Am., Modern Lang. Assn., Sacramento Turn Verein (v.p. 1976-77, sec. 1977-79), Medieval Assn. of the Pacific, Early English Text Soc. Home: 3320 M St Sacramento CA 95816-5336 Office: Calif State U 6000 J St Sacramento CA 95819-2605

MEINEL, ADEN BAKER, optics scientist; b. Pasadena, Calif., Nov. 25, 1922; s. John G. and Gertrude (Baker) M.; m. Marjorie Steele Pettit, Sept. 5, 1944; children: Carolyn, Walter, Barbara, Elaine, Edward, Mary, David. AB, U. Calif., Berkeley, 1947, PhD, 1949; DSc (hon.), U. Ariz., 1990, U. Ariz., 1990. Assoc. prof. Yerkes Obs., U. Chgo., Williams Bay, Wis., 1950-57; dir. Kitt Peak Nat. Obs., Tucson, 1958-60; prof. U. Ariz., Tucson, 1961-85; dir. Steward Obs., Tucson, 1962-67, Optical Scis. Ctr., Tucson, 1966-73; Disting. scientist Jet Propulsion Lab., Pasadena, 1985-93; ret., 1993; regent Calif. Luth. Coll., 1961-71; cons. USAF Spl. Projects Office, 1965-80. Co-author: Applied Solar Energy, 1976, Sunsets, Twilights and Evening Skies, 1983. Recipient Warner prize Am. Astron. Soc., 1954, Van Blesbroeck award Astron. Soc. Pacific, 1990, NASA Exceptional Scientific Achievement medal, 1993; Aden B. Meinel bldg. U. Ariz., dedicated 1993. Fellow Am. Acad Arts and Scis., Optical Soc. Am. (pres. 1972-73, Adolph Lomb medal 1952, Ives medal 1980), Internat. Optical Engring. Soc. (Goddard award 1984, Kingslake medal and prize, 1993). Home: 1600 Shoreline Dr Santa Barbara CA 93109-2024

MEINERT, JOHN RAYMOND, clothing manufacturing and retailing executive, investment banker; b. White Cloud, Mich., Aug. 11, 1927; m. Joyce Macdonell, Nov. 5, 1955; children: Elizabeth Tinsman, Pamela Martin. Student, U. Mich., 1944-45; B.S., Northwestern U., 1949. C.P.A. Ill., 1952. With Hart Schaffner & Marx/Hartmarx Corp., Chgo., 1950-90, exec. v.p., 1975-80, vice chmn., 1981-85, sr. vice chmn., 1985-86, chmn., 1987-90, chmn. emeritus, 1990—, also bd. dirs.; now prin., investment banking J.H. Chapman Group, Ltd., Rosemont, Ill.; bd. dirs. Evanston Hosp., The John Evans Club; trustee Amalgamated Ins. Fund, 1980-90; instr. acctg. Northwestern U., 1949; faculty Lake Forest Grad. Sch. Mgmt., 1994—; arbitrator Am. Arbitration Assn., 1993—. Bd. dirs. Better Bus. Bur.; chmn. U. Ill. Bus. Adv. Coun., 1989-90; fin. acctg. stds. adv. coun., 1989-92, Chgo. com. of coun. on fgn. rels., sister cities com. With U.S. Army, 1945-46. Recipient Alumni Merit award Kellogg Grad. Sch. Northwestern U., 1989. Mem. AICPAs (v.p. 1985-86, dir. 1975-78, coun. mem 1971-93, Gold Medal award 1987, trustee Benevolent Fund 1992—), Ill. CPA Soc. (pres. 1982-83, dir. 1966-68, 81-84, Hon. award), Clothing Mfrs. Assn. (dir. 1980-90, pres. 1982-87, chmn. 1987-90), Rotary/One Chgo. (pres. 1989-90, trustee found. 1991—), Chgo. C. of C. (bd. dirs.), Northwestern U. (Kellogg adv. coun., Alumni Merit award 1989, Kellogg Grad. Sch.), Univ. Club, Execs. Club, Rolling Green Country Club. Presbyterian (elder). Home: 634 Ironwood Dr Arlington Heights IL 60004-5818 Office: J H Chapman Group Ltd 9700 W Higgins Rd Des Plaines IL 60018-4796

MEING, DONALD WILLIAM, geography educator; b. Palouse, Wash., Nov. 1, 1924; s William August and Annie (Malsed) M.; m. Lee McAuliffe, June 29, 1946; children: Laurel, Kristin, Lee. B.S., Georgetown U., 1948; M.A., U. Wash., 1950, Ph.D., 1953. From asst. prof. to assoc. prof. U. Utah, Salt Lake City, 1950-59; assoc. prof. geography Syracuse U., N.Y., 1959-73, Maxwell prof. geography, 1973-89; Maxwell rsch. prof. Syracuse U., 1990—; lectr. St. Andrews U., Scotland, 1973, Charles Homer Haskins lectr. Am. Coun. Learned Socs., 1992; vis. prof. Hebrew U., Jerusalem, 1974; adv. editor Wadsworth Pub. Co., 1957-61, Harper & Row, N.Y., 1965-83; chief editorial cons. Nat. Geog. Soc., Washington, 1982-88. Author: On the Margins of the Good Earth, 1962, The Great Columbia Plain, fresh, England Texas, 1969, Southwest, 1971, The Shaping of America, Vol. 1: Atlantic America 1492-1800, 1986, Vol. 2: Continental America 1800-1867, 1993;

editor: The Interpretation of Ordinary Landscapes, 1979. Mem. N.Y. Council for Humanities, 1979-86. Served to 2d lt. U.S. Army, 1943-46. Recipient Emil and Kathleen Sick award in Western History, 1968, award of Merit Seattle Hist. Soc., 1968, award of Merit Am. Assn. State and Local History, 1969, Summerfield G. Roberts award Sons Republic of Tex., 1969, Faculty Enrichment award Can Embassy, 1980, Master Tchr. award Nat. Coun. for Geog. Edn., 1986, Charles P. Daly medal Am. Geog. Soc., 1986; Fulbright rsch. scholar U. Adelaide, 1958; Guggenheim fellow, 1966-67, NEH fellow, 1987-88. Fellow Brit. Acad. (corr.); mem. Assn. Am. Geographers (councilor 1965-67, Meritorious Contbn. award), Am. Antiquarian Soc. Office: Syracuse U Dept Geography Syracuse NY 13244-1090

MEINKE, PETER, writer, retired educator; b. Bklyn., Dec. 29, 1932; s. Harry Frederick Meinke and Kathleen Dorothy (McDonald) Lewis; m. Jeanne Clark, Dec. 14, 1957; children: Perrie Sue, Peter Thomas, Gretchen, Timothy Clark. AB, Hamilton Coll., 1955; MA, U. Mich., 1961; PhD, U. Minn., 1965. Tchr. Mountain Lakes (N.J.) High Sch., 1958-60; instr. Hamline U., St. Paul, 1961-66; prof. literature, dir. writing Eckerd Coll., St. Petersburg, Fla., 1966-93; writer-in-residence Hamline U., St. Paul, 1974, George Washington U., Washington, 1981-82, Thurber House, Columbus, Ohio, 1987, Davidson (N.C.) Coll., 1989, Austin Peay State U., Clarksville, Tenn., 1995; writer-in-residence, vis. disting. writer U. Hawaii, 1993. Author: Night Watch on the Chesapeake, 1987, The Piano Tuner, 1986 (Flannery O'Connor award for short fiction 1986), Trying to Surprise God, 1981, The Rat Poems, 1978, The Night Train and the Golden Bird, 1977, Underneath the Lantern, 1986, Liquid Paper: New and Selected Poems, 1991, Far From Home, 1987. With U.S. Army, 1955-57. Recipient Gustav Davidson award, 1976, Lucille Medwick award, 1984, Robert A. Staub Outstanding Tchr. award Eckerd Coll., 1990, Emily Dickinson award, 1992, Paumanok Poetry award, 1993; creative writing fellow Nat. Endowment for Arts, 1974, 89; named Fulbright Sr. Lectr., U. Warsaw, 1978-79. Mem. PEN, Poetry Soc. Am., Nat. Book Critics Circle. Avocations: sports, music. Home: 147 Wildwood Ln SE Saint Petersburg FL 33705-3222

MEINKE, ROY WALTER, electrical engineer, consultant; b. Cleve., Aug. 7, 1929; s. George F. and Marie (Reyer) M. BS, Miami U., Oxford, Ohio, 1952; postgrad. Ohio State U., 1952-53, 67-68; postgrad. in engring. Columbia Pacific U., 1985—. Asst. instr. dept. math. Ohio State U., Columbus, 1953; tchr. high sch., Edgerton, Ohio, 1953-54, Kingman, Ariz. 1954-56; aerodynamics engr. N.Am. Aviation, Los Angeles, 1956-57; instr. physics dept. Central State Coll., Edmond, Okla., 1957-58; elec. engr. Boeing Co., Seattle, 1958-62. Huntsville, Ala., 1962-74; mem. staff engring. mgmt. Lockheed Corp., Houston, 1974-88; ind. lectr., cons. on aerospace dynamic system, 1988—. Co-pilot Mercy Flight Systems, 1973-74; treas. Houston United Campus Christian Life Com., 1983; dir. S.E. Conf. Chs., 1969-73; rep. Tex. Conf. Chs., 1989-93; judge Harris County Optimists Club Youth Scholarship Fund, 1983-85. Recipient Apollo Achievement award NASA, 1970, Group Achievement awards, 1979, 82, 83; recipient Phase III Pilot Proficiency Wings Dept. Transp., 1982, Awareness Cert. of Appreciation, NASA, 1987. Mem. IEEE (sr.), AIAA (assoc. fellow 1991), AAAS. Mem. United Ch. of Christ. Home: 2935 Calder Dr # 8E League City TX 77573-6734

MEINWALD, JERROLD, chemist, educator; b. Bklyn., Jan. 16, 1927; s. Herman and Sophie (Baskind) M.; m. Yvonne Chu, June 25, 1955 (div. 1979); children: Constance Chu, Pamela Joan; m. Charlotte Greenspan, Sept. 7, 1980; 1 child, Julia Eve. PhB, U. Chgo., 1947, BS, 1948; MA, Harvard, 1950, PhD, 1952; Ph.D., U. Göteborg, 1989. Mem. faculty Cornell U., 1952-72, 73—, Goldwin Smith prof. chemistry, 1980—, mem. sci. directing group Cornell Inst. Rsch. chem. ecology, 1992—; research dir. Internat. Centre Insect Physiology and Ecology, Nairobi, 1970-77; A. Mellon Term prof., 1992-95; prof. chemistry U. Calif. at San Diego, 1972-73; chem. cons. Schering-Plough Rsch. Inst., 1975—; Procter & Gamble Pharms., 1958—, Cambridge Neurosci. Rsch., 1988-92; vis. prof. Rockefeller U., 1970; Camille and Henry Dreyfus Disting. scholar Mt. Holyoke Coll., 1981, Bryn Mawr Coll., 1983; Kolthoff lectr. U. Minn., 1985; Beckman lectr. Calif. Inst. Tech., 1986; Swiss "Troisième Cycle" Lectr., 1986; Russell Marker lectr. Pa. State U., 1987; mem. vis. com. chemistry Brookhaven Nat. Lab., 1969-72, chmn., 1972; mem. med. A chemistry study sect. NIH, 1963-67, chmn., 1965-67; mem. adv. bd. Petroleum Rsch. Found., 1971-73; mem. adv. coun. chemistry dept. Princeton U., 1978-83 ; mem. adv. bd. Rsch. Corp., 1978-83; mem. adv. bd. chemistry div. NSF, 1979-83; organizing chmn. Sino-Am. Symposium on Chemistry of Natural Products, Shanghai, 1980; mem. adv. bd. A.P. Sloan Found., 1985-91; Frontiers of Rsch. lectr. Coun. Chem. Rsch., 1987; mem. sci. adv. bd. Agridyne Corp., 1989-93; Carlton Coll. Convocation, 1992; Mary Aldrige lectr., American U., 1993; K. Pfister lectr. MIT, 1992, Hilldale lectr. U. Wis., 1991, Nat. Undergrad. Rsch. Symposium, Plenary lectr., Mpls., 1992; UNOCAL lectr. Calif. State U., Long Beach, 1992; Max T. Rogers lectr. Mich. State U., 1994; Jean Day lectr. Rutgers U., 1994, Max T. Rogers lectr., Mich. State U., 1994, Disting. Grad. Sch. lectr. U. Md., 1994. Mercer lectr. Lafayette Coll. Mem. bd. editors Jour. Organic Chemistry, 1962-66, Organic Reactions, 1968-78, Organic Synthesis, 1968-72, Jour. Chem. Ecology, 1974—, Insect Sci., 1979-90; contbr. articles to profl. jours. Sloan fellow, 1958-62, Guggenheim fellow, 1960-61, 76-77, NIH spl. postdoctoral fellow, 1967-68, Japan Soc. Promotion of Sci. fellow, 1983, Ctr. for Advanced Study in Behavioral Sci. fellow, 1990-91; NIH Fogarty internat. scholar, 1983-85; recipient Tyler Environ. Achievement prize U. So. Calif., 1990, Gustavas J. Esselen award for Chemistry in Pub. Interest, 1991. Mem. NAS (exch. scholar 1987), AAAS, Am. Acad. Arts and Scis., Am. Philos. Soc., Am. Chem. Soc. (chmn. organic divsn. 1969, E Guenther award 1985, Disting. Scientist award Kalamazoo sect. 1985, A.C. Cope Scholar award 1989), Internat. Soc. Chem. Ecology (pres. 1988, Silver medal 1991), Phi Beta Kappa, Sigma Xi (nat. lectr. 1965, 75, 92-94). Office: Cornell U Dept Chemistry Baker Lab Ithaca NY 14853-1301

MEIROVITCH, LEONARD, engineering educator; b. Maxut, Romania, Nov. 28, 1928; came to U.S., 1956, naturalized, 1964; s. Carol and Adelle (Schoenfeld) M.; m. Jo Anne Reifer, Oct. 15, 1960. BSc summa cum laude, Technion-Israel Inst. Tech., 1953; MS in Engring., UCLA, 1957, PhD, 1960. Structural engr. Water Planning for Israel, Tel Aviv, 1953-55; asst. sect. head Water Planning for Israel, 1955-56; asst. research engr., cons. in engring. UCLA, 1956-60; staff engr. IBM, Endicott, N.Y., 1960-62; asso. prof. Ariz. State U., 1962-66; prof. U. Cin., 1967-71, Va. Poly. Inst. and State U., Blacksburg, 1971-79; Reynolds Metals prof. Va. Poly. Inst. and State U., 1979-83, Univ. disting. prof., 1983—; cons. Goodyear Aerospace, Phoenix, 1962-63; cons. C.S. Draper Labs., Cambridge, Mass., 1976-78, Naval Research Lab., Washington, 1977-79, Intelsat, Washington, 1980-82. Author: Analytical Methods in Vibrations, 1967, Methods of Analytical Dynamics, 1970, Elements of Vibration Analysis, 1975, 2d edit., 1986, Computational Methods in Structural Dynamics, 1980, Introduction to Dynamics and Control, 1985, Dynamics and Control of Structures, 1990, also articles; assoc. editor Jour. Spacecraft and Rockets, 1971-76, Jour. Optimization Theory and Applications, 1984—; mem. internat. editorial bd. Jour. European Mechanics, 1977-93. Served with Israeli Army, 1948-49. Recipient Alumni award for rsch. excellence Va. Poly. Inst. and State U. 1981, Japan Soc. Mech. Engrs. medal, 1989, Alexander von Humboldt Sr. Rsch. award Germany, 1991; Am. Soc. Engring. Edn.-NASA fellow, 1964; NAS sr. rsch. assoc. Langley Rsch. Ctr., Hampton, Va., 1966-67. Fellow AIAA (Structures, Structural Dynamics and Materials award 1983, Pendray Aerospace Lit. award 1984, Mechanics and Control of Flight award 1987); mem. Sigma Xi, Tau Beta Pi. Home: 303 Neil St Blacksburg VA 24060-2542

MEIROWITZ, CLAIRE CECILE, public relations executive; b. Frankfurt, Fed. Republic Germany, Jan. 14, 1934; came to U.S., 1939; d. Karl and Margot (Herrmann) Bier; m. Richard Meirowitz, Sept. 12, 1954 (div., July, 1969); children: Diane, Laura, Linda; m. Joseph Spiegel, Apr. 20, 1975. AA, Nassau Community Coll., 1971; BA magna cum laude, Hofstra U., 1976; postgrad., N.Y. Inst. Tech., 1987-90. Pres., owner, editor, writer Profl. Editing Svcs., Massapequa Park, N.Y., 1972-76, 92—; editorial asst. United Technical Publs., Garden City, N.Y., 1976-77; publs. assoc. N.Y. Inst. Tech., Old Westbury, N.Y. 1977-79; asst. dir. coll. rels., dir. publs. SUNY, Old Westbury, 1979-87, dir. of community rels. and publs., 1987-92; pres. SUNY Coun. for Univ. Affairs and Devel., 1987-89; cons. Guarino Graphics, Greenville, N.Y., 1985-92, editor, copywriter, 1986-92. Manuscript editor: Jour. of Collective Negotiations in Pub. Sector, 1972-91, editor, 1991—, Jour. of Individual Employment Rights, 1992—; editor art catalog South Africa/South Bronx, 1981 (art excellence award 1982); author: New Student Pros-

pectus, The College at Old Westbury, 1979, Labor-Management Relations Among Government Workers, 1983; co-editor: Strategies for Impasse Resolution, 1992; contbr. articles to profl. jours. v.p., treas., sec., Taxpayers Edn. Assn., Hicksville, N.Y., 1962-68; mem. The Nature Conservancy, Cold Spring Harbor, N.Y., 1980—. Recipient Excellence in Profl. Svc. award SUNY at Albany, 1987, Disting. Svc. award SUNY Coun. Univ. Affairs, 1989, award for excellence in communications SUNY Westbury Alumni Assn., 1992, award for disting. leadership L.I. Women's Coun. for Equal Edn., Employment and Tng., 1992. Mem. L.I. Communicators Assn., Internat. Assn. of Bus. Communicators. Democrat. Jewish. Avocation: computers. Home: 167 Cadman Ave Babylon NY 11702-1607

MEISEL, ALAN, law educator; b. Newark, Dec. 24, 1946; s. Stanley and Beatrice (Katz) M.; m. Linda S. Serody, Mar. 6, 1982; children: Matthew, Julia. BA, Yale U., 1968, JD, 1972. Bar: Conn. 1972, Pa. 1973, U.S. Dist. Ct. Conn. 1972, U.S. Dist. Ct. (we. dist.) Pa. 1973, U.S. Ct. Appeals (3d cir.) 1985. Assoc. Goldstein & Peck, P.C., Bridgeport, Conn., 1972-73; prof. psychiatry U. Pitts., 1973—, prof. law, 1976—, co-dir. Ctr. Med. Ethics, 1986-91, dir., 1991—; of counsel Klett, Lieber, Rooney & Schorling, Pitts., 1983—; asst. dir. for legal studies Pres.'s Commn. for Study of Ethical Problems in Medicine and Biomed. and Behavioral Rsch., Washington, 1982; mem. ethics working group Presdl. Task Force on Healthcare Reform, 1993. Author: The Right to Die, 1989, 2d edit., 1995; co-author: Informed Consent: A Study of Decision Making in Psychiatry, 1984, Informed Consent: Legal Theory and Clinical Practice, 1987; contbr. articles to legal and med. jours. Grantee NIMH, grantee Pres.'s Commn. for Study of Ethical Problems in Medicine and Biomed. and Behavioral Research, 1981-82, Founds. Fund for Research in Psychiatry grantee, 1979-82, Legal Services Corp. grantee, 1985-87; fellow Hastings Ctr.; award for The Right to Die Am. Assn. Publs., 1989. Office: U Pitts Sch Law Pittsburgh PA 15260

MEISEL, GEORGE IRA, lawyer; b. Cleve., May 5, 1920; s. Herman George and Ethel Lynn (Wright) M.; m. Gladys Ulch, 1946; children: Scott, Craig, David, Keith. A.B., Case Western Res. U., 1942; LL.B., Harvard U., 1948. Bar: Ohio 1948. Assoc. Williams, Eversman & Morgan, Toledo, 1948-51; assoc. Squire, Sanders & Dempsey, Cleve., 1951-58, ptnr., 1958—, vice chmn. mgmt. com., 1980-81, chmn. mgmt com., 1981-86, sr. ptnr., 1986-87, ret., 1987; bd. dirs. Harris Corp., Melbourne, Fla., 1983-92. Pres. Cleve. Hearing & Speech Center, 1960-61; sec.-treas. Greater Cleve. Growth Assn., 1980-81, chmn. 1984-86. Served with USAAF, 1942-46. Mem. ABA (chmn. litigation sect. 1973-74), Ohio Bar Assn., Bar Assn. Greater Cleve. (pres. 1975-76), Am. Coll. Trial Lawyers, Internat. Assn. Def. Counsel (exec. com. 1977-80, sec.-treas. 1987-90) 6th Circuit Jud. Conf. Home: 13411 NW Wax Myrtle Trl Palm City FL 34990-4826 Office: Squire Sanders & Dempsey Society Center Cleveland OH 44115

MEISEL, GEORGE VINCENT, lawyer; b. St. Louis, Sept. 24, 1933; s. Leo Otto and Margaret (Duggan) M.; m. Joy C. Cassin, May 18, 1963. B.S. summa cum laude, St. Louis U., 1956, J.D. cum laude, 1958. Bar: Mo. 1958. Assoc. Grand Peper & Martin, St. Louis, 1961-64; ptnr. Grand Peper & Martin, 1965; jr. ptnr. Bryan Cave McPheeters & McRoberts, St. Louis, 1966-69; ptnr. Bryan Cave, St. Louis, 1970—. Served to 1st lt. USAF, 1958-61. Mem. ABA, Bar Assn. Met. St. Louis, Mo. Bar Assn. Roman Catholic. Clubs: Saint Louis, Mo. Athletic (St. Louis). Home: 2029 S Warson Rd Saint Louis MO 63124-1151

MEISEL, JEROME, electrical engineer; b. Cleve., Aug. 9, 1934; s. David and Anne Irene (Meisel) Marmorstein; children: Denise Lauren, David Marc. B.S. in Elec. Engring. (Union Carbide scholar), Case Inst. Tech., 1956, Ph.D., 1961; M.S. (Mpls. Honeywell fellow), MIT, 1957. Asst. prof. elec. engring. Case Inst. Tech., 1960-65; mem. tech. staff Bell Telephone Labs., Holmdel, N.J., 1965-66; mem. faculty Wayne State U., Detroit, 1966—; prof. elec. engring. Wayne State U., 1970—, acting chmn. dept., 1985-87; cons. in field. Author: Principles of Electromechanical Energy Conversion, 1966; also articles. Sr. mem. IEEE. Home: 156 Linden Rd Birmingham MI 48009-1609 Office: Wayne State U Dept Elec Engring Detroit MI 48202

MEISEL, JOHN, political scientist; b. Vienna, Austria, Oct. 23, 1923; s. Fryda and Ann M. BA, U. Toronto, 1948, MA, 1950; PhD in Polit. Sci., London Sch. Econs., 1959; LLD (hon.), Brock U. 1983, U. Guelph, 1985, Carleton U., 1990, U. Toronto, 1993; DU (hon.), U. Ottawa, 1983; D of Scis. Sociales, Laval U., 1988. Head dept. polit. studies Queen's U., Kingston, Ont., Can., 1963-67, Hardy prof. polit. sci., 1963-80; former chmn. Can. Radio-TV and Telecomms. Commn.; Sri Edward Peacock prof. polit. sci. emeritus Queen's U.; moderator symposia on finding common grounds for polit. issues confronting Yugoslavia, UN, Vienna, 1995. Author: The Canadian General Election of 1957, 1962, Papers on the 1962 Election, 1964, Ethnic Relations in Canadian Voluntary Assocations, 1972, Working Papers on Canadian Politics, 1975; editor: Internat. Polit. Sci. Rev., 1979—; contbr. articles to profl. jours. Decorated officer Order of Can.; recipient Killam award Can. Council, 1968, 73, Northern Telecom Internat. Can. Studies award of excellence, 1991. Fellow Royal Soc. Can. (pres. 1992-95). Home: Colimaison, Tichborne, ON Canada K0H 2V0 Office: Queen's U, Kingston, ON Canada K7L 3N6

MEISEL, LOUIS KOENIG, art dealer, art historian, writer; b. N.Y.C., Sept. 4, 1942; s. Sidney and Grace Elizabeth (Moak) M.; m. Susan Helene Pear, Mar. 26, 1966; 1 child, Ari Ron. Student, Columbia U., 1963, New Sch. for social Rsch., N.Y.C., 1964; BA, Tulane U., 1964. Pres. Eminent Publs., N.Y.C., 1964-78; owner Meisel Gallery, N.Y.C., 1967-72; pres. Louis K. Meisel Gallery, N.Y.C., 1973—; ptnr. Susan P. Meisel Gallery, N.Y.C., 1983—, Meisel Real Estate, N.Y.C., 1988—. Author: Photorealism, 1980, Richard Estes, 1988, Clarice Cliff, 1988, Charles Bell, 1991, Photorealism Since 1980, 1993. 2d lt. USAR, 1964-70. Mem. Internat. Soc. Appraisers, Appraiser Assn. Am., Maidstone Club (Easthampton). Jewish. Office: Gallery 141 Prince St New York NY 10012-5315

MEISEL, MARTIN, English and comparative literature educator; b. N.Y.C., Mar. 22, 1931; s. Joseph and Sally (Rössler) Mörsel; m. Martha Sarah Winkley, Dec. 22, 1957; children: Maude Frances, Andrew Avram, Joseph Stoddard. A.B., Queens Coll., 1952; M.A., Princeton U., 1957, Ph.D., 1960; postgrad., U. Rome, 1959. Instr. English Rutgers U., New Brunswick, N.J., 1957-58; instr. asst. prof., assoc. prof. Dartmouth Coll., Hanover, N.H., 1959-65; prof. English U. Wis., Madison, 1965-68; prof. English and comparative lit. Columbia U., N.Y.C., 1968—, Brander Matthews prof. dramatic lit., 1987—, chmn. dept., 1980-83, acting v.p. arts and scis., 1986-87, v.p. arts and scis., 1989-93; trustee Columbia U. Press, 1990—. Author: Shaw and the 19th Century Theater, 1963, Realizations: Narrative, Pictorial, and Theatrical Arts in 19th Century England (George Freedley Meml. award Theater Library Assn. 1984; Barnard Hewitt award Am. Theatre Assn. 1984), 1983; mem. editorial and adv. bds. Jour. Victorian Studies, PMLA, Jour. Contemporary Lit., Bull. Research in the Humanities, 19th Century Contexts. Served with U.S. Army, 1954-56. Fellow Guggenheim Found., 1963-64, 1987-88, Am. Council of Learned Secs., 1970-71, Inst. for Advanced Studies in the Humanities, Edinburgh, 1977, Huntington Library and Art Gallery, 1978, 80, 83, Nat. Humanities Ctr., 1983-84, Wilson Ctr., Smithsonian Instn., 1987-88. Mem. MLA, Acad. Lit. Studies, Am. Soc. Theatre Rsch. Home: 18 Bacon Hill Rd Pleasantville NY 10570-3502 Office: Columbia U 611 Philosophy Hall New York NY 10027

MEISEL, PERRY, English educator; b. Shreveport, La., Jan. 26, 1949; s. I.S. and Rebecca (Abramson) M. BA, Yale U., 1970, MPhil, 1973, PhD, 1975. Asst. prof. English NYU, N.Y.C., 1975-81, assoc. prof. English, 1981-87, prof. English, 1987—. Author: Thomas Hardy, 1972, The Absent Father, 1980, The Myth of the Modern, 1987; co-editor: Bloomsbury/Freud, 1985; editor: Freud, 1981. Mem. MLA, AAUP, PEN. Office: NYU Dept English 19 University Pl New York NY 10003-4501

MEISEL, PHILIP L, chemical company executive; b. Amsterdam, N.Y., Feb. 25, 1928; s. David and Bessie (Snukler) M.; m. Blanche Fay Long, Dec. 18, 1949; children—Myron, Lee, Robert, Neil. B.S., Union Coll., Schenectady, 1947. Chief exec. officer CPS Chem. Co., Old Bridge, N.J., 1955—. Office: C P S Chemical Co Inc PO Box 162 Old Bridge NJ 08857-0162

MEISEL, ROBERT P., financial company executive; b. Irvington, N.J., Apr. 6, 1955; s. Philip L. and Blanche Meisel. BA, U. Wis., 1976; MBA, JD, UCLA, 1981. Bar: Calif., N.Y. 2d v.p. Chase Manhattan Bank, N.Y.C., 1981-84; v.p. Dean Witter Reynolds, N.Y.C., 1984-85; sr. v.p. TSG Holdings, Inc., N.Y.C., 1985-90; pres. Triton Capital Group, Guttenberg, N.J., 1990—; chmn. of bd. CPS Chem. Co., Old Bridge, N.J., 1992—; bd. dirs. GBMZ Bedford, Inc., Dallas, 1990—. Mem. Phi Beta Kappa. Avocations: tennis, basketball, film, theater. Office: C P S Chemical Co Inc Old Waterworks Rd Old Bridge NJ 08857

MEISEL, STEVEN, advertising photographer; b. 1954; s. Lenny and Sally. Student, Parsons Sch. Design. Illustrator Women's Wear Daily; advt. photographer The Gap, Revlon, Valentino, Anne Klein, Calvin Klein, Gianfranco Ferré, Prada, Dolce and Gabbana, Lancome, Barney's, Donna Karan, Versace; photographer Madonna's Sex, 1992; free-lance photographer Vogue, Harper's Bazaar. Recipient Spl. award Photography Coun. Fashion Designers Am., 1992, Internat. Fashion Photography award Festival Internat. de la Photo de Mode, 1994. Office: Steven Meisel Studio 64 Wooster St 4th fl New York NY 10012

MEISELAS, SUSAN CLAY, photographer; b. Balt., June 21, 1948; d. Leonard and Murrayl (Groh) M. BA, Sarah Lawrence Coll., 1970; EdM, Harvard U., 1971; DFA (hon.), Parsons Sch./New Sch., N.Y.C., 1988. Photographic cons. Community Resources Inst., N.Y.C., 1972-74; artist-in-residence S.C. Arts Commn., 1974-75; photography tchr. New Sch., N.Y.C., 1975; free-lance photographer Magnum Photos, N.Y.C., 1976—, v.p., 1986-91. Author: Carnival Strippers, 1976, Nicaragua, 1981; co-editor: El Salvador, 1983; editor: Chile from Within, 1991; editor Learn to See, 1974; co-dir.: (film) Living at Risk, 1985, Pictures from a Revolution, 1991. Recipient Robert Capa gold medal Overseas Press Club, 1979, Leica award of excellence New Sch., 1981, Photojournalist of Yr. award Am. Soc. Mag. Photographers, 1981, award Nat Endowment for Arts, 1987, Hasselblad Found., 1994, Maria Moors Cabot prize Columbia U., 1994; MacArthur fellow, 1992. Office: Magnum Photos Inc 151 W 25th St New York NY 10001

MEISELS, GERHARD GEORGE, academic administrator, chemist, educator; b. Vienna, May 11, 1931; came to U.S., 1951, naturalized, 1961; s. Leo and Adele Josefa Maria (Seehofer) M.; m. Sylvia Claire Knopsnider, June 28, 1958; 1 dau., Laura Germaine. Student, U. Vienna, 1949-51, 52-53; M.S., U. Notre Dame, Ind., 1952, Ph.D., 1956. Postdoctoral research assoc. U. Notre Dame, 1955-56; chemist Gulf Oil Corp., Pitts., 1956-59; part time instr. Carnegie Inst. Tech., Pitts., 1956-58; chemist nuclear div. Union Carbide Corp., Tuxedo, N.Y., 1959-63; asst. group leader Union Carbide Corp., 1964-65; assoc. prof. U. Houston, 1965-70, prof., 1970-75, dept. chmn., 1973-75; prof., chmn. dept. chemistry U. Nebr., Lincoln, 1975-81, dean Coll. Arts and Scis., 1981-88; provost, COO U. South Fla., Tampa, 1988-94; dir. Coalition Sci. Literacy, 1994—; cons. Union Carbide Corp., Gearhart-Owen Industries. Editor: spl. issue Jour. Radiation Physics and Chemistry, 1980; contbr. writings in field to profl. publs. Sec., pres. Ramsey (N.J.) Jr. C. of C., 1959-64; active All Children's Hosp. Rsch. Bd. Fulbright fellow, Smith-Mundt fellow, 1951-52; sr. fellow Sci. Research Council, Eng., 1976. Mem. Am. Chem. Soc. (com. chmn.), Am. Soc. for Mass Spectrometry (charter, com. chmn., v.p. 1984-86, pres. 1986-88, bd. dirs. 1988-90), Nebr. Acad. Scis., AAAS, Am. Phys. Soc., Coun. Sci. Soc. Pres. (exec. bd. 1989-92, chmn. elect 1990, chmn. 1991, chmn. com. on sci. priorities), Coun. for Chem. Rsch. (bd. dirs. 1982-85), Sigma Xi. Clubs: Houston Kennel (bd. dirs. 1968-70), Cornhusker Kennel (pres., bd. dirs., del. to Am. Kennel Club 1976-81), St. Petersburg Dog Fanciers Assn. Home: 870 3rd Ave S Tierra Verde FL 33715-2223 Office: U South Fla 100 Fifth Ave S Saint Petersburg FL 33701

MEISEN, AXEL, chemical engineer, university administrator; b. Hamburg, Germany, Oct. 17, 1943; came to Can., 1966; s. Paul and Emmi (Schaaf) M.; children: Nadine Ramona, Kai Noel. B.Sc., Imperial Coll., 1965; M.Sc., Calif. Inst. Tech., 1966; Ph.D., McGill U., 1970. Registered profl. engr., B.C. Asst. prof. chem. engring. U. B.C., Vancouver, 1969-74, assoc. prof., 1975-79, assoc. dean, 1976-85, prof., 1979—, dean, 1985—; environ. engr. Imperial Oil Enterprise Ltd., Sarnia, Ont., 1974-75. Contbr. articles to profl. jours. Chmn. Can. Engring. Accreditation Bd., 1989-90. Fellow Inst. Can., Instn. Engrs. Ireland, Can. Acad. Engring.; mem. Assn. Profl. Engrs. B.C., Can. Soc. Chem. Engrs. (pres. 1994), Vancouver Club. Office: UC BC Office of Dean, 2006-2324 Main Mall, Vancouver, BC Canada V6T 1Z4

MEISLICH, HERBERT, chemistry educator emeritus; b. Bklyn., Mar. 26, 1920; s. Isidore and Bessie (Rose) M.; m. Estelle Kalechstein, July 1, 1951; children—Mindy, Debrah, Susan. A.B., Bklyn. Coll., 1940; A.M., Columbia U., 1947, Ph.D., 1950. With Edgewood Arsenal, Mo., 1942-44; asst. prof. chemistry CCNY, 1946-62, assoc. prof., 1963-68, prof., 1969-86, prof. emeritus, 1986—. Author: Introduction to Organic Chemistry, 1960, Fundamentals of Chemistry, 1966, 5th edit., 1980, Introduction to Chemistry, 1968, Schaum's Organic Chemistry, 1977, 2d edit., 1991, Schaum's 3000 Solved Problems in Organic Chemistry, 1993. Mem. New Milford (N.J.) Bd. Edn., 1967-81. Served to lt. (j.g.) USN, 1944-46. Sloan Kettering fellow, 1956. Mem. Am. Chem. Soc. (past mem. N.Y. sect., councilor). Home: 338 Lacey Dr New Milford NJ 07646-1128 Office: CUNY Dept Chemistry Convent Ave # 138th St New York NY 10027

MEISLIN, HARVEY WARREN, emergency healthcare physician, professional society administrator; b. June 19, 1946; s. Milton M. and Celia (Weiner) M.; m. Loretta Marie Bielski, Apr. 30, 1977; children: Justin, Jonathan, Megan. BS in Chemistry, Purdue U., 1968; MD, Ind. U., 1972. Diplomate Am. Bd. Emergency Medicine, Am. Bd. Med. Spltys. (del. 1990, fin. com. 1992, exec. com. 1994); cert. cardiac life support, ACLS instr., advanced trauma life support instr. Intern U. Chgo. Hosps. and Clinics, 1973-75, resident, 1975-77, dir. div. emergency medicine, 1975-77; asst. prof. internal and emergency medicine UCLA Emergency Med. Ctr., 1977-80, resident dir. emergency medicine, 1977-80; asst. prof. 1977-80 assoc. prof. dept. surgery emergency medicine Coll. Medicine, U. Ariz., Tucson, 1980-83, assoc. prof., 1983-85, prof., 1985—; chief emergency medicine U. Ariz., Tucson, 1980—; chief sect. emergency medicine dept. surgery Ariz. Health Scis. Ctr., Tucson, 1980—, dir. emergency svcs. Univ. Med. Ctr., 1980—, dir. Ariz. Emergency Med. Rsch. Ctr., 1990—; med. dir. MEDTRAN-Aeromed. Ambulance Corp., 1985-88; mem. emergency med. svc. com. Mid-South Health Planning Orgn., Chgo., 1974; coord. Mid-South Disaster Plan, Chgo., 1974; mem. com. revision of Disaster Plan Billings Hosp., 1974-76; mem. faculty Am. Hosp. Assn. Inst. Disaster Preparedness, 1975; vis. prof. dept. emergency medicine Denver Gen. Hosp., 1977; bd. trustees Emergency Med. Found., 1978-81; mem. med. adv. com. L.A. City Fire Dept., 1979-80; chmn.-elect Tuscon Met. EMS Coun., 1983-84, chmn., 1984-85; chmn. Tuscon Pre-Hosp. Care Coun., 1981; mem. trauma steering com. So. Ariz. Regional Trauma Ctr., 1986-88; mem. ETHICON emergency physicians adv. panel Johnson & Johnson Co., 1987-92; presenter and lectr. in field. Editor: Purdue Rivet, 1971-72, abstract sect. Annals Emergency Medicine, 1982-90, EMS sect., 1989-90; guest editor: Topics in Emergency Medicine, 1979; sci. editor: Drug Therapy, 1984—; mem. editorial bd.: Annals Emergency Medicine, 1977-90, Emergency Dept. News, 1979-87, Emergency Dept. and Ambulatory Care News, 1987-90, Digest of Emergency Medicine Care, 1981-87; contbr. articles and revs. to profl. jours. Mem. select med. adv. comm. City of Tuscon, 1981, med. dir. emergency med. svcs., 1982-83, 84-85; bd. dirs. so. Ariz. divsn. Am. Heart Assn., 1985-90; mem. emergency cardiac care com. so. divsn. Ariz. Heart Assn., 1986-88; mem. med. dirs. commn. dept. health svcs. State of Ariz., 1992—, also mem. Mex. border commn., 1991—. Recipient Pres. gavel and plaque Am. Bd. Emergency Medicine. Fellow Am. Coll. Emergency Physicians (State of Ill. chpt.: mem. sci. edn. com. 1975, mem. sci. edn. com. 1975-76, mem. grad./undergrad. edn. com. 1976-79, mem. ethics com. 1976-77, mem. surgery/trauma task force bd. cert. exam. 1976-77, bd. dirs. 1976-77, chmn. edn. com. 1976-77; State of Calif. chpt.: mem. hosp. and contract com. 1978-79, mem. EMS and legis. com. 1978-79, mem. spl. task force on emergency dept. distbn. 1979-80, mem. membership com. 1979-80, mem. legis. com. 1979-80, mem. sci. assembly planning com. 1980-81, bd. dirs. 1979-81, mem. rsch. com. 1981; State of Ariz. chpt.: bd. dirs. 1982-92, chmn. pub. rels. com. 1982-83, v.p. and sec. 1983-84, counselor 1984-87, mem. credentials com. 1986-91, chmn., 1987-90, mem. test com. 1986-87, mem. ad hoc com. for combined tng. 1987-88, chmn. task force on emergency medicine 1987-89, mem. exec. com.

1988—, mem. finance com. 1988—, sec./treas. 1989-90, mem. EMS com. 1990—, pres.-elect 1990-91, pres. 1991-92, chair standards com., mem. faculty Nat. Sci. Assembly 1974-76, Cert. Appreciation award 1990); mem. APHA, Am. Coll. Physician Execs., Am. Trauma Soc., Ariz. Med. Assn., Pima County Med. Soc. (bd. dirs. 1991—), Phi Rho Sigma. Avocations: racquetball, golf, skiing, automobiles. Office: U Ariz Med Ctr Sect Emergency Med 1501 N Campbell Ave Tucson AZ 85724-0002

MEISNER, DEE DOLORES ANNETTE, small business owner; b. Bismarck, ND, Dec. 29, 1936; d. Richard and Annie Gertrude (Binder) Gerlach; m. James Warren Meisner, Sept. 17, 1955; children: Terry L., John Warren. BA, U. N.D., 1973; MA, Ohio U., 1974; Graduate in Modeling, John Robert Powers, Mpls., 1980. Adminstrv. Asst. to pres. and chief exec. officer William Clairmont, Inc., Bismarck, N.D., 1977; owner Orgn. Communication Ctr., Bismarck, 1976—; co-owner Meisner Co., Bismarck, 1980—; oversee and adminstrn. Dick's Potpourri, Bismarck, 1987—; rsch. cons. United Meth. Chs. Bismarck 1979; bd. dir. of cur. and devel. First United Meth. Bismarck 1976-77; communication cons. Bismarck/Mandan Bus. and Orgn. Bismarck 1976—; spokesperson/rep. Plum Tree (Bus.) Bismarck 1986—. Composer and publisher several mus. compositions including Dakota Heritage Sonata #1 (1989 Centennial Selection U. Mary), cassette tape, Christmas Love 1987; author, publisher (children's newsletters) Fun Club, Adventure Science 1984-85, (book) Christmas Tree Angel 1988. Pres. Bismarck-Mandan Community Concerts 1978, drive chmn. 1960s; bd. dirs. and children's Edn. Com. Bismarck Art and Galleries Assn. 1987-93; orgn. com. Dakota West Arts Coun., Bismarck 1978. Recipient Citizen's Award Bismarck Schs. 1950; named Hon. Soc. Bismarck Schs. 1955, Midwest Spa Spls. Featured in Spa News 1981. Mem. Nat. Spa and Swimming Pool Inst., PEO (pres. 1970, other offices), Thursday Mus. (program chmn., pres. 1989-93, other offices, N.D. Fedn. Music Clubs (pres. 1991-93), Bismarck Art and Gallery Assn. (bd. dirs., offices), Symphony Conductor's Club (charter, com. mem.), Current Events Study Club. Avocations: photography, mus. art, gourmet-country cooking, swimming. Office: Meisner Co 925 E Main Ave Bismarck ND 58501-4571

MEISNER, GARY WAYNE, landscape architect; b. Terre Haute, Ind., Oct. 19, 1949; s. Ervin Gustav and Mary Lou (Maret) M.; children: Christopher Wayne, Kira Valora. BS in Landscape Architecture, Mich. State U., 1972. Lic. landscape architect, Ohio, Mich., Ind., Ill., Ky., W.Va. Designer Huron Clinton Metro Parks, Detroit, 1969, City of East Lansing, Mich., 1970, Fairfax County Park Authority, Annandale, Va., 1971; city design adminstr. Akron (Ohio) Dept. Planning and Urban Devel., 1972-79; prin. Bentley Meisner Assocs., Inc, Cin., 1979-94, Myers, Schmalenberger, Meisner Inc., Cin. and Columbus, Ohio, 1994—. Designer Akron Downtown Plan, 1978, King Sch. Plan, 1980 (honor award 1982), master plan Toyota Regional Office, 1983 (honor award 1986), Montgomery Cemetery, 1985 (honor award 1987), Falls at Cumberland Hill, 1987 (honor award 1988), Piatt Park, 1988 (honor award 1989), Cin. Mus. Ctr., 1990 (honor award 1990), Walk Across Am. Garden, 1990 (honor award 1991), Dayton Nat. Cemetery, 1993 (honor award 1994). Trustee Cin. Hillside Trust, 1987—, Capitol Square Renovation Found., Columbus, Ohio, 1987-93, Cin. Sculpture Coun., 1989—, Hubbard Ednl. Trust, 1988—. Recipient gov.'s commendation State of Ohio, 1985, Ohio Arts Coun. fellow, 1992-93, award Architecture Found. of Cin. 1995. Fellow Am. Soc. Landscape Architects (nat. trustee 1982-89, chmn. nat. community assistance team program 1983-86, chmn. editorial bd. Garden Design mag. 1986-90, chmn. nat. publs. bd. 1988-92, Nat. Com. Assistance Team commendation 1986, Trustee commendation 1989); mem. Am. Soc. Botanic Garden and Arboretum, Urban Land Inst., Am. Underground Space Assn. Mem. Unity Ch. Home: 4137 Jora Ln Cincinnati OH 45209 Office: Myers Schmalenberger Meisner Inc 2011 Madison Rd Cincinnati OH 45208

MEISNER, MARY JO, editor; b. Chgo., Dec. 24, 1951; d. Robert Joseph and Mary Elizabeth (Casey) M.; 1 child, Thomas Joseph Gradel. BS in Journalism, U. Ill., 1974, MS in Journalism, 1976. Copy editor Wilmington (Del.) News Jour., 1975-76, labor and bus. reporter, 1975-79; labor and gen. assignment reporter Phila. Daily News, 1979, city editor, 1979-83, met. editor, 1983-85; PM city editor San Jose (Calif.) Mercury News, 1985-86, met. editor, 1986-87; city editor The Washington Post, 1987-90; mng. editor The Ft. Worth Star-Telegram, 1991-93; editor and v.p. The Milw. Jour., 1993-95, v.p. and jour. editor, 1995—. Mem. AP Mng. Editors (bd. dirs. 1992—), Am. Soc. Newspaper Editors, Internat. Press Inst. (bd. dirs. 1994—), Pulitzer prize juror 1994). Office: The Milwaukee Jour 333 W State St Milwaukee WI 53203-1305*

MEISSNER, DORIS, federal commissioner; b. Nov. 3, 1941; d. Fred and Hertha H. (Tromp) Borst; m. Charles F. Meissner, June 8, 1963; children: Christine M., Andrew D. BA, U. Wis., 1963, MA, 1969. Asst. dir. student fin. aid U. Wis., 1964-68; exec. dir. Nat. Women's Polit. Caucus, 1971-73; asst. dir. office policy and planning U.S. Dept. Justice, 1975, exec. dir. cabinet com. illegal aliens, 1976, dep. assoc. atty. gen., 1977-80, acting commr. immigration and naturalization svc., 1981, exec. assoc. commr. immigration and naturalization svc., 1982-86; sr. assoc., dir. immigration policy project The Carnegie Endowment for Internat. Peace, 1993; commr. immigration and naturalization svc., 1993; adv. coun. U.S./Mex. project Overseas Devel. Coun., 1981-86; trustee Refugee Policy Group, 1987-93; adv. bd. Program for Rsch. on Immigration Policy Rand Corp./Urban inst., 1988-92; cons. panel to comptroller gen. GAO, 1989-93; with Coun. Fgn. Rels., 1990—, Washington Office Latin Am., 1989-93. White Ho. fellow, 1973-74. Mem. Nat. Women's Polit. Caucus (nat. adv. bd. 1976—), White House Fellows Alumni Assn. and Found. (sec., exec. com. 1979-82, Assn. Governing Bds. Colls. and Univs. (panel higher edn. issues 1990-92), Phi Kappa Phi, Mortar Board, Alpha Chi Omega. Office: Dept Justice Immigration & Naturalization Svc 425 I St NW Rm 7100 Washington DC 20536

MEISSNER, EDWIN BENJAMIN, JR., real estate broker; b. St. Louis, Dec. 27, 1918; s. Edwin B. and Edna R. (Rice) M.; m. Nina Renard, Dec. 17, 1946; children: Edwin Benjamin III, Wallace, Robert, Donald. B.S., U. Pa., 1940. Joined St. Louis Car Co., 1934, asst. to pres., v.p., exec. v.p., 1950-56, pres., gen. mgr., 1956-61; pres. St. Louis Car div. Gen. Steel Industries, Inc., 1961-67; sr. v.p., dir. Gen. Steel Industries, Inc., 1968-74; v.p. Bakewell Corp., 1974-85; real estate broker, v.p. Hilliker Corp., St. Louis, 1985—; dir. First Ill. Bank. Mem. pres.' com. St. Louis U.; bd. dirs. Washington U. Med. Ctr. Redevel. Corp., former Barnard Free Skin and Cancer Hosp., former James S. McDonnell USO; com. mem., bd. dirs. St. Louis Symphony Youth Orch.; mem. exec. com., outreach com. St. Louis Symphony Soc.; pres., bd. dirs. Humane Soc. Mo.; bd. mgrs. Ctrl. Inst. for Deaf; v.p. Gateway Ctr. Met. St. Louis; chmn. Ladue (Mo.) Police and Fire Commn.; mem. Jefferson Nat. Expansion Meml. Commn., Mo. Arts Coun.; mem. mil. affairs com. Regional Commerce. Mem. St. Louis Flood Assn. (dir.), Am. Ordnance Assn. (life), Internat. Assn. Chiefs of Police (assoc.), Mo. Assn. Chiefs of Police, Mo. Athletics Club, Westwood Country Club, Bridlespur Hunt Club, St. Louis Club, Beta Gamma Sigma. Home: 40 Roan Ln Saint Louis MO 63124-1480 Office: Hilliker Corp 2001 S Hanley Rd Ste 300 Saint Louis MO 63144-9999 also: Edwin B Meissner Jr 509 Olive St Ste 608 Saint Louis MO 63101-1855

MEISSNER, HAROLD C., window manufacturing company executive; b. 1917. With Andersen Corp., Bayport, Minn., 1954—, pres., until 1990, asst. chmn. bd., chief exec. officer, 1990—, also bd. dirs. Office: Andersen Corp 100 4th Ave N Bayport MN 55003-1046

MEISSNER, WILLIAM WALTER, psychiatrist, clergyman; b. Buffalo, Feb. 13, 1931; s. William Walter and Mary Emma (Glauber) M. BA, St. Louis U., 1956, PhL, 1957, MA, 1957; STL, Woodstock Coll., 1962; MD, Harvard U., 1967. Diplomate Am. Bd. Psychiatry and Neurology, Bd. Psychoanalysis. Entered S.J., 1951; intern Mt. Auburn Hosp., Cambridge, Mass., 1967-68; resident Mass. Mental Health Ctr., Boston, 1968-71; mem. instr. Boston Psychoanalytic Inst., 1971—, tng. and supervising analyst, 1980—; staff psychiatrist Mass. Mental Health Ctr., 1971-87, Cambridge (Mass.) Hosp., 1971-78; asst. clin. prof. psychiatry Harvard U. Med. Sch., 1973-76, assoc. clin. prof., 1976-81, clin. prof. psychiatry, 1981-87; prof. psychoanalysis Boston Coll., 1987—. Author: Annotated Bibliography in Religion and Psychology, 1961, Group Dynamics in the Religious Life, 1965, Foundations for a Psychology of Grace, 1966, The Assault on Authority:

Dialogue or Dilemma, 1971, Basic Concepts in Psychoanalytic Psychiatry, 1973, The Paranoid Process, 1978, Internationalization in Psychoanalysis, 1981, The Borderline Spectrum, 1984, Psychoanalysis and Religious Experience, 1984, Psychotherapy and the Paranoid Process, 1986, Life and Faith: Psychoanalytic Perspectives on Religious Experience, 1987, Treatment of Patients in the Borderline Spectrum, 1988, What is Effective in Psychoanalytic Therapy, 1991, Ignatius of Loyola: The Psychology of a Saint, 1992; mem. editorial bd. Psychoanalytic Inquiry, 1983—, Jour. Geriatric Psychiatry, 1980—, Rev. of Psychoanalytic Books, 1980-84, Psychoanalytic Study of Society, 1981—, Theol. Studies, 1981-91, Dynamic Psychotherapy, 1982-89, Internat. Forum for Psychoanalysis, 1983—, Internat. Jour. Psychoanalytic Psychotherapy, 1984—, Psychoanalytic Edn., 1990—, Bull. of Menninger Clinic, 1985—, Jour. Am. Psychoanalytic Assn., 1995—, Psychoanalysis and Psychotherapy, 1989—, Internat. Series in Psychology of Religion, 1990—, Am. Jour. Psychotherapy, 1993—. Recipient Deutsch prize Boston Psychoanalytic Inst., 1969. Fellow Am. Psychiat. Assn. (task force on treatments of psychiat. disorders 1989, Oskar Pfister award 1989), Mass. Psychiat. Soc., Ctr. for Advancement Psychoanalytic Studies; mem. Am. Psychoanalytic Assn. (councilor-at-large 1980-84), Internat. Psycho-Analytical Assn., Boston Psychoanalytic Inst., Am. Psychotherapy Seminar Ctr. (mem. prof. adv. com. 1991—), Sigma Chi, Psi Chi. Address: Boston Coll Carney Hall 420 D Chestnut Hill MA 02167-3806

MEISTAS, MARY THERESE, endocrinologist, diabetes researcher; b. Grand Rapids, Mich., July 22, 1949; d. Frank Peter and Anne Therese (Karsokas) M. MD, U. Mich., 1975. Diplomate Am. Bd. Internal Medicine, Am. Bd. Endocrinology. Intern, then resident in internal medicine Cleve. Clinic Hosp., 1975-78, endocrinology fellow, 1978-79; fellow in pediatric endocrinology Johns Hopkins Hosp., Balt., 1979-81; diabetes researcher Joslin Diabetes Ctr., Boston, 1981-86; assoc. in medicine Brigham and Women's Hosp., Boston, 1981-86; asst. in medicine, diabetes researcher Mass. Gen. Hosp., Boston, 1986-92. Contbr. articles to profl. jours. Mem. ACP, Am. Diabetes Assn., Am. Fedn. Clin. Research, Endocrine Soc. Office: Emerson Hosp 747 Main St Ste 111 Concord MA 01742

MEISTER, BERNARD JOHN, chemical engineer; b. Maynard, Mass., Feb. 27, 1941; s. Benjamin C. M. and Gertrude M. (Meister); m. Janet M. White, Dec. 31, 1971; children: Mark, Martin, Kay Ellen. B.S. in Chem. Engring., Worcester Poly. Inst., 1962; Ph.D. in Chem. Engring., Cornell U., 1966. Engring. researcher Dow Chem. Co., Midland, Mich., 1966—; sr. rsch. specialist, 1978-81, assoc. scientist 1981-85, sr. assoc. scientist, 1985-92, rsch. scientist, 1992—. Contbr. articles to profl. jours. Mem. Am. Inst. Chem. Engrs., Am. Chem. Soc., Soc. Plastics Engrs., Soc. Rheology, Sigma Xi. Mem. Ch. of Nazarene. Home: 2925 Chippewa Ln Midland MI 48640-4181 Office: Dow Chem Co 438 Bldg Midland MI 48640 Free the mind of things you can't change, and let it focus on things you can accomplish.

MEISTER, DORIS POWERS, investment management executive; b. Ames, Iowa, Sept. 12, 1954; d. James Phillip and Doris (Goess) P.; m. Gilbert Meister Jr., Oct. 18, 1980. AB, Smith Coll., 1976; MBA, U. Chgo., 1979. Mgr. currency Harris Trust & Savs. Bank, Chgo., 1976-78; sr. engagement mgr. McKinsey & Co. Inc., N.Y.C., London, 1979-84; dir., dept. head portfolio strategies dept., adminstrv. mgr. fixed income rsch. group C S First Boston, N.Y.C., 1984-90; exec. v.p., COO Christie, Manson & Woods Internat. Inc., N.Y.C., 1990-94; mng. dir. Copley Real Estate Advisors, Boston, 1994—. Bd. dirs. ArtsConnection, 1990, Am. Women's Econ. Devel. Corp., 1994. Named one of "Top 40 under 40" Execs., Crain's N.Y., 1992. Mem. Fin. Women's Assn., Women's Bond Club, Com. of 200, Women's Forum. Episcopalian. Office: Copley Real Estate Advisors 399 Boylston St Boston MA 02116

MEISTER, MARK JAY, museum director, professional society administrator; b. Balt., June 26, 1953; s. Michael Aaron and Yetta (Haransky) M.; m. Carla Stager, Aug. 7, 1977; children: Rachel, Kaitlin. AB, Washington U., St. Louis, 1974; MA, U. Minn., 1976; cert. mus. mgmt., U. Calif., Berkeley, 1983. Asst. lectr. St. Louis Art Mus., 1974; asst. coord. young people's program Mpls. Inst. Arts, 1975-76, coord. mobile program, 1976, coord. tchrs. resource svcs., 1976-77; dir. Mus. Art and History, Port Huron, Mich., 1978-79, Midwest Mus. Am. Art, Elkhart, Ind., 1979-81; exec. dir. Children's Mus., St. Paul, 1981-86; dir. Mus. Art, Sci. and Industry, Bridgeport, Conn., 1986-89; exec. dir. Archaeol. Inst. of Am., Boston, 1989—; adj. lectr. museology Kenyon Coll., Gambier, Ohio, 1977, art history Ind. U. South Bend, 1980-81; regional reviewer Inst. Mus. Svcs., Washington, 1985-86, 89; treas., vice chmn. Minn. Assn. Mus., St. Paul, 1983-86. Bd. dirs. Seaway Arts Coun., St. Clair County, Mich., 1978-79; mem. Mayor's Arts Adv. Com., Elkhart, 1981; mem. projects with industry bus. adv. coun. Goodwill Industries of Southwestern Conn., 1988-89; mem. exec. com., Conf. Adminstrv. Officers, Am. Coun. Learned Socs., 1994—. NEH museology fellow, Mpls. Inst. Arts, 1976-77, Kress fellow U. Minn. 1977-78, Bush leadership summer fellow, Bush Found., St. Paul, 1983; named One of Outstanding Young Men Am., 1981. Mem. Am. Assn. Mus., Am. Coun. Learned Socs., Conf. Adminstrv. Officers, Am. Soc. Assn. Execs. Office: Archaeol Inst of Am 656 Beacon St Boston MA 02215-2010

MEISTER, STEVEN GERARD, cardiologist, educator; b. Boston, Sept. 13, 1937; s. Harry and Edith (Segal) M.; m. Carol Anne Ross, Jan. 28, 1966; children: Laura Ilise, Elizabeth Lee. BA, Bowdoin Coll., 1958; MD, Tufts U., 1962. Diplomate: Am. Bd. Internal Medicine. Intern in medicine Ind. U. Med. Center, Indpls., 1962-63; asst. resident in medicine Boston VA Hosp., 1965-66, resident in medicine, 1966-67; research fellow in medicine Boston City Hosp., 1967-68, Peter Bent Brigham Hosp., Boston, 1968-70; research fellow in cardiology Tufts U., 1967-68, Harvard U., 1968-70; practice medicine specializing in cardiology Phila., 1970—; dir. cardiac catheterization lab. Med. Coll. Pa. and Hosp., 1973-79, acting dir. div. cardiology, 1978-79, dir. div. cardiology, 1979—; asst. prof. medicine U. Pa., Phila., 1970-73; assoc. prof. medicine Med. Coll. Pa. and Hosp., 1973-78, prof., 1978—; cons. cardiology VA hosps. Contbr. numerous articles on cardiology to profl. jours. Mem. Oversight Com. for Cardiac Catheterization. Capt. U.S. Army, 1963-65. Fellow ACP, Am. Coll. Cardiology; mem. Am. Fedn. Clin. Rsch., Am. Heart Assn. (Upper Atlantic rsch. com. 1977-79), Phila. Acad. Cardiology (v.p. 1988-89, pres. 1989-90).

MEITNER, PAMELA, lawyer, educator; b. Phila., Aug. 23, 1950; d. Alfred Victor Meitner and Claire Jane (Carroll) Harmer; m. William Bruce Larson, Sept. 13, 1980; 1 child, William Bruce, Jr. BS in chem. engring., Drexel U., 1973; JD, Del. Law Sch., 1977. Bar: Del. 1977, U.S. Dist. Ct. 1977. Engr. DuPont Co., Deepwater, N.J., 1973-77; lawyer DuPont Co., Wilmington, Del., 1977; prof. Del. Law Sch., Wilmington, 1985—; with U.S. Patent & Trademark Office. Commr. State Emergency Response Com., Dover, Del., 1986-90. Mem. Del. Bar Assn. Club: DuPont Country (Wilmington) (bd. govs. 1984-85). Home: 211 Welwyn Rd Wilmington DE 19803-2951 Office: DuPont Co Legal Dept 1007 Market St Wilmington DE 19898

MEITZEN, MANFRED OTTO, religious studies educator; b. Houston, Dec. 12, 1930; s. Otto Hugo and Laura Emma (Munsch) M.; m. Fredrica Haden Kilmer, May 16, 1970. BA, Rice U., 1952; MDiv, Wartburg Sem., 1956; PhD, Harvard U., 1961. Assoc. prof. religious studies Rocky Mountain Coll., Billings, Mont., 1961-65; assoc. prof. religious studies, chmn. dept. W.Va. U., Morgantown, 1965-70, prof., chmn. religious studies, 1970—, prof. religious studies W.Va. U. Mem., 1991—, chmn. program humanities Coll. Arts and Scis., 1972-77, mem. senate, 1968-82, 84—; vis. scholar Christ Ch. Coll., Oxford (Eng.) U., 1973; columnist Morgantown Dominion-Post, 1975-76, 80-89. Contbr. articles to profl. jours. and chpts. to books. Harvard Div. Sch. scholar, 1957, fellow, 1958; Rockefeller fellow, 1959-60; Sheldon Traveling fellow, 1961; W.Va. U. Study grantee, 1970; recipient Outstanding Tchr. award W.Va. U., 1971-72, Coll. Arts & Scis., 1979-80, 87-88, Outstanding Educator Am. award, 1974-75, W.Va. Assess. award, 1974-75, Golden Apple Tchg. award, 1995. Mem. Am. Guild Organists, Am. Acad. Religion, W.Va. Assn. for Humanities (pres. 1976-77), Harvard Alumni Assn., Univ. Profs. for Acad. Order (nat. 1st v.p. 1977-79, nat. pres. 1979, dir. 1974—, nat. sec.-treas. 1986-91), Nat. Assn. Scholars, Am. Rifle Assn., Rice U. Alumni Assn., Harvard Found. for Advanced Study and Rsch., Delta Phi Alpha. Lutheran. Home: 119 Forest Dr Morgantown WV 26505-2323 It is very important, particularly in our times, not to sell one's own ideas and convictions short in face of the increasing pressure in academe

and throughout society to comply with standardized opinion on moral, political and social issues.

MEITZLER, ALLEN HENRY, electrical engineering educator, automotive scientist; b. Allentown, Pa., Dec. 16, 1928; s. Herbert Henry and Estella Irene (Wagner) M.; m. Joan Catherine Egan, June 13, 1953; children: Thomas Joseph, Peter Michael, David Christopher. B.S., Muhlenberg Coll., Allentown, Pa., 1951; M.S., Lehigh U., 1953, Ph.D., 1955. Mem. tech. staff Bell Labs., Whippany and Murray Hill, N.J., 1955-72; prin. research scientist, research staff Ford Motor Co., Dearborn, Mich., 1972—; adj. prof. U. Mich.-Dearborn. Patentee ultrasonic and ferroelectric devices, automotive electronic devices and systems. Prof. Wackernagel scholar, 1947-51; Hood grad. fellow, 1954-55. Fellow IEEE, Acoustical Soc. Am.; mem. Am. Phys. Soc., Soc. Automotive Engrs., Am. Ceramic Soc. Republican. Home: 3055 Foxcroft St Ann Arbor MI 48104-2827 Office: Ford Motor Co Sci Rsch Staff PO Box 2053 Dearborn MI 48123-2053

MEIXNER, RICHARD, manufacturing executive, light. Sr. exec. v.p. Denon Digital Industries, Inc., Madison, Ga. Office: Denon Digital Industries Inc 1380 Monticello Rd Madison GA 30650*

MEIXSELL, BERRAE NEVIN (MIKE MEIXSELL), retail executive; b. Palmerton, Pa., June 28, 1936; s. Earl Henry and Beatrice Ellen (Walk) M.; m. Hilda Elizabeth Landis, July 5, 1960; children: Berrae Jr., Tracy Young, Pamela Thomas, Gail, Craig, Michele Utterback, Michael. Diploma, Lehighton High Sch., 1954. Asst. mgr., then mgr. G.C. Murphy Co., 1952-64, W.T. Grant Co., 1964-67; mgr., buyer Norman Purchasing Corp., Silver Spring, Md., 1967-83; dir. purchasing Oscar Robbins Corp., Pitts., 1983-86; dist. sales mgr. Shakespeare Fishing Tackle Corp., Pitts., 1986-88; pres. & CEO Nisito-Meixsell & Assocs., Ltd., Parker, Pa., 1988—. Elected ofcl. Butler County, Butler, Pa., 1992-93. Recipient Eagle Scout award Boy Scouts Am., 1952, Silver award Boy Scouts Am., 1954, award of merit Am. Legion, 1950. Republican. Lutheran. Avocations: hunting, fishing. Home: RR # 2 Box 311A Parker PA 16049 Office: Nisito-Meixsell & Assocs RR # 2 Box 311A Parker PA 16049

MEJIA, PAUL ROMAN, choreographer, dancer; b. Lima, Peru, Oct. 29, 1947; s. Pablo Enrique and Romana (Kryzanowska) M.; m. Suzanne Farrell, Feb. 21, 1969. Student, Sch. Am. Ballet, 1959. Dancer N.Y.C. Ballet, 1965-70; dancer Ballet of the XX Century, Belgium, 1970-75; guest dir. Stars of Am. Ballet, Ballet Guatemala, 1977-79; assoc. artistic dir., dancer, choreographer Chgo. City Ballet, 1981-87; dir., artistic dir. Ft. Worth Ballet, 1987—; dir. Cedar Islands Ballet Summer Camp, 1980—. Office: Ft Worth Ballet 6845 Green Oaks Rd Fort Worth TX 76116-1713

MEKLER, ARLEN B., lawyer, chemist; b. N.Y.C., May 4, 1943; s. Lev A. and Ethel (Fox) M.; m. Deborah Kay Nagle, Aug. 6, 1983; children: Jeffrey Arlen, Rebecca Ann, Ann-Marie Laura, Victoria Arlene, Lamar Adam, Lars Arlen. B.S. in Chemistry, Reed Coll.-San Jose State U., 1965; M.S. in Organic Chemistry, Iowa State U., 1955; Ph.D., Ohio State U., 1958; J.D., Temple U., 1972. Bar: Del. 1972, Pa. 1972, U.S. Supreme Ct. 1976. Sr. rsch. chemist E.I. du Pont de Nemours & Co., Wilmington, Del., 1958-69; ptnr. Mekler and Maurer, Wilmington, 1972—; chief appellate div. Office Pub. Defender, State of Del., 1973-77; pres. Del. Law Ctr., Wilmington, 1973—; instr. constl. law Wilmington Coll., 1976-80; dir. Bar Rev. Del., 1972—; mem. 3d Circuit Ct. Appeal Jud. Nominating Commn., 1977-81, 3d Circuit Ct. Appeals Jud. Conf. Contbr. monographs to legal pubs. Pres. Mental Health Aux. for Gov. Bacon Health Ctr., 1964-66; mem. Citizens Conf. for Modernization of State Legislatures, 1964-68; state chmn., Reform Commn. for Modernization Polit. Party Rules, 1965-68; pres. Del. Citizens for Fair Housing, 1965-69; state commr. Nat. Conf. on Uniform State Laws, 1972—; pres. Democratic Forum Del., 1966-70; mem. Del. Dem. Platform Com., 1966, 68, 72, 76; research dir. Del. Citizens for Humphrey-Muskie, 1968, Citizens for Biden, 1972, 78, 84, Citizens for McDowell, 1986—, Biden for Pres., 1986—; del. Dem. Nat. Conv., 1980; mem. social action com. Unitarian Ch., Wilmington, 1962-68. Recipient Keyman award, 1964, 65; State Govtl. Affairs award, 1964, 65. Mem. ABA, Del. Bar Assn. (com. on rules of criminal procedure 1973-74, supreme ct. com. on revision of criminal law 1973—, supreme ct. com. on rules of evidence 1976—, com. on revised rules of evidence 1976—, com. on revised rules of Del. Supreme Ct. 1974—, family law com. 1979—, continuing legal edn. com. 1981—), Pa. Bar Assn., Am. Chem. Soc., N.Y. Acad. Scis., Chem. Soc. (London), AAAS, Catalyst Club Phila., Wilmington Organic Chemists Club, ACLU (bd. dirs.), Sigma Xi, Phi Alpha Delta. Home: Brandywine Hills 714 W Matson Run Pky Wilmington DE 19802-1912 Office: PO Box 2285 Wilmington DE 19899-2285

MEL, HOWARD CHARLES, biophysics educator; m. Nancy Helene Shenon, June. 18, 1949; children—Amélie Catherine, Stéphanie Frances, Bartlett Woolsey. Student electronics and physics, Bowdoin Coll., 1945; student humanities and music, U. Geneva, Conservatoire de Musique, Geneva, 1946-47; B.S. with honors, U. Calif.-Berkeley, 1948, Ph.D. in Phys. Chemistry, 1953; postgrad., U. Brussels, 1953-55. Traffic mgr. Calo Pet Food Co., Oakland, 1948-50; instr. chemistry U. Calif.-Berkeley, 1955, USPHS fellow, lectr. med. physics, 1955-60, asst. prof., assoc. prof. biophysics, 1960-74, prof. biophysics, 1974-93, prof. emeritus, 1993—, dir. Lawrence Hall of Sci., 1981-82; faculty sr. scientist Lawrence Berkeley Lab. U. Calif. Berkeley, 1960—; dir. U. Calif. Study Ctrs., Bordeaux, Pau, Poitiers, France, 1986-89; dir. tng. grants Nat. Inst. Gen. Med. Scis., 1972-82; maître de recherche INSERM, U. Paris, 1974-75. Organizer, editor: Mason Katchalsky Meml. Symposium, 1977; editor for biophysics: Ency. Sci. and Tech., 4th edit., 1977; mem. editorial bd.: Blood Cells, 1974—, Cell Biophysics, 1978—, Rev. Sci. Instruments, 1975-78, Jour. Math. Biology, 1974-82; contbr. numerous articles to profl. jours.; patentee in field; researcher in cell membrane biophysics, hematopoiesis, biophys. instrumentation, and thermodynamic theory; inventor, developer stable-flow free-boundary method for analytical characterization & preparative separation of live cells and other particles, and of resistive pulse spectroscopy for characterization of geometrical, rheological, membrane-osmotic properties of cells, especially red blood cells. Former dir., mem. exec. com., chmn. music com. Oakland Symphony Orch. Assn.; v.p. Berkeleans for Acad. Excellence, 1970, Inverness Properties, Inc., 1965-75; bd. dirs. Pine Acres Homeowners Assn., 1983-86. Served to 1t (j.g.) USNR, 1943-46. Recipient Prix du Rayonnement de la Langue Francaise Acad. Francais, 1993; Fulbright fellow to Brussels, 1953-55; NSF sr. postdoctoral fellow, 1965-66. Fellow AAAS, Assn. Claude Bernard, Sigma Xi; mem. Biophys. Soc. (coun. 1969-71, founding), Am. Chem. Soc., Am. Inst. Physics, Am. Assn. Physics Tchrs., Soc. Gen. Systems Rsch., Internat. Soc. Biorheology, Internat. Union Pure and Applied Biophysics, Assn. Sci. Tech. Ctrs., Phi Beta Kappa, Sigma Phi Epsilon. Clubs: Faculty U. Calif.-Berkeley (dir. 1979-80); Bohemian (San Francisco); Sierra (San Francisco); Amphion (Berkeley), Mosswood Investment (Berkeley) (pres. 1958). Office: U Calif MCB-CDB Donner Lab Berkeley CA 94720-3206

MELADY, THOMAS PATRICK, university president, ambassador, author, public policy expert, educator; b. Norwich, Conn., Mar. 4, 1927; m. Margaret Judith Badum; children: Christina, Monica. BA, Duquesne U., 1950; MA, Cath. U. Am., 1952, PhD, 1954; hon. doctorates from 26 univs. Former mem. faculties Fordham and St. John's Univs.; founder Inst. African Affairs Duquesne U., 1957; cons. to founds., govts., corps., 1959-67; pres. Africa Service Inst.; prof. Afro-Asian affairs, chmn. dept. Asian studies and NonWestern civilization Seton Hall U., South Orange, N.J., 1967-69, expert, 1987-90; prof. Afro-Asian affairs, dir. Office of Internat. Studies, 1973-74; exec. v.p. prof. politics St. Joseph's U., Phila., 1974-76; pres. Sacred Heart U., Fairfield, Conn., 1976-86, prof. polit. sci. 1976-86, pres. emeritus, 1986—; asst. sec. for postsecondary edn. U.S. Dept. Edn., Washington, 1981-82; amb. to Burundi, 1969-72, amb. to Uganda, 1972-73; sr. adviser to U.S. del. to 25 UN Gen. Assembly, 1970; chmn. Conn. Conf. Ind. Colls., 1979-81; pres., chief exec. officer Conn. Pub. Expenditures Coun., 1986-89; U.S. amb. to The Holy See, Vatican City, 1989-93; 1993-94; exec. dir. Cath. Network of Vol. Svc., 1994—; disting. vis. prof. George Washington U. and St. John's U., 1993—. Author 13 books, including Ambassadors Story: The United States and The Vatican in World Affairs. Knighted by Pope Paul VI, 1968 and by Pope John Paul II, 1983, 91; honored by 4 countries; recipient Native Son award. Mem. Order of Malta.

MELAMED, ARTHUR DOUGLAS, lawyer; b. Mpls., Dec. 3, 1945; s. Arthur Charles and Helen Beatrix (Rosenberg) M.; m. Carol Drescher Weisman, May 26, 1983; children: Kathryn Henrie, Elizabeth Allyn. B.A., Yale U., 1967; J.D., Harvard U., 1970. Bar: D.C. 1970, U.S. Ct. Internat. Trade 1985, U.S. Ct. Appeals (9th cir.) 1971, U.S. Ct. Appeals (2d cir.) 1975, U.S. Ct. Appeals (D.C. cir.) 1978, U.S. Ct. Appeals (8th cir.) 1981, U.S. Ct. Appeals (fed. cir.) 1985, U.S. Ct. Appeals (4th cir.) 1989, U.S. Ct. Appeals (10th cir.) 1993, U.S. Supreme Ct. 1981. Law clk. U.S. Ct. Appeals for 9th Circuit, 1970-71; assoc. Wilmer, Cutler & Pickering, Washington, 1971-77; ptnr., 1978—; vis. prof. Georgetown U. Law Ctr., 1992-93, adj. prof., 1993-94. Contbr. articles to profl. jours. Class agt. Alumni Fund Yale U.; D.C. area chair Yale campaign, 1993—; mem. social scis. coun. com. Yale U., 1989-94; trustee Nat. Child Rsch. Ctr., 1990-93. Mem. ABA, D.C. Bar Assn., Am. Law Inst., Yale Club (N.Y.C.), Kenwood Country Club. Office: 2445 M St NW Washington DC 20037-1435

MELAMED, LEO, investment company executive; b. Bialystok, Poland, Mar. 20, 1932; came to U.S., 1941, naturalized, 1950.; s. Isaac M. and Fayga (Barakin) M.; m. Betty Sattler, Dec. 26, 1953; children: Idelle Sharon, Jordan Norman, David Jeffrey. Student, U. Ill., 1950-52; JD, John Marshall Law Sch., Chgo., 1955. Bar: Ill. 1955. Sr. ptnr. Melamed, Kravitz & Verson, Chgo., 1956-66; chmn., CEO Sakura Dellsher, Inc., Chgo., 1965—; mem. Chgo. Merc. Exch., 1953—; mem. bd. govs., 1967-91, chmn. bd., 1969-71, 75-77, chmn. exec. com. 1985-91, also spl. counsel; chmn. bd. Internat. Monetary Market, 1972-75, spl. counsel, 1976-91; mem. Chgo. Bd. Trade, 1969—; mem. corp. adv. bd. U. Ill., Chgo., 1991; mayor Chgo. Coun. Manpower and Econ. Advisors, 1972. Author: (sci. fiction novel) The Tenth Planet, 1987, Leo Melamed on the Markets, 1993; editor: The Merits of Flexible Exchange Rates, 1989. Trustee John Marshall Law Sch., 1991; coun. mem. U.S. Holocaust Meml. Mus. Named Man of Yr., Israel Bonds, 1975; recipient Am. Jewish Com. Human Rights medallion, 1991. Fellow Internat. Assn. Fin. Engrs. (sr.); mem. ABA, Am. Judicature Soc., Ill. Bar Assn., Chgo. Bar Assn., Nat. Bar. Econ. Rsch. (bd. dirs.), Econs. Club Chgo., Nat. Futures Assn. (chmn. 1982-89), Am. Contract Bridge League (life master), Union League Club, Chgo. Club, Standard Club. Avocations: writing, jogging. Office: Sakura Dellsher Inv Co Inc 30 S Wacker Dr Chicago IL 60606

MELAMEDE, ADA KARMI, architectural firm executive. Prin. Karmi Assocs., Tel Aviv, Israel. Prin. work (with Ram Karmi) Supreme Ct. of Israel. Office: Karmi Assocs, Tel Aviv Israel

MELAMID, ALEXANDER, economics educator, consultant; b. Freiburg, Fed. Republic Germany, Mar. 28, 1914; s. Michael and Zinaida (Gruenholz) M.; m. Ruth Caro, Nov. 28, 1940 (dec. July 1968); m. Ilse Hoenigsberg, Apr. 15, 1975; children: Diane H.C. Melamid Michaels, Suzanna C. Melamid Portnoy. BSc in Econs., London Sch. Econs., 1939; PhD, New Sch. for Social Research, 1952. Asst. prof. New Sch. for Social Research, N.Y.C., 1953-57; assoc. prof. NYU, 1957-65, prof., 1965-87, prof. emeritus, 1987—; v.p. Am. Geog. Soc., N.Y.C., 1975. Author: Turkey, 1956, History of Iran, 1968, New York City Region, 1985. Fellow Am. Geog. Soc. (hon., mem. council, Morse medal 1991); mem. Middle East Studies Assn. Am. Avocations: skiing. Office: NYU Dept Econs Washington Sq N New York NY 10003

MELBINGER, MICHAEL S., lawyer; b. Chgo., Sept. 5, 1958; s. Donald G. and Joyce A. (Haynes) M.; m. Karen Mary Melbinger, June 16, 1984; children: Peter Donald, Charlotte Anna. BA, U. Notre Dame, 1980; JD, U. Ill., 1983. Bar: Ill. 1983. Assoc. McDermott, Will & Emery, Chgo., 1983-88, ptnr., 1989-93; ptnr., head employee benefits dept. Schiff, Hardin & Waite, Chgo., 1993—; author, speaker Coll. for Fin. Planning, Denver, 1990—. Mem. editorial bd. Taxation for Lawyers, N.Y.C., 1989—, Employee Benefits Counselor, 1993—; contbr. articles to profl. jours. Precinct capt. Regular Rep. Orgn., Cook County, Ill., 1985—. Mem. Union League Club. Home: 623 W Campbell St Arlington Heights IL 60005-1419 Office: Schiff Hardin & Waite 7200 Sears Towers Chicago IL 60606

MELBY, EDWARD CARLOS, JR., veterinarian; b. Burlington, Vt., Aug. 10, 1929; s. Edward C. and Dorothy H. (Folsom) M.; m. Jean Day File, Aug. 15, 1953; children: Scott E., Susan J., Jeffrey T., Richard A. Student, U. Pa., 1948-50; D.V.M., Cornell U., 1954. Diplomate: Am. Coll. Lab. Animal Medicine. Practice veterinary medicine Middlebury, Vt., 1954-62; instr. lab. animal medicine Johns Hopkins U. Sch. Medicine, Balt., 1962-64; asst. prof. Johns Hopkins U. Sch. Medicine, 1964-66, assoc. prof., 1966-71, prof., dir. div. comparative medicine, 1971-74; prof. medicine, dean Coll. Vet. Medicine, Cornell U., Ithaca, N.Y., 1974-84; v.p. R & D SmithKline Beecham Animal Health, 1985-90, v.p. sci. and tech. assessment, 1990-91; ind. cons., 1992—; cons. VA, Nat. Research Council, NIH. Author: Handbook of Laboratory Animal Science, Vols. I, II, III, 1974-76. Served with USMC, 1946-48. Mem. Am., N.Y. State, Md., Pa. Veterinary Med. Assns., Am. Assn. Lab. Animal Sci., Am. Coll. Lab. Animal Medicine, AAAS, Phi Zeta. Home: PO Box 248 Charlotte VT 05445 Office: 1407 A Lime Kiln Rd Charlotte VT 05445

MELBY, JOHN B., composer, educator; b. Whitehall, Wis., Oct. 3, 1941; s. John B. Sr. and Margaret (Edmundson) M.; m. Carol A. Wurtz, July 7, 1961 (div. 1977); 1 child, John; m. Jane H. Thompson, June 15, 1978; children: Kirsten, Charles. MusB, Curtis Inst., 1966; MA, U. Pa., 1967; MFA, Princeton U., 1971, PhD, 1972. Assoc. prof. West Chester (Pa.) U., 1971-73; prof. music U. Ill., Urbana, 1973—; assoc. U. Ill. Ctr. for Advanced Studies, 1989-90. Composer numerous mus. works for live performers, computer-synthesized tape, vocal, chamber and orchestral music, works pub. by Am. Composers Edit., Merion Music Co., Margun Music, Inc.; recs. on Composers Recs., Inc., New World Records, Advance Records, Centaur Records, Zuma Records. Recipient 1st prize 7th Internat. Electroacoustic Music Awards, Bourges, France, 1979, Am. Acad./Inst. Arts and Letters award, 1984; Guggenheim fellow, 1983. Mem. BMI, Am. Composers Alliance. Democrat. Avocations: railroading, cooking, herpetology. Office: U Ill Sch Music 2136 Music Bldg 1114 W Nevada St Urbana IL 61801-3859

MELBY, ORVILLE ERLING, retired banker; b. Butte, Mont., Oct. 9, 1921; s. Ole and Esther (Jacobsen) M.; m. Arvilla L. Underland, Nov. 24, 1956; children—Steve E., James E., Ann-Margaret. B.A. magna cum laude, U. Wash., 1949. C.P.A., Wash., Oreg. Treas. Boeing Co., 1956-66; sr. v.p. fin. Continental Airlines, Los Angeles, 1966; v.p. Bank of Am., San Francisco, 1967; treas. Bendix Corp., Detroit, 1968; v.p., treas. Vought Aeronautics, Dallas, 1969-70, Bonanza Internat., Dallas, 1971-74; vice chmn. Rainier Nat. Bank, Seattle, 1974-87; bd. dirs. Health Care Property Investors, Los Angeles. Served with USAAF, 1942-46. Mem. Fin. Execs. Inst., Phi Beta Kappa. Presbyterian. Club: Mason. Home: 9439 Lake Washington Blvd NE Bellevue WA 98004

MELCHER, JERRY EUGENE, lawyer; b. Eugene, Oreg., June 26, 1945; s. Gordon Neil Wilcox and Irene Marie (Wagner) Mueller; m. Esther Donna Westby; children: Maureen Margit, Trenton Wilcox. BS, U. S.D., 1967; JD, Willamette U., 1970. Bar: Oreg. 1970, Alaska 1970, U.S. Dist. Ct. Alaska. Assoc. Hughes, Thorsness, Gantz, Powell & Brundin, Anchorage, Alaska, 1970-72, ptnr., 1972-89, prin. ptnr., 1980-89; ptnr. Heller, Ehrman, White & McAuliffe, Anchorage, 1989—. Mem. ABA, Oreg. State Bar Assn., Alaska State Bar Assn., Anchorage Bar Assn., Masons. Republican. Avocations: hunting, sports, fly fishing. Office: Heller Ehrman White & McAuliffe 1900 Enserch Ctr 550 W 7th Ave Anchorage AK 99501-3571

MELCHER, TRINI URTUZUASTEGUI, accounting educator; b. Somerton, Ariz., Dec. 1, 1931; d. Francisco Juan and Dolores (Barraza) Urtuzuastegui; m. Arlyn Melcher, Aug. 3, 1957 (div. Feb. 1972); children: Teresa Dolores, Michael Francis, Jocelyn Marie. BS, Ariz. State U., 1954, MBA, Kent State U., 1964; PhD, Ariz. State U., 1977. Acct. CPA firm, L.A., 1954-56; instr. L.A. Sch. Dist., 1956-58, Dolton (Ill.) Sch. Dist., 1958-61; asst. prof. Kent (Ohio) State U., 1962-72; prof. Calif. State U., Fullerton, 1976-89; founding faculty mem. Calif. State U., San Marcos, 1990—. Author: Intermediate Accounting Study Guide, 1984. Treas. Community Devel. Coun., Santa Ana, 1985-88, chmn. bd., 1989; mem. com. U.S. Dept. Labor, 1989—. Named Outstanding Educator, League of United Latin Am. Citizens, Stanton, Calif., 1987, Mex. Am. Women's Nat. Assn., Irvine, Calif., 1987; recipient Outstanding Faculty award Calif. State U. Sch. Bus., 1983,

Pub. Svc. award Am. Soc. Women CPAs, San Antonio, 1989; Affirmative Action grantee, 1990. Mem. AICPA (editorial bd. The Woman CPA), Am. Acctg. Assn., Calif. Soc. CPAs (Merit award 1991), Hispanic CPAs. Avocations: music, travel. Home: 2c24 Sequoia St San Marcos CA 92069 Office: Calif State U San Marcos CA 92069

MELCHERT, JAMES FREDERICK, artist; b. New Bremen, Ohio, Dec. 2, 1930; s. John Charles and Hulda Lydia (Egli) M.; m. Mary Ann Hostetler, June 18, 1954; children: Christopher, David, Renee. A.B., Princeton U., 1952; M.F.A., U. Chgo., 1957; M.A., U. Calif., Berkeley, 1961. Prof. art U. Calif., Berkeley, 1965-76, 81-84, 88-92, prof. emeritus, 1992—; dir. Am. Acad. in Rome, 1984-88; dir. Visual Arts Program, Nat. Endowment for Arts, Washington, 1977-81. Exhibited in one man shows at San Francisco Art Inst., 1970, San Francisco Mus. Modern Art, 1975, Holly Solomon Gallery, N.Y.C., 1991; group shows at Biennale de Paris, 1963, Whitney Mus., N.Y.C., 1966, 68, 70, Documenta 5, Kassel, Germany, 1972, Sydney (Australia) Biennal, 1976; commd. for Artwork (new Biology Bldg.) at MIT, 1993-94, Biomed. Rsch. Bldg. at Case Western Res. U., 1994. Recipient Adaline Kent award San Francisco Art Inst., 1970; Nat. Endowment for Arts artist fellow, 1973; hon. DFA, San Francisco Art Inst., 1984, Md. Inst. Coll. Arts, 1993. Home: 6077 Ocean View Dr Oakland CA 94618-1844

MELCONIAN, LINDA JEAN, state senator, lawyer; b. Springfield, Mass.; d. George and Virginia Elaine (Noble) Melconian. B.A., Mt. Holyoke Coll., 1970; M.A., George Washington U., 1976, J.D., 1978. Bar: Mass. Chief legis. asst. to Ho. of Reps. Speaker Thomas P. O'Neill, Jr., U.S. Congress, Washington, 1971-80; pros. atty. Hampden County Dist. Atty., Springfield, Mass., 1981-82; state senator Mass. Gen. Ct., Boston, 1983—; instr. Western New Eng. Coll., Springfield, 1978-82; Our Lady of the Elms Coll., Springfield, 1982-83. Chmn., Heart Fund Ball, Western Mass., 1983; incorporator Springfield Coll., 1982—; ex officio trustee Ella T. Grasso Found., Conn., 1982—; active Democratic State Com., Mass., 1983, Hampden County Dems. Recipient Appreciation award Vietnam Vets. of Greater Springfield, 1983; Equal Edn. for All Children award Bilingual Parents of Springfield, 1983; Appreciation award Vets.-Hampden County Council, 1984. Mem. Hampden County Bar Assn. Home: 257 Ft Pleasant Ave Springfield MA 01108-1521 Office: Mass State Senate Rm 213-b Boston MA 02133

MELCZEK, DALE J., bishop; b. Nov. 9, 1938. A.B., St. Mary Coll., Orchard Lake, Mich.; M.Div., St. John Sem., Plymouth, Mich.; M.A. in Edn., U. Detroit; postgrad., U. Notre Dame. Ordained priest Roman Cath. Ch., 1964, appointed aux. bishop, 1982. Assoc. pastor St. Sylvester Ch., Warren, Mich., 1964-70, co-pastor, 1970-72; pastor St. Christine Ch., Detroit, 1972-75; vicar West Detroit Vicariate, 1973-75; asst. vicar for parishes Archdiocese of Detroit, 1975-77, sec. to archbishop and vicar gen., 1977-82, archdiocesan consultor, 1972-83, aux. bishop, titular bishop of Trau, 1982—; regional bishop Detroit N.W. Region, 1983-92; apostolic adminstr. Diocese of Gary, Ind., 1992—; mem. adminstrv. bd. Nat. Conf. Cath. Bishops, chmn. Bishops' Com. on the Permanent Diaconate, 1992—.

MELCZER, JOSEPH T., III, lawyer; b. Phoenix, Aug. 8, 1948. BA, U. Santa Clara, 1970; JD, U. San Diego, 1974. Bar: Calif. 1974, Ariz. 1976. Ptnr. Snell & Wilmer, Phoenix. Mem. ABA, State Bar Calif., State Bar Ariz. (past mem. real estate adv. commn.). Office: Snell & Wilmer 1 Arizona Ctr Phoenix AZ 85004

MELDMAN, CLIFFORD KAY, lawyer; b. Milw., July 27, 1931; s. Edward H. and Rose (Bortin) M.; children: Mindy, David, Linda, James, Noah. JD, Marquette U., 1956. Bar: Wis. 1956. Ptnr. Meldman & Meldman, Milw., 1956-73; pres. Meldman & Meldman S.C., Milw., 1973—. Contbr. articles to profl. jours., also editor. Fellow Am. Acad. Matrimonial Lawyers (pres. 1982); mem. Milw. Bar Assn. (bd. dirs. 1984-86, pres. 1986-87, chmn. family law sect.), Wis. Bar Assn. (chmn. family law sect.). Home: 170 W Dean Cir Milwaukee WI 53217-2716 Office: Meldman & Meldman SC PO Box 17397 Milwaukee WI 53217-0397

MELDMAN, ROBERT EDWARD, lawyer; b. Milw., Aug. 5; s. Louis Leo and Lillian (Gollusch) M.; m. Sandra Jane Setlick, July 24, 1960; children—Saree Beth, Richard Samuel. B.S., U. Wis., 1959; LL.B., Marquette U., 1962; LL.M. in Taxation, NYU, 1963. Bar: Wis. 1962, fla. 1987, colo. 1990, U.S. Ct. Fed. Claims, U.S. Tax Ct. 1963, U.S. Supreme Ct. 1970. Practice tax law Milw., 1963—; pres. Meldman, Case & Weine, Ltd., Milw., 1975-85; dir. tax div. Mulcahy & Wherry, S.C., Milw., 1985-90; shareholder Reinhart, Boerner, Van Deuren, Norris & Rieselbach, S.C., 1991—; adj. prof. taxation U. Wis., Milw., 1970—, mem. tax adv. coun., 1978—; sec. Profl. Inst. Tax Study, Inc., 1978—; bd. dirs. Wis. Bar Found., 1988-94. Co-author: Federal Taxation Practice & Procedure, 1983, 86, 88, 92, Practical Tactics for Dealing with the IRS, 1994; contbr. articles to legal jours.; editor: Jour. Property Taxation. Recipient Adj. Taxation Faculty award UWM Tax Assn., 1987; named Outstanding Tax Profl. 1992 Corp. Reports Wis. Mag. and UWM Tax Assn. Mem. ABA, Fed. Bar Assn. (pres. Milw. chpt. 1966-67), Milw. Bar Assn. (chmn. tax sect. 1970-71), Wis. Bar Assn. (bd. dirs. tax sect. 1964-78, chmn. 1973-74), Am. Coll. Tax Counsel, Internat. Bar Assn., Marquette U. Law Alumni Assn. (bd. dirs. 1972-77), Milw. Athletic Club, Wis. Club, B'nai B'rith (trustee, Ralph Harris Meml. award Century Lodge 1969-70), Phi Delta Phi, Tau Epsilon Rho (chancellor Milw. chpt. 1969-71, supreme nat. chancellor 1975-76, v.p. Wis. chpt., tech. com. 1978—). Jewish (trustee congregation 1972-77). Home: 7455 N Skyline Ln Milwaukee WI 53217-3327 Office: Ste 2100 100 N Water St Ste 2100 Milwaukee WI 53202

MELDRUM, PETER DURKEE, venture capital/biotechnology company executive; b. Salt Lake City, June 26, 1947; s. Benjamin Nibley and Grace Natalie (Durkee) M.; m. Catherine Roper, June 16, 1970; children: Christopher Shawn. BS in Chem. Engring., U. Utah, 1970, MBA, 1974. Asst. to pres. Terra Tek, Inc., Salt Lake City, 1974-78; pres., chief exec. officer Resource Enterprises, Inc., Salt Lake City, 1978-81; pres., CEO, AgriDyne Techs., Salt Lake City, 1981-91, bd. dirs., 1979-93; pres., CEO, Founder's Fund Inc., 1991—; pres., CEO Myriad Genetics Inc., Salt Lake City, 1992—; bd. dirs. Dairy Equipment Co. Utah, Salt Lake City, Plantek Internat. Ltd., Singapore, Paradigm Bioscis. Inc., Cognetix Inc., Sonix Techs. Inc., Vaxsys Corp. Vice chmn. fundraising Salt Lake Boy's Club, 1978-79; bd. dirs. vice chmn. ARC Golden Spike, Salt Lake City, 1980-90; mem. State of Utah Council Sci. and Tech., 1984-89; adv. bd. High Tech Mktg. Rev., Austin, Tex., 1986-88; mem. Gov.'s Task Force on Entrepreneurship; mem. rev. panel Utah Tech. Fin. Corp., Gov.'s Com. on Biomed. Industry, 1988-91; mem. bioengring. adv. bd. U. Utah, bus. adv. bd. Coll. Bus. Weber State U.; bd. arbitrators NASD, 1991—. Served to 1st lt. USAR, 1970-72. Mem. Tau Beta Pi, Phi Kappa Phi, Beta Gamma Sigma. Republican. Presbyterian. Avocations: skiing, backpacking, basketball, racquetball. Home: 1808 Mohawk Way Salt Lake City UT 84108-3363 Office: Founder's Fund 390 Wakara Way Salt Lake City UT 84108-1255

MELE, ALFRED R., philosophy educator; b. Detroit, May 22, 1951; s. Alfred Emil and Rosemary (Pardo) M.; m. Constance, July 18, 1970; children: Al, Nick, Angela. BA, Wayne State U., 1973; PhD, U. Mich., 1979. Asst. prof. Philosophy Davidson (N.C.) Coll., assoc. prof., 1985-91, prof., 1991—. Author: Irrationality, 1987, Springs of Action, 1992, Autonomous Agents, 1995; contbr. articles to profl. jours. Fellow NEH, 1985-86, 92-93, Nat. Humanities Ctr., Rsch. Triangle Park, N.C., 1992-93. Mem. Am. Philos. Assn., So. Assn. Philosophy and Psychology, N.C. Philos. Soc. (pres. 1987-89). Avocations: racquetball, tennis. Office: Davidson Coll PO Box 1719 Davidson NC 28036

MELEIS, AFAF IBRAHIM, nurse sociologist, educator, clinician; b. Alexandria, Egypt, Mar. 19, 1942; d. Abdel Baki Ibrahim and Soad Hussein Hassan; m. Mahmoud Meleis, Aug. 21, 1964; children: Waleed, Sherief. BS magna cum laude, U. Alexandria, 1961; MS, UCLA, 1964, MA, 1966, PhD, 1968; D of Pub. Svc. (hon.), U. Portland, 1989. Instr. U. Alexandria, 1961-62; acting instr. UCLA, 1966-68, asst. prof. nursing, assoc. prof., 1968-75; assoc. prof., dean Health Inst., Kuwait, 1975-77; prof. nursing U. Calif., San Francisco, 1977—, also dir. Study Immigrant Health and Adjustment; vis. prof. colls. in Sweden, Brazil, Japan, Saudi Arabia, Kuwait, Egypt; 1st Centennial prof. Columbia U., N.Y.C., 1992-94; cons., speaker in field. author: theoretical Nursing: Development & Progress, 1985 (Book of Yr., am. Jour. Nursing, 1985), 2d edit., 1991; contbr. articles to rsch. and profl. jours. Recipient Helen Hahm award U. Calif. Sch. Nursing, San Francisco

1981, Teaching awards U. Calif., San Francisco, 1981, 85, Pres. Hosni Mubarak medal of Excellence, 1990; Kellogg Internat. fellow, 1986-89. Fellow Am. Acad. Nursing; mem. Coun. Nurse Researchers, Western Soc. Research in Nursing, Am. Nurses Assoc. Avocations: jogging, symphony, reading, international affairs, women's issues. Home: 39 Corte Ramon Greenbrae CA 94904-1228 Office: U Calif San Francisco Sch Nursing N511Y San Francisco CA 94143-0608

MELENDEZ, JOAQUIN, orthopedic assistant; b. San Gabriel, Calif., Aug. 16, 1929; s. Guadalupe and Gudelia (Maldonado) M.; m. Lola Hester Harris, Sept. 3, 1954. BS, Instituto del Estado, Chihuahua, Mex., 1949; AA, Foothill Coll., Los Altos Hill, Calif., 1973. Enlisted U.S. Army, 1950, advanced through grades to sgt. 1st class, ret., 1971; orthopedic asst. St. Vrain Valley Orthopedics (name now Longmont Orthopedics and Sports Medicine Clinic), Longmont, Colo., 1973—. Author: (poems) Saturday Night, 1990, Reflections, 1991, Freedom, 1992. With U.S. Army, 1950-71. Decorated Bronze Star with V, Meritorious Svc. medal with V; recipient marathon awards. Mem. Nat. Assn. Orthopedic Technologists, Colo. Acad. Physician Assts., Nat. Assn. Parlimentarians, Toastmasters Internat. (named Outstanding Div. Gov. 1988-89, recipient speech awards), Internat. Soc. Poets. Republican. Roman Catholic. Avocations: pub. speaking, writing, photography, running, hist. rsch. Home: 3331 Mountain View Ave Longmont CO 80503 Office: Longmont Orthopedics and Sports Medicine Clinic 1331 Linden St Longmont CO 80501

MELENDEZ, SARA E., academic administrator; b. San Juan, P.R., Jan. 20, 1941; d. Pablo and Lucia (Espinosa) M.; 1 child, Adam. BA, Bklyn. Coll., 1967; MS, L.I. U., 1974; EdD, Harvard U., 1981. Tchr. N.Y.C. Bd. of Edn., Bklyn.; asst. prof. U. Hartford (Conn.); dir. Minority Initiatives Am. Coun. on Edn., Washington; vice provost, dean arts and humanities U. Bridgeport (Conn.). Author: (book) Bilingual Education: A Sourcebook, 1987. Danforth fellow, Ford fellow. Mem. Soc. for Values in Higher Edn. (dir.). Office: Ctr for Applied Linguistics 1118 22nd St NW Washington DC 20037

MELENDY, DAVID RUSSELL, broadcast journalist; b. Corpus Christi, Tex., Oct. 19, 1948; s. Harold Orville and Marguerite Doris (Waller) M.; m. Lorna Sandra Katz, Mar. 19, 1972; children: Seth Howard, Andrew Scott. Student, George Washington U., 1966-70; BA magna cum laude, U. Hartford, 1972. News dir. Sta. WINY, Putnam, Conn., 1972-77; news anchor, reporter Sta. WPOP, Hartford, Conn., 1977-80; news dir. Sta. WNVR, Waterbury, Conn., 1980-81; news anchor Sta. WCBS-FM, N.Y.C., 1981; prodr., assignment editor, anchor, reporter AP Broadcast Svcs., Washington, 1981—; instr. journalism Briarwood Coll., Southington, Conn., 1977-81; mem. broadcast adv. com. Briarwood Coll., Southington, 1978-81. Prodr., writer, reporter (audio spl. report series) Star Wars: Strategic Defense Initiative, 1985, (daily audio feature) Flashback, 1986—. Publicity chmn. Woodstock (Conn.) Players Cmty. Theater, 1972-77; publicity chmn. Quinebaug Valley C.C. Found., Danielson, Conn., 1973-75, fundraising chmn., 1976; neighborhood coord. Am. Heart Assn., Washington, 1994; mem. Barker Found., Washington, 1983—. Mem. House and Senate Radio-TV Corr. Assn. Avocations: personal computers, photography, hiking, swimming. Office: AP Broadcast Svcs 1825 K St NW Washington DC 20006-1202

MELENDY, HOWARD BRETT, historian, educator; b. Eureka, Calif., May 3, 1924; s. Howard Burton and Pearl Marjorie (Brett) M.; m. Marian Ethel Robinson, Mar. 29, 1952; children: Brenda Dale, Darcie Brett, Lisa Marie. Student, Humboldt State Coll., 1942-45; A.B. in English., Stanford U., 1946, M.A. in Edn., 1948, Ph.D. in History, 1952. Tchr. Theodore Roosevelt High Sch., Fresno, Calif., 1950-54; instr. Fresno City Coll., 1954-55; faculty San Jose State Coll., 1955-69, prof. history, 1961-69, 79-93, head dept., 1958-65, chmn. dept., 1965-69, asst. v.p., 1968-69, acting acad. v.p., 1969, dean student studies, 1979-81, asso. acad. v.p. for undergrad. studies, 1981-83, univ. archivist, 1983-87, spl. advisor to dean engring., 1983-86, dir. Engring. Inst., 1986-87; interim dean for acad. devel. U. Hawaii, Honolulu, 1970, v.p. for community colls., 1970-73, prof. history, 1970-79; reader in Am. history advanced placement exam. Ednl. Testing Service, 1961-74; chmn. Hawaii Com. for Humanities, 1977-79. Author: (with Benjamin F. Gilbert) Governors of California, 1965, Oriental Americans, 1972, Asians in America, 1977, Chinese and Japanese Americans, 1984; Contbr. to: hist. jours., Ency. Brit.; contbr. chpts. to books. Mem. Santa Clara County Grand Jury, 1993—; bd. dirs. Rancho San Antonia Housing Corp., 1993—. Grantee Am. Philos. Soc., 1962, 74; Am. Council Edn. fellow in acad. adminstrn., 1967-68; Nat. Endowment for Humanities Edn. Planning grantee, 1975-76, 76-78. Mem. Am. Hist. Assn., NEA. Presbyterian (ruling elder). Office: San Jose State U One Washington Sq San Jose CA 95192

MELENEY, JOHN ALEXANDER, lawyer; b. N.Y.C., Dec. 11, 1950; s. John Coit and Lillian (Rhame) M.; m. Laura Marie Culley, Aug. 6, 1977; children: Anne Elizabeth, David Alexander, John Andrew. BA, Dartmouth Coll., 1972. B of Engring., 1974; JD, U. Chgo., 1977. Bar: Pa. 1977, Ill. 1980, U.S. Dist. Ct. (no. dist.) Ill. 1980, U.S. Ct. Appeals (7th cir.) 1988, U.S. Tax Ct. 1982. Assoc. Drinker, Biddle and Reath, Phila., 1977-79; assoc. Hopkins & Sutter, Chgo., 1979-83, ptnr., 1983—. Mem. ABA (tax sect. tax exempt fin. com. 1978—), Chgo. Bar Assn. Office: Hopkins & Sutter 3 First National Plz Chicago IL 60602

MELGAR, JULIO, retired mechanical engineer; b. Bklyn., July 4, 1922; s. Lorenzo and Maria (Lopez) M.; BME, U. Detroit, 1952. Mech. engr. Chance Vought Aircraft, Dallas, 1952-53, Wyatt C. Hedrick Architects and Engrs., Dallas, 1953, Zumwalt & Vinther, Cons. Engrs., Dallas, 1953-54, Joe Hoppe, Inc., Dallas, 1954-55, A.J. Boynton & Co., Dallas, 1956-57, Wyatt Metal and Boiler Works, Dallas, 1958, Tinker AFB, Okla., 1958-60; mech. engr. FAA, Ft. Worth, 1960-85, ret. 1985. Mem. Metroplex Recreation Coun., 1975—; mem. Am. Mus. Natural History, Ft. Worth Opera Guild, Dallas Opera Guild, Goodwill Industries; bd. dirs. Ft. Worth Opera Assn., Humane Soc. North Tex., Common Cause Disabled Am. Vets., Animal Protection Inst. With USMCR, 1943-45. Mem. ASME, Nat. Soc. Profl. Engrs., Am. Soc. Heating, Refrigerating and Air Conditioning Engrs., Profl. Soc. Protective Design, Fed. Bus. Assn., Amateur Athletic Union. Roman Catholic. Home: 6108 Menger Ave Dallas TX 75227-6228

MELHORN, WILTON NEWTON, geosciences educator; b. Sistersville, W.Va., July 8, 1921; s. Ralph Wilton and Pauline (Jones) M.; m. Agnes Leigh Beck, Aug. 25, 1961; children—Kristina L, Kimberly M. B.S., Mich. State U., 1942, M.S., 1951; M.S., N.Y. U., 1943; Ph.D., U. Mich., 1955. Hydrogeologist Mich. Geol. Survey, Lansing, 1946-49; hydrologist U.S. Weather Bur., Indpls., 1949-50; asst., then asso. prof. engring. geology Purdue U., Lafayette, Ind., 1954-70; head dept. geoscis. Purdue U., 1967-70, prof., 1970-91, prof. emeritus, 1991—; vis. prof. U. Ill. at Urbana, 1960-61, U. Nev., Reno, 1971-72, adj. prof., 1973-82; geol. cons. Cook County Hwy Commn., Chgo., 1955-56, Martin-Marietta Corp., Balt., 1964-66, Calif. Nuclear, Inc., Lafayette, 1966-68. Contbr. articles to tech. jours. Served to maj. USAAF, 1942-46. Fellow Geol. Soc. Am., AAAS; mem. Am. Assn. Petroleum Geologists, Soc. Econ. Geologists and Paleontologists, Speleological Soc., Ind. Acad. Scis. (pres. 1988, exec. officer 1992-94), Mich. Acad. Arts, Sci. and Letters, Am. Meteorol. Soc., Explorers Club , Sigma Xi, Sigma Gamma Epsilon. Home: 2065 S 9th St Lafayette IN 47905-2168

MELICAN, JAMES PATRICK, JR., lawyer; b. Worcester, Mass., Sept. 8, 1940; s. James Patrick and Abigail Helen (Donahue) M.; m. Debra A. Burns, Dec. 2, 1978; children: Marlane, James P., David, Molly, Megan. BA, Fordham U., 1962; JD, Harvard U., 1965; MBA, Mich. State U., 1971. Bar: Mich 1966, Calif. 1983. Supervising atty. product liability sect. Gen. Motors Corp., Detroit, 1971-73; atty.-in-charge trade regulation Gen. Motors Corp., 1973-77, atty.-in-charge mktg. and purchasing, 1977-80, asst. gen. counsel, 1980-81; gen. counsel Toyota Motor Sales, U.S.A., Inc., Torrance, Calif., 1981-82, v.p. gen. counsel, 1982-84; v.p., gen. counsel Internat. Paper Co., N.Y.C., 1984-87, sr. v.p., gen. counsel, 1987-91; exec. v.p. legal and external affairs Internat. Paper Co., Purchase, N.Y., 1991—; bd. dirs. Nat. Assn. Mfrs., Scitex Corp. Ltd.; bd. trustees Fordham Prep. Sch. Mem. ABA, NAM (bd. dirs.), Am. Law Inst., Assn. Bar City N.Y., Assn. Gen. Coun. (industry sector adv. com. on Paper and Paper Products for Trade Policy Matters; chair Lawyer's Adv. Com. to Bus. Roundtable Corp. Governance task force). Roman Catholic. Home: 46 Clearview Ln New Canaan CT 06840-3444 Office: Internat Paper Co 2 Manhattanville Rd Purchase NY 10577-2118

MELICH, DORIS S., public service worker; b. Salt Lake City, Apr. 8, 1913; d. Edward Harrison and Marie Cushing Snyder; m. Mitchell Melich, June 3, 1935; children: Tanya Marie Melich Silverman, Michael E., Nancy Lynne, Robert Allen. BA in Western History, U. Utah, 1934. Mem. Nat. Commn. Arthritis and Related Musculoskeltal Diseases, 1974-76, Nat. Arthritis Adv. Bd., 1977-84, 86-90; Utah del. Nat. Ho. of Dels. Arthritis Found., 1982-87; pres. Utah Arthritis Found. Bd., 1975-78, v.p., 1968-69, 73-74; Utah rep. Arthritis Found. Govt. Affairs, 1983—. Leader, founder 1st Girl Scouts Lone Troop U.S., Moab, Utah, 1947, regional selections com., 1958-67; active Utah Ballet Guild, Salt Lake Art Ctr., Utah Arts Coun., 1988—, Utah State Rep. Women, YWCA; trustee emeritus Arthritis Found. Recipient Cert. of Appreciation for Svc. Nat. Comm. Arthritis and Related Disease, 1976, Woman of Yr. Spl. award Utah Arthritis Found., 1980, Pyramid award Nat. Arthritis Found., 1986, Utan Coun. Girl Scouts award, 1987, Thanks Badge, 1963, Merit Honor award U. Utah Emeritus Club, 1978, Minute Man award Utah N.G., 1985; named to Nat. Women's Wall of Fame, Seneca Falls, N.Y., 1993. Mem. AAUW, Nat. Assistance League of Salt Lake City (charter mem.), Utah Women's Forum, Order Ea. Star, Alpha Delta Pi, Beta Sigma Phi (sponsor). Home: 900 Donner Way Apt 708 Salt Lake City UT 84108-2112

MELICH, MITCHELL, lawyer; b. Bingham Canyon, Utah, Feb. 1, 1912; s. Joseph and Mary (Kalembar) M.; m. Doris M. Snyder, June 3, 1935; children: Tanya (Mrs. Noel L. Silverman), Michael, Nancy, Robert A. LL.B., U. Utah, 1934. Bar: Utah 1934. Pvt. practice Moab, 1934-63, city atty., 1934-55; county atty. Grand County, 1940-42; sec., dir. Utex Exploration Co., Moab, 1953-62; pres., dir. Uranium Reduction Co., Moab, 1954-62; cons. to pres. Atlas Minerals, div. Atlas Corp., 1962-67; dir., treas. New Park Mining Co., 1962-65; assoc. Ray, Quinney & Nebeker, 1973—; solicitor Dept. Interior, Washington, 1969-73;. Mem. of Colorado River Com. of Utah, 1945-47; mem. Utah Water and Power Bd., 1947; chmn. Citizens Adv. Com. on Higher Edn., 1968; mem. nat. adv. council U. Utah, 1976—; Mem. Utah Senate, 1942-50, minority leader, 1949-50; mem. Utah Legislative Council, 1949-54; del. Republican Nat. Conv., 1952-72; mem. Rep. Nat. Com. for Utah, 1961-64; Rep. candidate for gov., 1964; cons. on staff Congressman Sherman P. Lloyd, Utah, 1967-68; bd. dirs. St. Marks Hosp., 1973-87; bd. regents U. Utah, 1961-65, also mem. devel. fund com., mem. nat. adv. council, 1968-73, 76—; mem. Utah Statewide Health Coordinating Coun., 1985; mem. Utah Fusion Energy Coun., 1989—. Recipient Disting. Alumni award U. Utah, 1969, Man of Yr. award, Arthritis Found., 1991. Mem. Am. Bar Assn., Utah State Bar, Utah Mining Assn. (pres. 1962-63), Kappa Sigma. Republican. Club: Alta Salt Lake Country (Salt Lake City). Lodges: Masons; Shriners. Home: 900 Donner Way Apt 708 Salt Lake City UT 84108-2112 Office: 400 Deseret Bldg 79 S Main St Salt Lake City UT 84111-1901

MELICHER, RONALD WILLIAM, finance educator; b. St. Louis, July 4, 1941; s. William and Lorraine Norma (Mohart) M.; m. Sharon Ann Schlarmann, Aug. 19, 1967; children: Michelle Joy, Thor William, Sean Richard. BSBA, Washington U., St. Louis, 1963; MBA, Washington U., 1965, DBA, 1968. Asst. prof. fin. U. Colo., Boulder, 1969-71, assoc. prof., 1971-76, prof. fin., 1976—, chmn. fin. div., 1978-86, 90; chmn. fin. and econ. div., 1993—; MBA/MS programs dir. U. Colo., Boulder, 1990-93, chmn. fin. and econ. div., 1993—; assoc. dir. space law bus. and policy ctr. U. Colo., 1986-87; rsch. cons. FPC, Washington, 1975-76, GAO, Washington, 1981, RCG/Hagler, Bailly, Inc., 1985—, Ariz. Corp. Commn., 1986-87, Colo. Dept. Pub. Utility Control, 1989, U.S. SEC, 1992—; cons. tech. edn. IBM Corp., 1985-91; dir. ann. Exch. Program for Gas Industry, 1975-94; instr. ann. program Nat. Assn. Regulatory Utility Commrs., Mich. State U., 1981—. Co-author: Real Estate Finance, 2d edit., 1984, 3d edit. 1989, Finance: Introduction to Markets, Institutions and Management, 7th edit., 1988, 8th edit., 1992, Financial Management, 5th edit., 1987; assoc. editor The Financial Rev., 1988-91. Recipient News Ctr. 4 TV Teaching award, 1987, MBA/MS Assn. Teaching award 1988; grantee NSF, 1974, NASA, 1986, 87; scholar W.H. Baughn Disting., 1989—, U. Colo. Pres.'s Teaching, 1989—. Mem. Fin. Mgmt. Assn. (mem. com. 1974-76, regional dir. 1975-77, assoc. editor 1975-80, v.p. ann. mtg. 1985, v.p. program 1987, pres. 1991-92, exec. com. 1991-93, bd. trustees 1992—, chmn. 25th Anniversary com. 1994-95), Am. Fin. Assn., Western Fin. Assn. (bd. dirs. 1974-76), Fin. Execs. Inst. (acad. mem. 1975—), Ea. Fin. Assn., Southwestern Fin. Assn., Midwest Fin. Assn. (bd. dirs. 1978-80), Alpha Kappa Psi, Beta Gamma Sigma. Presbyterian. Home: 6348 Swallow Ln Boulder CO 80303-1456 Office: U Colo Coll Bus PO Box 419 Boulder CO 80303

MELICK, GEORGE FLEURY, mechanical engineer, educator; b. Morristown, N.J., Sept. 7, 1924; s. George Fleury and Esther Purdy (Udall) M.; m. Florence Miriam Bevins, Dec. 28, 1946; children: Robert A., Linda S., Judith E., Karen L. BSE, Princeton U., 1944; MS, Stevens Inst. Tech., 1955; ME, Columbia U., 1963; MA, NYU, 1970. Registered profl. engr., N.J. Asst. chief engr. Worthington Corp., Harrison, N.J., 1946-55; asst. prof. Stevens Inst. Tech., Hoboken, N.J., 1955-58; assoc. in mech. engring. Columbia U., N.Y.C., 1958-61; assoc. prof. mech. engring., dean Rutgers U., New Brunswick, N.J., 1961-77; cons. engr. Stone & Webster Engring. Corp., Cherry Hill, N.J., 1977-87; dir. engring. mgmt. program Drexel U., Phila., 1987-91; chmn. bd. Anastasio & Melick Assocs., Egg Harbor, N.J., 1987—; cons. Worthington Corp., Harrison, 1956-65, Pub. Svc. Elec. & Gas, Newark, 1966-76. Author: John Mark and the Origin of the Gospels, 1979. Mem. countycom. Dem. Party, Franklin Twp., N.J., 1976. 1st lt. U.S. Army, 1945-52. Decorated Bronze Star medal. Mem. ASME (life), Am. Soc. Engring. Mgmt. (life), Am. Soc. Engring. Edn. (life), Soc. Bibl. Lit., Am. Acad. Religion (charter), Sigma Xi, Pi Tau Sigma. Presbyterian. Home: 6 Raven Ct Mount Laurel NJ 08054-3043 Office: Anastasio & Melick Assocs 543 Columbia Rd Egg Harbor City NJ 08215

MELICKIAN, GARY EDWARD, trade association executive; b. L.A., Apr. 2, 1935; s. Ara Harry Melickian and Virginia Anne (Gargan) Jardine; m. Greta Gail Rasbury, Aug. 20, 1955 (div. 1972); children: Mark Stanley, Lynn Anne; m. Sharon Anne McDaniel, July 28, 1989. Student, UCLA, 1953-55; EM, Colo. Sch. Mines, 1959; postgrad., U. So. Calif., 1961-67, Calif. Poly. Inst., 1969-71. Lic. geologist, Calif., Alaska, engring. geologist, Calif.; cert. profl. geologist. Geologist Humble Oil & Refining Co., L.A., 1959; civil engr. L.A. County Flood Control Dist., L.A., 1960; geophysicist Dames & Moore, L.A., 1961, project geologist, 1962-64, mgr. pers., 1965-66, mgr. pub. rels., 1967-69, prtnr., 1970-84; dir. mining Dames & Moore, Denver, 1970-80; dir. tech. svcs. Dames & Moore, Bethesda, Md., 1980-84; pres., bd. dirs. Consultation Networks, Inc., Washington, 1985-90, Expert Witness Network, Washington, 1985-90; dir. indsl. mktg. Am. Gas Assn., Arlington, Va., 1990—; technical project advisor Gas Rsch. Inst., Indsl. Gas Tech. Commercialization Ctr., Gas Tech. Can.; presenter in field. Contbr. articles to profl. jours. Fellow Geol. Soc. Am. (editor Engring. Geology newsletter 1966-67); mem. NSPE, ASME, Am. Inst. Profl. Geologists (pres. Calif. sect. 1971, bd. dirs. 1972-73, sec.-treas. 1982, Cert. of Merit 1982, 83), Soc. Mining Engrs. (bd. dirs. 1972-74, chmn. Peele award com., publs. com., program com.), Assn. Engring. Geologists (del. Internat. Geol. Congress, Prague), Hist. Earth Sci. Soc., Am. Soc. Metals, Tech. Assn. Pulp and Paper Industry, Assn. Iron and Steel Engrs., Assn. Energy Engrs. Avocations: art history, mineral collecting, stamps, western U.S. history, collecting rare books. Office: Am Gas Assn 1515 Wilson Blvd Arlington VA 22209-2402

MELILLO, JOSEPH VINCENT, producer, performing arts; b. New Haven, Conn., Nov. 15, 1948; s. Vincent and Viola (Fucci) M. BA, Sacred Heart U., 1968; MFA, Cath. U. Am., 1972. Adminstr. City Ctr. Music and Drama, N.Y.C., 1972-75; mktg. dir. The Walnut St. Theatre, Phila., 1975-76; dir. FEDAPT, N.Y.C., 1976-80; gen. mgr. New World Festival of Arts, Miami, Fla., 1982; dir. Next Wave Festival, N.Y.C., 1983-89; artistic dir. N.Y. Internat. Festival, N.Y.C., 1990-91; producing dir. Bklyn. Acad. Music, 1991—; trustee InGarde Arts, N.Y.C., 1991—; v.p. bd. dirs. Assn. Performing Arts Presenters, Washiington, 1991-93; cons.-specialist Opera Am., Washington, 1991-93. Editor: Market the Arts, 1980. Democrat. Avocations: reading, travel.

MELINSON, JAMES ROBERT, judge; b. Phila., Sept. 6, 1939; m. Monica Varrone, Apr. 27, 1963; children: Gregg, Keith, Megan. BA with honors, LaSalle U., 1961; JD, Temple U., 1968, M in Edn. Adminstrn., 1973. Bar: Pa. 1968. Gen. practice Meehan & Stoelker, Phila., 1968-82; chief negotiator Sch. Dist. Phila., 1976-85; gen. counsel Internat. Assn. Machinists & Aeroespace Workers, 1980-88, Whiting-Patterson Co., Inc., 1981-88; gen. practice James R. Melinson, P.C., 1982-88; judge Superior Ct. Pa., 1988-90, U.S. Dist. Ct. (ea. dist.) Pa., 1990—; English tchr. Olney High Sch., 1962-68, disciplinarian, 1968-73, vice-prin., 1968-76; cons./advisor labor rels. U.S. Dept. Def., 1982-85. Active Counseling or Referral Assistance, Inc., Irish Soc. Phila., Emerald Edn. Com., Friendly Sons of St. Patrick, Order Sons Italy Am., Police Athletic League, Am. Cath. Historical Soc. I. U.S Army arty., 1961-62. Recipient Pub. Svc. award Pa. Sch. Bds. Assn., President's award Phila. Assn. Sch. Adminstrs., 1985. Mem. ABA (judicial adminstrn. div.), KC, Am. Judges Assn., Am. Arbitration Assn., Fed. Bar Assn., Nat. Judicial Coll., Phila. Bar Assn., Nat. Assn. Edni. Negotiators, Soc. Profls. Dispute Resolution, Large City Negotiators Conf., Brehon Law Soc., Pa. Conf. State Trial Judges, Appellate Judges Conf., LaSalle U. Alumni Assn., Temple U. Law Alumni Assn. Office: US District Court 4614 US Courthouse 6th & Market St Philadelphia PA 19106

MELISSINOS, ADRIAN CONSTANTIN, physicist, educator; b. Thessaloniki, Greece, July 28, 1929; came to U.S. 1955, naturalized, 1970; s. Constantin John and Olympia (Abbott) M.; m. Mary Joyce Mitchell, June 7, 1960; children: Constantin John, Andrew William. Student, Royal Naval Acad., Greece, 1945-48; M.S., Mass. Inst. Tech., 1956, Ph.D., 1958. Naval cadet Greek Navy, 1945-48, commd. ensign, 1948, advanced through grades to lt., 1951; ret., 1954; teaching and research asst. Mass. Inst. Tech., 1955-58; instr. U. Rochester, N.Y., 1958-60; asst. prof. physics U. Rochester, 1960-63, assoc. prof., 1963-67, prof., 1967—, chmn. dept. physics and astronomy, 1974-77; vis. scientist CERN European Center for Nuclear Research, 1968-69, 77-78, 89-90; cons. Brookhaven Nat. Lab., 1970-72, 75-79. Author: Experiments in Modern Physics, 1966, (with F. Lobkowicz) Physics for Scientists and Engineers, 1975; (with A. Das) Quantum Mechanics, 1985, Principles of Modern Technology, 1990. Decorated Swedish Order of Sword. Fellow Am. Phys. Soc.; mem. Greek Nat. Acad. (corr.) Achievements include experimentation with elementary particles at most major high energy accelerators in the U.S. and Europe, experimentation with high power lasers. Home: 177 Whitewood Ln Rochester NY 14618-3223 Office: U Rochester Dept Physics Rochester NY 14627

MELKONIAN, HARRY G., lawyer, rancher; b. Bridgeport, Conn., June 18, 1949; s. Harry Artin and Hermina (Barsumian) M. BA, U. Rochester, 1971; JD cum laude, NYU, 1974. Bar: N.Y. 1975, Calif. 1977, U.S. Supreme Ct. 1984. Atty. Breed Abbott & Morgan, N.Y.C., 1974-76, Rifkind Sterling & Lockwood, Beverly Hills, Calif., 1976-78; atty. Buchalter Nemer Fields & Younger, L.A., 1978-81, ptnr., 1981-87; ptnr. White & Case, L.A., 1987—. Editor NYU Law Review, 1973-74. Trustee Project Literacy L.A., 1990-92; bd. govs. The Pilgrim Sch., L.A., 1992—; bd. dirs. HopeNet, L.A., 1990-91; chmn. bd. deacons 1st Congl. Ch. L.A., 1992-93, trustee, 1994—. Mem. Olympic Club, Calif. Club, Phi Alpha Delta. Republican. Avocations: fishing, hunting. Office: White & Case 633 W 5th St 19th Fl Los Angeles CA 90071

MELLA, ARTHUR JOHN, insurance company executive; b. New York, N.Y., Sept. 25, 1937; s. Anthony Arthur and Angela Helen (Morrongiello) M.; m. Louise Vetere, May 5, 1962; children: Douglas James, Gregory Arthur. BS, Fordham U., 1959. CPCU. Supr. Liberty Mut. Ins. Co. N.Y.C., 1960-70; v.p. The Home Ins. Co., N.Y.C., 1970-80, Skandia Am. Reinsurance Co., N.Y.C., 1980-85; sr. v.p. Reliance Reinsurance Corp., Phila., 1985—. With USNG, 1960-63. Mem. Fedn. Ins. and Corp. Counsel, Excess Surplus Lines Claims (pres. 1988-89, v.p. 1987-88, bd. dirs. 1986-87), Broker and Reins. Underwriting, Soc. CPCU. Republican. Roman Catholic. Avocations: gardening, book collecting, golf. Office: Reliance Reinsurance Co 1 Penn Center Plz Philadelphia PA 19103-1821

MELLBERG, LEONARD EVERT, physicist; b. Springfield, Mass., Dec. 18, 1935; s. Evert and Dorothy (Baker) M.; m. Margaret Ann Baker, Oct. 2, 1987. BS in Physics, U. Mass., 1961; MS in Physics, Trinity Coll., Hartford, Conn., 1968. Rsch. physicist Navy Underwater Sound Lab., New London, Conn., 1961-68, SACLANT Undersea Rsch. Ctr., LaSpezia, Italy, 1968-72, Office of Naval Rsch., London, 1968-72, Naval Underwater Systems Ctr., Newport, R.I., 1972-91; sr. scientist Marine Acoustics Inc., Newport, 1991-94; cons. Sci.Applications Internat. Corp., 1994—; mem. numerous govt. and profl. tech. adv. bds. and coms. Contbr. over 60 articles to profl. jours. Pres. Verdandi Swedish Cultural Found., Providence, 1992—; bd. dirs. Verdandi Chorus Am. Union Swedish Singers, Providence, 1992—. Recipient Civilian Navy Meritorious Svc. medal Dept. of Navy, 1991, Excellence in Sci. award Naval Underwater Systems Ctr., 1977, 84. Fellow Acoustical Soc. Am.; mem. IEEE (sr.), AIAA (svc. award 1977), Am. Geophys. Union. Achievements include research in ocean acoustic propagation, anti-submarine warfare acoustics, Arctic sea-ice ridges and lighter than air vehicles. Home: 20 Willow Ave Middletown RI 02842-4948 Office: Sci Applications Internat Corp 2 Shaws Cove Ste 203 New London CT 06320

MELLENBRUCH, GILES (JOHNNY) EDWARD, orchestra leader, lyricist; b. Hiawatha, Kans., May 9, 1911; s. William Bill and Mary Alice (Hanson) M.; m. Marie Lorraine Guy (dec. 1964); children: Gail Marie Smith, Joanne Kay Gillon; m. Leah Marie Cook, Feb. 25, 1967. BA in Music, U. Kans., 1932; BA in Econs., U. Kansas City, 1944. Band leader at many Kansas City night clubs and ballrooms in the 1930s, Hollywood, Calif, 1940s; recorded for Atlas Records, Movieland Records and others in 1930s and 40s. Treas. Christian Mission Outreach Inc., Aptos, Calif., 1989-94; founding mem. United We Stand Am., The Heritage Found. Recipient Minuteman Leadership Cert. award Am. Conservative Union, 1994. Mem. ASCAP, Local 47 AFM (life). Home: PO Box 244 Aptos CA 95001-0244

MELLENCAMP, JOHN (JOHN COUGAR), singer, songwriter; b. Seymour, Ind., Oct. 7, 1951; m. Vicky C. (div.); children: Michelle, Teddy Joe, Justice; m. Elaine Irwin, Sept. 5, 1992. Student, Vincennes U., Ind. Albums include Chestnut Street Incident, 1977, Biography, 1978, Johnny Cougar, 1979, Nothing Matters and What If It Did, 1980, Night Dancin, 1980, American Fool, 1982, Uh-huh, 1983, Scarecrow, 1985, The Lonesome Jubilee, 1988, Big Daddy, 1989, Whenever We Wanted, 1991, Human Wheels, 1993, Dance Naked, 1994; performed one song for Folkways: A Vision Shared (A Tribute to Woody Guthrie and Leadbelly), 1988; film actor, dir., soundtrack performer: Falling From Grace, 1992; TV appearance Bob Dylan: The 30th Anniversary Concert Celebration, 1993. Office: Champion Entertainment 130 W 57th St Apt 12B New York NY 10019-3312*

MELLETTE, M. SUSAN JACKSON, physician, educator, researcher; b. Raleigh, N.C., June 4, 1922; d. Donald Rough and Bessie Lou (Mull) Jackson; m. Peter A. Mellette, June 16, 1943; children: Susan E. Mellette Lederhouse, Peter Mason. AB, Meredith Coll., 1942; postgrad., U. N.C., 1942-43, U. Pa. Med. Sch., 1944; MD, U. Cin., 1947. Fels rsch. asst. U. N.C., Chapel Hill, 1942-43; intern Cleve. City Hosp., 1947-48; resident in internal medicine St. Barnabas Hosp., N.Y.C., 1949-51, Koch Hosp., St. Louis, 1952-54; rsch. assoc. U. Louisville, 1952; NIH rsch. fellow Med. Coll. Va., 1955-57, Damon Runyon cancer rsch. fellow, 1957-58; rsch. assoc. Med. Coll. Va., Richmond, 1958-60, asst. prof. internal medicine, 1960-69, assoc. prof., 1969-79, prof. internal and rehab. medicine, 1979-93, prof. emerita, 1993—, cancer coord., 1961-66, dir. Cancer Rehab. Program, 1974-93; mem. behavioral medicine study sect. NIH, Bethesda, Md., 1986-91; mem. cancer edn. com. Nat. Cancer Inst., NIH, 1974-78, mem. task force on rehab. rsch., 1990, mem. expert panel on advances in cancer treatment Nat Cancer Inst., 1992. Contbr. numerous articles and book chpts. on cancer treatment and rehab. to profl. publs. Mem. Commn. on Terminal Care Legislature Va., Richmond, 1982-83; adv. bd. Women's Bank, Richmond, 1979-81. Recipient Hoover award Va. Rehab. Assn., 1979, Nat. Brotherhood award NCCJ, 1987, Profl. of Yr. award Va. Assn. Professions, 1989. Fellow Am. Assn. Cancer Edn. (pres. 1975); mem. N.Y. Acad. Sci., Am. Congress Rehab. Medicine (chmn. cancer rehab. com. 1984-87), Am. Cancer Soc. (nat. svc. and rehab. com. 1982-92, nat. patient svcs. com. 1992-94, Profl. Edn. award Va. divsn. 1982), Am. Assn. Med. Colls., Med. Coll. Va. Alumni Assn.

(named disting. prof. 1995), Alpha Omega Alpha. Home: 1502 Wilmington Ave Richmond VA 23227-4430 Office: Med Coll Va Richmond VA 23298

MELLI, MARYGOLD SHIRE, law educator; b. Rhinelander, Wis., Feb. 8, 1926; d. Osborne and May (Bonnie) Shire; m. Joseph Alexander Melli, Apr. 8, 1950; children: Joseph, Sarah Bonnie, Sylvia Anne, James Alexander. BA, U. Wis., 1947, LLB, 1950. Bar: Wis. 1950. Dir. children's code revision Wis. Legis. Coun., Madison, 1950-53; exec. dir. Wis. Jud. Coun., Madison, 1955-59; asst. prof. law U. Wis., Madison, 1961-66, assoc. prof., 1966-67, prof., 1967-84; Voss-Bascom prof. U. Wis., 1985-93, emerita, 1993—; assoc. dean U. Wis., 1970-72, rsch. affiliate Inst. for Rsch. on Poverty, 1980; mem. spl. rev. bd. State of Wis. Dept. Health and Social Svcs., Madison, 1973—. Author: (pamphlet) The Legal Status of Women in Wisconsin, 1977, (book) Wisconsin Juvenile Court Practice, 1978, rev. edit., 1983, (with others) Child Support & Alimony, 1988, The Case for Transracial Adoption, 1994; contbr. articles to profl. jours. Bd. dirs. Am. Humane Assn., 1985—. Named one of five Outstanding Young Women in Wis., Jaycees, 1961; rsch. grantee NSF, 1983; recipient award for Outstanding Contbn. to Advancement of Women in State Bar of Wis., award for Lifelong Contbn. to Advancement of Women in the Legal Prof., 1994. Fellow Am. Acad. Matrimonial Lawyers (exec. editor jour. 1985-90); mem. Am. Law Inst. (reporter, cons. project on law of family dissolution), Internat. Soc. Family Law (v.p.), Wis. State Bar Assn. (reporter family law sect.), Nat. Conf. Bar Examiners (chmn. bd. mgrs. 1989). Democrat. Roman Catholic. Avocations: jogging, swimming, collecting art. Home: 2904 Waunona Way Madison WI 53713-2238 Office: U Wis Law Sch Madison WI 53706

MELLINK, MACHTELD JOHANNA, archaeologist, educator; b. Amsterdam, Holland, Oct. 26, 1917; came to U.S., 1949; d. Johan and Machteld (Kruyff) M. B.A., U. Amsterdam, 1938, M.A., 1941; Ph.D., Utrecht (Netherlands) U., 1943; LLD (hon.), U. Pa., 1987, Anatolian U., Turkey, 1990. Faculty Bryn Mawr Coll., 1949-88, prof. classical and Near Eastern archaeology, 1962-88, chmn. dept., 1955-83; staff mem. excavations Tarsus, Turkey, 1947-49, Gordion, Turkey, 1950-74; field dir. excavations Karatas-Semayuk, Lycia, Turkey, 1963—; Troy, 1988—; research asso. U. Mus., U. Pa., 1955-82, con. scholar, 1982—. Author: A Hittite Cemetery at Gordion, 1956; author: (with Jan Filip) Frühe Stufen der Kunst-Propyläen Kunstgeschichte XIII, 1974; editor: Dark Ages and Nomads c. 1000 B.C., 1964, Troy and the Trojan War, 1986, Elmali-Karatas I, 1992, II, 1994; contbr. articles to profl. jours. Recipient Lucy Wharton Drexel medal, 1994—. Fellow Am. Acad. Arts and Scis.; mem. Archaeol. Inst. Am. (pres. 1981-84, gold medal 1991), German Archaeol. Inst., Am. Oriental Soc., Am. Philos. Soc.; corr. mem. Royal Netherlands Acad. Scis., Austrian Archaeol. Inst. (corr.), Türk Tarih Kurumu (hon.), Am. Research Inst. Turkey (v.p. 1977-87, pres. 1988-92). Home: 264 Montgomery Ave Haverford PA 19041-1531

MELLINKOFF, DAVID, lawyer, educator; b. 1914. A.B., Stanford U., 1935; LL.B., Harvard U., 1939. Bar: Calif. 1939. Sole practice Calif., 1939-41, 46-64; lectr. UCLA Law Sch., 1964-65, prof., 1965-85, prof. emeritus, 1985—. Author: The Language of the Law, 1963, 11th printing, 1990, Lawyers and the System of Justice, 1976, Legal Writing: Sense and Nonsense, 1982, Mellinkoff's Dictionary of American Legal Usage, 1992; also articles. Served to capt. U.S. Army, 1941-46. Home: 744 Holmby Ave Los Angeles CA 90024-3320 Office: UCLA Law Sch 405 Hilgard Ave Los Angeles CA 90024-1301

MELLINKOFF, SHERMAN MUSSOFF, medical educator; b. McKeesport, Pa., Mar. 23, 1920; s. Albert and Helen (Mussoff) M.; m. June Bernice O'Connell, Nov. 18, 1944; children: Sherrill, Albert. BA, Stanford U., 1941, MD, 1944; LHD (hon.), Wake Forest U., 1984, Hebrew Union Coll., L.A., 1988. Diplomate Am. Bd. Internal Medicine, Am. Bd. Gastroenterology, Am. Bd. Nutrition. Intern asst. resident Stanford U. Hosp., San Francisco, 1944-45; asst. resident Johns Hopkins Hosp., Balt., 1947-49, chief resident, 1950-51, instr. in medicine, 1951-53; fellow in gastroenterology Hosp. of U. Pa., Phila., 1949-50; from asst. prof. to prof. medicine UCLA Sch. of Medicine, L.A., 1962-86; dean UCLA Sch. Medicine, L.A., 1962-86, emeritus prof. of medicine, 1990—; disting. physician of VA Wadsworth VA Medical Ctr., L.A., 1990-93; mem. sci. adv. panel Rsch. to Prevent Blindness, Inc., N.Y.C., 1975-93; mem. program devel. com. Nat. Med. Fellowships, Inc., N.Y.C., 1984—. Editorial bd. The Pharos, 1986; contbr. articles to profl. jours. Apptd. by Gov. of Calif. to McCone Com., 1965. Capt. U.S. Army, 1945-47. Recipient Abraham Flexner award Assn. Am. Med. Colls., 1981, J.E. Wallace Sterling Disting. Alumnus award Stanford U. Sch. of Medicine, 1987. Master ACP; fellow Royal Coll. of Physicians; mem. Am. Gastroenterol. Assn. Assn., of Am. Physicians, Inst. of Medicine of NAS, Am. Acad. of Arts and Scis., The Johns Hopkins Soc. of Scholars. Avocations: reading, hiking. Office: UCLA Sch of Medicine Dept of Medicine 44-143 CHS Los Angeles CA 90024

MELLINS, HARRY ZACHARY, radiologist, educator; b. N.Y.C., May 23, 1921; s. David J. and Ray (Hoffman) M.; m. Judith Alice Weiss, Dec. 26, 1950; children: Elizabeth, William, Thomas. A.B., Columbia Coll., 1941; M.D., L.I. Coll. Medicine, 1944; M.S. in Radiology, U. Minn., 1951; A.M. (hon.), Harvard U., 1970. Intern Jewish Hosp., Bklyn., 1944-45, asst. resident in radiology, 1945-46; resident in radiology U. Minn., Mpls., 1948-50, instr. radiology, 1950-52, asst. prof., 1952-53; clin. asst. prof. radiology Wayne State U., Detroit, 1953-56; dir. radiology Sinai Hosp., Detroit, 1953-56; prof., chmn. dept. radiology SUNY, Coll. Medicine, N.Y.C., 1956-69; chief radiology Kings County Hosp. Center, Bklyn., 1956-69; radiologist-in-chief State Univ. Hosp., Bklyn., 1966-69; prof. radiology Harvard Med. Sch., Boston, 1969-91, prof. radiology emeritus, 1991—; dir. diagnostic radiology Peter Bent Brigham Hosp., 1969-79; dir. diagnostic radiology Brigham and Women's Hosp., 1980-87, dir. edn. and tng., dept. radiology, 1987—; chief of radiology Harvard U. Health Svc., 1988—; nat. cons. in radiology to surgeon gen. U.S. Air Force, 1968-79; mem. radiation study sect. NIH, 1967-71; mem. subcom. for written exam. in diagnostic radiology Am. Bd. Radiology, 1970-75; mem. radiology tng. com. research tng. grants br. Nat. Inst. Gen. Med. Scis.; mem. diagnostic research adv. group div. cancer biology and diagnosis Nat. Cancer Inst., 1975-79; guest examiner Am. Bd. Radiology. Served to capt. M.C. USAAF, 1946-48. Mem. Bklyn. Radiol. Soc. (pres. 1965-66), N.Y. Roentgen Soc. (pres 1966-67), Assn. Univ. Radiologists (pres. 1969-70, Gold medal 1986), Soc. Uroradiology (pres. 1975-76), Am. Roentgen Ray Soc. (pres. 1977-79, Gold medal 1989), Radiol. Soc. N.Am., New Eng. Roentgen Ray Soc. (pres. 1986-87), Soc. Gastrointestinal Radiology, Alpha Omega Alpha. Office: Brigham and Women's Hosp 75 Francis St Boston MA 02115-6195

MELLINS, ROBERT B., pediatrician, educator; b. N.Y.C., Mar. 6, 1928; s. David J. and Ray H. (Hoffman) M.; m. Sue Mendelsohn, Apr. 19, 1959; children: Claude Ann, David Rustin. A.B., Columbia U., 1949; M.D., Johns Hopkins U., 1952. Intern Johns Hopkins Hosp., 1952-53; mem. epidemic intelligence svc., founder control ctr. Ctr. Disease Control, Chgo., 1953-55; resident in pediatrics N.Y. Hosp., 1955-56; resident in pediatrics Presbyn. Hosp., N.Y.C., 1956-57, dir. pediatric ICU, 1970-75; assoc. prof. pediatrics Columbia U., 1970-75, prof. pediatrics, 1975—, dir. Cystic Fibrosis Ctr., 1978-91, dir. pediatric pulmonary div., 1972—; founding mem. sect. on pulmonology Am. Bd. Pediatrics, 1985—; Christmas Seal prof. Can. Lung Assn., 1979-80; 1st Deans Disting. lectr. in clin. scis. Columbia U. Coll. P&S, 1982. Mem. editorial bd. Am. Rev. Respiratory Diseases, 1974-81, assoc. editor, 1980—; contbr. articles to med. jours. Bd. dirs. Am. Lung Assn., 1981-93, nat. v.p. 1987-89, bd. dirs N.Y. chpt., 1984—, v.p. 1994-96; bd. dirs. L.A. Jonas Found., 1970-78, 90—, Symphony of UN, 1990—; chmn. steering com. Multicenter Study of Heart and Lung Complicaitons of HIV Infection in Children, NIH, 1989—. Recipient Career Devel. award NIH, 1966-71, Career Scientist award Hlth. Rsch. Coun. N.Y.C. Hlth. Rsch. Coun., 1975, Stevens Triennial award for rsch. Columbia U., 1980, Health Edn. Rsch. award Nat. Asthma Edn. Program, 1992. Mem. Am. Pediatric Soc., Soc. Pediatric Rsch., Am. Physiol. Soc., Am. Soc. Pharmacology and Exptl. Therapeutics, Am. Acad. Pediatrics, Am. Thoracic Soc. (bd. dirs. 1974-75, 81-84, nat. pres. 1982-83, v.p.), Soc. Critical Care Medicine, Fleischner Soc. (pres. 1995—), Am. Acad. Allergy and Immunology, Alpha Omega Alpha. Home: 2 W 67th St New York NY 10023-6223 Office: Columbia U 630 W 168th St New York NY 10032-3702

MELLON, JOHN, publishing executive; b. 1940. Chmn. IPC mags., Reed Bus. Pub., Reed Regional Newspapers; CEO Reed Pub. Europe; dir. Reed

Internat., 1990—, exec. dir., 1992—; mem. Reed Elsevier Exec. Committee, 1994—; mem. adv. com. on advt. for the Ctrl. Office of Info. Office: IPC Magazines rm 1701, King's Reach Tower Stamford Street, London SE1 9LS, England

MELLON, PAUL, retired art gallery executive; b. Pitts., June 11, 1907; s. Andrew W. and Nora (McMullen) M.; m. Mary Conover, Feb. 2, 1935 (dec. Oct. 1946); children: Catherine Conover, Timothy; m. Rachel Lambert Lloyd, May 1, 1948. AB, Yale U., 1929, LHD (hon.), 1967; AB, Cambridge (Eng.) U., 1931, MA, 1938, LLD (hon.), 1983; Litt.D. (hon.), Oxford U., 1961; LL.D. (hon.), Carnegie Inst. Tech., 1967; DVM (hon.), Royal Vet. Coll., U. London, 1991. Pres. Nat. Gallery Art, Washington, to 1979; chmn. bd. trustees Nat. Gallery Art, 1979-85, hon. trustee, 1985—; trustee Andrew W. Mellon Found., N.Y.; assoc. fellow Berkeley Coll., Yale U.; hon. fellow Clare Coll., Cambridge, Eng.; St. John's Coll., Annapolis; Benjamin Franklin fellow Royal Soc. Arts, London, 1969. Served from pvt. to 1st lt. Cav. AUS, 1941-43; 1st lt. to maj. overseas service with OSS, 1943-45. Recipient Yale medal award, 1953; Horace Marden Albright Scenic Preservation medal, 1957; award for distinguished service to arts Nat. Inst. Arts and Letters, 1962; Benjamin Franklin medal Royal Soc. Arts, London, 1965; Skowhegan Gertrude Vanderbilt Whitney award, 1972, Nat. Medal of Arts, 1985, Thomas Jefferson Meml. Found. medal in architecture, 1989, Hadrian award World Monuments Fund, 1989, medal disting. philanthropy Am. Assn. Mus., 1993; decorated hon. knight comdr. Order Brit, Empire, 1974; decorated Knight Grand Officer of the Order of Orange Nassau, 1982. Fellow AAAS; mem. Scroll and Key Soc., Am. Philos. Soc. (Benjamin Franklin award 1989); hon. mem. AIA. Clubs: Metropolitan (Washington); Racquet and Tennis (N.Y.C.), Grolier (N.Y.C.), Links (N.Y.C.), Knickerbocker (N.Y.C.), Jockey (N.Y.C.), Nat. Steeplechase and Hunt Assn. (N.Y.C.); Society of the Dilettanti (London), Roxburghe (London), Buck's (London), English Jockey (hon.). Office: 1729 H St NW Washington DC 20006-3904

MELLON, RICHARD PROSSER, charitable foundation executive; b. Chgo., May 19, 1939; s. Richard King and Constance Mary (Prosser) M.; m. Gertrude Alice Adams, Apr. 28, 1962 (div. 1976); children: Richard Adams, Armour Negley; m. 2d Katherine Woodward Houker, Dec. 2, 1976. Student, U. Pitts, 1958-60; A.A. (hon.), Valley Forge Mil. Jr. Coll., 1970. Chmn. Richard King Mellon Found., Pitts., 1980—. Bd. dirs. Ducks Unltd. Found.; nat. trustee, mem. nat. exec. com. life mem. Ducks Unltd., Inc.; corporator Western Pa. Sch. for Blind. Served to 1st lt. USAR, 1958-67. Episcopalian. Clubs: Duquesne (Pitts.); Laurel Valley Golf (Ligonier), Rolling Rock (Ligonier), Rolling Rock-Westmoreland Hunt (Ligonier); Links (N.Y.C.); Nat. Steeplechase and Hunt Assn. (Ligonier). Home: Gen Delivery Ligonier PA 15658 Office: Mellon Found One Mellon Bank Center 500 Grant Street Pittsburgh PA 15219

MELLON, SEWARD PROSSER, investment executive; b. Chgo., July 28, 1942; s. Richard King and Constance Mary (Prosser) Mellon Burrell; m. Karen Leigh Boyd, Sept. 10, 1966 (div. 1974); children—Catharine Leigh, Constance Elizabeth; m. Sandra Springer Stout, 1975. Grad., Choate Sch., 1960; B.A., Susquehanna U., 1965, DH, 1993. With Mellon Nat. Corp., Pitts., 1965-69; with T. Mellon & Sons, Pitts., 1969-71; pres. Richard K. Mellon & Sons, Ligonier, 1971—; bd. dirs. Mellon Bank N.A., Mellon Nat. Corp. Trustee Richard King Mellon Family Found.; trustee, pres. Richard King Mellon Found.; chmn. real estate com., chmn. bd. mem. fin. and exec. com. Valley Sch. Ligonier. Mem. Western Pa. Conservancy (life), LoyalHanna Assn. (pres.), Lake Nona Club (Orlando), Vintage Club (Palm Springs, Calif.), Duquesne Club (Pitts.), Laurel Valley Golf Club (Ligonier), Rolling Rock Club, Rolling Rock Hunt, Phi Mu Delta. Republican. Home: Huntland Downs Box K Ligonier PA 15658-0780 Office: PO Box Rkm Ligonier PA 15658-0780

MELLOR, JAMES ROBB, electronics executive; b. Detroit, May 3, 1930; s. Clifford and Gladys (Robb) M.; m. Suzanne Stykos, June 8, 1953; children: James Robb, Diane Elyse, Deborah Lynn. BS in Elec. Engring. and Math., U. Mich., 1952, MS, 1953. Mem. tech. staff Hughes Aircraft Co., Fullerton, Calif., 1955-58; pres. Data Systems divsn. Litton Industries, Van Nuys, Calif., after 1958; exec. v.p. Litton Industries, Inc., Beverly Hills, Calif.; pres., COO AM Internat., Inc., L.A. to 1981; exec. v.p., dir. Gen. Dynamics Corp., Falls Church, Va., 1981-90, pres., 1990—, COO, 1990-93, CEO, 1993-94, chmn., CEO, 1994—; bd. dirs. Bergen Brunswig Corp., Kerr, Computer Scis. Corp. Patentee in fields of storage tubes and display systems; contbr. articles to profl. publs. 1st lt., Signal Corps, AUS, 1953-55. Mem. IEEE, Am. Mgmt. Assn., Armed Forces Comm. and Electronics Assn. (bd. dirs.), Computer and Bus. Equipment Mfrs. Assn. (former chmn.), L.A. Country Club, Calif. Club, Eldorado Club, Sigma Xi, Tau Beta Pi, Eta Kappa Nu, Phi Kappa Phi. Home: 7901 Sandalfoot Dr Potomac MD 20854-5449 Office: Gen Dynamics Corp 3190 Fairview Park Dr Falls Church VA 22042-4523

MELLOR, JOHN WILLIAMS, economist, policy consultant firm executive; b. Paris, Dec. 28, 1928; came to U.S., 1929; s. Desmond W. and Katherine (Beardsley) M.; m. Arlene Patton, June 15, 1951 (div. Sept. 1972); children: Michael, Brian, Mark (dec.); m. Uma Lele, Feb. 17, 1973 (div. Apr. 1992). BS, Cornell U., 1950, MS, 1951, PhD, 1954; Diploma, Oxford (Eng.) U., 1952. Prof. Cornell U., Ithaca, N.Y., 1953-75; chief economist USAID, Washington, 1975-77; dir. Internat. Food Policy Rsch. Inst., Washington, 1977-91; pres. John W. Mellor Assocs., Inc., Washington, 1991—; mem. bd. on agrl. NAS, 1989-92; mem. Agrl. Credit Commn., Res. Bank India, 1986-88. Author: Economics of Agricultural Development, 1966 (Am. Agrl. Econs. Assn. award 1978), Accelerating Food Production Growth in Sub-Saharan Africa, 1987, Agricultural Price Policy for Developing Countries, 1988 (hon. mention Am. Agrl. Econs. Assn. 1989). Mem. Internat. Commn. on Food and Peace, 1988—; Recipient Wihuri Internat. prize Wihuri Found., Helsinki, 1985, Presdl. End Hunger award The White House, 1987, Outstanding Alumni award Cornell U., 1987. Fellow AAAS, Am. Acad. Arts and Scis., Am. Agrl. Econs. Assn. (Best Pub. Rsch. award 1967). Avocations: sailing, skiing. Office: John Mellor Assocs Inc Ste PH23 801 Pennsylvania Ave NW Washington DC 20004

MELLOR, MICHAEL LAWTON, lawyer; b. Yorkshire, Eng., July 20, 1922; came to U.S., 1922; s. Bethel and Carmen (Lawton) M.; m. Mary Gordon, May 17, 1952 (dec.); children—Wendy, Jane, Christie. A.B., U. Calif.-Berkeley, 1943, LL.B., 1950. Bar: Calif. 1951. Assoc., Thelen, Marrin, Johnson & Bridges, San Francisco, 1950-62, ptnr., 1962-90, of counsel, 1990-93; dir. various bus. cos. Bd. dirs. San Francisco Attic Theatre, 1979-83, Robinson Jeffers Tor House Found., Carmel, Calif., 1980—, Pacific Vision Found., San Francisco, 1982—, Friends of San Francisco Pub. Library, 1984-92, Dance Through Time. Kentfield, Calif., 1986-92, Internat. Visitors Ctr., 1990—. 1st lt. U.S. Army, 1943-45; Philippines, Japan. Mem. ABA, Calif. State Bar, San Francisco Bar Assn. Democrat. Club: The Family (dir., sec.) (San Francisco). Home: 81 5th Ave San Francisco CA 94118 Office: Thelen Marrin Johnson & Bridges Two Embarcadero Ctr San Francisco CA 94111

MELLOR, ROBERT E., lawyer; b. 1943. BA, Westminster Coll., 1965; JD, So. Meth. U., 1968. Atty. legal dept. Union Oil Co. of Calif., 1968-73; atty. U.S. Leasing Internat. Inc., 1973-75; v.p. dir. Alexander & Bolton Inc., 1975-76; with Di Giorgio Corp., San Francisco, 1976-79, v.p., 1979-80, v.p., gen. counsel, 1980-81, v.p., sec, gen. counsel, 1981-87, sr. v.p., gen. counsel, sec., 1987, chief adminstrv. officer, exec. v.p., gen. counsel, sec.; now counsel Gibson, Dunn & Crutcher, San Francisco. Office: Gibson Dunn & Crutcher One Montgomery St 26th Plz San Francisco CA 94104

MELLORS, ROBERT CHARLES, physician scientist; b. Dayton, Ohio, 1916; s. Bert S. and Clementine (Steinmetz) M.; m. Jane K. Winternitz, Mar. 25, 1944; children: Alice J., Robert C., William K., John W. Ph.D., Western Res. U., 1940; M.D., Johns Hopkins, 1944. Diplomate Am. Bd. Pathology. Intern Nat. Naval Med. Ctr., Bethesda, Md., 1944-45; rsch. fellow medicine Meml. Center Cancer and Allied Diseases, N.Y.C., 1946-50; rsch. fellow pathology Meml. Ctr. Cancer and Allied Diseases, 1950-53, asst. attending pathologist, 1953-57, assoc. attending pathologist, 1957-58; sr. fellow Am. Cancer Soc., 1947-50; sr. clin. rsch. fellow Damon Runyon Meml. Fund, 1950-53; asst. attending pathologist Meml. Hosp., N.Y.C., 1953-57, assoc. attending pathologist, 1957-58; asst. attending pathologist Ewing Hosp.,

N.Y.C., 1953-57, assoc. attending pathologist, 1957-58; instr. biochemistry Western Res. U., 1940-42; rsch. assoc. Poliomyelitis Rsch. Ctr. and Dept. Epidemiology Johns Hopkins U. Sch. Hygiene, 1942-44; asst. prof. biology Meml. Ctr. Cancer and Allied Diseases, N.Y.C., 1952-53; asst. prof. pathology Sloan Kettering div. Cornell U., 1953-57, assoc. prof., 1957-58; prof. pathology Cornell U. Med. Coll., 1961-90, prof. emeritus, 1990—; assoc. attending pathologist N.Y. Hosp., 1961-72, attending pathologist, 1972-86; pathologist-in-chief, dir. labs., 1958-84, emeritus, 1984-85, hon. staff, 1986—; assoc. dir. rsch. Hosp. for Spl. Surgery, N.Y.C., 1958-69, dir. rsch., 1969-84, emeritus, 1984-85, scientist emeritus, 1986—; mem. rsch. adv. com. NIH, 1962-66; adv. com. Nat. Inst. Environ. Health Sci., 1966-69; com. nomenclature and classification of disease Coll. Am. Pathologists, 1960-64. Author: Analytical Cytology, 1955, 2d edit., 1959, Analytical Pathology, 1957. Served as lt. (j.g.), M.C. USNR, 1944-46. Recipient Kappa Delta award Am. Acad. of Orthopedic Surgeons, 1962. Fellow Royal Coll. Pathologists, Am. Soc. Clin. Pathology; mem. Am. Assn. Pathologists, Am. Assn. Immunologists, Am. Soc. Biochemistry and Molecular Biology, Am. Coll. Rheumatology, Am. Orthopedic Assn. (hon.). Home: 3 Hardscrabble Cir Armonk NY 10504-2222

MELLOTT, CLOYD ROWE, lawyer; b. McConnellsburg, Pa., Feb. 16, 1923; s. Wesley William and Alice (Cutshall) M.; m. Lois M. Williams, Aug. 16, 1952; children: Christopher R., Deborah L. BSEE, Carnegie Inst. Tech., 1947; LLB, U. Pitts., 1950, JD, 1968. Bar: Pa. 1951, U.S. Dist. Ct. (we. dist.) Pa. 1951, U.S. Ct. Appeals (3d cir.) 1952, U.S. Supreme Ct. 1968, various U.S. cts. appeal and U.S. dist. cts. Law clk. U.S. Dist. Ct. (we. dist.) Pa., Pitts., 1951-53; assoc. Smith, Buchanan, Ingersoll, Rodewald & Eckert, Pitts., 1953-58; ptnr. Eckert, Seamans, Cherin & Mellott, Pitts., 1958-93, of counsel, 1993—; mem. lawyers adv. com. U.S. Appeals for 3d Cir., 1984-86, chmn., 1986, permanent mem. U.S. 3d cir. jud. conf. chmn., 1989; chmn. Fund for Bicentennial Celebration of Common Pleas Ct. of Allegheny County, 1987-88. Trustee U. Pitts., 1979—; bd. visitors, Sch. Law, U. Pitts., 1978—, Sch. Engring., U. Pitts., 1979—; mem. various bds. and divs. of Pitts. Presbytery, Fox Chapel Presbyn. Ch., Pitts. 1st Lt. USAF, 1942-45, ETO. Decorated D.F.C., Air medal with three oak leaf clusters, Purple Heart; recipient Medallion of Distinction U. Pitts. Mem. ABA, Am. Judicature Soc., Pa. Bar Assn., Allegheny County Bar Assn. (chmn. civil lit. sect. 1981-82, fed. ct. sect. 1987-88), Duquesne Club, Pitts. Field Club, Allegheny Club (Pitts.), Lakewood Country Club (St. Petersburg, Fla.), Am. Legion. Republican. Office: Eckert Seamans Cherin & Mellott 42d Fl 600 Grant St Pittsburgh PA 15219-2702

MELLOTT, ROBERT VERNON, advertising executive; b. Dixon, Ill., Jan. 1, 1928; s. Edwin Vernon and Frances Rhoda (Miller) M.; m. Sarah Carolyn Frink, June 11, 1960; children: Lynn Mellott Finzer, Susan Mellott Dodge, David Robert. BA, DePauw U., 1950; postgrad. Grad. Sch., Ind. U., 1950-51, Law Sch., 1959-61, MA, 1983. TV producer, dir. Jefferson Standard Broadcasting Co., Charlotte, N.C., 1951-59; asst. studio mgr. GM., Flint, Mich., Chgo., 1961-62; TV and radio comml. supr. NW Ayer & Son, Chgo., 1962-65; TV and radio producer Foote, Cone & Belding Advt. Inc., Chgo., 1965-67, mgr. midwest prodn., 1967-69, mgr. comml. coordination, 1969-74, v.p., mgr. comml. svcs., Chgo., 1974-93 (ret.); cons. speech and broadcasting comm. Mem. media adv. com. Coll. of Dupage, Glen Ellyn, Ill., 1971-82; chmn. Cub Scout Com., Wheaton, Ill., 1978-79; bd. dirs. Chgo. Unltd., 1969-71. Mem. Am. Assn. Advt. Agys. (broadcast adminstrn. policy com., broadcast talent union rels. ANA-AAAA joint policy com. 1984-93), World Communication Assn., Internat. Platform Assn., Phi Delta Phi, Alpha Tau Omega. Republican. Mem. Evang. Christian Ch. Clubs: Chgo. Farmers, Ind. U. Alumni. Home: 26 W 130 Tomahawk Dr Wheaton IL 60187

MELLOY, MICHAEL J., federal judge; b. 1948; m. Jane Anne Melloy; children: Jennifer, Katherine, Bridget. Ba, Loras Coll., 1970; JD, U. Iowa, 1974. With O'Conner & Thomas P.C. (formerly O'Conner, Thomas, Wright, Hammer, Bertsch & Norby, Dubuque, Iowa, 1974-86; judge U.S. Bankruptcy Ct. (no. dist.) Iowa, 1986-92; apptd. chief judge U.S. Dist. Ct. (no. dist.) Iowa, Cedar Rapids, 1992—. With U.S. Army, 1970-72, USAR, 1972-76. Mem. ABA, Comml. Law League Am., Nat. Conf. Bankruptcy Judges, Eighth Cir. Judicial Coun. (bankruptcy judge rep., bankruptcy com.), Iowa State Bar Assn. (coun. mem. bankruptcy and comml. law sect.), Ill. State Bar Assn., Dubuque County Bar Assn., Linn County Bar Assn., Mason L. Ladd Inn of Ct., Rotary. Office: US Dist Ct 101 1st St Ste 304 Cedar Rapids IA 52401

MELLUM, GALE ROBERT, lawyer; b. Duluth, Minn., July 5, 1942; s. Lester Andrew and Doris Esther (Smith) M.; m. Julie Murdoch Swanstrom, July 23, 1966; children: Eric Scott, Wendy Jane. BA summa cum laude, U. Minn., 1964, JD magna cum laude, 1968. Bar: Minn. 1968. Assoc. Faegre & Benson, Mpls., 1968-75, ptnr., 1976—; mem. mgmt. com. Faegre & Benson, 1986—; mem. adv. bd. Quali Tech Inc., Chaska, Minn., 1985—; bd. dirs. Edn. Alternatives Inc., Mpls. Hockey chmn. LARC Bd., Mpls., 1980-85. Mem. ABA (fed. securities regulation com.), Minn. Bar Assn., Hennepin County Bar Assn. (exec. com. securities regulation com.). Republican. Lutheran. Avocations: tennis, golf, snow and water skiing, handball, boating. Home: 4889 E Lake Harriet Pky Minneapolis MN 55409-2322 Office: Faegre & Benson 2200 Norwest Ctr 90 S 7th St Minneapolis MN 55402

MELMON, KENNETH LLOYD, physician, biologist, pharmacologist, consultant; b. San Francisco, July 20, 1934; s. Abe Irving and Jean (Kahn) M.; m. Elyce Edelman, June 9, 1957; children: Bradley S., Debra W. AB in Biology with honors, Stanford U., 1956; MD, U. Calif. at San Francisco, 1959. Intern, then resident in internal medicine U. Calif. Med. Ctr., San Francisco, 1959-61; clin. assoc. surgeon USPHS, Nat. Heart, Lung and Kidney Inst., NIH, 1961-64; chief resident in medicine U. Wash. Med. Ctr., Seattle, 1964-65; chief div. clin. pharmacology U. Calif. Med. Ctr., 1965-78; chief dept. medicine Stanford U. Med. Ctr., 1978-84, Arthur Bloomfield prof. medicine, prof. pharmacology, 1978-86, prof. medicine and pharmacology, 1978—; assoc. dean postgrad. med. edn. Stanford U. Med. ctr., 1993—; dir. tech. transfer program Stanford U. Hosp., 1986—; mem. sr. staff Cardiovascular Rsch. Inst., chmn. joint commn. prescription drug use Senate Subcom. on Health, Inst. Medicine and HEW-Pharm. Mfrs. Assn.; mem. Nat. Bd. Med. Examiners, 1987—; pres Bio 2000, Woodside, Calif., 1983-85; cofounder Immulogic, Boston and Palo Alto, Calif., 1988; sci. advisor Syntex, Hoffman LaRoche, Pharmetrix, Microprobe, LXR, others; cons. FDA, 1965-82, Office Tech. Assessment, 1974-75, Senate Subcom. on Health, 1975—; bd. dirs. Pharmatrix, San Mateo, Calif., Immulogic, Boston, Microprobe, Seattle; cons. to govt.; founder Inst. Biol. and Clin. Investigation, Ctr. for Molecular and Genetic Medicine, Stanford Community of Internists and Stanford Med. Group. Author articles, chpts. in books, sects. encys.; Editor: Clinical Pharmacology: Basic Principles in Therapeutics, 3d edit., 1992, Cardiovascular Therapeutics, 1974; assoc. editor: The Pharmacological Basis of Therapeutics (Goodman and Gilman), 1984; mem. editorial bd. numerous profl. jours. Surgeon USPHS, 1961-64. Burroughs Wellcome clin. pharmacology scholar, 1966-71; John Simon Guggenheim fellow Weizman Inst., Israel, 1971, NIH spl. fellow, Bethesda, 1971. Fellow AAAS (nat. coun. 1985-89); mem. Am Fedn. Clin. Rsch. (pres. 1973-74), Am. Soc. Clin. Investigation (pres. 1978-79), Assn. Am. Physicians, Western Assn. Physicians (pres. 1983-84), Am. Soc. Pharmacology and Exptl. Therapeutics, Am. Soc. Clin. Pharmacology and Therapeutics (Oscar Hunter award in therapeutics 1994), Inst. Medicine of NAS, Am. Physiol. Soc., Calif. Acad. Medicine, Med. Friends of Wine, Phi Beta Kappa. Democrat. Jewish. Achievements include initiation of founding of Ctr. of Molecular and Genetic Medicine. Home: 51 Cragmont Way Woodside CA 94062-2307 Office: Stanford U Med Ctr Dept Medicine # S025 Stanford CA 94305

MELNER, SINCLAIR LEWIS, insurance company executive; b. Reno, Apr. 6, 1928; s. Abraham H. and Carol Rachel (Myers) M.; m. Roma F. Garner, Dec. 26, 1949; children: Catherine, Michael, Joan. B.S., U. Nev., 1949; M.S. in Internat. Affairs, George Washington U., 1969. Commd. 2d lt. U.S. Army, 1949; advanced through grades to lt. gen. U.S. Army, Ft. Benjamin Harrison, Ind., formerly comdg. gen.; later dep. chmn. NATO Mil. Command, Brussels; ret., 1984; v.p., corp. sec. Hudson Inst., 1984-88; sr. advisor Am. Amicable Life Ins. Co. Tex., 1989. Decorated Silver Star with oak leaf cluster, Def. Superior Service medal, Def. D.S.M., Army D.S.M., Legion of Merit with oak leaf cluster. Home: 301 E Braeburn Dr Phoenix AZ 85022-3621

MELNGAILIS, IVARS, solid state research executive; b. Riga, Latvia, Nov. 13, 1933; came to U.S., 1949; s. Janis and Jakobine (Zile) M.; m. Valda Dreimanis, June 6, 1964; children: Nils, Zinta. BS, Carnegie-Mellon U., 1956, MS, 1957, PhD, 1961. Mem. staff. Lincoln Lab., MIT, Lexington, 1961-67, asst. group leader, 1967-71, group leader, 1971-75, assoc. div. head, 1975—. Fellow IEEE; mem. Am. Phys. Soc., Am. Optical Soc. Office: MIT Lincoln Lab Solid State Div 244 Wood St Lexington MA 02173-6499

MELNICK, DANIEL, film producer; b. N.Y.C., Apr. 21, 1932; 1 son, Peter. Partner Talent Assos.; v.p., then sr. v.p. charge worldwide prodn. M.G.M., 1972-76; ind. film producer, 1976-77, 79—; in charge worldwide prodn. Columbia Pictures Industries Inc., 1977-78, pres. motion picture div., 1978; now independent prodr. Indie Prodn. Co. Producer films Straw Dogs, First Family, 1981, Making Love, 1982, Footloose, 1985, Quicksilver, 1986, Roxanne, 1987, Punchline, 1988, Mountains of the Moon, 1990, Total Recall, 1990, Air America, 1990, L.A. Story, 1991; exec. producer films That's Entertainment, That's Entertainment II, All That Jazz, Altered States, Footloose. Recipient Nat. Acad. TV Arts and Scis. Emmy award for Death of a Salesman and The Ages of Man. Office: Tristar Bldg 10202 W Washington Blvd # 204 Culver City CA 90232

MELNICK, GILBERT STANLEY, radiologist, educator; b. N.Y.C., July 31, 1930; s. Haskel and Ida (Palter) M.; m. Iris Dorothy Cohen, June 19, 1955 (div. Jan. 1983); children: Daniel, David, Deborah, Jeffrey; m. Noreen E. Moore, Apr. 28, 1984. BA, Cornell U., 1980; MD, SUNY, Bklyn., 1954. Diplomate: Am. Bd. Radiology. Intern Meadowbrook Hosp., Hempstead, N.Y., 1954-57; fellow in radiology U. Minn., Mpls., 1957-61; instr., then asst. prof. Yale U. Sch. Medicine, New Haven, 1961-66; dir. radiology St. Michael's Med. Ctr., Newark, 1967-82; chmn. dept. radiology N.J. Med. Sch., Newark, 1982-86, clin. prof. radiology, 1982, prof. clin. radiology, 1982-86, clin. prof. radiology, 1986—; clin. prof. radiology St. Physicians and Surgeons, Columbia U., 1987-90; asst. attending radiologist Christ Hosp., Jersey City, 1990—; chmn. radiology Morristown Meml. Hosp., 1986-90. Capt. U.S. Army, 1955-57. Fellow Am. Coll. Radiology; mem. AMA, Radiol. Soc. N.Am., Radiol. Soc. N.J. (treas. 1982, sec. 1983, pres. 1985-86), Essex PSRO (sec. 1982-88), Met Pro (trustee 1985), Axiom Group (trustee, vice-chmn 1987—). Democrat. Jewish. Office: Christ Hosp Dept Radiology PO Box 8184 Jersey City NJ 07308-8184

MELNICK, JOSEPH L., virologist, educator; b. Boston, Oct. 9, 1914; s. Samuel and Esther (Melny) M.; m. Matilda Benyesh, 1958; 1 dau., Nancy. A.B., Wesleyan U., 1936; Ph.D. (Univ. scholar), Yale, 1939; D.Sc., Wesleyan U., 1971; MD (hon.), Charles U., Prague, Czech Republic, 1993. Asst. in physiol. chemistry Yale Sch. Medicine, 1937-39; asst. in physiol. chemistry, Finney-Howell Research Found. fellow, 1939-41, NRC fellow in med. scis., 1941-42, research asst. in preventive medicine with rank of instr., 1942-44, asst. prof., 1944-48, research assoc., 1948-49, assoc. prof. microbiology, 1949-54, prof. epidemiology, 1954-57; chief virus labs., div. biologics standards NIH, USPHS, 1957-58; prof., chmn. virology and epidemiology Baylor Coll. Medicine, Houston, 1958-89; Disting. Svc. prof. Baylor Coll. Medicine, 1974—, dean grad. scis., 1968-91, dean emeritus, 1992—; mem. com. virus diseases WHO, 1957—; dir. WHO Internat. Center Enteroviruses, 1963-70, mem. cons. group on poliomyelitis vaccine, 1973—; dir. WHO Collaborating Center for Virus Reference and Rsch., 1970—; mem. com. on live poliovirus vaccines USPHS, 1958-61; virus reference bd. NIH, 1962-70, mem. dir. adv. com. on DNA Recombinants, 1976, mem. evaluation com. divsn. rsch. resources 1975-76; mem. human cancer virus task force Nat. Cancer Inst., USPHS, 1962-67; nat. adv. cancer coun. NIH, 1965-69; sec.-gen. Internat. Congresses Virology, Helsinki, Budapest, 1968-71; chmn. Internat. Conf. Viruses in Water, Mexico City, 1974; mem. rsch. coun. Am. Cancer Soc., 1971-75; mem. com. on hepatitis NAS/NRC, 1972-77; lectr. cons. Chinese Acad. Med. Scis., 1978, 79; mem. adv. com. Comparative Virology Orgn., 1978-86, mem. Internat. Task Force Hepatitis B Immunization, WHO, 1992; chmn. adv. com. on viral hepatitis Ctr. Disease Control, 1989, 95, mem. adv. com. respiratory and enteric viruses, 1991, mem. adv. com. evaluation U.S. polio cases, 1963-75, 76-84; cons. UN Devel. Program for Health Manpower and Svcs. of Palestinian People, 1981-83. Author: Textbook of Medical Microbiology; editor: Progress in Medical Virology and Monographs in Virology, also over 1000 rsch. papers in virology; editor-in-chief ofcl. jour. virology Intervirology, Internat. Union Microbiol. Socs., 1972-85. Chmn. Houston Acad. Medicine-Tex. Med. Ctr. Libr., 1987-88, bd. dirs. 1967-90; trustee Albert B. Sabin Vaccine Found., 1994—; chmn. U.S. Commn. on Polio Eradication, 1994—. Recipient Internat. medal (with Dr. Herdis von Magnus of Denmark), Argentinian Found. Against Infantile Paralysis, for research in immunity to poliomyelitis, 1949; Humanitarian award Jewish Inst. Med. Research, 1964; Modern Medicine Disting. Achievement award, 1965; Eleanor Roosevelt Humanities award, 1965; Indsl. Research-100 award (with Prof. Craig Wallis), 1971, 74; Inventor of Year award Houston Patent Law Assn., 1972; named to Nat. Found.'s Polio Hall Fame, 1958; Gold medal South African Poliomyelitis Research Found., 1979; Maimonides award State of Israel, 1980; Raymond E. Baldwin medal for Disting. Service, Wesleyan U., 1986. Fellow AAAS, Am. Pub. Health Assn., N.Y. Acad. Scis. (Freedman Found. award for research in virology 1973), Am. Acad. Microbiology; mem. Am. Soc. Microbiology, Am. Soc. Virology, Soc. Exptl. Biol. and Medicine (mem. council 1965-69), Am. Assn. Immunologists, Am. Epidemiol. Soc., Am. Assn. Cancer Research (pres. S.W. sect. 1968), Internat. Assn. Microbiol. Socs. (life, chmn. sec. on virology 1970-75, mem. exec. com. 1976-79, mem. internat. commn. microbiol. ecology 1972-87, mem. internat. com. on taxonomy of viruses 1966-83), Microbiol. Soc. Israel (hon.), Microbiol. Soc. Argentina (hon.), USSR Soc. Microbiologists and Epidemiologists (hon.), Chinese Soc. Med. Virology (hon.), Med. Soc. Bulgaria (hon.), Phi Beta Kappa, Sigma Xi.

MELNICK, ROB, research administrator; b. Mt. Vernon, N.Y., May 6, 1950. BA in Govt., Dartmouth Coll., 1972; postgrad., NYU, 1972; MA in Media, Ariz. State U., 1973, PhD in Ednl. Tech., 1980. Dir. media ctr., tchr. social studies Glendale (Ariz.) Union H.S., 1973-75; instr. dept. ednl. tech., assoc. dir. univ. media sys. Ariz. State U., Tempe, 1975-80; v.p. Desert Mountain Assocs. Inc., Phoenix, 1980-82; sr. rsch. fellow, v.p. Hudson Inst., Indpls., 1982-87; dir. Morrison Inst. for Pub. Policy Ariz. State U., Tempe, 1987—; cons. in areas of policy analysis, prodn. of pub. info. and program evaluation for numerous govt., corp., and ednl. orgns.; mass media presentations. Contbr. numerous articles to profl. jours. Bd. dirs. Noble Ctrs., Inc., Indpls., 1986, Phoenix Ctr. for Law-Related Studies, 1987—, Inst. for Ednl. Leadership of Ariz., 1990—, Succes by Six, 1990—, Work Force Solutions for Am.'s Future Inc., 1992—; mem. Phoenix Commn. on Edn., 1987-92; bd. dirs., sec. Ariz. Sch.-to-Work Partnership, Inc., 1990—; mem., moderator Gov.'s Task Force on Edn., 1991; mem., facilitator State Supt.'s Task Force on Sch. Violence, 1993, Gov.'s Task Force on Employment and Tng., 1993; other activities. Project dir., author or co-author numerous funded policy studies. Office: Morrison Inst Pub Policy Box 874405 Tempe AZ 85287-4405

MELNICK, VIJAYA LAKSHMI, biology educator, research center director; b. Kerala, India; came to U.S., 1959; m. Daniel Melnick, June 28, 1963; 1 child, Anil D. BS, Madras Agriculture Coll., India, 1959; MS, U. Wis., 1961, PhD, 1964, postgrad., 1964-66. Asst. prof. dept. biology Fed. City Coll., Washington, 1970-74; assoc. prof. dept. biology U. D.C., Washington, 1974-77, prof. biology, 1977—; dir. Ctr. for Applied Rsch. and Urban Policy, Washington, 1992—; sr. staff assoc. Internat. Ctr. Inter-Disciplinary Studies in Immunology Georgetown U. Med. Sch., 1978-85, assoc. dir. tech. transfer, edn. and community outreach Ctr. Inter-Disciplinary Studies in Immunology, 1985—; sr. rsch. scholar Ctr. for Applied Rsch. and Urban Policy, Washington, 1984-85; spl. asst. policy and bioethics Nat. Inst. Aging/NIH, Bethesda, Md., 1980-82; vis. prof., rsch. participant Carnegie program Oak Ridge Grad. Sch. Biomed. Sci., U. Tenn., 1974-78; vis. scientist Biology and Medicine Inst., Lawrence Livermore Labs., U. Calif., 1972-73; invited del. cell biologist to People's Republic of China, 1990; mem. health edn. adv. com. Internat. Med. Svc. for Health, Washington; mem. Nestle Infant Formula Audit Commn., 1981-91; mem. Mayor's Adv. Bd. on Infant and Maternal Health, 1987—; del. 1st Asian-Pacific Orgn. for Cell Biology Congress, Shanghai, 1990; mem. nat. coun. on rsch. in child welfare Child Welfare League Am., Inc., 1992—; mem. adv. coun. D.C. family policy seminar Georgetown U. Grad. Pub. Policy Program, 1993—; mem. adv. com. tng. program for postdoctoral program in devel. immunology Internat. Ctr. Interdisciplinary Studies in Immunology, Georgetown U. Med. Ctr., 1993—; mem. steering com. Nat. Consortium for African Am. Children,

Nat. Commn. to Prevent Infant Mortality, 1993—; host scientist Science in American Life exhibition Nat. Mus. Am. Hist. The Smithsonian Inst., 1994—. Recipient Outstanding Svc. award March of Dimes, 1987; postdoctoral fellow U. Wis. Med. Sch., 1964-66. Mem. APHA, AAAS, Am. Soc. Cell Biology, Assn. for Women in Sci., Am. Polit. Sci. Assn., Nat. Assn. Minority Med. Educators (legis. com. 1977—), Nat. Assn. for Equal Opportunities in Higher Edn. (sci. and tech. adv. com. 1982), N.Y. Acad. Sci., Sigma Xi, Sigma Delta Epsilon. Office: U DC Ctr Applied Rsch 4200 Connecticut Ave NW Washington DC 20008

MELNICK, WILLIAM, advertising executive; b. N.Y.C., Sept. 19, 1951; s. Lester and Evelyn (Rosenberg) M.; m. Jennifer Valentini, June 26, 1977. BFA, N.Y. U., 1975. Traffic mgr. Advt. Mktg., N.Y.C., 1975-76; media estimator Ogilvy & Mather Advt., N.Y.C., 1976-78; media buyer Calet, Hirsch & Spector, N.Y.C., 1978-79; sr. media planner Dancer Fitzgerald Sample, N.Y.C., 1979-85; media group supr. Dentso Young & Rubicam, N.Y.C., 1985-86; v.p., dir. media planning Earle Palmer Brown Co., Md., 1987-89; sr. v.p., media dir. Ketchum Advt., Phila., 1989-95; sr. v.p., dir. media svcs. Foote Cone Belding, Phila., 1995—; media cons. CIT Fin. Services, SHort Hills N.J. 1986. Vol. Rep. Party Rockland N.Y. 1983-85. Mem. Advt. Club Wash., Advt. Club Phila. Avocations: collecting antique reproductions, historical restorations, fishing, stamp collecting. Home: 1261 Taylor Dr Langhorne PA 19047-1253 Office: Foote Cone Belding 200 S Broad St Philadelphia PA 19102

MELNIK, ROBERT EDWARD, aeronautical engineer; b. N.Y.C., Nov. 19, 1933; s. Adam Edward and Anna Elizabeth (Petroccia) M.; m. Carol Joan Ceparano, Sept. 24, 1960; children: Joann, Christine. B.Aero.Engring., Poly. Inst. Bklyn., 1956, M.Aero. Engring., 1961, Ph.D., 1965. Research scientist Grumman Aerospace Corp. Bethpage, N.Y., 1956-66; head aerodynamics research group Grumman Aerospace Corp., 1966-73, dir. fluid mechanics, 1973-89. Assoc. editor: AIAA Jour, 1978-80; mem. editorial com.: Ann. Rev. Fluid Mechanics, 1982-87; contbr. articles to profl. jours. Bd. dirs. Family Service League of Suffolk, 1975—. Grumman rsch. fellow, 1989—. Fellow AIAA; mem. Am. Phys. Soc. Office: Grumman Aerospace Corp Bethpage NY 11714

MELNUK, PAUL D., diversified financial services company executive; b. Winnipeg, Man., Can., May 24, 1954; s. Martin William and Rita Clarice (Cochrane) M.; m. Donna Sturko, Oct. 21, 1989; children: Jillian, Andrew, Bryan, Kevin. B in Comm., U. Man., 1976. Joined Touche Ross & Co., 1976-80; v.p., contr. Can. Comml. Bank, 1980-86; corporate fin. rep. Pemberton Securities Inc., 1986-87; pres. WFL Capital Corp., 1987-88; pres., CEO Clark Refining & Mktg. Inc., St. Louis, 1988-93; pres., COO The Horsham Corp., St. Louis, 1993—. Home: 37 Countryside Ln Saint Louis MO 63131 Office: 8182 Maryland Ave Saint Louis MO 63105 also: 24 Hazelton Ave, Toronto, ON Canada M5R 2E2*

MELNYKOVYCH, ANDREW O., journalist; b. Mpls., Aug. 23, 1952; s. George and Oksana (Demianchuk) M.; m. Debra Denise Mamigonian, May 24, 1986; children: Alexander Vartan, Anna Emilia. BS in Biology, Yale U., 1975, M in Forest Sci., 1977; postgrad., U. Wyo., 1978-82. Lab. instr. dept. biochemistry U. Wyo., Laramie, 1982-83; corr. Casper (Wyo.) Star-Tribune, 1982-83, environ. writer, 1983-86, Washington reporter, 1986-90; environ. writer Louisville Courier-Jour., 1990—; contbg. writer High Country News, Paonia, Colo., 1987-90, The Post-Register, Idaho Falls, Idaho, 1989-90. Recipient George S. Polk award L.I. U., N.Y., 1989, 2d pl. Barnet Nover award Standing Com. of Corrs., Washington, 1989. Mem. Soc. Environ. Journalists. Avocations: birding, photography. Office: Louisville Courier-Jour 525 W Broadway St Louisville KY 40202-2206

MELO, THOMAS M., lawyer; b. San Bernardino, Calif., Apr. 12, 1952; s. Robert P. and Dorothy B. Melo; m. Tina L. Melo, July 9, 1983; children: Virginia, Caroline. BBA in Acctg., U. Ga., 1974; JD, U. Va., 1977. Bar: Tex. 1977; cert. labor law specialist Tex. Bd. Legal Specialization. Ptnr. Bracewell & Patterson, Houston, 1977—; frequent speaker on employment matters. Editor-in-chief, contbg. edidtor Employment Law Handbook; contbr. numerous articles on employment law to legal jours. Fellow Houston Bar Found.; mem. ABA, State Bar Tex., Houston Bar Assn., Tex. Assn. Bus. (bd. dirs., past chmn. employment rels. com.), Tex. Lyceum Assn. (bd. dirs.), Casa de Esperanza (devel. bd.), Houston Mgmt. Lawyers Forum (past chmn.). Office: Bracewell & Patterson 2900 S Tower Pennzoil Plz 711 Louisiana St Houston TX 77002-2716

MELOAN, TAYLOR WELLS, marketing educator; b. St. Louis, July 31, 1919; s. Taylor Wells and Edith (Graham) M.; m. Anna Geraldine Leukering, Dec. 17, 1944 (div. 1974); children: Michael David, Steven Lee; m. Jane Innes Bierlich, Jan. 30, 1975. B.S. cum laude, St. Louis U., 1949; M.B.A., Washington U., St. Louis, 1950; D of Bus. Admin., Ind. U., 1953. Advt. mgr. Herz Corp., St. Louis, 1941-42; sales promotion supr. Liggett & Myers Tobacco Co., St. Louis, 1942-43; asst. prof. mktg. U. Okla., Norman, 1953; asst., then assoc. prof. mktg. Ind. U., Bloomington, 1953-59; prof., chmn. dept. mktg. U. So. Calif., Los Angeles, 1959-69, prof. mktg., 1969-92, Robert E. Brooker prof. mktg., 1970-79, Robert E. Brooker prof. mktg. emeritus, 1991—; dean Sch. Bus. Adminstrn. U. So. Calif., 1969-71, assoc. v.p. acad. adminstrn. and research, 1971-81; prof. bus. adminstrn. U. Karachi, Pakistan, 1962; vis. prof. mktg. Istituto Post U. Per Lo Studio Dell Organizzazione Aziendale, Turin, Italy, 1964, U. Hawaii, 1993, Madrid Bus. Sch., 1993; disting. vis. prof. U. Witwatersrand, Johannesburg, 1978, U. Hawaii, 1993; editl. advisor bus. adminstrn. Houghton Mifflin Co., Boston, 1959-73; cons. to industry and govt., 1953%; bd. dirs Inst. Shipboard Edn. Author: New Career Opportunities, 1978, Innovation Strategy and Management, 1979, Direct Marketing: Vehicle for Department Store Expansion, 1984, Preparing the Exporting Entrepreneur, 1986, The New Competition: Dilemma of Department Stores in the 1980's, 1987, Franchise Marketing: A Retrospective and Prospective View of a Contractual Vertical Marketing System, 1988; co-author: Managerial Marketing, 1970, Internationalizing the Business Curriculum, 1968, Handbook of Modern Marketing, contbg. author, 1986; co-author, co-editor: International and Global Marketing: Concepts and Cases, 1994; bd. editors Jour. Mktg., 1965-72. Trustee World Affairs Coun. Orange County, 1994—. Lt. (j.g.) USMS, 1943-46. Mem. Am. Mktg. Assn. (pres. L.A. chpt. 1963-64), Order of Artus, Beta Gamma Sigma, Delta Pi Epsilon, Calif. Yacht Club, Univ. Club, Rotary. Home: 59 Lakefront Irvine CA 92714-4683 Office: U So Calif Los Angeles CA 90089-1421

MELODY, MICHAEL EDWARD, publishing company executive; b. Streator, Ill., Dec. 22, 1943; s. Giles Lambert and Rose Mary (Moreschi) M.; m. Carol Ann Weir, June 8, 1968 (div.) 1 dau., Alison Anne; m. Bonnie Kaye Binkert, Mar. 26, 1983. BA, Ala. Coll., 1966. Exec. editor, asst. v.p. Prentice-Hall, Inc., Englewood Cliff, N.J., 1974-79; v.p., editor-in-chief coll. div. Macmillan Pub. Co., N.Y.C., 1979-80, sr. v.p., pres. coll. div., 1980-87, pres. sch. div., 1987-88; v.p. higher edn. group Simon & Schuster, N.Y.C., 1988-90; sr. v.p. Houghton Mifflin Co., Boston, 1990-91, exec. v.p., 1991-95; prin. Michael E. Melody Cons., Boston, 1995—; chmn. bd. dirs Appleton & Lange, N.Y.C., 1989-90. Bd. overseers Huntington Theatre Co., Boston, 1993—. Served with USAR, 1967. Mem. Assn. Am. Pubs (vice chmn. coll. divsn. 1981-83, chmn. coll. divsn. 1983-86, exec. com. sch. divsn. 1987-88, exec. com. higher edn. divsn. 1990—), Nat. Assn. Coll. Stores (trustee 1986-87, 94-95).

MELONE, JOSEPH JAMES, insurance company executive; b. Pittston, Pa., July 27, 1931; s. Dominick William and Beatrice Marie (Pignone) M.; m. Marie Jane DeGeorge, Jan. 23, 1960; children—Lisa, Carol. B.S., U. Pa., 1953, M.B.A., 1954, Ph.D. in Econs., 1961. C.L.U., 1963 C.P.C.U., 1964. Asso. prof. ins. U. Pa., 1959-66, mem. pension research council, 1961-66; research dir. Am. Coll. Life Underwriters, 1966-68; v.p. Prudential Ins. Co., Boston, 1969-76; sr. v.p. Prudential Ins. Co., Newark, 1976-81, exec. v.p., 1981-84, pres., 1984-90; pres., COO Equitable Cos. Inc., 1992—, also bd. dirs.; chmn., CEO, exec. com., bd. dirs The Equitable Life Assurance Soc. U.S., 1991—; chmn., CEO Equitable Variable Life Ins. Co.; bd. dirs. Foster Wheeler Corp., Alliance Capital Mgmt., Donaldson, Lufkin & Jenrette, Equity and Law, AT&T Capital Corp., LICONY, ACLI. Author: Collectively Bargained Multi-Employer Pension Plans, 1961; co-author: Risk and Insurance, 1963, Pension Planning, 1966. Trustee Newark Mus.; chmn. ins. divsn. Cardinal's Commn. Laity N.Y. Archdiocese; ptnr. N.Y.C.

Partnership; bd. overseers Wharton Sch. U. Pa.; bd. dirs. Am. Coll., Huebner Found.-U. Pa.; bd. dirs Greater N.Y. couns. Boy Scouts Am. Mem. Am. Risk and Ins. Assn., Am. Soc. CLUs, Am. Coll. (trustee), Am. Inst. Property and Liability Underwriters (trustee), Pa. State U. Internat. Ins. Soc., Internat. Acad. Mgmt., Health Ins. Assn. Am. (bd. dirs., past chmn.), U.S.-Korea Bus. Coun., Morris County Country Club, Alpha Tau Omega. Home: 281 Hartshorn Dr Short Hills NJ 07078-1916 Office: Equitable Cos Inc 787 7th Ave New York NY 10019-6018

MELONI, ANDREW P., protective services official; b. Rochester, N.Y., Apr. 10, 1931; s. Andrew and Carrie (DeMaria) M.; m. Laura Ann Tiebe, June 28, 1952; children: Andrew, Michael, Philene Cromwell, Mary Therese Damiano, Stephen. BS, Empire State Coll., 1975. Desk dep. Monroe County Sheriff, Rochester, 1955-60, records sgt., 1960-63, records lt., 1963-65, asst. chief dep., 1965-68, undersheriff, 1968-73; pub. safety commr. Monroe County, Rochester, 1974-77; dir. security U. Rochester, 1977-79; sheriff Monroe County, Rochester, 1980—; commr. accreditation Commn. Accreditation Law Enforcement, Washington, 1993-94. Author: National Code of Ethics, 1991, National Standards for Sheriff & Deputy Sheriff, 1992. Mem. exec. com. Italian Charities, Rochester, 1981—, Rochester Fights Back Drug Com., 1990—. Staff sgt. U.S. Army, 1951-53. Recipient Hall of Fame award Aquinas Inst., 1993. Mem. Nat. Sheriffs Assn. (chmn. stds. and ethics com. 1983—), N.Y. State Sheriffs Ann. (mem. exec. com. 1981—). Republican. Roman Catholic. Avocations: coin collecting, jazz, golf. Office: Monroe County Sheriff's Office 130 Plymouth Ave S Rochester NY 14614

MELOON, ROBERT A., retired newspaper publisher; b. Davenport, Iowa, July 13, 1928; s. John and Evelyn Mae (Ede) Case; children: Mark Robert, Brian Alfred. Student pub. schs., Davenport. Reporter The Capital Times, Madison, Wis., 1957-71, assoc. editor, 1971-72, mng. editor, 1972-78, exec. editor, 1978-81, gen. mgr., 1981-83, exec. pub., 1983-93; also past bd. dirs., ret., 1993; dir. AP Mng. Editors, 1979; mem. media-law rels. com. State Bar Wis., 1980-89; founding mem., v.p. Wis. Freedom of Info. Coun., 1978-83. Mem. Newspaper Assn. Am., Wis. Newspaper Assn., Inland Press Assn. Unitarian. Home: 10 N Burberry Dr Madison WI 53719-3301

MELOY, SYBIL PISKUR, lawyer; b. Chgo., Dec. 1, 1939; d. Michael M. and Laura (Stevenson) Piskur; m. Paul W. Meloy, June 29, 1963 (div.); children: William S., Bradley M. B.S. in Chemistry with honors, U. Ill., 1961; J.D., Chgo. Kent Coll. Law, 1965. Bar: Ill. 1965, Fla. 1985, U.S. Dist. Ct. (no. dist.) Ill. 1965, U.S. Supreme Ct. 1972, U.S. Ct. Appeals (fed. cir.) 1983, U.S. Dist. Ct. (so. dist.) Fla. 1985. Patent chemist, patent atty., sr. atty., internat. counsel G.D. Searle & Co., Skokie, Ill., 1961-72; regional counsel Abbott Labs., North Chicago, Ill., 1972-78; pvt.practice, Arlington Heights, Ill., 1978-79; asst. gen. counsel Alberto Culver Co., Melrose Park, Ill., 1979-83; corp. counsel Key Pharms., Inc., Miami, Fla., 1983-86; assoc. Ruden, Barnett McCloskey, Smith, Schuster and Russell, Pa., 1987-89, ptnr., 1990-91; ptnr. Foley & Lardner, Miami, Washington 1991—; adj. prof. Univ. of Miami Sch. of Law, 1986—. Recipient Abbott Presdl. award, 1977; Bur. Nat. Affairs prize, 1965; Law Rev. prize for best article. Mem. ABA, Chgo. Bar Assn. (chmn. and vice chmn. internat. and fgn. law com.), Am. Patent Law Assn., Am. Chem. Soc., Licencing Execs. Soc., Phi Beta Kappa, Phi Kappa Phi. Patentee oral contraceptive, 1965; contbr. article on fertility control and abortion laws, book rev. on arbitration to law revs. Home: 1915 Brickell Ave Apt 1108C Miami FL 33129-1736 also: 1676 32nd St NW Washington DC 20007-5109 Office: Foley & Lardner 3000 K St NW Washington DC 20007-5109

MELROSE, BARRY JAMES, sportscaster, former professional hockey team coach; b. Kelvington, Sask., Can., July 15, 1956. Player various minor league teams 1973-77, 82-83, 83-86, 86-87; player Cin. Stingers, 1976-79, Winnipeg Jets, 1979-81, Toronto Maple Leafs, 1981-82, 82-83, Detroit Red Wings, 1983-84, 85-86; former gen. mgr., head coach Adirondack Red Wings; now head coach L.A. Kings, 1992-94; sportscaster ESPN, 1995—. Office: care ESPN ESPN Plz Bristol CT 06010*

MELROSE, KENDRICK BASCOM, manufacturing company executive; b. Orlando, Fla., July 31, 1940; s. Henry Bascom and Dorothy (Lumley) M.; children: Robert, Velia, Kendra. B.S. cum laude, Princeton U., 1962; M.Sc., MIT, 1965; M.B.A., U. Chgo., 1967. Mktg. mgr. Pillsbury Co., Mpls., 1967-69; dir. corp. planning Bayfield Techs., Inc., Mpls., 1969-70; with Toro Co. (mfrs. outdoor power equipment), Mpls., 1970—, exec. v.p. outdoor power equipment div., 1980-81, pres., 1981-88, chief exec. officer, 1988, also chmn. Congregationalist. Office: Toro Co 8111 Lyndale Ave S Minneapolis MN 55420-1196

MELSA, JAMES LOUIS, electrical engineer; b. Omaha, July 6, 1938; s. Louis F. and Anne (Pelnar) M.; m. Katherine Smith, June 25, 1960; children: Susan, Elisabeth, Peter, Jon, Jennifer, Mark. BSEE, Iowa State U., 1960; MSEE, U. Ariz., 1962, PhD, 1965. Asst. prof. elec. engring. U. Ariz., Tucson, 1965-67; prof. So. Meth. U., Dallas, 1967-73; prof., chmn. elec. engring. dept. U. Notre Dame, South Bend, Ind., 1973-84; v.p. rsch. and devel. Tellabs, Inc., Lisle, Ill., 1984-89; v.p. strategic planning and advanced tech., 1989-90, v.p., gen. mgr. data comms. div., 1990-93, v.p., strategic quality and process mgmt., 1993—; cons. in field; assoc. mem. tech. staff Radio Corp. Am., Tuscon, 1960-61. Author: Alternatives for Linear Multivariable Control, 1978; (with D.L. Cohn) Decision and Estimation Theory, 1978, A Step by Step Introduction to 8080 Microprocessor Systems, 1977; (with D.G. Schultz) State Functions and Linear Control Systems, 1967, Linear Control Systems, 1969; (with A.P. Sage) Estimation Theory: With Applications to Control and Communications, 1971, System Identification, 1971, Introduction to Probability and Random Process, 1973; (with J.D. Gibson) Nonparametric Detection with Applicaitons, 1975, Computer Programs for Computational Assistance in the Study of Linear Control Theory, 1973; (with C.E. Rohrs and D.G. Schultz) Linear Control Systems, 1993; contbr. articles to profl. publs.; mem. editorial bd. Jour. Computers and Elec. Engring., 1972—. Vice chmn. Am. Automatic Control Coun., 1972-74, chmn., 1974-77; bd. dirs. Nat. Engring. Consortium, 1975-79, Ctr. Communications and Signal Processing, N.C. State, 1986-88. Fellow IEEE (tech. editor Southwestern conf. 1970, chmn. nat. membership com. Control Systems Soc. 1972-81, v.p. mem. activities 1984-85, v.p. fin. 1984-85, 86, pres. 1988, mem. editorial bd. 1985—); mem. Tau Beta Pi, Pi Mu Epsilon, Eta Kappa Nu, Phi Kappa Phi, Sigma Xi. Home: 25w525 Johnson Dr Naperville IL 60540-8275 Office: Tellabs Inc 4951 Indiana Ave Lisle IL 60532-1698

MELSHEIMER, MEL P(OWELL), consumer products business executive; b. Los Angeles, July 9, 1939; s. Oscar Merrill M.; m. Sara Sturdevant, Sept. 1, 1962; children: Heidi, Erich, Douglas. A.B. in Econs., Occidental Coll., 1961; M.B.A., U. So. Calif., 1965. With United Calif. Bank, Los Angeles, 1962-66; sr. fin. analyst Ford Motor Co., Newport Beach, Calif., 1966-67; v.p., chief fin. officer Pepsi Cola Co. Pepsico, Inc., Purchase, N.Y., 1968-75; exec. v.p., chief operating officer AZL Resources, Inc., 1975-84; chmn. bd., chief exec. officer PHX Pacific, Inc., 1984-89; pres., chief exec. officer MPM Capital Corp., 1987-89; exec. v.p. Finevest Foods, Inc., Greenwich, Conn., 1989-92; pres., CEO Land-O-Sun Dairies Inc., 1991-92, Atlanta Dairies, Inc., 1991-92; exec. v.p., sec., chief oper. officer Dairy Holdings, Inc., Johnson City, Tenn., 1992-94; exec. v.p., COO, CFO Sonex Internat. Corp., Brewster, N.Y., 1994—; pres., CEO M.P. Melsheimer & Co., Ridgefield, Conn., 1995—. Served with U.S. Army, 1961-62.

MELSHEIMER, WILLIAM C., principal; b. Chgo., Nov. 3, 1940; s. Raymond C. and Gladys (Janar) M.; m. Nancy S. Melsheimer, July 29, 1987; children: David, Elizabeth, Michael Clevenger, Ami Clevenger. BA, North Cen. Coll. Naperville, Ill., 1962; MS in Edn., No. Ill. U. 1967. Tchr. Social Studies, prin. Jr. High Sch. Gower Sch. Dist. #62, Hinsdale, Ill.; prin. Jr. High Sch. Wilmette (Ill.) Pub. Schs. Contbr. articles to profl. jours. Mem. ASCD, NAESP, NASSP, NSDC, ISDC.

MELSHER, GARY W., lawyer; b. Cleve., Mar. 8, 1939. BS, Ohio State U., 1961; JD, Case Western Reserve U., 1964. Bar: Ohio 1964. Ptnr. Jones, Day, Reavis & Pogue, Cleve. Mem. Order of Coif. Office: Jones Day Reavis & Pogue North Point 901 Lakeside Ave E Cleveland OH 44114-1190

MELSOP, JAMES WILLIAM, architect; b. Columbus, Ohio, June 2, 1939; s. James Brendan and Juanita Kathryn (Van Scoy) M.; m. Sandra Lee Minnich, Sept. 21, 1957; children: Deborah Lee, Susan Elizabeth, Kathryn Anne. BArch, Ohio State U., 1964; MArch, Harvard U., 1965; MBA, U. Chgo., 1975. Reg. architect, profl. engr. Architect The Austin Co., Chgo., 1967-69, mgr. bus. devel., 1969-74, asst. dist. mgr., 1974-75; pres., mng. dir. Austin Brasil, Sao Paulo, 1975-78; asst. dist. mgr. The Austin Co., Roselle, N.J., 1978-80; dist. mgr. The Austin Co., 1980-81; v.p., dist. mgr. The Austin Co., Cleve., 1986, group v.p., dir., 1986—, exec. v.p. chief oper. officer, 1992, pres., CEO, 1992—, also bd. dirs. Mem. Am. Inst. Architects, Harvard Alum., Presidents' Club, Ohio State U. Pres. Club (Disting. Alumnus award 1989). Home: 3165 Trillium Trail Cleveland OH 44124-5205 Office: Austin Co 3650 Mayfield Rd Cleveland OH 44121-1734

MELTON, AUGUSTUS ALLEN, JR., airport executive; b. New Bern, N.C., Feb. 18, 1942; s. Augustus Allen and Margaret (Tucker) M.; m. Carole Yvonne Hawkins, Nov. 3, 1962 (div. 1984); children: Augustus Allen III, Harold David. B.S., Howard U., 1965. Ops. safety officer FAA, Washington, 1971-72; airport cert. and safety insp. FAA, Atlanta, 1972-75; airport cert. safety specialist FAA, Washington, 1976-79, airport mgr., 1980—. Office: Office of Airport Mgr Washington Nat Airport Washington DC 20001

MELTON, CHARLES ESTEL, physicist, educator; b. Fancy Gap, Va., May 18, 1924; s. Charlie Glenn and Ella (Ayers) M.; m. Una Faye Hull, Dec. 7, 1946; children—Sharon (Mrs. Lawrence Husch), Wayne, Sandra (Mrs. Glenn Allen). B.A., Emory and Henry Coll., 1952, D.Sc., 1967; M.S., Vanderbilt U., 1954; Ph.D., U. Notre Dame, 1964. Physicist Oak Ridge Nat. Lab., 1954-67; prof. chemistry U. Ga., Athens, 1967—; head dept. U. Ga., 1972-77. Author: Principles of Mass Spectrometry and Negative Ions, 1970, Ancient Diamond Time Capsules, Secrets of Life and the World, 1985, Primordial Petroleum, 1989; contbr. articles to profl. jours. Served with USNR, 1943-46. Recipient DeFriece medal Emory and Henry Coll., 1959, numerous research grants. Fellow AAAS; mem. Am. Phys. Soc., Am. Chem. Soc., Ga. Acad. Sci. Presbyterian. Home: 34 Glenn Carrie Rd Hull GA 30646-9802 Office: Univ Georgia Dept Chemistry Athens GA 30602

MELTON, DAVID REUBEN, lawyer; b. Milw., Apr. 4, 1952; s. Howard and Evelyn Frances (Cohen) M.; m. Nancy Hillary Segal, May 22, 1981; children: Michelle, Hannah. BA, U. Wis., 1974; JD, U. Chgo., 1977. Bar: Ill. 1977, U.S. Dist. Ct. (no. dist.) Ill. 1977, U.S. Ct. Appeals (7th cir.) 1981, U.S. Supreme Ct. 1982. Assoc. Karon, Morrison & Savikas, Chgo., 1977-83; ptnr. Karon, Morrison & Saviskas, Ltd., Chgo., 1983-87, Karon, Savikas & Horn, Ltd., Chgo., 1987-88, Keck, Mahin & Cate, Chgo., 1988—. Office: Keck Mahin & Cate 77 W Wacker Dr Ste 4900 Chicago IL 60606

MELTON, EMORY LEON, lawyer, publisher, state legislator; b. McDowell, Mo. June 20, 1923; s. Columbus Right and Pearly Susan (Wise) M.; student Monett Jr. Coll., 1940-41, S.W. Mo. State U., 1941-42; LLB, U. Mo., 1945; m. Jean Sanders, June 19, 1949; children—Stanley Emory, John Russell. Admitted to Mo. bar, 1944; individual practice law, Cassville, Mo., 1947—; pres. Melton Publs., Inc., pub. 2 newpapers, 1959—; pros. atty. Barry county (Mo.), 1947-51; mem. Mo. Senate, 1973—. Chmn., Barry County Republican Com., 1964-68. Served with AUS, 1945-46. Recipient award for meritorious public service St. Louis Globe-Democrat., 1976. Mem. Mo. Bar Assn. Baptist. Clubs: Lions, Masons. Office: PO Box 488 Cassville MO 65625-0488

MELTON, GARY BENTLEY, psychology and law educator; b. Salisbury, N.C., June 4, 1952; s. Harold Sumner Jr. and Marion Adair (Reeves) M.; m. Julia Ann Young, Aug. 25, 1973; children: Jennifer Lynn, Stephany Beth. BA, U. Va., 1973; MA, Boston U., 1975, PhD, 1978. Lic. psychologist, Nebr. Asst. prof. psychology Morehead (Ky.) State U., 1978-79, U. Va., Charlottesville, 1979-81; from asst. prof. to full prof. psychology and law U. Nebr., Lincoln, 1981-87, Carl A. Happold prof. psychology and law, 1987-94; prof. neuropsychiatry, law and psychology, dir. Inst. Families in Soc., U. S.C., Columbia, 1994—; dir. Consortium on Children, Families and the Law. Author: Child Advocacy: Psychological Issues and Interventions, 1983; (with others) Community Mental Health Centers and the Courts: An Evaluation of Community-Based Forensic Services, 1985; Psychological Evaluation for the Courts: A Handbook for Mental Health Professionals and Lawyers, 1987, Pediatric and Adolescent AIDS: Research Findings From the Social Sciences, 1992, Ethical and Legal Issues in AIDS Research, 1994; editor numerous books. Mem. U.S. Adv. Bd. on Child Abuse and Neglect, 1989-93, vice-chair, 1991-93. Recipient Frederick Howell Lewis award Psi Chi, 1993. Fellow APA (chmn. various coms., Disting. Contbn. to Psychology in Pub. Interest award 1985, Cert. of Recognition for Psychology in Pub. Interest 1981, Nicholas Hobbs award 1992, Harold Hildreth award 1992); mem. Am. Psychology-Law Soc. (pres. 1990-91), Nat. Com. to Prevent Child Abuse (Donna Stone award 1992). Democrat. Mem. Unitarian Ch. Office: Inst for Families in Soc Univ of SC Columbia SC 29208

MELTON, HOWELL WEBSTER, SR., federal judge; b. Atlanta, Dec. 15, 1923; s. Holmes and Alma (Combee) M.; m. Margaret Catherine Wolfe, Mar. 4, 1950; children—Howell Webster, Carol Anne. J.D., U. Fla., 1948. Bar: Fla. 1948. Mem. firm Upchurch, Melton & Upchurch, St. Augustine, St. Augustine, 1948-61; judge 7th Jud. Circuit of Fla., St. Augustine, 1961-77, U.S. Dist. Ct. (mid. dist.) Fla., Jacksonville, 1977—; past chmn. Fla. Conf. Cir. Judges, 1974; past chmn. coun. bar pres.'s Fla. Bar. Trustee Flagler Coll., St. Augustine. Served with U.S. Army, 1943-46. Recipient Disting. Service award St. Augustine Jaycees, 1953. Mem. ABA, St. Johns County Bar Assn., Jacksonville Bar Assn., Fed. Bar Assn., Fla. Blue Key, Phi Delta Theta, Phi Delta Phi. Methodist (past bd. trustees). Clubs: Ponce de Leon Country (St. Augustine), Marsh Creek Country (St. Augustine Beach), St. Augustine Fla. Office: Lodges: Masons, Kiwanis (past pres.). Office: US Dist Ct PO Box 52957 Jacksonville FL 32201-2957

MELTON, LYNDA GAYLE, reading specialist, educational diagnostician; b. Gatesville, Tex., Mar. 11, 1943; d. Dee and Myrtle (Dunlap) White; divorced; children: Melanie Gayle, William Matthew. BS, U. Tex., 1964; MA, U. North Tex., 1979, PhD, 1983, postgrad., 1993, 94; postgrad., Tex. Womans U., 1983. Cert. elem. tchr., spl. edn. tchr., supervision, spl. edn supr., learning disabilities tchr., orthpedically handicapped tchr., reading specialist, Tex., adminstrs., ednl. diagnostician. Tchr. 2d and 4th grades, spl. edn. tchr. Irving (Tex.) Ind. Sch. Dist., 1964-79, tchr., 1982-83; 4th grade tchr. Northwest Ind. Sch. Dist., Justin, Tex., 1980-81; asst. prin. Grapevine-Colleyville Ind. Sch. Dist., Tex., 1983-87; tchr. reading improvement Carrollton (Tex.)-Farmers Branch Ind. Sch. Dist., 1988-89; cons. lang. arts Edn. Svc. Ctr. Region 10, Richardson, Tex., 1989-91; pvt. practice diagnostic reading and ednl. diagnostician Grapevine, Tex., 1991—; reading clinician N.Tex. State U., Denton, 1980; instr. spl. edn. U. Tex., Dallas, 1983, U Tex., Arlington, 1988; vis. prof. Tex. Women's U., Denton, 1983, 84, 87-88. Contbr. Reading Rsch. Revisited, also revs. to Case Mgmt. Monthly Confs., Scottish Rite Hosp. and profl. jours. Mem. ASCD, Internat. Reading Assn. (North Tex. coun.), Learning Disabilities, Orton Disability Soc., Coun. for Exceptional Children, Phi Delta Kappa. Home: 30 Sonora Dr Trophy Club TX 76262 Office: 520 S Main Ste 106 Grapevine TX 76051

MELTON, MARIE FRANCES, university dean; b. Bayshore, N.Y.; d. Edward Kilgallon and Anne (Mohan) M. BS in Edn., St. John's U., Jamaica, N.Y., 1960, MS in Edn., 1975; MLS, Pratt Inst., Bklyn., 1961; EDD, St. John's U., Jamaica, N.Y., 1984. Dir. media ctr. Mater Christi High Sch., Astoria, N.Y. 1961-72; libr. sci. libr. St. John's U., Jamaica, N.Y., 1972-76, asst. dir., 1976-83, dir. Univ. Libr., 1983-89, dean Univ. Libr., 1989—. Mem., officer St. John's Prep Bd. of Trustees, Astoria, N.Y., 1980—, Holy Cross High Sch., Flushing, N.Y., 1979-89; chair Sunnyside Hist. Com., Sunnyside, N.Y., 1988-91. Mem. Am. Libr. Assn., Cath. Libr. Assn., N.Y. Libr. Assn., Council Nat. Libr. & Info. Assns. Roman Catholic. Office: St Johns University Utopia Pkwy Jamaica NY 11439

MELTON, RICHARD H., diplomat; b. Rockville, Md, Aug. 8, 1935; married; 3 children. BA, Cornell U., 1958; MA, U. Wis., 1971; grad., Nat. War Coll., 1979. Joined Fgn. Service, 1961, internat. relations officer, 1971-73; spl. asst. Bur. Inter-Am. Affairs Dept. of State, 1973-75; polit. officer U.S. Embassy, Lisbon, Portugal, 1975-78, London, 1979-82; dep. chief of mission U.S. Embassy, Montevideo, Uruguay, 1982-85; dir. Office of Cen. Am. and

Panamanian Affairs Dept. of State, 1985-87; amb. to Nicaragua, 1988, amb. to Brazil, 1989—. Served with U.S. Army, 1958-61. Office: Avenida das Nacoes Lote 3 Unit 3500 APO AA 34030 also: Am Embassy, Avenida das Nacoes Lote 3, Brasilia Brazil

MELTZER, ALLAN H., economist, educator; b. Boston, Feb. 6, 1928; s. George B. and Minerva I. (Simons) M.; m. Marilyn Ginsburg, Aug. 27, 1950; children: Bruce Michael, Eric Charles, Beth Denise. A.B., Duke U., 1948; M.A., UCLA, 1955, Ph.D., 1958. Univ. prof. polit. economy and pub. policy, 1991—; Lectr. econs. U. Pa., Phila., 1956-57; mem. faculty Carnegie Mellon U. Grad. Sch. Indsl. Adminstrn., Pitts., 1957—; prof. econs. Carnegie Mellon U. Grad. Sch. Indsl. Adminstrn., 1964—, Maurice Falk prof. econs. and social sci., 1970-80, John M. Olin univ. prof. polit. economy and pub. policy, 1980-91; Univ. prof. polit. economy and pub. policy Carnegie Mellon U. Grad. Sch. Indsl. Adminstrn., 1991—; vis. prof. U. Chgo., 1964-65, Fundacao Getulio Vargas, Rio de Janeiro, 1976-79, City U., London, 1979-86; vis. fellow Hoover Instn., 1977-78; vis. scholar Am. Enterprise Inst., Washington, 1989—; co-chmn. Shadow Open Market Com., 1974-89, chmn., 1989—; cons. U.S. Treasury, joint econ. com. U.S. Congress, 1960; com. on banking and currency U.S. Ho. of Reps., 1963-64; mem. Pres.'s Econ. Policy Adv. Bd., 1988-90; acting mem. Coun. Econ. Advisors, 1988-89; panel econ. advisors Congl. Budget Office, 1995—; cons., bd. govs. FRS, FDIC; dir. Cooper Tire & Rubber Co.; hon. advisor Inst. Monetary and Econ. Studies Bank of Japan, 1987—; bd. dirs. Sarah Scaife Found., Commonwealth Foun.; dir. Stillhalter Vision AG, Zurich, 1994—, Advanced Materials Group, 1994—. Author: Monetary Economics, 1989, Keynes's Monetary Theory: A Different Interpretation, 1988, (with Karl Brunner) Money and the Economy: Issues in Monetary Analysis, 1993, (with Alex Cukierman and Scott Richard) Political Economy, 1991; editor: (with Karl Brunner) Carnegie-Rochester Conf. Series, 1976-79, (with Charles Plosser), 1989—; contbr. articles to profl. jours. Recipient Award for Outstanding Achievement UCLA, 1983; Social Sci. Research Council fellow, 1955-56; Ford Found. fellow, 1962-63. Fellow Nat. Assn. Bus. Economists; mem. Am. Econ. Assn. (v.p. 1990), Western Econ. Assn. (pres. 1985-86), Am. Fin. Assn., Phila. Soc. (v.p. 1981-83), Cosmos Club. Avocations: research in macroeconomics, money, political economy. Office: Carnegie Mellon U Dept Econs Pittsburgh PA 15213

MELTZER, BERNARD DAVID, legal educator; b. Phila., Nov. 21, 1914; s. Julius and Rose (Welkov) M.; m. Jean Sulzberger, Jan. 17, 1947; children: Joan, Daniel, Susan. A.B., U. Chgo., 1935, J.D., 1937; LL.M., Harvard U., 1938. Bar: Ill. 1938. Atty., spl. asst. to chmn. SEC, 1938-40; assoc. firm Mayer, Meyer, Austrian & Platt, Chgo., 1940; spl. asst. to asst. sec. state, also acting chief fgn. funds control div. State 1941-43; asst. trial counsel U.S. staff Internat. Nuremberg War Trials, 1945-46; from professorial lectr. to disting. svc. prof. law emeritus U. Chgo. Law Sch., 1946—; counsel Vedder, Price, Kaufman & Kamnholz, Chgo., 1954-55, Sidley and Austin, Chgo., 1987-89; hearing commr. NPA, 1952-53; labor arbitrator; spl. master U.S. Ct. Appeals for D.C., 1963-64; bd. publs. U. Chgo., 1965-67, chmn., 1967-68; mem. Gov. Ill. Adv. Commn. Labor-Mgmt. Policy for Pub. Employees in Ill., 1966-67, Ill. Civil Service Commn., 1968-69; cons. U.S. Dept. Labor, 1969-70. Author: Supplementary Materials on International Organizations, 1948, (with W.G. Katz) Cases and Materials on Business Corporations, 1949, Labor Law Cases, Materials and Problems, 1970, supplement, 1972, 75, 2d edit., 1977, supplements, 1980, 82 (with S. Henderson), 3d edit. (with S. Henderson), 1985, supplement, 1988; also articles. Bd. dirs. Hyde Park Community Conf., 1954-56, S.E. Chgo. Commn., 1956-57. Served to lt. (j.g.) USNR, 1943-46. Mem. ABA (co-chmn. com. devel. law under NLRA 1959-60, mem. spl. com. transp. strikes), Ill. Bar Assn., Chgo. Bar Assn. (bd. mgrs. 1972-73), Nat. Acad. Arbitrators, Am. Law Inst., Am. Acad. Arts and Scis., Order of Coif, Phi Beta Kappa. Home: 1219 E 50th St Chicago IL 60615-2908 Office: U Chgo Law Sch 1111 E 60th St Chicago IL 60637-2702

MELTZER, BERNARD N(ATHAN), sociologist, educator; b. N.Y.C., Oct. 17, 1916; s. Philip and Anna (Kemper) M.; m. Ida Wasserman, June 11, 1944; children: Iris Jean, William Jay. B.A., Wayne State U., 1943, M.A., 1944; Ph.D., U. Chgo., 1948. Research assoc. U. Chgo., 1948-49; asst. prof. sociology McGill U., 1949-51; mem. faculty Central Mich. U., Mt. Pleasant, 1951-87; prof. sociology Central Mich. U., 1955-87, chmn. dept., 1959-87, prof. emeritus, 1987—. Author: Education in Society: Readings, 1958, The Social Psychology of George Herbert Mead, 1959, Symbolic Interaction: A Reader in Social Psychology, 3d edit., 1978, Symbolic Interactionism: Genesis, Varieties and Criticism, 1975; contbr. articles to profl. periodicals and books. Chmn. Isabella County Civil Rights Com., 1959. Recipient citation Mich. Acad. Sci., Arts and Letters, 1969; Ascher fellow social sci. U. Chgo., 1944; Univ. fellow sociology, 1945; Marshall Field fellow sociology, 1946; grantee Can. Social Sci. Research Council, 1950. Fellow Am. Sociol. Assn.; mem. Mich. Sociol. Assn. (pres. 1961-62), North Central Sociol. Assn. (v.p. 1971-72), Soc. Study Symbolic Interaction. Home: 318 E Cherry St Mount Pleasant MI 48858-2606

MELTZER, BRIAN, lawyer; b. Chgo., Apr. 15, 1944; s. Maurice and Ethel (Goldstein) M.; m. Rosemary Labriola, Sept. 11, 1982; children: Stuart Joseph, Alan Phillip, Martin Angelo. BA in Math., Cornell U., 1966; JD, Harvard U., 1969. Bar: Ill. 1969. Assoc. atty. D'ancona & Pflaum, Chgo., 1969-72; assoc. then ptnr. Schwartz & Freeman, Chgo., 1972-88; ptnr. Keck, Mahin & Cate, Chgo., 1988—. Office: Keck Mahin & Cate 1515 E Woodfield Rd Schaumburg IL 60173-6046

MELTZER, DANIEL J., law educator; b. 1951. AB, Harvard U., 1972, JD, 1975. Bar: Ill. 1975, D.C. 1978, Mass. 1983. Law clk. to Hon. Carl McGowan, 1975-76, law clk. to Hon. Potter Stewart, 1976-77; spl. asst., sec. Dept. Health, Edn. and Welfare, 1977-78; assoc. Williams & Connolly, 1979-81; asst. prof. Harvard U., Cambridge, Mass., 1982-87, prof., 1987—, assoc. dean, 1989-93. Office: Law Sch Harvard U Cambridge MA 02138

MELTZER, DAVID, author, musician; b. Rochester, N.Y., Feb. 17, 1937; s. Louis and Roseamunde (Lovelace) M.; m. Christina Meyer, Apr. 1, 1958; children—Jennifer, Margaret, Amanda, Adam Benjamin ben David. Student, Los Angeles City Coll., 1955-56, U. Calif. at Los Angeles, 1956-57. Mem. cons. bd. Coordinating Coun. of Lit. Mags.; instr. M.A. program in poetics New Coll., San Francisco, 1980—, coord. writing and lit. program in undergrad. humanites program, 1987—. Author: numerous books of poetry, including Tens, Selected Poems, 1973, Six, 1976, Two-Way Mirror: Notebook on Poetry, 1977, The Art, The Veil, 1981, The Name: Selected Poetry, 1973-83, 1983; editor: The San Francisco Poets, 1971, Birth, 1973, The Secret Garden: Anthology of the Classic Kabbalah, 1977, Birth: An Anthology of Ancient Texts, Songs, Prayers, and Stories, 1981, Death: An Anthology of Ancient Texts, Songs, Prayers, and Stories, 1983, The Book Within the Book: Approaching the Kabbalah, 1990, Arrows: Selected Poetry 1952-92, 1994, Reading Jazz, 1993; editor, pub.: bi-annual jour., Orf, 1968, The Agency, 1968, The Agency Trilogy, 1994, Out, 1995, also Tree Books; song-writer: Serpent Power, 1968, Poet Song, 1970; soundtrack for Chance, 1978. Bd. dirs. Before Columbus Found., 1977—. Coordinating Coun. of Lit. Mags. grantee, 1973-74, 81, Nat. Endowment of Arts grantee for creative writing, 1974, for pub., 1975, Calif. Arts Coun. grantee, 1979; recipient Tombstone award for poetry John Ryan Morris Meml. Found., 1992. Office: PO Box 9005 Berkeley CA 94709-0005

MELTZER, DONALD RICHARD, treasurer; b. Boston, Sept. 1, 1932; s. Leo N. and Betty (Flesher) M.; m. Mary Douglas Seelye, Dec. 7, 1963; children: Kimberly, Christopher. AB, Dartmouth Coll., 1954, MBA, 1955. Mgr. Peat, Marwick, Mitchell & Co., Boston, 1955-67; asst. controller United Fruit Corp., Boston, 1968-69, controller, 1969-70, v.p., controller, 1970-73; v.p., chief acctg. office United Brands Co., N.Y.C., 1973-74, v.p. fin. and adminstrn., 1974-76; v.p. fin., treas. Instron Corp., Canton, Mass. 1976-88; v.p. fin. and adminstrn., treas., chief fin. officer Dialogue, Inc., Braintree, Mass., 1988-90; corp. fin. cons., Sudbury, Mass., 1988—. Overseer Children's Hosp. Med. Ctr., Boston, 1980-94; fin. com. Town of Sudbury, Mass., 1967; chmn. bd. trustees First Parish Ch., Sudbury, 1970-71, treas., 1991-93; pres. Mass. Parents Assn. for Deaf and Hard of Hearing, Boston, 1976-77, bd. dirs., 1973-86. Mem. AICPA, Mass. Soc. CPAs, Fin. Execs. Inst., Am. Assn. Indsl. Mgmt. (bd. dirs. 1980-85), Walk 'N Mass Volkssport Club (co-pres. 1993—). Avocation: postal history, stamp collecting. Home: 341 Old Lancaster Rd Sudbury MA 01776-2035

MELTZER, HERBERT YALE, psychiatry educator; b. Bklyn., July 29, 1937; s. David and Estelle (Gross) M.; m. Sharon Rae Bittenson, June 12, 1960; children—David, Danielle. A.B., Cornell U., 1958; M.A., Harvard U., 1959; M.D., Yale U., 1963. Diplomate Am. Bd. Neurology and Psychiatry. Prof. U. Chgo., 1968-85; dir. biol. psychiatry lab. Ill. State Psychiat. Inst., Chgo., 1975-84; Bond prof. psychiatry Case Western Res. U., Cleve., 1985—; dir. psychiat. research Univ. Hosp., Cleve., 1985—. Editor: Neuropsychopharmacology; contbr. articles to profl. jours. Recipient Efran prize Am. Coll. Neuropsychopharmacology, 1981, Noyes prize for schizophrenia rsch. Commonwealth of Pa., 1990, Sachar award Columbia U., Gold medal Soc. Biol. Psychiatry, 1993. Mem. NIMH, Am. Coll. Neuropsychopharmacology (pres. 1984-85), Am. Psychiat. Assn., Soc. Biol. Psychiatry (editorial bd.), Nat. Alliance Rsch. Schizophrenia Affective Disorders (Lieber prize 1992). Avocation: music. Office: U Hosps Cleve 2074 Abington Rd Cleveland OH 44106-2602

MELTZER, JACK, consultant, retired college dean; b. Bayonne, N.J., Aug. 21, 1921; s. Louis and Debbie (Gold) M.; m. Rae Libin, June 26, 1944; children: Richard, Marc, Ellen. B.A., Wayne State U., 1941; M.A., U. Chgo., 1947. Dir. planning Michael Reese Hosp., Chgo., 1953-54; S.E. Chgo. Commn. and U. Chgo., 1954-58; propr. Jack Meltzer Assos. (planners), 1958-63; acting dir. Am. Soc. Planning Ofcls., 1967-68; prof. dir. Center Urban Studies, U. Chgo., 1963-71; prof. div. social scis., prof. Sch. Social Service Adminstrn., 1965-83; prof., dean Sch. Social Scis. U. Tex.-Dallas, 1983-86; pvt. practice cons., 1986—; cons. to govt. and industry, 1945—. Author book revs., articles, books. Village trustee, Park Forest, Ill., 1950-52, mem. plan commn., 1949; Served to capt. USAAF, World War II. Mem. AAUP, Am. Soc. Planning Ofcls. (past treas.), Am. Inst. Planners (past v.p. pvt. practice dept.), Nat. Assn. Housing and Renewal Ofcls., Am. Soc. Pub. Adminstrn. Home: 4550 N Park Ave Apt 803 Bethesda MD 20815-7237

MELTZER, JAY H., lawyer, retail company executive; b. Bklyn., Mar. 30, 1944; s. Solomon G. and Ethel L. (Kraft) M.; m. Bonnie R. Rosenberg, June 27, 1965; children: Wendy, Elizabeth, Jonathan. A.B., Dartmouth Coll., 1964; JD, Harvard U., 1967. Bar: N.Y. 1968, Mass. 1978, U.S. Dist. Ct. Mass. 1979. Law clk. to U.S. dist. judge, 1967-68; assoc. firm Shearman & Sterling, N.Y.C., 1968-72; with Damon Corp., Needham Heights, Mass., 1972-84; gen. counsel, sec. Damon Corp., 1973-84, v.p., 1979-84; v.p., corp. counsel The TJX Cos., Inc., Framingham, Mass., 1984-87, v.p., gen. counsel, sec., 1987-89, sr. v.p., gen. counsel, sec., 1989—. Dir. coun. Better Bus. Bur., 1990-93. Mem. ABA, Am. Soc. Corp. Secs., Am. Corp. Counsel Assn. (bd. dirs. N.E. chpt.), Retailers Assn. Mass. (bd. dirs., exec. com., sec.), New Eng. Corp. Counsel Assn. (bd. dirs.). Office: TJX Cos Inc 770 Cochituate Rd Framingham MA 01701-4630

MELTZER, MILTON, author; b. Worcester, Mass., May 8, 1915; s. Benjamin and Mary (Richter) M.; m. Hilda Balinky, June 22, 1941; children: Jane, Amy. Student, Columbia, 1932-36. adj. prof. history U. Mass., Amherst, 1977-80. Author: Mark Twain Himself, 1960; (with Walter Harding) A Thoreau Profile, 1962, Langston Hughes: A Biography, 1968, Bread and Roses, 1967, Brother, Can You Spare a Dime, 1968, Never to Forget: The Jews of the Holocaust, 1976, Dorothea Lange: A Photographer's Life, 1978; co-editor: Lydia Maria Child: Selected Letters, 1817-1880, 1982, The Terrorists, 1983, A Book about Names, 1984, The Black Americans, 1984, Ain't Gonna Study War No More, 1985, Mark Twain: A Writer's Life, 1985, Poverty in America, 1986, George Washington and the Birth of Our Nation, 1986, The Landscape of Memory, 1987, The American Revolutionaries, 1987, Benjamin Franklin: The New American, 1988, Rescue: The Story of How Gentiles Saved Jews in the Holocaust, 1988, Starting From Home: A Writer's Beginnings, 1988, Voices From the Civil War, 1989, Columbus and the World Around Him, 1990, The Bill of Rights: How We Got It and What It Means, 1990, Crime in America, 1990, Thomas Jefferson: Revolutionary Aristocrat, 1991, The Amazing Potato, 1992, Slavery: A World History, 1993, Lincoln: In His Own Words, 1993, Andrew Jackson and His America, 1993, Gold, 1993; (with Langston Hughes, C. Eric Lincoln, and Jon Michael Spencer) A Pictorial History of African-Americans, 1994, Cheap Raw Material: How Our Youngest Workers Are Exploited and Abused, 1994, Theodore Roosevelt, 1994, Who Cares? Millions Do: A Book About Altruism, 1994, Frederick Douglass: In His Own Words, 1995. Served with USAAF, 1942-46. Mem. Orgn. Am. Historians, Authors Guild, P.E.N. Address: 263 W End Ave New York NY 10023-2612

MELTZER, STEVEN LEE, lawyer; b. Rochester, N.Y., Sept. 6, 1946; s. Seymour Norman and Ruth (Pekarsky) M.; m. Harriet Vivian Lewis, Aug. 29, 1971; children: Debra, Scott, Jeremy. AB, Brown U., 1968; JD, MBA, Harvard U., 1973. Bar: Md. 1973, D.C. 1974. Assoc. Shaw, Pittman, Potts & Trowbridge, Washington, 1973-79, ptnr., 1980—, chmn. fin. com., 1985-88, chmn. corp. practice group, 1994—; mem. audit com., bus. users forum Nat. Info. Tech. Ctr., Md., 1992-94; gen. counsel Md. Info. Tech. Ctr., Rockville, 1994—; Suburban Md. High Tech. Coun., Rockville, 1995—; trustee New Eng. Inst. TEch., Warwick, R.I., 1974-89, chmn. bd. trustees, 1989—. Exec. editor Technology Law Notes, 1986—. Mem. 25th Reunion Gift com. Brown U., Providence, 1992—. Mem. Internat. Bar Assn., Info. Tech. Assn. Am., D.C. Bar Assn., Md. State Bar Assn., Harvard Bus. Sch. Club. Avocations: golf, tennis. Office: Shaw Pittman Potts & Trowbridge 2300 N St NW Washington DC 20037

MELVILLE, ROBERT SEAMAN, chemist; b. Worcester, Mass., Nov. 20, 1913; s. Carey Eyster and Maud Tesmer (Seaman) M.; m. Eleanor Elisabeth Vogel, Mar. 6, 1942; children: Robert Andrew, John Frederick, Margaret Ellen, Emily Jean, Martin Carroll. AB in Chemistry, Clark U., 1937; PhD in Biochemistry, State U. Iowa, 1950. Chief chemist St. Luke's Hosp., Chgo., 1950-54; chief biochemist VA Hosp., Iowa City, 1954-63; chief biochemist, lab. requirement specialist VA Cen. Office, Washington, 1963-65; health sci. adminstr. Nat. Inst. Gen. Med. Scis., NIH, Bethesda, Md., 1965-67, chief automated clin. lab. program, 1967-77, spl. asst. to dir. of biomed. engring., 1977-81; dir. In Vitro Diagnostic Device Standards div. Bur. Med. Devices, FDA, Silver Spring, Md., 1981-82; cons. in clin. scis., 1983—; clin. prof. pathology George Washington U. Med. Ctr., Washington, 1977—; pres. Trans-Tech. Biomed., 1983—. Contbr. articles on clin. lab. automation to profl. publs. With U.S. Army, 1942-46. Fellow AAAS, Am. Chem. Soc., Am. Assn. Clin. Chemistry (Joseph H. Rowe award 1972, Nat. Fisher award 1976, pres. 1969-70), Instrument Soc. Am., Assn. for Advancement of Med. Instrumentation; mem. Am. Bd. Clin. Chemists (pres. bd. dirs. 1978-81), Am. Inst. Chemists (chmn. cert. commn. in chem. engring. and chemistry 1981-84, 87-91, cert. chemist 1989—), Alpha Chi Sigma (Profl. Chemist award 1990), Lambda Chi Alpha. Unitarian. Club: Cosmos. Lodge: Masons. Home and Office: 11112 Kenilworth Ave PO Box 56 Garrett Park MD 20896-0056

MELVILL-JONES, GEOFFREY, physician, educator; b. Cambridge, Eng., Jan. 14, 1923; emigrated to Can., 1961, naturalized, 1974; s. Benett and Dorothy Laxton (Jotham) Melvill J.; m. Jenny Marigold Burnaby, June 21, 1953; children—Katharine F., Francis H., Andrew J., Dorothy H. B.A., Cambridge U., 1944, M.A., 1947, M.B.,B.Ch., 1949. House surgeon Middlesex (Eng.) Hosp., 1950; sr. house surgeon in otolaryngology Addenbrooke's Hosp., Cambridge, 1950-51; sci. officer Med. Research Council Gt. Britain, 1955-61; assoc. prof. physiology McGill U., Montreal, Que., Can. 1961-68; prof. McGill U., 1968-92, prof. emeritus, 1992—, Hosmer research prof., 1978-92, dir. aerospace med. research unit, 1961-89; adj. prof. dept. clin. neurosci., faculty medicine U. Calgary, 1992—; vis. prof. Stanford U., 1971-72, College de France, 1979, 95; Ashton Graybiel lectr. U.S. Naval Aerospace Lab., Fla. Author: Mammalian Vestibular Physiology, 1979, Adaptive Mechanisms in Gaze Control, 1985; contbr. numerous articles to profl. publs. Flying pers. med. officer RAF, 1951-55. Recipient SkyLab Achievement award NASA, 1974, Dohlman medal Toronto U., 1986, Wilbur Franks award Can. Soc. Aerospace Medicine, 1988. Fellow Can. Aero. and Space Inst., Aerospace Med. Assn. (Harry G. Armstrong Lectureship award 1968, Arnold D. Tuttle award 1971), Royal Soc. (London), Royal Soc. Can. (McLaughlin medal 1991), Royal Aero. Soc. (London) (Stewart Meml. award 1989, Buchanan Barbour award 1990); mem. U.K. Physiol. Soc., Can. Physiol. Soc., Can. Soc. Aviation Medicine, Internat. Collegium Otolaryngology, Soc. Neurosci., Bárány Soc. (Gold medal 1988). Office: U Calgary Dept Clin. Neurosci, 3330 Hospital Dr NW, Calgary, AB Canada T2N 4N1

MELVIN, BEN WATSON, JR., petroleum and chemical manufacturing executive; b. Nashville, Mar. 27, 1926; s. Ben Watson and Virginia (Darden) M.; m. Elizabeth Cooper Hershey, May 10, 1952; children—Ben W., Landis Anne, Thomas C., Mark C. B.Chem. Engring., U. Del., 1950. With E. I. duPont de Nemours & Co., Inc., Wilmington, Del., 1950-91, ret., 1991. Served with USAAF, 1944-46. Mem. AICE, Soc. Plastics Engrs., So. Chem. Industry, Wilmington Country Club.

MELVIN, BILLY ALFRED, clergyman; b. Macon, Ga., Nov. 25, 1929; s. Daniel Henry and Leola Dale (Seidell) M.; m. Marcia Darlene Eby, Oct. 26, 1952; children: Deborah Ruth, Daniel Henry II. Student, Free Will Baptist Bible Coll., Nashville, 1947-49; B.A., Taylor U., Upland, Ind., 1951; postgrad., Asbury Theol. Sem., Wilmore, Ky., 1951-53; B.D., Union Theol. Sem., Richmond, Va., 1956; D.D., Azusa (Calif.) Coll., 1968; LL.D. (hon.), Taylor U., 1984. Ordained to ministry Free Will Baptist Ch., 1951; pastor First Free Will Baptist Chs., Newport, Tenn., 1951-53, Richmond, 1953-57; pastor Bethany Ch., Norfolk, Va., 1957-59; exec. sec. Nat. Assn. Free Will Baptists, 1959-67; exec. dir. Nat. Assn. Evangelicals, 1967-95.

MELVIN, CHARLES EDWARD, JR., lawyer; b. Greensboro, N.C., July 13, 1929; s. Charles Edward and Mary Ruth (Plunkett) M.; m. Jacklyn McDaniel, Mar. 1, 1958; 1 child, Dana W. BS, U. N.C., 1951, JD with honors, 1956. Bar: N.C. 1956. Ptnr. Smith, Helms, Mulliss & Moore, Greensboro, 1958—. Capt. U.S. Army, 1952-54. Mem. N.C. Bar Assn. (chmn. real property sect. 1981), Am. Coll. Real Estate Lawyers, Greensboro C. of C. (pres. 1978). Office: Smith Helms Mulliss & Moore Ste 1400 PO Box 21927 300 N Greene St Greensboro NC 27420

MELVIN, DANIEL SEAN, radio station executive; b. Richmond, Va., Oct. 6, 1961; s. Thomas J. and Jane Louise (Abernathy) M. Student, Ga. State U., 1982-84; BA, U. Ga., 1985. Account exec. Sta. KMTN-FM, Jackson, Wyo., 1985-87, sales mgr., 1987; account exec., asst. sales mgr. Sta. KIZN AM-FM, Boise, Idaho, 1987-88, sales mgr., 1988, gen. mgr., 1988—; gen. mgr. Sta. WUOG-FM (U. Ga.), Athens, Ga., 1984-85. Writer, producer interview with G. Gordon Liddy, 1983. Avocations: skiing, running, tennis, bicycling. Office: Sta KIZN AM/FM 1002 W Franklin St Boise ID 83702-5431

MELVIN, JOHN LEWIS, physician, medical educator; b. Columbus, Ohio, May 26, 1935; s. John Harper and Ruth Eleanor (Wertenberger) M.; m. Carol Ann Pate, Apr. 10, 1991; children from a previous marriage: Megan Marie, Beth Anne, John Patrick, Mia Michelle. BS, Ohio State U., 1955, MD, 1960, M in Med. Sci., 1966. Rotating Intern Mt. Carmel Hosp., Columbus, 1960-61; resident in phys. medicine Univ. Hosp., Columbus, 1961, 63-66; asst. prof. Ohio State U., Columbus, 1966-69, assoc. prof., 1969-73; prof., chmn. dept. Med. Coll. Wis., Milw., 1973-91; prof., dep. chmn. dept. Temple U., Phila., 1992—; cons. to numerous U.S. govtl. agys., health care insts.; lectr. in field; research assoc. Ohio State Research Found., Columbus, 1966-68; assoc. coordinator Ohio State Regional Med. Program, Columbus, 1969-71; med. dir. Curative Rehab. Ctr., Milw., 1973-91; v.p. med. affairs Moss Rehab. Hosp., Phila., 1991—; dept. chmn. Einstein Med. Ctr., Phila., 1991—. Contbr. articles to profl. jours. Bd. dirs. Vis. Nurses Assn., Milw., 1974-83; mem. com. Mental Health Planning Council, Milw., 1974-75, Wis. Council Devel. Disabilities, Madison, 1979-80; mem. planning and evaluation com. Elizabethtown Hosp. for Children and Youth, Pa., 1977; advisor Nat. Multiple Sclerosis Soc., Milw., 1979-87; mem. Wis. Nicaragua Ptnrs., 1982-91; trustee Easter Seal Research Found., vice chmn., 1985, chmn. 1986-88. Served to capt. M.C., U.S. Army, 1961-63. Recipient cert. of appreciation Goodwill Industries, 1972, spl. recognition award Commn. Accreditation Rehab. Facilities, 1977, Performance award Wood VA Med. Ctr., 1978, Goldschmidt award Nat. Rehab. Hosp., 1990, cert. of appreciation Jour. Rehab. Adminstrn., 1982; Alumni Achievement award Ohio State U., 1985; grantee Rehab. Svcs. Adminstrn., 1979-91, Health Care Financing Adminstrn., 1984-85; Ford Found. fellow, 1951-53. Fellow Am. Acad. Cerebral Palsy and Devel. Medicine, Am. Acad. Phys. Medicine and Rehab. (sec. 1992—, Zeiter Lectr. award 1987); mem. Am. Bd. Phys. Medicine and Rehab. (Diplomate, chmn. 1988-93, chmn. residency Rev. Com. 1985-88), Am. Bd. Med. Specialists (exec. com. 1990-92), Med. Soc. Milw., Milw. Acad. Medicine, Wis. Soc. Phys. Medicine and Rehab., Am. Assn. Electromyography and Electrodiagnosis (pres. 1979-80), Am. Congress Rehab. Medicine (pres. 1987-88, gold medal 1971, 78, Gold Key award 1988), Am. Heart Assn., Am. Hosp. Assn. (sect. rehab. hosp., chmn. 1981), AMA (cert. of appreciation 1976, 82), Am. Paraplegia Soc., Assn. Acad. Physiatrists (pres. 1985-87), Internat. Fedn. Phys. Medicine and Rehab. (exec. com. 1980—, hon. sec. 1980-88, pres. elect 1995—), Internat. Rehab. Medicine Assn., Rehab. Internat. Med. Commn., Nat. Assn. Rehab. Facilities (pres. 1981-83, bd. dirs.), Coun. of Med. Splty. Socs. (pres. 1989-90), Alpha Omega Alpha. Home: 244 Delancey St Philadelphia PA 19106-4330 Office: Moss Rehab Hospital 1200 W Tabor Rd Philadelphia PA 19141-3099

MELVIN, NORMAN CECIL, lawyer; b. Balt., Aug. 21, 1916; s. Norman Cecil and Anna H. (Holzworth) M.; m. Louise A. Gillen, Feb. 10, 1945 (dec. Oct. 1958); children: Leigh G., Norman Cecil III; m. Virginia Brown Lester, Nov. 2, 1959; 1 dau., Susan A. A.B., Johns Hopkins U., 1939; LL.B., Harvard U., 1942. Bar: Md. 1942. Practice law Balt., 1946—; mem. firm Brown & Brune, 1946-52; gen. atty. Western Md. Ry. Co., 1952-66; gen. solicitor Western Md. Ry. Co., 1966-68, v.p., gen. counsel, 1968-75, dir., 1970-75; asst. peoples counsel Pub. Service Commn. Md., 1951-52; instr. U. Balt., 1957-66. Served to capt. AUS, 1942-46. Recipient Erskine M. Ross essay award ABA, 1950. Mem. ABA, Md. Bar Assn., Balt. Bar Assn., Soc. Colonial Wars (coun. 1966-69), SAR, Johns Hopkins Alumni Assn. (pres. 1968-70, Disting. Alumni award 1970, Heritage award 1980), Harvard Club, Johns Hopkins Club. Home: 4202 Wickford Rd Baltimore MD 21210-2930

MELVIN, RUSSELL JOHNSTON, magazine publishing consultant; b. New Castle, Pa., Nov. 16, 1925; s. Russell Conwell and Anna Katharine (Johnston) M.; m. Helen Margaret Connery, Aug. 6, 1949; children: Thomas Kirk, Meredith. B.A., U. Pa., 1949. Reporter Phila. Inquirer, 1949; copywriter, then asst. to circulation mgr. Time mag., 1949-53; with Newsweek mag., 1953-86, dir. Pacific edits., 1960-64, mng. dir. internat. edits., 1964-68, mng. editor internat. editorial service, 1969-86; cons. internat. affairs and profl. mem. Mag. Pubs. Am. (formerly Mag. Pubs. Assn.), N.Y.C. 1986—; v.p. Newsweek, Inc., 1965-85; founding editor The Journal, Tokyo, 1963; founding dir. Newsweek Feature Service, 1968; mem. UN Communications Adv. Coun. Served with USNR, 1942-46. Mem. Internat. Advt. Assn. (chmn., CEO 1980-85, exec. dir. Chgps. Corp. 1985-86, bd. dirs. 1988-91, mem. world coun. 1990), Internat. Fedn. Periodical Press (vice chmn., mem. exec. and mgmt. bd.), Univ. Club, Chappaqua Tennis Club. Episcopalian. Home: 153 Douglas Rd Chappaqua NY 10514-3104 Office: Mag Pubs Am 919 3rd Ave New York NY 10022-3903

MELVIN, T. STEPHEN, manufacturing company executive; b. Winter Haven, Fla., Mar. 12, 1938; s. Talmage Stephen and Doris Louise (Walker) M.; m. Beverly Sue Sauls. BIE with hons., U. Fla., 1960. Registered prof. engr., Fla. With Gen. Electric, various locations, 1960-70; v.p. mfg. Armor Elevator/A.O. Smith, Louisville, 1970-73; v.p. ops. Hamilton Std. div. United Technologies Corp., Windsor Locks, Conn., 1973-76; v.p., gen. mgr. Turbo Power & Marine/United Tech. Corp., Farmington, Conn., 1976-79; pres. Elliott Turbomachinery/United Tech. Corp., Jeannette, Pa., 1979-82; pres. eng. div. Pratt & Whitney div. United Techs. Corp., East Hartford, Conn., 1982-86; pres. aerospace div. AMCA Internat., Newington, Conn., 1986-87; pres. Smith & Wesson, Springfield, Mass., 1987-91; pres., chief exec. officer Datron, Inc., Windsor, Conn., 1992—. Mem. Suffield (Conn.) Country Club, Callawassie (S.C.) Country Club, Alpha Tau Omega. Republican. Episcopalian.

MELZACK, RONALD, psychology educator; b. Montreal, Que., Can., July 19, 1929; s. Joseph and Annie (Mandel) M.; m. Lucy Birch, Aug. 7, 1960; children: Lauren, Joel. BSc, McGill U., Montreal, 1950, MSc, 1951, PhD, 1954. Lectr. Univ. Coll., London, 1957-58; assoc. prof. MIT, 1959-63; lectr. psychology McGill U., $D, $D, $D, 1953-54, prof., 1963—, E.P. Taylor prof., 1986. Author: The Day Tuk Became a Hunter, and Other Eskimo Stories, 1967, Raven, Creator of the World, 1970, The Puzzle of Pain, 1973, Why the Man in the Moon is Happy, and Other Eskimo Creation Stories, 1977, (with P.D. Wall) The Challenge of Pain, 1982, 2nd edit., 1988, Pain Measurement and Assessment, 1983, (with P.D. Wall) Textbook of Pain,

1984, 3rd edit., 1994, (with D.C. Turk) Handbook of Pain Assessment, 1992. Recipient Molson prize Can. Coun., 1985, Gaston Labat award Am. Soc. Regional Anesthesia, 1989, J.J. Bonica award VI World Congress on Pain, 1990, Prix du Que. Marie-Victorin, 1994. Fellow APA, AAAS, Royal Soc. Can., Can. Psychol. Assn. (Disting. Contbns. to Psychol. Sci. award 1986, hon. pres. 1988-89); mem. Internat. Assn. Study of Pain (pres.). Home: 51 Banstead Rd, Montreal, PQ Canada H4X 1P1

MEMORY, JASPER DURHAM, academic administrator, physics educator; b. Raleigh, N.C., Dec. 10, 1936; s. Jasper Livingston and Margaret Moore (Durham) M.; m. Carolyn Hofler, June 4, 1961; children—Margaret Carolyn, Jasper William. B.S. summa cum laude, Wake Forest U., 1956; Ph.D., U. N.C., 1960. Successively asst. prof., assoc. prof. physics U. S.C., Columbia, 1960-64; assoc. prof. N.C. State U., Raleigh, 1964-67, assoc. dean, physics and math. scis., 1973-82, prof., 1967—, vice-provost, grad. dean, 1982-86; v.p. for research U. N.C. System, Chapel Hill, 1986—; bd. govs. Research Triangle Inst., Research Triangle Park, N.C., 1983-84, Triangle Area rsch. dir., 1981—; cons. NASA Langley, Hampton, Va., 1970-74, Ohio Bd. Regents, 1993-95, Ark. Bd. Regents, 1987; N.C. State U. rep. Oak Ridge Associated Univs., 1982-85, Grad. Record Exam. Bd., 1985-90, chair, 1989, Policy Coun., Test of English as a Fgn. Lang., 1987-88, chair, 1988. Author: Quantum Theory of Magnetic Resonance Parameters, 1968; (with others) NMR of Aromatic Compounds, 1982, High Resolution NMR in the Solid State: Fundamentals of CP/MAS, 1994. Recipient Outstanding Tchr. award N.C. State U., 1967, Disting. Alumni Service award Wake Forest U., 1981. Fellow Am. Phys. Soc.; mem. Am. Assn. Physics Tchrs., Phi Beta Kappa, Sigma Xi. Democrat. Presbyterian. Home: 124 Talon Dr Cary NC 27511 Office: Univ NC Gen Adminstrn Chapel Hill NC 27515-2688

MENAKER, RONALD HERBERT, banking executive; b. N.Y.C., Dec. 17, 1944; s. Harold L. Menaker and Gladys (Bleiberg) Ross; m. Kathleen Sager Thomas, Sept. 11, 1966; children: Meredith E., Kyri D. Student, Queen's Coll., 1965-66. Sr. v.p., head of corp. svcs. J.P. Morgan & Co., Inc., N.Y.C., 1966—; dir. J.P. Morgan Svcs., Wilmington, Del. Vice chmn., trustee N.Y. Downtown Hosp., N.Y.C., 1991—; pres. The Dog Mus., St. Louis, 1989—; trustee NYU Med. Ctr. Mem. Westminster Kennel Club (show chmn. 1990—). Avocations: fine arts, judging dogs. Office: JP Morgan & Co Inc 60 Wall St New York NY 10260

MENAKER, SHIRLEY ANN LASCH, psychology educator, academic administrator; b. Jersey City, July 22, 1935; d. Frederick Carl and Mary Elizabeth (Thrall) Lasch; m. Michael Menaker, June 4, 1955; children: Ellen Margaret, Nicholas. BA in English Lit., Swarthmore Coll., 1956; MA, Boston U., 1961, PhD in Clin. Psychology, 1965. Adminstrv. asst. N.J. State Fedn. Dist. Bds. Edn., Trenton, 1956-59; trainee clin. psychology Mass. Mental Health Ctr., Boston, 1960-61; intern clin. psychology Thom Guidance Clinic for Children, Boston, 1961-62; research assoc. ednl. psychology U. Tex.-Austin, 1964-67, asst. prof. ednl. psychology, 1967-70. assoc. prof., 1970-79, assoc. dean grad. sch., 1975-77, psychology cons. Research and Devel. Ctr. for Tchr. Edn., 1965-67, faculty investigator, 1967-74; assoc. prof. counseling psychology U. Oreg., Eugene, 1979-85, prof., 1985-87 , assoc. dean grad. sch., 1979-84, acting dean grad. sch., 1980-81, 82-83, dean grad sch., 1984-89, Silver Poet award, 1989, Editor's Choice faculty, U. Va., Charlottesville, 1987—. Bd. dirs. Nat. Grad. Record Exam. Bd. and Policy Council-Test of English as Fgn. Lang., Ednl. Testing Services, 1984-88. Contbr. articles to profl. jours. NIMH fellow, 1963-64. Office: U Va Adminstrn Madison Hall Charlottesville VA 22906-9014

MENARD, EDITH, English language educator, artist, poet, actress; b. Washington, Dec. 5, 1919; d. Willis Monroe and Edith Bercnenia (Gill) M. BS summa cum laude, Miner Tchrs. Coll., Washington, 1940; MA in English, Howard U., 1942; postgrad., NYU, 1944-46; MA in Teaching English, Columbia U., 1952; postgrad. in edn., George Washington U., 1966-79, 89-92, doctoral candidate, 1992—. Instr. English and speech Howard U., Washington, 1946-53; high sch. tchr. English D.C. Pub. Schs., Washington, 1953-73; chmn. dept. English Woodrow Wilson High Sch., Washington, 1972-73; adj. asst. prof. English fundamentals U. D.C., 1988-90; founder, dir. Miss Menard's Exclusive English Tutorial Svc., 1991—; substitute tchr. D.C. and Montgomery County (Md.) pub. schs. Contbr. articles and poetry to various publs., including At Day's End, 1994. Reader poetry to civic orgns.; vol. Washington Nat. Cathedral Assn., 1993—. Recipient Golden Poet award World of Poetry, 1988, Silver Poet award, 1989, Editor's Choice award The Nat. Libr. of Poetry, 1994; Julius Rosenwald fellow Yale U., 1943-44. Mem. Smithsonian Assocs. Episcopalian. Avocations: interior decorating and restoration, pub. speaking and politics, painting, writing. Home: Rittenhouse Apts 6101 16th St NW # 916 Washington DC 20011

MENARD, JOHN R., lumber company executive; b. 1940. With Menard Inc., Eau Claire, Wis., 1960—, pres., ceo. Office: Menard Inc 4777 Menard Dr Eau Claire WI 54703-9604*

MENASCO, WILLIAM WYATT, mathematics educator; b. Lancaster, Calif., Sept. 7, 1954; s. Lawrence Clifton and Dixie Lorene (Smith) M.; m. Melissa Ahn, Aug. 14, 1976; children: Timothy William, Ryan Wyatt. BA, UCLA, 1975; PhD, U. Calif., Berkeley, 1981. Hill asst. prof. Rutgers U., New Brunswick, N.J., 1981-84; asst. prof. math. U. Buffalo, 1984-91, assoc. prof., 1991-94, prof. math., 1994—. Contbr. articles to profl. jours. Am. Math. Soc. rsch. fellow, 1992-94; NSF rsch. grantee, 1983-87, 90-92, 92—. Mem. Am. Math. Soc. Avocations: fly fishing, clarinet playing. Office: U Buffalo Dept Math Diefendorf Hall Buffalo NY 14214

MENCER, GLENN EVERELL, federal judge; b. Smethport, Pa., May 18, 1925; s. Glenn Hezekiah and Ruth Leona (Rice) M.; m. Hannah Jane Freyer, June 24, 1950; children—Ruth Ann, Cora Jane, Glenn John. B.B.A., U. Mich., 1949, J.D., 1952. Bar: Pa. 1953, U.S. Dist. Ct. (we. dist.) Pa. 1953, U.S. Supreme Ct. 1958. Sole practice Eldred, Pa., 1953-64; dist. atty. McKean County, Pa., 1956-64; judge 48th Jud. Dist. Ct., Smethport, 1964-70, Commonwealth Ct. of Pa., Harrisburg, 1970-82, U.S. Dist. Ct., Erie, Pa., 1982—. Served with U.S. Army, 1943-45, ETO. Mem. Fed. Judges Assn., Pa. Bar Assn., McKean County Bar Assn. Republican. Methodist. Lodge: Masons (33 degree). Home: 30 W Willow St Smethport PA 16749-1524 Office: US Dist Ct Fed Courthouse PO Box 1820 Erie PA 16507-0820

MENCH, JOHN WILLIAM, retail store executive, electrical engineer; b. N.Y.C., Feb. 27, 1943; s. John William and Edna (Ilgen) M.; m. Rose Irene Miller, Aug. 12, 1962; 1 child, William Ilgen. BSEE, U. S.C., 1969; MBA, Ohio U., 1983; PhD, Calif. Coast U., 1994. Elec. engr. Uniroyal, Shelbyville, Tenn., 1969-74; facility engr. Kroger, Nashville, 1974-77; asst. mgr. facility engring. Kroger, Atlanta, 1977-79; Kroger mktg. area mgr. facility engring. Kroger, Columbus, Ohio, 1979-85; div. mgr. facility engring., v.p. Safeway Stores, Inc., Oakland, Calif., 1985-86; v.p. constrn., engring. Big V Supermarkets, Inc., Florida, N.Y., 1986—; pres. Mench & Assocs. Inc., 1994—. Author tech. manuals in field. Trustee Meth. Ch., 1987-93; bd. dirs. Goshen Day Care Ctr., 1988—; past v.p. Tri State V.W. Assn.; mem. exec. adv. bd. Ohio U. Coll. Bus. Adminstrn., 1992—; mem. bd. dirs. Elec. Distbn. Systems, 1993—. Mem. IEEE (sr.), Assn. Energy Engrs. (sr.) Republican. Methodist. Avocation: Volkswagens. Office: Big V 176 N Main St Florida NY 10921-1021

MENCHACA, PEGGY SUE BEARD, energy company executive; b. San Angelo, Tex., Mar. 25, 1938; d. Rufus Arch and Laura Enola (Davis) Beard; m. Elias Menchaca Jr., Feb. 7, 1957; children: Dana Menchaca Barber, Michael T., David R., Jay A. Cert. in ct. reporting/legal stenography, Alvin (Tex.) Community Coll., 1984; BA in Liberal Arts, Our Lady of the Lake U., 1993. Sec. to city mgr. and city atty. City of San Angelo, 1956-58; legal sec. Hardeman, Smith & Foy, San Angelo, 1959-65; with Enron Corp. (formerly HNG/InterNorth and Houston Nat. Gas Corp.), 1965—, successively exec. sec. to v.p. and gen. counsel, exec. sec. to sr. v.p. and gen. counsel, adminstrv. asst. to pres. and COO, adminstrv. asst. to chmn. and CEO, adminstr. corp. contbns., corp. sec., now v.p., sec.; bd. dirs. Houston Downtown Mgmt. Corp.; mem. Supreme Ct. Tex. Task Force on Gender Bias in Jud. Sys., 1991-94. Trustee Enron Found., bd. dirs., 1984—. Mem. Tex. Bar Assn. (legal assts. div.), Am. Soc. Corp. Secs. (v.p. Houston regional group 1989-90, pres. 1990-91), Inwood Forest Golf (Houston) Club. Avocation: skiing.

MENCHEL, DONALD, television executive; b. N.Y.C., Oct. 26, 1932; s. Abraham and Tessie (Green) M.; m. Barbara Winograd, Jan. 27, 1957; children: Pamela W., Terry G. B.A., Brandeis U., 1954. Film booker ABC Films, N.Y.C., 1956; with Telcom Assocs., N.Y.C., 1957-72; v.p. Telcom Assocs., 1961; exec. v.p. Telcom Assos., 1972; also dir.; dir. mktg. Time-Life TV, N.Y.C., 1972-75; v.p., dir. sales MCA TV, N.Y.C., 1975-77; exec. v.p. MCA TV, 1977-78, pres., 1978-89; pres. The Menchel Co., N.Y.C., 1989—. Trustee Brandeis U; bd. dirs. Literacy Vols. of N.Y.C. With U.S. Army, 1954-56. Mem. Internat. Radio and TV Soc.

MENCHER, BRUCE STEPHAN, judge; b. Washington, May 21, 1935; s. Emanuel and Bertha Miriam (Robbin) M.; m. Janet Patricia Whitfield, Nov. 24, 1974; children by previous marriage: Sean Robbin, Marc Nadzo. B.A., George Washington U., 1957, J.D. with honors, 1960. Bar: D.C. 1960. Gen. atty. Office Gen. Counsel, Dept. Agr., 1960-61; asst. corp. counsel for D.C., 1961-67; atty.-adviser Office Gen. Counsel, Bur. for Africa, AID, 1967-69; ptnr. Wilkes & Artis, Washington, 1969-75; assoc. judge Superior Ct. D.C., 1975-91; sr. judge, 1991—; presiding judge Family div. Superior Ct. D.C. 1988-90; professorial lectr. law George Washington U. Nat. Law Ctr., 1982-83; lectr. criminal justice Nat. Cathedral Sch./St. Albans Sch., 1985. Mem. gen. alumni gov. bd. George Washington U., 1972-80; life mem. Nat. Children's Center. Recipient Alumni Service award, 1975; recipient Judge of Yr. award Assn. Plaintiffs Trial Attys., 1983; Samuel Green award for disting. service to Washington legal community and Phi Delta Phi, 1985; Disting. Alumni Achievement award George Washington U., 1987. Mem. Am., D.C. bar assns., George Washington Law Assn. (exec. com. 1972-77), The Barristers (exec. com. 1981), Phi Delta Phi (pres. Barrister Inn 1974-75). Office: Superior Ct DC Rm 5520 500 Indiana Ave NW Washington DC 20001-2131 *While it may sound old-fashioned, I attribute my appointment to the bench, in large part, to hard work, dedication, a love of the law and respect for my fellow man. One should maintain his sense of balance, always try to understand the other person's position and, at all costs, maintain a sense of humor throughout.*

MENCHER, MELVIN, journalist, retired educator; b. Bklyn., Jan. 25, 1927; s. Peter and Theresa (Sherman) M.; m. Helen Chamberlain, Aug. 27, 1947; children: Thomas, Marianne, Nicholas. Student, U. N.Mex., 1943-44; B.A., U. Colo., 1947; postgrad. (Nieman fellow), Harvard, 1952-53. Reporter UP, 1947-50; state polit. corr. Albuquerque Jour., 1951-54; reporter Fresno (Calif.) Bee, 1954-58; asst. prof. journalism U. Kans., Lawrence, 1958-62; asst. prof. Columbia U., N.Y.C., 1962-65, assoc. prof., 1965-75, prof., 1975-90, assoc. dir. summer program for journalism edn. of minorities, 1971, prof. emeritus, 1990—. Contbg. author: Evaluating the Press, 1973; author: News Reporting and Writing, 1977, Basic Media Writing, 1983; editor: The FNMA Guide to Buying, Financing and Selling Your Home, 1973; contbr. articles to profl. jours. Mem. Soc. Profl. Journalists, Nat. Council Coll. Pubs. Advisers, Kappa Tau Alpha. Home: 450 Riverside Dr New York NY 10027-6821 Office: Grad Sch Journalism Columbia U New York NY 10027

MENCHER, STUART ALAN, sales and marketing executive; b. N.Y.C., Apr. 25, 1939; s. Meyer H. and Mildred B. (Finger) M.; m. Judith Leslie Schneider; children: Jane Lizabeth, Tracy Ellen. B in Mgmt. Engring., Rensselaer Poly. Inst., 1960; MBA, NYU, 1965. Sales rep. Sperry Rand Univac, Albany, N.Y., 1960-62; various sales and mktg. mgmt. positions IBM Corp., White Plains, N.Y., 1965-78; br. mgr. data processing div. IBM Corp., Harrison, N.Y., 1978-81; dr. mktg. ops. planning, bus. mktg. dept. AT&T, Basking Ridge, N.J., 1981-83; dir. market planning, sales and mktg. div. AT&T Info. Systems, Morristown, N.J., 1983; dir. data systems mktg. AT&T Info. Systems, Morristown, 1983-84, v.p. mktg., large bus. systems div., 1985-87; sr. v.p. sales and mktg. MCI Communications Corp., Washington, 1987-90; sr. v.p., gen. mgr. U.S. distbn. div. Motorola/Codex Corp., Mansfield, Mass., 1990-91; sr. v.p., gen. mgr. Teleport Communications, N.Y.C., 1992-93; sr. v.p. nat. sales and mktg., 1994—. Pres. Westfield Men's Coll. Scholarship Fund, N.J., 1977; coach Westfield Young Soccer Assn., 1976-81; mem. budget rev. com. United Fund, Westfield, 1983-85; mem. adv. bd. N.Y. Tech. Coll., 1993; mem. Mayor's Telecomms. Mutual Aid and Restoration Com. N.Y.C., 1992-93. Lt. USCGR, 1962-65. Avocations: golf, soccer coaching, sailing. Office: Teleport Communications Group 2 Teleport Dr Staten Island NY 10311-1004

MENCHIN, ROBERT STANLEY, marketing executive; b. Kingston, N.Y., Oct. 31, 1923; s. Abraham H. and Gertrude (Gorlin) M.; m. Marylin Barsky, Dec. 26, 1949; children: Jonathan, Scott. BA, NYU, 1948. Account exec. DKG Advt., N.Y.C., 1949-51; dir. spl. projects Am. Visuals Corp., N.Y.C., 1952-59; dir. advt. and pub. rels. Arthur Wiesenberger & Co., N.Y.C., 1959-65; pres. Wall St. Mktg. Communications, Inc., N.Y.C., 1967-77; dir. mktg. communications Chgo. Bd. Trade, 1977-83, v.p. communication and member rels., 1983-87; pres. Wall Street Mktg., Chgo., 1987—. With AUS, 1942-45. Mem. Am. Mktg. Assn., Pub. Rels. Soc. Am., Fin. Planners Assn. Author: The Last Caprice, 1964, Where There's a Will, 1977, The Mature Market: A Strategic Marketing Guide to America's Fastest-Growing Population Segment, 1989, New Work Opportunities for Older Americans, 1993. Home: Lake Point Tower 505 Lake Shore Dr Ste 1407-08 Chicago IL 60611

MENDE, ROBERT GRAHAM, retired engineering association executive; b. Newark, Dec. 4, 1926; s. Herman Ernest and Etta (Hillenbrand) M.; m. Joan B. Tamlyn, Apr. 12, 1958; children: Lisa Anne, Robert Graham Jr. Student, Mass. Inst. Tech.; BS, Webb Inst. Naval Architecture, 1951. Project engr. Foster Wheeler Corp., N.Y.C., 1953-56; dist. mgr., naval architect Bird-Johnson Co., N.Y.C., 1956-62; sr. naval architect J.J. Henry Co., Inc., N.Y.C., 1962-69; exec. dir. Soc. Naval Architects and Marine Engrs., 1969-91; mem. marine engring. coun. Underwriters Labs., Inc., 1969-91; ad hoc vis. com. Engrs. Coun. for Profl. Devel., 1970-72. Bd. dirs. Friends of World Maritime U., 1987-91; trustee Webb Inst. Naval Architecture, 1987-91. Lt. USNR, 1951-53. Fellow Royal Inst. Naval Architects, Soc. Naval Architects and Marine Engrs. (hon. life v.p., chmn. N.Y. sect. 1968-69, Vice Admiral E.S. Jerry Land medal 1991); mem. ASME, Am. Soc. Naval Engrs., Am. Soc. Assn. Execs., Coun. Engring. and Sci. Soc. Execs. (bd. dirs. 1988-91), Maritime Coll. Assn., N.E. Coast Inst. Engrs. and Shipbuilders, Webb Alumni Assn. (pres. 1970-72).

MENDEL, JERRY MARC, electrical engineering educator; b. N.Y.C., May 14, 1938; s. Alfred and Eleanor (Deutch) M.; m. Letty Susan Grossman, June 26, 1960; children: Jonathan, Aileen. BMechE cum laude, Poly. U., 1959, MEE, 1960, PhD in Elec. Engring., 1963. Registered profl. engr., Calif. Instr. elec. engring. Poly. Inst. Bklyn., 1960-63; engring. scientist and sect. chief McDonnell-Douglas Astronautics Co., Huntington Beach, Calif., 1963-74; prof. dept. elec. engring. systems U. So. Calif., L.A., 1974—, chmn. dept., 1991-94; dir. Signal and Image Processing Inst., L.A., 1991-94; pres., founder MENTECH, Culver City, Calif., 1983—; pres. United Signals and Systems, Inc., 1989—. Author: Discrete Techniques of Parameter Estimation: The Equation Error Formulation, 1973, Optimal Seismic Deconvolution: An Estimation Based Approach, 1983 (Phi Kappa Phi award 1985), Lessons in Digital Estimation Theory, 1987, Maximum-Likelihood Deconvolution, 1990, Lessons in Estimation Theory for Signal Processing Communications and Control, 1995; editor: Prelude to Neural Networks: Adaptive and Learning Systems, 1994; co-editor: Adaptive Learning and Pattern Recognition Systems, 1970. Fellow IEEE (centennial medal 1984); Disting. mem. IEEE Control Systems Soc. (pres. 1986). Office: U So Calif Dept Elec Engring Systems EEB 438 Los Angeles CA 90089-2564

MENDEL, MAURICE, audiologist, educator; b. Colorado Springs, Colo., Oct. 6, 1942; married; 3 children. BA, U. Colo., 1965; MS, Wash. U., 1967; PhD in Audiology, U. Wis., 1970. Asst. prof. audiology U. Iowa Hosp., 1970-74, assoc. rsch. scientist, 1975-76; assoc. prof. U. Calif., Santa Barbara, 1976-84, prof. audiology, 1984-88; chmn. dept. audiology and speech pathology Memphis State U., 1988-92; dean Sch. Audiology and Speech-Lang. Pathology U. Memphis, 1993—; program dir. speech and hearing sci. U. Calif., Santa Barbara, 1980-82. Fellow Am. Speech, Lang. and Hearing Assn., Soc. Ear Nose and Throat Advance in Children; mem. Am. Acad. Audiology, Internat. Elec. Response Audiology Study Group, Internat. Soc. Audiology, Tenn. Assn. Audiology and Speech-Lang. Pathologists, Sigma Xi. Achievements include research in middle components of the auditory evoked potentials and their subsequent clinical applications to hearing testing. Office: U Memphis CRISCI 807 Jefferson Ave Memphis TN 38105-5042

MENDEL, PERRY, day care company executive; b. Atlanta, Mar. 2, 1922; s. Max Lawrence and Esther (Kaufman) M.; m. Thelma Aronov, Oct. 13, 1946; children: Jake, Nan Valerie, Robin Leigh. Grad., Emory U., 1943. Pres. Quaker Supreme Chem. Corp., Montgomery, Ala., from 1951; pres. Kinder-Care Learning Ctrs. Inc., Montgomery, from 1969, chmn., chief exec. officer, until 1990; chmn., chief exec. officer Enstar Group Inc., 1990—. With USN, 1942-46. Jewish. Democrat. Office: Kinder-Care Inc PO Box 2151 2400 Presidents Dr Montgomery AL 36116-1616

MENDELEJIS, LEONARDO NIERMAN, artist; b. Mexico City, Nov. 1, 1932; s. Chanel and Clara (Mendelejis) N.; m. Esther Ptak, Feb. 16, 1957; children: Monica, Daniel, Claudia. BS in Physics and Math U. Mexico; degree in bus. adminstrn., U. Mex., 1959, degree in music, hon. degree, 1960. One-man shows, Proteo Gallery, 1958, 60, C.D.I. Gallery, 1956, Misrachi Gallery, 1964, Galeria Merkup, 1969, Mus. Modern Art, 1972, all Mexico City, Galeria Sudamericana, N.Y.C., 1958, Hammer Galleries, N.Y.C., 1960, I.F.A. Galleries, Washington, 1952, 62, 65, 68, 71, Edgardo Acosta Gallery, Beverly Hills, Calif., 1961, Art Collectors Gallery, Beverly Hills, 1966, Main St. Gallery, Chgo., 1961, Doll & Richard Gallery, Boston, 1963, Pucker Safrai Gallery, Boston, 1969, El Paso (Tex.) Mus Art, 1964, 71, Wolfard's Gallery, Rochester, N.Y., 1964, Pub. Library Rockville Centre, N.Y., 1964, Little Gallery, Phila., 1964, Neusteters Gallery Fine Arts, Denver, 1965, Judah L. Magnes Meml. Mus., Berkeley, Calif., 1967, Galerie Katia Granoff, Paris, 1969, Little Gallery, Phila., 1970, Aalwin Gallery, London, 1970, Gallery Modern Art, Scottsdale, Ariz., 1971, Mus. Contemporary Arts, Bogota, Colombia, 1973, 74, Galerie Dresdnere, Ont., Can., Casa de la Cultura, Cucuta, Colombia, 1974, also mus., galleries, Haifa, Israel, Rome, Italy, Toronto, Ont., Can., Paris, France, 1962—; exhibited group shows mus., Caracas, Venezuela, 1958, Mexico City, 1958—, Havana, Cuba, 1959, Tokyo, Japan, 1963, Paris, France, 1961, Nagoya, Japan, 1963, Kyoto, Japan, 1963, Osaka, Japan, 1963, Bogota, 1963, Santiago, Chile, 1963, Buenos Aires, Argentina, 1963, Rio de Janeiro, Brazil, 1963, Costa Rica, 1963, Panama, 1963, Oslo, Norway, 1965, Warsaw, Poland, 1965, Madrid, Spain, 1965, Stockholm, Sweden, 1966, Brussels, Belgium, 1966; also exhibitions at the Mus. Contemporary Art, Bogota, Colombia (diploma d'honneur of fine arts in Monaco), 1976, B. Lewin Galleries, Los Angeles, 1977, I.F. A. Galleries, Washington, 1977, Merrill Chase Galleries, Chgo., 1977, Am. Mus., Hayden Planetarium, N.Y.C., 1978, Cumberland Mus. of Sci. Ctr., Nashville, 1978, Fernback Sci. Ctr., Atlanta, 1978, Nahan Galleries, New Orleans, 1980, Broward Galleries, Pompano Beach, Fla., 1980, Mus. Sci. and Industry, Chgo., 1980, Galeria de Arte Misrachi, Mexico City, 1982, Calif. Mus. Sci. and Industry, 1982, Museo de Arte e Historia, Ciudad Juarez, Mexico, 1984, Centro de Artes Visuales e Investigaciones Esteticas, Mexico, 1984, Barbara Gillman Gallery, Miami, 1984, MIT Mus., Boston, 1984, Merrill Chase Galleries, Chgo., 1987, Museo de Arte Costarricense, Art Ctr. Galleries Hawaii Inc., 1988, Maison de L'Amerique Latine de Monaco, Monte Carlo, 1990, Centro Cultural San Angel, Mex.; also exhibited Expo, 1958, also numerous mus., univs., Eastern and Western U.S., Can., 1958—; executed murals, Sch. Commerce University City, Mexico, 1956, Bank San Francisco, 1965, physics bldg., Princeton, 1969; also executed stained glass windows, Mexican synagogues, 1968-69; executed tapestries Concert & Opera House, Salzburg, 1989, Majestic Theatre, San Antonio 1989, Theatre An Der Wein, Austria; prin. sculptures in including at Birmingham (Ala.) Mus. Art, Mexican Nat. U., Yeshiva U., N.Y., Hebrew U. Jerusalem, Sherman Bldg. Mount Scopus, City of Monterrey, Mex., Eleanor Roosevelt Inst., Denver, Wichita (Kans.) Airport; represented in permanent collections, Mus. Modern Art in Mexico, Atlanta Mus., Mus. Modern Art Haifa, Gallery Modern Art, N.Y.C., Phoenix Art Mus., Pan Am. Union, Washington, Detroit Inst. Arts, Bogota Mus. Contemporary Arts, Mus. Contemporary Arts, Madrid, Acad. Fine Arts, Honolulu, Tucson Art Center, Tel-Aviv Mus., Israel Mus., Jerusalem, Kennedy Art Center, Washington, Boston Mus. Fine Arts, U. Va., No. Ill. Univ., Chgo. Art Inst., New Orleans Mus. Art, other mus. and galleries. (Recipient 1st prize Mexican Contemporary Art, Art Inst. Mexico 1964, Palme d'or Beaux Arts, Monaco 1969, gold medal Tomasso Campanella Found. 1972). Patron Acad. St.rtin in the Fields, 1993—. Recipient Gold medal Internat. Parliament for Safety and Peace-U.S.A.-Italy, 1983; named Accademico D'Europe, Centro Studi di Ricerchi L'Accademia D'Europa, Italy; European Banner of Arts Prize, Italy, 1984, Oscar D'Italia, 1984; winner of world-wide competition to do a sculpture for U. Cen. Fla., Orlando, 1986. Life fellow Royal Soc. Arts (London, Eng.). Office: Reforma 16B San Angel, 01000 Mexico City 20, Mexico also: Str Reforma 16 Bis, Mexico City 20, Mexico also: Lublin Graphics 95 E Putnam Ave Greenwich CT 06830

MENDELL, OLIVER M., banking executive; b. N.Y.C., Apr. 4, 1925; s. M. Lester and Malvina Mendell; grad. Washington and Lee U., 1950; postgrad. Columbia U. Exec. Course, 1969; m. Shelley R. Disick, Sept. 24, 1962; children—Steven, David. Asst. treas. Bankers Trust Co., N.Y.C., 1950-56; v.p., dir. Queens Nat. Bank, N.Y.C., 1956-58; sr. v.p. Chem. Bank, N.Y.C., 1958—; dir. Cartier, Inc., 1967-69. Pres. Fifth Ave. Assn., 1978-82, chmn. 1982-87; trustee Washington and Lee U. Alumni, vice chmn. alumni fund campaign; bd. dirs. Citizens Budget Commn. N.Y., SSS, 1962-76, JFK Internat. Synagogue, Park 86th Apt. Corp., 1966-71, Joint Distbn. Com.; bd. govs. Sch. Banking and Money Mgmt., Adelphi U., 1975-82; gov. USO World Bd. Govs.; chmn. USO of Met. N.Y.; co-treas., bd. dirs. United Jewish Appeal Greater N.Y., Inc.; mem. adv. bd. Regional Emergency Med. Services Council of N.Y.C.; bd. dirs., mem. exec. com. Am. Jewish Com.; trustee Bernard J. Moncharsh Found., Inc., Temple Shaaray Tefila, 1971-74, Fedn. Jewish Philanthropies, B'nai Brith Banking Lodge; mem. com. legacies and bequests ARC; trustee NYU Real Estate Inst.; vice-chmn. steering com., treas. N.Y. Bus. Council for Clean Air, 1966-71; fellow Brandeis U. Served as navigator USAF, 1943-46. Recipient numerous civic awards. Mem. Assn. for Better N.Y. (mem. exec. com.), Phi Epsilon Pi (nat. budget com.), Omicron Delta Kappa. Clubs: Harmonie (N.Y.C.); Rockrimmon Country (Stamford, Conn.). Home: 1040 Park Ave New York NY 10028-1032 Office: Chem Bank 270 Park Ave New York NY 10017-2014

MENDELOVICI, EFRAIM ELIAHU, materials chemistry researcher; b. Botosani, Rumania, May 15, 1936; arrived in Venezuela, 1948; s. Heinic and Brana (Mates) Mendelovici; m., Nov. 1, 1968; 3 children. Licenciado in chemistry, Ctrl. U. Venezuela, Caracas, 1961; D in Agronomic Scis. with gran distinction, U. Louvain, Belgium, 1967. Prof. U. Los Andes, Merida, Venezuela, 1961-75; sr. investigator, lectr. Inst. Venezolano de Investigaciones Cientificas, Altos de Pipe, Venezuela, 1975—, chief materials physicochemistry lab., 1976—, head dept. materials sci., 1989—; vis. rschr., conferee Sidney and Beatrice Wolberg chair Israel Inst. Tech., Technion, Haifa, 1982-83; councillor at large Internat. Confedn. Thermal Analysis, Hatfield, Eng., 1992. Contbr. articles to sci. jours. Jewish. Avocations: music, bible study, jogging, swimming, chess. Office: IVIC, Apdo 21827, Caracas 1020A, Venezuela also: Bamco CCS 199-00 PO Box 025322 Miami FL 33102-5322

MENDELS, JOSEPH, psychiatrist, educator; b. Cape Town, Republic of South Africa, Oct. 29, 1937; came to U.S., 1964; s. Max and Lily (Tureski) M.; m. Ora Kark, Jan. 22, 1960; children: Gilla Avril, Charles Alan, David Ralph. MB, ChB, U. Cape Town, 1960; MD, U. Witwatersrand, Johannesburg, Republic of South Africa, 1965. Asst. prof., assoc. prof. psychiatry and pharmacology U. Pa., Phila., 1967-73; prof. U. Pa. and VA Hosp., Phila., 1973-80; med. dir. Fairmount Inst., Phila. 1980-81; prof. psychiatry and human behavior Thomas Jefferson Med. Ctr., 1985—; med. dir. Therapeutics, Inc.-Phila. Med. Inst., Phila. 1981-94; cons. NIMH, NIH, numerous pharm. cos., 1968—; lectr. to univs. and hosps. worldwide, 1968—. Author, editor: Concepts of Depression, 1971, Biological Psychiatry, 1973, Psychobiology of Affective Disorders, 1981; contbr. over 200 articles to med. jours. Fellow Internat. Coll. Neuropsychopharmacology; mem. Am. Psychiat. Assn. (Lester N. Hofheimer prize 1976). Office: 9 E Laurel Rd Stratford NJ 08080

MENDELSOHN, EVERETT IRWIN, science educator; b. Yonkers, N.Y., Oct. 28, 1931; s. Morris H. and May (Albert) M.; m. Mary B. Anderson, Sept. 14, 1974; children by previous marriage: Daniel Leeds, Sarah Ellicott, Joanna Moore; 1 stepson, Jesse Marshall Wallace. AB, Antioch Coll., 1953; postgrad., Marine Biol. Lab., Woods Hole, Mass., 1957; PhD, Harvard U.,

1960; DHL (hon.), R.I. Coll., 1977. Research assoc. sci. and pub. policy Grad. Sch. Pub. Adminstrn. Harvard U., 1960-65, assoc. prof. history of sci., 1965-69, prof. history of sci., 1969—, chmn. dept., 1971-78; overseas fellow Churchill Coll., U. Cambridge, Eng.; fellow Van Leer Jerusalem Inst., Israel, 1978; vis. fellow Zentrum für Interdizsciplinare Forschung, Bielefeld, W. Ger., 1978; fellow Wissenschafts Kolleg, Berlin, 1983-84; prof. invitée Conservatoire Nat. des Arts et Metiers, Paris, 1989, 90; dir. rsch. group on biomed. scis. Program on Tech. and Soc. Harvard U., 1966-68; mem. Soc. Fellows, 1957-60; Olaf Palme prof. U. Sweden, 1994. Author/editor: Heat and Life: The History of the Theory of Animal Heat, 1964, Human Aspects of Biomedical Innovation, 1971, Topics in the Philosophy of Biology, 1976, The Social Production of Scientific Knowledge, 1977, The Social Assessment of Science, 1978, Sciences and Cultures, 1981, A Compassionate Peace: A Future for the Middle East, 1982, 89, Transformation and Transition in the Sciences, 1984; Nineteen Eighty Four: Science Between Utopia and Dystopia, 1984, Science, Technology and the Military, 1988, Technology, Pessimism and Post-Modernism, 1993, Society as Biology, Biology as Society: Metaphors, 1994; editor: Jour. History Biology, 1967—; mem. editorial bd.: Sci, 1965-70, Social Studies of Sci, 1970-82, Ethics in Science and Medicine, 1973-80, Philosophy and Medicine, 1974-85, Sociology of Sciences, 1976—, Social Sci. and Medicine, 1981-92, Science in Context, 1986—, Social Epistemology, 1986—, Synthese, 1987—. Trustee Cambridge Friends Sch., The Sanctuary; bd. dirs. Inst. for Def. and Disarmament Studies; chmn. exec. com. Am. Friends Service Com. New Eng. regional office; mem. Commn. for Sci. and Cultural History of Mankind UNESCO; chmn. Harvard-Radcliffe Child Care Council.; mem. Cambridge Commn. for Nuclear Disarmament and Peace Edn.; pres. Inst. for Peace and Internat. Security. Fellow Swedish Collegium for Advanced Study in Social Scis., 1994; recipient Bowdoin prize, 1957. Fellow AAAS (v.p., chmn. sect. L, com. on arms control and nat. security), Am. Acad. Arts and Scis. (chmn. program Middle East Security Studies; mem. Academie Internat. d'Historie des Scis., History Sci. Soc. (council), Internat. Acad. History Medicine, Internat. Council Sci. Policy Studies (pres.), Am. Scandinavian Found. (fellowship com.). Home: 26 Walker St Cambridge MA 02138-2404*

MENDELSOHN, HAROLD, sociologist, educator; b. Jersey City, Oct. 30, 1923; s. Louis and Bessie (Yulinsky) M.; m. Irene Sylvia Gordon, Apr. 10, 1949; 1 dau., Susan Lynn. B.S., CCNY, 1945; M.A., Columbia U., 1946; Ph.D., New Sch. Social Research, 1956. Sr. survey analyst U.S. Dept. State, Washington, 1951-52; research assoc. Bur. Social Sci. Research, Am. U., Washington, 1952-56; assoc. mgr. mktg. communications McCann-Erickson Advt., N.Y.C., 1956-58; assoc. dir. Psychol. Corp., N.Y.C., 1958-62; prof. dept. mass communications U. Denver, 1962-89, prof. emeritus, 1989—, chmn., 1970-78, dean faculty social scis., 1984-86, spl. asst. to chancellor, 1986-88; Morton vis. disting. prof. Ohio U., spring 1981; cons. FTC, Denver Rsch. Inst., U.S. Consumer Product Safety Commn., The Gallup Orgn., Ford Found., Fedn. Rocky Mountain States, CBS, ABC, Children's TV Workshop. (Emmy award Nat. Acad. TV Arts Scis. 1968, Gold Camera award U.S. Indsl. Film Festival 1972); Author: Mass Entertainment, 1966, (with David H. Bayley) Minorities and the Police: Confrontation in America, 1969, (with Irving Crespi) Polls, Television and the New Politics, 1970, (with others) Television and Growing Up: The Impact of Televised Violence, 1972, (with Garrett O'Keefe) The People Choose a President, 1976; editor: Mass Communications series, 1967-69; contbr. articles to profl. jours. Mem. Denver Coun. Pub. TV, 1970-78; mem. U.S. Surgeon Gen.'s Sci. Adv. Com. on TV and Social Behavior, 1969-71; bd. dirs. Nat. Safety Coun., 1963-69; mem. pub. affairs adv. bd. Air Force Acad. Found., 1972-76; mem. cancer control and rehab. adv. com. Nat. Cancer Inst., 1976-81; mem. adv. coun., prevention dir. Nat. Inst. Alcoholism and Alcohol Abuse, 1977-82; trustee Colo. Med. Svc., Inc., 1973-78. Recipient award TV Bur. Advt., 1962, Nat. Life award Nat. Safety Council, 1967; Gold Eagle award, 1973; Silver award Internat. Festival Film and TV, 1974. Fellow Am. Psychol. Assn., Am. Sociol. Assn.; mem. Am. Assn. Pub. Opinion Research (pres. 1973-74), AAAS, N.Y. Acad. Scis., Sigma Delta Chi, Omicron Delta Kappa. Club: Chicago Press. Home: 1451 E Cornell Pl Englewood CO 80110-3013 Office: U Denver Dept Mass Communications Denver CO 80208

MENDELSOHN, JOHN, oncologist, hematologist, educator; b. Cin., Aug. 31, 1936; s. Joe and Sarah (Feibel) M.; m. Anne Charles, June 23, 1962; children: John Andrew, Jeffrey Charles, Eric Robert. BA, Harvard U., 1958, MD, 1963. Diplomate Am. Bd. Internal Medicine, Am. Bd. Hematology, Am. Bd. Med. Oncology. Intern, resident Peter Bent Brigham Hosp., Boston, 1963-65, 67-68; fellow in hematology Washington U. Sch. Medicine, St. Louis, 1968-70; asst. prof. to prof. medicine U. Calif., La Jolla, 1970-85, Am. Cancer Soc. prof. clin. oncology, 1982-85, dir. Cancer Ctr., 1977-85; prof. medicine Cornell U. Med. Coll., N.Y.C., 1985—; chmn. dept. medicine Meml. Sloan Kettering Cancer Ctr., N.Y.C., 1985—; mem. bd. sci. counselors, div. cancer treatment, Nat. Cancer Inst., 1986-90; bd. dirs. Am. Assn. Cancer Rsch.; cons. Hybritech, Genentech, Immunex, Bristol-Myers; founder, 1st dir. U. Calif. San Diego Cancer Ctr. Editor-in-chief: (textbook) The Molecular Basis of Cancer; mem. editorial bd. Jour. Immunology, Blood, Cancer Rsch., Jour. Clin. Oncology, Gworth Factors; editor-in-chief Clin. Cancer Rsch.; contbr. more than 100 articles in field of oncology to profl. jours. Mem. Gov.'s Cancer Adv. Coun., Calif., 1982-85; bd. dirs. Am. Cancer Soc., San Diego, 1981-85. Officer USPHS, 1965-67. Fulbright scholar U. Glasgow, Scotland, 1958-59; named Headliner of Yr. in Medicine, San Diego, 1985. Mem. Assn. Am. Physicians, Am. Soc. Clin. Investigation, Am. Soc. Clin. Oncology, Am. Assn. Cancer Rsch., Am. Soc. Hematology, Century Assn., Harvard Club N.Y., Phi Beta Kappa, Alpha Omega Alpha. Achievements include laboratory research establishing inhibition of tumor growth by antibodies against growth factor receptors. Avocations: tennis, music, history, hiking. Office: Meml Sloan-Kettering Cancer Ctr 1275 York Ave New York NY 10021-6007

MENDELSOHN, ROBERT VICTOR, insurance company executive; b. N.Y.C., July 18, 1946; s. Harold Victor and Mary Ellen (Muldoon) M.; A.B., Georgetown U., 1968; J.D., Harvard U., 1971; Bar: N.Y. 1971. Atty. firm Willkie Farr & Gallagher, N.Y.C., 1971-74; pres., dir. W.R. Berkley Corp., Greenwich, Conn., 1974-93; CEO Royal Group, Inc., Charlotte, N.C.; dir. Royal Ins., plc, London; dir. Am. Ins. Assn., Nat. Assn. Casualty & Surety Execs., 1994—. Trustee Jose Limon Dance Found., 1979—. Clubs: Innis Arden Golf, N.Y. Athletic, Riverside (Conn.) Yacht. Office: PO Box 1000 9300 Arrowpoint Blvd Charlotte NC 28201-1000

MENDELSOHN, WALTER, lawyer; b. N.Y.C., Jan. 22, 1897; s. Sigmund and Paula (Stieglitz) M.; m. Josephine Becker, Mar. 31, 1927; children—Sue (Mrs. Robert Mellins), Paul Richard. A.B., Yale U., 1918, LL.B., 1921. Bar: N.Y. bar 1921. Ptnr. Proskauer Rose Goetz & Mendelsohn and predecessors, N.Y.C., 1926—; Bd. dirs. 150 Central Park S. Corp. Mem. bd. Surprise Lake Camp, Welfare and Health Council; exec., adminstrv. coms. Am. Jewish Com., 1942—; bd. visitors State Tng. Sch. for Boys; chmn. trustees, chmn. bd., past pres. Jewish Bd. Guardians; trustee, past chmn. com. communal planning Fedn. Jewish Philanthropies; hon. trustee, past pres. Camp Ramapo; past trustee Inst. Internat. Edn.; trustee, pres. Henry Kaufmann Found., Edward de Rothschild Found. Served as pvt. U.S. Army, World War I; from maj. to lt. col. AUS, World War II; liaison officer SSS to under sec. war. Recipient Disting. Community Service award Brandeis U., Naomi and Howard Lehman Meml. award, Joseph M. Proskauer award, Horace Mann-Barnard Disting. Achievement award, Felix M. Warburg Meml. award. Mem. ABA, N.Y. State Bar Assn., Assn. Bar City N.Y., New York County Lawyers Assn., Am. Judicature Soc., Yale U. Law Sch. Assn. N.Y. (bd. dirs.), Yale Club, Harmonie Club. Home: 150 Central Park S New York NY 10019-1566 also: High Up Purdy's Station NY 10578 Office: Proskauer Rose Goetz & Mendelsohn 1585 Broadway New York NY 10036-8200

MENDELSON, ALAN CHARLES, lawyer; b. San Francisco, Mar. 27, 1948; s. Samuel Mendelson and Rita Rosalie (Spindel) Brown; children: Jonathan Daniel, David Gary; m. Agnés Marie Barbariol. BA with great distinction, U. Calif., Berkeley, 1969; JD cum laude, Harvard U., 1973. Bar: Calif. 1973. Assoc. Cooley, Godward et al., San Francisco, 1973-80; ptnr. Cooley, Godward, Castro, Huddleson & Tatum, Palo Alto, Calif., 1980-mng. ptnr. Cooley, Godward, Castro, Huddleson & Tatum Palo Alto, 1990-95; sec., acting gen. counsel Amgen Inc., Palo Alto, 1990-91; bd. dirs. Isis Pharms. Inc., CoCensys Inc., Senses Internat. Inc.; sec. Walker Interactive Sys., 1982—; Acuson, 1982-91, PetsMart, 1986—, Trans Ocean Ltd., 1988—, Arris Pharm. Corp., 1993—; mem. mgmt. com. Cooley, Godward,

Castro, Huddleson & Tatum, 1986—; chmn. Cos. Practice Group, 1990—. Chmn. Piedmont (Calif.) Civil Svc. Commn., 1978-80; den leader Boy Scouts Am., Menlo Park, Calif.; fundraiser Crystal Springs Upland Sch., Hillsborough, Calif., 1981—; coach Menlo Park Little League, 1982-86; pres., mem. exec. com., bd. dirs. No. Calif. chpt. Nat. Kidney Found., 1986—. With USAR, 1969-75. Recipient Disting. Svc. award Nat. Kidney Found., 1992; named U. Calif. Berkeley Alumni scholar, 1966, Scaife Found. scholar, 1966. Mem. Harvard U. Law Sch. Alumni Assn. (area rep. funds com. 1978—), Bohemian Club, Phi Beta Kappa. Jewish. Avocations: golf, tennis, softball, basketball, photography. Home: 1015 Continental Dr Menlo Park CA 94025-6651 Office: Cooley Godward Castro Huddleson & Tatum 5 Palo Alto Sq # 400 Palo Alto CA 94306-2122

MENDELSON, EDWARD JAMES, English literature educator; b. N.Y.C., Mar. 15, 1946; s. Ralph and Grace Bernice (Stein) M.; m. Cheryl Neel Noble, 1990; 1 child, James. B.A., U. Rochester, 1966; Ph.D., Johns Hopkins U., 1969. Instr. English Yale U., New Haven, 1969-70, asst. prof., 1970-76, assoc. prof., 1976-79; vis. assoc. prof. Columbia U., N.Y.C., 1979-80, assoc. prof. English, 1981-83, prof., 1983—; vis. assoc. prof. English Harvard U., Cambridge, Mass., 1977-78; lit. executor Estate of W.H. Auden. Author: Early Auden, 1981; editor: Homer to Brecht, 1977, Pynchon: A Collection of Critical Essays, 1978, The English Auden, 1978; editor: Complete Works of W.H. Auden, 1988—; contbg. editor PC Mag. Fellow Am. Council Learned Socs., 1974-75, NEH, 1980-81, Guggenheim Found., 1986-87. Mem. Acad. Lit. Studies, Societe Européene de Culture. Office: Columbia U Dept English 602 Philosophy Hall New York NY 10027

MENDELSON, ELLIOTT, mathematician, educator; b. N.Y.C., May 24, 1931; s. Joseph and Helen (Bienstock) M.; m. Arlene Zimmerman, Jan. 25, 1959; children—Julia, Hilary, Peter. A.B., Columbia U., 1952; M.A., Cornell U., 1954, Ph.D., 1955. Fellow U. Chgo., 1955-56; jr. fellow Soc. Fellows, Harvard U., 1956-58; Ritt instr. Columbia U., 1958-61; mem. faculty Queens Coll., CUNY, 1961—, prof. math., 1965—; dir., instr. NSF math. program for high sch. students, 1964-71; researcher axiomatic set theory and math. logic, especially ind. various important propositions of axiomatic set theory, axiom of choice, axiom of restriction. Author: Introduction to Mathematical Logic, 1964, Boolean Algebra and Switching Circuits, 1970, Number Systems, 1973, Beginning Calculus, 1985, 3000 Solved Problems in Calculus, 1988, Differential and Integral Calculus, 1990; contbr. articles to profl. jours. Mem. Am. Math. Soc., Math. Assn. Am., Assn. for Symbolic Logic, Phi Beta Kappa. Home: 10 Pinewood Rd Roslyn NY 11576-2420 Office: Queens Coll Flushing NY 11367

MENDELSON, HAIM, artist, educator, art gallery director; b. Siemiatycze, Bielsk, Poland, Oct. 15, 1923; s. David Cemach and Frieda (Konopiati) M.; m. Lita Joan Gordon, Mar. 30, 1955 (div. June 1966); children: Paul, Jan. Student, Am. Artists Sch., 1938-41, Saul Baizerman Sch. Art, 1940-43, Ednl. Alliance Art Sch., 1946. Tchr. Ednl. Alliance, N.Y.C., 1956-61; instr. CCNY, 1961-64; tchr. Columbia Grammar Sch., 1963-64, City and Country Sch., N.Y.C., 1964-91; dir. Hudson Guild Art Gallery, N.Y.C., 1971-94. One-man shows, Creative Galleries, N.Y.C., 1954, Caravan Gallery, N.Y.C., 1957, Chase Gallery, N.Y.C., 1960, Hudson Guild Art Gallery, N.Y.C., 1961, 76, 79, 82, 94, Yellow Poui Art Gallery, Grenada, W.I., 1973, 76, 79, 82, Ednl. Alliance, N.Y.C., 1976, Berkshire Artisans Gallery, Pittsfield, Mass., 1987, Hudson Guild, 1994; group shows include, Mus. Modern Art, N.Y.C., 1940-41, Pa. Acad. Fine Arts, 1965, Butler Inst. Am. Art, Ohio, 1965, 67, St. Paul Art Center, 1961, 66, NAD, N.Y.C., 1965, 68, 75, 77, 90, Bronx Mus. Arts, 1976, Prints U.S.A., 1982, Gallery Assn. N.Y. State, 1975-78; represented in permanent collections, N.Y. Public Library, Minn. Mus. Art, Edward Ulrich Mus., Wichita, Kans., St. Vincent Coll., Latrobe, Pa., Griffiths Art Center, Canton, N.Y., Manhattan Coll., Riverdale, N.Y., Flint (Mich.) Inst. Fine Arts; (portfolio drypoint engravings) Grass, 1963, The Artist and His Dead, 1975. Recipient numerous awards, prizes. Mem. Fedn. Modern Painters and Sculptors, Audubon Artists, Print Consortium, Am. Soc. Contemporary Artists. Home: 234 W 21st St # 63 New York NY 10011-3451 *Art is the avenue in which I express the significant experiences of my life. Out of feelings of expressive need, new forms and techniques spontaneously arise. The forms of the future are in life itself.*

MENDELSON, LEE M., film company executive, writer, producer, director; b. San Francisco, Mar. 24, 1933; s. Palmer C. and Jeanette D. (Wise) M.; m. Desiree Mendelson; children: Glenn, Linda, Jason, Sean. BA, Stanford U., 1954. With Sta. KPIX-TV, 1961-63; chmn. bd., pres. Lee Mendelson Film Prodns. Inc., Los Angeles and Burlingame, Calif., 1963—; guest instr. in communications Stanford U. Exec. producer, co-writer (miniseries) This Is America, Charlie Brown; producer: Charlie Brown, Cathy, Betty Boop, (TV spls.) John Steinbeck's Travels with Charley, American and Americans, The Fantastic Funnies, You Asked for It, Here Comes Garfield, (animated films) A Boy Named Charlie Brown, Snoopy Come Home, Race for Your Life Charlie Brown, Peanuts, Bon Voyage Charlie Brown (And Don't Come Back), Garfield and Friends, Mother Goose and Grim. Served to 1st lt. USAF, 1954-57. Recipient 7 Emmy awards, 3 Peabody awards. Mem. Writers Guild Am., Dirs. Guild Am. Office: 1440 Chapin Ave Ste 350 Burlingame CA 94010-4003

MENDELSON, LEWIS AARON, manufacturing company executive; b. Pitts., Apr. 11, 1935; s. Mendel M. and Florence G. (Goldfarb) M.; m. Catherine L. Anderson, Nov. 4, 1965; children: Matthew, Grant, Andrew. BBA, U. Pitts., 1956. Ptnr. Whitehead Plan, West Palm Beach, Fla., 1958-61, DeMarcellus, Knowlton, West Palm Beach, 1959-62; v.p. sales Pressure Pak, Inc., West Palm Beach, 1959-63, JetAir Corp., Dallas, 1964-65; exec. v.p., dir. Dazey Corp., Industrial Airport, Kans., 1966—, also bd. dirs. Republican. Avocations: walking, collecting antiques and western art. Office: Dazey Corp 1 Dazey Cir Industrial Airport KS 66031

MENDELSON, RALPH RICHARD, water heater manufacturing executive; b. Cleve., July 11, 1917; s. Louis Ralph and Ruth Margaret (Cohen) M.; m. Mary Adlaide Jones, Feb. 22, 1941 (div. 1982); children: Walton, Philip. BS in Mech. Engring., U. Mich., 1939; MA in Psychology, Cleve. State U., 1993. Staff Hotstream Heater Co., Cleve., 1941-48, v.p., 1948-59, pres., 1959-61; pres. Glass-Lined Water Heater Co., Lakewood, Ohio, 1961-82; cons. heating equipment design pvt. practice, Lakewood, 1882-87; lectr. psychology Cleve. State U., 1994—; instr. Cuyahoga C.C., 1986-93; leader-tchr. Case Western Reserve U., 1984-93—. Author: Solar Energy, 1978, Where Did I Put My Glasses? How You Can Improve Your Memory As You Grow Older, 1993; patentee water heater, infra-red heater. Bd. dirs. Urban League of Cleve., 1957-61, Merrick House, Cleve., 1972-86, pres. 1980-82; vis. com. Case Western Reserve U., 1972-80. Lt. USAAF, 1942-46. Mem. Assn. Energy Engrs., Oil Heat Inst. No. Ohio (bd. dirs. 1966-67, pres. 1969-70), Heights C. of C. (bd. dirs. 1953-60), Cleve. Play House. Democrat. Jewish. Home: 536 E 140th St Bratenahl OH 44108 Address: PO Box 10818 Cleveland OH 44110

MENDELSON, RICHARD DONALD, former communications company executive; b. N.Y.C., Dec. 2, 1933; s. George and Martha (Goodman) M.; m. Marilyn Miller, July 28, 1956; children: Sandra, Kenneth. BS, Wharton Sch. U. Pa., 1955; JD, NYU, 1959. Bar: N.Y., 1960; CPA, N.Y. Asst. atty. gen. N.Y. State Dept. Law, N.Y.C., 1959-70; v.p., treas. Petry TV, N.Y.C., 1971-75; v.p., dir. corp. devel. Katz Communications, Inc., N.Y.C., 1975-77, sr. v.p. ops., 1977-79, sr. v.p., chief fin. officer, 1979-81, v.p., chief operating officer, 1981-82, pres., chief oper. officer, 1982-89; free-lance writer, 1989—. Mem. Employee Stock Ownership Assn. Am. (pres. 1987-88, bd. dirs.). Home and office: 71 Saint George Pl Palm Bch Gdns FL 33418-4024

MENDELSON, ROBERT ALLEN, polymer scientist, rheologist; b. Cleve., 1930; s. Julius and Theodora Anne (Bloch) M.; m. Lura Lauzon, 1971; children: John A. Blackstone, Marie L. Taylor. BS in Indsl. Chemistry, Case Inst. Tech., 1952, PhD in Phys. Chemistry, 1956. From sr. rsch. chemist to sci. fellow rsch. dept. Monsanto Co., Texas City, Tex., 1956-71; sci. fellow Monsanto Co., Springfield, Mass., 1972-89, sr. sci. fellow, 1989-91; rheology focus area leader Baytown (Tex.) Polymers Ctr. Exxon Chem., 1991—; mem. com. for pub. policy Am. Inst. Physics, 1985-89; collaborator Univ. Rsch. Programs, Cornell U., 1989-91. Mem. editorial bd. Journal of Rheology, 1986—; contbr. articles to profl. jours.; patentee in field. Mem. Soc. Rheology (pres. 1989-91, v.p. 1987-89, sec. 1974-78), Am. Chem. Soc. (Arthur Doolittle award div. organic coatings and plastics 1982), Soc. Plas-

tics Engrs., AAAS. Home: 16503 Scenic Peaks Ct Houston TX 77059-5554 Office: Exxon Chem Co 5200 Bayway Dr Baytown Polymers Ctr Baytown TX 77522

MENDELSON, SOL, physical science educator, consultant; b. Checonovska, Poland, Oct. 10, 1926; came to U.S., 1927; s. David C. and Frieda (Cohen) M. BME, CCNY, 1955; MS, Columbia U., 1957, PhD, 1961. Prof. engring. CCNY, 1955-58; sr. scientist Sprague Electric Co., North Adams, Mass., 1962-64, Airborne Instruments Lab., Melville, N.Y., 1964-65; phys. metallurgist Bendix Rsch. Lab., Southfield, Mich., 1966-67; cons., rschr., writer, N.Y.C. and Troy, Mich., 1968-72; adj. prof. phys. sci. CUNY, 1972-87. Contbr. numerous articles to sci. jours. Mem. Am. Phys. Soc., Fedn. Am. Scientists, Sigma Xi, Tau Beta Pi, Pi Tau Sigma. Achievements include research on theory and mechanisms of Martensitic transformations. Home: 515 E 7th St Apt 5A Brooklyn NY 11218-4852

MENDENHALL, JOHN RYAN, retired lawyer, transportation executive; b. Des Moines, Jan. 17, 1928; s. Merritt Blake and Elizabeth M. (Ryan) M.; m. Joan Lois Schafer, June 23, 1950; children: Thomas, James, Jane, Julie, Robert, Jennifer. BS, U. Notre Dame, 1950; JD, Harvard U., 1953. Bar: Iowa 1953, U.S. Tax Ct. 1954, D.C. 1975, U.S. Ct. Claims 1975. Mem. tax staff Arthur Andersen & Co., Cleve., 1953-63, ptnr., 1963-66; dir. taxes Arthur Andersen & Co., Chgo., 1966-70; ptnr. Arthur Andersen & Co., Washington, 1970-74; Williams, Connolly & Califano, Washington, 1974-76; gen. tax counsel Union Pacific Corp., N.Y.C., 1977-80, v.p. taxes, 1980-93; bd. dirs. Empire Steel Castings, Reading, Pa. Co-author: Reforming the Tax Structure, 1973; contbr. articles on taxes to various jours. Bd. dirs. Cook County Hosp., Chgo., 1968-71, Inst. Rsch. on Econs. of Taxation, Washington, 1977-93, Burnside Plantation Inc., Bethlehem, Pa., 1989-93; trustee Convent of Sacred Heart, Greenwich, Conn., 1976-80; bd. govs. Bethlehem Area Found., 1989-93. With U.S. Army, 1946-47, Japan. Mem. ABA (tax sect., chmn. indexing com. 1985-86), Am. Coun. Capital Formation (bd. dirs. 1972-88), Bus. Roundtable (tax adv. group 1977-92), C. of C. (mem. tax com. 1972-92), Am. Law Inst. (tax adv. group 1974-88), Nat. Tax Assn. (pres. 1981-82), Nat. Chamber Found. (chmn. tax com. 1984-93), Chevy Chase (Md.) Club, Harvard Club (N.Y.C.), Met. Club (Washington), Belle Haven Club. Republican. Roman Catholic. Home: 47 Lafayette Pl Apt 6H Greenwich CT 06830

MENDENHALL, ONIEL CHARLES, retail executive; b. Seiling, Okla., Aug. 21, 1922; m. Trinidad Vasquez, Dec. 28, 1977; children: Oniel C. Jr., Janice L., Warren, Mark O. Student, Southwestern Okla. State. Mgr., owner Mendenhall Grocery, Seiling; owner several Red Bud Stores Alva and Enid, Okla. and Wichita; founder, owner, vice chair Fiesta Mart, Inc., Houston, 1971—; ethnic foods cons. FMI-AMI, Washington, 1985. Mem. Houston Ballet. Recipient Cmty. Leadership award Nat. Hispanic Inst. Houston, 1985. Mem. Food Mktg. Inst., Food Pac (pres. club, spl. recognition award 1984, 85), Produce Mktg. Assn., United Fresh Fruit and Vegetable Assn. (bd. dirs. 1993), Houston C. of C., Coll. Colleagues Fine Arts Mus. Republican. Methodist. Avocations: golf, seasonal hunting. Office: Fiesta Mart Inc PO Box 7481 5235 Katy Fwy Houston TX 77007-2210

MENDENHALL, ROBERT VERNON, mathematics educator; b. Geneva, Ind., Dec. 27, 1920; s. Carl and Lulu (Niswander) M.; m. Gay Dalrymple, Dec. 15, 1944; children—Lisa, Robin, Valerie. B.A. summa cum laude, Ohio State U., 1947, M.A., 1949, Ph.D., 1952. Instr. Ohio State U., 1951-53; sr. engr. N.Am. Aviation Corp., 1953-55; mathematician Vitro Labs., Inc., 1955; asst. prof. U. Miami, 1955-62; assoc. prof. Ohio Wesleyan U., 1962-66, prof. math., 1966-89, prof. emeritus, 1989—; cons. math Benares Hindu U., 1965, Andhra (India) U., 1966, U. Roorkee, India, 1970. Author: (with Herman Meyer) Techniques of Differentiation and Integration, 1966. Served with AUS, 1942-46, ETO. Mem. Am., Indian math. socs., Math. Assn. Am., Phi Beta Kappa, Sigma Xi. Home: 129 Oak Hill Ave Delaware OH 43015-2519

MENDEZ, ALBERT ORLANDO, industrialist, financier; b. Bogota, Colombia, Sept. 7, 1935; came to U.S., 1960; naturalized, 1968; s. Angelino Benjamin and Ana Isabel (Gutierre de Cetina) M.; children: Nicole C., Eric A. BS in Nuclear Physics, N.C. State U., 1961, MS in Nuclear Engring., 1963; MBA, U. Hartford, 1970. Physicist, mgr. mfg. Combustion Engring. Co., Windsor, Conn., 1963-67; mgr. corp. devel. and planning Gulf Oil Corp., Pitts., 1967-71; v.p. mktg., controller for Latin Am. Xerox Corp., Stamford, Conn., 1971-76; exec. v.p., chief operating officer, bd. dirs. Ogden Corp., N.Y.C., 1976-84; chmn., chief exec. officer, prin. shareholder Am. Indstl. Corp., Stamford, 1984—; chmn., chief exec. officer, prin. Argo-Tech Corp., Aerospace, Cleve., 1986-89; bd. dirs. Catalyst Energy Co., N.Y.C., 1st Prin. corp., N.Y.C., Demag, AG, Hamburg, Germany; gen. ptnr. Agnem Holdings Ltd. Partnership, New Canaan, Conn., 1984—; pres., chief exec. officer, bd. dirs., prin. shareholder Agnem Investment Co., New Canaan, 1983—; pres., chief exec. officer, prin. shareholder AM World Trade Corp., West Palm Beach, Fla. Contbr. articles to profl. jours. Mem. Internat. Platform Assn., Am. mgmt. Assn., Assn. of Corp. Dirs., The Conf. Bd., Am. Nuclear Soc., Palm Beach (Fla.) Polo Club. Office: 131 Pequot Ln New Canaan CT 06840-2023

MENDEZ-LONGORIA, MIGUEL ANGEL, law educator; b. 1942. AA, Tex. Southmost Coll., 1963; AB, George Washington U., 1965, JD, 1968. Bar: Tex. 1968, Calif. 1972. Law clk. U.S. Ct. Claims, D.C., 1968-69; legal asst. to Sen. Alan Cranston D.C., 1969-71; staff atty. Mexican-Am. Legal Def. Fund, San Francisco, 1971-72; dep. dir. Calif. Rural Legal Assistance, San Francisco, 1972-74; dep. pub. defender City of Monterey, Salinas, Calif., 1975-76; vis. prof. Santa Clara U., 1977; assoc. prof. Stanford (Calif.) U., 1977-84, prof., 1984—; vis. prof. U. Calif., Berkeley, 1982, U. Vt., 1986, U. San Diego, 1990-91; cons. Nat. Inst. Trial Advocacy; bd. dirs. Pub. Advs., Inc. Bd. Dirs. Latino Issues Forum. Mem. Order of the Coif. Office: Stanford Law Sch Nathan Abbott Way Stanford CA 94305

MENDIUS, PATRICIA DODD WINTER, editor, educator, writer; b. Davenport, Iowa, July 9, 1924; d. Otho Edward and Helen Rose (Dodd) Winter; m. John Richard Mendius, June 19, 1947; children: Richard, Catherine M. Graber, Louise, Karen M. Chooljian. BA cum laude, UCLA, 1946; MA cum laude, U. N.Mex., 1966. Cert. secondary edn. tchr., Calif., N.Mex. English teaching asst. UCLA, 1946-47; English tchr. Marlborough Sch. for Girls, L.A., 1947-50, Aztec (N.Mex.) High Sch., 1953-55, Farmington (N.Mex.) High Sch., 1955-63; chair English dept. Los Alamos (N.Mex.) High Sch., 1963-86; sr. technical writer, editor Los Alamos Nat. Lab., 1987—; adj. prof. English, U. N.Mex., Los Alamos, 1970-72, Albuquerque, 1982-85; English cons. S.W. Regional Coll. Bd., Austin, Tex., 1975—; writer, editor, cons. advanced placement English test devel. com. Nat. Coll. Bd., 1982-86, reader, 1982-86, project equality cons., 1985-88; book selection cons. Scholastic mag., 1980-82. Author: Preparing for the Advanced Placement English Exams, 1975; editor Los Alamos Arts Coun. bull., 1986-91. Chair Los Alamos Art in Pub. Pls. Bd., 1987-92; chair adv. bd. trustees U. N.Mex., Los Alamos, 1987-93; pres. Los Alamos Concert Assn., 1972-73; chair Los Alamos Mesa Pub. Libr. Bd., 1990-94. Mem. Soc. Tech. Communicators, AAUW (pres. 1961-63, state bd. dirs. 1993-94), DAR, Order of Ea. Star, Mortar Bd., Phi Beta Kappa (pres. Los Alamos chpt. 1969-72), Phi Kappa Phi, Delta Kappa Gamma, Gamma Phi Beta. Avocations: swimming, reading, hiking, astronomy, singing. Home: 124 Rover Blvd Los Alamos NM 87544-3634 Office: Los Alamos Nat Lab Diamond Dr Los Alamos NM 87544

MENDONSA, ARTHUR ADONEL, city official; b. Wauchula, Fla., Apr. 5, 1928; s. Arthur Abner and Mamie (Swafford) M.; m. Beverly Glover, Sept. 6, 1951; children—Arthur Adonel, George Andrew; m. Suzanne Danzig, Sept. 7, 1980. B.A., Emory U., 1952. M. City Planning, Ga. Inst. Tech. 1954. Planning dir. Gainesville-Hall County (Ga.) Planning Commn., 1954-56, 57-60; sr. planner Charleston (S.C.) County Planning Commn., 1956-57; exec. dir. Savannah-Chatham (Ga.) County Met. Planning Commn., 1960-62; city mgr. Savannah, 1962-67; 71—; dir. field svcs., asst. prof. Inst. Govt., U. Ga., Athens, 1967-69; exec. asst. to chmn. DeKalb County Bd. Commrs., Decatur, Ga., 1969-71; mem. Coastal Area Planning and Devel. Commn., 1972-90, chmn., 1983-85; mem. Ga. Gov.'s Adv. Council on Coastal Zone Mgmt., 1976-78, Ga. Coastal Mgmt. Bd., 1978-82. Author: Simplified Financial Management in Local Government, 1969. Recipient All-Pro City

Mgmt. Team City and State mags., 1986, 87, 88. Mem. Am. Inst. Planners (bd. examiners), Am. Soc. Pub. Adminstrn., Internat. City Mgrs. Assn. (Outstanding Mgmt. Innovator award 1979), Ga. City-County Mgrs. Assn. (pres. 1974-75), Kiwanis.

MENDOZA, GEORGE, poet, author; b. N.Y.C., June 2, 1934; s. George and Elizabeth Mendoza; m. Ruth Sekora, 1967; children: Ashley, Ryan. BA, State Maritime Coll., 1953; postgrad., Columbia U., 1954-56. Author over 100 books for children and adults published worldwide; many included in Boston U.'s George Mendoza Collection, established 1984; children's books on display at the Centre Nat. d'Art et de Culture Georges Pompidou. Works include: And Amedeo Asked, How Does One Become a Man?, (illustrated by Ati Forberg), 1959, The Puma and the Pearl, 1962, The Hawk Is Humming: A Novel, 1964, A Piece of String, Astor-Honor, 1965, Gwot! Horribly Funny Hairticklers (illustrated by Steven Kellog), 1967, The Crack in the Wall and Other Terribly Weird Tales (illustrated by Mercer Mayer), 1968, Flowers and Grasses and Weeds (illustrated by Joseph Low), 1968, The Practical Man (illustrated by Imero Gobbato), 1968, Hunting Sketches (illustrated by Ronald Stein), 1968, A Beastly Alphabet (illustrated by J. Low), 1969, The Digger Wasp (illustrated by Jean Zallinger), 1969, Herman's Hat (illustrated by Frank Bozzo), 1969, The Starfish Trilogy (illustrated by Ati Forberg), 1969, (compiler) The World From My Window: Poems and Drawings (children's writings), 1969, Are You My Friend? (illustrated by F. Bozzo), 1970, The Marcel Marceau Alphabet Book, 1970, The Thumbtown Toad (illustrated by Monika Beisner), 1970, The Inspector, 1970, The Good Luck Spider & other bad luck stories, 1970, The Fearsome Brat (illustrated by F. Bozzo), 1971, Fish in the Sky (illustrated by Milton Glaser), 1971, Moonfish and owl scratchings, 1971, Moonstring, 1971, The Hunter, the Tick and the Gumberoo, 1971, The Marcel Marceau Counting Book, 1971, The Scarecrow Clock (illustrated by Eric Carle), 1971, Big Frog, Little Pond, 1971, The Scribbler, 1971, The Christmas Tree Alphabet Book, 1971, Shadowplay, 1974, Lord, Suffer me to Catch a Fish, 1974, Fishing the Morning Lonely, 1974, (with Carol Burnett) What I Want to Be When I Grow Up, 1975, (with Zero Mostel) The Sesame Street Book of Opposites, 1975, Norman Rockwell's Americana ABC (illustrated by N. Rockwell), 1975, Doug Henning's Magic Book, 1975, Lost Pony, 1976, Norman Rockwell's Boys and Girls at Play, 1976, Secret Places of a Trout Fisherman, 1977, Norman Rockwell's Diary for a Young Girl (illustrated by N. Rockwell), 1978, Magic Tricks, 1978, Mon livre de magie (French edit. of My Book of Magic), Norman Rockwell's Scrapbook for a Young Boy (illustrated by N. Rockwell), 1979, (with Andres Segovia) Segovia, My Book of the Guitar, 1979, Need a House? Call Ms. Mouse! (illustrated by Doris Susan Smith), 1981, Alphabet Sheep (illustrated by K. Reidy), 1982, The Sheepish Book of Opposites, 1982, Silly Sheep and other sheepish rhymes, 1982, Norman Rockwell's Four Seasons, 1982, Norman Rockwell's Happy Holidays, 1983, Henri Mouse (illustrated by Joelle Boucher), 1985, Henri La Souris, 1987, Norman Rockwell's Patriotic Times, 1986, (with Ivan Lendl) Hitting Hot, 1986, (with Sam Snead) Slammin' Sam, 1986, Norman Rockwell's Love and Remembrance, 1986, Top Tennis, 1987, L'Album des Noeuds, 1988, Norman Rockwell's Old Fashioned American Cookbook, 1988, Hairticklers (illustrated by Gahan Wilson), 1989, The Hunter I Might Have Been, reprint 1989, Were You a Wild Duck, Where Would You Go? (illustrated by Jane Osborn-Smith), 1990, Traffic Jam (illustrated by David Stoltz), 1990; also author screenplays for Petals from a Poem Flower, You Show Me Yours and I'll Show You Mine and scripts for Sesame Street; numerous others; over 15 books of poetry including The Hunter I Might Have Been (Lewis Carroll Shelf award 1968), The Mist Men, Goodbye, River, Goodbye; also dozens of articles in The N.Y. Times, Herald Tribune, Stern, Vogue, Harper's Bazaar, Ms., Esquire, Town & Country, Sports Afield, Men's Journal, Philadelphia Inquirer; special travel corr. Toronto Globe & Mail, 1991-94. Cited by Pres. Reagan for Norman Rockwell's Patriotic Times. Avocation: trout and salmon fishing. Worldwide fishing expeditions recorded for TV spls. *I believe we are living in a world where people no longer see each other as individuals. We have become invisible. It is necessary to save our souls. Go out to a field and pick up a fallen leaf. Look at the veins that river the leaf. Follow them until nothing else matters except for the leaf in your hand. Then you will become visible. You will see others and others will see you.*

MENDYK, SANDRA L., English educator; b. Derby, Conn., Dec. 30, 1943; d. Andrew John and Michalina (Gagliardi) Mendyk. BS, So. Conn. State U., New Haven, 1983; MS in English, So. Conn. State U., 1991. Copy editor Valley Pub. Co., Derby, Conn.; tchr. 7th grade Saint Mary-Saint Michael Sch., Derby, head English Dept. with U.S. Army, 1976-80. Mem. Nat. Coun. Tchrs. English, Conn. Coun. Tchrs. English. Home: 33 Ells St Ansonia CT 06401-3010

MENEELEY, EDWARD STERLING, artist; b. Wilkes-Barre, Pa., Dec. 18, 1927; s. Edward Sterling and Louina Halter M. Student, Murray Art Sch., Wilkes-Barre, 1947-50, Sch. Visual Arts, N.Y.C., 1952-53. vis. lectr. Belleville Coll., St. Louis, Art Students League, N.Y.C.; lectr. Lehigh Valley Sch. System, 1987, Rogers College, Istanbul, Turkey, 1991; pres. ESM Documentations, N.Y.C.; fine arts cons. Arts Initiatives, Inc., N.Y.C.; founder Portable Gallery Press, 1957-67. One-man exhbs. include: Donovan Gallery, Phila., 1952, Parma Gallery, N.Y.C., 1962, Teuscher Gallery, N.Y.C., 1966, 68, Inst. Contemporary Arts, London, 1971, Victoria and Albert Mus., London, 1972, U. Sussex, Eng., 1972, Whitechapel Art Gallery, London, 1973, Demos Gallery, Athens, Greece, 1976, Frank Marino Gallery, N.Y.C., 1978, 79, 80, 81, 82, Sordoni Gallery, Wilkes (Pa.) Coll., 1981, Ericson Gallery, N.Y.C., 1980, Portfolio Gallery, Atlanta, 1983, Angela Flowers Gallery, London, 1985, J.T. Gallery, Jim Thorpe, Pa, 1987, 55 Mercer St., N.Y.C., 1987, Anita Shapolsky Gallery, N.Y.C., 1988, Bucknell U. Gallery Art, Lewisburg, 1988, Recent Painting & Sculpture, Coll. Misericordia, Dallas, Pa., 1989, Mixed Media, Craft Alliance Gallery, St. Louis, 1990, Provincetown (Mass.) Art Mus., 1993. Served with USNR, 1945-47, 50-52. Nat. Endowment Arts grantee; Pollock-Krasner Found. grantee, 1986, 90. Mem. Artist Club N.Y.C., Inst. Contemporary Arts London, Josiah White Soc., Weissport, Pa.

MENENDEZ, ADOFO, engineering company executive. Pres., COO K & M Engring. & Cons, Corp., Washington. Office: K & M Engring & Consulting Corp 2001 L St NW 500 Washington DC 20036*

MENENDEZ, CARLOS, financial executive, banker; b. Havana, Cuba, Apr. 16, 1938; s. Ramon and Rita (Leon) M.; m. Teresa Moran, Oct. 29, 1960; 1 child, Maria-Teresa. B.B.A., NYU, 1971. Asst. sec. Irving Trust Co., N.Y.C., 1970-72, asst. v.p., 1973-75, v.p., 1975-83; 2d v.p. Continental Bank, N.Y.C., 1972-73; sr. v.p., gen. mgr. Irving Trust Internat. Bank, Miami, Fla., 1983-87; sr. v.p. Latin Am. banking div. Irving Trust Co., 1987-88, Bank of N.Y., 1989-90; chief fin. officer Pacific Fruit Co., N.Y.C., 1990—; pres. Intercredit Bank, N.A., Miami, Fla., 1992—, Galo Worldwide Travel & Tours, N.Y.C., 1992—. Mem. Fla. Internat. Bankers Assn. (bd. dirs. 1985-87), Spain U.S. C. of C. (bd. dirs. 1985), Coun. of Ams. (corp. adv. bd. 1993—). Roman Catholic.

MENENDEZ, MANUEL, JR., judge; b. Tampa, Fla., Aug. 2, 1947; s. Manuel and Clara (Marin) M.; m. Linda Lee Stewart, Aug. 31, 1969; children: Jennifer Kay, Christine Marie. AA, U. Fla., 1967, BA, 1969, JD with Honors, 1972. Bar: Fla. 1972, U.S. Dist. Ct. (mid. dist.) Fla. 1973, U.S. Ct. Appeals (5th cir.) 1973, U.S. Ct. Claims 1974, U.S. Tax Ct. 1974, U.S. Ct. Customs and Patent Appeals 1974, U.S. Supreme Ct. 1976, U.S. Ct. Appeals (11th cir.) 1983, U.S. Ct. Appeals (D.C. cir.) 1984. Asst. U.S. atty. Dept. Justice, Jacksonville, Fla., 1973-77; chief asst. U.S. atty. Dept. Justice, Tampa, 1978-83; assoc. Law Office Jack Culp, Jacksonville, 1977-78; ptnr. Culp & Menendez, P.A., Jacksonville, 1978; county judge jud. br. State of Fla., Tampa, 1983-84, cir. judge jud. br., 1984—; dept. head, faculty mem. Fla. Coll. of Advanced Jud. Studies; faculty mem. pre-bench program Fla. New Judges Coll., 1993; faculty mem. Fla. Bar Prosecutor-Pub. Defender Advocacy Tng. Program, 1989-91, 94—. Exec. editor U. Fla. Law Rev., 1971-72. Mem. adv. bd. Salvation Army, 1988-91. Recipient Pub. Service Meritorious Achievement award West Tampa Civic Clubs Assn., 1983. Mem. ABA, Fla. Bar Bar Assn. (mem. criminal procedure rules com. 1988—, chmn., 1991—, mem. rules and jud. adminstrn. com., chmn., 1995-96), Fed. Bar Assn. (v.p. Jacksonville chpt. 1974-75, pres. Tampa Bay chpt. 1980-85), Hillsborough County Bar Assn. (media law com. 1984—, trial lawyers sect. 1985—), Liberty Bell award selection com. 1991-93, jud. evaluation com.

1993), Am. Judicature Soc., Am. Judges Assn., Am. Inns of Ct. (master of bench, pres. 1991—), U. Fla. Alumni Assn., U. Fla. Law Ctr. Assn., First U.S. Calvary Regiment Rough Riders Inc., Propellor Club, Tampa Gator Club. Avocations: fishing, golf, Univ. Fla. athletics, coaching little league sr. girls softball. Office: Hillsborough County Courthouse 419 N Pierce St Ste 370 Tampa FL 33602-4025

MENENDEZ, ROBERT, congressman, lawyer; b. N.Y.C., Jan. 1, 1954; s. Mario and Evangelina (Lopez) M.; m. Jane Jacobsen, June 5; children: Alicia, Robert. BA, St. Peter's Coll., 1976; JD, Rutgers U., 1979. Bar: N.J. 1980. Sole practice Union City, N.J., 1980-92; mem. 103d-104th Cngresses from 13th Dist. N.J., Dem. whip at large; mem. Congl. Arts Caucus. Mayor of Union City, 1986-92; sec. Union City Bd. Edn., 1978-82, trustee, 1974-78; pres. Alliance civic Orgn., 1982-92; mem. Gov.'s Hispanic Adv. Com., Trenton, N.J., 1984—; mem. Gov.'s Ethnic Adv. Com., Washington, 1985—. Recipient Cmty. Svc. award Gran Logia del Norte, 1981, Outstanding Svc. award Hispanic Law Enforcement, 1981, Outstanding Cmty. Svc. Revista Actualidades, 1982, Disting. Citizen award U. Medicine and Dentistry N.J., 1994, Man of Yr. award Kiwanis, 1994. Mem. N.J. Hispanic Elected and Apptd Ofcls. (chair), Hoboken Elks Club. Democrat. Roman Catholic. Avocations: chess, racquetball. Office: 1730 Longworth Bldg Washington DC 20515-3013 also: 911 Bergen Ave Jersey City NJ 07306

MENES, PAULINE H., state legislator; b. N.Y.C., July 16, 1924; d. Arthur B. and Hannah H. Herskowitz; m. Melvin Menes, Sept. 1, 1946; children: Sandra Jill Menes Ashe, Robin Joy Menes Elvord, Bambi Lynn Menes Gavin. BA in Bus. Econs. and Geography, Hunter Coll., N.Y.C., 1945. Economist Quartermaster Gen. Office, Washington, 1945-47; geographer Army Map Service, Washington, 1949-50; chief clk. Prince George's County Election Bd., Upper Marlboro, Md., 1963; substitute tchr. Prince George's County H.S.s, Md., 1965-66; mem. Md. Ho. of Dels., Annapolis, 1966—; mem. judiciary com., 1979—; mem. com. on rules and exec. nominations, 1979-94, 95—, chmn. spl. com. on drug and alcohol abuse, 1986—, chmn. Prince George's County del., 1993-95, parliamentarian, 1995—. Mem. Md. Arts Coun., Balt., 1968-95, Md. Commn. on Aging, Balt., 1975-95; bd. dirs. Prisoner's Aid Assn., Balt., 1971—. Recipient Internat. Task Force award Women's Yr., 1977; named to Hall of Fame Hunter Coll. Alumni Assn., 1986, Women's Hall of Fame Prince George County, 1989. Mem. NOW, Nat. Conf. State Legislators (com. on drugs and alcohol 1987), Md. NOW (Ann London Scott Meml. award for Legis. Excellence 1976), Nat. Order Women Legislators (pres. 1979-80), Women's Polit. Caucus, Bus. and Profl. Women, B'nai B'rith. Avocations: theater, music, dance show attending, stamp collector. Home: 3517 Marlbrough Way College Park MD 20740-3925 Office: Md Ho of Reps Rm 201 Lowe State Office Bldg Annapolis MD 21401

MENG, JIN, educator; b. Hangzhou, Zhejiang, China, Jan. 18, 1959; s. Guang-ging and Mei-fang (Lu) M. BA, Hangzhou U.; MS, Syracuse U. Tchr. Suichang High Sch., Zehjiang, China, 1983-85; lectr. Hangzhon U., Zehjiang, China, 1986-88; teaching asst. Syracuse U., N.Y., 1989-91, rsch. asst., 1990-91. Contbr. articles to profl. jours. Home: 430 Westcott St Syracuse NY 13210-2110 Office: Human Performance Lab 820 Comstock Ave Syracuse NY 13210-2810

MENG, JOHN C., food service executive; b. 1944. BA, Wabash Coll., 1966; MBA, Washington U., 1967. From supr. to plant mgr. Schreiber Foods, Green Bay, Wis., 1968-74, v.p., sec. treas., 1974-77, sr. v.p. fin., 1977-81, exec. v.p., 1981-85, pres., COO, 1985-89, CEO, 1989—. Office: Schreiber Food Inc 425 Pine St Green Bay WI 54301

MENGDEN, JOSEPH MICHAEL, investment banker; b. Houston, Sept. 28, 1924; s. Hippolyt Frederick and Amalia (Dittlinger) M.; m. Suzanne Miner, Sept. 30, 1950 (dec. July 1990); children: Anne Elise Mengden Giliberto, Amanda Mary, Michael Joseph, Charles Louis, Melissa Mary, Mary Miner Mengden Fitch; m. Dorothy Duggan, July 27, 1991. Ph.B., U. Notre Dame, 1949. V.p. Nat. Bank of Detroit, 1950-67; exec. v.p., dir. First of Mich. Capital Corp., Detroit, 1967-90, sr. cons., 1990—, chmn. bd., 1994—. Served to lt lt. USAAF, World War II. Decorated Air medal with 2 oak leaf clusters. Home: 321 Rivard Blvd Grosse Pointe MI 48230-1625 Office: 100 Renaissance Center 26th Fl Detroit MI 48243

MENGE, RICHARD CRAMER, electric utility executive; b. Ann Arbor, Mich., Aug. 28, 1935; s. Walter Otto and Elsie Belle (Cramer) M.; m. Mary Carolyn Poe, July 1, 1961; children: David, Peter, Karen. BA, U. Mich. 1957, MBA, 1961. Bus. trainee Am. Elec. Power Co., N.Y.C., 1961-63; personnel supr. Ind. Mich. Power Co., Lawrenceburg, Ind., 1963-65; with Ind. Mich. Power Co., Fort Wayne, Ind., 1965—, sr. v.p., 1988-89, pres., 1989—; also bd. dirs.; bd. dirs. Ind. Ky. Elec. Co., Madison, Ind., Am. Elec. Power Svc. Corp., Columbus, Ohio, Ft. Wayne Nat. Bank. Treas. Fort Wayne YMCA; chmn. Jr. Achievement of No. Ind., 1992-94; 1st lt. U.S. Army, 1957-59. Mem. Ind. Elec. Assn. (chmn. 1989), Ft. Wayne Downtown Assn. (pres. 1980), Greater Ft. Wayne C. of C. (chmn. 1994), Quest Club, Summit Club (v.p.) Rotary (pres. Ft. Wayne chpt. 1978). Lutheran. Home: 4415 Brixworth Ct Fort Wayne IN 46835-4609 Office: Ind Mich Power Co 110 E Wayne St Fort Wayne IN 46802-2604

MENGEDOTH, DONALD ROY, commercial banker; b. Naperville, Ill., Aug. 10, 1944; s. Orville Gustav and Bernice Lydia (Fries) M.; m. Stacy K. Halverson; children: Paul Bernard, Daniel Lawrence, Mary Bernice. BS, Marquette U., 1968, MBA, 1973. Ops. officer 1st Bank, N.A.-Milw., 1968-69, asst. v.p., 1969-71, v.p., 1971-73, sr. v.p., 1973-79; v.p. 1st Bank System, Inc., Mpls., 1979-82, sr. v.p., 1983-87; chmn., pres., chief exec. officer Community 1st Bankshares Inc., Fargo, N.D., 1987—; bd. dirs. Treasure Enterprises, Inc. Adv. bd. United Way Cass-Clay Campaign, Fargo, 1988-89; chmn. Cmty. 1st Polit. Action Com., Fargo, 1988-89; bd. dirs. Fargo Cath. Schs. Network Found., 1989-92; bd. dirs., vice-chmn. Red River Zool. Soc., 1993—; chmn. Diocesan God's Gift Appeals, Fargo, 1989. Mem. Am. Bankers Assn. (govt. rels. coun.), Am. Mgmt. Assn., N.D. Bankers Assn., S.D. Bankers Assn., Greater N.D. Assn., Fargo Country Club. Avocations: tennis, golf, hunting, reading. Office: Cmty 1st Bankshares 520 Main Ave Fargo ND 58124-0001

MENGEL, CHARLES EDMUND, physician, medical educator; b. Balt., Nov. 29, 1931; s. Charles LeRoy and Anna (Apgar) M.; m. Paula Padgett, June 5, 1978; children: Cheryl Lynn, Charles Edmund, Gregory John, Scott Alan, Carol Ann, Michael Daniel. A.B. in Chemistry, Lafayette Coll., 1953; M.D., Johns Hopkins U., 1957. Intern Johns Hopkins Hosp., 1957-58; resident Duke Hosp., 1958-59, 61-62; physician assoc. NIH, 1959-61; mem. faculty Duke U. Med. Sch., 1961-65; Doan prof., dir. hematology and oncology Ohio State U., 1965-69; prof. medicine U. Mo., Columbia, 1969-82; chmn. dept. U. Mo., 1969-81; pvt. practive gen. medicine Moberly, Mo., 1982-88; prof. medicine Kans. U. Med. Ctr., Kansas City, 1988—. Author textbook; contbr. articles to med. publs. Served with USPHS, 1959-61. Markle scholar acad. medicine, 1963. Mem. ACP, Am. Fedn. Clin. Research, Am. Soc. Hematology, Am. Soc. Clin. Investigation. Home: 3221 Meadow Rd Leavenworth KS 66048-4764 Office: VA Med Ctr Chief Med Ctr Leavenworth KS 66048

MENGEL, DAVID BRUCE, agronomy and soil science educator; b. East Chicago, Ind., May 1, 1948; s. Bill M. and Thelma Lee (Miller) M.; m. Susan Kay Haverstock, Aug. 30, 1968; children: David, Erin. BS in Agricultural Edn., Purdue U., 1970, MS in Agronomy, 1972; PhD in Soil Sci., N.C. State U., 1975. Cert. profl. agronomist, soil scientist. Asst. prof. agronomy La. State U., Crowley, 1975-79; asst. prof. agronomy Purdue U., West Lafayette, Ind., 1979-82, assoc. prof., 1982-86; prof. agronomy Purdue U., West Lafayette, 1986—. Mem. Am Soc. Agronomy, Soil Sci. Soc. Am., Internat. Soil Sci. Soc., Sigma Xi, Gamma Sigma Delta, Epsilon Sigma Phi, Delta Tau Delta. Avocations: fishing, woodworking. Office: Purdue U Dept Agronomy West Lafayette IN 47906

MENGEL, PHILIP RICHARD, investment banker; b. Memphis, Oct. 30, 1944; s. John P. and Marjorie Ann M.; m. Jayne E. Frutig, Dec. 20, 1980; 1 child, Jill Kathryn. AB, Princeton U., 1968; cert., Woodrow Wilson Sch. Pub. & Internat. Affairs, 1969. With Fiduciary Trust Co. N.Y., N.Y.C., 1968-77, mem. exec. com., 1973-77, v.p., 1970-77; pres., dir. Fiduciary Investment Corp., N.Y.C., 1973-77; founder, pres., dir. Mengel & Co., Inc.

(formerly Mengel, McCabe & Co., Inc.), N.Y.C., 1978—; chmn., pres. Mengel & Co., Inc., N.Y.C., 1983-90; pres., chief exec. officer Glen-Gery Corp., Wyomissing, Pa., 1990—, also bd. dirs.; bd. dirs. Brick Inst. Am., Ibstock Johnsen PLC (U.K.), 1993—; spkr. Practising Law Inst., various investment confs. Trustee St. Stephen's Sch, Rome, 1976-88, chmn. bd. 1978-82; co-chmn. Graham Windham Childcare Benefit, 1986-88. With USNR, 1962-64. Mem. Racquet and Tennis Club, U.S. Ct. Tennis Assn. (bd. dirs. 1993—), The Brook, Racquet Club of Phila., Tuxedo Club (gov. 1988—). Episcopalian. Office: 1166 Spring St Reading PA 19604-2238 also: 9 Three Kings Yard, London England

MENGELING, WILLIAM LLOYD, veterinarian, virologist, researcher; b. Elgin, Ill., Apr. 1, 1933; s. William Paul and Blanche Joyce (Wormwood) M.; m. Barbara Ann Kethcart, Aug. 23, 1958; children: Michelle, Michael. BS, Kans. State U., 1958, DVM, 1960; MS, Iowa State U., 1966, PhD, 1969. Diplomate M. Coll. Vet. Microbiologists (chmn. 1977-78, bd. dirs. 1975-77). Vet. clinician St. Francis Animal Hosp., Albuquerque, 1960-61; vet. med. officer Nat. Animal Disease Ctr., Ames, Iowa, 1961-69, rsch. leader, 1969—; rsch. leader U.S. Sr. Exec. Svc., 1991—; cons. numerous state, fed., pvt. U.S. and fgn. aggys.; collaborative prof., mem. grad. faculty Iowa State U. Co-editor: Diseases of Swine, 5th, 6th, 7th editions; contbr. articles to jours., chpts. to books. With U.S. Army, 1953-55. Recipient cert. appreciation USDA, 1978, George Fleming award Brit. Vet. Jour., 1978, Disting. Svc. award USDA, 1984, Gov.'s medal sci. State of Iowa, 1985, Vet. Med. Rsch. award Am. Feed Industry Assn., 1989, Leadership Merit awards USDA, 1989, 90, 91, 93. Mem. AVMA (Vet. Med. Rsch. award 1989), U.S. Animal Health Assn., Conf. Rsch. Workers in Animal Disease (pres. 1987-88, coun. 1981-86), Kiwanis (pres. 1975-76). Methodist. Avocations: wilderness survival, canoeing, camping, fishing. Address: 4220 Phoenix St Ames IA 50014-3922

MENGES, CARL BRAUN, investment banker; b. N.Y.C., Sept. 17, 1930; s. Hermann and Alice (Braun) M.; m. Cordelia Sykes, Apr. 24, 1965; children: James C., Benjamin W., Samuel G. B.A., Hamilton Coll., 1951; M.B.A., Harvard U., 1953. Salesman Owens Corning Fiberglas Corp., 1954-59, mktg. mgr., 1959-63; with instl. sales dept. Model Roland Co., N.Y.C., 1963-65; with instnl. sales dept., syndicate mgr., dir. internat. Donaldson, Lufkin & Jenrette Inc., 1965-77, mng. dir., 1972—, chmn. fin. services group, 1984-87, vice chmn. of bd., 1987—; chmn. bd. dirs. Winthrop Focus Funds, 1986—; bd. dirs. Med. Indemnity Assurance Corp., The Greenwall Found., G-Tech Corp. Trustee Hosp. for Spl. Surgery, 1977—, Hamilton Coll., Clinton, N.Y., trustee 1985—; v.p., treas., trustee The Allen-Stevenson Sch., N.Y.C., 1979-86, bd. dirs. Boys Club of N.Y. Mem. Union Club, Maidstone Club (gov. 1969-86, pres. 1982-86), Nat. Golf Links Am., Regency Whist Club, Colony Club, Leash Club, L.I. Wyandanch Club. Office: Donaldson Lufkin & Jenrette Securities Corp 140 Broadway New York NY 10005-1101

MENGES, CHRIS, cinematographer, film director; b. Kington, Eng., Sept. 15, 1940. Began career as cameraman with British TV, 1963. Cinematographer: Poor Cow, 1967, Gumshoe, 1970, Kes, 1970, Blackjack, 1979, Warlords of the 21st Century, 1982, Danny Boy Angel, 1983, Local Hero, 1983, Comfort and Joy, 1984, The Killing Fields (Academy Award, 1984), Marie, 1985, A Sense of Freedom, 1985, The Mission (Academy Award, 1986), 1986, Walter and June, 1986, Shy People, 1987, High Season, 1988, Singing the Blues in Red, 1988; film dir.: A World Apart, 1988 (Cannes Internat. Film Festival Grand Prize), Second Best, 1994. Office: United Talent Agy 9560 Wilshire Blvd Beverly Hills CA 90212-2427

MENGES, JOHN KENNETH, JR., lawyer; b. Louisville, Sept. 23, 1957; s. John Kenneth and Barbara Jean (Vick) M. BSBA, Boston U., 1979; JD, Harvard U., 1982. Bar: Tex. 1982. Assoc. Akin, Gump, Strauss, Hauer & Feld, Dallas, 1982-89, ptnr., 1989—. Pres. Dallas County Young Dems., 1985-88, Dallas Dem. Forum, 1990-91, bd. dirs. 1986-89; pres. sch. mgmt. Boston U., 1987—, bd. trustees, 1995—; bd. dirs. Save the Children Adv. Coun., Friends of Fair Park. Mem. ABA, Tex. State Bar Assn., Dallas Bus. League (pres. 1989), Dallas Coun. on World Affairs, Dallas Assn. Young Lawyers, Harvard U. Law Sch. Assn. Tex. (bd. dirs. 1984-87, 90-91, pres. 1993), Boston U. Nat. Alumni Coun. (Young Alumni award 1987). Democrat. Methodist. Avocation: basketball. Home: 3030 McKinney Ave # 401 Dallas TX 75204-2462 Office: Akin Gump Strauss Hauer & Feld 1700 Pacific Ave Ste 4100 Dallas TX 75201-4617

MENGUY, RENE, surgeon, educator; b. Prague, Czechoslovakia, Feb. 4, 1926; came to U.S., 1951, naturalized, 1957; s. Auguste and Beatrice (Adam) M.; m. Emilie Rigacci, Aug. 10, 1950; children—John, Ghislaine. B.A., U. Hanoi, Indochina, 1944; M.D., U. Paris, France, 1951; Ph.D., U. Minn., 1957. Fellow gen. surgery Mayo Clinic, 1952-57; mem. faculty U. Okla. Med. Sch., 1957-61, U. Ky. Med. Center, 1961-65; prof. surgery, chmn. dept. U. Chgo. Med. Sch., 1965-71; prof. surgery U. Rochester Med. Sch., 1971—; surgeon Genesee Hosp., 1971—; Mem. clin. research tomm. NIH, 1965-69; cons. VA, 1964—. Author: Peptic Ulcer, 1975; Mem. editorials bd. jours. in field.; Contbr. articles to profl. jours. Recipient citation French Expeditionary Corps, Hanoi, 1946; Fulbright travel grantee, 1951-52; recipient Alumni award meritorious research Mayo Found., 1956; John and Mary R. Markle scholar med. scis., 1958-63. Mem. A.C.S., Am. Fedn. Clin. Research, N.Y. Acad. Scis., Soc. Exptl. Biology and Medicine, Am. Assn. Cancer Research, Am. Gastroenterol. Assn., Soc. Univ. Surgeons, Soc. Surgery Alimentary Tract, Am. Physiol. Soc., Internat. Soc. Surgery, Surg. Biology Club, Soc. Clin. Surgery, Am. Surg. Assn., Acad. Chir. (Paris), Surg. Research Soc. So. Africa (corr.), Congrès Francais de Chirurgie (hon.), Sigma Xi. Home: 8 Highland Hts Rochester NY 14618-1116

MENINO, THOMAS M., mayor; b. Dec. 27, 1942; m. Angela Faletra; children: Susan, Thomas Michael, Jr. Degree in Community Planning, U. Mass., 1988; cert. in State and Local Govt. Program, Harvard U. Mem. City Coun., Boston, 1985—, pres., 1993; acting mayor Boston, 1993—; sr. rsch. asst. Joint Com. Urban Affairs, 1978-83. Contbr. articles to historic preservation jours. Regional chmn. Nat. Trust Historic Preservation; bd. dirs. Nat. League Cities, 1985—, mem. various coms. Office: Office of Mayor Boston City Hall 5th Fl Boston MA 02201*

MENIUS, ARTHUR CLAYTON, JR., former university dean; b. Salisbury, N.C., Apr. 30, 1916; s. Arthur Clayton and Maud Edna (Webb) M.; m. Lucille Clark Varner, Mar. 31, 1946; 1 son. Arthur Clayton III. A.B. in Physics and Math, Catawba Coll., 1937, D.Sc., 1969; Ph.D. in Physics, U. N.C., 1942. Sr. physicist Applied Physics Lab., Johns Hopkins, 1944-46, head battery group for proximity fuse project, 1945-46; prof. physics Clemson Coll., 1946-48; mem. faculty N.C. State U., Raleigh, 1949-81; prof. physics N.C. State U., 1949-55, head dept., 1956-60; dean N.C. State U. (Sch. Phys. and Math. Scis.), 1960-81; sec., v.p. Tharrington's Handcrafted 18th Century Furniture, Inc., 1984; cons. govt. agys. pvt. bus., 1950-81; chmn. Gov. N.C. Sci. Adv. Com., 1961-69, Atomic Energy Adv. Com. N.C., 1963-71; mem. N.C. Sci. and Tech. Bd.; N.C. State council rep. Oak Ridge Asso. Univs., 1963-69, mem. bd., 1969-76; edn. rep. So. Interstate Nuclear Bd. Author numerous monographs, articles profl. jours. Bd. govs. Research Triangle Inst. Fellow Am. Phys. Soc.; mem. N.C. Acad. Sci., Am. Inst. Physics, Sigma Xi, Phi Kappa Phi. Presbyn. Home: 541 Hertford St Raleigh NC 27609-6905

MENIUS, ESPIE FLYNN, JR., electrical engineer; b. New Bern, N.C., Mar. 5, 1923; s. Espie Flynn and Sudie Grey (Lyerly) M.; BEE, N.C. State U., 1947; MBA, U. SC., 1973; adopted children: James Benfield, Ruben Hughes, James Sechler, Steve Walden. With Carolina Power & Light Co., 1947-63, asst. to dist. mgr., Raleigh, Henderson, N.C., Sumter, S.C., 1947-50, elec. engr., Asheville, Southern Pines, Dunn, N.C., 1950-52, dist. engr. Hartsville, S.C., 1952-63; sr. elec. engr. Sonoco Products Co., Hartsville, 1963-74, engring. group leader, 1974-89, sr. profl. engr., 1989-91; profl. con. electrical engr., 1991—; instr. Florence-Darlington Tech. Ednl. Center. Mem. Hartsville Vol. Fire Dept., 1958—; Eagle Scout, Boy Scouts Am. 1938, scout troop leader New Bern, N.C., 1940-41, Raleigh, 1941-47, Henderson, 1948-49, Asheville, N.C., 1950, Southern Pines, N.C., 1951-52, Sumter, 1949-50, Hartsville, 1952-64; bd. mgrs. Nazareth Children's Home, Rockville, N.C., 1980—; chmn. bd. examiners City of Hartsville, 1980—; advocate Thornwell Children's Home, Clinton, S.C., 1990—; bd. dris. Darlington

(S.C.) County Youth Home, 1992—. Served with AUS, 1943-46. Recipient Silver Beaver award Boy Scouts Am., 1959, Citizenship award S.C. State Firemen's Assn., 1993; named Hartsville's Citizen of Year, Rotary, 1960. Registered profl. engr., N.C., S.C., Tenn., Ga., Fla. Mem. IEEE, AAAS, Nat. Assn. Engrs., Am. Legion, Knight of St. Patrick, Scabbard and Blade, Eta Kappa Nu, Pine Burr, Phi Eta Sigma, Theta Tau, Beta Gamma Sigma. Presbyn. (elder, tchr. men's Bible class). Club: Civitan (past dir.). Author articles in field. Home and Office: 423 W Richardson Cir Hartsville SC 29550-5437

MENK, CARL WILLIAM, executive search company executive; b. Newark, Oct. 19, 1921; s. Carl William and Catherine Regina (Murray) M.; m. Elizabeth Cullum, May 30, 1947; children: Carl, Elizabeth (dec.), Mary, Paul. BSBA, Seton Hall U., 1943; MA, Columbia U., 1950. Sr. v.p. P. Ballantine & Sons, Newark, 1946-69; pres. Boyden Assocs., Inc., N.Y.C. 1969-84; chmn. Canny, Bowen, Inc., N.Y.C., 1984—; dir. Howard Savs. Bank, 1980-91. 2d Lt., pilot USAAF, 1943-46. Mem. Union League N.Y., Spring Lake Golf Club, Bent Pine Golf Club, John's Island Club, Knights of Malta, Internat. Exec. Svc. Corps. Republican. Roman Catholic. Home: 950 Beach Rd Johns Island Vero Beach FL 32963 Office: Canny Bowen Inc 200 Park Ave New York NY 10166-4998

MENK, LOUIS WILSON, retired manufacturing company executive; b. Englewood, Colo., Apr. 8, 1918; s. Louis Albert and Daisy Deane (Frantz) M.; m. Mary Louise Menk; children: David Louis, Barbara Ann. Student, Denver U., 1937-38; grad., Advanced Mgmt. Program, Harvard U., 1953, Transp. Sch., Northwestern U., 1959; LL.D., Drury Coll., 1965, Denver U., 1966, Monmouth Coll., 1967. With U.P. R.R., 1936-40; with St. L.-S.F. R.R., 1940-65, telegrapher, 1940, chmn., pres., 1964-65; pres., dir. Burlington Lines, Chgo., 1965-66, No. Pacific R.R., St. Paul, 1966-70; pres. Burlington No. Inc., 1970-71, chmn., chief exec. officer, 1971-78, chmn. bd., 1978-81, also dir.; chmn., chief exec. officer Internat. Harvester, 1982, chmn., 1982-83; bd. dirs. Beverly Enterprises, Larimer Bank Corp.; chmn. bd. Black Mountain Gas Co. Presbyterian. Clubs: Desert Forest Golf (Carefree, Ariz.). Lodge: Masons. Home: 34815 N Arroyo Carefree AZ 85377 also: PO Box 1353 Carefree AZ 85377-1353

MENKE, ALLEN CARL, industrial corporation executive; b. Huntingburg, Ind., Feb. 16, 1922; s. William Ernest and Clara (Moenkhaus) M.; m. Virginia Lee MacDonald, Apr. 14, 1944; children: Janet, William, Sarah. B.S. in Mech. Engring, Purdue U., 1943, M.S., 1948. Instr. Purdue U., 1946-48; with Trane Co., 1948-68, v.p. sales, 1963-64, exec. v.p. sales, mfg. and engring., 1964-68; v.p. Borg-Warner Corp., Chgo., 1969-76; chmn., pres., chief exec. officer Artesian Industries, Northbrook, Ill., 1976-88. Pres. Met. Housing Devel. Corp.; founder, pres. Winnetka Interch. Coun.; bd. dirs., chmn. Presbyn. Home; past chmn. dean's adv. coun. Krannert Sch. Mgmt. Purdue U.; bd. dirs. McCormick Sem., U. Chgo.; active Kenilworth Union Ch. Served to 1st lt. AUS, 1944-46. Named Disting. Alumnus, Purdue U., 1965, Outstanding Engr. Grad., 1991, mem. Purdue Hall of Fame. Mem. Sigma Chi (Significant award). Presbyterian (elder). Lodge: Mason. Home: 1420 Tower Rd Winnetka IL 60093-1629

MENKELLO, FREDERICK VINCENT, computer scientist; b. Boston, Mar. 22, 1942; s. Albert Frederick and Angelina Marie (Tecci) M. BS, Boston U., 1964, MEd, 1965; PhD, Tex. A&M U., 1975. Commd. 2d lt. USAF, 1966, advanced through grades to lt. col.; scientist Environ. Tech. Applications Ctr., Washington, 1967-69; rsch. scientist NASA, Greenbelt, Md., 1969-70; sect. chief Global Weather Cen., Offutt AFB, Nebr., 1973-77; div. chief Mil. Airlift command, Scott AFB, Ill., 1978-82; br. chief Office Sec. Def., Washington, 1982-85; dir. Computer Acquisition Ctr., Hanscom AFB, Mass., 1985-86; ret., 1986; prin. engr. for R & D, Vitro Corp., Silver Spring, Md., 1986—. Mem. Assn. for Computing Machinery, Soc. for Indsl. and Applied Math., Phi Kappa Phi, Upsilon Pi Epsilon. Avocations: weightlifting, jogging, theater, reading. Office: Vitro Corp 45 W Gude Dr Rockville MD 20850

MENKEL-MEADOW, CARRIE JOAN, law educator; b. N.Y.C., Dec. 24, 1949; d. Gary and Margot (Sinn) M.; m. Robert Gary Meadow, Aug. 22, 1971. AB, Barnard Coll., 1971; JD, U. Pa., 1974. Bar: Pa. 1974, U.S. Dist. Ct. (ea. dist.) Pa. 1974, U.S. Ct. Appeals (3d cir.) 1976, Calif. 1979. Instr. law, dir. legal writing U. Pa., Phila., 1974-75, lectr., clin. supr., 1976-79; staff atty. Community Legal Svcs., Phila., 1977-79; prof. UCLA, 1979—; panel mem. Nat. Acad. Scis., Washington, 1986-87, Nat. Sci. Found., Washington, 1987—; cons. ABA, Chgo., 1979-84. Contbr. articles to profl. jours. Chairperson Ctr. for Study of Women UCLA; bd. dirs. Western Ctr. on Law and Poverty, L.A., 1980-86. Ctr. for Pub. Resources scholar, N.Y.C., 1984, 91; rsch. grantee NSF, 1980-83, Nat. Inst. for Dispute Resolution, Washington, 1984-86. Mem. Soc. Am. Law Tchrs. (trustee), Assn. Am. Law Schs. (alternative dispute resolution sect., law and social sci. sect., women in law sect., mem. accreditation com. 1987—), Ctr. for Law and Human Values (bd. dirs.), Law and Soc. Assn. (trustee), Phi Beta Kappa. Democrat. Avocations: dance, literature. Office: UCLA Sch Law 405 Hilgard Ave Los Angeles CA 90024-1301

MENKEN, ALAN, composer; b. 1950. Student, NYU. Composer, performer Lehman Engel Mus. Theatre Workshop at BMI; ptnr. with Howard Ashman. Composer: (theatre) Off-Broadway debut God Bless You, Mr. Rosewater, (with Howard Ashman) Little Shop of Horrors, Kicks, The Apprenticeship of Duddy Kravitz, Diamonds, Personals, Let Freedom Sing, Weird Romance, (films) Little Shop of Horrors, 1986 (Academy award nomination best original score 1986), The Little Mermaid, 1988 (Academy award best original score 1989, Academy award best original song 1989), Beauty and the Beast, 1990 (Academy award best original score 1991, Academy award best original score 1991), Newsies, 1992, Aladdin, 1992, (Academy award best original score 1993, Academy award best original song 1993, 3 Grammy awards 1994), Lincoln, 1992, Life With Mikey, 1993. Office: The Shukat Co 340 W 55th St/Ste 1A New York NY 10019

MENKEN, JANE AVA, demographer, educator; b. Phila., Nov. 29, 1939; d. Isaac Nathan and Rose Ida (Sarvetnick) Golubitsky; m. Matthew Menken, 1960 (div. 1985); children: Kenneth Lloyd, Kathryn Lee; m. Richard Jessor, Nov. 13, 1992. A.B., U. Pa., 1960; M.S., Harvard U., 1962; Ph.D., Princeton U., 1975. Asst. in biostats. Harvard U. Sch. Pub. Health, Boston, 1962-64; math. statistician NIMH, Bethesda, Md., 1964-66; research assoc. dept. biostats., Columbia U. N.Y.C., 1966-69; mem. research staff Office of Population Research Princeton U., N.J., 1969-71, 75-87, asst. dir., 1978-86, assoc. dir., 1986-87, prof. sociology, 1980-82, prof. sociology and pub. affairs, 1982-87; prof. sociology and demography U. Pa., Phila., 1987—; UPS Found. prof. social scis., 1987—; dir. Population Studies Ctr., 1989-95; mem. social scis. and population study sect., NIH, Bethesda, Md., 1978-82, chmn., 1980-82, population adv. com. Rockefeller Found., N.Y.C., 1981-93, com. on population and demography, NAS, Washington, 1978-83, com. on population, 1983-85, com. nat. stats., 1983-89, com. on AIDS research, 1987-94, cochair panel data and rsch. priorities for arresting AIDS in sub-Saharan Africa, 1994—, Commn. on Behavioral and Social Scis. and Edn., 1991-, sci. adv. com., Demographic and Health Surveys, Columbia, Md., 1985-90, Nat. Adv. Child Health and Human Devel. Council, 1988-91; cons. Internat. Centre for Diarrhoeal Disease Research, Bangladesh, Dhaka, 1984—. Author: (with Mindel C. Sheps) Mathematical Models of Conception and Birth, 1973; editor: (with Henri Leridon) Natural Fertility, 1979, (with Frank Furstenberg, Jr. and Richard Lincoln) Teenage Sexuality, Pregnancy and Childbearing, 1981, World Population and U.S. Policy: The Choices Ahead, 1986; contbr. articles to profl. jours. Bd. dirs. Alan Guttmacher Inst., N.Y.C., 1981-90, 93—. Nat. Merit scholar, 1957; John Simon Guggenheim Found. fellow, 1992-93, Ctr. for Advanced Study in Behavioral Scis. fellow, 1995-96. Fellow AAAS, Am. Statis. Assn.; mem. NAS, Am. Acad. Arts and Scis., Population Assn. am. (Mindel Sheps award 1982, pres. 1985), Am. Pub. Health Assn. (Mortimer Spiegelman award 1975, program devel. bd. 1984-87), Am. Sociol. Assn., Soc. for Study of Social Biology, Internat. Union for Sci. Study of Population (coun. 1989—), Sociol. Research Assn. (exec. com. 1991—). Office: U Pa Population Studies Ctr 3718 Locust Walk Philadelphia PA 19104-6298

MENKES, JOHN HANS, pediatric neurologist; b. Vienna, Austria, Dec. 20, 1928; came to U.S. 1940; s. Karl and Valerie (Tupler) M.; m. Miriam Trief, Apr. 14, 1957 (div. Feb. 1978); m. Joan Simon Feld, Sept. 28, 1980;

children: Simon, Tamara, Rafael C. AB, U. So. Calif., 1947, MS, 1951; MD, Johns Hopkins U., 1952. Diplomate Am. Bd. Pediatrics, Am. Bd. Neurology. Intern, jr. asst. resident Children's Med. Ctr., Boston, 1952-54; asst. resident pediatrics Bellevue Hosp., N.Y.C., 1956-57; resident neurology, trainee pediatric neurology Columbia-Presbyn. Med. Ctr., Neurological Inst. N.Y., N.Y.C., 1957-60; asst. prof. pediatrics Johns Hopkins U., Balt., 1960-63, assoc. prof., 1963-66, asst. prof. neurology, 1964-66, chief pediatric neurology div., 1964-66; prof. pediatrics and neurology UCLA, 1966-74, chief pediatric neurology div., 1966-70, prof. psychiatry, 1970-74; chief Neurology-Neurochem. Lab. Brentwood (Calif.) VA Hosp., 1970-74; clin. prof. psychiatry, neurology and pediatrics UCLA, 1974-77, clin. prof. pediatrics and neurology, 1977-84, prof. pediatrics and neurology, 1985-89, prof. emeritus pediatrics and neurology, 1989—; mem. metabolism study sect. NIH, 1966-70, project com. 1969-70; mem. adv. com. Nat. Inst. Child Health and Human Devel., 1985-87; mem. Coun. Child Neurology Soc., Dysautonomia Found., med. adv. bd. Nat. Orgn. Rare Diseases, Nat. Wilson's Disease Found.; trustee Dystonia Med. Rsch. Found., Vancouver, Can., 1985—. Author: Textbook of Child Neurology, 5th edit., 1995; (plays) The Last Inquisitor, 1985 (Drama-Logue Critics award 1985), The Salvation of Miguel Toruna, 1987; (screen plays) Miguel, Open Ward, 1989, The Countess of Sligo, 1992; contbr. numerous articles to pediatric and neurol. jours. Served with USAF, 1954-56. Mem. Am. Acad. Neurology, Am. Acad. Pediatrics, Am. Chem. Soc., Soc. for Pediatric Rsch., Sociedad Peruana de Neuro-Psychiatra (hon.), Am. Neurochem. Soc., Am. Neurol. Assn., Am. Pediatric Soc., Child Neurology Soc. (Hower award 1980), Dramatist Guild, PEN. Jewish. Home: 1201 Park Way Beverly Hills CA 90210-3334 Office: 9320 Wilshire Blvd Beverly Hills CA 90212-3216

MENKIN, CHRISTOPHER (KIT MENKIN), leasing company executive; b. Manhattan, N.Y., Jan. 1, 1942; s. Lawrence and Columbia (Riland) M.; children: Dashiel, Tascha, Ashley. Student, Julliard Sch. of Music, 1960, Santa Monica Coll., 1959-61, UCLA, 1961-64. News editor, dir. Sta. KRFC Radio, San Francisco, 1964-67; adminstrv. asst. to assemblyman Leo J. Ryan South San Francisco, 1967-68; mng. editor Sta. KGO TV News, San Francisco, 1968-69; news producer west coast Sta. ABC TV, Los Angeles, 1969; city mgr. City of San Bruno (Calif.), 1970; owner Menkin & Assocs., Santa Clara, Calif., 1971—; sr. ptnr. Am. Leasing, Santa Clara, 1971—; ptnr. Medallon Leasing, Santa Clara, 1974-80; pres. Monte Sereno Wine Co., Santa Clara, 1978—; dir. Meridian Nat. Bank, 1982-84. Chmn. nominating com. San Jose (Calif.) Symphony, 1988—; sec. Salvation Army, Santa Clara, 1968—, bd. dirs., 1990—, bd. dirs. San Jose chpt., 1990, vice chmn. county adv. bd., 1992; bd. dirs. Cmty. Against Substance Abuse, Los Gatos, Calif., 1988—, Valley Inst. of Theater Arts, Saratoga, Calif., 1987-88, San Jose Trolley, 1988—. Mem. UAEL (regional chmn. 1992-95, membership chmn. 1994—), Santa Clara Valley Wine Soc. (pres. 1988), Credit Profls. Santa Clara Valley (pres. 1990-91), Assn. Credit Grantors (past pres.), Credit Women Internat. (first male pres.), Santa Clara C. of C. (pres. 1973-76), Bay Area Exec. Club (sec.), Confrerie de la Chaine de Rotisseurs (charge de presse honaire), Royal Rose Soc. Gt. Britain (rep. No. Calif. 1990—). Democrat. Avocations: Rosarian, gardening, wine collecting, music, books. Office: Am Leasing 348 Mathew St Santa Clara CA 95050-3114

MENN, JULIUS JOEL, scientist; b. Danzig, Free City (now Poland), Feb. 20, 1929; came to U.S., 1950, naturalized, 1959; s. David Gregory and Regina (Ajzenstadt) M.; m. Alma R. Zito, Aug. 31, 1952 (div. 1981); children: Leslie, David (dec.), Diana (dec.); m. Dianne R. Sagner, Apr. 17, 1992. BS, U. Calif., Berkeley, 1953, MS, 1954, PhD, 1958. Dir. biochem. and insecticide rsch. Stauffer Chem. Co., Mountain View, Calif., 1957-79; dir. agrichem. research Zoecon Corp., Palo Alto, Calif., 1979-85; nat. program leader crop protection Agrl. Rsch. Svc., USDA, Beltsville, Md., 1985-88, assoc. dep. area dir. Beltsville Agrl. Rsch. Ctr., 1988-94, ret. 1994; chmn. Gordon Rsch. Conf., 1989; adj. prof. environ. toxicology San Jose State U., Calif., 1979-84; adj. prof. entomology U. Md., College Park, 1986—; mem. U.S./USSR Team on Environ. Pollution, 1974-85. Editor: Insect Juvenile Hormones, 1972, Insect Neuropeptides, 1991, 8 other tech. books; contbr. over 120 articles to profl. jours.; pioneered pesticide metabolism studies and research on selective insect control agents including juvenile hormones and neuropeptides; patentee in field. Recipient Bussart Meml. award Eastern Br. Entomol. Soc. Am., 1990, Ciba-Geigy Recognition award, Eastern Br. Entomol. Soc. Am. 1991, 92. Mem. Am. Chem. Soc. (fellow pesticide chem. div. 1973, chmn. 1976, councilor 1981-89, adv. bd. books dept. 1991-94, Burdick & Jackson Internat. award for rsch. in pesticide chem. 1979), Internat. Soc. Study Xenobiotics (councilor 1983-86), Cosmos Club (Washington).

MENNA, CHRISTINE ANN, public relations executive; b. Johnstown, Pa., Dec. 4, 1955; d. Joseph and Cecilia (Wojnaroski) Pisczek; m. Thomas Menna, Oct. 20, 1984; 1 child, Elizabeth. BA in Journalism, U. Pitts., 1977. Copywriter, account exec. Accent-Midstate Advt., Johnstown, Pa., 1977-85; mgr. corporate com. Crown Am. Realty Trust, Johnstown, 1985—; pub. rels. cons. Johnstown Chiefs, 1990—. Mem. adv. bd. Salvation Army, Johnstown, 1989—; bd. dirs. United Way, Johnstown, 1993—. Mem. Nat. Orgn. Underwater Instrs. (open water I diver), Internat. Coun. Shopping Ctrs. Avocations: sewing, ice skating, scuba diving. Office: Crown Am Realty Trust Pasquerilla Plz Johnstown PA 15901

MENNICKE, AUGUST THEODORE, church officer; b. Reeseville, Wis., July 4, 1931; s. Victor A.W. and Helen (Lau) M.; m. Joyce Scheidt, Aug. 21, 1954; children: Sheryll, Steven, David, Susan, Philip. Student, Concordia Coll., 1950; BA, St. Louis Concordia Sem., 1955; LittD (hon.), Concordia Coll., 1974; DD (hon.), Concordia Sem., 1974. Pastor St. John, Aitkin, Minn., 1955-62, Immanuel, Aitkin, Zion, Crosby, Minn., 1955-62, Prince of Peace, Ozark, Ala., 1962-63; exec. counselor Minn. North Dist., 1963-70, pres., 1970-86; 1st v.p. Luth. Ch.-Mo. Synod, St. Louis, 1986—. Author: My Devotions, 1978, Portals of Prayer, 1984, 90; contbr. essays and articles to jours.; mem. editl. com. for ofcl. publs., 1975-79. Mem. Coun. of Pres., 1970—, chmn., 1982-86; mem. steering com. Alive in Christ, 1984-86, Com. for Luth. Coop., 1986—; mem. bd. regents St. Louis and Ft. Wayne sems., 1986-92; bd. dirs. LSS of Minn., 1970-86; mem. steering com. Am. Bible Soc., 1994—. Office: 1333 S Kirkwood Rd Saint Louis MO 63122

MENNING, EDWARD LEE, veterinarian; b. Salem, Ohio, May 28, 1931; s. Edward Michael and Bernice Elaine (Althouse) M.; m. Carol Esther Patterson, Oct. 4, 1934; children: Karen Corinne, Michael Edward, Kimberly Ann. DVM, Ohio State U., 1955; MPH, U. Mich., 1965. Diplomate Am. Coll. Veterinary Preventive Medicine. Commd. USAF, 1955-80, advanced through grades to col., ret. 1980; career devel. officer USAF Surgeon Gen.'s Office, Washington, 1969-72; vet. staff officer USAF Surgeon Gen.'s Office, 1972-74; command veterinarian USAF Hdqr. Command, Andrews AFB, 1974-76; asst. surgeon gen. USAF Surgeon Gen.'s Office, Washington, 1976-80; exec. v.p. Nat. Assn. Fed. Veterinarians, Washington, 1980—; cons. in field; lectr. in field. Author: Environmental Sanitation, 1967, Cleaning and Sanitization of Food Contact Surfaces, 1984; co-editor: Yearbook of Agriculture Animal Health, 1984; contbr. articles to profl. jours. Recipient Disting. Service Medal, DOD, 1980, Disting. Alumnus, Ohio State U., 1980, others. Mem. Am. Vet. Med. Assn. (ho. of dels. 1976—), Conf. of Pub. Health Vets. (pres. 1975), Am. Pub. Health Assn. (governing council 1979), D.C. Vet. Med. Assn. (pres. 1986), Delta Omega. Methodist. Avocations: gardening, bridge, travel. Home: 3918 Keith Pl Annandale VA 22003-2546 Office: Nat Assn Fed Veterinarians 1023 15th St NW # 300 Washington DC 20005-2698

MENNINGER, EDWARD JOSEPH, public relations executive; b. N.Y.C., 1931; s. Edward Joseph and Pauline Loretta (Sessa) M.; m. Catherine Ann Giordano, Nov. 1, 1952 (div. 1978); children: Christopher, Catherine, Carl, Carolyn, Lisa; m. Ann Clementine Hunt, Jan. 5, 1979. B Social Sci. magna cum laude, Fordham U., 1952. Retail adv. sales promotion Sears, Roebuck and Co., N.Y.C., 1958-62; pub. rels. exec. Sears, Roebuck and Co., Chgo., N.Y.C., 1962-72; sr. buyer, buyer Sears, Roebuck and Co., N.Y.C., 1972-73; nat. mdse. mgr. Sears, Roebuck and Co., Chgo., N.Y.C., 1973-81; v.p., group mgr. Burson-Marsteller, N.Y.C., 1981-87, sr. v.p consumer retail mktg., 1987-92, mng. dir., 1992-93, exec. v.p., 1993—, also dir. employee devel. and tng. for N.Y.; lectr. in field. Contbr. articles to profl. jours. With M.I., U.S. Army, 1953-55. Mem. PRSA (accredited, edn. affairs commr. 1982-85, 87-88, v.p. Chgo. chpt. 1971-72, Chmn.'s Cert. of Recognition 1969, 73, 76, 84,

91, 92, Toth award Washington chpt. 1983, Silver Anvil award 1983, 89, 92, Big Apple award N.Y. chpt. 1991, 93, 94), Pub. Rels. Student Soc. Am. (profl. advisor 1983-84, Recognition award 1992), Am. Sch. Counselors Assn. (mem. bus. adv. bd. 1995). Office: Burson-Marsteller 230 Park Ave S New York NY 10003-1513

MENNINGER, ROY WRIGHT, medical foundation executive, psychiatrist; b. Topeka, Oct. 27, 1926; s. William Claire and Catharine (Wright) M.; m. Beverly Joan Miller, Mar. 4, 1973; children: Heather, Ariel, Bonar, Eric, Brent, Frederick, Elizabeth. AB, Swarthmore (Pa.) Coll., 1947; MD, Cornell U., 1951; DHL, Ottawa (Kans.) U., 1977; LittD, William Jewell Coll., Liberty Mo., 1985. Diplomate Am. Bd. Psychiatry and Neurology, 1959. Intern N.Y. Hosp., 1951-52; resident in psychiatry Boston State Hosp., 1952-53, Boston Psychopathic Hosp., 1953-56; from resident psychiatrist to assoc. med. psychiatrist Peter Bent Brigham Hosp., Boston, 1956-61; teaching and rsch. fellow Harvard U. Med. Sch., Boston, 1956-61; staff psychiatrist Menninger Found., Topeka, 1961-63, dir. dept. preventative psychiatry, 1963-67, pres., CEO, 1967-93; chmn., 1991—; bd. dirs. Bank IV Topeka N.A., CML Corp., The New Eng., U.S. Behavioral Health; mem. Karl Menninger Sch. Psychiatry, Topeka, 1972—, Ind. Sector, 1990—; clin. prof. psychiatry U. Kans. Med. Ctr., Wichita, 1977—; cons. Colmery-O'Neil VA Med. Ctr., Topeka, 1979—. Author: Trends in American Psychiatry: Implication for Psychiatry in Japan; co-author: The Medical Marriage, 1988, The Psychology of Postponement in the Medical Marriage; cons. editor Jour. Medical Aspects Human Sexuality, 1967-90; editor adv. bd. Parents mag., 1966-80, Clin. Psychiatry News, 1973—; reviewer Am. Jour. Psychiatry, 1980—. Mem. sponsoring com. Inst. Am. Democracy, 1967-70; mem. adv. group Horizons '76 Am. Revolution Bicentennial Commn.; adv. bd., steering com. Topeka Inst. Urban Affairs, 1967-70; adv. bd. Highland Park-Pierce Neighborhood House, Topeka, 1967-70; bd. dirs. Shawnee council Campfire Girls, Topeka, 1962-69, A.K. Rice Inst., Washington, Sex Info. and Edn. Council U.S., 1972-73, mem. edn. com., long range planning com., 1972-73; bd. dirs. Goals for Topeka, Topeka Inst. Urban Affairs, 1969-74, v.p., 1973; med. adv. com. VA Hosp., 1972-78; mem. Gov.'s Com. on Criminal Adminstrn., 1971-74; trustee People-to-People, Kansas City, Mo., 1967-69, Baker U., 1968-72, Midwest Research Inst., 1967-1986, 86—; mem. exec. com., 1970-86; vis. lectr. Fgn. Service Inst., State Dept., 1963-66; chmn. social issues com. Group Advancement Psychiatry, 1972-82; community adv. bd. Kans. Health Workers Union, 1968-70; adv. com. to bd. dirs. New Eng. Mut. Life Ins. Co., 1968-70. With U.S. Army, 1953-55. Recipient Disting. Svs. citation U. Kans., 1985; Pacific Rim Coll. Psychiatry fellow. Fellow Am. Psychiat. Assn. (life), Joint Info. Svc. (exec. com.), Am. Coll. Psychiatrists, Am. Orthopsychiat. Assn., Am. Coll. Mental Health Adminstrs.; mem. AAAS, Northeastern Group Psychotherapy (hon.), Physicians Social Responsibility, Kans. Psychiat. Soc., Greater Topeka C. of C. (dir.), Harvard Club (N.Y.C.). Episcopalian. Avocations: stamp collecting, chamber music, microcomputers. Office: Menninger Found PO Box 829 Topeka KS 66601-0829

MENNINGER, WILLIAM WALTER, psychiatrist; b. Topeka, Oct. 23, 1931; s. William Claire and Catharine Louisa (Wright) M.; m. Constance Arnold Libbey, June 15, 1953; children: Frederick Prince, John Alexander, Eliza Wright, Marian Stuart, William Libbey, David Henry. A.B., Stanford U., 1953; M.D., Cornell U., 1957; LittD (hon.), Middlebury Coll., 1982; DSc (hon.), Washburn U., 1982; LHD (hon.), Ottawa U., 1986; LLD (hon.), Heidelberg Coll., 1993. Diplomate Am. Bd. Psychiatry and Neurology, Am. Bd. Forensic Psychiatry. Intern Harvard Med. Service, Boston City Hosp., 1957-58; resident in psychiatry Menninger Sch. Psychiatry, 1958-61; chief med. officer, psychiatrist Fed. Reformatory, El Reno, Okla., 1961-63; assoc. psychiatrist Peace Corps, 1963-64; staff psychiatrist Menninger Found., Topeka, 1965—, coordinator for devel., 1967-69, dir. law and psychiatry, 1981-83, dir. dept. edn., dean Karl Menninger Sch. Psychiatry and Mental Health Scis., 1984-90, exec. v.p., chief of staff, 1984-93; pres., chief exec. officer Menninger Found., 1993—; clin. supr. Topeka State Hosp., 1969-70, sect. dir., 1970-72, asst. supt., clin., dir. residency tng. 1972-81; pres., chief exec. officer Menninger Clinic, Topeka, 1991—; staff Stormont-Vail Hosp., Topeka, 1984-94, assoc., 1994—; clin. prof. Kans. U. Med. Coll.; adj. prof. Washburn U., Wichita State U.; instr. Topeka Inst. for Psychoanalysis; mem. adv. bd. Nat. Inst. Corrections, 1975-88, chmn., 1980-84; cons. U.S. Bur. Prisons; mem. Fed. Prison Facilities Planning Council, 1970-73; bd. dirs. Mercantile Bank Topeka (formerly Mchts. Nat. Bank, Topeka). Syndicated columnist: In-Sights, 1975-83; author: Happiness Without Sex and Other Things Too Good to Miss, 1976, Caution: Living May Be Hazardous, 1978, Behavioral Science and the Secret Service, 1981, Chronic Mental Patient II, 1987; editor: Psychiatry Digest, 1971-74; mem. editorial bd. Bull. Menninger Clinic, 1985—; contbr. chpts. to books, articles to profl. jours. Mem. nat. health and safety com. Boy Scouts Am., 1970-92, chmn., 1980-85, mem. nat. exec. bd., 1980-90, mem. nat. adv. coun., 1990—; mem. Kans. Gov.'s Adv. Commn. on Mental Health, Mental Retardation and Community Mental Health Services, 1983-90; bd. dirs. Nat. Com. for Prevention Child Abuse, 1975-83; mem. nat. adv. health council HEW, 1967-71; mem. Nat. Commn. Causes and Prevention Violence, 1968-69, Kans. Gov.'s Penal Planning Coun., 1970; chmn. Kans. Gov.'s Criminal Justice Adv. Commn., 1991—, rsch. adv. com. U.S. Secret Svc., 1990—; trustee Kenworthy-Swift Found., 1980—; ruling elder 1st Presbyn. Ch., Topeka, 1992—. Served with USPHS, 1959-64. Fellow ACP, Am. Psychiat. Assn. (chmn. com. on chronically mentally ill 1984-86, chmn. Guttmacher award bd. 1990—), Am. Coll. Psychiatrists; mem. AAAS, AMA, Group for Advancement of Psychiatry (chmn. com. mental health svcs. 1974-77, 91—), Inst. Medicine NAS, Am. Psychoanalytic Assn. (chmn. com. on psychoanalysis, community and society 1984-93), Am. Acad. Psychiatry and Law, Stanford (Univ.) Assocs. Office: Menninger Found PO Box 829 Topeka KS 66601-0829*

MENNIS, EDMUND ADDI, investment management consultant; b. Allentown, Pa., Aug. 12, 1919; s. William Henry and Grace (Addi) M.; m. Selma Adinoff, Sept. 25, 1945; children: Ardith Grace, Daniel Liam. B.A., CCNY, 1941; M.A., Columbia U., 1946; Ph.D., NYU, 1961. Security analyst Eastman, Dillon & Co., N.Y.C., 1945-46; sr. research asst. Am. Inst. Econ. Research, Great Barrington, Mass., 1946-50; security analyst Wellington Mgmt. Co., Phila., 1950-61; dir. research Wellington Mgmt. Co., 1958-61, v.p., mem. investment com., 1958-66, economist, 1953-66; sr. v.p., chmn. trust investment com. Republic Nat. Bank, Dallas, 1966-72; sr. v.p., chmn. investment policy com. Security Pacific Nat. Bank, Los Angeles, 1973-81; pres., dir. Bunker Hill Income Securities, Inc., 1973-81; chmn. bd. Security Pacific Investment Mgrs., Inc., 1977-81; ind. cons. to investment mgmt. orgns., 1982—; Tech. cons. Bus. Council, Washington, 1962-66, 72-77, 79-81; econ. adviser sec. commerce, 1967-68; mem. investment adv. panel Pension Benefit Guaranty Corp., 1981-83. Assoc. editor: Financial Analysts Jour., 1960-88; editor: C.F.A. Digest, 1971-86, Bus. Econs., 1985—, Bank Funds Mgmt. Report, 1993—; author or editor books, chpts., numerous articles in field of econs. and investments. Trustee Fin. Analysts Research Found., 1981-86. Served to 1st lt. USAAF, 1942-45; to capt. USAF, 1951-53. Fellow Nat. Assn. Bus. Economists (coun. 1967-69), Fin. Analysts Fedn. (dir. 1970-72, Graham and Dodd award 1972, Molodovsky award 1972); mem. Am. Econ. Assn., Am. Fin. Assn., N.Y. Soc. Security Analysts, L.A. Soc. Fin. Analysts, Conf. Bus. Economists (vice chmn. 1977, chmn. 1978), Inst. Chartered Fin. Analysts (pres. 1970-72, trustee 1968-74, C. Stewart Sheppard award 1978). Home: 721 Paseo Del Mar Palos Verdes Estates CA 90274-1222 Office: PO Box 1146 Palos Verdes Estates CA 90274-6818

MENNUTI, MICHAEL THOMAS, medical educator; b. Trenton, N.J., Nov. 10, 1942; m. Nancy Lee Cleary, 1966; children: Jonathan Robert, Cara Elizabeth. BS, Georgetown U., 1964, MD, 1968. Diplomate Am. Bd. Ob-Gyn (dir. divsn. maternal-fetl medicine 1992-), Maternal Fetal Medicine, Clin. Genetics, Clin. Cytogenetics. Asst. instr. ob-gyn. Hosp. of U. Pa., Phila., 1969-73; clin. instr. ob-gyn. Wash. U. Sch. Med., Tacoma, 1974-75; asst. prof. ob-gyn. U. Pa. Sch. Medicine, Phila., 1975-81, asst. prof. human genetics, pediat., 1978-81, assoc. prof. ob-gyn. & human genetics, pediat., 1981-86, dir. residency tng., prof. ob-gyn. & human genetics, pediat., chmn. dept. ob-gyn., 1986—. Contbr. chpts. to books. Fellow Am. Coll. Ob-Gyn. (chmn., vice chmn., program chmn., sec. Dist. III 1978-94, chmn. Dist. III 1992—, chmn. com. ob practice 1994—), Coll. Physicians of Phila., Am. Gynecol. and Obstet. Soc.; mem. Am. Soc. Human Genetics, Am. Coll. Med. Genetics (founding), Alpha Omega Alpha. Office: U Pa Hosp Dept Ob-Gyn 3400 Spruce St Philadelphia PA 19104-4283

MENO, JOHN PETER, chorepiscopus; b. Carlinville, Ill., Aug. 22, 1942; s. John Victor and Margaret Mary (Cena) M.; m. Rolanda A. Abyad, Sept. 14, 1968; 1 child, Peter James. MA, Am. U. Beirut, 1969; STM, Union Theol. Sem., 1972. Ordained priest Syrian Orthodox Ch. of Antioch, 1972, elevated to chorepiscopus, 1983. Gen. sec. Archdiocese of Syrian Orthodox Ch. in U.S. and Can., Lodi, N.J., 1972—; cathedral rector St. Mark's Syrian Orthodox Cathedral, Teaneck, N.J., 1975—; co-sec. Standing Conf. of Oriental Orthodox Chs. in Am., N.Y.C., 1973—; co-chmn. U.S. Roman Cath.-Oriental Orthodox Cons., 1989—. Editor: Hymns of the Syrian Orthodox Church of Antioch, 1976. Recipient Golden Cross of the Archdiocese of the Syrian Orthodox Ch. in U.S., and Can., 1992. Home: 263 Elm Ave Teaneck NJ 07666 Office: Syrian Orthodox Archdiocese 49 Kipp Ave Lodi NJ 07644-2945

MENO, LIONEL R., state education official. Commr. edn. Tex. Edn Agy., Austin. Office: Tex Edn Agy 1701 N Congress Ave Austin TX 78701-1494

MENOHER, PAUL EDWIN, JR., army officer; b. West Palm Beach, Fla., July 20, 1939; s. Paul E. and Gladys (Maupin) M.; m. Kay I. Craddock; 1 child, Scott A.; m. Bebe Doris Etzler, Aug. 21, 1980. BA in Polit. Sci., U. Calif., Berkeley, 1961; MS in Internat. Rels., George Washington U., 1972. Commd. 2d lt. U.S. Army, 1961, advanced through grades to lt. gen.; student USN Coll. Command and Staff, Newport, R.I., 1971-72, U.S. Army War Coll., Carlisle, Pa., 1977-78; chief plans br. Hdqrs. U.S. Army Forces Command, Ft. McPherson, Ga., 1978-79, chief combat intelligence div. 1979-81; chief collection div. Hdqrs. U.S Army Europe, Heidelberg, Fed. Republic Germany, 1981-82; G2 VII Corps, Stuttgart, Fed. Republic Germany, 1982-84; comdr. 501st Mil. Intelligence Brigade, Seoul, Republic of Korea, 1984-86; dir. U.S. Army Intelligence and Electronic Warfare Master Plan, Washington, 1986-89; comdg. gen. U.S. Army Intelligence Agy., Washington, 1987-89, U.S. Army Intelligence Ctr., Ft. Huachuca, Ariz., 1989-93, U.S Army Intelligence and Security Command, Ft. Belvoir, Va., 1993-94; dep. chief of staff for intelligence Dept. Army, Washington, 1994—. Mem. Assn. U.S. Army, Armed Forces Comms. and Electronics Assn., Assn. Old Crows. Avocations: tennis, jogging. Office: Dept Army Hdqs The Pentagon Washington DC 20310

MENON, MANI, urological surgeon, educator; b Trichur, Kerala, India, July 9, 1948; came to U.S., 1972, naturalized 1977; s. Balakrishna and Sumathie Menon; m. Shameem Ara Begum, Oct. 17, 1972; children: Nisha, Roshen. MBBS, Madras U., India, 1971. Diplomate Am. Bd. Urology. Intern Bryn Mawr (Pa.) Hosp., 1973-74; resident Brady Urol. Inst., The Johns Hopkins Hosp., Balt., 1974-80; asst. prof. urology Washington U. Med. Ctr., St. Louis, 1980-83, assoc. prof., 1983; prof. urology, chmn. div. urology and transplant surgery U. Mass. Med. Ctr., Worcester, 1983—; prof. physiology, U. Mass. Med. Ctr., Worcester, 1986—. Mem. AAAS, Am. Assn. Genito Urinary Surgeons, Am. Urol. Assn. (Gold Cytoscope award 1990), Am. Fedn. Clin. Rsch., Am. Soc. Transplantation and Vascular Surgery, Rschrs. on Calculus Kinetics, Johns Hopkins Med. and Surg. Assn., Mass. Med. Soc., Mass. Soc. Med. Rsch. Avocations: tennis, puzzles, mystery fiction. Office: U Mass Med Ctr Div Urology Worcester MA 01655

MENON, PREMACHANDRAN RAMA, electrical engineering educator; b. Tapah, Perak, Malaysia, June 29, 1931; came to U.S., 1957; s. Rama and Bhargavi (Amma) M.; m. Mira Chuttani, Oct. 30, 1959;1 child, Ajay. BSc, Banaras Hindu U., Varanasi, India, 1954; PhD, U. Wash., 1962. Asst. prof. elect. engring. dept. U. Wash., Seattle, 1962-63; mem. tech. staff AT&T Bell Labs., Murray Hill, N.J., 1963-71, Naperville, Ill., 1971-86; prof. dept. elect. and computer engring. U. Mass., Amherst, 1986—. Co-author: Fault Detection in Digital Circuits, 1971; Theory and Design of Switching Circuits, 1976; author: (with others) Fault Tolerant Computing, 1986; contbr. articles to profl. jours. Recipient Disting. Tech. Staff award AT&T Bell Labs., 1982. Fellow IEEE (editor Trans. on Computer 1984-88, mem. program com. Internat. Test Conf. 1989-91, program com. VLSI test symposium 1992-95). Office: U Mass Elec & Computer Engring Amherst MA 01003

MENON, VIJAYA BHASKAR, recording and entertainment company executive; b. Trivandrum, India, May 29, 1934; s. Rama Krishna and Saraswathi M.; m. Sumitra Paniker, Jan. 21, 1972; children: Siddhartha Shankar, Vishnu Shankar. B.A. (hons.), U. Delhi, India, 1953; M.A., U. Oxford, Eng., 1956. Comml. mgr., mng. dir., chmn. A & R sales, mktg. and promotion divs. EMI Gramophone Co. of India, Ltd., 1957-70; mng. dir. EMI Internat. Services, Ltd., London, 1970-71; exec. v.p. Capitol Industries-EMI, Inc., Los Angeles, 1971, pres., chief exec. officer, 1971-87; chmn., chief exec. officer EMI Music Worldwide, 1978-90; chmn. bd. Capitol EMI-Music, Inc., 1987-90; dir. Internat. Cablecasting Techs., Inc., 1991—. Mem. Internat. Fedn. Phonographic Industry (pres. 1989-90, chmn. bd. 1990-91). Office: 9777 Wilshire Blvd Ste 904 Beverly Hills CA 90212-1902

MENOTTI, GIAN CARLO, composer; b. Cadegliano, Italy, July 7, 1911; came to U.S., 1928; s. Alfonso and Ines (Pellini) M. Grad. in composition, Curtis Inst. Music, 1933, Mus.B. (hon.), 1945. Tchr. Curtis Inst. Music, 1941-45. Writer chamber music, songs and operas; composer: (operas) Amelia al ballo, 1936, The Old Maid and the Thief, 1939, The Island God, 1942, The Medium, 1945 (Pulitzer Prize for music 1950), The Telephone, 1947, The Consul, 1949; Amahl and the Night Visitors, 1951, The Saint of Bleecker Street, 1954 (Pulitzer Prize for music 1955, Drama Critics' Circle Award 1955, New York Music Critics' Award 1955), Maria Golovin, 1958, The Last Savage, 1963, Labyrinth, 1963, Martin's Lie, 1964, Help, Help, the Globolinks, 1968, The Most Important Man, 1971, Arrival, 1973, Tamu-Tamu, 1973, The Egg, 1976, The Hero, 1976, The Trial of the Gypsy, 1978, Chip and His Dog, 1979, La loca, 1979, The Mad Woman, 1979, St. Teresa, 1982, A Bride from Pluto, 1982, The Boy Who Grew Too Fast, 1982, Goya, 1986, Giorino di Nozze, 1988; (symphonies/orchestral) Pastorale and Dance, 1934, (from Amelia al ballo) Prelude, 1937, (from The Old Maid and the Thief) Prelude, 1939, (from The Island God) Two Interludes, 1942, Piano Concert in F, 1945, Sebastian, 1945, Apocalypse, 1951, Introduction, March Shepherds' Dance, 1951, Violin Concerto, 1952, Triple Concerto a tre, 1970, Fantasia, 1975, Symphony No. 1: The Halcyon, 1976, Double Bass Concerto, 1983; (chamber/instrumental) Variations on a Theme of Schumann, 1931, Six Compositions, 1934, Four Pieces, 1936, Trio for a House-Warming Party, 1936, Poemetti per Maria Rosa, 1937, Ricercare e toccata, 1949, Suite, 1973, Cantilena scherzo, 1977; (vocal/choral) Baba's Aria, 1946, The Black Swan, 1946, Monica's Waltz, 1946, Lucy's Aria, 1947, Magda's Aria, 1950, Shepherd's Chorus, 1951, The Hero, 1952, The Death of the Bishop of Brindisi, 1963, Canti della lontananza, 1967, Landscapes and Remembrances, 1976, Missa o pulchritudo, 1979, Four Songs, 1981, Notturno, 1982, Muero porque no muero, 1982; (ballets) Sebastian, 1944, Errand in the Maze, 1947, The Unicorn, the Gorgon and the Manticore, or The Three Sundays of a Poet, 1956; writer own libretti.; Founder: Festival of Two Worlds, Spoleto, Italy, 1958; composer, artistic dir. Spoleto Festival USA, Charleston, S.C., 1988—. Recipient Guggenheim award, 1946, 47; Honary associate, Nat'l Inst. for Arts and Letters, 1953, Kennedy Ctr. award, 1984, N.Y.C. Mayor's Liberty award, 1986; George Peabody Medal, Johns Hopkins Univ., 1987; named Musician of Yr., Musical Am., 1991. Mem. ASCAP. Address: Yester House, Gifford East Lothian EH41 4JF, Scotland*

MENOYO, ERIC FELIX, lawyer; b. N.Y.C., May 9, 1944; s. Enrique and Frances (Villela) M.; m. Dierdre Caitlin Ryan, Aug. 12, 1967; children: Eric Edward, Sarah Micela. AB in English, Georgetown U., 1966, JD, 1969; LLM in Taxation, NYU, 1975. Bar: N.Y. 1969, Mass. 1976, U.S. Dist. Ct. (ea. dist.) Mass. 1976, U.S. Tax Ct. Appeals (1st cir.) 1976. Assoc. Barrett Smith Schapiro & Simon, N.Y.C., 1969-76; assoc. Palmer & Dodge, Boston, 1976-77, ptnr., 1978—; lectr. law Northeastern U., 1986-87, Mass. Continuing Legal Edn., Boston, 1978—. Trustee Nashoba-Brooks Sch. Concord (Mass.), Inc., 1984-90, 1st Parish Sudbury, 1979-82, Sudbury Valley Trustees, Inc., 1991—, pres., 1994—; mem. Pool Adv. Coun., Sudbury, Mass., 1987-89. Fellow Am. Coll. Trust and Estate Counsel; mem. ABA, Boston Bar Assn., Am. Law Inst., Larchmont Yacht Club. Unitarian. Avocations: sailing, hiking. Home: 388 Willis Rd Sudbury MA 01776-1332 Office: Palmer & Dodge 1 Beacon St Boston MA 02108-3106

MENSCER, DARRELL V., utility company executive; b. 1934. BS, N.C. State U., 1960. Sr. v.p. power supply Carolina Power and Light Co., 1973-80; with Pub. Service Co. of Ind., Plainfield, Ind., 1980—, now pres., chief operating officer. Served with USAF, 1952-56. Office: Pub Svc Co Ind Inc 1000 E Main St Plainfield IN 46168-1765

MENSCHEL, RICHARD LEE, investment banker; b. N.Y.C., Jan. 6, 1934; s. Benjamin and Helen (Goldsmith) M.; m. Ronay Arlt, Aug. 21, 1974; children: Charis, Sabina, Celene. B.S., Syracuse U., 1955; M.B.A., Harvard U., 1959. Assoc. securities sales adminstr. Goldman, Sachs & Co., N.Y.C. 1959-67; v.p. Goldman. Sachs & Co., N.Y.C., 1967-69; ptnr. securities sales Goldman, Sachs & Co., N.Y.C., 1969-88, mgmt. com., 1980-88, ltd. ptnr., 1988—. Co-chmn. City of N.Y. Transitional Gov. Search Panel, 1977; pres., bd. dirs. Joffrey Ballet Found., 1977-79; bd. dirs. Nat. Corp. Fund for Dance, 1977-79; trustee Fed. Protestant Welfare Agys., 1978-81; mng. dir. Horace W. Goldsmith Found., 1980—; bd. dirs. Mcpl. Art Soc., 1980-92; trustee, mem. exec. com. George Eastman House, Rochester, N.Y., 1980-94, Vera Inst. Justice, 1989—, Pierpont Morgan Libr., N.Y. Acad. Medicine; mem. vis. com. Harvard Grad. Sch. Bus. Adminstrn., 1985-91; dean's coun. Harvard Sch. Pub. Health, mem. com. on univ. resources; co-chair Harvard U. Campaign; trustee The Hastings Ctr., Nightingale Bamford Sch.; mem. adv. bd. Mus. Modern Art, Oxford, 1987—; co-chmn., trustee Hosp. for Spl. Surgery. 2d lt. USAF, 1955-56. Clubs: India House, Harvard. Home: 660 Park Ave New York NY 10021-5963 Office: Goldman Sachs & Co 85 Broad St New York NY 10004-2434

MENSCHEL, ROBERT BENJAMIN, investment banker; b. N.Y.C., July 2, 1929; s. Benjamin and Helen (Goldsmith) M.; m. Joyce Virginia Frank, Dec. 5, 1968; children: David F., Lauren E. BS, Syracuse U., 1951, LLD (hon.), 1991; postgrad., NYU, 1951-53. Mem. N.Y. Stock Exchange, N.Y.C., 1950-51; specialist HW Goldsmith and Co., N.Y.C., 1951-54; with Goldman, Sachs & Co., N.Y.C., 1954-66, gen. ptnr. instl. sales, 1966-78, ltd. ptnr., 1979—. V.p. bd. trustees, mem. fin. and exec. com. Temple Emanu-El, N.Y.; trustee Mus. Modern Art, mem. investment com., co-chmn. photography com.; trustee Inst. Advanced Study Princeton; trustee, exec. com. Syracuse U., Montefiore Hosp., N.Y., Guild Hall, East Hampton, past chmn. bd.; pres. bd. trustees, exec. com. Dalton Sch., N.Y.C.; past bd. advs. Grad. Sch. Inst. Internat. Bus. Pace U.; mem. exec. bd. N.Y. chpt. Am. Jewish Com.; bd. dirs., mem. fin. and budget com. N.Y. Pub. Library, N.Y.C.; bd. dirs. Parks Council; bd. dirs., v.p. Emanu-El Midtown YMHA; mng. dir. Horace W. Goldsmith Found.; bd. trustees Mus. Modern Art; bd. dirs. associated YM-YWHA; mem. Pres. Clinton's com. on the arts and the humanities. Recipient George Arents medal Syracuse U., 1984. Mem. Investment Assn. N.Y. Clubs: India House, City Athletic (N.Y.C.) Dunes Racquet (East Hampton, N.Y.). Home: 920 Fifth Ave New York NY 10021-4160 also: Further East Ln Amagansett NY 11930 Office: Goldman Sachs & Co 85 Broad St New York NY 10004-2434

MENSCHER, BARNET GARY, steel company executive; b. Laurelton, N.Y., Sept. 5, 1940; s. Samuel and Louise (Zaimont) M.; student Centenary Coll., 1958-59; B.B.A., U. Tex., 1963; m. Diane Elaine Gachman, June 12, 1966; children—Melissa Denise, Corey Lane, Scott Jay. Vice pres. mktg. Ella Gant Mfg., Shreveport, La., 1964-66; warehouse mgr., dir. material control Gachman Steel Co., Fort Worth, 1966-68, gen. mgr., Houston, 1968-70, v.p., sales mgr. Gulf Coast, 1971-76; pres. Menko Steel Service, Inc., Houston, 1979—; v.p., treas. Gachman Metal Co.; investment cons. D & L Enterprises, 1966—. Mem. solicitation com. United Fund, 1969-76; mem. Nat. Alliance of Businessmen Jobs Program, 1969—. Served with AUS, 1963-65. Mem. Tex. Assn. Steel Importers, Purchasing Agts. Assn. Houston, Credit Assn. Houston, Am. Mgmt. Assn., Assn. Steel Distbrs., Nat. Assn. Elevator Contractors, Phi Sigma Delta, Alpha Phi Omega. Home: 314 Tealwood Dr Houston TX 77024-6113 Office: PO Box 40296 Houston TX 77240-0296

MENSE, ALLAN TATE, research scientist, engineer; b. Kansas City, Mo., Nov. 29, 1945; s. Martin Conrad Mense and Nancy (Tate) Johnson; children from previous marriage: Melanie Georgia, Eileen Madelaine; m. Ramona Carol Stelford, Aug. 6, 1983. BS, U. Ariz., 1968; MS, U. So. Ariz., 1970; PhD, U. Wis., 1976. Scientist Oak Ridge (Tenn.) Nat. Lab, 1976-79; mem. sr. staff Sci. and Tech. commn. U.S. Ho. Reps., Washington, 1979-81; sr. scientist McDonnell Douglas Astro. Co., St. Louis, 1981-85; dep. chief scientist Dept. Def. Strategic Def. Initiative Orgn., Washington, 1985-86, chief scientist, 1986-88; v.p. for rsch. Fla. Inst. Tech., Melbourne, 1988-92; pres. Advanced Tech. Mgmt., Inc., Arlington, Va., 1992—; bd. dirs. F.I.T. Aviation, Inc. Contbr. over 60 articles to profl. jours. Mem. AIAA (sr. mem.), IEEE (chmn. energy com. 1985—, sr. mem.), Am. Def. Preparedness Assn., Am. Phys. Soc., Am. Nuclear Soc., Fla. Com. Nat. Space Club (charter), Navy League, Sigma Xi, Theta Tau. Episcopalian. Home and Office: Advanced Tech Mgmt Inc PO Box 2734 Arlington VA 22202-0734

MENSES, JAN, artist, draftsman, etcher, lithographer, muralist; b. Rotterdam, Netherlands, Apr. 28, 1933; emigrated to Can., 1960, naturalized 1965; s. Jan and Elisabeth Wilhelmina (Schwarz) M.; m. Rachel Régine Kadoch, Dec. 7, 1958; children: Salomon, Hnina Sarah, Nechamah Elisabeth Halo. Student, Acad. Fine Arts, Rotterdam, Officers Acad. Royal Dutch Air Force, 1953-55. lectr. in fine arts Concordia U., Montreal, 1973-76, others. One-man shows include Montreal Mus. Fine Arts, 1961, 65, 76, Isaacs Gallery, Toronto, Ont., Can., 1964, Delta Gallery, Rotterdam, 1965, Galerie Godard Lefort, Montreal, 1966, Gallery Moos, Toronto, 1967, Rotterdam Art Found., 1974, Galerie Mira Godard, Toronto, 1977, Montreal, 1978, Seasons Galleries, The Hague, 1980, U. B.C. Fine Arts Gallery, Vancouver, 1981, Galerie Don Stewart, Montreal, 1981, Mead Art Mus., Amherst, Mass., 1983, Agnes Etherington Art Mus., 1984, Blom and Dorn Gallery, N.Y.C., 1985, Marywood Coll. Mus., Scranton, Pa., 1985, Blom & Dorn Gallery, N.Y.C., 1986-93, Saraya-Wolfson Ctr., Safed, Israel, 1987, Mayanot Gallery, Jerusalem, 1987-88, Esperanza Gallery, Montreal, 1988, 89, Gallery Hamaavan Haradum, Safed, Israel, 1989-93, 94, Blom & Dorn Gallery, Hartford, Conn., 1995, Nora Gallery, Jerusalem, 1995, Artist's Colony, Safed, Isreal; over 300 group shows include Montreal World Exhbn., 1967, Salon Internat. Art, Basel, Switzerland, 1972, 74, Canadian Nat. Exhbn., 1972, Centennial Exhbn., Royal Can. Acad., Toronto, 1980, Que Biennale I, II, III, Montreal, 1977, 79, 81, Foire Internat. D'Art Contemporain Paris and Internat. Fair Koln Germany, 1986, Migdal Ha-Emek, Israel, 1988, Group of 8 Israel, Toronto, 1990, Royal Can. Acad. Show, Toronto, 1991; represented in permanent exhbn. Gallery Hamaayan Haradum, Safed; represented in permanent collections Museo Ciani di Villa Caccia, Lugano, Switzerland, The Art Gallery of Hamilton, Ont.,Can., Gallery of Nova Scotia-Halifax, Can, Jewish Public Libr. Collection, Montreal, Can., Cadillac Fairview Collection, Toronto, Can, Museum Modern Art, N.Y.C., Phila. Mus. Art, Solomon R. Guggenheim Mus., N.Y.C., Yivo Inst., N.Y.C., Bklyn. Mus., Art Inst. Chgo., Cleve. Mus. Art, Detroit Inst. Arts, Yale U., U. Montreal, Queens U., Kingston, Mead Art Mus., Amherst Coll., Jonathan Edwards Coll., New Haven, Victoria & Albert Mus., London, Vatican Mus., Rome, Quebec Art Bank, Concordia U., Montreal, Haifa Mus. Modern Art, Hebrew U., Jerusalem, Govt. of Que., Yad Vashem Holocaust Meml., Jerusalem, Museum Boymans-van Beuningen, Rotterdam, Stedelijk Mus. Amsterdam, Rijksmuseum, Amsterdam, Nat. Gallery Can., Ottawa, Gallery Stratford, Montreal Mus. Fine Arts, Musée d'Art Contemporain, Montreal, Que. Provincial Mus., Que. Art Bank, Art Bank of the Can. Coun., Ottawa, Ariz. State Mus., Tucson, Hebrew U., Jerusalem, City of Safed-Israel, Holocaust Meml. Ctr., Toronto, Lavalin Mus. Coll, Montreal, Oshawa Mus., Ont., Dept. External Affairs Govt. of Can., Ottawa, Can. Jewish Congress Mus., Montreal, Israel Mus., Jerusalem, McGill U., Montreal, Olympia & York Collection, Toronto, CBC Collection, Montreal, Kingston (Ont.) U. Mus. Collection, N.Y. Pub. Libr., Worcester (Mass.) Art Mus., Currier Gallery Art, Manchester, N.H., Art Gallery of U. N.H. Durham, Mus. Art. R.I. Sch. Design, Providence, Olympia & York Collection, Toronto, Collection Rishon Le'Zion, Jerusalem, Rose Art Mus., Brandeis U., Waltham, Mass., C.I.L. Collection Montreal, Tel Aviv U., McGill U. Coll., Montreal, Canadian Jewish Congress Mus., Montreal, Young Israel of Montreal (Coll.), Can., Confederation Art Ctr., Charlottetown-Prince Edward Island, Can.; paintings include Klippoth Series, 1963-78, Kaddish Series, 1964-80, Hechaloth Series, 1973—, Tikkun Series, 1978—; mural for Montreal Holocaust Meml. Center. Mem. Pres.'s Coun. of U. N.H. Served with Royal Dutch Air Force Res., 1953-55. Recipient 5 1st prizes Nat. Art Exhbn., Quebec, Que., 1960-65; Grand prize Concours Artistiques de la Province de Que., 1965; prize X and XI Winnipeg (Man., Can.) Shows, 1966, 68; prize IX Internat. Exhbn. Drawings and Prints, Lugano, 1966; prize Ofcl. Centennial Art Competition, Toronto; 1st prize Hadassah, 1969, 71, 82; Recipient Imago award U. Montreal, 1971; award Reeves of Can., 1969; Tigert award Ont. Soc. Arts, 1970; Loomis and Toles

award, 1972; J. I. Segal award J. I. Segal Fund Jewish Culture, 1975; Gold medal Accademia Italia Delle Arte, Italy, 1980; Gold medal Internat. Parliament U.S.A., 1982; Gran Premio delle Nazioni, Italy, 1983, European Banner of Arts with Gold medal, 1984, Oscar d' Italia, 1985, 1st prize III Que. Biennale, 1981, OSA award of merit, Toronto, 1981, 82; World Culture prize Italy, 1984; Golden Flame of World Parliament (U.S.A.) award, 1986; Ish Shalom award Jerusalem, 1993; numerous others; Can. Council sr. arts fellow, 1969-70, 71-72, 81-82; grantee, 1966-67, 67-68; travel grantee, 1968, 73. Mem. Royal Can. Acad. Arts, Acad. Italia Arte e del Lavoro, Acad. Nazioni, Maestro Accademico-Accademia Bedriacense (Italy), Jewish Am. Acad. Arts and Scis., Israeli Art Assn. (Telaviv), Israel Assn. Profl. Artists Safed, Acad. Europa, Academician of Italy, Israel Assn. Visual Art (Jerusalem). Jewish. Office: care Blom & Dorn Gallery 140 Huyshope Ave Hartford CT 06106 *My works have dealt with death, the eclipse of faith, exile, the Galut. They are shaped by my childhood experiences, real and imagined, in Nazi-occupied Europe; influenced by and rooted in my principles and standards of conduct as an Orthodox Jew in the post-holocaust/pre-Messianic era. They are an attempt to translate these experiences into visual contemporary terms (imagery conflicts and reconciliations of conflicts) in order to ascend from the personal/specific to the universal/general. They are a lament, an elegy, a denial and confirmation, an expression of the attitude of the soul in its debasement and dignity towards its Creator; a striving towards serenity in anticipation of the Redemption: a form of prayer.*

MENSINGER, PEGGY BOOTHE, retired mayor; b. Modesto, Calif., Feb. 18, 1923; d. Dyas Power and Margaret (Stewart) Boothe; m. John Logan Mensinger, May 25, 1952; children: John B., Stewart I., Susan B. AB in Polit. Sci, Stanford U., 1944. Reporter San Francisco Red Cross Chpt. News Bur., 1944; acting mgr. Boothe Fruit Co., Modesto, Calif., 1945; asst. dir. Stanford (Calif.) Alumni Assn., 1947; exec. sec. pub. exercises com. Stanford U., 1949-51; mem. Modesto City Council, 1973-79, mayor, 1979-87; ret., 1987; Mem. adv. bd. Agrl. Issues Ctr. U. Calif., 1988-94. Bd. dirs. Nat. coun. Girl Scouts U.S.A., 1978-87, Calif. Planning and Conservation League, 1980—; adv. bd. U. Calif. Agricultural Issues Ctr., 1988-94; Friends Outside Nat. Bd., 1991-93; chmn. Citizens Com. for Internat. Students, 1965-70; pres. Modesto PTA Coun., 1967-69, Modesto chpt. Am. Field Svc., 1969-70, Stanislaus County Hist. Soc., 1970-71; mem. state bd. Common Cause, 1973-75; chmn. Modesto City Cultural Commn., 1968-73; del. White House Com. on Families, L.A., 1980; chmn. Stanislaus Area Assn. Govts., 1976-77; chmn. air quality subcom. U.S. Conf. Mayors, 1985-87. Recipient Woman of Yr. award VFW Aux., 1980, Man of Yr. award Am. Legion, 1987, State of Calif. Legislature Women of Yr. Mem. Nat. League Am. Pen Women (assoc.), Stanford Assocs. (pres. 1985-87), Soroptimist (hon., Women Achievement award 1980), Phi Beta Kappa, Gamma Phi Beta. Unitarian. Home: 1320 Magnolia Ave Modesto CA 95350-5250

MENSON, RICHARD L., lawyer; b. Chgo., Nov. 10, 1943; s. John Lewis and Elizabeth Eileen (Carroll) M.; m. Lynne Patricia Lemke, Apr. 24, 1971; children: Melissa Lynne, Kristin Anne. BA, Ripon Coll., 1965; JD, Northwestern U., 1968; LLM in Taxation, George Washington U., 1973. Bar: Ill. 1968, U.S. Dist. Ct. (no. dist.) Ill. 1973, U.S. Ct. Mil. Appeals 1968, U.S. Ct. Claims 1973, U.S. Tax Ct. 1975. Commd. lt. U.S. Army, 1965, advanced through grades to capt., with JAG office, 1965-73, resigned, 1973; assoc. Gardner, Carton & Douglas, Chgo., 1973-77, ptnr., 1977—. Mem. bd. edn. Oak Grove Sch. Dist. #68, Libertyville, Ill., 1983-87; elder First Presbyn. Ch., Libertyville, 1979-83, mem. bd. deacons, 1975-79. Mem. ABA, Ill. State Bar Assn., Chgo. Bar Assn., Lake County Bar Assn., Legal Club of Chgo., Conway Farms Golf Club, Army Navy Country Club. Presbyterian. Home: 1000 Ashley Ln Libertyville IL 60048-3813 Office: Gardner Carton & Douglas Quaker Tower Ste 3400 321 N Clark St Chicago IL 60610-4795

MENTZ, HENRY ALVAN, JR., federal judge; b. New Orleans, Nov. 10, 1920; s. Henry Alvan and Lulla (Bridewell) M.; m. Ann Lamantia, June 23, 1956; children—Ann, Carli, Hal, Frederick, George. B.A., Tulane U., 1941; J.D., La. State U., 1943. Bar: La. 1943, U.S. Dist. Ct. (ea. dist.) La. 1944. With legal dept. Shell Oil, New Orleans, 1947-48; pvt. practice Hammond, 1948-82; judge U.S. Dist. Ct. (ea. dist.) La., 1982—; sr. judge, 1992—. Editor: Combined Gospels, 1976. Pres. La. Soc. Music and Performing Arts, La. Civic League, 1979-81; bd. dirs. Southeastern La. U. Found., Salvation Army; chmn. Tulane U. 50th Anniversary Reunion for 1991. Sgt. inf. U.S. Army, 1943-46, ETO. Decorated 2 Battle Stars, Bronze Star; recipient Disting. Svc. award AMVETS, 1950. Mem. S.R. Royal Soc. St. George (pres.), Boston Club of New Orleans, Delta Tau Delta. Republican. Episcopalian. Home: 2105 State St New Orleans LA 70118-6255 Office: US Dist Ct C-456 US Courthouse 500 Camp St New Orleans LA 70130-3313

MENTZER, JOHN RAYMOND, electrical engineer, educator; b. Arch Spring, Pa., June 16, 1916; s. Walter Ray and Katheryn Henderson (Barr) M.; m. Bernice Roslyn Simon, Feb. 17, 1945; children—Jacqueline Ferne, Richard Alan. B.S., Pa. State U., 1942, M.S., 1948; Ph.D., Ohio State U., 1952. Engr. Westinghouse Electric Corp., Balt., 1942-46, Ordnance Research Lab., 1946-48; research asso. Ohio State U., 1948-52; mem. staff Lincoln Lab., M.I.T., 1952-54; mem. faculty Pa. State U., 1954—, prof. engring. scis., 1956—, head dept. engring. sci. and mechanics, 1974-81, prof. emeritus engring. scis., 1981—. Author: Scattering and Diffraction of Radio Waves, 1955. Recipient Service award Pa. State U., 1979. Sr. mem. IEEE; mem. Am. Soc. Engring. Edn., AAAS, Sigma Xi. Home: 557 Clarence Ave State College PA 16803-3456 Office: 227 Hammond Bldg University Park PA 16802

MENUEZ, D. BARRY, religious organization administrator; b. Benton, Ohio, Feb. 28, 1933; s. Kyle LeRoy and Roxie Beulah (Rottman) M.; m. Mary Jane Sidley, Aug. 30, 1956 (div. 1974); children: Douglas, Stephanie, Jane, Ross; m. Jean Venable, June 30, 1989; 1 stepchild, Alan. BD, Kenyon Coll., 1955; MDiv, U. Chgo., 1971; LHD, Berkeley-Yale Div. Sch., 1990. Dir. office of ministries Episcopal Ch. Ctr., N.Y.C., dir. coun. for devel. of ministry, exec. adn. for mission and ministry, sr. exec. for missions ops., 1986—; trustee Indsl. Areas Found., Garden City, N.Y., 1974—. 1st lt. USAF, 1955-57. Recipient Disting. Christian Svc. award Seabury-Western Theol. Sem., 1988. Home: 199 Davis Ave White Plains NY 10605-3215 Office: Episcopal Ch Ctr 815 2nd Ave New York NY 10017-4503

MENUHIN, YEHUDI, violinist; b. N.Y.C., Apr. 22, 1916; s. Moshe and Marutha M.; m. Nola Ruby Nicholas, May 26, 1938; children: Zamira, Krov; m. Diana Gould, Oct. 19, 1947; children: Gerard, Jeremy. Educated by pvt. tutors; studied music under, Sigmund Anker, Louis Persinger, San Francisco, Georges Enesco, Rumania and Paris, Adolph Busch, Switzerland; MusD (hon.), U. Oxford, 1962, Queen's U., Belfast, 1965, U. Leicester, 1965; LLD (hon.), U. St. Andrews, 1963, U. Liverpool, 1963, U. Sussex, 1966, U. Bath, 1969; LittD (hon.), U. Warwick, 1968; MusD (hon.). U. London, 1969, U. Cambridge, 1970. Pres. Halle Orch., 1992; Established Yehudi Menuhin Sch. at Stoke D'Abernon, Eng.; pres. Internat. Music Council of UNESCO, Folkestone Menuhin Internat. Violin Competition, Royal Philharmonic Orch., 1982—. Completed his first round-the-world concert tour, 1935; appearing in 110 concert engagements; has toured in Latin Am., S.Am., Australia, South Africa and Pacific Islands; played 22 concerts during 12 day tour in Israel; filmed series of complete concert programs; opened Japan to world concert artists, 1951, concert tours in India, 1952, 54, also charity concerts various instns.; has own yearly summer festival in Gstaad, Switzerland, 1957—; debut as condr. symphony orch. in Am. with Am. Symphony Orch., Carnegie Hall, 1966, dir. Bath Festival, Eng., 1958-68, Bath Festival Orch.; presented his first festival at Windsor, 1969; held over 500 concerts for armed forces, Red Cross, others; followed U.S. Army into, France and Belgium, first artist to play in liberated Paris, Brussels, Bucharest, Budapest and Antwerp, also first in Moscow after cessation of hostilities; prin. guest condr. English Sting Orch., 1988—; author: The Violin: Six Lessons by Yehudi Menuhin, 1971, Theme and Variations, 1972, The Violin and Viola, 1976, The King, the Cut, and the Fiddle, 1983, Life Class, 1986, The Compleat Violinist: Thoughts, Exercises and Reflections of a Humanist Violinist, 1986; autobiography Unfinished Journey, 1977; co-author: The Music of Man, 1979. Goodwill Amb. UNESCO, 1992. Decorated officer Legion of Honor; chevalier de L'Ordre des Arts et des Lettres (France); Order of Leopold (Belgium); Ordre de la Couronne (Belgium); Order of Merit (West German Republic); knight comdr. Order Brit. Empire (Gt. Britain); Royal Order Phoenix (Greece), Order of Merit (Gt. Britain); recipient Jawaharlal Nehru award for Internat. Understanding India, 1968, Mendelssohn prize,

1986, 10 Grammy awards, Golden Viotti prize, 1987, Glenn Gould prize Glenn Gould Found., 1990, Wolf prize in Arts, 1991. Fellow World Acad. Art and Sci.; mem. and/or officer numerous U.S., fgn. orgns. Research in expansion violin concert repertoire; introduced many rare and important works both classical and modern. Office: care Columbia Artists Mgmt 165 W 57th St New York NY 10019-2201 also: Menuhin Festival, Gstaad-Saanen/Alpengala, CH-3780 Gstaad Switzerland also: SYM Music Co, PO Box 6160, London SW1W OXJ, England

MENYUK, PAULA, developmental psycholinguistics educator; b. N.Y.C., Oct. 2, 1929; d. Louis and Helen (Weissman) Nichols; m. Norman Menyuk, Mar. 5, 1950; children—Curtis R., Diane E., Eric D. B.S., NYU, 1951; Ed.M., Boston U., 1955, Ed.D., 1961. Chief lang. therapist Mass. Gen. Hosp., Boston, 1952-54; teaching fellow Boston U., 1957-60; NIMH postdoctoral fellow MIT, Cambridge, 1961-64, mem. research staff, 1964-72; prof. edn. Boston U., 1972, dir. div. vice chmn. faculty coun., 1981-87, chmn. faculty coun., 1990-91; cons. Children's Hosp., Boston, 1964-92, Kennedy Hosp., Boston, 1981-89, NIH, Bethesda, Md., 1972-80, 89-94, Nat. Found. March of Dimes, White Plains, N.Y., 1977-93; rsch. assoc. MIT, 1972-90. Author: Sentences Children Use, 1969, Acquisition and Development of Language, 1971, Language and Maturation, 1977, Language Development: Knowledge and Use, 1988, Early Language Development in Full-Term and Premature Infants, 1995. NIH fellow, 1958-64; Fulbright fellow, 1971, 88. Fellow Am. Speech, Lang. and Hearing Assn. (Disting. Svc. award 1976, highest honors 1992); mem. AAAS, Soc. Rsch. in Child Devel., Linguistic Soc. Am., Internat. Soc. Study Behavioral Devel., Am. Assn. Phonetic Scis. Home: 162 Mason Ter Brookline MA 02146-2772 Office: Boston U 605 Commonwealth Ave Boston MA 02215-1605

MENZEL, DANIEL BRUCE, toxicology educator; b. Cin., Sept. 27, 1934; s. Clifford Edward and Frances Lee (Hopkins) M.; m. Sally Fay McDonald, June 23, 1956; children: Robert Daniel, Lynn Margaret Menzel Micol, Carolyn Ann. BS, U. Calif., Berkeley, 1956, PhD, 1961. Registered profl. entomologist-toxicologist. Postdoctoral fellow NIH, Bethesda, Md., 1959; asst. prof. U. Calif., Berkeley, 1961-67; mgr. biology dept. Battelle Meml. Inst., Richland, Wash., 1967-70; dir. clin. rsch. Ross div. Abbott Lab., Columbus, Ohio, 1970-71; assoc. prof. pharmacology and medicine Duke U., Durham, N.C., 1971-73, prof. pharmacology and medicine, 1973-88; prof., chmn. dept. community and environ. medicine U. Calif., Irvine, 1989—; bd. dirs. U.S. EPA Sci. Adv. Bd., Washington, 1972—; NAS Environ. Scis. and Toxicology, Washington, 1972-79, 81-84, Nat. Drinking Water Adv. Coun., Washington, 1985-90, Govs. Task Force on Hazardous and Solid Waste, Raleigh, N.C., 1985, USAF Sci. Adv. Bd., Washington, 1986—; expert witness U.S. Congress Joint Com. on Commerce and the Environment, Washington, 1981-87; cons. Orange County Sheriff's Dept., Hillsborough, N.C., 1985; chmn. Carcinogens Working Group World Health Orgn., Geneva, 1985. Editor: Safe Drinking Water & Health, Vols. IV, V, VI, 1976, 80, 86; co-editor: Extrapolation Modelling, 1984, Toxicity of Organic Solvents, 1988—; founding editor jour. Toxicology Letters, 1975—; contbr. over 200 articles to profl. jours. With U.S. Army, 1957-59. Recipient medal Alexander von Humboldt Found., Bonn, Fed. Republic Germany, 1980, Kauffman medal Ohio Pharm. Soc., 1982; fellow Fogarty Internat., 1980. Fellow Acad. Toxicological Scis.; mem. Am. Inst. Nutrition, Am. Chem. Soc. (keynote speaker 1968), Am. Coll. Toxicology (sec. 1985-87), Am. Soc. for Pharmaceutics and Exptl. Therapy, Sigma Xi. Democrat. Episcopalian. Achievements include determination of the molecular weight of myosin; mechanism of toxicity of nitrogen dioxide and ozone. Home: 2 Young Irvine CA 92715-4055 Office: Univ Calif Dept Community and Environ Medicine Irvine CA 92715

MENZER, JOHN BRUCE, financial executive; b. Chgo., Mar. 27, 1951; s. John and Lorraine (Glugla) M. m. Kathleen A. Leahy, Oct. 23, 1976; 1 child, Christine. BBA in Pub. Acctg., Loyola U., 1972, MBA in Fin., 1980. CPA, Ill. Supr. acctg. systems Am. Internat., Mount Prospect, Ill., 1973-75; supr. audit Pannell, Kerr, Forster & Co., Chgo., 1975-77; sr. v.p. Bally Mfg. Corp., 1977-85; exec. v.p., chief operating officer, bd. dirs Ben Franklin Retail Stores, 1985—. Bd. dirs. Jr. Achievement, Chgo., 1973-75. Mem. Fin. Execs. Inst., Ill. State Soc. CPAs, Nat. Retail Mchts. Assn., Am. Inst. CPAs, Internat. Franchise Assn. (chmn. fin. and tax com., conf. coordinator). Avocations: golf, tennis. Home: 57 S Mundhank S Barrington IL 60010 Office: Ben Franklin Stores Inc PO box 5938 Chicago IL 60680

MENZER, ROBERT EVERETT, toxicologist, educator; b. Washington, Dec. 21, 1938; s. Russell Ernest and Ora Taylor (Oates) M.; m. Sara Lee Gribbon, Dec. 29, 1962; children: R. Eric, Paul D., Joan Coleraine. B.S. in Chemistry, U. Pa., 1960; M.S., U. Md., 1962; Ph.D., U. Wis., 1964. Instr. U. Wis., Madison, 1964; mem. faculty U. Md., 1964-89, asst. prof. entomology, 1964-69, assoc. prof., 1969-73, prof., 1973-89, assoc. dean grad. studies and research, 1974-77, acting dean, 1977-80, chmn. grad. program marine-estuarine-environ. scis., 1978-89, dir. Water Resources Research Ctr., 1981-89; dir. environ. rsch. lab. EPA, Gulf Breeze, Fla., 1989—; prof. emeritus U. Md., 1990—; chmn. hazardous substances data bank rev. panel Nat. Library Medicine, 1973—. Contbr. articles to profl. jours. Recipient U. Md. Alumni award, 1974. Fellow Washington Acad. Scis.; mem. AAAS, Am. Chem. Soc., Soc. Toxicology, Soc. for Environ. Toxicology and Chemistry, Sigma Xi, Phi Kappa Phi. Republican. Episcopalian. Club: Cosmos (Washington). Home: 90 Highpoint Dr Gulf Breeze FL 32561-4014 Office: Gulf Breeze Environ Rsch Lab 1 Sabine Island Gulf Breeze FL 32561

MENZIES, CARL STEPHEN, agricultural research administrator, ruminant nutritionist; b. Menard, Tex., Mar. 6, 1932; s. Alex L. and Marguerite (Watson) M.; m. Shirley W. Martin, Sept. 2, 1952; children: John S., Linda D. BS, Tex. Tech Coll., 1954; MS, Kans. State U., 1956; PhD, U. Ky., 1965. Instr. animal sci. Kans. State U., Manhattan, 1955-58, asst. prof., 1958-65, assoc. prof., 1965-69; rsch. asst. animal sci. U. Ky., Lexington, 1961-62; head, prof. S.D. State U., Brookings, 1969-71; resident dir. of rsch., prof. animal sci. Tex. Agrl. Experiment Sta., San Angelo, 1971—; cons. Pakistan project King Ranch, Kingsville, Tex., 1975; bd. dirs. small ruminant CRSP project U.S. AID, Davis, Calif., 1982—; mem. adv. com. sheep rsch. sta. USDA Agrl. Rsch. Sta., Dubois, Idaho, 1985—; mem. adv. bd. agrl. program Angelo State U., 1986—. Contbr. articles to profl. jours. Chmn. livestock com. Goals for San Angelo, 1988-90. Named to Manard Sch. Hall of Fame; recipient Appreciation for Svc. award Kand. Purebred Sheep Breeders Assn., 1968, Silver Ram award Am. Sheep Prodrs. Coun., 1988. Fellow Am. Soc. Animal Sci.; mem. Coun. Agrl. Sci. and Tech., San Angelo C. of C. (bd. dirs. 1990-93), Rotary, Sigma Xi, Gamma Sigma Delta, Phi Kappa Phi, Alpha Zeta. Avocations: ranching, producing registered sheep, outdoor activities. Office: Tex A&M U Agrl Rsch & Extension Ctr 7887 US Hwy 87 N San Angelo TX 76901-9714

MENZIES, IAN STUART, newspaper editor; b. Glasgow, Scotland, Mar. 11, 1920; came to U.S., 1944, naturalized, 1948; s. John S. and Gertrude (Mephius) M.; m. Barbara Edith Newton, June 16, 1945; children: Marla Ann, Gillian Jean, Alexa Stuart, Deborah Newton. Student, Royal Tech. Coll., 1937-39; Nieman fellow, Harvard U., 1961-62; L.H.D., Salem State Coll., 1978. Reporter Boston Globe, 1948-57, sci. editor 1957-63, fin. editor, 1963-65, mng. editor, 1965-70, assoc. editor, 1970-85; sr. fellow John McCormack Inst. Pub. Affairs, U. Mass., Boston, 1985—; vis. assoc. Joint Ctr. for Urban Studies, Mass. Inst. Tech.-Harvard, 1970-71. Mem. Hingham (Mass.) Sch. Com., 1962-68. Served to lt. Royal Naval Vol. Res., 1939-46. Decorated D.S.C.; recipient Pub. Service award Nat. Edn. Writers, 1961, Pub. Service award AAAS, 1963, Heywood Broun award, 1961, Sevellon Brown award, 1959, Rudolph Elie award, 1959, A.P. Big City award, 1958, U.P.I. award, 1959. Mem. Harvard Club, Hingham Yacht Club, Brit. Officers Club New Eng. Home: 479 Main St Hingham MA 02043-4705 Office: McCormack Inst U Mass Boston MA 02125

MEOLA, TONY, professional soccer player, actor; b. Belleville, N.J., Feb. 21, 1969; f. Vincent Meola. w. Colleen.: s. Vincent Meola, m. Colleen Meola. Student, U. Virginia, 1986-89. Goalkeeper CONCACAF World Cup Qualifying Games, 1989, U.S. World Cup Team, 1990, Brighton Football Club, England, 1990, Fort Lauderdale Strikers, Amer. Prof. Soccer League, 1991, U.S. Nat. Team, 1992-94, Long Island Roughriders, 1994—, U.S. World Cup Team, 1994; drafted ctr. fielder N.Y. Yankees; tried out as placekicker for N.Y. Jets, 1994. Appeared in play Tony N' Tina Wedding, 1995. Named Hermann Trophy winner, Mo. Athletic Club Player of Yr.,

1989, MVP U.S. Cup, 1993. mem., N.J. State H.S. Soccer Champions, 1986, NCAA Division I Co-Champions, 1989. Office: care Long Island Roughriders 1117 Old Country Rd Plainview NY 11803•

MEOTTI, MICHAEL PATRICK, state legislator, lawyer; b. New Britain, Conn., Oct. 30, 1953; s. Joseph John Sr. and Margaret Mary (O'Brien) M.; m. Pamela Goldman, June 16, 1990. BS in Fgn. Service cum laude, Georgetown U., 1975, JD cum laude, 1978. Atty. Updike, Kelly & Spellacy, P.C., Hartford, Conn., 1978-80; gen. counsel Ins. Assn. Conn., Hartford, 1980-85; counsel The Travelers Cos., Hartford, 1985-94; mem. Conn. State Senate, Hartford, 1987-95; ptnr. Shipman & Goodwin, Hartford, 1995—; chmn. environ. com. gen. assembly State of Conn., Hartford, 1987-89, transp. com., 1989-95. Mem. Bd. Edn., Glastonbury, Conn., 1979-83; mem. Town Council, Glastonbury, 1983-86, majority leader, 1985-86. Mem. Georgetown U. Alumni Club Conn. (pres. 1984-89). Democrat. Roman Catholic. Home: 56 Heather Glen Rd Glastonbury CT 06033-4161 Office: Shipman & Goodwin 1 American Row Hartford CT 06103

MERACHNIK, DONALD, superintendent of schools. AB, Upsma Coll., 1951; MS, City Coll. of N.Y., 1952; PhD, N.Y. U., 1961. Supt. Union County Regional H.S., Springfield, N.J., 1971—. Named Nat. Supt. of Yr. for N.J., Am. Assn. Sch. Adminstrs., 1993. Office: Union Co Regional HSD Jonathan Dayton Regional HS Mountain Ave Springfield NJ 07081

MERANUS, ARTHUR RICHARD, advertising agency executive; b. Bklyn., May 27, 1934; s. Herbert and Dorothy (Newman) M.; m. Phyllis Ochitell, Sept. 21, 1958; children—Lisa, Leonard, Steven. Grad., Cooper Union, 1956. With Gaynor & Ducas, N.Y.C., 1961-63; with Norman, Craig & Kummel, Inc., N.Y.C., 1963-65; with Cunningham & Walsh Advt. Inc., N.Y.C., 1965-87, sr. v.p., 1978-87, creative dir., 1979-81, dir. creative svcs., 1981-87; mng. dir. creative svcs. N.W. Ayer, N.Y.C., 1987-88, exec. v.p., mng. dir. creative svcs., 1988—, also bd. dirs. Recipient Clio award, Art Dirs. Club N.Y. award, One Show awards, Andy award, Effie award. Mem. Garden State Yacht Club (dir.). Office: NW Ayer & Ptnrs Inc Worldwide Plz 825 8th Ave 35th Fl New York NY 10019-7498

MERANUS, LEONARD STANLEY, lawyer; b. Newark, Jan. 7, 1928; s. Norman and Ada (Binstock) M.; m. Jane B. Holzman, Sept. 20, 1989; children: Norman, James M., David. LittB, Rutgers U., 1948; LLB, Harvard U., 1954. Bar: Ohio 1954. Assoc. Paxton & Seasongood, Cin., 1954-59, ptnr., 1959-85, pres., 1985-89; ptnr. Thompson, Hine and Flory, 1989—, ptnr.-incharge Cin. office, 1989-91, mem. firm mgmt com., 1991-93. Co-editor: Law and the Writer, 1978, 81, 85. Chmn. bd. dirs Jewish Hosp., 1982-86; trustee Andrew Jergens Found., 1962—. Mem. ABA, Ohio Bar Assn., Internat. Bar Assn., Cin. Bar Assn., Am. Arbitration Assn. (Ohio, Ind., Ky. regional adv. com., chmn. comml. arbitration com., Ohio panel large, complex arbitration cases), Union Internationale des Avocats. Office: Thompson Hine & Flory 312 Walnut St 14th Flr Cincinnati OH 45202-4029

MÉRAS, PHYLLIS LESLIE, journalist; b. Bklyn., May 10, 1931; d. Edmond Albert and Leslie Trousdale (Ross) M.; BA, Wellesley Coll., 1955; MS in Journalism, Columbia U., 1954; Swiss Govt. Exchange fellow, Inst. Higher Internat. Studies, Geneva, 1957; m. Thomas H. Cocroft, Nov. 3, 1968. Reporter, copy editor Providence Jour., 1954-57, 59-61; feature writer Ladies Home Jour. mag., 1957-58; editor Weekly Tribune, Geneva, Switzerland, 1961-62; copyeditor, travel sect. N.Y. Times, 1962-68; mng. editor Vineyard Gazette, Edgartown, Mass., 1970-74, contbg. editor, 1974—; assoc. editor Rhode Islander, Providence, 1970-76; travel editor Providence Jour., 1976—; editor Wellesley Alumnae mag., 1979—; assoc. in journalism U. R.I., 1974-75; adj. instr. Columbia U. Sch. Journalism, 1975-76. Author: First Spring: A Martha's Vineyard Journal, 1972, A Yankee Way With Wood, 1975, Miniatures: How to Make Them, Use Them, Sell Them, 1976, Vacation Crafts, 1978, The Mermaids of Chenonceaux and 828 Other Tales: An Anecdotal Guide to Europe, 1982, Exploring Rhode Island, 1984, Castles, Keeps and Leprechauns: Tales, Myths and Legends of Historic Sites in Great Britain and Ireland, 1988; co-author: Christmas Angels, 1979, Carry-out Cuisine, 1982, New Carry Out Cuisine, 1986, Eastern Europe: A Traveler's Companion, 1991, Rhode Island Explorer's Guide, 1995. Pulitzer fellow in critical writing, 1967. Mem. Soc. Am. Travel Writers. Home: Music St West Tisbury MA 02575-9999 Office: Providence Jour 75 Fountain St Providence RI 02902

MERBAUM, MICHAEL, psychology educator, clinical psychologist; b. N.Y.C., Nov. 6, 1933; s. Max J. and Molly (Rubin) M.; m. Marta Ettinger, Nov. 18, 1962; children: Tal, Marc. BA, Drake U., 1954; MA, U. Mo., Kansas City, 1956; PhD, U. N.C., 1961. Diplomate Am. Bd. Clin. Psychology. Staff psychologist U. Chgo., 1961-64; asst. prof. Bowling Green (Ohio) State U., 1964-66; assoc. prof. Adelphi U., N.Y.C., 1966-72; prof. U. Haifa, Israel, 1972-78; prof., dir. clin. tng. Washington U., St. Louis, 1978—; corp. psychologist Wetterau, Inc., St. Louis, 1988—. Editor: Personality: Readings in Theory and Research, 1964, 3d edit., 1978, Behavior Change Through Self-control, 1973. Mem. Am. Psychol. Assn., Assn. for Advancement Behavior Therapy. Democrat. Jewish. Avocations: tennis, reading, music. Home: 825 Fairfield Lake Dr Chesterfield MO 63017-5926 Office: Washington U Dept Psychology Saint Louis MO 63130

MERCER, DAVID ROBINSON, association executive; b. Van Nuys, Calif., Aug. 14, 1938; s. Samuel Robinson and Dorothy (Lenox) M.; m. Joyce Elaine Dahl, Aug. 23, 1958; children: Steven, Michael, Kimberly. BA, Calif. State U., L.A., 1961. Exec. dir. YMCA of L.A., 1963-69, sr. v.p., 1969-80; reg. mgr. Am. City Bur., Hoffman Estates, Ill., 1980-82; pres. YMCA of San Francisco, 1982-90; nat. exec. dir. YMCA of USA, Chgo., 1990—; cons. fin. devel. YMCAs throughout U.S., 1975—. Mem. The Family, Rotary (bd. dirs. 1987-89). Republican. Methodist. Avocations: golf, bridge, flying, back packing. Office: YMCA of USA 101 N Wacker Dr Chicago IL 60606

MERCER, DOUGLAS, lawyer; b. Sharon, Mass., Feb. 16, 1918; m. Pauline Loring Tobey, 4 children. AB, Harvard U., 1940, LLB, 1947. Bar: Mass. 1947. Ptnr. Ropes & Gray, Boston, 1957-90, of counsel, 1991—; moderator, panelist various Am. Law Inst.-ABA and other investment co. seminars. Former mem. and chmn. Planning Bd., Town of Weston, Mass., also former selectman, former mem. fin. com.; former trustee, treas. Social Law Library; chmn. Harvard Coll. Fund, 1975-77; chmn. Boston area Harvard Campaign for $350 Million; former mem. overseers resources com. Harvard U.; former trustee Groton Sch.; mem. corp. Belmont Hill Sch. Served to lt. comdr. USN, 1942-46, PTO. Mem. ABA, Boston Bar Assn. Clubs: The Country. Office: Ropes & Gray 1 Internat Pl Boston MA 02110-2624

MERCER, EDWIN WAYNE, lawyer; b. Kingsport, Tenn., July 19, 1940; s. Ernest LaFayette and Geneva (Frye) M. BBA, Tex. Tech U., 1963; JD, S. Tex. Coll. Law, 1971. Bar: Tex. 1971, U.S. Dist. Ct. (no. dist.) Tex 1975, U.S. Supreme Ct. 1976, U.S. Ct. Appeals (5th Cir.) 1979. Pvt. practice law Houston, 1971-73; gen. counsel, corp. sec. Alcon Labs., Inc., Ft. Worth, 1973-81; ptnr. Gandy Michener Swindle Whitaker Pratt & Mercer, Ft. Worth, 1981-84; v.p., gen. counsel, corp. sec. Pengo Industries, Inc., Ft. Worth, 1984-90, also bd. dirs. Bd. dirs. Soc. for Prevention Blindness, 1979—. Mem. ABA, State Bar Tex., Houston Bar Assn., Ft. Worth-Tarrant County Bar Assn., Coll. State Bar Tex., South Tex. Coll. Law Alumni Assn., Tex. Tech U. Ex-Assn., Ft. Worth Club, Delta Theta Phi, Phi Delta Theta. Methodist.

MERCER, LEE WILLIAM, lawyer, corporate executive, former government agency administrator; b. East Orange, N.J., July 16, 1943; m. Deborah Clare Robottom, Sept. 11, 1965 (div. Mar. 1980); children: James W., Charles A.; m. Deborah Anne O'Brien, Sept. 20, 1986; 1 child, Garrett W. BA, Dartmouth Coll., 1965; JD, Boston U., 1971, LLM in Tax, 1974. Ptnr. Sheehan, Phinney, Bass & Green, Manchester, N.H., 1971-80; counsel, legis. dir. U.S. Sen. Warren Rudman, Washington, 1981-84; v.p. The 1st Phillips Corp., Acton, Mass., 1985; dep. asst. sec. for trade adminstrn. U.S. Dept. Commerce, Washington, 1986-87, dep. under sec. for export adminstrn., 1887-89, dep. under sec. for tech., 1989-90; export mgr. Digital Equipment Corp., Washington, 1990-94; pres. U.S. Fiber Optics & Telecomms. Corp. Served to cpl. USMC, 1966-68. Mem. N.H. Bar Assn.

Republican. Office: Digital Equipment Corp 1331 Pennsylvania Ave NW Washington DC 20004-1703

MERCER, LEONARD PRESTON, II, biochemistry educator; b. Ft. Worth, Jan. 16, 1941; s. Leonard Preston and Margie (Miller) M.; m. Diane Cottingham, Feb. 6, 1963; children: Cindy Louise, Timothy Clayton, Megan Hope. BS in Chemistry, U. Tex., 1968; PhD in Biochemistry, La. State U., 1971. NIH postdoctoral fellow U. Ala., Birmingham, 1971-73; instr. U. South Ala., Mobile, 1973-74, asst. prof., 1974-77; asst. prof. Oral Roberts U. Sch. Medicine, Tulsa, 1977-80, assoc. prof., 1980-84, prof., chmn. dept., 1984-90, assoc. dean biomed. scis., 1989-90; prof., chmn. dept. nutrition and food sci. U. Ky., Lexington, 1990—; cons. in math. modeling phys. responses and neurochemistry of appetite control. Contbr. articles to profl. jours., chapters in books. Fellow Am. Coll. Nutrition; mem. Am. Inst. Nutrition, Am. Chem. Soc., Am. Soc. for Biochemistry, Soc. Math. Biology. Avocations: reading, computer programming. Home: 4633 Spring Creek Dr Lexington KY 40515-1506 Office: U Ky 212 Funkhouser Bldg Lexington KY 40506

MERCER, MELVIN RAY, electrical engineer, educator; b. Lubbock, Tex., Sept. 5, 1946; s. Dixie Melvin and Ollie Faye (Sheppard) M.; m. Sharry Billene Cannon, Sept. 9, 1967; children: Rebecca Raylene, Elizabeth Anne. BSEE, Tex. Tech U., 1968; MSEE, Stanford U., 1971; PhD in Elec. Engring., U. Tex., 1980. Registered profl. engr., Tex. Rsch. and devel. engr. GTE Sylvania, Mountain View, Calif., 1968-73; mem. tech. staff Hewlett-Packard Labs., Palo Alto, Calif., 1973-77; lectr. U. Tex., San Antonio, 1977-80; mem. tech. staff Bell Labs., Murray Hill, N.J., 1980-83; asst. prof. elec. and computer engring. U. Tex., Austin, 1983-87, assoc. prof., 1987-91, prof., 1991-95; prof. elec. engring., dept. chair Texas A&M, 1995—; lectr. Kilgore (Tex.) Jr. Coll., 1977; cons. Rothe Devel. Co., San Antonio, 1979, Lockheed Missiles and Space Co., Austin, 1983, IBM, Austin, 1984, 88-90, Harris Semiconductor, Dallas, 1983-86, State of Tex., Austin, 1984-85, CBS, N.Y.C., 1985-86, Teltech Resource Network, Mpls., 1986-93, Motorola Semiconductor, Austin, 1987-88, 91, TSSI, Beaverton, Ore., 1988—, MCC, Austin, 1989, Cimflex Teknowledge, Pitts., 1989-90, Integra-Test, L.I., N.Y., 1993, Teradyne, 1993-94, Sematech, 1994; advisor NSF, Washington, 1987-88, mem. engring. initiation awards evaluation panel, 1987, 1993; mem. program com. 1st MCC-Univ. Rsch. Symposium, 1987; lectr. in field. Contbr. articles to profl. jours.; patentee in field. Recipient Presdl. Young Investigator award NSF, 1986, Rsch. award Office Naval Rsch., 1986—, Advanced Projects Rsch. Adminstrn., 1992—; Werner W. Dornberger Centennial teaching fellow U. Tex., 1984-90, Engring. Found. Endowed Faculty fellow, 1990-91, Temple Found. Endowed Professorship #3 Engring., 1991—; grantee Univ. Rsch. Inst., 1983, Bur. Engring. Rsch., 1984, AT&T Info. Systems, 1985-88, Microelectronics and Computer Tech. Corp., 1985-90, Internat. Test Found., 1986-89, Semiconductor Rsch. Corp., 1989—, IBM Corp., 1989-92, Tex. Advanced Tech. Program, 1990-92, Motorola, 1991-92. Fellow IEEE (editor Design and Test of Computers mag. 1985-88); mem. Computer Soc. IEEE (vice chmn. Cen. Tex. chpt. 1983-85, chmn. 1985-86), Internat. Test Conf. (program com. 1986-89, program vice chmn. 1988, program chmn. 1989, Best Paper award Internat. Test Conf. 1982, honorable mention Internat. Test Conf. 1988, steering com. 1988-93, mktg. vice chair 1990, planning chmn. 1992-93), IEEE Design for Testability Workshop (program com. Vail, Colo. chpt. 1989—), Internat. Conf. on Computer-Aided Design (program com. 1987), Design Automation Conf. (Best Paper award 1991), Austin C. of C. (recruitment resource 1983-87), Tau Beta Pi, Eta Kappa Nu, Phi Kappa Phi, Phi Eta Sigma. Avocations: racquetball, swimming, scuba. Office: U Tex Dept Elec and Computer Engring ENS 143 Austin TX 78712-1084

MERCER, RICHARD JOSEPH, retired advertising executive, freelance writer; b. Elizabeth, N.J., Mar. 29, 1924; s. George Washington and Margaret Elizabeth (Walsh) M.; m. Muriel Davis, June 24, 1945; children: Richard George, Karen, James Davis, Lesley Ann. L.B. in Journalism, Rutgers U., 1949. Announcer, copywriter, news reporter Sta. WCTC, New Brunswick, N.J., 1946-49; assoc. creative dir., then v.p., dir. BBDO, Inc., N.Y.C., 1949-76; sr. v.p., creative exec. SSC&B, Inc., N.Y.C., 1977-83, exec. v.p. creative, 1983-85; sr. v.p., assoc. creative dir. McCann-Erickson, Inc., N.Y.C., 1985-87; part-time lectr. Rutgers U. Sch. Bus., New Brunswick, N.J., 1988-89; speaker in field. Chmn. Roselle (N.J.) Police Raise Referendum Com., 1958; promotion chmn. Cranford (N.J.) United Fund, 1960; publicity dir. Friends of Mendham (N.J.) Libr., 1974-75; bd. dirs. Friends of Nantucket Atheneum, 1991—; trustee Atheneum, 1993—. With A.C. USNR, 1943-45. Decorated Air medal; Recipient 10 Clio awards, 2 Effie awards, also Silver Key award Advt. Writers Assn. N.Y.C. Mem. NATAS, Air Force Assn. (life), Col. Henry Rutgers Soc. Roman Catholic. Home: 24 Pleasant St Nantucket MA 02554

MERCER, ROBERT B., automobile corporation executive. BA, Duke U., 1973; JD, U. Md., 1976. Bar: Md. 1976. V.p., sec., gen. counsel Volvo N.Am. Corp., N.Y.C., sr. v.p., sec., gen. counsel, 1990—. Office: Volvo N Am Corp 535 Madison Ave New York NY 10022-4212

MERCER, RONALD L., retired manufacturing executive; b. Camargo, Okla., Oct. 19, 1934; s. Joseph William and Lura (Dewald) M.; m. D. Yvonne Edwards, July 23, 1954; children: Gary D., Marla K., Lisa R., Michael D. BBA, So. Nazarene U., Bethany, Okla., 1970; HHD, So. Nazarene U., 1989; PMD, Harvard U., 1973. Br. sales mgr. Xerox Corp., Dallas, 1961-65; br. mgr. Xerox Corp., Oklahoma City, 1965-70; mgr. sales planning Xerox Corp., Rochester, N.Y., 1970-71; regional sales mgr. Xerox Corp., Chgo., 1971-74; regional v.p., gen. mgr. Xerox Corp., Greenwich, Conn., 1975-79; sr. v.p. Xerox Corp., Rochester, 1982-87; pres., chief exec. officer Xerox Can., Inc., Toronto, Ont., 1979-82; chmn., chief exec. officer Wilson Foods Corp. wholly owned subs. Doskocil Cos., Inc., Oklahoma City, 1988-89; pres., COO Doskocil Cos., Inc., 1989-91. Chmn. internat. Layman's Conf., Nashville, 1991; bd. dirs. So. Nazarene U., Internat. Ch. Nazarene, Kansas City, Kans; pres. Bethany (Okla.) Healthcare Corp. Republican. Mem. Ch. of Nazarene. Avocation: golf. Home: 7917 NW 38th St Bethany OK 73008-3141 Office: 3925 N Asbury Bethany OK 73008

MERCHANT, CARL WILLIAM, II, retail executive; b. Martinsburg, W.Va., Nov. 24, 1949; s. Carl William and Margery Ellen (Scenindiver) M.; m. Kathleen Mary Delaney, 1983; 1 child, Kaitlin Delaney. BS in Indl. Engring., W.Va. U., 1972; MBA, George Mason U., 1978. Mgr. mfg. Woodward & Lothrop, Washington, 1972-73; indsl. engr. Carolina Power & Light, Sanford, N.C., 1973-74; mgr. distbn. ops. Woodward & Lothrop, Washington, 1974-76, mgr. distbn. cen., 1976-80, v.p. constrn., 1980-81, v.p. store planning, 1981-82, sr. v.p. planning, ops., 1982—; mem. D.C. Constrn. Users Group (v.p.), 1984—; bd. dirs. W.Va. U. Faculty Adv. Bd., 1980—. Mem. Internat. Council Shopping Ctrs., Washington Bldg. Congress. Republican. Episcopal. Club: Washington Golf and Country. Avocations: golf, skiing, tennis. Office: Woodward & Lothrop Inc 1025 F St NW Washington DC 20004-1414

MERCHANT, CAROLYN, environmental history educator. AB in Chemistry, Vassar Coll., 1958; postgrad., U. Pa., 1958-59; MA in History of Sci., U. Wis., 1962, PhD in History of Sci., 1967. Prof. environ. history, philosophy and ethics dept. environ. sci., policy and mgmt. U. Calif., Berkeley, former chair dept. conservation and resource studies; vis. prof. Ecole Normale Superieure, Paris, 1986; Am. cultures fellow U. Calif., 1990; vis. fellow sch. social scis. Murdoch U., Perth, Australia, 1991; cons. for numerous TV and radio projects on sci., environment and soc.; lectr. in field. Author: The Death of Nature: Women, Ecology and the Scientific Revolution, 1980, 2d edit., 1990, Ecological Revolutions: Nature, Gender and Science in New England, 1989, Radical Ecology: The Search for a Livable World, 1992; editor: Major Problems in Environmental History: Documents and Essays, 1993, Key Concepts in Critical Theory: Ecology, 1994; contbr. articles to profl. jours. Grantee NSF, 1976-78, NEH, 1977, 81-83, Nathan Cummings Found., 1992; fellow Am. Coun. Learned Socs., 1978, Ctr. Advanced Study in Behavioral Scis., 1978; Fulbright Sr. Scholar, Umeå, Sweden, 1984. Achievements include research on the environmental history of California. Office: U Calif Dept Environ Sci Policy and Mgmt 570 Univ Hall Berkeley CA 94720

MERCHANT, DONALD JOSEPH, microbiologist; b. Biltmore, N.C., Sept. 7, 1921; s. Oscar Lowell and Bess Lee (Clark) M.; m. Marian Adelaide

Yeager, May 31, 1943; children—Nancy Adele, Barry Scott, Karen Ruth. A.B., Berea Coll., 1942; M.S., U. Mich., 1947, Ph.D., 1950. Instr. U. Mich., 1948-51, asst. prof., 1951-58, asso. prof., 1958-64, prof., 1964-69; dir., scientist W. Alton Jones Cell Sci. Center, Tissue Culture Assn., Lake Placid, N.Y., 1969-72; prof. U. Vt., 1969-72; prof., chmn. dept. microbiology and immunology Eastern Va. Med. Sch., Norfolk, 1973-86, prof. emeritus, 1986—; dir Tidewater Regional Cancer Network, 1974-88; cons. U.S. Army Biol. Lab., 1966-; mem. sci. adv. bd. Found. for Research on the Nervous System, Boston, 1965-69, Masonic Med. Research Lab., Utica, N.Y., 1970-75; mem. Nat. Prostatic Cancer Task Force, Nat. Cancer Inst., 1972-79, 83-86. Author: (with others) Handbook of Cell and Organ Culture, 1960, 2d edit., 1964; Editor: (with J.V. Neel) Approaches to the Genetic Analysis of Mammalian Cells, 1962, Cell Cultures for Virus Vaccine Production, 1968, (with others) Biology of Connective Tissues Cells, 1962; Contbr. (with others) chpts. to books, articles to profl. jours. Served with U.S. Army, 1944-46. Mem. Am. Acad. Microbiology, Am. Soc. Microbiology (past pres. Mich. br.), Soc. Exptl. Biology and Medicine, Am. Soc. Cell Biology, Tissue Culture Assn. (pres. 1964-68), Va. Acad. Sci., N.Y. Acad. Sci., Assn. Community Cancer Centers, Brit. Soc. Cell Biology, Royal Soc. Medicine. Presbyterian. Home: Apt 622 3100 Shore Dr Virginia Beach VA 23451

MERCHANT, ISMAIL NOORMOHAMED, film producer; b. Bombay, Dec. 25, 1936; arrived in U.S., 1958; s. Noormohamed and Hazrabi (Memon) Rehman. BA, St. Xavier's Coll., Bombay, 1958; MBA, NYU, 1960. V.p. Merchant Ivory Prodns. Inc., N.Y.C., 1962—. Prodr.: (films) Creation of Woman, 1960, The Householder, 1963, Shakespeare Wallah, 1965, The Guru, 1969, Bombay Talkie, 1970, Adventures of a Brown Man in Search of Civilization, 1971, Savages, 1972, Helen, Queen of the Nautch Girls, 1973 (dir.), Mahatma and the Mad Boy, 1973, Autobiography of a Princess, 1975, The Wild Party, 1975, Sweet Sounds, 1976, Roseland, 1977, Hullabaloo Over Georgie and Bonnie's Pictures, 1978, The Europeans, 1979, The Five-Forty-Eight, 1979, Jane Austen in Manhattan, 1980, Quartet 1981 (dir.), The Courtesans of Bombay, 1982, Heat and Dust, 1983, The Bostonians, 1984, A Room With A View, 1986, Maurice, 1987, The Perfect Murder, 1988, The Deceivers, 1988, Slaves of New York, 1988, Mr. and Mrs. Bridge, 1990, Howards End, 1992, The Remains of the Day, 1993, In Custody, 1993 (dir.), Jefferson in Paris, 1995; author: (books) Ismail Merchant's Indian Cuisine, 1986, The Making of the Deceivers, 1988, Ismail Merchant's Vegetarian Cuisine, 1991, Ismail Merchant's Florence, 1993, Ismail Merchant's Passionate Meals: The New Indian Cuisine for Fearless Cooks and Adventurous Eaters, 1994. Home: 400 E 52nd St New York NY 10022 Office: 250 W 57th St Ste 1913A New York NY 10107

MERCHANT, JUDITH MIRIAM, state agency administrator, educator, counselor; b. Burlington, Iowa, Aug. 27, 1940; d. Arnold Walter and Dorothy Lulu (Kretzschmar) Schmidt; m. Richard Ival Merchant, Dec. 19, 1961; children—Michael Brian, David Bradley. B.A. Summa cum laude, U. Iowa, 1962; M.A., Ball State U., 1974; cert. advanced grad. study Boston U., 1976. Adminstr. alcohol program Wash. Dept. Social and Health Services, Olympia, 1977-79, mgr. day care services, 1978-80, dir. bur. alcohol and substance abuse, 1980-81, exec. asst. to dept. sec. and dir intergovtl. relations, 1981-82, dir. div. income assistance, 1982-86; dep. dir. Mich. Dept. Social Services, 1986; dep. dir. Wash. Dept. of Fisheries, 1986-93; dir. Wash. State Energy Office Gov. Cabinet, 1993—; adminstr. alcohol and drug services, also educator secondary edn. Dept. Def., Fed. Republic of Germany, 1971-76; dep. dir. Wash. State Dept. Fisheries, 1986—. Ch. council Lutheran Ch. of Good Shepherd, Olympia, 1979-82; adv. com. Community Vol. Med. Program for Low-Income Families, Olympia, 1982—; bd. dirs. Wash. State Employees Credit Union, Olympia, 1983—. Recipient Service award VIIth Corps Hdqrs. U.S. Army, Fed. Republic of Germany, 1975. Mem. Nat. Assn. State Alcohol and Drug Dirs. (exec. bd. 1980-81), Am. Pub. Welfare Assn. (exec. bd.), Pacific Fisheries Mgmt. Coun., N. Pacific Mgmt. Coun., 1987-93, Nat. Assn. State Energy Officials (vice chair), We. Interstate Energy Bd. (mem. exec. com. 1994), European Congress Am. Parents and Tchrs. (v.p. 1972-74), Exec. Women in State Govt., Phi Beta Kappa. Home: 3724 Pifer Ct SE Olympia WA 98501-4160 Office: Energy Office PO Box 43165 Olympia WA 98504-3165

MERCHANT, MYLON EUGENE, physicist, engineer; b. Springfield, Mass., May 6, 1913; s. Mylon Dickinson and Rebecca Chase (Currier) M.; m. Helen Silver Bennett, Aug. 4, 1937; children—Mylon David, Helen Ann Merchant Alexander, Frances Sue Merchant Jacobson. B.S. magna cum laude, U. Vt., 1936, D.Sc. (hon.), 1973; D.Sc., U. Cinn., 1941; D.Sc. (hon.), U. Salford, Eng., 1980; D of Engring (hon.), GMI Engring. and Mgmt. Inst., 1994. Research physicist Cinn. Milacron, Inc., 1940-48, sr. research physicist, 1948-51, asst. dir. research, 1951-57, dir. phys. research, 1957-63, dir. sci. research, 1963-69, dir. research planning, 1969-81, prin. scientist, mfg. research, 1981-83; dir. advanced mfg. research Metcut Research Assocs., Inc., 1983-90; sr. cons. Inst. Advanced Mfg. Scis., Cinn., 1990—; adj. prof. mech. engring. U. Cin., 1964-69; vis. prof. mech. engring. U. Salford, Eng., 1973—. Bd. dirs. Dan Beard council Boy Scouts Am., 1967-80, pres.'s council, 1980—. Recipient Georg Schlesinger prize City of Berlin, 1980; Otto Benedikt prize Hungarian Acad. Scis., 1981; ; named to Automation Hall of Fame, 1995. Fellow Soc. Tribologists and Lubrication Engrs. (pres. 1952-53), Am. Soc. Metals Internat., Ohio Acad. Sci., Soc. Mfg. Engrs. (hon. mem., pres. 1976-77); mem. NAE, ASME (hon.), Internat. Instn. Prodn. Engring. Rsch. (hon., pres. 1968-69), Engrs. and Scientists of Cin. (pres. 1961-62), Fedn. Materials Socs. (pres. 1974), Phi Beta Kappa, Sigma Xi, Tau Beta Pi. Achievements include research on systems approach to manufacturing. Home: 3939 Erie Ave Apt 105 Cincinnati OH 45208-1913 Office: Inst of Advanced Mfg Scis 1111 Edison Dr Cincinnati OH 45216-2265

MERCHANT, ROLAND SAMUEL, SR., hospital administrator, educator; b. N.Y.C., Apr. 18, 1929; s. Samuel and Eleta (McLymont) M.; m. Audrey Bartley, June 6, 1970; children—Orelia Eleta, Roland Samuel, Huey Bartley. BA, NYU, 1957, MA, 1960; MS, Columbia U., 1963, MSHA, 1974. Asst. statistician N.Y.C. Dept. Health, 1957-60, statistician 1960-63; statistician N.Y. TB and Health Assn., N.Y.C., 1963-65; biostatistician, adminstrv. coord. Inst. Surg. Studies, Montefiore Hosp., Bronx, N.Y., 1965-72; resident in adminstrn. Roosevelt Hosp., N.Y.C., 1973-74; dir. health and hosp. mgmt. Dept. Health, City of N.Y., 1974-76; from asst. adminstr. to adminstr. West Adams Community Hosp., L.A., 1976; spl. asst. to assoc. v.p. for med. affairs Stanford U. Hosp., Calif., 1977-82, dir. office mgmt. and strategic planning, 1982-85, dir. mgmt. planning, 1986-90; v.p. strategic planning Cedars-Sinai Med. Ctr., L.A., 1990-94; cons. Roland Merchant & Assocs., L.A., 1994—; clin. assoc. prof. dept. family, community and preventive medicine Stanford U., 1986-88, dept. health rsch. and policy Stanford U. Med. Sch., 1988-90. Served with U.S. Army, 1951-53. USPHS fellow. Fellow Am. Coll. Healthcare Execs., Am. Pub. Health Assn.; mem. Am. Hosp. Assn., Nat. Assn. Health Services Execs., N.Y. Acad. Scis. Home: 27335 Park Vista Rd Agoura Hills CA 91301-3639

MERCIECA, CHARLES, philosophy and political science educator; b. Hamrun, Malta, Feb. 3, 1933; came to U.S. 1961; s. Carmelo and Julia (Brincat) M.; m. Sherry Jean Watson, May 15, 1950; children: Juliette, Alexander. BA in English, Loyola U., Malta, 1955; BA Philosophy, Aloisianum Coll., Varese, Italy, 1958; MS in Mgmt., Kans. State U., 1964; PhD, U. Kans., 1966. Prof. history, geography, philosophy and polit. sci. Ala. A&M U., Normal, 1967—; supr. Ala. A&M U., 1969-75, asst. to pres., 1987-91, dir. Inst. for Internat. Rels., 1988—; exec. v.p. Internat. Assn. of Educators for World Peace, Huntsville, Ala.; cons. UN, N.Y.C., 1973—; UNESCO, Paris, 1973—, Drug Rehab. prog., Montgomery, Ala., 1988—; vis. prof. Tver State U., Russia, 1992-93, U. Santa Ana, El Salvador, spring 1990. Author: Mismanagement in Higher Education, 1986 (citation 1987), Iscariots of Killversity, 1987 (citation 1988), Teaching Methods: On Making Classroom Instruction More Effective and Relevant, 1990, Education for Peace:: What It Entails, 1991, Administrative Skills and the Development of the Human Potential, 1992, Perspective of Yeltsin's Russia: Problems and Challenges, 1994. Recipient Kr. Col., 1983; Grand Cross of Honor & Merit, Federal Republic Germany, 1990; Albert Schweitzer Peace award, 1992. Mem. AAUP, NEA, Internat. Parliament for Safety and Peace (fed. magistrate 1987—), Internat. Assn. Educators for World Peace (sec.-gen. 1970-78, exec. v.p 1978—), World Constn. and Parliament Assn. (trustee mem.). Office: Internat Assn Educators World Peace PO Box 3282 Huntsville AL 35810-0282

MERCIER, EILEEN ANN, management consultant; b. Toronto, Ont., Can., July 7, 1947; d. Thomas Sidley and Frances Katherine (Boone) Falconer; m. Ernest Cochrane Mercier, Jan. 29, 1980; children: Jenny, Sheelagh, Peter, Michael, Stuart. BA with honors, Waterloo Luth. U., 1968; MA, U. Alberta, 1969; fellow, Instn. Can. Bankers, 1975; MBA, York U., 1977. Mgr. corp fin. Toronto-Dominion Bank, 1972-78, portfolio mgr. TD capital; dir., U.S. comm. ops Canwest Capital Corp., Toronto, 1978-81; mgr. fin. strategy & planning Gulf Can. Ltd., Toronto, 1981-86, mgr. corp. fin.; v.p. The Pagurian Corp., Toronto, 1986-87; v.p., treas. Abitibi-Price, Inc., Toronto, 1987-88, v.p. corp devel., 1989-90, sr. v.p., CFO, 1990-95; bd. dirs. John Labbatt Ltd.; bd. dirs. C.I.C.P.A. Bus. Ventures Fund Inc., Winpak Ltd. Bd. dirs. Toronto Hosp. Found., Metro Toronto YMCA; past chmn., mem. bd. govs. Wilfrid Laurier U., Waterloo, Ont. Recipient Outstanding Bus. Leader award Sch. Bus. & Econs., Wilfrid Laurier U., 1991. Office: Finvoy Mgmt Inc, 207 Queens Quay W Ste 6800, Toronto, ON Canada M5J 2P5

MERCIER, FRANCOIS, lawyer; b. Paris, France, Apr. 13, 1923; s. Oscar and Jeanne (Bruneau) M.; m. Lucile Rouleau, May 25, 1946; children—Genevieve, Madeleine, Jean Francois, Helene. B.A., Loyola Coll., Montreal, Que., Can., 1942; LL.B., U. Montreal, 1945. Bar: Called to bar Que 1945. Since practiced in Montreal; sr. partner Stikeman, Elliott and predecessors, 1964—; lectr. ins. law U. Montreal, 1945-58. Pres. La Librairie Fernand Nathan Can. Ltée.; vice chmn. Société des Hôtels Méridien Can., Ltée. Decorated officer Order of Can. Fellow Am. Coll. Trial Lawyers; mem. Can. bar assns., Montreal bar assns. Home: One Spring Grove Crescent, Outremont, PQ Canada H2V 3H8 Office: Stikeman Elliott, 1155 Dorchester St, Montreal, PQ Canada

MERCORELLA, ANTHONY J., lawyer, former state supreme court justice; b. N.Y.C., Mar. 6, 1927; s. Sante and Josephine (Bozzuti) M.; m. Maria G. Delucia, June 16, 1956; children: Anne Mercorella Flynn, Susan Mercorella Creavin, Robert, Carole. B.A., L.I. U., 1949; LL.D., Fordham U., 1952. Bar: N.Y. Law asst. City Ct., City of N.Y., 1955-62; chief law asst. Civil Ct. City of N.Y., 1962-65; mem. N.Y. State Assembly, 1965-72; councilman City N.Y., 1973-75; judge Civil Ct. City of N.Y., 1975-79; justice Supreme Ct., N.Y.C., 1980-84; ptnr. Wilson, Elser, Moskowitz, Edelman & Dicker, N.Y.C., 1984—; currently arbitrator and mediator in various dispute resolution systems. Served with USN, 1945-46, Europe, Pacific. Mem. ABA (del. N.Y. State Bar Assn.), N.Y. State Bar Assn., Assn. of Bar of City of N.Y., Bronx County Bar Assn. (pres. 1971), Columbian Lawyers Westchester County (pres. 1984). Office: Wilson Elser Moskowitz Edelman & Dicker 150 E 42nd St New York NY 10017-5639

MERCURIO, RENARD MICHAEL, real estate corporation executive; b. N.Y.C., June 22, 1947; s. Pasquale J. and Ann F. Mercurio; m. Abbie Gonzalez, June 29, 1968; children—Kristin, Allison. B.A., Queens Coll., N.Y.C., 1968; M.B.A., U. Rochester, 1969. CPA, N.Y.; lic. real estate broker, Calif. Sr. accountant Peat, Marwick & Mitchell, N.Y.C., 1969-73; mgr. Gulf & Western Industries, Inc., N.Y.C., 1973-78; v.p., treas. Famous Players Ltd., Toronto, Ont., Can., 1978-81; exec. v.p. Famous Players Realty Ltd., Toronto, 1981-84; v.p. Design Twenty-Seven Ltd., Toronto, 1984-87; pres. Renric Holdings, Ltd., 1987—; co-founder, pres. The Millennium Holistic Therapy Ctr., 1994—.—. Mem. AICPA, N.Y. State Soc. CPAs, Calif. Assn. Mortgage Brokers, Calif. Assn. Realtors.

MERDEK, ANDREW AUSTIN, publishing/media executive, lawyer; b. Portland, Maine, Oct. 11, 1950; s. Philip and Eleanor (Weiss) M.; m. Jeanne Mullen, July 22, 1983; children: David, Jonathan. AB, Middlebury Coll., 1972; JD, U. Va., 1978. Bar: D.C. 1978, U.S. Dist. Ct. D.C. 1979, U.S. Ct. Appeals (D.C. cir.) 1979, U.S. Supreme Ct. 1982. Reporter, editor Portland Press Herald, 1973-75; assoc. Dow, Lohnes & Albertson, Washington, 1978-86, ptnr., 1986-87; v.p., gen. mgr. Atlanta Constitution and Journal, 1987-92; v.p. legal affairs, corp. sec. Cox Enterprises Inc., Atlanta, 1993—. Mem. Order of Coif, Phi Beta Kappa. Home: 445 Mt Vernon Hwy NW Atlanta GA 30327-4313 Office: Cox Enterprises Inc 1400 Lake Hearn Dr NE Atlanta GA 30319-1464

MERDINGER, CHARLES JOHN, civil engineer, naval officer, academic adminstrator; b. Chgo., Apr. 20, 1918; s. Walter F. and Catherine (Phelan) M.; m. Mary McKelleget, Oct. 21, 1944; children: Anne, Joan, Susan, Jane. Student, Marquette U.; BS, U.S. Naval Acad., 1941; BCE, Rensselaer Poly. Inst., 1945, MCE, 1946; DPhil (Rhodes scholar), Brasenose Coll., Oxford U., Eng., 1949; LHD (hon.), Sierra Nev. Coll., 1987; LLD (hon.), U. Nev., 1994. Registered profl. engr., Wis. Commd. ensign U.S. Navy, 1941, advanced through grades to capt., 1959; served aboard USS Nevada, USS Alabama Atlantic and Pacific, 1941-44; design, constrn. pub. works Panama, 1946-47, Washington, Bremerton, Wash., Adak, Alaska and Miramar, Calif., 1949-56; comdg. officer, dir. U.S. Naval Civil Engring. Lab., Port Hueneme, Calif., 1956-59; pub. works officer U.S. Fleet activities, Yokosuka, Japan, 1959-62; head English, history and govt. dept. U.S. Naval Acad., Annapolis, Md., 1962-65; asst. comdr. ops. & maintenance Naval Facilities Engring. Command, Navy Dept., 1965-67; pub. works officer Seabees (NSA), DaNang, Vietnam, 1967-68; comdg. officer Western div. Naval Facilities Engring. Command, San Bruno, 1968-70; pres. Washington Coll., Chestertown, Md., 1970-73; v.p. Aspen (Colo.) Inst. Humanistic Studies, 1973-74; dep. dir. Scripps Instn. Oceanography, La Jolla, Calif., 1974-80; dir. Avco, 1978—. Author: Civil Engineering Through the Ages, 1963; contbr.: articles to Ency. Britannica; others. Mem. Md., Calif., Oreg. and Nev. Selection Coms. for Rhodes Scholars, sec. Nev. Com., 1982-89; exec. vol. Boy Scouts Am.; sec., mem. exec. com. Md. Ind. Coll. and Univ. Assn., 1971-72; mem. So. Regional Edn. Bd., 1971-73, Nat. Com. History and Heritage of Am. Civil Engring., 1965-72; alumni trustee U.S. Naval Acad., 1971-74; mem. council Rensselaer Poly. Inst., 1972—; trustee Found. for Ocean Research, 1976-80, Desert Research Inst. Found., Nev., 1983-92, U. Nev. Reno Found., 1986-93; chmn. bd. trustees Sierra Nevada Coll., 1980-87, chmn. bd. emeritus, 1987; commr. N.W. Assn. Commn. on Colls., 1988-93. Decorated Legion of Merit with combat V, Navy Meritorious Service medal, combat action ribbon; named All-Am. in lacrosse, 1945, Papal Knight Grand Cross Equestrian Order of Holy Sepulchre of Jerusalem, 1992; inducted into Rensselaer Athletic Hall of Fame, 1983; recipient Disting. Eagle Scout award, 1984. Fellow ASCE (Nat. History and Heritage award 1972), Explorers Club, Soc. Am. Mil. Engrs. (Toulmin medal 1952, 57, 61); mem. NSPE, Soc. History Tech., Am. Soc. Engring. Edn., Brasenose Soc., Pearl Harbor Survivors Assn., Nat. Eagle Scout Assn. (regent), Phalanx, Sigma Xi, Tau Beta Pi, Chi Epsilon. Roman Catholic. Clubs: Vincent's, Oxford. Home: 726 Tyner Way PO Box 7249 Incline Village NV 89452 also: 5538 Caminito Consuelo La Jolla CA 92037

MEREDITH, ALLEN KENT, real estate developer; b. Schenectady, Mar. 27, 1949; s. Jack Allen and Georgia (Pulliam) M.; m. Kim Myegaard, Sept. 23, 1978; 1 child, Alexis. BA in Econs., Stanford U., 1972; MBA, Harvard U., 1976. Assoc. Trammell Crow Co., Dallas, 1978-79; ptnr. Trammell Crow Co., Atlanta, 1980-84; div. ptnr. Trammell Crow Co., L.A., 1984-87; area ptnr. Trammell Crow Co., 1987-89, reg. ptnr., 1989—. Mem. Harvard Bus. Sch Assn., Stanford Buck Club, Regency Club of L.A., Capital City Country Club (Atlanta). Republican. Methodist. Avocation: marathon running. Home: 44 Tuscaloosa Ave Menlo Park CA 94027-4015 Office: Trammell Crow Co 950 Tower Lane Ste 1900 Foster City CA 94404

MEREDITH, BURGESS, actor; b. Cleve., Nov. 16, 1909; s. William George and Ida (Burgess) M.; m. Helen Berrian Derby, 1932 (div. 1935); m. Margaret H. Frueauff (Margaret Perry), 1936 (div. July 1938); m. Paulette Goddard, May 21, 1944 (div. July 1948); m. Kaja Sundsten, 1950; children: Jonathan Sanford, Tala Beth. Student. Amherst Coll., 1927-28, A.M. (hon.), 1939. Reporter, salesman, seaman, 1928-29; exec. dir. Actors Studio West, 1972—; artistic dir. Merle Oberon Theatre, L.A., 1972—; v.p. Actors Equity, 1938—, acting pres. spring 1938; chmn. adv. bd. Fed. Arts Projects, 1937. First small part with, Eva La Gallienne's Student Repertory Group, 1930; theatre appearances include Little Ol' Boy, 1933; She Loves Me Not, 1933, The Barretts of Wimpole Street, (with Katherine Cornell) Flowers of the Forest, 1935, Winterset, 1936 (Drama Critics award), High Tor, 1937 (Drama Critics award), Star Wagon, 1937, Five Kings, 1939, Liliom, 1941, Candida, 1942, Lincoln Portrait, 1943, The Playboy of the Western World, 1947, Winterset, 1947, Harvey, 1950, Let Me Hear the Melody, 1951, Lo and Behold! (dir.), 1951, The Remarkable Mr. Pennypacker, 1953, 58, Macbeth

(dir.), 1954, Teahouse of the August Moon, 1955, Major Barbara, 1956, Speaking of Murder (producer), 1957, Ulysses in Nighttown (dir.), 1958, 74, Enrico IV, 1958, God and Kate Murphy (dir.), 1959, The Vagabond King, 1959, A Thurber Carnival (dir.), 1960, An Evening with Burgess Meredith, 1960, Midgie Purvis (dir.), 1961, A Whiff of Melancholy (dir.), 1961, Blues for Mr. Charlie (dir.), 1964, Park Your Car in Harvard Yard, 1984; motion pictures include Winterset, 1936; There Goes the Groom, 1937, Spring Madness, 1938, Idiot's Delight, 1938, Of Mice and Men, 1939, Castle on the Hudson, 1940, Second Chorus, 1941, San Francisco Docks, 1941, That Uncertain Feeling, 1941, Tom, Dick and Harry, 1941, The Forgotten Village, 1941, Street of Chance, 1942, Welcome to Britain, 1943, Salute to France, 1944, The Yank Comes Back, 1945, Story of G.I. Joe, 1945, The Diary of a Chambermaid, 1946, Magnificent Doll, 1946, On Our Merry Way, 1948, Mine Own Executioner, 1948, Jigsaw, 1949, The Man on the Eiffel Tower, 1950, The Gay Adventure, 1953, Joe Butterfly, 1957, Universe, 1961, Advise and Consent, 1962, The Cardinal, 1963, In Harm's Way, 1965, Madame X, 1966, The Crazy Quilt, 1966, A Big Hand for the Little Lady, 1966, Batman, 1966, Hurry Sundown, 1967, Fortune Garden, 1968, Stay Away Joe, 1967, Mackenna's Gold, 1967, There Was a Crooked Man, 1969, The Yin and the Yang (also writer, dir.), 1970, A Fan's Notes, 1970, The Clay Pidgeon, 1970, Such Good Friends, 1971, The Man, 1972, B for Murder, 1973, Golden Needles, 1973, Day of the Locust, 1973, The Hindenburg, 1974, 92 in the Shade, 1975, Burnt Offerings, 1975, Rocky, 1976 (Acad. award nomination), The Sentinel, 1977, Foul Play, 1978, Magic, 1978, The Manitou, 1978, Rocky II, 1979, The Day the World Ended, 1979, Clash of the Titans, 1979, Final Assignment, 1979, The Last Chase, 1979, When Time Ran Out, 1980, True Confessions, 1980, Rocky III, 1982, Wet Gold, 1984, Santa Claus-The Movie, 1984, Outrage, 1986, Mr. Corbett's Ghost, 1986, No Thing, 1988, Full Moon in Blue Water, 1988, State of Grace, 1990, Rocky V, 1990, Grumpy Old Men, 1993, Camp Nowhere, 1994, Tall Tale, 1994; producer, writer: Diary of a Chambermaid, 1946; producer, actor: On Our Merry Way, 1947; dir.: Man On The Eiffel Tower, 1948, The Latent Heterosexual, 1969; writer, dir., narrator: film Afterglow (on the life Robert Frost), 1986; various TV appearances, including World of Disney; dir. others; directed, N.Y. Symphony, Carnegie Hall, 1969; narrator numerous commls.; film Houdini, 1979; co-host: Those Amazing Animals, ABC-TV, 1980-81; filmed: documentary Myths of Ancient Greece, 1981; singer, narrator the dragon in Puff the Magic Dragon, Part II, 1979; appeared as Penguin in TV series Batman, 1965-66; author: So Far, So Good. Served with AUS, 1942-44, ETO. Episcopalian. Club: Players (N.Y.C.)

MEREDITH, DALE DEAN, civil engineering educator, consultant; b. Centralia, Ill., Mar. 24, 1940; s. Leslie Edward Meredith and Beulah Marie (McClelland) Nattier; m. Linda Jean Hutson, July 3, 1965; children: Sarah Elizabeth, Laura Jane. AA, Centralia Twp. Jr. Coll., 1961; BS, U. Ill., 1963, MS, 1964, PhD, 1968. Registered profl. engr., N.Y., Ill. Asst. prof. U. Ill., Urbana, 1968-73; assoc. prof. civil engring. SUNY, Buffalo, 1973-79, prof., 1979—; chmn. Dept. Civil Engring., 1987—. Co-author: Design and Planning Engineering Systems, 1973, 2d edit., 1985; also over 50 articles. Vice pres. Baptist Conv. N.Y., Syracuse, 1982-84, 94—, chmn. exec. bd., 1987. Grantee U.S. Office Water Research and Tech., 1966-73, 75-78, U.S. Dept. Interior, 1968-79, U.S. Dept. Commerce, 1976-79, various pvt. cos., 1979—, N.Y. State Agys., 1980—. Fellow ASCE (chmn. exec. com. Water Resources Planning and Mgmt. div., 1988, editor jour. Water Resources Planning and Mgmt. 1982-84); mem. Am. Geophys. Union, Am. Soc. Engring. Edn., Am. Water Resources Assn. (editor Water Resources Bull. 1990-91), Internat. Assn. Water Resources, Water Environ. Fedn. Office: SUNY Dept Civil Engring Buffalo NY 14260-4300

MEREDITH, DAVID ROBERT, investor; b. Cleve., Apr. 9, 1940; s. Wilbur R. and Lillian B. M.; AB, Colgate U., 1962; PhD (Ford Found. grantee), MIT, 1966; student U.de Cuyo, 1961, U. de Tucuman, 1960; m. Sheila Kay Provost, Dec. 21, 1963; children—Karen, Adam, Alison. Labor cons. W.R. Meredith & Co., Cleve., 1958-65; labor asst. Mountain States Employers Coun., Denver, 1965-66; prin. McKinsey & Co., Inc., N.Y.C. and Cleve., 1966-75; pres. Meredith Assocs., Inc., Westport, Conn., 1975-81; chmn., chief exec. Pers. Corp. Am., Norwalk, 1980-94; pres. EM Internat., Wolfeboro, N.H., 1994—; bd. dirs. Gen Data Base Tech., Inc., Rotando Advt. Ptnrs., Meredith Marine; chmn. bd. Canberra Industries, 1978—, North Wind Power Co., 1976-78; rsch. and teaching asst. M.I.T., 1962-66; mem. Bus. Coun. for UN, 1989—. Fin. chmn. Weston Community Ctr., Inc., 1977; mem. Rep. Town Com., Weston, Conn., 1979-81, Weston Transit Study Commn., 1976-78; bd. dirs. Found. for a Greater Weston, Young Audiences of Conn., 1988-90; deacon Norfield Ch., 1975-81, fair chmn., 1977, treas., 1981-88, trustee, 1981-88, assoc. min. search com. chmn., 1990-91. NDEA fellow, 1962-65; FTES scholar, 1958-62; Williams scholar, 1960-61; recipient Osborne math. prize, Colgate U., 1962. Mem. Conn. Golf club (exec. com.), Aspetuck Valley Country Club, Bald Peak Club, Winged Foot Club, Ocean Reef Club, Loxahatchee Club, Princeton Club. Contbr. articles to newspapers, bus. and profl. jours. Home: 282 Locha Dr Jupiter FL 33458 Office: 428 Sewell Rd Wolfeboro NH 03894-1008

MEREDITH, EDWIN THOMAS, III, media executive; b. Chgo., Feb. 7, 1933; s. Edwin Thomas, Jr. and Anna (Kauffman) M.; m. Katherine Comfort, Sept. 4, 1953; children: Mildred M. (dec.), Dianna M., Edwin Thomas. Student, U. Ariz., 1950-53. With Meredith Corp., Des Moines, 1956—, varied mgmt. positions in mag., book and printing groups, 1956-65, asst. sec., bd. dirs. 1966-68, v.p., 1968-69, v.p., asst. to gen. mgr. mag. div., 1969-71; pres., chief exec. officer Meredith Corp., 1971-73; chmn. bd., chief exec. officer Meredith Corp., Des Moines, 1973-77, chmn. bd., 1977-88, chmn. exec. com., 1988—, also bd. dirs. Bd. dirs. Nat. Merit Scholarship Corp., Evanston, Ill., Iowa Natural Heritage Found, Des Moines; trustee Iowa Methodist Med. Ctr., Iowa 4-H Found., Ames; bd. govs. Drake U., Des Moines. With U.S. Army, 1953-56. Mem. Des Moines Club, Wakonda Club. Office: Meredith Corp 1716 Locust St Des Moines IA 50309-3023

MEREDITH, ELLIS EDSON, association and business executive; b. Mobile, Ala., Sept. 5, 1927; s. Charles Elmer and Eleanor Emery (Ellis) M.; m. Alice Foley; children: Shane Snowdon, Kent Williamson, Scott Emery; stepchildren: Scott Corcoran, Candace Corcoran. AB, U. Chgo., 1948, George Washington U., 1950. Exec. dir. Allied Florists Assn. of Greater Washington, 1952-55; legis. dir. Am. Assn. Nurserymen, 1955-58; asst. mgr. assn. dept. C. of C. U.S., 1958-60; pres. Am. Apparel Mfrs. Assn., Arlington, Va., 1960-84, Nat. Ctr. for Missing and Exploited Children, 1986-89; chmn. bd. dirs., CEO Allied Realty Corp.; chmn. Newsletters Inc., Food Execs. Internat. Found., 1989—; pres. Orgn. Mgmt., Inc.; bd. dirs. Phillips Van Heusen Corp., Internat. Apparel Fedn.; mem. adv. bd. Prodn. Group Internat. Fin. chmn. Md. Rep. Party, 1977-78; bd. visitors Sch. Pub. Affairs, U. Md.; bd. dirs., chmn. U. Md. Found. Mem. Am. Soc. Assn. Execs. (chmn. 1978-80), Greater Washington Soc. Assn. Execs. (pres. 1965-66), Met. Club, Nat. Press Club, Bethesda Country Club, Capital Hill Club. Episcopalian. Home: 7600 Carter Ct Bethesda MD 20817-1411

MEREDITH, GEORGE DAVIS, advertising agency executive; b. Milw., Aug. 7, 1940; s. George Wade and Carol (Catcott) M.; m. Ruth Lawrence, 1964 (div. 1968); 1 child, Hilary; m. Elizabeth Lee, Feb. 8, 1969; children: Sean, Daniel, Lisa. Student U. Ariz., 1958-60; BA, Fla. So. U., 1962; postgrad., Ind. U., 1963-66. With Spencer Mktg., Inc., N.Y.C., 1967-68, Force, Inc., Paterson, N.J., 1968-70; v.p., creative dir. Gianettino and Meredith, Inc., Short Hills, N.J., 1977—; pres. Derring-do Press; mem. founder com. Advt. Hall of Fame; Author: (poetry) Two for You, One for Me, 1967; contbr. articles to profl. jours.; Trustee Bloomfield (N.J.) Coll., 1982—; bd. dirs. Unity Concerts, Montclair, 1983—; mem. adv. coun. Reading is Fundamental, Inc.; nat. co-chmn. Yogi Berra/Montclair State U. Stadium Fund. Named to N.J. Advt. Hall of Fame, 1987. Mem. New Jersey Advt. (bd. dirs. 1978-81), Pi Delta Epsilon, Sigma Tau Delta, Omicron Delta Kappa, Sigma Chi. Home: 159 Upper Mountain Ave Montclair NJ 07042-1905 Office: Gianettino & Meredith Inc 788 Morris Tpke Short Hills NJ 07078-2698

MEREDITH, GEORGE (MARLOR), association executive, writer; b. Somerville, N.J., Apr. 21, 1923; s. Gilbert Judson and Dorothea (Pope) M. m. Elizabeth Jean Moore, Nov. 15, 1955; children: Gilbert Judson III, Scott Arthur. Student, Columbia U., 1941-44. Indsl. engring. writer Johns-Manville Corp., 1942-44; mng. editor Mast, 1944-47; editor Premium Practice, 1947-55; ptnr., editorial dir. Meredith Assocs., 1955-67, pres., 1967-88, chmn., 1989-91; pres. Meredith Rsch. Corp., 1962-74; mng. dir. Meredith & Henry, 1977-92, chmn., 1992—; exec. sec. Assn. Incentive Mktg., 1957-67, exec. dir., 1967-74, pub. rels. dir., 1972—; mng. dir. Eastman Editorial Rsch., 1979-87; exec. sec. Nat. Assn. Food Equipment Mfrs., 1957-59; exec. dir. Nat. Premium Mktg. Reps., 1963-66, dir. rsch. programs, 1964-67; dir. Mktg. New Bur., Red Bank, N.J., 1973-92; exec. dir. Trading Stamp Inst. Am., Assn. Retail Mktg. Svcs., 1979-91, editorial dir., 1991-92, pub. rels. dir., 1993—; mng. dir., Mktg. Comms. Execs. Internat., 1981-85, exec. dir. N.Y. chpt., 1981-82. Author: Effective Merchandising with Premiums, 1962, Creative Application of Sales Incentive Plans, 1972, (film) The Caine Coil, 1973, Incentives in Marketing, 1977, Incentives in Marketing & Motivation, 1994; editor: Premiums in Marketing, 1971; exec. editor, rsch. dir. Incentive Marketing Facts, 1968-87; rsch. dir. Incentive Mag., 1988-92; editor, pub. Sales Motivation Letter, 1973-74; editor The Register, 1979—, The Communicator, 1982-85, Creative Mktg. newsletter, 1989—; contbr. articles to profl. publs. Coord., moderator Premiums and Incentives Conf. NYU, 1972; pub. rels. dir. Soc. Incentive Travel Execs., 1974-79. Recipient Premium Man of Yr. award Nat. Premium Mfrs. Reps., 1973, Nat. Premium Sales Execs. Past Pres.'s award, 1966, Disting. Achievement award Premium Advt. Assn. Am., 1963. Mem. Overseas Press Club, Am. Soc. Assn. Execs., Incentive Fedn. (vice chmn. 1984-88, 89—, chmn. 1988-89), Assn. Incentive Mktg., Premium Mktg. Club N.Y., Am. Humanist Assn., Lions. Home: 3 Caro Ct Red Bank NJ 07701-2315

MEREDITH, JAMES HOWARD, association executive, farmer, consultant; b. Kosciusko, Miss., June 25, 1933; s. Moses Cap and Roxie (Patterson) M.; m. Mary June Wiggins, Dec. 16, 1956; children: John Howard, Joseph Howard, James Henry; m. Judy Alsobrooks, Mar. 1981; 1 child, Jessica Howard. Student, Jackson (Miss.) State Coll., 1960-62; B.A. in Polit. Sci, U. Miss., 1963; student, U. Ibadan, Nigeria, West Africa, 1964-65; J.D., Columbia U., 1968. Lectr. on black race and Africa at various univs. and colls., internat. cons. African-Am. bus. relations; pres. African Devel. and Reunification Assn.; vis. prof. African-Am. Studies U. Cin., 1984-85. Author: Three Years in Mississippi, 1966. Served with USAF, 1951-60. Mem. Phi Alpha Delta.

MEREDITH, JULIA ALICE, nematologist, biologist, researcher; b. Asheboro, N.C., Aug. 21, 1943; d. Ralph Shanklin and Kathryn Virginia (Corder) M.; m. Renato N. Inserra, Aug. 31, 1985. BA, U. Ky., 1965, MS, 1966; DSc, U. Cen. Caracas, Venezuela, 1977. Instr. zoology Cen. U. Venezuela, Maracay, 1967-69, asst. prof., 1969-76, assoc. prof., 1976-79, prof. nematology, 1980-86, 89-90, head dept., 1980-90; rsch. assoc. U. Fla., Gainesville, 1986-87, vis. prof., 1988; rsch. assoc. U. Fla. and Agrl. Rsch. Svc., 1988-1991—; cons. ministries agr. Colombia, 1967-71, Uruguay, 1971, Ecuador, 1977, 80, Venezuela, 1980-84; vis. prof. Va. Poly. Inst. and State U., Blacksburg, 1985. Author: (lab manuals) Nematologia Agricola, 1969, Field and Laboratory Methods, 1974; editor Nematropica, 1971-73; mem. editorial bd. Fitopatologia Venezolana, 1989-92. Rsch. grantee Nat. Coun. Sci. and Tech., Caracas, 1975, 84, Nat. Coun. for Sci. Devel., Caracas, 1988. Fellow European Soc. Nematologists; mem. Orgn. Nematologists of Tropical Am. (treas. 1974-75, pres. 1978-79, Disting. Svc. award 1988), Soc. Nematologists (edn. com. 1988-89), Venezuelan Phytopath. Soc., Internat. Soc. Chem. Ecology, Internat. Wildlife Fedn., Nat. Wildlife Fedn., Nat. Audubon Soc., Fla. Audubon Soc., Sigma Xi, Alpha Epsilon Delta, Phi Epsilon Phi. Methodist. Avocation: swimming. Office: USDA Agrl Rsch Svc IABBBRL 1700 SW 23rd Dr Gainesville FL 32608-1069

MEREDITH, MICHAEL, science educator, researcher; b. London, Jan. 15, 1942; came to U.S., 1967; s. Philip George and Dorothy Mary M.; married. BSc with honors, U. Birmingham, England, 1963; PhD, U. Pa., 1974. Rsch. assoc. Rockefeller U., N.Y., 1975-77, Worcester Found. Exptl. Biology, Shrewsbury, Mass., 1977-81; rsch. assoc. Fla. State U., Tallahassee, 1981-84, asst. prof., 1984-88, co-dir. program in neurosci., 1986—, assoc. prof., 1988-93, prof., 1993—; cons. site visits, grant revs. NIH, Washington, grant proposals, peer revs. NSF, Washington. Contbr. articles to profl. jours., chpts. to books. Pre-Doctoral Rsch. fellow NIH, 1970-73, Post-Doctoral Rsch. fellow, 1978-80; Rsch. grantee NIH, 1982-85, 88-91, 90-94, 94—, NSF, 1984-87, 87-90. Mem. Soc. Neurosci. (pres. local chpt. 1991-92, 94-95), Assn. Chemoreception Scis. (councillor 1981-83, chair membership 1986-88, program com. 1990-91, exec. chair elect 1995—), N.Y. Acad. Scis. Office: Fla State U Dept Biol Sci Tallahassee FL 32306-4075

MEREDITH, THOMAS C., academic administrator. Vice chancellor exec. affairs U. Miss., until 1988; pres. Western Ky. U., Bowling Green, 1988—. Office: Western Ky U Office of President Bowling Green KY 42101

MEREDITH, WILLIAM (MORRIS), poet, English language educator; b. N.Y.C., Jan. 9, 1919; s. William Morris and Nelley Atkin (Keyser) M. AB magna cum laude, Princeton U., 1940, Woodrow Wilson fellow, 1946-47. Copy boy, reporter N.Y. Times, 1940-41; instr. English Princeton U., 1946, 47-48, 49-50; asst. prof. English U. Hawaii, 1950-51; assoc. prof. Conn. Coll., 1955-65, prof. English, 1965-83; opera critic Hudson Rev., 1955-56; instr. Bread Loaf Sch. English, Middlebury Coll., 1958-62; dir. humanities Upward Bound program, Conn. Coll., 1964-68; poetry cons. Library of Congress, 1978-80; chancellor Acad. Am. Poets; mem. Conn. Commn. Arts, 1963-65. Author: (poetry) Love Letter from an Impossible Land, 1944 (Yale Series of Younger Poets award 1943), Ships and Other Figures, 1948, The Open Sea and Other Poems, 1958, The Wreck of the Thresher and Other Poems, 1964, Winter Verse, 1964, Year End Accounts, 1965, Two Pages from a Colorado Journal, 1967, Earth Walk: New and Selected Poems, 1970, Hazard, the Painter, 1975, The Cheer, 1980, Partial Accounts: New and Selected Poems, 1987 (Pulitzer Prize for poetry 1988); (prose) Reasons for Poetry and the Reason for Criticism, 1982, Poems Are Hard to Read, 1991; (libretto) The Bottle Imp, 1958; editor: Shelley, 1962, University and College Poetry Prizes, 1960-66, 1966, (with Mackie L. Jarrell) Eighteenth-Century Minor Poets, 1968, Poets of Bulgaria, 1985, Windows on the Black Sea: Bulgarian Poetry in Translation, 1992; translator: Guillaume Apollinaire's Alcools: Poems, 1898-1913, 1964; recs. include Selected Poems, 1977. Served with USAAF, 1941-42; to lt. USNR, 1942-46, PTO; to lt. comdr. USNR, Korea. Decorated Air medal with oak leaf cluster; recipient Harriet Monroe Meml. prize, 1944, Oscar Blumenthal prize, 1953, Loines prize Nat. Inst. Arts and Letters, 1966, Van Wyck Brooks award, 1971, Internat. Nicola Vaptsarov prize in lit., Sofia, Bulgaria, 1979, L.A. Times prize, 1987; Rockefeller grantee, 1948, 68; Hudson Rev. fellow, 1956; National Inst. of Arts and Letters grantee, 1958; Ford Found. fellow, 1959-60; Nat. Endowment for the Arts grantee, 1972, fellow, 1984; Guggenheim fellow, 1975-76; Acad. Am. Poets fellow, 1990. Mem. Nat. Inst. Arts and Letters. Office: 337 Kitemaug Rd Uncasville CT 06382-2208*

MERENDINO, K. ALVIN, surgical educator; b. Clarksburg, W.Va., Dec. 3, 1914; s. Biagio and Cira (Bivona) M.; m. Shirley Emojane Hill, July 6, 1943; children: Cira Anne Watts, Nancy Jane Napuunoa, Susan Hill Mitchell, Nina Francine Sarich, Maria King Merendino-Stillwell. BA, Ohio U., 1936, LLD (hon.), 1967; MD, Yale U., 1940; PhD, U. Minn., 1946. Diplomate Am. Bd. Surgery, Am. Bd. Thoracic Surgery. Intern Cin. Gen. Hosp., 1940-41; resident U. Minn. Hosp., Mpls., 1941-45; rsch. asst. Dr. Owen H. Wangensteen, 1942-43; trainee Nat. Cancer Inst., 1943-45; dir. program in postgrad. med. edn. in surgery Ancker Hosp., St. Paul, 1946-48; instr. dept. surgery U. Minn., Mpls., 1944-45, asst. prof. dept. surgery, 1945-48; assoc. prof. dept. surgery U. Wash., Seattle, 1949-55, dir. exptl. surgery labs., dept. surgery, 1950-72, prof. dept. surgery, 1955-81, prof. emeritus, 1981—, prof. and adminstrv. officer dept. surgery, 1957-64, prof., chmn., 1965-72; chmn. dept. surgery King Faisal Specialist and Rsch. Ctgr., Riyadh, Saudi Arabia, 1976, dir. med. affairs, 1976-79, dir. Cancer Therapy Inst., spl. cons. to Coun., supr. for exec. mgmt., assoc. dir. med. affairs, 1981-82; dir. ops. King Faisal Med. City, Riyadh, 1981-85; mem. adv. com. for med. rsch., Boeing Airplane Co., 1959-67, chmn., 1962l cons. Children's Orthopedic Hosp., Seattle, 1972-82; mem. adv. com. on heart disease and surgery for crippled children's svc., Wash. State Dept. Health and Div. Vocational Rehab., 1961; mem. surgery study sect. NIH, 1958-62, subcom. on prosthetic valves for cardiac surgery, chm. 1st Nat. Conf., 1960, mem. adv. com. 2d Nat. Conf. on Prosthetic Heart Valves, 1969, Surgery A study sect. chmn., 1970-72, Nat. Heart and Lung Inst. Tng. Com., 1965-69; cons. VA, Seattle, 1949-59, 65-81; mem. adv. com. on hosps. and clinics, USPHS, 1963-66; mem. surgery test com. Nat. Bd. Med. Examiners, 1963-67; mem. surgery resident rev. com., Conf. Com. on Grad. Edn. in Surgery, 1963-73, vice-chmn., 1972-73; chmn.

2d Saudi Arabian Med. Conf., Riyadh, 1978; mem. com. on postgrad. med. edn., Kingdom of Saudi Arabia Ministry of Health, 1978-79. Editor in chief: Prosthetic Valves for Cardiac Surgery, 1961; assoc. editor: Prosthetic Heart Valves, 1969; mem. editorial bd. Am. Jour. Surgery, 1958—, Jour. Surg. Rsch., 1961-69, Pacific Medicine and Surgery, 1964-68, King Faisal Hosp. Medicine Jour. (renamed Annals of Saudi Medicine), 1981-85; contbr. articles to profl. jours., chpts. to books; producer movies on surgery. Recipient cert. of merit Ohio U. Alumni Assn., 1957, Outstanding W.Va. Italian-Am. award W.Va. Italian Heritage Festival Inc., Clarksburg, W.Va., 1984, Spirit of Freedom award A. James Mancin, Sec. State W.Va., 1984, Disting. W. Virginian award State of W.Va., 1984, John Baird Thomas Meml. award Ohio U.; named Surgery Alumnus of Yr., U. Minn., 1981, Disting. Citizen Wash. State, Lt. Gov. John Cherberg, 1981; NIH grantee, 1951-76. Fellow ACS (numerous coms., bds.), Soc. of Univ. Surgeons (councilman at large 3 yrs.), Internat. Soc. Surgery; mem. Am. Surg. Assn. (adv. mem. com 1959-64, v.p. 1972-73), Am. Assn. for Thoracic Surgery, Halsted Soc., Henry N. Harkins Surg. Soc., N. Pacific Coast Surg. Assn., Seattle Surg. Soc., So. Surg. Soc. (Arthur H. Shipley award 1972), Am. Bd. Surgery 1958-64 (vice chmn. 1962-63, chmn. 1963-64, emeritus 1964—); University Club, Seattle Golf Club, Phi Beta Kappa, Sigma Xi, Beta Theta Pi (sec., pres.), Phi Beta Pi (hon.). Republican. Episcopalian. Avocations: golf, fly fishing, bird hunting, gardening. Home: The Highlands Seattle WA 98177 Office: U Wash Sch Medicine Dept Surgery Seattle WA 98195

MERGLER, H. KENT, investment counselor; b. Cin., July 1, 1940; s. Wilton Henry and Mildred Amelia (Pulliam) M.; m. Judith Anne Metzger, Aug. 17, 1963; children: Stephen Kent, Timothy Alan, Kristin Lee. BBA with honors, U. Cin., 1963, MBA, 1964. Chartered fin. analyst, chartered investment counselor. Portfolio mgr. Scudder, Stevens & Clark, Cin., 1964-68, exec. v.p., Chgo., 1970-73; v.p. Gibralter Rsch. and Mgmt., Ft. Lauderdale, Fla., 1968-70; ptnr., exec. v.p., pres., dir. and prin. Stein Roe & Farnham, Inc., Ft. Lauderdale, 1973-84, Chgo., 1984-91, also exec. com.; pres. Stein Roe Investment Trust; mng. ptnr. Loomis, Sayles & Co., Palm Beach Gardens, Fla., 1992—; bd. dirs. Gold Coast Mag., Inc., 1994—; arbitrator Nat. Assn. Security Dealers, Inc., 1976-82. Chmn. adminstrv. bd. Christ United Meth. Ch., Ft. Lauderdale, 1981-83; mem. fin. com. Kenilworth Union Ch., 1989-92, Broward Community Found. (Investment Com.), 1992—, chmn., 1994—, bd. dirs., 1995—, Martin County Econ. Coun., 1992—; bd. dirs. Pine Crest Prep. Sch., 1982-84, bd. advisors, 1984-87; mem. corp. adv. bd. U. Cin. Coll. Bus. Adminstrn., 1991-94; bd. dirs. Hibiscus House Children's Found., 1993—; bd. dirs. Coral Ridge Little League, 1976-84, pres., 1980-81. Mem. Fin. Analysts Soc. So. Fla. (bd. dirs. 1974-78, pres. 1975), Bond Club Ft. Lauderdale (dir. 1978-82), Tower Club (Ft. Lauderdale), Skokie Country Club (Glencoe, Ill.), Highlands Country Club (N.C.), Cullasaja Club (Highlands, N.C.), Sailfish Point Yacht and Country Club (Stuart, Fla.), City Club of Palm Beach, Beta Theta Pi, Beta Gamma Sigma. Republican. Home: 7036 SE Harbor Cir Stuart FL 34996 Office: 4400 PGA Blvd Ste 600 Palm Beach Gardens FL 33410

MERGLER, HARRY WINSTON, engineering educator; b. Chillicothe, Ohio, June 1, 1924; s. Harry Franklin and Letitia (Walburn) M.; m. Irmgard Erna Steudel, June 22, 1948; children—Myra A. L., Marcia B. E., Harry F. B.S., MIT, 1948; M.S., Case Inst. Tech., 1950, Ph.D., 1956. Aero. research scientist NACA, 1948-56; mem. faculty Case Inst. Tech., 1957—, prof. engring., 1962—, Leonard Case prof. engring., 1973—; dir. Digital Systems Lab., 1959—; vis. scientist, USSR, 1958; vis. prof. Norwegian Tech. U., 1962; cons. to industry, 1957—; editor Control Engring. mag., 1956—; pres. Digital/Gen. Corp., 1968-72; cons. Exploratory Research div. NSF. Author: Digital Systems Engineering, 1961, also articles, chpts. in books. Served with AUS, 1942-45. Recipient Case gold medal for sci. achievement Case Inst. Tech., 1980. Fellow IEEE (bd. dirs. 1987-89, v.p. 1989, Lamme medal 1978, Centennial medal 1984); mem. NAE, Indsl. Electronic Soc. (pres. 1977-79), Cleve. Engring. Soc., N.Y. Acad. Scis., Blue Key, Sigma Xi, Tau Beta Pi, Theta Tau, Pi Delta Epsilon, Zeta Psi. Home: 9658-23 Halyards Ct Fort Myers FL 33919

MERHIGE, ROBERT REYNOLD, JR., federal judge; b. N.Y.C., Feb. 5, 1919; s. Robert Reynold and Eleanor (Donovan) M.; m. Shirley Galleher, Apr. 24, 1957; children: Robert Reynold III, Mark Reynold. LLB, U. Richmond, 1942, LLD (hon.), 1976; LLM, U. Va., 1982; LLD (hon.), Washington and Lee U., 1990, Wake Forest U., 1994. Bar: Va. 1942. Ptnr. Bremner Merhige Montgomery & Baber, Richmond, 1945-67; judge U.S. Dist. Ct., Richmond, 1967—; guest lectr. trial tactics Law Sch. U. Va., Ewald disting. prof. law, 1987-88; adj. prof. Law Sch. U. Richmond, 1973-87; appeal agt. Henrico County Draft Bd., 1954-67; mem. NCAA spl. com. on discipline rules; profl.-in-residence, Zambia, Africa, 1994. Co-author: Virginia Jury Instructions. Mem. Richmond Citizens Assn.; mem. citizens adv. com. San. Dist. A, Henrico County. Served with USAAF, World War II. Decorated Air medal with four oak leaf clusters; recipient Amara Civic Club award, 1968, Spl. award City of Richmond, 1967; named Citizen of the Yr., 3d Dist. Omega Psi Phi, 1972, Citizen of the Yr., Richmond Urban League, 1977, Richmonder of Yr. Style mag., 1984, 87, Citizen of Yr., 1986; recipient Disting. Alumni award U. Richmond, 1979, Disting. Svc. award Nat. Alumni Coun., U. Richmond, 1979, Herbert T. Harley award Am. Judicature Soc., 1982, Athenian Ciitizen medal, 1979, Torch of Liberty award Anti-Defamation League of B'nai Brith, 1982, T.C. Williams Sch. of Law Disting. Svc. award, 1983, Pres.'s award Old Dominion Bar Assn., 1986, William J. Brennan award, 1986, Merit Citation award NCCJ, 1987, William B. Green award for professionalism U. Richmond, 1989, Marshall-Wythe medallion (William & Mary Faculty award), 1989. Fellow Va. Law Found.; mem. Va. Bar Assn., Richmond Bar Assn. (pres. 1963-64, Hill-Tucker award 1991, multi-dist. litigation panel 1990—), Am. Law Inst. (faculty), Va. Trial Lawyers Assn. (chmn. membership com. 1964-65, Disting. Svc. award 1977), Jud. Conf. U.S., Omicron Delta Kappa. Office: US Courthouse PO Box 630 Richmond VA 23205-0630

MERIDEN, TERRY, physician; b. Damascus, Syria, Oct. 12, 1946; came to U.S., 1975; s. Izzat and Omayma (Aidi) M.; m. Lena Kahal, Nov. 17, 1975; children: Zina, Lana. BS, Sch. Sci., Damascus, 1968; MD, Sch. Medicine, Damascus, 1972, doctorate cum laude, 1973. Diplomate Am. Bd. Internal Medicine. Resident in infectious diseases Rush Green Hosp., Romford, Eng., 1973; house officer in internal medicine and cardiology Ashford (Eng.) Group Univ. Hosps., 1973-74; sr. house officer in internal medicine and neurology Grimsby (Eng.) Group Univ. Hosps., 1974; registrar in internal medicine and rheumatology St. Annes Hosp., London, 1974-75; jr. resident in internal medicine Shadyside Hosp., Pitts., 1975-76; sr. resident in internal medicine, 1976-77; fellow in endocrinology and metabolism Shadyside Hosp. and Grad. Inst., Pitts., 1976-77; clin. asst. prof. U. Ill., Peoria, 1979; pres. Am. Diabetes Assn., Peoria, 1982-84; dir. Proctor Diabetes Unit, Peoria, 1984—, 1984—; adviser to the Gov. of Ill. on Diabetes. Mem. editorial bd. Diabetes Forecast mag., Clin. Diabetes, 1990; contbr. articles to profl. jours. Fellow ACP; mem. AMA (Recognition award 1985), ADA (chmn. profl. edn. and research 1980—, mem. editorial bd and Spanish lit bd, nat. bd. dirs. 1986—, vice chmn. nat. com. on diabetes edn. and affiliate services 1986—, Outstanding Service award 1984, Outstanding Diabetes Educator award 1986), Am. Cancer Soc. (Life Line award 1983), Am. Assn. Clin. Endocrinology (founding mem.), Am. Coll. Endocrinology, The Obesity Found. (Century award 1984, Recognition award 1985). Home: 115 E Coventry Ln Peoria IL 61614-2103 Office: 900 Main St Ste 300 Peoria IL 61602-1005

MERIDETH, FRANK E., JR., lawyer; b. 1944. BA, U. San Francisco, JD. Bar: Calif. 1970. Ptnr. Bryan Cave, Santa Monica, Calif. Office: Bryan Cave 120 Broadway Ste 500 Santa Monica CA 90401-2305

MERIGAN, THOMAS CHARLES, JR., physician, medical researcher, educator; b. San Francisco, Jan. 18, 1934; s. Thomas C. and Helen M. (Greeley) M.; m. Joan Mary Freeborn, Oct. 3, 1959; 1 son, Thomas Charles III. BA with honors, U. Calif., Berkeley, 1955; MD, U. Calif., San Francisco, 1958. Diplomate: Am. Bd. Internal Medicine. Intern in medicine 2d and 4th Harvard med. services Boston City Hosp., 1958-59, asst. resident medicine, 1959-60; clin. assoc. Nat. Heart Inst., NIH, Bethesda, Md., 1960-62; asso. Lab. Molecular Biology, Nat. Inst. Arthritis and Metabolic Diseases; NIH, 1962-63; practice medicine specializing in internal medicine and infectious diseases Stanford, Calif., 1963—; asst. prof. medicine Stanford U. Sch. Medicine, 1963-67, assoc. prof. medicine, 1967-72, head div. infectious diseases, 1966-92, prof. medicine, 1972—, George E. and Lucy Becker prof.

medicine, 1980—; dir. Diagnostic Microbiology Lab., Univ. Hosp., 1966-72, Diagnostic Virology Lab., 1969—, Ctr. AIDS Rsch. Stanford U., 1988—; hosp. epidemiologist, 1966-88; mem. microbiology rsch. tng. grants com. NIH, 1969-73, virology study sect., 1974-78; cons. antiviral substances program Nat. Inst. Allergy and Infectious Diseases, 1970—, mem. AIDS clin. drug devel. commn., 1986-94; mem. Virology Task Force, 1976-78, bd. sci. counselors, 1980-85; mem. U.S. Hepatitis panel U.S. and Japan Coop. Med. Sci. Program, 1979-90, AIDS subcom. Nat. Adv. Allergy and Infectious Diseases Coun., 1988-89; co-chmn. interferon evaluation Group Am. Cancer Soc., 1978-81; mem. vaccines and related biol. products adv. com. Ctr. for Drugs and Biols., FDA, 1984-88; mem. internat. adv. com. on biol. sci. Sci. Council, Singapore, 1985-88; mem. adv. com. J.A. Hartford Found., 1979-84; mem. Albert Lasker awards jury, 1981-84; mem. peer review panel U.S. Army Med. Rsch. and Devel. Com., 1986-88; nat. com. to rev. current procedures for approval New Drugs for Cancer and AIDS, 1989-90; mem. Com. to Study Use of Coms. within FDA, 1991-92. Contbr. numerous articles on infectious diseases, virology and immunology to sci. jours.; editor: Antivirals with Clinical Potential, 1976, Antivirals and Virus Diseases of Man, 1979, 2d edit., 1984, 3d edit., 1990, Regulatory Functions of Interferon, 1980, Interferons, 1982, Interferons as Cell Growth Inhibitors, 1986; assoc. editor: Virology, 1975-78, Cancer Research, 1987-91; co-editor: monograph series Current Topics in Infectious Diseases, 1975—, Cytomeglovirus Infect and Ganciclovir, 1988, Focus on Didanosine (ddI), 1990, Practical Diagnosis of Viral Infection, Textbook of AIDS Medicine, 1993; editorial bd.: Archives Internal Medicine, 1971-81, Jour. Gen. Virology, 1972-77, Infection and Immunity, 1973-81, Intervirology, 1973-85, Proc. Soc. Expt. Biology and Medicine, 1978-87, Reviews of Infectious Diseases, 1979-89, Jour. Interferon Research, 1980-89, Antiviral Research, 1980-86, Jour. Antimicrobial Chemotherapy, 1981-91, Molecular and Cellular Biochemistry, 1982-89, AIDS Research and Human Retroviruses, 1983—, Jour. Virology, 1984-89, Biotechnology Therapeutics, 1988—, Jour. Infectious Diseases, 1989—, Drug Investigation, 1989—, HIV: Advances in Research and Therapy, 1990—, Internat. Jour. Antimicrobial Agts. 1990—, The AIDS Reader, 1991—, AIDS, 1993, Clinical Immunotherapeutics, 1994—. Recipient Borden award for Outstanding Rsch., Am. Assn. Med. Colls., 1973, Merit award, Nat. Inst. Allergy and Infectious Diseases, 1988, Maxwell Finland award Infectious Diseases Soc. Am., 1988; Guggenheim Meml. fellow, 1972. Mem. Assn. Am. Physicians, Western Assn. Physicians, Am. Soc. Microbiology, Am. Soc. Clin. Investigation (coun. 1977-80), Am. Assn. Immunologists, Am. Fedn. Clin. Rsch., Western Soc. Clin. Rsch., Soc. Exptl. Biology and Medicine (publ. com. 1985-89), Infectious Diseases Soc. Am., Am. Soc. Virology, Inst. Medicine, Pan Am. Group for Rapid Viral Diagnosis, AMA, Internat. Soc. Interferon Rsch. (coun. 1983-89), Calif. Med. Assn., Santa Clara County Med. Soc., Cacad. Medicine, Royal Soc. Medicine, AAAS, Alpha Omega Alpha. Home: 148 Goya Rd Menlo Park CA 94028-7307 Office: Stanford U Sch Medicine Div Infectious Diseases Stanford CA 94305

MERINO CASTRO, JOSÉ TORIBIO, retired Chilean naval officer; b. Dec. 14, 1915; m. Margarita Maria Riofrio Bustos, 1952; children: M. Angelica, Carolina, Teresita. Ed., specialized as gunnery officer, Naval Acad., 1931-35. Naval service Maipo, 1936, Rancagua, 1939; instr. Blanco Encalada, 1940; divsn. officer Almirante Latorre, 1943; asst. officer USS Raleigh CL7, 1944-45; arty. officer DD Serrano, 1945, arty. officer DD Riqueline, 1947; with C&R O'Higgins, 1950-51; comdr. Corvette Papudo, 1952; staff officer Naval War. Coll. Staff Course, 1953-54; tech. adviser of armaments Chile Naval Mission, London, 1955-57; comdr. Navy Chile Transport, Angamos, 1959; prof. Naval War Coll., 1960-61; comdr. Destroyer Williams Chile Naval Mission, 1962, chief staff fleet, 1963, vice chief of gen. staff, 1964-68, head weapons bur., 1969, dir. gen. logistic navy, 1970, comdr. chieffleet, 1971, commdr. chief 1st Naval Zone, 1972-73; commdr. chief Navy, mem. Govt. Junta, 1973—, ret., 1990. Decorated Armed Forces medal III, II, I, Grand Star of Naval Merit, Cross for Naval Merit, Decoration of Pres. of Republic (Chile), Grand Cross Order (Spain), Order of Nat. Merit (South Korea), 1st Class Order of Rising Sun (Japan), Order of Star of South Africa, Legion of Merit (U.S.), Gran Mastre Orden de Mayo (Argentina), Cruz Peruana Naval Merit, (Peru), Grand Medal (Uruguay), Grand Cross Order of Quetzal (Guatemala), Cross Dist. Svcs. (Honduras), Grand Cross and Grand Star of Merit Fuerzas Armadas (Ecuador). Office: Chile Naval Mission 1736 Massachusetts Ave NW Washington DC 20036

MERIT, DENNIS ANDREW, zoo administrator; b. Rochester, N.Y., May 17, 1940; s. Dennis Andrew and Mary (Gilbert) M.; m. Gail Fitz, July 21, 1962; children: Laura, Jill. BS, U. Rochester, 1970; MA, Northeastern U., Chgo., 1977; PhD, U. Ill., Chgo., 1987. Lab. technician Rochester Gen. Hosp., 1958-60; rsch. asst. Rochester Eye Bank & Rsch., 1961-63, Rochester Gen. Hosp., 1960-63; lab. prep. U. Rochester, 1964-67, rsch. asst., 1963-67; curator mammals Lincoln Park Zoo, Chgo., 1968-75, asst. dir., 1975—. Fellow Am. Assn. Zool. Parks and Aquariums (bd. dirs. 1987—, chair honors awards 1972-75, chair wildlife conservation and mgmt. 1976-80, bd. mem. 1976-79, pres. elect 1992-93); mem. Internat. Union for Conservation of Nature (chari-edentate specialist 1980-89). Avocations: bird watching, hiking, photography, writing, travel. Office: Lincoln Park Zool Gardens 2200 N Cannon Dr Chicago IL 60614-3858

MERIWETHER, HEATH J., newspaper editor; b. Columbia, Mo., Jan. 20, 1944; s. Nelson Heath and Mary Agnes (Immele) M.; m. Patricia Hughes, May 4, 1979; children: Graham, Elizabeth. BA in History, BJ, U. Mo., 1966; MA in Teaching, Harvard U., 1967. Reporter Miami (Fla.) Herald, 1970-72, editor Broward and Palm Beach burs., 1972-77, exec. city editor, 1977-79, asst. mgr. editor news, 1979-80, mng. editor, 1981-83, exec. editor, 1983-87; exec. editor Detroit Free Press, 1987—. Served to lt. USNR, 1967-70. Journalism fellow Stanford U., 1980. Mem. AP Mng. Editors (bd. dirs. 1984-90). Roman Catholic. Avocation: tennis. Office: Detroit Free Press 321 W Lafayette Blvd Detroit MI 48226

MERIWETHER, JAMES BABCOCK, English language educator; b. Columbia, S.C., May 8, 1928; s. Robert Lee and Margaret (Babcock) M.; m. Nancy Anderson Callcott, July 29, 1955 (div. May 1992); children: Rebecca, Robert, George, Nicholas, Margaret; m. Anne M. Blythe, Nov. 14, 1992. BA, U. S.C., 1949; MA, Princeton U., 1952, PhD, 1958. Asst. prof. English U. Tex., Austin, 1958-59; asst. prof. English U. N.C., Chapel Hill, 1959-62, assoc. prof., 1962-64; prof. U. S.C., Columbia, 1964-70, McClintock prof. So. letters, 1970-90, dir. So. studies program, 1974-80, disting. prof. emeritus, 1990—, ret., 1994; appointed Bd. Fgn. Scholarships, Washington, 1982, 86, vice chmn., 1984, chmn. 1984-87; Fulbright prof. U. Paris, 1970-71, U. Bonn, 1980, Chinese U. Hong Kong, 1993. Author: The Literary Career of William Faulkner, 1961, others; editor: Essays, Speeches and Public Letters of William Faulkner, others; contbr. articles to profl. jours. Served with U.S. Army, 1953-56. Fellow Am. Coun. Learned Socs., 1960-61, Guggenheim Found., 1963-64, Earhart Found., 1989-90. Mem. MLA, Bibliographical Soc. Am., Am. Studies Assn., South Atlantic Modern Lang. Assn., Phi Beta Kappa. Home: 2526 Monroe St Columbia SC 29205

MERKELO, HENRI, electronics and computer scientist; b. Borky, Ukraine, June 12, 1939; came to U.S., 1960; s. Alexander and Natalia (Niushko) M. Certificat d'Aptitude Professionnelle, Coll. Moderne et Tech., Reims, France, 1956; MS, U. Ill., 1962, PhD, 1966. Translator Russian-Am. Math. Soc., Providence, 1961-63, Am. Phys. Soc., Am. Math. Soc., 1962-64; research scientist physics and thermodynamics Douglas Aircraft Co., Santa Monica, Calif., 1962; faculty U. Ill., Urbana, 1964—; dir. quantum electronics ultra high speed digital electronics rsch. lab., 1973—; dir. picosecond digital electronics U. Calif., Santa Barbara, 1982—; cons. Sangamo/ Schlumberger, Atlanta, 1977-80, AMP Inc., Harrisburg, Pa., 1983—, Stanfor Rsch. Inst., 1983, Hewlett Packard Corp., 1992; lectr. in field, U.S. and abroad. Fgn. editor, French translator Schlumberger, 1978-80; contbr. numerous articles to profl. jours.; patentee in field. Ford Found. fellow, 1960-62, RCA fellow, 1963, Kodak fellow, 1964; grantee NSF, 1970—, AMP, 1985—, IBM, 1988—, Hewlett-Packard, 1993—, other U.S. industries. Fellow IEEE (sr., chmn. computer elements workshop 1988, 89); mem. Am. Inst. Physics, Am. Physics Soc., Am. Optical Soc., Sigma Xi, Tau Beta Pi. Research directed to development of high speed and ultra high speed logic devices and networks for high speed computing and communication. Modeling and numerical simulation of high speed digital electronic and photonic networks. Picosecond and femtosecond switching phenomena.

Home: 7 Pine Cir Urbana IL 61801-7130 Office: U Ill Quantum Electronics Ultra High Speed Digital Elects 1406 W Green St Urbana IL 61801-2918

MERKER, FRANK FERDINAND, retired hospital administrator; b. Bklyn., July 2, 1909; s. August and Mathilda (Schmidt) M.; m. Edith Marjorie Greer, Feb. 6, 1937; 1 dau., Mathilda Sue. B.Engring., Johns Hopkins, 1931; M.D. Med. Coll. Va., 1943; postgrad., Menninger Sch. Psychiatry, 1946-49. With Balt. Gas & Electric Co., 1931, Glenn L. Martin Aircraft Co., 1933-35, Civilian Conservation Corps, 1935-40; intern U.S. Marine Hosp., Balt., 1944; resident psychiatry VA Hosp., Topeka, 1946-49; asst. sect. chief VA Hosp., 1949-51, sect. chief, 1952-54, asst. dir. profl. services, 1954-55, dir. profl. services, 1955-58; practice medicine specializing in psychiatry Topeka, 1946-58, Salem, Va., 1958-60, Roseburg, Oreg., 1960-66; dir. profl. services VA Hosp., Salem, 1958-60; dir. VA Hosp., Roseburg, 1960-66, Coatesville, Pa., 1966-69, Richmond, Va., 1969-72; dir. Southwestern State Hosp., Marion, Va., 1972-78, med. dir. forensic unit, 1978-80; psychiatrist Marion Correctional Treatment Center, 1980-82, Mt. Rogers Clinic, 1982-84; assoc. clin. prof. psychiatry Med. Coll. Va., 1969-81. Served to capt. M.C. USAAF, 1944-46. Fellow AAAS, Am. Psychiat. Assn.; mem. AMA. Home: 3804 Brandon Ave SW Apt 242 Roanoke VA 24018-7003

MERKER, STEVEN JOSEPH, lawyer; b. Cleve., Feb. 21, 1947; s. Steven Joseph and Laverne (Zamenik) M.; m. Janet L. Whyatt; children: Steven, Rena, Ashley. BS, Case Inst. Tech., 1968; MS, U. Fla., 1973. Bar: Ohio 1976, U.S. Dist. Ct. (no. dist.) Ohio, 1976, U.S. Dist. Ct. Colo. 1979, U.S. Ct. Appeals (10th cir.) 1979, U.S. Supreme Ct. 1989. Assoc. Jones, Day, Reavis & Pogue, Cleve., 1976-78; assoc. Davis, Graham & Stubbs, Denver, 1978-82, ptnr., 1983—, chmn. labor and employment group, 1989—. Legal counsel Coloradans for Lamm-Dick campaign, Denver, 1982, Nancy Dick for U.S. Senate Com., Denver, 1984, Cantrell for Dist. Atty., Jefferson County, Colo., 1984; bd. dirs. Very Spl. Arts, Colo., 1994—. Served as capt. USAF, 1969-72. Mem. ABA, Colo. Bar Assn., Denver Bar Assn. Office: Davis Graham & Stubbs PO Box 185 370 17th St Ste 4700 Denver CO 80202-5682

MERKERT, GEORGE, visual effects producer. Formerly exec. producer, producer Colossal Pictures, San Francisco; now producer MetroLight Studios, L.A. Recent visual effects projects include 7 effects shots (film) Total Recall; title sequence (TV pilot) Moe's World; also Apple Computers promotional film. Office: MetroLight Studios 5724 W 3rd St Ste 400 Los Angeles CA 90036-3078

MERKIN, WILLIAM LESLIE, lawyer; b. N.Y.C., Apr. 30, 1929; s. Jules Leo Merkin and Rae (Levine) Lesser; children—Monica Jo, Lance Jeffrey, Tiffany Dawn. B.A., U. Tex., Austin, 1950; J.D., St. Mary's U., San Antonio, Tex., 1953. Bar: Tex. 1953, U.S. Ct. Mil. Appeals 1954, U.S. Dist. Ct. (we. dist.) Tex. 1957, U.S. Ct. Appeals (5th cir.) 1969, U.S. Supreme Ct. 1970. Pvt. practice, El Paso, Tex., 1956-71; sr. ptnr. firm Merkin & Gibson, El Paso, 1972-78, Merkin, Hines & Pasqualone, 1978-90, ret.; lectr. U. Tex.-El Paso, 1978—; cons. in field. Served to capt. JAGC, U.S. Army, 1953-56. Mem. Tex. State Bar Assn., El Paso County Bar Assn., San Diego County Bar Assn., Soc. of Profls. in Dispute Resolution, Am. Trial Lawyers Assn., Tex. Trial Lawyers Assn., Common Cause, Internat. Wine and Food Soc. (pres. 1979-80), Am. Arbitration Assn. (part-time arbitrator), Del Norte Club (El Paso), B'nai B'rith (pres. 1961-62), Phi Delta Phi. Home: 1720 Avenida Del Mundo Coronado CA 92118

MERLIS, GEORGE, television producer; b. Bklyn., Feb. 7, 1940; s. Martin Richard and Ethel (Pollack) M.; m. Susan Haviland Crane, Nov. 21, 1963; children: James Duncan, Andrew Richard. B.A., U. Pa., 1960; M.S., Columbia U. Grad. Sch. Journalism, 1961. Sports editor Rome (Italy) Daily Am., 1961; reporter N.Y. World-Telegram and Sun, N.Y.C., 1962-65; asst. city editor N.Y. World-Telegram and Sun, 1965-67; day city editor World Jour. Tribune, N.Y.C., 1967; supr. editorial tng. program N.Y. News, N.Y.C., 1967-68; dir. pub. relations ABC News, N.Y.C., 1967-72; field producer Reasoner Report, 1972-75; exec. producer Good Morning America, 1975-81, CBS Morning News, 1981-83, Entertainment Tonight, 1983-84, Dick Cavett, USA, 1985, Great Weekend, 1987-88; supervising producer ABC-TV's Home Show, 1988-91; exec. producer Willard Scott's Home and Garden Almanac, 1994, Kitty Bartholomew You're Home, 1994; pres. Jaand Prodns., Inc.; founder, chmn. J-Nex TV News Services, Inc.; chmn. Sunrise News Co. Author: V.P. a Novel of Vice Presidential Politics, 1971, (with Al Ubell) Al Ubell's Energy-Saving Guide for Homeowners, 1980; contbr. articles to TV Guide. Mem. Nat. TV Acad. Arts and Scis., Home Video Acad. Arts and Scis., Internat. Assn. Bus. Communicators, N.Y. Newspaper Guild.

MERLISS, WILLIAM SIDNEY, retired architect, engineer; b. Okmulgee, Okla., Sept. 26, 1922; s. Sidney Samuel and Bonnie Bessie (Farr) M.; BArch., B. in Archtl. Engring., Okla. A&M U., 1950; m. Dorothy Halphen Kolb; children: Sherri Lynn Merliss Voebel, Benjamin Harrison, Virginia Jeanne Merliss Johnson. Architect, engr. Hudgins, Thompson & Ball, Oklahoma City, 1950; engr. Dow Chem. Co., Freeport, Tex., 1953-54; project engr. Walter P. Moore, Houston, 1954-55; cons. engr. W.S. Merliss & Assos., Houston, 1955-61; ptnr. Merliss, Jones and Robinson, Houston, 1961-77, Merliss & Jones, 1977-89, ret.; v.p. Aubibon Land Co.; dir. Freaky Fritters World Inc., Universal Domes Inc., Condo Domes Inc., Time Systems Inc.; chmn. bd. Bandit Messenger Service Inc., Houston and other locations. Adv. trustee Dorothy H. and Allison R. Kolb Ednl. Trust Found.; mgr. D. Kolb interests. Democrat precinct chmn., 1968-75. Served with USAF, 1941-45, 51-53. Decorated Purple Heart. Mem. AIA, Nat., Tex. socs. profl. engrs., Tex. Soc. Architects, L.A. Soc. Architects, Prestressed Concrete Inst., Gulf Coast Okla. State Alumni Assn. (pres. 1956-65), Kappa Kappa Psi. Republican. Jewish. Clubs: Baton Rouge City, Masons, Shriners, Consistory, Frolikers, Camelot, World Trade Ctr. New Orleans, Men of Bal Masque, Krewe of Tucumcari, Baton Rouge City, Big Timers (Baton Rouge). Home: 7420 Reinzi Blvd Baton Rouge LA 70809

MERLO, HARRY ANGELO, forest products executive; b. Stirling City, Calif., Mar. 5, 1925; s. Joseph Angelo and Clotilde (Camussa) M.; 1 son, Harry a. BS, U. Calif.-Berkeley, 1949, postgrad., 1949. Vice pres. Rockport Redwood Co., Cloverdale, Calif., 1967; v.p. No. Calif. div. Ga.-Pacific Corp., Samoa, Calif., 1967-69; v.p. Western lumber div. Ga.-Pacific Corp., Portland, Oreg., 1969-71, exec. v.p. Western timber, plywood and lumber operations, 1971-73; pres., chmn. bd. La.-Pacific Corp., Portland, 1973—; bd. dirs. World Forestry Ctr. Mem. Pres.'s Coun., Columbia Pacific coun. Boy Scouts Am.; former mem. nat. adv. coun. Salvation Army; trustee Hugh O'Brian Youth Found., Oreg. Mus. Sci. and Industry, Goodwill Industries; past chmn. bd. Am. Acad. Achievement; former western fin. chmn. U.S. Olympic commn.; past chmn., adv. bd. Salvation Army, Oreg.; past bd. dirs. Marshall U. Soc. Yaeger Scholars. Lt. USMCR. Named Man of Year Ga.-Pacific Corp., 1969; recipient Golden Plate award Am. Acad. Achievement, 1974; Horatio Alger award, 1980, Gold award for forest products industry The Wall St. Transcript, 1982, 83, 94, Disting. Svc. award La. Tech. U., 1984, Aubrey Watzek award Lewis and Clark Coll., 1984, Citizen of Merit award Assoc. Builders and Contractors, 1986, Piemontese Del Munde award, 1986, Merit award Calif. Parks & Recreation Soc., 1988, John J. Mulrooney award N.Am. Wholesale Lumber Assn., 1989, Hope award Nat. Multiple Sclerosis Soc., 1993. Mem. Calif. Redwood Assn. (past pres., bd. dirs.), Horatio Alger Assn. (pres., chmn.), Founders Club (bd. dirs.), Waverly County Club, Multnomah Athletic Club, Ingomar Club, Knight of the Vine. Office: La-Pacific Corp 111 SW 5th Ave Portland OR 97204-3604

MERMANN, ALAN CAMERON, pediatrics educator, chaplain; b. Bklyn., June 23, 1923; s. William Joseph and Ada Fletcher (McCree) M.; m. Constance Barnes, Sept. 4, 1948 (div. Mar. 1988); children: Edith, Constance, Sarah, Elizabeth; m. Cecily Allen Reynolds, Apr. 15, 1989. BA, Lehigh U., 1943; MD, Johns Hopkins U., 1947; MDiv, Yale U., 1979, MST, 1988. Diplomate Am. Bd. Pediatrics; med. license, Conn.; ordained to Christian ministry, United Ch. of Christ, 1979. Intern pediatrics Bellevue Hosp., N.Y.C., 1947-48, Johns Hopkins Hosp., Balt., 1948-49; asst. resident pediatrician N.Y. Hosp., N.Y.C., 1949-50; resident pediatrician Meml. Hosp., N.Y.C., 1950-51; rsch. fellow Sloane-Kettering Inst., N.Y.C., 1953-54; pvt. practice pediatrics Guilford, Conn., 1954-82; clin. instr. pediatrics Yale Sch. Medicine, 1954-59, asst. clin. prof. pediatrics, 1959-71, assoc. clin. prof. pediatrics, 1971-79, clin. prof. pediatrics, 1979—; trustee New Eng.

Coll., Henniker, N.H., 1969-91; fellow Branford Coll., Yale U., 1979—; mem. instnl. rev. bd. Union Carbide Corp., Danbury, Conn., 1991—; lectr. pastoral theology Yale Divinity Sch., 1979-82; asst. pastor First Congregational Ch., Guilford, 1979-82; assoc. pastor Ch. of Christ Congl., United Ch. of Christ, Norfolk, Conn., 1995—; chaplain Yale Sch. Medicine, 1982—; human investigation com., 1983-91, med. ctr. bioethics com., chair pediatrics ethics com., sch. medicine admissions com., com. on well-being of students. Contbr. articles to profl. jours. Lt. USNR, 1951-53. Fellow Am. Acad. Pediatrics. Democrat. Avocations: Dixieland, jazz, dancing, gardening. Home: 36 Eld St New Haven CT 06511

MERMIN, N. DAVID, physicist, educator, essayist; b. New Haven, Mar. 30, 1935; s. John and Eva (Gordon) M.; m. Dorothy E. Milman, June 9, 1957; children—Jonathan George, Elizabeth Ruth. A.B. summa cum laude, Harvard U., 1956, A.M., 1957, Ph.D., 1961. NSF postdoctoral fellow U. Birmingham, Eng., 1961-63; postdoctoral fellow U. Calif., San Diego, 1963-64; asst. prof. physics Cornell U., Ithaca, N.Y., 1964-67; assoc. prof. physics Cornell U., 1967-72, prof. physics, 1972-90, Horace White prof. physics, 1990—, dir. Lab. Atomic and Solid State Physics, 1984-90; Loeb lectr. Harvard U., Cambridge, 1980, Emil Warburg prof. U. Bayreuth, Germany, 1981, Walker Ames prof. U. Washington, Seattle, 1984; Wunsch lectr. Technion, Haifa, Israel, 1992; Japan Soc. for Promotion of Sci. fellow Nagoya U., 1982; Lorentz prof. U. Leiden, 1995. Author: Space and Time in Special Relativity, 1968, Solid State Physics, 1976, Boojums All the Way Through, 1990; contbr. articles to profl. jours. Sloan Found. fellow, 1966-68; Guggenheim Found. fellow, 1970-71. Fellow AAAS, Am. Acad. Arts and Scis., Am. Phys. Soc. (Julius Edgar Lilienfield prize 1989); mem. NAS. Avocation: piano. Home: 75 Hickory Rd Ithaca NY 14850 Office: Cornell U Lab Atomic and Solid State Phys Clark Hall Ithaca NY 14853-2501

MEROLLA, CARMINE RALPH, banker; b. N.Y.C., Nov. 8, 1931; s. Ralph and Nellie (Perrotta) M.; m. Sigrid Nagel, June 20, 1953; 1 child, Thomas E. BS, NYU, 1957, MBA, 1962; postgrad. Am. Inst. Banking, 1959. Sales rep. Internat. Corr. Schs., N.Y., 1953-57; asst. mgr., loan officer Chase Manhattan Bank, N.Y.C., 1957-63; v.p., loan adminstr. European Am. Bank, N.Y., 1963-70; dist. v.p., adminstrv. officer Chem. Bank, N.Y., 1970-74; pres., chief exec. officer, Guardian Bank N.A., Hempstead, N.Y., 1975-78, Bank of Long Island, N.Y., 1978—. Trustee, treas., bd. dirs. Good Samaritan Hosp., West Islip, N.Y.; founding chmn. L.I. Philharm.; bd. dirs. Suffolk County Boy Scouts Am.; bonded dep. sheriff Suffolk County, Riverhead, N.Y.; active Robert Morris Assn., N.Y., Suffolk County Grand Jurors, Riverhead, N.Y. Recipient Good Neighbor award Nat. Assn. Counties; Presdl. award for community svc. Pres. U.S., 1984, L.I. Disting. Leadership award, 1984, cert. Am. Cancer Soc., Good Scout award, Disting. Citizen award Suffolk County coun. Boy Scouts Am., 1985, Disting. Community Svc. award Anti-Defamation League B'nai B'rith, 1988. Mem. L.I. Coalition Fair Broadcasting (bd. dirs., founder), Suffolk County Pvt. Industry Coun. (co-founder), Am. Bankers Assn. (Community svc. award 1984), L.I. Assn. Commerce and Industry (bd. dirs., Bus. Achievement award). Clubs: Suffolk Ho Country, N.Y. Athletic, Magoun Landing Yacht, Point'o Woods. Home: 133 Boathouse Ln W Bay Shore NY 11706-8130

MEROLLA, MICHELE EDWARD, chiropractor; b. Providence, Feb. 20, 1940; s. Joseph and Viola (Horne) M.; m. Ednamarie H.; children: Michele Edward II, Matthew Joseph, Samantha Joan, Alexandra Marie. BSc, Bryant Coll., 1961; DC, Chiropractic Inst. N.Y., 1965; LHD, Logan Chiropractic Coll., St. Louis, 1973. Owner chiropractic clinics, New Bedford, Taunton, Somerset, Seekonk, Attleboro and Westport, Mass., 1965—. Daily Network radio talk show host Holistic Hotline. Mem. New Bedford City Coun., 1969-73, Airport Commn., 1972-75, Sch. Com., 1978-83, Recreation Commn., 1983-89; pres. New Bedford Aid Center, 1977; bd. dirs. Your Theatre Inc. Recipient Svc. award New England Chiropractic Coun., 1973. Mem. Southeastern Mass. Chiropractic Soc. (bd. dirs.), Mass. Chiropractic Soc., Am. Chiropractic Assn., N.Y. Acad. Sci., Fla. Chiropractic Soc., New Bedford Preservation Soc. (bd. dirs.). Editor: New England Jour. Chiropractic, 1965-75. Home: 62 Rear Manhattan Ave Fairhaven MA 02719 also: 3300 NE 23d Ave Lighthouse Point FL 33064 Office: 100 Bedford St New Bedford MA 02740-4896

MERON, THEODOR, law educator, researcher; b. Kalisz, Poland, Apr. 28, 1930; came to U.S., 1978, naturalized, 1984; s. Yhiel and Bluma (Lipschitz) Znamirowski; m. Monique Jonquet, Mar. 13, 1981; children: Daniel, Amos. M.J., Hebrew U., 1954; LL.M., Harvard U., 1955, S.J.D., 1957; diploma in Pub. Internat. Law, Cambridge U., Eng., 1957. Bar: Israel 1971, N.Y. 1984. Legal advisor to Fgn. Ministry of Israel, 1967-71; Israeli ambassador to Can., 1971-75; permanent rep. Geneva, 1977; prof. law Sch. Law, NYU, N.Y.C., 1978—; Carnegie lectr. Hague Acad. Internat. Law, 1980; Sir Hersch Lauterpacht Meml. lectr.; vis. fellow All Souls Coll., Oxford U., Eng., Max-Planck Inst., Heidelberg, Germany; vis. prof. Grad. Inst. Internat. Studies, Geneva, prof. law, 1991—; pub. mem. U.S. Del. Conf. on Human Dimension Conf. on Security and Cooperation in Europe, Copenhagen, 1990. Author: Investment Insurance in International Law, 1976, The United Nations Secretariat, 1977, Human Rights Law-Making in the United Nations, 1986, Human Rights in Internal Strife: Their International Protection, 1987, Human Rights and Humanitarian Norms as Customary Law, 1989, Henry's Wars and Shakespeare's Laws, 1993; editor: Human Rights in International Law, 1984; editor in chief: Am. Jour. Internat. Law; contbr. articles to profl. publs. Mem. bds. Helsinki Watch, Americas Watch, Blaustein Human Rights Inst., Coun. of Internat. Inst. Humanitarian Law, San Remo, Italy, Internat. League Human Rights. Rockefeller Found. fellow, 1975-76; Humanitarian Trust student Cambridge U., 1956-57. Mem. Am. Soc. Internat. Law (Cert. Merit 1987), French Soc. Internat. Law, Internat. Law Assn., Coun. on Fgn. Rels., UN Assn. of the U.S. (hon.). Office: NYU Law Sch 40 Washington Sq S New York NY 10012-1099

MEROW, JAMES F., federal judge; b. Salamanca, N.Y., Mar. 16, 1932; s. Walter and Helen (Smith) M.. AB, George Washington U., 1953, JD, 1956. Bar: Va. Trial atty. U.S. Dept. Justice, Washington, 1959-78; trial judge U.S. Ct. Claims, Washington, 1978-82, judge, 1982—. With JAGC, U.S. Army, 1956-59. Mem. ABA, Va. State Bar. Office: US Ct Fed Claims 717 Madison Pl NW Washington DC 20005-1011

MEROW, JOHN EDWARD, lawyer; b. Little Valley, N.Y., Dec. 20, 1929; s. Luin George and Mildred Elizabeth (Stoll) M.; m. Mary Alyce Smith, June 19, 1957; 1 child, Alison. Student, UCLA, 1947-48; B.S.E., U. Mich., 1952; J.D., Harvard U., 1958. Bar: N.Y. 1958, U.S. Supreme Ct. 1971. Assoc. Sullivan & Cromwell, N.Y.C., 1958-64, ptnr., 1965—, vice chmn., 1986-87, chmn., sr. ptnr., 1987-94; bd. dirs. Seligman Group Investment Cos., Commonwealth Aluminium orp., MYH Care Network, Inc.; bd. govs. N.Y. Hosp.; chmn. adv. bd. dirs. Am.-Australian Assn.; bd. dirs. The U.S.-New Zealand Coun., Mcpl. Art Soc. N.Y., trustee, mem. exec. com. U.S. Coun. Internat. Bus.; bd. dirs., sec. Met. Opera Club, 1986-94; trustee N.Y. Downtown Hosp. Chmn. bd. dirs. Am.-Australian Assn.; bd. dirs. The U.S.-New Zealand Coun., Mcpl. Art Soc. N.Y., chmn. Mcpl. Art Soc. Coun.; trustee, v.p. Am. Friends of Australian Nat. Gallery, Inc.; trustee, mem. exec. com. U.S. Coun. Internat. Bus.; bd. dirs., sec. Met. Opera Club, 1986-94; trustee N.Y. Downtown Hosp. Mem. ABA, N.Y. State Bar Assn., Assn. Bar City of N.Y. (chmn. com. on securities regulation 1974-77), Am. Law Inst. (advisor corp. governance project 1978-92), Coun. on Fgn. Rels., Internat. Bar Assn., Fgn. Policy Assn. (bd. govs.), Links Club, Pilgrims, Piping Rock Club, Down Town Assn., The Calif. Club, Union Club. Home: 350 E 69th St New York NY 10021-5706 also: 51 Fruitledge Rd Brookville NY 11545 Office: Sullivan & Cromwell 125 Broad St New York NY 10004-2498

MERRELL, JAMES LEE, religious editor, clergyman; b. Indpls., Oct. 24, 1930; s. Mark W. and Pauline F. (Tucker) M.; m. Barbara Jean Burch, Dec. 23, 1951; children: Deborah Lea Merrell Griffin, Cynthia Lynn Merrell Archer, Stuart Allen. A.B., Ind. U., 1952; M.Div., Christian Theol. Sem. 1956; Litt.D., Culver-Stockton Coll. 1972. Ordained to ministry Christian Ch., 1955; assoc. editor World Call, Indpls., 1956-66; editor World Call, 1971-73; pastor Crestview Christian Ch. Indpls., 1966-71; editor The Disciple, St. Louis, 1974-89; sr. v.p. Christian Bd. Publ., 1976-89; sr. minister Affton Christian Ch., St. Louis, 1989-94; interim chaplain Culver-Stockton

Coll., Canton, Mo., 1995—; bd. dirs. Horizons mag., 1995—. Author: They Live Their Faith, 1965, The Power of One, 1976, Discover the Word in Print, 1979, Finding Faith in the Headlines, 1985, We Claim Our Heritage, 1992. Chmn. bd. Kennedy Meml. Christian Home, Martinsville, Ind., 1971-73; trustee Christian Theol. Sem., 1978-81. Recipient Faith and Freedom award Religious Heritage of Am., 1983. Mem. Associated Ch. Press (award 1973, 79, 80, 81, 82, dir. 1974-75, 78-81, 1st v.p. 1983-85), Christian Theol. Sem. Alumni Assn. (pres. 1966-68), Religious Publ. Rels. Coun. (awards 1979, 80, 84, 87, 90, pres. St. Louis chpt. 1985-86), Sigma Delta Chi (award 1952), Theta Phi. Home: 5347 Warmwinds Ct Saint Louis MO 63129-3013 Office: Disciples 9625 Tesson Ferry Rd Saint Louis MO 63123-4365 *As a religious communicator and as a pastor, I have always believed in applying the same standards in the sacred realm as in the secular. I have tried to pursue the truth, to keep my constituency informed, to celebrate the noble in life, to fight against those who would lie, distort and hide God's truth in the name of some supposed good.*

MERRELL, JESSE HOWARD, writer; b. Shelby, Ala., Dec. 9, 1938; s. James Walton and Emma Thelma (Davis) M.; m. Betsy Lee Davis, Jan. 11, 1964 (div. 1979); children: Sandra, Mark, Brad, Carolyn, Gwen. Grad., Shelby High Sch., Columbiana, Ala., 1957. Pitcher Cin. Redlegs, 1958-62; reporter, news dir. WHAP Radio, Hopewell, Va., 1963; writer/editor Hopewell News, 1963-65; state editor Daily Progress, Charlottesville, Va., 1965-68; assoc. editor Transport Topics, Washington, 1968-75; spl. asst. to pres. Am. Trucking Assn., Washington, 1975-76; editor Transport Topics, Washington, 1976-77; pres. Merrell Ent., Washington, 1977—; pub. rels. com. Am. Movers Conf., Washington, 1969-72; instr. Dale Carnegie courses, Washington, 1974-81, 1st pres., 1980-81; cons. Mid. Atlantic Conf. Riverdale, Md., 1981-82, Contract Carrier Conf., 1977-82; speechwriter ICC, Washington, 1982. Author: (novel) A Christmas Gift, 1970; syndicated columnist Religion and the Times, Washington Welter, (genealogy) The Merrells of Alabama, 1995. With U.S. Army, 1960-62. Recipient Liberty award Congress of Freedom, Jackson, Miss., 1970, 71, Honor Cert., Freedoms Found., 1972, 1st place editorial writing Va. Press Assn., 1965, 1st place news writing, 1966. Mem. Nat. Press Club. Avocation: photography. Office: Merrell Ent 2610 Garfield St NW Washington DC 20008

MERRELL, STANLEY WILSON, manufacturing company executive; b. Cin., Jan. 25, 1929; s. Thurston and Helen Theodate (Dresser) M.; m. Lyda Lynn Stuart, June 15, 1956; children: Stanley Wilson III, Caroline Clark, Louise Theodate, Katherine Stuart. A.B., Princeton U., 1951; M.B.A., Harvard U., 1957. With TRW Inc., Cleve., 1957-67, Rockwell Internat., Pitts., 1967-70; v.p. J.P. Morgan & Co. Inc., N.Y.C., 1970-73; v.p. planning and devel. Gen. Instrument Corp., N.Y.C., 1973-76; v.p. corp. devel. Bausch & Lomb Inc., Rochester, N.Y., 1976-81, sr. v.p. adminstrn., 1981-88, sr. v.p., asst. to chmn. and pres., 1988—. Bd. dirs. Genesee Hosp.; past pres., trustee Allendale Columbia Sch., Rochester; trustee Ctr. Govt. Research; dir. United Way of Greater Rochester, Rochester Downtown Devel. Corp. Served to lt. (j.g.) USN, 1951-53. Baker scholar Harvard U., 1957. Republican. Episcopalian. Clubs: Country of Rochester, Genesee Valley (Rochester). Home: 3437 Elmwood Ave Rochester NY 14610-3427 Office: Bausch & Lomb Inc 1 Lincoln First Sq Rochester NY 14604

MERRELL, WILLIAM JOHN, JR., oceanography educator; b. Grand Island, Nebr., Feb. 16, 1943; s. William John and Dorothy Belle (Dye) M.; m. June Bearden, Oct. 12, 1970; children: Bethany Susan, Meredith Megan. BS, Sam Houston State U., 1965, MA, 1967; PhD, Tex. A&M U., 1971. Rsch. assoc. Dept. Oceanography, Tex. A&M U., 1970-71, 73-74, postdoctoral rsch. assoc., 1971-72, lectr., dep. dept. head, 1977-79, dep. dept. head, 1981-83, assoc. prof., 1981-85, prof., 1985—; co-investigator oceanography remote sensing project Tex. A&M U., 1969-70, dep. sea grant dir., 1977-78, asst. to dean geoscis., 1978-79, assoc. dir. Earth Resources Inst. 1978-79; dir. Earth Resources Inst. Coll. Geoscis., Tex. A&M U., 1983-84, assoc. dean, 1983-85, dir. div. atmospheric and marine scis., 1985; rsch. program mgmt. system officer Office Internat. Decade Ocean Exploration, NSF, 1972-73, exec. officer, 1974-77, asst. dir., 1985-87; oceanographer, mgr. Climate and Coastal Zone Br. Sci. Applications Inc., 1979-80; pres. Tex. A&M U., Galveston, 1987-91; v.p. rsch. policy Tex. A&M U., 1992-93; vice chancellor for strategic programs Tex. A&M U. System, Galveston, 1993—; pres. Tex. Inst. Oceanography, 1989-91; program mgr. Gulf of Mex. Topographic Features Synthesis, 1981-83; prin. investigator ocean drilling program, 1983-85; mem. exec. com. Joint Oceanographic Instn. for Deep Earth Sampling, Washington; bd. govs., Washington; mem. human exploration of space/space studies bd., chmn. ocean studies bd. com. NRC, chmn. internat. space programs com.; adv. com. on rsch. programs State of Tex.; adv. com. for Geosci., NSF. Contbr. articles to profl. jours. Bd. dirs. Galveston Hist. Fedn., William Temple Fedn., Galveston; bd. govs. Galveston Econ. Devel. Corp., Offshore Energy Mus., Houston; bd. counselors St. Mary's Hosp., Galveston; trustee Galveston Wharves. Recipient Disting. Svc. award NSF, 1987, Disting. Alumnus award Sam Houston State U., 1988, Disting. Achievement award Coun. for Geosciences and Earth Resources, 1990. Mem. Am. Assn. State Colls. and Univs. (vice chmn. com. on sci. and tech.), Nat. Assn. State Univ. and Land Grant Colls. (chmn. marine div.), The Oceanography Soc., Galveston C. of C. (bd. govs.), Sigma Xi (Disting. mem. award 1987), Sigma Phi Sigma, Alpha Chi, Phi Kappa Phi. Club: Vanda (Antarctica). Office: Tex A&M U PO Box 1675 Galveston TX 77553-1675

MERRIAM, DWIGHT HAINES, lawyer, land use planner; b. Norwood, Mass., Apr. 20, 1946; s. Austin Luther and Lillian Diana (Olsen) M.; m. Cynthia Ann Hayes, May 21, 1966 (div. June 1992); children: Sarah Ann Leilani, Jonathan Hayes. BA cum laude, U. Mass., 1968; M in Regional Planning, U. N.C., 1974; JD, Yale U., 1978. Bar: Conn. 1978, Mass. 1980, U.S. Dist. Ct. Conn. 1981, U.S. Dist. Ct. Hawaii 1984, U.S. Supreme Ct. 1990, U.S. Ct. Appeals (4th cir.) 1993. Land use planner Charles E. Downe, Newton, Mass., 1968; assoc. Byrne, Buck & Steiner, Farmington, Conn., 1978, Robinson, Robinson & Cole, Hartford, Conn., 1979-83; ptnr. Robinson & Cole, Hartford, 1984—; adj. prof. law Western New Eng. Coll., 1978-86, U. Conn., 1982, 84-87, U. Vt. Law Sch., 1994—; instr. planning U. Bridgeport, 1981-83, U. Conn., 1986-92; mem.faculty Nat. Coll. Dist. Attys., 1983-87, Nat. Jud. Coll., 1994—; instr. city and regional planning, Memphis State U., 1989, 94; speaker in field. Co-editor: Inclusionary Zoning Moves Downtown, 1985; contbr. over 40 articles and book revs. to profl. jours. Bd. dirs. Growth Mgmt. Inst., Washington, 1992—; Housing Edn. Resource Ctr., 1984-88, Housing Coalition for Capitol Region, Inc., 1984-86; bd. dirs. Conn. Fund for Environment, 1981-85, legal advr. com., 1985-88, legal advr. bd., 1978-81; mem. Environment 2000 environ. plan adv. bd. Conn. Dept. Enrion. Protection, 1987-91; assoc. Environ. Law Inst., 1987—; mem. housing task force Conn. Dept. on Aging, 1981; mem. Gov.'s Housing Task Force, Conn., 1980-81. USN, 1968-75. Vietnam; capt. USNR. Mem. ABA, Conn. Bar Assn. (exec. com. zoning & planning sect. 1985-87, 91—), Am. Planning Assn. (bd. dirs. 1988-90, chmn. planning & law divsn. 1984-86, exec. com. planning & law divsn. 1978-88, chmn. legis. com. Conn. chpt. 1978-80, editorial adv. bd. 1984-92), Nat. Inst. Mcpl. Law Officers (chmn. sect. on zoning, planning & land devel. 1988-89, sect. vice-chmn. 1987), Assn. State Floodplain Mgrs., Am. Inst. Cert. Planners (pres. 1988-90), Am. Coll. Real Estate Lawyers, U. N.C. Alumni Assn. Democrat. Unitarian. Avocations: sailing, skiing. Home: 1 Linden Pl Apt 410 Hartford CT 06106-1745 Office: Robinson & Cole 1 Commercial Plz Hartford CT 06103-3599

MERRICK, DAVID (DAVID MARGULOIS), theatrical producer; b. St. Louis, Nov. 27, 1912; s. Samuel and Celia Margulois; m. Etan Aronson. B.A., Washington U., St. Louis; LL.B., St. Louis U. Produced plays on Broadway: Fanny, 1954, The Matchmaker, 1955, Look Back in Anger, Romanoff and Juliet, Jamaica, 1957, The Entertainer, The World of Suzie Wong, La Plume de ma Tante, Epitaph for George Dillon, 1958, Destry Rides Again, Gypsy, Take Me Along, 1958, Irma La Douce, A Taste of Honey, Becket (Tony award), Do Re Mi, 1960, Carnival, 1961, Sunday in New York, 1961, Ross, 1961, Subways are for Sleeping, 1961, I Can Get It For You Wholesale, Stop the World—I Want to Get Off, Tchin Tchin, Oliver, 1962, Rehearsal, Luther (Tony award), 110 in the Shade, Arturo Ui, 1963, Hello Dolly (Tony award), Oh, What A Lovely War, 1964, The Roar of the Greasepaint—The Smell of the Crowd, Inadmissible Evidence, Cactus Flower, 1965, The Persecution and Assassination of Jean Paul Marat as Performed by the Inmates of the Asylum of Charenton Under the Direction of the Marquis de Sade, 1965 (Tony award), Philadelphia, Here I Come, Don't Drink the Water, I Do I Do, 1966, Rosencrantz and Guildenstern Are

Dead, 1967 (Tony award), Forty Carats, 1968, Promises, Promises, Play it Again Sam, Private Lives, 1969, Child's Play, 1970, Four in a Garden, 1971, A Midsummer Night's Dream, The Philanthropist, Mack and Mabel, Dreyfus in Rehearsal, 1974, Travesties (Spl. Tony award 1968), Red Devil Battery Sign, Very Good Eddy, 1975, 42nd Street, 1985-86 (Tony award 1980); produced films The Great Gatsby, 1974, Semi-Tough, 1977, Rough-Cut, 1980.

MERRICK, GEORGE BOESCH, aerospace company executive; b. Burlington, Iowa, Mar. 9, 1928; s. Dale McKeen and Marjorie May (Boesch) M.; m. Eleanor Gamble Moore, Sept. 1, 1951; children: Charles, Ellen, Elizabeth. B.S., U. Minn., 1949. With N.Am. Aviation (name changed to Rockwell Internat.), 1949; dir. Apollo Command and Service Module, Space div., 1966-72; v.p., program mgr. Apollo Program, 1972-74, v.p., program mgr. Space Shuttle Orbiter Program, 1974-76; pres. space div. Rockwell Internat., Downey, Calif., 1976-78; pres. space systems group Rockwell Internat., 1978-80, corp. v.p., 1980—. Recipient Pub. Service award NASA. Fellow Am. Astron. Soc., AIAA. Office: 2201 Seal Beach Blvd Seal Beach CA 90740-5603

MERRICK, ROSWELL DAVENPORT, association executive; b. Kings County, N.Y., July 20, 1922; s. George Roswell and Marguerite Regina M.; m. Gladys K. Kinley, June 26, 1948; children—Gregory, Susan, Peter. B.S., Springfield Coll., 1944; M.A., N.Y. U., 1947; Ed.D., Boston U., 1953. Assoc. prof., head basketball coach Central Conn. Coll., New Britain, 1946-53; asst. dean (Coll. div.); dir. div. health, phys. edn., recreation and athletics So. Ill. U., Carbondale, 1953-58; exec. dir. Nat. Assn. Sport and Phys. Edn., Reston, Va., 1958-91, U.S. Fitness and Sport Coun., 1991—. Contbr. articles to profl. jours. Mem. U.S. Olympic Com. Served with USAAF, 1944-46. Mem. AAHPERD, Mt. Vernon Yacht Club. Methodist. Address: 4739 Neptune Dr Alexandria VA 22309

MERRIER, HELEN, actress, director; b. Chgo., Mar. 10, 1932; d. Miner Thompson and Helen (Hembree) Coburn; m. Tom Meier, Dec. 23, 1954; 1 child, William Frank. BA, Mills Coll., 1954; BS, Northwestern U., 1955. Actress (radio) Ma Perkins, One Man's Family, Standard School House of the Air, 1934-52, (stage) Time and the Conways, Remains Theater, 1991, Cinderella, Milw., 1991, Chgo. theatres including Second City ETC, Organic Theatre, Center Theatre, Court, Drury Lane Oakbrook, Hull House, Kingston Mines, other theatres, including Cleveland Play House, Coconut Grove Playhouse, Fla., Evergreen Stage Co., L.A., M & W Prodns., Milw., Guthrie Theatre, Mpls., (musicals) Woman of Yr., Drury Lane, Evergreen Park, Ill., 1989, Sweeney Todd, Calo Theater, Chgo., 1991, Dreams of Defiance, N.Y.C., Chgo. and Ohio, Aristophanes' The Birds, Wisdom Bridge Theatre, Chgo., 1993, Dreams of Defiance, Theatre Bldg. Chgo., 1994, Adeline project, N.J., 1995, (film) Women in Treatment, 1990; dir. (stage) Center, Chgo., 1993. Women's bd. dirs. No. Ill. divsn. Salvation Army, 1965—; bd. dirs. Chgo. chpt. Prin. Found., 1972—, Women's Coll. Bd., 1956-66, Scottish Cultural Soc., 1976—; mem. Gaelic League, 1981-86, Celtic League, 1985—, Clan Irvine Assn., 1992—, Am. Anthrop. Soc., 1955-70, Am. Folklore Soc., 1955-70, Primitive Art Soc., 1975-85; mem. Apollo Chorus of Chgo., 1982-87, bd. mgmt., 1984-85. Mem. AFTRA, Actors Equity Assn. (Midwest adv. bd. 1983-84), Screen Actors Guild, Mills Coll. Club Chgo. (bd. dirs. 1962-81), Brit. Club Chgo., The Arts Club Chgo. Home: 915 Linden Ave Wilmette IL 60091-2712

MERRIFIELD, DONALD PAUL, university chancellor; b. Los Angeles, Nov. 14, 1928; s Arthur S. and Elizabeth (Baker) M. B.S. in Physics, Calif. Inst. Tech., 1950; M.S., U. Notre Dame, 1951; A.M., Ph.L. in Philosophy, St. Louis U., 1957; Ph.D., MIT, 1962; S.T.M., U. Santa Clara, Calif., 1966; S.T.D. (hon.), U. Santa Clara, Calif., 1969; D.H.L. (hon.), U. Judaism, 1984, Hebrew Union Coll.-Jewish Inst. Religion, 1986. Joined Soc. of Jesus, 1951; ordained priest Roman Cath. Ch., 1965; instr. physics Loyola U., Los Angeles, 1961-62; lectr. Engring. Sch., Santa Clara, 1965; cons. theoretical chemistry Jet Propulsion Lab., Calif. Inst. Tech., 1962-69; asst. prof. physics U. San Francisco, 1967-69; pres. Loyola Marymount U., Los Angeles, 1969-84, chancellor, 1984—. Bd. visitors UCLA; bd. dirs. Santa Marta Hosp. Found., European Am. Found. Mem. Sigma Xi. Home: Loyola Marymount U Xavier Hall Los Angeles CA 90045 *In today's world, we all stand in need of that pragmatic hope which allows us to see the possibilities for building a more just society and meeting the challenges before us. Without such hope we are paralyzed before our difficulties. With a less realistic hope, too idealistic, we are continually overwhelmed by failures. But with an openness to possibilities, we can move ahead with determination.*

MERRIFIELD, DUDLEY BRUCE, business educator, former government official; b. Chgo., June 13, 1921; s. Fred and Anna (Marshall) M.; m. Paula Sorensen, June 8, 1949; children: Bruce, Robert, Maryanna. A.B. in Chemistry, Princeton U., 1942; M.S. in Chemistry, U. Chgo., 1948, Ph.D. in Chemistry, 1950. Sr. rsch. chemist Monsanto, St. Louis, 1950-56; mgr. polymer rsch. Tex.-U.S. Chem. Co., Parsippany, N.J., 1956-63; dir. rsch. and devel. Petrolite Corp., St. Louis, 1963-68; v.p. tech. and ventures Occidental Petroleum Co., Houston, 1968-77; v.p. tech. and venture mgmt. Continental Group, Stamford, Conn., 1977-82; asst. sec. for productivity, tech. and innovation Dept. Commerce, Washington, 1982-89; undersec. econ. affairs, 1986-87; Walter Baldstrom prof. emeritus U Pa., Phila., 1989-94; pres., CEO Pinnacle Rsch. Inst. Devel. Co., 1991—; mem. adv. bd. Binat Research and Devel. Found., U.S., Israel, France, India, 1979—. Contbr. articles to profl. jours.; patentee in field. Mem. exec. com. Episcopal Ch., 1973-79; chmn. Princeton Alumni Coun., 1968-72. With USMC, 1943-46. Fellow AAAS, Inst. for Chemists; mem. Am. Chem. Soc., Indsl. Rsch. Inst. (dir., pres.-elect 1977-82 M. Holland Best Article award), Am. Mgmt. Assn. (trustee, chmn. rsch. coun.), Dirs. Rsch., Sigma Xi. Republican. Episcopalian. Office: U Pa Wharton Sch Bus Vance Hall 406 3733 Spruce St Philadelphia PA 19104-6301

MERRIFIELD, ROBERT BRUCE, biochemist, educator; b. Ft. Worth, Tex., July 15, 1921; s. George E. and Lorene (Lucas) M.; m. Elizabeth Furlong, June 20, 1949; children: Nancy, James, Betsy, Cathy, Laurie, Sally. B.A., UCLA, 1943, Ph.D., 1949. Clement Park Research Found., 1943-44; research asst. Med. Sch., UCLA, 1948-49; asst. Rockefeller Inst. for Med. Research 1949-53, assoc., 1953-57; asst. prof. Rockefeller U., 1957-58, assoc. prof., 1958-66, prof., 1966-92, John D. Rockefeller prof. 1984-92, emeritus prof., 1992—; Developed solid phase peptide synthesis; completed (with B. Gutte) 1st total synthesis of an enzyme, 1969. Assoc. editor: Internat. Jour. Peptide and Protein Research; contbr. articles to sci. jours. Recipient Lasker award biomed. rsch., 1969, Gairdner award, 1970, Intra-Sci. award, 1970, Nichols medal, 1973, Alan E. Pierce award Am. Peptide Symposium, 1979, Nobel prize in chemistry, 1984, Rudinger award European Peptide Soc., 1990, Chem. Pioneer award Am. Inst. Chemists, 1993. Mem. Am. Chem. Soc. (award creative work synthetic organic chemistry 1972, Hirschmann award in peptide chemistry 1990, Glenn T. Seaborg award 1993), NAS USA, Am. Soc. Biol. Chemists, Sigma Xi, Phi Lambda Upsilon, Alpha Chi Sigma. Office: Rockefeller U Dept Chemistry 1230 York Ave New York NY 10021

MERRIGAN, EUGENE T., financial company executive, marketing specialist; b. Mitchell, Nebr., Nov. 19, 1933; s. William M. and Catherine J. (Farner) M.; m. Joan L. Riha, Sept. 9, 1958; children: Craig, Curtis, Kyle, Kevin. BS in Mktg., U. Nebr., 1958. Various positions in ops. and mktg. Equifax, Inc., Atlanta, 1958-80, pres., gen. mgr. various bus. units, 1980-87, sr. v.p., 1987—, also bd. dirs. Served to cpl. U.S. Army, 1954-56. Republican. Roman Catholic. Lodge: Rotary. Avocations: tennis, golf. Office: Equifax Inc 1600 Peachtree St NW Atlanta GA 30309-2403

MERRILL, ARTHUR ALEXANDER, financial analyst; b. Honolulu, June 17, 1906; s. Arthur Merton and Grace Graydon (Dickey) M.; m. Elsie Louise Breed, Aug. 17, 1929; 1 child, Anne Louise Merrill Breiling. B.S. in Elec. Engring. U. Calif., 1927; M.B.A., Harvard U., 1929. Mem. engring. statistics, and mgmt. depts. Gen. Electric Co., Schenectady, also N.Y.C., 1927-61; fin. writer and analyst, pres. Merrill Analysis Inc., Haverford, Pa., 1961—. Author: How Do You Use a Slide Rule, 1961, Behavior of Prices on Wall Street, 1975, Battle of White Plains, 1975, Seasonal Tendencies in Stock Prices, 1975, Filtered Waves, Basic Theory, 1977, Bias in Hourly, Daily and Weekly Wave Patterns, 1979, Remembering Names, 1985; editor: Tech. Trends, 1961-88. Mem. Market Technicians Assn. (chartered, Ann. award

1977), Fin. Analysts Fedn., N.Y. Soc. Security Analysts, Mensa, Intertel, Soc. Preservation and Encouragement Barber Shop Quartet Singing Am., Sigma Xi, Theta Chi, Tau Beta Pi, Eta Kappa Nu. Republican. Congregationalist. Home and Office: 3300 Darby Rd Apt 3325 Haverford PA 19041-1071

MERRILL, ARTHUR LEWIS, retired theology educator; b. Tura, Assam, India, Sept. 14, 1930; s. Alfred Francis and Ida (Walker) M.; m. Barbara Jean Mayer, Aug. 18, 1951 (dec. June 1978); children: Margaret Jean, Katherine Merrill Nelson, Robert L.; m. Margaret Z. Morris, Sept. 11, 1985. BA, Coll. of Wooster, 1951; BD with distinction, Berkeley Bapt. Div. Sch., 1954; PhD, U. Chgo., 1962. Ordained to ministry United Ch. of Christ, 1954. Asst. prof. Bapt. Missionary Tng. Sch., Chgo., 1957-58; assoc. prof. Mission House Theol. Sem., Plymouth, Wis., 1958-62; assoc. prof. United Theol. Sem. Twin Cities, New Brighton, Minn., 1962-67, prof., 1967-95, Piper prof. bibl. interpretation, 1993-95. Author: United Theological Seminary of the Twin Cities: An Ecumenical Venture, 1993; co-author: Biblical Witness and the World, 1967; co-editor: Scripture in History and Theology, 1977; contbr. articles to profl. publs. ATS-Lilly postdoctoral fellow, 1966-67. Mem. Soc. Bibl. Lit., Am. Schs. Oriental Rsch., Israel Exploration Soc., Minn. Theol. Libr. Assn. (pres. 1994-95). Home: 214 Windsor Ct Saint Paul MN 55112-3367 Office: United Theol Sem 3000 5th St NW Saint Paul MN 55112-2598

MERRILL, CHARLES EUGENE, lawyer; b. San Antonio, Aug. 26, 1952; s. Charles Perry and Florence Elizabeth (Kupper) M.; m. Carol Ann Rutter, Apr. 28, 1984; children: Elizabeth C., Charles C. AB, Stanford U., 1974; JD, U. Calif., Berkeley, 1977. Bar: Mo. 1977, Calif. 1983, Ill. 1993. Ptnr. Husch & Eppenberger, St. Louis, 1977—. Mem. ABA, Bar Assn. of Met. St. Louis. Office: Husch & Eppenberger Ste 1300 100 N Broadway Saint Louis MO 63102

MERRILL, CHARLES MERTON, federal judge; b. Honolulu, Dec. 11, 1907; s. Arthur M. and Grace Graydon (Dickey) M.; m. Mary Luita Sherman, Aug. 28, 1931 (dec.); children: Julia Booth Stoddard, Charles McKinney. AB, U. Calif., 1928; LLB, Harvard, 1931. Bar: Calif. 1931, Nev. 1932. Sole practice Reno, 1932-51; judge Nev. Supreme Ct., 1951-59, chief justice, 1955-56, 59; judge U.S. Ct. of Appeals (9th cir.), San Francisco, 1959-74, sr. judge, 1974—. Mem. ABA, State Bar Nev. (gov. 1947-50), Am. Law Inst. (council 1960-). Office: US Ct of Appeals PO Box 193939 San Francisco CA 94119-3939*

MERRILL, DAVID NATHAN, ambassador; b. Balt.; s. Maurice B. and Ann (Nathanson) M.; m. Darlene J. Luke, 1976; four children. BA cum laude, Brandeis U., 1964; MA, Tufts U., 1965; MPA, Harvard U., 1974. Congl. liaison officer AID, 1976-79, rep. to Burma, 1979-83, deputy dir. legis. affairs, 1983-84, dir. East Asia affairs, 1984-87, mission dir. to Indonesia, 1987-90, dep. asst. adminstr., Europe Bur., 1990-94; U.S. amb. to Bangladesh, 1994—. Recipient Disting. Honor award AID, 1987, President's Meritorious Svc. award Dept. State, 1989. Mem. Am. Fgn. Svc. Assn. Office: Diplomatic Enclave, Madani Ave Baridhara GPO Box 323, Dhaka 1212, Bangladesh*

MERRILL, EDWARD CLIFTON, JR., emeritus university president; b. Asheville, N.C., Jan. 29, 1920; s. Edward Clifton and Alice (Tiddy) M.; m. Frances Bonkemeyer, June 2, 1946 (dec. Jan. 1993); children: Susan, Nancy, Ned, Ann. B.A., U. N.C., 1942; M.S., U. Tenn., 1948; Ph.D., George Peabody Coll., 1953; LL.D., Gallaudet U., 1969. Instr. Asheville-Biltmore Coll., 1946- 47; tchr., dean Lee Edwards High Sch., Asheville, 1948-51; instr. George Peabody Coll., also coordinator So. State Coop. Program Ednl. Adminstrn., 1953-55; assoc. prof. edn. Auburn U., 1955-57; summer vis. assoc. prof. edn. Coll. Edn., U. Fla., 1957; prof. edn., assoc. dean grad. studies Coll. Edn., U. Rochester, 1957-60; prof. edn. Coll. Edn., U. N.C., 1960-61; dean Coll. Edn., U. Tenn., 1961-69; pres. Gallaudet U., 1969-83, pres. emeritus, 1983—; dir. N.Y. Statewide In-Service Program Sch. Adminstrns., 1958-60; mem. N.Y. State Council Adminstrv. Leadership, 1957-60; dir. workshops and insts. U. Rochester, 1957-60; chmn. Assoc. Orgns. Tchr. Edn., 1966; mem. bd. Appalachia Ednl. Labs., Inc., Washington Ednl. TV Assn.; bd. dirs. Deafness Research Found., 1980-83, Nat. Captioning Inst., 1985—. Co-author: Community Leadership for Public Education, 1955, The Deaf Child in the Public School, 2d edit, 1978; Editor: Better Teaching in School Administration, 1955; Contbr. articles to profl. jours., chpts. to books. Bd. dirs. Nat. Assn. Hearing and Speech Agys., pres., 1971; bd. dirs. Nat. Captioning Inst., Inc., 1983—, vice-chmn., 1987-91. Recipient Disting. Service award Nat. Assn. of Deaf, 1978; Décoration au Mérite Social World Fedn. of Deaf, 1979; Daniel T. Cloud Leadership award, 1982; Disting. Service award Pres.'s Com. for Employment of the Handicapped, 1983; Disting. Service to Edn. award Council for Advancement and Support of Edn., 1983; Washingtonian of Yr., 1982. Mem. Am. Assn. Sch. Adminstrs. Home: 34 Saunooke Rd Asheville NC 28805-2801

MERRILL, EDWARD WILSON, chemical engineering educator; b. New Bedford, Mass., Aug. 31, 1923; s. Edward Clifton and Gertrude (Wilson) M.; m. Genevieve de Bidart, Aug. 19, 1948; children—Anne de Bidart, Francis de Bidart. A.B., Harvard, 1945; D.Sc., Mass. Inst. Tech., 1947. Research engr. Dewey & Almy div. W.R. Grace & Co., 1947-50; mem. faculty MIT, 1950—, prof. chem. engring., 1964—, Carbon P. Dubbs prof., 1973—; cons. in field, 1950—; cons. in biochem. engring. Harvard U. Health Services, 1982—. Author articles on polymers, rheology, med. engring. Pres. bd. trustees Buckingham Sch., Cambridge, 1969-74; trustee Browne and Nichols Sch., Cambridge, 1972-74, hon. trustee, 1974—. Fellow Am. Inst. for Med. and Biol. Engring., Am. Acad. Arts and Scis.; mem. Am. Chem. Soc., Am. Inst. Chem. Engrs. (Charles M.A. Stine award 1993), Soc. for Biomaterials. Patentee chem. and rheological instruments. Home: 90 Somerset St Belmont MA 02178-2010

MERRILL, GEORGE VANDERNETH, lawyer, investment executive; b. N.Y.C., July 2, 1947; s. James Edward and Claire (Leness) M.; m. Janice Anne Humes, May 11, 1985; 1 child, Claire Georgina. AB magna cum laude, Harvard U., 1968, JD, 1972; MBA, Columbia U., 1973. Bar: N.Y. 1973, U.S. Dist. Ct. (so. and ea. dists.) N.Y. 1974, U.S. Ct. Appeals (2d cir.) 1974. Assoc. Cleary, Gottlieb, Steen & Hamilton, N.Y.C., 1974-77, Hawkins, Delafield & Wood, N.Y.C., 1977-79; v.p. Irving Trust Co., N.Y.C., 1980-82; v.p., gen. counsel Listowel Inc., N.Y.C., 1982-84, bd. dirs., exec. v.p., gen. counsel, 1984-93, also bd. dirs. Pres. Arell Found., N.Y.C., 1985-93, also bd. dirs.; pres. Northfield Charitable Corp., N.Y.C., 1986-93; v.p., sec. Brougham Prodn. Co., N.Y.C., 1986-89, bd. dirs., sr. v.p., sec., 1990-93; v.p., sec. Marinetics Inc., N.Y.C., 1988-90, sr. v.p., sec., 1991-93, also bd. dirs., 1989-93; v.p. Sci. Design and Engring. Co., Inc., N.Y.C., 1987-88, bd. dirs., exec. v.p., 1989-93; v.p. Instl. Portfolio Mgmt., Shawmut Investment Advisors, 1993—. Recipient Detur award Harvard U., 1968, John Harvard scholar. Mem. ABA, Am. Mgmt. Assn., Assn. of Bar of City of N.Y., The Brook, Union Club, Down Town Assn., Racquet and Tennis Club, Pilgrims of U.S. Home: 60 Brenway Dr West Hartford CT 06117 Office: Shawmut Nat Corp 777 Main St Hartford CT 06115-2000

MERRILL, HARVIE MARTIN, manufacturing executive; b. Detroit, Apr. 26, 1921; s. Harvie and Helen (Nelson) M.; m. Mardelle Merrill; children—Susan, Linda. B.S. in Chem. Engring, Purdue U., 1942. Devel. engr. Sinclair Refining Co., 1946-47; research and gen. mgr. 3M Co., St. Paul, 1947-65; v.p. fabricated products Plastics div. Stauffer Chem. Co., N.Y.C., 1965-69; with Hexcel Corp. San Francisco, 1969-86, pres., chief exec. officer, 1969-86, chmn. bd., 1973-88; Calif.; bd. dirs. TIS Mortgage/Investment Co., Corp., San Francisco; adv. dir. Arrow Venture Ptnrs., N.Y.C. With USAF, 1942-46. Mem. Pacific-Union Club, Bohemian Club San Francisco, Villa Taverna (San Francisco), Burlingame Country Club. Home: 1170 Sacramento St San Francisco CA 94108-1943

MERRILL, J. MARK, financial management executive; b. Memphis, Dec. 6, 1959; s. John F. and Mary Louise (Oakley) M.; m. Ripple Kay Holland, Jan. 7, 1984; children: Sarah Elizabeth, John Mark. Jr. Student, Vanderbilt U., 1977-78; BS in Acctg., Christian Bros. Coll., 1981. CPA, Tenn. Auditor Deloitte Haskins & Sells, Memphis, 1981-82; audit supr. Watkins & Watkins, Memphis, 1982-84; mgr. fin. Danek Group, Inc., Memphis, 1984-88; v.p. fin. Danek Group, Inc., Memphis, 1988—. Mem. AICPA, Tenn. Soc. CPA's, Fin. Execs. Inst., Beta Gamma Sigma. Republican. Evangelical. Home:

8775 Birch Park Ln Germantown TN 38139-6555 Office: Danek Group Inc 3092 Directors Row Memphis TN 38131-0401

MERRILL, JEAN FAIRBANKS, writer; b. Rochester, N.Y., Jan. 27, 1923; d. Earl Dwight and Elsie (Fairbanks) M. B.A., Allegheny Coll., 1944; M.A., Wellesley Coll., 1945. Feature editor Scholastic Mags., 1947-50; editor Lit. Cavalcade, 1956-57; publs. div. Bank St. Coll. Edn., 1964-65. Children's books include Henry, the Hand-Painted Mouse, 1951, The Woover, 1952, Boxes, 1953, The Tree House of Jimmy Domino, 1955, The Travels of Marco, 1956, A Song for Gar, 1957, The Very Nice Things, 1959, Blue's Broken Heart, 1960, Shan's Lucky Knife (Jr. Lit. Guild selection), Emily Emerson's Moon, 1960 (Jr. Lit. Guild selection), The Superlative Horse (Jr. Lit. Guild selection), 1961 (Lewis Carroll Shelf award 1963), Tell About the Cowbarn, Daddy, 1963, The Pushcart War (Lewis Carroll Shelf award), 1964 (Boys Club Am. Jr. Book award), High, Wide & Handsome, 1964 (Jr. Lit. Guild selection), The Elephant Who Liked to Smash Small Cars, 1967, Red Riding, 1968, The Black Sheep, 1969, Here I Come—Ready or Not!, 1970, Mary, Come Running, 1970, How Many Kids are Hiding on My Block?, 1970, Please, Don't Eat My Cabin, 1971, The Toothpaste Millionaire (Dorothy Canfield Fisher Meml. award 1975-76), 1972 (Sequoyah award 1977), The Second Greatest Clown in the World, 1972, The Jackpot, 1972, The Bumper Sticker Book, 1973, Maria's House, 1974, The Girl Who Loved Caterpillars, 1992; poetry books edited include A Few Flies and I, 1969; libretto for chamber opera Mary Come Running, 1983. Fulbright fellow India, 1952-53. Mem. N.Am. Mycol. Assn., Authors League, Vt. Arts Coun., War Resisters League, Vt. Inst. Natural Sci., Dramatists Guild, Vt. Nat. Resources Coun., Vt. League Writers, Soc. Children's Book Writers, Fulbright Assn., Sierra Club, Phi Beta Kappa. *My interest in writing children's books may have derived from the impact certain books had on me as a child, and a wish to recreate the quality of that experience. As to my general motivation as a writer, I would say that it is to celebrate those aspects of the human experience that affirm the creative and life-reverencing instinct in man. I always hope that my stories may be essentially liberating, opening the reader to emotional, as well as intellectual experience, and that they may be entertaining, encouraging the capacity for joy by evoking the free play of a reader's curiosity, humor and inventiveness.*

MERRILL, JOSEPH HARTWELL, religious association executive; b. Norway, Maine, Jan. 16, 1903; s. Wiggin L. and Ella M. (Porter) M. Grad. high sch. Head retouching dept. Bachrach, Inc. (photographers), Newton, Mass., 1937-61; sec. Mass. Assn. Spiritualists, 1953-61; exec. sec. Nat. Spiritualist Assn. Chs., Milw., 1961-71; v.p. Nat. Spiritualist Assn. Chs., 1971-73, pres., 1973-94; v.p. Internat. Spiritualist Fedn. Spiritualists, London, 1975-81; lectr. social legislation for oldsters Townsend Orgn. Served with AUS, 1942-43. Address: 13 Cleveland Ave Lily Dale NY 14752

MERRILL, KENNETH COLEMAN, retired automobile company executive; b. South Bend, Ind., Feb. 20, 1930; s. Kenneth Griggs and Helen Shapley (Coleman) M.; m. Helen Jean Tagtmeyer, June 10, 1956; children: Barry, Diane, John. B.A., Cornell U., 1953; M.B.A., Ind. U., 1956. With Ford Motor Co., Dearborn, Mich., 1956-91; asst. controller Ford Motor Co., Dearborn, 1967-71, gen. asst. controller, 1971-73, controller N.Am. automotive ops., 1973-79, exec. dir. parts ops., 1979-80, exec. dir. bus. planning and trust mgmt., 1980-87; pres. Ford Motor Credit Co., Dearborn, 1987-91, ret., 1991; bd. dirs. Am. Dental Techs.; v.p. Wadsworth (Ohio) Ford. Pres. Plymouth (Mich.) Symphony Soc., 1969-70; vice chmn. bd. dirs. Detroit Inner City Bus. Improvement Forum, 1977-79; bd. dirs. Schoolcraft Coll. Found., 1982—; pres. 1984-86; bd. dirs. Crossroads, 1992-95, treas. 1994. Mem. Fin. Execs. Inst., Greater Detroit C. of C. (bd. dirs. 1988-91, exec. com. 1990-91), Detroit Econ. Club, Barton Hills Country Club, Oaks Club (Sarasota, Fla.), Beta Gamma Sigma, Psi Upsilon. Episcopalian (treas. 1973-74, 79—). Home: 1450 Maple St Plymouth MI 48170-1516

MERRILL, LELAND GILBERT, JR., retired environmental science educator; b. Danville, Ill., Oct. 4, 1920; s. Leland Gilbert and May (Babcock) M.; m. Virginia Gilhooley, Sept. 14, 1949; children: Susan Jane, Alison Lee. B.S., Mich. State U., 1942; M.S., Rutgers U., 1948, Ph.D., 1949. Research asst. entomology Rutgers U., 1946-49; asst. prof. entomology Mich. State U., 1949-53; mem. faculty Rutgers U., 1953-82, research specialist entomology, 1960-61, dean agr., 1961-71, dir. Inst. Environ. Studies, 1971-76, prof. center coastal and environ. studies, 1976-82; exec. sec. N.J. Acad. Sci., 1984-92. Served to maj. AUS, 1942-46. Medallist, Wrestling XIV Olympiad, 1948. Mem. AAAS, Entomol. Soc. Am., Coastal Soc., Sigma Xi, Alpha Gamma Rho, Phi Kappa Phi, Alpha Zeta, Epsilon Sigma Phi. Home: 49 Gulick Rd Princeton NJ 08540-4111

MERRILL, LINDSEY, music educator; b. Madisonville, Ky., Jan. 10, 1925; s. James E. and Della (Scott) M.; m. Martha Lynn Rowe, June 11, 1948; children: Jonathan Scott, Rebecca Rowe. Mus.B., U. Louisville, 1949; Mus.M., Yale U., 1950; Ph.D., U. Rochester, 1963. Mem. faculty Queen's Coll., N.C., 1950-53, Smith Coll., 1953-56; prof. music Bucknell U., 1957-67, chmn. dept., 1966-67; prof. dir. Sch. Music, dir. Blossom Festival Sch. Kent State U., 1967-75; dean Conservatory Music, U. Mo.-Kansas City, 1975-85; dir. Edn. Found. Ventura, Calif., 1986—; Music editor Merriam Webster 3d New Internat. Dictionary; cons. in field. Violinist, composer electronic music. Served with AUS, 1943-46. Mem. Pi Kappa Lambda.

MERRILL, MARTHA, instructional media educator; b. Anniston, Ala., Apr. 21, 1946; d. Walter James and Polly (McCarty) M. BA, Birmingham-So. Coll., 1968; MS, Jacksonville (Ala.) State U., 1974; PhD, U. Pitts., 1979. Social worker Tuscaloosa (Ala.) County Dept. Human Resources, 1968-71, Calhoun County Dept. Human Resources, Anniston, Ala., 1971-73; social scis./bus. libr. Jacksonville State U., 1974-86, prof. instrnl. media, 1987—. Mem. Friends of Libr. bd. Anniston-Calhoun County Pub. Libr., 1984—. Recipient Ala./SIRS Intellectual Freedom award. Intellectual Freedom Com., Ala. Libr. Assn., 1992. Mem. ALA (exec. bd., Intellectual Freedom Round Table 1987-93), Ala. Libr. Assn. (pres. 1990-91, Disting. Svc. award 1995), Ala. Assn. Coll. and Rsch. Libs. (pres. 1989-90), Southeastern Libr. Assn. (chair intellectual freedom com. 1986-88, chair resolutions com. 1990-92). Office: Jacksonville State U Dept Ednl Resources Coll Edn Jacksonville AL 36265

MERRILL, NEWTON PHELPS STOKES, financial executive; b. Mount Kisco, N.Y., Nov. 14, 1939; s. Edwin Katte Merrill and Helen (Phelps Stokes) Bush; m. Mary DuBois Schwarz, Apr. 30, 1966; children—N. Alexander, Eliot P., Mary S. B.A., Harvard Coll., 1961. Trainee, analyst Bank of N.Y., N.Y.C., 1961-66, investment officer, 1967-69, v.p. nat. div., 1970-75, sr. v.p., 1980-82, exec. v.p. regional banking, 1982-84; pres. v.p. Bank of N.Y. Co. Inc., N.Y.C., 1984-88, sr. exec. v.p., 1988—, also dir. various subs.; sr. exec. v.p. U.S. Comml. Banking, 1984—. Served with USAR, 1962-68. Republican. Episcopalian. Clubs: Harvard, Down Town Assn. (N.Y.C.). Avocations: sailing; skiing. Office: Bank NY Co Inc 1 Wall St New York NY 10005-2501

MERRILL, PHILIP, publisher; b. Balt.; m. Eleanor Merrill; children: Douglas, Catherine, Nancy. BA, Cornell U., 1955; PMD, Harvard Bus. Sch., 1963. Spl. asst. State. Deputy Sec. of State, Washington, 1961-68; counsellor undersec. of defense for policy Washington, 1981-83; asst. sec. gen. NATO, Brussels, Belgium, 1990-92; pub., chmn. Capital-Gazette Communications, Inc., Washingtonian Mag., Washington, 1968—; mem. policy bd. Dept. Defense, 1983-90. Del. USA Short Wave Treaty, USA Law of the Sea Treaty; trustee Cornell U., U. Md. Found., Aspen Inst.; bd. dirs. Ctr. Strategic and Internat. Studies, Johns Hopkins Sch. Advanced Internat. Studies; bd. dirs. Johnson Sch. Mgmt. Cornell U., Chesapeake Bay Found., Fed. City Coun., U. Md. Sch. Pub. Policy; mem. Gulf War Air Power Survey, 1991-92. Recipient Disting. Svc. medal U.S. Dept. Def., 1988. Mem. Coun. Fgn. Rels., Inst. Internat. Strategic Studies, Chief Execs. Orgn., World Pres. Orgn. Office: The Washingtonian Mag 1828 L St NW Washington DC 20036-5104

MERRILL, RICHARD AUSTIN, lawyer; b. Logan, Utah, May 20, 1937; s. Milton Rees and Bessie (Austin) M.; m. Elizabeth Duvall, Aug. 26, 1961; children—Patricia, John. AB, Columbia U., 1959, LLB, 1964; BA (Rhodes scholar), Oxford (Eng.) U., 1961, MA, 1965. Bar: N.Y. 1964, D.C. 1965, Va. 1980. Law clk. to Hon. Carl McGowan, U.S. Ct. Appeals for D.C., 1964-65, Va. bar, 1980; assoc. firm Covington & Burling, Washington, 1965-

69, spl. counsel, 1991—; assoc. prof. law U. Va., 1969-72, prof., 1972-75, Daniel Caplin prof. law, 1977—, Arnold Leon prof., 1985-88, dean sch. law, 1980-88, Albert C. Tate Jr. rsch. prof., 1989-91; gen. counsel FDA, Washington, 1975-77; cons. in field. Mem. Inst. Medicine (council) 1985-88, Nat. Acad. Scis., 1977—, Bd. on Toxicology and Environ. Health Hazards, 1979-85; bd. dirs. Immunex Corp. Author: (with Jerry L. Mashaw and Peter Shane) American Administrative Law, 2d edit., 1985, (with Peter B. Hutt) Food and Drug Law, 1980. Bd. trustees Thomas Jefferson Meml. Found. Mem. Am. Bar Found., Va. Bar Found., Am. Law Inst., Food and Drug Inst. (trustee). Office: U Va Sch Law Charlottesville VA 22901

MERRILL, RICHARD JAMES, educational director; b. Milw., Apr. 15, 1931; s. Henry Baldwin and Doris (Lucas) M.; m. Kathleen Emden Keely, June 14, 1953 (dec. Jan. 1974); children—Wendy Ann, Vicki Louise, Robin Kay, Christina Suzanne; m. Terry Bradley Alt, Aug. 10, 1974 (div. 1976); m. Shannon Ann Lynch, June 19, 1977. B.S., U. Mich., 1953; M.A., Columbia U., 1957, Ed.D., 1960. Tchr. sci. Ramona High Sch., Riverside, Calif., 1958-62; secondary sci. coordinator Riverside city schs., 1960-62; exec. dir. chem. edn. material study Harvey Mudd Coll. and U. Calif. at Berkeley, 1962-65; curriculum specialist Mt. Diablo Unified Sch. Dist., Concord, Calif., 1965-91, dir. curriculum, 1980-81; assoc. dir. Inst. for Chem. Edn. and Project Phys. Sci., U. Calif., Berkeley, 1990-94; bd. dirs. San Francisco Bay Area Sci. Fair; mem. sci. adv. com. Calif. Assessment Program, 1983-89, also mem. assessment adv. com. to state supt. pub. instrn., 1984-86; dir. N. Calif. W. Nev. Jr. Sci. and Humanities Symposium, 1993—. Author: (with David W. Ridgway) The CHEM Study Story, 1969; co-author: National Science Teachers Association Guidelines for Self-Assessment of Secondary Science Programs, 1975, Science Framework for California Public Schools, 1978, 84; co-author, editor: The Physical Science of Living in California, 1993. Bd. dirs. Ctr. for New Ams., Concord, Calif., 1984-91. Served from ensign to lt. (j.g.) USN, 1953-56. Mem. Nat. Sci. Tchrs. Assn. (past pres., past mem. exec. com.), Nat. Sci. Suprs. Assn., Elem. Sch. Sci. Assn. (coun. 1975-82, pres. 1983), Calif. Sci. Tchrs. Assn. (Disting. Svc. award 1990), Assn. Calif. Sch. Adminstrs., Acacia, Phi Delta Kappa. Home: 1862 2d Ave Walnut Creek CA 94596 Office: U Calif Lawrence Hall of Sci Berkeley CA 94720

MERRILL, ROBERT, baritone; b. Bklyn., June 4, 1919; s. Abraham and Lillian (Balaban) Miller; m. Marion Machno, May 30, 1954; children—David Robert, Lizanne. MusD (hon.), Gustavus Adolphus Coll., 1970. Ind. baritone N.Y.C. and on tour, 1945—. Baritone in concert, opera and on radio and TV; winner, Met. Auditions of the Air, 1945, debut in opera, 1945; operatic roles include Escamillo in Carmen, Germont in La Traviata, Valentine in Faust, Amonasro in Aida, Marcello in La Boheme, Don Carlo in La Forza del Destino, Sir Henry Ashton in Lucia de Lammermoor; sang in La Traviata condr. Arturo Toscanini over NBC network; singer with NBC, 1946—; opened Met. Opera season Rodrigo in Don Carlo, 1950; appeared in Toscanini's final opera performance and rec. as Renato in Un Ballo in Maschera; opened Met. season as Valentine in Faust, 1953, as Figaro in Barber of Seville, 1954, Rigoletto in Rigoletto; Barnaba in Gioconda, Scarpia in Tosca, Renato in Un Ballo in Maschera, Iago in Otello, Count di Luna in Il Trovatore, Tonio in Pagliacci, Gerard in Andrea Chenier, 1962, Sir Henry in Lucia, 1964, Valentine in Faust, 1965, Germont in La Traviata, 1966, Amonasro in Aida, 1969; also opened Met. Opera season, 1971; opened Royal Opera House-Covent Garden season as Germont in La Traviata, 1967, Met. Opera visit to Japan, Tokyo, 1975; appeared in concerts, London, Bournemouth, Geneva, Israel, 1975; rec. artist: RCA-Victor, Angel, London, Columbia labels; stage debut as Tevye in Fiddler on the Roof, 1970; author: (novel) The Divas, 1978, (autobiography) Once More From the Beginning, 1965, Between Acts, 1976. Mem. Nat. Council of the Arts, 1968-74. Recipient Music Ann. award for rec. Ah, Dite Alla Giovine, 1946, Best Opera Rec. award Nat. Acad. Rec. Arts and Scis., 1962, 64, Harriet Cohen Internat. Music award, 1961, Handel medal City N.Y., 1970, Medallion award Westchester C.C. Found., 1981, Nat. medal of the Arts, 1993, Internat. Dor L'Dor award B'nai B'rith, 1994; named Father of Yr. in Music, 1980. Mem. Opera Guild, AFTRA, AGVA, Actors Equity Assn., Screen Actors Guild, Am. Guild Mus. Artists. Club: Friars (monk 1968—). Avocations: golf, baseball, fine art. Achievements: 1st Am. opera singer to give 500 performances at Met. Opera, N.Y.C., 1973; ofcl. singer New York Yankees, 1969—; performer for Pres. Roosevelt, Truman, Eisenhower, Kennedy, Johnson, Nixon, Ford, Carter, Reagan; only singer to perform before both houses of Congress at Roosevelt Meml. Office: Robert Merrill Assocs Inc 79 Oxford Rd New Rochelle NY 10804-3712 *If you honestly feel that you are doing your best, it makes good criticism even sweeter and bad criticism less painful.*

MERRILL, RONALD THOMAS, geophysicist, educator; b. Detroit, Feb. 5, 1938; s. Robert Able and Freda (Havens) M.; m. Nancy Joann O'Byrne, Sept. 1, 1962; children: Craig Elliot, Scott Curtis. BS in Math., U. Mich., 1959, MS in Math., 1961; PhD in Geophysics, U. Calif., Berkeley, 1967. Asst. prof. oceanography U. Wash., Seattle, 1967-72, assoc. prof. geophysics and oceanography, 1972-77, prof. geophysics and geol. sci., 1977—, chmn. dept. geophysics, 1985-92. Author: (with M.W. McElhinny) The Earth's Magnetic Field, 1984; contbr. numerous articles to profl. jours. Recipient numerous rsch. grants from NSF, other founds. Fellow Am. Geophys. Union (pres. geomagnetism and paleomagnetism sect. 1988-90); mem. AAAS, Soc. Geomagnetism (Japan). Avocations: skiing, hiking, scuba diving, dancing. Office: U Wash Dept Geophysics AK-50 Seattle WA 98195

MERRILL, STEPHEN, governor. Student, U. N.H., Georgetown U. Former personal counsel to Sec. Air Force, Pentagon; atty. gen. State of N.H., Concord, 1985-89; gov. State of N.H., 1993—; mem. N.H. task force on Child Abuse and Neglect, former pres., legal counsel. Served to capt., USAF. Fellow ABA; mem. Ea. Assn. Attys. Gen. (chmn.), Phi Beta Kappa. Office: Office of the Governor State Capitol Concord NH 03301*

MERRILL, STEVEN WILLIAM, research and development executive; b. Oakland, Calif., Aug. 6, 1944; s. David Howard and Etha Nadine (Wright) M. BA in Chemistry, Calif. State U., 1986. Lic. pyrotechnic, Calif. Apprentice Borgman Sales Co., San Leandro, Calif., 1960-64; assembler Calif. Fireworks Display, Rialto, Calif., 1970; pyrotechnician Hand Chem. Industries, Milton, Ont., Can., 1972-74; dir. R&D Pyrospectaculars, Rialto, 1988—; owner, dir. Merrill Prodns. Ordnance, Crestline; experimenter in field, 1958—; chief chemist Baron Blakesly Solvents, Newark, Calif., 1987-88; court expert San Francisco Superior Ct., 1971, Victorville Calif.; Superior Ct. Counselor Xanthos, Inc., Alameda, Calif., 1970. Mem. AAAS, Am. Chem. Soc., Am. Stats. Assn., Am. Bd. Forensic Examiners, Internat. Platform Assn. Avocations: wood carving, sculpture, electronics. Home: PO Box 676 Crestline CA 92325-0676 Office: Merrill Prodns Ordnance PO Box 3327 PO Box 3327 Crestline CA 92325

MERRILL, THOMAS WENDELL, lawyer, law educator; b. Bartlesville, Okla., May 3, 1949; s. William McGill and Dorothy (Glasener) M.; m. Kimberly Ann Evans, Sept. 8, 1973; children: Jessica, Margaret, Elizabeth. BA, Grinnell Coll., 1971; DJur(Oxford U.), 1973; JD, U. Chgo., 1977. Bar: Ill. 1980, U.S. Dist Ct. (no. dist.) Ill. 1980, U.S. Ct. Appeals (5th cir.) 1982, U.S. Ct. Appeals (7th cir.) 1983, U.S. Ct. Appeals (9th and D.C. cirs.) 1984, U.S. Supreme Ct. 1985. Clk. U.S. Ct. Appeals (D.C. cir.), Washington, 1977-78, U.S. Supreme Ct., Washington, 1978-79; assoc. Sidley & Austin, Chgo., 1979-81, counsel, 1981-87, 90—; dep. solicitor gen. U.S. Dept. Justice, 1987-90; prof. law Northwestern U., Chgo., 1981—. Contbr. articles to profl. jours. Rhodes scholar Oxford U., 1971; Danforth fellow, 1971. Home: 939 Maple Ave Evanston IL 60202-1717 Office: Northwestern U Sch Law 357 E Chicago Ave Chicago IL 60611-3008

MERRILL, VINCENT NICHOLS, landscape architect; b. Reading, Mass., Apr. 28, 1912; s. Charles Clarkson and Bessie Louise (Nichols) M.; m. Anna Victoria Swanson, Jan. 20, 1943. AB, Dartmouth Coll., 1933; M in Landscape Architecture, Harvard U., 1937. Registered landscape architect, Mass. Office asst. Shurcliff & Shurcliff, Boston, 1937-42, 47-54, prin.; 1954-58; ptnr. Shurcliff & Merrill and predecessors Shurcliff, Shurcliff & Merrill, Boston, Mass., 1958-81; prin. Shurcliff & Merrill, Cambridge, Mass., 1981-89. Founder, bd. dirs. Charles River Watershed Assn., Auburndale, Mass., 1963-75; bd. dirs. Charles Basin Adv. Com., Boston, 1979-82; pres. Hubbard Edni. Trust, Cambridge, 1981-89, bd. dirs. 1989-95. Capt. U.S. Army, 1942-46, ETO. Recipient Gold medal Mass. Hort. Soc., 1988. Fellow Am. Soc. Landscape Architects; mem. Boston Soc. Landscape

Architects (pres. 1961-63), Hort. Club of Boston (pres. 1992-94). Avocation: home landscaping. Home and Office: 141 Old County Rd Lincoln MA 01773-3506

MERRILL, WILLIAM DEAN, architect, medical facility planning consultant; b. Portland, Oreg., June 1, 1915; s. Charles O. and Grace (Ruhl) M.; m. Bernice E. Wickham, Apr. 19, 1943; 1 child, Sue Ann Merrill Boardman. Student in Fine Arts and Forestry, Oreg. State U., 1936-38; student in Architecture, U. Oreg., 1939-42. Registered architect, Oreg.; Calif. Prin. W.D. Merrill, Architect, Portland, 1959-64; architect, ptnr. Bissell & Merrill, Architects, Stockton, Calif., 1964-68; architect Kaiser Found. Hosps. design and constrn., 1968-81; pvt. practice hosp. design and constrn., residential design and constrn., Bay Area, 1981-91; hosp. constrn. insp. State of Calif., 1984-93. Served as lt. (j.g.) USN, 1942-44, PTO. Mem. AIA (emeritus). Republican. Address: 14349 SE Sieben Pky Clackamas OR 97015-6319

MERRILL, WILLIAM DICKEY, architect; b. Honolulu, Mar. 21, 1909; s. Arthur Merton and Grace (Dickey) M.; m. Evelyn Gregory Selfridge, Oct. 23, 1936; children: Elizabeth, Thomas Selfridge. BA, U. Calif., Berkeley, 1930; MArch, Harvard U., 1932; PhD, Edinburgh U., 1974. Staff atchitect Am. Schs. Oriental Rsch., Jerusalem, 1933-35; assoc. C.W. Dickey, architect, Honolulu, 1936-42; ptnr. Merrill, Simms and Roehrig, architects, Honolulu, 1942-60; pres. Merrill, Roehrig, Onodera and Kinder, Inc., Honolulu, 1960-65; cons. architect Honolulu, 1965-81; mem. affiliate grad. faculty U. Hawaii, 1971. Prin. works include Neill Blaisdell Concert Hall, campus Mid-Pacific Inst., campus Kamehameha Elem. Sch., class rm. bldg. Kamehameha Girls Sch., Foremost Dairies, TH-3 Hawaii Housing Authority, other commnl., indsl., ednl. and mil. structures, hosps. in Hawaii. Mem. com. mgmt. Armed Svcs. YMCA, 1952-69; bd. dirs. Hawaiian Humane Soc., 1954-65, Hawaiian Mission Children's Soc., 1945-64. Fellow AIA (past pres. Hawaii, mem. emeritus). Home: 8545 Carmel Valley Rd Carmel CA 93923-9556

MERRILL, WILLIAM H., JR., lawyer, corporate professional; b. Indpls., Apr. 11, 1942; s. William H. and Jane (Robinson) M.; m. Winifred Jane Baur, July 25, 1964; children: Michele Jane, Betsy Diane. BS, Butler U., 1965; JD, Ind. U., 1967. Bar: Ind. 1967. Trust officer Mchts. Nat. Bank, Indpls., 1965-69; gen. counsel Everett I. Brown Co., Indpls., 1969-85; v.p.; gen. counsel Landeco, Inc., Indpls., 1970-85; pres. Bash Seed Co., Indpls., 1975—; gen. ptr. Meta Ptnrs., 1984—; pres. Meta Investment Co., 1988-90, Meta Mgmt. Co., 1988-90, Northwest Develop. Corp., 1975—, Scotts Garden Ctr., Inc., 1977—; bd. dirs. Custom Molded Products, Inc. Mem. Carmel (Ind.) City Plan Commn., 1975-85, pres. 1982-85. Mem. ABA, Ind. Bar Assn., Indpls. Bar Assn. Club: Crooked Stick Golf, Columbia. Home: 3725 W 106th St Carmel IN 46032-9607 Office: 3205 W 71st St Indianapolis IN 46268-2244

MERRILLS, ROY, telecommunications industry executive; b. 1934. Attended, Liverpool Coll. Tech., 1957. Formerly group v.p. Integrated Network Systems, Raleigh, N.C.; with Northern Telecom Ltd., 1957—; pres., chief exec. officer, dir. Northern Telecom Inc., Nashville, 1988—. Office: Northern Telecom Inc 200 Athens Way Nashville TN 37228-1397

MERRIMAN, ILAH COFFEE, financial executive; b. Amarillo, Tex., Mar. 22, 1935; d. Oran and Frances Elizabeth (Rocque) Coffee; children: Pamela, Michael. BS in Math., Tex. Tech. U. Cert. secondary tchr., Tex. Pres., chief exec. officer H&R Block Inc. of Houston; pres. H&R Block Inc., Tex.; exec. bd. Tex. Tech U. ex students assn., pres., 1989, past trustee; mem. steering com. Pres.'s Council, bd. dirs. Tex. Tech Double T Connection, Tex. Tech Found., Women's Basketball Tournament, Southwest Athletic Coun., past; mem. Tex. Tech U. enterprise fund Dallas Chpt.; dir. Cotton Bowl Assn. representing Tex. Tech U. Named Disting. Alumni, Texas Tech U., 1992; recipient Ernest T. Steward award Coun. Advancement and Support Edn., 1993. Mem. Dallas Mus. Fine Art, Dallas Shakespeare Festival, Dallas Symphony Assn., Dallas Hist. Soc., Cotton Bowl Assn. (exec. com.), Women's Basketball Coaches Assn. dir. nat. corp. bd.), Red Raider Club of Tex. Tech U. (past mem. exec. com.) Methodist.

MERRIMAN, JOE JACK, insurance company executive; b. Kansas City, Mo., Nov. 9, 1926; s. Jack Dawson and Sarah Elizabeth (Bryant) M.; m. Elaine Atha, Feb. 14, 1953; children: Mark, Marybeth, Michael. B.S. in Civil Engring, Northwestern U., 1946. With Merriman Mortgage Co., Kansas City, Mo., 1946-69; v.p. Merriman Mortgage Co., 1952-69, past dir.; pres., dir. United Investors Life Ins. Co., 1961-69, Waddell & Reed, Inc., 1965-69, Kansas City Securities Corp., 1964-69; past dir. United Funds, Inc.; pres. Continental Bankers Life Ins. Co., Mpls., 1971—; chmn. bd. Clin. Reference Lab, 1982-94, Fin. Assurance Inc., Kansas City, 1976—, United Fidelity Life Ins. Co., Kansas City, 1986—, Coll. Life Ins. Co., Kansas City, 1988—, Great So. Life Ins. Co., Dallas, 1989—, Loyalty Life Ins. Co., 1991, Nat. Farmers Union Life Ins. Co., 1991. Episcopalian. Office: 300 W 11th St Kansas City MO 64105-1618

MERRIMAN, JOHN ALLEN, lawyer, insurance executive; b. Knoxville, Iowa, Aug. 13, 1942; s. John W. and Doris (Henry) M.; m. Barbara Anne Beatty, Nov. 10, 1990. AB, Northwestern U., 1964; LLB, Columbia U., 1967. Bar: Iowa 1967, U.S. Dist. Ct. (no. and so. dists.) Iowa 1967. Assoc. Gamble, Riepe, Martin & Webster, Des Moines, 1967-69; counsel Equitable Life Ins. Co. Iowa, Des Moines, 1969-76; ptnr. Mumford, Schrage, Merriman & Zurek, P.C., Des Moines, 1976-86; assoc. gen. counsel Equitable of Iowa Cos., Des Moines, 1986-87, gen. counsel, sec., 1987—. Active state and local politics. Lt. USNR, 1968-79. Mem. Des Moines Club, Des Moines Golf and Country Club (dir. 1987-90). Republican. Avocations: golf, running. Office: Equitable of Iowa 604 Locust St Des Moines IA 50309-3705

MERRIN, SEYMOUR, computer marketing company executive; b. Bklyn., Aug. 13, 1931; s. Joseph and Esther Bella (Manelis) M.; m. Elaine Cohen, Sept. 4, 1960 (dec. May 1962); m. Elizabeth Jenifer Slack, Oct. 12, 1963; children: Charles Seymour, Mariamne Jenifer Weights. BS, Tufts Coll., 1952; MS, U. Ariz., 1954; PhD, Pa. State U., 1962. Geologist Magma Copper Co., Superior, Ariz., 1954; geologist U.S Geol. Survey, 1956-58; chemist IBM, Poughkeepsie, N.Y., 1962-64; mgr. package devel., mgr. reliability and failure analysis Sperry Semicondr. div. Sperry Rand, Norwalk, Conn., 1965-68; cons. materials tech. Fairfield, Conn., 1967-69; v.p., dir. Innotech Corp., Norwalk, 1969-74; div. mgr. Emdex div. Exxon Enterprises, Milford, Conn., 1974-78; chmn., dir. Computerworks, Westport, Conn., 1978-85; v.p., dir. personal computing service Gartner Group, Inc., Stamford, Conn., 1984-87; pres. Merrin Resources, Southport, Conn., 1987-89, Merrin Info. Svcs., Inc., Palo Alto, Calif., 1987—; bd. dirs. Micrografx Corp., Richardson, Tex.; mem. adv. panel Apple Computer Co., Cupertino, Calif., 1982-83; mem. adv. bd. Compaq Computer Corp., Houston, 1984-85, Computer and Software News, N.Y.C., 1984-89; mem. program adv. bd. Comdex, Boston, 1985—; lectr. in field. Contbr. numerous articles to profl. publs.; patentee in field. Served with U.S. Army, 1954-56. Fellow Geol. Soc. Am., Am. Inst. Chemists; mem. Assn. Better Computer Dealers (founder, pres. 1981-83, bd. dirs. 1981-84). Home: 143 Buckthorn Way Menlo Park CA 94025-3027 Office: 2275 E Bayshore Rd Palo Alto CA 94303-3220

MERRION, ARTHUR BENJAMIN, mathematics educator, tree farmer; b. Williamstown, N.J., Oct. 25, 1938; s. Anthony Robert and Eva May Merrion; m. Martha Jane Banse, Dec. 26, 1965 (div. May 1977); children: Benjamin Thomas, Elizabeth Jane. AB in Math., Pfeiffer Coll., 1965; MS in Numerical Sci., Johns Hopkins U., 1976. Navigations scientist Defense Mapping Agy. Hydrographic Ctr., Huntingtown, Md., 1966-78; fellow ops. rsch. analysis Sec. Army Pentagon, Washington, 1978-80; ops. rsch. analyst Asst. Sec. Army, Washington, 1980-86; tree farmer Huntingtown, Md. 1986—; instr. math. and stats. Embry-Riddle Aeronautical U., 1993-94. With U.S. Army, 1957-58. Avocations: chess, violin, judo, wrestling, ice skating. Home: 1080 Plum Point Rd Huntingtown MD 20639-9246

MERRISS, PHILIP RAMSAY, JR., corporate banker; b. N.Y.C., June 7, 1948; s. Philip Ramsay and Elisabeth (Paine) M.; m. Janet Henry Hylan, Oct. 27, 1973. AB in Econs. magna cum laude, Lafayette Coll., 1970, MBA with high distinction, Dartmouth Coll., 1972. Assoc. corp. fin. dept. A.G. Becker and Co. Inc., N.Y.C., 1972-73; fin. analyst corp. banking dept. Chase Manhattan Bank, 1973, asst. treas. N.Y.C. dist., 1974-75, 2d v.p. mining and

metals div., 1976-78, 2d v.p. petroleum div., 1978-79, v.p. global petroleum div., 1979-86, client exec., v.p. pub. utilities component, 1986-87, client exec., v.p. global energy component, 1987-89, credit supervising officer, div. exec., v.p. U.S. pvt. banking, 1989-94; credit exec. Chase Manhattan Pvt. Bank, N.Y.C., 1994—. Served to capt. U.S. Army, 1978. Tuck scholar Dartmouth Coll., 1972. Mem. Am. Econ. Assn., Fin Mgmt. Assn. Aircraft Owners and Pilots Assn., N.Y. Road Runners Club, Weston Gun Club, Yale Club, Fairfield County Fish and Game Club, Phi Beta Kappa. Republican. Episcopalian. Home: 100 Hillspoint Rd Westport CT 06880-5111 Office: Chase Manhattan Bank 1211 Ave of the Americas New York NY 10036-8701

MERRITT, BERNARD JASON, architect, urban and regional planner; b. London, Nov. 19, 1938; came to U.S., 1965, naturalized, 1970; s. Leonard Albert and Mary (Milne) M. BArch, U. Natal, Durban, Republic South Africa, 1962; cert. in architecture, Frank Lloyd Wright Sch. Architecture, Scottsdale, Ariz., 1967; MS in Urban & Regional Planning, U. Tex., 1983. Registered architect, Tex., Va., Ariz., Calif., N.Y.; cert. Nat. Coun. Archtl. Registration Bds. Prin. Bernard Jason Merritt Ltd., Durban, 1965-63; assoc. Frank Lloyd Wright Orgn., Scottsdale, 1968-75; pres. Bernard Jason Merritt Inc., Austin, La Grange, Tex., 1976—. Constrn. projects include office bldgs., chs., equine farms and racetracks, comml. correctional facilities, master planned communities and residences. Chmn. Capital Area Planning Coun., Fayette County, Tex., 1980; v.p. South Cen. Tex. for Performing Arts, Schulenburg, 1983-85. Regents scholar U. Natal, 1981, scholar Frank Lloyd Wright Found., 1967. Mem. AIA, Royal Inst. Brit. Architects, Inst. Couth African Architects, Am. Soc. Cons. Planners, Am. Planning Assn., Am. Inst. Cert. Planners (assoc.), COnstrn. Specifications Inst., Urban Land Inst., Am. Soc. Planning Ofcls., Nat. Space Soc., World Future Soc., Ex-Students Assn. U. Tex. (life), Internat. Platform Assn., Frisch Auf Country Club, Phi Kappa Phi (life). Avocations: furniture design, graphic art, carpentry, anthropology, archaeology. Office: 500 E Riverside Dr Apt 114 Austin TX 78704-1339 also: 5120 Woodway Dr Ste 9033 Houston TX 77056-1724 also: 8050 Airport Rd Georgetown TX 78628-3700

MERRITT, BETTY L., medical/surgical and mental health nurse; b. Greenville, S.C., Apr. 16, 1939; d. Milton and Lola (Wofford) Alexander; m. Otis Merritt Jr., Mar. 8, 1957; children: Belinda Lorezia, Otis III, Milton Otto, Glenda Frencestia, Lucinda Yvette. ADN, Community Coll. Balt., 1976; diploma, Balt. City Hosp. Sch. Nursing, 1973. LPN; cert. psychiat./mental health nurse, ANA. Student advisor Community Coll. Balt.; nurse coord. partial hospitalization svcs. Provident Hosp., Balt.; charge nurse Balt. City Hosp.; clin. nurse supr. Crownsville (Md.) State Hosp.; psychiat. and med.-surg. nurse Liberty Med. Ctr., Balt., alternate nurse mgr. dept. psychiatry; acting nurse Crownsville (Md.) State Hosp.; cons. psychiat. and mental health nursing Blue Cross/Blue Shield Md. Home: 3212 Burleith Ave Baltimore MD 21215-7908

MERRITT, BRUCE GORDON, lawyer; b. Iowa City, Iowa, Oct 4, 1946; s. William Olney and Gretchen Louise (Kuever) M.; m. Valerie Sue Edgerton, Dec. 28, 1969; children: Benjamin Carlyle, Alicia Marie. AB magna cum laude, Occidental Coll., 1968; JD magna cum laude, Harvard U., 1972. Bar: Calif. 1973. Assoc. Markbys, London, 1972-73; assoc. Nossaman, Krueger & Marsh, L.A., 1973-79, ptnr., 1979-81; asst. U.S. atty., L.A., 1981-85; ptnr. Hennigan & Mercer, L.A., 1986-88; ptnr. Debevoise & Plimpton, L.A., 1989—. Fellow Am. Coll. Trial Lawyers; mem. Calif. State Bar Assn. (exec. com. litigation sect. 1992—), L.A. County Bar Assn. (del. state bar conf. 1984-86), Phi Beta Kappa. Office: Debevoise & Plimpton 601 S Figueroa St Ste 3700 Los Angeles CA 90017-5742

MERRITT, CAROL RUTH, middle school educator; b. Des Moines, Nov. 5, 1944; d. Herbert Wesley and Anna Gelene (Satre) M. BS in Edn., Huntington (Ind.) Coll., 1966; MS in Psychology, Goddard Coll., Plainfield, Vt., 1982. Cert. tchr., Kans., Mo. Counselor, tchr. YMCA, Wichita, 1962-68; tchr. 5th grade Riverside Elem. Sch., Ft. Wayne, Ind., 1969-70, Lincoln Elem. Sch., Huntington, 1971-74; substitute tchr. St. Louis area, 1974-75; kindergarten tchr. Raymore, Mo., 1975-76; tchr. 7th grade St. Joseph Parochial Sch., Kansas City, Mo., 1978-79; tchr. 6th and 7th grades Rosedale Mid. Sch., Kansas City, Kans., 1979-84; tchr. 7th grade Coronado Mid. Sch., Kansas City, 1984-85; tchr. 6th, 7th and 8th grades Argentine Mid. Sch., Kansas City, 1986-93. Treas., Squire Pk. Neighborhood Assn., Kansas City, Mo., 1989-91; seminar leader Colonial Presbyn. Ch., Kansas City, Mo., 1980-90. Mem. NEA, Calif. Trails Assn. Avocations: painting, playing violin, swimming. Office: Argentine Mid Sch 22D And Ruby Kansas City KS 66106

MERRITT, DEBORAH FOOTE, state legislator, counselor; b. Peterborough, N.H., June 19, 1961; d. William Lewis and Mary Elizabeth (Moore) Foote. BA in Sociology, Bowdoin Coll., 1983; MPA, U. N.H., 1994. Tchr. math. Buckley Sch., Sherman Oaks, Calif., 1983-84, Chaminade Coll. Prep. Sch., Canoga Park, Calif., 1984-85; saleswoman Smith Barney, L.A., 1985-87, B.R. Stickle & Co., Chgo., 1987; trader Harris Trust, Chgo., 1988-90; bus. mgr. Merritt Chiropractic, Durham, N.H., 1990-94; state rep. N.H. Gen. Ct., Concord, 1993—; marketer Devel. Svcs. of Stafford County, Dover, 1994. Bd. dirs. Our House, 1993-94, counselor, 1994—. Mem. NOW, N.H. Women's Lobby, Gt. Dover C. of C., Planned Parenthood No. New Eng., Women's Legis. Lobby (vice chair Stratford County del. 1994—). Democrat. Home: 20 Cedar Point Rd Durham NH 03824 Office: Our House 35 3d St Dover NH 03820

MERRITT, DORIS HONIG, pediatrics educator; b. N.Y.C., July 16, 1923; d. Aaron and Lillian (Kunstlich) Honig; children: Kenneth Arthur, Christopher Ralph. B.A., CUNY, 1944; M.D., George Washington U., 1952. Diplomate Am. Bd. Pediatrics, Nat. Bd. Med. Examiners. Pediatric intern Duke Hosp., 1952-53; teaching and rsch. fellow pediatrics George Washington U., 1953-54; pediatric asst. resident Duke U. Hosp., 1954-55, cardiovascular fellow pediatrics, 1955-56, instr. pediatrics, dir. pediatric cardiorenal clinic, 1956-57; exec. sect. cardiovascular study sect., gen. medicine study sect. div. rsch. grants NIH, 1957-60; dir. med. rsch. grants and contracts Sch. Medicine Ind. U., 1961-62, asst. prof. pediatrics Sch. Medicine, 1961-68, asst. dean med. rsch. Sch. Medicine, 1962-65, asst. dir. med. rsch., aerospace rsch. application ctr. Sch. Medicine, 1963-65, assoc. dir. med. rsch. Sch. Medicine, 1965-68, asst. dean for rsch., office v.p. rsch. and dean advanced studies Sch. Medicine, 1965-67, dir. sponsored programs, asst. to provost Sch. Medicine, 1965-68, assoc. dean for rsch. and advanced studies, office v.p. and dean for rsch. and advanced studies Sch. Medicine, 1967-71, assoc. prof. pediatrics Sch. Medicine, 1968-73, prof. Sch. Medicine, 1973-80, prof. pediatrics, assoc. dean Sch. Medicine, 1988—; spl. asst. to dir. NIH, 1978-87, tng. and rsch. resource officer, 1980-87, acting dir. Nat. Ctr. Nursing Rsch., 1986-87; bd. dirs. Ind. Health Industry Reform; cons. USPHS, NIH div. rsch. grants Div. Health Rsch. Facilities and Resources, Nat. Heart Inst. 1963-78, Am. Heart Assn., 1963-67, Ind. Med. Assn. Commn. Vol. Health Orgns., 1964-67, Bur. Health Manpower, Health Profession's Constrn. Program, 1965-71, Nat. Library Medicine, Health Ctr. Libr. Constrn. Program, 1966-72; dir. office sponsored programs Ind. U.-Purdue U. Indpls. Office Chancellor, 1968-71, dean rsch. and sponsored programs, 1971-79; mem. Nat. Library Medicine biomed. communications rev. com., 1970-74; mem. com. to study rsch. capabilities acad. depts. ob-gyn Inst. Medicine, 1990-91. Contbr. articles to profl. jours. Chmn. Indpls. Consortium for Urban Edn., 1971-75; v.p. Greater Indpls. Progress Com., 1974-79; mem. Community Svc. Council, 1969-75; bd. dirs. Bd. for Fundamental Edn., 1973-77, Ind. Sci. Edn. Found., 1977-78, Community Addiction Svc. Agy., Inc., 1972-74; trustee Marian Coll., 1977-78; exec. com. Nat. Council U. Rsch. Adminstrs., 1977-78. Recipient Nat. Library Medicine, 1976-80; chmn. adv. screening com. for life scis. Council Internat. Exchange of Scholars, 1978-81; bd. dirs. Community Svc. Coun. Ind., 1989-94, Univ. Hosp. Consortium, Tech. Assessment Ctr., 1990-93; mem. Ind. Health Industry Forum, 1993—; chmn. scientific and tech. review bd. on biomedical and behavioral rsch. facilities NIH Ctr. for Rsch. Resources, 1994—. Served to lt. (j.g.) USNR. Fellow Am. Acad. Pediatrics; mem. AAAS, George Washigton U., Duke U. Med. Alumni Assns., Phi Beta Kappa, Alpha Omega Alpha., NIHNCRR (chair scientific and tech. rev. bd. on biomed. and biobehavioral rsch. facilities 1994-97). Office: Ind U Sch Medicine Ind U # Fh312 Indianapolis IN 46202 *The era in which I have lived and worked has been one of transition for women entering traditional male fields. What recognition and advancement I have achieved, have been due to maintaining high standards of performance on equal terms with my profes-*

sional peers. I consider the three essential ingredients of success to be competence, optimistic tenacity of purpose and an enduring sense of humor.

MERRITT, GILBERT STROUD, federal judge; b. Nashville, Tenn., Jan. 17, 1936; s. Gilbert Stroud and Angie Fields (Cantrell) M.; m. Louise Clark Fort, July 10, 1964 (dec.); children: Stroud, Louise Clark, Eli. BA, Yale U., 1957; LLB, Vanderbilt U., 1960; LLM, Harvard U., 1962. Bar: Tenn. 1960. Asst. dean Vanderbilt U. Law Sch., 1960-61, lectr., 1963-69, 71-75, assoc. prof. law, 1969-70; assoc. Boult Hunt Cummings & Conners, Nashville, 1962-63; city atty. City of Nashville, 1963-66; U.S. Dist. atty. for (mid. dist.) Tenn., 1966-69; ptnr. Gullett, Steele, Sanford, Robinson & Merritt, Nashville, 1970-77; judge U.S. Ct. Appeals (6th cir.), Nashville, 1977—; chief judge U.S. Ct. Appeals (6th cir.), 1989—; exec. sec. Tenn. Code Commn. 1977. Mng. editor: Vanderbilt Law Rev, 1959-60; contbr. articles to law jours. Del. Tenn. Constl. Conv., 1965; chmn. bd. trustees Vanderbilt Inst. Pub. Policy Studies. Mem. ABA, Fed. Bar Assn., Tenn. Bar Assn., Nashville Bar Assn., Vanderbilt Law Alumni Assn. (pres. 1979-80), Am. Law Inst., Order of Coif. Episcopalian. Office: US Ct Appeals 303 Customs House Nashville TN 37203

MERRITT, HOWARD SUTERMEISTER, retired art educator; b. Ithaca, N.Y., June 12, 1915; s. Ernest and Bertha (Sutermeister) M.; m. Florence Sederquest Hill, June 27, 1941; children—Jessica, Stephen, Jonathan, James. B.A., Oberlin Coll., 1936; M.F.A., Princeton U., 1942, Ph.D., 1958. Mem. faculty U. Rochester, N.Y., 1946-80; prof. emeritus U. Rochester, 1980—; cons. 19th Century Am. Painting, 1960—. Contbr. articles to various publs. Served with AUS, 1942-45. Decorated Bronze Star; Nat. Endowment for Humanities summer grantee, 1966-68. Mem. Coll. Art Assn. Home: 85 Bellevue Dr Rochester NY 14620-2703 Office: Dept of Fine Arts University Rochester Rochester NY 14627

MERRITT, JACK NEIL, retired army officer; b. Lawton, Okla., Oct. 23, 1930; s. Theodore and Lovell Wood; m. Rosemary Ralston, Oct. 31, 1953; children—Stephen Cahill, Grover Wood, Roger William. B.S., U. Nebr., Omaha, 1959; M.B.A., George Washington U., 1965; grad., F.A. Officer Advance Course, 1961, Air Command and Staff Coll., 1965, Indsl. Coll. Armed Forces, 1970; PhD (hon.), The Citadel. Commd. 2d lt. U.S. Army, 1953, advanced through grades to gen., 1985; served in various command and staff assignments U.S., Korea, Germany, 1953-65; served with (Army Gen. Staff, Pentagon), 1965-66; mem. staff (Asst. Sec. Def. for Systems Analysis), Washington, 1966-68; bn. comdr. (Riverine Arty.), Vietnam, 1968-69; staff (Asst. to Pres. for Nat. Security Affairs, White House), 1973-75; div. arty. comdr. Ft. Hood, Tex., 1973-74; chief of staff, 1974-75; asst. div. comdr. 1st Calvary Div., 1975-77; comdg. gen. U.S Army F.A. Center and comdt. U.S. Army F.A. Sch., Ft. Sill, Okla., 1977-80; comdt. U.S. Army War Coll., Carlisle, Pa., 1980-82; comdg. gen. Ft. Leavenworth, Kans., 1982-83; dir. joint staff Joint Chiefs of Staff, 1983-85; U.S. Rep. NATO Mil. Com., 1985-87; ret., 1987; pres. Assn. U.S. Army, Arlington, Va., 1988—; chmn. mil. profl. devel. com. West Point Study, 1977; adj. fellow Ctr. Strategic and Internat. Studies; mem. Commn. on West Point Honor Code, 1988-89. Bd. dirs. Atlantic Coun. Marshall Found.; chmn. adv. com. The Citadel; nat. adv. bd. Ga. Inst. Tech. Decorated D.S.M., Silver Star, Legion of Merit, D.F.C., Soldiers medal, Bronze Star, Air medal, Joint Commendation medal, Navy Commendation medal, Army Commendation medal; named to Okla. Hall of Fame. Mem. Internat. Inst. Strategic Studies, 1st Cavalry Div. Assn., 9th Inf. Div. Assn., Kappa Alpha. Office: Assn US Army 2425 Wilson Blvd Arlington VA 22201-3326

MERRITT, JAMES EDWARD, lawyer; b. Hickory, N.C., June 10, 1938; s. Eddy Schmidt and Dorothy (Hunt) M.; m. Joan L. Hiscock, June 14, 1960 (div. 1983); children: James Edward Jr., Catherine Hunt; m. Kristine McFadden, May 4, 1983. AB, Duke U., 1959; LLB, Harvard U., 1962. Bar: D.C. 1962, Calif. 1968; cert. tax specialist, Calif. Assoc. Pogue & Neal, Washington, 1962-64; trial atty. regional counsel IRS, San Francisco, 1964-68; assoc. Morrison & Foerster, San Francisco and Washington, 1968-72, ptnr., 1972—; lectr. Golden Gate U. San Francisco, 1970-74; cons. chief counsel IRS, Washington, 1983; mem. adv. bd. Tax Mgmt. Inc., N.Y.C., 1987—; mem. Prentice Hall Fed. Taxes Adv. Bd., 1989—. Contbr. articles to profl. jours. Mem. Asia Soc., Washington, 1986—. Fellow Am. Coll. Tax Counsel; mem. ABA (coun., air., sect. taxation 1990—), Bar Assn. D.C., Bar Assn. San Francisco (outstanding tax lawyer 1983), J. Edgar Murdock Inn of Ct. Avocations: travel, gardening, sports. Office: Morrison & Foerster 345 California St San Francisco CA 94104-2606

MERRITT, JAMES FRANCIS, biological sciences educator, administrator; b. Raleigh, N.C., July 21, 1944; s. Clifton and Emily (Rogers) M.; m. Sue Wall, Aug. 9, 1969; children—Ashley Grant, Bradley Gene, Carey Reid. B.S., E. Carolina U., 1966, M.S., 1968; Ph.D., N.C. State U., 1973. Asst. prof. biological scis. U. N.C. Wilmington, 1973-78, assoc. prof., chmn., 1978-89, dir. Ctr. Marine Scis. Rsch., Wilmington, 1989—. Contbr. articles to profl. jours. Chmn. PTA, Wilmington, 1983, Marine Expo Com., Wilmington, 1984—. E.G. Moss fellow N.C. State U., 1972. Mem. Am. Genetic Assn., N.C. Acad. Sci. (sect. chmn. 1975-76, vice pres. 1979-80), Chi Beta Phi (Outstanding Service award 1966). Avocations: fishing; woodworking. Home: 3523 Violet Ct Wilmington NC 28409-2541 Office: U NC at Wilmington Ctr Marine Sci Rsch 7205 Wrightsville Ave Wilmington NC 28403-7224

MERRITT, JOHN AUGUSTUS, geriatrician, educator; b. Greenwich, Conn., Nov. 1, 1931. AB, Dartmouth Coll., 1953; MD, Yale U., 1957. Diplomate Am. Bd. Internal Medicine, Am. Bd. Hematology, Am. Bd. Geriatric Medicine. Intern Upstate Med. Ctr., Syracuse, N.Y., 1958-59; resident in internal medicine Bostoon City Hosp., 1959-61, clin. fellow in hematology, 1961-62, rsch. fellow in hematology, 1962-63, assoc. vis. physician I and II med. svcs., 1966-70; asst. prof. medicine U. Md. Sch. Medicine, Balt., 1970-72; asst. prof., assoc. prof., prof. medicine U. Mass. Med. Sch., Worcester, 1972-88; chief geriatric medicine Hosp. of St. Raphael, New Haven, 1988—; asst. prof. dept. medicine Tufts U. Sch. Medicine, Boston, 1967-70; lectr. medicine Harvard U. Sch. Medicine, Boston, 1969-70; attending physician Boston VA Hosp., 1966-70; chief div. hematology York (Pa.) Hosp., 1970-72; chief div. medicine and geriatric medicine Worcester City Hosp., 1985-88; tng. Geriatric Edn. Ctr., Harvard U., 1986-87; asst. clin. prof. medicine Yale U. Sch. Medicine, New Haven, 1989—. Author textbooks; contbr. articles to med. jours. Fellow ACP; mem. Am. Geriatric Soc. (co-founder, bd. dirs. Mass. com.), Gerontol. Soc. Am., Nat. Coun. on Aging, Conn. Med. Soc. (ho. of dels., bd. govs.), New Haven County Med. Assn. Office: Hosp of St Raphael 1450 Chapel St New Haven CT 06511

MERRITT, JOHN C., investment banker; b. Glencove, N.Y., May 5, 1940; s. Wilbur M. and Irmgard Merritt; m. Janet H. Blum, July 22, 1961; children—Gregory John, Jacqueline Andrea. B.S. in Bus. Adminstrn., Babson Coll., 1961. Mcpl. bond analyst Drexel & Co., N.Y.C., 1961-64; with Drexel & Co., N.Y.C. and Phila., 1964-72, successively asst. v.p., v.p. and sr. v.p., also bd. dirs.; ptnr. Butcher & Singer Inc., Phila., 1972-79, also bd. dirs.; chmn. bd., chief exec. officer The Van Kampen Merritt Cos. Inc., Phila. and Oakbrook Terrace, Ill., 1979-94; former chmn. bd., CEO Xerox Fin. Svcs. Life Ins. Co., Oakbrook Terrace, Xerox Fin. Life Ins. Co. Calif., Xerox Life Mgmt. Co., Oakbrook Terrace., 1985-92; former gen. ptnr., bd. dirs. VMS Realty Ptnrs., Chgo., Chgo.-Wheaton Ptnrs.; former chmn., bd. dirs. Van Kampen Merritt U.S. Govt. Fund, Oakbrook Terrace, U.S. Govt. Trust and numerous subs., funds and trusts, Van Kampen Merritt Investment Adv. Corp., Ind. CashFlow Data Systems, Inc.; ltd. ptnr. Renck, Levy & Co., N.Y.C.; bd. dirs. McCarty, Crisanti & Maffei, Inc., N.Y.C. Trustee, bd. dirs. Calvary Luth. Ch., Medford, N.J.; mem. Babson Coll. Corp., Wellesley, Mass.; former bd. dirs., vice chmn. Mcpl. Securities Rulemaking Bd. Mem. Mcpl. Bond Club Phila. (past pres. bd. govs.). Office: The Van Kampen Merritt Cos Inc Mellon Bank Ctr 1735 Market St Ste 1300 Philadelphia PA 19103-7501 also: One Parkview Pla Oakbrook Terrace IL 60181

MERRITT, JOSHUA LEVERING, JR., retired engineering executive, consultant; b. Balt., July 28, 1931; s. Joshua Levering Sr. and Sarah Ethel (Sparks) M.; m. Eleanor Grace Williams , June 26, 1954; children: Nancy Lynn Mann, Debra Sue Stevens, Steven Edward. BSCE, Lehigh U., 1952; MSCE, U. Ill., 1955, PhD in Engring., 1958. Registered civil, structural, geotech. engr., Calif.; registered civil and structural engr., Nev.; registered

structural engr., Ill.; registered profl. engr., N.M. Rsch. asst., civil engr. U. Ill., Urbana, 1952-54, rsch. assoc., civil engr., 1954-58, asst. prof. civil engring., 1958-60, assoc. prof., 1960-66, prof., 1966-68; vis. prof. U. Ill., Urbana, Ill., 1968-69; mgr. hard rock silo devel. program TRW, 1968-70, mgr. facilities engring., 1970-71; pres. Merritt Cases, Inc., Redlands, Calif., 1971—; dir. Redlands ops. BDM Internat., Inc., 1986-91; mem. U.S. nat. com. on rock mechanics NRC, 1989-90; expert mem. panel on underground tech. devel. NRC, 1990; chmn. bd. appeal Dept Bldg. and Safety, San Bernardino County, Calif.; cons. in field, Urbana, 1958-68, Redlands, 1991—. Author more than 70 articles and rsch. reports. Fellow ASCE (local and nat. com.); mem. Am. Underground Space Assn., Structural Engrs. Assn. So. Calif., Inst. for Shaft Drilling Tech. (charter mem.), Internat. Soc. for Rock Mechanics, Internat. Soc. for Soil Mechanics and Found. Engrs., Internat. Tunnelling Assn., Seismol. Soc. Am., Am. Concrete Inst., Earthquake Engring. Rsch. Inst., Sigma Xi, Phi Kappa Phi, Chi Epsilon. Presbyterian. Achievements include research in fields of structural dynamics, earthquake engineering and behavior of materials.

MERRITT, LAVERE BARRUS, engineering educator, civil engineer; b. Afton, Wyo., Mar. 11, 1936; s. Joseph M. and Lera (Barrus) M.; m. Jackie Call, Jan. 5, 1956; children: Teri F., Lynn T., Rachel R., Shaun S. BSCE, U. Utah, 1963, MSCE, 1966; PhD, U. Wash., 1970. Registered profl. engr., Utah. Prof. civil and environ. engring. Brigham Young U., Provo, Utah, 1970—, chmn. dept. civil engring., 1986-92; spl. cons. Utah Div. Health, Salt Lake City, 1973-74; cons. engring. firms, 1970—. Chmn. Provo Met. Water Bd., Utah, 1978-87. Named Utah Engring. Educator of the Yr. Utah Joint Enring. Coun., 1987. Mem. ASCE (nat. dir. 1982-85), Am. Acad. Environ. Engrs., Water Environment Fedn. (nat. dir. 1981-84, Bedell award), Am. Water Works Assn., Assn. Environ. Engring. Profs., Sigma Xi. Republican. Mormon. Home: 562 E 3050 N Provo UT 84604-4264 Office: Brigham Young U 368 CB Provo UT 84602

MERRITT, LYNN GARNARD, trade association executive; b. Christiansburg, Ohio, May 2, 1930; s. Earl R. and Elizabeth (Huddleston) M.; m. Beverly J. Grauser, June 8, 1952; children: Richard, Peter. BA, Bowling Green U., 1952; MA, Millikin U., 1963. Tng. dir. Decatur (Ill.) Meml. Hosp., 1957-61; tng. cons. State of N.J., 1961-63; mgr. Life Office Mgmt. Assn., Atlanta, 1963-65, v.p., 1965-70, pres. 1970—. Lt. USAF, 1952-57. Mem. Atlanta C. of C., Union League Club, Capital City Club, Georgian Club, Kiwanis. Republican. Methodist. Office: LOMA 5770 Powers Ferry Rd NW Atlanta GA 30327-4350

MERRITT, NANCY-JO, lawyer; b. Phoenix, Sept. 24, 1942; d. Robert Nelson Meeker and Violet Adele Gibson; children: Sidney Kathryn, Kurt, Douglas. BA, Ariz. State U., 1964, MA, 1974, JD, 1978. Bar: Ariz 1978, U.S. Dist. Ct. Ariz. 1978, U.S. Ct. Appeals (9th cir.) 1984. Assoc. Erlichman, Fagerberg & Margrave, Phoenix, 1978-79, Pearlstein & Margrave, Phoenix, 1979-81, Corwin & Merritt, P.C., Phoenix, 1982-87; with Nancy-Jo Merritt & Assocs., P.C., Phoenix, 1987-88; shareholder Bryan Cave, Phoenix, 1988—. Author: Understanding Immigration Law, 1993; contbr. articles to profl. jours. Active Ariz. Coalition for Immigration Representation, Phoenix, 1988—. Fellow Ariz. Bar Found.; mem. ABA, Am. Immigration Lawyers Assn. (chairperson Ariz. chpt. 1985-87, several coms., Pro Bono award), Am. Immigration Law Found. (trustee), Ariz. Bar Assn. (immigration sect.), Nucleus Club. Democrat. Avocations: modern literature, South American literature, hiking, scuba diving, gardening. Office: Bryan Cave 2800 N Central Ave Fl 21 Phoenix AZ 85004-1007

MERRITT, ROBERT EDWARD, lawyer, educator; b. San Francisco, Jan. 31, 1941; s. Robert Edward and June Adele (Reynolds) M.; m. Robin Susan Kragen, July 2, 1966; children: Kim, Kevin, Kristin, Kate. BA, Sacramento State U., 1963; JD, U. Calif., Berkeley, 1966. Bar: Calif. 1967. Ptnr. Steinhart & Falconer, San Francisco, 1968-82, McCutchen, Doyle, Brown & Enersen, San Francisco, 1982—; lectr. U. Calif. Extension, Berkeley, 1976—, U. Calif. Extension, Davis, 1980—, U. Calif. Boalt Hall, 1989; mem. subdiv. adv. com. Calif. Dept. Real Estate, 1984—; cons. real property law subcom. U. Calif. Continuing Edn. of Bar, 1983—; mem. editorial bd. Land Use Forum, U. Calif. Continuing Edn. of Bar, 1991—. Author: Guide to Subdivision Sales Law, 1974, California Real Estate Forms and Commentaries Law and Business, Inc., 1985, California Subdivision Map Act Practice, 1987, Understanding Development Regulations, 1990; contbr. articles to profl. publs. Trustee Moraga (Calif.) Sch. Dist., 1977-89/. Named Citizen of Yr., Lesher Publs.-Moraga Kiwanis Club, 1983. Mem. ABA, State Bar Calif., Am. Coll. Real Estate Lawyers. Home: 227 Paseo Del Rio Moraga CA 94556-1628 Office: McCutchen Doyle Brown & Enersen 1331 N California Blvd Walnut Creek CA 94596

MERRITT, SUSAN MARY, computer science educator, university dean; b. New London, Conn., July 28, 1946; d. Nelson Alfred and Mary (Cory) M. BA summa cum laude, Cath. U. Am., 1968; MS, NYU, 1969, PhD, 1982; Cert., Inst. for Edn. Mgmt., Harvard U., 1985. Joined Sisters of Divine Compassion, 1975; permanent cert. tchr., N.Y. Systems programmer Digital Equipment Corp., Maynard, Mass., 1969-70; tchr. Good Counsel Acad. High Sch., White Plains, N.Y., 1970-75; adj. instr. computer sci. Pace U., White Plains, 1972-78, asst. prof., 1978-82, assoc. prof., 1982-85, prof., 1985—, chmn. dept., 1981-83, dean Sch. Computer Sci., 1983—; mem. gen. coun. Sisters Divine Compassion, 1988-92. Contbr. articles to profl. jours. Fellow Soc. for Values in Higher Edn.; mem. ACM (edn. bd. 1988—), Assn. Computer Sci. and Computer Engring. Chair (pres. 1989-90), Phi Beta Kappa, Sigma Xi. Roman Catholic. Office: Pace U 1 Martine Ave White Plains NY 10606

MERRITT, THOMAS BUTLER, lawyer; b. Toledo, Apr. 3, 1939; s. George Robert and Bernice (Gerwin) M.; m. Mary Jane Bothfeld, July 23, 1966; children—Thomas Butler, Haidee Soule, Theodore Bothfeld. A.B. magna cum laude, Harvard U., 1961, LL.B. cum laude, 1966. Bar: Mass. 1966, U.S. Supreme Ct. 1974, N.H. 1994. Law clk. to assoc. justice Arthur E. Whittemore Supreme Jud. Ct. Mass., Boston, 1966-67; assoc. Nutter, McClennen & Fish, Boston, 1967-69, Palmer & Dodge, Boston, 1969-73; asst. counsel to Gov. Mass., 1973; reporter of decisions Supreme Jud. Ct. Mass., Boston, 1974-94. Mem. Conservation Commn. Town of Sherborn, Mass., 1969-74, chmn., 1972-74; mem. corp. Tenacre Country Day Sch., Wellesley, Mass., 1972-84, trustee, 1973-78. Served to 1st lt. U.S. Army, 1962-63, capt. USAR, 1963-69. Mem. Mass. Bar Assn., N.H. Bar Assn., Fed. Bar Assn., Am. Law Inst., Am. Soc. Internat. Law, Internat. Law Assn. (Am. br.), Nat. Assn. Reporters of Jud. Decisions (pres. 1983-84). Episcopalian. Clubs: Union, Harvard (Boston). Office: Box 344 Hollis NH 03049-0344

MERRITT, WILLIAM ALFRED, JR., lawyer, telecommunications company executive; b. N.Y.C., Aug. 7, 1936; s. William Alfred and Florence Anne (O'Connor) M.; m. Christine Marie Cartnick, Sept. 27, 1969; children—William Tyler, Brian Edward, Elizabeth Cody. BA in Econs., Holy Cross Coll., Worcester, Mass., 1958; LLB, Harvard U., 1964. Bar: N.Y. 1965. Assoc. Olwine, Connelly, Chase, O'Donnell & Weyher, N.Y.C., 1964-68; atty. v.p. ops. and controls Bunge Corp., N.Y.C., 1968-83; exec. v.p. TIE/Communications Inc., Seymour, Conn., 1981-90; pres. Wiltel Communications Systems Inc, Rolling Meadows, Ill., 1991-92; gen. counsel Carolina Barnes Capital Inc., N.Y.C., 1992—; ptnr. Seaboard Equities Inc., Stamford, Conn., 1992—. Served to capt. USNR, 1958-80. Mem. Wee Burn Club. Avocations: skiing, boating, tennis. Home: 83 Brookside Rd Darien CT 06820-3505 Office: 2 Stamford Landing Ste 100 Stamford CT 06902

MERRY, ROBERT WILLIAM, publishing executive; b. Tacoma, Wash., Mar. 5, 1946; s. Robert Ellsworth and Carol Beatrice (Rasmussen) M.; m. Susan Diane Pennington, Sept. 20, 1969; children: Robert Ellsworth II, Johanna Lynn. Bachelor Journ. BA in Comms., U. Wash., 1968; MS in Journalism, Columbia U., 1972. Legis. reporter, gen. assignment reporter, copy editor Denver Post, 1972-74; reporter Nat. Observer Dow Jones & Co. Inc., 1974-77, reporter Wall St. Jour., 1977-86; exec. editor Roll Call, Newspaper of Capitol Hill, 1986-87; mng. editor Congl. Quar., Inc., Washington, 1987-89, exec. editor, 1990—, also bd. dirs.; appeared on CBS Face the Nation, NBC Meet the Press, ABC Good Morning Am., CNN Newsmakers, and Take Two, C-SPAN, numerous other local and Can. programs. Author: (chpt.) First Among Equals: Outstanding Senate Leaders of the Twentieth Century, 1991. With U.S. Army, 1968-71. Avocations: jogging, biking,

hiking, biography, movies. Office: Congl Quarterly Inc 1414 22nd St NW Washington DC 20037-1003

MERRYDAY, STEVEN D., federal judge; b. 1950. BA, U. Fla., 1972, JD, 1975. With Holland & Knight, Tampa, 1975-83; ptnr. Glenn, Rasmussen, Fogarty, Merryday & Russo, Tampa, 1983-91; federal judge U.S. Dist. Ct. (mid. dist.), Fla., 1992—. Mem. Fed. Bar Assn., The Fla. Bar, Hillsborough County Bar Assn. Office: US Courthouse 611 N Florida Ave Ste 310 Tampa FL 33602

MERSER, FRANCIS GERARD, manufacturing company executive, consultant; b. Boston, Jan. 23, 1930; s. Herbert Bartlett and Irene (Bonier) M.; m. Mary Elizabeth Snedeker, Aug. 8, 1936; children: Pamela Bartlett, Alison Gerrish. BS, Babson Coll., 1957; grad. Stanford exec. program, Stanford U., 1982. Product mgr. Dennison Mfg. Co., Framingham, Mass., 1960-70, mktg. mgr., 1970-75, div. gen. mgr., 1975-80, v.p., 1980-85, group v.p., 1985-90, ret., 1990; cons. Avery-Dennison Corp., Framingham, 1990—; overseer Myles Meml. Hosp., Damariscolta, Maine, 1979—. Approx. 35 patents in fastening methods. Served with USAF, 1951-55. Clubs: Cabadetis Boat, Cruising of Am., Manchester Yacht. Avocations: squash, racquetball, ocean racing. Office: Dennison Mfg Co Avery-Dennison Mfg Co 1 Clarks H1 Framingham MA 01701-8163

MERSEREAU, HIRAM STIPE, wood products company consultant; b. Portland, Oreg., Aug. 4, 1917; s. E.W. and Ruth (Stipe) M.; m. Margaret Daggett, Dec. 25, 1937; children: Hiram Stipe, John Bradford, Timothy Daggett. Student, George Washington U., 1936-37, Harvard U., 1959. With Weyerhauser Timber Co., Klamath Falls, Oreg., 1937-38, Alexander-Yawkey Lumber Co., Prineville, Oreg., 1938-52; gen. mgr. lumber div. Crossett Co., Ark., 1954-62; corp. sr. v.p., gen. mgr. So. div. Ga.-Pacific Corp., 1963-82, cons., 1982—; past dir. Citizens & So. Nat. Bank, Augusta, Appalachian Hardwood Mfrs. Inc., Merry Cos., Inc., Augusta. Past bd. dirs. Young Life, Ga. Conservancy, Jr. Achievement Augusta; bd. dirs. Augusta br. Boys Clubs Am., Augusta Cancer Fund; trustee Paine Coll., Augusta. Mem. Nat. Forest Products Assn. (exec. com., dir.). Republican. Presbyterian (elder). Home: 6 Turnberry Ln Sea Pines Plantation Hilton Head Island SC 29928

MERSEREAU, JOHN, JR., Slavic languages and literatures educator; b. San Jose, Calif., Apr. 16, 1925; s. John Joshua and Winona Beth (Roberts) M.; m. Nanine Landell, July 11, 1953; children: Daryl Landell, John Coates. AB, U. Calif., 1945, MA, 1950, PhD, 1957. Teaching fellow, Slavic dept. U. Calif., Berkeley, 1950-52, research asst., 1953-54; instr. Slavic dept. U. Mich., Ann Arbor, 1956-59, asst. prof., 1959-61, assoc. prof., 1961-63, prof., 1963—, chmn. dept., 1961-71, 85-89, prof. emeritus, 1990—, dir. Residential Coll., 1977-85; mem. Joint Com. Eastern Europe of Am. Council Learned Socs./Social Sci. Research Council, 1971-74, chmn., 1973-74. Author: Mikhail Lermontov, 1962, Baron Delvig's Literary Almanac: Northern Flowers, 1967, Translating Russian, 1968, Russian Romantic Fiction, 1983, Orest Somov, 1989; assoc. editor Mich. Slavic Publs., 1962—; contbr. articles to profl. jours. Served to lt. (j.g.) USNR, 1943-46, PTO. Calmerton Slavic scholar U. Calif., Berkeley, 1954-55; Ford Found. fellow, London and Paris, 1955-56, Guggenheim fellow, 1972-73; recipient Disting. Service award U. Mich., Ann Arbor, 1961. Mem. Am. Assn. Advancement Slavic Studies, U. Mich Research Club. Club: Waterloo Hunt (Grass Lake, Mich., sec. 1970-80); Commanderie de Bordeaux (Detroit). Avocations: flying, raising horses. Office: U of Mich Slavic Dept Ann Arbor MI 48109

MERSKY, ROY MARTIN, law educator, librarian; b. N.Y.C., Sept. 1, 1925; s. Irving and Rose (Mendelson) Mirsky; m. Deena Hersh, Feb. 3, 1951; children—Deborah, Lisa, Ruth. BS, U. Wis., 1948, JD, 1952, MALS, 1953. Bar: Wis. 1952, U.S. Supreme Ct. 1970, Tex. 1972, U.S. Ct. Appeals (5th cir.) 1981, N.Y. 1983. U.S. govt. documents cataloger U. Wis. Law Libr., 1951-52; reference asst. Madison (Wis.) Free Libr., 1952; pvt. practice law Wis., 1952-54; readers adv., reference and catalog libr., mcpl. reference libr. at City Hall, Milw. Pub. Libr., 1953-54; chief readers and reference svc. Yale Law Libr., 1954-59; dir. Wash. State Law Libr., 1959-63; exec. sec. Jud. Coun. Commn. Wash. Court Report, State of Wash., 1959-63; prof. law, law libr. U. Colo., Boulder, 1963-65; prof. law, dir. rsch. U. Tex., Austin, 1965-84, Elton M. Hyder Jr. and Martha R. Hyder Centennial prof. law, 1984—, adj. prof. Grad. Sch. Libr. and Info. Sci., 1976—; vis. prof. law, dir. law libr. N.Y. Law Sch., N.Y.C., 1982-84; M.D. Anderson Found. vis. prof. law Queen Mary and Westfield Coll. U. London, 1994; interim dir. Jewish Nat. and Univ. Libr., Hebrew U., 1972-73; cons. to legal pubs. and law schs.; panelist various confs.; lectr. in field. Author: A Treasure in Jerusalem, 1974, (with J. Myron Jacobstein) Fundamentals of Legal Research, 1977, 5th edit., 1990, Legal Research Illustrated, an Abridgement of Fundamentals of Legal Research, 1977, (with Jackstein, Dunn) 6th edit. 1994, (with Albert P. Blaustein) The First One Hundred Justices: Statistical Studies on the Supreme Court of the United States, 1978, (with Gary R. Hartman) A Documentary History of the Legal Aspects of Abortion in the United States, 1990, (with Jacobstein) Reports on Successful and Unsuccessful Nominations, 1987, 90; contbr. articles to profl. jours., chpts. to books; editor numerous books in field. Bd. dirs. ACLU Cen. Tex. chpt., pres. Austin chpt., 1969; bd. advisors Anti-Defamation League Austin lodge, 1974-78; bd. dirs. Hillel Found., 1980-83; bd. dirs. Tex. Com. for Humanities, 1978-80, chair, 1980-82, conf. facilitator, 1982. With U.S. Army, 1944-46, ETO. Decorated Bronze Star. Mem. ABA (com. sect. econs. of law practice 1982-86, Gavel com., various other coms.), AAUP (chmn. nominating com. 1979-80), Am. Bar Found., Am. Trial Lawyers Assn. (chair law libr. com. 1984—), Am. Law Inst., Assn. Am. Law Schs. (various coms.), Internat. Assn. Lawyers and Jurists (bd. govs. sect. 1980—), Coll. of Law Practice Mgmt., Nat. Bar Assn., Am. Assn. Law Libs. (chair various coms.), Am. Soc. Info. Sci. (pres. Tex./Okla. chpt. 1992-93), Scribes (bd. dirs. 1974—, book awards com. 1978-95, pres. 1991-93), Soc. Am. Law Tchrs. (bd. govs. 1979-88, nominations com. 1984), ALA , rsch. librs. group 1987, library edn. div.), Am. Soc. Indexers, Internat. Assn. Law Librs. (U.S. adv. council), Internat. Fedn. Libr. Assns., Nat. Librs. Assn. (pres. 1980-81), Spl. Libr. Assn., State Bar Tex. (com. Tex. Bar Jour. 1983-90), State Bar Wisc. (bd. mem. nonresident lawyers divsn. 1992—), Nat. Assn. Coll. and Univ. Attys., Tex. Assn. Coll. Tchrs., Tex. Humanities Alliance (bd. dirs. 1986—, pres. 1988), Tex. Supreme Ct. Hist. Soc. (bd. trustees 1988—), Order of Coif (mem. triennial book award com.), Am. Soc. of Inf. Sci. (pres. Tex./Okla. chpt. 1992-94). Home: 6412 Cascada Dr Austin TX 78750-8157 Office: U Tex Sch Law Tarlton Law Libr 727 E 26th St Austin TX 78705-3224

MERTE, HERMAN, JR., educator, mechanical engineer; b. Detroit, Apr. 3, 1929; s. Herman and Anna Marie (Mitterer) M.; m. Bernice Marie Brant, Sept. 17, 1952; children—Kenneth Edward, James Dennis, Lawrence Carleton, Richard Brant, Robert Paul. B.S. in Marine Engring. U. Mich., Ann Arbor, 1950, B.S. in Mech. Engring. 1951, M.S., 1956, Ph.D., 1960. Mem. faculty U. Mich., 1959—, prof. mech. engring., 1967—; vis. prof. Tech. U. Munich, Germany, 1974-75. Served to lt. (j.g.) USNR, 1952-55. NSF sr. postdoctoral fellow, 1967-68. Mem. ASME, Am. Soc. Engring. Edn., Am. Assn. U. Profs. Home: 3480 Cottontail Ln Ann Arbor MI 48103-1770 Office: U Mich Heat Transfer Lab 2148 G G Brown Lab Ann Arbor MI 48109

MERTEN, ALAN GILBERT, university dean; b. Milw., Dec. 27, 1941; s. Gilbert Ervin and Ruth Anna (Ristow) M.; m. Sally Louise Otto; children: Eric, Melissa. BS, U. Wis., 1963; MS, Stanford U., 1964; PhD, U. Wis., 1970. Asst. prof. U. Mich., Ann Arbor, 1970-74, assoc. prof., 1974-81, prof., 1981-86, assoc. dean, 1983-86; dean U. Fla., Gainesville, 1986-89; dean Johnson Grad. Sch. of Mgmt. Cornell U., Ithaca, N.Y., 1989—; bd. dirs. Comshare, Inc., Ann Arbor, Tompkins County Trust Co., Ithaca; mem. inf. sys. adv. coun. Whirlpool Corp., Benton Harbor, Mich., 1987—; mem. Fla. Gov.'s Select Com. on Workforce 2000, 1988-89. Author: Internal Control in U.S. Corporations, 1980, Senior Management Control of Computer-Based Information Systems, 1983. Bd. dirs. Univ. Musical Soc., Ann Arbor, 1985-86; mem. Airport Authority, Gainesville, Fla., 1986-89; mem. Speakers Adv. Com. on the Future, Tallahassee, Fla., 1987-88. Served to capt. USAF, 1963-67. Lutheran. Home: 532 Cayuga Heights Rd Ithaca NY 14850-1422 Office: Cornell U Dean Grad Sch Mgmt Ithaca NY 14853*

MERTENS, JOAN R., museum curator, art historian; b. N.Y.C., Oct. 10, 1946; d. Otto R. and Helen H. M. B.A., Radcliffe Coll., 1967; Ph.D.,

Harvard U., 1972. Curatorial asst. Met. Mus. Art, N.Y.C., 1972-73, asst. curator, 1973-76, assoc. curator, 1976-81, curator Greek and Roman dept., 1981—; curator, adminstr. Met. Mus. Art, 1983-90, mem. editorial bd. Mus. Jour., 1976—; adj. prof. NYU, Inst. Fine Arts, 1992—. Author: Attic White-Ground—Its Development, 1977, Greek Bronzes in the Metropolitan Museum of Art, 1985. Mem. Archaeol. Inst. Am., German Archael. Inst. (corr. mem.). Home: 124 E 84th St New York NY 10028-0915 Office: Met Mus Art Fifth Ave at 82nd St New York NY 10028

MERTENS, THOMAS ROBERT, biology educator; b. Fort Wayne, Ind., May 22, 1930; s. Herbert F. and Hulda (Burg) M.; m. Beatrice Janet Abair, Apr. 1, 1953; children—Julia Ann, David Gerhard. B.S., Ball State U., 1952; M.S., Purdue U., 1954, Ph.D., 1956. Research assoc. dept. genetics U. Wis.-Madison, 1956-57; asst. prof. biology Ball State U., Muncie, Ind., 1957-62, assoc. prof., 1962-66, prof., 1966-93, dir. doctoral programs in biology, 1974-93, disting. prof. biology edn., 1988-93; prof. emeritus Ball State U., 1993—. Author: (with A. M. Winchester) Human Genetics, 1983 (with R.L. Hammersmith) Genetics Laboratory Investigations, 9th edit., 1991, 10th edit., 1995; contbr. numerous articles to profl. jours. Fellow NSF, 1963-64, Ind. Acad. Sci., 1969; co-recipient Gustav Ohaus award for Innovative Coll. Sci. Teaching, Nat. Sci. Tchrs. Assn., 1986; recipient Dist. Service to Sci. Edn. citation Nat. Sci. Tchrs. Assn., 1987. Fellow AAAS; mem. Nat. Assn. Biology Tchrs. (pres. 1985, hon. mem. 1988), Am. Genetic Assn., Genetics Soc. Am. Lutheran. Home: 2506 W Johnson Rd Muncie IN 47304-3066 Office: Ball State U Dept Biology Muncie IN 47306

MERTIN, ROGER, photographer; b. Bridgeport, Conn., Dec. 9, 1942; s. George and Margaret (Marcinko) M. B.F.A, Rochester Inst. Tech., 1965; M.F.A, Visual Studies Workshop, Rochester, 1972. Assoc. prof. art U. Rochester, N.Y., 1981—. Exhibited in group shows at Internat. Mus. Photography, Rochester, 1966, 67, Nat. Gallery Can., Ottawa, 1969, Fogg Art Mus., Harvard U., Cambridge, Mass., 1974, Ctr. Cultureel Americain, Paris, 1976, U. Colo., Boulder, 1977, Mus. Modern Art, N.Y.C., 1978, Kunsthalle, Cologne, Fed. Republic Germany, 1980, Tampa (Fla.) Mus., 1983, Barbican Art Gallery, London, 1985; one-man shows include Internat. Mus. Photography, Rochester, 1966, U. Calif., Davis, 1969, Do Not Bend Gallery, London, 1970, Toronto (Can.) Gallery Photography, 1972, Light Gallery, N.Y.C., 1973, 75, 80, Galerie Stampa, Basel, Switzerland, 1974, Afterimage Gallery, Dallas, 1976, Ctr. for Contemporary Photography, Chgo., 1978, Visual Studies Workshop, Rochester, 1978, Sun Valley Ctr. for Arts and Humanities, Idaho, 1979, Rockwell Kent Gallery, Plattsburgh, N.Y., 1979, Light Work, Syracuse, N.Y., 1979, Friends of Photography, 1981; represented in permanent collections Mus. Modern Art, N.Y.C., Internat. Mus. Photography, Rochester, Visual Studies Workshop, Rochester, Mus. Fine Arts, Boston, Princeton (N.J.) U., Art Inst. Chgo., Mpls. Inst. Art, Bibliothèque Nat., Paris, Nat. Gallery Can., Ottawa, Australian Nat. Gallery, Canberra; author: Roger Mertin: Records 1976-78, 1978. Nat. Endowment Arts Photographer fellow, 1976; Photographers fellow Guggenheim Found., 1974, Creative Aritsts Pub. Service, 1974. Mem. Soc. Photog. Edn. Office: U Rochester Dept Art and Art History River Campus Sta Rochester NY 14627

MERTON, ROBERT C., economist, educator; b. N.Y.C., July 31, 1944; s. Robert K. and Suzanne (Carhart) M.; m. June Patricia Rose, June 4, 1966; children: Samantha June, Robert Frederick, Paul Jonathan. B.S. in Engring. Math., Columbia U., 1966; M.S. in Applied Math., Calif. Inst. Tech., 1967; Ph.D. in Econs., MIT, 1970; MA (hon.), Harvard U., 1989; LLD (hon.), U. Chgo., 1991; Doctorate (hon.), U. Paris, Dauphine, 1995. Instr. econs MIT, Cambridge, 1969-70; asst. prof. fin. Alfred P. Sloan Sch. Mgmt., 1970-73, assoc. prof., 1973-74, prof., 1974-80, J.C. Penney prof. mgmt., 1980-88; vis. prof. fin. Harvard U., Boston, 1987-88, George Fisher Baker prof. bus. adminstrn., 1988—; trustee Coll. Retirement Equities Fund; rsch. assoc. Nat. Bur. Econ. Rsch., 1979—; prin., founder Long-Term Capital Mgmt., L.P., Greenwich, Conn. Author: Continous-Time Finance, 1990, rev. edit., 1992; co-author: Casebook in Financial Engineering: Applied Studies of Financial Innovation, 1995, The Global Financial System: A Functional Perspective, 1995; editor: The Collected Scientific Papers of Paul A. Samuelson, vol. III, 1972, Finance Series, Basil Blackwell, 1987; mem. editl. bd. Internat. Econ. Rev., 1972-77, Jour. Fin., 1973-77, Jour. Money, Credit and Banking, 1974-79, Jour. Fin. Econs., 1974-83, Jour. Banking and Fin., 1977-79, 92—, Fin. India, 1988—, Geneva Papers on Risk and Ins., 1989—, Jour. Fixed Income, 1991—, Fin. Rev., 1992—; mem. adv. bd. The New Palgrave Dictionary of Money and Finance, Math. Fin., Rev. Derivatives Rsch., Nihon Finance Gakkai; contbr. articles to profl. jours. Recipient Leo Melamed prize U. Chgo. Sch. Bus., 1983, Roger Murray prize Inst. for Quantitative Rsch. in Fin., 1985, 86, Disting. Scholar award Ea. Fin. Assn., 1989, Internat. INA-Nat. Acad. Lincei prize Nat. Acad. Lincei, Rome, 1993, FORCE award for fin. innovation Fuqua Sch. Bus., Duke U., 1993, Fin. Engr. of Yr. award Internat. Assn. Fin. Engrs., 1993. Fellow Internat. Assn. Fin. Engrs. (v.p.), Econometric Soc., Am. Acad. Arts and Scis.; mem. NAS, Am. Fin. Assn. (dir. 1982-84, pres. 1986), Soc. for Fin. Studies (v.p. 1993), Tau Beta Pi, Sigma Xi. Office: Harvard U Grad Sch Bus Adminstrn Morgan 397 Soldiers Field Rd Boston MA 02163

MERTON, ROBERT K., sociologist, educator; b. Phila., July 4, 1910; s. Harry David and Ida (Rosoff) Schkolnick; m. Suzanne Carhart, 1934 (sep. 1968, dec. 1992); children: Stephanie, Robert C., Vanessa; companion Harriet Zuckerman, 1968-92, m. June, 1993. A.B., Temple U., 1931, LL.D. (hon.), 1956; M.A., Harvard U., 1932, Ph.D., 1936, LL.D. (hon.), 1980; L.H.D. (hon.), Emory U., 1965, Loyola U., Chgo., 1970, Kalamazoo Coll., 1970, Cleve. State U., 1977, U. Pa., 1979, Brandeis U., 1983, SUNY-Albany, 1986, New Sch. Social Rsch., 1995; Dr. honoris causa, U. Leyden, 1965, Jagiellonian U., Cracow, Poland, 1989; LL.D. (hon.), Western Res. U., 1966, U. Chgo., 1968, Tulane U., 1971, U. Md., 1982; Litt.D. (hon.), Colgate U., 1967, SUNY, 1984, Columbia U., 1985, SUNY, Albany, 1986, Oxford U., 1986; Dr. Social Sci. (hon.), Yale, 1968; D.Sc. in Econ. (hon.), U. Wales, 1968; Ph.D. (hon.), Hebrew U. of Jerusalem, 1980; PhD (hon.), U. Oslo, Norway, 1991. Tutor, instr. sociology Harvard U., 1936-39; prof., chmn. dept. Tulane U., 1939-41; asst. prof. to prof. sociology Columbia U., 1941-63, Giddings prof., 1963-74, univ. prof., 1974-79, spl. service prof., 1979-84, Univ. prof. emeritus, 1979—; assoc. dir. Bur. Applied Social Rsch., 1942-71; adj. faculty Rockefeller U., 1979—; George Sarton prof. hist. sci. U. Ghent, Belgium, 1986-88; adv. editor sociology Harcourt Brace [Jovanovich], 1947—; ednl. adv. bd. Guggenheim Found., 1963-79, chmn., 1971-79. Author: Science Technology and Society in the 17th Century England, 2d edit., 1970, Mass Persuasion, 2d edit., 1971, Social Theory and Social Structure, rev. edit., 1968, On the Shoulders of Giants, 1965, vicennial edit., 1985, post-Italianate edit., 1993, On Theoretical Sociology, 1967, The Sociology of Science, 1973, Sociological Ambivalence, 1976, Sociology of Science: An Episodic Memoir, 1979, Social Research and the Practicing Professions, 1982, Opportunity Structure, 1995; co-author: The Focused Interview, rev. edit., 1956, 3d edit., 1990, Freedom to Read, 1957; co-editor, co-author: Continuities in Social Research, 1950, Social Policy and Social Research in Housing, 1951, Reader in Bureaucracy, 1952, The Student-Physician, 1957, Sociology Today, 1959, Contemporary Social Problems, 4th edit., 1976, The Sociology of Science in Europe, 1977, Toward a Metric of Science, 1978, Qualitative and Quantitative Social Research: Papers in Honor of Paul F. Lazarsfeld, 1979, Sociological Traditions from Generation to Generation, 1980, Continuities in Structural Inquiry, 1981; co-editor Internat. Encyclopedia of the Social Scis., vol. 19, 1991, Social Sci. Quotations, 1992. Trustee Ctr. Advanced Study Behavioral Scis., 1952-75, Temple U., 1964-68, Inst. Sci. Info., 1968—; mem. bd. guarantors Italian Acad. for Advanced Studies in Am., 1992—. Recipient prize disting. scholarship humanities Am. Coun. Learned Socs., 1962, Commonwealth award for Disting. Svc. to Sociology, 1979, award Meml. Sloan-Kettering Cancer Ctr., 1981, Nat. Medal of Sci., 1994; Guggenheim fellow, 1962, MacArthur Prize fellow, 1983-88, elected corresponding fellow British Acad., 1994, Russell Sage Found. scholar, 1979—; NIH Lectureship in Recognition of Outstanding Sci. Achievement, 1964. Fellow Am. Acad. Arts and Scis. (Talcott Parsons prize 1979); mem. Nat. Acad. Scis., Am. Philos. Soc., Sociol. Rsch. Assn. (pres. 1968), Nat. Acad. Edn., Nat. Int. Medicine Am. Sociol. Soc. (pres. 1957, Disting. Scholarship award 1980), Eastern Sociol. Soc. (pres. 1969), History Sci. Soc., World Acad. Arts and Scis., Social Studies of Sci. Assn. (pres. 1975, Bernal prize), Royal Swedish Acad. Scis. (fgn.), Academia Europaea (fgn.), Brit. Acad. (fgn.). Home and Office: 450 Riverside Dr New York NY 10027-6821

MERTZ, DOLORES MARY, farmer, legislator; b. Bancroft, Iowa, May 30, 1928; d. John Francis and Gertrude (Erickson) Shay; m. H. Peter Mertz (dec. 1983), Dec. 27, 1951; children: Peter, Mary Simpson, David, Ann Cornicelli, Helen Powell, Janice, Carol. AA, Briar Cliff Coll., 1948. Pres. Coun. Cath. Women, Sioux City, Iowa, 1986-88; state regent Cath. Daughters of Am., Iowa, 1988—; county supr. Kossuth County, Iowa, 1983-89; legislator Iowa Ho. of Reps.(15th dist.), 1989—. Dem. precinct com. person, Kossuth County, Iowa, sec. 1975—. Recipient Womens Leadership award Iowa Lakes Community Coll., 1988; named Woman of Yr. Beta Sigma Phi Internat., West Bend, Iowa, 1989; recipient Iowa Lakes Community Coll. Disting. Svc. award, 1992, Guardian of Small Businesss award. Mem. Soroptomist Internat. (Woman of Distinction award 1987), Drama Club (pres. 1970's). Roman Catholic. Home: 607 110th St Ottosen IA 50570 Office: Iowa Ho of Reps State Capitol Des Moines IA 50319

MERTZ, EDWIN THEODORE, biochemist, emeritus educator; b. Missoula, Mont., Dec. 6, 1909; s. Gustav Henry and Louise (Sain) M.; m. Mary Ellen Ruskamp, Oct. 5, 1936; children: Martha Ellen, Edwin T.; m. Virginia T. Henry, Aug. 1, 1987. B.A., U. Mont., 1931, D.Sc. (hon.), 1979; M.S. in Biochemistry, U. Ill., 1933, Ph.D. in Biochemistry, 1935; D.Agr. (hon.), Purdue U., 1977. Research biochemist Armour & Co., Chgo., 1935-37; instr. biochemistry U. Ill., 1937-38; research assoc. pathology U. Iowa, 1938-40; instr. agrl. chemistry U. Mo., 1940-43; research chemist Hercules Powder Co., 1943-46; prof. biochemistry Purdue U., West Lafayette, Ind., 1946-76; emeritus Purdue U., 1976—; vis. prof. U. Notre Dame, South Bend, Ind., 1976-77; cons. in agronomy Purdue U., 1977-94; affiliate prof. crops and soils Mont. State U., Bozeman, 1995—. Author: Elementary Biochemistry, 1969; author, editor: Quality Protein Maize, 1992. Recipient McCoy award Purdue U., 1967; John Scott award City of Phila., 1967; Hoblitzelle Nat. award Tex. Research Found., 1968; Congressional medal Fed. Land Banks, 1968; Disting. Service award U. Mont., 1973; Browning award Am. Soc. Agronomy, 1974; Pioneer Chemist award Am. Inst. Chemists, 1976. Mem. AAAS, AAUP, Nat. Acad. Scis., Am. Soc. Biol. Chemists, Am. Inst. Nutrition (Osborne-Mendel award 1972), Am. Chem. Soc. (Spencer award 1970), Am. Assn. Cereal Chemists. Lutheran. Co-discoverer high lysine corn, 1963. Office: Montana State Univ Dept Plant and Soils Bozeman MT 59717

MERTZ, FRANCIS JAMES, academic administrator; b. Newark, Sept. 24, 1937; s. Frank E. and Marian E. (Brady) M.; m. Gail Williams, Apr. 11, 1964; children: Lynn, Christopher, Suzanne, David, Amy, Jonathan. BA, St. Peter's Coll., 1958; JD, NYU, 1961; LLD (hon.), Felician Coll., 1984, Stevens Inst. Tech., Hoboken, N.J., 1988. Bar: N.J. 1967. Exec. v.p. St. Peter's Coll., Jersey City, 1972-78; v.p.,chief fin. officer N.Y. Med. Coll., Valhalla, 1978-79; dir. adminstrn. Sage Gray Todd and Sims, N.Y.C., 1979-81; pres. Ind. Coll. Fund N.J., Summit, 1981-90, assn. Ind. Colls. and Univs. N.J., Summit, 1982-90, Fairleigh Dickinson U., Teaneck, N.J., 1990—; bd. dirs. UJB Fin., Princeton, N.J., United Jersey Bank, Nat. Assn. Ind. Colls. and Univs. Mem., officer Bd. Edn., Watchung, N.J., 1982-85; trustee, sec. St. James Found., Westfield, N.J., 1987—; bd. dirs. Ready Found., Tri County Scholarship Fund, Paterson, N.J., 1992—; trustee St. Peter's Prep. Sch., New Community Found., Acad. Decathlon of N.J., Libr. Sci. Ctr. Mem. N.J. State Bar Assn., University Club. Home: 167 Stanie Brae Dr Watchung NJ 07060-6233 Office: Fairleigh Dickinson U 1000 River Rd Teaneck NJ 07666

MERTZ, STUART MOULTON, landscape architect; b. Wayne, Pa., Dec. 4, 1915; s. Walter Smith and Elizabeth Armenia (Day) M.; m. Constance Coulter Buck, June 27, 1942 (dec. Mar. 17, 1978); children: Stuart Moulton, Maurice Walter; m. Theodora Lucks Hager, Oct. 13, 1979 (div. Dec. 1987); married, Sept. 13, 1988. B.S. in Landscape Architecture, Pa. State U., 1937; B.Landscape Architecture, Cornell U., 1938; travelling fellow, Am. Acad. Rome, 1938-40, fellow, 1940. With John Noyes, St. Louis, 1940-41; chief designer Harland Bartholomew & Assocs., St. Louis, 1941-49; pvt. practice landscape architecture St. Louis, 1949-83; sr. assoc. Austin Tao & Assocs., Inc., 1984-92; lectr. nurserymen's short course Tex. A & M Coll.; lectr. landscape architecture Iowa State U., also S.W. Park Tng. Inst., U. Kans., U. Ga., Mich. State U., others. Work includes 26 parks and playgrounds for City and County of St. Louis, St. John's Hosp., St. Lukes Hosp. West, Visitation Acad., Florissant Valley C.C., Bettendorf Stores, Meramec C.C., Barnwell Art and Garden Ctr., Shreveport, La. golf course and facilities design St. Andrew's Golf Club, St. Charles, Mo., site planning and recreational facilities design for Bellevive Country Club, Meadowbrook Country Club, Bogey Golf Club. Pres.: People's Art Center Assn., 1960-62, bd. dirs., 1959-63; bd. dirs. Spirit of St. Louis Fund, 1960-62; mem. adv. council U. Mo. Sch. Forestry, Fisheries and Wildlife, 1974-83. Served to 2d lt. USAAF, 1943-45. Recipient Centennial medal for disting. achievement in landscape architecture Am. Acad. in Rome, 1994. Fellow Am. Soc. Landscape Architects (chmn. St. Louis 1960-63, trustee Missouri chpt. 1954-60, nat. sec.-treas. 1963-67, nat. 2d v.p. 1967-69, chmn. Coun. of Fellows 1977-79, bd. soc. found. 1965-69, 71-75, sec.-treas. 1967-69); mem. Mo. Assn. Landscape Architects (pres. 1966-86), Sovestor's Investment Club (sec. 1988-92, pres. 1992-94), Cornell Club St. Louis (pres. 1955-56), Penn State Club, Chi Phi. Presbyterian. Home: 9009 Sedgwick Place Dr Saint Louis MO 63124-1890

MERTZ, WALTER, retired government research executive; b. Mainz, Germany, May 4, 1923; s. Oskar and Anne (Gabelmann) M.; m. Marianne C. Maret, Aug. 8, 1953. M.D., U. Mainz, 1951. Intern County Hosp., Hersfeld, Germany, 1952-53; resident Univ. Hosp., Frankfurt, Germany, 1953; vis. scientist NIH, Bethesda, Md., 1953-61; chief dept. biol. chemistry Walter Reed Army Inst. Research, Washington, 1961-69; mem. staff Nutrition Inst., Agrl. Research Service, Dept. Agrl., Beltsville, Md., 1969-72, chmn. inst., 1972-92; ret.; dir. Human Nutrition Research Ctr.; lectr. George Washington U. Med. Sch., 1963-73. Served with German Army, 1941-46. Recipient Osborne and Mendel award Am. Inst. Nutrition, 1971, Superior Performance award Dept. Agr., 1972, Lederle award in Human Nutrition, 1982, Internat. prize for Modern Nutrition, 1987, award for Disting. Svc., Dept. Agr., 1988. Mem. Am. Inst. Nutrition, Am. Soc. Biol. Chemists, Am. Soc. Clin. Nutrition. Home: 12401 St James Rd Rockville MD 20850-3744

MERVA, GEORGE ELLIS, agricultural engineer, educator, researcher; b. Guernsey County, Ohio; s. John and Julianna (Jugan) M.; m. Betty Lou Mnich, Oct. 31, 1959; children: Bernadette Marie, Monica Ann, Jacquelin Louise, Jennifer Kay, Michael Ellis. BSAE, Ohio State U., 1960, PhD, 1967. Registered profl. engr., Ohio. Asst. prof. agronomy Ohio Agrl. R&D Ctr., Wooster, Ohio, 1960-63; rsch. asst. Ohio State U., Columbus, 1963-67; asst. prof. agrl. engring. Mich. State U., East Lansing, 1967-70, assoc. prof. agrl. engring., 1970-74, prof., 1974—; external examiner Univ. Ife, Nigeria, 1977-78. Author: Physioengineering Principles, 1975, Physical Principles of the Plant Biosystem, 1994; patentee Velocity permeameter. With U.S. Army, 1953-55. Fellow Am. Soc. Agrl. Engrs.; mem. ASCE (pres.), Am. Soc. Engring. Edn., KC (co-organizer local chpt. 1981, dep. grand knight 1981, 83, grand knight 1994—), Kiwanis (community affairs chair 1990, bd. dirs. 1994—). Democrat. Byzantine Catholic. Avocations: accrodion, choir, travel. Office: Mich State U 213 A W Farrall Hall W East Lansing MI 48824

MERVIS, LOUIS, school system administrator. Chmn. Ill. Bd. Edn., Springfield. Office: Bd Edn 100 N 1st St Springfield IL 62777

MERWIN, DAVIS UNDERWOOD, newspaper executive; b. Chgo., June 22, 1928; s. Davis and Josephine (Underwood) M.; m. Nancy Snowden Smith Tailer, Nov. 14, 1958 (dec. Feb. 1995); children: Davis Fell, Laura Howell, James B. Tailer. AB, Harvard U., 1950; LLD (hon.), U. Wesleyan U., 1991. Pres. Evergreen Communications, Inc., Bloomington, Ill., 1969-80; pub. Daily Pantagraph, 1968-80; pres. Wood Canyon Corp., Tucson, 1989-93; bd. dirs. State Farm Growth, Balanced, Interim & Mcpl. Bond Funds, 1967, Crown C Cattle Co.; bd. dir., v.p. radio stas. WBD, WBNQ, WGOW, WSKZ, WJCW, WQUT, KLQ, WTCB, WXLY; dir. adv. bd. UPI, 1979-82. Bd. dirs. Fell Found.; bd. dirs., mem. exec. com. Adlai E. Stevenson Lectures; trustee emeritus Ill. Wesleyan U., Inland Daily Press Found., chmn. investment com., 1983-91; trustee Ill. Nature Conservancy, 1991-93. Served to capt. USMCR, 1950-53. Recipient Disting. Service award U.S. Jaycees, 1959. Mem. Am. Newspaper Pubs. Assn., Inland Daily Press Assn. (pres. 1977, chmn. bd. 1978). Republican. Unitarian. Clubs: Harvard (Chgo.);

Phoenix-SK, Hasty Pudding, Bloomington Country, Ristigouche Salmon. Office: 236 Greenwood Ave Bloomington IL 61704-7243

MERWIN, EDWIN PRESTON, educator; b. Revere, Mass., Oct. 13, 1927; s. George Preston and Edith Charlotte (Miller) M.; m. Marylynn Joy Bicknell, Nov. 3, 1979; 1 son by previous marriage, Ralph Edwin; stepchildren: Charles John Burns, Patrick Edward Burns, Stephen Allen Burns. BS, U. So.Calif., 1955, postgrad. Law Sch., 1955-57; postgrad., San Fernando Valley State Coll., 1965-66; M in Pub. Health (USPHS fellow), U. Calif. at Berkeley, 1970; PhD, Brantridge Forest (Eng.), 1971. Tng. officer Camarillo (Calif.) State Hosp., 1961-66; asst. coord. Mental Retardation Programs, State of Cal., Sacramento, 1966-67; project dir. Calif. Council Retarded Children, Sacramento, 1967-69; asst. dir. Golden Empire Comprehensive Health Coun., Sacramento, 1970-76, health care cons., 1976-77; gen. ptnr. EDRA Assocs., 1976—; cons. Calif. Dept. Health, 1977-78; cons. Calif. Office Statewide Health Planning and Devel., 1978-79; chief Health Professions Career Opportunity Program State of Calif., Sacramento, 1979-81; chief Health Personnel Info. and Analysis Sect., Office of Statewide Health Planning and Devel., 1981-82, asst. div. chief div. Health Professions Devel., 1982-84, asst. dep. dir., 1984-86; project dir. Alzheimers Disease Insts., Calif., 1986-87; chief Demonstration Project Sect. div. Health Projects and Analysis, 1987-89; chief Policy Analysis and Professsions Devel. Sect., 1989-93; tchr. Ventura (Calif.) Coll., 1962-66, Merritt Coll., Oakland, Calif., 1969; sr. adj. prof. Golden Gate U., 1976—; lectr. continuing edn. program U. Calif. at Berkeley; instr. Los Rios C.C. Dist., 1982—; mem. Task Force for New Health Care Sys. in Macedonia; mem. adv. com. Health Faculty, Golden Gate U., 1995—; cons. NIMH, HEW, Calif. Assn. Health Facilities. Mem. Health Adv. Council San Juan Sch. Dist., 1972-73; treas. Calif. Camping and Recreation Council, 1972-73. Bd. dirs. Sacramento Rehab. Facility, 1970-86, v.p., 1973-76, bd dirs Sacramento Vocational Svcs., 1986-93. Recipient Pres.'s award Golden Gate U., 1982. Mem. Am. Assn. Mental Deficiency, Calif. Pub. health Assn., Sacramento Mental Health Assn., Sacramento Assn. Retarded (life mem., dir., sec. award 1984), Nat. Assn. for Retarded Children, DAV (life), Am. Legion, Marines Meml. Assn. (life), AAAS, SCAPA Praetors U. So. Calif., Miles Merwin Assn. Founder, editor: T. Patrick Heck Meml. Case Series, 1982; co-author textbook: (with Dr. Fred Heck) Written Case Analysis, 1982; founder, cons. Internat. U. Am., 1995—; contbr. articles to profl. lit. Home: 8008 Archer Ave Fair Oaks CA 95628-5907 Office: Golden Gate U 3620 Northgate Blvd Ste 100 Sacramento CA 95834-1619

MERWIN, JOHN DAVID, lawyer, former governor; b. Frederiksted, St. Croix, V.I., Sept. 26, 1921; s. Miles and Marguerite Louise (Fleming) M.; m. Marjorie Davis Spaulding, Feb. 18, 1993. Student, U. Lausanne, Switzerland, 1938-39, U. P.R., 1939-40; B.Sc., Yale U., 1943; LL.B., George Washington U., 1948. Bar: Conn. V.I. 1949. Practice law St. Croix, V.I., 1949-50, 1953-57, 67-85; gen. counsel, v.p. Robert L. Merwin & Co., Inc., 1953-57; senator-at-large V.I. Legislature, 1955-57; govt. sec. for V.I., 1957-58, gov. V.I., 1958-61; rep. Chase Manhattan Bank, Nassau, Bahamas, 1961-65; exec. v.p. Equity Pub. Corp. Orford, N.H., 1965-67. Chmn. V.I. Port Authority, 1972-75; Rep. candidate for Pres. N.H. Primary Election, 1992; pres. The Nason Found., Cleve., 1981—. Served from 2d lt. to capt. F.A. AUS, 1942-46, 50-53. Decorated Bronze Star; Croix de Guerre with silver star. Mem. Internat., Conn., N.H., V.I. bar assns., Phi Delta Phi. Clubs: Tennis of St. Croix (V.I.); Yale (N.Y.C.). Home and Office: PO Box 778 Franconia NH 03580-0778

MERWIN, WILLIAM CHARLES, academic administrator; b. La Crosse, Wis., June 25, 1939; s. Donald Francis and Effie Marie (Haggerty) M.; m. Patricia Ann Byrne, Jan. 28, 1961 (div. Mar. 1980); children: John, Michael, William B.; m. Debra Lee Davis, Aug. 8, 1987. BS, U. Wis., La Crosse, 1961, MA, 1965; EdD, U. Ga., 1972. Tchr., coach Onalaske (Wis.) High Sch., 1961-65; tchr. W. Salem (Wis.) High Sch., 1965-68; asst. prof. U. Wis., La Crosse, 1968-73; chmn. dept. U. No. Fla., Jacksonville, 1973-77, assoc. v.p., 1977-81; provost, v.p. acad. affairs U. North Fla., Jacksonville, 1981-85; pres. No. Mont. Coll., Havre, 1985-89, SUNY, Potsdam, 1989—; bd. dirs. First Nat. Bank, Havre; bus. mgmt. cons. Outdoor World, Jacksonville, 1980-82, Amerifirst Savs. & Loan, Miami, Fla., 1980-82; ednl. cons. Clay, Duval, St. Johns Counties, Fla., 1973-82; pvt. practice econ. devel., venture capital, high tech. applications cons., Mont., 1985—. Author: Studies in State and Local History, 1967, Developing Competencies in Social Studies, 1974, Handbook on Contemporary Education "The Inquiry Method," 1975; (with others) Developing Competency Teaching Secondary Social Studies, Textbook for Teachers, 1974. Bd. dirs. United Way of Hill County, Havre, 1987—, Thomas Edison Found., 1987—; co-founder Havre Area Econ. Devel. Coalition, Havre, 1985-87. Named Tchr. of Yr., West Salem High, La Crosse, 1967, Prof. of Yr., U. North Fla., 1973; Fulbright scholar, Japan, 1966. Mem. Am. Assn. State Colls. and Univs. (econ. devel. task force 1985—), Havre Area C. of C. (bd. dirs. 1986—), Phi Kappa Phi. Democrat. Roman Catholic. Lodge: Rotary. Office: SUNY-Potsdam Office of Pres Potsdam NY 13676

MERWIN, WILLIAM STANLEY, poet; b. N.Y.C., Sept. 30, 1927. AB, Princeton, 1947. Tutor France and Portugal, 1949; to Robert Graves' son, Majorca, 1950; translator London, Eng. 1951-54. Playwright Poets' Theater, Cambridge, Mass., 1956-57; with Roger Planchon's Theatre de la Cite, Lyon, France, 1964-65; author: (poetry) A Mask for Janus, 1952, The Dancing Bears, 1954, Green with Beasts, 1956, The Drunk in the Furnace, 1960, The Moving Target, 1963, Collected Poems, 1966, The Lice, 1969, Animae, 1969, The Carrier of Ladders, 1970 (Pulitzer Prize for poetry 1971), (with A.D. Moore) Signs, 1970, Asian Figures, 1973, Writings to an Unfinished Accompaniment, 1973, The First Four Books of Poems, 1975, The Compass Flower, 1977, Feathers from the Hill, 1978, Finding the Islands, 1982, Unframed Originals, 1982, Opening the Hand, 1983, The Rain in the Trees, 1988, Selected Poems, 1988, Travels, 1993; (prose) The Miner's Pale Children, 1970, Houses and Travellers, 1977, Unframed Originals: Recollections, 1982, Regions of Memory, 1987, The Lost Upland, 1992; (plays) Darkling Child, 1956, Favor Island, 1957, The Gilded West, 1961; editor: West Wind: Supplement of American Poetry, 1961, The Essential Wyatt, 1989; poetry editor: Nation, 1962; translator numerous Spanish, French works; contbr. articles to lit. mags. Kenyon Rev. poetry fellow, 1954; Rockefeller fellow, 1956, grantee, 1969; Nat. Inst. Arts and Letters grantee, 1957; Arts Council Gt. Britain bursary, 1957; Rabinowitz Found. grantee, 1961; Ford Found. grantee, 1964-65; Chapelbrook Found. fellow, 1966; Acad. Am. Poets fellow, 1973; Guggenheim fellow, 1973, 83; recipient Bess Hokin prize Poetry Mag., 1962, Harriet Monroe Meml. prize Poetry Mag., 1967, PEN Translation prize, 1968, Shelley Meml. award, 1974, Bollingen prize for poetry Yale Univ. Libr., 1979. Mem. Nat. Inst. Arts and Letters. Office: care Atheneum Publishers 866 3rd Ave New York NY 10022-6221•

MERZ, CARL ALLEN, financial services company executive; b. Washington, Jan. 1, 1949; s. Albert Henry and Ruth Marie (Allen) M.; m. Renee Bradley; children: Christopher, Wendy. BS in Econs., U. Pa., 1970; MBA, Cornell U., 1972. CPA, N.Y. Mem. audit staff Price Waterhouse & Co., N.Y.C., 1972-80; asst. v.p. PaineWebber, N.Y.C., 1980-81, divisional v.p., 1981-82, corp. v.p., 1983-90; treas., CFO PaineWebber Cashfund, N.Y.C., 1981-85, PaineWebber R.M.A. Funds, N.Y.C., 1982-85; v.p. fin., CFO PaineWebber Futures, 1984-85; mng. dir., controller Cowen & Co., N.Y.C., 1990—. Mem. Am. Inst. C.P.A.s, N.Y. State Soc. CPAs Republican. Clubs: N.Y. Road Runners, N.Y. Thoroughbred Breeders. Home: 7 School House Ln Syosset NY 11791-2619 Office: Cowen & Co Fin Sq New York NY 10005

MERZ, JAMES LOGAN, electrical engineering and materials educator, researcher; b. Jersey City, Apr. 14, 1936; s. Albert Joseph and Anne Elizabeth (Farrell) M.; m. Rose-Marie Weibel, June 30, 1962; children: Kathleen, James, Michael, Kimarie. BS in Physics, U. Notre Dame, 1959; postgrad., U. Göttingen, Fed. Republic Germany, 1959-60; MA, Harvard U., 1961, PhD in Applied Physics, 1967; PhD (hon.), Lingköping U., Sweden, 1993. Mem. tech. staff Bell Labs., Murray Hill, N.J., 1966-78; prof. elec. engring. U. Calif., Santa Barbara, 1978-94, prof. materials, 1986-94, chmn. dept. elec. and computer engring., 1982-84, assoc. dean for rsch. devel.

Coll. Engring., 1984-86, acting assoc. vice chancellor, 1988, dir. semiconductor rsch. corp. core program on GaAs digital ICs, 1984-89, dir. Compound Semiconductor Rsch. Labs., 1986-92, dir. NSF Ctr. for Quantized Electronic Structures, 1989-94; Freimann prof. elec. engring. U. Notre Dame (Ind.), 1994—; NATO Advanced Study Inst. lectr. Internat. Sch. Materials Sci. and Tech., Erice-Sicily, Italy, 1990; mem. exec. com. Calif. Microelectronics Innovation and Computer Rsch. Opportunities Program, 1986-92; mem. NRC com. on Japan, NAS/NAE, 1988-90; mem. internat. adv. com. Internat. Symposium on Physics of Semiconductors and Applications, Seoul, Republic of Korea, 1990, Conf. on Superlattices and Microstructures, Xi'an, China, 1992; participant, mem. coms. other profl. confs. and meetings. Contbr. numerous articles to profl. jours.; patentee in field. Fulbright fellow, Danforth Found. fellow, Woodrow Wilson Found. fellow. Fellow IEEE, Am. Phys. Soc.; mem. IEEE Lasers and Electro-Optics Soc. (program com. annual mtg. 1980), IEEE Electron Device Soc. (sec. 1994, 95), Am. Vacuum Soc. (exec. com. electronic materials and processing divsn. 1988-89), Electrochem. Soc., Materials Rsch. Soc. (editl. bd. jour. 1984-87), Soc. for Values in Higher Edn., Inst. Electronics, Info. and Comm. Engrs. (overseas adv. com.), Sigma Xi, Eta Kappa Nu. Achievements include research in field of optoelectronic materials and devices: semiconductors and ionic materials; optical and electrical properties of implanted ions, rapid annealing; semiconductor lasers, detectors, solar cells, other optoelectronic devices; low-dimensional quantum structures. Office: U Notre Dame Dept Elec Engring 275 Fitzpatrick Hall Notre Dame IN 46556-5602

MERZ, MICHAEL, federal judge; b. Dayton, Ohio, Mar. 29, 1945; s. Robert Louis and Hazel (Appleton) M.; m. Marguerite Logan LeBreton, Sept. 7, 1968; children: Peter Henry, Nicholas George. AB cum laude, Harvard U., 1967, JD, 1970. Bar: Ohio 1970, U.S. Dist. Ct. (so. dist.) Ohio 1971, U.S Supreme Ct. 1974, U.S. Ct. Appeals (6th cir.) 1975. Assoc. Smith & Schnacke, Dayton, Ohio, 1970-75, ptnr., 1976-77; judge Dayton Mcpl. Ct., 1977-84; magistrate U.S. Dist. Ct. (so. dist.) Ohio, 1984—; adj. prof. U. Dayton Law Sch., 1979—. Bd. dirs. United Way, Dayton, 1981-95; trustee Dayton & Montgomery County Pub. Libr., 1991—. Mem ABA, Fed. Bar Assn., Am. Judicature Soc., Ohio State Bar Assn., Dayton Bar Assn. Republican. Roman Catholic. Office: US Dist Ct 902 Federal Bldg 200 W 2nd St Dayton OH 45402-1430

MERZBACHER, EUGEN, physicist, educator; b. Berlin, Germany, Apr. 9, 1921; came to U.S., 1947, naturalized, 1953; s. Siegfried and Lilli (Wilmersdoerffer) M.; m. Ann Townsend Reid, July 11, 1952; children: Celia, Charles, Matthew, Mary. Licentiate, U. Istanbul, 1943; A.M., Harvard U., 1948, Ph.D., 1950; DSc (hon.), U. N.C., Chapel Hill, 1993. High sch. tchr. Ankara, Turkey, 1943-47; mem. Inst. Advanced Study, Princeton, N.J., 1950-51; vis. asst. prof. Duke U., 1951-52; mem. faculty U. N.C., Chapel Hill, 1952—; prof. U. N.C., 1961—, acting chmn. physics dept., 1965-67, 71-72, Kenan prof. physics, 1969-91, Kenan prof. physics emeritus, 1991—, chmn. dept., 1977-82; vis. prof. U. Wash., 1967-68, U. Edinburgh, Scotland, 1986; Arnold Bernhard vis. prof. physics Williams Coll., 1993; vis. rsch. fellow Sci. and Engring. Rsch. Coun., U. Stirling, 1986; chair Internat. Conf. on Physics of Electronic and Atomic Collisions, 1987-89, chair APS task force on jour. growth, 1994-95. Author: Quantum Mechanics, 2d edit, 1970; also articles. NSF Sci. Faculty fellow U. Copenhagen, Denmark, 1959-60; recipient Thomas Jefferson award U. N.C., 1972; Humboldt sr. scientist award U. Frankfurt, Germany, 1976-77. Fellow Am. Phys. Soc. (pres. 1990), AAAS; mem. Am. Assn. Physics Tchrs. (Oerst medal 1992), AAUP, Sigma Xi. Achievements include research on applications of quantum mechanics to study atoms and nuclei. Home: 1396 Halifax Rd Chapel Hill NC 27514-2724

MESA, RICHARD, school superintendent. Supt. schs. Oakland (Calif.) Unified Sch. Dist. Office: Oakland Unified School District 1025 2nd Ave Oakland CA 94606-2212

MESA-LAGO, CARMELO, economist, educator; b. Havana, Cuba, Aug. 11, 1934; s. Rogelio M. and Ana Maria (Lago); m. Elena Mesa-Gross, Sept. 3, 1966; children: Elizabeth, Ingrid, Helena. LLB, U. Havana, 1956; LLD, U. Madrid, 1958; MA in Econs., U. Miami, 1965; PhD, Cornell U., 1968. Asst. prof. Cath U. Villanueva, Havana, Cuba, 1956-57, 59-61; research assoc. U. Miami, Fla., 1962-65; asst. prof. U. Pitts., 1968-71, assoc. prof., 1971-76, prof., 1976-81, disting. prof. econs. and Latin Am. affairs, 1981—; dir. Ctr. Latin Am. Studies, 1974-86; vis. prof. Oxford U., 1977, Mellon vis. prof. Fla. Internat. U., 1995, vis. prof. Inst. Univ. Ortega y Gasset, 1990-91; Bacardi chair U. Miami, 1994; regional advisor Econ. Commn. Latin Am., Santiago, Chile, 1983-84; rsch. assoc. Max-Planck-Inst., Munich, 1991-92; cons. in field. Author: Cuba in the 1970's, 1974, 2d edit. 1978, Social Security in Latin America, 1978, The Economy of Socialist Cuba, 1981 (A.P. Whitaker 1982), The Crisis of Social Security and Health Care: Latin American Experiences and Lessons, 1985, Ascent to Bankruptcy: Financing Social Security in Latin America, 1989, Health Care for the Poor in Latin America and the Caribbean, 1992, Cuba After the Cold War, 1993, Changing Social Security in Latin America, 1994 (Outstanding Book Choice award 1995), Are Economic Reforms Propelling Cuba To the Market?, 1994; former editor: Yearbook Cuban Studies. Recipient numerous rsch. grants, 1986—, Alexander von Humboldt sr. rsch. prize, 1990-91. Mem. Latin Am. Studies Assn. (pres. 1980), Caribbean Studies Assn. (eec. coun. 1973-74), Am. Econ. Assn., Assn. Comparative Econs., Internat. Assn. Labor Law and Social Security, Coun. on Fgn. Rels. and the Nat. Acad. of Social Ins., Spanish Club (Pitts., v.p.). Democrat. Roman Catholic. Office: U Pittsburgh Dept Econs 4M38 Forbes Quadrangle Pittsburgh PA 15260

MESAROS, KENNETH LEE, rancher, state senator; b. Great Falls, Mont., June 17, 1950; s. Albert and Hilda (Heiman) M.; m. Rebecca Lynn Mesaros; children: Mathew, Michael, Scot, Kimberly. BS in Agr. Edn., Mont. State U., 1973. Owner, operator Mesaros Ranch, Cascade, Mont., 1969—; senator State of Mont., Helena, 1992—; dir. Am. Inst. Cooperatives, Mpls., 1978; chmn., dir. Foothill Livestock Assn., Cascade County, Mont., 1982-88, Equity Co-op Assn., Ulm, Mont., 1977-84. Sch. bd. chmn. Sch. Dist. # 95, Deep Creek, Mont., 1986-90. Staff sgt. Mont. Air N.G., 1969-75. Mem. Mont. Stockgrowers Assn. (dir. 1990-94), Cascade Lions Club, Great Falls Elks Club. Republican. Roman Catholic. Avocations: hunting, fishing, skiing, golf. Home: 2191 Millegan Rd Cascade MT 59421

MESCH, BARRY, academic administrator; b. Birmingham, Ala., Jan. 19, 1943; s. Abraham Joseph and Vellie (Yablonsky) M.; m. Caryl L. Weinstein, June 5, 1965; children: Avram Joseph, Rachel Lisa, Elana Judith. BRE, Jewish Theol. Sem., N.Y.C., 1964; BS, Columbia U., 1964; PhD, Brandeis U., 1972. Asst.-to assoc. prof. dept. religion U. Fla., Gainesville, 1969, 75, dir. Ctr. for Jewish Studies, 1973-83; acting pres. Hebrew Coll., Brookline, Mass., 1991-92, provost, Stone-Teplow families prof. in Jewish Thought, 1990—; vis. assoc. prof. Haifa (Israel) U., 1977-78. Author: Studies in Joseph IBN Caspi, 1975. NEH grantee, 1985, 90. Mem. Am. Acad. Religion, Assn. for Jewish Studies, World Union Jewish Studies. Office: Hebrew Coll 43 Hawes St Brookline MA 02146-5495

MESCHES, ARNOLD, artist; b. Bronx, N.Y., Aug. 11, 1923; s. Benjamin and Anna (Grosse) M.; m. Sylvia Snetsky, Apr. 8, 1945 (div. 1972); children: Paul Elliot, Susan Jean; m. Jill Karen Ciment, Mar. 19, 1983. Student, Art Ctr. Sch., 1943-45, Jepson's Art Inst., 1945, Chouinard's Art Inst., 1945. Instr. painting U. So. Calif., L.A., 1950; instr. painting and drawing Kann Inst. Art, L.A., 1950-55, New Sch. of Art, L.A., 1955-58, Otis Art Inst., L.A., 1963-67, U. Calif., L.A., 1972-77, Otis/Parsons Art Inst., L.A., 1975-84; instr. advanced painting and drawing Parsons Sch. Design, N.Y.C., 1986; guest prof. grad painting Rutgers U., New Brunswick, N.J., 1985; instr. grad. painting and drawing NYU, N.Y.C., 1988—; art dir. Frontier mag., L.A., 1954-60; ct. rm. artist Walter Cronkite Program, CBS, L.A., 1968-70. One-man shows include L.A. Mcpl. Art Gallery, 1983, Civilian Warfare Gallery, N.Y.C., 1984, 85, Hallwalls, Buffalo, 1985, Haines Gallery, San Francisco, 1988, 91, 93, Jack Shainman Gallery, Niagara Falls, N.Y. and N.Y.C., 1985, 86, 89, Castellani Art Mus. and Burchfield Art Ctr., Buffalo, 1988, Madison Art Ctr., 1989 Carlo Lamagna Gallery, 1989, East Hampton Ctr. for Contemporary Art, 1990, Robert Berman Gallery, Santa Monica, 1990, E.M. Donahue Gallery, N.Y.C., 1991, 93, Brody's Gallery, Washington, 1992. Grantee John F. and Anna Lee Stacey Sch. Fund, 1954, 56, NEA, 1982, N.Y. Found. for Arts, 1991; Ford Found. Faculty grantee, 1979-80. Home: 254 E 7th St # 15-16 New York NY 10009-6053

MESCHKE, HERBERT LEONARD, state supreme court justice; b. Belfield, N.D., Mar. 18, 1928; s. G.E. and Dorothy E. Meschke; m. Shirley Ruth McNeil; children: Marie, Jean, Michael, Jill. B.A., Jamestown Coll., 1950; J.D., U. Mich., 1953. Bar: N.D. Law clk. U.S. Dist. Ct. N.D., 1953-54; practice law Minot, N.D., 1954-85; justice N.D. State Supreme Ct., 1985—; mem. N.D. Ho. of Reps., 1965-66, N.D. Senate, 1967-70. Mem. ABA, Am. Law Inst., Am. Judicature Soc., N.D. Bar Assn. Office: ND State Supreme Ct State Capitol 600 E Boulevard Bismarck ND 58505

MESCHUTT, DAVID RANDOLPH, curator, historian; b. N.Y.C., May 29, 1955; s. Philip Frederick and Mary Evelyn (Mahanes) M.; m. Sarah Caroline Bevan, July 14, 1990. BA in Journalism, Washington and Lee U., 1977; MA in History Mus. Studies, SUNY, Cooperstown, 1988. Rschr. Thomas Jefferson Meml. Found., Charlottesville, Va., 1977-78, Frick Art Reference Libr., N.Y.C., 1980-86; curator art West Point (N.Y.) Mus./U.S. Mil. Acad., 1988—; guest curator N.Y. State Hist. Assn., Cooperstown, 1986-87, Brandywine River Mus., Chadds Ford, Pa., 1992; cons. Curatorial office U.S. Dept. Treasury, Washington, 1988. Author: A Bold Experiment: John Henri Isaac Browere's Life Masks of Prominent Americans, 1988; co-author: The Portraits and History Paintings of Alonzo Chappel, 1992; assoc. editor and contbr. Am. Nat. Biography, Oxford U. Press, 1994—; contbr. articles to profl. jours. Nourse Found. fellow, 1986-87, Nat. Endowment for Arts fellow, 1987, Soc. Colonial Wars fellow, 1988, Andrew W. Mellon fellow Va. Hist. Soc., 1992, Anne S.K. Brown fellow Brown U., 1993. Mem. Assn. Historians Am. Art, Historians Brit. Art, Va. Hist. Soc., N.Y. State Hist. Assn. Methodist. Avocation: music. Office: West Point Mus US Mil Acad West Point NY 10996

MESCON, RICHARD ALAN, lawyer; b. Yonkers, N.Y., Oct. 14, 1945; s. Howard and Florence (Greenwald) M.; m. Eileen Etzi, Oct. 12, 1975 (div. 1984); children: Andrew, David; m. Veronica Day, May 6, 1988; 1 child, Hannah. BA, Cornell U., 1968; JD, Columbia U., 1972. Bar: N.Y. 1973, U.S. Dist. Ct. (so. and ea. dist.) N.Y. 1973, U.S. Ct. Appeals (2nd cir.) 1975, U.S. Ct. Internat. Trade 1983, U.S. Ct. Appeals (fed. cir.) 1984. Law clk. to Hon. David N. Edelstein U.S. Dist. Ct. (so. dist.), N.Y.C., 1972-73; assoc. Paul Weiss Rifkind Wharton & Garrison, N.Y.C., 1973-77; asst. U.S. atty. criminal divsn. so. dist. U.S. Dept. Justice, N.Y.C., 1977-83; ptnr. Kassel Neuwirth & Geiger, N.Y.C., 1983-85, Webster & Sheffield, N.Y.C., 1986-90, Morgan, Lewis & Bockius, N.Y.C., 1990—; adj. assoc. prof. law NYU, 1987-90. Mem. Assn. Bar City N.Y., Fed. Bar Coun. Office: Morgan Lewis & Bockius 101 Park Ave New York NY 10178-0060

MESEHA, GEORGE MANSOUR, mechanical engineer; b. El Mehala, El Garbia, Egypt, June 20, 1942; came to U.S., 1969; s. Mansour and Eleen Meseha; m. Nadia S. Girgis, Dec. 1, 1967; children: Lucy, Joseph. BSME, Poly. Inst., Cairo, 1965; MSME, Poly. Inst., N.Y.C, 1975; MS in Computer Engring., Rensselaer Poly. Inst., 1990. Field engr. Westinghouse, Cairo, 1965; devel. engr. Electric Cable of Egypt, Cairo, 1965-69; project engr. Columbia Cable and Electric, Bklyn., 1970-76; chief engr. Phelps Dodge Copper Products Co., Bayway, N.J., 1978-79; project mgr. Phelps Dodge Copper Products Co., Norwich, Conn., 1980-81, 1981-85, engring. mgr., 1985-92, div. engring. mgr., 1992—. Contbr. articles to profl. publs. Mem. ASTM, IEEE, Wire Assn. Internat. (mem. tech. com. 1989—), Soc. Mfg. Engrs. Achievements include design of effluent treatment system for acidic metallic water, first filtration system for rolling mill to filter the emulsion of rolling mill process, computer version system for in-line, nondestructive testing. Home: 81 Fairy Lake Rd Salem CT 06415 Office: Phelps Dodge Copper Prod 41 Wawecus St Norwich CT 06360

MESELSON, MATTHEW STANLEY, biochemist, educator; b. Denver, Col., May 24, 1930; s. Hymen Avram and Ann (Swedlow) M.; m. Jeanne Guillemin, 1986; children: Zoe, Amy Valor. Ph.B., U. Chgo., 1951, D.Sc. (hon.), 1975; Ph.D., Calif. Inst. Tech., 1957; Sc.D. (hon.), Oakland Coll., 1964, Columbia, 1971, Yale U., 1987, Princeton U., 1988. From research fellow to sr. research fellow Calif. Inst. Tech., 1957-60; assoc. prof. biology Harvard U., 1960—, prof. biology, 1964-76, Thomas Dudley Cabot prof. natural scis., 1976—. Recipient prize for molecular biology NAS, 1963, Eli Lilly award microbiology and immunology, 1964, Alumni medal U. Chgo., 1971; Lehman award 1975, Presidential award 1983, N.Y. Acad. Scis., 1975; Alumni Disting. Svc. award Calif. Inst. Tech., 1975; Leo Szilard award Am. Phys. Soc., 1978; MacArthur fellow, 1984-89. Fellow AAAS (Sci. Freedom and Responsibility award); mem. NAS, Inst. Medicine, Am. Acad. Arts and Scis., Fedn. Am. Scientists (chmn. 1986-88, Pub. Svc. award 1972), Coun. Fgn. Rels., Accademia Santa Chiara, Am. Philos. Soc., Royal Society (London), Académie des Sciences (Paris). Office: Harvard U Fairchild Biochem Bldg 7 Divinity Ave Cambridge MA 02138-2092

MESERVE, RICHARD ANDREW, lawyer; b. Medford, Mass., Nov. 20, 1944; s. Robert William and Gladys Evangeline (Swenson) M.; m. Martha Ann Richards, Sept. 20, 1966; children: Amy, Lauren. Ba, Tufts U., 1966; JD, Harvard U., 1975; PhD in Applied Physics, Stanford U., 1976. Bar: Mass. 1975, D.C. 1980, U.S. Supreme Ct. 1982. Law clk. Mass. Supreme Jud. Ct., Boston, 1975-76; law clk. to presiding justice U.S. Supreme Ct., Washington, 1976-77; legal counsel Pres. Sci. Adviser, Washington, 1977-81; ptnr. Covington & Burling, Washington, 1981—; chmn. com. to assess safety and tech. issues at Dept. Energy reactors, NAS, 1987-88, chmn. com. on fuel economy of automobiles and light trucks, 1991-92, chmn. com. on declassification of info. for Dept. Energy's environ. programs, 1994—; co-chmn. AAAS-ABA Nat. Conf. Lawyers and Scientist, 1988-94; bd. dirs. Carnegie Instn. Washington. Fellow AAAS, Am. Phys. Soc., Am. Acad. aRts and Scis.; mem. Phi Beta Kappa, Sigma Xi. Democrat. Home: 708 Berry St Falls Church VA 22042-2402 Office: Covington & Burling PO Box 7566 1201 Pennsylvania Ave NW Washington DC 20004-2401

MESERVE, ROBERT WILLIAM, lawyer; b. Chelsea, Mass., Jan. 12, 1909; s. George Harris and Florence Elizabeth (Small) M.; m. Gladys E. Swenson, Oct. 17, 1936 (dec. 1994); children: Roberta Ann Weil, William George, Richard Andrew, John Eric, Jeanne-Marthe. A.B., Tufts Coll., 1931; LL.B., Harvard, 1934; LL.D., Villanova U., 1972, Drury Coll., 1972, Suffolk U., 1972, St. Michael's Coll., 1972, Wm. Mitchell Law Sch., 1977, Tufts U., 1979, Vt. Law Sch., 1984. Bar: Mass. bar 1934. Asst. U.S atty. Boston 1936-41, 83-85; lectr. Boston Coll. Law Sch., 1938-40, Harvard Law Sch. 1957-61; assoc., then partner firm Nutter, McClennen & Fish, Boston, 1934-36, 41-43, 46-73; ptnr. firm Newman & Meserve, 1973-78; ptnr. Palmer & Dodge, 1978-83, of counsel, 1986—; Mem. Mass. Bd. Bar Examiners, 1961-71, sec., 1964-71; chmn. Mass. Bd. Bar Overseers, 1974-78; Mem. sch. com., Medford, Mass., 1936-40, chmn., 1940; by appt. of Chief Justice of the U.S. mem. adv. com. Federal Criminal Rules, 1966-71, adv. com. Federal Civil Rules, 1971-78, adv. com. Admission to Federal Bar Devitt Com. 1977-79, implementation com. Judicial Conf. U.S. Admission Attys. Federal Practiceing Com.; by Presidential appt. Asst. U.S. Atty., Boston, 1936-41, Spl. Asst., 1984-86,. Editor: Harvard Law Rev, 1933-34. Mem. bd. aldermen, Medford, 1941-43; Trustee Tufts Coll., 1955-79, chmn., 1965-70, emeritus, 1979—; pres. Boston Floating Hosp., 1960-65. Served to lt. (s.g.) USNR, 1943-46. Fellow Am. Bar Found. (pres. 1979-80, dir. 1975—), Am. Coll. Trial Lawyers (pres. 1968-69, bd. regents); mem. ABA (House Dels. 1961—, past chmn. standing com. fed. Judiciary, pres. 1972-73), Mass. Bar Assn., Mass. Bar Found., Middlesex County Bar Assn., Am. Law Inst., Boston Bar Assn. (past pres.), Am. Acad. Arts and Sci., Inst. Jud. Adminstrn. (pres. 1980-82), Phi Beta Kappa (pres. assoc. 1983-85). Democrat. Unitarian. Office: 1 Beacon St Boston MA 02108-3106

MESERVE, WALTER JOSEPH, drama studies educator, publisher; b. Portland, Maine, Mar. 10, 1923; s. Walter Joseph and Bessie Adelia (Bailey) M.; m. Mollie Ann Lacey, June 18, 1981; children by previous marriage—Gayle Ellen, Peter Haynes, Jo Alison, David Bryan. Student, Portland Jr. Coll., 1941-42; AB, Bates Coll., Lewiston, Maine, 1947; MA, Boston U., 1948; PhD, U. Wash., 1952. Instr. to prof. U. Kans., Lawrence, 1951-68; prof. dramatic lit. and theory Ind. U., Bloomington, 1968-88, assoc. dean rsch. and grad. devel., 1980-83, dir. Inst. for Am. Theatre Studies, 1983-88; disting. prof. drama ctr. CUNY, N.Y.C., 1988-93, disting. prof. emeritus, 1993—; v.p. Feedback Svcs., N.Y.C. 1983—. Author: History of American Drama, 1965, rev. edit. 1994, Robert Sherwood, 1970, An Emerging Entertainment, 1977, Heralds of Promise, 1986, A Chronological Outline of World Theatre, 1992; editor: Plays of WD Howells, 1960; editor in chief Feedback Theatrebooks, 1985—; co-editor jour. Am. Drama and Theatre,

1989-93; co-compiler: Who's Where in the American Theatre, 1990, 3rd edit., 1992, Musical Theatre Cookbook, 1993; mem. adv. bd. College Literature, 1990—; co-compiler: Playhouse America!, 1991, The Theatre Lover's Cookbook, 1992. With AC, U.S. Army, 1943-46. Fellow NEH, 1974-75, 83-84, 88-89, Rockefeller Found., 1979, Guggenheim Found., 1984-85. Mem. Cosmos Club.

MESERVE, WILLIAM GEORGE, lawyer; b. Medford, Mass., June 14, 1940; s. Robert William and Gladys Evangeline (Swenson) M.; m. Susan Mary Rycroft, Oct. 21, 1967; children: Daniel Scott, Susan Elizabeth, Jonathan Robert. BA, Tufts U., 1962; LLB, Harvard U., 1965; MSc, London Sch. Econs., 1966. Bar: Mass. 1966, U.S. Dist Ct. Mass. 1970, U.S. Ct. Appeals (1st cir.) 1973. Legal asst. to commr. FTC, Washington, 1966-67; staff counsel com. on commerce U.S. Senate, Washington, 1967-69; assoc. Ropes & Gray, Boston, 1970-76, ptnr., 1976—; geology field asst. McMurdo Sound, Antarctica, 1959-60, Inglefield Land, Greenland, summer 1965. Bd. visitors Fletcher Sch. Law and Diplomacy, Tufts U., Medford, 1971—; trustee Tufts U., 1979—, AFS Intercultural Programs Inc., N.Y.C., 1979-92, 93—, New Eng. Med. Ctr., Inc., Boston, 1988—; bd. dirs. United South End Settlements, Boston, 1979—; bd. govs. New Eng. Med. Ctr. Hosps., Boston, 1982-94. Fellow Am. Coll. Trial Lawyers; mem. ABA, Boston Bar Assn., Phi Beta Kappa. Democrat. Club: Appalachian Mountain (Boston) (rec. sec. 1977-78). Office: Ropes & Gray One International Pl Boston MA 02110

MESHBESHER, RONALD I., lawyer; b. Mpls., May 18, 1933; s. Nathan J. and Esther J. (Balman) M.; m. Sandra F. Siegel, June 17, 1956 (div. 1978); children: Betsy F., Wendy S., Stacy J.; m. Kimberly L. Garnaas, May 23, 1988; 1 child, Jolie M. BS in Law, U. Minn., 1955, JD, 1957. Bar: Minn. 1957, U.S. Supreme Ct. 1966. Prosecuting atty. Hennepin County, Mpls., 1958-61; pres. Meshbesher and Spence Ltd., Mpls., 1961—; lectr. numerous legal and profl. orgns.; mem. adv. com. on rules of criminal procedure Minn. Supreme Ct., 1971-91; cons. on recodification of criminal procedure code Czech Republic Ministry of Justice, 1994. Author: Trial Handbook for Minnesota Lawyers, 1992; mem. bd. editors Criminal Law Advocacy Reporter; mem. adv. bd. Bur. Nat. Affairs Criminal Practice Manual; contbr. numerous articles to profl. jours. Mem. ATLA (st. bd. govs. 1968-71), ABA, Minn. Bar Assn., Internat. Acad. Trial Lawyers, Am. Coll. Trial Lawyers, Am. Bd. Trial Advs., Am. Bd. Criminal Lawyers (v.p. 1983), Am. Acad. Forensic Scis., Nat. Assn. Criminal Def. Lawyers (pres. 1984-85), Minn. Trial Lawyers Assn., Minn. Assn. Criminal Def. Lawyers (pres. 1991-92), Trial Lawyers for Pub. Justice, Calif. Attys. for Criminal Justice. Avocations: biking, photography, travel, flying. Home: 2010 Sugarwood Dr Orono MN 55356-9339 Office: Meshbesher & Spence 1616 Park Ave Minneapolis MN 55404-1631

MESHEL, HARRY, state senator, political party official; b. Youngstown, Ohio, June 13, 1924; s. Angelo and Rubena (Markakis) Michelakis; children: Barry, Melanie. BSBA, Youngstown Coll., 1949; MS, Columbia U., 1950; LLD (hon.), Ohio U., Ohio Coll. Podiatric Medicine; LHD (hon.), Youngstown State U. Exec. asst. to mayor City of Youngstown, Ohio, 1964-68; urban renewal dir. City of Youngstown, Ohio, 1969; mem. 33d district Ohio Senate, Columbus, 1971-93; Dem. minority leader Ohio Senate, 1981-82, 85-90, pres. and majority leader, 1983-84, com. mem. econ. develop., sci. & tech., state & local govt., ways & means, commerce & labor, controlling bd., state employment compensation bd., fin. chmn., 1974-81, rules chmn., 1983-84, com. mem. rules, reference & oversight, 1985-90; state chair Ohio Dem. Party, 1993—; real estate broker; adj. prof. polit. sci. Ohio U.; faculty mem. (limited svc.) Youngstown State U.; div. mgr. investment firm; Ohio Senate special com. mem. Task Force on Drug Strategies, Ohio Acad. Sci. Centennial Celebration Commn., Motor Vehicle Inspection & Maintenance Program, Legis. Oversight Com., Ohio Boxing Commn., Correctional Inst. Inspection Com., Ohio Small Bus. & Entrepreneurship Coun., Gov.'s Adv. Coun. Travel & Tourism, Legis. Svc. Commn., Capital Sq. Rev. & Adv. Bd., others. Past pres., past lt. gov. Am. Hellenic Ednl. Prog. Assn. (AHEPA); precinct committeeman Mahoning County Dem. Party, ward captain, mem. exec. com.; campaign mgr. local candidates, county campaign mgr. presdl. candidates; del. Dem. Mid-Term Conv., 1981; founder Great Lakes/N.E. Legis. Coalition; chmn., founder Nat. Dem. State Legis. Leaders Assn.; dir. State Legis. Leaders Found.; state/fed. assembly, mem. communications com. Nat. Conf. State Legis., legis. mgmt. com., govt. opers. com.; chair fiscal affairs com. Midwest Conf. Coun. State Govts., task force on econs. & fiscal affairs; del., exec. com. Dem. Nat. Com.; mem. Dem. Leadership Coun., State Dem. Exec. Com.; exec. com. Assn. State Dem. Chairs; bd. trustees Nat. Hall of Fame for Persons with Disabilities; mem. St. Nicholas Greek Orthodox Ch. With USN, 1943-46. Decorated two Bronze Battle Stars; recipient Dist. Svc. award Office of Pres., Top Legislator award Ohio Union Patrolmen Assn., Dist. Citizen award Med. Coll. Ohio, City of Hope Leadership award, 1993, Legis. Leadership award Ohio Coalition for Edn. of Handicapped Children, Phillips Medal of Pub. Svc., Ohio U., John E. Fogarty award Gov.'s Com. of Employment of Handicapped, Gov.'s award, 1992, U. Cin. Award for Excellence, Lamp of Learning award Ohio Edn. Assn., Black Cultural Soc. award East Liverpool, Mahoning Valley Man of Yr. award, Mahoning Valley Econ. Devel. Corp., Office Holder of Yr. award Truman-Johnson Dem. Women, Best Interest of Children award Fathers of Equal Rights, Founders Day award Circle of Friends Found., Helping Hand award Easter Seal Soc., Honorary Riverboat Captain award Mahoning County Dem. Party, Community Svc. and Special Svcs. awards Eastern Orthodox Men's Soc., Periclean award AHEPA, Academy of Achievement award Nat. AHEPA Ednl. Found., Nat. Svc. Dem. award AHEPA, 1994, Disting. Citizen award Youngstown State U. Alumni Assn., numerous appreciation and recognition awards; recipient Outstanding Legislator awards Ohio Acad. Trial Lawyers, Ohio Assn. Pub. Sch. Employees, Ohio Rehab. Assn., League Ohio Sportsmen; recipient Dist. Svc. awards Youngstown State U., Ohio Edn. Assn., Ohio Union Patrolmen Assn., Ohio Disabled Vets., AFL-CIO Ohio Barbers Union, AFL-CIO Nat. Assn. of Theatre Owners of Ohio; named Guardian of the Menorah, Youngstown B'nai B'rith, Outstanding Dem., Fairfield Dem. Club, 1993. Mem. (life) NAACP, ACLU, AMVETS (Legislator of Yr. 1993), VFW, Am. Legion, Cath. War Vets (Dist. Legislator award), Vet. Boxers Assn. Mercer County, Pa., Trumbull County Boxers' Legends of Leather (Man of Yr. award Hall of Fame), William Holmes McGuffey Hist. Soc., Buckeye Elks Lodge (hon.); mem. Kiwanis Internat., Urbn League, Alliance C. of C., Southern Community Jaycees (hon.), Soc. for Preservation of Greek Heritage, Greek Am. Progressive Assn., Pan Cretan Assn., Arms Hist. Mus. Soc., Eagles, Moose, The Stambaugh Pillars. Office: Ohio Dems 37 W Broad St Ste 430 Columbus OH 43215-4132

MESHII, MASAHIRO, materials science educator; b. Amagasaki, Japan, Oct. 6, 1931; came to U.S., 1956; s. Masataro and Kazuyo M.; m. Eiko Kumagai, May 21, 1959; children: Alisa, Erica. BS, Osaka (Japan) U., 1954, MS, 1956; PhD, Northwestern U., 1959. Lectr. rsch. assoc. dept. materials sci. and engring. Northwestern U., Evanston, Ill., 1959-60, asst. prof., assoc. prof., then prof., 1960-88, chmn. dept. materials sci. and engring., 1978-82, John Evans prof., 1988—; vis. scientist Nat. Rsch. Inst. Metals, Tokyo, 1970-71; NSF summer faculty rsch. participant Argonne (Ill.) Nat. Lab., 1975; guest prof. Osaka U., 1985; Acta/Scripta Metallurgica lectr. 1993-95. Co-editor: Lattice Defects in Quenched Metals, 1965, Martensitic Transformation, 1978, Science of Advanced Materials, 1990; editor: Fatigue and Microstructures, 1979, Mechanical Properties of BCC Metals, 1982; contbr. 215 articles to tech. publs. and internat. jours. Recipient Founders award Midwest Soc. Electron Microscopists, 1987. Fellow ASM (Henry Marion Howe medal 1968), Japan Soc. Promotion of Sci.; mem. TMS-AIME, Japan Inst. Metals (Achievement award 1972). Home: 3051 Centennial Ln Highland Park IL 60035-1017 Office: Northwestern U Dept Materials Sci Eng Evanston IL 60208

MESHKE, GEORGE LEWIS, drama and humanities educator; b. Yakima, Wash., Oct. 7, 1930; s. George Joseph and Marye Elizabeth (Lopas) M. BA, U. Wash., 1953, MA, 1959, PhD in Drama, 1972. Cert. tchr., Wash. Tchr. English and drama Zillah High Sch., Wash., 1955-58; tchr. English and drama high sch., Bellevue, Wash., 1958-60, Federal Way, Wash., 1960-70; dir., actor Old Brewery Theatre, Helena, Mont., 1962-66; prof. drama Yakima Valley C.C., Yakima, 1970—; casting dir., dir. summer seminar Laughing Horse Summer Theatre, Ellensburg, Wash., 1989—; Inquiring Mind series Wash. State Humanities, 1989-91; regional dir. Am. Coll. Theatre Festival, Washington, 1980-86; arts dialogue J.F. Kennedy Ctr., Washington, 1987—. Author, producer Towers of Tomorrow, 1985. Regional bd. dirs. Common Cause, Yakima, 1971-73; active Wash. State Commn. Humanities. With U.S. Army, 1953-55, Austria. Recipient Gold medallion Kennedy Ctr., 1985, Wash. State Humanities medal, 1983, NISAD medallion, 1989. Mem. ACLU, Wash. Edn. Assn., N.W. Drama Assn., Am. Edn. Theatre Assn., Am. Fedn. Tchrs., Phi Delta Kappa. Democrat. Avocations: travel, mountain climbing, skiing, reading. Home: 5 North 42d Ave Yakima WA 98908 Office: Yakima Valley CC 16th And Nob Hill Blvd Yakima WA 98907

MESINGER, JOHN FREDERICK, psychologist, special education educator; b. Indpls., July 17, 1929; s. William F. and Thelma E. (Harden) M.; m. Marguerite E. Rudolf, June 12, 1954; children: Karen Mesinger-Miller, Stuart F., Brian W.L. AB in Psychology, Hamilton Coll., 1951; MA in Psychology, Butler U., 1952; PhD in Experimental Child Psychology, Pudue U., 1955. Lic. psychologist, Va., clin. psychologist, Pa. Clin. psychologist, spl. edn. supr. Allegheny County, Pa. Schs., Pitts., 1958-64; prof. spl. edn. dept. curriculum, instruction and spl. edn. U. Va., Charlottesville, 1964—; lectr. Sch. Edn. U. Pitts., 1959-63, Pa. State U., 1963-64, Syracuse U., 1966; mem. U. Va. Sch. Edn. Editl. Policy Bd., 1971; cons. Avonworth Union Sch. Dist., 1958-64, Easter Seal Soc., 1958-64; evaluator Allegheny County Juvenile Ct., 1958-64, Thornhill Instrn., 1958-64, Oak Hill Sch., 1958-64; mem. staff Consultative Resource Ctr. Sch. Desegregation, U. Va., 1968-69; co-dir. Ctr. Youth and Family Svcs., 1977-80; dir. Va. Educator Program, 1977-88, Beginning Tchr. Assistance Program, Region III, 1988-91; lectr. Internat. Conf. Children with Learning Disabilities, Washington, 1977, Nat. Adolescent Conf., Pensacola, Fla., 1984, Correctional Edn. Conf., San Francisco, 1987, Tri-State Optometric Conf. Reading, Pitts., 1963, Va. Mental Health Assn., 1965, Va. State Psychiat. Assn., 1972, Va. State Sch. Psychologists, 1974, Va. State CEC Conf., Roanoke, 1977, Va. Optometric Assn., Norfolk, 1977, Va. State Conf. Adminstrs. Spl. Edn., 1991, Va. Assn. Correctional Educators, 1991, Villages Conf. Menninger Found., Topeka, Kans., 1991; bd. dirs. Charlottesville-Albemarle Mental Health Assn., 1965-69, mem. adv. bd.; bd. dirs. Charlottesville-Albemarle chpt. ACLU, 1975-80, Adventure Bound Sch., 1980-84; chmn. adv. bd. Va. Rehab. Sch. Authority, 1975-78; cons. Va. State Dept. Spl. Edn., 1965—; mem. rev. teams SEA, 1965—; cons. Peking Med. Union, 1988, Va. Dept. Edn. Task Force, 1989-91. Author: Children and Youth in Need of Care and Supervision, 1978, (with others) Problems and Issues in Education of Exceptional Children, 1971, Contemporary Issues in Educational Psychology, 1987; consulting editor Behavioral Disorders, 1981-93, The Jour. of Correctional Edn. 1984—; contbr. 34 articles to profl. jours. Chmn. Pres.'s Com. Equal Ednl. and Employment Opportunities, Obligations and Rights, 1967-71. With U.S. Army, 1956-58. Grantee Bur. for Edn. of the Handicapped, 1964-65, NIMH, 1969, Law Enforcement Assistance Agy., 1973-75, Edwin Gould Found., 1981, Dept. Edn., 1981-83, Beginning Tchr. Assistance Program, 1989-90, 90-91. Mem. AAUP, Am. Orthopschiat. Assn., Pa. PTA (life), Correctional Edn. Assn. (lectr. internat. convs. 1990, 91), Coun. for Children with Behavioral Disorders (pres. Va. chpt. 1986-87, editor Jour. 1986-91), Coun. Exceptional Children (lectr. internat. convs. 1968, 70, 72, 79, 88, lectr. Va. state chpt. 1979), Sigma Xi, Alpha Kappa Delta, Phi Delta Kappa. Avocations: photography, fishing, gunsmithing, gardening. Office: U Va Curry Sch Edn 405 Emmet St Charlottesville VA 22903

MESIROV, LEON ISAAC, lawyer; b. Phila., Jan. 19, 1912; s. Isaac and Zippa (Robbins) M.; m. Sylvia W. Portner, June 25, 1935; children: Joan C. Rondell Sparens, Judy Lynn, Jill P. AB, U. Pa., 1931, LLB, 1934. Bar: Pa. 1934, U.S. Dist. Ct. (ea. dist.) Pa. 1934, U.S. Ct. Appeals (3d and Fed. cirs.) 1948, U.S. Ct. Internat. Trade 1948. Pvt. practice law Phila., 1934—; ptnr. Mesirov, Gelman, Jaffe, Cramer & Jamieson, Phila., 1959-88, counsel, 1988—. Commr. Phila. Civil Svc., 1952-70; pres. Jewish Community Rels. Coun., 1952-55, hon. pres., 1955—; commr. Phila. Fellowship Commn., 1952—, counsel, 1959—; sec. Jewish Y's and Ctrs., 1967-71; Trustee Fedn. Jewish Ags., 1960-71, Com. of Seventy, 1972—. Mem. ABA, Pa., Phila. bar assns., Order of Coif, Beta Sigma Rho. Jewish. Home: 2131 Saint James Pl Philadelphia PA 19103-4804 Office: Mesirov Gelman Jaffe Cramer & Jamieson 1735 Market St Philadelphia PA 19103-7598

MESKILL, THOMAS J., federal judge; b. New Britain, Conn., Jan. 30, 1928; s. Thomas J. M.; m. Mary T. Grady; children—Maureen Meskill Heneghan, John, Peter, Eileen, Thomas. B.S., Trinity Coll., Hartford, Conn., 1950, LL.D., 1972; J.D., U. Conn., 1956; postgrad., Sch. Law, NYU; LL.D., U. Bridgeport, 1971, U. New Haven, 1974. Bar: Conn. 1956, Fla. 1957, D.C. 1957, U.S. Ct. Appeals (2d cir.) 1975, U.S. Supreme Ct. 1971. Former mem. firm Meskill, Dorsey, Sledzik and Walsh, New Britain; mem. 90th-91st Congresses 6th Conn. Dist.; gov. Conn., 1971-75; judge U.S. Ct. Appeals (2d cir.), New Britain, Conn., 1975—; chief judge, 1992-93. Pres. New Britain Council Social Agys.; Asst. corp. council City of New Britain, 1960-62, mayor, 1962-64, corp. counsel, 1965-67; mem. Constl. Conv., Hartford, 1965. Served to 1st lt. USAF, 1950-53. Recipient Disting. Svc. award Jr. C. of C., 1964, Jud. Achievement award ATLA, 1983, Learned Hand medal for Excellence in Fed. Juridprudence, Fed. Bar Coun., 1994. Mem. Fla. Bar Assn., Conn. Bar Assn. (Henry J. Naruk Jud. award 1994), Hartford County Bar Assn., New Britain Bar Assn., KC. Republican. Office: US Ct Appeals 114 W Main St New Britain CT 06051-4223

MESKILL, VICTOR PETER, college president, educator; b. Albertson, N.Y., May 9, 1935; s. James Joseph and Ida May (Pfalzer) M.; m. Gail King Heidinger, 1986; children by previous marriage—Susan Ann, Janet Louise, Gary James, Glenn Thomas, Kenneth John, Matthew Adam. B.A., Hofstra U., 1961, M.A. (grad. scholar), 1962; Ph.D., St. John's U., 1967; postgrad. insts., Ohio State U., 1968, Harvard U., 1972; postgrad., NYU, 1973; ScD (hon.), Samara State Aerospace U., Russia, 1993, NYU, 1973; diploma, U. Pau and the Pays de l'Abour, France, 1994. Lab. asst., instr. biology Hofstra U., 1960-62; N.Y. State teaching fellow St. John's U., 1962-63; instr. biology Nassau (N.Y.) Community Coll., 1963-64; tchr. sci. Central High Sch. Dist. 2, Floral Park, N.Y., 1963-64; lectr. biology C.W. Post Coll., Greenvale, N.Y., 1963-64, instr. biology, 1964-67, asst. prof., 1967-68, assoc. prof., 1968-74, assoc. dir. Inst. for Student Problems, supr. student tchrs., 1967-68, asst. dean Coll., dean summer sch., coordinator Admissions Office, coordinator adult and continuing edn. programs, 1968-69; dean adminstrn. C.W. Post Ctr. of L.I. U., 1969-70, v.p. adminstrn., 1970-77, prof. biology, 1975-77; pres. Dowling Coll., Oakdale, L.I., 1977—; hon. prof. Minjiang U., Fuzhou, Peoples Republic of China, 1994; cons. in edn. and biology; chem. technician, detective Tech. Rsch. Bur., Nassau County Police Dept., 1958-63, mem. sci. adv. com., 1970; mem. adv. coun. Aerospace Edn. Coun. Inc., 1968; trustee, mem. state legis. com. Commn. Ind. Colls. and Univs.; mem. evaluation teams Mid. States Assn., 1971—; mem. higher edn. adv. com. N.Y. State Senate; mem. Nassau-Suffolk Comprehensive Health Planning Coun.; chmn. Internat. and Mediterranean Studies Group Conf. Author book; contbr. articles to profl. jours. Founding mem., vice chmn. bd. trustees Nassau Higher Edn. Consortium; bd. dirs. Suffolk County coun. Boy Scouts Am.; mem. N.Y. State Energy Rsch. and Devel. Authority, Town of Islip Devel. Commn.; chmn. bd. trustees L.I. Regional Adv. Coun. Higher Edn.; chmn. L.I. Mid Suffolk Bus. Action; bd. dirs. Southside Hosp., N.Y.; v.p. L.I. Forum for Tech.; commr. Suffolk County Vanderbilt Mus.; mem. Bus. Coun. N.Y.; hon. mem. U. Pau and Pays de l'Adour, Pau, France, 1994. NSF rsch. grantee, 1967-69; Named Tchr. of Year, Aesculapius Med. Arts Soc., C.W. Post Coll. of L.I. U., 1967; Disting. Faculty Mem. of Year, C.W. Post Ctr. L.I. U., 1977; recipient George M. Estabrook award Hofstra U., 1978, Higher Edn. Leadership award Corning Glass Works, 1987, Disting. Leadership award L.I., 1989. Mem. AAAS, Coun. Advancement and Support of Edn., Am. Assn. Collegiate Registrars and Admissions Officers, Am. Assn. Higher Edn., Am. Inst. Biol. Scis., Am. Soc. Zoologists, Am. Assn. U. Adminstrs., Nat. Assn. Biology Tchrs., Nat. Sci. Tchrs. Assn., Soc. Protozoologists, N.Y. Acad. Scis., Camilo José Cela Found. (hon.), Met. Assn. Coll. and Univ. Biologists (founder, mem. steering com.), Bus. Coun. N.Y., Oakdale C. of C. (founding mem., dir.), L.I. Assn. Commerce and Industry (v.p. edn., dir.), Alpha Chi, Kappa Delta Pi, Phi Delta Kappa, Sigma Xi, Beta Beta Beta, Alpha Eta Rho, Delta Mu Delta, Kappa Delta Rho, Univ. Club (N.Y.C.), Wings Club (N.Y.C.), Nat. Arts Club (N.Y.C.), Vanderbilt Mus. Bd. Trustee. Office: Dowling Coll Office of the Pres Oakdale NY 11769-1999

MESNIKOFF, ALVIN MURRAY, psychiatry educator; b. Asbury Park, N.J., Dec. 25, 1925; s. Nathan and Rachel (Feinberg) M.; m. Wendy Savin, June 15, 1952; children: Nathaniel, Rachel, Joel, Ann. A.B., Rutgers U., 1948; M.D., U. Chgo., 1954; cert. Psychoanalytic medicine, Columbia U.,

1962. Diplomate: Am. Bd. Psychiatry and Neurology. Pvt. practice, 1958—; collaborating psychoanalyst Columbia U. Psychoanalytic Ctr. for Tng. and Rsch., N.Y.C., 1962—; dir. Washington Heights Community, N.Y. State Psychiat. Inst. N.Y.C., 1965-68; prof. psychiatry SUNY, Bklyn., 1968-81; dir. South Beach Psychiat. Ctr., S.I., N.Y., 1968-75; regional dir. N.Y. State Dept. Mental Health, N.Y.C., 1975-78, dep. commr. research, 1978-81; Marion E. Kenworthy prof. Psychiatry Columbia U. Sch. Social Work, 1981-89; lectr. Union Theol. Sem., N.Y.C., 1989-90; cons. St. Vincent's Hosp., S.I., 1970-76; attending psychiatrist S.I. Hosp., 1972-76; sr. attending psychiatrist St. Luke's/Roosevelt Hosp. Ctr., N.Y., 1987—; cons. Ford Found., N.Y.C., 1980-81. Contbr. chpts. to books, articles to profl. jours. Bd. dirs. Reality House, 1967-74; mem. task force med. sch. enrollment and physician manpower N.Y. State Bd. Regents, 1973-75; mem. task force on gen. and splty. hosp. care N.Y. State Health Planning Commn., 1973-74. Served with U.S. Army, 1943-45. Grantee Ford Found., 1982. Fellow Am. Psychiat. Assn. (life); mem. Am. Psychoanalytic Assn., Assn. Psychoanalytic Medicine, Am. Friends Tel Aviv U. (chmn. 1974-75), Phi Beta Kappa. Jewish. Office: 360 Central Park W New York NY 10025

MESROBIAN, ARPENA SACHAKLIAN, publisher, editor, consultant; b. Boston; d. Aaron Harry and Eliza (Der Melkonian) Sachaklian; m. William John Mesrobian, June 22, 1940; children: William Stephen, Marian Elizabeth (Mrs. Bruce MacCurdy). Student, Armenian Coll. of Beirut, Lebanon, 1937-38; A.A., Univ. Coll., Syracuse (N.Y.) U., 1959, B.A. magna cum laude, 1971; MSsc, Syracuse U., 1993. Editor Syracuse U. Press, 1955-58, exec. editor, 1958-61, asst. dir., 1961-65, acting dir., 1965-66, editor, 1968-85, assoc. dir., 1968-75, dir., 1975-85, 87-88, dir. emeritus, 1985; dir. workshop on univ. press pub. U. Malaysia, Kuala Lumpur, 1985; cons. Empire State Coll. Book rev. editor: Armenian Rev., 1967-75; mem. publs. bd. Courier, 1970-94; mem. adv. bd. Armenian Rev., 1981-83; contbr. numerous articles, revs. to profl. jours. Pres. Syracuse chpt. Armenian Relief Soc., 1972-74; sponsor Armenian Assembly, Washington, 1975; mem. mktg. task force Office of Spl. Edn., Dept. Edn., 1979-84, Adminstrn. of Developmental Disabilities, HHS; mem. publs. panel Nat. Endowment for Humanities, Washington; bd. dirs. Syracuse Girls Club, 1982-87; pres. trustees St. John the Bapt. Armenian Apostolic Ch. and Community Ctr., 1991—. Named Post-Standard Woman of Achievement, 1980; recipient Chancellor's award for disting. service Syracuse U., 1985; Nat. award U.S. sect. World Edn. Fellowship, 1986; N.Y. State Humanities scholar. Mem. Women in Communications, Soc. Armenian Studies (adminstrv. council 1976-78, 85-87, sec. 1978, 85-87), Syracuse U. Library Assocs. (v.p. 1983-88), Am. Univ. Press Services (dir. 1976-77), Armenian Lit. Soc., Armenian Community Center, Assn. Am. Univ. Presses (v.p. 1976-77), UN Assn. (bd. dirs. 1983-88, v.p. 1985), Phi Kappa Phi, Alpha Sigma Lambda. Mem. Armenian Apostolic Ch. (trustee). Club: Zonta of Syracuse (pres. 1979-80, 1st v.p. 1985-86, dist. historian Dist. 2 Zonta Internat. 1993). Home: 4851 Pembridge Cir Syracuse NY 13215-1023

MESSEMER, GLENN MATTHEW, lawyer; b. Hartford, Conn., Jan. 7, 1947; s. Joseph M. and Mary S. Messemer; BSBA, Georgetown U., 1968; JD, U. Conn., 1971. Bar: Conn. 1972. Staff atty. Kaman Corp., Bloomfield, Conn., 1972-74, asst. sec., 1974-79, asst. v.p. 1979-81, v.p., sec., gen. counsel, 1981—; prof. bus. law Austin Dunham Barney Sch. Bus. Adminstrn., U. Hartford (Conn.), 1974-80; legal counsel Am. Helicopter Soc.; arbitrator Am. Arbitration Assn., 1978-82. Bd. dirs., trustee, regent U. Hartford, 1993—. Served with M.I., U.S. Army, 1968-75. Mem. ABA, Conn. Bar Assn. (founding; exec. com., sec.), Hartford County Bar Assn. Clubs: Hartford Golf, Hartford, Masons. Office: Kaman Corp Old Windsor Rd Bloomfield CT 06002

MESSENGER, GEORGE CLEMENT, engineering consultant; b. Bellows Falls, Vt., July 20, 1930; s. Clement George and Ethel Mildred (Farrar) M.; m. Priscilla Betty Norris, June 19, 1954; children: Michael Todd, Steven Barry, Bonnie Lynn. BS in Physics, Worcester Poly. U., 1951; MSEE, U. Pa., 1957; PhD in engring., Calif. Coast U., 1986. Rsch. scientist Philco Corp., Phila., 1951-59; engring. mgr. Hughes Semicondr., Newport Beach, Calif., 1959-61; div. mgr. Transitron Corp., Wakefield, Mass., 1961-63; staff scientist Northrop Corp., Hawthorne, Calif., 1963-68; cons. engr., Las Vegas, Nev., 1968—; lectr. UCLA, 1969-75; v.p., dir. Am. Inst. Fin., Grafton, Mass., 1970-78; gen. ptnr. Dargon Fund, Anaheim, Calif., 1983—; v.p., tech. dir. Messenger and Assoc., 1987—; registered investment adviser, 1989—. Co-author: The Effects of Radiation on Electronic Systems, 1986; contbg. author: Fundamentals of Nuclear Hardening, 1972; contbr. numerous articles to tech. jours.; patentee microwave diode, hardened semicondrs. Recipient Naval Rsch. Lab. Alan Berman award, 1982; Best Paper award HEART Conf., 1983, Spl. Merit award HEART Conf., 1983; fellow IEEE, 1976, annual merit award 1986, Pete Haas award HEART Conf., 1992. Mem. Rsch. Soc. Am., Am. Phys. Soc. Congregationalist. Home and Office: 3111 Bel Air Dr Apt 7F Las Vegas NV 89109-1510

MESSENGER, RON J., health facility administrator; b. 1944. MBA, U. So. Calif., 1968. Engr. CASH, L.A., 1968-73; v.p. Nat. Med. Enterprises, Santa Monica, Calif., 1973-84; pres. L.A. Cmty. Hosp., 1984—; Hollywood (Calif.) Cmty. Hosp., 1984—; pres., sec., CEO Paracelsus Healthcare Corp., Pasadena, Calif., 1984—. Office: Paracelsus Healthcare 155 N Lake Ave Ste 1100 Pasadena CA 91101-1835

MESSENKOPF, EUGENE JOHN, real estate and business consultant; b. N.Y.C., Jan. 26, 1928; s. John Philip and Helen Bessie (Holden) M.; m. Martha Ann Crane, Jan. 29, 1955; children: Diane, Nancy, Eugene John, Susan. BBA, Iona Coll., 1950; MBA, NYU, 1956. CPA, N.Y. Sec.-treas. KLM Process Co., N.Y.C., 1952-54; acct. Am. Tobacco Co., N.Y.C., 1954-56; staff acct. Peat, Marwick & Mitchell, N.Y.C., 1956-60; exec. v.p. Donaldson, Lufkin & Jenrette, Inc., N.Y.C., 1960-84, pres., chief exec. officer real estate div., 1977-84; pres., chief exec. officer Meridian Investing and Devel. Corp., 1977-84; pvt. practice cons., 1984—; mem. adv. bd. NYU Real Estate Inst., 1981-85; mem. exec. coun. small scale devel. Urban Land Inst., 1983-90; chmn. Wall St. Tax Com., N.Y.C., 1965-68; bd. dirs. SIA Acctg. Div., N.Y.C., 1965-79. Trustee, chmn. fin. com. Mt. Vernon Hosp., 1982-87. Served as sgt. AUS, 1950-52, Korea. Recipient Brother Loftus award Iona Coll., 1976. Mem. AICPA, N.Y. State Soc. CPAs, Fin. Execs. Inst. Republican. Roman Catholic. Walked 2000 mile Appalachian Trail, 1987.

MESSER, DONALD EDWARD, theological school president; b. Kimball, S.D., Mar. 5, 1941; s. George Marcus and Grace E. (Foltz) M.; m. Bonnie Jeanne Nagel, Aug. 30, 1964; children: Christine Marie, Kent Donald. BA cum laude, Dakota Wesleyan U., 1963; M. Divinity magna cum laude, Boston U., 1966, PhD, 1969; LHD (hon.), Dakota Wesleyan U., 1977. Asst. to commr. Mass. Commn. Against Discrimination, Boston, 1968-69; asst. prof. Augustana Coll., Sioux Falls, S.D., 1969-71; assoc. pastor 1st United Meth. Ch., Sioux Falls, 1969-71; pres. Dakota Wesleyan U., Mitchell, S.D., 1971-81, Iliff Sch. Theology, Denver, 1981—. Author: Christian Ethics and Political Action, 1984, Contemporary Images of Christian Ministry, 1989, Send Me? The Intineracy in Crisis, 1991, The Conspiracy of Goodness, 1992, Caught in the Crossfire: Helping Christians Debate Homosexuality, 1994, Calling Church and Seminary Into the 21st Century, 1995; contbr. articles to Face to Face, The Christian Century, The Christian Ministry. Active Edn. Commn. of U.S., 1973-79; co-chmn. Citizens Commn. Corrections, 1975-76; vice chmn. S.D. Commn. on Humanities, 1979-81. Dempster fellow, 1967-68; Rockefeller fellow, 1968-69. Mem. Soc. Christian Ethics, Am. Acad. Religion, Assn. United Meth. Theol. Schs. (v.p. 1986-91, pres. 1991-92). Democrat. Office: Iliff Sch Theology Office Pres 2201 S University Blvd Denver CO 80210-4798

MESSER, ROBERT H., obstetrician/gynecologist, educator; b. Ludington, Mich., Oct. 21, 1931; s. Harry Eaves and Mary Elizabeth (Haskell) M.; m. Emily Baker, June 12, 1955 (dec. Oct. 1981); children: Karen, Robert, Laura, Ellen; m. Dianne Marie Feldon Kimmens, Apr. 28, 1990. Grad., U. Wis., 1952; MD, U. Mich., 1956. Diplomate Am. Bd. Ob-Gyn. From intern to resident in ob-gyn. Univ. Hosp., Ann Arbor, Mich., 1956-61; instr. ob-gyn. U. Nebr., Omaha, 1963-65, asst. prof. med. ctr., 1965-68, assoc. prof., 1968-71, asst. dean grad. edn., 1969-72, prof., chmn. dept., 1971-74; prof. chmn. ob-gyn. U. N.Mex., Albuquerque, 1974-84; asst. chief staff Bernalillo County Med. Ctr., Albuquerque, 1977-78; prof., assoc. chair ob-gyn. regional acad. health ctr. Tex. Tech U., Lubbock, 1984-87, prof., assoc. chmn. dept. health scis. ctr., 1987-89, interim chmn. ob-gyn., 1989, prof., chmn., 1989—; staff

Univ. Med. Ctr. (formerly Lubbock Gen. Hosp.), 1988—; cons. Med. Educator Obstetrics and Gynecology, Washington, 1967; examiner Am. Bd. Obstetricians and Gynecologists, 1970—; mem. courtesy staff Immanuel Med. Ctr., Omaha, 1971-74, Presbyn. Hosp., Albuquerque, 1974-84; med. advisor, Bernalillo County pub. edn. com. Am. Cancer Soc., 1974-80; sci. advisor Applied Rsch. Fertility Regulation, 1974-80; cons. VA Hosp., Albuquerque, 1975-84, Nat. Bd. Med. Examiners, 1977-80, William Beaumont Army Med. Ctr., Albuquerque, 1980-81, Robert Wood Johnson Found. Rural Infant Care Program, 1980-82, N.Mex. S.W. Trophoblastic Disease Ctr., 1980-84; nat. liaison com. obstetrics and gynecology, 1976-81; dir. edn. postgrad. course ob-gyn., China, 1980, USSR, 1982, Australia, 1986, New Zealand, 1986; mem. provisional staff N.W. Tex. Hosp., Amarillo, 1984-87, VA Hosp., Amarillo, 1984-88, High Plains Bapt. Hosp., Amarillo, 1986-88, Lubbock Gen. Hosp., 1986-88; specialist site visitor Residency Review Com. Ob-Gyn. 1984—, chmn., 1989-90; health care com. State Health Dept., 1985-88; quality assurance com. N.W. Tex. Hosp., 1986-88; exec. com. Coun. Resident Edn. Ob-Gyn., 1988—. Co-author: (TV series) Nine to Get Ready; mem. editorial bd. Internat. Jour. of Gynecology and Obstetrics., 1978-84; reviewer Am. Jour. Ob-Gyn., 1989-90, Surgery, Gynecology and Obstetrics, 1992—; contbr. abstracts Commerce Clearinghouse Guide to Gynecol. and Obstet. Lit.; contbr. articles to profl. jours. Capt. USAF, 1961-63. Fellow Am. Coll. Ob-Gyn. (chmn. local arrangements dist. VI 1966, higher edn. program 1970-74, prize award com. 1970-73, learning resources commn. 1980-81, adv. com. March of Dimes); mem. AMA, GINE-DIPS (hon.), Am. Fertility Soc., Am. Assn. Ob-Gyn., Am. Gynecol. and Obstet. Soc., Assn. Profs. Gynecology and Obstetrics (pres. 1976), Internat. Corr. Soc. Ob-Gyn., Ctrl. Assn. Obstetricians and Gynecologists (v.p. 1988), S.W. Obstet. and Gynecology Soc., Tex. Med. Found., Tex. Med. Soc., Tex. Perinatal Assn., Nebr. Obstetrics and Gynecology Soc., N.D. Obstetrics and Gynecology Soc. (hon.), Ctrl. Travel Club, Gynecol. Travel Club, Norman F. Miller Gynecol. Soc. (pres. 1976, adv. coun.), Lubbock-Crosby-Garza County Med. Soc. (indigent health care com. 1990—), Kansas City Gynecology (hon.), Honolulu Obstet. Soc. (hon.), Phi Eta Sigma, Phi Kappa Phi, Alpha Omega Alpha, Phi Rho. Home: 4614 10th St Lubbock TX 79410 Office: Texas Tech U Health Scis Ctr Dept Ob-Gyn 3601 4th St Lubbock TX 79430

MESSER, THOMAS MARIA, museum director; b. Bratislava, Czechoslovakia, Feb. 9, 1920; came to U.S., 1939, naturalized, 1944; s. Richard and Agatha (Albrecht) M.; m. Remedios Garcia Villa, Jan. 10, 1948. Exch. student, Inst. Internat. Edn., 1939; student, Thiel Coll., Greenville, Pa., 1939-41; BA, Boston U., 1942; degree, U. Sorbonne, Paris, 1947; MA, Harvard U., 1951; DFA (hon.), U. Mass., 1962, U. of Arts, Phila., 1988. Dir. Roswell (N.Mex.) Mus., 1949-52; asst. dir. Am. Fedn. Arts, N.Y.C., 1952-53, dir. exhbns., 1953-55, dir. fedn., 1955-56, trustee, 1972-75; dir. Inst. Contemporary Art, Boston, 1957-61, Solomon R. Guggenheim Mus., N.Y.C., 1961-88, Peggy Guggenheim Collection, Venice, Italy, 1980-88, Solomon R. Guggenheim Found., N.Y.C., trustee 1980-90, dir. emeritus, 1990—; chief curator Schinn Kunsthalle, Frankfurt, 1994—; adj. prof. Harvard U., 1960, Barnard Coll., 1966, 71; prof. Hochschule fuer Angewandte Kunst, Vienna, Austria, 1984; prof. Goethe U., Frankfurt a.m., 1991-92, 93-94; pres. Assn. Art Mus. Dirs., 1974-75; founding mem. exec. com. Am. Arts Alliance, Washington, 1978-81; pres. The MacDowell Colony Inc., 1977-78, 93-94; mem. adv. bd. Palazzo Grassi, Venice, 1986—; trustee Fontana Found., Milan, 1988—; sr. cultural advisor Am.'s Soc., 1988—; sr. adv. visual arts, Caixa Found., 1991—; trustee, Inst. Internat. Edn. 1991—. Author: Edvard Munch, 1973; contbr. to mus. catalogues, art jours. Decorated chevalier Legion d'Honneur, France, 1980, Officier Legion d'Honneur, France, 1989; recipient Goethe medal Fed. Republic Germany; spl. fellow for study in Brussels Belgian-Am. Ednl. Found., 1953; sr. fellow Ctr. Advanced Studies, Wesleyan U., 1966. Mem. Internat. com. for Mus. and Collections Modern Art (hon. pres.), Met. Opera (N.Y.C.), Century Assn. (N.Y.C.). Home: 35 Sutton Pl New York NY 10022 Office: Americas Soc 680 Park Ave New York NY 10021-5009

MESSERLE, JUDITH ROSE, medical librarian, public relations director; b. Litchfield, Ill., Jan. 16, 1943; d. Richard Douglas and Nelrose B. (Davis) Wilcox; m. Darrell Wayne Messerle, Apr. 26, 1968; children: Kurt Norman, Katherine Lynn. BA in Zoology, So. Ill. U., 1966; MLS, U. Ill., 1967. Cert. med. libr. Libr., St. Joseph's Sch. Nursing, Alton, Ill., 1967-71, dir. med. info. ctr., 1971-76, dir. info. services, 1976-79, dir. ednl. resources and community relations, St. Joseph's Hosp., Alton, Ill., 1979-84; dir. Med. Ctr. Libr., St. Louis U., 1985-88; libr. Francis A. Countway Libr. for the Harvard Med. Sch. and Boston Med. Libr., 1989—; instr. Lewis and Clark Coll. 1975; cons. 1973—; instr. Med. Library Assn. Bd. dirs. Family Services and Vis. Nurses Assn., Alton, 1976-79. Mem. Med. Library Assn. (dir. 1981-84, pres. 1986-87, task force for knowledge and skills, 1988-92, Legis. task force 1986-90, search com. for exec. dir. 1979), Ill. State Libr. Adv. Com., Midwest Health Sci. Libr. Network (dir. health sci. council), St. Louis Med. Librs., Hosp. Pub. Relations Soc. of St. Louis, Nat. Libr. Medicine (biomed. libr. rev. com. 1983-92), AMA (com. on allied health edn. and accreditation 1991-94), Assn. Acad. Health Sci. Libr. Dirs. (pres. 1993, joint legis. task force 1992—, editorial bd. for ann. stats. 1989-94, Region 8 Adv. Bd. 1992-93), Am. Med. Informatics Assn. (planning com. 1990, publications com. 1994—), OCLC (spl. libr. adv. com. 1994—). Office: Countway Libr of Medicine 10 Shattuck St Boston MA 02115

MESSERSCHMITT, DAVID GAVIN, engineering educator; b. Denver, May 21, 1945; s. Darwin Erwin and Helen Marilla (Dentan) M.; m. Dorothy Margaret Seegers, May 2, 1970; 1 child, Laura Joanne. BS, U. Colo., 1967; MS, U. Mich., 1968, PhD, 1971. Mem. tech. staff Bell Labs., Holmdel, N.J., 1968-77; supr. Bell Labs., 1974-77; prof. dept. elec. engring. and computer sci. U. Calif., Berkeley, 1977—, chair dept. 1993—; bd. dirs. Teknetkron Communication Systems, Berkeley. Contbr. articles to profl. jours. Patentee in field. Recipient Pres.'s award U. Colo., 1967, named Outstanding Grad. Engr., 1967; NSF fellow, 1967. Fellow IEEE (bd. govs. communications soc. 1981-84); mem. NAE. Office: U Calif 231 Cory Hall Berkeley CA 94720

MESSICK, DON, actor; b. Buffalo, Sept. 7, 1926; s. Binford Earl and Lena Birch (Hughes) M.; m. Helen Marie McHugh; 1 child, Timothy Charles. Student, Ramsay Streett Sch. of Acting, Balt., 1943-45, Am. Theater Wing, N.Y.C., 1949-50. Ind. actor Los Angeles, 1946—, Hanna-Barbera Prodns., Los Angeles, 1957—. Voice of cartoon characters Scooby Doo (longest running animated TV series), Papa Smurf, Boo Boo Bear, Astro, Muttley, Droopy, others, Hamton (Warner Bros. animation's Tiny Toon Adventures); personal appearances in England, Russia, New Zealand, Australia. Served with U.S. Army, 1945-46. Mem. AFTRA, Screen Actors Guild. Avocation: rec. studio and comml. prodn. Office: PO Box 5426 Santa Barbara CA 93150-5426

MESSIER, MARK DOUGLAS, professional hockey player; b. Edmonton, Alta., Can., Jan. 18, 1961. With Indpls. Racers, 1978, Cin. Stingers, 1979; with Edmonton Oilers, 1979-91, team capt., 1988-91; with N.Y. Rangers, 1991—; player NHL All-Star Game, 1982-84, 86, 88-92, 94, Stanley Cup Championship Game, 1984, 85, 87, 88, 90, 94. Recipient Conn Smythe trophy, 1984, Lester B. Pearson award, 1989-90, 91-92, Hart trophy, 1990, 92; named NHL Player of Yr., 1989-90, 91-92; named to Sporting News All-Star Team, 1981-82, 82-83, 89-90, 91-92. Office: NY Rangers 4 Pennsylvania Plz New York NY 10001*

MESSIER, PIERRE, lawyer, manufacturing company executive; b. Montreal, Que., Can., Mar. 3, 1945; s. Lionel and Anita (Caron) M.; m. Ginette Piche, July 11, 1970; 1 child, Mathieu. B.A., Coll. St. Viateur, Outremont, Que., 1964; LL.L., U. Montreal, 1968; D.S.A., Ecole Hautes Etudes Commerciales, Montreal, 1973. Bar: Que. 1969. Assoc. firm Lemay & Messier, Montreal, 1969-75; v.p., sec. gen. counsel Can. Cement Lafarge, Ltd., Montreal, 1975-84; v.p., sec. Lafarge Corp., 1983-84; v.p. adminstrn. and legal affairs Norsk Hydro Can. Inc., Montreal, 1989—; v.p. Que. Bar Service Corp. Bd. dirs. Clinique Pedagogique de Montreal, Coll. Jean de Brebeuf, pres. Greenfield Park Bd. Revision, 1973-74; bd. dirs. Societe Progres Rive Sud, Longueuil, Que., 1974-75. Mem. ABA, Can. Bar Assn. (pres. young lawyers sect. 1976, nat. exec. 1977-78), Montreal Jr. Bar (treas. 1972), Que. Mfrs. Assn. (bd. dirs.), St. Denis Club (Montreal). Office: Norsk Hydro Canada Inc, 5 Place Ville-Marie # 1537, Montreal, PQ Canada H3B 2G2

MESSINEO, KAREN, newspaper publishing executive. V.p. and cfo The New York Times, N.Y.C. Office: The NY Times 229 W 43rd St New York NY 10036*

MESSING, ARNOLD PHILIP, lawyer; b. N.Y.C., Sept. 2, 1941; s. Louis Messing and Ruth Aaron; m. Esther S. Buchman, Oct. 1, 1967; 1 child, Noah. BA magna cum laude, NYU, 1962; JD, Yale U., 1965. Bar: N.Y. 1966, Mass. 1976, Pa. 1985, U.S. Dist. Ct. (so. and ea. dists.) N.Y., U.S. Dist. Ct. Mass. 1976, U.S. Ct. Internat. Trade 1977, U.S. Ct. Appeals (1st, 2d, 6th and D.C. cirs.), U.S. Supreme Ct. 1977, U.S. Tax Ct. 1984. Assoc. Cravath, Swaine & Moore, N.Y.C., 1967-76; ptnr. Gaston & Snow and predecessor firm, Boston, 1976-91, Choate, Hall & Stewart, Boston, 1991–. Served to sgt. USAFR, 1965-71. Mem. ABA, Boston Bar Assn., Mass. Bar Assn. Jewish. Home: 271 Mill St Newton MA 02160-2438 Office: Choate Hall & Stewart Exchange Pl 53 State St Boston MA 02109

MESSING, FRED M., health care executive; b. N.Y.C., Feb. 4, 1947; s. Saul and Jennie M.; m. Mary Ann White, Jan. 14, 1978; 1 child, Rachel Lynne. BBA, CCNY, 1968; MBA, George Washington U., 1974. Computer operator IBM, N.Y.C., 1967-68, assoc. computer systems engr., 1968-69; asst. hosp. adminstr. Bapt. Hosp. of Miami, 1974-79, assoc. hosp. adminstr., 1979-86, exec. v.p., chief operating officer, 1986–; Mem. com. S. Fla. Health Adminstry. Forum, Miami, 1975–. Capt. U.S. Army Med. Svc. Corps, 1969-72. Fellow Am. Coll. Healthcare Execs.; mem. Greater S. Dade C. of C. (bd. dirs. 1987–, v.p. 1989–), ACS (mem. on trauma Fla. chpt. 1987–). Office: Bapt Hosp of Miami 8900 N Kendall Dr Miami FL 33176-2118

MESSING, FREDERICK ANDREW, JR., action lobbyist; b. N.Y.C., Sept. 29, 1946; s. Frederick Andrew and Anne Messing; children: Camilla Beth, Frederick Andrew III. B.S., U. Md., 1972. Commnd. 2d lt. U.S. Army Res., 1967, advanced through grades to maj., 1987; inf. platoon leader 1st Air Cav, RVN, El Salvador, 1982-87; inf. platoon leader 1st Air CAV, RVN, 1967, Grenada, 1983, spl. forces officer, 1969-86, Congl. liaison for Army as G-13, 1974-77, resigned, 1977; exec. dir. Am. Conservative Union, Washington, 1977-79; pres. Nat. Def. Council, Washington, 1978-80; cons. Am. Security Coun., State Dept.; exec. dir. Conservative Caucus, 1979-84; exec. dir. Nat. Def. Council Found., 1984–; cons. Dept. Def., 1986, State Dept., 1991-93. Founder Vietnam Vets. for Reagan Com.; mem. Reagan Transition Team; mem. bd. regents James Monroe Law Office Mus. and Meml. Library, 1986–; cons. to Bush campaign, 1988, 92. Decorated Meritorious Service medal, Sr. Airborne badge, Combat Inf. badge, Can. Airborne badge, Air medal, German Airborne badge, Purple Heart with oak leaf cluster, Vietnamese Cross of Gallantry; recipient Leadership award Am. Conservative Union, 1979, Christian Action Coalition award, 1979, Ambassador of Mercy award Council Nat. Policy, 1984, commendation for refugee relief Pres. Reagan, 1984, Oustanding Service award U.S. Mil. Command El Salvador, 1986. Visited over 27 wars worldwide, and delivered over 134 tons of food and medicine to refugees worldwide. Home: 8600 Cherry Valley Ln Alexandria VA 22309-2124 Office: 1220 King St Ste #230 Alexandria VA 22314

MESSING, JOACHIM WILHELM, molecular biology educator; b. Duisburg, Germany, Sept. 10, 1946; came to U.S., 1978; s. Heinrich and Martha (Pfeifer) M; m. Rita C. Stremmer, Sept. 25, 1975; 1 child, Simon. MS, Free U., Berlin, 1971; Dr.Rer.Nat., LM U., Munich, 1975. Rsch. assoc. U. Calif., Davis, 1978-80; asst. prof. biochemistry U. Minn., St. Paul, 1980-82, assoc. prof., 1982-84, prof., 1984-85; univ. prof. molecular biology Waksman Inst. Rutgers U., Piscataway, N.J., 1985–, dir. rsch. Waksman Inst., 1985-88, dir. Waksman Inst., 1988–; mem. sci. adv. bd. Am. Cyanamid Co., Princeton, N.J., 1985-89, Metrigen, Inc., Piscataway, 1988-90; bd. dirs. Pharmacia Biotech., Inc., Piscataway. Co-author: An Introduction to Recombinant DNA Techniques: Basic Experiments in Gene Manipulation, 1988; co-editor: Molecular Biology of Plants: A Laboratory Course Manual, 1985; contbr. articles to profl. jours. Trustee Rutgers Preparatory Sch., Somerset, N.J., 1992–. Ranked first among sci. leaders of the decade as most cited U.S. scientist under 45 yrs. old The Scientist, 1990. Mem. AAAS, Am. Soc. Biol. Chemistry, Am. Soc. Microbiology, Internat. Soc. Plant Molecular Biology. Achievements include development of DNA purification techniques using genetic rather than physical methods; analysis of gene structure and organization, transposition and somatic recombination on the DNA sequence level in plants; discovery of high methionine maize; research on post-transcriptional regulation of gene expression and genomic imprinting. Office: Rutgers U Waksman Inst PO Box 759 Piscataway NJ 08855-0759*

MESSING, MARK P., advertising executive; b. Wellesley, Mass., Aug. 13, 1948; s. Richard F. and Gertrude (Walsh) M.; m. Tina M. Gallagher, Feb. 21, 1987; 1 child, Mark P. BA, Williams Coll., 1970. Account exec. Deutsch Shea & Evans, N.Y.C., 1970-72, Muller Jordan Herrick, N.Y.C., 1972-75, F. William Free & Co., N.Y.C., 1975; sr. v.p., mgmt. supr. Scali McCabe Sloves Inc., N.Y.C., 1976-91; sr. v.p., mgmt. dir. J. Walter Thompson, N.Y.C., 1991-93; mng. dir. Young and Rubicam, N.Y.C., 1993–; bd. dirs. Southampton (N.Y.) Commons Bd. Avocations: cooking, tennis, music. Office: Young & Rubicam Madison Ave New York NY 10017

MESSINGER, RICHARD C., engineering research and development consultant; b. Cin., Apr. 3, 1930; m. Barbara L. Jahns; children: Nancy, Marcy, David. Apprentice sch. grad., Cin. Milling Machine Co., 1952; ME, U. Cin., 1953; MBA, Xavier U., 1963. Co-op tech. trainee Cin. Milacron, Inc., 1948-53, field svc. engr., grinding machine specialist, 1953-54, sales project engr. grinding machine div., 1956-57, mgr. numerical control & computer programming, 1957-64, dir. patents and comml. devel., 1964-69, corp. dir. non-machine tool R&D, 1969-72, v.p. non-machine tool R&D, 1972-77, v.p. R&D, 1977-86, v.p. chief tech. officer, 1986-91, cons., 1991–; mem. nat. critical techs. panel, joint high level adv. panel Office Sci. and Tech. Policy; mem. commn. on engring. and tech. systems Nat. Rsch. Coun., liaison mem. mfg. studies bd.; liaison mem. nat. materials adv. bd., liaison mem. USAF studies bd.; mem. ad hoc industry group for internat. collaboration in advanced mfg. Dept. Commerce; mem. def. sci. bd. Dept. Def.; mem. exec. steering com. Ohio Advanced Tech. Ctr.; charter mem. Ohio Sci. Roundtable. Charter mem. Cin. Nature Ctr.; mem. Cin. Zool. Soc., Natural History Mus., Cin. Art Mus., Cisco Chain Riparian Owners Assn.; trustee, treas. Herman Schneider Found.; mem. scout exec. com. Boy Scouts Am. With USAF, 1954-56. Recipient award of Excellence U. Cin., Disting. Engring. Alumnus award U. Cin., Exec. Achievement award Xavier U., Carsey award Engring. Soc. Cin. Mem. Nat. Acad. Engring., Soc. Mfg. Engrs., Indsl. Rsch. Inst., Nat. Audubon Soc., Indian Hill Club, Tau Beta Pi, Pi Tau Sigma, Omicron Delta Kappa. Office: Cincinnati Milacron Inc 4701 Marburg Ave Cincinnati OH 45209 also: Cin Gear Co 5657 Wooster Pike Cincinnati OH 45227

MESSINGER, RUTH W., borough president; b. N.Y.C., Nov. 6, 1940; d. Wilfred and Marjorie (Goldwasser) Wyler; m. Eli C. Messinger, June 13, 1961 (div.); children: Daniel Solomon, Miriam Sara, Adam Carp; m. Andrew J. Lachman, Dec. 31, 1989. BA, Radcliffe Coll., 1962; MSW, U. Okla., 1964. Cert. social worker. Sch. adminstr. Children's Cmty. Workshop Sch., N.Y.C., 1968-74; coll. adminstr. Coll. for Human Svcs., N.Y.C., 1974-78; mem. coun. N.Y.C. Coun., 1978-90; borough pres. N.Y.C. Govt., 1990–. Bd. dirs. Women in Mcpl. Govt., Washington, 1981–; past mem. bd. dirs. Nat. League of Cities, Washington, mem. adv. coun., 1979–; mem. adv. bd. Jewish Fund for Justice, 1988–. Democrat. Jewish. Avocations: skiing, cooking. Home: 91 Central Park W New York NY 10023 Office: Office Borough President Municipal Bldg 19th Fl South One Centre St New York NY 10007

MESSINGER, SCOTT JAMES, advertising agency executive; b. Bklyn., Feb. 27, 1952; s. Nathaniel Bernard and Joy Black (Artson) M.; m. Michele Barbaro, Sept. 1988; children: Katherine Lydon, Zachary Ryan, Gabriella Lucia, Victoria Joy. BS in Journalism, Northwestern U., 1974, MS in Journalism, 1975. Asst. account exec. Ted Bates/N.Y., N.Y.C., 1977-78, account exec., 1978-79, account supr., 1979-80, v.p., account supr., 1980-84, sr. v.p., mgmt. rep., 1984-90, Scali McCabe Sloves, 1990–, exec. v.p. acct. dir., 1990–, dir. client svcs., 1991–, mng. dir., 1992-94; exec. dir. Lowe & Ptnrs./SMS, N.Y.C., 1994–. Roman Catholic. Avocations: running, skiing, tennis, squash. Home: 110 W 96th St Apt 11CD New York NY

10025-4333 Office: Lowe & Ptnrs/SMS 1111 Ave of Americas New York NY 10036

MESSITTE, PETER JO, judge; b. Washington, July 17, 1941; s. Jesse B. and Edith (Wechsler) M.; m. Susan P. Messitte, Sept. 5, 1965; children: Zachariah, Abigail. B.A. cum laude, Amherst Coll., 1963; J.D., U. Chgo., 1966. Bar: Md. 1969, D.C. 1969, U.S. Ct. Appeals (4th cir.) 1977, U.S. Supreme Ct. 1973, U.S. Ct. Appeals (D.C. cir.) 1982, U.S. Ct. Appeals (5th cir.) 1983. Assoc. Zuckert, Scoutt & Rasenberger, Washington, 1968-71; solo practice, Chevy Chase, Md., 1971-75; mem. Messitte & Rosenberg, P.A., Chevy Chase, 1975-81, Peter J. Messitte, P.A., Chevy Chase, 1981-85; assoc. judge Cir. Ct. for Montgomery County, Md., Rockville, 1985-93; judge U.S. Dist. Ct. Md., 1993–. Bd. dirs. Community Psychiat. Clinic, Montgomery County, Md., 1974-85, v.p., 1980-85, Peace Corps vol., Sao Paulo, Brazil, 1966-68; Md. del. Dem. Nat. Conv., N.Y.C., 1980. Recipient teaching citations Fed. Deposit Ins. Corp. Bank Exam. Sch., 1975, 79, Am. Inst. Banking, 1978; Elizabeth Scull award for Outstanding Svc. to Montgomery County, Md., 1993, Spl. citation Div. Roundtable Montgomery County, 1993, Contbr. Mental Health Community Psychiat. Clinic, 1986. Mem. ABA, Inter-Am. Bar Assn., D.C. Bar Assn., Md. Bar Assn., Montgomery County Bar Assn., Am. Law Inst., Fed. Bar Assn., Charles Fahy Inn of Ct. (master 1987-88), Montgomery County Inn of Ct. (pres. 1988-90), Jud. Inst. Md. (bd. dirs.). Jewish. Office: US Courthouse 6500 Cherrywood Ln Greenbelt MD 20770

MESSLER, ROBERT WILMER, JR., materials engineering educator, consultant; b. Kew Gardens, N.Y., Dec. 10, 1942; s. Robert W. and Alyce Rose (Braun) M.; m. Joan Barbara Bak, Apr. 27, 1974; children: Victoria Joan, Kerri Christine. B of Metall. Engring., Rensselaer Poly. Inst., 1965, PhD, 1971. Materials engr. Grumman Aerospace Corp., Bethpage, N.Y., 1970-73, devel. engr., 1973-78, group head advanced devel., 1978-80; dir. welding R & D Eutectic-Castolin Corp., Flushing, N.Y., 1980-84, v.p. tech. tng., 1983-84; assoc. dir. Ctr. Mfg. Productivity Rensselaer Poly. Inst., Troy, N.Y., 1984-91, adj. assoc. prof., 1986-91, assoc. prof., 1991–; pvt. practice materials cons., Ballston Lake, N.Y., 1991–. Author: Joining of Advanced Materials, 1993; co-inventor process for NDE of Cr plate, 1977; contbr. articles to profl. jours. NASA fellow, 1965-69. Fellow Am. Soc. Materials; mem. AIME, Am. Welding Soc. (A. F. Davis Silver medal 1982, Adams Meml. Educators award), Soc. Materials Engring., Tau Beta Pi, Sigma Xi. Avocations: golf, collecting X-Mas seals. Home: 3 Harvest Pl Ballston Lake NY 12019-9125 Office: Rensselaer Polytech Inst Dept Materials Engring Troy NY 12180

MESSMAN, JACK L., oil executive; b. Clarksburg, W.Va., Mar. 13, 1940; s. Marvin C. and Betty L. (Jones) M.; m. Ellen Frances Stiggins, Sept. 5, 1965; children—Valerie Lynne, Kyle Andrew. B.Chem. Engring., U. Del.-Newark, 1962; M.B.A., Harvard U., 1968. Ptnr. Butcher & Singer, Phila., 1971-73; pres. Norcross, Inc., West Chester, Pa., 1973-80; v.p. corp. devel. UGI Corp., Valley Forge, Pa., 1980-81; exec. v.p. Safeguard Scientifics, King of Prussia, Pa., 1981-83; pres., chief exec. officer Novell Data Systems, Inc., Orem, Utah, 1981-83; exec. v.p., chief fin. officer Warner Amex, N.Y.C., 1983-86; chmn., chief exec. officer Somerset House Corp., Houston, 1986-88; chief exec. officer, bd. dirs. USPCI, Inc., Oklahoma City, 1988-91; pres., CEO, Union Pacific Resources, Inc., Ft. Worth, 1991–; bd. dirs. Wawa, Inc. (Pa.), Novell Inc., Utah. Served to 1st lt. U.S. Army, 1963-65. Republican. Episcopalian. Clubs: Aronimink Golf (Newtorn Square, Pa.), River Crest Country (Ft. Worth), Shady Oaks Country (Ft. Worth). Office: Union Pacific Resources Inc 801 Cherry St Fort Worth TX 76101

MESSMER, DONALD JOSEPH, business management educator, marketing consultant; b. St. Louis, July 30, 1936; s. Edgar Louis and Lucille Louise (Straub) M.; m. Charlotte Jean Fox; 1 child, Angeline Charlotte. BSBA with honors, Washington U., St. Louis, 1969, PhD, 1974. Asst. mgr. M.A. Bell Co., St. Louis, 1956-61; dist. sales exec. U. S. Gypsum Co., St. Louis, 1962-65; br. sales exec. Victor Comptometer Corp., St. Louis, 1965-68; asst. prof. Coll. William and Mary, Williamsburg, Va., 1973-76, assoc. prof., 1976-81, prof., 1981–, J.S. Mack prof., 1982–, dir. exec. MBA program, 1988-91; pres. The Wessex Group, Ltd., Williamsburg, 1979–; bd. dirs. Williamsburg Winery, Ltd., Chateau Hotels, Ltd.; chmn. bd. dirs. Community Svcs. Coalition, Inc. Assoc. editor Decision Scis. jour., 1985-88; contbr. articles to profl. jours. Bd. dirs., treas. Community Action Agy., Williamsburg, 1984-91, United Way of Greater Williamsburg, 1985-91, pres., 1989. Mem. Decision Scis. Inst. (mktg. coord. 1985-86), Southeastern Decision Scis. Inst. (pres. 1985-86), Am. Mktg. Assn. (Dissertation award 1974), Rotary (bd. dirs. 1990-92), Alpha Mu Alpha, Beta Gamma Sigma. Republican. Avocations: fishing, golf. Office: Coll William and Mary Grad Sch Bus Williamsburg VA 23185-8795

MESSMORE, DAVID WILLIAM, construction executive, former psychologist; b. Indpls.; s. Max J. and Betty G. (Miller) M.; m. Sondra Renée Bastian, Aug. 22, 1981; children: Kristen Nicole, Eric Christian William David. AB in Social Sci., Calif. State Coll., Long Beach, 1968; PhD in Student Devel., Counseling and Clin. Psychology, Mich. State U., 1972. Lic. class A gen. contractor, Tex., Va.; lic. psychologist, Calif., Mich.; lic. sch. psychologist, Calif. Counselor Okemas (Mich.) Pub. Sch., 1970-72; psychologist Frederick Ctr. Day Hosp., Grand Rapids, Mich., 1972-73, Newport-Mesa Schs., Newport Beach, Calif., 1973-80; commr. Bd. Med. Quality Assurance, State of Calif. Psychol. com., Sacramento, 1980-82; pres. Bridgewater Constrn., Inc., Chesapeake, Va., 1987–; psychol. counselor Camp Highfields Residential Sch., Onondago, Mich., 1971; cons. The Open Door, Lansing, Mich., 1971-72, Juv. and Domestic Rels. Ct. of the Family Ct., State of Va., Chesapeake, 1989–; pres. Bridgewater Consultation Svcs., Chesapeake, 1989-91; intern Counseling Ctr. Calif. State U.; instr. Golden West Coll., Huntington Beach, Calif., 1977-78; advisor, counselor Dean of Students Mich. State U., 1969-71; coach City of Chesapeake, Parks/Recreation, commr. Transp./Safety, 1994-96. Author: (manual) The Impact of Divorce on Families, 1989; designer sch. crest Long Beach City Coll., 1965. Active Gt. Bridge Conf. com., Chesapeake, 1987-91; treas. Paint Your Heart Out, Chesapeake, 1993; coach parks and recreation dept. City of Chesapeake, 1994–. Served with USMC, 1959-63. Recipient Cert. of Appreciation Chesapeake Vols. in Youth Svcs., Inc., 1989, Outstanding Svc. award, 1990, Gov.'s award State of Va., 1990. Mem. Rotary Internat. (bd. dirs. Chesapeake club 1990-94, disting. svc. citation 1990), Nat. Youth Sports Coaches Assn., Delta Tau Delta (Iota chpt.). Avocations: tennis, reading, investments.

MESSMORE, THOMAS ELLISON, insurance company executive; b. Monongahela, Pa., June 30, 1945; s. Lindsay Ellison and Margaret (Hoffmann) M.; m. Sharon Weaver, Aug. 19, 1966; children: Lauren, Beth, Benjamin, William. BS in Indsl. Engring., W.Va. U., 1967; MBA, Harvard U., 1969. Chartered fin. analyst. Asst. treas. State Street Bank and Trust Co., Boston, 1969-72; fin. product mgr. Interactive Data Corp., Waltham, Mass., 1972-75; sr. v.p. Keystone Custodian Funds, Inc., Boston, 1975-80; sr. v.p. and chief fin. officer Keystone Mass. Group, Boston, 1981-83; sr. v.p. The Travelers Ins. Co., Hartford, Conn., 1984-94; pvt. cons. Hartford, 1994–; dir. Energy BioSystems Corp. Mem. Assn. for Investment Mgmt. and Rsch. Home and Office: 1090 Prospect Ave Hartford CT 06105-1125

MESSNER, HOWARD MYRON, professional association executive; b. Newark, June 10, 1937; s. Elias and Freda (Trachtenberg) M.; m. Aletha Bragg, 1960 (div. 1980); children: Jennifer, Linda, David; m. Melba June Meador, June 22, 1986. BA, Antioch Coll., 1960; MA, U. Mass., 1962. Mgmt. analyst Office Gov., Mass., 1960-61; staff asst. to adminstr. NASA, Washington, 1962-65; mgmt. analyst Bur. Budget, Washington, 1965-71; dir. adminstrn. EPA, Washington, 1971-75, asst. adminstr. for adminstrn., 1983-87; asst. dir. Congl. Budget Office, Washington, 1975-77, Office Mgmt. and Budget, Washington, 1977-83; controller Dept. Energy, Washington, 1983; exec. v.p., chief exec. officer Am. Cons. Engrs. Council, 1987–. Recipient William A. Jump Meml. award, 1971, Presdl. Disting. Exec. award, 1986, Outstanding Pub. Service award Nat. Capital chpt. Am. Soc. Pub. Adminstrn., 1986, Chancellor's medal U. Mass., 1988. Mem. Nat. Acad. Pub. Adminstrn., Am. Consortium for Internat. Pub. Adminstrn. (v.p.). Democrat. Jewish. Home: 1683 Justin Dr Gambrills MD 21054-2012 Office: Am Cons Engrs Coun 1015 15th St NW Washington DC 20005-2605

MESSNER, RICHARD STEPHEN, school system administrator; b. N.Y.C., Nov. 8, 1939; s. Blasius and Anna (Kuti) M.; m. Eugenia Mancuso, Oct. 22, 1968 (div. 1974); 1 child, Stephanie; m. Mary Theodorakis, May 28, 1976' stepchildren: Paul, Nicole. BS, Alderson-Broaddus Coll. 1961; MBA, Fairleigh Dickinson U., 1972; MEd, Rutgers U., 1980. Acctg. mgr. McGraw-Hill, Hightstown, N.J., 1968-71; bus. coord. Fairleigh Dickinson U., Rutherford, N.J., 1971-73; dep. treas. County of Somerset, Somerville, N.J., 1973-78; asst. dir. of adminstrv. svcs. Somerset County Vo-Tech, Bridgewater, N.J., 1978-82; dir. adminstrv. svcs. Somerset County Vocat. Tech., Bridgewater, 1982-85, asst. supt. for bus., 1985–, acting supt., 1987-88, supt. of schs., 1992–; bd. dirs. Edn. Svcs. Commn., Somerset County. Dep. mayor Franklin Twp., N.J., 1975, mayor, 1975-76; commr. Urban Enterprize Zone Authority, N.J., 1984–; treas. Somerset County Reps., 1985-91; bd. dirs. Somerset Alliance Future, 1992–, Greater Raritan Pvt. Industry Coun., 1992–. With U.S. Army, 1962-64; mem. Middlesex, Hunterdon, Somerset Pvt. Industry Coun., 1992–. Mem. Am. Soc. Bus. Officers Internat. (chmn. purchasing com. Reston, Va. chpt. 1986-88, legis. com. 1988–), N.J. Assn. Bus. Ofcls. (chmn. legis. com. Bordentown, N.J. chpt. 1985–), N.J. Assn. Sch. Adminstrs., Somerset County Adminstrs., Somerset County Bus. Ofcls. (v.p. Somerville chpt. 1991–), N.J. Edn. Assn. (adv. com. 1984–), VFW, Masons, Phi Delta Kappa. Baptist. Avocations: sports, World War II history, golf. Home: 32 Pin Oak Rd Skillman NJ 08558-1320

MESSNER, ROBERT THOMAS, lawyer, banking executive; b. McKeesport, Pa., Mar. 27, 1938; s. Thomas M. and Cecilia Mary (McElhinny) M.; m. Anne Margaret Lux, Dec. 3, 1966; children: Megan Anne, Michael Thomas. A.B., Dartmouth Coll., 1960; LL.B., U. Pa., 1963. Bar: Pa. 1965. With firm Rose, Schmidt & Dixon, Pitts., 1965-68; with G.C. Murphy Co., McKeesport, 1968-86; corp. sec. G.C. Murphy Co., 1974–, gen. counsel, 1975-86, v.p., 1976-86; v.p., gen. counsel, corp. sec. Dollar Bank, Pitts., 1986–; dir. G.C. Murphy Found. Bd. dirs. McKeesport YMCA, Dartmouth Pitts. YMCA, Mon-Yough Heritage Found., 1981-83, Braddock's Field Hist. Soc., 1994–; mem. adv. bd. Pa. Human Rels. Commn., 1968, 69; Rep. candidate for Pa. Legis., 1986, fin. adv. bd. Wilkinsburg, Pa., 1988–. 1st lt. U.S. Army, 1963-65. Decorated Commendation medal. Mem. ABA, Pa. Bar Assn. (chmn. corp. law dept. com.), Allegheny County Bar Assn., Am. Soc. Corp. Secs. (pres. Pitts. regional group, dir.), Am. Mgmt. Assn., Pa. Assn. Savs. Instns. (chmn. legal com. 1989–), Am. Corp. Counsel Assn., Theta Delta Chi. Clubs: Dartmouth Western Pa; Rivers, Gateway Ctr. (Pitts.). Home: 1061 Blackridge Rd Pittsburgh PA 15235-2719 Office: Dollar Bank Three Gateway Ctr Pittsburgh PA 15222

MESSNER, THOMAS G., advertising executive, copywriter; b. N.Y.C., Jan. 26, 1944; s. Malcolm V. Messner and Virginia M. Burkard; m. Terry Carol Bonaccolta, Nov. 28, 1971; 1 child, Zachary. Letter carrier U.S. Post Office, N.Y.C., 1965-67; copywriter Occidental Life Calif., L.A., 1967-68; mail boy D'Arcy Advt., N.Y.C., 1968; copywriter BBDO, N.Y.C., 1968-69, Doyle Dane Bernbach, N.Y.C., 1969-72; creative dir. Ally and Gargano, N.Y.C., 1972–; ptnr. Messner Vetere Berger Carey Schmetterer, N.Y.C., 1986-92, Messner Vetere Berger McNamee Schmetterer Euro RSCG, N.Y.C., 1992–; bd. dirs. Council for Study of Pub. Choice, Fairfax, Va., N.Y. Club for Art and Copy. Copywriter Ronald Reagan, 1984 presdl. campaign, Republican Nat. Com. N.Y., 1984, Andrew O'Rourke for Gov., N.Y., 1986, George Bush 1988 presdl. campaign. Roman Catholic. Office: Messner Vetere Berger McNamee Schmetterer Euro RSCG 350 Hudson St New York NY 10014-4504

MESSUD, FRANÇIS-MICHEL, manufacturing company executive; b. Toulon, France, June 29, 1931; m. Margaret D. Riches; children: Elizabeth C., Claire D. LLB, LLM, 1956; AM, Harvard U., 1961. With Pechiney Group, France, Greece, Australia, Can. and U.S., 1961-82; pres., chief exec. officer Pechiney World Trade (USA), Inc., Greenwich, Conn., 1982–. Served to lt. French Navy, 1956-59. Clubs: Harvard (N.Y.C.); Am. (Sydney, Australia). Office: Pechiney World Trade (USA) Inc 475 Steamboat Rd Greenwich CT 06830-7144

MESTER, JORGE, conductor; b. Mexico City, Apr. 10, 1935; came to U.S., 1946, naturalized, 1968; s. Victor and Margarita (Knöpfler) M. BS Juilliard Sch. Music, 1957, MS, 1958; studied conducting with Jean Morel, Leonard Bernstein., Abert Wolff. Faculty Juilliard Sch. Music, 1956-68, chmn. conducting studies, 1980–. Also condr., Juilliard Theatre Orch., 1961-62, Beaux Arts Trio, 1961-65; mus. dir., Louisville Orch., Greenwich Village Symphony, 1961-62, mus. dir., condr., Louisville Orch., 1967-79, artistic adviser, Kansas City Philharmonic, 1971-72, then music dir., Kansas City Philharmonic, 1973-77, music dir., Aspen Music Festival, 1970–, Festival Casals, 1978-85; music dir. Pasadena Symphony, 1984–; prin. guest condr., St. Paul Chamber Orch., 1978-79, guest condr., Orquesta Sinfonica Nacional de Mexico, Philharmonica Triestina, Spoleto Festival Orch., Japan Philharmonic, Yomiuri Nippon Symphony, Boston Symphony, Pitts. Symphony, New Orleans Philharmonic, Indpls. Symphony, N.Y.C. Opera, Phila. Orch., London Royal Philharmonic, Denver Symphony, Bach Aria Group, Cin. Orch., Rochester Philharmonic, Utah Symphony, Oreg. Symphony, Cin. Symphony, others; condr. dance season, Spoleto Festival, Grant Park, Chgo., Tanglewood, Mass., Harkness Dance Festival, 1964, Cosi Fan Tutte, 1964, L'Elisir D'Amore, rec. with, Columbia, Vanguard, Mercury, Desto, CRI, Cambridge records, also, Louisville 1st Edit. Recs. Named Ky. col., 1967; recipient Naumburg award, 1968, Ditson Conductors award, 1985. Office: care Aspen Music Festival 250 W 54th St 10th Fl E New York NY 10019 also: PO Box AA Aspen CO 81612

MESTRALLET, GÉRARD, association executive; b. Paris, Apr. 1, 1949; arrived in Belgium, 1991; s. Georges Julien Marie and Paule Andrée Augustine (Besnard) M.; m. Joëlle Emilienne Renée Arcens, Sept. 7, 1974; children: Stephanie, Caroline, Bastien. Student, Ecole Polytech., Paris, 1968, Ecole Aviation Civile, Paris, 1971, Inst. for Study of Politics, Toulouse, France, 1973, Ecole Nat. d'Adminstrn., Paris, 1978. Counsellor Minister Transp. Econs., Fins., & Budget, Paris, 1973-84; chargé de mission Suez, Paris, 1984-86, délt. adjoint indsl. affairs, 1986-91, dir. gen. adjoint, 1991–; CEO Soc. Gen. de Belgique, Brussels, 1991–. Office: Soc Gen de Belgique, Rue Royale 30, B-1000 Brussels Brabant, Belgium

MESTRES, RICARDO A., III, motion picture company executive; b. N.Y.C., Jan. 23, 1958; s. Ricardo Angelo Jr. and Ann (Farnsworth) M.; m. Tracy Stewart; children: Alexander Carson, Carrie Ann. AB, Harvard U., 1980. Creative exec. Paramount Pictures, L.A., 1981-82, exec. dir. prodn., 1982-84, v.p. prodn., 1984-85; v.p. prodn. Walt Disney Pictures, Burbank, Calif., 1985-86, sr. v.p. prodn., 1986-88; pres. prodn. Touchstone Pictures, Burbank, Calif., 1988-89; pres. Hollywood Pictures, Burbank, Calif., 1989-94; co-founder Great Oaks Entertainment, Burbank, 1995–. Mem. Acad. Motion Picture Arts and Scis. Office: Great Oaks Entertainment 500 S Buena Vista St Burbank CA 91521-0001

MESTRES, RICARDO ANGELO, JR., lawyer; b. N.Y.C., Aug. 12, 1933; s. Ricardo Angelo and Anita (Gwynne) M.; m. Ann Farnsworth, June 18, 1955; children: Laura, Ricardo III, Lynn, Anthony. AB, Princeton U., 1955; LLB, Harvard U., 1961. Bar: N.Y. 1962, U.S. Supreme Ct. 1970. Assoc. Sullivan & Cromwell, N.Y.C., 1961-67, ptnr., 1968–. Trustee Unitarian Ch. All Souls, N.Y.C., 1973-79, 84-87, Phillips Exeter Acad., 1989–. Served to lt. USN, 1955-58. Mem. ABA, N.Y. State Bar Assn., Assn. of Bar of City of N.Y. (corp. law, securities regulation law and state legis. coms.), Am. Law Inst., Phi Beta Kappa. Clubs: Downtown Assn. Links (N.Y.C.); Mill Reef (Antigua). Office: Sullivan & Cromwell 125 Broad St New York NY 10004-2400

MESZAR, FRANK, publishing executive, former army officer; b. East Chicago, Ind., Sept. 5, 1915; s. Frank Rach and Julia (Labois) M.; m. Carla Ruth Jorgensen, May 21, 1965; children—Frank, Sarah. B.S. in Civil Engring, U.S. Mil. Acad., 1940; grad., Army War Coll., 1955; M.B.A., Ga. So. Coll. Commd. 2d lt. U.S. Army, 1940, advanced through grades to brig. gen., 1965; chief aviation affairs Dept. Army, 1959-62; asst. dep. chief staff ops. U.S. Army Europe, 1962-65; asst. dep. chief staff Continental Army Command, Ft. Monroe, Va., 1965-67; comdg. gen. Army Flight Tng. Center, Hunter AFB, Ga., 1967-68; asst. comdg. gen. 1st Cav. Div., 1969-70; ret., 1970; v.p. finance U.S. Medicine, Inc., Washington, 1970–; treas. Profl. Lithography, Inc., Washington. Pres. Savannah Symphony Soc., 1970-79,

Savannah West Point Soc., 1972, Savannah Symphony Soc.; trustee Ga. Infirmary; hon. judge Chatham County, Ga.; vestryman , sr. warden St. John's Episc. Ch. Decorated D.S.M. with oak leaf cluster, Legion of Merit, D.F.C., Silver Star with oak leaf cluster, Bronze Star with 3 oak leaf clusters, Purple Heart with oak leaf cluster; Legion of Honor; Croix de Guerre (France). Clubs: Oglethorpe, Rotary. Home: 302 E 46th St Savannah GA 31405-2257 Office: US Medicine Ste 505/Lafayette Ctr Three 1155 21st St NW Washington DC 20036

MESZNIK, JOEL R., investment banker; b. Beirut, Oct. 3, 1945; s. Hans and Eugenie (Bagdadi) M.; m. Lynne Gladstein, Mar. 25, 1979; children: Daniel, Jared, Kara. BS, CCNY, 1967; MBA, Columbia U., 1970. Engr. Ebasco Svcs., N.Y.C., 1967-70; banker Citibank, N.Y.C., 1970-71, Newhouse Capital, N.Y.C., 1971-72, Matthews & Wright, N.Y.C., 1972-76; mng. dir. Drexel Burnham Lambert, N.Y.C., 1976-89; pres. Mesco Ltd., 1990—. Office: 122 E 42nd St Ste 4906 New York NY 10168

METCALF, ARTHUR GEORGE BRADFORD, electronics company executive; b. Boston, Nov. 1, 1908; s. Franklin B. and Emma A. (Maclachlan) M.; m. Mary G. Curtis, Feb. 22, 1935; children: Anne C., Helen C., Mary Lee, Hope S. Student, Mass. Inst. Tech., 1932; S.B., Boston U., 1935, LL.D., 1974; S.M., Harvard U., 1939; S.D., Franklin Pierce Coll., 1966. Engring. test pilot, 1930—; prof. math., physics Boston U., 1935; pres. Electronics Corp. Am., Cambridge, Mass., 1954—. Mil. editor: Strategic Rev; contbr. articles to profl. jours. Chmn. emeritus, bd. trustees, exec. com. Boston U.; bd. overseers Mus. Fine Arts, Boston; mem. trustee coun. Boston U. Med. Ctr.; chmn. U.S. Strategic Inst., Washington. Served to lt. col. AUS, WWII. Decorated Legion of Merit, Commendation medal.; Benjamin Franklin fellow Royal Soc. Arts London, 1972. Asso. fellow Royal Aero. Soc. (London), Inst. Aero. Scis.; mem. Am. Def. Preparedness Assn. (dir.), Phi Beta Kappa. Clubs: Harvard (Boston, N.Y.); Harvard Faculty (Boston), Algonquin (Boston); Edgartown (Mass.) Yacht; Army and Navy (Washington). Home: 45 Arlington St Winchester MA 01890-3732 Office: 125 Bay State Rd Boston MA 02215-1785

METCALF, CORWIN MOORE (MICKEY), business educator, businessman, consultant; b. Port Arthur, Tex., May 25, 1940; s. Richard Jackson and Loreah Alpha (Davis) M.; m. Pauline W. Ferry, May 10, 1960 (div. May 1965); 1 child, Richard Louis; m. Patricia Ann Crout, June 15, 1967 (div. May 1991); children: Allison Ann, James Moore; m. Janice Ann Frye, May 24, 1991. BA, Oglethorpe U., 1963; MBA, U. S.C., 1965; JD, Wake Forest U., 1988. Staff mktg., supply and distrbn. Gulf Oil Corp., Atlanta, Houston, 1966-70; v.p., div. mgr. Bank of S.W., Houston, 1970-75; v.p., mgr., comml. loan officer Merc. Nat. Bank, Dallas, 1975-78; exec. v.p., COO, Mid Continent Systems, Inc., West Memphis, Ark., 1978-80; pres., CEO, Automated Fleet Svcs., Greensboro, N.C., 1980-84, Silverscreen Mgmt. Co., Greensboro, 1987-93; pres., CEO Video Co. Inc., Greensboro, 1987-90; CEO, CFO, SCM Mktg. Ltd., Winston-Salem, N.C., 1990-91; assoc. prof. Elon Coll. N.C., 1993—, prin. TMG, 1993—. Capt. CAP, Greensboro, 1985-87. Mem. Fin. Execs. Inst., Airplane Owners and Pilots Assn., The Turnaround Mgmt. Assn., Am. Arbitration Assn., Phi Alpha Delta, Beta Sigma Phi. Avocation: flying. Home: 112 Georgetowne Dr Elon College NC 27244-9267 Office: Elon Coll Campus Box 2278 Elon College NC 27244-2020

METCALF, JACK, retired state senator; b. Marysville, Wash., Nov. 30, 1927; s. John Read and Eunice (Grannis) M.; m. Norma Jean Grant, Oct. 3, 1948; children: Marta Jean, Gayle Marie, Lea Lynn, Beverlee Ann. Student U. Wash., 1944-45, 47; BA, BEd, Pacific Luth. U., 1951. Tchr., Elma (Wash.) pub. schs., 1951-52, Everett (Wash.) pub. schs., 1952-81; mem. Wash. Ho. of Reps., 1960-64; mem. Wash. Senate, 1966-74, 80-92, U.S. congressman, Wash. 2nd Dist., 1995—; chmn. environment and natural resources com., 1988-92. Chmn. Honest Money for Am. Mem. Council State Govts., Wash. State Rep. Assn. (dir. 1959-61), Wash. Assn. Profl. Educators (state v.p. 1979-81, state pres. 1977-79). Mem. Nat. Conf. State Legislatures, Western States Recycling Coalition, South Whidbey Kiwanis, Deer Lagoon Grange. Republican. Home: 3273 E Saratoga Rd Langley WA 98260-9694 Office: US House Reps House Office Bldg 507 Cannon Washington DC 20515-4702

METCALF, JERRY D., wholesale food distribution company executive; b. 1938; married. BA, Kans. State U., 1961. Store mgr. Doebeles IGA Supermarket, 1952-63; v.p. div. ops. Fleming Cos., Inc., 1963-76; exec. v.p. S.M. Flickinger Co. Inc., Buffalo, 1976-77, pres., COO, 1977-81, chmn. bd., CEO, 1981—, now pres., dir.; chmn. bd., dir., CEO Scrivner, Inc., Oklahoma City, 1984—; Gateway Foods, Inc., 1989—; chmn. Scrivner Iowa; pres., chief exec. officer Scrivner Pa.; pres. Boogaart Supply, Inc. Office: Gateway Food Inc 201 Main St Ste 1000 La Crosse WI 54601

METCALF, KAREN, foundation executive; b. Reading, Mass., Dec. 12, 1936; d. Albion Edmund and Natalie Viola (Ives) M. AB, Vassar Coll., 1958; MBA, Harvard U., 1968. CFA. Sec. Radio Liberty Com., N.Y.C. 1958-60; rsch. asst. Air Inc., Cambridge, Mass., 1960-64; sys. analyst Keydata Corp., Watertown, Mass., 1964-66; customer edn. cons. Interactive Data Corp., N.Y.C., 1968; portfolio mgr. Scudder, Stevens & Clark, N.Y.C., 1969-81; v.p. fin. and adminstrn. N.Y. Cmty. Trust, N.Y.C., 1981—. Episcopalian. Avocations: travel, opera. Office: NY Cmty Trust 2 Park Ave New York NY 10016-9385

METCALF, LAURIE, actress; b. Edwardsville, Ill., June 15, 1955; 1 child, Zoe. Student, Ill. State U. Off-Broadway appearances: Balm in Gilead (debut, Theatre World award), 1984; stage appearances: Who's Afraid of Virginia Woolf?, 1982, Coyote Ugly, 1985, Bodies Rest, and Motion, 1986, Educating Rita, 1987 (Joseph Jefferson award best performance by principal actress in a play), Little Egypt, 1987, Killers, 1988, My Thing of Love, 1995; films: Desperately Seeking Susan, 1984, Making Mr. Right, 1987, Stars and Bars, 1988, Candy Mountain, 1988, Miles from Home, 1988, Uncle Buck, 1989, Internal Affairs, 1989, Pacific Heights, 1990, Frankie and Johnny, 1991, JFK, 1991, Mistress, 1992, A Dangerous Woman, 1993, Blink, 1994; TV series: Saturday Night Live, 1981, Roseanne, 1988— (Emmy award, Outstanding Supporting Actress in a Comedy Series, 1993, 94); TV appearances: The Equalizer, 1986, The Execution of Raymond Graham, 1985. Address: care ICM 8942 Wilshire Blvd Beverly Hills CA 90211*

METCALF, ROBERT CLARENCE, architect, educator; b. Nashville, Ohio, Nov. 7, 1923; s. George and Helen May (Drake) M.; m. Bettie Jane Sponseller, Sept. 15, 1943. Student, Johns Hopkins U., 1943; B.Arch., U. Mich., 1950. Draftsman G.B. Brigham, Jr., Architect, Ann Arbor, Mich., 1948-52; pvt. practice architecture Ann Arbor, 1953—; lectr. architecture U. Mich., Ann Arbor, 1955-58; asst. prof. U. Mich., 1958-63, asso. prof., 1963-68, prof., 1968-91, chmn. dept., 1968-74; dean U. Mich. (Coll. Architecture and Urban Planning), 1974-86; Emil Lorch prof. emeritus U. MIch., 1991—, dean emeritus 1991—; sec. Mich. Bd. Registration for Architects, 1975-79, chmn., 1980-82. Designer 127 bldgs., Ann Arbor, 1953—. Served with U.S. Army, 1943-46, ETO. Decorated Silver Star; recipient Sol King award for excellent teaching in architecture U. Mich., 1974; named Emil Lorch Professor of Architecture, 1989. Fellow AIA; mem. Mich. Soc. Architects, Assn. Collegiate Schs. Architecture, Phi Kappa Phi, Tau Sigma Delta. Home: 1052 Arlington Blvd Ann Arbor MI 48104-2816 Office: U Mich 2150 Art Architecture Bldg Ann Arbor MI 48109 also: 2211 Medford Ann Arbor MI 48104

METCALF, VIRGIL ALONZO, economics educator; b. Branch, Ark., Jan. 4, 1936; s. Wallace Lance and Luella J. (Yancey) M.; m. Janice Ann Maples, July 2, 1958; children: Deborah Ann, Robert Alan. BS in Gen. Agr., U. Ark., 1958, MS in Agrl. Econs., 1960; Diploma in Econs., U. Copenhagen, 1960; PhD in Agrl. Econs., U. Mo., 1964. Asst. prof. U. Mo., Columbia, 1964-65, asst. to chancellor, 1964-69, assoc. prof., 1965-69, prof., exec. asst. to the chancellor, 1969-71; prof. econs., v.p. administrn. Ariz. State U., Tempe, 1971-81, prof. Sch. Agribus. and Natural Resources, 1981-88, prof. internat. bus. Coll. of Bus., 1988—; asst. to the chancellor U. Mo., 1964-69 coord. internat. programs and studies, 1965-69, mem. budget com. 1965-71, chmn., co-chmn. several task forces; cons. Ford Found., Bogota, Colombia, 1966-67; mem. negotiating team U.S. Agy. for Internat. Devel., Mauritania, 1982, cons., Cameroon, 1983, agrl. rsch. specialist, india, 1984, agribus. cons., Guatemala, 1987, 88, asst. dir. Reform Coops. Credit Project, El Salvador, 1987-90; co-dir. USIA univ. linkage grant Cath. U., Bolivia, 1984-

89; cons. World Vision Internat., Mozambique, 1989. Contbr. numerous articles to profl. jours. Mem. City of Tempe U. Hayden Butte Project Area Com., 1979; bd. commrs. Columbia Redevel. Authority; mem. workable project com. City of Columbia Housing Authority. Econs. officer USAR, 1963, econ. analyst, 1964-66. Fulbright grantee U. Copenhagen, 1959-60, U. Kiril Metodij, Yugoslavia, 1973. Mem. Am. Assn. Agrl. Economists, Soc. for Internat. Devel., Samaritans (chmn. 1976, bd. dirs. 1976, mem. task force of health svc. bd. trustees 1974, health svc. 1974-78, chmn. program subcom. 1975), Kiwanis, Blue Key, Gamma Sigma Delta, Alpha Zeta, Alpha Tau Alpha. Democrat. Home: 1508 W Brooks St Chandler AZ 85224 Office: Ariz State U Tempe AZ 85287

METCALF, WILLIAM EDWARDS, museum curator; b. East Grand Rapids, Mich., Dec. 16, 1947; s. George Ellington and Ruthanne (Schnitzler) M.; m. Margaret Mary Finn, May 21, 1972 (annulled 1984); 1 son, Daniel F.; m. Jane Salinger, Oct. 26, 1991. B.A., U. Mich., 1969, M.A., 1970, Ph.D. in Classical Studies (Horace H. Rackham prize fellow), 1973. Asst. curator Roman and Byzantine coins Am. Numismatic Soc., N.Y.C., 1973-75; assoc. curator Am. Numismatic Soc., 1975-78, curator, dep. chief curator, 1978-79, chief curator, 1979—; adj. prof. art history and archaeology Columbia U., 1978—, adj. prof. history, 1993. Author: The Cistophori of Hadrian, 1980, The Silver Coinage of Cappadocia, Vespasian-Commodus, 1995; editor: Studies in Early Byzantine Gold Coinage, 1988, America's Gold Coinage, 1990, Mnemata: Papers in Memory of Nancy M. Waggoner, 1991; mem. adv. com. Lexicon Iconographicum Mythologiae Classicae, 1979—; mem. adv. bd. Am. Jour. Archaeology, 1980; editor book revs. Am. Jour. Numismatics, 1989; contbr. articles on Roman and Byzantine coinage and revs. to profl. jours. NEA fellow for mus. profls., 1978; mem. Inst. for Advanced Study, 1988-89. Mem. Am. Numismatic Soc., Royal Numismatic Soc., Am. Philol. Assn. (subcom. on classical bibliography 1979-89), Archaeol. Inst. Am. (exec. com. N.Y. 1976-80), Columbia U. Seminar on Classical Civilization, Internat. Numismatic Commn. Office: Am Numismatic Soc Broadway & 155th St New York NY 10032-7598

METCALF, WILLIAM HENRY, JR., architect; b. Memphis, Feb. 9, 1928; s. William Henry and Mary Myrtle (Tittle) M.; m. Barbara Ann Keller, Oct. 8, 1955; children: Ramsay Katherine, Anne Evelyn; m. Evelyn Byrd Gates, June 6, 1980. B.A., Yale U., 1949, B.Arch., 1951, M.Arch., 1952. Fellow div. architl. studies Nuffield Found., London, 1957-58; pvt. practice architecture Washington, 1958-66; partner Metcalf and Assos., Washington, 1966-89; ptnr. Metcalf Tobey & Ptnrs., Reston, Va., 1990—; vis. archtl. critic/lectr. Carnegie Inst. Tech., Howard U., Cath. U. Am., George Washington U., Tex. A&M U., Yale U. Prin. works include Health Centers, Lagos, Nigeria, 1964, Anne Arundel Gen. Hosp., Annapolis, Md., 1966, Fairfax Hosp., Falls Church, Va., 1967, Andrew Meml. Hosp., Tuskegee Inst., Ala., 1968, Montgomery Gen. Hosp., Olney, Md., 1969, Concentrated Care Center, Georgetown U., 1976; Am. embassy residence, also Cairo Am. Coll., 1977, St. Joseph's Hosp., Parkersburg, W.Va., 1977, Wilmington (Del.) Med. Center, 1977, Central Bank Bolivia, La Paz, 1978, Prospect Place, Washington, 1979, Intercultural Center, Georgetown U., 1980, Alleghany Valley Hosp., Natrona Heights, Pa., 1980, Smithsonian Instn. Mus. Support Center, Suitland, Md., 1981, Am. Embassy Office Bldg., Cairo, 1981, Phico Group corp. hdqrs., Mechanicsburg, Pa., 1985, Replacement Hosp., U. Va., Charlottesville, 1989, New Sci. Bldg., Va. Mil. Inst., Lexington, 1989. Bd. dirs. Innisfree Found. Served with USAF, 1953-56. Hopper fellow, 1951. Fellow AIA (Rehmann fellow 1957), Colegio de Arquitectos del Peru; mem. Am. Assn. Hosp. Planning, Internat. Hosp. Fedn. Presbyterian. Home: 201 Chain Bridge Rd Mc Lean VA 22101-1908 Office: Metcalf Tobey and Ptnrs 1750 Presidents St Reston VA 22090-5618

METCALFE, DARREL SEYMOUR, agronomist, educator; b. Arkansaw, Wis., Aug. 28, 1913; s. Howard Lee and Mabel (De Marce) M.; m. Ellen Lucille Moore, May 16, 1942; children: Dean Darrel, Alan Moore. Tchr. cert., U. Wis. at River Falls, 1931; B.S. in Agronomy, U. Wis., 1941; M.S., Kans. State U., 1942; Ph.D., Iowa State U., 1950. From instr. to prof. agronomy Iowa State U., 1946-56, asst. dir. student affairs, 1956-58; asso. dean, dir. resident instrn., asst. dir. agrl. expt. sta., agronomist U. Ariz., Tucson, 1958—; dean U. Ariz., 1978-82, dean emeritus, 1982—; Chmn. resident instrn. sect., div. agr. Nat. Assn. State Univs. and Land Grant Colls., 1958-59; mem. com. edn. agr. and natural resources Nat. Acad. Sci., 1966-70, mem. rev. panel for Egypt, 1980-81, mem. Internat. Edn. Com., Somalia and Kenya, 1980-82; U.S. rep. OECD Conf. Higher Edn. in Agr., Paris, 1963-65; trustee Consortium for Internat. Devel., 1978-82; mem. AID missions to Brazil, 1962, 64, 66, 69, 71, 72, 73, Sultan Qaboos U. Com., Oman, 1982-86. Co-author: Forages, 4th edit., 1985, Crop Production, rev. edits, 1957, 72, 80. Served with AUS, 1942-46, PTO. Named Hon. Alumnus U. Ariz., 1985. Fellow Am. Soc. Agronomy (Agronomic edn. award 1958, Agronomic Svc. award 1980, chmn. student activities sect. 1950-53, edn. div. 1956, editorial bd., tech. editor jour. 1961-65), Nat. Assn. Colls. and Tchrs. Agr. (E.B. Knight award 1967, pres. 1970-71, Disting. Educator award 1980, U. Ariz. Lifetime award), Kiwanis, Sigma Xi, Phi Kappa Phi, Phi Eta Sigma, Gamma Sigma Delta, Alpha Tau Alpha, Delta Theta Sigma, Acacia (medallion of merit 1966). Home: 5811 E 9th St Tucson AZ 85711-3221

METCALFE, TOM BROOKS, chemical engineering educator; b. Smithville, Tex., Feb. 26, 1920; s. Joseph Franklin and Ethel Louise (Taylor) M.; m. Gwendolyn Imogene Soward, July 3, 1944; children: Gwendolyn Jean Metcalfe Ellis, Linda Gail Metcalfe Gallup, Marilyn Louise, Carolyn Marguerite Metcalfe Montiel. BS, U. Tex., 1941, MS, 1947; PhD, Ga. Inst. Tech., 1953. Registered profl. engr.; Tex. Chemist Dow Chem. Co., Freeport, Tex., 1941-43; rsch. scientist U. Tex., 1947-50; rsch. engr. Ga. Inst. Tech., 1951-52, Shell Oil Co., Houston, 1952-62; asst. prof. U. Houston, 1953-56, rsch. prof., 1975; head dept. chem. engring. W.Va. Inst. Tech., 1962-63; prof., head dept. chem. engring. U. Southwestern La., 1963-82, Found. prof., 1982-85, adj. prof., 1985—; vis. prof. U. Tex., Austin, 1982; founder, pub. Pinehill Pub. Co.; cons. U.S. Bur. Public Rds.; U.S. Dept. Interior Office of Saline Water. Author: Radiation Spectra of Radionuclides, 1970, Chemical Engineering as a Career, 1966, Safe Handling of Radioactive Materials, 1964; Contbr. articles to profl. jours. Pres. Edgewood Civic Corp., 1954, 57, 59; mem. Mayor of Houston's Com. on Zoning, 1958-69; chmn. bd. dirs. U. Southwestern La. Wesley Found., 1966-67; mem. ofcl. bd. area Meth. ch. Lt. USNR, 1943-46, PTO. Fellow AIChE (nat. chmn. acad. dept. heads 1978-79, 80); mem. Soc. Engring. Edn., Masons, Sigma Xi, Phi Eta Sigma, Omega Chi Epsilon, Phi Lambda Upsilon, Tau Beta Pi. Home: 5907 Overlook Dr Austin TX 78731-4221 *Seek good and not evil; bless them who curse you; with God, all things are possible.*

METCALFE, WALTER LEE, JR., lawyer; b. St. Louis, Dec. 19, 1938; s. Walter Lee and Carol (Crowe) M.; m. Cynthia Williamson, Aug. 26, 1965; children—Carol, Edward. A.B., Washington U., St. Louis, 1960; J.D., U. Va., 1964. Bar: Mo. 1964. Ptnr. Armstrong, Teasdale, Kramer & Vaughan, St. Louis, 1964-81; sr. ptnr. Bryan Cave, St. Louis, 1982—. Bd. dirs. Grand Ctr., Inc. chmn.,1994—; bd. dirs. New England Patriots Football Club; sec., bd. dirs. Masters & Johnson Inst., St. Louis Regional Health Care Corp. Mem. ABA, Mo. Bar Assn., St. Louis Bar Assn. Episcopalian. Club: Bogey, Noonday. Home: 26 Upper Ladue Rd Saint Louis MO 63124-1675 Office: Bryan Cave 1 Metropolitan Sq Saint Louis MO 63102-2750

METEVIER, JAMES F., finance company executive; b. 1941. BSA, DePaul U., 1970. Asst. mgr., treas. ops. Standard Oil Co., 1962-66; asst. to treas. Pullman, Inc., 1966-68; fin. sales rep. Ford Motor Credit Co., 1968-70; pres. AFC Securities Inc., 1970-72; sr. v.p. corp. fin. Assocs. Corp. N.Am., 1972-81, exec. v.p., 1981-85, sr. v.p., 1985—. Office: Assocs Corp N Am PO Box 660237 250 E Carpenter Frwy Irving TX 75062

METHENY, PATRICK BRUCE, musician; b. Lee's Summit, Mo., Aug. 12, 1954. Student, U. Miami, Fla. Instr. dept. music U. Miami; mem. faculty Nat. Stage Band Camps, Fla., Berklee Coll. Music, Boston. Guitarist with Gary Burton, 1974; composer, 3 yrs, mus. dir. and guitarist, Pat Metheny Group, 1978—; performing tours in U.S., Europe, Can., Japan, USSR, S.Am.; rec. artist ECM Records, currently Geffen Records; composer for guitar and band: records include Bright Size Life, 1976, Watercolors, 1977, Pat Metheny Group, 1978, New Chautauqua, 1979, American Garage, 1980, 80/81, 1980, As Falls Wichita, So Falls Wichita Falls, 1981, Offramp, 1982, Travels, 1983, Rejoicing, 1983, Works, 1984, First Circle, 1984, Still Life (Talking), 1987,

Works II, 1988, Letter From Home, 1989, (with Roy Haynes and Dave Holland, Grammy award Best Jazz Composition 1990) Question and Answer, 1990, Secret Story, 1992, The Road to You, 1993 (Jazz Instrumental Grammy award, 1994); (with Ornette Coleman) Song X, 1986 (Best Jazz Album award Downbeat mag. Readers' Poll, 1986, Downbeat Readers Poll Jazz Album of Yr., Guitarist of Yr., 1989, USA Today, 1986, Best Jazz Colloboration Album award Cashbox mag., 1986, John Pareles Top Albums of 1986 award N.Y. Times); composer film scores: (with David Bowie) The Falcon and the Snowman, 1984, Twice in a Lifetime, 1985. Nominated for Grammy award, 1980, 81; recipient 7 Grammy awards; Outstanding Jazz Album award Boston Music Awards, 1986; named Best Jazz Musician Jazziz Readers' Poll, Best Jazz Guitarist Downbeat mag., 1986, Guitar Player mag., 1986, Guitar Player mag. Gallery of Greats, 1982-86, Outstanding Guitarist Boston Music Awards, 1986, Outstanding Jazz Fusion Group Boston Music Awards, 1986. Office: care Ted Kurland Assocs Inc 173 Brighton Ave Allston MA 02134-2003*

METHODIOS OF BOSTON See TOURNAS, METHODIOS

METHVIN, MILDRED E., judge; b. Alexandria, La., Oct. 24, 1952; d. DeWitt T. Jr. and Lallah Hill (Cunningham) M.; m. James T. McManus, Jan. 2, 1988; children: Michael James, Connor Hill; stepchildren: Christine Lynn, Matthew Robert, John Thomas. BA in Philosophy, Newcomb Coll., Tulane Univ., 1974; student, Tulane Univ. Law Sch., 1973-74; JD, Georgetown Univ. Law Ctr., 1976. Bar: La. 1977, D.C. 1977. Staff asst. to U.S. Rep. Gillis Long La., 1974-77; assoc. Gist, Methvin & Trimble, Alexandria, La., 1977-78; asst. U.S. atty. U.S. Dist. Ct. (we. dist.) La., Shreveport, 1979-81; staff atty. Dept. of Interior, Charleston, W. Va., 1981-83; magistrate judge U.S. Dist. Ct. (we. dist.) La., Lafayette, 1985—. Mem. La. Bar Assn., Nat. Assn. Women Judges, Fed. Magistrate Judges Assn., Am. Inn of Ct. Acadiana (pres. 1995-96). Avocations: travel, painting. Office: 705 Jefferson St Lafayette LA 70501-6090

METREY, GEORGE DAVID, social work educator, academic administrator; b. Milw., July 23, 1939; s. Richard Joseph and Catherine (Evans) M.; m. Cheryl Ann Mosca, June 21, 1969; 1 child, Mary Beth. A.B., Marquette U., 1961; M.S.W., Fordham U., 1963; Ph.D., NYU, 1970. Social worker N.J. Diagnostic Ctr., Edison, 1963-64, asst. social work supr., 1964-66, dir. psychiat. social work, 1966-70; coordinator undergrad. social work program Kean Coll., N.J., 1970-73, assoc. prof. social work, 1970-74, prof., 1974-79, chmn. dept. sociology, anthropology and social work, 1973-77, dir. social work program, acting assoc. dean Sch. Arts and Sci., 1977-79; dean Sch. Social Work, prof. R.I. Coll., Providence, 1979—; field instr. Fordham U. Sch. Social Service, 1966-70, adj. prof., 1969-77; adj. assoc. prof. Rutgers U. Grad. Sch. Social Work, 1972-73. Mem. program com. R.I. affiliate Am. Heart Assn., 1980—, bd. dirs., 1983-89, chmn. program com., 1985-87, exec. com., 1985-87; sec. bd. dirs. Ocean State Adoption Resource Exch., 1987-89, pres. bd. dirs., 1989-92. Recipient Fordham U. Grad. Sch. Social Service Outstanding Alumni, 1984. Mem. NASW (N.J. Social Worker of Yr. 1977, pres. 1978-80, parliamentarian 1981—, treas. R.I. chpt. 1986-87, mem. nat. competence cert. commn. 1989-91, nat. 2d v.p. 1978-80, chair nat. program com. 1981-83), Coun. on Social Work Edn. (dir. 1979-82), Acad. Cert. Social Workers, Nat. Assn. Deans and Dirs. Schs. Social Work (nominating com. 1993—, program com. 1993—), R.I. Cert. Ind. Social Workers, Alpha Phi Omega, Gamma Pi Mu, Alpha Delta Mu (regional v.p.). Roman Catholic. Home: 540 Waverly Rd Wyckoff NJ 07481-1229 Office: RI Coll Providence RI 02908

METROPOLIS, NICHOLAS CONSTANTINE, mathematical physicist; b. Chgo., June 11, 1915; s. Constantine Nicholas and Katharine (Ganas) M.; m. Patricia Hendrix, Oct. 15, 1955 (div. 1977); children: Katharine, Penelope, Christopher. BS, U. Chgo., 1936, PhD, 1941. Staff mem. Manhattan Project U. Chgo., 1942, asst. prof., 1946-48, prof., 1957-64; group leader Los Alamos Sci. Lab, Los Alamos, N.Mex., 1943-46, 1948-57, sr. fellow, 1965-85, emeritus, 1985—; cons. nat. labs. U. Ill. at Champaign-Urbana, 1970—; mem. com. for rsch. NSF, Washington, 1974-76; mem. tech. mission UN, Calcutta, India, 1961; mem. US-USSR Exch. State Dept., USSR, 1976; mem. 70th anniversary celebration Internat. Conf. on Quantum, Monte Carlo; J.R. Oppenheimer Meml. Lectr., Los Alamos, 1992; speaker 50th anniversary celebration Los Alamos Nat. Lab., 1993. Editor: J.R. Oppenheimer, 1984, The Los Alamos 40th Anniversary Vol.: New Directions in Physics; editorauthor: History of Computing, 1980, Essays in Applied Math., 1976; editor, contbr. MIT publ. Daedalus, 1993; mem. editl. bds. profl. jours., 1970—; contbr. articles to profl. jours. Mem. J.R. Oppenheimer Meml. Com., Los Alamos, 1965—; trustee Santa Fe Inst., 1985-88, bd. advisors, 1988—; sec., bd. dirs Global Pursuits, Inc., 1986—. U. Chgo. fellow, 1938-41; recipient Computer Pioneer medal IEEE, 1984. Fellow Am. Phys. Soc.; mem. AAAS, Am. Math. Soc., Soc. Indsl. and Applied Math., Am. Acad. Arts and Scis. (contbr. to Daedalus 1992). Home: 71 Loma Vista St Los Alamos NM 87544-3090 Office: Los Alamos Nat Lab Mail Stop B210 Los Alamos NM 87545

METROS, MARY TERESA, librarian; b. Denver, Nov. 10, 1951; d. James and Wilma Frances (Hanson) M. BA in English, Colo. Women's Coll., 1973; MA in Librarianship, U. Denver, 1974. Adult svcs. libr. Englewood (Colo.) Pub. Libr., 1975-81, adult svcs. mgr., 1983-84; libr. systems cons. Dataphase Systems, Kansas City, Mo., 1981-82; circulation libra. Westminster (Colo.) Pub. Libr. 1983; pub. svcs. supr. Tempe (Ariz.) Pub. Libr., 1984-90, libr. adminstr., 1990—. Mem. ALA, Pub. Libr. Assn., Ariz. Libr. Assn, Libr. Adminstrn. and Mgmt. Assn. Democrat. Home: 11860 E Purdue Ave Scottsdale AZ 85259 Office: Tempe Pub Libr 3500 S Rural Rd Tempe AZ 85282-5482

METSCH, JONATHAN MARTIN, health facility executive; b. Paterson, N.J., Mar. 28, 1945. BS in Polit. Sci., Queens Coll. CUNY, 1966; MPA, SUNY, Albany, 1967; DRPH, U. N.C., 1972. With med. svc. corps Wilford Hall USAF Med. Ctr., Lackland AFB, Tex., 1967-70; asst. prof. grad. program health care adminstrn. CUNY, N.Y.C., 1972-75; adminstr. Mt. Sinai Svcs., City Hosp. Ctr., Elmhurst, N.Y., 1975-79; sr. v.p. for adminstrn. Mt. Sinai Med. Ctr., N.Y.C., 1979-89; pres., CEO Jersey City Med. Ctr., Liberty HealthCare Sys., 1989—; CEO Greenville Hosp.; chmn. bd. trustees, CEO Liberty Health Plan, Inc.; CEO Meadowlands Hosp. Med. Ctr.; pres. bd. dirs. LHS Receivable Corp.; founder, vice chmn. bd. trustees Hudson Cradle, Inc.; adj. prof., preceptor Baruch Coll., N.Y.C., 1987—; adj. assoc. prof. health care mgmt. Mt. Sinai Sch. Medicine, N.Y.C., 1989—; adj. prof. Ctr. Pub. Svc. Seton Hall U., N.J., 1990—; clin. instr., preceptor NYU, 1992—. Office: Jersey City Med Ctr Exec Office 50 Baldwin Ave Jersey City NJ 07304-3154

METTE, JOE, museum director. Dir. California State Capitol Mus., Sacramento, Calif. Office: Calif State Capitol Museum State Capitol Rm B-27 Sacramento CA 95814

METTINGER, KARL LENNART, neurologist; b. Helsingborg, Sweden, Nov. 1, 1943; came to the U.S., 1989; s. Nils Allan and Anna Katarina (Hallberg) M.; m. Chesne Maree Ryman, Jan. 27, 1979. MD, U. Lund, 1973; PhD, Karolinska Inst., 1982. Intern Stockholm Hosps., 1973-74; resident Karolinska Hosp., Stockholm, 1974-77, clin. neurologist, 1977-85; med. dir. Kabi Hematology, Stockholm, 1985-87; dep. dont. neurologist U. Kabi Cardiovascular, Stockholm, 1987-89; med. dir. Ivax/Baker Norton Pharms., Miami, Fla., 1989-93, sr. clin. rsch. dir., 1993—; assoc. prof. Karolinska Inst., Stockholm, 1983-91; cons. neurologist Odenplan Med. Ctr., Stockholm, 1984-89. Author: Cerebral Thromboembolism, 1982, Refaat-Myths and Billions in Biotech, 1987; editor: Coronary Thrombolysis: Current Answers to Critical Questions, 1988, Controversies in Coronary Thrombolysis, 1989. V.p. Fla. Festival Philharmonic, Fort Lauderdale, 1991—. Lt. Swedish Army, 1979. Recipient Silver award Spanish Health Ministry, 1989, Classical Langs. award King Gustav V Found., 1963. Mem. Swedish Stroke Soc. (bd. dirs. 1984-86), Swedish Med. Soc., Swedish Christian Med. Soc. (bd. dirs. 1972-88, pres. 1983-88), Am. Heart Assn., N.Y. Acad. Scis., Nat. Found. for Advancement of Arts, Internat. Assn. Christian Physicians (exec. com. 1975-86). Achievements include 5 patents pending. Home: 1244 Sorolla Ave Coral Gables FL 33134-3516 Office: IVAX 8800 NW 36th St Miami FL 33178-2433

METZ, CHARLES EDGAR, radiology educator; b. Bayshore, N.Y., Sept. 11, 1942; s. Clinton Edgar and Grace Muriel (Schienke) M.; m. Maryanne Theresa Bahr, July, 1967 (div. 1988); children: Rebecca, Molly. BA, Bowdoin Coll., 1964; MS, U. Pa., 1966, PhD, 1969. Instr. radiology U. Chgo., 1969-71, asst. prof., 1971-75, assoc. prof., 1976-80, dir. grad. programs in med. physics, 1979-85, prof., 1980—, prof. structural biology, 1984-86; mem. diagnostic rsch. adv. group Nat. Cancer Inst., 1980-81; mem. sci. com. Nat. Coun. on Radiation Protection and Measurements, 1982—; Internat. Commn. on Radiation Units and Measurements, 1988—, chmn. sci. com., 1992—; cons. and lectr. in field. Assoc. editor Radiology jour., 1986-91, Med. Physics jour., 1992—; mem. editl. bd. Med. Decision Making, 1980-84; contbr. over 150 articles to sci. jours. and chpts. to books. Mem. Radiol. Soc. N.Am., Am. Physicists in Medicine, Soc. Med. Decision Making, Assn. Univ. Radiologists, Phi Beta Kappa, Sigma Xi. Office: U Chgo Dept Radiology MC2026 5841 S Maryland Ave Chicago IL 60637-1470

METZ, CRAIG HUSEMAN, legislative staff; b. Columbia, S.C., Aug. 26, 1955; s. Leonard Huseman and Annette (Worthington) M.; m. Karen Angela McCleary, Aug. 11, 1984; 1 child, Preston Worthington. BA, U. Tenn., 1977; JD, U. Memphis, 1986; cert., U.S. Ho. of Reps. Rep. Leadership Parlimentary Law Sch., 1987. Bar: S.C., D.C., U.S. Supreme Ct., U.S. Ct. Appeals (4th cir.), U.S. Ct. Fed. Claims. Intern U.S. Senator Strom Thurmond, Washington, summer 1976, Congressman Floyd Spence, Washington, summer 1977; canvass coord., liaison Campaign to Re-elect Congressman Floyd Spence, 1978; del., chmn. Shelby County Del. to 1983 Tenn. Young Rep. Fedn. Conv.; vice chmn. Shelby County Young Reps., 1983-84, chmn., 1984-85; Shelby County adminstr., asst. to Tenn. state exec. dir. Reagan-Bush Campaign, 1984; field rep. Campaign to Re-elect Congressman Floyd Spence, 1986; spl. asst. to Congressman Floyd Spence, 1986-88; counsel com. on labor and human resources U.S. Senate, 1988-90; commr.'s counsel U.S. Occupational Safety and Health Rev. Commn., Washington, 1990-91; dep. asst. sec. for congl. liaison U.S. Dept. Edn., Washington, 1991-93; asst. dir. Divsn. Congl. Affairs AMA, Washington, 1993; chief of staff Congressman Floyd Spence, Washington, 1993—. Judge nat. writing competition U.S. Constn. Bicentennial, S.C., 1987-88. Recipient award of merit Rep. Party of Shelby County, 1985, Outstanding Leadership award Shelby County Young Reps., 1985. Mem. ABA, Rep. Nat. Lawyers Assn. (state chmn. S.C. chpt. 1987-90), Federalist Soc., U.S. Capitol Hist. Soc., Freedoms Found. Valley Forge, Va. Hist. Soc., Assn. for Preservation of Va. Antiquities, Va. Geneal. Soc., U. So. Carolinians Soc., Nat. Trust for Hist. Preservation (Capital region assoc.), SAR, Newcomen Soc., St. David's Soc., St. Andrew's Soc. of Washington, Mil. Soc. of War of 1812, Vet. Corps. Arty. of State of N.Y., Gen. Soc. of War of 1912, Mil. Order of Loyal Legion of U.S., Order of St. John (hospitaller), Confederate Meml. Assn., Sons of Confederate Vets., Va. Geneal. Soc., Mil. Order Stars and Bars, Nat. Cathedral Assn., U. Tenn. Nat. Alumni Assn. Washington, Sigma Alpha Epsilon Found., Phi Alpha Delta (v.p. McKellar chpt., Outstanding Svc. award 1983). Republican. Episcopalian. Home: 8505 Westown Way Vienna VA 22182-2513 Office: 2405 Rayburn Bldg Washington DC 20515-4002

METZ, DOUGLAS WILBER, association executive, lawyer; b. Port Huron, Mich., Feb. 8, 1934; s. Wilber Leroy and Doris Mabel (Hurni) M. BA, Colgate U., 1955; JD, Wayne State U., 1957. Bar: Mich. 1957, D.C. 1968. Adminstrv. asst. Congressman Alexander Pirnie, Utica, N.Y., 1959-64; v.p. Booz-Allen & Hamilton, N.Y.C., 1964-74; dep. dir. Domestic Coun. Com. on Right of Privacy, White House, Washington, 1974-75; sr. staff ops. dir. Econ. Policy Bd., White House, 1975-76; assoc. dir., gen. counsel Coun. on Internat. Econ. Policy, Exec. Office of Pres., Washington, 1976-77; mng. dir., gen. counsel Wine and Spirits Wholesalers Am., Inc., Washington, 1977—; v.p., sec., gen. counsel WSSA Intermodal Svcs. Inc., 1970-90. Chmn. Cathedral Latin Sch. Bd., Cleve., 1971-72; mem. Bethesda (Md.) Fire Bd., 1976-78; bd. dirs. Sky Ranch Found., 1983—, Com. to Preserve Integrity of Am. Trademarks, 1988—; pres. Potomac Woods Civic Assn., 1986-87. Capt. USAF, 1957-59. Mem. ABA, Am. Soc. Assn. Execs. (bd. dirs., chmn. legal sect. 1990-91), Nat. Assn. Wholesalers (bd. dirs. 1984-87), Nat. Wine Coalition (treas.), U.S.-India Trade and Investment Coun. (gen. counsel, bd. dirs.), Univ. Club, Capitol Hill Club, George Town Club, Annapolis Yacht Club, Phi Beta Kappa. Office: 1023 15th St NW Fl 4 Washington DC 20005-2602

METZ, EMMANUEL MICHAEL, investment company executive, lawyer; b. Pitts., Sept. 19, 1928; s. Solomon and Gertrude (Krieger) M.; m. Janine Spaner, Apr. 3, 1964. BA, Dartmouth Coll., 1949; LLB, Harvard U., 1952; LLM, NYU, 1958. Bar: N.Y. 1952. Atty. ABC, N.Y.C., 1956-58; security analyst Standard & Poor's, N.Y.C., 1958-68; mng. dir. Oppenheimer & Co., Inc., N.Y.C., 1968—. Author: Street Fighting at Wall and Broad, 1982. Lt. USN, 1952-56. Home: 150 E 56th St New York NY 10022-3631 Office: Oppenheimer & Co Inc 200 Liberty St New York NY 10281-1003

METZ, FRANK ANDREW, JR., data processing executive; b. Winthrop, Mass., Jan. 28, 1934; s. Frank Andrew and Frances E. (Fallon) M.; married; children: Christopher, Lelia, Amy, Patrick, Joshua, Rebecca; m. Judith Ann Mapes, July 21, 1979. A.B., Bowdoin Coll., 1955. With IBM, 1955—; dir. fin. planning data processing group IBM, Harrison, N.Y., 1969-72; div. v.p. office products IBM, Franklin Lakes, N.J., 1972-75; asst. controller IBM, Armonk, N.Y., 1975-78, controller, 1978-80; v.p., asst. group exec. IBM, White Plains, N.Y., 1980-84, sr. v.p., group exec., 1984-86, sr. v.p., chief fin. officer, bd. dirs., 1986-93, ret., 1993; bd. dirs. Allegheny Power Systems, Monsanto Co., Norrell Corp. Trustee St. Luke's Roosevelt Hosp., N.Y.C., 1979—, chmn. 1994—; trustee Am. Mus. Natural History, 1986—. Served to 1st lt. Transp. Corps U.S. Army, 1956. Roman Catholic.

METZ, LAWRENCE ANTHONY, lawyer; b. Chgo., July 26, 1941; s. Florian Lawrence and Angeline M.; m. Lorraine Kutz, Aug. 14, 1965; children: Robert, Kathleen, Sandra, Diane, Jeanne. B.S.C., DePaul U., 1963, J.D., 1967. Bar: Ill. 1967. Atty. City Products Corp., Des Plaines, Ill., 1967-70; atty. Jewel Cos., Inc., Chgo., 1970-75, asst. sec., 1975-79, asst. gen. counsel, 1979-84; gen. counsel Osco Drug, Inc., Oak Brook, Ill., 1984-89, Jewel Food Stores, Melrose Pk., Ill., 1989-90, Jewel Cos., Inc., Chgo., 1990-93; sr. v.p., asst. gen. counsel Am. Stores Co., Chgo., 1993-94; sr. v.p., dep. gen. counsel Am. Stores Co., Salt Lake City, 1994-95, Melrose Park, Ill., 1995—. Bd. dirs. United Way of Suburban Chgo., 1977-79. Served with U.S. Army, 1963. Roman Catholic. Office: 420 E South Temple Salt Lake City UT 84111

METZ, MARILYN JOYCE, bank executive; b. Denver, Colo., Nov. 10, 1949; d. James C. and Lois M. (Roach) M.; m. Jack W. Calabrese, Apr. 15, 1977 (div. 1981); m. Frank C. Magowski, Oct. 13, 1986 (div.). Student, Colo. State U., 1968-72; diploma, Colo. Grad. Sch. Banking, 1983. With First Interstate Bank Denver, 1972-83; v.p., mgr. United Banks Colo., Denver, 1983-88; v.p., area mgr. First Interstate Bank Oreg., Portland, 1988-89; v.p., dist. mgr. 5 brs. 1st Interstate Bank Wash., Seattle, 1989-91; v.p., dist. mgr. 11 brs. 1st Interstate Bank, Bellevue, Wash., 1991—. Bd. dirs., Met. Child Dental Care Assn., 1985-87. Mem. Nat. Assn. Bank Women (state pres. Colo. 1986-87), Cherry Creek Commerce Assn., Seattle C. of C., Pres. Club Seattle. Republican. Avocations: travel, reading, skiing. Office: First Interstate Bank Bellevue Fin Ctr 225 108th Ave NE Bellevue WA 98004

METZ, MARY SEAWELL, university dean, retired college president; b. Rockhill, S.C., May 7, 1937; d. Columbus Jackson and Mary (Dunlap) Seawell; m. F. Eugene Metz, Dec. 21, 1957; 1 dau., Mary Eugena. BA summa cum laude in French and English, Furman U., 1958; postgrad., Institut Phonetique, Paris, 1962-63, Sorbonne, Paris, 1962-63; PhD magna cum laude in French, La. State U., 1966; HHD (hon.), Furman U., 1984; LLD (hon.), Chapman Coll., 1985; DLT (hon.), Converse Coll., 1988. Instr. French La. State U., 1965-66, asst. prof., 1966-67, 1968-72, assoc. prof., 1972-76, dir. elem. and intermediate French programs, 1966-74, spl. asst. to chancellor, 1974-75, asst. to chancellor, 1975-76; prof. French Hood Coll., Frederick, Md., 1976-81, provost, dean acad. affairs, 1976-81; pres. Mills Coll., Oakland, Calif., 1981-90; dean of extension U. Calif., Berkeley, 1991—; vis. asst. prof. U. Calif.-Berkeley, 1967-68; mem. commn. on leadership devel. Am. Coun. on Edn., 1981-90, adv. coun. Stanford Rsch. Inst., 1985-90, adv. coun. Grad. Sch. Bus., Stanford U.; assoc. Gannett Ctr. for Media Studies, 1985—; bd. dirs. PG&E, Pacific Telesis, PacTel & PacBell, Union

Bank, Longs Drug Stores, S.H. Cowell Found. Author: Reflets du monde francais, 1971, 78, Cahier d'exercices: Reflets du monde francais, 1972, 78, (with Helstrom) Le Francais a decouvrir, 1972, 78, Le Francais a vivre, 1972, 78, Cahier d'exercices: Le Francais a vivre, 1972, 78; standardized tests; mem. editorial bd.: Liberal Edn., 1982—. Trustee Am. Conservatory Theater. NDEA fellow, 1960-62,, 1963-64; Fulbright fellow, 1962-63; Am. Council Edn. fellow, 1974-75. Mem. Western Coll. Assn. (v.p. 1982-84, pres. 1984-86), Assn. Ind. Calif. Colls. and Univs. (exec. com. 1982-90), Nat. Assn. Ind. Colls. and Univs. (govt. rels. adv. coun. 1982-85), So. Conf. Lang. Teaching (chmn. 1976-77), World Affairs Coun. No. Calif. (bd. dirs. 1984-93), Bus.-Higher Edn. Forum, Women's Forum West, Women's Coll. Coalition (exec. com. 1984-88), Phi Kappa Phi, Phi Beta Kappa. Address: PO Box 686 Stinson Beach CA 94970

METZ, ROBERT ROY, publisher, editor; b. Richmond Hill, N.Y., Mar. 23, 1929; s. Robert Roy, Sr. and Mary (Kissel) M.; m. Susan Lee Blair, 1984; children: Robert Sumner, Christopher Roy. B.A., Wesleyan U., Middletown Conn., 1950. Copyboy N.Y. Times, 1951, asst. fgn. news desk, 1952; rewriteman cable desk I.N.S., 1953, overnight cable editor, 1954-56, asst. feature editor, 1956-58; asst. news editor Newspaper Enterprise Assn., 1958, news editor, 1959-63, mng. editor, 1963-66, exec. editor, 1966-68, v.p., 1967-71, editorial dir., 1968-71, pres., editor, dir., 1972-94; dir. Berkeley-Small Inc., 1974-77; chmn. Berkley-Small Inc., 1976-77; v.p., dir. United Feature Syndicate, 1976-77, pres., editor, 1978; pres., editor, dir. United Media, 1978-93, chmn., 1993-94; media cons., 1994—. Lutheran. Club: Union League (N.Y.C.). Home: 170 E 77th St New York NY 10021-1912

METZ, T(HEODORE) JOHN, librarian, consultant; b. Erie, Pa., Nov. 5, 1932; s. Theodore John and Dorothy Pearl (Schutte) M.; m. Dorothy Page Neff, June 11, 1955; 1 child, Margaret Elizabeth. Mus.B., Heidelberg Coll., 1954; M.A. in Music, Miami U., Oxford, Ohio, 1955; M.L.S., U. Mich., 1959. Librarian II U. Wis., Madison, 1959-61; asst. librarian Lawrence U., Appleton, Wis., 1961-67; dir. libraries U. Wis.-Green Bay, 1967-75; exec. dir. Midwest Region Library Network, Evanston, Ill., 1975-79; coll. librarian, assoc. prof. Carleton Coll., Northfield, Minn., 1979—; speaker, participant, coord. numerous confs. and insts., 1969—; chmn. several state libr. groups, 1971-76; mem. several nat. libr. adv. coms., 1974-80; bldg. cons. Carleton Coll., others, 1978—; mem. Citizen Amb. Rsch. Librs. del. to Ea. Europe, 1992. Author: MIDLNET Symposium Report, 1976. Chmn. Green Bay Symphony, 1971-76; mem. various bds. coms., relating to mus. activities; performer Green Bay and other orchs., 1955—. Library Service scholar U. Mich., 1957; Library Service fellow U. Mich., 1958. Mem. ALA, Assn. Coll. Research Libraries. Avocations: musical activities; hunting; fishing; gardening. Home: 1200 Elm St Northfield MN 55057-2906 Office: Carleton Coll Libr Northfield MN 55057-4097

METZENBAUM, HOWARD MORTON, senator; b. Cleve., June 4, 1917; s. Charles I. and Anna (Klafter) M.; m. Shirley Turoff, Aug. 8, 1946; children: Barbara Jo, Susan Lynn, Shelley Hope, Amy Beth. B.A., Ohio State U., 1939, LL.D, 1941. Chmn. bd. Airport Parking Co. Am., 1958-66, ITT Consumer Services Corp., 1966-68; chmn. bd. ComCorp, 1969-74, after 1975; U.S. senator from Ohio, 1974, 77—; mem. War Labor Bd., 1942-45, Ohio Bur. Code Rev., 1949-50, Cleve. Met. Housing Authority, 1968-70, Lake Erie Regional Transit Authority, 1972-73, Ohio Ho. of Reps., 1943-46, Ohio Senate, 1947-50; mem. Ohio Democratic Exec. Com., from 1966, Ohio Dem. Finance Com., from 1969. Trustee Mt. Sinai Hosp., Cleve., 1961-73, treas., 1966-73; bd. dirs. Council Human Relations, United Cerebral Palsy Assn., Nat. Council Hunger and Malnutrition, Karamu House, St. Vincent Charity Hosp., Cleve., St. Jude Research Hosp., Memphis; nat. co-chmn. Nat. Citizens' Com. Conquest Cancer; vice-chmn. fellows Brandeis U. Mem. ABA, Ohio Bar Assn., Cuyahoga Bar Assn., Am. Bar Assn., Am. Assn. Trial Lawyers, Order of Coif, Phi Eta Sigma, Tau Epsilon Rho. Office: Consumer Federation of America 1424 16th St NW Ste 504 Washington DC 20036*

METZER, PATRICIA ANN, lawyer; b. Phila., Mar. 10, 1941; d. Freeman Weeks and Evelyn (Heap) M.; m. Karl Hormann, June 30, 1980. BA with distinction, U. Pa., 1963, LLB cum laude, 1966. Bar: Mass. 1966, D.C. 1972, U.S. Tax Ct. 1988. Assoc., then ptnr. Mintz, Levin, Cohn, Glovsky and Popeo, Boston, 1966-75; assoc. tax legis. counsel U.S. Treasury Dept., Washington, 1975-78; shareholder, dir. Goulston & Storrs, P.C., Boston, 1978—; lectr. program continuing legal edn. Boston Coll. Law Sch., Chestnut Hill, Mass., spring 1974; mem. adv. com. NYU Inst. Fed. Taxation, N.Y.C., 1981-87; mem. practitioner liaison com. Mass. Dept. of Revenue, Mass., 1985-90; mem. editorial bd. Am. Jour. of Tax Policy, 1995—; speaker in field. Author: Federal Income Taxation of Individuals, 1984; contbr. chpts. to books and articles to profl. jours. Bd. mgrs. Barrington Ct. Condominium, Cambridge, Mass., 1985-86; bd. dirs. University Road Parking Assn., Cambridge, 1988—; trustee Social Law Libr., Boston, 1989-93. Mem. ABA (tax sect., chmn. subcom. allocations and distbns. partnership com. 1978-82, vice chmn. legis. 1991-93, chmn. 1993-95, com. govt. submissions, vice liaison 1993-94, liaison 1994—, North Atlantic region, regional liaison meetings com.), Mass. Bar Assn., Boston Bar Assn. (coun. 1987-89, chmn. tax sect. 1989-91), Fed. Bar Assn. (coun. on taxation, chmn. corp. taxation com. 1977-81, chmn. com. partnership taxation 1981-87), Boston Estate Planning Coun. (exec. com. 1975, 79-82), Am. Coll. Tax Counsel. Avocation: vocal performances (as soloist and with choral groups). Office: Goulston & Storrs PC 400 Atlantic Ave Boston MA 02110-3333

METZGER, BARRY, lawyer; b. Newark, June 11, 1945; s. William and Dorothy (Bagoon) M.; m. Jacqueline Sue Ivers, June 26, 1966; children: Darren Thomas, Rebecca Lynne. AB magna cum laude, Princeton U., 1966; JD cum laude, Harvard U., 1969. Bar: D.C. 1970. Asst. to Prin. Ceylon Law Coll., Colombo, 1969-71; dir. Asian programs Internat. Legal Ctr., N.Y.C., 1971-74; ptnr. Coudert Brothers, N.Y.C., 1974-76, resident in Hong Kong, 1976-84, Sydney, 1984-89, London, 1989—; mem. New South Wales Atty. Gen.'s Commn. on Comml. Dispute Resolution, Com. for Econ. Devel. Australia; arbitrator ICC Ct. Arbitration; v.p. Internat. Legal Aid Assn., 1972-80; pres. Harvard Legal Aid Bur., 1968-69; trustee Princeton-in-Asia. Editorial advisor: Internat. Fin. Law Rev.; editor: Legal Aid and World Poverty, 1974; contbr. articles to profl. jours. Sheldon Meml. fellow, 1969. Mem. ABA, Am. Bar City N.Y., Internat. Bar Assn. Democrat. Home: 6 Linnell Dr, London NW 117L3, England Office: Coudert Bros, 20 Old Bailey, London EC4M 7JP, England

METZGER, BOBBIE ANN, public relations executive; b. N.Y.C., June 10, 1948. BA in Journalism, Calif. State U., San Diego, 1970; MA in Internat. Rels., Calif. State U., Sacramento, 1980. Reporter, writer, producer Sta. KFMB-TV, San Diego, 1970-73; sr. cons., press liaison Assembly Retirement Com., Sacramento, 1973-76; press sec. for Gov. Jerry Brown Sacramento, 1976-80; press sec., assembly speaker Willie Brown Jr., Sacramento, 1980-84; pres., ptnr. Stoorza, Ziegaus, Metzger & Hunt, Sacramento, 1984—. Recipient Cappie award Sacramento chpt. Pub. Rels. Soc. Am., 1986, 92, Cappie Silver award, 1990, 92, Cappie Gold award, 1993, Silver Anvil award, 1989, Cipra award Inside PR, 1993. Mem. Internat. Assn. Bus. Communicators (Crystal award 1990, 92, 93, award of merit 1986, 90, award of excellence 1988), Sacramento Press Club, Bldg. Industry Assn. Superior Calif., Calif. Bldg. Assn., Sacramento Met. C. of C., Sacramento Area Commerce and Trade Orgn., Capitol Club. Avocations: travel, tennis. Office: Stoorza Ziegaus Metzger PO Box 189026 Sacramento CA 95818-9026

METZGER, BRUCE MANNING, clergyman, educator; b. Middletown, Pa., Feb. 9, 1914; s. Maurice Rutt and Anna Mary (Manning) M.; m. Isobel E. Mackay, July 7, 1944; children—John Mackay, James Bruce. A.B., Lebanon Valley Coll., 1935, D.D., 1951; Th.B., Princeton Theol. Sem., 1938, Th.M., 1939; A.M., Princeton U., 1940, Ph.D., 1942; L.H.D., Findlay U., 1962; D.D., St. Andrews U., Scotland, 1964; D.Theol., Münster U., Fed. Republic Germany, 1970; D.Litt., Potchefstroom U., South Africa, 1985. Ordained to ministry Presbyn. Ch., 1939. Teaching fellow N.T. Princeton Theol. Sem., 1938-40, mem. faculty, 1940—, prof. N.T. lang. and lit., 1954-64, George L. Collord prof. N.T. lang. and lit., 1964-84, emeritus, 1984—; vis. lectr. Presbyn. Theol. Sem. South, Campinas, Brazil, 1952, Presbyn. Theol. Sem. North, Recife, Brazil, 1952; mem. Inst. Advanced Study, Princeton, 1964-65, 73-74; scholar-in-residence Tyndale House, Cambridge, 1969; vis. fellow Clare Hall, Cambridge, 1974, Wolfson Coll., Oxford U., 1979, Macquarie U., Sydney, Australia, 1982, Caribbean Grad.

Sch. of Theology, Jamaica, 1990, Seminario Internacional Teológico Bautista, Buenos Aires, 1991, Griffith Thomas Lectrs., Dallas Theol. Sem., 1992; mem. mng. com. Am. Sch. Classical Studies, Athens, Greece; mem. Standard Bible com. Nat. Coun. Chs., 1952—, chmn., 1975—; mem. seminar N.T. studies Columbia U., 1959-80; mem. Kuratorium of Vetus-Latina Inst., Beuron, Germany, 1959—; adv. com. Inst. N.T. Text Rsch., U. Münster, 1961—; Thesaurus Linguae Graecae, 1972-80; Collected Works of Erasmus, 1977—; chmn. Am. com. versions Internat. Greek N.T., 1950-88; participant internat. congresses scholars, Aarhus, Aberdeen, Bangor, Basel, Bonn, Brussels, Cairo, Cambridge, Dublin, Exeter, Frankfurt, Heidelberg, London, Louvain, Manchester, Milan, Munich, Münster, Newcastle, Nottingham, Oxford, Rome, St. Andrews, Stockholm, Strasbourg, Toronto, Trondheim, Tübingen; mem. Presbytery, N.B. Author: The Saturday and Sunday Lessons from Luke in the Greek Gospel Lectionary, 1944, Lexical Aids for Students of New Testament Greek, 1946, enlarged edit., 1955, A Guide to the Preparation of a Thesis, 1950, An Introduction to the Apocrypha, 1957, Chapters in the History of New Testament Textual Criticism, 1963, The Text of the New Testament, Its Transmission, Corruption, and Restoration, 1964, 3d enlarged edit., 1992, (with H.G. May) The Oxford Annotated Bible with the Apocrypha, 1965, The New Testament, Its Background, Growth, and Content, 1965, Index to Periodical Literature on Christ and the Gospels, 1966, Historical and Literary Studies, Pagan, Jewish, and Christian, 1968, Index to Periodical Literature on the Apostle Paul, 1970, 2nd edit., A Textual Commentary on the Greek New Testament, 1971, 2d edit., 1994, The Early Versions of the New Testament, 1977, New Testament Studies, 1980, Manuscripts of the Greek Bible, 1981, The Canon of the New Testament, 1987, (with Roland Murphy) The New Oxford Annotated Bible with the Apocrypha, 1991. (with M.D. Coogan) The Oxford Companion to the Bible, 1993, Breaking the Code-Understanding the Book of Revelation, 1993; mem. editorial com.: Critical Greek New Testament, 1956-84; chmn. Am. com., Internat. Greek New Testament Project, 1970-88; sec. com. translators: Apocrypha (rev. standard version); editor: New Testament Tools and Studies, 18 vols., 1960-93, Oxford Annotated Apocrypha, 1965, enlarged edit., 1977; Reader's Digest Condensed Bible, 1982; co-editor: United Bible Societies Greek New Testament, 1966, 4th edit., 1993; compiler: Index of Articles on the New Testament and the Early Church Published in Festschriften, 1951, supplement, 1955, Lists of Words Occurring Frequently in the Coptic New Testament (Sahidic Dialect), 1961, Annotated Bibliography of the Textual Criticism of the New Testament, 1955, (with Isobel M. Metzger) Oxford Concise Concordance to the Holy Bible, 1962 (with R.C. Dentan and W. Harrelson), The Making of the New Revised Standard Version of the Bible, 1991; contbr. articles to jours. Chmn. standard bible com. Nat. Coun. Chs., 1977—. Recipient cert. Disting. Svc. Nat. Coun. Chs., 1957, Disting. Alumnus award Lebanon Valley Coll. Alumni Assn., 1961, citation of appreciation Laymen's Nat. Bible Assn., 1986, Disting. Alumnus award Princeton Theol. Sem., 1989, lit. competition prize Christian Rsch. Found., 1955, 62, 63, E.T. Thompson award, 1991. Mem. Am. Philos. Soc., Soc. Bibl. Lit. (pres. 1970-71, past del. Am. Coun. Learned Socs.), Am. Bible Soc. (bd. mgrs. 1948—, chmn. com. transls. 1964-70), Am. Philol. Assn., Studiorum Novi Testamenti Societas (pres. 1971-72), Cath. Bibl. Assn., N.Am. Patristic Soc. (past pres.), Soc. Textual Scholarship (pres. 1995), Am. Soc. Papyrologists; hon. fellow, corr. mem. Higher Inst. Coptic Studies, Cairo; corr. fellow Brit. Acad. (Burkitt medal in Bibl. studies 1994). Republican. Home: 20 Cleveland Ln Princeton NJ 08540 Office: Princeton Theol Sem Mercer St Princeton NJ 08542

METZGER, ERNEST HUGH, aerospace engineer, scientist; b. Nurnberg, Germany, Oct. 22, 1923; came to U.S., 1939, naturalized, 1943; s. Paul Arthur and Charlotte Babette (Kann) M.; m. Sarah Temple Grinnell, Nov. 19, 1956; children: Lisa Metzger Dunning, Charlotte Bennett, George Grinnell. B.S., CCNY, 1949; M.S., Harvard U., 1950. Automatic control engr. Bell Aerospace Co. div. Textron, Buffalo, 1950-54, tech. dir. inertial nav. systems, 1954-60, chief engr., inertial instruments, 1960-70, chief engr., gravity gradiometer systems, 1970-83, dir. gravity sensor systems, 1983-86, exec. dir. engring., 1986-89, cons., 1989—; mem. panel future navigation systems Nat. Acad. Sci., com. on geodesy NRC, 1988-89, accelerator criteria com. NASA, tech. com. navigation guidance and control, AIAA, 1989—; vis. lectr. dept. aernautics and astronautics Stanford U., 1990. Contbr. articles to profl. jours.; patentee in field. Served with AUS, 1943-46. Recipient Aerospace Pioneer award Niagara Frontier sect. AIAA, 1977; named to Niagara Frontier Aviation Hall of Fame, 1992. Mem. IEEE, Inst. Navigation (Thurlow award for outstanding contbn. to sci. navigation 1983), AAAS, Air Force Assn., N.Y. Acad. Scis., Explorers Club, Sigma Xi, Tau Beta Pi, Eta Kappa Nu. Clubs: Harvard, Buffalo Ski. Home: 90 High Park Blvd Buffalo NY 14226-4209 Office: Bell Aerospace Co PO Box 1 Buffalo NY 14240-0001

METZGER, FRANK, management consultant; b. Mainz, Fed. Republic Germany, Feb. 27, 1929; came to U.S., 1938; s. Paul Alfred and Anna (Daniel) M.; m. Lore Lichter, Dec. 21, 1952; children: Peter D., Mark S. BS in Indsl. Edn., N.Y. State Tchrs.'s Coll., 1951; MS in Psychology, Carnegie Mellon U., 1953, PhD in Indsl. Psychology, 1954. Lic. psychologist, N.Y., Ill. Supr. tech. adminstrn. Gen. Electric, Lynn., Mass., 1956-58; dir. mgmt. devel. Raytheon, Newton, Mass., 1958-59; asst. dir. personnel ITT, N.Y.C., 1959-69; sr. v.p. adminstrn. Nytronics Inc., Pelham, N.Y., 1969-71; sr. v.p. corp. and orgn. devel. CNA Fin. Corp., Chgo., 1971-75; pres. Metzger and Co. Inc., Chgo., 1975-76; sr. v.p. adminstrn. Bairnco Corp., N.Y.C., 1976-88; prin. Metzger & Co., Rye, N.Y., 1988—; bd. dirs. Genlyte Group Inc., Secaucus, N.J. Contbr. articles to profl. jours. Mem. Pres. Com. on Equal Opportunity, Washington, 1962-65. Served with signal corps. U.S. Army, 1954-56. Office: Metzger & Co 16 Norman Dr Rye NY 10580-2250

METZGER, HENRY, federal research institution administrator; b. Mainz, Germany, Mar. 23, 1932; came to U.S., 1938; naturalized, 1945; s. Paul Alfred and Anne (Daniel) M.; m. Deborah Stashower, June 16, 1957; children: Eran D., Renée V., Carl E. MD, Columbia U., 1957. Chief chem. immunology sect. Nat. Inst. Arthritis & Musculoskeletal & Skin Disease/NIH, Bethesda, Md., 1973—; Br. chief USPHS, Bethesda, 1983-94, sci. dir., 1987—; med. officer grade VI, 1975—; Carl Prausnitz Meml. lectr., 1982; Ecker Meml. lectr. Case Western Res. U., Cleve., 1984; Harvey Soc. lectr., 1984; Eli Nadel Meml. lectr. St. Louis U., 1987; Rodney Porter Meml. lectr., 1993; Burroughs-Wellcome lectr., 1994; R.E. Dyer lectr.; mem. health rsch. coun. BMFT, German Govt., 1994—. Editor: Fc Receptors & the Action of Antibodies, 1990; assoc. editor Ann. Rev. Immunology, 1982—; contbr. numerous articles to profl. jours.; mem. editorial bd. numerous sci. jours. Recipient Meritorious Svc. award USPHS, 1978, Disting. Svc. award, 1985, Joseph Mather Smith prize Columbia U., 1984. Fellow AAAS, Am. Acad. Allergy and Immunology; mem. NAS, Am. Assn. Immunologists (pres. 1991-92), Am. Soc. Biol. Chemists, Am. Soc. Cell Biology, Am. Rheumatism Assn., Internat. Union Immunological Soc. (pres. 1992—), Found. for Advanced Edn. in the Scis. (pres. 1990-92), Alpha Omega Alpha. Home: 3410 Taylor St Bethesda MD 20815-4024 Office: NIH Bldg 10 Rm 9N228 9000 Rockville Pike Bethesda MD 20892

METZGER, H(OWELL) PETER, writer; b. N.Y.C., Feb. 22, 1931; s. Julius Radley and Gertrude (Fuller) M.; m. Frances Windham, June 30, 1956 (div. July 1987); children: John, James, Lisa, Suzanne; m. Valerie A. Farnham, Jan. 12, 1990. B.A., Brandeis U., 1953; Ph.D., Columbia U., 1963. Mgr. advanced programs Ball Bros. Research Corp., Boulder, 1968-70; research assoc. Dept. Chemistry, U. Colo., Boulder, 1966-68; sr. research assistant N.Y. State Psychiat. Inst., N.Y.C., 1965-66; syndicated columnist N.Y. Times Syndicate, 1972-74, Science Critic, Newspaper Enterprise Assn., 1974-76; sci. editor Rocky Mt. News, Denver, 1973-77; mgr. public affairs planning Public Service Co. Colo., Denver, 1977—; cons. Environ. Instrumentation, 1970-72; dir. Colspan Environ. Systems, Inc., Boulder, Colo., 1969-72. Author: The Atomic Establishment, 1972; contbr. articles in field to profl. jours., nat. mags. Pres. Colo. Com. for Environ. Info., Boulder, 1968-72; mem. Colo. Gov.'s State Health Planning Council, 1969-72, Colo. Gov.'s Adv. Com. Underground Nuclear Explosions, 1971-74; mem. Gov.'s spl. project on energy policy mgmt. Heritage Found., 1980; mem. 1981 Presdl. Rank Rev. Bd. U.S. Office Personnel Mgmt., 1981; Bd. dirs. Wildlife-2000, 1970-72, Colo. Def. Council, 1972-75. USPHS fellow, 1955-65; prin. investigator, USPHS, 1963-65; mem. ACLU (state bd. 1968-71), Sigma Xi, Phi Lambda Upsilon. Clubs: Alpine. Address: 2595 Stanford Ave Boulder CO 80303-5332

METZGER, MARK KAVANAUGH, public relations company executive; b. Bethlehem, Pa., Aug. 13, 1951; s. A. Richard and Lucile (Kavanaugh) M.; m. Wendy J. Strothman, Nov. 25, 1978; children: Andrew R., Margaret A. BA, Brown U., 1973. Reporter The Express, Easton, Pa., 1973-76; newsman AP, Chgo., 1977-78; assoc. editor Crain Comm., Chgo. 1978-80, editor, 1980-83; sr. editor Inc. mag., Boston, 1983-85; account supr. Miller Comm. Inc., Boston, 1985-88, v.p., 1989-90, sr. v.p. 1990-94, exec. v.p. 1994—. Bd. dirs. Beacon Hill Nursery Sch., Boston, 1987-88. Recipient news writing award Pa. Newspaper Pubs. Assn., 1979. Avocation: sailing. Home: 1099 Massachusetts Ave Lexington MA 02177 Office: Mill Comm Inc Four Copley Pl Boston MA 02116

METZGER, ROBERT STREICHER, lawyer; b. St. Louis, Sept. 27, 1950; s. Robert Stanley and Jean Harriet (Streicher) M.; m. Stephanie Joy Morgan, Nov. 16, 1980; children: Michael, Kristen, Marisa. BA, Middlebury Coll., 1974; JD, Georgetown U., 1977. Bar: Calif. 1978, D.C. 1978. Legis. aide U.S. Rep. Robert F. Drinan, Washington, 1972-73; legis. asst. U.S. Rep. Michael J. Harrington, Washington, 1973-75; rsch. fellow Ctr. for Sci. and Internat. Affairs Harvard U., Cambridge, Mass., 1977-78; assoc. Latham & Watkins, L.A., 1978-84, ptnr., 1984-90; ptnr. Kirkland & Ellis, L.A., 1990-93, Hill, Wynne, Troop & Meisinger, L.A., 1993—; cons. Congl. Rsch. Svc., Washington, 1977-78. Contbr. articles to profl. jours. Mem. ABA (litigation pub. contracts sect.), Internat. Inst. for Strategic Studies, Jonathan Club. Office: Hill Wynne Troop & Meisinger 10940 Wilshire Blvd Los Angeles CA 90024

METZKER, RAY K., photographer; b. Milw., Sept. 10, 1931; s. William Martin and Marian Helen (Krueger) M. B.A., Beloit Coll., 1953; M.S., Inst. Design, Ill. Inst. Tech., 1959. Mem. faculty photography-film dept. Phila. Coll. Art, 1962-81, prof., chmn. dept., 1978-79; vis. assoc. prof. U. N.Mex., 1970-72; vis. adj. prof. R.I. Sch. Design, spring 1977; adj. Columbia Coll., Chgo., 1980-83; Smith Disting. vis. prof. art George Washington U., 1987-88. Author: Sand Creatures, 1979; one-man exhbns. include, Art Inst. Chgo., 1959, Mus. Modern Art, N.Y.C., 1967, Milw. Art Ctr., 1970, The Picture Gallery, Zurich, Switzerland, 1974, Marion Locks Gallery, Phila. 1978, 83, Internat. Ctr. Photography, N.Y.C., 1978, Light Gallery, N.Y.C., 1979, Shadai Gallery, Tokyo Inst. Polytechnics, 1992, Turner/Krull Gallery, L.A., 1992, Zelz Lieberman Gallery, Chgo., 1995, Lawrence Miller Gallery, 1984, 85, 87, 88, 90, 92, 94; represented in permanent collections, Mus. Modern Art, N.Y.C., Art Inst. Chgo., Smithsonian Inst., Washington, Met. Mus. Art, N.Y.C., Phila. Mus. Art, Bibliotheque Nat., Paris: 25 Yr. Retrospective, Mus. Fine Art, Houston and six other U.S. mus.; subject of monograph: Unknown Territory: Ray K. Metzker, 1984. Served with U.S. Army, 1954-56. Guggenheim fellow, 1966, 79; Nat. Endowment Arts fellow, 1974, 88; residency LaNapoule Art Found., France, 1989. Home: 733 S 6th St Philadelphia PA 19147-2109

METZLER, CYNTHIA A., federal agency administrator, lawyer. BA, Purdue U., 1970; JD, U. Ind., 1974; MS in Human Resources Devel. with distinction, Am. U. Atty., asst. dir. litigation Legal Svcs. Orgn. Ind., Indpls., 1979; from exec. asst. to spl. asst. to chmn. for new initiatives and programs Fed. Labor Rels. Authority, 1987—; assoc. dir. presdl. personnel The White House, Washington; assoc. administr. for administrn. Gen. Svcs. Administrn. U.S. Dept. Labor, asst. sec. administrn. and mgmt., 1994—. Mem. Clinton/Gore Transition Team. Office: Dept of Labor Administrn 200 Constitution Ave NW Washington DC 20210*

METZLER, DWIGHT FOX, civil engineer, retired state official; b. Kans., Mar. 25, 1916; s. Ross R. and Grace (Fox) M.; m. Lela Ross, June, 1941; children: Linda Diane, Brenda Lee, Marilyn Anne, Martha Jeanne. BSCE, Kans. U., 1940, CE, 1947; SM, Harvard U., 1948. Registered profl. engr., Kans., N.Y.; diplomate Am. Acad. Environ. Engrs. asst. engr. Kans. Bd. Health, 1940-42, san. engr., 1946-48; chief engr. Topeka, 1948-62; assoc. prof. dept. civil engring. U. Kans., 1948-59, prof., 1959-66; exec. sec. Kans. Water Resources Bd., Topeka, 1962-66; dep. commr. N.Y. State Dept. Health, Albany, 1966-70, N.Y. State Dept. Environ. Conservation, Albany, 1970-74; sec. Kans. Dept. Health and Environment, Topeka, 1974-79, dir. water supply devel., 1979-84, retired, 1984; cons. san. engring. Fed. Pub. Housing Authority, USPHS, 1943-46; housing cons. Chgo.-Cook County Health Survey, 1946; cons. water supply and water pollution control USPHS, 1957-66; adviser Govt. of India, 1960; mem. ofcl. exchange to USSR on environ.health research and practice, 1962; adviser WHO, 1964-84; cons., expert witness Occidental Chem. Co., Love Canal, 1990-91; mem. Water Pollution Bd., Internat. Joint Commn., 1967-74, Assembly of Engring. NRC, 1977-80. Contbr. articles to profl. jours. Chmn. Kans. Bible Chair Bd., 1957-66; chmn. com. for new bldg. U. Kans. Sch. Religion. Recipient Disting. Service award U. Kans., 1970, Disting. Engring. Service award U. Kans., 1984. Fellow Royal Soc. Health Gt. Britain (hon.), Am. Pub. Health Assn. (former mem. governing council, exec. bd., pres., chmn. action bd., Centennial award 1972, Sedgwick medal 1981), ASCE (sec. sanitary engring. div. 1959-61, chmn. 1963); mem. Am. Water Works Assn. (Fuller award 1954, Purification div. award 1958), Water Pollution Control Fedn. (Bedell award 1963, hon. mem. 1983), Kans. Pub. Health Assn. (Crumbine award 1965), Kans. Engring. Soc. (Outstanding Engr. award 1978), Nat. Acad. Engring., Kans. Rural Water Assn. (Engr. award 1990), Sigma Xi, Tau Beta Pi. Home: 900 SW 31st St Apt 325 Topeka KS 66611-2196

METZLER, GLENN ELAM, minister; b. Lititz, Pa., Nov. 22, 1945; s. Elam B. and Anna Mary (Martin) M.; m. Esther G. Stoltzfus, July 1, 1967; children: Gwenda L., Millie E., Danita K., Laurel M. BA in Family Counseling, U. Maine, Augusta and Farmington, 1981. Ordained to ministry Mennonite Ch., 1985. Dir. voluntary svc. Mennonite Ch., Hallowell, Maine, 1972-74; pastor Mennonite Ch., Augusta, 1975—; chmn. New Eng. Fellowship of Mennonite Chs., 1986—; carpenter, Augusta, 1979—. Bd. mem. Maine Interfaith Flood Recovery Inc., Waterville, Maine, 1987-88. Mem. Augusta Clergy Assn. Home: RR 1 Box 338 Readfield ME 04355-9733

METZLER, PHILIP LOWRY, JR., air force officer; b. Colorado Springs, Colo., Mar. 14, 1941; s. Philip Lowry Sr. and Elizabeth A. (Louk) M.; m. Patricia Louise Heintz, June 1, 1963; children: Paige Leslie, Philip L. III, Patrick L. BA, U. No. Colo., 1963; MS, Troy (Ala.) State U., 1974. Commd. 2d lt. USAF, 1963, advanced through grades to maj. gen., 1990; unit maintenance officer various assignments, 1963-70; advisor Air Force Pers. Ctr., San Antonio, 1970-73; comdr. Maintenance Squadron, Williams AFB, Ariz., 1974-76; chief maintenance evaluation Hdqrs. USAF in Europe, Ramstein, Fed. Republic Germany, 1976-79; chief aircraft overhaul Ogden (Utah) Air Logistics Ctr., 1980-83; dir. maintenance Sacramento Air Logistics Ctr., 1983-85, dir. materiel mgmt., 1985-86; dir. maintenance and supply Hdqrs. USAF, The Pentagon, 1986-87; dep. chief of staff for logistics Hdqrs. USAF in Europe, Ramstein, 1987-92; pres. Logistics Mgmt. Resources Inc., Ramstein, 1993—. V.p. North Atlantic coun. Girls Scouts U.S., Fed. Republic Germany, 1987-91. Decorated Bronze Star, Legion of Merit, Meritorious Svc. medal; named to Colorado Springs High Sch. Hall of Fame, 1991. Mem. Air Force Assn. (life). Home: 7127 Wintery Loop Colorado Springs CO 80919 Office: Log Mgmt Resources Colorado Springs CO 80919

METZLER, ROGER JAMES, JR., lawyer; b. East Orange, N.J., Feb. 4, 1945; s. Roger James and Dorothy Marie (Clark) M.; m. Marilyn Carol Schick, Apr. 19, 1969; children: Andrea C., Maria N. BS, Brown U., 1967; JD, Santa Clara U., 1975. Ptnr. Farrand, Cooper, Metzler & Bruiniers, San Francisco, 1975-88, McQuaid, Bedford, Clausen & Metzler, San Francisco, 1988-89, Keck, Mahin & Cate, Chgo. and San Francisco, 1990—. Avocation: soccer referee. Office: Keck Mahin and Cate 1 Maritime Plz Fl 23 San Francisco CA 94111-3404

METZLER, THOMAS M., service company executive; b. Bklyn., Nov. 29, 1944; s. Albert M. and Katherine A. (Gunn) M.; m. Janet L. Kraus, June 24, 1989; children: Christine M., Michael C. Grad. Adelphi U., 1985; grad. advanced mgmt. program, Harvard U., 1992. Supr. Am. Airlines, John F. Kennedy Airport, N.Y., 1967-75; sr. analyst Am. Airlines, N.Y.C., 1976-79; mgr. Am. Airlines, Memphis, 1979-82; dir. Learning Ctr. Am. Airlines, Dallas-Ft. Worth, 1982-84; v.p. AMR Svcs. Corp., Dallas-Ft. Worth, 1984-86, pres. airline svcs. div., 1986-89, pres., CEO, 1989—; bd. dirs. Am. Airlines Credit Union. Sgt. U.S. Army, 1964-66. Mem. Nat. Bus. Aircraft Assn., Am. Assocs. Airport Execs., Wings Club. Home: 3918 Fox Glen Dr

Irving TX 75062 Office: AMR Svcs Corp PO Box 619622 MD 4235 Fort Worth TX 75261-9622

METZNER, CHARLES MILLER, federal judge; b. N.Y.C., Mar. 13, 1912; s. Emanuel and Gertrude (Miller) M.; m. Jeanne Gottlieb, Oct. 6, 1966. A.B., Columbia U., 1931, LL.B., 1933. Bar: N.Y. 1933. Pvt. practice, 1934; mem. Jud. Council State N.Y., 1935-41; law clk. to N.Y. supreme ct. justice, 1942-52; exec. asst. to U.S. atty. Gen. Herbert Brownell, Jr., 1953-54; mem. firm Chapman, Walsh & O'Connell, 1954-59; judge U.S. Dist Ct. (so. dist.) N.Y., 1959—; Mem. Law Revision Commn. N.Y. State, 1959; chmn. com. administrn. magistrates system U.S. Jud. Conf., 1970-81; chmn. Columbia Coll. Coun., 1965-66. Pres. N.Y. Young Republican Club, 1941; Trustee Columbia U., 1972-84, trustee emeritus, 1984—; bd. dirs. N.Y.C. Ctr. Music and Drama, 1969-74. Recipient Lawyer Div. of Joint Def. Appeal award, 1961, Columbia U. Alumni medal, 1966, Founders award Nat. Coun. U.S. Magistrates, 1989. Mem. ABA, Am. Law Inst., Fed. Bar Coun. (cert. Disting. Jud. Svc. 1989).

METZNER, RICHARD JOEL, psychiatrist, psychopharmacologist, educator; b. L.A., Feb. 15, 1942; s. Robert Gerson and Esther Rebecca (Groper) M.; children: Jeffrey Anthony, David Jonathan; m. Leila Kirkley, June 26, 1993. BA, Stanford U., 1963; MD, Johns Hopkins U., 1967. Intern, Roosevelt Hosp., N.Y.C., 1967-68; resident in psychiatry Stanford U. Med. Center, 1968-71; staff psychiatrist div. manpower and tng. NIMH-St. Elizabeths Hosp., Washington, 1971-73; chief audiovisual edn. system VA Med. Center Brentwood, L.A., 1973-79, chmn. VA Dist. 26 Ednl. Task Force, 1976-78; asst. prof. psychiatry UCLA Neuropsychiat. Inst., 1973-80, assoc. clin. prof., 1980—, lectr. Sch. Social Welfare, 1975-84; pvt. practice medicine specializing in psychiatry, Bethesda, Md., 1972-73, L.A., 1973—; dir. Western Inst. Psychiatry, L.A., 1977—; pres. Psychiat. Resource Network, Inc., 1984—; Served with USPHS, 1968-71. Recipient 6 awards for film and videotape prods., 1976-80; diplomate Am. Bd. Psychiatry and Neurology (cons. 1974-78, producer audiovisual exam. programs 1975-77). Fellow Am. Psychiat. Assn.; mem. So. Calif. Psychiat. Soc., Mental Health Careerists Assn. (chmn. 1972-73), Phi Beta Kappa. Democrat. Jewish. Contbr. numerous articles to profl. publs., 1963—; producer, writer numerous ednl. films and videotapes, 1970—. Office: 9911 W Pico Blvd Ste 1570 Los Angeles CA 90035-2703

MEULEMAN, ROBERT JOSEPH, banker; b. South Bend, Ind., May 1, 1939; s. Joseph and Louise (Dutrieux) M.; m. Judith Ann Mc Comb, July 1, 1961; children Joseph, Jennifer, Rachel. BA, U. Notre Dame, 1961; MBA, Mich. State U., 1962. Investment analyst Nat. Bank of Detroit, 1965-68, Heritage Investment Advisors, Milw., 1968-72; sr. investment officer St. Joseph Bank and Trust Co., South Bend, 1972-81; pres., chief operating officer Amcore Bank N.Am., Rockford, Ill., 1981—. Bd. dirs. Swedish Am. Hosp. Found., Rockford, 1986—; Rockford Pro-Am., 1986—; campaign leader Crusader Clinic, Rockford, 1988. Served to 1st lt. U.S. Army, 1963-65. Mem. Chartered Fin. Analysts, Milw. Fin. Analysts, Rockford C. of C. (bd. dirs. 1985). Republican. Roman Catholic. Club: Rockford Country. Avocations: skiing, golf, tennis. Home: 5329 Gingeridge Ln Rockford IL 61114-5333 Office: Amcore Bank NA Rockford 501 7th St Rockford IL 61104-1242

MEULI, JUDITH K., communications executive, real estate developer, small business owner; b. Chippewa Falls, Wis., Jan. 15, 1938; d. Earle Joseph and Isabel M. (Dresel) M. B.S., U. Minn., 1963. Sr. designer Women's Graphic Comm., L.A., 1970—; real estate broker, 1990. Editor Nat. NOW Times, 1977-85, Financing the Revolution, 1973, NOW Acts, 1970-71; designer Women's Equality symbol, Human Liberation symbol, Woman Thinker in cloisonne, Women's Peace symbol; author: (with Toni Carabillo) The Feminization of Power, 1988, (with Toni Carabillo and June Bundy Csida) The Feminist Chronicles 1953-1993, 1993. Vice pres. L.A. chpt. NOW, 1969, chpt. coord., 1970, nat. bd. dirs., 1972, 75-77; sec. Fund for the Feminist Majority, 1987—; sec. Feminist Majority Found., 1987—; bd. dirs. 1987—. Recipient Los Angeles Feminist Achievement and Womens Rights Advocacy award, 1981, Women's Rights award NOW, 1982. Democrat. Home: 1126 Hi Point St Los Angeles CA 90035-2610

MEURLIN, KEITH W., airport terminal executive. Mgr. Wash. Dulles Internat. Airport. Office: Washington Dulles Intl Airport PO Box 17045 Washington DC 20041-0045

MEUSE, DAVID RUSSELL, investment banker; b. Cairo, Ill., Apr. 20, 1945; s. David L. and Jeanette (Settlemoir) M.; m. Mary Beth Busch, June 21, 1969; children: Lisa Marie, Charles David, Peter Alexander. BA in Polit. Sci., John Carroll U., 1967; postgrad., Cleve. State U., 1968-69. Ptnr. Ball, Burge, Kraus, Cleve., 1967-74, Prescott, Ball & Turben Co., Cleve., 1973-74, McDonald & Co., Columbus, Ohio, 1974-79; pres., chief exec. officer Charleston Securities Co., Columbus, 1979-81; pres. MRC Inc., Columbus, 1981-86; pres., bd. dirs. Meuse, Rinker, Chapman, Endres & Brooks, Columbus, 1986-90; chmn., chief exec. officer, bd. dirs. Banc One Capital Corp., Columbus, 1990-94; chmn., CEO Banc One Capital Holdings Corp., 1994—; bd. dirs. Banc One Capital Ptnrs. Corp., Banc One Capital Ptnrs. II, II, IV, V Corp., Cen. Benefits Blue Cross Blue Shield, Vacuform Industries, Inc., Nat. Housing & Rehab. Assn., Washington, Merich Capital, Merich Group, Inc., Merich Gen. Corp., Broad St. Capital, High St. Holding, High St. Capital, MRC Investment, Inc., Brencap Corp., Inmet Corp. Bd. dirs. Children's Hosp. Found.; Columbus; chmn. Columbus Assn. of Performing Arts. Mem. Columbus Country Club, Capital Club, Rocky Fork, New Albany Country Club. Republican. Office: Banc One Capital Corp 90 N High St Columbus OH 43215

MEUSER, FREDRICK WILLIAM, retired seminary president, church historian; b. Payne, Ohio, Sept. 14, 1923; s. Henry William and Alvina Maria (Bouyack) M.; m. Jeanne Bond Griffiths, July 29, 1951; children: Jill Martha, Douglas Griffiths. AB, Capital U., 1945, BD, 1948, DD (hon.), 1989; STM, Yale U., 1949, MA, 1953, PhD, 1956; DD (hon.), Tex. Luth. Coll., 1980, Capital U., 1989; LHD (hon.), Augustana Coll., 1985. Ordained to ministry Am. Lutheran Ch., 1948; asst. pastor 1st Luth. Ch., Galveston, Tex., 1948, Christ Luth. Ch., North Miami, Fla., 1949-51; campus minister Yale U., 1951-53; prof. ch. history Luth. Theol. Sem., Columbus, Ohio, 1953-78, dean grad. studies, 1963-69, pres., 1971-78; pres. Trinity Luth. Sem., Columbus, 1978-88; exec. sec. div. theol. studies Luth. Council in U.S.A., 1969-71; ed. World Council Chs., 1968, Luth. World Fedn., 1970; v.p. Am. Luth. Ch., 1974-80; mem. Commn. for a New Luth. Ch., 1982-86. Author: The Formation of the American Lutheran Church, 1958, Luther the Preacher, 1983; author: (with others) Church in Fellowship, 1963, Lutherans in North America, 1975; translator: (with others) What Did Luther Understand by Religion, 1977, The Reconstruction of Morality, 1979; editor: (with others) Interpreting Luther's Legacy, 1967. Recipient Disting. Churchman's award Tex. Luth. Coll., 1972, Joseph Sittler award Trinity Luth. Sem., 1990; named Outstanding Alumnus Capital U., 1977; Am. Assn. Theol. Schs. fellow, 1961-62. Mem. Am. Soc. Ch. History. Home: 6392 Claypool Ct Columbus OH 43213-3435 Office: 2199 E Main St Columbus OH 43209-3913

MEUTER, MARIA COOLMAN, lawyer; b. New Albany, Ind., July 17, 1915; d. William Edmund and Hundley Love (Wells) Coolman; m. Walter Frederick Meuter, Jan. 9, 1942; children: Stephen, Craig Frederick. Student, New Albany Bus. Coll., 1933; LLB, Jefferson Sch. Law, 1939; JD, U. Louisville, 1971. Bar: Ky. 1939, U.S. Ct. Internat. Trade, 1980. Clk. Fed. Land Bank of Louisville, 1933-41; exec. dir. Louisville Bar Assn., 1952-70; trial judge County Ct., Jefferson County, Louisville, 1962-70; assoc. dir. Law Alumni Affairs U. Louisville, 1970—; exec. dir. Continuing Legal Edn., U. Louisville, 1978-83; pvt. practice, Louisville, 1970—; life trustee Law Alumni Found. Vice pres. Beechmont Civic Club, Louisville, 1987-91. Named Disting. Alumnae, U. Louisville Sch. Law, 1976, Ky. col., 1968, Master of Steamboat Flotilla of Jefferson County, 1968. Mem. Ky. Bar Assn. (rec. sec. ho. of dels. 1964-68), Louisville Bar Assn., Jefferson County Women Lawyers (pres.), Nat. Assn. Bar Execs. (rec. sec. 1969-70), AAUW, DAR (com. chmn. John Marshall chpt. 1991), Daus. Am. Colonists, Colonial Dames, Law Alumni Assn. U. Louisville (treas., sec. 1970-75), South Fork Country Club. Republican. Episcopalian. Avocations: golf, bridge, Polynesian dance. Home: 1313 Marret Pl Louisville KY 40215-2368 also: 2855 Gulf Shore Blvd N Naples FL 33940-4339

MEVERS, FRANK CLEMENT, state archivist, historian; b. New Orleans, Oct. 10, 1942; s. Lloyd F. and Mary Ashley (Collins) M.; m. Kathryn Ann Hayes, Dec. 23, 1967; children: John F., Lauren K. BA in History, La. State U., 1965; PhD in Am. History, U. N.C., 1972; MA, La. State U., 1967. Editor Papers of James Madison, Charlottesville, Va., 1972-74, Papers of Josiah Bartlett, Concord, N.H., 1974-77, Papers of William Plumer, Concord, 1977-79; state archivist State of N.H., Concord, 1979—. Editor, author: New Hampshire: State That Made US a Nation, 1989. Mem. Pub. Libr. Bd. Trustees, Concord, 1979—. With U.S. Army, 1967-69, Korea. Episcopalian. Avocation: stamp collecting. Home: 29 Bradley St Concord NH 03301-6432 Office: NH State Archives 71 S Fruit St Concord NH 03301-2410

MEW, THOMAS JOSEPH, III (TOMMY MEW), artist, educator; b. Miami, Fla., Aug. 15, 1942; s. Thomas Joseph and Maude Edith (Perry) M.; m. Mary Ann Kelley, June 17, 1966; 1 son, Thomas Joseph. B.S., Fla. State U., 1962, M.A., 1964; Ph.D., N.Y. U., 1966. Grad. instr. Fla. State U., 1963; asst. prof. art Troy State U., 1966-68, Jacksonville U., 1968-70; prof., chmn. dept. art Berry Coll., 1970—, Dana prof. art; juror art shows: vis. artist; lectr. in field, cons. art; dir. Fluxus West/Southeast. Exhibited in one-man shows Parkway Gallery, Miami, 1962-63, 319 Gallery, N.Y.C., 1968, Meridian (Miss.) Mus., 1976, C.D.O. Gallery, Parma, Italy, 1978, Calif. State U., Sacramento, 1979, Miss. Mus. Art, Jackson, 1979, Art Inst. for Permian Basin, ITex, Arte Studio, Bergamo, Italy; group shows include High Mus., Atlanta, 1971, 72, 74, New Reform Gallery, Aalst, Belgium, 1975, U. Guelph, Ont., Can., 1975, Neuberger Mus., Purchase, N.Y., 1978, Arte Fiera, Bologna, Italy, 1979; represented in permanent collections, Kansas City Art Inst., Mildura Art Centre, Australia, Wichita Art Mus., Jacksonville (Fla.) Art Mus., Macon Mus. Art, AT&T, Harn Mus., U. Iowa; host: Cable TV show Art: The Mew View, 1978—; Filmmaker, 1966-69; contbr. articles to profl. jours. Bd. dirs. Rome Arts Council, 1984—; bd. dirs. Interface. Recipient Gellhorn award N.Y. U., 1966; Cowperthwaite grantee, 1972; Lilly Found. grantee, 1975; Gulf Life grantee, 1977. Mem. Southeastern Coll. Art Conf., Coll. Art Assn. Am., Am. Fedn. Arts, Nat. Art Edn. Assn., Am. Assn. Art Dealers. Home: 100 Saddle Trl Rome GA 30161-6841 Office: Berry Coll Art Dept Mount Berry GA 30149 *I've always moved in the direction of my dreams . . . always tried to make the great dream a reality.*

MEYAART, PAUL JAN, distilling company executive; b. Berchem, Belgium, Mar. 6, 1943; came to U.S., 1965; s. Joseph and Leonie (Devreese) M.; m. Mary-Ann Mota, Mar. 18, 1967; children—Peter, Antoine, Danielle. B.Commerce, U. Antwerp, Belgium, 1965; M.B.A. (Ford internat. fellow 1965-67, Fulbright grantee 1965-67), U. Chgo., 1967. Fin. planning mgr. Sinclair Belgium S. A., Brussels, 1967-70; controller-treas. Knoll Internat. Inc., N.Y.C., 1971-74; v.p. fin. treas. Boyle Midway div. Am. Home Products Co., N.Y.C., 1974-78; v.p. fin. and administrn., treas. Am. Distilling Co. Inc., N.Y.C., 1978—. Mem. Fin. Execs. Inst. Home: 231 S Stough St Hinsdale IL 60521 Office: 245 Park Ave New York NY 10167-0001

MEYBURG, ARNIM HANS, transportation engineer, educator, consultant; b. Bremerhaven, W. Ger., Aug. 25, 1939; came to U.S., 1965; s. Friedel and Auguste (Kleeberg) M.; m. Ruth Meyburg; 1 child, Jennifer Susan. Student, U. Hamburg, 1960-62, Free U. Berlin, 1962-65; M.S. (Fulbright travel grantee), Northwestern U., 1968, Ph.D., 1971. Research assoc. Transp. Center, Northwestern U., 1968-69; asst. prof. transp. engring. Cornell U., 1969-75, assoc. prof., 1975-78, prof., 1978—, acting chmn. dept., 1977-78, chmn. dept., 1980-85, dir. Sch. Civil and Environ. Engring., 1988—, chmn. bd. Univ. Transp. Rsch. Ctr.; vis. mem. faculties U. Calif., Irvine, Tech. U. Munich, Germany, (Fulbright lectr.) U. Sao Paulo, Brazil, 1984, Tech. U. Brunswick, W. Ger., 1985-86; Humboldt Found. research fellow, 1978-79; prin. investigator projects Dept. Transp., NSF, Nat. Coop. Hwy. Research Program, N.Y. State Dept. Transp., U.S. Dept. Transp. Author: (with others) Urban Transportation Modeling and Planning, 1975, Transportation Systems Evaluation, 1976, Survey Sampling and Multivariate Analysis for Social Scientists and Engineers, 1979, Survey Methods for Transport Planning, 1995; co-editor: (with others) Behavioral Travel-Demand Models, 1976, New Horizons in Travel-Behavior Research, 1981, Selected Readings in Transport Survey Methodology, 1992; contbr. articles to profl. jours., chpts. to books. NSF Research Initiation grantee, 1973; recipient Humboldt U.S. Sr. Scientist award, 1984, Fulbright sr. lectr. award, 1984. Mem. ASCE, AAUP, Transp. Rsch. Bd., Transp. Rsch. Forum, Regional Sci. Assn., Sigma Xi, Chi Epsilon. Office: Cornell U 220 Hollister Hall Ithaca NY 14853-3501

MEYE, ROBERT PAUL, retired seminary administrator, writer; b. Hubbard, Oreg., Apr. 1, 1929; s. Robert and Eva (Pfau) M.; m. Mary Cover, June 18, 1954; children: Marianne Meye Thompson, Douglas, John. BA, Stanford U., 1951; BD, Fuller Theol. Sem., 1957, ThM, 1959; DTheol magna cum laude, U. Basel, Switzerland, 1962; DD Eastern Bapt. Theol. Sem., 1990. Prof. No. Bapt. Theol. Sem., Lombard, Ill., 1962-77, dean, 1971-77; dean Sch. Theology, Fuller Theol. Sem., Pasadena, Calif., 1977-90, dean emeritus, 1992—; assoc. provost for Ch. Rels. and Christian Community, 1990-92, prof. N.T. interpretation, 1977-92, prof. emeritus, 92—. Author: Jesus and The Twelve; contbr. articles to profl. jours., dictionaries and encys. Served to lt. (j.g.) USN, 1946-47, 51-54, Korea. Am. Assn. Theol. Schs. grantee, 1970-71; 75-76. Mem. Nat. Assn. Bapt. Profs. of Religion, Studiorum Novi Testamenti Societas, Chgo. Soc. Bibl. Res., Soc. Bibl. Lit., Inst. Bibl. Research, Christianity Today Inst. Republican. Home: 1170 Rubio St Altadena CA 91001-2027 Office: Fuller Theol Sem 135 N Oakland Ave Pasadena CA 91182-0001

MEYER, ALBERT JAMES, educational administrator; b. Cleve., Sept. 24, 1929; s. Jacob Conrad and Esther Agnes (Steiner) M.; m. Mary Ellen Yoder, Aug. 21, 1954; children: Richard, Anne, Kathryn, Barbara, Elaine. BA, Goshen Coll., 1950; MA, Princeton U., 1952, PhD, 1954. Asst. in teaching and rsch. Princeton (N.J.) U., 1950-53; fellow U. Basel, Switzerland, 1953-54, rsch. assoc., 1956-57; dir. for France, rep. European peace sect. Mennonite Ctrl. Com., 1954-57; asst. prof. physics Goshen (Ind.) Coll., 1958-61, prof., rsch. prof., 1967-89, adj. rsch. prof., 1989—; acad. dean, prof. Bethel Coll., North Newton, Kans., 1961-66, Menno Simons lectr., 1993; exec. sec., pres. Mennonite Bd. Edn., Elkhart, Ind., 1967—; exec. for secretariat Puidoux Theol. Confs., 1955-57; former mem. staff Mennonite Student Svcs. Com.; former coord. com. on liberal arts edn. North Ctrl. Assn. Colls. and Secondary Schs.; vis. rsch. scientist U. Paris, 1974-75; vis. rschr. New Coll. Berkeley, 1986-87; presenter in field; former cons. Conrad Grebel Coll., U. Waterloo, Ont., Can.; mem. peace and social concerns com. Mennonite Ch. 1959-71; former mem. Continuation Com. of Hist. Peace Chs. Contbr. articles to denominational periodicals and sci. jours. Princeton U. exch. fellow and Charles Foster Kent fellow Nat. Coun. for Religion in Higher Edn., 1935-54. Mem. Denominational Execs. for Ch.-Related Higher Edn. (chmn. 1984-86), Am. Assn. for Higher Edn., Am. Assn. Physics Tchrs. Avocations: tennis, hockey, hiking. Home: 708 Emerson St Goshen IN 46526-3904 Office: Mennonite Bd Edn 500 S Main St Elkhart IN 46515-1142

MEYER, ALDEN MERRILL, environmental association executive; b. Buffalo, Mar. 21, 1952; s. Arthur Merrill Meyer and Susan (Rogers) Meyer Markle. BA, Yale U., 1975; MS, Am. U., 1990. Energy policy analyst Conn. Citizen Action Group, Hartford, 1975-78, Environ. Action Found., Washington, 1979-82; exec. dir. Environ. Action, Inc., 1983-85, League Conservation Voters, Washington, 1985-88; dir. climate change and energy policy Union of Concerned Scientists, Washington, 1989-92, legis. dir., 1992—; bd. dirs. Ams. for Environment, Washington 1983-87, chmn., 1985-87; bd. dirs. Urban Environment Conf., Washington, 1984-87, Zero Population Growth, 1989—; pres. bd. dirs. Safe Energy Communication Council, Washington, 1980-85; chmn. U.S. Climate Action Network, 1990—; mem. adv. coun. Nat. Renewable Energy Lab., 1993—; mem. state and local adv. bd. U.S. Dept. Energy, 1994—. Mem. Yale Whiffenpoofs, 1975. Democrat. Avocations: hiking; camping; skiing; singing. Home: 15 Montgomery Ave Takoma Park MD 20912-4614 Office: Union Concerned Scientists 1616 P St NW Washington DC 20036-1434

MEYER, ALICE K., investor; b. Corpus Christi, Tex., Sept. 26, 1928; d. Richard Mifflin and Mary Etta (Searcy) Kleberg; m. Richard Wells Reynolds, Alpr. 23, 1949 (div. Aug. 1970); children: Katherine Berkeley, Michael Mifflin, Alice Kleberg; m. Vaughan Benjamin Meyer, Dec. 23, 1972; children: Catherine H. Meyer Lange, Beverly Vaughan. BA, U. Tex., 1945-49. Treas. Laguna Gloria Art Mus., Austin, Tex.; trustee, chmn. Saint Mary's Hall, San Antonio, 1972-75. Mem. Jr. League, Austin (treas., pres.), San Antonio Mus. Assn. (trustee, treas. 1972—, chmn. 1987-91), The Argyle Club, Club Giraud, San Antonio Country Club, Phi Beta Kappa. Avocations: museum-going, travel. Home: 200 Patterson Ave Apt 906 San Antonio TX 78209-6269 Office: PO Box 6985 San Antonio TX 78209-0985

MEYER, ALICE VIRGINIA, state official; b. N.Y.C., Mar. 15, 1921; d. Martin G. and Marguerite Helene (Houzé) Kliemand; m. Theodore Harry Meyer, June 28, 1947; children: Robert Charles, John Edward. BA, Barnard Coll., 1941; MA, Columbia U., 1942. Tchr. pub. schs. Elmont, N.Y., 1942-43; tchr. Fairlawn (N.J.) High Schs., 1943-47; office mgr., sales rep. N.Y.C., 1948-55; substitute tchr. Pub. Schs., Easton, Conn., 1965-72; state rep., asst. minority leader Conn. State Legislature, Hartford, 1976-93; mem. Ct. Bd. of Govs. for Higher Edn., 1993—. Mem. bd. trustees Discovery Mus., 1980—, United Way Regional Youth Substance Abuse Project, Bridgeport, 1983-93; bd. dirs. Fairfield County Lit. Coalition, Bridgeport, 1988—, 3030 Park, 1993—; vice chmn. Easton Rep. Town Com., 1970-78; mem. strategic planning com. Town of Easton, 1993—; vice-chmn. adv. coun. on intergovtl. rels., 1988—; mem. Conn. Commn. on Quality Edn., 1992-93; supporter of Conn. small towns, 1988; mem. lt. gov's. commn. on mandate reduction, 1995. Named Legislator of Yr. Conn. Libr. Assn. 1985; Guardian Small bus. grantee Nat. Fedn. Ind. Bus., 1987. Mem. AAUW (past local pres. 1976, bd. dirs. 1982), LWV, Bus. and Profl. Women, Nat. Order Women Legislators (regional dir. 1987—, past pres. Conn. chpt.). Congregationalist. Avocations: swimming, sailing, bridge. Home: 18 Lantern Hill Rd Easton CT 06612-2218

MEYER, ANN JANE, human development educator; b. N.Y.C., Mar 11, 1942; s. Louis John and Theresa M B.A., U. Mich., 1964; M.A., U. Calif.-Berkeley, Ph.D., 1971. Asst. prof. dept. human devel. Calif. State U.-Hayward, 1972-77, assoc. prof., 1977-84, prof., chmn. dept., 1984—. Mem. Am. Psychol. Assn., Western Psychol. Assn., Western Gerontol. Soc. Office: Dept Human Devel Calif State U Hayward CA 94542

MEYER, ARMIN HENRY, retired diplomat, author, educator; b. Ft. Wayne, Ind., Jan. 19, 1914; s. Armin Paul and Leona (Buss) M.; m. Alice James, Apr. 23, 1949; 1 dau., Kathleen Alice. Student, Lincoln (Ill.) Coll., 1931-33; A.B., Capital U., 1935, LL.D., 1957; M.A., Ohio State U., 1941, LL.D.; LL.D., Wartburg Coll., S.D. Sch. Mines and Tech., 1972. Faculty Capital U., Columbus, Ohio, 1935-41; staff OWI, Egypt, Iraq, 1942-46; U.S. pub. affairs officer Baghdad, Iraq, 1946-48; pub. affairs adviser U.S. Dept. State, 1948-52; sec. Am. embassy, Beirut, Lebanon, 1952-55; dep. chief mission Kabul, Afghanistan, 1955-57; dep. dir. Office South Asian Affairs Dept. State, 1957-58, dep. dir. Office Near Eastern Affairs, 1958-59, dir. Office Nr. Ea. Affairs, 1959-61, dep. asst. sec. of state for Nr. Ea. and South Asian Affairs, 1961; U.S. ambassador to Lebanon, 1961-65, Iran, 1965-69, Japan, 1969-72; spl. asst. to sec. state, chmn. Cabinet Com. to Combat Terrorism, 1972-73; vis. prof. Am. U., 1974-75; dir. Ferdowsi project Georgetown U., 1975-79, adj. prof. diplomacy, 1975-86; dir. Internat. Affairs Ecology and Environ. Inc.; Woodrow Wilson vis. fellow, 1974—; cons. internat. bus. and environment, 1975—. Author: Assignment Tokyo: An Ambassador's Journal, 1974; co-author: Education in Diplomacy, 1987. Hon. mem. Lincoln Sesquicentennial Commn., 1959; bd. dirs. Washington Inst. Fgn. Affairs, 1979—, pres., 1988—. Recipient Meritorious Svc. award Dept. State, 1958, Superior Honor award 1973; decorated Order of Rising Sun, 1st class (Japan), 1982; inducted into Hall of Excellence Ohio Fedn. Ind. Colls., 1989. Mem. Sigma Psi. Lutheran. Home: 4610 Reno Rd NW Washington DC 20008-2941

MEYER, AUGUST CHRISTOPHER, JR., broadcasting company executive, lawyer; b. Champaign, Ill., Aug. 14, 1937; s. August C. and Clara (Rocke) M.; m. Karen Haugh Hassett, Dec. 28, 1960; children: August Christopher F., Elisabeth Hassett. BA cum laude, Harvard U., 1959, LLB, 1962. Bar: Ill. 1962. Ptr. Meyer, Capel, Hirschfeld, Muncy, Jahn and Aldeen, Champaign, Ill., 1962-77, of counsel, 1977—; owner, dir., officer Midwest TV, Inc., Sta. KFMB-TV-AM-FM, San Diego, Sta. WCIA-TV, Champaign, Ill. , Sta. WMBD-TV-AM, WMXP, Peoria, Ill., 1968—; pres. Sta. KFMB-TV-AM-FM, San Diego, Sta. WCIA-TV, Champaign, Ill. , Sta. WMBD-TV-AM, WMXP, 1976—; bd. dirs. BankIll.; spl. asst. atty. gen. State of Ill., 1968-76. Chmn. bd. trustees Carle Found. Hosp., Urbana, Ill. Mem. Ill. Bar Assn., Champaign County Bar Assn. Club: Champaign Country. Home: 1408 S Prospect Ave Champaign IL 61820-6837 Office: Midwest TV Inc PO Box 777 509 S Neil St Champaign IL 61820-5219 also: Sta KFMB PO Box 85888 7677 Engineer Rd San Diego CA 92111-1515

MEYER, B. FRED, small business executive, home designer and builder, product designer; b. Long Island, N.Y., Jan. 6, 1918; s. Barthold Fred and Edna May (Clark) M.; m. Mary E. Carman, July 18, 1951; children: Patricia Meyer Sauer, Susan Meyer Sachs. Student, Pratt Inst., 1935-39, Johns Hopkins U., 1946-48, Wayne State U., 1954-55. Registered builder, Fla. Project engr. Lear, Inc., Grand Rapids, Mich., 1948-51; group supr. design Ternstedt div. GM, Detroit, 1951-53, gen. supr. design, 1953-55; engring. exec. for mech. and elec. products GM, Warren, Mich., 1955-63, engring. exec. for new product design, 1963-71, product design exec. Fisher Body div., 1971-75; pres. BFM Assocs., Inc. (name Fred Meyer, Inc. 1990), Sarasota, Fla., 1975—. Patentee on pendulum type seat belt retractor, power window switch, power window actuator, 6-way seat switch, 6-way seat actuator, rear trunk pull-down mechanism, numerous others. Capt. USAAF, 1942-46, ETO. Mem. Oaks Country Club (Osprey, Fla.). Avocations: golf, computers, travel, tennis. Home and Office: 4131 Boca Pointe Dr Sarasota FL 34238

MEYER, BARRY MICHAEL, motion picture executive; b. N.Y.C., Nov. 28, 1943; s. Perry and Lillian Helen (Katz) M.; m. Barbara Patricia, June 12, 1966; children: Matthew, Elizabeth. BA, U. Rochester, 1964; JD, Case Western Res. U., 1967. Bar: N.Y. Legal counsel ABC, N.Y.C., 1968-70; dir. bus. affairs ABC, Los Angeles, 1970-71; dir. bus. affairs Warner Bros. TV, Los Angeles, 1971-73, v.p. bus. affairs, 1973-77, exec. v.p., 1977-84; exec. v.p. Warner Bros. Inc., Los Angeles, 1984—. Contbr. articles to profl. jours. Bd. dirs. San Fernando Valley Child Guidance Clinic, Calif. Mem. Hollywood Radio and TV Soc. (bd. dirs.), Nat. Acad. TV Arts and Scis. (bd. dirs.), Am. Mgmt. Assn. Office: Warner Bros Inc 4000 Warner Blvd Burbank CA 91522-0001

MEYER, BERNARD STERN, lawyer, former judge; b. Balt., June 7, 1916; s. Benjamin and Josephine Meyer; m. Elaine Strass, June 25, 1939 (div.); children: Patricia, Susan; m. Edythe Birnbaum, Apr. 18, 1975; m. Hortense Fox, Oct. 29, 1991. B.S., Johns Hopkins U., 1936; LL.B., U. Md., 1938; LL.D., Hofstra U., 1980, Western State U. Coll. Law, 1982, Union U., 1984. Bar: Md. 1938, D.C., N.Y. 1947. Assoc. Fisher & Fisher, Balt., 1938-41; with Office Gen. Counsel Treasury Dept., Washington, 1941-43; pvt. practice, N.Y.C., 1948-54; ptnr. Meyer, Fink, Weinberger & Levin, N.Y.C., 1954-58; justice N.Y. State Supreme Ct., 1958-72; of counsel Fink, Weinberger, Fredman & Charney, P.C., N.Y.C., 1973-79; ptnr. Meyer, English & Cianciulli, P.C., Mineola, N.Y., 1975-79; assoc. judge N.Y. Ct. Appeals, Albany, 1979-86; dep. atty. gen. in charge spl. Attica investigation State of N.Y., 1975; ptnr. Meyer, Suozzi, English & Klein P.C., Mineola, 1987—; assoc. spl. counsel Moreland Commn. To Study Workmen's Compensation Adminstrn. and Costs, 1955-57; mem. com. on govt. integrity State of N.Y., 1987-90. Contbr. articles to profl. jours. Founder United Fund L.I.; former mem. adv. bd. Commn. Law and Social Action, Am. Jewish Congress; chmn. Task Force on Permanency Planning for Foster Children, 1986-91; past pres., bd. dirs. Health and Welfare Coun. Nassau County; former mem. bd. dirs. Nassau-Suffolk region NCCJ, Nassau County coun. Boy Scouts Am., Nat. Ctr. for State Cts.; mem. Coalition for Effective Govt., 1991—. Lt. USNR, WWII. Recipient Disting. Svc. award L.I. Press, Presdl. medal Hofstra U., Disting. Alumnus award. Mem. ABA, Am. Bar Found., Am. Coll. Trial Lawyers, Am. Law Inst., N.Y. Bar Assn. (chmn. jud. sect.). N.Y. Bar Found., Assn. Bar of City of N.Y. (chmn. libr., matrimonial, election law com.), Nassau County Bar Assn. (Disting. Svc. medallion 1982), Am. Coll. Trial Lawyers, Nat. Conf. State Trial Judges (exec. com., past chmn.), Nat. Coll. State Judiciary (bd. dirs.), Assn. Supreme Ct. Justices (past pres., chmn. pattern jury instrn. com., 1962-79), Supreme Ct. Hist. Soc. (modern

courts com.), Nassau County Lawyers Assn. (award), Scribes, Order of Coif, Omicron Delta Kappa. Office: Meyer Suozzi English & Klein PC 1505 Kellum Pl Mineola NY 11501-4811

MEYER, BETTY JEAN, physical education educator; b. Hudson, S.D., Oct. 23, 1943; d. Thomas G. and Hazel Jeanette (Lundstrom) Eidsness; m. Edwin T. Meyer, Aug. 8, 1970. BS in Edn., So. State Coll., Springfield, S.D., 1967. Cert. tchr., Nebr. Tchr. instrumental and vocal music Geddes (S.D.) Pub. Sch., 1965-66; physical edn. tchr. Harmony (Minn.) Area Schs., 1967-70; physical edn., music tchr. Holy Trinity Grade Sch., Hartington, Nebr., 1970-71; instrumental, vocal music tchr., Holy Trinity Grade Sch., Hartington, 1979-80, physical edn. tchr., jr. high sch. coach, 1981-93; instrumental, vocal music tchr., asst. coach Wynot (Nebr.) Pub. Schs., 1971-75. Mem. AAHPERD, Nebr. Assn. for Health, Physical Edn., Recreation and Dance, Nat. Fedn. Interscholastic Coaches, Nebr. Coaches Assn. Roman Catholic. Avocations: softball, bowling, cross word puzzles. Home: 411 S Madison Hartington NE 68739 Office: Holy Trinity Grade Sch 502 S Broadway Hartington NE 68739

MEYER, BILL, newspaper publisher, editor; b. Pratt, Kans., Aug. 6, 1925; s. Otto William and Ruth Clarinda (Jones) M.; m. Joan Aileen Wight, Sept. ll, 1949; 1 child, Eric Kent. BS in Journalism, U. Kans., 1948. News editor Marion County Record, Hoch Pub. Co., Inc., Marion, Kans., 1948-67, editor, pub., 1967—; owner Cottonwood Valley Agy., Marion, 1990—; editor 99th Inf. Divsn. Assn., Marion, 1971—; lectr. media law Wichita (Kans.) State U., 1985; polit. interviewer St. KPTS-TV, Wichita, 1983-91; bd. dirs. Ctrl. Nat. Bank, Junction City, Kans.; mil. cons.; travel agt. Battlefield Tours, Slidell, La., 1990—. Past pres. Marion Sch. dist. Bd. Edn., Marion County Hosp. Dist.; bd. dirs. Marion Manor Nursing Home, Kans. Hist. Soc., 1985—; trustee, past pres. William Allen White Found., Lawrence, Kans.; mem. selection com. for judges, 8th Jud. Dist., 1994—. With U.S. Army, 1943-45, ETO. Recipient commendation Kans. Ho. of Reps., 1982, 99th Inf. Div. Assn., 1986, 89, named Hon. Col. Kans. Calvary, 1987, Hon. Ky. Col., 1990. Mem. Nat. Newspaper Assn., Kans. Press Assn. (pres. 1982-83, Boyd Community Svc. award 1979), Marion C. of C. (past bd. dirs.), Marion Country Club, Masons, Shriners, Kiwanis (pres. Marion 1957), Sigma Delta Chi. Republican. Methodist. Avocations: military vehicle restoration, flying, military history. Home: 425 Locust St Marion KS 66861-0099 Office: Hoch Pub Co Inc 117 South 3d St Marion KS 66861-0278

MEYER, BRUD RICHARD, pharmaceutical company executive; b. Waukegan, Ill., Feb. 22, 1926; s. Charles Lewis and Mamie Olive (Broom) M.; m. Betty Louise Stine (dec. 1970); children: Linda (Mrs. Gary Stillabower), Louise (Mrs. Donald Knochel), Janet (Mrs. Gerald Cockrell), Jeff, Karen, Blake, Amy; m. Barbara Ann Hamilton, Nov. 26, 1970. B.S., Purdue U., 1949. With Eli Lilly & Co., Indpls., 1949-87, indsl. engr., 1949-56, supr. indsl. engr., 1956-59, sr. personnel rep., 1960-64; personnel mgr. Eli Lilly & Co., Lafayette, Ind., 1964-67; asst. dir. Eli Lilly & Co., Lafayette, 1967-69, dir. adminstrn., 1969-79, dir. personnel and public relations, 1980-87, ret., 1987. Bd. dirs. Lafayette Home Hosp., 1977—, Hanna Community Ctr., 1983—; Tippecanoe Hist. Corp., 1985—; bd. dirs. United Way Tippecanoe County, 1970-76, pres., 1974; bd. dirs. Legal Aid Soc. Tippecanoe County, 1973—, Jr. Achievement, pres., 1979; bd. dirs. Lilly Credit Union 1969-75, pres., 1973-74; mem. Citizen's Com. on Alcoholism, 1966-72; bd. dirs. Greater Lafayette Community Centers, 1975-79, pres., 1977-78; mem., mng. dir. Battle Tippecanoe Outdoor Drama Bd. Served with USAAF, 1943-45. Mem. Pi Tau Sigma, Lambda Chi Alpha, C. of C. Greater Lafayette (bd. dirs., v.p. 1969-73), Battleground Hist. Soc. Methodist. Home: 4217 Trees Hill Dr Lafayette IN 47905-3451 Office: Eli Lilly & Co PO Box 7685 Lafayette IN 47903-7685

MEYER, C. RICHARD, architect. BArch, U. Calif., Berkeley, 1968. Registered architect, Wash. With The Callison Partnership, Seattle, 1977—, dir. quality assurance; mem. adv. bd. cert. program project mgmt. U. Wash.; contracts rev. panelist Soc. Archtl. Adminstrs.; mem. faculty Pacific real estate symposium N.W. Real Estate Inst.; guest lectr. Archtl. Registration Exam. Seminar; guest lectr. coll. architecture and urban planning U. Wash.; guest panelist Internat. Conf. of Bldg. Ofcls. Nat. Conf., 1991. Mem. AIA (treas. Seattle chpt., mem. steering com. Pacific NW regional conf., vice-chair nat. risk mgmt. com., mem. steering com. nat. practice com., liaison to Am. Arbitration Assn.), Nat. Inst. Bldg. Scis. Office: The Callison Partnership Ltd 1420 5th Ave # 2400 Seattle WA 98101-2343

MEYER, CHARLES APPLETON, former retailing executive; b. Boston, June 27, 1918; s. George von Lengerke and Frances (Saltonstall) M.; m. Suzanne Seyburn, June 15, 1940; children: Brooke M. Gray, Nancy M. Hovey. BA, Phillips Acad.; B.A., Harvard, 1939. With Sears, Roebuck & Co., 1939-69; beginning in New Haven store, successively mail order buyer Sears, Roebuck & Co., Boston; asst. buyer hdqrs. orgn.; staff asst. fgn. stores, mgr. fgn. adminstrn., pres. Sears, Roebuck & Co. (Sears subsidiary) Bogota, Colombia, 1939-55; v.p. Sears, Roebuck & Co. (Sears subsidiary) 1955-60, v.p., dir. southwestern ter., 1960-66, v.p., dir. eastern ter., 1966-69, v.p. corp. planning, 1973-78, sr. v.p. public affairs, 1978-81; ret., 1980; asst. sec. state for inter-Am. affairs, 1969-73; bd. dirs. Addison Capital Shares. Life trustee Children's Meml. Hosp. Chgo., Art Inst. Chgo., Lake Forest (Ill.) Coll.; trustee emeritus Phillips Acad., Andover, Mass. Capt. AUS, World War II. Clubs: Harvard (N.Y.); Racquet (Chgo.); Old Elm (Ft. Sheridan, Ill.); Shoreacres (Lake Bluff, Ill.); Metropolitan (Washington). Home: 1320 N Sheridan Rd Lake Forest IL 60045-1444 Office: 135 S La Salle St Chicago IL 60603-4105

MEYER, DANIEL JOSEPH, machinery company executive; b. Flint, Mich., May 31, 1936; s. John Michael and Margaret (Meehan) M.; m. Bonnie Harrison, June 22, 1963; children:—Daniel P., Jennifer. B.S., Purdue U., 1958; M.B.A., Ind. U., 1963. C.P.A., N.Y. Mgr. Touche, Ross & Co., Detroit, 1964-69; contr. Cin. Milacron, Inc., 1969-77, v.p. fin., treas., 1977-83, exec. v.p. fin. and adminstrn., 1983-86, pres., chief operating officer, 1987-90, pres., chief exec. officer, 1990-91, chmn., chief exec. officer, 1991-92, also bd. dirs.; bd. dirs. E.W. Scripps Inc., Hubbell Inc., Star Bank Corp. Served with U.S. Army, 1959. Mem. Am. Inst. C.P.A.'s. Club: Kenwood Country (Cin.). Home: 8 Grandin Ln Cincinnati OH 45208-3304 Office: Cin Milacron Inc 4701 Marburg Ave Cincinnati OH 45209-1025

MEYER, DENNIS IRWIN, lawyer; b. Dayton, Ohio, Oct. 20, 1935; s. Luther Edward and Mary (McGee) M.; m. Rita Murray, June 23, 1962; children: Matthew, Michael, Rita Catherine, Peter, Denise, Abigail. BS, U. Dayton, 1957; LLB, Georgetown U., 1960, LLM, 1962. Bar: Ohio 1960, D.C. 1962. Atty.-advisor U.S Tax Ct., Washington, 1960-62; ptnr. Baker & McKenzie, Washington, 1965—; bd. dirs. United Fin. Banking Cos., Vienna, Va., Splty. Retailing, College Park, Md., Oakwood Homes, Greensboro, N.C., Daily Express, Inc., Carlisle, Pa.; gen. ptnr. Potomac Investment Assoc., Md., 1976—. Mem. ABA, Internat. Fiscal Assn., Met. Club, 1925 F Street Club of Washington, Belle Haven Country Club, Avenel Golf Club, Robert Trent Jones Golf Club. Roman Catholic. Office: Baker & McKenzie 815 Connecticut Ave NW Washington DC 20006-4004

MEYER, DONALD GORDON, college dean, educator; b. St. Louis, Nov. 5, 1934; s. William Gordon and Grace Frances (Picraux) M.; m. Marilyn Lee Nathan, June 9, 1956; children: Wayne, Kathleen. BA, Blackburn Coll., 1956; MA, Northwestern U., 1959, PhD, 1965. Instr. econs. Oberlin (Ohio) Coll., 1959-60; lectr. Northwestern U., Evanston, Ill., spring 1960; mem. faculty Loyola U., Chgo., 1961—, assoc. prof. mktg., 1967-70, prof., chmn. dept., 1970—; dir. Loyola U. Grad. Sch. Bus., Chgo., 1975-77; dean Loyola U. Sch. Bus. Adminstrn., Chgo., 1977—; rsch. cons. Lerner Newspapers, 1964-72; mem. adv. bd. regional econ. seminars Ill. Bell Telephone Co., 1968-69; bd. dirs. Binks Mfg. Co. Trustee Blackburn Coll., Carlinville, Ill., 1973-82. Scholar Northwestern U., 1956-57; fellow, 1957-58; rsch. fellow, 1958-59; recipient Wall St. Jour. award, 1956. Mem. Am. Mktg. Assn., Am. Econs. Assn., Am. Inst. Decision Scis. (editor Mktg. Insights 1969). Home: 2306 Grant St Evanston IL 60201-2109 Office: Loyola U Sch Bus Adminstrn 820 N Michigan Ave Chicago IL 60611-2103

MEYER, DONALD RAY, psychologist, brain researcher; b. Rhineland, Mo., July 31, 1924; s. Julius Caesar and Annie Laurie (Wagner) M.; m. Patricia Lee Morgan, Dec. 31, 1957; 1 child, Julia Catherine. A.B., U. Mo., 1947; M.S., U. Wis., 1948, Ph.D., 1950. Asst. prof. psychology Ohio State

U., Columbus, 1950-51, assoc. prof. psychology, 1951-57, prof. psychology, 1957-85, prof. emeritus, 1985—; dir. lab. comparative and physiol. psychology Ohio State U., Columbus, 1958-85. Consulting editor to various jours.; contbr. articles to profl. jours. Served with USAF, 1943-46. Fellow AAAS, APA (pres. div. comparative and physiol. psychology 1975), Midwestern Psychol. Assn. (pres. 1971), Soc. Exptl. Psychologists, Am. Psychol. Soc., Phi Beta Kappa, Sigma Xi. Republican. Calvinist. Achievements include participation in Project Mercury, 1st manned space program. Avocation: arborist. Home: 476 Overbrook Dr Columbus OH 43214-3127 Office: Dept Psychology Ohio State U 1885 Neil Ave Columbus OH 43210-1222

MEYER, DONALD ROBERT, banker, lawyer; b. Phoenix, June 4, 1942; s. Donald Duncan and Eleanor M.; m. Virginia Whitesel, Sept. 3, 1966; 2 children. AB, U. Calif., Berkeley, 1964, JD, 1967; postgrad. Harvard U. Sch. Bus. Adminstrn., 1968. Bar: Calif. 1972. Lectr. Seoul Nat. Univ., Korea, 1969-70; assoc. Graham & James, San Francisco, 1971-76; asst. sec. Calif. First Bank (name now Union Bank), San Francisco, 1973—, v.p., 1976-78, gen. counsel, 1976—, sr. v.p., 1978—. Contbr.: Intro to the Law & Legal System of Korea, 1983. Mem. World Affairs Council, San Francisco, Sierra Club; co-chmn. San Francisco/Seoul Sister City Com., 1980-90; trustee Asian Art Found. of San Francisco, 1985-92; commr. Asian Art Mus., San Francisco, 1985-91. Recipient Key to Seoul, Korea, 1984. Mem. ABA, San Francisco Bar Assn., Am. Bankers Assn. (v.p. Calif. State 1982-83), Calif. Bankers Assn. (chmn. legal affairs com. 1982-84, svc. award 1989), Korean-Am. C. of C. (dir. San Francisco sec., bd. dirs. 1974-93), Soc. Calif. Pioneers, Univ. Club of San Francisco, Bohemian Club. Republican. Episcopalian. Office: Union Bank 350 California St San Francisco CA 94104-1402

MEYER, EDMOND GERALD, energy and natural resources educator, resources scientist, entrepreneur, former chemistry educator, university administrator; b. Albuquerque, Nov. 2, 1919; s. Leopold and Beatrice (Ilfeld) M.; m. Betty F. Knobloch, July 4, 1941; children: Lee Gordon, Terry Gene, David Gary. B.S. in Chemistry, Carnegie Mellon U., 1940, M.S., 1942; Ph.D., U. N.Mex., 1950. Chemist Harbison Walker Refractories Co., 1940-41; instr. Carnegie Mellon U., 1941-42; asst. phys. chemist Bur. Mines, 1942-44; chemist research div. N.Mex. Inst. Mining and Tech., 1946-48; head dept. sci. U. Albuquerque, 1950-52; head dept. chemistry N.Mex. Highlands U., 1952-59; dir. Inst. Sci. Rsch., 1957-63; dean Grad. Sch., 1961-63; dean Coll. Arts and Sci., U. Wyo., 1963-75, v.p., 1974-80, prof. energy and natural resources, 1981-87, prof. and dean emeritus, 1987—; exec. cons. Diamond Shamrock Corp., 1980; bd. dirs. Carbon Fuels Corp., First Nat. Bank, Laramie; sci. adviser Gov. of Wyo.; pres. Coal Tech. Corp., 1981—; cons. Los Alamos Nat. Lab., NFS, HHS, GAO, Wyo. Bancorp.; contractor investigator Rsch. Corp., Dept. Interior, AEC, NIH, NSF, Dept. Energy, Dept. Edn.; Fulbright exch. prof. U. Concepcion, Chile, 1959. Co-author: Chemistry-Survey of Principles, 1963, Legal Rights of Chemists and Engineers, 1977, Industrial Research & Development Management, 1982; contbr. articles to profl. jours.; patentee in field. Lt. comdr. USNR, 1944-46, ret. Recipient Disting. Svc. award Jaycees; rsch. fellow U. N.Mex., 1948-50. Fellow AAAS, Am. Inst. Chemists (pres. 1992-93, chmn. 1994—); mem. Assoc. Western Univs. (chmn. 1972-74), Am. Chem. Soc. (councilor 1962-90), Biophys. Soc., Coun. Coll. Arts and Scis. (pres. 1971, sec.-treas. 1972-75, dir. Washington office 1973), Laramie C. of C. (pres. 1984), Laramie Regional Airport Bd. (chair 1989-93, treas. 1994—), Sigma Xi. Home: 1058 Colina Dr Laramie WY 82070-5015 Office: U Wyo Laramie WY 82071-3825

MEYER, EDWARD HENRY, advertising agency executive; b. N.Y.C., Jan. 8, 1927; s. I.H. and Mildred (Driesen) M.; m. Sandra Raabin, Apr. 26, 1957; children: Margaret Ann, Anthony Edward. B.A. with honors in Econs., Cornell U., 1949. With Bloomingdale's div. Federated Dept Stores, 1949-51, Biow Co. (agy.), 1951-56; with Grey Advt., Inc., N.Y.C., 1956—; exec. v.p. Grey Advt., Inc., 1963-68, pres., chief exec. officer, 1968—, chmn. bd., 1970—; bd. dirs. May Dept. Stores co., Ethan Allan Interiors Inc., Harman Internat. Industries, Inc., Bowne & Co., Inc.; bd. dirs. trustee various mut. funds Merrill Lynch Asset Mgmt., Inc. Trustee Am. Mus. Natural History, Guggenheim Mus.; bd. dirs. NYU Med. Ctr., Film Soc. of Lincoln Ctr. With USCGR, 1945-47. Mem. Econ. Club (N.Y.C.), Century Country Club, Harmonie Club (N.Y.C.), Univ. Club (N.Y.C.). Office: Grey Advt Inc 777 3rd Ave New York NY 10017-1301

MEYER, EDWARD N., lawyer; b. Bklyn., Mar. 8, 1939. BS, U. Wis., 1960; LLB, Columbia U., 1963. Bar: N.Y. 1964, U.S. Dist. Ct. (so. and ea. dists.) N.Y. 1970, U.S. Supreme Ct. 1976. Ptnr. Winston & Strawn, N.Y.C. Mem. N.Y. State Bar Assn., N.Y. County Lawyers Assn. Office: Winston & Strawn 175 Water St New York NY 10038-4918

MEYER, EDWARD PAUL, advertising executive; b. Chgo., May 23, 1949; s. Edward and Eleanor Kathryn (DeJong) M.; m. Marsha L. Tower, Aug. 10, 1974; children: Paul Edward, Sarah Linnea. BA in Econs. and Bus. Adminstrn., Wheaton (Ill.) Coll., 1971, MA in Comm., 1983. Asst. dir. Wheaton Coll. Alumni Assn., 1972-81; v.p. corp. comm. The Yarmouth Group, Inc. (formerly Richard Ellis Co.), Chgo., 1981-88, sr. v.p., 1988—; cons. mktg. Service Auto Glass, Lombard, Ill., 1979—. Active with Coll. Ch. Wheaton, 1974—; pres., bd. dirs. Crusader Club Wheaton Coll., 1985-88; bd. dirs. Christian Svc. Brigade, Wheaton, 1985—, chmn., 1991—. Mem. Pub. Rels. Soc. Am., Internat. Assn. Bus. Communicators. Republican. Home: 1303 E Harrison Ave Wheaton IL 60187-4422 Office: The Yarmouth Group Two Prudential Pla Ste 1300 Chicago IL 60601

MEYER, EDWIN DALE, SR., school system administrator; b. Peoria, Ill., Sept. 2, 1943; s. Dale Lorenzo and Alice Eva (Bell) M.; m. Sharon Anne Allen, Dec. 26, 1966; children: Wendy Kimryn Meyer Rathmell, Edwin Dale II, John C. BS in Edn., Peru (Nebr.) State Coll., 1965; MS in Edn., U. Nebr., Kearney, 1974; EdS, U. Nebr., Omaha, 1985; EdD, Drake U., 1992. Tchr. Red Oak (Iowa) Community Sch. Dist., 1965-66, Bellevue (Nebr.) Pub. Schs., 1966-67, 69-78, Hildreth (Nebr.) Pub. Sch., 1968-69; grad. instr. ctrl. office adminstrn. Kearney State Coll., 1967-69; prin. Woodbine (Iowa) Ctrl. Sch. Dist., 1978-82; supr. schs. Sheffield (Iowa)-Chapin Ctrl. Sch. Dist., 1982-86, Missouri Valley (Iowa) Ctrl. Sch. Dist., 1986-93; supt. schs. Richland (Wis.) Sch. Dist., 1993—; presenter in field. Mem. Bellevue City Coun., 1976-79; bd. dirs. Monona Svcs. Industries, Missouri Valley, 1991-93; pres. Missouri Valley Devel. Coun., 1988-93; mem. Iowa Bus. and Edn. Task Force Com., 1987; active Boy Scouts Am. Doctoral fellow Iowa Scottish Rite, 1991. Mem. Masons, Kiwanis (pres.), Phi Delta Kappa. Republican. Roman Catholic. Avocations: beekeeping, rescue squad. Home: RR 3 Box 80 A-1 Richland Center WI 53581

MEYER, ERIC G., orchestra administrator; b. Washington, May 7, 1953; s. Rauer H. and Evelyn (Glad) M.; m. Pamela Sue Placeway, Nov. 27, 1976; children: Andrew Douglas, Bronwyn Elizabeth. BS in Econs., Coll. of Wooster, 1975. Asst. mgr. Tucson Symphony Orch., 1977-80, dir. devel., 1978-80, gen. mgr., 1980-88, exec. dir., 1988—. Mem. exec. com. Tucson Commn. on Arts, 1983, grants award com., 1984—. Mem. Am. Symphony Orch. League (bd. dirs. 1985), Met. Orch. Mgrs. Assn. (pres. 1986-87). Democrat. Presbyterian. Lodge: Rotary. Office: Tucson Symphony Soc 443 S Stone Ave Tucson AZ 85701-2399

MEYER, EUGENE CARLTON, retired editor; b. McGregor, Iowa, Dec. 10, 1923; s. Gilbert Nelson and Christine Winnifred (Henkes) M.; m. Maxine Beth Mallory, June 1, 1947; children—Bruce, Mary Lynn, John. B.S., Iowa State U., 1946. Farm news editor Sta. WHO, Des Moines, 1947-48; assoc. editor Hoard's Dairyman, Fort Atkinson, Wis., 1948-72, mng. editor 1972-88. Trustee Fort Atkinson Meml. Hosp., 1966-81, pres. bd. trustees, 1976-81. Navigator, USAAF. Recipient Disting. Service award Am. Dairy Sci. Assn., 1980, Disting. Grad. award Iowa State Dairy Sci. Club, Iowa State U., 1981, Agrl. Leadership award Alpha Gamma Rho, 1982, Award of Distinction U. Wis.-Madison, 1982, Disting. Citizen of Agr. Nat. Milk Producers, 1988, Henry A. Wallace award Iowa State U., 1989, Richard E. Lyng award, 1989; named Industry Person of Yr. World Dairy Expo, 1988. Mem. Nat. Dairy Shrine (pres. 1980, Guest of Hon. 1986). Republican. Methodist. Home: 524 Jackson St Fort Atkinson WI 53538-1356

MEYER, F. WELLER, bank executive; b. Washington, Dec. 15, 1942; s. Martin William and Sallie Rita (Weller) M.; m. Brenda Burton, Sept. 27, 1972; children: F. Weller Jr., Brandon Michael. BS, U. Md., 1977. V.p.

W.S. Steed Mortgage Co., Wheaton, Md., 1970-73; asst. dir. Mortgage Bankers Assn., Washington, 1973-77; mng. dir. Mortgage Systems Corp. Bethesda, Md., 1977-83; pres., chief executive officer Westmark Mortgage Corp., Rockville, Md., 1983-87, Acacia Fed. Savs. Bank, Annandale, Va. 1987—; dir. Acadia Fed. Savs. Bank, Acacia Svc. Corp., Annandale, Calvert Group Ltd., Am.'s Comty. Bankers, Va. Bankers Assn. Co-author: Residential Mortgage Underwriting, 1981, Construction Lending Commercial, 1981, Construction Lending Income Property, 1981, Income Property Underwriting, 1981. Dir. Make-A-Wish Found. of the Mid-Atlantic, No. Va. Comty. Found., Fairfax, Va., 1989; mem. Citizen's Housing Adv. Com., Montgomery County, Md., 1988-90. 1st lt. U.S. Army, 1967-70, Vietnam. Mem. Optimists (pres. Washington 1978-79). Republican. Roman Catholic. Avocations: golf, hunting, jogging. Home: 9809 Kendale Rd Rockville MD 20854-4246

MEYER, FRED JOSEF, advertising executive; b. Zurich, Switzerland, Jan. 1, 1931; came to U.S., 1959; s. Josef and Claire (Lehmann) M.; m. Beverly Ruth Carter, Apr. 9, 1961 (div. Feb. 1975); children: Fred Jay, Marcus Clinton, Michael Josef; m. Marie-Noelle Vigneron, Oct. 30, 1975. MS, Fed. Inst. Tech., Zurich, 1956; MBA, Harvard U., 1961; LLD (hon.), Sacred Heart U., 1981. Vice pres. plannng and adminstrn. Sandoz Inc., Hanover, N.J., 1971-73, exec. v.p., chief fin. officer, 1973-78; pres., chief exec. officer Sandoz U.S., Inc., Greenwich, Conn., 1978-81; mng. dir., chief exec. officer Wander Ltd., Berne, Switzerland, 1981-82; sr. v.p., chief fin. officer CBS Inc., N.Y.C., 1982-88; chief fin. officer, bd. dirs. Omnicom Group, Inc., N.Y.C., 1988—; bd. dirs. SBC Portfolio Mgmt. Internat., N.Y.C., Zurich-Am. Ins. Cos., Ill., AAAA Ins. Co., SoGen Internat. Fund, Inc., N.Y.C., SoGen Funds, Inc., N.Y.C., Sandoz Corp, SyStemix, Inc., Palo Alto, Calif. Mem. Fin. Execs. Inst., Econ. Club, Harvard Club (N.Y.C.), Greenwich Country Club. Republican. Presbyterian. Office: Omnicom Group Inc 437 Madison Ave New York NY 10022-7001

MEYER, FREDERICK JACOBS, architect; b. San Diego, June 24, 1931; s. Howald Arthor and Julia Ann (Kaufman) M.; m. Beverly N. Meyer, June 23, 1959; children: Airon Frederick, Ayrik Rudy. BA, Miss. State U., 1951, BArch, U. Calif., 1961. Archtl. misc. archtl. firms, San Diego, 1956-58; lighting design Hexhel Products, Berkeley, Calif., 1956-60; prin. Design Annex, Frederick J. Meyer, San Diego, 1966—; dir. Citizen Coordinate, San Diego, 1978; archtl. expert witness, 1988—. Prin. works include designer Lighting Test Lab., 1960; architect Innovative Energy Design, 1985, custom-designed residences & multiple complexes, 1975-90, comml. and govt. projects, 1985—. Legis. com. Am. Builders & Contractors, 1990-91, San Diego County, 1990-92, Internat. Conf. Bldg. Ofcls. Com., 1990-91. Fellow Am. Registered Architects; mem. Kiwanis, Optimists, Soc. Military Engrs., Soc. Cost Estimating, Internat. Toastmasters. Republican. Methodist. Avocations: art, photography, swimming, hunting, sports.

MEYER, G. CHRISTOPHER, lawyer; b. Fremont, Nebr., Mar. 27, 1948; s. Gerald William and Mildred Ruth (Clausen) M.; m. Linda Haines, Dec. 27, 1969; children: Katie, Stacy, Jon, Robert. Student, Grinnell (Iowa) Coll., 1966-69; BA, U. Kans., 1970; JD, U. Pa., 1973. Bar: Ohio 1973, U.S. Dist. Ct. (no. dist.) Ohio 1975, U.S. Ct. Appeals (6th cir.) 1982. Assoc. Squire, Sanders & Dempsey, Cleve., 1973-82, ptnr., 1982—. Mem. ABA, Ohio State Bar Assn., Greater Cleve. Bar Assn. Office: Squire Sanders & Dempsey 4900 Society Ctr 127 Public Sq Cleveland OH 44114-1304

MEYER, GEORGE GOTTHOLD, psychiatrist, educator; b. Frankfurt, Germany, Nov. 13, 1931; came to U.S., 1941, naturalized, 1946; s. Hans and Hilda (Lesser) M.; m. Paula Saslaw, June 17, 1953; children: Bruce Alan, Brian Lee, Barry Dale. B.A., Johns Hopkins U., 1951; M.D., U. Chgo., 1955. Diplomate: Am. Bd. Psychiatry and Neurology (asst. examiner 1979—). Intern USPHS Hosp., Staten Island, N.Y., 1955-56; resident in psychiatry U. Chgo. Hosps. and Clinics, 1958-60, chief resident, 1960-61, chief psychiat. inpatient service, 1966-69; mem. faculty U. Chgo. Med. Sch., 1961-69, assoc. prof. psychiatry, 1968-69; assoc. prof. psychiatry U. Tex. Med. Sch., San Antonio, 1969-71; prof. U. Tex. Health Sci. Ctr., San Antonio, 1971—; clin. prof., 1982—; dir. N.W. San Antonio Mental Health Ctr., 1969-74; mem. exec. bd. Crisis Ctr., San Antonio, 1971-75; cons. VA Hosp., San Antonio and Kerrville, Tex., Kerrville State Hosp., San Antonio State Hosp., Santa Rosa Children's Hosp., Jewish Family Service, 1980-86, Cath. Family Services; active staff Villa Rosa Hosp., Methodist Hosp.; courtesy staff Regional Hosp., Charter Real Hosp., Mission Vista Hosp., Methodist Hosp., Laurel Ridge Hosp., Afton Oaks Hosp., Med. Center Hosp.; psychiat. cons. Dallas Office, NIMH, 1970-81; also psychiatry edn. br., 1978-82; med. dir. Mexican Am. Unity Council, San Antonio, 1970-80; vis. lectr. psychiatry U. Edinburgh (Scotland) Med. Sch., 1966; vis. prof. psychiatry U. Man. (Can.), Winnipeg, 1977; mem. med. adv. bd. for driver licensing Tex. Dept. Health, 1973-78. Author 3 books; contbr. numerous articles to med. jours. Bd. dirs., cons. Ecumenical Ctr. Religion and Health San Antonio, 1974-86; bd. dirs. Cmty. Guidance Ctr. of Bexar County, 1979-81; bd. dirs., cons. Jewish Family Svc., San Antonio, 1980-86. Served with USPHS, 1955-58. NIMH career tchr. grantee, 1961-63; recipient Okie award Gov. Okla., 1969. Fellow Am. Psychiat. Assn. (life), APA; mem. Tex. and Bexar County Med. Assns., Tex., Bexar County, and World Psychiat. Assns., Am. Coll. Psychiatrists, Am. Assn. Geriatric Psychiatry, Biofeedback Soc. Tex. (dir. 1980-82), Sigma Xi, Alpha Omega Alpha, Phi Lambda Upsilon. Home: 2907 Marlborough Dr San Antonio TX 78230-4427 Office: 4499 Medical Dr Ste 267 San Antonio TX 78229-3712

MEYER, GEORGE HERBERT, lawyer; b. Detroit, Feb. 19, 1928; s. Herbert M. and Agnes F. (Eaton) M.; m. Carol Ann Jones, 1958 (div. 1981) children: Karen Ann, George Herbert Jr.; m. Katherine Palmer White, Nov. 12, 1988. A.B., U. Mich., 1949; J.D., Harvard U., 1952; cert., Oxford (Eng.) U., 1955; LL.M. in Taxation, Wayne State U., 1962. Bar: D.C. bar 1952, Mich. bar 1953. Assoc. firm Fischer, Franklin & Ford, Detroit, 1956-63; mem. firm Fischer, Franklin & Ford, 1963-74; established firm George H. Meyer, 1974-78; sr. mem. firm Meyer and Kirk, 1978-85; sr. ptnr. Meyer, Kirk, Snyder & Safford, Bloomfield Hills and Detroit, Mich., 1985—; curator Step Lively exhibit Mus. Am. Folk Art, N.Y.C., 1992; lectr. Am. Folk Art. Author: Equalization in Michigan and Its Effect on Local Assessments, 1963, Folk Artists Biographical Index, 1986, American Folk Art Canes: Personal Sculpture, 1992. Chmn. Birmingham (Mich.) Bd. Housing Appeals, 1964-68; vice chmn. Birmingham Bd. Zoning Appeals, 1966-69; mem. Birmingham Planning Bd., 1968-70; trustee, Bloomfield Village, Mich., 1976-80, pres., 1979-80; trustee Mus. Am. Folk Art, N.Y.C., 1987—; mem. exec. bd. Detroit Area coun. Boy Scouts Am., 1976—, counsel, 1986—; mem. nat. adv. bd. Folk Art Soc. Am., 1994—; trustee Detroit Sci. Ctr., 1985—. 1st lt. JAG, USAF, 1952-55, maj. Res. ret. Recipient Silver Beaver award Detroit Area coun. Boy Scouts Am., 1989. Mem. ABA, Detroit Bar Assn., Oakland County Bar Assn., State Bar Mich., Harvard Law Sch. Assn. Mich. (dir. 1959—, pres. 1970-78), Detroit Sci. Mus. Soc. (pres. 1961-74, chmn. 1974—), Am. Folk Art Soc., Prismatic Club, Detroit Club, Harvard Club (N.Y.C.), Detroit Club, Masons, Rotary, Phi Beta Kappa, Alpha Phi Omega. Republican. Unitarian. Home: 1228 Sandringham Way Bloomfield Hills MI 48301-2242 Office: Meyer Kirk Snyder & Stafford 100 W Long Lake Rd Ste 100 Bloomfield Hills MI 48304-2773

MEYER, GERALD JUSTIN, energy company executive; b. St. Louis, Oct. 3, 1940; s. Justin George and Cornelia Emilie (Moehlmann) M.; m. Pamela Jean Clapper, Aug. 10, 1963; children: Eric, Ellen, Sarah. B.S., St. Louis U., 1962; M.A., U. Minn., 1963. Editor Meredith Pub. Co., Des Moines, 1967-68; reporter Des Moines Tribune, 1968-69, St. Louis Post-Dispatch, 1969-73; pub. rels. counselor Fleishman-Hillard, Inc., St. Louis, 1973-75, v.p., ptnr., 1975-76; dir. external rels. McDonnell Douglas Corp., St. Louis, 1976-81, corp. v.p communications, 1981-88; corp. v.p. communications and pub. affairs J.I. Case Co., Racine, Wis., 1988-92; exec. dir. pub. rels. and publs. Marquette U., Milw., 1992-93; dir. comm. Centerior Energy Corp., Cleve., 1994—. Author: The Memphis Murders, 1973 (Mystery Writers Am.award 1973). Served to lt. j.g. USN, 1963-67. Nat. Merit scholar, 1958; Woodrow Wilson fellow, 1962; Nieman fellow, 1971. Mem. Pub. Rels. Soc. Am. Roman Catholic. Home: 6010 Elmwood Rd Rocky River OH 44116 Office: Centerior Energy Corp 6200 Oak Tree Blvd Independence OH 44131

MEYER, GREG CHARLES, psychiatrist; b. Bismarck, N.D., Aug. 17, 1935; s. Oscar Clarence and Agnes Josephine (Pearson) M. Degree in profl. engring., Colo. Sch. Mines, 1958, Alexander Hamilton Bus. Inst., 1960;

MME, U. So. Calif., 1965; MD, Marquette U., 1970. Diplomate Am. Bd. Psychiatry and Neurology. Engr. Minuteman-Thiokol, Brigham City, Utah, 1958-61; sr. engr. Saturn S-II N.Am. Aviation, Downey, Calif., 1962-65; design specialist Titan-Martin, Denver, 1965-66; rotating intern Weld Country Gen. Hosp., Greenly, Colo., 1970-71; psychiatric resident Ariz. State Hosp., Phoenix, 1971-74, psychiatrist, 1974-76; pvt. practice Mesa, Ariz., 1975-94; psychiatrist Ctrl. Ariz. Med. Ctr., 1995—; psychiatrist Ariz. Ctrl. Med. Ctr.; chmn. psychiatry Desert Samaritan Hosp., Mesa, 1982-86, 90-94, chmn. joint mental health, 1981-83, mem. edn. com., 1979-82, quality assurance com., 1979; mem. exec. com. Desert Vista Hosp., Mesa, 1988-94, chief of staff, 1989; chmn. psychiatry Mesa Luth. Hosp., 1984-85, mem. exec. com., 1984-85; mng. ptnr. Desert Samaritan Med. Bldg. II, Mesa, 1985-86; rsch., edn. com. East Valley Camel Back Hosp., 1989-90, quality assurance com., 1985; psychiatrist Ctrl. Ariz. Med. Ctr., 1995. Co-discoverer Larson-Meyer Transform. Coach Pop Warner Football, 1974. With USMCR, 1953-59. Mem. AMA, Am. Psychiatric Assn., Ariz. Med. Assn., Ariz. Psychiatric Assn., Phoenix Psychiatric Coun., Maricopa Country Med. Assn., Christian Med./Dental Assn., Triple Nine Soc. Republican. Lutheran. Avocation: multi engine instrument pilot, sailing, computers, canoeing, photography.

MEYER, HANK, public relations and publicity consultant; b. N.Y.C., Mar. 27, 1920; m. Lenore Mittlemark; 3 daus. BBA, U. Miami, 1942, D in Communication (hon.), 1987. Owner, operator public relations agy. Miami, Fla., 1946-49; public relations dir. City of Miami Beach, Fla., 1949-56; chmn., chief executive officer Hank Meyer Assocs., Inc., pub. relations cons., Miami, 1956—. Trustee emeritus U. Miami; hon. trustee Biscayne Coll., mem. adv. council Dept. Communication Fla. Internat. U.; founder, trustee U. Miami Symphony Club; sr mem. Orange Bowl Com.; chmn. Headliner Awards; former mem. United Fund Dade County; former mem. bd. govs. Dade Found.; mem. exec. com. to Miami Citizens Against Crime; mem. Greater Miami Coalition, Pillars- United Way of Dade County; mem. steering com. Rediscover Miami Beach; mem. exec. com. Anti-Defamation League. Served to chief petty officer USNR, World War II. Named to Fla. Public Relations Hall of Fame, 1966; recipient 1st Outstanding Alumnus award U. Miami, award United Fund, award Papanicolaou Cancer Research Inst.; silver medallion award NCCJ, service award U.S. Jr. C. of C., ann. award Civic League Miami Beach, 1956, Sand In My Shoes award Greater Miami C. of C., 1985, Community Svsc. award Advt. Fedn. Greater Miami, 1985; also numerous local, state and nat. service awards and certs. of appreciation. Mem. Am. Mcpl. Public Relations Assn. (v.p. 1950), Govt. Public Relations Assn. (pres. 1956), Public Relations Soc. Am. (pres. Fla. chpt. 1958-59), Fla. Public Relations Assn., Nat. Assn. Travel Orgns., Miami Beach C. of C. (trustee), Greater Miami C. of C. (gov.), Am. Legion, Omicron Delta Kappa, Sigma Delta Chi. Office: Hank Meyer Assocs Inc 2990 Biscayne Blvd PO Box 218 Miami FL 33137

MEYER, HARRY MARTIN, JR., retired health science facility administrator; b. Palestine Tex., Nov. 25, 1928. s. Harry Martin and Marjory Isabel (Griffin) M.; m. Mary Jane Martin, Aug. 19, 1949 (div. 1966); children: Harry, Mary, David; m. Barbara Story Chalfort, Nov. 21, 1966. BS Hendrix Coll., 1949, MD U. Ark., 1953; Diplomate Am. Bd. Pediatics, 1960. instr. biology Little Rock Coll., 1949, intern. Walter Reed Army Hosp., Washington, 1953-54, med. officer dep. virus and rickettsial diseases, Walter Reed Army Inst. Rsch., 1954-57, asst. resident dep. pediatrics, N.C. Meml. Hosp., Chapel Hill, 1957-59, head virology sect. div. biologics standards, NIH, Bethesda, Md., 1959-64, chief lab. of viral immunol., div. biologics standards, NIH, 1964-72, dir. bur. biologics FDA, Bethesda, 1972-82, dir. Ctr. for Drugs & Biologics, Rockville, Md., 1982-86, pres. med. research div. Am. Cyanamid Co., Pearl River, N.Y., 1986-93; retired 1993. Served to rear admiral USPHS, 1959-86, capt. U.S. Army, 1953-57. Mem. AMA, Am. Epidemiol. Soc., Am. Acad. Pediatrics, Am. Pediatric Soc. Protestant. Avocations: sailing, scuba diving, skiing, back packing. Contbr articles to profl. jours.; patentee in field.

MEYER, HARVEY KESSLER, II, retired academic administrator; b. Carlisle, Pa., Feb. 6, 1914; s. Harvey Kessler and Frances May (Shultz) M.; m. Jessie Irene Hamm, Feb. 22, 1935; children: Carol Frances, Harvey Kessler III, Howard Madison. BA, Berea (Ky.) Coll., 1936; MA, Eastern Ky. U., 1942; D Edn., U. Fla., Gainesville, 1951. Surveyor Wash. State Hwy. Engrs., 1932; furniture designer Berea Woodwork, 1932-36; lic. contractor Bailey Constrn. Co., Seattle, Wash., 1935, Alachua County, Fla., 1948-50; instr. U. Fla., Ocala, 1936-37; supr. Nat. Youth Adminstrn., Jacksonville, Fla., 1937-38; vocat. tchr. Richmond (Ky.) City Schs., 1938-40; asst. prof. Eastern Ky. U., Richmond, 1940-43; tchr. P.K.Yonge Lab. Sch., Gainesville, Fla., 1946-47, prin., 1947-48; assoc. prof. U. Fla., Gainesville, 1948-51, prof., 1951-65; assoc. dean acad. affairs Fla. Atlantic U., Boca Raton, 1965-68, grad. prof., 1968-73; dir. Indsl. Arts and Vocat. Edn., Managua, Nicaragua, 1955-57; founder Instituto Nacional Educacion Vocacional, Nicaragua; dir., trustee Moravian Theol. Sem., Bethlehem, Pa., 1976; dean radio and TV Fla. Inst. for Continuing Univ. Studies, 1962-65; adminstrv. cons. Brit.-Am. Investment Fund, Luxembourg City, Europe, 1969-71; owner, designer Plantation Glen, Alachua County, 1948-77, Hacienda Octlan, Clay County, N.C., 1975-78. Author: Technical Eduction in Nicaragua, 1958, Historical Dictionary Nicaragua, 1972, Historical Dictionary Honduras, 1976, rev. edit., 1994. Pres. Fla. dist. Moravian Ch., 1970-73, Melrose (Fla.) Library Assn., 1983—, pres., 1984-90, 92—; trustee Moravian Coll. and Sem., 1966-78. Comdr. USNR, ret.; naval aviation observer. Named Disting. Alumnus Berea Coll., 1986. Mem. Berea Coll. Alumni Assn. (pres. 1990-91), Rotary, Phi Kappa Phi, Phi Delta Kappa, Epsilon Pi Tau (trustee 1950—). Democrat. Avocations: boating, architecture, pistol shooting, furniture design and bldg., archeology. Home: 8146 Alderman Rd Melrose FL 32666-8818

MEYER, HELEN (MRS. ABRAHAM J. MEYER), retired editorial consultant; b. Bklyn., Dec. 4, 1907; d. Bertolen and Esther (Greenfield) Honig; m. Abraham J. Meyer, Sept. 1, 1929; children—Adele Meyer Brodkin, Robert L. Grad. pub. schs. With Popular Sci., McCall's mag., 1921-22; pres., dir. Dell Pub. Co., Inc., N.Y.C., 1923-57, Dell Distbg., Inc. from 1957, Dell Internat., Inc., from 1957; pres. Dell Pub. Co., Inc., Montville Warehousing Co., Inc.; chmn. bd. Noble & Noble Pubs., Inc.; v.p. Dellprint, Inc., Dunellen, N.J.; pres. Dial Press.; later editorial cons. Doubleday & Co. N.Y.C.; cons. Fgn. Rights, N.Y.C. Bd. dirs. United Cerebral Palsy. Named to Pub.'s Hall of Fame, 1986. Mem. Assn. Am. Pubs. (dir.). Home: 1 Claridge House Apt 608 Verona NJ 07044

MEYER, HORST, physics educator; b. Berlin, Germany, Mar. 1, 1926. BS, U. Geneva, 1949; PhD in physics, U. Zurich, 1953. Fellow Swiss Assn. Rsch. Physics and Math. Studies, Oxford, Eng., 1953-55; Nuffield fellow Clarendon Lab. U. Oxford, 1955-57; lectr., rsch. assoc. dept. engring. and applied physics Harvard U., Cambridge, Mass., 1957-59; from asst. prof. to prof. Duke U., Durham, N.C., 1959-84, Fritz London prof. physics, 1984—; vis. prof. Technische Hochschule, Federal Republic of Germany, 1965, Tokyo U., 1980, 81, 83; traveling fellow Japanese Soc. for Promotion Sci., 1971, vis. scientist, 1979; guest scientist Inst. Laue-Langevin, France, 1974, 75; Yamada Found. fellow, Japan, 1986; guest scientist USSR Acad. Sci., 1988; chmn. Gordon Conf. on Solid H2, 1990; western chmn. conf. quantum crystals, Almaty, Kazakhstan, 1995. Editor Jour. Low Temperature Physics, 1992—, mem. editorial bd., 1988-92; contbr. articles to profl. jours. Alfred P. Sloan fellow, 1961-65. Fellow Am. Phys. Soc. (Jesse Beams prize, 1982, Fritz London prize 1993). Exptl. rsch. on the properties of liquid and solid helium, solid hydrogen and deuterium, magnetic insulators, critical phenomena. Office: Duke U Dept Physics PO Box 90305 Durham NC 27708-0305

MEYER, HOWARD ROBERT, lawyer; b. N.Y.C., Feb. 5, 1938; s. Howard Wilton and Alice (Banks) M.; m. Beth Townsend Rowe, Mar. 23, 1959 (div. Mar. 1973); children: Jennifer, Rachel, Claudia; m. Marie Borrelli, June 27, 1982. AB, Syracuse U., 1962, JD, 1965. Atty.-in-charge criminal divsn. N.Y. County Legal Aid Soc., 1971-74, atty.-in-charge N.Y.C narcotics divsn., 1974-76; pvt. practice, 1976—. Home: 272 Barrow St Jersey City NJ 07302-4026

MEYER, IRWIN STEPHAN, lawyer, accountant; b. Monticello, N.Y., Nov. 14, 1941; s. Ralph and Janice (Cohen) M.; children: Kimberly B, Joshua A. BS, Rider Coll., 1963; JD, Cornell U., 1966. Bar: N.Y. 1966; CPA, N.J. Tax mgr. Lybrand Ross Bros. & Montgomery, N.Y.C., 1966-71;

mem. Ehrenkranz, Ehrenkranz & Schultz, N.Y.C., 1971-74; prin. Irwin S. Meyer, 1974-77, 82—; mem. Levine, Honig, Eisenberg & Meyer, 1977-78, Eisenberg, Honig & Meyer, 1978-81, Eisenberg, Honig, Meyer & Fogler, 1981-82. With U.S. Army, 1966-71. Mem. ABA, N.Y. Bar Assn., Am. Assn. Atty.-CPA, N.Y. Assn. Atty-CPA, N.J. Soc. CPA. Office: 1 Blue Hill Plz Ste 1006 Pearl River NY 10965-3104

MEYER, J. THEODORE, lawyer; b. Chgo., Apr. 13, 1936; s. Joseph Theodore and Mary Elizabeth (McHugh) M.; m. Marilu Bartholomew, Aug. 16, 1961; children: Jean, Joseph. B.S., John Carroll U., 1958; postgrad. U. Chgo.; J.D., DePaul U., 1962. Bar: Ill. 1962, U.S. Dist. Ct. (no. dist.) Ill. 1962. Ptnr. Bartholomew & Meyer, Chgo., 1963-83; mem. Ill. Gen. Assembly, House of Rep. 28th Legis. Dist., 1966-72, 74-82, chmn. House environ. study com., 1968; chmn. energy environ. com. and natural resources com.; mem. appropriations and exec. com.; chmn. Joint House/Senate com. to review state air and water plans, 1968; mem. Fed. State Task Force on Energy; chmn., founder Midwest Legis. Coun. on Environ., 1971; mem. State of Ill. Pollution Control Bd., Chgo., 1983—; mem. Joint Legis. Com. on Hazardous Waste in Lake Calumet Area, 1987; lectr. in field. Recipient Appreciation award Ill. Wildlife Fedn., 1972, Environ. Quality award Region V, EPA, 1974, Pro Bono Publico award Self-Help Action Ctr., 1975, Merit award Dept. Ill. VFW, 1977, Environ. Legislator of Yr. award Ill. Environ. Coun., 1978-79; Disting. Lawyer Legislator of Yr.; commd. hon. lt. aide-decamp Ala. State Militia; commd. Hon. Tex. Citizen. Fellow Chgo. Bar Found.; mem. ABA, Ill. Bar Assn., Chgo. Bar Assn., Nat. Rep. Legis. Assn., Nat. Trust Hist. Preservation, Nat. Wildlife Fedn., Ill. Hist. Soc., Beverly Tennis Club, Beverly Hills Univ. Club. Republican. Roman Catholic. Office: State of Ill Ctr 100 W Randolph St Ste 11500 Chicago IL 60601-3286

MEYER, JACKIE MERRI, publishing executive; b. Phila., Oct. 19, 1954; d. George Gilbert Meyer and Sylvia Magerman; m. W. Scot Carouge, May 23, 1982. BFA, The Cooper Union, N.Y.C., 1977. Art dir. Macmillan Pub. Co., N.Y.C., 1980-85; v.p., creative dir. Warner Books, N.Y.C., 1985—; tchr. Parsons Sch. Design, N.Y.C., 1984-85; lectr. Fashion Inst. Tech., N.Y.C., 1984-85, Am. Illustraton, N.Y.C., 1984; design cons. Adler and Adler, Bethesda, Md., 1985. Co-author: I Loathe New York, 1981. Fundraiser The Cooper Union, N.Y.C., 1977—. Recipient 170 profl. awards Alga, The Advt. Club, Desi Awards, Art Direction mag., Print mag., Graphis, Communication Arts. Mem. AFTRA, Soc. of Illustrators (bd. dirs. 1988—), Am. Inst. Graphic Arts, Art Dirs. Club (awards). Avocations: photography, gardening, landscape design. Office: Warner Books Inc 1271 Ave of the Americas 9th Fl New York NY 10020

MEYER, JAROLD ALAN, oil company research executive; b. Phoenix, July 28, 1938; s. Lester M. and Anita (Walker) M.; m. Diane Louise Wheeler; children: Ronald Alan, Sharon Lynne. BSChemE, Calif. Inst. Tech., 1960, MS, 1961. Mgr. process devel. Chevron Rsch., Richmond, Calif., 1978-82; tech. mgr. Chevron U.S.A., El Segundo, Calif., 1982-84; v.p. process rsch. Chevron Rsch., Richmond, 1984-86, pres., 1986—; sr. v.p. Chevron Rsch. and Tech., Richmond, 1990-93; ret., 1993; prin. J.A. Meyer Assocs., Martinez, Calif., 1993—; bd. dirs. Solvent Refined Coal Internat., Inc., San Francisco; mem. adv. bd. Surface Sci. and Catalysis Program Ctr. for Advanced Materials, Lawrence Berkeley Lab., 1988-91; mem. adv. coun. Lawrence Hall Sci., 1989-94; indsl. advisor Accreditation bd. for Engring. and Tech. Inventor petroleum catalysts; contbr. articles to profl. jours. Bd. visitors U. Calif., Davis, 1986-93, trustee found., 1989—. Mem. NAE, Am. Chem. Soc., Nat. Petroleum Refining Assn., Indsl. Rsch. Inst., Conf. Bd., Internat. Rsch. Mgmt. Coun., Sigma Xi, Tau Beta Pi. Avocations: electronics design and constrn., photography. Home and Office: 849 Corte Briones Martinez CA 94553-5950

MEYER, JEAN-PIERRE GUSTAVE, mathematician, educator; b. Lyon, Rhone, France, Aug. 5, 1929; s. Jules and Germaine (Becker) M.; m. Marilyn Joan Pettit, 1958; children: David, Susan, Steven, Alison, Nadine, Nicholas. BA, Cornell U., 1950, MS, 1951, PhD, 1954. Asst. prof. math. Syracuse (N.Y.) U., 1956; research assoc. math. Brown U., Providence, R.I., 1956-57; from asst. to assoc. to prof. Johns Hopkins U., Balt., 1957—, chmn. dept. math., 1985-90; dir. Japan-U.S. Math. Inst., 1992—. Co-author: Fundamental Structures of Algebra, 1963; contbr. articles to profl. jours. Served with U.S. Army, 1954-56. Grad. fellow NSF, 1953. Mem. Am. Math. Soc. Avocations: mineral collecting, archaeology. Home: 500 W University Pkwy Baltimore MD 21210 Office: Johns Hopkins U Dept Math Baltimore MD 21218

MEYER, JEROME J., diversified technology company executive; b. Caledonia, Minn., Feb. 18, 1938; s. Herbert J. and Edna (Staggemeyer) M.; m. Sandra Ann Beaudoin, June 18, 1960; children—Randall Lee, Lisa Ann, Michelle Lynn. Student, Hamline U., 1956-58; B.A., U. Minn., 1960. Devel. engr. Firestone Tire & Rubber Co., Akron, Ohio, 1960-61; v.p., gen. mgr. Sperry Univac, St. Paul, 1961-79; group v.p. Honeywell, Inc., Mpls., 1979-84; pres., chief operating officer Varian Assocs., Palo Alto, Calif., 1984-86, also bd. dirs.; pres., chief exec. officer Honeywell Inc., 1986-90; from pres. to CEO, CFO Tektronix Inc., Beaverton, Oreg., 1990—; dir. Magnetic Data Inc., Mpls., Keycom Electronic Pub. Co., Chgo., Honeywell Erickson Devel. Co., Anaheim, Calif. Bd. dirs. YMCA, West St. Paul, Minn., 1977. Clubs: Southview Country (West St. Paul) Palo Alto Hills Country, Mission Viejo Country. Avocation: golf. Office: Tektronix Inc PO Box 1000 26600 S W Pky Wilsonville OR 97070*

MEYER, JOHN, church administrator. Acting dir. Dept. of Stewardship of the Lutheran Church MO Synod International Ctr., St. Louis. Office: The Lutheran Church MO Synod Intl 1333 S Kirkwood Rd Saint Louis MO 63122-7295

MEYER, JOHN BERNARD, public relations executive; b. St. Louis, July 22, 1933; s. Bernard Charles and Virginia Marie (Hetherington) M.; m. Alberta Ruth Krohn, June 13, 1957; children: Margaret, Chrystal, Kathleen, Jennifer, Victoria. Student, So. Meth. U., 1951-53. TV network news corr. CBS News, Washington, 1962-75; anchor, corr. Mut. Radio Network, Washington, 1975-77; nat. dir. communications Gen. Aviation Mfrs. Assn., Washington, 1977-81; dir. corp. pub. relations Gates-Lear Jet Corp., Wichita, Kans., 1981-85; mgr. corp. pub. relations The Garrett Corp., L.A., 1985-87; mgr. mktg. comm. Allied Signal Controls and Accessories Divsn., Tucson, 1987—. Editor: Civil Aviation-Fuel Crisis, 1974 (Aviation/Space Writers award, 1975); producer: General Aviation Benefits, 1978 (Aviation/Space Writers award, 1979). Bd. dirs. Tucson-Pima Arts Coun., 1987—, pres. 1990—; bd. dirs. Ariz. Coun. Econ. Edn., Tucson, 1987—, Tucson Sympnony Orch., 1988-90, Metro YMCAs of Tucson 1989—. Mem. Aviation/Space Writers Nat. Found. (v.p., bd. dirs. 1987— Golden Quill award 1988), Pub. Rels. Soc. Am. (pres. Tucson chpt. 1985), Tucson Met. C. of C. (vice-chmn., bd. dirs. 1987—). Lutheran. Avocation: comml. aviation. Home: 17913 Sable Ridge Dr South Bend IN 46635-1035 Office: Allied Signal Controls & Accessories Divsn 11100 N Oracle Rd Tucson AZ 85737-9588

MEYER, JOHN EDWARD, nuclear engineering educator; b. Pitts., Dec. 17, 1931; s. Albert Edward and Thelma Elizabeth (Brethauer) M.; m. Gracyann Lenz, June 13, 1953; children: Susan Meyer Heydon, Karl, Karen Meyer Gleasman, Thomas. B.S., Carnegie Inst. Tech., 1953, M.S., 1953, Ph.D. (ASME Student award 1955), 1955. Engring. and mgmt. positions Westinghouse Bettis Atomic Power Lab., West Mifflin, Pa., 1955-75; vis. lectr. U. Calif., Berkeley, 1968-69; prof. nuclear engring. M.I.T., 1975—; cons. in field. Author papers in field. Recipient Bettis Disting. Service award, 1962, Outstanding Tchr. award nuclear engring. M.I.T., 1979, Alumni Merit award Carnegie Mellon U., 1987. Fellow Am. Nuclear Soc.; mem. ASME, Sigma Xi. Office: Rm 24-202 77 Massachusetts Ave Rm 24-202 Cambridge MA 02139-4307

MEYER, JOHN F., insurance company executive. Cfo, sr. v.p.-personal ins. fin. Fiemans Fund Insurance Co, Novato, Calif., until 1991, exec. v.p., cfo, 1991—. Office: Firemans Fund Insurance Co 777 San Marin Dr Novato CA 94998-0001

MEYER, JOHN FREDERICK, engineering and computer science educator, researcher, consultant; b. Grand Rapids, Mich., July 26, 1934; s. Frederick

Albert and Harriet (Stibbs) M.; m. Nancy Shaw Briggs, July 4, 1959; children: John, Patricia, James. B.S., U. Mich., 1957; M.S., Stanford U., 1958; Ph.D., U. Mich., 1967. Data systems engr. Douglas Aircraft Corp., Santa Monica, Calif., 1957; research engr. Caltech, Jet Propulsion Lab., Pasadena, Calif., 1958-67; asst. prof. U. Mich., Ann Arbor, 1968-71, assoc. prof., 1971-76, prof. elec. engring. and computer sci., 1976—; dir. Computing Research Lab. U. Mich., 1984-89; cons. Calif. Inst. Tech. Jet Propulsion Lab., 1979—, Indsl. Tech. Inst., Ann Arbor, 1985—, CIMSA, Paris, 1992, Bendix Advanced Tech. Ctr., Columbia, Md., 1977-85, Thomson CSF, Paris, 1975, Italtel, Milan, 1990—, Applied Scis. Corp., Reading, Mass., 1993—. Patentee Time Division Multiplexer, 1963 (NASA Inventions award 1964). Precinct chmn. 3d ward Democratic Party, Ann Arbor, 1971-74. Recipient Disting. Service Award U. Mich., 1964; IBM fellow, 1957. Fellow IEEE; mem. IEEE Computer Soc. (cert. of appreciation 1981, Meritorious Service award 1985); mem. Assn. Computing Machinery, AAAS. Home: 1946 Ridge Ave Ann Arbor MI 48104-6306 Office: U Mich 2214B Eecs Bldg Ann Arbor MI 48109

MEYER, JOHN ROBERT, economist, educator; b. Pasco, Wash., Dec. 6, 1927; s. Philip Conrad and Cora (Kemper) M.; m. Lee Stowell, Dec. 17, 1949; children: Leslie Karen, Ann Elizabeth, Robert Conrad. Student, Pacific U., 1945-46; BA, U. Wash., 1950; PhD (David A. Wells prize), Harvard U., 1955. Jr. fellow Harvard U., 1953-55, asst. prof., 1955-58, assoc. prof., 1958-59, prof. econs., 1959-68, prof. transportation and logistics, 1973-83; prof. Yale U., 1968-73; Harpel prof. capital formation and econ. growth Harvard U., 1983—; dir. Dun & Bradstreet, Rand McNally; vice chmn. Union Pacific Corp., 1982-83, now dir.; trustee Mut. Life. Ins. Co. N.Y., Pacific U. Author: (with others) The Investment Decision-An Empirical Inquiry, 1957, Economics of Competition in the Transportation Industry, 1959, The Urban Transportation Problem, 1965, The Economics of Competition in the Telecommunications Industry, 1980, Autos, Transit and Cities, 1981, Deregulation and the Future of Intercity Passenger Travel, 1987, Going Private: The International Experience with Tranaport Privatization, 1993, other books; contbr. articles to profl. jours. Mem. Presdl. Task Forces on Transp., 1964, 80, Presdl. Commn. on Population Growth and Am. Future, 1970-72; pres. Nat. Bur. Econ. Research, 1967-77. Served with USNR, 1946-48. Guggenheim fellow, 1958. Fellow Am. Acad. Arts and Scis., Econometric Soc.; mem. Am. Econ. Assn. (mem. exec. com. 1971-73), Council Fgn. Relations, Econ. History Assn. Home: 138 Brattle St Cambridge MA 02138-2202 Office: Harvard U Ctr Bus & Govt 79 Jfk St Cambridge MA 02138-5800

MEYER, JOSEPH B., state attorney general; b. Casper, Wyo., 1941; m. Mary Orr; children: Vincent, Warren. Student, Colo. Sch. Mines, 1963; BA, U. Wyo., 1964, JD, 1967; postgrad., Northwestern U., 1968. Dep. county atty. Fremont County, Wyo., 1967-69; assoc. Smith and Meyer, 1968-71; asst. dir. legis. svc. office State of Wyo., Cheyenne, 1971-87, atty. gen., 1987—; conductor numerous govt. studies on state codes including Wyo. probate, criminal, state adminstrn., banking, domestic rels., game and fish, state instn., employment security, worker's compensation, motor vehicle, others; conductor legis. rev. of adminstrv. rules; negotiator with Office of Surface Mining for Wyo. state preemption; instr. Wyo. Coll. Law, fall 1986; lectr. Rocky Mountain Mineral Law Found., 1977; chmn. Conf. Western Atty. Gen., 1992-93; mem. exec. com. Nat. Assn. Attys. Gen. Bd. dirs. Cheyenne Jr. League, 1982-85, Jessup PTO, 1980-81; instr. Boy Scouts Am. Mem. Rotary. Congregationalist. Avocations: golf, tennis, gardening, wood carving, rock hunting. Office: Office of Atty Gen 123 Capitol Bldg Cheyenne WY 82002

MEYER, JOYCE, special education educator. Special educ. teacher. Recipient Susan Phillips Gorin awd., Coun. for Exceptional Children, 1993. Office: 1820 N Delaney # 227 Gurnee IL 60031

MEYER, KARL ERNEST, journalist; b. Madison, Wis., May 22, 1928; s. Ernest Louis and Dorothy (Narefsky) M.; m. Sarah Nielsen Peck, Aug. 12, 1959 (div. 1972); children—Ernest, Heather, Jonathan; m. Shareen Blair Brysac, Jan. 6, 1989. B.A., U. Wis., 1951; M.P.A., Princeton U., 1953, Ph.D., 1956. Reporter N.Y. Times, N.Y.C., 1952, mem. editorial bd., 1979—; editorial writer Washington Post, 1956-65, chief London Bur., 1965-70, N.Y.C. corr., 1970-71; Washington corr. New Statesman, 1961-65; sr. editor, TV critic Saturday Rev., N.Y.C., 1975-79; corr. in residence Fletcher Sch. Law and Diplomacy, Tufts U., 1979; vis. journalist fellow Duke U., Durham, N.C., 1988; vis. prof. Yale U., 1983, 90, McGraw prof. in writing Princeton (N.J.) U., 1993-94. Author: The New America, 1961, (with Tad Szulc) The Cuban Invasion, 1962, Fulbright of Arkansas, 1963, The Pleasures of Archaeology, 1971, The Plundered Past, 1973, Teotihuacán, 1975, The Art Museum: Power, Money, Ethics, 1979, Pundits, Poets and Wits: An Omnibus of American Newspaper Columns, 1990. Recipient citatoin for excellence Overseas Press Club, 1960; Bronze medal Sigma Delta Chi, 1963; George Foster Peabody Broadcasting award 1983, Disting. Achievement award Sch. Journalism, U. Wis., 1985; Davenport Coll. of Yale U. fellow; Wisenschaftskolleg Inst. Adv. Studies (Berlin) fellow, 1994-95. Mem. PEN Club Internat., Coun. on Fgn. Rels., NYU Soc. Fellows, Century Assn. Home: 96 Eleven Oclock Rd Weston CT 06883 Office: NY Times 229 West 43d St New York NY 10036

MEYER, KARL WILLIAM, retired university president; b. Ft. Wayne, Ind., May 8, 1925; s. K.W. and L. (Hofacker) M.; m. Margery R. Hamman, Apr. 15, 1950; children—Mary, William, Frederick, Ann, Jean. A.B., Valpariaso U., 1948; M.F.S., U. Md., 1949; Ph.D., U. Wis., 1953; postgrad., U. Basel, Switzerland, 1948-49; postdoctoral fellow, U. Mich., 1958-59. Faculty Valparaiso U., 1952-53, Augustana Coll., 1953-55, Wis. State U., 1955-58; dean instrn., dir. grad. studies Wayne State Coll., 1959-63; asst. dir. bd. regents Wis. State Colls., Madison, 1963-64; pres. U. Wis.-Superior, 1964-87. Author: Karl Liebknecht: Man Without a Country, 1957; Contbr. articles to profl. jours. Served with USAAF, 1943-46, ETO. Home: 7012 S Maple Creek Rd Lake Nebagamon WI 54849-9220

MEYER, KATHLEEN MARIE, college educator; b. St. Louis, Oct. 29, 1944; d. Richard Henry and Leonora (Moser) Bailey; m. Thomas A. Meyer, Dec. 26, 1966; children: Richard, Amy, Mindy, Heidi. BA, Webster Coll., Webster Groves, Mo., 1966; MA, Fla. Atlantic U., 1981; postgrad., No. Ill. U., 1982—. Cert. secondary tchr., Mo., Ill. Tchr. English Notre Dame High Sch., St. Louis, 1966-67; tchr. English chmn. dept. Rosary High Sch. Aurora, Ill., 1981-1991; instr. English DeKalb Coll., Decatur, Ga., 1992—; mem. adv. bd. Univ. High Sch.; mem. joint enrollment coun. DeKalb Coll. Mem. ASCD, Nat. Coun. Tchrs. English.

MEYER, KENNETH MARVEN, academic administrator; b. Chgo., Nov. 27, 1932; s. Kenneth M. and Lorraine B. (Reiff) M.; m. Carol Jean Ebner, June 12, 1953; children: Keith, Kevin, Caryn. BD, Trinity Coll., 1954, MDiv, 1956; DMin., Luther Rice, 1978. Pastor Crystal Evang. Free Ch. in Am., Mpls., 1959-66, also bd. dirs.; pastor 1st Free Ch., Rockford, Ill., 1969-74; pres. Trinity Evangelical Div. Sch. and Coll., Deerfield, Ill., 1974-95, chancellor, 1995—; bd. dirs. Firstar Ill.; CEO Radio WMCU, Miami, Fla. Author: Guide to Financial Planning, 1987, (monograph) Turning Point Psalms, 1981. Mem. Nat. Assn. Evangelicals. Mem. Evangelical Free Ch. Avocations: money mgmt., reading. Office: Trinity Internat Univ Office of Chancellor 2065 Half Day Rd Deerfield IL 60015-1283

MEYER, KERSTIN, mezzo-soprano, music educator; b. Stockholm, Apr. 3, 1928; d. J.O. and Anna (Eriksson) M.; m. Björn Bexelius. Student, Royal Conservatory, Stockholm, Accademia Chigiana, Siena, Italy, Mozarteum, Salzburg, Austria. Chmn. Jussi Bjoerling Meml. Fund, Royal Opera Found.; Sch. Svanholm Fund, Kerstin Meyer Fund for young opera singers; prin. Swedish State Acad. Opera, Stockholm; dir. Swedish State Concert Bur., Royal Swedish Acad. Music, Swedish State Music Collections, European Cultural Found. in Amsterdam, Benjamin Britten Soc., Swedish Performing Rights Soc., Danish Conservatory of Music; prof. Mozarteum Salzburg; master tchr. Britten-Perce Sch. Advanced Mus. Studies, U.K. Debut in Il Trovatore, Stockholm, 1952; appeared with opera cos. in Buenos Aires, Salzburg, Vienna, Brussels, Vancouver, Copenhagen, Helsinki, Paris, London, Glyndebourne, Cardiff, Salzberg, Bayreuth, E. and W. Berlin, Hamburg, Tokyo, Munich, Cologne, Glasgow, Mexico City, Milan, Rome, Oslo, Edinburgh Festival, Moscow, Riga, Taschkent, N.Y.C., San Francisco, Santa Fe, San Diego, New Orleans, Boston, Tulsa, Cologne, Venice, Hong Kong, others, also maj. orchs. in, U.S., Europe, Australia, New Zealand, Far East; numerous radio TV appearances, recs.; translator opera librettos; producer various operas. Decorated Comdr. Order Brit. Empire, officer Italian Order of Merit, medal Litteris et Artibus; named Royal Ct. singer; recipient Swedish Wasa Order, Norwegian Royal medal, Bundesverdienstkrutz 1 Klasse, Germany. Mem. Royal Acad. Music (Prof. of Yr.). Office: Operahögskolanr, Strändvagen 82, S-11527 Stockholm Sweden*

MEYER, L. DONALD, agricultural engineer, researcher, educator; b. Concordia, Mo., Apr. 14, 1933; s. Lawrence Dick and Florence Malinda (Uphaus) M.; m. Loretta Lou Bush, Dec. 26, 1954; children: Dan W., James B., David J. Student, Cen. Coll., Fayette, Mo., 1950-51; BS in Agrl. Engring., U. Mo., 1954, MS in Agrl. Engring., 1955; PhD, Purdue U., 1964. Cert. profl. soil erosion and sediment control specialist; registered profl. engr., Ind. Agrl. engr. Agrl. Rsch. Svc., USDA, West Lafayette, Ind., 1955-73; agrl. engr. Nat. Sedimentation Lab., USDA, Oxford, Miss., 1973—; asst. prof., assoc. prof. Purdue U., West Lafayette, 1965-73; adj. prof. agr.-biol. engring. Miss. State U., Starkville, 1975—. Contbr. articles to profl. jours. Recipient Outstanding Performance award USDA Agrl. Rsch. Svc., 1959, 88, 89, 90, 91. Fellow Am. Soc. Agrl. Engrs. (dir. publs. 1968-69, chmn. soil and water div. 1972-73, Hancor award 1985), Soil and Water Conservation Soc.; mem. Soil Sci. Soc. Am. Office: USDA-ARS Nat Sedimentation Lab PO Box 1157 Oxford MS 38655-6004

MEYER, LASKER MARCEL, retail executive; b. Houston, Jan. 8, 1926; s. Lasker M. and Lucille (Dannenbaum) M.; m. Beverly Jean Goldberg; children: Lynn Meyer Brown, Susan Meyer Sellinger. Student, Rice U., 1942-43. Pres. Foley's, Houston, 1979, chmn., chief exec. officer, 1982-87; chmn., chief exec. officer Abraham and Straus, Bklyn., 1980-81; vice chmn. bd. Splty. Retailers, Inc., Houston, 1989-93; bd. dirs. BookTronics, Inc., Houston. Past chmn. bd. United Way Tex. Gulf Coast. Mem. Bentwater Yacht and Country Club. Jewish.

MEYER, LAWRENCE GEORGE, lawyer; b. East Grand Rapids, Mich., Oct. 2, 1940; s. George and Evangeline (Boerma) M.; children from previous marriage: David Lawrence, Jennifer Lynne; m. Linda Elizabeth Buck, May 31, 1980; children: Elizabeth Tilden, Travis Henley. BA with honors, Mich. State U., 1961; JD with distinction, U. Mich., 1964. Bar: Wis., 1965, Ill. 1965, U.S. Supreme Ct. 1968, D.C. 1972. Assoc. Whyte, Hirschboeck, Minahan, Hardin & Harland, Milw., 1964-66; atty. antitrust div. U.S. Dept. Justice, Washington, 1966-68; legal counsel U.S. Senator Robert P. Griffin, Mich., 1968-70; dir. policy planning FTC, Mich., 1970-72; ptnr. Patton, Boggs & Blow, Washington, 1972-85, Arent, Fox, Kintner, Plotkin & Kahn, Washington, 1985—. Contbr. articles on antitrust and trial practice to law jours.; asst. editor U. Mich. Law Rev., 1960-61. Bd. dirs. Hockey Hall of Fame, Toronto, 1993—. Recipient Disting. Svc. award FTC, 1972. Mem. ABA, D.C. Bar Assn., Wis. Bar Assn., Ill. Bar Assn., U.S. Senate Ex S.O.Bs Club, City Tavern Club, Congl. Country Club. Home: 8777 Belmart Rd Potomac MD 20854-1610 Office: 1050 Connecticut Ave NW Washington DC 20036-5303

MEYER, LAWRENCE ROBERT, journalist; b. Chgo., Nov. 27, 1941; s. Ferdnando Kolomon and Gertrude Meyer; m. Alviva Debra Sagalovitch, June 15, 1968; children: Ariel David, Evan Scher, Noa Anne. BA, U. Mich., 1963; MA, Columbia U., 1965, MS, 1965. Reporter Times-Herald Record, Middletown, N.Y., 1965-66, Louisville Times, 1968-69; reporter Washington Post, 1969-87, editor Nat. Weekly Edit., 1987—. Author: A Capitol Crime, 1977, False Front, 1979, Israel Now: Portrait of a Troubled Land, 1982. Sgt. USMC, 1966-68. Jewish. Home: 3311 Ross Pl NW Washington DC 20008 Office: Washington Post 1150 15th St NW Washington DC 20071

MEYER, LEONARD B., musician, educator; b. N.Y.C., Jan. 12, 1918; s. Arthur S. and Marion (Wolff) M.; m. Janet M. Levy; children: Marion L. Carlin, Erica Cecile. Student, Bard Coll., 1936-37; BA, Columbia, 1940, MA, 1948; PhD, U. Chgo., 1954; LHD, Grinnell Coll., Loyola U., Chgo., Bard Coll., U. Chgo. Faculty U. Chgo., 1946-75, head humanities sect., 1958-60, prof. music, 1961-75, chmn. music dept., 1961-70, Phyllis Fay Horton disting. svc. prof., 1972-75; Benjamin Franklin prof. music U Pa., 1975-88, Benjamin Franklin prof. emeritus, 1988—; fellow Ctr. for Advanced Studies, Wesleyan U., Middletown, Conn., 1960-61, Ctr. for Advanced Study in Behavioral Scis., Stanford, Calif., 1994; Ernest Bloch prof. music U. Calif. Berkeley, 1971, sr. fellow Sch. Criticism and Theory, 1975-88; resident scholar Bellagio Study and Conf. Ctr., 1982; Tanner lectr. Stanford U., 1984; Patten lectr. Ind. U., 1985. Author: Emotion and Meaning in Music, 1956 (with G. W. Cooper) The Rhythmic Structure of Music, 1960, Music, the Arts and Ideas, 1967, Explaining Music: Essays and Explorations, 1973, Style and Music: Theory, History and Ideology, 1994; gen. editor: Studies in the Criticism and Theory of Music; mem. editorial bd. Critical Inquiry, 1974—, Music Perception, 1983; contbr. articles to profl. jours. Guggenheim fellow, 1971-72. Fellow AAAS, Am. Acad. Arts and Scis.; mem. Am. Musicological Soc. (hon.), Soc. Music Theory, Soc. Music Perception and Cognition (bd. dirs.), Phi Beta Kappa. Home: 165 West End Ave Apt 23M New York NY 10023 Office: U of Pa Dept of Music Philadelphia PA 19104

MEYER, LOIS ANN, religious school system administrator; b. Cin., Oct. 20, 1937; d. Anthony Henry and Irma Elizabeth (Stuernberg) M. BS, Edgecliff Coll., Cin., 1967; MEd, Wright State U., 1972; PhD, Ohio State U., 1991. Joined Religious Community of Women, 1955; cert. tchr., prin., supr., Ohio; cert. tchr., sch. adminstr., supt., N.C. Tchr. Archdiocese of Cin., Cin., Mason, Dayton, Ohio, 1958-71; prin. Archdiocese of Cin., Mason/Hamilton, Millville, Ohio, 1971-81; asst. supt. Archdiocese of Cin., Dayton, 1981-87; grad. asst. Ohio State U., Columbus, 1987-90; supr. Diocese of Raleigh, N.C., 1991—. Co-author religious edn. cert. program, 1976. Mem., chmn. bd. trustees Chaminade-Julienne High Sch., Dayton, 1983-91. Recipient Outstanding Contbn. to Community award Kiwanis, Mason, 1974. Mem. ASCD, Cath. Edn. Assn., Am. Edn. Rsch. Assn., John Locke Soc., Wright State U. Alumni Assn., Edgecliff Coll. Alumni Assn., Ohio State U. Alumni Assn., Chief Adminstrs. of Cath. Edn., Phi Delta Kappa. Roman Catholic. Avocations: swimming, golfing, hiking, music, art. Office: Diocese of Raleigh Cath Schs Office 300 Cardinal Gibbons Dr Raleigh NC 27606-2108

MEYER, LOUIS B., superior court judge, retired state supreme court justice; b. Marion, N.C., July 15, 1933; s. Louis B. and Beulah (Smith) M.; m. Evelyn Spradlin, Dec. 29, 1956; children: Louis B. III, Patricia Shannon, Adam Burden. B.A., Wake Forest U., 1955, J.D., 1960; LLM, U. Va., 1992. Bar: N.C. 1960, U.S. Dist. (ea. dist.) N.C. 1960, U.S. Ct. Appeals (4th cir.) 1960, U.S. Supreme Ct. 1962. Law clk. Supreme Ct. N.C., Raleigh, 1960; spl. agent FBI, 1961-62; atty. Lucas, Rand, Rose, Meyer, Jones & Orcutt P.A., Wilson, N.C., 1962-81; assoc. justice Supreme Ct. N.C., Raleigh, 1981-95, ret., 1995. Former county chmn. Wilson County Dems., N.C.; former mem. N.C. State Exec. Com. Dem. Party. Served to 1st lt. U.S. Army, 1955-57. Mem. Wilson County Bar Assn. (former pres.), Wake County Bar Assn., 7th Jud. Dist. Bar Assn. (former pres.), N.C. Bar Assn. (former v.p.). Baptist. Lodge: Masons.

MEYER, MADELINE ANNA, librarian; b. Great Bend, Kans., Mar. 26, 1948; d. George Albert and Anna Millicent (Noel) M. Student, Cambridge U., Eng., 1967-68; BA, Valparaiso U., 1970; MA, U. Denver, 1981. Libr. Denver Pub. Library, 1971-76; lease records mgr. Vantage Cos., Dallas, 1976-77; libr. Lytham-St. Annes Coll., St. Annes-on-Sea, Lancashire, Eng. 1977-78; lease records asst. J. Grynberg & Assocs., Denver, 1978-79; travel cons. Free Spirit Travel, Aurora, Colo., 1979-82; libr. Aurora Pub. Library, 1982-83; customer svc. rep. Western Air Lines, Denver, 1983-85; libr. Mesa (Ariz.) Pub. Library, 1985-87, Scottsdale (Ariz.) Pub. Library, 1987—. Dep. registrar Election Com., Phoenix, 1985—. Mem. Ariz. State Library Assn., Nat. Mgmt. Assn., Cen. Ariz. Tall Soc. Democrat. Lutheran. Avocation: traveling. Office: Scottsdale Pub Libr 3839 N Civic Center Blvd Scottsdale AZ 85251-4467

MEYER, MARGARET ELEANOR, microbiologist, educator; b. Westwood, Calif., Feb. 8, 1923; d. Herman Henry and Eleanor (Dobson) M. B.S., U. Calif., Berkeley, 1945; Ph.D., U. Calif., Davis, 1961. Pub. health analyst USPHS, Bethesda, Md., 1945-46; swine Brucellosis control agt. Dept. Agr., Davis, 1946-47; bacteriologist U. Calif., Davis, 1947-61; research microbiologist U. Calif. (Sch. Vet. Medicine), 1961-77, prof. vet. pub. health and microbiologist exptl. sta., 1977—; research microbiologist U. Calif. Med. Sch., Los Angeles, 1961-77; supr. Brucella identifications lab. WHO, U. Calif.-Davis, 1964—, prof. vet. pub. health, 1973—; also dir. M.A. program in preventive vet. medicine; cons. subcom. on Brucella Internat. Com. Bacterial Taxonomy, 1962—, mem., 1966—; mem. 5th Pan Am. Congress Veterinary Medicine, Venezuela, 1966; mem. Internat. Congress Microbiology, Moscow, 1966, Mexico City, 1970, Munich, Ger., 1978, mem., officer, Eng. 1986; mem. Internat. Conf. Culture Collections, Tokyo, 1968; mem. adv. com. to Bergey's Manual Determative Bacteriology, 1967; cons. in resident Pan Am. Health Orgn., Zoonoses Lab., Buenos Aires, 1968; mem. brucellosis tech. adv. com. U.S. Animal Health Assn., 1977; FAO cons. on brucellosis control in dairy animals, Tripoli, Libya, 1981, mem. 3d internat. brucellosis symposium, Algiers, 1983; cons. Alaska Dept. Fish and Game, 1976, FAO, Libya, 1981, Bering Straits Reindeer Herders Assn., Nome, Alaska, 1981; invited speaker Internat. Symposium on Advances in Brucellosis Rsch., Tex. A&M U., 1989, Internat. Bison Conf.; resident cons. on brucellosis control in sheep and goats Am. Near East Refugee Aid, East Jerusalem, 1989; cons. on brucellosis in Yellowstone Nat. Pk., Nat. Pk. Svc., 1991—; invited mem. nat. symposium on brucellosis in the Greater Yellowstone Area, Jackson Hole, Wyo., 1994; cons. on brucellosis control in livestock for Armenia, 1994—. Contbr. articles to profl. jours. Bd. dirs. Carmichael Park and Recreation Dist., Calif., 1975. Recipient Research Career Devel. award USPHS-NIH, 1963. Fellow Am. Pub. Health Assn., Am. Acad. Microbiology; mem. Soc. Am. Microbiologists, N.Am. Conf. Animal Disease Research Workers, Am. Coll. Vet. Microbiologists (hon. affiliate), U.S. Animal Health Assn. (chmn. brucellosis tech. advisory com. 1978-79), Internat. Assn. Microbiol. Socs. (mem. 1st intersect. congress 1974), AAUW, No. Calif. Women's Golf Assn., U. Calif. Alumni Assn., Sigma Xi. Clubs: U. Calif. Faculty (Davis); El Dorado Royal Country (Shingle Springs, Calif.); Reno Women's Golf. Home: 5611 Fair Oaks Blvd Carmichael CA 95608-5503 Office: U Calif Sch Vet Medicine Dept Epidemiology & Preventive Medicine Davis CA 95616

MEYER, MAURICE WESLEY, physiologist, dentist, neurologist; b. Long Prairie, Minn., Feb. 13, 1925; s. Ernest William and Augusta (Warnke) M.; m. Martha Reba, Sept. 3, 1946; children—James Irvin, Thomas Orville. B.S., U. Minn., 1953, D.D.S., 1957, M.S., 1959, Ph.D., 1961. Teaching asst. U. Minn. Sch. Dentistry, 1954-55, USPHS fellow, 1955-56, rsch. fellow, 1956-57, mem. faculty, 1960—; prof. physiology, dentistry and neurology U. Minn., 1976-88, prof. emeritus, 1988—; investigator Ctr. Rsch. and Cerebral Vascular Disease, 1969—; dir. lab. Center Research and Cerebral Vascular Disease, 1975—; postdoctoral research fellow Nat. Inst. Dental Research, 1957-60, research fellow, 1958-61, mem. faculty, 1961—; asso. prof. neurology, 1974-80, mem. grad. faculty, 1973—; trainee Inst. Advanced Edn. in Dental Research, 1964—; vis. assoc. prof., also vis. research fellow dept. physiology and Sch. Dentistry Cardiovascular Research Inst., U. Calif., San Francisco, 1971. Contbr. articles to profl. jours. Served to col. Dental Corps AUS, 1943-50. Decorated D.F.C., Air medal with 3 oak leaf clusters. Fellow AAAS; mem. ADA, Minn. Dental Soc., Internat. Assn. Dental Research (pres. Minn. sect. 1967-68), Soc. Exptl. Biology and Medicine, Am. Physiol. Soc., Microcirculatory Soc., Am. Assn. Dental Schs. (chmn. 1972-73), Can. Physiol. Soc., Sigma Xi, Omicron Kappa Upsilon. Club: Masons. Home: 560 Rice Creek Ter NE Minneapolis MN 55432-4472 Office: U Minn 6-255 Millard Minneapolis MN 55455

MEYER, MAX EARL, lawyer; b. Hampton, Va., Oct. 31, 1918; s. Earl Luther and Winifred Katherine (Spacht) M.; m. Betty Maxwell Dodds, Sept. 22, 1945; children—Scott Maxwell, Ann Culliford. AB, U. Nebr., 1940, JD, 1942. Bar: Nebr. 1942, Ill. 1946. Assoc. firm Lord, Bissell & Brook, Chgo., 1945-53; ptnr. Lord, Bissell & Brook, 1953-85; chmn. Chgo. Fed. Tax Forum, 1965, U. Chgo. Ann. Fed. Tax Conf. 1972; mem. Adv. Group to Commr. of IRS, 1967; lectr. in field. Bd. dirs. Music Acad. of the West, chmn. 1993-94. Mem. ABA (mem. council tax sect. 1969-72), Ill. Bar Assn. (mem. council tax sect. 1973-76), Nebr. Bar Assn., Chgo. Bar Assn. (chmn. taxation com. 1959-61), Am. Coll. Tax Counsel. Republican. Presbyterian. Clubs: Legal, Law (Chgo.); Valley Club of Montecito, Birnam Wood Golf. Lodge: Masons.

MEYER, MELVIN A., lumber and hardware executive, freelance designer; b. Plymouth, Nebr., Mar. 27, 1933; s. Arthur and Selma (Niemeier) M.; m. Darlene Haecker, July 14, 1957; children: Rebecca Meyer Searcey, Joel. Grad., Plymouth High. Sch., 1950. Sales rep. Saek Lumber Co., Crete, Nebr., 1955-62; owner, mgr. Mel's Feed Svc., Wymore, Nebr., 1962-78, Wymore Lumber Co., 1978—. Designer: Vets. War Meml., Welsh Cemetary, Wymore, Nebr., 1993, Immanuel Luth. Ch. Meml., Plymouth, Nebr. 1986. Mem. coun. Our Saviors Luth. Ch., Wymore, 1991—; rescue capt. Wymore Vol. Fire Dept. Cpl. U.S. Army, 1953-55. Mem. Am. Legion (bd. dirs. 1981—, mem. exec. bd., Membership citation, Appreciation of Svc. award), Wymore C. of C., DAV, VFW. Republican. Avocations: golf, sports. Office: Wymore Lumber Co 116 E E St Wymore NE 68466-2122

MEYER, MICHAEL EDWIN, lawyer; b. Chgo., Oct. 23, 1942; s. Leon S. and Janet (Gorden) M.; m. Catherine Dieffenbach, Nov. 21, 1982; children: Linda, Mollie, Patrick, Kellie. BS, U. Wis., 1964; JD, U. Chgo., 1967. Bar: Calif. 1968, U.S. Supreme Ct. 1973. Assoc. Lillick & McHose, L.A., 1967-73; ptnr., 1974-90, mng. ptnr., 1986-87; ptnr. Pillsbury Madison Sutro, 1990—, mem. mgmt. com. 1990-92; judge pro tem Beverly Hills Mcpl. Ct., Calif., 1976-79, Los Angeles Mcpl. Ct., 1980-86; lectr. in field. Bd. dirs. Bldg. Owners and Mgrs. Assn. of Greater L.A., L.A. Coun. Boy Scouts Am., United Way Greater L.A. Recipient Good Scout award L.A. coun. Boy Scouts Am., 1992. Mem. ABA, Am. Arbitration Assn. (arbitrator), Calif. Bar Assn., L.A. Bar Assn., U. Chgo. Alumni Assn. So. Calif. (pres. 1980-82), Calif. Club, U. L.A. Club (dir. 1979-85, pres. 1984-85), L.A. Country Club. Jewish. Home: 4407 Roma Ct Marina Dl Rey CA 90292-7702 Office: Pillsbury Madison Sutro 725 S Figueroa Los Angeles CA 90017

MEYER, MICHAEL LOUIS, lawyer; b. Buffalo, Dec. 17, 1940; s. Bernard H. and Florence (Nusbaum) M.; m. Jo Ann Ackerman, Sept. 21, 1990. AB, Princeton U., 1962; LLB, Harvard U., 1965. Bar: Ill. 1965, D.C., 1978. Assoc. Schiff Hardin & Waite, Chgo., 1965-72, ptnr., 1972—. Lt. USN, 1965-68. Mem. ABA (mem. fed. regulation of security com.), Chgo. Bar Assn., Chgo. Coun. Lawyers, Chgo. Yacht Club, Metropolitan Club. Office: Schiff Hardin & Waite 7200 Sears Towers Ste 1200 Chicago IL 60606

MEYER, MILTON EDWARD, JR., lawyer, artist; b. St. Louis, Nov. 26, 1922; s. Milton Edward and Jessie Marie (Hurley) M.; m. Mary C. Kramer, Nov. 5, 1949; children: Milton E. III, Melanie M. Meyer Francis, Daniel K., Gregory N. B.S. in Bus. Adminstrn, Washington U., 1943; LL.B., St. Louis, U., 1950; LL.M., N.Y. U., 1953. Bar: Mo. 1950, Colo. 1956. Trust adminstr. Mississippi Valley Trust Co., St. Louis, 1946-50; asso. firm Burnett, Stern & Liberman, St. Louis, 1953-56; founding partner firm Hindry & Meyer, Denver, 1956-79; chmn. bd. Hindry & Meyer, 1970-79; spl. counsel Schmidt, Elrod & Wills, and predecessors, 1979-83, pres., 1980-82; sec. C.A. Norgren Co., Littleton, Colo., 1960-78; dir. C.A. Norgren Co., 1971-78. Contbr. articles to profl. jours. Bd. dirs. Nat. Club Assn., 1971-91, pres., 1976-78; bd. dirs., pres. Denver Community Concert Assn. 1960-64; bd. dirs. Sewall Rehab. Ctr., Denver, 1965-68, Carl A. Norgren Found., 1960-70, Denver Leadership Found. 1983-93; bd. dirs. Found. Colo. Women's Coll., 1984-86, chmn., 1984-86; bd. dirs. Conf. Amer. Pvt. Orgns., 1982-89, chmn., 1984-88; chmn. Denver Rotary's Artists of Am. Exhbn., 1990-92. With airborne inf. U.S. Army, 1943-46, 50-52. Mem. ABA, Colo. Bar Assn. Denver Bar Assn., Greater Denver Tax Counsels Assn. (founder, chmn. 1957), Denver Estate Planning Coun. (founder, pres. 1958), Am. Coll. Probate Counsel, Pastel Soc. Am., Pastel Soc. West Coast (Disting. Pastellist award), Internat. Assn. Pastel Socs. (founder, dir. 1994—), Cherry Hills Country Club, Pinehurst Country Club (pres. 1979-80), Denver Execs. Club, Hundred Club Denver, Rotary (bd. dirs. 1991-93), Phi Eta Sigma, Beta Gamma Sigma, Omicron Delta Kappa, Beta Theta Pi. Republican. Roman Catholic. Home and Studio: 5784 E Oxford Ave Cherry Hills Village CO 80111

MEYER, NICHOLAS, screenwriter, director; b. N.Y.C., Dec. 24, 1945; s. Bernard Constant and Elly (Kassman) M. B.A. in Theatre and Film, U. Iowa, 1968. Assoc. publicist Paramount Pictures, N.Y.C., 1968-69; story editor Warner Bros., N.Y.C., 1970-71. Writer, dir.: (films) Time After Time, 1979 (Avoriaz Film Festival grand prize, Academy of Science Fiction, Fantasy, and Horror Films award), Company Business, 1991, Star Trek VI:

The Undiscovered Country, 1991; writer: (films) Invasion of the Bee Girls, 1973, The Seven-Per-Cent Solution, 1976 (Academy award nomination best adapted screenplay 1976), Sommersby, 1993, (TV movies) Judge Dee, 1974, Please Stand By, 1975, The Night That Panicked America, 1975; dir.: (films) Startrek II: The Wrath of Khan, 1982, Volunteers, 1985, The Deceivers, 1988, (TV movies) The Day After, 1983; playwright, dir.: Loco Motives; author: (nonfiction) The Love Story, 1971, (novels) Target Practice, 1974 (Mystery Writers Guild award), The Seven-Percent Solution: Being a Reprint from the Reminiscences of John H. Watson, M.D., 1974 (Gold Dagger award British Crime Writers Assn.), The West End Horror: A Posthumous Memoir of John H. Watson, M.D., 1976, (with Barry J. Kaplan) Black Orchid, 1977, Confessions of a Homing Pigeon, 1981, The Canary Trainer, 1993. Recipient Anne Radcliffe award Count Dracula Soc. Mem. Authors Guild, Writers Guild. Democrat. Home: 2109 Stanley Hills Dr Los Angeles CA 90046-1529 Office: Creative Artists Agy 9830 Wilshire Blvd Beverly Hills CA 90212-1825*

MEYER, PATRICIA ANN, veterinarian; b. Greenwich, Conn., Jan. 13, 1945; d. William Charles and Dorothy Ann (Natter) M. BS, Mich. State U., 1967, DVM, 1967. Assoc. veterinarian Belmont (Mass.) Animal Hosp., 1968-69, Pieper Vet. Hosp., Middletown, Conn., 1969-70, Greenwich (Conn.) Animal Hosp., 1970-71, East Longmeadow (Mass.) Vet. Hosp., 1971-72, Clinton (Conn.) Vet. Hosp., 1972-74, MacDonald Vet. Hosp., Bloomfield, Conn., 1974-78, Manchester (Conn.) Vet. Clinic, 1978-83, Whitney Vet. Clinic, Orange, Conn., 1983-93; pvt. practice New Haven, 1993—. Fellow AVMA, Am. Animal Hosp. Assn., Conn. Vet. Med. Assn. (chmn. Acad. Vet. Medicine 1977—); mem. Baldwin Yacht Club, Hartford Ski Club, Hartford County Vet. Med. Assn. (sec.-treas. 1978—). Republican. Roman Catholic. Avocations: skiing, sailing. Home and Office: House Calls for Pets 146 Springside Ave New Haven CT 06515-1076

MEYER, PATRICIA MORGAN, neuropsychologist, educator; b. Delaware, Ohio, June 23, 1934; d. Thomas Wendell and Ceola (Drummond) Morgan; m. Donald Ray Meyer, Dec. 31, 1957; 1 dau., Julia Catherine. A.B., Ohio Wesleyan U., 1956; M.A., Ohio State U., 1958, Ph.D., 1960. Research assoc. Ohio State U., Columbus, 1960-76, prof. psychology, 1976-85, prof. psychology emeritus, 1985—. Editor Physiol. Psychology jour., 1980-85. Recipient Career award NIMH, Ohio State U., 1966-76. Fellow Am. Psychol. Assn. (bd. sci. affairs 1973-76), Midwestern Psychol. Assn., Psychonomic Soc., Soc. for Neurosci. Republican. Methodist. Avocation: videography. Home: 476 Overbrook Dr Columbus OH 43214-3127 Office: Ohio State U Dept Psychology 1885 Neil Ave Columbus OH 43210-1222

MEYER, PAUL JAMES, communications company executive; b. San Mateo, Calif., May 21, 1928; s. August Carl and Isabel (Rutherford) M.; m. Jane Gurley, Nov. 26, 1971; children: Paul James Jr., Larry, Bill, Janna, Leslie. DAviation Edn. (hon.), Embry-Riddle Aero. U., 1956; LHD (hon.), Ft. Lauderdale U., 1957; LittD (hon.), East Tex. Bapt. U., 1989. Mgr. sales Word, Inc., Waco, Tex., 1958-60; founder, chmn. bd. dirs. SMI/USA, Inc., Waco, 1960—; also Leadership Mgmt., Inc. Bd. dirs. Waco Boys Club, 1970—; mem. Nat. Rep. Fin. Com. With airborne U.S. Army, 1946-48. Mem. Am. Mgmt. Assn., Internat. Franchise Assn., Nat. Speakers Bur. Baptist. Avocations: tennis, snow skiing, scuba diving, bicycling, mountain hiking, flying. Office: PO Box 7411 Waco TX 76714-7411

MEYER, PAUL JOSEPH, lawyer; b. Oak Park, Ill., Nov. 27, 1942; s. Paul Gilbert and Frances Marie (O'Shea) M. B.A. summa cum laude, St. Mary's Coll., 1964; J.D. cum laude, U. Notre Dame, 1967. Bar: Ill. 1967, Ariz. 1970, U.S. Tax Ct. 1975, U.S. Supreme Ct. 1980. Law clk. to Hon. Walter V. Schaefer, Ill. Supreme Ct., 1967-68; sr. law clk. to Hon. Earl Warren U.S. Supreme Ct., Washington, 1968-69; assoc. Snell & Wilmer, Phoenix, 1969-71; mem. Meyer, Hendricks, Victor, Osborn & Maledon, Phoenix, 1971—. Trustee, Ariz. Heart Inst. Found.; St. Mary's Coll., Minn.; bd. dirs. Ariz. Coalition for Tomorrow, Phoenix Community Alliance. Ill. State scholar, 1960; Weymouth Kirkland scholar, 1964; William J. Brennan Law scholar, 1964. Mem. Am. Law Inst., ABA, Ariz. Bar Assn., Maricopa County Bar Assn., Notre Dame Law Assn. (bd. dirs.). Club: Phoenix Country, Arizona (Phoenix). Home: 1101 Crystal Point 1040 E Osborn Rd Phoenix AZ 85014 Office: 2929 N Central Ave Phoenix AZ 85012-2798

MEYER, PAUL REIMS, JR., orthopedic surgeon; b. Port Arthur, Tex.; s. Paul Reims and Evelyn (Miller) M.; m. Lesa W. Meyer; children: Kristin Lynn, Holly Dee, Paul Reims III, Stewart Blair. BA, Va. Mil. Inst., 1954; MD, Tulane U., 1958; MA of Mgmt., J.L. Kellogg Grad. Sch. of Mgmt. (Northwestern U.), 1992. Dir. Spine Injury Ctr. Northwestern U., Chgo., 1972—, prof. orthopaedic surgery, 1981—; cons. Nat. Inst. Disability and Rehab. Rsch. VA, Washington, 1978—, chmn. spinal cord injury subcom., 1983—, also chmn. sci. merit com.; clin. prof. surgery Dept. Surgery, USUHS; mem. adv. com. World Rehab. Fund, 1990—; mem. bd. councilors Am. Acad. Orthopaedic Surgeons, 1993—; orthopaedic cons. to Army Surgeon Gen. Author: Surgery of Spine Trauma, 1988; patentee cervical orthosis. Col. M.C., USAR. Fellow ACS, Am. Acad. Orthop. Surgeons; mem. Société Internationale de Chirurgie Orthopédique et de Traumatologie, Internat. Med. Soc. Paraplegia, Am. Trauma Soc. (bd. dirs. 1988—), Am. Orthop. Assn., Am. Spinal Injury Assn. (past pres.), Soc. Med. Cons. to Armed Forces, Mid-Am. Orthop. Assn. Roman Catholic. Avocations: photography, fishing, ham radio, aviation, boating. Office: Northwestern Meml Hosp 250 E Superior St Rm 619 Chicago IL 60611-2914

MEYER, PAUL WILLIAM, arboretum director, horticulturist; b. Cin., Aug. 30, 1952; s. Edward F. and Dorothy (Schroeder) M.; m. Debra L. Rodgers, May 16, 1990. BSc, Ohio State U., 1973; MSc, U. Del., 1976; diploma, U. Edinburgh, 1988. Curator Morris Arboretum U. Pa., Phila., 1976-91, dir., 1991—. Bd. dirs. The Henry Found., 1992-93; chair Springfield Twp. planning com., Montgomery County, Pa., 1993. Mem. Am. Assn. Botanical Gardens and Arboreta (bd. dirs.), The John Bartram Assn. (bd. dirs., v.p. 1984-85). Avocations: bicycling, swimming, backpacking, gardening. Office: Morris Arboretum of Univ Pa 9414 Meadowbrook Ave Philadelphia PA 19118-2624

MEYER, PAUL WILLIAM, biblical literature educator emeritus; b. Raipur, India, May 31, 1924; s. Armin Frederick and Hulda Dorothea (Klein) M.; m. Mary Louise Yonker, Sept. 3, 1948; children—Katherine Priode, Elizabeth Cooper. B.A., Elmhurst Coll., 1945; B.D., Union Theol. Sem., 1949, Th.D., 1955. Instr. Union Theol. Sem., N.Y.C., 1952-54; asst. prof. Div. Sch., Yale U., New Haven, 1954-62; assoc. prof. Div. Sch., Yale U., 1962-64; prof. N.T. interpretation Colgate Rochester (N.Y.) Div. Sch., 1964-70; prof. N.T. Div. Sch., Vanderbilt U., Nashville, 1970-78; Helen H.P. Manson prof. N.T. lit. Princeton (N.J.) Theol. Sem., 1978-89, prof. emeritus, 1989—; adj. visiting prof. dept. religious studies Univ. N.C., Chapel Hill, 1989—. Served with U.S. Army, 1943-45. Morse fellow Yale U., 1961-62; Fulbright research grantee U. Gottingen, W. Ger., 1961-62. Mem. Soc. Bibl. Lit. and Exegesis, Studiorum Novi Testamenti Societas, Am. Theol. Soc., AAUP. Presbyterian.

MEYER, PAULINE MARIE, retired special education educator; b. Gilead, Nebr., Dec. 15, 1928; d. Bernhard Martin and Helena Sophia (Vorderstrasse) Hellbusch; m. Calvin John, June 8, 1951 (dec. Nov. 1973); 1 child, Phyllis; m. Tim Gaspar. BA, U. Nebr., 1968, MA, 1972. Tchr. rural schs. Thayer County, Nebr., 1946-66; tchr. rural schs. Fairbury (Nebr.) Pub. Schs., 1966-91, ret., 1991. Mem. Bus. and Profl. Women's Club (pres. 1987-90), Delta Kappa Gamma (pres.). Democrat. Lutheran. Avocations: refinishing furniture, quilting, reading.

MEYER, PEARL, executive compensation consultant; b. N.Y.C.; d. Allen Charles and Rose (Goldberg) Weissman; m. Ira A. Meyer. BA cum laude, NYU, postgrad. Statis. specialist, exec. comp. div. Gen. Foods Corp., White Plains, N.Y.; exec. v.p. and cons. Handy Assocs., Inc., N.Y.C.; founder, pres. Pearl Meyer & Ptnrs., N.Y.C., 1989—; lectr. on exec. compensation at confs. and seminars. Contbr. numerous articles to profl. jours. Recipient Entrepreneurial Woman award Women Bus. Owners N.Y., 1983. Mem. Am. Mgmt. Assn., Am. Compensation Assn., Soc. for Human Resources Mgmt. (cert. accredited pers. diplomate), Women's Econ. Roundtable, Pers. Accreditation Inst., Women's Forum, Sedgewood Club, Atrium Club, Sky Club, Phi Beta Kappa, Pi Mu Epsilon, Kappa Pi Sigma. Clubs: Sedgewood,

Bd. Rm., Atrium, Sky. Office: Pearl Meyer & Partners Inc 300 Park Ave 21st Fl New York NY 10022-7402

MEYER, PETER, physicist, educator; b. Berlin, Jan. 6, 1920; came to U.S., 1952, naturalized, 1962; s. Franz and Frida (Lehmann) M.; m. Luise Schützmeister, July 20, 1946 (dec. 1981); children: Stephan S., Andreas S.; m. Patricia G. Spear, June 14, 1983. Dipl.Ing., Tech. U., Berlin, 1942; Ph.D., U. Goettingen, Germany, 1948. Faculty U. Goettingen, 1946-49; fellow U. Cambridge, Eng., 1949-50; mem. sci. staff Max-Planck Inst. fuer Physik, Goettingen, 1950-52; faculty U. Chgo., 1953—, prof. physics, 1965-90, prof. emeritus, 1990—, chmn. Dept. Physics, 1986-89; dir. Enrico Fermi Inst., 1978-83; cons. NASA, NSF.; mem. cosmic ray commn. Internat. Union Pure and Applied Physics, 1966-72; mem. space sci. bd. Nat. Acad. Scis., 1975-78. Recipient Alexander von Humboldt Sr. U.S. Scientist award, 1984, Llewellyn John and Harriet Manchester Quantrell award, 1971. Fellow Am. Phys. Soc. (chmn. div. cosmic physics 1972-73), AAAS; mem. NAS, Am. Astron. Soc., Am. Geophys. Union, Max Planck Inst. fuer Physik und Astrophysik (fgn.), Sigma Xi. Office: 933 E 56th St Chicago IL 60637-1460

MEYER, PHILIP EDWARD, journalism educator; b. Deshler, Nebr., Oct. 27, 1930; s. Elmer Edward and Hilda Grace (Morrison) M.; m. Sue Quail, Aug. 5, 1956; children: Caroline, Katherine, Melissa, Sarah. BS, Kans. State U., 1952; MA, U. N.C., 1963. Asst. state editor Topeka (Kans.) Daily Capital, 1954-56; reporter Miami (Fla.) Herald, 1958-62; Washington corr. Akron Beacon Jour., 1962-66; nat. corr. Knight-Ridder, Inc., Washington, 1967-78; dir. news research Knight-Ridder, Inc., Miami, 1978-81; William Rand Kenan Jr. prof. journalism U. N.C., Chapel Hill, 1981-93; Knight prof., 1993—. Author: Precision Journalism, 1973 (Sigma Delta Chi Disting. Service award 1974), The Newspaper Survival Book, 1985, Ethical Journalism, 1987, The New Precision Journalism, 1991; co-author: To Keep the Republic, 1975. Project dir. Russell Sage Found., N.Y.C., 1969-70. Served with USNR, 1952-54. Recipient Disting. Contbns. to Journalism award Nat. Press Found., 1994; Nieman fellow Harvard U., 1966-67, Freedom Forum Ctr. for Media Studies fellow, 1985. Mem. Am. Assn. for Pub. Opinion Rsch. (pres. 1989-90), World Assn. for Pub. Opinion Rsch. (pres. 1993-95), Assn. for Edn. in Journalism and Mass Communication, Nat. Press Club (D.C.). Democrat. Episcopalian. Avocation: photography. Home: 610 Croom Ct Chapel Hill NC 27514-6706 Office: UNC Sch Journalism & Mass Comm Howell Hall CB3365 Chapel Hill NC 27599

MEYER, PRISCILLA ANN, Russian language and literature educator, writer, translator; b. N.Y.C., Aug. 26, 1942; d. Herbert Edward and Marjorie Rose (Wolff) M.; m. William L. Trousdale, Sept. 15, 1974; 1 dau., Rachel V. B.A., U. Calif.-Berkeley, 1964; M.A., Princeton U., 1966, Ph.D., 1971. Lectr. in Russian lang. and lit. Wesleyan U., Middletown, Conn., 1968-71, asst. prof., 1971-75, assoc. prof., 1975-88, prof.—; vis. asst. prof. Yale U., 1973; tchr. John Lyman Elem. Sch., Middlefield, Conn., 1982, 83. Editor: Dostoevsky and Gogol, 1979; Life in Windy Weather (by Andrei Bitov), 1986; Find What The Sailor Has Hidden: Vladimir Nabokov's Pale Fire, 1988; co-editor: Essays on Gogol: Logos and the Russian Word, 1992; translator stories; contbr. articles to profl. jours. Sr. scholar exchange Internat. Research and Exchange Bd., 1973; Ford Found. grantee, 1964-68, 70. Mem. Am. Council Tchrs. Russian (dir. 1983-86), Am. Assn. Tchrs. Slavic and East European Langs., Am. Assn. for Advancement of Slavic Studies, Vladimir Nabokov Soc., Conn. Acad. Arts and Scis. Office: Russian Dept Wesleyan U Middletown CT 06459

MEYER, PUCCI, newspaper editor; b. N.Y.C., Sept. 1, 1944; d. Charles Albert and Lollo (Offer) M.; m. Thomas M. Anwe, Sept. 16, 1979. BA, U. Wis., 1966. Asst. editor Look mag., N.Y.C., 1970-71; editorial asst. Look mag., Paris, 1967-69; reporter Newsday, Garden City, L.I., N.Y., 1971-73; style editor N.Y. Daily News Sunday Mag., N.Y.C., 1974-76, assoc. editor, 1977-82, editor, 1983-86; sr. editor Prodigy, White Plains, N.Y., 1987; spl. projects editor N.Y. Post, N.Y.C., 1988-89, style editor, 1990-92, food editor, 1992-93, assoc. features editor, 1993—, travel editor, 1994—. Contbr. articles to various nat. mags. Recipient Pulitzer prize as mem. Newsday investigative team that wrote articles and book The Heroin Trail, 1973. Office: NY Post 210 South St New York NY 10002-7807

MEYER, RANDALL, retired oil company executive; b. Mt. Union, Iowa, Jan. 19, 1923; s. Carl Henry and Edythe (Stuck) M.; m. Barbara Swetman, Nov. 29, 1958; children: Warren, Gretchen, Kirsten. B.S. in Mech. Engring, U. Iowa, 1948; LL.D. (hon.), Iowa Wesleyan Coll., 1977. With Exxon Co. U.S.A. div. Exxon Corp., 1948-88; with tech. and mgmt. depts. Exxon Co. U.S.A., Baton Rouge and Houston, 1948-66; exec. asst. to pres. Exxon Corp., N.Y.C., 1966-67; sr. v.p., dir. Exxon Co. U.S.A., Houston, 1967-72, pres., 1972-88; bd. dirs., exec. com. Greater Houston Partnership; bd. dirs., chmn. Exec. Svc. Corps Houston; dir. M.D. Anderson Cancer Ctr. Outreach Corp. Trustee, mem. exec. com. Kinkaid Sch.; chmn. bd. visitors U. Tex. M.D. Anderson Cancer Ctr. Found.; bd. dirs., pres. Greater Houston Community Found.; bd. dirs. U. Iowa Found., Tex. So. U. Found. Mem. Am. Petroleum Inst. (bd. dirs.), Tex. Rsch. League, Sigma Xi, Tau Beta Pi, Omicron Delta Kappa, Pi Tau Sigma. Methodist. Office: Kellogg Tower Ste 975 601 Jefferson Houston TX 77002

MEYER, RAYMOND JOSEPH, former college basketball coach; b. Chgo., Dec. 18, 1913; s. Joseph E. and Barbara (Hummel) M.; m. Margaret Mary Delaney, May 27, 1939 (dec. 1985); children—Barbara (Mrs. Gerald Starzyk), Raymond Thomas, Patricia (Mrs. James Butterfield), Merianne (Mrs. James McGowan), Joseph, Robert. A.B., U. Notre Dame, 1938. Asst. coach U. Notre Dame, 1941-42; basketball coach DePaul U., Chgo., 1942—. Author: How To Play Winning Basketball, 1960, Basketball as Coached by Ray Meyer, 1967, Ray Meyer, 1 Coach, 1980, Coach, 1987. Named Coach of Yr. Chgo. Basketball Writers, 1943, 44, 48, 52, Coach of Yr. Nat. Assn. Basketball Coaches, 1978-79, Sportwriters Coach of Yr., 1978, Salvation Man of Yr., 1990; recipient Marine Corps Sportsman of Yr. award, 1979, Bunn award, 1981, Victor award, 1981, Lincoln Acad. award, 1988, Nat. Basketball Coach's Golden Jubilee award; inducted into Basketball Hall of Fame, 1979, Basketball Hall of Fame Chgo., 1981, Basketball Hall of Fame Ill., Golden Anniversay award Nat. Basketball Coaches, 1992. Mem. Nat. Basketball Coaches Assn. Roman Catholic. Home: 2518 W Cedar Glen Dr Arlington Heights IL 60005-4336 Office: 1011 W Belden Ave Chicago IL 60614-3205

MEYER, RICHARD CHARLES, microbiologist; b. Cleve., May 2, 1930; s. Frederick Albert and Tekla Charlotte (Schrade) M.; m. Carolyn Yvonne Patton, Apr. 6, 1963; children: Frederick Gustav, Carl Anselm. B.Sc., Baldwin-Wallace Coll., 1952; M.Sc., Ohio State U., 1957, Ph.D., 1961. Teaching and research asst. Ohio State U., 1956-61, research assoc., 1961-62; microbiologist Nat. Cancer Inst., NIH, Bethesda, Md., 1962-64; asst. prof. vet. pathology and hygiene and microbiology U. Ill., Urbana-Champaign, 1965-68; assoc. prof. U. Ill., 1968-73, prof., 1973-89, prof. emeritus, 1989—. Served with C.E. U.S. Army, 1952-54. Mem. Am. Acad. Microbiology, AAAS, Am. Inst. Biol. Sci., Am. Soc. Microbiology, Gamma Sigma Delta, Phi Zeta. Republican. Lutheran. Home: 1504 Buckthorn Ln Mahomet IL 61853-3632 Office: Dept Vet Pathobiology U Ill at Urbana-Champaign Urbana IL 61801

MEYER, RICHARD E., insurance agent. Exec. v.p. Johnson & Higgins, N.Y.C., 1957—. Office: Johnson & Higgins 125 Broad St New York NY 10004-2424

MEYER, RICHARD JONAH, broadcast executive, consultant; b. Bklyn., Feb. 15, 1933; s. Max and Evelyn (Berman) M.; m. Sylvia R. Marshall, Feb. 21, 1956 (div. 1974); children: Adina, Mahlon, Rachel; m. Susan Diane Harmon, Apr. 9, 1983. BA, Stanford U., 1954, postgrad., 1954, 60, MA, 1960; PhD, NYU, 1967; postgrad., Harvard U., 1978. Prodn. asst. Sta. KQED-TV, San Francisco, 1961; dir. ednl. TV Wichita (Kans.) State U., 1961-64; vis. Sta. WNET-TV, N.Y.C., 1972-82; gen. mgr. Sta. KCTS-TV, Seattle, 1972-82; pres., gen. mgr., chief exec. officer Stas. KERA-FM-TV, KDTN-TV, Dallas, Ft. Worth, Denton, Tex., 1982—; cons. SUNY-Albany, 1967-68, UNESCO, Paris, 1970—, Corp. for Pub. Broadcasting, Washington, 1971—, USIA, Washington, 1972—; broadcaster-in-residence, sr. fellow East-West Ctr., 1989; adj. prof. U. North Tex., 1990, U. Tex., Dallas, 1994. Contbr. chpts. to books; exec. producer (TV series) Communications and Edn., 1967. Bd. dirs. NAEB, 1971-73, Henry Art Gallery, Seattle, 1974,

PBS, 1979-84, Nat. Mus. Comm.; trustee Va. Mason Research Ctr., 1979, Goals for Dallas, 1988. Served with U.S. Army, 1956-58. Russell Sage fellow Columbia U., 1968. Mem. Nat. Assn. Underwater Instrs., Internat. Brecht Soc. Jewish. Club: City (Dallas). Office: Sta KERA-TV 3000 Harry Hines Blvd Dallas TX 75201-1098

MEYER, RICHARD SCHLOMER, food company executive; b. Rapid City, S.D., Dec. 31, 1945; s. Harm Henry Schlomer and Marie Charolette (Hoffman) Meyer; m. Bonnie June Francis, July 15, 1970; children: Jennifer June, Christina Francis, Robert Schlomer. BS, Wash. State U., 1968, MS, 1970; PhD, Cornell U., 1974. Sr. scientist Nestle Co., New Milford, Conn., 1974-76; mgr. research and devel. Armour & Co., Scottsdale, Ariz., 1976-81; v.p. and tech. mgr. research and devel. Griffith Labs., Alsip, Ill., 1981-82; v.p. tech. dir. research and devel. Kitchens of Sara Lee, Deerfield, Ill., 1982-84, Nalley's Curtice-Burns div. Agway, Tacoma, 1984-88; tech. v.p. Western regional lab. Curtice-Burns, Tacoma, 1988—; strategic planning com. N.W. Food Processor's Assn., Portland, Oreg., 1985—; pres. agrl. mktg. adv. bd. State of Wash., gov. coun. on agr. and environ., 1994—; pres. adv. bd. Wash. State U. Coll. Agr. and Home Econs., bd. trustees, 1992—; mem. U.S. Trade Misson to Indonesia, 1992; agrl. prof. Wash. State U.; adv. coun. on food processing Elec. Power Rsch. Inst., 1994—; adv. com. food sci. dept. Cornell U., 1994—. Contbr. articles to profl. jours.; holder 24 patents in field. Mem. exec. com. Cornell U., 1973-74, mem. adv. bd. food sci. dept., 1994; mem. bd. edn. New Milford Pub. Schs., 1975-81; bd. regents Wash. State U., 1969-70, pres. coll. agr. and home econs. adv. bd., mem. food svc. and human nutrition adv. bd.; Rep. state committeeman and precinct capt., Phoenix, 1979-81; mem. Oreg. State U. Food Sci. Dept.'s Indsl. Food Coun., 1990—; mem. Food Engring. Adv. Coun. U. Calif., Davis, 1994—; pres. Washington State Agrl. Mktg. Adv. Bd., 1991—; Food Industry rep. WSU-Kellogg Found. edn. system for U.S. Food Industry, 1994. NIH fellow, 1971, 72. Mem. Inst. Food Technologists, Internat. Rsch. Inst., Nutrition Today Soc., Wash. Agr. and Forestry Found., Can. Inst. Food Sci. and Tech., Am. Meat Sci. Assn., Coll. of Agr. and Home Econs. Alumni Assn. (pres. 1990-92), World Poultry Sci. Assn., Shriner, Masons, Phi Kappa Phi, Alpha Zeta. Mem. Christian Ch. Office: Nalley's/Agway 3303 S 35th St Tacoma WA 98409-4701

MEYER, RICHARD TOWNSEND, service company executive; b. Pitts., June 28, 1925; s. Howard Christian and Florence Leonore (Miller) M.; m. Faye Marie Cornell, Nov. 5, 1986; children Cynthia, Scott, Tracy, Richard, Lisa. BS, Allegheny Coll., 1949; postgrad., U. Buffalo, 1950-53; LLB, LaSalle U., Chgo., 1962. Eastern sales mgr. Hoover Co., Canton, Ohio, 1953-55; circulation dir. Time Inc., Chgo., 1955-62; v.p. sales Macmillan, Inc., Chgo., 1962-65; exec. v.p. mktg./sales Macmillan, Inc., N.Y.C., 1965; pres. chief exec. officer MacMillan Inc., N.Y.C., 1965-72; pres. R.T. Meyers Assoc., San Diego, 1972-80; chmn., pres., chief exec. officer Exec. Transitions Internat., Inc., Washington, 1980—. Lt. USN 1942-46, PTO. Mem. Pitts. Athletic Assn., Walden Country Club, Sigma Alpha Epsilon. Republican. Avocations: golf, racquetball, sailing. Home: 1409 Kensington Pl Crofton MD 21114-2615 Office: Exec Transitions Internat Inc Ste 1150 1655 Ft Myer Dr Arlington VA 22209-3105

MEYER, ROBERT, bank executive. Pres., chief exec. officer First Jersey Nat. Bank, Trenton, N.J. Office: 1st Jersey Nat Bank Cen E State & Montgomery Sts Trenton NJ 08605

MEYER, ROBERT ALLEN, human resource management educator; b. Wisconsin Rapids, Wis., May 31, 1943; s. Charles Harold and Viola Bertha (Stoeckmann) M.; 1 child, Timothy Charles. BA, Valparaiso (Ind.) U., 1966; MA, Mich. State U., 1967, PhD, 1972, postgrad., 1981. Asst. prof. Muskingum Area Tech. Coll., Zanesville, Ohio, 1972-74; adj. prof. U. Fla., Gainesville, 1974-80; dean acad. affairs Santa Fe Community Coll., Gainesville, 1974-80; asst. prof. Purdue U., W. Lafayette, Ind., 1982-84, Ga. State U., Atlanta, 1985-89; assoc. prof., program coord. U. N. Tex., Denton, 1989-91; Fulbright profl. scholar, Bangkok, 1991-92; coord. travel, tourism, hotel, restaurant mgmt. program U. Hawaii Manoa Campus, Honolulu, 1992—; investor, asst. mgr. LaSiene Restaurant, Ann Arbor, Mich., 1970-72; investor, cons. Cafe Brittany St. Thomas, U.S. V.I., 1974-80, owner, operator, Houston, 1980; pres. RTM Cons., Honolulu, Hawaii, 1989—; educator World Tourism Orgn., 1993—; mem. vis. ind. coun. C. of C., 1993—; club mgr. Assn. Am., 1994—. Contbr. articles to profl. jours. Recipient White House Commendation for Partnerships with Industry and Higher Edn.,1984, George Washington Medal of Honor for innovations in higher edn., Freedoms Found., 1985, 86, Achievement award in hospitality edn. Coun. of Hotel, Restaurant & Instl. Edn., 1987. Mem. Tarrant County Hotel and Motel Assn., Dallas Hotel Assn., Am. Soc. Tng. and Devel., Travel Ind. Assn. Tex., Hotel Sales & Mktg. Assn. (bd. dirs. 1985-89), Coun. of Hotel, Restaurant and Instl. Edn. (grad. com. 1989-90). Home: Apt 1608 2611 Ala Wai Honolulu HI 96815 Office: U Hawaii Manoa Campus 2560 Campus Rd Honolulu HI 96816

MEYER, SISTER ROBERTA, school system administrator. Supt. schs. Diocese of Lubbock, Tex. Office: Office of Schs Supt PO Box 98700 Lubbock TX 79499-8700

MEYER, RON, agent; b. 1944; m. Kelly Chapman; children Jennifer, Sarah, Carson. With Paul Kohner Agency, 1965-1970; agent William Morris Agency, Beverly Hills, CA, 1970-1975; co-founder, pres. Creative Artists Agency, Inc., Beverly Hills, CA, 1975—. Served with USMC. Office: Creative Artist Agy 9830 Wilshire Blvd Beverly Hills CA 90212-1825*

MEYER, RUSSEL WILLIAM, JR., aircraft company executive; b. Davenport, Iowa, July 19, 1932; s. Russell William and Ellen Marie (Matthews) M.; m. Helen Scott Vaughn, Aug. 20, 1960; children: Russell William, III, Elizabeth Ellen, Jeffrey Vaughn, Christopher Matthews, Carolyn Louise. B.A., Yale U., 1954; LL.B., Harvard U., 1961. Bar: Ohio 1961. Mem. firm Arter & Hadden, Cleve., 1961-66; pres., chief exec. officer Grumman Am. Aviation Corp., Cleve. 1966-74; exec. v.p. Cessna Aircraft Co., Wichita, Kans., 1974-75; chmn. bd., chief exec. officer Cessna Aircraft Co., 1975—; bd. dirs. Western Resources, 4th Fin. Corp., Coleman Corp.; presdl. appointee Aviation Safety Commn., 1987—; mem. Pres.'s Airline Commn., 1993. chmn. bd. trustees 1st Bapt. Ch., Cleve., 1972-74; bd. dirs. United Way, Wichita and Sedgwick County, Wichita State U. Endowment Assn.; trustee Wesley Hosp. Endowment Assn., Wake Forest univ.; bd. govs. United Way Am., 1993—. Served with USAF, 1955-58. Recipient Collier trophy Nat. Aeronautic Assn., 1986, George S. Dively award Harvard U., 1992. Mem. ABA, Ohio Bar Assn., Kans. Bar Assn., Cleve. Bar Assn., Gen. Aviation Mfrs. Assn. (chmn. bd. dirs. 1973-74, 81-82, 93-94), Wichita C. of C. (chmn. 1988—), Clubs: Wichita, Wichita Country, Castle Pines, Isleworth, Latrobe Country. Home: 600 N Tara Ct Wichita KS 67206-1830 Office: Cessna Aircraft PO Box 7704 1 Cessna Blvd Wichita KS 67215-1400

MEYER, RUTH ANN, physical education and dance educator; b. St. Louis, Oct. 24, 1944; d. Oliver Richard and Ruth Katherine (Popp) M. BS in Phys. Edn., Lindewood Coll., 1967; MS in Phys Edn., Western Ill. U., 1973; MA in Dance Edn., Lindewood Coll., 1977. Cert. tchr. Mo. Tchr. Normandy (Mo.) Sch. Dist. Garfield Elem., 1967—; speaker seminar U. Mo., St. Louis, 1974-75; tchr. Lindenwood Coll., St. Charles, Mo., 1977, Florissant (Mo.) Valley Community Coll., 1980; co-founder Mo. Dance Edn. Workshops, Mo., 1978-80; pres. St. Louis Women's Phys. Edn. Club, 1985, St. Louis Suburban Phys. Edn., 1975-76. Contbr. articles to profl. jours. Mem. Zion United Ch. Christ Outreach Com. (sec.), Florissant, 1990—. Tucson Creative Dance scholar, 1967. Mem. AAHPERD, Mo. Assn. Health Phys. Edn. Recreation and Dance (dance div. chair 1979-80, Helen Manley award 1984), Normandy Tchrs. Assn., Mo. Nat. Edn. Assn., Nat. Edn. Assn., Nat. Dance Assn. (children's dance commn. 1985). Democrat. Avocations: volleyball, stained glass, bingo, playing cards, church volunteering. Home: 1205 Hudson Rd Ferguson MO 63135-1443 Office: Normandy Sch Dist 7837 Natural Bridge Rd Normandy MO 63121

MEYER, RUTH KRUEGER, museum administrator, art historian; b. Chicago Heights, Ill., Aug. 20, 1940; d. Harold Rohe and Ruth Halbert (Bateman) Krueger; m. Kenneth R. Meyer, June 15, 1963 (div. 1978); 1 child, Karl Augustus. B.F.A., U. Cin., 1963; M.A., Brown U., 1968; Ph.D., U. Minn., 1980. Lectr. Walker Art Ctr., Mpls., 1970-72; instr. U. Cin., 1973-75; curator Contemporary Arts Ctr., Cin., 1976-80; dir. Ohio Found.

Arts, Columbus, 1980-83, Taft Mus., Cin., 1983-93; prof. Miyazaki (Japan) Internat. Coll., 1994—; adj. prof. The Union Inst., Cin., 1994. Pub. Dialogue Mag., Columbus, 1980-83; author: (exhbn. catalogues) Sandy Rosen Vestal Vases, 1986, Oblique Illusion: An Installation by Rick Paul, 1986, David Black an American Sculptor, 1983, Brad Davis: The Pines, 1984, The American Weigh, 1983, New Epiphanies, 1982, (with others) The Tafts Collection: The First Ten Years of Its Development, 1988, The Tafts of Pike St., 1988, (exhbn. catalogue) The History of Travel: Paintings by William Wegman, 1985-90, 1990, The Artist Face to Face: Two Centuries of Self-Portraits from the Paris Collection of Gerald Shurr, 1989, Tributes to the Tafts, 1991, The Taft Museum: Its Collection and Its History, 1995; contbr. articles to profl. jours. Recipient rsch. award Kress Found., 1967, 76; named Chevalier in the Order of Arts and Letters, Govt. of France, 1989. Mem. Internat. Assn. Art Critics, Coll. Art Assn. Democrat. Office: Miyazaki Internat College, 1405 Kano Kiyotake-Cho, Miyazaki 88916, Japan

MEYER, SANDRA W(ASSERSTEIN), bank executive, management consultant; b. N.J., Aug. 20, 1937; children—Jenifer Anne Schweitzer, Samantha Boughton Schweitzer. Student, U. Mich.; B.A. cum laude, Syracuse U., 1957; postgrad., London Sch. Econs., 1958. Advt. account exec. London Press Exchange, 1959-63; product mgr. Beecham Products Inc., Clifton, N.J., 1963-66; with Gen. Foods Co., White Plains, N.J., 1966-76; mktg. mgr. coffee div. Gen. Foods Co., 1973-74, dir. corp. mktg. planning, 1975-76; with Am. Express Co., N.Y.C., 1976-84; pres. communications div. Am. Express Co., 1980-84; mng. dir. Russell Reynolds Assocs., N.Y.C., 1985-89; sr. corp. officer corp. affairs Citicorp, N.Y.C., 1989-93; sr. partner Clark & Weinstock, N.Y.C., 1993—. Trustee Met. Opera Guild, East Hampton Guild Hall; mng. dir. Met. Opera Assn.; bd. dirs. St. Luke's Orch. Office: Clark & Weinstock 52 Vanderbilt Ave New York NY 10017-3808

MEYER, SCOTT D., public relations firm executive; b. Mpls., Oct. 7, 1949. BA in Journalism, U. Minn., 1972; postgrad., N.Y. Inst. of Fin. Asst. v.p., corp. rels. Piper, Jaffray & Hopwood, 1976-77; mgr. investor rels. Internat. Multifoods, 1977-79; dir. pub. rels. First Nat. Bank of Mpls., 1979-80; gen. mgr. pub. rels. Control Data Corp., 1980-84; exec. v.p. Dorn Pub. Rels., 1984-85, pres., from 1985; chmn., chief operating officer Mona, Meyer & McGrath, Mpls.; now vice chmn. Mona, Meyer, McGrath & Gavin Inc, Mpls. Office: Mona Meyer McGrath & Gavin Inc Ste 500 8400 Normandale Lake Blvd Bloomington MN 55437*

MEYER, SUSAN E., publisher; b. N.Y.C., Apr. 22, 1940; d. Ernest L. and Dorothy (Narefsky) M. BA, U. Wis., 1962. Asst. editor Collier Books, N.Y.C., 1962; mng. editor Watson-Guptill Publs., N.Y.C., 1963-70; editor-in-chief Am. Artist mag. N.Y.C., 1971-79; editorial dir. Am. Artist, Art and Antiques, Interiors, Residential Interiors, 1979-81; co-pub. Roundtable Press, Inc., 1981—; Dir. Ednl. Solutions, Inc., 1969-70; draft counselor Village Peace Center, 1967-70; tutor Empire State Coll., 1975-76; adj. prof. Union Grad. Sch., 1976-78. Author: (with Kent) Watercolorists at Work, 1972, Three Generations of the Wyeth Family, 1975, James Montgomery Flagg, 1974, 40 Watercolorists and How They Work, 1976, America's Great Illustrators, 1978, You Can Renovate Your Own Home, 1978, Norman Rockwell's People, 1981, Pasteups and Mechanicals, 1982, Treasury of the Great Children's Book Illustrators, 1983, How to Draw in Pen and Ink, 1985, Mary Cassatt, 1990, Norman Rockwell's World War II, 1991, Edgar Degas, 1994; editor: (with Guptill) Watercolor Painting Step-by-Step, 1966, (with Kent) 100 Watercolor Techniques, 1968, (with Kinstler) Painting Portraits, 1971, 87, (with Craig) Designing with Type, 1971, (with Guptill) Rendering in Pen and Ink, 1976, Rendering in Pencil, 1977, 20 Landscape Painters and How They Work, 1977, 20 Oil Painters and How They Work, 1978, 20 Figure Painters and How They Work, 1979; photographer: (with Buchman) Stage Makeup, 1971, Film and Television Makeup, 1973. Trustee Artists Fellowship, 1978-84, Little Red School House Inc., 1980-82, 1992—, Art Table Inc., 1981-84. Mem. Am. Book Producers Assn. (treas. 1984-89). Office: 80 5th Ave New York NY 10011-8002

MEYER, SYLVAN HUGH, editor, magazine executive, author; b. Atlanta, Oct. 7, 1921; s. David Norman and Ray (Levinsohn) M.; m. Annemie Heineman, Jan. 19, 1947; children: Erica, David, Jason. A.B. in Journalism, U. N.C., 1943; D.H.L. (hon.), Oglethorpe U., 1973; DL (hon.), Fla. Internat. U., 1994. Editor The Times, Gainesville, Ga., 1950-69; editor Miami (Fla.) News, 1969-73; editor, pres. Miami/South Fla. Mag., 1975-87; pub. South Florida Home & Garden Mag., 1984-87; pub. cons., 1988—; disting. vis. prof. Fla. Internat. U., Miami, 1973-75; project dir. Commn. on Future of South, 1974; chmn. 3d Century U.S.A., Bicentennial Commn. Dade County, 1973-76; chmn., Ga. adv. com. U.S. Commn. Civil Rights, 1958-65; mem. nat. adv. coun. ACLU, 1959—; mem. adv. bd. Pulitzer prize, 1968-73, bd. dirs., 1966-73; adv. com. sch. of communications FIU, 1985—; adj. prof. journalism, U. Miami, 1986-87. Author: (with Seymour C. Nash) Prostate Cancer: Making Survival Decisions, 1994. Mem. So. Growth Policy Bd., 1980-88; mem. exec. com. So. Regional Coun., 1980-86, 92—; mem. Speaker Ho. Rep. Com. on Future of Fla., 1985-89; chair Edn. for Info. Age campaign Fla. Internat. U. Lt. USNR, 1943-46. Nieman fellow Harvard U., 1951; recipient Disting. Svc. Editorial Writing award, 1957, award Sidney Hillman Found., 1961, Dept. of Army Patriotic Civilian Svc. award, 1961, Nat. Jour. award Am. Soc. Planning Ofcls., 1961, Civic award Miami Area Jewish Com. Human Rels., 1989. Mem. City/Regional Mag. Assn. (bd. dirs. 1983-88, pres. 1986-87, Lifetime Achievement award 1991), Am. Coun. on Edn. in Journalism, Greater Miami C. of C. (bd. govrs. 1970-74), U. N.C. Alumni Assn. (bd. dirs. 1973), Chattahoochee Country Club, La Gorce Country Club, Sigma Delta Chi, Tau Epsilon Phi, Sigma Delta Phi. Home and Office: 5500 Collins Ave Apt 901 Miami Beach FL 33140-2501 Address: Long Branch Rd Dahlonega GA 30355

MEYER, THOMAS J., chemistry educator; b. Dennison, Ohio, Dec. 3, 1941; s. Harold Arthur and Sybil (Reece) M.; m. Sandra L. Meyer, June 5, 1963; children: Tyler, Justin. BS, Ohio U., 1963; PhD, Stanford U., 1966. NATO postdoctoral research fellow U. Coll. London, 1967; asst. prof. chemistry U. N.C., Chapel Hill, 1968-72; assoc. prof. chemistry U. N.C., 1972-75, prof. chemistry, 1975—, M.A. Smith prof. chemistry, 1982-86, Kenan prof. chemistry, 1986—, chmn. dept. chemistry, 1985-90, dir. Curriculum in Applied Scis., 1991-94, vice chancellor for grad. studies and rsch., 1994—; ednl. cons. Dillard U., New Orleans, 1974; mem. exec. com. Material Research Ctr., U. N.C., 1974-77; mem. NATO ASI com. on mixed valence compounds in chemistry, physics and biology, Oxford U., 1979; mem. chem. dynamics rev. NSF, 1980; adv. com. proram in molecular biology and biotechnology U. N.C., 1986—; faculty instl. relations com. Sch. Medicine, 1986—; mem. dept. chemistry Haverford Review Com., 1986; mem. chemistry rev. com. Dept. Energy-SERI, 1986-88, chmn., 1987-88; mem. rev. com. for chemistry Argonne Nat. Lab., U. Chgo., 1987; chmn. outside rev. panel U. Rochester Sci. and Tech. Ctr., 1989-94, rev. com. for chemistry Brookhaven Nat. Lab., 1990-94. Bd. editors Inorganic Chemistry Jour., Am. Chem. Soc., 1985, Accounts Chem. Rsch., 1990—. Woodrow Wilson fellow, 1963-64; NSF grad. fellow, 1965-66, NATO postdoctoral fellow, 1967, Alfred P. Sloan fellow, 1975-77, Guggenheim fellow, 1983, Erskine fellow, 1985; recipient Tanner award for teaching excellence U. N.C., 1972, Dwyer medal U. NSW, Australia, 1989, Centenary medal Royal Soc. Chemistry, 1991, N.C. Disting. Chemist award N.C. Inst. of Chemists divsn. Am. Inst. Chemists, Inc., 1993. Fellow AAAS, NAS, Am. Acad. Arts and Scis.; mem. AAUP, Am. Chem. Soc. (exec. com. divsn. inorganic chemistry 1982-84, chair 1994, Charles H. Stone award Piedmont sect. 1982, Monsanto Co. award in inorganic chemistry 1990, So. Chemist of Yr. award Memphis sect. 1992, chair divsn. inorganic chemistry 1994). Office: U N C Dept Chemistry Cb 3290 Venable Hall Chapel Hill NC 27599

MEYER, THOMAS JAMES, editorial cartoonist; b. Fort Benning, Ga., May 8, 1955; s. Edward Charles and Carol (McCunniff) M. B.A., U. Wash. 1977. Congl. aide U.S. Ho. of Reps., Washington, 1977-79; free lance cartoonist, illustrator Washington Post, Fed. Times, Bus. Rev. of. Washington, 1979-81; editorial cartoonist San Francisco Chronicle, 1981—. Co-illustrator: The Church In A Democracy: Who Governs?, 1981. Mem. Am. Assn. Editorial Cartoonists. Roman Catholic. Office: San Francisco Chronicle 901 Mission St San Francisco CA 94103-2988*

MEYER, URSULA, library director; b. Free City of Danzig, Nov. 6, 1927; came to U.S., 1941; d. Herman S. and Gertrud (Rosenfeld) M. BA, UCLA,

1949; M.L.S., U. So. Calif., 1953; postgrad., U. Wis., 1969. Librarian Butte County (Calif.) Library, 1961-68; asst. pub. libraries div. library devel. N.Y. State Library, Albany, 1969-72; coordinator Mountain Valley Coop. System, Sacramento, 1972-73; chmn. 49-99 Coop. Library System, Stockton, Calif., 1974-85; dir. library services Stockton-San Joaquin County Pub. Library, 1974—. Higher Edn. Title II fellow, 1968-69. Active Freedom to Read Found. Mem. ALA (council 1979-83, chmn. nominating com. 1982-83, legis. com. 1985-87), Calif. Library Assn. (pres. 1978, council 1974-82), Am. Assn. Pub. Adminstrs., Sierra Club. AAUW, LWV, Common Cause. Lodges: Rotary, Soroptimists. Office: Stockton-San Joaquin County Pub Libr 605 N El Dorado St Stockton CA 95202-1907

MEYER, WILLIAM DANIELSON, retired department store executive; b. Mpls., May 5, 1923; s. J.A. and Florence (Danielson) M.; m. Betty Ann McBride, May 28, 1950; children—Patricia Ann, Janet Elizabeth, Jean Louise. B.S., U. Calif. at Los Angeles, 1947. With actuarial dept. Prudential Ins. Co. Am., Los Angeles, 1948-53; with Carter Hawley Hale Stores, Inc., Los Angeles, 1953-93; ret., 1993; asst. sec. Carter Hawley Hale Stores, Inc., 1962-64, sec., 1964-73, dir. employee benefits, asst. sec., 1973-93. Bd. dirs. Profit Sharing Coun., chmn. 1984-86; bd. dirs. Travelers Aid Soc., L.A., pres. 1976-77; trustee Profit Sharing Rsch. Found., U.S. Diving Found., 1994—, v.p. 1982-84, 90-94. Mem. Am. Soc. Corp. Secs., Personnel and Indsl. Relations Assn., Los Angeles C. of C., Gold Key, Sigma Pi (Founder's award 1992), Alpha Kappa Psi, Phi Phi. Republican. Presbyterian. Home: 1725 Durklyn Ct San Marino CA 91108-2035

MEYER, WILLIAM F., church administrator. Exec. dir. Higher Edn. Svc. of the Lutheran Ch. MO Synod Internat. Ctr., St. Louis. Office: Luth Ch Mo Synod Internat Ctr 1333 S Kirkwood Rd Saint Louis MO 63122-7295

MEYER, WILLIAM MICHAEL, mortgage banking executive; b. Fort Wayne, Ind., Oct. 21, 1940; s. Henry and Lola Mae (Leedy) M.; m. Phyllis Ann Ruetschilling, Aug. 12, 1961; children: Michael Dean, Blaine Aaron, Nathan Daniel, Andrea Rene. Degree in Bus., Ind. U., 1970. V.p. Waterfield Mortgage Corp., Fort Wayne, 1963-73, First Nat. Bank, Colorado Springs, Colo., 1973-78, Underwood Mortgage Co., Lawrenceville, N.J., 1978-79, Data Link Systems, South Bend, Ind., 1979-82; sr. v.p. Inland Mortgage Corp., Indpls., 1982—; bd. dirs. Ctrl. Ind. Quality Leadership Forum, Indpls. Mem. Mortgage Bankers Assn. (mem. com. 1979—), Ind. Mortgage Bankers (bd. dirs. 1992—), Rotary (Zionsville bd. dirs. 1990-93). Republican. Roman Catholic. Avocations: skiing, gardening, swimming, golf. Home: 3216 South 975 E Zionsville IN 46077

MEYER, WILLIAM TRENHOLM, defense company official, real estate executive, former army officer; b. Ancon, C.Z., May 28, 1937; s. Trenholm Jones and Virginia Blanche (Morgan) M.; m. Erna Charlotte Albert, Dec. 14, 1961; children: Cynthia L., Bonnie A., Christopher T., Tori L. BS, U. Nebr., 1965; grad. U.S. Army Command and Gen. Staff Coll., 1973. 2d lt. U.S. Army, 1961, advanced through grades to lt. col., 1976, ret., 1981; sr. engr. ManTech Internat. Corp., Sierra Vista, Ariz., 1981-82; mgr. field ops. RCA Sierra Vista, 1982-86; chief exec. officer MYCO, 1989; gen. ptnr., dir. Southwestern Investment Ltd. Partnership, Sierra Vista, 1983-89; mgr. advanced devel. GE, 1986—. Sustaining mem. Republican Nat. Com., 1983—, GE 1986-93, Martin Marietta, 1993—. Mem. Assn. Old Crows (regional dir. 1984-87, chpt. pres. 1983-84, 89-91, v.p. 1992—, Internat. Electronic Warfare-Intelligence medal 1983, Electronic Warfare special medal 1991), Armed Forces Communications and Electronics Assn., Ret. Officers Assn., Assn. U.S. Army. Roman Catholic. Clubs: Kings Tennis (pres. 1980, 87, 88), Aquatic (pres. 1981) (Sierra Vista). Home: 1902 N San Diego Cir Sierra Vista AZ 85635-9521 Office: Martin Marietta 2700 E Fry Blvd Ste 3B Sierra Vista AZ 85635-2828

MEYER-BAHLBURG, HEINO F. L., psychologist; b. Hamburg, Germany, Feb. 26, 1940; came to U.S., 1969; s. Wilhelm and Marie Luise Meyer-B. Vordiplom in Psychology, U. Hamburg, 1963, Diplom Psychology, 1966; Dr.rer.nat., U. Duesseldorf, 1970. Sci. asst. U. Duesseldorf, 1970; rsch. asst., then rsch. assoc. prof. psychiatry and pediatrics SUNY Med. Sch., Buffalo, 1970-77; rsch. scientist N.Y. State Psychiat. Inst., N.Y.C., 1977—; from assoc. clin. prof. med. psychology to prof. clin. psychology in psychiatry Columbia U. Coll. Physicians and Surgeons, 1978—; pediatric behavioral endocrinologist in psychiatry svc., then full prof. Presbyn. Hosp., N.Y.C., 1978—. Contbr. numerous articles to profl. publs. Recipient Disting. Sci. Achievement award Soc. for Sci. Study of Sex, 1993; grantee NIMH. Mem. AAAS, German Psychol. Soc., Soc. Pediatric Psychology, Am. Psychol. Assn., Internat. Acad. Sex Rsch., Internat. Soc. Rsch. Aggression, Deutsche Gesellschaft Sexualforschung, Am. Psychosomatic Soc., Internat. Soc. Psychoneuroendocrinology, Soc. Sci. Study Sex, Soc. Rsch. Child Devel., Soc. Sex. Therapy and Rsch., Lawson Wilkins Pediatric Endocrine Soc., Harry Benjamin Internat. Gender Dysphoria Assn., Internat. AIDS Soc. Office: Columbia U Dept Psychiatry 722 W 168th St Fl 10 New York NY 10032-2603

MEYERHOFF, ERICH, librarian, administrator; b. Braunschweig, Germany, Nov. 24, 1919; came to U.S., 1935; s. Karl and Irma Meyerhoff; m. Inge Zuber; children—Tina, C. Michael. B.S., CCNY, 1943; M.S., N.Y. Sch. Social Work, 1949; M.S.L.S., Columbia U., 1951, cert. advanced librarianship, 1974. Social worker various orgns., to 1951; reference librarian Columbia U. Med. Library, N.Y.C., 1951-57; librarian, asst. prof. Downstate Med. Ctr., SUNY, Bklyn., 1957-61; dir. Med. Library Ctr. N.Y., 1961-67; librarian Health Scis. Library, SUNY-Buffalo, 1967-70; librarian Cornell U. Med. Coll., N.Y.C., 1970-86, asst. dean, 1977-86; chief library service VA Med. Ctr. N.Y.C., 1986-88; archives librarian NYU Med. Ctr., 1980-91; adj. instr. biomed. communications Columbia U., 1976-81; cons. U. Mich., Ann Arbor, 1968, N.Y. Met. Reference and Research Library Agy., 1968-69, Coll. Physicians of Phila., 1969-70. Fellow Med. Library Assn. (cert., bd. dirs. 1972-76, chmn. various coms. 1968-72, 78-81, Inst. for Sci. Info. award 1981-82, Janet Doe lectr. 1977), N.Y. Acad. Medicine; mem. AAAS, AAUP, Spl. Libraries Assn., N.Y. Met. Sect. History of Sci. Soc., Archons of Colophon. Avocations: skiing; hiking; camping. Home: 90 La Salle St New York NY 10027-4719 Office: NYU Med Ctr Archives 550 1st Ave New York NY 10016-6402

MEYERHOFF, JACK FULTON, financial executive; b. Joliet, Ill., May 15, 1926; s. Charles F. and Helen (Ferguson) M.; m. Mary Margaret Williams, Jan. 2, 1949; children—Keith F., Greg H., Deborah S., Todd C. B.S., Miami U., Oxford, Ohio, 1947; postgrad., Ohio Wesleyan U., 1944-45; grad. Advanced Mgmt. Program, Harvard U., 1968. C.P.A., Ohio, Ill. Mgr. Arthur Andersen & Co., Chgo., Cin., Cleve., 1947-59; treas. MacGregor Sports, Cin., 1959-63; v.p., corp. controller Brunswick Corp., Chgo., 1963-77; chief fin. officer Brunswick Corp., 1972-77, v.p. corp. affairs 1977-80, v.p. human resources, 1980-81; chmn., chief exec. officer MarJac Assocs., Nokomis, Fla., 1981—; pres., dir. Charles Oxford Corp., Nokomis, 1984—; bd. dirs. Sherwood Med. Industries, Inc., Old Orchard Bank & Trust Co., Tech: Time Inc., Nokomis; organizer, vice chmn. bd. trustees Caldwell Trust Co., Venice, Fla., 1993—. Treas., bd. dirs. Cove Schs.; bd. dirs., pres. Skokie Valley Community Hosp., No. Ill. Indsl. Assn.; v.p., bd. dirs. Jr. Achievement; bd. dirs. Chgo. Responsibility Growth, Gulf Area Med. Properties, Venice Hosp.; chmn. bd. Venice Hosp. Found.; bd. dirs. J. Clifford MacDonald Handicapped Ctr. of Tampa, Sarasota Com. of 100, Triangle Econ. Devel. Council, Manatee Community Coll. Found.; mem. adv. council Miami U., Georgetown U., U. So. Fla. Served with USNR, 1944-46. Mem. Am. Inst. C.P.A.s, Ohio Soc. C.P.A.s, Ill. Soc. C.P.A.s, Fin. Execs. Inst., Nat. Assn. Accts., Harvard Bus. Sch. Alumni Assn., Miami U. Exec. Alumni Council (bd. dirs., treas.), Venice Area C. of C. (bd. dirs.), Sigma Alpha Epsilon, Delta Sigma Pi, Beta Alpha Psi, Beta Gamma Sigma. Methodist. Clubs: Venice Yacht, Mid America, Economic, Misty Creek Country, Saddlebrook Country. Lodges: Masons, Rotary. Home: 20 Inlets Blvd Nokomis FL 34275-4108 Office: MSW Assocs PO Box 1326 Nokomis FL 34274-1326

MEYERHOFF, JAMES LESTER, medical researcher; b. Phila., Dec. 12, 1937; s. Lester Bacharach and Natalie Hatch (Rosenberg) M. BA, U. Pa., 1962, MD, 1966. Diplomate Nat. Bd. Med. Examiners, Am. Bd. Psychiatry and Neurology; lic. physician, Md. Intern Misericordia Hosp., Phila., 1966-67; resident U. Chgo. Hosp., 1970-76; postdoctoral fellow Johns Hopkins U., 1970-71; rsch. assoc. Walter Reed Army Inst. Rsch. and Med. Ctr., Washington, 1971-72, head neurochemsitry sect., 1972-74, chief dept.

neuroendorcinology, 1974-76, chief neurochemistry and neurochemistry bd., 1976—; rsch. prof. psychiatry Uniformed Svcs. U. Health Scis., 1978; clin. assoc. prof. psychiatry Georgetown U., 1977. Contbr. numerous articles to profl. jours. Maj. M.C., U.S. Army, 1969-72. Fellow APA, Acad. Behavioral Medicine; mem. Internat. Soc. Neurochemistry, Soc. for Neurosci. Office: Walter Reed Army Inst Rsch & Med Ctr Washington DC 20307-5100

MEYEROWITZ, ELLIOT MARTIN, biologist, educator; b. Washington, D.C., May 22, 1951; s. Irving and Freda (Goldberg) M.; m. Joan Agnes Kobori, June 17, 1984; 2 children. A.B., Columbia U., 1973; M.Phil., Yale U., 1975, Ph.D., 1977. Research fellow Stanford U., Calif., 1977-79; asst. prof. biology Calif. Inst. Tech., Pasadena, 1980-85, assoc. prof. 1985-89, prof., 1989—. Mem. editorial bd. Trends in Genetics, Current Biology, Development, Cell; contbr. articles to profl. jours., 1978—. Jane Coffin Childs Meml. Fund fellow, 1977-79, Sloan Found. fellow, 1980-82. Fellow AAAS; mem. NAS, Genetics Soc. Am. (bd. dirs.), Internat. Soc. for Plant Molecular Biology (pres.), Am. Acad. Arts and Scis. Office: Calif Inst Tech Div Biology Pasadena CA 91125

MEYERS, ABBEY S., foundation administrator; b. Bklyn., Apr. 11, 1944; d. Herbert and Blossom (Ruben) Feldman; m. Jerrold B. Meyers, Oct. 23, 1966; children: David, Adam, Laura. AAS, N.Y.C. Community Coll., 1963. Comml. artist various advt. agys., N.Y.C., 1962-65; dir. patient svcs. Tourette Syndrome Assn., Bayside, N.Y., 1980-85; exec. dir., founder Nat. Org. for Rare Disorders, New Fairfield, Conn., 1985—; U.S. commr. Nat. Commn. on Orphan Diseases, Washington, 1986-89; mem. subcom. Human Gene Therapy NIH, Bethesda, Md., 1989-92; mem. recombinant DNA adv. com. NIH, 1992-96; mem. Health Care Payor Adv. Commn. on Conn. Commn. on Hosps. and Health Care, 1992-94. Author: (with others) Orphan Drugs and Orphan Diseases: Clinical Reality and Public Policy, 1983, (with others) Cooperative Approaches to Research and Development of Orphan Drugs, 1985, (with others) Tourette Syndrome: Clinical Understanding and Treatment, 1988, (with others) Physicians Guide to Rare Diseases, 1992. Bd. dirs. Nat. Orphan Drug and Device Found., N.Y.C., 1982-85; leader Coalition to Pass Orphan Drug Act of 1983, 1979-82. Recipient Pub. Health Svc. award NHS, 1985, Commr.'s Spl. citation FDA, 1988. Mem. Nat. Health Coun. (bd. dirs. 1989-94), Alliance of Genetic Support Groups (bd. dirs. 1987-89). Avocations: reading, horseback riding. Office: Nat Org for Rare Disorders PO Box 8923 Fairwood Profl Bldg New Fairfield CT 06812

MEYERS, ALBERT IRVING, chemistry educator; b. N.Y.C., Nov. 22, 1932; s. Hyman and Sylvia (Greenberg) M.; m. Joan Shepard, Aug. 10, 1957; children—Harold, Jill, Lisa. BS, NYU, 1954, PhD, 1957. Rsch. chemist Cities Svc. Oil Co., Cranbury, N.J., 1957-58; asst., assoc. prof., prof. La. State U., New Orleans, 1958-70; prof. Wayne State U., Detroit, 1970-72; prof. Colo. State U., Fort Collins, 1972—, disting. prof., 1986—, John K. Stille prof. chemistry, 1993—; spl. postdoctoral fellow Harvard U., Cambridge, 1965-66; cons. G.D. Searle Co., Skokie, Ill., 1972-84, Mid-West Rsch. Inst., Kansas City, Mo., 1974-77, Bristol-Myers Squibb Co., 1984-94, NIH, Bethesda, Md., 1977-79, 85-89, Syntex Co., 1989—, Smith Kline Beecham Co., 1994—. Editor Jour. Am. Chem. Soc., 1992—, Jour. Organic Chemistry, 1990—, Tetrahedron, 1990—; contbr. over 350 articles to profl. jours. Recipient Alexander von Humboldt award Fed. Republic of Germany, 1984, Disting. Alumni award NYU, 1990; named Man of Yr., New Orleans Jaycees, 1968, Boyd Prof. La. State U., 1969. Fellow AAAS, NAS; Royal Soc. Chemistry (silver medalist 1982), Phila. Organic Chemistry Soc. (Allan Day award 1987). Home: 1500 Hepplewhite Ct Fort Collins CO 80526-3822 Office: Colorado State Univ Dept Chemistry Fort Collins CO 80523

MEYERS, ANN ELIZABETH, sports broadcaster; b. San Diego, Mar. 26, 1955; d. Robert Eugene and Patricia Ann (Burke); m. Donald Scott Drysdale, Nov. 1, 1986; children: Donald Scott Jr., Darren John, Drew Ann. Grad., UCLA, 1978. Profl. basketball player N.J. Gems, 1979-80; profl. basketball player Ind. Pacers NBA, 1979; sports broadcaster Ind. Pacers, 1979-80; sportscaster men's basketball U. Hawaii, Honolulu, 1981-82; sportscaster men's and women's basketball UCLA, 1982-84, 89—; sportscaster volleyball, basketball, softball, tennis ESPN, 1981-94; sportscaster Olympic Games ABC, L.A., 1984; sportscaster volleyball, softball, tennis, basketball, soccer Sportsvision, 1985-87; sportscaster volleyball, basketball, softball Prime Ticket, 1985-95; sportscaster CBS-TV, 1991—; sportscaster Goodwill Games, WTBS, 1986, 90. Winner Silver medal Montreal Olympics, 1976, Gold medal Pan Am. Games, 1975, Silver medal, 1979, All-Am. UCLA, 1975, 76, 77, 78; 1st woman named to Hall of Fame UCLA, 1987; named to Women's Sports Hall of Fame, 1987, Orange County Sports Hall of Fame, 1985, Calif. H.S. Hall of Fame, 1990, Basketball Hall of Fame, 1993, Nat. H.S. Hall of Fame, 1995, NBC Hoop It Up, 1995. Office: c/o Lampros and Roberts 16615 Lark Ave # 101 Los Gatos CA 95030-2439

MEYERS, ARTHUR SOLOMON, library director; b. N.Y.C., Dec. 14, 1937; s. Nathan and Selma (Leeser) M.; m. Marcia Indianer, June 11, 1961; children: Naomi, Ruth. AB in History, U. Miami, 1959; MS in LS, Columbia U., 1961; MA in English, U. Mo., St. Louis, 1980; MA in History, Ball State U., Muncie, Ind., 1987. Cert. libr. I, Ind. Young adult libr. N.Y. Pub. Libr., N.Y.C., 1959-61; adult and young adult libr. Detroit Pub. Libr., 1963-67; adult and young adult specialist Enoch Pratt Free Libr., Balt., 1967-73; mgr. bras. and cmty. svc. St. Louis Pub. Libr., 1973-80; dir. Muncie Pub. Libr., 1980-86, Hammond (Ind.) Pub. Libr., 1986—; pres. Ednl. Referral Ctr., Lake County Ind., 1993-95; condr. workshops and insts. in field; presenter in field; past pres. N.W. Ind. Area Libr. Svcs. Authority; mem. AFL-CIO/ALA Reference and Adult Svcs. Divsn. Contbr. articles to profl. jours. Bd. dirs. Calumet Area Literacy Coun., Hammond Edn. Found.; mem. Hammond Mayor's Commn. on Disabilities; sec. Calumet Ethnic Heritage Alliance, Lake County, 1993-95. With U.S. Army, 1961-63. Mem. ALA (pres. reference and adult svcs. div. 1989-90), Ind. Libr. Fedn., Ind. Jewish Hist. Soc. (pres. 1993-95), Ind. Hist. Soc., Freedom To Read Found., ACLU, NAACP. Democrat. Jewish. Avocations: local and family history research, ethnic heritage research, reference book reviewing. Home: 6537 Kansas Ave Hammond IN 46323-1746 Office: Hammond Pub Libr 564 State St Hammond IN 46320-1532

MEYERS, CHRISTINE LAINE, publishing and media executive, consultant; b. Detroit, Mar. 7, 1949; d. Ernest Robert and Eva Elizabeth (Laine) M.; 1 child, Kathryn Laine; m. Oliver S. Moore III, May 12, 1990. BA, U. Mich., 1968. Editor, indsl. relations Diesel div. Gen. Motors Corp., Detroit, 1968; nat. advt. mgr. J.L. Hudson Co., Detroit, 1976-76, mgr. internal sales promotion, 1972-73, dir. pub., 1973-76; nat. advt. mgr. Pontiac Motor div., Mich., 1976-78; pres., owner Laine Meyers Assocs., Troy, Mich., 1978—; dir. Internat. Inst. Met. Detroit, Inc. Contbr. articles to profl. publs. Mem. bus. adv. council Cen. Mich. U., 1977-79; mem. pub. adv. com. on jud. candidates Oakland County Bar Assn.; mem. adv. bd. Birmingham Community Hosp., bd. dirs. YMCA, Mich., 1992—; Named Mich. Ad Woman of Yr., 1976, one of Top 10 Working Women Glamour mag., 1978, one of 100 Best and Brightest Advt. Age, 1987, one of Mich.'s top 25 female bus. owners Nat. Assn. Women Bus. Owners, One of Top 10 Women Owned Bus., Mich., 1994; recipient Vanguard award Women in Communications, 1986. Mem. Internat. Assn. Bus. Communicators, Adcraft Club, Women's Advt. Club (1st v.p. 1975), Women's Econ. Club (pres. 1976-77), Internat. Women's Forum Mich. (pres. 1986—), Internat. Inst. of Detroit (bd. dirs. 1986-89), Detroit C. of C., Troy C. of C., Mortar Board, Quill and Scroll, Pub. Relations Com. Women for United Found., Founders Soc. Detroit Inst. Arts, Fashion Group, Pub. Relations Soc. Am., First Soc. Detroit (exec. com. 1970-71), Kappa Tau Alpha. Home: 1780 Kensington Rd Bloomfield Hills MI 48304-2428 Office: Laine Meyers Inc 3645 Crooks Rd Troy MI 48084-1642

MEYERS, DALE (MRS. MARIO COOPER), artist; b. Chgo.; d. Walter Herman and Gertude (Pettee) Wetterer; m. Mario Cooper, Oct. 11, 1964; children: Dale (Mrs. John F. Hellegers), Steven R. Student, Glendale Coll., Corcoran Gallery Sch. Art, Washington, 1962-63, Art Student's League, N.Y.C., 1964-78. Instr. Art Students League, 1979—; ofcl. artist NASA, USCG.; lectr. Parson's Sch. Design, Nat. Acad. Sci. Author The Sketchbook, 1983; contbr.: Watercolor Bold and Free, Am. Artist mag, Diversion mag.; solo exhbns. include, West Wing Gallery, Ringwood (N.J.)

State Park, 1970, Manor Club, Pelham Manor, N.Y., 1970, Apollo Art Gallery, Oklahoma City, 1972, Quadrangle Gallery, Dallas, 1972, Galveston Ctr. for Arts, 1974, Fla. Gulf Coast Art Ctr., 1977, 86, Okura Hotel, Tokyo, Japan, 1977, Owensboro Mus. Art, 1983, Salmagundi Club, 1986, 88, Stehle-Reed Gallery, Midland, Tex., 1987, others; artist-in-residence, Galveston Arts Ctr., 1974, Owensboro Mus. Art, 1983, Asilomar, Calif., 1983, 84; group exhbns. include Two Hundred Years of Watercolor Painting in Am. Met. Mus. Art, 1966, Eyewitness to Space, Nat. Gallery Art, Washington, 1969, Smithsonian Instn., 1961-63, Corcoran Gallery, 1963, Museo de la Acuarela, Mexico City, 1968, 89, London (Ont., Can.) Mus. Art, 1971-72, Art Gallery Hamilton, Ont., Can., 1971-72, Ont. Inst. Edn., 1971-72, Butler Inst. Art, 1962—, Frye Mus., 1962—; represented in permanent collections, Calif. Palace of Legion of Honor, San Francisco, Nat. Acad. N.Y.C., Avon Fine Arts Collection, NASA, EPA, Museo de la Acuarela, Schumacher Gallery, Columbus, Ohio, Slater Mus., Conn., Portland (Maine) Mus., U. Utah Fine Arts Collection, Frye Mus., Seattle, Owensboro Mus. Art, Coll. Misericordia, Dallas, Pa, Canton Art Inst., Ohio, Arnot Mus., Elmira, N.Y.; internat. watercolor exhbn. Can., U.S., Gt. Britain, 1991-94, Chung Cheng Gallery, Taipei, 1994. Recipient Henry W. Ranger award Nat. Acad. Design, 1968, Samuel F.B. Morse medal, 1973, Anna Hyatt Huntington Bronze medal, 1971, Knickerbocker Artists Gold medal, 1981, 88, Allied Artists Am. award, 1969, Gold medal honor Nat. Arts Club, 1972, Anna Hyatt Huntington Gold medal, 1974, Adolf and Cara Obrig award Nat. Acad., 1974, 81, Walter Biggs award, 1976, Allied Arts Gold medal, 1978, Audubon ARtists Silver medal, 1984. Fellow Royal Soc. Arts (Grumbacher Gold medals 1988, 90); mem. Am. Watercolor Soc. (pres. 1993—, editor jours. 1962-79, Bronze medal honor award 1968, awards 1970, 72, 78, 79, 81, 82, 83, 85, 87, 89, 93), Nat. Acad. (academician), Allied Artists Am. (pres. 1975-78), Knickerbocker Artists, Art Students League N.Y., La. Watercolor Soc. (hon.), Ky. Watercolor Soc., Ohio Watercolor Soc. (hon.), Watercolor Soc. Mex., Fla. Watercolor Soc. (hon.), Audubon Artists, Salimagundi Club (medal of honor 1994). Address: 1 W 67th St New York NY 10023

MEYERS, DOROTHY, adult education educator, writer; b. Chgo., Jan. 9, 1927; d. Gilbert and Harriet (Levitt) King; m. William J. Meyers, Oct. 9, 1947; children: Lynn, Jeanne. BA, U. Chgo., 1945, MA, 1961, postgrad.; postgrad. Columbia U., New Sch. Social Rsch., Northwestern U. Instr. sr. adults, Chgo. Bd. and/City Colls. Chgo., 1961-78; coord. pub. affairs forum and health maintenance program City Colls. Chgo., 1975-78; lectr. adult program City Colls. Chgo., 1978-87; lectr., tchr. Dade County Adult Edn. Program, Miami, Fla., 1983-85; discussion leader Brandeis U. Adult Edn., 1985-86; cons., lectr. in field. Contbr. articles to profl. jours. Chmn. legis. PTA; discussion leader Great Decisions, 1984-86; chmn. civic assembly Citizens Sch. Com.; v.p. community rels. Womens Fedn. and Jewish United Fund; discussion leader LWV, Gt. Decisions, Fgn. Policy Assn.; program chmn. Jewish Community Ctrs., 1966-67, mem. sr. adult com.; bd. dirs. coun. Jewish Elderly, Open U.; mem. art and edn. com. Chgo. Mayor's Com. for Sr. Citizens and Handicapped; mem. com. on media Met. Coun. on Aging; active Bon Secour's Villa Maria Hosp.; founder Mt. Sinai Hosp., Miami Beach; sponsor Miami Heart Inst.; active Royal Notable Alzheimer Care Unit-Douglas Home Miami; com. mem. March of Dimes; amb. Project Newborn U. Miami Pre Natal Unit. Recipient Prima Donna award Men's Opera Guild-Fla., 1995. Mem. ASA, Gerontol. Assn., Nat. Coun. Aging, Nat. Coun. Jewish Women, Women's Auxiliary Jewish Community Ctr., Chgo. Met. Sr. Forum (media com.), Coun. Women Chgo. Real Estate Bd., Women in Communications, Chgo. Real Estate Bd., Nat. Assn. Real Estate Bds., Cultural Ctr. (Miami, Fla.), Mus. Art Ft. Lauderdale, Miami Internat. Press Club, Gastrointestinal Rsch. Found., Brandeis U., Art Inst. Chgo., Mus. Contemporary Art, Soc. Contemporary Art, Mus. Art Boca Raton, Brandeis Women's Auxiliary, Circumnavigator Club (Chgo. and Fla. chpts.). Office: 77 W Washington St Chicago IL 60602-2801

MEYERS, EDWARD, photographer, writer, publisher; b. Flushing, N.Y., Nov. 2, 1934; s. Gerson G. and Hester (Noble) M.; m. Marcia Rothman, June 29, 1958; children: Beth, Adam, Rosemarie. BFA, Rochester (N.Y.) Inst. Tech., 1957. Tech. editor Modern Photography mag., N.Y.C., 1957-66; photographer-writer N.Y.C., 1966-70; exec. editor Popular Photography mag., N.Y.C., 1971-86; assoc. pub. Silver Halide Press, N.Y.C., 1986—; lectr. Sch. Visual Arts, 1968—; U.S. corr. FotoPro Reflex mag., Italy, FotoVideo, Spain. Editor: Modern Photography Photo Almanac, 1967, 69; co-editor: The Official Depth of Field Tables, 1962. Served with U.S. Army, 1957-58. Recipient Alumni Achievement award Rochester Inst. Tech., 1972, Art Dir.'s Gold award, 1986. Mem. N.Y. Press Photographers Assn., Am. Soc. Picture Profls., N.Y.C. Audubon Soc., Joint Ethics Com. Home: 61-68 77th St Middle Village NY 11379

MEYERS, ERIC MARK, religion educator; b. Norwich, Conn., June 5, 1940; s. Karl D. and Shirlee M. (Meyer) M.; m. Carol Lyons, June 25, 1964; children: Julie Kaete, Dina Elisa. AB, Dartmouth Coll., 1962; MA, Brandeis U., 1964; PhD, Harvard U., 1969. Prof. religion, archeology, biblical studies, ancient hist. Duke U., Durham, N.C., 1969—; dir. Annenberg Inst., Phila., 1991-92; pres. Am. Schs. of Oriental Rsch., Balt., 1990—. Author 8 books; contbr. over 200 articles to profl. jours. Jewish. Avocation: singing Jewish. Home: 3202 Waterbury Dr Durham NC 27707-2416 Office: Duke U PO Box 90964 Bldg Durham NC 27708-0964

MEYERS, FREDERICK M., diversified industrial products and service company executive. Formerly chmn. Lukens Inc., Coatesville, Pa., vice chmn., 1988—. Office: Lukens Inc 50 S 1st Ave Coatesville PA 19320-3418

MEYERS, GERALD A., metal products executive. With Logan Aluminum Inc., Bowling Green, Ky., Alcan & Logan, U.S. and Canada; now pres., coo Ravenswood Aluminum Corp., W.Va. Office: Ravenswood Aluminum Corp RR 2 Ravenswood WV 26164

MEYERS, GERALD CARL, management consultant, author, educator, lecturer, former automobile company executive; b. Buffalo, Dec. 5, 1928; s. Meyer and Berenice (Meyers) M.; m. Barbara Jacob, Nov. 2, 1958. BS, Carnegie Inst. Tech., 1950, MS with distinction, 1954. With Ford Motor Co., Detroit, 1950-51, Chrysler Corp., Detroit and Geneva, 1954-62; with Am. Motors Corp., Detroit, 1962—; v.p. Am. Motors Corp., 1967-72, group v.p. product, 1972-75, exec. v.p., 1975-77, pres., 1977—; chief operating officer, 1977, chief exec. officer, 1977—, chmn., 1978-82; pres. Gerald C. Meyers Assocs., Inc., West Bloomfield, Mich.; Ford disting. prof. Carnegie Mellon U. Grad. Sch. Indsl. Adminstrn.; prof. Grad. Sch. Bus. Adminstrn., U. Mich., Ann Arbor. Served as 1st lt. USAF, 1951-53. Decorated French Legion of Honor. Mem. Econ. Club Detroit, Tau Beta Pi, Phi Kappa Phi, Omicron Delta Kappa. Office: 5600 W Maple Rd Ste 216B West Bloomfield MI 48322-3707

MEYERS, HOWARD L., lawyer; b. Dec. 22, 1948. BS, U. Del., 1970; JD, U. Va., 1973. Bar: Pa. 1973. Mng. ptnr. Morgan, Lewis & Bockius, Phila. Office: Morgan Lewis & Bockius 2000 One Logan Sq Philadelphia PA 19103

MEYERS, JAMES WILLIAM, judge; b. Natick, Mass., Sept. 16, 1942. BSA with high honors, Bentley Coll., 1964; JD, Harvard U., 1970. Bar: Mass., Calif. Sr. acct. Ernst & Ernst, Boston, 1964-67; trial atty. criminal div. Dept. Justice, Washington, 1970-72; chief appellate sect. Office U.S. Atty., So. Dist. Calif., 1972-76; judge U.S. bankruptcy Ct. (so. dist.) Calif. San Diego, 1976—; mem. bankruptcy appellate panel Ninth Cir. Ct. of Appeals, 1985—. Mem. ABA. Office: US Bankruptcy Ct Jacob Weinberger Courthouse 325 W F St Rm 210 San Diego CA 92101-6989

MEYERS, JAN, congresswoman; b. Lincoln, Nebr., July 20, 1928; m. Louis Meyers; children: Valerie, Philip. A.A. in Fine Arts, William Woods Coll., 1948; B.A. in Communications (hon.), U. Nebr.-Lincoln, 1951; LittD, William Woods Coll., 1986; LLD (hon.), Baker U., 1993. Mem. Overland Park (Kans.) City Coun., 1967-72; pres. Overland (Kans.) Park City Council; mem. Kans. Senate, 1972-84, chmn. pub. health and welfare com., local govt. com.; mem. 99th-103rd Congresses from 3rd Kans. Dist., 1985—, mem. com. internat. rels., chmn. sml. bus. com., mem. com. on econ. and ednl. opportunities. 3rd Dist. co-chmn. Bob Dole for U.S. Senate, 1968; chmn. Johnson County Bob Bennett For Gov., 1974; mem. Johnson County Cmty. Coll. Found.; bd. dirs. Johnson County Mental Health Assn. Recipient Outstanding Elected Ofcl. of Yr. award Assn. Cmty. Mental Health Ctrs. Kans., Woman of Achievement Matrix award Women in Communications, Disting.

Service award Bus. and Profl. Women Kansas City, William Woods Alumna award of distinction, Cmty. Svc. award Jr. League Kansas City, 1st Disting. Legislator award Kans. Assn. C.C.s, Outstanding Svc. award Kans. Library Assn., United Community Services, Kans. Pub. Health Assn., award Gov.'s Conf. Child Abuse and Neglect, Outstanding Legislator award Kans. Action for Children, Friend award Nat. Assn. County Park and Recreation Ofcls., 1987, Disting. Alumna award, 1991, numerous others. Mem. LWV (past pres. Shawnee Mission). Methodist. Office: US Ho of Reps Rayburn House Office Bldg 2303 Rayburn House Office Washington DC 20515

MEYERS, JOHN ALLEN, magazine publisher; b. Winnetka, Ill., Feb. 21, 1929; s. Fred W. and Ruth B. (Burras) M.; m. Jane Bowers, Sept. 18, 1954; children: Jennifer, Katherine, John. B.A., Mich. State U., 1951, Litt.D. (hon.), 1978; postgrad., Columbia U., 1965. Mgr. Cleve. Time mag., 1960-63, mgr. Chgo. 1963-65; mgr. Time mag., N.Y.C., 1965-68, worldwide advt. sales dir., 1968-72; v.p. Time, Inc., publisher Sports Illustrated mag., 1972-78; pub. Time mag., 1978-85; chmn. Time Inc. Mag. Co., 1985-88; chmn. emeritus Time Inc., 1988—; appointed presdl. bd. adv. on Pvt. Sector Initiatives; chmn. J.A.M. Enterprises; bd. dirs. Tambrands. Editor-in-chief Constitution mag. Pres., Found. for the U.S. Constn. Served with USMC, 1951-53. Decorated Purple Heart. Office: Time & Life Bldg 1221 Ave Of The Americas New York NY 10020-1001

MEYERS, MARLENE O., hospital administrator; m. Eugene Meyers; children: Lori, Lisa, Dean. BSc, U. Sask., 1962; MSc, U. Calgary, Alta., Can., 1976. Instr., chair Mount Royal Coll. Allied Health, Calgary, 1969-82; asst. exec. dir. Rockyview Hosp., Calgary, 1982-85; v.p. patient svcs. Calgary Gen. Hosp., 1985-91, pres., CEO, 1991-95; pres., CEO Meyers and Assocs. Health Care Mgmt. Cons., Calgary, 1995—; surveyor Can. Coun. on Health Facilities Accreditation, 1986—. Named Calgary Woman of Yr., 1982. Mem. Alta. Assn. RNs. Office: Meyers and Assocs, 139 Coleridge Rd NW, Calgary, AB Canada T2K 1X5

MEYERS, MARY ANN, writer, consultant; b. Sodus, N.Y., Sept. 30, 1937; d. Harold Galpin and Clarice Mildred (Daniel) Dye; m. John Matthew Meyers, Aug. 22, 1959; children: Andrew Christopher, Anne Kathryn. BA magna cum laude, Syracuse U., 1959; MA, U. Pa., 1965, PhD, 1976. Editorial asst. Ladies' Home Jour., Phila., 1959-62; asst. editor, asst. dir. news bur. U. Pa., Phila., 1962-65, asst. to pres., 1973-75, univ. sec., lectr. in Am. civilization, 1980-90; contbg. writer The Pennsylvania Gazette, Phila., 1965—; dir. coll. rels., editor Haverford Horizons, lectr. in religion Haverford (Pa.) Coll., 1977-80; pres. The Annenberg Found., St. Davids, Pa., 1990-92. Author: A New World Jerusalem, 1983; contbg. author: Death in America, 1975, Gladly Learn, Gladly Teach, 1978, Coping with Serious Illness, 1980, Religion in American Life, 1987; contbr. articles to profl. jours. Judge recognition program Coun. for Advancement and Support Edn., Washington, 1977-78, chair creative editing and writing workshop, 1978; mem. Picker Found. Program on Human Qualities in Medicine, N.Y.C. and Phila., 1980-83; del. Phila.-Leningrad Sister Cities Project, 1986; trustee U. Pa. Press, 1985—, vice chmn. U. Pa., 250th Anniversary Commn., 1987-90, mem. steering com. of bd. trustees, U. Pa., Annenberg Sch. for Communication, 1990-92, mem. bd. overseers, U. Pa., Sch. Arts and Scis., 1990—; mem. steering com. of bd. trustees Annenberg Ctr. for Communication, U. So. Calif., L.A., 1990-92, The Annenberg Washington Program in Communications Policy Studies of Northwestern U., Washington, 1990-92; trustee Am. Acad. Polit. and Social Sci., 1992—, World Affairs Coun. Phila., 1990—; dir. Diagnostic and Rehab. Ctr., Phila., 1993—. Recipient Excellence award Women in Communications, Inc., 1973-74, award for pub. affairs reporting Newsweek/Coun. for Advancement and Support Edn., 1977, Silver medal Coun. for Advancement and Support Edn., 1986. Mem. Cosmopolitan Club, Sunday Breakfast Club, Phi Beta Kappa. Roman Catholic. Avocations: reading, theater, classical music, biking. Home: 217 Gypsy Ln Wynnewood PA 19096

MEYERS, MORTON ALLEN, physician, radiology educator; b. Troy, N.Y., Oct. 1, 1933; s. David and Jeanne Sarah (Dunn) M.; m. Beatrice Applebaum, June 1, 1963; children—Richard, Amy. M.D., SUNY, Upstate Med. Coll., 1959. Diplomate: Am. Bd. Radiology. Intern Bellevue Hosp., N.Y.C., 1959-60; resident in radiology Columbia-Presbyn. Med. Ctr., N.Y.C., 1960-63; fellow Am. Cancer Soc., 1961-63; prof. dept. radiology Cornell U. Med. Center, N.Y.C., 1973-78; prof., chmn. dept. radiology SUNY Sch. Medicine, Stony Brook, 1978-91; prof. dept. radiology SUNY Sch. Medicine, 1991—; vis. investigator St. Mark's Hosp., London, 1976; spkr. Radiol. Soc. N.Am., 1986. Author: Diseases of the Adrenal Glands: Radiologic Diagnosis, 1963, Dynamic Radiology of the Abdomen: Normal and Pathologic Anatomy, 1976, 4th edit., 1994, Iatrogenic Gastrointestinal Complications, 1981; series editor: Radiology of Iatrogenic Disorders, 1981-86; editor: Computed Tomography of the Gastrointestinal Tract: Including the Peritoneal Cavity and Mesentery, 1986; founding editor in chief Abdominal Imaging, 1976—; mem. editorial bd. Iatrogenics, Surg. and Radiol. Anatomy; contbr. chpts. to med. textbooks, articles to med. jours.; speaker in field. Served to capt. M.C. U.S. Army, 1963-65. Fellow Am. Coll. Radiology; mem. AAAS, Am. Coll. Gastroenterology, Radiol. Soc. N.Am., Am. Roentgen Ray Soc., Am. Gastroenterol. Assn., Soc. Uroradiology, Soc. Gastrointestinal Radiologists, Assn. Univ. Radiologists, N.Y. Roentgen Ray Soc., N.Y. Acad. Gastroenterology, Phila. Roentgen Soc., Harvey Soc., N.Y. Acad. Scis., L.I. Radiologic Soc., Alpha Omega Alpha. Home: 14 Wainscott Ln East Setauket NY 11733-3816 Office: SUNY Health Scis Ctr Sch Medicine Dept Radiology Stony Brook NY 11794

MEYERS, NANCY JANE, screenwriter, producer; b. Phila., Dec. 8, 1949; d. Irving H. and Patricia (Lemisch) M. BA, Am. U., Washington, 1971. Co-writer, prodr.: (films) Private Benjamin (Acad. Award nominee, Writers Guild award 1980), Irreconcilable Differences, 1984, Baby Boom, 1987, Father of the Bride, 1991, I Love Trouble, 1994, Father of the Bride II, 1995. Mem. ASCAP, Acad. Motion Picture Arts and Scis., Writers Guild Am. West. Office: care ICM 8942 Wilshire Blvd Beverly Hills CA 90211-1908

MEYERS, PETER L., banker; b. Syracuse, N.Y., Mar. 19, 1939; s. Edwin Clark and Phyllis (Schiess) M.; m. Teresa Maley, Mar. 2, 1963; children: Gary, Gregory, Cheryl. BBA, Syracuse U., 1974. With Merchants Nat. Bank & Trust Co., Syracuse, N.Y., 1963-92, v.p., comml. loan officer, 1975-78, v.p., sr. loan officer, 1978-79, sr. v.p., 1979, exec. v.p., 1980-88, exec. v.p., COO, 1988, pres., CEO, 1988-92; vice chmn. OnBank & Trust Co., Syracuse, 1993—; dir. Security Mutual Life Ins. Co.; chmn. bd. dirs. N.Y. Bus. Devel. Corp. Bd. dirs. Met. Devel. Assn., Syracuse, YMCA; chmn. Syracuse Housing Partnership; sr. v.p. United Way Ctrl. N.Y., Mus. Sci. and Tech. Found.; trustee Erie Canal Mus.; bd. regents LeMoyne Coll.; active Syracuse Onondaga County Youth Bd., Onondaga Lake Mgmt. Conf. Mem. Am. Inst. Banking, Syracuse U. Alumni Assn., Onondaga Golf and Country Club. Avocations: golf, fishing. Office: OnBank & Trust Co 101 S Salina St PO Box 4983 Syracuse NY 13221

MEYERS, RICHARD JAMES, landscape architect; b. Columbus, Ohio, Jan. 25, 1940; s. Ralph Joseph and Margaret Mary (Kruse) M.; m. Mary Igoe, Jan. 12, 1963; children: Gregory James, Helen Marie, Andrew James. B.Landscape Arch., Ohio State U., 1961. Registered landscape architect, Ohio, Mich., Fla., Ind.; cert. Council Landscape Archtl. Registration Bds. Jr. planner Columbus Planning Commn. (Ohio), 1960-62; landscape architect Behnke-Nes & Assocs., Cleve., 1962-65, Arthur Hills & Assocs., Toledo, 1965-67; ptnr. Mortensen-Meyers Assocs., Toledo, 1967-69; prin. MMSS Inc., Toledo, 1969-71, The Collaborative, Inc., Toledo, 1973—; bd. dirs., past pres. Council Landscape Archtl. Registration Bd., Syracuse, N.Y., 1978-86, Ohio Bd. Landscape Architect Examiners, 1975-83. Mem. St. Vincent Hosp. and Med. Ctr. Assocs., Toledo, 1978-83; bd. dirs. Family Svcs. Greater Toledo, 1977-82; com. mem. Toledo Met. Area Coun. of Govt., 1972-79, 87-89, Toledo Bot. Gardens Design Rev. Bd., 1988-90, Downtown Toledo Vision, Inc., 1988—; vice-chmn. Toledo Lucas County Plan Commn., 1989—; Toledo Adminstrv. Bd. Zoning Appeals, 1994—, Met. Parks Com. of 25, 1991; chmn. campaign divsn. United Way, 1991; mem. adv. bd. U. Toledo-Stranahan Arboretum, 1994—. Dumbarton Oaks Jr. summer scholar, 1960; recipient First Honor Design award Am. Assn. Nurserymen, 1974. Fellow Am. Soc. Landscape Architects (merit design award Ohio chpt. 1975, 81, 83, 85, Outstanding Svc. to Profession award 1983, Ohio Chpt. medal 1984); mem. AIA, Ohio Chpt. of Am. Soc. Landscape Architects (v.p. 1974-76), Urban Land Inst., Soc. for Coll. and Univ.

Planning, Am. Forestry Assn., Am. Planning Assn., Rails to Trails Conservancy, Ohio Pks. and Recreation Assn., Heatherdowns Country Club (bd. dirs. 1983). *I am fortunate to be part of a profession dedicated to improving and beautifying our physical environment through the preservation and protection of our natural resources and by the sensitive blending of economic and social needs with these natural systems. Landscape architecture provides me with a great deal of personal satisfaction.*

MEYERS, RICHARD STUART, college president; b. Chgo., Sept. 6, 1938; m. Yasuko Kamata, Sept. 15, 1965; children—Anne Akiko, Toni Takiko. BM, DePaul U., 1961; MS, U. So. Calif., 1963, PhD, 1971. With Inglewood Unified Sch. Dist., Calif., 1967-68; with Dept. Def. Overseas Sch. System, Tokyo, 1964-67; jr. and sr. high sch. tchr. Palos Verdes Peninsula Unified Sch. Dist., Palos Verdes, Calif., 1962-64; instr. media coordinator Grossmont Coll., El Cajon, Calif., 1968-72; dean instrn. Cerro Coso Community Coll. Ridgecrest, Calif., 1972-75, pres., 1975-78; sec. to bd. trustees, supt. and pres. Pasadena City Coll., Calif., 1978-83; pres. Western Oreg. State Coll., Monmouth, 1983—; speaker; cons. Contbr. articles to profl. jours. Bd. dirs. United Way, Salem, Oreg., 1984-89; mem. Oreg. Internat. Trade Commn., 1983-86, bd. dirs. Oreg. Symphony Assn., 1985-90, pres., 1909—. Fulbright scholar, Egypt, 1975. Fellow Am. Leadership Forum; mem. Am. Assn. State Colls. and Univs., Pi Gamma Mu , Phi Delta Kappa. Republican. Lodge: Rotary. Home: 395 College St S Monmouth OR 97361-2015 Office: Western Oreg State Coll 345 Monmouth Ave N Monmouth OR 97361-1314

MEYERS, SHELDON, engineering company executive; b. N.Y.C., Sept. 6, 1929; s. Charles and Charlotte (Farb) M.; m. Anne Catherine Dietzel, Apr. 14, 1962; children—James, John, Catherine, Peter, Paul. B.Engring., SUNY, 1952; M.S.E., U. Mich., 1955; M.B.A., N.Y. U., 1967. Engr. Cities Svc. Oil Co., N.Y.C., 1955-56, Westinghouse Co., Pitts., 1957-58, Argonne (Ill.) Nat. Lab., 1958-69; engr., div. dir. AEC, N.Y.C., 1970-78; office dir., dep. asst. adminstr. EPA, dir. Office Air Quality Planning and Standards, 1982-83, dep. asst. adminstr. Office Air and Radiation, 1983-84; dep. asst. sec. Office of Nuclear Waste Mgmt., Dept. Energy, Washington, 1978-82; dir. Office Radiation, Washington, 1983-87; assoc. adminstr. internat. activities, 1987-88; v.p. Jacobs Engring., 1988—. Princeton U. fellow, 1964-65. Mem. ASME. Home: 3506 Dundee Dr Chevy Chase MD 20815-4741 Office: Jacobs 125 Broadway Ave Oak Ridge TN 37830

MEYERS, TEDSON JAY, lawyer; b. Bayonne, N.J., May 6, 1928; s. Irving and Norma Miriam (Anson) M.; m. Patricia Elizabeth Sullivan, Apr. 10, 1965 (div. Apr. 1978); children: Mary, John, Katherine; m. Lynn Scholz, Aug. 6, 1978 (div. Oct. 1992). Student, Ohio State U., 1945-47; BA, NYU, 1949, MA, 1950; JD, Harvard U., 1953. Bar: D.C. 1953, N.Y. 1957, U.S. Supreme Ct. 1971. Asst. counsel Office Gen. Counsel, Dept. Navy, Washington, 1955-56; assoc. Liebman, Eulau & Robinson, N.Y.C., 1956-58; staff counsel for govt. regulations ABC, N.Y.C., 1958-61; adminstrv. asst. to chmn. FCC, Washington, 1961-62; asst. to dir., dir. overseas ednl. TV projects Peace Corps, Washington, 1962-68; pvt. practice Washington, 1968-70; ptnr. Sullivan Beauregard Meyers & Clarkson, Washington, 1970-74, Peabody Lambert & Meyers, Washington, 1974-84, Reid & Priest, Washington, 1984—; adj. prof. comm. San Diego State U., 1993—; founding pres. Harvard Legis. Rsch. Bur., 1952-53; mem. White House Task Force on Ednl. TV Overseas, 1966-68, adv. coun on internat. telecommunication law U.S. State Dept., 1987—; bd. govs. Internat. Coun. on Computer Communication, 1986—; mem. bd. dirs. Internat. Ctr. Comms., 1994—. Contbr. conf. papers and articles to profl. publs. Mem. City Coun. Washington, 1972-75; bd. govs. Met. Washington Coun. Govts., 1973-75; chmn. Repub. fedn. of Am., 1977—; bd. dirs. U.S. Coun. for World Comm. Yr. 83, 1982-84; dir. The Arthur C. Clarke Found. of the U.S. Inc., 1987—. Lt. USMC, 1953-55, Korea. Rsch. fellow Carnegie Found., 1949. Mem. ABA (co-founder and chmn. internat. telecomm. com., sect. sci. and tech. 1982-85, coun. mem. sect. sci. and tech. 1983-87), Fed. Commn. Bar Assn., Internat. Inst. Comm., Royal TV Soc., Pacific Telecomm. Coun., Soc. Satellite Profls., Cosmos Club (pres. 1988-90), Cosmos Club Found. (trustee, chmn. 1985-88), Potomac Boat Club, Alpha Epsilon Pi. Avocations: photography, computers, sculling, bicycling, military music. Home: 5410 Macomb St NW Washington DC 20016 Office: Reid & Priest Ste 800 701 Pennsylvania Ave NW Washington DC 20004-2608

MEYERS, THEODORE A., food products executive; b. 1930. BS, Pa. State U., 1952; MBA, Harvard, 1966. V.p., treas. Washington Nat. Corp., Washington, 1966-74; v.p., fin. Inland Steel Co., Chgo., 1974-90; sr. v.p., CFO, dir. Wilson Foods Corp., Oklahoma City, 1990—. Office: Wilson Foods Corp 2601 NW Expressway St Oklahoma City OK 73112

MEYERS, WAYNE MARVIN, microbiologist; b. Huntingdon County, Pa., Aug. 28, 1924; s. John William and Carrie Venca (Weaver) M.; m. Esther Louise Kleinschmidt, Aug. 26, 1953; children: Amy, George, Daniel, Sara. BS in Chemistry, Juniata Coll., 1947; diploma, Moody Bible Inst., 1950; M.S. in Med. Microbiology, U. Wis., 1953, Ph.D. in Med. Microbiology, 1955; M.D., Baylor Coll. Medicine, 1959; DSc (hon.), Juniata Coll., 1986. Instr. Baylor Coll. Medicine, 1955-59; intern Conemaugh Valley Meml. Hosp., Johnstown, Pa., 1959-60; staff physician Berrien Gen. Hosp., Berrien Ctr., Mich., 1960-61; missionary physician Am. Leprosy Missions, Burundi and Zaire, Africa, 1961-73; prof. pathology Sch. Medicine U. Hawaii, Honolulu, 1973-75; chief microbiology divsn. Armed Forces Inst. Pathology, Washington, 1975-89, chief mycobacteriology, 1989—, registrar leprosy registry, 1975—; mem. leprosy panel U.S.-Japan Coop. Med. Sci. Program, 1976-83; mem. sci. adv. bd. Leonard Wood Meml., 1981-85, sci. cons. dir., 1985-87, sci. dir., 1987-90; cons., 1990—; rsch. affiliate Tulane U., 1981—; corp. bd. dirs. Gorgas Meml. Inst. Tropical and Preventive Medicine, Inc. Bd. dirs. Internat. Jour. Leprosy, 1978—; contbr. numerous chpts. and articles on tropical medicine to textbooks and jours. Adv. bd. Damien-Dutton Soc. for Leprosy Aid, Inc., 1983—, Am. Leprosy Missions, Inc., 1979-88, chmn. bd., 1985-88, program cons. to bd., mem. bd. reference, 1988—; mem. Hansen's Disease Ctr., Carville, La., 1983-85; chmn., 1985—. With U.S. Army, 1944-46. Allergy Found. Am. fellow, 1957, 58; WHO rsch. grantee, 1978-87. Mem. Internat. Leprosy Assn. (councillor 1978-88, pres. 1988-93), Internat. Soc. Tropical Dermatology, Am. Soc. Tropical Medicine and Hygiene, Am. Soc. Microbiology, Binford-Dammin Soc. Infectious Disease Pathologists (sec.-treas. 1988-91, pres. 1995-96), Internat. Soc. Travel Medicine, Sigma Xi. Achievements include researching human and experimental leprosy. Office: Armed Forces Inst Pathology Washington DC 20306-6000

MEYERS, WILLIAM HENRY, economics educator; b. Souderton, Pa., Nov. 24, 1941; s. Isaac Claude and Mary (Wismer) M.; m. Dalisay Hoborata Cuento, Jan. 1, 1972; children: Naila-Jean, Celina-Beth. BA in Math. and Physics, Goshen (Ind.) Coll., 1963; MS in Agrl. Econs., U. of The Philippines, Los Banos, 1972; PhD in Agrl. Econs., U. Minn., 1977. Team leader Internat. Vol. Svc., Can Tho, Vietnam, 1966-67; VEP coord. United Meth. Ch., Washington, 1968; rsch. fellow Internat. Rice Rsch. Inst., Los Banos, 1971-72; grad. asst. U. Minn., St. Paul, 1972-77; agrl. economist USDA, Washington, 1977-79; prof. econs. Iowa State U., Ames, 1979—; co-dir. Food and Agr. Policy Rsch. Inst., Ames, 1984—; assoc. dir. Ctr. for Agrl. and Rural devel., Ames, 1985—; exec. dir. MATRIC, Ames, 1987—; agr. policy cons. World Bank, Washington, 1992—; ad hoc group of experts East/West, OECD, Paris, 1993—; vis. prof. Inst. Agrl. Econs., Christian-Albrechts U., Kiel, Germany, 1991; agrl. economist Forecast Support Group and Food and Agrl. Policy Br., Econ. Rsch. Svc., USDA, Washington, 1977-79; rsch. fellow Internat. Rice Rsch. Inst., 1971-72; lectr. in field; cons. in field. Editor: Agrl. Econs., 1991-94, Iowa Ag Rev., 1995; editl. bd. Agrl. Econs., 1989-91; assoc. editor Am. Jour. Agrl. Econs., 1987-90; article referee Agrl. Econs. Rsch., Am. Jour. Agrl. Econs., North Ctrl. Jour. Agrl. Econs., Western Jour. Agrl. Econs., Can. Jour. Agrl. Econs.; contbr. numerous articles to profl. jours., chpts. to books. Mem. coun. of founders Baltic Mgmt. Found., Vilnius, Lithuania, 1991—. Rsch. grantee Mo. Valley Rsch. Assocs., 1982-83, USDA, 1982-83, Iowa Soybean Promotion Bd., 1984-86, Nat. Corn Devel. Found., 1982-86, Coop. State Rsch. Svc./USDA, 1983-95, ERS/USDA, 1986, US AID, 1984-87, 89-90, U.S. Feed Grains Coun., 1986-88, Iowa Lottery Funds, 1987-88, U.S. Agy. for Internat. Devel., 1988-90, Nat. Ctr. for Food and Agrl. Policy, Resources for Future, 1990-91, Agrl. Can., 1988-95, Asian Devel. Bank, 1990-92, Farm Credit Svc., 1992-93, Pioneer Hi-Bred Internat., 1994-95, others. Mem. Ames C. of C.,

Am. Agrl. Econs. Assn. (Disting. Policy Contbn. award 1991, Quality of Comm. award 1991), Assn. for Advancement of Baltic Studies, Am. Econs. Assn., Am. Assn. for Advancement of Slavic Studies, European Assn. Agrl. Economists, Internat. Agrl. Trade Rsch. Consortium, Internat. Assn. Agrl. Economists, Internat. Agribus. Mgmt. Assn., Western Agrl. Econs. Assn. (1994 Published Rsch. award), Gamma Sigma Delta, Phi Kappa Phi, Phi Beta Delta. Office: FAPRI Iowa State Univ 578 Heady Hall Ames IA 50011

MEYERSON, ADAM, magazine editor, foundation executive; b. Phila., Aug. 2, 1953; s. Martin and Margy Ellin (Lazarus) M.; m. Nina Hope Shea, Sept. 13, 1986; children: Thomas Abraham, William Ulysses, Henry Elijah. BA, Yale U., 1974; student, Harvard U., 1977-79. Mng. editor The Am. Spectator, Bloomington, Ind., 1974-77; editorial writer Wall St. Jour., N.Y.C., 1979-83; editor Policy Rev. The Heritage Found., Washington, 1983—, v.p. ednl. affairs, 1993—. Co-editor: The Wall Street Journal on Management, 1985. Bd. selectors Am. Inst. Pub. Svc., Washington, 1989—; mem. Coun. Fgn. Rels., 1980-85. Home: 5228 Chevy Chase Pky NW Washington DC 20015 Office: Heritage Foundation 214 Massachusetts Ave NE Washington DC 20002

MEYERSON, BERNARD STEELE, physicist; b. N.Y.C., June 2, 1954. PhD in Physics, CUNY, 1981. Fellow IBM Corp., Yorktown Heights, N.Y., 1980-81, mem. rsch. staff in physics, 1981—; adj. lectr. physics CUNY, 1976-80. Mem. Am. Phys. Soc. Office: IBM TJ Watson Rsch Ctr PO Box 218 Yorktown Heights NY 10598*

MEYERSON, MARTIN, university executive, educator; b. N.Y.C., Nov. 14, 1922; s. Samuel and Etta (Berger) M.; m. Margy Ellin Lazarus, Dec. 31, 1945; children: Adam, Laura (dec.), Matthew. BA, Columbia U., 1942; MCP, Harvard U., 1949; LLD, U. Pa., 1970; LLD (hon.), Queen's U., Can., 1968, Shiraz U., Iran, 1973, U. Edinburgh, 1976; also 17 other hon. doctorates including ScD, Ph D, LHD, LittD, 1967-94. Mem. staff Michael Reese Hosp., Chgo., 1945-47; asst. prof. coll. and grad. social scis. U. Chgo., 1948-52; assoc. Com. on Nat. Policy, Yale U., 1948; assoc. prof., city and regional planning U. Pa., 1952-56, prof., 1956-57, pres., 1970-81, pres. emeritus, 1981—, chmn. bd. dirs. U. Pa. Press, Inst. for Rsch. on Higher Edn. Fels Ctr. Govt., bd. dirs. Inst. Contemporary Art, Mahoney Inst. Neurosci., Lauder Inst. Mgmt. and Internat. Studies, co-chmn. Commn. for U. Pa. 250th Anniversary, 1987-90; Univ. prof. U. Pa. Found., 1977—, chmn., 1981—; exec. dir. Am. Council to Improve Our Neighborhoods, 1955-56, vice chmn., 1956-66; Frank Backus Williams prof. city planning and urban research Harvard U., 1957-63, acting dean Grad. Sch. Design, 1963; founding dir. Joint Center for Urban Studies, MIT and Harvard U., 1958-63; dean, prof. urban devel. Coll. Environ. Design, U. Calif., Berkeley, 1963-66; interim chancellor U. Calif., Berkeley, 1965; pres., prof. public policy SUNY, Buffalo, 1966-70; dir. visitor Inst. for Advanced Study, Princeton, N.J., 1983-84; pres. Found. for Internat. Exchange of Sci. and Cultural Info. by Telecommunications, Switzerland-U.S., 1986—; dir. Real Estate Research Corp., 1961-67, Marine Midland Bank, 1966-70, 1st Fidelity Bancorp., Scott Paper Co., Penn Mut. Life, Saint Gobain Corp., Certain Teed, Norton, Avatar, Universal Health Services; cons. to govts., pvt. firms U.S. and abroad, UN missions to Japan, Indonesia, Yugoslavia, 1958-65; sr. advisor Arthur D. Little, Inc., 1958-66, Taylor Internat., 1989—; cons. Sears Roebuck Found., 1958-69, Ford Found., various times; chmn. bd. Western N.Y. Nuclear Research Center, 1966-70; mem. adv. com. U.S. Census, 1958-61; adv. com. NASA, 1960-65; White House Office Sci. and Tech., 1962-66, White House task forces, 1960-69; mem. council Electric Power Research Inst., 1973-77; mem. U.S. del. UN Conf. on Sci. and Tech. for Less Developed Areas, 1963. Author: (with E. C. Banfield) Politics, Planning and the Public Interest, 1955, Housing, People and Cities, 1962, Face of the Metropolis, 1963, Boston, 1966, Gladly Learn and Gladly Teach, 1978; editor: Conscience of the City, 1970, McGraw-Hill Series; mem. editorial bd. Ency. Britannica, 1980—, Daedalus, 1972-90. Mem. Air Conservation Commn., 1962-66; mem. Bay Area Conservation and Devel. Commn., 1965-66; chmn. Assembly Univ. Goals and Governance, 1969-73; commr. N.Y. State Commn. on Post-Secondary Sch. Edn., 1976-77; hon. prof. Nat. U. Paraguay, 1969—; bd. dirs. Phila. Bicentennial Corp., 1970-76, Greater Phila. Partnership, 1973-81, Afro-Am. Film Found., 1966-70, Niagara U., 1968-70, Center for Community Change, 1968-72, Acad. Religion and Mental Health, 1970-78, Center for Ednl. Devel., 1967-70, Phila. Mus. Art, 1974—, Nat. Urban Coalition, 1969-78; trustee, Am. Coll., 1982-92, Curtis Inst. Music, 1987-94, Armand Hammer United World Coll.N. Mex., 1984—, Am. Schs. Oriental Rsch., 1985—, Tel Aviv U., Coll. Bd., 1986-92, Hebrew U., Internat. House Ctr., Monell Chem. Senses Ctr., chmn., 1993—, Fgn. Policy Rsch. Inst., 1981—, Panasonic Found., 1982—, Ctr. for Visual History, U.S. Com. on the Constl. System; founding dir. Internat. Centre for Study East Asian Devel. Japan; Inst. for Internat. Edn., 1971—, chmn., 1981-85; bd. dirs. Internat. Council Ednl. Devel., 1971—, Am. Council Financial Aid to Edn., 1975-81, Open Univ. Found., U.K., 1979-82; chmn. council pres. Nat. Accelerator Lab., 1972-73; co-chmn. Images (French TV), 1976-79, Salzburg Seminar Bd., 1978—, Marconi Fellowship Council, chair exec. com., 1978—; Internat. gov. tudies, London, 1966-84; mem. sr. exec. council Conf. Bd., 1970-77; trustee Aspen Inst., 1976—; chair adv. group for UN Centre for Regional Devel., Nagoya, Japan, 1983-93; chair internat. selection commn. Phila. Liberty Medal, 1988—; bd. overseers Koc Univ., Bosphorus, Turkey, 1994—; bd. dirs. Internat. Literacy Inst., 1995—. Decorated Commendatore Order of Merit (Italy); chevalier de l'Ordre Nat. de Mérite (France); Order of the Rising Sun, Gold and Silver Star (Japan); recipient Einstein medal Am. Technion Soc., 1976, Disting. Achievement award U. Calif. Berkeley, 1984, John Jay award Columbia U.; overseas fellow Churchill Coll., Cambridge U., 1983; hon. fellow Soc. for Tech. Communication, 1988; Meyerson Hall named in his honor U. Pa. Grad. Sch. Fine Arts; Meyerson Professorship named in his honor U. Pa. Fellow Am. Acad. Arts and Scis., Royal Soc. Arts (Franklin fellow), Am. Philos. Soc. Nat. Acad. Edn.; mem. Am. Soc. Planning Ofcls. (past dir.), Am. Inst. Planners (past gov., award winner), Internat. Assn. Univs. Paris (Am. dir. 1975—, v.p., interim pres. 1981-85, hon. pres. 1985—), Council Fgn. Relations, European Acad. Arts, Scis. and Letters (academician), Phi Beta Kappa (hon.). Clubs: Philadelphia, Century (N.Y.C.) Cosmos (Washington). Office: Univ Pa 225 Van Pelt Library Philadelphia PA 19104

MEYERSON, MORTON, communications executive; b. N.Y.C., Jan. 16, 1935; s. Rachel (Lochmond) M.; m. Roberta, Jan. 3, 1959; children: James, William, Jennifer, Alexander. BA, NYU, 1956. Reporter, editor Fairchild News Svc., N.Y.C., 1956-58, AP, N.Y.C., 1958-59; assoc. editor Biddle Survey, N.Y.C., 1961-65; editor, writer Eastman Dillon, N.Y.C., 1965-66; dir. communications Coopers & Lybrand, N.Y.C., 1966-83; nat. dir. comm. Arthur Young, N.Y.C., 1983-89; bd. dirs. Ernst & Young, N.Y.C. With USAFR, 1952-59. Mem. Overseas Press Club. Home: 21 Canterbury Rd Great Neck NY 11021-2123 Office: Ernst & Young 787 7th Ave New York NY 10019-6018

MEYERSON, SEYMOUR, retired chemist; b. Chgo., Dec. 4, 1916; s. Joseph and Rena (Margulies) M.; m. Lotte Strauss, May 22, 1943; children: Sheella, Elana. BA, Chgo., 1938, postgrad., 1938-39, 47-48; postgrad., George Williams Coll., 1939-40; DSc (hon.), Valparaiso U., Ind., 1995. Chemist Deavitt Labs., Chgo., 1941-42; inspector powder & explosives Kankakee Ordnance Works, Joliet, Ill., 1942; from chemist to rsch. cons. Standard Oil Co. (Ind.) Rsch. Dept., Whiting, Ind.-Naperville, Ill., 1946-84; mem. indsl. adv. coun. chemistry dept. U. Okla., Norman, 1967-69; invited spkr. James T. L. Waters Symposium, Pitts. Conf., Chgo. 1994. Charter mem. editorial adv. bd. Organic Mass Spectrometry jour., 1968-87, Mass Spectrometry Revs. jour., 1980-87; author, co-author 180 sci. publs. 2d lt. AUS, 1943-46, ETO. Mem. emeritus Am. Chem. Soc. (Frank H. Field and Joe L. Franklin award for outstanding achievement in mass spectrometry 1993), Am. Soc. for Mass Spectrometry. Achievements include many contributions to systematic chemistry of gas-phase organic ions; 2 patents in field. Home: 650 N Tippecanoe St Gary IN 46403-2262

MEYUNG, EUGENE J., insurance company executive; b. 1925; married. JD, U. Va., 1951. Regional v.p. State Farm Ins. Co., 1953-78; with Govt. Employees Ins. Co., 1978—, v.p., 1978-80, sr. v.p. 1980-81, exec. v.p., 1981-86, pres., dir., 1986—. Served to lt. USN, 1943-46. Office: Govt Employees Ins Co GEICO Plaza Washington DC 20076

MEZEY, ROBERT, poet, educator; b. Phila., Feb. 28, 1935; s. Ralph and Clara (Mandel) M.; m. Olivia Simpson (div.); children: Naomi, Judah, Eve. Student, Kenyon Coll., 1951-53; BA, U. Iowa, 1959; postgrad. Stanford U., 1960-61. Lectr. Western Res. U., Cleve., 1963-64, Franklin & Marshall Coll., Lancaster, Pa., 1965-66; asst. prof. Fresno (Calif.) State U., 1967-68, U. Utah, Salt Lake City, 1973-76; prof., poet-in-residence Pomona Coll., Claremont, Calif., 1976—. Author: (poems) White Blossoms, 1965, The Lovemaker, 1960 (Lamont award), The Door Standing Open, 1970, Selected Translations, 1981, Evening Wind, 1988 (Bassine citation, PEN prize 1989); editor: Naked Poetry, 1968, Collected Poems of Henri Coulette, 1990. With U.S. Army, 1953-55. Fellow Ingram Merrill, 1973, 89, Guggenheim Found., 1977, Stanford U., 1960, NEA, 1987; recipient Poetry prize Am. Acad. Arts and Letters, 1982. Avocations: tennis, chess. Home: 1663 Chattanooga Ct Claremont CA 91711-2917 Office: Pomona Coll Dept English 140 W 6th St St Claremont CA 91711-6335

MEZZACAPPA, DALE VERONICA, journalist; b. Jersey City, Feb. 1, 1951; s. Santo Michael and Eleanor Veronica (Dixon) Z.; 1 child, Matthew. AB, Vassar Coll., 1972. Staff reporter Suburbanite, Englewood, N.J., 1972-73, Ridgewood (N.J.) Newspapers, 1973-74; staff writer Bergen Record, Hackensack, N.J., 1974-79; N.J. corr. Phila. Inquirer, 1979-81, Trenton bur. chief, 1981-82, Washington corr., 1982-86, edn. reporter, 1986—. Nieman fellow Harvard U., 1990-91. Roman Catholic. Avocations: tennis, travel, reading. Office: Phila Inquirer 400 N Broad St Philadelphia PA 19130-4099

MEZZATESTA, MICHAEL PHILIP, art museum director. BA, Columbia Coll., 1970; mus. teaching cert., Inst. Fine Arts/Met. Mus. Art, 1976; MA, NYU, 1974, PhD, 1980. Curator European art Kimbell Art Mus., Ft. Worth, 1980-86; dir. Duke U. Mus. Art, Durham, N.C., 1987—; adj. prof. dept. art and art history Duke U.; visitor Inst. Advanced Study, Princeton, N.J., 1986; originator, coord. Kimbell Art Mus. theatre program; lectr. various museums and univs. Contbr. articles to profl. jours. Inst. Fine Arts NYU fellow, 1973-74, Ford Found. fellow, 1974-77, Am. Acad. in Rome fellow, 1977-79, John J. McCloy fellow Am. Coun. on Germany, 1982.

MEZZULLO, LOUIS ALBERT, lawyer; b. Balt., Sept. 20, 1944; m. Judith Scales, Jan. 2, 1970. BA, U. Md., 1967, MA, 1976; JD, T.C. Williams Law Sch., 1976. Bar: Va. 1976. Sales rep. Humble Oil (name now Exxon), Richmond, Va., 1970-72; acctg. Marcoin, Inc., Richmond, 1972-73; pvt. practice bookkeeping tax preparation Richmond, 1973-76; assoc. McGuire, Woods, Battle and Boothe, Richmond, 1976-79; dir. Mezzullo & McCandlish, Richmond, 1979—. Contbr. articles to profl. jours. Bd. dirs. Richmond Symphony; former pres. Southampton Citizens Assn., Richmond, 1986. Served with USAR, 1969-75. Mem. ABA (tax sect.), Am. Coll. Trust and Estate Counsel, Am. Coll. Tax Counsel, Va. State Bar (tax sect.), Va. Bar Assn., Am. Bar Found., Va. Law Found., Estate Planning Coun. Richmond, Trust Adminstrs. Coun., Willow Oaks Country Club. Home: 2961 Westchester Rd Richmond VA 23225-1842 Office: Mezzullo & McCandlish PO Box 796 Richmond VA 23206-0796

MFUME, KWEISI, congressman; b. Balt., Oct. 24, 1948; divorced; children: Donald, Kevin, Keith, Ronald, Michael. BS, Morgan State U.; MA, Johns Hopkins U., 1984. Mem. Balt. City Council, 1979-87, 100th-104th Congresses from 7th Md. dist., 1987—; chmn. congl. black caucus, ranking minority mem., mem. banking and fin. svcs. subcom. on gen. oversight and investigations, mem. small bus. com., mem. joint econ. com.; former adj. prof. polit. sci. Morgan State U., Balt. Baptist. Office: US Ho of Reps 2419 Rayburn HOB Washington DC 20515-2007*

MIAMIS, JAMES D., retail grocery chain executive; b. 1927. With Demoulas Supermarkets Inc., Tewksbury, Mass., 1948—, now exec. v.p. meat ops. Office: Demoulas Supermarkets Inc 875 East St Tewksbury MA 01876-1495

MIAN, FAROUK ASLAM, chemical engineer, educator; b. Lahore, Punjab, Pakistan, Aug. 10, 1944; came to U.S., 1969; s. Mohd Aslam and Qureshia Mian; m. Zahida Perveen, July 16, 1970; children: Shoaib F., Sophia F. BS in Chem. Engring., Inst. Chem. Tech., Punjab U., Lahore, 1964, MS in Chem. Engring., 1965; postgrad., Ill. Inst. Tech., Chgo., 1972-74. Registered profl. engr., Tex., Calif., Colo., La., Miss., Wis., Wyo.; registered environ. engr.; diplomate Am. Acad. Environ. Engrs. Chem. engr. Kohinoor/Didier-Werke, 1965-69, Nuclear Data, Inc., Palatine, Ill., 1969-71; prodn. supr. Searle Corp., Arlington Heights, Ill., 1971-74; lead process engr. Austin Co., Des Plaines, Ill., 1974-76, Crawford and Russell, Inc., Houston, 1976-77; supr. process Bechtel, Inc., Houston, 1977-80; process mgr. Litwin Corp., Houston, 1980; mgr. chems., product mgr. line Brown and Root, Inc., Houston, 1980—; chmn.'s adviser U.S. Congl. Adv. Bd., Am. Security Coun. Found., Washington, 1983, 84. Contbr. articles to profl. publs. Mem. AIChE, NSPE, Inst. Food Technologists. Achievements include engring. design/rsch. in petrochemicals, petroleum refining, inorganic/organic chemicals, specialty and fine chemicals, polymers, petroleum refining and coal gasification processes, chlor-alkali and electro-chems., food/pharms. Office: Brown and Root Inc PO Box 4574 Houston TX 77210-4574

MIANO, LOUIS STEPHEN, advertising executive; b. N.Y.C., July 28, 1934; s. Louis Clyde and Zefira (Palombo) M. BA, Dartmouth Coll., 1955; MA, Columbia U., 1958. Writer Look Mag., N.Y.C., 1960-61; editor Show Mag., N.Y.C. and L.A., 1961-63; assoc. producer ABC-TV, N.Y.C. and L.A., 1963-66; vice-chmn., dir. creative services AC&R Advt., N.Y.C., 1966-90; sec. EEE Theatrical Ventures, N.Y.C., 1974—; cons. in field. Co-producer plays: Design for Living, Corpse, The Seagull, Legends, Inner Voices, 1974-86. Trustee Marymount Manhattan Coll., N.Y.C., 1980—; cons. Home Box Office, 1991-92; bd. dirs. The Nat. Bd. of Rev. of Motion Pictures, 1995—; bd. dirs. Circle-in-the-Square. Mem. N.Y. Athletic Club. Home and Office: 430 E 57th St New York NY 10022-3061

MIASKIEWICZ, THERESA ELIZABETH, secondary educator; b. Salem, Mass., Aug. 29, 1933; d. Chester and Anastasia (Zmijewski) M. BA, Emmanuel Coll., Boston, 1954. Cert. tchr., Mass.; lic. real estate broker, Mass. Tchr. fgn. lang. dept. Salem Sch. Dept., 1954—; head tchr. Salem High Sch., 1954-94; 1990-94, retired, 1994; vol. Salem Hosp., 1994—; playground instr. City of Salem, summers, 1951-54; mem. vis. com. New Eng. Assn. Secondary Schs. and Colls. Vol. Salem Hosp., 1979-88, House of Seven Gables, Salem, summers 1987-89; active North Shore Med. Ctr. Aux. Mem. Am. Assn. Retired Persons (Nat. Retired Tchrs. Assn. divsn.), Ret. State county and Mcpl. Employees Assn., Mass. Ret. Tchrs. Assn., Mass. Fedn. Polish Women's Clubs (v.p. 1988-89, regional chmn. scholarship), Polish Bus. and Profl. Women's Club Greater Boston (past corr. sec., chmn. scholarship com., pres. 1988-89). Avocations: travel, floral design, cooking, reading, arts and crafts.

MICA, JOHN L., congressman; b. Binghamton, N.Y., Jan. 27, 1943; s. John and Adeline Resciniti M.; m. Patricia Szymanek, 1972; children: D'anne, Clark. AA, Miami (Fla.)-Dade C.C., 1965; BA, U. Fla., 1967. Chief of staff U.S. Senate; v.p. Winter Park (Fla.) Antique Mall; pres. M.K. Devel. Corp., Winter Park, Fla.; mem. Fla. Ho. of Reps., 1976-80; mem. appropriations com., mem. ethics com., mem. elections com., mem. community affairs com.; mem. transp. and infrastructre com., govt. reform and oversight com., chmn. civil svc. com. 103d Congress from 7th Fla. Dist., 1993—. Author: Factor affecting local government reorganization efforts in Florida, Urban and Environmental Issues. Active Beth Johnson Mental Health Bd., PTA Bd., Zora Neale Hurston Meml. Com. Recipient Outstanding Svc. award Fla. Conservative Union, Outstanding Svc. award Fla. Cancer Soc., Outstanding Svc. award Sertoma, Outstanding Young Men of Am. award; named as one of five outstanding Young Men in Fla. Mem. C. of C., Kiwanis, Winter Park Jaycees (Good Govt. award 1972), Fla. Jaycees Statewide (Good Govt. award 1973), Tiger Bay, Crime Line Bd. Republican. Episcopal. Office: PO Box 756 Winter Park FL 32790

MICCICHE, DANIEL JOHN, lawyer; b. Bklyn., Dec. 17, 1956; s. Rocco Joseph and Annette Louise (Izzo) M. BA, SUNY, Stony Brook, 1978; JD, U. Chgo., 1981. Bar: Tex. 1981, N.Y. 1988, U.S. Tax Ct. 1981, U.S. Dist. Ct. (no. dist.) Tex. 1983, U.S. Ct. Claims 1983, U.S. Ct. Appeals (5th cir.)

1983, U.S. Supreme Ct. 1984. Assoc. Akin Gump Strauss Hauer and Feld, Dallas, 1981-87; profl. corp. ptnr. Akin Gump Hauer and Feld, L.L.P., Dallas, 1988—. Mem. Dallas Mus. Art, Dallas Bus. League, Dallas Urban League, Sierra Club, Dallas Coun. on World Affairs, Amnesty Internat. Recipient Phillip Staudenraus award SUNY, Stony Brook, 1978, Louis Lefkowitz award Suffolk County (N.Y.) Bar Assn., 1978. Mem. ABA (tax sect.), Statre Bar Tex., Dallas Bar Assn., State Bar N.Y., Dallas Assn. Young Lawyers, Tex. Assn. Young Lawyers, Dallas Cross Country Club, Phi Beta Kappa. Roman Catholic. Avocations: running, sailing, swimming. Office: Akin Gump Strauss & Feld LLD 1700 Pacific Ave Ste 4100 Dallas TX 75201-4624

MICCICHE, SALVATORE JOSEPH, journalist, lawyer; b. Everett, Mass., Jan. 27, 1928; s. Calogero and Marianna M.; m. Theresa Ellen Miraglia, Oct. 11, 1953; children: Charles M., Marlene, Marcia E. B.S. in Journalism, Boston U., 1950; LL.B., Suffolk U., 1968. Bar: Mass. 1968, U.S. Dist. Ct. Mass. 1977. Reporter Portsmouth (N.H.) Herald, 1953-55; with Boston Globe, 1955-90, editorial writer, 1969-76, Washington bur., 1970-75, asst. to editor, 1975-77, mng. editor for adminstrn., 1977-80, ombudsman, 1980-82, assoc. editor for editorial dept. legal matters, 1982-85, asst. exec. editor, 1985, ret., 1990. Served with U.S. Army, 1950-52. Mem. Mass. Bar (barpress com. 1975-90), Boston Bar Assn., Orgn. Newspaper Ombudsmen (past dir.), Am. Soc. Newspaper Editors. Roman Catholic. Home: PO Box 152 33 Martha's Ln South Harwich MA 02661

MICCIO, JOSEPH V., business educator, consultant; b. Bklyn., May 1, 1915; s. Salvatore and Marian (Lauro) M.; m. Lillian Teves Pratt, Oct. 12, 1957; children: Kathryn, Michael. B.B.A. cum laude (econ. award), St. John's U., 1938; M.A. cum laude, NYU, 1940, Ed.D., 1965; LL.D., Fairleigh Dickinson U., 1963. C.P.A., N.Y. Accountant Rockwood & Co., Bklyn., 1932-39; controller Lightfoot, Schultz Co., N.J., 1939-42; controller, asst. to financial v.p. Republic Aviation Corp., L.I., 1942-45; controller-treas. Aircooled Motors, Inc., Syracuse, N.Y., 1945-50; gen. mgr. electronics div. Curtiss-Wright Corp., 1951-54, v.p. corp., 1953-64; pres., gen. mgr. Curtiss-Wright Corp. (Wright Aero. div.), Wood-Ridge, N.J., 1954-64, sr v.p., 1964-66, gen. mgr. plastics div., 1953-54; gen. mgr., exec. v.p. Columbia Protektosite Co. (wholly-owned subs.), 1951-54; chmn. bd. Redel Corp., Anaheim, Calif.; adj. prof. Fairleigh Dickinson U.; instr. NYU; prof. mgmt. and bus. policy U. Hawaii, 1966-69, prof., 1969—, chmn. Grad. Sch. Bus., 1966-69, assoc. dean Coll. Bus. Adminstrn., 1966-69; founder, chmn. bd. Hawaii Biotech. Group, Inc.; mgr. Hawaiian State Kitechs Bus. Incubator Facility in Honolulu; mem. state com. on employee stock ownership plans, Hawaii Govs. Task Force on Internat. Bus.; bd. dirs. Sun Fashions Inc., Cen. Pacific Supply Inc., IMUA Builders, Grace Pacific Corp., Hawkins Audio Comm., Inc.; adviser SBA; Hawaii del. Pres.'s Conf. Small Bus., 1980, 87; advisor Hawaii State Com. on E.S.O.P.'s, Hawaii State Spaceport Com. Contbr. articles to profl. jours. Trustee N.J. Symphony; bd. fellows Fairleigh Dickinson U.; mem. coun. St. John's U.; bd. regents Chaminade U., Honolulu. Recipient award of merit Aircraft War Prodn. Coun.; Founders award NYU; Profl. Mgr. award Soc. Advancement Mgmt., 1975; Outstanding Educator award and Excellence in Teaching award U. Hawaii Coll. Bus. Adminstrn., 1985, U. Pres. Citation for Teaching Excellence U. Hawaii, 1986, Bus. Advocate award for Region IX (Calif., Ariz., Nev., Hawaii) U.S. SBA, 1988. Fellow Soc. Advancement of Mgmt.; mem. N.Y. State Soc. CPAs, Fin. Execs. Inst., Am. Arbitration Assn., Am. Mgmt. Assn., Fin. Execs. Inst., Aerospace Industries Assn., Acad. Mgmt., Am. Inst. C.P.A.s, AIAA, Navy League U.S., Conquistadores del Cielo, Honolulu C. of C., Phi Delta Kappa, Phi Delta Epsilon, Beta Gamma Sigma (adv. com. to Hawaii Crime Com.). Clubs: Economic (N.Y.C.); Outrigger Canoe. Address: 2943 Kalakaua Ave Honolulu HI 96815-4649

MICH, CONNIE RITA, mental health nurse, educator; b. Nebr., Feb. 5, 1926; d. Henry B. and Anna (Stratman) Redel; m. Richard Mich. BSN, Alverno Coll.; postgrad., Marquette U.; MSN, Cath. U. Am. Asst. clin. dir. in-patient svcs. Fond du Lac (Wis.) County Health Ctr., 1974-78; head nurse, program coord. acute psychiat. unit St. Agnes Hosp., Fond du Lac, 1979-83; mental health clinician Immanuel Med. Ctr., Omaha, 1984-89; instr., clin. supr., asst. prof. psychiat. mental health Coll. St. Mary, Omaha, 1989-93; med. programs dir. Inst. Computer Sci. Ltd., 1989—; program dir. med. programs ICS Career Sch., Omaha; chair Examining Coun. on RNs; writer items State Bd. Test Pool Examination; pres. Milw. Coun. Cath. Nurses; vice chair Wis. Conf. Group Psychiat. Nursing Practice. Mem. Sigma Theta Tau, Pi Gamma Mu.

MICHA, DAVID ALLAN, chemistry and physics educator; b. Argentina, Sept. 12, 1939; came to U.S., 1969, naturalized, 1974; s. Simon David and Catalina (Cohen) M.; m. Rebecca Stefan, 1991; children: Michael F., Anna K. MS, U. Cuyo, Bariloche, Argentina, 1962; DSc, U. Uppsala, Sweden, 1966. Rsch. assoc. Theoretical Chemistry Inst. U. Wis., Madison, 1966-67; asst. rsch. physicist Inst. Pure and Applied Sci. U. Calif., La Jolla, 1967-69; assoc. prof. chemistry and physics U. Fla., Gainesville, 1969-74, prof., 1974—, dir. Ctr. Chem. Physics, 1982-91; vis. prof. U. Gothenborg, Sweden, 1970, Harvard U., 1972, 90, Max-Planck Inst., Gottingen, Germany, 1976, Imperial Coll., London, 1977, U. Calif., Santa Barbara, 1982, U. Col. and Weizmann Inst., Israel, 1983, U. Buenos Aires, 1988, Supercomputer Inst., Fla. State U., 1991; mem. adv. panel div. advanced sci. computing NSF, 1990-92. Mem. editorial bd. Internat. Jour. Quantum Chemistry, 1979-88, Few-Body Systems, 1985—; editor Finite Systems and Multiparticle Dynamics, 1990—; symposium procs.; contbr. several book chpts., over 130 articles to sci. jours. Recipient U.S. Sr. Scientist award A. Von Humboldt Found., 1976, Sr. Faculty Rsch. award Sigma Xi, 1985; Alfred P. Sloan Found. fellow, 1971-74; Nat. Bur. Standards JILA fellow, 1983. Fellow Am. Phys. Soc. (vice chmn. topical group on few-body sys. and multiparticle dynamics 1986-88, chmn. 1988-90); mem. Am. Chem. Soc. Office: U Fla 366 Williamson Hall Gainesville FL 32611

MICHAEL, ALFRED FREDERICK, JR., physician, medical educator; b. Phila.; s. Alfred Frederick and Emma Maude (Peters) M.; children: Mary, Susan, Carol. M.D., Temple U., 1953. Diplomate: Am. Bd. Pediatrics (founding mem. sub-bd. pediatric nephrology, pres. 1977-80). Diagnostic lab. immunology and pediatric nephrology intern Phila. Gen. Hosp., 1953-54; resident Children's Hosp. and U. Cin. Coll. Medicine, 1957-60; postdoctoral fellow dept. pediatrics Med. Sch., U. Minn., Mpls., 1960-63; asso. prof. Med. Sch., U. Minn., 1965-68, prof. pediatrics, lab. medicine and pathology, 1968—, dir. pediatric nephrology, Regents' Prof., head Dept. Pediatrics, 1986—; established investigator Am. Heart Assn., 1963-68. Mem. editorial bd. Internat. Year of Nephrology, Kidney Internat., Am. Jour. Nephrology, Clin. Nephrology, Am. Jour. Pathology; contbr. articles to profl. jours. Served with USAF, 1955-57. Recipient Alumni Achievement award in clin. scis. Temple U. Sch. Medicine, 1988; NIH fellow, 1960-63; Guggenheim fellow, 1966-67; AAAS fellow, 1995. Fellow Am. Acad. Pediatrics; mem. AMA, AAAS (fellowship award), Am. Assn. Immunologists, Am. Soc. Clin. Investigation, Assn. Am. Physicians, Am. Pediatric Soc., Soc. for Pediatric Research, Am. Assn. of Investigative Pathology, Am. Soc. Cell Biology, Central Soc. for Clin. Research, Am. Soc. Nephrology (coun., pres.-elect 1992—, pres. 1993), Internat. Soc. Nephrology, Soc. for Exptl. Biology and Medicine, Am. Fedn. Clin. Research, Soc. for Pediatric Nephrology, Northwestern Pediatric Soc., Minn. Med. Assn. Congregationalist. Office: U Minn Hosp Dept Pediatrics PO Box 391 Minneapolis MN 55455

MICHAEL, CAROLA, designer, weaver; b. Hamburg, Federal Republic of Germany, Apr. 18, 1921; came to U.S., 1939; d. Max and Selma (Marcus) Nussbaum; m. Walter O. Michael, Aug. 9, 1942; children: Michael L., Suzanne, Karen. Student, Gymnasium, Hamburg, 1938. Asst. to dir. Ednl. Ctr., Seattle, 1941-46; modern dance instr. Helen Bush Sch., Seattle, 1948-49; designer, weaver N.Y.C. 1960—; v.p., officer Artist Craftsmen, N.Y.C., 1960-70. Pres. PTA Elem. Sch. Flushing and Bayside, N.Y.; v.p. Jr. High, High Sch., Flushing and Bayside, 1960-70; chairperson, officer Queens Mus. Flushing, 1974—; designer, weaver textiles Mennonite Tabernacle Reprodn., Lancaster, Pa. Vol. Service award Mayor of N.Y.C., 1985, Citation of Honor Borough Pres., 1986. Office: The Queens Mus NY City Bldg Flushing Meadow Corona Park Flushing NY 11368

MICHAEL, DONALD NELSON, social scientist, educator; b. Chgo., Jan. 24, 1923; s. Albert Abraham and Jean (Lewis) M.; m. Margot Jean Murphy, Apr. 7, 1956; 1 child, Geoffrey William. S.B., Harvard U., 1946, Ph.D.,

1952; M.A. U. Chgo. 1948; D.Sc. (hon.), Marlboro Coll. 1964. Staff social scientist Weapons Systems Evaluation Group U.S., Joint Chiefs Staff, Washington, 1953-54; adviser Office Spl. Studies NSF, Washington, 1954-56; sr. research asso. Dunlap & Assocs., Stanford, Conn., 1956-59; sr. staff mem. Brookings Instn., Washington, 1959-61; dir. Peace Research Inst., Washington, 1961-63; resident fellow Inst. Policy Studies, Washington, 1963-66; prof. planning and pub. policy, program dir. Center Research Utilization Sci. Knowledge, Inst. Social Research, prof. psychology U. Mich., Ann Arbor, 1966-82, prof. emeritus, 1982—, NIMH spl. research fellow, 1968-70; vis. fellow Inst. Internat. Studies, U. Calif., Berkeley, 1972-73; rsch. assoc. Inst. Urban and Regional Design, U. Calif., Berkeley, 1980—; fellow Sch. Mgmt. and Strategic Studies, Western Behavorial Sci. Inst., La Jolla, Calif., 1981-92; lectr. 10th Ann. Lecture John Dewey Soc., 1967; mem. Commn. Study Orgn. Peace, 1965-74; sr. mgmt. cons. SRI Internat., 1980-88; hon. rsch. prof. Rsch. Ctr. Econ., Tech. and Social Devel. of State Coun., Shanghai, People's Republic China, 1988—; spl. researcher Shanghai Inst. for Sci. of Sci., 1988—; adj. faculty Saybrook Inst., San Francisco, 1983-91; bd. dirs. UN Assn., San Francisco chpt., 1989-92; mem. adv. bd. Resource Renewal Inst., Sausalito, Calif., 1991—; adv. bd. Commonweal, Bolivas Calif., 1993—. Author: Proposed Studies on the Implications of Peaceful Space Activities for Human Affairs, 1961, Cybernation: The Silent Conquest, 1962, The Next Generation, 1965, The Unprepared Society, 1968, On Learning to Plan —And Planning to Learn, 1973. Founding mem. nat. bd. U.S. Assn. for Club of Rome, 1978-81; mem. nat. bd. Citizen Involvement Network, 1975; mem. nat. bd. dirs. Girl Scouts U.S.A., 1969-72, Congl. Inst. for Future; mem. exec. bd. Wash. Assn. Scientists, 1961-66, chmn., 1963-64; bd. dirs. Rollo May Ctr. for Humanistic Studies, San Francisco, 1988—. With AUS, 1943-46. First recipient Aurelio Peccei prize L'eta Verde, Rome, 1987. Fellow AAAS, APA, Inst. Soc. Ethics Life Scis., Soc. for Psychol. Study Social Issues, World Acad. Art and Sci.; mem. Am. Soc. Cybernetics (founding bd. 1964-68), Internat. Soc. for Panetics (founding mem., founding bd. govs. 1991-94), N.Y. Acad. Scis., Fedn. Am. Scientists, Meridian Internat. Inst. (founding bd. 1992—), Club of Rome, Cosmos Club, Sigma Xi.

MICHAEL, ERNEST ARTHUR, mathematics educator; b. Zurich, Switzerland, Aug. 26, 1925; came to U.S., 1939; s. Jakob and Erna (Sondheimer) M.; m. Colette Verger Davis, 1956 (div. 1966); children: Alan, David, Gerard; m. Erika Goodman Joseph, Dec. 4, 1966; children: Hillary, Joshua. B.A., Cornell U., 1947; M.A., Harvard U., 1948; Ph.D., U. Chgo., 1951. Mem. faculty dept. math. U. Wash., Seattle, 1953—; asst. prof. U. Wash., 1953-56, assoc. prof., 1956-60, prof., 1960-93, prof. emeritus, 1993—; mem. Inst. for Advanced Study, Princeton, 1951-52, 56-57, 60-61, 68, Math. Research Inst., E.T.H., Zürich, 1973-74; vis. prof. U. Stuttgart, Ger., 1978-79, U. Munich, Fed. Republic Germany, 1987, 88, 92-93. Editor: Procs. Am. Math. Soc., 1968-71, Topology and Its Applications, 1972-94; contbr. articles to profl. jours. Served with USNR, 1944-46. Grantee AEC; Grantee Office Nav. Research; Grantee NSF; Grantee Guggenheim Found.; Grantee Humboldt Found. Mem. Am. Math. Soc., Math. Assn. Am., ACLU, Amnesty Internat. Jewish. Home: 16751 15th Ave NW Seattle WA 98177-3842

MICHAEL, GARY G., retail supermarket and drug chain executive; b. 1940; married. BS in Bus., U. Idaho, 1962. Staff acct. Ernst & Ernst, CPA's, 1964-66; with Albertson's, Inc., Boise, Idaho, 1966—, acct., 1966-68, asst. controller, 1968-71, controller, 1971-72, v.p., controller, 1972-74, sr. v.p. fin., treas., 1974-76, exec. v.p., 1976-84, vice chmn., CFO, corp. devel. officer, 1984-91, chmn., CEO, 1991—; also dir. Albertson's, Inc. Served to 1st lt. U.S. Army, 1962-64. Office: Albertson's Inc PO Box 20 Boise ID 83726*

MICHAEL, GARY LINN, architect; b. Portland, Oreg., Apr. 27, 1934; s. Donald Glenn and Ida Marie (Luoto) M.; m. Sandra Ann Schori, Sept. 16, 1956 (div. 1982); children: Brian Russell, Laura Joy, Jesse Daniel. B.Arch., U. Oreg., 1957; M.Arch., Yale U., 1965. Partner Campbell, Michael, Yost, Portland, 1965-68; prin. Architects & Planners Gary L. Michael, Portland, 1969-74; pres. Michael & Kuhns, Architects, Portland, 1974—; mem. Oreg. Bd. Architect Examiners, 1978-84; guest archtl. design critic Portland State U., U. Oreg.; guest lectr. pub. schs., colls., tchr. tng. seminars. Works include Mentor Graphics Child Development Center, Wilsonville, Oreg., 1991, Zach Studio and Residence, Elmira, Oreg., 1969, Cowles Bldg, Portland, 1973, Unthank Plaza Pub. Housing, Portland, 1977, Duniway Ctr., Portland, 1982, student housing at Wash. State U., U. Wash. U., U. Alaska, Portland State U., The Evergreen State Coll., So. Oreg. State Coll. Mem. Portland Sch. Dist. Eco-Aesthetics Bd., 1972-74; mem. citizens coordinating com. Oreg. Hwy. Div., 1973; chmn. Sensible Transp. Options for People, Portland, 1974; mem. Downtown Housing Adv. Com., 1978-81; chair adv. com. Milw. Riverfront Devel., 1987-89. Ion Lewis Traveling fellow, 1957. Fellow AIA (11 local design awards 1960-80, nat. design award 1973, pres. Portland chpt. 1972). Home: 11907 SE 19th Ave Milwaukie OR 97222 Office: Michael & Kuhns Archs PC 421 SW 6th Ave Portland OR 97204-1401

MICHAEL, GEORGE (GERGIOS KYRIAKOU PANAYIOTOU), musician, singer, songwriter; b. London, Eng., June 25, 1963; s. Jack and Lesley Panayiotou. Formed group The Executive with Andrew Ridgeley, 1979, band became Wham!, 1980-86. Albums with Wham! Fantastic, 1982, Make it Big, 1984, Music From the Edge of Heaven, 1985; album (with Queen) Five Live, 1993; solo releases Faith, 1987 (best dir. MTV Video award 1988, Best Pop Male Vocalist Am. Music award 1989, best soul R&B vocalist Am. Music award 1989, best soul R&B album Am. Music award 1989), Listen Without Prejudice, Vol. I, 1990; contbr. albums Two Rooms: Celebrating the Songs of Elton John and Bernie Taupin, 1991, Red, Hot & Dance, 1992, A Very Special Christmas II, 1992; duet (with Aretha Franklin) I Knew You Were Waiting For Me, 1987 (Grammy award best duo R&B 1987); prodr., writer Trojan Souls. Recipient Best New Video Artist award Am. Video Awards, 1985, Grammy nomination Wham! best pop performance by duo, 1985. Office: Columbia Records 2100 Colorado Ave Santa Monica CA 90404-3504*

MICHAEL, HAROLD LOUIS, civil engineering educator, consultant; b. Columbus, Ind., July 24, 1920; s. Louis Edward and Martha (Armuth) M.; m. Elsie Marie Ahlbrand, Aug. 15, 1943 (dec. Sept. 1951); m. Elizabeth Annette Welch, Dec. 12, 1954 (dec. Jan. 30, 1989); stepchildren: Betty, Ellen, Harold, Thomas Williams; 1 child, Edward Michael. BSCE with highest distinction, Purdue U., 1950, MSCE, 1951, DEng (hon.), 1992. Registered profl. engr., Ind. Grad. asst. Purdue U., 1950-51; dir. urban transp. studies Ind. State Hwy. Commn., 1951-54; research asst., instr. Purdue U., West Lafayette, Ind., 1952-54, asst. prof. hwy. engring., asst. dir. joint hwy. research project, 1954-56, assoc. prof. hwy. engring., assoc. dir. joint hwy. research project, 1956-61, prof. hwy. engring., head transp. and urban engring., assoc. dir. joint hwy. research project, 1961-78, head Sch. Civil Engring., prof. hwy. engring., dir. joint hwy. research project, 1978-91, prof. emeritus, 1991—; chmn. assoc. com. Transp. Rsch. Bd., NRC, 1976, mem. exec. com., 1973-79, chmn. or mem. adv. panels for Nat. Coop. Hwy. Research Programs, 1971-79; mem. adv. bd. Hwy. Extension and Research Program for Ind. Counties, 1971-91; chmn. Nat. Com. on Uniform Traffic Control Devices, 1971-74, mem.; chmn. Nat. Com. on Uniform Traffic Laws and Ordinances, 1990—, vice chmn. com. on ops., 1973-90; mem. adv. panel on nat. accident sampling system Nat. Hwy. Traffic Safety Adminstrn., 1978-80; mem. exec. res. U.S. Dept. Transp., 1967-83; mem. com. on transp. NRC, 1976-80; mem. bd. cons. Eno Found. Transp., 1978-82; chmn. Traffic Commn., West Lafayette, Ind., 1956—, chmn. transp. tech. com., Greater Lafayette, 1965—. Served to capt. U.S. Army, 1942-46, ETO; with USAR, 1946-64, ret. lt. col. Decorated Bronze Star; recipient citation for Disting. Service State Ind., 1967, Service award Ind. Soc. Profl. Engr., 1969, Disting. Service award Transp. Research Bd., 1976, Roy W. Crum award Transp. Research Bd., 1978, award in recognition of disting. service Ind. Soc. Profl. Engrs., 1978, Theodore M. Matson award, 1979, George S. Bartlett award Am. Assn. Hwy. and Transp. Ofcls., Am. Rd. and Transp. Builders Assn. and Transp. Research Bd., 1982; named Engr. of Yr., Ind. Soc. Profl. Engrs., 1972; Sagamore of Wabash, Ind. Fellow Inst. Transp. Engrs. (pres. 1974-75, Marsh award 1984), ASCE (hon., mem. ABET visitors com. 1978-83, G. Brooks Earnest Lecture award Cleve. sect. 1981, Laurie Prize 1981, Wilbur S. Smith award 1991); mem. NAE, NSPE (nat. dir. 1964-78), Am. Rd. and Transp. Builders Assn. (life, vice chmn. 1978-80, chmn. hwys. adv. council 1981-94, Disting. Svc. award 1994), Ind. Constructors, Inc. (hon. life), Am. R.R. Engring. Assn. (chmn. subcom. hwys. 1970-87), Am. Soc. Engring. Edn., Am. Pub. Works Assn. (trustee Research

Found. 1976-79), Inst. Transp. Engrs. (hon., Wilbur S. Smith Disting. Transp. Engring. Career Educator 1994), Rotary (dist. gov.), Theta Xi. Avocations: gardening; golf; stamp collecting; coin collecting. Home: 1227 N Salisbury St West Lafayette IN 47906-2415 Office: Purdue U Civil Engring Bldg West Lafayette IN 47907

MICHAEL, HENRY N., geographer, anthropologist; b. Pitts., July 14, 1913; s. Anthony M. and Albina (Dubska) M.; m. Ida Nemez, June 18, 1943; children: Susan Shelley, Richard Carleton, Andrew Paul. B.A., U. Pa., 1948, M.A., 1951, Ph.D., 1954. Instr. geography U. Pa., 1948-54; faculty Temple U., 1958-80, prof. geography, chmn. dept., 1965-73, prof., 1965-80; research assoc. Univ. Mus., Phila., 1959-82, sr. fellow, 1982—; mem. Bi-Nat. Commn. on Social Scis. and Humanities, Am. Council Learned Socs./Acad. Scis. USSR, 1975—. Editor: Anthropology of the North, 1959-72; editor, author: Dating Techniques for the Archaeologist, 1971, 73, 82; translator, editor various archaeol. and ethnographic works; mem. adv. publs. com. Mus. Applied Sci. Ctr. for Archaelogy, U. Pa., Anthropology and Archaeology of Eurasia-A Jour. of Transls., Alaska-Siberia Rsch. Ctr.; mem. editorial bd. Expedition-The Univ. Mus. Mag. Archaeology and Anthropology, U. Pa.; contbr. articles to profl. jours. Served to 1st lt. AUS, 1942-45. Decorated Purple Heart. Fellow Am. Anthrop. Assn., Arctic Inst. N.Am.; mem. Phila. Anthrop. Soc. (coun. 1954-90), Delaware Valley Assn. Geographers, Assn. Am. Geographers, Sigma Xi. Home: 2712 Pine Valley Ln Ardmore PA 19003-1719 Office: Univ Museum U Pa Philadelphia PA 19104

MICHAEL, JAMES HARRY, JR., federal judge; b. Charlottesville, Va., Oct. 17, 1918; s. James Harry and Reuben (Shelton) m. Barbara E. Puryear, Dec. 18, 1946; children: Jarrett Michael Stephens, Victoria von der Au. B.S., U. Va., 1940, LL.B., 1942. Bar: Va. 1942. Sole practice Charlottesville; ptnr. Michael & Musselman, 1946-54, J.H. Michael, Jr., 1954-59, Michael & Dent, 1959-72, Michael, Dent & Brooks Ltd., 1972-74, Michael & Dent, Ltd., 1974-80; assoc. judge Juvenile and Domestic Relations Ct., Charlottesville, 1954-68; judge U.S. Dist. Ct., Charlottesville, 1980—; mem. Va. Senate, 1968-80; exec. dir. Inst. Pub. Affairs, U. Va., 1952; chmn. Council State Govts., 1975-76, also mem. exec. com.; chmn. So. Legis. Conf., 1974-75. Mem. Charlottesville Sch. Bd., 1951-62; bd. govs. St. Anne-Belfield Sch., 1952-76. Served with USNR, 1942-46; comdr. Res. ret. Wilton Park fellow Wilton Park Conf., Sussex, Eng. 1971. Fellow Am. Bar Found.; mem. ABA, Va. Bar Assn. (v.p. 1956-57), Charlottesville-Albermarle Bar Assn. (pres. 1966-67), Am. Judicature Soc., 4th Jud. Conf., Va. Trial Lawyers Assn. (Va. disting. svc. award 1993), Assn. Trial Lawyers Am., Raven Soc., Sigma Nu Phi, Omicron Delta Kappa. Episcopalian (lay reader). Office: US Dist Ct 255 W Main St Rm 320 Charlottesville VA 22902-5058

MICHAEL, JERROLD MARK, public health specialist, former university dean, educator; b. Richmond, Va., Aug. 3, 1927; s. Joseph Leon and Esther Leah M.; m. Lynn Y. Simon, Mar. 17, 1951; children: Scott J., Nelson L. B.C.E., George Washington U., 1949; M.S.E., Johns Hopkins U., 1950; M.P.H., U. Calif., Berkeley, 1957; Dr. P.H. (hon.), Mahidol U., 1983; Sc.D. (hon.), Tulane U., 1984. Commd. ensign USPHS, 1950, advanced through grades to rear adm., asst. surgeon gen., 1966; ret., 1970; dean Sch. Pub. Health, U. Hawaii, Honolulu, 1971-92, prof. pub. health, 1971—; bd. dirs. Nat. Health Coun., 1967-78, Nat. Ctr. for Health Edn., 1977-90; mem. nat. adv. coun. on health professions edn., 1978-81; chmn. bd. dirs. Kuakini Med. Ctr., Honolulu; sec., treas. Asia-Pacific Acad. Consortium Pub. Health; vis. prof. U. Adelaide, 1993, George Washington, 1994; hon. prof. Beijing Med. U., 1994. Contbr. articles to profl. jours.; assoc. editor Jour. Environ. Health, 1958-80, Asia-Pacific Jour. of Pub. Health, 1990—. Served with USNR, 1945-47. Decorated D.S.M., comdr. Royal Order of Elephant (Thailand); recipient Walter Mangold award, 1961, J.S. Billings award for mil. medicine, 1964, gold medal Hebrew U. Jerusalem, 1982, San Karcil gold medal Govt. of Malaysia, 1989, Disting. Svc. award Gov. of Hawaii, 1989, Assn. Schs. Pub. Health, 1992, recognition of svc. award Pacific Island Health Officers Assn., 1992, USPHS awards, also others. Fellow Am. Public Health Assn.; mem. Am. Acad. Health Adminstrn., Am. Soc. Cert. Sanitarians, Nat. Environ. Health Assn., Am. Acad. Environ. Engrs. Democrat. Jewish. Club: Masons. Office: U Hawaii 1960 East-West Rd Honolulu HI 96822

MICHAEL, JOAN YVONNE JOHNSON, dean, psychologist; b. Pomoma, Calif., Jan. 1, 1935; d. William Frank and Madge Garnet (Simkins) Johnson; m. William Burton Michael, Aug. 26, 1966. AB, U. So. Calif., L.A., 1964, MS, 1965, PhD, 1967. Lectr. in ednl. psychology Immaculate Heart Coll., L.A., 1965-69, U. So. Calif., L.A., 1966; asst. prof. in ednl. psychology San Fernando Valley State Coll., Northridge, Calif., 1967-68; asst. prof. in ednl. psychology Calif. State U., Long Beach, 1968-70, assoc. prof., 1970-75, prof., 1975-83, assoc. dean grad. studies and rsch., 1977-83; dean Sch. Edn. U. Houston at Clear Lake, 1983-89; dean Coll. Edn. and Psychology N.C. State U., Raleigh, 1989—, dir. Lit. Sys. Ctr., 1989-94; chair task force prep for tchr. edn. Assn. Colls. and Schs. of Edn. in State Univ. and Land Grant Colls., 1993—; mem. task force assessing math. and sci. edn. in N.C. Glaxo Found. and N.C. Pub. Sch. Forum, Raleigh, 1995. Author chpt. to book, test manuals; asst. editor Ednl. and Psychology Measurement, 1965-85, assoc. editor, 1985-95; adv. editor Jour. Ednl. Measurement, 1983-84; contbr. articles to profl. jours. Mem. APA, Am. Psychol. Soc., Am. Edn. Rsch. Assn. Avocations: pvt. pilot, swimming, travel. Home: 123 Lochwood West Cary NC 27511 Office: NC State U Coll Edn and Psychology 208 Poe Hall, Box 7801 Raleigh NC 27695

MICHAEL, JONATHAN EDWARD, insurance company executive; b. Columbus, Ohio, Mar. 19, 1954; s. James Franklin and Mary Manetta (McCloud) M.; m. Lori Jeanette Fry, Sept. 1, 1973 (div. Feb. 1985); children: Amber Nicole, Jonathan Andrew. BA, Ohio Dominican Coll., 1977. CPA, Ohio. Acct. Coopers & Lybrand, Columbus, Ohio, 1977-82; chief acct. RLI Ins. Co., Peoria, Ill., 1982-84; controller, 1984-85, v.p. fin., CFO, 1985—; exec. v.p., 1991-94, pres., 1994—. Mem. Am. Inst. CPA's, Ins. Acctg. and Systems Assn. Cen. Ill. (treas. 1985, sec. 1986). Roman Catholic. Club: Mt. Hawley Country (Peoria). Avocation: golf. Home: 12706 Georgetowne Rd Dunlap IL 61525-9462 Office: RLI Ins Corp 9025 N Lindbergh Dr Peoria IL 61615-1431

MICHAEL, LARRY PERRY, broadcasting company executive; b. Chgo., Sept. 1, 1956; s. Perry Peter and Voula (Sakalleris) M.; m. Darlene Faith Coskey, Oct. 15, 1988; children: Olivia Diane, Anjelica Sharon. BA, U. Md., 1979. Producer MBS, Arlington, Va., 1980-82, mgr. sports ops., 1982-86, dir. sports, 1986-87; dir. sports Westwood One Inc., Arlington, 1987—; exec. prodr. Notre Dame U. football, 1984—; play-by-play announcer George Washington U., Washington, 1991-94; host (TV) Sport Edge...Play-by-Play, Westwood, 1990—. Recipient gold medal for 1988 summer Olympic coverage Internat. Radio Festival N.Y., 1989. Mem. Laconian Soc. Democrat. Greek Orthodox. Avocations: weightlifting, sports collecting, golf. Office: Westwood One Sports 1755 Jefferson Davis Hwy Arlington VA 22202

MICHAEL, M. BLANE, federal judge; b. Charleston, S.C., Feb. 17, 1943. AB, W.Va. U., 1965; JD, NYU, 1968. Bar: N.Y. 1968, U.S. Dist. Ct. (so. and ea. dists.) N.Y. 1968, W.Va. 1973, U.S. Ct. Appeals (4th cir.) 1974, U.S. Dist. Ct. (no. dist.) W.Va. 1975, U.S. Dist. Ct. (so. dist.) W.Va. 1981. Counsel to Gov. W.Va. John D. Rockefeller IV, 1977-80; atty. Jackson & Kelly, Charleston, W.Va., 1981-93; fed. judge U.S. Ct. Appeals (4th cir.), Charleston, W.Va., 1993—; active 4th Jud. Conf. Mem. ABA, W.Va. Bar Assn., Kanawha County Bar Assn., Phi Beta Kappa. Office: US Ct Appeals Fed Bldg 4th Fl Charleston WV 25301*

MICHAEL, PATRICIA ANN, physician, clinical systems research director; b. Highland Park, Ill., Aug. 25, 1953; d. Charles Joseph and Dorothy Josephine (Glomski) M. BSChemE, U. Ill., 1975; MBA, U. Chgo., 1979;

PhD in Biomed. Engring., U. N.C., 1982, MD, 1985. Postdoctoral fellow sect. on med. info. sci. U. Calif., San Francisco, 1986-88; med. applications analyst Rex Hosp., Raleigh, N.C., 1988-90, dir. clin. systems rsch., 1990—; adj. asst. prof. biomed. engring. U. N.C., Chapel Hill, 1989—; cons. Lexical Tech., Inc., Alameda, Calif., 1988-90. Contbr. articles to profl. jours. Recipient Postdoctoral traineeship Nat. Libr. Medicine, 1986-88. Mem. IEEE Computer Soc., Am. Med. Informatics Assn., Assn. Computing Machinery, Assn. MBA Execs. Avocations: choral music, science fiction and fantasy literature. Office: Rex Hosp 4420 Lake Boone Trail Raleigh NC 27604-3571

MICHAEL, SANDRA DALE, reproductive endocrinology educator, researcher; b. Sacramento, Calif., Jan. 23, 1945; d. Gordon G. and Ruby F. (Johnson) M.; m. Dennis P. Murr, Aug. 12, 1967 (div. 1974). BA, Calif. State Coll., Sonoma, 1967; PhD, U. Calif., Davis, 1970. NIH predoctoral and postdoctoral fellow U. Calif., Davis, 1970-73, asst. rsch. geneticist, 1973-74; asst. prof. SUNY, Binghamton, 1974-81, assoc. prof., 1981-88, prof. reproductive endocrinology, 1988—, dept. chair, 1992—; adj. prof. SUNY Health Sci. Ctr., Syracuse, N.Y., 1994—; mem. NIH Reproductive Endocrinology Study Sect., 1991—; cons., presenter in field; grant reviewer NIH, NSF, USDA and others. Contbr. articles to profl. jours. Vice chair Tri Cities Opera Guild, Binghamton, 1987-90, chair, 1990-92; mem. Harpur Forum, Binghamton, 1987—, SUNY Found., Binghamton, 1990—. Fulbright Sr. scholar Czech Republic, 1994; grantee NIMH, 1976-79, Nat. Cancer Inst., 1977-80, 83-87, Nat. Inst. Environ. Health Scis., 1979-80, NSF, 1981-83, NIH, 1987—. Mem. Endocrine Soc., Soc. for the Study of Reprodn., Soc. for Study of Fertility, Am. Soc. for Immunology of Reprodn., Women in Endocrinology (sec.-treas. 1992—), Soc. for Exptl. Biology and Medicine, N.Y. Acad. Sci., Sigma Xi. Avocations: golf, skiing, bridge, opera, literature. Office: State Univ of NY Dept Biol Scis Binghamton NY 13902

MICHAEL, WILLIAM BURTON, psychologist, educator; b. Pasadena, Calif., Mar. 6, 1922; s. William Whipple and Helen Augusta (Schultz) M.; m. Martha Walker Hennessey, Aug. 30, 1947 (dec. 1959); m. Joan Yvonne Johnson, Aug. 26, 1966. A.B., UCLA, 1943; M.S. in Edn., U. So. Calif. Los Angeles, 1945, M.A. in Psychology, 1946, Ph.D., 1947. Lic. psychologist Calif. Lectr. engring. math. Calif. Inst. Tech., Pasadena, 1942-45; asst. prof. psychology Princeton U., N.J., 1947-50; research assoc. Rand Corp., Santa Monica, Calif., 1951-52; dir. testing bur. U. So. Calif., Los Angeles, 1952-62, prof. edn. and psychology, 1957-62, 1967—; prof. edn. and psychology U. Calif., Santa Barbara, 1962-67; cons. in field; lectr. math, psychology and edn. U. So. Calif., 1944-47, others. Author: Teaching for Creative Endeavor, 1967; co-author: Psychological Foundations of Learning and Teaching, 2nd edit., 1974, Handbook in Research and Evaluation, 3rd edit., 1981, (standardized tests) Study Attitudes and Methods Survey, Dimensions of Self-Concept; editor Ednl. and Psychol. Measurement, 1985-95; cons. editor Jour. Pers. Evaluation in edn., Ednl. Rsch. Quar.; contbr. articles to profl. jours., chpts. to books. Mem., bd. dirs. Neuro-Psychiat. Clinic, Los Angeles and Pasadena, 1958—; mem. Los Angeles Philharmonic Assn., 1965—; advisor Sch. of Communication, Arcadia, Calif., 1981—. Fellow APA, mem. Am. Ednl. Rsch. Assn. (exec. com., editor Rev. Edn. Rsch. 1962-65), Western Psychol. Assn., Northeastern Ednl. Rsch. Assn., Nat. Coun. on Measurement in Edn., Calif. Ednl. Rsch. Assn. (pres. 1965), Phi Beta Kappa, Sigma Xi, Phi Kappa Phi, Psi Chi, Phi Delta Kappa. Independent. Congregationalist. Avocations: Music; travel; reading; ice cream gourmet. Home: 325 Callita Pl San Marino CA 91108-2311 Office: U So Calif Sch Edn 3470 University Ave Los Angeles CA 90007-3503

MICHAELCHECK, WILLIAM J., investment firm executive; b. Dyersburg, Tenn., Apr. 22, 1947; s. William Dooley and Frances Michaelcheck; m. Loretta Madison (div.); Pamela Jill Furer, Oct. 10, 1990. BA, Rhodes Coll., 1969; MBA, Harvard U., 1971. Sr. investment officer World Bank, Washington, 1971-75; ptnr. J.F. Eckstein and Co., N.Y.C., 1976-79; exec. v.p.; sr. mng. dir. Bear, Stearns and Co. Inc., N.Y.C., 1979—; adv. com. Chgo. Mercantile Exch.; bd. advisors banking law studies Boston U., 1990—. Trustee Rhodes Coll., Memphis, Nightingale-Bamford Sch., N.Y.C.; dir. devel. Internat. Sch. Am., Boston. Mem. Harvard Club N.Y.

MICHAELIDES, CONSTANTINE EVANGELOS, architect, educator; b. Athens, Greece, Jan. 26, 1930; came to U.S., 1955, naturalized, 1964; s. Evangelos George and Kalliopi Constantine (Kefallonitis) M.; m. Maria S. Canellakis, Sept. 3, 1955; children: Evangelos Constantine, Dimitri Canellakis. Diploma in Architecture, Nat. Tech. U., Athens, 1952; M.Arch., Harvard U., 1957. Practice architecture Athens, 1954-55, St. Louis, 1963—; asso. architect Carl Koch, Jose Luis Sert, Hideo Sasaki, Cambridge, Mass., 1957-59, Doxiadis Assos., Athens and Washington, 1959-60, Hellmuth, Obata & Kassabaum, St. Louis, 1962; instr. Grad. Sch. Design Harvard U., 1957-59, Athens Inst. Tech., 1959-60; asst. prof. architecture Washington U., St. Louis, 1960-64; assoc. prof. Washington U., 1964-69, prof., 1969-94; assoc. dean Washington U. Sch. Architecture, 1969-73, dean, 1973-93, dean emeritus, 1993—; vis. prof. (Sch. Architecture), Ahmedabad, India, 1970; counselor Landmarks Assn. St. Louis, 1975-79. Author: Hydra: A Greek Island Town: Its Growth and Form, 1967; contbr. articles to profl. jours. Mem. Municipal Common. on Arts, Letters, University City, Mo., 1975-81. Served to lt. Greek Army Res. 1952-54. Fellow AIA (Rsch. award 1963-64, Presdl. Citation 1992); mem. Tech. Chamber of Greece, Soc. Archtl. Historians, Modern Greek Studies Assn., Hellenic Soc. St. Louis (pres. 1991). Home: 735 Radcliffe Ave Saint Louis MO 63130-3139 Office: Washington U Sch Architecture 1 Brookings Dr Saint Louis MO 63130-4862

MICHAELIS, ARTHUR FREDERICK, health care company executive; b. N.Y.C., July 24, 1941; s. Paul F. and Rose (Landsberry) M.; m. Judith Anne Gordy, June 7, 1964; children: Bradley, Jennifer. BS, Bucknell U., 1963; MS, U. Wis., 1965, PhD, 1967; MBA, Fairleigh Dickinson U., 1976. Dir. quality control Sandoz, Inc., E. Hanover, N.J., 1970-71, dir. pharmacy and analytical chemistry, 1971-77, dir. pharm. devel., 1977-79; pres., applied tech. div. KV Pharm. Corp., St. Louis, 1979-80; dir., rsch. and devel. McNeil Consumer Products, Ft. Washington, Pa., 1980-81; v.p., rsch. and devel. Menley and James Lab, Phila., 1981-85; pres. Controlled Therapeutics, Malvern, Pa., 1985-91; chmn., dir. Polysystems Healthcare Ltd., E. Kilbride, Scotland, 1986-91, Controlled Therapeutics-Scotland, 1985-91; pres., dir. Advanced Med. Techs., 1989-91; founder, chmn., CEO Great Valley Pharms., Malvern, Pa., 1991—. Contbr. articles to profl. jours.; editorial bd.: Analytical Profiles of Drug Substances. Capt. U.S. Army, 1968-69. Fellow Am. Inst. Chemists; mem. AAAS, Am. Pharm. Assn., Acad. Pharm. Scis., N.J. Pharm. Quality Control Assn., N.Y. Acad. Scis., Chester Valley Golf Club (Malvern, Pa.), Morris County Golf Club (Convent Station, N.J.). Avocations: golf, woodworking, photography, fishing, fine wines. Office: Great Valley Pharm Inc 97 Great Valley Pkwy Malvern PA 19355-1316

MICHAELIS, ELIAS K., neurochemist; b. Wad-Medani, Sudan, Oct. 3, 1944; came to U.S., 1966; married, 1967; 1 child. BS, Fairleigh Dickinson U., 1966; MD, St. Louis U. Med. Sch., 1969; PhD in Physiology and Biophysics, U. Ky., 1973. Spl. fellow rsch. dept. physiology and biophysics U. Ky., 1972-73; from asst. prof. to rsch. prof. depts. human devel. and biochemistry, 1982-87; chair pharmacology and toxicology U. Kans., Lawrence, 1988—; dir. ctr. biomed. rsch. and Higuchi biosciis. rsch. ctr. U. Kans., 1988—. Mem. AAAS, Am. Soc. Neurochemistry, Am. Soc. Biochemistry and Molecular Biology, Internat. Soc. Biomedical Rsch. on Alcoholism, Soc. Neuroscience, N.Y. Acad. Sci. Achievements include research in characterization of L-glutamate receptors in neuronal membranes, in membrane protein isolation and chemical analysis, in characterization of membrane transport systems for amino acids, sodium, potassium, and calcium, in neuronal membrane biophysics, in molecular neurobiology.

MICHAELIS, MICHAEL, management and technical consultant; b. Berlin, June 8, 1919; s. George and Martha (Bluth) M.; m. Diana Odway Tead, Sept. 11, 1954; children: Ordway Peter, David Tead; m. Cintra McIlwain Williams, Mar. 19, 1966 (div. Nov. 1975); m. Caroline Crutcher Bishop, Mar. 17, 1984. B.Sc. in Engring., U. London, 1941. Research asst. group leader Research Labs. Gen. Electric Co., Ltd., 1935-45; staff physicist and cons. Gen. Electric Co., Ltd., 1945-49; dir. physics div. Radiochem. Centre, U.K. Atomic Energy Authority, 1949-51; cons. Arthur D. Little, Inc., Cambridge, Mass., 1951-52; staff cons. Arthur D. Little, Inc., 1952-61, sr. asso., 1957-61, head nuclear mgmt. cons. services, 1956-61, internat. bus. devel. services, 1959-61, policy adviser to several large corps, 1954-61, mgr.

Washington ops., 1963-72, sr. cons., 1972-81; pres., chief exec. officer Partners In Enterprise, Inc., 1981—; cons. to Pres.'s Spl. Asst. Sci. and Tech., 1961-63; exec. sec. The White House Panel on Civilian Tech., 1961-63; exec. dir. rsch. mgmt. adv. panel, com. on sci. and tech. U.S. Ho. of Reps., 1963-67; dep. coord. then Pres.-elect Carter's Task Force on Sci. and Tech. Policy, 1976; mem. tech. adv. bd. to U.S. Dept. Commerce, 1978-81; mem. citizens adv. coun. Congl. Caucus for Sci. and Tech., 1983-86; mem. nat. com. Am. Goals and Resources, Nat. Planning Assn., 1964-66; vice chmn. com. sci., tech. and economy, 1966-68; vice chmn. com. internat. affairs Atomic Indsl. Forum, 1958-60; assoc. with Anglo-Am. Radar Rsch. Project, World War II. Editor, project dir.: Federal Funding of Civilian Research and Development, 1976; Contbr. articles to publs., periodicals. Fellow AAAS (chmn. engring. sect. 1980-82, exec. dir. sr. scientists and engrs. program 1989-90); mem. IEEE (sr.), Sci. Film Assn. (founder 1943, coun., sec. 1943-48, v.p. 1948-51), Am. Nuclear Soc., Boston Com. Fgn. Rels., Royal Inst. Physics and Phys. Soc., Soc. Internat. Devel., Royal Instn. Elec. Engrs., Assn. Hosp. Physicists, Nat. Planning Assn., World Future Soc. (dir.), U.S. C. of C. (chmn. com. on govt.-industry rels. in sci. and tech. 1963-64), Interdisciplinary Comm. Assocs. Inc. (dir. 1969-79), Am. Econ. Assn., Am. Soc. Cybernetics, Am. Soc. for Pub. Adminstrn., Atlantic Coun. U.S. Home and Office: 6812 Meadow Ln Chevy Chase MD 20815-5018 *The Constitution of the U.S. diffuses power so as to better secure liberty. But it also intends that practice will integrate the dispersed powers into a workable government. It confers upon its branches autonomy but also reciprocity, separateness but also interdependence. It is incumbent on each of us to help make this system work, and to make it responsive to the human needs of our country and the world.*

MICHAELIS, PAUL CHARLES, engineering physicist executive; b. Bronx, N.Y., June 18, 1935; s. Paul Fredrick and Rose (Landsbury) M.; m. Geraldine A. DeCuollo, June 29, 1958; 1 son, Paul Charles. B.S. in Elec. Engring, Newark Coll. Engring., 1964, M.S. in Physics, 1967. With AT&T Bell Labs., Whippany, N.J., 1953—; assoc. mem. tech. staff Bell Telephone Labs., 1963-67, mem. tech. staff, 1967-82, supr., 1982—; lectr. USSR Acad. Scis., 1972. Contbr. articles to profl. jours.; patentee in optics, magnetics, mechanics and electronics. Mem. IEEE (Morris N. Liebmann award 1975), Am. Phys. Soc., AAAS, U.S. Naval Inst. Clubs: Watchung Lions (past pres.), Raritan Yacht (sec.). Home: 103 High Tor Dr Watchung NJ 07060-5408 Office: Bell Labs PO Box 903 67 Whippany Rd Whippany NJ 07981-1406

MICHAELS, ALAN RICHARD, sports commentator; b. Bklyn., Nov. 12, 1944; s. Jay Leonard and Lila Ruth (Ross) M.; m. Linda Anne Stamaton, Aug. 27, 1966; children—Steven, Jennifer. BA, Ariz. State U., 1966. TV/radio play-by-play announcer Cin. Reds, 1971-73, San Francisco Giants, 1974-76; sports commentator ABC TV Network, N.Y.C., 1976—. Recipient Nat. Sportscaster of Yr. award Nat. Sportscasters and Sportswriters Assn., 1980, 83, 86, Emmy award, 1987. Avocations: reading; tennis. Office: ABC Sports Inc 47 West 66th St New York NY 10023

MICHAELS, JAMES WALKER, magazine editor; b. Buffalo, June 17, 1921; s. Dewey and Phyllis (Boasberg) M.; m. Jean A. Briggs, June 1985; children: Robert Matthews, James Walker, Anne Phyllis. B.S. cum laude, Harvard U., 1942. Ambulance driver Am. Field Service, India and Burma, 1943-44; with USIS, New Delhi, Bangkok, 1944-46; fgn. corr. UP; bur. mgr. UP, New Delhi, 1946-50; with Forbes mag., N.Y.C., 1954—; mng. editor Forbes mag., 1956-61, editor, 1961—. Contbr. articles to mags. Office: Forbes Inc 60 Fifth Ave New York NY 10011-8865

MICHAELS, JENNIFER TONKS, foreign language educator; b. Sedgley, England, May 19, 1945; d. Frank Gordon and Dorothy (Compston) Tonks; m. Eric Michaels, 1973; children: Joseph, David, Ellen. BA, U. Edinburgh, 1967; MA, McGill U., 1971, PhD, 1974. Teaching asst. German dept. Wesleyan U., 1967-68; instr. German dept. Bucknell (Pa.) U., 1968-69; teaching asst. German dept. McGill U., Can., 1969-72; prodn. asst. Pub. TV News and Polit. program, Schenectady, N.Y., 1974-75; from asst. prof. to assoc. prof. Grinnell (Iowa) Coll., 1975-87, prof., 1987—; vis. cons. German dept. Hamilton Coll., 1981; cons. Modern Lang. dept. Colby Coll.; panelist NEH, 1985; spkr. in field. Author: D.H. Lawrence, The Polarity of North and South, 1976, Anarchy and Eros: Otto Gross' Impact on German Expressionist Writers, 1983, Franz Jung: Expressionist, Dadaist, Revolutionary and Outsider, 1989, Franz Werfel and the Critics, 1994; editl. bd. German Studies rev.; contbr. numerous articles, revs. to profl. jours. Mem. Sch. dist. adv. com. Grinnell Coll., 1989—. Mem. MLA (mem. various coms.), Soc. Exile Studies, German Studies Assn. (sec. treas. 1991-92, v.p. 1992-94, pres. 1995—, numerous coms.). Democrat. Avocations: travel, reading. Office: Grinnell Coll German Dept PO Box 805 Grinnell IA 50112-0810

MICHAELS, LORNE, television writer, producer; b. Toronto, Ont., Can.. Grad., U. Toronto, 1966. Chmn. bd. Broadway Video, N.Y.C. Creator, exec. producer: Saturday Night Live, NBC, 1975-80, 85—, Late Night with Conan O'Brien, 1993—; writer, co-producer 3 Lily Tomlin spls., Paul Simon spl.; exec. producer: (HBO spl.) Simon and Garfunkel, Concert in the Park, Paul Simon Born at the Right Time in Cen. Park, 1991, (ABC-TV spl) Rolling Stone's 30 Years of Rock 'n' Roll, 1988; writer, producer: (movie) Three Amigos; exec. producer (TV series) Night Music, NBC, Kids in the Hall, HBO, (spl.) Stones Retro, HBO; exec. producer and producer (spl.) Saturday Night 15th Anniversary Spl., 1989; producer 1(spl.), Wayne's World; producer, co-writer Steve Martin's Best Show Ever 81. Recipient 4 awards Writers Guild Am., 8 Emmy awards Nat. Acad. TV Arts and Scis. Office: Broadway Video 1619 Broadway New York NY 10019-7412

MICHAELS, WILLARD A., retired broadcasting executive; b. Omaha, May 13, 1917; s. Gus M. and Bessie (Kerstine) M.; m. Helen Louise Mintel, Nov. 20, 1938; children: Marcella, Lawrence Richard, Betty Michaels Westbrook. BA, Trinity U., 1940. Asst. sports editor San Antonio Express, 1937-40; sports announcer, sales mgr., gen. mgr. KABC, San Antonio, 1940-53; gen. mgr. KGBS-TV, 1954; v.p. WJBK-TV, Detroit, 1955-61; dir. Storer Broadcasting Co., Miami Beach, Fla., 1960-85; TV v.p. Storer Broadcasting Co., 1961-66, exec. v.p., 1966-67, pres., 1967-74, chmn., 1974-82, ret., 1982; chmn. New Boston Garden Corp. (Boston Bruins), 1974-82, v.p.; mem. exec. com. Northeast Airlines, 1965-72, pres., 1972; dir. Delta Airlines, 1972-90, adv. dir., 1990—. Bd. trustees Storer Found. Home: 12419 Winding Branch San Antonio TX 78230

MICHAELSON, ARTHUR M., lawyer; b. N.Y.C., May 16, 1927; s. Samuel H. and Augusta L. M.; m. Arline L. Kahn, June 30, 1957; children: Barbara L., Sarah E., David N. A.B., Columbia U., 1947; LL.B., Yale U., 1950. Bar: N.Y. 1950, U.S. Supreme Ct 1964. Partner Wachtel & Michaelson, N.Y.C., 1957-66; with McCrory Corp., N.Y.C., 1966-68, Glen Alden Corp., N.Y.C., 1968-73; partner Miller, Singer, Michaelson & Raives, N.Y.C., 1973-84; counsel Hofheimer Gartlir & Gross, 1984—. Author: (with J. Blattmachr) Income Taxation of Estates and Trusts, 1980, 85, 89. Bd. dirs. mem. exec. com. Amnesty Internat. of U.S.A., Inc., 1972-81, vice chmn., 1975-76. Served with USN, 1945-46. Mem. ABA, Assn. Bar City N.Y. Office: 633 3d Ave New York NY 10017

MICHAELSON, MARTIN, lawyer; b. Boston, Apr. 12, 1943; s. Eliot D. and Charlotte (Selib) M.; m. Anne Taylor, Aug. 30, 1987; children: Andrew M., Daniel M.; stepchildren: Rachel T., Hannah T. BA, U. Chgo., 1965; JD, Boston Coll., 1968. Bar: N.Y. 1968, D.C. 1973, U.S. Supreme Ct. 1973, Mass. 1983, U.S. Dist. Ct. N.Y. 1969, D.C. 1973, U.S. Ct. Appeals (1st, 2d, 3d, 4th, 9th cirs.). Atty. Cravath, Swaine & Moore, N.Y.C., 1968-71; legis. asst. Congressman Robert F. Drinan, Washington, 1971-73; atty. Hogan & Hartson, Washington, 1973-76, ptnr., 1976-83, 89—; dep. gen. counsel Harvard U., Cambridge, Mass., 1983-88, univ. counsel, 1989. Office: Hogan & Hartson Columbia Square 555 13th St NW Washington DC 20004-1109

MICHAELSON, RICHARD AARON, health science facility administrator; b. Newton, Mass., Feb. 7, 1952; s. Eliot David and Charlotte Natalie (Selib) M.; m. Allyn Joan Shaloff, Apr. 11, 1981; 1 child, David Benjamin. BA in Psychology, U. Rochester, 1973; MS in Mgmt., MIT, 1977. Research asst. MIT Ctr. Info. Systems Research, Cambridge, Mass., 1976-77; analyst IBM Biomed. Systems Group, Mt. Kisco, N.Y., 1977-79; staff fin. analyst IBM Gen. Bus. Group, White Plains, N.Y., 1979-80; dir. fin. planning MetPath, Inc., Teterboro, N.J., 1980-82, dir. fin. services, 1982-84, v.p. fin., chief fin.

officer, 1984-86, v.p. corp. devel., 1986—. Bd. dirs. United Jewish Assn. Fedn. of North N.J., 1987—. Club: MIT Sloan (N.Y.C.) (regional gov. 1986—). Home: 11-18 Fairhaven Pl Fair Lawn NJ 07410 Office: Unilab Corp 18448 Oxnard St Tarzana CA 91356

MICHAL, PHILIP QUENTIN, veterinarian, mayor; b. Rensselaer, Ind., May 15, 1940; s. Robert John and Doris Maurine (Yost) M.; m. Judith Lynn Price, June 9, 1963; children: David Scott, Richard Joseph, Christopher Thomas. DVM, Purdue U., 1964. Sole vet. practitioner in mixed practice Wingate, Ind., 1965-69, Crawfordsville, Ind., 1969-74; sole propr. small animal practice Crawfordsville, 1974-87; owner N.W. Vet. Hosp., Crawfordsville, 1987; mayor of Crawfordsville, 1987—. Elder, chmn. World Outreach, 1st Christian Ch., 1992. Mem. AVMA, Ind. Vet. Med. Assn. Kiwanis (past pres. Crawfordsville club), Moose. Mem. Christian Ch. (Disciples of Christ). Home: 102 N Davis St Crawfordsville IN 47933-1206 Office: 300 E Pike St Crawfordsville IN 47933-2537

MICHALAK, EDWARD FRANCIS, lawyer; b. Evanston, Ill., Sept. 6, 1937; s. Leo Francis Michalak and Helen Sopie (Wolinski) M.; m. Margaret Mary Minx, Jan. 2, 1978. BSBA, Northwestern U., 1959; LLB, Harvard U., 1962. Bar: Ill. 1962. Assoc. McDermott, Will & Emery, Chgo., 1963-69, ptnr., 1969—. Served to sgt. USAR, 1962-68. Mem. Ill. Bar Assn. Chgo. Bar Assn., Beta Gamma Sigma, Beta Alpha Psi. Roman Catholic. Club: Mid-Day (Chgo.). Avocations: golf, opera. Home: 3409 Summit Ave Highland Park IL 60035-1111 Office: McDermott Will & Emery 227 W Monroe St Chicago IL 60606-5016

MICHALAK, JANET CAROL, reading education educator; b. Buffalo, Mar. 22, 1949; d. Theodore and Thelma Ruth (Roesch) Vukovic; m. Gerald Paul Michalak, June 19, 1971; children: Nathan, Justin. BS in Edn., SUNY Coll. at Buffalo, Buffalo, 1970; MS in Edn., SUNY, Buffalo, 1971, EdD, 1981. Cert. tchr. nursery, kindergarten, grades 1-6, reading tchr., English tchr. grades 7-12, N.Y. Reading tchr. Tonawanda (N.Y.) Sch. System, 1971-80; instr. Niagara County C.C., Sanborn, N.Y., 1980-82, asst. prof., 1982-85, assoc. prof., 1985-91, prof., 1991—; adj. lectr. SUNY, Buffalo, 1990-91. Recipient Pres.'s award for Excellence in Teaching, Niagara County C.C., 1990, Nat. Inst. for Staff & Orgnl. Devel. Excellence award, 1991, SUNY Chancellor's award for Excellence in Teaching, 1991. Mem. Coll. Reading Assn., Internat. Reading Assn., N.Y. Coll. Learning Skills Assn., Niagara Frontier Reading Coun. (bd. dirs. 1986-88). Republican. Presbyterian. Avocation: reading. Home: 184 Montbleu Dr Getzville NY 14068-1329 Office: Niagara County CC 3111 Saunders Settlement Rd Sanborn NY 14132-9460

MICHALIK, EDWARD FRANCIS, construction company executive; b. Hartford, Conn., Apr. 4, 1946; s. Edward S. and Helen A. (Sito) M.; m. Dianne E. Del Cegno, 1967 (div. 1978); children: Marc Edward, Michael Donald; m. Cecilia C. Zoltanski, 1987; children: Alexander Edward, Gabrielle Therese. BBA, Nichols Coll., Dudley, Mass., 1969. Cost auditor Wigton-Abbott Corp., Plainfield, N.J., 1969-70; dir. cost control The John W. Cowper Co., Inc., Buffalo, 1970-73; v.p. Titan Group Inc., Paramus, N.J., 1973-76; exec. v.p. Harrison Western Corp., Denver, 1976-85; pres. The John W. Cowper Co., Inc., Buffalo, 1985-88, Adrian Devel., Inc., Buffalo and Denver, 1988-91; pres., CEO, bd. dirs. Sunburst Mine Svcs., Inc., Denver, 1991—. Mem. Associated Gen. Contracto of Am., The Beavers. Republican.

MICHALIK, JOHN JAMES, law school administrator; b. Bemidji, Minn., Aug. 1, 1945; s. John and Margaret Helen (Pafko) M.; m. Diane Marie Olson Dec. 21, 1968; children: Matthew John, Nicole, Shane. BA, U. Minn., 1967, JD, 1970. Legal editor Lawyers Coop. Pub. Co., Rochester, N.Y., 1970-75; dir. continuing legal edn. Wash. State Bar Assn., Seattle, 1975-81, exec. dir., 1981-91; asst. dean devel. & community rels. Sch. of Law U. Wash., 1991. Mem. Am. Soc. Assn. Execs., Nat. Assn. Bar Execs., Am. Mgmt. Assn., Nat. Trust Hist. Preservation, Ninth Jud. Cir. Hist. Soc., Univ. Faculty Club, Coll. Club Seattle. Lutheran. Office: U Wash Sch of Law 1100 NE Campus Pky Seattle WA 98105-6617

MICHALKO, JAMES PAUL, library association administrator; b. Cleve., May 13, 1950; s. Paul James and Lillian (Fanta) M.; 1 child, Alexandra. BA, Georgetown U., 1971; MLS, MBA, U. Chgo., 1974. Asst. to v.p. adminstrn. Technicare Inc. (formerly BCC Industries), Cleve., 1971-72; asst dir., adminstrn. U. Pa. Librs., Phila., 1974-80; dir. bus. and fin. Rsch. Librs. Group, Stanford, Calif., 1980-85, v.p. fin. and adminstrn., 1985-87, acting pres., 1988-89; pres. Rsch. Librs. Group, Mountain View, Calif., 1989—. Contbr. to Libr. Quar., Coll. & Rsch. Librs.; reviewer for Libr. Quar., Coll. & Rsch. Librs., Acad. of Mgmt. Rev., Jour. Acad. Librarianship, Jour. Libr. Adminstrn. Office: Rsch Librs Group Inc 1200 Villa St Mountain View CA 94041-1106

MICHALS, DUANE, photographer; b. McKeesport, Pa., Feb. 18, 1932; s. John Ambrose and Margaret Cecilia (Matik) M. B.A., U. Denver, 1953. Comml. photographer with works appearing in Life Magazine, Esquire mags., N.Y. Times and others; comml. clients include Eli Lilly Co., Revlon, Estee Lauder, Elizabeth Arden. One person shows: Museum fur Kunst und Gewerbe Hamburg, Germany, Galerie John A. Schweitzer, Montreal, Can., 1990, San Francisco Mus. of Modern Art, Internat. Mus. of Photography at George Eastman House, Rochester, 1991, Sidney Janis Gallery, N.Y.C.,1985; represented in permanent collections, Mus. of Modern Art, N.Y.C., Chgo. Art Inst., George Eastman House, Folkwang Mus., Essen, Fed. Republic Germany, Internat. Mus. Photography, Smithsonian Instn., Mus. N.Mex., U. N.Mex., UCLA, Norton Simon Mus., Calif., Mus. Ludwig, Cologne. Author: Sequences, 1970, The Journey of the Spirit After Death, 1971, Things Are Queer, 1973, Take One and See Mt. Fujiyama, 1976, Real Dreams, 1977, Merveilles d'Egypte, Homage to Cavafy, 1981, Duane Michals: Photographs with Written Text, Changes, A Visit with Magritte, 1982, Duane Michals Photographs de 1958 a 1982, Duane Michals: Sleep and Dream, Duane Michals Photographs/Sequences/Texts, 1958-84, The Nature of Desire, 1988, Portraits, 1990, Now Becoming Then. Served with U.S. Army, 1953-55. Nat. Endowment for the Arts grantee, 1976. Office: care Sidney Janis Gallery 110 W 57th St New York NY 10019-3319

MICHALS, GEORGE FRANCIS, investment and business development executive; b. Hungary, Sept. 14, 1935; came to Can., 1956, naturalized, 1961; s. Todor and Ilona (Sinkovich) Mihalcsics; m. Patricia Elizabeth Hoffman, June 18, 1971; children: Katherine, Julie, Elizabeth, Georgina. BComm, Sir George Williams U., Montreal, 1961; CA, McGill U., 1963. Chartered acct. McGill U., Montreal, 1963. Acct. Coopers & Lybrand, Montreal, 1963-68; from treas. to exec. v.p. Dominion Textile Co. Ltd., 1969-74; v.p. fin., sr. v.p., then exec. v.p. Genstar Corp., San Francisco, 1974-86; exec. v.p., chief fin. officer Can. Pacific Ltd., Montreal, 1987-90; pres. Baymont Capital Resources Inc., Toronto, 1990—; chmn. Phargo Group Inc. Mem. Mt. Royal Club. Home: RR 5, Orangeville, ON Canada L9W 2Z2 Office: Baymont Capital Resources, 141 Adelaide St W Ste 1506, Toronto, ON Canada M5H 3L5

MICHALSKI, THOMAS JOSEPH, city planner, developer; b. Waukesha, Wis., Jan. 28, 1933; s. Thomas and Anna (Benca) M. B.Arch., U. Mich., 1956, M.City Planning, 1959; postgrad., Magdalene Coll., U. Cambridge, Eng., 1988—. Urban renewal planner City of Milw., 1956-57; land planner, urban designer Baltimore County, Md., 1959-60; planning cons. City of N.Y., 1961-77; project mgr. Yanbu Indsl. Complex, Royal Comm., Saudi Arabia, 1980-83; cons. UN Ctr. for Human Settlements, Habitat Nairobi, Kenya, 1984—; bd. Community Housing Initiative Trust, 1993—; faculty U. Mich., 1994—; mem. faculty NYU, 1965-66, CUNY, 1970-71, Rollins Coll., 1992—; town planning cons. new town in Iran, 1977; mem. Community Bd. 8, N.Y.C., 1972-76, chmn. landmarks com.; cons. Islamic Devel. Bank, 1989—, Fla. Solar Energy Ctr. Affordable Living Conf., 1991. Author: In Search of Purpose: Essays on Planning the Human Environment, 1961, Human Values and the Emerging City, 1967. Founding mem. Friends of Cen. park; 1000 Friends of Fla., 1987—; pres. Brevard 21 Inc. 1988—; bd. govs. Coll. Architecture and Urban Planning, U. Mich., 1984-88; bd. ACLU, 1993—. Wis. Architects Found. scholar, 1953-56; Vincent Astor Found. grantee, 1971, World Wildlife Fund Successful Communities grantee, 1991. Fellow Am. Hort. Soc.; mem. Am. Planning Assn. (charter), Am. Inst. Cert. Planners, Royal Town Planning Inst., Town and Country Planning Assn.,

Internat. Fedn. Housing and Planning, Nat. Trust for Historic Preservation, Wis. Soc. Archtl. Historians, Mich. Urban Planning Alumni Soc. (bd. dirs. 1984-88), Audubon Soc. Fla. (chmn. conservation com. 1987-91), Assn. for Asian Studies, Worldwatch Inst., English-Speaking Union (London), Brevard County (Fla.) Democratic exec. com., U. Mich. Club (N.Y.C.), Delta Chi (Morrey Outstanding Alumnus award 1984). Roman Catholic. Address: 3325 Rivercrest Dr Melbourne FL 32935 *The educated person prepares mightily to do something constructive about that which is displeasing, to sustain that which is good, and to discriminate the one from the other.*

MICHALSKI, (ŻUROWSKI) WACTAW, adult education educator; b. Pierzchnica, Poland, Sept. 14, 1913; came to the U.S., 1951; s. Antoni and Józefa (Skrybuś) M.; m. Urszula Lewandowska, Nov. 12, 1959 (dec. 1986); 1 child, Anthony Richard. MA, Tchr.'s Coll., Poland, 1934; grad., Officer's Mil. Sch., Poland, 1934-35; postgrad., U. Wis. M.A.T.C., 1951-55. Lic. real estate broker, Wis. Tchr. jr. high sch. Poland, 1936-39; mgr. acctg. Ampco Metal Co., Milw., 1951-61; tchr., educator Marquette U., U. Wis. Ext., Milw., 1962-90, Milw. Area Tech. Coll., 1963—; real estate agt. Wauwatosa Realty Co., Milw., 1955—. Contbr. articles to profl. jours. With underground resistance, Poland, 1939-45; officer Holy Cross Brigade, Poland, 1944-55, which joined U.S. 3d Army, Czechoslovakia, 1945; Polish guard U.S. Army, Germany; officer Internat. Refugee Orgn., Germany, 1947-51. Recipient Polish Heritage award Pulaski Coun. Milw., 1992, Cert. of Appreciation State Hist. Soc. Wis., 1987, Vol. Svc. award Inner Agy. Coun. Volunteerism, 1986. Mem. Polish Am. Congress, North Am. Polish Ctr. Study, Polish Western Assn. Am. (Diploma of Merit 1988), Vets. Orgns. World War I, World War II. Roman Catholic. Avocations: chess, bridge. Home: 5505 Bentwood Ln Greendale WI 53129 Office: Wauwatosa Realty Co 5300 S 108th St Hales Corners WI 53130-1368

MICHAUD, HOWARD HENRY, conservation educator; b. Berne, Ind., Oct. 12, 1902; s. Justin Album and Bertha Amelia (Baumgartner) M.; m. Ruth M. Hefner, Aug. 19, 1928; 1 child, Ted C. AB, Bluffton Coll., 1925; MA, Ind. U., 1930. High sch. tchr. Ft. Wayne, Ind., 1925-45; chief naturalist Ind. State Parks, 1934-45; prof. conservation Purdue U., 1945-71, prof. emeritus, 1971—; head program of conservation edn. Pub. Sch. Ind., 1945-71; dir. Conservation Edn. Camp for Tchrs., 1946-59; del. conf. Internat. Union for Conservation of Nature and Natural Resources Conf., N.Y., 1949, Lucerne, Switzerland, 1966. Editor: (pamphlets on conservation) Ind. Dept. Pub. Instrn.; contbr. articles to profl. jours. Past mem. Bd. Pks. and Recreation, West Lafayette. Recipient Purdue Conservation award, 1945-71, Chase S. Osborn Wildlife award Purdue U., 1959, Sagamore of the Wabash award Gov. of Ind., 1991, Theodore Roosevelt award U.S. EPA, 1993; NSF grantee, 1960-61. Mem. Nat. Assn. Biology Tchrs. (pres. 1948), Ind. Audubon Soc. (past pres., Earl Brooks Conservationist of Yr. award 1986), Conservation Edn. Assn. (pres. 1956-57, v.p. 1953-55, Key Man award 1967), Ind. Acad. Sci. (pres. 1963), Soil Conservation Soc. Am. (hon.), Izaak Walton League Am. (div. pres. 1953), Am. Nature Study Soc., Am. Assn. Interpretive Naturalists (founder), Environ. Edn. Assn. Ind. Inc. (pres. 1972-73, editor newsletter 1972-88), Nat. Wildlife Fedn., Ind. Park and Recreation Assn. (Outstanding Svc. award 1984), Nat. Recreation and Park Assn., Pi Kappa Phi, Xi Sigma Pi. Democrat. Presbyterian. Lodge: Lafayette Noon Optimists (Optimist of Yr. award 1986). Avocations: travel, photography, lapidary. Home: 301 E Stadium Ave West Lafayette IN 47906-3049

MICHAUD, MICHAEL ALAN GEORGE, diplomat, writer; b. Hollywood, Calif., Aug. 22, 1938; s. George Emile and Nathalie Adele (Neagles) M.; m. Carmen Yvonne Mitchell, Sept. 1960 (div. 1963); m. M. Grace Russo, June 5, 1965; children: Jon C., Cassandra M., Jason M., Joshua M. BA, UCLA, 1960, M.A., 1963; postgrad., Georgetown U., 1978-79. Commd. fgn. service officer Dept. State, 1963; consular officer Dacca, East Pakistan, 1963-65; analyst Bur. Intelligence and Research/Dept. State, Washington, 1965-66; staff asst. Bur. Near Eastern and South Asian Affairs Dept. State, Washington, 1966-67; polit. officer Am. Embassy, Tehran, 1967-68, econ. officer, 1968-70; info. officer USIS, Bombay, India, 1970-72, co-dir., 1971-72; country officer for Iran Dept. State, 1972-74, country officer Australia, Papua New Guinea and Solomon Islands, Bur. East Asian Affairs, 1974-76; dep. dir. Office Internat. Security Policy, Bur. Politico-Mil. Affairs, 1976-78; trainee Georgetown U., Washington, 1978-79; officer-in-charge U.K. and Bermuda Affairs, Bur. European Affairs Dept. State, 1979-80; consul gen. Am. Consulate Gen. Belfast, No. Ireland, 1980-83; Una Chapman Cox fellow Fgn. Service Inst. Dept. State, 1983-84, div. chief fgn. service counseling and assignments, 1984-85, spl. asst. for space policy, 1985-86, dir. Office Advanced Tech., 1986-89; counselor sci., tech. and environ. affairs Am. Embassy, Paris, 1989-93; minister-counselor environ. sci. and tech. Am. Embassy, Tokyo, 1993—. Author: Reaching for the High Frontier, 1986; editor: Flotsam and Jetsam lit. ann., 1956; founding editor: Open Forum, 1974-76 (Honor award 1976); mem. editorial bd.: Fgn. Service Jour., 1977-79; contbr. numerous articles, papers, book revs., short stories to various publs. Recipient Superior Honor award Dept. State, 1966; recipient Meritorious Honor award Dept. State, 1976; Scott fellow, 1962. Fellow Brit. Interplanetary Soc.; mem. Internat. Inst. Strategic Studies, Internat. Inst. Space Law, Internat. Acad. Astronautics, AAAS, AIAA, Royal Soc. Asian Affairs, Planetary Soc., Nat. Space Soc., Am. Astron. Soc. Office: Am Embassy, 1 10 5 Akasaka, MinatoKu Tokyo 107, Japan

MICHAUD, NORMAN PAUL, association administrator, logistics consultant; b. Fall River, Mass., June 28, 1931; s. Amedee and Mary Veronica (Simcoe) M.; m. Helen P. Pettine, Oct. 11, 1952; children: Marianne, Norman, Elizabeth, Robert, Virginia. Cert. in Engring., U. Mass; student, Queens Coll., 1958-61. Commd. officer U.S. Army, 1948, advanced through grades to master sgt., 1956, ret., 1958; field engr. Raytheon Co., 1958-67; dept. mgr. Raytheon Svc. Co., Burlington, Mass., 1968-92; exec. dir. Soc. Logistics Engrs., Hyattsville, Md., 1992-95; pvt. practice logistics cons. Chelmsford, Mass., 1995—. Editor (tech. jour.) Logistics Spectrum, 1992-95, (newsletter) Soletter, 1992-95; contbr. articles to profl. jours. Pres. Chelmsford (Mass.) PTA, 1968-71, mem. coun., 1969-70. Fellow Soc. Logistics Engrs. (cert. profl. logistician, bd. dirs. 1985-95, exec. bd. 1986-92, Pres.'s award for merit 1992-93, Tech. Field award 1985). Roman Catholic. Home: 21 Radcliffe Rd West Chelmsford MA 01863

MICHEL, ANTHONY NIKOLAUS, electrical engineering educator, researcher; b. Rekasch, Romania, Nov. 17, 1935; came to U.S., 1952; s. Anton Michel and Katharina (Metz) Malsam; m. Leone Lucille Flasch, Aug. 17, 1957; children: Mary Leone, Katherine Jean, John Peter, Anthony Joseph, Patrick Thomas. B.S.E.E., Marquette U., 1958. M.S. in Math., 1964, Ph.D. in Elec. Engring., 1968; D.Sc. in Math., Tech. U. Graz (Austria), 1973. Registered profl. engr., Wis. Engr. in tng. U.S. Army C.E., Milw., 1958-59; project engr. AC Electronics div. Gen. Motors Corp., Milw., 1959-62; sr. research engr., 1962-65; asst. prof. elec. engring. Iowa State U. Ames, 1968-69, assoc. prof., 1969-74, prof., 1974-84; prof. and chmn. dept. elec. engring. U. Notre Dame, Ind., 1984-87, Frank M. Freimann prof. engring., chmn. dept. elec. and computer engring., 1987-88, dean coll. engring., 1988—; cons. Houghton Mifflin Co., 1975, Acad. Press, 1983; cons. editor William C. Brown Co. Pubs., Dubuque, Iowa, 1982-83. Author: (with others) Qualitative Analysis of Large Scale Dynamical Systems, 1977, Mathematical Foundations in Engineering and Science, 1981, Ordinary Differential Equations, 1982, Applied Linear Algebra and Functional Analysis, 1993, (with Derong Liu) Dynamical Systems with Saturation Nonlinearities, 1993, (with Kaining Wang) Qualitative Theory of Dynamical Systems, 1994; contbr. articles to profl. jours., chpts. to books. Research grantee NSF, 1972—; research grantee Dept. Def., 1968-72; Fulbright fellow Tech. U. Vienna, Austria, 1992. Fellow IEEE (mng. editor Trans. on Cirs. and Sys. 1981-83, Best Trans. Paper award 1978, 83, 93, Centennial medal 1984); mem. IEEE Cirs. and Sys. Soc. (pres. 1989, Myril B. Reed outstanding paper award 1993), Russian Acad. Engring. (hon.), Sigma Xi, Eta Kappa Nu, Pi Mu Epsilon, Phi Kappa Phi. Home: 17001 Stonegate Ct Granger IN 46530-9783 Office: U Notre Dame Coll Engring Notre Dame IN 46556

MICHEL, CLIFFORD LLOYD, lawyer, investment executive; b. N.Y.C., Aug. 9, 1939; s. Clifford William and Barbara Lloyd (Richards) M.; m. Betsy Shirley, June 6, 1964; children: Clifford Fredrick, Jason Lloyd, Katherine Beinecke. A.B. cum laude, Princeton U., 1961; J.D., Yale U., 1964. Bar: N.Y. 1964, U.S. Dist. Ct. (so. dist.) N.Y. 1968, U.S. Ct. Appeals (2d cir.) 1967, U.S. Supreme Ct. 1972. Assoc. Cahill Gordon & Reindel, N.Y.C.,

1964-67, Paris, 1967-69, N.Y.C., 1969-71; ptnr. Cahill Gordon & Reindel, Paris, 1972-76, N.Y.C., 1976—; bd. dirs. Alliance Capital Mgmt. Mut. Funds, Placer Dome Inc., Tempo Tech. Corp. Bd. dirs. Jockey Hollow Found., Michel Found., St. Mark's Sch., Morristown Meml. Hosp., Meml. Health Found., Atlantic Health Sys. Mem. ABA, N.Y. State Bar Assn., N.Y. County Lawyers Assn., Fed. Bar Assn., Am. Soc. Internat. Law. Republican. Clubs: City Midday, Racquet and Tennis, River; Shinnecock Hills Golf (N.Y.); Somerset Hills Country; Essex Hunt (N.J.); Sankaty Head Golf (Mass.); Golf de Morfontaine, Travellers (Paris). Home: St Bernards Rd Gladstone NJ 07934 Office: Cahill Gordon & Reindel 80 Pine St New York NY 10005-1702

MICHEL, DAVID J., metallurgist, crystallographer; b. Denison, Tex., July 24, 1942; married, 1966; 2 children. BS in Metall. Engring., U. Mo., 1964; MS in Metallurgy, Pa. State U., 1966, PhD in Metallurgy, 1968. Rsch. metallurgist U.S. Naval Rsch. Lab, Washington, 1972-73, head high temperature metals sect., 1973-91, assoc. supr. materials sci. & tech. divsn., 1991—; asst. metallurgist Homer Rsch. Lab., Bethlehem Steel Co.; 1964; rsch. asst. in metallurgy Pa. State U., 1964-68, fellow, 1968-69; metallurgist rsch. divsn. US AEC, 1969-71; rsch. asst. prof. materials sci. U. Cin., 1971-72; prof. George Washington U., 1979—; vis. scientist Carnegie-Mellon U., 1984-85. Recipient Nat. Capital award for Profl. Achievement Engring., Washington Coun. Engring. & Archtl. Soc., 1978. Fellow Am. Soc. Metals Internat. (George Kimball Burgess Meml. award 1993-94), Am. Inst. Mining, Metall. and Petroleum Engrs., Am. Crystallographers Assn., Internat. Metallurgists Soc. Achievements include research in radiation effects in materials, mechanical behavior of materials, intermetallic compounds, x-ray crystallography, alloy theory, phase equilibria, phase transformations in solids, electron microscopy, semiconductor alloys. Office: Naval Rsch Lab 4555 Overlook Ave SW Code 6300 Washington DC 20375-5000*

MICHEL, DONALD CHARLES, editor; b. Ventura, Calif., Nov. 17, 1935; s. Charles J. and Esther Caroline (Heilert) M.; m. Loretta Perron, May 4, 1963; children: Edwin, Robert, Christopher. B.A., UCLA, 1958, M.S., 1959. Editor San Fernando (Calif.) Sun, 1958-60; successively reporter, weekend editor, mng. editor Valley Times Today, West Hollywood, Calif., 1960-63; feature editor Houston Chronicle, 1963-68; asst. mng. editor features Chgo. Daily News, 1968-77; exec. v.p., editor Chgo. Tribune-N.Y. News Syndicate, 1977-84; v.p. adminstrn. and editorial devel. Los Angeles Times Syndicate, 1984—. Mem. Am. Sunday and Feature Editors, Features Coun., Sigma Delta Chi. Home: 3000 Adornos Way Burbank CA 91504-1609 Office: Los Angeles Times Syndicate Times Mirror Sq Los Angeles CA 90012

MICHEL, HARRIET R., association executive; b. Pitts., July 5, 1942; d. John and Vida (Fish) Richardson; m. Yves Michel, Apr. 13, 1968; children: Christopher, Gregory. BA, Juniata Coll., 1965; LHD (hon.), Baruch Coll., 1990. Dir. spl. projects Nat. Scholarship Svcs. & Fund for Negro Students, N.Y.C., 1971; asst. to Mayor Lindsay City of N.Y. for Anti-Drug Efforts, 1971-72; exec. dir. N.Y. Found., 1972-77; dir. Cmty. Youth Employment Program U.S. Dept. Labor, Washington, 1977-79; established Women Against Crime Found. John Jay Coll., N.Y.C., 1980-81; cons. U.S. Dept. Housing & Urban Devel., Washington, 1982; pres., CEO N.Y. Urban League, 1983-88; pres. Nat. Minority Supplier Develop. Coun., N.Y.C., 1988—; bd. dirs. Ctr. for Advance Purchasing Studies, Phoenix, Maxima Corp., Balt., N.Y.C. Partnership; mem. nat. adv. coun. U.S. Small Bus. Adminstrn., Washington, 1993—; lectr. in field; mem. del. Ctrl. Am. Peace and Democracy Watch, 1987; U.S. rep. Ditchley Found. Confs. London; cons. in field. Vice chair N.Y.C. Charter Revision Commn., 1986-91; bd. dirs. African Am. Inst., N.Y.C., 1985—, Citizens Com. of N.Y., 1984—, Juniata Coll., Huntington, Pa., 1989—, Trans Africa Forum, Washington, 1988—. Recipient 1st Non-Profit Leadership award new Sch. Social Rsch., 1988, Women on the Move award Anti-Defamation League of B'nai B'rith, 1990, Appreciation award Pres. Commn. Minority Bus. Devel., 1992, Bus. Advocate award Mayor of N.Y.C., 1993, Black Entrepreneurial award Wall St. Jour., 1994, others; named one of 50 Outstanding Internat. Bus. and Profl. Women by Dollars and Sense Mag., 1987. Mem. Assn. Black Found. Execs. (founder), Coun. on Founds. (bd. dirs.). Office: Nat Minority Supplier Devel Coun 15 W 39th St 9th Fl New York NY 10018

MICHEL, HENRY LUDWIG, civil engineer; b. Frankfurt, Germany, June 18, 1924; s. Maximilian Frederick and Loschka (Hepner) M.; m. Mary Elizabeth Strolis, June 5, 1954; children—Eve Musette, Ann Elizabeth. B.S.C.E., Columbia U., 1949. Registered profl. engr., Pa., N.Y. Pres., CEO, Parsons Brinckerhoff, Inc., 1975-90, chmn., 1990-94; chmn. Parsons Brinckerhoff, Internat., N.Y.C., 1975—; chmn. PBICSA, 1994—; guest lectr. NYU, Columbia U., Colo. State U., Cornell U., MIT; mem. svcs. policy adv. com. The U.S. Trade Rep.; mem. Design Profl. Coalition; instrumental in devel. and mgmt. of maj. transp. and pub. works projects in U.S. and abroad. Contbr. numerous articles on mgmt. and transp. engring. to engring. jours. Fellow ASCE, Soc. Am. Mil. Engrs., Instn. Civil Engrs.; mem. NAE, Internat. Rd. Fedn. (chmn. 1989-92, bd. dirs. 1977—), N.Y. Soc. Profl. Engrs., Constrn. Industry Pres. Forum (chmn. 1990-91), Civil Engring. Rsch. Found. (chmn. 1992—), Columbia U. Engring. Sch. Alumni Assn. (Egleston medal 1992, Alumni medal 1991), Am. European Comty. Assn. (bd. dirs. 1983—), Spain-U.S.C. of C. Home: 35 Sutton Pl New York NY 10022-2464 Office: Parsons Brinckerhoff Internat Inc 1 Penn Plaza New York NY 10119

MICHEL, JAMES H., ambassador, lawyer; b. St. Louis, Aug. 25, 1939; s. Paul J. and Margaret K. (Scheitlin) M.; m. Conception L. Trejo, Sept. 10, 1960; children—Mark, Kurt, Linda, Paul. J.D., St. Louis U., 1965. Bar: Mo. 1965, D.C. 1973. Atty. Dept. State, Washington, 1965-74, asst. legal adviser, 1974-78, dep. legal adviser, 1978-83, dep. asst. sec. for Inter-Am. affairs, 1983-87; ambassador to Guatemala, 1987-89; asst. adminstr. Latin Am. and Carribbean Bur. AID, Washington, 1990-93; pres. devel. assistance com. OECD, Paris, 1994—. Pres. St. Thomas More Fed. Credit Union, Arlington, Va., 1970-87. Recipient Superior awards Dept. State, 1971, 76, 83, Meritorious Exec. award, 1980, 87, Disting. award, 1981, Disting. Exec. award, 1982, 92. Mem. Fed. Bar Assn. (Tom C. Clark award 1982), D.C. Bar Assn., Mo. Bar Assn., Am. Soc. Internat. Law, Inter-Am. Bar Assn. Roman Catholic. Office: 2 rue André Pascal, Paris 75115, France

MICHEL, MARY ANN KEDZUF, nursing educator; b. Evergreen Park, Ill., June 1, 1939; d. John Roman and Mary (Bassar) Kedzuf; m. Jean Paul Michel, 1974. Diploma in nursing, Little Company of Mary Hosp., Evergreen Park, 1960; BS in Nursing, Loyola U., Chgo., 1964; MS, No. Ill. U., 1968, EdD, 1971. Staff nurse Little Co. of Mary Hosp., 1960-64; instr. Little Co. of Mary Hosp. (Sch. Nursing), 1964-67, No. Ill. U., De Kalb, 1968-69; asst. prof. No. Ill. U., 1969-71; chmn. dept. nursing U. Nev., Las Vegas, 1971-73; prof. nursing U. Nev., 1975—, dean Coll. Health Scis., 1973-90; pres. PERC, Inc.; mgmt. cons., 1993—; mgmt. cons. Nev. Donor Network, 1993; mem. So. Nev. Health Manpower Task Force, 1975; mem. manpower com. Plan Devel. Commn., Clark County Health Sys. Agy., 1977-79; mem. governing body, 1981-86; mem. Nev. Health Coordinating Coun., Western Inst. Nursing, 1991-96; mem. coordinating com. assembly instnl. adminstrs. dept. allied health edn. and accreditation AMA, 1985-88; mem. bd. advisors So. Nev. Vocat. Tech. Ctr., 1976-80; sec.-treas. Nev. Donor Network, 1988-89, bd. dirs., 1986-90, chmn. bd., 1988-90. Contbr. articles to profl. jours. Trustee Desert Spring Hosp., Las Vegas, 1976-85; bd. dirs Nathan Adelson Hospice, 1982-88, Bridge Counseling Assocs., 1982, Everywoman's Ctr., 1984-86; chmn. Nev. Commn. on Nursing Edn., 1972-73, Nursing Articulation Com., 1972-73, Nursing Articulation Com., 1972-73, Yr. of Nurse Com., 1978; moderator Invitational Conf. Continuing Edn., Am. Soc. Allied Health Professions, 1978; active Nev. Donor Network, Donor Organ Recovery, S.W. Eye and Tissue Banks. Named Outstanding Alumnus, Loyola U., 1983; NIMH fellow, 1967-68. Fellow Am. Soc. Allied Health Professions, 1991, (chmn. nat. resolutions com. 1981-84, treas. 1988-90, sec's award com. 1982-83, 92-93, nat. by-laws com. 1985, conv. chmn. 1987); mem. AAUP, Am. Nurses Assn., Nev. Nurses Assn. (dir. 1975-77, treas. 1977-79, conv. chmn. 1978), So. Nev. Area Health Edn. Coun., Western Health Deans (co-organizer 1985, chair, 1988-90), Nat. League Nursing, Nev. Heart Assn., So. Nev. Mem. Hosps. (mem. nursing recruitment com. 1981-83, mem. nursing practice com. 1983-85), Las Vegas C. of C. (named Woman of Yr. Edn.) 1988, Slovak Catholic Sokols, Phi Kappa Phi (chpt. sec. 1981-83, pres.-elect 1983, pres. 1984, v.p. Western region 1989-95, editl. bd.

jour. Nat. Forum 1989-93), Alpha Beta Gamma (hon.), Sigma Theta Tau, Zeta Kappa. Office: U Nev Las Vegas 4505 S Maryland Pky Las Vegas NV 89154-3018

MICHEL, PAUL REDMOND, federal judge; b. Philadelphia, Pa., Feb. 3, 1941; s. Lincoln M. and Dorothy (Kelley) M.; m. Sally Ann Clark, 1965 (div. 1987); children: Sarah Elizabeth, Margaret Kelley; m. Elizabeth Morgan, 1989. BA, Williams Coll., 1963; JD, U. Va., 1966. Bar: Pa. 1967, U.S. Supreme Ct., 1970. Asst. dist. atty. Dist. Atty's Office, Phila., 1967-71, dep. dist. atty. for investigations, 1972-74; asst. spl. prosecutor Watergate investigation Dept. Justice, Washington, 1974-75, dep. chief pub. integrity sect., Criminal div. and prosecutor "Koreagate" investigation, 1976-78, assoc. dep. atty. gen., 1978-81, acting dep. atty. gen., 1979-80; asst. counsel intelligence com. U.S. Senate, 1975-76, counsel and adminstrv. asst. to Sen. Arlen Specter, 1981-88; judge U.S. Ct. Appeals (Fed. cir.), Washington, 1988—; instr. appellate practice and procedure George Wash. U. Nat. Law Ctr., 1991—, appellate advocacy John Marshall Law Sch., Chgo. 2d lt. USAR, 1966-72. Office: US Ct Appeals Fed Cir 717 Madison Pl NW Ste 808 Washington DC 20439-0002

MICHEL, ROBERT CHARLES, retired engineering company executive; b. N.Y.C., July 14, 1927; s. Charles John and Helen Carolyn (Wagner) M.; m. Alice Virginia Kraissl, June 16, 1951; children: Richard Charles, Ann Florence, Susan Jean. SB in Chem. Engring., MIT, 1950, SM in Chem. Engring., 1951. Registered profl. engr., N.J. Chmn., pres. The Kraissl Co., Inc., Hackensack, N.J., 1986-92. Pres. Bd. Edn., River Edge, N.J., 1968-72. With USNR, 1945-46. Mem. Am. Inst. Chem. Engrs., ASME, ASM, Bergen County Soc. Profl. Engrs. (pres. 1960-61), U.S. Power Squadron, Palisades Power Squadron (comdr. 1982-83), Elks, Tau Beta Pi, Sigma Xi. Home: 470 Prospect St Glen Rock NJ 07452-1909 Office: The Kraissl Co Inc 299 Williams Ave Hackensack NJ 07601-5289

MICHEL, THOMAS MARK, internal medicine educator; b. Portland, Oreg., July 14, 1955. AB in Biochem. Scis., Harvard U., 1977; PhD in Biochemistry, Duke U., 1983, MD, 1984. Diplomate Am. Bd. Internal Medicine, Am. Bd. Cardiovasc. Disease. House officer, jr. and sr. resident in medicine Brigham and Women's Hosp., Boston, 1984-87, clin. and rsch. fellow in medicine cardiovasc. div., 1987-88, assoc. physician, staff physician cardiovasc. div., 1988—; clin. fellow in medicine Harvard U. Med. Sch., Boston, 1984-87, rsch. fellow dept. genetics, 1988-90; instr. medicine, 1988-89, asst. prof., 1989-95, assoc. prof., 1995—; tutor in biochem. scis. Harvard Coll., Harvard U., Cambridge, Mass., 1990—; lectr. molecular mechanisms of disease Harvard Med. Sch.-MIT health scis. and tech. program, 1990—; speaker at seminars, confs. and univs.; vis. lectr. U. Alta., U. Calgary, U. Alcala, Madrid, St. Bartholomew's Hosp., London; Cecilie Greig vis. prof. Hammersmith Hosp., Royal Postgrad. Med. Sch., London; plenary lectr. Nitriz Oxide Forum, Tokyo. Contbr. articles to med. jours. Recipient John J. Abel award in Pharmacology Am. Soc. for Pharacology Therapeutics, 1995, young scholar's award Am. Soc. Hypertension, 1991; Harvard nat. scholar Harvard U., 1973-77; fellow NIH, 1977-84. Fellow Am. Coll. Cardiology; mem. ACP, Am. Fedn. for Clin. Rsch., Henry Christian award for excellence in rsch. 1992, 93), Am. Heart Assn. (Established Investigator award 1993—, Clinican-Scientist award 1988-93), Am. Soc. for Biochemistry and Molecular Biology, Mass. Med. Soc. Office: Brigham & Women's Hosp Harvard Med Sch 75 Francis St Boston MA 02115-6195

MICHELI, FRANK JAMES, lawyer; b. Zanesville, Ohio, Mar. 23, 1930; s. John and Theresa (Carlini) M.; m. Doris Joan Clum, Jan. 9, 1954; children: Michael John, James Carl, Lisa Ann, Matthew Charles. Student, John Carroll U., Cleve., 1947-48, Xavier U., Cin., 1949-50; LL.D., Ohio No. U., Ada., 1953. Bar: Ohio 1953. Since practiced in Zanesville; partner Leasure & Micheli, 1953-65, Kincaid, Micheli, Geyer & Ormond, 1965-75, Kincaid, Cultice, Micheli & Geyer (and predecessor), 1982-92; ptnr. Micheli, Baldwin, Bopeley & Northrup, 1992—; Instr. bus. law Meredith Bus. Coll., Zanesville, 1956; lectr. on med. malpractice, hosp. and nurse liability. Dir. Public Service for, City of Zanesville, 1954. Mem. Internat. Assn. Ins. Counsel, Def. Rsch. Inst., Ohio Def. Assn., Am. Ohio bar assns., Am. Judicature Soc., Am. Arbitration Assn. (mem. nat. panel), Am. Bd. Trial Advs. (bd. dirs. Ohio chpt. 1991-95). Club: Elk. Home: 160 E Willow Dr Zanesville OH 43701-1249 Office: PO Box 2687 2806 Bell St Zanesville OH 43701

MICHELMAN, FRANK I., lawyer, educator; b. 1936. BA, Yale U., 1957; LLB, Harvard U., 1960. Bar: N.Y. 1961, Mass. 1967. Law clk. to assoc. justice William J. Brennan, U.S. Supreme Ct., Washington, 1961-62; asst. to asst. atty. gen., Tax Div., Dept. Justice, 1962-63; asst. prof. Harvard U., Cambridge, Mass., 1963-66, prof., 1966-93, Robert Walmsley Univ. prof., 1993—; cons. HUD, 1966; cons. Boston Model City Program, 1968-69; mem. Boston Home Rule Commn., 1969-71; mem. Gov.'s Task Force on Met. Devel., 1974-75. Mem. Am. Soc. for Polit. and Legal Philosophy, Am. Assn. Arts and Scis. Author: (with Sandalow) Materials on Government in Urban Areas, 1970. Office: Law Sch Harvard U Cambridge MA 02138

MICHELOTTI, CARL ANTHONY, electronics company executive; b. Chgo., Sept. 11, 1930; s. G. and Valentina (Parenti) M.; m. Arlene A. Macie, July 2, 1960; children: Mary Julie, Marc, Carl, Paul, Thomas. BEE, Fournier Inst. Lemont, Ill., 1952; MBA, DePaul U., 1963. Engring. mgr. Admiral Corp., Chgo., 1956-61; engring. mgr. Zenith Electronics Corp., Glenview, Ill., 1963-73, dir. systems engring., 1973-79, v.p. consumer product engring., 1979-84, pres. computer group, 1984—. Served with U.S. Army, 1954-56. Mem. IEEE, AMA. Lodge: K.C. Office: Zenith Electronics Corp 211 Hilltop Rd Saint Joseph MI 49085

MICHELS, EUGENE, physical therapist; b. Cin., May 16, 1926; s. Joseph and Anna (Bauer) M.; m. Genevieve Wilma Readinger, June 28, 1947; children: Karen, Timothy, Donald, Marian, Monica, Martha, David, Ann. B.S., U. Cin., 1950; cert. phys. therapy, U. Pa., 1951, M.A., 1965; Litt.D. (hon.), Thomas Jefferson U., 1985. Phys. therapist Grad. Hosp., U. Pa., Phila., 1951-58, mem. faculty dept. phys. therapy, 1965—, asst. prof., 1953-75, asso. prof., 1975-77; dir. phys. therapy Magee Meml. Hosp., Phila., 1958-65; assoc. exec. v.p. Am. Phys. Therapy Assn., 1977-88. Served with USNR, 1944-46. Recipient Lindback Found. Disting. Tchg. award, 1972; Pa. Phys. Therapy Assn. ann. achievement award named Carlin-Michels Achievement award in honor of Eleanor J. Carlin and Eugene Michels. Mem. Pa. Phys. Therapy Assn. (past pres.), Am. Phys. Therapy Assn. (past pres., Dorothy Briggs Meml. Sci. Inquiry award 1971, Golden Pen award 1977, Mary McMillan lectr. 1984, Catherine Worthingham fellow 1986, Eugene Michels New Investigator award established in his honor 1989, John Maley award sect. rsch. 1994), World Confedn. Phys. Therapy (pres. 1974-82). Democrat. Roman Catholic. Home: 7608 Wellesley Dr College Park MD 20740-3040

MICHELS, JOSEPH WILLIAM, anthropology and archaeology educator; b. Chgo., Nov. 1, 1936; s. Joseph William Michels and Helen Louise (White) Michels Read; m. Gabriele Ascher, Sept. 4, 1959; children—Dina Luise, Oren William. B.A. in Philosophy, UCLA, 1958, M.A. in Anthropology, 1963, Ph.D. in Anthropology, 1965. Cert. profl. archeologist. Asst. prof. anthropology Pa. State U., University Park, 1965-68, assoc. prof., 1969-73 prof., 1973—; assoc. dean research Liberal Arts Coll., 1984-88; asst. prof. anthropology U. Calif.-San Diego, 1968-69; cons. archaeometry MOHLAB, State College, 1980-88. Author: Dating Methods in Archaeology, 1973, The Kaminaljuyu Chiefdom, 1979; editor: Axum, 1979, Excavations at Kaminaljuyu, 1979; co-editor: Studies in Nuragic Archaeology, 1987. Grantee NSF, 1966-71, 74, 79-80, NEH, 1985. Fellow AAAS, Am. Anthrop. Assn.; mem. Soc. for Archaeol. Scis. (pres. 1985-86). Home: 1188 Smithfield St State College PA 16801-6427 Office: Pa State U Coll Liberal Art Dept Anthropology 409 Carpenter Bldg University Park PA 16802

MICHELS, ROBERT, psychiatrist; b. Chicago, Ill., Jan. 21, 1936; s. Samuel and Ann (Cooper) M.; m. Verena Sterba, Dec. 23, 1962; children—Katherine, James. B.A., U. Chgo., 1953; M.D., Northwestern U., 1958. Intern Mt. Sinai Hosp., N.Y.C., 1958-59; resident in psychiatry Columbia Presbyn.-N.Y. State Psychiat. Inst., N.Y.C., 1959-62; mem. faculty Coll. Physicians and Surgeons, Columbia U., N.Y.C., 1964-74; asso. prof. Coll. Physicians and Surgeons, Columbia U., 1971-74; psychiatrist student health service Columbia U., 1966-74; supervising and tng. analyst Columbia U. Center for Psychoanalytic Tng. and Research, 1972—; attending psychiatrist Vanderbilt Clinic, Presbyn. Hosp., N.Y.C., 1964-74; Barklie McKee

Henry prof. psychiatry Cornell U. Med. Coll., N.Y.C., 1974-93, chmn. dept. psychiatry, 1974-91; psychiatrist-in-chief N.Y. Hosp., 1974-91; Stephen and Suzanne Weiss dean Cornell U. Med. Coll., 1991—; provost for med. affairs Cornell U., 1991—; attending psychiatrist St. Luke's Hosp. Ctr., N.Y.C., 1966—. Co-author: The Psychiatric Interview in Clinical Practice, 1971; contbr. articles to profl. jours. Served with USPHS, 1962-64. Mem. Am. Psychiat. Assn., Am. Coll. Psychiatrists, N.Y. Psychiat. Soc., Royal Medico-Psychol. Assn., Psychiat. Research Soc., Assn. Research in Nervous and Mental Diseases, Assn. Acad. Psychiatry, Am. Psychoanalytic Assn., Internat. Psychoanalytic Assn., Center Advanced Psychoanalytic Studies, N.Y. County Health Services Rev. Orgn., N.Y. Acad. Scis., Alpha Omega Alpha. Office: Cornell U Med Coll 1300 York Ave New York NY 10021

MICHELSEN, CHRISTOPHER BRUCE HERMANN, surgeon; b. Boston, Aug. 18, 1940; s. Jost Joseph and Ingeborg Elizabeth (Dilthey) M.; B.A., Bowdoin Coll., 1961; M.D., Columbia U., 1969; m. Amy Lee; children: Heidi Elizabeth, Matthew Christopher, Joshua Jost. Intern Columbia Presbyn. Med. Center, N.Y.C., 1969-70, resident, 1970-71; orthopedic resident N.Y. Orthopedic Hosp., N.Y.C., 1971-73, jr. Anne C. Kane fellow, 1973-74, sr. Anne C. Kane fellow and hip fellow, 1974-75, traveling fellow, 1975-76; internat. A-O fellow, postgrad. fellow in biomechanics, instr. biomed. engring. Case-Western Res. U.; assoc. prof. clin. orthopaedic surgery Columbia Coll. Physicians and Surgeons; co-dir. combined orthopaedic neuro surg. spine svc.; chief orthopaedic spine surgery svc., chief orthopaedic svc. Allen Pavillion, CPMC, 1994. Col. USAR, 1961—. Diplomate Am. Bd. Orthopaedic Surgery. Fellow A.C.S., N.Y. Acad. Medicine, Am. Assn. for Surgery of Trauma, Am. Orthopaedic Assn., N.Am. Spine Soc., Am. Acad. Orthopaedic Surgeons, Internat. Coll. Surgeons; mem. AMA, Orthopaedic Research Soc., Am. Soc. for Bone and Mineral Research, Royal Soc. Medicine (affiliate). Home: 102-57 Shearwater Ct E Jersey City NJ 07305 Office: 5141 Broadway New York NY 10034-1159

MICHELSEN, W(OLFGANG) JOST, neurosurgeon, educator; b. Amsterdam, Holland, Aug. 20, 1935; came to U.S., 1936; s. Jost Joseph and Ingeborg Mathilde (Dilthey) M.; m. Constance Richards, Sept. 21, 1963 (div. 1987); children: Kristina, Elizabeth, Ingrid; m. Claude Claire Grenier, Mar. 30, 1988. AB magna cum laude, Harvard U., 1959; MD, Columbia U., 1963. Diplomate Am. Bd. Neurol. Surgery. Intern in surgery Case Wester Res. U. Hosps., Cleve., 1963-64; asst. resident in neurology Mass. Gen. Hosp., Boston, 1964-65; asst. resident, then chief resident neurol. surgery Columbia-Presbyn. Med. Ctr., N.Y.C., 1965-69; from instr. to assoc. prof. neurosurgery Columbia U. Coll. Physicians and Surgeons, N.Y.C., 1969-89, prof. clin. surgery, 1990—; fellow in neurosurgery Presbyn. Hosp., N.Y.C., 1969-71, dir. neuro vascular surgery, 1989-90; dir. neurosurgery St. Luke's Roosevelt Hosp. Ctr., N.Y.C., 1990—; prof. and chmn. dept. neurological surgery Albert Einstein Coll. Medicine, Bronx, N.Y., 1992—; dir. neurosurgery Montefiore Med Ctr, Bronx 1992—; asst. attending in neurosurgery, St. Luke's Hosp. Ctr., 1970—; cons. neurosurgeon Nyack (N.Y.) Hosp., 1972—, Englewood (N.J.) Hosp., 1972—; vis. prof. neurosurgery Tufts U., 1975, Emery U., 1977, Presbyn.-St. Luke's Hosp. Ctr., Chgo., 1978, Yale U., 1980; guest faculty Northwestern U., 1977, 78, U. Chgo., 1977, Colby Coll., 1980; mem. numerous panels on neurosurgery. Contbr. articles to profl. publs. 1st lt. U.S. Army, 1954-57. Grantee NIH, USPHS. Fellow ACS, Am. Heart Assn.; Mem. AMA, Am. Assn. Neurol. Surgeons (mem. sect. pediatric neurosurger), Neurosurg. Soc. Am. (v.p. 1984-85, pres. 1987-88), Congress Neurol. Surgeons, N.Y. Neurosurg. Soc. Neurosurg. Soc. State N.Y., N.Y. Acad. Scis., Assn. Rsch. in Nervous and Mental Diseases, Internat. Neurosurg. Soc., Internat. Pediatric Neurosurg. Soc., Explorers Club, N.Y. State Med. Soc., N.Y. County Med. Soc. Office: Montefiore Med Ctr 111 E 210th St Bronx NY 10467

MICHELSON, EDWARD J., journalist; b. Northampton, Mass., Apr. 3, 1915; s. Isadore Henry and Fannie (Avrich) M.; m. Dorothea Adair Pohlman, Feb. 3, 1938; children—Kathleen (Mrs. Howard J. Connolly), Paul, Emily (Mrs. Thomas D. Crews). B.A., Williams Coll., 1937. Reporter St. Louis Post-Dispatch, 1937-38; writer pub. relations div. Westinghouse Electric Co., 1939-40; day editor, internat. shortwave news div. CBS, 1941-44; spl. asst. Office Sec. War, 1946; mem. hist. sect. strategic services unit War Dept., 1946; asso. Robert S. Allen (syndicated columnist), 1946-50; Washington corr. N.Am. Newspaper Alliance, also New Eng. dailies, 1946—; Washington editor Forbes mag., 1956-63, Printer's Ink mag., 1958-63; mag. editor Ocean Sci. News, 1958-63, 1968; Washington editor Sci. and Tech. mag., 1969—; Exec. Enterprises Publs.; Research dir. pub. works subcom. on water resources U.S. Ho. of Reps., 1951. Contbr. to gen., financial, spl. bus. periodicals; Editor: (Wright Patman) Our American Government, 1948. Served with OSS, AUS, 1944-46. Mem. White House Corrs. Assn. Gargoyle Soc. Club: Cosmos. Home: #C-302 2300 Indian Creek Blv W Vero Beach FL 32966

MICHELSON, GERTRUDE GERALDINE, retired retail company executive; b. Jamestown, N.Y., June 3, 1925; d. Thomas and Celia Rosen; m. Horace Michelson, Mar. 28, 1947; children: Martha Ann (dec.), Barbara Jane. B.A., Pa. State U., 1945; LL.B., Columbia U., 1947; LLD with honors, Adelphi U., 1981; DHL with honors, New Rochelle Coll., 1983; LLD with honors, Marymount Manhattan Coll., 1988. With Macy's N.Y., N.Y.C., 1947—; mgmt. trainee Macy's N.Y., 1947-48, various mgmt. positions, v.p. employee personnel, 1963-70, sr. v.p. for labor and consumer relations 1970-72, dir. mem. exec. com., 1970—; sr. v.p. pers. labor and consumer rels. Macy & Co., Inc., 1972-79, sr. v.p. external affairs, 1979-80; sr. v.p. external affairs R.H. Macy & Co., Inc., 1980-92, sr. advisor, 1992—; bd. dirs. Quaker Oats Co., Chubb Corp., Gen. Electric Co., Stanley Works, Inc., Goodyear Tire & Rubber Co., Federated Dept. Stores, Inc.; bd. dirs. trustee Rand Corp.; former dep. chmn. N.Y. Fed. Reserve Bank; gov. Am. Stock Exch. Chmn. Helena Rubinstein Found., Markle Found.; chmn. emeritus bd. trustees Columbia U., Interracial Coun. Bus. Opportunity; life trustee Spelman Coll.; mem. adv. coun. Catalyst. Recipient Disting. Svc. medal Pa. State U., 1969. Mem. N.Y. City C. of C. (bd. dirs., mem. exec. com., vice chmn.), N.Y.C. Ptnrship. (vice chmn.), Women's Forum, Econ. Club N.Y. Home: 70 E 10th St New York NY 10003-5102 Office: R H Macy & Co Inc 151 W 34th St New York NY 10001-2124

MICHELSON, HAROLD, production designer; b. N.Y.C., Feb. 15, 1920; s. Max and Gussie (Reichel) M.; m. Lillian Farber, Dec. 14, 1947; children: Alan Bruce, Eric Neil, Dennis Paul. Student, Pratt Inst., 1938, NYU, 1939, Art Students League, 1942-44; Calif. Sch. Art, L.A., 1947-49. Illustrator Columbia Pictures, L.A., 1949-52; illustrator Paramount Pictures, L.A., 1953-58, art dir. prodn. designer, 1959-95; illustrator Warner Bros., Burbank, Calif., 1959-89; art dir. 20th Century Fox, Beverly Hills, Calif., 1959-89, visual cons., 1990-91; indl. prodn. designer, Hollywood, Calif., 1959-95; visual cons. Metro-Goldwyn-Mayer, Hollywood, 1992—; lectr. U. So. Calif., L.A., 1988-95; instr. UCLA, 1989-90, Maine Photog. Workshop, Rockport, Maine, 1991; mem. faculty Am. Film Inst., L.A. 1992-95. Exhibited in group show Storyboard-Le Cinema Dessiná, 1992. 1st lt. USAAF, 1941-45, ETO. Decorated Air medal with 7 oak leaf clusters. Mem. Soc. Motion Picture Art Dirs. (exec. bd. 1985-95), Acad. Motion Picture Arts and Scis. (membership bd. 1975—, 2 Acad. award nominations 1978, 84).

MICHELSON, IRVING, aerospace engineer; b. Jersey City, Jan. 4, 1922; s. Eli J. and Sadie H. (Ginsberg) M.; m. Larisa Rudaya; children: Ann Michelson Shoham, Louis, Linda Michelson Zelman, Julia Michelson Waldman, Elise Michelson Levin, Eliot, Jack. Student, George Washington U., 1938-41, 46; BS, Ga. Sch. Tech., 1943; postgrad., Brown U., 1943-44; MS, Calif. Inst. Tech., 1947, PhD in Aero. and Math., 1951. Lectr. U. Calif., L.A., 1951-54; rsch. scientist ODIN Assocs., Pasadena, Calif., 1954-57; prof. aero. engring., head dept. Pa. State U., 1957-60; prof. aerospace engring. Ill. Inst. Tech., 1960—; cons. govt., industry; Faculté des Scis. de Nancy (France), 1961—. Writer newspaper columns Math. at the Breakfast Nook, 1970—, Scientifically Speaking, 1974—; author: World Understanding, 1965, Man on the Moon, 1969; The Science of Fluids, 1970, Tides, 1976. Mem. adv. bd. Com. Pan Am. Policy, 1970—. Lt. (j.g.) USNR, 1944-46. Mem. Am. Astron. Soc., Am. Inst. Aeros. and Astronautics (chmn. edn. com. 1959-61), Am. Soc. Engring. Edn., AAUP, AAAS, Royal Soc. NSW, Chgo. Press Club, Sigma Xi, Kappa Kappa Psi. Discovered interelationship of earth-moon-sun distances and their mass ratios, 1964; introduced reciprocity concept in planetary mechanics, explanation of earth's rotational speed value, 1965-66; new formulation of ocean tide theory. Home and Office: 7061 N Kedzie Ave # 202 Chicago IL 60645

MICHELSON, LILLIAN, motion picture researcher; b. Manhattan, N.Y., June 21, 1928; d. Louis and Dora (Keller) Farber; m. Harold Michelson, Dec. 14, 1967; children: Alan Bruce, Eric Neil, Dennis Paul. Vol. Goldwyn Libr., Hollywood, Calif., 1961-69; owner Former Goldwyn Rsch. Libr., Hollywood, Calif., 1969—; ind. location scout, 1973—. Bd. dirs Beverlywood After Care Ctr., L.A., 1988—; mem. Friends of L.A. Pub. Libr. Office: care Paramount Pictures Bldg 264 5555 Melrose Ave Los Angeles CA 90038-3149

MICHELSON, STEPHAN, economist; b. Cambridge, Mass., Feb. 28, 1938; s. Morris and Harriet Ruth (Steinberg) M.; m. Mildred Ruth Howe, 1961 (div. 1962). B.A., Oberlin Coll., 1960; M.A., Stanford U., 1962, Ph.D., 1968. Dir research Ctr. for Community Econ. Devel., Cambridge, 1975-78; sr. fellow Urban Inst., Washington, 1978-79; pres. Econometric Research, Inc., Washington, 1979-85; pres. Longbranch Research Assocs., Inc., Takoma Park, 1985—. Contbr. to books and profl. jours. Office: Longbranch Research Assocs Inc 7918 Longbranch Pkwy Silver Spring MD 20912

MICHENER, CHARLES DUNCAN, entomologist, biologist, educator; b. Pasadena, Calif., Sept. 22, 1918; s. Harold and Josephine (Rigden) M.; m. Mary Hastings, Jan. 1, 1941; children: David, Daniel, Barbara, Walter. B.S., U. Calif., Berkeley, 1939, Ph.D., 1941. Tech. asst. U. Calif., Berkeley, 1939-42; asst. curator Am. Mus. Natural History, N.Y.C., 1942-46; assoc. curator Am. Mus. Natural History, 1946-48, research assoc., 1949—; assoc. prof. U. Kans., 1948-49, prof., 1949-89, prof. emeritus, 1989—, chmn. dept. entomology, 1949-61, 72-75, Watkins Disting. prof. entomology, 1959-89, acting chmn. dept. systematics, ecology, 1968-69, Watkins Disting. prof. systematics and ecology, 1969-89; dir. Snow Entomol. Museum, 1974-83, state entomologist, 1949-61; Guggenheim fellow. vis. research prof. U. Paraná, Curitiba, Brazil, 1955-56; Fulbright fellow U. Queensland, Brisbane, Australia, 1958-59; research scholar U. Costa Rica, 1963; Guggenheim fellow, Africa, 1966-67. Author: (with Mary H. Michener) American Social Insects, 1951, (with S.F. Sakagami) Nest Architecture of the Sweat Bees, 1962, The Social Behavior of the Bees, 1974, (with M.D. Breed and H.E. Evans) The Biology of Social Insects, 1982, (with D. Fletcher) Kin Recognition in Animals, 1987, (with R. McGinley and B. Danforth) The Bee Genera of North and Central America, 1994; contbr. articles to profl. jours.; editor: Evolution, 1962-64; Am. editor: Insectes Sociaux, Paris, 1954-55, 62-90; assoc. editor: Ann Rev. of Ecology and Systematics, 1970-90. Served from 1st lt. to capt. San. Corps AUS, 1943-46. Fellow Am. Entomol. Soc., Entomol. Soc. Am., Am. Acad. Arts and Scis., Royal Entomol. Soc. London, AAAS; mem. NAS, Linnean Soc. London (corr.), Soc. for Study Evolution (pres. 1967), Soc. Systematic Zoologists (pres. 1969), Am. Soc. Naturalists (pres. 1978), Internat. Union for Study Social Insects (pres. 1977-82), Kans. Entomol. Soc. (pres. 1950), Brazilian Acad. Scis. (corr.). Home: 1706 West 2d St Lawrence KS 66044

MICHENER, JAMES ALBERT, author; b. N.Y.C., Feb. 3, 1907; s. Edwin and Mabel (Haddock) M.; m. Patti Koon, July 27, 1935 (div.); m. Vange Nord, Sept. 2, 1948 (div.); m. Mari Yoriko Sabusawa, Oct. 23, 1955 (dec. 1994). A.B. summa cum laude, Swarthmore Coll., 1929; A.M., U. No. Colo., 1937; research study, U. Pa., U. Va., Ohio State U., Harvard U., U. St. Andrews, Scotland, U. Siena, Italy, Brit. Mus. London; research study (Lippincott Traveling fellow), 1930-33, numerous hon. degrees. Tchr. Hill Sch., 1929-31, George Sch., Pa., 1933-36; prof. Colo. State Coll. Edn., 1936-41; vis. prof. Harvard U., 1939-40; asso. editor Macmillan Co., 1941-49; mem. adv. com. on arts State Dept., 1957; mem. adv. council NASA, 1980-83; mem. U.S. Adv. Commn. on Info., 1971; mem. Citizen's Adv. Stamp Com., 1982-87; mem. Bd. for Internat. Broadcasting. Author: Unit in the Social Studies, 1940, Tales of the South Pacific, 1947 (Pulitzer prize), The Fires of Spring, 1949, Return to Paradise, 1951, The Voice of Asia, 1951, The Bridges at Toko Ri, 1953, Sayonara, 1954, Floating World, 1955, The Bridge at Andau, 1957, Rascals in Paradise, (with A. Grove Day), 1957, Selected Writings, 1957, The Hokusai Sketchbook, 1958, Japanese Prints, 1959, Hawaii, 1959, Report of the County Chairman, 1961, Caravans, 1963, The Source, 1965, Iberia, 1968, Presidential Lottery, 1969, The Quality of Life, 1970, Kent State, 1971, The Drifters, 1971, A Michener Miscellany, 1973, Centennial, 1974, Sports in America, 1976, Chesapeake, 1978, The Covenant, 1980, Space, 1982, Poland, 1983, Texas, 1985, Legacy, 1987, Journey, 1988, Alaska, 1988, Caribbean, 1989; (with John Kings) Six Days in Havana, 1989, The Novel, 1991, The World Was My Home, 1991, Writer's Workbook, 1992, Mexico, 1992, My Lost Mexico, 1992, Creatures of the Kingdom: Stories of Animals and Nature, 1993, Literary Reflections: Michener on Michener, Hemingway, Capote, and Others, 1993, Recessional, 1994; editor: Future of Social Studies for N.E.A., 1940. With USNR, 1944-46. Recipient U.S. Medal of Freedom, Disting. Svc. medal NASA, Golden Badge of Order of Merit, 1988. Mem. Phi Beta Kappa. Democrat. Mem. Soc. of Friends. Office: Tex Ctr for Writers PCL 3 ,102 Mail Code S5401 Austin TX 78713

MICHENFELDER, JOHN DONAHUE, anesthesiology educator; b. St. Louis, Apr. 13, 1931; s. Albert A. and Ruth J. (Donahue) M.; m. Margaret Grey Nice, Oct. 22, 1955 (dec. Nov. 1971); children: Carol, David, Joseph, Paul, Matthew, Laura; m. Mary Monica Milroy, Aug. 11, 1972; 1 child, Patrick. BS, St. Louis U., 1951, MD, 1955. Diplomate Am. Bd. Anesthesiology. Intern Presbyn. St. Luke's Hosp., Chgo., 1955-56; resident in internal medicine Presbyn. St. Luke's Hosp., 1956; resident in anesthesiology Mayo Clinic, Rochester, Minn., 1958-61, cons. in anesthesiology, 1961-91; prof. anesthesiology Mayo Med. Sch., Rochester, 1976—. Author: Anesthesia and the Brain, 1988, Clinical Neuroanesthesia, 1990. Lt. USN, 1956-58. NIH grantee, 1966-89, 91-95; Faculty Anaesthetists of Royal Coll. Surgeons Ireland fellow, 1982, Faculty Anaesthetists Royal Coll. Surgeons Eng. fellow, 1988. Mem. Am. Assn. Soc. Anesthesiologists (Excellence in Rsch. award 1990, Disting. Svc. award 1990), Inst. Med., Assn. Univ. Anesthetists (councilman 1975-78). Avocations: upland game bird hunting, gardening, reading, writing. Home: 325 First Ave NW Oronoco MN 55960 Office: Mayo Clinic Dept of Anesthesiology 200 1st St SW Rochester MN 55905-0001

MICHENFELDER, JOSEPH FRANCIS, public relations executive; b. Webster Groves, Mo., Mar. 30, 1929; s. Albert Aloysius and Ruth Josephine (Donahue) M.; m. Audrey Laurine Glynn, Aug. 8, 1970. BA, N.Y. State U., N.Y.C., 1951, STB, 1954, MRE, 1955; MS in Journalism, Columbia U., 1958. Projects dir. Maryknoll Headquarters, Ossining, N.Y., 1955-57; communications dir. Maryknoll Headquarters, Ossining, 1958-62; dir., chief exec. officer Noticias Aliadas, S.A., Lima, Peru, 1962-69; pub. rels. dir. Pub. Affairs Analysts, Inc., N.Y.C., 1970-72; exec. v.p. Pub. Affairs Analysts, Inc., 1973-89; sr. v.p. Napolitan Assocs./PAA Inc., N.Y.C., 1989-95; pres., CEO, 1995—; pres. IDOC/N.Am., Inc., N.Y.C., 1976—. Mng. Editor (polit. quarterly) POLITEIA, 1970-73; co-producer: TV documentary A Quiet Revolution, 1987. Trustee The Fund for Peace, 1994—; Coun. on Hemispheric Affairs, Washington, 1980—; cons. UNESCO WHO, Bogota, Lima, 1964-66; bd. dirs. Jobs for Youth, Inc., N.Y.C., 1978-84. Mem. Internat. Pub. Relations Assn., Internat. Assn. Polit. Cons., Columbia U. Journalism Alumni Fed. (pres. 1971-74), Ovrses Press Club, Columbia Club. Democrat. Avocations: theater arts, film, creative writing, ecology, Third World affairs. Office: Napolitan Assocs/PAA Inc 55 Fifth Ave New York NY 10003-4301

MICHERO, WILLIAM HENDERSON, retired retail trade executive; b. Fort Worth, June 19, 1925; s. William Alvin and Lela Belle (Henderson) M.; m. Nan Elaine Henderson, July 9, 1948; children—Jane Elaine Michero Christie, William Sherman, Thomas Edward. B.S. in Commerce, Tex. Christian U., 1948. Sec. Tandy Corp., Fort Worth, 1960-75; v.p Tandy Corp., 1970-75; with Tandycrafts, Inc., Fort Worth 1975-90; sr. v.p., sec. dir. Tandycrafts, Inc., 1979-83, chmn. bd., 1983-90, ret., 1990; Sec. B.F. Johnston Found., Fort Worth, 1962-90. Bd. dirs. David L. Tandy Found., Fort Worth, 1978—, Oakwood Cemetery Assn., 1979-89, Panther Boys Club, 1974-78, Fort Worth Mus. Sci. and History, 1973-75, United Way; chmn. Distributive Edn. Council, 1970. Served with U.S. Navy, 1943-46. Clubs: Fort Worth, Colonial Country. Home: 3704 Shady Ridge Ct Fort Worth TX 74109-1803 Office: 550 Bailey Ave Fort Worth TX 76107-2111

MICHIGAMI, MICHAEL MASAO, data processing executive; b. Mpls., Apr. 29, 1947; s. Masashi and Rose Sayoko (Tanada) M.; m. Christine Jeanne Flynn (div. June 1988); 1 child, Michael Thomas; m. Sharon Wilson Flynn; 1 stepchild, John C. Wilson IV. BA in Psychology, Trinity Coll., Hartford, Conn., 1969; MBA, The Wharton Sch., 1971. European contr. Data Gen. Europe, Paris, 1973-74; mgr. European Customer Svc. Tex. Instruments Europe, Villeneuve, Loubet, France, 1974-76; fin. adminstr. Tex. Instruments Consumer Electronics Group, Dallas, 1976-77; sr. assoc. Booz Allen & Hamilton, N.Y.C., 1977-81; mgr. strategic planning GE Credit Corp., Stamford, Conn., 1981-83; dir. strategic planning United Techs. Corp., Hartford, Conn., 1983-86; pres. Control Systems Div. United Techs. Corp., Farmington, Conn., 1986-89; pres., chief exec. officer Datapoint Corp., San Antonio, 1989—. Bd. dirs. The Planning Forum, Oxford, Ohio, 1989—, Greater Hartford ARC, Farmington, Conn., 1987-89, Hartford Symphony Orch., 1987—. 1st lt. USAF, 1971-73. Mem. Hartford Club, Hartford Golf Club. Republican. Episcopalian. Avocations: golf, tennis. Home: 24 Westwood Rd West Hartford CT 06117-2252 Office: Datapoint Corp 9725 Datapoint Dr San Antonio TX 78284-0001 Office: Digital Microwave Crop 170 Rose Orchard Way San Jose CA 95134

MICK, HOWARD HAROLD, lawyer; b. Newton, Kans., Oct. 21, 1934; s. Marvin Woodrow and Edith (Bergen) M.; m. Susan Siple, Sept. 5, 1957; children: Martha, Julie, Elizabeth. Student, U. Okla., 1952-54; BS, LLB, U. Colo., 1958. Bar: Colo. 1958, Mo. 1959. Assoc. Stinson, Mag & Fizzell, Kansas City, Mo., 1959-62; ptnr. Stinson, Mag & Fizzell, Kansas City, 1962—. Bd. dirs. Ctr. Mgmt. Assistance, Kansas City, Mo., 1984-88; mem. adv. coun. Kansas City Salvation Army, 1987—. Mem. ABA, Lawyers Assn. Kansas City, Kansas City Bar Assn., Rotary, Kansas City Club, Indian Hills Country. Democrat. Presbyterian. Avocations: golf, tennis, boating. Office: Stinson Mag & Fizzell PO Box 419251 Ste 2800 Kansas City MO 64141

MICKAL, ABE, retired physician; b. Talia, Lebanon, June 15, 1913; came to U.S., 1920, naturalized, 1920; s. Kalil and Hadda (Abu-Haider) M.; m. Lois Barnes, May 23, 1942; children: Annette, Marie Virginia, Schaffer, Joanne. B.S., La. State U., 1936, M.D., 1940. Intern Touro Infirmary, New Orleans, 1940-41; resident in ob-gyn Charity Hosp., New Orleans, and La. State U., 1945-48; mem. faculty La. State U. Med. Sch., 1949—, prof. ob-gyn, 1959-80, now emeritus prof., emeritus chmn., 1980—; v.p. med. affairs St. Judes Med. Ctr., New Orleans, 1985-95; retired, 1995; chmn. ob-gyn dept. La. State U. Med. Sch., 1988. Author numerous papers in field, chpts. in books. Served to maj. M.C. USAAF, 1942-46. Recipient Alumnus of Yr. award Med. Sch., La. State U., L Club award, 1980, Disting. Svc. award from the Am. Coll. Ob-Gyn., 1991—; named to Nat. Intercollegiate Found. and Hall of Fame, 1967. Mem. ACS, Am. Coll. Obstetricians and Gynecologists (Disting. Svc. award 1991, Outstanding Surgeons award 1992), Assn. Profs. Ob-Gyn. (past pres.), Am. Ob-Gyn Soc. (past sec., chmn. fin. com.), Am. Gynecol. Soc., Soc. Gynecol. Oncology, Infectious Disease Soc. Ob-Gyn. (council), So. Med. Assn., So. Ob-Gyn. Soc. (pres. 1973-86), Soc. Gynecol. Surgeons (pres. 1981), Orleans Parish Med. Soc., La. Med. Soc., New Orleans Ob-Gyn. Soc. (past pres.). Methodist. Home: 774 Topaz St New Orleans LA 70124-3624

MICKEL, JOSEPH THOMAS, lawyer; b. Monroe, La., Nov. 12, 1951; s. Toufick and Ruth Ella (Phelps) M.; m. Carlene Elise Nickens, Dec. 10, 1981 (div.); children: Thomas, Matthew. BA, La. State U., 1975; postgrad., Tulane U., 1977-78; JD, So. U., 1979. Bar: La. 1979, U.S. Dist. Ct. (mid. dist.) La. 1981, U.S.Ct. Appeals (5th cir.) 1981, U.S. Dist. Ct. (we. dist.) La. 1983, U.S. Ct. Mil. Appeals 1985, U.S. Supreme Ct. 1985. Staff atty. Pub. Defenders Office, Baton Rouge, La., 1979-80; assoc. Law Offices of Michael Fugler, Baton Rouge, 1981; asst. dist. atty. La. 4th Jud. Dist. Atty.'s Office, Monroe, 1982-84, 85-89; ptnr. Bruscato, Loomis & Street, Monroe, 1984-85; asst. U.S. atty. Western Dist. State of La., Lafayette, 1989—; adj. prof. Northeast La. U., Monroe, 1988; mem. U.S. Dept. Justice Organized Crime Drug Task Force, 1992-93. Mem. ABA. Republican. Presbyterian. Avocations: trapshooting, skeetshooting, bird hunting, fishing. Home: PO Box 91961 Lafayette LA 70509-1961 Office: US Atty Office 600 Jefferson St Ste 1000 Lafayette LA 70501-6964

MICKELSON, ARNOLD RUST, consultant, religious denominational official; b. Finley, N.D., Jan. 8, 1922; s. Alfred B. and Clara (Rust) M.; m. Marjorie Arveson, June 8, 1944; 1 son, Richard. BA, Concordia Coll., Moorhead, Minn., 1943, LLD (hon.), 1972; LLD (hon.), Calif. Luth. U., 1983, Luther Coll., 1987. Owner, mgr. Luther Book Store, Decorah, Iowa, 1946-48; credit supr. Gen. Motors Acceptance Corp., Fargo, N.D., 1948-53; mgr. Epko Film Service, Fargo, 1953-58; asst. to pres. No. Minn. dist. Evang. Luth. Ch., 1958-61, No. Minn. dist. Am. Luth. Ch., 1961-66; gen. sec. The Am. Luth. Ch., Mpls., 1967-82; coordinator Commn. for a New Luth. Ch., Mpls., 1982-87; pres. A.M. Cons., Amery, Wis., 1987—; councilor Luth. Council in U.S.A., 1966-82, sec., 1969-72, pres., 72-75; mem. U.S.A. Nat. Com. Luth. World Fedn., 1966-82, sec., 1966-69, 72-75, v.p., 1979-81, pres., 1981-82; mem. Consultation on Luth. Unity, 1970-76, sec., 1970-73, chmn., 1974-76; mem. Com. on Luth. Unity, 1976-82; del. 4th Assembly World Coun. Chs., Uppsala, Sweden, 1968, 5th Assembly, Nairobi, Kenya, 1975; chmn. Faith-in-Life Dialogue, Fargo-Moorhead, 1964, observer-trainer, Duluth, 1965; gen. sec. emeritus Am. Luth. Ch., 1982—; pres. Ctrl. Luth. Ch., Mpls., 1992-93. Mem. Conf. on Inflation, 1974, Mpls.-St. Paul Town Meeting Coun., 1968-76; bd. dirs. Midwest League, 1979—; bd. mgrs. Am. Bible Soc., 1979; trustee Suomi Coll., 1981—; mem. com. on hearing officers Evang. Luth. Ch. in Am., 1983—; pres. Luth. Leadership Inst., 1994—. With AUS, 1943-46. Recipient Civic Service award Eagles, 1965, Ch. award Suomi Coll., 1987, Judge Graven Lay Leadership award Wartburg Coll., 1990. Mem. Ch. Staff Workers Assn. (past pres.), Concordia Coll. Alumni Assn. (past pres.), Alpha Phi Gamma, Zeta Sigma Pi. Club: Mpls. Athletic. Home: 1235 Yale Pl Apt 409 Minneapolis MN 55403-1944 Office: AM Cons 1232 Marina Dr Amery WI 54001-5132

MICKELSON, ELLIOT SPENCER, quality assurance professional; b. Manti, Utah, Dec. 7, 1934; s. Rulon Spencer and Jessie (Chapman) M.; m. Zola G. Christensen, Sept. 6, 1957; children: Diana, Janet, Craig, Glenn, David. Degree in mech. engring. tech., U. Utah, 1977. Registered profl. engr., Calif.; cert. lead auditor U.S.A., Great Britain. Quality engr. Hercules Inc., Salt Lake City, 1961-80; mgr. quality assurance Cambelt Internat., Salt Lake City, 1980-87, dir. tech., 1990-92; dir. quality IRECO Inc., Salt Lake City, 1987-90, EnviroTech Pumpsystems, Salt Lake City, 1992—; cons. Quality Engring. and Mgmt. Systems, West Valley City, Utah, 1980—; chair program adv. com. Salt Lake Community Coll., West Valley City, 1979—. Author: Construction Quality Program Handbook, 1986, Quality Program Handbook, 1991, (with others) Quality Management for the Construction Project, 1987. Staff sgt. USAF, 1952-56. Recipient Dist. Award of Merit Boy Scouts Am., 1974. Fellow Am. Soc. for Quality Control (Internat. Inspector of Yr. 1974, Engr. of Yr. Salt Lake sect. 1982), Nat. Soc. Profl. Engrs., Am. Welding Soc., ASTM. Ch. Jesus Christ Latter Day Saints. Achievements include invention of mono-molded camflex and camwall belt tooling and process.

MICKELSON, H(ERALD) FRED, electric utility executive; b. Pratt, Kans., Oct. 4, 1938; s. Herald E. and Arvilla (Knight) M.; m. D. Joan Mickelson, Feb. 21, 1958; children: Mikel Tod, Janet Lynn. BS in Mgmt. Sci., Pepperdine U., 1974; postgrad. Mgmt. Policy Inst., U. So. Calif., 1978. Dist. mgr. So. Calif. Edison, Santa Ana, 1982-84; mgr. corp. communications So. Calif. Edison, Rosemead, 1984-85; div. ops. mgr. So. Calif. Edison, Santa Ana, 1985-86, San Bernardino, 1986-87; mgr. mktg. So. Calif. Edison, Rosemead, 1987-91; regional v.p. So. Calif. Edison, Santa Ana, 1992—. Officer, bd. dirs. Calif. divsn. Am. Cancer Soc., chmn. bd. Calif. divsn., 1993-94, nat. bd. dirs.; officer, mem. exec. com., bd. dirs United Way of Orange County, chmn. bd., 1995, chmn. bd., 1995; bd. dirs. ARC of Orange County, St. Joseph's Hosp. of Orange; chmn. Orange County Econ. Devel. Commn., 1993-94; adv. bd. St. Jude's Hosp. of Fullerton, Sch. Bus. and Econs. Chapman U.; officer, bd. dirs. Nat. Conf. Christians and Jews, presiding co-chmn., 1994—; officer, bd. dirs. Orange County Bus. Com. for the Arts, Orgn. Unified Concerned Homeowners; bd. govs. Orange County Transp. Coalition. Recipient Field Svcs. Builder award Am. Cancer Soc., 1992, Humanitarian award Orange County Human Rels. Commn., 1993, Comty. Leadership award Orange County Black C. of C., 1994; named one of Top 25 Bus. Leaders in Orange County, Orange County Bus. Jour., 1993-95. Mem. Edison Electric Inst. (customer svc. and mktg. bd. dirs.), Pacific Coast Electric Assn. (customer svc. and mktg. exec. com.), Orange County C. of C. (bd. dirs., exec. com., chmn. bd. 1994). Republican. Mem. Evangelical Free Ch. Avocations: carpentry, vocal musician, gardening, sports car restoration, antiques. Office: So Calif Edison Co 1325 S Grand Ave Santa Ana CA 92705

MICKELSON, SIG, broadcasting executive, educator; b. Clinton, Minn., May 24, 1913; s. Olaf and Harriet (Reinholdson) M.; m. Maybelle Brown, June 8, 1940 (dec. Apr., 1985); children: Karen Ann (Mrs. Christiaan De Brauw), Alan; m. Elena Mier y Teran, June 14, 1986. B.A., Augustana Coll., 1934, LLD, 1987; M.A., U. Minn., 1940. With CBS, N.Y.C., 1943-61; pres. CBS News, 1954-61; v.p., dir. Time-Life Broadcast, Inc., N.Y.C., 1961-70, Ency. Brit. Ednl. Corp., Chgo., 1970-72; prof., chmn. editorial dept. Medill Sch. Journalism, Northwestern U., Evanston, Ill., 1972-75; pres. RFE/RL, Inc., Washington, 1975-78; Disting. vis. prof. San Diego State U., 1978-79, exec. dir. Ctr. for Communications, 1979-82, adj. prof, 1984-90, Van Deerlin prof. communications, 1989-90; exec. dir. Ctr. for Communications Coun., 1989-90; Manship prof. journalism La. State U., 1991-93, disting. prof. comm., 1994—; research fellow Hoover Instn., 1981—; advisor Nat. News Council, 1973-80; ex-officio Bd. Internat. Broadcasting, 1975-78; dir. Stauffer Communications Inc. Author: The Electric Mirror, 1972, America's Other Voice, 1983, The First Amendment: The Challenge of New Technology, 1989, From Whistle Stop to Sound Bite, 1989, The Northern Pacific Railroad and the Selling of the West, 1993. Bd. regents Augustana Coll., 1983—. Mem. Radio TV News Dirs. Assn. (founder; v.p. 1946-48, pres. 1948-49), Internat. Inst. for Comm. (founder, chmn. 1970-71, chmn. exec. com. 1967-70, 71-73), Coun. on Fgn. Rels., Soc. Profl. Journalists. Clubs: Century Assn. (N.Y.C.); Cosmos (Washington). Home: 6443 Pasatiempo Ave San Diego CA 92120-3823

MICKELWAIT, LOWELL PITZER, lawyer; b. Glenwood, Iowa, Nov. 15, 1905; s. Wilbur W. and May I. (Pitzer) M.; m. Alice Semmes, July 18, 1936; children: Anne Nelson, John Semmes, Christie Betz. AB, U. Wash., 1928, LLB cum laude, 1930. Bar: Wash. 1930, U.S. Supreme Ct 1930. Practice in Seattle, 1930—; with firm Holman Mickelwait Marion Black & Perkins (now Perkins Coie), 1930-62; mng. partner Holman, Mickelwait, Marion, Black & Perkins, 1954-62, of counsel, 1972—; v.p. indsl. and pub. relations, dir. Boeing Co., Seattle, 1962-72; dir. Puget Sound Power & Light Co., 1960-77, Pacific N.W. Bell Tel. Co., 1966-76. Campaign chmn. Seattle-King County Community Chest, 1950, pres., 1953; pres. United Good Neighbour Fund, 1956, 61; chmn. Seattle-King County 1976 Bicentennial Commn., King County Design Commn., 1968-79; chmn. bd. Pacific Sci. Center Found., 1974, 75; chmn. bd. mgrs. Norman Archibald Charitable Found., 1976-91. Served to maj. USAAF, 1943-45. Mem. Am., Wash., Seattle bar assns., Seattle C. of C. (pres. 1972-73), Order of Coif, Phi Delta Phi, Phi Gamma Delta. Episcopalian. Clubs: Rainier, University, Golf. Home: 1630 43d Ave East Seattle WA 98112 Office: 1201 3rd Ave Seattle WA 98101-3000

MICKENS, GARFIELD JONES, songwriter, poet and philosopher; b. Camden, S.C., Mar. 13, 1941; s. Ernest Jones and Judabell Mary Mickens. Clothing presser Louis Levy Coat Co., Phila., 1955-60; master presser Joe Louis Coat Co., Phila., 1960-68, After Six Inc., Phila., 1968-85; ind. realtor Phila.; songwriter Hill Top Records, Rainbow Records, Hollywood, Calif., 1993—; poet, philosopher Mickens Pub. House, Phila., 1992—. Author: A Very Unusual Colored Person, 1993, "Hearken Unto Me", 1993, A Book of Poetry by Garfield Mickens, 1993; writer (songs) You Can't Preach, Sing, And Dance Your Way to Freedom, 1993, America, The Land That I Love So Well, 1993, Don't Pass My Jimmy Around, 1994. Girl Talk, Boy Talk, 1994. Democrat. Roman Catholic. Avocations: art, music, boating, collecting antiques. Home: 4943 Rubicam St Philadelphia PA 19144-1808

MICKEY, PAUL F(OGLE), JR., lawyer; b. Washington, Sept. 25, 1949; s. Paul Fogle and Margaret Snowden (Stanley) M.; m. Carol Lynne Forsyth, Mar. 19, 1977; children: Alison Langlands, Suzanne Snowden, Scott Forsyth. A.B. summa cum laude, Princeton U., 1971; J.D., U. Va., 1974. Bar: D.C. 1975, U.S. Supreme Ct. 1982. Law clk. to George E. MacKinnon, U.S. Ct. Appeals, D.C. Circuit, 1974-75; with office of legal adv. U.S. Dept. State, Washington, 1975-77; asso. firm Covington & Burling, Washington, 1977-79; v.p., gen. counsel Nat. R.R. Passenger Corp. (Amtrak), Washington, 1979-83, exec. v.p. law and pub. affairs, 1983-85; ptnr. Shaw, Pitman, Potts & Trowbridge, Washington, 1985—. Contbr. articles to legal revs. Mem., bd. govs. Nat. Cathedral Sch.; mem. corp. bd. dirs. Children's Hosp., Nat. Med. Ctr.; v.p., bd. dirs. St. Francis Ctr. Mem. ABA, D.C. Bar Assn. (chair subcom. on individual employment rights), Am. Arbitration Assn. (arbitrator), Met. Club, Chevy Chase Club. Episcopalian. Office: 2300 N St NW Washington DC 20037-1122

MICKIEWICZ, ELLEN PROPPER, political science educator; b. Hartford, Conn., Nov. 6, 1938; d. George K. and Rebecca (Adler) Propper; m. Denis Mickiewicz, June 2, 1963; 1 son, Cyril. B.A., Wellesley Coll., 1960; M.A., Yale U., 1961, Ph.D., 1965. Lectr. dept. polit. sci. Yale U., 1965-67; asst. prof. dept. polit. sci. Mich. State U., East Lansing, 1967-69; assoc. prof. Mich. State U., 1969-73, prof., 1973-80; prof. dept. polit. sci. Emory U., Atlanta, 1980-88; dean Grad. Sch. Arts and Scis. Emory U., 1980-85, Alben W. Barkley prof. polit. sci., 1988-93; James R. Shepley prof. pub. policy, prof. polit. sci. Duke U., Durham, N.C., 1994—, dir. DeWitt Wallace Ctr. for Comm. and Journalism Terry Sanford Inst. Pub. Policy, 1994—; vis. prof. Kathryn W. David Chair Wellesley Coll., 1978; vis. com. dept. Slavic lang. and lit. Harvard U., 1978-85, vice chmn. vis. com. Russian Research Ctr., Harvard U., 1986-92; mem. subcom. on communications and society Am. Council Learned Socs./Soviet Acad. Scis., 1986-90; mem. com. on internat. security studies, Am. Acad. Arts and Scis., 1988-90; fellow The Carter Ctr., 1985—; dir. Internat. Media and Communications Program; mem. area adv. com. for Ea. Europe and USSR, Coun. for Internat. Exchange of Scholars, 1987-90; mem. acad. adv. coun. The Kennan Inst. for Advanced Russsian Studies, 1989-93. Author: Soviet Political Schools, 1967, Media and the Russian Public, 1981, Split Signals: Television and Politics in the Soviet Union, 1988 (Electronic Book of Yr. award Nat. Assn. Broadcasters and Broadcast Edn. Assn. 1988: co-author: Television and Elections, 1992, Television/Radio News and Minorities, 1994; editor: Soviet Union Jour., 1980-90; co-editor: International Security and Arms Control, 1986, The Soviet Calculus of Nuclear War, 1986; editor, contbr.: Handbook of Soviet Social Science Data, 1973; mem. editorial bd. Jour. Politics, 1985-88. Founder, 1st chmn. bd. dirs. Opera Guild of Greater Lansing, Inc., 1972-74. Recipient Outstanding Svc. to Promote Dem. Media in Russia award Journalists Union of Russia, 1994; Ford Found. fgn. area tng. fellow, 1962-65; Guggenheim fellow, 1973-74; Sigma Xi grantee, 1973-74, Ford Found. grantee, 1985-85, 88-91, 92—, Rockefeller Found. grantee, 1985-87, W. Alton Jones Found. grantee, 1987-88, Eurasia Found. grantee, 1993-94; fellow The Carter Ctr. Mem. Am. Assn. for Advancement Slavic Studies (bd. dirs. 1978-81, mem. awards com., mem. endowment com. 1984-86, pres. 1987-88), Am. Polit. Sci. Assn.,Internat. Studies Assn. (v.p. N.Am. 1983-84), Dante Soc. Am., So. Conf. Slavic Studies (exec. com. 1983-84), Coun. Fgn. Rels. Office: Sanford Inst Pub Policy PO Box 90241 Duke U Durham NC 27708-0241

MICKLE, BILLY ARTHUR, state legislator, lawyer; b. London, July 7, 1945; m. Frances Bailey; 1 child. BS, Northeastern State U., 1967; JD, Oklahoma City U., 1974. Mcpl. judge City of Durant, 1974-80; assoc. dist. judge U.S. Dist. Ct., Bryan County, 1980-83; mem. Okla. State Senate, 1987—, also majority floor leader. Office: Mickle Rainbolt & Wilhite 211 N Fourth Durant OK 74701

MICKO, ALEXANDER S., financial executive; b. Munich, May 8, 1947; came to U.S., 1952, naturalized, 1957; s. Zygmunt and Maria (Huber) M.; m. Sharon E. Judge, June 7, 1969; 1 child, Brian A. BS, LaSalle U., 1969. CPA, N.J. Pa. Audit mgr. Price Waterhouse, Phila., 1970-77; asst. chief fin. investigations div. of Casino Gaming Enforcement, State of N.J., Trenton, 1977-79; v.p. fin. TeleScis., Inc., Mt. Laurel, N.J., 1979-87; v.p. fin., treas., sec. NET Atlantic, Inc., Thorofare, N.J., 1989-92; v.p., contr. AAA Mid-Atlantic, Inc., Phila., 1992—; owner AM Fin. Services, Medford, N.J., 1986—; cons. United Computer Services, Berlin. N.J., 1982—; lectr. in field.

Bd. dirs. Forest Hills Civic Assn., Williamstown, N.J., 1976. With USMC, 1969-75. Recipient Michael A. DeAngelis Outstanding Profl. Achievement award, LaSalle U., Phila., 1985. Mem. AICPA, N.J. Soc. CPAs, Pa. Inst. CPAs, Fin. Execs. Inst., Nat. Assn. Accts. Roman Catholic. Avocations: skiing, golf. Home: 5 Huntington Cir Medford NJ 08055-3315 Office: AAA Mid Atlantic Inc 2040 Market St Philadelphia PA 19103

MICKS, DON WILFRED, biologist, educator; b. Mt. Vernon, N.Y., Nov. 23, 1918; s. Wilfred Wallace and Bernice (Barbour) M.; m. Martha Millican, Feb. 15, 1944; children—Donald Frederick, Stephen Alan, Marjorie Ellen, Carol Jeanne. B.S., N. Tex. State U., 1940, M.S., 1942; Sc.D., Johns Hopkins, 1949. Faculty Med. Br. U. Tex., Galveston, 1949-86; prof., chmn. preventive medicine, community health Med. Br. U. Tex., 1966-86; prof. emeritus, 1993—; Scientist-biologist div. Environmental Health, WHO, Geneva, Switzerland, 1958-59; cons. WHO, Pakistan, 1969. Contbr. articles to profl. jours. Chmn. bd. St. Vincent's House, 1969-70; mem. adv. bd. Tex. Air Control Bd. Served to lt. USNR, 1942-45, PTO. Named Disting. Alumnus North Tex. State U., 1970; Fulbright sr. rsch. scholar U. Pavia, Italy, 1953-54; recipient Excellence in Teaching award, 1991; named suite dedication Ewing Hall, Dept. Preventive Medicine and Cmty. Health. Fellow Am. Pub. Health Assn., Royal Soc. Tropical Medicine and Hygiene, AAAS; mem. Assn. Tchrs. Preventive Medicine, Am. Soc. Exptl. Biology and Medicine, Am. Soc. Tropical Medicine and Hygiene, Internat. Soc. Toxinology, Entomol. Soc. Am., Am. Mosquito Control Assn., Sigma Xi. Episcopalian (vestryman 1968-70, 74-76).

MICOZZI, MARC STEPHEN, museum director, physician, educator; b. Norfolk, Va., Oct. 27, 1953; s. Edio Dominic and Huguette (Picon) M.; m. Carole Ann O'Leary, Oct. 8, 1982; 1 child, Alicia Madeleine. Cadet, USAF Acad., 1971-72; BA, Pomona Coll., 1974; MD, U. Pa., 1979, PhD, 1986. Diplomate Am. Bd. Pathology. Rsch. fellow City of Hope Nat. Med. Ctr., Duarte, Calif., 1973; chem. engr. Gould Corp., El Monte, Calif., 1974; Luce Found. scholar Mindanao, The Philippines, 1976-77; clin. applications chemist McDonnell-Douglas Corp., Pasadena, Calif., 1978; postdoctoral fellow Allied Inst. Environ. Health, Princeton, N.J., 1979; resident in pathology Pa. Hosp., Phila., 1980-83; med. examiner Dade County Med. Examiner's Office, Miami, Fla., 1983-84; sr. investigator Nat. Cancer Inst. Bethesda, Md., 1984-86; dir. Nat. Mus. Health and Medicine, Washington, 1986—; adj. prof. Uniformed Svcs. U. Health Scis., Bethesda, 1986—; vis. lectr. Georgetown U. Sch. Medicine, Washington, 1986—, Johns Hopkins U. Sch. Medicine, Balt., 1988—. Editor: Nutrition and Cancer, 1988; assoc. editor Health Care, Jour. Human Orgn., 1983-89; editor-in-chief: Journal of Alternative and Complimentary Medicine, 1994—; contbr. over 120 articles to med. jours., chpts. to books. Del. White House Conf. on Youth, Estes Park, Colo., 1971, UN Conf. on Human Environ., Stockholm, 1972, NATO Advanced Study Inst., Brussels, 1982; mem. Calif. Gov.'s Adv. Com., 1972-74. recipient performance mgmt. award U.S. Dept. Army, 1988-92. Fellow Human Biology coun., Soc. for Applied Anthropology, Am. Anthrop. Assn.; Am. Acad. Forensic Scis., Am. Pub. Health Assn., N.Y. Acad. Scis. Roman Catholic. Office: Nat Mus Health & Medicine 6825 16th St NW Washington DC 20306-0003

MICZEK, KLAUS ALEXANDER, psychology educator; b. Burghausen, Bavaria, Germany, Sept. 28, 1944; came to U.S., 1967; s. Erich and Irene (Wirthl) M.; m. Christiane Baerwaldt, Aug. 8, 1970; 1 child, Nikolai A. Tchrs. cert., Paedagogische Hochschule, Berlin, 1966; PhD, U. Chgo., 1972; Moses Hunt prof. psychiatry. Asst. prof. Carnegie-Mellon U., Pitts., 1972-74, assoc. prof., 1974-79; assoc. prof. Tufts U., Medford, Mass., 1979-83, prof., 1983-93, Moses Hunt prof., 1993—; cons. Duphar v.b., Weesp, The Netherlands, 1984—, Nat. Inst. Drug Abuse, Rockville, Md., 1984—; Boerhaave prof. U. Leiden, The Netherlands, 1987; mem. panel on violence, NAS, 1989-92. Editor: Pharmacology, 1983, Ethopharmacological Aggression Research, 1984; field editor, coord. editor Behavioral Pharmacology, Jour. Psychopharmacology; contbr. articles on psychopharmacology, 1973—. Rsch. grantee Nat. Inst. Drug Abuse, 1973—, Nat. Inst. Alcoholism and Alcohol Abuse, 1981—; recipient Solvay-Duphar award APA, 1993. Fellow Am. Psychol. Assn. (program chmn. 1981, pres. div. psychopharmacology 1990-91), Behavioral Pharmacological Soc. (pres. 1992-94), Internat. Soc. for Rsch. on Aggression (councilor 1987); mem. Soc. Neurosci., N.Y. Acad. Scis., Internat. Primatol. Soc. Office: Tufts U Dept Psychology 490 Boston Ave Medford MA 02155-5532

MIDDAUGH, ROBERT BURTON, artist; b. Chgo., May 12, 1935; s. John Burton and Mae Knight (Crooks) M. Student, U. Chgo., 1960-64; BFA, Art Inst. Chgo., 1964. curator art collection 1st Nat. Bank Chgo., 1971-83. Designed, executed ednl. display, Prehistoric Project at Oriental Inst. of U. Chgo., 1968; One-man shows include, Kovler Gallery, Chgo., 1965, 67, 69, Martin Schweig Gallery, St. Louis, 1970, 72, 79, 83, U. Wis., 1976, 81, 82, Fairweather Hardin Gallery, Chgo., 1977, 80, 83, 85, Rockford Art Mus., 1987, Zaks Gallery, Chgo., 1992, 93; group shows, including, Art Inst. Chgo., 1964, 66, 78, 79, Evanston (Ill.) Art Center, 1964, Joslyn Art Mus., Omaha, 1968, U. Notre Dame, 1969, Va. Mus. Fine Arts, Richmond, 1966; represented in permanent collections, Art Inst. Chgo., Boston Mus. Fine Arts, Fine Art Mus. of South, Mobile, Ala., Los Angeles County Mus., Phoenix Art Mus., Worcester (Mass.) Art Mus., Ill. State Mus., Springfield. Served with U.S. Army, 1958-60. Mem. Arts Club Chgo.

MIDDELKAMP, JOHN NEAL, pediatrician, educator; b. Kansas City, Mo., Sept. 29, 1925; s. George H. and Clara M. (Ordelheide) M.; m. Roberta Gill, Oct. 3, 1949 (div. 1970); children—Sharon Ann, Steven Neal, Susan Jean, Scott Alan; m. Lois Harper, Mar. 1, 1974. B.S., U. Mo., 1946; M.D., Washington U., St. Louis, 1948. Diplomate Am. Bd. Pediatrics. Intern D.C. Gen. Hosp., Washington, 1948-49; resident St. Louis Children's Hosp., 1949-50, 52-53; instr. pediatrics Washington U., 1953-57, asst. prof. pediatrics, 1957-64, assoc. prof., 1964-70, prof., 1970—; dir. ambulatory pediatrics St. Louis Children's Hosp., 1974-91. Author: Camp Health Manual, 1984; contbr. articles, chpts. to profl. publs. Served to comdr. M.C., USNR, 1943-66. NIH postdoctoral fellow, 1961-62. Mem. Am. Acad. Pediatrics, Am. Soc. Microbiology, Infectious Diseases Soc. Am., Am. Pediatric Soc., Ambulatory Pediatric Assn., Sigma Xi, Alpha Omega Alpha. Home: 8845 Paragon Cir Saint Louis MO 63123-1114 Office: 1 Childrens Pl Saint Louis MO 63110

MIDDENDORF, JOHN HARLAN, English literature educator; b. N.Y.C., Mar. 31, 1922; s. George Arlington and Margaret (Hofmann) M.; m. Beverly Bruner, July 14, 1943 (dec. 1983); children: Cathie Jean Middendorf Hamilton, Peggy Ruth Middendorf Brindisi; m. Maureen L. MacGrogan, Jan. 31, 1986. AB, Dartmouth Coll., 1943; AM, Columbia U., 1947, PhD, 1953. Lectr. English CCNY, 1946, Hunter Coll., 1946-49; faculty Columbia, 1947—, prof. English, 1965-89, prof. emeritus, 1990—, dir. grad. studies, 1971-74, vice-chmn., 1976-80; chmn. English test com. Coll. Entrance Exam. Bd., 1967-69. Contbr. articles, revs. to profl. jours.; Editor: English Writers of the Eighteenth Century, 1971; asst. editor: Johnsonian News Letter, 1950-58; co-editor, 1958-78, editor, 1978-90; assoc. editor: Yale edit. Works Samuel Johnson, 1962-66; gen. editor, 1966—. Served to lt. (j.g.) USNR, 1943-46. Faculty fellow Fund Advancement Edn., 1951-52; grantee Coun. Rsch. Humanities, 1958-59, Am. Philos. Soc., 1962, Am. Coun. Learned Socs., 1962, NEH, 1976-88. Mem. Johnsonians (sec.-treas. 1958-68, chmn. 1969, 79), Univ. Seminar on 18th Century European Culture (chmn. 1973-75, 85-87), Oxford Bibliog. Soc., Grolier Club, English Inst. (mem. supervisory com. 1963-66), Modern Lang. Assn., Conf. Brit. Studies, Soc. Textual Scholarship (adv. bd.), Am. Soc. 18th Century Studies, Phi Beta Kappa. Home: 404 Riverside Dr New York NY 10025-1861 Office: Columbia U Dept English New York NY 10027

MIDDENDORF, WILLIAM HENRY, electrical engineering educator; b. Cin., Mar. 23, 1921; s. William J. and Mary J. (Frommeyer) M.; m. Evelyn B. Taylor, Nov. 20, 1946; children—Judith A., Mark E., Jeffrey W., Craig A., Susan A. B. Elec. Engring., U. Va., 1946; M.S., U. Cin., 1948; Ph.D., Ohio State U., 1960. Mem. faculty U. Cin., 1948-91, prof. elec. engring., 1960-91, assoc. head. dept., 1986-91; prof. emeritus, 1991—; with Wadsworth Elec. Mfg. Co., Covington, Ky., U. 1966-90, dir. engring. and research, 1966-86, sr. cons., 1986-90; dir. research Cin. Devel. and Mfg. Inc., 1960-66. Author: Electric Circuit Analysis, 1956, Introductory Network Analysis, 1966, Engineering Design, 1969; author: Invention, 1981, Design of Devices and Systems, 1986, 2d edit., 1990; co-author: Product Liability, 1979; editor

book series: Marcel Dekker, Inc. (85 vols.), Continuing Edn. Series (30 vols.); contbr. to profl. publs.; holder 27 patents. Trustee St. Elizabeth Hosp., Covington, 1967-83, pres. bd., 1977-80. With USNR, 1943-46. Recipient Herman Schneider award Tech. Socs. of Cin., 1978, U. Cin. Public Service award, 1981, Rieveschl award for scholarly and creative works U. Cin., 1989; NSF fellow, 1958-59. Fellow IEEE (life); mem. Am. Soc. Engring. Edn. Home: 1941 Provincial Ln Covington KY 41011-1816 Office: Loc 30 Univ Cin Cincinnati OH 45221

MIDDLEBROOK, DIANE WOOD, English language educator; b. Pocatello, Idaho, Apr. 16, 1939; d. Thomas Isaac and Helen Loretta (Downey) Wood; m. Jonathan Middlebrook, June 15, 1963 (div. 1972); 1 child, Leah Wood Middlebrook; m. Carl Djerassi, June 21, 1985. BA, U. Wash., 1961; MA, Yale U., 1962, PhD, 1968. Asst. prof. Stanford (Calif.) U., 1966-73, assoc. prof., 1973-83, prof., 1983—, Howard H. and Jessie T. Watkins univ. prof., 1985-90, dir. Ctr. for Rsch. on Women, 1977-79. Author: Walt Whitman and Wallace Stevens, 1974, Words into Words: Understanding Modern Poems, 1980, Anne Sexton, A Biography, 1991, (poems) Gin Considered as a Demon, 1983; editor: Coming to Light: American Women Poets in the Twentieth Century, 1985. Founding trustee Djerassi Resident Artists Program, Woodside, Calif., 1980-83, chair, 1994; trustee San Francisco Art Inst., 1993. Ind. study fellow NEH, 1982-83, Bunting Inst. fellow Radcliffe Coll., 1982-83, Guggenheim Found. fellow, 1988-89, Rockefeller Study Ctr. fellow, 1990; recipient Yale Prize for Poetry; finalist Nat. Book award, 1991. Mem. MLA. Avocations: collecting art, theater. Home: 1101 Green St Apt 1501 San Francisco CA 94109-2006 Office: Stanford U Dept English Stanford CA 94305-2087

MIDDLEBROOK, ROBERT DAVID, electronics educator; b. England, May 16, 1929. BA, Cambridge U., England, 1952, MA, 1956; MS, Stanford U., 1953, PhD in Elec. Engring., 1955. Sr. tech. instr., mem. trade testing bd. Radio Sch. No. 3, Royal Air Force, Eng., 1947-49; asst. prof. electrical engring. Calif. Inst. Tech., Pasadena, 1955-58, assoc. prof., 1958-65, prof. electronics, 1965—; mem. hon. editorial adv. bd. Solid State Electronics, 1960-74; mem. WESCON tech. program com., 1964; lectr. 23 univs. and cos. in Eng., The Netherlands, Germany, 1965-66; mem. rsch. and tech. adv. coun. com. on space propulsion and power, NASA, 1976-77; gen. chmn. Calif. Inst. Tech. Indsl. Assocs. Conf. Power Electronics, 1982; cons. in field. Author: An Introduction to Transistor Theory, 1957, Differential Amplifiers, 1963, (with S. Cuk) Advances in Switched-Mode Power Conversion, Vols. I and II, 1981, 2d edit., 1983, Vol. III, 1983; mem. editorial bd. Internat. Jour. Electronics, 1976-82; presented 77 profl. papers; patentee in field. Recipient Nat. Profl. Group Indsl. Engrs. award, 1958, Indsl Rsch. 100 award Indsl. Rsch. Mag., 1980, award for the Best Use of Graphics Powercon 7, 1980, Powercon 8, 1981, William E. Newell Power Electronics award Inst. Elec. & Electronics Engrs., 1982, PCIM award for Leadership in Power Electronics Edn., 1990, Edward Longstreth Medal Franklin Inst., 1991. Fellow IEEE (exec. com. San Gabriel Valley sect. 1964-65, treas. 1977-78, gen. chmn. poer electronics specialists conf. 1973, AES-S elec. power/energy systems panel 1977-87, program chmn. applied electronics conf. 1986, 87), Instn. Elec. Engrs. (U.K.); mem. Inst. Radio Engrs. (Honorable Mention award 1958, subcom. 4.1 1956-62, chmn. L.A. chpt., 1960-61, vice chmn. Pasadena subsect. 1960-61), Sigma Xi. Achievements include research in new solid state devices, their development, representation and application; electronics education; power conversion and control. Office: Calif Inst Tech 116-81 Engring Applied Sci Pasadena CA 91125

MIDDLEBROOK, STEPHEN BEACH, lawyer; b. N.Y.C. BA, Yale U., 1958, LLB, 1961. Bar: Conn. 1961. Counsel Aetna Life and Casualty Co., Hartford, Conn., 1969-71, asst. gen. counsel, 1971-78, corp. sec., 1973-83, v.p., gen. counsel, 1981-88, sr. v.p., gen. counsel, 1988-90, sr. v.p., exec. counsel, 1990-94; spl. counsel Day, Berry & Howard, Hartford, 1994—; vis. fellow Rand, Santa Monica, Calif., 1994, cons., 1995—. Office: Day Berry & Howard City Place I Hartford CT 06103-3499

MIDDLEBROOKS, EDDIE JOE, environmental engineer; b. Crawford County, Ga., Oct. 16, 1932; s. Robert Harold and Jewell LaVerne (Dixon) M.; m. Charlotte Linda Hardy, Dec. 6, 1958; 1 child, Linda Tracey. B.C.E., U. Fla., 1956, M.S., 1960; Ph.D., Miss. State U., 1966. Diplomate: Am. Acad. Environmental Engrs.; registered profl. engr., Ariz., Miss., Utah; registered land surveyor, Fla. Asst. san. engr. USPHS, Cin., 1956-58; field engr. T.T. Jones Constrn. Co., Atlanta, 1958-59; grad. teaching asst. U. Fla., 1959-60; research asst. U. Ariz., 1960-61; asst. prof., asso. prof. Miss. State U., 1962-67; research engr. asst. dir. San. Engring. Research Lab., U. Calif.-Berkeley, 1968-70; prof. Utah State U., Logan, 1970-82, dean Coll. Engring., 1974-82; Newman chair natural resources engring. Clemson U., 1982-83; provost, v.p. acad. affairs Tenn. Tech. U., 1983-88; provost, v.p. acad. affairs U. Tulsa, 1988-90, prof. chem. engring., 1988-92, Trustees prof. chem. engring., 1990-92, acting pres., 1990; prof. civil engring. U. Nevada, Reno, 1992—; mem. nat. drinking water adv. council EPA, 1981-83; cons. EPA, UN Indsl. Devel. Orgn., Calif. Water Resources Control Bd., also numerous indsl. and engring. firms. Author: Modeling the Eutrophication Process, 1974, Statistical Calculations-How To Solve Statistical Problems, 1976, Biostimulation and Nutrient Assessment, 1976, Water Supply Engineering Design, 1977, Lagoon Information Source Book, 1978, Industrial Pollution Control, Vol. 1; Agro-Industries, 1979, Wastewater Collection and Treatment: Principles and Practices, 1979, Water Reuse, 1982, Wastewater Stabilization Lagoon Design, Performance and Upgrading, 1982, Reverse Osmosis Treatment of Drinking Water, 1986, Pollution Control in the Petrochemicals Industry, 1987, Natural Systems for Waste Management and Treatment, 1988, 2d edit., 1995; mem. editorial adv. bd. Lewis Pubs. Inc., Environment Internat., Environ. Abstracts; contbr. tech. articles to profl. jours. Fellow ASCE; mem. AAAS, Water Environment Fedn. (dir. 1979-81, 91-92), Eddy medal 1969), Assn. Environ. Engring. Profs. (pres. 1974), Utah Water Pollution Control Assn. (pres. 1976), Internat. Assn. on Water Quality, Am. Soc. Engring. Edn., Am. Acad. Environ. Engrs. (trustee 1992-95), Sigma Xi, Omicron Delta Kappa, Phi Kappa Phi (Disting. mem.), Tau Beta Pi, Sigma Tau. Home: 3855 Skyline Blvd Reno NV 89509-5661 Office: U Nevada at Reno Reno NV 89557

MIDDLEDITCH, LEIGH BENJAMIN, JR., lawyer, educator; b. Detroit, Sept. 30, 1929; s. Leigh Benjamin and Hope Tiffin (Noble) M.; m. Betty Lou Givens, June 27, 1953; children: Leigh III, Katherine Middleditch McDonald, Andrew B. BA, U. Va., 1951, LLB, 1957. Bar: Va. 1957. Assoc. James H. Michael, Jr., Charlottesville, Va., 1957-59; ptnr. Battle, Neal, Harris, Minor & Williams, Charlottesville, 1959-68; legal adviser U. Va., Charlottesville, 1968-72; ptnr. McGuire, Woods, Battle & Boothe, Charlottesville, 1972—; lectr. Grad. Bus. Sch., U. Va., Charlottesville, 1958, lectr. Law Sch., 1970-90. Co-author: Virginia Civil Procedure, 1978, 2d edition, 1992; contbr. articles to profl. jours. Pres. Ellen Bayard Weedon Found., 1984—; chmn. U. Va. Health Svcs. Found., 1988—; bd. mgrs. U. Va. Alumni, 1994—; bd. dirs. Va. Health Care Found., 1992—; trustee Claude Moore Found., 1991—; mem. Va. Health Planning Bd., 1989—; bd. visitors U. Va., 1990-91; trustee Thomas Jefferson Meml. Found., Monticello, 1994—. Fellow Am. Bar Found., Va. Bar Found., Am. Coll. Tax Counsel; mem. Va. State Bar (coun., chmn. bd. govs. various sects.), Charlottesville-Albemarle Bar Assn. (pres. 1979-80), U. Va. Law Sch. Alumni Assn. (pres. 1979-81), Va. C. of C. (pres. 1988-90), Omicron Delta Kappa. Episcopalian. Office: McGuire Woods Battle & Boothe PO Box 1288 Bldg Charlottesville VA 22902-1288

MIDDLEKAUFF, ROBERT LAWRENCE, history educator, administrator; b. Yakima, Wash., July 5, 1929; s. Harold and Katherine Ruth (Horne) M.; m. Beverly Jo Martin, July 11, 1952; children: Samuel John, Holly Ruth. B.A., U. Wash., 1952; Ph.D., Yale U., 1961. Instr. history Yale U., New Haven, Conn., 1959-62; asst. prof. history U. Calif.-Berkeley, 1962-66, assoc. prof., 1966-70, prof.; 1970-80, Margaret Byrne prof. history, 1980-83; dir. Huntington Library, Art Gallery and Bot. Gardens, San Marino, Calif., 1983-88; prof. history U. Calif., Berkeley, 1988-92, Preston Hotchkiss prof., 1992—; mem. council Inst. Early Am. History and Culture, Williamsburg Va., 1974-76, 85-88. Author: Ancients and Axioms, 1963, The Mathers, 1971, The Glorious Cause: The American Revolution, 1763-1789, 1982. Served to 1st lt. USMC, 1952-54, Korea. Recipient Bancroft prize, 1972; recipient Commonwealth Club Gold medal, 1983; fellow Am. Council Learned Socs., 1965, NEH, 1973, Huntington Library, 1977. Fellow Am. Acad. Arts and Scis.; mem. Am. Hist. Assn., Orgn. Am. Historians,

Soc. Am. Historians, Am. Antiquarian Soc., Assocs. Early Am. History and Culture (mem. exec. com.), Colonial Soc. Mass. (corr.). Home: 5868 Ocean View Dr Oakland CA 94618-1535 Office: Univ Calif Dept History Berkeley CA 94720

MIDDLETON, ANTHONY WAYNE, JR., urologist, educator; b. Salt Lake City, May 6, 1939; s. Anthony Wayne and Dolores Caravena (Lowry) M.; m. Carol Samuelson, Oct. 23, 1970; children: Anthony Wayne, Suzanne, Kathryn, Jane, Michelle. BS, U. Utah, 1963; MD, Cornell U., 1966. Intern, U. Utah Hosps., Salt Lake City, 1966-67; resident in urology Mass. Gen. Hosp., Boston, 1970-74; practice urology Middleton Urol. Assos., Salt Lake City, 1974—; mem. staff Primary Children's Hosp., staff pres., 1981-82; mem. staff Latter-Day Saints Hosp., Holy Cross Hosp.; assoc. clin. prof. surgery U. Utah Med. Coll., 1977—; vice chmn. bd. govs. Utah Med. Self-Ins. Assn., 1980-81, chmn. 1985-87. Bd. dirs. Utah chpt. Am. Cancer Soc., 1978-86; bishop, later stake presidency Ch. Jesus Christ Latter-day Saints; vice chmn. Utah Med. Polit. Action Com., 1978-81, chmn., 1981-83; chmn. Utah Physicians for Reagan, 1983-84; mem. U. Utah Coll. Medicine Dean's Search Com., 1983-84; bd. dirs. Utah Symphony, 1985—. editor (monthly pub.) AACU-FAX, 1992—. Capt. USAF, 1968-70. Mem. ACS, Utah State Med. Assn. (pres. 87-88), Am. Urologic Assn. (socioecons. com. 1987—, chmn. western sect. 1989—, western. sect. health policy com. chmn., 1990—), AMA (alt. del. to House of Dels. 1989-92, 94), Salt Lake County Med. Assn. (sec. 1965-67, pres. liaison com. 1980-81, pres.-elect 1981-83, pres. 1984), Utah Urol. Assn. (pres. 1976-77), Salt Lake Surg. Soc. (treas. 1977-78), Am. Assn. Clin. Urologists (bd. dirs. 1989-90, nat. pres. elect 1990-91, pres. 1991-92, nat. bd. chmn. urologic polit. action com. UROPAC, 1992—), Phi Beta Kappa, Alpha Omega Alpha, Beta Theta Pi (pres. Gamma Beta 1962). Republican. Contbr. articles to profl. jours. Home: 2798 Chancellor Pl Salt Lake City UT 84108-2835 Office: 1060 W 1st S Salt Lake City UT 84102-1501

MIDDLETON, CHARLES RONALD, educator, academic dean; b. Hays, Kans., Sept. 16, 1944; s. Charles Buster and Dorothy Bryant (Parsons) M.; m. Sandra Leigh Paulson, Dec. 19, 1964 (dec. 1986); children: Charles Christopher, Kevin Andrew, Kathryn Gillian. AB with honors, Fla. State U., 1965; MA, Duke U., 1967, PhD, 1969. Asst. prof. U. Colo., Boulder, 1969-77, assoc. prof., 1977-85, asst. dean, 1979-80, prof. history, 1985—, assoc. dean Coll. Arts and Scis., 1980-88, dean Coll. Arts and Scis., 1988—. Contbr. articles to profl. jours. Bd. dirs. Found. for World Health, Denver and Boulder, 1985-87, Boulder County AIDS Project (hon.), 1990—, The Consenting Adults Theatre Co., Washington, 1992—. Recipient Faculty Teaching Excellence award U. Colo., Boulder, 1978; research grantee Am. Philos. Soc., U. Colo., 1972. Fellow Royal Hist. Soc.; mem. N.Am. Conf. on Brit. Studies, Western Conf. on Brit. Studies (pres.-elect 1985-86, pres. 1986-87), Western Humanities Conf. (bd. dirs. 1990—), Am. Hist. Assn. (mem. com. gay and lesbian history), Am. Com. for Irish Studies, Brit. Politics Group, So. Conf. on Brit. Studies, Rotary, Coun. of Colls. and Arts and Scis. (bd. dirs. 1993—), Phi Beta Kappa, Phi Eta Sigma. Democrat. Avocations: fishing, cooking, travel, cycling. Home: 5685 Euclid Pl Boulder CO 80303-2952 Office: U Colo Arts and Scis Adminstrn Old Main I-42 Boulder CO 80309-0001

MIDDLETON, CHRISTOPHER, Germanic languages and literature educator; b. Truro, Cornwall, Eng., June 10, 1926; came to U.S., 1966; s. Hubert Stanley and Dorothy May (Miller) M. BA, U. of Oxford, Eng., 1951, PhD, 1954. Lectr. King's Coll., London, 1955-65; prof. Germanic langs. and lit. U. Tex., Austin, 1966—. Author: Selected Writings, 1989, Andalusian Poems, 1993, The Balcony Tree, 1992. Recipient transn. prize Schlegel-Tieck/Govt. Fed. Republic Germany, 1985, Anglo-Swiss Cultural Rels. prize Max Geilinger Stiftung, Zurich, Switzerland, 1987; Guggenheim Found. poetry fellow, 1974-75, NEA poetry fellow, 1980. Mem. Akademie der Künste Berlin. Office: U Tex Dept Of Germanic Langs Austin TX 78712

MIDDLETON, DAVID, physicist, applied mathematician, educator; b. N.Y.C., Apr. 19, 1920; s. Charles Davies Scudder and Lucile (Davidson) M.; m. Nadea Butler, May 26, 1945 (div. 1971); children: Susan Terry, Leslie Butler, David Scudder Blakeslee, George Davidson Powell; m. Joan Bartlett Reed, 1971; children: Christopher Hope, Andrew Bartlett, Henry H. Reed. Grad., Deerfield Acad., 1938; AB summa cum laude, Harvard U., 1942, AM, 1945, PhD in Physics, 1947. Teaching fellow electronics Harvard U., Cambridge, Mass., 1942, spl. rsch. assoc., Radio Rsch. Lab., 1942-45, NSF predoctoral fellow physics, 1945-47, rsch. fellow electronics, 1947-49, asst. prof. applied physics, 1949-54; cons. physicist Cambridge, 1954—, Concord, Mass., 1957-71, N.Y.C., 1971—; adj. prof. elec. engring. Columbia U., 1960-61; adj. prof. applied physics and communication theory Rensselaer Poly. Inst., Hartford Grad. Ctr., 1961-70; adj. prof. communication theory U. R.I., 1966—; adj. prof. math. scis. Rice U., 1979-89; U.S. del. internat. conf. Internat. Radio Union, Lima, Peru, 1975; lectr. NATO Advanced Study Inst., Grenoble, France, 1964, Copenhagen, 1980, Luneburg, Fed. Republic Germany, 1984; Naval Rsch. Adv. Com., 1976-77, Inst. of Def. Analyses: Supercomputing Rsch. Ctr. Sci. Adv. Bd., 1987-91; cons. physicist since 1946 Johns Hopkins U., SRI Internat., Rand Corp., USAF, Cambridge Rsch. Ctr., Comm. Satellite Corp., Lincoln Lab., NASA, Raytheon, Sylvania, Sperry-Rand, Inst. of Def. Analyses, Office of Naval Rsch., Applied Rsch. Labs., U. Tex., GE, Honeywell Transp. Systems Ctr. of Dept. Transp., Dept. Commerce Office of Telecom., NOAA, Office Telecom. and Info. Adminstrn., Sci. Applications Inc., Naval Undersea Warfare Ctr., 1995, Lawrence Livermore Nat. Labs., Planning Rsch. Corp. Applied Physics Labs. U. Wash., 1992—, others. Author: Introduction to Statistical Communication Theory, 1960, 87, Russian edit. Soviet Radio Moscow, 2 vols., 1961, 62, Topics in Communication Theory, 1965, 87, Russian edit., 1966; sci. editor: English edit. Statistical Methods in Sonar (by V.V. Ol'shevskii), 1978; mem. editorial bd. Info. and Control, Advanced Serials in Electronics and Cybernetics, 1971-82; contbr. articles to tech. jours. Recipient award (with W.H. Huggins) Nat. Electronics Conf., 1956; Wisdom award of honor, 1970; First prize 3d Internat. Symposium on Electromagnetic Compatibility Rotterdam, Holland, 1979; awards U.S. Dept. Commerce, 1978. Fellow AAAS, IEEE (life, awards 1977, 79), Am. Phys. Soc., Explorers Club, Acoustical Soc. Am., N.Y. Acad. Scis.; mem. Am. Math. Soc., Author's Guild Am., Electromagnetics Acad. MIT, Harvard Club (N.Y.C.), Cosmos Club (Washington), Dutch Treat (N.Y.C.), Phi Beta Kappa, Sigma Xi. Achievements include research in radar, telecommunications, underwater acoustics, oceanography, seismology, systems analysis, electromagnetic compatibility, communication theory; pioneering research in statistical communication theory. Home and Office: 127 E 91st St New York NY 10128-1601 also: MIND 48 Garden St Cambridge MA 02138-1561 also: 13 Harbor Rd Harwich Port MA 02646-2409

MIDDLETON, DONALD EARL, transportation company executive; b. Phila., Mar. 19, 1930; s. William Joseph and Marian May (Klotz) M.; m. Marilyn Ann Schmit, Feb. 27, 1954; children: David Earl, Donna Lynn, Linda Ann, Gary Lee. Student, Taylor Bus. Coll., Phila., 1948-49; cert. proficiency Accounts and Fins., U. Pa. Wharton Evening Sch., 1957; BBA, Roanoke Coll., 1979. With Norfolk and Western Ry. Co., Roanoke, Va., 1948—, asst. to sec., 1959-67, asst. sec., 1968-71, sec., 1972-82; corp. sec. Norfolk (Va.) So. Corp. (consolidation of Norfolk and Western Ry. with Norfolk So. Ry. Co.), 1982—; corp. sec. Atlantic Investment Co., Charlotte-So. Hotel Corp., Norfolk So. Found., Norfolk So. Properties, Inc., Rail Investment Co., Richmond-Washington Co.; asst. corp. sec. Norfolk and Western Ry. Co., Norfolk So. Ry. Co., Ctrl. of Ga. R.R. Co., N.Am. Van Lines, Inc., NS Crown Svcs., Inc., Pocahontas Land Corp., Va. Holding Corp., numerous others. Past pres. Fairfield Civic League; bd. dirs. Tidewater chpt. ARC; chmn. adv. com. Virginia Beach Svc., ARC; active ch. affairs Boy Scouts Am., Jr. Achievement. Mem. Am. Soc. Corp. Secs. (past chmn. nat. Jr. Achievement Com.), Va. C. of C., Hampton Roads C. of C., Harbor Club. Republican. Baptist. Office: Three Commercial Pl Norfolk VA 23510-2191

MIDDLETON, ELLIOTT, JR., physician; b. Glen Ridge, N.J., Dec. 15, 1925; s. Elliott and Dorothy (Thoman) M.; m. Elizabeth Blackford, Sept. 25, 1948; children: Elliott III, Ellen Alice, Blackford, James Jay. A.B., Princeton U., 1947; M.D., Columbia U., 1950. Diplomate: Am. Bd. Internal Medicine, Am. Bd. Allergy and Immunology. Intern Presbyn. Hosp., N.Y.C., 1950-51; resident in medicine Presbyn. Hosp., 1951-52; asst. in medicine immunochem. lab. Coll. Physicians and Surgeons, Columbia U.,

1952-53; clin. assoc. Nat. Heart Inst., 1953-55; fellow in allergy R.A. Cooke Inst. Allergy, Roosevelt Hosp., N.Y.C., 1955-56; practice medicine Montclair, N.J., 1956-69; dir. clin. services and research Children's Asthma Research Inst. and Hosp., Denver, 1969-76; assoc. clin. prof. medicine U. Colo., 1969-76; prof. medicine and pediatrics, dir. allergy div. Sch. Medicine, SUNY, Buffalo, 1976-92; attending physician Buffalo Gen. Hosp.; cons. in allergy Children's Hosp., VA Hosp., Buffalo. Editor-in-chief Allergy: Principles and Practice, 1978, 4th edit., 1993; editor Jour. Allergy and Clin. Immunology, 1983-88; contbr. numerous articles to jours. chpts. to books. Served with M.C. USNR, 1944-50; Served with M.C. USPHS, 1950-55. Fellow Am. Acad. Allergy and Immunology (pres. 1972, Disting. Svc. award 1991); mem. AAAS, Am. Assn. Immunologists. Episcopalian. Home: 36 Hodge Ave Buffalo NY 14222-2016 Office: Buffalo Gen Hosp 100 High St Buffalo NY 14203-1154

MIDDLETON, FRANK WALTERS, JR., lawyer; b. Texarkana, Tex., July 13, 1919; s. Frank Walters and Marian (Hodges) M.; m. Jane Lobdell Porter, Jan. 12, 1944; children: Frank Walters III, Vernon Porter, Jayne Lobdell. B.S. in Bus. Adminstrn, La. State U., 1948, J.D., 1947. Bar: La. 1947. Since practiced in Baton Rouge; ptnr. Taylor, Porter, Brooks & Phillips, Baton Rouge, 1952-90; dir. Capital City Press, La. TV Broadcasting Co., Inc., Baton Rouge Water Works Co.; regional dir. Premier Bank N.A. Chmn. adv. bd. Baton Rouge Salvation Army, 1949-50; mem. exec. bd. Istrouma area council Boy Scouts Am., 1950—; pres. council, 1964-67; mem. S.W. regional adv. com., 1967-92; vice pres. trustees Episcopal High Sch., Baton Rouge, 1964-75; mem. La. State U. Found., 1965-76; adv. bd. Our Lady of Lake Hosp., 1961-70; pres. Capitol area United Way, 1976; mem. council La. Law Inst., 1971—, sec., 1980-85, v.p., 1985-90, sr. officer, 1990—; bd. dirs. Baton Rouge Area Found., 1990-93, Our Lady of Lake Found., 1990—, sec., 1990—. Served to maj. USAAF, 1941-46. Recipient Silver Beaver, Silver Antelope awards Boy Scouts Am., 1967. Mem. La. Bar Assn., Baton Rouge Bar Assn. (pres. 1974), Baton Rouge Assembly, Baton Rouge C. of C. (v.p. 1965), Rotary (pres. Baton Rouge 1959), Baton Rouge Country Club, Baton Rouge City Club, Phi Delta Phi, Sigma Alpha Epsilon, Omicron Delta Kappa. Episcopalian (past sr. warden, vestryman). Home: 917 Steele Blvd Baton Rouge LA 70806-6930 Office: Taylor Porter Brooks & Phillips La Nat Bank Bldg Baton Rouge LA 70801

MIDDLETON, HARRY JOSEPH, library administrator; b. Centerville, Iowa, Oct. 24, 1921; s. Harry J. and Florence (Beauvais) M.; m. Miriam Miller, Oct. 29, 1949; children—Susan, Deborah, James Miller, Jennifer. Student, Washburn U., 1941-43; B.A., La. State U., 1947. Reporter AP, N.Y.C., 1947-49; news editor Archtl. Forum mag., N.Y.C., 1949-52; writer March of Time, N.Y.C., 1952-54; free lance writer, author, film dir., 1954-66; staff asst. to Pres. Lyndon B. Johnson, Washington, 1966-69; spl. asst. Pres. Lyndon B. Johnson, Austin, Tex., 1969-70; dir. Lyndon Baines Johnson Libr., U. Tex., Austin, 1970—. Author: Compact History of the Korean War, 1965, LBJ: The White House Years, 1990, Lady Bird Johnson: A Life Well-Lived, 1992. Mem. Am. Battle Monuments Commn., 1968—. Served with AUS, 1943-46, 50-52. Mem. Sigma Delta Chi. Home: 2201 Exposition Blvd Austin TX 78703-2209 Office: Lyndon Baines Johnson Libr & Mus 2313 Red River St Austin TX 78705-5702

MIDDLETON, HERMAN DAVID, SR., theater educator; b. Sanford, Fla., Mar. 24, 1925; s. Arthur Herman and Ruby (Emery Hart) M.; m. Amelia Mary Eggart, Dec. 1, 1945; children—Herman David, Kathleen Hart. B.S., Columbia U., 1948, M.A., 1949; Ph.D., U. Fla., 1964; postgrad., N.Y. U., 1950, Northwestern U., 1951. Instr. dir. drama and speech Maryville (Tenn.) Coll., 1949-50; instr., designer, tech. dir. theatre U. Del., 1951-55; asst. prof., head dept. drama U.N.C., Greensboro, 1956-59; assoc. prof., head dept. drama and speech U. N.C., 1959-65, prof., head dept., 1965-74, prof., 1974-79, Excellence Fund prof. dept. communication and theatre, 1979-90, prof. emeritus, 1990; designer Chucky Jack, Great Smokey Mountains Hist. Soc., Gatlinburg, Tenn., 1956, designer, dir., 1957; communications cons. N.C. Nat. Bank, 1968, Jefferson Standard Life Ins. Co., Greensboro, N.C., 1969, Gilbarco, Inc., Greensboro, 1969-70, 73. Drama critic, columnist: Sunday Star, Wilmington, Del., 1952; theatre editor: Players Mag, 1959-61; theatre columnist: Sunday editions Greensboro Daily News, 1959-62; contbr. articles to profl. jours. Mem. N.C. Arts Council Commn., 1964-66, Guilford County Bi-Centennial Celebration Commn., 1969-70; pres. Shanks Village Players, Orangeburg, N.Y.C., 1947-48, Univ. Drama Group, Newark, Del., 1954-55; bd. dirs. Broadway Theatre League Greensboro, 1958-60, Greensboro Community Arts Council, 1964-67, 69-72, Greensboro Community Theatre, 1983-86, Carolina Theatre Commn., 1990—; organizer-cons. The Market Players, West Market St. United Meth. Ch., 1979-82. Served with USN, 1943-46. Recipient O. Henry award Greensboro C. of C., 1966, Gold medallion Amoco Oil Co., 1973, Suzanne M. Davis award Southeastern Theatre Conf., 1975, Marian A. Smith Disting. Career award N.C. Theatre Conf., 1990. Mem. Am. Nat. Theatre and Acad. (organizer, exec. v.p. Piedmont chpt. 1957-60), Am. Theatre Assn. (chmn. bd. nominations 1971-72), Am. Coll. Theatre Festival (regional festival dir. 1973, 80, regional dir., mem. nat. com. 1978-80), Assn. for Theatre in Higher Edn. (founding mem. 1986-87), Speech Communication Assn. Am., Nat. Collegiate Players, Southeastern Theatre Conf. (bd. dirs. 1963-68, 87-92, pres. 1965, pres. pro-tem 1966), Carolina Dramatic Assn. (bd. dirs. 1958-59), N.C. Drama and Speech Assn. (pres. 1966-67), N.C. Theatre Conf. (co-organizer 1971, bd. dirs. 1984-92, pres. 1987-88), Assn. for Theater in Higher Edn., Phi Delta Kappa, Phi Kappa Phi, Theta Alpha Phi, Alpha Psi Omega. Democrat. Methodist. Home: 203A Village Ln Greensboro NC 27409-2502

MIDDLETON, J. HOWARD, JR., lawyer; b. Camden, N.J., Mar. 1, 1939; s. J. Howard and Helen Marie (Casper) M.; m. Betty Jo Bittinger, Aug. 22, 1965; children: J. Howard III, Lucia Katherine. BA, Haverford Coll., 1962; MDiv., Union Theol. Sem., 1965; JD, Georgetown U., 1972. Bar: Va. 1972, U.S. Dist. Ct. (ea. dist.) Va. 1973, U.S. Ct. Appeals (D.C. cir.) 1974, U.S. Supreme Ct. 1976, U.S. Ct. Claims 1978; ordained minister. Manpower analyst U.S. Dept. Labor, Washington, 1971-72; asst. atty. City of Alexandria, Va., 1972-76; dep. atty., 1976-78; sole practice Alexandria, Va., 1978-81; ptnr. Thomas & Fiske P.C., Alexandria, Va., 1981—; chmn. Alexandria mcpl. liaison com. Northern Va. Builders, 1986; active Va. legis. com. Washington Bd. Trade, Alexandria, 1986. Bd. dirs. Circle Terr. Hosp., Alexandria, 1986. Mem. ABA, Va. State Bar Assn., Alexandria Bar Assn., Am. Arbitration Assn. (panel of arbitrators), Unitarian Universalists Ministers Assn. Democrat. Office: Hazel Thomas 510 King St Ste 200 Alexandria VA 22314-3132

MIDDLETON, JACK BAER, lawyer; b. Phila., Jan. 13, 1929; s. Harry C. and Mildred Cornell (Baer) M.; m. Ann Dodge, Aug. 22, 1953; children: Susan D., Jack B. Jr., Peter C. AB, Lafayette Coll., 1950; JD cum laude, Boston U., 1956. Bar: N.H. 1956, U.S. Ct. Appeals (1st cir.) 1957, U.S. Supreme Ct. 1972. Assoc. McLane, Graf, Raulerson & Middleton, Manchester, N.H., 1956-62; ptnr., dir. McLane, Graf, Raulerson & Middleton, Manchester, 1962—; spl. justice Merrimack (N.H.) Dist. Ct., 1964-87; bd. dirs. Greater Manchester Devel. Corp., 1983-95; commr. Uniform State Laws, 1971-74; trustee New Eng. Law Inst., 1977-80. Author: (with others) Summary of New Hampshire Law, 1964, Compendium of New Hampshire Law, 1969, Trial of a Wrongful Death Action in New Hampshire, 1977; editor Boston U. Law Rev., 1954-56; contbr. articles to legal jours. Mem. Mt. Washington Commn., 1969—, Bedford (N.H.) Sch. Bd., 1960-66; mem. adv. bd. Merrimack Valley Coll.; trustee, sec. Mt. Washington Obs., 1957—; chmn. bd. trustees White Mountain Sch., 1976-79; campaign chmn. United Way Greater Manchester, 1987, bd. dirs., 1986-92, chmn., 1990-91; bd. dirs. N.H. Pub. Radio, 1988-91, gov., 1994—; bd. govs. N.H. Pub. TV, 1994—. Sgt. USMCR, 1950-52. Fellow ACTL (chmn. N.H. sect. 1988-90), Am. Bar Found. (life); mem. ABA (ho. dels. 1984—), New Eng. Bar Assn. (bd. dirs. 1977-88, pres. 1982-83), N.H. Bar Assn. (pres. 1979-80), Manchester Bar Assn., N.H. Bar Found. (bd. dirs. 1979-92), Nat. Conf. Bar Found. (trustee 1985-92, pres. 1989-90), Nat. Conf. Bar Pres. (exec. coun. 1987-95, pres. 1993-94), N.H. Bus. and Industry Assn. (bd. dirs. 1988—, sec. 1990—), Manchester C. of C. (bd. dirs. 1967-89, chmn. 1984-85), New Eng. Coun. (bd. dirs. 1991—). Office: McLane Graf Raulerson & Middleton 900 Elm St Manchester NH 03101-2007

MIDDLETON, JAMES ARTHUR, oil and gas company executive; b. Tulsa, Mar. 15, 1936; s. James Arthur and Inez (Matthews) M.; m. Victoria Middleton; children: Robert Arthur, James Daniel, Angela Lynn. B.A.,

Rice U., 1958, B.S. in Mech. Engring., 1959. With Atlantic Richfield Co., 1959—; design engr. Dallas, 1962-67; tech. planner, 1967-69; mgr. shale devel. Grand Junction, Colo., 1969-72; mgr. engring. dept. Los Angeles, 1972-74; mgr. Prudhoe Bay project Pasadena, Calif., 1974-80; v.p., mgr. corp. planning Los Angeles, 1980-81; pres. ARCO Coal Co., Denver, 1981-82; sr. v.p. ARCO Oil and Gas Co., Dallas, 1982-85, pres., 1985—, sr. v.p. parent co., 1981-87, exec. v.p. parent co., 1987—, also bd. dirs.; bd. dirs. Tex. Utilities Co., Dallas. Corp. rep. Circle Ten coun. Boy Scouts Am.; bd. dirs. L.A. coun. Boy Scouts Am., United Way Met. Dallas, Dallas Coun. on World Affairs, Jr. Achievement So. Calif. 2d lt. C.E., AUS, 1959-60. Recipient ASME Petroleum div. Oil Drop award. Mem. Soc. Petroleum Engrs. of AIME, Tex. Mid-Continent Oil and Gas Assn., Am. Petroleum Inst., Rocky Mountain Oil and Gas Assn., We. States Petroleum Assn. (bd. dirs.), L.A. C. of C. (bd. dirs.), L.A. Music Ctr. Founders, Ctr. for Strategic and Internat. Studies (CSIS)-Dallas Round Table, Am. Enterprise Forum Chief Execs. Round Table, Dallas Petroelum Club, Tower, Northwood, Calif. Club, Bel-Air Country Club, L.A. Country Club. Office: Arco 515 S Flower St Los Angeles CA 90071-2201

MIDDLETON, JAMES BOLAND, lawyer; b. Columbus, Ga., Aug. 19, 1934; s. Riley Kimbrough and Annie Ruth (Boland) M.; 1 child, Cynthia. BA in Psychology, Ga. State U., 1964; JD, Woodrow Wilson Coll. Law, 1972. Draftsman, paralegal and office mgr. to patent atty., Atlanta, 1955-68, for Jones & Thomas, Atlanta, 1968-72; Bar: Ga. 1972, U.S. Patent Office; assoc. Jones and Thomas, Atlanta, 1972-76; pvt. practice intellectual property, Decatur, Ga., 1976—. Mem. editorial bd. Atlanta Lawyer, 1973-82, assoc. editor, 1978-81, editor-in-chief, 1981-82. Dirs. arts coun. Unitarian-Universalist Congregation Atlanta, 1989-91; bd. dirs. Unitarian Universalist Endowment Fund, 1993—, vice chair, 1994—; bd. dirs., sec. Decatur Arts Alliance, 1990-94. With U.S. Army, 1957-59. Mem. ABA, Am. Intellectual Property Law Assn., Atlanta Bar Assn., DeKalb Bar Assn., State Bar of Ga. (editorial bd. jour. 1985-92, mem. patent trademark and copyright sect. 1972—, chmn. 1982-83, pub. rels. com. 1982-88), Fed. Cir. Bar Assn., Am. Arbitration Assn. (comml. panel 1983-94). Office: 315 W Ponce de Leon Ste 550 PO Box 1968 Decatur GA 30031-1968

MIDDLETON, LINDA JEAN GREATHOUSE, lawyer; b. Poplar Bluff, Mo., Sept. 22, 1950; d. Casper Scott and Anna Garnelle (Qualls) Greathouse; m. Roy L. Middleton, Sept. 27, 1969. BS cum laude, Ark. State U., 1972; JD, Baylor U., 1974. Bar: Tex., 1974; CPCU, CLU. Asst. v.p.; asst. sec., atty. Equitable Gen. Ins. Co., Ft. Worth, 1977-81; gen. counsel, corp. sec. Chilton Corp., Dallas, 1981-83; asst. corp. sec., sr. atty., mgr. pub. affairs Fina Oil and Chem., Dallas, 1983-85; sec. Parliamentarian, Dallas, 1985—. Sec. Homeowners Assn., Dallas, 1981—. Mem. Tex. Bar Assn., Dallas Bar Assn. Baptist. Avocations: oil painting, sewing, piano. Office: Fina Inc 8350 N Ctrl Expwy PO Box 2159 Dallas TX 75221

MIDDLETON, LOWELL GLENN, bank executive; b. Des Moines, May 31, 1948; s. Forrest Glenn and Melva L. (Miller) M.; m. Kathryn Sue Sirwaitis, Nov. 28, 1968; children: Trisha, Suzanne, Erin. BS, Ariz. State U. 1971. Sr. v.p. Security Pacific Bank, Phoenix, 1973—; chmn., bd. dirs. Consumer Credit Councelors of Ariz., Phoenix, 1983—; bd. dirs. Credit Data Southwest, Phoenix; assoc. mem. Robert Morris and Assocs. Mem. Am. Bankers Assn. (region 6B council 1988—), Ariz. Bankers Assn. (chmn. consumer credit com. 1985). Republican. Roman Catholic. Avocations: fishing, hunting, skiing, stained glass. Office: Security Pacific Bank PO Box 2511 Phoenix AZ 85002-2511

MIDDLETON, PAULETTE BAUER, atmospheric chemist; b. Beeville, Tex., Dec. 8, 1946; d. Paul Wylie and Lillian Grace (Schoppe) Bauer; m. John William Middleton, July 12, 1970; div. 1990; children: Mären Katherine, Erin Ann. BA, U. Tex., 1968, MA, 1971, PhD, 1973. Research asst., then instr. chemistry U. Tex., 1968-73; research assoc. chem. engring., 1973-75; postdoctoral fellow Nat. Ctr. Atmospheric Research, Boulder, Colo., 1975-76, sci. visitor, 1977-79, spl. project scientist, 1979, staff scientist, 1979-87; research assoc. then sr. research assoc. Atmospheric Scis. Research Ctr., SUNY, Albany, 1987—; lectr., seminar leader in field. NSF, DOE, EPA, EPRI grantee, 1982—. Author over 50 papers. Mem. Air Pollution Control Assn., AAAS. Office: Nat Ctr Atmospheric Rsch PO Box 3000 Boulder CO 80307-3000

MIDDLETON, TIMOTHY GEORGE, writer; b. Alton, Ill., Oct. 16, 1944; s. Elbert George and Freda Margaret Middleton; m. Joyce Elaine Rhea, Dec. 22, 1968; children: Brendan Mansfield, Michael Travis, Margaret Hart. BA, So. Ill. U. Pub. info. specialist So. Ill. U., Edwardsville, 1971-74; asst. mgr. pub. info. Ill. EPA, Springfield, 1974-76; reporter Metro-East Jour., East St. Louis, Ill., 1976-79; speech writer Fed. Res. Bank of St. Louis, 1979-81; reporter, copy editor Wall St. Jour., 1981-84; dep. mng. editor Crain's N.Y. Bus., 1984-92; mng. writer, 1992—. Author: Corporate and Foundation Fundraising, 1982, Grass Roots Fundraising, 1982; writer for Readers Digest, N.Y. Times, Bus. Week, Money Mag., Computer Life, Field and Stream, Worth, Modern Maturity; editorial cons.; radio personality WCBS-AM N.Y. Pres. bd. dirs. Edwardsville Pub. Libr., 1977-80; mem. St. Rose of Lima Sch. Bd., Short Hills, N.J., 1986-87; chmn. troop com. Boy Scouts Am., Short Hills, 1991-94. With U.S. Army, 1963-66. Fellow U. Mo., 1977. Mem. KC. Roman Catholic. Avocations: fishing, hunting. Home: 34 Pine Terrace E Short Hills NJ 07078

MIDELFORT, HANS CHRISTIAN ERIK, history educator; b. Eau Claire, Wis., Apr. 17, 1942; s. Peter Albert and Gerd (Gjems) M.; m. Corelyn Forsyth Senn, June 16, 1965 (div. Dec. 1981); children: Katarina, Kristian; m. Cassandra Clemons Hughes, May 25, 1985 (separated Aug. 1993); children: Sanford, Raphael, Lucy. BA, Yale U., 1964, MPhil, 1967, PhD, 1970. Instr. Stanford (Calif.) U., 1968-70; asst. prof. U. Va., Charlottesville, 1970-72, assoc. prof., 1972-87, prof., 1987—; vis. prof. Harvard U., Cambridge, Mass., 1985, Univ. Stuttgart, Germany, 1988, Univ. Bern, Switzerland, 1988. Author: Witch Hunting in Southwestern Germany, 1972 (Gustave Arlt prize 1972), Mad Princes of Renaissance Germany, 1994; translator: Revolution of 1525 (Peter Blickle), 1981, Imperial Cities and the Reformation (Bernd Moeller), 1972. Mem. Soc. Reformation Rsch. (pres. 1992-93). Office: U Va Dept History Charlottesville VA 22903

MIDGLEY, A(LVIN) REES, JR., reproductive endocrinology educator, researcher; b. Burlington, Vt., Nov. 9, 1933; s. Alvin Rees and Maxine (Schmidt) M.; m. Carol Crossman, Sept. 4, 1955; children: Thomas, Debra, Christopher. B.S. cum laude, U. Vt., 1955, M.D. cum laude, 1958. Intern U. Pitts., 1958-59, resident dept. pathology, 1959-61; resident dept. pathology U. Mich., Ann Arbor, 1961-63, instr. pathology, 1963-64, asst. prof., 1964-67, assoc. prof., 1967-70, prof., 1970—, dir. Reproductive Scis. Program; chmn. BioQuant of Ann Arbor, Inc., 1985-89. Contbr. articles to med. jours. Recipient Parke-Davis award, 1970; Ayerst award Endocrine Soc., 1977; Smith Kline Bio-Scl. Labs. award, 1985; NIH grantee, 1960—; Mellon Found. grantee, 1979-91. Mem. Soc. Study Reprodn. (pres. 1983-84), Endocrine Soc., Am. Assn. Pathology, Am. Physiol. Soc. Home: 3600 Tubbs Rd Ann Arbor MI 48103-9437 Office: U Mich Reproductive Scis Program 300 N Ingalls St Fl 11 Ann Arbor MI 48109-2007

MIDKIFF, DONALD WAYNE, program manager; b. Port, Tex., Sept. 26, 1940; s. Colvert Crockett Midkiff and Judy M. (Poss) Hinckley; m. Olga Maria Androvitch, June 21, 1961 (div. 1968); m. Manbeth Jean Crowell, Apr. 29, 1979. BS in Tech. Mgmt., Denver Tech. Coll., 1988; MS in Mgmt., Colo. Tech. Coll., 1994. With USAF, 1960, advanced through grades to sgt., 1968; electronics supr. Lockheed Aircraft, Jidda, Saudi Arabia, 1969-71; site mgr. Kentron Hawaii, Ltd., Pleiku, South Vietnam, 1971-73; supr. Kentron, Kwajalein, Marshall Islands, 1973-80, range ops. engr., 1980-84; ops. supr. Kentron PRC, Maui, Hawaii, 1984-85; ops. mgr. Kentron PRC, Colorado Springs, Colo., 1985-87; div. security mgr. PRC, Colorado Springs, Colo., 1987-89; program mgr. PRC Inc., Colorado Springs, Colo., 1989—; advisor Denver Tech. Coll., Colorado Springs, 1991—. CPR instr. Am. Red Cross, 1980-86; pres. Kwajalein Dive Club, 1981-83, Kwajalein Tennis Club, 1978-80. Recipient Group Achievement award NASA, 1992. Mem. AFCEA, Mensa, Nat. Contract Mgmt. Assn., Profl. Assn. Diving Instrs. (dive master). Republican. Avocations: golf, tennis, trap shooting, scuba diving, reading. Office: PRC Inc 985 Space Center Dr Ste 200 Colorado Springs CO 80915-3627

MIDKIFF, JOHN L., JR., health care administrator, retired army officer; b. Hamlin, W.Va., Oct. 26, 1932; s. John L. and Mary E. (Marcum) M.; m. Cathy. K. Hardwick; children—Cathy A. Martin, Karla J. Arndt. B.A. in Psychology, Marshall U., 1955; M.H.A., Baylor U., 1966; grad. U.S. Army Command and Gen. Staff Coll., Fort Leavenworth, Kans., 1970. Enlisted U.S. Army, 1953, advanced through grades to col., 1976; adminstrv. officer U.S. Army Dispensary, Pentagon, Washington, 1954-56; adminstrv. asst. Dental Surgeon, 5th U.S. Army, Chgo., 1957-59; comdr. 556th Med. Co., Ulm, Karlsruhe, Fed. Republic Germany, 1960-61; ops. officer 67th Med. Group, Republic Vietnam, 1970-71; ret., 1978; health care adminstr. Healthsouth Rehab. Corp., Birmingham, Ala., 1984-87, v.p. ops., 1985—; pres. Lacy Enterprises Inc., Chesapeake, Va., 1987—, Med. Mgmt. Services Co. Inc., 1987—; asst. dir. gen. services U. Md., Balt., 1978-79, assoc. dir. hosp. ops., 1979-83; dir. hosp. acquisition Lifemark Corp., Houston, 1983-84; cons. in field. Contbr. articles to profl. jours. Decorated Legion of Merit, Bronze Star, Meritorious Service medal with oak leaf cluster, Commendation medals, Nat. Def. Service medal, Republic of Vietnam Gallantry Cross, Civil Actions medal. Fellow Am. Coll. Hosp. Adminstrs.; mem. Am. Hosp. Assn., Ret. Officers Assn., Res. Officers Assn. Lutheran. Lodge: Masons. Home: PO Box 5070 Laurel MD 20726-5070 Office: Lacy & Assos Inc 4980 Alexis Dr Antioch TN 37213

MIDKIFF, ROBERT RICHARDS, financial and trust company executive, consultant; b. Honolulu, Sept. 24, 1920; s. Frank Elbert and Ruth (Richards) M.; m. Evanita Sumner, July 24, 1948; children: Mary Lloyd, Robin Starr, Shelley Sumner, Robert Richards Jr., David Wilson. BA, Yale U., 1942; grad. Advanced Mgmt. Program, Harvard U., 1962. Asst. sec. Hawaiian Trust Co., 1951-56, asst. v.p., 1956-57, v.p., 1957-65; dir. Am. Factors, Ltd., 1954-65; v.p. Amfac, Inc., 1965-68; exec. v.p., dir. Am. Security Bank, Honolulu, 1968-69, pres., dir., 1969-71; pres., chief exec. officer, dir. Am. Trust Co. Hawaii, Honolulu, 1971-93; chmn. bd. Bishop Trust Co. Ltd., Honolulu, 1984-93; pres., chief exec. officer Am. Fin. Svcs. of Hawaii, 1988-93; bd. dirs. Persis Corp., Honolulu. Co-chmn. Gov.'s Archtl. Adv. Com. on State Capitol, 1960-65; co-chmn. Gov.'s Adv. Com. on Fine Arts for State Capitol, 1965-69; past chmn., bd. dirs. Hawaii Visitors Bur.; past pres., bd. dirs. Downtown Improvement Assn.; bd. dirs. Lahaina Restoration Found., Archtl. Family Found., pres.; bd. dirs. Hawaii Community Found.; past chmn. Profit Sharing Research Found. 1st lt. AUS, 1943-46. Mem. Coun. on Founds., Profit Sharing Coun. Am. (bd. dirs.), Employee Stock Ownership Plan Assn. Am. (bd. dirs.), Small Bus. Coun. Am. (bd. dirs.), Pacific Club, Waialae Golf Club, Oahu Country Club, Phi Beta Kappa. Democrat. Episcopalian. Office: 4477 Kahala Ave Honolulu HI 96816-4924

MIDLARSKY, MANUS ISSACHAR, political scientist, educator; b. N.Y.C., Jan. 28, 1937; s. Max and Rachel (Potechin) M.; m. Elizabeth Steckel, June 25, 1961; children—Susan, Miriam, Michael. B.S., CUNY, 1959; M.S., Stevens Inst. Tech., 1963; Ph.D. (Ford Found. fellow), Northwestern U., 1969. Instr. polit. sci. U. Colo., Boulder, 1967-68, asst. prof., 1968-71, assoc. prof., 1971-74, prof., 1974-89, dir. Ctr. Internat. Relations, 1983-89; Moses and Annuta Back prof. internat. peace and conflict resolution Rutgers U., New Brunswick, N.J., 1989—; cons. USAF, 1968. Author: On War: Political Violence in the International System, 1975, The Disintegration of Political Systems: War and Revolution in Comparative Perspective, 1986, The Onset of World War, 1988; editor: Inequality and Contemporary Revolutions, 1986, Handbook of War Studies, 1989, 93, The Internationalization of Communal Strife, 1992, (with J. Vasquez and P. Gladkov) From Rivalry to Cooperation: Russian and American Perspectives on the Post-Cold War Era, 1994. Faculty fellow Richardson Inst. Conflict and Peace Research, London, 1977-78; faculty fellow Council Research and Creative Work, U. Colo., 1977-78; NSF grantee, 1973-76, 81-83, 83-85, 86-89; Nat. Endowment Humanities grantee, 1980, 83. Mem. Am. Polit. Sci. Assn. (pres. conflict processes sect. 1985-88) Internat. Studies Assn. (pres. West 1980-81, v.p. 1986-87), Am. Soc. Polit. and Legal Philosophy, Inter-Univ. Seminar in Armed Forces and Soc. Office: Rutgers U Dept Polit Sci Hickman Hall New Brunswick NJ 08903

MIDLER, BETTE, singer, entertainer, actress; b. Honolulu, Dec. 1, 1945; m. Martin von Haselberg, 1984; 1 child, Sophie. Student, U. Hawaii, 1 year. Debut as actress film Hawaii, 1965; mem. cast Fiddler on the Roof, N.Y.C., 1966-69, Salvation, N.Y.C., 1970, Tommy, Seattle Opera Co., 1971; nightclub concert performer on tour, U.S., from 1972; appearance Palace Theatre, N.Y.C., 1973, Radio City Music Hall, 1993; TV appearances include The Tonight Show, Bette Midler: Old Red Hair is Back, 1978, Gypsy, 1993 (Golden Globe award best actress in a mini-series or movie made for television 1994, Emmy nomination, Lead Actress - Special, 1994), Seinfeld, 1995; appeared Clams on The Half-Shell Revue, N.Y.C., 1975; recs. include The Divine Miss M, 1972, Bette Midler, 1973, Broken Blossom, 1977, Live at Last, 1977, The Rose, 1979, Thighs and Whispers, 1979, Songs for the New Depression, 1979, Divine Madness, 1980, No Frills, 1984, Mud Will Be Flung Tonight, 1985, Beaches (soundtrack), 1989, Some People's Lives, 1990; motion picture appearances include Hawaii, 1966, The Rose, 1979 (Academy award nomination best actress 1979), Divine Madness, 1980, Jinxed, 1982, Down and Out in Beverly Hills, 1986, Ruthless People, 1986, Outrageous Fortune, 1987, Oliver and Company (voice), 1988, Big Business, 1988, Beaches, 1988, Stella, 1990, Scenes From a Mall, 1991, For the Boys, 1991 (Academy award nomination best actress 1991), Hocus Pocus, 1993; appeared in cable TV (HBO) prodn. Bette Midler's Mondo Beyondo, 1988; author: A View From A Broad, 1980, The Saga of Baby Divine, 1983. Recipient After Dark Ruby award, 1973; Grammy awards, 1973, 1990; spl. Tony award, 1973; Emmy award for NBC Spl., Ol' Red Hair is Back, 1978; 2 Golden Globe awards for The Rose, 1979, Golden Globe award for The Boys, 1991; Emmy award The Tonight Show appearance, 1992. Office: Atlantic Records 75 Rockefeller Plz New York NY 10019-6907*

MIDORI (MIDORI GOTO), classical violinist; b. Osaka, Japan, Oct. 25, 1971. Attended, Juilliard Sch. Music; grad. Profl. Childrens Sch., 1990. Performer worldwide, 1981—. Recordings on Philips, Sony Classical, Columbia Masterworks; performed with N.Y. Philharmonic Orch., Boston Symphony Orch.; worldwide performances include Berlin, Chgo., Cleve., Phila., Montreal, London; recordings include Encore, Live at Carnegie Hall. Named Best Artist of Yr. by Japanese Govt., 1988; recipient Dorothy B. Chandler Performing Arts award, L.A. Music Ctr., 1989, Crystal award Ashani Shimbun Newspaper contbn. arts, Suntory award, 1994. Office: Sony Classical Sony Music Entertainment Inc 550 Madison Ave New York NY 10022-3211*

MIECH, ALLEN C., financial services company executive; b. 1939. Attended, U. Wis., 1960. With Transamerica Fin. Group. Inc., L.A., 1962—, br. mgr., 1965-68, dist. mgr., 1968-77, area mgr., 1977-79, asst. to pres., gen. mgr. br. Sys Lyon Moving & Storage, 1979-81, regional v.p., 1981-83, chief credit officer, 1983-84; exec. v.p. sales & mktg. ops., then pres. Transamerica Fin. Svcs. Calif., L.A., 1984—. With USNG, 1960-62. Office: TransAmerica Fin Svcs Calif 1150 S Olive St Los Angeles CA 90015-2211

MIEL, GEORGE JOSEPH, computer scientist; b. Paris, Sept. 7, 1943; s. Joseph and Josephine (Modlinska) M. BS, U. Ill., 1964, MS, 1965, PhD, U. Wyo., 1976. Mem. tech. staff Bellcomm, 1967-69, NASA, 1967-69; cons. Siemens A.G., Munich, 1969-70; computer scientist Applied Rsch. Labs., Ecublens, Switzerland, 1970-73; assoc. prof. U. Nev., Las Vegas, 1978-85; researcher Hughes Aircraft Co., Malibu, Calif., 1985—; prof. U. Nev., Las Vegas, 1991—; vis. asst. prof. U. Calgary, Can., 1976-78; vis. assoc. prof. Ariz. State U., Tempe, 1983-84; cons. on computer modelling, Las Vegas, 1994—. Contbr. numerous articles to profl. jours. Recipient numerous rsch. grants, Chauvenet prize Math. Assn. Am., 1986. Mem. IEEE, AIAA (vice chmn. com. on software sys 1993—), Aerospace Industries Assn. (chmn. computational sci. com. Washington 1989-91), soc. Indsl. Applied Math. (cons. and researcher). Office: # 324 220 E Flamingo Rd Las Vegas NV 89109 Office: PO Box 72226 Las Vegas NV 89170

MIELCUSZNY, ALBERT JOHN, wholesale distribution executive; b. Pitts., Oct. 30, 1941; s. Joseph John and Sophie (Krupa) M.; m. Constance Lorraine Snyder, Apr. 25, 1964; children: Alan, William. BS in Acctg., Duquesne U., 1964, MBA in Fin., 1972. CPA, Pa. Mgmt. trainee Jones & Laughlin Steel, Pitts., 1964-65; budget analyst Jones & Laughlin Steel, Aliquippa, Pa., 1967-68; acct. Touche Ross & Co., Pitts., 1968-72; asst. contr.

Servistar Corp. (previously Am. Hardware Supply Co.), Butler, Pa., 1972-74; contr. Servistar Corp., 1974-79, v.p. fin., treas., 1979-82, sr. v.p., CFO, 1982—; Treas. Butler County Community Devel. Corp., 1974—; bd. advisors Mellon Bank, Butler, 1980-86. Bd. dirs. Salvation Army, Butler, 1981-84. 1st lt. U.S. Army, 1965-67, Vietnam. Republican. Roman Catholic. Avocations: snow- and water-skiing, scuba diving, tennis. Office: Servistar Corp Servistar Way East Butler PA 16029

MIELE, ALFONSE RALPH, former government official; b. N.Y.C., Jan. 6, 1922; s. Angelo and Alesia (Laudadio) M.; m. Gloria I. Litrento, Nov. 22, 1942 (dec. Dec. 1977); children: Richard Lynn, Barbara Jo, Steven Arnold; m. Ann Carlino Valerio, Mar. 31, 1979 (dec. June 1988); m. Dorothy A. McGowan, July 7, 1990. AB in Litteris Gallicis with honors, Fordham U., 1942; postgrad., U. Nancy, France, 1945; MA, Columbia U., 1947, PhD, 1958. Commd. 2nd lt. U.S. Army, 1942; advanced through grades to col. USAF, 1961; served in 377th Automatic Weapons Bn., 1942-45; instr. French and pub. speaking Fordham Prep. Sch., N.Y.C., 1946-47; asst. prof. French and Russian U.S. Naval Acad., 1949-52; exec. officer to NATO comdrs., 1953-55; teaching asst. Columbia U., 1955-58; assoc. prof. French USAF Acad., 1958-60, prof., head dept. fgn. langs., 1960-67, assoc. dean, chmn. divsn. humanities, 1967-68; exec. v.p. Loretto Heights Coll., Denver, 1968-70; pres. Coll. St. Rose, Albany, 1970-72; prof. gen. edn. Schenectady County C.C., Schenectady, N.Y., 1972-73; dep. asst. adminstr. internat. aviation affairs FAA, Washington, 1973-75; edn. specialist, 1976—; asst. dir. pub. affairs U.S. Dept. Interior, Washington, 1975-76; chief negotiator civil aviation tech. agreement with USSR, 1973-75; project dir. Nat. Aviation Edn. Program for Am. Indians, 1978; asst. dir. Union County (N.J.) Coord. Agy. for Higher Edn., 1979-82; rep. Eckhart Assocs., 1983-88; relocation specialist Bradley/Wildman Co., Monument, Colo., 1989-92. Mem. Westfield (N.J.) Bd. Edn., 1985-88; bd. dirs. Pike's Peak chpt. ARC, 1990-93; pres. Colorado Springs World Affairs Coun., 1993-95. Decorated Bronze Star, Legion of Merit; chevalier Palmes Academiques France; recipient Encaenia award Fordham Coll., 1962. Mem. Monument C. of C. (bd. dirs. 1992-94). Home: PO Box 321 Monument CO 80132-0321 *Be ever curious and willing to dare. The sweet becomes even sweeter when the bitter is overcome. Each living moment is a learning experience and adds to the anticipation of better tomorrows. The journey of life is exciting—live with that thought in mind.*

MIELE, ANGELO, engineering educator, researcher, consultant, author; b. Formia, Italy, Aug. 21, 1922; came to U.S., 1952, naturalized, 1985; s. Salvatore and Elena (Marino) M. D.Civil Engring., U. Rome, Italy, 1944, D.Aero. Engring., 1946; DSc (hon.), Inst. Tech., Technion, Israel, 1992. Asst. prof. Poly. Inst. Bklyn., 1952- 55; prof. Purdue U., 1955-59; dir. astrodynamics Boeing Sci. Research Labs., 1959-64; prof. aerospace scis., math. scis. Rice U., Houston, 1964-88, Foyt Family prof. engring., 1988-93, Foyt prof. emeritus engring., aerospace scis., math. scis., 1993—; cons. Douglas Aircraft Co., 1956-58, Allison divsn. GM Corp., 1956-58, U.S. Aviation Underwriters, 1987, Boeing Comml. Airplane Co., 1989; Breakwell Meml. lectureship Internat. Astron. Fedn., 1994. Author: Flight Mechanics, 1962; editor: Theory of Optimum Aerodynamic Shaped, 1965, Math. Concepts and Methods in Sci. and Engring., 1974—; co-editor: Applied Mathematics in Aerospace Science and Engineering, 1994; editor in chief Jour. Optimization Theory and Applications, 1966—; assoc. editor Jour. Astronautical Scis., 1964-93, Applied Math. and Computation, 1975—, Optimal Control Applications and Methods, 1979—; mem. editorial bd. RAIRO-Ops. Rsch., 1990—; mem. adv. bd. AIAA Edn. Series, 1991—; contbr. numerous rsch. papers in aerospace engring., windshear problems, hypervelocity flight, math. programming, optimal control theory and computing methods. Pres. Italy in Am. Assn., 1966-68. Decorated knight comdr. Order Merit Italy, 1972; recipient Levy medal Franklin Inst. of Phila., 1974, Brouwer award AAS, 1980, Schuck award Am. Automatic Control Coun., 1988. Fellow AIAA (Pendray award 1982, Mechanics and Control of Flight award 1982, mem. adv. bd. Edn. Series 1991-94), Am. Astronautical Soc., Franklin Inst.; mem. NAE, Russian Acad. Scis. (fgn.), Internat. Acad. Astronautics, Acad. Scis. Turin (corr.). Home: 3106 Kettering Dr Houston TX 77027-5504 Office: Rice U Aero-Astronautics Group PO Box 1892 Houston TX 77251-1892

MIELE, ANTHONY WILLIAM, retired librarian; b. Williamsport, Pa., Feb. 12, 1926; s. Harry John and Louise Casale (Troyano) M.; m. Ruth Cassidy, Jan. 29, 1955; children—Terri Ann, Anthony William, Robert John, Elizabeth Ann. BA in Bus. Adminstrn, Marquette U., Milw., 1951; M.L.S., U. Pitts., 1966. Partner, mgr. restaurant Williamsport, 1960-66; dir. Elmwood Park (Ill.) Pub. Libr., 1967-68; asst. dir. Oak Park (Ill.) Pub. Libr., 1968-70; asst. dir. tech. services Ill. State Libr., Springfield, 1970-75; state librn. Ala. Pub. Libr. Service, Montgomery, 1975-86; coord. Libr. Svcs. and Constrn. Act, 1986-87; dir. library extension div. Ariz. Dept. Libr., Archives and Pub. Records, Phoenix, 1987-95; ret.; exec. dir. Ill. Nat. Libr. Week, 1970, ALA Nat. Libr. Week Commn., 1971-74; mem. Pub. Printer's Adv. Coun. Depository Librs., 1975-78, vice chmn., 1977-78; mem. CLSI Nat. Adv. Com., 1983-87; reader NEH, 1987; exhibits chair for confs. Mountain Plains Libr. Assn., Ariz. State Libr. Assn., Ariz. Edn. Media Assn., 1992; cochair ASLA/AEMA Annual Conf., 1993. Assoc. editor Govt. Publs. Rev., 1974-85; contbr. articles to profl. publs. Mayor Arrowhead Community, 1984; bd. dirs. Amigos Libr. Network, 1990-94. Recipient cert. of appreciation Am. Libr. Trustee Assn., 1986. Mem. ALA (chmn. govt. documents round table 1974-76, chair state libr. agy. sect. 1992-93, mem. coun. 1994—), Ill. Libr. Assn., Ala. Libr. Assn. (Exceptional svc. citation 1986), Ariz. State Libr. Assn. (Pres. award of recognition 1993), Nat Microfilm Assn., Spl. Libr. Assn., Chief Officers State Libr. Agys. (sec. 1978-80), Beta Phi Mu. Roman Catholic.

MIELE, JOEL ARTHUR, SR., civil engineer; b. Jersey City, May 28, 1934; s. Jene Gerald Sr., and Eleanor Natale (Bergida) M.; m. Faith Roseann Trombetta, July 21, 1952 (div. 1954); m. 2d Josephine Ann Cottone, Feb. 14, 1959; children: Joel Arthur, Jr., Vita Marie, Janet Ann. B.C.E., Poly. Inst. Bklyn., 1955. Registered profl. engr. N.Y., n.J., Fla.; profl. planner N.J. Civil engr. Yudell & Miele, Queens, N.Y., 1955-57; chief engr. Jene G. Miele Assocs., Queens, 1960-68; prin., CEO Miele Assocs., Queens, 1968-94; commr. N.Y.C. Planning Commn., 1990-94; commr. of bldgs. City of N.Y., 1994—. Patentee masonry wall constrn. Pres., bd. visitors Creedmoor State Hosp., 1979—; pres., bd. dirs. Peninsula Hosp. Ctr., 1990—, Peninsula Nursing Home, 1990—, Queen County Overall Econ. Devel. Corp., 1989-94; pres. Queens Borough Pub. Libr., 1979—; chmn. Cmty. Bd. 10, Queens, 1978-90; trustee, treas. Queens Pub. Comm. Corp., 1983—; exec. v.p. Queens coun. Boy Scouts Am., 1991—. Lt. (j.g.) USN, 1957-60; cpat. USNR, 1960-68. Named Italian-Am. of Yr. Ferrini Welfare League, Queens, 1980, Hon. Mem. of Queens Chpt. AIA, 1994, Prof. Affiliated Mem. (Hon.), N.Y. Soc. Architects, 1994; recipient Outstanding Cmty. Leader award Boy Scouts Am., 1987, Pride of Queens award, 1990, Pub. Servant Extraordinaire award United Cerebral Palsy of Queens, 1994, Good Scout award Greater N.Y. Coun. Boy Scouts Am., 1994. Fellow ASCE; mem. ASTM, NSPE (trustee polit. action com. 1988—), N.Y. State Soc. Profl. Engrs. (v.p. 1984-86, pres. 1988-89, nat. dir. 1987-90, Engr. of Yr. 1983, pres. Queens chpt. 1980-82), Soc. Am. Mil. Engrs., N.Y. State Assn. of Professions (founding), Ozone Howard C. of C. (pres. 1980-84, 86-91), Am. Parkinson Disease Assn. (dir. 1985—, exec. com. 1987—). Democrat. Congregationalist. Office: City of New York Dept of Buildings 60 Hudson St New York NY 10013-3315

MIELKE, CLARENCE HAROLD, JR., hematologist; b. Spokane, Wash., June 18, 1936; s. Clarence Harold and Marie Katherine (Gillespie) M.; m. Marcia Rae, July 5, 1964; children: Elisa, John, Kristina. BS, Wash. State U., 1959; MD, U. Louisville, 1963. Intern, San Francisco Gen. Hosp., 1963-64; resident in medicine Portland .VA Hosp., 1964-65, San Francisco Gen. Hosp., 1965-67; fellow in hematology U. So. Calif., 1967-68; teaching fellow, asst. physician instr. Tufts-New Eng. Med. Ctr. Hosps., Boston, 1968-71; sr. scientist Med. Rsch. Inst., San Francisco, 1971-90; chief hematology Presbyn. Hosp., San Francisco, 1971-82; asst. clin. prof. medicine U. Calif. Sch. Medicine, San Francisco, 1971-80, assoc. clin. prof., 1979-90, bd.92—dirs. Inst. Cancer Rsch.; trustee, bd. dirs. Med. Rsch. Inst. 1988—; dir. Health Rsch. and Edn. Ctr., Wash. State U., 1989—, prof. pharmocology, 1989—, prof. vet. medicine, 1989—, assoc. dean rsch., 1992—. Fellow ACP, Internat. Soc. Hematology, Am. Coll. Angiology; mem. Am. Soc. Internal Medicine, Internat. Soc. Thrombosis and Hemos-

tasis, Am. Heart Assn., N.Y. Acad. Scis., AMA, San Francisco Med. Soc., Am. Thoracic Soc., AAAS, Internat. Soc. Angiology. Editor emeritus, Jour. Clin. Aphersis, 1981; contbr. chpts. to books, articles to med. jours. Office: Wash State U Health Rsch & Edn Ctr West 601 First Ave Spokane WA 99204-0399

MIELKE, FREDERICK WILLIAM, JR., retired utility company executive; b. N.Y.C., Mar. 19, 1921; s. Frederick William and Cressida (Flynn) M.; m. Lorraine Roberts, 1947; children: Bruce Frederick, Neal Russell. AB, U. Calif., 1943; JD, Stanford U., 1949. Bar: Calif. 1950. Law clk. to Assoc. Justice John W. Shenk, Calif. Supreme Ct., 1949-51; with Pacific Gas and Electric Co., San Francisco, 1951-86; exec. v.p. Pacific Gas and Electric Co., 1976-79, chmn. bd., chief exec. officer, 1979-86; bd. dirs. The Bay Area Coun., Edison Electric Inst., 1979-82; dir. emeritus SRI Internat. Trustee Stanford U., 1977-87, Golden Gate U. 1977-79; mem. adv. coun. Stanford Grad. Sch. Bus., 1984-90; bd. dirs. Calif. C. of C. 1979-85, San Francisco C of C., 1977-79, Ind. Colls. No. Calif., 1969-79; chmn. bd. dirs. United Way of Bay Area, 1986-88. With USN, 1943-46. Mem. Calif. Bar Assn. Club: Electric of San Francisco. Office: Pacific Gas and Electric Co PO Box 770000 Mail Code H17 123 Mission St H17F San Francisco CA 94111-5401

MIELKE, PAUL WILLIAM, JR., statistician; b. St. Paul, Feb. 18, 1931; s. Paul William and Elsa (Yungbauer) M.; m. Roberta Roehl Robison, June 25, 1960; children: William, Emily, Lynn. BA, U. Minn., 1953, PhD, 1963; MA, U. Ariz., 1958. Teaching asst. U. Ariz., Tucson, 1957-58; teaching asst. U. Minn., Mpls., 1958-60, statis. cons., 1960-62, lectr., 1962-63; from asst. to assoc. prof. dept. statistics Colo. State U., Fort Collins, 1963-72, prof. dept. statistics, 1972—. Contbr. articles to Am. Jour. Pub. Health, Jour. of Statis. Planning and Inference, Ednl. and Psychol. Measurement, Biometrika, Earth-Sci. Revs. Capt. USAF, 1953-57. Fellow Am. Statis. Assn.; mem. Am. Meteorol. Soc. (Banner I. Miller award 1993), Biometric Soc. Achievements include proposal that common statistical methods (t test and analysis of variance) were based on counter intuitive geometric foundations and provided alternative statistical methods which are based on appropriate foundations. Home: 736 Cherokee Dr Fort Collins CO 80525-1517 Office: Colo State U Dept Stats Fort Collins CO 80523

MIERCORT, CLIFFORD ROY, coal mining company executive; b. Denver, Jan. 13, 1940; s. Frederic E. and Olga S. (Schlaepfer) M.; m. Barbara Dolan, Aug. 22, 1964; children: David Butler, Jennifer Dolan. BS in Archtl. Engring., U. Colo., 1964; MCE, U. Ill., 1966; advanced mgmt. program, Harvard U., 1983. Registered profl. engr., Colo., Kans., Mont., N.Mex., Tex. Supr. offshore oil drilling and production Shell Oil Co., New Orleans, 1966-69; oil production engr. Denver, 1969-71, staff engr., 1971-73; project mgr. mining venture Houston, 1973-76; asst. to pres. N.Am. Coal Corp., Cleve., 1976-77; v.p. SW div. N.Am. Coal Corp., Dallas, 1977-81, pres. SW div., 1981-87, pres., CEO, 1988—; bd. dirs. Bellaire Corp., The Coteau Properties Co., The Falkirk Mining Co., N.Am. Coal Royalty Co., The Sabine Mining Co., Am. Nat. Coal Assn. (bd. dirs. 1987), Nat. Mining Coun. (mem. coal policy com., mem. fin. and exec. coms.), Am. Inst. Mining Engrs., Soc. Profl. Engrs. Avocations: reading, traveling, gardening, refurbishing houses, golf. Office: N Am Coal Corp 14785 Preston Rd Ste 1100 Dallas TX 75240

MIGALA, LUCYNA JOZEFA, broadcast journalist, arts administrator, radio station executive; b. Krakow, Poland, May 22, 1944; d. Joseph and Estelle (Suwala) M.; came to U.S., 1947, naturalized, 1955; student Loyola U., Chgo., 1962-63, Chicago Conservatory of Music, 1963-70; BS in Journalism, Northwestern U., 1966. Radio announcer, producer sta. WOPA, Oak Park, Ill., 1963-66; writer, reporter, producer NBC news, Chgo., 1966-69, 1969-71, producer NBC local news, Washington, 1969; producer, coord. NBC network news, Cleve., 1971-78, field producer, Chgo., 1978-79; v.p. Migala Communications Corp., 1979—; program and news dir., on-air personality Sta. WCEV, Cicero, Ill., 1979—; lectr. City Colls. Chgo., 1981, Morton Coll., 1988. Columnist Free Press, Chgo., 1984-87. Founder, artistic dir., gen. mgr. Lira Ensemble (formerly The Lira Singers), Chgo., 1965—; mem., chmn. various cultural coms. Polish Am. Congress, 1970-80; bd. dirs. Nationalities Svcs. Ctr., Cleve., 1973-78; bd. dirs., v.p. Cicero-Berwyn Fine Arts Coun., Cicero, Ill.; mem. City Arts I and II panels Chgo. Office of Fine Arts, 1986-89, 94; v.p. Chgo. chpt. Kosciuszko Found., 1983-86; bd. dirs. Polish Women's Alliance Am., 1983-87, Ill. Humanities Coun., 1983-89, mem. exec. com., 1986-87; bd. dirs. Ill. Arts Alliance, 1989-92; founder, gen. chmn. Midwest Chopin Piano Competition (now Chgo. Chopin Competition), 1984-86; founding mem. ethnic and folk arts panel Ill. Arts Coun., 1984-87, 92—. Recipient AP Broadcasters award, 1973, Emmy award NATAS, 1974, Cultural Achievement award Am. Coun. for Polish Culture, 1990, Award of Merit Advocates Soc. Polish Am. Attys., 1991, Human Rels. Media award City of Chgo., 1992, Outstanding Achievement in Polish Culture award Minister of Fgn. Affairs, Rep. of Poland, 1994; Washington Journalism Ctr. fellow, spring 1969. Mem. Soc. Profl. Journalists. Office: Sta WCEV 5356 W Belmont Ave Chicago IL 60641-4103 also: The Lira Ensemble 3750 W Peterson Chicago IL 60659

MIGDAL, SHELDON PAUL, lawyer; b. Chgo., July 3, 1936; s. Joseph David M.; m. Barbara Simon, June 6, 1961; children: Pamela Anne, Andrew Alan. BS, U. Ill., 1958; JD, Northwestern U., 1961. Bar: Ill. 1961, CPA, Ill. Spl. trial atty. U.S. Dept. Justice, Washington, 1961-67; assoc. Dixon, Todhunter, Knouff & Holmes, Chgo., 1967; ptnr. Wildman, Harrold, Allen & Dixon, Chgo., 1968—. Pres., bd. dirs. Better Boys Found., Chgo., 1968—. Mem. ABA, Chgo. Bar Assn., Ill. Bar Assn., Chgo. Coun. of Lawyers. Home: 3552 N Pine Grove Ave Chicago IL 60657-1877

MIGDEN, CAROLE, county official; b. N.Y.C., Aug. 14, 1948. BA, Adelphi U., 1970; M in Psychology, Sonoma State U., 1976. Exec. dir. Operation Concern, San Francisco, 1981-89; mem. bd. suprs. City of San Francisco, 1991—; vice-chair San Francisco (Calif.) County Transp. Authority, 1994—; former commr. Calif. State Health Commn. Former chair San Francisco Dem. Party; chair Calif. Dem. Party Platform Com.; platform com. mem. Dem. Nat. Com.; past bd. mem. United Way, Lyon-Martin Women's Health Svcs., Hadassah, Western States Legal Found., San Francisco Women's Bldg. Recipient numerous cmty. awards. Jewish. Office: Bd Suprs City Hall Rm 308 401 McAllister St San Francisco CA 94102

MIGDEN, CHESTER L., association executive; b. N.Y.C., May 21, 1921; s. Albert and Louise (Jawer) M.; m. Dina Vohl, July 22, 1944; children: Barbara, Ann, Amy. B.A., CCNY, 1941; LL.B., Columbia U., 1947. Bar: N.Y. State 1947. Atty. NLRB, N.Y.C., 1947-51; various positions Screen Actors Guild Inc., Hollywood, 1952-81; nat. exec. sec. Screen Actors Guild Inc., 1973-81; v.p. Internat. Fedn. Actors, 1973-81, Calif. Labor Fedn., 1974-81, Associated Actors and Artistes Am., 1973-81; exec. dir. Assn. Talent Agts., 1982-94; ret., 1994; officer, trustee Producers-Screen Actors Guild pension, welfare plans, 1960-81; v.p. Motion Picture and TV Fund, 1975—; instr. extension program UCLA. Contbr. articles to profl. jours. Mem. Acad. Motion Picture Arts and Scis., Am. Arbitration Assn. (arbitrator), Labor Rels. Cons. Democrat.

MIGEON, CLAUDE JEAN, pediatrics educator; b. Lievin, Pas-De-Calais, France, Dec. 22, 1923; came to U.S., 1950, naturalized, 1967; s. André and Pauline (Descamps) M.; m. Barbara Lou Ruben, Apr. 2, 1960; children: Jacques, Jean-Paul, Nicole. M.D., Sch. Medicine, U. Paris, 1950. Fellow dept. pediatrics Sch. Medicine, Johns Hopkins U., 1950-52, asst. prof., 1954-60, asso. prof., 1960-71, prof. pediatrics, 1971—; instr. biochemistry U. Utah, 1952-54; pediatrician Johns Hopkins Hosp., 1954—; mem. diabetes and metabolism tng. grants com. NIH, 1963-67, gen. clin. research centers com., 1968-71, mem. endocrinology study sect., 1974-78; cons. Med. Research Council Can., 1969-85, others; vis. prof. Maadi Armed Forces Hosp., Cairo, 1985, Guy's Hosp., London, 1986. Mem. editorial bd.: Johns Hopkins Med. Jour., 1970-72, Jour. Clin. Endocrinology and Metabolism, 1971-77, Hormone Rsch., 1979—; contbr. articles to profl. jours. Fulbright fellow, 1950; Am. Field Service fellow, 1950-51; Andre and Bella Meyer fellow, 1951-52; recipient research career award NIH, 1964-85. Fellow AAAS; mem. Endocrine Soc. (coun. 1971-74, chmn. pub. affairs com. 1974-91, Ayerst award, Williams award), Soc. Pediatric Rsch. (emeritus), Am. Pediatric Soc., Lawson Wilkins Pediatric Endocrine Soc. (founding pres. 1972), Am. Soc. Clin. Investigation (emeritus), Am. Physiol. Soc., Japanese Clin. Endocrine Soc. (hon.), Found. for Am. Meml. Hosp. (bd. dirs. 1985—),

Soc. Francaise d'Endocrinologie (fgn. corr. mem.). Home: 502 Somerset Rd Baltimore MD 21210-2720 Office: CMSC 3-110 Johns Hopkins Hosp Baltimore MD 21205

MIGGINS, MICHAEL DENIS, retired career officer, arms control analyst; b. White Plains, N.Y., Aug. 8, 1944; s. Michael Joseph Miggins and M. Gabrielle (Daly) O'Neill; m. Kathleen Ann Isherwood, Oct. 22, 1966; children: Kristin D., Michael C. BA in Polit. Sci., Providence Coll., 1966; MA in Internat. Rels., St. John's U., 1972. Commd. lt. U.S. Army, 1966, advanced through grades to col., 1989; company comdr. and platoon leader 2nd Battalion, 325th Inf., 82nd Airborne Div., Ft. Bragg, N.C., 1966-68; dist. sr. advisor An Xuyen Province, Ca Mau, Vietnam, 1968-69; instr. ROTC St. John's U., Jamaica, N.Y., 1969-72; with joint security area Armistice Affairs div. UN Forces, Pan Mun Jom, Korea, 1973-74; ops. officer, company comdr., intelligence officer 4th Battalion, 6th Inf., Berlin (Germany) Brigade, Vietnam 1974-77; sec. gen. staff Army Combined Arms Test Activity, Ft. Hood, Tex., 1978-80; staff officer ODCSOPS Army Staff, Washington, 1980-84; br. chief priorities, programs and budget for Army Staff, 1984-85; exec. officer 1st brigade (armored) 1st Cavalry Divsn. U.S. Army, Ft. Hood, Tex., 1985-86, chief exercise divsn. III Corps., 1986-87; mem. joint staff, internat. negotiations divsn. Washington, 1987-91; U.S. del. mutual and balanced force reduction negotiations mandate talks Conventional Armed Forces in Europe Negotiation, Vienna, Austria, 1987-89; mil. advisor to U.S. rep. High Level Task Force NATO, Brussels, 1988-90; rep. to interagy. conventional arms control Joint Staff, Washington, 1990-91; sr. advisor to chmn. verification coord. com., internat. staff, polit. affairs divsn. NATO, Brussels, 1991-93; mgr. conventional arms ctrl. and open skies projects Ctr. Verification Rsch. Sci. Applications Internat. Corp., Newington, Va., 1994—. Decorated Silver Star, Bronze Star, Legion of Merit, Def. Superior Svc. medal, Meritorious Svc. medal, Army Commendation medal. Mem. Assn. U.S. Army, Army and Navy Club. Republican. Roman Catholic. Avocations: skiing, bicycling, jogging, military history. Home: 9352 Braymore Cir Fairfax Station VA 22039 Office: Ctr for Verification Rsch Cinder Bed Rd Newington VA 22122

MIGHELL, KENNETH JOHN, lawyer; b. Schenectady, N.Y., Mar. 17, 1931; s. Richard Henry and Ruth Aline (Simon) M.; m. Julia Anne Carstarphen, Aug. 24, 1961; children: Thomas Lowry, Elizabeth Anne. BBA, U. Tex., 1952, JD, 1957. Bar: Tex. 1957. Assoc. Scurry, Scurry, Pace & Wood, Dallas, 1957-61; asst. U.S. Atty. Justice Dept., Dallas, 1961-77; 1st asst. No. Dist. Tex., 1972-77; U.S. Atty. No. Dist., Tex., 1977-81; ptnr. Cowles & Thompson, 1981—. Chmn. bd. mgmt. Downtown Dallas YMCA, 1974-76; pres. Dallas Area Am. Lung Assn., 1985-87; bd. dirs. YMCA Met. Dallas, 1987—; chmn. adv. bd. Southwestern Law Enforcement Inst., 1994—. With USN, 1952-54; capt. USNR, 1954-78. Mem. ABA, Fed. Bar Assn., Dallas Bar Assn. (bd. dirs. 1984-89, chmn. 1989, v.p. 1990-91, pres. elect 1992, pres. 1993), Dallas Jr. Bar Assn. (pres. 1961), State Bar Tex. (bd. dirs. 1994-95), State Jr. Bar Tex. (bd. dirs. 1962), Nat. Assn. Former U.S. Attys. (pres. elect 1994). Democrat. Methodist. Office: 4000 Nations Bank Plz Dallas TX 75202

MIGHT, THOMAS OWEN, newspaper company executive; b. Fort Walton Beach, Fla., Apr. 22, 1951; s. Gerald William and Rosina (Bugner) M.; m. Sept. 22, 1973; children—Matthew, Daniel. B.S. in Indsl. Engring., Ga. Tech. U., 1972; M.B.A., Harvard Bus. Sch., 1978. Asst. to pub. Washington Post, 1978-80, mgr. plant, 1980-81, v.p. prodn., v.p. marketing; now pres., COO, divsn. Post-Newsweek cable The Washington Post Co., Phoenix. Served to capt. U.S. Army, 1972-76. Roman Catholic. Office: Washington Post Co Divsn Post-Newsweek Cable 4742 N 24 St Ste 270 Phoenix AZ 85016*

MIGIELICZ, GERALYN, photojournalist; b. St. Louis, Feb. 15, 1958; d. Edward J. and Mary Ann (McCarthy) M. BJ, U. Mo., 1979. Photographer Emporia (Kans.) Gazette, 1979-80; chief photographer St. Joseph (Mo.) News-Press & Gazette, 1980-83; photo editor, photographer Seattle Times, 1984; picture editor Rocky Mountain News, Denver, 1985-86; graphics editor San Jose (Calif.) Mercury News, 1986-92, dir. photography, 1992—. Recipient Individual Editing awards Soc. Newspaper Designers, 1988-92, Editing awards, 91-92; named for Overall Excellence in Editing, Picture of Yr. Contest, U. Mo., 1993. Office: San Jose Mercury News 750 Ridder Park Dr San Jose CA 95190

MIGLIARO, MARCO WILLIAM, electrical engineer; b. N.Y.C., Mar. 29, 1948; s. Marco Salvatore and Anna (Dalton) M.; children: Kristen Marie, Meredith Anne, Marie Angela, Marco Thomas; m. Jasoda Badlu, Nov. 19, 1988. BEE, Pratt Inst., 1969; postgrad., N.J. Inst. Tech., 1970-72. Registered profl. engr., N.Y., N.J., Pa., Mass., Fla. Engr. Am. Electric Power, N.Y.C., 1969-78; staff engr. Gibbs & Hill, Inc., N.Y.C., 1978-81; sr. cons. engr. Ebasco Svcs., Inc., N.Y.C., 1981-88; tech. mgr. ABB Impell Corp., Melville, N.Y., 1988-90; sr. staff specialist for nuclear engring. Fla. Power & Light, Juno Beach, 1990—; developer seminar on stationary batteries, 1987. Contbg. author: Handbook of Power Calculations, 1984; also articles. Recipient Meritorious Svc. award Am. Nat. Standards Inst., 1994. Fellow IEEE (bd. dirs. 1990-92, fin. com. 1990-92, dir. standards 1990-91, mem. exec. com. 1992, v.p. standards activities, 1992, Standards medal 1986, Standards Bd. Disting. Svc. award 1993); mem. IEEE Power Engring. Soc. (Disting. Svc. awrd 1988, 92). Avocations: fishing, travel. Home: PO Box 9253 Jupiter FL 33468-9253 Office: Fla Power & Light PO Box 14000 (JPN/JB) Juno Beach FL 33408-0420

MIGLIO, DANIEL JOSEPH, telecommunications company executive; b. Phila., June 23, 1940; s. Daniel Joseph and Eleanor (Zucca) M.; children: Paige Leslie, Marcus Daniel. BS in Econs., U. Pa., 1962. With So. New Eng. Telephone Co, 1962-84; acct. New Haven, Conn., 1962-67; budget coordinator New Haven, 1967-69; dist. traffic mgr. New London, Conn., 1969-72; gen. acctg. mgr. New Haven, 1972-74; div. ops. mgr. Hartford, Conn., 1974-78; gen. mgr. corp. planning New Haven, 1979-83, v.p. corp. planning and regulatory matters, 1983-84; sr. v.p. fin. and planning So. New Eng. Telecommunications Corp., New Haven, 1984—; bd. dirs. 1st Constn. Bank. New Haven. Charter mem., bd. dirs. Clinton (Conn.) Jaycees, 1967-68; chmn. allocations com., bd. dirs. United Way, New Haven, 1973-74, New Haven Symphony Orch., 1990—; bd. dirs., v.p., pres. Gateway Counseling, Essex, Conn., 1975-86; bd. govs. Old Saybrook (Conn.) Hist. Soc., 1979-80; trustee Rector's Concern, Old Saybrook, 1980-88; chmn. So. New Eng. Telephone Co. Polit. Action Com., New Haven, 1987—. Mem. U.S. Telephone Assn. (bd. dirs., exec. com. 1984—), Conn. Joint Coun. on Econ. Edn. (fin. chmn. 1988—), U. Pa. Club Greater Hartford, Univ. Club Hartford, Kappa Alpha. Republican. Episcopalian. Avocations: cross country skiing, hiking, golf, tennis. Office: So New England Telecom Corp 227 Church St Fl 15 New Haven CT 06510-1806

MIGLORE, JOSEPH JAMES, furniture manufacturing executive; b. Columbus, Ohio, May 12, 1945; m. Bonnie Chappell, Oct. 27, 1945; children: Shaun Ryan, Jamie Renee. BSBA, Ohio State U., 1971. Sr. acct. Ernst & Young, Columbus, 1971-74; asst. contr. Borden Chem. Co., Columbus, 1974-78; group contr. Borden Chem., Columbus, 1983-85; contr. Light Products, Grand Rapids, Mich., 1978-83; contr., treas. Haworth Inc., Holland, Mich., 1985-87, v.p. fin. and administrn., 1985-90; pres., CEO Ameriwood Industries, Grand Rapids, 1990—. Bd. advisors Holland Area Leadership Program, 1988-89, Columbus Area Leadership Program, 1976; mem. acctg. adv. bd. Grand Valley State Coll., Allendale, Mich., 1989—. With USAF, 1965-69. Mem. AICPA, Fin. Exec. Inst., Nat. Assn. Accountants, Ohio Soc. CPAs, Econs. Club. Grand Rapids, Beta Gamma Sigma. Home: 233 Foxdown Rd Holland MI 49424-2790 Office: Ameriwood Industries 171 Monroe NW Grand Rapids MI 49503

MIGNANELLI, JAMES ROBERT, manufacturing executive; b. Lawrence, Kans., May 20, 1932; s. Giacomo Mignanelli and Ida (Longo) Wlodyka; divorced; children: James T., Karen S., Suzanne J. Sales/mktg. AT&T, N. Andover, Mass., 1955-61; asst. sales engr. Transitron Corp., Wakefield, Mass., 1961-64; mgr. customer service ITT Corp., Lawrence, 1964-66, mgr. export and govt. sales, 1966-68, product mktg. engr., 1968-75; v.p. Plastronic Engring. Corp., Haverhill, Mass., from 1975, exec. v.p. Served in USN, 1951-54. Roman Catholic. Home: 7 Greenlawn Ave Methuen MA 01844-6223 Office: Plastronic Engring Corp 35 Walnut St Haverhill MA 01830-5692

MIGNANELLI, THOMAS D., automobile company executive. Formerly with Ford Motor Co., Detroit; v.p. mktg. Nissan Motor Corp., Carson, Calif., 1987-88, exec. v.p. ops., 1988-90; pres., chief exec. officer Nissan Motor Corp., 1990—. Office: Nissan Motor Corp PO Box 191 Gardena CA 90248-0191

MIGNONE, MARIO B., Italian studies educator; b. Benevento, Italy, July 26, 1940; came to U.S., 1960; s. Roberto and Palmina (Iannace) M.; m. Lois Dolores Pontillo, June 29, 1968; children: Pamela Anne, Cristina Maria, Elizabeth Maria. BA, CCNY, 1967; MA, Rutgers U., 1969, PhD, 1972. Prof. Italian lang. SUNY, Stony Brook, 1970—, dir. undergrad. studies, 1976-83, dir. grad. studies, 1983-87; founder, exec. dir. Ctr. for Italian Studies, chmn. French and Italian dept., Stony Brook, 1988—. Author: The Theater of Eduardo De Filippo, 1974, Abnormality and Anguish in the narrative of Dino Buzzati, 1981, Eduardo De Filippo, 1984, Pirandello in America, 1988; Columbus: Meeting of Cultures, 1993; Italy Today: A Country in transition, 1995; assoc. mng. editor Forum Italicum, 1986-94, editor, 1994—; contbr. articles to profl. jours. Mem. Am. Assn. Tchrs. Italian (pres. 1982-84). Home: 26 Hopewell Dr Stony Brook NY 11790-2339 Office: SUNY Dept French Italian Stony Brook NY 11794

MIGUE, JEAN LUC, economics educator; b. Montreal, Que., Can., Apr. 13, 1933; s. Joseph Alfred and Marie Laurence (Venne) M.; m. Renee Caron, Sept. 13, 1958; children—Paule, Pascal, Nicolas. B.A. in Econs, U. Montreal, 1953, M.A., 1956; Ph.D. in Econs, Am. U., 1968. Researcher Bank of Can., 1957-58; prof. Laval U., 1962-70; prof. econs. Nat. Sch. Public Adminstrn., Quebec, 1970—; mem. staff Econ. Council Can., 1973-74. Author: The Price of Health, 1974, Le Prix du Transport, 1978, Nationalistic Policies of Canada, 1979, L'Economiste et La chose Publique, 1979, The Public Monopoly of Education, 1989, Federalism and Free Trade, 1993. Massey Found. fellow, 1956. Fellow Royal Soc. Can.; mem. Am. Econ. Assn., Can. Econ. Assn., Public Choice Soc. Roman Catholic. Office: 945 Wolfe, Quebec, PQ Canada G1V 3J9

MIHALAS, DIMITRI MANUEL, astronomer, educator; b. Los Angeles, Mar. 20, 1939; s. Emmanuel Demetrious and Jean (Christo) M.; m. Alice Joelen Covalt, June 15, 1963 (div. Nov. 1974); children: Michael Demetrious, Genevieve Alexandra; m. Barbara Ruth Rickey, May 18, 1975 (div. Dec. 1992). B.A. with highest honors, UCLA, 1959; M.S., Calif. Inst. Tech., 1960, Ph.D., 1964. Asst. prof. astrophys. scis. Princeton U., 1964-67; asst. prof. physics U. Colo., 1967-68; assoc. prof. astronomy and astrophysics U. Chgo., 1968-70, prof., 1970-71; adj. prof. astrogeophysics, also physics and astrophysics U. Colo., 1972-80; sr. scientist High Altitude Obs., Nat. Center Atmospheric Research, Boulder, Colo., 1971-79, 82-85; prof. astronomy U. Ill., 1985—; astronomer Sacramento Peak Obs., Sunspot, N.Mex., 1979-82; cons. Los Alamos Nat. Lab, 1981—; vis. dept. astrophysics Oxford (Eng.) U., 1977-78; sr. vis. fellow dept. physics and astronomy Univ. Coll., London, 1978; mem. astronomy adv. panel NSF, 1972-75. Author: Galactic Astronomy, 2d edit, 1981, Stellar Atmospheres, 1970, 2d edit., 1978, Theorie des Atmospheres Stellaires, 1971, Foundations of Radiation Hydrodynamics, 1984; assoc. editor Astrophys. Jour., 1970-79, Jour. Computational Physics, 1981-87, Jour. Quantitative Spectroscopy, 1984—; mem. editorial bd. Solar Physics, 1981-89. NSF fellow, 1959-62; Van Maanen fellow, 1962-63; Eugene Higgins vis. fellow, 1963-64; Alfred P. Sloan Found. Research fellow, 1969-71; Alexander von Humboldt Stiftung sr. U.S. scientist awardee, 1984. Mem. U.S. Nat. Acad. Sci., Internat. Astron. Union (pres. commn. 36 1976-79), Am. Astron. Soc. (Helen B. Warner prize 1974), Astron. Soc. Pacific (dir. 1975-77). Home: 1924 Blackthorn Dr Champaign IL 61821 Office: Dept Astronomy U Ill 1002 W Green St Urbana IL 61801-3074

MIHALIC, DAVID ANTHONY, national park administrator; b. Litchfield, Ill., July 10, 1946; s. John Anthony and Geraldine Emily (Mills) M.; m. Jeri Lynn Andrews, June 25, 1988; children: Emily Victoria, Nicholas Charles. BS, So. Ill. U., 1968; MS, Mich. State U., 1974; grad. with distinction, Fed. Law Enforcement Tng. Ctr., Glynco, Ga., 1976. Environ. planner U.S. Army C.E., Ft. Worth, 1969-72; park ranger Glacier Nat. Park Nat. Park Svc., Mont., 1972-74; recreation planner Bur. Land Mgmt., Fairbanks, Alaska, 1974-76, Denver, 1977-78; dist. ranger Yellowstone Nat. Park Nat. Park Svc., Old Faithful, Wyo., 1978-81; supt. Yukon-Charley Rivers Nat. Res. Nat. Park Svc., Eagle City, Alaska, 1981-85; asst. supt. Great Smoky Mountains Nat. Park Nat. Park Svc., Tenn. and N.C., 1985-88; supt. Mammoth Cave Nat. Park, Nat. Park Svc., Ky., 1988-93; chief Office of Policy Nat. Park Svc. Hdqrs., Washington, 1993-94; supt. Glacier Nat. Park, West Glacier, Mont., 1994—; spl. advisor Bartrum River Area Devel. Dist., Bowling Green, Ky., 1988-94; instr. Albright Tng. Acad., Grand Canyon, Ariz., 1989—; adv. dir. Cave City Conv. Ctr., 1990-94; dir. Caveland Sanitation Authority, Cave City, Ky., 1988-94; dir. Flathead Basin Commn., 1994—, Flathead Vis. and Conv. Assn., 1994—. Contbr. articles to profl. jours. Scoutmaster Boy Scouts Am., Ft. Worth, 1971; mem. bldg. com. Our Lady of The Caves Ch., Horse Cave, Ky., 1990; councilman Eagle City, Alaska, 1984. Capt. U.S. Army, 1968-72. Named Supt. of Yr., Nat. Park Svc., 1994; named to Hon. Order Ky. Cols., 1988. Mem. Assn. Nat. Pk. Rangers (charter, regional rep. 1979-80, sec. award 1979, 89), Employee and Alumni Assn. Nat. Pk. Svc., Internat. Assn. Natural Resource Pilots, Rotary, Kiwanis (v.p Gatlinburg, Tenn. club 1987). Roman Catholic. Avocations: watercolor painting, flying commercial aircraft. Office: Glacier Nat Park West Glacier MT 59936

MIHALY, EUGENE BRAMER, consultant, corporate executive, writer, educator; b. The Hague, The Netherlands, Nov. 11, 1934; s. Eddy and Cecile (Bramer) Kahn; stepson of Eugene Mihaly; children: Lisa Klee, Jessica; 1 stepson, Russell C. DuBrow. AB magna cum laude, Harvard U., 1956; PhD, London Sch. Econs. and Polit. Sci., 1964. Aviation/space editor Hartford (Conn.) Courant, 1960-61; internat. economist AID, Washington, 1964-65; dep. dir. Peace Corps, Tanzania, 1966, dir., 1967-68; dep. dir. East Asia/Pacific bur. Peace Corps, Washington, 1969, dir. office program devel., evaluation and rsch., 1969-70; assoc. dir. Inst. Internat. Studies, U. Calif., Berkeley, 1970-72; pres. Mihaly Internat. Corp., 1972—; chmn. bd. Mihaly Internat. Can., Ltd., 1992—; sr. lectr. Haas Sch. Bus. U. Calif., Berkeley, 1991—. Author: Foreign Aid and Politics in Nepal: A Case Study, 1965; contbr.: Political Development in Micronesia, 1974, Management of the Multinationals, 1974; also articles to various pubs. Chmn. bd. dirs. Childreach (Plan Internat. U.S.A.); bd. dirs. Plan Internat., Inc.; trustee World Without War Coun.; chmn. Calif.-S.E. Asia Bus. Coun.; mem. Dist. Export Coun. No. Calif.; mem. adv. bd. World Resources Inst.; mem. U.S. nat. com. Pacific Econ. Coop. Mem. Coun. on Fgn. Rels., Signet Soc. San Francisco Com. on Fgn. Rels. Home: 170 Tremont Ste Apt 602 Boston MA 02111

MIHAN, RALPH GEORGE, lawyer; b. San Francisco, Mar. 30, 1941; s. Ralph William and Norma Rose (Holmes) M.; m. Eleanor Mae Green, Sept. 24, 1966; children: Gregory Scott, Jeffrey Matthew. BA, St. Mary's Coll., 1963; JD, U. San Francisco, 1966. Bar: Calif. 1966, U.S. Dist. Ct. (no. dist.) Calif. 1967, U.S. Ct. Appeals (9th cir.) 1967. Atty. U.S. Dept. Interior, San Francisco, 1967-74, field solicitor (area counsel) Office of the Solicitor, 1974—; lectr. Nat. Park Svc. Rangers Acad., 1976—. Dir. coach St. Raphael's Cath. Youth Orgn. Basketball Program, San Rafael, 1977-88, San Rafael Youth Soccer League, 1978-88, San Rafael Little League, 1979-89; commr. City San Rafael Pk. and Recreation Commn., 1982—. Recipient Outstanding Community Svc. award Calif. Pk. and Recreation Soc., 1983. Mem. San. Francisco Bar Assn., Fed. Bar Assn. (pres. San Francisco chpt. 1974-75, exec. com. 1976—, Outstanding Contbn. award 1977). Office: US Dept Interior Office of the Solicitor 600 Harrison St Ste 545 San Francisco CA 94107-1370

MIHAN, RICHARD, dermatologist; b. L.A., Dec. 20, 1925; s. Arnold and Virginia Catharine (O'Reilly) M.; student U. So. Calif., 1945; MD, St. Louis U., 1949. Rotating intern Los Angeles County Gen. Hosp., 1949-51, resident in dermatology, 1954-57; practice medicine specializing in dermatology, Los Angeles, 1957—; emeritus clin. prof. dept. medicine, dermatology and syphilology U. So. Calif. Served as lt. (j.g.) M.C., USNR, 1951-53, ret. as lt. comdr. Diplomate Am. Bd. Dermatology. Fellow ACP; mem. Internat. Soc. Tropical Dermatology, Soc. Investigative Dermatology, Pacific Dermatologic Assn. (exec. bd. 1971-74), Calif. Med. Assn. (chmn. dermatologic sect. 1973-74), AMA, Los Angeles Dermatol. Soc. (pres. 1975-76), Am. Acad. Dermatology, L.A. Acad. Medicine (pres. 1988-89), Calif. Club. Roman Catholic. Office: 1245 Wilshire Blvd Los Angeles CA 90017-4810

MIHICH, ENRICO, medical researcher; b. Fiume, Italy, Jan. 4, 1928; came to U.S., 1957; s. Milan and Rosina (Lenaz) M.; m. Renata Marisa Mustacchi, Sept. 25, 1954; 1 child, Sylvia. B.S., U. Milan, Italy, 1944, M.D., 1951, docent, 1962; MD (honoris causa), U. Marseille, 1986. Research asst. Inst. Pharmacology U. Milan, Italy, 1951, asst. prof., 1954-56; vis. research fellow Sloan Kettering Inst. Cancer Research, N.Y.C., 1952-54; head pharmacology lab. Valeas Pharm. Industry, Milan, 1954-56; sr. cancer research scientist dept. exptl. therapeutics Roswell Park Cancer Inst., Buffalo, 1957-59, assoc. cancer research scientist, 1959-66, prin. scientist, 1966-71, dir. dept. exptl. therapeutics and Grace Cancer Drug Ctr., 1971—, v.p. for sponsored programs, 1987—; prof. pharmacology SUNY-Buffalo, 1960—, research asst., 1960-66, research assoc., 1966-68, research prof. pharmacology, 1968-69, chmn. dept. pharmacology, 1969—; assoc. prof. biochem. pharmacology Sch. of Pharmacy, 1963-68, adj. prof. biochem. pharmacology, 1968—; cons., lectr. in field; participant numerous symposia; sci. advisor govt. agys., pvt. industry; mem. Nat. Cancer Adv. Bd., 1984-90. Author more than 230 books, articles, chpts. in books; editor-in-chief for N.Am. and Japan, Cancer Immunology and Immunotherapy; mem. editorial bd. Advances in Cancer Chemotherapy, Internat. Jour. Immunopharmacology, Cancer and Metastasis Revs., others; adv. editor Oncology Rsch., Selective Cancer Therapeutics jours. Recipient numerous grants for med. research; Fulbright travel fellow, 1952-53; Sloan Found. fellow, 1953-54; Myron Karon Meml. Lectr., 1981. Recipient Lifetime Sci. award Inst. Advanced Studies in Immunology and Aging, 1994; numerous grants for med. rsch.; Fulbright Travel fellow, 1952-53; Sloan Found. fellow, 1953-54; Myron Karon Meml. Lectr., 1981. Office: Grace Cancer Drug Ctr Roswell Park Cancer Inst Elm and Carlton Sts Buffalo NY 14263

MIHM, MARTIN CHARLES, JR., pathologist, educator; b. Pitts.; s. Martin Charles and Cecilia Matilda (Hepp) M. AB, Duquesne U., 1955; MD, U. Pitts., 1961; MA (with honors), Harvard U., 1989. Diplomate Am. Bd. Dermatology, Am. Bd. Pathology. Intern Mt. Sinai Hosp., N.Y.C., 1961-62, resident in medicine, 1963-64; resident in dermatology Mass. Gen. Hosp., Boston, 1964-67, resident in Pathology, 1968-72, chief dermatopathology, 1973-94; asst. prof. pathology Harvard U. Med. Sch., Boston, 1972-75, assoc. prof., 1975-79, chief dermatopathology, 1982-93; prof. pathology Mass. Gen. Hosp.-Harvard U., Boston, 1980-93; prof., chief dermatopathology, dermatology Albany (N.Y.) Med. Coll., 1993—; adj. prof. pathology Vanderbilt U., 1989—; chmn. pathology com. Intergroup Melanoma Study, 1983—; pathologist Malignant Melanoma Coop. Group, 1972-77; chief sr. adminstr. Wellman Labs., Mass. Gen. Hosp., 1985-93; cons. WHO, 1985—, chmn. pathology standing com., 1991—; vis. prof. pathology Harvard Med. Sch. Author: Primer of Dermatopathology, 1984, 2d edit., 1992, Problematic Pigmented Lesions, 1990; editor: Lymphoproliferative Disorders of the Skin, 1986, Pathbiology and Recognition Malignant Melanoma, 1988; contbr. articles to med. jours. Served to comdr. USPHS, 1967-69. Fellow ACP, Am. Acad. Dermatology, Am. Soc. Dermatopathology; mem. AMA (Harvard Med. Sch. rep. to med. sch. sect. 1991), Harvard Dermatology House Officer's Assn. (pres. 1982), Harvard Club (Boston, N.Y.C.), Alpha Omega Alpha, Pi Gamma Mu. Democrat. Roman Catholic. Home: 100 Memorial Dr Apt 87A Cambridge MA 02142-1330 Office: Albany Med Coll 47 New Scotland Ave Albany NY 12208-3479

MIHM, MICHAEL MARTIN, federal judge; b. Amboy, Ill., May 18, 1943; s. Martin Clarence and Frances Johannah (Morrissey) M.; m. Judith Ann Zosky, May 6, 1967; children—Molly Elizabeth, Sarah Ann, Jacob Michael, Jennifer Leah. B.A., Loras Coll., 1964; J.D., St. Louis U., 1967. Asst. prosecuting atty. St. Louis County, Clayton, Mo., 1967-68; asst. state's atty. Peoria County, Peoria, Ill., 1968-69; asst. city atty. City of Peoria, Ill., 1969-72; state's atty. Peoria County, Peoria, Ill., 1972-80; sole practice Peoria, Ill., 1980-82; U.S. dist. judge U.S. Govt., Peoria, Ill., 1982—; chief U.S. dist. judge U.S. Dist. Ct. (ctrl. dist.) Ill., 1994—; chmn. com. internat. jud. rels. U.S. Jud. Conf., 1994—, mem. com. jud. br., 1987-93; adj. prof. law John Marshall Law Sch., 1990. Past mem. adv. bd. Big Brothers-Big Sisters, Crisis Nursery, Peoria; past bd. dirs. Salvation Army, Peoria, W.D. Boyce council Boy Scouts Am., State of Ill. Treatment Alternatives to Street Crime, Gov.'s Criminal Justice Info. Council; past vice-chmn. Ill. Dangerous Drugs Adv. Council; trustee Proctor Health Care Found., 1991—. Recipient Good Govt. award Peoria Jaycees, 1978. Mem. Peoria County Bar Assn. (former bd. dirs., past chmn. profl. improvement com.). Roman Catholic. Office: US Dist Ct 204 Federal Bldg 100 NE Monroe St Peoria IL 61602-1003

MIHRAN, THEODORE GREGORY, retired physicist; b. Detroit, June 28, 1924; s. Miro Krikor and Zaroohi (Mesrobian) M.; m. Hermine Misirian, July 26, 1953 (dec. 1980); children: Gregory Charles, Joyce Hermine, Richard Theodore; m. Jean Wilson, Aug. 22, 1981; stepchildren: Mark Whitcomb, Susan Rebecca. A.B., Stanford U., 1944, M.S., 1947, Ph.D. (Fortescue fellow, 1948-49), 1950. Physicist Rsch. and Devel. Ctr., Gen. Electric Co., Schenectady, 1950-92; ret., 1992; vis. prof. elec. engring. dept. Cornell U., Ithaca, N.Y., 1963-64; adj. prof. Union Coll., Schenectady, 1960-61; lectr. Chalmers Inst., Gothenburg, Sweden, 1965; cons. in field. Contbr. articles to profl. publs. Pres., bd. dirs. Schenectady Symphony, 1962-63. Served with USN, 1944-46. Fellow IEEE (editor Trans. on Electron Devices 1970-73); mem. Am. Phys. Soc., Inst. Microwave Power, Sigma Xi, Phi Beta Kappa, Tau Beta Pi. Mem. Niskayuna Reformed Church. Patentee. Home: 898 Ash Tree Ln Niskayuna NY 12309-1723

MIKA, JOSEPH JOHN, library educator, consultant; b. McKees Rocks, Pa., Mar. 1, 1948; s. George Joseph and Sophie Ann (Stec) M.; children: Jason-Paul Joseph, Matthew Douglas, Meghan Leigh. BA in English, U. Pitts., 1969, M.L.S., 1971, Ph.D. in L.S., 1980. Asst. librarian, instr. Ohio State U. Mansfield, 1971-73; asst. librarian, asst. prof. Johnson State Coll. (Vt.), 1973-75; grad. asst., teaching fellow Sch. Libr. and Info. Sci. U. Pitts., 1975-77; asst. dean, assoc. prof. libr. svc. U. So. Miss., Hattiesburg, 1977-86, dir. libr. and info. sci. program, Wayne State U. Libr. and Info. Sci. program, 1986-94, prof., 1994—; cons. to libraries. Chair Mich Ctr. for the Book, 1994— Served to lt. col. USAR. Decorated D.S.M., Army Res. Components Achievement medal, Meritorious Svc. medal, Army Commendation medal. Mem. ALA (councilor 1983-86, chmn. constn. and bylaws com. 1985-86), Assn. Libr. and Info. Sci. Edn., (chmn. membership com. 1982-83, chmn. nominating com. 1982, exec. bd. 1986), Miss. Libr. Assn. (pres.-elect 1985), Mich. Libr. Assn. (chair libr. edn. com. 1989), Leadership Acad. (oversight com. 1989—), Assn. Coll. and Rsch. Librs. (chmn. 1982-83, chmn. budget com. 1982-83), Soc. Miss. Archivists (treas., exec. bd. 1981-83), Mich. Ctr. for The Book (chair 1994—), Beta Phi Mu (pres.-elect 1987-89, pres. 1989-91), Phi Delta Kappa. Lodge: Kiwanis (Hattiesburg). Contbr. articles to profl. jours. Home: 4332 Hillside Dr Ann Arbor MI 48105 Office: Wayne State U Libr and Info Sci Program 106 Kresge Library Detroit MI 48202

MIKALOW, ALFRED ALEXANDER, II, deep sea diver, marine surveyor, marine diving consultant; b. N.Y.C., Jan. 19, 1921; m. Janice Brenner, Aug. 1, 1960; children: Alfred Alexander, Jon Alfred. Student Rutgers U., 1940; MS, U. Calif., Berkeley, 1948; MA, Rochdale U. (Can.), 1950. Owner Coastal Diving Co., Oakland, Calif., 1950—, Divers Supply, Oakland, 1952—; dir. Coastal Sch. Deep Sea Diving, Oakland, 1950—; capt. and master rsch. vessel Coastal Researcher I; mem. Marine Inspection Bur., Oakland. marine diving contractor, cons. Mem. adv. bd. Medic Alert Found., Turlock, Calif., 1960—. Lt. comdr. USN, 1941-47, 49-50. Decorated Purple Heart, Silver Star. Mem. Divers Assn. Am. (pres. 1970-74), Treasury Recovery, Inc. (pres. 1972-75), Internat. Assn. Profl. Divers, Assn. Diving Contractors, Calif. Assn. Pvt. Edn. (no. v.p 1971-72), Authors Guild, Internat. Game Fish Assn., U.S. Navy League, U.S. Res. Officers Assn., Tailhook Assn., U.S. Submarine Vets. WWII, Explorer Club (San Francisco), Calif. Assn. Marine Surveyors (pres. 1988—), Soc. Naval Archs. and Marine Engrs., Masons, Lions. Author: Fell's Guide to Sunken Treasure Ships of the World, 1972; (with H. Rieseberg) The Knight from Maine, 1974. Office: 320 29th Ave Oakland CA 94601-2104

MIKALSON, JON DENNIS, classics educator; b. Milw., Aug. 1, 1943; s. John Martin and Evelyn Kathryn (Heuser) M.; m. Mary Helen Villemonte, Aug. 28, 1966; children: Melissa, Jacquelyn. BA, U. Wis., 1965; postgrad., Am. Sch. Classical Studies, Athens, Greece, 1968-69; PhD, Harvard U., 1970. Asst. prof. classics U. Va., Charlottesville, 1970-75, assoc. prof., 1975-84, prof., 1984—, chmn. dept. classics, 1978-90; vis. scholar Corpus Christi Coll., Cambridge, Eng., 1977-78; mem. Inst. for Advanced Study, Princeton,

N.J., 1984-85; Whitehead prof. Am. Sch. Classical Studies, 1995-96. Author: The Sacred and Civil Calendar of the Athenian Year, 1975, Athenian Popular Religion, 1983, Honor Thy Gods: Popular Religion in Greek Tragedy, 1991; contbr. articles to profl. and scholarly jours. James Rignall Wheeler fellow Am. Sch. Classical Studies, 1968-69, NEH fellow, 1977-78, Herodotus fellow Inst. for Advanced Study, 1984-85. Mem. Am. Philol. Assn., Am. Sch. Classical Studies, Archeol. Inst. of Am., Classical Assn. of Middle West and South (pres. so. sect. 1988-90), Classical Assn. of Va., Phi Beta Kappa, Phi Eta Sigma, Phi Kappa Phi. Club: Lions. Home: PO Box 664 Crozet VA 22932-9308 Office: University of Virginia Dept of Classics 146 Cabell Hall Charlottesville VA 22903-3196

MIKEL, SARAH ANN, librarian; b. Bklyn., Aug. 29, 1947; d. Robert H. and Sarah A. (Saver) Whalen; m. John R. Mikel, Oct. 21, 1977; 1 dau., Katherine Ann. B.A., U. Miami, 1969; M.A., U. Fla., 1971; M.A.L.S., Rosary Coll., River Forest, Ill., 1973. Editorial researcher Field Ednl. Enterprises, Chgo., 1971-72; librarian Purdue U., West Lafayette, Ind., 1973-75, U.S. Army Corps of Engrs., Rock Island, Ill., 1975-76, chief librarian, Washington, 1976-87, major command librarian, 1987-91; librr. dir. Nat. Def. Libr., Washington, 1991—; chmn. FEDLINK Users Group, 1980-83; mem. exec. adv. coun. FEDLINK, 1988-90; program chmn. Fed. Interagy. Field Librarians Workshop, 1983-84. Mem. Spl. Library Assn. (chmn. mil. librarians 1978-79), Army Lib. Inst. (chmn. 1988, 94, Army dep. functional chiefs rep. 1992-94). Home: 3343 Reservoir Rd NW Washington DC 20007-2312 Office: Nat Def Univ Ft Leslie J McNair 4th & P St SW Washington DC 20319

MIKELBERG, ARNOLD, meat packing company executive; b. N.Y.C., Apr. 28, 1937; s. Nathan and Frances (Levine) M.; m. Judith Pauline Weil, July 5, 1970; children: Hilary, Barrett. B.S., Mich. State U., 1958. Gen. mgr. Hygrade Food Products Corp., Detroit, 1958-70; v.p. South Chgo. Packaging Co., Chgo., 1970-71, Packers Provision Co., Highland Park, Ill., 1971-72, Frederick & Herrud, Detroit, 1972-78; sr. v.p., dir. John Morrell & Co., Northfield, Ill., 1978-88; exec. v.p. Thornapple Valley Inc., Southfield, Mich., 1988—; bd. dirs. Thornapple Valley Inc., Southfield. Mem. Am. Meat Inst. Republican. Office: Thorn Apple Valley Inc 18700 W 10 Mile Rd Southfield MI 48075-2699

MIKELS, RICHARD ELIOT, lawyer; b. Cambridge, Mass., July 14, 1947; s. Albert Louis and Charlotte Betty (Shapiro) M.; m. Deborah Gwen Katz, Aug. 29, 1970; children: Allison Brooke, Robert Jarrett. BS in Bus. Adminstrn., Boston U., 1969, JD cum laude, 1972. Bar: Mass. 1972, U.S. Dist. Ct. Mass. 1974, U.S. Ct. Appeals (1st cir.) 1978. Legal examiner ICC, Washington, 1972-74; ptnr. Riemer & Braunstein, Boston, 1974-80; ptnr., chmn. comml. law sect. Peabody & Brown, Boston, 1980-88; mem., chmn. comml. law sect. Mintz, Levin, Cohn, Ferris, Glovsky and Popeo, P.C., Boston, 1988—. Contbr. articles to profl. jours. Tng. adv. com. Jewish Vocat. Svc., Boston, 1991; vice-chair lawyers com. Combined Jewish Philanthropies, 1994, 95. Fellow Am. Coll. Bankruptcy; mem. ABA, Am. Bankruptcy Inst., Assn. Comml. Ins. Attys., Comml. Law League Am., Mass. Bar Assn., Boston Bar Assn. Home: 4 Barley Ln Wayland MA 01778-1600 Office: Mintz Levin Cohn Ferris Glovsky & Popeo PC Financial Center Boston MA 02111

MIKES, THOMAS LOUIS, optical design engineer; b. Cleve., Jan. 26, 1946; s. Frank Leo and Lottie Helen (Wiklinski) M.; m. Christine Mockler, Dec. 28, 1968 (div. Mar. 1984); children: Christine Veronica, Johanna Emily, Barbara Patricia. BS in Engring., Cath. U. Am., Washington, 1968, MS in Applied Physics, 1970. Physicist U.S. Naval Rsch. Lab., Washington, 1968-72; staff scientist systems div. AVCO, Wilmington, Mass., 1972-76, Sci. Application, Inc., Bedford, Mass., 1976-78; pres. Am. Holographic Inc., Littleton, Mass., 1976—. Mem. Optical Soc. Am. Achievements include patent for Low Profile Spectral Analysis System. Home: 605 Old Stonebrook Acton MA 01718 Office: Am Holographic Inc PO Box 1310 Littleton MA 01460-4310

MIKESELL, MARVIN WRAY, geography educator; b. Kansas City, Mo., June 16, 1929; s. Loy George and Clara (Wade) M.; m. Reine-Marie de France, Apr. 1, 1957. B.A., UCLA, 1952, M.A., 1953; Ph.D., U. Calif.-Berkeley, 1959. Instr. to prof. geography U. Chgo., 1958—, chmn. dept. geography, 1969-74, 83-86; del. U.S. Nat. Commn. for UNESCO. Author: Northern Morocco, 1961; editor: Readings in Cultural Geography, 1962, Geographers Abroad, 1973, Perspectives on Environment, 1974. Fellow Am. Geog. Soc. (hon.); mem. Assn. Am. Geographers (pres. 1975-76, Disting. Career award 1995). Club: Quadrangle. Home: 1155 E 56th St Chicago IL 60637-1530 Office: Com Geog Studies 5828 S University Ave Chicago IL 60637-1515

MIKESELL, RAYMOND FRECH, economics educator; b. Eaton, Ohio, Feb. 13, 1913; s. Otho Francis and Josephine (Frech) M.; m. Desyl DeLauder, July 6, 1937 (div.); children: George DeLauder and Norman DeLauder (twins); m. Irene Langdoc, Feb. 18, 1956. Student, Carnegie Inst. Tech., 1931-33; B.A. cum laude, Ohio U., 1935, M.A., 1935, Ph.D., 1939. Asst. prof. econ. U. Wash., 1937-41; economist OPA, Washington, 1941-42, U.S. Treasury Dept., 1942-46; rep. U.S. Treasury Dept., Cairo, Egypt, 1943-44; cons. U.S. Treasury Dept., 1946-47; on Middle East affairs FOA, 1953; chief fgn. minerals div. Pres.'s Materials Policy Commn., 1951-52; mem. staff Fgn. Econ. Policy Com. (Randall Com.), 1953-54; mem. U.S. Currency Mission to Saudi Arabia, 1948; spl. U.S. rep. to Israel, summer 1952; mem. U.S. mission to Israel, Ethiopia, summer 1953; prof. econs. U. Va., 1946-57; W.E. Miner prof. econs. U. Oreg., 1957—; dir. Inst. Internat. Studies and Overseas Adminstrn., 1958-60; assoc. dir. Inst. Internat. Studies and Overseas Adminstrn. U. Oreg., 1960-68; vis. prof. Grad. Inst. Internat. Studies, Geneva, 1964; sr. staff mem. Council Econ. Advisers, Exec. Office of Pres., 1955-56, cons. to Council Econ. Advisers, 1956-57; cons. Pan Am. Union, 1954-63, Dept. State, 1947-53, 63-67, 71-83, Ford Found., 1962, Dept. Commerce, 1962-64, ICA, 1952-53, 61-62, OAS, 1963-73, AID, 1964-71; mem. UN Econ. Commn. for Latin Am. working group on regional market, 1958; cons. Senate Fgn. Relations Com., 1962, 67, World Bank, 1968, Inter-Am. Devel. Bank, 1968-75; mem. panel advisers Sec. Treasury, 1965-69; sr. fellow Nat. Bur. Econ. Research, 1972-73. Author: U.S. Economic Policy and International Relations, 1952, Foreign Exchange in the Postwar World, 1954, The Emerging Pattern of International Payments, 1954, Foreign Investments in Latin Am, 1955, Promoting United States Private Investment Abroad, 1957, Agricultural Surpluses and Export Policy, 1958, (with H. Chenery) Arabian Oil, 1949, (with M. Trued) Postwar Bilateral Payments Agreements, 1955, (with J. Behrman) Financing Free World Trade with the Sino-Soviet Bloc, 1958, Public International Lending for Development, 1966, (with R.W. Adler) Public External Financing of Devel. Banks, 1966, Public Fgn. Capital for Private Enterprises in Developing Countries, 1966, The Economics of Foreign Aid, 1968, Financing World Trade, 1969, (with others) Foreign Investment in the Petroleum and Mineral Industries, 1971; Editor: U.S. Private and Government Investment Abroad, 1962, (with H. Furth) Foreign Dollar Balances and the International Role of the Dollar, 1974, Foreign Investment in the Copper Industry, 1975, The World Copper Industry, 1979, New Patterns of World Mineral Development, 1979, The Economics of Foreign Aid and Self-Sustaining Development, 1983, Foreign Investment in Mining Projects, 1983, Petroleum Company Operations and Agreements in the Developing Countries, 1984, Stockpiling Strategic Materials, 1986, Nonfuel Minerals: Foreign Dependence and National Security, 1987; (with John W. Whitney) The World Mining Industry: Investment Strategy and Public Policy, 1987, The Global Copper Industry: Problems and Prospects, 1988, (with Lawrence F. Williams) International Banks and the Environment, 1992; mem. editorial adv. bd. Middle East Jour., 1947-58; mem. bd. editors: Am. Econ. Rev., 1953-55. Mem. Econ. Assn., Pi Kappa Alpha, Alpha Kappa Psi. Unitarian. Home: 2290 Spring Blvd Eugene OR 97403-1860

MIKESELL, RICHARD LYON, lawyer, financial counselor; b. Corning, N.Y., Jan. 29, 1941; s. Walter Ray and Clara Ellen (Lyon) M.; m. Anna May Creese, Mar. 16, 1973; 1 child, Joel. BSChemE, U. Calif., Berkeley, 1962; LLB, Duke U., 1965; BA in Liberal Studies, UCLA, 1967. Bar: Calif. 1965, U.S. Supreme Ct., Ohio, Calif., U.S. Ct. Appeals (9th and 2d cirs.), U.S. Patent Office. Patent atty. Procter & Gamble, Cin., 1965-66, Rocketdyne divsn. N.Am. Aviation, L.A., 1966-69; pvt. practice law L.A., 1969-81; prin. Law Offices of R.L. Mikesell, L.A., 1981—; fin. counselor L.A. Police Dept.,

1986—; arbitrator Am. Arbitration Assn., L.A., 1980—. Pres. San Fernando Valley Fair Housing Coun., L.A., 1969-72, Valley Women's Ctr., L.A., 1990; line res. officer L.A. Police Dept., 1969-72. Named Res. Officer of Yr. L.A. Police Dept., 1990. Avocation: high power rifle shooting. Office: 14540 Hamlin St Ste B Van Nuys CA 91411-1626

MIKITA, JOSEPH KARL, broadcasting executive; b. nr. Richmond, Va., Oct. 3, 1918; s. John and Catherine (Wargofcak) M.; m. Mary Therese Benya, Nov. 26, 1942; children: Patty-Jane Mikita Cashman, Michael, M. Noël Mikita Garagiola. BS, Fordham U., 1939; MS, Columbia U., 1940. Treas., controller Capital Cities Broadcasting Co., Albany, N.Y., 1955-58; controller Westinghouse Broadcasting Co., Inc., N.Y.C., 1958-60, v.p. fin., 1960-64, v.p. fin. and adminstrn., 1964-65, sr. v.p., 1965-69, 1975—; also dir., exec. v.p. Westinghouse Electric Corp. for Broadcasting, Learning and Leisure Activities, N.Y.C., 1969-75; dir. Sutro Tower, Inc. Author: (with others) The Business of Broadcasting, 1964. Bd. dirs. Fordham U. Council, Albany County Workshop, Albany County Heart Assn., Citizens For Reasonable Growth, Boca Raton; chmn. bd. Instructional TV. Served to maj. AUS, 1940-45, ETO. Recipient Order of Merit (Silver), Westinghouse Electric Corp., Disting. Service Alumni award Fordham U., 1969. Mem. AICPA, Internat. Radio and TV Soc., N.Y. Soc. CPAs, Fin. Execs. Inst. (dir., past pres. Manhattan chpt.), Inst. Broadcasting Fin. Mgmt. (past dir.), Town Club, Westchester Country Club, Boca Raton Club, M.G.A. Club, JDM Country Club, Royal Palm Yacht and Country Club, Rotary (1st v.p. N.Y. club). Home: 3125 NE 7th Dr Boca Raton FL 33431-6906 Office: 90 Park Ave New York NY 10016-1302

MIKITKA, GERALD PETER, investment banker, financial consultant; b. Chgo., July 7, 1943; s. Michael and Helen (Cuprisin) M.; m. Nancy Lee Parker, Mar. 6, 1977; children: Richard, Jeffrey, Jennifer. B.S.B.A. in Fin., Roosevelt U., 1966, postgrad., 1967. Diplomate: registered investment advisor. Sr. investment exec. Shearson-Hayden, Stone, Chgo., 1967-73; chmn., pres. Capital Directions, Inc., Chgo., 1973—; pres. CDI Fin. Advisors, Chgo., 1974—; CDI Properties, Chgo., 1974—, CDI Communications, Inc., Chgo., 1978—, A.B. Properties Inc., Chgo., 1986—, Am. Eagle Realty Inc., Chgo., 1988—, Grand Caribbean Properties Inc., Chgo., 1988, Cain Estates Inc., Chgo., 1988—, Caribbean Sea Properties Inc., Chgo., 1989—. Served with U.S. Army, 1967-69. Mem. Nat. Assn. Securities Dealers, Securities Investment Protection Assn., Broadcast Fin. Mgmt. Assn., Nat. Radio Broadcast Assn., Internat. Assn. Fin. Planning. Lodge: Rotary.

MIKKELSON, DEAN HAROLD, geological engineer; b. Devils Lake, N.D., July 25, 1922; s. John Harold and Theodora (Eklund) M.; m. Delphene Doss, May 30, 1946; 1 child, Lynn Dee Hoffman. Student, N.D. State Coll., 1940-41; midshipman, U.S. Naval Acad., 1945; BS in Geological Engring., U. N.D., 1956. Registered profl. engr., Okla. 2d officer U.S. Lines, Quaker Lines-States Lines, Portland, Oreg., 1945-48; ptnr. J.I. Case Farm Machinery & Packard Automobile Franchises, Devils Lake, N.D., 1948-52; oil and gas lease broker Devils Lake, N.D., 1952-54; geologist Sohio Petroleum Co., Oklahoma City, 1956-58; geol. engr. Petrobras, Belem do Para, Brazil, 1958-60; pvt. practice Oklahoma City, 1961-78; pres., owner Dogwatch Petroleum, Inc., Oklahoma City, 1978—; agrl. pilot, N.D., Mont., Tex., N.Mex., summers, 1952-56. Contbr. articles to profl. jours. Candidate Okla. Rep. State Legislature, Oklahoma City, 1958; del. various county and state conv., N.D. and Okla., 1948-68. With N.D. N.G., 1938-40, U.S. Army Air Corps., 1942. Mem. Oklahoma City Geol. Soc., Masons, Shriners, Jesters, Am. Legion, Sportsmans Country Club. Republican. Avocations: hunting, fishing, golf, oil painting, singing. Office: Dogwatch Petroleum Inc 3022 NW Expy Ste 413 Oklahoma City OK 73112

MIKLASZEWSKI, JAMES ALAN, television news correspondent; b. Milw., July 8, 1949; s. Bernard Anthony Miklaszewski and LaVerne Dorothy (Venus) Montagano; m. Cheryl Ann Heyse; children: James Alexander, Jeffrey Alan. Reporter WISM Radio, Madison, Wis., 1970-71; new dir. WIZM Radio, LaCrosse, Wis., 1971-72; reporter WBAP Radio, Ft. Worth, 1972-75; news dir. KRXV Radio, Ft. Worth, 1975-80; corr. CNN, Dallas, N.Y.C., 1980-83; White House corr. CNN, Washington, 1983-84, nat. corr., 1984-85; Pentagon corr. NBC TV News, Washington, 1985-88, White House corr., 1988—. Recipient ACE award Nat. Cable Acad., 1983, Edward R. Murrow award Bnai Brith, 1985, Pres.' award Wesley Coll., 1994. Mem. White House Corrs. Assn. Methodist. Avocations: ornithology, golf. Office: NBC News Washington Bur 4001 Nebraska Ave NW Washington DC 20016-2733

MIKLOSHAZY, ATTILA, bishop. Ordained priest Roman Cath. Ch., 1961, consecrated bishop, 1989. Titular bishop Castel Minore; bishop Apostolate to Hungarians, Scarborough, Ont., Can., 1989—. Office: St Augustine's Sem, 2661 Kingston Rd, Scarborough, ON Canada M1M 1M3*

MIKON, ARNOLD, architect; b. Detroit, Feb. 12, 1943; s. Solomon and Sophie (Korman) M.; m. Deena Rochelle Polinsky, Mar. 28, 1976; children: Bradley, Beth, Renee. BArch, U. of Mich., 1966, MBA, 1969. Registered Architect, Ariz., Colo., Kans., Mich. Project architect Wakely Assocs., Inc., Warren, Mich., 1966-69; sr. v.p. and chief fin. officer Smith, Hinchman and Grylls Assocs., Inc., Detroit, 1969—; pres. Terra Devel. Corp., Detroit, 1975—. Bd. of Rev., City of Huntington (Mich.) Woods, 1977-78. mem. AIA, (Detroit Chpt.), Engring. Soc. Detroit, Detroit Bd. Realtors, Urban-Land Inst., Knollwood Country Club. Home: 25498 Sherwood Dr Huntington Wd MI 48070-1737 Office: Smith Group Inc 150 W Jefferson Ave Ste 100 Detroit MI 48226-4415

MIKOS, DAVID EDWARD, architect; b. Chgo., Mar. 7, 1955; s. Edward J. and Anne (Latala) M.; m. Miranda M. Jevtovic, Sept. 13, 1980; 1 child, Arielle Anne. BArch with highest honors, U. Ill., 1978. Cert. Nat. Coun. Archtl. Registration Bds. Staff architect Children's Meml. Hosp., Chgo., 1977-83; sr. health designer Perkins & Will Architects, Chgo., 1983-85; pres. Anderson Mikos Architects, Chgo., 1985—; lectr. U. Ill., Chgo., 1980-81. Prin. works include outpatient surg. facility MRI, Cancer Ctr. Ingall's Meml. Hosp., Harvey, Ill., Children's Meml. Hosp. U. Chgo. Med. Ctr., Northwestern Meml. Hosp., Erlanger Med. Ctr., Chattanooga, Western Res. Care System, Youngstown, Ohio, Michael Reese Hosp. and Med. Ctr., Med. Arts Clinic, Dixon, Ill., Surg. Ctr., Dixon, pvt. residences, Kenilworth, Ill. Wilmette, Ill., Chgo. Mem. AIA (nat. com. health, Chgo. chpt. com. health), Am. Assn. Hosp. Planning, Internat. Hosp. Fedn. Office: Anderson Mikos Architects 1420 Kensington Rd Hinsdale IL 60521-2143

MIKULAS, JOSEPH FRANK, graphic designer, educator, painter; b. Jacksonville, Fla., Sept. 15, 1926; s. Joseph and Marina (Zeman) M.; m. Joyce Gregory Haddock, Sept. 29, 1946; children—Joyce Marina Mikulas Abney, Juliana Claire Mikulas Catlin. Student Harold Hilton Studios, 1942-50. Art dir. Peeples Displays, Inc., 1945-50, 53-56, Douglas Printing Co. Inc., 1950-53, 56-59; ptnr., graphic design exec. Benton & Mikulas Assocs., Inc. Jacksonville, 1960-67; pres. Mikulas Assocs., Inc., Jacksonville, 1968-92, exec. graphic designer, retired dir. communications, adj. prof. advt. design Jacksonville U.; mem. advt. bd. Pub. TV. Chmn. Youth Resources Bur.; chmn. Mayor's Medal Com. Served with USAAF, 1945. Recipient Gold medal Am. Advt. Fedn., 4th dist., 1971; numerous other awards, 1960-81. Mem. Advt. Fedn. of Jacksonville (past pres. 1970), Jacksonville Watercolor Soc. Republican. Episcopalian. Clubs: San Jose Country, River, Art Dirs. of Jacksonville (past pres.). Lodges: Masons, Rotary (past pres. S. Jacksonville 1970, Paul Harris fellow), Torch of Jacksonville (past pres. 1977). Creator over 40 trademarks for local, regional, nat. and internat. use by corps. based in Jacksonville. Home: 2014 River Rd Jacksonville FL 32207-3906 Office: 3886 Atlantic Blvd Jacksonville FL 32207-2035

MIKULECKY, THOMAS J., city manager; b. Mpls., Aug. 11, 1938; s. Elston J. and Doris A. (Charkston) M.; m. Patricia Ann Chwierut, June 22, 1963; children: Joseph Michael, Christine Marie, Paul Thomas, Susan Jane. BA, U. Minn., 1960; MA, Tufts-Harvard Univs., 1961; PhD, U. Ariz., 1970. Urban programs analyst City of Tucson, Ariz., 1965-67; asst. to city mgr. City of Dallas, 1968-71; assoc. prof., dir. grad. program pub. adminstrn. So. Meth. U., Dallas, 1971-75; county mgr. Summit County, Breckenridge, Colo., 1975-78; city mgr. City of Bartlesville, Okla., 1978—; cons. Dallas Area Criminal Justice Council, 1974, Texarkana (Tex, and Ark.) Metro Plan, 1975. Editor: (handbook) What Makes Our City Run: A Handbook for Council, Board and Commisson Members, 1972, Handbook

for Administrators of Small Cities, 1975. Served to 1st lt. USMC, 1961-64. Mem. Internat. City Mgmt. Assn. (10 Yr. Recognition award), Am. Soc. Pub. Adminstrn. (pres. North Tex. chpt. 1973-74), City Mgmt. Assn. Okla. (bd. dirs. 1982-83, treas. 1983-84, pres. 1984-85, Mgmt. Innovation award 1981), Okla. Mcpl. League. Republican. Roman Catholic. Lodges: Rotary (bd. dirs. Bartlesville chpt. 1986-87), Moose. Office: City of Peoria Rm 207 City Hall Peoria IL 61602

MIKULSKI, BARBARA ANN, senator; b. Balt., July 20, 1936. BA, Mt. St. Agnes Coll., 1958; MSW, U. Md., 1965; LLD (hon.), Bowie State U., 1989, Morgan State U., 1990, U. Mass., 1991. Social worker Balt. Dept. Social Services, 1961-63, 66-70; Balt.; mem. Balt. City Council, 1971-76, 95th-99th Congresses from 3d Md. Dist., 1977-87; U.S. senator from Md., 1987—; adj. prof. Loyola Coll., 1972-76. ●

MIKULSKI, PIOTR WITOLD, mathematics educator; b. Warsaw, Poland, July 20, 1925; came to U.S., 1957; s. Julian and Zofia (Zalewska) M.; m. Barbara H. Mikulski, Sept. 2, 1960; 1 son, Antony F. B.S., Sch. Stats., Warsaw, Poland, 1951, M.S., 1952; Ph.D., U. Calif.-Berkeley, 1961. Adj. Sch. Stats., 1950-57, Inst. Math., Warsaw, Poland, 1952-57; teaching and research asst. U. Calif.-Berkeley, 1957-61; asst. prof. math. U. Ill., Urbana, 1961-62; asst. prof. U. Md., College Park, 1962-66, assoc. prof., 1966-70, prof., 1970. Assoc. editor: Am. Jour. Math. and Mgmt. Sci., 1982—; contbr. articles to profl. jours. Mem. Inst. Math. Stats., Polish Inst. Arts and Scis. Am. Home: 2525 Sandy Run Ct Annapolis MD 21401-7371 Office: U Md Dept Math College Park MD 20742

MIKUS, ELEANORE ANN, artist; b. Detroit, July 25, 1927; d. Joseph and Bertha (Englot) M.; m. Richard Burns, July 6, 1949 (div. 1963); children: Richard, Hillary, Gabrielle. Student, Mich. State U., 1946-49, U. Mex., summer 1948; B.F.A., U. Denver, 1957, M.A., 1967; postgrad., Art Students League, 1958, NYU, 1959-60. Asst. prof. Cornell U., Ithaca, N.Y., 1979-80, assoc. prof., 1980-92, prof. art, 1992-94, prof. emerita, 1994—; asst. prof. art Monmouth Coll., West Long Branch, N.J., 1966-70, prof. Cornell, Rome, 1989; vis. lectr. painting Cooper Union, N.Y.C., 1970-72, Central Sch. Art and Design, London, 1973-77, Harrow (Eng.) Coll. Tech. and Art, 1975-76. Exhibited in 14 one-person shows at, Pace Gallery, N.Y.C. and O.K. Harris Gallery, N.Y.C., Baskett Gallery, Cin., 1982, 84, 85; represented in permanent collections including, Mus. Modern Art, N.Y.C., Whitney Mus., N.Y.C., Los Angeles County Mus., Cin. Mus., Birmingham (Ala.) Mus. Art, Indpls. Mus. Art, Nat. Gallery Art, Washington, Victoria and Albert Mus., London, Library of Congress, Washington; subject of book Eleanore Mikus, Shadows of the Real (by Robert Hobbs and Judith Bernstock), 1991. Guggenheim fellow, 1966-67; Tamarind fellow, summer 1968; MacDowell fellow, summer 1969; grantee Cornell U., 1988. Mem. AAUP. Home: PO Box 6586 Ithaca NY 14851-6586 Office: Cornell U Dept Art Tjaden Hall Ithaca NY 14853 *I have always adhered in my paintings to an almost classic simplicity of expression; it is the simplicity of the child as seen through the eyes of the artist—impulsive, dramatic and yet close to the rhythm of childlike expression, born of an innocence which is all the more sophisticated for being so. It doesn't pretend—it just is.*

MIKVA, ABNER JOSEPH, lawyer, retired federal judge; b. Milw., Jan. 21, 1926; s. Henry Abraham and Ida (Fishman) M.; m. Zoe Wise, Sept. 19, 1948; children: Mary, Laurie, Rachel. JD cum laude, U. Chgo., 1951; DL (hon.), U. Ill. Am. U., Northwestern U., Tulane U.; DHL (hon.), Hebrew U. Bar: Ill. 1951, D.C. 1978. Law clk. to U.S. Supreme Ct. Justice Sherman Minton, 1951; ptnr. firm Devoe, Shadur, Mikva & Plotkin, Chgo., 1952-68, D'Ancona, Pflaum, Wyatt & Riskind, 1973-74; lectr. Northwestern U. Law Sch., Chgo., 1973-75, U. Pa. Law Sch., 1983-85, Georgetown Law Sch., 1986-88, Duke U. Law Sch., Durham, N.C., 1990-91, U. Chgo. Law Sch., 1992-93; mem. Ill. Gen. Assembly from 23d Dist., 1956-66, 91st-92d Congresses from 2d Dist. Ill., 94th-96th Congresses from 10th Dist. Ill., ways and means com., judiciary com.; chmn. Dem. Study Group; resigned, 1979; judge U.S. Circuit Ct. Appeals D.C., 1979-91, chief judge, 1991-94; counsel The White House, Washington, 1994—. Author: The American Congress: The First Branch, 1983. Served with USAAF, World War II. Recipient Page One award Chgo. Newspaper Guild, 1964; Best Legislator award Ind. Voters Ill., 1956-66; named one of ten Outstanding Young Men in Chgo., Jr. Assn. Commerce and Industry, 1961. Mem. ABA, Chgo. Bar Assn. (bd. mgrs. 1962-64), D.C. Bar Assn., Am. Law Inst., U.S. Assn. Former Mems. Congress, Order of Coif, Phi Beta Kappa. Office: The White House 1600 Pennsylvania Ave NW Washington DC 20500

MILAM, JOHN DANIEL, pathologist, educator; b. Kilgore, Tex., May 22, 1933; s. Ott G. and Effie (White) M.; m. Carol Jones Milam, Aug. 1, 1959; children: Kay, Beth, John Jr., Julie. BS, La. State U., 1955, MS, 1957, MD, 1960. Attending pathologist St. Luke's Episcopal Hosp., Houston, 1967-89; cons. in pathology Tex. Children's Hosp., Houston, 1979—; prof. lab. medicine M.D. Anderson Cancer Ctr., U. Tex., Houston, 1990—; prof. pathology and lab. medicine Utex-Houston Med. Sch., Houston, 1989—. Contbr. numerous articles to profl. jours., chpts., abstracts to books. Trustee Am. Bd. Pathology, 1985—, pres. 1995; bd. dirs. Harris County chpt. ARC, 1978—. Mem. Am. Assn. Blood Banks (pres. 1984, Disting. Svc. award 1988), Tex. Soc. Pathologists (George T. Caldwell award 1981). Republican. Baptist. Home: 11927 Arbordale Houston TX 77024 Office: U Tex Houston Med Sch Dept Pathology 6431 Fannin Rm 2022 Houston TX 77030

MILAM, WILLIAM BRYANT, diplomat, economist; b. Bisbee, Ariz., July 24, 1936; s. Burl Vivian and Alice Vera (Pierce) M.; m. Faith Adele Handley; step-children: Erika, Fred. AB, Stanford U., 1959; MA, U. Mich., 1972; postgrad., Am. U., 1973. Polit. officer Dept. of State, Washington, 1967-69; fin. economist Dept. of State, Washington and, U.S. Embassy, London, 1970-75; energy economist Dept. of State, Washington, 1975-77, dep. office dir., 1977-80, office dir., 1980-83; dep. chief of mission U.S. Embassy, Yaounde, Cameroon, 1983-85; dep. assc. sec. Dept. of State, Washington, 1985-90; ambassador to Bangladesh U.S. Embassy, Dhaka, Bangladesh, 1990-93; spl. negotiator Oceans, Environ., Sci. Dept. State, Washington, 1993—. Calif. State scholar, 1956-59; recipient James Clement Dunn award Dept. of State, 1981, Superior Honor award, 1983, Pres.'s Meritorious Svc. award U.S. Govt., 1990. Avocations: reading, golf, jogging. Home: 2749 Woodley Pl NW Washington DC 20008 Office: Bur Oceans Environ & Sci Dept State Rm 7831 2201 C St NW Washington DC 20520 Office: Bur Oceans Environ & Sci Dept State Rm 7831 2201 C St NW Washington DC 20520

MILAN, MARJORIE LUCILLE, early childhood educator; b. Ludlow, Colo., June 24, 1926; d. John B. and Barbara (Zenonian) Pinamont; m. John Francis Milan, June 18, 1949; children: Barbara, J. Mark, Kevin. BA, U. Colo., 1947, MA, 1978; PhD, U. Denver, 1983. Cert. tchr., adminstr., supt., Colo. Tchr. Boulder (Colo.) Pub. Schs., 1947-49, Denver Pub. Schs., 1949-51, 67—; adminstr. T. Tot Kindergarten, Denver, 1951-55; tchr. Colo. Women's Coll., Denver, 1956-67; adminstr. Associated Schs., Denver, 1956-67; adv. bd. George Washington Carver Nursery, Denver, 1960-85. Mem. Assn. Childhood Edn. (state bd. 1960—), Hall of Excellence 1991), Rotary (pres.-elect local chpt. pres. 1994-95), Philanthropic Ednl. Orgn., Phi Delta Kappa, Delta Kappa Gamma. Avocations: swimming, music. Home: 1775 Lee St Lakewood CO 80215-2855

MILAN, THOMAS LAWRENCE, accountant; b. Catonsville, Md., Nov. 23, 1941; s. Lawrence Francis and Mary Elizabeth (Freeley) M.; m. Mary Agnes LaCoste; children: Thomas Brian, Kathrine Mary. BS, U. Balt., 1965. CPA, Md., Va., Washington. With Ernst & Young, Balt., 1965-80, ptnr., 1976-80, Ernst & Young, Richmond, Va., 1980-88, regional dir. acctg. and auditing, Washington, 1988—; nat. dir. SEC practice Ernst & Young, 1989—. Mem. AICPA (chmn. SEC regulations com. 1994—), Annapolis Yacht Club, Commonwealth Club, TPC at Avenel, Beta Alpha. Republican. Roman Catholic. Avocations: boating, waterfowling, tennis. Home: 9721 Meyer Point Dr Rockville MD 20854-5420

MILANDER, HENRY MARTIN, community college president; b. Northampton, Pa., Apr. 17, 1939; s. Martin Edward and Margaret Catherine (Makovetz) M.; children: Martin Henry, Beth Ann. BS summa cum laude, Lock Haven U., Pa., 1961; MA, Bowling Green (Ohio) State U., 1962; EdS (Future Faculty fellow 1964), U. No. Iowa, 1965; EdD, Ill. State U.,

Normal, 1967. Instr. Wartburg Coll., Waverly, Iowa, 1962-64; asst. prof. Ill. State U., 1966-67; dean instrn. Belleville (Ill.) Area Coll., 1967-69; v.p. acad. affairs Lorain County Community Coll., Elyria, Ohio, 1969-72; pres. Olympic Coll., Bremerton, Wash., 1972-87. Northeastern Jr. Coll., Sterling, Colo., 1988—; pres. Bremers, Inc., 1986-87. Contbr. articles to profl. jours. Pres. Kitsap County Comprehensive Health Planning Council, 1975-76; pres. Logan County Colo. United Way, 1992-93. Recipient Faculty Growth award Wartburg Coll., 1963, Community Service award, 1975, Chief Thunderbird award, 1985. Mem. Am. Assn. C.C., Am. Assn. Sch. Adminstrs., N.W. Assn. Cmty. and Jr. Colls., Wash. Assn. C.C. (pres. 1984-85), Wash. C.C. Computing Consortium (chmn. bd. dirs. 1985-87), Puget Sound Naval Bases Assn. (pres. 1982-86), Wash. Assn. C.C. Pres. (pres. 1984-85), Bremerton Area C. of C. (pres. 1977-78), Colo. Assn. C.C. Pres. (pres. 1993-94), Rotary (pres. Sterling Club 1992-93), Kappa Delta Pi, Phi Delta Kappa. Lutheran. Home: 302 Delmar St Sterling CO 80751-3904 Office: Northeastern Jr Coll 100 College Dr Sterling CO 80751-2344

MILANICH, JERALD THOMAS, archaeologist, museum curator; b. Painesville, Ohio, Oct. 13, 1945; s. John Joseph and Jean Marie (Bales) M.; m. Maxine L. Margolis, Dec. 20, 1970; 1 child, Nara Bales. BA, U. Fla., 1967, MA, 1968, PhD, 1971. Cert. Soc. Profl. Archaeologists, 1975. Post doctoral fellow Smithsonian Inst., Washington, 1971-72; asst. prof. anthropology U. Fla., Gainesville, 1972-75; asst. curator Fla. Mus. Natural History, 1975-77; assoc. curator, 1977-81, chmn. dept. anthropology, 1981-83, 91—, curator, 1981—. Author: (with Samuel Proctor) Tacachale—Essays on the Indians of Florida and Southeastern Georgia during the Historic Period, 1978; (with Charles Fairbanks) Florida Archaeology, 1980; McKeithen Weeden Island, 1984; Early Prehistoric Southeast, 1985; (with Susan Milbrath) First Encounters, Spanish Explorations in the Caribbean and the United States, 1492-1570, 1989; The Hernando de Soto Expedition, 1990; Earliest Hispanic-Native America Interactions in the Greater American Southwest, 1991, (with Charles Hudson) Hernando de Soto and the Indians of Florida, 1993, Archaeology of Precolumbian Florida, 1994, Florida Indians and the Invasion of Europe, 1995. Recipient Ripley P. Bullen awards, 1980, Rembert Patrick Book award, 1994, 95; grantee NSF, 1970-71, 73-75, 77-81, 82, Wentworth Found., 1976-77, 81-84, 91, NEH, 1985, 87-89. Mem. Am. Anthrop. Assn., Soc. Am. Archaeology (exec. bd. 1990-93), Soc. Profl. Archeologists (pres. 1981-82), So. Anthrop. Soc., S.E. Archeol. Conf. (pres. 1986-88), Explorers Club. Office: Fla Mus Natural History Gainesville FL 32611

MILAVSKY, HAROLD PHILLIP, real estate executive; b. Limerick, Sask., Can., Jan. 25, 1931; s. Jack and Clara M. B in Commerce, U. Sask., Saskatoon, Can., 1953. Chief acct., treas., controller Loram Internat. Ltd. div. Mannix Co. Ltd., Calgary, Alta., Can., 1956-65; v.p., chief fin. officer Power Corp. Devels. Ltd., Calgary, Alta., Can., 1965-69; exec. v.p., bd. dirs. Great West Internat. Equities Ltd. (name now Trizec Corp. Ltd.), Calgary, Alta., Can., 1976-94; pres. Trizec Corp. Ltd., Calgary, Alta., Can., 1976-86, bd. dirs., 1976-94, chmn., 1986-93; chmn. Quantico Capital Corp., Calgary, 1994—; bd. dirs. Brascan Ltd., Toronto, Can., Toronto, London Life Ins. Co., London Ins. Group Ltd., Wascana Energy Inc., Regina, Nova Corp. Alberta, Calgary, Amoco Can., Calgary. Past dir. Terry Fox Humanitarian Award Program; past dir. Conf. Bd. Can.; past gov., Acctg. Edn. Found. Alta.; mem. Chancellor's Club, U. Calgary; hon. col. 14th Svc. Battalion, Calgary. Fellow Inst. Chartered Accts. Alta.; mem. Inst. Chartered Accts. Sask. and Alta., Can. Inst. Pub. Real Estate Cos. (past pres., bd. dirs.), Can. C. of C. (past chmn.), Internat. Profl. Hockey Alumni (founding dir.). Clubs: Petroleum, Ranchmen's, Glenmore Racquet (Calgary). Avocations: skiing, tennis, horseback riding. Office: Quantico Capital Corp, 1920-855 Second St, Calgary, AB Canada T2P 4J7

MILBANK, JEREMIAH, foundation executive; b. N.Y.C., Mar. 24, 1920; s. Jeremiah and Katharine (Schulze) M.; m. Andrea Hunter, July 19, 1947 (dec. Oct. 1982); children: Jeremiah III, Victoria Milbank Whitney, Elizabeth Milbank Archer, Joseph H.; m. Rose Jackson Sheppard, May 4, 1991. B.A., Yale U., 1942; M.B.A., Harvard U., 1948; L.H.D. (hon.), Ithaca (N.Y.) Coll., 1976, Sacred Heart U., Conn.; LL.D. Manhattan Coll. With J.M. Found., N.Y.C.; pres. J.M. Found., 1971—; pres. Cypress Woods Corp., 1972—. Author: First Century of Flight in America, 1942. Chmn. emeritus Boys & Girls Clubs Am.; hon. pres. Internat. Ctr. for the Disabled, 1991—; trustee Madison Ctr. for Ednl. Affairs; fin. chmn. Rep. Nat. Com., 1969-72, 75-77; mem. adv. com. Presdl. Librs. U. USAF Inst. 1943-46. Mem. Brook Club, River Club (N.Y.C.), Round Hill Club (Greenwich), Yale Club. Republican. Home: 535 Lake Ave Greenwich CT 06830-4515 Office: 60 E 42d St New York NY 10165-1651

MILBOURNE, WALTER ROBERTSON, lawyer; b. Phila., Aug. 27, 1933; s. Charles Gordon and Florie Henderson (Robertson) M.; m. Georgena Sue Dyer, June 19, 1965; children: Gregory Broughton, Karen Elizabeth, Walter Robertson, Margaret Henderson. A.B., Princeton U., 1955; LL.B., Harvard U., 1958. Bar: Pa. 1959. Assoc. firm Pepper, Hamilton & Sheetz, Phila., 1959-65, Obermayer, Rebmann, Maxwell & Hippel, Phila., 1965-67; ptnr. Obermayer, Rebmann, Maxwell & Hippel, 1968-84, Saul, Ewing, Remick & Saul, 1984—; bd. dirs. Pa. Lumbermen's Mut. Ins. Co., Phila. Reins. Corp.; co-chmn. Nat. Conf. Lawyers and Collection Agys., 1979-90; chmn. bus. litigation com. Def. Rsch. Inst., 1986-89, mem. law insts. com., 1989—. Chmn. mental health budget sect. Phila. United Fund, 1967-70. Served with Army N.G., 1958-64. Fellow Am. Coll. Trial Lawyers (mem. advancing the rule of law abroad com. 1992—); mem. ABA, Pa. Bar Assn., Phila. Bar Assn., Internat. Assn. Def. Counsel (exec. com. 1985-88), Assn. Def. Counsel, Union League, Merion Cricket Club, Princeton Club, Idle Hour Tennis Club (pres. 1968-68, Phila. Lawn Tennis Assn. (pres. 1969-70). Republican. Home: 689 Fernfield Cir Wayne PA 19087-2002 Office: Saul Ewing Remick & Saul 3800 Centre Sq W Philadelphia PA 19102

MILBRATH, ROBERT HENRY, retired petroleum executive; b. Apr. 17, 1912; s. Paul and Mabel (Volkman) M.; m. Margaret Ripperger, Jan. 19, 1940; children: Robert S., Constance, Susan. B.S., U.S. Naval Acad., 1934. With Standard Oil Co. N.J., 1934-74; v.p., gen. mgr. Esso Sociedad Anonima Petrolera Argentina, 1938-42, 45-50; area contact East Coast South Am., mktg. coordination, 1950-52; dir. Internat. Petroleum Co., 1954—, v.p., 1956; v.p., dir. Esso Export Corp. N.Y., 1957-59, exec. v.p., dir., 1959-61; pres., dir. chmn. exec. com. Esso Internat., Inc. (formerly Esso Export Corp.), 1961-66; exec. v.p. Esso Europe, 1966-68; logistics coordinator Standard Oil Co. (N.J.) (now Exxon Corp.), 1968-69, dir., v.p., 1969-70, dir., sr. v.p., 1970-73, ret., 1974. Cons. Boys Clubs Am. 1978-84. Served to lt. comdr. USNR; asst. naval attache 1942, Buenos Aires; chief Latin Am. sect. Army-Navy Petroleum Bd. 1943-45, Washington. Mem. U.S. Naval Acad. Alumni Assn. Republican. Clubs: Univesity (N.Y.C.), Ponte Vedra Club. Home: 214 Pablo Ct Ponte Vedra Beach FL 32082-1802

MILBURN, HERBERT THEODORE, federal judge; b. Cleveland, Tenn., May 26, 1931; s. He and Hazel (Shanks) M.; m. Elaine Dillow, Aug. 23, 1957; children: Blair Douglas, Elizabeth Elaine. Student, U. Chattanooga, 1949-50, Boston U., 1950-51; BS, East Tenn. State U., 1953; JD, U. Tenn., 1959. Bar: Tenn. 1959, U.S. Supreme Ct. 1971. Assoc. Folts, Bishop, Thomas, Leitner & Mann, Chattanooga, 1959-63; ptnr. Bishop, Thomas, Leitner, Mann & Milburn, Chattanooga, 1963-73; judge Hamilton County Cir. Ct., Chattanooga, 1973-83, U.S. Dist. Ct. (ea. dist.) Tenn., Chattanooga, 1983-84, U.S. Ct. Appeals (6th cir.), Chattanooga, 1984—; mem. faculty Nat. Jud. Coll. U. Nev., Reno, 1980, Tenn. Jud. Acad., Vanderbilt U., Nashville, 1982. Pres. Hamilton County Young Reps., Chattanooga, 1965; mem. Chancellor's Roundtable U. Tenn., Chattanooga, 1983-86; pres. Lakeside Kiwanis, 1964. With U.S. Army Security Agy., 1953-56. Recipient award Chattanooga Bd. Realtors, 1987, Outstanding Alumnus award East Tenn. State U., 1988; named Outstanding Young Rep., Hamilton County Young Reps., 1965. Mem. ABA, Tenn. Bar Assn. (commr. 1971-73, mem. profl. ethics and grievance com.), Chattanooga Bar Assn. (sec.-treas. 1967), Fed. Bar Assn. (life, chairperson U.S. jud. conf. com. on adminstrv. office of U.S. cts. 1994—), Am. Legion, East Tenn. State U. Found., Signal Mountain Golf and Country Club, Univ. Club Cin., Kiwanis. Republican. Episcopalian. Office: US Ct Appeals PO Box 750 Chattanooga TN 37401-0750

MILBURN, RICHARD ALLAN, management executive; b. Washington, May 30, 1933; s. Robert Andrew and Anna Janet (Schmidtman) M.; m. Joan (Frances) Hurst, Oct. 15, 1955; children: Jennifer Leigh, Michele Lynn. BS in Aeronautic and Space Engring. with honors, Okla. U., 1964, MS in Aerospace Engring., 1965. Commd. 2d lt. USAF, 1954, advanced through grades to col., 1980, interceptor pilot Aerospace Def. Command, 1955-64; designer, supr. constrn. ultra low speed wind tunnel Okla. U. Rsch. Inst., 1964-65, project engr. Aerospace Def. Command, 1965-68, chief weapons system div. Joint Chiefs of Staffs, 1968-71; asst. air attache, chief Fgn. Tech. Office Okla. U. Rsch. Inst., London, 1971-75; asst. dep. Near East activities, dep. East Asia Def. Security Assistance Agy., 1975-77; chief Mut. Def. Assistance Office Am. Embassy, Tokyo, 1977-80; chief rsch., devel., and systems acquisition Mgmt. Policy div. Hdqrs. USAF, 1980, ret., 1980; dir. def. programs Grumman Internat., Inc., 1980-82, v.p. def. programs, 1982-85, v.p. Washington ops., 1985-87, sr. v.p., 1987—; v.p. Northrop Grumman Internat., Arlington, Va., 1995—; chmn. aerospace and def. com., mem. exec. com. US/ROC Econ. Coun.; chmn. U.S. del. to NATO Indsl. Adv. Group, 1992—; bd. dirs. Robert C. Byrd Nat. Aviation Edn. and Tng. Ctr. Fellow AIAA (assoc.); mem. Nat. Security Industries Assn. (bd. dirs. Washington), Am. Def. Preparedness Assn. (bd. dirs. Washington), Am. League Export and Security Assistance (chmn., pres. 1994—), Royal Aero. Soc., Aerospace Industries Assn. (mem. internat. coun.), Order of Daedalians. Methodist. Home: 2200 Hunter Mill Rd Vienna VA 22181-3025 Office: Northrop Grumman Corp Ste 2400 1000 Wilson Blvd Arlington VA 22209-2230

MILBURN, RICHARD HENRY, physics educator; b. Newark, June 3, 1928; s. Richard Percy and Lucy Elizabeth (Karr) M.; m. Nancy Jeannette Stafford, Aug. 25, 1951; children—Sarah Stafford, Anne Douglas. A.B., Harvard U., 1948, A.M., 1951, Ph.D., 1954. Instr. Harvard U., Cambridge, Mass., 1954, 56-57, asst. prof., 1957-61; assoc. prof. physics Tufts U., Medford, Mass., 1961-65, prof., 1965—, John Wade prof., 1990—; Fulbright lectr., India, 1984. Trustee Cambridge Friends Sch., 1989-95. With U.S. Army, 1954-56. Sheldon travelling fellow, 1948-49; NSF fellow, 1952-53; Guggenheim fellow, 1960. Fellow Am. Phys. Soc. (past chmn. New Eng. sect.); mem. Am. Assn. Physics Tchrs., AAAS, AAUP. Research on high energy and elementary particles physics. Home: 1 Plymouth Rd Winchester MA 01890-3620 Office: Tufts Univ Medford MA 02155

MILCHAN, ARNON, film producer; b. Dec. 6, 1944. Prodr.: (plays) Tomb, It's So Nice To Be Civilized, Amadeus (Paris prodn.), (TV) MASADA, 1981, (films) The Medusa Touch, 1978, The King of Comedy, 1983, Once Upon a Time in America, 1984, Brazil, 1985, Stripper, 1986, Legend, 1986, Man on Fire, 1987, The Adventures of Baron Munchausen, 1989, Who's Harry Crumb, 1989, The War of the Roses, 1989, Big Man on Campus, 1990, Pretty Woman, 1990, Q&A, 1990, Guilty by Suspicion, 1991, JFK, 1991, The Mambo Kings, 1992, Memoirs of an Invisible Man, 1992, The Power of One, 1992, Under Siege, 1992, Sommersby, 1993, Falling Down, 1993, Made in America, 1993, Free Willy, 1993, The Nutcracker, 1993, That Night, 1993, Heaven and Earth, 1993, The New Age, 1993, Striking Distance, 1993, Six Degrees of Separation, 1993, Second Best, 1994, Boys on the Side, 1994, The Client, 1994. Office: Regency Enterprises 4000 Warner Blvd Bldg 66 Burbank CA 91522

MILDE, LESLIE NEWBERG, anesthesiologist, educator; b. Rochester, N.Y., Aug. 17, 1943; d. Frederick Johnson and Frances Stevenson Newberg; m. James Hans Milde, Dec. 31, 1984; children: Steven, Craig, Jade, Peggy Sue. AB, U. Rochester, 1965; MD, U. Calif., San Francisco, 1977. Diplomate Nat. Bd. Med. Examiners, Am. Bd. Anesthesiology. Cardiopulmonary technician Boston Children's Hosp., Harvard U., 1965-67, U. Calif., San Francisco, 1968-73; resident in internal medicine Kaiser Permanente Hosp., San Francisco, 1977-78; resident in anesthesiology Mass. Gen. Hosp., Harvard U., Boston, 1978-80, fellow in critical care medicine, 1980-81; fellow in neuroanesthesiology Mayo Grad. Sch. Medicine, Rochester, Minn., 1981-82; cons. anesthesiologist Mayo Clinic, Rochester, 1982-94, Scottsdale, Ariz., 1994—; prof. anesthesiology Mayo Med. Sch., Scottsdale, 1992—; assoc. examiner Am. Bd. Anesthesiology, 1989—. Editor: Clinical Anesthesia Procedures of Massachusetts General Hospital, 1982, Anesthesia Review, 1991; editor Jour. Neurosurg. Anesthesia. Mem. Am. Assn. Univ. Anesthesiologists (sci. adv. bd. 1985—). Avocations: refinishing antique furniture.

MILDON, MARIE ROBERTA, association executive; b. Pittsburg, Calif., Apr. 18, 1935; d. Samuel Ward and Roberta Alice (Trumpower) Wilson; m. James Lee Mildon, Sept. 17, 1958; 1 dau., Laura Marie. B.S., U. Nev.-Reno, 1983. News editor Seaside News Sentinel (Calif.), 1956-58; adminstrv. asst. for corp. devel. Crown Zellerbach, San Francisco, 1959-64; assoc. dir. Nat. Council Juvenile and Family Ct. Judges, Reno, Nev., 1969—; tng. dir. Nat. Coll. Juvenile Justice, Reno, 1971-72; apptd. cons. to task force on abused and neglected children Mo. Supreme Ct. Alt. trustee John Shaw Field Found., Reno, 1979-85; trustee Cystems, Inc., Juris/Amicus, Inc. Co-author: Model Statute for Termination of Parental Rights, 1976; Model Statute on Juvenile and Family Court Records, 1981; My World To Share, 1982. Editor: Judicial Concern for Children in Trouble, 1974; Juvenile and Family Law Jour., 1985—; prodn. editor Juvenile and Family Law Digest, 1986-88; mem. bd. cons. editors Jour. Emotional and Behavioral Problems, 1991—. Office: Juvenile and Family Ct Jour Nat Coun Juv & Family Ct Judges Box 8978 Reno NV 89507

MILDREN, JACK, lieutenant governor; b. Kingsville, TX, Oct. 10, 1949; s. Larry J. and Mary Glynne (Lamont) M.; m. Janis Susan Butler, Jan. 14, 1972; children: Leigh, Lauren, Drew. BBA, U. Okla., 1972. Cert. petroleum landman. Mem. Balt. Colts Football Club, 1972-73, New England Patriots Football Club, 1974; v.p. Saxon Oil Co., 1972-79; co-founder, pres. Regency Exploration Inc., 1977-88; oil indl. oper., 1988-90; lt. gov. State of Okla., Oklahoma City, 1990—. Bd. dirs. Children's Med. Rsch. Found., Arts Coun. Oklahoma City, Nat. Football League Players Found. and Hall of Fame, State Ctr. Com., Jim Thorpe Club; mem. Leadership Okla., Leadership Oklahoma City; mem. Com. to Devel. Biotech. Industry in Okla. Named All-Am. Football Player, 1971, Acad. All-Am., 1971, Nat. Football Found. Hall Fame, 1971, Most Valuable Player Sugar Bowl, 1972. numerous other athletic awards. Mem. Beta Gamma Sigma, Phi Delta Theta (past pres. bd. dirs). Meth. Office: Office Lt Gov State Capitol Rm 211 Oklahoma City OK 73105

MILDVAN, DONNA, infectious diseases physician; b. Phila., June 20, 1942; d. Carl David and Gertrude M.; m. Rolf Dirk Hamann; 1 child, Gabriella Kay. AB magna cum laude, Bryn Mawr Coll., 1963; MD, Johns Hopkins U., 1967. Diplomate Am. Bd. Internal Medicine and Infectious Diseases. Intern, resident Mt. Sinai Hosp., N.Y.C., 1967-70, fellow, infectious diseases, 1970-72; asst., assoc. prof. clin. medicine Mt. Sinai Sch. Medicine, N.Y.C., 1972-87; prof. medicine 1988-94; physician-in-charge infectious diseases Beth Israel Med. Ctr., N.Y.C., 1972-79, chief, div. infectious diseases, 1980—; prof. medicine Albert Einstein Coll. of Medicine, N.Y.C., 1994—; mem. AIDS charter rev. com., NIH/Nat. Inst. Allergy and Infectious Diseases, Bethesda, 1987—; cons. FDA, Rockville, 1987—; Ctrs. for Disease Control, Atlanta, 1985-86; among first to describe AIDS, "Pre-AIDS", AIDS Dementia, 1982, among first to study AZT, 1986; Keynote speaker, II Internat. Conf. on AIDS, Paris, 1986 and other achievements in field; Sophie Jones Meml. lectr. in infectious diseases U. Mich. Hosps., 1984. Contrb. numerous articles to profl. jours; co-editor two books, several book chpts. and abstracts on infectious diseases and AIDS. Recipient Woman of Achievement award AAUW, 1987; contract for antiviral therapy in AIDS, Nat. Cancer Inst./Nat. Inst. Allergy and Infectious Diseases, 1985-86, grant N.Y. State AIDS Inst., 1986-87, subcontract Nat. Inst. Allergy and Infectious Diseases, 1987-95; Henry Strong Denison scholar, Johns Hopkins U. Sch. Medicine, 1967. Fellow Infectious Diseases Soc. Am.; mem. Am. Soc. Microbiology, AAAS, Harvey Soc., Internat. AIDS Soc. Democrat. Jewish. Avocation: old movies. Office: Beth Israel Med Ctr 1st Ave New York NY 10003-7903

MILEDI, RICARDO, neurobiologist; b. Mexico City, Sept. 15, 1927; m. Ana Mela Garces, Dec. 17, 1955; 1 child, Rico. B.Sc., Instituto Cientifico y Literario, Chihuahua, Mex., 1945; M.D., U. Nacional Autónoma de Mex., 1955, Doctor Honoris Causa Universidad del Pais Vasco, 1992. Researcher Instituto Nacional de Cardiologia, Mex., 1954-56; fellow John Curtin Sch. Med. Res., Canberra, Australia, 1956-58; mem. faculty U. Coll., London, 1959-85, Foulerton research prof. of Royal Soc., 1975-85, head dept. biophysics, 1978-85; Disting. prof. dept. psychobiology U. Calif., Irvine, 1984—. Fellow Royal Soc. London, Am. Acad. Arts and Scis.; mem. NAS,

3d World Acad. Scis., (titular) European Acad. Arts, Scis., Humanities, N.Y. Acad. Scis., Hungarian Acad. Scis. (hon.), Mex. Acad. Scis. Home: 9 Gibbs Ct Irvine CA 92715-4032 Office: U Calif Dept Psychobiology Lab Cellular and Molecular Neurobiology Irvine CA 92717-4550

MILES, ARTHUR J., financial planner, consultant; b. N.Y.C., Sept. 2, 1920; s. Levi and Rachel Goldsworthy (Hiscock) M.; m. Pearl Cooper, Nov. 27, 1947; children: Beverly Miles Kerns, Douglas Robert. B.B.A., Pace U., 1958; M.B.A., NYU, 1963. With Dime Savs. Bank, N.Y.C., 1938-81, exec. v.p., treas., 1975-78, sr. exec. v.p., treas., 1978-81; pres. AJM Assocs., Floral Park, N.Y., then Sarasota, Fla., 1981—; newscaster Sta. WUSF-FM, Tampa, Fla.; bd. dirs. Cultural Instns. Retirement System, N.Y.C., 1968—; fin. cons. Bklyn. Inst. Arts and Scis., 1972—. Trustee, nat. treas. Alcoholics Anonymous, N.Y.C., 1970-79; tech. adviser N.Y.C Fin. Liason Com., 1975-76. Served to sgt., inf. U.S. Army, 1942-45, Philippines. Fellow Fedn. Fin. Analysts; mem. Nat. Assn. Bus. Economists, Internat. Assn. Fin. Planners, NYU Club, Marco Polo Club (N.Y.C.), Tournament Players Club. Republican. Office: AJM Assocs 8325 Shadow Pine Way Sarasota FL 34238-5624

MILES, CHRISTINE MARIE, museum director; b. Madison, Ind., Mar. 2, 1951; d. Leland Weber and Mary Virginia (Geyer) M.; B.A., Boston U., 1973; M.A., George Washington U., 1982; postgrad. Mus. Mgmt. Inst., 1985. Curatorial asst. Mus. of the City of N.Y., 1973-75; art gallery dir. South Street Seaport Mus., N.Y.C., 1975-77; researcher The Octagon, AIA Found., Washington, 1978-80; dir. Fraunces Tavern Mus., N.Y.C., 1980-86, Albany (N.Y.) Inst. History and Art, 1986—; bd. dirs. WMHT-TV, SUNY-Albany Found., Hist. Albany Found., Fedn. Hist. Svcs.; pres. Gallery Assn. N.Y. State, 1991-93; pres. N.Y. State Assn. Museums, Lower Manhattan Cultural Coun.; mus. aid panel N.Y. State Council on Arts, 1985-88. Author, writer/coordinator, compiler of catalogs in field. Mem. Am. Assn. Mus. Office: Albany Inst History & Art 125 Washington Ave Albany NY 12210-2296

MILES, DON CLIFFORD, architect; b. Ft. Knox, Ky., Sept. 17, 1942; s. Don and Kathrine Eva (Gray) M.; m. Pamela Wait, Aug. 6, 1972; children: Katherine Wait, Lesley Gray, Nicole Conel. BArch with honors, U. Wash., 1966; MArch, M of City Planning in Urban Design, Harvard U., 1971. Registered architect, Wash. Assoc. ptnr. Zimmer, Gunsul, Frasca Partnership, Seattle; cons., lectr. numerous orgns., cities, corps. Prin. projects include Pedestrian Corridor, Major Pub. Open Spaces, CBD Transit Ctr., Bellevue, Wash., Banfield Light Rail Project, Portland, Boise (Idaho) Downtown Major Pub. Open Space, Street Improvements and Transit Malls, Honolulu Rapid Transit Project, Revitalization of State St., Chgo., Midway Corridor Project, Mpls., High Capacity Transit Project, Seattle, Ctrl. Orange County Aerial Fixed Guideway, Mission Valley West Extension Light Rail Project, San Diego, Master Plan for Capitol of State of Wash., Seattle Union Sta. Redevel. Plan, Weyerhauser Corp. Campus, Quadrant Corp. site, Lake Union, Seattle, Whitman Coll. Bd. dirs. founder Project for Pub. Spaces, 1975—; bd. dirs. Seattle Children's Mus., 1978-82; trustee Queen Ann Community Coun., 1978-80. Fellow AIA, Inst. Urban Design. Avocations: skiing, jogging. Home: 611 W Comstock St Seattle WA 98119-3422 Office: Zimmer Gunsul Frasca 1191 2nd Ave Ste 800 Seattle WA 98101-2949

MILES, EDWARD LANCELOT, marine studies educator, consultant, director; b. Port-of-Spain, Trinidad, W.I., Dec. 21, 1939; came to U.S., 1959; s. Cecil Bannister and Louise (DuFont) M.; divorced; children: Anthony Roger, Leila Yvonne. BA, Howard U., 1962; PhD, U. Denver, 1965. Instr. Sch. Internat. Studies U. Denver, 1965-66, asst. prof., 1966-70, assoc. prof., 1970-74; prof. Inst. Marine Studies & Grad. Sch. Pub. Affairs U. Wash., Seattle, 1974—; dir. Sch. Marine Affairs, 1982-93, Virginia and Prentice Bloedel prof. marine studies and pub. affairs, 1994—; chief negotiator Micronesian Maritime Authority, 1980-90; chmn. ocean policy com. NAS/NRC, Washington, 1974-89; chmn. adv. com. on internat. programs NSF, Washington, 1990-92. Author: The Management of Marine Regions: The North Pacific, 1982. Mem. Coun. on Fgn. Rels., Inc., Seattle United Nations Assn., Harvard Club of N.Y.C., Sierra (adv. bd. N.Y.C. chpt. 1975-79). Avocations: literature, opera, history, music, skiing. Office: U Wash Sch Marine Affairs Wash # Hf-05 Seattle WA 98195

MILES, ELLEN GROSS, art historian, museum curator; b. N.Y.C., July 28, 1941; d. Mason Welch and Julia (Kernan) Gross; m. Nathan Reingold. BA, Bryn Mawr Coll., 1964; MPhil, Yale U., 1970, PhD, 1976. Registrar Corcoran Gallery Art, Washington, 1965-66; asst. to dir. Nat. Portrait Gallery, Washington, 1971-77; assoc. curator, 1977-84, curator dept. painting and sculpture, 1984—; guest curator Iveagh Bequest, Kenwood, London, 1979; vis. lectr. dept. Am. studies George Washington U., 1982. Co-author: American Colonial Portraits: 1700-1776, 1987; editor: The Portrait in 18th Century America, 1993; author: Saint-Mémin and the Neoclassical Profile Portrait in America, 1994, American Paintings of the Eighteenth Century, 1995. Rsch. grantee Smithsonian Instn., 1973-74, 79, 82, 87. Mem. Assn. Historians Am. Art, Am. Soc. for Eighteenth-Century Studies, Coll. Art Assn. Office: Nat Portrait Gallery 8th and F Sts NW Washington DC 20560

MILES, FRANK CHARLES, retired newspaper executive; b. Detroit, Jan. 1, 1926; s. Nelson and Ethel Jane (Mennill) M.; m. Catharine Estelle Coleman, Sept. 4, 1948; children—Barbara Ann, Diana Estelle. Student, Westervelt Bus. Coll., 1947-48. With Thomson Newspapers Ltd., Des Plaines, Ill., 1950—, Cambridge, Ont., 1950-52, 54-55; bus. mgr. Sarnia (Ont.) Obs., 1952-54; gen. mgr. Pembroke (Ont.) Obs., 1956-58, Moose Jaw (Sask) Times-Herald, 1958-62; pub. Austin (Minn.) Daily Herald, 1962-66; sr. v.p., gen. mgr. Thomson Newspapers Inc., Des Plaines, Ill., 1966-89; exec. v.p. acquisitions, 1990-91; ret.; also dir. Thomson Newspapers Inc., Des Plaines, Ill. Served with USNR, 1943-46. Mem. Am. Newspaper Pubs. Assn., Inland Daily Press Assn., Sigma Delta Chi. Republican. Mem. United Ch. of Christ. Home: 647 Wilton Ct Palatine IL 60067-3835

MILES, GORDON HUGH, restaurant company executive, lawyer; b. 1940. Bar: Nebr. 1964, U.S. Supreme Ct. 1964. With Wash. Walentine and Miles, until 1977; chmn. Vicorp Restaurants, Inc., 1977-86; chmn., dir. Rusty Pelican Restaurants, Inc.; chmn. Green Leaf Ventures Inc. and Papa Gino's Holdings, Inc., San Diego. Office: Green Leaf Ventures Inc 6610 Convoy Ct San Diego CA 92111-1009

MILES, JACK (JOHN RUSSIANO), journalist, critic; b. Chgo., July 30, 1942; s. John Alvin and Mary Jean (Murphy) M.; m. Jacqueline Russiano, Aug. 23, 1980; 1 child, Kathleen. LittB, Xavier U., Cin., 1964; PhB, Pontifical Gregorian U., Rome, 1966; student, Hebrew U., Jerusalem, 1966-67; PhD, Harvard U., 1971. Asst. prof. Loyola U., Chgo., 1970-74; asst. dir. Scholars Press, Missoula, Mont., 1974-75; postdoctoral fellow U. Chgo., 1975-76; editor Doubleday & Co., N.Y.C., 1976-78; exec. editor U. Calif. Press, Berkeley, 1978-85; book editor LA Times, 1985-91, mem. editl. bd., 1991-95; dir. Humanities Ctr. Claremont (Calif.) Grad. Sch., 1995—. Author: Retroversion and Text Criticism, 1984; God: A Biography, 1995; contbr. learned and popular articles to various periodicals; book reviewer. Guggenheim fellow, 1990-91; rsch. fellow Gould Ctr. for Humanistic Studies, Claremont McKenna Coll., 1991—. Mem. PEN, Nat. Book Critics Circle (pres. 1990-92), Am. Acad. Religion, Amnesty Internat. Episcopalian. Home: 3568 Mountain View Ave Pasadena CA 91107-4616 Office: Grad Humanities Ctr Claremont Grad Sch Claremont CA 91711

MILES, JANICE ANN, news reporter; b. Abilene, Tex., July 22, 1949; d. Theodore Winston and Clarice (Buie) M.; m. Martin Jerome Wiesenthal, Feb. 24, 1973; children: Alexis Ann Wiesenthal, Alison Claire Wiesenthal. BFA, U. Tex., 1971; postgrad., Trinity U., 1980. Social worker Tex. Dept. Human Svcs., San Antonio, 1971-79; TV news reporter Sta. KENS-TV, San Antonio, 1981—. Bd. dirs. Sunshine Cottage Sch. for Deaf Children, 1982-89, San Antonio Botanical Ctr., 1984-90, Univ. Presbyn. Children's Ctr., San Antonio 1986-90, San Antonio Day Hosp., 1990, San Antonio AIDS Found., 1995—, Alamo Theatre Arts Coun., 1995—, SIDS, 1994. Recipient Guardian Angel award Boysville, Inc., 1987, Barbara Jordan award Gov.'s Com. for Disabled Persons, 1988, 90, 92, Pat Weaver award Nat. Muscular Dystrophy Assn., 1989, Recognition award Lighthouse for the Blind, 1990, Tex. Child Welfare Bd. Media award, 1991, San Antonio award, 1992; named Media Person of Yr., San Antonio Planning com., 1993. Mem. Women in Communications Inc., San Antonio 100, San Antonio

Forum. Presbyterian. Avocations: acting, singing, Tex. history. Office: KENS-TV Eyewitness News 5400 Fredericksburg Rd San Antonio TX 78229-3504

MILES, JEANNE PATTERSON, artist; b. Balt.; d. Walter and Edna (Webb) M.; m. Frank Curlee, Dec. 31, 1935 (dec.); m. Johannes Schiefer, Feb. 11, 1939 (div.); 1 child, Joanna. BFA, George Washington U.; postgrad., Philips Meml. Gallery Sch., Atelier Gromaire, Grand Chaumiere, Paris. One-woman shows include Betty Parsons Gallery, N.Y.C., 1945, 52, 55, 56, 59, 77, 82, Grand Central Moderns, N.Y.C., 1968, Wesbeth Galleries, N.Y.C., 1972; group shows include N.Y. Rome Found., 1957, Walker Art Gallery, Mpls., 1954, Corcoran Biennial, Yale U. Mus., 1957, Chateau Gagnes, France, 1938, Whitney Mus., 1963, Nat. Fedn. Am. Art, 1963, Mus. Modern Art, 1966, Riverside Mus., N.Y.C., 1964, Guggenheim Mus., 1965-66, Geodok Am. Women Show, Hamburg and Berlin, 1972, Springfield (Mass.) Art Mus., 1975, Hunterton Art Center, Clinton, N.J., 1975, Betty Parsons Gallery, 1977, 82, Sid Deutch, 1978, 79, Marlyn Pearl Gallery, N.Y.C., 1986, 88, Bronx Mus. Art, 1986, George Washington, 1989, 55 Mercer St, N.Y.C., 1989, Marlyn Pearl Gallery, N.Y.C., 1991, Anita Shapalsky Gallery, N.Y.C., 1992, Shapalsky Gallery, 1993; represented in permanent collections NYU, Santa Barbara (Calif.) Mus., Muson Proctor Mus., Utica, N.Y., Rutgers Coll., U. Ariz., Guggenheim Mus., Cin. and Newark museums, White Art Mus., N.Y. State U. at Purchase, Cornell U., Ecumenical Inst., Garrison, N.Y., Graymoor, Garrison, Springfield Art Mus., Weatherspoon Art Mus., U. N.C., Wichita (Kans.) Mus., Mus. of Wichita, Mus. of St. Mary's (Md.) Coll., L.A. County Mus., Alexander Mus., La., also pvt. collections, N.Y.C. and France; traveling exhibits; poster and cover for catalogues, 1987-92; video tape showing of exhibits on cable TV, N.Y.C., 1989. Charles C. Ladd painting scholar Tahiti, 1938, 56, traveling scholar France, 1937-48; grantee Am. Inst. Arts and Letters, 1968, Mark Rothko Found., 1970-73, Pelham von Stoeffler Art Fund, 1974; invited residency (award) to Yaddo Art Colony, Saratoga Springs, N.Y., 50s and 60s, MacDowell Colony, N.H. Mem. Abstract Artists Am., George Washington U. Alumni Assn. (Disting. Achievement award 1987). *My paintings, I find, come out successfully when I keep a steady grip on an interior focus.*

MILES, JESSE MC LANE, retired accounting company executive; b. De Funiak Springs, Fla., June 17, 1932; s. Percy Webb and Dora (Pippin) M.; m. Catherine Rita Eugenio, July 18, 1959; children—Jesse Jr., Catherine, Teresa, John, Thomas, Robert. B.S.B.A., U. Fla., 1954. C.P.A., N.Y. Mem. staff, mgr., prin. Arthur Young & Co., N.Y.C., 1954-63, ptnr., 1963-89, dep. chmn.-internat., 1985-89; chmn. Arthur Young Internat., 1985-89; ptnr. Ernst & Young, 1989-92; co-chmn. Ernst & Young Internat., 1989-92; ret., 1992. Mem. AICPA, N.Y. Inst. CPAs, Burning Tree Country Club (Greenwich, Conn.), Blind Brook Club (Rye Brook, N.Y.), Boca Pointe Country Club (Boca Raton, Fla.), Adios Golf Club (Coconut Creek, Fla.). Home: 18 Red Coat Ln Greenwich CT 06830-3432

MILES, JIM, state official. Prof. of law Greenville Tech. Coll.; sec. of state S.C. Mem. Soc. Internat. Bus. Office: Sec of State PO Box 11350 Columbia SC 29211-1350

MILES, JOHN FREDERICK, retired manufacturing company executive; b. Fredericton, N.B., Can., Aug. 13, 1926; s . Ralph Edward and Hazel Jean (Young) M.; m. Frances Power, Oct. 2, 1950; children: John F., Robert D., Dalyce J., Leytha J. Sr. Matric, U. N.B., 1944; B.Sc. in Chem. Engring., Queen's U., Kingston, Ont., Can., 1948. Prodn. mgr. Dominion Steel & Coal Corp. Ltd., 1948-65, jr. engr., 1948-49, battery foreman coke ovens, 1949-51, gen. foreman coke ovens, 1951-56, rsch. engr. coke ovens and blast furnaces, 1956-57, asst. supt. blast furnace dept., 1957-58, asst. to gen. supt., 1958-60, asst. works mgr. Sidney Works, 1960-62, gen. mgr. Etobicoke Works, 1962-65; works mgr. Slater Steels—Hamilton Splty. Bar Div. (div. Slater Industries), Hamilton, Ont., Can., 1965-66, 1966-71, v. mfg., 1971-86, div. pres., 1986-91, pres., CEO, 1991-93, bd. dirs., 1991—. Mem. Assn. Profl. Engrs. Ont., Assn. Iron and Steel Engrs.

MILES, JOHN KARL, marketing executive; b. Indpls., June 17, 1937; s. Louis John and Rachel Anna (Robbins) M.; m. Nancy Margaret McCay, Aug. 22, 1959; children—John Karl, Ann McCay, James Vance. B.A., DePauw U., 1959; B.F.A., U. Ill., 1965, M.F.A., 1966. Design mgr. Arvin Industries Inc., Columbus, Ind., 1966-72; dir. design and mktg. Gen. Housewares Corp., Atlanta, 1972-77; exec. v.p. Homecrest Industries Inc., Wadena, Minn., 1977-88; pres. Crestmark Internat., Atlanta, 1988—; pres. bd. advisors Dallas Market Ctr., 1983-86; bd. dirs. Garden Window Network, Summer Casual Furniture Mfrs. Assn., pres. 1990-92, chair bd. 1993—, Atlantic Market Center Accessories Center, 1992. Inventor, designer electric heater, shoe buffer, bowling game table, electric scissors. Del. Wadena County Republican Conv., 1980-84; pres. Wadena Devel. Authority, 1986-87; mem. United Meth. Ch. Dist. Com. on Superintendency, 1985-88; lay leader Wadena United Meth. Ch., 1987; bd. dirs. Wadena Econ. Devel. Council, Community Edn. Adv. Com., Wadena. Served to 1st lt. USAF, 1959-62. Recipient Exec. of Yr. award Nat. Secs. Assn., Wadena, 1980. Mem. Summer and Casual Furniture Mfrs. Assn. (pres. bd. dirs. 1984—), Nat. Home Furnishings Coun. (bd. dirs. 1988—), Nat. Furnishings Coun. (bd. dirs. 1994), Wadena C. of C. (bd. dirs. 1985, pres. 1987, Citizen of Yr. 1988), Elks, Rotary. Methodist. Avocations: antiques, reading, drawing. Home: 601 Old Post Rd Madison GA 30650-1852 Office: Homecrest/Crestmark Internat 240 Peachtree St NW Atlanta GA 30303-1301

MILES, LELAND WEBER, university president; b. Balt., Jan. 18, 1924; s. Leland Weber and Marie (Fitzpatrick) M.; m. Mary Virginia Geyer, July 9, 1947; children: Christine Marie, Gregory Lynn. AB cum laude, Juniata Coll., 1946, MA, L.I.U., 1947, PhD, 1949; postgrad., Duke U., 1949; DLitt (hon.), Juniata Coll., 1969; LHD (hon.), Rosary Hill Coll., 1970; LLD (hon.), Far East U., 1979; DHC (hon.), U. Guadalajara (Mex.), 1984; Order of Merit, Alfred U., 1986. Assoc. prof. English Hanover Coll., 1949-50, prof., chmn. English dept., 1950-60; assoc. prof., asst. to head English dept. U. Cin., 1960-63, prof., 1963-64, founder humanities reading program for engrs., 1961; dean Coll. Arts and Scis., U. Bridgeport, Conn., 1964-67; pres. U. Bridgeport, 1974-87, founder Sch. Law, 1977, pres. emeritus, 1987—; pres. Alfred U., 1967-74; bd. dirs. United Illuminating, 1978-94, chmn. audit com., 1992-94, Grolier, 1984-88, Wright Managed Investment Funds, 1988—, Internat. Peace Acad., 1982-90, mem. adv. coun., 1990—; mem. adv. coun. Internat. Exec. Svc. Corps, 1993—; Danforth Visiting Union Theol. Sem., 1956; Lilly fellow Sch. Letters Ind. U., 1959; Am. Council Learned Socs. fellow Harvard, 1963-64; Sr. Fulbright Research scholar Kings Coll. U. London, 1964, vis. scholar, 1972; seminar leader, deans and presidents insts. Am. Council on Edn., 1973-79; chmn. bd. Acad. Collective Bargaining Info. Service, Washington, 1977-79; producer, moderator Casing the Classics CBS Sta. WHAS-TV, Louisville, 1958-61; moderator Aspen (Colo.) Inst. for Humanistic Studies, 1969-70; lectr. Keedick Lecture Bur., N.Y.C., 1956-83. Author: John Colet and the Platonic Tradition, 1961; editor: St. Thomas More's Dialogue of Comfort Against Tribulation, 1966; sr. editor: (with Stephen Graubard and later Stephen B. Baxter) Studies in British History and Culture, 1965-79; contbg. editor Nat. Forum, 1983-91, editorial advisor, 1991-94; contbr. articles to learned jours. Trustee Western N.Y. Nuclear Research Center, 1967-73; chmn. bd. Coll. Center Finger Lakes, 1968-71; chmn. bd. Empire State Found., 1969-71, chmn., 1971-73; mem. New Eng. Bd. Higher Edn., 1985-87, Ambs. Roundtable, 1986-92, Fuld Found./ Nat. League Nursing Adv. Council on Accreditation, 1986-88; chmn. Ettinger scholarship com. Ednl. Found. Am., 1987-93; bd. dirs. Conn. Grand Opera, 1978-89, Bridgeport Bus. Coun., 1982-88, Save the Children, 1988—; chmn. adv. coun. Save the Children, 1990—. 1st lt. USAAF, 1944-45; capt. USAF Res. Decorated DFC with oak leaf cluster, Crown Decoration of Honor 3rd Order Iran, 1978; chevalier l'Ordre des Palmes Académique (France), 1984; recipient Rosa and Samuel Sachs prize Cin. Inst. Fine Arts, 1961, Cultural medal Republic of China, 1983, Disting. Svc. award Greater Bridgeport Bar Assn., 1986, Outstanding Civilian Svc. medal Dept. Army, 1988. Fellow Royal Soc. Arts (life); mem. Renaissance Soc. Am., English Speaking Union, Internat. Assn. Univ. Pres. (pres.-elect 1978, pres. 1981-84, pres. emeritus 1984—, chief UN mission 1982—, World Peace award 1987, chmn. commn. on arms control edn. 1991—), Knights of Malta (order of the Orthodox Knights Hospitaller of St. John of Jerusalem, Russian orthodox br.), Phi Kappa Phi. Episcopalian. Clubs: Univ. (N.Y.C.); Country of Fairfield (Conn.). Office: 2425 Post Rd Southport CT 06490-1298

MILES, MICHAEL ARNOLD, consumer products executive; b. Chgo., June 22, 1939; s. Arnold and Alice (Morrissey) M.; m. Pamela L. Miles; children: Michael Arnold Jr., Christopher. BS, Northwestern U., 1961. Various mgmt. positions to v.p., account supr. Leo Burnett Co., Inc., 1961-71; with Heublein, Inc., 1971-82, sr. v.p. mktg. Ky. Fried Chicken, 1971-72, v.p. gen. mgr. grocery products, 1972-75, group v.p. internat. ops., 1976-77, v.p. group exec. Internat. group, chmn. food svc. and franchise group Ky. Fried Chicken, 1977-81, sr. v.p. foods, Louisville, 1981-82; pres., chief oper. officer Kraft Gen. Foods, Glenview, Ill., 1982-89, chief exec. officer vice chmn., Philip Morris Cos., Inc., 1989-91, dep. chmn., 1991, chmn., chief exec. officer, 1991-94. Bd. dirs. Jr. Achievement Chgo., Coun. Fgn. Rels., Nat. Multiple Sclerosis Soc., Lyric Opera Chgo.; mem. adv. coun. J.L. Kellogg Grad. Sch. Mgmt. Northwestern U., Evanston, Ill. Office: Philip Morris Cos Inc 120 Park Ave New York NY 10017-5592

MILES, RAYMOND EDWARD, former university dean, organizational behavior and industrial relations educator; b. Cleburne, Tex., Nov. 2, 1932; s. Willard Francis and Wilma Nell (Owen) M.; m. Lucile Dustin, Dec. 27, 1952; children: Laura, Grant, Kenneth. B.A. with highest honors, N. Tex. State U., 1954, M.B.A., 1958; Ph.D., Stanford U., 1963. Clk. Santa Fe R.R., Gainesville, Tex., 1950-55; instr. mgmt. Sch. Bus. N. Tex. State U., Denton, 1958-60; asst. prof. organizational behavior and indsl. relations Sch. Bus. Adminstrn. U. Calif.-Berkeley, 1963-68, assoc. prof., 1968-71, prof., 1971-, assoc. dean Sch. Bus. Adminstrn., 1978-81, dean, 1983-90; dir. Inst. Indsl. Relations, 1982-83; cons. various pvt., pub. orgns. Author: Theories of Management, 1975, (with Charles C. Snow) Organization Strategy, Structure and Process, 1978, (with Charles C. Snow) Fit, Failure, and the Hall of Fame, 1994; co-author: Organizational Behavior: Research and Issues, 1976, co-editor, contbg. author: Organization by Design: Theory and Practice, 1981. Served to 1st. lt. USAF, 1955-58. Mem. Indsl. Relations Research Assn., Acad. Mgmt. Democrat. Unitarian. Home: 8640 Don Carol Dr El Cerrito CA 94530-2733 Office: U Calif-Berkeley Walter A Haas Sch Bus 350 Barrows Hall Berkeley CA 94720

MILES, RICHARD, diplomat; b. Little Rock, Ark., 1937; m. Sharon O'Brien, June 18, 1960; children: Richard, Elizabeth. AA, Bakersfield Coll., 1960; AB, U. Calif., Berkeley, 1962; MA, Ind. U., 1964; grad., U.S. Army Russian Inst., Garmisch-Partenkirchen, Germany. With voter registration, political leadership tng. S.C. Voter Edn. Project, 1964-67; with Fgn. Svc., Oslo, Moscow, Belgrade, 1967-88; consul gen. Leningrad, 1988-91; prin. officer U.S. Embassy Office, Berlin, 1991-92; with Soviet, East European, Yugoslav Affairs, Politico-Military Bureau State Dept., amb. to Azerbaijan, 1992-93; dep. chief mission Am. Embassy, Moscow, 1993—. With USMC, 1954-57. Am. Polit. Sci. fellow for Sen. Ernest F. Hollings, 1983-84; fellow Harvard U. Ctr. Internat. Affairs, 1987-88. Office: Am Embassy Moscow APO AE 09721

MILES, RICHARD BRYANT, mechanical and aerospace engineering educator; b. Washington, July 10, 1943; s. Thomas Kirk and Elizabeth (Bryant) M.; m. Susan McCoy, May 14, 1983; children: Thomas, Julia. BSEE, Stanford U., 1966, MSEE, 1967, PhD in Elec. Engring., 1972. Rsch. assoc. elec. engring. dept. Stanford (Calif.) U., summer 1972; asst. prof. mech. and aerospace engring. dept. Princeton (N.J.) U., 1972-78, assoc. prof., 1978-82, prof., 1982—, chmn. engring. physics program, 1980—; lectr. Northwestern Poly. U., Xian, China, 1987. Contbr. articles to profl. publts., chpt. to book Advances in Fluid Mechanics Measurements, 1989; patentee in field. Bd. dirs. Fannie and John Hertz Found., Livermore, Calif., 1989—. Fannie and John Hertz Found. fellow, 1969-72; NSF summer trainee, 1972. Mem. AIAA (sr.), IEEE (sr.), Am. Phys. Soc., Optical Soc. Am. Office: Princeton U Mech & Aerospace Engring D-414 Eng Quad Olden St Princeton NJ 08544

MILES, ROBERT HENRY, management educator, university dean, consultant; b. Norfolk, Va., Mar. 10, 1944; s. Henry Bateman and Mildred Verda (Cuthrell) M.; m. Jane Irving Calfee, Aug. 27, 1966; children: Alexander Bateman, Holen Irving. BS, U. Va., 1967; MBA, Old Dominion U., 1969; PhD, U. N.C., 1974. Ops. analyst Ford Motor Co., Norfolk, 1968; project mgr. Advanced Rsch. Projects Agy. Office Sec. Def., Washington, 1970-71; asst. prof., co-founder Inst. Pub. Welfare Mgmt., U. Ala. Grad. Sch. Bus., Tuscaloosa, 1974-75; asst. prof. Sch. Orgn. and Mgmt. Yale U., New Haven, 1975-78; assoc. prof. Harvard Bus. Sch., Boston, 1978-85; vis. prof. Stanford Exec. Inst., 1985—; Isaac Stiles Hopkins prof. orgn. and mgmt. Emory U. Bus. Sch., Atlanta, 1987—, interim dir., 1989-91, dean faculty, 1991-93; mem. sec.'s adv. bd. U.S. Dept. Energy, Washington, 1993—; mem. adv. bd. orgn. studies program Nat. Ctr. for Higher Edn. Mgmt. Systems, Boulder, Colo., 1982-85; mem. adv. bd. McIntire Sch. Commerce, U. Va., Charlottesville, 1987—. Author: Macro-Organizational Behavior, 1980, (with J.R. Kimberly) The Organizational Life Cycle: Issues in the Creation, Transformation, and Decline of Organizations, 1980, Managing the Corporate Social Environment: A Grounded Theory, 1987; (in collaboration with K.S. Cameron) Coffin Nails and Corporate Strategies, 1982, (with A. Bhambri) The Regulatory Executives, 1983, (with W.A. Randolph) The Organization Game: A Simulation, 1979, 83, 93; mem. editorial bd. Adminstrv. Sci. Quar., 1978-86, Mgmt. Sci., 1979-82. 1st lt. U.S. Army, 1969-71. Recipient Disting. Svc. award Emory U. 1993. Mem. APA, Acad. Mgmt. (chmn. orgn. and mgmt. theory divsn. 1984-85), Strategic Mgmt. Soc., Harvard Club (Boston), Commerce Club (Atlanta), Cherokee Town Club (Atlanta), Beta Gamma Sigma. Unitarian Universalist. Avocations: boating, tennis. Home (summer): 177 Fox Hill Rd Chatham MA 02633

MILES, SAMUEL ISRAEL, psychiatrist; b. Munich, Mar. 4, 1949; came to U.S., 1949; s. Henry and Renee (Ringel) M.; m. Denise Marie Robey, June 26, 1977; children: Jonathan David, Justin Alexander. BS, CCNY, 1970; MD, N.Y. Med. Coll., 1974; PhD, So. Calif. Psychoanalytic Inst., 1986. Diplomate Am. Bd. Psychiatry and Neurology with added qualifications in forensic psychiatry. Intern D.C. Gen. Hosp., Washington, 1974-75; resident in psychiatry Cedars-Sinai Med. Ctr., Los Angeles, 1975-78; practice medicine specializing in psychiatry Los Angeles, 1978—; ind. med. examiner Calif. Dept. Indsl. Relations, 1984—, qualified med. examiner, 1991—; asst. clin. prof. psychiatry UCLA Sch. Med., 1978—; attending psychiatrist Cedars-Sinai Med. Ctr., 1978—, co-chmn. util. rev./qual. assurance com. dept. psychiatry, 1984-89, chmn. qual. assurance com. dept. psychiatry, 1990-91, mem. in-patient adv. com., 1983-85, 87-90, psychiatry adv. com., 1984-86; attending psychiatrist Brotman Med. Ctr., Culver City, Calif., 1978—; faculty mem. So. Calif. Psychoanalytic Inst., 1986—; mem. psychiat. panel Superior Ct., L.A. Co., 1990—, Fed. Ct., 1990—. Fellow Am. Acad. Psychoanalysis, Am. Orthopsychiat. Assn.; mem. Acad. Psychiatry and the Law, Calif. Psychiat. Assn. (manage and care com. 1991—), So. Calif. Psychiat. Soc. (coun. rep. 1985-88, 92—, chair pvt. practice com. 1988-92, sec. 1991-92, worker's compensation com. 1992—), Am. Coll. Legal Medicine, So. Calif. Psychoanalytic Inst. (pres. clin. assocs. orgn. 1981-82, mem. admissions com. 1988—, ethics stds. com. 1991-92, chair 1993—, exec. com. 1993—). Jewish. Avocations: flying, swimming. Office: 8631 W 3rd St # 425E Los Angeles CA 90048-5901

MILES, VIRGINIA (MRS. FRED C. MILES), marketing consultant; b. N.Y.C., Apr. 20, 1916; d. Samuel and Jeanette (Shalet) Goldman; m. Fred C. Miles, Mar. 24, 1940; 1 dau., Erica. B.A., Wellesley Coll., 1936; M.A., Columbia, 1938, Ph.D., 1940. Asso. dir. research R.H. Macy & Co., N.Y.C., 1940-46; instr. dept. psychology Coll. City N.Y., 1946-48; advt. research dir. Alexander Smith & Co., Yonkers, N.Y., 1948-50; v.p., research dir. McCann-Erickson Advt. Agy., N.Y.C., 1950-60; v.p. spl. planning Young & Rubicam, Inc., N.Y.C., 1960-71; sr. v.p. new product devel. Young & Rubicam, Inc., 1971-75; mktg. cons. Englewood, N.J., 1975—. Contbr. articles to profl. jours., trade mags. Active Urban Coalition. Mem. Advt. Women of N.Y., Am. Assn. Pub. Opinion Rsch., Am. Mktg. Assn., Internat. Advt. Assn., Sigma Zi. Democrat. Jewish. Avocations: reading, music, gardening, travel. Home and Office: 91 Glenbrook Pky Englewood NJ 07631-2105

MILES, WENDELL A., federal judge; b. Holland, Mich., Apr. 17, 1916; s. Fred T. and Dena Del (Alverson) M.; m. Mariette Bruckert, June 8, 1946; children: Lorraine Miles, Michelle Miles Kopinski, Thomas Paul. AB, Hope

Coll., 1938, LLD (hon.), 1980; MA, U. Wyo., 1939; JD, U. Mich., 1942; LLD (hon.), Detroit Coll. Law, 1979. Bar: Mich. Ptnr. Miles & Miles, Holland, 1948-53, Miles, Mika, Meyers, Beckett & Jones, Grand Rapids, Mich., 1961-70; pros. atty. County of Ottawa, Mich., 1949-53; U.S. dist. atty. Western Dist. Mich., Grand Rapids, 1953-60; U.S. dist. judge Western Dist. Mich., 1974—, chief judge, 1979-86, sr. chief judge, 1986—; cir. judge 20th Jud. Cir. Ct. Mich., 1970-74; instr. Hope Coll., 1948-53, Am. Inst. Banking, 1953-60; adj. prof. Am. constl. history Hope Coll., Holland, Mich., 1979—; mem. Mich. Higher Edn. Commn.; apptd. Fgn. Intelligence Surveillance Count, Washington, 1989—. Pres. Holland Bd. Edn., 1952-63. Served to capt. U.S. Army, 1942-47. Recipient Liberty Bell award, 1986. Fellow Am. Bar Found.; mem. Am., Mich., Fed., Ottawa County bar assns., Grand Rapids Bar, Am. Judicature Soc. Club: Torch. Lodges: Rotary; Masons. Office: US Dist Ct 236 Fed Bldg 110 Michigan Ave NW Grand Rapids MI 49503-2313

MILETICH, IVO, library and information scientist, bibliographer, educator, linguist, literature research specialist; b. Pucisca, Yugoslavia, Apr. 18, 1936; came to U.S., 1966, naturalized, 1972; s. Josip and Mandina (Bagich) M.; m. Mira Pilja, Mar. 11, 1967; children: George Edward, Marina Julie. AB, Acad. Edn., Split, Yugoslavia, 1960; AM in History, U. Skopje, Macedonia, Yugoslavia, 1966; cert. advanced study, English Inst., Chgo., 1969; MA in Libr. Sci., Rosary Coll., River Forest, Ill., 1971. Cert. libr., Va. Tchr. various schs. Yugoslavia, 1959-65; asst. bibliographer Slavic langs. and lit. Joseph Regenstein and Sam Harper Librs., U. Chgo., 1967-71; tchr. Croatian lang. co-edn. YMCA Community Coll., Chgo., 1969-71, 74—; bibliographer Old Dominion U., Norfolk, Va., 1971-74; assoc. prof. libr. sci., bibliographer Chgo. State U., 1974—; translator, interpreter English, Latin, Croatian, Serbian, Macedonian, Bulgarian, Old Ch. Slavic, Slovene, 1969—; interpreter Berlitz Trans. Ctr. Sch. Langs.; lectr. South Slavonic langs., lit., history and culture, Balkan states culture, heritage and folk lit., transl. techniques. Contbr. various confs., seminars, workshops, jours., transl. of articles, studies, work on dictionary, Berlitz Transl. Svc. transl. and interpretion. Recipient Cert. of Appreciation YMCA C.C., Chgo., 1976, certs. Beta Phi Mu, U. Pitts., 1972, Am. Transls. Assn., 1980, Internat. Bibliog. Centre, Cambridge, 1980, Assn. Coll. and Rsch. Librs., 1986. Mem. ALA, Am. Fedn. Tchrs., Assn. Coll. and Rsch. Librs., Chgo. Acad. Libr. Coun. Libr. of Congress (assoc.), Beta Phi Mu. Home: 618 Exchange Ave Calumet City IL 60409 Office: Chgo State U Rm Lib 203 95th St at King Dr Chicago IL 60628

MILEWSKI, BARBARA ANNE, pediatrics nurse, neonatal intensive care nurse; b. Chgo., Sept. 11, 1934; d. Anthony and LaVerne (Sepp) Witt; m. Leonard A. Milewski, Feb. 23, 1952; children: Pamela, Robert, Diane, Timothy. ADN, Harper Coll., Palatine, Ill., 1982; BS, Northern Ill. U., 1992; postgrad., North Park Coll. RN, Ill.; cert. CPR instr. Staff nurse Northwest Community Hosp., Arlington Heights, Ill., Resurrection Hosp., Chgo.; nurse neonatal ICU Children's Meml. Hosp., Chgo.; CPR instr. Stewart Oxygen Svcs., Chgo.; instr., organizer parenting and well baby classes and clinics; vol. Children's Meml. Hosp.; health coord. CEDA Head Start. Vol. first aid instr. Boy Scouts Am.; CPR instr. Harper Coll., Children's Meml. Hosp.; dir. Albany Park Community Ctr. Head Start, Chgo. Mem. Am. Mortar Bd., Sigma Theta Tau.

MILEY, GEORGE HUNTER, nuclear engineering educator; b. Shreveport, La., Aug. 6, 1933; s. George Hunter and Norma Angeline (Dowling) M.; m. Elizabeth Burroughs, Nov. 22, 1958; children: Susan Miley Hibbs, Hunter Robert. B.S. in Chem. Engring., Carnegie-Mellon U., 1955; M.S., U. Mich., 1956, Ph.D. in Chem.-Nuclear Engring., 1959. Nuclear engr. Knolls Atomic Power Lab., Gen. Electric Co., Schenectady, 1959-61; mem. faculty U. Ill., Urbana, 1961—; prof. U. Ill., 1967—, chmn. nuclear engring. program, 1975-86, dir. Fusion Studies Lab., 1976—, fellow Ctr. for Advanced Study, 1985-86; dir. rsch. Rochford Tech. Assocs. Inc., 1990—; vis. prof. U. Colo., 1967, Cornell U., 1969-70, U. New South Wales, 1986, Imperial Coll. of London, 1987; mem. Ill. Radiation Protection Bd., 1988—; mem. Air Force Studies Bd., 1990-94; chmn. tech. adv. com. Ill. Low Level Radioactive Waste Site, 1990—; chmn. com. on indsl. uses of radiation Ill. Dept. Nuclear Safety, 1989—. Author: Direct Conversion of Nuclear Radiation Energy, 1971, Fusion Energy Conversion, 1976; editor Jour. Fusion Tech., 1980—; U.S. assoc. editor Laser and Particle Beams, 1982-86, mng. editor, 1987-91, editor-in-chief, 1991—; U.S. editor Jour. Plasma Physics, 1995—. Served with C.E. AUS, 1960. Recipient Western Electric Tchg.-Rsch. award, 1977, Halliburton Engring. Edn. Leadership award, 1990, Edward Teller medal, 1995; NATO sr. sci. fellow, 1975-76, Guggenheim fellow, 1985-86, Japanese Soc. Promotion of Sci. fellow, 1994. Fellow IEEE, Am. Nuclear Soc. (dir. 1980-83, Disting. Svc. award 1980, Outstanding Achievement award Fusion Energy divsn. 1992), Am. Phys. Soc.; mem. Am. Soc. Engring. Edn. (chmn. energy conversion com. 1967-70, pres. U. Ill. chpt. 1973-74, chmn. nuclear divsn. 1975-76, Outstanding Tchr. award 1973), Sigma Xi, Tau Beta Pi. Presbyterian. Achievements include research on fusion, energy conversion, reactor kinetics. Office: U Ill 214 Nuclear Engring Lab 103 S Goodwin Ave Urbana IL 61801-2901 *My professional goal has been to insure that future generations have a plentiful supply of economical, readily available energy such as offered by fusion. Not only should this insure a continued improvement in the standard of living for persons in all nations, but it should help maintain peace which is threatened by the struggle to obtain and control limited natural sources of energy.*

MILEY, SAMUEL A., lawyer, electrical equipment company executive; b. Vincennes, Ind., Feb. 23, 1957. AB, Harvard U., 1979; JD, Northwestern U., 1982. Bar: Ill. 1982, Calif. 1986. With Sidley & Austin, Chgo., 1982-86, Sheppard, Mullin, Richter & Hampton, L.A., 1986-90; gen. counsel, v.p., sec. MagneTek, Inc., L.A., 1990—. Office: MagneTek Inc 11150 Santa Monica Blvd Los Angeles CA 90025

MILFORD, FREDERICK JOHN, retired research company executive; b. Cleve., July 1, 1926; s. Frederick Charles and Florence M.; m. Jean Irene Olson, Sept. 8, 1951; 1 child, Cheryl Lynn. B.S in Physics, Case Inst. Tech., 1949; Ph.D. in Physics, M.I.T., 1952. Instr. Case Inst. Tech., Cleve., 1952-56; asst. prof. Case Inst. Tech., 1956-59; div. cons. Battelle Columbus Labs., 1959-62, div. chief, 1962-64, sr. fellow, 1964-66, dir. research in phys. scis., 1966-73, scientist, 1973, dept. mgr., 1973-76, assoc. dir., 1976-85, chief scientist, 1985-87, v.p. spl. programs, 1987-89, ret., 1989; vis. prof. physics U. Wash., 1969. Author: (with J.R. Reitz) Foundations of Electromagnetic Theory, 1960, 4th edit., 1993. mem. adv. bd. Central Ohio Salvation Army. Served with USNR, 1945-46. George Eastman fellow, 1951-52; Focke scholar, 1948-49. Fellow Am. Phys. Soc.; mem. Masons, Army and Navy Club, Kit Kat Club. Home: 1411 London Dr Columbus OH 43221-1543

MILFORD, MURRAY HUDSON, soil science educator; b. Honey Grove, Tex., Sept. 29, 1934; s. Murray Lane and Vivian Ione (Hudson) M.; m. Marsha Ann Rasmussen, July 21, 1961; children: Rebecca Ione, Murray Daniel. BS in Agronomy, Tex. A&M, 1955, MS in Agronomy, 1959; PhD in Soil Science, U. Wis., 1962. Cert. profl. soil scientist. Rsch. assoc. Cornell U., Ithaca, N.Y., 1962-63; asst. prof. Cornell U., Ithaca, 1963-68, assoc. prof., 1968; assoc. prof. Tex. A&M U., College Station, 1968-74, prof., 1974—. Author: (lab. manual) Soils and Soil Science-Lab. Exercises, 1970. 1st lt. USAR, 1955-57. Fellow AAAS, Am. Soc. Agronomy, (pres. Tex. chpt 1982-83, Resident Edn. award 1978), Soil Sci. Soc. Am. (Edn. award 1988); mem. Soil and Water Conservation Soc.(pres. Tex. coun. of chpts. 1987). Democrat. Presbyterian. Home: 3606 Tanglewood Dr Bryan TX 77802-3320 Office: Tex A&M Univ Soil & Crop Scis Dept College Station TX 77843-2474

MILFORD, PEGGY R., communications executive; b. Fairmont, Minn., Oct. 1, 1945; d. Glenn E. and Truma (Niss) M. BA, St. Olaf Coll., 1967; MBA, U. Minn., 1983. V.p. quality assurance US West, Denver. Mem. Nat. Women's Polit. Caucus, Washington. Office: US West Communications 188 Inverness Dr W Englewood CO 80112

MILGRAM, JEROME H., marine and ocean engineer, educator; b. Phila., Sept. 23, 1938; s. Samuel J. and Fannie M. BSEE, MIT, 1961, BS in Naval Architecture and Marine Engring., 1961, MS, 1962, PhD in Hydrodynamics, 1965. Registered profl. engr., Mass. With Scripps Inst. Oceanography, San Diego, summer 1961; project engr. Block Assocs., Cambridge, Mass., 1961-67; asst. prof. MIT, Cambridge, 1967-70, assoc. prof., 1970-77, prof. ocean

engring., 1977-89, William I. Koch prof. marine tech., 1989—; rsch. assoc. in biophysics Harvard U. Med. Sch., 1974-76; vis. prof. in naval architecture and marine engring., U. Mich., 1988-89; design dir. Am. 3 Found., 1991-92. Contbr. articles to profl. jours. Recipient Am. Bur. Shipping award, 1961, Alan Berman Outstanding Rsch. Publ. award U.S. Naval Rsch. Lab., 1990, AT&T Design Innovation award, 1992. Mem. Soc. Naval Architects and Marine Engrs. (life), Nat. Acad. Engring. Patentee in field. Home: 322 Ridge St Arlington MA 02174-1703 Office: MIT 77 Massachusetts Ave Rm 5-320 Cambridge MA 02139-3594

MILGRIM, FRANKLIN MARSHALL, merchant; b. N.Y.C., Aug. 24, 1925; s. Charles and Sally (Knobel) M.; m. Carol E. Kleinman, Sept. 2, 1945; children: Nancy Ellen, Catherine. Grad. with honors, Woodmere (N.Y.) Acad., 1943; B.S. in Econs. with honors, Wharton Sch. U. Pa., 1949. Asst. mgr. Milgrim, Cleve., 1949-50; merchandiser, buyer H. Milgrim Bros., Inc., N.Y.C., 1950-52; v.p., dir., gen. merchandiser H. Milgrim Bros., Inc., 1952-57; pres., dir. Milgrim, Inc., Cleve. and Columbus, Ohio, 1957—; v.p., dir. Milgrim, Inc. (Mich.), Detroit, 1962-66, The 9-18 Corp., Cleve., 1969—; pres., treas., dir. Milgrim Suburban, Inc., 1963—, Milo, Inc., Columbus, 1966—, The Milgrim Co., Cleve., 1966—; pres., dir. Frankly Paul Bailey Inc., Cleve., 1965—; Dir., v.p. M and M Receivers Assn., Cleve., 1959-68. Pres. Severance Center Mchts. Assn., Cleveland Heights, 1963-66; Pres., bd. dirs. Greater Cleve. Area chpt. Nat. Council on Alcoholism, 1973—; chmn. bd. Alcoholism Services of Cleve., 1977—; fin. chmn. adv. council Salvation Army Harbor Light Complex, 1976—, chmn. bd. adv. council, 1981—; mem. Greater Cleve. adv. bd. Salvation Army, 1981—; founding bd. dirs. Sister Mary Ignatia Gavin Found.; foreman Cuyahoga County Grand Jury, 1986. Served with USNR, 1943-46. Clubs: Oakwood Country (Cleve.), Cleveland Mid-Day (Cleve.), City (Cleve.); Cleveland Playhouse; Turnberry (North Miami Beach, Fla.). Home: 1 Bratenahl Pl Cleveland OH 44108-1181 also: 4000 Towerside Terr # 1908 Miami FL 33138

MILGRIM, ROGER MICHAEL, lawyer; b. N.Y.C., Mar. 22, 1937; s. Isreal and Iola (Lash) M.; m. Patricia Conway, July 10, 1971; children: Justin, Alex. BA, U. Pa., 1958; LLB, NYU, 1961, LLM, 1962. Bar: N.Y., U.S. Supreme Ct. Assoc. Baker & McKenzie, Paris, 1963-65, Nixon Mudge et al, N.Y.C., 1965-68; mem. Milgrim Thomajan & Lee P.C., N.Y.C., 1968-92; ptnr. Paul, Hastings, Janogsky & Walker, N.Y.C., 1992—; adj. prof. sch. law NYU, N.Y.C., 1974—. Author: Milgrim on Trade Secrets, 1967, supplement, 1995, Milgrim on Licensing, 1990, supplement, 1995. Trustee Coll. Wooster, 1994—, Bklyn. Hosp., 1982-91. Mem. Knickerbocker Club, Phila. Cricket Club. Republican. Home: 14 Sutton Pl S New York NY 10022 Office: Paul Hastings Janofsky & Walker 399 Park Ave New York NY 10022-4697

MILGROM, FELIX, immunologist, educator; b. Rohatyn, Poland, Oct. 12, 1919; came to U.S., 1958; naturalized, 1963; s. Henryk and Ernestina (Cyryl) M.; m. Halina Miszel, Oct. 15, 1941; children: Henry, Martin Louis. Student, U. Lwow, Poland, 1937-41, U. Lublin, Poland, 1945; MD, U. Wroclaw, Poland, 1947; MD (hon.), U. Vienna, Austria, 1976, U. Lund, Sweden, 1979, U. Heidelberg, Fed. Republic Germany, 1979, U. Bergen, Norway, 1980; DSc (hon.), U. Med. Dent., N.J., 1991. Rsch. assoc., prof. dept. microbiology Sch. Medicine U. Wroclaw, 1946-54, chmn. dept., 1954; prof., head dept. microbiology Sch. Medicine, Silesian U., Zabrze, Poland, 1954-57; rsch. assoc. Svc. de Chime Microbienne, Pasteur Inst., Paris, 1957; rsch. assoc., prof. dept. bacteriology, immunology Sch. Medicine, U. Buffalo, 1958-62; assoc. prof., then prof. and disting. prof. microbiology Sch. Medicine, SUNY, Buffalo, 1962—, chmn. dept., 1967-85. Author: Studies on the Structure of Antibodies, 1950; co-editor: International Convocations on Immunology, 1969, 75, 79, 85, Principles of Immunology, 1973, 2d edit., 1979, Principles of Immunological Diagnosis in Medicine, 1981, Medical Microbiology, 1982; editor in chief Internat. Archives of Allergy and Applied Immunology, 1965-91; contbg. editor Vox Sanguinis, 1965-76, Transfusion, 1966-73, Cellular Immunology, 1970-83, Transplation, 1975-78; contbr. numerous articles to profl. jours. Recipient Alfred Jurzykowski Found. prize, 1986, Paul Ehrlich and Ludwig Darmstaedter prize, 1987. Mem. Am. Assn. Immunologists, Transplantation Soc. (v.p. 1976-78), Am. Acad. Microbiology, Coll. Internat. Allergologicum (v.p. 1970-78, pres. 1978-82), Sigma Xi. Achievements include research on the serology of syphilis, Tb, rheumatoid arthritis, organ and tissue specificity including blood groups, transplantation and autoimmunity. Home: 474 Getzville Rd Buffalo NY 14226-2555

MILGROM, PAUL ROBERT, economics educator; b. Detroit, Apr. 20, 1948; s. Abraham Isaac and Anne (Finkelstein) M.; m. Jan Thurston, Dec. 10, 1977; children: Joshua, Elana. AB in Math. with high honors, U. Mich., 1970; MS in Stats., Stanford U., 1978, PhD in Bus., 1979; MA (hon.), Yale U., 1983. Actuarial trainee Met. Life Ins. Co., 1970-71; conulting actuary Nelson and Warren, Inc., 1972-75; asst. prof. managerial econs. and decision scis. Kellogg Grad. Sch. Mgmt. Northwestern U., 1979-81, assoc. prof., 1981-82, prof., 1982-83; prof. econs. and mgmt. Yale U., 1983-85, Williams Bros. prof. mgmt. studies, prof. econs., 1985-87; prof. econs. Stanford U., 1987—; dir. Stanford Inst. Theoretical Econs., 1989-91; vis. rsch. assoc. econs. Stanford U., 1981; vis. prof. Yale U., 1982-83; Ford vis. prof. econs. U. Calif., Berkeley, 1986-87; IBM rsch. chair Northwestern U., 1981; Williams Bros. chair mgmt. studies Yale U., 1985; Olin disting. lectr. Princeton U., 1988; past cons. Rexnord Corp., Southern New Eng. Telephone Co., Rand Corp., Arctic Slope Regional Corp., Georgia Pacific, Exxon, Bishop, Barry et. al.; lectr. in field. Author: (with John Roberts) Economics, Organization and Management, 1992, (with John Roberts), Instructor's Manual for Economics, Organization and Management, 1992; assoc. editor Jour. Econ. Theory, 1983-87, Rand Jour. Econs., 1985-89, Econometrica, 1987-90, Jour. Fin. Intermediation, 1989-92, Games and Econ. Behavior, 1990-92; co-editor Am. Econ. Review, 1990-93; contbr. over 50 articles to profl. jours. Recipient Leonard J. Savage Meml. Thesis award, 1980, Rsch. grant NSF, 1980, 82, 85, 88-91, 89, 91, Rsch. award Actuarial Edn. and Rsch. Fund, 1983, John Simon Guggenheim fellowship, 1986, Best Paper of Yr. award, 1987, Rsch. grant Ctr. Econ. Policy, 1988, 90. Fellow Am. Acad. Arts and Scis., Econometric Soc. (plenary lectr. 5th World Congress 1985), Morse Coll., Inst. Advanced Studies Hebrew U. Jerusalem, Ctr. Advanced Study in Behavioral Scis., Soc. Actuaries (Triennial Paper prize 1976); mem. Am. Econ. Assn. Office: Stanford Univ Dept Econs Stanford CA 94305

MILHAVEN, JOHN GILES, religious studies educator; b. N.Y.C., Sept. 1, 1927; s. John Michael and Rose (Burns) M.; m. Anne Teresa Lally, May 21, 1970; 1 child, Shelly. B.A., Woodstock Coll., 1949. M.A. in Teaching, Licentiate in Philosophy, 1950; Licentiate in Theology, Facultés Théologiques de la Compagnie de Jésus d'Enghien, Belgium, 1957; Ph.D. in Philosophy, U. Munich, Germany, 1962. Instr. philosophy Canisius Coll., Buffalo, 1951-53; assoc. prof. philosophy Fordham U., N.Y.C., 1961-66; assoc. prof. moral theology Woodstock Coll., Md., 1966-70; assoc. prof. religious studies Brown U., Providence, 1970-76; prof. religious studies Brown U., 1976—; lectr. med. ethics Georgetown U. Med. Sch., Washington, 1966-68. Author: Towards a New Catholic Morality, 1970, Good Anger, 1989, Hadewijch and Her Sisters: Other Ways of Loving and Knowing, 1993; contbr. articles to various pubs. Mem. Am. Acad. Religion, Soc. Christian Ethics, Cath. Theol. Soc. Am. Roman Catholic. Home: 20 Penrose Ave Providence RI 02906-5620 Office: Brown U Dept Religious Studies Providence RI 02912 *I believe I succeeded when I effectively shared with others something of my evasive but persistent experience of human life as important.*

MILHORAT, THOMAS HERRICK, neurosurgeon; b. N.Y.C., Apr. 5, 1936; s. Ade Thomas and Edith Caulkins (Herrick) M.; children: John Thomas, Robert Herrick. BA, Cornell U., 1957, MD, 1961. Intern, asst. resident in gen. surgery N.Y. Hosp.-Cornell Med. Ctr., 1961-63; clin. assoc. dept. surgery, neurology Nat. Inst. Neurol. Diseases and Blindness, Bethesda, 1963-65; asst. resident, chief resident in neurosurgery N.Y. Hosp.-Cornell Med. Ctr., 1965-68, asst. neurosurgeon NIH, 1968-71; assoc. prof. neurol. surgery, assoc. prof. child health and devel. George Washington U. Sch. Medicine, Washington, 1971-74; prof. child health and devel. George Washington U., Washington, 1974-81, prof. neurol. surgery, 1974-81; chmn. dept. neurosurgery Children's Hosp. Nat. Med. Ctr., Washington, 1971-81; prof. neurol. surgery, dept. chmn. SUNY Health Sci. Ctr., Bklyn., 1982—; neurosurgeon-in-chief Kings County Hosp. Ctr.; regional chmn. neurol.

surgery L.I. Coll. Hosp., 1986—, Coney Island Hosp., 1986—; program dir. Neurosurgery Rsch. Tng. Program, 1982—. Author: Hydrocephalus and Cerebrospinal Fluid, 1972, Pediatric Neurosurgery, 1978, Cerebrospinal Fluid and the Brain Edemas, 1987, (with M.K. Hammock) Cranial Computed Tomography in Infancy and Childhood, 1981; contbr. 180 articles to sci. publs. and chpts. to books. Chmn. bd. Internat. Neurosci. Found., pres., 1986—. Served to lt. comdr. USPHS, 1963-65. Recipient 1st prize in pathology, Cornell U. Med. Sch. Dept. Ob-Gyn., 1960, Charles L. Horn prize Cornell Med. Sch., 1961, Best Paper award ann. combined meeting N.Y. Acad. Medicine/N.Y. Neurosurg. Soc., 1965, Pudenz award for Excellence in CSF Physiology, 1994; named one of N.Y.'s Best Doctors, N.Y. Mag., 1992. Mem. AAAS, Internat. Soc. Pediat. Neurosurgery, Am. Assn. Neurol. Surgery, Am. Assn. Neurol. Surgery (pediat. sect.), Am. Acad. Pediatrics (surg. sect.), Soc. Pediat. Rsch., N.Y. Acad. Medicine, N.Y. Soc. Neurosurgery (pres. 1988-90), Bklyn. Neurol. Soc. (pres. 1988-95), Soc. Neurosci., Internat. Soc. Neurosci., Soc. Neurol. Surgeons, Nat. Coun. Scientists NIH, Med. Club Bklyn., Sigma Xi. Avocations: golf, billiards, gardening. Office: SUNY Health Sci Ctr Bklyn 450 Clarkson Ave PO Box 1189 Brooklyn NY 11203

MILHOUS, ROBERT E., advertising executive; b. 1937; married. BS, Purdue U., 1960. Advt. salesman Gen. Telephone Co., Calif., 1960-63; with B&B Advt. Co., Stanton, Calif., 1963-68; now chmn. bd. dirs., chief exec. officer Treasure Chest Advt. Co., Glendora, Calif.; also bd. dirs. Served U.S. Army, 1958-60. Office: Treasure Chest Advt Co Inc 511 W Citrus Edge St Glendora CA 91740-5098

MILHOUSE, PAUL WILLIAM, bishop; b. St. Francisville, Ill., Aug. 31, 1910; s. Willis Cleveland and Carrie (Pence) M.; m. Mary Frances Noblitt, June 29, 1932; children: Mary Catherine Milhouse Hauswald, Pauline Joyce Milhouse Vermillion, Paul David. A.B., U. Indpls. (formerly Ind. Cen. U.), 1932; D.D., U. Ind. (formerly Ind. Cen. U.), 1950; B.D., Am. Theol. Sem., 1937, Th.D. 1946; L.H.D., Westmar Coll., 1965; S.T.D., Oklahoma City U., 1969; D.D., So. Meth. U., 1969. Ordained to ministry United Brethren Ch., 1931; pastor Birds, Ill., 1928-29, Elliott, Ill., 1932-37, Olney, Ill., 1937-41; pastor 1st Ch., Decatur, Ill., 1941-51; asso. editor Telescope-Messenger, 1951-58; exec. sec. gen. council Evang. United Brethren Ch., 1959-60, bishop, 1960-68; bishop United Meth. Ch., 1968—; presiding bishop Southwestern Area, Evang. United Brethren Ch., 1960-68; presiding bishop Okla., 1968-80; pres. Coun. United Meth. Bishops, 1977-78; bishop-in-residence Oklahoma City U., 1980-91, U. Indpls., 1992-95. Author: Enlisting and Developing Church Leaders, 1946, Come Unto Me, 1946, Lift Up Your Eyes, 1955, Doorways to Spritual Living, 1950, Except the Lord Build the House, 1949, Christian Worship in Symbol and Ritual, 1953, Laymen in the Church, 1957, At Life's Crossroads, 1959, Phillip William Otterbein, 1968, Nineteen Bishops of the Evangelical United Brethren Church, 1974, Organizing for Effective Ministry, 1980, Theological and Historical Roots of United Methodists, 1980, Detour Into Yesterday, 1984, Okla. City U., Miracle at 23d and Blackwelder, 1984, Transforming Dollars into Service, A History of Methodist Manor, 1987, St. Lukes of Oklahoma City, 1988; also articles; editor: Facing Frontiers, 1960. Trustee Westmar Coll., 1960-68, Western Home, 1960-68, So. Meth. U., 1968-80, Oklahoma City U., 1968-80, hon. life trustee, 1980—, Francis E. Willard Home, 1968-80, Meth. Manor, 1968-80, Boys Ranch, 1968-80, Last Frontier coun. Boy Scouts Am., 1968-80; hon. life trustee United Theol. Sem. Recipient Disting. Alumnus award Ind. Central U. now U. Indpls., 1978; Disting. Friend award Oklahoma City U., 1979; Disting. Service award Oklahoma City U., 1980; Top Hand award Oklahoma City C. of C., 1980; Bishop Paul W. Milhouse award Okla. City U., 1990. Mem. Mark Twain Writers Guild, Epsilon Sigma Alpha, now Alpha Chi. *Life is a gift to be lived in harmony with the purpose of God, who holds us accountable.*

MILIC, LOUIS TONKO, English educator; b. Split, Yugoslavia, Sept. 5, 1922; came to U.S., 1936, naturalized, 1945; s. Tonko L. and Helen (Gross) M.; m. Patricia A. Langwell, May 27, 1950 (div. Sept. 1960); 1 dau., Barbara; m. Ann Mulford Boyer, Sept. 24, 1960 (div. Oct. 1970); children: Pamela, Antonia, Byrd Jones; m. Jan Louise Lundgren, Nov. 20, 1970. A.B., Columbia U., 1948, M.A., 1950, Ph.D., 1963. Instr., Mont. State Coll., 1952-54; lectr. Columbia U., 1955-58, instr., 1958-63, asst. prof., 1963-67, assoc. prof. Tchrs. Coll., 1967-69; prof. English, Cleve. State U., 1969-91, prof. emeritus, 1991—, chmn. dept., 1969-78. Author: A Quantitative Approach to the Style of Jonathan Swift, 1967, Style and Stylistics: An Analytical Bibliography, 1967, Stylists on Style, 1969; co-author: The English Language: Form and Use, 1974; editor: Modernity of the Eighteenth Century, 1971, The Gamut, 1983-92; gen. editor: New Humanistic Research series, 1972-80; book rev. editor Computers and the Humanities, 1966-72; compiler The Augustan Prose Sample, The Century of Prose Corpus. Served with USAAF, 1943-46. Am. Council Learned Socs. and IBM fellow, 1967; NEH fellow, 1980. Mem. Internat. Assn. Univ. Profs. English, Assn. Computers in Humanities, Am. Soc. 18th Century Studies, Midwest MLA (exec. com. 1972-75), Henry Sweet Soc., Dictionary Soc. N.Am. (sec.-treas. 1990—), Assn. for Lit. and Linguistic Computing, Rowfant Club. Home: 3111 Chelsea Dr Cleveland OH 44118-1220 *The world is a lucky accident. Its chance opportunities for the inquisitive mind are limitless. I have always found it hard to avoid studying everything, because of this richness, which is tantalizing and yet without permanent meaning.*

MILIC-EMILI, JOSEPH, physician, educator; b. Sezana, Slovenia, May 27, 1931; arrived in Can., 1963; s. Joseph Milic-Emili and Giovanna Milic-Emili Perhavec; m. Ann Harding, Nov. 2, 1957; children: Claire, Anne-Marie, Alice, Andrew. MD, U. Milan, 1955; Dr honoris causa, U. Montpellier, France, 1994. Asst. prof. physiology and exptl. medicine McGill U., Montreal, Que., Can., 1963-65, assoc. prof., 1965-69, prof., 1970—, dir. Meakins-Christie Labs., 1979—; vis. prof. Lab. de Physiologie Faculte de Medecine Saint-Antoine, Paris, Svc. de Pneumologie Hosp. Beaujon, Paris, 1978-79, 94-95, chmn. dept. physiology, 1973-78; vis. cons. medicine Royal Postgrad. Med. Sch., London, 1969-70; vis. cons. aeronautics Imperial Coll. Tech., London, 1969-70; asst. prof. physiology U. Liege, Belgium, 1958-60; asst. prof. U. Milan, 1956-58. Mem. editorial bd. Am. Jour. Physiology, 1970-76, Jour. Applied Physiology, 1970-76, Rev. Française des Maladies Respiratoires, 1979—, Rivista de Biologia, 1979-86, Am. Rev. Respiratory Disease, 1982-89, Reanimation, Soins Intensifs, Medicine d'Urgence, 1984—. Mem. applied physiology and bioengring. study sect. NIH, 1975-78. Decorated Order of Can.; recipient Gold medal C. Forlanini u. Pavia, Italy, 1982, Am. Coll. Chest Physicians medal, 1984, Harry Wunderly medal Thoracic Soc. Australia, 1988; named Dr. Honoris Causa, U. Louvain, Belgium, 1987, Kunming Med. Coll., China, 1987; Harvard U. fellow, Boston, 1960-63; author one of 100 most-cited articles in clin. rsch. of 1960s; named one of 1,000 most-cited contemporary scientists, 1965-78. Fellow Royal Soc. Can., Slovenian Acad. Scis. (fgn. corr.); mem. Soc. Belge de Physiologie, Assn. Physiologistes de Langue Française, Am. Physiol. Soc., Can. Physiol. Soc., Can. Soc. for Clin. Investigation (assoc. editor Clin. Investigative Medicine 1981-86), Italian Physiol. Soc., Can. Thoracic Soc. Med. Rsch. Coun. (mem. grants com. 1980). Home: 4394 Circle Rd, Montreal, PQ Canada H4W 1Y5 Office: McGill U Meakins-Christie Labs, 3626 St Urbain St, Montreal, PQ Canada H2X 2P2

MILIDRAG, GEORGE D., engineering company executive; b. 1931. Chmn. bd. dirs. Engring. Tech. LTD, Trpy, Mich. Office: Engring Tech LTD 777 Chicago Dr Troy MI 48083*

MILIORA, MARIA TERESA, chemist, psychotherapist, psychoanalyst, educator; b. Somerville, Mass., June 29, 1938; d. Andrew and Maria Civita (Gallinaro) Migliorini. BA cum laude, Regis Coll., 1960; PhD, Tufts U., 1965; MSW, Boston U., 1985. Rsch. asst. Tufts U., Medford, Mass., 1960-64; rsch. assoc. Tufts U., 1965-66; assoc. prof. Suffolk U., Boston, 1965-68; asso. prof. Suffolk U., 1968-71, prof., 1971—, chmn. dept. chemistry, 1972-84, mem. presdl. search com., 1980; faculty rep. univ. strategic planning com. Suffolk U., Boston, 1992—; faculty Boston Inst. for Psychotherapy, 1992—; faculty mem. Tng. and Rsch. Inst. for Self Psychology, N.Y.C., 1994—; research asso. Bio-Research Inst., Cambridge, Mass., 1968. Contbr. articles to profl. jours. Faculty rep. to trustees Joint Coun. on Univ. Affairs, Suffolk U., 1973-77, 79-81; convenor Pres.'s Commn. on Status of Women, 1974-78, speaker ednl. policy com., 1972-73; chair cultural diversity CLAS Curriculum, 1991—. Mem. AAUP (chpt. pres. 1970), NASW, Am. Chem. Soc. (alt. councillor 1976-79, 82—, councillor 1979-82; bd. dirs. Northeastern

sect. 1976—, chmn. pub. rels. sect. 1977-79), Mass. Acad. Clin. Social Work, Nat. Assn. for Advancement Psychoanalysis, Nat. Membership Com. on Psychoanalysis, Sigma Xi (chpt. pres. 1972-73), Sigma Zeta (chpt. sect. 1970—), Alpha Lambda Delta, Delta Epsilon Sigma. Home: 41 Irving St Newton MA 02159-1611 Office: Suffolk University Beacon Hill Boston MA 02114

MILIUS, JOHN FREDERICK, film writer, director; b. St. Louis, Apr. 11, 1944; s. William Styx and Elizabeth (Roe) M.; 3 children. Ed., U. So. Calif. instr. motion pictures script analysis U. So. Calif., fall 1973, advanced motion picture script analysis, spring 1974. Films include: (screenwriter) Devil's 8, 1969, Evel Kenieval, 1971, Jeremiah Johnson, 1972 (Heritage Wrangler Award), The Life and Times of Judge Roy Bean, 1973, Magnum Force, 1973, Apocalypse Now, 1979 (with Francis Ford Coppola, Academy Award nominee Best screenplay), Clear and Present Danger, 1994; (story) Extreme Prejudice, 1987; (dir.; screenwriter) Dillinger, 1973, The Wind and the Lion, 1975 (National Bell Ringers ednl. award, Writers Guild nom. for Best Orig. Screenplay), Big Wednesday, 1978, Conan the Barbarian, 1981, Red Dawn, 1984, Farewell to the King, 1989, Flight of the Intruder, 1991; (exec. prodr.) Hardcore, 1979, Used Cars, 1980; (exec. prodr., co-screenwriter) 1941, 1979; (co-screenwriter, story) Geronimo: An American Legend, 1993. Recipient Nat. Student Film Festival award U. So. Calif., 1968; numerous gun shooting awards; honored by Winchester for The Wind and the Lion. Office: care Jeff Berg International Creative Mgmt 8942 Wilshire Blvd Beverly Hills CA 90211*

MILIUS, RICHARD A., organic chemist; b. Lawrence, Mass., Nov. 10, 1950; s. Leo and Teresa (Liehr) M.; m. Amy L. Dingley, Sept. 29, 1979; children: James, Elena. BS, Marquette U., 1972; PhD, Northeastern U., 1981. Rsch. chemist Miles Labs., Inc., Elkhart, Ind., 1972-74; chemist New Eng. Nuclear Corp., Boston, 1974-77; rsch. assoc. Harvard Med. Sch., Boston, 1981-84; tech. dir. Rsch. Biochems. Internat., Natick, Mass., 1984-94; dir. sponsored rsch. Rsch. Biochems. Internat., Natick, 1994—; chmn. small bus. rsch. rev. com. NIMH, Washington, 1991-93; instr. Univ. Coll. Northeastern U., Boston, 1988-92. Co-chmn. Norwood/Brockton chpt. Open Door Soc. Mass., 1989-90. Recipient Marie Curie award European Assn. Nuclear Medicine, 1992. Mem. AAAS, Am. Chem. Soc., Soc. Neurosci., Soc. Nuclear Medicine. Achievements include patents for astatinated organic compounds, iodinated neuroprobe for mapping monoamine reuptake sites. Office: Rsch Biochems Internat 1 Strathmore Rd Natick MA 01760-2418

MILKMAN, ROGER DAWSON, genetics educator, molecular evolution researcher; b. N.Y.C., Oct. 15, 1930; s. Louis Arthur and Margaret (Weinstein) M.; m. Marianne Friedenthal, Oct. 18, 1958; children: Ruth Margaret, Louise Friedenthal, Janet Dawson Milkman Lussenhop, Paul David. A.B., Harvard U., 1951, A.M., 1954, Ph.D., 1956. Student, asst., instr., investigator Marine Biol. Lab., Woods Hole, Mass., 1952-72, 88—; instr., asst. prof. U. Mich., Ann Arbor, 1957-60; assoc. prof., prof. Syracuse U., N.Y., 1960-68; prof. biol. scis. U. Iowa, Iowa City, 1968—, chmn. univ. genetics PhD program, 1992-93; vis. prof. biology Grinnell Coll., 1990. Translator: Developmental Physiology, 1970; editor: Perspectives on Evolution, 1982, Experimental Population Genetics, 1983, Evolution jour., 1984-86; mem. editl. bd. Molecular Phylogenetics and Evolution; contbr. articles to profl. jours. Sec. Soc. Gen. Physiologists, 1963-65, Am. Soc. Naturalists, 1980-82; alumni rep. Phillips Acad., Andover, Mass., 1980-94. NSF grantee, 1959—; USPHS grantee, 1984-87. Fellow AAAS; mem. Am. Soc. for Microbiology, Genetics Soc. Am., Am. Soc. of Marine Biol. Lab., Soc. Study Evolution, Soc. for Gen. Microbiology (U.K.), Soc. Molecular Biology and Evolution, Internat. Soc. for Molecular Evolution (NIH genetics study sect. 1986-87). Jewish. Avocation: mountain hiking. Home: 12 Fairview Knoll NE Iowa City IA 52240-9147 Office: U Iowa Dept Biol Scis 138 Biology Building Bldg Iowa City IA 52242-1324

MILLANE, LYNN, town official; b. Buffalo, N.Y. Oct. 14, 1928; d. Robert P. Schermerhorn and Justine A. (Ross) m. J. Vaughan Millane, Jr.; Aug. 16, 1952 children: Maureen, Michele, John, Mark, Kathleen. EdB, U. Buffalo, 1949, EdM, in Health Education 1951. Mem. Amherst Town Bd., 1982—; dep. town supr., 1990—; pres., E. J. Meyer Hosp. Jr. Bd., 1962-64; pres. Aux. to Erie County Bar Assn., 1966-68; pres. Women's Com. of Buffalo Philharm. Orch., 1976-78, v.p. adminstrn., 1975-76, v.p. pub. affairs, 1974-75, chmn. adv. bd., 1978-82; v.p. Buffalo Philharm. Orch. Soc., Inc., 1976-78, mem. coun., trustee, 1979-87, bd. overseers, 1987-92; dir. 8th judicial dist. N.Y. State Assn. of Large Towns, 1989-90, 90-91; bd. dirs. oper. bd. Millard Fillmore Suburban Hosp., 1992-2001; 1st v.p. Fans for 17, 1980-82; 1st. v.p. Friends of Baird Hall, SUNY-Buffalo, 1980-82; exec. bd. mem. Longview Protestant Home for Children, 1979-85, 2d v.p., 1982-85; bd. dirs. ARC, Town of Amherst br., 1982-91, by-laws com., 1981, 84, chmn. sr. concerns com., 1982-91, liaison code of ethics com., 1987-89; bd. dirs. Amherst Symphony Orch. Assn., 1981-87, roster chmn., 1982-84, nominating chmn., 1985-86, vice-chmn. 50th anniversary com. 1994—; nat. music com. Women's Assn. for Symphony Orchs. in Am. and Can., 1977-79; coun. mem. Am. Symphony Orch. League; sec. Amherst Sr. Citizen's Adv. Bd., 1980-81, liaison from Amherst Town Bd., 1982—; founder, liaison 1st adult day svcs. adv. bd. Town of Amherst, 1988; liaison to ad hoc cable TV com., 1992—; mem. 1st records mgmt. adv. bd., liaison ethics bd. Town of Amherst, 1994—, dep. supr. 1990—; liaison to the Alternate Fuel and Clean Cities Com., 1994-95; dir.-at-large community adv. coun. SUNY-Buffalo, 1981-91; co-assoc. chmn. maj. gift div. capital campaign Daeman Coll., 1983-84; co-chmn. Women United Against Drugs Campaign, 1970-72; founding mem. Lunch and Issues, Amherst, 1981—; mem. edn. com. Network in Aging of Western N.Y., Inc., 1982-89, bd. dirs., 1982-89, housing com., 1987-89; bd. dirs. Amherst Elderly Transp. Corp., 1982—; committeeman dist. Town of Amherst Republican Com.; treas. Town and Country Rep. Club, 1980-81; mem. nominating com. Fedn. Rep. Women's Clubs Erie County, 1980; exec. bd. mem. Women's Exec. Coun. of Erie County Rep. Com., 1969-71; dir. Amherst Rep. Women's Club, 1963-65; delegate N.Y. State Govs. Conf. on Aging, 1995, White House Conf. on Aging, 1995. Named Homemaker of Yr., Family Circle Mag., 1969; Woman of Substance, 20th Century Rep. Women, 1983; Woman of Yr., Buffalo Philharm. Orch. Soc., Inc., 1982; Outstanding Woman in Community Svc., SUNY-Buffalo, 1985; recipient Good Neighbor award Courier Express, 1978; Merit award Buffalo Philharm. Orch., 1978; award Fedn. Rep. Women's Clubs Erie County, 1982; Disting. Svc. award Town of Amherst Sr. Ctr., 1985; Susan B. Anthony award Interclub Coun. of Western N.Y., 1991, Community Svc. award Amherst Rep. Com., 1991, D.A.R.E. award Town of Amherst Police Dept., 1994, Disting. Svc. award Amherst Adult Day Care and Vis. Nurses Assn., 1994. Mem. Amherst C. of C. (VIP dinner com. 1984), LWV, SUNY-Buffalo Alumni Assn. (life, presdl. advisor 1977-79), Zonta (pres. Amherst chpt. 1986-88, Zontian of Yr. 1992), Pi Lambda Theta (hon.). Office: 5583 Main St Buffalo NY 14221-5409

MILLAR, GORDON HALSTEAD, mechanical engineer, agricultural machinery manufacturing executive; b. Newark, Nov. 28, 1923; s. George Halstead and Dill E. (McMullen) M.; m. Virginia M. Jedryczka, Aug. 24, 1957; children—George B., Kathryn M., Juliet S., John G., James H. B.M.E., U. Detroit, 1949, D.Sc. (hon.), 1977; Ph.D., U. Wis., 1952; L.H.D., West Coast U., 1984; D.Sc. (hon.), Western Mich. U., 1986. Registered profl. engr., Fla., Ill., Iowa, Mich., Minn., Ohio. Supr. new powerplants Ford Motor Co., 1952-57; engring. mgr. Meriam Instrument Co., Cleve., 1957-59; dir. new products McCulloch Corp., Los Angeles, 1959-63; with Deere & Co., 1963-84; v.p. engring. Deere & Co., Moline, Ill., 1972-84; exec. assoc. Southwest Research Inst., 1987; mem. Fed. Adv. Com. Indsl. Innovation, 1979; chmn. West Ctrl. Ill. Ednl. Telecom. Corp.; pres. Accreditation Bd. for Engring. and Tech., 1983-85; pres., fellow Accreditation Bd. for Engring. and Tech. Contbr. articles to profl. jours.; patentee in field. Chmn. Quad Cities chpt. United Way, 1976-77; bd. dirs.; adv. council Bradley U. Coll. Engring. and Tech.; mem. exec. com. Illowa council Boy Scouts Am., 1977-79. Served with U.S. Army, World War II. Decorated Purple Heart; recipient Alumnus of Year award U. Detroit, 1976, Comdrs. medal for pub. svc. Dept. Army, 1989. Fellow ASME (hon. life mem.), Soc. Automotive Engrs. (pres. 1984, bd. dirs. 1984-86, mem. nat. nominating com.); mem. NAE, NSPE, Engrs. Joint Coun., Indsl. Rsch. Inst., Engring. Soc. Detroit, Am. Soc. Agrl. Engrs., Ill. Soc. Profl. Engrs., Moline C. of C., Aviation Coun. Home: 1840 Wiley Post Trl Daytona Beach FL 32124-6756

MILLAR, JAMES ROBERT, economist, educator, university official; b. San Antonio, Tex., July 7, 1936; s. James G. and Virginia M. (Harrison) M.; m. Gera Ascher, July 4, 1965; children: Leo Schaeg (dec.), Mira Gail. B.A., U. Tex., 1958; Ph.D. in Econs, Cornell U., 1965. Asst. prof. dept. econs. U. Ill., Urbana, 1965-70, assoc. prof., 1970-72, prof., 1973-89, assoc. vice chancellor for acad. affairs, 1984-89, dir. internat. programs and studies, 1984-89; prof. econs. and internat. affairs George Washington U., Washington, 1989—, dir. Inst. for European, Russian and Eurasian Studies, 1989—, assoc. dean Elliott Sch. Internat. Affairs, 1989-95, acting dean, 1994; mem. acad. coun. Kennan Inst. Advanced Russian, 1975-84; young faculty exchangee Moscow State U., 1966; cons. to congressmen and various U.S. govt. depts., 1972—; dir. Soviet Interview Project, 1981-88; sec., bd. dirs. Midwest Univs. Consortium for Internat. Activities, 1984-88, chmn. bd., 1988-89. Author: The ABCs of Soviet Socialism, 1981, The Soviet Economic Experiment, 1990; editor, contbr. The Soviet Rural Community, 1971; editor: Slavic Rev., Am. Quar. Soviet and East European Studies, 1975-80; editor, contbr. Politics, Work and Daily Life, A Survey of Former Soviet Citizens, 1987; editor, contbr. Cracks in the Monolith: Party Power in the Brezhnev Era, 1992, The Social Legacy of Communism, 1994; contbr. articles on studies on Soviet/Russian economy and econ. history to scholarly jours. Served with Q.M.C. U.S. Army, 1960. Ford Found. fgn. area fellow, 1961-64; sr. scholar rsch. travel grantee to USSR, 1972; Am. Coun. Learned Socs./USSR Acad. Scis. travel exchangee, 1979; fellow Woodrow Wilson Internat. Ctr. for Scholars, 1988-89, Guggenheim fellow, 1995-96. Mem. AAAS, Econ. History Assn., Assn. Evolutionary Econs., Am. Assn. Advancement Slavic Studies (del. Am. Coun. Learned Soc. 1992—), Am. Coun. Learned Soc. (sec., bd. dirs. 1995—, mem. exec. com. del., chair 1993-95, mem. joint com. with Social Sci. Rsch. Coun. 1990-95), Am. Assn. Pub. Opinion Rsch., N.Y. Acad. Sci. Home: The Westchester 4000 Cathedral Ave NW Apt 143B Washington DC 20016-5249 Office: George Washington U Inst Eur Russ Eurasian Studies 2130 H St NW Ste 601 Washington DC 20052-0001

MILLAR, JEFFERY LYNN, columnist; b. Houston, July 10, 1942; s. Daniel Lynn Millar and Betty Ruth (Shove) Coons; m. Lynne McDonald, Dec. 21, 1964 (div. Aug. 1983); m. Peggy V. Watson, Apr. 1, 1994. BA, U. Tex., 1964. Reporter Houston Chronicle, 1964-65, film critic, 1965—, columnist, 1972—. Writer, co-creator: (comic strip) Tank McNamara, Universal Press Syndicate, Kansas City, 1974—. Office: Houston Chronicle PO Box 4260 Houston TX 77210-4260

MILLAR, JOHN DONALD, occupational and environmental health consultant, educator; b. Newport News, Va., Feb. 27, 1934; s. John and Dorothea Virginia (Smith) M.; m. Joan M. Phillips, Aug. 17, 1957; children: John Stuart, Alison Gordon, Virginia Taylor. B.S., U. Richmond, 1956; M.D., Med. Coll. Va., 1959; D.T.P.H., London Sch. Hygiene and Tropical Medicine, 1966. Cert. specialist in Gen. Preventive Medicine, 1969. Intern U. Utah Affiliated Hosps., Salt Lake City, 1959-60, asst. resident in medicine, 1960-61; chief Epidemic Intelligence Svc., Ctr. for Disease Control, USPHS, HEW, Atlanta, 1961-63, dep. chief surveillance sect. epidemiology br., 1962-63, chief smallpox unit, 1963-65, dir. smallpox eradication program, 1966-70, dir. Bur. State Svcs., 1970-78, asst. dir. Ctr. for Disease Control for Pub. Health Practice, 1979-80; dir. Ctr. for Environ. Health Atlanta, 1980-81; dir. Nat. Inst. for Occupation Safety and Health, Atlanta, 1981-93; pres. Don Millar & Assocs., Inc., Atlanta, 1993—; adj. prof. occupational and environ. health Sch. Pub. Health Emory U., Atlanta; cons. on smallpox, smallpox eradication, immunization programs and occupational and environ. health WHO; mem. WHO expert adv. panel on occupational health. Contbr. articles to profl. jours. Recipient Surgeon Gen's. Commendation medal, 1965, Okeke prize London Sch. Hygiene and Tropical Medicine, 1966, Presdl. award for mgmt. improvement, 1972, W.C. Gorgas medal Assn. Mil. Surgeons U.S., 1987, Lucas lectr. Faculty Occupational Medicine Royal Coll. Physicians, London, 1987, Outstanding Med. Alumnus award Med. Coll. Va., 1988; also recipient Equal Employment Opportunity award, 1975, Medal of Excellence, 1977, Joseph W. Mountin lectr. award, 1986, all from Ctrs. for Disease Control, Disting. Svc. medal USPHS, 1983, 88, Exemplary Svc. medal Surgeon Gen. U.S., 1988, Giants in Occupational Medicine lectr. U. Utah, 1989, William S. Knudsen award Am. Coll. Occupational Medicine, 1991, presdl. citation APA, 1991, William Steiger Meml. award Am. Conf. Govtl. Indsl. Hygienists, 1993, Health Watch award for outstanding contbns. toward improving health of minority popvulations, 1992, Award of Merit Minerva Edn. Inst., 1993, Alumni Disting. Svc. award U. Richmond, 1993; named to Order Bifurcated Needle, World Health Orgn., 1978, Faculty Occupational Medicine, Royal Coll. Physicians, London, 1990. Office: Don Millar & Assocs Inc Ste 201 3243 Wake Robin Trail Atlanta GA 30341-5721

MILLAR, JOHN FRANCIS, industrial products company executive; b. Teaneck, N.J., Jan. 23, 1936; m. Doris Connolly; children: Michael R., Cynthia A. BS in Fin., Fairleigh Dickinson U., 1961. Sr. auditor Hurdman & Cranstoun CPAs, NYC, 1961-64; dir. treas. ops. Keuffel & Esser Co., Morristown, N.J., 1964-76; treas., chief fin. officer Batt Bates & Co., Washington, 1976-77, Joseph Dixon Crucible Co., Jersey City, 1977-83, Dixon Ticonderoga Co., Vero Beach, Fla., 1983-85; exec. v.p. chief ops. officer indsl. products Dixon Ticonderoga Co., Lakehurst, N.J., 1985-90; bd. dirs. Dixon Ticonderoga Co., Vero Beach. Served with U.S. Army, 1954-56. Mem. Am. Chem. Soc., Am. Powder Metal Inst., Metal Powder Prodrs. Assn. (bd. dirs.), Nat. Assn. Accts., Ind. Lubricants Mfrs. Assn. Republican. Roman Catholic. Home: 1780 Rolling Ridge Ln Toms River NJ 08755-1004 Office: Dixon Ticonderoga Co Ridgeway Blvd Lakehurst NJ 08733

MILLAR, RICHARD WILLIAM, JR., lawyer; b. L.A., May 11, 1938. LLB, U. San Francisco 1966. Bar: Calif. 1967, U.S. Dist. Ct. (cen. dist.) Calif. 1967, U.S. Dist. Ct. (no. dist.) Calif. 1969, U.S. Dist. Ct. (so. dist.) Calif. 1973, U.S. Supreme Ct. Assoc. Iverson & Hogoboom, Los Angeles, 1967-72; ptnr. Eilers, Stewart, Pangman & Millar, Newport Beach, Calif., 1973-75, Millar & Heckman, Newport Beach, 1975-77, Millar, Hodges & Bemis, Newport Beach, 1979—. Fellow Am. Bar Found.; mem. ABA (litigation sect., trial practice com., ho. of dels. 1990—), Calif. Bar Assn. (lectr CLE), Orange County Bar Assn. (chmn. bus. litigation sect. 1981, chmn. judiciary com. 1988-90), Balboa Bay Club, Bohemian Club (San Francisco). Home: 2546 Crestview Dr Newport Beach CA 92663-5625 Office: Millar Hodges & Bemis One Newport Pl Ste # 900 Newport Beach CA 92660

MILLAR, SALLY GRAY, nurse; b. Madison, Wis., Dec. 8, 1946; d. William Llewellyn and Janet Josephine (Dean) M. Student, U. Iowa, 1964-65; R.N., St. Joseph Hosp. Sch. Nursing, 1968; M.B.A., Simmons Coll. Grad. Sch. Mgmt., 1985. Staff nurse Bryn Mawr (Pa.) Hosp., 1968-69; team leader, cardiac surg. intensive care unit Mass. Gen. Hosp., Boston, 1969-78, head nurse, respiratory/surg. intensive care unit, 1978-81, clin. nurse leader, intensive care nursing service, 1981-85, project dir. patient classification system, 1985-86; dir. nursing info. systems, 1986—. Editor: Focus on Critical Care, 1978-80; editor-in-chief: Methods in Critical Care, 1980, Procedure Manual for Critical Care, 1985. Mem. Am. Assn. Critical Care Nurses (pres. 1980-81, dir. 1976-82), Soc. Critical Care Medicine. Republican. Roman Catholic. Home: 849 Boston Post Rd E Apt 3-e Marlborough MA 01752-3700 Office: Mass Gen Hosp 32 Fruit St Boston MA 02114-2620

MILLARD, CHARLES WARREN, III, museum director, writer; b. Elizabeth, N.J., Dec. 20, 1932; s. Charles Warren and Constance Emily (Keppler) M. A.B. magna cum laude, Princeton U., 1954; M.A., Harvard U., 1963, Ph.D., 1971. Asst. to dir. Fogg Art Mus. Harvard U., Cambridge, Mass., 1963-64; asst. to dir. Dumbarton Oaks, Washington, 1965-66; dir. Washington Gallery Modern Art, 1966-67; teaching fellow Harvard U., 1968-69; curator 19th Century European art Los Angeles County Mus. Art, 1971-74; chief curator Hirshhorn Mus. and Sculpture Garden Smithsonian Instn., Washington, 1974-86; adj. prof. Johns Hopkins U., Balt., 1983-86; dir. Ackland Art Mus. U. N.C., Chapel Hill, 1986-93, adj. prof., 1986-93; chmn. vis. com. to fine arts dept. Boston U., 1977-80. Author: The Sculpture of Edgar Degas, 1977; art editor Hudson Rev., 1972-87; contbr. articles to profl. jours. Served with USN, 1956-59.

MILLARD, JAMES MICHAEL, oral surgeon; b. San Bernardino, Calif., Sept. 16, 1945; s. Joseph Eugene and Patricia Isabel (Gormley) M.; m.

Nancy Jeanne Bedwell, June 15, 1968; children: Timothy, Meridith, Megan, Matthew. DDS, UCLA, 1970. Resident in oral and maxillofacial surgery Highland Hosp., Oakland, Calif., 1973-77; pvt. practice oral and maxillofacial surgery, Wenatchee, Wash., 1977-78; pvt. practice, Spokane, Wash., 1978—; cons. VA Med. Ctr., Spokane, 1979—. Capt. USAF, 1970-73. Fellow Am. Assn. Oral Maxillofacial Surgeons, Am. Coll. Oral Maxillofacial Surgeons; mem. ADA, Wash. State Dental Assn., Spokane Dist. Dental Soc. (pres. 1988—), Wash. State Soc. Oral Maxillofacial Surgeons, Western Soc. Oral Maxillofacial Surgeons, Rotary. Republican. Roman Catholic. Avocations: golf, skiing, fly fishing. Home: 8928 E Day Rd Mead WA 99021-8720 Office: 123 W Francis Ave Spokane WA 99205-6348

MILLARD, JOHN ALDEN, lawyer; b. Buenos Aires, Argentina, Nov. 4, 1940; s. Alden Shultz and Lois (Guthrie) M.; m. Carey Barbara French, Sept. 7, 1966; children—John Alden, James Guthrie, Alexander French. B.A., Harvard U., 1963, LL.B., 1967. Bar: N.Y. 1968. Assoc., Shearman & Sterling, N.Y.C., 1967-75, ptnr., 1976—. Served with U.S. Army, 1963-64. Mem. Assn. Bar City N.Y. Office: 599 Lexington Ave New York NY 10022-6030

MILLARD, KENNETH E., communications company executive; b. 1946. BBA, U. Wis., 1969, JD, 1972. With Wis. Telephone Co., 1972-78, 80-83, AT&T, 1978-80; past sr. v.p. Am. Info. Techs. Corp.; pres., chief exec. officer, dir. Mich. Bell Telephone Co., 1989—. Office: Oncor Comms Inc 6707 Democracy Blvd Fl 8 Bethesda MD 20817

MILLARD, NEAL STEVEN, lawyer; b. Dallas, June 6, 1947; s. Bernard and Adele (Marks) M.; m. Janet Keast, Mar. 12, 1994; 1 child, Kendall Layne. BA cum laude, UCLA, 1969; JD, U. Chgo., 1972. Bar: Calif. 1972, U.S. Dist. Ct. (cen. dist.) Calif. 1973, U.S. Tax Ct. 1973, U.S. Ct. Appeals (9th cir.) 1987, N.Y. 1990. Assoc. Willis, Butler & Schiefly, Los Angeles, 1972-75; ptnr. Morrison & Foerster, Los Angeles, 1975-84, Jones, Day, Reavis & Pogue, Los Angeles, 1984-93, White & Case, L.A., 1993—; instr. Calif. State Coll., San Bernardino, 1976; lectr. Practising Law Inst., N.Y.C., 1983-90, Calif. Edn. of Bar, 1987-90; adj. prof. USC Law Ctr., 1994—. Mem. citizens adv. com. L.A. Olympics, 1982-84; trustee Altadena (Calif.) Libr. Dist., 1985-86; bd. dirs. Woodcraft Rangers, L.A., 1982-90, pres., 1986-88; bd. dirs. L.A. County Bar Found., 1990; mem. energy commn. County and City of L.A., 1995—. Capt. U.S. Army, 1970-72. Mem. ABA, Calif. Bar Assn., N.Y. State Bar Assn., L.A. County Bar Assn. (trustee 1985-87), Pub. Counsel (bd. dirs. 1984-87, 90-93), U. Chgo. Law Alumni Assn. (bd. dirs. So. Calif. chpt. 1981—), Calif. Club, Phi Beta Kappa, Pi Gamma Mu, Phi Delta Phi. Office: White & Case 633 W 5th St Ste 1900 Los Angeles CA 90071-2038

MILLARD, PETER TUDOR, English language educator; b. Treorchy, Rhondda, Wales, U.K., July 21, 1932; s. Percival and Catherine (Davies) M. B.A. with hons., McGill U., Montreal, 1959, Oxford (Wadham Coll.), Eng., 1961; D.Phil., Oxford U. (Linacre Coll.), Eng., 1970. Lectr. U. of Sask., Saskatoon, 1964-70, asst. prof., 1970-74, assoc. prof., 1974-86, prof., 1986—; head Dept. of English, 1985—, pres. Faculty Assn., 1987-88. Author: Dmytro Stryjek: Trying the Colours, 1988, (short stories) The Malahat Review, 1985-87; editor: Roger North's Life of Dr. John North, 1984; contbg. editor Inuit Art Quar.; contbr. articles to various jours. Trustee Mendel Art Gallery, Saskatoon, 1971-74; pres. Saskatoon Human Rights Assn., 1980-83, Saskatoon Gay Community Ctr., 1974-75. Can. Coun. fellow, 1968; Social Scis. and Humanities Rsch. Coun. fellow, 1979 and rsch. grantee, 1985. Avocation: art. Office: 308 Skyline Dr Box 1372, Gibsons, BC Canada V0N 1V0

MILLARD, RICHARD STEVEN, lawyer; b. Pasadena, Calif., Feb. 6, 1952; s. Kenneth A. and Kathryn Mary (Paden) M.; m. Jessica Ann Edwards, May 15, 1977; children: Victoria, Elizabeth, Andrew. AB, Stanford U., 1974; JD magna cum laude, U. Mich., 1977. Bar: Calif. 1977, Ill. 1985. Assoc. Heller, Ehrman, White & McAuliff, San Francisco, 1977-81; assoc. Mayer, Brown & Platt, Chgo., 1982-83, ptnr., 1984—. Mem. ABA, Order of Coif. Office: Mayer Brown & Platt 190 S La Salle St Chicago IL 60603-3410

MILLARD, STEPHENS FILLMORE, electronics company executive; b. Balt., Dec. 5, 1932; s. Lyman Clifford and Frances Louise (Stephens) M.; m. Suzanne Taylor, Nov. 2, 1957 (div. 1990); children: Anne, Stephens, William; m. Linda Dyer, 1995. BS in Econs., U. Pa., 1955; MBA, Northwestern U., 1963. Dist. sales mgr. Olin Mathieson Chem. Corp., Chgo., 1958-63; Western Sales mgr. Champion Papers, Inc., San Francisco, 1963-70; U.S. sales mgr. MacMillan Bloedel, Ltd., Vancouver, B.C., Can., 1970-72; dir. new product devel. Crown Zellerbach Corp., San Francisco, 1972-75; Midwestern sales mgr. paper group Internat. Paper Co., Chgo., 1975-79; v.p. mktg. Mead Corp., Dayton, Ohio, 1979-83; co-founder, sr. v.p. Packet Techs., Inc. (now Stratacom, Inc.), Cupertino, Calif., 1983-86; co-founder, Cable Data, Inc., Equatorial Communications, Telebit, Inc., Metricom, Inc., Com-21; assoc. prof. mgmt. Golden Gate U., 1970-75; vis. lectr. Simon Frasier U., 1973; bd. adv. Sch. of Bus. San Francisco State U., 1995—. Dir. alumni assn. giving Northwestern U., 1966; trustee Severn Prep. Sch., Severna Park, Md.; chmn. devel. com. Santa Fe Inst., 1993; bd. visitors Nat. Def. U., Ft. McNair, Washington, 1994— (Nat. War Coll., Armed Forces Staff Coll., Industrial Coll. of the Armed Forces); adv. bd. San Rafael Bionomics Inst., Calif., 1995—. Recipient Rolland Marshall Teel award Severn Sch., 1994. Served to 1st lt., U.S. Army, 1955-57. Mem. Northwestern U. Grad. Sch. Bus. Alumni Assn. (nat. pres. 1967-68), Wharton Sch. Alumni Assn. (v.p.), Active Core Execs., The February Group. Republican. Episcopalian. Home: 5 Fremontia Portola Valley CA 94028-8032

MILLARD, WENDA HARRIS, magazine publisher; b. Alexandria, Va., July 9, 1954; d. Roger and Joan Marie (Kelliher) Harris; m. William John Millard III, Oct. 8, 1983. BA in English, Trinity Coll., 1976; MBA, Harvard U., 1983. Sales promotion mgr. Am. Home mag., 1976-77, Ladies' Home Jour., 1977-79; sales devel. mgr. N.Y. mag., 1979-81; gen. mgr. Working Woman Ventures, 1983-85; pub. Adweek mag., N.Y.C., 1985-89; gen. mgr., ptnr. The Peer Group, Westport, Conn., 1989—; exec. producer Working Woman radio report, Nat. Commn. on Working Women, 1984. Contbr. articles to profl. jours.; editor Fashion Capital News, 1980. Mem. nominating com. bd. trustees Trinity Coll., Hartford, Conn., 1980—. Named one of 100 Young Women of Promise, Good Housekeeping mag. 1985. Mem. Advt. Women N.Y., Women in Communications, Women's Equity Action League, Advt. Club N.Y. (bd. dirs. chmn. Andy award 1988, 89), Harvard Club (N.Y.C.). Republican. Home: 31 Buttonwood Ln Darien CT 06820 Office: Family Circle 110 5th Ave New York NY 10011-5693

MILLENSON, DEBRA ANN, lawyer; b. Cleve., July 24, 1947; d. Morton B. and Judith Leah (Rehmar) M. BA, Mich. State U., 1967; JD, U. Mich., 1970. Bar: La. 1970, U.S. Dist. Ct. (mid. dist.) La. 1970, U.S. Ct. Appeals (5th cir.) 1970, U.S. Supreme Ct. 1974, U.S. Dist. Ct. D.C. 1974, D.C. 1976, U.S. Dist. Ct. (we. dist.) Tex. 1978. Staff atty. Lawyers Constn. Def. Com., New Orleans, 1970-72; pvt. practice law New Orleans, 1972-73; trial atty. EEOC, Washington, 1973-82; sr. trial atty. U.S. Dept. Labor, Washington, 1982—. Author: (with others) Employment Discrimination Law, 1981—. Chair ACLU, Va., 1976-78. Mem. ABA (subcom. chmn. labor and EEO com. 1985—). Avocations: volleyball, spectator sports, sailing. Office: US Dept Labor Office of Solicitor 200 Constitution Ave NW Washington DC 20210-0001

MILLER, ALAN B., hospital management executive; b. N.Y.C., Aug. 17, 1937; s. Daniel and Mary (Blumenthal) M.; m. Jill K. Stein, Oct. 5, 1968; children: Marc Daniel, Marni Elizabeth, Abby Danielle. BA, Coll. William and Mary, 1958; MBA, U. Pa., 1960. V.p. Young & Rubicam,Inc., N.Y.C., 1964-69; sr. v.p. Am. Medicorp., Inc., L.A., 1970; pres., chief exec. officer Am. Medicorp., Inc., Phila., 1973-77; chmn. bd., 1977; chmn. bd. Hosp. Underwriting Group, 1977-78; founder, pres., chmn. bd. Universal Health Svcs., King of Prussia, Pa., 1978—; chmn., founder UHT-Real Estate Trust, King of Prussia, 1986—; formerly health care adviser Fed. Mediation and Conciliation Svc.; bd. mem. Leonard Davis Inst. U. Pa.; past mem. adv. bd. Temple U. Sch. Bus.; chmn., pres. Universal Health Svcs. Real Estate Investment Trust, N.Y. Stock Exch. 1986—; bd. dirs. Genesis Health, GMIS, Inc. Trustee Penn Mut. Life; former trustee Coll. of William and Mary; bd. dirs. Penjerdel Coun., pres. Opera Co. of Phila. Capt. USAR.

Mem. Phila. C. of C. (bd. dir.). Home: 57 Crosby Brown Rd Gladwyne PA 19035-1512 Office: Universal Health Svcs Inc 367 S Gulph Rd King Of Prussia PA 19406

MILLER, ALAN GERSHON, lawyer; b. Boston, Feb. 24, 1931; s. Harold Louis and Etta (Futransky) M.; m. Maxine Schreiber, July 2, 1951 (div. 1971); m. Natalie Cohen, Oct. 6, 1977; 1 child, Geoffrey Paul. AB, U. Ill., 1952; JD, Harvard U., 1955. Bar: Mass. 1955, U.S. Dist. Ct. Mass. 1956, Fla. 1978. Assoc. Morrison, Mahoney & Pearlman, Boston, 1955-59; ptnr. Morrison, Mahoney & Miller, Boston, 1959—. Co-author: Business Interruption Insurance, 1986. Mem. ABA, Internat. Bar Assn., Boston Bar Assn., Fedn. Ins. Corp. & Counsel, Def. Rsch. Inst., Fla. Bar Assn., Soc. of CPCU's. Office: Morrison Mahoney & Miller 250 Summer St Boston MA 02210-1134

MILLER, ALAN JAY, financial consultant, author; b. Bklyn., July 11, 1936; s. Louis and Claire (Maltz) M.; m. Susan Ruth Morris, Oct. 29, 1961; children—Laurie Ann, Adam Louis. B.A., Cornell U., 1957. Chartered fin. analyst. Pres. Analysis-in-Depth Inc., N.Y.C., 1965-67; mng. editor Value Line Investment Survey, N.Y.C., 1967-68; research dir. Emanuel Deetjen & Co., N.Y.C., 1968-69; exec. v.p., dir. Intersci. Capital Mgmt. Corp., N.Y.C. 1969-71; pres., dir. ICM Equity Fund Inc., N.Y.C., 1970-71, ICM Fin. Fund Inc., N.Y.C., 1970-71; v.p., assoc. research dir. Bache & Co., Inc., N.Y.C., 1972, G.H. Walker & Co., Inc., N.Y.C., 1972-73; 1st v.p., assoc. research dir. Blyth Eastman Dillon & Co. Inc., N.Y.C., 1974-76; dir. research E.F. Hutton & Co., Inc., N.Y.C., 1976-81, sr. v.p., 1976-80, exec. v.p., 1981-88; dir. Hutton Investment Mgmt., 1976-88; mng. dir. SLH Asset Mgmt. Shearson Lehman Hutton, Inc, N.Y.C., 1988-90; sr. v.p. Martin E. Segal Co., N.Y.C., 1990-92; adj. assoc. prof. Columbia U. Grad. Sch. Bus., 1978-79; mem. faculty N.Y. Inst. Fin., 1977—; adj. prof. Adelphi U. Coll., 1993—. Author: Socially Responsible Investing: How to Invest with Your Conscience, 1991, Standard and Poor's 401(k) Planning Guide, 1995. Mem. N.Y. Soc. Security Analysts, Fin. Analysts Fedn.

MILLER, ALAN ROBERT, lawyer; b. Chgo., Dec. 22, 1939; s. George James and Catherine (McCarthy) M.; m. Patricia Burke, Dec. 27, 1961; children: Julie, Nancy, Stephen. Student, Xavier U., 1957-60; JD summa cum laude, DePaul U., 1964; LLM, Harvard U., 1990. Bar: Ill. 1964, U.S. Supreme Ct. 1968, Minn. 1979, Mass. 1982, N.Y. 1985, numerous fed. dist. cts. and cir cts. of appeal. Hearing officer EPA State of Ill., spl. asst. atty. gen.; assoc./ptnr. Epton, Mullin, Miller and Druth, Chgo., 1964-79; sr. ptnr. Robins, Kaplan, Miller and Ciresi, Mpls., 1979-82, Boston, 1982—; adj. prof. New Eng. Sch. Law, Boston, 1987—; lectr. in field. Contbr. to profl. jours. Mem. ABA (chair property ins. law com. tort and ins. practice sect. 1988-89, vice chair commi. torts com. 1991—, chmn. TIPS task force on legal edn. 1989—), Mass. Bar Assn., Minn. Bar Assn., N.Y. State Bar Assn., Chgo. Bar Assn., Fedn. Ins. and Corp. Counsel (property ins. and ins. issues com.), Def. Rsch. Inst., Nat. Forum for Property Loss Profls. (faculty 1985—), Loss Execs. Assn. Office: Robins Kaplan Miller & Ciresi Ste 2200 222 Berkeley St Boston MA 02116

MILLER, ALAN STANLEY, ecology center administrator, law educator; b. Detroit, Dec. 22, 1949; s. Ralph and Ruth (Leeman) M.; m. Susan O'Hara, Aug. 25, 1973; 1 child, Joanna. AB in Goverment, Cornell U., 1971; JD, U. Mich., 1974, M of Pub. Policy, 1974. Bar: Mich. 1974, D.C. 1975. Rsch. atty. Environ. Law Inst., Washington, 1974-77; atty. ABA, Washington, 1978-79, Natural Resources Def. Coun., Washington, 1979-84; assoc. World Resources Inst., Washington, 1984-86; asst. prof. law Widener U., Wilmington, Del., 1988-89; exec. dir. Ctr. Global Change, College Park, Md., 1989—; prof. Vermont Law School, South Royal, Vt., 1991-93; head EPA Transition Team for Pres. Clinton Wash. D.C. 1992, Energy Task Force State of Md. Annapolis, Md. 1991-92; bd. dirs. Environmental Exchange; adjunct prof. Maryland Law Sch. 1989—; vis. assoc. prof. U. Iowa Coll. of Law 1979, Wash. Coll. of Law Am. U., Wash., D.C. 1986, Duke U. N.C. 1990, Vt. Law Sch 1991, 92; mem. adv. bd. Office Tec. Assessment, Washington, 1989. Co-author: (book) International Regulation Flourocarbons, 1980; (monographs) Growing Power, The Sky is the Limit, 1985, Environmental Regulation, 1992. Bd. dirs. Solar Light Fund, 1988. Fulbright scholar Macquarie Univ., Australia, 1977-87, Fulbright scholar Tokyo Univ. Law Sch., Japan, 1987-87; Stratospheric Ozone Protection award U.S. EPA Washington, D.C. 1992. Mem. ABA (global climate com. 1992-93). Avocations: jogging white-water rafting, writing. Office: Center Global Change 7100 Baltimore Ave # 401 College Park MD 20740-3627

MILLER, ALBERT JAY, retired librarian, educator; b. Beaver Falls, Pa., Dec. 7, 1927; s. Joseph Jefferson and Alberta Mae (Shaffer) M. B.S., Geneva Coll., 1952; M.L.S., Rutgers U., 1958; postgrad., U. Chgo., 1960-61, U. Pitts., 1963-68, U. Mich., 1969. Librarian West Allegheny Jr. High Sch., Imperial, Pa., 1959-60, Butler (Pa.) Area Sr. High Sch., 1962-67; librarian Pa. State U. New Kensington, 1969-89, tchr.-librarian continuing edn. dept., 1970-89, ret., 1989. Author: A Selective Bibliography of Existentialism in Education and Related Topics, 1969, Confrontation, Conflict and Dissent, 1972, Death: A Bibliographical Guide, 1977; book and media rev. editor: Learning Today, 1978—, mem. editorial bd., 1979—. Instr. water safety ARC, New Kensington, 1969—, Citizens Gen. Hosp., 1971-72; active Boy Scouts Am., 1970—; bd. dirs. Westmoreland County, Butler County mental health assns.; mem. Allegheny-Kiski Human Relations Council, 1976-77; bd. dirs. Allegheny-Kiski Sr. Citizens Center, 1976-77, fund raising chmn., 1989-90; bd. corporators Geneva Coll., Beaver Falls, Pa., 1987—; Sunday Sch. tchr. Manchester Ref. Presbyn. Ch., 1970—, elder, 1984—, clk. of session, 1984—; Sabbath Sch. supt., 1990; mem., pub. rels. dir. Twirling Unltd, Akron, OHio; baton twirler Kensington Firemens Band; mem. Alle-Kiski Revitalization Corp. Mem. NEA, Pa. Edn. Assn., ALA, Pa. Library Assn. Democratic. Home: 417 Charles Ave New Kensington PA 15068-5335

MILLER, ALLAN JOHN, lawyer; b. Beachwood, Ohio, Oct. 17, 1921; s. Carl Frederick and Rhoda (Warren) M.; m. Marjorie Hewitt Pirtle, Aug. 10, 1946; children: James W., Patricia Anne. B.B.A., Fenn Coll., 1946; LL.B., Western Res. U., 1948; D (hon.), Dyke Coll., Cleve., 1986. Bar: Ohio 1948. With Standard Oil Co., Ohio, 1948-77; treas. Standard Oil Co., 1967-77; mem. firm Kiefer, Knecht, Rees, Meyer & Miller, Cleve., 1977-80; dir. United Screw & Bolt Corp. Chmn. bd. dirs. Luth. Med. Ctr., Cleve., 1967-82; pres. Luth. Med. Ctr. Med. Staff Found., 1979-85; bd. dirs. Christian Residencies Found., 1972-77, St. Luke's Hosp. Assn., 1973-84; chmn. bd. trustees Dyke Coll., Cleve., 1971-86. With AUS, 1943-46, PTO. Mem. Cleve. Treas.'s Club, Cleve. Soc. Security Analysts. Presbyterian. Club: Capri Isles Golf Club (Venice, Fla.). Home: 1364 Capri Isles Blvd Venice FL 34292-4459

MILLER, ANDREW PICKENS, lawyer; b. Fairfax, Va., Dec. 21, 1932; s. Francis Pickens and Helen (Hill) M.; m. Penelope Farthing, Nov. 18, 1990; children: Julia Lane, Andrew Pickens, Elise Givhan, Winfield Scott, Lucia Holcombe. A.B. magna cum laude, Princeton U., 1954; postgrad., New Coll., Oxford (Eng.) U., 1954-55; LL.B., U. Va., 1960. Bar: Va. 1960, U.S. Supreme Ct. 1967, D.C. 1979. Asso. Penn, Stuart & Stuart, 1960-62; partner Penn, Stuart & Miller, Abingdon, Va., 1963-69; atty. gen. Va., 1970-77; partner Mays, Valentine, Davenport & Moore, Richmond, Va., 1977-78, Dickstein, Shapiro & Morin, Washington, 1979—. Pres., Young Democratic Clubs Va., 1966-67; chmn. Washington County Dem. Com., 1967-69; Dem. nominee for U.S. Senate from Va., 1978; bd. dirs. Barter Found., 1962-69; trustee King Coll., 1966-74; mem. adv. bd. Ams. for Effective Law Enforcement, 1973-77, Center for Oceans Law and Policy, 1975-79; vice-chmn. Va. Bd. Corrections, 1983-86. Served to 1st lt. AUS, 1955-57. Fellow Am. Bar Found.; mem. So. Conf. Attys. Gen. (vice chmn. 1972-73, chmn. 1973-74), Nat. Assn. Attys. Gen. (exec. com. 1973-74, chmn. antitrust com. 1971-76, Wyman Meml. award 1976), ABA (ho. dels. 1971-76, mem. action commn. to reduce ct. costs and delay 1979-84, chmn. pub. election law com. 1986-87, commn. on pub. understanding about the law, 1992—, co-chair program devel. com., govt. and pub. lawyers divsn. 1993—), Va. Bar Assn. (chmn. young lawyers sect. 1967-68, exec. com 1985-88), Am. Judicature Soc. (dir. 1973-76, exec. com. 1974-76), Soc. of the Cin. (Va. standing com. 1986-89, 93—, asst. sec., 1992—), The John Marshall Found. (pres. 1987-89), Phi Beta Kappa, Omicron Delta Kappa. Presbyn. Home: 15003 35th St NW Washington DC 20007-2729 Office: Dickstein Shapiro & Morin Morin LLP 2101 L St NW Washington DC 20037-1526

MILLER, ANTHONY BERNARD, physician, medical researcher; b. Woodford, Eng., Apr. 17, 1931; married, 1952; 5 children. BA, U. Cambridge, 1952, MB, BChir, 1955. House officer Oldchurch Hosp., Romford, Eng., 1955-57; med. registrar Luton and Dunstable Hosp., Eng. 1959-62; mem. sci. staff Med. Research Council Tb and Chest Disease Unit London, 1962-71; assoc. prof. preventive medicine and biostats. U. Toronto, 1972-76, prof., 1976—, chmn. dept., 1992—, dir. grad. program in epidemiology, 1986-91; dir. epidemiology unit Nat. Cancer Inst. Can., Toronto, 1971-86; dir. Nat. Breast Screening Study, 1980—, WHO Collaborating Ctr. on Evaluation of Screening for Cancer, 1991—; Nat. Health scientist, 1988-93; mem. working cadre Bladder Cancer Project, U.S., 1973-75; mem. epidemiology com. Breast Cancer Task Force, U.S., 1973-77, chmn., 1975-77; mem. Fed. Task Force Cervical Cytol. Screening, Can., 1974-76, 80-81, Union Internat. Contre le Cancer com., controlled therapeutic trials, 1978-82, Multidisciplinary project breast cancer, 1978-82, chmn. project on screening, 1982-93; mem. sci. council Internat. Agy. Research Cancer, Lyon, 1981-85, chmn., 1985; mem. com. on diet, nutrition and cancer NRC of U.S., 1980-83, mem. oversight com. radioepidemiologic tables, 1983-84, com. on diet and health, 1986-89, com. on dietary guidelines implementation, 1988-91, chmn. com. on environmental epidemiology, 1990-94; chmn. Ont. Task Force on Primary Prevention of Cancer, 1994-95. Served with RAF, 1957-59. Mem. Can. Oncology Soc. (sec.-treas. 1975-79, pres. 1980-81), Soc. Epidemiology Research, Internat. Epidemiology Assn., Am. Soc. Preventive Oncology (pres. 1983-85), Am. Coll. Epidemiology (bd. dirs. 1987-89). Office: U Toronto Dept Preventive, Medicine and Biostats, McMurrich Bldg, Toronto, ON Canada M5S 1A8

MILLER, ANTHONY G., advertising executive; b. Sydney, Australia, Aug. 25, 1942; s. Gordon James and Patricia (Fuller) M.; m. Karen Frances Wilson, Oct. 14, 1967; children: Ryan, Adam, Kelly Ann. Mgmt. trainee McCann-Erickson, Sydney, 1963-65; with J. Walter Thompson, N.Y.C., 1969-73, v.p. 1970-73; with MacLaren Advt., Toronto, 1966-69, 73—; gen. mgr. MacLaren Advt., Montreal, 1973-79; exec. v.p. gen. mgr. MacLaren Advt. Ltd., Toronto, 1979-80, pres., CEO, from 1980; now chmn. MacLaren Lintas Inc., Toronto; chmn., CEO Lintas: N.Y.C., N.Y., 1991—. Liberal. Mem. Ch. of England. Office: MacLaren Lintas Inc, 20 Dundas St, Toronto, ON Canada M5G 2H1

MILLER, ARJAY, retired university dean; b. Shelby, Nebr., Mar. 4, 1916; s. Rawley John and Mary Gertrude (Schade) M.; m. Frances Marion Fearing, Aug. 18, 1940; children: Kenneth Fearing, Ann Elizabeth (Mrs. James Olstad). B.S. with highest honors, UCLA, 1937; LL.D. (hon.), 1964; postgrad., U. Calif.-Berkeley, 1938-40; LL.D. (hon.), Washington U., St. Louis; LL.D., Whitman Coll., 1965, U. Nebr., 1965, Ripon Coll., 1980. Teaching asst. U. Calif. at Berkeley, 1938-40; research technician Calif. State Planning Bd., 1941; economist Fed. Res. Bank San Francisco, 1941-43; asst. treas. Ford Motor Co., 1946-53, controller, 1953-57, v.p., controller, 1957-61, v.p. finance, 1961-62, v.p. of staff group, 1962-63, pres., 1963-68, vice chmn., 1968-69; dean Grad. Sch. Bus., Stanford U., 1969-79, emeritus, 1979—; former chmn. Automobile Mfrs. Assn., Econ. Devel. Corp. Greater Detroit; councillor The Conf. Bd.; past chmn., life trustee Urban Inst.; mem. Public Adv. Commn. on U.S. Trade Policy, 1968-69, Pres.'s Nat. Commn. on Productivity, 1970-74. Trustee Internat. Exec. Svc. Corps.; hon. trustee The Brookings Instn.; bd. dirs. Wm. and Flora Hewlitt Found., S.R.I. Internat.; dir. Pub. Policy Inst. Calif.; former pres. Detroit Press Club Found.; former chmn. Bay Area Coun. Capt. USAAF, 1943-46. Recipient Alumnus of Year Achievement award UCLA, 1964; Distinguished Nebraskan award, 1968; Nat. Industry Leader award B'nai B'rith, 1968. Fellow Am. Acad. Arts and Scis. Presbyterian. Clubs: Pacific Union, Bohemian.

MILLER, ARLYN JAMES, oil company executive; b. LeMars, Iowa, Aug. 31, 1940; s. Clarence Theodore and Irene (DeSmet) M.; m. Loyola E. Valdes, Nov. 11, 1978. BBA, U. Iowa, 1962. CPA, Colo. Staff acct. Peat, Marwick, Mitchell & Co., Denver, 1962-65; acct. Hamilton Brothers Oil Co., Denver, 1965-69, treas., 1969—, v.p., 1978-80, sr. v.p., 1980-81, exec. v.p., chief fin. officer, 1981—; bd. dirs. Luth. Community Health Svcs., Wheat Ridge, Colo., Tejas Gas Corp., Houston, Luth. Med. Ctr. and Luth. Hosp., Wheat Ridge. Mem. AICPA. Republican. Roman Catholic. Clubs: Lakewood Country (Colo.), Denver Petroleum. Home: 1682 Montane Dr E Golden CO 80401 Office: Hamilton Oil Co Inc 1560 Broadway Ste 2200 Denver CO 80202-5153

MILLER, ARNOLD, electronics executive; b. N.Y.C., May 8, 1928; s. Sam and Mina (Krutalow) M.; m. Beverly Shayne, Feb. 5, 1950; children: Debra Lynn, Marla Jo, Linda Sue. BS in Chemistry, UCLA, 1948, PhD in Phys. Chemistry, 1951. Registered profl. engr., Calif. Rsch. phys. chemist Wrigley Rsch. Co., Chgo., 1951; supr. phys. chemistry Armour Rsch. Found., Chgo., 1951-54, mgr. chemistry and metals, 1954-56; chief materials sci. dept. Borg-Warner Rsch. Ctr., Des Plaines, Ill., 1956-59; dir. rsch. Rockwell Corp., Anaheim, Calif., 1959-66, dir. microelec. ops., 1967-68; group exec. materials ops. Whittaker Corp., L.A., 1968-70; pres. Theta Sensors, Orange, Calif., 1970-72; mgr. xeroradiography Xerox Corp., Pasadena, Calif., 1972-75; corp. dir. rsch. and adv. devel. Xerox Corp., Stamford, Conn., 1975-78; corp. dir. rsch. and adv. devel. Xerox Corp., El Segundo, Calif. 1978-81, v.p. electronics div., 1981-84, pres. electronics div., 1984-87; corp. officer Xerox Corp., Stamford, 1984-87; pres. Tech. Strategy Group, Fullerton, Calif., 1987—; bd. dirs. Spectro Diode Labs, San Jose, Calif., Semicondr. Rsch. Corp., Colorep Inc., Carlsbad, Calif.; bd. dirs., chair audit com. Merisel Computer Products, El Segundo, Calif.; mem. vis. com. on materials sci. U. So. Calif., L.A., 1966-68; mem. State of Calif. Micro Bd., 1984—. Editorial adv. bd. Advances in Solid State Chemistry; co-editor Electronics Industry Development; contbr. numerous articles to profl. jours. and monographs; patentee in field. Mem. civilian adv. group Dept. Commerce, 1959-60; mem. 5th decade com., also adv. com. on engring. and mgmt. program UCLA, 1984—; mem. com. on scholarly communication with People's Republic of China, Tech. Transfer Task Force, Nat. Acad. Sci., Washington, 1985-85; bd. dirs. Orange County Pacific Symphony, Fullerton, Calif., 1982—; mem. univ.'s adv. bd. Calif. State U.-Fullerton, 1986—, chair, 1991—; v.p., bd. dirs. Heritage Pointe Home for the Aging, 1987—; chmn. Indsl. Assocs sch. of engring. and computer sci. Calif. State U., 1987—, trustee continuing learning ctr., 1993—; mem. Overseas Devel. Coun., 1988—; mem. Nat. Com. U.S.-China Rels., 1990—. Recipient Sci. Merit award Navy Bur. Ordnance/ Armour Rsch. Found., 1952, IR-100 award, 1964, 69. Fellow AAAS; mem. IEEE, AIME, Am. Chem. Soc., So. Calif. Coalition Edn. Mfg. Engring. (bd. dirs. 1994—), Soc. Photog. and Instrumentation Engrs. and Scientists, Elec. Industry Assn. (past chmn. microelectronics), Phi Beta Kappa, Sigma Xi, Phi Lamda Upsilon. Home: 505 E Westchester Pl Fullerton CA 92635-2706 Office: Tech Strategy Group PO Box 5769 Fullerton CA 92635-0769

MILLER, ARTHUR, playwright, author; b. N.Y.C., Oct. 17, 1915; s. Isadore and Augusta (Barnett) M.; m. Mary Grace Slattery, Aug. 5, 1940 (div. 1956); children: Jane Ellen, Robert; m. Marilyn Monroe, June 1956 (div. 1961); m. Ingeborg Morath, Feb. 1962; children: Rebecca Augusta, Daniel. AB, U. Mich., 1938, LHD, 1956. Assoc. prof. drama U. Mich., 1973-74. Author: (plays) Honors at Dawn, 1936 (Avery Hopwood award for playwriting U. Mich. 1936), No Villain: They Too Arise, 1937 (Avery Hopwood award for playwriting U. Mich. 1937), Man Who Had All the Luck, 1944 (Nat. prize Theatre Guild 1944), That They May Win, 1944, All My Sons, 1947 (N.Y. Drama Critics Circle award 1947, Tony award best play 1947, Donaldson award 1947), Death of a Salesman, 1949 (N.Y. Drama Critics Circle award 1949, Tony award best play 1949, Donaldson award 1949, Pulitzer prize in drama 1949), The Crucible, 1953 (Tony award best play 1953, Donaldson award 1953, Obie award 1958), A View from the Bridge, 1955, A Memory of Two Mondays, 1955, After the Fall, 1964, Incident at Vichy, 1964, The Price, 1968, Fame, 1970, The Reason Why, 1970, The Creation of the World and Other Business, 1972, Up From Paradise, 1974, The Archbishop's Ceiling, 1976, The American Clock, 1980, Some Kind of Love Story, 1983, Elegy for a Lady, 1983, Playing for Time, 1986, Danger: Memory!, 1986, The Last Yankee, 1990, The Ride Down Mt. Morgan, 1991, Broken Glass, 1994; (play adaptation) Enemy of the People (Ibsen), 1950; (screenplays) The Story of G.I. Joe, 1945, The Witches of Salem, 1958, The Misfits, 1961, The Hook, 1975, Everybody Wins, 1990; (teleplays) Death of a Salesman, 1966, The Price, 1971, Fame, 1978, Playing for Time, 1980 (George Foster Peabody award 1981, Outstanding Writing Emmy award 1981), All My Sons, 1987, An Enemy of the People, 1990, The American Clock, 1994; author: Situation Normal, 1944, Focus, 1945, Jane's Blanket, 1963, I Don't Need You Anymore, 1967, In Russia, 1969, In the

Country, 1977, The Theatre Essays of Arthur Miller, 1978, Chinese Encounters, 1979, Salesman in Beijing, 1987, Timebends: A Life, 1987, The Misfits and Other Stories, 1987, (novella) Homely Girl, 1994; exec. prodr. Death of a Salesman, 1985 (Outstanding Drama/Comedy Spl. Emmy award 1985). Recipient Bur. New Plays prize Theatre Guild, 1938, Nat. Assn. Ind. Schs. award, 1954, Gold Medal for drama Nat. Inst. Arts and Letters, 1959, Anglo-Am. award, 1966, Creative Arts award Brandeis U., 1970, Lit. Lion award N.Y. Pub. Libr., 1983, John F. Kennedy Lifetime Achievement award, 1984, Algur Meadows award So. Meth. U., 1991. Home: Tophet Rd Roxbury CT 06783

MILLER, ARTHUR HAWKS, JR., librarian, consultant; b. Kalamazoo, Mar. 15, 1943; s. Arthur Hawks and Eleanor (Johnson) M.; m. Janet Carol Schroeder, June 11, 1967; children: Janelle Aileen, Andrew Hawks. AB, Kalamazoo Coll., 1965; student U. Caen, Calvados, France, 1963-64, Lake Forest Grad. Sch. Mgmt., 1990-91; AM in English, U. Chgo., 1966, AM in Librarianship, 1968; PhD, Northwestern U., 1973. Reference libr. Newberry Libr., Chgo., 1966-69, asst. libr. pub. svcs., 1969-72; coll. libr. Lake Forest (Ill.) Coll., 1972-94, archivist and libr. for spl. collections, lectr. English dept., 1993—; mem. Ill. Libr. Computer Sys. Policy Coun., Chgo., 1982-87, 92-94. Pres. Lake Forest/Lake Bluff Hist. Soc., 1982-85, Lake County Hist. Soc., 1985—, Ill. Ctr. for Book Bd., 1992-93, v.p. 1993—; trustee Ragdale Found., 1986—, sec., 1987-92, pres., 1992—. Mem. ALA (chmn. history sect. 1982-83, chmn. coll. sect. 1986-87), Melville Soc. Am., Ill. Libr. Assn. (chmn. pub. policy com. 1988-90), Pvt. Acad. Libs. of Ill. (v.p. 1988-90, pres. 1990-92), Caxton Club (pres. 1978-80, coun. mem. 1988-91), Rotary. Presbyterian. Home: 169 Wildwood Rd Lake Forest IL 60045-2462 Office: Lake Forest Coll Donnelley Library 555 N Sheridan Rd Lake Forest IL 60045

MILLER, ARTHUR RAPHAEL, legal educator; b. N.Y.C., June 22, 1934; s. Murray and Mary (Schapin) M.; m. Ellen Monica Joachim, June 8, 1958 (div. 1978); 1 child, Matthew Richard.; m. Marilyn Tarmy, 1982 (div. 1988.); m. Sandra L. Young, 1992. A.B., U. Rochester, 1955; LL.B., Harvard U., 1958; student, Bklyn. Coll., 1952, 55, CCNY, 1955. Bar: N.Y. 1959, U.S. Supreme Ct. 1959, Mass. 1983. With Cleary, Gottlieb, Steen & Hamilton, N.Y.C., 1958-61; assoc. dir. Columbia Law Sch. Project Internat. Procedure, N.Y.C., 1961-62; instr. Columbia U. Law Sch., 1961-62; assoc. prof. U. Minn. Law Sch., 1962-65; prof. law U. Mich. Law Sch., 1965-72; vis. prof. Harvard U. Law Sch., 1971-72, prof., 1972-86, Bruce Bromley prof., 1986—; rsch. assoc. Mental Health Research Inst., 1966-68; dir. project computer assisted instn. Am. Assn. Law Schs., 1968-75; spl. rapporteur State Dept. concerning chpt. II of Hague Conv., 1967; del. U.S.-Italian Conf. Internat. Jud. Assistance, 1961, jud. conf. Mont. Supreme Ct., 1975; mem. adv. group Nat. Acad. Sci. Project on Computer Data Banks, 1970-78; mem. spl. adv. group to chief justice Supreme Ct. on Fed. Civil Litigation; mem. com. on automated personal data systems HEW, 1972-73; chmn. Mass. Security and Privacy Council, Mass. Commn. on Privacy; mem. U.S. Commn. New Technol. Uses Copyrighted Works, 1975-79; reporter U.S. Supreme Ct.'s Adv. Com. on Civil Rules, 1978-86, mem. 1986-91; faculty Fed. Jud. Ctr.; reporter study on complex litigation Am. Law Inst.; bd. dirs. Research Found. on Complex Litigations, 1975-80. Author: (with others) New York Civil Practice, 8 vols., Civil Procedure Cases and Materials, 6th edit., 1993, (with C.A. Wright) Federal Practice and Procedure: Civil, 28 vols., 1969—, (with others) CPLR Manual, 1967, The Assault on Privacy: Computers, Data Banks, and Dossiers, 1971, Miller's Court, 1982; host syndicated TV shows In Context, Miller's Law, Miller's Court, Headlines on Trial; legal expert Good Morning America. Served with AUS, 1958-59. Recipient Nat. Emmy award for The Constitution, That Delicate Balance. Mem. ABA, Am. Law Inst. Office: Harvard U Law Sch Cambridge MA 02138 also: Good Morning Am 147 Columbus Ave New York NY 10023-5900

MILLER, B. JACK, investment company executive; b. N.Y.C., Mar. 1, 1945; s. Bertram Jackson and Charlotte (Kea) M.; m. Lynsie Schaberg; children: Molly, Andrew. AB, Princeton U., 1966; MBA, U. Mich., 1968. Various positions Eli Lilly and Co., Indpls., 1968-80, dir. benefit plan investments, 1980-88; v.p. benefit investments Philip Morris Cos. Inc., N.Y.C., 1988-89, v.p., corp. contr., 1989-92; v.p. J.P. Morgan Investment Mgmt., N.Y.C., 1992—; trustee Bison Money Mkt. Funds, Indpls. Served with M.I., USAR, 1964-74. Mem. Fin. Execs. Inst., Princeton Club N.Y. Avocations: golf, bridge. Office: JP Morgan Investment Mgmt 522 Fifth Ave New York NY 10036

MILLER, BARRY, research administrator, psychologist; b. N.Y.C., Dec. 25, 1942; s. Jack and Ida (Kaplan) M.; m. Susan Hallermeier; children: Eric, Arianne, Kristina, Barrie. BS in Psychology, Bklyn. Coll., 1965; MS in Psychology, Villanova U., 1967; PhD in Psychiatry, Med. Coll. Pa. 1971. Instr. psychology Villanova (Pa.) U., 1971-73; asst. dir. dept. behavioral sci., med. rsch. scientist Ea. Pa. Psychiatric Inst., Phila., 1971-73, sr. med. rsch. scientist, 1973-80; dir. Pa. Bur. Rsch. and Tng., Harrisburg, 1973-81; asst. prof. psychology U. Pa. Med. Sch., Phila., 1975-78, clin. prof. psychology, 1978—; assoc. prof. psychiatry Med. Coll. Pa., Phila., 1981-90, rsch. assoc. prof. medicine, 1983-90, assoc. dean for rsch., 1981-90; Odir. for rsch. devel. Albert Einstein Healthcare Network, Phila., 1990-95; dir. The Permanente Med. Group Rsch. Inst., Oakland, Calif., 1995—; adj. assoc. prof. psychiatry Med. Coll. Pa., Phila., 1990—; rsch. assoc. prof. psychiatry Temple U. Sch. Med., Phila., 1990—; mem. sci. and tech. task force Pa. Econ. Devel. Partnership, Harrisburg, 1987-88, adv. com. Clin. Rsch. Ctr. Psychopathology of Elderly, Phila., 1985-88; mem. cancer control prgram Pa. Dept. Health, 1994; vis. rsch. assoc. prof. Med. Coll. Pa., Phila., 1991—. Contbr. articles to profl. jours.; mem. editorial bd. Jour. Mental Health Adminstrn., 1988—, assoc. editor, 1989—. Bd. dirs. Community Mental Health Ctr. 6A, Phila., 1973-75, Northwest Jewish Youth Ctrs., Phila., 1974-75; mem. Lafayette Hill Civic Assn., 1973-86, Citizens Coun. Whitemarsh (Pa.) Twp., 1975-86. Grantee HHS, NIH. Fellow Pa. Psychol. Assn.; mem. AAAS, Am. Psychol. Assn., Assn. Mental Health Adminstrs., Assn. Univ. Tech. Mgrs., Soc. Rsch. Adminstrs. Avocation: tennis. Office: The Permanente Med Group Rsch Inst Ste 400 1800 Harrisoon St Oakland CA 94612

MILLER, BARRY RIXMANN, lawyer; b. Tempe, Ariz., Feb. 8, 1945; s. Ray E. and Dorothy (Rixmann) M.; m. Patricia A. Cunningham, Aug. 10, 1968; children—Christy, Brandy, Ann. B.S. with honors, U. Ill., 1967; J.D. with honors, U. Ill., 1970. Bars: Ill. 1970, Tex. 1972, U.S. Tax Ct. 1972. Mem. firm Andrews & Kurth, Houston, 1972-79, ptnr., 1979—, mgmt. com., 1990-92. Treas. Askew PTO, 1980. Served to 1st lt. U.S. Army, 1970-72. Decorated Army Commendation medal. James Scholar, 1963; recipient Bronze Tablet, U. Ill., 1967. Mem. Tex. Bar Assn., ABA (sect. on taxation), Order of the Coif, Beta Alpha Psi, Phi Alpha Mu, Sigma Chi. Republican. Contbr. articles to profl. jours. Office: Andrews & Kurth LLP 4200 Texas Commerce Towers Houston TX 77002

MILLER, BEN NEELY, physician; b. Smyrna, S.C., Dec. 20, 1910; s. Benjamin Neely and Addie Jane (Whitesides) M.; m. Ruth Elizabeth Gambill, Dec. 27, 1938; children: Elizabeth Gambill, Jane Adelaide, Ben Neely. B.S., M.D., Duke U., 1935. Diplomate: Am. Bd. Internal Medicine. Med. resident Duke Hosp., Durham, N.C., 1935-37; instr. U. Ala. Med. Sch., 1937-38; practice of internal medicine Columbia, S.C., 1938-91; vis. lectr. U. S.C., 1967-70; clin. prof. medicine U. S.C. (Sch. Medicine), 1977-91; past chief staff Providence, Baptist, Columbia hosps.; med. cons. S.C. State Hosp., 1938-83, S.C. Dept. Vocat. Rehab. Bd. dirs. United Community Services, 1959-62, public-at-large trustee, 1963-66; med. adv. com. United Health and Med. Research Found. S.C.; mem. S.C. Pollution Control Authority, 1970-73; trustee Duke U. Recipient award S.C. Order of the Palmetto, 1983. Fellow A.C.P., Am. Coll. Allergists, Am. Acad. Allergy; mem. AMA, Southeastern Allergy Assn. (pres. 1955-56), Duke Alumni Assn. (pres. 1960-61), Duke Med. Alumni Assn. (pres. 1955-61), S.C. Med. Assn. (sec. 1962-68, pres. 1970-71), S.C. Soc. Internal Medicine (past pres.), Columbia Med. Soc. (pres. 1950). Presbyterian (elder). Club: Forest Lake Country (Columbia). Home: Presbyn Home Box 107 700 Da Vega Dr Lexington SC 29073

MILLER, BENJAMIN K., state supreme court justice; b. Springfield, Ill., Nov. 5, 1936; s. Clifford and Mary (Luthyens) M. BA, So. Ill. U., 1958; JD,

Vanderbilt U., 1961. Bar: Ill. 1961. Ptnr. Olsen, Cantrill & Miller, Springfield, 1964-70; prin. Ben Miller-Law Office, Springfield, 1970-76; judge 7th jud. cir. Ill. Cir. Ct., Springfield, 1976-82, presiding judge Criminal div., 1977-81, chief judge, 1981-82; justice Ill. Appellate Ct., 4th Jud. Dist., 1982-84, Ill. Supreme Ct., Springfield, 1984—; chief justice Ill. Supreme Ct., 1991-93; adj. prof. law U. Ill., Springfield, 1974—; chmn. Ill. Cts. Commn., 1988-90; mem. Gov.'s Adv. Coun. on Criminal Justice Legis., 1977-84; mem. Ill. State Justice Commn., 1995—; mem. Ad Hoc Com. on Tech. in Ctrs., 1985—. Mem. editorial rev. bd. Illinois Civil Practice Before Trial, Illinois Civil Trial Practice. Pres. Cen. Ill. Mental Health Assn., 1969-71; bd. govs. Aid to Retarded Citizens, 1977-80; mem. Lincoln Legals Adv. Bd., 1988—. Lt. USNR, 1964-67. Mem. ABA (bar admissions com. sect. of legal edn. and admissions to bar 1992—), Ill. State Bar Assn. (bd. govs. 1970-76, treas. 1975-76), Sangamon County Bar Assn., Women's Bar Assn. of Ill., Cen. Ill. Women's Bar Assn., Am. Judicature Soc. (bd. dirs. 1990—), Abraham Lincoln Assn. (bd. dirs. 1988—). Office: Supreme Ct Ill 1st Of America Ste 560 Springfield IL 62701

MILLER, BENNETT, physicist, former government official; b. N.Y.C., Jan. 18, 1938; s. Meyer Leon and Henrietta (Abramowitz) M.; m. Patricia Dawn Schoenhut, June 3, 1961; children: Beth Ann, Jeffrey Martin. A.B. magna cum laude (U.S. Rubber Co. scholar), Columbia U., 1959, M.A. (Eugene Higgins fellow), 1961, Ph.D., 1965. Research assoc. plasma physics lab. Columbia U., 1965-69, adj. asst. prof. physics, 1969; adj. assoc. prof. physics Fairleigh Dickinson U., 1967-69; asst. prof. nuclear engring. Ohio State U., cons. Battelle Meml. Inst, Columbus, Ohio, 1969-70; physicist div. controlled thermonuclear research U.S. Dept. Energy (formerly AEC and ERDA), Washington, 1970-74; dep. asst. dir. for research, acting chief exptl. plasma research br. U.S. Dept. Energy (formerly AEC and ERDA), 1974-75, asst. dir. research, 1975-76; dir. Office Plans, Budget and Program Implementation Solar, Geothermal and Advanced Energy Systems, U.S. Dept. Energy, 1976-78, program dir. solar, geothermal, electric and storage systems, 1978-80, dep. asst. sec. solar energy, 1980-81; v.p. energy programs McLaren Hart Inc. (formerly Fred C. Hart Assocs., Inc.), 1981-83; pres. Alternate Gas, Inc., Washington, 1983—, Miller Energy Corp., 1987—; v.p. tech. Kira, Inc., 1992—. Assoc. editor Jour. Solar Engring, 1980-84; contbr. articles to profl. jours. Pres. Columbia Coll. Class of 1959 Alumni, 1965-69, 84-89; v.p. Watkins Mill Elem. Sc. PTA, Gaithersburg, Md., 1970-71, pres., 1972-73. Finalist White House Fellows Program, 1966; recipient Spl. Achievement certificate AEC, 1973; Exceptional Service award Dept. Energy, 1979; Presdl. citation for meritorious service, 1980; hon. Woodrow Wilson fellow, 1960. Mem. Nat. Wood. Energy Assn. (v.p., vice-chmn. 1983-84, chmn. 1984-85, bd. dirs. 1983-87), bd. of dir., Sunergy Inc., 1993—. Phi Beta Kappa. Home and Office: 7805 Fox Gate Ct Bethesda MD 20817-4100

MILLER, BERNARD JOSEPH, JR., advertising executive; b. Louisville, July 31, 1925; s. Bernard J. Sr. and Myrtle (Herrington) M.; m. Jayne Hughes, Aug. 7, 1948 (div. Oct. 1970); children: Bernard J. III, Jeffrey, Janet Marie.; m. Brita Naujok, Nov. 24, 1970; 1 child, Brian. BS, Ind. U., 1949. Merchandising mgr. Brown-Forman Distillers, Inc., Louisville, 1949-54; v.p. Phelps Mfg. Co., Terre Haute, Ind., 1954-60; pres. Columbian Advt. Inc., Chgo., 1960-87, chmn., 1987—. 2d lt. USAF, 1943-46, PTO. Mem. Point of Purchase Advt. Inst. (dir. 1970-73), Saddle and Cycle Club (bd. dirs. 1987-90). Avocations: tennis, downhill skiing, collecting first edition autographed books. Office: Columbian Advt Inc 201 E Ohio St Chicago IL 60611-3234

MILLER, BETTY JEAN, feature film distribution company executive; b. Cleve., Nov. 13, 1958; d. Lester Theodore and Edith Frances (Dressel) M.; m. Paulo Carlos de Oliveira, July l4, 1984. AB magna cum laude, Brown U., 1980. Pres., owner Gingham Girls & Guys, Cleve., 1972-77; music paralegal Mitchell, Silberberg & Knupp, L.A., 1981; asst. Sotheby Parke Bernet, L.A., 1982; dir. music contracts adminstrn. Columbia Pictures, L.A., 1982-84; dir. adminstrn. Kodiak Films, L.A., 1985-87; v.p. corp. projects Skouras Dictures, Inc., L.A., 1987—. Mem. Women in Film Internat. (steering com., festival liaison 1985-87), Am. Film Mktg. Assn. (outreach com. 1986-87), NAFE. Office: Skouras Pictures Inc l040 N Las Palmas Ave Hollywood CA 90038

MILLER, BEVERLY WHITE, college president; b. Willoughby, Ohio; d. Joseph Martin and Marguerite Sarah (Storer) White; m. Lynn Martin Miller, Oct. 11, 1945 (dec. 1986); children: Michaela Ann, Craig Martin, Todd Daniel, Cass Timothy, Simone Agnes. AB, Western Res. U., 1945; MA, Mich. State U., 1957; PhD, U. Toledo, 1967; LHD (hon.), Coll. St. Benedict, St. Joseph, Minn., 1979; LLD (hon.), U. Toledo, 1988. Chem. and biol. researcher, 1945-57; tchr. schs. in Mich., also Mercy Sch. Nursing, St. Lawrence Hosp., Lansing, Mich., 1957-58; mem. chemistry and biology faculty Mary Manse Coll., Toledo, 1958-71; dean grad. div. Mary Manse Coll., 1968-71, exec. v.p., 1968-71; acad. dean Salve Regina Coll., Newport, R.I., 1971-74; pres. Coll. St. Benedict, St. Joseph, Minn., 1974-79, Western New Eng. Coll., Springfield, Mass., 1980—; cons. U.S. Office Edn., 1980; mem. Pvt. Industry Coun./Regional Employment Bd., exec. com., 1984-94; cons. in field. Author papers in field. Corporator Mercy Hosp., Springfield, Mass. Recipient President's citation St. John's U., 1979; also various service awards. Mem. AAAS, Am. Assn. Higher Edn., Assn. Cath. Colls. and Univs. (exec. bd.), Internat. Assn. Sci. Edn., Nat. Assn. Ind. Colls. and Univs. (govt. rels. adv. com., bd. dirs. 1990-93, exec. com. 1991-93, treas. 1992-93), Nat. Assn. Biology Tchrs., Assn. Ind. Colls. and Univs. of Mass. (exec. com. 1981—, vice chmn. 1985-86, chmn. 1986-87), Nat. Assn. Sci. Teaching, Springfield C. of C. (bd. dirs.), Am. Assn. Univ. Adminstrs. (bd. dirs. 1989-92), Delta Kappa Gamma, Sigma Delta Epsilon. Office: Western New Eng Coll Office of the President 1215 Wilbraham Rd Springfield MA 01119-2693

MILLER, BRIAN KEITH, airline executive; b. Cin., Aug. 12, 1958; s. Charles Eugene and Vera Adeline (Garrison) M.; m. Victoria Lee Vaughan, Oct. 20, 1990. BBA, Tex. A&M U., 1980. CPA, Tex. From audit staff to audit mgr. Ernst and Young, Dallas, 1980-86; corp. controller and treas. Metro Airlines, Inc., Dallas, 1986-90, v.p. controller and treas., 1990-91, sr. v.p., chief fin. officer, sec., treas., 1991-92, pres., 1992-94; v.p., CFO Lone Star Airlines, Ft. Worth, 1994—. Steering com. Dallas Bus. Forum, 1989-92; active The 500, Inc., Dallas, 1983-86. Mem. AICPA, Treasury Assn., Fin. Execs. Inst., Tex. Soc. CPA's. Avocation: travel. Office: Lone Star Airlines 131 E Exchange Ave Ste 222 Fort Worth TX 76106

MILLER, BURTON LEIBSLE, sales executive; b. L.A., July 17, 1944; s. Kenneth Wilbur and Dorothy (Leibsle) M.; m. April Suydam, Dec. 22, 1969 (div. 1983); children: Brandon, Gregory; m. Linda L. Reynolds, Aug. 11, 1990. BSCE, San Jose State U., 1968; MS in Engring., U. So. Calif., 1977. Civil engr. USN, San Bruno, Calif., 1968-74; cost engr. Bechtel Corp., L.A. 1974-79; supr. Bechtel Corp., Saudi Arabia, 1979-81; project mgr. Bechtel Corp., San Francisco 1981-84; Bay Area Contractors, San Francisco, 1984—; dist. sales mgr. ISC San Francisco, 1994—; cons. KMD/Kimco Mgmt. Co., San Francisco, 1989-90. Mem. World Affairs Coun. San Francisco, 1991, C. of C. San Francisco, 1986. Recipient Commendation, V.P. Dan Quayle, 1992, Cert. of Appreciation, Pres. George Bush, 1989, Cert. of Appreciation, Congressman Bob Mitchel, 1991. Mem. Commonwealth Club of Calif., Olympic Club, Project Mgmt. Inst. Republican. Avocations: snow skiing, scuba diving, real estate investment. Home: 1035 Cabrillo St San Francisco CA 94118 Office: ISC Cir # 249 5 Thomas Mellon Circle San Francisco CA 94134

MILLER, C. ARDEN, physician, educator; b. Shelby, Ohio, Sept. 19, 1924; s. Harley H. and Mary (Thuma) M.; m. Helen Meihack, June 26, 1948; children—John Lewis, Thomas Meihack, Helen Lewis, Benjamin Lewis. Student, Oberlin Coll., 1942-44; M.D. cum laude, Yale, 1948. Intern, then asst. resident pediatrics Grace-New Haven Community Hosp., 1948-51; faculty U. Kans. Med. Center, 1951-66, dir. childrens rehab. unit, 1957-60, dean Med. Sch., dir., 1960-66; prof. pediatrics and maternal and child health U. N.C. Chapel Hill, 1966—, vice chancellor health scis., 1966-71, chmn. dept. maternal and child health, 1977-87; chmn. exec. com. Citizens Bd. Inquiry into Health Services for Am., 1968-71. Mem. editorial bd.: Jour. Med. Edn., 1960-66; Author numerous articles in field. Trustee Appalachian Regional Hosps., 1974-84, Alan Guttmacher Inst., Planned Parenthood Fedn. Am. Markle scholar in med. scis., 1955-60; recipient Robert H. Felix Distinguished Service award St. Louis U., 1977, Martha Mae Eliot award in pub. health, 1984, Sedgewick Meml. medal Am. Pub.

Health Assn., 1986, O. Max Gardner award U. N.C. 1987. Fellow Royal Soc. Health (hon.), Clare Hall Cambridge (Eng.) U. (life); mem. Am. Pub. Health Assn. (chmn. action bd. 1972-75, pres. 1974-75), Soc. Pediatric Research, Assn. Am. Med. Colls. (v.p. 1965-66), Inst. of Medicine of Nat. Acad. Sci., Sigma Xi, Alpha Omega Alpha, Delta Omega. Home: 908 Greenwood Rd Chapel Hill NC 27514-3910

MILLER, CALVIN FRANCIS, geology educator; b. Escondido, Calif., Aug. 6, 1947; s. Wells Wait and Alice Atherton (Bakeman) M.; m. Molly Beth Fritz, Apr. 19, 1971; children: Spring Alice, Zachary Fritz. BA, Pomona Coll., Claremont, Calif., 1969; MS, George Washington U., 1973; PhD, UCLA, 1977. Instr. Pomona Coll., Claremont, Calif., 1976-77; asst. prof. Vanderbilt U., Nashville, 1977-84, assoc. prof., 1984-89, prof., 1989—, chair dept. geology, 1991—; vis. rsch. assoc. prof. Rensselaer Polytechnic Inst., Troy, N.Y., 1984-85. Assoc. editor Jour. Geophys. Rsch., Washington, 1995—. Lt. USCG, 1969-73. Grantee NSF, 1977—. Mem. Am. Geophys. Union, Geol. Soc. Am. (assoc. editor Bull. 1989-94), Mineral. Soc. Am. Achievements include understanding the growth histories and geochemical significance of accessory minerals in the crust, the origins of peraluminous granites, and the history of the crust of Ea. Calif. and So. Nev. Home: 6744 Pennywell Dr Nashville TN 37205 Office: Vanderbilt U Dept Geology Box 6028, Sta B Nashville TN 37235

MILLER, CANDICE S., state official; b. May 7, 1954; m. Donald G. Miller; 1 child, Wendy Nicole. Student, Macomb County C.C., Northwood Inst. Sec., treas. D.B. Snider, Inc., 1972-79; trustee Harrison Twp., 1979-80, supr., 1980-92; treas. Macomb County, 1992-95; sec. of state State of Mich., Lansing, 1995—; chair Mich. State Safety Commn., 1995—; mem. M-59 Task Force Strategy Com. Mem. community coun. Selfridge Air Nat. Guard Base. Mem. Govt. Finance Officers Assn., Mich. Assn. County Treas., Macomb County Treas. and Assessors Assn., Boat Town Assn., Ctrl. Macomb C of C. Harrison Twp. Indsl. Corridor. Avocations: boating, yachting. Office: PO Box 16248 Lansing MI 48901

MILLER, CARL DUANE, transportation company executive; b. Tulare, Calif., Aug. 24, 1941; s. Carl D. and Ida Ferne (Martin) M.; m. Cheryl Rae Henard, Mar. 29, 1961; children: Kelli R. Walker, Lori Leigh Elmore, Craig D. Student, Coll. of Sequoias, 1959-60, Am. Inst. Banking, 1964-69. Ops. supr. Crocker Citizens Nat. Bank., Tulare, 1964-69, Am. Nat. Bank, Tulare, 1969-70; Modesto terminal mgr. Kings County Truck Lines, 1970-75; Fresno outbound supr. Calif. Motor Express, 1975-77; terminal mgr. System 99 Transport, Tulare, 1977-80; pres., CEO Cal-Western Transport, Tulare, 1980-90, Daystar Transp., Tulare, 1990—; dir. Silver Arrow Express, Regency Transport Inc.; cons. Calif. Milk Producers, Artesia, Calif., 1990; transp. cons. Calif. Coop. Creamery, Petaluma, Calif., 1990; speaker world govt. and world monetary system various sv. clubs. Mem. City Coun., City of Tulare, 1979-83, mayor, 1983-87, Bd. Pub. Utilities, 1978; bd. mem. Nat. Coun. for Drugs and Alcohol, Tulare, 1980—; mem. exec. bd. Tulare County Econ. Devel.; transp. com. League of Calif. Cities. With USAF, 1960-64; v.p. Little League Baseball, Babe Ruth Baseball. Louis Pasteur fellow Scripps Clinic Rsch. Coun. Mem. NRA, AMVETS, Am. Legion, Am. Mgmt. Assn., Elks, Lions (v.p.). Republican. Avocations: restoring old cars. Home and Office: Daystar Transp Inc 2511 E Vassar Ct Visalia CA 93292

MILLER, CARL EUGENE, marketing executive; b. Sacramento, Calif., Aug. 20, 1942; s. Carl E. and Helen L. (Ries) M.; m. Joan P. Welch, Aug. 30, 1969; children: Carl Edward, Scott William. BS in Econs., U. Pa., 1964; MBA, U. Wash., 1970. Sales rep. Continental Co., San Francisco, 1964-68, mktg. staff, 1968-69; acct. mgr. Xerox Corp., Richland, Wash., 1971-74; equipment sales specialist Western region Xerox Corp., L.A., 1974-76; equipment sales mgr. Xerox Corp., Seattle, 1976-78; N.W. dist. mgr. Compugraphic Corp., Seattle, 1978-81; mktg. mgr. bus. systems div. Compugraphic Corp., Wilmington, Mass., 1981-83, mgr. Original Equipment Mfr., 1983-85; v.p. sales Tegra Inc., Billerica, Mass., 1985-86; v.p. sales and mkt. Butler Automatic Inc., Canton, Mass., 1986—. Scoutmaster, Amherst N.H., 1982-85 (unit commr. 1991—). Mem. Nat. Printing Equipment and Supply Assn. (bd. dirs. 1988—, chmn. govt. affairs com. 1988-91). Avocations: skiing, running. Home: 32 Nathan Lord Rd Amherst NH 03031-3004 Office: Butler Automatic Inc 480 Neponset St Canton MA 02021-1970

MILLER, CARL GEORGE, manufacturing executive; b. Milw., Oct. 3, 1942; s. Carl Conrad and Agnes Frances (Patla) M.; m. Patricia Ann Smith, Apr. 27, 1968; children: Gregory, Brian. BS, St. Louis U., 1964. CPA, Mo. Audit mgr. Ahrens & McKeon, CPAs, St. Louis, 1967-73; supr. internal audit Gen. Dynamics Corp., St. Louis, 1973-75, mgr. fin. analysis, 1975-78, dir. fin. analysis, 1978-80; v.p., contr. Quincy (Mass.) Shipbldg. div. Gen. Dynamics Corp., 1980-86; v.p. fin. Cessna Aircraft Co., Wichita, Kans., 1986-88; v.p., contr. Ft. Worth div. Gen. Dynamics Corp., Ft. Worth, 1988-90; v.p., contr. TRW, Inc., Cleve., 1990—. Mem. adv. coun. So. U. and A&M Bus. Sch., Case Western Reserve U. Acctg. Dept. Mem. AICPA, Fin. Execs. Inst. (com. on corp. reporting), Mfr. Alliance for Productivity and Innovation (fin. coun. II), Mo. Soc. CPA, Mayfield Country Club, Delta Sigma Pi (pres. 1963-64). Republican. Lutheran. Avocations: traveling, reading. Office: TRW Inc 1900 Richmond Rd Cleveland OH 44124-3760

MILLER, CAROLINE, editor-in-chief. Exec. editor Variety mag., N.Y.C., 1989-92; editor-in-chief Lear's mag., N.Y.C., 1992-94, Seventeen mag., N.Y.C., 1994—. Office: Seventeen 850 Third Ave New York NY 10022*

MILLER, CARROLL GERARD, JR. (GERRY MILLER), lawyer; b. San Antonio, Tex., Dec. 12, 1944; s. Carroll Gerard Sr. and Glyn (Roddy) M.; m. Sylvia Louise Mertins, Mar. 7 1971 (dec. 1982); children: Glyn Marie Bennett, Roddy Gerard, Gina Louise. AS, Del Mar Coll., 1965; BS, U. Houston, 1967; JD, Tex. Tech. U., 1970. Bar: Tex. Ct. Criminal Appeals 1970, U.S. Dist. Ct. (so. dist.) Tex. 1971, U.S. Ct. Appeals (5th cir.) Tex. 1973, U.S. Supreme Ct. 1974, U.S.C. Ct. Appeals (D.C. 1986), Colo. 1987, D.C. 1989. Assoc. Allison, Madden, White & Brin, Corpus Christi, Tex., 1970-71; asst. city atty. City of Corpus Christi, 1971; asst. dist. atty. Nueces County Dist. Attys. Office, Corpus Christi, 1971-73; asst. city atty. civil div. City of Corpus Christi, 1973-74; atty. Corpus Christi Police Dept.-City of Corpus Christi, 1974-77; pvt. practice Corpus Christi, 1973—; adj. prof. Bee County Coll., Beeville, Tex., 1973-74, Tex. A & I U., Corpus Christi, 1975-76. Past treas. and diaconate First Presbyn. Ch., Corpus Christi; bd. dirs., incorporator Iron Curtain Outreach; 20/20 coun. Open Doors. Mem. SAR, SCV, Assn. Trial Lawyers Am., Tex. Criminal Def. Lawyers Assn., Nat. Criminal Def. Lawyers Assn., Coll. State Bar Tex., Sons of Republic Tex., Crime Stoppers, Inc. (past dir.), Bay Yacht Club (dir.). Republican. Avocations: sailing, scuba diving, photography. Home: 1209 Sandpiper Dr Corpus Christi TX 78412-3821 Office: 719 S Shoreline Blvd Ste 302 Corpus Christi TX 78401-3548

MILLER, CHARLES A., lawyer; b. Oakland, Calif., Feb. 7, 1935; s. Frank and Janice (Greene) M.; m. Jeanette Segal, Sept. 27, 1964; children: Amy Guitel, Jennifer Fay, Charlotte Irene, Ira David. AB, U. Calif., Berkeley, 1955, LLB, 1958. Law clk. to assoc. justice U.S. Supreme Ct., Washington, 1958-59; assoc. Covington & Burling, Washington, 1959-67, ptnr., 1967—; mem. criminal justice coordinating bd., Washington, 1977-78; chmn. hearing com. Bd. on Profl. Responsibility, Washington, 1980-86. Pres. U. Calif. Alumni Club, Washington, 1962-70; mem. various coms. and adv. bds. Washington Pub. System, 1972-79; chmn. lawyers com. Washington Performing Arts Soc., 1984-86; bd. dirs. Dumbarton Concert Series, Washington, 1986—, chmn., 1990—. Fellow Am. Coll. Trial Lawyers; mem. ABA, D.C. Bar Assn., U. Calif. Alumni Assn. (trustee 1989-92). Democrat. Jewish. Club: Burning Tree (Bethesda, Md.). Office: Covington & Burling 1201 Pennsylvania Ave NW PO Box 7566 Washington DC 20044

MILLER, CHARLES DALY, lumber company executive; b. Hartford, Conn., 1928; married. Grad., Johns Hopkins U. Sales and mktg. mgr. Yale & Towne Mfg. Co., 1949-59; assoc. Booz, Allen & Hamilton, 1959-64; with Avery Internat. Corp., Pasadena, Calif., 1964—; v.p., mng. dir. Materials Europe, 1965; v.p. Fasson Internat. Ops., 1968; group v.p. materials group Avery Internat. Corp., Pasadena, 1969-75, pres., COO, 1975-77, pres., CEO, 1977-83; bd. dirs.,chmn., CEO Avery Dennison Corp. (formerly Avery Internat. Corp.), Pasadena, 1983—. Office: Avery Dennison Corp PO Box 7090 Pasadena CA 91109-7090

MILLER, CHARLES E., judge; b. Washington, Sept. 26, 1944; s. Charles Edward Miller and Mary (Cox) M.; 1 child, Samantha McGill Cox. BA, So. Meth. U., 1971, JD, 1972. Bar: Tex. 1972. Assoc., Roseborough & Curlee, Dallas, 1972-77; judge County Criminal Ct. #7, Dallas, 1977-82, Ct. Criminal Appeals, Austin, Tex., 1983-94; state judge at large, 1995—; adj. prof. criminal law So. Meth. U. Law Sch., Dallas, 1980-82. Author and lectr. in field. mem. nat. adv. coun. Nat. Victim Ctr., nat. steering com. Victims Constitutional Amendment Network, adv. bd. Victims Organized to Ensure Rights and Safety, victim assistance com. Tex. Young Lawyers Assn., exec. bd. People Against Violent Crime. Served with U.S. Army, 1966-70. Named Disting. Mil. Grad., Officer Candidate Sch., Ft. Sill., Okla., 1968, Best Dallas Misdemeanor Ct. Judge, 1982, Best Dallas Criminal Ct. Judge, 1982; decorated Army Commendation medal, 1970; recipient Sunny von Bulow Nat. Victim Advocacy Ctr. Appreciation cert., 1987, U.S. Dept. Justice Victims of Crime Appreciation cert., 1992, Victims Organized to Ensure Rights and Safety Advocate for Justice award, 1993, People Against Violent Crime Appreciation cert., 1993. Mem. State Bar Tex. (chmn. criminal law sect. 1981-82, crime victim & witness, 1994, cert. specialist in criminal law). Republican. Baptist. Home: 1705 Wild Basin Ldg Austin TX 78746-2820 Office: Ct Criminal Appeals Supreme Ct Bldg Austin TX 78711

MILLER, CHARLES EDMOND, library administrator; b. Bridgeport, Conn., Aug. 3, 1938; s. Edmond and Irene Ovelia (Boudreaux) M.; m. Alice Ann Phillips, June 2, 1962; children—Alison, Charles Edmond, Catherine, Susan. Student, U. Hawaii, 1957-58; B.A., McNeese State U., 1964; M.S. in L.S, La. State U. 1966. Tchr. Lake Charles (La.) High Sch., 1964-65; mem. staff La. State U. Library, Baton Rouge, 1966-69; assoc. dir. Tulane U. Library New Orleans, 1969-73; dir. Fla. State U. Library, Tallahassee, 1973—; vis. coms. So. Assn. Colls. and Schs.; bd. dirs. SOLINET, 1979-81, 85-86, corp. v.p, vice chmn., 1980-81; cons. in field; adv. com. State Librr. Fla.; bd. dirs. Ctr. for Rsch. Librs., 1976-77, 91—, sec. 1993-94, 94—; mem. policy bd. Fla. Libr. Network; pres. Assn. Southeastern Rsch. Librs., 1982-84. Asst. editor: La. Library Assn. Bull, 1967; contbr. articles to profl. jours.; book revs. to Southeastern Librarian. Served with USMCR, 1956-59. Mem. ALA, Fla. Libr. Assn. (dir. 1979-81), Southeastern Libr. Assn., Assn. Coll. and Rsch. Librs., bd. dirs. 1985-90, v.p., pres.-elect 1987-88, pres. 1988-89), Fla. Ctr. Libr. Automation (chmn. bd. dirs. 1985-90), Rsch. Librs. Group (exec. com. 1988-90, bd. dirs. 1991-94), Phi Kappa Phi, Beta Phi Mu, Sigma Tau Delta.

MILLER, CHARLES EDWARD, JR., financial executive; b. Balt., Sept. 4, 1950; s. Charles E. and Mary Frances (Sterling) M.; m. Linda Sue Caviness, Aug. 4, 1973; children: Matthew, Adam. BS in Mgmt., Va. Poly. & State U., 1973. Div. merchandiser W.T. Grant Co., Harrisonburg, Va., 1973-74; chief acct. Estate Life, Roanoke, Va., 1974-76; asst. controller Founders Life, Tampa, Fla., 1976-78; controller Harvest Life Ins. Co., Orlando, Fla., 1978-82, v.p., treas., asst. sec., 1982-85; sr. v.p., CFO Harcourt Gen. Ins. Cos., Orlando, 1985-89, exec. v.p., CFO, 1989—. Fellow Life Mgmt. Inst. Republican. Baptist. Avocations: golf, swimming. Office: Harcourt Gen Ins Cos 6277 Sea Harbor Dr Orlando FL 32887-0001

MILLER, CHARLES F., insurance executive; b. Vicksburg, Miss., July 20, 1932; s. Charles Fritz and Georgine (White) M.; m. J. Maxine Loftin, June 9, 1952; ch8ildren: Lori G., Leslie M., Marc A., Julie A., Joy S. BS in Geology, McNeese Coll., 1952. CLU. Sales rep. Metro. Life Ins. Co., New Orleans, 1960-62; staff mgr. Metro. Life Ins. Co., Nashville, 1962-65; field trainer Metro. Life Ins. Co., Louisville, 1965-68; dist. mgr. Metro. Life Ins. Co., Paducah, Ky., 1968-75; v.p. mktg. Capital Holding, Louisville, 1975-83; sr. v.p., chief mktg. officer Tenneco Security Trust Life, Dallas, 1983-87; br. mgr./fin. planner Metro. Life Ins. Co., Augusta, 1988—. With USN, 1952-55. Mem. Gen. Agts. and Mgrs. Assn. (pres. 1981). Home: 108 Stone Mill Dr Augusta GA 30907-1612

MILLER, CHARLES HAMPTON, lawyer; b. Southampton, N.Y., Jan. 25, 1928; s. Abraham E. and Ethel (Simon) M.; m. Mary Fried, Aug. 26, 1956; children—Cathy Lynn, Steven Scott, Jennifer Lee. B.A., Syracuse U., 1949; LL.B., Columbia U., 1952. Bar: N.Y. 1952, Republic Korea 1954, U.S. Ct. Appeals (2d cir.) 1969, U.S. Supreme Ct. 1969, U.S. Ct. Appeals (3d cir.) 1972, U.S. Ct. Appeals (7th cir.) 1973; cert. mediator and early neutral evaluator (so. and ea. dists.) N.Y., 1994—. Asst. counsel Waterfront Commn. N.Y. Harbor, 1954-56; asst. atty. U.S. Atty. for So. Dist. N.Y., 1956-58; assoc. Cole & Deitz, N.Y.C., 1958-61; assoc. Marshall Bratter Greene Allison & Tucker, N.Y.C., 1961-64, ptnr., 1964-82; ptnr. Hess Segall Guterman Pelz Steiner & Barovick, N.Y.C., 1982-86, Loeb and Loeb, N.Y.C., 1986—; mem. faculty Continuing Legal Edn. Columbia U. Law Sch., 1976-82. Served with U.S. Army, 1952-54. Fellow Am. Bar Found.; mem. ABA, N.Y. State Bar Assn. (chmn. fed. ct. com. 1976-79, vice chmn. com. on specialization 1976-79, mem. fin. com. 1980-81), Assn. Bar City N.Y., Fed. Bar Council. Home: 171 Ralph Ave White Plains NY 10606-3813 Office: Loeb and Loeb 345 Park Ave New York NY 10154

MILLER, CHARLES LESLIE, civil engineer, planner, consultant; b. Tampa, Fla., June 5, 1929; s. Charles H. and Myrle Iona (Walstrom) M.; m. Roberta Jean Pye, Sept. 9, 1949; children—Charles Henry, Stephen, Jonathan, Matthew. BCE, MIT, 1951, MCE, 1958. Registered profl. engr., Mass., Fla., Tenn., N.H., R.I., P.R. Successively field engr., project engr., exec. engr. Michael Baker, Jr., Inc. (cons. engrs.), Rochester, Pa., 1951-55; asst. prof. surveying, dir. photogrammetry lab. Mass. Inst. Tech., 1955-59, asso. prof. civil engring., head data engring. div., 1959-61, prof. civil engring., 1961-77, head dept., 1961-70, dir. urban systems lab., 1968-75, dir. civil engring. systems lab., 1961-65, dir. inter-Am. program civil engring., 1961-65, asso. dean engring., 1970-71; cons. engr., 1955—; chmn. bd., sr. cons., pres. CLM Systems, Inc., C.L. Miller Co., Inc.; advisor Commonwealth of P.R; dir. Geo-Transport Found.; Chmn. Pres.-elect's Task Force on Transp., 1968-69. Author: The COGO Book, 1990; contbr. articles to tech. jours. Recipient Outstanding Young Man of Greater Boston award. Fellow ASCE, Am. Acad. Arts and Scis.; mem. Am. Inst. Cons. Engrs., Am. Soc. Engring. Edn. (George Westinghouse award), Am. Soc. Photogrammetry, Am. Congress Surveying and Mapping, Am. Rd. Builders Assn., Transp. Rsch. Bd., Assn. Computing Machinery, Sigma Xi, Chi Epsilon, Tau Beta Pi. Originator of DTM, COGO, ICES, CEAL computer systems. Office: CL Miller Co 5601 Mariner Dr Tampa FL 33609-3407

MILLER, CHARLES Q., engineering company executive; b. 1945. BA, Balt. Polytechnic Inst., 1963; BS in Mech. Engring. and Math., U.S. Naval Acad., Annapolis, 1967; MS in Applied Mechanics, Stanford U., 1970; JD, Rutgers U., 1980. Ensign US Navy, 1970-79; with Raytheon Engineers and Constructors, Phila., 1979—, now CEO. Office: Raytheon Engrs & Constructors 30 S 17th St Philadelphia PA 19103 also: United Engrs & Constructors 30 S 17th St Philadelphia PA 19103-4021*

MILLER, CHARLES S., clergy member, church administrator. Exec. dir. Division for Church in Society of the Evangelical Lutheran Church in America, Chicago, Ill. Office: Evangelical Lutheran Church Am 8765 W Higgins Rd Chicago IL 60631

MILLER, CHRISTINE ODELL COOK, federal judge; b. Oakland, Calif., Aug. 26, 1944; d. Leo Marshall and Carolyn Grant (Odell) Cook; m. Dennis F. Miller, Sept. 10, 1994. BA, Stanford U., 1966; JD, U. Utah, 1969. Bar: Utah 1969, D.C. 1972, Calif. 1982. Clk. to chief judge U.S. Ct. Appeals (10th cir.), 1969-70; trial atty. U.S. Dept. Justice, Washington, 1970-72, Fed. Trade Commn., Washington, 1972-74; litigation Hogan & Hartson, Washington, 1974-76; spl. counsel Pension Benefit Guaranty Corp., Washington, 1976-78; asst. gen. counsel U.S. Ry. Assn., Washington, 1978-80; litigation Shack & Kimball P.C., Washington, 1980-83; judge U.S. Ct. of Fed. Claims, Washington, 1983—. Mem. State Bar Assn. Calif., D.C. Bar Assn., Order of Coif. Republican. Presbyterian. Club: University. Avocation: gemology. Office: US Ct of Fed Claims 717 Madison Pl NW Washington DC 20005-1086

MILLER, CLARENCE ALPHONSO, chemical engineering educator; b. Houston, Sept. 1, 1938; s. Clarence Alphonso and Frances Marie (Kuykendall) M.; m. Ann Hilary Williams, May 22, 1965; 1 child, Sian Frances. BA, BS, Rice U., 1961; PhD, U. Minn., 1969. Asst. prof., chem. engring. Carnegie Mellon Univ., Pitts., 1969-74, assoc. prof., chem. engring. 1974-77, prof., chem. engring. 1977-81; prof., chem. engring. Rice U.,

Houston, 1981—, chair, dept. chem. engring., 1989—. Editorial bd. Colloids and Surfaces, 1987—; co-author: Interfacial Phenomena, 1985. Lt. USN, 1961-65. Fellow Am. Inst. Chem. Engrs. (chair interfacial phenomena programming 1990—); mem. Am. Chem. Soc., Soc. Petroleum Engrs., Sigma Xi (pres. Carnegie-Mellon chpt. 1976-77). Episcopalian. Office: Rice U PO Box 1892 Houston TX 77251-1892

MILLER, CLIFFORD ALBERT, merchant banker, business consultant; b. Salt Lake City, Aug. 6, 1928; s. Clifford Elmer and LaVeryl (Jensen) M.; m. Judith Auten, Sept. 20, 1976; 1 child, Courtney; children by previous marriage, Clifford, Christin, Stephanie. Student, U. Utah, 1945-50, UCLA, 1956. Pres. Braun & Co., L.A., 1955-82, chmn., 1982-87; exec. v.p. Gt. Western Fin. Corp., Beverly Hills, Calif., 1987-91; chmn. Clifford Group, Inc., bus. cons., 1992—; mng. dir. Shamrock Holdings, Inc., 1992—, Shamrock Capital Advisors, L.P., 1992—; bd. dirs. First Am. Corp., First Am. Bankshares, Inc., Washington, Shamrock Broadcasting , Inc., Burbank, Calif., L.A. Gear, Inc., Santa Monica, Calif.; cons to White House, 1969-74. Trustee Harvey Mudd Coll., Claremont, Calif., 1974—; chmn. bd. trustees, 1991; chmn. bd. dirs. L.A. Master Chorale, 1989-93, chmn. emeritus, 1993; mem. chmn.'s coun. Music Ctr. Unified Fund Campaign. Mem. UCLA Chancellor's Assocs., Skull and Bones, The Lakes Country Club, Calif. Club, Wilshire Country Club, Jeremy Golf and Country Club, Pi Kappa Alpha. Office: Shamrock Holdings Inc 4444 Lakeside Dr Burbank CA 91505

MILLER, CURTIS HERMAN, bishop; b. LeMars, Iowa, May 3, 1947; s. Herman Andrew and Verna Marion (Lund) M.; m. Sharyl Susan Vander-Tuig, June 2, 1969; children: Eric, Nathan, Paul. BA, Wartburg Coll., 1969; MDiv., Wartburg Sem., 1973; DD (hon.), Wartburg Coll. 1987. Assoc. pastor Holy Trinity Luth. Ch., Dubuque, Iowa, 1973-75; pastor St. Paul Luth. Ch., Tama, Iowa, 1975-82; coord. for congl. life Am. Luth. Ch. Iowa dist., Storm Lake, 1982-87; bishop Western Iowa Synod Evang. Luth. Ch. in Am., Storm Lake, 1987—. Bd. regents Waldorf Coll., Forest City, Iowa, 1987—; bd. dirs. Luth. Social Svcs. of Iowa, Des Moines, 1987. Office: Evang Luth Ch Am Western Iowa Synod 318 E 5th St Storm Lake IA 50588-2312

MILLER, DAN, congressman; b. Mich., 1943; m. Glenda Darsey; children: Daniel, Robyn. Grad. U. Fla., 1964; MBA, Emory U.; PhD, La. State U. Ptnr. Miller Enterprises, Bradenton, Fla.; restaurant owner Memorial Pier, Fla., 1977—; instr. Ga. State U., U. South Fla., Sarasota; mem. 103d-104th Congresses from 13th Fla. Dist., 1993—; mem. appropriations com. mem. budget com. Active Rep. Leader's Task Force on Health. Mem. Manatee C. of C. Episcopalian. Office: US Ho of Reps 117 Cannon HOB Washington DC 20515-0913*

MILLER, DANIEL NEWTON, JR., geologist, consultant; b. St. Louis, Aug. 22, 1924; s. Daniel Newton and Glapha (Shuhardt) M.; m. Esther Faye Howell, Sept. 9, 1950; children: Jeffrey Scott, Gwendolyn Esther. B.S. in Geology, Mo. Sch. Mines, 1949, M.S., 1951; Ph.D., U. Tex., 1955. Intermediate geologist Stanolind Oil and Gas Co., 1951-52; sr. geologist Pan Am. Petroleum Corp., 1955-60, Monsanto Chem. Co., 1960-61; cons. geologist Barlow and Haun, Inc., Casper, Wyo., 1961-63; prof. geology, chmn. dept. So. Ill. U., 1963-69; state geologist, dir. Wyo. Geol. Survey, 1969-81; adj. prof. geology U. Wyo., 1969-81; asst. sec. energy and minerals Dept. Interior, 1981-83; geol. cons., 1983-89; dir. Anaconda Geol. Documents Collection U. Wyo., 1989-92; mem. Interstate Oil Compact Commn., 1969-81. Co-editor: Overthrust Belt of Southwestern Wyoming, 1960; gen. editor: Geology and Petroleum Production of the Illinois Basin, 1968; Contbr. articles to profl. jours. Served with USAAF, 1942-46. Decorated Air medal; recipient award merit So. Ill. U., 1967. Mem. Assn. Am. State Geologists (pres. 1979-80, chmn. govt. liaison com. 1970-71), Am. Assn. Petroleum Geologists (pres. Rocky Mountain sect. 1987, Pub. Svc. award), Am. Inst. Profl. Geologists (pres. 1992, Ben H. Parker Meml. medal 1993, Martin Van Couvering Meml. award 1994), Assn. Am. State Geologists (pres. 1979-80, hon. mem. 1982), Rocky Mountain Assn. Geologists (Disting. Pub. Svc. award). Achievements include patent for exhausto-port for automobiles. Home: 402 Colony Woods Dr Chapel Hill NC 27514-7908 *Use everything you know, in everything you do, all the time.*

MILLER, DARWIN LEON, healthcare administrator; b. Post, Tex., Oct. 1, 1933; s. Thomas Jefferson and Orbie Penelope (Landmon) M.; m. JoAnn Moreman, Nov. 2, 1956; children: J. Scott, G. Tim, L. David. Student, Tex. Tech. U., 1951-53, 55-56, Grand Canyon Coll., 1971-72, U. Ala., 1972-74; cert. health adminstr., Trinity U. Grad. Sch., 1976. Performance supr. U.S. Dept. Agriculture, Post, 1956-60; dist. scout exec. Boy Scouts Am., Midland/Lubbock, Tex., 1960-68; adminstrv. asst., chief of staff U.S. VA, Phoenix, Birmingham, Dallas, 1968-89; clin. adminstr. U.S. Dept. Vet. Affairs, Ft. Worth 1989—. Active Ft. Worth Med. Dist., 1990-93; bd. dirs. Dallas-Ft. Worth Fed. Exec. Bd., 1991-93, chmn. vet. affairs com., 1992-93; bd. dirs. Southside Med. Dist., Ft. Worth, 1993;. Recipient Outstanding Svc. award State of Tex., 1992. Mem. Rotary. Avocations: exercise, camping. Home: 1109 Briarcliff Dr Arlington TX 76012-5320

MILLER, DAVID, lawyer, advertising executive; b. Fort Worth, Dec. 12, 1906; s. Max and Tillie (Hoffman) M.; m. Rosalie Agress, Jan 31, 1929; children—Allan David, Martha Sally. A.B. cum laude, U. Tex., 1926; LL.B. cum laude, Harvard, 1929. Bar: N.Y. State bar 1931. With law firm of Jones, Clark & Higson, N.Y. City, 1929-33; pvt. practice with Harold W. Newman, Jr., 1937-44; mem. law firm of Engel, Judge & Miller, 1944-74; counsel RFC, Washington, 1933-34; asst. gen. counsel Md. Casualty Co., Balt., 1934-36; with Office of Gen. Counsel, Securities & Exchange Commn., 1936-37; v.p. and gen. counsel Young & Rubicam, Inc. (Advt. agy.), 1951-71, sec., dir., sr. v.p., 1971; counsel Squadron, Ellenoff & Plesent, 1974—; v.p., sec., gen. counsel The Music Project for TV, Inc., 1973—; Trustee Motion Picture Players Welfare Fund, Am. Fedn. TV & Radio Artists Pension and Welfare Fund.; Cons. joint policy com. Am. Assn. Advt. Agys.- Assn. Nat. Advertisers. Lecturer on radio and TV law for professional groups.; Editor: Harvard Law Review, 1927-29. Mem. Am. Bar Assn., Assn. Bar City N.Y., N.Y. County Lawyers' Assn., Am. Assn. Advt. Agencies (cons. broadcast business affairs com.), Phi Beta Kappa. Club: Harvard (N.Y.). Home: 30 Arleigh Rd Great Neck NY 11021-1327 Office: 551 5th Ave New York NY 10176-0001

MILLER, DAVID ANDREW BARCLAY, physicist; b. Hamilton, Scotland, Feb. 19, 1954; came to U.S., 1981; s. Matthew Barclay and Martha Sanders (Dalling) M.; m. Patricia Elizabeth Gillies, Aug. 13, 1976; children: Andrew Donald, Susan Rachel. BS, St. Andrews U., Scotland, 1976; PhD, Heriot-Watt U., Edinburgh, Scotland, 1979. Postdoctoral rsch. assoc. Heriot-Watt U., 1979-80, lectr., 1980-81; mem. tech. staff AT&T Bell Labs., Holmdel, N.J., 1981-87, head photonics switching device rsch. dept., 1987-92, head advanced photonics rsch. dept., 1993—. Contbr. 170 articles to profl. jours.; holder 30 patents. Recipient Prize of Internat. Commn. for Optics, 1991. Fellow Royal Soc. London, Optical Soc. Am., Adolph Lomb medal 1986, R.W. Wood prize 1988), Am. Phys. Soc., IEEE (pres. lasers and electroptics soc. 1995). Avocations: playing clarinet and saxophone. Home: 64 Hance Rd Fair Haven NJ 07704-3210 Office: AT&T Bell Labs 101 Crawfords Corner Rd Rm 4b4 Holmdel NJ 07733-1900

MILLER, DAVID EDMOND, physician; b. Biscoe, N.C., June 6, 1930; s. James Herbert and Elsie Dale (McGlaughon) M.; m. Marjorie Willard Penton, June 4, 1960; children: Marjorie Dale, David Edmond. AB, Duke U., 1952, MD, 1956. Diplomate Am. Bd. Internal Medicine (subspecialty bd. cardivasular disease). Interned: ctr. Duke U., Durham, N.C., 1956-57, resident in internal medicine, 1957-58, 59, 60, research fellow cardiovascular disesase, 1958-59, 61, assoc. internal medicine and cardiology, 1963-79, clin. asst., prof. medicine cardiology, 1979—; practice medicine specialising in internal medicine Durham, 1964—; attending physician internal medicine div. cardiology Watts Hosp., Durham, 1964-76, chief medicine, 1975-76; attending physician cardiology divsn. internal medicine Durham Regional Hosp. (formerly Durham County Gen. Hosp.), 1976—, chmn. dept. internal medicine, 1976-82, pres. med. staff, 1980-81; adv. com. Duke Med. Ctr. Contbr. articles to profl. jours. Council clin. cardiology N.C. chpt. Am. Heart Assn., 1963—. Served to lt. comdr. USNR, 1961-63. Fellow ACP, Am. Coll. Cardiology; mem. AMA, So. Med. Assn., N.C. Med. Soc. (del. ho. of dels. 1981, 82, 83), N.C. Durham-Orange County Med. Soc., Am. Soc. Internal Medicine, N.C. Soc. Internal Medicine (exec. coun. 1984-92), Am.

Fedn. Clin. Rsch. Methodist. Clubs: Capitol City, Hope Valley Country, University Club, Duke Faculty Club. Home: 1544 Hermitage Ct Durham NC 27707-1680 Office: 2609 N Duke St Ste 403 Durham NC 27704

MILLER, DAVID EMANUEL, physics educator, researcher; b. Bethel, Vt., Aug. 30, 1943; s. Manuel Southworth and Lucille (Shurtleff) M. BA, U. Vt., 1965; MA, SUNY, Stony Brook, 1967, PhD, 1971; Habilitation in Theoretical Physics, U. Bielefeld, Fed. Republic Germany, 1978. Instr. physics SUNY, Stony Brook, 1970-71; Wissenschaftlicher asst. Freie U., Berlin, 1972-75; scientist U. Bielefeld, 1975-78, Heinrich-Hertz Stipendium, 1977-78; privat dozent U. Bielefeld, 1978-83, univ. prof., 1987—; asst. prof. of physics Pa. State U., Hazelton, 1983-86, assoc. prof., 1986-92, mem. faculty senate, 1988—, prof., 1992—. Recipient Heinrich-Hertz stipendium, 1977-78. Mem. Am. Phys. Soc., Am. Assn. Physics Tchrs., Deutsche Physikalische Gesellschaft, Deutscher Hochschulverband, N.Y. Acad. Sci., Am. Math. Soc., Phi Beta Kappa, Sigma Xi. Home: PO Box 611 Conyngham PA 18219-0611 Office: Pa State U High Acres Hazleton PA 18201

MILLER, DAVID EUGENE, soil scientist, researcher; b. Scipio, Utah, July 31, 1926; s. Henry and Josie (Peterson) M.; m. Jo Ann Peterson, Mar. 17, 1950; children: Ross H., Dale E., Diane. BS, Utah State U., 1950; MS, Colo. State U., 1953; PhD, Wash. State U., 1959. Cert. agronomy, crops and soils profl. Asst. agronomist Colo. State U., Grand Junction, 1950-53; soil scientist USDA Agrl. Rsch. Svc., Grand Junction, 1953-54; rsch. soil scientist USDA Agrl. Rsch. Svc., Prosser, Wash., 1958-89, ret., 1989; acting instr. soils Wash. State U., Pullman, 1954-58. Contbr. numerous articles to profl. jours. Sgt. U.S. Army, 1944-46, ETO. Fellow Am. Soc. Agronomy, Soil Sci. Soc. Am. (chair S-6 1982-83); mem. Western Soc. Soil Sci. (pres. 1979-80), Internat. Soc. Soil Sci, Soil and Water Conservation Soc. Mem. LDS Ch. Avocations: camping, sports, gardening, travel. Home: 965 Campbell Dr Prosser WA 99350-1307

MILLER, DAVID HEWITT, environmental scientist, writer; b. 1918; m. Enid Woodson Brown; 1 child. AB cum laude, UCLA, 1939, MA, 1944, PhD, U. Calif., Berkeley, 1953; DLitt (hon.), U. Newcastle, 1979. Meteorologist U.S. Corps Engrs., 1941-43; forecaster TWA, 1943-44; climatologist Quartermaster Gen.'s Office, 1944-46; meteorologist, hydrologist Coop. Snow Investigations, San Francisco, 1946-53; geographer U.S. Natick (Mass.) Labs., 1953-59; meteorologist, hydrologist U.S. Forest Svc., 1959-64; prof. geography U. Wis., Milw., 1964-75, prof. atmospheric scis., 1975—; sr. acad. meteorologist NOAA, 1981-82; Fulbright lectr., Australia, 1966, 71, 79; exchange scientist Acad. Scis., Moscow, 1969; mem. adv. com. climatology Nat. Acad. Scis., 1958-64. Author: Snow Cover and Climate, 1955, (with others) Snow Hydrology, 1956, Heat and Water Budget of Earth's Surface, 1965, Energy at the Surface of the Earth, 1981, Water at the Surface of the Earth, 1982; editor: Climate and Life (M.I. Budyko), 1974. NSF fellow, 1952-53. Fellow AAAS (life); mem. Am. Geophys. Union (life, mem. transl. bd. 1972-76), Am. Meteorol. Soc. (profl. life), Ecol. Soc. Am., Assn. Am. Geographers, Inst. Australian Geographers, Internat. Assn. Landscape Ecology, Phi Beta Kappa, Sigma Xi. Office: Univ Wis Dept Geoscis PO Box 413 Milwaukee WI 53201-0413

MILLER, DAVID JERGEN, insurance executive; b. Rochester, N.Y., Dec. 2, 1933; s. Harry Jacobs and Beatrice Lucille (Crippen) M.; m. Luanne Ashton Zahniser (div. 1980); children: Frances Z. Miller Kinney, David Stewart; m. Doris Elaine Reibsome, 1981. BA, Ohio Wesleyan U., 1956; postgrad., Plymouth State Coll., 1983. Agt., brokerage mgr. Conn. Mut. Life Ins. Co., Rochester, N.Y., 1958-65; br. mgr. Continental Assurance Co., Rochester, 1965-70; gen. agt. Continental Casualty Co., Rochester, 1970-77, Manhattan Life Ins. Co., Rochester, 1970-77; regional supt. agys. Standard Security Life Ins. Co. N.Y., N.Y.C., 1977-80; regional v.p. Maine Fidelity Life Ins. Co., Keene, N.H., 1980-88; nat. mktg. dir. Colonial Life and Accident Ins. Co., Columbia, S.C., 1988-89; mng. gen. agt. Capitol Bankers Life Ins. Co., Milw., 1989-93. Contbr. articles to profl. jours. Board dirs. Walpole (N.H.) Hist. Soc., 1983-86; chmn., bd. dirs. Town Congl. Soc., 1983-86. With U.S. Army, 1956-58. Fellow Life Mgmt. Inst.; mem. Am. Soc. CIUs and Chartered Fin. Cons., Voluntary Employee Benefit Bd. (exec. com. 1986-88). Methodist. Home and Office: 403 E 4th St Bloomsburg PA 17815-1915

MILLER, DAVID W., lawyer; b. Indpls., July 1, 1950; s. Charles Warren Miller and Katherine Louise (Beckner) Dearing; m. Mindy Miller, May 20, 1972; children: Adam David, Ashley Kay, Amanda Katherine Kupfer. BA, Ind. U., Bloomington, 1971; JD summa cum laude, Ind. U., Indpls., 1976. Bar: Ind. 1977. Investigator NLRB, Indpls., 1971-76; assoc. Roberts & Ryder, Indpls., 1977-80, ptnr., 1981-86; ptnr. Baker & Daniels, Indpls., 1986—; bd. dirs. Everybody's Oil Corp., Anderson, Ind. Mem. Ind. Bar Assn. (chmn. labor law sect. 1981-82). Republican. Office: 300 N Meridian St Ste 2700 Indianapolis IN 46204-1755

MILLER, DAVID WILLIAM, historian, educator; b. Coudersport, Pa., July 9, 1940; s. Arthur Charles and Kathryn Marie (Long) M.; m. Margaret Vick Richardson, Aug. 22, 1964; 1 child, Roberta Neal. BA, Rice U., 1962; MA, U. Wis., 1963; PhD, U. Chgo., 1968. Instr. history Carnegie Mellon U., Pitts., 1967-68, asst. prof., 1968-73, assoc. prof., 1973-80, prof., 1980—; dir. Ctr. for Hist. Info. Sys. and Analysis, 1994—. Author: Church, State and Nation in Ireland, 1898-1921, 1973, Queen's Rebels: Ulster Loyalism in Historical Perspective, 1978; editor: Peep o'Day Boys and Defenders: Selected Documents on the Disturbances in County Armagh, 1784-1796, 1990; assoc. editor: New Dictionary of National Biography, 1994—; mem. editl. bd.: Hist. Methods, 1991-93; prin. developer: (interactive atlas) Great American History Machine, 1994. Sr. research fellow Inst. Irish Studies Queen's U., Belfast, Northern Ireland, 1975-76. Mem. Am. Hist. Assn., Am. Conf. for Irish Studies. Democrat. Presbyterian. Avocations: walking, singing. Office: Carnegie Mellon Univ Dept of History Schenley Park Pittsburgh PA 15213

MILLER, DECATUR HOWARD, lawyer; b. Balt., June 29, 1932; s. Lawrence Vernon and Katherine Louise (Baum) M.; m. Sally Burnam Smith, Nov. 23, 1963; 1 dau., Clemence Mary Katherine. B.A., Yale U., 1954; LL.B., Harvard U., 1959. Bar: Md. 1959. Assoc. Piper & Marbury, Balt., 1959-62, 1963-66, assoc., ptnr., 1967-94, mng. ptnr., 1974-87, chmn., 1987-94; Md. Securities commr., 1962-63. Trustee Enoch Pratt Free Libr., 1975—, v.p., 1977-85, pres., 1985-89; bd. dirs. Balt. Symphony Orch., 1970—, v.p., 1978-86, 88-90, pres., 1990-92; trustee Calvert Sch., 1976-89, pres., 1982-87; trustee Walters Art Gallery, 1987-91; bd. dirs. United Way Ctrl. Md., 1988-91, The Leadership, 1990-93, Empower Balt. Mmgt. Corp., 1995—; bd. dirs. Coll. Bound Found., 1990—, chmn., 1994—; bd. dirs. Greater Balt. Com., 1988—, chmn., 1992-94; mem. bd. sponsors Sellinger Sch. Bus. and Mgmt. Loyola Coll., 1990—; mem. Mayor's Bus. Adv. Coun., 1993—; mem. bd. visitors U. Md. Baltimore County, 1994—. With U.S. Army, 1954-56. Mem. ABA, Md. Bar Assn., Balt.Bar Assn., Am. Law Inst., Am. Bar Found., Md. Bar Found., Elkridge Club, 14 W. Hamilton St. Club, Ctr. Club, Elizabethan Club, Lawyers Round Table. Home: 26 Whitfield Rd Baltimore MD 21210-2928 Office: Piper & Marbury 36 S Charles St Baltimore MD 21201-3020

MILLER, DENNIS, comedian; b. Pitts., Nov. 3, 1953; m. Ali Espley, 1988; 2 children, Holden, Marlon. BA, Point Park Coll. Stand-up comic, cast mem. Saturday Night Live, 1985-91; prodr., writer, host Dennis Miller Show, 1992; exec. prod., writer, host Dennis Miller Live, 1994—. HBO spls. include: Mr. Miller Goes to Washington, 1988, host 13th Annual Young Comedians Show, 1989, (also prodr., writer) Black & White, 1990, They Shoot HBO Specials, Don't They?, 1993; host Freedomfest: Nelson Mandela's 70th Birthday Celebration, The America's Choice Awards, 1990, 43d Annual Primetime Emmy Awards Presentation, 1991; albums include The Off-White Album, 1989; film appearances include: Disclosure, 1994, The Net, 1995. Recipient Best Writing for a Variety/Music Program for Dennis Miller Live, 1994. Address: Internat Creative Mgmt Inc 8899 Beverly Blvd Los Angeles CA 90048 also: Internat Creative Mgmt Inc 8942 Wilshire Blvd Beverly Hills CA 90211

MILLER, DENNIS EDWARD, corporate executive; b. Detroit, Dec. 21, 1951; m. Deborah Ann Keith, Feb. 12, 1977. BS, Austin Peay State U., 1973; MBA, U. South Fla., 1981. CPA. Chief exec. officer Hosp. Corp. of Am., Bennettsville, S.C., 1976-84; div. v.p. Westworld Community Healthcare, Waco, Tex., 1984-86; group v.p. Nat. Healthcare, Inc., Dothan, Ala., 1986-87; COO Healthcare Connections, Brentwood, Tenn., 1988; cons. VHA Physician Svcs., Inc., Dallas, 1988-90; asst. adminstr., CFO Clarksville (Tenn.) Meml. Hosp., 1990; Franklin, Tenn., 1990; sr. v.p., COO Eastside Ventures, Inc., Birmingham, Ala., 1990-93; sr. v.p. Ea. Health System, Inc., Birmingham, 1993—; chmn. Minority Leadership Task Force, Ea. Health System, Inc., 1994-95. Sec. Ala. Health Svcs. Bd.; mem. Literacy Coun. Ala., Ala. Hosp. Assn. State Legis. Com.; mem. Birmingham Regional Healthcare Exec. Forum. Fellow Am. Coll. Healthcare Execs. (diplomate credentials com.), Hosp. Fin. Mgmt. Assn.; mem. AICPA, Tenn. Soc. CPAs, Birmingham C. of C. (membership com.), Birmingham East Rotary Club (v.p.), Mensa, Shriners. Avocations: hunting, fishing, gardening, antique collecting. Office: Ea Health System Inc 48 Medical Park Dr E Birmingham AL 35235-3401

MILLER, DON ROBERT, surgeon; b. Highland, Kans., July 6, 1925; s. Pleasant V. and Lucy Anna (Hammond) M.; m. Geraldine Ellen Nelson, Sept. 6, 1947; children: Don R., Laurie, Todd, Marcia, Kristen, Felicia. A.B., Westminster Coll., 1944; M.D., U. Kans., 1948. Mem. faculty U. Kans., Kansas City, 1957-73; prof. surgery U. Kans., 1970-73; prof. surgery U. Calif. Irvine, 1973-92, prof. emeritus, 1992—, vice chmn., chief dept. surgery, pres. med. staff, 1989-91; dir. surgery Orange County (Calif.) Med. Center, 1973-77. Contbr. articles to profl. jours. Gov. 1988-92. Served with USNR, 1943-45, 50-52. Spl. research fellow Zurich, Switzerland, 1965-66. Fellow A.C.S., Am. Coll. Cardiology; mem. Am. Soc. Univ. Surgeons, Am. Surg. Assn., Soc. Vascular Surgery, Am. Assn. Thoracic Surgery, Am., Central, Western surg. assns., Internat. Cardiovascular Soc., Sigma Xi, Alpha Omega Alpha. Research extracorporeal circulation, myocardial function. Home: 743 Louisiana St Lawrence KS 66044-2339

MILLER, DON WILSON, nuclear engineering educator; b. Westerville, Ohio, Mar. 16, 1942; s. Don Paul and Rachel (Jones) M.; m. Mary Catherine Thompson, June 25, 1966; children: Amy Beth, Stacy Catherine, Paul Wilson Thompson. BS in Physics, Miami U., Oxford, Ohio, 1964, MS in Physics, 1966; MS in Nuclear Engring., Ohio State U., 1970, PhD in Nuclear Engring., 1971. Rsch. assoc. Ohio State U., Columbus, 1966-68, univ. fellow, 1968-69, tchg. assoc., 1969-71, asst. prof. nuclear engring., 1971-74, assoc. prof., 1974-80, chmn. nuclear engring. program, 1977—, prof., 1980—, dir. nuclear reactor lab., 1977—; sec., treas. Cellar Lumber Co., Westerville, Ohio, 1972-84, 85—; cons. Monsanto Rsch. Corp., Miamisburg, Ohio, 1979, NRC, Washington, 1982-84, Scantech Corp., Santa Fe, 1984—, Neoprobe Corp., Columbus, 1990, Electric Power Rsch. Inst., Palo Alto, Calif., 1992-94; mem. adv. com. on reactor safeguards NRC, Washington, 1995—. Patentee in field; contbr. articles to profl. jours. Mem. Westerville Bd. Edn., 1976-91, pres., 1977-78, 86-88; mem. Ohio Sch. Bd.'s Assn., Columbus, 1976-91; mem. fed. rels. com. Nat. Sch. Bd.'s Assn., Washington, 1984-86. With USAR, 1960-68. Named Tech. Person of Yr. Columbus Tech. Coun., 1979; named to All Region Bd. Ohio Sch. Bd's. Assn., 1981, 86; recipient Coll. of Engring Rsch. award Ohio State U., 1984, Achievement award Mid Ohio Chpt Multiple Sclerosis Soc., 1988. Fellow Am. Nuclear Soc. (chmn. edn. div. 1986-87, bd. dirs. 1989-91, chair human factors div. 1993-94, cert. appreciation 1991); mem. IEEE, Am. Soc. Engring. Edn. (chmn. nuclear engring. div. 1978-79, Glenn Murphy award 1989), Nuclear Dept. Heads Orgn. (chmn. 1985-86), Westerville Rec. Assn. (Friend of Edn. award 1992), Rotary (Courtright Community Svc. award 1989), Kiwanis, Hoover Yacht Club, Alpha Nu Sigma (chmn. 1991-93). Avocations: sailing, Am. history, traveling, amateur radio. Home: 172 Walnut Ridge Ln Westerville OH 43081-2464 Office: Ohio State U Dept Mech Engring Nuclear Engring Program 206 W 18th Ave Columbus OH 43210-1154

MILLER, DONALD, art critic; b. Pitts., Dec. 21, 1934; s. LeRoy Gatskell and Alyse G. (McFarland) M. B.A., U. Pitts., 1956, M.A., 1975. Art critic Pitts. Post-Gazette, instr. Carnegie-Mellon U., Pitts., 1979-80; lectr. Community Coll. Allegheny County, 1973, Westmoreland Mus. Art, 1973; art critic Sta. KDKA-TV, 1970-71. Author: (with others) Organic Vision: The Architecture of Peter Berndtson, 1980 (Merit award Pa. Soc. Architects 1981), Malcolm Parcell Wizard of Moon Lorn, 1985. Contbr. articles to profl. jours., also chpts. to various books. Chmn. Art and Antiques auction, Sta. WQED-TV, 1976. Recipient Golden Quill award Pitts. Press Club, 1980, 87, Forbes medal Ft. Pitt Mus., 1986. Rescue Artists Pitts. (hon.), 100 Friends of Pitts. Art, Pitts. Bibliophiles, Phi Beta Kappa. Democrat. Home: Gateway Towers Pittsburgh PA 15222 Office: Pitts Post-Gazette 50 Blvd Of The Allies Pittsburgh PA 15222

MILLER, DONALD E., rubber company executive; b. Denver, Dec. 17, 1930; s. Alex H. and Nina A. (Schlatter) M.; m. Barbara J. Rehm, June 15, 1952; children: Steven, David. Grad., Colo. Sch. Mines, 1953. With Gates Rubber Co., Denver, 1963—; field sales mgr. indsl. sales Gates Rubber Co., 1963-66, v.p. mfg., 1966-69, v.p. auto-hardware sales, 1969-73, v.p. mktg., 1973-81, group v.p. automotive, 1981-82, pres., 1982—; pres., chief oper. officer, dir. Gates Corp. 1st lt. U.S. Army, 1954-56. Presbyterian. Home: 5965 E Princeton Cir Englewood CO 80111-1038 Office: Gates Rubber Co PO Box 5887 900 S Broadway Denver CO 80209-4010

MILLER, DONALD EUGENE, aerospace electronics executive; b. Providence, Mar. 20, 1947; s. Meyer Samuel and Beatrice (Wattman) M.; m. Deborah Neary Miller, Mar. 14, 1987. BA, Boston U., 1968; JD, U. Pa., 1972. Law clk. Assoc. Justice Alfred H. Joslin Supreme Ct., Providence, 1972-73; prin., lawyer Temkin, Marolla & Zurier, Providence, 1973-81, Temkin & Miller, Ltd., Providence, 1981-91; sr. v.p., gen. counsel The Fairchild Corp., Chantilly, Va., 1991—. Author: (treatise) Buying and Selling a Small Business, 1987. Mem. R.I. Bar Assn., Mass. Bar Assn. Avocations: dog breeding, table tennis. Home: 10704 Riverwood Dr Potomac MD 20854-1332 Office: Fairchild Corp PO Box 10804 300 W Service Rd Chantilly VA 22094

MILLER, DONALD EUGENE, minister, educator; b. Dayton, Ohio, Dec. 2, 1929; m. Phyllis Gibbel, Aug. 19, 1956; children: Bryan Daniel, Lisa Kathleen, Bruce David. Student, Manchester Coll., 1947-49; MA, U. Chgo., 1952; postgrad., United Theol. Sem., 1955-56; BD, Bethany Theol. Sem., 1958; PhD, Harvard U. 1962; postgrad., Yale U., 1968-69, Cambridge (Eng.) U., 1975-76. Ordained minister Ch. of the Brethern, 1957. Dir. material aid Brethren Svc. Commn. in Europe, 1952-54; tchr. Madison Twp. High Sch., Trotwood, Ohio, 1954-55; social worker Dayton, 1954-56; tchr. Gregory Sch., Chgo., 1957-58; interim pastor Salem Ch. of the Brethern, Dayton, 1959; assoc. prof. Christian Edn. and Ethics Bethany Theol. Sem., Oak Brook, Ill., 1961-70, prof., 1970-82, dir. grad. studies, 1973-86, Brightbill prof. ministry studies, 1982-86; gen sec. Ch. of the Brethern Gen. Bd., Elgin, Ill., 1986—; lectr. Pastoral Psychotherapy Inst., Park Ridge, Ill., U. Chgo., Princeton Theol. Seminary, Princeton, N.J.; guest tchr. Theol. Coll. No. Nigeria, 1983. Author: a Self Instruction Guide Through Brethern History, 1976, The Wingfooted Wanderer: Conscience and Transcendence, 1977, The Self Study of the Chicago Cluster of Chicago Schools, 1981, Story and Context: An Introduction to Christian Education, 1986, The Gospel and Mother Goose, 1987; (with Warren F. Groff) The Shaping of Modern Christian Thought, 1968; (with Jack L. Seymour) Marking Choices, 1981, Contemporary Approaches to Christian Education, 1982, Theological Approaches to Christian Education, 1990; (with Robert W. Neff and Graydon F. Snyder) Using Biblical Stimulations, vol. 1, 1973, vol. 2, 1975; (with James N. Poling) Foundation for a Practical Theology of Ministry, 1985; designer programs include Edn. for A Shared Ministry, 1976-86, Tng. in a Ministry, 1984; TV host Christianity and the Arts, 1963. Mem. faith and order commn. Nat. Counc. Chs., 1976-81; del. to Russian Orth. Chs., 1967. Fellow Case Study Inst., 1972; rsch. fellow U. Chgo., 1951-52; teaching fellow Harvard U., 1960-61; faculty fellow Am. Assn. Theol. Schs. Faculty, 1968-69. Mem. Assn. for Profl. Edn. for Ministry (editor yearbook 1972, pres. 1976), Assn. Profs. and Researchers in Religious Edn. (pres. 1968), Am. Theol. Soc., Am. Soc. Christian Ethics, Religious Edn. Assn. Office: Ch of the Brethren 1451 Dundee Ave Elgin IL 60120-1674

MILLER, DONALD KEITH, venture capitalist, asset management executive; b. Akron, Ohio, Feb. 2, 1932; s. Clinton Raymond and Hazel Elizabeth (Curl) M.; m. Barbara Dewees Duff, Sept. 25, 1971 (div. 1983); children: Prescott Clinton, Barclay St. John; m. Priscilla Corwith Barker, Sept. 17, 1988. BS, Cornell U., 1954; MBA, Harvard U. 1959. Asst. treas. Chase Manhattan Bank, N.Y.C., 1959-62; asst. to v.p. Electric Bond & Share,

N.Y.C., 1962-66; gen. ptnr. G.H. Walker & Co. Inc., N.Y.C., 1966-74; sr. v.p. White Weld & Co., N.Y.C., 1974-77; mng. dir. Blyth Eastman Paine Webber Inc., N.Y.C., 1978-86; chmn. Greylock Fin., N.Y.C., 1987—, Christensen Boyles Corp., Salt Lake City, 1987—; chmn., CEO Thomson Adv. Group L.P., Stamford, Conn., 1990-93, vice chmn., 1993—; pres., CEO PIMCO Inc., 1993—; bd. dirs. PIMCO Advisors L.P., Newport Beach, Calif.; bd. dirs., chmn. audit com. RPM, Inc., Medina, Ohio, 1972—, Huffy Corp., Dayton, Ohio, 1988—, bd. dirs., mem. exec. com. 1st lt. U.S. Army, 1954-57. Avocation: tennis, squash. Home: 588 Round Hill Rd Greenwich CT 06831-2724 Office: Greylock Fin 399 Park Ave Fl 28 New York NY 10022-4614

MILLER, DONALD LESESSNE, publishing executive; b. N.Y.C., Jan. 10, 1932; s. John H. and Mamie (Johnson) M.; m. Ann Davie, Aug. 12, 1951 (div. 1981); children: Lynn, Mark; m. Gail Aileen Wallace, June 27, 1981. BA, U. Md., 1967; cert., Harvard Grad. Sch. Bus. Adminstrn., 1969. Enlisted U.S. Army, 1948, advanced through grades to maj., 1966, ret., 1968; spl. asst. to pres., mgr. corp. recruitment Inmont Corp., N.Y.C., 1968-70; v.p. indsl. relations Seatrain Shipbldg. Corp., N.Y.C., 1970-71; dep. asst. sec. def. U.S. Dept. Def., Washington, 1971-73; v.p. personnel mgmt. Columbia U., N.Y.C., 1973-78; dir. personnel devel. and adminstrn. Internat. Paper, N.Y.C., 1978-79; v.p. employee relations Consol. Edison N.Y., N.Y.C., 1979-86, Dow Jones & Co., Inc., N.Y.C., 1986—; bd. dirs. Bank of N.Y. and Bank of N.Y. Co., N.Y.C., ACMC, Burlingame, Calif. Author: An Album of Black Americans in the Armed Forces, 1969. Chmn. bd. Associated Black Charities, N.Y.C., 1982-94; bd. dirs. United Way, N.Y.C. and Tri-State, 1981-93; trustee Pace U., 1979—. Decorated Legion of Merit; decorated Commendation Medal; recipient Disting. Civilian Service medal Dept. Def., 1973, Disting. Alumnus award U. Md., 1977. Mem. Alpha Sigma Lambda, Pi Sigma Alpha, Phi Kappa Phi, Alpha Phi Alpha, Sigma Pi Phi. Office: Dow Jones & Co Inc 200 Liberty St New York NY 10281-1003

MILLER, DONALD MORTON, physiology educator; b. Chgo., July 24, 1930; s. Harry Madison and Anna Loraine (Zeller) M.; 1 son, Tad Michael. A.B. in Zoology, U. Ill., Urbana, 1960, M.A. in Physiology, 1962, Ph.D. (NIH fellow), 1965; NIH postgrad. fellow, UCLA, 1965-66. Insp. Buick Jet div. Gen. Motors Corp., Willow Springs, Ill., 1953-55; sci. asst. Organic Chemistry Lab., U. Ill., 1960-62, counselor residence halls, 1960-63, teaching asst. physiology, 1960-64; mem. faculty So. Ill. U., Carbondale, 1966—, prof. physiology, 1966-94, retired, 1995, vis. prof., 1995; adj. prof. McKendree Coll., Lebanon, Ill., 1986-88, Queensland U. of Tech., Brisbane, Australia, 1989; Damon lectr., 1973-74; lectr. trauma edn. Ill. Hwy. Div., So. Ill. Health Manpower Consortium, Critical Care Nurse Program; judge Ill. Jr. Acad. Sci; vis. instr. Nakajo, Japan, 1992. Contbr. articles to profl. jours. Treas. Jackson County chpt. ARC, 1973-79; active CAP, 1968-79. Served with USAF, 1955-59. USPHS summer grantee, 1962, 73, NIH grantee, 1968-80, NASA grantee, 1973-85, Coll. Sea Grant Program grantee, 1983-88, U.S. Army Med. Rsch. Inst. grantee, 1987-92. Mem. Am. Physiol. Soc., Biophys. Soc., Am. Microscopic Soc., Neurosci. Soc., Am. Soc. Zoologists, N.Y. Acad. Scis., Am. Soc. Photobiology (charter), Am. Soc. Parasitologists (ednl. policies com.), Am. Midwest Conf. of Parasitologists (pres. 1980-81 sec.-treas. 1985-93), Am. Trauma Soc., Sigma Xi (past chpt. pres.), Chi Gamma Iota. Clubs: Elks, Lions. Home: #9 New Swan Lake Rd Murphysboro IL 62966-9761

MILLER, DONALD MUXLOW, accountant, administrator; b. Luverne, Minn., Feb. 21, 1924; s. Henry Clay and Mildred Eva (Muxlow) M.; m. Eunice Jean Gibson, Feb. 19, 1944; children: SueRilla M., Donna Jean Eichten, Patsy Ann Pushee. Student, Metro State, St. Paul, Minn., 1973-84. Lic. pub. acct. Mgr. Hines & Paulus, CPA, Worthington, Minn., 1952-65; commandant Minn. Vets. Home, Mpls., 1965-68; prin. D.M. Miller, Acct., 1968-70, 76-78; asst. sec. Minn. State Senate, St. Paul, 1970-72; comptr. Western Oil Co., Mpls., 1972-76; commr. Dept. Vet. Affairs, State of Minn., St. Paul, 1978-81; prin. D.M. Miller & Assoc., Ltd., Mpls., 1981—; chief exec. officer MARD, Inc., Mpls., 1985-95; v.p. Miller, Micketts & Assocs. Ltd., Mpls., 1993—. Trustee Heart Professorship Found., 1987-91; pres. Legionville Sch. Patrol Camp, Brainerd, Minn., 1963-64; pres. bd. govs. Big Island Vets. Camp, Mpls., 1986-88. 2nd lt. USAAC, 1942-46; 1st lt. USAF, 1951-52. Recipient Volunteer of the Year award Kidney Found., 1975. Mem. Nat. Soc. Pub. Accts., Minn. Assn. Pub. Accts., VFW, Nat. Assn. State Vets. Homes (hon. life mem., reg. v.p. 1967-68), Nat. Assn. State Dirs. Vets. Affairs (reg. v.p. 1978-79), Minn. Gaming Assn. (exec. sec. 1987-92), Accreditation Coun. for Accountancy, Am. Legion (hon. life mem., comdr. Minn. 1962-63, com. chmn. 1980-84, pres. Minn. Found. Bd. 1990-91), Masons, Shriners. Presbyterian. Avocation: golf. Office: Miller Micketts & Assocs Ltd 9033 Lyndale Ave S Ste 201 Minneapolis MN 55420-3537

MILLER, DONALD ROSS, management consultant; b. Huntington, N.Y., Aug. 5, 1927; s. George Everett and Ethel May (Ross) M.; m. Constance Higgins, 1948 (div. 1955); children: Donald Ross Jr., Cynthia Lynn, Candace Lee; m. Janet Heyman Behr, Apr. 15, 1965; children: Jeffrey Lawrence, Wendy Lorraine. BS/BEA, MIT, 1950. Cert. mgmt. cons. Inst. of Mgmt. Cons. Staff engr. Stop & Shop, Inc., Boston, 1950-56; v.p., dir. Cresap, McCormick and Paget, Inc., N.Y.C., 1956-76; mng. dir. Donald R. Miller Mgmt. Cons., Forest Hills, N.Y., 1977—; bd. dirs. Nash Finch Co., Mpls., chmn. bd. dirs. 1995—. Author: Management Practices Manual, 3 vols., 1963, (booklet) Management of Managerial Resources, 1969. Bd. dirs. Queens Mus. Art, Flushing, N.Y., 1982-93, pres., 1988-92; pres. Lexington House, Forest Hills, 1984—. With U.S. Maritime Svc., 1945-46, ETO, U.S. Army, 1946-48. Mem. Nat. Assn. Corp. Dirs., Inst. Mgmt. Cons. (cert. com. 1986—), Sky Club. Episcopal. Avocations: tennis, reading. Home: 68-10 108th St Forest Hills NY 11375 Office: PO Box 649 Forest Hills NY 11375

MILLER, DONALD SPENCER, geologist, educator; b. Ventura, Calif., June 12, 1932; s. Spencer Jacob and Marguerite Rachael (Williams) M.; m. Carolyn Margaret Losee, June 12, 1954; children: Sandra Louise, Kenneth Donald, Christopher Spencer. BA, Occidental Coll., 1954; MA, Columbia U., 1956, PhD, 1960. Asst. prof. Rensselaer Poly. Inst., Troy, N.Y., 1960-64, assoc. prof., 1964-69, prof., 1969—, chmn. dept. geology, 1969-94, emeritus prof., 1994—; research assoc. geology Columbia U., 1960-63; research fellow geochemistry Calif. Inst. Tech., Pasadena, summer 1963; NSF Sci. Faculty fellow U. Bern, Switzerland, 1966-67; sci. guest prof. Max-Planck Inst. Nuclear Physics, Heidelberg, Fed. Republic Germany, 1977-78, vis. prof., summer 1979, guest scientist, Aug. 1979, 80, 81, 82; vis. prof. Isotope Geology Lab., U. Berne, summer 1979; participant NATO exchange program Demokritos Inst., Athens, Greece, Sept. 1983, 85; vis. rsch. fellow U. Melbourne, Australia, summer 1988; mem. nat. screening com. Inst. Internat. Edn., 1988-91. Pres., treas. Troy Rehab. and Improvement, Inc., 1968-74; mem. Troy Zoning Bd. Appeals, 1970-85. Fellow Geol. Soc. Am.; mem. Am. Geophys. Union, Geochem. Soc., Nat. Assn. Geol. Tchrs., Sigma Xi, Sigma Pi Sigma. Home: 2198 Tibbits Ave Troy NY 12180-7015 Office: Rensselaer Poly Inst Dept Earth Environ Sci Troy NY 12181

MILLER, DOROTHY ANNE SMITH, cytogenetics educator; b. N.Y.C., Oct. 20, 1931; d. John Philip and Anna Elizabeth (Hellberg) Smith; m. Orlando Jack Miller, July 10, 1954; children: Richard L., Cynthia K., Karen A. BA in Chemistry magna cum laude, Wilson Coll., Chambersburg, Pa., 1952; PhD in Biochemistry, Yale U., 1957. Rsch. assoc. dept. ob-gyn Columbia U., N.Y.C., 1964-72, from rsch. assoc. to asst. prof. dept. human genetics-devel., 1973-85; prof. depts. molecular biology and genetics and pathology Wayne State U., Detroit, 1985-94, prof. dept. pathology, 1985—, prof. Ctr. for Molecular Medicine and Genetics, 1994—; vis. scientist clin. and population cytogenetics unit Med. Rsch. Coun., Edinburgh, Scotland, 1983-84; vis. prof. dept. genetics and molecular biology U. la Sapienza, Rome, 1988; vis. disting. fellow La Trobe U., Melbourne, Australia, 1992. Contbr. numerous articles to sci. jours. Grantee March of Dimes Birth Defects Found., 1974-93, NSF, 1983-84. Mem. Am. Soc. Human Genetics, Genetics Soc. Am., Genetics Soc. Australia, Phi Beta Kappa. Presbyterian. Home: 1915 Stonycroft Ln Bloomfield Hills MI 48304-2339 Office: Wayne State U 540 E Canfield St Detroit MI 48201-1998

MILLER, DUANE KING, health and beauty care company executive; b. N.Y.C., Mar. 1, 1931; s. Henry Charles and Helen Marion (King) M.; A.B. in Econs. and Fin., NYU, 1951; m. Nancy L. Longley, June 6, 1954; children—Cheryl L., Duane L. Vice pres. mktg. Warner-Chilcott div. Warner

Lambert Co., Morris Plains, N.J., 1970-72, pres. div., 1973-77, exec. v.p. Am. Optical div. and pres. Am. Optical Internat. div., Southbridge, Mass., 1978; pres. biol. and proprietary products divs., v.p. Revlon Health Care Group, Revlon Corp., Tuckahoe, N.Y., 1978-80, pres. ethical, proprietary and vision care divs., 1981-82, corp. v.p. parent co., 1982, pres. Revlon Health Care Group, 1983-92, corp. exec. v.p. parent co., 1984-92, pres. Revlon Health Beauty Care and Internat. Group, 1988-92, ret., 1992; pres. DKL Properties, health care cons. Promedex Techs., 1992—. Mem. Republican Nat. Com. Mem. Am. Mgmt. Assn., Am. Mktg. Assn. (pres. N.J. chpt. 1967-68), Sales Exec. Club N.Y. Clubs: Princeton N.Y.; Cripple Creek (Del.) Golf; Masons, Shriners. Author: (with others) Marketing Planning for Chief Executives and Planners, 1966. Home: 8 Western Dr Colts Neck NJ 07722-1271 Office: 1 Bethany Rd Ste 44 Hazlet NJ 07730-1662

MILLER, DUANE LEON, insurance company executive; b. Oskaloosa, Iowa, July 31, 1937; s. Marvin L. and Cora Mae (Ver Steeg) M.; m. Suzanne Schoon, May 1, 1958; children—Debra, Jeffrey. Student, Central Coll., Pella, Iowa, 1955-57; B.A. in Math, U. Iowa, 1959; M.B.A., Ill. State U., Normal, 1972. C.P.A., Ill. With Ill. Agrl. Assn. (and its affiliate), 1959-81; asst. v.p. fin., asst. treas. Ill. Agrl. Assn. (and its affiliate), Bloomington, 1971-72; v.p. fin., treas. Ill. Agrl. Assn. (and its affiliate), 1972-74; exec. v.p., chief exec. officer Country Life Ins. Co., Country Mut. Ins. Co., Mid-Am. Ins. Co., Country Casualty Ins. Co., Country Capital Mgmt. Co., CC Services, Inc. and 3 related, Bloomington, 1974—; pres. Ill. Ins. Info. Service, 1978-79. Bd. dirs. Brokaw Hosp., Normal, 1976-84, pres., 1980-82; pres. United Way of McLean County, Ill., 1977. Mem. Nat. Assn. Ind. Insurers (governing bd.), Conf. Casualty Ins. Cos. (past dir.), Nat. Assn. Ind. Insurers Safety Assn. (gov.), Am. Inst. C.P.A.'s. Presbyterian. Office: 1701 N Towanda Ave Bloomington IL 61701-2040

MILLER, DWIGHT RICHARD, cosmetologist, corporate executive, hair designer; b. Johnstown, Pa., Jan. 24, 1943. Grad., Comer & Doran Sch., San Diego; DSci. (hon.), London Inst. for Applied Rsch., 1973. Cert. aromatherapist; lic. cosmetologist, instr.; Brit. Mastercraftsman. Styles dir. Marinello-Comer, Hollywood, Calif., 1965-67; expert Pivot Point Internat., Chgo., 1967-68; styles dir. Lapins, L.A., 1969; dir. Redken, L.A., 1970, Vidal Sassoon, London, 1971-74; world amb. Pivot Point, New Zealand and Australia, 1974-75; internat. artistic dir. Pivot Point, Chgo., 1975-78; internat. dir., co-founder Hair Artists Inst. & Registry, 1978-81; internat. artistic dir. Zotos Internat., Darien, Conn., 1981-87, Matrix Essentials, Inc., Solon, Ohio, 1987-92; bd. dirs., v.p. creative, internat. artistic dir. Anasazi Exclusive Salon Products, Inc., 1992—; judge hairdressing competitions including Norwegian Masters, Australian Nat. Championships; pres. Intercrimpers, London, 1974-75. Author: Sculptic Cutting Pivot Point 75, Prismatics, 1983; prod., dir. 15 documentaries, numerous tech. and industry videos; contbr. articles, photographs to popular mags.; developer several profl. product lines including Vidal Sassoon-London, Design Freedom, Bain de Terre, Ultra Bond, Vavoom!, Systeme Biolage, Anasazi. With USMC, 1960-64. Named Artistic Dir. Yr. Am. Salon mag.; presented with Order of White Elephant, 1976; recipient London Gold Cup for Best Presentation London Beauty Festival, 1982, Dr. Everett G. McDonough award for Excellence in Permanent Waving, World Master award Art and Fashion Group, 1992. Mem. Cercle des Arts et Techniques de la Coiffure, Intercoiffure, Haute Coiffure Franchaise, Soc. Cosmetic Chemists, Hair Artists Great Britain, Internat. Assn. Trichogists, Nat. Cosmetologists Assn. (HairAmerica), Am. Soc. Phytotherapy and Aromatherapy, HairChicago (hon.), Art and Fashion Group (pres. 1993), 'Dressers MC (pres. 1990—), London's Alternative Hair Club (patron). Address: 13900 Watt Rd Novelty OH 44072-9741

MILLER, E. HITE, banker, holding company executive. Pres. First Citizens Bancorp of S.C., Columbia, First Citizens Bank TR of S.C., Columbia. Office: First Citizens Bancorp 1230 Main St Columbia SC 29201-3248

MILLER, E. WILLARD, geographer; b. Turkey City, Pa., May 17, 1915; s. Archie Howard and Tessie Bernella (Master) M.; m. Ruby Skinner, June 27, 1941. MA, U. Nebr., 1939; PhD, Ohio State U., 1942. Instr. Ohio State U., 1941-43; asst. prof. geography and geology Western Res. U., 1943-44; asso. prof. geography Pa. State U., University Park, 1945-49; prof. Pa. State U., 1949—, chief div. geography, 1945-53, head dept. geography, 1954-63; asst. dean for resident instrn. Coll. Earth and Mineral Scis., 1964-72, asso. dean, 1972-80, asst. dean for resident instrn. and continuing edn., 1967-69; dir. Acad. Year Inst., Earth Scis., NSF, 1967-71; geographer OSS, Washington, 1944-45; spl. research on Arctic environ. problems for Q.M. Gen., U.S. Army, 1947-50; geographic adviser Thomas Y. Crowell Co., hon. chmn. Nat Coun. for Geographic Edn. 21st Century Endowment Fund, 1994—. Author: Careers in Geography, 1948 (rev. 1955), (with others) The World's Nations: An Economic and Regional Geography, 1958, A Geography of Manufacturing, 1962, An Economic Atlas of Pennsylvania, 1964, (with G. Langdon) Exploring Earth Environments: A World Geography, 1964, Energy Resources of the United States, 1968, Mineral Resources of the United States, 1968, A Geography of Industrial Location, 1970, A Socio-Economic Atlas of Pennsylvania, 1974, Manufacturing: A Study of Industrial Location, 1977, Industrial Location: A Bibliography, 1978, Physical Geography: Earth Systems and Human Interactions, 1985, Pennsylvania: A Keystone to Progress, 1986, (with Ruby M. Miller) During Business In and With Latin America, 1987, (with Ruby M. Miller) Economic, Political and Regional Aspects of the World's Energy Problems, 1979, The Third World: Natural Resources, Economics, Politics and Social Conditions, 1981, Africa: A Bibliography on the Third World, 1981, The American Coal Industry: Economic, Political and Environmental Aspects, 1980, Manufacturing in Nonmetropolitan Pennsylvania, 1980; (with Ruby M. Miller) Latin America: A Bibliography on the Third World, 1982, South America: A Bibliography in the Third World, 1982, Middle America: A Bibliography on the Third World, 1982, Industrial Location and Planning: Theory, Models and Factors of Localization: A Bibliography, 1984, Industrial Location and Planning: Localization, Growth and Organization: A Bibliography, 1984, Industrial Location and Planning: Regions and Countries: A Bibliography, 1984; Pennsylvania: Architecture and Culture: A Bibliography, 1985, United States' Foreign Relation: Western Europe, 1987, United States' Foreign Relations: Soviet Union and Eastern Europe, 1987, United States' Foreign Relations: United States and Canada, 1987, Industrial Parks, Export Processing Zones, and Enterprise Zones: A Bibliography, 1987, The 1976 Presidential Elections: A Bibliography, 1987, The 1980 Presidential Election: A Bibliography, 1987, The 1984 Presidential Election: A Bibliography, 1987, The Third World: Economic Development, 1988, The Third World: Government and Political Relations, Social Conditions, Population, Urbanization, Education, and Communications, 1988, The Third World: Economic Activities, 1988, Natural Resources and Commerical Policy, 1988, others; editl. dir.: Earth and Mineral Scis. Bull, 1967-69; editor: (with S.K. Majumdar) Pennsylvania Coal: Resources, Technology and Utilization, 1983, Hazardous and Toxic Wastes: Management and Health Effects, 1984, Solid and Liquid Wastes: Managment Methods and Socioeconomic Considerations, 1984, Management of Radioactive Materials and Wastes: Issues and Progress, 1985, Environmental Consequences of Energy Production, 1987, Ecology and Restoration of the Delaware River Basin, 1988, A Geography of Pennsylvania, 1995; (with S.K. Majumdar, R.F. Schmalz) Management of Hazardous Materials and Wastes: Treatment, Minimization and Environmental Impacts, 1989, (with Ruby M. Miller) Environmental Hazards: Air Pollution, 1989, (with S.K. Majumdar and R.R. Parizek) Water Resources in Pennsylvania, 1990, (with S.K. Majumdar and R.F. Schmalz) Environmental Radon, 1990; (with Ruby M. Miller) Environmental Hazards: Radioactive Wastes and Materials, 1990, Environmental Hazards: Toxic Materials and Hazardous Wastes, 1991; (with S.K. Majumdar, L.M. Rosenfeld, P.A. Rubba and R.F. Schmalz) Science Education in the United States, Issues, Crises and Priorities, 1991; (with S.K. Majumdar and John Cahir) Air Pollution, 1991, (with G. Forbes, R.F. Schmalz and S.K. Majumdar) Natural and Technological Disasters, 1992, (with S.K. Majumdar, L.S. Kalkstein, B.M. Yarnal, and L.M. Rosenfeld) Global Climatic Change: Implications Challenges and Mitigation Measures, 1992, (with Ruby M. Miller) Water: Quality and Availability, 1993, (with S.K. Majumdar, L.S. Kalkstein, B.M. Yarnal and L.M. Rosenfeld) Global Climatic Change: Implications, Challenges and Mitigation Measures, 1992, (with S.K. Majumdar et al) Conservation and Resource Management, 1993, (with S.K. Majumdar, D.E. Baker, E.K. Brown, J.R. Pratt and R.F. Schmalz) Conservation and Resource Management, 1993, (with Ruby M. Miller) Energy and American Society, 1993, (with others) Biological Diversity: Problems and Challenges, 1994; assoc. editor The Pennsylvania Geographer, Jour. of Pa. Acad. Scis.;

media materials editor: Jour. Geography, 1981-84; contbg. editor: Producers Monthly Mag; editor Middle States Geographer, 1991—; contbr. articles to sci. jours. Recipient cert. of merit from OSS, Whitbeck award Nat. Coun. Geog. Edn., 1950, Pa. Gov.'s citation for Contbn. to Commonwealth, 1975, Pa. Dept. Commerce Sec.'s Meritorious Svcs. award, 1975, Disting. Alumnus Clarion U., 1989; named Hon. Alumnus Pa. State U., 1991. Fellow AAAS, Am. Geog. Soc., Explorers Club, Nat. Coun. Geog. Edn.; mem. Am. Inst. Mining, Metall. and Petroleum Engrs., Am. Soc. Profl. Geographers (sec, 1945-48, pres. 1948), Assn. Am. Geographers (Honors award 1990), Pa. Geog. Soc. (pres. 1962-63, dir. 1965—, Meritorious Service award 1974, 84, 93), Pa. Acad. Sci. (pres. 1966-68, editorial bd. Procs. 1985—, Spl. Services award 1976, 87, Appreciation award 1992), Obelisk Soc., Mount Nittany Soc. of Pa. State U., Pres.'s Club of Pa. State U., George Atherton Soc. Pa. State U., Sigma Xi, Pi Gamma Mu, Beta Gamma Sigma. Home: 845 Outer Dr State College PA 16801-8234

MILLER, EDMOND TROWBRIDGE, civil engineer, educator, consultant; b. Pitts., Dec. 9, 1933; s. George Ellsworth and Billie Sue (Watson) M.; m. Nancy Lee Cooper, July 21, 1956; children: Carol Anne, Nancy Ruth, Laura Elizabeth. B.C.E., Ga. Inst. Tech., 1955, M.S.C.E., 1957; C.E., MIT, 1963; Ph.D., Tex. A&M U., 1967. Registered profl. engr., Ala., Fla. asst. prof. civil engring. U. Ala., Tuscaloosa, 1963-64, assoc. prof., 1967-71, prof., 1971-75; v.p. William S. Pollard Cons., Memphis, 1976-77; chmn. dept. civil engring. U. Louisville, 1977-81; prof. U. Ala., Birmingham, 1981—, chmn. dept. civil engring., 1981-90, interim dean Sch. Engring., 1984; instr. civil engring. Tex. A&M U., 1964-67. Served to capt. C.E. AUS, 1956-57. Automotive Safety Found. fellow, 1964-65; recipient Outstanding Achievement in Edn. award Ky. Soc. Profl. Engrs., 1980. Fellow ASCE (dist. 9 council 1978-80), Inst. Transp. Engrs.; mem. Am. Soc. Engring. Edn., Transp. Research Bd., Sigma Xi, Chi Epsilon, Tau Beta Pi, Chi Epsilon. Christian Scientist. Home: 2566 Dalton Dr Pelham AL 35124-1448 Mailing Address: PO Box 158 Pelham AL 35124-0158 Office: U Ala Birmingham Dept Civil & Environ Engring Birmingham AL 35294

MILLER, EDMUND KENNETH, retired electrical engineer, educator; b. Milw., Dec. 24, 1935; s. Edmund William and Viola Louise (Ludwig) M.; m. Patricia Ann Denn, Aug. 23, 1958; children: Kerry Ann, Mark Christopher. BSEE, Mich. Tech. U., 1957; MS in Nuclear Engring., U. Mich., 1958, MSEE, 1961, PhD in Elec. Engring., 1965. Rsch. assoc. U. Mich., Ann Arbor, 1965-68; sr. scientist MB Assocs., San Ramon, Calif., 1968-71; group leader engring. rsch. div. Lawrence Livermore Lab., Livermore, Calif., 1971-78, leader engring. rsch. div., 1978-83, leader nuclear energy systems div. 1983-85; regents prof. elect. and computer engring. U. Kans., 1985-87; mgr. electromagnetics Rockwell Sci. Ctr., Thousand Oaks, Calif., 1987-88; dir. electromagnetics rsch. operation Gen. Rsch. Corp., Santa Barbara, Calif., 1988-89; group leader MEE div. Los Alamos (N.Mex.) Nat. Lab., 1989-93, ret., 1993. Stocker vis. prof. of elec. and computer engring., Ohio u., Athens, 1994—. Editor: Time Domain Measurements in Electromagnets, 1986; past assoc. editor Radio Sci.; assoc. editor IEEE Potentials, 1985-91, editor, 1992—; assoc. editor IEEE AP-S mag.; co-editor (with L. Medgyesi-Mitschang and E.H. Newman) Computational Electromagnetics, 1991; editorial bd. Internat. Jour. Numerical Modeling, 1990—, Computer Applications in Engring. Edn., 1992—; editor: Jour. Electromagnetic Waves and Applications, 1991—, Jour. of Applied Computational Electromagnetics Soc., IEEE Computer Soc. Mag. Computational Sci. and Engring., 1994—; contbr. 100 articles to profl. jours. Singer Lyra Male Chorus, Ann Arbor, Mich., 1966-68, Livermore Civic Chorus, 1969-71. Fellow IEEE (mem. press. bd. 1991—), mem. Am. Phys. Soc., Optical Soc. Am., Acoustical Soc. Am., Am. Soc. Engring. Edn., Electromagnetics Soc. (past bd. dirs.) Internat. Sci. Radio Union (past chmn. U.S. Commn. A), Applied Computational Electromagnetics Soc. (past pres.). Office: Ohio Univ 330 Stoker Ctr Athens OH 87501

MILLER, EDWARD ALBERT, lawyer; b. N.Y.C., May 4, 1931; s. Paul Leslie and Marguerite Teresa (Lotte) M.; m. Sachiko Makishima, Sept. 19, 1959; children: Juliet Kyoko, Janet Akiko. B.A., Yale U., 1953, LL.D., 1956. Bar: D.C. 1956, N.Y. 1960. Assoc. Winthrop, Stimson, Putnam & Roberts, N.Y.C., 1960-72; from v.p. to sr. v.p., gen. counsel Harper & Row Pubs., Inc., N.Y.C., 1972-87; pvt. practice law N.Y.C., 1987—. Served to lt. USNR, 1956-60. Mem. ABA, Assn. Bar City N.Y., Assn. Am. Pubs. (chmn. lawyers com. 1980-82).

MILLER, EDWARD BOONE, lawyer; b. Milw., Mar. 26, 1922; s. Edward A. and Myra (Munsert) M.; m. Anne Harmon Chase Phillips, Feb. 14, 1969; children by previous marriage: Barbara Miller Anderson, Ellen Miller Gerkens, Elizabeth Miller Lawhun, Thomas; stepchildren: T. Christopher Phillips, Sarah Phillips Parkhill. B.A., U. Wis., 1942, LL.B., 1947; student, Harvard Bus. Sch., 1942-43. Bar: Wis. 1947, Ill. 1948. With firm Pope, Ballard, Shepard & Fowle, Chgo., 1947-51, 52-70, ptnr., 1953-70, 75-93, mng. partner, 1979-82, chmn. labor and employment law dept., 1975-76, 87-88, 90-91; of counsel Seyfarth, Shaw, Fairweather, and Geraldson, Chgo., 1994—; mem. adv. com. Ctr. for Labor Mgmt. Dispute Resolution, Stetson U., 1984—; Instl. Indsl. Rels., Loyola U., 1987-91, Kent Pub. Employee Labor Rels. Conf., 1988—, Ill. Ednl. Labor Rels. Bd., 1988—; exec. asst. to industry mems. Regional Wage Stblzn. Bd., Chgo., 1951-52, industry mem., 1952; chmn. NLRB, Washington, 1970-74; mem. panel of labor law experts Commerce Clearing House, 1987—; dir. Chgo. Wheel & Mfg. Co., 1965-70, 75-88, Andes Candies, Inc., 1965-68, 75-80. Mem. Gov. Ill. Commn. Labor-Mgmt. Policies for Pub. Employees, 1966-67; chmn. Midwest Pension Conf., 1960-61; mem. labor relations com. Ill. C. of C., 1953-70; bd. dirs. Am. Found. Continuing Edn., 1960-69. Served to lt. USNR, 1943-46. Mem. ABA (NLRB practice and procedures com., internat. labor law com.), Ill. Bar Assn., Wis. Bar Assn., Chgo. Assn. Commerce and Industry (chmn. labor relations com. 1980-86, bd. dirs. 1987—), Order of Coif. Republican. Congregationalist. Clubs: Legal (Chgo.), Law (Chgo.), Cliff Dwellers (Chgo.); North Shore Country (curling mem.). Home: 632 Chatham Rd Glenview IL 60025-4402

MILLER, EDWARD DANIEL, banker; b. 1940; married. Grad., Pace U. With Mfrs. Hanover Trust Co., N.Y.C., 1959—, former sr. v.p. consumer credit, sr. v.p., dep. gen. mgr. br. banking group, 1980-82, exec. v.p., head retail banking div., 1982-85, sector exec. v.p. retail banking, 1985-88; vice chmn. Mfrs. Hanover Corp. and Mfrs. Hanover Trust Co., 1988—; vice chmn. Chem. Banking Corp., N.Y.C., 1992-93, pres., 1994—, also bd. dirs. Office: Chem Bank 270 Park Ave New York NY 10017-2014

MILLER, EDWARD DAVID, non-profit association administrator; b. Bradenton, Fla., July 5, 1934; s. Louis and Pauline (Goldman) M.; m. Denise Daniel, Dec. 26, 1973. BA, Fla. So. Coll., 1958; MA, Appalachian State U., 1966; EdS, Coll. U., 1976; EdD, U. Ark., 1988. Cert. tchr., D.C., Fla. Assoc. exec. Nat. Bus. Edn. Assn., Washington, 1969-73; pres., chief exec. officer Future Bus Leaders Am., Washington, 1973—. Chmn. nat. coordinating coun. Vocational Student Orgn., Washington, 1980—, Nat. Adv. Coun. for Vocat. Edn., Washington, 1983-86; commr. Nat. Commn. for Employment Policy, Washington, 1983-85. With U.S. Army, 1957-59. Named to Hon. Order Ky. Cols., 1970, Hon. Citizen City of Stateboro, Ga., 1975, One of Outstanding Commrs. Nat. Commn. for Employment Policy, 1983. Mem. Am. Vocat. Assn., Am. Soc. Assn. Execs., Nat. Bus. Edn. Assn., Nat. Assn. State Suprs. Vocat. Edn. Republican. Avocations: music, collecting fine art and gems. Office: FBLA PBL Inc 1912 Association Dr Reston VA 22091-1502

MILLER, EDWARD DORING, JR., anesthesiologist; b. Rochester, N.Y., Feb. 1, 1943; s. Edward D. and Natalie (Sadam) M.; m. Leslie Coombs, June 15, 1968 (dec. Apr. 1987); children: Sara Davenport, Katherine Coombs; m. Lynne Perkins, Apr. 30, 1988. AB, Ohio Wesleyan U., 1964; MD, U. Rochester, 1968. Diplomate Am. Bd. Anesthesiology, Am. Coll. Anesthesiology; cert. critical care medicine. Intern University Hosp., Boston, 1968-69; anesthesia resident Peter Bent Brigham Hosp., Boston, 1969-71; fellow in physiology Harvard Med. Sch., Boston, 1971-73; dir. anesthesia research Brooke Army Med. Ctr., Ft. Sam Houston, Tex., 1973-75; asst. prof. anesthesiology U. Va. Med. Ctr., Charlottesville, Va., 1975-79, assoc. prof. anesthesiology, 1979-82, prof. anesthesiology, 1982-83, prof. anesthesiology, surgery, 1983-86; E.M. Papper prof. anesthesiology, chmn. dept. Columbia U. Coll. Physicians and Surgeons, N.Y.C. 1986-94; Mark C. Rogers prof., chmn. dept. anesthesiology and Johns Hopkins U., Balt.,

1994—; sr. scientist physiology, pharmacology Hosp. Necker, Paris, 1981-82; examiner Am. Bd. Anesthesiology; v.p. clin. faculty U. Va., 1983-85, pres. 1985-86. Editor Anesthesia and Analgesia, 1982-92; contbr. numerous articles to profl. jours. Pres. Barracks-Rugby-Preston Neighborhoods, Va., 1977-79; vestry Christ Episc. Ch., Va., 1985-86. Served to maj. M.C., U.S. Army, 1973-75. Recipient Research Career Devel. award Nat. Inst. Gen. Med. Scis., 1978-83; NIH grantee, 1977-87, Inst. Nat. de la Sante et de la Recherche Medicale grantee, 1981-82. Mem. Assn. U. Anesthetists (sec. 1984-87), Am. Soc. Anesthesiologists, Am. Physiol. Soc., Internat. Anesthesia Research Soc. (trustee 1988—), Soc. Critical Care Medicine, Soc. Cardiovascular Anesthesiologists, Assn. Univ. Anesthesiologists (pres. 1990-92), Found. for Anesthesia Edn. and Rsch. (bd. dirs. 1986—), Up Med. Bd. Presbyn. Hosp. Home: 15 Meadow Rd Baltimore MD 21212 Office: Johns Hopkins U Sch Medicine 600 N Wolfe St Blalock 1415 Baltimore MD 21287-4965

MILLER, ELDON EARL, corporate business publications consultant, retired manufacturing company executive; b. Hutchinson, Kans., Jan. 1, 1919; s. Robert Dewalt and Martha Velva (Stauffer) M.; m. Margaret Borgsdorf, Mar. 26, 1950. B.A., UCLA, 1941. Formerly newspaper editor, mag. editor, pub. relations cons., polit. writer; with Purex Industries, Inc., Lakewood, Calif., 1950-85; asst. sec. Purex Industries, Inc., 1971-72, v.p. corp. relations, 1972-85, cons. bus. publs., corp. relations, 1985—. Republican. Presbyterian. Home and Office: 26685 Westhaven Dr Laguna Hills CA 92653-5767

MILLER, ELLIOTT CAIRNS, retired bank executive, lawyer; b. Cambridge, Mass., May 4, 1934; s. James Wilkinson and Mary Elliott (Cairns) M.; m. Mary Killion, July 2, 1960; children: Jonathan Vaill, Stephen Killion. Grad., Matthew Whaley Sch., Williamsburg, Va., 1952; A.B., Harvard Coll., 1956; J.D., U. Mich., 1961; LL.M., Boston U., 1970. Bar: Conn. 1962. Assoc. Robinson & Cole, Hartford, Conn., 1961-66, ptnr., 1967-72; v.p., counsel Savs. for Savs., Hartford, Conn., 1972-73; sr. v.p., 1973-78, exec. v.p., 1978, pres., chief exec. officer, dir., 1979-90; pres., chief exec. officer Soc. for Savs. Bancorp Inc., 1987-90; bd. dirs. nat. council Savs. Inst., Washington, 1984-88. Trustee, chmn. Kingswood-Oxford Sch., West Hartford, 1977-87; trustee Coordinating Coun. on Founds., 1987-90; bd. dirs Downtown Coun., Hartford, 1975-90; trustee Greater Hartford Arts Coun., 1980-88; trustee Wadsworth Atheneum, 1990—; trustee Hartford Stage Co., 1973-85, hon. trustee, 1985—; corporator Hartford Hosp., Mt. Sinai Hosp., Inst. of Living, Hartford Pub. Libr. With U.S. Army, 1956-58. Mem. Conn. Bar Assn. Home: 4 Stratford Rd West Hartford CT 06117-2838

MILLER, EMANUEL, retired lawyer, banker; b. N.Y.C., Jan. 22, 1917; s. Mayer and Helen (Stein) M.; m. Ruth Marcus, Jan. 3, 1942; children—Linda Alice, Henry Ward, Marjorie Joan. B.A. Bklyn. Coll., 1937; LL.B., St. Lawrence U., Bklyn., 1941. Bar: N.Y. bar 1942. With Harold W. Zeamans, Flushing, N.Y., 1950-51; firm White & Case, N.Y.C., 1951-53; with Bankers Trust Co., N.Y.C., 1953-89; v.p., counsel Bankers Trust Co., 1976-89, ret., dir. various affiliates; lectr. in field. Contbr. legal publs. Served with U.S. Army, 1942-45. Mem. Am., N.Y. State bar assns., Iota Theta. Club: Indian Spring Golf (Boynton Beach, Fla.). Home: 6370 Evian Pl Boynton Beach FL 33437-4909

MILLER, EMILIE F., state senator; b. Chgo., Aug. 11, 1936; d. Bruno C. and Etta M. (Senese) Feiza; m. Dean E. Miller; children: Desireé M., Edward C. BS in Bus. Adminstrn., Drake U., 1958. Asst. buyer Jordan Marsh Co., Boston, 1958-60, Carson, Pirie, Scott & Co., Chgo., 1960-62; dept. mgr., asst. buyer Woodward & Lothrop, Washington, 1962-64; polit. cons. various cos., Va., 1980-87; legis. aide Senator Adelard Brandt, Va., 1980-83; legis. cons. Va. Fedn. Bus. Profl. Women, 1986-87; senator Va. Gen. Assembly, Richmond, 1988-92; mem. Edn. and Health com., Gen. Laws com., Local Gov. com., Rehab. and Social Scis. com.; bus. tng. seminars Moscow, Nizhny Novgorod, Russia, 1993, Novgorod, St. Petersburg, 1995. Guest editorial writer Va. Sun, 1981; host, producer weekly TV program, Channel 61. Mem. State Cen. Com. Dem. Party Va., Richmond, 1974—; chmn. Va. Assoc. Dem. County and City Chmn., 1980, Fairfax County Dem. Com., 1976-80; past v.p. Women's Nat. Dem. Club.; bd. dirs. Mental Health Assn. No. Va., 1980—, State Mental Health and Mental Retardation Bd., 1982-88; fin. dir. Saslaw for Congress, 1984; state labor coord. Robb-Davis-Baliles Joint Campaign; bd. dirs. Stop Child Abuse Now, 1988; chmn. Va. Assn. Community Svcs. Bd., 1980-82; v.p. Fairfax County Coun. of Arts, exec. com., internat. childrens festival; mem. exec. bd. Mantua Citizens' Assn., 1985-87, nat. alumni bd. J.A. Achievement, BRAVO adv. com. for the first Gov.'s Awards for the Arts in Va., 1979-80; lay tchr. St. Ambrose Cath. Ch., 1963-80; del. to White House Conf. on Children, 1970; chmn. Va. Coalition for Mentally Disturbed, 1992—; bd. dirs. Ctr. Innovative Tech., 1992-94, Ct. Appointed Spl. Advocates, 1993—. Recipient Disting. Grad. award Jr. Achievement, 1973, Woman of Achievement award Fairfax (Va.) Bd. Suprs., 1982, Cmty. Svc. award Friends of Victims Assistance Network, 1988, Founders award Fairfax County Coun. of Arts, 1989, Mental Health Assn. award, 1991, Psychology Soc. of Washington Cmty. Svc. award, 1993. Mem. Va. Assn. Female Execs. (v.p. 1992—), Fairfax County Coun. Arts (v.p. 1988—), Fairfax County C. of C., Ctrl. Fairfax C. of C., Bus. and Profl. Women's Fedn. Va. (bd. dirs., pres. 1994—), Tower Club (Fairfax), Downtown Club (Richmond). Roman Catholic. Avocations: Cubs fan, tennis, art. Home: 8701 Duvall St Fairfax VA 22031-2711

MILLER, ERIC, zoologist; b. Gt. Falls, Mont., Mar. 27, 1942; s. Chester and Doris (Day) Millers; m. Margaret, Aug. 11, 1965; children: Charleen Millers, Andrew Miller. Student, Costa Mesa Coll., 1965; PhD in Zoology, U. N.Mex., 1969. Zoologist San Diego Zoo, 1966-76, Met. Zoo, San Francisco, 1977-87, A. Park Zoo, Santa Ana, Calif., 1988—. Home: 2537 S Pruce Santa Ana CA 92704

MILLER, ERNEST CHARLES, management consultant; b. Bronx, N.Y., July 14, 1925; s. Ernest Philip and Elizabeth (Hellwig) M.; m. Edith Grosvenor Porterfield, Nov. 11, 1947 (div. Oct. 3, 1963); children: Laura Lee, Marcy Rogers, Ernest Charles; m. Tung-fen Lin, Jan. 8, 1985. A.B., Yale U., 1945; M.A., U. Pa., 1949. Lic. psychologist, N.Y. Instr. U. Pa., 1947-51, cons., 1950-53; br. mgr., bd. dirs. Richardson, Bellows, Henry & Co., Inc., 1953-55; mgr. personnel tech. Am. Standard, Inc., 1955-59; mng. prin. Hellwig, Miller & Assocs., Westport, Conn., 1959-61; sr. assoc. Cresap, McCormick & Paget, Inc., N.Y.C., 1961-63; with Am. Mgmt. Assns., N.Y.C., 1964-83; pres. AMACOM div. Am. Mgmt. Assns., 1978-81, group v.p. AMA Publs. Group, 1981-83; pres. Miller, Hellwig Assocs., 1984—. Author works in strategic planning, orgn. devel., human resources, exec. compensation and mgmt. Bd. dirs. La Jolla Inst. for Allergy and Immunology; mem. Columbia U. All-Univ. Seminar, China Internat. Bus. Orgn. and Mgmt. NEH fellow, 1980. Mem. Am. Psychol. Assn., Japan Soc., Soc. Indsl. and Orgnl. Psychology, Inc. Episcopalian. Office: Miller Hellwig Assocs 150 W End Ave New York NY 10023

MILLER, EUGENE, business educator, university official; b. Chgo., Oct. 6, 1925; s. Harry and Fannie (Prosterman) M.; m. Edith Sutker, Sept. 23, 1951 (div. Sept. 1965); children: Ross, Scott, June; m. Thelma Gottlieb, Dec. 22, 1965; stepchildren: Paul Gottlieb, Alan Gottlieb. BS, Ga. Inst. Tech., 1945; AB magna cum laude, Bethany Coll., 1947, LLD, 1969; diploma, Oxford (Eng.) U., 1947; MS in Journalism, Columbia U., 1948; MBA, NYU, 1959; postgrad., Pace U., 1973—. Reporter, then city editor Greensboro (N.C.) Daily News, 1948-52; S.W. bur. chief Bus. Week mag., Houston, 1952-54; asso. mng. editor Bus. Week mag., N.Y.C., 1954-60; dir. pub. affairs and communications McGraw-Hill, Inc., 1960-63, v.p., 1963-68; sr. v.p. pub. rels. and investor rels., exec. com. N.Y. Stock Exch., N.Y.C., 1968-73; sr. v.p. CNA Fin. Corp., Chgo., 1973-75; chmn. Eugene Miller & Assos., Glencoe, Ill., 1975-77; v.p. USG Corp., Chgo., 1977-82, sr. v.p., 1982-85; mem. mgmt. com., 1982-91, exec. v.p., chief fin. officer, 1985-87, elected vice chmn., chief fin. officer, 1987-91, mem. exec. com., also bd. dirs.; prof., asst. dean Coll. Bus., Fla. Atlantic U., 1991—; adj. profl. mgmt. NYU, 1963-75; prof. bus. adminstrn. Fordham U., 1969-75; prof. fin., chmn. dept. Northeastern Ill. U., 1975-78; lectr. to bus. and ednl. groups; bd. dirs. P.O.B. Pub. Co., Wayne, Mich., SafeCard Svcs., Inc., Cheyenne, Wyo., 1993—, vice chmn.; bd. dirs. MFRI, Inc., Chgo., Teletech Holding Inc., Denver; dir., adv. bd. Comtel Corp., Boulder, Colo.; editor-in-residence U. Oreg., 1992; cons. to sec. Dept. Commerce, 1961-66; adv. bd. dirs. Nationwide Acceptance Corp., Chgo., exec.-in-residence U. Ill., 1991, U. Wis., 1991, U. Toronto, 1992. Author

syndicated bus. column, 1964-86; author: Your Future in Securities, 1974, Barron's Guide to Graduate Business Schools, 1977, 9th edit., 1995; contbg. editor: Public Relation Handbook, 1988, Boardroom Reports, 1985—; mem. adv. bd. CEO Mag., 1991—; exec.-in-residence POHL fellow U. Wyo., 1992. Trustee Bethany Coll.; mem. alumni bd. Columbia U. Sch. Journalism. Comdr. USNR, World War II, ret. Recipient Outstanding Achievement award Bethany Coll., 1963, 50th Anniversary award Bethany Coll., 1963, 50th Anniversary award Sch. Journalism Columbia U., Honors award Sch. Journalism Columbia U., 1963, Honors award Sch. Journalism Ohio U., 1964, Disting. Svc. award in investment edn. Nat. Assn. Investment Clubs, 1980, Roalman award Nat. Investor Rels. Inst., 1987. Fellow Pub. Rels. Soc. Am.; mem. Am. Fin. Assn., Nat. Assn. Bus. Economists, Soc. Am. Bus. Writers (founder), Assn. Corp. Growth Fin. Execs. Inst., Arthur Page Soc., Mid-Am. Club, St. Andrew's Country Club, Sigma Delta Chi, Alpha Sigma Phi. Home: 7351 Ballantrae Ct Boca Raton FL 33496-1423 Office: Fla Atlantic U 777 Glades Rd Boca Raton FL 33431-0991

MILLER, EUGENE ALBERT, banker; married. B.B.A., Detroit Inst. Tech., 1964; grad., Sch. Bank Adminstrn., Wis., 1968. With Comerica Bank-Detroit (formerly The Detroit Bank, then Detroit Bank & Trust Co.), 1955—, v.p., 1970-74, controller, 1971-74, sr. v.p., 1974-78, exec. v.p., 1978-81, pres., 1981-89, chief exec. officer, 1989—, chmn., 1990—; with parent co. Comerica Inc. (formerly DETROITBANK Corp.), 1973—, treas., 1973-80, pres., 1981—, chief exec. officer, 1989-92, chmn. bd., 1990-92; pres., COO Comerica Inc. (merger with Manufacturers Nat. Corp.), Detroit, 1992—; also bd. dirs. Comerica Inc. (formerly DETROITBANK Corp.); chmn., CEO Comerica Bank (merged with Manufacturers Nat. Corp.), Detroit, 1993—; chmn., CEO Comerica Inc., Detroit, 1993—, also bd. dirs. Office: Comerica Inc 500 Woodward Ave Detroit MI 48275-3382

MILLER, EWING HARRY, architect; b. Toledo, Ohio, Oct. 5, 1923; s. Ewing Harry and Esther Alice (Graves) M.; m. Gladys Jacquelyn Good, Dec. 18, 1948 (dec.); children: Victoria Alice, Paul Ewing. B.A., U. Pa., 1947, M.A., 1948. Draftsman Harbeson, Hough, Livingston & Larson, Phila., 1948; designer Nolen & Swinburne, Phila., 1950-52; project architect Gilboy & O'Malley, London, 1953-55; partner Miller, Vrydagh & Miller, Terre Haute, Ind., 1955-65; pres. Ewing Miller Partnership, Terre Haute, 1965-70; pres. Archonics Corp., 1970-76, chmn. bd., 1976-79; sr. ptnr. for design Archonics Design Partnership, Indpls., 1979-84; assoc. ptnr. architecture eastern region U.S. Howard Needles, Tammen & Bergendoff, 1985-92; archtl. cons. Design & Bldg. Industry, 1992—; gen. ptnr. Lockerbie Devel. Co., 1978-86, Lockerbie Glove Devel. Co., 1983-86, East St. Devel. Co., 1979-86. Contbr. articles to profl. jours.; archtl. critic Indpls. Monthly Mag. Major archtl. works include: various bldgs. Ind. U., including grad. biology lab., Ind. State U., master plan and edn. bldgs., residence halls and power ctr., Southwestern Ind. U., master plan and edn. bldgs., Ind. and Ohio Laborers Tng. Center, Prairie Elem. Sch., Indpls. Westin Conv. Hotel; various office parks, Indpls. Pub. Transp. Corp. facility, addition to Duesenberg Factory; master plan Ind. State Govt. Complex, State of Ind. and design of new state office bldg.; prin. in charge printing facility House of Rep. Architect of the Capitol, prin. in charge of Prospectus Development Study for design and restoration of Old Exec. Office Bldg., Washington; master plan for remodeling The Pentagon, Washington; prin. in charge design for remodeling Dept. of State, Washington. Mem. Ind. Gov.'s Commn. on Aging, 1959-62; pres. Gov.'s Commn. on Comprehensive Health Planning, Ind., 1970-75, Behavioral Research Found., 1965-85; bd. mgrs. Sheldon Swope Art Gallery, 1965-80, pres. 1965-73; bd. dirs. Center for Exploration of Values and Meaning, 1978-85, Herron Art Gallery, 1980-88; chmn. Indpls. Arts and Cultural Alliance, 1983. Recipient design citation, biennial awards program Ind. Soc. Architects; Honor awards, triennial design awards East Central Region AIA; Archtl. award of excellence Am. Inst. Steel Constrn.; 1st Honor award and winner Internat. Competition for Housing, Indpls.; award of excellence for univ. bldgs. Am. Sch. and Univ. Mag., 1985; Ind. Soc. Architects Honor award restoration of Circle Theater, various office bldgs., 1985, 86. Fellow AIA (mem. com. on design, chmn. com. on architecture for edn., mem. Vision 2000 study, architecture in coming decade), Lambda Alpha Hon. Soc. Home and Office: 2230 Birch Rd Port Republic MD 20676-2640 also: The Pennsylvania Apt 601 Pennsylvania Ave NW Washington DC 20004

MILLER, FRANCES SUZANNE, historic site curator; b. Defiance, Ohio, Apr. 17, 1950; d. Francis Bernard Johnson and Nellie Frances (Holder) Culp; m. James A. Batdorf, Aug. 7, 1970 (div. Aug. 1979); 1 child, Jennifer Christine Batdorf; m. Rodney Lyle Miller, Aug. 8, 1982 (div. Apr. 1987). BS in History/Museology, The Defiance Coll., 1990; AS in Bus. Mgmt., N.W. Tech. Coll., 1986. With accts. receivable dept. Ohio Art Co., Bryan, Ohio, 1984-87; leasing agent Williams Met. Housing Authority, Bryan, 1987-91; curator, property mgr. James A. Garfield Nat. Historic Site, Mentor, Ohio, 1991—. Mem. AAUW (pres. 1993-95, treas. 1995-97), Nat. Trust Hist. Preservation, Ohio Mus. Assn., Ohio Assn. Host. Soccs. and Mus., Cleve. Restoration Soc., Phi Alpha Theta. Avocations: needlework, reading. Office: James A Garfield Nat Historic Site 8095 Mentor Ave Mentor OH 44060

MILLER, FRANK L., JR., army officer; b. Atchinson, Kans., Jan. 27, 1944; s. Frank L. and Evelyn (Wilson) M.; m. Paulette Duncan, Sept. 28, 1968; children: Frank L. III, Michael W., Toni K. BA, U. Wash., 1973; MS, Troy State U., Eng., 1979. Commd. 2d lt. U.S. Army, 1966, advanced through grades to maj. gen., 1992; disting. grad. student U.S Army Command and Gen. Staff Coll. Ft. Leavenworth, Kans., 1977, Naval War Coll., Newport, R.I., 1984; chief of staff Free World's Ctr. for Fire Support, Ft. Sill, Okla., 1988-89; comdg. gen. III Corps Arty., Ft. Sill, 1989-92; dir. ops. Forces Command, Ft. McPherson, Ga., 1992—. Decorated DFC, Legion of Merit with two oak leaf clusters, Bronze Star with two oak leaf clusters, Meritorious Svc. medal, Air medal with 19 oak leaf clusters; Cross of Gallantry with silver star (Vietnam). Mem. Assn. U.S. Army, F.A. Assn. Office: Hdqs Forces Command J3 Fort McPherson Marshall Hall Atlanta GA 30310

MILLER, FRANK WILLIAM, legal educator; b. Appleton, Wis., May 15, 1921; s. Frank Paul and Ruth Margaret (Arft) M.; m. Lucille Gloria Rinnan, Sept. 8, 1945; children: Deborah Lynn, Patrica Elizabeth. B.A., U. Wis., 1946, LL.B., 1948, S.J.D., 1954. Bar: Wis. 1948. Mem. faculty Washington U., St. Louis, 1948-91, Coles prof. criminal law and adminstrn., 1962-64, James Carr prof. criminal jurisprudence, 1964-91, prof. emeritus, 1991—; Dan Hopson Disting. prof. So. Ill. U., Carbondale, 1992; summer vis. prof. law U. Ark., 1952, 54, 56, Stetson U., 1955, U. Wis., 1957, U. Tex., 1975, 85; vis. prof. law So. Ill. U. at Carbondale, 1973-74, summers 1976-81; chmn. Pub. round table council criminal law Assn. Am. Law Schs., 1961; chmn. Pub. Defender Adv. Com. St. Louis County, 1962. Author: (with A.C. Becht) Factual Causation in Negligence and Strict Liability Cases, 1961, Prosecution: The Decision to Charge a Suspect with a Crime, 1969; editor: (with R.O. Dawson, Dawson, Dix, Raymond I. Parnas) Criminal Justice Administration, 1976, 4th edit., 1991, (with Dawson, Dix, Parnas) The Police Function, 1982, 5th edit., 1991, Sentencing and The Correctional Process, 1976, The Juvenile Justice Process, 1976, 3d edit., 1985, The Mental Health Process, 1976, Prosecution and Adjudication, 1982, 4th edit., 1991. Served with AUS, 1942-45. Recipient citation for outstanding teaching Washington U. Alumni Fedn., 1965, Washington U. Law Alumni Assn., 1991. Mem. ABA, Am. Law Inst. (Guttmacher award 1977), Order of Coif. Democrat. Office: Washington Univ Sch Of Law Saint Louis MO 63105

MILLER, FRANKLIN RUSH, retired internist, educator; b. Bloomington, Ill., Aug. 24, 1902; s. Frank Ira and Sadie Jackman (Kimball) M.; m. Anne McAllister, July 10, 1931 (div. 1940); 1 child, Franklin Rush; m. Ellen Newhall, Apr. 5, 1941; children: Ellen Newhall Lewis, Mary Caroline Miller Thorington, Cushman Newhall. BS, Ill. Wesleyan U., 1923; MD, Harvard U., 1927. Diplomate Am. Bd. Internal Medicine. Resident Huntington Meml. Hosp., Boston, 1927-28; intern Boston City Hosp., 1928-29; asst. and fellow in bacteriology and pathology Rockefeller Inst., N.Y.C., 1929-31; chief med. resident Lakeside Hosp./Univ. Hosps., Cleve., 1931-32; from demonstrator to asst. prof. Western Res. U. Med. Sch., Cleve. 1931-39; asst. prof., then assoc. prof. Jefferson Med. Coll., 1939-55; assoc. prof. medicine, neurology U. Kans., 1957-60; assoc. prof. medicine, then vis. prof. medicine Hahnemann U., Phila., 1960-81; chief of internal medicine Snyder Clinic Assn., Winfield, Kans., 1960-81; ret., 1981; chief internal medicine Snyder

Clinic, Winfield, 1954-60; acting supt. Winfield State Hosp. and Tng. Ctr., 1958-59, supt., 1959-60. Contbr. articles to profl. jours. Mem. ACP, AAAS, AMA, Am. Assn. Cancer Rsch., Am. Soc. Clin. Investigation, Am. Soc. Exptl. Pathology, Soc. Exptl. Biology and Medicine, Internat. Homotological Assn., Am. Soc. Hemotology, Am. Therapeutic Soc, Phila. Coll. Physicians, Am. Assn. Pathologists, N.Y. Acad. Scis., Alpha Omega Alpha, Sigma Chi, Phi Chi. Home: 1910 Dee Ave Winfield KS 67156-1510

MILLER, FREDERICK, pathologist; b. N.Y.C., Apr. 5, 1937; s. Alex and Sarah M.; m. Emilie J. Kronish, June 2, 1962; children: David, Allison. B.S., N.Y., 1956; M.D., N.Y. U., 1961. Diplomate: Am. Bd. Pathology. Intern Bellevue Hosp., N.Y.C., 1961-62, resident, 1962-63; practice medicine specializing in pathology, 1965—; clin. assoc., attending physician Nat. Inst. Arthritis and Metabolic Diseases, 1963-65; resident chief pathology dept. NYU Med. Ctr., 1965-67; attending pathologist Bellevue and Univ. Hosps., N.Y.C., 1967; asst. prof. pathology NYU, 1967-70, assoc. prof., 1970; assoc. prof. SUNY, Stony Brook, 1970-75, prof., 1975—, chmn. dept. pathology, 1977—, Marvin Kuschner prof. pathology, 1991, dir. lab. for arthritis and related diseases, 1976—; dir. labs. Univ. Hosp., Stony Brook, 1978—, pathologist-in-chief, 1979—. Contbr. articles to med. jours. Served with USPHS, 1963-65. Recipient Bausch and Lomb medal for research, 1961; Pres.'s award SUNY, Stony Brook, 1990, Chancellor's award, 1990, Aescalapius award, 1993; NIH grantee, 1963-87. Mem. AAAS, Harvey Soc., Soc. Clin. Immunology, Am. Soc. Investigative Pathology, Am. Soc. Clin. Pathologists (award 1961), Internat. Acad. Pathology, N.Y. Acad. Sci., Am. Assn. Immunologists, Am. Pathology Chairmen, Suffolk Orchid Soc. (pres.), Sigma Xi, Alpha Omega Alpha. Hort. authority on roses and orchids. Home: 46 Manchester Ln Stony Brook NY 11790-2826 Office: SUNY Stony Brook Dept Pathology Hsc Stony Brook NY 11794

MILLER, FREDERICK POWELL, agronomy educator; b. Springfield, Ohio, Oct. 17, 1936; s. Edwin S. and Marcella (Powell) M.; m. Marilyn Ellen Miller (dec. Dec. 1991); m. Jann M. Ricchetti, Mar. 12, 1993. Student, Wittenberg Coll., Springfield,Ohio, 1954-56; B.Sc., Ohio State U., 1958, M.S., 1961, Ph.D., 1965. Cert. prof. soil scientist, Am. Registry of Cert. Profls. in Agronomy, Crops, Soils. Asst. prof. dept. agronomy U. Md., College Park, 1965-69, assoc. prof., 1969-74, prof., 1974-82; head and prof. dept. agronomy U. Ark., Fayetteville, 1982-86; prof., chmn. dept. agronomy Ohio State U., 1986-94, dir., prof., Sch. Natural Resources, 1994—; vis. assoc. prof. dept. soil sci. U. Calif.-Davis, 1972-73; vis. prof. U. Fla., Gainesville, 1980. Fellow AAAS, Am. Soc. Agronomy, Soil Sci. Soc. Am. (div. chmn. 1979-80, pres. 1991, past pres. 1992); mem. Soil Conservation Soc. Am. Office: Ohio State Univ Dept Agronomy Columbus OH 43210

MILLER, FREDERICK ROBESON, banker; b. Oakland, Calif., Oct. 11, 1927; s. Charles Lennon and Juliet Robeson (Chamberlain) M.; m. Nancy McDaniel, July 19, 1952; children: Susan Chase Miller Clark, Stephen Robeson, Elizabeth Rockwell. B.A., Yale U., 1952. With J.P. Morgan & Co., Inc., 1952-54; v.p. Phila. Nat. Bank, 1954-69; pres. Waterbury Nat. Bank, Conn., 1969-71, City Nat. Bank, Bridgeport, Conn., 1971-72, Conn. Nat. Bank, Bridgeport, 1973-83; also chief exec. officer, vice chmn. Conn. Nat. Bank; vice chmn. Hartford Nat. Corp., until 1984. Served with U.S. Army, 1946-47. Mem. Tubac Valley Country Club. Republican. Episcopalian. Home: PO Box 1503 Tubac AZ 85646-1503

MILLER, FREDERICK STATEN, music educator, academic administrator; b. Lima, Ohio, Dec. 12, 1930; s. Donald Frederick and Esther Lillian (Moore) M.; m. Florence Dorothy Mistak, June 20, 1959; children: Jennifer Leigh, John Staten. B of Music Edn., Northwestern U., 1957, M in Music, 1958; D of Music Performance, U. Iowa, 1974. Mem. music faculty U. Ark., Fayetteville, 1958-64; asst. dir. bands Northwestern U., Evanston, Ill., 1964-70, assoc. dean, sch. music, 1970-76; dean, sch. music DePaul U., Chgo., 1976-95; bd. dirs. Concertante de Chgo., 1985—; accreditation evaluator North Cen. Assn., Boulder, Colo., 1982—, Nat. Assn. Schs. Music, Washington, 1981—. Composer/arranger numerous pub. works for band; editor music pubis. Served with USN, 1948-52. Mem. ASCAP, Nat. Assn. Schs. Music (hon. life, regional chmn. 1982-84, instl. rep., treas. 1984-88, v.p. 1988-91, pres. 1991-94), Pi Kappa Lambda (bd. regents 1970-74). Roman Catholic. Clubs: University (Chgo.); Sheridan Shore Yacht (Wilmette, Ill.). Avocations: sailing, cooking, jazz performance. Home: 1322 Greenwood Ave Wilmette IL 60091-1624 Office: DePaul Univ Sch Music 804 W Belden Ave Chicago IL 60614-3214

MILLER, FREDERICK WILLIAM, publisher, lawyer; b. Milw., Mar. 18, 1912; s. Roy W. and Kathryn (Oehlers) M.; m. Violet Jane Bagley, Mar. 31, 1939. B.A., U. Wis., 1934, LLB, 1936. Bar: Wis. 1936. Assoc. Tenney & Davis, Madison, 1935-36; atty. State of Wis., Madison, 1936-77; pub. The Capital Times Co., Madison, 1979—, also dir.; dir. Madison Newspaper, Inc., 1970—, chmn. bd., 1980—; dir. Evjue Found., Inc., Madison, 1957—. Trustee Evjue Charitable Trust, Madison, 1970—. Mem. Wis. Bar Assn. Clubs: Madison Club, Univ. Club. Home: 2810 Arbor Dr Madison WI 53711-1826 Office: Capital Times Co PO Box 8056 1901 Fish Hatchery Rd Madison WI 53713-1248

MILLER, GABRIEL LORIMER, physicist, researcher; b. N.Y.C., Jan. 18, 1928; s. Hugh Lorimer and Olga (Katzin) M.; m. Natalie Coffin, May 20, 1962; children: Matthew, Jonathan, Katharine. BS in Physics, London U., 1949, MS in Math., 1952, PhD in Physics, 1957. Sr. demonstrator Birkbeck Coll. London U., 1953-57; physicist Brookhaven Nat. Lab., Upton, L.I., N.Y., 1957-63; mem. tech. staff AT&T Bell Labs., Murray Hill, N.J., 1963-82, head dept. interactive systems rsch., 1982—; vis. prof. U. Aarhus, Denmark, 1969-70, Rutgers U., New Brunswick, N.J., 1972-73; mem. vis. coms. Oak Ridge, Lawrence Berkeley and Brookhaven nat. labs. Contbr. numerous pubis. on instrumentation, measurement and sensors; holder over 30 patents; past assoc. editor Rev. Sci. Instruments. Fellow IEEE (mem. nuclear instruments com. 1960—, Centennial medal 1984), Am. Phys. Soc.; mem.IEEE Indsl. Electronics Soc. (assoc. editor Robotics 1985-). Bohmische Phys. Soc. Home: 614 Boulevard Westfield NJ 07090-3210

MILLER, GALE TIMOTHY, lawyer; b. Kalamazoo, Sept. 15, 1946; s. Arthur H. and Eleanor (Johnson) M.; m. Janice Lindvall, June 1, 1968; children: Jeremy L., Amanda E., Timothy W. AB, Augustana Coll., 1968; JD, U. Mich., 1971. Bar: Mich. 1971, Colo. 1973, U.S. Dist. Ct. Colo. 1973, U.S. Ct. Appeals (10th cir.) 1979. Trial atty. FTC, Washington, 1971-73; assoc. Davis, Graham & Stubbs, L.L.C., Denver, 1973-77, ptnr., mem., 1978—. Bd. dirs. Sr. Housing Options, Inc., 1980-93; chair Colo. Lawyers Com., 1989-91, bd. dirs. 1987—, Individual Lawyer of Yr. 1994. Mem. ABA (antitrust sect. task force on model civil antitrust jury instrns. 1984—), Colo. Bar. Assn. (sec.-treas. antitrust sect. 1991—), Denver Bar Assn. Democrat. Lutheran. Office: Davis Graham & Stubbs LLC PO Box 185 Denver CO 80201-0185

MILLER, GARY EVAN, psychiatrist, mental health services administrator; b. Cleve., Aug. 19, 1935; s. Henry M. and Mollie (Price) M.; m. Karen Ann Marie Barrett, Sept. 16, 1972; children: Anna Charis, Rebecca Elizabeth. MD, U. Tex., Galveston, 1960. Diplomate in psychiatry, addiction psychiatry, and geriatric psychiatry Am. Bd. Psychiatry and Neurology. Intern Montefiore Hosp., N.Y.C., 1960-61; resident in psychiatry Univ. Hosps. Cleve., 1961-62, Austin (Tex.) State Hosp., 1963-65; dep. commr. mental health services Tex. Dept. Mental Health and Mental Retardation, 1967-70; dir. Rio Grande State Center for Mental Health and Mental Retardation, Tex. Dept. Mental Health, Harlingen, 1966-67; asst. commr., dir. Rochester regional office N.Y. State Dept. Mental Hygiene, 1970-72; clin. asst. prof. psychiatry U. Rochester Sch. Medicine and Dentistry, 1970-72; asst. clin. prof. psychiatry SUNY, Buffalo, 1970-72; cons. mental health Ga. Dept. Human Resources, Atlanta, 1972; dir. div. mental health Ga. Dept. Human Resources, 1972-74; clin. prof. psychiatry Emory U. Sch. Medicine, Atlanta, 1972-74; vice chmn. Ga. State Planning and Adv. Council for Devel. Disabilities Services and Constrn., 1972-73; cons. mental health services orgn. and adminstrn., 1974-76; dir. mental health and devel. services State of N.H. Concord, 1976-82; commr. Tex. Dept. Mental Health and Mental Retardation Austin, 1982-88; clin. prof. psychiatry U. Tex. Health Sci. Ctr., Houston; adj. assoc. prof. psychiatry U. Tex. Health Sci. Ctr., San Antonio; dir. profl. svcs. HCA Gulf Pines Hosp., Houston, 1988-94, chief of staff, 1993; clin. dir. adult psychiatry Cypress Creek Hosp., Houston, 1994—; assoc. clin. psychiatry Post Oak Psychiatry Assocs., Houston, 1988-

90; pres. Alternative Svcs. Network, Houston, 1990—; clin. dir. adult psychiatry Cypress Creek Hosp., Houston, 1994—, pres.-elect med. staff, 1995; dir. state alcoholism program in Ga., 1972-74, also, South Tex. region, 1966-67; mem. faculty U. S.C. Sch. Alcohol and Drug Studies, 1975; bd. dirs. nat. patient rights policy research project NIMH, 1981; Bd. dirs. Genessee Regional Health Planning Council, Rochester, 1970-72. Contbr. articles to profl. jours. Served as capt. M.C., U.S. Army, 1962-63. Recipient Cert. of Recognition, Ga. Psychol. Assn., 1973. Fellow Am. Psychiat. Assn. (cert. in adminstrv. psychiatry 1983); mem. AMA, Am. Soc. Addiction Medicine (cert. alcoholism and other drug dependencies 1993), N.H. Psychiat. Soc. (pres. 1981-82), Nat. Assn. State Mental Health Program Dirs. (bd. dirs. 1984-88, sec. 1986-88), N.H. Med. Soc., Am. Acad. Psychiatry and the Law, Am. Assn. Psychiat. Adminstrs. (pres. Tex. chpt.), Tex. Med. Assn., Tex. Soc. Psychiat. Physicians, Mental Health Assn. Houston and Harris County (bd. dirs. 1989—, v.p. advocacy 1990—), Alpha Omega Alpha. Home: 5314 Westminister Ct Houston TX 77069 Office: 530 Wells Fargo Dr Ste 110 Houston TX 77090-4026

MILLER, GARY J., political economist; b. Urbana, Ill., Jan. 2, 1949; s. Gerald J. and Doris Elaine (Miner) M.; m. Anne Colberg, Jan. 29, 1971; children: Neil, Ethan. BA, U. Ill., 1971; PhD, U. Tex., 1976. Asst. prof. Calif. Inst. Tech., Pasadena, 1976-79; assoc. prof. Mich. State U., East Lansing, 1979-86; Taylor prof. of polit. economy Washington U., St. Louis, Mo., 1986—. Author: Cities by Contract, 1981, Reforming Bureaucracy, 1987, Managerial Dilemmas, 1992. NSF grantee, 1981, 83, 92. Mem. Phi Beta Kappa, Phi Kappa Phi. Democrat. Office: Washington U Sch of Bus 1 Brookings Dr Saint Louis MO 63130-4862

MILLER, GAVIN, lawyer; b. N.Y., Mar. 8, 1926; s. George Gavin and Catherine (Schurman) M.; m. Camilla Congreve Strong, Aug. 15, 1959 (dec. Mar. 1982); children: Emily, Louise, Catherine; m. Suzanne Techentin, Feb. 17, 1991. AB, Harvard U., 1950, LLB, 1953. Bar: N.Y. 1955, Calif. 1962. Assoc. Davis, Polk & Wardwell, N.Y.C., 1953-61; assoc. Kindel & Anderson, L.A., 1961-63, ptnr., 1963-66; ptnr. Agnew, Miller & Carlson, L.A., 1966-81, Hufstedler, Miller, Carlson & Beardsley, 1981-90, Heller, Ehrman, Smith & McAuliffe, L.A., 1990—. With AUS, 1944-46. Mem. ABA, State Bar Calif., L.A. County Bar Assn. (trustee 1978-84, v.p. 1980-81, sr. v.p. 1981-82, pres.-elect 1982-83, pres. 1983-84), N.Y. State Bar Assn., Nature Conservancy (trustee So. Calif. chpt. 1974-80), California Club, University Club, (N.Y.C., L.A.), Phi Beta Kappa. Office: Heller Ehrman Smith & McAuliffe 601 S Figueroa St 40th fl Los Angeles CA 90017-3874

MILLER, GENE EDWARD, newspaper reporter and editor; b. Evansville, Ind., Sept. 16, 1928; m. Electra Sonia Yphantis, Apr. 13, 1952 (dec. May 1993); children: Janet Irene, Theresa Jean, Thomas Raphael, Roberta Lynn. A.B. in Journalism, Ind. U., 1950, LL.D. (hon.), 1977; Nieman fellow, Harvard U., 1967-68. Reporter Jour.-Gazette, Ft. Wayne, Ind., 1950-51, Washington Bur. Wall St. Jour., 1953-54, Richmond (Va.) News Leader, 1954-57, Miami (Fla.) Herald, 1957—. Author: Invitation To A Lynching, 83 Hours Till Dawn. Served with AUS, 1951-53. Recipient Pulitzer prize for local reporting, 1967, 76. Office: 1 Herald Plz Miami FL 33132-1609

MILLER, GENEVIEVE, retired medical historian; b. Butler, Pa., Oct. 15, 1914; d. Charles Russell and Genevieve (Wolford) M. AB, Goucher Coll., 1935; MA, Johns Hopkins U., 1939; PhD, Cornell U., 1955. Asst. in history of medicine Johns Hopkins Inst. of History of Medicine, Balt., 1943-44, instr., 1945-48, rsch. assoc., 1979-94; asst. prof. history of medicine Sch. Medicine, Case Western Res. U., Cleve., 1953-67, assoc. prof., 1967-79, assoc. prof. emeritus, 1979—; research assoc. in med. history Cleve. Med. Library Assn., 1953-62, curator Howard Dittrick Mus. of Hist. Medicine, 1962-67, dir. Howard Dittrick Mus. Hist. Medicine, 1967-79. Author: William Beaumont's Formative Years: Two Early Notebooks 1811-1821, 1946; The Adoption of Inoculation for Smallpox in England and France (William H. Welch medal Am. Assn. for History of Medicine 1962), 1957; Bibliography of the History of Medicine of the U.S. and Canada, 1939-1960, 1964; Bibliography of the Writings of Henry E. Sigerist, 1966; Letters of Edward Jenner and Other Documents Concerning the Early History of Vaccination, 1983; assoc. editor Bull. of History of Medicine, 1944-48, acting editor, 1948, mem. adv. editorial bd. 1960-92; mem. bd. editors Jour. of History of Medicine and Allied Scis., 1948-65; editor Bull. of Cleve. Med. Library, 1954-72; editor newsletter Am. Assn. for History of Medicine, 1986—; contbr. articles in field to profl. jours. Am. Council Learned Socs. fellow, 1948-50; Dean Van Meter fellow, 1953-54. Alumna trustee Goucher Coll., Balt., 1966-69. Hon. fellow Cleve. Med. Library Assn.; mem. Am. Assn. for History of Medicine (pres. 1978-80, mem. council 1960-63), Am. Hist. Assn., Internat. Soc. for History of Medicine, Soc. Archtl. Historians, Phi Beta Kappa; corr. mem. fgn. socs. for history of medicine. Democrat. Home and Office: Judson Manor 1890 E 107th St Apt 816 Cleveland OH 44106-2245

MILLER, GEOFFREY PARSONS, law educator; b. Princeton, Oct. 17, 1950; s. Robert Parsons and Daphne (Haynes) M.; m. Joan R. Falk; children: Jason, Forrest. AB, Princeton U., 1973; JD, Columbia U., 1978. Bar: D.C. Law clk. to Hon. Carl McGowan Washington, 1978-79, law clk. to Hon. Byron R. White, 1979-80; atty., advisor U.S. Dept. Justice, Washington, 1980-82; assoc. atty. Ennis, Friedman, Bersoff & Ewing, Washington, 1982-83; asst. prof. U. Chgo., 1983-87, prof. law, assoc. dean, 1987-89, Kirkland and Ellis prof., 1989—. Contbr. articles to profl. jours. Office: U Chgo Law Sch 1111 E 60th St Chicago IL 60637-2702

MILLER, GEORGE, mayor; b. Detroit; m. Roslyn Girard; 4 children. BA, U. Ariz., 1947, MEd, 1952. Tchr. high schs., owner, prin. painting contracting co., until 1989; mayor City of Tucson, 1991—. Active mem. Dem. Party So. Ariz., 1960—, treas. Pima County div., state chmn. Presdl. Del. Selection Reform Commn.; bd. dirs. Tucson Jewish Community Ctr., Anti-Defamation League of B'nai B'rith; councilman Tucson City Coun., 1977-91, also vice mayor. With USMC, WWII. Decorated Purple Heart; recipient recognition award United Way, Community Svcs. Support award Chicanos Por La Causa (2), cert. appreciation San Ignacio Yaqui Coun., Old Pasqua, Man of Yr. award So. Ariz. Home Builders Assn. Office: Office of Mayor PO Box 27210 Tucson AZ 85726-7210*

MILLER, GEORGE, film director; b. Brisbane, Australia, Mar. 3, 1945. MD, U. NSW, Australia. Former physician St. Vincent's Hosp., Sydney, Australia. Films include: dir, writer: Violence in the Cinema, Part I, 1971, Devil in Evening Dress, 1973, Frieze, an Underground Film, 1973, Mad Max, 1979, The Road Warrior-Mad Max II, 1982, Mad Max: Beyond the Thunderdome, 1985, Lorenzo's Oil, 1992; dir.: Twilight Zone: The Movie, 1983, The Witches of Eastwick, 1987; assoc. prodr.: Chain Reaction, 1980; exec. prodr.: The Year My Voice Broke, 1988, Dead Calm, 1989, Flirting, 1990. Office: Kennedy Miller Prodns, 30 Orwell St Kings Cross, Sydney 2011, Australia*

MILLER, GEORGE, congressman; b. Richmond, Calif., May 17, 1945; s. George and Dorothy (Rumsey) M.; m. Cynthia Caccavo, 1964; children: George, Stephen. B.A., San Francisco State Coll., 1968; J.D., U. Calif., Davis, 1972. Legis. counsel Calif. senate majority leader, 1969-73; mem. 94th-104th Congresses from 7th Calif. dist., 1975—; chmn. subcom. on oversight and investigations, 1985—, chmn. subcom. on labor stds., 1981-84, chmn. select com. on children, youth and families, 1983-91, chmn. com. on natural resources, 1991-94; mem. com. on edn. and lab., dep. majority whip, 1989-94; vice chair Dem. Policy Com., 1995—. Mem. Calif. Bar Assn. Office: House of Representatives House Office Bldg 2205 Rayburn Washington DC 20515

MILLER, GEORGE ARMITAGE, psychologist, educator; b. Charleston, W.Va., Feb. 3, 1920; s. George E. and Florence (Armitage) M.; m. Katherine James, Nov. 29, 1939; children: Nancy, Donnally James. BA, U. Ala., 1940, MA, 1941; AM, Harvard U., 1944, PhD, 1946; Doctorat honoris causa, U. Louvain, 1976; D Social Sci. (hon.), Yale U., 1979; DSc honoris causa, Columbia U., 1980; DSc (hon.), U. Sussex, 1984, New Sch. Social Rsch., 1993; LittD (hon.), Charleston U., 1992. Instr. psychology U. Ala., 1941-43; research fellow Harvard Psycho-Acoustic Lab., 1944-48; asst. prof. psychology Harvard U., 1948-51, assoc. prof., 1955-58, prof., 1958-68, chmn. dept psychology, 1964-67, co-dir. Ctr. for Cognitive Studies, 1960-67; prof. Rockefeller U., N.Y.C., 1968-79; adj. prof. Rockefeller U., 1979-82; prof.

psychology Princeton U., 1979-90, James S. McDonnell Disting. Univ. prof. psychology, 1982-90, James S. McDonnell Disting. Univ. prof. psychology emeritus, 1990—, program dir. McDonnell-Pew Program in Cognitive Neurosci., 1989-94; assoc. prof. MIT, 1951-55; vis. Inst. for Advanced Study, Princeton, 1972-76, 82-83, mem., 1950, 70-72; vis. prof. Rockefeller U., 1967-68; vis. prof. MIT, 1976-79, group leader Lincoln Lab., 1953-55; fellow Ctr. Advanced Study in Behavioral Scis., Stanford U., 1958-59; Fulbright research prof. Oxford (Eng.) U., 1963-64; Sesquicentennial prof. U. Ala., 1981. Author: Language and Communication, 1951, (with Galanter and Pribram) Plans and the Structure of Behavior, 1960, Psychology, 1962, (with Johnson-Laird) Language and Perception, 1976, Spontaneous Apprentices, 1977, Language and Speech, 1981, The Science of Words, 1991; editor Psychol. Bulletin, 1981-82. Recipient Disting. Service award Am. Speech and Hearing Assn., 1976, award in behavioral scis. N.Y. Acad. Scis., 1982, Hermann von Helmholtz award Cognitive Neurosci. Inst., 1989, Nat. Medal Sci. NSF, 1991, Gold Medal Am. Psychological Found. 1990, Nat. Medal of Sci. 1991, Louis E. Levy medal Franklin Inst., 1991; Guggenheim fellow, 1986, William James fellow Am. Psychological Assn., 1989; Fondation Fyssen Priz Internat. for cognitive sci., 1992. Fellow Brit. Psychol. Assn. (hon.); mem. NAS, AAAS (chmn. sect. J 1981), Am. Psychol. Assn. (pres. 1968-69, Disting. Scientific Contbn. award 1963, William James Book award divsn. gen. psychology 1993), Eastern Psychol. Assn. (pres. 1961-62), Acoustical Soc. Am., Linguistic Soc. Am., Am. Statis. Assn., Am. Philos. Soc., Am. Physiol. Soc., Psychometric Soc., Soc. Exptl. Psychologists (Warren medal 1972), Am. Acad. Arts and Scis., Psychonomic Soc., Royal Netherlands Acad. Arts and Scis. (fgn.), Sigma Xi. Home: 753 Prospect Ave Princeton NJ 08540-4080 Office: Princeton Univ Dept Psychology Green Hall Princeton NJ 08544

MILLER, GEORGE DAVID, retired air force officer, marketing consultant; b. McKeesport, Pa., Apr. 5, 1930; s. George G. and Nellie G. (Cullen) M.; m. Barbara Aex; 1 child from previous marriage: George David Jr. BS, U.S. Naval Acad., 1953; MS in Aerospace Engring, Air Force Inst. Tech., 1966; postgrad., Nat. War Coll., 1970-71. Commd. 2d lt. U.S. Air Force, 1953, advanced through grades to lt. gen., 1981; ops. officer, comdr. 22d Spl. Ops. Squadron, Nakhon Phanom Royal Thai AFB, Thailand, 1970-71; dep. comdr. for ops., vice comdr., comdr. 55th Strategic Reconnaissance Wing, Offutt AFB, Nebr., 1971-74; comdr. 17th Air div., 307th Strategic wing, U-Tapao Airfield, Thailand, 1974-75; comdr. 57th A Div. Minot AFB, N.D., 1975-76; asst. dep. chief staff ops. hdqrs. SAC, Offutt AFB,, Nebr., 1976-77; dep. dir. single integrated operational plan Joint Strategic Target Planning Staff, Joint Chiefs of Staff, 1977-79; dir. plans, dep. chief of staff ops., plans and readiness Hdqrs. USAF, Washington, 1979-80; asst. dep. chief staff ops., plans and readiness Hdqrs. USAF, 1980-81; vice comdr.-in-chief SAC, Offutt AFB, Nebr., 1981-84; sec.-gen. U.S. Olympic Com., 1984-87; cons. Sports Mktg. and Def. Programs, 1984—. Pres., exec. dir. Morris Animal Found., 1989-92; pres., CEO Nat. Fire Protection Assn., 1992—; chmn. bd. NFPA Rsch. Found.; pres. Learn Not to Burn Found.; trustee U.S. Naval Acad. Found., Jesse Owens Found.; dir. Nat. Inst. Bldg. Scis. Decorated D.S.M., Def. D.S.M., Legion of Merit, D.F.C. with 3 oak leaf clusters, Air medal with 18 oak leaf clusters, others. Mem. Air Force Assn., Am. Legion, Masons, Scottish Rite, Shriners, Daedalians. Republican. Lutheran. Home: 20 Philips Pond Natick MA 01760 Office: NFPA PO Box 9101 1 Batterymarch Pk Quincy MA 02269-9101

MILLER, GEORGE DEWITT, JR., lawyer; b. Detroit, Aug. 20, 1928; s. George DeWitt and Eleanor Mary Miller; m. Prudence Brewster Saunders, Dec. 28, 1951; children: Margaret DeWitt, Joy Saunders. BA magna cum laude, Amherst Coll., 1950; JD with distinction, U. Mich., 1953. Bar: Mich. 1953, U.S. Dist. Ct. (so. dist.) Mich. 1953, U.S.C. Appeals (6th cir.) 1960, U.S. Tax Ct. 1960. Assoc. Bodman, Longley & Dahling, Detroit, 1957-61, ptnr., 1962—. Trustee, mem. Matilda R. Wilson Fund, 1993—; trustee Henry Ford Maplegrove Ctr./Kingswood Hosp., 1995—. Capt. USAF, 1953-56. Recipient Commendation medal. Mem. ABA, State Bar Mich., Detroit Bar Assn., Detroit Club, Grosse Pointe Club, Orchard Lake Country Club, Order of Coif, Phi Beta Kappa. Episcopalian. Avocation: sailing. Home: 320 Dunston Rd Bloomfield Hills MI 48304-3415 Office: Bodman Longley & Dahling 100 Renaissance Ctr Ste 34 Detroit MI 48243-1006

MILLER, GEORGE H., historian, educator; b. Evanston, Ill., Aug. 5, 1919; s. Donald Crandon and Janet Gordon (Hall) M. BA, U. Mich., 1941, MA, 1946, PhD in History, 1951; MA, Harvard U., 1949, LHD (hon.), Ripon Coll., 1985. Instr. history U. Mich., Ann Arbor, 1951-54; from asst. prof. to prof. Ripon (Wis.) Coll., 1954-81; ret., 1981; bd. curators State Hist. Soc. Wis., Madison, 1980—, pres., 1989-91; dir. Wis. History Found., Madison, 1989—. Author: Railroads and the Granger Laws, 1971; co-author: Ripon College: A History, 1990; editor: A History of Ripon, Wisconsin, 1964. Mem., pres. Ripon Hist. Soc., 1962—; bd. dirs. Wis. Humanities Commn., Madison, 1973-79. With AUS, 1941-45. Recipient honor medal DAR, 1986; fellow Ford Found., 1951. Mem. Univ Club (Chgo.). Home: 511 Union St Ripon WI 54971-1661

MILLER, G(EORGE) WILLIAM, merchant banker, business executive; b. Sapulpa, Okla., Mar. 9, 1925; s. James Dick and Hazle Deane (Orrick) M.; m. Ariadna Rogojarsky, Dec. 22, 1946. B.S. in Marine Engring, U.S. Coast Guard Acad., 1945; J.D., U. Calif. at Berkeley, 1952; hon. degree, Babson Coll, Boston U., Brown U., Bryant Coll., Fairfield U., Fla. State U., R.I. U. Bar: Calif. 1952, N.Y. 1953. Asst. sec. Textron Inc., 1956-57, v.p., 1957-60, pres., chief oper. officer, 1960-68, chmn., chief exec. officer, 1967-74, chmn., chief fin. officer, 1974-78; chmn. Fed. Res. Bd., Washington, 1978-79; sec. of Treasury Washington, 1979-81; chmn. G. William Miller & Co. Inc., Washington, 1981—; chmn., chief exec. officer Federated Dept. Stores, Inc., 1990-92; bd. dirs. Federated Dept. Stores Inc., Repligen Corp., Georgetown Industries, Inc., Kleinwort Benson Australian Income Fund, Inc., Ralphs Supermarkets, Inc., De Bartolo Realty Corp.; chmn. supervisory com. Schroder Venture Trust; past chmn. adv. coun. Pres.'s Com. EEO, 1963-65; mem. coun. Nat. Found. Humanities, 1966-67; bd. dirs. USCG Acad. Found., 1969-78, pres. 1973-77, chmn., 1977-78; chmn. U.S. Indsl Payroll Savs. Bond Com., 1977, Pres.'s Com. HIRE, 1977; co-chmn. Polish-U.S. Econ. Coun., 1977-78, U.S.-USSR Trade and Econ. Coun., 1977-78, Pres.'s Cir. NAS, 1989-92. Bd. dirs. Washington Opera, Wolf Trap Found. Officer USCG, 1945-49. U. Calif.-Berkeley fellow. Mem. State Bar Calif., Nat. Alliance Businessmen (dir. 1968-78, chmn. 1977-78), Conf. Bd. (trustee 1972-78, chmn. 1977-78), Bus. Council, Order of Coif, Phi Delta Phi. Clubs: Lyford Cay (Nassau); Acoaxet (Westport, Mass.); Brook (N.Y.C.); Burning Tree (Washington), Chevy Chase (Washington). Office: 1215 19th St NW Washington DC 20036-2487

MILLER, GERALD E., bishop. Bishop Allegheny dist. Evang. Luth. Ch. in Am., Altoona, Pa. Office: Evang Luth Ch in Am 701 Quail Ave Altoona PA 16602-3010

MILLER, GERALD RAYMOND, communications educator; b. Muscatine, Iowa, Oct. 18, 1931; s. Raymond Russell and Mabel Anna (Bridges) M.; m. Pearl Ann Parsons, Aug. 2, 1952; children: Patricia Anne Miller Bender, Greg Anthony, Caleb Drew. BA, U. Iowa, 1957, MA, 1958, PhD, 1961. Instr. U. Iowa, Iowa City, 1958-61; asst. prof. U. Washington, Seattle, 1961-62; from asst. prof. to full prof. Mich. State U., East Lansing, 1963—, Univ. Disting. prof., 1991—. Author, editor books; contbr. numerous jours. to profl. pubis. Served to pvt. U.S. Army, 1952-54, Korea. Recipient Disting. Faculty award Mich. State U., 1973, Joint Resolution of Tribute Mich. Legislature, 1974. Fellow Internat. Communication Assn. (pres. 1979), Am. Psychol. Assn.; mem. Speech Communication Assn. Democrat. Unitarian. Home: 1323 Beech St East Lansing MI 48823-3638 Office: Mich State U Communication Dept East Lansing MI 48824

MILLER, GERRI, magazine editor, writer; b. Bklyn., Mar. 2, 1954; d. Norman and Isobel (Rand) M. BA, SUNY, Binghamton, 1976. Assoc. editor Sixteen Mag., N.Y.C., 1977-80; editor, then exec. editor Sterling/Macfadden, N.Y.C., 1981—. Avocations: travel, reading, rock concerts, crossword puzzles. Office: Metal Edge TV Picture Life Sterling/Macfadden 233 Park Ave S New York NY 10003

MILLER, G(ERSON) H(ARRY), research institute director, mathematician, computer scientist, chemist; b. Phila., Mar. 2, 1924; m. Mary Alexa Heath, Jan. 28, 1961; children: Byron, Alexandra. BA, Pomona Coll., 1949; MEd in Counseling and Pers., Temple U., 1951; PhD. in Ednl. Psychology, U. So. Calif., 1957; MS in Math., U. Ill., 1982. Jr. high sch. and jr. coll. instr. math. L.A. Sch. Dist., 1953-57; assoc. prof. Western Ill. U., Macomb, 1957-60; prof. Towson State U., Balt., Md., 1960-61; prof. math. and edn. Parsons Coll., Fairfield, Iowa, 1961-65; prof. Tenn. Technol. U., Cookeville, 1966-68; prof. math. and computer sci. Edinboro (Pa.) U., 1968-71, 81-89; asst. dir. Institutional Rsch. Edinboro U., Pa., 1972-80; dir. Studies On Smoking, Inc. and SOS Stop Smoking Clinic, Edinboro, 1972—; spkr. state, nat. and internat. profl. meetings; condr. seminars on smoking and health London, Fed. Republic Germany, Alaska, New Brunswick, N.J., Chgo., Costa Rica; dir. Nat. Study Math. Requirements for Scientists and Engrs., 1966-73. Contbr. numerous articles to profl. jours. Pres. Edinboro YMCA, 1972-83; bd. dirs. Common Cause, Harrisburg, Pa., 1975-80; Sgt. USAAF, 1943-46, PTO. Grantee U.S. Office Edn., 1968, 70, No Other World, 1973, NAS, 1980, ITT Life Ins. Corp., 1983, Erie Community Found., 1987. Fellow Am. Inst. Chemists (hon., cert. profl. chemist); mem. AAAS, APHA, Am. Assn. World Health, Am. Chem. Soc., Am. Soc. for Engring. Edn., Internat. Assn. Pure and Applied Chemists, Internat. Soc. for Preventive Oncology, Math. Assn. Am., Am. Diabetes Assn., Erie County Diabetes Assn., Nat. Coun. Math. Tchrs., Sch. Sci. and Math. Assn., N.Y. Acad. Scis. (hon.), Acad. Sr. Profls. (hon.). Home and Office: Studies on Smoking Inc 125 High St Edinboro PA 16412-2552 also: 25 Crescent Pl S Saint Petersburg FL 33711

MILLER, GIFFORD HUBBS, geologist; b. Washington, Feb. 28, 1946; s. Robert Rush and Frances (Hubbs) M.; m. Midra Gay McCalmont, Nov. 13, 1971; children: Luke, Obadiah. BA, U. Colo., 1970, PhD, 1975. Postdoctoral fellow Carnegie Inst., Washington, 1974-75; asst. prof. INSTAAR, Dept. Geol. Scis., U. Colo.-Boulder, 1975-77, assoc. prof., 1980-92, prof. 1992—, chair 1993—, assoc. dir., 1980-82, Quaternary geologist, 1982—; mem. sci. adv. com. NSF, 1983-85; councilor in biochem. and geophysics, AMQUA, 1986-90; dir. Ctr. Geochronological Research U. Colo., 1986—; vis. prof. U. Bergen, Norway, 1979-80; vis. fellow Rsch. Sch. Earth Scis. Australian Nat. U., Canberra, 1991-92. Contbr. articles to profl. jours. and books. Research grantee NSF, 1976—. Fellow Geol. Soc. Am. Office: Univ of Colorado Ctr For Geochronological Res University of Colorado CO 80309-0450

MILLER, GLENN, library director, retired; b. Saginaw, Mich., Dec. 5, 1937; s. H.H. and Evelyn Miller; m. Janice Gase, Aug. 11, 1962; children: Anne, Thomas, John. AA, Bay City (Mich.) Jr. Coll., 1960; BA in Polit. Sci., U. Mich., 1962, MLS, 1963. City librarian Southfield, Mich., 1963-66; dir. Genessee County Libr. System, Flint, Mich., 1967-69; asst. dir. Orlando (Fla.) Pub. Libr., 1969-70; dir. Orange County Libr. System, Orlando, 1970—; cons. in field. Bd. dirs. Additions of Orange County, 1974-77, Sta. WMFE Pub. TV, Orlando, 1970-76; bd. trustees Lucerne Hosp., Orlando, 1974-79. Mem. ALA (chmn. constitution and by-laws com. 1973-76), Pub. Library Assn. of ALA (bd. dirs. 1974-77), Southeastern Library Assn., Fla. Library Assn. (chmn. edn. com. 1978-79, legis. and planning com. 1978-79, pres. 1977-78).

MILLER, GORDON K., lawyer; b. Madison, Wis., Oct. 17, 1949. BBA, U. Wis., 1971, JD, 1974. Bar: Wis. 1974. Mem. Michael, Best & Friedrich, Milw. Mem. ABA. Office: Michael Best & Friedrich 100 E Wisconsin Ave Milwaukee WI 53202-4108*

MILLER, H. TODD, lawyer; b. Buffalo, N.Y., Sept. 19, 1947; s. Henry Opel and Irene Teresa (Hauck) M.; m. June Diehl Lancaster, Aug. 1, 1970; children: Catharine Maclay, Todd Lancaster, Peter Hames. BA, SUNY, Buffalo, 1969; JD, Duke U., 1971. Bar: N.C. 1971, D.C. 1973. Jud. clerk to Hon. Charles R. Simpson U.S. Tax Ct., Washington, 1971-73; assoc. atty. Hogan & Hartson, Washington, 1973-78, ptnr., 1979—. Mem. Phi Beta Kappa, Order of the Coif. Episcopalian. Office: Hogan & Hartson Columbia Sq 555 13th St NW Washington DC 20004-1109

MILLER, HAINON ALFRED, lawyer, investor; b. Kosciusko, Miss., Oct. 9, 1930; s. J. Wesley and Louise (Johnston) M.; m. Lillian Henderson, June 4, 1956; children: Nadalyn, Philip, Kendall, Melissa, Lyon. BA, Miss. Coll., 1951; LLB Tulane U., 1954. Bar: Miss. 1954, U.S. Dist. Ct. (no. and so. dists.) Miss. 1954, U.S. Ct. Appeals (5th cir.) 1972. Sole practice Greenville, Miss., 1954-92; mem. Miss. Senate, Jackson, 1987-95. Mem. Miss. Ho. of Reps., 1968-83; sec. Washington County Dem. Exec. Com., 1955-60. Recipient Disting. Service award U.S. Jr. C. of C., 1957, Humanized Edn. award Miss. Assn. Educators, Jackson, 1979. Mem. Kiwanis (It. gov. dist. 1959). Baptist. Office: New Capitol Bldg Jackson MS 39215

MILLER, HARBAUGH, lawyer; b. Wilkinsburg, Pa., July 23, 1902; s. Charles Shively and Ella (Harbaugh) M.; m. Ruth M. Davis, Nov. 8, 1952. B.S., U. Pitts., 1922, J.D., 1925. Bar: Pa. 1925. Since in pvt. practice law; patnr. Miller & Entwisle, Pitts. Pres. Goodwill Industries, 1958-61, YMCA Pitts., 1956-58; trustee U. Pitts., 1945-60, 66-72, trustee emeritus, 1973—; trustee Western Theol. Sem., 1955-58. Fellow Am. Bar Found., Am. Coll. Trust & Estate Counsel; mem. ABA (ho. of dels.), Am. Law Inst., Am. Judicature Soc., Pa. Bar Assn., Allegheny County Bar Assn. (pres. 1955), Pitts. Coun. Chs. (pres. 1951-53), SAR (pres. Pitts. 1940), U. Pitts. Alumni Assn. (pres. 1940), Univ. Club, Duquesne Club, Masons, Shriners, Pitts. Athletic Assn., Phi Delta Theta, Omicron Delta Kappa, Beta Gamma Sigma, Phi Delta Phi. Presbyterian. Home: 154 N Bellefield Ave Pittsburgh PA 15213-2655 Office: 614 Oliver Bldg Pittsburgh PA 15222-2404

MILLER, HAROLD ARTHUR, lawyer; b. St. Marie, Ill., Aug. 18, 1922; s. Arthur E. and Luletta (Noé) M.; m. Michele H. Rogivue, Nov. 23, 1947; children: Maurice H., Jan Leland, Marc Richard. BS in Acctg., U. Ill., 1942, JD, 1950. Bar: Ill. 1950, U.S. Dist. Ct. Ill. 1950, U.S. Tax Ct. 1950. Fgn. svc. officer U.S. State Dept., Paris, France, 1945-48; ptnr. Filson, Williamson & Miller, Champaign, Ill., 1950-60, Williamson & Miller, Champaign, 1960-72, Miller & Hendren, Champaign, 1972—; atty. Christie Clinic Assn., Champaign, 1960-88; atty. pub. schs. dists., Champaign & Vermilion Counties, Ill., 1960—; atty. for municipalities in Champaign County, Ill., 1970—. Author: Estate Planning for Doctors, 1961. Bd. dirs., officer Urbana Sch. Dist., 1957-69; chmn., trustee Parkland Coll. Champaign, 1971-91; founding bd. mem. CCDC Found., Champaign-Urbana Ednl. Found., Moore Heart Found., Christie Found.; life mem. PTA. With inf. U.S. Army, 1942-45, ETO. Mem. ABA, Am. Judicature Soc., Ill. and Local Bar Assns., Ill. Trial Lawyers Assn., Alpha Kappa Psi. Presbyterian. Office: Miller & Hendren Attys 30 Main 300 Champaign IL 61820

MILLER, HAROLD EDWARD, retired manufacturing conglomerate executive, consultant; b. St. Louis, Nov. 23, 1926; s. George Edward and Georgenia Elizabeth (Franklin) M.; m. Lilian Ruth Gantner, Dec. 23, 1949; children—Ellen Susan, Jeffrey Arthur. B.S.B.A., Washington U., St. Louis, 1949. Vice pres. Fulton Iron Works Co., St. Louis, 1968-71; pres. Fulton Iron Works Co., 1971-79, chmn. bd., 1979-90; v.p. Katy Industries Inc., Elgin, Ill., 1976-77; exec. v.p. Katy Industries Inc., 1978-90, also dir., to 1990; pres. HM Consulting, Palatine, Ill., 1990—; dir. Vigel Machine Tool Co., Tecumseh, Ont., Can.; internat. cons. Vigel Spa, Italy. Served with U.S. Army, 1945-46. Mem. Sugar Equipment and Service Exporters Assn., Internat. Machine Tool Builders Assn., Cutting Tool Mfrs. Assn. Presbyterian. Clubs: Barrington Tennis, Inverness Golf.

MILLER, HARRY B(ENJAMIN), lawyer; b. Lexington, Ky., Jan. 4, 1924; s. Harry Benjamin Miller and Ann (Walcutt) Winn; m. Patricia Griffin, Mar. 22, 1946; children: Thomas, Robin, John, Harry Benjamin III. LLM, U. Ky., 1948. Bar: Ky. 1948, U.S. Dist. Ct. (ea. dist.) Ky. 1948, U.S. Ct. Appeals (6th cir.) 1952, U.S. Supreme Ct. 1962. Pres. Miller, Griffin & Marks, P.S.C., Lexington, 1962—. Mng. editor U. Ky. Law Rev., 1948. Treas. Ky. Dem. State Party, Frankfort, 1960-68. Mem. Order of Coif. Presbyterian. Avocation: golf. Home: 111 Woodland Ave Lexington KY 40502-6415 Office: Miller Griffin & Marks PSC Security Trust Buildin Ste 700 Lexington KY 40507

MILLER, HARRY BRILL, scenic designer, director, acting instructor, lyricist, interior designer; b. Jersey City, Jan. 26, 1924; s. Max Joseph Miller and Lillian (Hirsch) Grodjesk. BA, U. Mich., 1946; MA, Smith Coll., 1948. Set designer, asst. scenic designer various Broadway, Off Broadway and summer shows, N.Y.C., 1948-72; scenic designer NBC-TV, N.Y.C., 1950-63; art dir. MPO-Video Prodns., N.Y.C., 1962; scenic dir. CBS-TV, N.Y.C.,

1963-91; indsl. show designer Norelco, Thompson CSF, Engelhard, N.Y.C., 1958-75; interior designer Interior Comml. Constrn. Assocs., Hialeah, Fla., 1969-70; dir., writer Miramar Minstrels, N.Y.C., 1979-95; dir. PACT Theatre, N.Y.C., 1995; acting tchr. Emmanuel Midtown Young Men and Young Women's Hebrew Assn., N.Y.C., 1989-90. Set designer (TV shows) Princeton '54, '55, '56 (Peabody 1954, 55), The Price is Right, 1962-63, Jackie Gleason Show, 1969-70, CBS News and Special Events, 1986-91, (mus. show) Nashville at the Garden, 1972; art dir. (TV show) Guiding Light, 1978-86 (2 Emmys 1984, 85), The Edge of Night, 1964-69; prodn. designer TV show Captain Kangaroo, 1970-78 (various Peabody awards); set design asst. (Broadway mus.) Funny Girl, 1964, (Broadway play) Sign in Sidney Brustein's Window. Sgt. U.S. Army, 1943-46. Recipient Teaching Assistantship French Govt., Paris, 1948. Mem. United Scenic Artists, Miramar Ski Club (trip chair 1991-93). Avocations: skiing, dancing, swimming, painting, acting. Address: 333 W 56th St Apt 7B New York NY 10019-3770

MILLER, HARRY CHARLES, JR., physician, urologist, educator; b. Ridgewood, N.J., Sept. 22, 1928; s. Harry Charles and Ruth G (McDermott) M.; m. Kari L. Palmer, June 14, 1969; children: Harry C., Carolynn A., Barbara J., Janet E., Jennifer T., Sandra L. AB, Amherst Coll., 1950; MD, Yale U., 1954. Intern Duke U. Hosp., Durham, N.C., 1954-55; resident U. Rochester Med. Ctr., N.Y., 1959-62; pvt. practice specializing in urology Washington, 1973—; asst. prof. urology U. Rochester Health Sci. Ctr., 1962-71; assoc. prof. U. Okla. Health Sci. Ctr., Oklahoma City, 1971-73; prof., chmn. dept. urology George Washington U. Med. Ctr., Washington, 1973—. Served with U.S. Army, 1955-57. Mem. AMA, ACS, Am. urol. Assn. (exec. com., pres. Mid-Atlantic sect., bd. dirs. 1989—), Am. Acad. Pediat., Societe Internationale d'Urologie, Soc. Pediat. Urology, Soc. Univ. Urologists, Am. Assn. Clin. Urologists (sec.-treas., pres.-elect., pres. 1993-94), Beekeepers Assn. No. Va. (treas. 1976-79), Great Falls Grange, River Bend Golf and Country Club, Urology Polit. Action Com. (treas. 1992—). Office: George Washington U Med Ctr 2150 Pennsylvania Ave NW Washington DC 20037-2396

MILLER, HARRY GEORGE, education educator; b. Waukesha, Wis., Feb. 15, 1941; s. Harry Fricke and Ethel Ruth (D'Amato) M.; m. Mary Frances Shugrue, June 20, 1964; children: Alicia, Michael, Anne, Dierdre, Courtney. B.A., Carroll Coll., 1963; M.Ed., U. Nebr., 1967, Ed.D., 1970. Tchr. Westside Community Schs., Omaha, 1964-67; demonstration tchr. East Edn. Complex, Lincoln (Nebr.) Pub. Schs., 1967-68; instr. curriculum research Tchrs. Coll., U. Nebr., Lincoln, 1968-70; faculty So. Ill. U., Carbondale, 1970—; asso. prof. edn., dept. secondary edn. So. Ill. U., 1972—, chmn. dept. secondary edn., 1973-75, prof., chmn. dept. ednl. leadership, 1975—; dean, prof. Coll. Tech. Careers 1980-89; assoc. v.p. acad. affairs So. Ill. U., 1989-92; dean, prof. Ctr. Adult and Continuing Edn. The Am. U., Cairo, 1992—; rsch. prof. Ministry Edn., Thailand, 1978; vis. prof. Ministry Edn., Sabah, East Malaysia, 1980, Korea, 1985; vis. prof. Vladimir State U., Russia, 1989; vis. prof. PRC, 1991; cons. to various orgns. and instns., 1969-74. Author: Beyond Facts: Objective Ways to Measure Thinking, 1976, Adults Teaching Adults, 1977, Responsibility Education, 1977, The Adult Educator: A Handbook for Staff Development, 1978, An Introduction to Adult and Continuing Education, 1979, The Education of Adults, 1981, The Life-long Learning Experience, 1986, Grassroots, 1992, Veiled Voices, 1993; also monographs; mem. editorial bd. Traning, 1976. Mem. Ill. Migrant Council, 1974; Adv. bd. Evaluation and Devel. Center, Rehab. Inst., Carbondale, 1974-80; bd. dirs. St. Joseph's Hosp. Fulbright grantee Republic of Togo, 1982. Mem. Pub. Adult and Continuing Edn. Assn., Rural Edn. Assn., Ill. Coun. for Social Studies (hon.), Community Svcs. Assn. Cairo (bd. dirs. 1994—), Greater Cleve. Coun. for Social Studies (hon.), Ednl. Coun. fo 100 Inc., Coll. of Cons., Godlen Key, Phi Delta Kappa, Kappa Delta Pi, Omicron Tau Theta. Democrat. Roman Catholic. Club: K.C. Office: The Am U Ctr for Adult and Con Edn, PO Box 2511 113 Sharia Kass Aini, Cairo Egypt

MILLER, HARVEY ALFRED, botanist, educator; b. Sturgis, Mich., Oct. 19, 1928; s. Harry Clifton and Carmen (Sager) M.; m. Donna K. Hall, May 9, 1992; children: Valerie Yvonne, Harry Alfred, Timothy Merk, Tanya Merk. B.S., U. Mich., 1950; M.S., U. Hawaii, 1952; Ph.D., Stanford U., 1957. Instr. botany U. Mass., 1955-56; instr. botany Miami U., 1956-57, asst. prof., 1957-61; assoc. prof., curator herbarium, 1961-67; prof., chmn. program in biology Wash. State U., 1967-69; vis. prof. botany U. Ill., 1969-70; prof., chmn. dept. biol. scis. U. Cen. Fla., 1970-75, prof., 1975-94; v.p. Marine Research Assocs. Ltd., Nassau, 1962-65; assoc. Lotspeich & Assocs., natural systems analysts, Winter Park, Fla., 1979—; botanist U. Mich. Expdn. to Aleutian Islands, 1949-50; prin. investigator Systematic and Phytogeographical Studies Bryophytes of Pacific Islands, NSF, 1959, Miami U. Expdn. to Micronesia, 1960; dir. NSF-Miami U. Expdn. to Micronesia and Philippines, 1965; prin. investigator NSF bryophytes of So. Melanesia, 1983-86; research assoc. Orlando Sci. Ctr., Orlando; vis. prof. U. Guam, 1965; cons. tropical botany, foliage plant patents, also designs for sci. bldgs.; adj. prof. botany Miami U., 1985—, vis. prof. botany, 1994—; field researcher on Alpine meadows in Irian Jaya, 1991, 1992. Author: (with H.O. Whittier and B.A. Whittier) Prodromus Florae Muscorum Polynesiae, 1978, Prodromus Florae Hepaticarum Polynesiae, 1983; Field Guide to Florida Mosses and Liverworts, 1990; editor: Florida Scientist, 1973-78; contbr. articles to sci. jours. Mem. exec. bd. and chmn. scholarship and grant selection com. Mercury Seven Found., 1985—. Recipient Acacia Order of Pythagoras; recipient Acacia Nat. award of Merit; Guggenheim fellow, 1958. Fellow AAAS, Linnean Soc. London; mem. Pacific Sci. Assn. (chmn. sci. com. for botany 1975-83), Assn. Tropical Biology, Am. Inst. Biol. Scis., Am. Bryol. Soc. (v.p. 1962-63, pres. 1964-65), Brit. Bryol. Soc., Bot. Soc. Am., Internat. Assn. Plant Taxonomists, Internat. Assn. Bryologists, Mich. Acad. Sci. Arts and Letters, Hawaiian Acad. Sci., Am. Soc. Plant Taxonomists, Fla. Acad. Sci. (exec. sec. 1976-83, pres. 1980), Nordic Bryol. Soc., Acacia, Explorers Club, Sigma Xi, Phi Sigma, Beta Beta Beta. Home: PO Box 6004 Oxford OH 45056 Office: Miami U Dept Botany Oxford OH 45056

MILLER, HARVEY R., lawyer, bankruptcy reorganization specialist; b. Bklyn., Mar. 1, 1933; married;. Grad., Columbia U. Law Sch., 1959. Ptnr. Weil Gotshal and Manges, N.Y.C. Office: Weil Gotshal & Manges 767 Fifth Ave New York NY 10153-0002

MILLER, HARVEY S. SHIPLEY, foundation trustee; b. Phila., Sept. 28, 1948; s. Frank Leroy and Betty Charlotte (Elfont) M. BA, Swarthmore Coll., 1970; JD, Harvard U., 1973. Bar: N.Y. 1973. Assoc. Debevoise & Plimpton, N.Y.C., 1973-75; curator and dir. appt. collections and spl. exhbns. Franklin Inst., Phila., 1975-81; v.p. Energy Solutions, Inc., N.Y.C., 1982-84; pres., chief exec. officer, dir. Daltex Med. Scis., Inc., N.Y.C., 1983-86, dir. exec. com., 1983-94, chief operating officer, vice chmn., 1986-91, pres., chief operating officer, 1991-93; sole trustee, CEO The Judith Rothschild Found., N.Y.C., 1993—. Author: Milton Avery: Drawings and Paintings, 1976, It's About Time, 1979; author; editor: New Spaces: Exploring the Aesthetic Dimensions of Holography, 1979; co-author: Rapid Inactivation of Infectious Pathogens by Chlorhexidine-coated Gloves, 1992; contbr. articles to profl. jours. Mem. vis. com. on photography George Eastman House, Rochester, N.Y., 1976-78; trustee Milton and Sally Avery Arts Found., N.Y.C., 1983—, The Franklin Inst., Phila., 1993—, Phila. Mus. Art, 1985—, exec. com., 1993—; assoc. trustee U. Pa., 1981—; bd. govs. Print Club, Phila., 1976-87; bd. overseers U. Pa. Sch. Nursing, 1981—, Edith C. Blum Art Inst. Bard Coll., 1984-87; bd. dirs., mem. corp. MacDowell Colony, N.Y.C., 1982-85; exec. bd. dirs. Fabric Workshop, Phila., 1976-86; mem. prints and drawings and photographs trustees adv. com. Phila. Mus. Art, 1974—, trustee, 1985—, investment com., 1989—, exec., devel. and exhbn. coms., 1993—; bd. assocs. Swarthmore Coll. Librs., Phila., 1978-86; treas., dir. Arcadia Found., Norristown, Pa., 1981—; chmn. adv. bd. Inst. Contemporary Art U. Pa., 1982-84; trustee, vice chmn. coms. on instrn. Pa. Acad. Fine Arts, 1982-91, trustee emeritus, 1991—, chmn. collections and exhbns. com., 1985-87; trustee N.Y. Studio Sch., 1974-80, U. of the Arts, 1979-86; mem. exec. bd. Citizens for Arts in Pa., 1980; bd. dirs. Once Gallery, Inc., 1974-75, Wildlife Preservation Trust Internat., Inc., 1990—; mem. Mayor's Cultural Adv. Coun., Phila., 1987-91; chair Mayor's Art-in-City Hall Program, Phila., 1992-95; trustees coun. Nat. Gallery Art, Washington, 1995—; mem. collections com. Nat. Gallery of Art. Mem. Bar of City of N.Y., Athenaeum, Libr. Co. Phila., Am. Philos. Soc., Hist. Soc. Pa., Phila. Art Alliance, Union League of Phila., Harvard Club of N.Y.C., Swarthmore Club Phila., Phi

Sigma Kappa. Republican. Episcopalian. Home: Moorhope Mathers Ln Fort Washington PA 19034 Office: 1110 Park Ave New York NY 10128-1201

MILLER, HASBROUCK BAILEY, financial and travel services company executive; b. Gloversville, N.Y., Aug. 1, 1923; s. Edward Waite and Lorraine (Taylor) M.; m. Elizabeth J. Wilson, Jan. 5, 1949; children: Kimberly Elizabeth, Stacey Wilson, Hasbrouck Bailey, Sloan Taylor. B.A., Hamilton Coll., 1944; postgrad., U. Lausanne, Switzerland, 1946, Sch. Advanced Internat. Studies, Washington, 1947, Stanford Grad. Sch. Bus., 1961. With Am. Express Co. (and subsidiaries), 1948—, v.p., sec., 1964-65, sr. v.p., 1965-68, exec. v.p., 1968-83; exec. v.p. Am. Express Internat., Inc., 1960-83; ret., 1983. Served with OSS, AUS, 1942-45. Mem. Morris County Golf Club (Convent Station, N.J.). Home: Fox Hollow Rd Morristown NJ 07960

MILLER, HENRY FORSTER, architect; b. Sept. 16, 1916; s. Rutger Bleecker and Dorothy (Forster) M.; m. Maria Stockton Bullitt, Apr. 6, 1942; children: Maria, Andrew, Dorothy, Steven, Henry Jr. BA, Yale U., 1938, MArch, 1948. Registered architect, Conn., R.I., Mass. Instr. archtl. design Yale Sch. Architecture, New Haven, 1948-49; assoc. dir. facilities planning office Yale U. New Haven, 1974-90; assoc. Harold H. Davis Architect, New Haven, 1949-56; ptnr. Davis, Cochran & Miller, New Haven, 1956-69, Davis, Cochran, Miller, Baerman, Noyes, New Haven, 1969-74; pvt. practice Orange, Conn., 1990—; pres. Conn. Bldg. Congress, 1957-58. Prin. works include Booth Meml. Boys Club Bldg. (Archtl. Design award 1971), Columbus Sch. New Haven (HUD Design Excellence award 1970). Mem. bd. govs. New Haven Boys and Girls Club, 1956-93; v.p. Comty. Coun. Greater New Haven, 1964-66; apptd. mem. State Housing Commn., Conn., 1970-72; mem. Conn. Rev. Bd. for Nat. Register of Hist. Places, 1974-81; founding dir. Conn. Trust for Hist. Preservation, 1975-86, pres., 1975-77; bd. dirs. New Haven Preservation Trust. Maj. F.A. AUS, 1941-46, ETO. Fellow AIA (Conn. state preservation coord. 1965-90); mem. Conn. Soc. Architects (exec. com. 1967-69), Mory's Assn. Democrat. Roman Catholic. Avocations: tennis, hiking, drawing, painting. Home and Office: 30 Derby Ave Orange CT 06477-1403

MILLER, HENRY FRANKLIN, lawyer; b. Phila., May 19, 1938; s. Lester and Bessie (Posner) M.; m. Barbara Ann Gendel, June 20, 1964; children: Andrew, Alexa. AB, Lafayette Coll., 1959; LLB, U. Pa., 1964. Bar: Pa. 1965. Law clk. U.S. Dist. Ct. Del., Wilmington, 1964-65; assoc. Wolf, Block, Schorr & Solis-Cohen, Phila., 1965-71, ptnr., 1971—. Pres. Soc. Hill Synagogue, Phila., 1978-79, Big Brothers/Big Sisters Assn. of Phila., 1980-81, Jewish Family & Children's Agy., Phila., 1986-88. 1st lt. U.S. Army, 1959-60. Mem. Am. Coll. Real Estate Lawyers. Avocations: swimming, hiking, reading. Office: Wolf Block Schorr & Solis-Cohen 12th Fl Packard Bldg 15th and Chestnut Sts Philadelphia PA 19118-3743

MILLER, HERBERT ELMER, accountant; b. DeWitt, Iowa, Aug. 11, 1914; s. Elmer Joseph and Marian (Briggs) M.; m. Lenore Snitkey, July 1, 1938; 1 dau., Barbara Ruth. A.B., State U. Iowa, 1936, M.A., 1937; Ph.D., U. Minn., 1947; Dr. h.c., Free U. Brussels, 1982; D.H.L. (h.c.), De Paul U., 1983. C.P.A., Iowa. Acctg. prof. U. Minn., U. Mich., Mich. State U., 1938-70; ptnr. Arthur Andersen & Co., Chgo., 1970-78; dir. Sch. Acctg., U. Ga., Athens, 1978-83. Co-author: Finney-Miller accounting series, 1950-70; editor, contbr.: C.P.A. Rev. Manual, 1951-79. Mem. AICPA (bd. dirs. 1968-70), Am. Acctg. Assn. (pres. 1965-66), Federated Schs. Acctg. (pres. 1982), Beta Gamma Sigma, Beta Alpha Psi (nat. pres. 1961-62). Home: 145 S Stratford Dr Athens GA 30605-3025

MILLER, HERBERT JOHN, JR., lawyer; b. Mpls., Jan. 11, 1924; s. Herbert John and Catherine (Johnson) M.; m. Carey Kinsolving, Apr. 3, 1948; children—John Kinsolving William Grady. Student, U. Minn., 1941-43; B.A., George Washington U., 1948, LL.B., 1949. Bar: D.C. 1949. Asso. Kirkland, Fleming, Green, Martin & Ellis, Washington, 1949-58; partner Kirkland, Ellis, Hodson, Chaffetz and Masters, 1958-61; asst. atty. gen., criminal div. Dept. Justice, 1961-65; partner Miller, Cassidy, Larroca & Lewin, Washington, 1965—; chmn. U.S. del. Conferees Attys. Gen. Ams., Mexico City, 1963, Mins. of Govt., Interior and Security of Cen. Am., Panama, and U.S., 1964, 65; chmn. Pres.'s Commn. on D.C. Crime, 1965-67. Capt. AUS, 1943-46. Mem. ABA, Am. Coll. Trial Lawyers, D.C. Bar Assn. (pres. 1970-71), Order of Coif, Phi Delta Phi, Alpha Delta Phi. Club: Congressional (Washington). Home: 17017 Whites Store Rd Boyds MD 20841-9665 Office: Miller Cassidy Larroca & Lewin 2555 M St NW Washington DC 20037-1302

MILLER, HOPE RIDINGS, author; b. Bonham, Tex.; d. Alfred Lafayette and Grace (Dupree) Ridings; m. Clarence Lee Miller, Sept. 26, 1932 (dec. Jan. 1965). B.A., U. Tex.; M.A., Columbia; D.Litt., Austin Coll. Society editor Washington Post, 1938-45; Washington corr. Town and Country mag., 1944-46, The Argonaut mag., 1945-49; Washington columnist Promenade mag., 1945-51; syndicated column McNaught, 1945-50; asso. editor Diplomat mag., 1952-55, editor in chief, 1956-66; television prodn. staff Metromedia, Inc., 1966-70; Washington editor Antique Monthly, 1976-89; mem. editorial adv. bd. Horizon mag., 1978-89. Author: Embassy Row: The Life and Times of Diplomatic Washington, 1969, Great Houses of Washington, 1969, Scandals In The Highest Office: Facts and Fictions in the Private Lives of Our Presidents, 1973; script for cassette tape Circling Lafayette Square, 1976. Mem. women's bd. Columbia Hosp., Friends of the Folger Library, Washington Heart Assn. Mem. Nat. Press Club, Hist. Soc. Washington, Friends of LBJ Libr., Am. News Women's Club, The Circle of the Nat. Gallery of Art, Stephen F. Austin Soc., Am. Archives of Art, Smithsonian Assocs., Author's Guild, Nat. Mus. Women in the Arts, Sulgrave Club, Phi Mu. Home: Norwood Apts 1868 Columbia Rd NW Washington DC 20009

MILLER, HUGH EDWARD, business executive; b. Franklin, Pa., July 4, 1935; s. Edward L. and Martha (Carr) M.; m. Angela Jones, Mar. 25, 1958; children—Susan D., Michael H., Brian E., Kathryn M. B.A., B.S., Rice U., 1958, postgrad., Internat. Bus. Sch., Harvard U., Vevey, Switzerland, 1974. Salesman Jefferson Chem. Co., Houston, 1957-69; with Atlas Chem. Industry NV, Everberg, Belgium, 1969-79; v.p., gen. mgr. splty. chems. ICI Ams. Inc., Wilmington, Del., 1979-80; pres. Stuart Pharmacy subs. ICI Ams. Inc., Wilmington, 1980-85; sr. v.p. ICI Ams. Inc., Wilmington, 1985—, prin. exec. officer advanced materials and electronics, 1985-89, vice chmn., 1989—; dir. Wilmington Trust Co., Diamond State Telephone Co., Wilmington. Bd. dirs. United Way Del., Wilmington, 1980-85, Med. Ctr. Del., Wilmington, 1981—. Mem. Pharm. Mfrs. Assn. (bd. dirs. 1982-86), Sigma Xi. Republican. Episcopalian. Clubs: Kennett Square Country (bd. dirs. 1983-85) (Pa.); Greenville Country (Wilmington). Avocations: golf; skiing. Office: ICI Ams Inc Concord Pike New Murph Wilmington DE 19803

MILLER, I. GEORGE, physician, educator, researcher; b. Chgo., Apr. 18, 1937; s. Irving George and Florence (Levy) M.; m. Arlette Goldmuntz, Mar. 25, 1962; children: Lisa, John, David. A.B., Harvard U., 1958, M.D., 1962. Intern Univ. Hosp., Western Res., U., Cleve., 1962-63; resident Univ. Hosp., Western Res., U., Cleve., 1963-64; epidemiology intelligence oficer Communicable Disease Ctr. USPHS, Atlanta, 1964-66; research fellow in medicine Harvard U. Med. Sch., Boston, 1966-69; asst. prof. pediatrics, epidemiology, biophysics and biochemistry Yale Sch. Medicine, New Haven, 1969-72, J.F. Enders prof., 1979—; mem. exptl. virology study sect. NIH, 1974-77; mem. sci. adv. com. Damon Runyon Fund, 1979-85, dir., 1985—; Leukemia Soc. Am., 1976-81. Contbr. numerous articles, chpts. to profl. publs.; editorial bd.: Jour. Virology, 1981—, Virology, 1982. Recipient epidemic Intelligence Service Alumni Assn. prize, 1967; Macy faculty scholar, 1977, Am. Cancer Soc. scholar, 1990; Howard Hughes Med. Inst. investigatorship, 1972-80. Fellow Infectious Diseases Soc. (Squibb award 1982, Enders award 1989); mem. Am. ABA, Am. Coll. Trial Lawyers, D.C. Bar Assn. Soc., Am. Soc. Virology, Assn. Am. Physicians. Jewish. Home: 95 Alden Ave New Haven CT 06515-2718 Office: Yale U Sch Medicine Dept Biochemistry PO Box 6666 New Haven CT 06511-8198*

MILLER, IRIS ANN, landscape architect, urban designer, educator; b. Pitts., Jan. 6, 1938; d. Bernard and Sadye (Topel) Ress; m. Lawrence Alan Miller, Jan. 24, 1959; children: Bradley Stuart, Richard Lyle, Stefan Ress. BS cum laude, U. Pitts., 1959, MEd in Secondary Edn., 1961; postgrad. in psychology and counseling, U. Md., 1962-68; MArch, Cath. U. Am.,

1979. Tchr. various pub. and pvt. schs., Pitts., Monroeville, Pa., Montgomery County, Md., 1959-61, 63-64; free lance landscape design Washington, 1965-81; architecture design and research O'Neil and Manion Architects, Bethesda, Md., 1979, 81; architecture design and drawing Frank Schlesinger Architects/Planners, Washington, 1979-80; prin. Iris Miller Urbanism and Landscape Design, 1982—; cons. architecture design Washington, 1982—; vis. lectr. Cath. U. Am., Washington, 1983-86, vis. asst. prof., 1987-93, adj. asst. prof., 1993—; dir. landscape and architecture studies, 1986-89, dir landscape studies, 1990—; urban design cons. Techworld, Washington, 1984-86; devel. dir. Tech 2000 Mus., 1985-86; dir., presenter lectr. series Resident Assoc. Program Smithsonian Instn., Washington, 1982, 83, 85, 87, 89; dir., founder 7th, 8th, and 9th Sts. Group Streetscape project, Washington, 1986—, others; founder Charrette urban design seminar, Washington, Dallas, Alexandria, Va., St. Louis and Cleve., 1982-89; initiator, participant Sarasota (Fla.) Regional Urban Design Assistance R/UDAT team, 1983, seminar Nat. Gallery Art, Washington, 1984, Nat. Arboretum, 1988, symposia Cath. U. of Am., 1987—; founder, co-dir. symposium Libr. Congress, 1995; dir., mem. steering com. numerous confs. in field; invited participant, Congress for New Urbanism, 1994—, U.S. Embassy Amman, Jordan, 1992, U. Va., 1993, Ecole Nationale Superieure du Paysage/Versailles, France, 1993, U. Osaka, Japan, 1993. Tokyo Inst. Tech. U., 1993, SUNY, Buffalo, 1994, U. Colo., Denver, 1994, Mayors Inst. on City Design, St. Louis, 1994; jury critic Cath. U. Am., 1980-94, U. Puerto Rice, U. Va., 1993. Author, co-editor (book): Urban Design: Visions and Reflections, 1991, Capital Visions: Reflections on a Decade of Urban Design Charrettes and a Look Ahead, 1995; (map and text) Visions of Washington: Composite Plan of Urban Interventions, 1991; contbr. articles to profl. publs.; curator, author exhbn. and catalogue on Washington Maps Sumner Sch. Mus., 1987, 92, U. Md., 1993, Embassy of France, 1993, SUNY Buffalo, 1994, U. Calif., Berkeley, 1994, U. Toronto, 1995; curator, author map exhbn. ACSA Am. Meeting, Montreal, 1994; co-curator, author exhbn. and catalogue Octagon Mus., 1987; project dir., curator Paris-Washington Exhbn., 1987—; landscape architecture design and drawing Georgetown Day H.S., Washington, 1988, W.Va. Wesleyan Coll. Campus plan for religious art ctr., 1992, L'Iris Espace et Animation Cultural Ctr., Francheville, France, 1993, Washington Hebrew Congregation Meml. Park Info. pavilion and landscape renovation, 1993-94; recent landscape projects include Kahn Residence, Arlington, Va., 1993-94, Marks Residence, Silver Spring, Md., 1993, Nesse, Lewis Residence, Silver Spring , Md., 1992, Friedman Residence, Washington, 1992, Drysdale Hershon Residence, Washington, 1991, Miller Residence, Washington, 1990—, Sexton Residence, Kenwood, Chevy Chase, Md., 1990, Romano Residence, Fairfax Station, Va., 1989, Mushinski Residence, Bethesda, Md., 1989, 8th St. Mall Washington, 1987-88, Mishkin, Jennis Residence, Bethesda, 1988, Cramer Residence, Bethesda, 1988; recent home design and renovations include Sexton Residence, Chevy Chase, Md., 1994, Miller Jayapal Residence, San Francisco, 1993, Marks Residence, Silver Spring, Md., 1993, Miller Residence, Washington, 1991, Mishkin Jennis Residence, Bethesda, 1988. Co-chmn. stamp com. Bicentennial Washington, 1987-90; founding mem. Washington Network, 1986-89; mem. adv. panel L'Enfant Forum, Washington, 1987-90, Hist. Georgetown Found., 1989-92; trustee John J. Sexton Fund for Local Govt. Sth. Pub. Affairs, U. Md., College Park, 1983—; dir., founder Pub.-Pvt. Partnership and Univ. Scholarship Outreach Inner-City High Sch. Program, Cath. U. Am., Washington Pub. Schs., 1985—; dir., founder Intern Exch. Program Landscape Architecture, France-U.S.A., Cath. U. Am., U. Va., Friends of Vieilles Maisons Francaises, 1991—; mem. historic landscape com. U.S/ Internat. Coun. on Monuments and Sites, 1990—; active Cultural Alliance Greater Washington, Nat. Trust for Historic Preservation, Ikebana Internat., Hist. Soc. Washington, Nat. Bldg. Mus., alumni coun. Sch. Architecture and Planning, Cath. U. Am., 1986—. Travel rsch. grantee Cath. U. Am., 1978, 79, Rsch. grantee Govt. France, 1985; grantee NEA (2), 1982, grantee D.C. Commn. on Arts, 1991, 92; recipient Program Devel. award Cath. U. Am., 1978. Mem. Am. Planning Assn., U.S.-Internat. Coun. on Monuments and Sites (program speaker 1987, 92, 93, hist. landscapes com. 1990—), Friends Vieilles Maisons Francaises (program speaker 1987, 92), AIA (assoc., regional and urban design com. 1982—, chmn. edn. subcom 1987—, chmn. founder data base on design edn. and urban design 1993, urban design exhbn. and panel, 1989—, chmn. edn. conf. 1983, chmn. newsletter 1993, edn. com. D.C. chpt. 1981-83, Charrette co-chmn., program devel. award 1982), Assn. Collegiate Schs. Architecture (speaker N.E. region conf. 1989, speaker ann. meeting 1991-92, chmn. panel on urban design 1989—, chair Collegiate Exhbn. for Excellence in Urban Design, 1990—, author conf. procs. 1991-93 , Citation for Urban Design 1993), Am. Soc. Landscape Architects (Potomac chpt. strategic planning com., 1994—), Inst. Urban Design, Friends of Vieilles Maisons Francaises, Alpha Epsilon Phi (pres. D.C. alumni 1965-67). Avocations: photography, Japanese flower arranging, tennis, jogging. Home: 3820 52nd St NW Washington DC 20016-1924 Office: 914 11th St NW Washington DC 20001-4408

MILLER, IRVING FRANKLIN, chemical engineering educator, academic administrator; b. N.Y.C., Sept. 27, 1934; s. Sol and Gertrude (Rochkind) M.; m. Baila Hannah Milner, Jan. 28, 1962; children—Eugenia Lynne, Jonathan Mark. B.S. in Chem. Engring. N.Y. U., 1955; M.S., Purdue U., 1956; Ph.D., U. Mich., 1960. Research scientist United Aircraft Corp., Hartford, 1959-61; from asst. prof. to prof., head chem. engring. Poly. Inst. Bklyn., 1961-72; prof. bioengring., head bioengring. program U. Ill., Chgo., 1973-79, acting head systems engring. dept., 1978-79, assoc. vice chancellor for research, dean Grad. Coll., 1979-85, prof. chem. engring., head chem. engring., 1986—, dir. Ctr. for Advanced Edn. and Rsch., 1989-90, dir. Office of Spl. Projects, 1990-92, dir. bioengring. program, 1992—; cons. to industry, also Nat. Acad. Scis., NIH. Editor: Electrochemical Bioscience and Bioengineering, 1973; Contbr. articles profl. jours. Mem. Am. Inst. Chem. Engrs., Am. Chem. Soc., AAAS, Biomed. Engring. Soc., N.Y. Acad Scis. Home: 2600 Orrington Ave Evanston IL 60201-1750 Office: PO Box 4348 Chicago IL 60680-4348

MILLER, ISRAEL, rabbi, university administrator; b. Balt., Apr. 6, 1918; s. Tobias and Bluma (Bunchez) M.; m. Ruth Joan Goldman, Oct. 16, 1945; children: David, Michael, Deborah, Judith. B.A. magna cum laude, Yeshiva Coll., 1938, D.D., 1967; M.A., Columbia U., 1949. Ordained rabbi, 1941. Rabbi Kingsbridge Heights Jewish Center, Bronx, 1941-68; rabbi emeritus Kingsbridge Heights Jewish Center, 1968—; asst. to pres. Yeshiva U. N.Y.C., 1968-70; v.p. Yeshiva U., 1970-80, sr. v.p., 1980-94, sr. v.p. emeritus, 1994—; counselor B'nai B'rith Hillel Found., Hunter Coll., Bronx, 1951-60; lectr. homiletics Yeshiva U., 1954-55; prof. applied rabbinics Rabbi Isaac Elchanan Theol. Sem., 1968—. Editor: Sermon Manual, 1951. V.p. Bronx Coun. Am. Jewish Congress, 1954-60, Bronx Coun. Jewish Edn., 1964-68; pres. Rabbinical Coun. Am., 1964-66, hon. pres., 1966-68; mem. exec. com. World Zionist Orgn., 1971-76; chmn. Am. Jewish Conf. on Soviet Jewry, 1965-67, Am. Zionist Council, 1967-70; pres. Am. Zionist Fedn., 1970-74, hon. pres., 1974—; v.p. Religious Zionists Am., 1966-68; religious cons., retreat master Dept. Def. in. Europe, 1954, 63-64, Alaska, 1958, Japan, 1960; Vice chmn. Conf. Pres.'s Am. Jewish Orgns., 1969-74; chmn. Conf. Pres.'s Major Am. Jewish Orgns., 1974-76; vice chmn. N.Y. Jewish Community Rels. Coun., 1976—; exec. com. Bronx coun. Boy Scouts Am., 1951-58; mem. Nat. Citizens Com. Community Rels., 1946—; bd. dirs. Nat. Jewish Welfare Bd., v.p., 1969—; chmn. Commn. Jewish Chaplaincy, 1962-65; bd. dirs. Bd. Jewish Edn. N.Y.C., Nat. Jewish Community Relations, United Israel Appeal, 1968—; bd. dirs., acting pres. Conf. on Jewish Material Claims Against Germany, 1983, pres., 1984—; pres. Conf. on Jewish Material Claims Against Austria, 1984—; sec. Meml. Found. for Jewish Culture, 1973-94, mem. bd. dirs. ad personam, 1994—; bd. govs. Jewish Agy. for Israel, 1971-76; vice chmn. Am. Israel Pub. Affairs Com., 1983-91; mem. Jerusalem Com., 1990—; bd. dirs. The Jerusalem Found., 1985—; hon. chmn. Jewish Nat. Fund. Served as chaplain USAAF, 1945-46. Recipient Bernard Revel award Yeshiva Coll. Alumni Assn., 1961, Nat. Rabbinic Leadership award Union of Orthodox Jewish Congregations, 1966, 81, Shofar award Boy Scouts Am., 1965, Frank L. Weill award Nat. Jewish Welfare Bd., 1972, Louis Lipsky Meml. award Am. Jewish League for Israel, 1993, Dr. Harris J. Levine award B'nai Zion, 1979; named Man of Yr. Nat. Coun. Young Israel, 1976. Mem. Am. Zionist Youth Found. (life), Jewish War Vets. (nat. chaplain 1962-63), Assn. Jewish Chaplains Armed Forces (pres. 1955-56), Rabbinical Alumni Yeshiva U. (pres. 1960-62). Home: 2619 Davidson Ave Bronx NY 10468-4103 Office: Yeshiva U 2540 Amsterdam Ave New York NY 10033-2807 *In life I have found the verbs more important than the nouns and adjectives. We show who we are by how we act, respond, love or hate.*

MILLER, IVAN LAWRENCE, lawyer; b. Cleve., Feb. 2, 1914; s. Ralph and Sarah (Kichler) M. B.A., Case Western Res. U., 1936, LL.B., JD, 1938; postgrad., Grad. Sch. Bus. Adminstrn., Harvard U., 1943, Inns of Ct. (Middle Temple), London, Eng., 1945. Bar: Ohio 1938, U.S. Supreme Ct. 1960. Pvt. practice Cleve., 1938—; with Ziegler, Metzger & Miller, 1968—; hon. consul of Belgium, Ohio, 1962—; legal adviser Brit. Consulate Gen., 1947-92, Can. Consulate Gen. and Trade Commn., 1964—; v.p., trustee, legal counsel Maison Francaise. Mem. bd. overseers Case Western Res. U., 1973-76. Maj. (QM) US Army, 1941-45. Decorated Bronze Star; Belgian Mil. Cross 1st Class, Knight Order Crown (Belgium); Civic medal First Class (Belgium); officer Order of Brit. Empire; Knight Order of Leopold (Belgium); chevalier dans l'Ordre des Palmes Academiques (France); chevalier dans l'Ordre Nat. du Merite (France); named Consul of Yr. in U.S., 1974; recipient Law Alumni Assn. award, 1986, Disting. Alumni award Case Western Res. U., 1990. Fellow Ohio State Bar Found. (life); mem. ABA, Fed. Bar Assn. (pres. Cleve. 1974-75), Ohio Bar Assn., Cleve. Bar Assn. (past trustee), English Speaking Union (Cleve. past pres., nat. bd. dirs.), Sch. of Law Alumni Assn. (past pres.), Nat. Alumni Coun. Case Western Res. U. (past pres.), Cleve. World Trade Assn., Soc. Benchers (chmn.), Union Club, Wig and Pen Club (Eng.), Link (Eng.), Rotary (Internat. award 1987), No. Ohio Golf Assn. (emeritus legal counsel 1988—). Home: 2482 Derbyshire Rd Cleveland OH 44106-3289 Office: 2020 Huntington Bldg Cleveland OH 44115-1441

MILLER, J. PHILIP, television producer, director, educator; b. Barberton, Ohio, July 10, 1937; s. Cloy M. and Mary (Yoder) M.; children—Kimberly Lowell, Marc Cloy. B.A., Haverford Coll., 1959; EdM, Harvard U., 1960. Tchr. public schs. Newton and Lexington, Mass., 1959-63; dir., lead guitarist profl. folksinging trio Boston, 1963-66; prodn. coordinator, prodn. asst. Candid Camera, N.Y.C., 1966-67; unit mgr., assoc. producer NBC-TV, N.Y.C., 1967-73; instr. TV prodn. NYU; freelance producer, dir. N.Y.C., 1973—; exec. producer Miller Greenewood Prodns., N.Y.C., 1982-83; sr. spls. producer WCVB-TV, Boston, 1983-85; asst. prof. broadcasting and film Coll. Communication Boston U., 1985-89, assoc. prof., 1989—; dir., writer, head writer Kids-TV series showtime, N.Y.C., 1989-90. Programs include Go Show, 1973-75, Special Treat, 1975, 77, First Tuesday, 1970-71, Tonight Show, 1969, Christmastime with Mr. Rogers, 1978, 3-2-1 Contact, 1979, The Bloodhound Gang, 1979, Getting the Most Out of Television, 1980. Recipient Emmy awards, 1976, 84, 86; Peabody award, 1975; Ohio State award, 1985, 86; Chgo. Internat. Film Festival Cert., 1975, Silver Circle award Nat. Acad. TV Arts and Scis., 1994. Mem. Dirs. Guild Am., Writers Guild Am., Nat. Acad. TV Arts and Scis., Assn. Ind. Video and Filmmakers, Phi Delta Kappa. Avocations: photography, tennis. Home: 161 W Newton St Boston MA 02118-1204 Office: Boston U Coll of Communication 640 Commonwealth Ave Boston MA 02215-2422

MILLER, JACK DAVID R., radiologist, physician, educator; b. Johannesburg, South Africa, Apr. 15, 1930; s. Harold Lewis and Inez (Behrman) M.; m. Miriam Sheckter, Dec., 1988. B.Sc., M.B., Ch.B., U. Witwatersrand, Johannesburg, 1956. Diplomate: Am. Bd. Radiology. Intern Coronation Hosp., Johannesburg, 1957-58; resident in radiology Passavant Meml. Hosp., Chgo., 1959-62, Wesley Meml. Hosp., Chgo., 1959-62; fellow in radiology Northwestern U. Med. Sch., 1962-63; chmn. dept. radiology U. Hosp., Edmonton, Alta., Can., 1971-83; clin. prof. radiology U. Alta., 1971—. Fellow Royal Coll. Physicians Can., Am. Coll. Radiology. Office: U Alberta Dept Radiology Edmonton, AB Canada

MILLER, JACK RICHARD, federal judge; b. Chgo., June 6, 1916; s. Forest W. and Blanche M.; m. Isabelle M. Browning, Aug. 1, 1942; children: Janice Lee (Mrs. Robert Amott), Mrs. Judy Flynn, James Forrest, Mrs. A.H. Studenmund. A.B. cum laude, Creighton U., 1938, LL.D. (hon.) 1966; M.A., Cath. U., Washington, 1939; J.D., Columbia U., 1946; postgrad., State U. Iowa Coll. Law, 1946; LL.D. (hon.), Loras Coll., 1967, Iowa Wesleyan Coll., 1969, Yonsei U., South Korea, 1976. Bar: Iowa 1946, Nebr. 1946, D.C. 1949. Atty. Office Chief Counsel, IRS, Washington, 1947-48; professorial lectr. taxation George Washington U., 1948; asst. prof. tax law Notre Dame, 1948-49; pvt. practice tax law Sioux City, Iowa, 1949-60; mem. Iowa Ho. of Reps., 1955-56, Iowa Senate, 1957-60; U.S. senator from Iowa, 1961-73; judge U.S. Ct. Customs and Patent Appeals, Washington, 1973-82, U.S. Ct. Appeals (fed. cir.), Washington, 1982—; now sr. judge U.S. Ct. Appeals (fed. cir.). Contbr. numerous articles on tax and patent law to legal periodicals. Served from 1t. to 1t. col. USAAF, 1942-46; brig. gen. USAF Res. (ret.). Mem. ABA, Iowa, Nebr., D.C. Bar Assns., Am. Law Inst. (life), Am. Patent Law Assn., Am. Legion, VFW, Amvets, KC, Rotary. Office: US Ct Appeals Federal Circuit 717 Madison Pl NW Washington DC 20439-0002

MILLER, JACQUELINE WINSLOW, library director; b. N.Y.C., Apr. 15, 1935; d. Lynward Roosevelt and Sarah Ellen (Grevious) W.; 1 child, Percy Scott. BA, Morgan State Coll., 1957; MLS, Pratt Inst., 1960; grad. profl. seminar, U. Md., 1973. Cert. profl. librarian. With Bklyn. Pub. Library, 1957-68; head extension services New Rochelle (N.Y.) Pub. Library, 1969-70; br. adminstr. Grinton Will Yonkers (N.Y.) Pub. Libr., 1970-75; dir. Yonkers Pub. Library, 1975—; mem. adj. faculty grad. libr. studies Queens Coll., CUNY, 1989, 90. Mem. commr.'s com. Statewide Libr. Devel., Albany, N.Y., 1980; mem. N.Y. Gov.'s Commn. on Librs., 190, 91; bd. dirs. Community Planning Coun., Yonkers, N.Y., 1987; mem. Yonkers Black Women's Polit. Caucus, 1987; pres. bd. Literacy Vols. of Westchester County, 1991-92. Recipient Yonkers Citizen award Ch. of Our Saviour, 1980, 2d Ann. Mae Morgan Robinson award Yonkers chpt. Westchester Black Women's Polit. Caucus, 1992, 3d Ann. Equality Day award City of Yonkers, 1992, African-Am. Heritage 1st award YWCA, 1994; named Outstanding Profl. Woman Nat. Assn. Negro Bus. and Profl. Women's Clubs Inc., 1981. Mem. ALA (councilor 1987-91), N.Y. State Libr. Assn., Pub. Libr. Dirs. Assn. (exec. bd.), N.Y. State Pub. Libr. Dirs. Assn., Westchester Libr. Assn., Yonkers C of C. (bd. dirs. 1992-95), Rotary (Yonkers chpt.). Office: Yonkers Pub Libr 7 Main St Yonkers NY 10701-2711

MILLER, JAMES, construction company executive; b. Scotland, Sept. 1, 1934; s. Sir James and Lady Ella Jane M.; m. Kathleen Dewar, 1959; 3 children; m. 2d, Iris Lloyd Webb, 1969; 1 child. MA in Engring. Sci., Oxford (Eng.) U., 1958. With Miller Group Ltd. (formerly James Miller & Ptnrs.), Edinburgh, Scotland, 1958—; chmn. Miller Group Ltd. (formerly James Miller & Ptnrs.), 1970—; chmn. Fedn. Civil Engring. Contractors, 1985-86, pres., 1990-93; bd. dirs. Brit. Linen Bank Ltd., Bank of Scotland; mem. Scottish adv. bd. Brit. Petroleum, 1990—. Chmn. Ct. Heriot-Watt U., 1990—. Mem. City Livery Club, Merchants of City of Edinburgh (master 1992-94). Avocation: shooting. Office: Miller Group Ltd Miller Hse, 18 S Groathill Ave, Edinburgh EH4 2LW, Scotland

MILLER, JAMES ALEXANDER, oncologist, educator; b. Dormont, Pa., May 27, 1915; s. John Herman and Emma Anna (Stenger) M.; m. Elizabeth Cavert, Aug. 30, 1942; children: Linda Ann, Helen Louise; m. Barbara Butler, Dec. 21, 1988. B.S. in Chemistry, U. Pitts., 1939; M.S., U. Wis., 1941, Ph.D. in Biochemistry, 1943; D.Sc. (hon.), Med. Coll. Wis., 1982, U. Chgo., 1991. Finney-Howell fellow in cancer research U. Wis., Madison, 1943-44; instr. oncology U. Wis., 1944-46, asst. prof., 1946-48, asso. prof., 1948-52, prof., 1952-85, Wis. Alumni Research Found. prof. oncology, 1980-82, Van Rensselaer Potter prof. on oncology, 1982-85, prof. emeritus, 1985—; mem. advisory coms. Nat. Cancer Inst., Am. Cancer Soc., 1950—. Contbr. numerous articles on chemical carcinogenesis and microsomal oxidations to profl. jours. Recipient awards (with E.C. Miller): Langer-Teplitz award Ann Langer Cancer Research Found., 1962; Lucy Wortham James award James Ewing Soc., 1965; G.H.A. Clowes award Am. Assn. Cancer Research, 1969; Bertner award M.D. Anderson Hosp. and Tumor Inst. 1971; Papanicolaou award Papanicolaou Inst. Cancer Research, 1975; Rosenstiel award Brandeis U., 1976; award Am. Cancer Soc., 1977; Bristol-Myers award in cancer research, 1978; Gairdner Found. ann. award Toronto, 1978; Founders award Chem. Industry Inst. Toxicology, 1978; 3M Life Sci. award Fedn. Am. Socs. Exptl. Biology, 1979; Freedman award N.Y. Acad. Sci., 1979; Mott award Gen. Motors Cancer Research Found., 1980, Noble Found. Research award, 1986, 1st E. C. Miller and J. A. Miller Disting. Lectureship in Exptl. Oncology award Rutgers U., 1989. Fellow Am. Acad. Arts and Scis., Wis. Acad. Scis., Arts and Letters; mem. Am. Assn. for Cancer Research (hon.), Am. Soc. Biol. Chemists, AAAS, Japanese Cancer Soc. (hon.), Am. Chem. Soc., Soc. Toxicology, Soc. for Exptl. Biology and

Medicine, Nat. Acad. Scis. Home: 5517 Hammersley Rd Madison WI 53711-3556 Office: U Wis Mcardle Lab Madison WI 53706

MILLER, JAMES CHRISTOPHER, paper industry information systems specialist; b. Augsburg, Germany, Oct. 20, 1951; came to U.S., 1955, naturalized, 1969; s. William Edwin and Martha (Isele) M.; B.S. in Acctg., Pa. State U., 1973; M.S. in Computer Sci., Rensselaer Poly. Inst., 1975; M.B.A., U. New Haven, 1980; m. Lynette Marie Murri, Aug. 25, 1973; children—Meghan Leigh, Margo Elizabeth. Fin. and EDP auditor United Techs. Corp., Hartford, Conn., 1973-74, fin. systems analyst, 1974-76, asst. mgr. corp. acctg., 1976-77; sr. analyst The Upjohn Co., North Haven, Conn., 1977-79; cons. bus. systems Am. Can Co., Greenwich, Conn., 1980-81, mgr. systems planning, 1981-82, assoc. dir. systems support, 1982; mgr. mgmt. info. systems James River Corp., Richmond, Va., 1983, dir. mgmt. info. systems, 1984-86, v.p. mgmt. info. systems, 1986-90, v.p info. tech., 1990-93, v.p. info. tech. Hallmark Cards, Inc., Kansas City, Mo., 1993—; instr. info. systems Conn. Tech. Colls., Waterbury and Thames Valley; instr. bus. adminstrn. Western Conn. State U., Ancell Sch. Bus.; chmn. MIS adv. coun. Bloch Sch. Bus. U. Mo., Kansas City. Republican. Roman Catholic. Home: 3405 W 132nd St Leawood KS 66209 Office: James River Corp Richmond Plaza 5th floor 110 S 7th St Richmond VA 23219-3904

MILLER, JAMES CLIFFORD, III, economist; b. Atlanta, June 25, 1942; s. James Clifford and Annie (Moseley) M.; m. Demaris Humphries, Dec. 22, 1961; children: Katrina Demaris, John Felix, Sabrina Louise. BBA, U. Ga., 1964; PhD in Econs., U. Va., 1969. Asst. prof. Ga. State U., Atlanta, 1968-69; economist U.S. Dept. Transp., Washington, 1969-72; assoc. prof. econs. Tex. A&M U., College Station, 1972-74; economist U.S. Coun. Econ. Advs., Washington, 1974-75; asst. dir. U.S. Council Wage and Price Stability, Washington, 1975-77; resident scholar Am. Enterprise Inst., 1977-81; adminstr. Office Info. and Regulatory Affairs, Office Mgmt. and Budget and exec. dir. Presdl. Task Force on Regulatory Relief, Washington, 1981; chmn. FTC, Washington, 1981-85; dir. Office Mgmt. and Budget, Washington, 1985-88; disting. fellow, chmn., counsellor Citizens for a Sound Economy, 1988—; disting. fellow Ctr. for Study of Pub. Choice George Mason U., 1988—; pres., chmn. bd. Econ. Impact Analysts, Inc., 1978—. Author: Why the Draft?: The Case for a Volunteer Army, 1968, Economic Regulation of Domestic Air Transport: Theory and Policy, 1974, Perspectives on Federal Transportation Policy, 1975, Benefit-Cost Analyses of Social Regulation: Case Studies from the Council on Wage and Price Stability, 1979, Reforming Regulation, 1980, The Economist as Reformer, 1989, Fix the U.S. Budget: Urgings of an "Abominable No-Man," 1994. Thomas Jefferson fellow, 1965-66, DuPont fellow, 1966-67, Ford Found. fellow, 1967-68. Mem. Am. Econ. Assn., Pub. Choice Soc., So. Econ. Assn. (exec. com. 1980-81, v.p. 1990-91), Adminstrv. Conf. U.S. (vice chmn. 1987-88). Republican. Presbyterian. Office: Citizens for Sound Economy 1250 H St NW Washington DC 20005-3952

MILLER, JAMES EDWARD, computer scientist, educator; b. Lafayette, La., Mar. 21, 1940; s. Edward Gustave and Orpha Marie (DeVilbis) M.; m. Diane Moon, June 6, 1964; children—Deborah Elaine, Michael Edward. B.S., U. La.-Lafayette, 1961, Ph.D. 1972; M.S., Auburn U., 1964. Systems engr. IBM, Birmingham, Ala., 1965-68; asst. prof. U. West Fla., Pensacola, 1968-70, chmn. systems sci., 1972-86; grad. researcher U. La.-Lafayette, 1970-72; computer systems analyst EPA, Washington, 1979; prof., chmn. computer sci. and stats. U. So. Miss., Hattiesburg, 1986-92; prof. U. So. Miss., 1992—; program evaluator Computer Sci. Accreditation Commn., 1986—, cons., lectr. in field; co-dir. NASA/Am. Soc. Engring. Edn. Summer Faculty Fellowship Program-Stennis Space Flight Ctr., 1990—. Author numerous articles for tech. publs. Mem. Computer Soc. of IEEE, Assn. Computing Machinery (editor Computer Sci. Edn. spl. interest group bull. 1982—), Data Processing Mgmt. Assn. (dir. edn. spl. interest group 1985-86), Info. Systems Security Assn., Internat. Assn. Math. and Computer Modeling. Democrat. Methodist. Avocations: Research on computer crime, computer sci. edn. and optimal sensor deployment. Office: U So Miss Computer Sci & Stat PO Box 5106 Hattiesburg MS 39406-5106

MILLER, JAMES EDWIN, JR., English language educator; b. Bartlesville, Okla., Sept. 9, 1920; s. James Edwin and Leona (Halsey) M.; m. Barbara Anderson, July 3, 1944 (dec. 1981); children: James E. III, Charlotte Ann; m. Kathleen Farley, Mar. 15, 1990. B.A., U. Okla., 1942; M.A., U. Chgo., 1947, Ph.D., 1949. Asst. prof. English U. Nebr., Lincoln, 1953-56; prof., chmn. dept. U. Nebr., 1956-62, Charles J. Mach Regents prof. English, 1961-62; prof. English U. Chgo., 1962—, chmn. dept., 1978-84, Helen A. Regenstein prof. lit., 1983-90, prof. emeritus, 1990—; vis. prof. Northwestern U., 1962, U. Hawaii, 1964, The Sorbonne, Paris, 1984-85, 86, Beijing, China, 1994; Fulbright lectr., Italy, 1958-59, Kyoto, Japan, 1968, Australia, 1976; Otto Salgo prof. Am. studies, Budapest, Hungary, 1991-93. Author: A Critical Guide to Leaves of Grass, 1957, (with Bernice Slote and Karl Shapiro) Start with the Sun, 1960, Walt Whitman, 1962, rev. 1990, Reader's Guide to Herman Melville, 1962, F. Scott Fitzgerald: His Art and His Technique, 1964, J.D. Salinger, 1965, Quests Surd and Absurd: Essays in American Literature, 1967, Word Self, Reality: The Rhetoric of Imagination, 1972, T.S. Eliot's Personal Waste Land, 1977, The American Quest for a Supreme Fiction: Whitman's Legacy in the Personal Epic, 1979, Leaves of Grass: America's Lyric-Epic of Self and Democracy, 1992; Editor: Complete Poetry and Selected Prose of Walt Whitman, 1959, Myth and Method: Modern Theories of Fiction, 1960, Dimensions of Poetry, 1962, Dimensions of the Short Story, 1964, Whitman's Song of Myself: Origin, Growth, Meaning, 1964, Dimensions of Literature, 1967, The Arts and The Public, 1967, Theory of Fiction: Henry James, 1972, Heritage of American Literature, 2 Vols., 1991. Capt. U.S. Army, 1942-46, 50-52. Recipient Walt Whitman award Poetry Soc. Am., 1958, Poetry Chap Book award, 1961; Distinguished Service award Nat. Council Tchrs. English, 1975; Guggenheim fellow, 1969-70; Nat. Endowment for Humanities sr. fellow, 1974-75. Mem. Modern Lang. Assn., Nat. Council Tchrs. of English (editor Coll. English 1960-66, pres. 1970), Am. Studies Assn., Assn. Depts. English (exec. council 1981-84, pres. 1984); AAUP (council 1964-67), Midwest Modern Lang. Assn. (pres. 1961-62), Phi Beta Kappa. Home: 5536 S Blackstone Ave Chicago IL 60637-1834

MILLER, JAMES GEGAN, research scientist, physics educator; b. St. Louis, Nov. 11, 1942; s. Francis John and Elizabeth Ann (Caul) M.; m. Judith Anne Kelvin, Apr. 23, 1966; 1 child, Douglas Ryan. A.B., St. Louis U., 1964; M.A., Washington U., 1966, Ph.D, 1969. Asst. prof. physics Washington U., St. Louis, 1970-72, assoc. prof., 1972-77, prof. physics, 1977—, dir. lab. for ultrasonics, 1987—, research asst. prof. medicine, 1976-81, research assoc. prof. medicine, 1981-88, research prof. medicine, 1988—. Contbr. articles to profl. jours.; patentee in field. Recipient I-R 100 award Indsl. Research Devel. Mag., 1974, 78; NIH, NASA grantee. Fellow Am. Inst. Ultrasound in Medicine, Acoustical Soc. Am.; mem. IEEE (gov. com. Ultrasonics, Ferroelectrics and Frequency Control Soc. 1978-80, 86-88, 92-94), Am. Phys. Soc., Sigma Xi (nat. lectr. 1981-82). Home: 444 Edgewood Dr Saint Louis MO 63105-2016 Office: Washington U Box 1105 Dept Physics Saint Louis MO 63130

MILLER, J(AMES) GORMLY, retired librarian, educator; b. Rochester, N.Y., Jan. 5, 1914; s. James Billings and Marian (Robinson) M.; m. Mildred Catharine Bevan, Sept. 6, 1939; children: Susan Miller Milligan, James Gormly, Paul B. AB, U. Rochester, 1936; BSLS, Columbia U., 1938. Asst. librarian Rochester Pub. Library, 1938-42; research asst. Bur. Adult Edn. N.Y. State Dept. Edn., 1946; librarian Cornell U.-N.Y. State Sch. Indsl. and Labor Relations, 1946-62, assoc. prof., then prof., 1949-70, 74-77, asst. dir. personnel and budget univ. libraries, 1962-70, libraries dir., 1975-79, librarian, 1979-80, prof. emeritus, 1980—; acting Univ. librarian Cornell U., 1985-86; dep. chief central library and documentation br. ILO, Geneva, 1970-74; trustee Finger Lakes Library System, 1967-69; pres. bd. trustees South Central Research Library Council, 1980-83, 1993-94, 1984-85; cons. in field. Author profl. articles, reports. Alderman Ithaca (N.Y.) Common Council, 1959-63, 68; commnr. Ithaca Civil Service Commn., 1983-86. Served with U.S. Army, 1943-46. Mem. Am. Soc. for Info. Sci., ALA, N.Y. State Library Assn., Indsl. Relations Research Assn. Democrat. Anglican. Home: Eastwood Commons 7 Wildflower Dr # D Ithaca NY 14850-6230 Office: Cornell Univ 349 Ives Hall Ithaca NY 14853-3901

MILLER, JAMES HUGH, JR., retired public utility executive; b. New Orleans, Oct. 14, 1922; s. James Hugh and Helen (Piguet) M.; m. Juliet deVilliers, Nov. 22, 1945; children: Juliet Miller Beale, James Hugh, Robert Boyd, Mary Ashley Miller Crosier. BEE, Tulane U., 1943. Jr. engr. Ala. Power Co., Mobile, 1946-58; supr. transmission lines Ala. Power Co., Birmingham, 1958-60, asst. to pres., 1960-62, asst. mgr. elec. ops., 1962-68, sr. v.p., 1968-75; exec. v.p. Ga. Power Co., Atlanta, 1975-82, pres., 1982-87. Home: 2170 Mount Paran Rd NW Atlanta GA 30327-2924

MILLER, JAMES L., food products executive; b. 1948. Grad., Cornell U., 1972. V.p. sales, then gen. mgr Sysco Corp., Houston, 1972-83; v.p., gen. mgr., exec. v.p., COO no. divsn. PYA/Monarch, Inc., Balt., 1983-89; pres., COO J.P. Foodservice, Inc., Hanover, Md., 1989—. Office: J P Foodservices Inc 7250 Parkway Dr Hanover MD 21076

MILLER, JAMES LYNN, lawyer; b. Fairmont, W.Va., June 1, 1951; s. Robert Ogden Jr. and Dora Alice (Ward) M.; m. Maureen Clancy, Apr. 16, 1983; children: James Clancy, Bailey Ward. BA, Calif. State U., Humboldt, 1973; JD, U. Calif., Berkeley, 1976. Bar: Calif. 1976, Hawaii 1988. From assoc. to ptnr. Brobeck, Phleger & Harrison, San Francisco, 1976—. Republican. Avocation: fishing. Office: Brobeck Phleger & Harrison Spear St Tower 1 Market Pla San Francisco CA 94105

MILLER, JAMES ROBERT, lawyer; b. McKeesport, Pa., Aug. 2, 1947; s. Robert Charles and Ethel Margaret (Yahn) M.; m. Kathleen Ann Galka, June 6, 1975; children: Jesse J., Cassidy A. BA, NYU, 1969; JD, Duquesne U., 1972. Bar: Pa. 1972, U.S. Dist. Ct. (we. dist.) Pa. 1974, U.S.Ct. Appeals (3d cir.) 1978, U.S. Ct. Appeals (11th cir.) 1989, U.S. Supreme Ct. 1990. Law clerk to Hon. James C. Crumlish, Jr. Commonwealth Ct. of Pa., Phila., 1972-74; with Dickie, McCamey & Chilcote, Pitts., 1974—. Mem. ABA, Am. Coll. Trial Lawyers, Pa. Bar Assn., Acad. Trial Lawyers. Avocation: sports. Office: Dickie McCamey & Chilcote Two PPG Pl Ste 400 Pittsburgh PA 15222

MILLER, JAMES RUMRILL, III, finance educator; b. Phila., Dec. 21, 1937; s. James Rumrill and Elizabeth Pleasants (King) M.; m. Bettie M. Studer, May 1, 1989; children from previous marriage: Elizabeth, Katharine, Kerry. A.B., Princeton U., 1959; M.B.A. (Woodrow Wilson fellow), Harvard U., 1962; Ph.D., M.I.T., 1966. Systems analyst MITRE Corp., Bedford, Mass., 1962-67; asst. prof. bus. adminstrn. Stanford U., 1967-69, asso. prof., 1970-73, prof., 1973—; Walter and Elise Haas prof. bus. adminstrn., 1977—; asso. dean Stanford U. (Bus. Sch.), 1974-76; cons. in field. Author: Professional Decision Making, 1970; contbr. numerous articles to profl. jours. Mem. Phi Beta Kappa. Republican. Episcopalian. Home: 264 Foster St # 2 Boston MA 02135-4622 Office: Stanford U Bus Sch Stanford CA 94305

MILLER, JAMES VINCE, university president; b. Waynetown, Ind., July 16, 1920; s. J. Vince and Hazel B. (Spore) M.; m. Mildred Mae Hockersmith, June 13, 1943; children: Maryllyn Jean, Rachel Katherine. B.A. in Philosophy and English, U. Indpls., 1942; M.Div. in History and Lit., United Sem., Dayton, Ohio, 1945; postgrad., Earlham Coll., 1945-46; Ph.D. in Philosophy, Boston U., 1955; LL.D. (hon.), Otterbein Coll., 1971, U. Indpls., 1979. Ordained to ministry Evang. United Brethren Ch., 1945; pastor Greensfork, Ind., 1944-46, Stow, Mass., 1946-48; faculty dept. philosophy and religion Bates Coll., Lewiston, Maine, 1950-64; prof. Bates Coll., 1960-64, chmn. dept., 1958-64; acad. dean Otterbein Coll., Westerville, Ohio, 1964-68; v.p. for acad. affairs, acad. dean Otterbein Coll., 1968-71; pres. Pacific U., Forest Grove, Oreg., 1971-83, pres. emeritus, 1983—; pres. Nat. Coll. of Naturopathic Medicine, Portland, Oreg., 1989-93, pres. emeritus, 1993—; adj. prof. Union Grad. Sch., 1970-78, San Francisco Theol. Sem., 1979-86; chmn. N.W. Assn. Pvt. Colls. and Univs., 1974-76; treas. Oreg. Ind. Coll. Assn., 1974-75, 76-78, chmn., 1978-79; adv. com. Oreg. Ednl. Coordinating Commn., 1976-79; chmn. council for higher edn. United Ch. Bd. Homeland Missions, 1975-76; former mem. spl. com. on future of edn. in Oreg., Oreg. Ednl. Coordinating Commn.; mem. Oreg. Bd. Optometry, 1988-92; bd. dirs. Terwilliger Plz., Inc. Methodist. Lodge: Rotary.

MILLER, JAN DEAN, metallurgy educator; b. Dubois, Pa., Apr. 7, 1942; s. Harry Moyer and Mary Virginia (McQuown) M.; m. Patricia Ann Rossman, Sept. 14, 1963; children: Pamela Ann, Jeanette Marie, Virginia Christine. B.S., Pa. State U., 1964; M.S., Colo. Sch. of Mines, 1966, Ph.D., 1969. Research engr. Anaconda Co., Mont., 1966, Lawrence Livermore Lab., Calif., 1972; asst. prof. metallurgy U. Utah, Salt Lake City, 1968-72, assoc. prof., 1972-78, prof., 1978—; cons. on processing of mineral resources to various cos. and govt. agys. Editor: Hydrometalurgy, Research, Development, and Plant Practice, 1983. Contbr. over 200 articles to profl. jours. First commercial plant using air-sparged hydrocyclone tech. for deinking flotation in wastepaper recycling plant, 1992, patentee, 1983. Bethlehem Steel fellow, 1964-68; recipient Marcus A. Grossman award Am. Soc. Metals, 1974; Van Diest Gold medal Colo. Sch. Mines, 1977; Mellow Met award U. Utah, Salt Lake City, 1978, 82, 94, Stefanko award coal divsn. Soc. Mining Engrs., 1988, Extractive Metallurgy Tech. award, Metall. Soc., 1988, Richards award Am. Inst. Mining, Metall. and Petroleum Engrs., 1990, Extractive and Processing Lectr. award The Minerals, Metals and Materials Soc., 1992, Disting. Achievement medal Colo. Sch. of Mines, 1994. Mem. AIME (chmn. mineral processing div. 1980-81), Fine Particle Soc., AIME (Henry Krumb lectr. 1987), NAE, Am. Chem. Soc., Soc. Mining Engrs. (bd. dirs. 1980-83, program chmn. 1982-83, Taggart award, 1986), Metall. Soc., Soc. Mining, Metall. and Exploration (Disting. mem., Antoine M. Gaudin award 1992). Baptist. Clubs: Salt Lake Swim and Tennis; U. Utah Faculty. Office: U Utah Dept Metallurgy Salt Lake City UT 84112

MILLER, JASON, playwright; b. Scranton, Pa., Apr. 22, 1939; s. John and Mary M.; m. Linda Gleason, 1963 (div. 1973); children: Jennifer, Jason, Jordan, Joshua. Student, Cath. U.; B.A., U. Scranton, 1961. Author: (plays) Lou Gehrig Did Not Die of Cancer, 1967, Perfect Son, 1967, The Circle Lady, 1967, Nobody Hears a Broken Drum, 1970, That Championship Season, 1971 (Pulitzer prize for drama 1973, Tony award best play 1973, N.Y. Drama Critics Circle award best play 1972), It's a Sin to Tell a Lie; (poetry) Stone Step, 1968, (teleplays) The Reward, 1980, Marilyn: The Untold Story, 1980; dir., writer: (film) That Championship Season, 1982; actor: (theatre) Pequod, 1969, The Happiness Cage, 1970, Subject to Fits, 1971, Long Day's Journey into Night, 1971, Juno and the Paycock, 1971, That Championship Season, 1987, (films) The Exorcist, 1973 (Academy award nomination best supporting actor 1974), The Nickel Ride, 1975, The Ninth Configuration, 1980, Monsignor, 1982, Toy Soldiers, 1984, Light of Day, 1987, The Exorcist III, 1990, Rudy, 1993, (TV movies) A Home of Our Own, 1975, F. Scott Fitzgerald in Hollywood, 1976, The Dain Curse, 1978, Vampire, 1979, Henderson Monster, 1980, The Best Little Girl in the World, 1981, A Touch of Scandal, 1984, Deadly Care, 1987, A Mother's Courage: The Mary Thomas Story, 1989. Office: Mickey Freiberg/Rich Shepard The Artists Agy 10000 Santa Monica Blvd Ste 305 Los Angeles CA 90067*

MILLER, JAY ALAN, civil rights association executive; b. Cleve., Feb. 8, 1928; s. Herbert Phillip Miller and Ruth Weisbach; m. Joyce Dannen, Feb. 1, 1952 (div. Oct. 1964); children: Joshua, Adam, Rebecca; m. Maryanne Carol Dust, Jan. 1, 1989; stepchild, Joshua Kalin. Student, Roosevelt U., 1948; BSc, U. Ill., 1950. Organizer Amalgamated Clothing Workers, Chgo., 1950-52; bus. agt., edn. dir. Amalgamated Clothing Workers, Wilkes-Barre, Pa., 1956-61; organizer United Packing House Workers, Chgo., 1952-53; reporter Cleve. Press, 1954-56; peace edn. dir. Am. Friends Svc. Com., Chgo., 1961-65; exec. dir. ACLU of Ill., Chgo., 1965-71, 78—, ACLU of No. Calif., San Francisco, 1971-74; assoc. dir. legis. office ACLU, Washington, 1975-78. Pres. AFL-CIO Labor Coun., Hazelton, Pa., 1959-61, mem. trade union delegation to USSR, 1960; chmn. Turn Toward Peace, Chgo., 1962-64; coord. Com. for a Test Ban Treaty, Ill. and Wis., 1962-63; dep. dir. Ill. Rally for Civil Rights, Chgo., 1964. With U.S. Army, 1946-48, PTO. Home: 2573 N Clark St Chicago IL 60614-1717 Office: ACLU 203 N La Salle St Ste 1405 Chicago IL 60601-1210

MILLER, JEANNE-MARIE ANDERSON (MRS. NATHAN J. MILLER), English language educator, academic administrator; b. Washington, Feb. 18, 1937; d. William and Agnes Catherine (Johns) Anderson m. Nathan John Miller, Oct. 2, 1960. BA, Howard U., 1959, MA, 1963, PhD, 1976.

Instr. dept. English Howard U., Washington, 1963-76, asst. prof., 1976-79, assoc. prof., 1979-92, prof., 1992—; also asst. dir. Inst. Arts and Humanities, 1973-75, asst. acad. planning, office v.p. for acad. affairs, 1976-90; cons. Am. Studies Assn., 1972-75, Silver Burdett Pub. Co., Nat. Endowment for Humanities, 1978—; adv. bd. D.C. Libr. for Arts, 1973—, John Oliver Killens Writers Guild, 1975—, Afro-Am. Theatre, Balt., 1975—. Editor, Black Theatre Bull., 1977-86; Realism to Ritual: Form and Style in Black Theatre, 1983; assoc. editor Theatre Jour., 1980-81; contbr. articles to profl. jours. Mem. Washington Performing Arts Soc., 1971—, Friends of Sta. WETA-TV, 1971—, Mus. African Art, 1971—, Arena Stage Assos., 1972—, Washington Opera Guild, 1982—, Wolf Trap Assocs., 1982—, Fod Found. fellow, 1970-71. So. Fellowships Fund fellow, 1972-74; Howard U. Rsch. grantee, 1975-76, 94-95, Am. Coun. Learned Socs. grantee, 1978-79, Nat. Endowment Humanities grantee, 1981-84. Mem. Nat. Coun. Tchrs. of English, Coll. English Assn., Am. Studies Assn., Am. Theatre Assn., AAUP, AAUW, D.C. LWV, Common Cause, ACLU, Am. Acad. Polit. and Social Sci., Coll. Lang. Assn., MLA, Am. Assn. Higher Edn., Nat. Assn. Women Deans, Administrs. and Counselors, Friends Kennedy Ctr. for Performing Arts, Pi Lambda Theta. Democrat. Episcopalian. Home: 504 24th St NE Washington DC 20002-4818

MILLER, JEFFREY CLARK, lawyer; b. Boston, Aug. 17, 1943; s. Andrew Otterson and Jeanne (White) M.; m. Susanne Jackson, Oct. 23, 1970; children: Gordon, Andrew, Katharine, Eric. BA, Yale U., 1965; JD, Cornell U., 1968. Bar: N.Y. 1970. Assoc. Miller, Montgomery, Spalding & Sogi, N.Y.C., 1968-69; sec. Jamaica Water & Utilities Inc., Greenwich, Conn., 1969-72; assoc. Reid & Priest, N.Y.C., 1972-86, ptnr., 1986-93; asst. gen. coun. Northeast Utilies Svc. Co., Berlin, Conn., 1993—. Bd. dirs. Wilson Point Porperty Owners Assn., Norwalk, Conn., 1972-74, pres., 1988-92; trustee St. Luke's Sch., New Canaan, Conn., 1992—, chmn., 1995—. Mem. N.Y. State Bar Assn. (sec. pub. utility com. 1983-87). Home: 1 Valley Rd Norwalk CT 06854-5010 Office: Northeast Utilities Svc Co PO Box 270 Hartford CT 06141-0270

MILLER, JEFFREY GRANT, law educator; b. Muncie, Ind., Aug. 15, 1941; s. Robert G. and Virginia (Bell) M.; m. Georgia Callahan, Feb. 19, 1988; children: Elizabeth, Scott. AB, Princeton U., 1963; LLB, Harvard U., 1967. Bar: Mass. 1968, D.C. 1987. Rsch. asst. Harvard Law Sch., Cambridge, Mass., 1976-78; assoc. Bingham, Dana & Gould, Boston, 1968-71; enforcement dir. chief U.S. EPA, Boston, 1971-73, dir. enforcement div., 1973-75; dep assist adminstr. for water enforcement U.S. EPA, Washington, 1975-79, acting asst. adminstr. for enforcement, 1979-81; ptnr. Bergson, Borkland, Margolis & Adler, Washington, 1981-86, Verner, Liipfert, Washington, 1986-87; of counsel Perkins Coie, Washington, 1987—; prof. law Pace U., White Plains, N.Y., 1987—; bd. dirs. EnviroSource, Inc., Stamford, Conn.; sec.-treas. Environ. Law Inst., 1987-90. Author: Citizen Suits: Private Enforcement of Federal Pollution Control Laws, 1987, (with T. Colosi) Fundamentals of Negotiation, 1989; mem. editl. adv. bd. Environ. Law Reporter, 1983—. Mem. ABA (chmn. water quality com. 1986-88). Avocations: backpacking, hiking, white water canoeing.

MILLER, JERRY HUBER, retired university chancellor; b. Salem, Ohio, June 15, 1931; s. Duber Daniel and Ida Claire (Holdereith) M.; m. Margaret A. Setter, 1958; children: Gregory, Joy, Carol, Beth, David. BA, Harvard U., 1953; MDiv., Hamma Sch. Theology, 1957; DD (hon.), Trinity Luth. Sem., 1981. Ordained to ministry Luth. Ch., 1957. Research assoc., intern Cornell U., Ithaca, N.Y., 1955-56; instr. Wittenberg U., Springfield, Ohio, 1956-57; parish pastor Ch. of Good Shepherd, Cin., 1957-62; asst. to pres. Ohio Synod Luth. Ch. Am., 1962-66; sr. campus pastor, dir. campus ministry U. Wis., Madison, 1966-69; regional dir. Nat. Luth. Campus Ministry, Madison, 1969-76; exec. dir. Nat. Luth. Campus Ministry, Chgo., 1977-81; pres. Calif. Luth. U., Thousand Oaks, 1981-92, chancellor, 1992-94, pres. emeritus, 1994—; ret. Venturra County Maritime Mus., Channel Islands Harbor, Calif., 1994; chmn. Los Robles Bank, Thousand Oaks; mem. exec. com. Coun. Ind. Colls., Washington, Assn. Ind. Calif. Colls. and Univs., 1981-92, Coun. Luth. Colls., Luth. Ednl. Conf. N.Am., 1977-94. Editor: The Higher Disciplines, 1956; contbr. articles to profl. jours. Bd. dirs. Wittenberg U., Augustana Coll., Rock Island, Ill., United Way, Thousand oaks, Ventura County chpt. ARC, Thousand Oaks, YMCA; chmn. bd. dirs. Los Robles Hosp. Named Man of Yr., Salem, 1975; Siebert Found. fellow, 1975. Mem. Am. Assn. Higher Edn., Council Advancement and Support Edn., Harvard Alumni Assn., Western Coll. Assn. (bd. dirs.), Conejo Valley C. of C. (bd. dirs.), Conejo Symphony Orch. (bd. dirs.). Club: Harvard (Ill., Ohio, Wis., Calif.), YMCA (regional bd. dirs.), Rotary. Avocations: skiing, golfing, hiking, travelling.

MILLER, JESSE D., lawyer; b. Chgo., June 13, 1930; s. Jesse B. and Rose Veronica (Jasnoch) M.; m. Geraldine Rae Richardson, Apr. 7, 1967; children: Nancy, Craig, Cynthia, Steven, Traci, Christian. BS summa cum laude, UCLA, 1956; JD, Harvard U., 1959. Assoc. Foley, Sammond & Lardner, Milw., 1959-64, Keatinge & Sterling, L.A., 1964-65; ptnr. Iverson & Hogoboom (now Iverson, Hatch & Miller), L.A., 1965-69, Law Offices of Jesse D. Miller, L.A., 1969-74, Miller & Mandel, L.A., 1974-82; mng. ptnr. Pepper Hamilton & Scheetz, L.A., 1982-89, Fulbright & Jaworski, L.A., 1990—; affiliate Stanford Ctr. Conflict and Negotiation, 1989—; mem. adv. com. Ctr. Pub. Resources, 1983—; ptnr. gambling casino, Cripple Creek, Colo.; owner standardbred racehorse. With US Army, 1951-53. Mem. ABA (chmn. litigation sect. litigation mgmt. subcom. 1989—), Calif. Dental Assn. (hon.), Phi Beta Kappa, Beta Gamma Sigma. Avocation: golf.

MILLER, JIM, film editor. Editor: (TV pilots) Feel the Heat, 1993, The Wizard, 1986, (TV movies) Two Fathers' Justice, 1985, Alice in Wonderland, 1985, (films) (with Dede Allen) The Breakfast Club, 1985, Blue City, 1986, (with Allen) The Milagro Beanfield War, 1988, (with Allen) Let It Ride, 1990, (with Allen) The Addams Family, 1991, (with Arthur Schmidt) Addams Family Values, 1993, For Love or Money, 1993. Office: 3926 Corte Cancion Thousand Oaks CA 91360*

MILLER, JOANNE LOUISE, middle school educator; b. Milton, Mass., Apr. 4, 1944; d. Joseph Louis and Marion Theresa (Saulnier) Fasci; m. William Frederick Miller, Dec. 4, 1962; 1 child, Robert Joseph. BS, U. Oreg., 1972, MS in Curriculum and Instrn., 1973; EdD, Brigham Young U., 1980; postgrad., Oreg. State U., 1995. Lic. counselor, tchr., adminstr., Oreg. Tchr. South Lane Sch. Dist., Cottage Grove, Oreg., 1973—, lang. arts div. chairperson, 1975-78, 89-90, reading coord., 1978-79, 7th grade block chairperson, 1982-92, mid. sch. talented and gifted coord., 1992-93, counselor, 1991-93; mem. Oreg. State Assessment Content Panel Reading, Salem, 1987-88; mem. Oreg. Lang Arts Curriculum Devel. Com., Salem, 1985-87; del. to Citizen Amb. Program of People to People Internat. 1st U.S.-Russia Joint Conf. on Edn., Moscow, 1994. Vol. Am. Cancer Soc., Am. Diabetes Assn., 1990—. Mem. ACA, NEA, Internat. Reading Assn., Am. Sch. Counselor Assn., Oreg. Counseling Assn., Oreg. Edn. Assn., South Lane Edn. Assn., Oreg. Reading Assn., Delta Kappa Gamma, Alpha Rho State (v.p. 1995—). Democrat. Roman Catholic. Avocations: travel, reading. Home: 85515 Appletree Dr Eugene OR 97405-9738 Office: Lincoln Mid Sch 1565 S 4th St Cottage Grove OR 97424-2955

MILLER, JOEL E., accountant, finance company executive; b. Boston, Mar. 3, 1941; s. Morris I. and Florence (Engleman) M.; m. Irene Mazur, Apr. 12, 1964; children: Jason, Michael, Eric. BA, Rutgers U., 1963, MBA, 1964. CPA, N.Y. Acct. Arthur Andersen & Co., N.Y.C., 1964—, ptnr., 1974-87; chief fin. officer, adminstrv. mng. dir. L.F. Rothschild & Co., Inc., N.Y.C., 1987—. Co-author: (guide) Audit of Brokers and Dealers in Securities. Mem. AICPA (stockbrokerage com. 1983-86, commodities futures com. 1981-82), N.Y. State Soc. CPA's (commodities futures com. 1987), First Wednesday Group, Securities Industry Assn., Pitts. C. of C. (bd. dirs.). Home: 2 Renee Ct Edison NJ 08820-3634 Office: L F Rothschild & Co Inc 222 Broadway New York NY 10038-2510

MILLER, JOEL STEVEN, solid state scientist; b. Detroit, Oct. 14, 1944; s. John and Rose (Schpok) M.; m. Elaine J. Silverstein, Sept. 20, 1970; children: Stephen D., Marc A, Alan D. BS in Chemistry, Wayne State U., 1967; PhD, UCLA, 1971. Mgr. rsch. Occidental Rsch. Corp., Irvine, Calif., 1979-83; supr. rsch. Cen. R & D Lab. E. I. Du Pont Nemours & Co., Wilmington, Del., 1983-93; prof. chemistry U. Utah, 1993—; adj. prof. materials sci., 1994—; bd. dirs. Inorganic Synthesis Corp., Chgo.; vis. prof.

U. Calif., Irvine, 1980, Weizmann Inst., Rehovot, Israel, 1985, U. Pa., Phila., 1988, U. Paris-Sud, 1991. Editor 8 books; mem. adv. bd. Jour. Chemistry Materials, 1990—, Jour. Materials Chemistry, 1991—, Advanced Materials, 1990—; contbr. more than 250 articles to sci. jours. Indsl. fellow in material sci. Northwestern U., 1991-93. Mem. Am. Chem. Soc. (chmn. solid state subdiv. 1989). Achievements include discovery and development of molecular-based conductors and magnets. Office: U Utah Dept Of Chemistry Salt Lake City UT 84108

MILLER, JOHN A., JR., public relations executive. Chmn., CEO Miller Comms., Boston. Office: Miller Comm Copley Sq 607 Boylston St Boston MA 02116*

MILLER, JOHN ALBERT, university administrator, marketing consultant; b. St. Louis County, Mo., Mar. 22, 1939; s. John Adam and Emma D. (Doering) M.; m. Eunice Ann Timm, Aug. 25, 1968; children: Michael, Kristin. AA, St. Paul's Coll., 1958; BA with high honors, Concordia Sr. Coll., 1960; postgrad., Wash. U., St. Louis, 1960-64; MBA, Ind. U., 1971, D.B.A. in Mktg., 1972. Proofreader, editor Concordia Pub. House, St. Louis, 1960-62, periodical sales mgr., 1964-68; asst. prof. Drake U., Des Moines, 1971-74; cons. FTC, Washington, 1974-75; vis. assoc. prof. Ind. U., Bloomington, 1975-77; assoc. prof. U. Colo., Colorado Springs, 1977-79, prof., 1977-86, prof. mktg., resident dean, 1980-84; v.p. market devel. Peak Health Care Inc., Colorado Springs, 1984-85; dean, prof. mktg. Valparaiso (Ind.) U., 1986—; cons. and rschr. govt. and industry; dir. health maintenance orgn.; bd. dirs. Ind. Acad. Social Scis., 1988-90; adv. bd. N.W. Ind. Small Bus. Devel. Ctr., 1988-91; consulting dean USIA project to form Polish Assn. of Bus. Schs., 1995. Author: Labeling Research The State of the Art, 1978; contbr. articles to profl. jours. Mem. Colorado Springs Symphony Orch. Coun., 1980-86; cons. Citizens Goals of Colorado Springs, 1985-86, Jr. League Colorado Springs, 1981-82; bd. dirs. Christmas in April, 1991—. With U.S. Army, 1962-64. U.S. Steel fellow, 1970-71. Mem. Assn. Consumer Rsch. (chmn. membership 1978-79), Am. Mktg. Assn. (fed. govt. liaison com. 1975-76), Am. Acad. Advt., Ind. Acad. Social Scis. (bd. dirs. 1988-90), Greater Valparaiso C. of C. (accreditation com. 1991, planning com. 1989-92, chair 1992), Am. Assembly Collegiate Schs. Bus. (internat. affairs com. 1991-93, mem. peer rev. team 1994, com. mem., seminar leader, faculty mem. for various seminars and workshops 1992—), Beta Gamma Sigma, Alpha Iota Delta. Lutheran. Avocations: racquetball, walking. Home: 1504 Del Vista Dr Valparaiso IN 46383-3322 Office: Valparaiso U Valparaiso IN 46383

MILLER, JOHN B., lawyer; b. New Britain, Conn., Nov. 16, 1952; s. Hugh Wilson and Edith (Hinton) M.; m. Joan Whitten, Aug. 22, 1981; children: John, Douglas, Mary. SB, MIT, 1974, SM, 1974; JD, Boston U., 1977, LLM Taxation, 1982. Bar: Mass. 1977, D.C. 1991, U.S. Dist. Ct. Mass. 1978, U.S. Ct. Appeals (1st cir.) 1978, U.S. Ct. Appeals (5th cir.) 1987, U.S. Ct. Appeals (fed. cir.) 1982, U.S. Claims Ct. 1982. Patent counsel Orion Rsch., Inc., Cambridge, Mass., 1977-80; assoc. Gadsby & Hannah, Boston, 1980-84; ptnr. Gudsby & Hannale, Boston, 1985-92, of counsel, 1993—. Author: (monograph) Architect Engineer Liability, 1991. Mem. ABA (chair elect section pub. contract law, 1993—). Office: 125 Summer St Ste 1500 Boston MA 02110-1616

MILLER, JOHN DAVID, manufacturing company executive; b. Utica, N.Y., Mar. 24, 1945; s. David Gordon and Eleanor Katherine (Brant) M., m. Ann Geraldine Johnston, Feb. 25, 1968; children: Shannon, Adra. BSME, Rochester Inst. Tech., 1968. Jr. engr. Pall Corp., Cortland, N.Y., 1968-70; staff engr., 1970-71; group leader Pall Corp., Cortland, N.Y., 1971-76, mgr. filter design, 1976-78, v.p.; tech. dir., 1978-86, sr. v.p., 1986—. Patentee filter equipment. Mem. ASME. Democrat. Unitarian. Avocations: song writing, sculpture, rowing, squash. Home: 511 Kline Rd Ithaca NY 14850-2305 Office: Pall Corp 3669 State Route 281 Cortland NY 13045-8857

MILLER, JOHN DAVID, agronomist; b. Todd, N.C., Aug. 9, 1923; s. Reuben Patterson and Chessie (Graham) M.; BS, N.C. State U., 1948, MS, 1950; Ph.D., U. Minn., 1953; m. Frances McCollum, June 9, 1946 (dec.); children—John David, Glenn, Mary; m. 2d Jimmie Heard, Mar. 24, 1984. Research fellow U. Minn., 1953; asst. prof. Kans. State Coll., 1953-57; research agronomist Agrl. Research Service, U.S. Dept. Agr., Blacksburg, Va. and Tifton, Ga., 1957-75, research leader, 1972-79, sr. agronomist, 1975-91. Dist. commr. Boy Scouts Am., 1971-74. Served with AUS, 1943-46. Decorated Bronze Star medal. Mem. Am. Soc. Agronomy, Phi Kappa Phi, Gamma Sigma Delta, Sigma Xi. Clubs: Toastmasters, Lions. Home: 801 E 12th St Tifton GA 31794-4115 Office: USDA Coastal Plain Sta Agrl Rsch Svcs Tifton GA 31793

MILLER, JOHN EDWARD, army officer; b. Paragould, Ark., May 8, 1941; s. Wardlow Knox and Anna Mae (Danford) M.; m. Joan Carolyn Capano, Oct. 5, 1968; children: C. Claire, J. Andrew, JoAnna M., Mary Ellen. BS in Math., S.W. Mo. State U., 1963; MS in Ops. Rsch., Ga. Inst. Tech., 1971; postgrad., Yale U., 1991. Commd. 2d lt. U.S. Army, 1963, advanced through grades to lt. gen., 1993; student U.S. Army Command and Gen. Staff Coll., Ft. Leavenworth, Kans., 1974; bn. comdr. 4th Brigade, 4th Inf. Div., Wiesbaden, Fed. Republic Germany, 1977-79; ops. officer 8th Inf. Div., Badkreuznach, Fed. Republic Germany, 1979-81; student U.S. Army War Coll., Carlisle, Pa., 1982; div. chief Office Dep. Chief of Staff for Rsch. Devel. and Acquisition, Dept. Army, Washington, 1982-84; brigade comdr., chief of staff 9th Inf. Div., Ft. Lewis, Wash., 1984-87; asst. for combat devels. U.S. Army Tng. and Doctrine Command, Ft. Monroe, Va., 1987-88; asst. div. comdr. 8th Inf. Div., Baumholder, Fed. Republic Germany, 1988-89; dep. comdt. U.S. Army Command and Gen. Staff Coll., Ft. Leavenworth, 1989-91; comdt. 101st Airborne Div., Ft. Campbell, Ky., 1991-93, Combined Arms Command, Ft. Leavenworth, Kans., 1993—; comdt. U.S. Army Command and Gen. Staff Coll., Ft. Leavenworth, 1993—. Recipient Outstanding Alumni award, S.W. Mo. State U. 1993. Mem. Assn. U.S. Army, Army Aviation Assn. Am., 101st Airborne Divsn.Assn. Republican. Avocations: tennis, skiing. Office: Combined Arms Command Fort Leavenworth KS 66027

MILLER, JOHN FRANCIS, association executive, social scientist; b. Canton, Ill., Aug. 3, 1908; s. Frank Lewis and Minnie Grace (Eyerly) M.; m. Ruth Roby, May 29, 1937; children: Joan, Kent R. Dana R. AB, U. Ill., 1929, AM, 1930; postgrad., Columbia U., 1930-31, 34-35; German-Am. student exch. fellow, U. Frankfurt on Main, 1931-33. Staff Commn. Inquiry on Pub. Svc. Pers., 1934-35, Regent's Inquiry Character and Cost Pub. Edn. 1936; cons. Pres.'s Com. on Adminstrv. Mgmt., 1936-37, Com. Civil Svc. Improvement, 1939, Inst. Pub. Adminstrn., 1937-38, Pub. Adminstrn. Clearing House, 1938; chief field svc. Nat. Resources Planning Bd., 1938-43; asst. dir. Nat. Planning Assn., 1943-50, asst. chmn., 1951-71, exec. sec., 1951-71, pres., 1971-79, vice chmn., 1977-89; trustee Nat. Planning Assn. Washington, 1977—; sec. Canadian-Am. Com., 1957-76, N.Am. sec. Brit.-N.Am. Com., 1969-85. Author: Veteran Preference in the Public Service, 1935. Trustee, mem. adv. com. Nat. Conf. on Family, 1946-49; mem. adv. council social security Senate Com. on Finance, 1947-48. Mem. The Planning Forum, Am. Econ. Assn., Am. Polit. Sci. Assn., Am. Hist. Assn., Phi Beta Kappa, Cosmos Club (Washington), Univ. Club (N.Y.). Home: Washington Hill Rd Chocorua NH 03817 Office: Nat Planning Assn 1424 16th St NW Ste 700 Washington DC 20036-2211

MILLER, JOHN HENRY, clergyman; b. Ridgeway, S.C., Dec. 3, 1917; s. Fletcher and Frances Helo (Turner) M.; BA, Livingstone Coll., 1941; M. Div., Hood Theol. Sem., 1945; postgrad. Hartford Theol. Sem. Found., 1954; m. Bernice Frances Dillard, June 27, 1945; children: George Frederick, John Henry. Ordained to ministry AME Zion Ch., 1939-40; ordained bishop, 1972. Bishop, 10th Dist., 1972-80, 8th Dist., Dallas, 1980-84, 7th Dist., 1984-88, 5th Dist, 1988—, ret.; mem. Gov.'s Advocacy Com. on Children and Youth, 1985—; chmn. bd. AME Zion Ch. Trustee Livingstone Coll.; former chmn. bd. Lomax-Hannon Jr. Coll.; chmn. bd. Black Reps. N.C. 1985—; chmn. hon. degrees com. L.C. Mem. NAACP, World Meth. Council, Alpha Phi Alpha. Republican. Clubs: Masons, Elks. Office: African Meth Episcopal Zion Ch 8605 Caswell Ct Raleigh NC 27613-1101

MILLER, JOHN LAURENCE, professional golfer; b. San Francisco, Apr. 29, 1947; s. Laurence O. and Ida (Meldrum) M.; m. Linda Strouse, Sept. 17, 1969; children: John Strouse, Kelly, Casi, Scott, Brent, Todd. Student,

Brigham Young U., 1965-69. Profl. golfer, 1969—; Pres. Johnny Miller Enterprises, Inc. Author: Pure Golf, 1976, Johnny Miller's Golf for Juniors, 1987. Named PGA Player of Yr., 1974. Winner U.S. Open at Oakmont County Club, 1973, Otago Golf Classic; New Zealand, 1972, Lancome Trophy tournament, Paris, 1973, Dunlop Phoenix, Japan, 1974, World Cup individual and team titles, 1973, 75, So. Open, 1971, Los Angeles Open, 1981, Inverrary Classic, 1980, 83, Los Angeles Open, 1981, Crosby Nat., Heritage and Tournament of Champions, 1974, Westchester Classic, World Open and Kaiser Internat., 1974 Brit. Open, Bob Hope Classic, Tucson Open, 1974-76, 81, San Diego Open, 1982, Chrysler Team Invitational, 1983, AT&T Nat. Pro Am., 1987, 94; NBC commentator for golf. Office: PO Box 2260 Napa CA 94558-0060*

MILLER, JOHN RICHARD, interior designer; b. Washington, Feb. 11, 1927; s. John Henry and Helen (Vermillion) M.; m. Audrey Gene Owens, Nov. 6, 1946; children: Pamela Dawn, Felicity Amanda, Timothy John. Diploma in interior design, Colbert Inst., Washington, 1950. Designer Hollidge Interiors, Washington, 1950-51; pres. Miller's Interiors Inc., Temple Hills, Md., 1951—; bd. dirs. St. Barnabas Venture, Temple Hills. Author: Training for Design Related Trades, 1976; columnist Washington Star, 1971-79. Mem. Pres.'s Com. on Employment of Handicapped, 1978-82, White House Design Com., 1969-74, Presdl. Barrier Free Design Com., 1972-80. With USN, 1944-46, PTO. Fellow Am. Soc. Interior Designers (pres. Potomac chpt. 1973-80, nat. dir. 1960-74, chmn. opportunity guidance coun. 1972-74); mem. Nat. Soc. Interior Designers (pres. Potomac chpt. 1974-76), Tantallon Country Club (Oxon Hill, Md.). Democrat. Episcopalian. Avocations: tennis, reading. Home: 13710 Piscataway Dr Fort Washington MD 20744 Office: Millers Interiors Inc PO Box 441711 Ft Washington MD 20749-1711

MILLER, JOHN ROBERT, environmental recycling company executive; b. Lima, Ohio, Dec. 28, 1937; s. John O. and Mary L. (Zickafoose) M.; m. Karen A. Eier, Dec. 30, 1961; children: Robert A., Lisa A., James E. BSChE with honors, U. Cin., 1960, D.Comml. Sc. hon., 1983. With Standard Oil Co., Cleve., 1960-86, dir. fin., 1974-75, v.p. fin. 1975-78, v.p. transp., 1978-79, sr. v.p. tech. and chems., 1979-80, pres., COO, 1980-86; bd. dirs. Cleve.; pres., CEO TBN Holdings, Pepper Pike, Ohio, 1986—; bd. dirs. Am. Waste Svcs., Inc., Eaton Corp., Man Gill Chem.; former chmn. Fed. Res. Bank, Cleve. Mem. Pepper Pike Club, Chagrin Valley Hunt Club, Country Club, Nat. Assn. of Chem. Recyclers (bd. dirs.), Chagrin Valley Hunt Club, Country Club, Tau Beta Pi. Office: 3550 Lander Rd Cleveland OH 44124-5729

MILLER, JOHN T., JR., lawyer, educator; b. Waterbury, Conn., Aug. 10, 1922; s. John T. and Anna (Purdy) M.; children: Kent, Lauren, Clare, Miriam, Michael, Sheila, Lisa, Colin, Margaret. AB with high honors, Clark U., 1944; JD, Georgetown U., 1948; Docteur en Droit, U. Geneva, 1951; postgrad., U. Paris, 1951. Bar: Conn. 1949, D.C. 1950, U.S. Ct. Appeals (3d cir.) 1958, U.S. Ct. Appeals (D.C. cir.) 1952, U.S. Ct. Appeals (5th cir.) 1957, U.S. Supreme Ct. 1952. With Econ. Cooperation Adminstn. Am. Embassy, London, 1950-51; assoc. Covington & Burling, 1952-53, Gallagher, Connor & Boland, 1953-62; pvt. practice Washington, 1962—; adj. prof. law Georgetown U. Law Ctr., Washington, 1959—; mem. Panel on Future of Internat. Ct. Justice. Co-author: Regulation of Trade, 1953, Modern American Antitrust Law, 1948, Major American Antitrust Laws, 1965; author: Foreign Trade in Gas and Electricity in North America: A Legal and Historical Study, 1970, Energy Problems and the Federal Government: Cases and Material, 7th edit., 1994; contbr. articles, book revs. to legal publs. Trustee Clark U., 1970-76, De Sales Sch. of Theology, 1993—; bd. advisors Georgetown Visitation Prep. Sch., 1978-94, bd. trustees, 1994—; former fin. chmn. troop 46 Nat. Capital Area coun. Boy Scouts Am. Served to 1st lt. U.S. Army, 1943-46, 48-49. Recipient 10 yr. teaching award Nat. Jud. Coll. 1983. Mem. ABA (coun., chmn. adminstrv. law sect. 1972-73, ho. dels. 1991-93), AAUP, D.C. Bar Assn., Fed. Energy Bar Assn. (pres. 1990-91), Internat. Bar Assn., Internat. Law Assn., Internat. Club, Congl. Country Club, Prettyman-Leventhal Am. Inn of Ct. (master, pres.), Sovereign Mil. Order of Malta (knight). Republican. Roman Catholic. Home: 4721 Rodman St NW Washington DC 20016-3234 Office: 1001 Connecticut Ave NW Washington DC 20036-5504

MILLER, JOHN ULMAN, minister, author; b. N.Y.C., Dec. 9, 1914; s. Clarence James and Edythe Gladys (Shaffer) M.; m. Marcella E. Hubner, June 12, 1937; children: John U., Mark C. (dec.), Mary Kay (Mrs. Charles Bolin, dec.), Gretchen (Mrs. Ernest Micka). BA cum laude, Taylor U., 1937; MA, Butler U., 1942; DD, Geneva (Wis.) Theol. Coll., 1968. Ordained to ministry Bapt. Ch., 1937; pastor First Bapt. Ch., Bluffton, Ind., 1946-49, Boston, 1949-56; pastor Tabernacle Ch., Utica, N.Y., 1956-63, United Ch. of Christ, Hagerstown, Ind., 1963-66, St. John's Evang. Ch., Louisville, 1967-77; Participant Churchmen Weigh News, WNAC, Boston, 1953-56; preacher Meml. Chapel; instr. religion N.Y. Masonic Home, Utica, 1957-62; broadcast weekly services WKBV, Richmond, Ind., 1965-66; preacher Fellowship Chapel WHAS, Louisville, 1967-77; maintains 24 hour Dial-A-Prayer, Louisville, 1968-77; minister Royal Poinciana Chapel, Palm Beach, Fla., 1978-84; ret., 1984. Author: Only to the Curious, The Voice of St. John, Providence on Pilgrimage, Two Wonders I Confess, Stop! Look! Listen!, He Opened the Book, Christian Ethic in the Sermon on the Mount, Windows on the Agony, Prayers Under Pressure, 1989. Chmn. Campaigns Crippled Children, Tb, U.S.O., 1946-49. Capt. USAAF, 1942-45, PTO. Named Community Leader Am. News Pub. Co., 1969. Mem. Ind.-Ky. Conf. United Ch. of Christ, Bach Soc. Louisville. Home: 4409 Green Pine Dr Louisville KY 40220-1542 *Reverence is my name—the unwritten law of the universe, the invisible order of time, the cardinal virtue of life. Call me sovereign, for so I am, the gift of God to the world of man. Follow me, if you will, and I will disclose to you the life of God in the affairs of man. Charity is my attitude—the most pure of all gifts in the world, the ever redemptive spirit of time, the reconciling power of love. Call me sovereign, for so I am, the gift of God to the world of man. Seek me, if you will, and I will disclose to you the blessings of the eternal in the world of the temporal. Justice is my goal—the incredible design of the universe, the rightness of all things, the inescapable oughtness of life. Call me sovereign, for so I am, the gift of God to the world of man. Pursue me if you will and I will disclose to you the triumph of right amid the shadows of wrong.*

MILLER, JOHN W., management and financial consultant; b. Canton, Mo., Aug. 29, 1933; s. Robert Walton and Leona Elizabeth (Bailey) M.; m. Marilyn Jean Peterson, June 26, 1955 (dec. 1982); children: Melanie, Melinda, John II; m. Ruth Kincaid Kitchens, June 4, 1983; stepchildren: Susan, John M., Richard. BS, U.S. Mil. Acad., 1955; postgrad., U.S. Command & Gen. Staff Coll., 1970-71; MPA, U. Mo., Kansas City, 1973. Commd. U.S. Army, 1955-80; inspector gen. U.S. Army, Alaska, Vietnam, 1967-72; advisor German Ministry of Def., Bonn, 1973-76; program dir. Ft. Knox, Ky., 1976-77, multiple program dir., 1977-78, dep. dir. personnel and community activity, 1978-80; exec. dir. Ala. Med. Rev., Inc., Birmingham, 1980-84; chief exec. officer Ala. Quality Assurance Found., Birmingham, 1982-93; mgmt. and fin. cons., pres. MilleVest Co., 1993—. Contbr. articles to profl. jours. Dir. fin. Birmingham Opera Theater, 1994—. Decorated Legion of Merit; recipient Outstanding Scholarship award, U. Mo., 1973. Mem. AMPRA (legis. com. 1985-87), Green Valley Country Club, West Point Soc. Ala. (pres. 1993—), Phi Kappa Phi. Avocations: golf, tennis, skiing. Office: 90 Bagby Dr Ste 11 Homewood AL 35209

MILLER, J(OHN) WESLEY, III, lawyer, author; b. Springfield, Mass., Oct. 3, 1941; s. John Wesley Jr. and Blanche Ethel (Wilson) M. AB, Colby Coll., 1963; AM, Harvard U., 1964, JD, 1981. Bar: Mass. 1984, U.S. Dist. Ct., 1984, U.S. Supreme Ct. 1993. Instr. English Heidelberg Coll., Tiffin, Ohio, 1964-69, U. Wis., 1969-77; real estate broker, 1977-84; founder Miller-Wilson Family Papers, Vt., Madison (Wis.) People's Poster and Propaganda Collection. Author: The Millers of Roxham, 1958, Giroux Genealogy, 1958, Symphonic Heritage, 1959, Community Guide to Madison Murals, 1977, Aunt Jennie's Poems, 1986; founding editor: Hein's Reprints of Legal Poetry Series, 1985—; editor: The Curiosities and Law of Wills, 1989, The Lawyers Alcove, 1990, Famous Divorces, 1991, Legal Laughs, 1993; founding editor: Law Libr. Series. Microform Conservation Arts Law Letters Collection, 1991; exhibitor A Salute to Street Art, State Hist. Soc. Wis., 1974; represented in permanent collections U. Vermont, Colby Coll. Archives, State Hist. Soc. Wis., Boston Pub. Libr.; contbr. The Poems of Ambrose Philips, 1969,

Dictionary of Canadian Biography, 1980, Collection Building Reader, 1992; also numerous articles on Am. street lit., bibliography, ethics, history, edn., law, religion, librarianship, mgmt. of archives. Mem. MLA, Am. Philol. Assns., Milton Soc., New Eng. Historic Geneal. Soc., Vt. Hist. Soc., Wis. Acad. Scis., Arts & Letters, Social Law Library, Pilgrim Soc., Ancient and Hon. Arty. Co., Mayflower Soc., Soc. Colonial Wars, Sons and Daus. of the Victims of Colonial Witch Trials, Mensa. Office: 5 Birchland Ave Springfield MA 01119-2708

MILLER, JOHN WILLIAM, JR., bassoonist; b. Balt., Mar. 11, 1942; s. John William and Alverta Evelyn (Rodemaker) M.; m. Sibylle Weigel, July 12, 1966; children: Christian Desmond, Andrea Jocelyn, Claire Evelyn. BS, M.I.T., 1964; MusM with highest honors, New Eng. Conservatory, 1967, Artist's Diploma, 1969. Instr. bassoon Boston U., 1967-71, U. Minn., 1971—; prin. bassoonist, founding mem. Boston Philharmonia Chamber Orch., 1968-71; prin. bassoonist Minn. Orch., Mpls., 1971—; dir. Boston Baroque Ensemble, 1963-71, John Miller Bassoon Symposium, Towson, Md., 1984—; mem. Am. Reed Trio, 1977—; faculty Sarasota Music Festival, 1986—; Affinis Seminar, Japan, 1992; vis. faculty Banff Ctr. for Arts, 1987. Soloist on recs. for Cambridge, Musical Heritage Soc., Pro Arte. Recipient U.S. Govt. Fulbright award, 1964-65, Irwin Bodky award Cambridge Soc. Early Music, 1968. Mem. Internat. Double Reed Soc., Minn. Bassoon Assn. (founder). Home: 706 Lincoln Ave Saint Paul MN 55105-3533 Office: 1111 Nicollet Mall Minneapolis MN 55403-2406

MILLER, JONATHAN WOLFE, theater and film director, physician; b. London, July 21, 1934; s. Emanuel Miller; m. Helen Rachel Collet, 1956; 3 children. Ed. St. John's Coll., Cambridge U.; M.B., B.Ch., Univ. Coll. Hosp. Med. Sch., London; D.Litt. (hon.), U. Leicester, 1981; Dr. (hon.), Open U., 1983. Dir. Nottingham Playhouse, 1963-69; assoc. dir. Nat. Theatre, 1973-75; mem. Arts Council, 1975-76; vis. prof. drama Westfield Coll., U. London, 1977-78; artistic dir., Old Vic, 1988-90. Co-author, actor in Beyond the Fringe, 1961-64; dir. Under Plain Cover, Royal Ct. Theatre, 1962, The Old Glory, N.Y.C., 1964, Prometheus Bound, Yale Drama Sch., 1967, Oxford and Cambridge Shakespeare Co. prodn. of Twelfth Night, on tour in U.S., 1969; dir. for Nat. Theatre, London: The Merchant of Venice, 1970, Danton's Death, 1971, The School for Scandal, 1972, The Marriage of Figaro, 1974; other prodns. include: The Tempest, London, 1970, Prometheus Bound, London, 1971, The Taming of the Shrew, Chichester, Eng., 1972, The Seagull, Chichester, 1973, The Malcontent, Nottingham, Eng., 1973, The Family in Love, Greenwich Season, 1974, The Importance of Being Earnest, 1975, All's Well That Ends Well, Measure For Measure, Greenwich Season, 1975, Three Sisters, 1977; dir. operas Arden Must Die, Sadler's Well Theatre, 1974, The Cunning Little Vixen, Glyndebourne, 1975, 77, Katya Kabanova, New York, 1991, Marriage of Figaro, Vienna State Opera, 1991, Robert Devereux, Monte Carlo, 1992, Die Gezeichnete, Zurich, 1992, Maria Stuarda, Monte Carlo, 1993, The Secret Marriage, Opera North, 1993; (for English Nat. Opera) The Marriage of Figaro, 1978,The Turn of the Screw, 1979, 91, Arabella, 1980, Otello, 1981, Rigoletto, 1982, 85, Fidelio, 1982, 83, Don Giovanni, 1985, The Magic Flute, 1986, Tosca, 1986, The Mikado, 1986, 88, The Barber of Seville, 1987, Cosi fan Tutte, 1995, Pelleas et Melisande, Met. Opera, N.Y.C.; (for Kent Opera) Cosi Fan Tutte, 1975, Rigoletto, 1975, Orfeo, 1976, Eugene Onegin, 1977, La Traviata, 1979, Falstaff, 1980, 81, Fidelio, 1982, 83, 88, La Scala: La Fanciulla del West, 1991, Manon Lescaut, 1992; (for Maggio Musicale, Florence) Don Giovanni, 1990, Cosi fan Tutte, 1991, Marriage of Figaro, 1992, (Met. Opera, N.Y.) Pelleas et Melisande, 1995; dir. Broadway play Long Day's Journey Into Night, 1986, The Taming of the Shrew at Royal Shakespeare Co., Stratford, 1987, Andromache, One Way Pendulum, Bussy D'Ambois, all at Old Vic, 1988, The Tempest, 1988, Turn of the Screw, 1989, King Lear, 1989, The Liar, 1989; films include: Take a Girl Like You, 1969; TV films include: Whistle and I'll Come to You, 1967, Alice in Wonderland, 1967, The Body in Question series, 1978, Henry the Sixth, part one, 1983, States of Mind series, 1983; exec. producer Shakespeare TV series, 1979-81; author: McLuhan, 1971, The Body in Question, 1978, Subsequent Performances, 1986; editor: Freud: The Man, His World, His Influence, 1972, The Don Giovanni Book, 1990. Decorated Order Brit. Empire; named dir. of Yr. Soc. West End Theatre Awards, 1976; recipient Silver medal Royal TV Soc., 1981; fellow Univ. Coll. London; hon. fellow St. John's Coll., Cambridge U.; research fellow in history of medicine Univ. Coll., London U., 1970-73. Office: care IMG Artists, Media House 3 Burlington Ln, London W4 2TH, England

MILLER, JOSEPH CALDER, history educator, historical consultant, editor; b. Cedar Rapids, Iowa, Apr. 30, 1939; s. John William and Harriet Eleanor (Calder) M.; divorced; children: Julia Carolyn, John Russell, Laura Andrée. BA, Wesleyan U., 1961; MBA, Northwestern U., 1963; MA, U. Wis., 1967, PhD, 1972. Asst. prof. U. Va., Charlottesville, 1972-75, assoc. prof., 1975-82, prof., 1982-89, Commonwealth prof., 1989—, dean Coll. Arts & Scis., 1990-95, Commonwealth prof. of history, 1995—. Author: Way of Death, 1988 (Herskovitz prize, spl. citation Conf. Latin Am. Historians 1988), Kings and Kinsmen, 1976; editor: The African Past Speaks, 1980; compiler Slavery: Worldwide Bibliography, 1985, Slavery and Slaving in World History: A Bibliography, 1900-1991, 1993; editor Jour. African History, 1990—. NEH fellow, 1978-79, 85. Mem. Am. Coun. Learned Socs. (study fellow 1974-75), Soc. Sci. Rsch. Coun. (rsch. grant 1987), African Studies Assn. (treas. 1988-93, bd. dirs. 1986-89), Am. Hist. Assn. (rsch. div. 1987-89), Can. Assn. African Studies. Avocations: theater, music, roadrunning. Office: U Va Corcoran Dept History University Station Charlottesville VA 22903

MILLER, JOSEPH EDWARD, JR., media company executive; b. Seattle, Jan. 4, 1945; s. Joseph Edward and Kathleen Bell (Campbell) M.; m. Ingrid Maria Exner, Mar. 5, 1965 (div. July 1972); 1 child, Nancy Marie; m. Barbara Leigh Gregson, May 25, 1986. AA, Montgomery Coll., 1974; BS, U. Md., 1976, MA, 1978. Mktg.-mgr. Inst. Modern Lang., Silver Spring, Md., 1974-75; pres. JEMPRO Films Ltd., Silver Spring, 1975-79; writer/dir. WRAMC Inst. of Rsch., Washington, 1979-81; lobbyist The Am. Legion, Washington, 1981-86; ptnr. Miller-Gregson Prodns., Sherman Oaks, Calif., 1986—; cons. Renaissance Communications, Silver Springs, 1983-88, Loreen Arbus Prodns., L.A., 1988, Boss Film Corp., 1989, Four Point Entertainment, 1989, 90, 91, Varied Directions, Inc., 1990, Group W Prodns., 1990, 91, Blair Entertainment, 1990, CBS Entertainment, 1991, Fox TV, 1991, Barry Weitz Prodns., 1991, Carolco TV, 1991, Multi-Media TV, 1992, Prodrs. Video Inc., 1992, Lewisfilm, Ltd., 1991-93, USA Network, 1993. Author: House on Thayer Hill, 1988. Orgn. fund raiser United Way, Washington, 1984-85; bd. dirs. Vietnam Veterans Inst., Washington, 1981—; With U.S. Army, 1962-72. Decorated Bronze Star, Air medal with oak leaf cluster, Purple Heart with oak leaf cluster; Recipient Honor award Assn. of Mil. Surgeons Internat., 1979, spl. recognition award Walter Reed Army Inst. of Research, 1981. Mem. Ind. Media Producers Assn., Alpha Sigm Lambda, Phi Kappa Phi, Phi Theta Kappa. Republican. Presbyterian. Avocations: photography, tennis, Vietnam veterans' advocate.

MILLER, JOSEPH HILLIS, comparative literature educator; b. Newport News, Va., Mar. 5, 1928; s. Joseph Hillis and Nell (Critzer) M.; m. Dorothy Marian James, Apr. 2, 1949; children: Robin Leigh, Matthew Hopkins, Sarah Elizabeth. BA, Oberlin Coll., 1948; MA, Harvard U., 1949, PhD, 1952; MA, Yale U., 1972; hon. degree, U. Fla., Bucknell U., U. Zaragoza. Instr. English Williams Coll., Williamstown, Mass., 1952-53; asst. prof. Johns Hopkins U., Balt., 1953-59, assoc. prof., 1959-63, prof. English, 1963-68, chmn. dept. English, 1964-68, prof. English and humanistic studies, 1968-72; prof. English Yale U., New Haven, 1972-75, Gray prof. rhetoric, 1975-76, chmn. dept. English, 1976-79, Frederick W. Hilles prof. English, 1976-86, prof. comparative lit., 1979-86, dir. lit. maj., 1980-83; Disting. Prof. of English and Comparative Lit. U. Calif., Irvine, 1986—; vis. prof. U. Hawaii, 1956, Harvard U., 1962, 72, Swarthmore Coll., 1967, U. Va., 1968, U. Wash., 1971, U. Zurich, 1972, U. Calif. Sch. Criticism, Irvine, 1979, Dartmouth Sch. Criticism and Theory, 1986, 92, Tulane U., 1987; Danforth Seminar lectr. U. Chgo., 1959; Ward-Phillips lectr. U. Notre Dame, 1967; fellow Wesleyan Ctr. for Humanities, 1971; vis. prof., fellow Coun. of Humanities, Princeton U., 1974; dir. Nat. Endowment for Humanities Summer Seminars, 1974, 77, 80. Author: Charles Dickens: The World of His Novels, 1958, The Disappearance of God: Five Nineteenth-Century Writers, 1963, Poets of Reality: Six Twentieth-Century Writers, 1965, The Form of Victorian Fiction: Thackeray, Dickens, Trollope, George Eliot, Meredith, and Hardy, 1968, Thomas Hardy: Distance and Desire, 1970, Charles Dickens and George Cruikshank, 1971, Fiction and Repetition, 1982, The

Linguistic Moment, 1985, The Ethics of Reading, 1987, Versions of Pygmalion, 1990, Hawthorne and History, 1991, Victorian Subjects, 1991, Tropes, Parables, Performatives, 1991, Theory Now and Then, 1991, Ariadne's Thread, 1992, Illustration, 1992; editor: Modern Lang. Notes, 1953-61, ELH, 1953—, The Act of the Mind: Essays on the Poetry of Wallace Stevens, 1965, William Carlos Williams: A Collection of Critical Essays, 1966, Aspects of Narrative, 1971, Thomas Hardy, The Well-Beloved, 1976; mem. adv. bd.: Diacritics, 1975—, Ga. Rev., 1975—, Critical Inquiry, 1974—, Poetics Today, 1979—, Oxford Lit. Rev., 1978—, Studies in English Lit, 1979—, Genre, 1980—, Yale Jour. of Criticism, 1987—, Signature, 1988—. Trustee Keuka Coll. 1971-80. Recipient E. Harris Harbison Disting. Teaching award Danforth Found., 1968; Guggenheim fellow, 1959-60, 65-66; Nat. Endowment for Humanities sr. fellow, 1975, 86- 87; Carnegie fellow U. Edinburgh, 1981. Fellow Soc. Values in Higher Edn.; mem. Acad. Arts and Scis., Conn. Acad. Arts and Scis.; mem. MLA (research com. 1968-69, exec. council 1970-73, PMLA 1975-77, 2d v.p. 1984, 1st v.p. 1985, pres. 1986), Coll. English Assn. (dir. 1977-80), English Inst. (supr. com. 1968-70, chmn. 1970), New Eng. Coll. English Assn. (pres. 1975-76), Phi Beta Kappa (lectr. 1977-78). Office: U Calif Irvine Dept English and Comp Lit Irvine CA 92717*

MILLER, JOSEPH IRWIN, automotive manufacturing company executive; b. Columbus, Ind., May 26, 1909; s. Hugh Thomas and Nettie Irwin (Sweeney) M.; m. Xenia Ruth Simons, Feb. 5, 1943; children: Margaret Irwin, Catherine Gibbs, Elizabeth Ann Garr, Hugh Thomas, II, William Irwin. Grad., Taft Sch., 1927; AB, Yale U., 1931, MA (hon.), 1959, LHD (hon.), 1979; MA, Oxford (Eng.) U., 1933; LLD, Bethany Coll., 1956, Tex. Christian U., Ind. U., 1958, Oberlin Coll., Princeton, 1962; LL.D., Hamilton Coll., 1964, Columbia, 1968, Mich. State U., 1968, Dartmouth, 1971, U. Notre Dame, 1972, Ball State U., 1972, Lynchburg Coll., 1985; L.H.D. (hon.), Case Inst. Tech., 1966, U. Dubuque, 1977; Hum.D., Manchester U., 1973, Moravian Coll., 1976. Assoc. Cummins Engine Co., Inc., Columbus, Ind., 1934—; v.p. gen. mgr. Cummins Engine Co., Inc., 1934-42, exec. v.p., 1944-47, pres., 1947-51, chmn. bd., 1951-77, chmn. exec. com., 1977—; pres. Irwin-Union Bank & Trust Co., 1947-54, bd. dir., 1937—, chmn., 1954-75; chmen. exec. com. Irwin Union Corp., 1976-90; bd. dirs. Irwin Fin. Corp., 1990—; mem. Commn. Money and Credit, 1958-61, Pres.'s Com. Postal Reorgn., 1968, Pres.'s Com. Urban Housing, 1968; chmn. Pres.'s Com. on Trade Rels. with Soviet Union and Eastern European Nations, 1965, Nat. Adv. Commn. on Health Manpower, 1966; vice chmn. UN Commn. on Multinat. Corps., 1974; adv. council U.S. Dept. Commerce, 1976; mem. Study Commn. on U.S. Policy Toward So. Africa, 1979-81. Pres. nat. Coun. Chs. of Christ U.S.A., 1960-63; trustee Nat. Humanities Ctr., 1978-90, Carnegie Instn., Washington, 1988-91; mem. cen. and exec. coms. World Coun. Chs. 1961-68; trustee Ford Found., 1961-79, Yale Corp., 1959-77, Urban Inst., 1966-76, Mayo Found., 1977-82; fellow Branford Coll. Recipient Rosenberger award U. Chgo., 1977, 1st MacDowell Colony award, 1981; hon. fellow Balliol Coll., Oxford (Eng.) U.; Benjamin Franklin fellow Royal Soc. Arts. Fellow Am. Acad. Arts and Scis., Royal Inst. Brit. Architects (hon.); mem. Am. Bus. Conf. (co-chmn. 1985-87), Soc. Indsl. and Bus. Econs. (hon.) Am. Philos. Soc., Ind. Acad. Bus. Coun., Conf. Bd. (sr.), Phi Beta Kappa, Beta Gamma Sigma. Mem. Christian Ch. Office: 301 Washington St Columbus IN 47201-6743

MILLER, JUDSON FREDERICK, lawyer, former military officer; b. Tulsa, Dec. 5, 1924; s. Herbert Frederick and Martha (Davidson) M.; m. June Hirakis, Aug. 4, 1967; children by previous marriage: Kathleen, Shelley, Douglas, Judson Frederick. BS, U. Md., 1961; postgrad., Army War Coll., 1961-62; MA, George Washington U., 1962; JD, U. Puget Sound, 1980. Bar: Wash. 1981. Commd. 2d lt. U.S. Army, 1943, advanced through grades to maj. gen., 1975; platoon leader, co. comdr. 4th Cav. Group, Europe, 1944-46, 82d Airborne Div., 1947-50; with 187th Airborne RCT and Hdqrs. 8th Army, 1950-52; instr. Armored Sch., 1953-56; bn. comdr. 14th Armored Cav., 1958-60; with Hdqrs. U.S. Strike Command, 1963-65; brigade comdr., chief of staff 4th Inf. Div., Vietnam, 1966-67; mem. gen. staff Dept. Army, 1967-68; dep. comdg. gen. Ft. Ord, Cal., 1968-69; asst. chief of staff Hdqrs. Allied Forces Central Europe, 1969-71; asst. comdr. 3d Inf. Div., Germany, 1971-73; chief of staff I Corps Group, Korea, 1973-75; dep. comdg. gen. VII Corps, Germany, 1975-77; ret., 1977; assoc. F.G. Enslow and Assocs., Tacoma, 1981—. Decorated Silver Star, Legion of Merit, Bronze Star with V device and oak leaf cluster, Joint Service Commendation medal, Air medal with 8 oak leaf clusters, Purple Heart, Vietnamese Gallantry Cross with palm; named to Okla. Mil. Acad. Hall of Fame, 1988. Mem. ABA, Assn. U.S. Army. Club: Tacoma Country, Lakewood Racquet. Home: 8009 75th St SW Tacoma WA 98498-4817 Office: Tacoma Mall Office Bldg 4301 S Pine St Ste 205 Tacoma WA 98409-7205

MILLER, KEITH, insurance company executive; b. Peoria, Ill., Apr. 24, 1938; s. Dustin and Mary (Keith) M.; m. Deanna Yaeger, Aug. 16, 1959; children: Linda Leigh, Lori Jane. BS in Mktg., U. Ill., 1960. CLU, ChFC. Agt. Penn Mutual life Ins. Co., Milw., 1960—; founder Miller, Miller & Donavan (now M Fin. Corp. Wis.), Milw., 1969, chmn. bd., 1976—; bd. dirs. Kickhaefer Mfg. Co., Port Washington, Wis. Capt. U.S. Army, 1960-68. Mem. Internat. Forum, Assn. for Advanced Life Underwriting (pres. 1991), Milw. Estate Planning Coun. (pres. 1991), Milw. Chpt. CLUs (past pres.), Milw. Estate Counselors Forum (past pres.), Tripoli Country Club (pres. 1983-87), Milw. Athletic Club, Million Dollar Round Table. Episcopalian. Avocations: golf, tennis. Office: M Fin Corp of Wis 5150 N Port Washington Rd Milwaukee WI 53217-5470

MILLER, KEITH WYATT, pharmacology educator; b. Chard, Eng., Mar. 31, 1941; Married: 2 children. BA, Oxford U., Eng., 1963, D.Phil., 1967; AM, Harvard U., 1984. NSF fellow in chemistry U. Calif., Berkeley, 1967-69; research fellow in pharmacology Oxford U., Eng., 1969-71; instr. Harvard U., 1971-73; asst. prof. pharmacology Harvard U. Med. Sch., Boston, 1973-76, assoc. prof. pharmacology, 1976-83, Mallinckrodt prof. pharmacology dept. anesthesia, 1983—; Christensen vis. fellow, St. Catherine's Coll., Oxford, UK, 1991; dir. Harvard Anaesthesia Ctr. Mem. Internat. Electron Paramagnetic Resonance Soc., Am. Chem. Soc., Am. Soc. Pharmacology and Exptl. Therapeutics, Biophys. Soc., Brit. Pharmacol. Soc., Brit. Biophys. Soc., Am. Soc. Anesthesiologists, Internat. Cell Research Orgn., AAAS, Internat. Soc. Biomed. Rsch. Alcoholism, Rsch. Soc. Alcoholism, Assn. U. Anesthetists. Office: Harvard Med Sch MA General Hosp Dept Anesthesia/14 Fruit St Boston MA 02114-2698*

MILLER, KEN LEROY, religious studies educator, consultant, writer; b. San Antonio, July 29, 1933; s. Eldridge and Paskel Dovie (Vick) M.; m. Eddie Juanell Crawford, June 14, 1953 (dec. Apr. 1981); children: Kimberly Miller Stern, Kerry, Karen Miller Davis; m. Carolyn Gayle Jackson, May 4, 1982; children: Sheila Stanley, Keith Conatser. BA, Abilene Christian U., 1958; MEd, Trinity U., 1965; EdD, Ariz. State U., 1975. Cert. tchr., Tex. Tchr. SAn Antonio Ind. Sch. Dist., 1957-58; tchr., adminstr. N.E. Ind. Sch. Dist., San Antonio, 1958-69; min. edn. MacArthur Park Ch. of Christ, San Antonio, 1960-69; prin. Ralls (Tex.) Ind. Sch. Dist., 1969-70; minister of edn. S.W. Ch. of Christ, Phoenix, 1970-74; adminstr., tchr. Lubbock (Tex.) Christian Sch./U., 1974-77; minister of edn. Sunset Ch. of Christ, Lubbock, 1977-82; prof. religious edn. Harding U. Searcy, Ark., 1987—; curriculum cons. Sweet Pub. Co., Ft. Worth, 1988-91; leader internat. and nat. religious edn. workshops and seminars. Author: Moral and Religious Stages of Development, 1975, (curriculum) Old Testament Personalities, 1980, Organization, Administration, Supervision of the Bible School, 1993, Recruiting, Training, Retaining Teachers in the Bible School, 1993, Curriculum for the Bible School, 1993; editor: Recipes for Living and Teaching, 1982, (curiculum) Growing in Knowledge, 1977-90, The MINNITH series, 1991-95; guest editor, contbr. Christian Family 1984. With U.S. Army, 1954-56. Mem. Christian Educators, Christian Edn. Assn., Religious Edn. Assn., Assn. Secondary Schs. and Colls., Alpha Psi Omega, Sigma Tau Delta. Republican. Mem. Ch. of Christ. Avocations: fishing, hunting, reading, travel, writing, poetry readings. Home: 5 Robinwood Dr Searcy AR 72143-8920 Office: Harding U 900 E Center Box 792 Searcy AR 72149-0001

MILLER, KENNETH ALLEN, electrical engineer; b. Flushing, N.Y., Dec. 19, 1944; s. Marvin David and Inez Eleanor (Fischer) M.; B.E.E., U. Mich., 1966; M.B.A., Hofstra U., 1972; children—Johanna, Kena. Engr., Kahn Research Labs., L.I. N.Y., 1967-69, 71-74; mgr. systems engring. Comtech Labs., L.I., 1974-78; exec. v.p., ctrl. mgr. Satellite Transmission Systems,

Inc., L.I., 1978—. Contbr. articles to profl. jours. Served as 1st lt. Signal Corps, U.S. Army, 1969-71. Mem. IEEE (chmn. symposium on advances in satellite communications 1984). Democrat. Office: Satellite Transmission Systems 125 Kennedy Dr Hauppauge NY 11788-4015*

MILLER, KENNETH EDWARD, sociologist, educator; b. N.Y.C., June 17, 1929; s. Joseph F. and Irene (Edersheim) M.; m. Andrée Nora Barthelemy, Feb. 14, 1959 (div. Nov. 1984); children: Jennifer Andrée, Christopher Kenneth; m. Janet Sue Daniels, May 21, 1990. B.A., U. Ala., 1953, M.A., 1956; Ph.D., Duke, 1965; MS, Drake U., 1986. Asst. to pres., dir. devel. Jacksonville (Fla.) U., 1957-60; dir. Health Council, asso. dir. Community Planning Council, Birmingham, Ala., 1960-62; asst. prof. sociology Emory U., Atlanta, 1966-70; acting chmn. dept. sociology Drake U., 1969-70; prof. sociology Drake U., Des Moines, 1970—; chmn. dept. Drake U., 1970-79, 82-88, asst. to dean for grad. studies, 1991-92; Research sociologist U. Ala., 1956-57; research asso. U.S. Civil Service Commn., summer 1968. Served with USN, 1946-48. Postdoctoral research fellow Duke, 1965-66. Mem. Midwest Sociol. Soc. Home: 2129 NW 140th St Clive IA 50325-8730 Office: Drake Univ Dept Sociology Des Moines IA 50311

MILLER, KENNETH GREGORY, air force officer; b. Bryan, Tex., July 28, 1944; s. Max Richard and Catherine Mae (Sultzman) M.; m. Ann Marguerite Perpich, Nov. 25, 1966; children: Keith G., Deborah J., Craig S. BS in Aero. Engring., Purdue U., 1966; MS in Systems Mgmt., U. So. Calif., 1970, grad., Nat. War Coll., Washington, 1986; postgrad., U. Va., 1988. Commd. 2d lt. USAF, 1966, advanced through grades to brig. gen., 1990; with Office Sec. Def., Washington, 1980-81; various positions to dir. field ops. F-16 System Program Office, Wright-Patterson AFB, Ohio, 1981-86; chief engring. div. Sacramento Air Logistics Ctr., McClellan AFB, Calif., 1986-87; dir. materiel mgmt. Ogden (Utah) Air Logistics Ctr., Ga., 1987-89; vice comdr. Acquisition Logistics Div., Wright-Patterson AFB, 1989-90; comdr. contract mgmt. div. Air Force Systems Command, Kirtland AFB, N.Mex., 1990; comdr. western dist. Def. Contract Mgmt. Command, L.A., 1990-91; dir. C-17 Program Office, Wright-Patterson AFB, 1991-93; dep. asst. sec. of AF for acquistion Washington, 1993-94; dir. supply Hdqs. USAF, Washington, 1994—. Decorated Legion of Merit; recipient award of merit Freedom Found. Mem. Nat. Contract Mgmt. Assn. (bd. advisors 1990-92), Soc. Logistics Engrs. Office: Hdqs USAF/LGS The Pentagon Rm 4E260 Washington DC 20330-1060

MILLER, KENNETH MERRILL, computing services company executive; b. Lowell, Mass., Dec. 13, 1930; s. Harry Dow and Marjorie Louise (Morris) M.; m. Mary Jo Putnam, June 8, 1952 (div. Aug. 1979); children: Debra, Pamela, Carol; m. Eileen Anne Durnin, Feb. 4, 1980; 1 child, Andrew. BS, Am. U., 1964; MBA, Syracuse U., 1966. Commd. 2d lt. U.S. Army, 1953, advanced through grades to col., 1974; assigned to France, Fed. Republic Germany, Korea, Vietnam; ret., 1978; v.p. Robert W. Baird & Co., Inc., Milw., 1978-79; sr. v.p. Automatic Data Processing, Inc., Roseland, N.J., 1979—. Decorated Legion of Merit with three oak leaf clusters, Bronze Star, Purple Heart. Mem. Ont. Club (Toronto). Office: ADP Inc, 4 King St W, Toronto, ON Canada M5H 1B6

MILLER, KENNETH MICHAEL, electronics executive; b. Chgo., Nov. 20, 1921; s. Matthew and Tillie (Otto) M.; student Ill. Inst. Tech., 1940-41, UCLA, 1961; m. Dolores June Miller, Jan. 16, 1943 (dec. Dec. 1968); children: Barbara Anne Reed, Nancy Jeanne Hathaway, Kenneth Michael, Roger Allan; m. Sally J. Ballingham, June 20, 1970. Electronics engr. Rauland Corp., Chgo., 1941-48; gen. mgr. Lear, Inc., Santa Monica, Calif., 1948-59; v.p., gen. mgr. Motorola Aviation Electronics, Inc., Culver City, Calif., 1959-60; v.p., gen. mgr. Instrument div. Daystrom, Inc., Los Angeles, 1961; gen. mgr. Metrics div. Singer Co., Bridgeport, Conn. and Los Angeles, 1962-65; v.p., gen. mgr. Lear Jet Corp., 1965-66; pres., dir. Infonics Inc., 1967-68; v.p., gen. mgr. Computer Industries, Inc., 1968-69; dir. ops., tech. products group Am. Standard Corp., McLean, Va., also v.p., gen. mgr. Wilcox Electric div., Kansas City, Mo., 1969-71; pres. Wilcox Electric, Inc. subs. Northrop Corp., Kansas City, 1971-72, v.p., dir. World Wide Wilcox, Inc. subs., McLean, Va., 1971-72; pres., chief exec. officer Penril Corp., Rockville, Md., 1973-86, dir. 1973-86, pres. K-M Miller and Assocs., Rockville, Md., 1986—; dir., mem. investment com. Palmer Nat. Bank, Washington. Mem. regional planning coun. Community Mental Health Svcs. Bridgeport, 1966; mem. Bridgeport Capital Fund Com.; trustee Park City Hosp.; vice dir. Montgomery County Arts Council; bd. dirs. U. Bridgeport; mem. Md. State Com. High Tech. Recipient Job Makers award Mfrs. Assn. Bridgeport, 1963. Fellow Radio Club Am. (dir., chmn. grants-in-aid com.); mem. AIAA. IEEE, Aircraft Owners and Pilots Assn., Am. Mgmt. Assn., Armed Forces Communications and Electronics Assn. (life), Electronic Industries Assn., Instrument Soc. Am. (life), Nat. Aero. Assn., Soc. Non-Destructive Testing, Soc. Automotive Engrs., Air Force Assn., Am. Radio Relay League (life), Amateur Satellite Corp. (life), Am. Def. Preparedness Assn. (life), Aero. Elec. Soc. (life), Nat. Capital DX Assn. (pres. 1987-88), Assn. Old Crows (life), Mfrs. Assn. Bridgeport (dir.), Bridgeport Engring. Inst., Bridgeport C. of C. (pres. 1964), Quarter Century Wireless Assn. (life, Disting. Svc. award 1994), Soc. Wireless Pioneers. Clubs: Rolling Hills Country (Wichita); Algonquin (Bridgeport). Mem. adv. bd. Washington Bus. Jour.; contbr. articles to profl. jours. Home and Office: 16904 George Washington Dr Rockville MD 20853-1128

MILLER, KENNETH RAYMOND, biologist, educator; b. Rahway, N.J., July 14, 1948; s. Claude Ray and Marion Ruth (Hamill) M.; m. Jody Annette Zanot, June 10, 1972; children: Lauren Beth, Tracy Erin. BS in Biology, Brown U., 1970; PhD, U. Colo., 1974. Asst. prof. Harvard U., Cambridge, Mass., 1974-80; assoc. prof. Brown U., Providence, 1980-82, assoc. prof., 1982-86, prof., 1986—. Author: Biology: Discovering Life, 1991, Biology, 1991; contbr. articles to profl. jours. Grantee NIH, 1977—, NSF, 1982—. Mem. AAAS, Am. Soc. Cell Biology (chmn. edn. com. 1986-90). Office: Brown U PO Box G-b589 Providence RI 02912

MILLER, KENNETH ROY, management consultant; b. Uniontown, Pa., Oct. 22, 1902; s. Franklin Pierce and Annabelle (Darby) M.; m. Mary E. Hunnicutt, June 14, 1930; 1 son, Stephen Goodrich. Student, Emerson Inst., 1922-23, George Washington U., 1923-25; LL.D., Lebanon Valley Coll., 1957, Fla. Atlantic U., 1975. Dir. conservation dept. Acacia Mut. Life Ins. Co., Washington, 1926-28; asst. supt. agencies Occidental Life Ins. Co., Raleigh, N.C., 1928-31; cons. Life Ins. Agy. Mgmt. Assn., Hartford, 1931-38; supt. agencies Atlantic Life Ins. Co., Richmond, Va., 1938-41; prin. dir. Nat. Fed. Sales Execs., N.Y.C., 1941-42; asst. to program vice chmn., dir. ops. analysis WPB, Washington, 1942-43; with NAM, N.Y.C., 1943-64; asst. to exec. v.p., asst. treas., treas., bus. mgr., sr. v.p. NAM, 1943-55, mng. dir., 1955-57, gen. mgr., 1957-62, group v.p., 1962-63, sr. v.p., adviser, 1963-64; prin. Kenneth R. Miller & Assos (mgmt. and fin. cons.), Boca Raton, Fla., from 1964. Bd. dirs., past pres., dir. emeritus Fla. Atlantic U. Found., Boca Raton; founder, sponsor dept. ocean engring. Fla. Atlantic U.; former mem. Boca Raton Airport Authority; retired chmn. bd. Caldwell Theatre Co.; former chmn. adv. council Music Guild of Boca Raton; mem. Friends of Caldwell Playhouse; former moderator Congl. Ch. of Boca Raton; citizens adv. com. Boca Raton Downtown Redevel. Agy. Mem. Economic Roundtable (treas., exec. com.), English-Speaking Union (past pres. Boca Raton br.), Phi Sigma Kappa, Pi Delta Epsilon. Club: Bankers (Boca Raton) (past pres.). Address: 699 SW 5th St Boca Raton FL 33486-4615

MILLER, KENNETH WILLIAM, holding company executive, financier; b. Albany, N.Y., Sept. 25, 1947; s. Kenneth Carpenter and Rose May (Chatfield) M.; m. Barbara Ann Tortorici, Aug. 5, 1967; children: Justin Carpenter, Jason Chatfield. BBA, SUNY, Albany, 1970. Exec. v.p. chief operating officer Texgas Corp., Houston, 1981-84; chief exec. officer The Edge Group, Inc., Houston, 1984—; Edge Mgmt. Group, Inc., Houston, 1984—; Superior Energy Group, Ltd., Houston, 1985-94, Gulf Butane Co. Houston, 1985-89, Auto-Quip Leasing Co., Houston, 1986—, MetroGas Corp., Mpls., 1986-89, MetroGas Supply Corp., Houston, 1986—, TRICO, Inc., Savannah, Ga., 1986-90, Tri-County Gas & Appliance Co., Tifton, Ga., 1986-90, Delta Storage and Distbn. Co., Hattiesburg, Miss., 1987-94, Edge Fin. Group, Inc., Atlanta, N.Y.C. and Houston, 1989—, Edge Realty Group, Inc., Houston, 1991—, AMC Funding, Inc., Houston, Little Rock, 1992—; Edge Ins. Holdings, Houston, 1993—, Edge Transp. Group, Inc., Houston, 1994-95; CEO Harper Energy Group, Atlanta, 1994—, DaVinci Sci. Corp., L.A., 1995—; mem. adv. commn. N.Y. Cotton Exch., N.Y.C.,

1984-87; del. to USSR Am. People Amb. Program, 1989, Western Europe, 1990; bd. dirs. ProLine Golf Corp., Cardio Dynamics Internat. Pres. Hidden Dunes Community Assn., Destin, Fla., 1988-90. With USAR, 1968-74. Mem. Nat. Propane Gas Assn. (bd. dirs. 1984-95), Gov.'s Club, Pine Forest Country Club, Willow Fork Country Club, West Side Tennis Club. Avocations: tennis, water sports, scuba diving, gold, skiing. Office: The Edge Group Inc Ste 380 16225 Park Ten Pl Houston TX 77084-5150

MILLER, KIRK, lawyer. BA, U. Calif., Riverside; JD, Syracuse U., 1976. Bar: Colo. 1976, Calif. 1980, Tex. 1993. Assoc. Hughes & Dorsey, Denver, 1977-79; v.p., assoc. gen. counsel Am. Med. Internat., Inc., Dallas, 1979-88, v.p., sec., gen. counsel, 1988-91; with McGlinchey Stafford Lang, Dallas, 1991-94; sr. v.p., sec., gen. counsel Kaiser Found. Health Plan, Inc., Kaiser Found. Hosps., Inc., Oakland, Calif., 1994; instr. Syracuse U., 1975-76. Mem. ABA (co-vice chair com. health care fraud and abuse). Office: Kaiser Found Health Plan 1 Kaiser Plz Oakland CA 94612

MILLER, L. MARTIN, accountant, financial planning specialist; b. N.Y.C., Sept. 17, 1939; s. Harvey and Julia (Lewis) M.; m. Judith Sklar, Jan. 21, 1962; children: Philip, Marjorie. BS, Wharton Sch., U. Pa., 1960. CPA; CFP; accredited fin. planning specialist. Jr. acct. Deloitte, Haskins & Sells, N.Y.C., 1960-62, sr. acct., Phila., 1962-64; mng. partner Cogen, Sklar LLP, Phila., 1964—; treas. Coronet Container Co., Inc., Phila., & Val Mar Realty Corp., N.Y.C.; dir. Penn Internat. Trading Co., Phila.; mng. dir. CPA Tax Forum, 1966-69; underwriting mem. Lloyds of London, 1978—, chmn. Mid-Atlantic region, 1991-92; mem. faculty Wharton Sch. U. Pa., 1992—; lectr., discussion leader on fin. and taxation; columnist Montgomery and Bucks County Dental News. Mem. Phila. Rep. com., 1963-67; chmn. Lower Merion Twp. scholarship fund, 1975-78; bd. dirs. Penn Valley Civic Assn., 1973-79, Gladwyne Civic Assn., 1992—; mem. Lower Merion Planning Commn., 1978-82, Gov.'s Tax Study Commn.; pres. Mensa Edn. and Rsch. Found., 1984-86; mem. SEC Forum on Small Bus. Capital Formation, 1983; apptd. to Pa. State Bd. Accountancy, 1985-94, chmn., 1990-91; elected sch. bd. dir. Lower Merion Twp., 1993—, also chmn. fin. com. Served with U.S. Army, 1961-62. Recipient Outstanding Achievement award Germantown Civic Assn., 1965. Mem. Pa. Inst. CPAs (edn. com. 1975-78, bd. dirs. 1979-81, bylaws chmn. 1980-83), Nat. Assn. State Bds. Accountancy (edn. com. 1987, nominating com. 1989, experience com. 1990), AICPAs (nat. tax commn. 1979-82, exec. com. self regulation div. for CPA firms 1984-87, acctg. and rev. services com. 1985-88, ethics div. 1985-88, specialization bd. 1989-90, ethics exec. com. 1990-93, mem. curriculum and acctg. edn. 1993—), Little 10 Acctg. Assn. (edn. chmn. 1980-84), Main Line C. of C. (govt. affairs com. 1991—), Mensa (internat. fin. officer 1970-74), Beta Alpha Psi. Clubs: Masons (past master) Plays and Players (treas. 1978-79). Author: Accountants Guide to S.E.C. Filings, 1968; contbr. articles to profl. jours. Home: 204 Dove Ln Haverford PA 19041-1902 Office: Cogen Sklar LLP 150 Monument Rd Bala Cynwyd PA 19004-1725

MILLER, LARRY D., broadcasting executive; b. Chadron, Nebr., June 14, 1943; s. John and Lettie Leota (Maiden) M.; m. Karen Eva Galey, Dec. 28, 1963; children: Bradley James, Jill Marie. BA in History, Chadron State Coll., 1969; MSc in Journalism, Iowa State U., 1974. News dir. sta. KCSR, Chadron, 1966-67; asst. mgr., news dir. KDUH-TV Duhamel Broadcasting Co., Scottsbluff, Nebr., 1967-69; news dir. KMA May Broadcasting Co., Shenandoah, Iowa, 1969-70; news dir., instr. sta. KOSU Okla. State U., Stillwater, 1971-7e; dir. news and pub. affairs sta. KLRN/KUT U. Tex., Austin, 1973-76; asst. prof., sta. mgr. Okla. State U., Stillwater, 1977-80; sta. mgr. Okla. Edn. TV Authority, Tulsa 1980-85; dep. exec. dir. S.D. Pub. Broadcasting, Vermillion, 1985-93; exec. dir. Miss. Authority Edn. TV, Jackson, 1993—; pres., CEO EdNet Inst., Inc., Jackson, 1993—. Bd. dirs. Internat. Ballet competition, Miss. Rural Econ. Devel. coun. Commdr. U.S. Naval Res., 1962—. Named Outstanding Young Man, U.S. Jaycees, 1978, Ambassador Good Will, Indep. Order Foresters, 1984. Mem. Found. Pub. Broadcasting (bd. dirs.), Naval Res. Assn. (pres. Tulsa chpt. 1984), Oil Capital C. of C. (pres. 1983), Metro C. of C. (bd. dirs. 1983). Methodist. Avocations: genealogy, amateur radio, photography. Home: 140 Pinevale St Brandon MS 39042 Office: 3825 Ridgewood Rd Jackson MS 39211

MILLER, LARRY JOSEPH, oil and gas company executive; b. Huntington, W.Va., Aug. 20, 1932; s. Thomas Emerson and Etta Alice (Staley) M.; m. Phyllis June Queen, Jan. 25, 1957; children: Kristen Staley, Kimberly Anne, Katherine Crawford. BSBA, Ohio State U., 1957. Various positions Ford Motor Co., Dearborn, Mich., 1957-71; dir. planning Allis-Chalmers Corp., Milw., 1971-74; v.p. fin. and adminstrn. Fiat-Allis, Inc. B.V., Chgo., 1974-79; sr. v.p. fin., chief fin. officer Fox-Stanley Products, Inc., San Antonio, 1979-81; v.p. fin. Internat. Harvester Credit Corp., Schaumburg, Ill., 1981-84; exec. v.p. oil and gas exploration and prodn. Pyramid Energy, Inc., San Antonio, 1984—; bd. dirs. Harco Nat. Ins. Co., Milw., Internat. Harvester Credit Corp., Toronto, Ont., Can., Pyramid Energy, Inc., MJB Acquisition Corp. Fundraiser United Fund, San Antonio, 1981, mem. budget rev. com., 1982. With U.S. Army, 1953-54, ETO. Mem. Fin. Execs. Inst. Republican. Episcopalian. Home: 14073 Mint Trail Dr San Antonio TX 78232-3505 Office: Pyramid Energy Inc 10101 Reunion Pl San Antonio TX 78216-4160

MILLER, LAURENCE GLENN, art gallery owner and director; b. N.Y.C., Oct. 8, 1948; s. Tobias and Lilyan (Saposnik) M.; m. Lorraine Koziatek, Apr. 9, 1983. BS, U. Wis., 1972, MA, 1973; postgrad., U. N.Mex., 1973-74. Assoc. dir. LIGHT Gallery, N.Y.C., 1974-80; instr. New Sch. for Social Research, N.Y.C., 1976-80; pres. Laurence Miller Gallery, N.Y.C., 1984—. Mem. Assn. Internat. Photographic Art Dealers (bd. dirs. 1985-86, 90-93). Avocations: racquetball, fishing. Office: 138 Spring St New York NY 10012-3854

MILLER, LAWRENCE A., lawyer; b. Cleve. Dec. 3, 1946. BA with highest distinction, Northwestern U., 1969; student, New Coll. Oxford U. Eng.; JD, Yale U., 1976. Bar: Ill. 1976. Ptnr. Sidley & Austin, Washington. Office: Sidley & Austin 1722 I St NW Washington DC 20006-3705

MILLER, LAWRENCE EDWARD, lawyer; b. Trenton, N.J., May 18, 1944; s. Lawrence William and Cathryn (Brennan) M.; m. Michele Bongiovanni. Mar. 4, 1978; children: Lawrence Michael, Kristin Michele. BA, Villanova U., 1966; JD, Boston Coll., 1969; diploma Pvt. Internat. Law, The Hague, Netherlands, 1969; MA, Princeton U., 1970. Bar: N.J. 1969, N.Y. 1972, U.S. Supreme Ct. 1973. Assoc. Donovan Leisure Newton & Irvine, N.Y.C., 1971-76; sec., asst. gen. counsel Asarco Inc., N.Y.C., 1977-86; v.p., sec., gen. counsel Lac d'Amiante du Que. Ltee, Que., Can., 1982-86; ptnr. LeBoeuf, Lamb, Greene & MacRae, N.Y.C., 1986—. Contbr. articles to profl. jours. Mem. ABA, Fed. Bar Assn. N.J. (v.p.), Bedens Brook Club (Skillman, N.J.). Democrat. Roman Catholic. Office: LeBoeuf Lamb Greene & MacRae 125 W 55th St New York NY 10022

MILLER, LEE ANNE, artist, educator; b. Salt Lake City. B.S., Utah State U., Logan, 1960; M.F.A., Cranbrook Acad. Art, 1961; postgrad., Pratt Graphic Art Ctr., N.Y.C., 1962-63. Instr. painting and drawing Cleve. Inst. Art, 1964-66; instr. intaglio printmaking and painting E. Tex. State U., Commerce, 1966-68; assoc. prof. printmaking and painting, chmn. dept. art and art history U. Mo., Kansas City, from 1968; prof., chair dept. art Wayne State U., Detroit, 1978-81; dean Sch. Art Cooper Union for the Advancement of Sci. and Art, N.Y.C., 1981-91, prof. art, 1981—; project coordinator Women Artists, 1977; mem. curatorial panel Contemp Issues: Works by Women on Paper, 1977; mem. discipline screening com. art Fulbright Sr. Scholar awards, 1984-87. One-woman shows include Chgo., Salt Lake City, Cleve., Ohio, Kansas City, Mo. and Manhattan, Kans., 1976-77; Contemp Issues: Works by Women on Paper, Los Angeles, Utah and Tex., 1977-78; Contact: Women and Nature, Greenwich, Conn., 1977; Nat. Print. Exhbn., Honolulu Acad. Arts, Okla. Art Ctr., Oklahoma City, SUNY-Potsdam, Bradley U., Peoria, Ill. and Wichita Art Assn., Kans., Detroit Inst. Fine Arts, Nelson Gallery Art, Kansas City, Mo., Witte Meml. Mus., San Antonio, Springfield Art Mus., Mo., Dallas Mus. Fine Arts; exhibited in group shows include Watercolor USA, 1968-74, 17th Dixie Ann. Montgomery Mus. Fine Arts, Ala., 1976, 7 for 76 Bicentennial, Eastern Ill. U., 1976, Colorprint USA, 1976-77, The Transforming Landscape, Women's Views of Nature, N.Y.C., 1986, Elaine Benson Gallery, Easthampton, N.Y., 1986, East-West Ctr., Honolulu, 1990, Rocky Mountain Nat. Watermedia Exhbn., Colo., 1994. Recipient Purchase award 9th Ann. Prints, Drawings

and Crafts Exhbn., Ark. Arts Ctr., 1976, 2d place award 36th Ann. Cedar City Nat. Exhbn., Utah, 1977, resolution of tribute Mich. Senate, 1979, Outstanding Alumna award Utah State U., 1987; Fulbright fellow Slade Sch. of Art, London, 1962-63, Tamarind Inst. grantee, 1975-76. Office: Cooper Union Sch Art 41 Cooper Square New York NY 10003-7183

MILLER, LELAND BISHOP, JR., food processing and financial consultant; b. Bloomington, Ill., June 17, 1931; s. Leland Bishop and Nellie (Jolly) M.; m. Alice P. Elder; children: Susan Elizabeth, James Bishop, Steven Robert. B.S. in Chem. Engring, U. Ill., 1954, M.S. in Chem. Engring, 1955, M.B.A., 1978. Research engr. Exxon Research & Engring., Linden, N.J., 1955-58; research asst. Purdue U., 1958-59; with A. E. Staley Mfg. Co., Decatur, Ill., 1959-85; dir. corp. planning A.E. Staley Mfg. Co., 1971-73, asst. treas., 1973-77, corp. treas., 1977-81, v.p., treas., 1981-85; v.p., treas. Staley Continental Inc., Rolling Meadows, Ill., 1985-88; exec. v.p., chief fin. officer MultiFresh Systems, Inc., Hoffman Estates, Ill., 1989-90; exec. v.p. MWT Ltd., Inc., Barrington, Ill., 1990-93; fin. cons., 1993—; pres. Indsl. Devel. Research Council, 1973-74. State v.p. United Cerebral Palsy of Ill., 1971-72; pres. United Cerebral Palsy of Macon County, Ill., 1972-73; bd. dirs. Progress Resource, Inc., Decatur. Served to 1st lt. U.S. Army, 1955-57. Mem. Am. Mgmt. Assn. (fin. council), Fin. Mgmt. Assn., Nat. Assn. of Corp. Treas., Alpha Chi Sigma, Phi Lambda Upsilon, Sigma Chi.

MILLER, LENORE, labor union official; b. Union City, N.J., Mar. 10, 1932; d. Louis and Lillian (Bergen) Shapiro; m. Louis Miller, Dec. 25, 1952; 1 child, Jessica. BA, Rutgers U., 1952; postgrad., Purdue U., 1952-56, New Sch. Social Research, 1957. Sec., asst. to pres. Panel of Ams.; sec., asst. to pres. Retail, Wholesale & Dept. Store Union, AFL-CIO, CLC, N.Y.C., 1958-78, v.p., 1978-80, sec.-treas., 1980-86, pres., 1986—; vice chair civil rights com. AFL-CIO, 1990—; exec. bd. AFL-CIO Indsl. Union Dept., Washington, 1980-82, AFL-CIO Food & Beverage Trades Dept., Washington, 1980—, Maritime Trades Dept., 1986; v.p. Transp. Trades Dept. AFL-CIO, 1992—; vice-chmn. Nat. Trade Union Coun. for Human Rights, N.Y.C., 1980—; mem. Nat. BD. Workers Def. League, 1979-81—. Pres. Commn. Tariff & Trade, 1994—; mem. com. Am. Trade Union Coun. for Histadrut & Afro-Asian Inst., N.Y.C., 1980—; bd. dirs. Health Security Action Coun., 1986; chmn. RWDSU Welfare and Pension Plan, 1986. Mem. adv. com. AFL-CIO Com. on Polit. Edn., Washington, 1978—, Frontlash, 1978—; bd. dirs. A. Philip Randolph Ednl. Fund, 1988, Cen. Labor Rehab. Coun. N.Y.; charter trustee Rutgers U., 1988-94; pres. Jewish Labor Com., 1989; mem. platform com. Dem. Nat. Conv., 1992; mem. Pres. Commn. on Family and Med. Leave, 1993—. Named to Acad. of Women Achievers YWCA, 1987. Mem. AFL-CIO (v.p. 1987—, mem. exec. coun.), Douglass Soc. Office: Retail Wholesale & Dept Store Union AFL-CIO CLC 30 E 29th St Fl 4 New York NY 10016-7925

MILLER, LEONARD DAVID, surgeon; b. Jersey City, July 8, 1930; s. Louis Abner and Esther (Levy) M.; children—Steven Lawrence, Jason Lloyd. A.B., Yale U., 1951; M.D., U. Pa., 1955. Intern Hosp. of U. Pa., Phila., 1955-56; resident Hosp. of U. Pa., 1956-57, 59-65; practice medicine, specializing in surgery Phila., 1965—; vice chmn. dept. research and surgery U. Pa., 1972-75, acting chmn., 1975-78, John Rhea Barton prof., 1978-83, chmn. dept. surgery, 1978-83; dir. Harrison Dept. Surgery. Mem. editorial bd.: Annals of Surgery, 1973—. Served to capt., M.C. USAF, 1957-59. Recipient Lindback award for disting. teaching, 1969, Student award for clin. teaching, 1965. Mem. Am. Surg. Assn., AAAS, Soc. for Surgery of Alimentary Tract, Nat. Soc. Med. Research (rep.), Soc. Univ. Surgeons, Am. Soc. Surgery of Trauma, Coll. Physicians of Phila., N.Y. Acad. Sci., Sigma Xi, Alpha Omega Alpha. Office: Univ Pa Hosp Dept Surgery 4 Silverstein 3400 Spruce St Philadelphia PA 19104

MILLER, LEONARD DOY, army officer; b. Minden, La., Feb. 14, 1941; s. Doy Bracken and Jewel (Krouse) M.; m. Mona Carolyn Hall, Dec. 22, 1962; children: Doy Michael, Mark Leonard. BS, Northwestern State U. La., 1964. Commd. 2d lt. U.S. Army, 1964, advanced through grades to brig. gen., 1989; student U.S. Army Command and Gen. Staff Coll., Ft. Leavenworth, Kans., 1973-74; ops. officer 9th Inf. Div. Arty., Ft. Lewis, Wash., 1977; bn. comdr. 1st Bn., 11th F.A., 9th Inf. Div., Ft. Lewis, 1977-79; student Nat. War Coll., Washington, 1979-80; action officer Orgn. Joint Chiefs of Staff, Washington, 1980-81; dep. div. chief, exec. officer Office Chief of Legis. Liaison, Washington, 1981-83; comdr. 5th Inf. Div. Arty., Ft. Polk, La., 1983-86; div. chief Office Chief of Legis. Liaison, Washington, 1986-87; chief of staff 5th Inf. Div., Ft. Polk, 1987-88; dep. chief Office Chief of Legis. Liaison, Washington, 1988-90; comdr. V Corps Arty., Frankfurt, Germany, 1990-92; comdr. field command Defense Nuclear Agy., Kirtland AFB, N.Mex., 1992—. Decorated Legion of Merit, Bronze Star, Meritorious Svc. medal, Def. Meritorious medal. Mem. Assn. U.S. Army. Baptist. Avocations: fishing, woodworking. Home: Box 16 RR 5 Box 16 Minden LA 71055-9070 Office: Field Command Defense Nuclear Agy Kirtland AFB NM 87117

MILLER, LEROY BENJAMIN, architect; b. Cleve., Dec. 24, 1931; s. Harry Simon and Carol Jane (Goldberg) M.; m. Sue Firestone, July 1, 1956; children: Laurie, Janet, David, Matthew. BArch. U. Mich., 1956. Registered architect, Calif. From assoc. to v.p. Daniel Dworsky & Assocs., L.A., 1958-66; prin., pres. Leroy Miller Assocs., L.A., Santa Monica, Calif., 1966—; tchr. Calif. State Poly. Coll., Pomona, 1971-72. Exhibited in group shows, 1976, 84, 94. Pres. Leo Baeck Temple, L.A., 1991-93. Cpl. U.S. Army, 1956-58. Fellow AIA (Design awards L.A. chpt. 1966, 69, 72, 89). Democrat. Jewish. Avocations: writing, music, skiing, racquetball. Office: Leroy Miller Assocs 2800 Olympic Blvd Santa Monica CA 90404-4119

MILLER, LESLEY JAMES, JR., state representative; b. Tampa, Fla., Apr. 21, 1951; s. Lesley James and Shaddie Alice (Robinson) M.; m. Gwendolyn Martin, Nov. 27, 1982; children: Le'Jean Michelle, Lesley James III. BA in Polit. Sci., U. South Fla., 1978. Customer rels. rep. Tampa Electric Co., 1978-87; pres. Lesley Miller Cons., Tampa, 1988-89; v.p. COO Greater Tampa Urban League, 1989-90; human resources recruiter Time Customer Svc., Inc., Tampa, 1990-91; mem. City of Tampa City Coun., 1991; mem Fla. Ho. of Reps., Tampa, 1992—; pres. Miller, Miller and Assocs., Tampa, 1990—. Mem. Fla. Commn. on Mental Health, Tallahassee, 1993—, Planning Commn., Hillsborough County, Fla., 1987-91, City Conv. Facilities Bd., Tampa, 1987-91, City County Cable TV Bd., Tampa, 1987-91; dir. Tampa Hillsborough Urban League, 1977—. With USAF, 1971-74. Recipient Milestone award Tampa Hillsborough Urban League, 1993, Achievement award Charmettes, Inc., 1993, Outstanding Support award Fla. Consortium Urban Leagues, 1993, Disting. Alumnus award U. South Fla., 1985. Mem. Masons (32d degree), Kappa Alpha Psi (life). Democrat. Baptist. Avocations: singing, reading, travel. Home: 2505 E 38th Ave Tampa FL 33610-7617 Office: Fla Ho of Reps PO Box 5993 Tampa FL 33675-5993

MILLER, LESLIE ANNE, lawyer; b. Franlin, Ind., Nov. 4, 1951; d. G. Thomas and Anne (Gaines) Miller; m. Richard B. Worley, Feb. 14, 1987. AB cum laude, Mt. Holyoke Coll., South Hadley, Pa., 1973; MA in Polit. Sci., Eagle Inst. Politics, New Brunswick, N.J., 1974; JD, Dickinson Sch. of Law, Carlisle, Pa., 1977. Bar: Pa. 1977, U.S. Dist. Ct. (ea. dist.) Pa. 1977, U.S. Ct. Appeals (3d cir.) 1980, U.S. Dist. Ct. (ea. dist.) Pa. 1987. Assoc. LaBrum & Doak, Phila., 1977-81; ptnr. LaBrum & Doak, 1981-86, Goldfein & Joseph, Phila., 1986—; mem. Jud. Inquiry and Rev. Bd., 1990—, chair, 1993. Chmn. Con. on Jud. Selection and Retention, Phila., 1987-89; mem. Open Space Task Force Com., Lower Merion Twp., Pa., 1990—; bd. dirs. Med. Coll. Pa., 1985—, sec., 1987-92, chair presdl. search com., 1993, chair presdl. inauguration, 1987, chair com. on acad. affairs 1989—; bd. dirs. United Hosps., 1991—; bd. dirs. St. Christopher's Hosp. for Children, 1991—, vice chair, bd. dirs 1992—. Recipient Mary Lyon award, Mt. Holyoke Alumni Assn., 1985, Alumnae Medal of Honor, 1988, Hon. Alumnae award, 1989, Pres. award 1993. Fellow Am. Bar Found., Pa. Bar Found.; mem. ABA, Pa. Bar Assn. (bd. govs. 1990-93, gender bias task force 1993, chair comm. on jud. selection and retention 1989, chair Andrew Hamilton Ball 1989, trustee Phila. Bar Found. 1990—), Pa. Bar Assn. (ho. dels. 1981—, bd. govs. 1980-83, 84-87, 91-93, chair young lawyers div. 1982-83, sec. 1984-87, chair ho. dels. 1991-93, chair commn. on status of women in the profession 1993), Pa. Bar Inst., Phila. Assn. Def. Counsel, Def. Rsch. Inst. Democrat. Lutheran. Avocations: collecting Am. antiques, gardening, running. Office: Goldfein & Joseph 17th Fl Packard Bldg Philadelphia PA

19102 Office: St Chris Hosp Children 100 W Laurel Ave Cheltenham PA 19012

MILLER, LEVI, publishing administrator; b. Millersburg, Ohio, Sept. 15, 1944; s. Andrew A. and Mattie (Schlabach) M.; m. Gloria E.; children: Jakob, Hannah, Elizabeth. Student, Kent State U., 1963-64; BA in English/History, Malone Coll., 1968; MA in English, Bowling Green State U., 1976. Tchr. English pub. schs. Orocovis, P.R., 1968-71; editor Mennonite Pub. House, Scottdale, Pa., 1971-82, dir. congl. lit. divsn., 1990—; tchr., pastor Eastern Mennonite Bd. Missions, Caracas, Venezuela, 1982-84; program dir. Laurelville Mennonite Ch. Ctr., Mt. Pleasant, Pa., 1984-90; sec. Allegheny Mennonite Conf., 1976-79. Contbr. articles to profl. jours.; author: Ben's Wayne, 1989, Our People, 1983, 2d edit. 1992; editor Allegheny Conf. News, 1979-82; editor Found. Series for Youth and Adults, Mennonite Pub. House, 1981-83. Mem. sch. bd. Southmoreland Sch. Dist., Scottdale, 1989-93. Home: 903 Arthur Ave Scottdale PA 15683-1543 Office: Mennonite Pub House 1600 Walnut St Scottdale PA 15683

MILLER, LEWIS NELSON, JR., banker; b. 1944. BA, Washington and Lee U., 1966; postgrad., U. Va., 1972. With 1st & Mchts. Nat. Bank, 1969-70; planning mgr. Cen. Fidelity Bank N.A., Richmond, Va., 1972-73, planning officer, then asst. v.p., 1973-75, v.p., 1975-76, sr. v.p., mgr. fin. group, 1976-78, chief fin. officer, 1978-79, exec. v.p., 1979-82, exec. v.p., chief adminstrv. officer, from 1982; with Cen. Fidelity Banks Inc., Richmond, 1972—, sr. v.p., 1980-82, corp. exec. officer, 1983-83; exec. v.p. Cen. Fidelity Banks Inc., Richmond, Va., 1983-84; pres., later also treas., bd. dirs. Cen. Fidelity Banks Inc., Richmond, from 1984. Lt. USN, 1966-69. Office: Cen Fidelity Banks Inc PO Box 27602 1021 E Cary St Richmond VA 23219-4000

MILLER, LILLIE M., nursing educator; b. Atlanta, Nov. 16, 1937; d. George W. and Lillie M. (Reese) McDaniel; m. Harold G. Miller, June 30, 1962; children: Daren K., Lisa K. Diploma in nursing, Jewish Hosp. of Cin., 1959; BSN, U. Cin., 1961; MEd, Temple U., 1970; MSN, Villanova U., 1987. RN, Pa.; cert. sch. nurse, cert. clin. specialist in med.-surg. nursing ANCC. Instr. sch. nursing Jewish Hosp. Cin., 1959-62; instr. Phila. Gen. Hosp. Sch. Nursing, 1962-67; sch. nurse Norristown (Pa.) Area Sch. Dist., 1967-70; nursing instr. Villanova U., Villanova, Pa., 1988; asst. prof. Montgomery County C.C., Blue Bell, Pa., 1983-93, assoc. prof, 1993—; advisor Student Nurses Assn. Pa. Recipient Pi Tau Delta scholarship, Chapel of Four Chaplains. Mem. ANA, Nat. League for Nursing, Pa. League for Nursing, Jewish Hosp. Alumni Assn., Temple U. Alumni Assn., Villanova U. Alumni Assn., Sigma Theta Tau.

MILLER, LINDA B., political scientist; b. Manchester, N.H., Aug. 7, 1937; d. Louis and Helene (Chase) M. A.B. cum laude, Radcliffe Coll., 1959; M.A., Columbia U., 1961, Ph.D., 1965. Asst. prof. Barnard Coll., 1964-67; research asso. Princeton U., 1966-67; research asso. Harvard U., 1967-71, 76-81, lectr. polit. sci., 1968-69; assoc. prof. Wellesley (Mass.) Coll., 1969-75, prof. polit. sci., 1975—, chmn. dept., 1985-89. Author: World Order and Local Disorder: The United Nations and Internal Conflicts, 1967, Dynamics of World Politics: Studies in the Resolution of Conflicts, 1968, Cyprus: The Law and Politics of Civil Strife, 1968; co-author, co-editor: Ideas and Ideals: Essays on Politics in Honor of Stanley Hoffmann, 1993; also articles and monographs. Internat. Affairs fellow Coun. Fng. Rels., 1973-74, Rockefeller Found. fellow, 1976-77, Oceanographic Instn. sr. fellow, 1979-80, 82-83, NATO social sci. rsch. fellow, 1982-83. Mem. Inst. Strategic Studies, Internat. Studies Assn., Coun. Fgn. Rels., Phi Beta Kappa. Home: PO Box 415 South Wellfleet MA 02663-0415 Office: Wellesley Coll Wellesley MA 02181

MILLER, LIZ RODRIGUEZ, public library system director, librarian; b. Tucson, Feb. 22, 1954; d. Tony S. Martinez and Maria (Corral) Rodriguez; m. Marc Alan Miller, Nov. 5, 1972; children: Andrea Eve, Matthew Luke, Meredith C. BA in Spanish, U. Ariz., 1976, MLS, 1978. Unit mgr. S. Tuscon Libr., 1978-80; activities coord. community cable com. City of Tuscon, 1980; info./reference mgr. Tuscon Pub. Libr., 1981-84, agy. mgr., 1984-85, regional mgr., 1985-87, asst. dir. pub. svcs., 1987-89; dep. exec. dir. divsn. ALA Libr. Adminstrn. & Mgmt. Assn., Chgo., 1990; dep. dir. Tuscon Pima Libr., 1990-91, libr. dir., 1991—. Co-editor: Great Library Propotion Ideas V, 1990; contbr. articles to profl. jours. Mem. adv. bd. libr. power grant Tuscon Unified Sch. Dist., 1992—; bd. dirs. Tuscon area Literacy Coalition, 1992—; active Hispanic Profl. Action Com., 1992—. Mem. ALA (mem. pres. program com. 1987, mem. nominating com. 1991-93), REFORMA (chair elections com. 1983-84, 85, chair conf. program 1987, pres. 1987-88), Am. Soc. Pub. Adminstrn., Libr. Adminstrn. and Mgmt. Assn. (mem. cultural diversity com. 1991-92, chair 1992-93, mem. nominating com. 1992-93), Pub. Libr. Assn. (mem. Pub. Libr. Assn.-Libr. Adminstrn. and Mgmt. Assn. cert. com. 1991-92, chair 1992-93, chair Allie Beth Martin Award com. 1987-88, mem. 1989), Ariz. State Libr. Assn. (chair svcs. to Spanish-speaking Roundtable 1980-82, pres. pub. libr. divsn. 1984-85, chair ann. conf. 1986), U. Ariz. Hispanic Alumni Assn., Beta Phi Mu. Office: Tuscon Pima Library PO Box 27470 101 N Stone Ave Tucson AZ 85726-7470*

MILLER, LLOYD DANIEL, real estate agent; b. Savannah, Mo., May 25, 1916; s. Daniel Edward and Minnie (Wiedmer) M.; m. Mabel Gertrude Kurz, June 9, 1939; children—Sharon Miller Schumacher, Donna Miller Bodinson, Rosemary Rae, Jeffrey Lloyd. B.S. in Agrl. Journalism, U. Mo., 1941. Reporter, feature writer, photographer, market editor Corn Belt Farm Dailies, Chgo., Kansas City, Mo., 1941-43; asst. agrl. editor U. Mo., 1946; dir. pub. relations Am. Angus Assn., Chgo., 1946-67, St. Joseph, Mo., 1967; asst. sec., dir. pub. relations Am. Angus Assn., 1968, exec. sec., 1968-78, sr. cons., 1978-81; realtor The Prudential Summers Realtors, 1978—; mem. U.S. Agrl. Tech. Adv. Com. on Livestock and Livestock Products for Trade Negotiations, 1975-79. Bd. dirs. Mo. Western State Coll. Found., 1976-82, pres., 1978-79; deacon Wyatt Park Bapt. Ch.; chmn. Heartland Ctr., Heartland Hosp. West, 1987-89, bd. dirs. 1987-95. With AUS, 1943-45. Recipient Silver Anvil award Pub. Relations Soc. Am., 1962, Faculty-Alumni award U. Mo.-Columbia, 1975. Mem. Nat. Assn. Realtors, St. Joseph Area C. of C. (pres. 1969, dir., chmn. agri-bus. coun. 1971), St. Joseph Regional Bd. Realtors (pres. 1986), Realtors Land Inst. (v.p. Mo. chpt. 1987-90), Am. Angus Heritage Found., Masons (32 deg.), Shriners, Kiwanis, Sigma Delta Chi. Home: 3208 Miller Rd Saint Joseph MO 64505-1532 Office: 1007 E St Maartens Dr Saint Joseph MO 64506

MILLER, LOUIS HOWARD, biologist, researcher; b. Balt., Feb. 4, 1935; s. David and Daisy (Arenson) M.; m. Nancy Jo Harned, Sept. 26, 1959; 1 child, Jennifer. BS, Haverford Coll., 1956; MD, Washington U., St. Louis, 1960; MS in Parasitology, Columbia U., 1964. Asst. prof. then assoc. prof. Coll. of P & S, Columbia U., N.Y.C., 1967-71; head malaria rsch. NIAID, NIH, Bethesda, Md., 1971-92, chief lab. malaria rsch., 1992—. Contbr. articles to profl. jours. Capt. U.S. Army, 1965-67. Recipient Paul Ehrlich/Ludwig Darmstaedter prize, 1989. Fellow Royal Soc. Tropical Med. Hygiene, Queensland Inst. Med. Rsch., ACP; mem. Am. Soc. Tropical Medicine & Hygiene (pres. 1988), NAS, Inst. of Medicine, Assn. Am. Physicians. Office: NIH Building 4 Rm 126 Bethesda MD 20892

MILLER, LOUIS RICE, lawyer; b. Frankfort, Ind., Feb. 28, 1914; s. Louis A. and Josephine (Rice) M.; m. Jean Preston Russell, Feb. 1, 1941; 1 child, Mary Melissa. A.B., U. Chgo., 1935, J.D., 1937. Bar: Ill. 1938. Assoc. Gardner, Carton & Douglas, Chgo., 1937-40; atty. Armour & Co., Chgo., 1940-71, Phoenix, 1971-79; v.p., chief legal officer Armour & Co. (acquired by Greyhound Corp. 1970), 1967-79; v.p., gen. counsel Greyhound Corp. (now The Dial Corp.), Phoenix, 1972-79. Served with AUS, 1941; Served with USNR, 1942-45. Mem. ABA, Assn. Gen. Counsel. Club: Paradise Valley Country (Phoenix). Home: 7541 N Shadow Mountain Rd Paradise Valley AZ 85253-3311 Office: Dial Corp Phoenix AZ 85077-2212

MILLER, LOWELL DONALD, pharmaceutical company research executive; b. Chgo., Jan. 20, 1933; s. Nick William and Otillie M.; m. Marian N. Couranz, Aug. 22, 1959; children—Lowell Donald, Jeanette L. B.S., U. Mo., 1957, M.S. in Biochemistry, 1958, Ph.D. in Biochemistry, 1960. Dir. biol. sci. Neisler Labs., Decatur, Ill., 1960-69; assoc. dir. biomed. sci. Warren-Teed, Columbus, Ohio, 1969-71; pres. Lab. Exptl. Biology St. Louis, 1971-73; sci. dir. Marion Labs., Kansas City, Mo., 1973-78, corp. v.p. research and devel., 1978-87, sr. v.p. research and devel., 1987-89; cons.,

1989—; bd. dirs. Air Methods, Syntello. Contbr. numerous articles to profl. jours. Bd. dirs. Kansas City Eye Bank, 1981-90. Served with U.S. Army, 1953-55. Fellow Am. Inst. Chemists; mem. Soc. Toxicology, Am. Soc. Clin. Chemists, Am. Chem. Soc.

MILLER, LOYE WHEAT, JR., journalist, corporate communications specialist; b. Knoxville, Tenn., Mar. 20, 1930; s. Loye Wheat and Sara Vance (Davis) M.; children: Lissa Wethey, Loye Wheat. AB, Dartmouth Coll. 1951; MS in Journalism, Columbia U., 1952. Mem. staff Charlotte (N.C.) observer, 1955-59, asst. city editor, 1959; corr. Washington bur. Time mag., 1959-64, 69-70; chief Midwest news bur. Time-Life mags., 1964-69; corr. Washington bur. Knight-Ridder Newspapers, 1970-77; chief Washington bur. Chgo. Sun-Times, 1977-78; corr. Washington Bur. Gannett Newspapers, 1978-79; chief polit. writer Newhouse Newspapers, 1979-85; dir. pub. affairs U.S. Dept. Edn., Washington, 1985-88, U.S. Dept. Justice, Washington, 1988-89; dir. pub. info. Northrop Corp., Arlington, Va., 1989—. Lt. (j.g.) USNR, 1952-55. Home: 1672D Beekman Pl NW Washington DC 20009-4009 Office: 1000 Wilson Blvd Arlington VA 22209-2230

MILLER, LYLE G., bishop. Bishop Sierra Pacific dist. Evang. Luth. Ch. in Am., Oakland, Calif. Office: Evang Luth Ch in Am 401 Roland Way Ste 215 Oakland CA 94621-2034

MILLER, MADELYN SUE, advertising executive, food and travel writer; b. Chgo., Mar. 4, 1947; d. Seymour and Estelle (Klotwogg) Jensky. Student, NYU, 1966-67; B.A. in Journalism, U. Mich., 1968; m. Howard Brian Miller, May 26, 1968; children: Mallorie Ann, Gregory Scott. Copywriter Young & Rubicam, Detroit, 1968-69, Yaffe Stone August, Huntington Woods, Mich., 1969-70, Dancer Fitzgerald Sample, N.Y.C., 1970-71, Neiman-Marcus, Dallas, 1975-76; sr. copywriter Tracy Locke, Dallas, 1976-81; pres. Madelyn Miller, Inc., Dallas, 1982—. Mem. adv. bd. Dallas Art Inst.; mem. Leadership Dallas; chmn. counselor's program PRSSA. Recipient Clio award, 1981; Matrix award Outstanding Dallas Woman in Advt., 1981, Effie award, 1980, Addy award (2), 1980, Bravo award (4) Detroit Art Dirs. Club, 1981, numerous others. Mem. S.W. Assn. Advt. Agys. (bd. dirs.), Dallas Soc. Visual Communications (Bronze medal, Bronze award 1979, cert. of merit 1979), Women in Communications (student pres. 1968, nat. task force on entrepreneurship, scholarship com.), Dallas Advt. League (cert. of merit 1979), Internat. Assn. Bus. Communicators, Pub. Rels. Soc. Am., Bus. and Profl. Advt. Assn., Am. Inst. Graphic Artists, Northwood Inst. Am. Women in Radio and TV, Dallas C. of C. (pub. rels. chmn., small bus. coun.), Internat. Food, Wine and Travel Writers Assn. (bd. dirs.), Nat. Spkrs. Assn., Mensa (nat. adv. bd. advt. and pub. rels.), CEO Club, Hadassah Nat. Fedn. Jewish Women's Club, Leadership Dallas. Home: 9619 Rocky Branch Dr Dallas TX 75243-7528 Office: PO Box 743242 Dallas TX 75374-3242

MILLER, MALCOLM LEE, retired lawyer; b. Canton, Ohio, Jan. 4, 1923; s. Thomas Maxwell and Margaret (Unkefer) M.; m. Laura Washburn; children: Stephen Washburn, Ann Mayo. JD, Ohio State U., 1949. Bar: Ohio 1950. Assoc. Law Office of Paul R. Gingher, Columbus, Ohio, 1950-53; assoc. Gingher & Christensen, Columbus, 1953-58, ptnr., 1958-86; of counsel Baker & Hostetler, Columbus, 1986-87; asst. counsel legal dept. Columbus Mut. Life Ins. Co., 1987-89; asst. counsel Columbus Life Ins. Co., 1989-90. Bd. dirs. Columbus Area chpt. ARC, 1972-94. 2d lt. USAAF, 1943-45. Mem. Columbus Bar Assn., Phi Delta Phi. Home: 1427 London Dr Columbus OH 43221-1543

MILLER, MARC DOUGLAS, airline pilot; b. New Orleans, Oct. 28, 1953; s. Harold and Danielle (Graff) M.; m. Denice Kaye Duchemin, Apr. 24, 1983; children: Catherine Rachael, Audrey Rose. BS, Tulane U., 1975, MS, 1976. Lic. FAA airline transport pilot; cert. flight instr. Regional airline capt. Scheduled Skyways, Inc., Fayetteville, Ariz., 1983-85; nat. airline capt. Am. West Airlines, Phoenix, 1985—. Percussionist Mesa (Ariz.) Symphony Orch., 1985—. Served to lt. USN, 1976-82; lt. comdr. USNR, 1983—. Mem. Aircraft Owners and Pilots Assn. Republican. Jewish. Avocations: numismatics, baseball, swimming, skiing. Home: 15 W Vinedo Ln Tempe AZ 85284-1323 Office: Am West Airlines 222 S Mill Ave Tempe AZ 85281-2869

MILLER, MARGARET HAIGH, librarian; b. Ashton-under-Lyne, Lancashire, Eng., Feb. 26, 1915; came to U.S., 1915, naturalized, 1919; d. Errwood Augustus and Florence (Stockdale) Savage; m. Mervin Homer Miller, June 30, 1940; children: Nancy Elaine Reich, Edward Stockdale, Jane Elizabeth Miller-Dean. B.S. in Edn., Millersville U., 1937; M.S. in L.S., U. So. Calif., 1952; postgrad. in supervision Calif. State U.-Northridge, 1957-59. High sch. librarian Phoenixville Sch. Dist. (Pa.), 1937-40; jr. high sch. librarian Los Angeles Unified Sch. Dist., 1952-55, coordinating librarian, 1955-62, coll. head librarian, 1959-62, supr. library services, 1962-83; lectr. children's lit. U. So. Calif., Los Angeles, 1959-76, advisor Sch. Library and Info. Sci., 1980-83; resource person Nat. Council for Accreditation Tchr. Edn., Washington, 1976-85; cons. Pied Piper Prodns., Glendale, Calif., 1978—, David Sonnenshein Assocs., Los Angeles, 1983-85, Baker & Taylor Co., Inc., N.Y.C., 1979-83, H.W. Wilson Co., N.Y.C., 1975—, Mook & Blanchard, La Puente, Calif., 1985—, Enslow Pub., Inc., Hillside, N.J, 1986—. Mem. Los Angeles area planning com. Library of Congress Yr. of the Young Reader, 1989. Editor: Book List for Elementary School Libraries, 1966; Books for Elementary School Libraries, 1969; Children's Catalog, 13th edit., 1976; Multicultural Experiences in Children's Literature, Grades K-6, 1978; Periodicals for School Libraries, Grades K-12, 1977; Multicultural Experiences in Literature for Young People, Grades 7-12, 1979; Baker & Taylor School Selection Guide, K-12, 1980, 81, 82, 83; Supplement to Multicultural Experiences in Children's Literature, 1982; Special Books for Special People: A Bibliography about the Handicapped, 1982. Bibliographer: Concepts in Science, Levels 1 through 6 students' edits. (P. Brandwein et al), 1972; Concepts in Science Teacher's Education, 1972. Columnist, book reviewer Los Angeles Times, various jours. Recipient Dorothy McKenzie award for disting. contbn. outstanding svc. in field of children's literature. Mem. Los Angeles Sch. Library Assn. (cons. 1952-83), Calif. Assn. Sch. Librarians (pres. So. sect. 1971-72, state pres. 1975-76, many coms. 1952-77), Calif. Media and Library Educators Assn. (various coms. 1977—), ALA (many coms.), Young Adult Svcs., Am. Assn. Sch. Librarians, Assn. Library Service to Children, Friends Children and Lit. (dir. 1979—, pres. 1987-88), So. Calif. Council on Lit. for Children and Young People (dir. 1961—, pres. 1973-74, 1st v.p. 1986, 3d v.p. 1987-88, awards chair 1989, 90, 91), Calif. Library Assn., Young Adult Reviewers Booklist Com. (sec. 1995), Assn. Adminstrs. Los Angeles Unified Sch. Dist., Women's Nat. Book Assn (Los Angeles chpt.), Beta Phi Mu (dir. 1977-79, 84-86, pres. 1979-80), Pi Lambda Theta (chpt. pres. 1964-66, 91-92), Delta Kappa Gamma (chpt. sec. 1962-64), Phi Delta Kappa (contest essay judge). Republican. Home: 4321 Matilija Ave Sherman Oaks CA 91423

MILLER, MARGERY K., lawyer; b. Phila., Jan. 16, 1947. BA, Smith Coll., 1968; JD cum laude, U. Pa., 1972. Bar: Pa. 1972. Ptnr. Reed Smith Shaw & McClay, Phila. Office: Reed Smith Shaw & McClay 2500 1 Liberty Pl Philadelphia PA 19103

MILLER, MARILYN LEA, library science educator. AA, Graceland Coll., 1950; BS in English, U. Kans., 1952; AMLS, U. Mich., 1959, PhD of Librarianship and Higher Edn., 1976. Bldg.-level sch. libr. Wellsville (Kans.) High Sch., 1952-54; tchr.-libr. Arthur Capper Jr. High Sch., Topeka, Kans., 1954-56; head libr. Topeka High Sch., 1956-62; sch. libr. cons. State of Kans. Dept. of Pub. Instrn., 1962-66; from asst. to assoc. prof. Sch. Librarianship Western Mich. U., Kalamazoo, 1966-73; assoc. prof. libr. sci. U. N.C. Chapel Hill, 1977-87; prof., chair dept. libr. and info. studies U. N.C., Greensboro, 1987—; vis. faculty Kans. State Tchrs., Emporia, 1960, 63, 64, 66, U. Minn., Mpls., 1971, U. Manitoba, Winnipeg, Can., 1971; vis. prof. Appalachian State U., Boone, N.C., 1987; mem. adv. bd. sch. libr. media program Nat. Ctr. for Ednl. Statistics, 1989, mem. user rev. panel, 1990; chair assoc. dean search com. Sch. Edn., 1988, coord. Piedmont young writers conf., 1989-94, chair race and gender com., 1990-93, SACS planning and evaluation com., 1990, 91, learning resources ctr. adv. com., 1993-93; hearing panel for honor code U. N.C. Greensboro, 1988-91, assn. women faculty and adminstrv. staff, 1987—, faculty coun., 1987—, univ. libr. com., 1987-88, com. faculty devel. in race and gender scholarship, 1990-92; lectr. and cons. numerous confs., seminars in field. Mem. editorial bd. The Emergency

Librarian, 1981—, Collection Building: Studies in the Development and Effective Use of Library Resources, 1978—; contbr. numerous chpts. to books, and articles to profl. jours., procs. and revs. Selected as one of four children's libr. specialists to visit Russian sch. and pub. librs., Moscow, Leningrad, Tashkent, 1979; hon. del. White House Conf. on Libr. and Info. Svcs., Washington, 1991; head del. Romanian Summer Inst. on Librarianship in U.S., 1991; citizen amb. People to People Internat. Program, People's Republic of China, 1992, Russian and Poland, 1992, Russia, 1994. Recipient Freedom Found. medal, 1962, Disting. Svc. to Sch. Librs. award Kans. Assn. Sch. Librs., 1982, Disting. Svc. award Graceland Coll., 1992, Disting. Alumnus award Sch. Libr. and Info. Studies, U. Mich., 1988; Delta Kappa Gamma scholar, 1972. Mem. ALA (chair rsch. com., exec. dir. 1994, pres. 1992-93, adv. com. Nat. Ctr. Ednl. Stats. 1984, standing com. libr. edn. 1987-91, chair 1989-90, chair Chgo. conf. resolutions 1972, awards com. 1971-72, chair 1973-75, resolutions com. 1976-78, yearbook adv. com. 1988-90, Disting. Svc. award Am. Assn. Sch. Librs. 1993, other coms.), Am. Assn. Sch. Librs. (nominating com. 1980, pub. com. 1981-82, v.p.-pres.-elect 1985-86, chair search com. exec. dir. 1985, pres. 1986-87), Assn. for Ednl. Comms. and Tech., Assn. for Libr. and Info. Sci. Edn., Assn. of Libr. Svc. to Children (bd. dirs. 1976-81, pres. 1979-80, rsch. com. 1982-85, chair 1984-85, chair nominating com. 1984, other coms.), N.C. Libr. Assn. (edn. libr. com. 1978-80, 82-86, exec. bd. status of women roundtable 1989—), N.C. Assn. Sch. Librs., Southeastern Libr. Assn. (chair libr. educators sect. 1990-92), So. Assn. of Colls. and Schs. (mem. accreditation team 1988). Office: U NC at Greensboro Dept Libr And Studies Greensboro NC 27412

MILLER, MARK, newspaper editor. BA in English, Grinnell Coll., 1976. Mng. editor Crain's Chgo. Bus., 1983-89, editor, 1989-93; dep. mng. editor, columnist Chgo. Sun-Times, 1993—; mem. exec. com. Com. on Fgn. Affairs. Guest radio and TV shows including Chicago Tonight with John Callaway, Sta. WTTW. Office: Chgo Sun Times 401 N Wabash Ave Chicago IL 60611-3532

MILLER, MARSHALL LEE, lawyer; b. Chattanooga, Tenn., Oct. 18, 1942. BA, Harvard U., 1964; student, Oxford U., Eng. Heidelberg U., Germany; JD, Yale U., 1970. Bar: D.C. 1971, Va. 1970, U.S. Supreme Ct. 1979. Spl. asst. to adminstr. U.S. EPA, 1971-73; assoc. dep. atty. gen. U.S. Dept. Justice, 1973-74; asst. sec. labor (acctg.), dep. adminstr. OSHA, 1975-76; ptnr. Gabeler, Baise & Miller, Washington; bd. dirs. Electronic Warfare Assocs. Bd. editors: Yale Law Jour.; Soviet Mil. editor: Armed Forces Jour., 1983-87; author books internat. and environ. topics. Bd. dirs. Bulgarian-Am. Enterprise Fund, Electronic Warfare Assocs., Am. Coun. of Internat. Living. Office: Gabeler Baise & Miller Washington Sq 1050 Connecticut Ave NW Ste 1250 Washington DC 20036-5303

MILLER, MARTIN JOHN, lawyer; b. N.Y.C., Aug. 31, 1943; s. John and Marianne (Boguslaw) M.; m. Elaine Pouletsos, Oct. 28, 1978; children—Catherine, Kassia, Diana, Alexander. B.A., Colgate U., 1965; J.D., Duke U., 1968. Bar: N.C. 1968. Staff atty. Mecklenburg Legal Aid, Charlotte, N.C., 1968-70; legis. asst. Congressman H. Robison, D.C., 1970-71; legis. counsel Pharm. Mfg. Assn., D.C., 1971-73, Am. Home Products Co., N.Y.C., 1973-75; pres. State and Fed. Assocs., D.C., 1975—. V.p. Widewater Fire and Rescue, Va., 1982-85; bd. dirs. Children's Hospice Internat., 1990—; chmn. 2020 Visioning Com., 1994—. Recipient Wall St. Jour. award for Excellence in Econs., 1965. Democrat. Home: 158 Waller Point Dr Stafford VA 22554-3220 Office: State and Fed Assoc Inc 1101 King St Ste 600 Alexandria VA 22314-2944

MILLER, MARVIN EDWARD, building materials company executive; b. Far Rockaway, N.Y., Jan. 28, 1929; s. Philip J. and Dorothy B. (Verby) M.; m. Beverly Kolikof, June 7, 1953; children: Lisa, Deborah, James. BS, Ind. U., 1949; MS, Columbia U., 1950. Salesman M. Verby Co., Jamaica, N.Y., 1953-56; pres. Miller Supply Corp., White Plains, N.Y., 1956-74, chmn. bd., 1975—; pres. Grip-Rite Ltd., Hong Kong, 1979—; chmn., co-chief exec. officer PrimeSource, Inc., 1990—. Bd. dirs., v.p. Westchester Jewish Community Svcs., Hartsdale, N.Y., 1985. With AUS, 1951-53. Mem. Masons, Shriners. Republican. Avocation: tennis. Home: 17153 Ericarose Ct Boca Raton FL 33496-5939 Office: PrimeSource Inc 1800 John Connally Dr Carrollton TX 75006-5403

MILLER, MARY ALICE, nursing educator; b. Searcy, Ark., May 21, 1941; d. Victor D. Sr. and Ida G. Wall. BSN, Union Coll., 1963; MS, Loma Linda U., 1964; cert. GNP, U. Colo. Health Scis. Ctr., Denver, 1977; PhD, U. Colo., Boulder, 1987. RN, Colo. Staff nurse, team leader Belinda Hosp., Port Hueneme, Calif., 1964, Loveland (Colo.) Meml. Hosp., 1965; instr. Union Coll., Denver, 1965-67; prof. nursing and health care mgmt. dept. Met. State Coll., Denver, 1967—; prof., chmn. dept. nursing and health care mgmt., 1987-91, assoc. dean, 1990—. Contbr. articles to profl. publs. Fed. Nurse Practitioner grantee. Mem. Nat. League Nursing (bd. dirs., bd. rev.), Am. Cancer Soc. (bd. dirs. Adams unit), Colo. Nurses Assn. (mem. various coms.).

MILLER, MARY HELEN, public administrator; b. Smiths Grove, Ky., June 30, 1936; d. Walter Frank and Lottie Belle (Russell) Huddleston; m. George Ward Wilson, Sept. 12, 1958 (div. Sept. 1973); children: Ward Glenn, Amy Elizabeth Huddleston; m. Francis Guion Miller Jr., June 6, 1981. BA, Western Ky. U., 1958. Tchr. Fayette County Schs., Lexington, Ky., 1958-60, Seneca High Sch., Louisville, 1960-63, Shelby County High Sch., Shelbyville, Ky., 1963-69; rsch. analyst Legis. Rsch. Com., Frankfort, Ky., 1973-79, asst. dir., 1979-83, 90-91; chief exec. asst. Office Gov., Frankfort, 1983-87, 93—; legis. liaison, 1991-93; cabinet sec. Natural Resources and Environ. Protection Cabinet, Frankfort, 1987-88; sales assoc. W. Wagner, Jr. Comml. Real Estate, Louisville, 1989-91. Author: (constl. revision) Citizens Guide To/Perspective, 1978, (booklet) A Look at Kentucky General Assembly, 1979, A Guide to Education Reform, 1990, (handbook) Gubernatorial Transition in Kentucky, 1991. Mem. Leadership Ky. Alumni, Frankfort, 1986, Waterfront Devel. Corp. Bd., Louisville, 1986-87, Greater Louisville Partnership, Econ. Devel., 1988—, Shelbyville 2000 Found. Bd., 1991-92; mem., sec. Regional Airport Authority Bd., Louisville, 1986-89; pres. Shelby County Community Theatre Bd., Shelbyville, 1989-90. Mem. Pendennis Club, Jefferson Club. Democrat. Episcopalian. Avocations: reading, theatre, gardening, antiques. Home: 1116 W main St Shelbyville KY 40065 Office: State Capitol Frankfort KY 40601

MILLER, MARY HOTCHKISS, lay worker; b. Washington, Dec. 4, 1936; d. Ronald and Esther LeMoyne (Helfer) H.; m. Ronald Homer Miller, May 20, 1961; 1 child, Timothy Ronald. BA, Western Md. Coll. 1958; MRE, Union Theol. Sem. 1960; Cert., Windham House, N.Y.C., 1960. Dir. Christian Edn. Bruton Parish ch., Williamsburg, Va., 1960-61; dir. Christian Edn. (part-time) All Saints Episcopal Ch., Bklyn., 1961-62; adminstrv. and program asst., Christian Social Rels. Dept., Exec. Coun. Episcopal Ch. U.S.A. Episcopal Ch. Ctr., N.Y.C., 1967-72; nat. treas., chmn. Episcopal Peace Fellowship, Washington, N.Y.C., 1972-85; exec. sec. Episcopal Peace Fellowship, Washington, 1989—; bd. dirs., exec. com. Nat. Campaign for Peace Tax Fund, Washington, 1989—; bd. dirs., consultative coun. Nat. Interreligious Svc. Bd. for COs, Washington, 1989—. Contbr. articles to Witness mag. and jours., newsletters in field; book reviewer for The Living Ch., 1978—; designer ch. vestments and banners. Democrat. Office: Episcopal Peace Fellowship PO Box 28156 Washington DC 20038

MILLER, MAURICE JAMES, accountant; b. Barron, Wis., May 14, 1926; s. James Martin and Fern (Harvey) M.; m. Marguerite Joyce Mielke, Nov. 1, 1952; children: Maureen J., Mark J. B.B.A., U. Wis., 1951, J.D., 1955. Bar: Ill., Wis. 1955. ; C.P.A. Wis. Assoc. Sidley & Austin, Chgo., 1955-62, ptnr., 1963-90, counsel, 1991—. Trustee William H. Miner Found., 1994—. With U.S. Army, 1944-46. Mem. ABA, Chgo. Bar Assn., Phi Alpha Delta. Republican. Methodist. Clubs: Chicago, Mid-Day. Home: 925 Brand Ln Deerfield IL 60015-3403 Office: Sidley & Austin 1 First Nat Plz Chicago IL 60603

MILLER, MAX DUNHAM, JR., lawyer; b. Des Moines, Oct. 17, 1946; s. Max Dunham and Beulah (Head) M.; m. Melissa Ann Dart, Jan. 10, 1969 (div. July 1975); 1 child, Ann Marie Victoria; m. Caroline Jean Armendt, Sept. 19, 1981; children: Alexander Bradshaw, Benjamin Everrett. BS with high honors, Mich. State U., 1968; postgrad., George Washington U., 1970-71; JD, U. Md., 1975. Bar: Md. 1976, U.S. Dist. Ct. Md. 1976, U.S. Ct.

Appeals (4th cir.) 1981, U.S. Supreme Ct. 1982. Engr. U.S. Dept. of Def., Aberdeen Proving Ground, Md., 1968-72; law clk. to presiding judge Md. Cir. Ct., Higinbothom in Bel Air, Md., 1975-76; asst. county atty. Harford County, Bel Air, 1976-79; assoc. Lentz & Hooper P.A., Balt., 1979-81; ptnr. Miller, Olszewski & Moore, P.A., Bel Air, 1981-94; prin. Law Offices of Max D. Miller, P.A., 1994—; county atty. Harford County, Md., 1983-88. Mem. Md. Bar Assn., Assn. Trial Lawyers Am., Md. Trial Lawyers Assn., Harford County Bar Assn., Phi Kappa Phi, Phi Eta Sigma. Avocations: carpentry, sailing, canoeing. Home: 308 Whetstone Rd Forest Hill MD 21050-1332 Office: 5 S Hickory Ave Bel Air MD 21014-3732

MILLER, MAYNARD MALCOLM, geologist, educator, research foundation director, explorer, state legislator; b. Seattle, Jan. 23, 1921; s. Joseph Anthony and Juanita Queena (Davison) M.; m. Joan Walsh, Sept. 15, 1951; children: Ross McCord, Lance Davison. BS magna cum laude, Harvard U., 1943; MA, Columbia U., 1948; PhD (Fulbright scholar), St. John's Coll., Cambridge U., Eng., 1957; student, Naval War Coll., Air War Coll., Oak Ridge Inst. Nuclear Sci.; D of Sci. (hon.), U. Alaska, 1990. Registered profl. geologist, Idaho. Asst. prof. naval sci. Princeton (N.J.) U., 1946; geologist Gulf Oil Co., Cuba, 1947; rsch. assoc., coordinator, dir. Office Naval Rsch. project Am. Geog. Soc., N.Y.C., 1948-52; staff scientist Swiss Fed. Inst. for Snow and Avalanche Rsch., Davos, 1952-53; instr. dept. geography Cambridge U., 1953-54, 56; assoc. producer, field unit dir. film Seven Wonders of the World for Cinerama Corp., Europe, Asia, Africa, Middle East, 1954-55; rsch. assoc. Lamont Geol. Obs., N.Y.C., 1955-57; sr. scientist dept. geology Columbia U., N.Y.C., 1957-59; asst. prof. geology Mich. State U., East Lansing, 1959-61, assoc. prof., 1961-63; prof. Mich. State U., Lansing, 1963-75; dean Coll. Mines and Earth Resources U. Idaho, Moscow, 1975-88, prof. geology, dir. Glaciological and Arctic Scis. Inst., 1975—; dir., state geologist Idaho Geol. Survey, 1975-88; elected rep. Legislature of State of Idaho, Boise, 1992—; prin. investigator, geol. cons. sci. contracts and projects for govt. agys., univs., pvt. corps., geographic socs., 1946—; geophys. cons. Nat. Park Svc., NASA, USAF, Nat. Acad. Sci.; organizer leader USAF-Harvard Mt. St. Elias Expdn., 1946; chief geologist Am. Mt. Everest Expdn., Nepal, 1963; dir. Nat. Geographic Soc. Alaskan Glacier Commemorative Project, 1964-74; organizer field leader Nat. Geographic Soc. Joint U.S.-Can. Mt. Kennedy Yukon Meml. Mapping Expdn., 1965, Muséo Argentino de Ciencias Naturales, Patagonian expdn. and glacier study for Inst.. Geologico del Peru & Am. Geog. Soc., 1949-50, participant adv. missions People's Republic of China, 1981, 86, 88, geol. expdns. Himalaya, Nepal, 1963, 84, 87, USAF mission to Ellesmere Land and Polar Sea, 1951; organizer, ops. officer USN-LTA blimp geophysics flight to North Pole area for Office Naval Rsch., 58; prin. investigator U.S. Naval Oceanographic Office Rsch. Ice Island T-3 Polar Sea, 1967-68, 70-73; dir. lunar field sta. simulation program USAF-Boeing Co., 1959-60; co-prin. investigator Nat. Geographic Soc. 30 Yr. Remap of Lemon & Taku Glaciers, Juneau Icefield, 1989-92; exec. dir. Found. for Glacier and Environ. Rsch., Pacific Sci. Ctr., Seattle, 1955—, pres., 1955-85, trustee, 1960—, organizer, dir. Juneau (Alaska) Icefield Rsch. Program (JIRP), 1946—; cons. Dept. Hwys. State of Alaska, 1965; chmn., exec. dir. World Ctr. for Exploration Found., N.Y.C., 1968-71; dir., mem. adv. bd. Idaho Geol. Survey, 1975-88; chmn. nat. coun. JSHS program U.S. Army Rsch. Office and Acad. Applied Sci., 1982-89; sci. dir. U.S. Army Rsch. Office-Nat. Sci. and Humanities Symposia program, 1991—; disting. guest prof. China U. Geoscis., Wuhan, 1981-88, Changchun U. Earth Scis., People's Republic of China, 1988—; affiliate prof. U. Alaska, 1986—. Author: Field Manual of Glaciological and Arctic Sciences; co-author books on Alaskan glaciers and Nepal geology; contbr. over 200 reports, sci. papers to profl. jours., ency. articles, chpts. to books, monographs; producer, lectr. 16 mm. films and videos. Past mem. nat. exploring com., nat. sea exploring com. Boy Scouts Am.; mem. nat. adv. bd. Embry Riddle Aero. U.; bd. dirs. Idaho Rsch. Found.; pres. state divsn. Mich. UN Assn., 1970-73; mem. Centennial and Health Environ. Commns., Moscow, Idaho, 1987-94. With USN, 1943-46, PTO. Decorated 11 battle stars; named Leader of Tomorrow Seattle C. of C. and Time mag., 1953, one of Ten Outstanding Young Men U.S. Jaycees, 1954; recipient commendation for lunar environ. study USAF, 1960, Hubbard medal (co-recipient t. Everest expdn. team) Nat. Geographic Soc., 1963, Elisha Kent Kane Gold medal Geog. So. Phila., 1964, Karo award Soc. Mil. Engrs., 1966, Franklin L. Burr award Nat. Geog. Soc., 1967, Commendation Boy Scouts Am, 1970, Disting. Svc. commendation plaque UN Assn. U.S.A., Disting Svc. commendation State of Mich. Legislature, 1975, Outstanding Civilian Svc. medal U.S. Army Rsch. Office, 1977, Outstanding Leadership in Minerals Edn. commendations Idaho Mining Assn., 1985, 87; recipient numerous grants NSF, Nat. Geographic Soc., others, 1948—. Fellow Geol. Soc. Am., Arctic Inst. N.Am., Explorers Club; mem. councilor AAAS (Pacific divsn. 1978-88), AIME, Am. Geophys. Union, Internat. Glaciological Soc. (past councilor), ASME (hon. nat. lectr.), Am. Assn. State Geologists (hon.), Am. Assn. Amateur Oarsmen (life), Am. Alpine Club (past councilor, life mem.), Alpine Club (London), Appalachian Club (hon. corr.), Brit. Mountaineering Assn. (hon., past v.p.), The Mountaineers (hon.), Cambridge U. Mountaineering Club (hon.), Himalyan Club (Calcutta), English Speaking Union (nat. lectr.), Naval Res. Assn. (life), Dutch Treat Club, Circumnavigators Club (life), Adventurers Club N.Y. (medalist), Am. Legion, Harvard Club (N.Y.C. and Seattle), Sigma Xi, Phi Beta Kappa (pres. Expdion chpt. Mich. State U. 1969-70), Phi Kappa Phi. Republican. Methodist. Avocations: skiing, mountaineering, photography. Home: Col E 1st St Moscow ID 83843-2814 Office: U Idaho Coll Mines & Earth Resources Mines Bldg Rm 204 Moscow ID 83843 also: House of Reps Idaho State House Boise ID 83720 also: Found for Glacier & Environ Rsch 4470 N Douglas Hwy Juneau AK 99801-9403

MILLER, MELVIN HOWARD, state legislator; b. Bklyn., July 24, 1939; s. Henry and Frieda (Chaiet) M.; m. Elizabeth Mohr, 1961; children: Susan, Lawrence. BA, Bklyn Coll., 1961; LLB, NYU Sch. Law, 1964. Assoc. O'Dwyer & Bernstein, N.Y.C., 1964-67, Joseph Keller, 1967-69, Bluestone, Kleigman & Israel, 1969-71; ptnr. Sherman, Adolf & Miller, 1971-91; assemblyman 44th assembly dist. N.Y. State, 1971; Speaker of the House N.Y. State Assembly, Albany, 1987, mem. rules com. Mem. Flatbush Com. for Youth, Midwood Community Coun. With U.S. Army, 1957. Mem. N.Y. County Bar Assn., Fidelity Lodge, KofP. Democrat. Jewish. Office: House Speaker State Capitol Albany NY 12224

MILLER, MERLE LEROY, retired manufacturing company executive; b. College Springs, Iowa, Dec. 20, 1922; s. Otis John and Hilda Edith (Reiff) M.; m. Doris Marie Young, June 4, 1944; children: Mark, Kevin, Jean. B.S. in Mech. Engring., U. Mo.-Columbia, 1944. Engr. Peerless Pump Div., Quincy, Ill., 1946; engr. John Deere Co., Waterloo, Iowa, 1946-55, sr. engr., 1955-59, project engr., 1959-65, sr. div. engr., 1965-84; dir. Council for Agr. Sci. and Tech., Ames, Iowa, 1981—. Patentee transmission valve, transmission housing. Served to lt. USN, 1942-53. Fellow Am. Soc. Agr. Engrs.; mem. Soc. Automotive Engrs., Pi Tau Sigma, Tau Beta Pi. Republican. Am. Baptist. Club: JD Suprs. (Waterloo).

MILLER, MERTON HOWARD, finance educator; b. Boston, Mass., May 16, 1923; s. Joel L. and Sylvia F. (Starr) M. AB, Harvard U., 1943; PhD, Johns Hopkins U., 1952. With Treasury Dept., 1944-47, Fed. Res. Bd., 1947-49; asst. lectr. London Sch. Econs., 1952; asst. prof., then assoc. prof. Grad. Sch. Indsl. Adminstrn., Carnegie Inst. Tech., Pitts., 1958-61; prof. banking and fin. Grad. Sch. Bus. U. Chgo., 1961—. Co-author: Theory of Finance, 1972, Macroeconomics, 1974, Financial Innovation and Market Volatility, 1991. Recipient Nobel prize in econs., 1990. Fellow Econometric Soc.; mem. Am. Fin. Assn. (pres. 1976), Am. Econ. Assn., Am. Statis. Assn. Office: U Chgo Grad Sch Bus 1101 E 58th St Chicago IL 60637

MILLER, MICHAEL EVERETT, chemical company executive; b. Indiana, Pa., Sept. 4, 1941; s. Everett Michael and Elizabeth Mary (Becker) M.; m. Eleanor Ann Flyn, June 19, 1965; children: Elizabeth Anne, Christopher. BS in History, St. Louis U., 1963, MS in History, 1965; grad. Advanced Mgmt. Program, Stanford U., 1982. Tchr. Ferguson/Florissant Sch. System, St. Louis, 1965; sales rep. inorganic chems. div Monsanto Chem. Co., St. Louis, 1965, dir. mktg., cycle-safe, 1976-77, dir. mktg. detergents and phosphates, 1977-80, comml. dir., water treatment chems., 1980-83, gen. mgr., detergent materials, 1983-86, v.p., gen. mgr., detergents div., 1986-88, v.p. rubber chems. and instruments div. and Asia Pacific, 1988-89, córp. v.p. adminstrn., 1989-93; sr. v.p. ops. The Chem. Group, 1993, group v.p. indsl. products, 1993, pres. splty. and engineered products, 1995—; bd. dirs. Watlow Electric Mfg. Co. St. Louis, Physicians Health

Plan; adv. bd. Emerson Electric Ctr. for Bus. Ethics, St. Louis U. Vice chmn. bd. trustees Fontbonne Coll., St. Louis, 1990. Mem. Algonquin Golf Club. Avocations: golf, skiing, racquetball, restoration of early model Corvettes.

MILLER, MICHAEL I., lawyer; b. Chgo., Apr. 9, 1937. BA, Northwestern U., 1957, JD, 1960. Bar: D.C. 1960, Ill. 1960. Ptnr. Sidley & Austin, Chgo. Office: Sidley & Austin 1 First Nat Plz Chicago IL 60603

MILLER, MICHAEL JON, survey engineer, local government manager; b. Parkers Prairie, Minn., Mar. 17, 1950; s. Buford Kenneth and Gretchen Cena (Sharp) M.; m. Terry Lynn Peck, May 20, 1972; children: Livia Mica, David Peter. BS. U. Wis., Platteville, 1972; M of Pub. Adminstrn., Ariz. State U., 1988. Cert. profl. land surveyor, Wis., Ariz.; soil tester, Wis. Chief of surveys Hovelsrud Cons. Assn., Richland Ctr., Wis., 1972-78; ops. mgr. Tech, Advisors, Inc., Phoenix, 1978-82; profl. surveyor Coe and Van Loo, Inc., Phoenix, 1982-83; survey engr. City of Phoenix, 1983—; land surveyor mem. Ariz. Bd. Tech. Registration, sec., 1990-91, vice chmn., 1991, chmn., 1991-92, vice chmn. 1993-94, chmn. 1994-95. Contbr. articles to profl. jours. Dep. registrar Dem. Party of Ariz., Phoenix, 1983—; clk. Phoenix Friends Meeting, 1985-86; recording clk. Intermountain Yearly Meeting of Religious Soc. of Friends, 1984-85. Fellow Congress Surveying and Mapping (membership chmn. 1987-88); mem. Nat. Soc. Profl. Surveyors (gov. for Ariz. 1985-89), Western Fedn. Land Surveyors (state del. 1988-89), Ariz. Profl. Land Surveyors (sec. 1983-84, pres. 1985-86, Outstanding award 1981), Nat. Coun. Examiners for Engrs. and Surveyors, Am. Pub. Works Assn., Am. Soc. for Pub. Adminstrn., World Clown Assn., Internat. Jugglers Assn., Greater Ariz. Bicycle Assn. Democrat. Avocations: hist. research, writing, juggling, bicycling. Home: 4026 E Campbell Ave Phoenix AZ 85018-3709

MILLER, MICHAEL PAUL, toy company executive; b. N.Y.C., Dec. 20, 1938; s. Samuel and Florence (Gordon) M.; m. Susan Arlene Portnoy, June 13, 1964; children—Andrew Laurence, Scott Leigh. B.B.A., Hofstra U., Hempstead, N.Y., 1969. Sr. v.p. real estate Toys R Us, Inc., Paramus, N.J., 1977—. Board dirs. Jewish Community Ctr., Greater Morris, N.J., 1985—, pres., 1987—; United Jewish Ctrs.; trustee Morris Mus. Found., 1989; v.p. bd. edn. Plainview/Old Bethpage (N.Y.) Cen. Sch. Dists. With U.S. Army, 1956-61. Mem. Nat. Assn. Corp. Real Estate Execs., Internat. Coun. Shopping Ctrs., Columbia Soc. Real Estate Appraisers, Masons. Republican. Avocations: golf, jogging.

MILLER, MICHAEL RADGIFF, film editor; b. N.Y.C., Aug. 7, 1952; s. Irving Arthur and Augusta Shirley (Schiff) M.; m. Iris Judith Rosenkrantz, Jan. 9, 1982; children: Adam Harold, Natasha Sarah. BS, Cornell U., 1974. Film editor Raising Arizona Fox, N.Y.C., 1987; film editor D.O.A. Disney, L.A., 1988; film editor Patty Hearst Atlantic, N.Y.C., 1989; film editor Miller's Crossing Fox, N.Y.C., 1990; film editor Mr. Destiny Disney, L.A., 1990, film editor Medicine Man, 1992, film editor Swing Kids, 1993; film editor With Honors Warners, L.A., 1994, film editor Boys on the Side, 1995; panelist student editing competition Am. Film Inst., L.A., 1990. Contbr. articles to profl. jours. Recipient Emmy award nominations for best editing NATAS, 1982. Mem. IATSE (local 771 and 776), Am. Cinema Editors. Jewish. Office: care Lawrence Mirisch The Mirisch Agency 10100 Santa Monica Blvd Ste 700 Los Angeles CA 90067

MILLER, MILDRED, opera singer, recitalist; b. Cleve.; d. William and Elsa (Friedhofer) Mueller; m. Wesley W. Posvar, Apr. 30, 1950; children: Wesley, Margot Marina, Lisa Christina. MusB, Cleve. Inst. Music, 1946; hon. doctorate, Cleve. Ins. Music, 1983; artists' diploma, New England Conservatory Music, 1948, hon. doctorate, 1966; MusD (hon.), Bowling Green State U., 1960; hon. doctorate, Washington and Jefferson U., 1988. founder, pres. artistic dir. Opera Theater of Pitts., 1978—. Operatic debut in Peter Grimes, Tanglewood, 1946; appeared N.E. Opera Theater, Stuttgart State Theater, Germany, 1949-50, Glyndebourne Opera, Edinburgh Festival; debut as Cherubino in Figaro, Met. Opera, 1951; 23 consecutive seasons Met. Opera; radio debut Bell Telephone Hour; TV debut Voice of Firestone, 1952; appeared in films including Merry Wives of Windsor (filmed in Vienna), 1964; Vienna State Opera debut, 1963, appearances with San Francisco, Chgo. Lyric, Cin. Zoo, San Antonio, Berlin, Munich, Frankfurt, Pasadena, Ft. Worth, Kansas City, Pitts., Tulsa and St. Paul operas. Bd. dirs. Gateway to Music. Recipient Frank Huntington Beebe award for study abroad, 1949, 50, Grand Prix du Disque, 1965, Outstanding Achievements in Music award Boston C. of C., 1959, Ohioana Career medal, 1985, Outstanding Achievement in Opera award, Slippery Rock U., 1985, YWCA Ann. Tribute to Women award, 1989; named one of outstanding women of Pitts. Pitts. Press-Pitts. Post-Gazette, 1968, Person of Yr. in Music, Pitts. Jaycees, 1980. Mem. Nat. Soc. Arts and Letters (pres. 1989-90, Gold medal 1984), Keystone Salute, Pa. Fedn. Music Clubs (Keystone Salute 1994), Disting. Daus. Pa. (pres. 1991-93), Tuesday Mus. Club, Phi Beta Kappa, Phi Delta Gamma, Sigma Alpha Iota. Office: PO Box 110108 Pittsburgh PA 15232-0608*

MILLER, MILTON ALLEN, lawyer; b. Los Angeles, Jan. 15, 1954; s. Samuel C. and Sylvia Mary Jane (Silver) M.; m. Mary Ann Toman, Sept. 10, 1988; 1 child, Mary Ann. AB with distinction and honors in Econs., Stanford U., 1976; JD with honors, Harvard U., 1979. Bar: Calif. 1979, U.S. Ct. Appeals (9th cir.) 1979, U.S. Dist. Ct. (cen.; no. and so. dists.) Calif., U.S. Supreme Ct. 1989. Law clk. U.S. Ct. Appeals (9th cir.), Sacramento, 1979-80; assoc. Latham & Watkins, L.A., 1979-87, ptnr., 1987—. chmn. ethics com. Latham & Watkins. Author: Attorney Ethics; articles editor Harvard Law Rev., 1978-79. Mem. Am. Cancer Soc., L.A. Mem. ABA, Calif. State Bar Assn. (com. on profl. responsibility), L.A. County Bar Assn. (chmn. profl. responsibility and ethics com.), Assn. Trial Lawyers Am., Phi Beta Kappa. Office: Latham & Watkins 633 W Fifth St Ste 4000 Los Angeles CA 90071 Notable cases include Raquel Welch vs. MGM Corp.; served as trial and insurance counsel in San Juan Dupont Plaza Hotel Fire litigation.

MILLER, MILTON HOWARD, psychiatrist; b. Indpls., Sept. 1, 1927; came to Can., 1971; s. William and Helen L. (Lefkovits) M.; m. Harriet Sanders, June 27, 1948; children—Bruce, Jeffrey, Marcie. B.S., Ind. U., 1946, M.D., 1950; diploma in psychiatry Menninger Sch., Topeka, 1953. Intern Indpls. Gen. Hosp., 1950-51; resident Menninger Sch. Psychiatry, Topeka, 1951-53; with psychiatry Univ. Hosps., U. Wis., Madison, 1955-71; prof. Univ. Hosps., U. Wis., 1955-71, chmn., 1962-71; dir. Wis. Psychiat. Inst., 1962-71; vis. prof. Nat. Taiwan U., Taipei, 1969-70; prof. psychiatry U. B.C., Vancouver, 1972-78; head dept. psychiatry U. B.C., 1972-78; dir. WHO-U. B.C. Mental Health Tng. Centre, Vancouver, 1974-78; dep. dir coastal region Dept. of Mental Health, L.A. County, 1978-86; chmn. dept. psychiatry Harbor-UCLA Med. Ctr., Torrance, Calif., 1978—; prof., vice chmn. dept. psychiatry UCLA, 1978—; dep. med. dir. Dept. of Mental Health, L.A., 1986—; cons. in field. Author: Psychiatry: A Personal View, 1981; Contbr. articles to profl. jours. Fellow Am. Psychiat. Assn., Royal Coll. Psychiatry; mem. Can. Psychiat. Assn., Royal Coll. Physicians and Surgeons (examiner 1973—), Can. Med. Assn., World Fedn. for Mental Health (mem. exec. bd. 1973—) Home: 809 Esplanade Redondo Beach CA 90277 Office: Harbor-UCLA Med Ctr Dept Psychiatry Torrance CA 90509-2910 For many years I worked hard for my parents and myself. Later I worked hard for my wife, children, friends and self. These last years I've been including strangers and it's better.

MILLER, MORGAN LINCOLN, textile manufacturing company executive; b. New Rochelle, N.Y., Feb. 11, 1924; s. Harry H. and Belle M.; m. Marjorie Leff, June 8, 1952; children—Betsy, Harry Robert, Amy, Cindy. B.A., Lehigh U., Bethlehem, Pa., 1947. With Nat. Spinning Co., Inc., 1959—; exec. v.p. Nat. Spinning Co., Inc., N.Y.C., from 1964; now vice chmn. Nat. Spinning Co., Inc., pres. Nat. Yarn Crafts subs., 1978—; pres. Nat. Yarn Crafts subs. Jr. Accent Dress Mfg. Co., 1956—, Coquet Bathing Suit Mfg. Co., 1954—; Bd. dirs BHC Comm., Inc. V.p. Westchester (N.Y.) Reform Temple, 1971, Westchester Jewish Community Svcs., White Plains, N.Y., 1970; trustee Beth Israel Med. Ctr. Served with USNR, 1942-45. Named Industry Man of Year United Jewish Appeal, 1980. Mem. Craft Yarn Coun. Am., Beach Point Club. Republican. Office: 183 Madison Ave New York NY 10016-5113

MILLER, MORRIS FOLSOM, banker; b. Omaha, Mar. 17, 1919; s. Max Arnold and Phebe (Folsom) M.; m. Nancy Keegan, July 26, 1952 (dec. Jan. 1977); children: Jay, Louise, Paul; m. Barbara Osborne Cunningham, Feb. 12, 1978 (dec. June 1986); m. Kathryn Klok Lewis, June 20, 1987. A.B., U. Mich., 1940. With Gering (Nebr.) Nat. Bank, 1946, Am. Nat. Bank, Kimball, Nebr., 1946-47, Boone (Iowa) State Bank, 1947-51; with Omaha Nat. Bank, 1951-80, asst. v.p., 1953-54, v.p., 1954-58, exec. v.p., 1958-62, pres., 1962-70, chmn., 1969-77, vice chmn., 1977-80, also past dir. Past dir. Creighton U., Omaha Pub. Power Dist.; past chmn. and past bd. dirs. Health Future Found., 1986-88; past receiver Midlands Community Hosp. Served with AUS, 1941-46; with USAF, 1951-52. Mem. Mid Am. Bankcard Assn. (past chmn., dir.), Omaha C. of C. (past pres.). Home: Box 454 Dubois WY 82513 Office: Firstier Bank PO Box 3443 Omaha NE 68103-0443

MILLER, NAN LOUISE, museum director; b. Atlanta, Aug. 6, 1948; d. William Mitchell and Harriet Irene (Wilkie) Schotanus; B.S., Kans. State U., 1970; postgrad. UCLA, 1979-80, Media Communications, 1981, Weist Barron Sch. TV, 1982, East Tenn. State U., 1982-83; m. Robert W. Miller Jr., Oct. 31, 1981. Buyer, Jones Store Co., Kansas City, Mo., 1971-75, Harzfeld's, Kansas City, 1975-76; exec. sales rep. Monet, Los Angeles, 1976-80; mgr. corp. buying offices Trifari, N.Y.C., 1980-82, field mktg. coordinator and media pub. relations rep., 1981-82; co-owner, v.p. mktg. Devel. Resources Corp., Kingsport, Tenn., 1982-89; exec. dir. Hands On! Regional Mus., Johnson City, Tenn., 1989-93, Richmond (Va.) Children's Mus., 1993—. Mem. Nat. Soc. Fundraising Execs., Assn. Youth Mus. (bd. dirs. nat. coun.), Am. Assn. Mus., S.E. Mus. Conf., Va. Assn. Mus., Nat. Coun. Assn. Youth Mus. (treas.), Jr. League of Richmond, Rotary Club Richmond, Chi Omega. Presbyterian. Home: 3600 Noble Ave Richmond VA 23222-1834 Office: Richmond Children's Mus 740 Navy Hill Dr Richmond VA 23219

MILLER, NAOMI, art historian; b. N.Y.C., Feb. 28, 1928; d. Nathan and Hannah M. B.S., CCNY, 1948; M.A., Columbia U., 1950, NYU, 1960; Ph.D., NYU, 1966. Asst. prof. art history R.I. Sch. Design, 1963-64; asst. prof. U. Calif.-Berkeley, 1969-70; asst. to assoc. prof. Boston U., 1964—, prof. art history, 1981—; vis. prof. U. B.C., Vancouver, 1967, Hebrew U., Jerusalem, 1980, U. Padua, 1990; vis. scholar I Tatti, 1984-85. Author: French Renaissance Fountains, 1977, Heavenly Caves, 1982, Renaissance Bologna, 1989; co-author: Fons Sapientiae: Garden Fountains in Illustrated Books, 16th-18th Centuries, 1977, Boston Architecture 1975-90, 1990; book rev. editor: Jour. Soc. Archtl. Historians, 1975-81, editor, 1981-84; articles, catalogues. Jr. fellow NEH, 1972-73; sr. fellow Dumbarton Oaks, 1976-77, 83-89; vis. sr. fellow Ctr. for Advanced Study in Visual Arts, 1988, 95. Mem. Coll. Art Assn., Soc. Archtl. Historians, Renaissance Soc. Office: 725 Commonwealth Ave Boston MA 02215-1401

MILLER, NEAL ELGAR, psychologist, emeritus educator; b. Milw., Aug. 3, 1909; s. Irving E. and Lily R. (Fuenfstueck) M.; m. Marion E. Edwards, June 30, 1948; children: York, Sara. B.S., U. Wash., 1931; M.S., Stanford U., 1932; Ph.D., Yale U., 1935; D.Sc., U. Mich., 1965, U. Pa., 1968, St. Lawrence U., 1973, U. Uppsala, Sweden, 1977, LaSalle Coll., 1979, Rutgers U., 1985. Social sci. research fellow Inst. Psychoanalysis, Vienna, Austria, 1935-36; asst. research psychologist Yale U., 1933-35; instr., asst. prof., research assoc. asst. psychol. Inst. Human Relations, 1936-41, assoc. prof., research assoc., 1941-42, 46-50, prof. psychology, 1950-52, James Rowland Angell prof. psychology, 1952-66; fellow Berkeley Coll., 1955—; prof. Rockefeller U., N.Y.C., 1966-81; prof. emeritus Rockefeller U., 1981—; research affiliate Yale U., 1985—; expert cons. Am. Inst. Research, 1946-62; spl. cons. com. human resources Research and Devel. Bd., Office Sec. Def., 1951-53; mem. tech. adv. panel Office Asst. Sec. Def., 1954-57; expert cons. Ops. Research Office and Human Resources Research Office, 1951-54; bd. of sci. counsellors Nat. Inst. of Aging, 1987-90; bd. gov.s and mem. of exec. com. N.Y. Acad. of Scis., 1987. Author: (with J. Dollard et al) Frustration and Aggression, 1939, (with Dollard) Social Learning and Imitation, 1941, Personality and Psychotherapy, 1950, Graphic Communication and the Crisis in Education, 1957, N.E. Miller: Selected Papers, 1971; contbr. chpts. to psychol. handbooks; editor: Psychological Research on Pilot Tng., 1947. Chmn. bd. sci. dirs. Roscoe B. Jackson Meml. Lab., Bar Harbor, Maine, 1962-76, hon. trustee, 1980—; bd. sci. counsellors NIMH, 1957-61; fellowship com. Founds. Fund for Research in Psychiatry, 1956-61; mem. central council Internat. Brain Research Orgn., 1964; v.p. bd. dirs. Foote Sch., 1964-65; chmn. NAS/NRC Com. on Brain Scis., 1969-71; bd. sci. counsellors Nat. Inst. Child Health and Human Devel., 1969-72; v.p. Inst. for Advancement of Health, 1982-90. Maj. USAAC., 1942-46; officer in charge research, Psychol. Research Unit 1, Nashville 1942-44; dir. psychol. research project Hdqrs. Flying Tng. Command, Randolph Field, Tex. 1944-46. Recipient Warren medal for exptl. psychology, 1954, Newcomb Cleveland prize, 1956; Nat. medal of Sci., 1964, Kenneth Craik Rsch. award U. Cambridge, 1966, Wilbur Cross medal Yale U., 1966, Alumnus Summa Laude Dignitatus U. Wash., 1967, Disting. Alumnus award Western Wash. State Coll., Gold medal award Am. Psychol. Found., 1975, Mental Health Assn. rsch. achievement award, 1978, Inst. for Advancement of Health Sci. and Art of Health award, 1988, Disting. Scholar award Internat. Soc. for Behavioral Medicine, 1990; establishment of Neal E. Miller Disting. Lectr. in Neurosci./ Am. Psychol. Assn., 1995—. Fellow Am. Acad. Arts and Scis. (council 1979-83), Brit. Psychol. Soc. (hon. fgn.), Internat. Soc. Rsch. on Aggression (life); mem. Am. Philos. Soc., N.Y. Acad. Scis. (hon. life), Spanish Soc. Psychology (hon.), Am. Psychol. Assn. (council reps. 1954-58, pres. exptl. div. 1952-53, pres. 1960-61, pres. div. health psychology 1980-81, Disting. Sci. Contbn. award 1959, award for Disting. Contbns. to Knowledge 1983, citation for Outstanding Lifetime Contribution to Psychology 1991, Divsn. Health Psychology Centennial award for outstanding achievement 1992), Eastern Psychol. Assn. (pres. 1952-53), NRC (div. anthropology and psychology 1950-53, chmn. 1952-53), Nat. Acad. Sci. (chmn. sect. psychology 1965-67, chmn. com. brain sci. 1969-71, sr. fellow Inst. of Medicine 1983—; bd. mental health and behavioral medicine 1980-85), German Soc. of Behavioral Medicine and Behavior Modification (hon.), Soc. Exptl. Psychologists, AAAS, Soc. Neurosci. (pres. 1971-72, pres. award for Career of Outstanding Neuroscience Rsch. Teaching and Svc, 1994), Biofeedback Soc. Am. (pres.-elect 1983, pres. 1984, Outstanding Rsch. award 1987), Acad. Behavioral Medicine Research (pres. 1978-79, Neal E. Miller New Investigar award established 1989), Sigma Xi (pres. Rockefeller U. chpt. 1968-69), Phi Beta Kappa. Club: Mory's Grad. Club (New Haven), Grad. Club Assn. Office: Yale U Dept Psychology PO Box 208-205 New Haven CT 06520-8205

MILLER, NEIL AUSTIN, biology educator; b. Grand Rapids, Mich., Apr. 9, 1932; s. Kennith C. and Marjorie (Linsenmeyer) M.; m. Sally Bond, June 23, 1961; children: Anne C., Mary Leigh. AS, Grand Rapids Jr. Coll., 1956; BS, Mich. State U., 1958; MS, Memphis State U., 1964; PhD, So. Ill. U., 1968. Asst. prof. Western Ky. Coll., Bowling Green, 1964-65; fellow So. Ill. U., Carbondale, 1965-68; prof. U. Memphis, 1968—, Consulting prof., 2004; ecologist Hall, Blake and Assocs.; cons. Continental Engring., Inc.; wetland ecologist cons.; environ. cons. Republic of Estonia. With USCG, 1950-53. Named Tenn. Conservation Educator of Yr., 1983. Baptist. Home: 6898 Trowbridge Cv Memphis TN 38138-1822 Office: U Memphis Biology Dept Life Sci 225 Memphis TN 38152

MILLER, NEIL S., financial officer, advertising executive; b. N.Y.C., July 30, 1958; s. Irving Israel Maltz and Lenore (Goldstein) M.; m. Karen Joyce Salomon, Nov. 22, 1987; children: Lindsay Alexandra, Jacqueline Olivia. BS, SUNY, Buffalo, 1980; MBA, SUNY, Binghamton, 1982. CPA, N.Y. Staff auditor Peat Marwick Mitchell & Co., N.Y.C., 1982-83; ops. auditor Gulf & Western Industries, N.Y.C., 1983-84; spl. projects acct. Mickelberry Corp., N.Y.C., 1984-86; v.p. fin. Ptnrs. & Shevack Inc. subs. Mickelberry Comms., Inc., N.Y.C., 1986-87; sr. v.p. fin. Ptnrs. & Shavack Inc. subs. Mickelberry Comms., Inc., N.Y.C., 1987-89, exec. v.p. chief fin. officer, 1989—. Mem. AICPA, Am. Mgmt. Assn., N.Y. State Soc. CPAs (com. chief fin. officers and advt.), Advt. Agy. Fin. Mgmt. Group. Avocations: skiing, motorcycling. Home: 594 W Saddle River Rd U Saddle Riv NJ 07458-1115 Office: Ptnrs & Shevack Inc 1211 Avenue Of The Americas New York NY 10036-8701

MILLER, NEWTON EDD, JR., communications educator; b. Houston, Mar. 13, 1920; s. Newton Edd and Anastasia (Johnston) M.; m. Edwina Whitaker, Aug. 30, 1942; children: Cathy Edwina, Kenneth Edd. B.S., U.

Tex., 1939, M.A., 1940; Ph.D., U. Mich., 1952; LL.D., U. Nev., Reno., 1974. Tutor U. Tex., Austin, 1940-41; instr. U. Tex., 1941-45, asst. prof. speech, 1945-47; research asst. Navy Conf. Research, 1947-52; mem. faculty U. Mich., Ann Arbor, 1947-65; successively lectr., instr., asst. prof. speech U. Mich., 1947-55, assoc. prof., 1955-59, prof., 1959-65, asst. dir. summer session, 1953-57, assoc. dir., 1957-63, asst. to v.p. acad. affairs, 1963-65; chancellor U. Nev., Reno, 1965-68; pres. U. Nev., 1968-73, U. Maine, Portland-Gorham, 1973-78; emeritus, 1987—, interim gen. mgr. Sta. WNKU, 1985-86; mem. adv. com. to commr. of edn. U.S. Office of Edn., Accreditation and Instl. Eligibility, 1976-79, acting chmn., 1977-78; mem. Judicial Edn. Study Group Am. Univ. Law Inst., 1977-78; mem. Nat. Accreditation Commn. for Agys. Serving Blind and Physically Handicapped, 1988—, pres., 1991-92. Author: Post War World Organization, Background Studies, 1942, (with J.J. Villareal) First Course in Speech, 1945, (with W.M. Sattler) Discussion and Debate, 1951, Discussion and Conference, 2d edit., 1968, (with Stephen D. Boyd) Public Speaking: A Practical Handbook, 1985, 2d edit., 1989; co-editor: Required Arbitration of Labor Disputes, 1947. Pres. bd. dirs. Perry Nursery Sch., 1956-57, Sierra Community Orch., 1989-94; mem. Ann Arbor Bd. Edn., 1959-65, Washtenaw County Bd. Edn.; sec. bd. dirs. Behringer Crawford Mus.; bd. dirs Sierra Arts Found., 1992—; pres. Reno/Sparks Theater Cmty. Coalition, 1994—; mem. Nev. Humanities Com., 1994—. Mem. Mich. Assn. Sch. Bds. (dir.), N.W. Assn. Colls. and Secondary Schs. (chmn. higher commn. 1971-73), Am. Forensic Assn. (pres. Midwest sect. 1950-53), Central States Speech Assn. (pres. 1958-59), Mich. Speech Assn. (exec. sec. 1950-55), Speech Communication Assn. (chmn. fin. bd.), Assn. Western U. (chmn. 1971-72), Delta Sigma Rho (nat. v.p. 1948-52), Phi Kappa Phi. Address: 1480 Ayershire Ct Reno NV 89509-5248

MILLER, NICOLE JACQUELINE, fashion designer; b. Ft. Worth, Tex., Mar. 20, 1951; d. Grier Bovey and Jacqueline (Mahieu) M. BFA, RISD, 1973; cert. de coursspeciale, École de la Chambre Syndicale de la Couture Parisienne, Paris, 1971. Asst. designer Clovis Ruffin, N.Y.C., 1974; designer Raincheetahs, N.Y.C., 1974-75, P.J. Walsh, N.Y.C., 1975-82, Nicole Miller, N.Y.C., 1982—. Recipient Dallas Fashion award, 1991; named RISD Alumni of Yr., 1992. Mem. Fashion Group, Fashion Roundtable, CFDA, N.Y. Athletic Club. Avocations: skiing, ice skating, waterskiing, wind surfing. Office: 525 7th Ave Fl 20 New York NY 10018-4901

MILLER, NORMAN, psychology educator, researcher; b. N.Y.C., Nov. 29, 1933; s. Arthur and Pearl (Doudera) M.; divorced 1975; 1 dau., Carrie Ellen. B.A., Antioch Coll., Yellow Springs, Ohio, 1956; M.S., Northwestern U., 1957; Ph.D., 1959. Asst. prof. Yale U., New Haven, 1959-65; assoc. prof. U. Calif., Riverside, 1966-68; assoc. prof. U. Minn., Mpls., 1966-68, prof., 1968-70; prof. psychology U. So. Calif., Los Angeles, 1970—, now Mendel B. Silberberg prof. Editor: Jour. Personality and Social Psychology, Interpersonal Rels. and Group Processes. Jame McKeen Cattell fellow, 1978; Guggenheim fellow, 1984-85; Fulbright Research fellow Bar-Ilan U. Israel, 1984-85. Office: U Southern Calif Dept Psychology 3620 Mc Clintock Ave Los Angeles CA 90007-4010*

MILLER, NORMAN CHARLES, JR., newspaper editor; b. Pitts., Oct. 2, 1934; s. Norman Charles and Elizabeth (Burns) M.; m. Mollie Rudy, June 15, 1957; children—Norman III, Mary Ellen, Teri, Scott. B.A., Pa. State U. 1956. Reporter Wall Street Jour., San Francisco, 1960-63; reporter Wall Street Jour., N.Y.C., 1963-64; bur. chief Wall Street Jour., Detroit, 1964-66; Washington corr. Wall Street Jour., 1966-72, Washington Bur. chief, 1973-83; nat. editor Los Angeles Times, 1983—. Author: The Great Salad Oil Swindle, 1965. Served to lt. (j.g.) USN, 1956-60. Recipient Disting. Alumnus award Pa. State U., 1978; George Polk Meml. award L.I. U., 1963; Pulitzer Prize, 1964. Roman Catholic. Club: Gridiron (Washington). Avocation: tennis. Office: Los Angeles Times Times Mirror Sq Los Angeles CA 90012

MILLER, NORMAN L., lawyer; b. Detroit, Jan. 31, 1936; m. Carol Miller; children: Norman L. Jr., Kristina A., Katherine A., Thomas A. BA, U. Mich., 1957, JD, 1960. Asst. dean U. Detroit Law Sch., 1965-66; spl. asst. atty. gen. State of Mich., 1966-70; dep. mayor City of Detroit, 1970-74; v.p., legal counsel Western Fin. Corp., Phoenix, 1974-81; ptnr. Rawlins, Burrus & Lewkowitz, P.C., Phoenix, 1981-84; pres., CEO Ariz. League Savings Instns., Phoenix, 1984-89; sr. ptnr. O'Connor, Cavanagh, et al, Phoenix, 1990—; chief judge Ariz. Ct. of Mil. Appeals, 1993—. chmn. Xavier Preparatory Sch. Bd., Phoenix, 1980-85, Maricopa County (Ariz.) Parks and Recreation Com., 1983—; mem., treas. Indsl. Devel. Authority, Phoenix, 1985-90; mem., chair Ariz. State Retirement Sys., 1991—. Capt. JAGC, USNR; U.S. Mil. Judge. Fellow State Bar of Ariz. (chmn. sect. on real property trust & probate law, mem. sect. on bus. law); mem. ABA (sect. on bus. law), State Bar Mich. (State Bar Fla., State Bar Ariz. Office: O'Connor Cavanagh et al 1 E Camelback Rd Ste 1100 Phoenix AZ 85012-1656

MILLER, NORMAN RICHARD, diversified manufacturing company executive; b. Balt., Mar. 7, 1922; s. Samuel and Tobie Hildreth (Engleman) M.; m. Nancy Lee Rosenthal, 1967; children: Hilary S., Dana A. B.S. in Indsl. Engring., Ga. Inst. Tech., 1947; M.B.A., Harvard U., 1950. Indsl. cons. George S. Armstrong & Co., Inc., N.Y.C., 1950-51; ind. mgmt. cons. Italy, 1952-56; founder Italian Postgrad. Bus. Sch., Turin, 1953-55; dir. analysis and bus. planning RCA, 1957-61, v.p. div. bus. planning, 1962-68, v.p., gen. mgr. Graphic Systems Div., 1968-71; cons. Office Sci. and Tech., 1971-72; pres., chief exec. officer, dir. Lynch Corp., N.Y.C., 1972-73; pres., v.p., dir. Radiation Dynamics, Inc., Westbury, N.Y., 1973-76; v.p. Diebold Group, N.Y.C., 1976-82; pres., dir. Conn. Corridor Cellular Communications Cos., Inc., West Hartford, Conn., 1982-87, Broadcast Enterprises Inc., N.Y.C., 1985-92; pres. Twenver, Inc., Denver, 1986-93, Continental Divide PCS Ltd., 1993—. Pres. Merce Cunningham Dance Found., 1976-83; trustee Phila. Mus. Art, 1967-89; trustee, mem. exec. com. Am. Fedn. Arts, 1982-90; mem. Boulder County Cultural Com., 1993—, Sci. and Cultural Facilities Dist., Denver, 1993—, Denver Found. Arts and Culture, 1994—. 2d lt. AUS, 1943-46. Mem. Inst. Aero. Scis., Ga. Tech. Alumni Assn., Harvard Club (N.Y.C.), Tau Beta Pi, Omicron Delta Kappa, Phi Delta Epsilon, Phi Epsilon Pi. Home: 5411 Sunshine Canyon Dr Boulder CO 80302

MILLER, ORLANDO JACK, physician, educator; b. Oklahoma City, Okla., May 11, 1927; s. Arthur Leroy and Iduma Dorris (Berry) M.; m. Dorothy Anne Smith, July 10, 1954; children: Richard Lawrence, Cynthia Kathleen, Karen Ann. B.S., Yale U., 1946, M.D., 1950. Intern St. Anthony Hosp., Oklahoma City, 1950-51; asst. resident in obstetrics and gynecology Yale-New Haven Med. Center, 1954-57, resident, instr., 1957-58; vis. fellow dept. obstetrics and gynecology Tulane U. Service, Charity Hosp., New Orleans, 1958; hon. research asst. Galton Lab., Univ. Coll., London, 1958-60; instr. Coll. Physicians and Surgeons Columbia U., N.Y.C., 1960, asso. dept. obstetrics and gynecology, 1960-61, asst. prof., 1961-65, asso. prof., 1965-69, prof. dept. human genetics and devel., dept. obstetrics and gynecology, 1969-85; asst. attending obstetrician, gynecologist Presbyn. Hosp., N.Y.C., 1964-65, assoc., 1965-70, attending obstetrician and gynecologist, 1970-85; prof. molecular biology, genetics and ob-gyn. Wayne State U. Sch. Medicine, Detroit, 1985-94, prof. Ctr. for Molecular Medicine and Genetics, 1994—, chmn. dept. molecular biology and genetics, 1985-93, dir. Ctr. for Molecular Biology, 1987-90; bd. dirs.Am. Bd. Med. Genetics, 1983-85, v.p., 1983, pres., 1984, 85; mem. human genome Study Sect. NIH, 1991-94. Editor: Cytogenetics, 1970-72; assoc. editor: Cytogenetics and Cell Genetics, 1972—, Birth Defects Compendium, 1971-74; mem. editorial bd. com. Genomics, 1987-93, assoc. editor, 1993—; mem. editorial bd. Cytogenetics, 1961-69, mem. Jour. Human Genetics, 1969-74, 79-83, Gynecologic Investigation, 1970-77, Teratology, 1972-74, Cancer Genetics and Cytogenetics, 1979-84, Jour. Exptl. Zoology, 1989-92, Chromosome Rsch., 1994—; mem. adv. bd. Human Genetics, 1978—; cons: Jour. Med. Primatology, 1977—; contbr. articles to med. and sci. jours., chpts. to textbooks. Mem. sci. adv. com. on rsch. Nat. Found. March of Dimes, 1967-95; mem. sci. rec. com. Basil O'Connor starter grants, 1973-77, 86-94; mem. human embryology and devel. study sect. NIH, 1970-74, chmn., 1972-74; mem. com. for study of inborn erros of metabolism NRC, 1972-74; mem. sci. adv. com. virology and cell biology Am. Cancer Soc., 1974-78, mem. sci. adv. com. cell and devel. biology, 1986-90; U.S. rep. permanent com. Internat. Congress of Human Genetics, 1986-91. With AUS, 1951-53. James Hudson Brown Jr. fellow Yale U., 1947-48; NRC fellow, 1953-54; Population Council fellow, 1958-59; Josiah Macy Jr. fellow, 1960-61; NSF sr.

postdoctoral fellow U. Oxford, 1968-69; vis. scientist U. Edinburgh, 1983-84; Disting. vis. fellow, Fogarty Internat. fellow LaTrobe U., Melbourne, Australia, 1992. Fellow AAAS; mem. AAAS, Am. Genetic Assn., Am. Soc. Cell Biology, Am. Soc. Human Genetics (bd. dirs. 1970-73, 86-90), Genetics Soc. Am., Genetics Soc. Australia, Am. Soc. Microbiologists, Human Genome Orgn., Acad. Scholars, Wayne State U. (life), Sigma Xi. Presbyterian. Home: 1915 Stonycroft Ln Bloomfield Hills MI 48304-2339 Office: 540 E Canfield St Detroit MI 48201-1928

MILLER, PAMELA GUNDERSEN, city official; b. Cambridge, Mass., Sept. 7, 1938; d. Sven M. and Harriet Adams Gundersen; A.B. magna cum laude, Smith Coll., 1960; m. Ralph E. Miller, July 7, 1962; children—Alexander, Erik, Karen. Feature writer Congressional Quar., Washington, 1962-65; dir. cable TV franchizing Storer Broadcasting Co., Louisville, Bowling Green, Lexington, and Covington, Ky., 1978-80, 81-82; mem. 4th Dist. Lexington, Fayette County Urban Council, 1973-77, councilwoman-at-large, 1982—, vice-mayor, 1984-86, 89-93, mayor, 1993—; dep. commr. Ky. Dept. Local Govt., Frankfort, 1980-81; pres. Pam Miller, Inc., 1984—, Community Ventures Corp., 1985—. Mem. Fayette County Bd. Health, 1975-77, Downtown Devel. Commn., 1975-77; alt. del. Dem. Nat. Conv., 1976; bd. dirs. YMCA, Lexington, 1975-77, 85-90, Fund for the Arts, 1984-93, Council of Arts, 1978-80, Sister Cities, 1978-80; treas. Prichard Com. for Acad. Excellence, 1983—. Named Woman of Achievement YWCA, 1984, Outstanding Woman of Blue Grass, AAUW, 1984. Mem. LWV (dir. 1970-73), Profl. Women's Forum, NOW, ACLU, Land and Nature Trust of the Bluegrass. Home: 140 Cherokee Park Lexington KY 40503-1304 Office: 200 E Main St Lexington KY 40507-1315

MILLER, PATRICIA G., lawyer; b. Northfield, Vt., Nov. 20, 1933. BS, U. Colo., 1957; JD, U. Pitts., 1976. Bar: Phila. 1976. Ptnr. Reed Smith Shaw & McClay, Pitts. Office: Reed Smith Shaw & McClay James H Reed Bldg 435 6th Ave Pittsburgh PA 15219-1886*

MILLER, PATRICIA LOUISE, state legislator, nurse; b. Bellefontaine, Ohio, July 4, 1936; d. Richard William and Rachel Orpha (Williams) Miller; m. Kenneth Orlan Miller, July 3, 1960; children: Tamara Sue, Matthew Ivan. RN, Meth. Hosp. Sch. Nursing-Indpls., 1957; BS, Ind. U., 1960. Office nurse A.D. Dennison, MD, 1960-61; staff nurse Meth. Hosp., Indpls., 1959, Community Hosp., Indpls., 1958; representative, State of Ind., Dist. 50, Indpls., 1982-83, senator, State of Ind., Dist. 32, Indpls., 1983—, mem. edn. com., 1984-90, health welfare and aging com. 1983-90, labor and pension com. 1983-94, legis. apportionment and elections coms., chmn. interim study com. pub. health and mental health Ind. Gen. Assembly, 1986; chair Senate Environ. Affairs, 1990-92, Health and Environ. Affairs, 1992—; mem. election com., 1992—; mem. budget subcom. Senate Fin. Com., 1995— . Mem. Bd. Edn., Met. Sch. Dist. Warren Twp., 1974-82, pres., 1979-80, 80-81; mem. Warren Twp. Citizens Screening Com. for Sch. Bd. Candidates, 1972-74, 84, Met. Zoning Bd. Appeals, Div. I, appointed mem. City-County Council, 1972-76; bd. dirs. Central Ind. Council on Aging, Indpls., 1977-80; mem. State Bd. of Voc. and Tech. Edn., 1978-82, sec., 1980-82; mem. Gov.'s Select Adv. Commn. for Primary and Secondary Edn., 1983; precinct committeeman Republican Party, 1968-74, ward vice chmn., 1975-78, ward chmn., 1978-85, twp. chmn., 1985-87; vice chmn. Marion County Rep., 1986—; del. Rep. State Conv., 1968, 74, 76, 80, 84, 86, 88, 90, 92, 94, sgt. at arms, 1982, mem. platform com., 1984, 88, 90, 92, co-chmn. Ind. Rep. Platform Com., 1992; del. Rep. Nat. Conv., 1984, alternate del., 1988, Rep. Presdl. Elector Alternate, 1992; active various polit. campaigns; bd. dirs. PTA, 1967-81; pres. Grassy Creek PTA, 1971-72; state del. Ind. PTA, 1978; mem. child care adv. com. Walker Career Center, 1976-80, others; bd. dirs. Ch. Fedn. Greater Indpls., 1979-82, Christian Justice Center, Inc., 1983-85, Gideon Internat. Aux., 1977—; mem. United Meth. Bd. Missions Aux. of Indpls., 1974-80, v.p., 1974-76; bd. dirs. Lucille Raines Residence, Inc., 1977-80; exec. com. S. Ind. Conf. United Meth. Women, 1977-80, lay del. S. Ind. Conf. United Meth. Ch., 1977—, fin. and adminstrn. com., 1979-88, planning and research com., 1980-88, co-chmn. law adv. com., chmn. health and welfare, conf. council ministries, also mem. task force, bd. ordained ministry, also panel, chmn. com. on dist. superintendency, dist. council on ministries; sec. Indpls. S.E. Dist. Council on Ministries, 1977-78, pres., 1982; chmn. council on ministries Cumberland United Meth. Ch., 1969-76; chmn. stewardship com. Old Bethel United Meth. Ch., 1982-85, fin. com., 1982-85, adminstrv. bd., mem. council on ministries, 1981-85; co-chair Evangelism Com., 1994—; jurisdictional del. United Meth. Ch., 1988, 92; alternate del. United Meth. Ch. Gen. Conf., 1988, delegate, 1992; mem. health and human svcs. com. Midwest Legis. Conf., 1995. Recipient Phi Lambda Theta Honor for outstanding contbr. in field of edn., 1976; Woman of the Year, Cumberland Bus. and Profl. Women, 1979; Ind. Voc. Assn. citation award, 1984, others. Mem. Indpls. Dist. Dental Soc. Women's Aux., Ind. Dental Assn. Women's Aux., Am. Dental Assn. Women's Aux., Council State Govt. (intergovtl. affairs com.), Nat. Conf. State Legislatures (health com. vice chmn. 1994—), Warren Twp. Rep. Franklin Rep., Lawrence Rep., Center Twp. Rep., Fall Creek Valley Rep., Marion County Council Rep. Women, Ind. Women's Rep., Indpls. Women's Rep., Ind. Fedn. Rep. Women, Nat. Fedn. Rep. Women, Beech Grove Rep., Perry Twp. Rep. Home: 1041 Muessing Rd Indianapolis IN 46239-9614

MILLER, PATRICK DWIGHT, JR., religion educator, minister; b. Atlanta, Oct. 24, 1935; s. Patrick Dwight and Lila Morse (Bonner) M.; m. Mary Ann Sudduth, Dec. 27, 1958; children: Jonathan Sudduth, Patrick James. AB, Davidson Coll., 1956; BD, Union Theol. Sem., Va., 1959; PhD, Harvard U., 1964. Ordained to ministry Presbyn. Ch., 1963. Pastor, minister Trinity Presbyn. Ch., Traveler's Rest, S.C., 1963-65; asst. prof. Bibl. studies Union Theol. Sem., Richmond, Va., 1966-68, assoc. prof., 1968-73, prof., 1973-84, dean of faculty, 1979-83; prof. of Old Testament Theology Princeton (N.J.) Theol. Sem., 1984—. Author: The Divine Warrior in Early Israel, 1973, The Hand of the Lord, 1977, Sin and Judgment in the Prophets, 1982, Interpreting the Psalms, 1986, Deuteronomy, 1990, They Cried to the Lord, 1994; editor: Theology Today, 1990—. Mem. Soc. of Bibl. Lit. (sec.-treas. 1987-88), Colloquium for Bibl. Rsch. (rev. standard version translation com. 1974—). Democrat. Presbyterian. Home: 89 Mercer St Princeton NJ 08540-6826 Office: Princeton Theol Sem CN821 Princeton NJ 08542

MILLER, PATRICK WILLIAM, research administrator, educator; b. Toledo, Sept. 1, 1947; s. Richard William and Mary Olivia (Rinna) M.; m. Jean Ellen Thomas, Apr. 5, 1974; children: Joy, Tatum, Alex. BS in Indstrl. Edn., Bowling Green State U., 1971, MEd in Career Edn. and Tech., 1973; PhD in Indstrl. Tech. Edn., Ohio State U., 1977. Tchr. Montgomery Hills Jr. High Sch., Silver Spring, Md., 1971-72, Rockville (Md.) High Sch., 1973-74; asst. prof. Wayne State U., Detroit, 1977-79; assoc. prof., grad. coord. indstrl. edn. and tech. Western Carolina U., Cullowhee, N.C., 1979-81; assoc prof. U. No. Iowa, Cedar Falls, 1981-86; dir. grad. studies practical arts and vocat.-tech. edn. U. No. Iowa, Columbia, 1986-89; devel. editor Am. Tech. Pubs., Homewood, Ill., 1989-90; proposal mgr. Nat. Opinion Rsch. Ctr. U. Chgo., 1990—; pres. Patrick W. Miller and Assocs., Munster, Ind., 1981—; presenter, advisor and cons. in field. Author: Nonverbal Communication: Its Impact on Teaching and Learning, 1983, Teacher Written Tests: A Guide for Planning, Creating, Administering and Assessing, 1985, Nonverbal Communication: What Resarch Says to the Teacher, 1988, How To Write Tests for Students, 1990; mem. editl. bd. Jour. Indsl. Tchr. Edn., 1981-88, Am. Vocat. Edn. Rsch. Jour., 1981-85, 94—; Tech. Jour., 1982-84, Jour. Indsl. Tech., 1984—, Jour. Vocat. and Tech. Edn., 1987-90, Human Resource Devel. Quar., 1989—; also articles. Sec. U. No. Iowa United Faculty, Cedar Falls, 1983-84, pres., 1984-86. Lance cpl. USMC, 1966-68, Vietnam. Recipient editl. recognition award Jour. Indsl. Tchr. Edn., 1984, 86, 87; named One of Accomplished Grads. of Coll. Tech., Bowling Green State U., 1995. Mem. ASTD, Am. Edn. Rsch. Assn., Am. Vocat. Assn., Am. Vocat. Assn., Am. Vocat. Edn. Rsch. Assn., Nat. Assn. Indsl. Tech. (chmn. rsch. grants 1982-87, pres. industry devin. 1991-92, chmn exec. bd. 1992-93, past pres. 1993-94, Leadership award 1992, 93), Nat. Assn. Indsl. and Tech. Tchrs. Educators (pres. 1988-89, past pres. 1989-90, trustee 1990-93, Outstanding Svc. award 1988, 90), Nat. Assn. Vocat. Edn. Spl. Needs Pers., Internat. Tech. Edn. Assn., Coun. Tech. Tchr. Edn., Epsilon Pi Tau, Phi Delta Kappa. Office: Univ Chgo Nat Opinion Rsch Ctr 1155 E 60th St Chicago IL 60637-2745

MILLER, PAUL, health care products company executive. AB, Rutgers U., 1960, LLB, 1962. Bar: N.Y. 1963. Assoc. Kaye, Scholer, Fierman,

Handler & Hays, 1963-65, Rubin, Baum & Levin, 1965-66; ptnr. Miller & Zimet, 1966-70; counsel Leasing Cons., Inc., 1970-71; assoc. gen. counsel, asst. sec. Pfizer, Inc., N.Y.C., 1983-86, v.p., gen. counsel, 1986-92, sr. v.p., gen. counsel, 1992—. Office: Pfizer Inc 235 E 42nd St New York NY 10017-5703

MILLER, PAUL AUSBORN, adult education educator; b. East Liverpool, Ohio, Mar. 22, 1917; s. Harry A. and Elizabeth (Paula) M.; m. Catherine Spiker, Dec. 9, 1939 (dec. Dec. 1964); children—Paula Kay, Thomas Ausborn; m. Francena Lounsbery Nolan, Jan. 15, 1966. B.S., U. W.Va., 1939; M.A., Mich. State U., 1947, Ph.D., 1953. County agrl. agt. in W.Va., 1939-42; extension specialist sociology and anthropology Mich. State U., East Lansing, 1947-55; asst. prof. Mich. State U., 1947-52, asso. prof., 1953, prof., 1953-61, provost, 1959-61; pres. W.Va. U., Morgantown, 1962-66; asst. sec. for edn. HEW, 1966-68; disting. prof. edn., dir. univ. planning studies U. N.C., Charlotte; prof. adult edn. N.C. State U. at Raleigh, 1968-69; pres. Rochester (N.Y.) Inst. of Tech., 1969-79, pres. emeritus, 1979—, prof., 1979-93; sr. program cons. W.K. Kellogg Found., 1979-83; adj. prof. rural sociology U. Mo.-Columbia, 1994—. Author: Community Health Action, 1953; co-author: Patterns for Lifelong Learning, 1973; contbr. to publs. in field. Mem. Colombian Commn. Higher Edn., 1960-61. Served as 1st lt. USAAF, 1942-46. Fellow Am. Sociol. Assn.; mem. Rural Sociol. Soc., Phi Kappa Phi, Epsilon Sigma Phi. Home: 1909 Walden Ct Columbia MO 65203-5407

MILLER, PAUL DEAN, breeding company executive, geneticist, educator; b. Cedar Falls, Iowa, Apr. 4, 1941; s. Donald Hugh and Mary (Hansen) M.; m. Nancy Pearl Huser, Aug. 23, 1965; children: Michael, Steven. BS, Iowa State U., 1963; MS, Cornell U., 1965, PhD, 1967. Asst. prof. animal breeding Cornell U., Ithaca, N.Y., 1967-72; v.p. Am. Breeders Service, DeForest, Wis., 1972—; adj. prof. U. Wis., Madison, 1980—. Contbr. articles to profl. jours. Mem. Beef Improvement Fedn. (disting. service award 1980), Am. Soc. Animal Sci., Am. Dairy Sci. Assn., Nat. Assn. Animal Breeders (dir. 1983, v.p. 1986). Republican. Home: 3665 Windsor Rd De Forest WI 53532-2727 Office: Am Breeders Service 6908 River Rd DeForest WI 53532

MILLER, PAUL FETTEROLF, JR., investment company executive; b. Phila., 1927; s. Paul Fetterolf and Katharine Mills (Thompson) M.; m. Ella Warren Shafer, June 14, 1952; children: Ella Warren, Katharine Shafer, Paul Fetterolf III. BS, U. Pa., 1950, LLD (hon.), 1982, LLD (hon.), Washington & Lee U., 1988. Chartered fin. analyst. Founding ptnr. Miller, Anderson & Sherrerd, West Conshohocken, Pa., now ltd. ptnr.; bd. dirs. Mead Corp., Rohm & Haas Co., SPS Techs., Hewlett-Packard. Trustee U. Pa., Ford Found., 1982-94, Colonial Williamsburg; mem. bd. overseers Wharton Sch. Mem. Fin. Analysts Phila., World Wildlife Fund (dir.), Merion Golf Club, Merion Cricket Club, Philadelphia Club, Useppa Island Club, Beta Theta Pi. Home: 115 Maple Hill Rd Gladwyne PA 19035-1305 Office: One Tower Bridge West Conshohocken PA 19428

MILLER, PAUL GEORGE, computer company executive; b. Louisville, Dec. 13, 1922; s. George Moore and Pauline Louise (Koob) M.; m. Doris Kahl Ingram, Feb. 17, 1979; children: George, James, Randolph. B.M.E. Purdue U., 1948; B.S., U.S. Naval Acad., 1946; B.S. in Electronics Engring., Mass. Inst. Tech., 1949, postgrad. in Nuclear Sci., 1949. Gen. mgr. control systems div. Daystrom (later acquired by Control Data Corp.), La Jolla, Calif., 1957-65; v.p., gen. mgr. communications and spl. systems group Control Data Corp., Mpls., 1965-67; v.p., group gen. mgr. computer systems and devel. Control Data Corp., 1967-69, sr. v.p., mktg. group exec., 1970-72, sr. v.p., 1973—; pres. Control Data Mktg. Co.; chmn., chief exec. officer Comml. Credit Co., 1977-83; bd. dirs. Merrill Corp., Bon Secours Health System; chmn. and treas. LSC, Inc. Served to lt. USN, 1946-57. Recipient Distinguished Alumnus award Purdue U., 1968. Mem. IEEE (sr.); Sigma Xi, Tau Beta Pi, Eta Kappa Nu, Delta Tau Delta. Home: II203 Falls Rd Lutherville MD 21093 Office: PO Box 725 Brooklandville MD 21022-0725

MILLER, PAUL J., lawyer; b. Boston, Mar. 27, 1929; s. Edward and Esther (Kalis) M.; children—Robin, Jonathan; m. Michal Davis, Sept. 1, 1965; children—Anthony, Douglas. B.A., Yale U., 1950; LL.B., Harvard U., 1953. Bar: Mass. 1953, Ill. 1957. Assoc. Miller & Miller, Boston, 1953-54; assoc. Sonnenschein Nath & Rosenthal, Chgo., 1957-63, ptnr., 1963—; bd. dirs. Oil-Dri Corp. Am., Chgo. Trustee Latin Sch. of Chgo., 1985-91. 1st lt. JAGC, U.S. Army, 1954-57. Fellow Am. Bar Found.; mem. Tavern Club, Saddle and Cycle Club, Law Club, Phi Beta Kappa. Avocations: jogging; sailing. Office: Sonnenschein Nath & Rosenthal 233 S Wacker Dr Ste 8000 Chicago IL 60606-6404

MILLER, PAUL JAMES, coffee company executive; b. San Mateo, Calif., Aug. 23, 1939; s. Paul and Rita M.; m. Patricia Ann Deruette, Aug. 22, 1964; children—Mike, Britt, Brian. B.S. in Bus. Adminstrn. with honors, San Jose (Calif.) State U., 1962, M.B.A. in Mktg, Santa Clara (Calif.) U., 1964. With Hills Bros. Coffee, Inc., San Francisco, 1964—, advt. mgr., then dir. mktg., 1971-75, pres., 1975-83, chmn. bd., 1983-89, pres., chief exec. officer, dir., 1989-91; pres., chief exec. officer Nestle Beverage Co., San Francisco, 1991—. Mem. Am. Mgmt. Assn., Grocery Mfrs. Assn. Am., Better Bus. Bur. San Francisco, Conf. Board, U.S. C. of C., Calif. C. of C. Clubs: World Trade, Olympic. Office: Nestle Beverage Co 345 Spear St San Francisco CA 94105-1673

MILLER, PAUL LUKENS, investment banker; b. Phila., Dec. 6, 1919; s. Henry C.L. and Elsie (Groff) M.; m. Adele Olyphant, Nov. 4, 1950; children: Paul L. (dec.), Hilary, Beverly, Leslie. Student, William Penn Charter Sch., Phila., 1937; A.B., Princeton U., 1941. With First Boston Corp., N.Y.C., 1946—; v.p. First Boston Corp., 1955-64, dir., 1959-78, pres., 1964-78, sr. advisor, 1978—. Served to maj., F.A. AUS, 1941-46. Clubs: Ivy (Princeton); Links, River (N.Y.C.). Office: First Boston Corp Park Ave Plaza 55 E 52 St New York NY 10055

MILLER, PEGGY MCLAREN, management educator; b. Tomahawk, Wis., Jan. 12, 1931; d. Cecil Glenn and Gladys Lucille (Bame) McLaren; m. Richard Irwin Miller, June 25, 1955; children: Joan Marie, Diane Lee, Janine Louise. BS, Iowa State U., 1953; MA, Am. U., 1959; MBA, Rochester Inst. Tech., 1979; PhD, Ohio U., 1987. Instr. Beirut Coll. for Women, 1953-55, U. Ky., Lexington, 1964-66, S.W. Tex. State U., San Marcos, 1981-84; home economist Borden Co., N.Y.C., 1955-58; cons. Consumer Cons., Chgo., Springfield, Ill., 1972-77; sr. mktg. rep. N.Y. State Dept. Agr., Rochester, 1978-79; asst. prof., coord. bus. and mgmt. Keuka Coll., Keuka Park, N.Y., 1979-81; lectr. mgmt. Ohio U., Athens, 1984—. Co-editor: Fifty States Cookbook, 1977; contbr. articles to profl. jours. Mem. Soc. for Advancement of Mgmt. (advisor campus chpt.), Mortar Bd., Phi Kappa Phi. Home: 17 Briarwood Dr Athens OH 45701-1302 Office: Ohio U Copeland Hall Athens OH 45701

MILLER, PENELOPE ANN, actress; b. Jan. 13, 1964; d. Mark and Beatrice (Ammidown) M. Studies with Herbert Berghof. Appeared in (plays) The People From Work, 1984, Biloxi Blues, 1984-85, Moonchildren, Our Town (Tony Award nom.), (TV shows) The Guiding Light, 1984, As the World Turns, 1984, The Popcorn Kid, (films) Adventures in Babysitting, 1987, Biloxi Blues, 1988, Big Top Pee-Wee, 1988, Miles From Home, 1988, Dead-Bang, 1989, Downtown, 1990, The Freshman, 1990, Kindergarten Cop, 1990, Awakenings, 1990, Other People's Money, 1991, Year of the Comet, 1992, The Gun in Betty Lou's Handbag, 1992, Chaplin, 1992, Carlito's Way, 1993 (Golden Globe nom.), The Shadow, 1994. Mem. Actors' Equity Assn., AFTRA.

MILLER, PHILIP BOYD, retail executive; b. Balt., June 4, 1938; s. Robert Boyd and Claire Elise (Hossfeld) M.; m. Anne Gorman, Dec. 23, 1985; 1 child, Philip Graham; children from previous marriage: Laura, Brandt, Heather. Student, McDonogh Sch., Tulane U., John Hopkins U. Divisional mdse. mgr. Filene's, Boston, 1962-70; v.p.and mgr. Wallach's, N.Y.C., 1970-73, Bloomingdale's, N.Y.C., 1975-77; vice chmn. Lord & Taylor, N.Y.C., 1977-83; pres. Neiman-Marcus, Dallas, 1979-83; chief exec. officer, chmn. bd. Marshall Field and Co., Chgo., 1983-90; chmn., CEO Saks Fifth Ave., N.Y.C., 1990—, COO, 1993, CEO, 1993—. Mem. Chgo. Urban League Bus. Adv. Council, 198690, Mid-Am. Com., Chgo., 1985-90, Chgo. Cen. Area Com., 1984-90, Econ. Devel. Corp., Chgo., 1986-90; bd. dirs.

Rehab. Inst., 1986-87, Lyric Opera Chgo., 1984—, Dallas Opera, 1980—. Mem. Nat. Retail Merchants Assn., Ill. Retail Merchants Assn., Greater State Stree Council (chmn. 1986-87), Northwestern Univ. Assocs. Clubs: Econ. (Chgo.), Chicago. Office: Saks Fifth Avenue 12 E 49th St New York NY 10017*

MILLER, PHILIP EFREM, librarian; b. Providence, Feb. 18, 1945; s. Jacob and Natalie (Rouslin) M.; m. Zenia Weiner, Dec. 20, 1969; 1 son, Paul Jeremy. B.S.L., Georgetown U., 1967; M.S., U. Mich., 1968, A.M.L.S., 1973; Ph.D., NYU, 1984. Acting librarian Hebrew Union Coll., N.Y.C., 1973-76, asst. librarian, 1976-78, librarian, 1978—. Author: Karaite Separatism in 19th Century Russia, 1993. Mem. Assn. Jewish Libraries (pres. 1982-84), Jewish Book Coun. (exec. bd. 1977—), Am. Soc. for Jewish Music (exec. bd. 1990—), Assn. Jewish Studies. Home: 56 Truman Dr Marlboro NJ 07746-1122 Office: Hebrew Union Coll-Jewish Inst of Religion Klau Libr 1 W 4th St New York NY 10012-1105

MILLER, PHILLIP EDWARD, environmental scientist; b. Waterloo, Iowa, May 29, 1935; s. Joe Monroe and Katherine Elva (Groom) M.; m. Cathy Ann Love, Sept. 15, 1962; children: Eric Anthony, Bryan Edward, Stefan Patrick, Gregory Joseph. BA in Sci. Edn., U. No. Iowa, 1961; MA in Sci. Edn., U. Iowa, 1964; postgrad., U. Wis., 1966-68. Physics and chemistry tchr. Millersburg (Iowa) Community High Sch., 1961-62; supervising tchr. NSF Insvc. Inst. U. Iowa, Iowa City, 1962-64; instr. biology, area coord. Office Equal Opportunity Western Ky. U., Bowling Green, 1964-66; sci. editor, journalism instr.-sci. and tech. Mich. State U., East Lansing, 1968-74; asst. prof. agr., forestry and home econs. U. Minn., St. Paul, 1974-77; sr. editor atomic energy div. E.I. du Pont de Nemours and Co., Aiken, S.C., 1977-89; sr. scientist environ. protection dept. Westinghouse Savannah River Co., Aiken, 1989—; pres. Agy. for Book Authors, Collectors and Understanding of Sci., Aiken, 1994—; panelist 26th Internat. Tech. Comm. Conf., L.A., 1979; participant Dept. Energy/Westinghouse Sch. for Environ. Excellence, Cin., 1991; invited contbr. to proceedings of the 1st Tatarstan Symposium on Energy, Environment and Econs., Kazan, Tatarstan, Russia, 1992. Mem. publs. com. Cen. Assn. Sci. and Math. Techs., Iowa City, 1969-72; editor Nat. Task Force on Agrl. Energy R&D, Washington, 1976; editor, contbr. Minn. Sci. Mag., 1974-77; contbr. several hundred med., sci. and engring. articles including to Procs. of Iowa Acad. Sci., Sch. Sci. and Math., Am. Biology Tchrs., Procs. of Internat. Communication Conf., and Procs. of Westinghouse Computer Symposium. Pres. Savannah River Rifle & Pistol Club, Aiken, 1981-82, Aiken Toastmasters, 1984; judge speech contests Optimist and 4-H Club Contests, Aiken, 1985-86. Sgt. U.S. Army, 1955-58. Decorated Disting. Marksman Badge gold medal; recipient 1st place sci. writing Argonne Labs. Assn., 1973, Profl. Achievement Permanent Profl. cert. Iowa State Bd. of Pub. Instrn., 1974, Blue Ribbon, Am. Assn. Agrl. Coll. Editors, Tex. A&M, 1976. Mem. AAAS, N.Y. Acad. Scis., Am. Chem. Soc., Phi Delta Kappa, Sigma Xi. Achievements include research in the causes and timing of pre-adolescent initial interest in science; discovery that low-zinc root environment causes delay of development and acceleration of senescence in tobacco plants. Office: Westinghouse Savannah River Co Environ Protection Dept Aiken SC 29801

MILLER, RALPH BRADLEY, lawyer, former state legislator; b. Fayetteville, N.C., May 19, 1953; s. Raymond David and Margaret Virginia (Hale) M.; m. Esther Susan Hall, Dec. 19, 1981. BA, U. N.C., 1975; MSc, London Sch. Econs., 1978; JD, Columbia U., 1979. Bar: N.C. 1979, U.S. Dist. Ct. (ea. dist.) N.C. 1980, U.S. Ct. Appeals (4th cir. 1980), U.S. Dist. Ct. (mid. dist.) N.C. 1983. Law clk. to Hon. J. Dickson Phillips Jr. U.S. Ct. Appeals (4th cir.) 1979-80; assoc. Allen, Steed & Allen, Raleigh, N.C., 1980-82, Barringer, Allen & Pinnix, Raleigh, N.C. 1982-84, LeBoeuf, Lamb, Leiby & MacRae, Raleigh, N.C., 1985-88; prin. Nichols, Miller & Sigmon, Raleigh, N.C., 1988-90; pvt. practice Raleigh, N.C., 1991—; mem. N.C. Ho. of Reps., Raleigh 1993-94. Chmn. Wake County Dem. Com., 1985-87; mem. state exec. com. N.C. Dem. Com., 1985-89, 91—; mem. N.C. Environ. Rev. Commn., 1994-95. Mem. ATLA, N.C. Bar Assn., Wake County Bar Assn., N.C. Acad. Trial Lawyers, Am. Judicature Soc., Greater Raleigh C. of C., Raleigh Civitan Club. Democrat. Episcopalian. Home: 3211 Coleridge Dr Raleigh NC 27609-7201 Office: 4006 Barrett Dr Raleigh NC 27609-6604

MILLER, RALPH ELI, consulting economist; b. N.Y.C., Feb. 28, 1941; m. Avis Dimond, 1965; children: Ethan, Jeremy, Gabriel, Justin, Ezra. AB in Math. summa cum laude, Harvard U., 1961, AM in Econs., 1963, postgrad. in Econs. Cons. The Rand Corp., Santa Monica, Calif., 1963-67; acting asst. prof. Econs. U. Calif., Berkeley, 1966-69; economist Leon H. Keyserling, Washington, 1969-72, Fed. Power Commn., Washington, 1972, Antitrust Div. Dept. Justice, Washington, 1972-73; chief energy acctg. and modeling systems divsn. Fed. Energy Adminstrn., Washington, 1973-75; exec. v.p. J.W. Wilson & Assocs., Inc., Washington, 1975-80; pres., v.p. and prin. Exeter Assocs., Inc., Bethesda, Md., 1981-85; cons. economist pvt. practice, Chevy Chase, Md., 1985—; expert witness on pub. utility rates. Author or co-author of numerous reports on energy, utility rates, utility production etc; editor: The Unofficial Guide to Graduate Life at Harvard, 14th edit., 1965. Pres. Harvard Grad. Student Assn., 1964-65. Mem. Phi Beta Kappa. Home and Office: 5502 Western Ave Chevy Chase MD 20815

MILLER, RAYMOND EDWARD, computer science educator; b. Bay City, Mich., Oct. 9, 1928; s. Martin Theophil and Elizabeth Charlotte (Zierath) M.; m. Marilyn Lueck, June 18, 1955; children: Patricia Ann, Laura Jean, Donna Lyn, Martha Eileen. BS in Mech. Engring., U. Wis., 1950; BEE, U. Ill., 1954, MS in Math., 1955, PhD in Elect. Engring., 1957. Design engr. IBM, Endicott, Poughkeepsie, N.Y., 1950-51; mem. rsch. staff IBM, Yorktown Heights, N.Y., 1957-81; dir., prof. Ga. Inst. Tech., Atlanta, 1980-89, prof. emeritus, 1989—; dir. Ctr. Excellence in Space Data and Info. Scis. NASA, Greenbelt, Md., 1988-93; prof. U. Md., College Park, 1989—; pres. Computing Scis. Accreditation Bd., N.Y.C., 1985-87. Author: Switching Theory, Vols. I and II, 1965; editor: (with J.W. Thatcher) Complexity of Computer Computation, 1972; patentee in field. Lt. USAF, 1951-53. Fellow AAAS, IEEE; Assn. for Computing Machinery, IEEE Computer Soc. (v.p. edn. acts 1991-92). Lutheran. Avocations: tennis, fishing. Office: U Md Dept of Computer Sci A V Williams Bldg College Park MD 20742

MILLER, RAYMOND F., banker; b. N.Y.C., Apr. 21, 1941; s. Raymond F. and Ann Catherine (Cassidy) M.; children: Christopher Kurt, Gretchen Ann. B.S in Fin., Lehigh U., 1963. Nat. div. staff mem. Bankers Trust Co., N.Y.C., 1963-71; gen. mgr. Bankers Trust Co. London, 1972-80; sr. v.p. Bankers Trust Co. N.Y.C., 1973-91; head Asia Pacific group, 1980-83; head central group world corp. dept. Pacific group, London, 1983-86, mng. dir. investment banking dept., 1986—. Mem. Far East-Am. Council of Commerce and Industry (dir. 1980-83). Congregationalist. Office: Bankers Trust Co 280 Park Ave New York NY 10017-1216

MILLER, RAYMOND JARVIS, agronomy educator; b. Claresholm, Alta., Can., Mar. 19, 1934; came to U.S., 1957, naturalized, 1975; s. Charles Jarvis and Wilma Macy (Anderson) M.; m. France Anne Davidson, Apr. 28, 1956; children—Cheryl Rae, Jeffrey John, Jay Robert. B.S. (Fed. Provincial grantee 1954-56, Dan Baker scholar 1954-56), U. Alta., Edmonton, 1957; M.S., Wash. State U., 1960; Ph.D., Purdue U., 1962. Mem. faculty N.C. State U., 1962-65, U. Ill., 1965-69; asst. dir., then assoc. dir. Ill. Agrl. Expt. Sta., 1969-73; dir. Idaho Agrl. Expt. Sta., 1973-79; dean U. Idaho Coll. Agr., 1979-85, v.p. for agr.; dean Coll. Agr. and Coll. Life Sci. U. Md., College Park, 1986-89, vice chancellor agr. and natural resources, 1989-91; pres. Md. Inst. for Agrl. and Natural Resources, 1991-93, prof. agronomy, 1986—. Author numerous papers in field. Pres. Idaho Rsch. Found., 1980-85; bd. govs. Agrl. Rsch. Inst., 1979-80; chmn. legis. subcom. Expt. Sta. Com. on Policy, 1981-82; chmn. bd. div. agr. Land Grant Assn., 1985-86; co-chmn. Nat. Com. Internat. Sci. Edn. Joint Coun., USDA, 1991—; bd. dirs. C.V. Riley Found., 1985-93; chmn. budget com. Bd. Agr., Nat. Assn. State Univs. and Land Grant Colls., 1993. Grantee Internat. Congress Soil Sci., 1960, Purdue U. Research Found., summers 1960, 61. Fellow AAAS, Am. Soc. Agronomy, Soil Sci. Soc. Am.; mem. Internat. Soc. Soil Sci., Clay and Clay Minerals Soc., Am. Chem. Soc., Am. Soc. Plant Physiologists, Elks, Lions, Sigma Xi, Phi Kappa Phi, Gamma Sigma Delta, Alpha Zeta. Home: 3319 Gumwood Dr Hyattsville MD 20783-1934 Office: HJ Patterson Hall Univ Md College Park College Park MD 20783

MILLER, REED, lawyer; b. Fairmont, W.Va., Dec. 1, 1918; s. Maurice Entler and Lillian Moore (Reed) M.; m. Emilie Morrison Crawford, Feb. 20, 1943; children: Michael Reed, George Crawford, Richard Clinton. AB, W.Va. U., 1939, LLB, 1941. Bar: W.Va. 1941, N.Y. 1945, D.C. 1946. Assoc. Arnold & Fortas, 1946-47; assoc. Arnold, Fortas & Porter, Washington, 1947-59, ptnr. 1959-65; ptnr. Arnold & Porter, Washington, 1965—; mem. vis. com. Coll. Law, W.Va. U., 1981-86. Trustee N.Y. Ave. Presbyn. Ch., Washington, 1967-69, 88-91. Served to maj. U.S. Army, 1941-46. Mem. ABA, Fed. Communications Bar Assn. (pres. 1976, mem. exec. com.), Army Navy Country Club (Arlington, Va.), Columbia Country Club, Kenwood Golf and Country Club, Phi Beta Kappa, Beta Theta Pi. Avocation: skiing.

MILLER, REGINALD WAYNE, professional basketball player; b. Riverside, Calif., Aug. 24, 1965. Student, UCLA. Basketball player Indiana Pacers, 1987—. Named to NBA All-Star Team, 1990, 94, Dream Team II, 1994. Office: Indiana Pacers 300 E Market St Indianapolis IN 46204*

MILLER, RENE HARCOURT, aerospace engineer, educator; b. Tenafly, N.J., May 19, 1916; s. Arthur C. and Elizabeth M. (Tobin) M.; m. Marcelle Hansotte, July 16, 1948 (div. 1968); children: Christal L., John M.; m. Maureen Michael, Nov. 20, 1973. B.A., Cambridge U., 1937, M.A., 1954. Registered profl. engr., Mass. Aero. engr. G.L. Martin Co., Balt., 1937-39; chief aero. and devel. McDonnell Aircraft Corp., St. Louis, 1939-44; mem. faculty aero. engring. MIT, Cambridge, 1944—, prof., 1957-86, Slater prof. flight transp., 1962-86; head dept. aeros. and astronautics MIT, 1968-78, prof. emeritus, 1986—; v.p. engring. Kaman Aircraft Corp., Bloomfield, Conn., 1952-54; mem. tech. adv. bd. FAA, 1964-66; mem. Aircraft panel Pres.'s Sci. Adv. Com., 1960-72, Army Sci. Adv. Panel, 1966-73; chmn. Army Aviation Sci. Adv. Group, 1963-73; mem. Air Force Sci. Adv. Bd., 1959-70; com. on aircraft aerodynamics NASA, 1960-70. Contbr. articles to profl. jours. Recipient U.S. Army Decoration for Meritorious Civilian Service, 1967, 70; recipient L.B. Laskowitz award N.Y. Acad. Scis., 1976. Fellow Am. Helicopter Soc. (hon. tech. dir. 1957-59, editor jour. 1957-59, Klemin award, Hon. Nikolski lectr. 1983), AIAA (hon., pres. 1977-78, Sylvanus Albert Reed award), Royal Aero. Soc. (Great Britain); mem. Nat. Acad. Engring., Internat. Acad. Astronautics, Academie National de L'Air et de L'Espace France. Home: San Jose New Rd, Penzance Cornwall TR18 4PN, England Office: MIT Dept Aeros and Astronautics 33-411 Cambridge MA 02139

MILLER, REUBEN GEORGE, economics educator; b. Phila., Mar. 28, 1930; s. George and Edna (Fuchs) M.; m. Sylvia Raigla, June 9, 1955. B.A., LaSalle Coll., 1952; diploma, U. Stockholm, 1954; M.A., U. Mont., 1956; Ph.D., Ohio State U., 1966. Asst. instr. Ohio State U., 1954-57; acting asst. prof. Oberlin (Ohio) Coll., 1957-58; asst. prof. U. Mass., Amherst, 1959-67; assoc. prof. econs. Smith Coll., Northampton, Mass., 1967-70; chmn. div. social scis.; mem. adv. staff Computer Sci. Corp., Washington; cons. Dept. Def.; Fulbright-Hayes lectr. econs. Coll. Law, Nat. Taiwan U., Republic China, 1965-66. Contbr. articles to profl. jours. Am.-Scandinavian Found. fellow, 1952-53; Research Tng. fellow Social Sci. Research Council, 1958-59. Mem. Am. Econ. Assn., Am. Fin. Assn., Royal Econ. Soc. Office: Sweet Briar Coll Dept Econs Sweet Briar VA 24595

MILLER, RICHARD ALAN, economist, educator; b. Springfield, Ohio, Feb. 25, 1931; s. Ross and Beatrice Miller; m. Joan Taylor Walton, July 7, 1956; children: Carol Elizabeth, Jean Anne, Eric Ross. B.A., Oberlin Coll., 1952; M.A., Yale U., 1957; MA (hon.), Wesleyan U., 1972. Mem. faculty Wesleyan U., Middletown, Conn., 1960—, chmn. dept. econs., 1968-69, 71-73, 75-76, 92-94, Andrews prof., 1995—; vis. lectr. Yale U., New Haven, 1961-62, vis. assoc. prof., 1967-68, vis. prof., 1973, 83, 85, 95; vis. assoc. prof. U. Calif., Berkeley, 1969-70; vis. prof. U. Adelaide, Australia, 1981; vis. lectr econs. U. Conn., Storrs, 1983; economist Econ. Policy Office, Antitrust Div., U.S. Dept. Justice, Washington, 1973-74, cons., 1974-75; cons. antitrust sect. State Conn., 1980, 82; dir. Kawanhee, Inc., Maine, 1975-81, 82-86. Contbr. articles on indsl. orgn. and antitrust econs. to profl. jours. Mem. cert. adv. coun. Dept. Edn., State Conn., 1982-86; mem. coms. Bd. for State Acad. Awards. State Conn., 1978—; dean faculty of Cons. Examiners., 1985-87; trustee Conn. Joint Coun. Econ. Edn., 1982-85. Served to lt. (j.g.) USNR, 1952-55. Ford Found. fellow Yale U., 1958-59; NSF fellow MIT, 1964-65, Wesleyan U., 1965-69; Shelby Cullom Davis Found. grantee Wesleyan U., 1979-82; Fulbright fellow N.Z. Inst. Econ. Research, 1986, 88. Mem. Am. Econs. Assn., Royal Econ. Soc., So. Econ. Assn. Congregationalist. Home: 83 Paterson Dr Middletown CT 06457-5138 Office: Wesleyan U Dept Econs Middletown CT 06459

MILLER, RICHARD ALAN, lawyer, former merger and acquisition and forest products company executive; b. Cleve., July 29, 1939; s. Joshua Spencer and Martha (Harris) M.; m. Virginia Bell McCully, June 23, 1962; children: Cynthia Lynn (dec.), Alexander James. B.B.A., U. Mich., 1961, J.D., 1964. Bar: Ariz. 1964, Ill. 1969, Wis. 1989, Fla. 1994; lic. real estate broker, Ill., Wis. Assoc. Fennemore, Craig, von Ammon and Udall (now Fennemore Craig), Phoenix, 1964-69; ptnr. Fennemore, Craig, von Ammon and Udall (now Fennemore Craig), 1970-71; exec. v.p. Southwest Forest Industries, Inc., Phoenix, 1972-86; pres., chief exec. officer Knox Lumber Co., St. Paul, 1986; v.p. F.H. Fin. Corp., Milw., 1987-88; owner Hammett, Williams & Miller, Delavan, Wis., 1989-91; of counsel Brennan, Steil, Basting & MacDougall, S.C., Delavan, 1991—. Mem. Ariz. Bar Assn., Ill. Bar Assn, Wis. Bar Assn., Fla. Bar Assn.

MILLER, RICHARD B., publishing executive; b. Cleve. 1926. Grad., Princeton U., 1949. Exec. v.p. McGraw-Hill, Inc., N.Y.C. Office: McGraw-Hill Inc 1221 Ave Of The Americas New York NY 10020-1001

MILLER, RICHARD DWIGHT, professional association executive; b. Topeka, Jan. 21, 1929; s. Amzie Keith and Josephine Amelia (Reese) M.; m. Phyllis Ann Pease, June 11, 1949; children: Rebecca Lynn Miller Shanahan, Susan Kay Barker. BS, Ind. U., 1951, MS, 1958; PhD, Purdue U., 1963. Prin. Jimtown High Sch., Elkhart, Ind., 1958-60; asst. supt. schs. Elkhart Community Schs., 1961-62, supt., 1973-83; asst. supt. schs. Richmond (Ind.) Community Schs., 1962-64; supt. Baugo Community Schs., Elkart, 1964-65, Logansport (Ind.) Community Schs., 1965-69, East Allen County Schs., New Haven, Ind., 1969-73, Elkhart Community Schs., 1973-83; dep. exec. dir. Am. Assn. Sch. Adminstrs., Arlington, Va., 1983-85, exec. dir., 1985-94. Served to sgt. U.S. Army, 1952-54. Mem. Am. Soc. Assn. Execs., Am. Assn. Sch. Adminstrs. (pres. 1980-81), Greater Washington Soc. Assn. Exec. Office: Amer Assn of School Adminstrs 13850 Tonbridge Ct Bonita Springs FL 33923

MILLER, RICHARD HAMILTON, lawyer, broadcasting company executive; b. Cleve., July 18, 1931; s. Ray Thomas and Ruth (Hamilton) M.; m. Ernestine Bowman, Aug. 25, 1985; children: James M., Suanne R., Elizabeth M., Judith K., William P., Matthew W. A.B., U. Notre Dame, 1953, J.D., 1955. Bar: Ohio 1955. Since practiced in Cleve. as mem. firm Miller & Miller; asst. prosecutor Cuyahoga County, 1957-60; pres. Cleve. Broadcasting, Inc., 1966-70, Searles Lake Chem. Corp., Los Angeles, 1966-69, Miller Broadcasting Co., Cleve., 1970-87, Hollywood Bldg. Systems, Inc., Meridian, Miss., 1974-86; mng. partner Miller & Co., Cleve., 1974—; former owner, dir. Cleve. Profl. Basketball Co., Cleve. Baseball, Inc. Dir. gen. counsel Mail Marketing Inc., 1974—, R.W. Sidley, Inc., 1966—; gen. chmn. N.E. Ohio March of Dimes, 1971-73; adv. council Catherine Horstman Home Retarded Children, 1969-73; mem. Cuyahoga Democratic Exec. Com., 1955-66. Served to capt. AUS, 1956-57. Mem. Ohio, Cuyahoga County, Cleve. bar assns., Cleve. Citizens League. Clubs: K.C. (Cleve.), Variety (Cleve.), Notre Dame (Cleve.) (pres. 1964-65), Cleve. Athletic (Cleve.) (dir. 1971-74); Shaker Heights (Ohio) Country. Office: The Park 1700 E 13th St Ste 20T Cleveland OH 44114-3238

MILLER, RICHARD IRWIN, education educator, university administrator; b. Fairbury, Nebr., Feb. 1, 1924; s. Carl W. and Iva Mae (Wilburn) M.; m. Peggy J. McLaren, June 25, 1955; children: Joan Marie, Diane Lee, Janine Louise. B.S., U. Nebr., 1947; M.Ed., Springfield Coll., 1948; Ed.D., Columbia U., 1958. Instr. Pa. State U., 1957-58; observer UN, 1958-60; assoc. dir. project on instrn. NEA, 1960-63; assoc. dir. Ctr. Study of Instrn., 1963-64; prof. edn. U. Ky., Lexington, 1964-69, chmn. dept. social philosophy Founds. in Edn., 1967-69, dir. program for ednl. change, 1964-69; v.p. acad. affairs, dean Baldwin-Wallace Coll., Berea, Ohio, 1970-72; assoc. dir. Ill. Bd. Higher Edn., Springfield, 1972-77; prof. higher edn., v.p. for ednl. services SUNY, Brockport, 1977-80; vis. fellow Cornell U., Ithaca, N.Y., 1980-81; v.p. for acad. affairs, prof. S.W. Tex. State U., San Marcos, 1981-84; prof., coordinator higher edn. Ohio U., Athens, 1984—; ednl. advisor ABA, 1959-63; mem. adv. bd. Ctr. for Info. on Am., 1965-70; dir. nat. evaluation program Elem. and Secondary Edn. Act Title III, 1967-68; exec. sec. Pres.'s Nat. Adv. Council Supplementary Ctrs. and Services, 1968-69; cons. Com. Econ. Devel., U.S. Office Edn., 1967-70; cons. edn. Mead Ednl. Service, Inc. div. Mead Corp., also coordinator spl. ednl. seminars. Author: Dag Hammarskjod and Crisis Diplomacy, 1961, Education in a Changing Society, 1963, Teaching About Communism, 1966; editor: (with Ole Sand) Schools for the Sixties, 1963, ESEA Title III: Catalyst for Change, 1967, The Nongraded School, 1968, Perspectives on Educational Change, 1967, Evaluating Faculty Performance, 1972, Developing Programs for Faculty Evaluation, 1974, Assessment of College Performance, 1979, Institutional Assessment for Self-Improvement, 1981, Evaluating Faculty for Promotion and Tenure, 1987, (with Ed Holzapfel) Issues in Personnel Management, 1988; editor: Evaluating Major Components in Two-Year Colleges, 1988, Major American Higher Education Issues and Challenges in the Nineties, 1990; editor, chpt. contbr.: Applying the Deming Method to Higher Education, 1991. Served with USAF, 1942-43. Recipient Nat. Pacesetter award in edn. Nat. Council Supplementary Centers and Services. Mem. Am. Assn. Higher Edn. (nat. planning group), Nat. Council Social Studies (research council 1967-70), Am. Assn. Univ. Adminstrs. (bd. dirs. 1972), Phi Delta Kappa. Presbyn. Club: Cosmos (Washington). Lodge: Rotary. Home: 17 Briarwood Dr Athens OH 45701-1302

MILLER, RICHARD JACKSON, lawyer; b. Milw., July 17, 1946; s. Wayne D. and Margarite M. (Von Sitany) M.; m. Irene Nikki Tsacoyeanes, May 28, 1972; children: Nicole Elizabeth, Andrew James, Katherine M., Penelope Constance. BA, U. N.C., 1968; JD, U. Va., 1971. Bar: N.Y. 1973, U.S. Dist. Ct. (so. dist.) N.Y. 1975, U.S. Ct. Appeals (2d cir.) 1975, Fla. 1988. Assoc. Brown and Wood, N.Y.C., 1971-78, Wood and Dawson, N.Y.C., 1978-82; ptnr. Alexander and Green, N.Y.C., 1982-86, Mudge, Rose, Guthrie, Alexander & Ferdon, West Palm Beach, Fla., 1986—; Contbr. articles to profl. jours., chpt. to book. Capt. USAR, 1972-79. Mem. ABA, Fla. Bar Assn., N.Y. State Bar Assn., Palm Beach County Bar Assn., University Club (N.Y.). Episcopalian. Avocations: golf, tennis. Office: Mudge Rose Guthrie Alexander & Ferdon 515 N Flagler Dr Ste 900 West Palm Beach FL 33401-4334

MILLER, RICHARD JEROME, bank executive; b. Erie, Pa., May 8, 1939; s. Richard A. and Irene (Strahl) M.; children by previous marriage: Edward Scott, Lisa Ann, Sondra Lynn; m. Suzanne Marie Johnson, Oct. 22, 1983. BS, Lehigh U., 1961; MA, New Sch. N.Y.C., 1964; postgrad. NYU, 1964-68. With Chase Manhattan Bank, N.Y.C., 1961-82, v.p., 1974-82; v.p. E.F. Hutton Credit Corp./Chrysler Capital Corp., Greenwich, Conn., 1982-88, The CIT Group, N.Y.C., 1988-90; dir. Miller/Davis & Assocs., N.Y.C., 1991—; v.p. Nat. Westminster Bank, N.Y.C., 1991—. Mem. Waldwick Bd. Edn., N.J., 1968-72, v.p., 1971-72; pres. Columbia Condominium. Mem. Am. Econ. Assn., Western Fin. Assn., Fin. Mgmt. Assn. Republican. Roman Catholic. Office: Miller/Davis & Assocs 60 E 42nd St Ste 2120 New York NY 10165

MILLER, RICHARD KIDWELL, artist, actor, educator; b. Fairmont, W.Va., Mar. 15, 1930; s. Maurice Entler and Lillian (Reed) M.; m. Teresa Marie Robinson, Apr. 27, 1957. Student, Pa. Acad. Fine Arts, 1948-49; BA, Am. U., Washington, 1953; MFA, Columbia U., 1956. Instr. painting Scarsdale (N.Y.) Community Sch., 1970-75; asst. prof. Kansas City Art Inst., 1968-69. Participated extensively in profl. theater as actor and singer, including roles in Broadway prodn. Baker Street; actor stock cos. including Fiddler on the Roof; one-man art shows include Trans-Lux Gallery, Washington, 1950, Watkins Gallery, Washington, 1951, Bader Gallery, Washington, 1954, Balt. Mus. Art, 1955, Graham Gallery Ltd., N.Y.C., 1960, 62, 65, Argas Gallery, Madison, N.J., 1966, Jefferson Place Gallery, Washington, 1966, Albrecht Gallery Art, St. Joseph, Mo., 1969, L.I. U., 1973, Aaron Berman Gallery, N.Y.C., 1983, Westbeth Gallery, N.Y.C., 1982; group shows include Corcoran Gallery Art, 1950-51, 53, Pa. Acad. Fine Arts, 1951, 64, Carnegie Internat., 1961, Salon de National, Paris, 1954, Whitney Mus., 1958, U. Nebr., 1963, Martha Jackson Gallery, N.Y.C., 1973, others; represented in permanent collections Hirshhorn Mus. and Sculpture Garden, Washington, Phillips Collection, Washington, Rochester Mus. Art, Albrecht Gallery, U. Ariz., also numerous private collections; featured in Jan. edit. Am. Artist mag., 1988, Christian Sci. Monitor, 1990, World Artists (Claude Marks), 1991. Washington Times Herald scholar, 1944, 45, 46; Gertrude Whitney scholar, 1948-53, 55-56; Fulbright fellow, 1953-54. Address: 222 West 83d St Apt 8C New York NY 10024 *I have an insatiable need to express myself—I suppose I was born with it. I was given more than one talent to satisfy this need, and for that I thank God. I have endeavored to use these talents to the absolute best of my ability. I can do no more than that. Some times I have succeeded, and many times I have failed, but the real joy and meaning is in the doing. All the pain has been worth it.*

MILLER, RICHARD L., architectural executive; b. Salina, Kans., Jan. 31, 1941; s. L. William and Inez Corine (DeMars) M.; m. Sharalena Miller, June 22, 1963; children: Lora Miller Vinson, Scott Miller. Student, Kansas Wesleyan U., 1959-61; BArch, U Kans., 1966, postgrad., 1966-67. Registered architect, 38 states and V.I. Assoc. Earl Swensson Assocs., Nashville, 1967-73, pres., 1973—; mem. hosp. licensure task force State of Tenn. Dept. Pub. Health, 1975, Ambulatory Surg. Treatment Ctr. Act Task Force, 1976-77, SCARAB, Hon. Archtl. Frat.; Nursing Home Task Force, 1977-78; participant Internat. Pub. Health Seminar, Budapest, 1984; speaker Fla. HRS seminars, 1986, 90; mem. ann. faculty health care forum on health facilities design, 1990. Mem. Leadership Nashville, 1993-94. Mem. Am. Inst. Architects (mem. com. architecture for health 1980), Tenn. Soc. Architects (mem. ad hoc fire com. 1975). Mem. Christian Ch. Avocations: golfing, kite flying, sailing. Office: Earl Swensson Assocs 2100 W End Ave Ste 1200 Nashville TN 37203-5239

MILLER, RICHARD MCDERMOTT, sculptor; b. New Philadelphia, Ohio, Apr. 30, 1922; s. J. Harry and Clela Belle (McDermott) M.; m. Audrey F. Miller, 1942; 1 dau., Sue Ann (Mrs. Kenneth Hartz); m. Gloria B. Bley, Mar. 18, 1961. Student, Cleve. Inst. Art, 1940-42, 49-51. Prof. emeritus Queens Coll., CUNY. One man shows include Peridot Gallery, N.Y.C., 1964, 66, 67, 69, Washburn Gallery, N.Y.C., 1971, 74, 75, 77, Canton (Ohio) Art Inst., 1980, 20-yr retrospective Artists Choice Mus., N.Y.C., 1984, Springfield (Mo.) Mus. Art, 1985, Friends of Figurative Sculpture Gallery, N.Y.C., 1987-94, Philharm. Ctr., Naples, Fla., 1991; represented in numerous pub. and pvt. collections; author: Figure Sculpture in Wax and Plaster, 1971. Served with AUS, 1942-46. Mem. Sculptors Guild, NAD (pres. 1989-92), Century Assn. Address: 53 Mercer St New York NY 10013-2617

MILLER, RICHARD SHERWIN, legal educator; b. Boston, Dec. 11, 1930; s. Max and Mollie (Kruger) M.; m. Doris Sheila Lunchick, May 24, 1956; children: Andrea Jayne Armitage, Matthew Harlan. B.S.B.A., Boston U., 1951, J.D. magna cum laude, 1956; LL.M., Yale U., 1959. Bar: Mass. 1956, Mich. 1961, Hawaii 1977. Pvt. practice law Boston, 1956-58; assoc. prof. law Wayne State U., Detroit, 1959-62, prof., 1962-65; prof. Ohio State U., Columbus, 1965-73, dir. clin. and interdisciplinary program, 1971-73; prof. U. Hawaii, Honolulu, 1973-95, prof. emeritus, 1995—, 1995—, dean, 1981-84; vis. prof. law USIA/U. Hawaii, Hiroshima U., Japan, fall 1986, Victoria U., Wellington, N.Z., spring 1987; del. Hawaii State Jud. Conf., 1989-92. Author: Courts and the Law: An Introduction to our Legal System, 1980; editor: (with Roland Stanger) Essays on Expropriations, 1967; editor-in-chief: Boston U. Law Rev., 1955-56; contbr. articles to profl. jours. Mem. Hawaii Substance Abuse Task Force, 1994—. 1st lt. USAF, 1951-53. Sterling-Ford fellow Yale U., 1958-59; named Lawyer of Yr. Japan-Hawaii Lawyers Assn., 1990. Mem. ABA, Hawaii State Bar Assn., Hawaii ACLU, Am. Law Inst. CIV (founding mem., master of the bench), Am. Law Inst., Honolulu Community-Media Coun. (chair 1994—). Office: U Hawaii Richardson Sch Law 2515 Dole St Honolulu HI 96822-2386

MILLER, RICHARD STEVEN, lawyer; b. Mt. Vernon, N.Y., Dec. 5, 1951; s. Norman and Mildred (Curtis) M. BA, U. Pa., 1974; JD, NYU, 1977. Bar: N.Y. 1978, U.S. Dist. Ct. (so. and ea. dists.) N.Y. 1978, U.S. Ct. Appeals (2d cir.) 1978. Asst. dist. atty. Kings County, N.Y., 1977-79; with Hahn & Hessen, N.Y.C., 1979-82, Levin & Weintraub & Crames, N.Y.C., 1982-87; counsel, then ptnr. Rogers & Wells, N.Y.C., 1987-91; ptnr. Dewey Ballantine, N.Y.C., 1991—. Mem. ABA, Internat. Bar Assn., Am. Bankruptcy Inst. Office: Dewey Ballantine 1301 Ave of the Americas New York NY 10019-6092

MILLER, RICHARD ULRIC, business and industrial relations educator; b. N.Y.C., Sept. 6, 1932; s. Luther Cedric and Frances Elizabeth (Wells) M.; m. Louise Elaine O'Donnell, Jan. 6, 1954; children: Elizabeth Louise, Richard Christopher. B.B.A. cum laude, U. Miami, Coral Gables, Fla., 1958; M.S., Cornell U., 1960, Ph.D., 1966. Instr. U. Ariz., Tucson, 1960-62; asst. prof. SUNY-Buffalo, 1965-66; vis. prof. U. Tex., Austin, 1971-72; from asst. prof. to prof. bus. and indsl. relations U. Wis.-Madison, 1966-94; assoc. dean. sch. bus. U. Wis., Madison, 1994—; dir. Indsl. Rels. Rsch. Inst., 1973-77, 90-93; arbitrator Am. Arbitration Assn., Fed. Mediation and Conciliation Svc., Wis. Employment Rels. Commn., 1978—. Co-author: Collective Bargaining in Hospitals, 1978, Labor Relations in Urban Transit, 1977, Canadian Labour in Transition, 1971. Served with USN, 1951-55. Doherty fellow, 1964; Latin Am. studies fellow Cornell U., 1965. Mem. Indsl. Relations Research Assn. (sec.-treas. 1973-77), Phi Kappa Phi, Beta Gamma Sigma. Office: U Wis Grad Sch Bus 4106 Grainger Hall 975 Univ Ave Madison WI 53706-1323

MILLER, RICHARD WESLEY, telecommunications company executive; b. Buffalo, Nov. 22, 1940; s. John Irwin and Rose Mary (Mirco) M.; m. Sharon Ann Betzler, Jan. 28, 1967; children: Barbara Ann, Thomas Andrew. B.B.A., Case Western Res. U., 1967; M.B.A., Harvard U., 1970. With Nat. City Bank, Cleve., 1961-68, credit officer, 1966-68; with Penn Central Corp., N.Y.C., 1970-82; v.p. fin., then exec. v.p. subs. Penn Central Corp. (Arvida Corp.), Boca Raton, Fla., 1972-79, corp. sr. v.p. fin., chief fin. officer, 1979-82; exec. v.p., chief fin. officer RCA Corp., N.Y.C., 1982-85, exec. v.p. consumer products and entertainment, 1985-86; sr. v.p. consumer electronics bus. Gen. Electric Co., 1986-88; pres., chief exec. officer Thomson Consumer Electronics, 1988; ptnr. Am. Indsl. Ptnrs., 1988-89; pres. Wang Labs., 1989-90, chief oper. officer, 1989-93, chmn., chief exec. officer, 1990-93, dir., 1989-93; exec. v.p. and CFO AT&T, Basking Ridge, N.J., 1993—; tchr. Interracial Coun. Bus. Opportunity, N.Y.C., 1971-72; dir. AT&T Capital Corp. Pres. Econ. Council Palm Beach County, Fla., 1977-78; trustee Fla. Atlantic U., 1977-79, bd. advisors, 1975-79; mem. Gov. Fla. Com. on Energy, 1976; chmn. Housing Adv. Bd. Boca Raton, 1977-78; bd. dirs. South Fla. Coordinating Council, 1977-79; mem. vis. com. Harvard U., 1981-86. Named Bus. Man of Yr. Palm Beach County, 1978. Mem. Urban Land Inst. (chmn. recreational devel. coun. 1979), Harvard U. Bus. Sch. Assn. (pres. 1980, exec. coun.), Electronics Industries Assn. (bd. govs. 1987-88), U.S.C. of C. (dir. 1994—). Office: 295 N Maple Ave Rm 44913 Basking Ridge NJ 07920-1002*

MILLER, ROBERT, advertising executive; b. N.Y.C., June 2, 1923; s. Samuel and Adele (Elswit) M.; m. Frances Fitzgerald, June 10, 1944 (dec. 1978); children: Marc Robert, William Fitzgerald, Daniel Bates, Ellen Minette (Mrs. John Meyer); m. sandra Gold Patelmo, 1980. Student, NYU, 1940-42, Syracuse U., 1943. Newsroom employee N.Y. Daily Mirror, 1942; with Miller Advt. Agy., Inc., N.Y.C., 1946—, v.p., 1948-54, chmn. bd., 1954-57, pres., 1958—; pres. Miller Advt. Service Corp., 1956-62; pres. Miller Advt. Agy. Ill., Inc., 1965-73, also bd. dirs.; bd. dirs. Hereford Ins. Co., Inc., 1988-94. Contbg. editor Madison Avenue mag., 1975-78. Bd. govs. Roslyn Democratic Club, 1957-61, 68-73; mem. Nassau County Dem. Com., 1958-61, 68-73; Bd. dirs. Shalom Peace Found. Served to 1st lt. USAAF, 1942-46. Mem. Am. Legion. Home: 301 E 52d St New York NY 10022 also: 17 Shelly Dr Ellenville NY 12428 Office: Miller Advt Agy Inc 71 5th Ave New York NY 10003-3004

MILLER, ROBERT ALLEN, hotel executive; b. Chgo., Nov. 26, 1945; s. Jerome David and Leah Ester (Pollack) M.; m. Diana Marie Hall, Dec. 29, 1967; children: David, Allison, Brian. BSBA, U. Fla., 1967. CPA, Fla. Auditor, acct. Arthur Young & Co., Tampa, Fla., 1967-72; chief fin. officer Fleetwing Corp., Lakeland, Fla., 1972-78; pres. Am Resorts Corp., Lakeland, 1978-84; v.p. Marriott Corp., Bethesda, Md., 1984—. Office: Marriott Ownership Resorts PO Box 890 Lakeland FL 33802

MILLER, ROBERT ARTHUR, state supreme court chief justice; b. Aberdeen, S.D., Aug. 28, 1939; s. Edward Louis and Bertha Leone (Hitchcox) M.; m. Shirlee Ann Schlim, Sept. 5, 1964; children: Catherine Sue, Scott Edward, David Alan, Gerri Elizabeth, Robert Charles. BSBA, U. S.D., 1961, JD, 1963. Asst. atty. gen. State of S.D., Pierre, 1963-65; pvt. practice law Philip, S.D., 1965-71; state atty. Haakon County, Philip, 1965-71; city atty. City of Philip, 1965-71; judge State of S.D. (6th cir.), Pierre, 1971-86, presiding judge, 1975-86; justice S.D. Supreme Ct., Pierre, 1986—, now chief justice; trustee S.D. Retirement System, Pierre, 1974-85, chmn. 1982-85; mem. faculty S.D. Law Enforcement Tng. Acad., 1975-85. Mem. S.D. State Crime Commn., 1979-86; mem. adv. commn. S.D. Sch. for the Deaf, 1983-85, Communications Svcs. to Deaf, 1990—; cts. counselor S.D. Boy's State, 1986—. Mem. State Bar of S.D., S.D. Judges' Assn. (pres. 1974-75). Roman Catholic. Lodge: Elks. Avocations: golf, hunting. Office: US Supreme Ct SD 500 E Capitol Ave Pierre SD 57501-5070

MILLER, ROBERT BRANSON, JR., retired newspaper publisher; b. Battle Creek, Mich., Aug. 10, 1935; s. Robert Branson and Jean (Leonard) M.; m. Pattricia E. Miller; children: Melissa Ann, Gregory Allen, Jennifer Lynn, Jeffrey William. Grad., Hotchkiss Sch., Lakeville, Conn., 1953; BA, Mich. State U., 1959. Advt. salesman State Jour., Lansing, Mich., 1959-61; circulation sales rep. State Jour., 1961-62, reporter, 1962-65, nat. advt. mgr., 1965-66; asst. to pub. Idaho Statesman, Boise, 1966-69, pub., 1971-79; pub. Daily Olympian, Olympia, Wash., 1969-71; pub. Battle Creek Enquirer, 1979-90, chmn., 1990-91. Bd. dirs. Battle Creek chpt. ARC, Big Bros./Big Sisters; sr. advisor United Way; trustee Cheff Ctr. for the Handicapped; trustee Miller Found., Battle Creek. With USNR, 1956-58.

MILLER, ROBERT C., telecommunications industry executive; b. 1930. Grad., Va. Poly. Inst. & State U. Sr. v.p. NEC Am., Inc., 1978-83, exec. v.p., also bd. dirs. Office: NEC Am Inc 8 Old Sod Farm Rd Melville NY 11747-3148

MILLER, ROBERT CARL, library director; b. May 9, 1936. BS in History and Philosophy, Marquette U., 1958; MS in Am. History, U. Wis., 1962; MA in Libr. Sci., U. Chgo., 1966. Head telephone reference Library of Congress, Wash., 1959-60; reference librarian Marquette U., Milw., 1960-62, acquisition librarian, 1962-66; head tech. services/librarian Parsons Coll., Fairfield, Iowa, 1966-68; head acquisitions dept. U. of Chgo. Library, Ill., 1968-71; assoc. dir (reader services) U. of Chgo. Library, 1971-73; assoc dir (gen. service) U. of Chgo, 1973-75; dir. of libraries U. Mo., St. Louis, 1975-78; dir of libraries U. of Notre Dame, Ind., 1978—; vis. prof. IBIN-U. Warsaw, Poland, 1992, 93. Contbr. to prof. jour. Fellow Woodrow Wilson Found. (sr.), Coun. on Libr. Resources; mem. ALA, Polish Inst. of Arts and Letters of Am. Roman Catholic. Home: 17650 Tanager Ln South Bend IN 46635-1315 Office: U Notre Dame U Library 221 Theodore M Hesburgh Notre Dame IN 46556

MILLER, ROBERT CARMI, JR., microbiology educator, university administrator; b. Elgin, Ill., Aug. 10, 1942; s. Robert C. and Melba I. (Steinke) M.; m. Patricia A. Black, Aug.28, 1964; children: Geoffrey T., Christopher J. BS in Physics, Trinity Coll., Hartford, Conn., 1964; MS in Biophysics, Pa. State U., 1965; PhD in Molecular Biology, U. Pa., 1969. USPHS trainee U. Pa., Phila., 1966-69; postdoctoral fellow U. Wis., Madison, 1969-70; rsch. assoc., Am. Cancer Soc. postdoctoral fellow MIT, Cambridge, 1970-71; asst. assoc. prof. U. B.C., Vancouver, 1971-79, prof. microbiology, 1980—, head dept. microbiology, 1982-85, dean sci., 1985-88, v.p. rsch., 1988—, mem. exec. coun., sr. appointments com., mem. univ. senate, 1985, devel. com., 1986—; vis. prof. Inst. Molecular Biology U. Geneva, Switzerland, 1976; mem. program subcom. Internat. Congress of Biochemistry, 1979; mem. grants com. on genetics Med. Rsch Coun., 1980-82; mem. Grants Panel A Nat. Cancer Inst., 1981-85; biotech. com. B.C. Sci.

Coun., 1981-87, univ./industry program grant com., 1987—; biotech. com. Med. Rsch. Coun., 1983; assoc. com. for biotech. NRC, 1983—; strategic grant com. biotech. NSERC, 1985-87; bd. dirs. Paprican, Discovery Found., Sci. Coun. B.C., TRIUMF. Assoc. editor Virology, 1974-85, Jour. Virology, 1975-84; contbr. 100 articles to profl. jours.; author research papers. Recipient Merit award Am. Chem. Soc., gold medal Nat. Sci. Coun. B.C., 1993; grantee Natural Sci. and Engring. Rsch. Coun., 1971—, Med. Rsch. Coun., 1981, 86, 89—, Nat. Cancer Inst., 1982-85, 86. Mem. Can. Biochem Soc., Am. Soc. Microbiol., Sigma Xi. Office: Univ of BC, Faculty of Sci, Vancouver, BC Canada V6T 1Z1*

MILLER, ROBERT CHARLES, retired physicist; b. State College, Pa., Feb. 2, 1925; s. Lawrence P. Miller and Eva Mae (Gross) Wiedemann; m. Virginia Callaghan, Aug. 30, 1952; children: Robin Kingon Storey, Jeffrey Lawrence Miller, Lauren Wray Lynch. AB, Columbia U., 1948, MA, 1952, PhD, 1956. Staff mem. Johns-Manville Research Ctr., Finderne, N.J., 1948-49; teaching asst. in physics Columbia U., N.Y.C., 1949-51, lectr. in physics, 1951-53; mem. tech. staff Bell Telephone Labs., Murray Hill, N.J., 1954-63, head solid state spectroscopy research dept., 1963-67; staff mem. Inst. Defense Analyses, Arlington, Va., 1967-68; head optical elec. research dept. Bell Telephone Labs., Murray Hill, 1968-77; mem. tech. staff AT&T Bell Labs., Murray Hill, 1977-84, disting. mem. tech. staff, 1984-88, ret., 1988; cons. Office of Sec. Def., Arlington, Va., 1968-75. Inventor (with Dr. J.A. Giordmaine) Optical Parametric Oscillator, 1965 (co-recipient R.W. Wood prize, 1986); contbr. articles to profl. jours. Served with U.S. Army, 1943-46, ETO. RCA predoctoral fellow Columbia U., 1953-54. Fellow Am. Phys. Soc.; mem. AAAS, N.Y. Acad. Scis., Sigma Xi. Avocations: sailing, sports cars, tennis. Home: 65 Eaton Ct Cotuit MA 02635-2908

MILLER, ROBERT DANIEL, lawyer; b. Houston, May 3, 1960; s. Robert Thomas and Joyce (Danielson) M.; m. Lisa Anne Davis, May 23, 1987. BA, Rice U., 1982; JD, U. Tex., Austin, 1985. Bar: Tex. 1985. Legis. aide Senator Don Henderson, Austin, Tex., 1983; assoc. Liddell, Sapp, Zivley, Hill & LaBoon, L.L.P., Houston, 1985-91, ptnr., 1992—; sec., treas. Com. for Jud. Merit Election, Tex., 1987-89. Chmn. Battleship Tex. Adv. Bd., 1988-92; mem. fin. com. Houston Conv. Fund, 1991-95, Leadership Houston Class X, 1991-92; bd. dirs. Citizens Commn. on Tex. Judiciary, 1991-95, Greater Houston Preservation Alliance, 1994—, Tex. Lyceum, 1994—, Vote Tex., 1995—. Named one of Five Outstanding Young Houstonians, Jaycees, 1992. Mem. State Bar Tex., Houston Bar Assn., Tex. Assn. Bank Counsel, Houston Club, Order of Coif, Phi Delta Phi, Omicron Delta Epsilon. Republican. Office: Liddell Sapp Zivley Hill & LaBoon LLP 3400 Texas Commerce Twr Houston TX 77002

MILLER, ROBERT EARL, engineer, educator; b. Rockford, Ill., Oct. 4, 1932; s. Leslie D. and Marcia V. (Jones) M. B.S., U. Ill., 1954, M.S., 1955, Ph.D., 1959. Asst. prof. theoretical and applied mechanics U. Ill., Urbana, 1959-61; asso. prof. U. Ill., 1961-68, prof., 1968—; cons. in field to industry U.S. Army; in various positions in industry, summers, 1963-68. Contbr. articles to profl. jours. Mem. AIAA, Am. Soc. Engring. Edn. (Disting. Engring. award 1991), ASCE. Office: U Ill 216 Talbot Lab 104 S Wright St Urbana IL 61801-2935

MILLER, ROBERT G., retail company executive; b. 1944. With Albertson's Inc., 1961-89, exec. v.p. retail ops., 1989-91; chmn. bd., CEO Fred Meyer Inc., Portland, Oreg., 1991—. Office: Fred Meyer Inc 3800 SE 22d Ave Portland OR 97202-2918*

MILLER, ROBERT H., soil scientist, dean; b. Fremont, Wis., Sept. 19, 1933; married, 1957; 3 children. BS, Wis. State U., 1958; MS, U. Minn., 1961, PhD in Soil Microbiology, 1964. From asst. to full prof. agronomy Ohio State U., 1964-81; head and prof. dept. soil sci. N.C. State U., 1982-89; dean natural resources U. R.I., 1989—; Fulbright lectr., 1974-75. Fellow Am. Soc. Agronomy (bd. dirs. 1978-81), Soil Sci. Soc. Am. (bd. dirs. 1978-81); mem. Am. Soc. Microbiology, Sigma Xi. Achievements include research on plant rhizosphere microorganisms and their interactions with plants; ecology and physiology of Rhizobium japonicum; chemistry of soil organic matter; recycling of organic wastes in soil; international development. Office: U RI Ri Agrl Expt Sta Kingston RI 02881*

MILLER, ROBERT HAROLD, otolaryngologist, educator; b. Columbia, Mo., July 2, 1947; s. Harold Oswald and Ruth Nadine (Ballew) M.; m. Martha Guillory, Apr. 18, 1981; children: Morgan Guillory, Reed Thurston. BS in Biology, Tulane U., 1969, MD, 1973; cert. in otolaryngology-head/neck surg., UCLA Med. Ctr., 1978. Diplomate Am. Bd. Otolaryngology. From asst. prof. to assoc. prof. otolaryngology-HNS Baylor Coll. Medicine, Houston, 1978-87; prof., chmn. otolaryngology-HNS Tulane Sch. Medicine, New Orleans, 1987—; bd. dirs. Am. Bd. Otolaryngology; vice chief of staff Tulane Hosp., 1991—. Mem. editl. bd. Archives of Otolaryngology, 1986—, Head & Neck Surgery, 1987—. Named Outstanding Young Man, Houston C. of C., 1980. Fellow ACS, Am. Soc. Head & Neck Surgery, Am. Acad. Oto-Head & Neck Surgery (Disting. Svc. award 1994, Honor award 1991), Triological Soc. (exec. sec. 1992—). Avocations: tennis, computers. Home: 205 Brockenbraugh Ct Metairie LA 70005 Office: Tulane U Sch Medicine 1430 Tulane Ave New Orleans LA 70112

MILLER, ROBERT HASKINS, retired state chief justice; b. Columbus, Ohio, Mar. 3, 1919; s. George L. and Marian Alice (Haskins) M.; m. Audene Fausett, Mar. 14, 1943; children: Stephen F., Thomas G., David W., Stacey Ann (dec.). A.B., Kans. U., 1940, LL.B., 1942; grad., Nat. Coll. State Trial Judges, Phila., 1967. Bar: Kans. 1943. Practice in Paola, 1946-60; judge 6th Jud. Dist. Kans., Paola, 1961-69; U.S. magistrate Kans. Dist., Kansas City, 1969-75; justice Kans. Supreme Ct., Topeka, 1975-88, chief justice, 1988-90, ret., 1990; chmn. Kans. Jud. Coun., 1987-88. Contbg. author: Pattern (Civil Jury) Instructions for Kansas, 2d edit, 1969. Served with AUS, 1942-46. Mem. Kans. Bar Assn., Wyandotte County Bar Assn., Shawnee County Bar Assn., Am. Legion, Phi Gamma Delta, Phi Delta Phi. Presbyterian. Office: Supreme Ct Kans-Jud Ctr 301 SW 10th Ave Topeka KS 66612

MILLER, ROBERT HENRY, English educator; b. Defiance, Ohio, Aug. 10, 1938; s. Richard Carl and Elizabeth Jane (Sowers) M.; m. Diane Sue Partee, June 5, 1960; children: Rebecca, Rachel, Amy. BA, Bowling Green State U., 1960, MA, 1961; PhD, Ohio State U., 1968. Instr. Mich. Tech. U., 1961-64; prof., chmn. Renaissance lit. and culture, modern novel U. Louisville, 1968—. Author: Understanding Graham Greene, 1990, Handbook of Literary Research, 1987, 95; editor: Harington's Catalogue of Bishops, 1979; contbr. poems to poetry mags. and articles to scholarly mags. Mem. AAUP, MLA, ACLU. Democrat. Roman Catholic. Avocations: fishing, baseball, bicycling. Home: 2440 Saratoga Dr Louisville KY 40205-2023 Office: U Louisville Dept English Louisville KY 40292

MILLER, ROBERT J., financial executive; b. Prague, Czechoslovakia, June 27, 1949; came to U.S., 1978; children: Mark Peter, Peter John. MS in Engring., Czech Inst. Tech., Prague, 1969; PhD, Sch. Architecture, Prague, 1978. Investment officer Preferred Capital Investments, Dallas, 1985-89; ptnr. Miller, Myslivec & Scott, Ltd., Rockville, Md., 1990-92; sr. ptnr. Am. Adv. Group, Inc., Washington, 1992—; exec. dir. Czech and Slovak Svc. Ctrs., Washington, 1993—; appeared on numerous TV and radio programs on Ctrl. Europe econ. and polit. issues. Author: Global Investments, 1980; contbr. articles to profl. pubs. Mem. Am. Czech and Slovak Assn. (pres.). Jewish. Office: Czech & Slovak Svc Ctrs 1511 K St NW Ste 1030 Washington DC 20005

MILLER, ROBERT JAMES, association executive; b. Mansfield, Ohio, Jan. 27, 1926; s. Dennis Cornelius and Mabel (Snyder) M.; m. Jerri Ann Burran, June 5, 1952; children: Robert James Jr., Dennis Burran. Student, Heidelberg Coll., 1946-47; BS, U. N.Mex., 1950, MA, 1952; postgrad., Miami U., Central Ohio, 1951-55; MBA, Fla. Atlantic U., 1978. Asst. exec. sec. Phi Delta Theta Hdqrs., Oxford, 1951-54, adminstrv. sec., 1954-55, exec. v.p., 1955-91; pres. Phi Delta Theta Found., Oxford, 1984—; bus. mgr. The Scroll, Oxford, 1955-91; adviser Western Regional Interfraternity Conf. 1973-76; speaker numerous meetings, mgr. various convs., confs. Editor: Phikeia—The Manual of Phi Delta Theta, 1951, 19 edits., 1989, Phis Sing, 1958, Constitution and General Statutes of Phi Delta Theta, Fraternity Education Foundations, 1962, Directory of Phi Delta Theta, 1973; also 2

workbooks. Chmn. United Appeal, Oxford, 1960; bd. dirs. U. N.Mex. Alumni Assn., 1961-68; pres. Fedn. of Clubs, Oxford, 1964, McGuffey PTA, 1971, Miami U. Art Mus., 1993-94, McCullough-Hyde Hosp., Oxford, 1966, chmn. endowment adv. com., 1988-89; vol. leader Boy Scouts Am., Oxford, 1966-79. Recipient Citizen of Yr. award City of Oxford, 1968, citation Theta Chi, 1967, Order of Interfrat. Svc. Lambda Chi Alpha, 1994, Meritorious Svc. award Boy Scouts Am., 1977, others; Interfrat. Inst. fellow Ind. U., 1988. Mem. Nat. Interfraternity Conf. (various coms. 1954—, cert. of svc. 1981, 85, gold medal, 1992), Am. Soc. Assn. Execs. (cert.), Cin. Soc. Assn. Execs., Fraternity Execs. Assn. (pres. 1962-63, svc. citations 1980, 85, 90, Disting. Svc. award 1991), Fraternity Scholarship Assn., Fraternity Editors Assn., Edgewater Conf. (pres. 1978-79), Summit Soc., Country Club Oxford (bd. dirs.), Order of Symposiarchs, Order of Omega, Rotary (founder Oxford club 1965, pres. 1966, Merit award 1974, dist. gov. S.W. Ohio 1978-79, study group exchange leader South Africa 1992), Blue Key, Phi Delta Kappa, Omicron Delta Kappa. Home: 170 Hilltop Rd Oxford OH 45056-1572 Office: Phi Delta Theta Ednl Found 2 S Campus Ave Oxford OH 45056-1801

MILLER, ROBERT JAMES, lawyer; b. Dunn, N.C., Jan. 14, 1933; s. Robert James and Edith (Crockett) M.; m. Patricia L. Shaw, Sept. 29, 1984; children: Patricia Ann, Susan Ballantine, Nancy Crockett. B.S., N.C. State U., 1956; M.F., Yale U., 1962, M.S., 1965, Ph.D., 1967; J.D., N.C. Central U., 1984. Registered land surveyor. Forester W.Va. Pulp & Paper Co., 1956-59, Tilghman Lumber Co., 1959-61; asst. in instrn. and research Yale U., New Haven, 1962-65; assoc. prof. biology Radford (Va.) Coll., 1965-67, prof., chmn. biology dept., 1967-68, dean div. natural scis., 1968-71, v.p. for acad. affairs, 1971-73; prof. law, dean of coll. St. Mary's Coll., Raleigh, N.C., 1973-85; atty. Patton, Boggs & Blow, Raleigh, N.C., 1985-89; pvt. practice, 1989—; mediator N.C. Gen. Ct. of Justice; ecol. cons.; arbitrator Am. Arbitration Assn., Better Bus. Bur. Author: The Assimilation of Nitrogen Compounds by Tree Seedlings, 1957, Some Ecological Aspects of Dry Matter Production, 1962, Liberal Arts and the Individual, 1972, Liberal Arts: an Educational Philosophy, 1973, Laboratory Notebook: General Biology, 1976, Educational Malpractice, 1984. Mem. Am. Soc. Plant Physiologists, Ecol. Soc. Am., ABA, Am. Immigration Lawyers Assn., N.C. Acad. Trial Lawyers, N.C. Bar Assn., Sigma Xi, Phi Kappa Phi, Xi Sigma Pi. Episcopalian. Lodges: Masons; Shriners. Home: 3404 Lake Boone Trl Raleigh NC 27607-6756

MILLER, ROBERT JAMES, fundraising company executive; b. Rochester, Minn., Nov. 8, 1944; s. Robert Harrison and Beverly Anne (Vaughn) M.; m. Donna M. Hofner, June 17, 1967 (div. 1987); children: Laura Anne, Stephen James; m. Josephine M. Rose, Oct. 8, 1988; 1 child, Erica Rose Miller. BA, Alfred U., 1967; MBA, CUNY, 1970. Grants specialist U.S. Dept. Health & Human Svcs., Washington, 1972-76; pres. Robert J. Miller & Assocs. Inc., Buffalo, 1976—; commd. 2d lt. U.S. Army, 1967, advanced through grades to Maj., 1976, resigned, 1977; lectr. on grant devel., 1977—. Author (text) Personnel Administration, 1973, Program Evaluation, 1974; contbg. author Newsletter for Nat. Soc. of Fundraising Execs. Bd. Trustees Clarence (N.Y.) Ctrl. Schs., 1976-80. Recipient Bronze Star U.S. Army, Vietnam, 1970. Mem. Nat. Soc. of Fund Raising Execs. (bd. dirs. 1993—), Jr. Achievement Western N.Y. (bd. dirs. 1992—). Republican. Avocations: private pilot, skiing. Home: 41 Summershade Ct East Amherst NY 14051-1677 Office: Robert J Miller & Assocs 124 Delaware St Tonawanda NY 14150-3421

MILLER, ROBERT JOSEPH, governor, lawyer; b. Evanston, Ill., Mar. 30, 1945; s. Ross Wendell and Coletta Jane (Doyle) M.; m. Sandra Ann Searles, Oct. 17, 1949; children: Ross, Corrine, Megan. BA in Polit. Sci., U. Santa Clara, 1967; JD, Loyola U., Los Angeles, 1971. First legal advisor Las Vegas (Nev.) Met. Police Dept., 1973-75; justice of the peace Las Vegas Twp., 1975-78; dep. dist. atty. Clark County, Las Vegas, 1971-73, dist. atty., 1979-86; lt. gov. State of Nev., 1987-89, acting gov., 1989-90, gov., 1991—. Chmn. Nev. Commn. on Econ. Devel., Carson City, 1987-91, Nev. Commn. on Tourism, Carson City, 1987-91; mem. Pres. Reagan's Task Force on Victims of Crime, 1982; chmn. Nev. divsn. Am. Cancer Soc., 1988-90. Mem. Nat. Dist. Atty.'s Assn. (pres. 1984-85), Western Govs. Assn. (chair-elect 1992-93, chmn. 1993-93), Nat. Govs. Assn. (past chmn. com. on justice and pub. safety, chmn. legal affairs com. 1992-94, lead gov. on trasp. 1992—) Nev. Dist. Atty.'s Assn. (pres. 1979, 83). Democrat. Roman Catholic. Home: Gov Mansion 606 N Mountain St Carson City NV 89703 Office: State of Nev Office of Gov Capitol Bldg Carson City NV 89710

MILLER, ROBERT L., publishing company executive. MBA, Columbia Bus. Sch., 1971. Former ops. mgr. internat. Time-Life Books Inc., N.Y.C.; former bus. mgr. Sports Illustrated mag., from 1979, former gen. mgr., from 1981, former pub., from 1983; former exec. v.p. Time Inc. Mags.; now v.p. internat. sales Berlitz Pub. Co., Inc., N.Y.C. Office: Berlitz Pub Co Inc 257 Park Ave South New York NY 10010

MILLER, ROBERT L., JR., federal judge; b. 1950; m. Jane Woodward. BA, Northwestern U., 1972; JD, Ind. U., 1975. Law clk. to presiding justice U.S. Dist. Ct. (no. dist.) Ind., 1975; judge St. Joseph Superior Ct., South Bend, Ind., 1975-86, chief judge 1981-83; judge U.S. Dist. Ct. (no. dist.) Ind., South Bend, Ind., 1985—. Office: US Dist Ct 325 Fed Bldg 204 S Main St South Bend IN 46601-2122

MILLER, ROBERT LINDSEY, bishop; b. Eagle Grove, Iowa, June 24, 1933; m. Doris Mandsager; children: Tedd, Darrell, Diane. BA, St. Olaf Coll., 1966. Pastor Luth. congregations, St. Louis Park, Minn., Riverside and Santa Barbara, Calif., First Luth. Ch., Fullerton, Calif.; bishop Pacifica Synod, Evang. Luth. Ch. in Am., Yorba Linda, Calif., 1988—. Office: Evang Luth Ch in Am 23655 Via Del Rio Yorba Linda CA 92687-2718

MILLER, ROBERT LOUIS, university dean, chemistry educator; b. Chgo., Jan. 26, 1926; s. Sam P. and Ida (Reich) M. m. Virginia Southard, Oct. 26, 1947 (dec. Sept. 1973); children: Ruth, Stephen, Martin, Andrew; m. Bonnie Seay Berard, Nov. 28, 1975; children: Edouard, Derek. Ph.B., U. Chgo., 1947, B.S., 1949, M.S., 1951; Ph.D., Ill. Inst. Tech.; Ph.D. (NSF Sci. faculty fellow), 1963. Mem. faculty U. Ill. Chgo. Circle Campus, 1953-67, asst. dean Coll. Liberal Arts and Scis., 1963-65, assoc. dean Coll. Liberal Arts and Scis., 1965-67; prof. chemistry U. N.C.-Greensboro, 1968—, dean arts and scis., 1968-85, acting dean Grad. Sch., 1989-91, spl. asst. to the provost, 1993-94; acting assoc. provost, 1994—; Am. Council Edn. adminstrv. intern SUNY-Binghamton, 1967-68. Mem. exec. com. of com. environ. affairs Piedmont Council Govts., 1971-76; mem. Greensboro Task Force on Energy; chmn. residential and transp. subcom Greensboro Energy Commn.; mem. Bd. Edn., Oak Park, Ill., 1965-66; bd. dirs. Hospice at Greensboro, 1981-87, pres., 1982-84, vol. 1988-89; vol., mem. bd. dirs. Cities in Schs., 1988-92; bd. dirs. Gilbert Pearson Audubon Soc., Greensboro Civil Liberties Union, Weatherspoon Gallery, 1981-85. Served with AUS, 1944-46, ETO. Mem. AAAS, Sigma Xi (treas. chpt.). Home: 1702 Natchez Trce Greensboro NC 27455-3226

MILLER, ROBERT NOLEN, lawyer; b. Monmouth, Ill., May 30, 1940; s. Robert Clinton and Doris Margaret (Nolen) M.; m. Diane Wilmarth, Aug. 21, 1965; children: Robert Wilmarth, Anne Elizabeth. BA, Cornell Coll., Mt. Vernon, Iowa, 1962; JD, U. Colo., 1965. Bar: Colo. 1965. Assoc. firm M. Quiat, Denver, 1965-66, Fischer & Beaty, Ft. Collins, Colo., 1966-70; dist. atty. Weld County Dist. Atty.'s Office, Greeley, Colo., 1971-81; U.S. atty. U.S. Dept. Justice, Denver, 1981-88; chief counsel litigation and security US West Inc., Englewood, Colo., 1988-93; of counsel Patton, Boggs & Blow, Denver, 1993-94, LeBoeuf, Lamb, Greene & Mac Crae, Denver, 1994—; instr. bus. law Am. U., U.S.C., Myrtle Beach, 1966-69. Co-author: Deathroads, 1978. Bd. dirs. Boys Club, Greeley, 1974-78, 1st Congl. Ch., Greeley, 1975-78; Rep. candidate for atty. gen. Colo., 1977-78. Capt. USAF, 1966-69. Recipient Citizen of Yr. award Elks Club, Greeley. Mem. Fed. Bar Assn. (pres. chpt. 1983-84), Colo. Dist. Atty's Coun. (pres. 1976-77), Colo. Bar Assn., Weld County Bar Assn., Rotary (pres. local chpt. 1980-81). Republican. Avocations: fishing, hunting, golf, tennis, reading. Office: LeBoeuf Lamb Greene MacRae Ste 1975 633 17th St Ste 2800 Denver CO 80202

MILLER, ROBERT REESE, trade association executive; b. Cin., Nov. 14, 1934; s. Louis and Lucille D. (Cantwell) M.; m. Jimmie Lorraine Mote, Aug. 15, 1965; children: Tracy Lou, Kimberly Kristin. BS, U. Okla., 1959. Ter.

mgr. Walker div. Tenneco, Shreveport, La., 1961-64; dist. mgr. Garlock, Inc., Chgo., 1964-68; regional mgr. Ideal Corp., Bklyn., 1968-69, nat. sales mgr., 1970-73, v.p., 1973-74; group v.p. Parker Hannifin Automotive, Bklyn., 1975-86; pres. Gen. Automotive Splty., North Brunswick, N.J., 1986-89; v.p. Wagner div. Cooper Industries, Parsippany, N.J., 1989-91; chmn. Motor and Equipment Mfrs. Assn., Englewood Cliffs, N.J., 1985-87; pres., CEO, Motor and Equipment Mfrs. Assn., Research Triangle Park, N.C., 1991—; chmn. Automotive Anti-Counterfeiting Task Force, 1983-87; mem. automobile parts adv. com. U.S. Dept. Commerce, Washington, 1993-95; responsible for achieving passage of trade mark counterfeit bill making product counterfeiting a criminal offense. Contbr. articles to profl. publ. Recipient Pursuit of Excellence award Automotive Warehouse Distbrs. Assn., 1991. Mem. Automotive Sales Coun. (pres. 1985-87), Fedn. N.Am. Automotive Parts Mfrs. (sec.-gen. 1993-95), Durham C. of C. (bd. dirs. 1995—), Treyburn Country Club, Univ. Club, Detroit Soc. Clubs. Avocations: reading, golf, deep sea fishing, tennis. Office: Motor-Equipment Mfrs Assn 10 Laboratory Dr Box 13966 Research Triangle Park NC 27709-3966

MILLER, ROBERT STEVENS, JR., finance professional; b. Portland, Oreg., Nov. 4, 1941; s. Robert Stevens and Barbara (Weston) M.; m. Margaret Rose Kyger, Nov. 9, 1966; children: Christopher John, Robert Stevens, Alexander Lamont. AB with distinction, Stanford U., 1963; LLB, Harvard U., 1966; MBA, Stanford U., 1968. Bar: Calif. bar 1966. Fin. analyst Ford Motor Co., Dearborn, Mich., 1968-71; spl. studies mgr. Ford Motor Co. Mexico City, 1971-73; dir. fin. Ford Asia-Pacific, Inc., Melbourne, Australia, 1974-77, Ford Motor Co., Caracas, Venezuela, 1977-79; v.p., treas. Chrysler Corp., Detroit, 1980-81, exec. v.p. fin., 1981-90, vice chmn., 1990-92; sr. ptnr. James D. Wolfensohn, Inc., N.Y.C., 1992-93; chmn. bd. dirs. Morrison Knudsen Corp., 1995—; bd. dirs. Fed.-Mogul, U.S. Bancorp, Fluke, Polk & Talbot, Coleman, Symantec.

MILLER, ROBERT T., political science educator; b. Ogburn, Tex., Feb. 17, 1920; s. Francis James and Edna Jeannette (Stokes) M.; m. Ann Vardaman, Dec. 22, 1949; children—Robert T., Laurie Anne Smith. B.A., Baylor U., 1941, M.A., 1941; Ph.D., U. Tex., 1954. Adminstrv. asst. Congressman W.R. Poage, Washington, 1961-62; from asst. prof. to prof. polit. sci. Baylor U., Waco, Tex., 1946—, R.W. Morrison Disting. prof. polit. sci., 1990—, chmn. dept., 1962-90, assoc. dean Coll. Arts and Scis., 1979-84, vice provost instructional programs, 1984-87, dean of continuing edn. and faculty devel. 1987-90. Co-author: Church and State in Scripture, History and Constitutional Law, 1958, Toward Benevolent Neutrality: Church, State and the Supreme Court, 1977, 4th edit., 1992; author (with others) Readings on Church and State, 1989. Mem. McLennan County. Com. Dem. Party, Tex., 1965—; mem. dist. com. Grievance Com., Tex. State Bar, Waco, 1980-86. Served to lt. comdr. USNR, 1942-46. Mem. Am. Polit. Sci. Assn., AAUP, So. Polit. Sci. Assn., Southwestern Social Sci. Assn., Omicron Delta Kappa. Baptist. Home: 4908 Ridgeview Dr Waco TX 76710-1725 Office: Baylor Univ Dept Of Polit Sci Waco TX 76798

MILLER, ROBERT WILEY, educational foundation executive; b. Linden, Calif., June 8, 1928; s. Raymond Wiley and Florence Estelle (Burke) M.; m. Betty Ruth Brown, Nov. 15, 1953; children—Janet Ruth, Stephen Wiley. B.A., Coll. of Pacific, Stockton, Calif., 1950; M.B.A., Harvard U., 1956; LL.D. (hon.), Lincoln Meml. U., 1978; L.H.D. (hon.), Samford U., 1978; Litt.D. (hon.), Rider Coll., 1981. Dir. program in pub. relations Columbia U., 1960-65; dir. bus.-govt. relations program, dir. Center Study Pvt. Enterprise, Univ. A.L., 1965-70; dir. Office Domestic Bus. Policy, Dept. Commerce, 1970-71; exec. dir. White House Conf. Indsl. World Ahead, 1971-72; asst. dir. Council Internat. Econ. Policy, White House, 1972-73; spl. asst. for Bicentennial affairs White House, 1973-74; sr. asst. adminstr. Am. Revolution Bicentennial Adminstrn., 1974-75; pres. Freedoms Found. at Valley Forge, Pa., 1975-94, pres. emeritus, 1994—; mem. pres.'s Adv. Council Pvt. Sector Initiatives, 1983-85. Vice chmn. pub. relations com. Nat. council Boy Scouts Am., 1965-76; trustee Am. U., 1976-82, Valley Forge Mil. Acad. and Jr. Coll., 1991—. Served with AUS, 1951-53. Recipient Medal of Honor D.A.R., 1978; Silver Helmet Americanism award AMVETS, 1978; named Alumnus of Year U. Pacific, 1976. Mem. Cosmos Club (Washington), Union League (pres. 1995—), Phila. Country Club, Masons. Office: Union League of Phila 140 S Broad St Philadelphia PA 19102-3083

MILLER, ROBERT WILLIAM, personal property appraiser, writer; b. Phila., Apr. 28, 1922; s. Stuart Parmalee and Ruth Anne (Mills) M.; m. Judith Bayard Wood, Sept. 1948 (div. Feb. 1951); m. Bettie Lucy Hays, Apr. 28, 1962. Student, NYU, 1945-46, Fenster Sch. Writing, N.Y.C., 1945-47, Dickinson Coll., 1948-49. Copywriter Ruthraff & Ryan, N.Y.C., 1944-46; writer various publs., 1944-60; ind. personal property appraiser N.W. Fla., 1960—; writer Wallace-Homestead Book Co., Des Moines, 1971-86; lectr., mus. cons. on antiques, Gt. Britain, France, Italy, Fed. Republic Germany, 1963—; cons. McClung Mus., Knoxville, Tenn., 1968-72, Houston Mus., Chattanooga, 1970-78. Host TV talk show Antiques and Collectibles, PBS, 1968-72; author 34 books on antiques and collectibles. Dir. Swim Program for Handicapped, Oak Ridge, Tenn., 1954-68; scoutmaster, cubmaster Boy Scouts of Am. Troop #120, Oak Ridge, 1962-68. Vol. Am. Field Svc., 1943-44, CBI. Decorated 1939-45 Star, Burma Star, War Medal (Gt. Britain); recipient Nat. award Nat. Recreation Assn., 1960. Mem. Appraisers Assn. Am., Nat. Geog. Soc. Presbyterian. Avocations: scuba diving, fishing, collecting antique cars. Home: 100 Greenwood Dr Panama City Beach FL 32407-5424

MILLER, ROBERTA BALSTAD, science administrator; b. Mpls., June 25, 1940; d. Gerhard Oliver and Laverne K. (Anderson) Balstad; m. Gary David Lange, Nov. 26, 1959 (div. 1968); m. Floyd John Miller, June 15, 1969; 1 child, Aaron Gerhard. BA, U. Minn., 1964, MA, 1970, PhD, 1973. Rsch. assoc. AIA, Washington, 1974; staff assoc. Social Sci. Rsch. Coun., Washington, 1975-81; exec. dir. Consortium Social Sci. Assns., Washington, 1981-84; divsn. dir. NSF, Washington, 1984-93; pres., CEO Consortium for Internat. Earth Sci. Info. Network (CIESIN), University Center, Mich., 1993—; adj. prof. natural resources policy and behavior U. Mich., 1993—; guest scholar Woodrow Wilson Internat. Ctr. for Scholars, 1994; sr. assoc. mem. St. Anthony's Coll., U. of Oxford, Eng., 1991-92; mem., chmn. NATO adv. panel on Advanced Sci. Insts./Advanced Rsch. Workshops, Brussels, 1988-91; chmn. adv. bd. Luxembourg Income Survey, 1987-91. Author: City and Hinterland, 1979; editor (with Harriet Zuckerman) Scientometrics, 1979; contbr. articles to profl. jours.; translator poetry of Jorge Luis Borges, 1989, 90, 91. Mem. bd. trustees Newport Schs., Kensington, Md., 1986-91, St. Anthony's Coll. Trust, 1994—. Recipient NSF Meritorious Svc. award, 1993. Mem. AAAS (com. mem., chmn. 1987—), U.S. Man in the Biosphere Program (mem. com., chmn. 1989-91), Internat. Social Sci. Coun. (mem. com. 1991—, v.p. 1992-94), Am. Hist. Assn., Am. Lit. Translators Assn., Coun. on Fgn. Rels., Cosmos Club. Lutheran. Home: 3909 Jocelyn St NW Washington DC 20015-1905 Office: CIESIN 2250 Pierce Rd University Center MI 48710

MILLER, ROBERTA DAVIS, editor; b. Oklahoma City, Aug. 18, 1931; s. Robert Rutter and Lenora (Baldwin) Davis; children: Wendy, Jane, Elisabeth. Student, Okla. U., 1948-50, Central State U., 1950-51. Editor Golden Books, Western Pub. Co., 1963-71; pub. Sesame St. Mag., Electric Co. Mag., Children's TV Workshop, N.Y.C., 1971-76; editor-in-chief Pizzazz Mag., Cadence Pub. Co., N.Y.C., 1976-78; v.p., dir. lit. properties United Media, N.Y.C., 1978-85, v.p. internat. pub., 1986-93, v.p., dir. pub., 1993-94; prin. Roberta D. Miller Assocs. Internat., N.Y.C., 1994—. Mem. Authors Guild, Nat. Cartoonists Soc., Newswomen's Club N.Y. Office: 42 E 12th St New York NY 10003-4640

MILLER, ROBIN DAVIS, professional society administrator; b. Phila., May 22, 1962; d. Neil Monas and Julia (Kraft) Mann; m. Stephen Michael Miller, Apr. 17, 1993; 1 child, Benjamin Preston. BA, U. Pa., 1983; MA, U. Coll., Oxford, Eng., 1985; JD, U. Pa., 1988. Bar: N.Y. 1989, Pa. 1991. Litigator Rogers & Wells, N.Y.C., 1988-90, Kornstein Veisz & Wexler, N.Y.C., 1990-91, Drinker Biddle & Reath, Phila., 1991-93; exec. dir. Authors Guild Found., N.Y.C., 1993—, Authors League Am., N.Y.C., 1993—, Authors Guild, N.Y.C., 1993—; bd. dirs. Copyright Clearance Ctr., Danvers, Mass. Bd. dirs. Ralston House, Phila., 1992-93; del. Libr. of Congress ACCORD com. on Copyright Law, Washington, 1993-94. Mem. N.Y. Bar Assn., Pa. Bar Assn., Authors Registry, Inc. (bd. dirs.). Jewish. Office: Authors League of Am 330 W 42d St 29th Fl New York NY 10036

MILLER, RODGER DALE, private investigator, intelligence analyst; b. Onnalinda, Pa., July 7, 1945; s. Louis Grant and Anna Eve (Sherman) M.; m. Jeanne Ellen Flinn, Nov. 15, 1969; children: Ginger Louise, Spring Leanne. Cert. in Crime Investigation, Wichita State U., 1967; cert. in Dactaloscopy, U. Calif., Santa Barbara, 1969; AA in Liberal Arts, Allen Hancock Coll., 1971; BA in Ancient History, Calif. State U., Chico, 1974. Lic. pvt. investigator, Calif.; cert. in law enforcement; cert. diplomatic courier; cert. space analyst. Coal miner A.R. Burkett Coal Co., Beaverdale, Pa., 1959-62; police investigator Wichita (Kans.) Police Dept., 1966-69; sheriff, coroner investigator Santa Barbara (Calif.) County Sheriff's Dept., 1969-74; owner heavy equip. Redding, Calif., 1974-82; lead intelligence analyst GTE Govt. Systems/Space, Sunnyvale, Calif., 1986-89; lead planner analyst Martin-Marietta Space Corp., Denver, 1989-91; qualified mgr., owner All Answers Detective Agy., Redding, 1991—; cons. analyst various U.S. agencies, Washington, 1982—; tech. cons. authors/motion picture industry, Calif., 1986—. Author: (text) Orbits of Artificial Bodies, 1983; author rsch. treatise Cave Paintings as Graffiti, 1977; author (fingerprints) Dactaloscopy, 1970. Staff sgt. U.S. Army, 1962-66, 82-86, Vietnam. Decorated Silver Star with V device, 1965, Bronze Star with V device, 1966. Mem. Nat. Rifle Assn., Am. Legion, Greater Redding C. of C. Republican. Southern Baptist. Avocations: photography, fishing, boating, reading, target shooting. Home: 3336 Meadow Oak Dr Cottonwood CA 96022 Office: All Answers Detective Agy 2750 Eureka Way Ste 112 Redding CA 96001

MILLER, RONALD ALFRED, family physician; b. Orange, Calif., Sept. 27, 1943; s. Alfred Casper and Inez Geraldine (Gunderson) M.; m. Jean Ilene Andrews, June 18, 1966; children: Jon, Lauri, Bryan. BA, Pacific Luth. U., 1965; MD, U. Wash., 1969. Diplomate Am. Bd. Family Practice (bd. dirs. 1985-90, pres. bd. 1989-90). Intern in medicine Parkland Meml. Hosp. Dallas, 1969-70; gen. practice residency USPHS Gallup Indian Med. Ctr., Gallup, N.Mex., 1970-72; prin. Family Physicians' Clinic, Whitefish, Mont., 1972—; assoc. clin. prof. U. Wash., Seattle, 1975—; coord. community clin. unit in family medicine, U. Wash., Whitefish, 1975—; bd. dirs. Utah Med. Ins. Assn., Salt Lake City, 1987—. Bd. dirs. Whitefish Housing Authority, 1977-82; mem. alumni bd. Pacific Luth. U., Tacoma, 1976-81, pres., 1979-80; mem. Glacier Community Chorale, Whitefish, 1984—, bd. dirs., 1990—. Lt. comdr. USPHS, 1970-72. Mem. Am. Acad. Family Physicians (com. on continuing med. edn. 1977-81, com. on edn. 1984-89, Mead Johnson award Grad. Edn. in Family Practice 1972), Mont. Acad. Family Physicians (bd. dirs., sec./treas. v.p., pres. 1982-83, del. nat. congress 1978-84), Rotary, Alpha Omega Alpha. Republican. Lutheran. Avocations: hunting, fishing, skiing, backpacking, choral singing. Home: 721 Iowa Ave Whitefish MT 59937-2338 Office: Family Physicians Clinic 401 Baker Ave Whitefish MT 59937-2435

MILLER, RONALD ANTHONY, distribution company executive; b. Lebanon, Pa., Mar. 7, 1940; s. Milton Leo and Annette Miller; m. Jane Carson (dec. Feb. 1988); children: Kathleen Marie, David Anthony; m. Terry Jeanne Kapp, June 17, 1989. A in Bus., Harrisburg (Pa.) Community Coll., 1989; BSBA, Columbia Pacific U., 1989. Mgr. data processing Lebanon (Pa.) County Govt., 1964; v.p. Keystone Ctrs. Inc., Lebanon, 1964-77; sr. v.p. distbn. Rite Aid Corp., Shermantown, Pa., 1977—. With USN 1958-63. Mem. Warehouse Edn. Rsch. Coun., Nat. Assn. Chain Drug Stores, Coun. Logistics Mgmt. Office: Rite Aid Corp Hunter Ln Camphill PA 17011

MILLER, RONALD BAXTER, English language educator; author; b. Rocky Mount, N.C., Oct. 11, 1948; s. Marcellus Cornelius and Elsie (Bryant) M.; m. Jessica Garris, June 5, 1971; 1 child, Akin Dasan. BA magna cum laude, N.C. Ctrl. U., 1970; AM, Brown U., 1972, PhD, 1974. Asst. prof. English Haverford Coll., Haverford, Pa., 1974-76; assoc. prof. English, dir. Black lit. program U. Tenn., Knoxville, 1977-81, prof. English, dir. Black lit. program, 1982-92, Lindsay Young prof. liberal arts and English, 1986-87; prof. English, dir. Inst. for African Am. Studies U. Ga., Athens, 1992—; instr. summer sch. Roger Williams Coll., Bristol, R.I., 1973; lectr. SUNY, 1974; Melville prof. Xavier Univ., New Orleans, 1988; Irvine Found. visiting scholar Univ. San Francisco, 1991. Author: (reference guide) Langston Hughes and Gwendolyn Brooks, 1978, The Art and Imagination of Langston Hughes, 1989 (Am. Book award 1991), (monograph) Southern Trace in Black Critical Theory: Redemption of Time, 1991; editor, contbr.: Black American Literature and Humanism, 1981, Black American Poets Between Worlds, 1940-60, 1986; co-editor: Call and Response in African American Literature, 1995; mem. editorial bd. Tenn. Studies in Lit., 1991-93, Black Fiction Project (Yale/Cornell/Duke), 1985—, U. Ga. Press, 1994—; contbr. numerous articles and revs. to profl. jours. Recipient Golden Key award Nat. Golden Key, 1990, 95, Alpha award for disting. svc. U. Ga.-Athens, 1993; Nat. Rsch. Coun. sr. fellow, 1986-87, NEH fellow, 1975, Ford Found. fellow, 1972-73, NDEA fellow, 1970-72; Lilly Sr. Teaching fellow U. Ga.-Athens, 1994; Nat. Fellowships Fund dissertation grantee, 1973-74, others. Mem. MLA (exec. com. Afro-Am. Lit. Discussion Group 1980-83, chair 1982-83, mem. del. assembly 1984-86, com. on langs. and lits. of Am. 1993—), Langston Hughes Soc. (pres. 1984-90). Office: U Ga Inst African Am Studies Athens GA 30602

MILLER, RONALD EUGENE, regional science educator; b. Seattle, Sept. 1, 1933; s. Eugene H. and Nellie A. (Myers) M. B.A., Harvard U., 1955; M.A., U. Wash., 1957; Ph.D., Princeton U., 1961. Asst. prof. regional sci. U. Pa., Phila., 1962-65; assoc. prof. U. Pa., 1965-71, prof., 1971—, chmn. dept., 1981-84. Author: Input-Output Analysis, 1985; Dynamic Optimization and Economic Applications, 1979; Modern Mathematical Methods for Economics and Business, 1972; also articles; editor Jour. Regional Sci., 1965—. Mem. Am. Econ. Assn., Regional Sci. Assn. Home: 137 Elfreths Aly Philadelphia PA 19106-2005 Office: U Pa Regional Sci Dept 3718 Locust Walk Philadelphia PA 19104-6209

MILLER, RONALD GRANT, journalist; b. Santa Cruz, Calif., Feb. 28, 1939; s. Fred Robert and Evelyn Lenora (Mosher) M.; m. Darla-Jean Irene Rode, Nov. 2, 1963. AA, Monterey Peninsula Coll., 1958; BA, San Jose State U., 1961. Reporter Santa Cruz (Calif.) Sentinel, 1959-62; reporter, chief news bur. San Jose (Calif.) Mercury News, 1962-77, editor T.V., 1977—; syndicated TV columnist Knight Ridder Syndicate, 1978—; commentator, critic Sta. KLOK, San Jose, 1981-83; panelist, guest speaker various orgns., 1978—; nat. judge Cablacce awards, 1987. Author: (forward) Les Brown's Encyclopedia of Television, 1992; contbr. articles, short fiction to various mags. Recipient Nat. Spot News Photo award Sigma Delta Chi, 1961, Outstanding Alumnus award San Jose State U. Dept. Journalism and Mass Comm., 1985, Nat. Headline award Press Club Atlantic City, 1994. Mem. TV Critics Assn. (nat. pres. 1981). Democrat. Home and Office: 1554 Arbor Ave Los Altos CA 94024

MILLER, RONALD M., manufacturing executive; b. Bklyn., Aug. 30, 1944; s. Samuel L. and Kitty M.; m. Carole J. Schaps, June 9, 1966; children: Elisa, Deborah. BSEE, Poly. Inst., Bklyn., 1966, MS in Ops. Rsch., 1969. Sr. electronic engr. Grumman Aerospace Corp., Bethpage, N.Y., 1966-72; dir. program mgmt. Gould Inc., Simulation Systems div., Melville, N.Y., 1972-81; v.p. ops. EMS Devel., Farmingdale, N.Y., 1981-85; pres., chief exec. officer Marks Polarized Corp., Deer Park, N.Y., 1985-89, also chmn. bd. dirs., 1985—; pres., chief exec. officer Marks Polarized Corp., Hauppauge, N.Y., 1989—; pres., chmn. bd. dirs. Upward Tech. Corp., 1989-92, sec., COO, bd. dirs., 1989—; pres. Image Analytics Corp., 1992—; adj. lectr. Hofstra U. Hempstead, N.Y., 1969-70; bus. cons. Aerospace Industry, Long Island, N.Y., 1978—. Sr. arbitrator Better Bus. Bur., Farmingdale, 1981—; arbitrator Am. Arbitration Assn., Garden City, N.Y., 1980—. Mem. L.I. Forum for Tech. (v.p., bd. dirs. 1987—), Navy League of U.S. (life), Am. Def. Preparedness Assn. (life). Avocations: amateur radio. Home: 38 Fairfield Dr Dix Hills NY 11746-7137 Office: Marks Polarized Corp 275 Marcus Blvd # D Hauppauge NY 11788-2022

MILLER, ROSS HAYS, retired neurosurgeon; b. Ada, Okla., Jan. 30, 1923; s. Harry and Helen (Rice) M.; m. Catherine Railey, May 2, 1943; children—Terry Hays, Helen Stacy. B.S., East Central State Coll., Ada, 1943; M.D., U. Okla., 1946; M.S. in Neurosurgery, U. Minn., 1952. Diplomate Am. Bd. Neurol. Surgery (chmn. exam. com. 1978-84). Intern St. Luke's Hosp., Cleve., 1946-47; fellow in neurosurgery Mayo Clinic, Rochester, Minn., 1950-54; instr. in neurosurgery Mayo Med. Sch., 1954-63, asst. prof. neurosurgery, 1963-73, asso. prof., 1973-75, prof., chmn. dept. neurosurgery, from 1975, now ret.; vis. prof. neurol. surgery Med. U. S.C., Med. Coll. Ga., Augusta. Contbr. numerous articles to med. publs. Trustee East Central State U. Found. Served as capt., M.C. U.S. Army, 1947-49, Korea. Named to Okla. Hall of Fame, 1977, Athletic Hall of Fame, East Central U. Okla. 1977; recipient Disting. Alumnus award East Central U. Okla., 1974, Mayo Found. Disting. Alumnus award, 1992. Mem. AMA, ACS, Am. Assn. Neurol. Surgeons (chmn. com. profl. practice 1976-79, dir. 1976-79, v.p. 1979, rep. to Council Med. Splty. Socs. 1980-84), Congress Neurol. Surgeons (exec. com. 1963-65), Minn. Soc. Neurol. Scis., Neurosurg. Soc. Am. (v.p. 1975), Soc. Neurol. Surgeons (v.p. 1983), Sigma Xi.

MILLER, RUSH GLENN, JR., university dean, librarian; b. Atlanta, Mar. 13, 1947; s. Rush Glenn and Gene (Ramsey) M.; m. Johnnye Mize, July 21, 1967; children: Lisa, Glenn, John, Edward. BA in History, Delta State Coll., Cleveland, Miss., 1969; MA in History, Miss. State U., 1971, PhD in medieval History, 1973; MLS, Fla. State U., 1974. Asst. prof. U. Miss., Oxford, 1974-75; dir. libr. svcs. Delta State U., 1975-82; dir. libr. Sam Houston State U., Huntsville, Tex., 1982-86; dean librs. Bowling Green (Ohio) State U., 1986-94; dir. univ. libr. sys. U. Pitts., 1994—; del. White House Conf. on Librs., Washington, 1979; del. to users coun. Online Computer Libr. Ctr., Inc., Dublin, Ohio, 1992-94. Contbg. author: Diversity and Multiculturalism in Libraries, 1994, also others; editor Miss. Librs., 1982-84; contbr. articles to profl. jours. Recipient Past President's award Miss. Libr. Assn., 1976. Mem. ALA (various coms. 1976—), Southeastern Libr. Assn. (exec. bd. 1976-82), Acad. Libr. Assn. Ohio. Democrat. Methodist. Avocations: golf, reading. Office: U Pitts Hillman Libr Pittsburgh PA 15260

MILLER, SAM SCOTT, lawyer; b. Ft. Worth, July 26, 1938; s. Percy Vernon and Mildred Lois (MacDowell) M.; m. Mary Harrison FitzHugh, May 10, 1969. BA, Mich. State U., 1960; JD, Tulane U., 1964; LLM, Yale U., 1965. Bar: La. 1965, N.Y. 1966, Minn. 1969. Assoc. Simpson Thacher & Bartlett, N.Y.C., 1965-68; sr. counsel Investors Diversified Services, Mpls., 1968-73; ptnr. Ireland Gibson Reams & Miller, Memphis, 1973-74; gen. counsel Paine Webber Group, Inc., N.Y.C., 1974-87, sr. v.p., 1976-87; ptnr. Orrick, Herrington & Sutcliffe, N.Y.C., 1987—; adj. prof. NYU Law Sch., 1986-90; vis. lectr. Yale Law Sch., 1980-85, Inst. for Internat. Econs. and Trade, Wuhan, China, 1983, U. Calif., 1986; mem. dean's coun. Tulane U. Law Sch., 1979—; trustee Omni Mut., Inc., 1988—; ombudsman Kidder Peabody Group, 1988—; ombudsman Kidder Peabody Group, 1988—, Charles Schwab & Co., 1991—, Gruntal & Co., 1995—. Contbr. articles to profl. jours.; editor-in-chief: Tulane Law Rev, 1964-65; bd. editors Securities Regulation Law Jour., 1982—. Bd. dirs. Guthrie Theatre Found., Mpls., 1971-74; bd. dirs. Minn. Opera Co., 1971-74, Yale U. Law Sch. Fund., 1981—; bd. govs. Investment Co. Inst., 1980-87. Mem. ABA (chmn. subcom. market regulation 1985-93), Assn. Bar City N.Y. (treas. and mem. exec. com. 1994—, chmn. broker-dealer investment co. and regulations subcom. 1982-83), Internat. Bar Assn., Securities Industry Assn. (chmn. fed. regulation com. 1976-78), Down Town Assn., Knickerbocker Club, Order of Coif, Omicron Delta Kappa. Democrat. Baptist. Office: Orrick Herrington et al 599 Lexington Ave New York NY 10022-6030

MILLER, SAMUEL MARTIN, apparel company finance executive; b. N.Y.C., Jan. 31, 1938; s. Irving Nathaniel and Estelle (Furman) M.; m. Kay Shapiro, Dec. 23, 1963; children: Jennifer, Suzanne. BBA magna cum laude, CCNY, 1964. With Coopers & Lybrand, N.Y.C., 1964-72; supervising sr. acct. Coopers & Lybrand, 1968-69, audit mgr., 1969-72; corp. controller Manhattan Industries, Inc., Glen Rock, N.J., 1972-74; v.p., corp. controller Manhattan Industries, Inc., 1974-76, v.p., treas., controller, 1976-83, v.p., sec.-treas., controller, 1983-88; sr. v.p. fin., CFO, mem. policy com. Liz Claiborne Inc., North Bergen, N.J., 1988—. Served with USN, 1957-59. Recipient Haskin's award N.Y. State Uniform C.P.A. Exam. Mem. AICPA, Am. Arbitration Assn., Am. Apparel Mfrs. Assn. (chmn. fin. mgmt. com.), Fin. Execs. Inst. (CFO adv. com.), Nat. Assn. Accts., N.Y. State Soc. CPAs (chief fin. officer com.), Beta Gamma Sigma, Beta Alpha Psi. Office: Liz Claiborne Inc One Claiborne Ave North Bergen NJ 07047

MILLER, SARAH PEARL, librarian; b. Wilkensburg, Pa., Aug. 31, 1938; d. Samuel Henry and Anna Deborah (Shirley) Lyons; m. Paul Victor Miller, Apr. 15, 1989; children: Cheryl, Michael, Daniel, Lorel. BS, Indiana U. of Pa., 1960; MREM, Denver Conservative Bapt. Sem., 1965; MA, U. Denver, 1966. Libr. Denver Conservative Bapt. Sem., 1966—. Mem. Am. Theol. Libr. Assn. (bd. dirs. 1978-81, 90-91, index bd. 1983-90). Home: 15707 E Grand Ave Aurora CO 80015-1708 Office: Denver Conservative Bapt Sem Carey S Thomas Libr PO Box 10000 PO Box 10000 Denver CO 90250-0100

MILLER, SHELDON IRVIN, psychiatrist, educator; b. Cleve., June 29, 1938; s. Edward A. and Evelyn Miller; m. Sarah Johnston, June 18, 1961; children: Lynn, David. AB, Oberlin Coll., 1960; MD, Tufts U., 1964. Diplomate Am. Bd. Psychiatry and Neurology. Clin. prof. psychiatry U. Calif., Irvine, 1982-84; dir. acute inpatient svc. Sheppard & Enoch Pratt Hosp., Towson, Md., 1983-86; clin. prof. psychiatry U. Md., Balt., 1984-86; chief of svc. psychiatry U. Medicine and Dentistry-N.J.-Univ. Hosp., Newark, 1986-91; chmn. psychiatry St. Barnabas Med. Ctr., Livingston, N.J., 1987-91; prof., chmn. psychiatry U. Medicine and Dentistry-N.J., Newark, 1986-81; dir. Stone Inst. Psychiatry Northwestern Meml. Hosp., Chgo., 1991—; program reviewer Residency Rev. Com., Chgo. Editor: Clinical Text Addictive Disorders, 1991, (jour.) Am. Jour. Addictions, 1990—; contbr. articles to sci. and psychiat. jours. Bd. dirs. Mental Health Assn., Ill., 1992—; advisor Abraham Low Inst., Ill., 1992—; pres., bd. trustees Essex County Nat. Coun. Alcoholism, N.J. 1990-91. Lt. comdr. USPHS, 1968-70. Alcohol dependence grantee NIMH, 1990; fetal alcohol syndrome grantee Nat. Inst. on Alcohol Abuse and Alcoholism, 1983. Fellow ACP, Am. Psychiat. Assn. (com. mem. practice guidelines com.); mem. The Am. Acad. of Psychiatry on Alcohol and Addictions (exec. com., pres. 1987-89), Assn. Acad. Psychiatrists, Rsch. Soc. on Alcoholism, Am. Acad. Psychiat. Assn. Chairs. Depts. of Psychiatry, Am. Bd. Psychiatry & Neurology (bd. dirs. 1991—), Sigma Xi. Avocations: photography, biking, hiking. Office: Northwestern U Med Sch 303 E Superior #561 Chicago IL 60611

MILLER, STANFORD, reinsurance exeutive, arbitrator, lawyer; b. Kansas City, Mo., Nov. 15, 1913; s. Hugh and Gertrude Anna (Kraft) M.; m. Gloria Goble, July 11, 1942 (div. 1958); 1 child, Hans Hugh; m. Beverly Breuer, Apr. 19, 1962; 1 son, Bradford Channing. B.A., U. Kans., 1934; J.D., U. Chgo., 1938. Bar: Mo. 1938. lectr. in field. Author: (with Robert D. Brown) Health Insurance Underwriting, 1962; also articles. Bd. dirs. Kansas City, Boy Scouts Am., Community Living Opportunities; trustee emeritus U. Kansas City. Mem. Mo. Bar Assn., Reins. Assn. Am. (past chmn.), Health Ins. Assn. Am. (former sec., dir.), Am. Humanics Assn. (trustee), Am. Arbitration Assn. (panel of arbitrators), Phi Alpha Delta, Alpha Tau Omega. Clubs: Rotary, Profl. Men's, Mission Hills Country. Home: 2709 Tomahawk Rd Shawnee Mission KS 66208-1827 Office: 6700 Antioch Ste 400 Merriam KS 66204

MILLER, STANLEY CUSTER, JR., physicist, retired educator; b. Kansas City, Mo., July 30, 1926; s. Stanley Custer and Verda (Storer) M.; m. Elene G. Josephson, Nov. 27, 1957 (dec.); children: Gloria Diane, James Kenneth, Richard Eric (dec.). BS in Engring. Physics, U. Colo., 1948; PhD in Physics, U. Calif. at Berkeley, 1953. Mem. faculty U. Colo., Boulder, 1953-90; prof. physics U. Colo., 1961-90. Author: Principles of Physics, 2 vols, 1966, Irreducible Representations of Space Groups, 1967, Principles of Modern Physics, 1970, Kronecker Product Tables, 1979. Served with USNR, 1944-46. Mem. Am. Phys. Soc. Home: 2570 S Dayton Way Apt 306A Denver CO 80231-3975

MILLER, STEPHANIE LEE, federal agency administrator; b. Los Angeles, Mar. 7, 1950; d. Robert Wilson and Estella Elizabeth (Halle) Lee; m. Phillip Van Miller, June 13, 1976 (div. Oct. 1981). B.A., Calif. State U.-Dominquez Hills, 1971; M.A., Occidental Coll., 1975. Cons. Coro Found., Los Angeles, 1973-77; fundraiser Legal Def. Fund NAACP, Los Angeles, 1978-79; owner, mgr. Contact Calif., Beverly Hills, 1979-81; spl. asst. Dept. Commerce, Washington, 1981-83; asst. sec. pub. affairs HHS, Washington, 1983-89; dir. Office Comml. Space Transp. Dept. Transportation, Washington, 1989—; mem. U.S. del. to Internat. Women's Conf., Nairobi, Kenya,

1985, UN Commn. on Status of Women, 1987. Vice chmn. community and govt. affairs council United Way, Los Angeles. Mem. Los Angeles C. of C. (bd. dirs. women's div.). Nat. Council Negro Women, Delta Sigma Theta. Republican. Home: 116 G St SW Washington DC 20024-4303 Office: Dept Transp 400 7th St SW Washington DC 20590-0001

MILLER, STEPHEN RALPH, lawyer; b. Chgo., Nov. 28, 1950; s. Ralph and Karin Ann (Olson) M.; children: David Williams, Lindsay Christine. BA cum laude, Yale U., 1972; JD, Cornell U. 1975. Bar: Ill. Assoc. McDermott, Will & Emery, Chgo., 1975-80, income ptnr., 1981-85, equity ptnr., 1986—, mgmt. com. mem., 1992-95; mem. spl. task force on pre-employment benefits Fin. Acctg. Standards Bd., Norwalk, Conn., 1987-91. Contbr. articles to profl. jours. Mem. Chgo. Coun. on Fgn. Rels., 1978—; trustee police pension bd., Wilmette, Ill., 1992—; bd. trustees Seabury Western Theol. Sem., Evanston, Ill. Mem. ABA, Ill. Bar Assn., Chgo. Bar Assn., Midwest Benefits Coun., Yale Club Chgo., Mich. Shores Club, Chgo. Athletic Assn., Hundred Club Cook County, Legal Club of Chgo. Avocations: sailing, water skiing, cross-country skiing. Office: McDermott Will & Emery 227 W Monroe St Ste 3100 Chicago IL 60606-5096

MILLER, STEVE, television director, producer; b. L.A., Sept. 13, 1951; s. Nathan H. and Shirley Ann (Watstein) M.; m. Lee Keiter, June 22, 1975; children: Jeffrey, Brian, David. BA in Telecommunications, U. So. Calif. 1973. Producer, dir. TV program: The Love Report, Eye on Hollywood, Entertainment Tonight, Christmas Eve at the Music Ctr., Dads, The Car Man, Together with Shirley and Pat Boone, Summer Faire, The Voyager Spacecraft Meets Saturn; dir. home videos Shape Up with Arnold Schwarzenegger, Mickey, Donald, Goofy & Friends, How to Use Your IBM PC; dir., producer commls. and corp. videos; contbr. articles to profl. jours. Mem. Dirs. Guild Am., Acad. TV, Arts and Scis.

MILLER, STEVEN H., museum dicetor; b. Phila., 1947; m. Jane McClure Pelson; children: Andrew Steven, Katherine Ann. BA, Bard Coll., 1970; cert. in conservation sci., Internat. Ctr. for Study of Preservation and Restoration of Cultural Property, Rome, 1978. Asst. to sr. curator Mus. of City of N.Y., N.Y.C., 1971-72, asst. curator paintings, prints and photographs, 1973-77, curator prints and photographs, 1977-79, curator, dept. head fine art collections, history and spl. collections, 1979-85, sr. curator, 1985-87; asst. dir. Maine State Mus., 1987-91; dir. of mus. Western Res. Hist. Soc., Cleve., 1991-95; exec. dir. The Bennington (Vt.) Mus., 1995—; adj. prof. mus. studies Case Western Res. U.; lectr. NYU, 1978-87, Columbia U., N.Y.C., 1981, 82, New Sch. for Social Rsch., N.Y.C., 1978, 83, Maine State Mus., 1987-91. Contbr. articles to profl. jours. Bd. govs. Bard-St. Stephen's Alumni Assn.; mem. fellowship gift com. Hist. Deerfield, Mass.; mem. landmarks preservation com. Shaker Heights, Ohio; former mem. hist. preservation com. City of Gardiner, Main, former mem. hist. preservation commn.; former mem. adv. com. Blaine House Restoration, Maine; former mem. art adv. com. Gracie Mansion Conservancy, N.Y.C.; former mem. adv. coun. Mus. Moving Image, Astoria, N.Y. Mem. Am. Assn. Mus. (mem. mus. advocacy team, mem. mus. accreditation vis. com.), Maine Assn. Mus. (co-founder, charter coun. mem.), Nat. Arts Club. Home: 5 Apple Tree Ln Bennington VT 05201*

MILLER, STEVEN MAX, humanities educator; b. Portland, Ind., Feb. 9, 1950; s. J. Max and Belva Kathryn (Kitty Booher) M.; m. Fran Felice Koski, May 30, 1985 (div. Aug. 7, 1992). BA in Eng., Coll. of William and Mary, 1972; MA in English Lang. and Lit., Ind. U., 1975, PhD in English Lang. and Lit., 1985. Sr. libr. asst. cataloger rare books and spl. collections Lilly Libr., Bloomington, Ind., 1972-76; assoc. instr. English Ind. U., Bloomington, 1975-82; asst. prof. English Millersville (Pa.) U., 1985-94; assoc. prof. English Millersville (Pa.) U., 1994—; faculty sponsor Iota Phi chpt. Sigma Tau Delta Millersville (Pa.) U., 1986—; asst. prof. English Murray (Ky.) State U., 1989-90; cons. women writers project Brown U., Providence, 1990—; reader nat. teaching exam. Ednl. Testing Svc., Princeton, N.J., 1990-92. Contbr. articles to profl. jours. Grantee NEH, 1991, 92. Mem. MLA, John Donne Soc. Am., Spenser Soc., English Assn. Pa. State Univs. (nominating com. 1987), Bibliog. Soc. Am. Episcopalian. Avocations: gardening, marbling paper. Office: Millersville U Dept English Chryst Bldg Millersville PA 17551

MILLER, SUSAN HEILMANN, publishing executive; b. Yuba City, Calif., Jan. 13, 1945; d. Paul Clay and Helen Christine (Sterud) Heilmann; m. Allen Clinton Miller III, June 24, 1967. BA, Stanford U., 1966; MS, Columbia U., 1969; PhD, Stanford U., 1976. Info. officer Montgomery County Schs. Rockville, Md., 1970-71, Palo Alto Schs., Calif., 1969-70, 71-73; news-features editor Bremerton Sun, Wash., 1976-80; night city editor Peninsula Times Tribune, Palo Alto, 1980-81; exec. editor News-Gazette, Champaign, Ill., 1981-85; dir. editorial devel. Scripps Howard Newspapers, Cin., 1985-90, v.p. editorial, 1990-93; pres., editor The Monterey (Calif.) County Herald, 1993—. Contbr. articles to profl. jours. Bd. dirs. Vol. Illini Projects, U. Ill., 1983-85, Washington Journalism Ctr., 1985-90, New Directions for News, 1988-91; mem. Pulitzer Prize Nominating Jury, 1986-87, accrediting com. Accrediting Council on Journalism and Mass Communication, 1986-89. Mem. Am. Soc. Newspaper Editors (bd. dirs. 1985-92), Newspaper Assn. Am., Nat. Press Found. (assoc.), Internat. Newspaper Fedn. Newspaper Pub. (mem. newspaper mktg. bureau), Assoc. Press Mng. Editors (bd. dirs.1984-91), Ill. AP Mng. Editors (bd. dirs. 1984-85). Clubs: Executive (Champaign, Ill.) (bd. dirs. 1984-85). Office: PO Box 271 8 Upper Ragsdale Dr Monterey CA 93940-0271

MILLER, SYDELL LOIS, cosmetics executive, marketing professional; b. Cleve., Aug. 10, 1937; d. Jack Harvey Lubin and Evelyne (Saltzman) Brower; m. Arnold Max Miller, Oct. 19, 1958; children: Lauren Beth, Stacie Lynn. Student, U. Miami, 1955-56. Mgr. Hair Salon, Cleve., 1958-60; pres., owner Women's Retail Store, Cleve., 1960-72; exec. v.p. Ardell, Inc., Solon, Ohio, 1972-84; exec. v.p. and owner Matrix Essentials, Inc., Solon, 1980—; pres. Lauren Stacy Mktg., Inc., Solon, 1972—. Editor ednl. books and newsletter, Salons 1981—. Mem. Mt. Sinai Hosp. Aux., Cleve., 1972—, Beachwood (Ohio) Mus., 1981—, Cleve. Fashion Group. Mem. Am. Beauty Assns. (bd. dirs. 1988—, named Woman of Yr. 1985), Beauty and Barber Supply Inst., Inc., Cosmetic, Toiletry and Fragrance Assn., Inc., Spirit of Life (hon.), City of Hope. Avocations: collecting art and antiques, interior design, reading. Office: Matrix Essentials Inc 30601 Carter St Cleveland OH 44139

MILLER, TERRY ALAN, chemistry educator; b. Girard, Kans. Dec. 18, 1943; s. Dwight D. Miller and Rachel E. (Detjen) Beltram; m. Barbara Hoffmann, July 16, 1966; children: Brian, Stuart. BA, U. Kans., 1965; PhD, Cambridge (Eng.) U., 1968. Disting. tech. staff Bell Telephone Labs, 1968-84; vis. asst. prof. Princeton U., 1968-71; vis. lectr. Stanford U., 1972; vis. fgn. scholar Inst. Molecular Sci., Okazaki, Japan, summer 1983; Ohio eminent scholar, prof. chemistry Ohio State U., Columbus, 1984—; chair Molecular Spectroscopy Symposium, Columbus, 1992—. Mem. editl. bd. Jour. Chem. Physics, 1978-81, Jour. Molecular Spectroscopy, 1982-87, Laser Chemistry, 1986—, Rev. of Sci. Instruments, 1986-89, Jour. Phys. Chemistry, 1989—, Jour. Optical Soc. Am., 1989-95, Chemtracts, 1989-90, Ann. Revs. Phys. Chemistry, 1989-94; contbr. more than 245 articles to profl. jours. Marshall fellow Brit. Govt., 1965-67, NSF fellow, 1967-68; William F. Meggard Awd., 1993, Optical Soc. Am. Fellow Optical Soc. Am. (Meggars award 1993), Coblentz Soc. (Bomem-Michaelson award 1995), Am. Phys. Soc.; mem Am. Chem. Soc. (councilor). Office: Ohio State U 120 W 18th Ave Columbus OH 43210-1106

MILLER, TERRY MORROW, lawyer; b. Columbus, Ohio, Mar. 11, 1947; s. Robert E. and Elizabeth Jane (Morrow) M.; m. Martha Estella Johnson, Mar. 20, 1976; 1 child, Timothy. BS, Ohio State U., 1969, JD, 1975. Bar: Ohio 1975, U.S. Ct. Appeals (6th cir.) 1979, U.S. Supreme Ct. 1980. Asst. atty. gen. State of Ohio, Columbus, 1975-77; ptnr. Miller & Noga, Columbus, 1977-81; assoc. Vorys, Sater, Seymour and Pease, Columbus, 1981-85; ptnr. Vorys, Sater, Seymour & Pease, Columbus, 1986—. Sgt. U.S. Army, 1969-71, Okinawa. Mem. Ohio State Bar Assn., Columbus Bar Assn. Avocations: golf, Ohio history. Home: 288 E North Broadway Columbus OH 43214-4114 Office: Vorys Sater Seymour et al PO Box 1008 52 E Gay St Columbus OH 43215-3161

MILLER, TEVIE, supernumary justice, academic administrator; b. Edmonton, Alta., Can., Jan. 1, 1928; s. Abe William and Rebecca (Griesdorf) M.; m. Arliss June Toban, June 24, 1951; children: Catherine Dolgoy, Joshua Miller, Lisa Shadlyn. BA, U. Alta., 1949, LLB, 1950, LLD (hon.), 1991; LLD (hon.), U. Alta., 1991. Bar: Alta. 1951. Sr. ptnr. Miller, Miller, Witten, Edmonton, 1974; judge Alta. Dist. Ct., 1974; dep. judge N.W. territories, 1976; appointed to trial div. Supreme Ct. Alta., 1976; dep. judge Yukon territory, 1978; judge Ct. of Queen's Bench of Alta., 1974-84, assoc. chief justice, 1984-93; chancellor U. Alta., Edmonton, 1986-90; sessional lectr. law U. Alta., bd. govs., 1986-90; chmn. bd. Banff (Alta.) Sch. Advanced Mgmt., 1982-92. Former pres., former conv. chmn. Edmonton Liberal Assn.; liberal candidate Edmonton West Fed. Riding, 1968. Served to sub-lt. Royal Can. Navy. Recipient Torch of Learning award Hebrew U. of Jerusalem, 1992; honoree Edmonton Jewish Community Negev Dinner, 1972, Faculty Club of U. Alta. Avocations: sailing, travel. Office: Law Cts Bldg 6th Floor, 1A Sir Winston Churchill Sq, Edmonton, AB Canada T5J 0R2

MILLER, THEODORE NORMAN, lawyer; b. Chgo., Oct. 9, 1942; s. Alexander Hyman and Bertha Helen (Swidler) M.; m. Marylyn Sue Zax, June 21, 1964; children—Henry, Amy. B.A., U. Mich., 1964; LL.B., Yale U., 1967. Bar: Ill. 1967, U.S. Dist. Ct. (no. dist.) Ill. 1967, U.S. Ct. Appeals (7th cir.) 1968, U.S. Supreme Ct. 1972. Law clk. U.S. Ct. Appeals (7th cir.), 1967-68; assoc. Sidley & Austin, Chgo., 1968-73, ptnr., 1973—. Mem. ABA, Chgo. Bar Assn., Chgo. Council Lawyers. Office: Sidley & Austin 1 First Nat Plz Chicago IL 60603

MILLER, THEODORE ROBERT, surgeon, educator; b. Phila., Mar. 13, 1907; s. Robert and Regina (Ramspacher) M.; m. Helen E. Reiser, July 31, 1934. Student, Swarthmore Coll., Yale, Stockholm U.; MD, Temple U., 1933. Diplomate Am. Bd. Surgery. Intern Hackensack (N.J.) Hosp., 1933-34, resident, 1934-36, asst. attending surgeon, chief tumor clinic, 1936-39, adj. cons. neoplastic diseases, 1947-52, cons. in surgery, 1959—; asst. attending surgeon City Hosp., N.Y.C.; asst. resident, fellow Meml. Hosp., N.Y.C., 1939-42; clin. asst. surgeon gastric and mixed tumor services Meml. Hosp., 1947-49, asst. attending surgeon, gastric and mixed tumor services, 1949-59, asso. attending surgeon, 1959-64, attending surgeon chief bone tumor service, 1964-74, sr. attending surgeon, 1974-77, emeritus surgeon, 1977—, chief spl. surgery service, 1964-70; fellow Am.-Scandinavian Found., 1946-47; asso. surgeon Pack Med. Group, N.Y.C., 1947-69, asso. radiotherapist, 1947-69; instr. in surgery Cornell U. Med. Coll., 1952-62, clin. asst. prof., 1962-64, clin. asso. prof. surgery, 1964-70, clin. prof. surgery, 1970-78, emeritus clin. prof. surgery, 1978—; clin. prof. surgery Rutgers U. Med. Coll.; courtesy staff N.Y. Infirmary-Beekman Downtown, Princeton Med. Ctr. Contbr. articles to profl. publs. Served from capt. to lt. col. M.C. AUS, 1942-46. Fellow ACS, AMA, AAAS, N.Y. Acad. Medicine; mem. N.Y. State, County N.J. State, Middlesex County med. socs., Am. Radium Soc. (pres. 1959-60), N.Y. Cancer Soc., Del. Valley Orthol. Club, N.Y. Surg. Soc., James Ewing Soc. (pres. 1967-68), N.Y. Acad. Scis., Academia Peruana de Cirguia (corr.), Sociedad Venezolana de Cirugia (corr.), Academia de Zulia (Venezuela) (corr.), Yale Club (N.Y.C. and Princeton), Phi Sigma Kappa. Home: 3-311 David Brainerd Dr Jamesburg NJ 08831

MILLER, THERESA ANN, management consultant; b. St. Charles, Mo., Apr. 1, 1945; d. Ford Emmett Wilkins and Alice Mary (Farmer) Wilkins Burrow. Cert. secretarial, N.E. Mo. State Tchrs Coll., 1964; AA, St. Louis Community Coll., 1976; BSBA, Lindenwood Coll., 1983, MBA, 1990; MBA Cert. Internat. Bus., 1991. With McDonnell Douglas Aerospace-East, St. Louis, 1985—, supr. master files dept., 1984—, sect. mgr. office svcs., 1987—, auditor self-governance audit program, 1991—, sr. analyst command media, 1993-94, 1994—. Mem. NAFE, Nat. Notary Assn., Lindenwood Coll. Alumni Club (past pres. St. Charles chpt.), Mgmt. Club McDonnell Douglas Aerospace. Roman Catholic. Avocations: snow skiing, scuba diving, boating, cooking, golfing. Home: 15618 Coventry Farm Dr Chesterfield MO 63017-7386 Office: McDonnell Douglas Aerospace PO Box 516 Saint Louis MO 63166-0516

MILLER, THOMAS HULBERT, JR., former marine corps officer; b. San Antonio, June 3, 1923; s. Thomas Hulbert and Dora S. (Bartlett) M.; m. Ida Mai Giddings, May 11, 1943; children: Jacqueline Mai, Jo Ann. Student, U. Tex. Lic. comml. single and multi-engine pilot; lic. flight instr. Commd. 2d lt. USMC, 1943, designated naval aviator, 1943, advanced through grades to lt. gen., 1975; service in Pacific, Korea; chief staff 3d Amphibious Force Vietnam, 1970; comdg. gen. 2d Marine Aircraft Wing, 1972; dep. comdr., later comdg. gen. Fleet Marine Forces Pacific, 1975; dep. chief staff aviation Hdqrs. USMC, 1975-79, ret., 1979; cons. Applied Physics Lab., Johns Hopkins U., Nat. Acad. Sci., Def. Sci. Bd.; mem. FAA Blue Ribbon Panel on Civil Pilot and Maintenance Pers. Availability. Chmn. joint bd. U.S. Space Camp and Mercury Seven Found.; chmn. exec. bd. Mercury Seven Found.; mem. exec. bd. Washington Airports Task Force, Air & Space Heritage Coun. Decorated D.S.M., Legion of Merit (2), D.F.C. (4), Air medal (15), Navy Commendation medal; recipient Grey Eagle award; Silver Hawk award; Am./Brit. John Curtis Wilkinson Sword award for Anglo/Am. aerospace contbn.; Paul E. Haueter award Am. Helicopter Soc.; named one of Va.'s Pioneers of Aviation. Mem. Soc. Exptl. Test Pilots, Marine Corps Aviation Assn., Assn. Naval Aviation, Naval Aviation Mus. Found., Daedalians, Golden Eagles, Am. Radio Relay League, Masons. President-ian. Holder 500 kilometer closed course world speed record F4H-1 Phantom II aircraft, 1960; first American to fly British Harrier aircraft, 1968. Home: 3689 N Harrison St Arlington VA 22207-1843 *I believe a balanced life must include equal emphasis on moral, professional (work) and recreational activity. This activity must be guided by a strong Christian faith, moral and professional integrity, loyalty and a humble recognition of others rights. And, although we all are imperfect, we should strive to achieve perfection in these characteristics and never accept or receive those things that we do not work for.*

MILLER, THOMAS J., state attorney general; b. Dubuque, Iowa, Aug. 11, 1944; s. Elmer John and Betty Maude (Kross) M.; m. Linda Cottington, Jan. 10, 1981; 1 child, Matthew. B.A., Loras Coll., Dubuque, 1966; J.D., Harvard U., 1969. Bar: Iowa bar 1969. With VISTA, Balt., 1969-70; legis. asst. to U.S. Congressman P.G. Culver, 1970-71; legal edn. dir. Balt. Legal Aid Bur., also mem. part-time faculty U. Md. Sch. Law, 1971-73; pvt. practice McGregor, Iowa, 1973-78; city atty. McGregor, 1975-78, Marquette, Iowa; atty. gen. of Iowa, 1979-91, 95—; ptnr. Faegre & Benson, Des Moines, 1991-95. Pres. 2d Dist. New Democratic Club, Balt., 1972. Mem. Am. Bar Assn., Iowa Bar Assn., Common Cause. Roman Catholic. Office: Office of the Atty Gen Hoover State Office Bldg Des Moines IA 50309*

MILLER, THOMAS L., insurance company executive. Pres., ceo, Blue Cross Blue Shield of Kans., Topeka, 1983—. Office: Blue Cross Blue Shield of Kans 1133 SW Topeka Blvd Topeka KS 66629-0002

MILLER, THOMAS MARSHALL, air transportation executive; b. Mineral Wells, Tex., Oct. 19, 1910; s. Van Dorn and Ida (Crockett) M.; m. Edith Mae Blake, July 8, 1936; children: Kay (Mrs. Robert Amick), Thomas Marshall, Robert, Philp, James. LL.B., Houston Law Sch., 1935. Office mgr. Dun & Bradstreet, Inc., Houston, 1936-42; v.p. traffic and sales Chgo. & So. Air Lines, Inc., Memphis, 1942-53; sr. v.p. mktg., dir. Delta Air Lines, Inc., Atlanta, 1973-87, advis. cons., 1973-91, adv., 1973-95; advr. dir., 1995—. Pres. Air Traffic Conf. Am., 1964. Mem. Am., Ga. bar assns., Inst. Cert. Travel Agts. (vice chmn. emeritus). Republican. Episcopalian. Home: One Yonah Dr NE Atlanta GA 30309

MILLER, THOMAS ROBBINS, lawyer, publisher; b. Chgo., Mar. 8, 1938; s. William Whipple and Helen (Robbins) M.; m. Tran Tuong Nhu, July 3, 1974; children: Toby, Teddy, Nathalie, Gabriella. BA, Yale U., 1960; LLB, Stanford U., 1965; cert., Parker Sch. Fgn. and Comparative Law, Columbia U., 1966. Bar: N.Y. 1966, Calif. 1974. Assoc. Webster & Sheffield, N.Y.C., 1965-68; sole practice N.Y.C., 1968-74, Berkeley, 1974-89; pub. Laseract Miller Pubs., Berkeley, 1974-89; sr. ptnr. Thomas R. Miller, A Profl. Law Corp., Oakland, Calif., 1989—; founder, pres. Internat. Children's Fund, Berkeley, 1974—; cons. Peace Corps, Washington, 1961, Ctr. for Constl. Rights, UNICEF, N.Y.C., 1973-76; dep. dir. Calif. Rural Legal Assistance, San Francisco, 1977-79. Named 1 of 10 Outstanding Young Men in U.S.,

U.S. Jaycees, 1974. Democrat. Office: 725 Washington St Oakland CA 94607-3924

MILLER, THOMAS WILLIAMS, former university dean; b. Pottstown, Pa., July 2, 1930; s. Franklin Sullivan and Margaret (Williams) M.; m. Edythe Edwards, Dec. 20, 1952; children: Theresa, Thomas, Christine, Stefanie. B.S. in Music Edn, West Chester (Pa.) State Coll., 1952; M.A., East Carolina U., Greenville, N.C., 1957; Mus.A.D. (Univ. fellow), Boston U., 1964. Dir. instrumental music Susquenita (Pa.) High Sch., 1955-56; instr. trumpet East Carolina U., 1957-61; asst. dean East Carolina U. (Sch. Music), 1962-68, dean, 1969-71; vis. prof. U. Hawaii, Honolulu, 1968; dean Sch. Music Northwestern U., Evanston, Ill., 1971-89. Contbr. articles to profl. jours. Assoc. Nat. Arts, 1989. Served with AUS, 1952-55. Named Distinguished Alumnus West Chester State Coll., 1975. Mem. Nat. Arts Assn., Music Educators Nat. Conf. (life), Nat. Assn. Schs. Music (hon. life, grad. commr. 1974-79, v.p. 1979-82, pres. 1982-85, chmn. grad. com. 1985-86, bd. dirs. 1986-89), Coll. Music Soc., Pi Kappa Lambda (nat. pres. 1976-79), Phi Mu Alpha Sinfonia (hon. mem., Orpheus award 1989), Sigma Alpha Iota. Home: 3121 Walden Ln Wilmette IL 60091-1139 Office: Sch of Music Northwestern U Evanston IL 60208

MILLER, THORMUND AUBREY, lawyer; b. Pocatello, Idaho, July 14, 1919; s. Roy Edmund and Lillian (Thordarson) M.; m. Hannah A. Flansburgh, Feb. 10, 1946; children: Karen Lynette Van Gerpen, Christine Alison Westall. BA, Reed Coll., 1941; LLB, Columbia U., 1948; grad., Advanced Mgmt. Program, Harvard Bus. Sch., 1961. Bar: Calif. 1949, D.C. 1951, U.S. Supreme Ct. 1960. Assoc. McCutchen, Thomas, Matthews, Griffiths & Greene, San Francisco, 1948-50; atty. So. Pacific Transp. Co., Washington, 1950-56; asst. gen. atty. So. Pacific Transp. Co., 1956-59, gen. atty., 1959-66; sr. gen. atty. So. Pacific Transp. Co., San Francisco, 1966-75, gen. solicitor, 1975-79, gen. commerce counsel, 1979-83, dir., mem. exec. com., 1983-87, v.p., gen. counsel, 1983-89; gen. counsel So. Pacific Communications Co., San Francisco, 1970-79, dir., 1970-81; pvt. practice law Atherton, Calif., 1989—. Pres. Wood Acres Citizens Assn., Bethesda, Md., 1955-56; mem. exec. com. Holbrook Palmer Recreation Park Found., 1979—, pres. 1982-84; bd. dirs. Atherton Civic Interest League, 1981—, pres. 1992-94; mem. Atherton Park and Recreation Commn., 1991-95; mem. alumni bd. Reed Coll., 1971-72, trustee, 1987—; bd. dirs. Assocs. of U. Calif. Press, 1994—. Mem. ABA, Calif. Bar Assn., Assn. Transp. Law, Logistics and Policy, World Trade Club. Presbyterian.

MILLER, TIMOTHY ALDEN, plastic and reconstructive surgeon; b. Inglewood, Calif., Dec. 11, 1938; s. Henry Bernard and Florence Algena (Maddock) M.; 1 child, Matthew Christopher. Student, U. Calif., Berkeley; MD, UCLA, 1963. Diplomate Am. Bd. Surgery, Am. Bd. Plastic Surgery (bd. dirs. 1991—). Intern Vanderbilt U. Hosp., Nashville, 1963-64; resident in surgery, dept. surg. pathology UCLA, 1966-67, resident, then chief resident gen. and thoracics sugery, 1967-69, acting asst. prof., 1969-70, prof. surgery, 1981—; asst. surg. resident John Hopkins Hosp., 1967; fellow plastic and reconstructive surgery U. Pitts., 1970-72; chief plastic surgery West L.A. VA Med. Ctr., 1973—; dir. Am. Bd. Plastic Surgery, 1991—. Author: (novel) Practice to Deceive, 1991; assoc. editor Jour. Plastic & Reconstructive Surgery, 1987-93, co-editor, 1994—. Trustee Children's Inst. Internat., 1995—. Capt. U.S. Army, 1964-66, Vietnam. Decorated Bronze Star; recipient Thomas Symington award Pitts. Acad. Medicine, 1971. Mem. Am. Soc. for Plastic Surgery (chmn. jud. coun. 1991—), Am. Soc. for Aesthetic Plastic Surgery (bd. dirs. 1990-92), Plastic Surgery Ednl. Found. (bd. dirs. 1991—). Avocations: tennis, novel writing. Office: UCLA Med Ctr 200 Medical Plz Ste 669 Los Angeles CA 90095-6960

MILLER, TOM POLK, retired architect; b. Houston, Nov. 17, 1914; s. Enoch Lester and Willie Elvie (Chumley) M.; m. Isabel Mount, Aug. 10, 1947; children: Crispin Mount, Abigail Mount. BA, Rice U., 1936, BArch, 1937. Registered architect, Tex., Calif. Draftsman, designer Salisbury & McHale, Houston, 1937-38, Wirtz & NcGinty, Houston, 1939-40, Robert & Co., Corpus Christi, Tex., 1940-41; assignee Civilian Pub. Service, Ark., Calif., Ind., Fla. and Oreg., 1942-46; draftsman, designer Kemper Nomland, Los Angeles, 1946-47, 48-49, Frick & Frick, Pasadena, Calif., 1950-51, Walter Reichardt, Los Angeles, 1951-52, De Witt & Swank, Dallas, 1952-54; prin. Mount-Miller, Houston, 1947-48, Denton, Tex., 1954-89; prin. Mount Miller McCain, Denton, 1989—. Editor The Illiterati and The Untide Press, 1945-52, The Denton Voice, 1970-74, Arkwork Rev., 1979-83; contbr. articles to profl. jours. Mem. Denton County Dem. Com., 1960-67; mem. Denton Hist. Landmark Commn., 1980-92, vice chmn., 1980-82; mem. The Fine Arts at Waldport, 1944-46, exec. sec. 1945, Am. Inst. Architects, 1957—, Anthropology Group Dallas, 1953—, The Forum, Denton, 1968—. Recipient Community Arts Recognition award Greater Denton Arts Council, 1982, State Service Recognition award Tex. Civil Liberties Union, 1986. Mem. AIA (emeritus), Interfaith Forum for Religion Art and Architecture (emeritus), Soc. Archtl. Historians, Nat. Trust for Hist. Preservation, Am. Solar Energy Soc., ACLU, War Resisters League, Fellowship of Reconciliation, Nat. Ataxia Found. Democrat. Unitarian Universalist. Avocations: music, piano, writing, travel, photography. Home and Office: 711 W Sycamore St Denton TX 76201-5999

MILLER, VERNON DALLACE, minister; b. McClure, Ill., Sept. 27, 1932; s. Homer Lee and Marie Kathleen (White) M.; m. Alice Elizabeth Wright, July 25, 1954; children: Ronald, Philip, Elizabeth, Annette, Douglas. Student, Moody Bible Inst., 1950-53, S.E. Mo. State, 1954, So. Ill. U., 1956-57; BA, Cedarville Coll., 1963, LittD, 1988. Ordained to min. Bapt. Ch., McClure, 1953. Pastor Camp Creek Bapt. Ch., Murphysboro, Ill., 1953-54, Bible Fellowship Bapt. Ch., Carterville, Ill., 1954-57, Faith Bapt. Ch., Mattoon, Ill., 1957-60, Immanuel Bapt. Ch., Arcanum, Ohio, 1961-63; editor, bus. mgr. Regular Bapt. Press, Chgo., 1963-70; pres. Ch. Bldg. Cons., Chgo., 1971-87; exec. editor, treas. Gen. Assn. of Regular Bapt. Chs., Schaumburg, Ill., 1987—; trustee Awana Youth Assn., Streamwood, Ill., 1965-83, Grand Rapids (Mich.) Bapt. Coll. and Sem., 1981-91, Shepherds Bapt. Ministries, Union Grove, Wis., 1965—. Editor: (mag.) The Baptist Bulletin, 1987—. Del. Ill. Small Bus. Com., Springfield, Ill., 1984. Mem. Christian Ministries Mgmt. Assn. Republican. Office: Regular Bapt Press 1300 N Meacham Rd Schaumburg IL 60173-4888

MILLER, VICTORIA LOREN, designer, art director; b. San Francisco, May 25, 1957; d. Leon and Malvina (Hoffman) M. BFA, UCLA, 1979; postgrad., Art Ctr. Coll. Design, Pasadena, Calif., 1979, 80, UCLA, 1980-82, Otis/Parsons, L.A., 1981. Designer Bright and Assocs., L.A., 1979-80, Richard Runyon Design, L.A., 1980-83; art dir. Grey Entertainment Media, Santa Monica, Calif., 1984; prin. Victoria Miller Design, Santa Monica, Calif., 1984—; freelance art dir. Backer Spielvogel Bates, L.A. 1987-88; designer Sussman/Prejza & Co., Santa Monica, 1984, The Mednick Group, L.A., 1988-89. Label designer for Grand Cru Vineyards (Clio award 1985); designed represented in permanent collection Libr. Congress; pub. in Print Regional Ann., ADLA Ann.; Am. Corp. Identity, Letterheads 5, Vision mag.; contbr. articles to profl. publs. Mem. Am. Inst. Graphic Arts, Mus. Contemporary Art (photography coun.), Art Dirs. Club. Republican. Jewish. Avocations: contemporary art, photography, dance, tennis, cycling. Home and office: 10650 Kinnard Ave # 311 Los Angeles CA 90024-5983

MILLER, WALTER NEAL, insurance company consultant; b. N.Y.C., Nov. 26, 1929; s. Morton and Kathryn (Gersten) M.; m. Nancy Louise Clapp, Sept. 11, 1954; children—Scott, Timothy, David, Kathryn, Amy. B.A., Swarthmore Coll., 1951. With N.Y. Life Ins. Co. N.Y.C. 1951-86; v.p., actuary Prudential Ins. Co., Newark, 1986-93; sr. v.p., chief actuary Prudential Preferred Fin. Svcs., Liberty Corner, N.J., 1993-94; pvt. practice cons., 1994—. Author: (with others) Analysis of Actuarial Theory for Variable Life Insurance, 1969; contbr. (with others) articles to profl. jours. Mem. Soc. Actuaries, Am. Acad. Actuaries. Home: 470 Grandview Ave Wyckoff NJ 07481-2546

MILLER, WALTER RICHARD, JR., banker; b. N.Y.C., Nov. 20, 1934; s. Walter Richard and Ann M. (Phelan) M.; m. Joan M. Groark; children: Kathryn A., Margaret E., Jennifer M., Walter Richard III. AB, Dartmouth Coll., 1955, MBA, Columbia U., 1957; PhD, NYU, 1965. Dir. mktg., v.p. Mellon Nat. Corp., Pitts., 1965-78; sr. v.p. First Atlanta Corp., 1979-81; exec. v.p. Norwest Corp., Mpls., 1981-86; pres., chief exec. officer First Constn. Fin. Corp., New Haven, 1987—, also bd. dirs.; pres., CEO First

Constn. Bank, New Haven, 1987-90, Fin. Mktg. and Planning Co., Whitneyville, Conn., 1990—; exec.-in-residence Quinnipiac Coll., 1990—; pres. CIRRUS Sys., Inc. Contbr. articles, chpts. to profl. publs. Bd. dirs. St. Paul Chamber Orch., Minn. Pub. Radio, Sci. Mus. Minn., Quinnipiac Coll., Hamden, Conn., Quinnipiac Coun. Boy Scouts Am., The Mus. of Am. Theatre; chmn. bd. Orchestra New England. With USAF, 1958. Teaching fellow NYU, N.Y.C., 1960; Ford Found. fellow NYU, 1962. Mem. Interbank Card Assn. (internat. chmn., bd. dirs.), Am. Mktg. Assn. (contbg. editor), Bank Mktg. Assn. (bd. dirs., chmn. mktg. planning council, chmn. mktg. mgmt. council), Somerset Club, New Haven County Club, Quinnipiack Club, Lawn Club. Home: 2 Marshall Rd Hamden CT 06517 Office: Fin Mktg-Planning Co 3 Marshall Rd Whitneyville CT 06517

MILLER, WARREN, bishop. Bishop Ch. of God in Christ, Cleve. Office: Ch of God in Christ 3618 Beacon Dr Cleveland OH 44122-6009

MILLER, WARREN EDWARD, political scientist; b. Hawarden, Iowa, Mar. 26, 1924; s. John Carroll and Mildred Ovedia (Lien) M.; m. Ruth S. Jones, May 1981; children by previous marriage: Jeffrey Ralph, Jennifer Louise. B.S., U. Oreg., 1948, M.S., 1950; Ph.D., Maxwell Sch. Citizenship and Public Affairs, Syracuse U., 1954; Ph.D. (hon.), U. Goteborg, Sweden, 1972. Asst. study dir. Survey Research Ctr., Inst. Social Research, U. Mich., 1951-53, study dir., 1953-56, research assoc., 1956-59, program dir., 1959-68, research coordinator polit. behavior program, 1968-70, prin. investigator nat. election studies, 1977—; dir. Ctr. Polit. Studies, Inst. Social Research, 1970-81; program dir. Ctr. Polit. Studies, 1982—; asst. prof. polit. sci. Ctr. Polit. Studies, Inst. Social Research, 1956-58, asso. prof., 1958-63, prof., 1963-93, Arthur W. Bromage prof. polit. sci., 1981-82; prof. polit. sci. Ariz. State U., 1981—; fellow Ctr. Advanced Study in Behavioral Scis., 1961-62; exec. dir. Inter-univ. Consortium for Polit. and Social Rsch., 1962-70, assoc. dir., 1978—; vis. prof. U. Tilburg, Netherlands, 1973, U. Geneva, 1973, European U. Inst., Florence, Italy, 1979; vis. Disting. prof. Ariz. State U., 1981; trustee Inst. Am. Univs., 1970—; Regents' prof., Ariz. State U., 1988—. Author: (with others) books including The Voter Decides, 1954, American Voter, 1960, Elections and the Political Order, 1966, (with T.E. Levitin) Leadership and Change: Presidential Elections from 1952-1976, 77, (with M.K. Jennings) Parties in Transition, 1986, Without Consent, 1988, (with others) The American National Election Studies Data Sourcebook, 1952-1978, 80, The American National Election Studies Data Sourcebook, 1952-86, 89; contbr. (with others) articles to profl. publs.; editorial bd.: (with others) Am. Polit. Sci. Rev, 1966-71, Computers and the Humanities, 1969-71, Social Science History, 1976-91, Social Science Rev., 1973; editorial adv. bd.: (with others) Sage Electoral Studies Yearbook, 1974. Served with USAAF, 1943-46. Recipient Disting. Alumnus award Maxwell Sch. Citizenship and Public Affairs, Syracuse U., 1974, Disting. Faculty Achievement award U. Mich., 1977; honored in the creation of the Warren E. Miller award for Intellectual Accomplishment and Svc. Am. Polit. Sci. Assn. sect. on Elections, Pub. Opionion and Voting Behavior, 1995, creation of the Warren E. Miller award for Meritorious Svc. to Social Scis. Inter-Univ. Consortium for Polit. and Social Rsch., 1993. Fellow Am. Acad. Arts and Scis.; mem. AAAS, Am. Polit. Sci. Assn. (pres. 1979-80), Internat. Polit. Sci. Assn. (coun. 1969-73), M.W. Polit. Sci. Assn., Internat. Soc. Polit. Psychology, So. Polit. Sci. Assn., Social Sci. History Assn. (pres. 1979-80), Norwegian Acad. Sci. and Letters. Office: Ariz State U Dept Polit Sci Tempe AZ 85287

MILLER, WARREN LLOYD, lawyer; b. Bklyn., July 18, 1944; s. Allan and Ella (Faecher) M.; m. Jana Lee Morris, May 13, 1978; children: Lindsey Beth, Alan Gregory, William Brett. BA with high univ. honors, Am. U., 1966; JD with honors, George Washington U., 1969. Bar: Va., 1969, D.C., 1969, U.S. Supreme Ct., 1981. Law clk. to Hon. Edward A. Beard Superior Ct. D.C., 1968-69; asst. U.S. atty. for D.C., 1969-74; ptnr. Stein, Miller & Brodsky, 1974-85; pres. Warren L. Miller, P.C., 1986—; of counsel Reed, Smith, Shaw & McClay, 1986-93; lectr. Georgetown U. Law Sch., 1970-71, Am. U. 1971-72; guest speaker various TV programs and legal forums; mem. Jud. Conf. D.C. Cir., 1984—. contbr. articles to profl. jours. Parliamentarian credentials and rules coms. Rep. Nat. Conv., 1984, mem. D.C. Law Revision Commn., 1987-91 (apptd. by Pres. Reagan), U.S. Commn. for Preservation of Am.'s Heritage Abroad, 1992— (apptd. by Pres. Bush); fundraiser Rep. Nat. Com. and Pres. Bush, 1988-92; co-chmn. dinner for V.P. Bush, 1988; vice chmn. Pres.'s Dinner, 1989; mem. dinner com. Bush-Quayle '92 Dinner, 1991; co-chmn. Pres.'s Club, Washington, 1990-92; co-chmn. fundraiser for U.S. Senator Christopher Bond, 1992; chmn. fundraiser for Supr. Ernest Berger, 1994; bd. dirs. Found. for Buchenwald and Mittelbau-Dora Memls., 1994—. Mem. Congl. Country Club (Bethesda, Md.), Phi Delta Phi, Omicron Delta Kappa, Pi Gamma Mu. Office: 2300 N St NW Ste 600 Washington DC 20037-1122

MILLER, WILBUR HOBART, business diversification consultant; b. Boston, Feb. 15, 1915; s. Silas Reuben and Muriel Mae (Greene) M.; m. Harriett I. Harmon, June 20, 1941; children: Nancy Iber Miller Harray, Warren Harmon, Donna Sewall Miller Davidge. B.S., U. N.H., 1936, M.S., 1938; Ph.D., Columbia U., 1941. Rsch. chemist Am. Cyanamid Co., Stamford, Conn., 1941-49, Washington tech. rep., 1949-53, dir. food industry devel., 1953-57; tech. dir. products for agr. Cyanamid Internat. Am. Cyanamid Co., N.Y.C., 1957-60; sr. scientist Dunlap & Assos., Darien, Conn., 1960-63, sr. assoc., 1963-66; coord. new product devel. Celanese Corp., N.Y.C., 1966-67, mgr. comml. rsch., 1967-68, dir. corp. devel., 1969-84; bus. diversification cons., 1984—; lectr. on bus. and soc. Western Conn. State Coll., 1977-79. Contbr. sci. papers to profl. jours.; patentee in field. Chmn. Stamford Forum for World Affairs, 1954-87, hon. chmn. 1987—; mem. adv. bd. Ctr. for Study of Presidency, 1980—; bd. dirs. Stamford Symphony, 1974-80, v.p., 1978-80; bd. dirs. Stamford Hist. Soc., 1988, v.p., 1991-92, pres. 1993—; pres. Coun. for Continuing Edn. Stamford, 1963, bd. 1960-70; elder United Presby. Ch., nominating com., 1960-63; pres. Interfaith Coun. of Stamford, 1973; internat. fellow U. Bridgeport, 1985—; mem. pres.'s coun. U. N.H., 1982—. Recipient outstanding achievement award Coll. Tech., U. N.H., 1971, Am. Design award, 1948, Golden Rule Award J.C. Penney & Co., 1986; Univ. fellow Columbia U., 1940-41. Fellow AAAS, Am. Inst. Chemists (councillor N.Y. chpt. 1984-85); mem. Am. Chem. Soc. (news svc. adv. bd., 1948-53), N.Y. Acad. Scis., Société de Chimie Industrielle (v.p. fin. Am. sect. 1980-84, dir. 1984—), Inst. Food Tech., Soc. for Internat. Devel., Am. Acad. Polit. and Social Scis., Stamford Hist. Soc., Chemists Club (N.Y.C., treas. 1982-84), Sigma Xi, Alpha Chi Sigma, Phi Kappa Phi. Home: 19 Crestview Ave Stamford CT 06907-1906

MILLER, WILBUR RANDOLPH, retired university educator and administrator; b. Elsberry, Mo., Nov. 12, 1932; s. Charles Clifton and Pauline Jean (Dryden) M. Student, SE Mo. U., 1951-53; BEd, U. Mo., 1954, MEd, 1955, EdD, 1960. Cert. secondary tchr., Mo. Tchr. indsl. arts Hazelwood Sch. Dist., St. Louis, 1955-56, U. Lab. Sch., Columbia, Mo., 1956-60; indsl. tchr. educator Purdue U., West Lafayette, Ind., 1960-63; asst. prof. U. Mo., Columbia, 1963-67, assoc. prof. and chmn. dept. coll. edn., 1967-76, prof. and assoc. dean coll. edn., 1976-86, dean coll. edn., 1986-91, prof., dean emeritus, 1992; chmn. adv. coun. Fed. Rsch. Ctr. in Vocat. Edn., Ohio State U., Columbus, 1981-84; internat. edn. cons. 1992—; adj. edn. adv. bd. DeVry Inc., Evanston, Ill., 1986—; mem. pvt. tech. sch. accreditation commn., 1994—. Author: Teaching Children Through Construction Activities, 1985, Instructors and Their Jobs, 1990, The Golf Primer, 1991, Handbook for College Teaching, 1995; editor: (series) Basic Industrial Arts, 1978; contbr. more than 40 articles to profl. jours. Pres., bd. dirs. Lenoir Inc., Columbia, 1977-84; mem. Woodhaven Sch. Bd., Columbia, 1982-83. With USNR, 1955-63. Recipient U. Faculty/Alumni award, 1985. Mem. Nat. Assn. Indsl. Tchr. Educators (pres., officer 1965-74), Am. Indsl. Arts Assn. (v.p. 1980), Mo. Vocat. Assn. (pres. 1974-75), Mo. Assn. Colls. for Tchr. Edn. (pres. 1987-90), Am. Vocat. Assn. (Outstanding Svc. award 1979). Mem. Disciples of Christ Ch. Club: Faculty (Columbia) (officer 1977-82). Lodge: Kiwanis. Avocations: golf, travel, home maintenance. Office: PO Box 71 Sautee Nacoochee GA 30571-0071

MILLER, WILLARD, JR., mathematician, educator; b. Ft. Wayne, Ind., Sept. 17, 1937; s. Willard and Ruth (Kemerly) M.; m. Jane Campbell Scott, June 5, 1965; children—Stephen, Andrea. S.B. in Math., U. Chgo., 1958; Ph.D. in Applied Math., U. Calif.-Berkeley, 1963. Vis. mem. Courant Inst. Math. Scis., NYU, 1963-65; mem. faculty U. Minn., 1965—, prof. math., 1972—, head Sch. Math., 1978-86; co-prin. investigator Inst. Math. and its Applications, 1980-94, assoc. dir., 1987-94; assoc. dean Inst. of Tech.,

1994—. Author: Lie Theory and Special Functions, 1968, Symmetry Groups and Their Applications, 1972, Symmetry and Separation of Variables, 1977; assoc. editor Jour. Math. Physics, 1973-75, Applicable Analysis, 1978-90. Mem. AAAS, Soc. Indsl. and Applied Math. (mng. editor Jour. Math. Analysis 1975-81), Am. Math. Soc., Sigma Xi. Home: 4508 Edmund Blvd Minneapolis MN 55406-3629 Office: Univ Minn Sch Math Minneapolis MN 55455

MILLER, WILLIAM ALVIN, clergyman, author; b. Pitts., Jan. 1, 1931; s. Christ William and Anna Ernestine (Wilhelm) M.; m. Marilyn Mae Miller, Aug. 8, 1953; children: Mark William, Eric Michael. BA, Capital U., 1953; MDiv, Luth. Theol. Sem., Columbus, Ohio, 1957; MST, Andover Newton Theol. Sch., Newton Centre, Mass., 1958, D of Ministry, 1974. Ordained to ministry Luth. Ch.; lic. marriage & family therapist, Minn. Pastor St. James Luth. Ch., Balt., 1958-66; chaplain Fairview Hosp., Mpls., 1966-73, dir. dept. religion & health, 1973-87; instr. Fairview Sch. Nursing, Mpls., 1967-75, Luther Northwestern Theol. Sem., St. Paul, 1973-85; pres. Woodland Pub. Co., Wayzata, Minn., 1979—; dir. Woodland Pastoral Assocs., Mpls., 1987—; assoc. pastor Cen. Luth. Ch., Mpls., 1989-94; chair bd. dirs. Luth. Social Svcs. Md., Balt., 1963-65; administr. Dialogue 88, Mpls., 1987-88. Author: Why Do Christians Break Down?, 1973, Big Kids' Mother Goose, 1976, When Going to Pieces Holds You Together, 1976, You Count, You Really Do!, 1976, Mid Life, New Life, 1978, Conversations, 1980, Make Friends With Your Shadow, 1981, Prayers at Mid Point, 1983, The Joy of Feeling Good, 1986, Your Golden Shadow, 1989, 91, Meeting the Shadow, 1991; assoc. editor Jour. Pastoral Care, Decatur, Ga., 1984-88; contbr. articles to profl. jours. Chaplain, Jr. C. of C., Randallstown, Md., 1962-64; bd. dirs. Am. Protestant Health Assn., Schaumburg, Ill., 1983-89. Fellow Coll. Chaplains (pres. 1985-87), Assn. Mental Health Clergy (Anton T. Boisen award 1989); mem. Assn. Clin. Pastoral Edn. (supr.), Am. Assn. Marriage & Family Therapy. Avocations: cabinetmaking, skiing, publishing, construction. Home: 2005 Xanthus Ln Minneapolis MN 55447 Office: 2005 Xanthus Ln Minneapolis MN 55447

MILLER, WILLIAM CHARLES, lawyer; b. Jacksonville, Fla., Aug. 6, 1937; s. Charles and Mary Elizabeth (Kiger) M.; m. Hadmut Gisela Larsen, June 10, 1961; children: Monica Lee, Charles Andreas. BA, Washington and Lee U., 1958, LLB, 1961; LLM, N.Y. U., 1963; postgrad., Harvard U., 1978. Bar: Fla. 1961, Calif. 1984, Ind. 1987, U.S. Supreme Ct. 1968. Counsel to electrochem., elastomers and internat. depts. E.I. duPont de Nemours & Co., Wilmington, Del., 1963-66; counsel S. Am. ops. Bristol-Myers Co., N.Y.C., 1967-69; internat. counsel Xerox Corp., Stamford, Conn., 1969-79; assoc. gen. counsel Xerox Corp., Stamford, 1979-80; v.p., gen. counsel, sec. Max Factor & Co., Hollywood, Calif., 1981-85, Boehringer Mannheim Corp., Indpls., 1985-92; v.p., gen. counsel Collagen Corp., Palo Alto, Calif., 1992—. Bd. dirs. Southwestern Legal Found., 1975-85. Fulbright scholar, 1959-60; Ford Found. fellow, 1961-62; Hague Acad. fellow, 1963; German Govt. grantee, 1962-63; Kappa Sigma scholar, 1959. Mem. Internat. Bar Assn., ABA, Calif. Bar Assn., Fla. Bar Assn., Ind. Bar Assn., Masons, Elks, Phi Beta Kappa, Phi Eta Sigma, Delta Theta Phi. Republican. Mem. Christian Ch. Home: 4931 Monaco Dr Pleasanton CA 94566-7671

MILLER, WILLIAM EVANS, JR., retired lawyer; b. Pitts., May 8, 1923; s. William Evans and Elisabeth (Looney) M.; m. Phyllis Evans, Sept. 9, 1950 (dec. Oct. 7, 1982); children: Jonathan, David; m. Sandra Hawkins, June 14, 1986. A.B., Amherst Coll.; LL.B., U. Pa. Bar: Pa. Assoc. Reed Smith Shaw McClay Pitts., 1949-64, ptnr., 1964-88; ret., 1988. Served to lt. (j.g.) USN, 1943-46, PTO. Mem. Wildwood Club, University Club, Masons. Republican. Christian Scientist. Home: 4554 William Flynn Hwy Allison Park PA 15101-1427

MILLER, WILLIAM FREDERICK, research company executive, educator, business consultant; b. Vincennes, Ind., Nov. 19, 1925; s. William and Elsie M. (Everts) M.; m. Patty J. Smith, June 19, 1949; 1 son, Rodney Wayne. Student, Vincennes U., 1946-47; BS, Purdue U., 1949, MS, 1951, PhD, 1956; D.Sc., 1972. Mem. staff Argonne Nat. Lab., 1955-64, assoc. physicist, 1956-59, dir. applied math. div., 1959-64; prof. computer sci. Stanford U., Palo Alto, Calif., 1965—; Herbert Hoover prof. pub. and pvt. mgmt. Stanford U., 1979—, assoc. provost for computing, 1968-70, v.p. for research, 1970-71, v.p., provost, 1971-78; mem. Stanford Assocs., 1972—; pres., chief exec. officer SRI Internat., Menlo Park, Calif., 1979-90; chmn. bd., chief exec. officer SRI Devel. Co., Menlo Park, David Sarnoff Research Ctr., Inc., Princeton, N.J.; profl. lectr. applied math. U. Chgo., 1962-64; vis. prof. math. Purdue U., 1962-63; vis. scholar Ctr. for Advanced Study in Behavioral Scis., 1976; bd. dirs. Varian Assocs. Inc., 1st Interstate Bancorp, 1st Interstate Bank Calif., Pacific Gas and Electric Co., Regis McKenna, Inc., Scios-Nova, Inc.; mem. adv. coun. BHP Internat.; mem. computer sci. and engring. bd. Nat. Acad. Sci., 1968-71; mem. Nat. Sci. Bd., 1982-88; mem. corp. com. computers in edn. Brown U., 1972-79; mem. policy bd. EDUCOM Planning Coun. on Computing in Edn., 1974-79, chmn., 1974-76; ednl. adv. bd. Guggenheim Meml. Found., 1976-80; com. postdoctoral and doctoral rsch. staff NRC, 1977-80, mem. computer sci. and telecommunications bd., Nat. Inst. Standards Tech. bd. assessment; mem. internat. adv. panel Nat. Sci. and Tech. Bd., Singapore. Assoc. editor: Pattern Recognition Jour, 1968-72, Jour. Computational Physics, 1970-74. Served to 2d lt. F.A. AUS, 1943-46. Recipient Frederic B. Whitman award United Way Bay Area, 1982. Fellow IEEE, Am. Acad. Arts and Scis., AAAS; mem. Am. Math. Soc., Am. Phys. Soc., Soc. Indsl. and Applied Math., Assn. Computing Machinery, Nat. Acad. Engring., Sigma Xi, Tau Beta Pi. Office: Stanford U Grad Sch Bus Stanford CA 94305

MILLER, WILLIAM FREDERICK, trust company executive; b. Webster, N.Y., May 7, 1935; s. Roy McDermott and Katherine (Faist) M.; m. Jean Ann Macdonald, May 2, 1959; children: Susan Jane Miller Selden, William Scott, Anne Macdonald Miller Cannella. BA, U. Rochester, 1957. CLU; chartered fin. cons.; cert. fin. planner. Various positions Equitable Life Assurance Soc. U.S., New Haven, Ft. Wayne, Ind., 1957-64; div. dir. advanced underwriting Equitable Life Assurance Soc. U.S., Cin., L.A., Atlanta, 1964-73; dir. individual fin. planning Trust Co. Bank, Atlanta, 1974-78, 81-85; group dir. personal fin. planning Coopers & Lybrand, Atlanta, 1978-81; v.p., trust officer Trust Co. Bank, Atlanta, 1985—. Contbr. articles to profl. jours. Bd. dirs. Young Life Atlanta Inner City, 1985—, chmn., 1988; mem. fin. dept. Episc. Diocese Atlanta, 1973-83. Sgt. U.S. Army, 1957-58. Mem. CLU's bd. dirs. Atlanta chpt. 1973-74), Atlanta Estate Planning Coun. (bd. dirs. 1981-82), Internat. Assn. for Fin. Planning (bd. dirs. Atlanta chpt. 1984-85), Internat. Bd. Cert. Fin. Planners, Registry Fin. Planning Practitioners, Dunwoody Country Club. Republican. Avocations: golf, tennis, boating, hiking. Office: Trust Co Bank 25 Park Pl NE Atlanta GA 30303-2900

MILLER, WILLIAM GREEN, ambassador; b. N.Y.C., Aug. 15, 1931; m. Suzanne Lisle; 2 children. BA, Williams Coll., Oxford U., U.K.; MA, Oxford U., U.K.; postgrad., Harvard U. With Fgn. Svc., 1959; vice consul, polit. officer Isfahan, Iran, 1959; polit. officer Tehran, Iran, 1962-64; line officer, exec. secretariat Dept. of State, 1965-66; mem. Sr. Interdepartmental Group, 1966-67; spl. asst. fgn. affairs and def. Senator John Sherman Cooper, 1967-72; staff dir. Senate Select Com. Emergency Powers, 1973-75, Senate Select Com. to Study Govtl. Ops. with Respect to Intelligence Communities, 1975-76, Senate Select Com. Intelligence, 1976-81; assoc. dean, adj. prof. internat. politics Fletcher Sch. Law and Diplomacy, 1981-82, rsch. assoc., 1983-85; faculty assoc. Harvard Ctr. Middle Eastern Studies, 1983-86; pres. Am. Com. U.S.- Soviet Rels., 1986-92; U.S. amb. to Ukraine, 1993—; cons. D.H. Sawyer and Assocs., Ltd., N.Y.C., 1985; bd. dirs. Internat. Found., pres. 1986-92; pres. Com. Am.- Russian Rels., cons. Catherine T. MacArthur Found., 1992-93. Contbr. articles to profl. jours. Rsch. fellow Harvard Ctr. Sci. and Internat. Affairs, 1984-86, John F. Kennedy Sch. of Govt. fellow Harvard U., 1986. Mem. Nat. Acad. Pub. Diplomacy, Nat. Acad. Pub. Adminstrn., Internat. Inst. Strategic Studies, Coun. Fgn. Rels., Children of the 21st Century, Middle East Inst. Office: 10 Yuria Kotsyubinskovo, 252053 Kiev 53, Ukraine

1976-81, assoc. mng. ptnr., 1981—. Office: Fin Rels Bd John Hancock Ctr 875 N Michigan Ave Chicago IL 60611-1779

MILLER, WILLIAM HUGHES, theoretical chemist, educator; b. Kosciusko, Miss., Mar. 16, 1941; s. Weldon Howard and Jewel Irene (Hughes) M.; m. Margaret Ann Westbrook, June 4, 1966; children: Alison Leslie, Emily Sinclaire. B.S., Ga. Inst. Tech., 1963; A.M., Harvard U., 1964, Ph.D., 1967. Jr. fellow Harvard U., 1967-69; NATO postdoctoral fellow Freiburg (Germany) U., 1967-68; asst. prof. chemistry U. Calif., Berkeley, 1969-72, assoc. prof., 1972-74, prof., 1974—, dept. chmn., 1989-93; fellow Churchill Coll., Cambridge (Eng.) U., 1975-76; hon. prof. Shandong U., People's Republic of China, 1994. Alfred P. Sloan fellow, 1970-72; Camille and Henry Dreyfus fellow, 1973-78; Guggenheim fellow, 1975-76, Christensen fellow St. Catherine's Coll., Oxford, 1991; recipient Alexander von Humboldt-Stiftung U.S. Sr. Scientist award 1981-82, Ernest Orlando Lawrence Meml. award, 1985. Fellow AAAS, Am. Acad. Arts and Scis., Am. Phys. Soc. (Irving Langmuir award 1990); mem. NAS, Am. Chem. Soc. (theoretical chemistry award 1994), Internat. Acad. Quantum Molecular Sci. (Ann. prize 1974). Office: U Calif Dept Chemistry Berkeley CA 94720

MILLER, WILLIAM IAN, legal educator; b. 1946. B.A., U. Wis., 1969, M of Philosophy, 1973, PhD, 1975; JD, Yale U., 1980. Bar: Wis. 1980. Assoc. prof. U. Houston, 1981-85; prof. U. Mich., Ann Arbor, 1985—; vis. assoc. prof. U. Mich., An Arbor, 1984-85; vis. prof. Yale U., fall 1988. Mem. Law and Soc. Assn., Am. Soc. Legal History, Am. Hist. Assn. Office: U Mich Law Sch 625 S State St Ann Arbor MI 48109-1215

MILLER, WILLIAM JONES, lawyer; b. Cleve., Apr. 20, 1938; s. William John and Virginia Katheryn (Harris) M.; divorced; children: Cheray, Jason. BA, Yale U., 1960; JD, U. Miami, 1965. Bar: Fla. 1965, Ohio 1967. Assoc. Grimditch & Assoc., Pompano Beach, Fla., 1965-67; ptnr. Arter & Hadden, Cleve., 1967-81; shareholder Carlton, Fields, Ward, Emmanuel, Smith & Cutler, Tampa, Fla., 1981-95. Chmn. editorial com. Cleve. Bar Jour., 1973-74. Chmn. Yale U. Alumni Cleve., 1978-81; mem. exec. bd. Fed. Bar Assn. Middle Dist. Fla., Tampa. Sgt. USAR, 1963-68, then col. Mem. ABA, Maritime Law Assn. U.S., Propeller Club of Tampa Bay (pres. 1990-91), The Author's Guild. Republican. Presbyterian. Avocations: writing, golf, reading. Office: 147 Wisteria Dr Longwood FL 32779

MILLER, WILLIAM LAWRENCE, government official; b. Medford, Oreg., May 12, 1937; s. Oliver William Miller and Ida Lucile Lowry; m. Jo Anne Carmen Clifton, Jan. 29, 1961; children: William Scott, Douglas Britton. B.S. in Chemistry, U. Calif.-Davis, 1963, M.S. in Geology, 1967. Assoc. chemist Aerojet Gen. Corp., Sacramento, 1963-64; chemist Bur. of Mines, Reno, 1966-70; program analysis officer U.S. Dept. Interior, Washington, 1970-71; staff metallurgist Bur. Mines, Washington, 1971-77; chief div. metallurgy Bur. Mines, 1977-79, chief research directorate staff, 1979-82, asst. dir. minerals and materials research, 1982-87, chief office regulatory projects coordination, 1988-91; chief div. regulatory and policy analysis Bur. Mines, Washington, 1991—; alt. mem. coordinating com. on materials research and devel. Fed. Council Sci. and Tech., Washington, 1969. Recipient Meritorious Service award and silver medal U.S. Dept Interior, 1982. Mem. Am. Chem. Soc., Metall. Soc., AIME, Geol. Soc. Washington, Mining and Metall. Soc. Am., Sr. Execs Assn. Office: US Dept of Interior Bur of Mines 810 Seventh St NW Washington DC 20241-0002

MILLER, WILLIAM LEE, writer, social ethics educator; b. Bloomington, Ind., Apr. 21, 1926; s. Arthur Lemoine and Lova June (McCain) M.; m. Betty Lou Horton, July 29, 1949 (div. Apr. 1981); children: Rebecca, Cynthia, David, Andrew; m. Linda Curtis Moore, June 12, 1981. AB, U. Nebr., 1947; BD summa cum laude, Yale U., 1950, PhD, 1958. Instr. Yale U., New Haven, 1951-53; asst. prof. Smith Coll., Northampton, Mass., 1953-55; staff writer The Reporter Mag., N.Y.C., 1955-58; assoc. prof. Yale U., 1958-69; prof. Ind. U., Bloomington, 1969-82; prof. U. Va., Charlottesville, 1982—, chmn. Miller Ctr. Profl. Ethics Insts.; cons. Ford Found., N.Y.C., 1969-77; dir. The Poynter Ctr., Bloomington, 1971-79; moderator Aspen (Colo.) Inst. Seminars, 1973-85. Author: Piety Along the Potomac, 1964, Of Thee Nevertheless I Sing, 1975, Yankee From Georgia, 1978, The First Liberty, 1986. Staff writer Pres.'s Com on Urban Housing, Washington, 1968; alderman 15th ward, New Haven, 1964-68; editorial asst. to U.S. Vice Pres., Washington, 1968. Mitchell Prize Essay, Woodlands (Tex.) Conf., 1979; Annenberg Disting. Scholar, U. So. Calif., 1981; guest scholar Woodrow Wilson Ctr., Washington, 1981, 82; research grantee Lilly Endowment, 1982-85. Mem. Soc. for Christian Ethics. Democrat. Presbyterian. Home: 1830 Yorktown Dr Charlottesville VA 22901-3037 Office: U Va Dept Religious Studies Charlottesville VA 22903

MILLER, WILLIAM LEE, minister; b. Mammoth Spring, Ark., Dec. 27, 1926; s. William L. and Janie Katherine (Murrell) M.; m. Marion Evelyn O'Neal, Mar. 23, 1947 (div. 1976); children: Georgia Katherine Miller Beach, William Lee III; m. Judith Ann Bell, Nov. 28, 1977. AB, Phillips U., 1950, LittD, 1968; postgrad., U. Ark., 1951-52, Tex. Christian U., 1958, U. Ky., 1961; BD, Lexington Theol. Sem., 1961. Ordained to ministry Christian Ch. (Disciples of Christ), 1950. Pastor 1st Christian Ch., Rogers, Ark., 1952-59; v.p. Bd. Higher Edn., Indpls., 1962-68; pres. Bd. Higher Edn. Christian Ch. (Disciples of Christ), 1968-77; v.p. devel. Nat. City Christian Ch. Corp., Washington, 1977-82; upper Midwest regional min., pres. Christian Ch. (Disciples of Christ), Des Moines, 1982-93; dir. Christian Ch. Found., Indpls., 1968-77, 84-93; trustee Bethany Coll., W.Va., 1972-85, Culver Stockton Coll., 1970-77, 82—, Tougaloo Coll., Jackson, Miss., 1970-76, Christian Theol. Sem., Indpls., 1987—. Precinct committeeman Dem. Party, Indpls., 1968-72; mem. Reagan First Inaugural Religious Com.; bd. dirs. St. Louis Christian Home, 1956-59; chmn. Coop. Coll. Registry, Washington, 1963-70; mem. Disciples of Christ Ch. With USCG, 1945-47. Mem. Disciples of Christ Hist. Soc., Coun. Christian Unity (exec. com. 1968-77), Nat. Evangelistic Assn. (bd. dirs. 1983-86), Am. Assn. Higher Edn., Masons, KT, Sigma Chi. Home: 113 Kellam Ct Manteo NC 27954 Office: Miller Devel Assocs PO Box 194 Manteo NC 27954-0194

MILLER, WILLIAM NAPIER CRIPPS, lawyer; b. Long Branch, N.J., June 7, 1930; adopted s. Julia (Erwin) M.; m. Carolyn Anderson, Jan. 19, 1951 (div. 1969); children: Bruce Douglass, Jennifer Erwin; m. Hannelore Steinbeck, Dec. 4, 1970; A.A., Coll. Marin, 1949; student, U. Calif.-Berkeley, 1949-51, J.D., 1955. Bar: N.Y., Calif. 1956, U.S. Supreme Ct. 1983. Assoc. Mudge, Stern, Baldwin & Todd, N.Y.C., 1955-58; assoc. Pillsbury, Madison & Sutro, San Francisco, 1959-65, ptnr., 1966—; staff NYU Law Sch., 1957-58; ct. adv. com. Calif. State Assembly Judiciary Com., 1979-80. Bd. dirs. Laguna Honda Hosp., San Francisco, 1966—; bd. visitors U. Calif.-Hastings Law Sch. Served with USAF, 1951-52. Recipient Bur. Nat. Affairs award U. Calif.-Hastings, 1955; recipient Thurston Soc. award, 1953. Fellow Am. Coll. Trial Lawyers; mem. ABA, San Francisco Bar Assn., Order of Coif, St. Francis Yacht Club, World Trade Club (San Francisco), Silverado Country Club (Napa, Calif.). Home: 16 George Ln Sausalito CA 94965-1890 Office: Pillsbury Madison & Sutro PO Box 7880 San Francisco CA 94120-7880

MILLER, WILLIAM RICHEY, JR., lawyer; b. Oklahoma City, Apr. 4, 1947; s. William Richey and Edna Rosalind (Nielsen) M.; m. Susan Hammond, Aug. 2, 1970; children: Brooke, Karen. BA, Pomona Coll., Claremont, Calif., 1969; MA, Claremont Grad. Sch., 1972; JD, Lewis and Clark Coll., 1975. Bar: Oreg. 1975, U.S. Dist. Ct. Oreg. 1976, U.S. Ct. Appeals (9th cir.) 1976. Staff atty. Oreg. Ct. Appeals, Salem, 1975-76; with firm Griffith, Bittner, Abbott & Roberts, Portland, Oreg., 1976-83; ptnr. Davis Wright Termaine, Portland, 1983—; adj. prof. Lewis and Clark Law Sch., 1975-78. Bd. dirs. Portland Civic Theatre, 1988-91, Am. Lung Assn. Oreg., Portland, 1985-88, Oreg. Bus. Com. for the Arts, Portland, 1991-93. Mem. Oreg. State Bar (sect. chair 1990-91), Comml. Fin. Assn., Oreg. Bankers Assn., Lewis and Clark Alumni Assn. (bd. dirs. 1989-92). Presbyterian. Home: 843 Lakeshore Rd Lake Oswego OR 97034 Office: Davis Wright Tremaine Ste 2300 1300 SW 5th Ave Portland OR 97201

MILLER, WILLIAM TALBOT, lawyer; b. Baton Rouge, Mar. 27, 1943; s. Don P. and Zola Lynn (Talbot) M.; m. Leslie H., Feb. 4, 1968; children: Adrienne Karen, Stephanie Kate. BS cum laude, Princeton U., 1965; JD with honors, U. Tex., 1969. Bar: Tex. 1969. Ptnr. Andrews & Kurth, Houston, 1969—; bd. dirs. W.S. Farish & Co., Houston. Assoc. editor Tex.

Law Rev., 1967. Trustee, bd. dirs. Hamill Found., Houston, David Malcolm Found., Houston; councilman City of Bunkerhill Village, 1987. Lt. USN, 1969-73. Fellow Am. Coll. Probate Counsel; mem. ABA, Tex. Bar Assn. Houston Bar Assn. Republican. Episcopalian. Avocations: hunting, fishing.

MILLER, WILLIAM VENCILL, medical administrator; b. Kansas City, Mo., Feb. 21, 1940; s. John Pearse and Joy (Vencill) M.; m. Jeanne Wilmes Miller, Aug. 17, 1984; children: Joyce, John, Daniel, Mitchell. BA, U. Mo., 1962, MD, 1966. Diplomate Am. Bd. Pathology. Intern U. Rochester, N.Y., 1966-67; clin. assoc. NIH, Bethesda, Md., 1967-69; resident and fellow U. Mo., 1969-71; asst. prof. dept. pathology U. Ky., 1971-73; clin. prof. Washington U., 1973-91, St. Louis U., 1973-91, U. Tex., 1992—; dir. histocompatibility lab. U. Mo. Med. Ctr., 1969-71; dir. Cen. Ky. Blood Ctr., Lexington, 1971-73, U. Ky. Hosp. Blood Bank, Lexington, 1971-73; med. dir. U. Ky. Med. Ctr., 1971-73; dir. blood bank St. Louis U. Hosps., 1974-80; blood bank cons. Cardinal Glennon Hosp. for Children, 1977-80; dir. labs. St. Louis U. Hosps. for Children, 1977-81; pres., chief exec. BloodCare, Dallas, 1991—; mem. med. adv. bd. Primus Corp. Inc., Kansas City, Mo., 1991-95, Biorelease Inc. 1991—, dir. 1989-91, Biocyte, Inc. 1992-94. Author: HLA Without Tears, 1979; sr. editor: Transfusion Therapy, 1983, 86. bd. dirs. Sta. KWMU Pub. Radio, St. Louis 1983-85, Nat. Mus. of Transport, St. Louis, 1987-91; chmn. Mayor's Task Force on Homeless, St. Louis, 1983-85; lt. comdr. USPHS, 1967-69. Recipient Dist. Citizen award St. Louis Jaycees, 1976, Dist. Alumnus award U. Mo., 1991. Mem. AMA, FDA (adv. com. on blood and blood products 1979-85, chmn. 1984-85, cons. 1986), Am. Nat. Red Cross (mem. pres. adv. com., chmn. nat. com. histocompatable blood transfusion, spl. com. bd. govs. plasma fractionation facility, chmn. spl. com. on blood resource sharing), Am. Assn. Blood Banks (chmn. com. tech. manual 1970-78, com. standards 1971-83), Am. Blood Commn. (bd. dirs. 1979-83, pres. 1983-85), Am. Soc. Clin. Pathologists, Am. Soc. Hematology, Am. Assn. Tissue Banks, Am. Coun. Transplantation (founding dir. 1984-85), Am. Soc. Histocompatibility and Immunogenetics (founding dir.), Internat. Soc. Blood Transfusion, South Central Assn. Blood Banks, AIDS Found. St. Louis (dir. 1988-91), U.S. Sailing Assn., Nat. Corvette Restorers Soc., Fort Worth Boat Club. Avocations: Sailing, Automobile Restoration, Folk and Bluegrass Music, Photography and Contemporary Art. Office: BloodCare 9000 Harry Hines Blvd Dallas TX 75235

MILLER, YVONNE BOND, state senator, educator; b. Edenton, N.C.; d. John and Pency Bond. BS, Va. State Coll., Petersburg, 1956; postgrad., Va. State Coll., Norfolk, 1966; MA, Columbia U., 1962; PhD, U. Pitts., 1973; postgrad., CCNY, 1976. Tchr. Norfolk Pub. Schs., 1956-68; asst. prof. Norfolk State U., 1968-71, assoc. prof., 1971-74, prof., 1974-88, head dept. early childhood/elem. edn., 1984-87; mem. Va. Ho. Dels., Richmond, 1984-87, mem. edn. com., health, welfare and instns. com., militia and police com., 1983-87; mem. Va. Senate, Richmond, 1987—; now mem. commerce and labor com., gen. laws com., transp. com., rehab. and social svcs. com. Va. Senate; Va. Dems. vice chair; mem. Nat. Dem. Com.; cons. to chs., parent orgns. and community groups. Commr. Ea. Va. Med. Authority; adv. bd. Va. Div. Children; active C.H. Mason Meml. Ch. of God in Christ. 1st black woman to be elected to Va. Legislature, 1983, 1st black woman to be elected to Va. Senate, 1987. Mem. Nat. Alliance Black Sch. Educators (bd. dirs.), Va. Assn. for Early Childhood Edn., Nat. Assn. Dem. Chairs, Zeta Phi Beta (past officer). Office: 960 Norchester St Norfolk VA 23504-4021 also: Norfolk State U 2401 Corprew Ave Norfolk VA 23504-3907 also: Va Senate Gen Assembly Bldg Rm 365 Richmond VA 23219

MILLER, ZELL BRYAN, governor; b. Young Harris, Ga., Feb. 24, 1932; s. Stephen Grady and Birdie (Bryan) M.; m. Shirley Carver, Jan. 14, 1954; children: Murphy Carver, Matthew Stephen. Student, Young Harris Coll.; AB, MA, U. Ga. Dir. Ga. Bd. Probation, 1965-66; dep. dir. Ga. Dept. Corrections, 1967-68; exec. sec. to Gov. Ga., 1968-71; mem. State Bd. Pardons and Paroles, Atlanta, 1973-75; lt. gov. State of Ga., 1975-90, gov., 1990—; prof. polit. sci. and history U. Ga., Young Harris Coll., 1959-64. Author: The Mountains Within Me, Great Georgians, They Heard Georgia Singing. Mem. Ga. Senate, 1960-64; mayor Young Harris, 1959; exec. dir. Democratic Com. Ga., 1971-72; pres. Coun. State Govts., 1991—; vice chmn. So. Gov.'s Assn., 1991—; bd. dirs. Towns County Hosp. Authority. Served with USMC, 1953-56. Mem. Ga. Sch. Food Services Assn. (life), Ga. Peace Officers Assn. (life), Gridiron Soc. U. Ga., Blue Key, Lions Club. Methodist. Office: Office of Governor State Capitol Rm 203 Atlanta GA 30334*

MILLER-LANE, BARBARA See LANE, BARBARA MILLER

MILLETT, KATHERINE MURRAY (KATE MILLETT), political activist, sculptor, artist, writer; b. St. Paul, Sept. 14, 1934; m. Fumio Yoshimura, 1965. BA magna cum laude, U. Minn., 1956; postgrad. with 1st class honors, St. Hilda's Coll. Oxford, Eng., 1956-58; PhD with distinction, Columbia U., 1970. Instr. English U. N.C. at Greensboro, 1958; file clk. N.Y.C., kindergarten tchr., 1960-61; sculptor, Tokyo, 1961-63; tchr. Barnard Coll., 1964-70; tchr. English Bryn Mawr (Pa.) Coll., 1970; disting. vis. prof. Sacramento State Coll., 1972-73; founder Women's Art Colony Farm, Poughkeepsie, N.Y. Author: Sexual Politics, 1970, The Prostitution Papers, 1973, Flying, 1974, Sita, 1977, The Basement, 1979, Going to Iran, 1982, The Loony Bin Trip, 1990, The Politics of Cruelty, 1994; co-prodr., co-dir. film Three Lives, 1970; one-woman shows Minami Gallery, Tokyo, Judson Gallery, N.Y.C., 1967, Noho Gallery, N.Y.C., 1976, 79, 80, 82, 84, 86, 93, Women's Bldg., L.A., 1977; one-woman drawings Andre Wanters Gallery, Berlin, 1980, Courtland Jessup Gallery, Provincetown, Mass., 1991, 92, 93, 94. Mem. Congress of Racial Equality; chmn. adv. com. NOW, 1966, active supporter women's liberation groups. Mem. Phi Beta Kappa. Office: 295 Bowery New York NY 10003

MILLETT, RALPH LINWOOD, JR., retired newspaper editor; b. Memphis, Oct. 30, 1919; s. Ralph Linwood and Alice (Campbell) M.; m. Mary Virgina Smith, Dec. 10, 1944; children—Mary Jo, Alice Virginia, Jan Vasco, Ralph Linwood III. Student, U. Wyo., 1938-40; BJ., U. Mo., 1942. Copy reader, copy desk chief, news editor Knoxville (Tenn.) News-Sentinel, 1947-66, editor, 1967-84; ret., 1984. Served to lt. USNR, 1942-45. Mem. Am. Soc. Newspaper Editors, Sigma Chi, Sigma Delta Chi, Kappa Tau Alpha. Presbyterian. Club: Cherokee.

MILLEY, JANE ELIZABETH, academic administrator; b. Everett, Mass., May 20, 1940; d. Walter R. and Florence (Leach) M. MusB, Boston U., 1961; MA in Music, Columbia U., 1966; PhD in Higher/Post Sec. Edn.-Adminstrn., Syracuse (N.Y.) U., 1977. Coord., founder, pianist Elmira (N.Y.) Coll. Fine Arts Trio, 1967-75; instr. music Elmira Coll., 1967-70, asst. prof. music, 1970-75, dir. arts and scis. program, 1974-75; rsch. assoc. Syracuse U., 1975-76, adminstrv. asst. to dean Coll. Arts and Scis., 1976-77; div. dean humanities and fine arts Sacramento City Coll., 1977-80; assoc. dean sch. fine arts, prof. music Calif. State U., Long Beach, 1980-81, interim dean, sch. fine arts, prof. music, 1981-82, dean, sch. fine arts, prof. music, 1982-84; arts advisor to chancellor Calif. State Univ. System, 1983-84; chancellor N.C. Sch. Arts U. N.C., Winston-Salem, 1984-89; cons. to pres. Sonoma State U., Rhonert Park, Calif., 1989-90; sr. fellow Am. Assn. State Colls. and Univs., Santa Rosa, Calif., 1989-90; provost, v.p. acad. affairs SUNY, Oswego, 1990-94; provost Simmons Coll., Boston, 1994—; speaker, cons. in field. Author: (with J. Sturnick and C. Tisinger) Women at the Helm, 1991; contbr. articles to profl. jours. Ex officio bd. dirs. Regional Arts Found., 1982-84, N.C. Scenic Studios, 1984-89, N.C. Dance Theatre, 1984-89, N.C. Shakespeare Festival, 1984-89; bd. dirs. Sacramento Film Festival, 1979-80, Long Beach Grand Opera, 1980; charter mem., founder Sacramento Expttl. Theatre, 1978-84. Commendation for excellence Los Rios Community Coll. Bd. Trustees, 1980, Sacramento City Coll., 1980. Mem. AAUW (found. adv. com. 1987-89), Am. Assn. State Colls. and Univs. (chmn. arts com. 1986-89), Nat. Assn. State Univs. and Land Grant Colls. (U. N.C. rep. commn. on arts 1986-89), Internat. Coun. Fine Arts Deans, N.C. Women's Forum, N.Y. Edn. Consortium, N.Y. State Sea Grant Inst. (bd. govs. 1991—), Oswego County Opportunities (bd. dirs. 1991—), Kappa Delta Pi, Pi Kappa Lambda. Office: 300 The Fenway Boston MA 02100

MILLGATE, JANE, language professional; b. Leeds, Eng. June 8, 1937; d. Maurice and Marie (Schofield) Barr; m. Michael Millgate, Feb. 27, 1960.

B.A. with honors, Leeds U., Eng., 1959, M.A., 1963; Ph.D., U.Kent, Eng., 1970. Instr. U. Toronto, Ont., 1964-65, lectr., 1965-70, asst. prof., 1970-72, assoc. prof., 1972-77, prof. English, 1977—, vice-dean arts and scis., 1983-87; mem. bd. regents Victoria U., Toronto, 1981-86. Author: Macaulay, 1973, Walter Scott, 1984, 2d edit., 1987, Scott's Last Edition: A Study in Publishing History, 1987. Editor: Editing 19th Century Fiction, 1978. Contbr. articles to profl. jours. Doctoral fellow Can. Council, 1968-70; research fellow Can. Council, 1972, 74-75, Social Scis. and Humanities Research Council Can., 1980-81, 85-87, 88-90, 91-94, Connaught Rsch. fellow, 1995—. Fellow Royal Soc. Can., Royal Soc. Edinburgh; mem. Victorian Studies Assn. (pres. 1978-80), Assn. Can. Univ. Tchrs. English (pres. 1980-82), Can. Fedn. for Humanities (exec. 1981-83, 95—), Assn. Scottish Studies, Soc. for History of Authorship, Reading and Pub., Bibliog. Soc. Home: 75 Highland Ave, Toronto, ON Canada M4W 2A4 Office: U Toronto, Victoria Coll, Toronto, ON Canada M5S 1K7

MILLGATE, MICHAEL (HENRY), retired English educator; b. Southampton, Eng., July 19, 1929; arrived in Can., 1964; s. Stanley and Marjorie Louisa (Norris) M.; m. Jane Barr, Feb. 27, 1960. BA, Cambridge U., 1952, MA, 1956; postgrad., U. Mich., Ann Arbor, 1956-57; PhD, U. Leeds, 1960. Tutor Workers' Ednl. Assn., Eng., 1953-56; lectr. English lit. U. Leeds, 1958-64; prof., chmn. dept. English York U., Ont., Can., 1964-67; prof. English U. Toronto, 67-94, univ. prof., 87-94; Carpenter lectr. Ohio Wesleyan U., 1978; vis. scholar Meiji U., 1985. Author: William Faulkner, 1961, American Social Fiction, 1964, The Achievement of William Faulkner, 1966, Thomas Hardy: His Career as a Novelist, 1971, Thomas Hardy: A Biography, 1982, Testamentary Acts: Browning, Tennyson, James, Hardy, 1992; editor: Tennyson: Selected Poems, 1963, Thomas Hardy, The Life and Work of Thomas Hardy, 1985, William Faulkner Manuscripts, 20 (4 vols.), 21 (2 vols.), 22 (4 vols.), 23 (2 vols.), 1987, New Essays on Light in August, 1987, Thomas Hardy, Selected Letters, 1990; co-editor: Transatlantic Dialogue, 1966, Lion in the Garden, 1968, The Collected Letters of Thomas Hardy, Vol. I, 1978, Vol. II, 1980, Vol. III, 1982, Vol. IV, 1984, Vol. V, 1985, vol. VI, 1987, Vol. VII, 1988, Thomas Hardy's Studies, Specimens Etc. Notebook, 1994. Can. Coun. leave fellow, 1968-69, S.W. Brooks fellow U. Queensland, 1971; Killam sr. rsch. scholar, 1974-75; Guggenheim Meml. fellow, 1977-78, Connaught sr. fellow, 1979-80; Social Sci. and Humanities Rsch. Coun. Can. leave fellow, 1981-82, grantee, 1977—; Can. Coun. grantee, 1973-77; Killam rsch. fellow, 1986-88. Fellow Royal Soc. Lit., Royal Soc. Can.; mem. MLA (adv. com. for Edit. Am. Authors 1971-74, com. on scholarly edits. 1985-89), Brit. Assn. Am. Studies (exec. com. 1961-64), Victorian Studies Assn. Ont. (pres. 1970-72), Thomas Hardy Soc. (v.p. 1973—), Bibliog. Soc. Am., Soc. for Study So. Lit. (exec. coun. 1972-76, 81-83), Soc. Textual Scholarship, Tennyson Soc. Home: 75 Highland Ave, Toronto, ON Canada M4W 2A4

MILLHONE, JOHN PAUL, federal laboratory administrator; b. Des Moines, Iowa, Nov. 15, 1931; s. Paul L. and Margaret M. (Griffith) M.; m. Carole Malone, Sept. 8, 1954; children: Paul, Kirk, Mark. BJ, U. Mo., 1960. Reporter Columbia (Mo.) Tribune, 1957-60, AP, Jefferson City, Mo., 1960; reporter, Capitol corr. Detroit Free Press, 1960-65, chief editorial writer, 1965-67; editorial writer Des Moines Register, 1967-74; dir. Iowa Energy Policy Coun., Des Moines, 1974-75, Minn. Energy Agy., St. Paul, 1975-79; dir. office of bldg. tech. U.S. Dept. Energy, Washington, 1979-90, dep. asst. sec. for bldg. tech., 1990-94; sr. fellow Advanced Internat. Studies unit Battelle Pacific N.W. Lab., Washington, 1994—; chmn. Internat. Energy Agys. Working Party on End Use Tech., Paris, 1980-82. Editor: Energy Technologies Procs., 3 vols., 1981l; contbr. numerous articles to profl. jours. With U.S. Army, 1954-56. Cited for Outstanding Contbns., Am. Coun. for Energy Efficient Economy, 1988; Fed. Leadership award U.S. Energy Assn. Avocation: running. Office: Battelle Pacific NW Lab 370 L'Enfant Promenade SW Washington DC 20024-2115

MILLIAN, KENNETH YOUNG, public policy consultant; b. Washington, Sept. 29, 1927; s. John Curry and Myrtle (Young) M.; m. Alva Randolph Clarke, Sept. 10, 1949; children: John R., Kenneth Y. Jr., Kathleen M. Gilbert, Elizabeth W. Allen. BA, U. Md., 1951; MA in Internat. Rels., George Washington U., 1969; Diploma, Nat. War Coll., Washington, 1969; MS in Bus., Columbia U., 1980. Officer U.S. Navy, 1951-76; corp. exec. W.R. Grace & Co., N.Y.C. 1976-93; corp. v.p., dir. govt. rels. W.R. Grace & Co., Washington, 1982-88; corp. v.p., dir. environ. policy W.R. Grace & Co., N.Y.C., 1988-93; ret., 1993; pres. Millian Assocs., Washington, 1993—; pres. Found. for Pres.' Pvt. Sector Survey on Cost Control, 1986-92. Labor columnist Japan Times, 1955-57. Bd. govs. Wesley Sem., Washington, 1988—. Democrat. Methodist. Avocations: sailing, golf. Office: Millian Assocs 11 Dupont Circle NW Ste 300 Washington DC 20036-1207

MILLICAN, BILL T., construction company executive; b. Cooper, Tex., Aug. 4, 1925; s. Walter Hugh and Lucinda (Brackeen) M.; m. Virginia Louise Trice, June 26, 1949; children: Mary Jenny, Rebecca. BSCE, Tex. Tch U., 1949; grad. advanced mgmt. program, Harvard U., 1969. Registered profl. engr., Tex. With Suggs Constrn. Co., Big Spring, Tex., 1949-51, Carl E. Maxey Co., J.D. Leftwich Co., Maxey & Leftwich, Lubbock, Tex., 1951-58, Charles Ramsey Co., Lubbock, 1958-60, C.H. Leavell Co., El Paso, Tex., 1960-61; gen. contractor Lubbock, 1961-63; with Henry C. Beck Co., Dallas, 1963-68, exec. v.p., mgr. Western div., Houston, since 1968, also bd. dirs. With USNR, 1942-46. Mem. Houston Club, Warwick Club, Univ. Club. Mem. Ch. of Christ. Office: HCB Contractors 1401 Elm St Dallas TX 75202-2910

MILLICHAP, JOSEPH GORDON, neurologist, educator; b. Wellington, Eng., Dec. 18, 1918; came to U.S., 1956, naturalized, 1965; s. Joseph P. and Alice (Flello) M.; m. Mary Irene Fortey, Feb. 25, 1946 (dec. Oct. 1969); children: Martin Gordon, Paul Anthony; m. Nancy Melanie Kluczynski, Nov. 7, 1970; children: Gordon Thomas, John Joseph. M.B. with honors in Surgery, St. Bartholomew's Med. Coll., U. London, Eng., 1946, M.D. in Internal Medicine, 1951, diploma child health, 1948. Diplomate: Am. Bd. Pediatrics, Am. Bd. Neurology and Child Neurology, Am. Bd. Electroencephalography. Intern, resident St. Bartholomew's Hosp., 1946-49, Hosp. Sick Children, London, 1951-53, Mass. Gen. Hosp., Boston, 1958-60; pediatric neurologist NIH, 1955-56; USPHS fellow neurology Mass. Gen. Hosp., Boston, 1958-60; cons. pediatric neurology Mayo Clinic, 1960-63; pediatric neurologist Children's Meml. Hosp., Northwestern Med. Center, Chgo., 1963—; prof. neurology and pediatrics Northwestern U. Med. Sch., 1963—; Cons. surgeon gen. USPHS; mem. med. adv. bds. Ill. Epilepsy League, Muscular Dystrophy Found., Cerebral Palsy Found., 1963—; vis. prof. Gt. Ormond St. Hosp., U. London, 1986-87. Author: Febrile Convulsions, 1967, Pediatric Neurology, 1967, Learning Disabilities, 1974, The Hyperactive Child with MBD, 1975, Nutrition, Diet and Behavior, 1985, Dyslexia, 1986, Progress in Pediatric Neurology, 1991, Vol. II, 1994, Environmental Poisons in Our Food, 1993, A Guide to Drinking Water, Hazards and Health Risks, 1995; editor Jour. Pediatric Neurology Briefs; contbr. articles to profl. jours., chpts. to books. Chmn. research com. med. adv. bd. Epilepsy Found., 1965—. Served with RAF, 1949-51. Named New Citizen of Year in Met. Chgo., 1965; recipient Americanism Medal D.A.R., 1972; USPHS research grantee, 1957. Fellow Royal Coll. Physicians; mem. Am. Neurol. Assn., Am. Pediatric Soc., Am. Soc. Pediatric Research, Am. Acad. Neurology, Am. Soc. Pharmacology and Exptl. Therapeautics, Soc. Exptl. Biology and Medicine, Am. Bd. Psychiatry and Neurology (asst. examiner 1961—), A.M.A. Episcopalian. Home: PO Box 11391 Chicago IL 60611-0391 Office: Northwestern Meml Med Ctr PO Box 11391 Chicago IL 60611-0391

MILLIGAN, ARTHUR ACHILLE, retired banker; b. Oxnard, Calif., Oct. 29, 1917; s. John Leslie and Julia (Levy) M.; m. Jeanne Welch, Dec. 12, 1942; children: Michael S., Marshall C. B.A., Stanford U., 1938. Pres., CEO Bank of A. Levy, Oxnard, Calif. 1955-82, chmn. bd., 1982-87, chmn. exec. com., 1988-95; dir. Oxnard Frozen Foods Corp., Oxnard, 1958-90; chmn. Real Estate Investment Trust of Calif., Santa Monica, 1968-87, chmn., 1988-91. Served to lt. USN, 1942-45. Mem. Ind. Bankers So. Calif. (pres., 1958), Western Ind. Bankers (pres. 1961), Calif. Bankers Assn. (pres. 1964), Am. Bankers Assn. (pres. 1978). Republican. Club: Valley (dir. 1969-73, 1985-87, 88—, pres. 1990-92) (Montecito). Lodges: Elks, Rotary (pres. 1949—).

MILLIGAN, GLENN ELLIS, psychologist; b. Emporia, Kans., Nov. 12, 1919; s. Ellis S. and Clara (Kriete) M.; m. Phyllis Eaton, Aug. 26, 1945

(div.); children: Douglas, Gregory, David; m. Janice Barron Dawes, Oct. 10, 1970; 1 step-dau., Virginia. BS, Kans. State Tchrs. Coll., 1941, MS, 1942; postgrad., U. Chgo., 1943-44; Ed.D., Colo. State Coll., 1951. Head dept. edn. Findlay (Ohio) Coll., 1946-55; psychologist Columbus (Ohio) Pub. Schs., 1955-56; asso. prof. edn. Ohio Wesleyan U., Delaware, 1956-60; exec. dir. Am. Assn. Mental Deficiency, Columbus, 1960-65; cons. mental retardation Vocat. Rehab. Adminstrn., HEW, 1965-67; psychologist spl. edn. Montgomery County Pub. Schs., Rockville, Md., 1967—; Lectr. Catholic U. Am. Editor: (1st) Mental Retardation, 1963-64, (with others) Directory of Residential Facilities for the Mentally Retarded, 1965. Fellow Am. Assn. Mental Deficiency; mem. Am. Psychol. Assn., NEA (life). Home: 5208 Elsmere Ave Bethesda MD 20814-5731 Office: Montgomery County Pub Schs Spring Mill Field Office 11721 Kemp Mill Rd Silver Spring MD 20902-1722

MILLIGAN, JOHN DRANE, historian, educator; b. N.Y.C., Oct. 11, 1924; s. Carl Glover and Hazel Gray (Drane) M.; m. Joyce Mary Jervis, Nov. 16, 1946; children: Jacqueline M., Paula J., Mary M., Elizabeth Y. B.A., U. Mich., 1952, M.A., 1953, Ph.D., 1961. Teaching asst. U. Mich., 1951-52, teaching fellow, 1954-56; from asst. prof. to prof. history SUNY, Buffalo, 1962—; dir. grad. programs in history SUNY, 1963-68, 94—; dir. undergrad. programs in history, 1979-86, acting dept. chmn., summers, 1977, 78-80, 88; vis. prof. McMaster U., Hamilton, Ont., Can., summer 1964, 69-70. Author: Gunboats Down the Mississippi, 1965, From the Fresh-Water Navy, 1861-1864, 1970; also chpts. in books, articles in jours., encys. Mem. Ann Arbor chpt. NAACP, exec. bd., 1956-61; mem. ACLU, exec. bd., 1959-61; mem. campaign coms. for various candidates for local and nat. office, 1960-76; mem. Buffalo NAACP, Buffalo Housing Opportunities Made Equal, Citizens Council on Human Relations, Physicians for Social Responsibility, Common Cause, Amnesty Internat.; faculty chmn. United Fund dr., 1977; active Foster Parents Plan, 1955—; adoptive parent Internat. Social Services; founder charitable trust for minority coll. scholarships. Served with USAAF, 1943-46, USAFR, 1946-56. James B. Angell scholar U. Mich.; grantee Research Found. SUNY; grantee U.S. Naval Inst.; Citation of Civil War Round Table; Moncado Award of Am. Mil. Inst. Mem. Am. Hist. Assn., Assn. Am. Historians, So. Hist. Assn., Buffalo and Erie County Hist. Soc., Afro-Am. Hist. Soc., Soc. Civil War Historians, Buffalo Council for Responsibility in Fgn. Policy (founding), Soaring Soc. Am., Aircraft Owners and Pilots Assn., Niagara Soaring Club, Cambria Flying Soc., Silver Wings Assn., Civil War Round Table, Tau Sigma Delta, Phi Kappa Phi, Phi Alpha Theta. Home: 21 Allenhurst Rd Buffalo NY 14214-1201 Office: SUNY History Dept Buffalo NY 14260 *If an individual cannot influence for the better the course of humankind, one can sometimes influence for the better the life of another individual.*

MILLIGAN, LAWRENCE DRAKE, JR., consumer products executive; b. Lake Forest, Ill., Apr. 6, 1936; s. Lawrence Drake Sr. and Mary Catherine (Cliggit) M.; m. Lucy Shepard, Oct. 20, 1962; children: Michael D., Carolyn S. BA, Williams Coll., 1960. Nat. sales mgr. Bar Soap and Household Cleaning Products div. Procter & Gamble, Cin., 1974-78; gen. mgr. spl. products Procter & Gamble, Cin., 1979-80, gen. mgr. food service and lodging products, 1980-84, v.p. food service and lodging products, 1984, v.p. food products, 1984-87, v.p. sales in Europe, 1987-89, v.p. sales, customer devel. internat., 1989—; sr. v.p. worldwide sales Procter & Gamble, 1990—. Served as sgt. USMC, 1955-58. Republican. Home: 7475 Old Hickory Ln Cincinnati OH 45243-1454 Office: Procter & Gamble Co 1 Procter Gamble Plz Cincinnati OH 45202

MILLIGAN, MANCIL WOOD, mechanical and aerospace engineering educator; b. Shiloh, Tenn., Nov. 21, 1934; s. Mancil Abernathy and Ivy (Wood) M.; m. Arlys Joyce Cushman, Sept. 15, 1956; children: Mancil Wood, Matthew Wayne. B.S., U. Tenn., 1956, M.S., 1958, Ph.D., 1963; postgrad., U. Wash., 1958, Stanford U., 1964. Research engr. Boeing Co., Seattle, 1956-57, 58-59; instr. mech. engring. U. Tenn., Knoxville, 1957-58; prof. mech. and aerospace engring. U. Tenn., 1959—, head mech. and aerospace engring., 1973-82; cons. to more than 100 industries, 1959—. Mem. ASME, AIAA, Am. Soc. Engring. Edn., Tech. Soc. Knoxville, Pi Tau Sigma, Tau Beta Pi, Sigma Gamma Tau. Home: 10214 Emory Rd Luttrell TN 37779-2942

MILLIGAN, SISTER MARY, theology educator, religious consultant; b. Los Angeles, Jan. 23, 1935; d. Bernard Joseph and Carolyn (Krebs) M. BA, Marymount Coll., 1956; Dr. de l'Univ., U. Paris, 1959; MA in Theology, St. Mary's Coll., Notre Dame, Ind., 1966; STD, Gregorian U., 1975; D. honoris causa, Marymount U., 1988. Tchr. Cours Marymount, Neuilly, France, 1956-59; asst. prof. Marymount Coll., Los Angeles, 1959-67; gen. councillor Religious of Sacred Heart of Mary, Rome, 1969-75, gen. superior, 1980-85; asst. prof. Loyola Marymount U., Los Angeles, 1977-78, provost, 1986-90, prof., 1990—, dean liberal arts, 1992—; pres. bd. dirs. St. John's Sem., Camarillo, Calif., 1986-89; mem. exec. com. Internat. Union Superiors Gen. Rome, 1983-85; mem. planning bd. spiritual renewal program Loyola Marymount U., Los Angeles, 1976-78. Author: That They May Have Life, 1975; compiler analytical index Ways of Peace, 1986; contbr. articles to profl. jours. Vis. scholar Grad. Theol. Union, Berkeley, 1986. Mem. Calif. Women in Higher Edn., Coll. Theology Soc., Cath. Biblical Assn. Democrat. Roman Catholic. Office: Loyola Marymount U 7101 W 80th St Los Angeles CA 90045-2699

MILLIGAN, ROBERT F., state agency administrator; b. Teaneck, N.J., Dec. 27, 1932; m. June; 4 children. BS in Engring., U.S. Naval Acad.; MBA, U. Rochester; postgrad., U. Md. Commd. USMC, advanced through grades to lt. gen.; comdr. pre-positioning ATO, ETO; comdr. U.S. Forces in Caribbean; comdg. gen. Fleet Marine Forces, Hawaii; ret., 1991; comptr. State of Fla., Tallahassee, 1994—; mem. Fla. Cabinet. Republican. Office: Office of Comptr Dept Banking and Fin Plaza Level Place, Capitol Bldg Tallahassee FL 32399

MILLIKAN, CLARK HAROLD, physician; b. Freeport, Ill., Mar. 2, 1915; s. William Clarance and Louise (Chamberlain) M.; m. Gayle Margaret Gross, May 2, 1942 (div. Apr. 1966); children: Terri, Clark William, Jeffry Brent; m. Janet T. Holmes, July 21, 1966 (div. Dec. 1987); m. Nancy Futrell, Dec. 28, 1987. Student, Parsons (Kans.) Jr. Coll., 1935; MD, U. Kans., 1939. Diplomate Am. Bd. Psychiatry and Neurology. Intern St. Luke's Hosp., Clev. 1939-40, asst. resident medicine, 1940-41; from resident neurology to asst. prof. neurology State U. Iowa, Iowa City, 1941-49; staff Mayo Clinic, Rochester, Minn., 1949—, cons. neurology, 1958—; dir. Mayo Center for Clin. Research in Cerebrovascular Disease; prof. neurology Mayo Sch. Medicine; physician-in-chief pro tem Cleve. Clinic, 1970; prof. neurology U. Utah Sch. Medicine, Salt Lake City, 1976-87, U. Miami (Fla.) Sch. Medicine, 1987-88; scholar in residence, dept. neurology Henry Ford Hosp., Detroit, 1988-92; prof. neurology Sch. of Medicine Creighton U., Omaha, 1992-94; clin. prof. neurology Med. Coll. Ohio, Toledo, 1994—; Asst. chmn., editor trans. 2d Princeton Conf. Cerebrovascular Disease, 1957, chmn. confs., 1961, 64; chmn. com. classification and nomenclature cerebrovascular disease USPHS, 1955-69; mem. council Nat. Inst. Neurologic Diseases and Blindness, NIH, USPHS, 1965-69, div. regional med. program, 1965-68; A.O.A. lectr. Baylor U., Waco, Tex., 1952; James Mawer Pearson Meml. lectr., Vancouver, B.C., Can., 1958; Conner Meml. lectr. Am. Heart Assn., 1961; Peter T. Bohan lectr. U. Kans., 1965, 73. Editor: Jour. Stroke, 1970-76; assoc. editor, 1976—. Recipient Outstanding Alumnus award U. Kans., 1973. Fellow ACP, Am. Acad. Neurology (founding chmn. sect. on stroke and vascular neurology 1994), Royal Soc. Medicine; mem. AMA, AAUP, AAAS, Assn. Rsch. Nervous and Mental Disease (pres. 1961), Am. Neurol. Assn. (1st v.p. 1969-70, pres. 1973-74), Minn. Med. Assn., Four County Med. Soc. South Minn., Cen. Neuropsychiat. Assn., N.Y. Acad. Sci., Am. Heart Assn. (chmn. coun. cerebrovascular disease 1967-68, Gold Heart award 1976, Spl. Merit award 1981), Nat. Stroke Assn. (pres. 1986), Sigma Xi.

MILLIKEN, CHRISTINE TOPPING, legal association administrator, lawyer. BApin Polit. U., Geo. Wash. U., 1970, JD, Catholic U. Am., 1976. Bar: DC, U.S. Supreme Ct. Legislative cons. Harvard U., 1976-77; v.p. and gen. counsel Nat. Assn. Ind. Colls. and Univs., 1977-86; exec. dir. and gen. counsel Nat. Assn. of Attys. Gen., 1986—; mem. The Washington Ctr., 1982—, chair 1987-94; mem. Ind. Sector Founding Bd., Ethics Task Force,

Mgmt. Com., chair Govt. Rels. Com. Office: Nat Assn Attys Gen 444 N Capitol St NW Washington DC 20001-1512*

MILLIKEN, JOHN GORDON, research economist; b. Denver, May 12, 1927; s. William Boyd and Margaret Irene (Marsh) M.; m. Marie Violet Machell, June 13, 1953; children: Karen Marie, Douglas Gordon, David Tait, Anne Alain. BS, Yale U., 1949, BEng, 1950; MS, U. Colo., 1966, PhD, 1969. Registered profl. engr., Colo. Engr. U.S. Bur. Reclamation, Denver, 1950-55; asst. to plant mgr. Stanley Aviation Corp., Denver, 1955-56; prin. mgmt. engr., dept. mgr. Martin-Marietta Aerospace Div., Denver, 1956-64; mgmt. engr. Safeway Stores, Inc., Denver, 1964-66; sr. rsch. economist, prof., assoc. div. head U. Denver Rsch. Inst., 1966-86; pres. Univ. Senate, 1980-81; prin Milliken Chapman Rsch. Group, Inc., Littleton, Colo., 1986-88, Milliken Rsch. Group, Inc., Littleton, 1988—; vis. fellow sci. policy rsch. unit U. Sussex, Eng., 1975-76; bd. dirs. Sci. Mgmt. Corp.; cons. mgmt. engr. Author: Aerospace Management Techniques, 1971, Federal Incentives for Innovation, 1974, Recycling Municipal Wastewater, 1977, Water and Energy in Colorado's Future, 1981, Metropolitan Water Management, 1981, Technological Innovation and Economic Vitality, 1983, Water Management in the Denver, Colorado Urban Area, 1988, Benefits and Costs of Oxygenated Fuels in Colorado, 1990, Water Transfer Alternatives Study, 1994, Colorado Springs Water Resources Plan Alternative Assessment Study, 1995; contbr. articles to profl. jours. Bd. dirs. Southeast Englewood Water Dist., 1963—, South Englewood San. Dist., 1965—; bd. dirs. South Suburban Park and Recreation Dist., 1971—; chmn., 1990-92; chmn. Dem. Com. of Arapahoe County, 1969-71, 5th Congl. Dist. Colo., 1972-73, 74-75; mem. exec. com. Colo. Faculty Adv. Coun., 1981-85; mem. Garrison Diversion Unit Commn., 1984; trustee Colo. Local Govt. Liquid Asset Trust, 1986—, chmn., 1991-93; bd. dirs. Colo. Spl. Dist. Assn. Property and Liability Pool, 1989—. With M.C. U.S. Army, 1945-46. Recipient Adlai E. Stevenson Meml. award, 1981, hon. title "Amicus Universitatis," U. Denver, 1994. Mem. Acad. Mgmt., Nat. Assn. Bus. Economists, Yale Sci. and Engring. Assn., Am. Water Works Assn., Sigma Xi, Tau Beta Pi, Beta Gamma Sigma, Sigma Iota Epsilon. Congregationalist. Home and Office: 6502 S Ogden St Littleton CO 80121-2561

MILLIKEN, ROGER, textile company executive; b. N.Y.C., Oct. 24, 1915; s. Gerrish and Agnes (Gayley) M.; m. Justine V. R. Hooper, June 5, 1948; children: Justine, Nancy, Roger, David, Weston. Student, Groton Sch., 1929-33; A.B., Yale U., 1937; LL.D. (hon.), Wofford Coll., Rose-Hulman Inst. Tech., Phila. Coll. Textiles and Sci., Brenau Coll., The Citadel; D. Textile Industry (hon.), Clemson U.; D.H.L. (hon.), Converse Coll. CEO Milliken & Co., 1947-83, chmn., chief exec. officer, 1983—; bd. dirs. Merc. Stores Co., W.R. Grace & Co.; chmn. bd. Inst. Textile Tech., 1948—; bd. dirs. Am. Textile Mfrs. Inst., S.C. Textile Mfrs. Assn. Chmn. Greenville-Spartanburg Airport Commn.; trustee Wofford Coll., S.C. Found. Ind. Coll. Mem. Bus. Council, Textile Inst. (Eng.) (companion mem.). Clubs: Union League, Links, Augusta Nat. Golf, Yeamans Hall. Office: Milliken & Co 1045 6th Ave New York NY 10018*

MILLIMET, ERWIN, lawyer; b. N.Y.C., Oct. 7, 1925; s. Maurice and Henrietta (Cohen) M.; m. Mary Malia; children: Robert, James, Rachel, Sarah. BA magna cum laude, Amherst Coll., 1948; LLB cum laude, Harvard U., 1951. Bar: N.Y. 1952. Formerly sr. ptnr., chmn. exec. com. Stroock & Stroock & Lavan, N.Y.C., ret. 1991. Mem. bd. visitors U. San Diego Law Sch.; active Nat. Support Group for Africa; founder Citizens for Am., Washington, 1984; mem. Rep. Presdl. Task Force; mem. Rep. Club, N.Y.C. and Washington. Served with inf. U.S. Army, 1943-46. Mem. N.Y. State Bar Assn., Assn. of Bar of City of N.Y., Fed. Bar Assn., Phi Beta Kappa.

MILLIMET, JOSEPH ALLEN, retired lawyer; b. West Orange, N.J., July 23, 1914; s. Morris and Dorothy (McBlain) M.; m. Elizabeth Gray Gingras, Jan. 10, 1942; children: Madlyn Ann (Mrs. Angus Deming), Lisa Gray (Mrs. Silas Little, III), Rebecca Allen (Mrs. James Smith), Peter Joseph (dec.). A.B., Dartmouth Coll., 1936; LL.B., Yale U., 1939; LLD (hon.), U. N.H., 1992. Bar: N.H. 1939. Pvt. practice Concord and Manchester, N.H.; sr. ptnr. Devine, Millimet, Stahl & Branch, and predecessors (now Devine Millimet & Branch), Manchester, 1947-93, ret.; with FCC, 1941-42. Mem. N.H. Bd. Bar Examiners 1953-61, legislative counsel to gov. N.H., 1963-66; chmn. Commn. to Revise N.H. Constn., 1964, 74, 84; mem. Commn. Uniform State Laws, 1965-73. Served with USCG, 1942-45. Fellow Am. Coll. Trial Lawyers; mem. N.H. Bar Assn. (pres. 1962-63), ABA. Democrat. Home: 1655 N River Rd Manchester NH 03104 Office: Devine Millimet & Branch 111 Amherst St Manchester NH 03105-0719

MILLING, BERT WILLIAM, JR., federal judge; b. Mobile, Ala., Mar. 5, 1946; s. Bert William and Marjorie Anne (Smith) M.; m. Priscilla Pitman, Apr. 15, 1966; children: Brooks Pitman, Jeremy Bacon, Maran Celeste. AB in Philosophy, Coll. William and Mary, 1968; JD, U. Ala., 1971. Bar: Ala. 1971. Legal officer 212th Arty. Group, Fort Lewis, Wash., 1971-72; legal asst. officer Judge Advocate Gen.'s Office, Ft. Sill, Okla., 1972-74; spl. asst. atty. gen. Dist. Atty.'s Office, Mobile, 1974-75, asst. dist. atty., 1977-78; assoc. Sintz, Pike, Campbell & Duke, Mobile, 1975-77; ct. referee Juvenile Div. of Cir. Ct., Mobile, 1978-81; counsel U.S. Senate Com. on Jud., Subcom. on Security & Terrorism, Washington, 1981-83; asst. U.S. atty. Justice Dept., Mobile, 1983-86; U.S. magistrate judge U. S. Dist. Ct. Ala., Mobile, 1986—. Capt. U.S. Army, 1971-74. Mem. Ala. Bar Assn., Mobile Bar Assn. Avocations: jogging, reading. Office: US Courthouse 113 Saint Joseph St Mobile AL 36602-3606

MILLING, MARCUS EUGENE, SR., geologist; b. Galveston, Tex., Oct. 8, 1938; s. Robert Richardson and Leonora Mildred (Currey) M.; m. Sandra Ann Dunlay, Sept. 21, 1959; 1 child, Marcus Eugene Jr. BS in Geology, Lamar U., 1961; MS in Geology, U. Iowa, 1964, PhD in Geology, 1968. Cert. petroleum geologist. Rsch. geologist Exxon Prodn. Rsch. Co., Houston, 1968-76; prodn. geologist Exxon Co. U.S.A., Kingsville, Tex., 1976-78; dist. exptl. geologist Exxon Co. U.S.A., New Orleans, 1978-80; mgr. geol. rsch. Arco Oil and Gas Co., Plano, Tex., 1980-86; chief geologist Arco Oil and Gas Co., Dallas, 1986-87; assoc. dir. Bur. Econ. Geology U. Tex., Austin, 1987-92; exec. dir. Am. Geol. Inst., Alexandria, Va., 1992—; vice-chmn. Offshore Tech. Conf., Dallas, 1984-87; dir. Geosci. Inst. for Oil and Gas Recovery Rsch., Austin, 1988-91. NSF fellow, 1966. Fellow Geol. Soc. Am. (councilor 1986-89); mem. Am. Assn. Petroleum Geologists, Soc. Petroleum Engrs., Am. Inst. Profl. Geologists, Blue Key, Sigma Xi. Home: 11457 Hollow Timber Ct Reston VA 22094-1980 Office: Am Geol Inst 4220 King St Alexandria VA 22302-1507

MILLING, R(OSWELL) KING, bank executive, lawyer; b. New Orleans, Aug. 7, 1940; s. Robert E. and Claudia (Pipes) M.; m. Anne McDonald, June 20, 1964; children—Roberts Clay II, Roswell King Jr., Michael Delery. BA, Washington and Lee U., 1962; LLB, Tulane U., 1965. Bar: La. 1965, U.S. Dist. Ct. (ea. dist.) La. 1965, U.S. Ct. Appeals (5th cir.) 1965, U.S. Sup. Ct. 1979, U.S. Ct. Appeals (11th cir.) 1981. Assoc. Milling, Saal, Saunders, Benson & Woodward (now Milling, Benson, Woodward, Hillyer, Pierson & Miller), New Orleans, 1965-69, ptnr., 1969-84; pres. Whitney Nat. Bank, New Orleans, 1984—, also bd. dirs.; Whitney Holding Corp., New Orleans; past pres. Bur. Govtl. Research, New Orleans. mem. Met. Area Com.; La. Civil Service League; past chmn. Upper Pontalba Bldg Commn.; bd. trustees Dillard U., N.O. Marine Inst.; bd. dirs. Downtown Devel. Dist., L.A. Civil Svc. League. Mem. La. State Bar Assn., ABA. Office: Whitney Nat Bank 228 St Charles Ave New Orleans LA 70130-2615

MILLIS, ROBERT LOWELL, astronomer; b. Martinsville, Ill., Sept. 12, 1941; married, 1965; 2 children. BA, Ea. Ill. U., 1963; PhD in Astronomy, U. Wis., 1968. Astronomer Lowell Obs., Flagstaff, Ariz., 1967-86, assoc. dir., 1986-90, dir., 1990—. Mem. Am. Astron. Soc., Astronomy Soc. Pacific, Internat. Astronomy Union, Divsn. Planetary Sci. (sec.-treas. 1985-88, chmn. 1994-95). Achievements include research in planetary satellites and ring systems; occultation studies of solar system objects; research on comets. Office: Lowell Observatory 1400 W Mars Hill Rd Flagstaff AZ 86001-4499

MILLMAN, HOWARD J., artistic director; b. Bklyn., Apr. 28, 1931; s. Philip and Dorothy (Feldman) M.; m. Joyce Noreen Skjellerup, June 3, 1953; children: David, Devora. BA, Hartwick Coll., 1952; MS, Purdue U., 1953; PhD, Fla. State U. Asst. prof. drama MontClair (N.J.) State Coll., 1960-61;

entertainment dir. U.S. Army, N.C. and Europe, 1961-68; mng. dir. Asolo Theatre, Sarasota, Fla., 1968-80; prodn. artistic dir. GeVa Theatre, Rochester, N.Y., 1982—; cons. Found. for Encouragement of Am. Profl. Theatre, N.Y.C., 1982. Dir. (plays) Front Page, 1970, Macbeth, 1974, Boy Meets Girl, 1976, History of American Film, 1982, Quilters, 1983, The Immigrant, 1987, Inherit the Wind, 1987, I'm Not Rappaport, 1989, Frankie & Johnny, 1989, A Stone Carver, 1991, Man of La Mancha, 1991. With U.S. Army, 1953-55. Recipient Disting. Alumnus award Hartwick Coll., 1989. Mem. Soc. Stage Dirs. and Choreographers. Democrat. Jewish. Avocation: golf. Office: GeVa Theatre 75 Woodbury Blvd Rochester NY 14607-1795

MILLMAN, JODE SUSAN, lawyer; b. Poughkeepsie, N.Y., Dec. 28, 1954; d. Samuel Keith and Ellin Sadenberg (Bainder) M.; m. Michael James Harris, June 20, 1982; children: Maxwell, Benjamin. BA, Syracuse U., 1976, JD, 1979. Bar: N.Y. 1980, U.S. Dist. Ct. (so. and ea. dists.) N.Y. 1982, U.S. Supreme Ct. 1983. Asst. corp. counsel City of Poughkeepsie, 1979-81; assoc. Law Office of Lou Lewis, Poughkeepsie, 1981-85; pvt. practice Poughkeepsie, 1985—; staff counsel City of Poughkeepsie Office of Property Devel., 1990—; gen. mgr. WCZX-Communicatons Corp. Contbg. author: Kaminstein Legislative History of the Copyright Law, 1979. Pres. Dutchess County (N.Y.) Vis. Bur., 1980-82; bd. dirs. Poughkeepsie Ballet Theater, 1982, Jewish Community Ctr., 1988; mem. assigned counsel program Dutchess County Family Ct., 1985—; trustee Greater Poughkeepsie Libr. Dist., 1991—. Mem. ABA, N.Y. State Bar Assn., Dutchess County Bar Assn. (chmn. pub. rels. 1991—), Mid-Hudson Women's Bar Assn., Poughkeepsie Area C. of C. (econ. devel. com. 1994—). Democrat. Jewish. Office: 97-99 Cannon St Poughkeepsie NY 12601-3140

MILLMAN, RICHARD GEORGE, architect, educator; b. St. Johns, Mich., Feb. 12, 1925; s. Harold Fildew and Elizabeth Hill (Van Deusen) M.; m. Mary Louise Manley, June 17, 1950; children: John Richard, Ruth Barbara. BArch. U. Mich., 1951, MArch, 1962. Registered architect, Mich., Ohio, Ala. Job capt. Smith Hinchman & Grylls, Detroit, 1951-52; designer assoc. Eliot Robinson, AIA, Birmingham, Mich., 1952-55; designer Eero Saarinen Assocs., Bloomfield Hills, Mich., 1955-56; assoc. Chas. W. Lane Assocs. Inc., Ann Arbor, Mich., 1956-59; prin. Kainlauri, MacMullan, Millman, Ann Arbor, 1959-62; assoc. prof. Ohio U., Athens, 1962-68; prof. Auburn (Ala.) U., 1968—, head architecture dept., 1968-73, 84-85, head indsl. design dept., 1988-89; prof. Mid. East Tech. U., Ankara, Turkey, 1966-67,King Faisal U., Dammam, Saudi Arabia, 1979-81. One man shows include Dhahran Art Group, Saudi Arabia, 1981, Peet Gallery, Auburn U., 1983, 91; author: Washtenaw Community Coll., 1962, Auburn U. Tour Guide, 1990. With U.S. Army, 1943-46, ETO, PTO. Recipient Cert. of Honor Ala. Hist. Commn., 1977; Alumni scholar U. Mich., 1961; Fulbright lectr. Econ. Com., Mid. East Tech. U., 1966. Mem. AIA (treas. Ala. coun. 1969, v.p. 1970, pres. 1972, emeritus 1990, Auburn chpt. pres. 1970, emeritus), Nat. Coun. Archtl. Registration Bd. (cert.), Auburn Arts Assn. Avocations: painting, photography. Home: 736 Brenda Ave Auburn AL 36830-6038 Office: Auburn U Architecture Dept 104 Dudley Hall Auburn AL 36849-5121

MILLMAN, ROBERT BARNET, psychiatry and public health educator; b. N.Y.C., 1939. BA, Cornell U., 1961; MD, SUNY, 1965. Intern in internal medicine NYU div. Bellevue Hosp., N.Y.C., 1965-66; with rsch. and adminstrn NIH, Washington, 1966-68; resident in internal medicine N.Y. Hosp., 1968-70; resident in psychiatry Payne Whitney Psychiat. Clinic, 1974-77, assoc. attending psychiatrist, 1977-89, attending psychiatrist, 1989—; project dir. adolescent devel. program, dept. pub. health Dept. Pub. Health, 1970—, acting chmn., 1992—; clin. affiliate in medicine Payne Whitney Psychiat. Clinic, 1977—; assoc. prof. clin. psychiatry Cornell U., N.Y.C., 1980-84, Disting. prof. psychiatry and pub. health, 1986—; vis. assoc. physician Rockefeller U., 1972-79; dir. Substance Abuse Svcs., N.Y. Hosp., 1980—; chmn. tech adv. group on drugs, N.Y.C., 1989-92; chmn. com. on alcohol and drugs N.Y. Acad. Med., 1988—; med., psychiat. advisor Major League Baseball, 1992—, Assocs. Tennis Profls.; adv. com. Robert Wood Johnson Found., 1990—. Mem. N.Y. Acad. Medicine, Am. Psychiat. Assn., Am. Pub. Health Assn., Acad. Med. Educators and Rschrs. in Substance Abuse, Am. Soc. on Addiction Medicine. Office: Cornell U Med Coll Dept Pub Health 1300 York Ave New York NY 10021-4805*

MILLNER, ROBERT B., lawyer; b. N.Y.C., Apr. 20, 1950; s. Nathan and Babette E. (Leventhal) M.; m. Susan Brent, June 5, 1983; children: Jacob, Daniel, Rebecca. BA, Wesleyan U., 1971; JD, U. Chgo., 1975. Bar: Ill. 1975. Law clk. to Hon. George C. Edwards U.S. Ct. Appeals for 6th Cir., Cin., 1975-76; with Sonnenschein Nath & Rosenthal, Chgo., 1976—, ptnr., 1982—; mem. Panel of Bankruptcy Trustees, Chgo., 1992—. Editorial bd. Jour. Corp. Disclosure and Confidentiality, 1989-92; contbr. articles to profl. jours. Trustee Anshe Emet Synagogue, Chgo., 1990-93; mem. gov. coun. Am. Jewish Cong. midwest region, 1989—. Fellow Am. Bar Found.; mem. ABA (co-chair bankruptcy and insolvency com. litigation sect. 1992—), Am. Bankruptcy Inst., Shakespearean Assn. of Am. (v.p. Stratford chpt. 1992—), Chgo. Bar Assn., Comml. Bar Assn. (hon. overseas mem.), Legal Club, Standard Club, Wesleyan Alumni Club Chgo. (pres. 1988-90), Phi Beta Kappa. Office: Sonnenschein Nath & Rosenthal 8000 Sears Towers Chicago IL 60606

MILLNER, THOMAS, manufacturing and holding company executive. Pres. The Pilliod Cabinet Co., High Point, N.C., Pilliod Holding Co., Swanton, Ohio. Office: The Pilliod Cabinet Co 1403 Eastchester Dr High Point NC 27265-2307

MILLO, APRILE ELIZABETH, opera singer; b. N.Y.C., Apr. 14, 1958; d. Giovanni and Margarita (Girosi) M. Grad., Hollywood High Sch., 1976. Operatic debut in Aida, Utah Opera, Salt Lake City, 1980; European debut in Aida, Karlsruhe Opera House, 1982; appeared in Ernani, La Scala Teatro, Milan, 1982, Simon Boccanegra, Met. Opera, N.Y.C., 1984; prin. artist, Met. Opera, 1984—; appeared as Elizabetta in Don Carlo, Teatro a Bologna, Italy, 1987, Aida, Met. Opera, 1989; recs. include A Recital with Eugene Kohn, 1986, Aida Sony Classical, 1990, Lusia MIller Classical, 1991, Il Trovatore Sony Classical, 1991; video Deuctle Grammaphone Un Ballo in Maschera, 1991. Recipient Voce Verdiane award Verdian Voice Competition, Busetto, Italy, 1978, Monserrat Caballe Verdi award Francisco Viñas Competition, Barcelona, Spain, 1979, Richard Tucker Found. award, N.Y.C., 1985, Maria Callas award Maria Callas Found., Frankfort, Fed. Republic Germany, 1986, Showstopper award N.Y. Woman mag., 1987. Roman Catholic. Avocations: tennis, sports, reading. Office: Met Opera Assn Inc Lincoln Ctr New York NY 10023 also: Columbia Artists Mgt Inc Crittenden Anson Div 165 W 57th St New York NY 10019

MILLON, HENRY ARMAND, fine arts educator, architectural historian; b. Altoona, Pa., Feb. 22, 1927; s. Henri Francois and Louise (de Serent) M.; m. Emily Dees, June, 1953; m. Judith Rice, Dec. 27, 1966; children: Henri, Hadrian, Phoebe, Aaron. BA, Tulane U., 1947, BS, 1949, BArch, 1953; AM, Harvard U., 1954, MArch, 1955, PhD, 1964; LHD (hon.), Tulane U., 1995. Asst. prof. MIT, Cambridge, 1960-69, prof., 1969-80, vis. prof., 1981—, pres. univ. Film Study Ctr., 1972-73, trustee Film Study Ctr., 1967-73; dean Ctr. for Advanced Study in Visual Arts, Nat. Gallery Art, Washington, 1979—; mem. bd. visitors Fine Arts Sch. Boston Mus., 1972-78; mem. rsch. grants panel NEH, 1972-73, rsch. tools panel, 1983; dir. Am. Acad. in Rome, 1974-77, trustee, 1977—, vice chmn., 1982—; mem. adv. coun. Sch. Architecture, Princeton U., 1970-73, adv. coun. dept. art and archeology, 1972-73, 80-84; mem. cons. Nat. Survey Historic Sites and Bldgs., Nat. Pk. Svc. div. U.S. Dept. Interior, 1969-80; vice chmn. Boston Landmarks Commn., 1970-73; panelist Gladys Krieble Delmas Found., 1979—; chmn. adv. bd. architecture and design TV series Guggenheim Prodns., 1980-88; vis. com. Dept. Fine Arts Harvard U., 1982-84, Sch. Hist. Studies Inst. Advanced Study, 1978, Arthur M. Sackler Gallery Smithsonian Instn., 1986-92; mem. U.S. Nat. Com. History of Art, 1980—; alt. del. Internat. Com. History of Art, 1981-85, del., 1985—; sec. sec. working group Thesaurus Artis Universalis, 1983-89; hon. mem. Boston Archtl. Ctr., 1982—; chmn. sr. fellows com. history of landscape architecture program Dumbarton Oaks, 1983-89; convenor archtl. drawing arts group, 1983—; mem. adv. com. Getty Art Hist. Info. Program, 1983-91, mem. internat. repertory of lit. of art history, 1985-90, adv. com. Bibliography of the History of Art, 1986—; vice chmn. Coun. Am. Overseas Rsch. Ctrs., 1984-90;

pres. Found. for Documents of Architecture, 1987-93; trustee Nat. Bldg. Mus., 1988-94. Author: Baroque and Rococco Architecture, 1962, Key Monuments of the History of Architecture, 1964, Filippo Juvarra: Drawings from the Roman Period, 1704-1714, 1984, (with Craig H. Smyth) Michelangelo Architect, 1988; editor: (with Linda Nochlin) Art and Architecture in the Service of Politics, 1978, Studies in Italian Art and Architecture 15th through 18th Centuries, 1980; co-editor: The Renaissance From Brunelleschi to Michelangelo: The Representation of Architecture, 1994. With USNR, 1944-46. Fulbright fellow, Italy, 1957, Am. Acad. Rome fellow, 1957-60. Mem. Soc. Archtl. Historians (pres. 1968-70), Coll. Art Assn. (bd. dirs. 1982-85), AIA Found. (mem. octagon com. 1986-88), Renaissance Soc., Am. Acad. Arts and Scis., Am. Philos. Soc., Deputazione Subalpina di Storia Patria, Soc. Preservation New Eng. Antiquities, Am. Inst. Archeology, Am. Soc. 18th Century Studies, Academia delle Scienze di Torino. Home: 8051 Parkside Ln NW Washington DC 20012-2252

MILLS, AGNES EUNICE KARLIN, artist, printmaker, sculptor; b. N.Y.C., Apr. 2, 1915; d. Herman Karlin and Celia (Ducoffe) Karlin; m. Saul Mills, May 10, 1910 (dec. Nov. 1993); children: Karen, Marghe Mills Thysen. Grad., Cooper Union Art Sch., N.Y.C., 1938; BFA, Pratt Inst., 1975; student, NYU. One-woman shows include Carus Gallery, N.Y.C., Unitarian Soc., Manhasset, N.Y., Harbor Gallery, Cold Spring Harbor, N.Y., North Truro Art Gallery, Cape Cod, Mass., Alfredo Valente Gallery, N.Y.C., Robbins Gallery, East Orange, N.J., Nuance Galleries, Tampa, Friends of Tampa Ballet, Graphic Eye Coop Gallery, Pt. Washington, N.Y., City Ctr. Gallery, N.Y.C., Lincoln Ctr. Art Gallery, N.Y.C., North Shore Cmty. Arts Ctr., Great Neck, N.Y., Delray Beach Works in Progress Gallery, Boca Raton Cmty. Ctr., Palm Beach Pub. Libr.; exhibited in group shows at Alfredo Valente Gallery, N.Y.C., Audubon Soc., N.Y.C., Bowdoin Coll. Mus. Art, Brunswick, Maine, Brandeis U., Waltham, Mass., Bklyn. Mus. Art, Brown U., Providence, Butler Inst. Am. Art, Youngstown, Ohio, Colgate U. Libr., Hamilton, N.Y., Cornell U. Ithaca, N.Y., East Hampton (N.Y.) Guild Artists, Gallery K, Woodstock, N.Y., Graphic Eye Coop Gallery, Port Washington, N.Y., Heckscher Mus., Huntington, N.Y., Hunterdon County Mus., Clinton, N.J., Joan Avnet Gallery, Great Neck, N.Y., Lincoln Ctr. Libr. Performing Arts, N.Y.C., Madison Gallery, N.Y.C., Boca Raton City Hall, Boca Raton Cmty. Ctr., Boca Raton Libr.; represented in permanent collections at Boca Raton Mus. Art, Nat. Women in the Arts Mus. Home: Ste L 9 144 8903 Glades Rd Boca Raton FL 33434-4023 Studio: 9763 Majorca Pl Boca Raton FL 33434-3713

MILLS, ANDREW GEOFFREY, financial executive; b. Leicester, Eng., June 6, 1952; s. John Alfred and Noreen Mary (Burgess) M.; m. Gail O'Connell, Aug. 20, 1983; children: Victoria Ann, Christopher John. BA, Oxford (Eng.) U., 1973; MBA, Harvard U., 1979. Sales exec. Courtaulds Ltd., London, 1973-75; regional mgr. Courtaulds Ltd., N.Y.C., 1975-77; mgr. Boston Cons. Group, 1979-84; pres. Bus. Rsch. Group, Boston, 1984-86, Tech. Data Internat., Boston, 1986-89, Thompson Fin. Networks, Boston, 1989—; bd. dirs. 1st Call Corp., Boston, Tech. Data Internat., Ltd., London, Tech. Data Internat. (Far East) Inc., Tokyo; pres., bd. dirs. 1st Call Internat., Boston. Mem. H.B.S.O.B.R.F.C. (capt. 1980-86). Avocations: rugby, skiing, cycling, theater. Office: Thompson Fin Networks 22 Pittsburgh St Boston MA 02210

MILLS, BRADFORD, merchant banker; b. N.Y.C., Dec. 16, 1926; s. Dudley Holbrook and Louise (Morris) M.; m. Cheryl Ann Di Paolo; children: Elizabeth Lee, Bradford Alan, Barbara Louise, Ross Dudley. BA cum laude in Econs, Princeton U., 1948; postgrad., Oxford (Eng.) U., 1950-51. Asst. to dir. overseas terr. div. ECA, Paris, 1948-50; F. Eberstadt & Co., N.Y.C., 1954-62; ptnr. F. Eberstadt & Co., 1960-62; mng. ptnr. N.Y. Securities Co., 1962-70; chmn. dir. Specialized Svcs., Inc., Atlanta, 1968-85; pres., CEO Overseas Pvt. Investment Corp., Washington, 1971-73; dir. Overseas Pvt. Investment Corp., 1971-75; chmn. bd., dir. F. Eberstadt & Co. Internat., 1973-74; mng. ptnr. Bradford Assocs., 1974-92; ltd. ptnr. Bradford Investment Ptnrs. Ltd., 1992—; CEO Overseas Pvt. Investors Ltd., Overseas Pvt. Equities, Overseas Equity Investors, Inc., U.S. Precision Glass Inc.; bd. dirs. The Sunbelt Cos., Inc., DentureCare, Inc., The Princeton Packet, Futronix Corp. Pres. Mills Found.; trustee, treas. Millbrook (N.Y.) Sch., 1978—; trustee Med. ctr. Princeton. Mem. Coun. Fgn. Rels. Clubs: Blooming Grove (Pa.); Links, Princeton, Leash; Anglers of N.Y.; Nassau, Bedens Brook (Princeton). Home: 15 Van Kirk Rd Princeton NJ 08540-4207 Office: 22 Chambers St Princeton NJ 08542-3719

MILLS, CELESTE LOUISE, hypnotherapist, professional magician; b. L.A., May 16, 1952; d. Emery John and Helen Louise (Bradbury) W.; m. Robert Richardson Feigel, Apr. 11, 1971 (div. 1973); m. Peter Alexander Mills, June 12, 1991. (div. 1992). BBA, Western State U., Doniphan, Mo., 1987; PhD in Religion, Universal Life Ch. Univ., 1987; grad., Hypnotism Tng. Inst., Glendale, Calif., 1990. Cert. hypnotherapist. Credit mgr. accounts receivable Gensler-Lee Diamonds, Santa Barbara, Calif., 1973-74, Terry Hinge and Hardware, Van Nuys, Calif., 1975-78; credit mgr., fin. analyst Peanut Butter Fashions, Chatsworth, Calif., 1978-82; personal mgr. Charter Mgmt. Co., Beverly Hills, Calif., 1982-83; co-owner, v.p. Noreen Jenney Communicates, Beverly Hills, 1983-85; corp. credit mgr., fin. analyst Cen. Diagnostic Lab., Tarzana, Calif., 1985-89; credit mgr., fin. analyst Metwest Clin. Lab., Inc., Tarzana, Calif., 1989-90; pvt. practice, 1990—; cons. Results Now, Inc., Tarzana, 1986-87. Prodr., host (TV) Brainstorm, 1993—. Mem. NAFE, Nat. Assn. Credit Mgmt., Credit Mgrs. Assn. So. Calif., Credit Ednl. Found., Nat. Humane Ednl. Found., Credit Mgrs. Assn. Trade Groups (bd. govs. 1988-89), Nat. Clin. Lab. Trade Group (chmn. 1988-89), Med. and Surg. Suppliers Trade Group (vice-chmn. 1988-89, chmn. 1989-90), Soc. Am. Magicians, Acad. Magical Arts, Internat. Brotherhood of Magicians, Am. Advanced Ethical Hypnosis, Am. Coun. Hypnotist Examiners. Avocations: scuba diving, sailing.

MILLS, CHARLES G., photography company executive; b. 1935; married. Grad., Auburn U., 1960. With Olan Mills, Inc., Chattanooga, Tenn., 1962—, now treas., also bd. dirs. Served with U.S. Army, 1962-63. Office: Olan Mills Inc 4325 Amnicola Hwy Chattanooga TN 37406

MILLS, CHARLES GARDNER, lawyer; b. Griffin, Ga., Feb. 29, 1940; s. Charles G. and Marguerite (Powell) M. AB, Yale U., 1962; JD, Boston Coll., 1967. Bar: N.Y. 1967, U.S. Dist. Ct. (so. and ea. dists.) 1972, U.S. Ct. Appeals (2d cir.) 1975, U.S. Supreme Ct., 1977, U.S. Ct. Claims 1991. Assoc. Smart & McKay, N.Y.C., 1967-68, Smart & Mills, N.Y.C., 1969-71, Eaton & VanWinkle, N.Y.C., 1971-82, Payne, Wood & Littlejohn, Glen Cove, Melville, N.Y., 1982-91. With U.S. Army, 1964-64, ETO. Mem. Nassau County Bar Assn., N.Y. State Bar Assn., Assn. of the Bar of the City of N.Y., Rotary (pres. Glen Cove club 1989-90), Am. Legion (comdr. Locust Valley, N.Y. post 1988-90, comdr. Nassau County comm. 1990-91). Republican. Roman Catholic. Office: 56 School St Glen Cove NY 11542-2512

MILLS, CYNTHIA SPRAKER, association administrator; b. Williamsburg, Va., June 11, 1962; d. Charles E. and Marceil H. (Harris) S.; m. John E. Mills, Oct. 18, 1986. BA in History and Psychology, Queens Coll., 1984; MA in Medieval Studies, U. of York, Eng., 1986. Fin. aid officer Rutledge Edn. Sys., Charlotte, N.C., 1987-88; assoc. dir. Younger Bros. & Sys., Inc., Charlotte, 1988-90; asst. exec. editor Nat. Assn. Coll. Aux. Svcs., Staunton, Va., 1990-93; exec. dir. Pilot Internat. & Pilot Internat. Found., Macon, Ga., 1993—; presenter in field. Contbr. articles to profl. publs. Chair Pacesetters divsn. United Way of Staunton/West Augusta County, 1992; mem. adv. bd. Edn. Exch., Ind., 1991-93; mem. Commonwealth/Cmty. Alliance for Drug Rehab. and Edn. of Staunton/Augusta County, Inc., 1991-93. Rotary Found. scholar, 1986, Queens Coll. Presdl. scholar, 1980-84. Mem. Ga. Soc. Assn. Execs. (membership com. 1991—, staff mgmt. com. 1994-95, chair tech. spl. interest group 1994-95, bd. dirs. 1995—), Am. Soc. Assn. Execs. (cert., membership com. 1991—), Notable Accomplishment award 1991, mem. Chmn.'s Honor Roll 1992, mem. Chmn.'s Round Table for Membership Recruitment 1994), Am. Biog. Inst. (rsch. bd. advisors), Nat. Ctr. for Nonprofit Bds., Svc. Club Leaders Conf. Republican. Lutheran. Office: Pilot Internat & Found PO Box 4844 Macon GA 31213

MILLS, DANIEL QUINN, business educator, consultant, author; b. Houston, Nov. 24, 1941; s. Daniel Monroe and Louise (Quinn) M.; m. Joyce Smith, Jan. 2, 1970; children: Lisa Ann, Shirley Elizabeth. B.A., Ohio Wesleyan U., 1963; M.A., Harvard U., 1965, Ph.D., 1968. Prof. MIT, Cambridge, 1968-75, Harvard Bus. Sch., Boston, 1976—; impartial umpire Plan to Settle Disputes in Constrn., 1973-79, Trans-Alaska Pipeline, 1975-78, AFL-CIO Internal Disputes Plan, 1975-82; commr. Nat. Commn. on Employment Policy, Washington, 1982-86. Author: Industrial Relations in Construction, 1971, Labor, Government and Inflation, 1975, Labor-Management Relations, 1978, 5th edit., 1993, Construction Industry, 1979, The New Competitors, 1985, Not Like Our Parents: The Baby-Boom Generation, 1987, The IBM Lesson, 1988, The Rebirth of the Corporation, 1990, The GEM Principle, 1994. Mem. Am. Econ. Assn., Indsl. Relations Research Assn., Phi Beta Kappa. Mem. United Ch. of Christ. Office: Harvard U Harvard Bus Sch Soldiers Field Rd Allston MA 02134-1805

MILLS, DAVID B., museum director. Dir. Newfoundland (Can.) Mus., St. John's. Office: Newfoundland Museum, 283-285 Duckworth St, Saint John's, NF Canada A1C 1G9

MILLS, DAVID HARLOW, psychologist, association executive; b. Marshalltown, Iowa, Dec. 26, 1932; s. Harlow Burgess and Esther Winifred (Brewer) M.; m. Janet Louise Anderson, June 15, 1957 (div. 1984); children: Ross Harlow, Anne Louise; m. Susan S. Greene, Aug. 3, 1984. BS, Iowa State U., 1955, MS, 1957; PhD, Mich. State U., 1964. Postdoctoral fellow USPHS U. Ill., Champaign, 1964-65; asst. prof. psychology Iowa State U., Ames, 1965-68; assoc. prof. Iowa State U., 1968-69; asst. dir. Iowa State U. (Counseling Center), 1967-69; mem. faculty U. Md., College Park, 1969-81; prof. psychology U. Md., 1972-81, asst. dir. counseling center, 1969-81; adminstrv. officer Am. Psychol. Assn., Washington, 1981-86; pvt. practice Bangor, Maine, 1989—, Blue Hill, Maine, 1990—; cons. Iowa Women's Reformatory, 1966-69, VA, Rockwell City, Iowa, 1966-69; rsch. assoc. Nat. Register Health Svcs. Providers in Psychology; mgmt. cons. Ctr. Creative Leadership U. Md., 1980—; mem. Maine Bd. Psychologists; mem. examination com. Assn. State and Provincial State Psychology Bds., 1995—. Contbr. articles to profl. jours. Pres. Woodmoor-Pinecrest Citizens Assn., Silver Spring, Md., 1973-74; mem. com. higher edn. Allied Civic Group Montgomery County, 1974, sr. fellow Consortium of Univs. of the Washington D.C. Met. Area., 1987—. Served with U.S. Army, 1957-61. Fellow APA (bd. dirs. 1986-90, dir. ethics 1986—, ethics cons. 1990—); mem. Internat. Assn. Counseling Svcs. (accrediting bd. 1972-74, v.p. 1975-77, pres. 1977-79). Democrat. Unitarian. Home: RR 1 Box 323A Little Deer Isle ME 04650-9714 Office: 277 State St Ste 214 Bangor ME 04401-5439

MILLS, DON HARPER, pathology and psychiatry educator; b. Peking, Republic of China, July 27, 1927; came to U.S., 1928; s. Clarence Alonzo and Edith Clarissa (Parrett) M.; m. Lillian Frances Snyder, June 11, 1949; children: Frances Jo, Jon Snyder. BS, U. Cin., 1950, MD, 1953; JD, U. So. Calif., 1958. Diplomate Am. Bd. Law in Medicine. Intern L.A. County Gen. Hosp., 1953-54, admitting physician, 1954-57, attending staff pathologist, 1959—; pathology fellow U. So. Calif., L.A., 1954-55, instr. pathology, 1958-62, asst. clin. prof., 1962-65, assoc. clin. prof., 1965-69, clin. prof., 1969—, clin. prof. psychiatry and behavioral sci., 1986—; asst. in pathology Hosp. Good Samaritan, L.A., 1956-65, cons. staff, 1962-72, affiliating staff, 1972-91; dep. med. examiner Office of L.A. County Med. Examiner, 1957-61; instr. legal medicine Loma Linda (Calif.) U. Sch. Medicine, 1960-66, assoc. clin. prof. humanities, 1966—; cons. HEW, 1972-73, 75-76, Dept. of Def., 1975-80; bd. dirs. Am. Bd. Law in Medicine, Inc., Chgo., 1980-86; med. dir. Profl. Risk Mgmt. Group, 1989—. Column editor Newsletter of the Long Beach Med. Assn., 1960-75, Jour. Am. Osteopathic Assn., 1965-77, Ortho Panel, 1970-78; exec. editor Trauma, 1964-88, mem. editorial bd., 1988—; mem. editorial bd. Legal Aspects of Med. Practice, 1972-90, Med. Alert Communications, 1973-75, Am. Jour. Forensic Medicine and Pathology, 1979-87, Hosp. Risk Control, 1981—; contbr. numerous articles to profl. jours. Bd. dirs. Inst. for Med. Risk Studies, 1988—. Fellow Am. Coll. Legal Medicine (pres. 1974-76, bd. govs. 1970-78, v.p. 1972-74, chmn. malpractice com. 1973-74, jour. editorial bd. 1981—); mem. Am. Acad. Forensic Scis. (pres. 1986-87, v.p. 1984-85, exec. com. 1971-74, gen. program chmn. 1966-67, chmn. jurisprudence sect. 1966-67, 73-74, jour. editorial bd. 1965-79); mem. AMA (jour. editorial bd. 1973-77), Calif. Med. Assn., L.A. County Med. Assn., AAAS, ABA, L.A. County Bar Assn., Am. Judicature Soc., Am. Soc. Hosp. Attys., Calif. Soc. Hosp. Attys. Home: Ste 2606 700 E Ocean Blvd Long Beach CA 90802 Office: 911 Studebaker Rd Ste 250 Long Beach CA 90815

MILLS, DONALD MCKENZIE, librarian; b. Virden, Man., Can., Feb. 25, 1946; s. Earl Townsend and Mable Elizabeth (Davies) M.; m. Kathrine Ann Richards, Aug. 26, 1968; children—Jennifer, Susan. B.A., U. Winnipeg, Man., Can., 1968; M.L.S., U. B.C., Vancouver, Can., 1972. Chief librarian St. Albert Pub. Library, Alta., Can., 1972-75; children's coordinator Kamloops Pub. Library, B.C., Can., 1975-78; chief librarian West Vancouver Pub. Library, B.C., Can., 1978-82, Winnipeg Pub. Library, Man., Can., 1982-87, Mississauga (Ont.) Pub. Library, 1987—. Mem. ALA, Can. Library Assn., Ontario Libr. Assn. Office: Mississauga Libr Sys, 301 Burnham Thorpe Rd, Mississauga, ON Canada L5B 3Y3

MILLS, DONNA, actress; b. Chgo., Dec. 11, 1945. Student, U. Ill. Began career with stage prodns. Chgo. area; appeared on Broadway in Don't Drink the Water; regular in TV series The Secret Storm, Dan August, The Good Life, 1971-72, Knots Landing, 1980-89, Love Is a Many Splendored Thing, 1967; appeared in various TV films including Haunts of the Very Rich, 1972, Rolling Man, 1972, Night of Terror, 1972, The Bait, 1973, Live Again, Die Again, 1974, Who is the Black Dahlia?, 1975, Beyond the Bermuda Triangle, 1975, Look What's Happened to Rosemary's Baby, 1976, Smash-Up on Interstate 5, 1976, Fire!, 1977, Curse of the Black Widow, 1977, The Hunted Lady, 1977, Superdome, 1978, Doctors' Private Lives, 1978, Waikiki, 1980, He's Not Your Son, 1984, Outback Bound, 1988, The Lady Regrets, 1989, The World's Oldest Living Bridesmaid, 1990, Runaway Father, 1992, False Arrest, 1991, The President's Child, 1992; actress, co-prodr. In My Daughter's Name, 1992; mini series Hanging By a Thread, 1979, Bare Essence, 1982, Intimate Encounters, 1986; motion pictures (debut) The Incident, 1967, Play Misty for Me, 1971. Address: 822 S Robertson Blvd # 200 Los Angeles CA 90035*

MILLS, EDWIN SMITH, economics educator; b. Collingswood, N.J., June 25, 1928; s. Edwin Smith and Roberta (Haywood) M.; m. Barbara Jean Dressner, Sept. 2, 1950; children: Alan Stuart, Susan Dorinda; m. Margaret M. Hutchinson, Jan. 22, 1977. B.A., Brown U., 1951; Ph.D., U. Birmingham, Eng., 1956. Asst. lectr. Univ. Coll. North Staffordshire, Eng., 1953-55; instr. Mass. Inst. Tech., 1955-57; mem. faculty Johns Hopkins, Balt., 1957-70; prof. econs. Johns Hopkins, 1963-70, chmn. dept. econs., 1966-69; prof. econs. and pub. affairs, Gerald L. Thilbe prof. urban studies Princeton U., 1970-75, prof. econs., 1975-87, chmn. dept., 1975-77; Gary Rosenberg prof. real estate and fin. Kellog Sch. Mgmt. Northwestern U., Evanston, Ill., 1987—; vis. research fellow Cowles Found., Yale, 1961; sr. profl. staff Council Econ. Advisers, 1964-65. Author: The Burden of Government, 1986. Served to 2d lt. AUS, 1946-48. Mem. Am. Econ. Assn., Phi Beta Kappa. Home: 430 W Roslyn Pl Chicago IL 60614-2713 Office: Northwestern U Ctr Real Estate Rsch Kellogg Graduate School 2001 Sheridan Rd Evanston IL 60208-0814

MILLS, EUGENE SUMNER, college president; b. West Newton, Ind., Sept. 13, 1924; s. Sumner Amos and Lela (Weatherly) M.; m. Dorothy Frances Wildman, Oct. 22, 1945; children: David Wahlen, Sara Anne. A.B., Earlham Coll., 1948; M.A., Claremont Grad. Sch., 1949, Ph.D., 1952; postgrad., Harvard, 1958-59; LLD (hon.), N.H. Coll., 1979, U. N.H., 1988; LHD (hon.), Earlham Coll., 1987. Instr. psychology Whittier (Calif.) Coll., 1950, asst. prof., chmn. dept., 1952-55, assoc. prof., chmn. dept., 1955-60, prof. psychology, chmn. dept., 1960-62; faculty U. N.H., Durham, 1962-79; prof. psychology U. N.H. 1962-79, chmn. dept., 1962-65, dean Grad. Sch., coordinator research, 1963-67; dean U. N.H. (Coll. Liberal Arts), 1967-70, acad. v.p. 1970-71, provost, 1971-74, provost, acting pres., 1974, pres., 1974-79; pres. Whittier (Calif.) Coll. and Whittier Coll. Sch. of Law, 1979-89; prof. psychology Whittier (Calif.) Coll., 1979-89, emeritus prof. psychology, pres. emeritus, 1989—; vis. prof. U. Victoria, B.C., summers 1958, 60, bd. dirs. Elderhostel, Inc., 1977—, chmn. 1984-90; bd. dirs. Fedco Inc. (chmn). mem. N.H. Psychol. Assn., 1962-79, pres., 1969-70, bd. dirs. 1967-70. Author: George Trumbull Ladd: Pioneer American Psychologist, 1969, The Story ofElderhostel, 1993; contbr. articles to profl. jours. Danforth Found. grantee; NSF grantee. Fellow Am. Psychol. Assn.; mem. Western Psychol.

Assn., Sigma Xi, Phi Kappa Phi., Omicron Delta Kappa. Mem. Soc. of Friends.

MILLS, FRANCES JONES, state official; b. Gray, Ky.; d. William Harrison and Bertie (Steely) Jones. Student, Union Coll., Eastern Ky. State Coll.; grad., Cumberland Coll., Williamsburg, Ky. Public sch. tchr.; mem. Ky. Ho. of Reps., 1961-62, asst. to speaker, 1963-65; dir. women's activities Ky. Civil Def., 1965-72; clk. Ky. Ct. Appeals, 1972-76; treas. Commonwealth of Ky., Frankfort, 1976-80, sec. of state, 1979-83, treas., 1984-88, 1992—; bd. dirs. Ky. Lottery Corp.; vice chmn. Ky. Investments Commn.; mem. Ky. Personal Svc. Contract Rev. Commn., 1976—, Ky. Tchrs. Retirement Bd., 1976—; pres. Nat. Conf. Appellate Ct. Clks., 1975-76. Author: Civil Def. booklet What Would You Do?. Del. Dem. Nat. Conv., 1964, 68, 76, alt., 1972; bd. dirs. Ky. Lottery Corp., Ky. Mountain Laurel Festival; vice chmn. Ky. Investments Commn.; mem. devel. com. Cumberland Coll. Named Southeastern Ky. Outstanding Woman, 1973, Bus. and Profl. Women's Club Woman of Achievement, 1978, 88; named to Cumberland 100 Disting. Grads. Mem. AMA Aux., Whitley County Med. Aux., Nat. Assn. State Treas. (v.p. so. region). Baptist. Clubs: Order Eastern Star, Bus. and Profl. Women's. Office: Treasury Dept New State Capitol Buil Frankfort KY 40601

MILLS, FREDERICK VANFLEET, art educator, watercolorist; b. Bremen, Ohio, June 5, 1925; s. Frederick William and Juanita Ellen (VanFleet) M.; m. Lois Jean Rademacher; children: Mark Steven (dec.), Michael Sherwood, Mollie Sue, Merre Shannon, Randal Dean, Susan Lynn, Todd Patrick, Shondra Marie. BS, Ohio State U., 1949; MS, Ind. U., 1951, EdD, 1956; postgrad., U.S. Army Staff and Command Coll., 1973-76. Tchr. art, supr. Celina (Ohio) Pub. Schs., 1949-51; instr. univ. h.s. Ind. U., 1951-55; prof. art, art edn., chmn. dept. art edn. Ind. U., Bloomington, 1959-65; vis. prof. U. Tex.-Austin, 1965; chmn. dept. related arts, crafts and interior design U. Tenn., Konxville, 1966-68; prof. art, chmn. dept. art Ill. State U., 1968-85, prof. emeritus, 1985—; prof. art Lincoln Coll., Normal, 1986—; rsch. reader humanities HEW, 1968-69; resource person arts, edn. and Ams. panel Rockefeller Report Am Coun. Arts in Edn., 1977-78; cons. Latin Am. Fulbright Scholarship Program Harvard U., 1981-82; mem. com. III. Fine Arts Rev. for Capital Devel. Bd., 1987—, planning com. Nat. Inst. Advanced Studies in Art and Design and Archives of Am. Art Sch., 1988—, rsch. com. Nat. Sch. Art and Design. One-man shows include McLean County Arts Ctr., Bloomington, Ill., Lincoln (Ill.) Coll., Ill. Agriculture Assn. Credit Union Art Exhbn. Series, Bloomington, Suzette Schochet Gallery, Newport, R.I.; represented in permanent collections Wonderlin Gallery, Normal, Ill., State Farm Ins. Co., Kemper Fin. Securities/Kemper Fin. Fund, First of Am. Bank, Ill., Diamond Star Motors Corp., Easter Seal Assn., City of Vladimir, Russia, City of Asahikawa, Hokkaido, Japan, County of McLean, City of Bloomington, Town of Normal; author, editor: The Status of the Visual Arts in Higher Education, 1976, New Perspectives in Visual Arts Administration, 1977, Issues in the Administration of Visual Arts, 1978, Politics and the Visual Arts, 1979, The Visual Arts in the Ninth Decade, 1980; editor Western Arts Bull., 1958-62; contbr. to profl. jours. Pres. Ill. Alliance Art Edn., 1975-77, Ill. Task Force for Arts Edn. in Gen. Edn., 1976-77; mem. Tenn. Arts Commn., 1967-68, Nat. Alliance Arts Edn./Kennedy Ctr., 1975-77; charter trustee Ill. Summer Sch. for Arts, v.p., v.p. Found. Bd., 1988-94; bd. dirs., co-founder Sugar Creek Arts Festival, Normal, 1985—; chair major gifts com. Normal Theater Restoration Project, 1992—; bd. dirs., v.p. McLean County Arts Ctr., Bloomington, 1980-90, sponsor Skilled Crafts award, 1968—. Served to maj. USAR; Col. III. Militia. Recipient Recognition award Alliance for Arts Edn., 1984, Outstanding Svc. award Ill. Alliance Arts Edn., 1984, 1994 Ornament of Yr./Artist of Yr. award; subject articles, TV interviews. Mem. Nat. Council Art Adminstrs. (charter, sr. rsch. editor bd. dirs. 1973-81), Nat. Assn. Schs. Art (instnl. del. 1974-84, nominating com. 1977-78, rsch. com. 1976-77), Western Arts Assn. (pres. 1962-64), Coll. Art Assn., Nat. Art Edn. Assn. (dir. 1964-66), Scabbard and Blade, Phi Delta Kappa, Delta Tau Delta, Delta Phi Delta. Club: Rotary Internat. Office: Ctr Frst # 119 Normal IL 61761 *As I reflect on my life and career up to this point, I feel that consistency and humaneness are two words that come to mind. It seems extremely important to be consistent when a person relates to others, and if that is coupled with humaneness and consideration of the value of others, being aware of their strengths and weaknesses, their likes and dislikes, it becomes easier to relate to them in this most complex world of ours.*

MILLS, GEORGE ALEXANDER, science administrator; b. Saskatoon, Sask., Can., Mar. 20, 1914; s. George Robison and Leafa (Johnson) M.; m. Roberta Walker Mills, June 15, 1940; children: Richard, Sandra, Marilyn, Janice. B.Sc., U. Sask., 1934, M.Sc., 1936; Ph.D., Columbia U. Instr., Dartmouth Coll., 1939-40; with Houdry Process Co., 1940-68; with U.S. Bur. Mines, 1968-75, chief coal div., 1968-75; dir. fossil energy research ERDA, 1975-77; exec. dir. Ctr. Catalytic Sci. and Tech., U. Del., Newark, 1981-84, sr. scientist Ctr. Catalytic Sci and Tech., 1984—. Contbr. numerous articles to profl. jours. Mem. Nat. Acad. Engring., Am. Inst. Chemists (Pioneer award), Am. Chem. Soc. (Storch award, Murphree award), AAAS, Am. Inst. Chem. Engring., Catalysis Soc. Presbyterian. Patentee in field. Home: Cokesbury Village # 48 726 Loveville Rd Hockessin DE 19707 Office: Dept Chem Engring U Del Newark DE 19716

MILLS, GEORGE MARSHALL, insurance and financial consultant; b. Newton, N.J., May 20, 1923; s. J. Marshall and Emma (Scott) M.; m. Dorothy Lovilla Allen, Apr. 21, 1945; children: Dianne (Mrs. Thomas McKay III), Dorothy L.A. (Mrs. Edward Sphatt). BA, Rutgers U., 1943; MA, Columbia U., 1951, profl. cert., 1952. CLU; CPCU; chartered fin. cons. Pres. George M. Mills Inc., North Brunswick, N.J., 1946-75; pres. CORECO, Inc., Newark, 1960-78; risk mgr. N.J. Hwy. Authority, Woodbridge, 1976-95; pres. George M. Mills, P.A., North Brunswick, N.J., 1995—; cons. Govs.'s Com. on Bus. Efficiency in Pub. Schs., 1979-80; cons. Risk Mgmt. Ins., Real Estate. Bd. dirs. Alpha Chi Rho Ednl. Found., vice-chmn. 1991—; workshop Easter Seal Soc.; mem. Gov.'s Task Force on Sound Mcpl. Govt., 1981-82; pres. Nat. Interfrat. Conf., 1979-80. With USNR, 1943-46. Mem. Am. Coll. Life Underwriters, Am. Coll. Property Liability Underwriters, Internat. Bridge Tunnel and Turnpike Assn. (chmn. risk mgmt. com. 1980-95, mem. bus. ins. risk mgmt. bd. 1988-95, Matthew J. Lenz Jr. medal 1989, Paul K. Addams award 1992), New Brunswick Hist. Soc., English Speaking Union, Rutgers U. Alumni-Faculty Club, Alpha Chi Rho (nat. councillor 1964-70, nat. pres. 1970-73, nat. treas. 1975-78), Kappa Kappa Psi, Tau Kappa Alpha, Phi Delta Phi. Mem. Reformed Ch. Am. Home: 1054 Hoover Dr North Brunswick NJ 08902-3244

MILLS, GORDON LAWRENCE, financial executive; b. N.Y.C., Feb. 21, 1933; s. Dudley H. and Louise M. (Morris) M.; m. Margaret Devereux Aydelotte, Dec. 13, 1958 (div. 1993); children: Julia H., Thomas B.; m. Signa Lynch Read, Nov. 9, 1993. AB cum laude, Princeton U., 1954; MBA, Harvard U., 1958. Chartered fin. analyst. Sr. analyst White Weld & Co. (now Merrill Lynch), N.Y.C., 1958-62; v.p. Mut. Life Ins. Co., N.Y.C., 1962-74; gen. mgr. pension The Continental Group (formerly Continental Can), Stamford, Conn., 1974-81; v.p. Lipper Analytical Service, Greenwich, Conn., 1981-83; mgr. benefit plans fin. mgmt. Texaco Inc., White Plains, N.Y., 1983-90; chmn. bd. advisors S.E.I. Internat., Greenwich, 1991—; mng. ptnr. Manchester (Vt.) Capital Mgmt., 1994—; Vt. state sen. cand. Natural Law Party, 1994; lectr. Fin. Mgmt. of Multinat. Corps., N.Y.C., 1975-80, Cornell Sch. Indsl. Rels., 1978, Internat. Counsel Adv. Bd. Can. Assn. Pension Mgmt., 1976; pres. Am. Capital Corp. Greenwich, 1981-83; cons. Venture Capital Partnerships, N.Y.C., 1981-83. Author: Pension Management-AMA, 1983; editor of Conn. Venture Group newsletter, Stamford, 1981-83. Profl. magician UN Hospitality Com., 1979; bd. dirs. N.Y.C. Mission Soc., Soc. 1963-85, exec. com. mem., investment com. chmn., United Hosp. Fund Greater N.Y., 1974-80, Nat. Audubon Soc. Greenwich, 1979-86, Allegheny Power Systems Inc, 1973-81, Home for Old Men and Aged Couples, N.Y.C., 1974-80; fin. com. chmn., Amsterdam House. 1st lt., arty. U.S. Army, 1954-56. Mem. Sentinel Pension Inst. (bd. advs., lectr. 1975—), Pension Group East (founding mem., lectr., Internat. counsel adv. bd. Can. Assn. Pension Mgmt. 1975-78), The Links Club (N.Y.C.), Clove Valley Rod and Gun Club, Holland Lodge. Office: Box 416 Brookside Bldg Hist Rte 7A Manchester VT 05254

MILLS, JAMES SPENCER, author; b. Milw., May 20, 1932; s. Ralph Erskine and Elisabeth Amsden (Stevens) M. Student, Erskine Coll., 1950-51; BA, Princeton U., 1956. Reporter Worcester (Mass.) Telegram and Evening Gazette, summer 1955, Corpus Christi (Tex.) Caller Times, 1958, UPI, 1959; reporter, corr., writer, editor Life mag., 1960-66. Author: The Panic in Needle Park, 1966, The Prosecutor, 1969, Report to the Commissioner, 1972, One Just Man, 1974, On the Edge, 1975, The Seventh Power, 1976, The Truth about Peter Harley, 1979, The Underground Empire: Where Crime and Governments Embrace, 1986, The Power, 1990, Haywire, 1995. Served with USNR, 1956-58. Address: care Marvin Kalickstein 2547 Joel Pl Oceanside NY 11572-1331

MILLS, JAMES STEPHEN, medical supply company executive; b. Chgo., Sept. 29, 1936; s. Irving I. and Beatrice (Shane) M.; m. Victoria L. Krisch, Mar. 23, 1973; children: Charles, Donald, Margaret. B.S. in Bus., Northwestern U. Vice pres. sales Mills Hosp. Supply Co., Chgo., 1961-66; pres. Medline Industries Inc., Northbrook, Ill., 1966-75, chmn. bd., 1975—. Served with AUS, 1958-64. Jewish. Home: 500 N Green Bay Rd Lake Forest IL 60045-2146 Office: Medline Industries Inc 1 Medline Pl Mundelein IL 60060

MILLS, JAMES THOBURN, association executive; b. Balt., Nov. 30, 1923; s. Victor Garfield and Beatrice M. (Moore) M.; m. Frances Clagett Keller, June 16, 1951; children—Elizabeth R. Mills Durkee, Hilary F. Mills Lambert, Frances T. Mills Wonnell, Margaret K. B.A., Princeton U., 1947; LL.B., Yale U., 1950. Bar: N.Y. 1951. Assoc. Burke & Burke, N.Y.C., 1950-51; assoc. Mudge, Stern, Baldwin & Todd, N.Y.C., 1951-56; with Sperry & Hutchinson Co., N.Y.C., 1956-80; pres. Sperry & Hutchinson Co., 1978-80, chmn. bd., chief exec. officer, 1980-81, also dir.; pres. The Conference Board, Inc., N.Y.C., 1982-88; bd. dirs. Union Camp Corp., Wayne, N.J. Pres. Montclair (N.J.) Art Mus., 1990—. 1st lt. U.S. Army, 1943-46. Decorated Bronze Star medal, Purple Heart. Clubs: University (N.Y.C.); Montclair Golf (N.J.). Avocations: golf; skiing. Home: 102 Inwood Ave Montclair NJ 07043 Office: Montclair Art Mus 3 S Mountain Ave Montclair NJ 07042

MILLS, JERRY WOODROW, lawyer; b. Springfield, Mo., July 17, 1940; s. Woodrow Wilson and Billie Louise M.; m. Marion Cargile, Mar. 27, 1964; children: Eric E., Brendon W. BSEE, Tex. A&M U., 1963; JD, Georgetown U., 1967. Bar: Tex. 1967, U.S. Patent Office 1967. Ptnr. Richards, Harris & Hubbard, Dallas, 1970-82, Baker, Mills & Glast, Dallas, 1982-90; sr. ptnr. Baker & Botts, Dallas, 1990—; adj. prof. So. Meth. U. Law Sch., 1994—. Bd. dirs. Dallas Legal Svcs. Project, 1972-75. Fellow Tex. Bar, Dallas Bar; mem. ABA, Tex. State Jr. Bar Assn. (treas. 1975, dir.), Dallas Jr. Bar Assn. (pres. 1971, Outstanding Young Lawyer award 1975), Dallas Bar Assn. (bd. dirs. 1983-85). Methodist. Home: 4301 Overhill Dr Dallas TX 75205-4328 Office: Baker & Botts 800 Trammell Crow Ctr 2001 Ross Ave Dallas TX 72501-4332

MILLS, JOHN JAMES, research director, mechanical engineering educator; b. Motherwell, Scotland, May 12, 1939; came to U.S., 1966; s. John Thompson King and Esther Houston (Leitch) M.; m. Dorothea Becker, Mar. 27, 1971; children: Jennifer, Julia, Janine, Ian. BS in Physics, U. Glasgow, Scotland, 1961; PhD in Applied Physics, U. Durham, Eng., 1965. Rsch. fellow dept. elec. engring. Imperial Coll., London, 1964-66; from scientist to sr. scientist IIT Rsch. Inst., Chgo., 1966-71; sr. fellow Inst. Silicatforschung der Fraunhofergesellschaft, Fed. Republic of Germany, 1972-73; sect. leader Inst. Werkstofftechnic, Fed. Republic of Germany, 1973-75; sr. scientist Martin Marietta Labs., Balt., 1975-79, mgr. aluminum fabrication R&D, 1979-84, mgr. mfg. tech. R&D, 1984-88, project dir., 1988-90; dir. Automation & Robotics Rsch. Inst., U. Tex. at Arlington, 1990—, Agile Aerospace Mfg. Rsch. Ctr. Author: (chpt.) Properties of Pure Aluminum, 1984; contbr. articles to profl. jours. Recipient rsch. fellowship British Oxygen Co., 1964-66, A. von Humboldt fellowship Inst. Silicatforschung der Fraunhofergesellschaft, 1972-73, Outstanding Achievement award Martin Marietta Labs., 1981. Mem. ASME (at large dir. mfg. tech. operating group bd.), Soc. Mfg. Engring., Am. Soc. Metals, Am. Inst. Mining and Metall. Engring., Am. Phys. Soc., Ft. Worth C. of C. (bd. dirs. East Area Coun. 1991—). Avocations: wine making, rowing, cabinet making. Office: Automation and Robotics Rsch 7300 Jack Newell Blvd S Fort Worth TX 76118

MILLS, JON K., psychologist, educator. AS in Criminal Justice, Parkland Coll., 1985; BS in Psychology with honors, So. Ill. U., 1987, MA in Rehab. Counseling with honors, 1988; postgrad., Vanderbilt U., 1992. Cert. rehab. counselor. Crisis intervention trainer, hotline supr. Synergy Crisis Intervention Agy., Carbondale, Ill., 1986-87; individual and family counselor, 1987; individual and group therapist Evaluation and Devel. Ctr., Carbondale, Ill., 1987-88, Youth Options: Substance Abuse Svcs., Marion, Ill., 1988; intern Jackson County Community Mental Health Ctr., Carbondale, 1988; diagnostic extern Elgin (Ill.) State Mental Health Ctr., 1989-90; staff therapist Davis Ctr. for Emotional Devel., Glen Ellyn, Ill., 1989-90; therapy extern Roosevelt U., Chgo., 1990—; counselor coord. Copley Weight Mgmt. Copley Meml. Hosp., Aurora, Ill., 1989—; predoctoral intern Michael Reese Hosp. and Med. Ctr., Chgo., 1991; asst. prof. dept. psychology Lewis U., Romeoville, Ill., 1992—; staff psychologist Inst. for Behavioral Svcs., Oak Brook, Ill., 1993—; teaching asst. for tests and measurements Rehab. Inst., So. Ill. U., 1987-88; teaching asst. Ill. Sch. of Profl. Psychology, Chgo., 1989-90; adj. faculty dept. of psychology Waubonsee Community Coll., Sugar Grove, Ill., 1990—, Coll. of Dupage, Naperville, 1989—; faculty mem. social sci. dept. Joliet (Ill.) Jr. Coll., 1990—. Contbr. numerous articles to profl. jours. Vol. Crisis Hotline Jackson County Community Mental Health Ctr., Carbondale, 1987. Recipient numerous scholarships, Tchg. fellow Vanderbilt U. Dept. Philosophy, Nashville, 1994—. Mem. APA, Ill. Group Psychotherapy Soc., Chgo. Assn. for Psychoanalytic Psychology, Phi Kappa Phi, Gamma Beta Phi. Avocations: vocal, guitar, harmonica. Home: 301 31st Ave N Apt C-2 Nashville TN 37203

MILLS, KEVIN LEE, government executive; b. Frederick, Md., Oct. 21, 1951; s. John Lee and Doris Jean (Comer) M.; m. Karen June Davis, Dec. 30, 1972; children: Colin Walter, Elizabeth Anne. BS in Polit. Sci. and Econs., Frostburg (Md.) State U., 1973; MS in Tech. Mgmt., Am. U., 1979; postgrad., George Mason U. Sr. computer analyst System Devel. Corp., McLean, Va., 1976-81; project mgr. Tesdata Systems Corp., McLean, 1981-82; computer scientist Nat. Bur. of Stds., Gathersburg, Md., 1982-84; group leader Nat. Bur. of Stds., Gathersburg, 1984-87; divsn. chief Nat. Inst. Stds. and Tech., Gathersburg, 1987—; cons. in field. Contbr. articles to profl. jours. Capt. USMC, 1972-78. Mem. IEEE (sr.). Avocations: hiking, writing, reading. Office: Nat Inst Stds and Tech Bldg 225 Rm B217 Gaithersburg MD 20899

MILLS, LINDA S., public relations executive; b. San Antonio, June 26, 1951; d. Frank M. and Betty A. (Young) M. BA, St. Mary's U., 1971. Asst. dir. Paseo Del Rio Assn., San Antonio, 1971-74; mktg. officer Frost Nat. Bank, San Antonio, 1974-79; account exec. Fleishman-Hillard Inc., St. Louis, 1979-81, v.p., sr. ptnr., 1981-85, exec. v.p., sr. ptnr., 1985—, dir. corp. planning, 1986—; bd. dirs. Fleishman-Hillard U.K. Ltd., London, Fleishman-Hillard France, Paris. Mem. adv. bd. St. John's Mercy Med. Ctr. Mem. Pub. Relations Soc. Am., Noonday Club. Office: Fleishman Hillard Inc 200 N Broadway Saint Louis MO 63102-2730

MILLS, LISTON OURY, theology educator; b. Wilmington, N.C., Aug. 7, 1928; s. Leonard Liston and Ruby Preston (Oury) M.; m. Jennie Ellen Windsor, Dec. 28, 1962; 1 child, Sarah Elizabeth. BA, Davidson Coll., 1950; BD, So. Bapt. Theol. Sem., 1953, ThM, 1957, ThD, 1964. Ordained to ministry So. Bapt. Conv., 1953. Asst. pastor 5th Ave. Bapt. Ch., Huntington, W.Va., 1957-58; pastor Kent (Ind.) Bapt. Ch., 1960-62; successively instr, asst. prof., assoc. prof. Vanderbilt U. Div. Sch., Nashville, Oberlin Alumni prof. pastoral theology and counseling, 1962—; Alexander Heard disting. svc. prof., 1991-92, acting dean, 1989; vis. prof. Earlham Grad. Sch. Theology, Richmond, Ind., 1965, St. Luke's Sch. Theology, Sewanee, Tenn., 1972, 73, 74, 83, So. Bapt. Theol. Sem., 1980, Lexington (Ky.) Theol. Sem., 1981; vis. lectr. Yale U. Div. Sch., New Haven, 1969; cons. Tenn. Dept. Mental Health, Nashville, 1964-65, Tenn. Personnel Dept., Nashville, 1967-68, VA Med. Ctr., Nashville, 1972—, Chief of VA Chaplains, Washington, 1975, 78; Ingersoll lectr. Harvard U., Cambridge, Mass., 1971; Upperman lectr. Tenn. Technol. U., Cookeville, 1973; Stringfellow lectr. Drake U., Des

Moines, 1974. Editor: Perspectives on Death, 1969; assoc. editor: Dictionary of Pastoral Care and Counseling, 1990; editor Pastoral Psychology, 1974-82; contbr. articles to jours. Bd. dirs. Family and Children's Svc., Nashville, 1978-81, Tenn. Pastoral Counseling Ctrs., Nashville, 1984-91, St. Thomas Home Health Care, Nashville, 1986-89. 1st lt. U.S. Army, 1953-55. Recipient Obert Kempson award for disting. svc. S.E. Region Assn. for Clin. Pastoral Edn., 1994; named Alumni Educator of Yr., Vanderbilt U., 1984, Pastoral Theologian of Yr., Pastoral Psychology Jour., 1994; fellow So. Bapt. Theol. Sem., 1959-62, Assn. Theol. Schs., 1968-69. Mem. Soc. for Sci. Study of Religion, Assn. for Profl. Edn. for Ministry (pres. 1972-74), Assn. for Clin. Pastoral Edn., Soc. for Pastoral Theology, Omicron Delta Kappa. Office: Vanderbilt U Div Sch Nashville TN 37240

MILLS, LOIS JEAN, legislative aide, former education educator; b. Chgo., Oct. 20, 1939; d. Martin J. and Annabelle M. (Hrabik) Rademacher; m. Frederick V. Mills, Dec. 1, 1974; children: Todd, Susan, Randal, Merre, Mollie, Michael, Mark. BS in Edn., Ill. State U., Normal, 1962, MS in Edn. 1969. Lectr. elem. curriculum Ill. State U.; in-svc. advisor for elem., gifted, critical thinking and study skills, coop. learning Title I State Bd. Edn., Springfield, Ill.; elem. tchr., supr. Metcalf Lab. Sch. Ill. State U.; legis aide to Asst. Majority Leader Senator John Maitland, Jr., Ill. Gen. Assembly, 1991—. Contbr. articles to profl. jours. Pres. Leadership Ill.; vice chmn. McLean County Regional Planning Commn.; pres. governing bd. Lake Bloomington Assn.; mem. mgmt. com. McLean County 21st Century Com.; bd. govs. Ill. Lincoln Excellence in Pub. Svc. Series, other civic activities. Recipient Exemplary Tchr. awards Ill. State U. Student Elem. Edn. Bd., Women of Distinction award YWCA of McLean County. Mem. NAFE, Ill. State U. Alumni Assn. (nat. pres.), McLean County Rep. Women's Club (pres.), Ill. Rep. Committeewoman's Roundtable, Ill. Fedn. Rep. Women, Nat. Fedn. Rep. Women. Home: K-162 Lake Bloomington RR 2 Box 60A Hudson IL 61748-9414

MILLS, LORNA HENRIETTA, banker; b. Long Beach, Calif., Feb. 5, 1916; d. James Herbert and Henrietta (Waller) M. Grad., Johnston's Bus. Inst., 1936. Stenographer, clk. Laguna Fed. Savs., Laguna Beach, Calif., 1936-38, asst. sec.-treas., 1938-57, pres., mgr., 1957-82; pres. Laguna div. (merger Great American First Savs. Bank), Laguna Beach, 1982—; vice chmn. Great Am. First Savs. Bank, San Diego, 1982—, also bd. trustees. Past dir. Laguna Beach C. of C., Orange County C. of C. Mem. Dacowits, DAR. Republican. Reorganized Ch. of Jesus Christ of Latter-day Saints. Club: Soroptomists (Laguna Beach) (past pres.). Became 1st woman mem. of Laguna Beach Rotary Club. also: Gt Am First Savs Bank San Diego Fed Bldg 600 B St San Diego CA 92183

MILLS, MARTHA ALICE, lawyer; b. Lansing, Mich., May 11, 1941; d. Edward Lucien and Muriel (Eastman) M.; m. A. Patrick Papas, Mar. 17, 1940. BA cum laude, Maclester Coll., St. Paul, 1964; JD cum laude, U. Minn., 1965. Bar: U.S. Ct. Appeals (5th cir.) 1967, U.S. Ct. Appeals (7th cir.) 1970, (6th cir.) 1987, U.S. Supreme Ct., 1970. City atty. Fayette, Miss., 1969; chief counsel Lawyer's Com. for Civil Rights Under Law, Cairo, Ill., 1969-71, Lawndale Legal Svcs. Office, Chgo. Legal Svcs., 1971; assoc. Schiff, Hardin and Waite, Chgo., 1971-75; instr. IIT Chgo. Kent Coll. of Law, 1976-82; owner Martha A. Mills, Ltd., 1976-79; ptnr. Cotton, Watt, Jones and King, Chgo., 1980-86, Foss, Schuman, Drake and Barnard, Chgo., 1986-88, Gottlieb and Schwartz, Chgo., 1989-90; of counsel Schaefer, Rosenwein & Fleming, Chgo., 1990-92, Smith, Williams & Lodge, Chgo., 1992—; fed. defender panel, U.S. Dist. Ct. for the No. Dist. Ill., Ea. Div., 1974—; bd. dirs. Legal Assistance Found., 1989—. Contbr. articles to legal publs. Fellow Am. Coll. Trial Lawyers; mem. ABA (governing coun. litigation sect. 1979-84, Chgo. Bar Assn., 7th Cir. Bar Assn. Avocations: reading, computers, languages, telecommunications. Home: 1021 W Bryn Mawr Ave Chicago IL 60660-4643

MILLS, MICHAEL JAMES, architect; b. Streator, Ill., Feb. 18, 1951; s. Harry Nelson and Ruth Ludia (Piel) M.; m. Kathryn Louise Brewington, June 6, 1974 (div. Feb. 1977); m. Beverly Jane Ballard, Mar. 14, 1981; children: Kevin Charles, Jeffrey Ross, Caroline Ruth. BA, Princeton U., 1973; cert., ICCROM, 1979; MS, Columbia U., 1980. Registered architect, N.J., S.C., N.Y., D.C., Pa., Mich.; lic. profl. planner, N.J. Draftsman John Milner Assocs., West Chester, Pa., 1973-74, John Diehl & Assocs., Princeton, N.J., 1974-75; project mgr. Heritage Studies, Princeton, N.J., 1975-76; draftsman Short and Ford Architects, Princeton, N.J., 1976-78; apprentice architect The Ehrenkrantz Group, N.Y.C., 1979-80; apprentice architect Short & Ford & Ptnrs., Princeton, 1980-83, assoc., 1983-87; partner Short & Ford & Ptnrs. (name changed to Ford, Farewell, Mills and Gatsch Architects 1992), Princeton, 1987-92, 1992—; cons. Burlington County Hist. Dist. Commn., Burlington, N.J., 1983-93. Contbr. articles to profl. jours. Chmn. Hopewell Planning Bd., 1985-89. Excellence in Architecture N.J Soc. Architects, 1989, 92, hon. mention, 1983. Mem. AIA, Assn. Preservtion Tech., Nat. Trust for Hist. Preservation, N.J. Soc. Architects, U.S.-Internat. Coun. on Monuments and Sites. Presbyterian. Avocations: guitar, photography, tennis. Office: Ford Farewell Mills and Gatsch Architects 864 Mapleton Rd Princeton NJ 08540-9538

MILLS, MIKE, popular musician; b. Macon, Ga.. Student, U. Ga. Bass guitarist R.E.M., 1980—. Rec. albums include Chronic Town, 1982, Murmur, 1983 (Gold record, Rolling Stone Critics Poll Best Album of Yr. 1983), Reckoning, 1984 (Gold record), Fables of the Reconstruction, 1985 (Gold record), Life's Rich Pageant, 1986 (Gold record), Dead Letter Office, 1987 (Gold record), Document, 1987 (Platinum record), Eponymous, 1988 (Platinum record), Green, 1988 (Platinum record), Out of Time, 1991 (Platinum record, 7 Grammy nominations, Best Pop Vocal Group Grammy award 1992), Automatic for the People, 1993 (4 Grammy nominations), Monster, 1994; appeared on Robbie Robertson's album, Storyville, 1991; perfomed on "Backbeat" soundtrack, 1994. Named Rolling Stong Artist of Yr., 1992. Office: Warner Bros Records 3300 Warner Blvd Burbank CA 91505-4694*

MILLS, NANCY ANNE, elementary education educator; b. Madisonville, Ky., Oct. 2, 1937; d. Leslie Owen and Ruby A. (Baker) Hawkins; m. Orton Leroy Mills, May 11, 1957; children: Charles Leroy, Roy Leslie. BS in Edn., Ind. U., South Bend, 1970, MS in Edn., 1972; Ednl. Specialist degreee, Ind. U., 1978. Cert. elem. tchr., Ind. Tchr. elem. South Bend Schs., 1972—; gifted cadre' Purdue U-For Ind., Lafayette, 1988—; presenter workshops; cons. econ. edn. Chmn. new ch. com. Nazarene Ch., South Bend, 1990; supr. students with Student Exch., France, 1991-95. Named Woman of Yr., Profl. and Bus. Womans Club, 1989; Inst. for Chem. Edn. grantee, 1989. Mem. Ind. Coun. Econ. Edn. (cons. 1987—, Tchr. of Yr. for State of Ind. 1992), Delta Kappa Gamma. Avocations: sewing, travel. Home: 16320 Wellington Pky Granger IN 46530 Office: Muessel Sch 1213 California Ave South Bend IN 46628-2701

MILLS, NANCY STEWART, chemistry educator; b. Osceola, Nebr., Mar. 31, 1950; d. Robert Lees and Margaret Eva (Stewart) M.; m. Mark Alan Hurd, Aug. 20, 1977; children: Caroline Margaret Mills Hurd, William Clark Mills Hurd. BA, Grinnell Coll., 1972; PhD, U. Ariz., 1976. Asst. prof. Carleton Coll., Northfield, Minn., 1977-79; asst. prof. Trinity U., San Antonio, 1979-83, assoc. prof., 1983-89, prof., 1979—, chmn. chemistry dept., 1990-93; mem. dept. rev. team Bowdoin Coll., Brunswick, Maine, 1986, Macalester Coll., St. Paul, 1989, Albion Coll., 1991; councilor Coun. on Undergrad. Rsch., 1991—. Contbr. articles to profl. jours. Grantee NSF, Welch Found., Petroleum Rsch. Fund, Rsch. Corp., 1977—; Camille and Henry Dreyfus Found. scholar, 1994; recipient Outstanding Teaching and Campus Leadership award Sears Roebuck Found., 1990, Z.T. Scott Fellowship for outstanding teaching Trinity U., 1992. Mem. AAUP, Sigma Xi. Avocations: backpacking, reading, sewing, singing. Home: 137 Alta Ave San Antonio TX 78209-4508 Office: Trinity U 715 Stadium Dr San Antonio TX 78212-7200

MILLS, OLAN, II, photography company executive; b. 1930; married. G-rad., Princeton U., 1952. With Olan Mills, Inc., Chattanooga, 1950—, now chmn., sec., also bd. dirs. Office: Olan Mills Inc 4325 Amnicola Hwy Chattanooga TN 37406

MILLS, PETER RICHARD, advertising executive; b. Nanango, Queensland, Australia, Mar. 28, 1939; s. Frederick Richard and Muriel Estelle

(Fischer) M.; m. Nicole Poulin, July 2, 1982; children: Duncan, David, Alexander, Maxine. Student, York U., Toronto, 1964-65. Copy/contact Jackson Wain Publicity Ltd., Brisbane, Australia, 1957-60; copywriter T. Eaton Co., Toronto, Can., 1960-62; bus. mgr. Southam Publs. Inc., Toronto, 1962-66; account exec. J. Walter Thompson, Vancouver, Toronto, 1966-70; gen. mgr. J. Walter Thompson, Montreal, Can., 1970-75; chief oper. office J. Walter Thompson, Toronto, Can., 1975-79; gen. mgr. J. Walter Thompson, N.Y.C., 1979-82; chmn., chief exec. officer J. Walter Thompson, Australia, 1982-88; pres., chief exec. officer Comcore/BBDO, Toronto, Can., 1986-91; pres., No. Am. div. BBDO Worldwide Inc., Southfield, Mich., 1991-93; chmn., pres., CEO Ross Roy Commns., Bloomfield Hills, Mich., 1993—. Mem. Nat. Yacht Club, Toronto. Avocations: scuba diving, sailing, skiing, reading. Office: Ross Roy Commns Inc 100 Bloomfield Hills Pky Bloomfield Hills MI 48304

MILLS, RICHARD, state education official. Commr. edn. Vermont. Office: Vt Dept Edn State Office Bldg Montpelier VT 05620-0001

MILLS, RICHARD HENRY, federal judge; b. Beardstown, Ill., July 19, 1929; s. Myron Epler and Helen Christine (Greve) M.; m. Rachel Ann Keagle, June 16, 1962; children: Jonathan K., Daniel Cass. BA, Ill. Coll., 1951; JD, Mercer U., 1957; LLM, U. Va., 1982. Bar: Ill. 1957, U.S. Dist. Ct. Ill. 1958, U.S. Ct. Appeals 1959, U.S. Ct. Mil. Appeals 1963, U.S. Supreme Ct. 1963. Legal advisor Ill. Youth Commn., 1958-60; state's atty. Cass County, Virginia, Ill., 1960-64; judge Ill. 8th Jud. Cir., Virginia, 1966-76, Ill. 4th Dist. Appellate Ct., Virginia, 1976-85, U.S. Dist. Ct. (cen. dist.) Ill., Springfield, 1985—; adj. prof. So. Ill. U. Sch. Medicine, 1985—; mem. adv. bd. Nat. Inst. Corrections, Washington, 1984-88, Ill. Supreme Ct. Rules Com., Chgo., 1963-85. Contbr. articles to profl. jours. Pres. Abraham Lincoln coun. Boy Scouts Am., 1978-80. With U.S. Army, 1952-54, Korea, col. res.; maj. gen. Ill. Militia. Recipient George Washington Honor medal Freedoms Found., 1969, 73, 75, 82, Disting. Eagle Scout Boy Scouts Am., 1985. Fellow Am. Bar Found.; mem. ABA (joint com. profl. sanctions), Ill. Bar Assn., Chgo. Bar Assn., Cass County Bar Assn. (pres. 1962-64, 75-76), Sangamon County Bar Assn., 7th Cir. Bar Assn., Am. Law Inst., Fed. Judges Assn., Army and Navy Club (Washington), Sangamo Club, Masons (33 degree). Republican. Home: 2112 Augusta Dr Springfield IL 62704-3103 Office: US Dist Ct PO Box 2327 Springfield IL 62705-2327

MILLS, ROBERT GAIL, retired physicist; b. Effingham, Ill., Jan. 20, 1924; s. Gail A. and Helen June (Taylor) M.; m. Mary Addie Steer, May 25, 1946; children: Susan Elizabeth, Robert William. BS in Engring., Princeton U., 1944; MA, U. Mich., 1947; PhD, U. Calif., Berkeley, 1952. Rsch. assoc. U. Mich., Ann Arbor, 1946-47, U. Calif., 1950-52; Rockfeller Found. nat. rsch. fellow U. Zurich, Switzerland, 1952-54; instr. elec. engring. Princeton (N.J.) U., 1943-44, rsch. assoc., 1945-46, rsch. assoc., mem. profl. rsch. staff, 1954-74, prof., 1975-87; ret., 1987. Chief petty officer USNR, 1944-45. Fellow IEEE, Am. Nuclear Soc.; mem. Am. Phys. Soc., Plasma and Nuclear Scis. Soc. (Centennial medal 1974, Disting. Svc. award 1975). Home: 150 Prospect Ave Princeton NJ 08540-5247

MILLS, ROBERT HARRY, church administrator; b. Moncton, N.B., Can., Mar. 3, 1933; s. Harry Earl and Evelyn Perl (Cosman) M.; m. Karen Barbara Keirstead, Dec. 26, 1953 (dec. June 1991); children: Deborah Karen, Michael Robert, Stephen Gordon, David Richard, Katrina Marie. BA, Mt. Allison U., Sackville, N.B., 1954; diploma in theology, Pine Hill Divinity Hall, Halifax, N.S., Can., 1956. Ordained to ministry United Ch. Can. 1956. Minister religion Port Mouton (N.S.) Pastoral Charge, 1956-59, Tatamagouche (N.S.) Pastoral Charge, 1959-65, St. Andrew's United Ch., Wolfville, N.S., 1965-67, Bridgewater (N.S.) United Ch., 1967-75, Wesley United Ch., St. John's, Nfld., Can., 1975-82, Fairview United Ch., Halifax, N.S., 1982-89; exec. sec. maritime conf. United Ch. Can., Sackville, 1989-95; ret., 1995; sec. settlement com. maritime conf. United Ch. Can., 1963-67, chmn., 1967-71, chmn. transfer com. gen. coun., 1970-71, chmn. staff com. Newfound and Labrador conf., 1978-82, sec. Halifax Presbyn., 1983-87. Avocation: music.

MILLS, ROBERT LAURENCE, physicist, educator; b. Englewood, N.J., Apr. 15, 1927; s. Frederick Cecil and Dorothy Katherine (Clarke) M.; m. Elise Ackley, July 21, 1948; children—Katherine, Edward, Jonathan, Susan, Dorothy. A.B. Columbia Coll., 1948; B.A., Cambridge (Eng.) U., 1950, M.A., 1954; Ph.D., Columbia, 1955. Research asso. Brookhaven Nat. Lab., Upton, N.Y., 1953-55; mem. Sch. Math. Inst. for Advanced Study, Princeton, 1955-56; asst. prof. physics Ohio State U., Columbus, 1956-59; asso. prof. Ohio State U., 1959-62, prof., 1962—. Author: Propagators for Many-Particle Systems, 1969, Space, Time and Quanta, 1994. Recipient (with C.N. Yang) Rumford prize for devel. of generalized gauge invariant field theory (Yang-Mills Theory), 1980. Mem. Am. Phys. Soc., AAUP, Fedn. Am. Scientists. Home: 2825 Neil Ave Apt 816 Columbus OH 43202-2077

MILLS, ROBERT LEE, president emeritus; b. Erlanger, Ky., Nov. 13, 1916; s. John Clifford and Dixie Lee (Morris) M.; m. Mildred Sizer, June 24, 1942; children: Robert Lee, Dixie Louise, Barbara Jean. A.B. in Math. and Physics, U. Ky., 1938, M.A. in Ednl. Adminstrn, 1941, Ed.D., 1951; LLD William Jewell Coll., 1971. Tchr. Covington (Ky.) pub. schs., 1938-41; head hydraulics br. Air Force Tech. Sch., Lincoln, Nebr., 1942-44; mem. supervisory staff electromagnetic plant Oak Ridge, 1944-48; research asst. U. Ky., Lexington, 1948-51; dean admissions, registrar U. Ky., 1954-57; dir. research, head bur. adminstrn. and finance Ky. Dept. Edn., 1951-54; chmn. dept. ednl. adminstrn. U. Tex., Austin, 1957-59; pres. Georgetown (Ky.) Coll., 1959-78, chancellor, 1978-86, pres. emeritus, 1987—; exec. sec. Ky. Adv. Commn. Ednl. Policy, 1952-54; v.p. Ky. Assn. Colls. and Secondary Schs., 1962-63, exec. com., 1959-64, pres., 1963-64; chmn. exec. com. Ky. Ind. Coll. Found.; mem. Ky. Commn. on Higher Edn., 1967-70, Ky. Govt. Council, 1968-72; adviser Texas Assn. Sch. Bds., 1957-59. Contbr. articles to profl. jours. Cons. Pres.' Com., White House Conf. Edn., 1955; mem. Ky. Devel. Council, 1961-65, Ky. Constn. Revision Assembly, 1964-66. Recipient Distinguished Alumni award U. Ky., 1963, Centennial award, 1964. Mem. Nat., Ky. edn. assns., Newcomen Soc. So. Assn. Bapt. Colls. (pres. 1965-66), Bapt. World Alliance (chmn. men's dept. 1965-67), So. Assn. Colls. and Schs. (commn. on colls 1971-77), Kappa Delta Pi, Phi Delta Kappa, Phi Kappa Tau. Democrat. Baptist. Lodge: Kiwanis.

MILLS, RODNEY DANIEL, engineering company executive; b. Niagara Falls, N.Y., Nov. 26, 1942; s. Russell Thomas and Golda Marie (Rowe) M.; m. Alana Rae French, June 12, 1965 (div. 1971); children: Thomas Andrew, Robert Daniel; m. Sharon Louise Maggart, May 13, 1972; 1 child, Melinda Marie. Student, Tri-State U., 1961-64, Purdue U., 1966-72. Draftsman Kunkle Valve Co., Inc., Fort Wayne, Ind., 1965-67; draftsman Cen. Soya Co. Inc., Fort Wayne, 1967-74, sr. draftsman 1974-76, staff engr., 1976-80, engr., 1980-84, project engr., 1984-90, engring. purchasing mgr. 1990—. Pres. Three Rivers Youth Soccer Assn., 1987-91; active United Soccer Boosters, 1988—. Recipient Rick Trowski Nat. Humanitarian award United Soccer Boosters, 1990. Home: 7131 Winnebago Dr Fort Wayne IN 46815-6422 Office: Cen Soya Co Inc PO Box 2507 Fort Wayne IN 46801-2507

MILLS, RUSSELL ANDREW, newspaper publisher; b. St. Thomas, Ont., Can., July 14, 1944; s. Gerald Armond and Phyllis Marie (Hulse) M.; m. Judith Elizabeth Zimmerman, Mar. 25, 1967; children—Lara, Colin, Patrick. B.A., U. Western Ont., 1967, M.A., 1968. Reporter London Free Press, Ont., Can., 1965-67; city editor Oshawa Times, Ont., Can., 1970-71; asst. mng. editor The Ottawa Citizen, Ont., Can., 1973-75, editor, 1975-84, gen. mngr. 1984-86, pub., 1986-89; pres. Southam Newspaper Group, Toronto, 1989—

MILLS, SAMUEL DAVIS, JR., professional football player; b. Neptune, N.J., June 3, 1959. Student, Montclair State U. With Cleve. Browns, 1981, Toronto Argonauts, CFL, 1982, Phila. Stars, USFL, 1982; linebacker New Orleans Saints, 1986-95, Carolina Panthers, 1995—. Named USFL All-Star Team Inside Linebacker by Sporting News, 1983, 85, NFL All-Pro Team Inside Linebacker by Sporting News, 1991-92. Played in Pro Bowl, 1987, 88, 91, 92. Office: Carolina Panthers 227 W Trade St Ste 1600 Charlotte NC 28002*

MILLS, STEPHEN NATHANIEL, computer software company executive; b. Boston, Apr. 18, 1942; s. Nathaniel and Alice Mary (Lerner) M.; m. Lorraine Hill Ransom, Mar. 27, 1966 (div. Apr. 1993); children: Nathaniel Stephen, George Robert, Barbara Ransom (dec.), Priscilla Alden; m. Patricia Punch Meadows, Mar. 5, 1994; stepchildren: James Christopher, Katherine Alexandra. Student, MIT, 1959-61; BS, Regents Coll., 1989. Programmer analyst Cambridge (Mass.) Computer Assocs., 1966-68; sr. programmer, analyst Computer Fulfillment, Winchester, Mass., 1968-69; software Engring., Inc., Norton, Mass., 1969-73; product devel. mgr. Pecan Software Corp., Roswell, Ga., 1987-88; pres. Software Eclectics, Inc., Alpharetta, Ga., 1988—; cons. in field; mem. Lang. Test Mgmt. Coun., Inst. Cert. Computer Profls., Des Plaines, Ill., 1994—; adj. faculty Gwinnett Tech. Inst., Lawrenceville, Ga., 1992, Chattahoochee Tech. Inst., Marietta, Ga., 1992. Sgt. USAR, 1964-70. Mem. IEEE Computer Soc., Southeastern Software Assn., Data Processing Mgmt. Assn. (Atlanta bd. dirs. 1992-93), Assn. Computing Machinery, Mensa (Boston chpt. pres. 1967-68, Little Rock newsletter editor 1978). Avocation: aviation. Office: Software Eclectics Inc 10955 Jones Bridge Rd # 131 Alpharetta GA 30202-7343

MILLS, THEODORE MASON, sociologist, educator; b. Fairfield, Ind., May 6, 1920; s. Charles S., Sr. and Pearl (Mason) M.; m. Mary Jane Seaman, June 21, 1947; children: Duncan Kimball, Peter Benjamin, Sarah Jane. A.B., Guilford Coll., 1941; M.A., Haverford Coll., 1942; Ph.D., Harvard U., 1952. Lectr. sociology, also research assoc. Lab. of Social Relations of Harvard U., 1952-55, asst. prof. sociology and gen. edn., 1956-60; assoc. prof. sociology, dir. interaction lab. Yale U., 1960-68; prof. SUNY, Buffalo, 1968—, chmn. dept. sociology, 1968-72, prof. emeritus, 1989; also dir. Social Scis. Interaction Lab.; cons. USN, Family Service N.Y., Niagara Internat. Inst., A.K. Rice Inst., Prentice-Hall pubs.; Mem. Math. Seminar for Social Scientists, 1950; vis. Fulbright prof. U. Oslo, 1955-56, vis. prof., 1973-74; fellow Ctr. Advanced Study in Behavioral Scis., Social Sci. Research Council, 1951-52. Author: (with others) Group Structure and the Newcomer, 1957, Group Transformation: an Analysis of a Learning Group, 1964, The Sociology of Small Groups, 1967, 2d edit., 1984, translations Japanese, German, Spanish, Indonesian, and Danish, (with Stan Rosenberg) Readings on the Sociology of Small Groups, 1970; (with Michael P. Farrell and Dan Gilbertson) film Fathers and Sons; A Study in Group Dynamics, 1972; Assoc. editor: Sociometry, 1963-66, Personality and Social Systems. Mem. Guilford (Conn.) Dem. Com., 1962-65. Served with Am. Friends Service Com. China Convoy, 1942-46. Mem. Am. Sociol. Assn., Am. Anthrop. Assn., Soc. Exptl. Psychology, Am. Psychol. Assn., Sociol. Research Assn., Eastern Sociol. Soc. Home: 156 Mariner St Buffalo NY 14201-1413 Office: Social Scis Interaction Lab Ellicott Complex SUNY Amherst NY 14261

MILLS, WILLIAM HAROLD, JR., construction company executive; b. St. Petersburg, Fla., July 24, 1939; s. William Harold and Caroline (Bonfoey) M.; m. Sylvia Ludwig, Jan. 4, 1962 (div. 1975); children—William Harold III, Robert Michael, Leslie Anne; m. Kimberly Keyes, May 4, 1985 (div. 1988); m. Gigi Alice Schmidt, Aug. 1, 1990. Grad., Woodberry Forest Sch., 1954-57; B.S. in Civil Engring., U. Fla., 1961. Cert. Class A gen. contractor, Fla. V.P. bus. devel. Mills & Jones Constrn., St. Petersburg, Fla., 1964-68; v.p. Wellington Corp., Atlanta, 1968-71; exec. v.p. Mills & Jones Constrn., St. Petersburg, Fla., 1971-79; pres., chmn. Federal Constrn. Co., St. Petersburg, 1979-88, vice chmn., 1988-90; pres., chair Univ. Housing Svcs., Inc., St. Petersburg; mem. adv. com. St Petersburg Port, 1993—. Pres. St. Petersburg Progress, Inc., 1986-87; active mem. Suncoasters, St. Petersburg, 1974—, St. Anthony's Devel. Found., St. Petersburg, 1983—; past chmn. Pinellas Marine Inst., St. Petersburg; past chmn. Blue Ribbon Zoning Com. City of St. Petersburg; former mem. Pinellas County Construction Licensing Bd., Tampa Bay Aviation Adv. Com., United Fund Pinellas County; mem. U. S. Fla. Campus Adv. Bd. Named Hon. Royal Navy Liaison Officer Her Majesty's Royal Navy, 1984—. Mem. ASCE, NSPE, Am. Mgmt. Assn., Mensa, St. Petersburg Area C. of C. (bd. govs. 1983-86), Fla. Sports Adv. Coun., Order of Salvador/Salvador Dali Mus., St. Petersburg Yacht Club, Dragon Club, Les Ambassadeurs Club (London), Vinoy Croquet Club (pres.) Annabel's Club (London) Useppa Island Club (bd. govs.), Sigma Alpha Epsilon, U.S. Croquet Assn. Republican. Episcopalian. Home: 1260 Brightwaters Blvd Saint Petersburg FL 33704 Office: Ste 201 1325 Snell Isle Blvd Saint Petersburg FL 33704

MILLS, WILLIAM HAYES, lawyer; b. Gordo, Ala., Mar. 30, 1931; s. Early S. and Bama (Cameron) M. LL.B., U. Ala., 1956. Bar: Ala. 1956. Since practiced in Birmingham; partner Rogers, Howard, Redden & Mills, 1961-79, Redden, Mills & Clark, 1979—; arbitrator Fed. Mediation and Conciliation Service, Am. Arbitration Assn. Served with AUS, 1948-50, 50-51. Mem. ABA, Ala., Birmingham bar assns., Am., Ala. trial lawyers assns. Baptist. Home: 2105 Williamsburg Way Birmingham AL 35223-1740 Office: Redden Mills & Clark 940 1st Alabama Bank Bldg Birmingham AL 35203

MILLS (KUTZ-HARDER), HELGA, religious organization executive. BA with honors, U. Western Ontario, Vancouver, 1965; MA, U. British Columbia, Vancouver, 1965; PhD in English Renaissance Lit., U. N.C., Chapel Hill, 1976. Specialist instr. English, German Fisher Park High Sch., Ottawa, Can., 1959-63; sessional instr. to instr. dept. English U. British Columbia, Vancouver, Can., 1964-67; sessional instr. to prof. dept English U. Windsor, Ontario, Can., 1970-78, 82-85; missionary United Ch. Can., Tokyo, Japan, 1978-82; interm program dir. United Ch. Can., Windsor, Can., 1982-83; mem. program office United Ch. Can., 1985-91; exec. sec. United Ch. Can. Toronto Conf., 1991-94; prin. St. Paul's United Coll., U. Waterloo, Ont., Can., 1994—. Contbr. to articles to religious mags. Gov. Gen. Gold medalist, 1959, Deutsche Akademische Austauschdienst scholar, 1961, Can. Coun. scholar 1963, U. British Columbia Grad. scholar, 1964. Office: U Waterloo, St Paul's United Coll, Westmount Rd, Waterloo, ON Canada N2L 3G5

MILLSAPS, FRED RAY, investor; b. Blue Ridge, Ga., Apr. 30, 1929; s. Samuel Hunter and Ora Lee (Bradshaw) M.; m. Audrey Margaret Hopkins, June 22, 1957; children: Judith Gail, Stephen Hunter, Walter Scott. A.B., Emory U., 1951; postgrad., U. Wis. Sch. Banking, 1955-57, Harvard Bus. Sch., 1962; LLD, Fla. So. Coll., 1991. Auditor Fed. Res. Bank, Atlanta, 1953-58, asst. v.p., 1958-62, v.p., 1962-64; fin. v.p. Fla. Power & Light Co., 1965-69; pres., dir. First Nat. Bank of Ft. Lauderdale, Fla., 1969-73; chmn., pres. Landmark Banking Corp. of Fla., Ft. Lauderdale, 1971-78; chmn. Landmark Union Trust Bank of St. Petersburg, Fla., 1976-78; bd. dirs. Templeton Mut. Funds, , Shipp Corp., Toronto, Ont. Chmn. com. of 100 Broward County Indsl. Devel. Bd., 1972-77; chmn. South Fla. Coordinating Coun., 1979-81, WPBT Community TV Found. of South Fla., 1973-75, Fla. So. Coll., Lakeland, Broward Performing Arts Authority, Honda Classic, Broward Workshop, Holy Cross Health Corp.; mem. Fla. Coun. of 100. Mem. Tower Club, Inverrary Club, Coral Ridge Country Club. Methodist.

MILLSAPS, RITA RAE, elementary school educator; b. Magdalena, N.Mex., Jan. 14, 1937; d. Samuel Thomas Martin and Geneva Opal (Nicholson) Martin Freeman; m. Daryl Ray Millsaps, June 26, 1955; children: Michael (dec.), Kathleen, Marian, Larry. Student, Delta Community Coll., 1981-82; BA, Calif. State U., Sacramento, 1986, MEd in Curriculum and Instrn., 1993. Cert. elem. educator, Calif. Mem. ASCD, Internat. Reading Assn. Home: PO Box 1413 San Andreas CA 95249-1413

MILLSAPS, SHELBY J., nurse, college educator; b. Coalfield, Tenn., Oct. 24, 1940; d. Oscar W. and Lois Kathleen (East) Justice; m. Charles H. Millsaps, Oct. 27, 1961. Diploma Erlanger Hosp., Chattanooga, 1961; B.S., U. Chattanooga, 1968; M.S.N., Med. Coll. Ga., 1976. Staff nurse Victory Meml. Hosp., Bklyn., 1961-63; instr. Erlanger Hosp., Chattanooga, 1963-74; instr. Cleveland State Community Coll., Tenn., 1974-77, dir., 1977—. Mem. Tenn. Nurses Assn. (chmn. practice 1984—), Chattanooga Nurses Assn., Chattanooga League Nursing, Cleveland Diabetic Assn. (sec. 1983—), Deans and Dirs. (chmn. 1984-85), Sigma Theta Tau. Republican. Baptist. Office: Cleveland State Community Coll Cleveland TN 37411

MILLSAPS, WILLIAM HOBART, JR., newspaper editor; b. Chattanooga, July 1, 1942; s. William Hobart and Myra Sue (Bryant) M.; m. Nancy Dickenson Hurt; children: Katherine Gail Millsaps Renick, Camerian Sue. Student, U. Tenn., 1960-66. Sports writer The Knoxville (Tenn.), 1963-66; sports writer Richmond (Va.) Times-Dispatch, 1966-71, assoc.

sports editor, 1972, exec. sports editor, 1973-76, sports editor, 1977-91, mng. editor, 1992-93, exec. editor, 1994—; pres. U.S. Basketball Writers Assn., 1986, AP Sports Editors, 1980; pres. Leadership Metro Richmond Alumni Assn., 1995. Recipient 11 Va. Sports Writer of Yr. awards Nat. Sportscasters and Sportswriters Assn. Mem. AP Mng. Editors, Am. Soc. Newspaper Editors, Willow Oaks Country Club Richmond, Downtown Club Richmond. Presbyterian. Avocations: reading, golf.

MILLSON, JOHN ARTHUR, former mayor; b. Windsor, Ont., Can., Feb. 29, 1952; s. Arthur Eric and Eleanor Blanche (Chandler) M.; m. Susan Marie Young (div. June 1989); children: Erica, Jody, Katie, John Jr.; m. Gail Diane Campbell, May 18, 1990. Grad. secondary sch., Windsor. Owner Fisher's Flowers, Windsor, 1978-90; mem. city coun. City of Windsor, 1982-88, mayor, 1988-92; police commr. Windsor Police Force, 1988-91; devel. commr. Windsor-Essex County Devel. Commn., Windsor, 1985-91.

MILLSPAUGH, MARTIN LAURENCE, real estate developer, urban development consultant; b. Columbus, Ohio, Dec. 16, 1925; s. Martin Laurence and Elisabeth (Park) M.; m. Meredith Plant, May 10, 1952; children: Elisabeth, M. Laurence, Meredith, Thomas. AB summa cum laude, Princeton U., 1949. Reporter, columnist Richmond News Leader, Va., 1949-53; urban affairs writer Balt. Evening Sun, 1953-57; asst. commr. Urban Renewal Administrn., Washington, 1957-60; dep. gen. mgr. Charles Ctr., Balt., 1960-65; pres., chmn., chief exec. officer Charles Ctr.-Inner Harbor Mgmt., Inc., 1965-85; exec. v.p., pres., vice chmn. Enterprise Devel. Co., Columbia, Md., 1985—, also bd. dirs.; pres. Enterprise Internat. Devel. Co., Columbia, 1988-91, vice chmn., 1991—; cons. to pvt. developers and local pub. agys., Mass., Va., S.C., Fla., Calif., Sydney, 1987—; conducted seminars in Nagasaki and Kagoshima, Japan, 1991-92; lectr. Columbia U., Princeton U., Johns Hopkins U., U. Md., U. New Orleans, NYU, Acad. Polit. Sci., AAAS, Lambda Alpha Internat., 1991, U.K. Inst. Travel and Tourism, 1993, Can. Water Resources Assn., 1991, and numerous other profl. confs. and seminars. Author: (with others) The Human Side of Urban Renewal, 1958; author, editor (monograph) Baltimore's Charles Center, 1964; author (newspaper series) Design for Living (hon. mention Heywood Broun award 1957), 1957; profl. appearances include USIA Worldnet TV, 1990, VOA, 1994, CBS Sunday News, 1994; contbr. articles to profl. jours. Trustee Enoch Pratt Free Libr., Balt., 1965-85, Gilman Sch., 1975-80, Bryn Mawr Sch. for Girls, 1978-81; bd. dirs. Planned Parenthood Assn. Md., 1962-65, Roland Park Civic League, 1962-64, sec., 1963-64, Blue Cross of Md., Inc., 1970-80, Balt. Symphony Orch. Assn., 1974-78, YMCA of Greater Balt. area, 1977-81; Md. Internat. Coun., Balt., 1992—, mem. long range planning com., 1994—; mem. chair nominating com., mem. task force Twentieth Century Fund, N.Y.C., 1984-85; mem. adv. coun. real estate devel. program Columbia U. Grad. Sch. Architecture and Planning, 1985-94; mem. bd. advisors Fight-Blight Fund, Balt., 1961-62, Waterfront Ctr., Washington, 1987-90; mem. adv. bd. Nat. Aquarium, Balt., 1988—, Sch. Bus. Mgmt. Morgan State U., Real Estate Inst., Sch. Continuing Studies Johns Hopkins U., 1994—; mem. pres.'s adv. bd. U. Md. Balt. County, 1989-94; mem. adv. panel Ctr. Strategic and Internat. Studies, Washington, 1993-94; active U.S. Senate Productivity Award Selection Com. for Md., 1987. Served to sgt. USAF, 1944-46, PTO. Recipient Disting. Service award U.S. Housing and Home Fin. Agy., Washington, 1960. Mem. Urban Land Inst. (exec. group internat. coun. 1989—, award of excellence 1980, chair adv. panel for city of Harrisburg, Pa. 1984, internat. com. 1987-88, Balt. dist. coord. 1987-91, vice chmn. dist. coun. com. 1991-94), Greater Balt. Com. (urban affairs coun. 1982-84, J. Jefferson Miller award for civic accomplishment 1981), Coun. on Urban Econ. Devel., Internat. Downtown Assn., Internat. New Town Assn. (mem. adv. panel for waterfront devel. for City of Malmo, Sweden 1987), Phi Beta Kappa, Lambda Alpha. Democrat. Episcopalian. Clubs: Center, Balt., 14 W Hamilton St (Balt.); Ivy (Princeton, N.J.). Home: 203 Ridgewood Rd Baltimore MD 21210-2538 Office: Enterprise Devel Co 600 American City Bldg Columbia MD 21044

MILLSTEIN, IRA M., lawyer, lecturer; b. N.Y.C., Nov. 8, 1926; s. Harry M. and Birdie E. (Rosenbaum) M.; m. Diane G. Greenberg, July 3, 1949; children: James Eliot, Elizabeth Jane. B.S., Columbia U., 1947, LL.B., 1949. Bar: N.Y. 1949, U.S. Supreme Ct. 1973. Atty. antitrust div. Dept. Justice, Washington, 1949-51; assoc. firm Weil Gotshal & Manges, N.Y.C., 1951-57, ptnr., 1957—; chmn. bd. advisors Ctr. for Law and Econ. Studies, Columbia U., 1987—, adj. prof., dir. Henley Program on bus. and law, 1987-89; fellow faculty govt. John F. Kennedy Sch. Govt., Harvard U., 1983-87; disting. faculty fellow Yale U. Sch. of Mgmt., 1980-82, Sloan fellow, 1982-83, Lester Crown vis. faculty fellow, Yale U.Sch. Orgnl. Mgmt., 1992—; mem. coun. Adminstrv. Conf. U.S., 1978-81. Author: (with Katsh) The Limits of Corporate Power, 1981; contbr. articles to profl. jours. Mem. Nat. Commn. on Consumer Fin., 1969-72, chmn., 1971-72; chmn. N.Y.C.'s Spl. Com. on Inquiry into Energy Failures, 1977-82, N.Y. State Energy Planning Bd., 1978-82, Gov. Cuomo's Task Force on Pension Fund Investment, 1988—; vice chmn. bd. overseers Albert Einstein Coll. Medicine, Yeshiva U., Bronx, N.Y., 1981—; chmn. bd. trustees Cen. Pk. Conservancy. Decorated chevalier Nat. Order of Merit, France; Harlan Fiske Stone scholar, 1948-49. Mem. ABA (chmn. antitrust law sect. 1977-78, chmn. antitrust law sect.'s task force report on antitrust div. 1988-89), N.Y. State Bar Assn. (chmn. antitrust law sect. 1967-68), Met. Club, Quaker Ridge Golf Club. Home: 1240 Flagler Dr Mamaroneck NY 10543-4601 Office: Weil Gotshal & Manges 767 5th Ave New York NY 10153-0001

MILLSTEIN, RICHARD ALLEN, federal agency administrator; b. N.Y.C., Jan. 21, 1945; s. Abraham and Minnie (Zahn) M.; m. Nancy Louise Karelitz, Aug. 10, 1968; children: Danna Karen, Eric Jon, Todd David. BA, NYU, 1964; JD cum laude, Boston U. 1968. Bar: N.Y. 1968. Spl. asst. to dir. NIMH, Chevy Chase, Md., 1968-70; from legal asst. to acting chief legis. svcs. br. NIMH, Rockville, Md., 1970-73; chief legis. svcs. unit Alcohol, Drug Abuse and Mental Health Adminstrn., Rockville, 1973-77, 78-79, assoc. administr. planning, policy analysis and legis., 1979-85, assoc. administr. for policy coordination, 1986-87; profl. staff liaison Pres.'s Commn. on Mental Health The White House, Washington, 1977-78, sr. staff mem. Drug Abuse Policy Office, 1987-88; exec. asst. to asst. sec. for health HHS, Washington, 1985-86; dep. dir. Nat. Inst. on Drug Abuse, Rockville, 1988-92, acting dir., 1992—. Editor Periodic Summaries of Proposed and Enacted Fed. Legis., 1971-77; columnist On the Federal Scene Administrs. in Mental Health, 1973-76; contbr. articles to profl. jours. Bd. dirs., chmn. youth commn., sec., v.p. Congregation Har Shalom, Potomac, Md., 1984-85, 87-89. Recipient cert. appreciation Spanish Heritage Pub. Health Svc. Workers, 1981, Equal Employment Opportunity award Parklawn Asian/Pacific Am. Community, 1985, Superior Svc. award USPHS, 1986; Meritorious Exec. Rank award Pres. of U.S., 1988, Disting. Exec. Rank award, 1991. Mem. Commd. Officers' Assn. of USPHS, Md. Congress Parents and Tchrs. (hon. life). Office: HHS Nat Inst Drug Abuse 5600 Fishers Ln Rockville MD 20857-0001

MILLSTONE, DAVID J., lawyer; b. Morgantown, W.Va., 1946. AB, Johns Hopkins U., 1968; JD, U. W.Va., 1971. Bar: W.Va. 1971, Ohio 1971, Fla. 1980. Ptnr. Squire, Sanders & Dempsey, Cleve. Mem. ABA (internat. coord. labor and employment practice). Office: Squire Sanders & Dempsey 4900 Society Ct 127 Public Sq Cleveland OH 44114-1304

MILMAN, DORIS HOPE, pediatrics educator, psychiatrist; b. N.Y.C., Nov. 17, 1917; d. Barnet S. and Rose (Smoleroff) Milman; m. Nathan Kreeger, June 15, 1941; 1 child, Elizabeth Kreeger Goldman. BA, Barnard Coll., 1938; MD, NYU, 1942. Intern Jewish Hosp., Bklyn., 1942-43, resident, 1944-46, fellow in pediatrics, 1946-47; postgrad. extern in psychiatry Bellevue Hosp., N.Y.C., 1947-49; pediatric psychiatry attending Jewish Hosp., Bklyn., 1950-56; asst. prof. pediatrics Health Sci. Ctr. at Bklyn. SUNY, 1956-67, assoc. prof. pediatrics, 1967-73, prof. pediatrics, 1973-93, prof. emeritus, 1993—; acting chmn. dept. pediatrics, 1973-75, 82; pvt. practice child and adolescent psychiatry, Bklyn., 1950-90; vis. prof. Ben Gurion U. of the Negev, Beersheva, Israel, 1977. Mem. adv. bd. N.Y. Assn. for the Learning Disabled, N.Y.C., 1975-80. Recipient Disting. Alumna award Barnard Coll., 1986, Solomon R. Berson Achievement award NYU Sch. Medicine, 1991; Grace Potter Rice fellow Barnard Coll., 1938-39. Fellow Am. Acad. Pediatrics (emeritus). Am. Psychiat. Assn. (life), mem. Am. Orthopsychiat. Assn. (life), Am. Pediatric Soc. (emeritus), N.Y. Pediatric Soc. (emeritus), AAAS. Home: 126 Westminster Rd Brooklyn NY 11218-

3444 Office: Health Sci Ctr at Bklyn SUNY Box 49 450 Lenox Rd Brooklyn NY 11203-2020

MILMOE, PATRICK JOSEPH, lawyer; b. Oct. 2, 1939; s. Hugh A. Milmoe and Mary Frances (O'Connell) Steenken; m. Carolyn Mann, Nov. 30, 1963; children: Mary Frances Chrysicus, Caroline Peugh, Hugh. BA, Coll. William and Mary, 1959; JD, U. Va., 1962. Bar: N.Y. 1962, Va. 1962, Fla. 1989. Assoc. Davis Polk & Wardwell, N.Y.C., 1965-72; ptnr. Hunton & Williams, Richmond, Va., 1972—; pres. DARE Marina, Inc., Virginia Beach, Va., 1992—; chmn. States Roofing Corp., Norfolk, Va., 1994—; pres. Virginia Beach Marlin Club, Inc., 1980—. Trustee Village of Atlantic Beach, N.Y., 1965-72; bd. dirs. St. Joseph's Villa, Richmond, Va., 1985-91. Capt. U.S. Army, 1963-65. Mem. Am. Coll. Real Estate Lawyers. Avocations: boating, fishing. Office: Hunton & Williams 951 E Byrd St Richmond VA 23219-4040

MILNE, JAMES, secretary of state; b. Barre, Vt., July 8, 1950; m. Judith Garigliano; children: Honah Lee, Heather, Joseph, Elizabeth. BS in Pharmacy, Mass. Coll. Pharmacy, 1974. City clk., treas. City of Barre (Vt.), 1988-94; sec. of state State of Vt., 1995—; pharmacist, mgr. Allan Milne Pharmacy, 1974-88. Mem. Aldrich Pub. Libr. (bd. trustees), Nat. Ski Patrol, Mutuo, Inc.; chair Barre Basketball Tournament Com.; dir. Granite Mutual Ins. Co. Mem. Vt. Municipal Clks. and Treas. Assn., Vt. Jaycees (pres. 1979-80), U.S. Jaycees (nat. v.p. 1980-81), Barre Elks Lodge, Barre Country Club, Barre Rotary Club (pres. 1985-86). Republican. Office: PO Box 992 Barre VT 05641 also: Sec of State Barre City Clerk 41 Beacon St Barre VT 05641*

MILNER, BRENDA ATKINSON LANGFORD, neuropsychologist; b. Manchester, Eng., July 15, 1918; emigrated to Can., 1944; d. Samuel and Leslie (Doig) Langford. BA, Cambridge (Eng.) U., 1939, MA, 1949, ScD, 1972; PhD, McGill U., 1952; DSc (hon.), 1991;, LLD (hon.), Queen's U., 1980; ScD (hon.) U. Manitoba, 1982, U. Lethbridge, 1986, Mt. Holyoke Coll., 1986, U. Laval, 1987, U. Toronto, 1987; LHD (hon.), Mt. St. Vincent U., 1988; Hon. D. U. de Montréal, 1988; DSc (hon.) Wesleyan U., 1991, Acadia U., 1991, U. St. Andrews, 1992. Exptl. officer U.K. Ministry of Supply, 1941-44; prof. agrégé Institut de Psychologie, Université de Montréal, 1944-52; rsch. assoc. psychology dept. McGill U., Montreal, 1952-53, lectr. dept. neurology and neurosurgery, 1953-60, asst. prof., 1960-64, assoc. prof., 1964-70, prof. psychology, 1970-73; Dorothy J. Killam prof. Montreal Neurological Inst., 1993—; head neuropsychology rsch. unit Montreal Neurol. Inst., 1953-90; Clothworkers fellow Girton Coll., Cambridge, 1972-73. Mem. editorial bd. Neuropsychologia, 1973-93, Behavioral Brain Rsch., 1980-88, Hippocampus, 1990—. Career investigator Med. Rsch. Coun. Can., 1964—; recipient Disting. Sci. Contbn. award Am. Psychol. Assn., 1973; Karl Spencer Lashley award Am. Philos. Soc., 1979; Izaak Walton Killam Meml. prize Can. Coun., 1983; Hermann Von Helmholtz prize Cognitive Neuroscience Inst., 1984; Officier de l'Ordre nat. du Que., 1985; Ralph W. Gerard prize Soc. for Neuroscience USA, 1987; named Officer Order of Can., 1984; William James fellow Am. Psychol. Soc., 1989. Wilder Penfield prize Province of Quebec, 1993. Fellow APA, AAAS, Royal Soc. London, Royal Soc. Can. (McLaughlin medal 1994), Can. Psychol. Assn.; mem. Am. Epilepsy Soc., Am. Neurol. Assn., Association de Psychologie Scientifique de Langue Française, Brit. Soc. Exptl. Psychology, Exptl. Psychol. Soc., Psychonomic Soc., Eastern Psychol. Assn., Internat. Neuropsychology Symposium, Internat. Brain Rsch. Orgn. (exec. sec. 1993—), Soc. Neurosci. (Ralph W. Gerard prize 1987), NAS (frgn. assoc.), Am. Acad. Neurology (assoc.), Assn. Rsch. in Nervous and Mental Diseases (assoc.), Royal Soc. Medicine (affiliate), Sigma Xi. Office: McGill University Montreal Neurol Inst 3801 University St, Montreal, PQ Canada H3A 2B4

MILNER, CLYDE A., II, historian; b. Durham, N.C., Oct. 19, 1948; s. Charles Fremont and Eloyse (Sargent) M.; m. Carol Ann O'Connor, Aug. 14, 1977; children: Catherine Carol, Charles Clyde. AB, U. N.C., 1971; MA, Yale U., 1973, MPhil, 1974, PhD, 1979. Admissions counselor Guilford Coll., Greensboro, N.C., 1968-70; acting instr. Yale U., New Haven, Conn., 1974-75; research fellow McNickle Ctr., Chgo., 1975-76; instr. Utah State U., Logan, 1976-79, asst. prof., 1979-82, assoc. prof., 1982-88, prof., 1988—; reader of manuscripts History Book Club, Inc., 1986—. Author: With Good Intentions, 1982; editor Major Problems in the History of the American West, 1989; assoc. editor: The Western Historical Quarterly, 1984-87, co-editor, 1987-89; editor, 1990—; co-editor: Churchmen and the Western Indians, 1985, Trails: Toward a New Western History, 1991, Oxford History of the American West, 1994 (Western Heritage award for non-fiction Nat. Cowboy Hall of Fame 1995). Recipient Paladen Writing award The Montana Mag. Western History, 1987, Faculty Svc. award Associated Students Utah State U., 1987, Outstanding Social Science Researcher award Utah State U., 1983. Mem. Western History Assn., Orgn. Am. Historians, Phi Alpha Theta, Phi Beta Kappa. Society of Friends. Home: 1675 E 1400 N Logan UT 84341-2975 Office: Utah State U Utah State U Dept of History Logan UT 84322

MILNER, HAROLD WILLIAM, hotel executive; b. Salt Lake City, Nov. 11, 1934; s. Kenneth W. and Olive (Schoettlin) M.; m. Susan Emmett, June 19, 1959 (div. 1976); children—John Kenneth, Mary Sue; m. Lois Friemuth, Aug. 14, 1977; 1 dau., Jennifer Rebecca. B.S., U. Utah, 1960; M.B.A., Harvard, 1962. Instr. Brigham Young U., Provo, Utah, 1962-64; v.p. Gen. Paper Corp., Mpls., 1964-65; dir. finance Amalgamated Sugar Co., Ogden, Utah, 1965-67; corp. treas. Marriott Corp., Washington, 1967-70; pres., chief exec. officer, trustee Hotel Investors, Kensington, Md., 1970-75; pres., chief exec. officer Americana Hotels Corp., Chgo., 1975-85, Kahler Corp., Rochester, Minn., 1985—. Author: A Special Report on Contract Maintenance, 1963. Served as lt. AUS, 1960. Mem. Minn. Bus. Partnership (dir. 1991—). Mem. Ch. Jesus Christ Latter-day Saints. Home: 4010 Maywood Rd SW Rochester MN 55902-1011 Office: Kahler Corp 20 2nd Ave SW Rochester MN 55902

MILNER, HOWARD M., real estate developer, international real estate financier; b. L.A., Sept. 21, 1937; s. David Daniel and Rose (Devron) M.; m. Shirley Glogow, Oct. 24, 1964 (div. 1978); children: Mara Lynn, Debra Faye. AA in Architecture, L.A. City Coll., 1960; cert. real estate, UCLA, 1962. Sr. store planner Broadway Dept. Stores, L.A., 1959; exec. v.p. Palm Properties Inc., Van Nuys, Calif., 1959-69; v.p. Network Cinema Corp., L.A., 1969-79, Hesa Global Investments Ltd., Beverly Hills, Calif., 1979-86; pres., chief exec. officer Lyons Internat. Realty and Devel. Inc., L.A., 1986-87, Howard M. Milner and Assocs., North Hollywood, Calif., 1987—; cons. Swiss-Am. Investment Trust, North Hollywood, 1979—; adj. sr. assoc. Visa Enterprises Inc., Beverly Hills., 1986—; sr. assoc. cons. AMF Roadmaster Mfg. Co., North Hollywood, 1986—; developed nat. expansion Internat. House Pancakes, Copper Penny Coffee Shops, Fotomat Corp., Jerry Lewis Cinema Theatres, K-Mart Shopping Ctrs.; lectr. in field. Contbr. articles on real estate to profl. jours. Life mem., fin. sec. City of Hope, L.A.'s mem. Mayor's Comml. Devel. Com., Brea, Calif., Mayor's Redevel. Com., L.A. and Hollywood; actively City of Hope Cancer Rsch. Found., Duarte, Calif. With U.S. Army, 1957-59. Recipient Civic Appreciation award Mayor of L.A., 1987; Architecture scholar Ford Motor Co., 1954, Architecture scholar East L.A. Coll., 1955; Eagle Scout award Boy Scouts Am., 1952. Mem. AIA, Am. Inst. Indsl. Engrs., Am. Inst. Plant Engrs., Am. Assoc. Mil. Engrs., Calif. Apt. and Motel Mgrs. Assn., Calif. Notary Assn., Calif. Real Estate Assn., Constrn. Specifications Inst., Real Estate Mgmt. Internat. Coun. Shopping Ctrs., Internat. Real Estate Fedn., Nat. Home Builders Assn. Am., Nat. Franchise Assn. Am., Real Estate Cert. Inst., Young Home Builders Coun. Am., L.A. C. of C., San Fernando C. of C., Saugus-Newhall C. of C., Van Nuys C. of C., Toastmasters, Masons, Shriners. Democrat. Jewish. Avocations: walking, jogging, racquetball, golf, cooking. Office: 1st Interstate Bank Bldg 4605 Lankershim Blvd # 413 North Hollywood CA 91602-1818

MILNER, IRVIN MYRON, lawyer; b. Cleve., Feb. 5, 1916; s. Nathan and Rose (Spector) M.; m. Zelda Winograd, Aug. 15, 1943. A.B. cum laude, Western Res. U. (now Case Western Res. U.), 1937, J.D., 1940, LL.M., 1970. Bar: Ohio 1940, U.S. Dist. Ct. (no. dist.) Ohio 1946. Pvt. practice Cleve., 1946—; exec. sec., counsel Men's Apparel Club Ohio, Cleve., 1947-48; adj. instr. Sch. Law, Case Western Res. U., 1965-66; spl. counsel Ohio Office Atty. Gen., 1963-70; legal counsel Korean Am. Assn., 1973-95, Greater Cleve., 1973—. Mem. Cleve. Fgn. Consular Corps, 1970—, hon.

consul Rep. of Korea for Cleve., 1970—; bd. dirs. Internat. Human Assistance Programs, Inc., 1973-79, voting corp. mem., 1980-88. Served with U.S. Army, 1941-45, ETO. Decorated Order Diplomatic Svc. Merit-Heung-in medal (Republic of Korea), 1975; named to Disting. Alumni Hall of Fame, Cleveland Heights (Ohio) High Sch., 1983. Fellow Internat. Consular Coll., Ohio Bar Found.; mem. ABA (small bus. com., corp. bus. law sect 1971-74), Greater Cleve. Internat. Lawyers Group, Cleve. Bar Assn., Cuyahoga County Bar Assn. (pres. 1975-76, award of special Merit 1976, Pres.' award 1988, co-chmn. jud. standards com. 1987-88, life trustee), Ohio State Bar Assn. (council dels. 1976-86, com. on legal ethics and profl. conduct 1984—), Cuyahoga County Bar Found. (sec. treas. 1980-84, bd. dirs. 1984—), Cuyahoga County Coun. Ohio VFW (comdr. 1958, Merit award 1958), Greater Cleve. Vets Coun. (pres. 1957, Merit award 1983), Am. Security Coun. (nat. adv. bd.), Western Res. Coll. Alumni Assn. (bd. dirs. 1982-88), Tau Epsilon Rho (chancellor Cleve. Grad. chpt. 1987-88), Delta Phi Alpha. Republican. Jewish. Club: Cleve. City. Lodges: Masons 32 degree, Rotary. Office: Standard Bldg #1148 1370 Ontario St Cleveland OH 44113-1701

MILNER, MAX, food and nutrition consultant; b. Edmonton, Alta., Can., Jan. 24, 1914; came to U.S., 1939, naturalized, 1944; s. Morris Abram and Rose (Lertzman) M.; m. Elizabeth Banen, Aug. 9, 1942; children—Ruth Sharon, Marcia Ann. B.Sc., U. Sask., 1938; LL.D. (hon.), 1979; M.S., U. Minn., 1941, Ph.D., 1945. Research chemist Pillsbury Mills Inc., Mpls., 1939-40; prof. grain sci. and industry Kans. State U., Manhattan, 1947-59; sr. food technologist UNICEF, N.Y.C., 1959-71; chief nutrition br. AID, 1966-67; dir. secretariat protein calorie adv. group UN, 1971-75; assoc. dir. internat. nutrition program M.I.T., 1975-78; exec. officer Am. Inst. Nutrition, Bethesda, Md., 1978-84; mem. U.S. Wheat Industry Council, 1980-83; mem. expert evaluation panel Bd. Internat. Food and Agrl. Devel., 1983—; chmn. Gordon Research Conf. Food and Nutrition, 1968; Gen. Food Co. (Can.) disting. internat. lectr., 1975. Co-author: Protein Resources and Technology, 1978, Postharvest Biology and Biotechnology, 1978; Editor: Protein-enriched Cereal Foods for World Needs, 1969, Nutrition Improvement of Food Legumes by Breeding, 1975; Contbr. articles to profl. jours., chpts. to monographs. Bd. dirs., exec. com. Meals for Million/Freedom From Hunger Found., 1975-83, cons. in field. Fellow AAAS, Inst. Food Technologists (Internat. award 1968, lectr. sci. series 1971-72, Disting. Food Service award N.Y. sect. 1975), Am. Inst. Nutrition; mem. Am. Chem. Soc., Am. Assn. Cereal Chemists. Home: 10401 Grosvenor Pl Apt 721 Rockville MD 20852-4635 As a child of immigrant parents with minimal formal education, my career, like that of many Americans with this kind of background, is a testimonial to the unique role of the Canadian and American system of open higher education, available to all able to qualify for admission. It is to such institutions that I owe a profound debt.

MILNER, PETER MARSHALL, psychology educator; b. Silkstone Common, Eng., June 13, 1919; s. David William and Edith Anne (Marshall) M.; m. Susan Walker, Oct. 13, 1970; 1 son, David Elliot. B.S., Leeds U., 1941; M.S., McGill U., Ph.D., 1954. Sr. sci. officer U.K. Ministry Supply, 1941-48; research asso. physics McGill U., 1948-50, research asst., prof. dept. psychology, 1950-92, prof. emeritus, 1992—, chmn. dept., 1980-83. Author: Physiological Psychology. Fellow Am. Psychol. Assn., Canadian Psychol. Assn.; mem. Sigma Xi. Home: 4032 Vendôme, Montreal, PQ Canada H4A 3N1 Office: McGill U Dept Psychology, 1205 Dr Penfield Ave, Montreal, PQ Canada H3A 1B1

MILNER, SCOTT T., chemical engineer. Recipient John H. Dillon medal Am. Physical Soc., 1994. Studies the behavior of polymer brushes, self-assembling polymer structures and sheared polymer solutions. Office: Exxon Rsch & Engring Clinton Twnshp Route 22 E Annandale NJ 08801*

MILNER, THIRMAN L., mayor; b. Hartford, Oct. 29, 1933; s. Marshall Henry and Grace (Allen) M.; children by previous marriage—Theresa, Gary. Mem. Conn. Ho. of Reps., 1979-81, Democratic whip, 1979-81, sec. Conn. legis. black caucus, 1979-81, chmn. mcpl. affairs and home rule subcoms., 1979-81; mayor City of Hartford, 1981-87; state senator, Conn., 1987—; formerly minority bussings acct. rep. Oasis Oil Co.; pub. relations dir. and exec. asst. Community Renewal Team; exec. asst. N.Y.C. Against Poverty. Weekly columnist Northend Agt., 1974-80. Bd. dirs. St. Francis Hosp., Hartford Hosp. Mem. NAACP (life), Nat. Conf. Mayors, Conn. Govt. Assn. Methodist. Address: 19 Colebrook St Hartford CT 06112-1522

MILNES, ARTHUR GEORGE, electrical engineer, educator; b. Heswall, Eng., July 30, 1922; came to U.S., 1957, naturalized, 1964; s. George and Marion (Teasdale) M.; m. Mary Laverne Wertz, Dec. 4, 1955; children: Sheila Rae, Brian George, John Teasdale. B.Sc., U. Bristol, Eng., 1943, M.Sc., 1947, D.Sc., 1956. With Royal Aircraft Establishment, 1943-57, prin. sci. officer, 1952-57; mem. faculty Carnegie-Mellon U., Pitts., 1957—; prof. elec. engring. Carnegie-Mellon U., 1960—, assoc. head dept., 1966-69, Buhl prof., 1973—; cons. to industry on semiconductor devices, 1957. Author: Transductors and Magnetic Amplifiers, 1957, (with D.L. Feucht) Heterojunctions and Metal-Semiconductor Junctions, 1972, Deep Impurities in Semiconductors, 1973, Semiconductor Devices and Integrated Electronics, 1979; contbr. articles to profl. jours. FOA research fellow Nat. Acad. Scis.- Royal Soc. London, 1954. Fellow Instn. Elec. Engrs. (London), IEEE (J.J. Ebers award 1982, van der Ziel award 1993), Am. Phys. Soc. Home: 1417 Inverness Ave Pittsburgh PA 15217-1157

MILNES, SHERRILL EUSTACE, baritone; b. Downers Grove, Ill., Jan. 10, 1935; s. James Knowlton and Thelma (Roe) M.; children by previous marriage—Eric, Erin; m. Nancy Denise Stokes, Sept. 28, 1969; 1 son, Shawn. Student, North Central Coll., Ill.; B in Music Edn., Drake U., 1957, M in Music Edn., 1958; postgrad., Northwestern U., 1958-61; studied with Boris Goldovsky, Rosa Ponselle, Andrew White, Hermanes Baer; postgrad. hon. degree, Ripon Coll., Drake U., Coe Coll., Westminster Choir Coll., SUNY, Potsdam. Operatic debut Goldovsky Opera Co., N.Y.C., 1960; leading baritone N.Y.C. Opera Co., Met. Opera Co., 1964—; European debut in Macbeth, Vienna, 1970; appearances major world opera cos. including Covent Garden, London, L'Opera, Paris, Staasoper, Vienna, Austria, Teatro Colon, Argentina, La Scala, Milan, Hamburg, Munich, Salzburg, Frankfurt, Berlin, Zurich, as well as continued appearances in the U.S. in San Antonio, Cin., Miami, Houston, Pitts., Chgo., Balt.; numerous TV, concerts, recitals, recordings (RCA, Deutsche Grammophon, Angel/EMI, London, Decca, Philips, CBS). Recipient Order of Merit, Comdr. of the Rep. of Italy, 1984; Ford Found. award, 1962. Mem. Affiliate Artists, Inc. (past pres., chmn. devel. com. 1966—, chmn. emeritus), Tucker Found. (v.p.), Phi Mu Alfa Sinfonia (life). Office: care Herbert Barrett 1776 Broadway Ste 584 New York NY 10019-2001*

MILNES, WILLIAM ROBERT, JR., insurance company executive; b. St. Louis, Jan. 11, 1946; s. William Robert and Patricia June (Hargate) M.; m. Rebecca Jane Richards, Oct. 14, 1983; children: Bill, Julie, Kristen, David. BSBA in Acctg., U. Mo., 1968, MBA in Fin., 1971. CPA 1980. Budget analyst Chrysler Corp., St. Louis, 1968; plant acctg. supr., acctg. analyst Monsanto Corp., St. Louis, 1971-74; mgr., cost & budget Mo. Hosp. Svcs. Inc., St. Louis, 1974-76; dir. fin., controller Mo. Hosp. Svcs. Inc., 1976-78, v.p. fin., 1978-82, sr. v.p. Hosp. care Corp., Cin., 1982-84; group sr. v.p., treas., chief fin. officer fin. svcs. Community Mutual Ins. Co., Cin., 1984-91, exec. v.p. corp. svcs., chief fin. officer, 1991—; bd. dirs. Health Plans Capital Svcs. Corp., Chgo., Blue Cross Blue Shield Assn., Nat. Employee Benefits Com., Chgo.; bd. dirs., chmn. audit com. Exec. & Employee Benefits Plans Inc., Columbus, Ohio, 1990—; bd. dirs., sec., treas. CMIC Holding Co., Cin., 1986—; bd. dirs., chmn. investment com. Community Nat. Assurance Co., Columbus, 1983—. Chmn. Anderson Twp. Bicentennial, 1991—; bd. dirs. Nat. Employee Benefits Bd., Chgo. With USMC, 1967-70. Mem. Fin. Execs. Inst. Avocations: golf, bicycling, fishing. Office: Community Mutual Ins Co 221 E 4th St Cincinnati OH 45202-4124

MILNIKEL, ROBERT SAXON, lawyer; b. Chgo., Aug. 17, 1926; s. Gustav and Emma Hazel (Saxon) M.; m. Virginia Lee Wylie, July 26, 1969; children: Robert Saxon Jr., Elizabeth Wylie. A.B., U. Chgo., 1950, JD, 1953. Bar: Ill. 1953, U.S. Dist. Ct. 1954. Assoc. Traeger, Bolger & Traeger, Chgo., 1953-57, Heineke, Conklin & Schrader, Chgo., 1958-66; ptnr. Peterson & Ross, Chgo., 1966—. With USN, 1944-46, PTO. Mem. Beta Theta Pi (pres. chpt. and alumni assn.), Cliffdwellers Club (bd. dirs. Arts Found.). Republican.

Lutheran. Home: 601 Ridge Rd Kenilworth IL 60043-1042 Office: Peterson & Ross 200 E Randolph Dr # 7300 Chicago IL 60601-6401

MILNOR, WILLIAM ROBERT, physician; b. Wilmington, Del., May 4, 1920; s. William Robert and Virginia (Sterling) M.; m. Gabriella Mahaffy, Aug. 19, 1944; children—Katherine Alexander, William Henry. A.B., Princeton U. 1941; M.D. Johns Hopkins U., 1944. Diplomate: Am. Bd. Internal Medicine. Intern, resident Johns Hopkins Hosp., 1944-46; research fellow Nat. Heart Inst., 1949-51; physician-in-charge heart sta. Johns Hopkins Hosp., 1951-60, physician, 1952—; mem. faculty Johns Hopkins Med. Sch., 1951—, prof. physiology, 1969—; vis. fellow St. Catherine's Coll., Oxford (Eng.) U., 1968; mem. med. adv. panel Am. Inst. Biol. Scis., 1971—; assessor Nat. Med. Research Council of Australia, 1976—. Author: Hemodynamics, 2d edit., 1989, Cardio-vascular Physiology, 1990; contbr. articles to med. textbooks, med. jours. Served to capt. M.C. USAAF, 1946-48. Fellow A.C.P.; mem. Am. Physiol. Soc., Am. Fedn. Clin. Research, Biomed. Engring. Soc., Am. Heart Assn. (chmn. research com. 1966), Heart Assn. Md. (past pres.). Clubs: L'Hirondelle, Princeton, 14 W Hamilton St. Office: Johns Hopkins Med Sch 725 N Wolfe St Baltimore MD 21205-2105

MILONE, ANTHONY M., bishop; b. Omaha, Sept. 24, 1932. Grad., North American Coll. (Rome). Ordained priest Roman Catholic Ch., 1957. Ordained titular bishop of Plestia and aux. bishop Diocese of Omaha, 1982; apptd. bishop Mont. Diocese, Great Falls-Billings, 1987—. Office: PO Box 1399 121 23rd St S Great Falls MT 59403*

MILONE, FRANCIS MICHAEL, lawyer; b. Phila., June 18, 1947; s. Michael Nicholas and Frances Theresa (Fair) M.; m. Maida R. Crane, Nov. 25, 1991; children: Michael, Matthew. Ba., LaSalle Coll., 1969; MS, Pa. State U., 1971; JD, U. Pa., 1974. Bar: Pa. 1974, U.S. Dist. Ct. (ea dist.) Pa. 1974, U.S. Dist. Ct. (mid. dist.) Pa. 1979, U.S. Dist. Ct. (ea. dist.) Mich. 1983, U.S. Ct. Appeals (3d cir.) 1978, U.S. Ct. Appeals (4th and 5th cirs.) 1979, U.S. Supreme Ct. 1979. Assoc Montgomery, McCraken, Walker & Rhoads, Phila., 1974-77; ptnr. Morgan, Lewis & Bockius, Phila., 1977—. Mem. ABA (labor and litigation sects.), Pa. Bar Assn., Phila. Bar Assn. Home: 1020 Cedar Kd Newton Square PA 19073-2808 Office: Morgan Lewis & Bockius 2000 One Logan Sq Philadelphia PA 19103

MILORO, FRANK P., church official, religious studies educator; b. Wilmington, Del., Jan. 26, 1947; m. Constance Ann Evanisko, Apr. 20, 1969; children: Alexandra, Stephanie, Christopher. Grad. summa cum laude, Saviour Sem., 1969; grad. with high honors, St. Vincent Coll., 1972; attended, U. Pitts. Ordained to Diaconate and Priesthood, 1969. Assigned St. John's Ch., Ligonier, Pa., 1969-72, St. Stephen's Ch., Latrobe, Pa., 1969-72, St. John's Ch., Rahway, N.J., 1972-76; dir. Camp Nazareth, diocesan dir. youth, 1976-86; dean Christ the Saviour Sem.; elevated to dignity of Very Rev., 1985; assoc. pastor Christ the Saviour Cathedral; sec. to bishop, instr. homiletics and parish administr.; diocesan chancellor Am. Carpatho-Russian Orthodox Diocese, 1990—; chaplain Ea. Orthodox residents Polk Ctr., Commonwealth Pa., established chapel; sr. spiritual advisor A.C.R.Y. Assoc. editor The Ch. Messenger. Office: 312 Garfield St Johnstown PA 15906-2122

MILOSH, EUGENE JOHN, international trade association executive; b. N.Y.C., Nov. 18, 1933; s. John Peter and Natalie (Stack) M.; children: Wendy, Dara. AB, Dickinson Coll., 1955; postgrad. in acctg., U. N.C., 1957; MA in Internat. Econ., New Sch. for Social Rsch., 1962. Mgr. market devel. Union Carbide Corp., Danbury, Conn., 1957-73; v.p. US-USSR Trade and Econ. Coun., N.Y.C., 1973-80; pres. Am. Assn. Exporters and Importers, N.Y.C., 1980—; adv. bd. World Trade Inst., N.Y.C., 1982—; mem. adv. com. Com. on Customs Ops., Dept. Treasury, Washington, 1987—, Com. on Retailing, Dept. Commerce, Washington, 1986—; mem. steering com. Retail Industry Trade Action Com., Wshington, 1988—; Congl. testimony on trade related matters. Contbr. articles to profl. jours. 1st Lt. M.I., 1955-57. Mem. Chem. Assn. Execs. Coun. (steering com.). Republican. Episcopalian. Avocations: writing, home repair, tennis, sailing. Home: 145 Jonathan Rd New Canaan CT 06840-2117 Office: American Assn of Exporters And Importers 11 W 42nd St New York NY 10036-8002

MILOSZ, CZESLAW, poet, author, educator; b. Lithuania, June 30, 1911; came to U.S., 1960, naturalized, 1970; s. Aleksander and Weronika (Kunat) M. M Juris, U. Wilno, Lithuania, 1934; LittD (hon.), U. Mich., 1977; honoris causa, Harvard U., 1989, Jagellonian U., Poland, 1989, U. Rome, Italy, 1992. Programmer Polish Nat. Radio, 1935-39; diplomatic service Polish Fgn. Affairs Ministry, Warsaw, 1945-50; vis. lectr. U. Calif., Berkeley, 1960-61; prof. Slavic langs. and lits. U. Calif., 1961-78, prof. emeritus, 1978—. Author: The Captive Mind, 1953, Native Realm, 1968, Post-War Polish Poetry, 1965, The History of Polish Literature, 1969, Selected Poems, 1972, Bells in Winter, 1978, The Issa Valley, 1981, Separate Notebooks, 1984, The Land of Ulro, 1984, The Unattainable Earth, 1985, Collected Poems, 1988, Provinces, 1991, Beginning With My Streets, 1992, A Year of the Hunter, 1994, Facing the River, 1995. Recipient Prix Littéraire Européen Les Guildes du Livre, Geneva, 1953, Neustadt Internat. prize for lit. U. Okla., 1978, citation U. Calif., Berkeley, 1978, Nobel prize for lit., 1980, Nat. Medal of Arts, 1990; Nat. Culture Fund fellow, 1934-35; Guggenheim fellow, 1976. Mem. AAAS, Am. Acad. Arts and Scis., Am. Acad and Inst. Arts and Letters, Polish Inst. Letters and Scis. in Am., PEN Club in Exile. Office: U Calif Dept Slavic Langs Lits Berkeley CA 94720

MILSOM, ROBERT CORTLANDT, banker; b. Butler, Pa., Dec. 15, 1924; s. Robert C. and M. Ethel (Leyland) M. BS, John Carroll U., 1948. With PNC Bank (formerly Pitts. Nat. Bank), 1948-90; asst. sec., asst. cashier customer relations div. PNC Bank, 1953-56, asst. v.p. loan div., 1956-60, v.p. charge comml. loan group, 1960-65, sr. v.p. charge comml. banking div., 1965-68, exec. v.p., 1968-72, pres., 1972-85, chmn., CEO, 1985-90, also bd. dirs., 1972—; vice chmn., dir. PNC Bank Corp, 1972-90; bd. dirs. PNC Bank N.A., PNC Equity Mgmt. Corp., Exec. Svc. Corps., Foxwall Med. Svc.; chmn. bd. trustees Mercy Hosp. Pitts., 1994—. Bd. dirs. Pitts. Mercy Health System, Inc., Pitts. Ballet Theatre, Regional Indsl. Devel. Corp.; hon. trustee John Carroll U., Cleve.; mem. adv. bd. Mon Valley Renaissance program California U. Pa. Mem. Duquesne Club of Pitts., Fox Chapel Golf Club of Pitts., Laurel Valley Golf Club, Rolling Rock Club. Office: PNC Bank 5th Ave & Wood St Pittsburgh PA 15222

MILSOME, DOUGLAS, cinematographer. Cinematographer: (TV movies) Great Expectations, 1989, Lonesome Dove, 1989, Mily of Spies-Parts I and II, 1990, (films) Race to a Yankee Zephyr, 1984, Wild Horses, 1984, Full Metal Jacket, 1987, The Beast, 1988, Hawks, 1989, Desperate Hours, 1990, If Looks Could Kill, 1991, (with Dante Spinotti) The Last of the Mohicans, 1992, Body of Evidence, 1993. Office: Smith/Gosnell/Nicholson & Assoc PO Box 1166 1515 Palisades Dr Pacific Palisades CA 90272*

MILSTEIN, ALBERT, lawyer; b. Germany, Dec. 29, 1946. BA magna cum laude, Yeshiva U., 1969; JD, U. Chgo., 1972. Bar: Ill. 1972. Ptnr. Winston & Strawn, Chgo. Mem. Chgo. Bar Assn., Ill. State Bar Assn. Office: Winston & Strawn 35 W Wacker Dr Chicago IL 60601-1614

MILSTEIN, ELLIOTT STEVEN, legal educator, academic administrator; b. Hartford, Conn., Oct. 19, 1944; s. Samuel M. and Mildred K. Milstein; m. Bonnie Myrun, Oct. 1, 1967 (div. Oct. 1992); 1 child, Jacob. BA, U. Hartford, 1966; JD, U. Conn., 1969; LLM, Yale U., 1971. Bar: Conn. 1969, D.C. 1972, U.S. Dist. Ct. Conn. 1969, U.S. Ct. Appeals (D.C.) 1972. Lectr. in law U. Conn. Clin. Program. 1969-70; staff atty. New Haven Legal Assistance Assn., 1971-72; asst. prof. law, dir. clin. programs Washington coll. law Am. U., 1972-74, assoc. prof., dir. clin. programs, 1974-77, prof., dir. clin. programs, 1977-88, interim dean, 1988-90, dean, 1990—, assoc. dean Law Sch., 1977-78, interim pres., 1993-94, dean Washington Coll. Law, 1994—; co-dir. Nat. Vets. Law Ctr., 1978-84; cons. Calif. Bar Bd. of Bar Admissions, lawyer tng. Practising Law Inst., N.Y.C.; chmn. D.C. Law Students in Ct. Program, 1982-83; mem. Law Tchrs. for Legal Services. Ford Urban Law fellow, 1971-72. Mem. Soc. Am. Law Tchrs., Assn. Am. Law Schs. (chmn. sect. clin. edn. 1982, mem. accreditation com. 1984-86, chmn standing com. clin. edn. 1993—), ABA (skills tng. com. 1983-85, govt. rels. com. 1992—), ACLU. Democrat. Home: 3216 Brooklawn Ct Bethesda MD

20815 Office: Am U Washington Coll Law 4400 Massachusetts Ave NW Washington DC 20016-8001

MILSTEIN, LAURENCE BENNETT, electrical engineering educator, researcher; b. Bklyn., Oct. 28, 1942; s. Harry and Sadie (Kaplan) M.; m. Suzanne Barbara Hirschman, Oct. 3, 1969; children—Coreen Roxanne, Renair Marissa. B.E.E., CUNY, 1964; M.S.E.E., Poly. Inst. Bklyn., 1966, Ph.D. in Elec. Engring., 1968. Mem. tech. staff Hughes Aircraft Co., El Segundo, Calif., 1968-69, staff engr., 1969-72, sr. staff engr., 1972-74; asst. prof. Rensselaer Poly. Inst., Troy, N.Y., 1974-76; asst. prof. U. Calif.-San Diego, La Jolla, 1976-79, assoc. prof., 1979-82, prof. elec. engring., 1982—, chmn. dept., 1984-88; cons. Hughes Aircraft Co., Culver City, Calif., 1976-78, Lockheed Missiles & Space Co., Sunnyvale, Calif., 1978-93, Motorola Satellite Communications, 1992—, InterDigitel Communications Corp., 1992—, various govt. agys., pvt. cos., 1975—. Co-editor: Tutorials in Modern Communications, 1983; Spread Spectrum Communications, 1983; contbr. articles to profl. jours. Recipient Outstanding Tchr. award Warren Coll., U. Calif.-San Diego, La Jolla, 1982; grantee Army Rsch. Office, 1977-80, 81-84, 86-89, 91-94, Office of Naval Rsch., Arlington, Va., 1982—, TRW, San Diego, 1983-89, 92-95, NSF, 1993—. Fellow IEEE Comms. Soc. (bd. govs. 1983, 85-87, 93-95, v.p. for tech. activities 1990-91), IEEE Info. Theory Soc. (bd. govs. 1989-94). Jewish. Office: U Calif-San Diego Dept Elec and Computer Engring La Jolla CA 92093

MILSTEIN, MONROE GARY, retail executive; b. N.Y.C., Jan. 14, 1927; s. Abe Herman and Ann Ethel (Isaacs) M.; m. Henrietta Haas, Dec. 22, 1949; children—Lazer, Andrew, Stephen. B.S., NYU, 1946. Pres. Monroe G. Milstein Inc., N.Y.C., 1947—; chmn. bd., pres., chief exec. officer Burlington Coat Factory Warehouse Corp., N.J., 1972—; dir. Fidelity Bank & Trust Co. of N.J., 1972—. Trustee, pres. bd. Long Beach Pub. Library, N.Y., 1967-76; pres. bd. trustees Nassau Library System, Roosevelt Field, N.Y., 1971-73. Recipient Man of Yr. awards Coat and Suit Buyers Assn., 1984, Long Beach C. of C., Youth Service award B'nai B'rith. Mem. Am. Gen. Mdse. Assn., U.S. C. of C. Jewish. Clubs: Dads (Long Beach) (pres. 1969). Lodge: B'nai B'rith (v.p. 1960-62). Avocations: fishing; reading; music.

MILSTEIN, RICHARD SHERMAN, lawyer; b. Westfield, Mass., May 9, 1926; s. Abraham and Sarah (Yudman) M. BA, Harvard U., 1948; JD, Boston U., 1952. Bar: Mass. 1952, U.S. Supreme Ct. 1959. Ptnr. Ely & King, Springfield, Mass., 1954—, Chaplin & Milstein, Boston, 1984-91; dir. Mass. Continuing Legal Edn., 1969-80; cons. dir., 1980—. Commr. Springfield Parking Authority, 1984-90; trustee Springfield Symphony Orch., Cmty. Music Sch., Springfield, 1994—, Springfield Libr. Mus. Assn., Applewood at Amherst, Vis. Nurses Western Mass.; overseer Mass. Supreme Jud. Ct. Hist. Soc., 1995—; trustee, life mem. Sta. WGBY-TV, pub. TV, Springfield; mem. adv. com. Springfield Fine Art Mus., 1988—, chmn., 1988-90; trustee Baystate Hosp., v.p., 1995—; vice chmn. Westfield Acad.; chmn. Horace Smith Fund, 1977-93. Lt. comdr. USCGR, 1952-64. Fellow Am. Coll. Trust and Estate Counsel, Mass. Bar Found. (life); mem. Am. Law Inst. (life), Am. Bar Found. (life). Home: 47 Mattoon St Springfield MA 01105-1715 Office: Ely & King 1350 Main St Springfield MA 01103

MILSTEN, DAVID RANDOLPH, lawyer; b. Coalgate, Okla., Sept. 29, 1903; s. Morris and Etta (Goldstein) M.; m. Minnie Gottlieb, Nov. 16, 1930 (dec. June 1991); children: Donald E., Suzanne Parelman. BA, U. Okla., 1925, LLB, 1928; postgrad., Yale Law Sch., 1926. Bar: Okla. 1928. Practiced in Tulsa, 1928—; asst. county atty. Tulsa County, 1930-32. Author: An Appreciation of Will Rogers, 1935, Howdy Folks (Official State of Okla. poem about Will Rogers), 1938; (poetry) Before My Night, 1962, The Morning After, 1968, Thomas Gilcrease, 1969, Will Rogers, The Cherokee Kid, 1987. Pub. speaker, lectr., founder, chmn. Benevolent and Welfare Fund Tulsa County Bar Assn.; mem. Will Rogers Commn. Okla., 1978-93; chmn. bd. Tulsa Salvation Army, 1954-55; pres. Tulsa Opera, 1953-55, bd. dirs., 1951—; pres. Thomas Gilcrease Inst. Am. History and Art, Tulsa, 1967-68, chmn. bd., 1969-70, bd. dirs., 1954-72, life bd. dirs. emeritus, 1972—. Recipient Commendation Okla. Hist. Soc., Disting. Svc. award Okla. Heritage Assn. for State of Okla., 1990; inductee Hall of Fame, Tulsa Hist. Soc., 1994. Mem. Sigma Alpha Mu (nat. historian, past supreme prior). Jewish (bd. dirs., past pres. Temple Israel, hon. life pres.), Mason (33 deg., past potentate, Shriner). Home and Office: 3905 S Florence Pl Tulsa OK 74105-3731 *Throughout my adolescent and adult life my credo has been that there is no right way to do a wrong thing and there is no wrong way to do a right thing, and there is no compromise with efficiency.*

MILSTEN, ROBERT B., lawyer; b. Tulsa, Nov. 6, 1932; s. Travis I. and Regina (Jankowsky) M.; m. Jane Herskowitz, June 24, 1956; children: Stuart Paul, Leslie Jane. B.S., Ind. U., 1954; LL.B., U. Okla., 1956; postgrad., So. Meth. U., 1959. Bar: Okla. 1956, U.S. Ct. of Appeals 1956, U.S. Tax Ct 1956. Practiced in Oklahoma City, 1962—; govt. atty. Office Chief Counsel, IRS, 1958-62; atty. Fuller, Smith, Mosburg & Davis, 1962-63; atty. Andrews, Davis, Legg, Bixler, Milsten & Price, Inc. (and predecessor firm), 1964—, mem. firm, 1966—, dir., 1977-82. Past pres., trustee Temple B'nai Israel. Served as lt., JAGC USAF, 1956-58. Mem. ABA (com. civil and criminal tax penalties sect. taxation 1976—), Okla. Bar Assn., Oklahoma County Bar Assn., Fed. Bar Assn. (2d v.p. local chpt. 1976), Econ. Club Okla., Quail Creek Golf and Country Club, Men's Dinner Club , Phi Delta Phi (treas. 1955-56). Office: 500 W Main St Oklahoma City OK 73102-2220

MILTON, CATHERINE HIGGS, public service organization executive; b. N.Y.C., Jan. 6, 1943; d. Edgar Homer and Josephine (Doughty) Higgs; m. A. Fenner Milton (div.); m. Thomas F. McBride, Aug. 25, 1974; children: Raphael McBride, Luke McBride. BA, Mt. Holyoke Coll., 1964, PhD (hon.), 1992. Reporter, travel writer Boston Globe, 1964-68; with Internat. Assn. Chiefs Police, Washington, 1969-70; asst. dir. Police Found., Washington, 1970-75; program dir. Ctr. for Female Offenders ABA, Washington, 1975-77; spl. asst. U.S. Treasury Dept., Washington, 1977-80; project staff Spl. Com. Aging/Senate, Washington, 1980-81; spl. asst. to pres., exec. dir. Stanford (Calif.) U. Haas Ctr. for Public, 1981-91; exec. dir. Commn. for Nat. and Cmty. Svc., Washington, 1991-93; v.p. Corp. for Nat. Svc., Washington, 1993—; mem. U.S. Atty. General's Task Force on Family Violence 1981-82; chair nat. forum Kellogg Found., 1990. Author: Women in Policing, 1972, Police Use of Deadly Force, 1976; co-author: History of Black Americans, 1965, Team Policing, Little Sisters and the Law, 1970. Bd. mem. Youth Svc. Calif., L.A., 1986-91, Truma Found., San Francisco, 1982-90; spl. advisor Campus Compact, Providence, 1986-91. Nat. Kellogg Found. fellow, Battle Creek, Mich., 1985-88; recipient Dedication and Outstanding Efforts award Bd. Suprs., Santa Clara, Calif., 1989, Outstanding Vol. Contbn. award Strive for Five, San Francisco, 1991, Dinkelspiel award Stanford U., 1991; named Outstanding Campus Adminstr. COOL, 1987. Avocations: backpacking, skiing, hiking, travel. Home: 837 Cedro Way Stanford CA 94350 Office: Corp Nat Svc Presidio Leadership Ctr PO Box 29995 San Francisco CA 94129

MILTON, CHAD EARL, lawyer; b. Brevard County, Fla., Jan. 29, 1947; s. Rex Dale and Mary Margaret (Peacock) M.; m. Ann Mitchell Bunting, Mar. 30, 1972; children: Samuel, Kathleen, Kelsey. BA, Colo. Coll., 1969; JD, U. Colo., 1974; postgrad., U. Mo., 1976-77. Bar: Colo. 1974, Mo. 1977, U.S. Dist. Ct. Colo. 1974, U.S. Dist. Ct. (we. dist.) Mo. 1977. Counsel Office of Colo. State Pub. Defender, Colo. Springs, 1974-76; pub. info. officer, counsel Mid-Am. Arts Alliance, Kansas City, Mo., 1977-78; claims counsel Employers Reinsurance Corp., Kansas City, Mo., 1978-80; v.p., asst. gen. counsel Media/Profl. Ins., Kansas City, Mo., 1981—; reporter, photographer, editor Golden (Colo.) Daily Transcript, 1970; investigator, law clk. Office of Colo. State Pub. Defender, Denver, Golden, 1970-74; assoc. Gage, Tucker, Hodges, Kreamer, Kelly & Varner (now Gage & Tucker), Kansas City, 1973; participant Annenberg Project on the Reform of Libel Laws, Washington, 1987-88; adj. prof. comm. & advt. law Webster U., 1989—; lectr. in field. Pres. bd. dirs. Folly Theater, 1992-94. Mem. ABA (chair intellectual property law com. of the torts and ins. practice sect., forum com. on comm. law), Mo. Bar Assn., Kansas City Met. Bar Assn., Libel Def. Resource Ctr. (editorial bd., exec. com.). Avocations: tennis, golf, skiing, sailing, antique maps. Home: 8821 Alhambra Shawnee Mission KS 66207 Office: Media/Profl Ins 2 Pershing Sq 2300 Main St Ste 800 Kansas City MO 64108

MILTON, JOHN CHARLES DOUGLAS, nuclear physicist; b. Regina, Sask., Can., June 1, 1924; s. William and Frances Craigie (McDowall) M.; m. Gwendolyn Margaret Shaw, Oct. 10, 1953; children: Bruce F., Leslie J.F., Neil W.D., Theresa M. A.M. in Music, U. Man., 1943, B.Sc. with honors, 1947; M.A., Princeton U., 1949, Ph.D. in Physics, 1951. Asst. research officer Atomic Energy Can., Ltd., Chalk River, Ont., 1951-57; assoc. research officer Atomic Energy Can., Ltd., 1957-62, sr. research officer, 1962-70, prin. research officer, 1970—, head nuclear physics br., 1967-83, dir. physics div., 1983-85, v.p. physics and health scis., 1986-90, researcher emeritus, 1990—; vis. scientist Lawrence Berkeley Lab., 1960-62, Centre de Recherches, Strasbourg & Bruyeres-le-Chatel, 1975-76; chmn. nuclear physics grants Natural Sci. and Engring. Research Council, 1977-82. Fellow Royal Soc. Can., Am. Phys. Soc.; mem. Can. Assn. Physicists (pres. 1992). Home: 3 Alexander Pl, Deep River, ON Canada K0J 1P0 Office: Chalk River Nuclear Lab, Chalk River, ON Canada K0J 1J0

MILTON, JOHN RONALD, English language educator, author; b. Anoka, Minn., May 24, 1924; s. John Peterson and Euphamia Alvera (Swanson) M.; m. Leonharda Allison Hinderlie, Aug. 3, 1946; 1 dau., Nanci Lynn. B.A., U. Minn., 1948, M.A., 1951; Ph.D., U. Denver, 1961. Instr. English and philosophy Augsburg Coll., Mpls., 1949-57; mem. faculty Jamestown (N.D.) Coll., 1957-63, prof. English, chmn. dept., 1961-63; prof. English, U. S.D., Vermillion, 1963—; chmn. dept. U. S.D., 1963-65; editor S.D. Rev., 1963—, dir. writing program, 1965—; vis. prof. N.D. State U., summer 1966, Ind. State U., summer 1966, Bemidji (Minn.) State Coll., 1969; chmn. Dakota Press, publ. U. S.D., 1968-81. Author: (poetry) The Loving Hawk, 1962, Western Plains, 1964, The Tree of Bones, 1965, This Lonely House, 1968, The Tree of Bones and Other Poems, 1973, The Blue Belly of the World, 1974; (novel) Notes to a Bald Buffalo, 1976; (biography) Oscar Howe, 1972, Crazy Horse, 1974; (history) South Dakota: A Bicentennial History, 1977; (criticism) The Novel of the American West, 1980; also interviews, essays, stories, revs., articles; editor: The American Indian Speaks, 1969, Three West, 1970, American Indian II, 1971, The Literature of South Dakota, 1976. Served with U.S. Army, 1943-46. Recipient Gov.'s award for achievement in arts, 1978, Western Am. award, 1984, Western Writers Am. award, 1987, S.D. Hall of Fame Writer of the Year, 1993; Spl. Recognition award S.D. State Hist. Soc., 1978, U. S.D., 1980, S.D. Hist. Assn. award, 1992; Wurlitzer Found. fellow, 1965; Hill Found. grantee, 1966, 69, 70, 81; grantee Whitney Found., 1970, 72, U. S.D., 1963, 64; grantee S.D. Arts Council, 1969, 70, 74, lit. fellowship, 1987; Nat. Endowment Arts writing fellow, 1976-77; fellow S.D. Arts Council, 1987. Mem. Am. Studies Assn. (regional bd. 1957-59), Western Lit. Assn. (pres. 1971, editl. bd. 1966-80, exec. coun. 1966-68), Western History Assn. Home: 630 Thomas St Vermillion SD 57069-3631 Office: Univ SD Box 111 University Exchange Vermillion SD 57069

MILTON, LYNN LEONHARDA, elementary and secondary school educator; b. Minneota, Minn., Apr. 7, 1924; d. John and Mathilde (Bockman) Hinderlie; m. John Ronald Milton, Aug. 3, 1946; 1 child, Nanci. BA, U. Minn., 1949. Cert. tchr., Minn., Colo., S.D. Visual art tchr. Humboldt High Sch., St. Paul, 1949-57, Vermillion (S.D.) Middle Sch., 1972—; tchr. Kuns Miller Jr. High Sch., Denver, 1960-61; occupational therapist N.D. State Hosp., Jamestown, 1959-60. Exhibited prin. works in numerous shows in Minn., N.D., S.D. Mem. Nat. Art Edn. Assn. (State Art Educator award 1983), S.D. Art Educators (pres. 1980-83), S.D. Alliance for Art Edn. (pres. 1985-88). Democrat. Lutheran. Avocations: reading, visual artwork, travel. Home: 630 Thomas St Vermillion SD 57069-3631 Office: Vermillion Middle Sch Princeton St Vermillion SD 57069

MILTON, RICHARD HENRY, retired diplomat; b. Bowling Green, Ky., Sept. 30, 1938; s. Lester Thomas and Rose Ann (Jesse) M.; m. Evy M. Miller, Aug. 28, 1964; children—Christopher, Ann. Student, W.Va. U., 1956-57; B.A., Marshall U., 1960, M.A., 1964. Tchr. Columbus, Ohio, 1960-61; tchr. Sidney, Ohio, 1964-65; fgn. service officer U.S. Dept. State, Washington, 1965-94; dep. asst. dir. ACDA, Washington, 1982-83; consul gen. U.S. consulate gen., Guayaquil, Ecuador, 1984-87; polit. advisor U.S Space Command, Peterson AFB, Colo., 1987-90, 92-94; v.p. Am. Fgn. Svc. Assn., U.S. Dept. State, Washington, 1990-91; vis. prof. U.S. Coast Guard Acad., New London, Conn., 1979-81; court appointed spl. adv. El Paso County Juvenile Ct., 1992—. Pres. Community Welfare Assn., Warsaw, Poland, 1975; mem. gifted edn. com. Ledyard Pub. Schs., Conn., 1980. Served to 1st lt. U.S. Army, 1961-63. Congl. fellow Am. Polit. Sci. Assn., 1974-75. Mem. Am. Fgn. Service Assn., Consular Officers Assn. (pres. 1983-84), Sr. Fgn. Service Assn. Avocation: antique automobiles. Home: 2022 Devon St Colorado Springs CO 80909-1618

MILTON, ROBERT MITCHELL, chemical company executive; b. St. Joseph, Mich., Nov. 29, 1920; s. Clare Leon and Frances Thornton (Mitchell) M.; m. Mary Wills Bridges, June 22, 1946; children: Mrs. M. Gillian Sanders (dec.), Mrs. Suzanne M. Padilla, David Wills. B.A., Oberlin Coll., 1941; M.A., Johns Hopkins U., 1943, Ph.D., 1944. C.Y. War Project Johns Hopkins U., Balt., 1943-45, rsch. assoc., 1945-46; with Union Carbide Corp., 1946-85, rsch. chemist, 1946-51, rsch. supr., 1951-54, mgr. devel. lab., 1954-58, asst. mgr. new products, 1958-59, asst. dir., then dir. rsch. Linde div., 1959-73, exec. v.p. Showa UNOX, Showa Union Good div., 1973-77, dir. agrl. bus. devel., v.p. Keystone Seed Co. div., 1977-79; assoc. corp. dir. product safety and liability Union Carbide Corp., Danbury, Conn., 1980-85; pres. R. Milton Assocs., Inc., 1986—; cons. U.S. Naval Tech. Mission to Europe, 1945; mem. adv. bd. hyperbaric medicine SUNY, 1966-73; mem. NRC panel on environ. protection, safety and hazardous materials of Com. on Chem. Engring. Frontiers, 1985-87. Inventor Linde molecular sieve adsorbents and catalysts, hi-flux tubing; patentee in field. Mem. AAAS, Am. Chem. Soc. (Jacob F. Schoellkopf medal 1963), Am. Inst. Chem. Engrs., Am. Inst. Chemists (dir.-at-large 1982-87, pres. elect 1988-89, pres. 1990-91, chmn. bd. dirs. 1992-93, Chem. Pioneer award 1980), Wawashkamo Golf Club (pres. emeritus), Mackinac Island Yacht Club, Johns Hopkins Club, Phi Beta Kappa, Sigma Xi. Home office: 18800 Sandpointe Bay #310 Tequesta FL 33469 also: PO Box 326 Mackinac Island MI 49757

MILTON, WILLIAM HAMMOND, III, trust company executive; b. Schenectady, Mar. 3, 1925; s. William Hammond Jr. and Lois (Preston) M.; m. Maryanna Kennedy, July 26, 1956; children: Alexander, William. Maryanna. BA, Union Coll., Schenectady, 1950; postgrad., Rutgers U., 1961. Statistician Guaranty Trust Co., N.Y.C., 1950-51; trust salesman Schenectady Trust Co., 1953-63, v.p., 1963-74, bd. dirs., sec., 1972—, sr. v.p., 1974-84, exec. v.p., 1984—; pres. Bank Fiduciary Funds, N.Y.C., 1965-67; bd. dirs., sec. Trustco Bank Corp N.Y., Schenectady, 1982—. Founder, treas. Schenectady Found., 1966—. Served to 1st lt. USAAF, 1943-46, USAF, 1951-53. Avocations: sailing, Lotus 1-2-3. Office: TrustCo Bank NY 320 State St Schenectady NY 12305-2302

MILUM-WOOD, JOAN, hospital administrator; b. Miami, Fla., Nov. 25, 1937; d. James R. and Ruth K. (Still) Worline; divorced; children: Jenine M. Milum Weaver, Elizabeth J. BSN, Capital U., 1959. Cert. nursing adminstr. advanced. Dir. nursing Wyandot Manor ECR, Upper Sandusky, Ohio; asst. dir. nursing Lima (Ohio) Meml. Hosp.; v.p. nursing Candler Gen. Hosp, Savannah, Ga.; Gwinnett Hosp. System, Lawrenceville, Ga.; Appt. by Gov. Joe Frank Harris Access to Health Care Commn., 1989-90. Mem. ACHE, AHA, VHA (nursing adminstrv. coun.), Ga. Orgn. Nurse Exec. (com. chair), Ga. Nurses Assn. (com. mem.). Home: 3703 Madrid Cir Norcross GA 30092-4542

MILUNAS, J. ROBERT, health care organization executive; b. Aug. 7, 1947; s. Joseph John M.; m. Glenetta Graham; children: Amy, Joseph, Anna Kate. BS, Tulane U., 1969; postgrad., Samford U., 1973; MBA, Ga. State U., 1977. Mgr. internal and govt. reporting, corp. contr.'s staff Arvin Industries Inc., Columbus, Ind., 1977-80; mgr. consol. acctg., corp. contr.'s staff Mattel Inc., Hawthorne, Calif., 1980-82; asst. contr. Times Mirror Cable TV Inc., Irvine, Calif., 1982-83; Western Div. contr. SCA, Santa Ana, Calif., 1983-84; v.p., corp. contr. Tchrs. Mgmt. Investment Corp., Newport Beach, Calif., 1984-86; v.p., chief fin. officer Beech Tree Inc., Irvine, 1987-89; v.p. fin. and administrn. ConsumerHealth Inc., Newport Beach, Calif., 1989-93; pres. Aegis Consulting Svcs., Mission Viego, Calif., 1993—. 1st lt. U.S. Army Transp. Corps., 1969-71. Decorated Bronze Star. Home: 27692 Bahamonde Mission Viejo CA 92692-3232 *Life is a precious gift to be* *nurtured daily through interaction with friends and family and helping others achieve their potential.*

MIMNAUGH, JOHN M., advertising executive; b. Portchester, N.Y., July 17, 1936; s. John F. and Malvina (Irving) M.; m. Susan Swan, Nov. 1968, (Div. Feb. 1978); m. Susan Ryan, Nov. 9, 1981; children: Susan, Adele, Jennifer. BA, Lehigh U., Bethlehem, 1958. Public info. officer USAF, 1958-61; asst. dir. of pr Charles Hoyt Co., NYC, 1961-65; copywriter Rumrill Hoyt Inc., NYC, 1965-69; exec. v.p. Gilbert, Whitney & Johns, Whippany, NJ. Pres. Jaycees, Waldwick, 1967, Highlands Community Assn., 1968; Chmn. Waldwick Evangelism Community Methodist Church, 1967-68; Committeeman (Bergen County) Republican Committee, 1967. Served as 1st lt. USAF, 1958-61. Republican. Methodist. Gardening, Woodwork. Home: 15 Ogden Pl Morristown NJ 07960-5248 Office: Gilbert Whitney & Johns 110 S Jefferson Rd Whippany NJ 07981-1027

MIMS, FORREST MARION, III, science writer; b. Houston, Sept. 4, 1944; s. Forrest Marion and Ollieve Elizabeth (Dunn) M.; m. Minnie Chavez, June 15, 1985—. Freelance sci. writer Albuquerque, 1970-76, San Marcos, Tex., 1976-85, Seguin, Tex., 1985—. Columnist Popular Electronics mag., San Marcos, 1975-85, Modern Electronics mag., Seguin, 1985—; editor Sci. Probe!, Seguin, 1990-92; author: Getting Started in Electronics, 1983, Forrest Mims's Computer Projects, 1985, Siliconnections, 1986, Understanding Digital Computers, 1987; contbr. columns to Sci. Am.; co-founder Sci. Probe!, The Amateur Scientist's Jour. Capt. USAF, 1966-70, Vietnam. Recipient IR-100 award Indsl. Rsch., 1972, Rolex award for Enterprise, 1993. Mem. IEEE, AAAS, Am. Geophysical Union, Optical Soc. of Am. Baptist. Achievements include design of eyeglass-mounted infrared travel aids for the blind, small rockets guided by ram air, miniature instruments to measure total column ozone, volcanic aerosols, water vapor, and solar ultraviolet radiation. Home and Office: 433 Twin Oak Rd Seguin TX 78155-7423

MIMS, WILLIAM CLEVELAND, state legislator, lawyer; b. Harrisonburg, Va., June 20, 1957; s. David Lathan and Lurleen Shirley (Stovall) M.; m. Jane Ellen Rehme, Dec. 20, 1980; children: Katherine Grace, Emily Anne, Sarah Joy. AB, Coll. of William & Mary, 1979; JD, George Washington U., 1984; LLM, Georgetown U., 1986. Bar: Va. Legis. asst. Congressman Paul Trible, Washington, 1981-82; dep. legis. dir. Senator Paul Trible, Washington, 1983-85; chief of staff Congressman Frank Wolf, Washington, 1986-87; atty. Hazel & Thomas, P.C., Leesburg, Va., 1987-91, Worcester, Mims & Atwill, P.C., Leesburg, 1993—; mem. Va. Gen. Assembly, Richmond, 1991—; mem. adv. bd. Farmers & Merchants Nat. Bank, Sterling, Va., 1991-93. Bd. dirs. Dulles Area Transp. Assn., Herndon, Va., 1994—, Marshall Home Preservation Fund, Leesburg, 1992—, Youth for Tomorrow, 1995—; treas., bd. dirs. Loudoun Bar Assn., Leesburg, 1988-89; chmn. Loudoun Rep. Com., Leesburg, 1988-91; dist. rep. Nat. Eagle Scout Assn., 1992—. Recipient commendation Com. for Dulles, 1986; named Outstanding Local Chmn. Rep. Party of Va., 1991. Mem. Va. Bar Assn., Va. Trial Lawyers Assn., Christian Legal Soc., Loudoun C. of C. Republican. Episcopalian. Office: Worcester Mims & Atwill PC PO Drawer 741 Leesburg VA 22075-2820

MINAHAN, DANIEL FRANCIS, manufacturing company executive, lawyer; b. Orange, N.J., Dec. 3, 1929; s. Alfred A. and Katherine (Kelly) M.; m. Mary Jean Gaffney, May 2, 1953; children: Daniel F. Jr., John A. AB magna cum laude, U. Notre Dame, 1951; JD magna cum laude, U. Conn., 1964; grad., Advanced Mgmt. Program, Harvard, 1975. Bar: Conn. 1964, U.S. Supreme Ct. 1964, U.S. Ct. of Appeals (2d cir.), U.S. Dist. Ct. Conn. 1967. Mgr. indsl. engring. Uniroyal, Inc., Naugatuck, Conn., 1952-59, mgr. indsl. relations, 1959-64; dir. labor relations Uniroyal, Inc., N.Y.C., 1964-66; v.p. indsl. relations and labor counsel Phillips Van Heusen Corp., N.Y.C., 1966-69; v.p. personnel-adminstrn. Broadway-Hale Stores, Inc., Los Angeles, 1969-70; v.p. employee relations, sec. Magnavox-N.Am., Philips Corp., 1970-73, v.p. ops., group exec., 1973-83, sr. v.p. adminstrn., 1984-89, exec. v.p., 1989-93, vice chmn., 1993; vice chmn. nat. found. bd. Robert Anderson Sch. Mgmt., U. N.Mex., 1993—; mem. trustees adv. coun., Fairfield U. Co-author: The Developing Labor Law, 1971. Chmn. bd. Internat. Fedn. Keystone Youth Orgns., London and Chgo., 1984-88; trustee U. Conn. Law Sch.; vice-chmn. nat. found. bd. Anderson Sch. Mgmt., U. N.Mex., 1993—. With USMC. Mem. ABA, Conn. Bar Assn., Assn. Bar City N.Y., NAM, Rsch. Inst. Am., Harvard Advanced Mgmt. Assn., Bur. Nat. Affairs, Internat. Platform Assn., Stanford Rsch. Inst. Internat., Washington Internat. Corp. Circle, Econ. Strategy Inst., Unim of Indsl. and Employers Confed. of Europe, Bruxelias, Harvard Club, Club Internat. (Chgo.), Belfrey Club (London). Office: c/o Office of the Dean U N Mex Robert Anderson Sch Bus Albuquerque NM 87131

MINAHAN, JOHN C., JR., federal judge; b. Melbourne, Australia, Mar. 1, 1943; came to U.S., 1946; s. John C. and Mavis V. (Monahan) M.; m. Ann K. Parmelee, Jan. 31, 1 970; children: Keith, Eliot. BS, U. Calif., Berkeley, 1965; JD, Creighton U., 1973; LLM, Harvard U., 1976. Bar: Nebr. 1973, U.S. Dist. Ct. Nebr. 1973, U.S. Ct. Appeals (8th cir.) 1984. Prof. Vt. Law Sch., South Royalton, Vt., 1974-77; ptnr. Kutak Rock & Campbell, Omah, 1977-82; prin. Dixon Dixon & Minahan, P.C., Omah, 1982-87; bankruptcy judge U.S. Dist. Ct. Nebr., Lincoln, 1987—; adj. prof. U. Nebr. Sch. of Law, Lincoln, 1987—. Contbr. articles to profl. jours. Capt. USMC, 1965-69, Vietnam. Mem. Fed. Bar Assn., Nebr. Bar Assn., Lincoln Bar Assn., Nat. Conf. of Bankruptcy Judges, Am. Legion. Avocations: skiing, shortwave radio, competitive shooting. Office: US Bankruptcy Ct 463 Federal Bldg 100 Centennial Mall N Lincoln NE 68508-3803

MINAHAN, JOHN ENGLISH, author; b. Albany, N.Y., Apr. 30, 1933; s. John English and Constance Madeline (Langdon) M.; m. Verity Ann Hill, Apr. 27, 1966. Student, Cornell U., 1955-57, Harvard U., 1958-59, Columbia U., 1959-60. Staff writer Time mag., 1960-61; chief TV writer J. Walter Thompson Co., N.Y.C., 1961-65; free-lance writer N.Y.C., 1965-73, L.A., 1976-79, Miami, 1981—; editor, pub. American Way mag., N.Y.C. 1973-76; contbg. editor L.A. mag., 1978-79; dir. corp. communications The Wackenhut Corp., Coral Gables, Fla., 1990—; cons. Universal-MCA Inc., 1976-79; instr. novel writing workshop Harvard U. Ctr. Lifelong Learning, 1987-89. Author: novels A Sudden Silence, 1963, The Passing Strange, 1965, Jeremy, 1973, Sorcerer, 1977, Nine/Thirty/Fifty-Five, 1977, Almost Summer, 1978, Nunzio, 1978, The Complete American Graffiti, 1979, Eyewitness, 1981, The Great Hotel Robbery, 1982, The Great Diamond Robbery, 1984, Mask, 1985, The Face Behind the Mask, 1986, The Great Pyramid Robbery, 1987, The Great Harvard Robbery, 1988, The Great Grave Robbery, 1989; biography The Dream Collector, 1972, The Quiet American: A Biography of George R. Wackenhut, 1994; translation from French The Fabulous Onassis, 1972; screenplays A Sudden Silence, 1965, The Passing Strange, 1979; TV play First Flight, 1968; contbg. editor book and theater revs.: Miami Herald, 1983—; also articles in N.Y. Times, Saturday Rev., Time-Life Spl. Reports. Recipient Doubleday award, 1960. Mem. Nat. Soc. Lit. and Arts, Alpha Delta Phi. Club: Harvard of Miami, Faculty of Harvard U. Office: The Wackenhut Corp 1500 San Remo Ave Coral Gables FL 33146

MINAMI, ROBERT YOSHIO, artist, graphic designer; b. Seattle, May 1, 1919; s. Kichitaro and Suma (Fujita) M.; m. Shizu Tashiro, May 30, 1953; 1 child, Ken. Artist; student, Art Inst., Chgo., 1957, Am. Acad. Art, Chgo., 1980-81. Graphic artist Filmack Studios, Chgo., 1947-48, S. Taylor & Leavitt Assocs., Chgo., 1949-50; head graphic designer NBC-TV, Chgo., 1950-82; fine artist Robert Minami's Studio, Oceanside, Calif., 1983—; artist Goodman Theatre Design, Chgo., 1955-56. Active Supporters for City Couns., Oceanside, 1984—. Recipient Merit award Artist Guild Chgo., 1956, People's Choice award Carlsbad Oceanside Art League, 1986, Dick Blick award, 1992, 1st place award Mixed Media Collage, 1993, Nat. Watercolor award Watercolor West, 1994. Mem. San Diego Watercolor Soc., United Scenic Artists (life), Am. Fine Art Connection, San Diego Art Inst., Nat. Watercolor Soc. (assoc.), Watercolor West Juried Assn. Avocations: painting, travel, movies, concerts, opera.

MINARD, EVERETT LAWRENCE, III, journalist, magazine editor; b. Seattle, Nov. 19, 1949; s. Everett Lawrence Jr. and Nancy M.; m. Elizabeth Anne Bailey, Sept. 15, 1979. BA in Econs., Trinity Coll., Hartford, Conn., 1972; postgrad., New Sch. for Social Rsch., 1972-74. Reporter, staff writer,

mgr. European, West Coast/Asia burs. Forbes mag., 1974-89; mng. editor Forbes mag., N.Y.C., 1989—. Dir. Grace Ch. Sch., Bklyn., 1988—. Mem. Seattle Yacht Club, Heights Casino Club, Lawrence Beach Club. Office: Forbes Inc 60 Fifth Ave New York NY 10011-8865

MINARD, FRANK PELL LAWRENCE, investment manager; b. Newark, May 19, 1945; s. Duane E. Jr. and Elizabeth (Lawrence) M.; m. Lynne Stewart, June 19, 1982; children: Rachel S, Courtney S., Margaret P. BA in English, U. N.C., 1968; MBA in Fin., Rutgers U., 1975. Asst. treas. N.J. Bell Co., Newark, 1972-78; mgr. analysis and planning AT&T, N.Y.C., 1978-80; v.p., head eastern region Bankers Trust, N.Y.C., 1980-81; v.p. investment adviser Equitable Life Co., N.Y.C., 1981-83; mng. dir. Oppenheimer Capital Co., N.Y.C., 1983-93; exec. v.p. Paine Webber Inc., N.Y.C., 1993—; chmn., bd. dirs. Investor Responsibility Rsch. Ctr., Washington, 1986—; bd. dirs. Investor Responsibility Rsch. Ctr., chmn. 1990-92; chmn., CEO Mitchell Hutchins Asset Mgmt., 1993—. Bd. dirs. Westover Sch., 1989—. With USN, 1968-72, Vietnam. Mem. Assn. Investment Mgmt. Sales Execs. (bd. dirs. 1986-89, pres. 1988-89), Investment Mgmt. Cons. Assn. (bd. dirs. 1988—), Montclair Golf Club, Mauna Lani Golf Club, Willowbend Golf Club, Los Campanas (Santa Fe). Avocations: golf, tennis, farming. Home: 519 Rockaway Valley Rd Boonton NJ 07005-1307 Office: Paine Webber 1285 Ave Americas New York NY 10019

MINARIK, JOSEPH JOHN, economist, researcher; b. Lancaster, Pa., July 27, 1949; s. Joseph John and Helen Elizabeth (Mikus) M.; m. Eileen Marie Dowds; children: Mara Christina, Sara Elizabeth. B.A., Georgetown U., 1971; M.A., Yale U., 1972, M.Phil, 1973, Ph.D, 1974. Rsch. assoc. Brookings Instn., Washington, 1974-81; dept. asst. dir. Congl. Budget Office, Washington, 1981-84; sr. rsch. assoc. Urban Inst., Washington, 1984-88; exec. dir. Joint Econ. Com. U.S. Congress, Washington, 1988-90; exec. dir. for policy, chief economist House Budget Com., 1991-93; assoc. dir. econ. policy Office Mgmt. and Budget, 1993—. Author: Making Tax Choices, 1985, Making America's Budget Policy, 1989; contbr. articles to profl. jours. Fellow NSF, 1971-74, Yale U., 1971. Mem. Am. Econ. Assn., Nat. Tax Assn. Democrat. Home: 11656 Mediterranean Ct Reston VA 22090-3401 Office: Economic Policy 244 Old Executive Bldg Washington DC 20503

MINC, HENRYK, mathematics educator; b. Lodz, Poland, Nov. 12, 1919; came to U.S., 1960, naturalized, 1966; s. Izrael and Haja (Zyngler) M.; m. Catherine Taylor Duncan, Apr. 16, 1943; children: Robert Henry, Ralph Edward, Raymond. MA with honors, Edinburgh U. (Scotland), 1955, PhD, 1959. Tchr. Morgan Acad., Dundee, Scotland, 1956-58; lectr. Dundee Tech. Coll., Scotland, 1957-58, U. B.C., Vancouver, Can., 1958-59, asst. prof., 1959-60; assoc. prof. U. Fla., Gainesville, 1960-63; vis. prof. Technion Israel Inst. Tech., Haifa, 1969-80; prof. U. Calif.-Santa Barbara, 1963-90, emeritus, 1990—; referee and reviewer for math. jours. Author: A Survey of Matrix Theory and Matrix Inequalities, 1964, translated into Russian, 1972, Chinese, 1990; Introduction to Linear Algebra, 1965, translated into Spanish, 1968; Modern University Algebra, 1966; Elementary Linear Algebra, 1968, translated into Spanish, 1971; New College Algebra, 1968; Elementary Functions and Coordinate Geometry, 1969; Algebra and Trigonometry, 1970; College Algebra, 1970; College Trigonometry, 1971; Integrated Analytic Geometry and Algebra with Circular Functions, 1973; Permanents, 1978, translated into Russian, 1980, Chinese, 1991; Nonnegative Matrices, 1988, trans. into Chinese, 1991; contbr. over 80 research papers to profl. jours. 2d. lt. Polish Army, 1940-48. France, U.K. Recipient Lester Ford award Math. Assn. Am., 1966, rsch. contract Office Naval Rsch., 1985-88. Air Force Office Sci. Rsch. grantee, 1960-83, Lady Davis fellow, 1975, 78. Fellow Soc. Antiquaries of Scotland; mem. Am. Math Soc., Internat. Linear Algebra Soc., Inst. Antiquity and Christianity, Scottish Soc. Santa Barbara (chieftain), Scots Lang. Soc., Saltire Soc., Assn. for Scottish Lit. Studies, Coll. of Piping, Burns Fedn., James Hogg Soc., Santa Barbara Elks Lodge, Clan Fraser Soc. N.Am. Democrat. Home: 4076 Naranjo Dr Santa Barbara CA 93110-1213 Office: U Calif Dept Math Santa Barbara CA 93106

MINCER, JACOB, economics educator; b. Tomaszow, Poland, July 15, 1922; came to U.S., 1948; s. Isaac and Dora (Eisen) M.; m. Flora Kaplan, 1951; children—Deborah, Carolyn. B.A., Emory U., 1950; Ph.D., Columbia U., 1957; LLD honoris causa, U. Chgo., 1991. Asst. prof. CUNY, 1954-59; assoc. prof. Columbia U., N.Y.C., 1960-62; prof. econs. Columbia U., 1962—; Mem. research staff Nat. Bur. Econ. Research, N.Y.C., 1960—. Author: Schooling, Experience and Earnings, 1974, Studies in Human Capital, ;882, Studies in Labor Supply, 1993; author, editor: Economic Forecasts and Expectations, 1969. Contbr. numerous articles to profl. publs. Postdoctoral fellow U. Chgo., 1957-58; Guggenheim fellow, N.Y.C., 1971. Fellow Am. Statis. Assn., Econometric Soc., Am. Econ. Assn. (Disting.); mem. Am. Acad. Arts and Scis., Nat. Acad. Edn. Home: 448 Riverside Dr New York NY 10027-6818 Office: Columbia U Dept Econs 118th St at Amsterdam Ave New York NY 10027

MINCHIN, MICHAEL M., JR., food industry consultant; b. Los Angeles, Sept. 5, 1926; s. Michael M. and Daisy (Salmon) M.; m. Carolyn Brown, June 1, 1961; children: Michael M. III, Montgomery. B.A. cum laude, Stanford U., 1948; postgrad., Stanford U., Law, 1948-49; M.B.A. cum laude, Harvard U., 1951. Asst. to Sec. of Def., Washington, 1951; asst. to pres. Emporium-Capwell, San Francisco, 1951-53; v.p. Erwin Wasey, Inc., Los Angeles, 1958-65; sr. v.p., gen. mgr. Erwin Wasey, Inc., 1965-73, exec. v.p., also dir., chmn. exec. policy com., 1973-80; v.p. mktg. Collins Foods Internat., Los Angeles, 1973—; exec. v.p. S.R.I., Inc., 1980—; bd. dirs. Sizzler Restaurants Internat. Inc. Home: 15401 Mulholland Dr Los Angeles CA 90077-1624 Office: Collins Foods Internat Inc PO Box 35910 Louisville KY 40232-5910

MINCY, HOMER F., school system administrator. Supt. Upper Arlington (Ohio) City Sch. Dist. State finalist Nat. Supt. Yr. award, 1992. Office: Upper Arlington City Sch Dist 1950 N Mallway Dr Upper Arlington OH 43221-4398

MINDELL, EUGENE ROBERT, surgeon, educator; b. Chgo., Feb. 24, 1922; s. Leon and Tillie (Rosenthal) M.; m. June A. Abrams, Sept. 19, 1945; children: Barbara, Ruth, David, Douglas. BS, U. Chgo., 1943, MD, 1945. Diplomate Am. Bd. Orthopaedic Surgery (bd. dirs 1977-84, pres. 1983-84). Resident in orthopaedic surgery U. Chgo. Clinics, 1948-52; instr. U. Chgo., 1952; mem. faculty dept. orthopaedic surgery Sch. Medicine SUNY, Buffalo, 1953—, prof. Sch. Medicine, 1964—; chmn. dept. SUNY Sch. Medicine, Buffalo, 1964-88, dir. orthopaedic oncology Sch. Medicine, 1988—; mem. bd. mgrs. Erie County Med. Ctr., 1990—. Assoc. editor Jour. Bone and Joint Surgery, 1984-88, trustee, 1990—; contbr. articles to profl. jours. Lt. (j.g.) M.C. USNR, 1946-48. Recipient Dean's award SUNY at Buffalo Sch. Medicine, 1986, Disting. Svc. award Alumni U. Chgo. Sch. Medicine, 1990; NRC fellow, 1949-50. Fellow ACS; mem. Am. Acad. Orthopaedic Surgeons (bd. dirs. 1991), Am. Orthopaedic Assn. (v.p. 1990-91), Assn. Orthopaedic Chmn., Am. Assn. Surgery of Trauma, Am. Orthopaedic Rsch. Soc. (pres. 1972-73, residency rev. com. 1985-91), Musculoskeletal Tumor Soc. (pres. 1989-90, Coun. Musculoskeletal Specialty Socs. (chmn. elect 1991, chmn. 1992). Jewish. Home: 85 Depew Ave Buffalo NY 14214-1509 Office: 100 High St Buffalo NY 14203-1154

MINDES, GAYLE DEAN, education educator; b. Kansas City, Mo., Feb. 11, 1942; d. Elton Burnett and Juanita Maxine (Mangold) Taylor; BS, U. Kans., 1964; MS, U. Wis., 1965; EdD, Loyola U., Chgo., 1979; m. Marvin William Mindes, June 20, 1969 (dec.); 1 son, Jonathan Seth. Tchr. pub. schs., Newburgh, N.Y., 1965-67; spl. educator Ill. Dept. Mental Health, Chgo., 1967-69; spl. edn. supr. Evanston (Ill.) Dist. 65 Schs., 1969-74; lectr. Northeastern Ill. U., Chgo., 1974, Loyola U., Chgo., 1974-76, Coll. St. Francis, Joliet, Ill., 1976-79, North Park Coll., Chgo., 1978; cons. Chgo. Head Start, 1978-79; asst. prof. edn. Oklahoma City U., 1979-80; vis. asst. prof., rsch. assoc. Roosevelt U. Coll. Edn., Chgo., 1983-87, prof., dir. R&D, dir. tchr. edn., dir. early childhood, dir. grad. edn. ctr., Roosevelt U. Coll. Albert A. Robin campus, 1993; prof. sch. edn. De Paul U., 1993—; chair Roosevelt U. Senate, 1986-89; co-chair ILAEYC Bldg. Bridges; cons. Ill. Resource Ctr., Arts Coun. Oklahoma City, Indian Affairs Commn., 1979-80, Bensenville Pub. Schs., Lincolnwood (Ill.) Pub. Schs., Chgo. Pub. Schs., Atwood Sch. Dist, Chgo. Assn. Retarded Citizens, Nat. Assn. Tech. Tng. Schs., Ill. State Bd. Edn., Itasca Pub. Schs., Decatur Pub. Schs., Robin Scholarship Found.; 1982—, Rasho Media, Ill. Facilities Fund for Childcare;

alt. rep. faculty coun. Sch. Edn. De Paul U., mem. faculty adv. com. to univ. plan. and info. tech.; mem. tng. sub-com. adv. Ill. Dept. Children & Family Svcs., 1993—; mentor, cons. to partnerships project tng. early intervention svcs. U. Ill., Champaign; early childhood panelist Ill. Initiative for Articulation between Ill. Bd. Higher Edn. and Ill. Cmty. Coll. Bd.; education panelist for Early Childhood Assessment System. Assoc. editor Ill. Sch. R & D; Ill. Div. Early Childhood Edn. Adv. Com. to Ill. Bd. Edn.; alternate rep to faculty council Sch. Edn. De Paul U.; co-chair early childhood panelist for early childhood assessment system, Bansenville Pub. Schs.; meditor: Depaul U. Sch. Edn. Newsletter. Co-author: Planning a Theme Based Curriculum for 4's or 5's, 1993; contbr. articles to profl. jours. Bd. dirs. North Side Family Day Care, 1981; northside affiliates Mus. Contemporary Art, 1991—; trustee Roosevelt U., 1987-93; mem. edn. adv. com. Okla. Dept. Edn., 1979-80; mem. adv. bd. bilingual early childhood program Oakton Community Coll.; mem. adv. bd. early childhood tech. assistance project Chgo. Pub. Schs., Lake View Mental Health, 1986-90; mem. regional com. Lake View Citizens Coun. Day Care Ctr., 1978-79, local planning coun. Ill. Dept. Child and Family Svcs., childcare block grant tng. sub. com.; co-chair Ill. Assn. for Edn. Young Children Building Bridges Project; chmn. teen com. Florence G. Heller JCC, membership com.; mem. adv. bd. Harold Washington Coll. Child Devel., regional tech. assistance grant LICA; mem. parents com. Francis W. Parker Sch. Graduate Faculty Assn. scholar, 1965; U. Wis. fellow in mental retardation, 1964-65; U. Kans. scholar, 1960. Fellow Am. Orthopsychiat. Assn.; mem. AAUP, ASCD, AAUW, Assn. Children with Learning Disabilities, Nat. Assn. for Edn. Young Children (tchr. edn. bd. 1990—), Am. Ednl. Rsch. Assn., Coun. for Exceptional Children, Ill. Coun. for Exceptional Children (mem. multicultural affairs com. divsn. early childhood), Ill. Assn. for Edn. Young Children, Coun. for Adminstrs. Spl. Edn., Am. Assn. U. Women, Coun. on Children with Behavioral Disorders, Soc. for Rsch. in Child Devel., Foun. for Excellence in Teaching (selection com. Golden Apple 1989-94), Alpha Sigma Nu, Phi Delta Kappa, Pi Lambda Theta. Office: DePaul Univ Sch Of Edn Chicago IL 60614

MINDLIN, PAULA ROSALIE, educator; b. N.Y.C., Nov. 27, 1944; d. Simon S. and Sylvia (Naroff) Bernstein; m. Alfred Carl Mindlin, Aug. 14, 1965; 1 child, Spencer Douglas. BA in Edn., Queens Coll., 1965; MS in Edn., Queens Coll., 1970, Specialist Sch. Adminstrn, 1973. Tchr. Dist. 16 Pub. Sch., Bklyn., 1965-68; reading tchr. Dist. 29 Pub. Sch. and Dist. 16, Bklyn., 1968-85; instr. insvc. courses Comty. Sch. Dist. 29, Queens Village, N.Y., 1984-93; reading coord. Reading/Comms. Arts Program Comty. Sch. Dist. 29, Queens, N.Y., 1985—; dir. reading Cmty. Sch. Dist. 29, Queens Village, N.Y., 1990-93, reading coord., 1993—; adj. lectr. York Coll., 1989, program dir.; mem. profl. adv. bd. Queens Coll. Reading Program, 1995—. Recipient Chpt. I Program Nat. Recognition award U.S. Sec. Edn., 1993, Queensboro Educator of Yr. award, 1994. Mem. ASCD, Internat. Reading Assn., Nassau Reading Coun., Queensboro Reading Coun. (pres. 1994-96), Phi Delta Kappa. Avocations: reading, gardening, boating. Office: Dist 29 Queens 1 Cross Island Plz Rosedale NY 11422

MINDLIN, RICHARD BARNETT, market research executive; b. Kansas City, Mo., Apr. 9, 1926; s. Harold Saul and Ann (Copeland) M.; m. Susan Dorothy Weinberg, Feb. 6, 1954; children: Steven, Edward, Andrew. Student, U. of South, 1943-46, Columbia U., 1947-48. Mdse. mgr. Kaufmann's Dept. Store, Pitts., 1951-54; founder, pres. Coach House Stores, Kansas City, Mo., 1955-76, Richard B. Mindlin Assocs., mktg. and new product research and devel., Shawnee Mission, Kans., 1963—. Author books and articles to profl. jours. Chmn. bd. dirs. Bacchus Charity, 1960; bd. dirs. Kaw council Boy Scouts Am., 1964-66; pres. bd. trustees Kansas City Mus. History and Sci.; trustee Menorah Med. Center, Kansas City, Mo. Served to 1t. (j.g.) USNR, 1943-45. Club: Oakwood Country (Kansas City, Mo.) (dir. 1981-84). Home and Office: 4101 W 90th St Shawnee Mission KS 66207-2325

MINEAR, JUDITH, school system administrator. Supt. schs. Diocese of Wheeling-Charleston, W.Va. Office: Office Schs Supt 11-13th St PO Box 230 Wheeling WV 26003

MINEKA, SUSAN, psychology educator; b. Ithaca, N.Y., June 2, 1948; d. Francis Edward and Muriel Leota (McGregor) M. BA in Psychology magna cum laude, Cornell U., 1970; PhD, U. Pa., 1977. Lic. psychologist, Ill. Prof. psychology U. Wis., Madison, 1974-85, U. Tex., Austin, 1986-87; prof. Northwestern U., Evanston, Ill., 1987—. Editor Jour. Abnormal Psychology, 1990-94; contbr. articles to profl. jours. Grantee NSF and NIMH, 1977-89. Fellow APA (chair bd. sci. affairs 1994, pres. divsn. 12 sect. 3, 1995), Am. Psychol. Soc.; mem. Psychonomic Soc., Midwestern Psychol. Assn. (pres.-elect 1995-96), Assn. for Advancement Behavior Therapy, Internat. Primatol. Soc., Internat. Soc. for Rsch. on Emotion, Soc. for Rsch. in Psychopathology (mem. exec. bd. 1992-94), Phi Beta Kappa, Sigma Xi. Democrat. Home: 1825 N Lincoln Plz Apt 1609 Chicago IL 60614-5337 Office: Northwestern U Psychology Dept Evanston IL 60208

MINER, A. BRADFORD, journalist; b. Columbus, Ohio, Oct. 30, 1947; s. Robert Bradford and Margaret L. (Earnhart) M.; m. Sydny H. Weinberg, Apr. 29, 1984; children: Robert Bradford II, Jonathan Frederick. BA, Ohio U., 1970. Mgr., Gaylord Enterprises, Columbus, 1974-77; sales planning mgr. Bantam Books, N.Y.C. 1977-80, sr. editor, 1980-84; editor hardcover and paperback books Harper & Row, N.Y.C., 1984-86; nat. sales mgr. Sea-Tex Inc. div. Balson-Hercules Group, N.Y.C., 1987-89; lit. editor National Review, 1989-91; co-editor Nat. Rev. Coll. Guide, 1991, rev. 1993; Olin prof. Adelphi U., 1994—. Editor Good Order, 1994; pres. Religion Pub. Group, N.Y.C., 1983-84. Mem. Fulton J. Sheen Soc. (trustee). Republican. Roman Catholic. Club: N.Y. Athletic.

MINER, DENNIS KANE, chemical engineer, consultant; b. Chambersburg, Pa., Jan. 13, 1944; s. Byers A. and Lois J. (Kane) M.; m. Ellen K. Cleary, Dec. 24, 1965 (div. Apr. 1989); children: Chance C., Race K.; m. Sandra Neubaum, Oct. 31, 1992; stepchildren: Mark Taylor, Matthew Taylor. B-SChemE, Tri-State U., 1964; MS in Mgmt., Meridian Environ. & Tech. Mgmt. Inst., St. Louis, 1975. Team mgr. Proctor & Gamble, Mehoopany, Pa. and, Cape Girardeau, Mo., 1971-73; dept. mgr. Pfizer, Inc., East St. Louis, Ill., 1973-75; plant mgr. Van Straaten Chem. Co., Aurora, Ill., 1975-77; prodn. mgr. Textron, Cairo, Ill., 1977-79; cons. Meridian Engrs. & Assocs., St. Louis, 1979-81; gen. contractor LTD Constrn. Co., Harrisburg, Pa., 1981-85; salesman Engrs., Inc., Harrisburg, 1985-86; bus. mgr. Brinjac, Kambic & Assocs., Harrisburg, 1986-87; salesman Automatic Operators, Balt., 1987; cons. Gannett Fleming, Harrisburg, 1988—. Co-author: Naturality, 1979. Bd. dirs. Jackson (Mo.) C. of C., 1978; Big Bro., YMCA, Aurora, 1975; mem. com. Pa. Chamber of Bus. and Industry, Harrisburg, 1989—. Capt. U.S. Army, 1964-70, Pa. Army Nat. Guard, 1983—. Decorated Disting. Flying Cross, Bronze Star, Meritorious Svc. medal, Pa. Meritorious Svc. medal. Fellow Am. Prodn. and Inventory Control Soc.; mem. Am. Mgmt. Assn., U.S. Nat. Guard Assn. (Legion De Lafayette award 1992. Republican. Avocations: racquetball, metaphys. studies, classical music. Home: PO Box 464 Lemoyne PA 17043-0464 Office: Gannett Fleming 207 Senate Ave Camp Hill PA 17011-2316

MINER, EARL HOWARD, retired trust banker; b. Donnellson, Iowa, Jan. 26, 1923; s. T. Ralph and Carrie T. (Talbot) M.; m. Marian Aumann, May 30, 1944; children: Marcia, Susan, Scott. B.A., Iowa Wesleyan Coll., 1947; J.D., U. Iowa, 1948. Bar: Iowa 1948, Mich. 1965. Atty. Mt. Pleasant, Iowa, 1948-55; trust officer Nat. Bank Burlington, Iowa, 1955-57; v.p. 1st Trust Co., St. Joseph, Mo., 1957-62; investment editor Trusts & Estates Mag., N.Y.C., 1962-64; v.p.-trust officer St. Louis Union Trust Co., 1972-79, Citizens Trust Co., Ann Arbor, Mich., 1979-88; ret., 1988; instr. Iowa Wesleyan Coll., part-time 1949-50; county atty., Henry County, Iowa, 1951-55. Chmn. bd. dirs. Mary Free Bed Hosp., Grand Rapids, 1977-79; pres. Green Valley Cmty. Coordinating Coun., 1995—. With USAAF, World War II. Decorated D.F.C. Air medal with 2 oak leaf clusters. Mem. Iowa Bar Assn., State Bar Mich., Mich. Bankers Assn. (chmn. trust div 1970-71, 86-87), Lambda Chi Alpha, Phi Alpha Delta. Republican. Presbyterian (elder). Home: 1473 W Via De La Gloria Green Valley AZ 85614

MINER, EARL ROY, English educator; b. Marshfield, Wis., Feb. 21, 1927; s. Roy Jacob and Marjory M.; m. Virginia Lane, July 15, 1950; children:

Erik Earl, Lisa Lane. B.A. summa cum laude, U. Minn., 1949, M.A., 1951, Ph.D., 1955. Instr. English Williams Coll., 1953-55; mem. faculty dept. English UCLA, 1955-72, prof., 1964-72; prof. English Princeton U., 1972-74, Townsend Martin Class of 1917 Prof. English and comparative lit., 1974—; vis. fellow U. Canterbury, 1985; mem. joint com. for Japanese Studies Social Sci. Rsch. Coun., 1979-83; disting. vis. prof. Emory U., 1989; vis. prof. UCLA, 1990, Stanford U., 1994; mem. Com. on Scholarly Communications with Peoples Republic China, 1983-87. Author numerous books including The Japanese Tradition in British and American Literature, 1958, The Metaphysical Mode from Donne to Cowley, 1969, The Restoration Mode from Milton to Dryden, 1974, The Princeton Companion to Classical Japanese Literature, 1985, Comparative Poetics, 1991; co-author: Literary Transmission and Authority, 1993; assoc. editor: The New Princeton Ency. of Poetry and Poetics, 1993; assoc. gen. editor: Calif. edit. Works of John Dryden, 1964-72, editor 3 vols.; author articles. Am. Coun. Learned Socs. fellow, 1962-63; Guggenheim Found. fellow, 1977-78; fellow Woodrow Wilson Internat. Ctr. for Scholars, 1982-83; U. Calif. Humanities Res. Inst. fellow, 1990; vis. prof. Internat. Rsch. Ctr. for Japanese Studies, 1993-94; recipient Yamagata Banto Prize Osaka Prefectural Govt., 1987, Koizumi Yakumo prize, 1991; decorated Order of the Rising Sun with Gold Rays and Neck Ribbon Japanese Govt., 1994. Mem. Am. Soc. for 18th Century Studies (pres. 1981-82), Milton Soc. Am. (pres. 1982-83), Am. Comparative Lit. Assn. (adv. bd. 1977-80, 86-89), Internat. Comparative Lit. Assn. (exec. coun. 1986-88, pres. 1988-91). Office: Princeton U 22 Mccosh Princeton NJ 08544-0001

MINER, JOHN BURNHAM, industrial relations educator, writer; b. N.Y.C., July 20, 1926; s. John Lynn and Bess (Burnham) M.; children by previous marriage: Barbara, John, Cynthia, Frances; m. Barbara Allen Williams, June 1, 1979; children: Jennifer, Heather. AB, Princeton U., 1950, PhD, 1955; MA, Clark U., 1952. Lic. psychologist, N.Y. Rsch. assoc. Columbia U., 1956-57; mgr. psychol. svcs. Atlantic Refining Co., Phila., 1957-60; faculty mem. U. Oreg., Eugene, 1960-68, prof., chmn. dept. orgnl. sci. U. Md., College Park, 1968-73; rsch. prof. Ga. State U., Atlanta, 1973-87; pres. Orgnl. Measurement Systems Press, Buffalo, 1976—; prof. Human Resources SUNY, Buffalo, 1987—; chmn. dept. orgn. and human resources, 1989-92; cons. McKinsey & Co., N.Y.C., 1966-69; vis. lectr. U. Pa., Phila., 1959-60; vis. prof. U. Calif., Berkeley, 1966-67, U. South Fla., Tampa, 1972; researcher on orgnl. motivation, theories of orgn., human resource utilization, bus. policy and strategy, entrepreneurship. Author many books and monographs including Personnel Psychology, 1969; Personnel and Industrial Relations, 1969, 73, 77, 85; The Challenge of Managing, 1975; (with Mary Green Miner) Policy Issues Personnel and Industrial Relations, 1977; (with George A. Steiner) Management Policy and Strategy, 1977 (James A. Hamilton-Hosp. Adminstrs. Book award 1982, 86), (with M.G. Miner) Employee Selection Within the Law, 1978; Theories of Organizational Behavior, 1980; Theories of Organizational Structure and Process, 1982; People Problems: The Executive Answer Book, 1985; The Practice of Management, 1985; Organizational Behavior: Performance and Productivity, 1988, Industrial-Organizational Psychology, 1992, Role Motivation Theories, 1993; (with Donald P. Crane) Human Resource Management: The Strategic Perspective, 1995; contbr. numerous articles, papers to profl. jours. Served with AUS, 1944-46, ETO. Decorated Bronze Star, Combat Infantryman's Badge; named Disting. Prof. Ga. State U., 1974. Fellow APA, Acad. of Mgmt. (editor Jour. 1973-75, pres. 1977-78), Soc. for Personality Assessment, Am. Psychol. Soc.; mem. Soc. for Human Resource Mgmt., Indsl. Rels. Rsch. Assn., Internat. Cou. for Small Bus., Strategic Mgmt. Soc., Internat. Pers. Mgmt. Assn., Human Resource Planning Soc., Transit Valley Country Club. Republican. Home: 11054 Howe Rd Akron NY 14001-9473 Office: SUNY Dept Orgn and Human Resources Jacobs Mgmt Ctr Buffalo NY 14260

MINER, JOHN RONALD, agricultural engineer; b. Scottsburg, Ind., July 4, 1938; s. Gerald Lamont and Alice Mae (Murphy) M.; m. Betty Katheron Emery, Aug. 4, 1963; children--Saralena Marie, Katherine Alice, Frederick Gerald. B.S. in Chem. Engring. U. Kans., 1959; M.S.E. in San. Engring. U. Mich., 1960; Ph.D. in Chem. Engring. and Microbiology, Kans. State U., 1967. Lic. profl. engr., Kans., Oreg. San. engr. Kans. Dept. Health, Topeka, 1959-64; grad. research asst. Kans. State U., Manhattan, 1964-67; asst. prof. agrl. engring. Iowa State U., 1967-71, assoc. prof., 1971-72; assoc. prof. agrl. engring. Oreg. State U., 1972-76, prof., 1976—, head dept., 1976-86, acting assoc. dean Coll. Agrl. Sci., 1983-84, assoc. dir. Office Internat. Research and Devel., 1986-90, extension water quality specialist, 1991—; environ. engr. FAO of UN, Singapore, 1980-81; internat. cons.; cons. to livestock feeding ops., agrl. devel. firms. Co-author book on livestock waste mgmt.; author 3 books of children's sermons; contbr. numerous articles on livestock prodn., pollution control, control of odors associated with livestock prodn. to profl. publs. Mem. Am. Soc. Agrl. Engrs. (bd. dirs. 1985-87), Water Pollution Control Fed., Sigma Xi, Gamma Sigma Delta, Alpha Epsilon, Tau Beta Pi. Presbyterian. Office: Dept Bioresource Engring Oregon State University Corvallis OR 97331

MINER, ROBERT GORDON, creative promotional consultant, auctioneer, writer, publisher, actor; b. Blue Island, Ill., Jan. 29, 1923; s. Glen Ernest and Catherine (Leytze) M.; m. Betty Anne Clegg, May 23, 1944; children: Patricia L. Miner Jolin, Stephen C., David N. Student, Knox Coll., 1941-42; M.B.A., U. Chgo., 1950; grad., U.S. Army Command and Gen. Staff Coll., 1968. Payroll auditor Employers Group Ins. Cos., 1946-49; advt. salesman Cole & Mason (pub. reps.), 1949-54, partner, 1955-56; asst. pub. Flower Grower mag., Williams Press, 1956-61, pub., 1961-67; owner Media Design Assos., Westport, Conn., 1967-71; pres. Early Am. Soc., Inc. (pub. Early Am. Life), Harrisburg, Pa., 1971-81; owner, pub. Old Main Books, 1981-87; creative promotional cons., auctioneer, appraiser St. Thomas, V.I., 1987-94; adj. prof. humanities U. V.I., 1994—. Author: Handbook of Gardening, 1966; Complete Gardening Guide, 1969, Flea Market Handbook, 1981, rev., updated edit., 1990; columnist Virgin Islands Bus. Jour.,1994—; film appearances: My Father the Hero, 1993, Kawasaki Jet Ski Promo film and Geman TV program; contbr. articles to profl. jours. Served from 2d lt. to capt. AUS, 1942-46; col. Res. ret. Decorated Bronze Star. Republican. Episcopalian. Clubs: St. Thomas Yacht, Navy League. Home: 8-24 Estate Nazareth 6501 Red Hook Plz Ste 201 Saint Thomas VI 00802

MINER, ROGER JEFFREY, federal judge; b. Apr. 14, 1934; s. Abram and Anne M.; m. Jacqueline Mariani; 4 children. BS, SUNY; LLB cum laude, N.Y. Law Sch., 1956, LLD (hon.), 1989; postgrad., Bklyn. Law Sch., Judge Advocate Gen.'s Sch., U. Va.; LLD (hon.), Syracuse U., 1990. Bar: N.Y. 1956, U.S. Ct. Mil. Appeals 1956, Republic of Korea 1958, U.S. Dist. Ct. (so. and ea. dists.) N.Y. 1959. Ptnr. Miner & Hudson, N.Y., 1959-75; justice N.Y. State Supreme Ct., 1976-81; judge U.S. Dist. Ct. (no. dist.) N.Y., 1981-85, U.S. Ct. Appeals (2d cir.), Albany, N.Y., 1985—; conf. counsel City of Hudson, 1961-64; asst. dist. atty. Columbia County, 1964, dist. atty., 1968-74; adj. lectr. criminal law State U. System, N.Y., 1974-79; adj. prof. law N.Y. Law Sch., 1986—; lectr. state and local bar assns.; lectr. SUNY-Albany, 1985; N.Y. Law Sch. Bd. Trustees; mem. jud. coun. 2d Cir. N.Y. Law Sch. Bd. Trustees; 2d Cir. Com. on Hist. and Commemorative Events, 1989-94; Cameras in the Courtroom Com., No. Dist. Historical Com., 1981-85; State, Fed. Judicial Coun. of N.Y., 1986-91, chmn. 1990-91; Judicial Conf. of the U.S. Mng. editor N.Y. Law Sch. Law Rev.; contbr. articles to law jours. 1st lt. JAGC, U.S. Army, 1956-59, capt. USAR ret. Recipient Dean's medal for Disting. Profl. Svc., N.Y. Law Sch.; Disting. Alumnus award, Charles W. Froessel award for Valuable Contbn. to Law. Albany Jewish Fedn. award, Abraham Lincoln award, Community Svc. award Kiwanis, others; named Columbia County Man. of Yr., 1984, Ellis Island medal of Honor. Mem. ABA, N.Y. State Bar Assn., Assn. of Bar of City of N.Y., Columbia County Bar Assn., Am. Law Inst., Am. Judicature Soc., Fed. Judges Assn., Fed. Bar Coun., Am. Soc. Writers on Legal Subjects, Assn. Trial Lawyers Am., Columbia County Magistrates Assn., Supreme Ct. Hist. Soc., Columbia County Hist. Soc., N.Y. Law Sch. Alumni Assn. (hon. mem., bd. dirs.), B'nai Brith, Elks (past exalted ruler). Jewish. Office: US Ct Appeals PO Box 858 Albany NY 12201-0858

MINER, THOMAS HAWLEY, international entrepreneur; b. Shelbyville, Ill., June 19, 1927; s. Lester Ward and Thirza (Hawley) M.; m. Lucyna T. Minciel, July 1, 1988; children: Robert Thomas, William John. Student, U.S. Mil. Acad., 1946-47; BA, Knox Coll., 1950; JD, U. Ill., 1953. Bar: Ill. 1954. Atty. Continental Ill. Nat. Bank & Trust Co., Chgo., 1953-55; pres. Harper-Wyman Internat. (S.A.), Venezuela and Mex., 1955-58, Hudson Internat. (S.A.), Can. and Switzerland, 1958-60, Thomas H. Miner & Assoc.,

Inc., Chgo., 1960—; chmn. Miner, Fraser & Gabriel Pub. Affairs, Inc., Washington, 1982-88, Miner Systems, Inc., 1981—; bd. dirs. Lakeside Bank; chmn. Ill. dist. export coun. U.S. Dept. Commerce, 1971-76; sec. Consular Corps Chgo., 1986-88. Chmn. bd. dirs. Sch. Art Inst. Chgo., 1977-81; bd. govs., life mem., sustaining fellow Art Inst. Chgo.; former chmn. UN Assn., Chgo.; founder, chmn. Mid-Am. Com., 1968—; former mem. bd. dirs. UNICEF, NAM, Internat. Trade Policy Com. and Working Group on Commonwealth of Ind. States and Ea. Europe; trustee 4th Presbyn. Ch., Chgo.; bd. advisors Mercy Hosp.; vice chmn. Chgo. Sister Cities; mem. adv. bd. Internat. Inst. Edn.; bd. dirs. Internat. Sister Cities. With USNR, 1945-46; mem. Pres. Coun. U. Ill. Found. Capt. U.S. Army, 1946-47. Decorated commendatore Ordine al Merito della Repubblica Italiana; recipient Alumni Achievement award Knox Coll., 1974, Gold Medallion award Internat. Visitors Ctr. Chgo., 1989; named One of Chgo.'s 10 Outstanding Young Men, 1962, Chicagoan of Year Chgo. Assn. Commerce and Industry, 1968, Alumni of Month Coll. Law U. Ill., Nov. 1970, Aug. 1984; hon. consul Republic of Senegal, 1970-88. Mem. Am. Mgmt. Assn., Chgoland C. of C., Mid-Am.-Arab C. of C. (founder, former pres.), Chgo. Bar Assn., Chgo. Com., Chgo. Coun. Fgn. Rels. (past dir.), Coun. of the Ams., Internat. Trade Club (past dir., pres.), Japan-Am. Soc., Nat. Coun. U.S.-China Trade, Nat. Acad. Scis. (pres. coun.), English Speaking Union (dir., past chmn.), Trade and Econs. Coun. USA-CIS (dir.), U.S.-Russia Bus. Coun., Mus. Contemporary Art, Newcomen Soc. N.Am., U.S.-Arab C. of C. (bd. dirs.), U.S.-Mex. C. of C. (bd. dirs.), Thomas Minor Soc., Chgo. Club, Econ. Club, Chgo. Farmers Club, Mid-Am. Club, Internat. Club (Washington), Desiree Club, Univ. Club (Milw.), Hillsboro Club (Fla.), Tryall Golf and Beach Club (Jamaica), Rotary, Phi Delta Phi, Phi Gamma Delta. Office: 150 N Michigan Ave Chicago IL 60601-7508 also: 2400 Virginia Ave NW Washington DC 20037

MINES, HERBERT THOMAS, executive recruiter; b. Fall River, Mass., Jan. 30, 1929; s. Abraham and Fanny (Lepes) M.; B.S. in Econs., Babson Coll., 1949; M.S. in Indsl. and Labor Relations, Cornell U., 1954; m. Barbara Goldberg, Oct. 23, 1960; 1 child, Susan. Supr., asst. buyer, employment supr. G. Fox & Co., Hartford, Conn., 1949-52; adminstr. div. mg.-exec. devel. and orgn. planning R.H. Macy & Co., N.Y.C., 1954-66; v.p. personnel Neiman Marcus Co., Dallas, 1966-68, sr. v.p. personnel, 1968-70; v.p. personnel Revlon, Inc., N.Y.C., 1970-73; pres. Bus. Careers, Inc., 1973-78, chmn., 1978-81; pres. Exec. Search and Cons. Div., Wells Mgmt. Corp., 1978-81; pres. Herbert Mines Assocs., Inc., 1981-93, chmn., CEO 1993—. Bd. dirs. Fashion Inst. Tech., Am. Jewish Com., Assn. of Exec. Cons. Contbr. articles to trade publs. Office: 815 Pirates Cove Mamaroneck NY 10543

MINETA, NORMAN YOSHIO, congressman; b. San Jose, Calif., Nov. 12, 1931; s. Kay Kunisaku and Kane (Watanabe) M.; m. Danealia; children: David, K., Stuart S. B.S., U. Calif.-Berkeley, 1953; D of Pub. Svc., Santa Clara U., 1989; HHD (hon.), Rust Coll., 1993. Agt./broker Mineta Ins. Agy., San Jose, 1956-89; mem. adv. bd. Bank of Tokyo in Calif., 1961-75; mem. San Jose City Council, 1967-71; vice mayor City of San Jose, 1969-71, mayor, 1971-75; mem. 94th-104th Congresses from 13th (now 15th) Calif. dist., 1975—; subcom. surface transp., 1989-92, former dep. Dem. whip, ranking minority mem. transp. and infrastructure com.; chmn. fin. com. Santa Clara County (Calif.) Council Chs., 1960-62; commr. San Jose Human Relations Commn., 1962-64, San Jose Housing Authority, 1966—. Precinct chmn. Community Theater Bond Issue, 1964; mem. spl. gifts com. Santa Clara County council Boy Scouts Am., 1967; sec. Santa Clara County Grand Jury, 1964; bd. dirs. Wesley Found., San Jose State Coll., 1956-58, Pacific Neighbors, Community Council Cen. Santa Clara County, Japan Soc., San Francisco, Santa Clara County chpt. NCCJ, Mexican-Am. Community Services Agy.; mem. exec. bd. No. Calif.-Western Nev. dist. council Japanese Am. Citizens League, 1960-62, pres. San Jose chpt., 1957-59; bd. regents Smithsonian Instn., 1979—; chmn. Smithsonian vis. com. for Freer Gallery, 1981—; mem. bd. regents Santa Clara U. Served to lt. AUS, 1954-56. Mem. Greater San Jose C of C, Nat. Assn. Indsl. Ins. Agts., Calif. Assn. Indsl. Ins. Agts., San Jose Assn. Ind. Ins. Agts. (dir. 1960-62), North San Jose Optimists Club (pres. 1956-58), Jackson-Taylor Bus. and Profl. Assn. (dir. 1963). Methodist. Office: US Ho of Reps 2221 Rayburn HOB Washington DC 20515 Personal philosophy: My two greatest responsibilities are accountability and accessibility to everyone I represent, and to anyone who comes to me for help.

MING, SI-CHUN, pathologist, educator; b. Shanghai, China, Nov. 10, 1922; came to U.S. 1949, naturalized, 1964; s. Sian-Fan and Jan-Teh (Kuo) M.; m. Pen-Ming Lee, Aug. 17, 1957; children—Carol, Ruby, Stephanie, Michael, Jeffrey, Eileen. M.D., Nat. Central U. Coll. Medicine, China, 1947. Resident in pathology Mass. Gen. Hosp., Boston, 1952-56; assoc. pathologist Beth Israel Hosp., Boston, 1956-67; asst. prof. pathology Harvard U. Med. Sch., 1965-67; assoc. prof. U. Md., 1967-71; prof. Temple U., Phila., 1971-93, prof. emeritus, 1993—, acting chmn. dept. pathology, 1978-80, dep. chmn. dept. path., 1980-86; emeritus prof. Temple U., 1993—; mem. Internat. Study Group on Gastric Cancer; U.S. rep. WHO Collaborating Ctr. for Primary Prevention, Diagnosis and Treatment of Gastric Cancer; coun. Internat. Gastric Cancer Assn. 1994—. Author: Tumors of the Esophagus and Stomach, 1973, supplement, 1985, Precursors of Gastric Cancer, 1984, Pathology of the Gastrointestinal Tract, 1992. Nat. Cancer Inst. sr. fellow Karolinska Inst. Stockholm, 1964-65; named hon. prof. Tianjin Med. U., Shanghai Second Med. U. and Fourth Mil. Med. U., China, 1988—. Mem. AAAS, U.S. Canadian Acad. Pathology, Am. Soc. Investigative Pathology, Am. Gastroenterol. Assn., N.Y. Acad. Scis. Achievements include development of classification method for stomach carcinoma based on the growth pattern of the cancer. Office: 3400 N Broad St Philadelphia PA 19140-5104

MINGE, DAVID, congressman, lawyer, law educator; b. Clarkfield, Minn., 1942; m. Karen Aaker; children: Erik, Olaf. BA in History, St. Olaf Coll., 1964; JD, U. Chgo., 1967. Atty. Faegre & Benson, Mpls., 1967-70; prof. law U. Wyo., 1970-77; atty. Nelson, Oyen, Torvik, Minge & Gilbertson, 1977-93; mem. 103d-104th Congresses from 2nd Minn. Dist., 1993—; mem. agrl. com.; cons. Ho. Jud. Com., Subcom. Adminstrv. Law U.S. Congress, 1975; formerly atty. Minn. Valley Coop. Light and Power Assn., 1984-93; chair Agrl. Law Sect., Minn. State Bar Assn. 1990-92, adv. bd. Western Minn. Legal Svcs., 1978-84; bd. dirs. Legal Advice Clinics, Ltd., Hennepin County, Western Minn. Vol. Atty. Program. Clk. Montevideo Sch. Bd., 1989-92; dir. Montevideo Community Devel. Corp.; steering com. Clean Up the River Environ., 1992 ; co-coord. Montevideo area CROP Walk for the Hungry, Multi-church Vietnamese Refugee Resettlement Com., Montevideo, 1978-90; bd. dirs. Montevideo United Way, Model Cities Program, Kinder Kare; chair AFS Montevideo chpt. Mem. Minn. Bar Assn., Chippewa County Bar Assn. (chair), Montevideo C. of C., Kiwanis (pres.). Office: 1415 Longworth HOB Washington DC 20515-2302*

MINGLE, JAMES JOHN, lawyer. AB in English, St. Joseph's Coll., Phila., 1968; JD, U. Va., 1973. Bar: Md. 1974, Va. 1990. Asst. to pres. Frostburg State Coll., 1973-77, adj. prof. bus. law, 1975-77; asst. atty. gen. State of Md., 1977-89; chief counsel U. Md., Balt., 1981-89; gen. counsel U. Va., Charlottesville, 1989-95, lectr. law, 1994-95; univ. counsel, sec. Cornell U., Ithaca, N.J., 1995—; adj. prof. law U. Md., 1984-88; asst. to bus. mgr. Phila. 76ers NBA Club, 1968-69; city atty. City of Frostburg, Md., 1974-76. Mem. Nat. Assn. Coll. and Univ. Attys.

MINGLE, JOHN ORVILLE, engineer, educator, lawyer, consultant; b. Oakley, Kans., May 6, 1931; s. John Russell and Beulah Amelia (Johnson) M.; m. Patricia Ruth Schmitt, Aug. 17, 1957; children: Elizabeth Lorene, Stephen Roy. B.S., Kans. State U., Manhattan, 1953, M.S., 1958; Ph.D., Northwestern U., 1960; J.D., Washburn U., 1980. Bar: Kans., Wyo., U.S. Patent Office; registered profl. engr., Kans. Tng. engr. Gen. Electric Co., Schenectady, 1953-54; mem. faculty Kans. State U., 1956-90, prof. nuclear engring., 1965-90, prof. emeritus, 1990—, Black & Veatch Disting. prof., 1973-78; dir. Inst. Computational Research in Engring., 1969-88; exec. v.p., patent counsel Kans. State U. Research Found., 1983-88; instr. Northwestern U., 1958-59; vis. prof. U. So. Calif., 1967-68; cons. to govt. and industry. Author: The Invarient Imbedding Theory of Nuclear Transport, 1973; also articles. Bd. dirs. Laramie Regional Airport, 1994—. Officer AUS, 1954-56. Mem. ABA (chairperson sci. and tech. phys. scis. com. 1982-92), NSPE (sect. exec. com. 1985-87, chmn. 1985-86), Am. Nuclear Soc. (sect.

pres. 1976-77), Am. Inst. Chem. Engrs. (profl. devel. com. 1982—), Am. Soc. Engring. Edn. (chmn. Midwest sect. 1984-87, exec. com. 1984-87), Profl. Engrs. in Edn. (vice chmn. 1978-80, workshop chairperson 1983), Kans. Engring. Soc. (past chpt. pres.), Kans. Bar Assn., Licensing Execs. Soc., Sigma Xi (past chpt. pres., lectr.), Soc. Univ. Patent Adminstrs. (exec. com. 1985-87, v.p. cen. region 1985-87). Home: 1409 Downey St Laramie WY 82070-1867 The "workaholic" doctrine has been highly chastised by our modern society which seems to place great emphasis upon leisure; however those who are most slothful appear to be its loudest critics. Yet, this doctrine still remains one of the most viable methods for the dedicated person to make a lasting contribution to our society.

MINICHELLO, DENNIS, lawyer; b. Cleve., June 9, 1952; s. Ernest Anthony and Mary Theresa (Rocci) M.; m. Janine Stevens, Feb. 14, 1987. BA in Econs., Ohio U., 1974, MA in Econs., 1974; JD, Northwestern U., 1978. Bar: U.S. Dist. Ill., U.S. Ct. Appeals (7th cir.), Supreme Ct. Ill., U.S. Supreme Ct. Assoc. Haskell & Perrin, Chgo., 1978-84; ptnr. Tribler & Marwedel, Chgo., 1984-89, Keck, Mahin & Cate, Chgo., 1989—. Contbr. articles to profl. jours. Bd. dirs. Great Lakes Naval and Maritime Mus. Fulbright scholar, 1974-75. Mem. ABA, Ill. State Bar Assn., Chgo. Bar Assn. (mem. transp. com.), Maritime Law Assn. (proctor), Casualty Adjusters Assn. Chgo., The Propeller Club U.S. (pres. 1983-84), Port Chgo., Met. Club. Roman Catholic. Avocations: sailing, reading, running. Office: Keck Mahin & Cate 77 W Wacker Dr Chicago IL 60601-1629

MINICK, MICHAEL, publishing executive; b. Albany, N.Y., Mar. 26, 1945; s. Jason and Ruth Isabelle (Solomon) M. Student, U. Va., 1963-66; BA in History, L.I. U., 1968. Editorial dir. Mag. Mgmt., N.Y., 1969-73; mng. editor Gentlemen's Quarterly, N.Y.C., 1975-76; pub., ptnr. Beauty Digest, N.Y., 1978-90; pub. Pa. Ofcl. Wine and Liquor Quar., N.Y.C., 1985—, Ohio Liquor Quar., 1990—. Author: The Kung Fu Exercise Book-Health Secrets of Ancient China, 1974, The Wisdom of Kung Fu, 1974; contbr. numerous articles to popular mags. Mem. 25 Yr. Club of Ind. Distbrs., Pa. Wine and Spirit Assn. Democrat. Home: 24 Fifth Ave Apt 930 New York NY 10011-8819 Office: Wine and Liquor Quars Inc 24 Fifth Ave Ste 930 New York NY 10011

MINICUCCI, RICHARD FRANCIS, lawyer, former hospital adminstrator; b. N.Y.C., Jan. 16, 1947; s. Daniel Michael and Marie Felice (Trotta) M.; m. Nancy Jean Moran, Aug. 16, 1969; children: Jonathan, Elizabeth, Richard. BA, Rutgers Coll., 1969; MHA, Duke U., 1971; JD, Memphis State U., 1976. Bar: Tenn. 1977, N.Y. 1978. Adminstrv. asst. Duke Hosp., Durham, N.C., 1971; health planner Mid-South Med. Ctr. Coun., Memphis, 1971-73; dir. adminstrn. Memphis & Shelby County Hosp. Authority, 1973-77; assoc. Hayt Hayt & Landau, Great Neck, N.Y., 1977-81, ptnr., 1981-89; ptnr. Nixon Hargrave Devans & Doyle, Garden City, N.Y., 1989—; lectr. various health law assns. Editor: New York Environmental Law Handbook, 2d edit.; author: Residency Training Program Accreditation, 1st-5th edits.; editor-in-chief Accreditation Alert. Co-chmn. fund raising Luth. High Sch., Brookville, N.Y., 1991. Capt. U.S. Army, 1971-79. Mem. Am. Acad. Hosp. Attys., N.Y. State Bar Assn., Nassau Bar Assn., Nat. Health Lawyers Assn. Republican. Roman Catholic. Avocations: tennis, skiing, hockey, travel. Office: Nixon Hargrave Devans & Doyle 990 Stewart Ave Garden City NY 11530

MINICUCCI, ROBERT A., management consultant; b. Waterbury, Conn., May 7, 1952; s. Arnold A. and Mary (Garafola) M.; m. Jill Hanau, June 18, 1988; children: Robert A. Jr., Alexandra H. BA, Amherst (Mass.) Coll., 1975; MBA, Harvard U., 1979. CPA. Staff acct. Price Waterhouse, Boston, 1975-77; assoc. Lehman Bros., N.Y.C., 1979-82; v.p. Lehman Bros., 1982-85, sr. v.p., 1985-88, mng. dir., 1988-91; sr. v.p., treas. Am. Express Co., 1991-92; CFO First Data Corp., N.Y.C., 1992-93; gen. ptnr. Welsh, Carson, Anderson & Stowe, N.Y.C., 1993—; bd. dirs. Attachmate Corp., Telescis., Inc., Servantis Sys. Inc., Strategic Mortgage Svcs., Inc., Seer Techs., Inc. Home: 7 Hilltop Rd S Norwalk CT 06854-5001 Office: Welsh Carson Anderson Stowe Ste 3601 One World Financial Ctr New York NY 10281

MINIKES, MICHAEL, investment banker; b. N.Y.C., May 17, 1943; s. Jack and Kate (Jaffee) M.; m. Cheryl Gumora, Dec. 26, 1965; children: Peter, Joanna. B.A., Queens Coll., 1965; M.B.A., NYU, 1968. C.P.A., N.Y. Ptnr. Oppenheim Appel Dixon, N.Y.C., 1965-78; gen. ptnr. Bear Stearns & Co., N.Y.C., 1978—; sr. mgr. treas., dir., 1985—; dir. Securities Industry Automation Corp. Chmn. SIA Net Capital Com., N.Y.C., 1983—; treas. Central Park Community Fund, 1978-80. Mem. N.Y. Soc. C.P.A.s, Securities Industry Assn. Home: 960 Park Ave New York NY 10028-0325 Office: 245 Park Ave New York NY 10167-0001

MINISH, ROBERT ARTHUR, lawyer; b. Mpls., Dec. 25, 1938; s. William Arthur and Agnes Emilia (Olson) M.; m. Marveen Eleanor Allen, Sept. 16, 1961; 1 children: Roberta Ruth. BA, U. Minn., 1960, JD, 1963. Bar: Minn. 1963. Assoc. Popham, Haik, Schnobrich & Kaufman, Ltd., Mpls., 1963-67, ptnr., 1967—; bd. dirs. Braas Co., Mpls. Mem. ABA, Minn. Bar Assn. Avocations: fishing, traveling. Home: 331 Pearson Way NE Minneapolis MN 55432-2418 Office: Popham Haik Schnobrich & Kaufman 3300 Piper Jaffray Tower 222 S 9th St Minneapolis MN 55402

MINISI, ANTHONY S., lawyer; b. Newark, Sept. 18, 1926; s. Anthony F. and Leonora (Petoia) M.; m. Rita Marie Hentz, Jan. 8, 1949; children: Claire, Anthony J., Joseph J. Brian A. BS, U. Pa., 1948, JD, 1952. Player, N.Y. Giants, NFL, 1948; law clk. to presiding judge Ct. of Common Pleas #6, Phila., 1952-54; sr. ptnr. Wolf, Block, Schorr and Solis-Cohen, Phila., 1954—; past pres., vice chmn. Robert E. Maxwell Meml. Football Club, Eastern Assn. Intercoll. Football Ofcls. Past chmn. Com. of Seventy, Phila.; former mem., past pres. Bd. of Edn., Tredyffrin/Easttown Joint Sch. Dist.; mem., past chmn. bd. supr. Easttown Twp.; past v.p. Cmty. Svcs. Planning Coun., Phila.; trustee U. Pa.; trustee, mem. exec. com. U. Pa. Health Svcs.; mem. Clin. Care Assocs. U. Pa. Health Sys.; former mem., vice-chmn. Pa. State Bd. Law Examiners. Served to maj. USAR. Mem. ABA (ho. of dels.), Pa. Bar Assn., Phila. Jr. Bar Assn. (past pres.), Def. Lawyers Am., Assn. Trial Lawyers Am., Phila. Bar Assn. (bd. of govs., past chmn.), Phila. Trial Lawyers Assn., Fed. Bar Assn. Republican. Roman Catholic. Clubs: Lawyers (past pres.), Justinian Soc., Union League (Phila.). Office: Wolf Block Schorr & Solis-Cohen SE Corner 15th & Chestnut Sts Philadelphia PA 19102

MINISTER, KRISTINA, speech communication educator; b. Dayton, Ohio, Aug. 27, 1934; d. Roy J. and Margaret (Chatterton) Arndt; m. Edward Minister, Mar. 1959 (div. 1972); children: Matthew, Margaret; m. Hal W. Howard, Sept. 10, 1977 (dec. Sept. 1993). BFA, Ohio U., 1958; MA, Columbia U., 1962; PhD, Northwestern U., 1977. Instr. speech St. John's U., Bklyn., 1962-65, Bowdoin Coll., Brunswick, Maine, 1969-71; asst. prof. speech communication U. Ariz., Tucson, 1974-77, Calif. State U., Northridge, 1978-79; vis. asst. prof. communication Ariz. State U., Tempe, 1979-82; oral historian Oral History Ctr., Inc., Phoenix, 1982-89; prof. comm. Midway (Ky.) Coll., 1989—; cons. oral history to bus., families, mus. and schs., 1982-89. Author: Oral History: The Privilege You Inherit, 1985; contbr. scholarly essays to various publs. Actor Cmty. Profl. Theatre. Mem. NOW, Women in Comm., Inc., Speech Comm. Assn., Oral History Assn., Am. Folklore Soc. Democrat. Unitarian Universalist. Avocations: race walking, aerobic dance, travel. Office: Midway Coll 512 E Stephens St Midway KY 40347-1120

MINISTER, MICHAEL E., lawyer; b. Athens, Ohio, Feb. 14, 1944. BS, Ohio State U., 1966; JD, Capital U., 1974. Bar: Ohio 1974. Dir. adminstrn. City of Worthington, Ohio, 1970-73, city mgr., 1974, dir. law, 1975—; ptnr. Baker & Hostetler, Columbus, Ohio. Lt. (j.g.) USN, 1967-69. Mem. ABA. Office: Baker & Hostetler 65 E State St Ste 2100 Columbus OH 43215-4260

MINK, ERIC P., newspaper columnist; b. St. Louis, Dec. 15, 1947; s. Joseph and Ida (Novack) M.; m. Claudia Eve Gellman, Mar. 22, 1970. BA, George Washington U., 1969. Consumer affairs editor, mng. editor The Midwest Motorist, St. Louis, 1973-77; consumer reporter, columnist St. Louis Post Dispatch, 1977-79, TV critic, 1979—; critic-at-large, commentator KSD-FM/KUSA Gannett Radio, St. Louis, 1987—; juror Banff (Alta.,

Can.) TV Festival, 1989, Alfred I. duPont-Columbia U. awards in broadcast journalism, N.Y.C., 1989—. Recipient Citation for excellence in consumer reporting Nat. Press Club, Washington, 1978, Lowell Mellett award citation Pa. State U. Sch. Communications, 1987. Office: St Louis Post Dispatch 900 N Tucker Blvd Saint Louis MO 63101-1069

MINK, JOHN ROBERT, dental educator; b. Peru, Ill., Sept. 8, 1927; s. Monte Franklin and Marcella (White) M.; m. Barbara Joanne Merrell, June 21, 1952; children: Sarah, Teresa, Kathleen, Mary, James, Elizabeth. B.A., Ind. U., 1951; D.D.S. with honors, 1956, M.S. in Pedodontics, 1961. Diplomate Am. Bd. Pedodontics (bd. examiners). Instr. Ind. U., Indpls., 1957-60, asst. prof., 1960-62; dir. dental Clinic Handicapped Children, James Whitcomb Riley Hosp. for Children, Indpls., 1957-62; mem. faculty U. Ky., Lexington, 1962—, chmn. dept. pedodontics, 1962-74, prof. pedodontics, 1966—, asst. dean clin. affairs Coll. Dentistry, 1974-80, assoc. dean clin. affairs, 1980-85; prof., chmn. dept. pediatric dentistry U. Ky. and U. Louisville, 1985-88; dir. U. Ky. Med. Plaza Dental Clinic, 1985-89; cons. pedodontics USPHS, 1969-72, U.S. Army, Fort Knox, 1969—, ADA, 1972—, Ft. Jackson, 1987—, Ft. Lewis, 1989. Pres. Vols. Bur. Lexington, Ky., 1972-73; bd. dirs. Vol. Action Ctr., 1978—; bd. dirs. Margaret Hall Sch., Versailles, Ky., chmn. bd., 1976—; pres. Margaret Hall Found., 1980—. Served with AUS, 1946-47. Fellow Am. Acad. Pedodontics, Internat. Coll. Dentists (dep. regent 1990—); mem. Am. Soc. Dentistry for Children (pres. Ky. chpt. 1967—), Ky. Assn. Pediatric Dentists (sec.-treas. 1979—), Am. Assn. Dental Schs., Blue Grass Dental Soc. (pres. 1985-86), Pierre Fauchard Acad., Ind. U. Pediatric Dentistry Alumni Assn. (pres. 1993—), Delta Upsilon, Delta Sigma Delta (Delta Epsilon chpt., sec.-treas. 1992-94, pres.-elect 1994), Omicron Kappa Upsilon. Home: 5411 Parkers Mill Rd Lexington KY 40513-9711 Office: U Ky Coll Dentistry Chandler Med Ctr Lexington KY 40504

MINK, PATSY TAKEMOTO, congresswoman; b. Paia, Maui, Hawaii, Dec. 6, 1927; d. Suematsu and Mitama (Tateyama) Takemoto; m. John Francis Mink, Jan. 27, 1951; 1 child, Gwendolyn. Student, Wilson Coll., 1946, U. Nebr., 1947; BA, U. Hawaii, 1948; LLD, U. Chgo., 1951; DHL (hon.), Chaminade Coll., 1975, Syracuse U., 1976, Whitman Coll., 1981. Bar: Hawaii. Pvt. practice Honolulu, 1953-65; lectr. U. Hawaii, 1952-56, 59-62, 79-80; atty. Territorial Ho. of Reps., 1955; mem. Hawaii Ho. of Reps., 1956-58, Ter. Hawaii Senate, 1958-59, Hawaii State Senate, 1962-64, 89th-94th Congresses from 2nd Hawaii dist., 101st-104th Congresses from 2d dist. Hawaii, 1989—; mem. econ. and ednl. opportunity com., mem. budget com.; mem. U.S. del. to UN Law of Sea, 1975-76, Internat. Woman's Yr., 1975, UN Environ. Program, 1977, Internat. Whaling Commn., 1977; asst. sec. of state U.S. Dept. State, 1977-78. Charter pres. Young Dem. Club Oahu, 1954-56, Ter. Hawaii Young Dems., 1956-58; del. Dem. Nat. Conv., 1960, 72, 80; nat. v.p. Young Dem. Clubs Am., 1957-59; v.p. Ams. for Dem. Action, 1974-76, nat. pres., 1978-81; mem. nat. adv. com. White House Conf. on Families, 1979-80; mem. nat. adv. coun. Federally Employed Women. Recipient Leadership for Freedom award Roosevelt Coll., Chgo., 1968, Alii award 4-H Clubs Hawaii, 1969, Nisei of Biennium award, Freedom award Honolulu chpt. NAACP, 1971, Disting. Humanitarian award YWCA, St. Louis, 1972, Creative Leadership in Women's Rights award NEA, 1977, Human Rights award Am. Fedn. Tchrs., 1975, Feminist of Yr. award Feminist Majority Found., 1991, Margaret Brent award ABA, 1992. Office: US Ho of Reps 2135 Rayburn HOB Washington DC 20515*

MINKEL, HERBERT PHILIP, JR., lawyer; b. Boston, Feb. 11, 1947; s. Herbert Philip and Helen (Sullivan) M. A.B., Holy Cross Coll., 1969; J.D., NYU, 1972. Bar: Mass. 1973, N.Y. 1976, U.S. Dist. Ct. Mass. 1973, U.S. Dist. Ct. (so. dist.) N.Y. 1976. Law clk. U.S. Dist. Ct. Mass., Boston, 1972-73; assoc. Milbank, Tweed, Hadley & McCloy, N.Y.C., 1973-79; ptnr. Fried, Frank, Harris, Shriver & Jacobson, N.Y.C., 1979-94; adj. assoc. prof. NYU Law Sch., 1987-94; mem. adv. com. on bankruptcy rules Jud. Conf. U.S., 1987-93. Contbg. editor 5 Collier on Bankruptcy, 15th edit. 1979-94; contbr. articles to profl. jours.; co-author American Bankers Association Bankruptcy Manual, 1979. Root-Tilden scholar, NYU, 1969-72. Mem. ABA, Nat. Bankruptcy Conf., N.Y. Bar Assn., Assn. of Bar of City of N.Y. Office: 360 E 88th St New York NY 10128-4983

MINKER, JACK, computer scientist, educator; b. Bklyn., July 4, 1927; s. Harry and Rose (Lapuck) M.; m. Rita Goldberg, June 24, 1951 (dec. Oct. 11, 1988); children: Michael Saul, Sally Anne. B.A. cum laude with honors in Math., Bklyn. Coll., 1949; M.S. in Math., U. Wis., 1950; Ph.D. in Math., U. Pa., 1959. Grad. teaching asst. U. Wis., 1949-50; tchr. math. Erasmus Hall High Sch., Bklyn., 1950-51; engr. Bell Aircraft Corp., Buffalo, 1951-52; mgr. info. tech. sect. RCA, Bethesda, Md., 1952-63; dir. tech. staff Auerbach Corp., Washington, 1963-67, tech. cons., 1967-72; mem. Faculty NIH Grad. Sch., 1965-66; vis. mem. faculty U. Md., 1967-68, assoc. prof. computer sci., 1968-71, prof., 1971—, 1st chmn. dept. computer sci., 1974-79; cons., speaker, lectr. in field; cons. NSF, 1979-82, chmn. adv. bd. on computer sci., 1980-82; prof. Inst. Advanced Computer Studies, 1986—; vice-chmn. Com. Concerned Scientists, 1973—; past mem. U.S. Nat. Com. for Refch. Info. Documentalists. Author: (with H. Gallaire and J.M. Nicolas) Logic and Data Bases a Deductive Approach, 1984; editor: (with H. Gallaire and J.M. Nicholas) Advances in Data Base Theory, vol. 1, 1980, vol. 2, 1984, (with H. Gallaire) Logic and Data Bases, 1978, Foundation of Deductive Databases and Logic Programming, 1988, (with J. Lobo and A. Rajasekar) Foundations of Disjunctive Logic Programming, 1992; contbr. numerous articles to profl. publs.; publs. reviewer. Served with U.S. Army, 1945-46. Nat. Bur. Standards investigator, 1970-73, grantee, 1975-76; grantee NASA, 1969-81, NSF, 1971—, Air Force Office of Sci. Rsch., 1982-94, Army Rsch. Office, 1985-90. Fellow AAAS, ACM, IEEE (mem. editorial bd. Expert Info. Systems jour.), Am. Assn. Artificial Intelligence (founding); mem. Assn. Computing Machinery (chmn. nat. program com. 1968-69, vice chmn. com. on sci. freedom and human rights 1979-89, Outstanding Contbn. award Assn. Computer Machines, 1985). Jewish. Office: U Md Dept Computer Sci Inst Advanced Computer Studies College Park MD 20742

MINKLE, L. STEVEN, manufacturing executive, light. CFO Nimbus Mfg. Inc., Ruckersville, Va., Nimbus CD Internat., Inc., Ruckersville, Va. Office: Nimbus USA Inc Rt 629 Ruckersville VA 22968 also: Nimbus CD Internat Inc Rt 629 Ruckersville VA 22968*

MINKOFF, JACK, economics educator; b. N.Y.C., Jan. 29, 1925; s. Isidore and Yetta (Fine) M.; m. Anne B. Johnson, June 19, 1948; children—Ellen, Paul. A.B., Cornell U., 1948; A.M., Columbia U., 1950, Ph.D. (Ford Found. fellow), 1960. Instr. econs. Western Res. U., 1952-53; instr. econs. Sarah Lawrence Coll., 1959-60; prof. econs., chmn. dept. social sci. Pratt Inst., Bklyn., 1960—; acting dean Sch. Liberal Arts and Scis. Pratt Inst., 1985-86, dean, 1986-93, acting provost, 1993—. Served with USAAF., 1943-45. Fellow Social Sci. Research Council, 1950-51. Mem. Phi Beta Kappa. Home: 57 Ruxton Rd Great Neck NY 11023-1528 Office: Pratt Inst Brooklyn NY 11205

MINKOWITZ, MARTIN, lawyer, former state government official; b. Bklyn.; s. Jacob and Marion (Kornblau) M.; 1 son from previous marriage, Stuart Allan. AA, Bklyn. Coll., 1959, BA, 1961; JD, Bklyn. Law Sch., 1963, LLM, 1965. Bar: N.Y. 1963, U.S. Supreme Ct. 1967, U.S. Tax Ct. 1974, all four U.S. Dist. Cts. N.Y. Ptnr. firm Minkowitz & Rosenbluth, N.Y.C., 1964-76; gen. counsel State of N.Y. Workers' Compensation Bd., N.Y.C., 1976-81; gen. counsel, dep. supt. State of N.Y. Ins. Dept., N.Y.C., 1981-88; instr. CUNY, 1975; ptnr. Stroock & Stroock & Lavan, N.Y.C., 1988—; mem. adv. bd. Coll. Ins., 1987-90; adj. prof. law N.Y. Law Sch., N.Y.C., 1982—; lectr. ABA, N.Y.C. of C, Practicing Law Inst., N.Y. State Bar Assn., Nat. Assn. Ins. Commrs., Nat. Conf. Ins. Legis.; hearing officer N.Y.C. Transp. Dept., 1970-75; cons. City Council, N.Y.C., 1969. Author: (with others) Rent Stabilization and Control, 1973; (with others) Handling the Basic Workers' Compensation Law Case, 1982, 85, 87; co-author Workers Compensation Insurance and Law Practice-The Next Generation, 1989; commentaries to McKinney's Laws, 1982—; mem. editorial bd. Jour. Occupational Rehabilitation U. Rochester, 1991—; contbr. numerous articles to profl. jours. Bd. dirs., sec. Kingsbay YM-YWHA, Bklyn., 1978—; pres. bd. dirs. Shore Terrace Co-op., Bklyn., 1982-83; co-chmn. exec. bd., met. council, nat. v.p. Am. Jewish Congress, N.Y.C., 1983-91; bd. dirs. Met. Coord. Coun. on Jewish poverty, 1993—; Nat. Conf. Christians and Jews (dir. N.Y. divsn.). Recipient cert. meritorious service Bklyn. Law Sch., 1963, Outstanding Pub.

Service award Ind. Ins. Agts. Assn., 1988, citation outstanding performance State of N.Y. Workers' Compensation Bd., 1981, Disting. Leadership award N.Y. Claims Assn., 1986, City of Peace award State of Israel Bonds, 1986, Brotherhood award NCCJ, 1994. Mem. N.Y. County Lawyers Assn. (chmn. unlawful practice of law com. 1982-86, mem. profl. ethics com. 1985-91, chair worker's compensation com. 1988-91), N.Y. State Bar Assn. (chmn. unlawful practice of law com. 1981-83, mem. com. on profl. ethics 1981-84, chmn. com. profl. discipline 1988-92), Bklyn. Law Sch. Alumni Assn. (v.p. bd. dirs. 1984-92, pres. elect 1993-94, pres. 95—). Office: Stroock Stroock & Lavan 7 Hanover Sq New York NY 10004-2616

MINKOWYCZ, W. J., mechanical engineering educator; b. Libokhora, Ukraine, Oct. 21, 1937; came to U.S., 1949; s. Alexander and Anna (Tokan) M.; m. Diana Eva Szandra, May 12, 1973; 1 child, Liliana Christine Anne. B.S. in Mech. Engring., U. Minn., 1958, M.S. in Mech. Engring., 1961, Ph.D. in Mech. Engring, 1965. Asst. prof. U. Ill., Chgo., 1966-68, assoc. prof., 1968-78, prof., 1978—; cons. Argonne Nat. Lab, Ill., 1970-82, U. Hawaii, Honolulu, 1974—. founding editor-in-chief Jour. Numerical Heat Transfer, 1978—; editor Internat. Jour. Heat and Mass Transfer, 1968—, Internat. Communications In Heat and Mass Transfer Jour., 1974—; editor book series: Computational and Physical Processes in Mechanics and Thermal Sciences, 1979—; editor: Rheologically Complex Fluids, 1972, Handbook of Numerical Heat Transfer, 1988; contbr. articles to profl. jours. Recipient Silver Circle for Excellence in Teaching, U. Ill.-Chgo., 1975, 76, 81, 86, 90, 94, Harold A. Simon award Excellence in Teaching, 1986, Ralph Coats Roe Outstanding Tchr. award Am. Soc. Engring. Edn., 1988, U. Ill. Disting. Tchr. award, 1989. Fellow ASME (Heat Transfer Meml. award 1993); mem. Sigma Xi, Pi Tau Sigma. Republican. Ukrainian Catholic. Office: U Ill Dept Mech Engring Mail Code 251 842 W Taylor St Chicago IL 60607-7022

MINNELLI, LIZA, singer, actress; b. Los Angeles, Mar. 12, 1946; d. Vincente and Judy (Garland) M.; m. Peter Allen, 1967 (div. 1972); m. Jack Haley, Sept. 15, 1974 (div.); m. Mark Gero, Dec. 4, 1979 (div. 1992). Appeared in Off-Broadway revival of Best Foot Forward, 1963; recorded You Are For Loving, 1963, Tropical Nights, 1977, Liza Minelli at Carnegie Hall, 1987; appeared with mother at London Palladium, 1964; appeared in Flora, the Red Menace, 1965 (Tony award), The Act, 1977 (Tony award), The Rink, 1984; nightclub debut at Shoreham Hotel, Washington, 1965; films include Charlie Bubbles, 1967, The Sterile Cuckoo, 1969, Tell Me That You Love Me, Junie Moon, 1970, Cabaret, 1972 (Oscar award), That's Entertainment, 1974, Lucky Lady, 1975, A Matter of Time, 1976, Silent Movie, 1976, New York, New York, 1977, Arthur, 1981, Rent A Cop, Arthur on the Rocks, 1988, Stepping Out, 1991; albums include: Results, 1989; appeared on TV in own spl. Liza With a Z, 1972 (Recipient Emmy award); other TV appearances include Goldie and Liza Together, 1980, Baryshnikov on Broadway, 1980, The Princess and the Pea, Showtime, 1983, A Time to Live, 1985, Sam Found Out, 1988, Liza Minnelli Live from Radio City Music Hall, PBS (Emmy nomination, Music Program Performance, 1993); internat. tour with Frank Sinatra, Sammy Davis Jr., 1988. Awarded the Brit. equivalent of the Oscar for Best Actress, 1972, Italy's David di Donatello award (twice), the Valentino award. Office: care PMK 1776 Broadway, 8th Floor New York NY 10019-2002

MINNER, RUTH ANN, state senator; b. Milford, Del., Jan. 17, 1935; m. Roger Minner. Student Del. Tech. and Community Coll. Office receptionist Gov. of Del., 1972-74; mem. Del. Ho. of Reps., 1974-82; mem. Del. Senate, 1982-92; lt. gov. State of Del., Dover, 1993—; mem. Dem. Nat. Com., 1988. Home: RD 3 Box 694 Milford DE 19963 Office: Office Lt Gov Tatnall Bldg 3rd Fl Dover DE 19901*

MINNERLY, ROBERT WARD, headmaster; b. Yonkers, N.Y., Mar. 21, 1935; s. Richard Warren and Margaret Marion (DeBrocky) M.; m. Sandra Overmire, June 12, 1957; children: Scott Ward, John Robert, Sydney Sue. AB, Brown U., 1957; MAT, U. Tex., Arlington, 1980. Tchr., coach Rumsey Hall Sch., Washington, Conn., 1962-64; tchr., coach Berkshire Sch., Sheffield, Mass., 1964-70, asst. head, 1969-70, headmaster, 1970-76; dir. Salisbury (Conn.) Summer Sch. Reading and English, 1970; prin. upper sch. Ft. Worth Country Day Sch., 1976-86; headmaster Charles Wright Acad., Tacoma, Wash., 1986—; cons. Tarrant County Coalition on Substance Abuse, 1982-84; mem. mayor's task force Tacoma Edn. Summit, 1991-92. Contbr. articles to profl. jours. Bd. dirs. Tacoma/Pierce County Good Will Games Art Coun., 1989; mem. exec. com. Am. Leadership Forum, 1991-95; mem. Broadway Ctr. for Performing Arts, Tacoma, 1988-94, mem. exec. com., 1990-93. Named Adminstr. of Yr. Wash. Journalism Edn. Assn., 1991. Mem. Pacific N.W. Assn. Ind. Schs. (chmn. long-range planning com. 1989-92, exec. com. 1990-92, 91, v.p. 1994). Republican. Presbyterian. Home: 4214 39th Avenue Ct NW Gig Harbor WA 98335-8029 Office: Charles Wright Acad 7723 Chambers Creek Rd W Tacoma WA 98467-2099

MINNICH, DALE E., religious administrator. Assoc. gen. sec. Gen. Svcs. Commn. Office: Ch of the Brethren 1451 Dundee Ave Elgin IL 60120

MINNICH, NELSON HUBERT JOSEPH, historian, educator; b. Cin., Jan. 15, 1942; s. Hubert Jakob Matthäus and Alberta Mary Rosella (Pfadt) M. AB in Philosophy, Boston Coll., 1965, MA in History, 1969; STB in Theology, Gregorian U., 1970; PhD in History, Harvard U., 1977. Instr. Loyola Acad., Wilmette, Ill., 1966-68; teaching fellow, asst. Harvard U., Cambridge, Mass., 1972-73, 74-76; instr. Cath. U. of Am., Washington, 1977, asst. prof., 1977-83, assoc. prof., 1983-93, prof., 1993—. Co-editor: Studies in Catholic History in Honor of John Tracy Ellis, 1985; author: The Fifth Lateran Council (1512-17) Studies on Its Membership, Diplomacy and Proposals for Reform, 1993, The Catholic Reformation: Council, Churchmen, and Controversies, 1993; assoc. editor The Cath. Hist. Rev., 1977-90, adv. editor, 1991—; editor Melville Studies in Church History, 1988—; contbr. chpts. to books, numerous articles to profl. jours. and encys. Grantee, Societas Internationalis Historiae Concilium Investigandae, 1982, 84, 86, 87, 90, Am. Philos. Soc., 1984, NEH, 1978, Am. Coun. Learned Socs., 1986, Cath. Univ. Am. faculty rsch., 1981, 90, 93-95; recipient fellowship Harvard U., 1972-73, 73-74, Villa I Tatti: The Harvard U. Ctr. for Italian Renaissance, 1979, Am. Acad. in Rome, 1979-80, Am. Coun. Learned Socs., 1979-80, 1990, NEH, 1986; recipient scholarship Harvard U., 1971-73, 74-76, Richard Krautheimer, 1980, Carl Meyer prize, 1977. Mem. Am. Cath. Hist. Assn., Gesellschaft zur Herausgabe des Corpus Catholicorum, Erasmus of Rotterdam Soc., Sixteenth Century Studies Conf. Avocations: dancing, local politics, gardening, travel, genealogy. Home: 5713 37th Ave Hyattsville MD 20782-3821 Office: Cath U of Am 423 Caldwell Hall Washington DC 20064

MINNICH, VIRGINIA, retired medical researcher, educator; b. Zanesville, Ohio, Jan. 24, 1910; d. Rufus Humphrey and Ollie (Burley) M.; m. Jerry Hajek, Oct. 23, 1987. BS in Home Econs, Ohio State U., 1937; MS in Nutrition, Iowa State Coll., 1938; ScD (hon.), Williams Woods Coll., Fulton, Mo., 1972. Research asst., then research assoc. medicine, div. hematology Washington U. Sch. Medicine, St. Louis, 1939-78; prof. medicine, 1974-78, prof. emeritus, 1978—. Contbr. articles to profl. jours. Recipient Alumni award home econs. Ohio State U., 1975; named St. Louis Woman of Achievement Group Action Council, 1947; award for founder of thalassemia research in Thailand, Mahidol U. Bangkok, 1985; Fulbright-Hays grantee Turkey, 1964. Mem. Am. Fedn. Clin. Research, Soc. Exptl. Biology and Medicine, Internat., Am. socs. hematology, Sigma Xi, Omicron Nu, Phi Upsilon Omicron. Office: Washington U Med Sch Dept Medicine Saint Louis MO 63110 *I discovered at an early age that there are many obstacles on the road to success. My friends and family helped me over the hurdles and they were the ones who were instrumental in the achievement of my goals.*

MINNICK, CARLTON PRINTESS, JR., bishop; b. Greensboro, N.C., Sept. 8, 1927; s. Carlton Printess and Catherine (Johnson) M.; m. Mary Ann Adams, Sept. 5, 1946; children: Mary Ann, Gregory Carlton, Patte Carroll, Jonathan Allan. Student, U. Va., 1944-45; BA, Lynchburg Coll., 1954; BD, Union Theol Sem. in va., 1957, MTh, 1958. On trial Va. Conf., 1954, ordained deacon United Meth. Ch., 1955, full connection, 1956, elder, 1957. Pastor Mt. Airy charge United Meth. Ch., 1951-54, pastor Goochland charge, 1954-58; pastor St. James Meth. Ch. United Meth. Ch., Ferrum, 1958-1963; pastor Westhampton Meth. Ch. United Meth. Ch., Richmond,

1963-67; pastor Mt. Olivet United Meth. Ch. Arlington, 1973-78; supt. Alexandria Dist. United Meth. Ch., 1978-80, bishop, 1980—, resident bishop Jackson, Miss. area, 1980-84; bishop United Meth. Ch., Raleigh, N.C., 1984&. Office: United Meth Ch PO Box 10955 Raleigh NC 27605-0955

MINNICK, MALCOLM DAVID, lawyer; b. Indpls., July 5, 1946; s. Malcolm Dick and Frances Louise (Porter) M.; m. Heidi Rosemarie Klein, May 24, 1972. BA, U. Mich., 1968, JD, 1972. Bar: Calif. 1972, U.S. Dist. Ct. (cen. dist.) Calif. 1972, U.S. Ct. Appeals (9th cir.) 1984, U.S. Dist. Ct. (no. dist.) Calif. 1986, U.S. Supreme Ct. 1986. Assoc. Lillick McHose & Charles, Los Angeles, 1972-78; ptnr. Lillick & McHose, Los Angeles, 1978-91, Pillsbury, Madison & Sutro (formerly Lillick & McHose), San Francisco, 1991—; group mgr. Creditors Rights and Bankruptcy Group, 1993—; panelist Calif. Continuing Edn. of Bar, L.A., 1982-86, 88, Practicing Law Inst., 1992, 93, 94; bd. govs. Fin. Lawyers Conf., L.A., 1981-84; mem. exec. com. Lillick & McHose, 1982-85. Co-author: Checklist for Secured Commercial Loans, 1983. Mem. ABA (corp., banking and bus. law sect.), Calif. Bar Assn. (Uniform Comml. Code com. 1983-86), L.A. County Bar Assn. (exec. com. comml. law and bankruptcy sect. 1987-90), Bar Assn. San Francisco (comml. law and bankruptcy sect.), L.A. Country Club, Univ. Club (bd. dirs. 1983-86, pres. 1985-86). Avocation: golf. Office: Pillsbury Madison & Sutro 235 Montgomery St 14th Fl San Francisco CA 94104-2902

MINNICK, MALCOLM L., JR., clergy member, church administrator. Exec. dir. Division for Outreach of the Evangelical Lutheran Church in America, Chicago, Ill. Office: Evangelical Lutheran Church Am 8765 W Higgins Rd Chicago IL 60631-4101

MINNICK, WALTER CLIFFORD, building materials company executive; b. Walla Walla, Wash., Sept. 20, 1942; s. Walter Lawrence and Dorothy (Waldron) M.; children from previous marriage: Amy Louise, Adam Wade; m. A.K. Lienhart. BA summa cum laude in Econs., Whitman Coll., 1964; MBA with high distinction, Harvard U., 1966, JD magna cum laude, 1969. Bar: Oreg. and Wash. bars. Assoc. firm Davies, Biggs, Strayer, Stoel & Boley, Portland, Oreg., 1969-70; staff asst. to pres. Domestic Council, Washington, 1971-72; dep. asst. dir. Office Mgmt. and Budget, Washington, 1972-73; with T.J. Internat., Boise, Idaho, 1974-95, v.p. div. ops., 1976-79, pres., COO, 1979-95, pres., CEO, 1986-95, also past chmn. bd. dirs., trustee; pvt. investigator, 1995—; bd. dirs. Eljer Corp., MacMillan Bloedel, Ltd. Trustee, past chmn. Albertson Coll. of Idaho; past chmn. bus. adv. coun. Boise State U. Sch. Bus., bus. com. Coll. Idaho; mem. exec. com. Idaho Bus. Coun.; mem. Gov. Coun. of the Wilderness Soc. With U.S. Army, 1970-72. Named Idaho Bus. Leader of Yr., 1992. Mem. Wash. State Bar Assn., Oreg. State Bar Assn., Idaho Conservation League, Nature Conservancy, Boise Fgn. Affairs Soc. (mem. exec. com.), Bogus Basin Recreation Assn. (past chmn.). Unitarian. Office: T J Internat Inc Box 65 380 E Parkcenter Blvd Boise ID 83706-3962

MINNIGH, JOEL DOUGLAS, library director; b. Greenville, Pa., Apr. 9, 1949; s. Wendell Ellsworth and Frances Alene (Hyde) M.; m. Margaret Beth Crowther, Dec. 26, 1972; children: Bradley Dean, Douglas Knox. BA, Allegheny Coll., 1971; MLS, U. Pitts., 1975. Cert. libr., Pa. Asst. libr. Wilkinsburg (Pa.) Pub. Libr., 1976-77, head libr., 1977—. Bd. dirs. Goodwill Industries Pitts., 1980-90; vice chmn. bd. dirs. Bach Choir Pitts., 1984-87; sec., bd. dirs. United Meth. Ch. Union, Pitts., 1987-88; elder, deacon Fox Chapel Presbyn. Ch., 1987—; v.p. Friends of Music Libr.-Carnegie Libr., 1988—. Recipient honor Goodwill Industries Pitts., 1990, citation Pa. Senate, 1991. Mem. Pa. Libr. Assn. (treas. S.W. chpt. 1988-89), Allegheny County Libr. Assn. Republican. Avocations: travel, cooking, gardening, music, reading. Home: 1009 Blackridge Rd Wilkinsburg PA 15235 Office: Wilkinsburg Pub Libr 605 Ross Ave Pittsburgh PA 15221-2195

MINNIX, BRUCE MILTON, television and theatre director; b. Hendersonville, N.C., Apr. 26, 1923; s. Bruce Milton and Jane Irene (Leverett) M.; m. Corinne McClure, Aug. 5, 1950; 1 child, Tracy Logue. B.A., U. N.C., 1948. mem. faculty New Sch., N.Y.C., 1977-80; adj. prof., Bklyn., 1985; AT&T sales tng. program, 1987. Dir. numerous TV shows including: U.S. Steel Hour, 1961-62, Merchant of Venice, 1962, Essay on Doors, 1963, Never Too Young, 1965-66, On Being Black, 1969, The Haggadah Oratorio, 1981, Search for Tomorrow, 1968-74, All My Children, 1978-79, Another World, 1981, Texas, 1981-82, Body Talk, 1983, As the World Turns, 1985-86; The Cradle Will Rock, 1986 (Emmy nomination), Minolta Tng. series Minolta Info. Network, 1980-81; dir. Citibank, 1984, N.J. Bell (AT&T), 1985; dir. Victorian Cape May A Video Visit to a Town out of Time, 1988 (Bronze medal Houston Film Festival), dir. Pitney Bowes Copier Intro 1992, Time Warner Cable 1991; producer, writer: Mt. Washington Valley, A Video Visit in Four Seasons, 1990; Actor: Music Video by Little Texas What Might Have Been, 1993. Mayor, City of Cape May, N.J., 1972-76; founding mem., 3-term pres. Mid-Atlantic Center for Arts. Served with USN, 1943-45. Mem. Dirs. Guild Am.

MINOGUE, JOHN P., academic administrator, priest, educator; b. Chgo.. B in Philosophy, St. Mary's Sem.; MDiv, Deandreis Inst. Theology, 1972; M in Theology, DePaul U., 1975; D in Ministry, St. Mary of the Lake Sem., 1987. Ordained Vincentian priest, 1972. Vincentian priest Congregation of the Mission; instr. theology, dir. clin. pastoral placement programs St. Thomas Sem., Denver, 1972-76; instr. grad. theology, asst. then acad. dean DeAndreis Inst., 1976-83; pres. DePaul U., Chgo., 1993—; trustee DePaul U., 1991—; bd. mems. DePaul U. Corp., 1981-91; adj. prof. Sch. New Learning DePaul U., 1984—; instr. law and med. ethics Coll. Law DePaul U., 1989—; asst. prof. clin. ob.-gyn. Northwestern U.; instr. health care ethics St. Joseph Coll. Nursing, Joliet, Ill., Northwestern Sch. Nursing, Chgo.; cons. nat. heatlh care ethics, patient decision-making. Office: De Paul U 25 E Jackson Blvd Chicago IL 60604

MINOGUE, ROBERT BROPHY, retired nuclear engineer; b. Covington, Ky., Jan. 31, 1928; s. Joseph and Catherine Ann (Brophy) M.; m. Marie Joan Clarke, June 12, 1954; children: Patrick, Margaret, Marie, Francis. B.S., Thomas More Coll., 1949; M.S., U. Cin., 1951; grad., Oak Ridge Sch. Reactor Tech., 1952. Registered profl. engr., Calif. Nuclear engr., then head nuclear tech. sect. naval reactors br. AEC, Washington, 1952-56; head research reactor design and enngring., then head nuclear power plant engring. sect. Gen. Atomic div. Gen. Dynamics Corp., 1957-67; chief spl. projects br. div. reactor standards AEC, Washington, 1967-72, asst. dir., then dep. dir. regulatory standards, 1972-74; dir. office standards devel. Nuclear Regulatory Commn., Washington, 1975-80, dir. office research, 1980-86; pvt. practice Temecula, Calif., 1986—; U.S. mem. sr. adv. group Safety Standards IAEA, 1974-86; mem. Com. on Interagy. Radiation Research and Policy Coordination, 1982-86. Author: Reactor Shielding Design Manual, 1956; patentee: Triga Research Reactor. Served with AUS, 1946-48. Recipient Bernard F. Langer award, ASME, 1982. Mem. ASTM (dir. 1975-76, 77-80). Roman Catholic. Home and Office: 29743 Marhill Cir Temecula CA 92591-1809

MINOR, CHARLES DANIEL, lawyer; b. Columbus, Ohio, May 28, 1927; s. Walter Henry and Helen Margaret (Bergman) M.; m. Mary Jo Klinker, Dec. 27, 1950; children: Daniel, Amy. B.S. in Bus. Administrn, Ohio State U., 1950, J.D. summa cum laude, 1952. Bar: Ohio 1952. Mem. firm Vorys, Sater, Seymour and Pease, Columbus, 1952—, ptnr., 1957-93, of counsel, 1993—; bd. dirs. Inland Products, Inc., Worthington Industries, Inc. Served with USNR, 1945-46. Mem. Columbus, Ohio State bar assn. Republican. Clubs: Scioto Country, The Golf, The Columbus, Double Eagle. Office: Vorys Sater Seymour & Pease 52 E Gay St Columbus OH 43215-3161

MINOR, GEORGE GILMER, JR., drug and hospital supply company executive; b. 1912; married. BS, Va. Mil. Inst., 1934. With Owens & Minor, Inc., Richmond, 1934—, sec., treas., 1940-41, v.p. 1941-47, pres., 1947-78, chief exec. officer, from 1947, chmn., 1978—, also bd. dirs. Office: Owens & Minor Inc 4800 Cox Rd Glen Allen VA 23060-6292*

MINOR, GEORGE GILMER, III, drug and hospital supply company executive; b. 1940; married. BA, Va. Mil. Inst., 1963; MBA, U. Va., 1966. With Owens & Minor, Inc., Richmond, Va., 1963—, mgr. sales Acme Candy Co. div., 1966-68, mgr. retail mktg., 1968-73, div. mgr. wholesale drug br.,

1973-77, v.p., 1977-80, exec. v.p., 1980-81, pres., chmn., CEO, 1981—, also bd. dirs. Office: Owens & Minor Med Inc 4800 Cox Rd Glen Allen VA 23060

MINOR, JOSEPH EDWARD, civil engineer, educator; b. Corpus Christi, Tex., June 2, 1938; s. William Smoot Jr. and Irene (Schiller) M.; m. Treva Ann Edmiston, Sept. 3, 1960; children: Joseph Edward Jr., Sharon Diane. BSCE, Tex. A&M U., 1959, M of Engring., 1960; PhD, Tex. Tech U., 1974. Registered profl. engr., Tex., Mo., Fla. Sr. rsch. engr. Southwest Research Inst., San Antonio, 1962-69; P. Whitfield Horn prof. Tex. Tech U., Lubbock, 1969-88; Thomas Reese prof., chmn. dept. civil engring. U. Mo., Rolla, 1988-93; pres. Insulating Glass Cert. Council, N.Y., 1986-89. Contbr. articles to profl. jours. Served with USAR. Recipient Disting. Engr. award Tex. Tech U., 1989; Nat. Def. fellow, 1959-60; Fulbright scholar, 1978. Fellow ASCE (pres. Tex. sect. 1984-85); mem. Nat. Soc. Profl. Engrs., Am. Meteorol. Soc. Presbyterian. Avocation: fishing. Office: Joseph E Minor PE Consulting Engineer PO Box 603 Rockport TX 78381-0603

MINOR, MARILYN T., engineering company executive. BS, Am. U.; postgrad., So. Ill. U. Pres. Mitech Inc., Rockville, Md., 1984—. Office: Mitech Inc 9430 Key West Ave 100 Rockville MD 20850*

MINOR, RALEIGH COLSTON, management consultant; b. Charlottesville, Va., June 3, 1936; s. Charles Venable and Louise (Minetree) M.; m. Nancy Ettinger, Oct. 12, 1963; children: Eves Scott Minetree, Catherine Colston. BA in Econs., U. Va., 1958, MBA in Fin., 1960. Cert. mgmt. cons. With NCNB Charlotte, N.C., 1961-63; sales rep. IBM, Balt., 1963-65; various positions C&O/B&O R.R., Clev., Balt., 1965-69; v.p., chief fin. officer Info. Industries, Inc., Phila., 1969-71; chief fin. officer Quechee (Vt.) Lakes Corp., 1971-73, Hope Products, Inc., Fitchburg, Mass., 1973-75; pres. Standard Pyroxoloid Corp., Fitchburg, 1975-76; prin. Pace Cons. Group, Hartford, Conn., 1976-86; prin., founder, treas. Allomet Ptnrs. Ltd., N.Y., Ga., 1986—; chief operating officer Cuisinarts, Stamford, 1989-90; guest lectr. Darden Sch. U. Va., 1986-91. Contbr. articles to profl. jours. Dir. LUK, Inc., Fitchburg, 1975-80. Lt. U.S. Army, 1961. Mem. Turnaround Mgmt. Assn. (founder), Inst. Mgmt. Cons., Newcomen Soc. U.S., The Landings Club. Episcopalian. Avocations: reading, bridge, tennis, golf. Office: Allomet Ptnrs Ltd 325 E 77th St New York NY 10021

MINOR, ROBERT ALLEN, lawyer; b. Washington, Oct. 20, 1948; s. Robert Walter and Joan (Allen) M.; m. Sue Ellyn Blose, June 13, 1981; children: Robert Barratt, Sarah Allen. AB in English, Duke U., 1970; JD, Ohio State U., 1975. Bar: Ohio 1975, U.S. Dist. Ct. (so. dist.) Ohio 1976, D.C. 1979. Assoc. Vorys, Sater, Seymour & Pease, Columbus, Ohio, 1975-82, ptnr., 1982—. Author seminar articles. With U.S. Army, 1970-72. Mem. ABA, Ohio Bar Assn., Columbus Bar Assn., Athletic Club Columbus, Scioto Country Club. Republican. Presbyterian. Office: Vorys Sater Seymour & Pease PO Box 1008 52 E Gay St Columbus OH 43216-1008

MINOR, ROBERT WALTER, lawyer; b. Columbus, Ohio, Dec. 15, 1919; s. Walter Henry and Helen Margaret (Bergman) M.; m. Joan Allen, Sept. 13, 1947; children—Robert Allen, Mary Ann, Emily, Julia. B.A., Ohio State U., 1940, J.D. summa cum laude, 1948. Bar: Ohio 1949, D.C. 1977, U.S. Supreme Ct. 1952. Asst. counsel Senate Investigating Com., 1948-49; adminstrv. asst. U.S. Senator John W. Bricker, 1949-53; apptd. 1st asst. dep. atty. gen. Washington, 1953; apptd. commr. ICC, 1956; v.p. law N.Y. Central R.R., 1958-67, v.p. exec. dept., 1967-68; sr. v.p. Penn Central Co., 1968-70; counsel Vorys, Sater, Seymour & Pease, Columbus, 1971-73, 90—; ptnr. Vorys, Sater, Seymour & Pease, 1974-90. Lt. col. inf. U.S. Army, 1942-46. Decorated Bronze Star, Purple Heart; recipient Centennial Achievement award Ohio State U., 1970. Mem. ABA, Fed. Bar Assn., Internat. Bar Assn., Ohio State Bar Assn., Empire State C. of C. (pres.), Ohio C. of C. (chmn.), Scioto Country Club (Columbus), Athletic Club (Columbus), Army and Navy Club (Washington), Wilderness Country Club (Naples, Fla.). Order of Coif, Phi Delta Phi, Beta Theta Pi. Republican. Mem. Ref. Ch. Am. (deacon). Home: 2384 W Lane Ave Columbus OH 43221-3602 Office: 52 E Gay St Columbus OH 43215-3108

MINOR, RONALD RAY, minister; b. Aliceville, Ala., Nov. 3, 1944; s. Hershel Ray and Minnie Ozell (Goodson) M.; m. Gwendolyn Otella Newsome, July 25, 1970; 1 child, Rhonda Rene. BA in Ministerial, Southeastern Bible Coll., 1971, BA in Secondary Edn., 1973; DDiv, Southern Bible Coll., 1984. Ordained to ministry Penecostal Ch. of God, 1968. Gen. sec., treas. Pentecostal Ch. of God, Joplin, Mo., 1979—; dist. supt. Pentecostal Ch. of God, Philadelphia, Miss., 1975-79; pastor Pentecostal Ch. of God, Bartow, Fla., Orient Park Tabernacle, Tampa, Fla.; pres. Pentecostal Young People's Assn., Fla. and Miss.; sec. Gen. Bd. Pentecosatal Ch. of God, Joplin, 1979; bd. dirs. Nat. assn. Evangs., Wheaton, Ill., 1981—; adv. coun. Am. Bible Soc., N.Y.C., 1979—; sec. Commn. Chaplains, Washington, 1991—. Home: 2625 E 13th St Joplin MO 64801-5353 Office: Pentecostal Ch of God 4901 Pennsylvania Ave Joplin MO 64804-4947

MINOW, JOSEPHINE BASKIN, civic worker; b. Chgo., Nov. 3, 1926; d. Salem N. and Bessie (Sampson) Baskin; m. Newton N. Minow, May 29, 1949; children: Nell, Martha, Mary. BS, Northwestern U., 1948. Asst. to advt. dir. Mandel Brothers Dept. Store, Chgo., 1948-49; tchr. Francis W. Parker Sch., Chgo., 1949-50; vol. in civil and charitable activities, 1950—; bd. dirs. Juvenile Protective Assn., Chgo., 1958—; pres. Juvenile Protective Assn., 1973-75; bd. dirs. Parnham Trust, Beaminster, Dorset, Eng. Founder, coord. Children's div. Hospitality and Info. Svc., Washington, 1961-63; mem. Caucus Com., Glencoe, Ill., 1965-69; co-chmn. spl. study on juvenile justice Chgo. Community Trust, 1978-80; chmn. Know Your Chgo., 1980-83; bd. dirs. Chgo. Coun. Fgn. Rels.; trustee Chgo. Hist. Soc., Ravinia Festival Assn.; mem. women's bd. Field Mus., U. Chgo.; founding mem., v.p. women's bd. Northwestern U., 1978; bd. govs. Chgo. Symphony, 1966-73, 76—; mem. Citizens Com. Juvenile Ct. of Cook County; exec. com. Northwestern U. Libr. Coun., 1974—. Recipient spl. award Chgo. Sch. and Workshop for Retarded, 1975, Children's Guardian award Juvenile Protective Assn., 1993. Mem. Hebrew Immigrant Aid Soc. (bd. dirs. 1977—, award 1988), Casino Club, Friday Club, Northmoor Country Club. Democrat. Jewish. Office: Chgo Hist Soc Clark St at North Ave Chicago IL 60614

MINOW, MARTHA L., law educator; b. 1954. AB, U. Mich., 1975; EdM, Harvard U., 1976; JD, Yale U., 1979. Bar: Mass. 1981. Law clk. to presiding justice U.S. Ct. Appeals (D.C. cir.), 1979-80; law to Assoc. Justice Thurgood Marshall U.S. Supreme Ct., 1980-81; asst. prof. Harvard U., Cambridge, Mass., 1981-86, prof., 1986—. Trustee, judge Baker Guidance Ctr., 1983—; bd. dirs. ABF, 1985—. Mem. Law and Soc. Assn. Faculty, Brandeis U. Club. Office: Harvard U Law Sch Cambridge MA 02138

MINOW, NEWTON NORMAN, lawyer; b. Milw., Jan. 17, 1926; s. Jay A. and Doris (Stein) M.; m. Josephine Baskin, May 29, 1949; children: Nell, Martha, Mary. B.S., Northwestern U., 1949, J.D., 1950, LL.D. (hon.), 1965; LL.D. (hon.), U. Wis., Brandeis U., 1963, Columbia Coll., 1972, Govs. State U., 1984, De Paul U., 1989, RAND Grad. Sch., 1993; hon. degree, U. Notre Dame, 1994. Bar: Wis. 1950, Ill. 1950. With firm Mayer, Brown & Platt, Chgo., 1950-51, 53-55; law clk. to chief justice Fred. M. Vinson, 1951-52; adminstrv. asst. to Ill. Gov. Stevenson, 1952-53; spl. asst. to Adlai E. Stevenson in presdl. campaign, 1952, 56; ptnr. firm Stevenson, Rifkind & Wirtz, Chgo., N.Y.C. and Washington, 1955-61; chmn. FCC, Wash., 1961-63; exec. v.p., gen. counsel of the Ency. Brit., Chgo., 1963-65; ptnr. Sidley & Austin, Chgo., 1965-91, of counsel, 1991—; trustee, past chmn. bd. Rand Corp.; past chmn. Chgo. Ednl. TV, now hon. chmn.; chmn. pub. rev. bd. Arthur Andersen & Co., 1974-83; bd. dirs. Aon Corp., Foote, Cone & Belding Comm. Inc., Tribune Co. Sara Lee Corp., AON Corp., Manpower, Inc.; chmn. bd. trustees Carnegie Corp. of N.Y.; Annenberg Univ. prof. comm. policy and law Northwestern U., 1987—; dir. Annenberg Washington Program, 1987—. Author: Equal Time: The Private Broadcasters and the Public Interest, 1964; co-author: Presidential Television, 1973, Electronics and the Future, 1977, For Great Debates, 1987; contbr.: As We Knew Adlai. Trustee Notre Dame U., 1964-77, 83—, Mayo Found., 1973-81; trustee Northwestern U., 1975-87, life trustee, 1987—; co-chmn. presdl. debates LWV, 1976, 80; bd. govs. Pub. Broadcasting Svc., 1973-80, chmn. bd., 1978-80; chmn. bd. overseers Jewish Theol. Sem., 1974-77; trustee Chgo. Orchestral Assn., 1975-87, life trustee, 1987—. Served with AUS, 1944-46. Named

1 of Am.'s 10 Outstanding Young Men 1961; recipient George Foster Peabody Broadcasting award, 1961; Ralph Lowell award, 1982. Fellow Am. Bar Found., Am. Acad. Arts and Scis.; mem. ABA, Ill. Bar Assn., Chgo. Bar Assn., Northwestern U. Alumni Assn. (Alumni medal 1978), Comml. Club (pres. 1978-88), Chgo. Club, Century Club (N.Y.C.). Democrat. Office: Sidley & Austin 1 First Nat Pla Chicago IL 60603 Office: Carnegie Corporation NY 437 Madison Avenue New York NY 10022

MINSHALL, DREXEL DAVID, retired manufacturing company executive; b. Bridgeport, Nebr., Nov. 1, 1917; s. Charles D. and Minnie C. (Nordell) M.; m. Betty Jane Tesdell, Feb. 12, 1938 (dec. June 1971); children—Drexel David, Carol J. Minshall Preston; m. Roylynn Hurlburt McAllister, Apr. 19, 1974. Student, Colo. U., 1934-38. Sales mgr. Gates Rubber Co., Denver, 1939-61; v.p. mktg. Perfect Circle Corp., Hagerstown, Ind., 1961-65; pres. Dana Parts Co. div. Dana Corp., Toledo, Ohio, 1965-67, group v.p., 1967-73, sr. group v.p., 1973-79; pres. Service Parts Worldwide, 1979-81; chmn. bd. Dana Western Hemisphere Trade Corp., Toledo, 1970-81; dir. Dana World Trade Corp., Ludwig Motors Corp., Corp. HZ, Caracas, Venezuela, Arcamsa, Rosario, Argentina, Brown Bros. Ltd., London, Eng.; pres. Double D Mktg. Corp. Bd. dirs. Community Chest, 1972-75; trustee Toledo Boys Club, 1967-82. Mem. Automotive Service Industries Assn. (past pres.), Automotive Hall of Fame (past chmn.), Automotive Acad., Nat. Inst. Automotive Service Excellence (bd. dirs. 1972-86, past chmn.), Motor Automotive Parts Assn. (bd. dirs. mfrs. council 1971-81, past chmn.), Motor and Equipment Mfrs. Assn. (product v.p. 1972-75), Alpha Tau Omega. Clubs: Toledo, Inverness; Atlantis Golf (Fla.). Lodges: Masons, Shriners. Contbr. articles to profl. jours. Home: 620 Estates Way Atlantis FL 33462

MINSKER, ROBERT STANLEY, consultant, former industrial relations executive; b. Pitts. Jan. 1, 1911; s. Theodore Kühne and Isabella Lavinia (Trumbor) M.; BS, U. Ill., 1934; postgrad. Pa. State U., 1938-39; m. Marion Elizabeth Warner, May 29, 1937; children: Norma (Mrs. Leo Jerome Brown II), Robert S., James D. With Owens-Ill., Inc., Toledo, Ohio, 1934-76, pers. dir. Clarion (Pa.) plant, 1936-40, per. dir. Columbus (Ohio) plant, 1940-44, mgr. indsl. rels. Alton, 1945-72, adminstr. workmen's compensation, safety and health Ill. and pub. affairs Ill. Plants, 1972-76; dir. Germania Fin. Corp., 1963-82, Germania Bank 1953-82, hon. dir., 1982-91; assoc. faculty So. Ill. U., 1959-64; bd. dirs., chief exec. officer Midwestern Comm. Inc. Lectr., cons. Chmn. Madison County Savs. Bond Campaign, 1959-61; active Boy Scouts Am.; pres. Piasa Bird Council, 1949-51, mem. exec. bd., 1952-90; mem. grievance com. panel State of Ill. Dept. Pers., 1967-80; vice chmn. Higher Edn. Coordinating Council Met. St. Louis, 1966-70; founder Board Pride, Inc., 1966—. Mem. Bd. Edn., 1957-70, pres. 1961-70. Bd. dirs., treas., sec., exec. com. Alton Meml. Hosp., 1969-88, dir. emeritus 1988—, bd. dirs. Alton Meml. Hosp. Found., 1986-91; Jr. Achievement, United Fund.; bd. dirs. Community Chest, v.p. 1949-54, 61-66, gen. chmn., 1949-50; adminstr., sec., vice chmn. Alton Found., 1955—; trustee Lewis and Clark Community Coll., sec. bd., 1970-77; bd. dirs. McKendree Coll., 1981—; mem. pres. council U. Ill. Found., Alton Police Chief Adv. Com., 1994—. Recipient Silver Beaver award Boy Scouts of Am., 1951, Achievement award U.S. Treasury Dept., 1951, Hall of Fame award Piasa Bird Council, 1969, Alton Citizens' award, 1988, Southwestern Ill. Leadership Council award, 1989, Lovejoy Human Rights award, 1989, Pride Outstanding Citizen award, 1988; named to Lewis and Clark Hall of Fame, 1987, Impact Community Svc. award, 1992. Mem. Alton C. of C. (chmn. pub. rels. 1951-54), U. Ill. Varsity "I" Assn., U. Ill. Alumni Assn., Nature Conservation Assn. (a founder), Acacia, Alpha Phi Omega. Methodist. Clubs: Masons, (32 deg.), K.T., Shriners. Home: 2018 Chapin Pl Alton IL 62002-4631

MINSKY, MARVIN LEE, mathematician, educator; b. N.Y.C., Aug. 9, 1927; s. Henry and Fannie (Reyser) M.; m. Gloria Anna Rudisch, July 30, 1952; children: Margaret, Henry, Juliana. B.A., Harvard U., 1950; Ph.D., Princeton U., 1954. Mem. Harvard Soc. Fellows, 1954-57; with Lincoln Lab., MIT, 1957-58, prof. math. 1958-61, prof. elec. engring., 1961—, Donner prof. sci., 1974-90, dir. artificial intelligence group MAC project, from 1958, dir. artificial intelligence lab., 1964-74; Toshiba prof. media arts and scis. MIT, 1990—. Author: Computation, 1967, Semantic Information Processing, 1968 (with S. Papert) Perceptrons, 1969, rev. eidt., 1987, The Society of Mind, 1985, (with H. Harrison) The Turing Option, 1992. Served with USNR, 1945-46. Recipient Turing award Assn. for Computing Machinery, 1970, Japan prize Sci. and Tech. Found., Japan, 1990, Internat. Joint Conf. on Artificial Intelligence Rsch. Excellence award, 1991. Fellow IEEE; mem. NAE, NAS, Am. Acad. Arts and Scis. Office: MIT Media Lab Cambridge MA 02139-4307

MINTER, DAVID LEE, English literature educator; b. Midland, Tex., Mar. 20, 1935; s. Kenneth Cruse and Frances (Hennessey) M.; m. Cynthia Caroline Sewell, Dec. 22, 1957; children: Christopher Sewell, Frances Elizabeth. B.A., N. Tex. State U., 1957, M.A., 1959; B.D., Yale U., 1961, Ph.D., 1965. Univ. lectr. Hamburg (W. Ger.) U., 1965-66; lectr. Yale U., 1966-67; asst. prof. Rice U., Houston, 1967-69, assoc. prof., 1969-74, prof., 1974-80; prof. English Emory U., Atlanta, 1981-89, Asa G. Candler prof. Am. lit., 1989-90, dean Coll. Arts and Scis., 1981-90, v.p. arts and scis., 1984-90; Libbie Shearn Moody prof. English Rice U., Houston, 1990—. Author: The Interpreted Design as a Structural Principle in American Prose, 1969, William Faulkner: His Life and Work, 1980, A Cultural History of the American Novel: Henry James to William Faulkner, 1994; editor: Twentieth-Century Interpretations of Light in August, 1969, The Norton Critical Edit. of the Sound and the Fury, 1987, 93; co-editor: The Harper American Literature, 1986, 93, The Columbia Literary History of the United States, 1987; also articles and revs. Fulbright Travel fellow, 1966; Nat. Endowment for Humanities fellow, 1969-70; Am. Council Learned Socs. grantee, 1975; Fred Harris Daniels fellow, 1980. Mem. MLA, Am. Lit. Group, Am. Studies Assn., Phi Beta Kappa. Methodist. Home: 5 Sunset Blvd Houston TX 77005-1836 Office: Rice U Dept English PO Box 1892 Houston TX 77251-1892

MINTER, EDGAR FREDERICK, industrial executive; b. Pottstown, Pa., Apr. 9, 1935; s. Edgar F. and Kathryn E. (Wendling) M.; m. Barbara H. Craig, July 2, 1937; children: Edgar III, Craig. BSME, Lehigh U., 1957. Product mgr. turbocompressor div. Joy Mfg. Co., Buffalo, 1966-79, gen. mgr. turbocompressor div., 1979-86, pres. IC group, 1986-88; pres. turbocompressor div. Cooper Industries, Buffalo, 1988—. Mem. Am. Soc. Mech. Engrs., Brookfield C. of C. (Clarence, N.Y.), Tau Beta Pi. Republican. Lutheran. Avocations: skiing, golf. Office: Cooper Industries Turbocompressor Div 3101 Broadway St Buffalo NY 14227-1034

MINTER, JERRY BURNETT, electronic component company executive, engineer; b. Ft. Worth, Oct. 31, 1913; s. Claude Joe and Roxie (Ayers) M.; m. Monica Rose Hanlon, Mar. 2, 1940; children: Claude, Mark, Bryon, Claire, Maureen. BSEE, MIT, 1934. Engr., Boonton (N.J.) Radio Corp., 1935-36, Ferris Instruments Co., Boonton, 1936-39; v.p., chief engr. Measurements Corp., Boonton, 1939-53; pres. Components Corp., Denville, N.J., 1946—. Contbr. numerous articles to tech. jours.; patentee in field. Pilot, CAP, Morristown, N.J., 1947-50. Fellow IEEE (life, past chmn. no. N.J. sect.), Audio Engring. Soc. (past pres.), Radio Club Am. (life, pres. emeritus, past pres., Armstrong Medal 1968); mem. Am. Soc. for Metals (life), Am. Inst. Aero. and Astronautics, N.Y. Acad. Scis., Soc. Motion Picture TV Engrs. (life), Internat. Soc. Photo-Optical Instrumentation Engrs., Quiet Birdmen. Home: 48 Normandy Heights Rd Morristown NJ 07960-4613 Office: Components Corp 6 Kinsey Pl Denville NJ 07834

MINTER, PHILIP CLAYTON, retired communications company executive; b. Sydney, Australia, Aug. 9, 1928; cme to U.S., 1957; s. Roy Dixon and Adeline Claire (Bradly) M.; m. Mary Bashford Schettler, Jan. 24., 1959; children: Elizabeth C., Margaret S. BSc with honours, U. Sydney, 1951; MS, U. Wyo., 1958; PhD, U. Wis., 1960. Tchr. King's Sch., Parramatta, Australia, 1951-57; mng. dir. Motivational Rsch. Assocs., Sydney, 1960-62; dir. rsch. Nat. Fund Raising Coun., Sydney, 1962-65; project dir. USDA, Ft. Collins, Colo., 1965-67; chief info. pesticides program USPHS, Atlanta, 1967-68; mgr. data bases div. Pa. Rsch. Assocs., Phila., 1968-70; pres. Ednl. Communications Inc., King of Prussia, Pa., 1970-94; pres. Svc. Tng. Ltd., Kenilworth, Eng., 1976-88; cons. Westinghouse Learning Corp., 1972. Author: Handbook for Pesticide-Chemicals Program Coordinators, 1967. Recipient Terry Magill award Australia Soc., N.Y., 1994. Mem. Soc. Automotive Engrs., Sci. Rsch. Soc. Am., Royal Heritage Soc. (bd. dirs.), U.

Wis. Alumni Assn. (bd. dirs. Delaware Valley br.), Australian/Am. C. of C. Phila. (exec. dir.), Union League, Brit. Officers Club Phila. (pres. 1992-93), Sloane Club (London), Sigma Xi. Republican. Episcopalian. Home: RR 5 Box 352 Malvern PA 19355-9800 Office: PO Box 902 Southeastern PA 19399-0902

MINTER, STEVEN ALAN, foundation executive, social worker; b. Akron, Oct. 23, 1938; s. Lawrence L. and Dorothy (Knox) M.; m. Dolores Kreicher, Apr. 8, 1961; children: Michele, Caroline, Robyn. BA in Edn., Baldwin-Wallace Coll., 1960, LHD (hon.), 1974; M in Social Adminstrn., Case Western Reserve U., 1963, LHD (hon.), 1989; LHD (hon.), Findlay (Ohio) Coll., 1984, Kent (Ohio) State U., 1988, Oberlin Coll., 1988, Lake Erie Coll., 1990. Lic. social worker. Dir. Cuyahoga County Welfare Dept., Cleve., 1969-70; commr. Mass. Dept. Pub. Welfare, Boston, 1970-75; assoc. dir., program officer The Cleve. Found., 1975-80, 1981-83, exec. dir., 1984—; under sec. U.S. Dept. Edn., Washington, 1980-81; mem. bd. overseers Florence Heller Grad. Sch. Advanced Studies in Social Welfare, Brandeis U.; bd. dirs. Goodyear Tire and Rubber Co., Akron, Ohio, Soc. Corp., Cleve., Consol. Natural Gas, Pitts. Rubbermaid Inc., Wooster, Ohio. Contbr. articles to profl. jours. Trustee Coll. of Wooster, Ohio, 1977—, Found. Ctr. 1990—, Leadership Cleve.; bd. dirs. Am. Assn. for Higher Edn., 1993—, Cleve. Initiative for Edn., 1991—. Recipient Disting. Svc. award Jr. C. of C. of Cleve., 1969, Disting. Svc. award Case Western Res. U. Sch. Applied Social Svcs., 1985, Ohio Govs. award, 1991; named Black Profl. of the Yr., Cleve. Black Profl. Assn., 1985. Mem. Nat. Acad. Pub. Adminstrs., NAACP (life), Assn. Black Found. Execs., NASW, Pepper Pike (Ohio) Club, Union. Democrat. Presbyterian. Home: 2878 Woodbury Rd Cleveland OH 44120-2426 Office: The Cleve Found 1422 Euclid Ave Ste 1400 Cleveland OH 44115-2001

MINTO, CLIVE, retail company executive; b. Cardiff, Wales, Aug. 17, 1945; arrived in Can., 1969; s. Clifford and Doris (Parkhouse) M.; m. Frances Betty Lloyd, Sept. 23, 1967; children: Anna, Emma. B.S. in math. and stats. with honors, U. Birmingham, Eng., 1966. Mktg. exec. Rank Xerox (Europe), London, 1966-69; account exec. Maclaren Advt., Toronto, Ont., Can., 1969-70; mgr. personal products div. Lever Detergents, Toronto, 1970-77; dir. mktg. Pepsi-Cola Can. Ltd., Toronto, 1977-80, pres., chief exec. officer, 1983-87; mng. dir. Pepsi-Cola Africa, Johannesburg, Republic of South Africa, 1980-81; v.p. No. European region Pepsico Internat., London, 1981-83; exec. v.p. Can. Tire Corp. Ltd., Toronto, 1987—. Office: Can Tire Corp Ltd, 2180 Yonge St, Toronto, ON Canada M4P 2V8

MINTON, DWIGHT CHURCH, manufacturing company executive; b. North Hills, N.Y., Dec. 17, 1934; s. Henry Miller and Helen Dwight (Church) M.; m. Marian Haven Haines, Aug. 4, 1956; children: Valerie Haven, Daphne Forsyth, Henry Brewster. B.A., Yale U., 1959; M.B.A., Stanford U., 1961. With Church & Dwight Co., Inc., Princeton, N.J., 1961—; asst. v.p. Church & Dwight Co., Inc., 1964-66, v.p., 1966-67, pres., 1967-81, chief exec. officer, 1969—, chmn., 1981—, dir., 1966—; bd. dirs. Crane Corp., Medusa Cement Corp., Chem. Bank N.J., N.A., First Brands Corp. Trustee Atlanta U., 1971-88, Morehouse Coll., 1971—, Spelman Coll., 1971-80; v.p., bd. dirs. Greater Yellowstone Coalition, 1991—. With U.S. Army, 1956-57. Mem. Chem. Mfrs. Assn. (bd. dirs. 1980-83), Grocery Mfrs. Am. (dir. 1983-87). Clubs: Seawanhaka Corinthian Yacht, Racquet and Tennis, Yale, Links. Office: Church & Dwight Co Inc 469 N Harrison St Princeton NJ 08543-5297

MINTON, JERRY DAVIS, lawyer, former banker; b. Ft. Worth, Aug. 13, 1928; s. Robert Bruch and Anna Elizabeth (Davis) M.; m. Martha Drew Fields, Nov. 28, 1975; children: Marianne, Martha, John Morgan. B.B.A., U. Tex., Austin, 1949, J.D.; 1960; grad. cert., Nat. Trust Sch., Northwestern U., 1960. Of counsel Michener, Larimore, Swindle, Whitaker, Flowers et al., 1991—; vice chmn. 1st Nat. Bank Ft. Worth, 1982-87, 88; chmn. & CEO 1st City Bank Ft. Worth, 1986-91. Mem. Ft. Worth Air Power Council. Pilot USAF, 1951-55, pilot Tex. Air N.G., 1955-57; capt. USAFR Ret.). Decorated D.F.C., Air medal with 3 oak leaf clusters. Mem. State Bar Tex., Tarrant County Bar Assn., Ft. Worth C. of C. Found. (trustee), Mil. Order World Wars, SAR, Soc. Descendants of George Washington's Army at Valley Forge, Mil. Order Stars and Bars, Sons of Confederate Vets., Ft. Worth Club, River Crest Country Club, Breakfast Club, Sigma Iota Epsilon, Phi Delta Phi. Episcopalian. Home: 5404 El Dorado Dr Fort Worth TX 76107-3236 Office: 301 Commerce St Ste 3500 Fort Worth TX 76102-4135

MINTON, JOHN DEAN, historian, educator; b. Cadiz, Ky., July 29, 1921; s. John Ernest and Daisy Dean (Wilson) M.; m. Betty Jo Redick, June 8, 1947; children—John Dean, James Ernest. A.B. in Edn, U. Ky., 1943, M.A. in History, 1947; Ph.D., Vanderbilt U., 1959. Instr. history U. Miami, Fla., 1951; tchr. Broward County Pub. Sch. System, U. Miami evening div., 1951-53; prin. Trigg County (Ky.) High Sch., 1953-58; prof. history Western Ky. U., Bowling Green, 1958-86, ret., dean Grad. Coll., 1964-71, v.p. for adminstrv. affairs, 1970-79, interim pres., 1979, v.p. for student affairs, 1981-86, part-time prof., 1986—. Author: The New Deal in Tennessee, 1932-1938, 1979; contbr. articles to profl. jours. Mem. Gen. Bd. Discipleship, United Meth. Ch.; mem. Louisville Bd. Discipleship; lay speaker Louisville Conf. Meth. Ch.; bd. dirs. Higher Edn. Found., Meth. Ch., Jesse Stuart Found. Served with USNR, 1943-46. Mem. NEA, Ky. Edn. Assn., So. Hist. Assn., Ky. Hist. Soc., Bowling Green C. of C. (bd. dirs.), Civitan Club (pres. Cadiz 1956), Phi Alpha Theta, Phi Eta Sigma, Kappa Delta Pi. Home: 645 Ridgecrest Way Bowling Green KY 42104-3818

MINTON, JOSEPH PAUL, retired safety organization executive; b. Houston, Oct. 20, 1924; s. Joseph Marion and Stella (Fite) M.; m. Nancy Fettig, June 19, 1948; children—Joan M., Michael J., Jean A., Mary B., John E., Diane C. B.S. in Air Transp., Purdue U., 1949; Grad., U.S. Air Force Air Command and Staff Coll., 1958. Commd. 2d lt. U.S. Air Force, 1944, advanced through grades to col., 1966; combat U.S. Air Force, Burma, World War II; assignments in crew, staff and command U.S. Air Force, ret., 1967; v.p. Purdue Airlines Inc., Lafayette, Ind., 1967-68, pres., chief exec. officer, 1969-71; mng. dir., chief exec. officer Saber Air Ltd., Singapore, 1971-73; sr. v.p. Brit. Caledonian Airways, N.Y.C., 1974-76; mng. dir. Nat. Transp. Safety Bd., Washington, 1977-78; exec. dir. Nat. Safety Council, Washington, 1978-88. Decorated D.F.C. with oak leaf cluster, Air medal with 3 oak leaf clusters, 3 battle stars, Air Force Commendation medal with oak leaf cluster. Republican. Roman Catholic. Address: Ste 108 1720 Lake Shore Crest # 15 Reston VA 22090

MINTON, YVONNE FAY, mezzo-soprano; b. Sydney, Australia; d. Robert Thomas and Alice Violet M.; m. William Barclay, Aug. 24, 1965; children—Malcolm Alexander, Alison Elizabeth. Ed., Sydney Conservatorium of Music, 1960-61. Mezzo-soprano with all maj. orchs. in, Australia, 1958-61; moved to, London, 1961, joined, Royal Opera House, Covent Garden, 1965-70, guest artist, Cologne (W. Ger.) Opera, 1969—, U.S. debut as Octavian in Der Rosenkavalier, 1970; appeared, with Lyric Opera, Chgo., 1970, Met. Opera, N.Y.C., 1973, San Francisco Opera, 1974, Paris Opera, 1974, Bayreuth, 1974, Salzburg, 1978; sings regularly with maj. symphony orchs. throughout world, 1968—; recs. include The Knot Garden, 1970, Cosi Fan Tutte, 1971, Lulu, 1979; maj. vocal works include Mahler songs with, Chgo. Symphony. Comdr. Order Brit. Empire, 1980. Hon. mem. Royal Acad. Music. Office: care Ingpen & Williams, 14 Kensington Ct, London England W85DN

MINTZ, ALBERT, lawyer; b. New Orleans, Oct. 19, 1929; s. Morris and Goldie (Goldblum) M.; m. Linda Barnett, Dec. 19, 1954; children—John Morris, Margaret Anne. B.B.A., Tulane U., 1948, J.D., 1951. Bar: La. bar 1951. Since practiced in New Orleans; ptnr. Montgomery, Barnett, Brown, Read, Hammond & Mintz, Hurwitz-Mintz Realty Cos., New Orleans.; bd. dirs. Sunbelt Mfg. Inc., Strauss Distrbrs. Mem. adv. bd. Law Sch. Tulane U.; chmn., dir. adv. bd. Tulane Summer Lyric Tehater; bd. dirs. Tulane Ctr. Stage Talent and Shakespearean Theatre; bd. dirs. Jewish Community Ctr., New Orleans, 1965-72, Jewish Fedn. 1968-73, Home for Jewish Aged, 1968-71, Jewish Family Svc. New Orleans, 1968-72; trustee, bd. mgrs. Touro Infirmary Hosp. and Found.; trustee Jewish Endowment Found.; charter mem. La. Hist. Assn. Mem. ABA, La. Bar Assn. (lectr., pub. on corp., tax, real estate law), New Orleans Bar Assn. (exec. com. 1971-74), Am. Law Inst., U.S. Hist. Assn., New Orleans C. of C. (chmn. com. civic affairs and state legis. 1968-69), Phi Delta Phi, Omicron Delta Kappa, Zeta Beta Tau.

Jewish. Clubs: Internat. House, Plimsoll of Internat. Trade Mart, Petroleum, New Orleans Athletic. Home: 2017 Jefferson Ave New Orleans LA 70115-5618 Office: 3200 Energy Ctr 1100 Poydras St New Orleans LA 70163-3200

MINTZ, DONALD EDWARD, psychologist, educator; b. N.Y.C., July 19, 1932; s. Irving and Pauline Lynore (Arenson) M.; children: Peter Graham, Hayley Ilana. A.B., Columbia U., 1954, Ph.D., 1961. Research assoc. Princeton U., 1959-63; asst. prof. psychology City Coll., CUNY, 1963-67, assoc. prof., 1967-73, chmn. dept., 1971-74, prof., 1973—; acting dean Sch. Architecture and Environ. Studies, 1982-85; pvt. practice psychotheraphy N.Y.C., 1979—. Author: Dynamics of Response, 1965; contbr. articles to profl. jours. Served to lt. USN, 1954-57. NSF predoctoral fellow, 1957. Fellow N.Y. Acad. Sci.; mem. Am. Psychol. Assn., AAAS, Psychonomic Soc., Assn. Advancement Behavior Therapy, Eastern Psychol. Assn.; N.Y. Acad. Scis., Phi Beta Kappa, Sigma Xi. Democrat. Jewish. Club: Stuyvesant Yacht. Home: 10 W 15th St New York NY 10011 Office: CCNY New York NY 10031

MINTZ, HARRY, artist, educator; b. Warsaw, Poland, Sept. 27, 1909; s. Zysman and Rachel Sari (Milgram) M.; m. Rosabelle Truglio, Sept. 1, 1958; children: William Zysman, Sari Rachel. M.F.A., Warsaw Acad. Fine Arts, 1927. Tchr. art Evanston Art Ctr., 1940-70, North Shore Art League, 1950-59; prof. emeritus Art Inst. Chgo.; vis. prof. Washington U., St. Louis, 1954-55; faculty Art Inst. Chgo., 1955-70, now emeritus prof. advanced painting. One man shows, Art Inst. Chgo., Heller Gallery, N.Y.C., Feingarten Galleries, Chgo. and Beverly Hills, Calif., 1961, Ruth Volid Gallery, Chgo., 1986, Galleria del Arte, Guadalajara, Mex., 1987, others; exhibited local, nat., internat. shows, Art Inst. Chgo., 1932—also N.Y. World's Fair, 1940, Whitney Mus. Am. Art, N.Y.C., Pa. Acad. Fine Arts, Carnegie Internat., Pitts., Venice Biennale, Italy, Palace Legion of Honor, San Francisco, Mus. Modern Art, N.Y.C., Old Town Art Fair, 1953-93, 94, WFMT Art Exhbt., 1989, others; represented in permanent collections, Art Inst. Chgo., Whitney Mus., Warsaw Acad. Fine Arts, Mus. Art Tel-Aviv, Mus. Modern Art Rio de Janeiro, Evansville (Ind.) Mus., Notre Dame U., Northwestern U., Columbus U. (Ohio), others. Recipient awards Art Inst. Chgo., 1937, 39, 45, 46, 49, 52, 54, 55, 61, Palace Legion of Honor Nat. Exhbn. San Francisco, 1946, Palace Legion of Honor Nat. Exhbn. U. Chgo., 1953, Palace Legion of Honor Nat. Exhbn. Union League Exhibit, Chgo., 1959, Palace Legion of Honor Nat. Exhbn. Old Orchard, Chgo., 1958-73, Palace Legion of Honor Nat. Exhbn. Sarasota (Fla.) Nat. Exhibit, 1959, others. Mem. Renaissance Soc., Chgo. Soc. Artists, Inc. Home: 429 W Briar Pl Chicago IL 60657-4768

MINTZ, M. J., lawyer; b. Phila., Oct. 29, 1940; s. Arthur and Lillian (Altenberg) M.; children: Robert A., Christine L.; m. Judith E. Held. B.S., Temple U., 1961, J.D., 1968. Bar: D.C.; C.P.A., Pa., D.C. Atty. adv. to judge U.S. Tax Ct., Washington, 1968-70; asst. gen. counsel Cost of Living Council, Washington, 1971-73; ptnr. Dickstein, Shapiro & Morin, Washington, 1973—; adj. prof. George Mason U. Law Sch., Va., 1974-78; adv. Employee Retirement Income Security Act of 1974, Adv. Council, Washington, 1982-85. Contbr. articles to profl. jours. Apptd. by Pres. Reagan to advisory com. Pension Benifit Guaranty Corp., 1987; reapptd. and designated chmn. by Pres. George Bush; rep. candidate Fairfax County Bd. of Suprs., 1971. Fellow Nat. Assn. Watch & Clock Collectors; mem. ABA, Am. Inst. C.P.A.s, Antuquarian Horological Soc. (London). Clubs: Cosmos, Belle Haven Country, Met. Club of Washington. D.C., Chappaquiddick Beach. Avocations: antiquarian horologist.

MINTZ, MARSHALL GARY, lawyer; b. Detroit, May 28, 1947. BA, UCLA, 1968, JD, 1971. Bar: Calif. 1972. Law clk. appellate dept L.A. County Superior Ct., 1971-72; ptnr. Kelly & Lytton, L.A., Calif., 1995—; moderator, panelist Calif. Continuing Edn. of Bar, 1980—; mem. arbitration adminstrv. com. L.A. County Superior Ct., 1979, mem. 1984 Olympics spl. settlement panel. Mem. ABA, State Bar Calif., L.A. County Bar Assn. (arbitrator arbitration and client rels. com. 1978-90), Assn. Bus. Trial Lawyers (bd. govs. 1976-77, program chmn. 1976). Office: Kelly & Lytton Ste 1450 1900 Avenue of the Stars Los Angeles CA 90067

MINTZ, MORTON ABNER, author, former newspaper reporter; b. Ann Arbor, Mich., Jan. 26, 1922; s. William and Sarah (Solomon) M.; m. Anita Inez Franz, Aug. 30, 1946; children—Margaret Ruth, Elizabeth Diane (dec.), Roberta Joan, Daniel Robert. A.B. in Econs, U. Mich., 1943. Reporter St. Louis Star-Times, 1946-50; reporter, asst. city editor St Louis Globe-Democrat, 1951-58; reporter Washington Post, 1958-88. Author: The Therapeutic Nightmare, 1965, By Prescription Only, 1967, The Pill: An Alarming Report, 1969, At Any Cost: Corporate Greed, Women, and the Dalkon Shield, 1985, (with Jerry S. Cohen) America, Inc.: Who Owns and Operates the United States, 1971, Power, Inc.; Public and Private Rulers and How to Make Them Accountable, 1976, (with others) In the Name of Profit: Profiles in Corporate Irresponsiblity, 1972, More Bucks, Less Bang: How the Pentagon Buys Ineffective Weapons, 1983. Recipient Heywood Broun, Raymond Clapper, George Polk awards for journalism, 1962, A.J. Liebling award, 1974, Worth Bingham Meml. award, 1976, Columbia Journalism award, 1983.

MINTZ, NORMAN NELSON, investment banker, educator; b. N.Y.C., Sept. 18, 1934; s. Alexander and Rebecca (Nelson) M.; m. Marcia Lynn Belford, Aug. 27, 1966; children: Geoffrey Belford, Douglas Nelson. AB, Bucknell U., 1955; PhD, NYU, 1966. Asst. gen. mgr. Ross Products Inc., N.Y.C., 1957-59; media analyst Benton & Bowles Inc., N.Y.C., 1960; asst. prof. fin. Syracuse U., 1965-69; asst. prof. econs. Columbia U., N.Y.C., 1968-72; assoc. dean Grad. Sch. Arts and Scis. Columbia U., 1972-77, dep. provost, 1977-80, acting provost, 1978-79, sr. v.p., 1982-85; exec. v.p. for acad. affairs, 1982-89, exec. v.p., ret., 1990—; mng. dir. Loeb Ptnrs. Corp., 1990—; economist U.S.-P.R. Commn. on Status of P.R., 1965-66; bd. dirs. Alcide Corp., Doehler-Jarvis, Sr. Network, Inc., Inncom, Inc., Comm. Mgmt. Sys., Inc., Exxel/Atmos, Inc., Gladwin Corp. Author: Monetary Union and Economic Integration, 1970; contbr. articles to profl. jours. Dir. Conf. on Jewish Social Studies, 1975-94, N.Y.C. Coun. on Econ. Edn., 1993—. Served with Signal Corps U.S. Army, 1955-57. Earhart Found. fellow, 1963-65. Mem. Am. Econ. Assn., Am. Fin. Assn., Royal Econ. Soc., India House Club, Phi Beta Kappa, Omicron Delta Epsilon. Office: care Loeb Ptnrs 61 Broadway New York NY 10006-2704

MINTZ, RICHARD I., federal official; b. Bklyn., Aug. 10, 1961; s. Walter and Sandra (Ullman) M.; m. Helaine Greenfeld, Sept. 1, 1991. BA in Internat. Rels., Union Coll., 1983. Assoc. prodr. CBS News, 1983-85; press. sec. N.E.-Midwest Congrl. Coalition, 1985-86; media dir. Nat. Abortion Rights Action League, 1986-88; v.p. Ogilvy, Adams & Rinehart, 1988-91; dir. staff Hillary Rodham Clinton, dep. mgr. Clinton-Gore Campaign, Calif. 1991-92; dir. comm. Presdl. Inaugural Com., 1992-93; dir. pub. affairs Dept. Transp., Washington, 1993—. Office: Dept Transp Pub Affiars 400 7th St SW Rm 10414 Washington DC 20590

MINTZ, SEYMOUR STANLEY, lawyer; b. Newark, Mar. 7, 1912. A.B., George Washington U., 1933, J.D., 1936. Bar: D.C. 1936. Atty. Office of Undersec. of Treasury, 1937-38, Office of Chief Counsel, IRS, 1938-42; assoc. Hogan & Hartson, Washington, 1946-49; ptnr. Hogan & Hartson, 1949-84, counsel, 1985—. Contbr. articles to profl. jours. Fellow Am. Coll. Tax Counsel; mem. ABA, D.C. Bar Assn., Am. Law Inst., Order of Coif. Office: Hogan & Hartson 555 13th St NW Washington DC 20004-1109

MINTZ, SHLOMO, conductor, violist, violinist; b. Moscow, Oct. 30, 1957; came to U.S., 1974; s. Abraham and Eve (Labko) M.; m. Corina Ciacci; children: Eliav David, Alexander. Diploma, Juilliard Sch. Music, 1979. Violin solo recordings include Violin Concertos by Mendelssohn and Bruch (Grand prix du Disque Diapason d'or), 1981, Complete Sonatas and Partitas for Solo Violin by J.S. Bach, The Miraculous Mandarin-Two Portraits (with Abbado/Chicago Symphony Orchestra) by Bartok, Compositions and Arrangements (with Clifford Benson, piano) by Kreisler, Violin Concerto; also Bruch: Violin Concerto Number 1 (with Abbado/Chgo. Symphony Orchestra) by Mendelssohn, Twenty-Four Caprices by Paganini, Two Violin Concertos (with Abbado/London Symphony Orchestra) by Prokofiev, The Four Seasons (with Stern, Perlman, Mehta) by Vivaldi, Vivaldi violin concertos, Vols. I & II (with Israel Chamber Orch.), 1992, Collection String Symphonies, Vol. III to X, (with Israel Chamber Orch.), 1992, Violin and

Viola Sonatas by Chostakovich (with V. Postnikova); apptd. music advisor, chief condr., soloist Israel Chamber Orch., 1989—. Recipient Premio Accademia Musicale, Chigiana Siena, Italy, 1984. Uses Zahn violin made by Stradivarius, and a Carlo-Guiseppe Testrove viola. Office: ICM Artists Inc 40 W 57th St New York NY 10019*

MINTZ, SIDNEY WILFRED, anthropologist; b. Dover, N.J., Nov. 16, 1922; s. Solomon and Fromme Leah (Tulchin) M.; m. June Mirken, May 1952 (div. Dec. 1962); children: Eric Daniel, Elizabeth Rachel; m. Jacqueline Wei, June 6, 1964. BA, Bklyn. Coll., 1943; PhD, Columbia U., 1951; MA, Yale U., 1963. Mem. faculty dept. anthropology Yale U., New Haven, 1951-74; prof. Yale U., 1963-74; prof. anthropology Johns Hopkins U., Balt., 1974—; vis. prof. anthropology MIT, 1964-65. Princeton U., 1975-76; directeur d'études associé E.P.H.E., Paris, 1970-71; professeur associé Coll. de France, Paris, 1988; editor Yale U. Press Caribbean Series, 1957-74; Lewis Henry Morgan lectr. U. Rochester, 1972; Christian Gauss lectr. Princeton U., 1979; Harry Hoijer lectr. UCLA, 1981; Duijker Found. lectr., Amsterdam, 1988; Rodney lectr. U. Warwick, 1993. Author: (with others) People of Puerto Rico, 1956, Worker in the Cane, The Life History of a Puerto Rican Sugar Cane Worker, 1960, Caribbean Transformations, 1974, Sweetness and Power, 1985, (with Richard Price) The Birth of African-American Culture, 1992. Served with USAAF, 1943-46. Recipient William Clyde DeVane medal Yale U., 1972, Huxley medalist Royal Anthropol. Inst., 1994; named Social Sci. Rsch. Coun. Faculty Rsch. fellow, 1958-59, Guggenheim fellow, 1957, Fulbright fellow, 1966-67, 70-71, NEH fellow, 1978-79, Smithsonian Inst. Regents' fellow, 1986-87. Fellow Am. Anthrop. Assn.; mem. Am. Ethnol. Soc. (v.p., pres.-elect 1967-68), Royal Anthrop. Soc. Gt. Britain and Ireland, Am. Acad. Arts and Scis., Sigma Xi. Office: Johns Hopkins U Dept Anthropology Baltimore MD 21218

MINTZ, STEPHEN ALLAN, real estate company executive, lawyer; b. N.Y.C., May 21, 1943; s. Irving and Anne (Medwick) M.; m. Dale Leibson, June 19, 1966; children: Eric Michael, Jaclyn Leibson. AB, Cornell U., 1965; JD cum laude, Harvard U., 1968. Bar: N.Y. 1969. Assoc. Proskauer, Rose, Goetz & Mendelsohn, N.Y.C., 1968-76, ptnr., 1976-80; v.p. Integrated Resources, Inc., N.Y.C., 1980-84, 1st v.p., 1984-86, sr. v.p., 1986-89, exec. v.p., 1989-94; chmn. Resources Hotel Mgmt. Svc. Inc., 1986-94; pres. Resources High Equity, Inc., 1991-94, Stemin Assocs., Rye, N.Y., 1994—. Mem. ABA, N.Y. State Bar Assn. Democrat. Jewish. Home: 11 Eve Ln Rye NY 10580-4113 Office: Stemin Assocs 11 Eve Ln Rye NY 10580-4113

MINTZ, WALTER, investment company executive; b. Vienna, Austria, Feb. 23, 1929; came to U.S., 1938, naturalized, 1945; s. Maximilian and Ilse (Schueller) M.; m. Sandra Jane Earl, Aug. 27, 1971. B.A., Reed Coll., 1950; postgrad. in econs, Columbia, 1950-51, 53-54. Asso. editor Barrons mag., 1951-53, 54-56; with Shearson Hammill Co., 1956-70, dir. research, 1962-69, exec. v.p. charge investment div., 1965-70; partner Cumberland Assocs., investment mgmt., 1970-85; spl. ltd. ptnr. Cumberland Ptnrs., investment ptnrship., 1982—; bd. dirs. Merrill Lynch Phoenix Fund, Merrill Lynch Fed. Securities Trust, Merrill Lynch Retirement Series Fund. Trustee Reed Coll. 1971—, vice chmn. bd. trustees, 1991—; trustee Manhattan Inst., 1990—, vice chmn., 1994—; bd. dirs. Citizens Union of N.Y.C., 1980—. Mem. N.Y. Soc. Security Analysts (bd. dirs. 1969-75). Home: 2 E 88th St New York NY 10128-0555 Office: Cumberland Assocs 1114 Avenue Of The Americas New York NY 10036-7701

MINTZBERG, HENRY, management educator, researcher, writer; b. Montreal, Que., Can., Sept. 2, 1939; s. Myer and Irene M.; children: Susan, Lisa. B.Eng., McGill U., 1961; B.A., Sir George Williams U., 1962; S.M., M.I.T., 1965, Ph.D., 1968; hon. degree, U. Venice, 1983, U. Lund, 1989, U. Lausanne, 1991, U. Montreal, 1993. Operational research analyst Can. Nat., 1961-63; mem. faculty mgmt. McGill U., Montreal, 1968—, INSEAD, Fontainebleau, France, 1994—; vis. prof. Carnegie-Mellon U., 1973, Universite d'Aix-Marseille, 1974-76, Ecole des Hautes Etudes Commerciales de Montreal, 1977-78, London Bus. Sch., 1990, INSEAD, France, 1992, 93-94. Author: The Nature of Managerial Work, 1973, The Structuring of Organizations, 1979, Power In and Around Organizations, 1983, The Strategy Process, 1988, Mintzberg on Management, 1989, The Rise and Fall of Strategic Planning, 1994; contbr. articles to profl. jours. Fellow Royal Soc. Can., Acad. Mgmt., Internat. Acad. Mgmt.; mem. Strategic Mgmt. Soc. (pres. 1988-91). Office: McGill U Faculty Mgmt, 1001 Sherbrooke W, Montreal, PQ Canada H3A 1G5

MINTZER, DAVID, physics educator; b. N.Y.C., May 4, 1926; s. Herman and Anna (Katz) M.; m. Justine Nancy Klein, June 26, 1949; children: Elizabeth Amy, Robert Andrew. B.S. in Physics, Mass. Inst. Tech., 1945, Ph.D., 1949. Asst. prof. physics Brown U., 1949-55; research asso. Yale U., 1955-56, assoc. prof., dir. lab. marine physics, 1956-62; prof. mech. engring. Northwestern U., Evanston, 1962-91, prof. physics and astronomy, 1968-91, prof. emeritus mech. engring., prof emeritus physics and astronomy, 1991—; assoc. dean McCormick Sch. Engring. and Applied Sci., 1970-73, acting dean, 1971-72, v.p. for rsch., dean sci., 1973-86, spl. asst. to pres., 1986-87, prof. emeritus mech. engring., physics and astronomy, 1991—; mem. mine adv. com. Nat. Acad. Sci.-NRC, 1963-73; mem. Ill. Gov.'s Commn. on Sci. and Tech., 1987-88; mem. adv. bd. Applied Rsch. Lab. Pa. State U., 1976-82, chmn., 1980-81. Contbr. numerous chpts. to books, papers to profl. publs. Trustee EDUCOM interuniv. communications coun., 1975-83, vice chmn., 1977-78, chmn., 1978-81; trustee Adler Planetarium, 1976-92, life trustee, 1992—; bd. dirs. Rsch. Park, Inc., evanston, 1986-92, treas., 1986-91; trustee Ill. Math. and Sci. Acad., 1986—, mem. exec. com., 1989—, chmn. alliance coun., 1991-93; chmn. bd. dirs. Heartland Venture Capital Network, Inc., 1987-90; bd. dirs. Tech. Innovation Ctr., Inc., 1990-92, treas., 1990-92. Fellow Am. Phys. Soc., Acoustical Soc. Am.; mem. ASME, Am. Astron. Soc., Sigma Xi, Tau Beta Pi, Pi Tau Sigma. Research on underwater acoustics and rarefied gas dynamics. Office: Northwestern U Technol Institute Evanston IL 60208

MINUDRI, REGINA URSULA, librarian, consultant; b. San Francisco, May 9, 1937; d. John C. and Molly (Halter) M. B.A., San Francisco Coll. for Women, 1958; M.L.S., U. Calif.-Berkeley, 1959. Reference librarian Menlo Park (Calif.) Pub. Library, 1959-62; regional librarian Santa Clara County (Calif.) Library, 1962-68; project coordinator Fed. Young Adult Library Services Project, Mountain View, Calif., 1968-71; dir. profl. services Alameda County (Calif.) Library, 1971, asst. county librarian, 1972-77; library dir. Berkeley Pub. Library, 1977-94; lectr. U. San Francisco, 1970-72, U. Calif., Berkeley, 1977-81, 91-93; lectr. San Jose State U., 1994—; cons., 1975—; adv. bd. Miles Cutter Ednl., 1992—. Bd. dirs. Cmty. Memory, 1989-91, Berkeley Cmty. Fund, 1994—, chair youth com., 1994—; mem. bd. mgrs. cen. br. Berkeley YMCA, 1988-93. Recipient proclamation Mayor of Berkeley, 1985, 86, 94, Citation of Merit Calif. State Assembly, 1994; named Woman of Yr. Alameda County North chpt. Nat. Women's Polit. Caucus, 1986, Outstanding Alumna U. Calif. Sch. Library and Info. Scis., Berkeley, 1987. Mem. ALA (pres. 1986-87, council 1979-88, 90-94, Grolier award 1974), Calif. Library Assn. (pres. 1981, council 1965-69, 79-82), LWV (dir. Berkeley chpt. 1980-81). Author: Getting It Together, A Young Adult Bibliography, 1970; contbr. articles to publs. including School Library Jour., Wilson Library Bulletin. Office: Reality Mgmt 836 The Alameda Berkeley CA 94707-1916

MINYARD, JAMES PATRICK, JR., chemist, educator; b. Greenwood, Miss., May 11, 1929; s. James Patrick and Mary Louise (Duke) M.; m. Mary Louise Whitesell, Aug. 11, 1956; children: Mary Susan, Thomas James, Barbara Lynn, Carol Ann, William Patrick. B.S. in Chemistry, Miss. State U., 1951, Ph.D. in Organic Chemistry, 1967; postgrad., Calif. Inst. Tech., 1951-52. Field engr. Minyard Well Co., Belzoni, Miss., 1954-58; asst. chemist Miss. State Chem. Lab., Miss. State U. Mississippi State, 1958-59, chemist, 1959-64; instr. chemistry, 1959-64; state chemist Miss. State Chem. Lab., 1967-91, emeritus state chemist, 1991—; prof. chemistry Miss. State U., 1967-91, prof. chemistry emeritus, 1991—; rsch. chemist Boll Weevil Rsch. Lab., Agrl. Rsch. Svc., USDA, 1964-67; cons. chemist numerous legal firms, Balt., Jackson, Miss., Indpls., N.Y.C., New Orleans, Mpls.; cons., advisor U.S. FDA, USDA, TVA, Nat. Fertilizer Devel. Ctr., U.S. EPA; mem. Miss. Gov.'s Coun. Environ. Quality, 1973-74. Author: mgr. nat. databases FEEDCON and FOODCONTAM (info. toxic chems. in foods and animal feed), 1980—; contbr. articles to profl. jours., numerous chpts. in books; patentee in field. Served with U.S. Army, 1952-54. Gen. Edn. Bd.

scholar, 1951; recipient Agrl. Research Service, USDA research group Award Merit, 1975, Commr's Spl. Citation USPHS, FDA, 1987. Fellow Assn. Ofcl. Analytical Chemists (bd. dirs. 1978-83, pres. 1981, chmn. editorial bd. 1977-81), Am. Chem. Soc. (bd. dirs., mem. coun. com. on environ. improvement, chmn. pesticide subcom., chmn. 1977, councillor div. agrochems., outstanding chemist of yr. award Miss. sect. 1990); mem. AAAS, ASTM, Plant Growth Regulators Soc. Am., Am. Assn. Plant Food Control Ofcls. (bd. dirs. 1984-89, pres. 1987-88), Assn. Am. Pesticide Control Ofcls., Assn. Food and Drug Ofcls., Nat. Acad. Sci., Coun. State Agys. Agr., Oktibbeha County C. of C., Soc. Environ. Toxicology and Chemistry, Sigma Xi, Phi Eta Sigma, Phi Kappa Phi, Phi Lambda Upsilon. Methodist. Office: Mississippi State Chemical Lab PO Box Cr Mississippi State MS 39762-5622

MIRABELLA, GRACE, magazine publishing executive; b. Maplewood, N.J., June 10, 1930; d. Anthony and Florence (Belfatto) M.; m. William G. Cahan, Nov. 24, 1974. BA, Skidmore Coll., 1950. Mem. exec. tng. program Macy's, N.Y.C., 1950-51; mem. fashion dept. Saks Fifth Ave., N.Y.C., 1951-52; with Vogue mag., N.Y.C., 1952-54, 56-88; assoc. editor Vogue mag., 1965-71, editor-in-chief, 1971-88; founder, publ. dir. Mirabella Mag., 1988—; mem. pub. relations staff Simonetta & Fabiani, Rome, Italy, 1954-56; hon. bd. dirs. Catalyst; lectr. New Sch. Social Rsch.; adv. bd. mem. Columbia Grad. Sch. Journalism, Leeds Castle, London. Mem. Meml. Sloat-Kettering Cancer Ctr. Women's Soc., bd. adv. Harvard Sch. Pub. Health Ctr. for Cancer Prevention. Decorated cavalier Order of Merit Republic of Italy; recipient Outstanding Grad. Achievement award Skidmore Coll., 1972, Coty Fashion Critics award, 1980, Fashion Critics award Parsons Sch. Design, 1985; Woman of Distinction award Birmingham-So. Coll., 1985, Girl Scouts Am. Leadership award, 1987, Excellence in Media award Susan G. Komen Found., 1987, Equal Opportunity award NOW, 1987; officer Order of Merit, Republic of Italy; 1987; Mary Ann Magnin award, 1988; Achievement award Am. Assn. Plastic and Reconstructive Surgery, 1988; Spl. Merit award Coun. Fashion Designers Am., 1989, Life and Breath award N.Y. Lung Assn., 1990, Matrix award Assn. Edn. in Journalism Mass Comm., 1991, AEJMC award, 1992, St. Francis Cabrini Humanitarian award, 1992, Heart of N.Y. award Am. Heart Assn., N.Y.C. Meals-on-Wheels honor, 1994, Nat. Italian-Am. Found. hon., 1994. Mem. Women's Forum N.Y. Office: Mirabella Mag 200 Madison Ave New York NY 10016-3903

MIRABELLI, MARIO V., lawyer; b. Elizabeth, N.J., July 5, 1939. AB, Georgetown U., 1961; LLB, Am. U., 1964. Bar: D.C. 1966. Trial atty. Bur. Deceptive Practices, FTC, Washington, 1967-69, Divsn. Corp. Fin., Br. Adminstrv. Proceedings, SEC, Washington, 1969-73; ptnr. Baker & Hostetler, Washington. Office: Baker & Hostetler Washington Sq 1050 Connecticut Ave NW Ste 1100 Washington DC 20036-5304

MIRABELLO, FRANCIS JOSEPH, lawyer; b. Ft. Lauderdale, Fla., Mar. 2, 1954; s. Frank Guy and Mary (Sorce) M.; m. Marianna Hay O'Neal, Aug. 5, 1978; childen: Diana H., A. Paul. BS in Civil Engring., Princeton U., 1975; JD, Harvard U., 1978. Bar: Calif. 1978, Pa. 1981, Fla. 1983. Assoc. Irell & Manella, Los Angeles, 1978-81; ptnr. Morgan, Lewis & Bockius, Phila., 1981—; lectr. law Villanova (Pa.) U. Law Sch., adj. prof. law U Pa., Phila. Mem. ABA (chmn. tax sect. subcom.). Club: Martins Dam, Merion Cricke. Avocation: tennis. Office: Morgan Lewis & Bockius 2000 One Logan Sq Philadelphia PA 19103

MIRACLE, GORDON ELDON, advertising educator; b. Olympia, Wash., May 28, 1930; s. Gordon Tipler and Corine Adriana (Orlebeke) M.; m. Christa Stoeter, June 29, 1957; children: Gary, Gregory, Glenn. BBA, U. Wis., 1952, MBA, 1958, PhD, 1962. Case officer, civilian intelligence analyst U.S. Army, Fed. Republic Germany, 1955-57; instr. commerce U. Wis. Grad. Sch. Bus. Madison, 1958-60; instr., then asst. prof. mktg. U. Mich., Ann Arbor, 1960-66; assoc. prof. advt. Mich. State U., East Lansing, 1966-70, chmn. PhD program in mass media, 1973-74, chmn. dept., 1974-80, prof. advt., 1970—; vis. prof. mktg. mgmt. N. European Mgmt. Inst., Oslo, 1972-73; cons., lectr. in field. Author: Management of International Advertising, 1966; co-author: International Marketing Management, 1970, Advertising and Government Regulation, 1979, Instructor's Manual for International Marketing Management, 1971, European Regulation of Advertising: Supranational Regulation of Advertising in the European Economic Community, 1986, Voluntary Regulation of Advertising: A Comparative Analysis of the United Kingdom and the United States, 1987, (in Korean) Cultures in Advertising: Advertising in Cultures, 1990; contbr. articles to scholarly and profl. jours.; editor: Marketing Decision Making: Strategy and Payoff, 1965, Sharing for Understanding, Proc. Ann. Conf. Am. Acad. Advt., 1977. Served with AUS, 1952-55. Ford Found. fellow, 1961-62, 64; Am. Assn. Advt. Agys. fellow Marsteller, Inc., 1967; Advt. Ednl. Found. fellow McCann-Erikson Hakuhodo, 1985; Fulbright rsch. fellow Waseda U., Tokyo, 1985; numerous grants. Fellow Am. Acad. Advt. (treas., exec. com. 1978-79); mem. Acad. Internat. Bus. (sec., exec. com. 1973-75), Am. Mktg. Assn., Internat. Advt. Assn. (ednl. accreditation com. 1993-95), Adcraft Club Detroit. Home: 10025 Oak Island Dr Laingsburg MI 48848-8718 Office: Mich State U Dept Advt East Lansing MI 48824

MIRACLE, ROBERT WARREN, retired banker; b. Casper, Wyo.; m. Maggie Zanoni; children—Mark, John. BS in Law, U. Wyo., 1951; grad. with honors, Pacific Coast Banking Sch. With Wyo. Nat. Bank (now Norwest Bank Casper N.A.), 1954-91; exec. v.p. Wyo. Nat. Bank of Casper, 1967; pres., chief exec. officer Wyo. Nat. Bank of Casper (now Norwest Bank Casper N.A.)ú, 1968-87; chmn. Wyo. Nat. Bank of Casper (formerly Norwest Bank Casper N.A.), 1983-91; also bd. dirs.; pres., chief exec. officer, dir. Wyo. Nat. Bancorp. (formerly Affiliated Bank Corp Wyo.), Casper, 1970-91; instr. bank mgmt. U. Colo. 1971-75. Bd. dirs. United Fund of Natrona County, Wyo., 1963-85, campaign co-chmn., 1973-78; trustee The Myra Fox Skelton Found., 1963—, Goodstein Found., 1992—; bd. dirs., pres. Investment in Casper, 1967-70; Wyo. treas. Radio Free Europe, 1967-72; trustee Casper Coll. Foun., 1967-91, pres., 1973-75, 85-91; trustee U. Wyo. Found., 1972-87; chmn. Casper Downtown Improvement Assn., 1974-75; bd. dirs. Cen. Wyo. Fair Bd., 1974-79, pres., 1977-78; dir. Mountain States Employers Coun., 1979-91. Capt. USMC, 1951-53. Recipient James C. Scarboro Meml. award Colo. Sch. Banking., 1977; Disting. Service in Bus. award U. Wyo. Coll. Commerce and Industry, 1980. Mem. Wyo. Bankers Assn. (chmn. legis. com. 1969-80, pres. 1974-75), Am. Bankers Assn. (mem. governing coun. 1974-75, 81-83), Am. Mgmt. Assn., Rocky Mountain Oil and Gas Assn., Newcomer Soc. in N.Am., Casper C. of C. (pres. 1965-66, Disting. Svc. award 1981), FVW, Casper Petroleu, Casper Country (pres. 1993-94), Masons, Lions. Office: Petroleum Bldg PO Box 2733 Casper WY 82602-2733

MIRAGEAS, EVANS JOHN, record company executive; b. Ann Arbor, Mich., Nov. 17, 1954; s. Xenophon John and Constance (Collins) M. BA, U. Mich., 1976. Producer WUOM, Ann Arbor, Mich., 1973-82; sr. prodr. WFMT, Chgo., 1982-89; artistic adminstr. Boston Symphony, 1989-94; sr. v.p. artists and repertoire Decca Records Ltd., London, 1994—. Bd. mem. Classical Action, N.Y.C., 1992—. Greek Orthodox. Office: Decca Records Ltd, 347-353 Chiswick High Rd, London W4 4HS, England

MIRAND, EDWIN ALBERT, medical scientist; b. Buffalo, July 18, 1926; s. Thomas and Lucy (Papier) M. B.A., U. Buffalo, 1947, M.A., 1949; Ph.D., Syracuse (N.Y.) U., 1951; D.Sc. (hon.), Niagara (N.Y.) U., 1970, D'Youville Coll., Buffalo, 1974. Successively undergrad. asst., grad. asst., instr. U. Buffalo, 1946-48; teaching fellow Syracuse U., 1948-51; instr. Utica (N.Y.) Coll., 1950; mem. staff Roswell Park Meml. Inst., Buffalo, 1951—; head W. Seneca labs. 1961—, assoc. inst. dir., head dept. edn., 1967—, dir. cancer rsch., 1968-73, head dept. viral oncology, 1970-73, head dept. biol. resources, 1973—; rsch. prof. biology Grad. Sch., prof. biochem. pharmacology Sch. Pharmacy, SUNY, Buffalo, 1955—, dean Roswell Park grad. div. SUNY, 1967—; rsch. prof. biology Grad. Sch.; mem. human cancer virus task force, clin. cancer edn. com. NIH. Mem. editorial bd. Jour. Surg. Oncology, Cancer Rsch., Jour. Cancer Edn., Cancer jour.; contbr. articles to profl. jours. Mem. U.S. nat. com. Union Internat. Contra Cancer; profl. edn. com. cancer control Nat. Cancer Inst; liaison mem. Pres.'s Nat. Cancer Adv. Bd.; mem. N.Y. State Health Research Council; mem. Gov.'s AIDS Adv. Council, 1982—; sec. N.Y. State Cancer Programs, Inc., 1984—; bd. dirs. Network in Aging of Western N.Y., Inc., 1986—. Recipient Billings Silver medal AMA, 1963, Margaret Hays Edwards award in edn., SUNY, Buffalo,

1993, Citation award in sci. coll. arts and scis., 1964, award sci. rsch. mammalian tumor viruses Med. Soc. State N.Y., 1963. Life mem., fellow N.Y. Acad. Sci.; fellow AAAS; mem. Am. Cancer Soc. (state pub. edn. com. 1982—, nat. adv. com. on research personnel 1985—), Assn. Gnotobiotics (pres. 1968-69, dir. 1975-78), Internat. Assn. for Gnotobiology (pres. 1981-84), Assn. Am. Cancer Insts. (sec.-treas. 1968—), Am. Assn. Cancer Research, Radiation Research Soc., Am. Soc. Zoologists, Soc. Exptl. Biology and Medicine, Am. Assn. for Cancer Edn., Buffalo Acad. Medicine, Am. Soc. Hematology, Internat. Soc. Hematology, Pub. Health Cancer Assn. Am., Internat. Union Against Cancer (chmn. U.S. nat. com. 1979—, sec.-gen. 13th Internat. Cancer Congress), Hematology Soc., Am. Soc. Preventive Oncology, Buffalo Hist. Soc. (life), Buffalo Fine Arts Acad. (life), Sigma Xi. Home: S-6178 Hunters Creek Rd South Wales NY 14139 Office: Roswell Park Meml Inst 666 Elm St Buffalo NY 14263-0001

MIRANDA, CONSTANCIO FERNANDES, civil engineering educator; b. Raia-Goa, India, Dec. 4, 1926; came to U.S., 1960, naturalized, 1966; s. Alex Fernandes and Maria Marcelina (Viegas) M.; m. Joan Mary Menezes, Mar. 3, 1957; children: Steven Alex, Christopher Gerard, Kenneth Michael, Marie Lynn. Student, Karnatak Coll. Dharwar, 1944-46; B Engring. (civil), U. Bombay, 1949; MS in Civil Engring. U. Notre Dame, 1962; PhD in Structural Engring. Ohio State U., 1964; MA in Math, U. Detroit, 1974. Registered profl. engr., Ind., Ohio, Mich., Ky., Wis., W.Va., N.C., Fla. With civil engring. projects Govt. Bombay, 1950-60; teaching asst., then instr. U. Notre Dame, 1960-62; instr., rsch. assoc. Ohio State U., 1962-64; mem. rsch. staff U. N.Mex., 1964-65; mem. faculty U. Detroit, 1965-88, prof. civil engring., 1966-88, chmn. dept., 1965-72, prof. structural and systems engring., 1973-88, assoc. dean Coll. Engring., acting dean, 1972-73, ret., 1989; cons. civil, structural, systems engring., applied maths. and computer applications, 1989—; bd. dir. Profl. Adv. Soc. Ctr., 1973-75; staff engr. EPA, N.C., 1976-77. Contbr. articles to jours. Named Engring. Tchr. of Yr. Engring. Joint Coun., U. Detroit, 1967, 76; Distinguished Alumnus Ohio State U., 1973. Mem. ASCE, Am. Soc. Engring. Edn., Sigma Xi, Chi Epsilon, Tau Beta Pi, Pi Mu Epsilon. Home: 100 Silvercliff Trl Cary NC 27513-2803

MIRANDA, ROBERT NICHOLAS, publishing company executive; b. Bklyn., July 9, 1934; s. John and Florence Miranda; m. Marilyn H. Pils, May 25, 1958; children: Marilyn, Robert, Susan, Lori, Jennifer. A.A. in Acctg. and Bus. Adminstrn., SUNY-Farmingdale. Pres. Pergamon Press, Inc., Elmsford, N.Y., 1985-92; chmn., chief exec. officer Cognizant Communication Corp., Elmsford, 1992—; bd. dirs., exec. v.p., vice chmn. Soc. and Assoc. Svc. Corp., McLean, Va., 1979-82; bd. dirs., chmn. electronics com. Copyright Clearance Ctr., 1984-93. Pub. Acupuncture and Electro Therapeutics Research, Analgesia, Bird Behaviour, Cancer Prevention International, Festival Management and Event Tourism, Gene Expression, Life Support and Biosphere Science, Technology: Journal of Franklin Inst. Served with USNR, 1954-59. Mem. Council Sci. Editors, Internat. Soc. Intelligent Systems (founder, bd. dirs., fin. dir. 1992—). Avocations: hunting; fishing; horseback riding. Office: Cognizant Comm Corp PO Box 217 Croton On Hudson NY 10520

MIRANOWSKI, JOHN ALFRED, agricultural economist; b. Norfolk, Va., May 26, 1944; s. John Bernard and Helene Katherine (Haberman) M.; m. Joan Goldthwaite, Aug. 17, 1968; children: John Todd, Anne Christine. BS in Agrl. Bus. with honors, Iowa State U., 1966; AM in Econs., Harvard U., 1969, PhD in Econs., 1975. Tchg. fellow econs., econs. tutor Harvard U., Cambridge, Mass., 1969-71; instr. Northeastern U., Boston, 1971-74; asst. prof. Iowa State U., 1975-80, assoc. prof., 1980-84; dir. resources and tech. div. Econ. Rsch. Svc., USDA, Washington, 1984—; exec. coord. sec.'s policy coordination coun., 1990-91, spl. asst. to dep. sec., 1990-91; Gilbert F. White vis. fellow Resources for Future, 1981-82; cons. Abt Assocs. Inc., 1971-74, project dir., 1973; numerous presentations in field; mem. U.S. del. ad hoc com. on agr. and environ. OECD, 1989-92, head U.S. del. joint working party on agr. and environ., 1993—; mem. exec. com. Gt. Plains Agrl. Coun., 1989-93; vis. lectr. U. Calif., Berkeley, 1987; mem. com. on impact of emerging agrl. trends on fish and wildlife habitat, NRC, NAS, 1980-82. Co-editor: Agricultural and Resource Economics, 1993; mem. editl. coun. Jour. Environ. Econs. Mgmt., 1986-89; contbr. articles and book revs. to profl. jours., numerous chpts. to books. Grad. Price fellow Harvard U.;Ralston Purina scholar, Eli Lilly Advanced Curriculum scholar Iowa State U., George Chase Christian scholar Harvard U.; grantee EPA, 1979-81, Resources for Future, 1981-82, Econ. Rsch. Svc., 1978-79. Mem. Am. Econ. Assn., Am. Agrl. Econs. Assn. (quality of rsch. discovery award com. 1977-80, bd. dirs., exec. bd. 1987-90), Assn. Environ. and Resource Economists (bd. dirs., exec. bd. 1989-93), Northeastern Agr. and Resource Econs. Assn., So. Agrl. Econs. Assn., Western Agrl. Econs. Assn., Cardinal Key, Phi Eta Sigma, Phi Kappa Phi, Alpha Zeta. Home: 5711 Ogden Rd Bethesda MD 20816-1260 Office: Econ Rsch Svc Resources Tech Div 1301 New York Ave NW Ste 524 Washington DC 20005-4708

MIRANTE, ARTHUR J., II, real estate company executive; b. Hackensack, N.J., Aug. 25, 1943; s. Arthur J. and Mildred (Spaluzzi) M.; m. Elizabeth McMillan, Oct. 2, 1993; children: Arthur, Claudia, Matthew. BS, Coll. of the Holy Cross, 1965; JD, St. John's U., 1968. Bar: 1968. Sole practice N.Y.C., 1966-71; asst. to gen. counsel Cushman & Wakefield, N.Y.C., 1971-77, gen. counsel 1977-81, nat. dir. asset mgmt., 1981-82, exec. v.p., dir. N.Y. area, 1982-84, pres., chief exec. officer, 1984—. Home: 211 E 70th St New York NY 10021 Office: Cushman & Wakefield Inc 51 W 52nd St CBS Bldg New York NY 10019

MIRCHANDANEY, ARJAN SOBHRAJ, mathematics educator; b. Hydrabad, Sind, India, Aug. 13, 1923; s. Sobhraj Gurmukhdas and Jamuna Mohanlal (Advani) M.; m. Padma Kalachand Lalwani, Oct. 20, 1958; 1 child, Haresh. B.A. Bombay, India, 1943; MS, U. Bombay, 1946; PhD, U. Conn., 1984. Asst. prof. math. D.G. Nat. Coll., U. Bombay, 1943-47; lectr. Jai Hind Coll. U. Bombay, 1949-60, lectr. postgrad. classes, 1953-78, prof. math. Jai Hind Coll., 1960-69, prof., head dept. math. Jai Hind Coll., 1969-78; asst. prof. math. No. Ill. U., DeKalb, 1979-80, Knox Coll., Galesburg, Ill., 1982-85; prof. math. Defiance (Ohio) Coll., 1986—; coord. math. coll. sci. improvement program for Bombay colls., 1971-74; vis. prof. math. St. Lawrence U., Canton, N.Y., 1978; vis. asst. prof. Cornell U., Ithaca, N.Y., 1985-86; postgrad. lectr. U. Bombay, 1953-78; external examiner Shivaji U., Kolhapur, India, 1972-74; presenter Internat. Congress on Relativity and Gravitation, Munich, 1988, Internat. Congress History of Sci., Munich, 1989. Author: A Course in Elementary Trigonometry, 1954, 3d edit., 1965; contbr. to profl. jour. and book. Mem. Nat. Ctr. for Performing Arts, Bombay, 1969-78. Grantee Defiance Coll., 1989. Mem. Am. Math. Soc., Math. Assn. Am. Achievements include research in field theory of electromagnetics and photic field theory. Home: 700 Ralston Ave Apt 36 Defiance OH 43512-1567 Office: Defiance Coll 701 N Clinton St Defiance OH 43512-1695

MIRELS, HAROLD, aerospace engineer; b. N.Y.C., July 29, 1924; s. Hyman and Lily (Efron) M.; m. Nell Segal, Oct. 4, 1953; children: Lily, Laurence Franklin, Jeremy Mark. BSME, Cooper U., 1944; MSME, Case Inst. Tech., 1949; PhD in Aero. Engring., Cornell U., 1953. Sect. head NACA, Cleve., 1944-57; br. chief NASA, Cleve., 1957-61; dept. head Aerospace Corp., El Segundo, Calif., 1961-78, assoc. dir., 1978-84, prin. scientist, 1984-93; cons., 1993—. Co-inventor continuous wave chem. laser. Recipient Tech. Achievement award Cleve. Tech. Socs., 1960. Fellow AIAA (Fluid and Plasmadynamics award 1988), Am. Phys. Soc.; mem. Nat. Acad. Engring. Home: 3 Seahurst Rd Palos Verdes Peninsula CA 90274-3700

MIRER, FRANKLIN EMANUEL, industrial hygienist; b. Bklyn., May 4, 1946; s. Lewis H. and Janet (Emanuel) M.; m. Jeanne Ellen Cohn, Sept. 12, 1971; children: Michael Lewis, Elisabeth Anna. AB, Columbia Coll., 1966; PhD, Harvard U., 1972. Rsch. fellow Sch. Pub. Health Harvard U., Boston, 1972-75; indsl. hygiene cons. dept. social security UAW, Detroit, 1975-82, dir. internat. union dept. health and safety, 1982—; mem. adv. com. NAS, Washington, 1981-83, 90—, Office of Tech. Assessment, Washington, 1989-92, Nat. Toxicology Program, Rsch. Triangle Park, N.C., 1987-89; mem. injury adv. com. Ctrs. for Disease Control, Atlanta, 1991—. Democrat. Office: UAW 8000 E Jefferson Ave Detroit MI 48214-3963

MIRES, DENNIS BURNARD, architect; b. Hollister, Calif., Feb. 27, 1944; s. Gene and Doris Genevieve (Clark) M.; m. Tecla Millman, Dec. 31, 1966;

children—Amy Sara, Jonathan Clark. B.Arch., U. Calif.-Berkeley. Registered architect, N.H., Mass., Maine, Vt. Sr. draftsman Carroll & Greenfield, Boston, 1971-72; architect Michael B. Ingram, Architect, Manchester, N.H., 1972-80; prin. Dennis B. Mires, The Architect, Manchester, 1980—; interior design instr. Manchester Inst. Arts and Scis., 1979, N.H. Voc-Tech Coll., 1981; design instr. Kids' Coll., Manchester, 1984-85. Instr. Explorer Scouts, Arch. Post, Manchester, N.Y., 1977-78; tchr. Unitarian Universalist Ch. Sch., Manchester, 1978-82. Served to capt. USAF, 1967-71. Recipient Excellence in Architecture award, AIA, 1984. Mem. AIA (dir.), Nat. Council Archtl. Registration Bds. Home: 40 N Bend Dr Manchester NH 03104 Office: Dennis B Mires The Architect 697 Union St Manchester NH 03104-3632

MIRICK, HENRY DUSTIN, architect; b. Washington, Aug. 6, 1905; s. Henry Brown and Blanche Mitchell (Swope) M.; m. Marion Winsor, June 24, 1933; children: Marion Mirick Dick, Henry Dustin, Heath Mirick Kennedy, Richard. B.A., Princeton, 1927; B. Arch., U. Pa., 1930, M. Arch., 1931. Ptnr. Mirick, Pearson, Batcheler, Phila., 1935—. Works include monograph on large baths Hadrians Villa, Trivoli, Italy; works include Pennwalt, Nat. Bd. Med. Examiners bldgs., Friends Cen. Shipley Sch., Agnes Irwin Sch., Haverford Sch., Episcoal Schs., Pa. State U. natatorium and labs., Bryn Mawr Hosp., Lankenau Hosp., Jefferson Hosp., U. Pa. Hosp., Medford Leas, Dunwoody, Cathedral Village retirement communities, Mus. Dr. Albert Barnes, Phila., Nat. Scis. Phila. auditorium and labs., James Murphy House, Episcopal Acad., St. Christopher's Ch., Parish House, Ch. of the Redeemer, Bryn Mawr, Humming Bird house, African Plains, Bear Mountain, Phila. Zoo, Sunnybrook, Buena Vista and Whitemarsh country clubs. Pres. Lower Merion Bd. Hist. Review, 1963-66; mem. Lower Merion Planning Commn., 1955-69; Trustee Acad. Natural Scis., 1965-78, emeritus, 1985—; bd. dirs. Pa. Environ. Council, Phila. Zool. Soc., 1963—Harriton Assn., Wharton Community Center, 1951-63; bd. dirs., treas. Phila. com. World Wildlife Fund; treas. Conservation Projects Inc.; chmn. bd. Montgomery Country Day Sch., 1965-67; bd. dirs. Dunwoody Retirement Community, 1976-82, emeritus, 1986—; mem. vestry Ch. of the Redeemer, Bryn Mawr, 1977-80; overseer Strawbery Banke, Portsmouth, N.H., 1981-84. Served to lt. col. AUS, 1942-45 (commendation medal). Recipient Rome prize in architecture, 1930, AIA merit citations; fellow Am. Acad. Rome, 1933. Fellow AIA (pres. Phila. 1970, chmn. Phila. charitable trust 1971-74); mem. Pa. Soc. Architects, Phila. C.C. (bd. dirs. 1970-75), Pa. Hort. Soc. (pres. 1959-62), Pa. Soc. Promoting Agr. (v.p. 1980-83, pres. 1983-84), Am. Arbitration Assn., Shakspere Soc., Delaware Valley Ornithol. Club, Tau Sigma Delta, Delta Psi. Clubs: Merion Cricket, Philadelphia, Rittenhouse, Art Alliance Phila., Princeton, Pohoqualine Fish Assn., Wilderness (Phila.); Quadrangle (Princeton), Am. Alpine Club. Home: 101 Cherry Ln Ardmore PA 19003 Office: 262 South 23rd St Philadelphia PA 19103

MIRISCH, LAWRENCE ALAN, motion picture agent; b. Los Angeles, CA, Oct. 10, 1957; s. Walter and Patricia (Kahan) M. BA Radio & TV, Film, Calif. State U., Northridge, 1980. Apprentice film editor, 1975-77, 2nd asst. dir., 1978-81; agent The Gersh Agency, Los Angeles, CA, 1982-84, Adams, Ray & Rosenberg, Los Angeles, CA, 1984, Triad Artists, Los Angeles, CA, 1984-92; pres. The Mirisch Agency, Los Angeles, CA, 1992—; mem. Mot. Picture Editors Guild, 1975; Directors Guild of Amer., 1978; Academy of Motion Pictures Arts & Sciences, 1987; Amer. Cinema Editors, 1988; adv. bd., Amer. Film Inst., 1990; special products comm., Dir. Guild of Amer., 1991. bd. of governors, Cedars Sinai Hosp., 1991. Office: The Mirisch Agency 10100 Santa Monica Blvd Suite 700 Los Angeles CA 90067

MIRISCH, MARVIN ELLIOT, motion picture producer; b. N.Y.C., Mar. 19, 1918; s. Max and Josephine (Urbach) M.; m. Florene Smuckler, Dec. 28, 1941; children—Donald, Carol, Lynn. B.A., Coll. City N.Y., 1940. With contract and print depts., then office mgr. Grand Nat. Films, Inc., N.Y.C., 1936-40; organized theatre concession bus. Theatres Candy Co., Inc., Milw., 1940; exec., corporate officer Allied Artists Pictures Corp., Hollywood, Calif., 1953-57; co-organizer Mirisch Co., Inc. (motion picture producers), Hollywood, Calif., 1957; v.p., dir. Mirisch Co., Inc. (motion picture producers), 1957—; chmn., chief exec. officer Mirisch Prodns., Inc., 1968—; Chmn. permanent charities com. Motion Picture and TV Industries. (Recipient Best Picture of Year award Acad. Motion Picture Arts and Scis. for The Apartment, 1961, West Side Story, 1962, In the Heat of the Night 1968, Producer of Year award Nat. Assn. Theatre Owners 1972). Bd. govs. Cedars-Sinai Med. Ctr. Mem. Assn. Motion Picture and TV Producers Am. (dir., vice-chmn.), Los Angeles Art Inst., Acad. Motion Picture Arts and Scis. (bd. govs., 1st v.p.). Jewish. Clubs: Motion Picture Pioneers, Hillcrest Country. Office: Office 100 Universal C Plz North Hollywood CA 91606

MIRISCH, WALTER MORTIMER, motion picture producer; b. N.Y.C., Nov. 8, 1921; s. Max and Josephine (Urbach) M.; m. Patricia Kahan, Oct. 11, 1947; children: Anne, Andrew, Lawrence. Student, CCNY, 1938-40; BA, U. Wis., 1942, HHD (hon.), 1989; I.A., Harvard Grad. Sch. Bus., 1943. Producer, exec. producer Allied Artists Pictures Corp., 1946-57; producer, v.p. charge prodn. Mirisch Co., Inc., Los Angeles, 1957—; pres.-exec. head prodn. Mirisch Corp., Inc., 1969—. Prodns. include The Magnificent Seven, In the Heat of the Night (Acad. award for best picture of year 1968), Two for the Seesaw, The Hawaiians, The Organization, Toys in the Attic, Mr. Majestyk, Midway, Gray Lady Down, Same Time Next Year, Romantic Comedy, Prisoner of Zenda, 1979, Dracula, 1979. Pres., bd. dirs. Motion Picture Permanent Charities, 1960-61; bd. dirs. Ctr. Theatre Group, Los Angeles, Cedars-Sinai Med. Ctr.; adv. bd. Calif. State U., Northridge; bd. govs. The Los Angles Music Ctr. Decorated Order Arts et Lettres (France); recipient medal UCLA, 1989. Mem. Acad. Motion Picture Arts and Scis. (pres. 1973-77, gov. 1964-70, T2—, Motion Picture Acad. Jean Hersholt award 1983, Motion Picture Acad. Irving Thalberg award 1977), Producers Guild Am. (pres., dir. 1959-62), Motion Picture Assn. Am. (dir. 1961—), Wis. Alumni Assn. (dir. 1967-73).

MIRKIN, ABRAHAM JONATHAN, surgeon; b. Flushing, N.Y., Aug. 17, 1910; s. Samuel and Anna (Jaffe) M.; m. Miriam G. Klawan, Jan. 26, 1936; children: Louise, Lawrence Stanley. A.B., Cornell U., 1931; M.D., NYU, 1935. Diplomate: Am. Bd. Surgery. Intern, then resident Sinai Hosp., Balt., 1935-41; mem. surg. staff Meml. and Sacred Heart hosps., both Cumberland, Md; pres. med. staff Meml. Hosp., 1966-67; instr. Traffic Inst., Northwestern U., 1964, 68, 72, 74, 76, 78, 80, 82; med. adv. bd. Fla. Dept. Hwy. Safety and Motor Vehicles, 1977—; mem. Com. on Uniform Laws and Ordinances, 1969-72. Gen. chmn. Nat. Conf. on Aging Drivers, 1974. Served to maj. M.C. AUS, 1942-46. Fellow A.C.S. (chmn. hwy. safety com. Md. chpt. 1967-68), Southeastern Surg. Congress; mem. AMA (past chmn. med. aspects automotive safety), Allegany County Med. Soc. (pres. 1947-48), Assn. for Advancement of Automotive Medicine (bd. dirs. 1957-60, 79-81, pres. 1957-59), Soc. Automotive Engrs. (com. on automotive safety), Med.-Chirurg. Faculty Md. (subcom. on traffic safety 1970-76), Fla. Med. Assn., Cedars-Sinai Med. Ctr. (bd. dirs.), Allegany County (Md.) Med. Soc. (pres. 1948-50). Home and Office: 2003 N Ocean Blvd #203 Boca Raton FL 33431

MIRKIN, BERNARD LEO, clinical pharmacologist, pediatrician; b. Bronx, N.Y., Mar. 31, 1928; s. Max and Esther M.; m. Phyllis Korduner, Aug. 1954 (dec. 1982); children: Lisa Mia, Mara Rebecca; m. Sarah Solotaroff, 1986; stepchildren: Jennifer, Rachel, Jacob. AB, NYU, 1949; PhD, Yale U., 1953; MD, U. Minn., 1964. Asst. prof. pharmacology SUNY, Downstate Med. Center, 1954-60; Ford Found. postdoctoral fellow Karolinska Inst., Stockholm, 1960-61; USPHS post-doctoral fellow Yale U., 1961-62; resident in pediatrics U. Minn. Hosp., Mpls., 1964-66; asst. prof. U. Minn. Med. Sch., Mpls., 1966-67; assoc. prof. U. Minn. Med. Sch., 1967-72; prof. pediatrics and pharmacology U. Minn. Health Sci. Ctr., 1972-89; prof. pediatrics and pharmacology Northwestern U. Med. Sch., Chgo., 1989—; head, dir. rsch. Children's Meml. Inst. for Edn. and Rsch., Children's Meml. Hosp., Chgo., 1989—; assoc. dean Rsch. Northwestern U. Med. Sch., 1994—; cons. NIH, Office of Technology Assessment, U.S. Congress, WHO, U.S. Pharmacopeia, Pharm. Mfrs. Assn. Found.; vis. fellow Jesus Coll., Oxford U., 1974. Author: Perinatal Pharmacology and Therapeutics, 1976, Clinical Pharmacology: A Pediatric Perspective, 1978. postdoctoral fellow Karolinska Inst. Stockholm 1960-61. Served with M.C. U.S. Army, 1954-56. Mem. Am. Fedn. Clin. Research, Soc. Pediatric Rsch., Am. Assn. Cancer Rsch., Am. Pediatrics Soc., Am. Soc. Pharm. Exptl. Therapeutics. Home: 427 Greenleaf St Evanston IL

60202-1328 Office: Childrens Meml Inst Edn and Rsch Mailcode # 117 2300 N Childrens Plz Chicago IL 60614-3394

MIRMAN, IRVING R., scientific adviser; b. Syracuse, N.Y., July 29, 1915; s. Saniel I. and Rebecca (Raichlin) M.; m. Beatrice Wolff, Aug. 14, 1942; children—Robert, Marsha, Kenneth. B.E.E., N.Y. U., 1942; postgrad., Harvard-Mass. Inst. Tech., 1942-43, Poly. Inst. Bklyn., 1947-51, Air U., 1952, 56, 59, George Washington U., 1956, Colgate U., 1957, Syracuse U., 1958, Am. U., 1964-65. Registered profl. engr. Mass. Elec. engr. Central N.Y. Power Co., Syracuse, 1937-41; project engr. Watson Labs., Red Bank, N.J., 1946-50; mem. tech. staff Rome Air Devel. Ctr., N.Y., 1950-51; chief program staff Rome Air Devel. Ctr., 1951-55, asst. sci. dir., 1955-57, assoc. dir. R & D, 1957-59; dir. tech. planning and ops. Capehart Corp., N.Y., 1959-60; v.p. Capehart Corp., 1960-63; sci. cons. Anser Corp., Baileys Cross Roads, Va., 1963; sci. adviser, dep. chief staff research and devel. in sci. and tech. Dept. Air Force, Washington, 1963-66; sci. adviser S.E. Asia matters Dept. Air Force, 1966-72; spl. asst. to comdr. Hdqrs. Air Force System Command, 1966-76; dep. dir. SHAPE Tech. Center, The Hague, Netherlands, 1976-80; pres. Decision Process Systems, Washington, 1980—. Served to capt. USAF, 1942-46. Recipient Meritorious Civilian award Dept. Air Force, 1958, also Distinguished Civilian award, 1976. Fellow A.A.A.S.; sr. mem. IEEE; mem. Am. Inst. Aeros. and Astronautics, N.Y. Acad. Sci., Research Engring. Soc. Am. Home: 5729 Fairway Park Dr # 20203 Boynton Beach FL 33437-1764

MIRMAN, JOEL HARVEY, lawyer; b. Toledo, Dec. 3, 1941; s. Benjamin and Minnie (Krapifko) M.; m. Denise M. Dembinski, June 12, 1982; children: Lisa, Julie, Benjamin. BBA, Ohio U., 1963; JD, Ohio State U., 1966. Bar: Ohio 1966, U.S. Dist. Ct. (so. dist.) Ohio 1966, U.S. Supreme Ct. 1972. Ptnr. Topper, Alloway, Goodman, DeLeone & Duffey, Columbus, Ohio, 1966-85, Benesch, Friedlander, Coplan & Aronoff, 1986-93; shareholder Buckingham, Doolittle & Burroughs, Columbus, Ohio, 1994—; lectr. Ohio CLE Inst., Columbus, 1972—. Author direct examination CLE materials; contbr. articles to profl. jours. Mem. Ohio Elections Commn., 1976-80, vice-chmn. 1980. Mem. Capital Club, Worthington Hills Country Club, Worthington Hills Civic Assn. (pres. 1992-93), Assn. Trial Lawyers Am. (chmn. family law sects. 1993-94). Office: Buckingham Doolittle & Burroughs 88 E Broad St Ste 1600 Columbus OH 43215-3506

MIROJNICK, ELLEN, costume designer; b. N.Y.C., July 7, 1949; d. Abe and Sunny (Schneider) Schneid; 1 child, Lili. Student, Sch. Visual Arts, N.Y.C., 1967-68, Parsons Sch. Design, N.Y.C., 1968-70. Head designer Happy Legs Inc., N.Y.C., 1970-76; freelance costume designer, 1976—. Costume designer: (films) French Quarter, 1977, Reckless, 1984, The Flamingo Kid, 1984, Remo Williams: The Adventure Begins, 1985, Nobody's Fool, 1986, Fatal Attraction, 1987, Wall Street, 1987 (Cutty Sark Men's Wear award for costume in menswear 1988), Cocktail, 1988, Talk Radio, 1988, Black Rain, 1989, Always, 1989, Narrow Margin, 1990, Jacob's Ladder, 1990, Switch, 1991, Mobsters, 1992, Basic Instinct, 1992, Chaplin, 1992 (Brit. Acad. award nomination 1993), Cliffhanger, 1993, Intersection, 1993, Speed, 1994; asst. costume designer: (films) Endless Love, 1981, Fame, 1984. Mem. Acad. Motion Picture Arts and Scis. Avocation: painting.

MIRON, MURRAY SAMUEL, psychologist, educator; b. Allentown, Pa., Aug. 7, 1932; s. Murray R. and Myrtle E. (Hurlbut) M.; m. Helen Kutuchief, July, 1954 (div. June 1972); 1 child, Melinda; m. Cheryl Adamy, Aug. 5, 1973; 1 child, Murray Thomas. MA, U. Ill., 1956, PhD, 1960. From asst. prof. to assoc. prof. U. Ill., Urbana, 1960-70; prof. Syracuse (N.Y.) U., 1956; threat assessor, FBI, Washington, 1972-92, U.S. Dept. Energy, Washington, 1980—, U.S. Dept. State, 1989—. Author: Hostage, 1979; co-author: Cross-Cultural Universals of Affective Meaning, 1976; contbr. 50 articles to profl. jours. Negotiatior Onandaga Sheriff's Office and Syracuse Police Dept., 1980-84; forensic cons. Onondaga Dist. Atty., Syracuse, 1992—. Recipient Gold Badge Internat. Assn. of Chiefs of Police, 1977. Fellow Am. Bd. Forensic Examiners (bd. cert. in document examination and psychol. profiling); mem. Am. Psychol. Soc., Am. Soc. Indsl. Security, Internat. Assn. Bomb Tech. & Investigation. Achievements include pioneering rsch. in resolution of disputed communication origins, cross-cultural rsch. in meaning, psycholinguistic profiling of anonymous communications. Office: Psycholinguistic Rsch Ctr 2200 E Genesee St Ste C Syracuse NY 13210

MIROW, SUSAN MARILYN, psychiatry educator; b. Manhattan, N.Y., Feb. 15, 1944. BA in Biology, Temple U., 1964; PhD in Anatomy, N.Y. Med. Coll., 1970; MD, Med. Coll. Pa., 1973. Diplomate Nat. Bd. Med. Examiners, Am. Bd. Psychiatry and Neurology. Intern in medicine and psychiatry Temple U. Hosp., Phila., 1973-74, resident in psychiatry, 1973-75; pvt. practice psychiatry Salt Lake City, 1976—; clin. asst. prof. psychiatry U. Utah Sch. Medicine, Salt Lake City, 1976—; clin. asst. prof. psychiatry Neuropsychiat. Inst. U. Utah; mem. staff Salt Lake Regional Med. Ctr., 1976—, Latter Day Saints Hosp., 1985—; prin. investigator Marine Biol. Lab., Woods Hole, Mass., 1968; research investigator Temple U. Dept. Biology, summer 1971, Hosp. Joint Diseases, N.Y.C., 1969-70; clin. dir. Utah State Hosp., Provo, 1980-82; psychiat. extern Phila. Child Guidance Clin, 1973, neurology clk. Med. Coll. Pa. Dept. Neurology, 1973, cons. psychiatrist Adolescent Residential Treatment Ctr., Salt Lake City, 1976-77; vis. prof. St. George's U., Grenada, 1990—; psychiat. cons. Divsn. Youth Corrections, Salt Lake City, 1992—; lectr. in field. Contbr. articles to profl. jours. NSF fellow 1965-69; grantee John Polachek Research Found., 1969-70; recipient Weisman award Excellence Child Psychiatry, 1973. Fellow Am. Psychiat. Assn.; mem. AAAS, AMA, Utah State Med. Assn. (impaired physician's com. 1983—), Salt Lake County Med. Soc., N.Y. Acad. Scis., Soc. Clin. and Exptl. Hypnosis, Internat. Soc. Clin. Hypnosis, Utah Soc. Clin. Hypnosis (sec. 1982-83), Am. Soc. Clin. Hypnosis. Office: 73 G St Salt Lake City UT 84103-2951

MIROWSKI, PHILIP EDWARD, economics educator; b. Jackson, Mich., Aug. 21, 1951; s. Edward and Elizabeth (Kapusinski) M.; m. Pamela Margaret Cook, June 14, 1986. BA, Mich. State U., 1973; MA in Econs., U. Mich., 1976, PhD in Econs., 1979. Asst. prof. U. Santa Clara, Calif., 1978-81; asst. prof. Tufts U., Medford, Mass., 1981-84, assoc. prof. econs., 1984-90; Carl Koch prof. econs. and history and philosophy of sci. U. Notre Dame, Ind., 1990—; vis. assoc. prof. Yale U., New Haven, 1987-89; vis. prof. Tinbergen Inst., Erasmus U., Rotterdam, Holland, 1991. Author: Reconstruction of Economic Theory, 1986, Against Mechanism, 1988, More Heat Than Light, 1989; Rowman & Littlefield series editor Studies in Worldly Philosophy; editor: Natural Images in Economics, 1994, Edgeworth on Chance, 1994; mem. editorial bd. History Polit. Econ., Duke U., 1986—, Social Concept, 1988-94, Review of Polit. Economy, 1994—; contbr. articles to profl. jours. Mem. Am. Econs. Assn., History Sci. Soc., History Econs. Soc., Soc. for Social Studies of Sci. Office: U Notre Dame Dept Econs Notre Dame IN 46556

MIRREN, HELEN, actress; b. London, 1946. First appeared with Nat. Youth Theatre; appeared as Cleopatra in Antony and Cleopatra, Old Vic, 1965; joined Royal Shakespeare Co., 1967; appeared as Castiza in The Revenger's Tragedy and Diana in All's Well That Ends Well; other roles include: Cressida in Troilus and Cressida, Royal Shakespeare Co., Stratford, Eng., 1968; Hero in Much Ado About Nothing, Stratford, 1968; Win-the-Fight Littlewit in Bartholomew Fair, Aldwych, 1969; Lady Anne in Richard III, Stratford, Ophelia in Hamlet, Julia in The Two Gentlemen of Verona, Stratford, 1970 (last part also at Aldwych); Tatyana in Enemies, Royal Shakespeare Co., Aldwych, 1971; title role in Miss Julie, Elynae in The Balcony, The Place, 1971; with Peter Brook's Centre Internationale de Recherches Theatrales, Africa and U.S., 1972-73; Lady Macbeth, Royal Shakespeare Co., Stratford, 1974, and Aldwych, 1975; Maggie in Teeth 'n' Smiles, Royal Ct., 1975; Nina in The Seagull and Ella in The Bed Before Yesterday, Lyric for Lyric Theatre Co., 1975, Antony and Cleopatra, The Roaring Girl, Henry VI-Parts 1, 2, 3, 1977-78, Measure for Measure, 1979, The Duchess of Malfi, 1980-81, Faith Healer, 1981, Royal Shakespeare Co., Barbican, 1983, Extremities, 1984, Madame Bovary, 1987, Two Way Mirror, 1988, Sex Please We're Italian, 1991, A Month in the Country, 1994 (Tony nominee - Lead Actress in a Play, 1995); films include: Age of Consent, 1969, Savage Messiah, O Lucky Man!, 1973, Caligula, 1977, The Long Good Friday, Excalibur, 1981, Cal, 1984 (Best Actress award Cannes Film Festival 1984), 2010, 1984, White Knights, 1984, Heavenly Pursuits, 1985, The

Mosquito Coast, 1986, Pascali's Island, 1987, When The Whales Came, 1988, Bethune, Making of a Hero, 1988, The Cook, The Thief, His Wife, and Her Lover, 1989, The Comfort of Strangers, 1990, Where Angels Fear to Tread, 1991, The Gift, 1991, The Hawk, 1991, The Prince of Jutland, 1991, The Madness of King George, 1994 (Acad. award nominee for Best Supporting Actress), Prime Suspect; TV appearances include: Behind the Scene, Cousin Bette, Coffin for the Bride, Jackanory, The Changeling, Bellamira, The Philanthropist, Mussolini And Claretta Petacci, The Collection, The Country Wife, Blue Remembered Hills, The Serpent Son, Quiz Kids, Midsummer Night's Dream, After the Party, Cymbeline, Coming Through, Cause Celebre, Miss Julie, The Apple Cart, The Little Minister, As You Like It, Mrs. Reinhardt, Soft Targets, 1982, Heavenly Pursuits, 1985, Red King White Knight, 1988, Prime Suspect, 1991 (Best Actress award BAFTA 1991), Prime Suspect 2, 1992, Prime Suspect 3, 1993 (Emmy award, 1994). Mem. PTO. Office: Ken McReddie Ltd, 91 Regent St, London WIR TTB, England*

MIRRIELEES, JAMES FAY, III, publishing executive; b. Cin., Nov. 2, 1939; s. James Fay and Alicia Lucille (Beatty) M.; m. Gillian C. Hanlon, July, 1986; 1 child, Hillary Evan, from previous marriage. BA, U. Cin. Editorial dir. McGraw-Hill Pub. Co., N.Y.C., 1975-77; v.p. Holt-Rinehart & Winston, N.Y.C., 1977-79; pres. CBS Coll. Pub., N.Y.C., 1979-81, 83-85, CBS Internat. Pub., 1981-83; mng. dir. European ops. Ashton-Tate, London, 1985-86; pres. Somerset House Edn. and Profl. Pubs., 1986-87; chief exec. officer Raintree Pub. Inc., 1987-88; chmn., pres. Raintree I Ltd. Partnership, 1988-91; pres. Coronet/MTI Film & Video, Deerfield, Ill., 1991-93; v.p. mktg. Edunetics Corp., Arlington, Va., 1993-95; v.p. bus. devel. Jennings & Keefe Media, 1995—. Democrat. Home: 104 Princess St Alexandria VA 22314-2325 Office: 1975 N Pierce St Arlington VA 22209-2505

MIRRO, JOHN, engineering company executive. Student, MIT, Cambridge, Mass. Pres. Conmec, Inc., Bethleham, Pa. Office: Conmec Inc 1480 Valley Center Pky Bethlehem PA 18017*

MIRRO, RICHARD ALLEN, bank executive; b. Pitts., Oct. 9, 1951; s. Amaria Joseph and Agnes Elizabeth (Kassa) M.; m. Candace West. BA in Math. and Econs., St. Vincent Coll., 1972; MA in Math. Econs., Duquesne U., 1975. Mktg. officer Mellon Bank, Pitts., 1972-75; mgr. computer systems CACI, Inc., Roslyn, Va., 1976; banking ins. sales mgr. GE Info. Svc. Co., Rockville, Md., 1976-78; v.p. Transaction Tech., Inc., N.Y.C., 1978-81; prin. Booz Allen & Hamilton, N.Y.C., 1981-82; sr. v.p. Marine Midland Bank, N.A., N.Y.C., 1982-85; v.p. First Boston Capital Group, Tarrytown, N.Y., 1985-86; pres. Chase Home Mortgage Co., Tampa, Fla., 1986-89; sr. v.p. Chase Manhattan Bank, 1989—. Republican. Avocations: home remodeling, automobile restoration. Office: Chase Home Mortgage Corp 4915 Independence Pky Tampa FL 33684-5700

MIRSE, RALPH THOMAS, former college president; b. Carrsville, Ky., Aug. 8, 1924; s. Ralph Thomas and Ruth Catherine (Morris) M.; m. Blanche Allen, May 10, 1945; children: Ralph Allen, Deborah Lynn, Sally Ann. BA, Asbury Coll., Wilmore, Ky., 1943; ThM, Asbury Theol. Sem., 1946; PhD, Boston U., 1962; LHD (hon.), Lakeland Coll., Sheboygan, Wis., 1977; LLD (hon.), Buena Vista Coll., Storm Lake, Iowa, 1978; LittD (hon.), Heidleberg Coll., Tiffin, Ohio, 1981; DEd (hon.), Sungshin Women's U., Seoul Korea, 1983; DFA (hon.), Columbia Coll., 1988; DD (hon.), Oklahoma City U., 1988. Ordained to ministry United Methodist Ch., 1947; pastor Meth. Chs., in Ky., 1947-57; exec. sec. New Eng. Conf. United Meth. Ch., 1960-65, exec. sec. nat. div., 1965-70; v.p. Baker U., Baldwin, Kans., 1970-74; pres. Lakeland Coll., 1974-77, Columbia Coll., 1977-88, ret., 1989; part-time dir. ednl. devel. U. S.C., Hilton Head, 1989—; mem. Gov. S.C. Adv. Bd. Social Services, S.C. Adv. Council Pvt. Colls.; mem. bd. S.C. Ptnrs. of Ams. Author: The Methodist Minister, 1960, The Self-Image of the Methodist Minister, 1962, The Changing Face of New England, 1964, Community Planning Studies, 1970. Decorated Order of the Palmetto, 1986. Mem. Am. Assn. Higher Edn., Counc. Advancement and Support Edn., Am. Acad. Polit. and Social Sci., Nat. Conf. Small Pvt. Colls. (pres., dir.), S.C. Found. Pvt. Colls., S.C. Coll. Counc., Internat. Assn. Univ. Pres.' (exec. com.), Am. Coun. on Edn. Republican. Clubs: Forest Lake, Summit (Columbia); Univ. (N.Y.C.); Hyannis (Mass.) Yacht. Lodges: Rotary, Shrine. Office: 10 Office Park Rd Hilton Head Island SC 29928-4602

MIRSKY, ARTHUR, geologist, educator; b. Phila., Feb. 8, 1927; s. Victor and Dorothy M.; m. Patricia Shorey, Dec. 22, 1961; 1 dau., Alexis Catherine. Student, Bklyn. Coll., 1944-45, 46-48; B.A., U. Calif., 1950; M.S., U. Ariz., 1955; PhD., Ohio State U., 1960. Cert. geologist, Ind. Field uranium geologist AEC, S.W. U.S., 1951-53; consulting uranium geologist Albuquerque, 1955-56; asst. dir. Inst. Polar Studies, Ohio State U., 1960-67; adj. asst. prof., 1964-67; asst. prof. geology Ind. U.-Purdue U., Indpls., 1967-70, asso. prof., 1970-74; prof. Ind. U.-Purdue U., Indpls., 1974-94; prof. emeritus Ind. U.-Purdue U., Indpls., 1994—, coord. geology, 1967-69, chmn. dept. geology, 1969-93. Contbr. articles to profl. jours. Served with USN, 1945-46. Mem. Am. Inst. Profl. Geologists, Geol. Soc. Am., Nat. Assn. Geology Tchrs., Am. Geol. Inst., Soc. Econ. Paleontologists and Mineralogists, AAAS, AAUP, Ind. Acad. Sci., Sigma Xi. Office: Indiana U-Purdue U Dept Geology 723 W Michigan St Indianapolis IN 46202-5132

MIRSKY, PHYLLIS SIMON, librarian; b. Petach Tikva, Israel, Dec. 18, 1940; d. Allan and Lea (Prizant) Simon; m. Edward Mirsky, Oct. 21, 1967; 1 child, Seth. BS in Social Welfare, Ohio State U., 1962; postgrad., Columbia U., 1962-63; AMLS, U. Mich., 1965. Caseworker field placement Children's Aid Soc., N.Y.C., 1962-63; hosp. libr. hosp. and instns. divsn. Cleve. Pub. Libr., 1963-64; reference libr. UCLA Biomed. Libr., 1965-68, reference/acquisitions libr., 1968-69, head coms./continuing edn. Pacific S.W. Regl. Med. Libr. Sv., 1969-71, asst. dir. Pacific S.W. Regl. Med. Libr. Sv., 1971-73, faculty coord. Biomed. Libr. program Cen. San Joaquin Valley Area Health Edn. Ctr., 1973-77, assoc. dir. Pacific S.W. Regl. Med. Libr. Sv., 1973-79; head reference sect., coord. libr. assoc. program Nat. Libr. of Medicine, Bethesda, Md., 1979-81; asst. univ. libr., scis. U. Calif.-San Diego, La Jolla, 1981-86, acting univ. libr., 1985, 92-93, asst. univ. libr. adminstrv. and pub. svcs., 1986-87, assoc. univ. libr. adminstrv. and pub. svcs., 1987-92, assoc. univ. libr., 1993—; guest lectr. Libr. Schs. UCLA and U. So. Calif., 1967-78, Grad. Sch. Libr. Sci. Cath. U., Washington, 1980, Grad. Sch. Libr. and Info. Sci. UCLA, 1984; mem. task force on role of spl. libr. nationwide network and coop. programs Nat. Commn. on Libr. and Info. Svcs./Spl. Libr. Assn., 1981-83; facilitator AASLD/MLA Guidelines Scenario Writing Session, L.A., 1984; mem. users coun. OCLC Online Computer Libr. Ctr., Inc., 1991-94; U. Calif.-San Diego rep. Coalition for Networked Info., 1992—; instr. Assn. Rsch. Librs., Office Mgmt. Studies, Mgmt. Inst., 1987; peer reviewer Coll. Libr. Tech. and Cooperation Grant Program U.S. Dept. Edn., 1988—; cons. Nat. Libr. Medicine, Bethesda, Md., 1988, San Diego Mus. Contemporary Art Libr., La Jolla, Calif., 1993—; Salk Inst., 1995. Contbr. articles to profl. jours. and bulls. NIH fellow Columbia U., 1962-63; sr. fellow UCLA/Coun. on Libr. Resources, 1987. Mem. ALA (site visitors panel com. on accreditation 1990-92, libr. adminstrv. and mgmt. assn. 1990-92), Med. Libr. Assn. (bd. dirs. 1977-80), Med. Libr. Group Soc. Calif. and Ariz. (sec. 1970-71, v.p. 1971-72, pres. 1972-73), Documentation Abstracts, Inc. (bd. dirs. 1985-90, vice chair bd. dirs. 1988-90), Med. Libr. Assn. (pres. 1984-85), U. Mich. Libr. Sch. Alumni Assn. Office: U Calif-San Diego Univ Libr 0175G 9500 Gilman Dr La Jolla CA 92093-0175

MIRSKY, SONYA WOHL, librarian, curator; b. N.Y.C., Nov. 12, 1925; d. Louis and Anna (Steiger) Wohl; m. Alfred Ezra Mirsky, Aug. 24, 1967 (dec. June 1974). B.S. in Edn., CCNY, 1948; M.S.L.S., Columbia U., 1950. Asst. libr. Rockefeller U., N.Y.C., 1949-60, assoc. libr., 1960-77, univ. libr., 1977-91, univ. libr. emeritus, 1991—; trustee Med. Libr. Ctr. N.Y., 1965-91, v.p., 1980-88; cons. libr. mgmt. Mem. Bibliog. Soc. Am., Bibliog. Soc. Can., Bibliog. Soc. Gt. Britain, Soc. Bibliography of Natural History. Home: Sutton Ter 1161 York Ave Apt 4F New York NY 10021-7945 Office: Rockefeller U Libr 1230 York Ave New York NY 10021-6399

MIRZA, DAVID BROWN, economist, educator; b. Dayton, Ohio, Feb. 28, 1936; s. Youel Benjamin and Althea (Brown); m. Leona Lousin, June 20, 1965; children: Sara Anush, Elizabeth Ann. AB, Earlham Coll., 1958; PhD, Northwestern U., 1973. Instr. Dartmouth Coll., Hanover, N.H., 1961-63, Kalamazoo (Mich.) Coll., 1963-69; assoc. prof. econs. Loyola U., Chgo.,

1969—, chmn. dept. econs., 1978—; dir. Inst. Futures Trading, 1973—; dir. Mid-Am. Commodities Exch., Chgo., 1978-86; trustee Earlham Coll., Richmond, Ind., 1988—. Mem. found. bd. Earlham Coll., Richmond, 1991—. Mem. Am. Econ. Assn. Mem. Soc. of Friends. Home: 795 Lincoln Ave Winnetka IL 60093-1920 Office: Loyola Univ Chgo 820 N Michigan Ave Chicago IL 60611-2103

MIRZA, SHAUKAT, engineering educator, researcher, consultant; b. Bhopal, India, Aug. 1, 1936; s. Mirza Afaq Beg and Birjees Jehan; m. Ferzana Beg, June 24, 1967; children: Sabah Jehan, Mazin. BS in Engring., Aligarh U., 1956; MS in Civil Engring., U. Wis.-Madison, 1960, PhD in Engring. Mechanics, 1962. Sr. lectr. Delhi Coll. Engring., India, 1962-64; prof. Indian Inst. Tech., New Delhi, 1964-69; prof. mech. engring. U. Ottawa, Ont., Can. 1969—, vice dean R & D faculty engring; vis. engr. Westinghouse Nuclear Europe, Brussels, 1976-77; vis. engr. Def. Rsch. Establishment, Ottawa, 1987-88; cons. Govt. of India, New Delhi, 1967-68, Atomic Energy Can., 1974-80, Bell No. Research, Ottawa, 1981-82. Vis. prof. Worcester (Mass.) Polytech. Inst., 1994-95, Ecole Nat. Superieur d'Ingenieur de Const. Aero., Toulouse, France, 1994. Invited keynote speaker various internat. profl. confs.; contbr. rsch. articles, tech. reports to publs. Recipient Pres.'s gold medal, Roorkee U., India, 1958. Mem. ASME, Assn. Profl. Engrs. Ont. Office: U Ottawa Faculty Engring, 770 King Edward Ave, Ottawa, ON Canada K1N 6N5

MISA, KENNETH FRANKLIN, management consultant; b. Jamaica, N.Y., Sept. 24, 1939; s. Frank J. and Mary M. (Soszka) M.; BS cum laude in Psychology, Fairfield U., 1961; MS in Psychology, Purdue U., 1963; PhD in Psychology (Fellow 1963-66), St. John's U., 1966. Staff psychologist Rohrer, Hibler & Replogle, Los Angeles, 1966-67; assoc. A.T. Kearney, Inc., Los Angeles, 1968-71; sr. assoc., 1972-74, prin., 1975-78, v.p., partner, 1979-86; pres. HR Cons. Group, 1987—. Cert. mgmt. cons.; lic. psychologist, Calif. Mem. Am. Psychol. Assn., Am. Psychol. Soc., Calif. State Psychol. Assn., Soc. for Human Resources Mgmt., Human Resources Planning Soc., Indsl. Rels. Rsch. Assn., Soc. for Indsl. and Organizational Psychology, World Affairs Coun. of L.A., Town Hall of So. Calif., Glendale C. of C., Jonathan Club. Republican. Roman Catholic. Home: 924C S Orange Grove Blvd Pasadena CA 91105-1741 Office: HR Cons Group 100 N Brand Blvd Ste 200 Glendale CA 91203-2614

MISBRENER, JOSEPH MICHAEL, labor union official; b. Crucible, Pa., June 17, 1924; s. Martin and Catherine (Schneider) M.; m. Dorothy Rose Lakatos, Dec. 31, 1963; children: Robert Norman, Michael Frank, Deneen Marie, Patricia Ann. Grad., North High Sch., 1942. Sec., treas. local chpt. Oil Chem. and Atomic Workers Internat. Union AFL-CIO, Lawndale, Calif., 1961-63; internat. rep. Oil Chem. and Atomic Workers Internat. Union AFL-CIO, Denver, 1963-76, asst. to pres., 1976-81, v.p., 1981-83; pres. Oil Chem. and Atomic Workers Internat. Union AFL-CIO, 5, 1983-91; U.S. rep. U.S. Petroleum Worker Internat. Labor Orgn. Conf., Geneva, 1980; v.p. indsl. union dept. AFL-CIO, Washington, 1983-91, food and allied svcs. dept., 1983-91. Civil svc. commr. City of Martinez (Calif.), 1969-70; mem. energy crisis com. City of L.A., 1972-76; mem. Long Beach (Calif.) Manpower Adv. Coun., 1972-76; mem. L.A. County Labor Fedn. Manpower Com., 1972-76. Cpl. U.S. Army, 1942-46. Mem. Export Processing Industry Coalition, Labor-Industry Coalition for Internat. Trade, Workers Inst. Safety and Health (trustee 1983), Nat. Petroleum Coun. Democrat. Roman Catholic. Avocations: golf, gardening. Office: Oil Chem & Atomic Workers Internat Union PO Box 2812 Denver CO 80201-2812 Home: 2650 S Garland St Denver CO 80227-2936

MISCHER, DONALD LEO, television director and producer; b. San Antonio, Mar. 5, 1940; s. Elmer Frederick and Lillian Alma. B.A., U. Tex., 1961, M.A., 1963. Mem. faculty U. Tex., 1962-63; producer/dir. USIA, Washington, 1965-68; with Charles Guggenheim Prodns., 1969-71; pres. Don Mischer Prodns., pres. Mischer Enterprises, Inc., Beverly Hills, Calif., prodr., dir., and program packager for network television programs, 1971—. Television programs include: The Kennedy Center Honors: A Celebration of the Performing Arts (Emmy Awards 1987,8); The Tony Awards (Emmy Awards 1987-88); Michael Jackson's Super Bowl XXVII Halftime Show; Baryshnikov by Tharp (Emmy Award 1985); Gregory Hines, Tap Dance America; Carnegie Hall: Live at 100; It's Garry Shandling's Show; Mowtown 25: Yesterday, Today, Tomorrow (Emmy Award 1983); The Muppets Celebrate Jim Henson; Motown Returns to the Apollo (Emmy Award 1985); Baryshnikov in Hollywood, Goldie and Liza Together, Shirley MacLaine—Illusions, Making Television Dance with Twyla Tharp, An Evening with Robin Williams, Am. Film Inst. Salute to Gene Kelly; producer additional programs with Bob Hope (Bob Hope: The First 90 Years - Emmy award Outstanding Variety, Music or Comedy Special, 1993), Barbara Walters, Goldie Hawn, others. Recipient: Primetime Emmy awards (10), Director's Guild awards for Outstanding Directorial Achiement (8), NAACP Image awards (3), Peabody award, Golden Rose of Montreux award, Gabriel award, Ohio State award. Mem. Dirs. Guild Am., Nat. Acad. TV Arts and Scis. Gov., Am. Film Inst. Office: Brillstein-Grey Entertainment 9200 Sunset Blvd Ste 428 Los Angeles CA 90069

MISCHER, WALTER M., diversified company executive, bank holding company executive; b. 1923; married. With Stone & Webster, 1943-46; chmn. bd. Allied Bancshares Inc., Houston, from 1971; chmn. bd. Mischer Corp., Houston, from 1969, chief exec. officer, from 1969; sr. chmn. bd. First Interstate Bank Tex.; now pres. Southern Investors, Houston. Office: Southern Investors 2727 N Loop West Houston TX 77008-5008

MISCHER, WALTER M., JR., health facility administrator; b. 1950. Grad., U. Tex., 1973. With Mischer Corp., Houston, 1974—; pres.; chmn. bd., pres., CEO Herman Hosp. Inc., Houston, 1991—. Office: Hermann Hosp 6411 Fannin St Houston TX 77030

MISCHKE, CARL HERBERT, religious association executive, retired; b. Hazel, S.D., Oct. 27, 1922; s. Emil Gustav and Pauline Alvina (Polzin) M.; m. Gladys Lindloff, July 6, 1947; children: Joel, Susan Mischke Blahnik, Philip, Steven. B.A., Northwestern Coll., Watertown, Wis., 1944; M.Div., Wis. Luth. Sem., Mequon, 1947. Ordained to ministry Evang. Lutheran Ch. Parish pastor Wis. Synod, 1947-79; pres. Western Wis. Dist. Evang. Luth. Ch., Juneau, 1964-79; v.p. Wis. Luth. Synod, Milw., 1966-79, pres., 1979-93; retired, 1993. Address: 1034 Buena Vista Dr Sun Prairie WI 53590-2031

MISCHKE, CHARLES RUSSELL, mechanical engineering educator; b. Glendale, N.Y., Mar. 2, 1927; s. Reinhart Charles and Dena Amelia (Scholl) M.; m. Margaret R. Bubeck, Aug. 4, 1951; children: Thomas, James. BSME, Cornell U., 1947, MME, 1950; PhD, U. Wis., 1953. Registered mechanical engr. Iowa, Kans. Asst. prof. mech. engring. U. Kans., Lawrence, 1953-56; assoc. prof. mech. engring. U. Kans., 1956-57; prof., chmn. mech. engring. Pratt Inst., N.Y.C., 1957-64; prof. mech. engring. Iowa State U., Ames, 1964—, Alcoa Found. prof., 1974. Author: Elements of Mechanical Analysis, 1963, Introduction to Computer-Aided Design, 1968, Mathematical Model Building, 1972; editor: Standard Handbook of Machine Design, 1986, Mechanical Engineering Design, 5th edit., 1989, eight Mechanical Designers Workbooks, 1990. Scoutmaster Boy Scouts Am., Ames. With USNR, 1944-75, mem. Res. ret. Recipient Ralph Teetor award Soc. Automotive Engrs., 1977, best book award Am. Assn. Pubs., 1986, Legis. Teaching Excellence award Iowa Assembly, 1990, Ralph Coates Roe award Am. Soc. for Engring. Edn., 1991. Fellow ASME (life, Machine Design award 1990); mem. Am. Soc. Engring. Edn. (Centennial cert. 1993), Am. Gear Mfrs. Assn., Scabbard and Blade, Cardinal Key, Sigma Xi, Phi Kappa Phi, Pi Tau Sigma. Avocations: model bldg., railway history. Office: Iowa State U 3029 Black Ames IA 50011

MISCHKE, FREDERICK CHARLES, manufacturing company executive; b. Benton Harbor, Mich., Sept. 21, 1930; s. Fred William and Clara Adeline (Ruhno) M.; m. Kathleen Ann Schultz, Nov. 19, 1955 (dec. Aug. 1980); children: Stephanie Ann, Michael Frederick, Eric William; m. Lori Ann Leonard, Dec. 23, 1983. AA, Lake Mich. Coll., 1956; BBA, Western Mich. U., 1958. CPA, Ind., Mich. Staff acct. Lybrand, Ross Bros. & Montgomery, Chgo., 1958-63; supr. acctg. Lybrand, Ross Bros. & Montgomery, Niles, Mich., 1963-65; v.p., treas. Skyline Corp., Elkhart, Ind., 1965-91, ret., 1991. Vol. Svc. Corps. of Ret. Execs., 1992—, local v.p., 1993—; chmn. Meml. Eondowment Fund Luth. Ch., 1995—. Mem.

AICPA, Ind. Assn. CPAs (Civic Achievement award, 1976), Mich. Assn. CPAs, Fin. Execs. Inst. (Michiana chpt. pres. 1974-75), Nat. Assn. Accts., U.S. Power Squadron. Republican. Lutheran. Club: Elcona Country (pres. 1975). Lodge: Rotary (local pres. 1976-77). Avocations: photography, boating, golf, bowling. Home: 23322 Greenleaf Blvd Elkhart IN 46514-4508

MISCHLER, PAUL, grain company executive. Exec. v.p.-finance Garnac Grain Co. Inc., Shawnee Mission, Kans., 1958—. Office: Garnac Grain Co Inc 7101 College Blvd Ste 800 Shawnee Mission KS 66210-1891

MISENER, ALAN FRANCIS, science educator; b. Montague, Mass., Mar. 4, 1944; s. Alan Miller and Mary Lillian (Roache) M.; m. Christine Ann Camandona; children: Eric, Craig, Darren. BS, U. Mass., 1967; MS, Wesleyan U., 1973; MA, SUNY, Stonybrook, 1971. Cert. tchr., N.Y. Tchr. Three Village Schs., Setauket, N.Y., 1967—. Avocations: golf, vocal music. Office: Three Village Schs Nichols Rd Setauket NY 11733

MISER, HUGH JORDAN, systems analyst, operations researcher, consultant; b. Fayetteville, Ark., May 23, 1917; s. Wilson Lee and Nellie (Pyle) M.; m. Josephine Spence Lehmann, June 24, 1944; children: James Spence, Wendel Lee, Andrew Lehmann, Emily Margaret. BA magna cum laude, Vanderbilt U., 1938; MS, Ill. Inst. Tech., 1940; PhD, Ohio State U., 1946. Tchr. math. Ill. Inst. Tech., Chgo., 1938-40, 42-44, Ohio State U., Columbus, 1940-42, 45-46; acting chmn. dept. math. Lawrence Coll., Appleton, Wis., 1944; ops. analyst Hdqrs. 20th Air Force, Washington and Guam, 1945; asst. prof. math. Williams Coll., Williamstown, Mass., 1946-49; ops. analyst Hdqrs. USAF, Washington, 1949-59, dep. asst. ops. analysis, 1951-59, acting asst. for ops. analysis, 1958-59; dir. operational scis. lab. Rsch. Triangle Inst., Durham, N.C., 1959-60; dir. applied sci. div. ops. evaluation group MIT, Cambridge, Mass., 1960-62; asst. to dir. systems planning and rsch. Mitre Corp., Bedford, Mass., 1962-65; v.p. Travelers Rsch. Ctr., Inc., Hartford, Conn., 1965-69; with U. Mass., Amherst, 1969—, prof. indsl. engring. and ops. rsch., 1969-80, acting head dept. indsl. engring. and ops. rsch., 1975-76, head dept., 1976-79, prof. emeritus, 1980—; leader craft of systems analysis, exec. editor publs. Internat. Inst. Applied Systems Analysis, Laxenburg, Austria, 1979-82, acting head communications, 1980-81; cons., sec., chief of staff USAF, 1967-68; cons. ops. analysis office hdqrs. USAF, 1968-71; mem. NAS Evaluation Panel for Inst. Applied Tech., Nat. Bur. Standards, 1969-72, Evaluation Panel for Tech. Analysis Div., 1967-69, 72-73, chmn. 1969-72; mem. commerce tech. adv. bd. Panel on Noise Abatement, 1968-71; cons. info. systems programs NSF Office Sci. Info. Svc., 1969-74, Ctr. for the Environment and Man Inc., Hartford, 1970-79, Rensselaer Poly. Inst. of Conn., Hartford, 1970, Am. Acad. Arts and Scis., Cambridge, 1983-85; chmn. rsch. adv. com. Ins. Inst. for Hwy. Safety, Washington, 1967-69; cons., mem. systems and program analysis panel Gen. Acctg. Office, Washington, 1972-76; mem. internat. advisory com. Systems Practice jour. Co-author: Basic Mathematics for Engineers, 1944, Basic Mathematics for Science and Engineering, 1955; co-editor: Handbook of Systems Analysis, Vol. 1, 1985, Vol. 2, 1988, Vol. 3, 1995. Moderator First Ch. of Christ, Congl., Farmington, Conn., 1986-88; pres. New World Chamber Ensemble, Inc., Simsbury Conn., 1986-88, 90-92, 93-94. Recipient Arthur S. Flemming award U.S. Jr. C. of C., 1952. Fellow AAAS; mem. Ops. Rsch. Soc. Am. (founding mem. 1952, sec. 1958-61, v.p. 1961-62, pres. 1962-63, rep. to NRC 1967-73, editor Bull. 1959-61, editor Ops. Rsch. 1968-74, George E. Kimball medal 1975), Inst. Mgmt. Scis., Can. Operational Rsch. Soc. (Harold Larnder prize 1990), Am. Math. Soc., Math. Assn. Am., Soc. for Indls. and Applied Math., Inst. Math. Stats., Am. Statis. Assn., Conn. Acad. Sci. and Engring. (founding mem. 1976), Ops.-Rsch./Mgmt.-Sci. Found. Inc. (pres. 1987-91), Operational Rsch. Soc., Assn. Pub. Policy and Mgmt., Phi Beta Kappa, Sigma Xi. Home and Office: 199 South Rd Farmington CT 06032-2522

MISH, FREDERICK CRITTENDEN, editor; b. Hagerstown, Md., Feb. 11, 1938; s. Joseph Dubbs and Edith Louise (Crittenden) M.; m. Judith Elizabeth Solberg, Mar. 15, 1969; children—Stephen Crittenden, Andrew Dubbs, David Rogneby. BA, Yale U., 1959; MA, U. Minn., 1967, PhD, 1973; LHD (hon.), York Coll., 1995. Instr. English, Severn Sch., Severna Park, Md., 1959-61; chmn. dept. English Severn Sch., 1963-65; teaching assoc. U. Minn., Mpls., 1965-71; asst. editor G & C Merriam Co., Springfield, Mass., 1973-74, assoc. editor, 1974, sr. editor, 1974-75, joint editorial dir, 1975-78; editorial dir. Merriam-Webster Inc., 1978-93, v.p., editor-in-chief, 1993—. Editor-in-chief: The Merriam-Webster Book of Word Histories, 1976, 6000 Words: A Supplement to Webster's Third, 1976, Webster's School Dictionary, 1980, Webster's Beginning Dictionary, 1980, Webster's Vest Pocket Dictionary, 1981, Webster's Ninth New Collegiate Dictionary, 1983, Merriam Webster's Collegiate Dictionary, 10th Edit., 1994, 9, 000 Words: A Supplement to Webster's Third, 1983, 12,000 Words: A Supplement to Webster's Third, 1986, Webster's Intermediate Dictionary, 1986, Webster's Word Histories, 1989, The New Merriam Webster Dictionary, 1989, Addenda Section 1993: A Supplement to Webster's Third, The Merriam-Webster Dictionary, 1994. Advisor Noah Webster Found., 1979—; trustee Davis and Elkins Coll., 1986-95. With U.S. Army, 1961-63. S. H. Monk teaching fellow, 1971-72. Mem. MLA, Nat. Coun. Tchrs. English (commn. on English lang. 1981-83), Linguistic Soc. Am., Am. Dialect Soc., Am. Name Soc., Dictionary Soc. N.Am. Home: 45 Harwich Rd Longmeadow MA 01106-1207 Office: Merriam Webster Inc 47 Federal St PO Box 281 Springfield MA 01102-0281

MISHELL, DANIEL R., JR., physician, educator; b. Newark, May 7, 1931; s. Daniel R. and Helen Mishell; m. Carol Goodrich; children: Sandra, Daniel III, Tana. BA, Stanford U., 1952, MD, 1955. Diplomate Am. Bd. Ob-Gyn. (examiner 1975—, bd. dirs., dir. subspecialty divsn. reproductive endocrinology 1985-89, pres. 1986-90, chmn. 1990-94). Intern L.A. County Harbor Gen. Hosp., Torrance, 1955-56; resident in ob-gyn. Bellevue Hosp., N.Y.C., 1956-57, UCLA-Harbor Gen. Hosp., Torrance, 1959-63; rsch. fellow Univ. Hosp., Uppsala, Sweden, 1961-62; asst. prof. dept. ob-gyn. Sch. Medicine, UCLA, 1963-68, assoc. prof., 1968-69; prof. U. So. Calif., L.A., 1969—, assoc. chmn. dept., 1972-78, chmn. dept., 1978—. Editor in chief Contraception, 1969—; editor Jour. Reproductive Medicine, 1982—; Year Book of Obstetrics and Gynecology, 1987—, Year Book of Infertility, 1989—; adv. com. Core Jours. in Obs-gyn., 1982—; mem. editorial bd. New Trends in GYN and OB, 1985—. Capt. USAF, 1957-59. Recipient Lester T. Hibbard award U. So. Calif., L.A., 1983, Joseph Bolivar DeLee Humanitarian award Chgo. Lying-In Hosp., 1985, Arthur and Edith Wippman Sci. Rsch. award Planned Parenthood Fedn. Am., 1992, Disting. Scientist award Soc. Gynecologic Investigation, 1994. Mem. Am. Gyn-Ob Soc., Am. Fertility Soc., Am. Coll. Obstetricians and Gynecologists, Am. Fedn. Clin. Rsch., Endocrine Soc., Soc. for Gynecologic Investigation (pres. 1985-86), L.A. Lb-Gyn. Soc. (v.p. 1984-85, pres. 1985-86), Assn. Profs. Gynecology and Obstetrics (exec. coun. 1982-85), Pacific Coast Fertility Soc. (pres. 1973-74), Salerni Collegium, L.A. Athletic Club, Phi Beta Kappa, Alpha Omega Alpha. Avocations: tennis, fishing. Office: U So Calif Dept Ob-Gyn 1240 N Mission Rd Los Angeles CA 90033-1078

MISHER, ALLEN, college president, retired; b. Feb. 12, 1933; m. Patricia Ann Kelley, Jan. 5, 1956; children: Robert, Lynda, David, Karen. BSc in Pharmacy, Phila. Coll. Pharmacy and Sci., 1959; PhD in Physiology, U. Pa., 1964. V.p. rsch. Smith, Kline & French, Inc., Phila., 1971-77, v.p. mfg., 1977-78; pres. Smith Kline Med. Diagnostics Co., Phila., 1978-82; sr. v.p. Nat. Med. Care, Boston, 1982-84; pres. Phila. Coll. Pharmacy and Sci., 1984—; bd. dirs. U.S. Health Care, U.S. Biosci., G.D. Searle, Inc. Home: 6 Roselawn Ln Malvern PA 19355-3316 Office: Phila Coll Pharmacy and Sci 600 South 43d St Philadelphia PA 19104

MISHKIN, EDWIN D., lawyer; b. N.Y.C., Feb. 1, 1937; s. Abraham and Esther Mishkin; m. Harriet Furgang, June 17, 1959; children: Andrew, David. Student, Union Coll.; BS in Law, Northwestern U., 1958, LLB, 1960. Assoc. Cleary, Gottlieb, Steen, and Hamilton, N.Y.C., 1960-70, ptnr., 1970—. Mem. N.Y. County Lawyers Assn. (bd. dirs.). Home: 8 E 83rd St New York NY 10028-0418 Office: 1 Liberty Plz New York NY 10006-1401

MISHKIN, JEFFREY ALAN, lawyer; b. N.Y., Sept. 7, 1948; s. Arthur Lawrence Mishkin and Bette (Beraha) Jaffe; m. Janet Paula Steel, Dec. 26, 1971; children: Paul Steel, Douglas William. BA, State U. of N.Y., Albany, 1969; JD, Cornell U., 1972. Bar: N.Y. 1973, U.S. Dist. Ct. (no. dist.) N.Y. 1973, U.S. Dist. Ct. (so. and ea. dists.) N.Y. 1974, U.S. Ct. Appeals (2d cir.)

1974, U.S. Supreme Ct. 1980, U.S. Ct. Appeals (9th cir.) 1986, U.S. Ct. Appeals (3d cir.) 1988, U.S. Ct. Appeals (4th cir.) 1987, U.S. Ct. Appeals (1st and 7th cirs.) 1990, U.S. Ct. Appeals (DC circuit), 1992. Staff atty. Legal Aid Soc. N.Y.C., N.Y.C., 1972-73; assoc. Proskauer, Rose, Goetz & Mendelsohn, N.Y.C., 1973-80, ptnr., 1980-92; sr. v.p. legal and bus. affairs Nat. Basketball Assn., N.Y.C., 1993—; adj. prof. law Cardozo Law Sch., N.Y.C., 1984-89. Mem. ABA, N.Y. State Bar Assn., Assn. of Bar of City of N.Y. Home: 2 E End Ave Apt 4F New York NY 10021-1151 Office: NBA 645 5th Ave New York NY 10022-5910

MISHKIN, MORTIMER, neuropsychologist; b. Fitchburg, Mass., Dec. 13, 1926; married; 2 children. AB, Dartmouth Coll., 1946; MA, McGill U., Montreal, Can., 1949, PhD, 1951. Asst. in research and physiology and psychiatry Yale U. Med. Sch., New Haven, Conn., 1949-51; research assoc. Inst. of Living, Hartford-Conn. and NYU Bellevue Med. Ctr., N.Y.C., 1951-55; research psychologist, sect. on neuropsychology NIMH, Bethesda, Md., 1955-75, research physiologist, Lab. of Neuropsychology, 1976-78, chief, sect. on cerebral mechanisms, Lab. of Neuropsychology, 1979-80, chief Lab. of Neuropsychology, 1980—, assoc. dir. basic rsch. DIRP, 1994—; part-time instr. psychology Howard U., 1956-58; vis. scientist Nencki Inst. Exptl. Biology, Warsaw, Poland, winter 1958, 68, Tokyo Met. Inst. Neuroscis., summer 1978, Oxford U. Dept. Exptl. Psychology, summer 1979; mem. psychol. scis. panel NIH, 1959-61, exptl. psychology study sect., 1965-69; mem. NIMH Assembly of Scientists Council, 1962-64, 72-74; mem. NIMH Scientist Promotion Rev. Com., 1984-86; mem. adv. com. Cognitive Neurosci. Inst., 1982-86; mem. NIH Fogart Internat. Scholars-in-Residence Adv. Panel, 1985-89; adv. bd. McDonnell-Pew Program Cognitive Neurosci., 1989-94; review com. Brain rsch., Human Frontier Sci. program, 1992-94, chmn. 1993—. Cons. editor Jour. Comparative and Physiol. Psychology, 1963-73, Exptl. Brain Research, 1965—, Brain Research, 1974-78; cons. editor Neuropsychologia, 1963, mem. editorial bd., 1978-81; editorial bd. Human Neurobiology, 1981-87, Neuropsychologia, 1963-92; Exptl. Brain Rsch., 1965—, Brain Rsch., 1974-78, Human Neurobiology, Jour. Cognitive Neurosci., 1989—, Jour. NIH Rsch., 1989—, Cerebral Cortex, 1990—, Advances in Neurobiology, 1990—, Handbook Behavioral Neurology, 1990, Current Opinion in Neurobiology, 1991—, Behavioral and Neural Biology, 1992—; reviewing editors Sci., 1985-93; assoc. editor Neuroreport, 1990—; contbr. over 170 articles to profl. jours.; also abstracts and books revs. Served to lt. (j.g.) USNR. Fellow AAAS (chair-elect 1990-91, chair 1991-92, past chair 1992-93), Am. Psychol. Assn. (officer, mem. at large 1964-66, coun. rep. 1967-69, pres. 1968-69); mem. NAS (officer, chmn. 1989-92), Ea. Psychol. Assn., Internat. Brain Research Orgn. (officer, rep.-at-large governing coun. 1993—), Internat. Neuropsychol. Soc., Internat. Neuropsychol. Symposium, Internat. Primatological Soc., Internat. Soc. Neuroethology, Soc. Exptl. Psychologists, Soc. Neurosci. (officer, pres.-elect 1985-86, pres. 1986-87, past pres. 1987-88), Sigma Xi, Phi Beta Kappa. Achievements includes research in behavioral and cognitive neuroscience in primates. Office: NIMH Lab Neuropsychology Bldg 49 Rm 1B80 49 Convent Dr MSC 4415 Bethesda MD 20892-4415

MISHKIN, PAUL J., lawyer, educator; b. Trenton, N.J., Jan. 1, 1927; s. Mark Mordecai and Bella (Dworetsky) M.; m. Mildred Brofman Westover; 1 child, Jonathan Mills Westover. AB, Columbia U., 1947, JD, 1950; MA (hon.), U. Pa., 1971. Bar: N.Y. State bar 1950, U.S. Supreme Ct. bar 1958. Mem. faculty Law Sch. U. Pa., Phila., 1950-72; prof. law U. Calif., Berkeley, 1972-75, Emanuel S. Heller prof., 1975—; Cons. City of Phila., 1953; reporter study div. jurisdiction between state and fed. cts. Am. Law Inst., 1960-65; mem. faculty Salzburg Seminar in Am. Studies, 1974; Charles Inglis Thompson guest prof. U. Colo., 1975; John Randolph Tucker lectr., 1978, Owen J. Roberts Meml. lectr., 1982; vis. fellow Wolfson Coll., Cambridge U., 1984; vis. prof. Duke U. Law Sch., 1989. Author: (with Morris) On Law in Courts, 1965, (with others) Federal Courts and the Federal System, 2d edit, 1973, 3d edit, 1988; contbr. articles to profl. jours. Trustee Jewish Publ. Soc. Am., 1966-75; mem. permanent com. Oliver Wendell Holmes Devise, 1979-87. With USNR 1945-46. Rockefeller Found. rsch. grantee, 1956; Center for Advanced Study in Behavioral Scis. fellow, 1964-65. Fellow Am. Acad. Arts Scis., Am. Bar Found.; mem. Am. Law Inst., Order of Coif, Phi Beta Kappa. Home: 91 Stonewall Rd Berkeley CA 94705-1414 Office: U Calif Sch Law Boalt Hall Berkeley CA 94720

MISHLER, CLIFFORD LESLIE, publisher; b. Vandalia, Mich., Aug. 11, 1939; s. Nelson Howard and Lily Mae (Young) M.; m. Sandra Rae Knutson, Dec. 21, 1963 (dec. July 8, 1972); m. Sylvia M. Leer, Feb. 27, 1976; children: Sheila, Sharon, Susan. Student, Northwestern U., 1957-58. Author, pub. ann. edits. Ann. Studies U.S. and Can. Commemorative Medals and Tokens, 1958-63; assoc. editor Numismatic News, Krause Publs., Iola, Wis., 1963-64; editor Numismatic News, Krause Publs., 1964-66, numismatic editor all publs., 1966-75, exec. v.p., pub. all numismatic publs., 1975-78, exec. v.p., pub. all products, 1978-88, sr. v.p., pub. all Numismatic products, 1988-89, sr. v.p. ops., 1989-90; pres. Krause Publs., Iola, Wis., 1991—; bd. dirs. First State Bank Iola, 1972-83, Scandinavia Telephone Co., 1981—; ex-officio dir. Iola Old Car Show, Inc., 1985—; mem. coins and medals adv. panel Am. Revolution Bicentennial Commn., 1970-75; mem. ann. assay commn. U.S. Mint, 1973. Co-author: Standard Catalog of World Coins, ann. 1972—; contbr. articles New Book Knowledge, an. 1969-81. Bd. dirs. William R. Higgins, Jr. Found., 1991—. Fellow Am. Numismatic Soc. (life mem.); mem. Am. Numismatic Assn. (life mem., medal of merit 1983, Farran Zerbe meml. disting svc. award 1984, Glen Smedley meml. dedicated svcs. award 1991), Token and Medal Soc. (life mem., pres. 1976-78, editor jour. 1964-68, disting. svc. award 1966, 80), Numismatics Wis. (life mem., pres. 1974-76, meritorious svc. award 1972), Soc. Internat. Numismatics (award of excellence 1981), Blue Ridge Numismatic Assn. (life mem., hall of fame 1994), Tex. Numismatic Assn. (life mem., hall of fame 1993), Ind. State Numismatic Assn. (life mem., founders award 1993), Ctrl. States Numismatic Soc. (life mem., medal of merit 1984), Iola Lions. Home: 100 Island Dr Iola WI 54945-9485 Office: 700 E State St Iola WI 54990-0001

MISHLER, JACOB, federal judge; b. N.Y.C., Apr. 20, 1911; s. Abraham and Rebecca M.; m. Lola Mishler, Sept. 1, 1936; m. Helen Mishler, Aug. 26, 1970; children: Alan, Susan Lubitz; stepchildren: Bruce Shillet, Gail Shillet Unger. Degree, NYU, 1931, JD, 1933. Pvt. practice L.I. City, N.Y., 1934-50; ptnr. Mishler & Wohl, 1950-59, 60; judge N.Y. State Supreme Ct., 1959; sr. judge U.S. Dist. Ct. (ea. dist.), Uniondale, N.Y., 1961—; mem. U.S. Jud. Conf., Dist. Judge Rep., 2nd cir., 1974-77. Office: US Dist Ct LI Courthouse Uniondale Ave at Hempstead Tpk Uniondale NY 11553-1259

MISHLER, JOHN MILTON (YOCHANAN MENASHSHEH BEN SHAUL), natural sciences educator, academic administrator; b. Cairo, Ill., Sept. 25, 1946; s. John Milton and Mary Jane (Woodbury) M.; m. Mary Therese Stember, Apr. 15, 1972 (div. Nov. 1981); m. Sigrid Ruth Elizabeth Fischer, Dec. 15, 1981; 1 child, Joshua Evan. AA with honors, Orange Coast Coll., Costa Mesa, Calif., 1966; AB in Molecular Biology, U. Calif., San Diego, 1969, ScM in Engring. Scis., 1971; DPhil in Immunohematology, St. John's Coll., Oxford U., 1978. Cert. community coll. instr., Calif. Clin. coord. McGaw Labs., Costa Mesa, 1972-78; rsch. fellow Royal Postgrad. Med. Sch., Eng., 1977-78, Med. U., Cologne, Fed. Republic Germany, 1978-80; br. chief Nat. Heart, Lung and Blood Inst. NIH, Bethesda, Md., 1980-82; prof. med., basic life scis. and pharmacol. U. Mo., Kansas City, 1983-89, asst. vice chancellor, 1983-85, div. div. basic med. scis., 1985-86, assoc. vice chancellor, 1985-89; prof. nat. scis. U. Md. Ea. Shore, Princess Anne, 1989-94, dean grad. studies and rsch., 1989-91; prof. biology Delaware Valley Coll. Sci. and Agrl., Doylestown, Pa., 1994—, dean of Coll., 1994—; frequent nat. and internat. lectr.; chmn. 13 nat. and internat. meeting sects. Author: Pharmacology of Hydroxyethyl Starch. Use in Therapy and Blood Banking, 1982; editor or co-editor 6 sci. monographs; mem. editorial rev. bd. Jour. Soc. Rsch. Adminstrs., 1987-91; book rev. editor Grants Mag., 1987-89; contbr. more than 100 articles to profl. jours. Bd. dirs. Bucks Assn. for Retarded Citizens, 1995—. Sr. rsch. fellow Alexander von Humboldt Foun. (West Germany), 1978-80; recipient Outstanding Adminstrn. Svc. award U. Mo., Kansas City, 1987, Excellence award Soc. Rsch. Adminstrn., 1989, Cert. Appreciation, 1991. Fellow Internat. Soc. Haematology, Royal Coll. Pathologists; mem. Am. Soc. Hematology, German Soc. Hematology, Nat. Coun. Univ. Rsch. Adminstrn., Nat. Assn. State Univs. and Land-Grant Colls. (mem. exec. com. coun. on rsch. policy and grad. edn. 1990-91), Coun. Grad. Schs., N.Y. Acad. Scis., Sigma Xi. Jewish. Avocations: reading, writing, music. Office: Delaware Valley Coll 700 E Butler Ave Doylestown PA 18901-2699

MISHLER, WILLIAM, II, political science educator; b. Miami, Fla., Oct. 14, 1947; s. William Thomas Earle and Marie Kathryn (Schmitz) M.; m. Mary Catherine Tanner, Aug. 5, 1972. BA, Stetson U., 1969; MA, Duke U., 1972, PhD, 1973. Asst. prof. Duke U., Durham, N.C., 1972-78; assoc. prof. SUNY, Buffalo, 1978-82, prof., chmn., 1984-86; dir. polit. sci. program NSF, Washington, 1982-84; prof., chmn. U. S.C., Columbia, 1986-89, prof., 1989—; vis. prof. U. Strathelyde, Glasgow, Scotland, 1976-77; vis. scientist, dir. polit. sci. program NSF, Washington, 1990-91. Author: Influence in Parliament, Political Participation in Canada, Representative Democracy in the Canadian Provinces, Resurgence of Conservatism, Controversies in Political Economy; mem. editorial bds. Jour. Politics, 1982-88, Legis. Studies Quar., 1988-91. Capt. U.S Army, 1972. Mem. Am. Polit. Sci. Assn., So. Polit. Sci. Assn., Midwest Polit. Sci. Assn., Can. Polit. Sci. Assn., Internat. Studies Assn., Assn. Can. Studies (U.S. chpt.). Office: Dept Govt & Internat Studies U SC Columbia SC 29208

MISKEL, CECIL G., academic dean. Dean grad. sch. edn. U. Utah, Salt Lake City, until 1988; dean sch. edn. U. Mich., 1988—. Office: U Mich Sch Edn Ann Arbor MI 48108

MISKIMIN, HARRY ALVIN, history educator; b. Orange, N.J., Sept. 8, 1932; s. Harry Alvin and Anne Wylie (Hamilton) M.; m. Alice Augusta Schwenk, Aug. 29, 1953 (div. May 1988); children: Sidonie Ann Miskimin Clauss (dec.), Matthew Charles; m. Patricia E. Behre, Dec. 22, 1989. BA, Yale, 1954, MA, 1958, PhD, 1960. From instr. to prof. history Yale U., New Haven, 1960—; assoc. prof., 1964-71, prof. history, 1971—, chmn. dept. history, 1986-89, Charles Seymour Prof. of History, 1991—; pres. Yale chpt. AAUP, 1979-82. mem. exec. com. Conn. conf., 1982-87. Author: Money, Prices and Foreign Exchange in Fourteenth Century France, 1963, The Economy of Early Renaissance Europe 1300-1460, 1969, The Economy of Later Renaissance Europe 1460-1600, 1977, Money and Power in Fifteenth Century France, 1984, Cash, Credit and Crisis in Europe 1300-1600, 1989; gen. editor: The Economic Civilization of Europe, vols. I-IV; editor (with A. Udovitch and D. Herlihy) The Medieval City, 1977; contbr. articles to profl. jours. Treas. Conn. Cystic Fibrosis Assn., 1961, trustee 1969-72; bd. dirs. Woodbridge (Conn.) Town Libr., 1973-76, treas. 1974-76; mem. Woodbridge Dem. Town Com., 1972-85; zoning commr. Town of Woodbridge, 1976-85. With U.S. Army, 1955-57. Morse fellow Yale U., 1964-65, Guggenheim fellow, 1968, Am. Coun. Learned Socs. fellow, 1981. Me. Econ. History Assn., Econ. History Soc., Mory's Assn. Avocations: carpentry, gardening, swimming. Office: Yale U Dept History PO Box 1504A New Haven CT 06520-7425 also: 130 Center Ln Centerville MA 02632

MISKOWSKI, LEE R., retired automobile executive; b. Stevens Point, Wis., Mar. 27, 1932; s. Paul P. and Marie Grace (Glazer) M.; m. Billie Poulson, 1963; children: Christine, Katherine. BBA, U. Wis., 1954, MBA, 1957. V.p. Ford of Europe Ford Motor Co., Cologne, Fed. Republic Germany, 1977-80; gen. mktg. mgr. Ford div. Ford Motor Co., Dearborn, Mich., 1980-83, v.p., gen. mgr. parts and svc. div., 1989-91, v.p., gen. mgr. Lincoln-Mercury div., 1991-94; ret. Ford Motor Co., 1994. Contbr. articles to trade jours. Trustee Hospice of S.E. Mich., Detroit, 1988-94; mem. bd. Mich. Parkinson Found., Detroit, 1992-94. With U.S. Army, 1954-56. Mem. Oakland Hills Country Club. Roman Catholic. Avocations: tennis, snow skiing, reading, extensive travel.

MISLOW, KURT MARTIN, chemist, educator; b. Berlin, Germany, June 5, 1923; came to U.S., 1940, naturalized, 1946; s. Max and Ida (Bingen) M.; m. Jacqueline Ford, 1966; children: Christopher, John. B.S., Tulane U., 1944, D.Sc. (hon.), 1975; Ph.D., Calif. Inst. Tech., 1947; D. honoris causa, Free U., Brussels, 1974, Uppsala U., 1977; Düsseldorf U., 1994. Instr. NYU, 1947-51, asst. prof., 1951-56, asso. prof., 1956-60, prof., 1960-64; Hugh Stott Taylor prof. chemistry Princeton, 1964-88, chmn. dept. chemistry, 1968-74, prof. emeritus, 1988—; vis. prof. Stanford U., 1960, Calif. Inst. Tech., 1994; M.S. Kharasch vis. prof. U. Chgo., 1989; Univ. lectr. U. London, 1965; J.A. McRae Meml. lectr. Queen's U., 1967; H.A. Iddles lectr. U. N.H., 1972; Solvay lectr. and medalist Free U. Brussels, 1972; E.C. Lee lectr. U. Chgo.; A.A. Vernon lectr. Northeastern U., 1976; PPG lectr. Ohio U., 1977; J. Musher Meml. lectr. Hebrew U. Jerusalem, 1978; North Country lectr., 1978; Honor lectr. Ariz. State U., 1981; E. Ritchie meml. lectr. Sydney U., 1983; Fuson lectr. U. Nev., 1983; Research Scholar lectr. Drew U., 1983, McGregory lectr. Colgate U., 1984; Sandia lectr. U. Alta., 1984; Purves lectr. McGill U., 1985; Arnold lectr. So. Ill. U., 1985; Bergmann lectr. Yale U., 1986; H.C. Brown lectr. Purdue U., 1988; Irvine lectr. U. St. Andrews, 1988; Eyring lectr. Ariz. State U., 1989; Disting. Scientist lectr. Bard Coll., 1991; Syntex Disting. lectr. Colo. State U., 1991; Disting. scientist lectr. Bard Coll., 1991; J.W.T. Spinks lectr. U. Saskatchewan, 1992; Bristol-Myers-Squibb disting. lectr. Syracuse U., 1992; Churchill fellow Cambridge U., 1974-75; mem. adv. panel chemistry NSF, 1963-66; mem. panel medical and organic chemistry NIH, 1963-66. Author: Introduction to Stereochemistry, 1965; also numerous articles; bd. editors: Jour. Organic Chemistry, 1965-70; mem. editl. adv. bd. Monatshefte für Chemie, Topics in Stereochemistry, Accounts of Chem. Rsch., Chem. and Engring. News, Bull des Sociétés Chimiques Belges, Symmetry, Jour. Math. Chemistry. Recipient Prelog medal, ETH Zurich, 1986, W.H. Nichols medal, 1987, Sci. Achievement award medal CCNY, 1988, Disting. Alumni award Calif. Inst. Tech., 1990, Chirality medal, 1993, Cope scholar award, 1995; Guggenheim fellow, 1957-58, 74-75, Alfred P. Sloan fellow, 1959-63, Sherman Fairchild disting. scholar Calif. Inst. Tech., 1990, 91, 94. Fellow AAAS, Am. Acad. Arts and Scis.; mem. Nat. Acad. Scis., Am. Chem. Soc. (James Flack Norris award 1975), Chem. Soc. London, AAUP, Phi Beta Kappa, Sigma Xi, Phi Lambda Upsilon.

MISNER, CHARLES WILLIAM, physics educator; b. Jackson, Mich., June 13, 1932; s. Francis deSales and Madge B. (Mee) M.; m. Susanne Elisabeth Kemp, June 13, 1959; children: Benedicte Elisabeth, Francis Frithjof, Timothy Charles, Christopher Kemp. B.S., U. Notre Dame, 1952; M.A., Princeton U., 1954, Ph.D., 1957. Instr. Princeton U., (N.J.), 1956-59 asst. prof., 1959-63; assoc. prof. physics U. Md., College Park, 1963-66, prof., 1966—; vis. fellow Inst. for Theoretical Physics, U. Calif., Santa Barbara, 1980-81, All Souls Coll., Oxford, Eng., 1973; vis. faculty Calif. Inst. Tech., 1972, Princeton U., 1969. Author: (with Wheeler and Thorne) Gravitation, 1973, (with Patrick J.Cooney) Spreadsheet Physics, 1991; contbr. articles to profl. jours. Recipient Sci. Centennial award U. Notre Dame, 1965, Dannie Heineman prize (with R. Arnowitt and S. Deser) for math. physics Am. Phys. Soc., 1994; NSF sr. postdoctoral fellow, 1966-67; Guggenheim fellow, 1972-73; Eistein Centennial lectr., 1979. Fellow Am. Phys. Soc., Royal Astron. Soc. AAAS; mem. Philosophy of Sci. Assn., Am. Math. Soc. Fedn. Am. Scientists. Democrat. Roman Catholic. Home: 1009 Crest Park Dr Silver Spring MD 20903-1339 Office: U Md Dept Physics College Park MD 20742-4111

MISRA, JAYADEV, computer science educator; b. Cuttack, Orissa, India, Oct. 17, 1947; s. Sashibhusan and Shanty (Kar) M.; m. Mamata Das, Nov. 30, 1972; children: Amitav, Anuj. B Tech, Indian Inst. Tech., Kanpur, 1969; PhD, Johns Hopkins U., 1972. Staff scientist IBM, Gaithersburg, Md., 1973-74; from asst. prof. to prof. computer sci. U. Tex., Austin, 1974—. Regents chair in computer sci., 1992—; vis. prof. Stanford (Calif.) U., 1983-84; cons. on software and hardware design. Contbr. articles to profl. jours. Guggenheim fellow, 1988-89. Fellow IEEE, Assn. Computing Machinery (Samuel N. Alexander Meml. award 1970). Office: Univ Tex Dept Computer Sci Austin TX 78712-1188

MISRA, RAGHUNATH PRASAD, physician, educator; b. Calcutta, W. Bengal, India, Feb. 1, 1928; came to U.S., 1964; s. Guru Prasad and Anandi M.; m. Therese Rettenmund, Sept. 13, 1963; children: Sima, Joya, Maya, Tara. BSc with honors, Calcutta U., 1948; MBBS, Med. Coll., Calcutta, 1953; PhD, McGill U., Montreal, Que., 1965. Diplomate Am. Bd. Anatomical and Clin. Pathology. Asst. prof., dir. kidney lab. U. Louisville Sch. Medicine, 1964-68; asso. investigator dir. kidney lab Mt. Sinai Hosp., Cleve., 1968-73; asst. prof. Case Western Reserve Med. Sch., Cleve., 1973-76; asst. prof., dir. kidney lab. La State U. Sch. Medicine, Shreveport, 1976-80, assoc. prof., 1980-86; prof. La. State U., Sch. of Medicine, Shreveport, 1986—, dir. Ocular Pathology Lab., 1988—; cons. VA Med. Ctr., Shreveport, 1977—, EA Conway Meml. Hosp., Monroe, La., 1980—. Author: Atlas of Skin Biopsy, 1983. Pres. India Assn. of Shreveport, 1979, 81. Recipient Tallisman Fellowship, Mt. Sinai Hosp., 1970-73. Fellow Am.

Coll. Pathologists; Am. Soc. Clin. Pathologists, U. Calcutta Med. Alumni Assn. Am. (pres. 1992-93), Sigma Xi (pres. 1987-89). Democrat. Hindu. Avocations: photography, travel. Office: La State U Sch Medicine 1501 Kings Hwy Shreveport LA 71103-4228

MISRACH, RICHARD LAURENCE, photographer; b. L.A., July 11, 1949; s. Robert Laskin and Lucille (Gardner) M.; m. Debra Bloomfield, Jan. 18, 1981 (div. 1987); 1 son, Jacob Luke; m. Myriam Weisang, Apr. 17, 1989. A.B. in Psychology, U. Calif., Berkeley, 1971. Instr. Students Studio, U. Calif., Berkeley, 1971-77; vis. lectr. U. Calif-Berkeley, 1982; lectr. U. Calif.-Santa Barbara, 1984; juror Nat. Endowment Arts, 1986, Whitney Biennial, 1991. Exhbns. include Musée d'Art Moderne, Paris, 1979, Mus. Modern Art, N.Y.C., 1978, Whitney Mus. Am. Art, N.Y.C., 1981, Grapestake Gallery, San Francisco, 1979, 81, Young-Hoffman Gallery, Chgo., 1980, Centre Georges Pompidou, Paris, 1983, Oakland Mus., 1982, San Francisco Mus. Modern Art, 1983, Centre Georges Pompidou, Paris, 1983, Los Angeles County Mus. Art, 1984, Fraenkel Gallery, San Francisco, 1985, 89, 91, Oakland Mus., 1987, Min Gallery, Tokyo, 1975-87, U. Art Mus., Berkeley, numerous others; one person exhbns. at Art Inst. Chgo., 1988, Milw. Art Mus., 1988, Carpenter Ctr., Harvard U., 1988, Fotomamm, Inc., N.Y., 1989, 91, Photographers Gallery, 1990, Parco Gallery, Tokyo, 1990, Arles Festival, France, 1990, Jan Kesner Gallery, 1990, 91; art commn. cover Time mag., July 4, 1988; books include: Telegraph 3 A.M, 1974, Grapestake Gallery, 1979, (A Photographic Book), 1979, Hawaii portfolio, 1980, Graecism dye-transfer portfolio, 1982, Desert Cantos, 1987, (Internat. Ctr. of Photography award, 1988), Bravo 20: The Bombing of the American West, 1990 (Pen Ctr. U.S.A. West award for nonfiction 1991), Houston Ctr. for Photography, 1985, Light Gallery, N.Y.C., 1985, Martin Gallery, Washington, 1985, Richard Misrach, Minn. Gallery, 1988, Violent Legacies, Aperture, 1992. Guggenheim fellow, 1978; Ferguson grantee, 1976; NEA grantee, 1973, 77, 84, 92; AT&T commn., 1979; Eureka fellow, 1991; NEA fellow, 1992-93; recipient Koret Israel prize, 1992. Photographs are the shadows of reality much like dreams. On the one hand, they appear to literally transcribe the real world, while on the other, they defy our linear concept of time and meaning. Because the primary illusion of photography is fact, it is the most powerful art medium of our time.

MISS, MARY, artist; b. N.Y.C., 1944; d. David and Jeannette K. BA, U. Calif., Santa Barbara, 1966; MFA, Rhinehart Sch. Sculpture, Md. Art Inst., 1968. guest lectr. UCLA, Columbia U., San Francisco Art Inst., Archtl. Assn., London, Princeton U., N.J., U. Wash., Seattle. One-woman shows include Mus. Modern Art, N.Y.C., 1976, Nassau County Mus. Fine Arts, Roslyn, N.Y., 1978, Fogg Art Mus. Harvard U., Cambridge, Mass., 1980, Max Protetch Gallery, N.Y.C., 1980, Brown U. and U. R.I., Kingston, 1981, Laumeier Sculpture Park, St. Louis, 1982, U. Calif., Santa Barbara, 1983, Inst. Contemporary Art, London, 1983, Protetch-McNeil Gallery, N.Y.C., 1984, Danforth Mus. Art, Framingham, Mass., 1986, Archtl. Assn., London, 1987, Harvard U. Sch. Art and Design, 1990, Freedman Gallery Albright Coll., Reading, Pa., 1991; group shows include LaJolla Mus., 1986, L.A. County Mus., 1985, Whitney Mus. Am. Art, N.Y.C., 1981, Akademie der Kunst, Berlin, 1976, Williams Coll. Mus. Art, Williamstown, Mass., 1976, Bklyn. Mus. Art, 1977, Solomon R. Guggenheim Mus., N.Y.C., 1977, John Weber Gallery, N.Y.C., 1977, Max Protech Gallery, 1978, 80, Indpls. Mus. Art, 1980, Venice Biennale, Italy, 1980, 1981, Inst. Contemporary Art, Boston, 1980, Des Moines Art Ctr., 1980, L.A. Inst. Contemporary Art, 1980, Mus. Art R.I. Sch. Design, Providence, 1981, Neuer Berliner Kunstverein, Berlin, German Democratic Republic, 1982, U. South Fla., Tampa, 1983, The Clocktower Inst. for Art and Urban Resources, N.Y.C., 1983, Inst. Contemporary Art U. Pa., Phila., 1983, Sidney Janis Gallery, N.Y.C., 1984, L.A. County Mus. Art, 1985, Hudson River Mus., Yonkers, N.Y., 1985, Cleve. Ctr. for Contemporary Art, 1985, Contemporary Arts Ctr., Cin., 1987, Queen's Mus., N.Y.C., 1987, Making Their Mark: Women Artists Move Into the Mainstream 1970-85, Cin., 1989, New Orleans, 1989, Denver, Colo., 1989, Phila., 1989, Mus. Modern Art, N.Y.C., 1992, Bklyn. Mus., 1993, Berkshire Mus., Pittsfield, Mass., 1993, Weatherspoon Gallery, U. N.C., Greensboro, 1993, Art Devf. Gallery, Paris, 1993, John Weber Gallery, N.Y.C., 1993; represented in permanent collections: Mus. Modern Art, N.Y.C., Guggenheim Mus., N.Y.C., Allen Meml. Art Mus., Oberlin, Ohio; prin. works include wood panel cut-outs Battery Park City Landfill, N.Y.C., Sunken Pool, Greenwich, Conn., Blind Set, Lewiston, N.Y., Perimeters/Pavilions/Decoys, Nassau County Mus., Roslyn, Veiled Landscape, XIII Winter Olympics, Lake Placid, N.Y., Staged Gates, Hills and Dales Park, Dayton, Ohio, Mirror Way, Fogg Mus. Harvard U., Field Rotation, Govs. State U., Park Forest South, Ill., Study for a Courtyard: Approach to a Stepped Pool, Inst. Contemporary Art, London, Pool Complex: Orchard Valley, St. Louis, Arrivals and Departures: 100 Doors, Dallas Mus., Study for an Entry, Danforth Mus., Framingham, Mass., Hayden Sq., Tempe, Ariz., urban pavilion Archtl. Assn., London, South Cove, Battery Pk. City, N.Y.C., Univ. Hosp., Seattle, (reflecting pools, walkways and pergola to be viewed from waiting room), 1990, Albright Coll., Reading, Pa. (cen. ct. new art ctr.), 1991; subject of various articles. Bd. dirs. Am. Acad. in Rome. John Simon Guggenheim Meml. Found. fellow, 1986; grantee Nat. Endowment for Arts, 1974, 75, N.Y. State Coun. on Arts, 1973, 76; project grant Mott C.C., Flint, Mich., 1974; recipient Brandeis U. Creative Arts award, 1982; Am. Acad. Rome resident, 1989. Office: PO Box 304 Canal St Sta New York NY 10013

MISSAN, RICHARD SHERMAN, lawyer; b. New Haven, Oct. 5, 1933; s. Albert and Hannah (Hochberg) M.; m. Aileen Louise; children: Hilary, Andrew, Wendy. B.A., Yale U., 1955, J.D., 1958. Bar: N.Y. 1959, U.S. Dist. Ct. (so. and ea. dists.) N.Y. 1979, U.S. Ct. Appeals (2d cir.) N.Y. 1993. Assoc. Kaye, Scholer, Fierman, Hays & Handler, N.Y.C., 1962-67; ptnr. Schoenfeld & Jacobs, N.Y.C., 1968-78, Walsh & Frisch, N.Y.C., 1979-80, Gersten, Savage & Kaplowitz, N.Y.C., 1980-87, v.p., gen. counsel, Avis, Inc., 1987-88; pvt. practice, N.Y.C., 1988—; spl. prof. law Hofstra U., 1988—; mem. panel of mediators U.S. Dist. Ct. (ea. dist.) N.Y. Revision author: Corporations, New York Practice Guide (Business and Commercial). Mem. ABA, N.Y. State Bar Assn., Fed. Bar Council, Assn. of Bar of City of N.Y. (com. on corrections, chmn. subcom. on legis., com. on juvenile justice, chmn. subcom. on juvenile facilities, past com. corrections, com. on atomic energy, mem. com. on mcpl. affairs, com. on housing and urban devel.), Yale Club. Office: 100 Park Ave 35th Fl New York NY 10017

MISSAR, CHARLES DONALD, librarian; b. Cleve., July 16, 1925; s. Charles Frank and Genevieve Catherine (Buechele) M.; m. Margaret Mary du Fief, Feb. 17, 1962; children: Charles David, Stephen du Fief. Student, Sacred Heart Sem., Detroit, 1943-45, St. Mary's Sem., Cleve., 1945-49; BA, John Carroll U., 1951; MLS, Cath. U. Am., 1960. Referral specialist Libr. of Congress, Washington, 1963-66; ERIC info. specialist U.S. Office Edn., Washington, 1966-72; head Ednl. Reference Ctr. Nat. Inst. Edn., Washington, 1973-78, supervisory libr., 1978-85; sr. libr. U.S. Dept. Edn., 1985-86; sr. editor ERIC Processing and Reference Facility, CSC Psq., 1986—; agy. rep. Fed. Libr. Com., Washington, 1978-86; ann. lectr. Fed. Libr. Resources Workshop, CUA, Washington, 1981—. Editor: Management of Federally Sponsored Libraries: Case Studies and Analysis, 1995; editor monthly jour. Tech. Abstract Bull., 1958-60; mem. editorial bd. Online Mag., 1977-80. Recipient Superior Svc. Group award U.S. Office Edn., 1968, Superior Performance award Nat. Inst. Edn., 1974, 84; inductee Spl. Libraries Assn. Hall of Fame, 1991. Mem. ALA, D.C. Libr. Assn. (treas. 1973-74), Spl. Librs. Assn. (chmn. edn. divsn. 1980-81, chmn. 1989-90), Am. Soc. Info. Sci. (chmn. info. svcs. for edn. group 1984-86), John Carroll Soc., Cleve. Club, Serra Club (pres. 1992-93, 94—). Roman Catholic. Home: 5617 32nd St NW Washington DC 20015-1622 Office: CSC Profl Svcs Group 1301 Piccard Dr Ste 300 Rockville MD 20850-4305

MISSIMER, THOMAS MICHAEL, geologist; b. Lancaster, Pa., Mar. 10, 1950; s. Jacob M. and Lorraine L. (Bilodeau) M.; A.B. in Geology, Franklin and Marshall Coll., 1972; M.S. in Geology, Fla. State U., 1973; PhD in Marine Geology and Geophyics, 1995. Hydrologist, U.S. Geol. Survey, Ft. Myers, Fla., 1973-75; research assoc. sedimentology U. Miami, Coral Cables, Fla., 1975-76; pres. Missimer & Assocs., Inc., Cape Coral, Fla., 1976-91; vice chmn. ViroGroup, Inc., 1991-93; pres. Missimer Internat., Inc. 1993—, bd. Fla. Profl. Geologists, 1991-95, vice chmn. 1993, chmn. 1994. Mem. citizens planning adv. com. Bd. Lee County (Fla.), 1981-82, chmn. 1982-83. Registered profl. geologist, Fla., Ga., ind. Mem. Geol. Soc. Am., Am. Inst. Profl. Geologists (cert. profl. geol. scientist), Am. Water Resources Assn., Am. Water Works Assn., AAAS, Am. Inst. Hydrology (cert. profl.

hydrogeologist), Am. Soc. Groundwater Engrs. and Scientists (cert. hydrogeologist), Fla. Acad. Scis. (chmn. earth and planetary sci. sect. 1973-74, 1995), Southeastern Geol. Soc. Republican. Author Water supply development for membrane water treatment facilities, 1994; contbr. hydrogeol. and geol. studies of Southeastern U.S. to sci. jours. RecipientBest Paper award, Internat. Desalination Assoc., D.C., World Conf. on Desalination, 1991. Home:3214 McGregor Blvd Fort Myers FL 33901-6723 Office: Missimer Internat Inc 8140 McGregor Blvd Fort Myers FL 33914

MISTACCO, VICKI E., foreign language educator; b. Bklyn., Nov. 18, 1942; d. Anthony Sebastian and Lucia (Lalli) M. B.A., NYU, 1963; M.A., Middlebury Coll., 1964; M. Philosophy, Yale U., 1968, Ph.D., 1972. Instr. French, Wellesley Coll., Mass., 1968-72, asst. prof. French, 1972-78, assoc. prof. French, 1978-84, prof. French, 1984—, intern. nat. adv. bd. Sweet Briar Jr. Yr. in France, Va., 1978—. Contbr. articles to profl. jours. Fulbright fellow, 1963-64; Woodrow Wilson fellow, 1964-65, 1966-67; NEH fellow, 1983-84, 94-95. Mem. MLA, N.E. MLA, Am. Assn. Tchrs. French, Phi Beta Kappa. Democrat. Roman Catholic. Avocations: photography; travel. Office: Wellesley Coll Dept French 106 Central St Wellesley MA 02181-8203

MITAU, LEE R., lawyer; b. St. Paul, 1948. AB cum laude, Dartmouth Coll., 1969; JD magna cum laude, U. Minn., 1972. Bar: Minn. 1972, N.Y. 1973. Law clk. to Hon. George E. MacKinnon U.S. Ct. Appeals (D.C. cir.), 1972-73; ptnr. Dorsey & Whitney, Mpls.; adj. prof. law William Mitchell Coll. Law, 1982-83. Office: Dorsey & Whitney 220 S 6th St Minneapolis MN 55402

MITBY, NORMAN PETER, college president; b. Cashton, Wis., May 21, 1916; s. Chester M. and Margaret (Murray) M.; m. Luvern J. Jensen, June 15, 1941; children: John C., Margaret N. BS, Whitewater (Wis.) State Coll., 1938; postgrad., U. Wis., 1947-48; MS, Stout State U., 1949. Tchr. high sch., vocat. sch. Cornell, Wis., 1938-41, Antigo, Wis., 1941-46; asst. dir. LaCrosse (Wis.) Vocat. and Adult Schs., 1946-54; dir. vocat. and adult sch. Oshkosh, Wis., 1954-55, Green Bay, Wis., 1955-60, Madison, Wis., 1960-67; dist. dir. tech. and adult edn. dist. Madison Area Tech. Coll., 1967, pres., 1967-88; prof. Stout State U. Grad. Sch., Menomonie, Wis.; mem. adv. council U. Wis. Schs. Edn., Madison and Milw., 1961-64; cons., examiner North Central Assn. Colls. and Secondary Schs., 1970-88; mem. pres.'s adv. com. Assn. Community Coll. Trustees, 1978-79; mem. joint adminstrv. com. on acad. programs U. Wis. Vocat., Tech. and Adult Edn. System, 1985-88. Mem. Community Welfare Council Madison, 1960-63, mem. needs and priorities com., 1964; sponsor Wis. Heart Assn.; chmn. pub. employees div. Cancer Fund drive, 1963; mem. Mayor's Com. for Employment Handicapped, 1964-68, Nat. Adv. Com. on Health Occupations Tng., 1964-68; chmn. gov.'s adv. com. Title I, Higher Edn. Act, 1965-74; mem. adv. council Midwest Community Coll. Leadership Council, 1968-73; mem. Wis. Gov.'s Adv. Council on Vocat. Edn., 1969-74, Wis. Gov.'s Health Planning and Policy Task Force, 1971-73; adv. com. Wis. State Bd. Nursing, 1972-74; mem. Wis. Council Safety, 1960-73; bd. dirs. Madison Civic Music Assn. 1960-88, Oakwood Found. Inc., 1990—. Recipient Disting. Svc. Alumni award U. Wis.-Whitewater, Spl. award NAACP, 1987, cert. recognition Phi Delta Kappa-U. Wis. chpt., 1987, Rotary Sr. Svc. award, 1992; named to Madison Area Tech. Coll. Athletic Hall of Fame, 1989. Mem. Am. Assn. Community and Jr. Colls. (dir. 1975-78, Leadership award 1988), Am. Vocat. Assn. Merit award Region 3 1988), Wis. Assn. for Vocat. and Adult Edn. (Disting. Svc. award 1988), Wis. Assn. Dirs. Vocat. and Adult Edn. (pres. 1960-61), Sigma Tau Gamma, Epsilon Pi Tau, Delta Pi Epsilon. Clubs: Rotarian, Elk, Nakoma Golf. Home: 4413 Waite Ln Madison WI 53711-2845

MITCHEL, F(REDERICK) KENT, retired food company executive; b. Orange, N.J., June 2, 1927; s. E. Kent and Arlene (Lee) M.; m. Elizabeth L. Rich, June 25, 1955 (div. 1990); children: Pamela, Peter; m. Susan Holden Colcock, 1990. AB, Dartmouth Coll., 1950; postgrad., Harvard U., 1970. With Gen. Foods Corp., 1950-86; v.p. mktg., then v.p. corp. comm. Gen. Foods Corp., White Plains, N.Y., 1970-79; v.p. mktg. staffs Gen. Foods Corp., 1979-86; pres. Mktg. Sci. Inst., Cambridge, Mass., 1987-89, chmn., 1990-91; pres. Fair Tide Assocs. Ltd., Sandwich, N.H., 1987—; artistic dir. Harleysville Ins. Cos. Assn. Nat. Advertisers; trustee Mktg. Sci. Inst., chmn., 1990-91; past chmn. Nat. Advt. Rev. Coun., Advt. Coun.; bd. dirs. Nutrasweet Co., Advt. Rsch. Found., 1987-93. Bd. dirs. Squam Lakes Assn., 1989-91. Mem. Univ. Club (N.Y.C.), Harvard Club Boston. Episcopalian.

MITCHELL, ALFRED HENRY, state government official; b. Brewton, Ala., Feb. 26, 1948; s. James Fred and Sybil Francis (Wiggins) M.; m. Jackie Mae Ferguson, Aug. 30, 1969; children: Henry, Jason, Cary. BA, Auburn U., 1972. Asst. plant mgr. Judy Bond, Inc., Brewton, Ala., 1972-77; cen. finishing plant mgr., 1977-79; plant mgr. Ozark (Ala.) Mfg. Co., 1979-83; asst. fin. dir. State of Ala., 1983-86; fin. dir., 1986-87; asst. to speaker of house Ala. Ho. of Reps., 1987—. Bd. dirs. Ozark YMCA, 1981-82; pres. Dale County (Ala.) United Fund, 1982-83; mem. Ala. Hist. Records Adv. Bd., 1984, Ala. DeSoto Commn., 1985, Dale County Dem. Exec. Com., 1982. Named one of Outstanding Young Men Am., 1985. Mem. Dale County C. of C., Escambia County (Ala.) Hist. Soc., Reapportionment Task Force of Nat. Conf. State Legis. Democrat. Baptist. Home: 2318 Old Pike Rd Pike Road AL 36064-2529 Office: House Speakers Office State House 11 S Union St Montgomery AL 36130-0001

MITCHELL, ANDREA, journalist; b. N.Y.C., Oct. 30, 1946; d. Sydney and Cecile Mitchell. B.A., U. Pa., 1967. Polit. reporter KYW Newsradio, Phila., 1967-76; polit. corr. Sta. KYW-TV, Phila., 1972-76; corr. Sta. WTOP-TV, Washington, 1977-78; gen. assignment and energy corr. NBC News, Washington, 1978-81; White House corr. NBC News, 1981-88, chief congl. corr., 1989-92, chief White House corr., 1993-94; chief fgn. affairs corr. NBC News, Washington, 1995—, 1994—; instr. Gt. Lakes Colls. Assn., 1974-76; co-anchor Summer Sunday, USA, NBC-TV News, 1984, substitute anchor Meet the Press, 1988—. Overseer Coll. Arts and Scis. U. Pa., 1989—, trustee, 1991—; mem. nat. adv. bd. Girl Scouts U.S. Recipient award for pub. affairs reporting Am. Polit. Sci. Assn., 1969, Pub. Affairs Reporting award AP, 1976, AP Broadcast award, 1977; named Communicator of the Yr., Phila. chpt. Women in Comms., 1976, Woman of the Yr., Phila. chpt. Am. Women in Radio and TV, 1989, Lucretia Mott award Woman's Way, 1991. Mem. White House Corrs. Assn. Office: NBC News 4001 Nebraska Ave NW Washington DC 20016-2733

MITCHELL, ARTHUR, dancer, choreographer, educator; b. N.Y.C., Mar. 27, 1934; s. Arthur and Willie Mae M. Student, Sch. Am. Ballet.; D. Arts (hon.), Columbia Coll., Chgo., 1975; cert. of competence, Peter U., 1978; DFA (hon.), City Coll., CUNY, 1979, N.C. Sch. Arts, 1981, L.I. U. Sch. Bus. Pub. Adminstrn., 1982, Fordham U., 1983, Princeton U., 1986, Williams Coll., 1986, Juilliard Sch., 1990; DHS (hon.), Urbana Coll., 1979; DA (hon.), Harvard U., 1987. With William Dollar's Ballet Theatre Workshop, 1954, John Butler Co., 1955; prin. dancer N.Y.C. Ballet, 1955-72; artistic dir., founder Am. Negro Dance Co. N.Y.C., 1966—; founder, dir., choreographer Dance Theatre of Harlem, N.Y.C., 1969—; former resident choreographer, artistic dir. Nat. Ballet Co., Brazil; tchr. dance Karel Shook Studio, Melissa Hayden Sch., Cedarhurst, L.I., Jones-Haywood Sch. Ballet, Washington. dancer in Kiss Me, Kate, Orpheus, Carmen Jones, Allegro, Creation of the World, Episodes, House of Flowers, numerous others; choreographer (with Rod Alexander) Newport Jazz Festival, Rhythmetron, 1971, Ode to Otis, 1969, Lil' Gal, 1969, Tones, 1970, Biosfera, 1970, Fun and Games, 1970, Holberg Suite, 1970, Manifestations, 1975, Concerto for Jazz Band and Orch., 1971, Fête Noire, 1971, Spiritual Suite: Dance In Praise of His Name, 1976, Breezin', 1977, The Greatest, 1977, El Mar, 1977, Doin' It, 1978, Porgy and Bess, 1985, Phoenix Rising, 1987, John Henry, 1988, Ribbon In The Sky, 1990, Bach Passacaglia, 1993; co-choreographer Broadway prodn. Shinbone Alley; dancer, choreographer, actor: Spoleto Festival of Two Worlds, 1960; TV prodns. A Streetcar Named Desire dance prodn., PBS, Songs of Mahler, Dance in America: Dance Theatre of Harlem, PBS, Stravinsky's Firebird, PBS, Creole Giselle, NBC, Fall River Legend, A&E. Active Nat. Conf. on Social Welfare, 1973, U.S. Dept. State Dance Adv. Panel, Pres. Task Force on Arts and Humanities, 1981, Commn. for Cultural Affairs, N.Y.C., 1982, Arts and Entertainment Adv. Bd. N.Y.C. Partnership, Inc., 1983, Nat. Coun. of Arts, 1987; named to Pres. Commn.

on White House Fellowships, 1991. Recipient Changers award Mademoiselle Mag., 1970, North Shore Commn. Arts Ctr. award, 1971, Capezio Dance award, 1971, Ann. Excellence award John F. Kennedy Ctr. for Performing Arts, 1980, Am. Dance Guild award, 1982, Ebony Mag. Am. Black Achievement award, 1983, Pres.'s Cabinet award, U. Detroit, 1983, Paul Robeson award Actors Equity Assn., 1986, Lion of the Performing Arts award N.Y. Pub. Library, 1986, Arnold Gingrich Meml. award, 1987, Banquet of Golden Plate, 1989, Harkness Disting. Artist award Adelphi U., 1990, Disting. Svc. to Arts award Am. Acad. of Arts and Letters, 1994, Zenith award for Fine Arts, 1994, Handel Medallion, City of New York, 1993, Barnard Medal of Distinction Barnard Coll., 1994, Lifetime Achievement award Sch. Am. Ballet, 1995; named to NAACP Image Awards Hall of Fame, 1986; Kennedy Center Honor for Lifetime Achievement, 1993; Conroy fellow St. Paul's Sch., Concord, N.H., 1982, MacArthur fellow, 1994. Office: Dance Theatre Harlem 466 W 152nd St New York NY 10031-1896

MITCHELL, ARTHUR HARRIS, newspaper columnist; b. St. John, N.B., Can., Nov. 8, 1916; s. Stuart Campbell and Marjorie (Harris) M.; m. Mary Moliawko, Nov. 6, 1944; children: John Stuart, Marjorie Starr. Student, Columbia Sch. Journalism, 1945-46. Travelling freelance writer various U.S., Can. mags., 1946-48; syndicated newspaper columnist, 1971—; editor Mitchell Press Ltd., Vancouver, B.C.; founding editor Can. Pulp and Paper Industry mag., Western Homes & Living mag., 1948-66; editor Can. Homes mag., Southstar Publs. Ltd., Toronto, Ont., 1967-80; Can. cons. Time-Life Books, N.Y.C., 1976-82. Author: You Wanted to Know, 1971, Easy Furniture Finishing, 1974, The Basement Book, 1977. Served with Brit. and U.S. Mcht. Marine, 1940-45. Home: TH28 270 Timberbank Blvd, Scarborough, ON Canada M1W 2M1

MITCHELL, BERT BREON, literary translator; b. Salina, Kans., Aug. 9, 1942; s. John Charles and Bernita Maxine (Breon) M.; m. Lynda Diane Fink, July 21, 1965; children:—Kieron Breon, Kerry Archer. B.A., U. Kans., 1964; Ph.D., Oxford U., 1968. Asst. prof. German and comparative lit. Ind. U., Bloomington, 1968-71, assoc. prof., 1971-78, prof., 1978—, assoc. dean Coll. Arts and Scis., 1975-77, chmn. comparative lit., 1977-85, dir. Wells Scholars Program, 1988—. Author: James Joyce and the German Novel, 1922-1933, 1976, Beyond Illustration; the Livre d'Artiste in the Twentieth Century, 1976, The Complete Lithographs of Delacroix's Faust and Manet's The Raven, 1981; editor: Literature and the Other Arts, 1978, Metamorphosis and the Arts, 1979, Paul Morand, Fancy Goods/Open All Night, 1984; translator: Heartstop (Martin Grzimek), 1984, Selected Stories (Siegfried Lenz), 1989, The Musk Deer and Other Stories (Vilas Sarang), 1990, Looking Back (Lou Andreas-Salomé), 1991, Shadowlife (Martin Grzimek), 1991, Laura's Skin (J.F. Federspiel), 1991, The Color of the Snow (Rüdiger Kremer), 1992, Knife Edge (Ralf Rothmann) 1992, In the Kingdom of Enki (Vilas Sarang), 1993, On the Glacier (Jürgen Kross), 1994, The Silent Angel (Heinrich Böll), 1994. Rhodes scholar, 1964-68; Danforth fellow, 1964-68, Woodrow Wilson fellow, 1964, Alexander-von-Humboldt fellow, 1971, Translation fellow Nat. Endowment for Arts, 1989; recipient Frederic Bachman Lieber Meml. award for disting. teaching, 1974, hon. citation Columbia Translation Ctr., 1990. Mem. MLA (chair William Riley Parker prize selection com. 1994), Am. Comparative Lit. Assn., Am. Lit. Translators Assn. (pres. 1985-87, Alta prize for disting. translation 1992), Am. Translators Assn. (com. lit. transl. 1983-84, German Lit. prize for disting. translation 1987, chmn. honors and awards com. 1992), P.E.N., James Joyce Found., Franz Kafka Soc., Samuel Beckett Soc., So. Comparative Lit. Assn., Brit. Comparative Lit. Assn., Internat. Comparative Lit. Assn. Office: BH402 Indiana University Bloomington IN 47405

MITCHELL, BRADFORD WILLIAM, insurance executive, lawyer; b. Lewiston, Maine, Aug. 14, 1927; s. William Henry and Marietta Edna (Ramsdall) M.; m. Frances T. Cantwell, June 20, 1953; children:—Mark, Scott, Patrick, Paula, Kristen. Student U. Maine, 1947-49; LL.B., Boston U., 1952. Bar: Maine 1952, Mass. 1952, N.H. 1967, Pa. 1976, U.S. Supreme Ct. 1971, U.S. Ct. Mil. Appeals 1974. Asst. gen. counsel Am. Mut. Liability Ins. Co., Wakefield, Mass., 1959-67, asst. v.p. 1963-67; gen. counsel Nat. Grange Mut. Ins. Co., Keene, N.H., 1967-73, corporate sec., 1971-75, exec. v.p., 1973-75; pres., dir. Harleysville Ins. Cos., Pa., 1976-93, chief exec. officer, 1977-93; chmn. bd. dirs. Harleysville Group Inc., Harleysville Mut. Ins. Co., 1977—; dir. Harleysville Nat. Bank & Trust; former CEO Harleysville Group Inc., chmn. bd. dirs., Harleysville Life Ins. Co., Harleysville Mut. Ins. Co. Inc., Worcester Ins. Co. Campaign chmn. Am. Cancer Soc., Keene, 1973, Monadnock United Fund, Keene, 1974; bd. dirs. Valley Forge council Boy Scouts Am., 1979—; bd. dirs. North Pa. United Way, Lansdale, 1980—, campaign chmn., 1984. Served with JAGC, U.S. Army, 1952-59; lt. col. Res. ret. Mem. ABA, Disciplinary Bd. Pa., Nat. Assn. Ind. Insurers (bd. govs. 1977—), vice chmn. 1983, chmn. 1984), Pa. Assn. Mut. Ins. Cos. (pres. 1983). Republican. Home: 10 Pine Hill Rd Sergeantsville NJ 08557 Office: Harleysville Inc Cos 355 Maple Ave Harleysville PA 19438

MITCHELL, BRENDA K., state secretary; 1 child, Corrie Nelson. BA, Fordham U., 1973; MA in Urban Affairs, Hunter Coll., 1974; D in Pub. Adminstrn., Nova U., 1981. Dir. community econ. revitalization project City Ventures Corp., 1980-83; bus. mgr. Control Data Corp. Bus. Tech. Ctr., 1983-87; dep. sec. for policy planning adminstrn. amd program mgmt. Dept. of Commerce, Pa., 1987-90; spl. asst. to gov. Pa., 1990-91; sec. Commonwealth of Pa. Pa. Dept. of State; alternate rep. Appalachian Regional Commn., Washington; gov.'s liaison Dept. of Community Affairs, Labor and Industry; mem. Gov.'s Adv. Commn. on African Am. Affairs. V.p. Phila. Regional Port Authority, West Parkside Phila. Bus. Assn.; co-founder, pres. Harrisburg chpt. Nat. Forum for Black Pub. Adminstrs.; past bd. dirs. Ben Franklin Partnership Advanced Tech. Ctr. for Southeastern Pa., Phila. Fund Community Devel.; past trustee United Way of Southeastern Pa.; trustee Lincoln Univ.; mem. Pa. Bd. Fin. and Revenue, Pa. Mcpl. Retirement System, Pa. State U. Econ. Decel. Coun., Econs. Am. Office: PA State Dept 302 N Office Bldg Harrisburg PA 17120

MITCHELL, BRIANE NELSON, lawyer; b. Seattle, July 4, 1953; s. Robert Max and Frances Marie (Nelson) M.; m. Suzanne Harmatz; children: Brianne Nelson, Brittany Suzanne. AB, Columbia U., 1975; JD, U. Idaho, 1978. Law clk. U.S. Ct. Appeals (9th cir.), 1978-80; assoc. Debevoise & Plimpton, N.Y.C., 1980-84; assoc. Paul, Hastings, Janofsky & Walker, L.A., 1984-86, ptnr., 1986-93; ptnr. McCambridge, Deixler & Marmaro, L.A., 1993—. Mem. ABA, Idaho Bar Assn., N.Y. State Bar Assn., Calif. Bar Assn. Office: McCambridge Deixler Marmaro & Goldberg 2029 Century Park East Ste 2700 Los Angeles CA 90067

MITCHELL, BRUCE TYSON, lawyer; b. San Francisco, Nov. 6, 1928; s. John Robert and Lorraine C. (Tyson) M.; m. Adrienne Means Hiscox, Oct. 14, 1951; 1 son, Mark Means. AB with great distinction, Stanford U., 1949, JD, 1951. Bar: Calif. 1952, U.S. Dist. Ct. (no. dist.) Calif 1952, U.S. Ct. Appeals (9th cir.) 1952, U.S. Supreme Ct. 1971. Estate adminstr. Crocker Nat. Bank, San Francisco, 1955-57; atty. Utah Internat. Inc., San Francisco, 1957-87; sec. Utah Internat. Inc., 1974-87, sr. counsel, 1961-87; mem. non-securities panel arbitrators N.Y. Stock Exch., Pacific Stock Exchange, NASD Bd. Arbitrators. Chmn. San Mateo County Rep. Cen. Com., 1964-70; mem. Calif. Rep. Central Com., 1964-74, 77-83; alt. del. Rep. Nat. Conv., 1968; co-chmn. San Mateo (Calif.) County Pres. Ford Com., 1976; mem. bd. visitors sch. law Stanford U., 1980-83; exec. v.p., bd. dirs. San Francisco Jr. C. of C., 1961; bd. dirs. No. Calif. chpt. Arthritis Found., 1972-85, 1987-92, St. Francis Hosp. Found., San Francisco. Lt. (j.g.) USNR, 1952-55, Japan. Mem. ABA, Calif. Bar Assn., San Francisco Bar Assn., Am. Judicature Soc., Am. Soc. Corp. Secs. (v.p. 1976-77, dir. 1976-79), Assn. Former Intelligence Officers, Commonwealth Club of Calif. (pres. San Francisco 1973), Pacific Union Club, Olympic Club, Capitol Hill Club, Travelers Century Club, Masons. Congregationalist. Home: 165 Redwood Dr Hillsborough CA 94010 Office: 400 Montgomery St Ste 1002 San Francisco CA 94104-1277

MITCHELL, BURLEY BAYARD, state supreme court chief justice; b. Oxford, N.C., Dec. 15, 1940; s. Burley Bayard and Dorothy Ford (Champion) M.; m. Mary Lou Willett, Aug. 3, 1962; children: David Bayard, Catherine Morris. B.A., N.C. State U., 1966; J.D., U. N.C. 1969. Bar: N.C. 1969, U.S. Ct. Appeals (4th cir.) 1970, U.S. Supreme Ct. 1972. Asst. atty. gen. State of N.C., Raleigh, 1969-72, dist. atty., 1973-77, judge Ct. Appeals, 1977-79, sec. crime control, 1979-82; justice Supreme Ct. N.C.

Raleigh, 1982-94; chief justice Supreme Ct. of N.C., Raleigh, 1995—. Served with USN, 1958-62, Asia. Recipient N.C. Nat. Guard Citizen Commendation award, 1982. Mem. ABA, VFW, N.C. Bar Assn., Mensa, Am. Legion. Democrat. Methodist. Home: 820 Glen Eden Dr Raleigh NC 27612-5038 Office: Supreme Ct NC PO Box 1841 Raleigh NC 27602-1841

MITCHELL, CAROL ANN, nursing educator; b. Portsmouth, Va., Aug. 31, 1942; d. William Howell and Eleanor Bertha (Wesarg) M.; m. David Alan Friedman, June 17, 1971 (div. 1988). Diploma, NYU, 1963; BS, Columbia U., 1968, MA, 1971, EdM, 1974, EdD, 1980; MS, SUNY, Stony Brook, 1990. Charge nurse Nassau County Med. Ctr., East Meadow, N.Y., 1963-65; staff nurse Meml. Hosp., N.Y.C., 1965-68; head nurse, supr. Community Hosp. at Glen Cove (N.Y.), 1969-71; assoc. prof. dept. nursing Queensborough Community Coll. CUNY, Bayside, 1971-80; assoc. prof. Marion A. Buckley Sch. Nursing Adelphi U., Garden City, N.Y., 1981-88; ednl. cons. Nat. League for Nursing, N.Y.C., 1980-81; prof. sch. nursing SUNY, Stony Brook, 1988-92, chmn. adult nursing, 1988-92; prof., chair Coll. Nursing East Tenn. State U., 1992—; mem. faculty Regents Coll. degrees in nursing program USNY, Albany, 1978-91, cons., 1978—; faculty cons. geriatrics Montefiore Med. Ctr., 1991-93. Editor Scholarly Inquiry in Nursing Practice jour., 1983—; contbr. articles to profl. jours. Robert Wood Johnson clin. nurse scholar postdoctoral fellow U. Rochester (N.Y.), 1983-85. Mem. Am. Nurses Assn., Nat. League for Nursing, Gerontol. Soc. Am., N.Am. Nursing Diagnosis Assn., Soc. for Research in Nursing Edn. Avocations: reading, gardening, cycling, travel, cooking.

MITCHELL, CAROLYN COCHRAN, college official; b. Atlanta, Dec. 27, 1943; d. Clemern Covell and Agnes Emily (Veal) Cochran; m. W. Alan Mitchell, Aug. 30, 1964; 1 child, Teri Marie. AB magna cum laude, Mercer U., 1965, M in Svc. Mgmt., 1989. Caseworker Ga. Dept. Family & Children Svcs., Macon, 1965-67, Covington, 1967-69; presch. dir. Southwestern Theol. Sem., Ft. Worth, 1969-70; presch. tchr., dir. Noah's Ark Day Care, Bowden, Ga., 1970-72, First Bapt. Ch., Bremen, Ga., 1972-75, Roebuck Park Bapt. Ch., Birmingham, Ala., 1975-79; freelance office mgr. and bookkeeper Macon, 1979-84; asst. to pres. Ga. Wesleyan Coll., Macon, 1984—; exec. dir. Ga. Women of Achievement, 1991-95; dir. Macon Arts Alliance, 1987-91; mem. Cultural Plan Oversight Com., 1989-90. Mem. Get Out the Vote Task Force, Macon, 1981—, Macon Symphony Guild, 1986-91; dep. registrar Bibb County Bd. Elections, Macon, 1981-95. Mem. AAUW (bd. dirs. Ga. chpt., v.p. 1991-93, chair coll.-univ. rels. 1993-94, v.p. treas., historian Macon chpt., Named Gift honoree 1988), NAFE, Am. Mgmt. Assn., Presdl. Assts. in Higher Edn., Women's Polit. Orgn. Macon, Sigma Mu. Democrat. Unitarian. Office: Ga Wesleyan Coll 4760 Forsyth Rd Macon GA 31297-4299

MITCHELL, CHARLES ARCHIE, financial planning consultant, engineer; b. Kodia Kanal, Madras, India, May 3, 1926; came to U.S., 1932; s. Charles Archie and Ethel Blanche (Nutter) M.; m. Betty Louise Johnson, June 15, 1947; children: Cynthia E., Charles Archie Jr., Susan L. BSEE, Worcester (Mass.) Poly. Inst., 1946; MBA, Harvard U., 1954; CFP, Coll. of Fin. Planning, 1974. Sales engr. Johnson Steel & Wire Co., Worcester, 1947-50; dist. sales mgr. GE, Plainville, Conn., 1954-61; v.p. mktg. Dictograph Co., Danbury, Conn., 1962-63; dir. corp. planning GCA Corp., Bedford, Mass., 1963-65; div. mgr. Polaroid Corp., Cambridge, Mass., 1965-66; rep. Hayden Stone, Inc., Boston, 1966-69; div. mgr. Westamerica Fin. Corp., Boston, 1971-77; officer, dir. MHA Mgmt. Corp., Braintree, Mass., 1977-89; pres., dir. Mitchell Fin. Corp., Falmouth, Mass., 1989—. Contbr. articles to profl. jours. Instr. Northeastern U., Boston, 1962-66, Mass. Dept. of Edn., Cambridge, 1966-69. Lt. USN, 1943-47, 51-53, Korea. Mem. Internat. Assn. Fin. Planners (treas., bd. dirs. 1975-76), Inst. Cert. Fin. Planners (ea. v.p. nat. bd. dirs. 1974-79), Nat. Assn. Life Underwriters, Cape Cod Estate Planning Coun., Cape Cod Curling Club, Woods Hole Golf Club, Woods Hole Yacht Club, Masons, Shriners. Avocations: sailing, curling, golf. Office: PO Box 550 Falmouth MA 02541-0550

MITCHELL, CLAYBOURNE, JR., retired utilities executive; b. Chgo., Jan. 13, 1923; s. Claybourne and Ethel Emma (Osby) M.; m. Isabella Ophelia Skerrett; 1 dau., Mary Faith. Assoc. in Engring. Sci., Flint Jr. Coll., 1948; B.S. in Physics, U. Mich., 1950, M.S. in Physics, 1959. Dir. research Controlled Power Corp., Farmington, Mich., 1968-74; gen. dir. engring. research dept. Detroit Edison, 1974-77, mgr. personnel services, 1977-79, asst. v.p. planning and research, 1979-80, v.p. planning and research, 1980-88. Inventor, patentee: system for periodically reversing elec. energy through a load; co-inventor photon detector sliderule; co-patentee resolution voltage controllable interferometer, micromeasurement apparatus, apparatus for infrared scanning. Served to master sgt. USAAF, 1943-46, PTO. Mem. Engring. Soc. Detroit, Detroit Sci. Ctr. Mem. Unity Ch.

MITCHELL, DANIEL RAY, lawyer; b. Fremont, Ohio, Aug. 7, 1939; s. Daniel Ray and Ruth Esther (Murphy) M.; m. Sally Jo Meadors, June 20, 1964; children: Susan, Jill. BS, Ohio State U., 1961; JD, Harvard U., 1966. Asst. v.p. tax Brunswick Corp., Skokie, Ill., 1977-81; mgr. tax planning Amoco Corp., Chgo., 1981-86, gen. tax counsel, 1986—; v.p., 1991—. Mem. ABA, Am. Inst. CPA's. Home: 1148 Oak St Winnetka IL 60093-2132 Office: Amoco Corp 200 E Randolph Dr # 2406 Chicago IL 60601-6401

MITCHELL, DANIEL WERTZ, banking executive; b. Phoenix, Jan. 23, 1928; s. s. Larry Roy and Audrey (Wertz) M.; m. Nancy Evelyn Byrd, Apr. 4, 1928; children: Daniel L., Douglas R., Karen. BS, Ind. U., 1950. Chmn. Old Nat. Bancorp, Evansville, Ind. Served in U.S. Army, 1946-47. Mem. Robert Morris Assocs.(nat. pres. 1976-77). Republican. Lutheran. Office: Old Nat Bank in Evansville 420 Main St PO Box 718 Evansville IN 47705

MITCHELL, DAVID L., phycology researcher. Prof. U. Tex. MD Anderson Cancer Ctr., Houston. Recipient Luigi Provasoli award Phycological Soc. Am., 1992. Office: U Tex MD Anderson Cancer Ctr Houston TX 77030*

MITCHELL, DAVID T., electronic computing equipment company executive; b. 1942. Prodn. control mgr. Honeywell Inc., Mpls., 1966-69; dir. mfg. planning Memorex Corp., Santa Clara, Calif., 1969-72; dir. materials Fairchild Camera and Instrument Corp., Mountain View, Calif., 1972-75; pres. Castell Inc., Santa Ana, Calif., 1975-77; dir. materials Bendix Corp., San Francisco, 1977-78; gen. mgr. Commodore Bus. Machines Inc., Santa Clara, 1978-80; pres., chief operating officer Seagate Tech., Scotts Valley, Calif., 1980-92, also bd. dirs.; pres. COO Conner Peripherals, San Jose, Calif., 1992—, also dir. Capt. USMC, 1963-66. Office: Conner Peripherals 3081 Zanker Rd San Jose CA 95134

MITCHELL, DAVID WALKER, lawyer; b. Oakland, Calif., Nov. 11, 1935; s. Theodore Boyd and Helen Louise (Walker) M.; m. Carolyn Hilliard Graves, July 29, 1961; children: Sarah, Betsy. AB in History, Stanford U., 1957; JD, Harvard U., 1960. Bar: Calif. 1961. Assoc. Kindel & Anderson, L.A., 1961-65, Weir, Hopkins, Donovan, San Jose, Calif., 1965-68; ptnr. Hopkins, Mitchell & Carley, San Jose, 1968-87, McCutchen, Doyle, Brown & Enersen, San Jose, 1987-93, Hoge, Fenton, Jones & Appel, San Jose, 1993—. Bd. dirs. Peninsula Open Space Trust, Menlo Park, Calif., 1982—; pres., 1984-92; bd. dirs. Santa Clara Community Found., San Jose, 1977-94; chair bd. trustees United Way Santa Clara County, 1983-85. Fellow Am. Bar Found., Am. Leadership Forum (sr.); mem. Santa Clara County Bar Assn. (trustee 1972-75), San Jose C of C. (bd. dirs. 1975-80). Mem. United Ch. of Christ. Avocations: music, hiking. Office: Hoge Fenton Jones Appel Ste 1400 60 S Market St San Jose CA 95113-2396

MITCHELL, DENNIS A., Olympic athlete, track and field; b. Feb. 20, 1966. Student, U. Fla. Olympic runner Barcelona, Spain, 1992. Recipient 4x100m relay Track and Field Gold medal, 100m Bronze medal, Olympics, Barcelona, 1992. Office: US Olympic Com 1750 E Boulder St Colorado Springs CO 80909-5746

MITCHELL, DONALD E., rehabilitation counselor, transition counselor; b. Kansas City, Mo., Jan. 19, 1948; s. Rosa E. Mitchell. BA, Southwestern Coll., 1970; MS in Community Counseling, Emporia State, 1983, MS in Vocat. Rehab. Counseling, 1986; postgrad., U. Kans., Pitts. State U., Emory U. Registered profl. counselor. Svc. technician, sales and sheet metal installer Lee's Cooling and Heating, Independence, Kans., 1976-82; dir. partial hosp. facility, case mgr. Iroquis Ctr. for Human Devel., Greensburg, Kans., 1983-85; job coach Kans. Social Rehab. Svc., Topeka, 1985-86; title IV counselor Independence Community Coll., 1986-87; transition counselor Kans. Rehab. Svcs., Chanute, 1988—. Mem. VEWAA (membership chmn.) Nat. Rehab. Assn., Kans. Rehab. Assn., Chi Sigma Iota. Home: 200 E Pecan St Independence KS 67301-2530 Office: Kans Rehab Svcs 1500 W 7th St Chanute KS 66720

MITCHELL, DONALD J., former congressman; b. Ilion, N.Y., May 8, 1923; m. Margaretta Wilson Levee, 1945; children: Gretchen, Cynthia, Allen. Student, Hobart and William Smith Coll., 1946-47, LLD (hon.); BS in Optometry, Columbia U., 1949, MA in Edn., 1950; LLD (hon.), Pa. Coll. Optometry; D Ocular Scis. (hon.), So. Coll. Optometry. Optometrist; mem. 93d-97th Congresses from, N.Y.; Councilman Town of Herkimer, 1954-56; mayor Village of Herkimer, 1956-59; mem. sr. assoc. faculty Nat. Emergency Tng. Ctr.; pres. Mohawk Valley Conf. Mayors, 1959; mem. N.Y. State Assembly, 1965-72, majority whip, 1968-72; bd. dirs. Comml. Travelers Mut. Ins. Co. Bd. dirs. Herkimer chpt. Cub Scouts, Cen. N.Y. Assn. for the Blind, Herkimer County United Fund, ea. chpt. Nature Conservancy. With USNR, 1942-45, 51-53. Named Optometrist of Yr. N.Y. State Optometric Assn., 1971; recipient Pub. Svc. award, 1965, award of distinction SUNY State Coll. Optometry Alumni Assn., Patriot of Yr. award N.Y. Res. Officers Assn., Nat. Security award U.S. Civil Def.; Jimmy Doolittle fellow Aerospace Edn. Found. of Air Force Assn. Mem. Nat. Soc. State Legis. (gov. 1971), Am. Civil Def. Assn. (mem. 1988—), Am. Legion, VFW. Republican. Methodist. Clubs: Rod and Gun, Masons, Elks, Kiwanis. Home: Herkimer NY 13350

MITCHELL, DOUGLAS FARRELL, trust company executive, lawyer; b. Pleasant Hill, Ill., Oct. 28, 1940; s. Henry C. and Opal V. Mitchell; m. Pamella Locke; children: Michael, Deborah. BS, U. Ill., 1964; JD, DePaul U., 1969; MBA, U. Chgo., 1976. Asst. sec. No Trust Co., Chgo., 1964-72, 2d v.p., 1972-78, v.p., 1978-86, sr. v.p., 1986—. Bd. dirs. United Charities, Chgo., 1988-92. Mem. Ill. State Bar Assn., Chgo. Bar Assn. Home: 1836 Prairie St Glenview IL 60025-2922 Office: No Trust Co 50 S La Salle St Chicago IL 60603-1003

MITCHELL, EARL NELSON, physicist, educator; b. Centerville, Iowa, Aug. 30, 1926; s. Earl Nelson and Nina (Swank) M.; m. Marlys Marie Panning, July 23, 1955. A.B. magna cum laude, U. Iowa, 1949, M.S., 1951; Ph.D., U. Minn., 1955. Research scientist Sperry Rand Corp., St. Paul, 1955-58; asst. prof., then assoc. prof. physics U. N.D., Grand Forks, 1958-62; vis. assoc. prof., then assoc. prof. and prof. physics U. N.C., Chapel Hill, 1962-91, prof. emeritus, 1991—, asst. chmn. dept., 1968-76, prof. physics emeritus, 1991—; lectr. Hamline U., 1956, 57; cons. Sperry Rand Corp., 1958-62. Contbr. articles to profl. jours.; author textbooks. Mem. Chapel Hill Planning Bd., 1970-71; pres. Chapel Hill Concert Series, 1967-70; mem. bd. for missions to deaf Luth. Ch. Mo. Synod, 1958-64. Served in USNR, 1945-46. Mem. AAAS, Am. Phys. Soc., Am. Assn. Physics Tchrs., Am. Soc. Enologists (bd. dirs. ea. sect. 1984-91, pres. elect 1988, pres. 1989, past pres. 1990), Soc. Wine Educators, N.C. Grape Coun., N.C. Wine Growers Assn. (pres. 1994—), Phi Beta Kappa, Sigma Xi, Phi Eta Sigma. Democrat. Office: U NC Chapel Hill NC 27599

MITCHELL, EARL WESLEY, clergyman; b. Excelsior Springs, Mo., Mar. 16, 1931; s. Earl Van and Ora Leah (Butterfield) M.; m. Mary Lou Bell, June 8, 1956; children: Susan Yvonne, Randall Bruce. Ordained to ministry Christian Union Ch., 1971. Min. Vibbard (Mo.) Christian Union Ch., 1962-69, Liberty (Mo.) Christian Ch., 1969-77, Barwick Christian Union Ch., Cameron, Mo., 1977-80, Independence (Mo.) Christian Ch., 1980—; mem. state sec. bd. Christian Union Mo., area rep. Mo., Christian Union USA, mem. gen. exec. bd., former editor C.U. Witness. Sgt. USAF, 1951-55. Avocations: music, woodworking, painting, photography. Home and Office: Christian Union 17500 Hidden Valley Rd Independence MO 64057-1718

MITCHELL, EDWARD FRANKLIN, utility company executive; b. Harrisonburg, Va., Dec. 23, 1931; s. Charlotte Elaine M. m. Suzanne S. Sublette, Aug. 20, 1955; children: Karen Mitchell Holland, Brian. B.E.E., U. Va., 1956; M.E.A., George Washington U., 1960. Registered profl. engr., D.C. With Potomac Electric Power Co., Washington, 1956—, v.p. elec. engring., 1971-76, sr. v.p. system engring. and ops., 1976-80, exec. v.p., chief operating officer, 1980-83, former pres., former chief operating officer, also dir.; chief exec officer Potomac Electric Power Co., Washington, DC, 1989—, also chmn., 1993—; mem. bd. visitors U. Md. Engring. Coll.; dir. Acacia Mut. Life. Mem. Vienna (Va.) Town Council, 1963-66; mem. Vienna Planning and Zoning Commn., 1963-66; elder Vienna Presbyterian Ch.; active Md. Bus. Coun., Met. Washington Bd. Trade.; bd. dirs. Nat. Rehab. Hosp. Served with USN, 1950-52. Home: 9409 Duxford Ct Rockville MD 20854-4342 Office: Potomac Electric Power Co 1900 Pennsylvania Ave NW Washington DC 20068-0002*

MITCHELL, EDWARD JOHN, economist, retired educator; b. Newark, Aug. 15, 1937; s. Edward Charles and Gladys (Werner) M.; m. Mary Josephine Osborne, June 14, 1958; children: Susan, Edward. B.A. summa cum laude, Bowling Green State U., 1960; postgrad. (Social Sci. Research Council fellow), Nuffield Coll., Oxford U. Eng., 1963-64, Ph.D. in Econs. (NDEA fellow 1960-63, NSF fellow 1964-65), 1966. Lectr. in econs. Wharton Sch., U. Pa., 1964-65; economist Rand Corp., 1965-68; mem. Inst. Advanced Study, Princeton, N.J., 1968-69; sr. economist Pres.'s Council Econ. Advs., Washington, 1969-72; vis. assoc. prof. econs. Cornell U., 1972-73; assoc. prof. bus. econs. U. Mich., 1973-75, prof., 1975-88, prof. emeritus bus. econs. and pub. policy, 1988—; pres. Edward J. Mitchell Inc., Ann Arbor, 1977—; dir. nat. energy project Am. Enterprise Inst., 1974-76; pres. Fountainhead Investment Co., 1984—. Author: U.S. Energy Policy: A Primer, 1974, Dialogue on World Oil, 1974, Financing the Energy Industry, 1975, Vertical Integration of the Oil Industry, 1976, The Deregulation of Natural Gas, 1983; contbr. articles to profl. jours. Home: 310 Penny Ln Santa Barbara CA 93108-2601 Office: Grad Sch Bus U Mich Ann Arbor MI 48109

MITCHELL, EHRMAN BURKMAN, JR., architect; b. Harrisburg, Pa., Jan. 25, 1924; s. Ehrman Burkman and Alice (DeCevee) M.; m. Hermine Strickler, Sept. 25, 1948; children: Eric Ehrman, Marianne. AB, U. Pa., 1947, BArch, 1948; LHD (hon.), Spring Garden Coll., 1989. Asso. architect Bellante & Clauss, 1951-58; partner Mitchell/Giurgola, Assocs., Phila., 1958-85; dir. Wyck Assn.; lectr. Ohio State U., U. Ariz., U. Utah, Cath. U. Am., Washington U., St. Louis, U. Notre Dame, Dartmouth Coll., U. Ky., U. Md., Temple U.; Phila. lectr. U. Nebr.; lectr. Calif. Poly. State U., U. Brasilia, Boston Archtl. Ctr., Pa. State U., Clemson U., Cornell U.; bd. overseers Temple U. Arch. Sch., U. Pa. Grad. Sch. Fine Arts; arch. design panels U. Pa. Prin. works Nat. hdqrs. Am. Coll. Life Underwriters, Bryn Mawr, Pa. also, Adult Learning Research Center; office bldg. Penn Mut. Life Ins. Co., Phila., Ins. Co. N.Am., Phila.; U. Wash. Law Sch. and Library, Seattle, USIS Cultural Center, Brasilia, Brazil, A.B. Volvo Co. mfg. plant, Chesapeake, Va., New Parliament House, Canberra, Australia. Pres. Citizens Coun. Whitemarch Twp., Montgomery County, Pa., 1963-65, dir., 1963-67; mem. Del. Valley Citizens Transp. Com., 1964—; Citizens Coun. Montgomery County, 1964—; mem. archtl. rev. panel U.S. Fed. Res. System; bd. regents Am. Archtl. Found. With USNR, 1943-46. Recipient Gold medal Artists Guild Phila., Hazlett award Pa. Coun. Arts, 1985, plaque honor Mexican Fedn. Architects; fellow U. Pa. Mus. Fellow Royal Archtl. Inst. Can. (hon.), Royal Australian Inst. Architects; mem. AIA (chpt. dir. Phila. 1965-68, coll. fellows 1969—, nat. dir. 1973-75, v.p. 1977, 1st v.p. 1978, pres. 1979, gold medal Phila. chpt. 1964, 72, 74, silver medal 1973, Nat. Honor award 1974, 75, archtl. firm award 1976), Pa. Soc. Architects (dir. 1966—), sec. 1966, v.p. 1967, pres. 1968, silver medal 1974, 75, 77), AIM (pres.'s council 1967), Inst. Contemporary Art, Pa. Acad. Fine Arts, Greater Phila. C. of C., Pan Am. Fedn. Architects, NAD, Societe Arquitecto Mexicanos, Beta Theta Pi. Clubs: Philadelphia, Carpenter's Co., St. Andrew's Soc. (Phila.). Home: 600 E Cathedral Rd E-101 Philadelphia PA 19128-1929

MITCHELL, GARY EARL, physicist, educator; b. Louisville, July 5, 1935; s. Earl Raymond and Delma Kathlene (Lockard) M.; m. Carolyn Fey Stutz, Aug. 4, 1957; children: Scott Frederick, Karen Lee (dec.). BS, U. Louisville,

1956; MA, Duke U., 1958; PhD, Fla. State U., 1962. Research assoc. Columbia U., N.Y., 1962-64, asst. prof., 1964-68; assoc. prof. N.C. State U., Raleigh, 1968-74, prof. physics, 1974—, assoc. head physics dept., 1982—. Contbr. numerous articles to sci. publs. Sr. scientist Alexander Von Humboldt Found., Bonn, Fed. Republic Germany, 1975. Recipient Alumni Disting. Prof. award N.C. State U. Fellow Am. Phys. Soc.; mem. numerous sci. assns. Avocation: history. Home: 2913 Harriman Dr Durham NC 27705-5423 Office: NC State U Dept Physics PO Box 8202 Raleigh NC 27695-8202

MITCHELL, GEORGE ERNEST, JR., animal scientist, educator; b. Duoro, N.Mex., June 7, 1930; s. George Ernest and Alma Thyrza (Hatley) M.; m. Billie Carolyn McMahan, Mar. 14, 1952; children: Leslie Dianne, Karen Leigh, Cynthia Faye. B.S., U. Mo., 1951, M.S., 1954; Ph.D., U. Ill., 1956. Asst. prof. animal sci. U. Ill., 1956-60; assoc. prof. U. Ky., Lexington, 1960-67; prof. U. Ky., 1967—, dir. grad. studies in animal scis., 1964—, coord. beef cattle and sheep, 1974-90. Contbr. articles to profl. jours. Served with USAF, 1951-53. Fulbright research scholar New Zealand, 1973-74; Rsch. scholar Japan Soc. for Promotion of Sci., Japan, 1989. Mem. Am. Soc. Animal Sci. (sec. 1969-70, v.p. 1970-71, pres. So. sect. 1971-72, rsch. fellow 1989, Disting. Svc. award 1994), Am. Dairy Sci. Assn., Am. Inst. Nutrition, AAAS, Council for Agrl. Sci. and Tech., Sigma Xi, Alpha Zeta, Gamma Sigma Delta, Omicron Delta Kappa. Democrat. Methodist. Home: 690 Hill N Dale Rd Lexington KY 40503-2164 Office: So U Ky 809 W P Garrigus Bldg Lexington KY 40546

MITCHELL, GEORGE FREDERICK, association executive; b. N.Y.C., Oct. 18, 1937; s. Joseph Michael and Ruth Ann (McEvoy) M.; m. Lorraine Wanda Nalwak, Nov. 3, 1962; children: Michael A., Susan A., Karen L., Kathleen A. BS, Syracuse U., 1970; postgrad., Boston U., 1971. Cert. assn. exec. Asst. mgr. underwriting Utica (N.Y.) Mut. Ins. Co., 1962-68; dir. pub. rels. and publs. Soc. Chartered Property and Casualty Underwriters, Media, Pa., 1971-75; exec. dir., treas. Northeastern Loggers' Assn., Old Forge, N.Y., 1976—; mem. regional adv. bd. Norstar Bank of Utica, 1985-93; dir. Am. Hardwood Export Coun., Washington, 1986—; guardian Nat. Fedn. Ind. Bus. N.Y., 1986—. Contbr. articles to trade jours. Trustee, treas. Old Forge (N.Y.) Libr. Assn., 1978-86; mem., pres. Sch. Bd., Town of Webb Union Free Sch. Dist., Old Forge, 1979-87. With USAF, 1956-62. Mem. Nat. Coun. Forestry Assn. Execs. (pres. 1989-90), Am. Soc. Assn. Execs., Nat. Assn. Expo Mgrs., N.Y. Forest Owners' Assn. (dir., membership ssec. 1980-86). Roman Catholic. Avocations: ice skiing, canoeing, bicycling. Office: Northeastern Loggers Assn PO Box 69 Old Forge NY 13420-0069

MITCHELL, GEORGE HALL, lawyer; b. Houston, Oct. 24, 1939; s. David Eaton and Adelia Eveline (Hall) M.; m. Nancy Duffey, June, 1962; children: Cathleen McRoberts, Bradley Duffey. BA, U. Ariz., 1962, JD, 1965. Bar: Ariz. 1965, U.S. Dist Ct. Ariz. 1965, U.S. Supreme Ct. 1972. Atty.-at-law O'Connor, Cavanagh, Phoenix, 1965—; bd. dirs. State Capital Law Firm Group, Raleigh, N.C. Legal Counsel Theodore Roosevelt Coun. Boy Scouts Am., Phoenix, 1988-93, pres. Grand Canyon Coun., 1994— (Silver Beaver award); precinct committeeman Rep. Party, Dist. 25, Phoenix, 1991; dist. rep. Rep. State Com., Ariz., 1991; past chmn. bd. dirs. All Saints Episcopal Day Sch.; past sr. warden All Saints Episcopal Ch. James E. West fellow, 1994. Mem. ABA, State Bar Ariz., Maricopa County Bar Assn., Internat. Assn. Def. Counsel (chmn. property ins. com. 1989-91), Arizona Town Hall, Thoeodore Roosevelt Rough Riders (pres. 1986), Phoenix County Club, Rotary (pres. Club No. 100 1985, Paul Harris fellow). Avocations: study of World War II, golf. Office: O'Connor Cavanagh 1 E Camelback Rd Ste 1100 Phoenix AZ 85012-1691

MITCHELL, GEORGE P., gas and petroleum company executive; b. Galveston, Tex., 1919; married. BS, Tex. A&M U. 1940. Exploration engr., geologist Amoco Prodn. Co., 1940-41, cons. geologist, engr., 1940-41; pres. Mitchell Energy & Devel. Corp., 1947-72, chmn. bd. dirs., CEO, 1972—; with Mitchell Energy & Devel. Corp., The Woodlands, Tex., 1947—, chmn., pres., 1972—, chief exec. officer, from 1972, also bd. dirs.; pres. George Mitchell & Assocs. Served to maj. U.S. Army, 1942-46. Office: Mitchell Energy & Devel 2201 Timberloch Pl PO Box 4000 The Woodlands TX 77380

MITCHELL, GEORGE WASHINGTON, JR., physician, educator; b. Balt., Apr. 30, 1917; s. George Washington and Katharyne Eugenia (Diggs) M.; m. Anne Jenkins Shriver, Dec. 19, 1942 (div. 1954); children: Beverly Shriver, George Washington III, Anne Jenkins, Edward Diggs; m. Mary Elizabeth McKay, Sept. 14, 1957; children—Bruce McKay, Katharyne Wilcox. A.B., Johns Hopkins, 1938, M.D., 1942. Diplomate: Am. Bd. Ob-Gyn (dir.). Intern Johns Hopkins Hosp., 1942, resident, 1946-49; gynecologist in chief New Eng. Med. Center Hosp., Boston, 1950-81; prof. ob-gyn Tufts U. Sch. Med., 1954-81, prof. emeritus, 1981—, chmn. dept., 1956-81; prof. ob-gyn U. Tex., San Antonio, 1981—; chief of gynecology U. Tex. Health Scis. Center, San Antonio, 1981-92; cons. Surgeon Gen. Navy. Served with USNR, 1943-46. Recipient Pub. Svc. award USN, 1977; named to Soc. Scholars Johns Hopkins U., 1991. Fellow ACS, ACOG, Am. Gynecol. and Obstet. Soc.; mem. AMA, Am. Fertility Soc., Soc. Pelvic Surgeons, Mass. Med. Soc., Obstet. Soc. Boston, New Eng. Ob-Gyn. Soc., Soc. Gynecol. Oncologists, So. Atlantic, Tex. Ob-Gyn. Soc., N.Am. Ob-Gyn. Soc., S.W. Ob-Gyn. soc., Johns Hopkins Med. and Surg. Assn., Soc. of Scholars Johns Hopkins U. Office: Dept Obstetrics and Gynecology U Texas Health Sci Center San Antonio TX 78284

MITCHELL, GLENN R., hospital administrator; b. Miller, S.D., May 25, 1929; married. BA, U. S.D., 1953; MA, U. Minn., 1956. Adminstrv. resident U. Minn. Hosp. & Clinic, Mpls., 1955-56, adminstrv. asst., 1956-57, asst. dir., 1957-63, assoc. dir., 1963-66; asst. adminstr. Johns Hopkins Hosp., Balt., 1966-71; adminstr. Sentara Norfolk Gen. Hosp., Norfolk, Va., 1971-72; exec. dir. Med. Ctr. Hosp., Norfolk, Va., 1972-82; pres. Sentara Health System, Norfolk, Va., 1982—. Mem. Va. Hosp. Assn. Home: 509 Bunker Dr Virginia Beach VA 23462 Office: Sentara Health System #300 6015 Poplar Hall Dr Norfolk VA 23502

MITCHELL, HERBERT HALL, former university dean, educational consultant; b. New Market, Ala., Dec. 10, 1916; s. Walter Hall and Vera Pearl (Johnston) M.; m. Audrey Elizabeth Taylor, Oct. 30, 1942; children: William Hall, Robert Michael, Richard Lee, Mary Ann. B.S., U. Ala., 1939, M.S., 1950; Ph.D., U. N.C. 1954. Asst. to dean of men U. Ala., 1939-42, asst. dean of men, 1942-43, asst. to dean of students, 1946-48; instr. U. N.C. 1948-51; asst. prof. Ala. Poly. Inst., 1951-55, assoc. prof., 1955-56; prof., head dept. bus. adminstrn. Miss State U., 1956-60; prof., chmn. dept. bus. adminstrn. Va. Poly. Inst., 1960-61, dean Sch. Bus., 1961-81, dean emeritus, 1981—; dean Coll. Commerce and Bus. Adminstrn. U. Ala., 1981-86, dean emeritus, 1986—; ednl. cons. and lectr., 1986—; vis. prof. finance grad. program in England and Germany U. Ark., 1972; mem. adv. bd. Intercollegiate Case Clearing House, Harvard U., 1973-76, 77-78. Contbr. articles to jours. Bd. dirs. Ala. Council Econ. Edn., 1982—; trustee Joint Council on Econ. Edn., 1982-86. Capt. Transp. Corps, AUS, 1943-46, col. Res., ret. Edn. fellow Joseph T. Ryerson & Son, Inc., Chgo., summer 1956. Mem. So Bus. Adminstrn. Assn. (pres. 1968-69), Am. Assembly Collegiate Schs. Bus. (dir. 1973-80, v.p. 1977, pres. 1978), Anderson Soc., Ret. Officers Assn., Univ. Club, West Ala. Ret. Officers Club (pres. 1989), Indian Hills Country Club, Phi Eta Sigma, Delta Sigma Pi, Beta Alpha Psi, Omicron Delta Epsilon, Beta Gamma Sigma (nat. bd. govs. 1980-84), Omicron Delta Kappa (G. Burke Johnston award 1981), Mu Kappa Tau, Gamma Iota Sigma. Methodist. Home: 82 The Highlands Tuscaloosa AL 35404-2915

MITCHELL, HOWARD ESTILL, human resources educator, consultant; b. Indpls., Aug. 13, 1921; s. Estill and Emma (Howard) M.; m. Nadine Wilson Harris, July 21, 1946; 1 son, Howard Estill Jr. B.S., Boston U., 1943; Ph.D., U. Pa., 1950; D.F.A., Phila. Coll. Art, 1969. Asst. chief clin. psychologist VA Mental Hygiene Clinic, Phila., 1953-57; chief psychologist Lankenaw Hosp., Phila., 1957-59; asst. prof. family study in psychiatry U. Pa. Sch. Medicine, Phila., 1955-66; dir. U. Pa. Human Resource Ctr., 1964-84; prof. human resources U. Pa. Grad. Sch. Fine Arts, Phila., 1967, 1907 Found. Prof. urbanism and human resources, 1967-73; UPS prof. mgmt. and human resources Wharton Sch. U. Pa., 1974-92, emeritus UPS prof. mgmt. and human resources, 1992—; dir. U. Pa. Univ. Ctr. Transit Research and Mgmt. Devel., 1981-84; chmn. bd. Change Technologies, Inc., Phila., 1981-

85; pres. Mitchell and Mitchell Assn., Phila. 1983—; cons. Barton-Aschman Assocs., Evanston, Ill., 1982—; IBM Human Resources Forum, Armonk, N.Y., 1983, Squibb Corp., 1984—, Skadden, Arps, 1985—, Ford Motor Co., 1986—, Gen. Motors Corp., 1986—, Covington & Burling, 1987—, others. Mem. bd. Com. of Seventy, Phila., 1975-78; mem. vestry Old Christ Ch., 1978—; chieftain Segamores of the Wabash, State of Ind., 1989. Served to 1st lt. U.S. Army, 1943-46. Named Albert Hill Cup Prof. of Yr., Sigma Kappa Phi, 1983, 91; fellow W.T. Grant Found., 1950-51. Fellow Am. Psychol. Assn.; mem. Pa. Psychol. Assn. (pres. 1959-60, 50th Anniversary past pres. award 1983), Am. Acad. Mgmt., Am. Soc. Tng. and Devel., Am. Pub. Transp. Assn., Friars Sr. Soc. U. Pa. (hon. mem.). Democrat. Episcopalian. Club: Franklin Inn (Phila.). Office: Mgmt Dept Wharton Sch U Pa 3620 Locust Walk Philadelphia PA 19104-6302

MITCHELL, JAMES AUSTIN, insurance company executive; b. Cin., Dec. 16, 1941; s. James Austin and Jeannette Louise (Stiles) M.; 1 child, J. David. A.B., Princeton U., 1963. CLU; chartered fin. cons.; FSA. Various positions Conn. Gen. Life Ins. Co., Hartford, 1963-73, v.p., controller, 1973-77; v.p., chief fin. officer Aetna Ins. Co., Hartford, 1977-82; pres. Cigna RE Corp., Hartford, 1982-84; pres., chief exec. officer IDS Life Ins. Co., Mpls., 1984—; dir. IDS Fin. Services and Affiliated Cos., Mpls. Mem. exec. com. Mpls. Inst. Arts, 1987—; bd. dirs. Mpls. YMCA. With U.S. Army, 1964-70. Fellow Soc. Actuaries; mem. Soc. C.L.U.s. Republican. Presbyterian. Club: Minneapolis. Avocations: tennis; skiing; reading. Home: 2685 N Shore Dr Wayzata MN 55391-9351 Office: IDS Life Ins Co 2900 IDS Tower 10 Minneapolis MN 55474

MITCHELL, JAMES KENNETH, civil engineer, educator; b. Manchester, N.H., Apr. 19, 1930; s. Richard N. and Henrietta (Moench) M.; m. Virginia D. Williams, Nov. 24, 1951; children: Richard A., Laura K., James W., Donald M., David L. B.C.E., Rensselaer Poly. Inst., 1951; M.S., M.I.T., 1953; D.Sc., 1956. Mem. faculty U. Calif., Berkeley, 1958-93, prof. civil engring., 1968-89, chmn. dept., 1979-84, Edward G. and John R. Cahill prof. civil engring., 1989-92, Edward G. and John R. Cahill prof. civil engring. emeritus, 1993—; Berkeley citation, 1993; Via prof. civil engring. Va. Poly. Inst. and State U., Blacksburg, 1994—; geotech. cons., 1960—. Author: Fundamentals of Soil Behavior, 1976, 2d edit., 1993; contbr. articles to profl. jours. Asst. scoutmaster Boy Scouts Am., 1975-82; mem. Moraga (Calif.) Environ. Rev. Com., 1978-80. Served to 1st lt. AUS, 1956-58. Recipient Exceptional Sci. Achievement medal NASA, 1973, Berkeley Citation, 1993. Fellow ASCE (hon., Huber prize 1965, Middlebrooks award 1962, 70, 73, Norman medal 1972, 95, Terzaghi lectr. 1984, Terzaghi award 1985, pres. San Francisco sect. 1986-87); mem. Nat. Acad. Engring., Am. Soc. Engring. Edn. (Western Electric Fund award 1979), NRC (geotech. bd. chmn. 1990-94, bd. on infrastructure and constrn. environ. 1994—, transp. rsch. bd. exec. com. 1983-87), Internat. Soc. Soil Mechanics and Found. Engring. (v.p. N.Am. 1989-94), Earthquake Engring. Rsch. Inst., Brit. Geotech. Soc. (Rankine lectr. 1991), Sigma Xi, Tau Beta Pi. Office: Va Tech Dept Civil Engring Blacksburg VA 24061-0105

MITCHELL, JAMES LOWRY, lawyer, former government official; b. Evanston, Ill., May 20, 1937; s. David B. and Sara (McGinn) M.; children: Caitlin, Andrew. BA, Cornell U., 1959; LLB, Yale U., 1962. Bar: Ill. 1962, D.C. 1977, N.Y. 1985. Assoc. Mayer, Brown & Platt, Chgo., 1966-69, ptnr., 1970-72, 77-84; spl. asst. to sec. for policy devel. U.S. Dept. Commerce, Washington, 1972-73; gen. counsel HUD, Washington, 1973-74, under sec., 1974-75; assoc. dir. Office Mgmt. and Budget, Washington, 1975-77; dep. gen. counsel Citicorp/Citibank, N.Y.C., 1984-90; exec. v.p., gen. counsel 1st Fidelity Bancorp, Newark, 1990—. Lt. USN, 1962-66. Mem. ABA, Assn. of Bar of City of N.Y., Capitol Hill Club. Office: 1st Fidelity Bancorp 550 Broad St Newark NJ 07102-4517

MITCHELL, JAMES WINFIELD, science administrator; b. Durham, N.C., Nov. 16, 1943; s. Willie Lee and Eunice H. (Hester) M.; m. June 4, 1964; children: Veronica, Duane, Tonya. BS, N.C. A&T State U., 1965; PhD, Iowa State U., 1970. Mem. tech. staff AT&T Bell Labs., Murray Hill, N.J., 1970-72; supr. AT&T Bell Labs., Murray Hill, 1972-75, dept. head, 1975-85, rsch. fellow, head process and chem. engring. rsch. dept., 1985—. Author or co-author of 65 publs. in field; patentee in field. Trustee Drexel U., Rutgers U. AT&T fellow, 1985; recipient IR100 award, 1982, P.I. Julian award 1981. Fellow Am. Inst. Chem. (recipient R & D award 1989); mem. New York Acad. Sci., NAE, Bd. Chem. Sci. and Tech., Omega Psi Phi (pres. 1986-88). Avocations: bowling, archery, golf. Office: AT&T Bell Labs Dept Process/ChemE Rsch 600 Mountain Ave New Providence NJ 07974-2010

MITCHELL, JANET BREW, health services researcher; b. N.Y.C., Oct. 20, 1949; d. Robert Moscrip Mitchell and Dorothy Brennan; m. Jerry Lee Cromwell, June 15, 1980; children: Alexander, Genevieve. BA with highest honors, U. Calif., San Diego, 1971; MSW, UCLA, 1973; PhD, Brandeis U., 1976. Rsch. asst. Brandeis U./Worcester Tng. Program in Social Rsch. & Psych., Waltham, Mass., 1973-75; sr. analyst Abt Assocs., Cambridge, Mass., 1975-77; asst. prof. Boston U. Sch. Medicine, 1977-80; pres. Ctr. for Health Econs. Rsch., Waltham, Mass., 1980—; mem. com. on monitoring access to health care svcs. Inst. Medicine, 1989-92; mem. nat. adv. com. Robert Wood Johnson Health Care Fin. Fellows, 1988-93; cons. VA, 1982-85, NIH, 1983-85, Health Care Financing Adminstrn., 1979—; advisor Physician Reimbursement Study, Congl. Budget Office, 1984-85; mem. adv. panel on physicians & heat tech. Office of Tech. Assessment, 1984-85; mem. health care tech. study sect. Nat. Ctr. for Health Svcs. Rsch., 1984-88; psychiat. social worker UCLA Med. Ctr., 1971-72; med. social worker U. So. Calif., 1972-73. Univ. Hosp. San Diego, 1973. Author (with F.A. Sloan & J. Cromwell) Private Physicians and Public Programs, 1978; contbr. chpts. to 8 books; contbr. numerous articles to profl. jours. Thesis grantee VA, 1976-77. Office: Ctr for Hlth Econ Rsch 300 5th Ave Waltham MA 02154

MITCHELL, JOHN DIETRICH, theatre arts institute executive; b. Rockford, Ill., Nov. 3, 1917; s. John Dennis Royce and Dora Marie (Schroeder) M.; m. Miriam Pitcairn, Aug. 25, 1956; children: John Daniel, Lorenzo Theodore, Barbarina Mitchell Heyerdahl. BSS, Northwestern U., 1939, MA, 1941; EdD, Columbia U., 1956; HHD (hon.), Northwood U., 1986. Dir.-producer Am. Broadcasting Co., N.Y.C., 1942-46; assoc. editor Samuel French, Publ., N.Y.C., 1946-48; assoc. prof. Manhattan Coll., N.Y.C., 1948-58; pres. Inst. for Advanced Studies in the Theatre Arts, N.Y.C., 1958—; founder, pres. Eaton St Press, Key West, Fla., 1994; founder, pres. Eaton St. Press, Key West, Fla., 1994; bd. dirs. Beneficia Found., Jenkintown, Pa. Author: Staging Chekhov, 1990, Actors Talk, 1991, Gift of Apollo, 1992; author: (aka Jack Royce) The Train Stopped at Domodossola, 1993, Murder at the Kabuki, 1994, Dressed to Murder. Trustee Northwood U., Midland, Mich., 1972-91; patron Met. Opera, N.Y.C.; mem. Cmty. Ch. Key West. Named Hon. conch Key West (Fla.) Commrs., 1994. Mem. Met. Mus., Key West Arts and Hist. Soc., Tennessee Williams Fine Arts Ctr. (founder), Key West Literary Seminar (emeritus), Nippon Club N.Y.C., NY Athletic Club. Avocations: Tai Chi Chuan, swimming, collecting musical recordings, books. Home: 703 Eaton St Key West FL 33040 Office: Inst for Advanced Studies in Theatre Box 399 331 W 57th St New York NY 10019 also: Eaton Street Press 524 Eaton St # 30 Key West FL 33040

MITCHELL, JOHN FRANCIS, electronics company executive; b. Chgo., Jan. 1, 1928; s. William and Bridie (Keane) M.; B.S. in Elec. Engring., Ill. Inst. Tech., 1950; m. Margaret J. Gillis, Aug. 26, 1950; children—Catherine (Mrs. Dennis Miller), John, Kevin. Exec. v.p., asst. chief oper. officer Motorola Inc. Schaumburg, Ill., 1953-80, pres., 1980-87, chief oper. officer, 1986-87, vice chmn., 1988—; also bd. dirs. Served to lt. (j.g.) USNR, 1950-53. Mem. IEEE (sr.). Club: Inverness (Ill.) Country. Patentee in field. Office: Motorola Inc 1303 E Algonquin Rd Schaumburg IL 60196

MITCHELL, JOHN HENDERSON, retired army officer, management consultant; b. Atlanta, Sept. 9, 1933; s. William Lloyd and Jessie (Henderson) M.; m. Joan Ann Cameron, Apr. 8, 1961; children—John Cameron, Christopher Lloyd, Colin MacKenzie. BA in Bus. Adminstrn., St. Bonaventure U., 1956, PhD in Sci. 1991; MA in Pub. Adminstrn. Shippensburg State U., 1973. Commd. 2d lt. U.S. Army 1956, advanced through grades to maj. Army., 1982; comdr. 8th Battalion, 6th Arty., 1st Infantry div. U.S. Army, Vietnam, 1968; chief officer assignments, field arty. br., Officer

Personnel Directorate U.S. Army, Washington; chief of staff 8th div. U.S. Army, 1973-75; asst. dept. chief of staff for personnel, Hdqrs. U.S. Army Europe and 7th Army U.S. Army, Heidelberg, Fed. Republic Germany, 1975-77; div. arty. comdr., chief of staff, 1st Inf. Div. U.S. Army, Ft. Riley, Kan., 1977-79; comdr., Field Command, Def. Nuclear Agy. U.S. Army, Kirtland AFB, N.Mex., 1979-81; dir. Human Resources Devel. Office, dept. chief staff for pers. U.S. Army, Washington; U.S. comdr. Berlin, 1984-88; ret., 1989; pres. Intersystems, Inc., Englewood, Colo., 1989—; POM Enterprises, Inc., Colo. Springs, Colo. Bd. dirs. Nat. Safety Council, 1982-84. Decorated D.S.M. with oak leaf cluster, Legion of Merit with oak leaf cluster, D.F.C. with oak leaf cluster, Bronze Star with oak leaf cluster and V., Air medals. Mem. Assn. U.S. Army, VFW, Army Navy Club, Army War Coll. Alumni, Soc. of First Inf. Div. Republican. Roman Catholic. Avocations: tennis, history, reading. Home: 375 Hidden Creek Dr Colorado Springs CO 80906-4386 Office: POM Enterprises Inc PO Box 60171 Colorado Springs CO 80960-0171

MITCHELL, JOHN McKEARNEY, manufacturing company executive; b. N.Y.C., Sept. 20, 1938; s. James William and Genevieve (McKearney) M.; AB, Dartmouth Coll., 1960; MBA, Amos Tuck Sch. Bus., 1961; m. Melinda Marsters, Aug. 25, 1962; children: Peter Marsters, Jeffrey Dewing. Acct., Ernst & Whinney, N.Y.C., 1962-64; asst. MIS mgr., mgr. acctg. Sperry Corp., Univac Internat. Div., N.Y.C., Bluebell, Pa., 1964-68; planning analyst, mgr. treas. ops., asst. contr. Sybron Corp., Rochester, N.Y., 1968-80; corp. contr. Condec Corp., Old Greenwich, Conn., 1980-83; exec. v.p. Powell Duffryn (U.S.A.) Ltd., 1983-86; pres. 1986-88; pres. Vt. Marble Co., Proctor, 1988-89, Pluess-Staufer Ind. Inc., 1990—; bd. dirs. Canadiagua Enterprises. , Bd. dirs. Park Ridge Hosp., Greese, N.Y., 1971-80; chmn. bd. dirs. Conn. Ballet Theatre, Stamford, Conn., 1983-88. 1st lt., inf., U.S. Army, 1961-62. Mem. Fin. Execs. Inst., Dartmouth Club. Republican. Home: Otis Ho RR 1 Box 257B Danby VT 05739-9754

MITCHELL, JONI (ROBERTA JOAN ANDERSON), singer, songwriter; b. Ft. Macleod, Alta., Can., Nov. 7, 1943; d. William A. and Myrtle M. (McKee) Anderson; m. Chuck Mitchell (div.); m. Larry Klein, Nov. 21, 1982. Student, Alta. Coll. Albums include Song to a Seagull, Clouds, Ladies of the Canyon, Blue, For the Roses, Court and Spark, 1974, Miles of Aisles, The Hissing of Summer Lawns, 1975, Hejira, 1976, Don Juan's Reckless Daughter, Mingus (Jazz Album of Year and Rock-Blues Album of Year, Downbeat mag. 1979), Shadows and Light, 1980, Wild Things Run Fast, 1982, Dog Eat Dog, 1985, Chalk Mark in a Rainstorm, 1988, Night Ride Home, 1991, Turbulent Indigo, 1994. Recipient Grammy award for Best Folk Performance, 1969, Grammy award for Best Arrangement Accompanying Vocalists (with Tom Scott), 1974. Address: care Peter Asher Mgmt 644 N Doheny Dr Los Angeles CA 90069-5526

MITCHELL, JOSEPH NATHAN, retired real estate executive; b. Winnipeg, Man., Can., Oct. 10, 1922; came to U.S., 1931, naturalized, 1936; s. Edward David and Anna (Copp) M.; m. Beverly Edna Henigson, Oct. 27, 1946; children: Jonathan Edward, Jan Ellen, Karin Helene. Student, UCLA, 1940-42. Pres. Beneficial Standard Corp. and Beneficial Standard Life Ins. Co., 1967-85, chmn., 1985-89; pres. Am. Investors & Cons. Inc., L.A. 1989—; past mem. internat. bd. Ampal-Am. Israel Corp., N.Y.C.; v.p. exec. com. Jackson-Mitchell Pharms., Inc., Santa Barbara, Calif.; exec. com. L.A. Children's Bur. Found., 1988-89; chmn. Mayor's Task Force-Capital Financing Subcom., 1988-89; chmn. bd. Cedars-Sinai Med. Ctr., 1991-93. Chmn. Los Angeles Appeal, State of Israel Bonds, 1967, also past mem. exec. com., cabinet; mem. Mayor's Steering Com. on Urban Coalition, Mayor's Ad Hoc Com. on Aging, 1980, L.A. Citizens Olympic Adv. Commn., 1980-81, Dist. Atty.'s Adv. Council, Greater L.A. Urban Coalition, L.A. Mayor's Fin. Task Force; past mem. bd. dirs., exec. com., nat. campaign cabinet United Jewish Appeal; chmn. bd. Cedars-Sinai Med. Ctr.; past mem. exec. com. Jewish Fedn.-Coun. Greater L.A.; bd. dirs., past v.p., gen. chmn. United Jewish Welfare Fund, 1952; trustee, mem. adv. bd., past v.p. Jewish Community Found.; bd. dirs. ops. mgmt. coun. United Way, 1972-73, also mem. exec. com.; chmn. United Way L.A., Music Ctr. Unified Fund Campaign, 1981; dir., pres. Edward D. and Anna Mitchell Family Found.; vice chmn. bd. govs. Performing Arts Coun., 1980-81; chmn. L.A. C. of C., 1979. Served with AUS, 1942-46, ETO. Mem. Am. Technion Soc. (past nat. v.p., bd. govs.), U.S.C. of C., Calif. C. of C. (past nat. v.p., Calif.-Israel C. of C., L.A. C. of C. (bd. dirs., chmn., pres. 1977). Clubs: Hillcrest Country (Los Angeles) (past treas., dir.), Los Angeles (Los Angeles); Tamarisk Country (Palm Springs, Calif.). Office: Am Investors & Cons Inc 6310 San Vicente Blvd Ste 500 Los Angeles CA 90048-5426

MITCHELL, JOSEPH (QUINCY), writer; b. Fairmont, N.C., July 27, 1908; s. Averette Nance and Elizabeth Amanda (Parker) M.; m. Therese Dagny Engelsted Jacobsen, Feb. 27, 1931 (dec. Oct. 1980); children: Nora (Mrs. John L.R. Sanborn), Elizabeth (Mrs. Henry Curtis). Student, U. N.C., 1925-29. Reporter N.Y. World, N.Y.C., 1929-30, N.Y. Herald Tribune, 1930-31, N.Y. World Telegram, 1931-38; writer New Yorker, N.Y.C., 1938—. Author: My Ears Are Bent, 1938, McSorley's Wonderful Saloon, 1943, Old Mr. Flood, 1948, The Bottom of the Harbor, 1960, Joe Gould's Secret, 1965, (with Edmund Wilson) Apologies to the Iroquois, With a Study of the Mohawks in High Steel, 1960, Up in the Old Hotel, 1992. Vestryman Grace Ch., N.Y.C., 1978-84; mem. N.Y.C. Landmarks Preservation Commn., 1982-87; mem. restoration com. South Street Seaport Mus., 1972-80. Recipient Gold medal for lit. State N.C., 1984, Disting. Alumnus award U. N.C., 1993, Brendan Gill prize Mcpl. Art Soc., 1993, Amb. Book award English-Speaking Union, 1993. Mem. Am. Acad. Arts and Letters, Soc. Archtl. Historians, Soc. Indsl. Archeology, Friends of Cast-Iron Architecture, James Joyce Soc., Gypsy Lore Soc. Club: Century Assn. (N.Y.C.). Home: 44 W 10th St New York NY 10011-8762 Office: The New Yorker 20 W 43d St New York NY 10036

MITCHELL, KENDALL, writer, literary critic; b. Chgo.; s. John Kendall Southgate and Ann (Leichsenring) M. BA, Yale U., 1946. Instr. Am. U. of Beirut, 1946-49; pub. rels. dir., dir. publis. Bldg. Owners and Mgrs. Assn. Internat., Chgo., 1951-76; cons. Bldg. Mgrs. Assn., Chgo., 1976-85; writer, reviewer Chgo. Tribune and Chgo. Sun Times, 1977—; lectr. journalism Roosevelt U., Chgo., 1981—. Author: A Chair By The Fire, 1951; translator: Lebanon, 1949. With USAAF, 1942-43. Mem. Nat. Book Critics Circle, Elizabethan CLub, Alpha Delta Phi. Episcopalian. Home: 318 South Blvd Evanston IL 60202-3019

MITCHELL, KIM SARAHJANE, lawyer; b. Geneseo, Ill., Nov. 19, 1954; d. Edward Franklin and Lorraine Marie (Jung) Kittrell; m. Gary Everett Mitchell, May 19, 1979. BA, U. Notre Dame, 1976; JD, U. Mich., 1979. Bar: Ill. 1979, U.S. Dist. Ct. (no. dist.) Ill. 1979, Mich. 1988. Law clk Ill. Appellate Ct. for 2d Dist., Waukegan, 1979-81; atty. Interstate United Corp., Chgo., 1981-85; asst. gen. counsel Canteen Corp., Chgo., 1985-87; corp. counsel Amway Corp., Grand Rapids, Mich., 1987—. Mem. ABA, Ill. Bar Assn., Mich. Bar Assn. Office: Amway Corp 7575 E Fulton St Ada MI 49355

MITCHELL, LANSING LEROY, federal judge; b. Sun, La., Jan. 17, 1914; s. Leroy A. and Eliza Jane (Richardson) M.; m. Virginia Jumonville, Apr. 18, 1938; children—Diane Mitchell (Mrs. Donald Lee Parker), Lansing Leroy. B.A., La. State U., 1934, LL.B., 1937. Bar: La. 1937. Pvt. practice Pontchatoula, 1937-38; spl. agt. FBI, 1938-41; atty. SEC, 1941-42; asst. U.S. atty. Eastern Dist. La., 1946-53; also engaged in pvt practice; ptnr. Deutsch, Kerrigan & Stiles., New Orleans, 1953-66; U.S. dist. judge Eastern Dist. La., 1966—. Commn. nat. security com. New Orleans C. of C., 1963-66; vice chmn. New Orleans Armed Forces Day, 1964, 65, New Orleans Heart Fund campaign, 1959-60; mem. New Orleans Municipal Auditorium Adv. Com., 1957-61, New Orleans Municipal Com. Finance, 1955-67, Small Bus. Adv. Council La., 1963-66; pres. Camp Fire Girls Greater New Orleans, 1965-67; La. chmn. Lawyers for Kennedy-Johnson, 1960. Served to lt. col. AUS, 1942-46; col. Res. (ret.). Decorated Royal Order St. George Royal Order Scotland. Mem. ABA, Inter-Am. Bar Assn., La. Bar Assn., New Orleans Bar Assn., Maritime Law Assn. U.S., Judge Adv. Assn., Soc. Former Spl. Agts. FBI, Am. Legion, Mil. Order World Wars, VFW, Navy League Assn. U.S. Army (pres. La. 1964-65, pres. New Orleans 1961-64, v.p. 4th Army region 1963-66), Soc. Mayflower Descendants in State of La. (assoc.), Scabbard and Blade, SAR, S.R., Soc. War 1812 La., Pi Kappa Alpha, Phi Delta Phi, Theta Nu Epsilon. Clubs: Mason (33 degree, New Orleans)

(Shriner), Press (New Orleans), Paul Morphy Chess (New Orleans), Southern Yacht (New Orleans), Bienville, Pendennis (New Orleans); Tchefuncta Country (Covington, La.). Office: US Dist Ct C-508 US Courthouse 500 Camp St New Orleans LA 70130-3313 *To serve my country as a soldier, praying that I need never be called to arms again; to serve the people as a jurist, knowing that I too shall someday be judged; to serve my family as a shepherd, finding that my love for them begets greater loving.*

MITCHELL, LEE MARK, communications executive, investment fund manager, lawyer; b. Albany, N.Y., Apr. 16, 1943; s. Maurice B. and Mildred (Roth) M.; m. Barbara Lee Anderson, Aug. 27, 1966; children: Mark, Matthew. A.B., Wesleyan U., 1965; J.D., U. Chgo., 1968. Bar: Ill. 1968, D.C. 1969, U.S. Supreme Ct. 1972. Assoc. Leibman, Williams, Bennett, Baird & Minow, Chgo. and Washington, 1972-74; ptnr., 1974-84, 92-94; exec. v.p. and gen. counsel Field Enterprises, Inc., Chgo., 1981-83, pres. and chief exec. officer, 1983-84; pres., chief exec. officer Field Corp., 1984-92; prin. Golder, Thoma, Cressey, Rauner, Inc., Chgo., 1994—; bd. dirs. Paging Network, Inc., Washington Nat. Corp.; Northwestern Meml. Mgmt. Corp.; PTN Pub. Co., Learning Scis. Corp.; chmn. NOTIS Systems, Inc., 1987-91. Author: Openly Arrived At, 1974, With the Nation Watching, 1979; co-author: Presidential Television, 1973. Mem. LWV Presdl. Debates Adv. Com., Washington, 1979-80, 82; U.S. del. Brit. Legis. Conf. on Govt. and Media, Ditchley Park, Eng., 1974; bd. visitors U. Chgo. Law Sch., 1984-86, Medill Sch. Journalism, Northwestern U., 1984-91; bd. govs. Chgo. Met. Planning Coun., pres., 1988-91; mem. midwest regional adv. bd. Inst. Internat. Edn., 1987—; trustee Ravinia Festival Assn., Northwestern U., bd. dirs. Japan-Am. Soc. Chgo. Mem. ABA, Fed. Comm. Bar Assn., Econ. Mid-Am. Club (trustee), Mid-Day Club, Chgo. Club, Comml. Club Chgo. Home: 135 Maple Hill Rd Glencoe IL 60022 Office: Golder Thoma Cressey Rauner Inc 6100 Sears Tower Chicago IL 60606-6402

MITCHELL, LEONA PEARL, soprano; b. Enid, Okla., Oct. 13, 1949; d. Hulon and Pearl Olive (Leatherman) M.; married. BA, Oklahoma City U., 1971, MusD (hon.), 1979. With San Francisco Opera, spring, 1973, fall, 1974, 77. Appeared at Edinburgh (Scotland) Festival, 1977, Sacria Umbria Festival, Perugia, Italy, 1977, on concert tour, Australia, 1978; has sung with most maj. symphonies throughout U.S.; European debut Barcelona, Spain, 1974; Met. Opera debut as Micaela, 1975; also appeared films and TV shows; recs. include Porgy and Bess with Cleve. Orch., 1975. Winner San Francisco Opera auditions, 1971; named Ambassadress of Enid, 1978, Okla. Hall of Fame, 1983. Mem. Am. Guild Musicians Assn. Sigma Alpha Iota, Alpha Kappa Alpha. Mem. Ch. of God in Christ. Performed for Pres. Ford, 1976, Pres. Carter, 1978, 79. Office: Orgn Internat Opera et Concert, 19,rue Vignon, F-7 5008 Paris France*

MITCHELL, MAURICE B., publishing executive, educator; b. N.Y.C., Feb. 9, 1915; s. Jacob and Beatrice (Weinstein) M.; m. Mildred Roth, Mar. 1937; 1 child, Lee Mark; m. Mary V. Rowles, Nov. 1951; children: Keith Edward, Deborah Irene; m. Linda Merry Stewart, Nov. 1991. Student, NYU, 1932-35; LLD (hon.), U. Denver, 1958, W.Va. Wesleyan U., 1978; LHD (hon.), Nat. Coll. Edn., 1969, Nat. U., San Diego, 1986; LittD (hon.), Colo. State U., 1971. With N.Y. Times, 1935-36; editor Gouverneur (N.Y.) Press, 1936-37; asst. pub. Ogdensburg (N.Y.) Jour., 1938-39, Rochester (N.Y.) Times-Union, 1940; nat. advt. mgr. Albany (N.Y.) Knickerbocker-News, 1941-43; with CBS, Washington, also N.Y.C., 1945-48, Nat. Assn. Broadcasters, Washington, 1948-49; mng. dir. Broadcast Advt. Bur./TVB, N.Y.C., 1949-50; with NBC, 1950; v.p., assoc. program service div. Muzak Corp., N.Y.C., 1950-53; dir. Muzak Corp., 1953-58; pres., dir. Ency. Brit. Films, Inc., 1953-62; pres. Ency. Brit., Inc. (Chgo. and all subs.), 1962-67; dir. Ency. Brit. Edn. Corp., 1977-94; chancellor U. Denver, 1967-77, emeritus, 1978—; pres. Ctr. for Study Dem. Instns./Fund for Republic, 1977-78; chmn. Pacific Basin Inst., Santa Barbara, Calif., 1978—; dir. Washington program com. policy studies Annenberg Found., 1983-85, cons., 1986-92; chmn. Internat. Acad., Santa Barbara, 1988-93, dir. Ctr. for Study of the Environment, Santa Barbara,1993—; co-founder, chmn. Westview Press, Boulder, Colo., 1975-83; chmn. Denver Br. Fed. Res. Bank, 1971-76; bd. dirs. Fed. Res. Bank of Kansas City. Contbr. articles on edn. and communications to profl. jours. Mem. U.S. Commn. on Civil Rights, 1968-74; chmn. Calif. Ednl. Tech. adv. com., 1981-83, Denver Community Edn. Council on Integration Pub. Schs., 1974-76; trustee Freedoms Found.; chmn. Colo. com. Rhodes Scholarship Trust, 1974-77, Calif. Commn., 1978-80; citizens bd. U. Chgo.; mem. adv. com. U.S. Army Command and Gen. Staff Coll., Dept. Army, 1975-78; chmn. Western Regional Judges Truman Scholarships, 1976-82; dir. Nat. Public Radio, 1977-82, chmn., 1979-82; bd. assos. Nat. Coll. Edn.; trustee Com. Econ. Devel., 1957-62; bd. dirs. Fgn. Policy Assn., World Affairs Center and Nat. Citizens on Internat. Coop., 1966-71, chmn., 1980; bd. dirs., Inst. Internat. Edn., 1978-85, African Student Aid Fund; trustee Nat. U., San Diego. Recipient George Washington medal Freedoms Found., 1969; VFW medal of Merit, 1970; Cert. of Recognition for disting. service to edn. Phi Delta Kappa, 1971; Golden Plate award Am. Acad. Achievement, 1972; Civis Princeps award Regis Coll., Denver, 1973; Meritorious award Denver Met. NAACP, 1973; Malcolm Glenn Wyer award Adult Edn. Council Met. Denver, 1975; B'nai B'rith award, 1976; Human Relations award Beth Joseph Synagogue, Denver, 1976; award NCCJ, 1974. Mem. Colo. State Hist. Soc. (dir.), Phi Beta Kappa, Beta Alpha Psi, Omicron Delta Kappa, Beta Gamma Sigma, Alpha Kappa Psi, Cosmos Club (Washington), Chgo. Club, Mid-Am. Club (Chgo.), Santa Barbara Club, La Cumbre Country Club, Masons (32 deg., Knight Commdr., Ct. of Honor). Home: 1455 E Mountain Dr Santa Barbara CA 93108-1216

MITCHELL, MAURICE MCCLELLAN, JR., chemist; b. Lansdowne, Pa., Nov. 27, 1929; s. Maurice McClellan and Agnes Stewart (Kerr) M.; m. Marilyn M. Badger, June 14, 1952. BS in Chemistry, Carnegie-Mellon U., 1951, MS in Chemistry, 1957, PhD in Phys. Chemistry, 1960. Group leader rsch. and devel. U.S. Steel Corp., Pitts., 1951-61; br. head phys. chemistry rsch. and devel. Melpar Inc., Falls Church, Va., 1961-64; group leader rsch. and devel. Atlantic Richfield Co., Phila., 1964-73; dir. rsch. and devel. Houdry div. Air Products and Chems., Inc., 1973-81; dir. rsch. and devel. Ashland (Ky.) Oil Inc., 1981-86, v.p. rsch. and devel., 1986-93; vis. lectr. dept. chem. Coll. Arts and Scis. Ohio U. Southern Campus, Ironton, 1993—. Contbr. articles to profl. jours.; patentee in field. Fellow Am. Inst. Chemists; mem. Am. Chem. Soc., Am. Inst. Chem. Engrs., Catalysis Soc. N.Am. (pres. 1985-89), AAAS, Sigma Xi. Home: 2380 Hickory Ridge Dr Ashland KY 41101-3604 Office: Ohio U So Campus 1804 Liberty Ave Ironton OH 45638-2214

MITCHELL, MICHAEL KIEHL, elementary and secondary education educator, minister; b. Phila., Pa., Oct. 27, 1932; s. Robert Bartow and Louise Room (Keyser) M.; m. Gloria (Nell) Wilburn, Nov. 12, 1960; children: Donald Kiehl, Robert Alan. B in Edn., U. Miami, 1955, MEd, Tex. A&M U., 1975, PhD, 1978. Cert. elem. and secondary edn., Fla., Tex., Alaska; lic. comml. pilot. Tchr. math. Dade County Pub. Schs., Miami Springs, Fla., 1955-60; tchr. elem. Greenwood Sch. Dist., Midland, Tex., 1961-63; from tchr. social studies, English to tng. coord. Midland (Tex.) Sch. Dist., 1963-75; prin. rsch. investigator Tex. A&M U., College Station, 1977-78; project dir. Edn. Profl. Devel. Consortium, Richardson, Tex., 1978-79; sr. rsch. scientist Am. Airlines, Dallas, 1979-83; pres. North Rsch. Inc., Anchorage, Alaska, 1983-84; vocat. edn. curriculum specialist Anchorage Sch. Dist., 1984-87; sci. tchr., dept. head McLaughlin Youth Ctr. Anchorage (Alaska) Sch. Dist., 1987—; adj. prof. U. Alaska, Anchorage, 1987-89; evaluation team N.W. Accreditation Assn., Anchorage, 1985; asst. min. United Meth. Ch., 1990-94; min. Christian Cmty. Fellowship, 1994—, 1st United Meth. Ch., Anchorage, 1990; instr. Flight and Ground Sch. Dir., v.p. Anchorage Comty. Theater, 1984-89; marriage commr. 3d Jud. Dist. Alaska, Anchorage, 1989-93; vol. United Way, Anchorage, 1984-90, Tony Knowles for Gov. Campaign, Anchorage, 1990, 94, Mark Begich for Mcpl. Assembly Campaign, 1991, Cheryl Clementson for Mcpl. Assembly Campaign, 1993. With U.S. Army, 1955-57. Tex. Edn. Agy. fellow, Austin, 1975, Ednl. Profl. Devel. fellow, 1975-78. Mem. Am. Correctional Edn. Assn., Alaska Airmans Assn. (bd. dirs. 1983-89), Screen Actors Guild, Mensa, Am. Legion, Clowns of Am., Nat. Sci. Tchrs. Assn., Alaska Sci. Tchrs. Assn., Alaskan Aviation Safety Found., Tex. Assn. Aerospace Tchrs., Phi Delta Kappa, Phi Kappa Phi. Avocations: commercial pilot, professional acting, FAA accident prevention counselor. Home: 6626 Foothill Dr Anchorage AK 99504-2620 Office: McLaughlin Youth Cen High 2600 Providence Dr Anchorage AK 99508-4678

MITCHELL, MILTON, lawyer; b. Rochester, N.Y., Apr. 6, 1916; s. Mark and Pauline (Amberg) M.; m. Marion Irene Lieberman, Nov. 1, 1942; children: Mark, Martha. J.D. with honors, George Washington U., 1942. Bar: D.C. 1941, U.S. Supreme Ct. 1966. Atty. Bur. Customs, Washington, 1945-50; asst. chief protocol Dept. State, Washington, 1950-64, sr. atty., 1964-69; lectr., prof. internat. law Nat. Law Ctr., George Washington U., Washington, 1964-80; professional lectr. diplomatic and consular law; gen. counsel Accuracy in Media, Inc., Washington, 1973-90. Bd. dirs. Community Action Council, Rossmoor Leisure World, Silver Spring, Md., 1979-85. Served to lt. USNR/World War II. Mem. Fed. Bar Assn., D.C. Bar Assn., Am. Acad. Philately (dir., pres.), Soc. Philatelic Americans, Royal Philatelic Soc. Can. Republican. Clubs: Lawyer (Washington); Diplomatic and Consular Assn., Aspen Hill Tennis. Address: 3401 Hallaton Ct Silver Spring MD 20906-1833 *I have always felt that one of cardinal principles of my life was to 'tell it like it is'— to have the courage to present my views on important subjects, no matter whether they met with agreement or disagreement. It was never my policy to curry favor with important people just to please them or to advance my station in life. I have always felt I first have to live with myself, and I have found that most people valued my sincerity, whether or not they agreed with my position.*

MITCHELL, NANCY K., nurse; b. Charleston, Ark., Oct. 11, 1937; d. Daniel G. and Jocie M. (Fitzgerald) Keith; m. Wallace L. Hufschmid, Sept. 29, 1956 (div. Feb. 1971); children: Ramona, Kimley, Donald, Rebecca. Diploma Nursing, Sparks Meml. Hosp., Ft. Smith Ark., 1958; BS, St. Joseph's Coll., North Windham, Maine, 1984; MBA, Oklahoma City U., 1987. Staff nurse St. John's Hosp., Tulsa, 1958-62; night nursing sup. Capitol Hill Hosp., Oklahoma City, 1963-66; staff nurse Bapt. Med. Ctr. of Okla., Oklahoma City, 1962-63, 1966-68, night nursing supr., 1968-71, clin. supr., 1971-72; night nursing supr. St. Anthony Hosp., Oklahoma City, 1973, Veterans Med. Ctr., Oklahoma City, 1973-80; dir. nursing South Community Hosp., Oklahoma City, 1980-92; ret., 1992. Republican. Mem. Ch. of Christ.

MITCHELL, ORLAN E., clergyman, former college president; b. Eldora, Iowa, Mar. 13, 1933; s. Frank E. and Alice G. (Brown) M.; m. Verlene J. Huehn, June 10, 1952; children: Jolene R., Stephen M., Nadene A., Timothy M., Mark E. B.A., Grinnell Coll., 1955; B.D., Yale U., 1959, M.Div., 1965; D.Min., San Francisco Theol. Sem., 1976. Ordained to ministry United Ch. of Christ, 1959; pastor chs. Sheridan Twp., Iowa, 1954-55, New Preston, Conn., 1956-59, Clarion, Iowa, 1959-69, Yankton, S.D., 1969-77; pres. Yankton (S.D.) Coll., from 1977; now conf. minister Iowa Conf. United Ch. Christ. Mem. Sch. Bd., Clarion, Iowa, 1965-69, mem., Yankton, S.D., 1973-77, pres., 1976; bd. dirs. Lewis and Clark Mental Health Center. Mem. S.D. Found. Pvt. Colls., S.D. Assn. Pvt. Colls., Colls. of Mid-Am. Democrat. Lodges: Kiwanis; Masons. Office: 600 42nd St Des Moines IA 50312-2701

MITCHELL, OTIS CLINTON, JR., history educator; b. Spearville, Kans., Jan. 10, 1935; s. Otis Clinton and Joeanna Esther (Woodring) M.; m. Darlene Foley, Aug. 20, 1966. A.B., Wichita U., 1957; M.A., Kans. State Coll., 1960; Ph.D., U. Kans., 1964. Instr. history Wichita State U., 1963-64; mem. faculty U. Cin., 1964—, prof. history, 1975—, also chmn. dept. history. Author: Two Totalitarians, 1965, The Western Cultural Way, 1965, A Concise History of Western Civilization, 2d edit, 1976, Fascism: An Introductory Perspective, 1978, The Great European Revolutionary Era of 1789-1815, 1979, A Concise History of Brandenburg-Prussia to 1786, 1980; co-author: The World Since 1919, 1971; editor, contbr.: Nazism and the Common Man, 2d edit, 1981, Hitler Over Germany, 1983, Two German Crowns, 1985, Hitler's Nazi State, 1987, Otto von Bismarck: Germany's Iron Chancellor, 1992; editor: Studies in Historical Europe, 1986, Thirty Year's War, 1993, Blood Purge, 1993, A German History, 3 Vols., 1994. Dir. civic com. Hidden Valley Lake, Ind., 1975; bd. dirs. Hidden Valley Lake P.O.A., 1978-79. Served with AUS, 1957-59. Grantee Taft Fund Fellowship, 1969-74, 77, 82, 89; recipient Outstanding Tchr. award Ohio Acad. History, 1983, Excellence in Teaching award U. Cin., 1985, Nat. Excellence in Teaching award Am. Assn. Higher Edn., 1989. Mem. Phi Alpha Theta. Home: Hidden Valley Lake 19912 Longview Dr Lawrenceburg IN 47025-9061 Office: Univ Cin Dept History Cincinnati OH 45221

MITCHELL, PAMELA ANN, airline pilot; b. Otis AFB, Mass., May 6, 1955; d. Gene Thomas and Rose Margaret (Jones) Mitchell; m. Robert Carroll Stephens, May 26, 1984 (div. Dec. 1992). BFA, Colo. State U., 1975; postgrad., Webster Coll., 1981. Lic. pilot Ill., comml. instr., airline transport pilot, jet rating, Boeing 747 and 727, Boeing 747-400. Flight attendent United Airlines, Chgo., 1976-80; charter pilot Air Aurora, Sugar Grove, Ill., 1978-80; owner, operator Deliverance, Unltd. Ferry Co., Aurora, Ill., 1978-81; flight test pilot Cessna Aircraft Co., Wichita, Kans., 1981-82, nat. spokeswoman, 1982-83; airline pilot Rep. Airlines, Mpls., 1983-84, Northwest Airlines, Mpls., 1985—; pres., ptnr., artist Aerographics Jacksonville, Fla., 1986-90. Mem. Safety Coun. Airline Pilots Assn., 99's Internat. Women Pilots Assn., Mooney Aircraft Pilots Assn. (exec. bd.), Internat. Women Airline Pilots Soc. (mem. exec. bd.), Nat. Aviation Club, N.W. Airline Ski Team (capt.), Kappa Kappa Gamma. Republican. Presbyterian. Avocations: piano, snow skiing, tennis, travel, golf. Home: 12502 Mission Hills Cir Jacksonville FL 32225 Office: Northwest Airlines Minn/St Paul Internat Airport Saint Paul MN 55111

MITCHELL, PAULA RAE, nursing educator; b. Independence, Mo., Jan. 10, 1951; d. Millard Henry and E. Lorene (Denton) Gates; m. Ralph William Mitchell, May 24, 1975. BS in Nursing, Graceland Coll., 1973; MS in Nursing, U. Tex., 1976; postgrad. N.Mex. State U. RN, Tex., Mo.; cert. childbirth educator. Command capt. U.S. Army, 1972; ob-gyn. nurse practitioner U.S. Army, Seoul, Korea, 1977-78; resigned, 1978; instr. nursing El Paso (Tex.) Community Coll., 1979-85, dir. nursing, 1985—, acting div. chmn. health occupations, 1985-86, div. chmn., 1986—; curriculum facilitator, 1984-86; ob-gyn. nurse practitioner Planned Parenthood, El Paso, 1981-86, mem. med. com.; cons. in field. Author: (with Grippando) Nursing Perspectives and Issues, 1989, 93; contbr. articles to profl. jours. Founder, bd. dirs. Health-C.R.E.S.T., El Paso, 1981-85; mem. pub. edn. com. Am. Cancer Soc., El Paso, 1983-84, mem. profl. activities com., 1992-93; mem. El Paso City-County Bd. Health, 1989-91; mem. Govt. Applications Rev. Com., Rio Grande Coun. Govts., 1989-91; mem. collaborative coun. El Paso Magnet High Sch. for Health Care Professions, 1992-94. Decorated Army Commendation medal, Meritorious Svc. medal. Mem. Nat. League Nursing (mem. resolutions com. Assocs. Degree coun. 1987-89, accreditation site visitor, AD coun. 1990—, mem. Tex. edn. com. 1991-92, Tex. 3rd v.p. 1992-93), Am. Soc. Psychoprophylaxis Obstetrics, Nurses Assn. Am. Coll. Obstetricians & Gynecologists (cert. in ambulatory women's health care; chpt. coord. 1979-83, nat. program rev. com. 1984-86, corr. 1987-89), Advanced Nurse Practitioner Group El Paso (coord. 1980-83 legis. committee 1984), Am. Phys. Therapist Assn. (commn. on accreditation, site visitor for phys. therapist assistant programs 1991—), Orgn. Assoc. Degree Nursing (Tex. membership chmn. 1985-89, chmn. goals com 1989—, mem nat. bylaws com., 1990—), Am. Vocat. Assn., Am. Assn. Women Community & Jr. Colls., Tex. Orgn. Nurse Execs., Nat. Coun. Occupational Edn. (mem. articulation task force 1986-89, program standards task force 1991-93), Nat. Coun. Instructional Adminstrs., Tex. Soc. Allied Health Profls., Tex. Nurses Assn., Nat. Soc. Allied Health Profls. (mem. edn. com. 1993—), Sigma Theta Tau, Phi Kappa Phi. Mem. Christian Ch. (Disciples of Christ). Home: 4616 Cupid Dr El Paso TX 79924-1726 Office: El Paso C C PO Box 20500 El Paso TX 79998-0500

MITCHELL, PETER KENNETH, JR., educational consultant, association administrator; b. Bklyn., June 12, 1949; s. Peter Kenneth and Joan Marie (Hayes) M.; m. Susan Veitch Mitchell, June 25, 1983; 1 child, Elyse Alexandra. BA, SUNY, Geneseo, 1970; MS in French, LI. U., 1975; cert. of French lang. proficiency, U. de Neuchatel, Switzerland, 1969. Tchr. French and Spanish Middle Country Sch. Dist., Selden, N.Y., 1972-81; tech. asst. to dir. internat. affairs dept. Am. Fedn. Tchrs., Washington, 1981-82; asst. to gen. sec. internat. fedn. of Free Tchrs. Unions, Amsterdam, 1982-90; exec. dir. Internat. Reading Assoc., Newark, Del., 1990-91; owner Insights Out Assocs., Newark, Del., 1992—; dir. mktg. Jr. Achievement Del., 1994—. Author numerous ednl. publs. Mem. ACLU, Am. Soc. Assn. Execs., N.Y. State United Tchrs., Washington U. Club, Amnesty Internat. Avocations: reading, music, tennis. Office: Insights Out Assocs PO Box 9652 Newark DE 19714-9652

MITCHELL, PETER MCQUILKIN, educational administrator; b. Ft. Dodge, Iowa, Oct. 15, 1934; s. Granger and Majorie (McQuilkin) M.; m. Lou Cushing Harden, Sept. 16, 1961; children: Andrew, Thomas. BA in Polit. Sci., Marquette U., 1956; MA in History, U. Colo., 1960, PhD, 1965. Asst. v.p. acad. affairs Seton Hall U., South Orange, N.J., 1971-73, v.p. acad. affairs, 1973-77, v.p./ provost, 1977-79; pres. Stockton State Coll., Pomona, N.J., 1979-83; vice chancellor Higher Edn. Coordinating Coun., Boston, 1983-94; pres. Mass. Maritime Acad., Buzzards Bay, 1994—; cons. acad. personnel; panelist NEH. Contbr. arricles to profl. jours. Am. Council on Edn. intern, 1972-73. Mem. Am. Assn. State Colls and Univs. Office: Mass Maritime Acad 101 Academy Dr Buzzards Bay MA 02532

MITCHELL, R. CLAYTON, JR., state legislator; b. Chestertown, Md., Apr. 16, 1936; m. Marie A. Whitsett; children: Clayton A., John C., Michael R. Student, Goldey Beacom Jr. Coll., 1958. Mem. Kent County (Md.) Dem. Cen. Com., 1962-66; chmn. Kent County Commrs., 1966-70; del. Md. Ho. of Dels., Annapolis, 1970—, speaker, 1987—; bd. dirs. 2d Nat. Bank Md. Mem. bd. visitors and govs. Washington Coll., Chestertown, 1987; life mem. Md. Vol. Fire Assn. Md. Recipient William Collington award Johns Hopkins U., 1984; named Legis. of Yr., KC, 1972, one of 6 Best Legislators in Md., Md. Assn. Counties, 1984. Democrat. Roman Catholic. Avocations: golf, farming. Office: State Cir H-101 State House Annapolis MD 21401

MITCHELL, RALPH, microbiologist; b. Dublin, Ireland, Nov. 26, 1934; came to U.S., 1956; s. Samuel and Sara (Miller) M.; m. Muriel Harris, 1957; children—Susan, Tricia, Dara. B.A., Trinity Coll., Dublin, 1956; M.S., Cornell U., 1959, Ph.D., 1961; M.A. (hon.), Harvard U., 1971. Sr. scientist Weizmann Inst. Sci., Rehovot, Israel, 1962-65; asst. prof. applied biology, div. engring. and applied physics Harvard U., 1966-69, assoc. prof., 1969-70, Gordon McKay prof. applied biology, div. applied scis., 1970—; mem. exec. com. Tyler Ecology Prize. Editor: Water Pollution Microbiology, vol. 1, 1971, vol. 2, 1978; author: Introduction to Environmental Microbiology, 1974; editor-in-chief: Microbial Ecology, 1976—. Mem. AAAS, Am. Soc. Microbiology, Internat. Water Pollution Control Fedn. Office: Harvard U Div Applied Sci Pierce Hall Cambridge MA 02138

MITCHELL, RALPH MELVIN JR., naval officer; b. Easton, Pa., Oct. 30, 1944; s. Ralph Melvin and Betty (Hummer) M.; m. Shirley Anne Petty, June 11, 1966; children: Amy, Anne, Stephanie. BS, U.S. Naval Acad., 1966; MBA, U. Pa., 1976, MSE in Computer Sci., 1976; advance mgmt. program, Harvard U., 1987. Commd. ensign USN, 1966, supply officer U.S. Naval Ships, 1969-86; personal aide, comdt. 4th Naval Dist. USN, Phila., 1969-71; dir. advance planning Naval Supply Ctr. USN, San Diego, 1976-78; dir. data processing Navy Fin Ctr. USN, Cleve., 1980-82; dir. aircraft engines Aviation Supply Office USN, Phila., 1982-84; dir. navy stock fund Naval Supply Systems Command USN, Washington, 1986-88; exec. asst. to dep. under sec. Dept. Def., Washington, 1988—. Mem. Washington Navy Supply Corps Assn. (chmn. ann. fund drive 1987-88, trustee 1987-88, pres. 1988-89, nat. bd. dirs. 1989—). Republican. Roman Catholic. Avocations: tennis, basketball. Office: Dept Def Office Under Sec Rm 3E1014 Pentagon Arlington VA 20301

MITCHELL, RICHARD BOYLE, advertising executive; b. St. Louis, June 20, 1947; s. Samuel West and Blair (Boyle) M.; m. Deborah Mead Boas, June 1, 1968; children: Rebecca, Jessica. BS in Mktg., NYU, 1969. Account exec. D.L. Blair Corp., N.Y.C., 1967-70, NW Ayer Adv. Agy., N.Y.C., 1970-74; sr. account exec. Ted Bates Agy., N.Y.C., 1974-75; sr. v.p. DKG Advt., N.Y.C., 1975-81, McCaffrey/McCall, N.Y.C., 1981-86; pres., CEO Marshall Jaccoma Mitchell Advt., N.Y.C., 1986—. Commr. Wilton (Conn.) Police Dept., 1984—. Served with USAR, 1969-75. Democrat. Roman Catholic. Club: Wilton Riding. Avocations: mil. history, running, weight lifting. Home: 43 Collinswood Rd Wilton CT 06897-1811 Office: Marshall Jaccoma Mitchell Adv 41 Madison Ave New York NY 10010-2202

MITCHELL, RICHARD DALE, journalist, writer; b. San Jose, Calif., Nov. 27, 1952; s. Maurice Dale Mitchell and Mary Margaret (Woody) Gron; m. Lori-Lyn Sumako, May 3, 1987; 1 child, Chelsea Pearl. BA in Am. Studies, Calif. State U., Fullerton, 1974. Music critic Oreg. Jour., Portland, 1978-82, Willamette Week, Portland, 1983, The Oregonian, Portland, 1984-85; music critic, sports columnist Willamette Week, 1986; freelance writer L.A., 1987; arts and entertainment reporter The Bakersfield Californian, 1988; music critic Houston Chronicle, 1989—. Author: Garth Brooks: One of A Kind, Workin' on A Full House, 1993; jazz columnist Request Mag., 1990—; contbr. New Country Music Mag., 1994—. Mem. adv. com. Houston Blues Soc.; active Amnesty Internat., ACLU. Avocations: athletics, physical fitness, playing the drums, reading. Office: Houston Chronicle 801 Texas St Houston TX 77002-2996

MITCHELL, ROBERT, province official; b. Preeceville, Sask., Can., Mar. 29, 1936; s. Charles Stuart M. and Beda Annette Abrahamson; m. Sandra Gail Stolson, Oct. 18, 1968; children: Janet Maureen, Roberta June, Stephanie Arbonna, Shannon Elizabeth, Donna Gailynn, Alison T. Marie. BA, U. Sask., 1957, LLB, 1959. Assoc. Salloum & Hagemeister, 1961-64; ptnr. Pierce, Hleck, Kanuka, Mitchell & Thuringer, 1964-70; dir. legal svcs. and legis. rsch. Labour Can., 1970-72; dir. legal svcs. Dept. of Regional Economic Expansion, 1973; labor rels. expert Internat. Labour Orgn., 1973-74; dep. min. Sask. Labour, 1974-79; sr. ptnr. Mitchell Taylor Mattison Ching, 1979-91; mem. Sask. Legis. Assembly, 1986; re-elected, 1991; Min. of Justiceand Atty. Gen. Province of Sask., Saskatoon, Can., 1991—; Provincial Sec. and Min. Human Resources, Labour and Employment Province of Sask., Can., 1991-92; now Min. of Indian and Metis Affairs Province of Sask., Regina, Can.; opposition critic Trade & Investment; chmn. Bd. of Inquiry, 1979-81; chief fed. negotiator Inuit Land Claim, 1980-82; cons. Labour Legis. Govt. of Yukon, 1981-84, province of Man., 1984; auditor gen. adv. com. Labrador, Can., 1984; del. to C.P.A. Registration Seminar, P.E.I., 1988. Author: Mega-Projects, 1981. Mem. United Ch. Mem. law Soc. of Sask. NDP. Avocations: golf, canoeing. Office: Dept of Justice, 1874 Scarth St, Regina, SK Canada S4P 3V7 Home: 70 Degeer Cres, Saskatoon, SK Canada S7H 4P7°

MITCHELL, ROBERT ARTHUR, university chancellor; b. N.Y.C., Jan. 19, 1926; s. George P. and Vera A. (Duffy) M. Novitiate, student, St. Andrew-on-Hudson, Poughkeepsie, N.Y., 1947; A.B. (summa cum laude), Woodstock Coll., 1949, Ph.L. (summa cum laude), 1950; S.T.L.(magna cum laude), Facultes S.J. de Louvain, Belgium, 1957; Th.D., U. Strasbourg, France, 1965; (hon.), Le Moyne Coll., 1990, Loyola U., 1991; U. Detroit, 1992. Joined S.J., 1943, ordained priest, Roman Cath. Ch., 1956. Instr. in philosophy LeMoyne Coll., 1950-53, asst. prof. theology, 1958-59, acad. dean, 1959-63, assoc. prof. theology, acad. dean, 1965-66; pres. Loyola Coll., Shrub Oak, 1966; provincial N.Y. State Province (S.J.), 1966-72; pres. Jesuit Conf., chmn. Am. Jesuit Provincials, Washington, 1972-76; dir. Woodstock Theol. Ctr., 1976-79; pres. U. Detroit, 1979-90, chancellor, 1990-92; consultant, Higher Education to Jesuit U.S. Provincials, 1992—; acting pres. Le Moyne Coll., Syracuse, N.Y., 1993-94; pres. Le Moyne Coll. 1994—; bd. dirs. Economic Club of Detroit, 1979-92, Detroit Econ. Growth Corp., 1983-92, Detroit Symphony Orchestra, 1981-89, Woodstock Theological Ctr., 1977-83, Georgetown U., 1976-82, 1983-92; bd. trustees, Loyola Marymount U., 1986, St. Peter's Coll., 1992, U. Detroit, 1979, Sta. WTVS/Channel 56, 1979-86, 1988-92, Michigan Cancer Foundation, 1985-92, New Detroit, Inc., 1979-92, Fordham U., 1966-74, Le Moyne Coll., 1994—; bd. dirs. Georgetown U., New Detroit, Inc., Detroit Symphony Orch., United Way; trustee Boston Coll., Loyola Marymount U., Mich. Cancer Found.; mem. adv. bd. United, Detroit Sci Ctr., Met. Affairs Corp.; dir. Greater Detroit Interfaith Roundtable NCCJ. Clubs: Econ. of Detroit (dir.). Detroit Athletic, Renaissance. Office: Le Moyne College Office of the Pres Syracuse NY 13214

MITCHELL, ROBERT C., federal judge; Judge, U.S. Dist. Ct. (we. dist.) Pa., Pitts. Office: US District Court 524 US Post Office and Courthouse 700 Grant St Pittsburgh PA 15219-1952

MITCHELL, ROBERT DALE, consulting engineer; b. Worthington, Minn., Aug. 2, 1910; s. Karl V. and Margaret Dumont (Steigleder) M.; m. Carol Sherman Northrop, June 17, 1939; children—Constance Remington, Robert Brown. B.S., S.D. State U., 1932; S.M. (grad. fellow), Harvard U., 1939.

Engr. J. Emberg, Madison, S.D., 1932-35; instr. S.D. State U., 1935-37; engr. Malcolm Pirnie, N.Y.C., 1939-42; project engr., partner Malcolm Pirnie, 1945-70, sr. v.p., sec., chief engr., 1970-75, cons., 1975—. Served to maj. San Corps AUS, 1942-45. Recipient Distinguished Engr. award S.D. State U., 1977. Mem. ASCE, Am. Water Works Assn., Am. Cons. Engrs. Council, New Eng. Water Works Assn. (Commemorative award 1963). Home: 487 Brackett Rd Rye NH 03870-2204 Office: 2 Corporate Park Dr White Plains NY 10602

MITCHELL, ROBERT EDWARD, urban planner, international development specialist, educator; b. Detroit, May 16, 1930; s. Arthur and Elizabeth (Wayne) M.; m. Sylvia Ann Sheppard, Aug. 26, 1950 (div. 1993); children: Anthony Edward, Maude Wayne, Adam Arthur. BA in Oriental Civilizations, U. Mich., 1952; M.A., Harvard U., 1955; Ph.D. in Sociology, Columbia U., 1962. Instr., project dir. Bur. Applied Social Research, Columbia U., 1956-62; coord. internat. rsch. program, dep. dir. Survey Research Center, U. Calif.-Berkeley, 1962-66; dir. Hong Kong Urban Family Life Survey, dir. Social Survey Research Centre, Chinese U., Hong Kong, 1966-69; prof. urban and regional planning, dir. Survey Data Center Fla. State U., Tallahassee, 1969-78; exec. dir. Fla. Gov.'s Task Force on Housing and Community Devel., 1971-73; mem. UN Ad Hoc Meeting Experts on Social Aspects of Housing in Urban Areas, 1970; mem. tech. mission to Jordan Dept. State, 1973; behavioral sci. adv. urban devel. Nr. East Bur., Office Tech. Support, AID, Dept. State, Washington, 1979—, devel. ofcl., 1980—; AID duty tours, Egypt, Yemen and Guinea-Bissau; cons. in field. Author: The Needs of Hong Kong Manufacturing Industry for Higher Level Manpower, 1968, Levels of Emotional Strain in Southeast Asian Cities: A Study of Individual Responses to the Stresses of Urbanization and Industrialization, Family Life in Urban Hong Kong, 1972, Pupil, Parent and School, 1972, Housing, Urban Growth, and Economic Development, 1972; Contbr. articles to profl. jours. Mem. Am. Sociol. Assn.

MITCHELL, ROBERT EVERITT, lawyer; b. Port Washington, N.Y., June 14, 1929; s. Everitt and Alice (Fay) M.; m. Anne Nordquist, Nov. 2, 1957; children: Anne C. Mitchell Coneys, Maura A. Kelly, Michael E. BS, U. Mich., 1952; JD, Georgetown U., 1956. Bar: N.Y. 1957, U.S. Dist. Ct. (so. dist.) N.Y. 1958, U.S. Supreme Ct. 1966. Assoc. Sullivan & Cromwell, N.Y.C., 1956-63; v.p., sec., gen. counsel Lambert & Co. Inc., N.Y.C., 1963-65; ptnr. Campbell & Mitchell, Manhasset, N.Y., 1965-80; asst. gen. counsel J.P. Stevens & Co. Inc., N.Y.C., 1980-82, gen. counsel, 1982-88; pvt. practice Peconic, N.Y., 1988—. Atty. Village Baxter Estates, Port Washington, 1967-83; Counsel Mobilized Community Resources, Roslyn, N.Y., 1969-80; asst. scout master Troop 1001 Boy Scouts Am., Port Washington, 1976-79; justice Village Sands Point, N.Y., 1966-85. Served to lt. USNR, 1952-55. Mem. ABA. Republican. Roman Catholic. Clubs: Manhasset Bay Yacht (Port Washington) (commodore 1972-73); N.Y. Yacht (N.Y.C.). Avocations: sailing, fishing, camping, platform tennis, music. Home and Office: 3905 Wells Rd Peconic NY 11958

MITCHELL, ROBERT GREENE, industrial manufacturing executive, consultant; b. Abington, Pa., July 20, 1925; s. James Henry and Nellie Edna (Greene) M.; m. Alma Maerker Honsberger, Mar. 6, 1948; children: Scott Craig, Donna Lynn, Sandra Lee. B.S., Drexel U., 1948. Cert., CPIM. Dept. mgr. Internat. Plastics, Dover, Del., 1949-52, quality control mgr., 1952-59, mfg. mgr. Indsl. div., 1959-60; v.p. ops. The Wool "O" Co., Phila., 1960-65; mfg. mgr. Plymouth Rubber, Canton, Mass., 1965-68; chief indsl. engr., spl. projects Vanity Fair Mills, Monroeville, Ala., 1968-75; v.p. materials mgmt. The H.W. Gossard Co., Chgo., 1975-76; v.p. adminstrn., 1977; v.p. adminstrn., mem. exec. com. Knickerbocker Toy Co., Middlesex, N.J., 1977-79; pres. H&R Block, Prince Frederick, Md., 1979-85; sr. mfg. cons. Sperry Corp. (now UNISYS Corp.), Lutherville, Md., 1980-87, Hunt Valley, Md., 1987-89; ret., 1989. 1st lt. USAF, 1943-46. Mem. Am. Soc. Quality Control (cert. quality engr., chmn. textile div. 1959-60), Am. Prodn. and Inventory Control Soc. Lodge: Lions (dir. 1954-56, pres. 1955-56). Patentee in field. Home and Office: 22 Hillside Ct Huntingtown MD 20639-9406

MITCHELL, ROBERT LYNN, business supply company executive; b. Lufkin, Tex., July 28, 1933; s. Sherman M. and Zula (Chandler) M.; m. Eileen Agnes Parma, Sept. 13, 1958; children: Pamela Eileen, Robert Gary, Gregory Michael. BBA in Mktg., North Tex. State U., 1959. Sales rep. Graybar Electric Co., Dallas, 1959-62; mgr. regional sales personnel Allstate Ins. Co., Dallas, 1962-66; mgr. regional personnel Xerox Corp., Dallas, 1966-69; com. mgmt. services Arthur Young & Co., Dallas, 1969; v.p. mktg. Ennis (Tex.) Bus. Forms, Inc., 1969-83, exec. v.p., 1983-85, pres., 1985—. Served with U.S. Army, 1954-56. Roman Catholic. Lodge: KC. Home: 1901 W Baldridge St Ennis TX 75119-8004 Office: Ennis Bus Forms Inc 107 N Sherman St Ennis TX 75119-3954

MITCHELL, ROGER LOWRY, agronomy educator; b. Grinnell, Iowa, Sept. 13, 1932; s. Robert T. and Cecile (Lowry) M.; m. Joyce Elaine Lindgren, June 26, 1955; children: Laura, Susan, Sarah, Martha. B.S. in Agronomy, Iowa State Coll., 1954; M.S., Cornell U., 1958; Ph.D. in Crop Physiology, Iowa State U., 1961. Mem. faculty Iowa State U., 1959-69, prof. agronomy, 1966-69, prof. charge farm operation curriculum, 1962-66; prof. agronomy, chmn. dept. U. Mo., Columbia, 1969-72, 81-83; dean agr., dir. expt. sta. U. Mo., 1983—, dean extension, 1972-75; v.p. agr. Kans. State U., Manhattan, 1975-80; exec. dir. Mid-Am. Internat. Agrl. Consortium, 1981; exec. bd. divsn. agr. Nat. Assn. State Univs. and Land Grant Colls., 1978-80, 85-90, chmn., 1988-89; mem. bd. agr. NRC/NAS, 1983-86. Author: Crop Growth and Culture, 1970; co-author: Physiology of Crop Plants, 1985. Served to 2d lt. USAAF, 1954-56. Danforth fellow, 1956-61; Acad. Adminstrn. fellow Am. Council Edn., 1966-67. Fellow AAAS (chmn. sect. O 1980-81), Am. Soc. Agronomy (pres. 1979-80), Crop Sci. Soc. (pres. 1975-76); mem. Soil Sci. Soc. Am., Coun. Agrl. Sci. and Tech., Sigma Xi, Gamma Sigma Delta, Alpha Zeta, Phi Kappa Phi. Home: 502 W Lathrop Rd Columbia MO 65203-2804

MITCHELL, ROY SHAW, lawyer; b. Sherwood, N.Y., Jan. 16, 1934; s. Malcolm Douglas and Ruth Landon (Holland) M.; m. Nancy Elizabeth Bishop, Aug. 27, 1955; children: Mark E., Jeffrey B., Jennifer R. BS, Cornell U., 1957; JD with honors, George Washington U., Washington, D.C., 1959. Bar: D.C. 1959, Ohio 1960, Va. 1967, U.S. Claims Ct. 1963, U.S. Supreme Ct. 1965. Atty. Squire, Sanders & Dempsey, Cleve., 1960-61, Hudson & Creyke, Washington, 1961-67, Lewis, Mitchell & Moore, Vienna, Va., 1967-87, Morgan, Lewis & Bockius, Washington, 1987—; vice-chmn. Ameribanc Savs. Bank, Annandale, Va., 1980-95; trustee Ameribanc Investors Group, Annandale, 1980-95. Co-author: (with others) Handbook of Construction Law and Claims, 1982, 89; contbr. numerous articles to profl. jours. Fellow ABA (pub. contract law sect.), Va. Bar Assn., D.C. Bar Assn. Presbyterian. Avocation: boating. Home: 5 Jefferson Run Rd Great Falls VA 22066 Office: Morgan Lewis & Bockius 1800 M St NW Washington DC 20036-5802

MITCHELL, RUSSELL HARRY, dermatologist; b. Erie, N.D., Oct. 19, 1925; s. William John and Anna Lillian (Sögge) M.; B.S., B.A., U. Minn., Mpls., 1947, B.M., M.D., 1951; postgrad. U. Pa. Med. Sch., 1968-69; m. Judith Lawes Douvarjo, May 24, 1968; children: Kathy Ellen, Gregory Alan, Jill Elaine, Crystal Anne. Intern, Gorgas Hosp., C.Z., 1951-52; resident in dermatology U.S. Naval Hosp., Phila., 1967-70; asst. chief out-patient dept. Gorgas Hosp., 1954-56; chief med. and surg. wards Ariz. State Hosp., Phoenix, 1965; commd. lt. (j.g.) M.C., U.S. Navy, 1953, advanced through grades to capt., 1968; svc. in Vietnam; ret., 1981; pvt. practice specializing in dermatology, Leesburg, Va., 1971-98; mem. staff Loudoun Meml. Hosp. 1975—; dermatologist Nat. Naval Med. Center, Bethesda, Md., 1973-81; asst. prof. Georgetown U. Med. Sch., 1975-85. Pres. Archaeol. Soc. Panama, 1962-64. Decorated Bronze Star with combat V; Vietnam Gallantry Cross with palm and clasp; Condecoratíón Vasco Nuñez de Balboa in orden de Caballero (Panama); diplomate Am. Bd. Dermatology. Fellow Am. Acad. Dermatology, Am. Acad. Physicians, Explorers Club; mem. AMA, Assn. Mil. Surgeons, Assn. Mil. Dermatologists (life), Am. Soc. Contemporary Medicine and Surgery, Soc. Am. Archaeology, Royal Soc. Medicine, Pan Am. Med. Assn., Loudoun County Med. Soc., Dermatology Found., Marine's Meml. Club (assoc.), Internat. Platform Soc., Phi Chi. Contbr. articles to med. and archaeol. publs. Home: RR 2 Box 99 Leesburg VA 22075-9008 Office: 823J S King St Leesburg VA 22075-3916

MITCHELL, TAMARA O., judge; b. Mobile, Ala., Apr. 19, 1952; d. Maurice E. and Harriett (Roth) Olen; m. George E. Mitchell, Mar. 17, 1981. BS, U. South Ala., Mobile, 1974; JD, Whittier Coll., L.A., 1980. Bar: Calif. 1980, Ala. 1981. Pvt. practice Mobile, 1981-83; ptnr. Grodsky & Mitchell, Mobile, 1983-91; judge U.S. Bankruptcy Ct., Birmingham, Ala., 1992—. Mem. Nat. Conf. Bankruptcy Judges, Calif. State Bar, Ala. State Bar (exec. bd. bankruptcy sect. 1989-90, vice chairperson, chairperson com. on lawyer pub. rels. 1990-92, com. on bench and bar rels.), Mobile Bar Assn. (treas. 1991), Birmingham Bar Assn. Avocation: horseback riding. Office: US Bankruptcy Ct 1800 5th Ave N Birmingham AL 35203-2111

MITCHELL, TERENCE EDWARD, materials scientist; b. Haywards Heath, Sussex, Eng., May 18, 1937; came to U.S., 1963, naturalized, 1978; s. Thomas Frank and Dorothy Elizabeth (Perrin) M.; m. Marion Wyatt, Dec. 5, 1959; children: Robin Norman, Jeremy Neil. BA, St. Catharine's Coll., Cambridge (Eng.) U., 1958, MA, 1962, PhD in Physics, 1962; ScD, U. Cambridge, 1994. Research fellow Cavendish Lab., Cambridge, 1962-63; asst. prof. metallurgy Case Inst. Tech., 1963-66; assoc. prof. Case Western Res. U., 1966-75, prof., 1975-87, adj. prof., 1987—, chmn. dept., 1983-86, dir. high voltage electron microscopy facility, 1970-82, co-dir. materials research lab., 1982-83; vis. scientist NASA at Ames Lab., Stanford U. and Electric Power Research Inst., Palo Alto, Calif., 1975-76; scientist Ctr. Materials Sci. Los Alamos (N.Mex.) Nat. Lab., 1987—, lab fellow, 1991—; lab fellows chair Los Alamos (N.Mex.) Nat. Lab., 1993—; chmn. steering com. Electron Microscopy Ctr. Argonne (Ill.) Nat. Lab., 1979-83; cons. in field; mem. vis. com. metals and ceramics div. Oak Ridge Lab., 1987-91; vis. com. solid state scis. div. Ames Lab., 1987-89; sci. adv. com. Sci. and Tech. Ctr. for Superconductivity, 1989-93. Materials sci. editor Microscopy Rsch. and Technique, 1986—; sr. editor North Am., 1994—; contbr. articles to profl. jours. Pres. Cleve. Ethical Soc., 1970-72; bd. dirs Am. Ethical Union, 1972-74; steward Los Alamos Unitarian Ch., 1992-94; mem. policy com. Univ. Materials Coun., 1986-89; mem. policy com. Argonne Electron Microscopy Steering Com., chmn. 1978-82. Electric Power Research Inst. fellow, 1975-76; NSF grantee, 1966-88; Dept. Energy grantee, 1970-86, 87—; NIH grantee, 1969-72; NASA grantee, 1974-77, 81-87; USAF Office Sci. Research grantee, 1974-85; U.S. Army Research Office grantee, 1970-75, 79-83, EPRI grantee, 1986-89. Fellow Am. Soc. Metals, Am. Phys. Soc., Am. Ceramics Soc. (assoc. editor jour.), Los Alamos Nat. Lab.; mem. Metall. Soc. (editl. bd. 1981—), Electron Microscopy Soc. Am. (program chmn. 1981-82, dir. 1984-86, pres.-elect 1994, pres. 1995), Materials Rsch. Soc., Soc. Francaise de Microscopie Electronique (sci. com. 1982-90). Office: Los Alamos Nat Lab Ctr Materials Sci Ms # K-765 Los Alamos NM 87545

MITCHELL, THEODORE R., dean, education educator; b. San Rafael, Calif., Jan. 29, 1956; s. Theodore Robert and Genevieve Dolores (Doose) M.; m. Christine Marie Beckman, July 8, 1995. BA, Stanford U., 1978, MA, 1980, PhD, 1983. Asst. prof. Dartmouth Coll., Hanover, N.H., 1981-86, assoc. prof., 1986-87, chair dept. edn., 1987-91; dep. to pres. and provost Stamford (Calif.) U., 1991-92; dean Sch. Edn. and Info. Studies UCLA, 1992—; trustee Stanford U., 1985-90, Thetford (Vt.) Acad., 1989-91; bd. dirs. L.A. Edn. Partnership, L.E.A.R.N., L.A. Author: Political Education, 1985. Bd. dirs. Children Now, Oakland, Calif., 1994—. Office: UCLA Sch Edn & Info Studies 405 Hilgard Ave Los Angeles CA 90024

MITCHELL, THOMAS WAYNE, newspaper editor; b. Chillicothe, Mo., Dec. 20, 1945; s. Thomas Alan and Doris Lilly (Brammer) M.; m. Mary Kay Kolar, Sept. 10, 1967 (div. 1981); 1 child, Jonathan Robert; m. Janette Olene Corey, June 5, 1982; 1 child, Morgan Allison. BJ, U. Mo., 1967. Reporter Kansas City (Mo.) Star, 1967-71, state capital corr., 1971-78; metro editor Binghamton (N.Y.) Press, 1978-81; city editor San Diego Tribune, 1981-88; editor Marietta (Ga.) Daily Jour., 1988-89; v.p. editor Anderson (S.C.) Independent-Mail, 1989—. Dir. Brighter Christmas Fund Charity, Anderson, 1989—. Sgt. U.S. Army, 1967-69, Vietnam. Decorated Bronze Star, Commendation medal. Mem. Am. Soc. Newspaper Editors, S.C. Press Assn. (freedom of info. com. 1989—, bd. dirs. 1994—), Anderson Area C. of C. Presbyterian. Avocations: travel, reading, gardening. Home: 109 Cameron Way Anderson SC 29621-1501 Office: Anderson Independent-Mail 1000 Williamston Rd Anderson SC 29621-6508

MITCHELL, W. J. T., English language, literature and visual arts educator; editor; b. Anaheim, Calif., Mar. 24, 1942; s. Thomas Miles and Leona Marie (Gaertner) M.; m. Janice Misurell, Aug. 11, 1968; children: Carmen, Gabriel. B.A., Mich. State U., 1963; M.A., Johns Hopkins U., Ph.D., 1968. Asst. prof. Ohio State U., Columbus, 1968-73, assoc. prof., 1974-77; prof. English, art, and design U. Chgo., 1977-89, Gaylord Donnelley Disting. Svc. prof., 1989—, chair English dept., 1989-91; prof. Sch. Criticism and Theory Northwestern U., Evanston, Ill., 1983, Dartmouth Coll., 1990; vis. prof. Canterbury U., New Zealand, 1987, Beijing Fgn. Studies U., 1988; editor Critical Inquiry U. Chgo. Press, 1977—. Author: Blake's Composite Art, 1978, Iconology, 1986, Picture Theory, 1994; editor: Language of Images, 1980 (outstanding issue of a learned jour. Conf. Editors Learned Jours. 1981), On Narrative, 1982, Politics of Interpretation, 1983, Against Theory, 1985, Art and the Public Sphere, 1992, Landscape and Power, 1994. Nat. Endowment Humanities fellow, 1976, 86; Guggenheim fellow, 1982; Am. Philos. Soc. grantee, 1967, 72; Fairchild Disting. scholar Calif. Inst. Tech., 1993. Mem. MLA, Am. Soc. 18th Century Studies, Conf. Editors Learned Jours., Johnson Soc., PEN (Poets, Editors, and Novelists), Acad. Lit. Studies. Democrat. Club: Quadrangle (Chgo.). Office: Critical Inquiry U Chgo 1050 E 59th St Chicago IL 60637-1512

MITCHELL, W. RANDLE, JR., textile company executive; b. 1934. BS, U. Pa., 1956, MBA, 1965. Mgr. fin. reporting and analysis internat. div. Merck & Co., 1965-68; various positions to sr. v.p. Wellington Mgmt. Co., Boston, 1969-78; v.p., treas., chief fin. officer Amoskeag Co, Boston, from 1979; exec. v.p., chief fin. officer Fieldcrest Cannon Inc., Eden, N.C., 1985—; pres. & CEO Amoskeag, Boston, 1993—. Lt. comdr. USN, 1956-58, 61-62. Office: Amoskeag Co 4500 Prudential Ctr Boston MA 02199

MITCHELL, WARREN L., utility company executive; b. 1937. BSAS, Pepperdine U., MBA, 1976. With So. Calif. Gas Co., 1958—, v.p., 1981-90, pres., 1990—; also bd. dirs. Office: So Calif Gas Co 555 W 5th St ML 29A0 Los Angeles CA 90013-1011

MITCHELL, WILLIAM ALLEN, air force officer, political geography educator; b. Waco, Tex., Apr. 21, 1940; m. Joan Mary Woodill, May 31, 1958; children: Bill, Jim, John, Brian. BS in Geography and Bus., East Tex. State U., 1965; MA in Geography, U. Calif., L.A., 1969; PhD in Geography, U. Ill., 1974. Commd. 2d lt. USAF, 1965, advanced through grades to col., 1986, ret., 1991; dir. intercultural edn. USAF Acad., 1980-83, prof., head geography, 1985-86; prof. nat. security affairs, 1986-88; seminar dir. Am. War Coll., 1987, Air War Coll.; vis. prof. dept. polit. sci. Baylor U., Waco, Tex., 1993; adj. faculty U. Md., 1970, U. Colo., Colorado Springs, 1975-80, Troy State U., Montgomery, 1974-80. Author: (with John Kolars) The Euphrates River and The Southeast Anatolia Development Project, 1991; contbr. articles to profl. jours. Decorated U.S. Legion of Merit, Bronze Star, Humanitarian award for Kurdish Relief Efforts, Commendation medal, Humanitarian award for Turkish Earthquake Relief Effort, Orgn. Excellence award, Vietnam Cross of Gallantry with bronze palm, Humanitarian award for Armenian Earthquake relief, Spl. Rsch. award for intercultural edn. Dept. Air Force; named Outstanding Young Man of Am., 1976; recipient rsch. and travel grants NSF Quick Response to Earthquakes, 1978, 80, 84, 92, Inst. Turkish Studies, 1985, Atlantic Coun. of the U.S.-NATO Discussion Series Assoc. to Brussels, 1988, German Marshall fund grant to Turkey, 1988, others. Mem. Phi Kappa Phi. Baptist. Home: 501 Brint Ln Waco TX 76706-6207 Office: Baylor Univ PO Box 97276 Waco TX 76798-7276

MITCHELL, WILLIAM B., electronics company executive; b. 1935; married. BSME, Lamar State Coll. Tech. 1958; MEEE, So. Meth. Univ., 1965. With Gen. Dynamics, Ft. Worth, 1958-61; system design engr. Tex. Instruments Inc., 1961-68, with advanced weapon design, 1968-76, with HARM missile design, 1976-77, mgr. HARM missile program, 1977-80, mgr. def. suppression, 1980-84, v.p., pres. def. system and electronic group, 1984-87, exec. v.p., pres. def. system and electronic group, 1987—, also bd. dirs. Office: Tex Instruments Inc 13500 N Central Expy Dallas TX 75243

MITCHELL-RANKIN, ZINORA MONA, judge; b. Washington, Apr. 16, 1956; d. Walter, Sr. and Mary Lucinda (Sharpe) Mitchell; m. Michael Lee Rankin, May 14, 1988; 1 child, Everett. BA, Spelman Coll., 1976; JD, George Washington U., 1979. Bar: D.C. 1979. Law clk. voting rights divsn. U.S. Civil Rights Commn., Washington, 1977-78; law clk. divsn. of advice Nat. Labor Rels. Bd., Washington, 1978-79; trial atty. U.S. Dept. Justice, Washington, 1979-82; asst. U.S. atty. U.S. Attys.' Office, Washington, 1982-89; assoc. judge Superior Ct., Washington, 1990—; adj. prof. trial practice Nat. Law Ctr., Washington, 1990-92. Vol. Big Sister Program, greater metro. area, Washington, 1992—; mem. task force youth violence D.C. Ct. Appeals, 1994—. Recipient Mentor to Women Lawyers award Law Assn. for Women, 1994. Mem. William B. Bryant Inn of Ct. (master 1988-93). Avocations: reading, travel, jazz. Office: DC Superior Ct 500 Indiana Ave NW Washington DC 20001

MITCHELSON, BONNIE ELIZABETH, politician, nurse; b. Winnipeg, Man., Can., Nov. 28, 1947; d. Henry Alfred and Millie Christine (Leslie) Bester; m. Donald Mitchelson, Aug. 30, 1969; children: Michele, Scott. Diploma in nursing, Winnipeg, 1969. Nurse various hosps., Winnipeg, 1968-86; legis. dep. health critic Urban Affairs Critic, 1986-87; minister responsible for status of women and for lotteries, 1988-93; minister Ministry of Culture, Heritage and Citizenship, Winnipeg, 1988-93; ministry Ministry of Family Svcs., 1993—. Avocations: downhill skiing, boating, reading.

MITCHUM, ROBERT CHARLES DURMAN (CHARLES MITCHUM), actor; b. Bridgeport, Conn., Aug. 6, 1917; m. Dorothy Spence, Mar. 16, 1940; children: Jim, Petrine, Chris. Ed., N.Y.C. pub. schs. Motion picture debut in Hopalong Cassidy film, 1944; producer, actor motion pictures including Nightkill, Thunder Road; film appearances include The Story of G.I. Joe, 1945, Undercurrent, 1946, Till the End of Time, 1946, Pursued Locket, 1947, Til the End of Time, 1946, Desire Me, 1947, Crossfire, 1947, Out of the Past, 1947, Rachel and the Stranger, 1948, Blood on the Moon, 1948, Red Pony, 1949, Where Danger Lives, 1950, My Forbidden Past, 1951, The Racket, 1951, Macao, 1952, The Lusty Men, 1952, One Minute to Zero, 1952, Angel Face, 1953, River of No Return, Track of the Cat, She Couldn't Say No, 1954, Not as a Stranger, 1955, The Night of the Hunter, 1955, The Man with the Gun, 1955, Bandido, 1956, Foreign Intrigue, 1956, Heaven Knows Mr. Allison, 1957, Fire Down Below, 1957, The Enemy Below, 1957, Thunder Road, 1958, The Hunters, 1958, The Angry Hills, 1959, The Wonderful Country, 1959, Home from the Hill, 1960, A Terrible Beauty, 1960, The Grass is Greener, 1960, The Sundowners, 1960, The Longest Day, 1962, Cape Fear, 1962, Two for the Seesaw, 1962, The List of Adrian Messenger, 1963, Rampage, 1963, Man in the Middle, 1964, What a Way to Go, 1964, Mr. Moses, 1965, The Way West, 1967, El Dorado, 1967, Anzio, 1968, Five Card Stud, 1968, Secret Ceremony, 1968, Villa Rides, 1968, Young Billy Young, 1969, The Good Guys and the Bad Guys, 1969, Ryan's Daughter, 1971, Wrath of God, 1972, The Friends of Eddie Coyle, 1973, The Yakusa, 1974, Battle of Midway, 1975, Farewell My Lovely, 1975, The Amsterdam Kill, 1975, The Last Tycoon, 1976, The Big Sleep, 1977, Matilda, 1978, That Championship Season, 1982, Breakthrough, 1984, The Ambassador, 1984, Maria's Lovers, 1985, Mr. North, 1988, Scrooged, 1988, Cape Fear (Martin Scorsese remake) 1991, Tombstone, 1994; TV appearances include The Hearts and Davies Affiar, Reunion at Fairborough, Promises to Keep, Thompson's Lost Run, Brotherhood of the Rose, 1989, Jake Spanner, Private Eye, 1989; starring role in TV mini-series The Winds of War, 1983, War and Remberance, 1988; TV series: A Family for Joe, 1990, Family Man, 1990. Subject of book: It Sure Beats Working, 1972. Office: Taylor and Lieberman 10866 Wilshire Blvd Los Angeles CA 90024-4300*

MITFORD, JESSICA, author; b. Batsford Mansion, Eng., Sept. 11, 1917; d. Lord and Lady Redesdale; m. Esmond Romilly, June 1937; 1 dau., Constancia; m. Robert Treuhaft, June 21, 1943; 1 son, Benjamin. Author: Life itselfmanship, 1956, Daughters and Rebels, 1960, The American Way of Death, 1963, The Trial of Dr. Spock, 1969, Kind and Usual Punishment-The Prison Business, 1973, A Fine Old Conflict, 1977, Poison Penmanship: The Gentle Art of Muckraking, 1979, Faces of Philip: A Memoir of Philip Toynbee, 1984, Grace Had an English Heart: The Story of Grace Darling, Heroine and Victorian Superstar, 1988, The American Way of Birth, 1992.

MITGANG, HERBERT, author, journalist; b. N.Y.C., Jan. 20, 1920; s. Benjamin and Florence (Altman) M.; m. Shirley Kravchick, May 13, 1945; children: Esther, Lee, Laura. LLB, St. John's Law Sch., 1942. Bar: N.Y. 1942. Sports stringer Bklyn. Eagle, 1938-39; screen writer Universal-Internat. Pictures, 1945; copy editor, reviewer N.Y. Times, N.Y.C., 1945-54; supervising editor Sunday Times drama sect., 1955-62; editorial writer, mem. editorial bd. N.Y. Times, 1963-64, 67-76, publishing, cultural corr., book critic, 1976-94; asst. to pres., exec. editor CBS News, 1964-67; instr. English evening divsn. CCNY, 1948-49; vis. lectr. English, guest fellow Silliman Coll., Yale U., 1975-76; lit. advisor White House Libr., 1977-81. Writer, producer: (film documentaries) Henry Moore: Man of Form, D-Day Plus 20 Years, Sandburg's Prairie Years, Anthony Eden on Vietnam; author: Lincoln as They Saw Him, 1956; (novel) The Return, 1959, The Man Who Rode the Tiger: The Life and Times of Judge Samuel Seabury, 1963 (Gavel award Am. Bar Assn.), Working for the Reader, 1970, Get These Men Out of the Hot Sun, 1972, The Fiery Trial: A Life of Lincoln, 1974, The Montauk Fault, 1981, Kings in the Counting House, 1983, Dangerous Dossiers: The Secret War Against America's Authors, 1988, Words Still Count With Me: A Chronicle of Literary Conversations, 1995; editor: Washington, D.C., in Lincoln's Time, 1958, Civilians Under Arms: Stars and Stripes, Civil War to Korea, 1959, The Letters of Carl Sandburg, 1968, America at Random, 1969, Spectator of America, 1971; (play) Mister Lincoln, 1980, Knight Errant, 1995; contbr. to the New Yorker, Art News, Am. Heritage, The Progressive. Mem. exec. bd. Newspaper Guild of N.Y., CIO, 1948-49. Served with counter-intelligence sect. 5th wing USAAF, 1942-43, MTO; Army corr., mng. editor Stars and Stripes, Oran-Casablanca and Sicily edits. 1943-45. Decorated six battle stars, Knight Order of Merit (Italy); recipient George Polk Career award L.I. U., 1993, 25 Yr. News Achievement award Soc. of Silurians, 1993, Lit. Lions award N.Y. Pub. Libr. Fellow Soc. Am. Historians (bd. dirs.); mem. Authors League (council 1962—, pres. fund 1976—), Dramatists Guild, Authors Guild (pres. 1971-75), Internat. P.E.N. (U.S. del. London). Jewish. Club: Century Assn. (N.Y.C.). Office: 203 E 72d St New York NY 10021

MITHUN, RAYMOND O., advertising agency executive, banker, real estate and insurance executive; b. Warren, Minn., Mar. 20, 1909; s. Louis and Alma (Anderson) M.; m. Doris Berg, Aug. 9, 1932; children—Lewis, John, Raymond, Jr. A.B., U. Minn., 1930. From printers devil to editor Buffalo Jour., 1922; bur. mgr., 1924; editor Minn. Daily, 1929; pub. Wright Co. Press, 1929-30; city editor Mankato (Minn.) Free Press, 1930; copywriter, radio dir., account exec. Batten, Barton, Durstine & Osborn, Inc., 1930-32; founder, chmn. Campbell-Mithun, Inc., Mpls., 1933; chmn. Mithun Enterprises; owner State Bank of Chanhassen, Minn. Admitted to Advtg. Hall Fame, 1989. Mem. Delta Upsilon, Sigma Delta Chi (Journalism award 1930). Clubs: Minneapolis, Minikahda (Mpls.); Tavern (Chgo.); Minnesota (St. Paul); El Dorado (Palm Desert), Thunderbird (Palm Desert); Woodhill Country (Wayzata, Minn.). Home: 630 Indian Mound St Wayzata MN 55391-1709 Office: 900 Wayzata Blvd E Wayzata MN 55391-1836

MITLYNG, ERROL PAUL, financial executive; b. Montevideo, Minn., Oct. 10, 1936; m. Barbara Ann Lundin, Sept. 20, 1938; children: James, Nancy, David. BS, U. Nebr., 1960. CPA, Ill. Audit staff Ernst & Whinney, Chgo., 1960-66; asst. v.p. Wylain Inc., Michigan City, Ind., 1966-72; v.p., controller Wylain Inc., Dallas, 1972-80; sr. v.p. fin., treas. The Marley Co., Mission Woods, Kans., 1980—, also bd. dirs. B. dirs. KCPT, Kansas City, Mo., 1986—. Mem. Am. Inst. CPA's. Fin. Execs. Inst. Office: Marley Co 1900 Shawnee Mission Pky Shawnee Mission KS 66205-2001

MITOVICH, JOHN, association executive; b. Youngstown, Ohio, Feb. 8, 1927; s. John and Rose (Elieff) M.; m. Rebecca E. Webb, Aug. 1, 1953; children: Jon, Rosemary, Victoria, Janet, Martha, Matthew; m. Mary Lou Brennan, Nov. 27, 1985; m. Nancy Lexow Reichard, July 14, 1990. B.S. in Journalism, Ohio U., 1951. Advt. and pub. relations specialist Gen. Electric Co., Schenectady, 1955-57, Pittsfield, Mass., 1957-58; pub. affairs specialist Gen. Electric Co., Lynn, Mass., 1958-62; mgr. community relations Gen.

Electric Co., Johnson City, N.Y., 1962-64; cons. community and govt. relations Gen. Electric Co., N.Y.C., 1964-66; exec. v.p. Rockford (Ill.) C. of C., 1966-70; pres. Southwestern Area (Conn.) Assn. Commerce and Industry, 1970-90; pres., chief exec. officer Metropool Ridesharing Corp., 1980-85; vice chmn. Greater Stamford Conv. and Visitors Bur., 1987-90; pres. SACIA/West, Albuquerque, N.Mex., 1990—; lectr. econ. devel./western style U. Zagreb (Croatia) Sch. of Mgmt., 1991. Mem. bd. selectmen, North Reading, Mass., 1961-62, chmn. indsl. devel. commn., 1962-66; mem. Rockford Mayor's Urban Devel. Adv. Commn., 1966-68, Ill. Gov. Commn. on Urban Area Govt., 1969-70; founder-dir. Winnebago County (Ill.) Opportunities Industrialization Center, 1968-70, Met. Rockford Housing Devel. Corp., Forward Rockford, Inc., 1969-70; mem. Gov.'s Commn. Services and Expenditures, 1971; corp. chmn. N.Mex. Project Uplift, 1992; active N.Mex. Total Quality Mgmt. Coun. Task Force, 1992, Albuquerque Shared Vision Community Devel., 1993. Served with USMC, 1952-54. Recipient Gen. Electric Mgmt. award, 1958, Associated Industries Mass. award, 1958, Freedoms Found. disting. service award; 1965, Rockford Community Leadership award, 1970, Disting. Salesman's award Southwestern Conn. Sales and Mktg. Exec., 1974, Walter H. Wheeler Jr. Bus. Leadership award, 1990; Dwight B. Havens acad. scholar Acad. Orgn. Mgmt., 1976. Mem. Conn. Assn. C. of C. Execs. (v.p. 1979, pres. 1981-82), Greater Albuquerque C. of C. Republican. Methodist. Home: 6316 Wilmington Dr NE Albuquerque NM 87111-6424 *A good man isn't good for everything: knowing this is the best guide toward the pursuit of one's life goals.*

MITRA, SANJIT KUMAR, electrical and computer engineering educator; b. Calcutta, West Bengal, India, Nov. 26, 1935; came to U.S., 1959; MS in Tech., U. Calcutta, 1956; MS, U. Calif., Berkeley, 1960, PhD, 1962; D of Tech. (hon.), Tampere (Finland) U., 1987. Asst. engr. Indian Statis. Inst. Calcutta, 1956-58; from teaching asst. to assoc. Univ. Calif., Berkeley, 1958-62; asst. prof. Cornell U., Ithaca, N.Y., 1962-65; mem. tech. staff Bell Telephone Labs., Holmdel, N.J., 1965-67; prof. U. Calif., Davis, 1967-77; prof. elec. and computer engring. U. Calif., Santa Barbara, 1977—, chmn. dept. elec. and computer engring., 1979-82; dir. Ctr. for Info. Processing Rsch., 1993—; cons. Lawrence Livermore (Calif.) Nat. Lab., 1974—; cons. editor Van Nostrand Reinhold Co., N.Y.C., 1977-88; mem. adv. bd. Coll. Engring., Rice U., Houston, 1986-89; mem. adv. coun. Rsch. Inst. Math. and Computing, U. Groningen, The Netherlands, 1995—. Author: Analysis and Synthesis of Linear Active Networks, 1969, Digital and Analog Integrated Circuits, 1980; co-editor: Modern Filter Theory and Design, 1973, Two-Dimensional Digital Signal Processing, 1978, Miniaturized and Integrated Filters, 1989, Multidimensional Processing of Video Signals, 1992, Handbook for Digital Signal Processing, 1993. Named Disting. Fulbright Prof., Coun. for Internat. Exch. of Scholars, 1984, 86, 88, Disting. Sr. Scientist, Humboldt Found., 1989. Fellow AAAS, IEEE (Edn. award Crcts. and Systems Soc. 1988, disting. lectr. Crcts. and Systems Soc. 1991—), Internat. Soc. Optical Engring.; mem. Am. Soc. for Engring. Edn. (F.E. Terman award 1973, AT&T Found. award 1985), European Assn. for Signal Processing. Achievements include patents for two-port networks for realizing transfer functions; non-reciprocal wave translating device. Office: Univ Calif Dept Elec Computer Eng Santa Barbara CA 93106

MITRANO, JOSEPH CHARLES, school principal; b. Rochester, N.Y., Sept. 22, 1940; s. Charles V. and Anna Marie (Robinson) M. BA, St. John's Coll., 1963; MA, U. Detroit, 1967; STB, U. Toronto, Ont., Can., 1969; EdS. Cert. tchr., adminstr., Calif., ednl. specialist. Tchr. Cath. Cen. Sch., Detroit, 1965-70, counselor, 1970-75; dean St. John Fisher Coll., Rochester, 1976-84, tchr., 1980-84; counselor U. Toronto, 1985-86; prin. Bishop O'Dowd High Sch., Oakland, Calif., 1986—; bd. dirs. Elan Engring., Novi, Mich., Fred M. Tinker, Inc., Fairport, N.Y. Mem. Assn. Secondary Sch. Prins., Nat. Assn. Sch. Pers. Adminstrs., Calif. Adminstrs. Assn., Basilian High Sch. Prins. (pres.), Oakland C. of C. Roman Catholic. Avocations: golf, traveling, antique cars. Office: Bishop O'Dowd High Sch 9500 Stearns Ave Oakland CA 94605-4799

MITSCH, RONALD ALLEN, chemical company executive; b. St. Paul, July 26, 1934; s. Raymond Otto and Evelyn Eva Marie (Goodrow) M.; m. Marilyn Jean Martin, Nov. 26, 1955; children: Jeffrey, Gregory, RaeAnne. BS in Chemistry, Hamline U., 1956; MS, U. Nebr., PhD, 1960. Sr. chemist 3M-Contract Engring., St. Paul, 1960-64; research specialist 3M-Contract Research, St. Paul, 1964-66; supr. 3M-Synthesis Research, St. Paul, 1966-67, mgr., 1967-69; mgr. 3M-Spl. Elastomers Project, St. Paul, 1969-70; tech. dir. 3M-Chem. Research Lab., St. Paul, 1970-73, 3M-BS&CP Div. Lab., St. Paul, 1973-79; mng. dir. 3M Netherlands, 1979-81; v.p. research and devel. 3M-Life Scis. Sector, St. Paul, 1981-85; group v.p. 3M-Traffic & Personal Safety Products-Life Scis. Sector, St. Paul, 1985-90, sr. v.p. R & D, 1990—; bd. dirs. Shigematsu Works Co. Ltd., Tokyo, Medimorphics, Inc., St. Paul. Author, co-author 31 tech. publs.; 19 patents in field. Trustee Children's Hosp., St. Paul, 1984—, Hamline U., St. Paul, 1986—. Mem. Am. Chem. Soc. (div. fluorine chemistry). Republican. Roman Catholic. Club: White Bear Yacht (Minn.). Office: 3M Ctr 220-13W-39 3M Center # 39 Saint Paul MN 55144-1000

MITSCHER, LESTER ALLEN, chemist, educator; b. Detroit, Aug. 20, 1931; s. Lester and Mary Athelda (Pounder) M.; m. Betty Jane McRoberts, May 29, 1953; children: Katrina, Kurt, Mark. B.S., Wayne U., 1953, Ph.D., 1958. Research scientist, group leader Lederle Labs., Pearl River, N.Y., 1958-67; prof. Ohio State U., Columbus, 1967-75, U. Kans., Lawrence, 1975—; chmn. dept. medicinal chemistry U. Kans., 1975-92; intersearch prof. Victorian Coll. of Pharmacy, Monash U., Melbourne, Australia, 1975—; cons. NIH, Am. Cancer Soc., Abbott Labs., Searle Labs., DuPont Merck Labs. Author: (with D. Lednicer) The Organic Chemistry of Drug Synthesis, Vol. 1, 1976, Vol. 2, 1980, Vol. 3, 1984, Vol. 4, 1990, The Chemistry of the Tetracycline Antibiotics, 1978; contbr. over 190 articles to profl. jours. Recipient Disting. Alumnus award Wayne State U., 1980, Research Achievement award Acad. Pharm. Scis., 1980, Volweiler research award Am. Assn. Colls. Pharmacy, 1985, Higuchi-Simmons award U. Kans., 1986. Mem. AAAS, Am. Soc. Pharmacognosy (pres. 1992-93), Am. Chem. Soc. (former chmn. councilor medicinal chemistry div., Bristol-Myers Smissman rsch. award 1989), Chem. Soc. London, Japanese Antibiotics Assn., Soc. Heterocyclic Chemistry. Presbyterian. Office: Dept Medicinal Chemistry U Kans Lawrence KS 66045-2506

MITSEFF, CARL, lawyer; b. Detroit, Nov. 16, 1928; s. Frank H. and Katherine (Schaffer) M.; m. Phyllis Schlitters, June 28, 1952; children: C. Randall, Bradley Scott, Julie, Emily, Faye. B.S., Wayne State U., 1952, LL.B., 1955. Bar: Mich. 1956. Practiced in Detroit, 1956—; staff atty. Burroughs Corp., 1955-60; mem. firm LeVasseur, Mitseff, Egan & Capp, 1960-80, Mitseff & Baril, 1980-85, Fitzgerald, Hodgman, Cox, Cawthoren & McMahon, 1986-90, Cox & Hodgman, 1990—; spl. asst. atty. gen. State of Mich.; lectr. in field. Mem. ABA, State Bar Mich., Internat. Assn. Ins. Counsel, Internat. Assn. Indsl. Accident Bds. and Commns., Detroit Athletic Club (bd. dirs.), Beavers (pres.), Lochmoor Club, Grosse Pointe Yacht Club, Pi Kappa Alpha, Delta Theta Phi. Home: 612 N Brys Dr Grosse Pointe MI 48236-1247 Office: 1000 First Federal Bldg Detroit MI 48226

MITTELSTADT, CHARLES ANTHONY, advertising executive; b. Eau Claire, Wis., Mar. 19, 1918; s. Frederick William and Pearl (White) M.; m. Angelica Farber, Feb. 20, 1957; children—Nancy Lee, Charles Anthony II, Monica, Simone. B.S., U. Wis., 1942, postgrad., 1945-47; grad., Advanced Mgmt. Program, Harvard, 1960. Radio announcer sta. WIBA, Madison, Wis., 1945-47; account exec. Foote, Cone & Belding, Chgo., 1948-52, Campbell-Mithun, Chgo., 1953-54; mktg. dir. Tatham-Laird, Chgo., 1955-56; exec. v.p. The Marschalk Co., N.Y.C., 1957-64, also bd. dirs.; chmn. plans bd., mgr. Interpub. Group Cos., Inc., Frankfurt, Germany, 1964-66; pres., chief operating officer Erwin Wasey, Inc., Los Angeles, 1967-69; sr. v.p., mgr. Ctr. for Advt. Services Interpub. Group of Cos., Inc., 1969-92, cons., 1991—. Trustee, v.p. N.Y. Foundling Hosp., 1979—. Mem. Wis. Alumni Club, Harvard Alumni Club, N.Y. Athletic Club (N.Y.C.), Westchester Country Club (bd. govs., v.p. 1988-93), Am. Yacht Club. Home: 12 Griswold Rd Rye NY 10580-1802 Office: Interpublic Group of Cos Inc 1271 Ave Of The Americas New York NY 10020-1300

MITTELSTAEDT, GERARD E., library director; b. Sheboygan, Wis., Jan. 27, 1948; s. Arthur R. and Gelane M. (Merget) M.; m. Mona S. Althaus,

May 18, 1985; 1 child, Jennifer S. BA in Geography, U. Tex., 1970, MLS, 1978. Reference libr. McAllen (Tex.) Meml. Libr., 1978, head audio/video svcs., 1979, asst. dir., 1979, dir., 1980—; mem. planning com. South Tex. Libr. System, Corpus Christi, 1980—; chmn., adv. Hidelgo County Libr. System, McAllen, 1985-86. Mem. Am. Libr. Assn., Tex. Libr. Assn., Valley Libr. Assn. (pres. 1987-88), Joshua Slocum Soc. (life), Beta Phi Mu. Roman Catholic. Avocation: sailing. Home: 2011 Daffodil Mcallen TX 78501 Office: 601 N Main Mcallen TX 78501

MITTEMEYER, BERNHARD THEODORE, university official, surgeon, retired army officer; b. Paramaribo, Suriname, Oct. 30, 1930; (parents Am. citizens); s. John Frederick and Hannah (Roy) M.; children: Thomas Theodore, Jan Charles, Robert James, Sarah Ann. BS in Biology, Moravian Coll., 1952, LLD (hon.), 1982; MD, Temple U., 1956; student, Army Med. Field Svc. Sch., Ft. Sam Houston, Tex., 1957, Command and Gen. Staff Coll., Ft. Leavenworth, Kans., 1961, Army Sr. Svc. Coll., Carlisle, Pa., 1970; DSc (hon.), Wm. Jewell Coll., 1985. Diplomate Am. Bd. Urology, Am. Bd. Quality Assurance and Utilization Rev. Physicians. Intern Santa Barbara (Calif.) Cottage and County Hosps., 1956-57; commd. lt. U.S. Army, 1957; advanced through grades to lt. gen., 1981, ret., 1985; bn. surgeon, div. surgeon 101st Airborne Div., Fort Campbell, Ky., 1957-59; resident, gen. surgery Fitzsimons Army Med. Ctr., Denver, 1959-61; resident urol. surgery Tripler Army Med. Ctr., Honolulu, 1962-65; asst. chief urology svc. Walter Reed Army Med. Ctr., Washington, 1971-74, chief, 1974-76, chief dept. surgery and urology svc., 1976-77; clin. prof. surgery (urology), Dept. Surgery Uniformed Svc. U. of the Health Scis., Bethesda, Md., 1976—; comdr. U.S. Army, Med. Command U.S. Army Hosp. Eighth Army, Seoul, Republic of Korea, 1977-78, chief med. corps affairs, 1978-80; comdg. gen. Walter Reed Army Med. Ctr., Washington, 1980-81; surgeon gen. Dept. of Army, Washington, 1981-85, ret.; sr. v.p., corp. med. dir. Whittaker Health Svcs., Los Angeles, 1985-86; provost, vice chmn. Tex. Tech U Health Scis Ctr., Lubbock, 1986—, prof. surgery, 1986—; interim dean Sch. Medicine, 1988-90; vis. prof., guest lectr. in urology Georgetown U., U. Mo., U. Pitts., Korea U., Pa. State U., U. Mass., U. Va., N.C. Bowman Gray Sch. Medicine, Armed Forces Inst. Pathology, Walter Reed Army Inst. Rsch., 1975—; cons. in urology to U.S. Army Surgeon Gen., 1974-77; pres. selection bd. for grad. med. edn., U.S. Army Med. Dept., 1978-80; clin. and nonclin. presentations to med. congresses, seminars, univs.; mem. med. adv. com. to Spl. Com. on Post-Secondary Med., Dental and Allied Health Edn., 1987-88. Contbr. articles to profl. jours.; producer films and exhibits. Med. adv. com. to Climate for Econ. Vitality Task Force of Tex. Strategic Econ. Policy Commn., 1988; advisor to bd. regents Uniformed Svcs. U. of Health Scis., Bethesda, Md., 1980-81, mem. ex officio, 1981-85; bd. commrs. U.S. Soldiers' and Airmen's Home, Washington, 1981-85; bd. trustees Moravian Coll., 1982-86; bd. dirs Lubbock Symphony Orch., Sci. Spectrum, Lubbock Conv. and Visitors Bur. Decorated D.S.M., Legion of Merit with oak leaf cluster, D.F.C, Meritorious Svc. medal, Bronze Star with V device for valor, Air medal with oak leaf cluster, Army Commendation medal, Vietnam Campaign Ribbon with three campaign stars, Comenius award Moravian Coll., 1978, Founders medal Assn. Mil. Surgeons, 1978, Alumni Achievement award in health policy, Temple U. Sch. Medicine, 1988. Fellow Am. Coll. Physician Execs. (mem. coun. 1989—, bd. dirs. 1986-88, v.p. bd. regents 1988), ACS (N. Tex. chpt.), Am. Coll. Quality Assurance and Utilization Rev. Physicians; mem. AMA (ho. dels. 1981-85), Tex. Med. Assn. (cons. coun. med. edn. 1987—), Lubbock-Crosby-Garza County Med. Soc., Am. Urol. Assn. (South Cen. sect.), Soc. Gov. Svc. Urologists, Soc. Univ. Urologists, Uniformed Svcs. U. Surg. Assocs., Am. Acad. Med. Dirs., Soc. Med. Cons. to Armed Forces, Assn. of U.S. Army, AF Assn., Lubbock C. of C., (Armed Svc. com. 1988—), Sci. Spectrum, Lubbock (bd. dirs. 1988—). Republican. Methodist. Home: PO Box 65285 Lubbock TX 79464-5285 Office: Tex Tech U Health Scis Ctr 3601 4th St Lubbock TX 79430-0001

MITTEN, DAVID GORDON, classical archaeologist; b. Youngstown, Ohio, Oct. 26, 1935; s. Joe Atlee and Helen Louise (Boyd) M.; children: Claudia Antonia Sabina, Eleanor Elizabeth. BA, Oberlin Coll., 1957; MA in Classical Archaeology, Harvard U., 1958, PhD in Classical Archaeology, 1962. Instr. dept. fine arts Harvard U., Cambridge, Mass., 1962-64, Francis Jones asst. prof. classics, 1964-68, assoc. prof., 1968-69, James Loeb prof. classical art and archaeology, 1969—, curator ancient art Harvard U. Art Mus., 1976—; assoc. dir. Harvard-Cornell Sardis Expdn., 1976—; Whitehead vis. prof. archaeology Am. Study of Classical Studies, Athens, Greece, 1990-91. Author: (with S.F. Doeringer) Master Bronzes from the Classical World, 1967, Classical Bronzes: Mus. Art, RISD, 1975, (with Arielle P. Kozloff) The Gods Delight: The Human Figure in Classical Bronze, Cleve. Mus. Art, 1988. Woodrow Wilson fellow Harvard U., 1958; Fulbright fellow Am. Sch. Classical Studies at Athens, 1959-60; Archaeol. Inst. Am. Olivia James fellow, 1969-70; John Simon Guggenheim Found. fellow, 1976-77. Mem. Archaeol. Inst. Am., Assn. Field Archaeology (co-founder), Am. Schs. Oriental Rsch., Brit. Sch. Archaeology (Athens, Greece), Am. Numismatic Soc. Office: Sackler Mus 316 Harvard Univ 485 Broadway Cambridge MA 02138

MITTER, SANJOY K., electrical engineering educator; b. Calcutta, India, Dec. 9, 1933. PhD, Imperial Coll., Eng., 1965. Prof. elec. engring. MIT, Cambridge, 1973—; dir. Lab. Info. and Decision Systems, 1981-86, co-dir Lab. Info. and Decision Systems, 1986—, dir. Ctr. Intelligent Control Systems, 1986—. Fellow IEEE; mem. Nat. Acad. Eng. Office: MIT Lab Info & Decision Systems Bldg 35 Rm 308 Cambridge MA 02139-4307

MITTERMEIER, JANICE, commercial airport executive. Airport dir. John Wayne Airport, Costa Mesa, Calif. Office: John Wayne Airport Orange County 3151 Airway Ave Bldg K-101 Costa Mesa CA 92626

MITTERMILLER, JAMES JOSEPH, lawyer; b. Washington, Apr. 13, 1953; s. Jack and Alice Marie (Froeba) M.; m. Elizabeth Gaillard Simons, June 23, 1979; children: Samuel Stoney, Paul Andrew, Laurie Alice, Claire Mary. Student, U. Heidelberg, 1973-74; BA, Claremont Men's Coll., 1975; JD, U. Calif. Berkeley, 1978. Bar: Calif., U.S. Dist. Ct. (so., ctrl. and ea. dists.) Calif., U.S. Ct. Appeals (9th cir.), U.S. Supreme Ct. Assoc. Sheppard, Mullin, Richter & Hampton, L.A., 1978-86, ptnr., 1986—; panelist Calif. Continuing Edn. of Bar, L.A. and San Diego, 1984—. Dir. Legal Aid Soc. of San Diego, 1990—. Recipient Wiley Manuel Pro Bono award Calif. State Bar, 1992. Mem. Assn. Bus. Trial Lawyers, Am. Inss of Ct., Claremont McKenna Coll. Alumni Assn. San Diego (bd dirs.), La Jolla Youth Soccer League (bd. dirs.). Avocations: swimming, surfing. Office: Sheppard Mullin Richter & Hampton 501 W Broadway 19th Fl San Diego CA 92101

MITTLER, DIANA (DIANA MITTLER-BATTIPAGLIA), music educator and administrator, pianist; b. N.Y.C., Oct. 19, 1941; d. Franz and Regina (Schilling) Mittler; m. Victor Battipaglia, Sept. 5, 1965 (div. 1982). BS, Juilliard Sch., 1962, MS, 1963; DMA, Eastman Sch. Music, 1974. Choral dir. William Cowper Jr. High Sch. and Springfield Gardens Jr. High Sch., Queens, N.Y., 1963-68, coordinator of music Flushing High Sch., Queens, 1968-79; asst. prin. music Bayside High Sch., Queens, 1979-86; assoc. prof. music Lehman Col. CUNY, 1986-87, prof., 1987—, choral dir., 1986—; dir. ednl. projects New World Records, 1987—; ednl. cons. Flushing Coun. on Culture and the Arts; cons. Sta. WNET; assoc. condr. Queens Borough-Wide Chorus, 1964-70; pianist, founder Con Brio Chamber Ensemble, 1978; faculty So. Vt. Music Festival, 1979-83; soloist with N.Y. Philharmonic, 1956; solo and chamber music appearances; examiner N.Y.C. Bd. Edn. Bd. Exams., 1985—. Author: 57 Lessons for the High School Music Class, 1983, Franz Mittler: Austro-American Composer, Musician and Humourous Poet, 1993. Choral dir. and accompanist various charitable, religious, mil., civic holiday functions. N.Y. State Regents scholar, 1958-62; scholarships, Juilliard Sch. and Eastman Sch. Music. Contbr. articles to music publs.; performance Internat. Summer Acad. Mozarteum, Salzburg, Austria, 1995. Mem. Golden Key Soc., Am. Choral Dirs. Assn., Music Edn. Nat. Conf., Sonneck Soc. Democrat. Home: 10857 66th Ave Flushing NY 11375-2247 Office: Lehman Coll Music Dept Bedford Pk Blvd W Bronx NY 10468

MITZELFELD, JIM, newspaper reporter; b. Royal Oak, Mich., Apr. 26, 1961; s. Thomas Henry and Audrey Mae (Howard) M.; m. Lisa Jeanne Grayson, Sept. 28, 1985. BA in Journalism, Mich. State U., 1984; postgrad., U. Mich. Law Sch., 1993-. Intern newspaper reporter The Times, Hammond, Ind., 1981; editor-in-chief The State News, East Lansing, Mich., 1982-83; intern reporter Democrat & Chronicle, Rochester, N.Y., 1983; newspaper reporter The Oakland Press, Pontiac, Mich., 1984-85, The Flint (Mich.) Jour., 1985-86, UP Internat., Lansing, 1986, AP, Lansing, 1986-88, The Detroit News, Dearborn, Mich., 1988-90; state capitol reporter The Detroit News, Lansing, 1990-93; intern law clk. to Judge David W. McKeague U.S. Dist. Ct. for We. Dist. Mich., 1994; summer assoc. Butzel Long, Lansing, 1994. Polit. commentator Off the Record Pub. TV, 1986-93. Recipient Nat. Best of Gannett Runner-Up award, 1991, Top Well Done prize Best of Gannett, 1993, 2d place prize Mich. Assoc. Press Editorial Assn., 1994, Pulitzer Prize for beat reporting, 1994; named one of 18 In People Detroit Monthly, 1993; honored by Mich. Senate for pub. svc., 1993. Mem. Soc. Profl. Journalists (Journalist of Yr. Detroit Chpt. 1994), Mich. State U. Alumni Assn., State News Alumni Assn. (pres., co-founder 1991-93). Episcopalian. Avocations: travel, golf, photography, videography, hockey. Home: 5395 Wild Oak Dr East Lansing MI 48823 Office: U Mich 1905 Anderson Ave Ann Arbor MI 48104•

MITZNER, KENNETH MARTIN, electrical engineer; b. Bklyn., May 7, 1938; s. Louis Bernard and Dora (Sandler) M.; m. Ruth Maria Osorio, Dec. 26, 1968; children: Camille Lorena, Esther Jeannette, Sharon Michelle. BS, MIT, 1958; MS, Calif. Inst. Tech., 1959, PhD, 1964. Mem. tech. staff Hughes Aircraft, Malibu, Calif., 1959-64; prin. engr. B-2 divsn. Northrop Corp., Pico Rivera, Calif., 1964-94; instr. U. Calif., Santa Barbara, 1964-65; lectr. in field. Author: (handbook) Demonstrations Against Abortion & Death Selection, 1970; contbr. articles to profl. jours. Pres. Mobilization for the Unnamed, Torrance, Calif., 1970—; bd. dirs. Ams. United for Life, 1971-94, Nat. Right to Life Com., 1980-81, Jewish Life Issues Com., Solana Beach, 1983—; sec. Calif. Pro Life Coun., Sacramento, 1972; mem. L.A. County Select Citizens Com. on Life Support Policies, L.A., 1983-85;. Named Patron of Life Calif. Pro Life Coun., 1976, Pres's award, 1979; Howard Hughes fellow, 1959-64; grantee Fullbright Found., Govt. Italy, 1961-62. Fellow IEEE; mem. U.S. Nat. Commn. Internat. Union Radio Sci. (del. to 20th gen. assembly), Electromagnetics Acad. Avocations: historic research, stamp collecting.

MIURA, ROBERT MITSURU, mathematician, researcher, educator; b. Selma, Calif., Sept. 12, 1938; emigrated to Can., 1975; s. Richard Katsuki and Frances Yoneko (Yukutake) M.; m. Kathryn Bannai; children: Derek Katsuki, Brian Robert, Jared Bannai Nagae, Sean Takeo. BS, U. Calif.-Berkeley, 1960, MS, 1962, MA, Princeton U., 1964, PhD, 1966. Rsch. assoc. Princeton U. Plasma Physics Lab., 1965-67; assoc. rsch. scientist Courant Inst. Math. Sci., N.Y.C., 1967-68; asst. prof. math. NYU, 1968-71; assoc. prof. math. Vanderbilt U., 1971-75; assoc. prof. math. U. B.C., Vancouver, B.C., Can., 1975-78, prof., 1978—; chmn. joint com. on math. in life scis. Am. Math. Soc.-Soc. Indsl. and Applied Math., 1981-84. Editor: Backlund Transformations, 1976, Nonlinear Phenomena in Physics and Biology, 1981, Some Mathematical Questions in Biology-Neurobiology, 1982, Muscle Physiology, 1986, DNA Sequence Analysis, 1986, Plant Biology, 1986; assoc. editor Can. Applied Math. Quar., Japan Jour. Indsl. and Applied Math.; adb. bd. Jour. Math. Biology; co-editor-in-chief Methods and Applications of Analysis; contbr. articles to profl. jours. Mem. steering com. Ctr. Math. Rsch., U. Montreal, 1990-94. John Simon Guggenheim fellow, 1980-81; U. B.C. hon. Killam fellow, 1980-81. Mem. Am. Math. Soc., Soc. Indsl. and Applied Math., Can. Applied Math. Soc., Can. Math. Soc., Soc. Math. Biology, AAAS, Sigma Xi. Office: U BC Dept Math, 1984 Mathematics Rd, Vancouver, BC Canada V6T 1Z2

MIX, JUDITH ANN, nursing education administrator; b. Casco, Wis., May 5, 1941; d. Edward Joseph and Ruby (DeChamps) Wendricks; m. Thomas Mix, Aug. 20, 1966. B. Nursing, U. Wis., 1967; M. Nursing, U. Cin., 1977, Ed.D., 1983. Nurse Holy Family Hosp., Manitowoc, Wis., 1962-65, St. Marys Hosp., Milw., 1965-67; instr. nursing St. Francis Hosp., Cin., 1967-72, nursing edn. adminstr., 1972-80; nursing educator administr. Great Oaks Joint Vocational Sch., Cin., 1980-82, Green Bay Tech. Inst., Wis., 1982—. Mem. Am. Nurses Assn., Am. Vocational Assn., Sigma Theta Tau. Office: N E Wis Tech 2740 W Mason St Green Bay WI 54303-4966

MIX, TERRY PLATT, banker; b. Moscow, Idaho, June 2, 1940; s. Gainford William and Rachel (Belle) M.; m. Judith Joan Mix, Sept. 15, 1962 (div. 1984); 1 child, Michelle; m. Ann Larner, Oct. 12, 1985. BA in Agrl. Sci., U. Idaho, 1963. Regional credit supr., br. mgr. Seafirst Bank, Seattle, 1967-84, sr. v.p., region mgr., 1984—. Bd. dirs. Jr. Achievement, Everett, Wash., 1982-83. Capt. U.S. Army, 1963-67, Vietnam, col. Wash. Army N.G., 1969—. Mem. Lynnwood C. of C. (pres. 1977-78), Rotary. Home: 4610 176th Ave SE Issaquah WA 98027-9083

MIXON, ALAN, actor; b. Miami, Fla., Mar. 15, 1933; s. James E. and Matilda (Beers) M. Student, U. Miami, 1951-52. Appeared in: premiere prodn. play Sweet Bird of Youth, Miami, 1956, N.Y.C., 1956; appeared in: premiere prodn. play View from the Bridge, Chgo. and San Francisco, 1957, 59, Royal Hunt of the Sun, Broadway and Hollywood, 1966; New York prodns. include Suddenly Last Summer, 1958, Desire Under the Elms, 1963, Trojan Women, 1963-64, The Alchemist, 1964, Sign in Sidney Brustein's Window, 1964-65, The Child Buyer, 1964-65, The Devils, 1965-66, A Whitman Portrait, 1966, Black Comedy, 1966-67, Unknown Soldier and His Wife, 1967, Iphegenia in Aulis, 1967-68, Love Suicide at Schofield Barracks, 1972, Small Craft Warnings, 1972, Mourning Becomes Electra, 1972, Equus, 1974-75, Benito Cereno, 1976; London prodn. Whitman Portrait, 1969; TV appearances include Theatre in America. Served with AUS, 1953-54.

MIYA, TOM SABURO, retired pharmacologist, educator; b. Hanford, Calif., Apr. 6, 1923; s. Katsunosuke and Harue (Takeuchi) M.; m. Midori Sakamoto, Aug. 14, 1948; 1 child, Pamela Anne. BS, U. Nebr., 1947, MS, 1948, DSc (hon.), 1986; PhD, Purdue U., 1952. Faculty Purdue U., Lafayette, Ind., 1948-56, 58-77, prof. pharmacology, 1958-77, head dept. pharmacology and toxicology, 1963-77; head dept. pharmacology U. Nebr., 1956-57; dean. prof. Sch. Pharmacy, U. N.C., Chapel Hill; also prof pharmacology, chmn. toxicology program Sch. Medicine, U. N.C., 1977-92, ret., 1992; bd. dirs. N.C. Biotech. Ctr.; mem. rev. com. U.S. Pharmacopeia XVIII, XIX, pharmacology-toxicology program com. Nat. Inst. Gen. Med. Scis., NIH program rev. com. divsn. rsch. resources, 1973-77, chmn. chem. and biol. info. handling rev. com., 1975-76, NRC-Nat. Acad. Scis. toxicology info. com. chmn. 1977-80, NIH nat. environ. health adv. coun., bd. of grants Am. Found. Pharm. Edn., 1994-99. Author: (with Holck, Yim, Mennear and Spratto) Laboratory Guide in Pharmacology, 4th edit, 1973; assoc. editor: Toxicology and Applied Pharmacology; contbr. articles to profl. jours. Mem. AAAS, Am. Assn. Colls. Pharmacy (chmn. sect. tchrs. biol. scis. 1965-66, pres. 1975-76, Disting. Educator award 1985), Am. Pharm. Assn. (Rsch. Achievement award in pharmacodynamics 1964), Am. Soc. Pharmacology and Exptl. Therapeutics, Am. Chem. Soc., Soc. for Exptl. Biology and Medicine (pres. Ohio Valley sect. 1972-74), Soc. Toxicology (mem. council 1975-77, pres. 1979-80, Merit award 1984, Toxicology Edn. award 1989), N.Y. Acad. Scis., Acad. Pharm. Scis. (chmn. elect sect. pharmacology and biochemistry 1970), Rotary (bd. dirs. 1971-73). Sigma Xi, Rho Chi, Phi Lambda Upsilon, Kappa Psi. Office: Univ NC CBN 7360 Beard Hall Chapel Hill NC 27599

MIYAGAWA, ICHIRO, physicist; b. Hiratsuka, Kanagawa, Japan, Mar. 5, 1922; s. Shigejiro and Tsuma (Itoh) M.; m. Mitsuko Yamada, Feb. 10, 1950; children: Shigeru, Haruyo, Mari. BS, Nagoya (Japan) U., 1945; DSc, U. Tokyo, 1954. Asst. prof. U. Tokyo, 1959-62; vis. asst. prof. Duke U., Durham, N.C., 1961-63; asst. prof. physics U. Ala., Tuscaloosa, 1965-66, assoc. prof., 1966-70; prof. U. Ala., 1970-80, Univ. Research prof. physics, 1980-92, prof. emeritus, 1992—; advisor Office External Affairs, U. Ala. System, 1992—; cons. Redstone Arsenal, 1966-72. Contbr. articles to profl. jours. USPHS grantee; EPA grantee; NIH grantee. Fellow Am. Phys. Soc.; mem., AAAS, Sigma Xi. Home: 4905 10th Ct E Tuscaloosa AL 35405-5113 Office: U Ala PO Box 870324 Tuscaloosa AL 35403-1957 *Finding truth in any work or in any matter, however simple, is rewarding, although painful in many cases. Successful people in every spectrum of society are master discoverers of truth.*

MIYAKE, AKIO, biologist, educator; b. Kyoto, Japan, June 29, 1931; s. Yoshikazu and Yukie (Yamazaki) M.; m. Sadako Harada, Mar. 15, 1965 (dec. June 1986); children: Akiko, Toshio; m. Terue Harumoto, Dec. 30, 1988; 1 child, Yuka. BS, Kyoto U., 1953, D of Science, 1959. Asst. Osaka (Japan) City U., 1953-63; visiting scholar Ind. U., Bloomington, 1959-61;

lectr. Kyoto (Japan) U., 1963-70; group leader Max-Planck Inst. for Molecular Genetics, West Berlin, 1970-74; visiting scholar U. Pisa, Italy, 1975-77, U. Münster, West Germany, 1978-83; prof. U. Camerino, Italy, 1983—. Contbr. articles on sexual reprodn. in microorganisms to profl. jours. and books. Recipient Zool. Soc. of Japan Prize, 1981. Mem. Zool. Soc. Japan, Genetics Soc. of Japan, AAAS, Soc. Protozoologists. Avocations: origin and evolution of life, Italian opera music. Home: Corso Italia 150, I-62022 Castelraimondo Italy Office: U Camerino Dept Cell Biol, Via F Camerini 2, I-62032 Camerino Italy

MIYAKE, ISSEY, fashion designer; b. Hiroshima, Japan, Apr. 22, 1938. Student, Tama Art U., Tokyo, 1959-63, La Chambre Syndicale de la Couture Parisienne, Paris, 1965. Asst. designer Guy Laroche, Paris, 1966-68; asst. designer Hubert de Givenchy, Paris, 1968-69; designer Geoffrey Beene, N.Y.C., 1969-70; founder Miyake Design Studio, N.Y.C., 1970—, Issey Miyake, Inc., N.Y.C., 1971—. Exhbns. of work include: Seibu Mus. Art, Tokyo, 1977, Musee des Arts Decoratifs, Paris, 1978, MIT, Cambridge, 1982, San Francisco Mus. Modern Art, 1983, Touko Mus. of Contemporary Art, Tokyo, 1990; represented in permanent collections: Met. Mus. Art, N.Y.C., Victoria and Albert Mus., London. Author: Issey Miyake: East Meets West, 1978, Issey Miyake: Bodyworks, 1983. Office: Issey Miyake USA Corp 3 W 18th St 7th Floor New York NY 10011

MIYAKODA, KIKURO, meteorologist, lecturer; b. Yonago, Tottori, Japan, Nov. 7, 1927; came to U.S., 1965; s. Kanae and Kimiyo (Nishimura) M.; m. Toyoko Fukuda, Jan. 8, 1954; 1 child, Noriko Miyakoda Hall. BA, U. Tokyo, 1953, DSc, 1961. Assoc. prof. U. Tokyo, 1957-65; rsch. meteorologist Geophysical Fluid Dynamics Lab., Washington, 1964-68; rsch. meteorologist Geophysical Fluid Dynamics Lab., Princeton, N.J., 1968-79, supervisory meteorologist, 1979—; lectr., Princeton U., 1969—, Rutgers U., Newark, 1982-90. Author: Weather Forecast, 1975. Recipient Gold medal U.S. Dept. of Commerce, 1972, 88. Fellow Am. Meteorol. Soc. (Carl-Gustaf Rossby medal 1991); mem. Japan Meteorol. Soc. (Soc. award, 1956, Fujiwara award 1983). Office: Princeton U Geophys Fluid Dynamics Lab PO Box 308 Princeton NJ 08542-0308

MIYAMOTO, OWEN, state agency administrator. Airport adminstr. Hawaii State Dept. of Transp., Honolulu, HI. Office: Honolulu Internat Airport 400 Rodgers Blvd Ste 700 Honolulu HI 96819-1880

MIYAMOTO, RICHARD TAKASHI, otolaryngologist; b. Zeeland, Mich., Feb. 2, 1944; s. Dave Norio and Haruko (Okano) M.; m. Cynthia VanderBurgh, June 17, 1967; children: Richard Christopher, Geoffrey Takashi. BS cum laude, Wheaton Coll., 1966; MD, U. Mich., 1970; MS in Otology, U.So. Calif., 1978. Diplomate Am. Bd. Otolaryngology. Intern Butterworth Hosp., Grand Rapids, Mich., 1970-71, resident in surgery, 1971-72; resident in otolaryngology Ind. U. Sch. Medicine, 1972-75; fellow in otology and neurotology St. Vincent Hosp. and Otologic Med. Group, L.A., 1977-78; asst. prof. Ind. U. Sch. Medicine, Indpls., 1978-83, assoc. prof., 1983-88; prof. 1988—; chmn. 1987, chief Otology and Neurotology dept. Otolaryngology, Head and Neck Surgery, Ind. U., 1982—, chmn. dept. Otolaryngology, 1987—, Arilla DeVault prof.; 1991; chief Otolaryngology, Head and Neck Surgery Wishard Meml. Hosp., 1979—. Mem. editorial bd. Laryngoscope, Am. Jour. of Otology, Otolaryngology-Head and Neck Surgery, European archives of Oto-Rhino-Laryngology, Anales de Otorrinolaringologia Mexicana; contbr. articles to profl. jours. Mem. adv. coun. Nat. Inst. Deafness and other communication disorders, 1989—; mem. med. adv. bd. Alexander Graham Bell Assn. for the Deaf, The Ear Found. Served to maj. USAF, 1975-77. Named Arilla DeVault Disting. investigator Ind. U., 1983. Fellow Am. Acad. Otolaryngology (gov. 1982—), ACS, Am. Otological, Rhinological, and Laryngological Soc. (Thesis Disting. for Excellence award), Am. Neurotology Soc. Am. Auditory Soc. (mem. exec. com. 1985—); mem. Otosclerosis Study Group (coun. 1993—), Am. Otol. Soc. (coun. 1992—), Marines Meml. Assn., Wheaton Coll. Scholastic Honor Soc., Cosmos Club of Washington, Columbia Club of Ind., Royal Soc. Medicine London, Collegium Oto-Laryngologicum Amecitiae Sacrum; Alpha Omega Alpha. Avocation: tennis. Office: Indiana U Sch Med Riley Hosp Rm 0860 702 Barnhill Dr Indianapolis IN 46202-5230 also: Sch Medicine Ind U Indianapolis IN 46204•

MIYAOKA, K., grain company executive. With Tomen Am. Inc., N.Y.C., 1960-91, pres., ceo, 1991—. Office: Tomen Am Inc 1285 Avenue of the Americas New York NY 10019

MIYARES, BENJAMIN DAVID, editor, publisher, consultant; b. Tampa, Fla., July 23, 1940; s. Benigno and Mary Carolyn (Dominguez) M.; m. Martha Suzanne Urban, May 14, 1966; children—David, Jeffrey, Beth. B.A. in Journalism, St. Bonaventure U., Olean, N.Y., 1962. News dir. radio sta. WSET, Glens Falls, N.Y., 1962-63; with subs. Edgell Communications, Inc. (magazines for industry), N.Y.C., 1963-89; editor Food and Drug Packaging mag., 1968-89, editorial dir. company, 1975-89, corp. v.p., 1977-80, exec. editor, 1980-89; publisher Candy Marketer, 1985-87, Instructor, 1987; pres. BDM Enterprises, Mktg./Communications Cons., Bay Village, Ohio, 1989—; cons. in packaging field. Pres. council Nat. Packaging Week, 1975; editorial com. Am. Bus. Press, 1973-74. Served with AUS, 1963. Fellow Inst. Packaging Profls. (v.p. 1976-78, pres. 1978-79). Office: BDM Enterprises 31408 Narragansett Ln Cleveland OH 44140-1068

MIYASAKI, GEORGE JOJI, artist; b. Kalopa, Hawaii, Mar. 24, 1935. BFA, Calif. Coll. Arts and Crafts, 1957, MFA, 1958. Asst. prof. art Calif. Coll. Arts and Crafts, Oakland, 1958-64; mem. faculty dept. art U. Calif., Berkeley, 1964-94; prof. emeritus U. Calif. John Hay Whitney fellow, 1957-58; Tamarind printing fellow, 1961; Guggenheim fellow, 1963-64; Nat. Endowment for Arts fellow, 1980-81, 85-86. Mem. Nat. Acad. of Design. Home: 2844 Forest Ave Berkeley CA 94705-1309

MIYATA, GEN, history of religion educator; b. Kyoto, Japan, Feb. 11, 1933; s. Zenichiro and Ine (Yoshida) M.; m. Hiroko Fujiwara, Feb. 3, 1968; children: Kenichi, Mamoru, Teizo. BA, Tokyo U., 1956, MA, 1958. Lectr. Tenri (Japan) U., 1964-70, assoc. prof., 1970-79, 1979—, chairperson dept. religious studies, 1981-87, 89-91, 92-93, dean faculty letters, 1987-89, 91-92, dean faculty human studies, 1993—; vis. prof. Ind. U., Bloomington, 1980-81. Mem. Japanese Assn. for Am. Studies (councilor 1972—), Japanese Assn. for Religious Studies (dir. 1989—). Tenrikyo. Office: Tenri U, 1050 Somanouchi cho, Tenri Nara, Japan 632

MIYAZAWA, AKIRA, advertising executive; b. Tokyo, Oct. 28, 1932; s. Koji and Kyoko M.; m. Atsuko Uda, Oct. 19, 1958; 1 child, Kentaro. LLB, Tokyo U., 1956; cert. in advanced mgmt. program, Harvard U., 1980. Bus. Analyst Peoples Fin. Corp., Tokyo, 1956-64; v.p. McCann-Erickson Hakuhodo Inc., Tokyo, 1980-81, sr. v.p., 1981-82, exec. v.p., 1982-85, dir., 1985—. Mem. Japan Fedn. of Econ. Orgns., Japan Assn. of Corp. Execs., Tokyo Am. Club. Avocations: golf, reading books. Office: McCann-Erickson Inc, Shin Aoyama Bldg E 1-1, Minami-Aoyama 1-chome, Minata-ku, Tokyo 107, Japan

MIZE, JOE HENRY, industrial engineer, educator; b. Colorado City, Tex., June 14, 1934; s. Kelly Marcus and Birtie (Adams) M.; m. Betty Bentley, Mar. 16, 1961; 1 dau., Kelly Jean. B.S. in Indsl. Engring, Tex. Tech. Coll. 1958; M.S. (Research Found. grantee) in Indsl. Engring, Purdue U., 1963, Ph.D., 1964. Registered profl. engr., Ala., Okla. Indsl. engr. White Sands Missile Range, N.Mex., 1958-61; grad. research asst. Purdue U., Lafayette, Ind., 1961-64; asso. prof. engring. Auburn (Ala.) U., 1964-69; dir. Auburn (Ala.) U. (Computer Center), 1965-66; prof. engring. Ariz. State U., Tempe, 1969-72; prof., head Sch. Indsl. Engring. and Mgmt. Okla. State U., Stillwater, 1972-80; dir. Univ. Ctr. for Energy Research Okla. State U., 1980-83, Regents prof., 1982—; cons. to Air War Coll., 1968-69, U.S. Army, Ops. Analysis Standby Unit, U. N.C., 1965-69, various mfg. firms, 1964—; program adv. Office of Mgmt. and Budget, Exec. Office of the President, Washington, 1974-79; adv. to NSF, 1974-79, Nat. Center for Productivity and Quality of Work Life, 1973-78; chmn. tech. adv. council So. Growth Policies Bd., 1975-77; accrediting visitor Engrs. Council for Profl. Devel., 1973-80. Author: (with J.G. Cox) Essentials of Simulation (translated into Japanese 1970), 1968, Prosim V.: Instructor's Manual, 1971, Student's Manual, 1971, (with C.R. White and George H. Brooks) Operations Plan-

ning and Control, 1971, (with J.L. Kuester) Optimization Techniques with Fortran, 1973, (with W.C. Turner and K.E. Case) Introduction to Industrial and Systems Engineering, 3d edit., 1993 (named Book of Yr., Am. Inst. Indsl. Engrs. 1979), Guide to Systems Integration, 1991; contbr. articles to profl. jours., more. Recipient Disting. Engring. Alumnus award Purdue U., 1978. Mem. Am. Inst. Indsl. Engrs. (exec. v.p. 1978-80, pres. 1981-82, H.G. Maynard Innovative Achievement award 1977, Gilbreth Indsl. Engring. award 1990), Am. Soc. for Engring. Edn. (sec. govt. rels. com. 1975-76), Nat. Soc. Profl. Engrs., Okla. Soc. Profl. Engrs. (Outstanding Engring. Achievement award 1977, Outstanding Engr. in Okla. 1981), Inst. Mgmt. Scis., Coun. Indsl. Engring. Acad. Dept. Heads (chmn. 1975-76), NAE, Nat. Rsch. Coun., Sigma Xi, Tau Beta Pi, Alpha Pi Mu. Office: Oklahoma State U Indsl Engring Dept Stillwater OK 74078

MIZE, LARRY, professional golfer. Profl. golfer, 1981—; PGA tour victories include: Memphis Classsic, 1983, Masters, 1987, Northern Telecom Open, 1993, Buick Open, 1993. mem. U.S. Ryder Cup Team, 1987. Office: care PGA 100 Ave of the Champions Palm Beach Gardens FL 33410•

MIZEL, LARRY A., housing construction company executive; b. 1942; married. Alumnus, U. Denver, 1967. Chmn. bd., chmn. exec. com., dir. MDC Holdings Inc., 1972-88, chmn. bd., chief exec. officer, 1988—. Office: MDC Holdings Inc 3600 S Yosemite St Denver CO 80237-1812

MIZGALA, HENRY F., physician; b. Montreal, Nov. 28, 1932; s. Louis and Mary (Ropeleski) M.; m. Pauline Barbara Delaney, Oct. 26, 1957; children: Paul Stephen, Cynthia Louise, Liane Mary, Melanie Frances Mizgala Dressler, Nancy Elizabeth Mizgala Lewis. B.A. magna cum laude, Loyola Coll., Montreal, 1953; M.D., C.M., McGill U., 1957. Rotating intern, then resident in medicine St. Mary's Hosp., Montreal, 1957-59; asst. physician St. Mary's Hosp., 1963-66; resident in medicine Royal Victoria Hosp., Montreal, 1959-60; Dazian fellow cardiology Mt. Sinai Hosp., N.Y.C., 1960-61, USPHS fellow cardiology, 1961-62; resident in cardiology Montreal Gen. Hosp., 1962-63, assoc. physician, 1966-74; asst. physician, cons. cardiology Lachine (Que.) Gen. Hosp., 1964-80; cardiologist Montreal Heart Inst., also dir. CCU, 1974-80; cons. Centre Hosp. Baie des Chaleurs, Gaspe, Que., 1975-80; hon. cons. Montreal Heart Inst., 1980—; prof. medicine U. B.C., 1980—; cardiologist The Vancouver (B.C.) Hosp. and Health Scis. Ctr.; cons. B.C. Cancer Agy., Vancouver, 1981—; cons. staff Univ. Hosp., U. B.C. site, 1981-94; mem. faculty McGill U. Med. Sch., Montreal, 1968-74; assoc. prof. medicine McGill U. Med. Sch., 1973-74; assoc. prof., then prof. Montreal U. Med. Sch., 1974-81; prof. medicine, head div. cardiology U. B.C., 1980-87. Mem. editorial bd. Can. Jour. Cardiol, 1988—, Jour. Am. Coll. Cardiology, 1992—; contbr. numerous articles to med. jours. Fellow Royal Coll. Phys. and Surg. Can., Am. Coll. Cardiology, Am. Heart Assn. (council clin. cardiology); mem. Can. Med. Assn., Can. Cardiovascular Soc. (treas. 1974-90), Que. Med. Assn., B.C. Med. Assn., Montreal Cardiac Soc., Que. Fedn. Med. Specialists, Que. Heart Found., Can. Heart Found., B.C. and Yukon Heart and Stroke Found. (bd. dirs., sr. bd. dirs.), Alpha Omega Alpha. Office: U BC Div Cardiology Dept Med, 2775 Heather St Rm 326, Vancouver, BC Canada V5Z 3J5

MIZRAHI, ABRAHAM MORDECHAY, cosmetics and health care company executive, retired physician; b. Jerusalem, Apr. 16, 1929; came to U.S., 1952, naturalized, 1960; s. Solomon R. and Rachel (Haliwa) M.; m. Suzanne Eve Glasser, Mar. 15, 1956; children: Debra, Judith, Karen. B.S., Manchester Coll., 1955; M.D., Albert Einstein Coll. Medicine, 1960. Diplomate: Am. Bd. Pediatrics, Nat. Bd. Med. Examiners. Intern U. N.C., 1960-61; pediatric resident Columbia-Presbyn. Med. Center, N.Y.C., 1961-63; NIH fellow in neonatology Columbia-Presbyn. Med. Center, 1963-65; assoc. dir. Newborn Service Mt. Sinai Hosp., N.Y.C.; also dir. Newborn Service Elmhurst Med. Center, 1965-67; staff physician Geigy Pharm. Corp., N.Y.C., 1967-69; head cardio-pulmonary sect. Geigy Pharm. Corp., 1969-71; sr. v.p. corp. med. affairs USV Pharm. Corp., Tuckahoe, N.Y., 1971-76; v.p. health and safety Revlon, Inc., N.Y.C., 1976-89, sr. v.p. human resources, 1989-94; ret., 1994; assoc. in pediatrics Columbia U., 1963-67; cons. in neonatology Misericordia-Fordham Med. Ctr., 1987-89; clin. affiliate N.Y. Hosp.; clin. assoc. prof. Cornell U. Med. Coll., 1982—. Contbr. articles to profl. jours. Trustee Westchester (N.Y.) Jewish Center. Mem. AMA, N.Y. State and County Med. Assn., Am., N.Y. acads. medicine, Am. Soc. Clin. Pharmacology and Therapeutics, Am. Pub. Health Assn., Am. Occupational Med. Assn. Home: 7 Jason Ln Mamaroneck NY 10543-2108 *The principles that have guided my life are old Biblical concepts. Firstly, that God had created Adam and Eve and all Men are, therefore, brothers and sisters. Secondly, God created Man and, therefore every human being has a spark of God in him. It, therefore, follows that killing diminishes God's presence on earth and saving of a human being increases His presence.*

MIZRAHI, ISAAC, fashion designer; b. Bklyn., Oct. 14, 1961; s. Zeke and Sarah M. Attended, Parsons Sch. Design, 1982. Design asst. Perry Ellis, 1982-84, Jeffrey Banks, 1984-85, Calvin Klein, 1985-87; founder Isaac Mizrahi, 1987—, added menswear line, 1990—. Designed costumes Twyla Tharp's ballet Brief Fling, Am. Ballet Theatre. Recipient Perry Ellis new fashion talent award Coun. Fashion Designers Am., 1989; named Best Womenswear Designer 1989 Coun. Fashion Designers Am., 1990. Office: 104 Wooster St New York NY 10012

MIZROCH, JOHN F., lawyer; b. Norfolk, Va., Sept. 28, 1948; s. Solomon B. and Muriel G. Mizroch; m. Martha Melissa Bankston; children: Zachary, Elliott, Brandon. BA, U. Va., 1970, MA, 1972; JD, Coll. of William and Mary, 1975. Bar: Va. 1975, D.C. 1977, Colo. 1980, Tex. 1985. Asst. commonwealth atty. Commonwealth Atty. Office, Arlington, Va., 1975-76; fgn. service officer USIA, Washington, 1976-79; pvt. practice real estate devel., Winter Park, Colo., 1980-84; v.p., counsel VCMI, Dallas, 1984-86; gen. counsel W.O. Bankston, Enterprise, Dallas, 1986-87; dep. asst. sec. commerce Office of Trade Adjustment Assistance, Dept. Commerce, Washington, 1987-89; advisor to minority Joint Econ. Com. of Congress, Washington, 1989-90; mng. dir., gen. coun. R.J.M. Internat., Washington, 1991-93; exec. dir. U.S. Environ. Tech. Export Coun., 1993—. Town councilman Winter Park Town Council, 1982-84. Mem. ABA. Home: 4825 V St NW Washington DC 20007-1510

MIZUNO, MASARU, retail executive. Office: Marubeni America Corp 450 Lexington Ave New York NY 10017-3911

MLAY, MARIAN, government official; b. Pitts., Sept. 11, 1935; d. John and Sonia M.; A.B., U. Pitts., 1957; postgrad. (Univ. fellow) Princeton U., 1969-70; J.D., U. Pitt., 1977. Mgmt. positions HEW, Washington, 1961-70, dep. dir. Chgo. region, 1971-72, dir. div. consol. funding, 1972-73, dep. dir. office policy devel. and planning USPHS, Washington, 1973-77; dir. program evaluation EPA, Washington, 1978-79, dep. dir. Office of Drinking Water, 1979-84, dir. Office of Ground Water Protection, 1984-91, dir. Oceans and Coastal Protection, 1991-95; sr. rschr. Nat. Acad. Pub. Adminstrn. 1995—. Bd. dirs. D.C. United Fund, 1979-80. Recipient Career Edn. award Nat. Inst. Public Affairs, 1969. Mem. ABA, D.C. Bar (steering com. energy, environment and natural resources sect.). Author: articles in field. Home: 3747 1/2 Kanawha St NW Washington DC 20015-1838 Office: Nat Acad Pub Adminstrn 1120 G St NW Ste 850 Washington DC 20005

MLOCEK, SISTER FRANCES ANGELINE, financial executive; b. River Rouge, Mich., Aug. 4, 1934; d. Michael and Suzanna (Bloch) M. BBA, U. Detroit, 1958; MBA, U. Mich., 1971. CPA, Mich. Bookkeeper Allen Park (Mich.) Furniture, 1949-52, Gerson's Jewelry, Detroit, 1952-53; jr. acct. Meyer Dickman, CPA, Algaze, Staub & Bowman, CPAs, Detroit, 1953-58; acct., internal auditor Sisters, Servants of Immaculate Heart of Mary Congregation, Monroe, Mich., 1959-66, asst. gen. treas., 1966-73, gen. treas., 1973-76; internal auditor for parishes Archdiocese of Detroit, 1976-78; asst. to exec. dir. Leadership Conf. of Women, Silver Spring, Md., 1978-83; dir. of fin. Nat. Conf. of Cath. Bishops/U.S. Cath. Conf., Washington, 1989-94; CFO Sisters Servants of the Immaculate Heart of Mary, Monroe, Mich., 1994—; trustee Sisters, Servants of Immaculate Heart of Mary Charitable Trust Fund, Monroe 1984—. Author: (manual) Leadership Conference of Women Religious/Confernce of Major Superiors of Men, 1981. Treas. Zonta Club of Washington Found., Washington, 1983-88, pres. 1992-93; bd. dirs. Our Lady of Good Counsel High Sch., Wheaton, Md., 1983-89. Mem.

AICPA, D.C. Inst. CPAs (mem. not-for-profit com. 1992-94, CFOs com. 1990-94. Democrat. Roman Catholic. Office: Sisters Servants Immaculate Heart Mary 610 W Elm Ave Monroe MI 48162-7909

MLSNA, TIMOTHY MARTIN, lawyer; b. Berwyn, Ill., Feb. 13, 1947; s. Theodore Joseph and Dorothy Clara (Kurth) M.; m. Kathryn Kimura, Oct. 4, 1975; children: Lauren Marie, Matthew Christopher, Michael Timothy. BS, MacMurray Coll., 1969; JD, Northwestern U., 1974. Bar: Ill. 1974, U.S. Dist. Ct. (no. dist.) Ill. 1974. Assoc. McDermott, Will & Emery, Chgo., 1974-80, ptnr., 1980-81; ptnr. Kirkland & Ellis, Chgo., 1981-94, head of employee benefits dept., 1984-94; pres. Timothy M. Mlsna, P.C., Chgo., 1995—. Trustee MacMurray Coll., Jacksonville, Ill., 1987—, The Associated Colls. of Ill., 1994—. Home: 28 Chatham Ln Oak Brook IL 60521-2349 Office: Timothy M Mlsna PC 200 E Randolph Dr Chicago IL 60601-6401

MLYNIEC, WALLACE JOHN, law educator, lawyer, consultant; b. Berwyn, Ill., July 10, 1945; s. Casimir Adele and Adeline Mary (Kaczka) M. B.S., Northwestern U., 1967; J.D., Georgetown U., 1970. Bar: D.C. 1971, Alaska 1971, U.S. Dist. Ct. D.C. 1971, U.S. Ct. Appeals (D.C. cir.) 1971, U.S. Supreme Ct. 1974. Exec. dir. ABA standards U.S. Cir. Jud. Conf. Project on ABA Standards, Washington, 1971-73; dir. Juvenile Justice Clinic, Georgetown U., Washington, 1973—, prof. law, 1973—; coord. clin. edn, 1986-89, assoc. dean, 1989—; cons. Nat. Adv. Com. on Juvenile Justice, Washington, 1979-80; cons. pvt. and pub. agys. on juvenile and criminal justice, 1974—; chmn. Juvenile Justice Adv. Group, D.C., 1980-82; mem. Nat. Resource Ctr. on Child Abuse and Neglect. Meyer Found. grantee, 1980-82; Swedish Bicentennial fellow, 1985. Mem. Am. Assn. Law Schs. (mem. com. on polit. interference 1983-84, chair 1991, standing com. on clin. edn.), ABA (mem. adv. com. on family ct. rules 1984), D.C. Bar Assn. (chmn. juvenile justice sect. 1973). Democrat.

MNOOKIN, ROBERT HARRIS, lawyer, educator; b. Kansas City, Mo., Feb. 4, 1942; s. I.J. and Marion (Sittenfeld) M.; m. Dale Seigel, June 16, 1963; children—Jennifer Leigh, Allison Heather. A.B., Harvard U., 1964, LL.B., 1968. Bar: D.C. 1970, Calif. 1971. Fulbright scholar Econometric Inst., Netherland Sch. Econs., 1964-65; assoc. Howard, Prim, Smith, Rice & Downs, San Francisco, 1970-72; of counsel Howard, Prim, Smith, Rice & Downs, 1972-93; vis. prof. Stanford U. Sch. Law, 1980-81, prof. law, 1981-89, Adelbert H. Sweet prof. law, 1989-93; Samuel Williston prof. Harvard Law Sch., Cambridge, Mass., 1993—; dir. harvard negotiation rsch. project Harvard, Cambridge, Mass., 1993—; lectr. U. Calif., Berkeley, 1972, dir. childhood and govt. project, 1972-74, acting prof. law, 1974, prof. law, 1975-81; dir. Stanford Ctr. on Conflict and Negotiation, 1988-93; vis. fellow Wolfson Coll. and Centre for Socio-Legal Studies, Oxford, Eng., 1978; fellow Center for Advanced Studies in Behavioral Scis., 1981-82; vis. prof. Harvard Law Sch., 1990-91; arbitrator IBM-Fujitsu Arbitration, 1985—. Author: Child, Family and State, 3rd edit. 1995, In the Interest of Children, 1985, Dividing The Child, 1992; Contbr. articles in field to profl. jours. Mem. overseer's com. to visit Law Sch., Harvard U., 1972-78; trustee Berkeley Pub. Library, 1973-80, chmn., 1975-77, vice chmn., 1978-80. Mem. ABA, Calif. Bar Assn. Home: 10 Follen St Cambridge MA 02138-3503 Office: Hauser 416 Harvard Law Sch Cambridge MA 02138

MO, LUKE WEI, physicist, educator; b. Shangtung, China, June 3, 1934; s. Si-leng and Shu-feng (Lo) M.; m. Doris Chang, Dec. 31, 1960; children: Curtis L., Alice. B.S. in Elec. Engring, Nat. Taiwan U., 1955; M.S. in Physics, Nat. Tsinghua U., Taiwan, 1959; Ph.D., Columbia U. 1963. Research asso. Columbia U., N.Y.C., 1963-64; research physicist Stanford (Calif.) Linear Accelerator, 1965-69; asst. prof. physics U. Chgo., 1969-76; prof. physics Va. Poly. Inst. and State U., Blacksburg, 1976—. Contbr. articles to profl. jours. Served with Taiwan Air Force, 1955-56. Recipient Alumni Research Excellence award Va. Poly. Inst. and State U., 1980, Guggenheim fellow, 1981, NSF grantee, 1969—. Fellow Am. Phys. Soc. Office: Dept Physics Va Poly Inst and State U Blacksburg VA 24061

MO, ROGER SHIH-YAH, electronics engineering manager; b. Shanghai, Rep. of China, Mar. 10, 1939; s. Maurice Chun-Dat and Mary (Shen) M.; m. Amy Chun-Muh Chang, June 21, 1964; 1 child, Karen Voong-Tsun. BSEE, MIT, 1962; MSEE, Northeastern U., Boston, 1964, PhD, 1967; MBA, Pepperdine U., 1980. Engr. Raytheon Corp., Sudbury, Mass., 1967-69; on tech. staff Xerox, El Segundo, Calif., 1969-74, mgr. memory, 1974-77, mgr. cirs. and subsystems, 1977-81, area mgr., 1981-87, program mgr., 1987-89, imaging systems mgr., 1989-92, systems design mgr., 1992—; sr. lectr. West Coast U., L.A., 1978-87, chmn. acad. standards com., 1981-82. Contbr. articles to profl. jours. Bd. dirs. The Wellness Community Los Angeles, 1989—. Mem. IEEE, Chinese Am. Assn. of So. Calif. (bd. dirs. 1983-87). Democrat. Roman Catholic. Lodge: Flip Flap (local chmn. 1974, nat. chmn. 1976). Avocations: golf, table tennis, photography. Home: 6852 Verde Ridge Rd Palos Verdes Penin CA 90275-4638 Office: Xerox Corp 701 S Aviation Blvd El Segundo CA 90245-4806

MOAKLEY, JOHN JOSEPH, congressman; b. Apr. 27, 1927; m. Evelyn Duffy, 1957. LLB, Suffolk U., 1956. Bar: Mass. 1957. Pvt. practice Boston, 1957-72; mem. 93rd-104th Congresses from 9th Mass. dist., 1973—; ranking minority mem. com. on rules. Chmn. com. on rules Mass. Senate, 1964-70; mem. Boston City Coun., 1971-72, chmn. appropriations and fin. com. With USNR, 1943-46. Office: US Ho of Reps 235 Cannon HOB Washington DC 20515*

MOAK-MAZUR, CONNIE J., investment consultant, marketing professional; b. Ft. Worth, Feb. 5, 1947; d. David Clark and Dorothy Carol (Jackson) Moak; m. Jay Mazur, May 31, 1987. BBA, N. Tex. State U., 1969. Cert. bus. edn. tchr. V.p Lionel D. Edie & Co., N.Y.C., 1969-77; mgr. Peat, Marwick, Mitchell & Co., N.Y.C., 1977-80; v.p Shaw Data, N.Y.C., 1980, Fred Alger Mgmt., N.Y.C., 1980-82; ptnr. Glickenhaus & Co., N.Y.C., 1982-93; mng. dir. Wasserstein Perella Capital, 1993—; speaker in field. Contbr. articles to profl. jours. Mem. Fin. Women's Assn., Am. Pension Conf., Internat. Found. Employee Benefit Plans, Assn. Investment Mgmt. Sales Execs. (bd. dirs., pres.). Avocations: downhill skiing, jogging, horseback riding. Home: 150 E 69th St Apt 19C New York NY 10021-5704 Office: Wasserstein Perella 31 W 52d St New York NY 10019

MOATES, G. PAUL, lawyer; b. Los Angeles, May 26, 1947; s. Guy Hart and Virginia Rose (Mayolett) M.; m. Paulette Anita Minkus, Mar. 21, 1970; 1 child, Amanda Frances. B.A., Amherst Coll., 1969; J.D., U. Chgo., 1975. Bar: Ill. 1975, D.C. 1976, U.S. Ct. Appeals (D.C. cir.) 1976, U.S. Supreme Ct. 1980, U.S. Ct. Appeals (6th cir.) 1984, U.S. Ct. Appeals (3d cir.) 1991, U.S. Ct. Appeals (7th cir.) 1993. Assoc. firm Sidley & Austin, Washington, 1975-82, ptnr., 1982—. Contbr. articles to profl. jours. Served with U.S. Army, 1970-73. Mem. ABA, Ill. Bar Assn., D.C. Bar Assn. Office: Sidley & Austin 1722 I St NW Washington DC 20006-3705

MOAWAD, ATEF, obstetrician-gynecologist, educator; b. Beni Suef, Egypt, Dec. 2, 1935; came to U.S., 1959; s. Hanna and Baheya (Hunein) M.; m. Ferial Fouad Abdel Malek, Aug. 22, 1966; children: John, Joseph, James. Student, Cairo U. Sch. Sci., 1951-52; MB, BCh, Cairo U. Sch. Medicine, 1957; MS in Pharmacology, Jefferson Med. Coll., 1963. Diplomate Am. Bd. Ob-Gyn; licentiate Med. Coun Can. Rotating intern Cairo U. Hosp., 1958-59, Elizabeth (N.J.) Gen. Hosp., 1959-60; resident in ob-gyn. Jefferson Med. Coll. Hosp., Phila., 1961-64; lect. dept. pharmacology U. Alta., Can., 1966; asst. prof. dept. ob-gyn. and pharmacology U. Alta., Can., 1967-70, assoc. prof. 1970-72; assoc. prof. dept. ob-gyn. and pharmacology U. Chgo., 1972-75, prof. dept. ob-gyn. and pediatrics, 1975—, co-dir. perinatal ctr., 1974-80; obstetrician-gynecologist, chief obstetrics, co-dir. perinatal ctr. The Chgo. Lying-in Hosp. U. Chgo. 1980—; vis. investigator dept. ob-gyn. U. Lund, Sweden, 1969. Co-author book chpts., jour. articles. Mem. perinatal adv. com. Chgo. March of Dimes, 1977—, health profl. adv. com., 1983—; mem. perinatal adv. bd. com. State of Ill., 1978—; mem. Chgo. Maternal Child Health Adv. Com., chmn., 1991—; mem. Mayor's Adv. Com. on Infant Mortality, 1991—. Fellow Jefferson Med. Coll., 1960-61, Case Western Reserve U., 1964-65; grantee Brush Found., 1966-67, Maternal Fetal Medicine Unites Network NIH, 1994; recipient award Phila. Obstet. Soc., 1964, Disting. Teaching award Am. Profs. Gynecology and Obstetrics, 1993. Fellow Am. Coll. Ob-Gyn. (Purdue-Frederick award 1978), Royal Coll. Surgeons (Can.); mem. Soc. for Gynecol

Investigation, Pharmacol. Soc. Can., Am. Gynecol. and Obstet. Soc., Soc. Perinatal Obstetricians, N.Y. Acad. Scis., Chgo. Gynecol. Soc., Can. Med. Assn., Christian Med. Soc., Edmonton Obstetrics Soc. Office: U Chgo Dept Ob-Gyn 5841 S Maryland Ave Chicago IL 60637

MOBBS, MICHAEL HALL, lawyer; b. Lawrenceburg, Tenn., Dec. 25, 1948; s. Hershel Leon and Doris (Davis) M.; m. Ellene Winn, June 19, 1976; children: Michael Hall Jr., Clifton Stevenson, Ellene Glenn. BA summa cum laude, honors with exceptional distinction in Russian studies, Yale U., 1971; JD, U. Chgo., 1974. Bar: Ala. 1974, D.C. 1978, U.S. Supreme Ct. 1980. Assoc. Bradley, Arant, Rose & White, Birmingham, Ala., 1974-77; assoc. Stroock & Stroock & Lavan, Washington, 1977-81, ptnr., 1990-93; ptnr. Squire, Sanders & Dempsey, 1994—; rep of sec. def. to Strategic Arms Reduction Talks, Washington and Geneva, 1982-85; spl. counsel to head of del. and rep. of sec. def. to Negotiations on Nuclear and Space Arms, Washington and Geneva, 1985; asst. dir. of U.S. Arms Control and Disarmament Agy., Washington, 1985-87. Ford Fund scholar, 1967-71; Bates fellow, 1970; recipient Fellows' prize Jonathan Edwards Coll. Yale U., 1971. Mem. Ala. State Bar, ABA (com. on Soviet and East European law, mem. com. on central and eastern european law initiatives), Am. Soc. Internat. Law, D.C. Bar, Fed. Bar Assn., Phi Beta Kappa. Democrat. Clubs: Yale of N.Y.C.; City Tavern (Washington). Author: (with George G. Lorinczi) An Importer's Roadmap to U.S. Import Restrictions, 1980, CBMs For Stabilizing the Strategic Nuclear Competition, 1986, Remarks on Verification of Arms Control Agreements, 1988, (with William J. Vanden Heuvel) Overview of the Laws Governing Foreign Investment in the USSR, 1990, On the Road in Eastern Europe, 1991, Environmental Protection in the CIS and Eastern Europe: Emerging Trends May Affect Your Business, 1993. Home: 636 E Capitol St NE Washington DC 20003-1233 Office: Squire Sanders & Dempsey PO Box 407 1201 Pennsylvania Ave NW Washington DC 20004-2401

MOBERG, DAVID OSCAR, sociology educator; b. Montevideo, Minn., Feb. 13, 1922; s. Fred Ludwig and Anna E. (Sundberg) M.; m. Helen H. Heitzman, Mar. 16, 1946 (dec. Oct. 16, 1992); children: David Paul, Lynette, Jonathan, Philip; m. Marlys Taege, July 23, 1994. AA, Bethel Jr. Coll., 1942; AB, Seattle Pacific Coll., 1947; MA, U. Wash., 1949; PhD, U. Minn., 1952. Assoc. instr. U. Wash., Seattle, 1948-49; faculty Bethel Coll., St. Paul, 1949-68, prof. sociology, 1959-68, chmn. dept. social scis., 1952-68; prof. sociology Marquette U., Milw., 1968-91; prof. emeritus, 1991—, chmn. dept. sociology and anthropology, 1968-77; cons. Nat. Liberty Found., 1970-71, Interfaith Coalition on Aging, 1973-75, nat. adv. bd., 1980-89; guest rschr. Sociology of Religion Inst., Stockholm, summer 1978; adj. prof. San Francisco Theol. Sem., 1964-73, McCormick Theol. Sem., 1975-78, 81-82; vis. prof. U. So. Calif., 1979, Princeton Theol. Sem., 1979, So. Bapt. Theol. Sem., 1982; adv. bd. Ecumenical Ministry with Mature Adults, 1983-92; resource scholar Christianity Today Inst., 1985—; bd. dirs. Fairview Elder Enterprises, 1990—. Author: The Church as a Social Institution, 1962, 2d edit. 1984, (with Robert M. Gray) The Church and the Older Person, 1962, 2d edit., 1977, Inasmuch: Christian Social Responsibility in the 20th Century, 1965, White House Conference on Aging: Spiritual Well-Being Background and Issues, 1971, The Great Reversal: Evangelism and Social Concern, 1972, 2d edit, 1977, Wholistic Christianity, 1985; also articles, chpts. in symposia.; editor: International Directory of Religious Information Systems, 1971, Spiritual Well-Being: Sociological Perspectives, 1979, Rev. Religious Research, 1968-72, Jour. Am. Sci. Affiliation, 1962-64, Adris Newsletter, 1971-76; co-editor Research in the Social Scientific Study of Religion, 1986—; assoc. editor Social Compass, 1968—; mem. editorial bd. Christian Univ. Press, 1979-84, Perspectives on Sci. and Christian Faith, 1988—; Fulbright lectr. U. Groningen, Netherlands, 1957-58, Fulbright lectr. Muenster U., West Germany, 1964-65. Fellow Am. Sci. Affiliation (editor jour. 1962-64, publs. com. 1984-91, social Ethics com. 1985-88), Gerontol. Soc. Am.; mem. Am. Sociol. Assn., Internat. Sociol. Assn. (sociology of religion research com. 1972—), Wis. Sociol. Assn. (pres. 1969-71), Midwest Sociol. Assn. (Wis. bd. dirs. 1971-73), Assn. Devel. Religious Information Systems (coordinator ADRIS 1971—, editor ADRIS newsletter 1971-76), Religious Research Assn. (editor Rev. Religious Research 1968-72, contbg. editor 1973-77, assoc. editor 1983—, bd. dirs. 1959-61, 68-72, pres. 1981-82, H. Paul Douglass lectr. 1986), Assn. for Sociology of Religion (exec. coun. 1971-73, pres. 1976-77), Soc. for Sci. Study Religion (exec. council 1971-74), Evangelicals for Social Action (planning com. 1973-75), Christian Sociol. Soc. (steering com. 1973-81, newsletter lit. reviewer 1981-93), Family Research Coun. (assoc. 1985-88, rsch. network 1989—), Psychologists Interested in Religious Issues (profl. affiliate, 1984—), Midwest Coun. for Social Research on Aging (fellow 1961-64, 87—), Am. Soc. on Aging, Forum on Religion and Aging, Fairview Elder Enterprises (bd. dirs. 1990—). Home: 7120 W Dove Ct Milwaukee WI 53223-2766 Office: Marquette U Dept Social & Cultural Sci Milwaukee WI 53233 *As I try to live with eternity's values in view, my entire lifetime seems to grow ever briefer instead of lengthier.*

MOBERLY, DAVID LINDSEY, foundation executive; b. Irvine, Ky., Apr. 25, 1929; s. Earl and Blanche (Finney) M.; m. Peggy Compton, Dec. 30, 1951; children—Kent, Lynn. A.B., U. Ky., 1951; postgrad., Am. U., 1950; M.A., U. Ky., 1953; Ph.D., Kent State U., 1965. Tchr. Jefferson County Bd. Edn., Louisville, 1951-54; dean of boys Jefferson County Bd. Edn., 1954-55, asst. prin., 1955-57; ednl. adv. AID, U.S. State Dept., Tripoli, Benghazi, Libya, 1957-61; edn. program officer, research and survey team AID, U.S. State Dept., Nairobi, Kenya, 1961-62; instr. resident project coordinator in Tanzania Kent State U., 1962-65; supt. schs. Bd. Edn., Tallmadge, Ohio, 1966-67, Warren, Ohio, 1967-71, Cleve. Heights, 1971-74; supt. schs. Evanston (Ill.) Twp. High Sch., 1974-76, Seattle Sch. Dist. 1, 1976-81; pres. Seattle Found., 1981-84; nat. edn. mgr. Deloitte, Hoskins & Sells, 1984-89; asst. state supt. State of Wash., 1989—; spl. participant documentary on problems in edn. ABC-TV, 1976. Area chmn. Ohio's Right-to-Read project, 1969-71; chmn. alumni com. for edn. com. Kent State U., 1968-71; mem. nat. adv. bd. Corp. for Pub. Broadcasting; U.S. del. to World Orgn. of Teaching Profession in Rome, Italy, 1958; Mem. Seattle council Boy Scouts Am.; bd. dirs. Jr. Achievement; trustee Pacific Sci. Center Found., Seattle; mem. Pvt. Sector's Initiative Bd., Seattle. Mem. NEA, Am. Assn. Sch. Adminstrs., Wash. Assn. Sch. Adminstrs., Mcpl. League, Seattle C. of C., Kappa Delta Pi, Phi Delta Kappa. Club: Rotarian. Home: 3045 44th Ave W Seattle WA 98199-2401

MOBERLY, LINDEN EMERY, educational administrator; b. Laramie, Wyo., Jan. 4, 1923; s. Linden E. and Ruth (Gathercole) M. BS, Coll. Emporia, 1952; MS, Kans. State Tchrs. Coll., 1954; m. Viola F. Mosher, Apr. 29, 1949. Tchr. sci., Florence, Kans., 1952-54, Concordia, Kans., 1954-56, Grand Junction, Colo., 1957-60; asst. prin. Orchard Mesa Jr. High Sch., Grand Junction, 1960-66, prin., 1967-84; field cons. Nat. Assn. Secondary Sch. Prins., 1985—. Sgt. USMC, 1941-46. Recipient Outstanding Secondary Prin. award Colo. Assn. Sch. Execs., 1978. Mem. NEA, VFW, Nat. Assn. Secondary Prins. (bd. dir. 1979-83), Colo. Edn. Assn. (bd.dir. 1968-71), Colo. North Central Assn. Colls. and Secondary Schs., Colo. Assn. Secondary Sch. Prins. (bd. dir. 1974-77), Lions, Sons of the Revolution, Marine Corps League (life), VFW (life), Masons (award of Excellence 1990). Home: 2256 Kingston Rd Grand Junction CO 81503-1221

MOBERLY, ROBERT BLAKELY, lawyer, educator; b. Madison, Wis., Sept. 17, 1941; s. Russell Louis and Hildegarde (Reimer) M.; m. Lynne Webb; children—Laura, Richard, Reed. B.S., U. Wis., 1963, J.D., 1966. Bar: Wis. 1966, Tenn. 1977, Fla. 1984 (faculty affiliate). Law clk. Wis. Supreme Ct., 1966-67; arbitrator, trial examiner, mediator Wis. Employment Relations Commn., 1966-71; practice law Milw., 1971-73; prof. U. Tenn. Coll. Law, Knoxville, 1973-77, U. Fla., 1977—; vis. prof. U. Ill. Inst. for Labor Rels., 1973, U. Louvain, Belgium, 1975, Polish Acad. Scis., 1981; mem. arbitration panels, Fed. Mediation and Conciliation Svc., Am. Arbitration Assn., Nat. Mediation Bd.; prin. investigator U.S. Labor Dept., 1988; mem. com. on mediation and arbitration Fla. Supreme Ct., 1989—, chair arbitration subcom., standards of conduct subcom. Author: Public Employment Labor Relations, 1974, Arbitration and Conflict Resolution, 1979; contbr. articles to profl. jours. Mem. Nat. Acad. Arbitrators (chmn. S.E. region 1976-79), ABA (Fla. Bar Assn. (exec. council labor law sect. 1986-88), Indsl. Relations Research Assn., Soc. Profls. in Dispute Resolution, Internat. Soc. Labor Law and Social Legislation (mem. exec. bd. 1989-92), Assn. Am. Law Schs. (chair labor law sect. 1989). Office: U Fla Coll Law Gainesville FL 32611

MOBIUS, MICHAEL, chemicals executive; b. 1950. With Stinnes AG, Germany, 1978-91; pres. Stinnes Corp., N.Y.C., 1991—. Office: Stinnes Corporation 605 3rd Ave 44 New York NY 10158

MOBLEY, EMILY RUTH, library dean, educator; b. Valdosta, Ga., Oct. 1, 1942; d. Emmett and Ruth (Johnson) M. AB in Libr., 1964, AM in Libr. Sci., 1967, postgrad. Tchr. Ecorse (Mich.) Pub. Schs., 1964-65; adminstrv. trainee Chrysler Corp., Highland Park, Mich., 1965-66, engring. libr., 1966-69; libr. II Wayne State U., Detroit, 1969-72, libr. III, 1972-75; staff asst. GM Rsch. Labs. Libr., Warren, Mich., 1976-78, supr. reader svcs., 1978-81; libr. dir. GMI Engring. & Mgmt. Inst., Flint, Mich., 1982-86; assoc. dir. for pub. svcs. & collection devel., assoc. prof. libr. sci. Purdue U. Libr., West Lafayette, Ind., 1986-89, acting dir. librs., assoc. prof. libr. sci., 1989, dean librs., prof. libr. sci., 1989—; adj. lectr. U. Mich. Sch. Libr. Sci., Ann Arbor, 1974-75, 83-86; mem. editorial bd. Reference Svcs. Rev., 1989—; grants reader Libr. of Mich., 1980-81; project dir. Mideastern Mich. Region Libr. Cooperation, 1984-86; cons. Libr. Coop. of Macomb, 1985-86, Clark-Atlanta U., 1990, 91; mem. search com. for new dir. of libr. Smithsonian Instn., 1988; mem. GM Pub. Affairs Subcom. on Introducing Minorities to Engring. Author numerous publs.; mem. editl. bd. Infomanage, 1993—; presenter in field. Mem. corp. vis. com. for libris. MIT, 1990—; mem. Ind. Statewide Libr. Automation Task Force, 1989-90; mem. state tech. strategy subcom. on info. tech. & telecommunications Ind. Corp. for Sci. & Tech., 1989; mem. nat. adv. com. of Libr. of Congress, 1988; trustee Libr. of Mich., 1983-86, v.p., 1986, long range plan com., 1979-82, task force on document access and delivery, 1977-79; info. project mem. Rep. Nat. Conv., 1980; bd. dirs. Small Farms Assn., Southfield, Mich. Recipient Bausch & Lomb award for Scientific Achievement, 1960, Cert. for Outstanding Performance in Acad. Achievement State of Mich. Ho. of Reps., 1976, Spl. Tribute for Outstanding Contbns. Libr. of Mich. Bd. Trustees, 1986, Disting. Alumnus award U. Mich. Sch. Libr. Studies, 1989; U. Mich. Regents Alumni scholar, 1960-64; CIC doctoral fellow in libr. sci., 1973-76. Mem. ALA (com. on accreditation, subcom. to rev. 1972, standards for accreditation 1988-89, OLOS minority internship com. 1988-89, nominating com. 1992-93, mem. coun. resolutions com. 1993—), Assn. Coll. & Rsch. Libris. (task force on libr. sch. curriculum 1988-89, com. on profl. edn. 1990-92), Libr. Adminstrn. & Mgmt. Assn., Assn. Rsch. Libris. (bd. dirs. 1990-93), Spl. Libris. Assn. (pres. 1987-88, fellow 1991, numerous coms. and other offices), Alpha Kappa Alpha. Office: Purdue U Librs Stewart Ctr West Lafayette IN 47907

MOBLEY, JOHN HOMER, II, lawyer; b. Shreveport, La., Apr. 21, 1930; s. John Hinson and Beulah (Wilson) M.; m. Sue Lawton, Aug. 9, 1958; children: John Lawton, Anne Davant. AB, U. Ga., 1951, JD, 1953. Bar: Ga. 1952, U.S. Dist. Ct., D.C. Ptnr. Kelley & Mobley, Atlanta, 1956-63, Gambrell & Mobley, 1963-83; sr. ptnr., Sutherland, Asbill & Brennan, 1983—. Chmn. Cities in Schs. of Ga.; dir. Cities in Schs. Capt. JAGC, USAF, 1953-55. Mem. ABA, D.C. Bar, State Bar Ga., Atlanta Bar Assn., Am. Judicature Soc., Atlanta Lawyers Club, Phi Delta Phi. Clubs: Atlanta Athletic, Atlanta Country, Commerce, Piedmont Driving, Georgian (Atlanta), N.Y. Athletic, Metropolitan (Washington). Home: 4348 Sentinel Post Rd NW Atlanta GA 30327-3910 Office: Sutherland Asbill & Brennan 999 Peachtree St NE Atlanta GA 30309-3996

MOBLEY, KAREN RUTH, art gallery director; b. Cheyenne, Wyo., Aug. 26, 1961; d. David G. and Marlene G. (Franz) M. BFA, U. Wyo., 1983; MFA, U. Oka., 1987. Sales assoc. Morgan Gallery, Kansas City, Mo., 1984-85; grad. asst. U. Okla. Mus. Art, Norman, 1985-87; dir. Univ. Art Gallery N.Mex. State U., Las Cruces, 1988-93; exec. dir. Nicolaysen Art Mus., Casper, Wyo., 1993—; guest artist Okla. City Community Coll., 1986. Paintings exhibited in numerous exhbns. including Phoenix Triennial, 1990, New Am. Talent, Lagua Gloria Art Mus., Austin, Tex., 1992, Adair Margo Gallery, El Paso, 1992, 93, 94. Wyo. Arts Coun. Individual Artist grantee 1994; named Outstanding Young Women Am. Mem. Am. Assn. Mus., Mountain Plains Mus. Assn., N.Mex. Mus Assn., Coll. Art Assn., Phi Beta Kappa, Phi Kappa Phi. Home: PO Box 1574 Casper WY 82602 Office: Nicolaysen Art Mus 400 E Collins Casper WY 82601

MOBLEY, MARK, music critic, feature writer; b. Pitts., May 19, 1964; s. Dozier Mell and Carolyn (Estridge) M. MusB in Percussion Performance, Fla. State U., Tallahassee, 1985; MusM, Peabody Conservatory, 1987. Music critic, feature writer The Virginian-Pilot, Norfolk, Va., 1987—. Office: The Virginian-Pilot 150 W Brambleton Ave Norfolk VA 23510-2018

MOBLEY, TONY ALLEN, university dean, recreation educator; b. Harrodsburg, Ky., May 19, 1938; s. Cecil and Beatrice (Bailey) M.; m. Betty Weaver, June 10, 1961; 1 child, Derek Lloyd. BS, Georgetown Coll., 1960; MS, Ind. U., 1962, D Recreation, 1965; MRE, So. Sem., Louisville, 1963. Chmn. dept. recreation and pks. Western Ill. U., Macomb, 1965-72, Pa. State U., University Park, 1972-76; prof., chmn. recreation and pks. dean Sch. Health, Phys. Edn. and Recreation Ind. U., Bloomington, 1976—; chair health adv. coun. White River Park Commn., State of Ind., 1979—; v.p Ind. Sports Corp., Indpls., 1983-89; bd. dirs. Nat. Inst. for Fitness and Sport, Indpls., 1984—; J.B. Nash scholar, lectr. Am. Assn. Leisure and Recreation, Reston, Va., 1985. Contbr. over 50 articles to profl. jours. Bd. dirs. Monroe County YMCA, Bloomington, 1984-88. Am. Coun. Edn. adminstrv. internship fellow, N.C. State U., 1970-71. Fellow Am. Acad. Pk. and Recreation Adminstrn. (pres. 1985-86); mem. Nat. Recreation and Pk. Assn. (pres. 1978-79, Nat. Disting. Profl. award 1981), Assn. Rsch., Adminstrn., Profl. Couns. and Socs. (pres. 1986-87, award 1987), Am. Alliance Health, Phys. Edn., Recreation and Dance (Coll. and Univ. Adminstrs. Coun. Honor award 1986), Soc. Pk. and Recreation Edn. (pres. 1974-75, award 1978), Ind. Pk. and Recreation Assn. (Outstanding Profl. award 1985). Avocations: golf, travel. Office: Ind U Sch Health Phys Edn & Rec Recreation Rm 111 Bloomington IN 47405

MOBLEY, WILLIAM HODGES, management educator; b. Akron, Ohio, Nov. 15, 1941. BA, Denison U., 1963; PhD, U. Md., 1971. Mgr. employee relations research PPG Industries, Pitts., 1971-73; prof. U. S.C., Columbia, 1973-80; head dept. of mgmt. Tex. A&M U., College Station, 1980-83, dean. coll. of bus. adminstrn., 1983-86, exec. dep. chancellor, 1986-88, pres., 1988-93; chancellor Tex. A&M U. Sys., College Station, 1993-94; prof. mgmt. Tex. A&M U., College Station, 1994—; cons. Indsl. Psychologist, College Station, 1980—; bd. dirs. So. Region Inst. for Internat. Edn., Pool Energy Svc., Da Vinci Sci. Co.; vis. fellow Cornell U., 1994; vis. prof. Hong Kong U. of Sci. and Tech., 1995. Author: Employee Turnover, 1982. Bd. dirs. Amma Found., 1991—, Internat. Food and Agrl. Devel. and Econ. Coop., U.S. Agy. Internat. Devel., 1992-94; mem. trilateral task force on N.Am. Higher Edn. Coop., USIA, 1993—; mem. Pres. Bush's Commn. on Minority Bus. Devel., 1990-92. Fulbright scholar Found. for Scholarly Exchange, Republic China, 1978-79; recipient DAAD, Rep. Germany, 1984; Fellow NDEA U.S. Dept. of Edn., 1968-71. Fellow APA, Am. Psychol. Soc. Home: 431 Chimney Hill Dr College Station TX 77840 Office: Grad Sch Bus Tex A&M Univ College Station TX 77843-4221

MOCH, ROBERT GASTON, lawyer; b. Montesano, Wash., June 20, 1914; s. Gaston and Fleeta Belle (Metcalf) M.; m. Barbara M. Kent, Sept. 2, 1940 (dec.); children: Marilynn A., Michael K., Robert M.; m. LaVerne I. Miller, May 29, 1968. BA magna cum laude, U. Wash., 1936; JD, Harvard Coll., 1941. Bar: Wash. 1941, Wash. 1945. Asst. crew coach U. Wash., 1936-39; head crew coach Mass. Inst. Tech., 1939-44; practiced in Boston, 1941-44, Seattle, 1945—; asso. Herrick, Smith, Donald, Farley & Ketchum, 1941-44, Eggerman, Rosling & Williams, 1945-50, Weter, Roberts & Shefelman, 1950-53; ptnr. Roberts & Shefelman, 1953-87; of counsel Foster, Pepper & Shefelman, 1988—; Del. Nat. Conf. on Law and Poverty, 1965, Nat. Defender Conf., 1969; chmn. King County Pub. Defender Adv. Com., 1970. Mem. U. Wash. Crew, 1933-36. Recipient Olympic Gold medal, 1936; named to Helms Rowing Hall of Fame, U. Wash. Hall of Fame. Mem. ABA, Wash. Bar Assn., Seattle-King County Bar Assn. (past trustee, com. chmn.), U. Wash. Alumni Assn. (pres. 1978-79, Disting. Svc. award 1968), Wash. Alumni Advs. (pres. 1985-87), Rainier Club, Rotary, Phi Beta Kappa, Beta Gamma Sigma, Alpha Kappa Psi, Phi Delta Phi, Phi Gamma Delta. Mem. Christian Ch. Home: 22509 SE 42nd Ter Issaquah WA 98027-7229 Office: Foster Pepper & Shefelman 1111 3rd Ave Ste 3400 Seattle WA 98101-3299

MOCHARY, MARY VERONICA, lawyer; b. Budapest, Hungary, Sept. 7, 1942; d. Alexander and Elizabeth (Aranyi) Kasser; m. Stephen E. Mochary, Sept. 25, 1965 (div. 1990); children: Alexandra Veronica, Matthew Neal. BA, Wellesley Coll., 1963; JD, U. Chgo., 1967. Bar: Ark. 1968, N.J. 1970. Ptnr. Fayetteville, Ark., 1968-70, Mochary & Mochary, Montclair, N.J., 1970-85, Cerny & Mochary, Montclair, 1980-84, Lane & Mittendorf, Woodbridge, N.J., 1984-85; legal advisor U.S. Dept. State, Washington, 1985-89, spl. negotiator real estate issues, 1989-92; cons. Hughes, Hubbard & Read, Washington, pres. Technopulp, Inc., Montclair, 1982—, Iamco, Inc., Montclair, 1982—; ptnr. Kand M Co., Montclair, 1982—, Atlantic Highlands Real Estate, Montclair, 1982-89. Mayor Twp. of Montclair, 1980-84; mgr. Kasser Art Found., Montclair, 1982—; Rep. candidate U.S. Senate, State of N.J., 1984; co-chmn. re-election campaign Tom Kean for Gov., N.J., 1985; treas. Com. N.J. Rep. Women in 1985; mem. regional adv. bd. Anti-Defamation League of B'nai B'rith, Montclair Library Bd., 1980—, Montclair Twp. Council, 1980—; chmn. Rep. Task Force Women's Polit. Caucus N.J., Overseas Neighbors Internat., 1985; bd. dirs. Am. Hungarian Found., 1970—, Found. Edul. Alternatives, Urban League, 1985—. Raoul Wallenberg Com. of U.S., 1985—, Nat. Mus. for Women in the Arts, Washington, 1994—; mem. Women's Internat. Forum, 1992—; founder, bd. dirs. WISH;. Recipient Disting. Service award Am. Hungarian Found., 1984. Mem. ABA, N.J. Bar Assn., Ark. Bar Assn., N.J. Conf. Mayors, N.J. Elected Women Ofcls., Suburban Essex Bus. and Profl. Women (named Woman of Yr. 1985), Wellesley Club (pres. N.J. chpt. 1983-84), Women's Internat. Forum, Adirondack League Club, Ocean Reef Club, Angler's Club (Key Largo, Fla.), Rappahannock County Garden Club. Avocations: skiing, travelling, politics, assisting charitable orgns. and conservation, gardening. Office: 26 Park St Montclair NJ 07042-3443 also: 2700 Virginia Ave NW Washington DC 20037-1908

MOCHRIE, DOTTIE, professional golfer; b. Saratoga Springs, NY, 1966. Student, Furman University. Top ranked player LPGA Tour, 1992. 3 time NCAA All-American; recipient Rolex Player of the Year Award, 1992; recipient Vare Trophy, 1992. Winner tournaments including Mazda Classic, 1989, Crestar Classic, 1990, Nabisco Dinah Shore, 1992, Sega Women's Championship, 1992, Welch's Classic, 1992, Sun-Times Challenge, 1992, LPGA Leading Money Winner, 1992. Address: care LPGA 2570 Volusia Ave Ste B Daytona Beach FL 32114-7103*

MOCHRIE, RICHARD D., physiology educator; b. Lowell, Mass., Feb. 17, 1928; s. William Blair and Helen (Stephens) M.; m. Helene Mary Buchanan, Aug. 19, 1950; children: Barbara Jean Washer, Steven Howard, Lois Ann Blair. B.S., U. Conn., 1950, M.S., 1953; Ph.D., N.C. State U., 1958. Research technician U. Conn.,1950-53; grad. asst. N.C. State U., 1953-54, instr., 1954-58, asst. prof., 1958-61, assoc. prof., 1961-72, prof. lactational physiology and nutrition, 1972-89, prof. emeritus, 1989—, faculty rep. athletics 1983-88; U.S. organizer U.S.-Auralian Forage Workshop, also co-editor procs. Author: Lactation Laboratory Outline, 1971; contbr. numerous articles to sci. jours.; Ruminant Nutrition and Metabolism to Ency. Biochemistry, 1967. Precinct com. chmn., county conv. del. Cary and Wake County (N.C.) Dem. Party, 1972—; mem. Cary Recreation Commn., 1989-92, chmn., 1964-70; mem. Wake County Parks and Recreation Commn. 1977, chmn., 1978-83; bd. dirs. Raleigh YMCA; master track and field ofcl.; v.p. N.C. U.S.A. Track & Field, pres., 1992-94. With AUS, 1946-47. Recipient Upjohn Co. citation for contbn. to quality milk mgmt., 1978; inducted into Chelmsford (Mass.) H.S. Hall of Fame, 1995. Mem. Nat. Mastitis Coun. (dir. 1973-86, v.p. 1975, pres. 1976, disting. svc. award 1978), Am. Dairy Sci. Assn. Found. (charter), Assn. Ofcl. Analytical Chemists (assoc. referee), Interstate Milk Shippers, N.C. Recreators Found. (chmn. 1981-89), Nat. Recreation and Park Assn. (citizen bd. mem. divsn. 1984-94, bd. dirs. 1984-90), Atlantic Coast Conf. (mem. 1986), N.C. Recreation and Park Soc. (bd. dirs. 1981-85, Citation award 1986), N.C. State U. Faculty Club (bd. dirs. 1990-92, pres. 1991-92), Cary Exch. (pres. 1963-64), Dairy Shrine, Gamma Sigma Delta (cert. of merit 1978), Sigma Chi, Pi Alpha Sigma, Sigma Xi. Democrat. Presbyterian (deacon 1959-61). Home: 505 S Dixon Ave Cary NC 27511-3254

MOCK, DAVID CLINTON, JR., internist; b. Redlands, Calif., May 6, 1922; s. David Clinton and Eithel (Benson) M.; m. Marcella Enriqueta Fellin, Nov. 13, 1952. A.B., U. So. Calif., 1944; M.D., M.H.D., Hahnemann Med. Coll., 1948. Intern Hahnemann Hosp., Phila., 1948-49; resident San Mateo (Calif.) County Hosp., 1949-51, 54, VA Hosp., Oklahoma City, 1954-55; research fellow in exptl. therapeutics U. Okla., Oklahoma City, 1956-57, L.N. Upjohn fellow, 1958, dir. exptl. therapeutics unit, 1959-62; dir. preceptorship program, 1968-76; assoc. prof. medicine U. Okla., Oklahoma City, 1963-72, prof., 1972-84, emeritus prof. medicine, 1984—, assoc. dean med. student affairs, 1970-76, assoc. dean postdoctoral edn., 1976-82, dir. continuing med. edn., 1980-83, dir. Transitional Yr. program, 1980-84, dir. History of Medicine program, 1982-84; assoc. mem. Faculty of Homeopathy Royal London Homeopathic Hosp., Eng.; pres., dir. Coachella Valley Fruit Co., Inc., Indio, Calif. Lt. comdr. USPHS, 1951-53; now capt. Res. Fellow ACP; mem. Am. Fedn. Clin. Research, N.Y. Acad. Scis. Unitarian. Home: 570 Alameda Blvd Coronado CA 92118-1617

MOCK, FRANK MACKENZIE, lawyer; b. South Bend, Ind., May 17, 1944; s. Frank Carlton and Julia (Baughmann) M.; m. Virginia Johns, Dec. 31, 1974 (div. Feb. 1991); children: Shannon, John, Bridget. BA, Duke U., 1966, JD, 1969. Bar: Fla. 1969. Assoc. Mahoney, Adams, Criser, Jacksonville, Fla., 1969-74, ptnr., 1977-92; gen. counsel Builders Investment Group, Valley Forge, Pa., 1974-77; ptnr. Baker & Hostetler, Orlando, Fla., 1992—. Mem. ABA, Duval County Bar Assn., Orange County Bar Assn., Dade County Bar Assn., Palm Beach County Bar Assn., Turnaround Mgmt. Assn. Republican. Episcopalian. Avocations: hiking, fishing, reading. Home: 2147 Santa Antilles Rd Orlando FL 32806-1533 Office: Baker & Hostetler 200 S Orange Ave Orlando FL 32801-3410

MOCK, HENRY BYRON, lawyer, writer, consultant; b. Greenville, Tex., Feb. 1, 1911; s. Henry Byron and Helena (Edmonds) M.; m. Mary Morris, Nov. 11, 1949. A.B., U. Ariz., 1933; J.D., Georgetown U., 1939, George Washington U., 1940. Asst. sec. to Congresswoman Isabella Greenway of Ariz., 1934-35; office mgr., legal research asst., recreation div. WPA, Washington, 1935-38; asst. atty. WPA, 1938; legal adv. President's Adv. Com. on Edn., 1938-39; asst. solicitor Dept. Interior, 1939-41; chief counsel U.S. Grazing Service, Salt Lake City, 1941-42; adminstr. region IV U.S. Bur. Land Mgmt., Colo., Utah, 1947-54; area adminstr. U.S. Bur. Land Mgmt. Idaho, Ariz., Utah, Nev., 1954-55; exec. resource cos., 1955—; adj. prof. law U. Utah, 1979—. Contbr. profl. publs. Chmn. Dept. Interior storm relief com. Western U.S., 1949; mem. U.S. Pub. Land Law Rev. Commn., 1964-70, vice chmn., 1965-70; mem. Interior Oil Shale Com., 1964. Served pvt. to capt. with AUS, 1942-46, MTO. Mem. D.C., Va., Utah bar assns. Bar Supreme Ct. of U.S., Am., Fed. bar assns., U.S.C. of C., Bar of Ct. Mil. Appeals, Am. Inst. Mining and Metall. Engrs., Am. Soc. Range Mgmt., Am. Soc. Pub. Adminstrn. (past Utah pres.), Western Polit. Sci. Assn., Am. Forestry Assn., Pi Kappa Alpha. Clubs: Rotary (Salt Lake City), Alta (Salt Lake City). Home and Office: 900 Donner Way No 101 Salt Lake City UT 84108

MOCK, RANDALL DON, lawyer; b. Oklahoma City, Aug. 9, 1943; s. John Haskell and M. Louise M.; m. Sally Merkle, June 4, 1966; children: Adam Peterson, Caroline Louise. BBA, U. Okla., 1965, JD, 1968; LLM in Taxation, NYU, 1970. Bar: Okla. 1968, U.S. Tax Ct. 1970, U.S. Supreme Ct. 1974; CPA. Dir. Mock, Schwabe, Waldo, Elder, Reeves and Bryant, Oklahoma City; dir., sec. Okla. Bar Profl. Liability Ins. Co. Editor: Oklahoma Law Review, Tax Law Review; co-author: Oklahoma Corporate Forms. Pres. Okla. City Estate Planning Coun., 1987-88, dir., 1980-88; pres. Okla. City Tax Lawyers Group, 1973; dir., mem. exec. com. Met. YMCA; dir. The Beacon Club; trustee Westminster Day Sch. Fellow Am. Coll. Tax Counsel; mem. Okla. Bar Assn. (sect. taxation), Order of Coif. Office: Mock Schwabe Waldo Elder Reeves & Bryant 15th Fl 1 Leadership Sq 211 N Robinson Ave Oklahoma City OK 73102-7101

MOCK, ROBERT CLAUDE, architect; b. Baden, Fed. Republic of Germany, May 3, 1928; came to U.S. 1938, naturalized, 1943; s. Ernest and Charlotte (Geismar) M.; m. Belle Carol Bach, Dec. 23, 1952 (div.); children: John Bach, Nicole Louise; m. Marjorie Reubenfeld, Dec. 20, 1964. BArch.,

Pratt Inst., 1950; MArch, Harvard U., 1953. Registered architect, N.Y., Conn., N.J., Nat. Council Archtl. Registration Bds. Architect George C. Marshall Space Center, Huntsville, Ala., 1950-51; archtl. critic Columbia Sch. Architecture, N.Y.C., 1953-54; dir. facility design Am. Airlines, N.Y.C., 1955-60; founder Robert C. Mock & Assocs. (architects and engrs.), N.Y.C., 1960—; Mem. Mayor's Panel of Architects, N.Y.C. Prin. works include: Shine Motor Inn, Queens, N.Y., 1961 (recipient 1st prize motel category Queens C. of C. 1961), temporary terminal bldg. Eastern Air Lines, La Guardia Airport, N.Y.C., 1961, cargo bldgs United Airlines and Trans World Airlines, Kennedy Airport, N.Y.C., Bridgeport (Conn.) Airport, 1961, Eastern Air Lines Med. Ctr., Kennedy Airport, 1962, ticket office Trans World Airlines Fifth Ave., N.Y.C., 1962, terminal bldgs. Eastern Air Lines and Trans World Airlines, La Guardia Airport, N.Y.C., 1963, 7 bldgs. Mfrs. Hanover Trust Co., 1964-66, kitchen and commissary bldg. Lufthansa German Airlines, 1964, Ambassador Club, La Guardia Airport, 1964, Happyland Sch., N.Y.C., 1965, cargo bldgs. Alitalia and Lufthansa German Airlines, Kennedy Airport, 1965, FAA-Nat. Prototype Air Traffic Control Tower, 1966; Lufthansa German Airlines; Irish Internat. Airlines, El Al Israel Airlines, Varig Brazilian Airlines; passenger terminals Kennedy Airport, 1970; Swiss Air Cargo Terminal, Lufthansa German Airlines, cargo terminals El Al Israel airline cargo terminal, Kennedy Airport, 1972, passenger terminal Aerolineas Argentina, 1974, N.Am. hdqrs. Aerolineas Argentinas, N.Y.C., 1974, corp. hdqrs. Am. Airlines, 1977, N.Am. hdqrs. Varig Brazilian Airlines, N.Y.C., 1977, Norel-Ronel Indsl. Pk., Hollywood, Fla., 1979, N.Am. hdqrs. Irish Internat. Airlines, N.Y.C., 1979, corp. hdqrs. Bankers Trust Co., N.Y.C., 1980, cargo terminal Air India, cargo terminal Flying Tiger, Kennedy Airport, 1982, 2 flight kitchen bldgs. Ogden Food Corp., Kennedy Airport, 1984, 88 and LaGuardia Airport, 1987, Greenwich Assn. Retarded Citizens Sch., 1983, passenger terminal extension Varig Brazilian Airlines, 1985, 3 restaurants La Guardia Airport, 1987, residences Palm Beach, Fla., 1989-92, Bethesda, Md., 1993, Fenwick Island, Del., 1994, Potomac Falls, Md., 1995. Recipient United Way Vol. of Yr. award, 1984. Mem. Am. Arbitration Assn. Clubs: City, Harvard, Admirals Cove. Office: 185 Byram Shore Rd Greenwich CT 06830-6909

MOCK, THEODORE JAYE, accounting educator; b. Traverse City, Mich., May 28, 1941; s. Raymond Doris and Georgeann (Lardie) M.; m. Mary Jo Icenhower, Mar. 25, 1962; children: Christopher, Cameron. B.S. in Math., Ohio State U., 1963, M.B.A. in Fin., 1964; Ph.D. in Bus. Adminstrn., U. Calif.-Berkeley, 1969. Dir. AIS Research Ctr. UCLA, 1969-73; dir. Ctr. Acctg. Research, Arthur Andersen Alumni prof. acctg. U. So. Calif., 1982—; vis. prof. Norwegian Sch. Econs. and Bus., Bergen, 1988, Bond U., Gold Coast, Australia, 1990, 92, So. Cross U., Lismore, Australia, 1994; adj. prof. U. Limburg, The Netherlands, 1991—; bd. dirs. Maastricht (The Netherlands) Acctg. Rsch. Ctr., U. Limburg 1991—. Author: (monographs) Risk Assessment, 1985, Internal Accounting Control (Am. Acctg. Assn. Wildman medal), 1983, Measurement and Accounting Information Criteria, 1976, Impact of Future Technology on Auditing, 1988, Auditing and Analytic Review, 1989; mem. editorial bd. Auditing: A Jour. of Practice and Theory, 1983-86, 88-93, editor, 1993—; mem. editorial bd. The Acctg. Rev., 1972-78. Recipient CPA Faculty Excellence award Calif. CPA Found. for Edn. and Rsch., 1983; Fulbright scholar U. Otago, Dunedin, New Zealand, 1988, U. Limburg, Maastricht, The Netherlands, 1993. Mem. Acctg., Orgns. and Soc. (editorial bd. 1978-93), Am. Acctg. Assn. (dir. 1982-84, acad. vice chmn. auditing sect. 1990-91, chair auditing sect. 1991-92). Office: U So Calif Sch of Acctg Los Angeles CA 90089-1421

MOCKARY, PETER ERNEST, clinical laboratory scientist, researcher; b. Zghorta, Lebanon, Jan. 6, 1931; came to U.S., 1953; s. Ernest Peter and Evelyn (Kaddo) M.; m. Yvette Fadlallah, Aug. 27, 1955; children: Ernest, Evelyn, Paula, Vincent, Marguerite. BA in Philosophy, Coll. des Freres, Tripoli, Lebanon, 1948; BA in Medicine, Am. U. Beirut, 1950, postgrad., 1950-52. Cert. clin. lab. technologist, Calif.; cert. clin. lab. scientist Nat. Certification Agy. Chief hematology unit VA Wadsworth Med. Ctr., West Los Angeles, Calif., 1956-81; CEO Phoenicia Trading Co., 1981-88; dir. Coagulation Lab., Orthopaedic Hosp., L.A., 1988—; lab. supr. Westside Hosp., L.A., 1964-79; lectr. hematology UCLA, West Los Angeles, 1970-78. Pres. World Lebanese Cultural Union, L.A., 1978-79. With U.S. Army, 1954-56. Recipient outstanding performance award lab. svc. VA Wadsworth Med. Ctr., 1972-76. Republican. Roman Catholic. Avocations: billiards, reading, classical music. Home: 3103 Gilmerton Ave Los Angeles CA 90064-4319 Office: Orthopaedic Hosp 2400 S Flower St Los Angeles CA 90007-2697

MOCKLER, ESTHER JAYNE, political party administrator, state legislator; b. Jackson, Wyo., Sept. 21, 1957; d. Franklin and Nancy (Fisher) Mockler. BA in Polit. Sci., Wellesley Coll., 1980. Mem. Wyo. Ho. of Reps., 1992—; exec. dir. Wyo. Dem. Pary, Cheyenne, 1993—. Office: PO Box 2036 Cheyenne WY 82003-2036

MOCKO, GEORGE PAUL, minister; b. Little Falls, N.Y., Feb. 15, 1934; s. George and Anna (Swancara) M.; m. Elizabeth Carol Davidson, Sept. 2, 1956; children: David, Paul, Kristopher, Elissa. BA, Hartwick Coll., 1956; BD, Phila. Sem., 1959, STM, 1972; DD (hon.), Gettysburg Coll., 1978. Ordained to ministry Evang. Luth. Ch. in Am., 1959. Pastor Jacob's and Outwood Chs., Pine Grove, Pa., 1959-62; assoc. pastor St Mark's Ch. Wilmington, Del., 1962-65, sr. pastor, 1965-78; sr. pastor Ascension Evang. Luth. Ch., Towson, Md., 1978-91; bishop Del.-Md. Synod Evang. Luth Ch. in Am., Towson, 1991—. Author books; contbr. articles to profl. jours. Home: 501 Sussex Rd Baltimore MD 21286-7609 Office: Evang Luth Ch in Am 7604 York Rd Baltimore MD 21204-7570 *Colossians speaks of Christ as the one in whom "all things hold together". I know that Christ is the one who holds me together. Proclaiming and living his life, the church holds our society together.*

MODANO, MICHAEL, professional hockey player; b. Livonia, Mich., June 7, 1970. Right wing/center Minn. North Stars, 1988-93, Dallas Stars, 1993—; player World Hockey League East All-Star Game, 1988-89, NHL All-Rookie Game, 1989-90, NHL All-Star Game, 1993. Office: Dallas Stars 901 Main St Ste 2301 Dallas TX 75202*

MODDERMAN, MELVIN EARL, health administrator; b. Coopersville, Mich., Nov. 13, 1940; s. Ray J and Alberta Ruth (Sietsema) M.; m. Ida Sue Evans, Sept. 6, 1969; children: Scott David, Christopher Braeden, Geoffrey Alan. BS, U. Mich., 1963; MHA, Baylor U., 1968; MBA, St. Mary's U., San Antonio, 1976; D in Bus. Adminstrn., George Washington U., 1982. With 36th med. battalion U.S. Army, Hanau, Fed. Republic Germany, 1963-66; project officer hosp. constrn. Office Surgeon Gen., Dept. Army, Washington, 1968-70; adminstr. 3d Surg. Hosp., U.S. Army, Vietnam, 1970-71; asst. prof. grad. program Baylor U. AHS, Ft. Sam Houston, Tex., 1971-75; policy analyst Office Surgeon Gen., Dept. Army, Washington, 1976-79, chief pers. policy, 1981-83, dep. dir. pers., 1983-84; prof. and program dir. grad. program Baylor U. AHS, Ft. Sam Houston, Tex., 1984-88; chmn. health care adminstrn. Acad. Health Scis., Ft. Sam Houston, 1988-90; dep. comdr. for adminstrn., chief exec. officer Ireland Army Community Hosp., Ft. Knox, Ky., 1990-92; adminstr. Lincoln Trail Hosp., Radcliff, Ky., 1992—; mem. geographic distbn. tech. subpanel Grad. Med. Edn. Nat. Adv. Com., 1979-81. Ruling elder Arlington (Va.) Presbyn. Ch., 1981-83; chmn. com. Eagle Dist. Boy Scouts Am. Troop 497, 1988-90. Accrediting Commn. on Edn. for Health Svcs. Commn. fellow, 1985. Fellow Am. Coll. Healthcare Execs. (regent U.S. Army 1990-92); mem. Ky. Hosp. Assn., Fed. Exec. Assn. Home: 217 W French St Elizabethtown KY 42701-1901 Office: Lincoln Trail Hosp Adminstr's Office 3909 S Wilson Rd Elizabethtown KY 42701-8425

MODE, CHARLES J., mathematician, educator; b. Bismarck, N.D. Dec. 29, 1927; s. Charles and Fannie E. (Hansen) M.; m. Eleanore L. Perdelwitz, 1 dau., Martha Lisa. B.S. in Genetics, N.D. State U., 1952; M.S. in Genetics, Kans. State U., 1953; Ph.D. in Genetics, U. Calif., Davis and Berkeley, 1956; postgrad. in stats. (Univ. fellow), N.C. State U., 1956-57. Asst. prof. math. Mont. State U., 1957-59, asso. prof., 1960-62, prof., 1963-66, mem. genetics group, 1957-66; asso. prof. math. stats. SUNY, Buffalo, 1966-70; prof. math. Drexel U., 1970—; cons. to industry. Author: Multitype Branching Processes - Theory and Applications, 1971, Stochastic Processes in Demography and their Computer Implementation, 1985; contbr. numerous articles to profl. publs.; assoc. editor: Math. Biosics, 1975—. Mem. Inst. Math. Stats., Biometric Soc., Am. Math. Soc., AAAS, Popula-

tion Assn. Am., Sigma Xi, Phi Kappa Phi, Pi Mu Epsilon. Lutheran. Home: 502 Balsam Rd Cherry Hill NJ 08003-3202 Office: Drexel Univ Dept Math Philadelphia PA 19104

MODE, PAUL J., JR., lawyer; b. Columbus, Ohio, Feb. 23, 1938; s. Paul J. and Dorothy O. Mode; m. Elaine Rush, June 13, 1961; children: Rebecca D., David B. BME with distinction, Cornell U., 1961; LLB magna cum laude, Harvard U., 1967. Bar: D.C. U.S. Supreme Ct. Assoc. Wilmer, Cutler & Pickering, Washington, 1967-70, 73-74, ptnr., 1975—, mem. mgmt. com., 1983-86, chmn. mgmt. com., 1987—; chief counsel U.S. Senate Subcom. on Constl. Amendments, Washington, 1970-73; panelist Ctr. for Pub. Resources Panel of Disting. ADR Neutrals, 1989—. Author: (with others) Litigation, vol.12, No.4, 1986; mem. editorial bd. Harvard Law Rev., 1966-67, Alternatives to the High Cost of Litigation, 1991—; contbr. articles to profl. jours. Mem. issues staff Robert F. Kennedy Presdl. campaign, 1968. Lt. (j.g.) USN, 1961-64. Avocations: tennis, collecting antique maps. Home: 2750 Brandywine St NW Washington DC 20008-1040 Office: Wilmer Cutler & Pickering 2445 M St NW Washington DC 20037-1435

MODEL, IRIS, cosmetics executive. With Clinique Labs., Inc., N.Y.C. 1975—; now sr. v.p. Office: Clinique Lab Inc 767 5th Ave 38 New York NY 10153

MODEL, PETER, molecular biologist; b. Frankfort, Germany, May 17, 1933; s. Leo and Jane (Ermel) M.; m. Pat Goldman, 1961 (div. 1981); 1 child Paul; m. Marjorie Russel, June 21, 1981; 1 child Sascha. BA, Stanford U., 1954; PhD, Columbia U., 1965. Rsch. assoc. Columbia U., N.Y.C., 1965-1967; fellow Rockefeller U., N.Y.C., 1967-69, mem. faculty, 1969—, prof., 1987—; bd. dirs. Biotechnica Inst., Cambridge, Mass., 1981-86. Mem. editorial bd. Jour. Virology, Virology; contbr. articles to profl. jours. Bd. dirs. United Help, N.Y., 1980, Self Help Community Svc., N.Y., 1980. 1st Lt. U.S. Army, 1954-56. Mem. Am. Soc. Virology, Am. Soc. Microbiology, Am. Soc. for Biochemistry and Molecular Biology. Democrat. Office: Rockefeller U Lab of Genetics 1230 York Ave New York NY 10021-6341

MODELL, ARTHUR B., professional football team executive; b. Bklyn. June 23, 1925; m. Patricia Breslin, July 25, 1969; stepchildren: John, David. Owner, pres. Cleve. Browns football team, 1961—; pres. Nat. Football League, 1967-70. Office: Cleveland Browns Cleveland Stadium 80 First Ave Berea OH 44017*

MODELL, JEROME HERBERT, anesthesiologist, educator, dean; b. St. Paul, Sept. 9, 1932; s. William and Frieda (Singer) M.; m. Shirley Graves, Nov. 25, 1977; children: Charles, Jack, Julie. B.A., U. Minn., 1954, B.S., 1957, M.D., 1957. Intern U.S. Naval Hosp., St. Albans, N.Y., 1957-58; resident U.S. Naval Hosp., 1958-60; practice medicine specializing in anesthesiology Gainesville, Fla., 1969—; attending staff U.S. Naval Hosp., St. Albans, 1960-61; chief anesthesiology U.S. Naval Hosp., Pensacola, Fla., 1961-63; assoc. prof. dept. anesthesiology U. Miami (Fla.) Sch. Medicine, 1963-69; prof., chmn. dept. anesthesiology U. Fla. Coll. Medicine, Gainesville, 1969-92, sr. assoc. dean clin. affairs, 1990-95; assoc. v.p. U. Fla. Health Sci. Ctr. Affiliations, 1992—. Author: The Pathophysiology and Treatment of Drowning and Near-Drowning, 1971, (with others) Introduction to Life Support, 1973; also numerous scientific articles. Served to lt. comdr. USN, 1957-63. Recipient NIH Research Career Devel. award. Mem. AMA, AAAS, Assn. U. Anesthetists, Am. Soc. Anesthesiologists, N.Y. Acad. Scis., Am. Coll. Chest Physicians. Home: PO Box 14347 Gainesville FL 32604-4347

MODELL, JOHN, historian, educator; b. N.Y.C., June 3, 1941; s. Walter and Merriam (Levant) M.; m. Judith Schachter, June 2, 1963; children: Jennifer, Matthew Thelonious. AB, Columbia U., 1962, MA, 1963, PhD, 1969; postgrad. (Social Sci. Research Council research tng. fellow), U. Pa., 1969-70. Research asst. Bur. Applied Social Research, Columbia U., 1962-65; lectr. Kingsborough Community Coll., 1965-66; dir. research Japanese Am. Research Project, UCLA, 1966-69; asst. prof. history U. Minn., 1969-72, assoc. prof., 1972-77, prof., 1977-83; prof. Carnegie Mellon U., 1983—, acting dean Coll. Humanities and Social Scis., 1985-87; Cardozo vis. prof. history Yale U., 1991; rsch. assoc. Phila. Social History Project, U. Pa., 1974-85; mem. adv., planning com. Ctr. for Coordination of Study of Social Indicators, Social Sci. Rsch. Coun., 1980-85; mem. com. child devel. rsch. and pub. policy NRC, 1981-86; mem. coun. Inter-Univ. Consortium for Polit. and Social Rsch., 1982-86; mem. MacArthur Found. Rsch. Network on Successful Pathways through Middle Childhood; mem. Network Program on Aging and Social Change, Nat. Inst. Aging. Author: The Economics and Politics of Racial Accommodation: The Japanese of Los Angeles 1900-1942, 1977, Into One's Own: From Youth to Adulthood in the United States, 1920-75, 1989, (with others) The Economic Basis of Ethnic Solidarity, 1981, Recent Social Trends in the United States 1960-90, 1991; editor, author: (with others) The Kikuchi Diary: Chronicle of an American Concentration Camp, 1973; editor: (with others) Theory, Method, and Practice in Social and Cultural History, 1992, Children in Time and Place: Developmental and Historical Insights, 1993; mem. editorial bd. Jour. Social History, 1985—, Historical Methods, 1985-87, Pub. Opinion Quar., 1987-91, Jour. of Research in Adolescence, 1990-93, The Historian, 1990-91. John Simon Guggenheim Meml. fellow, 1978-79. Home: 2048 Beechwood Blvd Pittsburgh PA 15217-1744 Office: Carnegie Mellon U Dept History Pittsburgh PA 15213

MODELL, MICHAEL STEVEN, lawyer, business executive; b. Bklyn., Mar. 11, 1953; s. William D. and Shelby Modell. BA in Internat. Svc., Govt. Pub. Adminstrsn., Am. U., 1974; JD, St. Johns U., Jamaica, N.Y., 1977. Bar: N.Y. 1978, Fla. 1978, U.S. Dist. Ct. (so. dist.) N.Y. 1979, U.S. Dist. Ct. (ea. dist.) N.Y. 1979. Pres. Henry Modell and Co., Inc. (Modell's Sporting Good), N.Y.C., 1988—; bd. dirs. Empire Blue Cross & Blue Shield, Nat. Retail Fedn. Foster parent Save the Children Found., N.Y.C., 1970—; big brother Big Brother Orgn., N.Y.C., 1970-80; v.p., trustee Crohns and Colitis Found. of Am., N.Y.C., 1968—. Mem. Young Pres.' Orgn., Real Estate Bd. of N.Y., Pi Sigma Alpha, Seawane Club (Hewlett), Friars Club (N.Y.C.). Office: Modells Sporting Goods 34-24 Vernon Blvd Long Island City NY 11106-5124

MODER, JOHN JOSEPH, academic administrator, priest; b. St. Louis, Apr. 9, 1948; s. Helen (Freihaut) M. BA in English and Philosophy, St. Mary's U., San Antonio, 1970; MA in Philosophy, Fordham U., 1972, PhD in Philosophy, 1977; M Div, U. St. Michael's, 1979. Joined Soc. of Mary, ordained priest Roman Cath. Ch., 1979. Mem. faculty Assumption High Sch., East St. Louis, Ill., 1973-75, Vianney High Sch., St. Louis, 1975-77; faculty mem. Irish Christian Bros. Sch., Mono Mills, Ont., Can., 1977-79; asst. prof. philosophy St. Mary's U., San Antonio, 1979-86, assoc. prof. philosophy, trustee, co-chmn. peace commn., 1986-88, pres., 1988—. Bd. advisors Communities-in-Schs., San Antonio, 1988—. Mem. Am. Cath. Philos. Assn., Am. Cancer Soc., Hispanic Assn. Colls, World Affairs Coun., Greater San Antonio C. of C., Rotary Club of San Antonio. Avocations: hiking, reading, travel, running. Office: St Mary's U Office of Pres 1 Camino Santa Maria St San Antonio TX 78228-8572

MODERACKI, EDMUND ANTHONY, music educator, conductor; b. Hackensack, N.J., July 18, 1946; s. Edmund Joseph and Helen Theresa (Fisher) M. BA, Montclair State Coll., 1968, postgrad., 1970-71; MA, Hunter Coll., 1970, postgrad., 1970-72; postgrad., Newark State Coll., 1969-70, Seton Hall U., 1970, Rutgers U., 1976-78, Ctr. for Understanding Media, 1973. Tchr. music pub. schs. River Vale, N.J., 1968—; asst. condr. Ridgewood (N.J.) Symphony Orch., 1969—, trustee, pres., 1986-87, 94-95; asst. conductor Adelphi Chamber Orch., 1994—; tuba soloist Rutherford Cmty. Band, Ridgewood Village Band, Waldwick Band, Ridgewood Concert Band, 1978—, Ridgewood Concert Band, 1983—; guest condr., 1985, 86, 88, 93; mgr. All Bergen High Sch. Band, 1994. Town historian River Vale; mem. steering com. Bergen County Teen Arts, 1991—. Recipient County Exec. Vol. award, 1991, Tchr. Recognition award Gov. of State of N.J., 1990; Bergen County PTA fellow, 1976. Mem. NEA, Music Educators Nat. Conf., N.J. Orch. Assn. (trustee 1981-85), N.J. Edn. Assn. (bd. assembly alt. 1983-93, mem. state membership com. 1986—), River Vale Edn. Assn. (pres. 1981-83, 88-91), Brigade Am. Revolution (bd. dirs. at large 1991—, info. officer 1989—, civilian music supt. 1992—), Phi Mu Alpha Sinfonia, Kappa

Delta Pi. Home: 531 Westwood Ave River Vale NJ 07675-5526 Office: Woodside Sch River Vale NJ 07675

MODEROW, JOSEPH ROBERT, package distribution company executive; b. Kenosha, Wis., 1948. Grad., Calif. State U., Fullerton, 1970; JD, Western State U., 1975. Bar: Calif. 1975, U.S. Dist. Ct. (cen. dist.) Calif. 1975, U.S. Supreme Ct. 1982. Now sr. v.p., sec., gen. counsel, dir. United Parcel Svc. Am., Inc., Atlanta, Ga. Office: United Parcel Svc Inc 55 Glenlake Pky NE Atlanta GA 30328

MODESTINO, JAMES WILLIAM, electrical engineering educator; b. Boston, Apr. 27, 1940; s. William and Mary Elizabeth (Dooley) M.; m. Leone Marie MacDougall, Aug. 25, 1962; children: Michele Marie, Lee Ann. BS, Northeastern U., 1962; MS, U. Pa., 1966; MA, Princeton U., 1968, PhD, 1969. Mem. tech. staff Gen. Telephone Electronics Labs., Waltham, Mass., 1969-70; asst. prof. Northeastern U., Boston, 1970-72; prof. Rensselaer Poly. Inst., Troy, N.Y., 1972-93, inst. prof., 1993—, dir. Ctr. for Image Processing Rsch., co-dir. Internat. Ctr. for Multimedia Edn.; dir. Ctr. for Image Processing Rsch.; co-dir. Internat. Ctr. Multimedia Edn.; vis. prof. U. Calif., San Diego, 1981-82; vis. faculty fellow GE Corp. R&D Ctr., 1988-89; pres. Modcom Inc., Ballston Lake, N.Y., 1981—; v.p. ICUCOM Inc., Troy, N.Y., 1986—. Recipient Sperry Faculty award Sperry Corp., 1986. Fellow IEEE (S.O. Rice Prize Paper award 1984, gov. Info. Theory Soc. 1988—). Avocations: sailing, jogging, tennis, skiing. Office: Rensselaer Poly Inst 110 8th St Troy NY 12180-3522

MODIANO, ALBERT LOUIS, gas, oil industry executive; b. N.Y.C., Sept. 10, 1953; s. Sam A. and Eve Modiano; m. Carolyn Elizabeth Barker, Sept. 29, 1979; children: Aaron, Sarah Anne. BA cum laude, Hobart Coll., 1975; MA, U. Chgo., 1977; postgrad., Harvard U., 1992. Assoc. Am. Petroleum Inst., Washington, 1981-87; dep. dir. Office of Oil Policy U.S. Dept. Interior, Washington, 1987-89; dep. dir. U.S. Minerals Mgmt. Svc., Washington, 1989-93; v.p. Mid Continent Oil & Gas Assn., Washington, 1993—. Mem. Phi Beta Kappa. Office: Mid Continent Oil Gas Assn 801 Pennsylvania Ave NW 840 Washington DC 20004-2615

MODIC, STANLEY JOHN, business editor, publisher; b. Fairport Harbor, Ohio, Dec. 29, 1936; s. Frank and Mary (Zakrajsek) M.; m. Albina DiMichele, May 27, 1961; children—Mark Francis, Laurel Marie. BS in Commerce, Ohio U., 1958. Reporter The Telegraph, Painesville, Ohio, 1960-63; city editor The Telegraph, 1964-65; asst. editor Steel Mag., Cleve., 1965-67; news editor Steel Mag., 1968-70; mng. editor Industry Week (formerly Steel Mag.), Cleve., 1970-72; exec. editor Industry Week (formerly Steel Mag.), 1972; editor Industry Week, 1972-86; sr. editor Industry Week (formerly Steel Mag.), 1986-89; editor-in-chief Purchasing World Mag., 1989-90; editor-in-chief Tooling and Prodn. Mag., 1990—, pub., editor in chief, 1991—. Mcpl. clk. Fairport Harbor, 1960-61; mem. Fairport Harbor Village Council, 1962-63, pres., 1962-63. Recipient G.D. Crane award Am. Bus. Press, 1991. Mem. Am. Soc. Mag. Editors, Am. Soc. Bus. Press Editors, Am. Fedn. Musicians, Press Club (pres. Cleve. chpt. 1978-79), Am.-Slovenian Club, KC, Elks, Sigma Delta Chi (pres. Cleve. chpt. 1975-76). Clubs: K.C. (Cleve.), Press (Cleve.) (pres. 1978-79); Am.-Slovenian (Fairport Harbor). Home: 5842 Woodhill St Painesville OH 44077-5167 Office: 29100 Aurora Rd Cleveland OH 44139-1855

MODIGLIANI, FRANCO, economics and finance educator; b. Rome, June 18, 1918; came to U.S., 1939, naturalized, 1946; s. Enrico and Olga (Flaschel) M.; m. Serena Calabi, May 22, 1939; children: Andre, Sergio. D. Jurisprudence, U. Rome, 1939; D. Social Sci., New Sch. Social Rsch., 1944; LLD (hon.), U. Chgo., 1967; D. honoris causa, U. Louvain, Belgium, 1974, Istituto Universitario di Bergamo, 1979, Hartford U.; LHD (hon.), Bard Coll., 1985, Brandeis U., 1986, New Sch. Social Research, 1985; LLD, Mich. State U., 1989; D (hon.), U. Ill., 1990, U. Valencia, Spain, 1992. Instr. econs. and statistics N.J. Coll. Women, New Brunswick, 1942; instr., then asso. econs. and statistics Bard Coll., Columbia, 1942-44; lectr., asst. prof. math. econs. and econometrics New Sch. Social Rsch., 1943-44, 46-48; rsch. asso., chief statistician Inst. World Affairs, N.Y.C., 1945-48; rsch. cons. Cowles Commn. Rsch. in Econs. U. Chgo., 1949-54; asso. prof., then prof. econs. U. Ill., 1949-52; prof. econs. and indsl. adminstrn. Carnegie Inst. Tech., 1952-60; vis. prof. econs. Harvard U., 1957-58; prof. econs. Northwestern U., 1960-62; vis. prof. econs. MIT, 1960-61, prof. econs. and finance, 1962—, Inst. prof., 1970-88, Inst. prof. emeritus, 1988—; Fellow polit. economy U. Chgo., 1948; Fulbright lectr. U. Rome, also, Palermo, Italy, 1955; mem. Shadow Fin. Regulatory Com., 1994—. Author: The Debate Over Stabilization Policy, 1986, Il Caso Italia, 1986, The Collected Papers of Franco Modigliani, 3 vols., 1980, 4th and 5th vols., 1989; co-author: National Incomes and International Trade, 1953, Planning Production, Inventories and Work Forces, 1960, The Role of Anticipations and Plans in Economic Behavior and Their Use in Economic Analysis and Forecasting, 1961, New Mortgage Designs for Stable Housing in an Inflationary Environment, 1975, (with Frank J. Fabozzi) Capital Markets: Institutions and Instruments, 1991, (with Frank J. Fabozzi) Mortgage and Mortgage-Backed Security Markets, 1992, (with Frank J. Fabozzi, Michael G. Ferri) Foundations of Financial Markets and Institutions, 1994. Recipient Nobel prize in econ. sci., 1985; Cavaliere Di Gran Crose Repubblica Italiana, 1985, Premio Coltura for Econs., Repubblica Italiana, 1988, Premio APE award, 1988, Graham and Dodd award, 1975, 80, James R. Killian Jr. Faculty Achievement award, 1985, Lord Found. prize, 1989, Italy Premio Columbus, 1989, Italy Premio Guido Dorso, 1989, Italy Premio Stivale D'oro, 1991, Italy Premio Campione D'Italia, 1992; named hon. citizen of Town of Modigliana, Italy, 1993. Fellow NAS, Am. Econ. Assn. (v.p. 1971, 1976), Econometric Soc. (coun. 1960, v.p. 1961, pres. 1962), Am. Acad. Arts and Scis., Internat. Econ. Assn. (v.p. 1977-83, hon. pres. 1983—); mem. Am. Fin. Assn. (pres. 1981), Accademia Nazionale dei Lincei (Rome) (mem. shadow fin. regulatory com. 1994—).

MODIGLIANI, LAZZARO G., chemicals executive; b. 1932. PhD in Chem. Engring., Polytechnic Inst., Milan, Italy, 1962. With Badger Co., Inc., 1965—, now pres., CEO; with Badger Engrs., Inc., Cambridge, Mass., 1975—, now pres., CEO. Office: Badger Engrs Inc 1 Broadway Cambridge MA 02142-1190

MODINE, MATTHEW AVERY, actor; b. Loma Linda, Calif., Mar. 22, 1959; m. Caridad Rivera, 1979; 2 children: Bowman, Ruby. Appeared in films Baby, Its You, 1983, Private School, 1983, Streamers, 1983 (Best Actor award, Venice Film Festival 1983), The Hotel New Hampshire, 1984, Mrs. Soffel, 1984, Birdy, 1984, Vision Quest, 1985, Full Metal Jacket, 1987, Orphans, 1987, Married to the Mob, 1988, Gross Anatomy, 1989, Memphis Belle, 1990, Pacific Heights, 1990, Wind, 1992, Equinox, 1993, And the Band Played On, HBO, 1993 (Emmy nominee for Lead Actor in a Special, 1994), Short Cuts, 1993, The Browning Version, 1994, Bye Bye, Love, 1995, Fluke, 1995; numerous TV commls.; dir. of short film, Smoking, 1994, Jacob, 1994. Office: William Morris Agy 151 El Camino Beverly Hills CA 90211*

MODLIN, GEORGE MATTHEWS, university chancellor emeritus; b. Elizabeth City, N.C., July 13, 1903; s. John William and Nannie E. (Matthews) M.; m. Virginia Pendleton Brinkley, June 2, 1928. A.B., Wake Forest (N.C.) U., 1924, LL.D., 1947; M.A., Princeton, 1925, Ph.D., 1932; Dr. Laws, Stetson U., 1942, Hampden-Sydney Coll., 1971, U. Richmond, 1971. Asst. in econs. Princeton U., 1927-28, instr., 1928-32, asst. prof., 1932-38; part-time lectr. econs. Rutgers U., 1936-38; prof. econs., dean Sch. Bus. Adminstrn. U. Richmond, Va., 1938-46, pres., 1946-71, chancellor, 1971-86, chancellor emeritus, 1986—; mem. pub. panel War Labor Bd., 1943-45. Author: (with F.T. De Vyver) Development of Economic Society, 1936, rev., 1946, (with A.M. McIsaac) Social Control of Industry, 1938. Trustee, pres. Keesee Ednl. Fund, 1963—; trustee, v.p. Titmus Found., 1971—; trustee Va. Found. Ind. Colls., pres., 1956-58. Mem. Richmond C. of C. (pres. 1951), So. U. Conf. (pres. 1955), So. Assn. Bapt. Schs. and Colls. (pres. 1952), Assn. Va. Colls. (pres. 1952), Assn. Am. Colls. (pres. 1962), Phi Beta Kappa, Kappa Alpha, Beta Gamma Sigma, Omicron Delta Kappa. Clubs: Country of Virginia, Commonwealth; University (N.Y.C.). Office: Univ of Richmond Richmond VA 23173

MODLIN, HOWARD S., lawyer; b. N.Y.C., Apr. 10, 1931; s. Martin and Rose Modlin; m. Margot S., Oct. 18, 1956; children: James, Laura, Peter. AB, Union Coll., Schenectady, 1952; JD, Columbia U., 1955. Bar: N.Y.

1956, D.C. 1973. Assoc., Weisman, Celler, Spett & Modlin, N.Y.C., 1956-61; ptnr., 1961-76; mng. ptnr., 1976—; sec., dir. Gen. DataComm Industries, Inc., Middlebury, Conn.; dir. Am.-Book-Stratford Press, Inc., N.Y.C., Fedders Corp., Liberty Corner, N.J., Trans-Lux Corp., Norwalk, Conn. Chmn. bd. dirs. Daus. of Jacob Geriatric Ctr., Bronx, N.Y. Mem. ABA, Assn. Bar City N.Y., D.C. Bar Assn. Office: Weisman Celler Spett & Modlin 445 Park Ave New York NY 10022-2606

MODUGNO, MARIA, publishing executive. V.p., editor-in-chief, children's division Little, Brown and Co. Inc., Boston. Office: Little Brown & Co Inc 34 Beacon St Boston MA 02108-3703

MOE, ALDEN JOHN, university dean; b. Cookston, Minn., Apr. 9, 1939; s. Melvin Truman and Martha Mathilde (Njus) M.; m. Margery Elizabeth Sharbono, Aug. 1959 (div. 1983); m. Elayne Ackerman, Jan. 2, 1984; children: Christine Marie, Perry Wayne. BS, U. Minn., 1963; MA, Clarke Coll., Dubuque, Iowa, 1967; PhD, U. Minn., 1971. Tchr. St. Anthony Village, Minn., 1963-66; instr. Clarke Coll., 1967-69, U. Minn., 1969-71; from asst. to assoc. prof. Purdue U., West Lafayette, Ind., 1971-82; prof. La. State U., Baton Rouge, 1982-85, assoc. dean, 1985-88; dean of edn. Lehigh U., Bethlehem, Pa., 1988—. Author: Vocabulary of First Grade Children, 1982, Ginn Word Book for Teachers, 1983, Occupational Literacy Education, 1986, Keystones for Reading, 1988, Analytical Reading Inventory, 5th edit., 1995. Mem. Internat. Reading Assn. (bd. dirs. 1980-83), Am. Ednl. Rsch. Assn., nat. Conf. Rsch. in English. Democrat. Avocations: flying, playing bridge, reading mysteries, collecting antiques. Home: 5606 Meadow Dr Orefield PA 18069-9027 Office: Lehigh U Dean of Edn Bethlehem PA 18015

MOE, CHESNEY RUDOLPH, physics educator; b. Ont., Can., Oct. 6, 1908; s. Oscar and Edith (Miller) M.; m. Berthe Newton, Aug. 24, 1935 (dec. Sept. 1950); 1 son, Ronald; m. Bernice Woolman, July 21, 1951 (dec. May 1993); 1 dau., Donna. A.B., Stanford, 1929, A.M., 1931; Ph.D., U. So. Calif., 1941. Registered profl. engr., Cal. Asst. in physics San Diego State U., 1929-30, instr., 1931-35, asst. prof., 1935-39, asso. prof., 1939-45, prof. physics, 1945—, chmn. dept. physics, 1948-51, 53-56, 61-64, asso. chmn. div. phys. scis., 1956-61; cons. in acoustics Tracor, San Diego, 1965-74, Jet Propulsion Lab., Pasadena, 1968-70; dir. Electronics Investment Corp., 1959-63. Served as comdr. USNR, 1942-46, 1951-57; capt. Res. ret. Fellow Acoustical Soc. Am. (contbr. to jour.); mem. Sigma Xi, Phi Delta Kappa, Sigma Pi Sigma, Kappa Sigma. Home: 750 State St # 206 San Diego CA 92101-6033

MOE, ORVILLE LEROY, racetrack executive; b. Spokane, Wash., Nov. 26, 1936; s. Clarence Orville and Georgia Maria (Lombard) M.; m. Deonne Wesley Schultz, Jan. 11, 1953; children: Susan Marie, Terry Ann. Co-owner Moe's Sudden Svc. Fuel Co., Spokane, Wash., 1956-74; sec. Gold Res. Mining Corp., Spokane, 1973-89, Bonanza Gold Corp., Spokane, 1973-85; pres., founder Spokane Raceway Park, Inc., 1971—; regional v.p. Am. Hot Rod Assn., Kansas, Mo., 1968-84, mktg. dir., 1978-84; co-producer Internat. Car Show Assn., Spokane, 1969-90. Co-producer Spokane Auto Boat Speed Show, 1964—. Mem. Nat. Rep. Senatorial Com., 1984—, mem., trustee Rep. Presdl. Task Force, mem. 1992 Presdl. Trust Rep. Nat. Com. Mem. ISCA, Eagles, Am. Hot Rod Assn. (exec. v.p. Spokane, Wash. 1986—), Internat. Footprint Assn., Am. Auto Racing Assn. (regional v.p.). Republican. Avocations: auto racing, mining, collecting and rebuilding autos, fishing, ice hockey. Office: Spokane Raceway Park Inc 101 N Hayford Rd Spokane WA 99204-9510

MOE, PALMER L., gas company executive; b. Billings, Mont., 1944. BSBA, U. Denver, 1966. Mem. audit staff to mng. ptnr. Arthur Anderson Co., 1965-83; pres., chief oper. officer Valero Energy Corp., San Antonio, 1983—; vice chmn., bd. dirs. Valero Transmission Co., Valero Refining and Mktg. Co., Valero Natural Gas Co.; bd. dirs. Valero Storage, Valero Offshore Inc., Valero Offshore Properties Inc., Valero Producing Co. Served with USAR, 1963-69. Office: Valero Energy Corp 530 McCullough Ave San Antonio TX 78215-2104

MOE, RICHARD PALMER, lawyer; b. Duluth, Minn., Nov. 27, 1936; s. Russell James and Virginia Mary (Palmer) M.; m. Julia Neimeyer, Dec. 26, 1964; children—Eric Palmer, Andrew Neimeyer, Alexandra Julia. B.A., Williams Coll., 1959; LL.B., U. Minn., 1966. Bar: Minn. 1967, D.C. 1979, N.Y. 1991. Adminstrv. asst. to mayor City of Mpls., 1961-62; lt. gov. State of Minn., 1963-66; fin. dir. Minn. Democratic Farmer-Labor Party, 1967-69, chmn., 1969-72; adminstrv. asst. to Sen. Walter F. Mondale of Minn., Washington, 1972-76; chief of staff Vice Pres. Walter F. Mondale, 1977-81; counsel Davis Polk & Wardwell, Washington, 1981-85, ptnr., 1985-92; pres. Nat. Trust for Hist. Preservation, Washington, 1992—. Office: Nat Trust for Hist Preservation 1785 Massachusetts Ave NW Washington DC 20036-2117

MOE, STANLEY ALLEN, architect, consultant; b. Fargo, N.D., May 28, 1914; s. Ole Arnold and Freda Emily (Pape) M.; m. Doris Lucille Anderson, May 25, 1937; children: Willa Moe Crouse, Myra Moe Parsons. BArch, U. Minn., 1936; D of Engring. (hon.), U. N.D., 1993. lic. architect several states; NCARB cert. Project architect several firms in Midwest, 1936-42; project architect U.S. Army Corps Engrs., Africa, 1942-43; ptnr. H.S. Starin, Architects & Engrs., Duluth, Minn., 1943-47; sr. ptnr. Moe & Larsen, Architects & Engrs., L.A., 1947-54; ptnr. gen. mgr., exec. v.p. Daniel, Mann, Johnson & Mendenall, L.A., 1954-71, corp. v.p., 1972-79; prin. Stanley A. Moe, AIA, L.A., 1979—; dir. design of major mil. projects in Eritrea, Sudan, Yemen for Allied Forces, 1942-43; chmn. control com. DMJM & Assocs., 1958-63; designer of prototype, eng. and operational facilities for Titan I Ballistic Missile program for USAF; project dir. Space Shuttle facilities Kennedy Space Ctr., 1973; project dir. for design of aircraft maintenance complex Iranian Aircraft Industries, 1978; project mgr. for design of major med. facility program Min. of Def. and Aviation, Saudi Arabia, 1975-76; project mgr. design of Boufarik Internat. Airport, Algeria, 1983. Pres. San Fernando Valley Young Reps., 1952, Van Nuys (Calif.) Jaycees, 1950. Recipient Dsiting. Svc. award for cmty. svc. Van Nuys Jaycees, 1949, Sioux award U. N.D. Alumni Assn., 1985, Trustees Soc. award U. Minn., 1992. Mem. AIA (Calif. coun.), Delta Tau Delta. Republican. Presbyterian. Avocations: world travel, hunting, fishing, historic restoration. Home and Office: 447 S Plymouth Blvd Los Angeles CA 90020-4706

MOE, THOMAS O., lawyer; b. Des Moines, 1938. BA, U. Minn., 1960, LLB, 1963. Bar: Minn. 1963. Ptnr. Dorsey & Whitney P.L.L.P, Mpls., 1964-89; mng. ptnr. Dorsey & Whitney P.L.L.P., Mpls., 1989—. Mem. Order of Coif. Office: Dorsey & Whitney 220 S 6th St Minneapolis MN 55402-1498

MOE, TOMMY (THOMAS SVEN MOE), skier, former Olympic athlete; b. Missoula, Mont., 1970. Gold medalist, men's Downhill alpine skiing Olympic Games, Lillehammer, Norway, 1994; Silver medalist, men's Super-G alpine skiing Olympic Games, 1994; skier Fedn. Ski World Cup Circuit. Office: US Skiing Assn PO Box 100 Park City UT 84060

MOECK, WALTER F., conductor, music director; b. Milw., Mar. 18, 1922; s. Walter Ernst and Verena Helen (Klein) M.; m. Barbara Conklin; children: Karen, Richard, Stephen. MusB in Trumpet, Eastman Sch. Music, 1947; studies with Pierre Monteux, L'Ecole Monteux, 1951-53; MA in Conducting, U. Iowa, 1955; D in Fine Arts & Music (hon.), London Inst. Applied Rsch., 1993. Instr. brass Univ. Ala., Tuscaloosa, 1947-54, condr. symphony, 1950-54; assoc. condr. Birmingham (Ala.) Symphony, 1948-60; condr. Southeastern Composers Symphony, Tuscaloosa, 1950-54; mus. dir. Birmingham Ballet Co., 1955-62; mus. dir., condr. Ala. Pops Symphony, Birmingham, 1955-73, L.A. Repertoire Orch., 1975-88, San Fernando Valley Theater of Performing Arts, L.A., 1977-88, Am. Philharmonia New Project, L.A., 1978—; instr. Birmingham Southern Coll., Samford U., Montevallo U., Indian Springs Sch., 1954-68; cons., judge various mus. orgns., L.A. and Birmingham, 1947—; tchr. writing various groups and individuals, L.A. 1968—; guest condr. New Orleans Philharm., 1980, Burbank (Calif.) Symphony Orch., 1972, Bakersfield (Calif.) Philharm., 1971, Phila. Symphony Orch., 1953; condr., musical dir. Fine Arts Orch. Scottsdale/Phoenix, Sun City Concert Band. Composer: Trumpet Etudes (2 vols.),

1980, various warm-up exercises for all brass instruments, 1980; contbr. articles to Brass Warm-Ups, 1974. Mayor, pres. Town of Hoover, Ala., 1966; pres. Ch. Coun., L.A., 1973-74; mem. Pres. George Bush's Presdl. Task Force, Nat. Rep. Senatorial Com., Nat. Rep. Congrl. Com., Nat. Rep. Com. With U.S. Army, 1943-46. Recipient Key to City of Birmingham, 1986, Merit medal Pres. Bush, 1990, Man of the Yr. award Internat. Biog. Centre of Cambridge, Eng., 1993; Walter Moeck Week proclaimed in his honor musicians of Birmingham, 1986. Fellow Internat. Inst. of Arts and Letters (life); mem. Calif. Symphony Assn. Republican. Roman Catholic. Avocations: golf, reading, hiking. Home: 14507 W Trading Post Dr Sun City West AZ 85375-5794 Office: Fine Arts Orch Scottsdale Coll 9000 E Chaparral Rd Scottsdale AZ 85250-2614

MOECKEL, BILL REID, retired university dean; b. Pekin, Ill., Sept. 2, 1925; s. Willis E. and Daisy M. M.; m. Pauline C. Fox, Sept. 1, 1946; children—Steven, Cindy, Nancy. B.S., U. Ill., 1948, M.S., 1949, Ph.D., 1953. Instr. mktg. U. Mo., 1949-51; asst. prof. Ga. State U., 1953-54; asso. dean Sch. Bus., Ohio State U., 1954-67; dir. USAF Sch. Logistics, 1958-65; dean Sch. Bus., Miami U., Oxford, Ohio, 1967-87. Served with AUS, 1943-46. Mem. Am. Assembly Collegiate Schs. Bus. (nat. pres. 1981-82), Air Force Inst. Tech. Assn. Grads, Beta Gamma Sigma (nat. pres. 1976-78), Alpha Delta Sigma, Omicron Delta Kappa, Alpha Kappa Psi, Pi Sigma Epsilon, Mu Kappa Tau, Beta Alpha Psi.

MOEHLE, JACK P., civil engineer, engineering executive. BSCE, U. Ill., 1977, MSCE, 1977, PhD, 1980. Registered civil engr., Calif. From asst. to assoc. prof. U. Calif., Berkeley, 1980-90, prof., 1990—, Roy W. Carlson Disting. prof. civil engring., vice-chair tech. svcs. civil engring., 1990-91, dir. earthquake engring. rsch. ctr., 1991—; tech. advisor Double Deck Peer Rev. Panel, Caltrans, 1990—; mem. sci. adv. com. Nat. Ctr. Earthquake Engring. Rsch.; proposal reviewer NSF; cons. in field; bd. dirs. Calif. Univs. Rsch. Earthquake Engring., Cooperating Orgns. No. Calif. Earthquake Rsch. and Tech. Contbr. articles to profl. jours.; reviewer tech. papers. Recipient Chi Epsilon Excellence Teaching award, 1986; Regents Jr. Faculty fellow, 1981. Fellow Am. Concrete Inst. (chmn. detail and proportion earthquake resisting structural elements and systems com. 1988—, mem. various coms.); mem. ASCE (publs. sec. com. seismic effects, Huber Rsch. prize 1990), Structural Engrs. Assn. Calif. (mem. seismology com., reinforced concrete com., bd. dirs.), Earthquake Engring. Rsch. Inst. Office: U Calif Berkeley Earthquake Engring Rsch Ctr 1301 S 46th St Richmond CA 94804-4603*

MOEHLMAN, MICHAEL SCOTT, lawyer; b. Columbus, Ohio, Apr. 11, 1938; s. Arthur Henry and Marguerite Caroline M.; m. Carol Jean Shafer, Sept. 28, 1963; 1 son, Matthew. B.A., Harvard U., 1960; LL.B., U. Tex., 1963. Bar: Tex. 1963. Ptnr. Baker & Botts, Houston, 1963—. Bd. dirs. St. Martin's Episcopal Children's Ctr. Mem. ABA (com. bank securities, com. bus. bankruptcy, com. savs. instns.) Tex. Bar Assn. (com. revision corp. law), Houston Bar Assn. (judicature com.), Am. Judicature Soc., Houston Bar Found. (chmn. bd. dirs.), Phi Delta Phi. Episcopalian. Clubs: Houston (chmn. fin. com., bd. dirs.), Houston Racquet, Houston Yacht, Harvard (Boston), St. Charles Bay Hunting. Office: Baker & Botts 1 Shell Plz 30th Fl Houston TX 77002

MOELING, WALTER GOOS, IV, lawyer; b. Quantico, Va., Feb. 16, 1943; s. Walter Goos III and Dorothy (Tritle) M.; m. Nell Frances Askew, Aug. 27, 1965; children: Charles H., Christine E. BA, Duke U., 1965, JD, 1968. Bar: Ga. 1968. Assoc. Powell, Goldstein, Frazer & Murphy, Atlanta, 1968-75, ptnr., 1975—. Bd. dirs. Children's Rehab. Ctr., Atlanta, 1982, The Gatchell Home, Atlanta, 1983; bd. dirs. REACH, Inc., 1989, chmn., 1993. Mem. ABA (banking com. 1986—), Ga. Bar Assn., Ga. Bankers Assn. (assoc., chair bank counsel sect. 1992—), Community Bankers Assn. (assoc.), Ga. League Savs. Instns. (assoc.), Capital City Club, Willow Point Country Club. Democrat. Unitarian. Avocations: golf, fly-fishing. Office: Powell Goldstein Frazer & Murphy 191 Peachtree St NE Ste 16 Atlanta GA 30303-1741

MOELLEKEN, WOLFGANG WILFRIED, Germanic languages and literature educator; b. Jan. 14, 1934; s. August and Emmy (d'Oliva) M.; m. Melita Anne Hildebrandt, Dec. 27, 1958; children: Brent Roderick Wilfred, Alan Patrick Wilfred, Sonja Melita Clarice. Student, U. Cologne, 1955-57; BE, U. N.Mex., 1961; MA, U. Wash., 1962, PhD, 1965. Asst. prof. U. Calif., Riverside, 1964-67; assoc. prof. U. Va., 1967-68, SUNY, Stony Brook, 1968-69; prof. U. Calif., Davis, 1969-77; prof. Germanic langs. and lits., head dept. fgn. langs. and lits. Purdue U., 1977-79; prof. Germanic langs. SUNY, Albany, 1979—, chmn. dept., 1979-82, 88-92; vis. prof. Univ. Augsburg, Univ. Marburg; dir. Ctr. for German Speech Islands in Am.; corr. mem. Rsch. Ctr. on Multilingualism, Brussels. Author numerous books and monographs; editor: German Lang. and Lit. Monographs, 1976—; founding editor: Purdue U. Monographs in Romance Langs., Davis Medieval Texts and Studies; contbr. articles to profl. jours. Calif. Humanities Inst. grantee and fellow; Regents fellow; Am. Council Learned Socs. grantee; Am. Philos. Soc. grantee; SUNY Research Found. fellow; Austrian Govt. fellow; Deutsche Forschungsgemeinschaft research and teaching prof.; NEH grantee; Fulbright sr. research fellow. Mem. Belgian Rsch. Assn. (rsch. prof.). Office: SUNY Dept Germanic Langs Li Albany NY 12222

MOELLENBECK, ALBERT JOHN, JR., engineering executive; b. St. Louis, Aug. 4, 1934; s. Albert John and Josephine Marie (Fruth) M.; m. Charlotte Anne Zimmerman, Nov. 26, 1960; children: Albert, Mary, Cheryl, Joan. BSCE, U. Mo., Rolla, 1960; postgrad., Harvard U., 1979. Registered prof. engr., Calif., N.Y., N.J., N.Mex. Engring. technician Calif. Divsn. Hwys., Sacramento, 1956-59; sr. engr. Calif. Dept. Water Resources, Sacramento, 1960-66; constrn. mgmt. engr. nuclear energy divsn. GE, San Jose, Calif., 1967-70; project mgr. R. Parsons Co., Pasadena, Calif., 1971-73; CEO, pres. Nuclear Power Svcs., N.Y.C., 1973-87; CEO BioTech Industries, Wyckoff, N.J., 1988-92; prin. A.J. Moellenbeck P.A., 1992—; expert lectr. U. Calif., Berkeley, 1963-66; expert examiner Calif. P & V Stds., Sacramento, 1964-68; expert instr. San Jose State U., 1967-69. Chief editor: Professional Engineering Examination Handbook, 1968; contbr. tech. articles to jours. With USN, 1952-55. Mem. ASME (nuclear codes com. 1972—, award 1990), ASCE, Am. Nuclear Soc. Achievements include patent for upflow biol. reactor treatment system. Home: 36 Wilderness Gate Santa Fe NM 87501

MOELLER, A. DIANE, health facility administrator; b. West Point, Iowa, July 11, 1935. Diploma in Nursing, 1959; bachelors degree, Viterbo Coll., 1962, masters degree, 1966. Adminstr. resident St. Elizabeth Hosp., Elizabeth, N.J., 1965-66; asst. adminstr. Sacred Heart Hosp., Idaho Falls, Idaho, 1966-67, adminstr., 1967-71; dir. family health ctr. program Coll. Medicine U. Utah, Salt Lake City, 1971-75; exec. dir. Utah Group Health Plan, Salt Lake City, 1975-76; dir. quality assurance and program devel. Intermountain Health Care, Inc., Salt Lake City, 1976-78, v.p. profl. svcs., 1978-82; v.p. mem. svcs. Cath. Health Assn., St. Louis, 1982-87; pres., CEO Cath. Health Corp., Omaha, 1987-93, CEO, 1993—. Contbr. articles to profl. jours. Mem. Am. Coll. Hosp. Adminstrs. (svc. com.), Am. Hosp. Assn., Utah Hosp. Assn. Home: 924 S 117th Ct Omaha NE 68114 Office: Cath Health Corp 920 S 107th Ave # 200 Omaha NE 68114-4719

MOELLER, ACHIM FERDINAND GERD, art dealer, consultant, publisher; b. Heidelberg, Fed. Republic Germany, July 21, 1942; came to U.S., 1967; s. Friedrich Hermann and Liselotte Gerda Emilie (Kehrer) m. Danièle Poli, Mar. 24, 1971 (div. 1978); children: Frédèric, Bèatrice; m. Colette Jeannine Estiveau, Aug. 11, 1986; 1 child, Stephanie. Baccalauréat, Lycée Français, Sarrebruck, Germany, 1961. Asst. mgr. Kunsthaus Lempertz, Cologne, Fed. Republic Germany, 1964-66; student econs. Wildenstein & Co., N.Y.C., 1966-67; dir., v.p. Marlborough Gallery, N.Y.C., 1967-71; pres. Achim Moeller Ltd., London, 1971-85, Achim Moeller Fine Art Ltd., N.Y.C., 1983—; curator in chief John C. Whitehead Collection, Washington, N.Y.C., 1981—; expert Lyonel Feininger, N.Y.C., 1980—. Pub., editor, author: (exhbn. catalogs) Lyonel Feininger, 1969, 75, 85, 86, 90, (book catalogs) Kirchner-Heckel, 1975, Kandinsky, 1977, Ph. Guston, 1977, Julius Bissier, 1987, John C. Whitehead Collection, 1987, Feininger-Tobey, The Complete Correspondence, 1991, Feininger in Paris, 1892-1911, 1992. Mem. Pvt. Art Dealers Assn. U.S.A., French Nat. Syndicate of Art Dealers, Confedn. Internat. de Negociants en Oeuvres d'Art, Rotary Internat. (Paul Harris fellow), Am. Coun. of Germany, Nat. Arts Club. Avocations: violin, literature, chess, photography, contemporary art. Office: 52 E 76th St New York NY 10021-2755

MOELLER, AUDREY CAROLYN, energy company executive, corporate secretary; b. Pitts., May 10, 1935; d. Nicholas William and Edith Tecla (Russman) M. Grad. high sch., Pitts. Legal sec. Equitable Resources Inc., Pitts., 1955-72, asst. corp. sec., 1972-80, corp. sec., 1980-86, v.p., corp. sec., 1986—; also corp. sec. Equitable Resources Inc. subs.; dir. EOT Capital Corp., EREC Capital Corp. Com. mem. United Way Allegheny County, Pa., 1978, United Way Southwestern Pa., 1984. Mem. Loyal Christian Benefit Assn. (nat. coun. 1993), Am. Soc. Corp. Secs. (asst. sec., chmn. membership Pitts. chpt. 1995), Pa. Assn. Notaries. Democrat. Roman Catholic. Avocations: choral singing, golf. Home: 1015 Edward Dr Pittsburgh PA 15227-3917 Office: Equitable Resources Inc 420 Blvd Of The Allies Pittsburgh PA 15219

MOELLER, DADE WILLIAM, environmental engineer, educator; b. Grant, Fla., Feb. 27, 1927; s. Robert A. and Victoria (Bolton) M.; m. Betty Jean Radford, Oct. 7, 1949; children: Garland Radford, Mark Bolton, William Kehne, Matthew Palmer, Elisabeth Anne. BS in Civil Engring., Ga. Inst. Tech., 1947, MS in Environ. Engring., 1948; PhD in Nuclear Engring., N.C. State U., 1957. Commd. jr. asst. san. engr. USPHS, 1948, advanced through grades to san. engr. dir., 1961; research engr. Los Alamos Sci. Lab., 1949-52; staff asst. Radiol. Health Program, Washington, 1952-54; research asso. Oak Ridge Nat. Lab., 1956-57; chief radiol. health tng. Taft San. Engring. Center, Cin., 1957-61; officer charge Northeastern Radiol. Health Lab., Winchester, Mass., 1961-66; assoc. dir. Kresge Center Environ. Health, Harvard Sch. Pub. Health, 1966-83; prof. engring. in environmental health, head dept. environmental health scis., 1968-83, dir. Office of Continuing Edn., 1982-84, assoc. dean continuing edn., 1985-93; environ. cons., 1993—; pres. Dade Moeller & Assocs., Inc., 1993—; cons. radiol. health. Author: (textbook) Environmental Health, 1992; contbr. articles to profl. jours. Chmn. Am. Bd. Health Physics, 1967-70; mem. Nat. Coun. Radiation Protection and Measurements, 1968—; mem. com. 4 Internat. Commn. on Radiol. Protection, 1978-85; chmn. nat. air pollution manpower devel. adv. com. U.S. EPA, 1972-75; mem. adv. com. reactor safeguards U.S. NRC, 1973-88, chmn., 1976, chmn. adv. com. nuclear waste, 1988-93. Fellow Am. Pub. Health Assn., Am. Nuclear Soc.; mem. Am. Acad. Environ. Engrs., Nat. Acad. Engring, Health Physics Soc. (pres. 1971-72), AAAS. Home and Office: 147 River Island Rd New Bern NC 28562-3656

MOELLER, DONALD JOSEPH, academic administrator, educator; b. Covington, Ky., Dec. 27, 1933; s. Arthur Edward and Ida (Knauf) M.; married, 1969; children: Kristi Lee, Susan Jean. BA, St. Paul Seminary, 1953; STB, Gregorian U., Rome, 1955, Licentiate in Sacred Theology, 1957; Licentiate in Sacred Scripture, Pontifical Biblical Inst., 1960. Ordained priest Roman Cath. Ch., 1957. Asst. pastor St. Stephen Parish, Newport, Ky., 1960-66, St. James Parish, Ludlow, Ky., 1966-68, St. Agnes Parish, Ft. Wright, Ky., 1969; laicized, 1969; asst. prof. Thomas More Coll., Edgewood, Ky., 1960-69, asst. dean, 1966-69; assoc. prof. theology St. Ambrose U., Davenport, Iowa, 1969—, provost, academic v.p., 1974—. Del. to local and state Dem. Party caucuses; alt. rep. Ky. Assn. Higher Edn., 1966-68. Mem. Am. Acad. Religion, Soc. Bibl. Lit., Coll. Theology Soc., Am. Assn. Higher Edn. Democrat. Avocations: golf, walking, travel. Home: 2901 Camden Dr Bettendorf IA 52722-3324 Office: St Ambrose U 518 W Locust St Davenport IA 52803-2829

MOELLER, JAMES, state supreme court justice; b. Valley, Nebr., Nov. 14, 1933; s. Hans and Marie Grace (Shumaker) M.; m. Nancy Lee Kiely, Dec. 16, 1961; children: Amy Jo, Linda Anne. BA, Nebr. Wesleyan U., 1954; JD with high distinction, George Washington U., 1959. Bar: Ariz. 1959, U.S. Dist. Ct. Ariz. 1959, U.S. Ct. Appeals (9th cir.) 1961. Assoc. Lewis and Roca, Phoenix, 1959-64, ptnr., 1964-70; ptnr. Moeller Hover Jensen & Henry, Phoenix, 1970-77; judge Maricopa County Superior Ct., Phoenix, 1977-87; assoc. justice Ariz. Supreme Ct., Phoenix, 1987-92, vice chief justice, 1992—. Editor-in-chief George Washington U. Law Rev., 1958-59. Bd. dirs. Found. for Blind Children, Scottsdale, Ariz., 1964-70, Ariz. Found. Prevention of Blindness, Phoenix, 1966-70; Rep. committeeman, Phoenix and Scottsdale, 1965-69. Served with U.S. Army, 1954-56. Mem. ABA, Am. Judicature Soc., Ariz. Bar Assn., Maricopa County Bar Assn. Methodist. Avocations: travel, puzzles, history. Office: Ariz Supreme Ct 432 Ariz Courts Bldg 1501 W Washington Phoenix AZ 85007

MOELLER, JERRY G., health care facility executive; b. Holdenville, Okla.; s. John Joseph and Johnnie V. (Dean) M.; m. Barbara Pierce; children: Jeff, Julie. Student, U. Tulsa; MS in Healthcare Adminstrn., Trinity U., 1974. V.p. ops. Bapt. Med. Ctr., Oklahoma City, 1974-80; exec. dir. North Clark Community Hosp., Charlestown, Ind., 1980-83; dir. ops. Hosp. Corp. Am., Baton Rouge, 1983-85; adminstr. Med. Ctr. of Baton Rouge, 1985—. Founder Friends of ALS, Baton Rouge, 1983—; mem. United Way, Baton Rouge, 1985; bd. dirs. Shenandoah Civic Assn., Baton Rouge, 1984. Fellow Am. Coll. Healthcare Execs.; La. Assn. of Bus. and Industry (bd. dirs. 1985), La. Healthcare Assn. (pres. SE chpt. 1985-86). Republican. Roman Catholic. Lodge: Rotary. Avocations: golf, fishing. Office: Quorum Health Resources Inc Intensive Resources Div 2515 Park Plz Nashville TN 37203

MOELLER, ROBERT CHARLES III, fine arts consultant; b. Providence, Jan. 22, 1938; s. Robert Charles Jr. and Eleanor Frances (Dowling) M.; m. Dorothy Jean Westby, July 12, 1958 (div. 1974); children: Kristen Read, Robert Charles IV; m. Laurie Anne Lochridge, July 30, 1994. Grad. Choate Sch., 1955; B.A., Washington and Lee U., 1959; M.A., Harvard U., 1963. With Collyer Insulated Wire Co., R.I., 1960-62; research assoc. Duke, 1967, instr., 1968; dir. Art Mus., 1968-69, asst. prof., 1968-69; asst. curator dept. European decorative arts and sculpture Mus. Fine Arts, Boston, 1970; curator Mus. Fine Arts, 1971-80, curatorial rep., 1971-72; pvt. practice art cons. Jackson, Wyo. Teaching fellow Harvard, 1964-65; N.E.A. grantee, 1972-73. Home and Office: PO Box 20339 Jackson WY 83001-7000

MOELLER, ROBERT JOHN, management consultant; b. Mpls., July 20, 1938; s. Ben G. and Catheryn D. M.; m. Sharon Lee Holmberg, Sept. 1, 1962; children: Mark Thomas (dec.), Maria Therese. BBA, U. Minn., 1962, MBA, 1965; grad. exec. mgmt. program, Columbia U., 1972; grad. exec. internat. mgmt., Mankato U., 1990. Asst. brand mgr. toiletries Procter & Gamble, Cin., 1965-68; group product mgr. No. div. Am. Can Co., Greenwich, Conn., 1968-71, dir. mktg. Dixie div., 1971-73; v.p. mktg. and sales Tonka Toy Co., Mpls., 1973-77; v.p. mktg. and sales Toro Co., Mpls., 1977-79, v.p. gen. mgr. outdoor appliance div., 1979-80, v.p. gen. mgr. irrigation div., 1980-84, exec. v.p. internat. and irrigation div., 1984-88; pres., chief oper. officer Mackay Envelope Corp., Mpls., 1988-90; sr. v.p. mktg. Excel div. Cargill, Inc., 1991-94; pres. Moeller & Assoc., 1994—; bd. dirs. Data Map. Trustee Voyageur Outward Bound, 1993—; bd. dirs. State of Minn. Prison Industries, St. Paul, 1984—; commr. Chaska (Minn.) Planning Commn., 1988—; pres. Dist. 112 Edn. Found., Chaska, 1987-92; pres. Chaska Civic Theatre, 1978-80; chmn. Jonathan Archtl. Rev. Commn., 1976-78. With USN, 1955-61. Avocations: running, skiing, sailing, tennis, music.

MOELLERING, JOHN HENRY, aviation maintenance company executive; b. Ft. Wayne, Ind., Feb. 4, 1938; s. Robert Charles and Irene Pauline (Nolde) M.; m. Karla Louise Fritzsche, Dec. 21, 1963; children: John Henry, Matthew C., Ann Elizabeth. BS, US Mil. Acad., 1959; MS, U. Calif., Berkeley, 1962; postgrad., Army Command and Gen. Staff Coll., 1971-72, Army War Coll., 1976-77. Registered profl. engr., La. Commd. 2d lt. U.S. Army, 1959, advanced through grades to lt. gen., 1985; aide de camp Combat Devel. Command, 1961-63; command and staff 24th Inf. Div., Fed. Republic Germany, 1964-67; ops. officer Engr. Group, Vietnam, 1967-68; instr. civil engring., asst. prof. history U.S. Mil. Acad., 1968-71; with Office Army Chief of Staff, Pentagon, 1972-73; White House staff, 1973-74; bn. comdr. 101st Airborne Div., 1974-76; dist. engr. Vicksburg, Miss., 1977-79; exec. to Army Chief of Staff, Pentagon, 1979-81; asst. div. comdr. 9th Inf. Div., Ft. Lewis, Wash., 1981-82; commandant West Point, N.Y., 1982-84; comdg. gen. Ft. Leonard Wood, Mo., 1984-85; asst. to chmn. Joint Chiefs of Staff, Pentagon, Washington, 1985-87; chief exec. officer Lear Siegler Mgmt. Svcs. Corp., Oklahoma City, 1990-93; exec. v.p., COO UNC Inc, Annapolis, Md., 1993—. Editor, contbr.: Evolution of Modern Warfare, 1969, Battalion Commanders Speak Out, 1977. Chmn. Class of '59 fund com. U.S. Mil.

Acad., 1984-89; bd. dirs. Last Frontier coun. Boy Scouts Am.; bd. dirs. U. Okla. Sch. Continuing Edn. and Pub. Svc.; v.p.Oklahoma County unit Am. Cancer Soc.; mem. Def. Sci. Bd., The Pentagon. Decorated Def. DSM, Army DSM, Legion of Merit, Bronze Star; White House fellow, 1973-74. Mem. Econ. Club Okla., Oklahoma City Club C. of C. (bd. dirs.), Phi Kappa Phi. Home: 1526 Shipsview Rd Annapolis MD 21401-5740 Office: 3100 N I-35 175 Admiral Cochrane Dr Annapolis MD 21401-7307

MOELLERING, ROBERT CHARLES, JR., internist, educator; b. Lafayette, Ind., June 9, 1936; s. Robert Charles and Irene Pauline (Nolde) M.; children: Anne Elizabeth, Robert Charles, Catherine Irene; m. Mary Jane Ferraro, July 11, 1987. BA, Valparaiso U., 1958, DSc, 1980; MD cum laude, Harvard U., 1962. Diplomate: Am. Bd. Internal Medicine. Intern Mass. Gen. Hosp., Boston, 1962-63, resident, 1963-64, postdoctoral fellow in infectious diseases, 1967-70, resident, 1966-67, mem. infectious disease unit and asst. physician, 1970-76, assoc. physician, 1976-83, hon. physician, 1983—, cons. bacteriology, 1972-87; instr. medicine Harvard U. Med. Sch., Boston, 1970-72, asst. prof., 1972-76, assoc. prof., 1976-80, prof., 1980—; chmn. dept. medicine, physician-in-chief New Eng. Deaconess Hosp., 1981—; Shields Warren-Mallinckrodt prof. clin. rsch. Harvard U. Med. Sch., Boston, 1981-89, Shields Warren-Mallinckrodt prof. med. rsch., 1989—; mem. subcom. on susceptibility testing Nat. Com. for CLin. Lab. Standards, 1976-88; mem. subcom. on antimicrobial agts. and chemotherapy, 1978-80; subcom. on antimicrobial disc. diffusion susceptibility testing, 1980-88. Mem. editorial bd. Antimicrobial Agts. and Chemotherapy, 1977-81, editor, 1981-85, editor-in-chief, 1985—; editor European Jour. Clin. Microbial Infectous Diseases, 1990—; consulting editor Infectious Disease Clinics N.Am., 1986—; editor Les Infections, 1983; editorial bd. New Eng. Jour. Medicine, 1977-81, European Jour. Clin. Microbiology, 1981—, Jour. Infectious Diseases, 1981-85, 89-93 Infectious Disease Alert, 1981-92, Pharmacotherapy, 1982—, Antimicrobial Agts. Ann., 1984-87, Zentralblatt Fur Bacteriologie, Microbiologie and Hygience, 1984—, Jour. of Infection, 1986—, Innovations, 1986-90, Infectious Disease Clinics N. Am., 1986—, Residents Forum in Internal Medicine, 1988-90, Diagnostic Microbiology and Infectious Disease, 1989-90, Internat. Jour. Antimicrobial Agts., 1990—, Infectious Diseases in Clin. Practice, 1991-92. Served with USPHS, 1964-66. Grantee USPHS, NIH. Fellow ACP, Am. Acad. Microbiology, Infectious Diseases Soc. Am. (v.p. 1988-89, pres. elect 1989-90, pres. 1990-91, past pres. 1991-92); mem. Am. Soc. Microbiology, Am. Clin. and Climatol. Assn., Internat. Soc. Chemotherapy, Am. Soc. Clin. Investigation, Assn. Am. Physicians, European Soc. Clin. Microbiology, Am. Fedn. Clin. Rsch., Assn. Profs. Medicine, Roxbury Clin. Records Club, Mass. Med. Soc. (councilor), Brit. Soc. Antimicrobial Chemotherapy, Coun. Biology Editors, Alpha Omega Alpha, Phi Kappa Psi. Home: 49 Longfellow Rd Wellesley MA 02181-5220 Office: New Eng Deaconess Hosp Dept Medicine 110 Francis St Boston MA 02215-5501

MOELMANN, LAWRENCE R., lawyer; b. Oak Park, Ill., Oct. 13, 1947. AB magna cum laude, Princeton U., 1970; JD, U. Mich., 1973. Bar: Ill. 1973, U.S. Dist. Ct. (no. dist.) Ill. 1973, U.S. Ct. Appeals (7th cir.). Ptnr. Hinshaw & Culbertson, Chgo. Mem. ABA (fidelity and surety law com., tort and ins. practice sect. 1978—, vice-chair 1992—), Ill. State Bar Assn., Cook County Bar Assn., Defense Rsch. Inst. (chair fidelity and surety com. 1995—), Internat. Assn. Defense Counsel (fidelity and surety com., chair 1992-93), Nat. Bond Claims Assn., Surety Claims Inst. Address: Hinshaw & Culbertson 222 N LaSalle St Ste 300 Chicago IL 60601-1081

MOELY, BARBARA E., psychology researcher, educator; b. Prairie du Sac, Wis., July 17, 1940; d. John Arthur and Loretta Ruth (Giese) M.; children: John Jacob Moely Wiener, David Andrew Moely Wiener. Student Carroll Coll., 1958-60; BA, U. Wis., 1962, MA, 1964; PhD, U. Minn., 1968. Asst. prof. U. Hawaii, Honolulu, 1967-71; rsch. psychologist UCLA, 1971-72; asst. prof. Tulane U., New Orleans, 1972-75, assoc. prof. psychology, 1975-85, prof., 1985—, dept. chmn., 1992—. Contbr. articles to profl. jours. Grantee U.S. Office Edn., Handicapped Pers. Preparation, 1977-80, Tulane U., 1973, 75, '77, 78, 83-84, grant for Mental Hygiene, City of New Orleans, 1983-84, Nat. Inst. Edn., 1983-84, La. Edn. Quality Support Fund, 1988, 89, 91, 92. Mem. AAUP (v.p. La. conf. 1992-93, sec. 1993—, pres. Tulane 1992-94), APA, Soc. Research in Child Devel., Am. Ednl. Rsch. Assn., Southwestern Soc. for Rsch. in Human Devel. (pres. 1986-88), Phi Beta Kappa (pres. Alpha chapter La. 1981-82, sec. 1995—). Office: Tulane Univ Dept Psychology New Orleans LA 70118

MOEN, RODNEY CHARLES, state senator, retired naval officer; b. Whitehall, Wis., July 26, 1937; s. Edwin O. and Tena A. (Gunderson) M.; m. Catherine Jean Wolfe, 1959; children: Scott A., Jon C., Rodd M., Catherine J., Daniel M. Student Syracuse U., 1964-65; BA, U. So. Calif., 1972; postgrad. Ball State U., 1975-76. Contbg. editor Govt. Photography, 1970-74; gen. mgr. Western Wis. Communications Corp., Independence, Wis., 1976-83; mem. Wis. Senate, 1983—, mem. health, human svcs. and aging com., 1983—. Lt. USN, 1955-76, Vietnam. Democrat. Lodge: Lions. Home: 2119 Dewey St Whitehall WI 54773-0215 Office: State Capitol PO Box 7882 Madison WI 53707-7882

MOENS, PETER B., biology researcher and educator; b. Sukabumi, Indonesia, May 15, 1931; s. Pieter B. and Anneke D. (Ritsema van Eck) M.; m. Marja Schroder, May 8, 1953; children: Richard, Theodore, Vivian, Cecilia, Francis. B.S. in Forestry, U. Toronto, 1959, M.A., 1961, Ph.D. 1963. Lectr. biology York U., Downsview, Ont., Can., 1963-64; asst. prof. York U., 1964-67, asso. prof., 1967-71, prof., 1971—, chmn. dept. biology, 1981-84. Editor: Genome; Chromosoma, 1988—. Fellow Royal Soc. Can.; mem. Genetics Soc. Am., Can. Soc. Cell Biology, Genetics Soc. Can. (pres. 1979), Am. Soc. Cell Biology. Office: York U, Dept Biology, Downsview, ON Canada M3J 1P3

MOERDLER, CHARLES GERARD, lawyer; b. Paris, Nov. 15, 1934; came to U.S., 1946, naturalized, 1951; s. Herman and Erna Anna (Brandwein) M.; m. Pearl G. Hecht, Dec. 26, 1955; children: Jeffrey Alan, Mark Laurence, Sharon Michele. BA, L.I.U., 1953; JD, Fordham U., 1956. Bar: N.Y. 1956, U.S. Supreme Ct. 1962. Asso. firm Cravath, Swaine & Moore, N.Y.C., 1956-65; spl. counsel cons. City of N.Y. and judiciary N.Y. State Assembly, 1960-61; commmr. bldgs. City of N.Y., 1966-67; sr. ptnr., chmn. litigation dept. Stroock & Stroock & Lavan, N.Y.C., 1967—; bd. dirs., gen. counsel, dir. N.Y. Post Co., Inc., 1987-92; cons. housing, urban devel. and real estate to Mayor of N.Y.C., 1967-73; mem. com. on character and fitness of applicants for admission to Bar, Appellate div. 1st Dept., N.Y., 1977—; commmr. N.Y. State Ins. Fund, 1978—, vice chmn., 1986-94, chmn., 1995—; mem. Mayor's Com. on Judiciary, 1994—. Mem. editorial bd. N.Y. Law Jour., 1985—; assoc. editor Fordham Law Rev., 1956. Asst. dir. Rockefeller nat. presdl. campaign com., 1964; adv. bd. Sch. Internat. Affairs Columbia U., 1977-80; bd. govs. L.I.U., 1966, trustee, 1985-91; chmn. Community Planning Bds. 8 and 14, Bronx County, 1977-78; nat. bd. govs. Am. Jewish Congress, 1966 bd. overseers Jewish Theol. Sem. Am., 1983—; trustee St. Barnabas Hosp., Bronx, N.Y., 1985—. Recipient Walker Metcalf award L.I. U., 1966. Mem. Am. Bar Assn., N.Y. State Bar Assn., N.Y. County Lawyers Assn., Internat. Bar Assn., Assn. of Bar of City of N.Y., Free Sons of Israel, World Trade Ctr. Club, Metro. Club. Home: 7 Rivercrest Rd Bronx NY 10471-1336 Office: Stroock Stroock & Lavan 7 Hanover Sq New York NY 10004-2616

MOESCHL, STANLEY FRANCIS, electrical engineer, management consultant; b. Cin., Mar. 14, 1931; s. Stanley F. and Matilda F. (Trenkamp) M.; m. Kathleen K. Koebel, Aug. 21, 1954; children: Stanley, Melissa, Deborah, Karen. BSEE, Purdue U., 1957. Engr. Honeywell Space Div., St. Petersberg, Fla., 1957-60; engring. mgr. 1969-77; dir. engring. Honeywell Avionics Div., Mpls., 1977-80; v.p. gen. mgr. Honeywell Space Div., St. Petersberg, 1980-82, Honeywell Avionics Div., Mpls., 1982-88; pres. Sundstrand Data Control, Redmond, Wash., 1988-92; bd. mem. Com. of 100, St. Petersberg, 1980-82, Wash. Round Table, Seattle, 1989-92. Bd. dirs. Jr. Achievement, Mpls. 1983-86, Seattle, 1989-92. With USCG, 1951-54, Korea. Mem. IEEE, AIEE, Eta Kappa Nu, Tau Beta Pi. Home: 4575 S Landings Dr Fort Myers FL 33919-4635

MOESER, ELLIOTT, principal. Prin. Nicolet High Sch., Glendale, Ill. Recipient Blue Ribbon Sch. award, 1990-91. Office: Nicolet High Sch 6701 N Jean Nicolet Rd Glendale WI 53217-3799

MOFFAT, DONALD, actor; b. Plymouth, Eng., Dec. 26, 1930; s. Walter George and Kathleen Mary (Smith) M.; m. Anne Murray Ellsperman, May 22, 1954 (div. Aug. 1968); children: Kathleen Wendy, Gabriel Robin; m. Gwen Arner, May 1969; children: Lynn Marie, Catherine Jean. Student, Royal Acad. Dramatic Art, 1952-54. Actor: (plays) including War and Peace, 1964, Man and Superman, 1964, The Hostage, 1964, Judith, 1964, The Wild Duck, 1965-66, You Can't Take It With You, 1965-66, Krapps's Last Tape, 1965, Right You Are, 1966, School for Scandal, 1966, Above Repertory, 1967, Cherry Orchard, 1967-68, Cock-a-Doodle Dandy, 1968-69, Hamlet, 1968-69, Chemin de Fer, 1969, Hadrian VII, 1970, Father's Day, 1970-71, Trial Catonsville Nine, 1971, Hotel Paradiso, 1971, The Tavern, 1973, Childs Play, 1973, Forget-Me-Not Lane, 1973, The Miser, 1974, The Kitchen, 1975, Heartbreak House, 1976, Misalliance, 1976, Waiting for Godot, 1977, Terra Nova, 1979, Painting Churches, 1983, Play Memory, 1983, Passion Play, 1984, The Iceman Cometh, 1985-86, Henry IV Part I, 1987, Titus Andronicus, 1989, Uncommon Ground, 1991, The Heiress, 1995; (television) Armistead Maupin's Tales of the City, 1993; (films) Rachel, Rachel, 1968, R.P.M, 1969, Great Northfield, Minnesota Raid, 1970, Showdown, 1972, Terminal Man, 1973, Eleanor and Franklin, 1977, On the Nickel, 1979, Strangers, 1979, Health, 1979, Promises in the Dark, 1979, Popeye, 1980, The Thing, 1983, The Right Stuff, 1983, Alamo Bay, 1985, Far North, 1988, Music Box, 1989, Class Action, 1990, Kaleidescope, 1990, Regarding Henry, 1991, Babe Ruth, 1991, Housesitter, 1991, A Clear and Present Danger, 1994; dir.: Akron (Ohio) Shakespeare Festival, 1961, McCarter Theatre, Princeton (N.J.) U., 1963, 66, Playhouse-in-the-Park, Cin., 1964, Assn. Producing Artists Repertory, 1966-67, 68-69, Father's Day N.Y., 1971; assoc. artistic dir.: Gt. Lakes Shakespeare Festival, 1963; mng. artist: L.A. Actors' Theatre, 1976-77. With Royal Arty., 1949-51. Office: care William Morris Agency 151 El Camino Beverly Hills CA 90212

MOFFAT, JOHN WILLIAM, physics educator; b. Copenhagen, Denmark, May 24, 1932; s. George William and Esther (Winther) M. PhD, Trinity Coll., Cambridge (Eng.) U., 1958; DSc, U. Winnipeg, 1989. Sr. research fellow Imperial Coll., London, Eng., 1957-58; scientist Research Inst. Advanced Studies, Balt., 1958-60; prin. scientist Research Inst. Advanced Studies, 1961-64; scientist CERN, Geneva, Switzerland, 1960-61; asso. prof. dept. physics U. Toronto, Ont., Can., 1964-67; prof. U. Toronto, 1967—. Contbr. articles to profl. jours. Dept. Sci. and Indsl. Research fellow, 1958-60; NRC Can. grantee, 1965. Fellow Cambridge Philos. Soc. (Eng.); mem. N.Y. Acad. Scis., Can. Astron. Soc., Internat. Union Astronomers. Office: Univ of Toronto, Dept Physics, Toronto, ON Canada

MOFFATT, DAVID JOHN, anatomy educator; b. Cheadle, Staffordshire, Eng., July 23, 1939; s. John and Mary (Simpson) M.; m. Barbara Sims, July 4, 1964; children: Wendy J., Keith J. BSc, U. Bristol, Eng., 1961, MBChB, 1964. Demonstrator anatomy U. Bristol, Eng., 1965-67; research assoc. U. Bristol, U. Bristol, Eng., 1967-68; asst. prof. U. Iowa, Iowa City, 1968-71, assoc. prof., 1971-79; prof., chmn. dept. anatomy U. Mo.-Kansas City, 1979-85, prof., coordinator of anatomy, 1985—; vis. prof. various univs.; cons. Assoc. Med. Schs. Mid-East, Lebanon, 1975. Author: dir. 8 vols. programmed learning materials, 1974, author computer aided instruction materials in anatomy, 1984-95. Active Boy Scouts Am., Kansas City, Mo., 1979—; adviser in sci. Lee's Summit Sch. Dist. R7, Mo., 1980—; vice chair Nat. United Ch. Christ Assn. Scouters. Fellow Brit. Assn. Clin. Anatomists (corr.); mem. Assn. Med. Schs. Mid-East, Assn. Anatomy Chairmen, Am. Assn. Anatomists, Anat. Soc. Gt. Brit. and Ireland, Midwest Assn. Anatomists (past pres.). Mem. United Ch. Christ. Home: 3612 NW Lake Dr Lees Summit MO 64064-1805 Office: U Mo Kansas City Sch Medicine 2411 Holmes St Kansas City MO 64108-2741

MOFFATT, HUGH McCULLOCH, JR., hospital administrator, physical therapist; b. Steubenville, Ohio, Oct. 11, 1933; s. Hugh McCulloch and Agnes Elizabeth (Bickerstaff) M.; m. Ruth Anne Colvin, Aug. 16, 1958; children: David, Susan. AB, Asbury Coll., 1958; cert. in phys. therapy, Duke U., 1963. Lic. in phys. therapy and health care adminstrn., Alaska. Commd. officer USPHS, 1964, advanced through grades to capt.; therapist USPHS, N.Y.C., 1964-66, Sitka, Alaska, 1970-72; therapist cons. USPHS, Atlanta, 1968-70; clinic adminstr. USPHS, Kayenta, Ariz., 1972-73; hosp. dir. USPHS, Sitka, 1973-78; therapist cons. Idaho Dept. Health, Boise, 1966-68; contract health officer USPHS, Anchorage, 1978-89, ret., 1989; phys. therapy cons. Ocean Beach Hosp., Ilwaco, Wash., 1989—; Harbors Home Health Svcs., Aberdeen, Wash., 1990—; therapist cons. Our Lady of Compassion Care Ctr., Anchorage, 1979—, Alaska Native Med. Ctr., Anchorage, 1988—. With U.S. Army, 1955-57. Mem. Am. Phys. Therapy Assn., Commd. Officers Assn. USPHS, Res. Officers Assn., Ret. Officers Assn., Am. Assn. Individual Investors, Am. Assn. Ret. Persons, Eagles. Avocations: automobile repairs, woodworking, camping, fishing, church choir.

MOFFATT, JOYCE ANNE, performing arts executive; b. Grand Rapids, Mich., Jan. 3, 1936; d. John Barnard and Ruth Lillian (Pellow) M. BA in Lit., U. Mich., 1957, MA in Theatre, 1960; HHD (hon.), Sch. Psychology, San Francisco, 1991. Stage mgr., lighting designer Off-Broadway plays, costume, lighting and set designer, stage mgr. stock cos., 1954-62; nat. subscription mgr. Theatre Guild/Am. Theatre Socs., N.Y.C., 1965-67; subscription mgr. Theatre, Inc.-Phoenix Theatre, N.Y.C., 1963-67; cons. N.Y.C. Ballet and N.Y.C. Opera, 1967-70; asst. house mgr. N.Y. State Theater, 1970-72; dir. ticket sales City Ctr. of Music and Drama, Inc., N.Y.C., 1970-72; prodn. mgr. San Antonio's Symphony/Opera, 1973-75; gen. mgr. San Antonio Symphony/Opera, 1975-76, 55th St. Dance Theater Found., Inc., N.Y.C., 1976-77, Ballet Theatre Found., Inc./Am. Ballet Theatre, N.Y.C., 1977-81; v.p. prodn. Radio City Music Hall Prodns., Inc., N.Y.C., 1981-83; artist-in-residence CCNY, 1981—; propr. mgmt. cons. firm for performing arts N.Y.C., 1983—; exec. dir. San Francisco Ballet Assn., 1987-93; mng. dir. Houston Ballet Assoc., 1993-95; gen. ngr. Chgo. Music and Dance Theater, Inc., 1995—; cons. Ford Found., N.Y. State Coun. on Arts, Kennedy Ctr. for Performing Arts.; mem. dance panels N.Y. State Coun. on Arts, 1979-81; mem. panels for Support to Prominent Orgns. and Dance, Calif. Arts Coun., 1988-92. Appointee San Francisco Cultural Affairs Task Force, 1991; mem. bd. Tex. Inst. for Arts in Edn., 1994—; trustee of I.A.T.S.E. Local 16 Pension and Welfare Fund, 1991-94. Mem. Assn. Theatrical Press Agts. and Mgrs., Actors Equity Assn., United Scenic Artists Local 829, San Francisco Visitors and Conv. Bur. (bd. dirs.). Club: Argyle (San Antonio). Office: Chicago Music & Dance Theater Mezz Level 203 No LaSalle Chicago IL 60601

MOFFATT, KATY (KATHERINE LOUELLA MOFFATT), musician, vocalist, songwriter; b. Ft. Worth, Nov. 19, 1950; d. Lester Huger and Sue-Jo (Jarrott) M. Student, Sophie Newcomb Coll., 1968, St. John's Coll., 1969-70. Rec. artist Columbia Records, 1975-79, Permian/MCA Records, 1982-84, Enigma Records, L.A., 1985, Wrestler Records, L.A., 1987-88, Red Moon Records, Switzerland, 1988-93, Philo/Rounder Records, 1989-93, Round Tower Music, U.K., Ireland, Europe, 1993—, Watermelon Records, U.S., 1994—. Folksinger, Ft. Worth, 1967-68; musician, vocalist, songwriter, rec. artist: (films) Billy Jack, 1970, Hard Country, 1981, The Thing Called Love, 1993; prodn. asst. film, Sta. KIII-TV, Corpus Christi, 1970, audio engr., Sta. KRIS-TV, Corpus Christi, 1970; musician, vocalist in blues band, Corpus Christi, 1970; receptionist, bookkeeping asst., copywriter, announcer, Sta. KFWT, Ft. Worth, 1971, musician, vocalist, songwriter, Denver, 1971-72, on tour, 1973, 75—, Denver, 1974, on tour, 1976-79, European tour, 1977, Can. tour, 1984-85, on tour in Europe, U.S., Can. and Asia, 1985—; albums include Katy, 1976, Kissin' In The California Sun, Am. release, 1977, internat. release, 1978, A Town South of Bakersfield, 1985, Walkin' on the Moon, European release, 1988, U.S. release, 1989, Child Bride, 1990, (duet album with brother Hugh) Dance Me Outside, 1992, (Switzerland only) Indoor Fireworks, 1992, The Greatest Show On Earth A.K.A. The Evangeline Hotel, 1994, Hearts Gone Wild, 1994; singles include Take it as it Comes, 1981, Under Loved and Over Lonely, 1983; songs include The Magic Ring, 1971; Gerry's Song, 1973, Kansas City Morning, 1974, Take Me Back To Texas, 1975, (Waitin' For) The Real Thing, 1975, Didn't We Have Love, 1976, Kissin' in the California Sun, 1977, Walkin' on the Moon, 1989. Named one of 4 Top New Female Vocalists, Cashbox Singles Awards, 1976; nominee for Top New Femal Vocalist, Acad. Country Music, 1985; recipient Record World Album award, 1976. Mem. Am. Fedn. Musicians, AFTRA, SAG.

MOFFATT, LESLIE MACK, aluminum company executive; b. New Orleans, Sept. 6, 1928; s. Frank Leslie and Vesta Jane (Sanders) M.; m. Carolyn Joyce Guess, Sept. 6, 1952; children: Leslie S., Vance P., Neil S. BA, Southeastern La. U., 1949. Mgr. bus. planning Gen. Electric Co., Decatur, Ill., 1950-64; exec. v.p. Croft Metals, McComb, Miss., 1964-72; pres. Better Bilt Aluminum, Smyrna, Tenn., 1972—. Served to lt. U.S. Army, 1952-54. Recipient Disting. Citizenship award Rutherford Courier, 1979. Republican. Presbyterian. Home: 4080 Port Cleburne Ct Hermitage TN 37076-3119 Office: Better-Bilt Aluminum Smyrna Indsl Pk PO Box 277 Smyrna TN 37167-0277

MOFFET, HUGH LAMSON, pediatrician; b. Monmouth, Ill., Jan. 6, 1932; s. Victor Logue and Helen (Sipfle) M.; m. Donna Mae Pienschke, Sept. 20, 1984; children: Cynthia, Sandra, Douglas. AB, Harvard U., 1953; MD, Yale U., 1957. Instr. Bowman Gray Sch. Medicine, Winston-Salem, N.C., 1957-60; asst. prof. Northwestern U., Chgo., 1960-68, assoc. prof., 1968-71; assoc. prof. U. Wis., Madison, 1971-75, prof., 1975—; head div. infectious diseases Children's Meml. Hosp., Chgo., 1960-71. Author: (book) Clinical Microbiology, 1975, 2d rev. edit., 1980, Pediatric Infectious Diseases, 1975, 3d rev. edit., 1989. Capt. USAR, 1953-68.

MOFFETT, B. J., church administrator. Dir. of Benevolence Ch. of God. Office: Church of God PO Box 2430 Cleveland TN 37320

MOFFETT, CHARLES SIMONTON, museum director, curator, writer; b. Washington, Sept. 19, 1945; s. Charles Simonton M. and Faith Atherton Locke Phelps; m. Jane Pettigrew Daniels, July 28, 1979; children: Kate Serena, Charles Locke. B.A., Middlebury Coll., 1967; M.A., NYU, 1970. Ford Found. fellow Nelson Gallery Art, Kansas City, Mo., 1969-70; expert Sotheby Parke Bernet, N.Y.C., 1970-71; guest asst. curator Met. Mus., N.Y.C., 1974-75, assoc. curator, 1976-81, curator European paintings, 1981-83; curator-in-charge Fine Arts Mus. San Francisco, 1983—, chief curator, summer 1987; sr. curator paintings Nat. Gallery Art, Washington, 1987-92; dir. The Phillips Collection, Washington, 1992—; art adv. panel IRS, 1980-83; organizer mus. exhbns., author catalogues; spl. exhbns. panel NEA, 1987; project dir. publs. grant from J. Paul Getty Trust to Fine Arts Mus. San Francisco, 1987. Trustee San Francisco Day Sch., 1987, Middlebury Coll., 1987-90. Andrew Mellon fellow Met. Mus. Art, 1975; travel grantee Met. Mus. Art, 1980; recipient award for best exhbn. Soho News Arts Awards, 1978; co-recipient Prix Bernier for Manet 1832-1883, 1983, recipient Alumni Achievement award Middlebury Coll., 1985, Kaufman award Nat. Gallery Art, 1989. Episcopalian. Office: The Phillips Collection 1600 21st St NW Washington DC 20009-1003

MOFFETT, JAMES ROBERT, oil and gas company executive; b. Houma, La., Aug. 16, 1938; s. Robert E. and Mary G. (Pollack) M.; m. Louise C. Hohmann, June 5, 1960; children: Crystal Louise, James R. B.S., U. Tex., 1961; M.S., Tulane U., 1963. Cons. geologist oil and gas industry New Orleans, 1964-69; v.p. founding ptnr. McMoRan Exploration Co., New Orleans, 1969-74; pres., chief exec. officer McMoRan Oil & Gas Co., New Orleans, 1974-81, 81-85; chmn., chief exec. officer McMoRan Oil & Gas Co., from 1985; dir. McMoRan Oil & Gas Co., New Orleans, from 1974; vice-chmn. Freeport McMoRan Inc., New Orleans, 1981-85, chmn., chief exec. officer, 1985—, dir., 1981—. Mem. Nat. Petroleum Council, Washington, 1979, Commn. on the Future of South, 1986; bd. dirs. La. Energy Nat. PAC, Metairie, La., 1979, World Trade Ctr., New Orleans, Am. Cancer Soc. Greater New Orleans, Bus. Task Force Edn., Inc.; chmn. bd. La. Coun. Fiscal Reform; chmn. bus. coun. New Orleans and River Region, 1985-87. 2nd lt. U.S. Army, 1961-68, capt. Res. ret. Recipient T award Ex Students Assn. U. Tex., 1960, Hornblower Yr. award Pub. Relations Soc. Am., 1986, Vol. Yr. award Urban League Greater New Orleans, 1987; Minnie Stevens Piper Found. scholar U. Tex., 1960, Jacques E. Yenni, S.J. award Loyola U. of New Orleans for Outstanding Community Svc., Jr. Achievement Bus. Hall of Fame award, 1987, Loyola U. of New Orleans' Integritas Vitae award, 1988; named One of Ten Outstanding Persons of 1985 Inst. for Human Understanding, New Orleans. Mem. All Am. Wildcatters, New Orleans Geol. Soc., Petroleum Club New Orleans, Greater New Orleans Mktg. Com. (exec. com. 1987), Geology Found U. Tex. (adv. council 1972-85), Devel. bd. U. Tex., La. Ind. producers Royalty Owners Assn. South La. Mid-Continent Oil Gas Assn. (v.p.), Dinner Steering Com. (Disting. Citizen award 1983, 85 Boy Scouts Am. New Orleans div.), Green Wave Club. Republican. Office: Freeport-McMoRan Inc 1615 Poydras St New Orleans LA 70112-1217

MOFFETT, KENNETH LEE, superintendent schools; b. Mt. Vernon, Wash., May 6, 1935; s. Charles R. and Edith May (Barker) M.; m. Diane Muriel Buckley, July 30, 1966; children: Kendis Charlene, Patrick Charles. BA, Western Wash. State U., 1957; MA, Calif. State U., Los Angeles, 1958-60; EdD, U. So. Calif., 1972. Tchr. pub. schs., Inglewood, Calif., 1957-61, 63-65, asst. prin., 1965-69, prin., 1969-73; tchr. U.S. Dependent Sch. Pirmasens, Fed. Republic Germany, 1961-62, asst. prin., Erlangen, Fed. Republic Germany, 1962-63; asst. supt. Inglewood Sch. Dist., Calif., 1973-76; supt. Lennox Sch. Dist., Calif., 1976-86; supt. ABC Unified Sch. Dist., Cerritos, Calif., 1986—; mem. adv. bd. Ad Hoc Com. on Mental Health for Tchrs., Los Angeles, 1980-81; chmn. scholarship com. Bank of Am., 1979-84. Mem. adv. com. Los Angeles Area council Boy Scouts Am., 1981-83; mem. support group for U. So. Calif., 1978-84; bd. dirs. Centinela Valley Guidance Clinic, Inglewood, 1978-82. Recipient Service awards PTA, Inglewood, 1973, Lennox, 1982, Am. Assn. of Sch. Admnstrs. Nationl Supt. of the Year, 1994. Mem. Centinela Valley Admnstrs. Assn. (charter pres. 1979-80), Assn. Calif. Sch. Admnstrs. (region chmn. 1980-82, Service award 1982), Centinela Valley Supts. Group (chmn. 1980-84), Centinela Valley Trustees and Admnstrs. Assn. (sec.-treas. 1977-78). Republican. Methodist. Office: ABC Unified Sch Dist 16700 Norwalk Blvd Artesia CA 90701-1838

MOFFETT, THOMAS DELANO, music educator; b. Smiths, Ala., Sept. 19, 1942; s. Early Moffett and Estella Sparks; m. Gloria Jean Marshall, Dec. 22, 1968; children: Stephanie Viloria, Marlon Delano. BS, Fla. A&M U., 1963; MEd, Auburn U., 1972. EdD, 1981. Cert. tchr., Ga. Band dir. Drake High Sch., Auburn, Ala., 1963-66, Talbotton Rd. Jr. High Sch., Columbus, Ga., 1966-78; asst. prin. Waddell Elem. Sch., Columbus, Ga., 1978-81; prin. St. Mary's Elem. Sch., Columbus, Ga., 1981-90, Dimon Elem. Sch., Columbus, Ga., 1990; music supr. Muscogee County Sch. Dist., Columbus, Ga., 1990-93; assoc. prof. music Troy (Ala.) State U., 1993—. Active membership drive YMCA, Columbus, 1991; mem. adv. bd. Boy Scouts Am. Pack 120, Columbus, 1981-89. Recipient citation Achievement in Edn., Omega Psi Phi, 1981, Past President's award Muscogee Elem. Prins. Assn., 1989; named Boss of Yr., Muscogee Assn. Edn. Office Personnel, 1989. Mem. NEA, Music Educators Nat. Conf., Ala. Educators Assn., Troy State Educators Assn., Phi Delta Kappa. Democrat. Methodist. Avocations: golf, bowling, singing, saxophone. Home: 1111 Knight Dr Columbus GA 31906 Office: Troy State U Smith Hall Troy AL 36082

MOFFITT, CHARLES WILLIAM, insurance sales executive; b. Altoona, Pa., Mar. 24, 1932; s. Charles William and Beatrice Jeanette (Shellenberger) M.; m. Marianne Foley Potter, May 23, 1980; children: Michelle Ann Hunt, Charles William III, Deborah K.; stepchildren: Christopher Potter, Kimberly Bryan. B.A., Pa. State U., 1957. Examiner Pa. R.R., Buffalo, 1957-62; asst. to pres. White Cross Stores, Inc., Monroeville, Pa., 1962-65; sec. White Cross Stores, Inc., 1965-70, v.p. adminstrn., sec., 1970-72; dir. labor relations and legal affairs Revco D.S., Inc., Cleve., 1972-75; asst. v.p. personnel Revco D.S., Inc. 1974-75; pres. Fashion Wearhouse, Inc., Altoona, Pa., 1975-87; owner Omega Advt. Co.; pres. Olympus I, Inc., 1980-87; agt. Prin. Fin. Group, 1988-90, Variable Annuity Life Ins. Co., 1990—. Co-author: Mincemeat Cartoons, Altoona Mirror Newspaper. Bd. dirs. Bedford Springs Music Festival, 1984-87, Blair County Arts Found., 1987-91. Republican. Roman Catholic. Home and Office: 2033 Southpoint Dr Hummelstown PA 17036

MOFFITT, DONALD EUGENE, transportation company executive; b. Terre Haute, Ind., May 22, 1932; s. James Robert and Margaret Mary (Long) M.; m. Billie Duffy, Feb. 21, 1989; 1 child, Jaime. BA, Ind. State U., 1954; postgrad., Ind. U., 1956; grad., Advanced Mgmt. Program, Harvard U., 1972. Acct. Foster Freight Lines, Indpls., 1955-56; with Consol. Freightways Inc., San Francisco, 1956-88, v.p. planning, 1961-69; v.p. fin., motor carrier subs. Consol. Freightways Corp. Del., 1969-75; v.p. fin., treas.

parent co. Consol. Freightways Inc., San Francisco, 1975-81; exec. v.p. Consol. Freightways Inc., Palo Alto, Calif., 1981-86; vice chmn. parent co. bd. Consol. Freightways, Inc., Palo Alto, Calif., 1986-88; chmn., CEO Circle Express, Indpls., 1988-90; pres., CEO Consol. Freightways, Inc., Palo Alto, Calif., 1990—, chmn., CEO, 1995—, also bd. dirs.; chmn. bd. dirs. all subsidiaries Consolidated Freightways, Inc., 1990—. Bd. dirs. Bay Area Coun., Calif. Bus. Roundtable, Conf. Bd., Boy Scouts Am., ARC; bd. dirs., exec. com. Hwy. Users Fedn.; bd. trustees Automotive Safety Found.; bus. adv. coun. Northwestern U. Transp. Ctr. Mem. Nat. C. of C. (Washington) (bd. dirs.). Office: Consol Freightways Inc 3240 Hillview Ave Palo Alto CA 94304-1201

MOFFITT, GEORGE, JR., foreign service officer; b. N.Y.C., June 18, 1918; s. George and Margaret (Buchanan) M.; m. Lois Anderson, July 7, 1946; children: Katherine M., Margaret Louise. Student, U. Wis., 1950-51. With indsl. firm, 1937-39; fgn. service officer in Haiti, Iraq, Can., Belgium, Burma, Netherland Antilles, Cyprus,, Washington 1939—; counselor of embassy Brussels, 1966-71; polit. adviser to comdr.-in-chief Allied Forces, So. Europe, 1971—. Bd. dirs. Fulbright Found. for Belgium and Luxembourg; vice chmn. Burlington Bicentennial Commn.; chmn. Conn. Adv. Coun. on Aging, 1979-80, Conn. Coalition on Aging, 1979-80; bd. dirs. Conn. Assn. for Human Svcs., 1980-81, Conn. Regional Planning Agy., 1985-87; corporator Wheeler Clinic; mem. Conn. Gov.'s Commn. on Energy Assistance, 1987—; Bristol (Conn.) Bd. Pub. Welfare, 1988-92; hon. pres. Burlington Libr. Assn., mem., 1979-88. Home: 2 Chimney Crest Ln Bristol CT 06010-7969

MOFFITT, PHILLIP WILLIAM, magazine editor; b. Kingsport, Tenn., Sept. 11, 1946; s. Wallace and Claire Matilda (Allen) M. BS, U. Tenn., 1968, MS, 1971. Co-founder 13-30 Pub. (now Whittle Communications), Knoxville, Tenn., 1971, editor, 1971-79, pres., 1976—; editor-in-chief 13-30 Publs. Group, Knoxville, Tenn., 1979-86; editor, pres. Esquire Magazine, N.Y.C., 1979-84, editor-in-chief, pres., 1984-86; chmn. Light Source Computer Images, Inc., 1989—. Co-author: The Power to Heal, 1990, Medicine's Great Journey, 1992; contbr. columns to Esquire Mag., 1979-88. Bd. dirs. C.J. Jung Found. Mem. Mag. Pubs. Assn. (bd. dirs. 1984—). Home and Office: 1 Pelican Point Belvedere Tiburon CA 94920-2456

MOFFITT, ROBERT ALLEN, economics educator; b. Houston, Aug. 10, 1948; s. Herbert Franklin and Evelyn (Sinderson) M. BA, Rice U., 1970; MA, Brown U., 1972, PhD, 1975. Rsch. economist Mathematica, Inc., Princeton, N.J., 1975-78; asst. prof. econs. Rutgers U., New Brunswick, N.J., 1978-83, assoc. prof., 1983-84; assoc. prof. econs. Brown U., Providence, 1984-87, prof., 1987—. Editor: Jour. Human Resources, 1985-91; co-editor: Rev. Econs. and Statistics, 1991—; contbr. articles to profl. jours. Mem. Am. Econ. Assn., Econometric Soc., Population Assn. Am. Office: Brown U Dept Econs Providence RI 02912

MOGABGAB, WILLIAM JOSEPH, epidemiologist, educator; b. Durant, Okla., Nov. 2, 1921; s. Anees and Maude (Jopes) M.; m. Joy Roddy, Dec. 24, 1948 (div. July 1988); children: Robert (dec.), Ann, Kay, Edward R., Jean, Robert Mark Berryman, William J.M. Berryman; m. Rose Warren Berryman, July 18, 1988. B.S., Tulane U., 1942, M.D., 1944. Diplomate Am. Bd. Internal Medicine, Am. Bd. Microbiology. Intern Charity Hosp. La., New Orleans, 1944-45, resident, 1946-49, vis. physician, 1949-51; sr. vis. physician, 1971-75; cons., 1976—; mem. faculty Tulane U. Sch. Medicine, 1948—, prof. medicine, 1962-92; cons. infectious diseases, epidemiology, internal medicine New Orleans Dept. Health, 1992—; vis. investigator, asst. physician Hosp. Rockefeller Inst. Med. Research, N.Y.C., 1951-52; chief infectious disease VA Hosp., Houston, 1952-53; asst. prof. medicine Baylor U. Coll. Medicine, 1952-53; head virology div. NAMRU 4, USNTC, Great Lakes, Ill., 1953-55; cons. infectious disease VA Hosp., New Orleans, 1956—; cons. FDA Orphan Products Devel. Grants Program, 1984—. Assoc. mem. commn. influenza Armed Forces Epidemiological Bd., 1959-71; mem. New Orleans Mayor's Health Adv. Com., 1983—. With UNS, 1945-46; comdr. USNR, ret. 1981. Fellow Nat. Found. Infantile Paralysis, 1951-52. Fellow ACP, Am. Acad. Microbiology, Infectious Disease Soc. Am., Am. Coll. Epidemiology; mem. Soc. Exptl. Biology and Medicine, So., Central socs. clin. research, Am. Fedn. Clin. Research, Am. Soc. Cell Biology, Am. Soc. Microbiology, Am. Soc. Clin. Investigation, Tissue Culture Assn., Am. Pub. Health Assn., Am. Soc. Internal Medicine, Am. Soc. Clin. Pharmacology and Therapeutics, So. Med. Soc., AMA, AAAS, Am. Soc. Internal Medicine, Southwestern Assn. Clin. Biology, Soc. Epideniol. Research, Am. Soc. Virology. Research, publns. agts. of and vaccines for respiratory infections, viruses, mycoplasma, new antibiotics. Home: 3 Fortress Rd New Orleans LA 70122-1336

MOGEL, LEONARD HENRY, author; b. Bklyn., Oct. 23, 1922; s. Isaac and Shirley (Goldman) M.; m. Ann Vera Levy, Oct. 23, 1949; children: Wendy Lynn, Jane Ellen. B.B.A., Coll. City N.Y., 1947. Salesman N.Y. Printing Co., N.Y.C., 1946-48; sales mgr. Pollak Printing Co., N.Y.C., 1948-52; advt. dir. Diners Club, Inc., N.Y.C., 1952-56; pub. Diners Club for Signature and Bravo mags., 1956-67; pres. Leonard Mogel Assos., Inc. (nat. advt. reps.), N.Y.C., 1952-67; prin. owner San Francisco Warriors Profl. Basketball Team, 1963-64; pres. Twenty First Century Communications Inc., N.Y.C., 1967-72; pub. Cheetah and Weight Watchers mags., 1967-75; dir. Regents Pub. Co. div. Simon & Schuster, 1960-67; advt. cons. Harvard Lampoon, 1968; pub. Nat. Lampoon, 1970-86, Ingenue mag., 1971-73, Ingenue mag., 1973-75, Heavy Metal mag., 1977-86; adj. prof. N.Y. U. Sch. Continuing Edn., 1973-78; panelist Folio Mag. Pub. Conf., 1975-76. Exec. producer: (feature films) Heavy Metal, 1981; author: Everything You Need to Know to Make It in the Magazine Business, 1979, Making It in the Media Professions, 1988, Making It in Advertising, 1993, Making It in Public Relations, 1993, Making It in Broadcasting, 1994, Making It in Book Publishing, 1995. Sponsor Albert Einstein Med. Coll., Birch Wathen Sch., N.Y.C. Served with AUS, 1942-46, CBI. Mem. Soc. Illustrators.

MOGEL, WILLIAM ALLEN, lawyer, educator, author; b. N.Y.C., Mar. 7, 1942; s. Harry H. and Therese M.; m. Judith; children: Elisabeth, Andrew. B.A. cum laude, Hobart Coll., 1963; LL.B., U. Pa., 1966. Bar: D.C. 1967, Md. 1971. Ptnr., Morley Caskin, Washington, 1991—; adj. instr. Am. U., Washington, 1982—; active Washington Bd. Trade. Author: Transportation & Marketing of Natural Gas, 1985, 86, Natural Gas: Current Federal and State Developments, 1987; editor-in-chief: Energy Law Jour., 1980—; editor: Natural Gas Yearbook, 1988-92; co-editor: Energy Law & Transactions; contbr. articles to profl. jours. Trustee Hobart Coll., 1983-88. Served to capt. U.S. Army, 1966-69. Mem. Fed. Energy Bar Assn. Home: 8806 Transue Dr Bethesda MD 20817-6931 Office: Morley Caskin 1225 Eye St NW Washington DC 20005

MOGELEVER, BERNARD, public relations executive; b. Newark, Oct. 15, 1940; s. Louis J. and Kate (Rosenblatt) M.; m. Diane Hinkley, Feb. 1966; children: Elisa, Jonathan G. BA, Rutgers U., New Brunswick, N.J., 1962. News & feature writer S.I. Advance, N.Y., 1965-66; pub. rels. writer The Nat. Found., N.Y.C., 1966-68; exec. A.A. Schechter Assocs., N.Y.C., 1968-73; sr. v.p. Harshe-Rotman & Druck, Inc., N.Y.C., 1973-82; exec. v.p. Ruder Finn & Rotman, N.Y.C., 1982-85; sr. v.p. Burson-Marsteller, 1985-91; pres. Mogelever Comm., Inc., N.Y.C., 1991—. Lt. USAF, 1962-65.

MOGERMAN, SUSAN, state agency administrator. Ceo and dir. State of Illinois, Historic Preservation Agency, Springfield, Ill. Office: State Ill-Hist Preservation Agy Old State Capitol Springfield IL 62701

MOGGRIDGE, BILL G., product designer, consultant; b. London, June 25, 1943; came to U.S., 1979; s. Harry William and Helen Mary Ferrier (Taylor) M.; m. Karin Helbig Hansen, Apr. 15, 1966; children: Eric Giffard, Alex Zacho. NDD with distinction, Ctr. Sch. Art and Design, London, 1965. Founder Moggridge Assocs., product designers, London, 1969-91, ID Two, San Francisco, ptnr-ptnr.; ptnr. IDEO Product Devel., San Francisco, Palo Alto, Calif., Chgo., Boston, London, Tokyo, 1991—; external examiner Coun. Nat. Acad. Awards (U.K.), 1972-74. Designer microscope (Brit. design award 1976), grid compass computer (IDEA Excellence award 1981), telephone (IDEA Excellence award 1983), word processor (IDEA Excellence award 1984). Fellow Royal Soc. Arts (sr., Royal Designer for Industry award 1988), Chartered Soc. Designers; mem. Indsl. Designers Soc. Am. Home: 979 Lincoln Ave

Palo Alto CA 94301 Office: IDEO Product Devel 700 High St Palo Alto CA 94301-1632

MOGIL, BERNARD MARC, judge; b. N.Y.C., May 13, 1949; s. Roman and Musia (Mosiewcka) Mogilanski; m. Terry Gerbs, Nov. 21, 1975; 4 children. BA, CCNY, 1970; postgrad. in law, Ind. U., 1970-71; JD, N.Y. Law Sch., 1974. Bar: N.Y. 1975, Fla. 1974, U.S. Ct. Appeals (2nd cir.) 1975, U.S. Dist. Ct. (so. dist. and ea. dist.) N.Y. 1975, U.S. Dist. Ct. 1978. Asst. gen. counsel N.Y.C. Health Dept., 1975-76; assoc. Hayt, Hayt & Landau, Great Neck, N.Y., 1976-81; spl. asst. atty. gen. N.Y. Medicaid fraud prosecutor, N.Y.C., 1981-84; sole practice Garden City, N.Y., 1984-86; judge Nassau County Dist. Ct., Hempstead, N.Y., 1987-90, Nassau County Ct., Mineola, N.Y., 1991—; pilot Civil Air Patrol, Garden City, 1982-86; chief counsel Nassau County Conservative Party, 1982-86. Contbr. articles to profl. jours. Chief counsel, lt. col. Civil Air Patrol N.Y. Wing, Garden City, 1980-86; mgr. Little League Baseball, Syosset, N.Y., 1991-92, Great Neck, N.Y., 1993. Mem. N.Y. State Bar Assn., Fla. Bar Assn., D.C. Bar Assn., Nassau County Bar Assn., Flying Judges Assn. Ltd. (pres.). Conservative. Jewish. Avocations: music, private aircraft flying, linguistics, firearms. Home: 9 Willow Ln Great Neck NY 11023-1138 Office: County Ct Nassau County 262 Old Country Rd Mineola NY 11501-4255

MOGIL, H(ARVEY) MICHAEL, meteorologist, educator; b. N.Y.C., July 9, 1945; s. Nathan and Linda (Balansky) M.; m. Sheila Rose Schleiderer, Mar. 13, 1965 (div. 1987); children: Fredrika Sharon, Allyn Keith; m. Barbara G. Levine, Feb. 6, 1988. BS in Meteorology, Fla. State U., 1967, MS in Meteorology, 1969. Cert. cons. meteorologist. Cons. How the Weatherworks, Rockville, Md., 1979—; trainer NOAA, Washington, 1985—; instr. U. Mo., Columbia, 1989-92, Loyola Coll., Balt., 1992—; co-chair Project "Sky Awareness Week", Rockville, 1991—; adv. bd. Rockville Consortium for Sci., 1990—. Contbr. numerous articles to profl. jours.; creator video tape tchr. guide Our Sea of Clouds, 1992, A Hurricane: Through the Eyes of Children, 1993; co-author: Weather Study Under a Newspaper Umbrella, 1989, The Amateur Meteorologist, 1993. Mem. Nat. Sci. Tchrs. Assn. (reviewer 1983—), Nat. Earth Sci. Tchrs. Assn., Nat. Weather Assn. (chmn. tng. com. 1986-89, Mem. of the Yr. 1988), Am. Meteorol. Soc. Avocations: biking, reading, gardening, travel.

MOGK, JOHN EDWARD, legal educator, association executive; b. Detroit, Feb. 10, 1939; s. Clifford Anthony and Evelyn Lenore (Paselk) M.; m. Lylas Heidi Good, Aug. 23, 1964; children: Marya, Tenley, Matthew. BBA, U. Mich., 1961, JD with distinction, 1964; diploma in comparative law, U. Stockholm, 1965. Bar: N.Y. 1966, Mich. 1970. Assoc. atty. Shearman & Sterling, N.Y.C., 1964-68; mem. faculty Wayne State U. Sch. Law, 1968—, dir. grad. studies, 1990—; chmn. MERRA Rsch. Corp., 1977-94, pres., 1974-94; cons. econ. and urban devel., arbitrator. Editor Michigan International Lawyer and Utilities Law Rev.; contbr. articles to profl. jours. Chmn. Mich. TOP Task Force, 1972; vice chmn. Mich. Constrn. Code Commn., 1973; mem. exec. com. Southeastern Mich. Coun. Govts., 1970; chmn., adviser Jefferson-Chalmers Redevel. Program, 1969-73; chmn. Detroit Sch. Boundary Commn., 1970; mem. Detroit Bd. Edn., 1970; mgr. Detroit Empowerment Zone Proposal, 1994. Named Outstanding Wayne State U. Assoc. Prof., 1971, Outstanding Wayne Law Sch. Prof., 1977, 83, 93, Outstanding Young Man in Detroit, 1972, One of Ten Outstanding Young Men in U.S., 1973, One of Four Outstanding Vols. in U.S., 1974; recipient Presdl. citation Wayne State U., 1977, State of Mich., 1988, 94; Am.-Scandinavian fellow, 1965; vis. fellow U. Warwick, Eng., 1985-86. Mem. ABA, Mich. Bar Assn., Assn. of Bar of City of N.Y. Home: 1000 Yorkshire Rd Grosse Pointe MI 48230-1432

MOGOL, ALAN JAY, lawyer; b. Balt., July 29, 1946; s. Jesse and Kitty (Stutman) m.; m. Ellen Epstein, June 19, 1969; children: Andrew Stephen, Jonathan David. BA with distinction, U. Va., 1968, JD, 1971. Bar: Md. 1972, U.S. Dist. Ct. Md. 1972, U.S. Ct. Appeals (4th cir.) 1972, U.S. Supreme Ct. 1978. Assoc. Ober, Kaler, Grimes & Shriver, Balt., 1971-77, ptnr., 1978—, chmn. bus. dept., 1980-81, 84-85, 1991—; lectr. on continuing edn. Md. Inst. Continuing Profl. Edn. for Lawyers, 1988-92, trustee, 1990-93; spkr. seminars Nat. Health Lawyers Assn., Washington, 1986-87, Rocky Mountain Mgmt., Denver, 1987, Med. Imaging Expo., 1995, Washington, 1995. Co-author: (book chpt.) in Structuring the Secured Loan Agreement, 1991; contbr. articles on ins. and equipment leasing to jours., newspapers. Bd. dirs. Transitional Living Coun., Balt., 1972-92; bd. trustees Md. Inst. of Continuing Profl. Edn. for Lawyers, 1990-93. Mem. ABA, Equipment Leasing Assn. Am. (lawyers com. 1986-89, program com. 1986-91, spkr. seminars 1986—), Md. Bar Assn. (uniform comml. code com. 1988—, co-chmn. 1990-91, chmn. 1991-93, exec. com. 1994—). Avocation: tennis. Office: Ober Kaler Grimes & Shriver 120 E Baltimore St Baltimore MD 21202-1643

MOGUL, LESLIE ANNE, marketing communications executive; b. Balt., Mar. 9, 1948; d. Harry and Elaine (Blaustein) M.; m. William Kasper. AS, Miami Dade Jr. Coll., 1969; BA, Temple U., 1976. Accredited pub. rels. Account exec. Gray & Rogers, Inc., Phila., 1976-80; pres. Leslie Mogul, Inc., Phila., 1980-84; v.p. McKinney, Inc., Phila., 1984-87; assoc. dir. comm. Scripps Meml. Hosps., San Diego, 1987-93; dir. pub. rels. Scripps Health, San Diego, 1993, dir. customer rels. and mktg., 1994—. Recipient over 25 awards local and nat. pub. rels. and comm. orgns. Mem. Pub. Rels. Soc. Am. (dir.-at-large 1993-94), Alumni Leadership Calif. Office: Scripps Health PO Box 28 La Jolla CA 92038

MOHAIDEEN, A. HASSAN, surgeon, healthcare consultant; b. Ramanathapuram, India, Aug. 14, 1940; s. Abdul and Mariam (Pitchai) Kader; m. Zarina M. Meera, May 30, 1965 (dec. July 1986); children: Ahamed, Mariam, Najeeba, Azeema; m. Laurie J. Kucich, June 23, 1989; 1 child, Yasmin Sara. MD, U. Madras, India, 1965. Diplomate Am. Bd. Surgery, Am. Bd. Quality Assurance and Utilization. Intern Govt. Stanley Hosp., Madras, 1965-66, Good Samaritan Hosp., West Islip, N.Y., 1967-68; resident in gen. surgery L.I. Coll. Hosp., Bklyn., 1968-73, asst. attending surgeon, 1973-76, assoc. attending surgeon, 1976-78, attending surgeon, 1978—, chief divsn. vascular surgery, 1980-93, dir. vascular lab., 1981-93; v.p., managed care and exec. vice-chmn. dept. surgery The Bklyn.-Caledonian Hosp. Ctr. (affiliate of NYU), 1994—; asst. surgeon G.H.Q. Hosp., Ramnad, India, 1966-67; assoc. attending surgeon Meth. Hosp., Bklyn., 1982-90, attending surgeon, 1991; asst. attending surgeon Bklyn. Caledonian Med. Ctr., 1973-85, mem. courtesy staff, 1985—; attending physician Victory Meml. Hosp., Bklyn., 1982—; vis. physician Kings County Hosp. Ctr., Bklyn., 1973—; clin. instr. in surgery Downstate Med. Ctr., SUNY, Bklyn., 1973-78, clin. asst. prof. surgery, 1978—; mem. exec. com. of medical staff Long Island Coll. Hosp., Bklyn., 1979—, treas. medical staff, 1982-85, pres. 1985-87, medical chmn. Guild Ball com., 1981, mem. quality assurance com. dept. surgery, 1988—, chmn. credentials com., 1990—, quality assurance and risk mgmt. com., 1990—; bd. dirs. Aetna Health Plans of N.Y., aids advisory com., 1990—, standards com., 1986—, quality assurance com., mem. credentials com. Prucare, 1988—. Contbr. articles to med. jours. Fellow ACS (com. on Long Island dist. applicants, 1988—), Royal Coll. Physicians and Surgeons Can. (cert.), Internat. Coll. Surgeons; mem. AMA (Physician's Recognition award), AAAS, Am. Coll. Physician Execs., Med. Soc. of State of N.Y., N.Y. State Soc. of Surgeons, N.Y. Acad. of Scis., Med. Soc. of County of Kings (mediation com., 1979-85), Bklyn. Surg. Soc., Soc. for Non-Invasive Vascular Technicians, Kings Physicians I.P.A. (pres./medical dir., 1985—), Bklyn. Physicians I.P.A. (v.p., 1985—). Avocations: photography, computers, walking. Office: 705 86th St Brooklyn NY 11228

MOHAMMAD, SHAIKH NOOR, electronics engineer, educator; b. Paruldihi, India, Dec. 27, 1946; came to U.S., 1979; s. Shaikh Abdul and Shaikh Ayesha Jalil. PhD, Indian Inst. Tech., Kharagpur, India, 1977; DSc, Calcutta (India) U., 1982. Rsch. associate Indian Inst. Tech., Kharagpur, 1977-79, Case Western Res. U., Cleve., 1979-82; vis. prof. Indian Inst. Tech., Kharagpur, 1982-84; visitor Case Western Res. U., Cleve., 1985-87, U. Ill., Urbana, 1988-89; electronics engr. Semiconductor R&D Corp., IBM, Hopewell Junction, N.Y., 1989—; prof. electr. enc. engring. SUNY, New Paltz, 1990—. Contbr. over 100 articles to profl. jours. Mem. IEEE (sr., Electron Devices Soc. mid-Hudson sect. 1991—, Disting. Svcs. award 1992), Am. Phys. Soc. Achievements include patents and patents pending in field of bipolar transistors; research in bipolar transistors and related devices; in field effect transistors; in photovoltaics and optoelectronics; in solid-state electronics; in quantum mechanical study of materials structure. Office: IBM Semiconductor R&D Ctr 1580 State Route 52 Hopewell Junction NY 12533-6526

MOHAN, D. MIKE, transportation company executive; b. Chico, Calif., Apr. 10, 1945; s. Alfred and Velda June (Clark) M.; m. Dixie Watson, June 21, 1969; children—Laurel, Patrick, Christopher. B.A., U. Calif.-Berkeley, 1967, M.B.A., 1968; A.M.P., Harvard U., 1983. With So. Pacific Transp. Co., 1968—; asst. to pres. So. Pacific Transp. Co., San Francisco, 1981-82; v.p.-maintenance So. Pacific Transp. Co., 1982-83, exec. v.p., 1983-88, also dir.; pres., chief oper. officer So. Pacific Transp. Co., San Francisco, Denver & Rio Grande Western R.R., 1988—; bd. dirs. Rio Grande Industries. Mem. Nat. Freight Traffic Assn., Assn. Am. R.R.s (bd. dirs.). Avocations: sports; hiking. Office: So Pacific Transp Co 1 Market Plz San Francisco CA 94105-1019

MOHAN, J. PATRICK, lawyer; b. Balt., Apr. 10, 1948; s. Joseph F. and Laura (Reed) M.; m. Linda Lee, Aug. 26, 1972; children—Brian, Michael, Bradley, Timothy, Kerry. B.S., Ohio State U., 1970; J.D., U. San Francisco, 1973; LL.M., Georgetown U., 1977. Bar: Calif. 1973, U.S. Dist. Ct. (no dist.) Calif. 1973. U.S. Ct. Appeals (9th cir.) 1974, Ohio 1977, Ill. 1980. Atty., Chevron Oil Co., New Orleans, 1973-75; atty. U.S. SEC, Washington, 1975-77; assoc. atty. Moritz, McClure, Hughes & Kerscher, Columbus, Ohio, 1977-79; corp. counsel, asst. sec. A.E. Staley Mfg. Co., Decatur, Ill., 1979-85; asst. gen. counsel and asst. sec. Staley Continental, Inc., Rolling Meadows, Ill., 1985-87, v.p., gen. counsel, asst. sec., 1987-88; exec. v.p. adminstrn., gen. counsel, sec. Staley Mfg. Co., Decatur, Ill., 1988—. Home: 3010 E Fulton Ave Decatur IL 62521-4541 Office: A E Staley Mfg Co 2200 E Eldorado St Decatur IL 62521-1599

MOHAN, JOHN J., lawyer; b. St. Louis, May 22, 1945; s. John Joseph and Virginia Loretta (Durkin) M.; m. Elaine Bronwyn Lipe, May 29, 1982; children: Bryn Elizabeth, John Robert. BS Indsl. Engring., St. Louis U., Sch. Engring. and Earth Scis., 1967; JD, St. Louis U., 1971. Bar: Mo. 1971, Ill. 1971, U.S. Dist. Ct. (we. dist.) Mo. 1971, U.S. Dist. Ct. (ea. dist.) Mo. 1980, U.S. Dist. Ct. (so. dist.) Ill. 1981, U.S. Ct. Appeals (8th cir.) 1987. Asst. prosecuting atty. St. Louis County, 1971-72; asst. cir. atty. St. Louis Cir. Atty's. Office, 1972-74; spl. asst. state's atty. St. Clair County Atty's. Office, Belleville, Ill., 1974—; assoc. Lashley, Caruthers, Theis, Rava & Hamel, St. Louis, 1979-80; ptnr. Schreiber, Tueth & Mohan, Clayton, Mo., 1981-83, Danis, Reid, Murphy, Tobben, Schreiber & Mohan, Ladue, Mo., 1983-87, Hinshaw & Culbertson, St. Louis, 1987—. Mem. U. Mo. Law Sch. Found. Scholarship. Mem. ABA, Am. Arbitration Assn. (cert. mediator, arbitrator 1988—), Ill. Arbitration and Mediation Midwest (cert. mediator, arbitrator 1985—), Ill. State Bar Assn., Mo. Bar, Bar Assn. Metropolitan St. Louis, St. Clair County Bar, St. Louis County Bar, Defense Rsch. Inst., Mo. Orgn. Defense Lawyers, Maritime Law Assn., Phi Delta Phi. Home: 529 Big Horn Basin Ct Ballwin MO 63011 Office: Hinshaw & Culbertson 1010 Market St Ste 350 Saint Louis MO 63101

MOHIUDDIN, SYED MAQDOOM, cardiologist, educator; b. Hyderabad, India, Nov. 14, 1934; came to U.S., 1961, naturalized, 1976; s. Syed Nizamuddin and Amat-Ul-Butool Mahmoodi; m. Ayesha Sultana Mahmoodi, July 16, 1961; children: Sameena J., Syed R., Kulsoom S. M.B., B.S., Osmania U., 1960; M.S., Creighton U., Omaha, 1967; D.Sci., Laval U., Que., Can., 1970. Diplomate: Am. Bd. Internal Medcine (cardiovascular disease). Intern Altoona (Pa.) Gen. Hosp., 1961-62; resident in cardiology Creighton Meml. Hosp., also St. Joseph Hosp., Omaha, 1963-65; mem. staff Creighton Meml. Hosp., also St. Joseph Hosp., 1965—; prof. adjoint Laval U. Med. Sch., 1970; practice medicine specializing in cardiology Omaha, 1970—; prof. Creighton U. Med. Sch., 1977—, assoc. dir. div. cardiology, 1983—; prof. pharmacy practice Creighton U. Sch. Pharmacy, 1986—; cons. Omaha VA Hosp. Research fellow Med. Research Council Can., 1968; grantee Med. Research Council Can., 1970; grantee NIH, 1973. Fellow ACP, Am. Coll. Cardiology (gov. for Nebr. 1987-90), Am. Coll. Clin. Pharmacology, Am. Coll. Chest Physicians; mem. AAAS, Am. Heart Assn. (fellow coun. clin. cardiology, bd. dirs. 1973-75), Am. Fedn. Clin. Rsch., Nebr. Heart Assn. (chmn. rsch. com. 1974-76, dir. 1973—), Gt. Plains Heart Com. (Nebr. rep. 1976-84, pres. 1977-78), N.Y. Acad. Scis., Nebr. Cardiovascular Soc. (pres. 1980-81). Democrat. Islam. Home: 12531 Shamrock Rd Omaha NE 68154-3529 Office: 601 N 30th St Omaha NE 68131-2100

MOHL, ALLAN S., social worker; b. Passaic, N.J., Feb. 10, 1933; s. Milton and Ruth (Meisler) M.; m. Judith Klein, Dec. 21, 1958; children: Barbara, Eric, Adam. BA, NYU, 1954, MA, 1956, MSS, 1960; PhD, Columbia Pacific U., 1991. Diplomate Clin. Social Work. Dir. resdl. social svcs. Queens Soc. for Prevention of Cruelty of Children, Queens, N.Y., suprv. of incest; psychotherapist in pvt. practice Ardsley, N.Y.; cons. Tip Neighborhood House, Bronx; dir. family svcs. Tip Neighborhood House; sch. social worker Com. on Spl. Edn., Dist. 28, N.Y.; condr. workshop on incestuous families and child sexual abuse; unit dir. Children's Village, Dobbs Ferry, N.Y.; cons. Parents Anonymous, South Bronx, N.Y. Contbr. articles to profl. jours. Former chmn. of Gen. Social Svcs. Adv. Counsel #6; active participant Bronx Task Force on Child Abuse and Neglect; group leader Project Enable, South Bronx, N.Y. With U.S. Army, 1956-58. NIMH grantee. Mem. NASW, Am. Assn. Marriage and Family Therapy, Am. Orthopsychiat. Assn., N.Y. State Soc. Clin. Social Wk. Psychotherpaists, Internat. Assn. Counselors and Therapists. Home: 8 Shorthill Rd Ardsley NY 10502-2020

MOHLEJI, SATISH CHANDRA, electrical engineer; b. New Delhi, India, Aug. 16, 1940; came to U.S. 1970; s. Raghbir Singh and Kashmiro Devi (Sharma) M.; m. Manjula Sharma, Apr. 5, 1972; children: Anjali, Shalini, Nandita. BE with hons., U. Bombay, India, 1962; M.Engring., Tech. U. N.S., Can., 1967; PhD, U. Windsor, Can., 1970; MS in Mgmt. Sci., Am. U., Washington, 1988. Registered profl. engr., Ont., 1967-79. Asst. engr. World Wide Engrs. pvt. Ltd., New Delhi, 1962-63, Dodsal Pvt. Ltd., New Delhi, 1963-64; engr. trainee Richard Zimmerman, K.G. Stuttgart, Germany, 1964; engr. Std. Elec. Lorenz, Stuttgart, 1964-65, Lear Siegler, Inc., Grand Rapids, Mich., 1970-71; lead engr MITRE Corp., McLean, Va., 1971—. Contbr. articles to profl. jours. Mem. rsch. adv. panel Aviation Wk. and Space Tech. Pub., 1986-87. Fellow AIAA (assoc., chmn. aircraft ops. tech. com.); mem. IEEE (sr.) Internat. Fedn. Automatic Control (chmn. air traffic control automation tech. com.) RTCA (spl. com. SC-166 tech. working group, chmn. 1989-92). Avocations: photography, gardening. Home: 12324 Ox Hill Rd Fairfax VA 22033-2407 Office: The MITRE Corp 7525 Colshire Dr Mc Lean VA 22102-7500

MOHLER, BRIAN JEFFERY, diplomat; b. Niskayuna, N.Y., May 28, 1948; s. Donald and Rosemary (Brown) M. BA, Johns Hopkins U., 1970, MA, 1972. Economist Congl. Rsch. Svc. Libr. of Congress, Washington, 1973-74; staff asst. Bur. Econ. Affairs, Washington, 1974-76, economist, 1979-82; consul Am. Consulate Gen., Strasbourg, France, 1976-78; desk officer European community affairs Bur. European Affairs, Washington, 1982-84; petroleum attache Am. Embassy, Riyadh, Saudi Arabia, 1986-88, counselor for econ. affairs, 1988-90; dep. chief of mission Am. Embassy, Abu Dhabi, United Arab Emirates, 1990-93; desk officer Japanese affairs Bur. East Asian and Pacific Affairs, Washington, 1984-86, dep. dir. of econs. for Japanese affairs, 1993—. 2d lt. U.S. Army, 1972, capt. USAR, 1972-85. Recipient Superior Honor award Dept. of State, 1993, Meritorious Honor award, 1987. Mem. Am. Fgn. Svc. Assn., Confrerie de la Chaine des Rotisseurs, Sigma Nu. Roman Catholic. Home: 6711 Washington Blvd # C Arlington VA 22213-1006 Office: Office of Japanese Affairs Dept of State 2201 C St NW Washington DC 20520-0001

MOHLER, MARY GAIL, magazine editor; b. Milaca, Minn., Dec. 15, 1948; d. Albert and Deane (Vedders) M.; m. Paul Rodes Trautman, June 5, 1976 (div. 1994); children: Elizabeth Deane, David Albert Rodes, Theodore DeForest Lloyd. B.A., U. Calif.-Davis, 1974; M.A. in Lit., SUNY-Stony Brook, 1976. Asst., then editor-reporter Family Circle Mag., N.Y.C., 1979-81; editorial coordinator Ladies' Home Jour., N.Y.C., 1981, assoc. articles editor, 1982; mng. editor, 1982-93, sr. editor, 1994—; editor in chief Ladies' Home Jour. Parent's Digest. Medieval philosophy fellow SUNY-Binghamton, 1978. Mem. MLA, Am. Soc. Mag. Editors, Phi Beta Kappa.

Clubs: Medieval; Overseas Press. Office: Ladies' Home Jour 100 Park Ave New York NY 10017-5516

MOHLER, RONALD RUTT, electrical engineering educator; b. Ephrata, Pa., Apr. 11, 1931; s. David Wealand and Elizabeth (Rutt) M.; m. Nancy Alice Strickler, May 6, 1950; children: Curtis Gene, Pamela Louise, Susan Lynn, Anita Marie, John Scott, Andrew Thomas, Jennifer Lee, Lisa Nancy. B.S. (scholarship), Pa. State U., 1956; M.S., U. So. Calif., 1958; Ph.D., U. Mich., 1965. Designer, trainee Textile Machine Works, Rockwell Internat. Corp., Reading, Pa., 1949-56; staff mem. Hughes Aircraft Co., Culver City, Calif., 1956-58, Los Alamos Sci. Lab., 1958-65; asso. prof. elec. engring. U. N.Mex., Albuquerque, 1965-69; prof. elec. engring. and aerospace mech. and nuclear engring. U. Okla., 1969-72, prof., chmn. info. and computing scis., 1970-72; dir. Systems Research Center, 1969-72; adj. prof. elec. engring. and nuclear engring. U. N.Mex., Los Alamos Grad. Center, 1959-65; cons. Sandia Corp., Albuquerque, 1966-69, Aerojet-Gen. Corp., Sacramento, 1966; vis. assoc. prof. system sci. UCLA, 1968-69; cons. community health project OEO, Oklahoma City, 1970-71; prof. elec. and computer engring. Oreg. State U., Corvallis, 1972—; head dept. Oreg. State U., 1972-79, 90; pres. Pace Tech., Inc., 1982—; vis. prof. U. Rome, 1973, 75, Imperial Coll., London, 1978-79, U.S. Naval Postgrad. Sch., 1983-85, Australian Nat. U., 1988; cons. Optimization Software, Los Angeles, 1973—, Bonneville Power Adminstrn., 1975—, Internat. Inst. Applied Systems Analysis, 1988—. Author: Optimal Control of Nuclear Reactors, 1970, Bilinear Control Processes, 1973, Nonlinear Systems: Dynamics and Control, vol. 1, 1991, Applications to Bilinear Control, vol. II, 1991, Disease Dynamics, 1993; editor: Theory and Application of Variable Structure Systems, 1972, Variable Structure Systems with Application to Biology and Economics, 1975, Recent Developments in Variable Structure Systems, Economics and Biology, 1979, Nonlinear Time Series and Signal Processing, 1988, assoc. editor Annals of Nuclear Energy, 1973—; contbr. jours. Chmn. St. Stephens Sch. Bd., Norman, 1970-72. Recipient NATO award, 1979; rsch. grantee NSF, 1966—, Sandia Labs., 1966-68, ONR, 1981-92, NASA, EPRI, BPA, 1990—; AEC fellow, 1961-65, Hughes fellow, 1956-58; Acad. Sci. exch. scientist to USSR and China, 1980, US-CIS (USSR) Commn. on Engring. Edn., 1991—. Fellow IEEE (local chmn. 1975); Mem. Am. Soc. Engring. Edn., Control System Soc., Sigma Xi, Tau Beta Pi, Pi Tau Sigma. Democrat. Pioneer rsch. on bilinear systems and worldwide collaboration. Home: 2050 NW Dogwood Dr Corvallis OR 97330-1102

MOHLER, STANLEY ROSS, physician, educator; b. Amarillo, Tex., Sept. 30, 1927; s. Norton Harrison and Minnie Alice (Ross) M.; m. Ursula Luise Burkhardt, Jan. 24, 1953; children: Susan Luise, Stanley Ross, Mark Hallock. B.A., U. Tex., 1953, M.A., 1953, M.D., 1956. Diplomate: Am. Bd. Preventive Medicine. Intern USPHS Hosp., San Francisco, 1956-57; med. officer Center Aging Research, NIH, Bethesda, Md., 1957-61; dir. Civil Aeromed. Rsch. Inst., FAA, Oklahoma City, 1961-66; chief aeromed. applications div. Civil Aeromed. Rsch. Inst., FAA, Washington, 1966-78; prof., vice chmn. dept. community medicine, dir. aerospace medicine Wright State U. Sch. Medicine, Dayton, Ohio, 1978—; rsch. assoc. prof. preventive medicine and pub. health U. Okla. Med. Sch., 1961—; vice chmn. Am. Bd. Preventive Medicine, 1978—, sec.-treas., 1980—. Author articles in field. Bd. dirs. Sr. Citizens Assn. Oklahoma City, 1962—, Flying Physicians Assn., 1961—. Served with AUS, 1946-48. Recipient Gail Borden Research award; Boothby award Aerospace Med. Assn., 1966; FAA Meritorious Service award, 1974. Fellow Geriatrics Soc., Aerospace Med. Assn. (pres. 1983, Harry G. Moseley award 1974, Lyster award 1984), Am. Coll. Preventive Medicine, Gerontol. Soc.; mem. AMA, Aircraft Owners and Pilots Assn. (Sharples award 1984, Hubertus Strughold award 1991), Alpha Omega Alpha. Home: 6539 Reigate Rd Dayton OH 45459-3214 Office: Wright State U Sch Medicine PO Box 927 Dayton OH 45401-0927

MOHN, MELVIN PAUL, anatomist, educator; b. Cleve., June 19, 1926; s. Paul Melvin and Julia (Jacobik) M.; m. Audrey Faye Lonergan, June 28, 1952; children—Shorey Faye, Andrew Paul. A.B., Marietta Coll., 1950; Sc.M., Brown U., 1952, Ph.D. in Biology, 1955. Instr. SUNY Downstate Med. Ctr., Bklyn., 1955-59, asst. prof., 1959-63; asst. prof. anatomy U. Kans. Sch. Medicine, Kansas City, 1963-65, assoc. prof., 1965-72, prof., 1972-89, prof. emeritus, 1989—; cons. Nat. Med. Audiovisual Ctr., Atlanta, 1972; vis. lectr. U. Miami Sch. Medicine, Fla., 1966. Bd. dirs. U. Kans. Med. Ctr. Credit Union, 1968-77, Kansas City Youth Symphony, 1972-77; mem. U.S. Pony Club, 1964-71, Med. Arts Symphony, 1945-71, 90—, Spring Hill Chorale, 1990—. Served with USN, 1944-46, PTO. McCoy fellow, 1950, Arnold biology fellow, 1954. Fellow AAAS; mem. Am. Soc. Zoologists, Am. Assan. Anatomists, Am. Inst. Biol. Sci., Phi Beta Kappa, Sigma Xi, Beta Beta Beta. Republican. Methodist. Club: Lions, Rotary, Lodge: Masons. Home: Yankee Bit Farm 23595 W 223rd St Spring Hill KS 66083-4029 Office: U Kans Med Ctr Dept Anatomy 39th and Rainbow St Kansas City KS 66103

MOHNEY, RALPH WILSON, minister; b. Paris, Ky., May 20, 1918; s. Silas Phillip and Clarine (Wilson) M.; m. Nell Marie Webb, Dec. 31, 1948; children—Richard Bentley, Ralph Wilson. B.A., Transylvania Coll., 1940; B.D., Vanderbilt U., 1943; S.T.M., Boston U., 1945; postgrad., Harvard, Garrett Bibl. Inst.; D.D., Emory and Henry Coll., 1959. Ordained elder Meth. Ch., 1944; pastor Winter Street Congl. Ch., Bath, Me., 1943-45, Manker Meml. Meth. Ch., Chattanooga, 1945-50, Washington Pike Meth. Ch., Knoxville, 1950-56; supt. Kingsport dist. Holston Conf. Meth. Ch., 1956- 59; pres. Tenn. Wesleyan Coll., 1959-65; sr. minister Centenary Meth. Ch., 1945-66, First Centenary United Meth. Ch., Chattanooga, 1967-81, First Broad St. United Meth. Ch., Kingsport, Tenn., 1981-87; asst. dir. Growth Plus Ministries Gen. Bd. Discipleship, Chattanooga, 1988-92, Disting. evangelist in residence, 1991—; staff mem. Large Ch. Initiative, 1988-89; Staley Disting. lectr. Columbia Coll., 1973, Emory and Henry Coll., 1975, Pfeiffer Coll., 1976, Union Coll., 1977; del. World Conf. Christian Youth, Oslo, Norway, 1947; adult counselor Meth. Youth Caravan to Poland., 1947; chmn. Holston Conf. Commn. on World Peace, 1952-56; leader Annual Lenten Pilgrimage to Holy Land, 1973-80; pres. Holston Council on Finance and Administrn., 1968-76, mem., 1976-84; mem. Gen. Council Finance and Adminstrn., 1976-84, mem. exec. com., 1976-80; chmn. Commn. on Christian Higher Edn., 1956-59; rec. del. Gen. Conf. Meth. Ch., del. jurisdictional conf. Meth. Ch., 1960, 68; del. Meth. Ch. (Gen. Conf.), 1976; mem. Gen. Bd. Christian Social Concerns, 1960-72, World Council Meth. Ch., 1966-70; mem. steering com. United Meth. TV Presence and Ministry, 1979-81; mem. S.E. radio and film commn. Meth. Ch., 1968-76; dir. Holston Conf. Found., 1984-92; exchange minister Eng., 1984, New Zealand, 1987. Co-author: Parable Churches, 1989, Churches of Vision, 1990, Vision 2000: Planning for Ministry Into the Next Century, 1991. Bd. dirs. E. Tenn. State Coll. Wesley Found., 1955-59, U. Tenn. Wesley Found., 1956-62; pres. Athens United Fund, 1965, Affiliated Ind. Colls. Tenn., 1963-65, Chattanooga Meth. Ministers Assn., 1966-67, Chattanooga Clergyman's Assn., 1968. Mem. Pi Kappa Alpha, Pi Kappa Delta. Club: Kiwanis. Home: 1004 Northbridge Ln Chattanooga TN 37405-4214

MOHOLY, NOEL FRANCIS, clergyman; b. San Francisco, May 26, 1916; s. John Joseph and Eva Gertrude (Cippa) M.; grad. St. Anthony's Sem., Santa Barbara; STB, Faculte de Theologie, Universite Laval, Quebec, Que., Can., 1944, STL 1945, STD, 1948; Joined Franciscan Friars, 1935; ordained priest Roman Catholic Ch., 1941; tchr. fundamental theology Old Mission Santa Barbara, 1942-43, sacred theology, 1947-58; tchr. langs. St. Anthony's Sem., 1943-44; Am. adminstr. (handling affairs of the cause in U.S.) Cause of Padre Junipero Serra, 1950-55, vice postulator, 1958—; retreat master San Damiano Retreat, Danville, Calif., 1964-67. Mem. Ann. Assay Commn. U.S. Mint, 1964. Occupied numerous pulpits, assisted in several Franciscan Retreat Houses; condr. series illustrated lectrs. on cause of canonization of Padre Junipero Serra to students of all Franciscan study houses in U.S., summer 1952, also speaker in field at various clubs of Serra Internat. in U.S., Europe and Far East, on NBC in documentary with Edwin Newman, Padre Serra, Founding Father, 1985, PBS on Firing Line with William F. Buckley: Junipero Serra—Saint or Sinner, 1989, CBS, ABC broadcasts and conducted own local TV series. Mem. Bldg. Com. for Restoration Hist. Towers and Facade of Old Mission Santa Barbara, 1950-53; exec. dir., treas. Old Mission Restoration Project, 1954-58; mem. Calif. Hist. Landmarks Adv. Com., 1962-71, Calif. Hist. Resources Commn., 1971-76, Calif. Bicentennial Celebration Commn., 1967-70; pres. Serra Bicentennial commn., 1983-86, dir. Old Spanish Days in Santa Barbara, Inc., 1950-58, Nat. and internat. authority on Saint Irenaeus, mariology, Calif. history (particularly history of

Father Serra). Decorated Knight comdr. Order of Isabella la Catolica, 1965. Pres. Father Junipero Serra 250th Anniversary Assn., Inc., 1964—. Named hon. citizen Petra de Mallorca, 1969, Palma de Mallorca, 1976; recipient Cross of Merit Sovereign Mil. Order of Knights Malta, 1989. Mem. Mariol. Soc. Am., Native Sons Golden West, Associacion de los Amigos de Padre Serra, K.C., Calif. Missions Study Assn. Author: Our Last Chance, 1931; Saint Irenaeus; the Father of Mariology, 1952; The California Mission Story, 1975; The First Californian, 1976; co-author (with Don DeNevi) Junipero Serra, 1985; producer phonograph records Songs of the California Missions, 1951, Christmas at Mission Santa Barbara, 1953, St. Francis Peace Record, 1957; producer VCR The Founding Father of the West, 1976. Home: The Old Mission 2201 Laguna St Santa Barbara CA 93105-3611 Office: Serra Cause The Old Mission Santa Barbara CA 93105-3611

MOHR, JAY PRESTON, neurologist; b. Mar. 5, 1937; s. John G. and Marguerite F. Mohr; A.B., Haverford Coll., 1958; M.S., U. Va., 1963, M.D., 1963; m. Joan L. Seal, Mar. 10, 1962; children—Thea, Gregory. Intern, then asst. resident in medicine Mary Imogene Bassett Hosp., Cooperstown, N.Y., 1963-65; asst. resident in neurology N.Y. Neurol. Inst., Columbia-Presbyn. Med. Ctr., N.Y.C., 1965-66; fellow in neurology Mass. Gen. Hosp., Boston, 1966-69; instr. neurology Johns Hopkins U. Med. Sch., also U. Md. Med. Sch., 1969-71; assoc. neurologist Mass. Gen. Hosp., also asst. prof. Harvard U. Med. Sch., 1972-78; prof. neurology, chmn. dept. U. South Ala. Med. Sch., Mobile, 1978-83; Sciarra prof. clin. neurology Columbia U. Coll. Physicians and Surgeons, N.Y.C., 1983—; dir. cerebrovascular research N.Y. Neurol. Inst., N.Y.C., 1983—. Served as maj. M.C., U.S. Army, 1969-72. Diplomate Am. Bd. Neurology and Psychiatry. Fellow Am. Acad. Neurology; mem. Am. Neurol. Assn., Am. Heart Assn. (stroke council) Sigma Xi. Democrat. Quaker. Contbr. articles to med. jours. Home: PO Box 1014 Shelter Island Heights NY 11965-1014 Office: NY Neurol Inst 710 W 168th St New York NY 10032-2603 also: Presbyn Hosp Columbia-Presbyn Med Ctr New York NY 10032-3784

MOHR, JOHN LUTHER, biologist, environmental consultant; b. Reading, Pa., Dec. 1, 1911; s. Luther Seth and Anna Elizabeth (Davis) M.; m. Frances Edith Christensen, Nov. 23, 1939; children: Jeremy John, Christopher Charles. A.B. in Biology, Bucknell U., 1933; student, Oberlin Coll., 1933-34; Ph.D. in Zoology, U. Calif. at Berkeley, 1939. Research asso. Pacific Islands Research, Stanford, 1944-46; asst. prof., 1946-47, asst. dept. biology, 1947-54, asso. prof., 1954-57, prof., 1957-77; chmn. dept., 1960-62, prof. emeritus, 1977—; vis. prof. summers U. Wash. Friday Harbor Labs., 1956, '57; marine borer and pollution surveys harbors So. Calif., 1948-51, arctic marine biol. research, 1952-71; chief marine zool. group U.S. Antarctic research ship Eltanin in Drake Passage, 1962, in South Pacific sector, 1965; research deontology in sci. and academia; researcher on parasitic protozoans of anurans, crustaceans, elephants; analysis of agy. and industry documents, ethics and derelictions of steward agy., sci. and tech. orgns. as they relate to offshore and coastal onshore oil activities, environ. effects of oil spill dispersants and offshore oil industry discharges and naturally occurring radioactive material NORMs. Active People for the Am. Way; mem. Biol. Stain Commn., 1948-80, trustee, 1971-80, emeritus trustee, 1981—, v.p., 1976-80. Recipient Guggenheim fellowship, 1957-58. Fellow AAAS (coun. 1964-73), So. Calif. Acad. Scis., Sigma Xi (exec. com. 1964-67, 68, 69, chpt. at large bd. 1968-69); mem. Am. Micros. Soc., Marine Biol. Assn. U.K. (life), Am. Soc. Parasitologists, Western Soc. Naturalists (pres. 1960-61), Soc. Protozoologists, Am. Soc. Tropical Medicine and Hygiene, Am. Soc. Zoologists, Ecol. Soc. Am., planning and Conservation League, Calif. Native Plant Soc., Am. Inst. Biol. Scis., Save San Francisco Bay Assn., Ecology Ctr. Soc. Calif., Assn. Forest Svc. Employees Environ. Ethics, Common Cause, Huxleyan, Sierra Club, Phi Sigma, Theta Upsilin Omega. Democrat. Home: 3819 Chanson Dr Los Angeles CA 90043-1601

MOHR, L. THOMAS, newspaper executive; b. Endicott, N.Y., Dec. 25, 1955; s. Lionel Charles and Anne (Tredwell) M.; m. Pageen Rogers, July 13, 1985; children: Mary Catherine, Jack. BA with honors, Queens U., Kingston, Ont., Can., 1979; MBA, U. Calif., Berkeley, 1987. Gen. mgr. Foster City (Calif.) Progress, 1981-82; classified advt. mgr. Peninsula Times Tribune, Palo Alto, Calif., 1982-85, mktg. mgr., 1985-86, advt. sales dir., 1986-87; dir. mktg. and advt. sales Bakersfield Californian, 1987-90; classified advt. dir. Star Tribune, Mpls., 1990-93, v.p., 1993—. Bd. dirs. March of Dimes, Mpls., 1994—. Mem. Newspaper Assn. Am. (bd. dirs. classified fedn. 1993—, co-chair classified task force, 1994—). Republican. Roman Catholic. Avocations: running, tennis, golf, cross country skiing. Home: 3080 Quinwood Ln N Plymouth MN 55441 Office: Star Tribune 425 Portland Ave Minneapolis MN 55488-0001

MOHR, ROGER JOHN, advertising agency executive; b. Milw., Sept. 8, 1931; s. Reinhold and Clara (Meissner) M.; m. Pauline Spicuzza, Oct. 18, 1958; children: Gregory, Mary Margaret, Kristin, Thomas, Kathleen. B.S. in Speech, Marquette U., 1953; postgrad. radio and TV, Northwestern U., 1955-56. Staff announcer radio sta. WBKB, West Bend, Wis., 1952, WCAN, Milw., 1952-54; with Arthur Meyerhoff Assos., Inc., Chgo., 1956-80; pres. Arthur Meyerhoff Assos., Inc., 1965-80; pres. BBDO, Chgo., 1980-82, chmn., 1982-90, vice chmn. internat., 1991-93. Chmn. Lake Bluff (Ill.) Plan Commn., 1972-75; mem. Lake Forest (Ill.) Plan Commn., 1994—; bd. dirs. Chgo. City Ballet, 1982-84, Off the Street Club, 1976-78; mem. adv. coun. Marquette U. Sch. Comm., 1993—. Served with AUS, 1954-55. Mem. Am. Assn. Advt. Agys. (chmn. Chgo. coun. 1966-67, sec., treas., nat. bd. dirs. 1976-77), Evans Scholars Alumni Assn. (pres. 1964-65), Western Golf Assn. (bd. dirs. 1980—, v.p. 1994—), Knollwood Club (bd. govs. 1985-85, 89-92), Tavern Club (bd. govs., v.p. 1988-94). Home: 2000 Knollwood Rd Lake Forest IL 60045-1137

MOHRAZ, JUDY JOLLEY, college president; b. Houston, Oct. 1, 1943; d. John Chester and Mae (Jackson) Jolley; m. Bijan Mohraz; children: Andrew, Jonathan. BA, Baylor U., 1966, MA, 1968; PhD, U. Ill., 1974. Lectr. history Ill. Wesleyan U., 1972-74; asst. prof. history So. Meth. U., Dallas, 1974-80, coordr. women's studies, 1977-81, assoc. prof. history, 1980-84, asst. provost, 1983-88, asst. provost for student academics, 1988-94; pres. Goucher Coll., Towson, Md., 1994—; cons. Ednl. Testing Svc., Princeton, N.J., 1984-93, Nat. Park Svcs., Seneca Falls, N.Y., 1992-93. Trustee The Lamplighter Sch., 1991-94, St. Mark's Sch., 1993-94; adv. bd. U. Tex. Southwestern Med. Sch., 1992-94; active Leadership Dallas, 1994. Recipient Disting. Alumni award Baylor U., 1993; named Woman of Merit, Omicron Delta Kappa, 1993. Home: Pres House 1021 Dulaney Valley Rd Baltimore MD 21204 Office: Goucher Coll Office of Pres 1021 Dulaney Valley Rd Baltimore MD 21204

MOHRFELD, RICHARD GENTEL, heating oil distributing company executive; b. Camden, N.J., Dec. 30, 1945; s. Herbert Henry and Elizabeth Weldon (Gentel) M.; m. Ann Bacon, June 20, 1971 (div. 1975); m. Janice Lee Strickland, July 1, 1978; children: Kathryn Elizabeth, Christopher Hall. BSc in Geology, Dickinson Coll., 1971. Staff geologist Temple U., Phila., 1971-74; pres. Mohrfeld Inc., Collingswood, N.J., 1974—; bd. dirs. South Jersey Savs. & Loan Assn., Turnersville, N.J. Bd. dirs. Boy Scouts Am., Camden County, N.J., 1985—; trustee, treas. Knight Park Trustees, Collingswood, 1986—; trustee Health Care Support Found., Inc., 1994—. Sgt. USAF, 1969-71. Mem. Air Conditioning Contractors Am. (pres. 1986-88), Fuel Mchts. Assn. N.J. (pres. 1992-94), Rotary (pres. Collingswood 1980-81). Episcopalian. Avocations: travel, photography. Office: 24 Lees Ave Collingswood NJ 08108-1926

MOHRMAN, KATHRYN, academic administrator. Pres. The Colo. Coll., Colo. Springs. Office: Colorado College Office of the President 14 E Cache La Poudre St Colorado Springs CO 80903-3243

MOHRMANN, LEONARD EDWARD, JR., chemist, chemical engineer; b. Winston Salem, N.C., June 14, 1940; s. Leonard E. and Helen (Bean) M.; m. Sue Ross, June 18, 1966; children: Leonard III, Vaden, Nelwyn Ann. BS in Chemistry, U. Tex., 1963; PhD in Chemistry, Fla. State U., 1971; BSChemE, Tex. A&M U., 1980. Cert. profl. chemist. Tech. lab. coord. Tex. A&M U., College Sta., 1971-81, rsch. assoc., 1981-82; chemist, chemical engr. Tex. Dept. Health, Austin, 1982-92, Tex. Water Commn., Austin, 1992-93, Fugro Environ., Inc. formerly Fugro McClelland, Houston, 1993-95, Tex. Dept. Health, Austin, 1995—. Contbr. articles to sci. jours. Active Mathcounts program Tex. Soc. Profl. Engrs., Austin, 1991-92, Jr. Achievement Program, Houston, 1994-95. Recipient Appreciation cert. Tex. Soc. Profl. Engrs., 1993. Achievements include development of Texas regulations for special waste disposal, medical waste handling and disposal, special waste program for municipal waste. Office: Tex Dept Health Bur Labs 1100 W 49th Austin TX 78757

MOHRMANN, ROBERT E., wholesale distribution executive; b. 1945. BS, St. Louis U., 1968. Internal auditor Associated Dry Goods Corp., 1967-68; fin. officer U.S. Correctional Tng. Facility, 1968-70; sr. acct. Price Waterhouse and Co., St. Louis, 1968-74; mgr. gen. acct. Mallinckrodt Inc., St. Louis, 1974-76; ops. mgr. Wetterau Inc., Hazelwood, Mo., 1976-92; vice-chmn., pres., CEO Supervalu Holdings Inc., Hazelwood, Mo., 1992—. Mem. AICPA, Fin. Execs. Inst., Nat. Assn. Accts. Office: Supervalu Holdings Inc 8920 Pershall Rd Hazelwood MO 63042-2883

MOHS, FREDERIC EDWARD, surgeon, educator; b. Burlington, Wis., Mar. 1, 1910; s. Frederic Carl and Grace Edith (Tilton) M.; m. Mary Ellen Reynolds, June 18, 1934; children: Frederic Edward, Thomas James, Jane Ann. MD, U. Wis., 1934. Intern Multnomah County Hosp., Portland, Ore., 1934-35; Bowman Cancer Research Fellow U. Wis. Med. Sch., 1935-38, asso. in cancer research, instr. in surgery, 1939-42, asst. prof. chemosurgery, 1942-48, asso. prof. chemosurgery, 1948-69, clin. prof. surgery, 1969-85, emeritus prof. surgery, spl. cons., 1985—. Author: Chemosurgery: Microscopically Controlled Surgery for Skin Cancer; Contbr. articles, papers on treatment of cancer by means of Mohs micrographic surgery. Recipient Lila Gruber award for cancer rsch. Am. Acad. Dermatology, Internat. Facial Plastic Surgery award 3d Internat. Symposium on Plastic and Reconstructive Surgery of Head and Neck, Discovery award Dermatology Found., 1995. Fellow AMA; mem. AAAS, Am. Assn. Cancer Rsch., Dane County Med. Soc. (pres. 1959- 60), Am. Coll. Mohs Micrographic Surgery and Cutaneous Oncology (founder, 1st pres.). Home: 3616 Lake Mendota Dr Madison WI 53705-1475

MOIR, ALFRED KUMMER, art history educator; b. Mpls., Apr. 14, 1924; s. William Wilmerding and Blanche (Kummer) M. A.B., Harvard U., 1948, A.M., 1949, Ph.D., 1953. From instr. to assoc. prof. Newcomb Coll., Tulane U., 1952-62; mem. faculty U. Calif., Santa Barbara, 1962-91, prof. art history, 1964-91, prof. emeritus, 1991—, chmn. dept., 1963-69; dir. Edn. Abroad Program U. Calif., Italy, 1978-80; cons. for acquisitions Isaac Delgado Mus. Art, 1953-57; v.p. Friends La. State Mus., 1959-62, Friends New Orleans Pub. Libr., 1959-62; pres. So. Calif. Art Historians, 1964-66, 67-69; chmn. Tri-Counties Com. to Rescue Italian Art, 1967-68; art historian in residence Am. Acad. Rome, 1969-70, 80; vis. prof. U. Minn., 1973; hon. curator of drawings U. Calif.-Santa Barbara Art Mus., 1985-94;. Author: (with others) Art in Italy, 1600-1700, 1965, The Italian Followers of Caravaggio, 2 vols, 1967, Caravaggio's Copyists, 1976, Caravaggio, 1982, Van Dyck, 1994; editor: (with others) Seventeenth Century Italian Drawings in the Collection of Janos Scholz, 1974, European Drawings in the Santa Barbara Museum of Art, 1976, Regional Styles of Drawing in Italy 1600-1700, 1977, Old Master Drawings from the Feitelson Collection, 1983, Old Master Drawings from the Collection of John and Alice Steiner, 1985, (with others) Van Dyck's Antwerp, 1991, Anthony Van Dyck, 1994. Trustee Santa Barbara Free Sch., 1968-69; gov. Brooks Inst. Art Gallery, 1968-69. Served with AUS, 1943-46. Named hon. alumnus Tulane U., 1963, Outstanding Alumnus of 1993, The Blake Sch., Mpls., 1993. Mem. AAUP, Coll. Art Assn., Medieval Acad. Am., Soc. Archtl. Historians, Renaissance Acad. Am., Soc. Fellows of Am. Acad. in Rome, Ateneo Veneto (fgn. mem.). Clubs: Harvard (La. pres. 1959-62, Boston), University Calif. at Santa Barbara Faculty (pres. 1968). Office: U Calif Dept Art History Santa Barbara CA 93106

MOIR, ROBERT JESSE, manufacturing company executive, lawyer; b. N.Y.C., Mar. 15, 1942; s. William E. and Edith M. (Lane) M. B.A., U. Va., 1964; J.D., Georgetown U., 1972. Bar: Colo. 1972, U.S. Dist. Ct. Colo. 1972. Assoc. Holland & Hart, Denver, 1972-76; corp. counsel Ideal Basic Industries, Inc., Denver, 1976-81, v.p. legal affairs, 1981-85, v.p., sec., gen. counsel, 1985-90; v.p., sec., gen. counsel Holnam Inc., 1990—. Served to lt. USN, 1964-69. Decorated Bronze Star. Mem. ABA, Mich. Bar Assn., Colo. Bar Assn., Am. Corp. Counsel Assn., Denver Bar Assn. (chmn. legal services com. 1982-83). Office: Holnam Inc 6211 Ann Arbor Rd Dundee MI 48131

MOISE, EDWIN EVARISTE, mathematician, educator; b. New Orleans, Dec. 22, 1918; s. Edwin Evariste and Annie Josephine (Boatner) M.; m. Mary Lorena Leake, May 28, 1942 (div. 1980); children: Edwin Evariste, Claire Mary. Student, La. State U., 1935-37; B.A., Tulane U., 1940; Ph.D. in Pure Math., U. Tex., 1947; M.A. (hon.), Harvard, 1960. Instr. math. U. Mich., 1947-49, from asst. prof. to prof. math., 1951-60; James Bryant Conant prof. edn. and math. Harvard U., 1960-71; vis. prof. Centro de Investigación y de Estudios Avanzados, Instituto Politecnico Nacional, Mexico City, 1970-71; Disting. prof. Queens Coll., CUNY, 1971-80, 81-87, now emeritus; Hudson prof. Auburn U., 1980-81; Temp. mem. Inst. Advanced Study, Princeton, 1949-51, 56-57; mem. writing team Sch. Math. Study Group, summers 1958-60. Author: Elementary Geometry from an Advanced Standpoint, 1963, (with Floyd L. Downs, Jr.) Geometry, 1964, Number Systems of Elementary Mathematics, 1965, Calculus: Part I, 1966, Calculus: Part II, 1967, Geometric Topology in Dimensions 2 and 3, 1977, Introductory Problem Courses in Analysis and Topology, 1982. Served with USNR, 1942-46. Mem. MLA, Am. Math Soc. (mng. editor bull. 1958-63, v.p. 1973-74), Math. Assn. Am. (v.p. 1965, pres. 1967-68), Phi Beta Kappa. Home: 77 Bleecker St Apt 323E New York NY 10012-1553

MOIZE, JERRY DEE, lawyer; b. Greensboro, N.C., Dec. 19, 1934; s. Dwight Moody and Thelma (Ozment) M.; m. Margaret Ann Wooten, Aug. 13, 1976; 1 child, Jerry Dee Jr. AB cum laude, Elon (N.C.) Coll., 1957; JD, Tulane U., New Orleans, 1960; diploma, Army Command & Gen. Staff Sch., USAR, 1981. Bar: Colo. 1961, U.S. Dist. Ct. Colo. 1961, U.S. Ct. Mil. Appeals 1962, U.S. Supreme Ct. 1965, N.C. 1965. Legal clk. Air Def. Commd., Colorado Springs, Colo., 1960-61, assistance officer, 1962-63; chief legal assistance divsn. 2nd Army, Ft. Meade, Md., 1964-65; staff JAG, Indiantown Gap Mil. Reservation, 1965; law clk. to hon. Eugen Gordon U.S. Dist. Ct. (mid. dist.) N.C., Winston-Salem, 1965-66; dir. Legal Aid Soc. Forsyth County, Winston-Salem, 1966-69; exec. dir. Forsyth Bail Project, Winston-Salem, 1968-69, Lawyer Referral Svc. of Bar of 21st Jud. Dist., Winston-Salem, 1968-69; staff atty. office of gen. counsel FAA, Washington, 1969-70, acting chief admin. & legal resources, 1970-71; staff atty. office of gen. counsel Dept. Housing & Urban Devel., Washington, 1971; area counsel Jackson (Miss.) field office Dept. Housing & Urban Devel., 1971-83, chief counsel Jackson (Miss.) field office, 1983-94; chief counsel Office Gen. Counsel Miss., Jackson, 1994—; lectr. U. W.Va. Conf. on Poverty Law, 1968. Editor N.C. Legal Aid Reporter, 1968-69, N.C. Legal Aid Directory, 1968, Avlex Legal Index (2nd supplement), 1971; contbr articles to profl. jours., articles to splty. mags. Dem. candidate N.C. Ho. of Reps., Guilford County, 1964; mem. military com. Forsyth County N.C. Red Cross, 1967-68; pack leader Andrew Jackson coun. Boy Scouts Am., 1986-92; active Project Adv. Group U.S. Office Econ. Opportunity Legal Svcs. Program, 1968-69, Adv. Com. on Housing & Urban Devel., Miss., Law Rsch. Inst. 1963-81, Pilot Mountain Preservation & Park Com., Winston-Salem, 1968-70; mem. Race Com. Whitworth Hunt Races, 1973-76. Capt. AUS, 1960-65; ret. lt. col. USAR, 1966-87. Decorated Meritorious Svc. medal, Army Commendation medal with one oak leaf cluster. Mem. Fed. Bar Assn., N.C. State Bar, Miss. Hist. Assn., Miss. Track Club, Iron Bridge Hunt Club (v.p. 1964-65), Whitworth Hunt Club (founder, master of foxhounds 1975-76), The Austin Hunt (joint master of foxhounds 1976-79), Caledonian Soc. Miss., Sons of Confederate Vets., Pi Gamma Mu. Republican. Episcopal. Avocations: riding to hounds, running, book collecting. Home: Ivanhoe 935 Bellevue Pl Jackson MS 39202 Office: Dept Housing & Urban Devel Miss State Office 9th Fl Fed Bldg 100 W Capitol Jackson MS 39269

MOJICA, AGNES, academic administrator. Chancellor Internat. Am. U., San German, P.R. Office: Inter Am U Office of the Chancellor San German PR 00753

MOJICA, AURORA, association executive; b. Mayaguez, P.R., Feb. 19, 1939; d. Luis Martinez and Anna Celida Montalvo; m. Aristides Mojica, Jan. 19, 1957 (div. July 1967); children: Ty, Marc Anthony, Raymond

Francis, Sharai, Angeles. BS in Mgmt. and Labor Rel., Cornell U., 1979; postgrad., Boston U.; M in Tng. and Edn. Asst. dir. Attica Commn., N.Y.C., 1974, South Bklyn. Health Ctr., N.Y.C., 1975-79; sec. to the dept., dir. cmty. rels. (1st woman apptd.) Fire Dept. N.Y.C., 1979-81; dir. pub. cmty. rels. WYC Koff Heights Hosp., N.Y.C., 1981-84, Interfaith Adopt-A-Bldg., N.Y.C., 1984-86; dir. women health svcs. Woodhull Med. and Mental Health Ctr., N.Y.C., 1986-87; dir. individual and family grants program Fed. Emergency Mgmt. Agy., P.R., 1987-88; exec. dir. Nat. Image, Inc., Washington, 1988-90; pres. Wall St. chpt. Nat. Image, Inc.; regional tng. dir., safety rep. N.Y. State Dept. Transp., Long Island City, 1990—; cons. Agy. for Internat. Devel., Mex., Costa Rica and Peru, 1981—; trainer Venezuela and P.R., Cornell U. P.R. Studies, N.Y., 1971—; trainer and bd. dirs. Neighborhood Reinvestment, N.Y.C., 1984-86. Bd. dirs. Dialogue on Diversity, Washington. Recipient Susan B. Anthony award for Pub. Svc., NOW, N.Y.C., 1981, Pub. Svc. award U.S. Dept. Labor, 1985, Gov. award for excellence, 1994, Women of Achievement award N.Y. State Dept. Transportation, 1994, Advisors Program for Women award Gov. N.Y., 1994; cert. of Recognition Sesame Street CTW, N.Y.C. 1983;. Named Hispanic Woman of the Yr. in Health Hispanic Woman's Network, Bklyn., 1987; Nat. Hispana Leadership Inst. fellow, 1990, 91. Roman Catholic. Office: NY State Dept Transp Hunters Point Plz 47-40 21st St Long Island City NY 11101

MOJTABAI, ANN GRACE, author, educator; b. N.Y.C., June 8, 1937; d. Robert and Naomi (Friedman) Alpher; m. Fathollah Mojtabai, Apr. 27, 1960 (div. 1966); children: Chitra, Ramin. B.A. in Philosophy, Antioch Coll., 1958; M.A. in Philosophy, Columbia U., 1968, M.S. in L.S., 1970. Lectr. philosophy Hunter Coll., CUNY, 1966-68; librarian CCNY, 1970-76; fellow Radcliffe Inst. Ind. Study, Cambridge, Mass., 1976-78; Briggs-Copeland lectr. in English Harvard U., 1978-83; writer-in-residence U. Tulsa, 1983—, Yaddo Found., Saratoga, N.Y., 1975, 76. Author: Mundome, 1974, The 400 Eels of Sigmund Freud, 1976, A Stopping Place, 1979, Autumn, 1982, Blessed Assurance, 1986, Ordinary Time, 1989, Called Out, 1994. Recipient Richard and Hinda Rosenthal award Am. Acad. and Inst. Arts and Letters, 1983, Lillian Smith award So. Regional Council, 1986, Lit. Acad. award AAAL, 1993; Guggenheim fellow, 1981-82. Mem. PEN, Mark Twain Soc., Tex. Inst. Letters, Phi Beta Kappa. Home: 2102 S Hughes Amarillo TX 79109-2212 Office: U Tulsa Dept English 600 S College Ave Tulsa OK 74104-3189

MOK, NGAIMING, mathematics educator; b. Hong Kong, May 22, 1956; came to U.S., 1975; s. Mau-Hong and Lai-Chun (Tai) M.; m. Julia Kwanyiu Ko, Aug. 20, 1982; 1 child, Vivienne Ting-Ting. Student, U. Chgo., 1975-76; MA, Yale U., 1978; PhD, Stanford U., 1980. Instr., then asst. prof. Princeton (N.J.) U., 1980-84; prof. U. Paris, 1985; assoc. prof. Columbia U., N.Y.C., 1985-89; prof. math. Columbia U., 1989—. Author: Metric Rigidity Theorems on Hermitian Locally Symmetric Spaces, 1989; contbr. articles to math. jours. Sloan Found. fellow, 1984-86; NSF grantee, 1980—. Mem. Am. Math. Soc. Office: Columbia U Dept Math New York NY 10027

MOKHAYESH, CARL, retired electrical engineer; b. Damascus, Syrian Arab Republic, Feb. 14, 1941; came to U.S., 1961; s. Mahmood and Naemeh (Nasri) M.; m. Mary Frances Beafore, Mar. 28, 1970. Student, U. Mo., 1962-65; BSEE, Detroit Inst. Tech., 1970; MSEE, Wayne State U., 1975. Sr. plant engr., Great Lakes Div. National Steel, Ecorse, Mich., 1965-92; ret., 1992; cons. various overseas firms. Mem. IEEE. Avocations: tennis, golf, racquetball, swimming, backgammon, chess, traveling.

MOKODEAN, MICHAEL JOHN, lawyer, accountant; b. Canton, Ohio, Dec. 24, 1923; s. Michael and Elizabeth (Stroia) M.; m. Jean Cristea, Apr. 17, 1950 (dec.); children: Michael Dan, Christine Ann; m. Josephine Woodward, Jan. 28, 1995. B.S. in Edn, Kent (Ohio) State U., 1948; J.D., William McKinley Sch. Law, Canton, 1955. Bar: Ohio 1955; C.P.A., Ohio. Agt. IRS, Canton, 1950-56; self-employed atty. C.P.A., Canton, 1957-69; tax accountant Elmer Fox & Co., Las Vegas, Nev., 1969; mgr. tax and ins. Diebold, Inc., Canton, 1969-74; sec., house counsel Diebold, Inc., 1974-78, v.p. legal, 1978-87, cons., 1987-89; part-time instr. tax accounting Walsh Coll., N. Canton, 1963-64, bd. advisers, 1976—; bd. advisers Stark Tech. Coll., Canton, 1972-76. Bd. advisers Doctors' Hosp., Massillon, Ohio, 1986—. With AUS, 1943-46. Mem. Brookside Country Club. Roman Catholic. Home: 2607 Charing Cross Rd NW Canton OH 44708-1575

MOKRASCH, LEWIS CARL, neurochemist, educator; b. St. Paul, May 9, 1930; s. Lewis and Anna (Dvorak) M.; m. Jane Carolyn Church, Apr. 20, 1974. B.S. magna cum laude, Coll. St. Thomas, 1952; Ph.D., U. Wis., 1955. Research assoc. dept. psychiatry and neurology La. State U. Med. Center, New Orleans, 1956-57; assoc. prof. dept. biochemistry La. State U. Med. Center, 1971-76, prof., 1976-92, prof. emeritus, 1992—, acting head dept., 1978-79; instr. medicine U. Kans. Med. Center, Kansas City, 1957-59, assoc. in medicine, dir. neurochemistry lab., 1959-62; asst. biochemist McLean Hosp., Belmont, Mass., 1960-64, assoc. biochemist, 1964-71; assoc. dept. biol. chemistry Harvard Med. Sch., Boston, 1964-67; asst. prof. 1967-71; adj. assoc. prof. biology Hellenic Coll., Brookline, Mass., 1969-71; staff scientist Neurosciences Research Programs, Brookline, 1970-71; vis. prof. neurology Duke U. Med. Center, 1981-82; lectr. in field. Author book written on myelin; contbr. articles to profl. jours.; book reviewer for jours. Sci. and FASEB. Pres. Belmont Preservation Soc., 1969; candidate Bd. Selectman, Belmont, 1969; active Met. Opera Guild, Piedmont Opera Guild, Winston Salem Piedmont Triad Symphony Guild, Reynolda Ho. Mus. Am. Art. Grantee NIMH, 1973-74, Nat. Inst. Neurol. Disability and Blindness, 1957-90, Schlieder Found., 1971-72, 83-84, La. Bd. Regents, 1986-88. Fellow Am. Assn. Clin. Chemists; mem. AAUP, Am. Soc. Neurochemistry (local chmn. 1974), Am. Soc. Biol. Chemists, Soc. Neurosci. (pres. local chpt. 1974-75), Soc. Rsch. Adminstrs. (membership chmn. New Eng. sect.), Nat. Citizens Coalition Nursing Home Reform, Nat. Taxpayers Union, Nat. Alliance Sr. Citizens, Am. Assn. Individual Investors (pres. Piedmont chpt.), Peoples Med. Soc. Libertarian. Achievements include first demonstration of adaptive enzyme regulation in animals and allosteric control of fructose bisphosphatase, of incorporation of hydrouracil into transfer RNA, of thermogenic mechanism for arousing hibernators, of metabolic control in hibernation, of altered hydrophobic proteins in neurological disorders, of biosynthesis of hydrophobic proteins and mitochondrial proteins in brain in vitro, of altered transport processes in cells of neurological disease victims, of defective transport of acetylcholine precursors into cells of Alzheimer's victims and that such transport is modulatable; development of coestimation method for ketoses, aldoses, and pentoses; first isolation in pure form of receptor hydrophobic proteins from mammalian brain. Home: 1422 Reynolda Rd Winston Salem NC 27104-1016 *Before I entered Science, I regarded it as a Priesthood of individuals dedicated to the service of humanity, whose common goal was the enhancement of human life and the remedying of its ills. After 30 years in Science, I hold this thesis more strongly and have found many colleagues who agree with it. I am certain now that the failures and abuses of Science derive from the use of it for the goals of wealth, fame and power.*

MOLDAW, STUART G., venture capitalist, retail clothing stores executive; b. 1927. Student, Syracuse U. With Allied Stores, N.Y.C., 1949-51, G. Fox Co., Hartford, Conn., 1951-55; founder Foxmoor Casuals, 1959; co-founder U.S. Venture Ptnrs., 1981; chief exec. officer Ross Store Inc., Newark, Calif. from 1987, chmn. bd., 1988—. Office: Ross Stores Inc PO Box 728 8333 Central Ave Newark CA 94560-3440

MOLDEN, HERBERT GEORGE, publisher; b. Taunton, Mass., June 14, 1912; s. Ernest William and Edith (Parker) M.; m. Eleanor Caswell, Aug. 26, 1935; children: Marilyn (Mrs. Robert Erb), Parker C. Ph.B., Brown U., 1934. Head history dept. Storm King Sch., Cornwall on Hudson, N.Y., 1934-44; salesman, promotion mgr., exec. editor Macmillan Co., 1944-60; v.p. McCormick-Mathers Pub. Co., Inc., Wichita, Kans., 1960-61; with Am. Book Co., 1961-69, pres., 1968—; pres. Cambridge Book Co., 1970-78, H.G. Molden Co. Inc., Fairfield, Conn., 1978—; v.p., dir. N.Y. Times Media Co., 1971-76. Mem. Phi Beta Kappa.

MOLDENHAUER, JUDITH A., graphic design educator; b. Oak Park, Ill., Feb. 28, 1951; d. Raymond L. and Jean Marie (Carqueville) M. BFA, U. Ill., 1973; MA, Stanford U., 1974; MFA, U. Wis., 1977. Design supr. N.E. Mo. State U., Kirksville, Mo., 1977-79; asst. prof. design, design dept. Kans.

City Art Inst., Mo., 1979-83; asst. prof. art, graphic design Sch. Art U. Mich., Ann Arbor, 1983-92; vis. lectr. Wayne State U., 1990-92, asst. prof. graphic design, 1992—, area coord. graphic design, 1992—; free-lance designer The Detroit Inst. Arts, Toledo (Ohio) Mus. Art, Burroughs Corp. (Unisys) Detroit, Detroit Focus Gallery; vis. designer N.S. Coll. Art and Design, 1986; juror Ohio Mus. Assn., 1986, collaborator Presdl. Initiative "Healthy Start: prenatal and pre-conceptional booklets and ednl. modules designs, 1992—. Contbr. articles to profl. jours. Co-recipient grant Nat. Endowment for Arts, 1988; recipient Rackham grant U. Mich., Ann Arbor, 1987, award of distinction, merit award Am. Assn. Museums, 1985, 86, Excellence Design award Beckett Paper Co., 1991, Gold award for softcover books Printing & Publishing Competition, 1994. Mem. Am. Ctr. Design, Univ. and Coll. Designers Assn. (merit award 1979, gold award 1979), Coll. Art Assn. (chmn. panel 1991), Women's Caucus for Art (panel chmn. 1987), Amnesty Internat., Women in Design (excellence award Chgo. 1985, Sierra Club, Audubon Soc. Lutheran. Office: Wayne State U Dept Art and Art History 150 Community Arts Ctr Detroit MI 48202

MOLDENHAUER, WILLIAM CALVIN, soil scientist; b. New Underwood, S.D., Oct. 27, 1923; s. Calvin Fred and Ida (Killam) M.; m. Catherine Ann Maher, Nov. 26, 1947; children—Ann Maher, Patricia, Barbara, James, Thomas. B.S., S.D. State U., 1949; M.S., U. Wis., 1951, Ph.D., 1956. Soil surveyor S.D. State U., Brookings, 1948-54; soil scientist U.S. Dept. Agr., Big Spring, Tex., 1954-57; soi. scientist U.S. Dept. Agr., Ames, Iowa, 1957-72, Morris, Minn., 1972-75; rsch. leader Nat. Soil Erosion Rsch. Lab., Agrl. Rsch. Svc. U.S. Dept. Agr., West Lafayette, Ind., 1975-85; prof. dept. agronomy Purdue U., West Lafayette, 1975-85, prof. emeritus, 1985—. Contbr. articles to profl. jours. Served with U.S. Army, 1943-46. Fellow Am. Soc. Agronomy, Soil Sci. Soc., Soil Conservation Soc. Am. (pres. 1979), World Assn. Soil and Water Conservation (pres. 1983-85, exec. sec. 1985—). Home and Office: 317 Marvin Ave Volga SD 57071-9140

MOLEN, GERALD ROBERT, film producer; b. Great Falls, Mont., Jan. 6, 1935; s. Gerald Richard Molen and Edith Lorraine (Meyer) Burris; m. Patricia Jane Lindke, July 29, 1954; children: Steven Robert, Lorion Marie Molen Bunyea. Grad., Van Nuys (Calif.) High Sch., 1953. Transp. mgr. Universal City (Calif.) Studios, 1967-70; transp. coord. Ind. Producers, Hollywood, Calif., 1971-79; freelance prodn. mgr. Hollywood, 1980-91. Prodn. mgr.: (films) Postman Always Rings Twice, 1980, Tootsie, 1982, A Soldiers Story, 1983, The Color Purple, 1985; assoc. prodr.: (film) Batteries Not Included, 1986; exec. prodr.: (films) Bright Lights, Big City, 1987, A Far Off Place, 1993, The Flintstones, 1994, Little Rascals, 1994; prodr.: (films) Hook, 1991, Jurassic Park, 1992, Schindlers List, 1993 (Acad. award, Golden Globe award 1994); appeared in films: Rain Man, 1988 (also co-prodr.), Days of Thunder, 1990 (also exec. prodr.), Jurassic Park, 1992. Sgt. USMC, 1953-56. Mem. Dirs. Guild Am., SAG. Republican. Avocations: golf, travel, movies. Home: 17156 Balinger St Northridge CA 91325-1928

MOLEN, JOHN KLAUMINZER, lawyer; b. Gary, Ind., June 13, 1952; s. Franklin B. and Jane Anne (Klauminzer) M.; m. Susan Wilson Blair, Aug. 10, 1985; children: Mary Wilson, Elisabeth Blair. AB with honors, U. N.C., 1974, MBA, 1978, JD with honors, 1978. Bar: Ala. 1978. Assoc. Bradley, Arant, Rose & White, Birmingham, Ala., 1978-84, ptnr., 1984—. Mem. Rotary Club Birmingham-Sunrise. Presbyterian. Avocations: sailing, swimming. Office: Bradley Arant Rose & White 2001 Park Pl Ste 1400 Birmingham AL 35203

MOLER, EDWARD HAROLD, lawyer; b. Oklahoma City, May 26, 1923; s. Harold Stanley and Rosemary (Callahan) M.; m. Donna Blocksom Cram, Sept. 12, 1964; children: John Frederick, Shelley Elizabeth, Christopher Bryan. BA, U. Okla., 1947, LLB, 1948. Bar: Okla. 1948, U.S. Supreme Ct. 1951. Pvt. practice law Oklahoma City, 1948-52, 61—; asst. mcpl. counselor, 1952-59, mcpl. counselor, 1959-61; spl. justice Okla. Supreme Ct., 1977. Trustee Oklahoma City Mcpl. Improvement Authority, 1960-61; bd. dirs. Mummers Theatre, Inc., 1969—; bd. dirs. Greater Oklahoma City YMCA, 1981-91. 2d lt. USAAF, 1943-45. Mem. ABA, Okla. Bar Assn., Oklahoma County Bar Assn. (bd. dirs. 1963-67, pres. 1968), Rotary, Phi Delta Phi, Phi Gamma Delta (pres. local chpt. 1946, pres. Nu Omega Housing Assn. 1963-65). Home: 2540 NW Grand Blvd Oklahoma City OK 73116-4110 Office: City Pl Oklahoma City OK 73102

MOLER, ELIZABETH ANNE, federal agency administrator, lawyer; b. Salt Lake City, Jan. 24, 1949; d. Murray McClure and Eleanor Lorraine (Barry) M.; m. Thomas Blake Williams, Oct. 19, 1979; children: Blake Martin Williams, Eleanor Bliss Williams. BA, Am. U., 1971; postgrad., Johns Hopkins U., 1972; JD, George Wash. U., 1977. Bar: D.C. 1978. Chief legis. asst. Senator Floyd Haskell, Washington, 1973-75; law clk. Sharon, Pierson, Semmes, Crolius & Finley, Washington, 1975-76; profl. staff mem. com. on energy and natural resources U.S. Senate, Washington, 1976-77, counsel, 1977-86, sr. counsel, 1987-88; commr. FERC, Washington, 1988-93, chair, 1993—. Mem. ABA, D.C. Bar Assn. Democrat. Home: 1537 Forest Ln Mc Lean VA 22101-3317 Office: FERC 825 N Capitol St NE Rm 9000 Washington DC 20426

MOLER, JAMES CLARK, marketing research executive; b. West Union, Ohio, Nov. 17, 1930; s. Joseph Adam and Kathryn Susan (Clark) M.; m. Barbara Lucille Painter, Sept. 14, 1953 (div. 1973); children: Kathy, James. BBA, U. Cin., 1953. Various positions Burgoyne, Inc., Cin., 1956-62, v.p. client svc., 1962-65, exec. v.p., 1965-69; pres. J.C. Moler and Assocs., Cin., 1969-71, B&B Rsch. Svcs., Inc., Cin., 1971—. Lt. USN, 1953-56. Mem. Am. Mktg. Assn., Mkgt. Rsch. Assn. Avocations: woodworking, stamp collecting, tennis. Office: B&B Rsch Svcs Inc 8005 Plainfield Rd Cincinnati OH 45236-2500

MOLHO, ANTHONY, history educator; b. Thessaloniki, Greece, July 12, 1939; came to U.S., 1956; s. Saul and Lily (Alcalay) M.; m. Brenda Neff, Sept. 3, 1961 (div. 1982); children: Elizabeth, Lilla; m. Lynn M. Gunzberg, Dec. 23, 1984. Student, U. Florence, Italy, 1962-64; BA, Western Res. U., 1959, PhD, 1965. Tchr. The Hawken Sch., Cleve., 1969-61; instr. history U. Vt., Burlington, 1964-65; asst. prof. Mich. State U., East Lansing, 1965-66, assoc. prof., 1966-70; prof. Brown U., Providence, 1974-86, Munro-Goodwin-Wilkinson prof. European History, 1986—, chmn. dept. history, 1979-83, chmn. program in renaissance studies, 1986-89; vis. prof. U. Florence, 1983-1985. Author: Florentine Public Finances in the Early Renaissance, 1971; co-editor: Alle Bocche della Piazza, 1986, Marriage Alliance in Late Medieval Florence, 1994, Origini dello Stato, 1994. NEH fellow, 1968-69, 78-79, Villa I Tatti fellow, Florence, 1971-72, 74-75, The Getty Trust fellow, 1989-90, Guggenheim fellow, 1994-95. Mem. Soc. for Italian Hist. Studies (pres. 1989). Office: Brown Univ Dept of History Box N Providence RI 02912

MOLHO, EMANUEL, publisher; b. N.Y.C., Jan. 27, 1936; s. Isaac Emanuel and Alvira (Altchek) M.; m. Brenda Nadel, Sept. 25, 1965; children—Deborah Rochelle, Brian Emanuel. B.A., N.Y. U., 1957; M.B.A., Wharton Sch., U. Pa., 1960. Pres. French & European Publs., Inc., N.Y.C., 1961—, French & Spanish Book Corp., 1967—, Brendeman Pub. Cons., 1977—; pres., dir. Librairie de France, Inc., 1961—. Recipient Orden de Merito Civil Spain, 1975. Mem. Am. Booksellers Assn., French-Am. C. of C. in U.S. (exec. com.). French Am. Club. Office: Librairie de France Rockefeller Center Promenade 610 5th Ave New York NY 10020-2497

MOLHOLM, KURT NELSON, federal agency administrator; b. Denver, June 24, 1937; s. Ervin Maurice and Helen Pauline (Nelson) M.; m. Sonja Dell Williams, Aug. 17, 1967; children: Kevin William, Paul Nelson. BS, U. Oreg., 1959; MS, George Washington U., 1974. Computer specialist D.L.A. Adminstrv. Support Ctr., Alexandria, Va., 1963-65; with Hdqrs. Def. Logistics Agy., Alexandria, 1965-85, chief planning and policy office, 1975-76, chief ADP/T tech div., 1984-85; adminstr. Def. Tech. Info. Ctr. Alexandria, 1985—; pres. Nat. Fedn. Abstracting and Info. Svcs., Phila., 1993-94, treas., 1990-93; del. Va. Govs. Conf. Librs. Info. Svcs., 1990, Fed. Libr. Pre-White House Conf. on Librs. Info. Sci., 1990; vice chmn. Fed. Libr. and Info. Info. Com., 1992-93; chmn. Commerce, Energy, NASA, NLM, Def. Info. Group, 1991-94; mem. NATO Agard Tech. Info. Panel, 1985-91. 1st lt. U.S. Army. 1st lt. U.S. Army, 1960-63. Recipient Meritorious award William A. Jump Meml. Found., 1973. Mem. Internat. Coun. on Sci. and Tech. Info. Methodist. Office: Def Tech Info Ctr Cameron Sta Alexandria VA 22304

MOLHOLT, PAT, university official; b. Fond du Lac, Wis., Oct. 19, 1943; d. Elmore Harrison and Leona Ann (Reschke) Leu; divorced; children: Rebecca Marie, Stephanie Anne. BS, U. Wis., 1966, MLS, 1970; postgrad., Rensselaer Poly. Inst., 1985—. Library intern Milw. Pub. Library, 1966-67; astronomy librarian, dept. astronomy U. Wis., Madison, 1970-73; physics librarian U. Wis. Libraries, Madison, 1973-77; asst. prof. dir. U. Wyo. Sci. and Tech. Library, Laramie, 1977-78; assoc. dir. Rensselaer Poly. Inst. Libraries, Troy, N.Y., 1978-92, affirmative action advisor to pres., 1988-92; asst. v.p., assoc. dean scholarly resources Columbia U., N.Y.C., 1992—; co-dir. art and architecture thesaurus program J. Paul Getty Trust, Williamstown, Mass., 1983-86; rsch. analyst U.S. Dept. Edn., Washington, 1987-88; pres. Universal Serials and Book Exch., 1988-89; trustee Capital Dist. Libr. Coun., 1986-89; bd. visitors U. Pitts. Sch. Libr. and Info. Studies, 1993-95; mem. adv. bd. libr. sci. program Wayne State U., Detroit, 1992-95. Contbr. articles to profl. jours. Mem. adv. bd. Sch. Info. and Pub. Policy, SUNY-Albany, 1989; mem. steering com. N.Y. Gov.'s Conf. on Libr. and Info. Svcs., 1989-90; active N.Y. State Regent's Vis. Com. on State Archives, 1991—. Fellow Spl. Librs. Assn. (pres. 1983-84, John Cotton Dana award 1989); mem. ALA, NSF (mem. adv. bd., divsn. networking comm. rsch. and infrastructure 1991-92), Sci. Libr. Assn., Am. Soc. Info. Sci. (chair tech. program com. mid-yr. meeting, 1994). Office: Columbia U Health Scis 701 W 168th St Rm 201 New York NY 10032

MOLINA, MARIO JOSE, physical chemist, educator; b. Mexico City, Mexico, Mar. 19, 1943; came to U.S., 1968; s. Roberto Molina-Pasquel and Leonor Henríquez; m. Luisa Y. Tan, July 12, 1973; 1 child, Felipe. Bachillerato, Acad. Hispano Mexicana, Mexico City, 1959; Ingeniero Químico, U. Nacional Autónoma de México, 1965; postgrad., U. Freiburg, Fed. Republic Germany, 1966-67; Ph.D., U. Calif., Berkeley, 1972. Asst. prof. U. Nacional Autónoma de México, 1967-68; research assoc. U. Calif.-Berkeley, 1972-73; research assoc. U. Calif-Irvine, 1973-75, asst. prof. phys. chemistry, 1975-79, assoc. prof., 1979-82; sr. rsch. scientist Jet Propulsion Lab., 1989-88; prof. dept. earth, atom and planet sci., dept. chemistry MIT, Cambridge, 1989—, Martin prof. atmospheric chemistry. Mem. Pres.'s Com. of Advisors on Sci. and Tech. Recipient Tyler Ecology award, 1983, Esselen award for chemistry in pub. interest, 1987. Mem. NAS, Am. Chem. Soc., Am. Phys. Soc., Am. Geophys. Union, Pres.'s Com. on Advisors on Sci. and Tech., Sigma Xi. Achievements include discovering the theory that fluorocarbons deplete ozone layer of stratosphere. Home: 8 Clematis Rd Lexington MA 02173-7117 Office: MIT Dept of EAPS 54-1312 77 Massachusetts Ave Cambridge MA 02139-4307 *We have to understand our environment to find out if we are tampering with it. One of our accomplishments has been to call attention to society's potential altering of the atmosphere.*

MOLINAR, LUPE RODRIQUEZ, librarian, library director; b. Marathon, Tex., June 6, 1942; d. Luciano and Ignacia (Ramirez) Rodriquez; m. Victor O. Molinar, July 29, 1961; 1 child, Lynn Molinar Bigwall. AA, N.Mex. Jr. Coll., 1989. Cert. libr., Tex. Store clk., waitress Big Bend (Tex.) Nat. Pk., 1960-64; cafeteria worker Sul Ross State U., Alpine, Tex., 1964-65; nurse's aide Twilight Acres, Seminole, Tex., 1969-75; circulating clk. Gaines Co. Libr., Seminole, Tex., 1975-76, processing clk., 1976-91, libr., 1991—. Vol. Voters Registration, Seminole, 1980—; chair St. James Fall Festival, Seminole, 1994; bd. trustees Seminole Ind. Sch. Dist., 1994—. Mem. Tex. Libr. Assn., Guadalupanas Soc. (pres. 1988-89). Democrat. Roman Catholic. Avocations: music, reading, handicrafts. Home: 400 NW H Seminole TX 79360 Office: Gaines County Libr 704 Hobbs Hwy Seminole TX 79360-3402

MOLINARI, SUSAN K., congresswoman; b. S.I., N.Y., Mar. 27, 1958; d. Guy V. and Marguerite (Wing) M.; m. Bill Paxon, 1994. BA, SUNY, Albany, 1980, MA, 1982. Former intern for State Senator Christopher Mega; former rsch. analyst N.Y. State Senate Fin. Com.; former fin. asst. Nat. Rep. Gov.'s Assn.; civic community liaison Rep. Nat. Com., 1983-84; minority leader N.Y.C. Council, 1986-90; mem. 101st-104th Congresses from 14th (now 13th) N.Y. dist., 1990—; mem. budget com., chmn. transp. and infrastructure subcom. on railroads. Roman Catholic. Office: US Ho of Reps 2435 Rayburn HOB Washington DC 20515*

MOLINDER, JOHN IRVING, engineering educator, consultant; b. Erie, Pa., June 14, 1941; s. Karl Oskar and Carin (Ecklund) M.; m. Janet Marie Ahlquist, June 16, 1962; children: Tim, Karen. BSEE, U. Nebr., 1963; MSEE, Air Force Inst. Tech., 1964; PhD EE, Calif. Inst. Tech., 1969. Registered profl. engr., Calif. Project officer Ballistic Systems Div., Norton AFB, Calif., 1964-67; sr. engr. Jet Propulsion Lab., Pasadena, Calif., 1969-70; prof. engring. Harvey Mudd Coll., Claremont, Calif., 1970—; part-time lectr. Calif. State U., Los Angeles, 1970-74; mem. tech. adv. panel Kinemetrics, Pasadena, 1985-86; part-time mem. tech. staff Jet Propulsion Lab., Pasadena, 1974—; rep. NASA Hdqrs., Washington, 1979-80; vis. prof. elec. engring. Calif. Inst. Tech., 1982-83. Contbr. articles to profl. jours. Served to capt. USAF, 1963-67. Mem. IEEE. Avocations: bicycling, reading, computers. Office: Harvey Mudd Coll Dept of Engring 301 East 12th St Claremont CA 91711

MOLINE, JON NELSON, philosopher, educator, college president; b. Ft. Worth, May 12, 1937; s. Paul Ross and Elsie Virginia (Nelson) M.; m. Sandra Lois Reininger, Aug. 13, 1960; children—Kevin, Eric. A.B., Austin Coll., 1960; Ph.D., Duke U., 1964; LHD, Austin Coll., 1995. Asst. prof. U. Wis., Madison, 1964-69; assoc. prof. U. Wis., 1969-73, prof. philosophy, 1973-86, prof. environ. studies, 1974-86; faculty adviser U. Wis. (Nat. Humanities Faculty), 1976-82; v.p., dean St. Olaf Coll., Northfield, Minn., 1987-94; pres. Tex. Lutheran Coll., Seguin, 1994—; vis. assot. prof. U. Ill. at Chgo., 1969; vis. assoc. prof. U. Tex., Austin, 1971-72; fellow Nat. Humanities Center, 1979-80. Pres. Madison Symphony Orch., 1975-77; bd. dirs. Fund for Improvement Post-Secondary Edn., 1985-91; mem. Nat. Coun. on the Humanities, 1991—, vice-chair, 1993—. Vis. fellow Inst. for Research in Humanities, 1973, 75-76; Spencer Found. fellow, 1974; Rockefeller Found. humanities fellow, 1975-86. Office: Texas Lutheran College St Olaf Coll 1000 W Court St Seguin TX 78155

MOLINE, SANDRA LOIS, librarian; b. San Antonio, Dec. 13, 1938; d. Udo F. and Olivia Marie (Link) Reininger; m. Jon Nelson Moline, Aug. 13, 1960; children: Kevin, Eric. BA in Chemistry, Austin Coll., 1960; postgrad., Duke U., 1962-64; MA in History of Sci., U. Wis., 1976, MLS, 1977. Tchr. chemistry and physics Durham (N.C.) High Sch., 1960-64; head physics libr. U. Wis., Madison, 1977-88; head reference svcs. Sci. & Engring. Libr. U. Minn., Mpls., 1988-94; libr. reader's svc. Luth. Coll., 1994—; reader Svcs. Libr., Tex. Luth. Coll., 1994—. Mem. Spl. Librs. Assn. (physics, astronomy, math, sci.-tech. divsns.). Librs. Assembly (sec., treas. 1980, pres. 1983), Madison Acad. Staff Assn. (steering com. 1980-83, pres. 1982). Home: 605 Fleming St Seguin TX 78155

MOLINO, PATRICIA MARY, communications executive; b. Jersey City, N.J., Nov. 20, 1946; d. Nicholas and Jean (Rocco) M.; m. Ronald J. Sullivan. BS, NYU, 1968, MA, 1987. Writer Am. Mus. Nat. History, N.Y.C., 1968-69; dir. pub. affairs Bot. Garden, N.Y.C., 1969; dir. pub. rels. Hunter Coll. CCNY, 1970-74; dir. communications Deutsch, Shea & Evans, N.Y.C., 1975; dir. pub. info. Meml. Sloan-Kettering Cancer Ctr., N.Y.C., 1976-84; pres. Patricia Molino Communications, N.Y.C., 1985-89; sr. v.p. healthcare Makovsky & Co., N.Y.C., 1989; pres. Molino & Assocs., N.Y.C., 1989—. Bd. dirs. Family Dynamics, N.Y.C., 1986—. Mem. AAAS, Pub. Relations Soc. Am., N.Y. Acad. Scis. Avocation: real estate. Office: 245 5th Ave Ste 2404 New York NY 10016-8728

MOLINOFF, PERRY BROWN, biology educator; b. Smithtown, N.Y., June 3, 1940; s. Henry Charles and Thelma (Brown) M.; m. Marlene Sirota, 1963; children: Jeffrey, Sharon. BS, Harvard U., 1962, MD, 1967. Intern U. Chgo. Hosp. & Clinics, 1967-68; research assoc. NIMH, Bethesda, Md., 1968-70; vis. fellow Univ. Coll., London, 1970-72; asst. prof. U. Colo. Health Sci., Denver, 1972-76; assoc. prof. U. Colo. Health Sci., 1976-80, prof., 1980-81; prof., chmn. research U. Pa., Phila., 1981-94, prof., chmn. pharmacology, 1982-94; v.p.C.N.S. drug discovery Bristol-Myers Squibb, Wallingford, Conn., 1995—. Editor: Basic Neurochemistry, 1989, Biology of Normal and Abnormal Brain Function, 1990; editorial adv. bd. Molecular Pharmacology, 1976—. Med. adv. bd. Dysautonomia Found., 1977—. Lt. comdr. USPHS, 1968-70. Mem. Soc. Neurosci. (membership com.), Am. Heart Assn. (research com.), John Morgan Soc. (sec.-treas.1988—), Pa. Heart Assn.

Home: 234 Edgewood Ave Smithtown NY 11787-1856 Office: Bristol-Myers Squibb S Rsch PkwyP O Box 5100 Wallingford CT 06492-7600

MOLITEUS, MAGNUS, pharmaceutical and biotechnology company executive; b. Arvika, Sweden, Mar. 11, 1939; came to U.S., 1977; s. Erik and Karen (Allden) Nilsson; m. Margareta Lundberg, Dec. 30, 1961 (div. Feb. 1983); children: Ulrika, Elisabeth; m. Christina Ofverholm, Aug. 24, 1983; 1 child, Marcus. MS, Uppsala U., 1963, postgrad., 1965-66. Sales rep. Geigy, Gothenburg, Sweden, 1963-65; regional mgr. Pharmacia Internat. AB, Uppsala, 1965-70, chief exec. officer, 1976-77; dir. mktg. Pharmacia AB, Uppsala, 1970-73; chief exec. officer Pharmacia France S.A., Paris, 1973-76, Pharmacia Inc., Piscataway, N.J., 1977—; sr. v.p. Pharmacia AB, Uppsala, 1985—. Served to capt. Swedish Army Res. Mem. Health Industry Mfrs. Assn. (bd. dirs.), Swedish Am. C. of C. (chmn. 1989-92), Royal Round Table. Lutheran. Avocation: tennis. Office: Pharmacia Inc 800 Centennial Ave Piscataway NJ 08854-3911

MOLITOR, GRAHAM THOMAS TATE, lawyer; b. Seattle, Apr. 6, 1934; s. Robert Franklin and Louise Margaret (Graham) M.; m. Carlotta Jean Crate, July 30, 1960; children: Graham Thomas Tate, Anne Therese, Christopher Robert. B.S., U. Wash., 1955; LL.B., Am. U., 1963. Bar: D.C. 1963. Research asst. U. Wash., Seattle, 1957; bailiff U.S. Criminal Ct. D.C., 1958-59; legis. counsel U.S. Ho. of Reps., Washington, 1961-63; dir. candidate research Rockefeller for Pres. Com., 1963-64, 68; D.C. counsel, asst. dir. govt. relations Nabisco, Inc., Washington, 1964-70; dir. govtl. relations Gen. Mills, Inc., Washington, 1970-77; pres., chief exec. officer Public Policy Forecasting, Inc., Potomac, Md., 1977—; prin. ptnr. Public Policy Communicators, 1989-91; prin., ptnr. Pub. Policy Action Inst., Potomac; adv. bd. Creative Bus. Strategies, Inc.; adj. prof. Grad. Sch. Bus., Am. U., Washington, 1969-75, 79-85, Montgomer Coll., Rockville, Md., 1987-88; dir. rsch. White House Conf. on Indsl. World Ahead, 1971-72; mem. White House Adv. Com. on Social Indicators, 1975-76; chmn. Commn. on the Future of Montgomery County, 1986-88; guest lectr. numerous univs.; del. White House Confs. on Food, Nutrition and Health, 1969-71, White House Conf. on Youth, 1970; bd. dirs. First Global Conf. on the Future, Inc., Can., 1980—. Contbg. editor Food Tomorrow Newsletter, 1976-77; co-editor, chmn. editorial bd. Ency. of the Future, 1991—; mem. bd. editors Hudson Inst. Study of World Health, 1975-77; editorial bd. Bus. Tomorrow Newsletter, 1977-79; bd. advs. New Mktg. Technologies Monitor, 1983-85; polit. editor: On the Horizon, 1993—; contbr. articles to profl. jours. Mem. Food Adv. Bd., N.Y.C., 1980—. Served to 1st lt. U.S. Army, 1958-61. Recipient Disting. Service award Grocery Mfrs. Am., 1973-74, Disting. Service award Nat. Consumer Info. Center, 1974, Disting. Service award Am. Mgmt. Assn., 1975. Mem. Washington Bus.-Govt. Rels. Coun., Washington Indsl. Roundtable, E.D. Export Coun., World Future Soc. (gen. chmn. 2d Gen. Assembly 1975, v.p.; dir. 1981-94, v.p., legal counsel 1994—, Disting. Svc. award 1975), Univ. Club, Phi Kappa Sigma, Phi Alpha Delta. Republican. Presbyterian. Home and Office: 9208 Wooden Bridge Rd Rockville MD 20854-2416

MOLITOR, SISTER MARGARET ANNE, nun, former college president; b. Milford, Ohio, Sept. 19, 1920; d. George Jacob and Mary Amelia (Lockwood) M. B.A., Our Lady of Cin. Coll., 1942; M.Ed., Xavier U., 1950; LL.D.; M.A., Catholic U. Am., 1963, Ph.D., 1967. Joined Sisters of Mercy, 1943; tchr. elementary schs. Cin., 1946-50, secondary schs., Cin. and Piqua, Ohio, 1951-60; faculty Edgecliff Coll., Cin., 1962-73; pres. Edgecliff Coll., 1973-80; archivist Cin. Province Sisters of Mercy; research cons. various religious communities. Bd. dirs. Citizens Com. on Youth; trustee Chatfield Coll., Clermont Mercy Hosp., Mercy St. Theresa Retirement Ctr.; mem. Area Coun. Planning Task Force, Cin. Community Devel. Adv. Coun.; pres. Better Housing League of Greater Cin. Recipient Woman of Year award Cin. Enquirer, 1977, 200 Greater Cincinnatians Bicentennial award, 1988. Mem. Greater Cin. Consortium Colls. and Univs. (pres. 1980). Address: 2335 Grandview Ave Cincinnati OH 45206

MOLITOR, PAUL LEO, professional baseball player; b. St. Paul, Aug. 22, 1956; m. Linda Kaplan; 1 child, Blaire. Student, U. Minn., 1975-77. With Milw. Brewers, 1978-92, Toronto Blue Jays, 1992—; mem. Am. League All-Star Team, 1980, 85, 88, 91-94. Named Am. League Rookie of Yr. Sporting News, 1978, Sporting News Coll. All-America Team, 1977; recipient Silver Slugger award, 1987, 88, 93, World Series MVP award, 1993, Midwest League MVP award. Office: Toronto Blue Jays, 300 Bremner Blvd Gate No 9, Toronto, ON Canada M5V 3B3*

MOLL, CHARLES J., III, lawyer; b. Phila., Dec. 21, 1953; m. Christine K. Moll; children: Mark, Alexander. AB with distinction, Cornell U., 1976; JD with honors, George Washington U., 1979. Bar: Conn. 1979, Calif. 1981. Atty., advisor U.S. Tax Ct., Washington, 1979-81; assoc. Morrison & Foerster, San Francisco, 1981-88, ptnr., 1989—. Mem. ABA (chair young lawyers tax com. 1985-88, environ. tax com. sect. taxation, 1989-92),San Francisco Barristers' Club (tax sect.), San Francisco Tax Litigation Club. Office: Morrison & Foerster 345 California St San Francisco CA 94104

MOLL, CLARENCE RUSSEL, university president emeritus, consultant; b. Chalfont, Pa., Oct. 31, 1913; s. George A. and Anna A. (Schmidt) M.; m. Ruth E. Henderson, Nov. 19, 1941; children: Robert Henderson, Jonathan George. BS, Temple U., 1934, EdM, 1937; LHD, Pa. Mil. Coll., 1949; PhD, NYU, 1955; LLD, Temple U., 1963; ScD, Chungang U., Seoul, Korea, 1969; LLD, Swarthmore Coll., 1970, Gannon U., 1981; LittD, Delaware Valley Coll., 1976; PedD, Widener U., 1981. Instr. physics and chemistry Conshohocken (Pa.) High Sch., 1935-37; instr. sci. Freehold (N.J.) High Sch., 1937-38; instr. physics, chemistry Memorial High Sch., Haddonfield, N.J., 1938-42; instr. electronics and radar US Navy, Phila., 1942-43; assoc. prof. physics and electrical engring. Pa. Mil. Coll., Chester, Pa., 1943-45; registrar, coordinator engring. program Pa. Mil. Coll., 1945-47, dean admissions, student personnel, prof. coll., 1947-56, v.p., dean personnel services, 1956-59, pres. coll., 1959-72; pres. Widener U. (formerly PMC Colls.), 1972-81, chancellor, 1981-88, pres. emeritus, 1988—; pres. RC Assocs., Inc., 1981—; instr. electronics Temple U. 1944-46; headmaster Pa. Mil. Prep. Sch., 1945-47; bd. dirs. Fedders Corp., Ironworkers Sav. Bank. Author: numerous mag. articles. History of Pennsylvania Military College. Chmn. Pa. Commn. Ind. Colls., 1969, Found. for Ind. Colls. Pa., 1970; chmn. Com. for Financing Higher Edn. in Pa., 1975; bd. dirs. Crozer Chester Med. Ctr. (hon.); trustee Pa. Inst. Tech.; mem. Am. Assn. Homes and Svcs. for Aging, Continuing Care Accrediting Commn. Recipient Horatio Alger award, 1962, Disting. Alumnus award Temple U., 1964, B'nai B'rith Citizen Service award, 1966, Distinguished Citizen award, 1971, Themis award Del. County Bar, 1976, Good Citizenship award Phila. Bar, 1976, Exec. of Yr. award Soc. Advancement Mgmt., 1978. Mem. Assn. Mil. Colls. and Schs. (pres. 1969), Pa. Assn. Colls. and Univs. (pres. 1970, Sheepskin award 1982), Am. Soc. Engring. Edn., Springhaven Club (Wallingford, Pa.), Racquet Club, University Club (Wilmington, Del.), Tau Beta Pi, Phi Delta Kappa, Alpha Sigma Lambda, Phi Kappa Phi. Home: 1960 Dog Kennel Rd Media PA 19063-1008 Office: Widener U Chester PA 19013

MOLL, JOHN EDGAR, wholesale grocery company executive; b. Sikeston, Mo., Mar. 25, 1934; s. John A. and Letha A. (McDowell) M.; m. Marjorie Ellison, May 1, 1954; children—John Steven, Lynn Moll Rassieur, Nancy Moll Janeway, Julie Ann Moll Peters. Student Southeast Mo. State Coll. 1952-54, Program Mgmt. Devel. Harvard U., 1964. Office mgr. Malone & Hyde, Inc., Sikeston, 1957-64, div. mgr., 1964-70, div. mgr., Nashville, 1970-72, regional v.p., Nashville, 1972-76, v.p., Memphis, 1976-78, exec. v.p., 1978-88, pres. 1988-89; exec. v.p. Fleming Foods Inc., 1988-89, pres., 1989—. Exec. bd. Last Frontier coun. Boy Scouts Am.; co-chmn. shipping container com. Food Mktg. Inst. Served with USAF, 1953-57. Mem. Nat. Am. Wholesale Grocers Assn. (bd. govs.), Food Mktg. Inst. (co-chmn. shipping container com.), Oklahoma City C. of C. (bd. dirs.). Republican. Baptist. Office: Fleming Cos Inc 6301 Waterford Blvd Oklahoma City OK 73118-1124

MOLL, JOHN LEWIS, electronics engineer; b. Wauseon, Ohio, Dec. 21, 1921; s. Samuel Andrew and Esther (Studer) M.; m. Isabel Mary Sieber, Oct. 28, 1944; children: Nicolas Josef, Benjamin Alex, Diana Carolyn. B.Sc. Ohio State U., 1943, Ph.D., 1952; Dr. h.c., Faculty Engring., Katholieke U. Leuven, (Belgium), 1983. Elec. engr. RCA Labs., Lancaster, Pa., 1943-45; mem. tech. staff Bell Telephone Labs., Murray Hill, N.J., 1952-58; mem.

faculty Stanford U., 1958-69, prof. elec. engring., 1959-69; tech. dir. optoelectronics Fairchild Camera and Instrument Corp., 1969-74; dir. integrated circuits labs. Hewlett-Packard Labs., Palo Alto, Calif., 1974-80; dir. IC structures research, sr. scientist Hewlett-Packard Labs., 1980-87, dir. Superconductivity Lab., 1987-90, mem. tech. staff, 1990—. Author: Physics of Semi Conductors, 1964; co-author Computer Aided Design and VLSI Device Development, 1985, rev. edit., 1988; inventor (with Ebers) first analytical transistor model, 1953, still valid and useful for circuit design. Guggenheim fellow, 1964; recipient Howard N. Potts medal Franklin Inst., 1967, Disting. Alumnus award Coll. Engring., Ohio State U., 1970, Benjamin C. Lamme medal Coll. Engring. Ohio State U., 1988, Vladimir Karapetoff Eminent Members' award Eta Kappa Nu, 1995. Fellow IEEE (Ebers award 1971, Thomas A. Edison medal 1991), Am. Acad. Arts and Scis.; mem. Am. Phys. Soc., Nat. Acad. Engring., Nat. Acad. Scis., N.Y. Acad. Scis. Home: 4111 Old Trace Rd Palo Alto CA 94306-3728 Office: PO Box 10350 3500 Deer Creek Rd Bldg 26M Palo Alto CA 94303-0867

MOLL, LLOYD HENRY, banker; b. Reading, Pa., June 26, 1925; s. Lewis J. and Katie (Rothermel) M.; m. Luise G. Keiper, Oct. 25, 1947; children: Lloyd E., Darryl M. BA, Albright Coll., Reading, 1952. Aircraft engine installer War Dept., 1942-47; tire inspector Firestone Tire & Rubber Co., Pottstown, Pa., 1947-48; asst. mgr. Household Fin. Corp., Reading, 1952-57; v.p. Meridian Asset Mgmt. Inc. and Meridian Trust Co. (formerly Am. Bank & Trust Co. of Pa.), Reading, 1957-94; v.p. sales and mktg. Investors Trust Co., Wyomissing, Pa., 1995—; co-founder, past dir. Estate Planning Council of Berks County. Served with AUS, 1945-47. Mem. Am. Inst. Banking. (dir., chmn. bank relations Berks County chpt., pres. 1972-73), Toastmasters (pres. Reading club 1992), Optimists (pres. Reading club 1978-79). Democrat. Home: 213 W 39th St Crestwood Reading PA 19606 Office: Investors Trust Co 2201 Ridgewood Rd #180 Wyomissing PA 19610-1190 *Although it has been known to fail me on occasion I try to live by my understanding of the "Golden Rule." When it does fail me I'm usually able to discount such failure by recounting in my mind the many times it has been a two-way street or by convincing myself that I didn't try hard enough in this particular instance. All too often it comes to me much later that the other fellow's interpretation of the "Golden Rule" was far superior to mine. When this happens I have added to my learning. When it does not happen, it forces me to try that much harder to avoid "PERFECTION".*

MOLL, WILLIAM GENE, broadcasting company executive; b. Sikeston, Mo., Dec. 25, 1937; s. John Alexander and Letha Ann (McDowell) M.; m. Marilyn Lewis, Aug. 2, 1957; children: David William, Craig Lewis. Student, So. Ill. U., 1955-57, Anderson Coll., 1957-58; B.S. in Edn., S.E. Mo. State Coll., 1960; M.A., U. Tex., 1963. Announcer, program dir. Sta. KSIM, Sikeston, Mo., 1954-57, 58-59; announcer Sta. WCBC, Anderson, Ind., 1957; announcer, writer, dir.; news anchor KFVS-TV, Cape Girardeau, Mo., 1959-62; producer, dir., writer KLRN-TV, Austin, Tex., 1962-64; mgr. sta. ops. KLRN-TV, San Antonio, 1964-69; v.p., gen. mgr. WSMW-TV, Worcester, Mass., 1969-72; with KENS-TV, San Antonio, 1972-87, pres., gen. mgr., 1977-81, chmn., 1981-87; pres., chief exec. officer Harte-Hanks TV Group, 1979-81; pres., chief exec. officer Harte-Hanks Communications, Inc., 1981-87. Bd. dirs. San Antonio Art Inst., 1974—, chmn., 1978-81; bd. dirs. Goodwill Industries, 1973-87, pres., 1987-88; bd. dirs. San Antonio Symphony Soc., 1979-85, United Way San Antonio, 1979-82, Friends of the McNay, 1979-81, Media-Advt. Partnership for Drug-Free Am., 1987—; exec. bd. Alamo Area council Boy Scouts Am. Mem. Tex. Assn. Broadcasters (dir. 1976—, sec.-treas. 1981—, pres. 1983), TV Bur. of Advt. (bd. dirs. 1980—, sec. 1981-83, chmn. 1983-85, pres./chief exec. officer 1987—), CBS TV Affiliates Assn. (bd. dirs. 1980-83), Internat. Radio TV Found. (bd. dirs. 1985-88), Advt. Council (bd. dirs. 1987—), Electronic Media Rating Council (bd. dirs. 1987—). Clubs: Torch (San Antonio), Giraud (San Antonio); Oak Hills Country. Office: WKRC-TV 1906 Highland Ave Cincinnati OH 45219-3161

MOLLARD, JOHN DOUGLAS, engineering and geology executive; b. Regina, Sask., Can., Jan. 3, 1924; s. Robert Ashton and Nellie Louisa (McIntosh) M.; m. Mary Jean Lynn, Sept. 18, 1952; children: Catherine Lynn, Jacqueline Lee, Robert Clyde Patrick. BCE, U. Sask., 1945; MSCE, Purdue U., 1947; PhD, Cornell U., 1952. Registered profl. engr., profl. geologist Sask., Alta. and B.C., Can. Resident constrn. engr. Sask. Dept. Hwys and Transp., 1945; grad. asst. Purdue U., West Lafayette, Ind., 1946-47; rsch. engr. sch. civil engring. Cornell U., Ithaca, N.Y., 1950-52; air surveys engr., soil and water conservation and devel. Prairie Farm Rehab. Adminstrn., Govt. of Can., 1947-50; chief, airphoto analysis and engring. geology divsn. Prairie Farm Rehab. Adminstrn., Govt. of Can., Regina, 1953-56; pres. J.D. Mollard and Assocs. Ltd., Regina, 1956—; aerial resource mapping surveys tech. adv. Colombo plan, Govts. Ceylon and Pakistan, 1954-56; advisor Shaw Royal Commn. on Nfld. Agr.; Disting. lectr. series Ea. Can. Geotech. Soc., 1969; Cross Can. disting. lectr. Can. Geotech Soc., 1993; C.J. Mackenzie Disting. Grad. Meml. lectr. Coll. Engring. U. Sask., 1994; guest lectr., vis. lectr., instr. over 50 short courses on remote sensing interpretation aerial photos and satellite imagery numerous univs., cities and provinces in Can., also Cornell U., Ithaca, N.Y., Harvard U., Cambridge, Mass., U. Calif., Berkeley, U. Wis., Madison, U. Hawaii, 1952—. Author: Landforms and Surface Materials of Canada, 7 edits.; co-author: Airphoto Interpretation and the Canadian Landscape, 1986; contbr. over 100 articles to profl. pubs. Organizer, canvasser United Appeal campaigns; former bd. dirs. Regina Symphony Orch. Recipient Engring. Achievement award Assn. Profl. Engrs. Sask., 1984, Massey medal Royal Can. Geog. Soc., 1989. Fellow ASCE, Geol. Soc. Can., Geol. Soc. Am., Am. Soc. Photogrammetry and Remote Sensing (award for contbns. airphoto interpretation and remote sensing 1979), Internat. Explorers Club; mem. Engring. Inst. Can. (Keefer medal 1948), Assn. Cons. Engrs. Can., Can. Geotech. Soc. (1st R.M. Hardy Meml. Keynote lectr. 1987, Thomas Roy award with engring. geology divsn. 1989, R.F. Legget award 1992), Regina Geotech. Soc., Geol. Soc. Sask., Can. Soc. Petroleum Engrs., Regina YMCA (former dir.), Rotary (former dir. Regina club). Mem. United Ch. of Can. Avocations: jogging, reading, golf, tennis, nature study. Home: 2960 Retallack St, Regina, SK Canada S4S 1S9 Office: JD Mollard/Assoc 810 Avord Tower, 2002 Victoria Ave, Regina, SK Canada S4P 0R7

MOLLEGEN, ALBERT THEODORE, JR., engineering company executive; b. Meridian, Miss., Aug. 13, 1937; s. Albert Theodore and Harriette Ione (Rush) M.; m. Glenis Ruth Gralton, Feb. 16, 1962; children: Glenis Ione, Marion Anne. BEE, Yale U., 1961; postgrad. Poly. Inst. Bklyn., 1965-67. Cir. designer Melpar Inc., Falls Church, Va., 1958-59; system engr., group supr. Arma div. AMBAC Industries, N.Y.C., 1961-67; dept. mgr. Mystic Oceanographic Co. (Conn.), 1967-71; v.p., group mgr. Analysis & Tech. Inc., North Stonington, Conn., 1971-76, pres., CEO, 1976-91, chmn., CEO, bd. dirs., 1991—; bd. dirs. Continental Dynamics, Inc., Reston, Va., Automation Software, Inc., No. Kingston. R.I., Benthos, Inc., No. Falmouth, Mass., Philips Cir. Assemblies/Slatersville (R.I.) Inc., SEATECH, Groton, Conn. Applied Sci. Assocs., Inc., Butler, Pa., Gen. Systems Solutions, Inc., Groton, Ct., Naval Submarine League, Annandale, Va., Profl. Svcs. Coun., Vienna, Va. Inventor towed array rangefinder; writer numerous tech. reports. Chmn. Mystic Area Ecumenical Coun., 1970-72; treas. Seabury deanery Episcopal Diocese Conn., 1974-76, mem. diocesan fin. policy com., 1975, missionary strategy com., 1976-78, chmn. stewardship com., 1982-89, del. diocesan conv., 1974—, del. nat. gen. conv., 1991, alt. del. nat. gen. conv., 1982, 85, 88. Mem. Am. Soc. for Quality Control, IEEE, Am. Mgmt. Assn., Acoustical Soc. Am., Nat. Contract Mgmt. Assn., Ops. Rsch. Soc. Am., Inst. Mgmt. Scis., Navy League U.S., Am. Def. Preparedness Assn., Am. Soc. Naval Engrs. Surface Navy Assn., The Newcomer Soc. Home: 337 Pleasant St Willimantic CT 06226-3311 Office: Analysis & Tech Inc PO Box 220 North Stonington CT 06359-0220

MOLLENAUER, LINN FREDERICK, physicist; b. Washington, Pa., Jan. 6, 1937. B of Engring. in Physics, Cornell U., 1959; PhD in Physics, Stanford U., 1965. Asst. prof. physics U. Calif., Berkeley, 1965-72; rsch. staff mem. AT&T Bell Labs, Holmdel, N.J., 1972—. Co-editor: (with J.C. White) Tunable Lasers, 1987. Recipient Rank prize in Photonics, 1991, Ballantine medal Franklin Inst., 1986. Fellow AAAS, Optical Soc. Am. (R.W. Wood prize 1982), mem. IEEE (sr.), Nat. Acad. Engring. Office: AT&T Bell Labs Rm 4C-306 Crawfords Corner Rd Holmdel NJ 07733

MOLLER, HANS, artist; b. Wuppertal-Barmen, Germany, Mar. 20, 1905; came to U.S., 1936, naturalized, 1944; s. Ernst and Auguste (Heer) M.; m. Helen Rosenblum, Feb. 28, 1933. Student, Art Sch., Barmen, Germany, 1919-27, Berlin Acad., 1927-28. tchr. graphic design and painting Cooper Union, N.Y.C., 1944-56. One man shows include Bonestell Gallery, N.Y.C., 1942-43, Arts Club Chgo., 1945, U. Mich., 1945, Kleeman Galleries, N.Y.C., 1945, 47, 48, 49, 50, Pen and Palette Gallery, St. Louis, 1949, Grace Borgenicht Gallery, N.Y.C., 1951, 53, 54, 56, Fine Arts Assocs., 1957, Otto Gerson Gallery, 1960, Albert Landry Gallery, N.Y.C., 1962, Midtown Gallery (now Midtown Payson Galleries), 1964, 67, 70, 73, 76, 79, 81, 84, 87, Allentown Art Mus., Pa., 1969, 80, 93, Norfolk Mus., Va., 1970, Muhlenberg Coll., Allentown, 1977, Lehigh U., 1977, Madison (Conn.) Gallery, 1987, Hobe Sound (Fla.) Gallery, 1989, Baum Sch. Art, Allentown Art Mus., 1995, Torsteu Bröhan Gallery, Düsseldorf, Germany, 1995; exhibited in group shows at Colby Coll., F.A.R. Coll., Durand-Ruel Galleries, N.Y.C., Nierendorf Gallery, N.Y.C., Pa. Acad., Phila., Chgo. Art Inst., Whitney Mus. and Met. Mus., N.Y.C., Nat. Acad. N.Y., Bklyn. Mus., Corcoran Gallery, Washington, Va. Mus. Fine Arts, Richmond, Walker Art Center, Mpls., Worcester Mus. Mass., Phila. Print Club, Nat. Inst. Arts and Letters, N.Y.C., Maine Coast Artists, Rockport, 1991, Forty Years Maine Painting, 1952-92; included in, Mass. Pepsi Cola Show, N.Y.C., 1946; represented in permanent collections NAD, N.Y.C, Pa. Acad., Phila., The Michener Found., Mus. Modern Art, N.Y.C., Bklyn. Mus., Nat. Gallery Victoria, Australia, Staedtisches Mus., Wuppertal, Fed. Republic Germany, Walker Art Center, Mpls., Yellowstone Art Center, Billings, Mont., Phillips Meml. Gallery, Washington, Whitney Mus., N.Y.C., Detroit Inst. Art, Cummer Gallery, Jacksonville, Fla. N.Y. Pub. Library, Allentown Art Mus., Princeton U., Butler Inst. Am. Art, Youngstown, Ohio, Sunrise Found., Charleston, W.Va., Portland Mus. Art, Maine, Guggenheim Mus., N.Y.C., Nat. Mus. Am. Art, Washington, Va. Mus. Fine Art, Richmond, also univ. assns., pvt. collections, retrospective exhbn., 1926-56, 1956-62, Olsen Found. at U. Bridgeport, Bennington Coll., Dartmouth Coll., Trinity Coll., Mt. Holyoke Coll., Middlebury Coll., U. Vt., Portland Sch. Art, Bates Coll., U. Maine. Recipient first purchase prize Nat. Religious Art Exhbn., 1964, Edwin Palmer Meml. prize N.A.D., 1968, 80, Samuel Finley Breese Morse medal, 1969, Murry Kupferman prize Audubon Artists, 1973, Andrew Carnegie prize N.A.D., 1974, Hibbard Meml. award, 1975, purchase prize Childe Hassam Fund, 1966, 70, 76, 1st prize and merit medal Butler Inst. Am. Art, 1978, Edwin Palmer Meml. prize Nat. Acad. N.Y., 1980, 92, Andrew Carnegie prize, 1985. Mem. NAD, Audubon Artists Inc. (Gold medal and prize 1992). Home: 2207 W Allen St Allentown PA 18104-4327

MOLLER, WILLIAM RICHARD, JR., banker; b. N.Y.C., Mar. 14, 1941; s. William Richard and Inga Elinor (Olsen) M.; m. Molly Ann Tarkington, July 11, 1970; children: William Richard III, Sally McLaughlin, Katherine Tarkington. BA in English, Widener U., 1965; diploma, Am. Inst. Banking, 1976; postgrad., Rutgers U., Stonier Grad. Sch. Banking, 1983. Dir. alumni relations Widener U., Chester, Pa., 1970-71; asst. sec. Chemical Bank, N.Y.C., 1971-78; asst. v.p. Putnam Trust Co., Greenwich, Conn., 1978-80; v.p. Putnam Trust Co., Greenwich, 1980-82, v.p., sec., 1982-84, sr. v.p., sec., 1984—. Dir., treas Greenwich Emergency Med. Service, 1986-89; mem. Greenwich Hosp. Bd. Incorporators, 1985—. Capt. with U.S. Army, 1965-70, Vietnam. Mem. Am. Soc. Corp. Secs., Nat. Assn. Bus. Economists, Econs. Club Conn., Am. Bankers Assn. (com. of 52 1983—, adv. com. Stonier Grad. Sch. bd. 1985-88, govt. rels. coun. 1990-93, mem. community bankers coun. 1993—), Conn. Bankers Assn. (chmn. polit. action com. 1985—, legis. com.), Greenwich C. of C. (dir./treas. 1984—), Greenwich Country Club, Union Club, Rotary. Avocations: tennis, music, reading. Home: 130 Hendrie Ave Riverside CT 06878-1931 Office: Putnam Trust Co 10 Mason St Greenwich CT 06830-5431

MOLLER-GUNDERSON, MARK ROBERT, minister, administrator; b. Evanston, Ill., Feb. 1, 1950; s. Robert Leroy Gunderson and Marcia Louise (Scheuvnemann) G.; m. Mary Ann Moller, Sept. 1, 1973; children: David, Maria. BS, U. Ill., 1972; MDiv, Luth. Sch. Theology, 1976. Pastor Pilgrim Luth. Ch., Portland, Oreg., 1977-82, St. Matthew Luth. Ch., Madison, Wis., 1982-87; asst. to bishop Greater Milw. SYNOD, 1988-92; exec. dir. Evang. Luth. Ch. Am., Chgo., 1992—; chaplain Fire Dept., Portland, 1978-82, Milw., 1991-92, Park Ridge, Ill., 1994—. Chair Oreg. Fair Share, 1977-82, Citizen Action, 1978-84. Avocations: sailing, biking, triathlons, cross country skiing, running. Office: Evang Lutheran Ch in Am 8765 Higgins Rd Chicago IL 60631

MOLLER-GUNDERSON, MARY ANN, clergy member, church administrator. Exec. dir. Division for Congregational Ministries of the Evangelical Lutheran Church in America, Chicago, Ill. Office: Evang Luthern Ch in Am 8765 W Higgins Rd Chicago IL 60631

MOLLICA, JOSEPH A., pharmaceutical executive; b. 1940. Various positions, sr. v.p. drug devel. Ciba-Geigy, Ardsley, N.Y., 1966-88; v.p. med. products E.I. Du Pont De Nemours & Co., Inc., Wilmington, Del., 1988-91, dir. r&d, CEO, 1991—. Office: EI DuPont De Nemours & Co Inc Barley Mill Plz # P-25 Wilmington DE 19898

MOLLIGAN, PETER NICHOLAS, lawyer; b. New Orleans, Mar. 8, 1938; s. Peter Nicholas and Violet Augusta (Scheeler) M.; children: Liza J., Jessica L., Rene N. BA, La. State U., 1960; JD, San Francisco Law Sch., 1970. Bar: Calif. 1970. Claims mgr. Govt. Employees Ins. Co., San Francisco, 1963-70; trial atty., pres., CEO Molligan, Cox & Moyer, San Francisco, 1970—; pro-tem judge San Francisco Supreme Ct., 1989—. Lt. (j.g.) USN, 1960-65. Fellow Am. Coll. Trial Lawyers; mem. Am. Bd. Trial Advocates, Nat. Bd. Trial Advocates, ATLA, Calif. Trial Lawyers Assn. Avocations: tennis, chess. Office: Molligan Cox & Moyer 703 Market St San Francisco CA 94103-2102

MOLLMAN, JOHN PETER, book publisher, consultant electronic publishing; b. Belleville, Ill., Feb. 8, 1931; s. Kenneth John and Maurine (Farrow) M.; m. Jane Michael Kendall, Aug. 22, 1953; children—Sarah Chase, Eric Cleburne. B.Arts, Washington U., St. Louis, 1952. Advt. specialist Gen. Electric Co., Schenectady and Boston, 1952-54; mgr. Enterprise Printing Co., Millstadt, Ill., 1956-66; gen. mgr. Monarch Pub. Co., N.Y.C., 1966-67; dir. prodn. Harper & Row Pubs., N.Y.C., 1967-74; pub. Harper's Mag. Press, N.Y.C., 1971-74; v.p. prodn. Random House Inc., N.Y.C., 1974-81; sr. v.p. World Book-Childcraft Inc., Chgo., 1981-88; pres. World Book Pub., 1988-91; pub. cons., 1991-92; dir. intellectual property devel. Multimedia Publishing Microsoft, 1992—. Chmn. graphics standards rsch. com. NEH; mem. vis. com. Washington U., pub. com. Art Inst. of Chgo. With U.S. Army, 1954-56. Mem. Assn. Am. Pubs., Siwanoy Club (Bronxville, N.Y.), Sigma Delta Chi, Omicron Delta Kappa. Unitarian. Home: 4511 103d Ln NE Kirkland WA 98033 Office: Microsoft 1 Microsoft Way Redmond WA 98052

MOLLO, JOHN, film costume designer, military historian; b. London, Mar. 18, 1931; s. Eugene Simonovitch and Ella Clara (Cockell) M.; m. Margaret Ann Mollo, Apr. 4, 1966 (div. 1966); m. Louise Alexandra Mary Mollo, Aug. 12, 1968; 1 child, Thomas Frederick George. Student, Farnham Sch. Art, 1947-49. Print. Hist. Rsch. Unit, London, 1964-70, Mollo Publs., London, 1970-90, John Mollo Assocs., Hungerford, Eng., 1981—. Costume designer for films Star Wars, 1977 (Academy award best costume design 1977), Alien, 1978, The Empire Strikes Back, 1978, Outland, 1980, Gandhi, 1982 (Academy award best costume design 1982), The Lords of Discipline, 1982, Greystoke, 1983, King David, 1984, Revolution, 1985, Cry Freedom, 1986, White Hunter, Black Heart, 1989, Chaplin, 1991, Rudyard Kipling's Jungle Book, 1994, others; mil. adviser The Jewel in the Crown, 1981; hist. advisor The Charge of the Light Brigade, Barry Lyndon, others; author: Military Fashion, 1972, Uniforms of the American Revolution, 1975,, Acting capt., inf. Royal Army, 1950-56, Hong Kong and Eng. Recipient 2 Acad. awards; nominee: 2 Acad. awards. Mem. Soc. for Army Hist. Rsch. Acad. Motion Picture Arts and Scis. Avocations: painting, listening to music, collecting watercolors and militaria.

MOLLO-CHRISTENSEN, ERIK LEONARD, oceanographer; b. Bergen, Norway, Jan. 10, 1923; came to U.S., 1951, naturalized, 1955; s. Axel and Helga (Holmboe) Mollo-C.; m. Johanna D. Waller, Nov. 20, 1948; children—Jan E., Peter E., Anne. S.B. in Aero. Engring. Mass. Inst. Tech., 1948, S.M., 1949, Sc.D., 1954. With Norwegian Def. Research Establish-

ment, 1949-51, sr. sci. officer, 1951; grad. student, then research assoc. Mass. Inst. Tech., 1951-55, prof. aeronautics, 1955-84, prof. meteorology, 1964-73, prof. oceanography, 1973-84; prof. oceanography NASA/Goddard Space Flight Ctr., 1983-90, assoc. dir. earth scis., 1990-91, ret., 1991; cons. to industry from 1955. Guggenheim fellow, 1957. Fellow Am. Phys. Soc.; mem. AIAA (Von Karman award 1970), Am. Meteorol. Soc., Am. Geophys. Union., Am. Acad. Arts and Scis. Home: 10 Barberry Rd Lexington MA 02173-8026

MOLLOHAN, ALAN B., congressman, lawyer; b. Fairmont, W.Va., May 14, 1943; s. Robert H. and Helen (Holt) M.; m. Barbara Whiting, Aug. 7, 1976; children: Alan, Robert, Andrew, Karl, Mary Kathryn. AB in Polit. Sci., Coll. William and Mary, 1966; JD, W.Va. U., 1970. Assoc. law firm, 1970-82; mem. 98th-104th Congresses from 1st W.Va. dist., 1983—; mem. appropriations com., budget com. Mem. ABA, W.Va. Bar, Moose, Elks. Baptist. Office: US Ho of Reps Office of Postmaster 2242 Rayburn Ho Office Bldg Washington DC 20515*

MOLLOY, BRIAN JOSEPH, lawyer; b. Jersey City, July 19, 1953; s. Joseph G. and Agnes L. (Mullaney) M.; m. Christina M. Cencek, June 14, 1975; children: Brooke Leigh, Evan Joseph. BA, Kean Coll. of N.J., 1975; JD, Seton Hall U., 1978. Bar: N.J. 1978, U.S. Dist. Ct. N.J. 1978, U.S. Ct. Appeals (3d cir.) 1987, U.S. Supreme Ct. 1987. Ptnr. Wilentz, Goldman & Spitzer P.A., Woodbridge, N.J., 1978—. Mem. ABA, N.J. Bar Assn., Middlesex County Bar Assn. Home: 31 Hawthorne Dr Westfield NJ 07090-1947 Office: Wilentz Goldman & Spitzer PO Box 10 90 Woodbridge Ctr Dr Ste 900 Woodbridge NJ 07095-1146

MOLLOY, JAMES B., corrugated packaging executive. Pres., COO Tri-Pack Corp., Chgo., CEO. Office: Tri-Pack Corp 2828 S Lock St Chicago IL 60608-5444*

MOLLOY, MICHAEL JOHN, public relations professional; b. Phila., July 19, 1939; s. William John and Florence Hope (Buckley) M.; m. Johnise Josette Retossa, June 26, 1965; children: Johnie Michelle, Michael John Jr. BA, Coll. William and Mary, Williamsburg, Va., 1962. Reporter The Daily Press, Gloucester, Va., 1962-66; state news editor The Daily Press, Newport News, Va., 1967-68; asst. editor New Dominion mag., Newport News, Va., 1966-67; editor publs. Newport News Shipbldg. and Dry Dock Co., 1968-70; with Va. Power, 1970-94; staff project adminstr. Va. Power, Fairfax, 1989-94. Mem. County Planning Commn., Warrenton, Va., 1987-94, chmnn., 1989, 94. Mem. Pub. Rels. Soc. Am., Soc. Profl. Journalists, Warrenton-Fauquier C. of C. (pres. 1984), John Marshall Club (pres. 1990), Fauquier Springs Country Club. Avocations: golfing, gardening, traveling. Home: 7907 Sir Topas Dr Warrenton VA 22186-8613

MOLLOY, SYLVIA, Latin American literature educator, writer; b. Buenos Aires, Argentina, Aug. 29, 1938; came to U.S. 1967; d. Herbert Edward and Margarita Marta (Chasseing) M. Licence es Lettres, U. Paris, 1960, Diplome D'Etudes Superieures, 1961, Doctorat de U. Paris, 1967. Asst. prof. Spanish SUNY, Buffalo, 1967-69; asst. prof. Spanish Vassar Coll., Poughkeepsie, N.Y., 1969-70; asst. prof. Spanish Princeton U., Princeton, N.J., 1970-73, assoc. prof., 1973-81, Emory L. Ford prof., 1981-86; prof. Spanish Yale U., New Haven, 1986-90; ALbert Schweitzer prof. of Humanities NYU, 1990—. Author: La Diffusion de la Litterature Hispanoamericaine en France, 1972, Las Letras de Borges, 1979, En Breve Carcel, 1981, At Face Value: Autobiographical Writing in Spanish America, 1991; co-author Women's Writing in Latin America, 1991; author short stories and contbr. articles to profl. jours.; cons., editorial bd. Revista Iberoamericana, 1979-81, 1985—, Latin Am. Literary Rev., 1985—, Revista de Filología, Buenos Aires, 1985—. fellow Am. Philos. Soc., 1970, NEH, 1976; Social Sci. Research Council grantee, 1983; Guggenheim Found. fellow, 1986-87. Mem. MLA, Asociacion Internacional de Hispanistas, Instituto Internacional de Literatura Iberoamericana.

MOLM, JOHN RALPH, lawyer; b. Dubuque, Iowa, Oct. 25, 1947; s. Ralph Fredrick and Eva Marie (Nusbaum) M.; m. Linda Beth Dahl, June 10, 1970 (div. June 1980); m. Harrilee Cheshire, Apr. 12, 1985. BA, N.D. State U., 1970; JD, Georgetown U., 1973. Bar: N.C. 1973, Ga. 1976, U.S. Dist. Ct. (no. dist., mid. dist.) Ga., U.S. Ct. Appeals (5th cir., 11th cir., D.C.), U.S. Supreme Ct. Atty. N.C. Utilities Commn., Raleigh, 1973-76; ptnr. Troutman Sanders, Atlanta, 1976—. Pres. Brookwood Hills Civic Assn., Atlanta, 1990. Mem. Lawyers Club. Avocations: gardening, hiking, running, reading. Home: 4911 Quebec St NW Washington DC 20016-3230 Office: Troutman Sanders 5200 Nationsbank Plaza 600 Peachtree St NE Atlanta GA 30308-2214

MOLNAR, ANTHONY WILLIAM, publishing and training company executive; b. Weehawken, N.J., Sept. 30, 1938; s. Anthony George Molnar and Margaret J. (Bleidorn) Saunders; m. Barbara Ann Stootkoski, Sept. 24, 1960; children: Sandra Lynn, Susan Gail, Melissa Mary. AAS, Pace Coll., 1965, BBA, 1968, MBA, 1974; advanced mgmt. program, Harvard U., 1984. Sr. acctg. supr. Abex Corp., N.Y.C., 1959-68; asst. contr. GAB Bus. Services Inc., N.Y.C., 1968-77, v.p. treas., 1974-77; contr. Macmillan Pub. Co., N.Y.C., 1977-78; with John Wiley & Sons Inc., N.Y.C., 1978-88, sr. v.p., chief fin. officer, 1986-88; pres., chief exec. officer Wilson Learning Corp., 1987-88, Your Better Self, Inc., Bedminster, N.J., 1988-91; fin. dir. Nat. Consumer Ins. Co., 1991-94; contr. Stat-A-Matrix, Inc., Edison, N.J., 1994—. With USNR, 1957-59. Mem. Fin. Execs. Inst.

MOLNAR, DONALD JOSEPH, landscape architecture educator; b. Springfield, Ill., Dec. 24, 1938; s. Joseph and Mabel Irene (Woods) M.; m. Carol Jeanette Smith, Aug. 22, 1958; children: Elaina Deanne, Amy Lynn, Holly Suzanne. BFA in Landscape Architecture, U. Ill., 1960, MFA in Landscape Architecture, 1964. Landscape architect Simonds and Simonds, Pitts., 1961-63; landscape architect campus planning U. Ill., Urbana, 1963-72; asst. dir., planner capital programs U. Ill., Urbana and Chgo., 1971-81; assoc. prof. landscape architecture Purdue U., West Lafayette, Ind., 1981-85, dir. landscape architecture coop. program, 1983—, prof. landscape architecture, 1985—, chair landscape architecture program, 1987—, dir. internat. exch. landscape architecture, 1988—; cons. to architect, engrs., park agys., 1964—, MObile Homes Mfr. Assn., Chgo., 1966-76. Author: Anatomy of a Park, 2d edit., 1986; illustrator: Anatomy of a Park, 1971, Visual Approach to Park Design, 1980; developer software CompuPave, 1992. Mem., program coord. Champaign (Ill.) Devel. Coun., 1966-78. Named Hon. Parks Commr., Champaign Park Dist., 1981. Fellow Am. Soc. Landscape Architects (licensing com. Ill. chpt. 1968-70, registration com. Ind. chpt. 1982-85, pres. 1991-92, award 1982). Avocations: travel, computers. Office: Purdue U Landscape Architecture Prog 1165 Horticulture Bldg West Lafayette IN 47907-1165

MOLNAR, LEWIS K., health facility administrator. With Continental Ill. Bank, Chgo., 1961-62; ceo Shriner's Hosp. Crippled Children, Tampa, Fla., 1962—. Office: Shriner's Hosp Crippled Children 2900 N Rocky Point Dr Tampa FL 33607-1435

MOLNAR, THOMAS, philosophy of religion educator, author; b. Budapest, Hungary, June 26, 1921; s. Alexander and Aurelie (Blon) M. M.A. in French Lit., Université de Bruxelles, 1948, M.A. in Philosophy, 1948; Ph.D., Columbia U., 1952; PhD honoris causa, U. Mendoza (Argentina), 1986. Prof. French and world lit. Bklyn. Coll., 1957—; prof. philosophy of religion U. Budapest, 1991—; adj. prof. European intellectual history L.I. U., 1967—; guest prof. polit. philosophy Potchefstroom U. South Africa, 1969; guest prof. philosophy Hillsdale Coll., Mich., 1973-74; vis. prof. Yale U., 1983; vis. prof. philosophy U. Dijon, France, 1990; prof. philosophy of religion U. Budapest, 1991—, permanent vis. prof. philosophy of religion dept. philosophy, 1991—. Author: Bernanos, His Political Thought and Prophecy, 1960, The Future of Education, 1961, The Decline of the Intellectual, 1962, The Two Faces of American Foreign Policy, 1962, Africa, A Political Travelogue, 1965, Utopia, The Perennial Heresy, 1967, Sartre, Ideologue of Our Time, 1968, Ecumenism or New Reformation?, 1968, The Counter-Revolution, 1969, La Gauche vue d'en face, 1970, L'Animal politique, 1974, The European Dilemma, 1974, God and the Knowledge of Reality, 1974, Le Socialisme san visage, 1976, Authority and Its Enemies, 1976, Christian Humanism, A Critique of the Secular City and

its Ideology, 1978, Le Modèle dé figuré, l'Amérique de Tocqueville à Carter, 1978, Theists and Atheists, A Typology of Non-Belief, 1980, Politics and the State: A Catholic View, 1982, Le Dieu Immanent, 1982, Tiers-Monde, Idéologie Réalité, 1982, L'Eclipse du Sacre, 1986, The Pagan Temptation, 1987, Twin Power: Politics and the Sacred, 1988, L'Europe entre Parenthèses, 1990, Philosophical Grounds, 1991, The Church, Pilgrim of Centuries, 1991, L'Américanologie, Le triomphe du modèle planétaire?, 1991, Az Ideális éllam kritikája, 1991, L'Hégémonie libérale, 1992, The Emerging Atlantic Culture, 1994, Archetypes of Thought, 1995; also numerous articles in Am. and European scholarly jours. Relm Found. grantee for travel and study in French-speaking Africa, 1963-64, for travel in S.Am., 1966, for writing Sartre, Ideologue of Our Time, 1967; Earhart Found. grantee, 1992. Home: 238 Heights Rd Ridgewood NJ 07450-2414

MOLNAU, CAROL, state legislator; b. Sept. 17, 1949; m. Steven F. Molnau; 3 children. Attended, U. Minn. Mem. Minn. Ho. of Reps., 1992—. Active Our Saviors Luth. Ch., 4-H, Chaska City Coun. Mem. Agrl. Com., Econ. Devel., Infrastructure & Regulation Fin.-Transportation Fin. Divsn., Fin. Inst. & Ins.: Internat. Trade & Economic Devel. Republican. Home: 495 Pioneer Trl Chaska MN 55318 Office: 287 State Office Bldg Saint Paul MN 55155

MOLONEY, JAY, agent. Agent Creative Artists Agy. Office: Creative Artists Agy 9830 Wilshire Blvd Beverly Hills CA 90212*

MOLONEY, THOMAS E., lawyer; b. Rockville Ctr., N.Y., Jan. 9, 1949. BS, U. Dayton, 1971; JD, U. Notre Dame, 1974. Bar: Ohio 1974. Ptnr. Baker & Hostetler, Columbus, Ohio. Office: Baker & Hostetler Capital Sq 65 E State St Ste 2100 Columbus OH 43215-4260

MOLONEY, THOMAS JOSEPH, lawyer; b. Bklyn., Oct. 14, 1952; s. Thomas J. and Grace (Molloy) M.; m. Molly K. Heines, Dec. 26, 1976. AB, Columbia U., 1973; JD cum laude, NYU, 1976. Bar: N.Y. 1977, U.S. Dist. Ct. (so. dist.) N.Y. 1977, U.S. Dist. Ct. (ea. dist.) N.Y. 1978, U.S. Ct. Appeals (2d cir.) 1981. Assoc. Cleary, Gottlieb, Steen & Hamilton, N.Y.C., 1976-84, ptnr., 1984—; bd. dirs. N.Y. Lawyers for Pub. Interest, N.Y.C., 1986-91. Asst. counsel Gov.'s Jud. Nominating Com., N.Y.C., 1981-85. Mem. ABA, Am. Bankruptcy Inst., Assn. of Bar of City of N.Y. (bankruptcy, corp. reorganization coms. 1983-86, chair com. legal assistance), Order of Coif. Avocations: chess, golf, dance, travel, wine. Office: Cleary Gottlieb Steen & Hamilton 1 Liberty Plz New York NY 10006-1401

MOLONEY, THOMAS WALTER, consulting firm executive; b. N.Y.C., Feb. 8, 1946; s. Thomas Walter and Anne (Heney) M. BA, Colgate U., 1967; MA, Columbia U., 1970, MPH, 1973, MBA, 1975. Program dir. Nat. Ctr. for Deaf-Blind, New Hyde Park, N.Y., 1971-72; spl. asst. to dir. and dean N.Y. Hosp., N.Y.C., 1973-74; asst. v.p. Robert Wood Johnson Found., 1975-80; sr. v.p. The Commonwealth Fund, N.Y.C., 1980-92; dir. pub. policy and health programs The Inst. for Future, 1992—; vis. lectr. Princeton (N.J.) U., 1975-80; bd. dirs. Grantmakers in Health, N.Y.C., 1984—, chmn. bd., 1984-88; mem. health adv. com. GAO, 1987—; mem. health adv. coun. Johns Hopkins U. Sch., Hygiene and Pub. Health, Balt., 1989-91; bd. dirs. Found. Health Svcs. Rsch., Washington, 1985-92; mem. bd. visitors Med. Sch., U. Calif. at Davis, 1988—; mem. vis. com. Grad. Sch. Mgmt. and Urban Policy New Sch. for Social Rsch., N.Y.C., 1988-92; mem. Nat. Bd. Examiners, 1986-90; mem. sr. adv. bd. global leadership program U. Mich. Grad. Sch. Bus., Ann Arbor, 1988—; mem. press. com. The N.Y. Acad. Scis., 1987-90; policy scholar The Eisenhower Ctr. Columbia U., N.Y.C., 1992—; Inst. Health Policy Studies U. Calif., San Francisco, 1992—. Author books; editor: New Approaches to the Medicaid Crisis, 1983; contbr. articles to profl. jours. bd. dirs. New Eng. Med. Ctr., Boston, 1982-89. Policy scholar Inst. Health Policy Studies U. Calif., San Francisco, 1992—, Eisenhower Ctr. Columbia U., 1992—. Fellow AAAS; mem. Inst. Medicine, Nat. Acad. Scis., Nat. Acad. Social Ins., N.Y. Acad. Medicine, N.Y. Acad. Scis. (pres' com. 1987-90). Home: 72 Norwood Ave Montclair NJ 07043-1935 Office: Inst for the Future 630 5th Ave Fl 11 New York NY 10111-0001

MOLONY, MICHAEL JANSSENS, JR., lawyer; b. New Orleans, Sept. 2, 1922; s. Michael Janssens and Marie (Perret) M.; m. Jane Waguespack, Oct. 21, 1951; children: Michael Janssens III (dec.), Leslie, Megan, Kevin, Sara, Brian, Ian, Duncan. JD, Tulane U., 1950. Bar: La. 1950, D.C. 1979, U.S. Dist. Ct. (ea. and mid. dists.) La. 1951, U.S. Ct. Appeals (5th cir.) 1953, U.S. Supreme Ct. 1972, U.S. Dist. Ct. (w. dist.) La. 1978, U.S. Ct. Appeals (11th and D.C. cirs.) 1981. Ptnr., Molony & Baldwin, New Orleans, 1950; assoc. Jones, Flanders, Waechter & Walker, 1951-56; ptnr. Jones, Walker, Waechter, Poitevent, Carrere & Denegre, 1956-75, Milling, Benson, Woodward, Hillyer, Pierson & Miller, 1975-91, Chaffe, McCall, Phillips, Toler & Sarpy, 1991-92, Sessions & Fishman, 1993—; instr., lectr. Med. Sch. and Univ. Coll. Tulane U., 1953-59; mem. Eisenhower Legal Com., 1952. Bd. commrs. Port of New Orleans, 1976-81, pres., 1978, vice-chmn. past pres. coun., 1985—, mem. bd. rev. Associated Br. Pilots, 1990—; bd. dirs. La. World Expn. Inc., 1974-84; bd. dirs., exec. com. New Orleans Tourist and Conv. Commn., 1971-74, 78, chmn.; family attractions com. 1973-75; chmn. La. Gov.'s Task Force on Space Industry, 1971-73; chmn. La. Gov.'s Citizens' Adv. Com. Met. New Orleans Transp. and Planning Program, 1971-77; mem. La. Gov.'s Task Force Natural Gas Requirements, 1971-72; mem. Gov.'s Proaction Commn. for Higher Edn., 1995—; mem. Goals Found. Coun. and ex-officio mem. Task Force. Met. New Orleans Goals Program, 1969-72, vice chmn. ad hoc planning com. Goals Met. New Orleans, 1969-73; vice chmn. Port of New Orleans Operation Impact, 1969-70, mem. Met. Area Com., New Orleans, 1970-84; trustee, Pub. Affairs Rsch. Coun. La., 1970-73, mem. exec. com. Bus./Higher Edn. Coun., U. New Orleans, 1980-94; bd. dirs., 1980—, v.p. 1986-88, pres., 1988-90, chmn. Task Force on Higher Edn. Funding, 1990-95, chmn. pres. coun., Task Force on Edn./Econ. Devel. Alliances, 1993-95; mem. Mayor's Coun. on Internat. Trade and Econ. Devel., 1978; mem. Mayor's Transition Task Force Econ. Devel., 1994; bd. dirs. mem. exec. com. La. Partnership for Tech. and Innovation, 1989—; bd. dirs. Acad. Sacred Heart, 1975-77, Internat. House, 1985-86, U. New Orleans Found., 1991—; mem. vis. com. Loyola Sch. Bus. Adminstrn., Loyola U., New Orleans, 1981—, trustee Loyola U., 1985-91, vice chmn. bd. trustees, 1990-91; mem. Dean's Coun. Tulane U. Law Sch., 1988—, vice chmn. building com., 1991-95; bd. dirs., mem. exec. com. Internat. Trade Mart, chmn. internat. bus. com., 1983-85; World Trade Ctr.-New Orleans (bd. dirs. 1983—, mem. Port Activity com. 1985-91, transp. com. 1991-94); chmn. Task Force on Internat. Banking, 1982; mem. Mayor's Task Force on Drug Abuse, 1989-90. Capt. JAGDR, USAAF, 1942-46, PTO, La. Gov.'s Proaction Commn. for Higher Edn. Recipient Leadership award AIAA, 1971, Yenni award Loyola U., New Orleans, 1979, New Orleans Times Picayune Loving Cup, 1986, First Citizen of the Learning Soc. Dean's award UNO Met. Coll., 1992; also various civic contbn. awards; co-recipient Silver Anvil award Pub. Rels. Soc. Am., 1991. Mem. ABA (antitrust law, labor and employment law and litigation sects., com. equal opportunity law, chmn. regional com. liaison with equal opportunity commn., office of fed. contract compliance programs), D.C. Bar Assn., Fed. Bar Assn., La. Bar Assn. (past sec.-treas., bd. govs. 1957-60, editor jour. 1957-59, sec. spl. supreme ct. com. on drafting code jud. ethics), New Orleans Bar Assn. (dir. legal aid bur. 1974-77, chmn. standing com. legis. 1968, vice chmn. standing com. pub. rels. 1970-71), Am. Judicature Soc., La. Law Inst. (asst. sec.-treas. 1950-76), Am. Arbitration Assn. (bd. dirs., chmn. reg. adv. coun., mem. spl. panel large complex arbitration/mediation cases, Whitney North Seymour Sr. award 1991), So. Inst. Mgmt. (founder), AIM, U.S. C. of C. (urban and regional affairs com. 1970-73), La. C. of C. (bd. dirs. 1963-66), New Orleans Area C. of C. (v.p. met. devel. anfairs 1969, past chmn. labor rels. coun., bd. dirs. 1970-78, pres.-elect 1970, pres. 1971, dir., exec. com. 1972, ex officio mem. bd. dirs. 1979—), Bienville Club, City Club, English Turn Golf and Country Club, Pickwick Club, Plimsoll Club, Serra Club, So. Yacht Club, Sigma Chi (pres. alumni chpt. 1956). Roman Catholic. Home: 3039 Hudson Pl New Orleans LA 70131-5337 Office: Sessions & Fishman 201 Saint Charles Ave New Orleans LA 70170-3500

MOLPUS, DICK, state official; b. Philadelphia, PA, Sept. 7, 1949; s. Richard and Frances (Blount) M.; m. Sally Nash, May 27, 1971; children—Helen Nash, Richard Gregory. BBA, U. Miss., 1971. V.p. mfg. Molpus Co., Phila., 1971-80; exec. dir. Gov.'s Office Fed.-State Programs, Jackson, Miss., 1980-83; sec. of state State of Miss., Jackson, 1984—; dir. Citizens Bank and Trust Co. Vice pres. Miss. Agr. and Forestry Mus., 1979;

campaign dir., chmn. bd. United Givers Fund, Nehshoba County, Miss., 1979-80; bd. dirs. Miss. PTA, 1980—; founder Parents for Pub. Schs. orgn., 1989. Recipient Friends of Children award Miss. Assn. Elem. Sch. Adminstrs., 1984, Pub. Ofcl. of Yr. award Miss. chpt. Am. Soc. for Pub. Adminstrn., 1985. Mem. Miss. Forestry Assn. (bd. dirs. 1980-87), Nat. Assn. Secs. of State (pres. 1992), Sigma Chi, Omicron Delta Kappa, Pi Sigma Alpha (Theta Beta chpt.). Avocations: hiking, tennis, running, reading. Office: 401 Mississippi St PO Box 136 Jackson MS 39205

MOLSON, ERIC H., beverage company executive; b. Montreal, PQ, Can., Sept. 16, 1937; s. Thomas Henry Pentland and Celia Frances (Cantlie) M.; m. Jane Mitchell, Apr. 16, 1966; 3 children. AB, Princeton U., 1959. With The Molson Cos. Ltd., Montreal, chmn. bd., 1988—. Office: The Molson Cos Ltd, 1555 Notre Dame St E, Montreal, PQ Canada H2L 2R5

MOLTZ, JAMES EDWARD, brokerage company executive; b. Williamsport, Pa., July 25, 1932; s. George N. and Margaret L. (Abell) M.; m. Barbara Vance, Sept. 8, 1956; children: George Wilson, James Clay, John Thomas. BS, Williams Coll., 1954; MBA, Wharton Sch., U. Pa., 1956. Chartered fin. analyst. Fin. analyst Cyrus J. Lawrence Inc., N.Y.C., 1957-62, rsch. dir., 1962-64, gen. ptnr., 1964-71, mng. ptnr., 1971-73; chmn., pres. C.J. Lawrence/Deutsche Bank Securities Corp., N.Y.C., 1973—; mem. exec. com. Deutsche Bank N.Am. Holding; dir. McLean McCarthy, Inc. Mem. fin. com. Williams Coll.; trustee Sterling and Francine Clark Art Inst., Darien (Conn.) Libr., Williamsport (Pa.) Found., Williamsport-Lycoming Found.; elder Noroton (Conn.) Presbyn. Ch.; trustee Woods Hole Oceanographic Inst. Mem. Fin. Analysts Fedn., N.Y. Soc. Security Analysts (former dir.), Rockefeller Ctr. Club, Union League Club (N.Y.), Wee Burn Country Club (dir.), Windsor Club (Vero Beach). Home: 29 Indian Spring Trl Darien CT 06820-2109 Office: Deutsche Bank Securities Corp 1290 Avenue Of The Americas New York NY 10104-0012

MOLTZ, MARSHALL JEROME, lawyer; b. Chgo., May 22, 1930; s. Nathan and Rose (Nathanson) M.; m. Rita G., Dec. 26, 1954; m. 2d, Mary Ann, Nov. 4, 1967; children: Alan J., Michelle S. Yastrow, Marilyn F. Moltz-Hohmann, Julie A., Steven E., Rachel N. BS, Northwestern U., 1951, JD, 1954. Bar: Ill. 1954, Mo. 1954. Assoc. John B. Moser, Chgo., 1957; assoc. Goldberg, Devoe, Shadur & Mikva, Chgo., 1957-58; assoc. Lester Plotkin, Chgo., 1958-59; sole practice, Chgo., 1959-65; ptnr. Moltz & Spagat, Chgo., 1966-67; sole practice, Chgo., 1967-68; ptnr. Moltz & Wexler, Chgo., 1968-80; sole practice Chgo. 1980—; pres. Mercury Title Co.; faculty mem. profl. liab. in real estate transactions ABA Regional Inst., 1993; mem. Blue Ribbon com. Cook County Recorder of Deeds; speaker real estate law; atty. Counseling Ctr. of Lake View Mental Health Organ., Chgo. With M.I., U.S. Army, 1955-56; ETO. Recipient Louden Wigmore prize Northwestern U. Law Sch., 1954. Mem. ABA, Ill. State Bar Assn., Chgo. Bar Assn. (mem. real property law com. 1958—, chmn. Torrens sub-com. 1968-75, vice chmn. real property law com. 1974-75, chmn. real property law com. 1975-76, speaker and faculty mem. various seminars 1993, 94), VFW, Phi Alpha Delta (law fraternity). Author course outlines Ill. Inst. Continuing Legal Edn., 1972, 73; editorial bd. Northwestern U. Law Rev., 1953-54. Home: 112 Harvard Ct Glenview IL 60025-5917 Office: 77 W Washington St Ste 1620 Chicago IL 60602-2903

MOLTZON, RICHARD FRANCIS, manufacturing executive; b. Bklyn., Nov. 20, 1941; s. Arthur G. and Joan (Paladino) M.; m. Susan A. Anderson, Feb. 15, 1981; children: Paige, Kimberly, Michael, Keir. BS in Info. Systems Mgmt., U. Md., 1970. Various positions IBM Corp., various locations, 1965-70; plant mgr. Telex Terminal Communications, Inc., Raleigh, N.C., 1970-75, Carnes Co. div. Wehr Steel, Sanford, N.C., 1975-76; gen. mgr. Modular Computer Systems, Inc., Ft. Lauderdale, Fla., 1980-87; v.p. ops. Profile Corp., Pompano Beach, Fla., 1987-88; dir. mfg. AMF, Inc., Herndon, Va., 1976-79, Documation, Inc., Melbourne, Fla., 1979-80, Concurrent Computer Corp., Oceanport, N.J., 1988-89; v.p. mfg. Internat. Tech. Corp., Clearwater, Fla., 1989-90; pres. The Realty Authority, Inc., 1990-92; ops. mgr. Combustion Tec, Inc., Orlando, Fla., 1992—. With U.S. Army, 1961-64. Mem. KC (chancelor 1987, 88), Omicron Delta Kappa. Roman Catholic. Avocations: golf, jogging, writing, scuba diving, exotic birds. Office: Combustion Tec Inc PO Box 607693 Orlando FL 32860-7693

MOLYNEAUX, DAVID GLENN, newspaper travel editor; b. Marion, Ind., Oct. 16, 1945; s. Glenn Ingersol and Barbara Wingate (Draudt) M.; m. Ann Louise Geery, Aug. 8, 1970; children: Miles David, Rebecca Susan. BS in Econs., Miami U., Oxford, Ohio, 1967. Reporter The Plain Dealer, Cleve., 1967-75, city editor, 1976-78, assoc. editor, 1979-80, editorial page editor, 1980-82, travel editor, 1982—. Editor: 75 Years-An Informal History of Shaker Heights, 1987. Trustee Shaker Heights Pub. Libr., 1987—. With U.S. Army, 1968-70. Mem. Cleve. Press Club. Office: Plain Dealer 1801 Superior Ave E Cleveland OH 44114-2107*

MOLZ, FRED JOHN, III, hydrologist, educator; b. Mays Landing, N.J., Aug. 13, 1943; s. Fred John Jr. and Viola Violet (MacDonald) M.; m. Mary Lee Clark, Dec. 17, 1966; children: Fred John IV, Stephen Joseph. BS in Physics, Drexel U., 1966, MCE, 1968; PhD in Hydrology, Stanford U., 1970. Hydraulic engr. U.S. Geol. Survey, Menlo Park, Calif., 1970; asst. prof. Auburn (Ala.) U., 1970-74, alumni assoc. prof., 1974-76, alumni assoc. prof., 1976-80, asst. dean research, 1979-84, dir. Eng. exptl. sta., 1981-84; prof., 1980-84, Feagin prof., 1984-89, Huff eminent scholar, 1990—; cons. Battelle N.W., Richland, Wash., 1982-83, 84-85, Argonne (Ill.) Nat. Labs., 1983-85, Electric Power Rsch. Inst., Menlo Park, Calif., 1984—, U.S. Nuclear Regulatory Commn., 1991—. Author: (with others) Numerical Methods in Hydrology, 1971, Modeling Wastewater Renovation, 1981; contbr. articles to profl. jours. Recipient Disting. Faculty award Auburn U. Alumni Assn., 1987; grantee EPA, 1983, 86, 90, U.S. Dept. Edn., 1991, NSF, 1992. Mem. Am. Geophys. Union (Horton award 1992), Am. Soc. Agronomy, Nat. Ground Water Assn., Am. Inst. Hydrology. Avocations: reading, travel, investing. Home: 1224 Ferndale Ct Auburn AL 36830-6731 Office: Auburn Univ Dept of Civil Engring Harbert Engring Ctr Auburn AL 36849

MOLZ, OTIS, oil industry executive. Chmn. Farmland Industries Inc., Kansas City, Mo., 1993—. Office: Farmland Industries Inc 3315 N Oak Trafficway Kansas City MO 64116-2775*

MOLZ, REDMOND KATHLEEN, public administration educator; b. Balt., Mar. 5, 1928; d. Joseph T. and Regina (Barry) M. B.S., Johns Hopkins U., 1949, M.A., 1950; M.A.L.S., U. Mich., 1953; D.L.S., Columbia U., 1976. Librarian I and II Enoch Pratt Free Library, Balt., 1953-56; pub. relations officer Free Library of Phila., 1958-62; editor Wilson Library Bull. H.W. Wilson Co., Bronx, N.Y., 1962-68; chief planning staff Bur. Libraries and Learning Resources U.S. Office Edn., Washington, 1968-73; prof. library sci. Sch. Library Service Columbia U., N.Y.C., 1976-80, Melvil Dewey prof., 1980-93; prof. pub. affairs Sch. Internat. and Pub. Affairs, Columbia U., N.Y.C., 1993—; cons. U.S. Nat. Commn. Libraries and Info. Sci., Washington, 1974-75, U.S. Adv. Commn. Intergovtl. Relations, Washington, 1979-80. Author: Federal Policy and Library Support, 1976 (Ralph R. Shaw award 1977), National Planning for Library Service, 1935-75, 1984, Library Planning and Policy Making: The Legacy of the Public and Private Sector, 1990, The Federal Roles in Support of Public Library Services, 1990, The Federal Roles in Support of Academic and Research Libraries, 1991; co-editor: The Metropolitan Library (anthology), 1972; author TV script Portraits in Print, 1959. Recipient Leadership Tng. award Fund for Adult Edn., 1956-57; recipient Disting. Alumnus award Sch. Library Sci. U. Mich., 1969, George Virgil Fuller award Columbia U., 1975, Johns Hopkins U. scholar, 1949-50, Horace H. Rackham fellow U. Mich., 1952-53, Columbia U. scholar, 1974-76, Tangley Oaks fellow, 1975-76; Council Library Resources Inc. Officers' grantee, 1974. Mem. ALA (councilor 1972-74, 76-80, exec. bd. 1976-80, chmn. legis. com. 1985-86), Freedom to Read Found. (dir. 1972-79, pres. 1977-79). Office: Columbia U Sch Internat & Pub Affairs New York NY 10027

MOLZ, ROBERT JOSEPH, manufacturing company executive; b. Yonkers, N.Y., Mar. 15, 1937; s. Philip and Maria Hilda (Geist) M.; m. Diane Ruth Horowitz, July 31, 1960; children—Jennifer Ann, Erica Beth. B.S., CCNY, 1960, M.A., 1966; Ph.D., N.Y. Med. Coll., 1969. Tech. services supr. E.I. DuPont de Nemours Co. Inc. Wilmington, Del.; 1971-73, product mgr., 1973-75, quality assurance mgr. clin. systems div., 1976,

---

research and devel. mgr. clin. systems div., 1976-84, asst. dir. research and devel. div. agrl. chem. dept., 1984-86, dir. departmental plans div., med. products dept., 1986-88, dir. med. scis. programs, cen. R&D, 1988-91, dir. new bus. devel., Cen. R&D, 1991-92, exec. dir. rsch. support, 1992—. Mem. Am. Chem. Soc. Roman Catholic. Home: 306 Dove Dr Newark DE 19713-1212 Office: EI DuPont de Nemours Co Inc Cen R&D Market St Wilmington DE 19801

MOLZEN, DAYTON FRANK, consulting engineering executive; b. Newton, Kans., Jan. 6, 1926; s. Walter N. and Ionia Maude (Gordon) M.; m. Margaret Jean Hanna, Aug. 13, 1949; children: George Walter, Lucena Ann. B.S., Kans. State U., 1950. Project engr. Kans. Hwy. Commn., Garden City, 1950-51; design engr. Wilson & Co., Engrs., Albuquerque and Salina, Kans., 1953-60; civil engr., pres. D.F. Molzen and Assocs., Inc., Albuquerque, 1960-74; pres. Molzen-Corbin & Assos., Albuquerque, 1974—. Served with A.C. U.S. Army, 1942-45; Served with USAF, 1951-53. Fellow Am. Cons. Engrs. Coun. (nat. bd. dirs. 1982-85, exec. dir. N.Mex. 1985-93); mem. ASCE, Cons. Engrs. Coun. (past pres.), Am. Pub. Works Assn. Clubs: Masons, Shriners, Rotary, Appaloosa Horse (past pres. N.Mex., nat. dir.). Home: 3216 Calle De Estella NW Albuquerque NM 87104-3003 Office: 2701 Miles Rd SE Albuquerque NM 87106-3228

MOMADAY, NAVARRE SCOTT, English educator, author; b. Lawton, Okla., Feb. 27, 1934; s. Alfred Morris and Natachee (Scott) M.; m. Gaye Mangold, Sept. 5, 1959; children: Cael, Jill, Brit; m. Regina Heitzer, July 21, 1978; 1 dau., Lore. AB, U. N.Mex., 1958; AM, Stanford U., 1960, PhD, 1963. Asst. prof. U. Calif., Santa Barbara, 1963-65, assoc. prof. English, 1968-69; assoc. prof. English and comparative lit. U. Calif., Berkeley, 1969-73; prof. English and comparative lit. Stanford U., 1973-82, from 1985; prof. English and comparative lit. U. Ariz., Tucson, 1982-85, Regents Prof. English; cons. Nat. Endowment for Humanities, Nat. Endowment for Arts, 1970—. Author: Owl in the Cedar Tree, 1965, The Journey of Tai-me, 1967 (pub. as The Way to Rainy Mountain, 1969), House Made of Dawn, 1968 (Pulitzer Prize for fiction 1969), Colorado: Summer/Fall/Winter/Spring, 1973 (Western Heritage award 1974), Angle of Geese and Other Poems, 1974, The Gourd Dancer, 1976, The Names: A Memoir, 1976, The Ancient Child, 1989, In the Presence of the Sun, 1991, Circle of Wonder: A Native American Christmas Story, 1993, The Native Americans: Indian Country, 1993; co-author: American Indian Photographic Images, 1868-1931, 1982; editor: The Complete Poems of Frederick Goddard Tuckerman, 1965, American Indian Authors, 1972. Trustee, Museum of Am. Indian, Heye Found., N.Y., 1978—. Guggenheim fellow, 1966-67; Nat. Inst. Arts and Letters grantee, 1970; recipient Acad. Am. Poets prize for "The Bear", 1962, Premio Letterario Internazionale Mondello Italy, 1979. Mem. MLA, Am. Studies Assn., PEN. Office: Univ Ariz Dept English Tucson AZ 85721-0001*

MOMMAERTS, WILFRIED FRANCIS HENRY MARIA, physiologist, educator; b. Broechem, Belgium, Mar. 4, 1917; came to U.S., 1948, naturalized, 1956; s. Hendrik David and Maria (van Damme) M.; m. Elizabeth Barbara Batyka, July 29, 1944 (dec.); children—Robert Wilfried Anthony, Edina Maria, Quentin Francis. Student, U. Leiden, Netherlands, 1934-39; PhD, Kolozsvar, Hungary, 1943; Dr. honoris causa, U. Dijon, 1976. Faculty Am. U., Beirut, 1945-48, Duke U., 1948-53, Western Res. U., 1953-56; coordinator Commonwealth Fund Med. Curriculum Expt., 1955-56; spl. Rockefeller fellow U. Coll., London, 1956; prof. medicine, physiology, dir. L.A. County Heart Assn. Cardiovascular Rsch. Lab. U. Calif., 1956-87; emeritus prof. UCLA, 1987-88, chmn. dept. physiology, 1966-87; mem. Roger Wagner L.A. Master Chorale; Commonwealth Fund fellow Centre des Recherches sur les Macromolecules, Strasbourg, 1963-64; chmn. physiology tng. com. NIH, 1967-71; vis. prof. U. Dijon, 1973-74; mem. Internat. Commn. on Genetic Experimentation, 1980—; researcher Max Planck Inst. for Med. Rsch., Heidelberg, Fed. Rep. Germany; chmn. planning com. European Union Socs. Exptl. Biology, 1987-90. Author: Muscular Contraction, a Topic in Molecular Physiology, 1950; contbr. articles to profl. jours. Recipient award for outstanding contbn. to sci. knowledge Los Angeles County Heart Assn., 1967, award of merit, 1972; Samuel Racz medal, Budapest, 1985, Alexander von Humboldt prize, 1986. Mem. Am. Physiol. Soc., Am. Soc. Biol. Chemists, Biophys. Soc., Am. Acad. Arts and Scis., Royal Belgian Acad. Medicine, Hungarian Physiol. Soc. (hon.), others. Republican. Episcopalian. Home: 969 Hilgard Ave Penthouse 05 Los Angeles CA 90024

MOMMSEN, KATHARINA, German language and literature educator; b. Berlin, Sept. 18, 1925; came to U.S., 1974, naturalized, 1980; d. Hermann and Anna (Johannsen) Zimmer; m. Momme Mommsen, Dec. 23, 1948. Dr.phil., U. Tübingen, 1956; Dr. habil., Berlin Free U., 1962. Collaborator Acad. Scis., Berlin, 1949-61; assoc. prof. Free U., Berlin, 1962-70; prof. German Carleton U., Ottawa, Can., 1970-74; Albert Guerard prof. lit. Stanford U., 1974—; vis. prof. U. Giessen, Tech. U. Berlin, 1965, State U. N.Y., Buffalo, 1966, U. Calif., San Diego, 1973. Author over 150 publs. on 18th-20th century German and comparative lit.; editor: Germanic Studies in America. Mem. Internat. Assn. Germanic Langs. and Lit., Goethe Soc., Schiller Soc. Home: 980 Palo Alto Ave Palo Alto CA 94301-2223 Office: Stanford U Dept German Stanford CA 94305

MONA, DAVID L., public relations executive; b. Mpls., May 4, 1943. BA in Journalism and Mass Communication, U. Minn, 1965. Reporter, editor Sta. WCCO-TV, 1962-65; reporter Mpls. Tribune, 1965-69; mgr. media rels. Luth. Brotherhood, 1969-70; dir. corp. communications Internat. Multifoods, 1970-78; v.p. communications The Toro Co., 1978-81; pres. David L. Mona Assocs., from 1981; now chief exec. officer Mona, Meyer, McGrath & Gavin. Office: Mona Meyer McGrath & Gavin Ste 500 8400 Normandale Lake Blvd Bloomington MN 55437-3889*

MONACELLI, AMIETO, professional bowler. Top money leader, top average Pro Bowlers Assn., 1990. Office: c/o Pro Bowlers Assn 1720 Merriman Rd Akron OH 44313-5252

MONACELLI, GIANFRANCO, publishing executive; b. Milan, July 19, 1939; came to U.S., 1965; s. Rodolfo and Isabella (Paolillo) M.; m. Eugenia Hyman, Dec. 20, 1965; children: Nurit, Fausto, Alexander. Dr., U. Turin, Italy, 1963, Acad. Santa Cecilia, Italy, 1964; BS, Mannes Coll., 1967; postgrad., Columbia U., 1969. Gen. mgr. Rizzoli Internat. Bookstore, N.Y.C., 1969-72, v.p., 1972-75; exec. v.p. Rizzoli Internat. Publs., Inc., N.Y.C., 1975-93, Rizzoli Editore Corp. N.Y.C., 1975-89; sr. v.p. RCS Rizzoli Corp., N.Y.C., 1989-93; pres. USITAL Ltd., N.Y.C., 1993—; The Monacelli Press, Inc., N.Y.C., 1994—; vis. com. U. Miami, Coral Gables, Fla., 1988-89. Trustee Mannes Coll., N.Y.C., 1979-81; pres. Weathersfield Music Festival, Vert., 1993—. Mem. Century Assn., Am.-Italy Soc. (pres. 1993-94).

MONACHINO, FRANCIS LEONARD, music educator. MMus, Tulane U., 1967—. With Tulane U., New Orleans, 1967—, now Dawnman prof. performing arts. Office: Tulane U Grad Sch Dept of Music New Orleans LA 70118*

MONACO, ANTHONY PETER, surgery educator, medical institute administrator; b. Phila., Mar. 12, 1932; s. Donato Charles and Rose (Consalvi) M.; m. Mary Louise Oudens, June 4, 1960; children: Anthony Peter, Marck Churchill, Christopher Donoto, Lisa Oudens. B.A. in Chemistry, U. Pa., 1952; M.D. magna cum laude, Harvard U., 1956. Diplomate: Am. Bd. Surgery, Am. Bd. Thoracic Surgery. Prof. surgery Harvard Med. Sch., Boston, 1977—; mem. bd. acad. advisors, 1974-83; chief transplantation div. Sears Surg. Research Lab. Boston City Hosp., 1967-73; sci. dir. Cancer Research Inst., New Eng. Deaconess Hosp., Boston, 1980—; chief div. organ transplantation Cancer Research Inst., New Eng. Deaconess Hosp., 1975—; mem. surgery study sect. NIH, 1973-77, mem. clin. sci. study sect., 1983—; mem. adv. com. endstage renal disease Bur. Quality Assurance, HEW, 1975-76; mem. merit rev. bd. immunology VA, Washington, 1977-80. Author: Biology of Tissue Transplantation, 1964; editor: Transplantation Procedures, 1970, 81; jour. Transplantation, 1969—. Trustee New Eng. Organ Bank, Boston, 1970—, chmn., 1981—; bd. dirs. Kidney Found. Mass., 1978-81; mem. Harvard Med. Sch. Alumni Council, 1979-81. Recipient nat. scholar Harvard Med. Sch., 1952-56; recipient Henry Asbury Christian award

---

Harvard Med. Sch., 1956, Lederle Med. Faculty award Harvard Med. Sch., 1968. Mem. Transplantation Soc. (charter, v.p. 1971-74, pres. 1985, internat. pres. 1986), Am. Soc. Transplant Surgeons (charter, treas. 1982-85, pres. 1985—), Am. Surg. Assn., Soc. Univ. Surgeons, ACS (pres. Mass. chpt. 1985). Club: Harvard (Boston). Home: 25 Farlow Rd Newton MA 02158-2407 Office: Harvard Med Sch-Surgery Boston MA 02218

MONACO, JOSEPH R., metals company executive; b. N.Y.C., June 7, 1945; s. Joseph Mario and Rose (Micelotta) M.; m. Carol Ann Romano, Sept. 7, 1968. BA, Queens Coll., 1965. Traffic mgr. N.J. Zinc, N.Y.C., 1965-70; asst. to pres. Internat. Minerals and Metals, N.Y.C., 1970-73; asst. v.p. Brandeis, Goldschmidt & Co., N.Y.C., 1973-76, v.p., 1976-81; sr. v.p. Pechiney World Trade, Secaucus, N.J., 1981—; cons. Habits, Inc., N.Y.C. With U.S. Army, 1965-67. Mem. Minor Metals Assn. Club: Vertical (N.Y.C.). Avocations: physical training, tennis, golf. Office: Pechiney World Trade USA Inc 500 Plaza Dr Secaucus NJ 07094-3602

MONACO, MICHAEL P., finance company executive; b. 1948. BS, Villanova U., 1970; MBA, Fairleigh Dickinson U., 1981. Mgr. fin. reporting W.T. Grant Co., 1965-76; sr. auditor Ernst & Whinney, 1970-73; internal auditor Coca-Cola Bottling Co. N.Y. Inc., 1973-74, asst. contr., 1976-81; sr. v.p., comptr. Am. Express Co., N.Y, until 1990, exec. v.p., chief fin. officer, 1990—. Office: Am Express Co Am Express Tower World Fin Ctr New York NY 10004

MONACO, PAUL, academic administrator, educator, artist, writer; b. Niskayuna, N.Y., Sept. 11, 1942; s. Angelo M. and Birdena (O'Melia) M.; m. Victoria O'Donnell, 1993. BS, Columbia U., 1965; MA, U. N.C., 1966; PhD, Brandeis U., 1974. Asst. prof. hist. Brandeis U., Waltham, Mass., 1973-75; prof. arts and humanities U. Tex., Dallas, 1975-85, dir. grad. studies arts and humanities, 1976-80; dept. head, prof. media and theatre arts Mont. State U., Bozeman, 1985—; bd. dirs. U. Film and Video Assn., 1988-91, 95—, Bozeman Film Festival, 1985— (pres. 1987-90); mem. Hist. Preservation Com., Bozeman, 1988-90, Mont. Com. for Humanities, Missoula, 1989-93; regional coord. Nicholls Screenwriting Awards, 1989-91. Author: Cinema and Soc., 1976, Modern Europe Culture . . . 1983, Ribbons in Time, 1988 (ALC 10 best award 1988); prodr., dir.: Montana: 2nd Century, 1990 (Mont. broadcasters award 1991); prodr., dir., co-writer: Home to Montana, 1988; dir. Women, War and Work, 1994, Way of the Trout, 1994, I Often Thought of Berlin, 1989. Bd. mem. Mont. Ballet Co., Bozeman, 1986-90. Recipient Fulbright Prof. award U.S., Germany, 1982-83, 92. Home: 290 Low Bench Rd Gallatin Gateway MT 59730-9741

MONAGHAN, EILEEN, artist; b. Holyoke, Mass., Nov. 22, 1911; d. Thomas F. and Mary (Doona) Monaghan; m. Frederic Whitaker. Student, Mass. Coll. Art. Represented in collections NAD, Okla. Mus. Art, Hispanic Soc., High Mus. Art, Atlanta, Norfolk museums, U. Mass., Springfield (Mass.) Mus. Fine Art, Reading (Pa.) Art Mus., Charles and Emma Frye Mus., Seattle, Kans. State U., Wichita, St. Lawrence U., N.Y., NAD, also in numerous pvt. collections, ann. exhbns., nat. and regional watercolor shows; author: Eileen Monaghan Whitaker Paints San Diego, 1991. Recipient Wong award Calif. Watercolor Soc., Ranger Fund purchase Nat. Acad. Design, Allied Artists Am., DeYoung Mus. show award, Soc. Western Artists award, 1st award Springville (Utah) Mus., numerous others. Mem. NAD (academician, Obrig prize, Walter Biggs Meml. award), Am. Watercolor Soc. (Silver medal, Dolphin fellow), Watercolor West Soc. (hon.), San Diego Watercolor Soc. (hon.), Providence Watercolor Club (award), Phila. Watercolor Club. Address: 1579 Alta La Jolla Dr La Jolla CA 92037-7101

MONAGHAN, HENRY P., lawyer, educator; b. 1934. B.A., U. Mass. 1955; LL.B., Yale U., 1958; LL.M., Harvard U., 1960. Bar: Mass. 1958. Law clk. U.S. Ct. Appeals (4th cir.), 1958-59; assoc. Foley, Hoag & Eliot, Boston, 1960; asst. prof. Boston U., 1963, assoc. prof., 1965, prof., 1966-79; Robert S Stevens prof., Cornell U., Ithaca, N.Y., 1979-82; Harlan Fiske Stone prof. constl. law Columbia U. Law Sch., N.Y.C., 1984—. Office: Columbia U Sch Law 435 W 116th St New York NY 10027-7201

MONAGHAN, THOMAS JUSTIN, prosecutor. U.S. atty. Dept. Justice, Omaha, 1993—. Office: US Attys Office PO Box 1228 Omaha NE 68101-1228

MONAGHAN, THOMAS STEPHEN, restaurant chain executive; b. Ann Arbor, Mich., Mar. 25, 1937; m. Marjorie Zybach, Aug. 25, 1962; children—Mary, Susan, Margaret, Barbara. Student, Ferris State Coll., U. Mich.; Ph.D. (hon.), Cleary Coll., 1982, Madonna Coll., 1983, Eastern Mich. U., 1984, So. Fla. U., 1985. Ptnr. Dominick's Pizza, Ypsilanti, Mich., 1960-65; pres., chmn. bd. founder Domino's Pizza, Inc., Ann Arbor, Mich., 1960—; owner Detroit Tigers, 1983-92. Author: (autobiography) Pizza Tiger. Bd. dirs. Cleary Coll., Ypsilanti, Henry Ford Hosp., Detroit, Detroit Renaissance, U. Steubinville, Ohio, St. Joseph's Hosp. Devel. Bd., Ann Arbor. Served with USMC, 1956-59. Named Entrepreneur of Yr. Harvard U. Bus. Sch., 1984, Pizzaman of Yr. Nat. Assn. Pizza Owners, 1984; recipient Golden Plate award Am. Acad. Achievement, 1984, Golden Chain award Multi Unit Franchise Svc. Orgn., 1986, Horatio Alger award, 1986, Restaurant Bus. Leadership award, 1986, Pope John Paul II Family Fidelity award 1988, Pine Mission's Knights of Charity award, 1990, Semper Fidelis award USMC, 1990. Mem. Internat. Franchise Assn. (Entrepreneur of Yr. 1986), Nat. Restaurant Assn. (Silver Plate award 1985), Mich. Restaurant Assn., Ypsilanti C. of C., U. Mich. Pres.'s Club, Ann Arbor Pres.'s Assn., Missionary Vehicle Assn. (bd. dirs.), AIA (hon.), Mich. Soc. Architects (hon.). Club: Barton Hills Country (Ann Arbor). Lodge: K.C. Avocations: collecting Frank Lloyd Wright furniture and memorabilia, classic cars. Office: Domino's Pizza Inc 30 Frank Lloyd Wright Dr Ann Arbor MI 48105-9755

MONAHAN, DAVID EMORY, lawyer; b. San Diego, Nov. 19, 1937; s. James Stanley and Lillian (Emory) M.; m. Patricia Ann Bailey, Apr. 18, 1959 (div. 1981); children: James, Michael, Leslie. BS, Calif. Maritime Acad., 1958; LLB, Loyola U., L.A., 1966. Bar: Calif. 1966. Assoc. Gray, Cary, Ware & Freidenvich (formerly Gray, Cary, Ames & Frye), San Diego, 1966-72, ptnr., 1972—. Mem. Am. Coll. Trial Lawyers, Am. Bd. Trial Advocates (pres. San Diego chpt.), Internat. Assn. Def. Counsel, Nat. Assn. R.R. Trial Counsel. Home: 5855 La Jolla Corona Dr La Jolla CA 92037-7406 Office: Gray Cary Ware & Freidenvich 1st Interstate Pla 401 B St San Diego CA 92101-4223

MONAHAN, EDWARD CHARLES, academic administrator, marine science educator; b. Bayonne, N.J., July 25, 1936; s. Edward C. and Helen G. (Lauenstein) M.; m. Elizabeth Ann Eberhard, Aug. 27, 1960; children: Nancy Elizabeth, Carol Frances, Eilis Marie. B of Engring. Physics, Cornell U., 1959; MA, U. Tex. 1961; PhD, MIT, 1966; DSc, Nat. U. Ireland, Dublin, 1984. Rsch. asst. Woods Hole (Mass.) Oceanographic Inst. 1964-65; asst. prof. physics No. Mich. U., Marquette, 1965-68; asst. prof. oceanography Hobart and William Smith Coll., Geneva, N.Y., 1968-69; asst. prof. dept. meteorology, oceanography U. Mich., Ann Arbor, 1969-71; assoc. prof. dept. atmosphere and ocean sci., 1971-75; dir. edn. and rsch. Sea Edn. Assn., Woods Hole, 1975-76; statutory lectr. phys. oceanography U. Coll., Galway, Ireland, 1976-86; prof. marine scis. U. Conn., Avery Point, 1986—; dir. Conn. Sea Grant Coll. Program, Avery Point, 1986—. Editor: Oceanic Whitecaps and Their Role in Air-Sea Exchange Processes, 1986, Climate and Health Implications of Bubble-Mediated Sea-Air Exchange, 1989; contbr. more than 250 articles to profl. jours. Recipient more than 115 rsch. grants, 1966—. Fellow Royal Meteorol. Soc.; mem. AAUP, Am. Geophys. Union, Am. Meteorol. Soc. (profl.), Am. Soc. Limnology and Oceanography, Acoustical Soc. Am., Internat. Assn. Theoretical and Applied Limnology, Irish Meteorology Soc., Irish Marine Assn., European Geophys. Soc., The Oceanography Soc. (life). Avocation: recreational sculling.

MONAHAN, FRANCES DONOVAN, nursing educator; b. Lawrence, Mass., Aug. 29, 1943; d. Francis Jeremiah and Isabel Rita (Torpey) Donovan; m. William Thomas Monahan; children: Michael McCain, Kerryane Torpey. AB in Psychology, Emmanuel Coll., 1964; BS in Nursing, Columbia U., 1966; MS in Med. Surg. Nursing, Boston U., 1968; PhD in Nursing, NYU, 1980. RN, N.Y. Staff nurse Lawrence Gen. Hosp., 1967,

Columbia Presbyn. Hosp., N.Y.C., 1969; instr. Beth Israel Hosp. Sch. Nursing, N.Y.C., 1969-71; from asst. to assoc. prof. Dept. Nursing Rockland Community Coll., Suffern, N.Y., 1971-82, prof., chmn., 1983—; staff nurse Columbia Presbyn. Hosp., N.Y., 1969; camp nurse Model Cities Program, Highland Falls, N.Y., summer 1972-73, Ladycliff Coll., 1971-74; adj. faculty State U. Coll. at New Paltz, N.Y., 1985-86, fall 1987; site visitor accreditation Nat. League for Nursing, N.Y., 1987—; mem. bd. rev. assoc. degree coun. Nat. League for Nursing, 1992-98, chair, 1995; mem. faculty Regents Coll., 1992—. Co-author: Writing Across the Curriculum Handbook of Strategies, 1983, Pocket Companion to Nursing Care of Adults, 1994; editor: Nursing Care of Adults, 1994; contbg. author Pathophysiology; contbr. articles to profl. jours. Mem. adv. bd. Nursing Coll. New Paltz, 1984—; bd. dirs. Orange County Ballet, 1988-90. Recipient Excellence in Practice award Rockland County Nurse Recognition Day, 1995. Mem. ANA, Am. Nursing Dianosis Assn. (charter), Nat. League for Nursing (site visitor for accreditation 1987, bd. rev. assoc. degree coun.), Mid-Atlantic Regional Nursing Assn., N.Y. State Assn. Degree Nursing Coun., NYU Alumnae Assn., Sigma Theta Tau. Avocations: reading, computing, crocheting, gardening. Office: Rockland C C 145 College Rd Suffern NY 10901-3699

MONAHAN, JOHN T., law educator, psychologist; b. N.Y.C., Nov. 1, 1946; s. John Joseph and Dorothy (King) M.; m. Linda Costa, Aug. 24, 1969; children: Katherine, John. BA, SUNY, 1968; PhD, Ind. U., 1972. Asst. prof. U. Calif., Irvine, 1972-80; prof. U. Va., Charlottesville, 1980-84, Doherty prof., 1985—; dir. mental health law MacArthur Found., Chgo., 1988—. Author: Predicting Violent Behavior, 1981 (Guttmacher award 1981), Social Science in Law, 1994. Recipient Disting. Contbn. Pub. Policy award APA, Washington, 1990. Home: 939 Rosser Ln Charlottesville VA 22903-1645 Office: U Va Sch Law 580 Massie Rd Charlottesville VA 22903-1789

MONAN, JAMES DONALD, college president; b. Blasdell, N.Y., Dec. 31, 1924; s. Edward Roland and Mary Gertrude (Ward) M. AB, Woodstock Coll., 1948, PhL, 1949, STL, 1956; PhD, U. Louvain, 1959; post-doctoral research, Munich, Oxford, Paris; LHD (hon.), Le Moyne Coll., 1973, St. Joseph's Coll., 1973, New Eng. Sch. Law, 1975, Northeastern U., 1975; LLD (hon.), Harvard U., 1982, Loyola U., Chgo., 1987, Nat. U. Ireland, 1991. Prof. philosophy Le Moyne Coll., Syracuse, N.Y., 1960-68; v.p., acad. dean Le Moyne Coll., 1968-72; pres. Boston Coll., Chestnut Hill, Mass., 1972—; cons. to N.Y. Jesuit Provincial for Higher Edn., 1966-72; dir. First Nat. Bank Boston, Bank of Boston Corp. Author: The Philosophy of Knowing, 1952, A Prelude to Metaphysics, 1967, Moral Knowledge and Its Methodology in Aristotle, 1968. Chmn. edn. div. Boston United Way, 1974; chmn. steering com. of coll. pres. under phase II of ct.-ordered desegregation Boston Pub. Sch. System, 1974-76, Coun. for Aid to Edn., 1985—, The Partnership, 1984—; Sr. Thea Bowman Black Cath. Ednl. Found., 1989—, Gov.'s Internat. Trade Adv. Bd., 1992—; bd. dirs. Nat. One to One, 1991—; co-chair Greater Boston One-to-One, 1992—; trustee Le Moyne Coll., 1961-69, Fordham U., 1969-75, Boston Coll., 1972—, Canisius Coll., 1976-82, Georgetown U., 1979-84, Sta WGBH, 1972—; exec. com. Boston Higher Edn. Ptnrship, 1988—; mem. com. to Review and Implement Apostolic Constitution Ex Corde Ecclesiae, 1991—. Mem. Assn. Jesuit Colls. and Univs. (dir., chmn. exec. com. 1983-86), Assn. Ind. Colls. and Univs. Mass. (exec. com. 1988-91, chmn. 1977-78), Nat. Assn. Ind. Colls. and Univs., Harvard Bd. Overseers (com. to visit grad. sch. bus. adminstrn., 1987-93), Nat. Collegiate Athletic Assn. (pres.'s commn. 1984-88), Metaphys. Soc. Am., Jesuit Philos. Assn., Soc. Phenomenology and Existential Philosophy, Soc. Ancient Greek Philosophy. Home: Boston Coll Chestnut Hill MA 02167

MONASEE, CHARLES ARTHUR, healthcare foundation executive; b. Gary, Ind., Apr. 29, 1942; s. Sam Hasell and Phyllis (Kresham) M.; m. Lyra Ann Halper, Jan. 28, 1950; children—Pam, Lisa. B.S., U. Chgo., 1944. With Am. Cmty. Stores, 1955-80, pres., 1968-80; pres. Am. Community Stores Corp., Omaha, 1971-80; exec. v.p. parent co. Cullum Companies, 1976-80; group pres. Riekes Group, ALCO Standard Corp., 1980-84; pres. Health Future Found., 1984—. Pres., bd. dirs. United Way Midlands, 1977-78; bd. dirs. Omaha Symphony Assn., 1968-94, Boys Town, 1973-79, Creighton U., Omaha, 1976—, Ctr. Human Nutrition, 1987—; past chmn. bd. Joslyn Mus.; trustee Nebr. Meth. Hosp., 1974-86, Temple Israel, Omaha; nat. trustee NCCJ, 1986-89; bd. govs. Boys Clubs Omaha, 1975—; past mem. adv. coun. U. Nebr. Med. Ctr., 1978-88; pres. Omaha Jewish Cmty. Ctr., 1972-75; active SAC Hdqs. Consultation Com., 1976-92. Lt.col. USAF, 1943-55. Decorated Bronze Star. Mem. Air Force Assn., Plaza Club. Home: 9977 Spring St Omaha NE 68124-2654

MONAT, WILLIAM ROBERT, university official; b. Biwabik, Minn., Oct. 9, 1924; s. William Stephen and Milda Aleta (Sundby) M.; m. Josephine Ann Sclafani, Sept. 9, 1951; children: Lise Ann, Kathryn, Margaret, William Michael, Eric. A.A., Virginia (Minn.) Jr. Coll., 1947; B.A. magna cum laude, U. Minn., 1949, Ph.D., 1956; postgrad., Wayne U., 1949-50. Asst. prof. Wayne U., 1954-57; exec. asst. to Gov. Mich., 1957-60; asso. prof. Pa. State U., 1960-65, prof. polit. sci., 1965-69; asso. dir. Inst. Pub. Adminstrn., 1962-69; majority budget dir. Pa. Ho. of Reps., 1968-69; prof., chmn. dept. polit. sci. No. Ill. U., De Kalb, 1969-71, provost, 1976-78, Regency prof., 1986-92; Regency prof. emeritus, 1992—; pres. No. Ill. U., De Kalb, 1978-84; chancellor Ill. Bd. Regents, 1984-86; prof., dean faculties Baruch Coll., City U. N.Y., 1971-74; v.p. acad. affairs, 1974-76; cons. USPHS, 1958, Office of Sec. Dept. Labor, 1963-64, Bur. Labor Stads., 1966, Office of Gov. Pa., 1968; bd. dirs. 1st Nat. Bank DeKalb, 1981—, Castle Bancgroup, Inc., 1993—, bd. dirs. Castle Mortgage Co., 1995—. Author: Labor Goes to War, 1965, The Public Library and its Community, 1967, Politics, Poverty and Education, 1968; Editor: Public Adminstration in Era of Change, 1962; Contbr. articles to profl. jours. Mem. Gov.'s Commn. on Sci. and Tech., 1983-87; trustee Grad. Sch. Polit. Mgmt., N.Y., 1986—. With AUS, 1943-46. Recipient Outstanding Achievement award U. Minn., 1981; decorated Bronze Star medal. Mem. Am. Polit. Sci. Assn., Am. Soc. Pub. Adminstrn., Phi Beta Kappa. Home: 1605 Mayflower Dr De Kalb IL 60115-1723

MONCREIFF, ROBERT P., lawyer; b. Evanston, Ill., Mar. 26, 1930; s. W. Philip and Maxine E. M.; m. Elisabeth M.; children: Anne, Philip, Jane. BA, Yale U., 1952; MA, Oxford U., Eng., 1954; LLB, Harvard U., 1957. Bar: Mass. 1957. Assoc. Palmer & Dodge, Boston, 1957-62, ptnr., 1963-95; of counsel Boston, 1995—. City councillor, Cambridge, Mass., 1970-74. Office: Palmer & Dodge 1 Beacon St Boston MA 02108-3106

MONCRIEF, JAMES LORING, educational administrator; b. Limestone County, Ala., Sept. 19, 1935; m. Sue Evans; 4 children. BS, Samford U., 1958; MS, U. So. Miss., 1959; postgrad., Fla. State U., 1961, Ga. So. U., 1979-82, U. S.C., 1984—. Instr. dept. social scis. U. So. Miss., Hattiesburg, 1958-59; chmn. dept. social scis. North Fla. Jr. Coll., Madison, 1959-62; asst. prof. social scis. Jacksonville (Ala.) State U., 1962-64; exec. dean Jefferson State Coll., Birmingham, Ala., 1964-68; dir. community coll. mental health workers project So. Regional Edn. Bd., Atlanta, 1968-70; dir. career edn. and tng. N.C. Dept. Mental Health, Raleigh, 1970-71; asst. prof., coord. dir. health related professions U. Tex./Pan Am., Edinburg, 1971-74; tchr., asst. prin., prin. Chatham-Savannah (Ga.) Bd. Edn., 1974-78; prin. Williamsburg-Blakeley High Sch., Kingstree, S.C., 1978-86, Gaffney (S.C.) Sr. High Sch., 1986-92, Laurens (S.C.) Dist. 55 H.S., 1992-94; dist. obligate administr., exec. dir. secondary programs Sch. Dist. Pickens County, Easley, S.C., 1994—; past adj. assoc. prof. div. allied health East Carolina U., Greenville, N.C.; past asst. prof., coord. div. health related professions, U. Tex./Pan Am. Contbr. to profl. publs. Bd. dirs., exec. com., project rev. com. Pee Dee Health Systems Agy.; deacon West End Bapt. Ch., Gaffney, S.C.; mem. blue ribbon com. Williamsburg County Civic Auditorium; bd. dirs. Boys Club Am., Cherokee County div. Am. Heart Assn.; past pres. S.C. High Sch. League; bd. advisers Cherokee Pastoral Counseling Ctr., Gaffney; active S.C. Bus. Edn Partnership for Excellence Edn. With U.S. Marines, Korea, Vietnam. Fullbright scholar Brazil, 1962. Mem. Cherokee C. of C., Lions, Christian Businessmen's Com., Laurens C. of C., Rotary. Office: Sch Dist Pickens County 1348 Griffin Mill Rd Easley SC 29640-6997

MONCURE, JAMES ASHBY, historian; b. Abingdon, Va., June 4, 1926; s. Walter R.D. and Harriet Ashby (Ogburn) M.; m. Jennie Bruce Belk, June 15, 1952; 1 son, James Ashby. BA, U. Richmond, 1949; MA, Columbia U.,

1953, PhD, 1960. Mem. faculty U. Richmond, 1954-74, prof. English history, 1967-74; dean U. Richmond (Univ. Coll.), 1968-74, dir. univ. summer sch. study abroad program, 1963-70; v.p. for acad. and student affairs Elon Coll., 1974-83, prof. history, 1974-87; Pres. Richmond Experiment Internat. Living, 1957-59, Duntreath Community Assn., 1959-61, Richmond Internat. Council, 1967-69. Editor white paper on activities of Va. Gen. Assembly, 1958, 60, 62 for Va. C. of C., Research Guide to European Historical Biography, 1991, 93, 8 vols. Bd. dirs. English Speaking Union, YMCA, Experiment Internat. Living, E.R. Patterson Edn. Found. Served with inf., M.C. AUS, 1944-46, 50-51. Decorated Bronze Star medal, Combat Inf. badge; Richmond Community ambassador to Eng., 1954. Mem. Experiment Nat. Alumni Assn. (bd. dirs.), Am. Hist. Assn., Archeol. Inst. Am., Conf. Brit. Studies, Va. Social Sci. Assn., Omicron Delta Kappa, Pi Sigma Alpha, Phi Alpha Theta, Cross Keys. Baptist (chmn. bd. deacons). Home: 3336 Seven Lks West End NC 27376

MONCURE, JOHN LEWIS, lawyer; b. Houston, Nov. 4, 1930; s. Walter Raleigh Daniel and Margaret (Atkins) M.; m. Norma Steed, Dec. 29, 1954 (dec. June 1982); children—John Carter, Michael Lewis, Douglas Lee, Stuart Richard, Mary Margaret; m. Margaret Edmonston, Nov. 12, 1983. B.B.A., U. Houston, 1953; J.D., U. Tex., 1956. Bar: Tex. 1956. Assoc. Butler, Binion, Rice, Cook & Knapp, Houston, 1956-68; ptnr. Prappas, Moncure & Eidman, Houston, 1969-86, John L. Moncure and Assocs., Houston, 1987—; lectr. bus. law U. Houston, 1958-59, 68-69. Mem. sch. bd. St. Thomas Episcopal Sch., Houston, 1965-78; mem. vestry St. Thomas Episc. Ch., 1975-78. Named Distinguished Alumni Coll. Bus., U. Houston, 1968. Fellow Am. Coll. Probate Counsel; mem. Am., Tex., Houston bar assns., Assn. Christian Schs. (trustee), Coll. Bus. Alumni Assn. U. Houston (pres., dir.), U. Houston Alumni Fedn. (treas., dir.), Sigma Alpha Epsilon. Democrat. Home: 1100 Richmond Ave Apt 10 Houston TX 77006-5447 Office: 1200 River Oaks Tower 3730 Kirby Dr Houston TX 77098-3914

MONDALE, JOAN ADAMS, wife of former vice president of U.S.; b. Eugene, Oreg., Aug. 8, 1930; d. John Maxwell and Eleanor Jane (Hall) Adams; m. walter F. Mondale. Dec. 27, 1955; children—Theodore, Eleanor Jane, William Hall. BA, Macalester Coll., 1952. Asst. slide librarian Boston Mus. Fine Arts, 1952-53; asst. in edn. Mpls. Inst. of Arts, 1953-57; weekly tour guide Nat. Gallery of Art, Washington, 1965-74; hostess Washington Whirl-A-Round, 1975-76. Author: Politics in Art, 1972. Mem. bd. govs. Women's Nat. Dem. Club; hon. chmn. Fed. Coun. on Arts and Humanities, 1978-80; bd. dirs. Associated Coun. of Arts, 1973-75, Reading Is Fundamental, Am. Craft Coun., N.Y.C., 1981-88, J.F.K. Center Performing Arts, 1981-90, Walker Art Ctr., Mpls., 1987-93, Minn. Orch., Mpls., 1988-93, St. Paul Chamber Orch., 1988-90, Northern Clay Ctr., 1988-93, St. Paul, 1988-93, Nancy Hauser Dance Co., Mpls., 1989-93, Minn. Landmarks, 1991-93; trustee Macalester Coll., 1986—. Presbyterian. Office: Unit 45004 Box 200 APO AP 96337-5004

MONDALE, THEODORE ADAMS, state senator; b. Mpls., Oct. 12, 1957; s. Walter Frederick and Joan (Adams) M.; m. Pamela Burris, June 12, 1988; children: Louis F., Amanda J., Berit C. BA in History, U. Minn., 1985; JD, William Mitchell Coll. Law, 1988. Assoc., law firm Larkin, Hoffman Daly & Lindgren, 1988-91; state senator Minn. State Senate, St. Paul, 1990—; v.p. pub. programs United HealthCare; legal counsel United HealthCare Corp., Mpls. Press aide Carter for Pres. Com., 1976; surrogate speaker Carter Reelection Com., 1979-80, Mondale for Pres. Com., 1983-84; midwest dir. Dukakis for Pres. Com., 1988. Home: 3800 France Ave S Saint Louis Park MN 55416 Office: Minn Senate 226 State Capitol Saint Paul MN 55155

MONDALE, WALTER FREDERICK, former vice president of United States, diplomat, lawyer; b. Ceylon, Minn., Jan. 5, 1928; s. Theodore Sigvaard and Claribel Hope (Cowan) M.; m. Joan Adams, Dec. 27, 1955;children: Theodore, Eleanor, William. BA cum laude, U. Minn., 1951, LLB, 1956. Bar: Minn. 1956. Law clk. Minn. Supreme Ct.; pvt. practice law, 1956-60; atty. gen. State of Minn. 1960-64; U.S. senator from Minn., 1964-77, v.p. of U.S., 1977-81; mem. Nat. Security Council, 1977-81; mem. firm Winston & Strawn, 1981-87; ptnr. Dorsey & Whitney, Mpls., 1987-93; U.S. amb. to Japan Tokyo, 1993—. Author: The Accountability of Power—Toward a Responsible Presidency, 1975; mem. Minn. Law Rev. Dem. nominee for Pres. U.S., 1984. With U.S. Army, 1951-53. Mem. Minn. Law Review. Presbyterian.

MONDAVI, ROBERT GERALD, winery executive; b. Virginia, Minn., June 18, 1913; s. Cesare and Rosa (Grassi) M.; m. Marjorie Declusin, 1940 (dec.); children: Robert, Timothy, Marcia; m. Margrit Biever, 1980. BA, Stanford U., 1936. Dir. Sunny St. Helena Wine Co., St. Helena, Calif., 1937-45; v.p., gen. mgr., Charles Krug Winery, St. Helena, 1943-66; pres. Robert Mondavi Winery, Oakville, Calif., 1966—, now chmn. bd. Office: Robert Mondavi Winery PO Box 106 Oakville CA 94562-0106

MONDAY, JOHN CHRISTIAN, manufacturing company executive; b. West Bend, Wis., June 29, 1925; s. Leo John and Emilie Suzanne (Klapper) M.; m. Alyce S. Riesch, Aug. 20, 1949 (div. Jan. 1981); children: Linda Lee Monday Orlando, John Scott; m. Virginia M. Clayton, Jan. 29, 1981. BA in Math. and Econs., Ripon Coll., 1949; BSBA, MIT, 1951; MBA, U. Wis. 1954. Dir. research Hevi Duty Elec. Co., 1951-54, div. mgr., 1954-59; v.p., gen. mgr. Hubbard Aluminum Products Co., Pitts. and Abingdon, Va., 1959-65; pres. Am. Vitrified Products Co., Cleve., 1965-69; exec. v.p., bd. dirs. Intermark Inc., La Jolla, Calif., 1969-91; pres., chmn. Specialties Engring. Corp, San Diego 1991—; pres., bd. dirs. Specon Inc.; pres., chmn. bd. dirs. Spltys. Engring. Corp., 1976—; San Diego; pres. Specon Inc., La Jolla, 1981—. Author: Radiography of Copper Casting, 1951. Mem. Com. of 25, Washington, 1967-69; Trustee Johnston Meml. Hosp., 1963-65, Va. Highlands Found., 1963-65; dir. Street and Hwy. Safety Lighting Bur., 1959-65; regional chmn. ednl. council M.I.T., 1969-82. Served with AUS, 1943-46. Mem. ASTM (mem. D 33 com., subcom. chmn., steel structures painting coun.), Nat. Elec. Mfrs. Assn., Am. Mgmt. Assn., Clay Pipe Assn. (vice chmn. 1965-69), Nat. Assn. Corrosion Engrs., La Jolla Country Club (San Diego), Baillage La Chaine des Rotisseurs (Bailli of La Jolla). Republican. Presbyterian. Avocation: golfing. Home: 5192 Chelsea St La Jolla CA 92037-7908

MONDER, STEVEN L., orchestra executive; b. Mar. 12, 1945, Newark. B in Mus. Edn., Coll. Conservatory of Music, 1968, M in Mus. Edn., 1970. Tchr. orch., chorus, humanities McAuley HIgh Sch., Cin., 1970-71; prodn. mgr. Cin. Symphony Orch., 1971, asst. mgr., 1971-74, mgr., 1974-76, gen. mgr., 1976-89, exec. dir., 1989—; prodn. stage mgr. Cin. Opera Co., 1970, 71, adminstr., 1973; tchr. orch., chorus, humanities McAuley High Sch., Cin., 1970-71. Office: Cin Symphony Orch 1241 Elm St Cincinnati OH 45210-2267

MONDLIN, MARVIN, retail executive, antiquarian book dealer; b. Bklyn., July 1, 1927; s. Samuel and Thelma (Schultz) M.; m. Phyllis Grossman, Oct. 23, 1962 (div. 1968); 1 child, Gerri; m. Irene Szmulewicz, Sept. 4, 1970. Student, Cornell U., 1945; student of Aesthetic Realism, with Eli Siegel, 1945-68; student, CCNY, 1948, Bklyn. Coll., 1969-71. Ptnr. Amory Books, N.Y.C., 1953-59; clk. Strand Book Store, N.Y.C., 1951, estate book buyer, 1959-71, 74-76; sr. exec. v.p., 1976—; bus. mgr. Definition Press, N.Y.C., 1957; cataloger U. Cath. de Louvain, Belgium, 1972. Proofreader, copy editor Dover Publs., N.Y.C., 1958; editor Yearbook of Internat. Assocs., 1974. Mem. Antiquarian Booksellers Assn. Am., Appraisers Assn. Am., Bibliog. Soc. Am., Bibliog. Soc. London, Am. Photog. Hist. Soc., European Soc. History of Photography. Avocations: photography, nonsilver processes lab. work, natural history, horticulture, music. Home: 889 Broadway New York NY 10003-1212 Office: Strand Book Store 828 Broadway New York NY 10003-4805

MONDRY, IRA, electronic appliance company executive. Pres., CEO, dir. Highland Superstores Inc., Plymouth, Mich. Office: Highland Superstores Inc 909 N Sheldon Rd Plymouth MI 48170-1000*

MONE, PETER JOHN, lawyer; b. Brockton, Mass., Apr. 8, 1940; s. Edward Patrick and June E. (Keliher) M.; m. Sharon Lee Bright, Oct. 9, 1965; children: Kathleen, Peter. AB, Bowdoin Coll., 1962; JD, U. Chgo., 1965. Ptnr., Baker & McKenzie, Chgo., 1968—. Mem. Winnetka Caucus, Ill.,

1984-85. Served to capt. U.S. Army, 1966-67; Vietnam. Decorated Purple Heart, Bronze Star, Air medal. Fellow Am. Coll. Trial Lawyers; mem. Soc. Trial Lawyers, Chgo. Trial Lawyers Club, Internat. Assn. Def. Counsel (Ill. Supreme Ct. Ad Hoc Rules com.), Skokie Country Club. Democrat. Roman Catholic. Avocations: photography, golf, paddle tennis, softball. Home: 1035 Sunset Rd Winnetka IL 60093-3622 Office: Baker & McKenzie 1 Prudential Plz 130 E Randolph St Chicago IL 60601-6206

MONE, ROBERT PAUL, lawyer; b. Columbus, Ohio, July 23, 1934; s. Henry P. and Ann E. (Freedlund) M.; m. Lucille L. Willman, May 3, 1960; children: Robert, Maria, Andrew, Richard. BA, U. Dayton, 1956; JD, U. Notre Dame, 1959. Bar: Ohio 1959. Law clk.to presiding judge U.S. Dist. Ct. (no. dist.) Ohio, Cleve., 1960-62; assoc. George, Greek, King, et al, Columbus, 1962-66, ptnr., 1966-79; ptnr. McConnaughey, Stradley, et al, Columbus, 1979-81, Thompson, Hine and Flory, Columbus, 1981—. Cpl. U.S. Army, 1959-60. Mem. ABA, Ohio State Bar Assn., Fed. Energy Bar Assn., Columbus Bar Assn., Nat. Generation and Transmission Coop. Lawyers Assn. (1st pres.), Rotary. s. Home: 2300 Tremont Rd Columbus OH 43221-3706 Office: Thompson Hine & Flory 10 W Broad St Columbus OH 43215-3418

MONEO, JOSÉ RAFAEL, architecture educator; b. Tudela, Navarra, Spain, May 9, 1937; s. Rafael and María Teresa (Vallés); m. Belén Feduchi; children: Belén, Teresa, Clara Matilde. Degree in architecture, Madrid, 1961, DArch, 1963; DArch (hon.), Harvard U., 1986. Postgrad. fellow Spanish Acad., Rome, 1963-65; prof. architecture Barcelona, Spain, 1971-80, Madrid, 1981-84; prof. architecture Sch. Design, Harvard U., Cambridge, Mass., 1985—, chmn. dept. architecture, 1985—. Prin. works include Bankinter, Madrid, Logronó Hall, Merida Roman Art Mus., Atocha Sta., Madrid, Seville (Spain) Airport, Auditorium of Barcelona, Auditorium of San Sebastian, Thyssen-Bornemesza Mus., Madrid, Wellesley Coll. Davis Mus., Miro Collection Mus., Mallorca, Diagonal Bldg., Barcelona. Recipient Arnold W. Brunner Mem. prize in Architecture, Am. Acad. Arts and Letters, 1994. Office: Harvard U Dept Architecture Cambridge MA 02138

MONEY, ARTHUR L., electronics executive; b. Stockton, Calif.; m. Sharon Money; children: Jennifer, David. BSME, San Jose State Coll., 1965; MSME, U. Santa Clara, 1970. Data analysis of space and missile sys. Lockheed Missiles and Space Co., 1962-72; engr., then mgr. and dir. various units ESL Inc., Sunnyvale, Calif., 1972-84, v.p., gen. mgr. signals, analysis and sys. divsn., 1984-89, v.p. advanced programs and devel., 1989-90, pres., 1990—. Chmn. United Way campaign Santa Clara County, 1993; bd. dirs. Valley Med. Ctr. Found., Am. Leadership Forum, Santa Clara County Mfg. Group, Silicon Valley Art Fund, San Jose U. Sch. Engring. Mem. AIAA, Am. Electronics Assn., Navy League Am., Assn. Old Crows, Planetary Soc., Am. Def. Preparedness Assn., Security Affairs Support Assn. Office: ESL Inc PO Box 3510 495 Java Dr Sunnyvale CA 94088-3510

MONEY, JOHN WILLIAM, psychologist; b. Morrinsville, N.Z., July 8, 1921; came to U.S., 1947, naturalized, 1962; s. Frank and Ruth (Read) M. M.A. with honors, Victoria U. Coll., N.Z., 1943; postgrad., U. Pitts., 1947; Ph.D., Harvard U., 1952; DHL (hon.), Hofstra U., 1992. Jr. lectr. philosophy and psychology U. Otago, N.Z., 1945-47; part-time vis. lectr. Bryn Mawr Coll., Pa., 1952-53; mem. faculty Johns Hopkins U., 1951—, prof. med. psychology, 1972-86, assoc. prof. pediatrics, 1959-86, prof. emeritus med. psychology and pediatrics, 1986—; psychologist Johns Hopkins Hosp., 1955—, founder psychohormonal research unit, 1951, founding mem. gender identity com., 1966—; vis. prof. pediatrics Albert Einstein Coll. Medicine, 1969 and U. Nebr. Coll. Medicine, 1972; vis. prof. endocrinology Harvard U., 1970; vis. prof. obstetrics and gynecology U. Conn., 1975; Rachford lectr. Children's Hosp. Cin., 1969; bd. dirs. Sex Info. and Edn. Council U.S., 1965-68, Neighborhood Family Planning Center, 1970-82; mem. task force homosexuality NIMH, 1967-69; mem. study sect. devel. and behavioral scis., NIH, 1970-74; mem. task force on nomenclature Am. Psychiat. Assn., 1977-79, 85-87; pres. Am. Found. Gender and Genital Medicine and Sci., 1978—; bd. advisors Elysium Inst., 1980—; mem. adv. bd. Internat. Council Sex Edn. and Parenthood, 1981—; mem. external com. for rev. of Inst. for Sex Research, Indiana U., 1980; mem. sci. advd. bd. The Kinsey Inst. for Research in Sex, Gender, and Reproduction, 1982—; Kan Tongpo vis. prof. dept. psychiatry U. Hong Kong, 1994. Editorial bds. numerous jours.; field editor: Medicine and Law: An Internat. Jour., 1982—. Recipient Hofheimer prize Am. Psychiat. Assn., 1956; Gold medal Children's Hosp., Phila., 1966; citation Am. Urol. Assn., 1975; Harry Benjamin medal of honor Erickson Ednl. Found., 1976; Outstanding Contbn. award Md. Psychol. Assn., 1976; Lindemann lectr. pediatrics Cornell U., 1983; Bernadine Disting. lectr. U. Mo., 1985; Maurice W. Laufer Meml. lectr. Bradley Hosp. and Brown U., 1986; Disting. Scholar award Harry Benjamin Internat. Gender Dysphoria Assn., 1987; Outstanding Research Accomplishments award Nat. Inst. Child Health and Human Devel., 1987; named Sexologist of Yr. Polish Acad. Sex. Sci., 1988, Gloria Scientae award, 1991, Lifetime Outstanding Sci. Contrbn. award Internat. Community Profls. for Treatment Sex Offenders, 1991, Richard J. Cross award Robert Wood Johnson Med. Sch., 1992, Career Achievement award N.Y. Soc. Forensic Scis., 1994, Coun. Sex Edn. and Parenthood award, 1994; James McKeen Cattell fellow Am. Psychol. Soc., 1993; subject of book John Money: A Tribute (E. Coleman, editor), 1991. Fellow AAAS (life), Soc. Sci. Study Sex (charter, pres. 1974-76, award 1976, Past Pres. award 1987), Harriet Lane Alumni Soc., Nat. Inst. Rsch. Sex. Edn., Counseling and Therapy (hon.); mem. APA (master lectr. 1975, Disting. Sci. award 1985), Deutsche Gesellschaft für Sexualforschung, Internat. Orgn. Study Human Devel., Soc. Pediatric Psychology, Lawson Wilkins Pediatric Endocrine Soc. (founder), Am. Assn. Sex Educators, Counselors and Therapists (hon. mem., awards 1976, 85), European Soc. Pediatric Endocrinology (corr.), Internat. Acad. Sex Rsch. (charter, award 1991), Assn. Sexologists (life), Columbian Sexological Soc. (hon.), Internat. Soc. Psychoneuroendocrinology, N.Y. Acad. Scis., Med. Soc. Med. Rsch., Internat. Coll. Pediatrics, Czechoslovak Sexology Soc. (hon.), New Zealand Soc. on Sexology (hon. life), Sociedad Brasileira de Sexologia (hon.), Sociedad Andaluza de Sexolgia (hon.), Canadian Sex Rsch. Forum (hon.), Nat. Inst. Rsch. in Sex Edn., Counseling and Therapy (India, hon. chmn. internat. adv. bd.), Asian Fedn. for Sexology (hon.), Associacion de Especialistas en Sexologia (hon.). Home: 2104 E Madison St Baltimore MD 21205-2337 Office: Johns Hopkins Hosp Baltimore MD 21205 *It has always been my policy to combine research with clinical care, academic teaching and public education. I have combined a lifelong interest in travel and in research by lecturing on all continents except Antarctica.*

MONEYPENNY, EDWARD WILLIAM, petroleum exploration and production executive; b. Long Branch, N.J., Jan. 28, 1942; s. Edward Henry and Eleanor Kathleen (O'Hagen) M.; BS in Acctg., St. Joseph's U., 1964; MS in Acctg. Sci., U. Ill., 1967; m. Connie Wills, Feb. 19, 1966; children—Matthew, Jonathan, Christopher. Audit mgr. Coopers & Lybrand, Phila., 1970-76; mgr. corp. acctg. Sun Co., Inc., Radnor, Pa., 1976-78; v.p. fin. adminstrn. Sun Prodn. Co., Dallas, 1978-81; exec. v.p. fin. and CFO Oryx Energy Co. (formerly Sun Exploration & Prodn. Co.), Dallas, 1981-91; sr. v.p. fin., CFO Oryx Energy Co., Dallas, 1992-94, exec. v.p. fin., bd. dir. and CFO, 1994—; mng. gen. ptnr. Sun Energy Ptnr. L.P. Bus. adv. coun. U. Ill. Sch. Bus., 1994—. 1st lt. U.S. Army, 1967-70. CPA, Tex. Mem. AICPA, Fin. Execs. Inst., Tex. Soc. CPAs. Home: 4712 Stonehollow Way Dallas TX 75287-7524 Office: Oryx Energy Co 13155 Noel Rd Dallas TX 75240-5090

MONFORT, KENNETH, cattle production and meat processing company executive; b. 1928. Mem. Colo. Ho. of Reps., 1965-69; pres. Monfort of Colo. Inc., Greeley, 1969—, co-chmn., sr. v.p., 1976, pres., chief exec. officer, 1980—, also bd. dirs.; pres., chief operating officer ConAgra Redmeat Cos.; ret. 1989. Office: ConAgra Redmeat Cos care Shirley Bernhart 1930 Aa St # G Greeley CO 80631-9663

MONG, ROBERT WILLIAM, JR., managing editor; b. Fremont, Ohio, Jan. 22, 1949; s. Robert William and Betty (Dwyer) M.; m. Carla Beth Sweet, July 25, 1975 (div. 1979); m. Diane Elizabeth Reischel, Jan. 23, 1988; children: Eric Robert, Elizabeth Diana. BA, Haverford (Pa.) Coll., 1971. Reporter Cin. Post, 1973-75, Capital Times, Madison, Wis., 1975-77; city editor Madison Press Connection, 1977-79; asst. city editor Dallas Morning News, 1979-80, bus. editor, 1980-81, projects editor, 1981-83, asst. mng. editor, 1983-88, dep. mng. editor, 1988-90, mng. editor, 1990—. Mem. Am.

Soc. Newspaper Editors. Office: Dallas Morning News Comm Ctr PO Box 655237 Dallas TX 75265-5237

MONGAN, AGNES, museum curator, art historian, educator; b. Somerville, Mass., 1905. B.A., Bryn Mawr Coll., 1927; spl. student, Fogg Mus., Harvard U., 1928-29; A.M., Smith Coll., 1929, L.H.D. (hon.), 1941; Litt.D. (hon.), Wheaton Coll., 1954; L.H.D. (hon.), U. Mass., 1970; D.F.A. (hon.), LaSalle Coll., 1973, Colby Coll., 1973, U. Notre Dame, 1980, Boston Coll., 1985. Research asst. Fogg Mus., Harvard U., Cambridge, Mass., 1929-37; keeper of drawings Fogg Mus., Harvard U., 1937-47, curator of drawings, 1974-75, asst. dir., 1951-64, assoc. dir., 1964-68, acting dir., 1968-69, dir., 1969-71, cons., 1972—; Martin A. Ryerson lectr. fine arts Harvard U., 1960-75; vis. dir. Timken Art Gallery, San Diego, 1971-72; Kreeger-Wolf disting. vis. prof. Northwestern U., 1976; Bingham vis. prof. U. Louisville, 1976; Waggoner vis. prof. U. Tex., Austin, 1977, vis. prof. fine arts, 1981; Samuel H. Kress prof.-in-residence Nat. Gallery Art, Washington, 1977-78; vis. prof. fine arts U. Calif.-Santa Barbara, 1979; vis. dir. Met. Mus. and Arts Ctrs., Coral Gables, Fla., 1980; Brazilian Govt. lectr., 1954; Amy Sackler Meml. lectr. Mt. Holyoke Coll., 1966-67; vis. prof. fine arts U. Tex. Austin, 1981; Baldwin lectr. Oberlin Coll., 1966; lectr. throughout U.S., Can., Japan; organized numerous exhbns.; leader, lectr. yearly tours Europe to Friends of the Fogg groups. Former mem. editorial bd. Art Bull.; mem. adv. bd. Arte Veneta, Venice; editor: Heart of Spain (Georgiana Goddard King), 1941; One Hundred Master Drawings, 1949; contbr. to exhbn. and catalogue In Pursuit of Perfection: The Art of J.-A.-D.-Ingres, 1983; contbr. catalogue In Quest of Excellence, 1983; intro. to catalogue The Fine Line, 1985, exhbn. catalogue Ingres and Delacroix, Germany and Belgium, 1986; contbr. Silverpoint Drawings in the Fogg Art Museum, 1987, Some Brief Comments on Left-Handedness for Fogg Old Master Drawings Symposium, 1987; contbr. to books in field. Trustee, mem. com. Inst. Contemporary Art, Boston, 1940-60; a founder, v.p. Pan-Am. Soc. New Eng., 1940-62; mem. U.S. Nat. Commn. for UNESCO, 1954-57, White House Com. for Edn. in Age of Sci., 1961; trustee Chaplebrook Found.; mem. vis. com. art dept. Wheaton Coll., 1961-68; mem. vis. com. to U. Mass., Smith Coll., to 1970; mem. council for arts MIT; mem. adv. bd. Skowhegan Sch. Painting and Sculpture, 1974—; mem. exec. com. Save Venice, Council for Villa I Tatti; mem. vis. com. dept. textiles Boston Mus. Fine Arts; bd. dirs. Brit. Inst.; mem. exec. com. Somerville Hist. Soc.; vice chmn. Com. for Restoration of Italian Art. Decorated Palms d'Academie (France), cavaliere ufficiale (Italy); recipient Julius Stratton award Friends of Switzerland, 1978, Signet Soc. Medal for Achevement in the Arts Harvard U., 1986, 350th Harvard medal for Extraordinary Service, 1986, Benemerenti medal Vatican, 1987; honored by Women's Caucus for the Arts, 1987; Benjamin Franklin fellow Royal Acad. Art; Inst. Internat. Edn. grantee, 1935; Fulbright scholar, 1950. Fellow Am. Acad. Arts and Scis.; mem. Coll. Art Assn. (bd. dirs. 1949-54), Am. Assn. Art Mus. Dirs. (assoc.), Academie de Montauban, Phi Beta Kappa (hon.). Office: Fogg Museum Harvard U Art Museums Cambridge MA 02138

MONGAN, JAMES JOHN, physician; b. San Francisco, Ca., Apr. 10, 1942; s. Martin and Audrey Vera (Cunningham) M.; m. Jean Trotter Holmes, Apr. 22, 1972; children—John Holmes, Sarah Holmes. Student, U. Calif., Berkeley, 1959-62; A.B., Stanford U., 1963, M.D., 1967. Intern Kaiser Found. Hosp., San Francisco, 1967-68; med. officer USPHS, Denver, 1968-70; profl. staff mem. U.S. Senate Fin. Com., Washington, 1970-77; dep. asst. sec. for health HEW, Washington, 1977-79; asso. dir. human resources Domestic Policy Staff, White House, 1979-81; asst. surgeon gen. USPHS, 1979-81; exec. dir. Truman Med. Center, U. Mo., Kansas City, 1981—; dean sch. medicine U. Mo., Kansas City, 1987—; mem. health adv. com. GAO. Commr. Dept. Vets. Affairs Commn. on Future Structure of Vets. Health Care, 1990-91; mem. Pew Health Profesions Commn., Kaiser commn. on Future of Medicaid, Joint Commn. Users Adv. Group; trustee Pembroke Hills Sch., Kansas City, Mo.; bd. dirs. Midwest Rsch. Ins., Kansas City, Mo. With USPHS, 1968-70; trustee Kaiser Family Found., 1982—. Commonwealth Fund Health Adv. Com. Mem. NAS (Inst. Medicine), Am. Hosp. Assn. (trustee 1988-91), Am. Assn. Teaching Hosps. (bd. dirs. coun. teaching hosps. 1984-90). Home: 831 Westover Rd Kansas City MO 64113-1121 Office: U Mo Kansas City Sch Med 2411 Holmes St Kansas City MO 64108-2741

MONGE, JAY PARRY, lawyer; b. N.Y.C., Mar. 15, 1943; s. Joseph Paul and Dorothy Emma (Oschmann) M.; m. Julia T. Burdick, June 25, 1966 (div. 1994); children: Justin Parry, Lindsay Newton; m. Elizabeth Ann Tracy, 1994. AB, Harvard U., 1966; LLB, U. Va., 1969. Bar: Ill. 1969, N.Y. 1981. Assoc. Mayer, Brown & Platt, Chgo., 1969-75, ptnr., 1976-79; ptnr. Mayer, Brown & Platt, N.Y.C., 1980—, mng. ptnr., 1981-94. Contbr. legal commentaries Ill. Inst. Continuing Legal Edn., 1974, 78, 81, 84, 87, 93. Mem. ABA, Assn. Bar City N.Y., Chgo. Club, Onwentsia Club, Sky Club. Office: Mayer Brown & Platt 1675 Broadway New York NY 10019

MONHOLLON, LELAND, lawyer; b. Corbin, Ky., Nov. 8, 1925; s. Lewis Tom and Thelma (Prewitt) M.; m. Gawinna Owens, 1946 (div. 1969); 1 child, Patricia Lynn; m. Alice Faye Burden, July 3, 1970. JD, U. Ky., 1952. Bar: Ky. 1952. Supervising adjustor Travelers Ins. Co., Louisville, 1955-69; pvt. practice law Madisonville, Ky., 1969—. With USN, 1943-46, PTO, USNR, 1963-69. Mem. Ky. Bar Assn., Hopkins County Bar Assn., Am. Legion, VFW. Republican. Baptist. Home: 185 Threadneedle Dr Madisonville KY 42431-6439 Office: 111 S Main St Madisonville KY 42431-2555

MONIA, JOAN, management consultant; b. Teaneck, N.J., Mar. 20, 1938; d. James Anthony and Anne Linden (Cairns) McCaffrey; m. Charles Anthony Monia, Dec. 30, 1961; 1 child, Clare Ann Woodman. BA, Ohio Dominican U., 1960. Info. specialist Battelle Meml. Inst., Columbus, Ohio, 1960-62; project leader Douglas Aircraft Corp., Huntington Beach, Calif., 1962-64; programmer analyst McDonnell Aircraft Corp., St. Louis, 1965-66; project mgr. Sanders Assocs., Nashua, N.H., 1966-70; database adminstrn. project leader Mass. Blue Cross, Boston, 1970-74; data strategist Factory Mut. Enging. Corp., Norwood, Mass., 1974-78; mgr. data resource planning Digital Equipment Corp., Maynard, Mass., 1978-84; sr. mem. tech. staff GTE Govt. Systems Corp., Needham, Mass., 1984-91; prin. DMR Group, Inc., Waltham, Mass., 1991—. Recipient Sci. medal Bausch & Lomb, 1956. Avocation: painting. Home: 175 Anderson Rd Marlborough MA 01752 Office: DMR Group Inc 404 Wyman St Waltham MA 02154

MONICAL, ROBERT DUANE, consulting structural engineer; b. Morgan County, Ind., Apr. 30, 1925; s. William Blaine and Mary Elizabeth (Lang) M.; m. Carol Arnetha Dean, Aug. 10, 1947 (dec. 1979); children: Mary Christine, Stuart Dean, Dwight Lee; m. Sharon Kelly Eastwood, July 13, 1980; 1 stepson, Jeffrey David Eastwood. B.S.C.E., Purdue U., 1948, M.S.C.E., 1949. Engr. N.Y.C. R.R., Cin., 1949-51, So. Rwy., Cin., 1951; design engr. Pierce & Gruber (Cons. Engrs.), Indpls., 1952-54; founder, partner Monical & Wolverton (Cons. Engrs.), Indpls., 1954-63; founder, partner Monical Assocs., Indpls., 1963—, pres., 1975—; v.p. Crawle-Whittaker, Inc. (Engrs. and Land Surveyors), Miami Beach, Fla., 1975-90; Mem. Ind. Adminstrv. Bldg. Council, 1969-75; chmn., 1973-75; mem. Meridian St. Preservation Commn., 1971-75, Ind. State Bd. of Registration for Profl. Engrs. and Land Surveyors, 1976-84, chmn., 1979, 83. Served with USNR, 1943-46, USAAF, 1948-53. Mem. ASCE (Outstanding Civil Engr. award Ind. sect. 1987), Cons. Engrs. Ind. (pres. 1969, Cons. Recognition award 1986), Am. Cons. Engrs. Council (pres. 1978-79), Ind. Soc. Profl. Engrs. (Engr. of Yr. 1980), Nat. Soc. Profl. Engrs., Prestressed Concrete Inst., Am. Concrete Inst., Post-Tensioning Inst., Am. Inst. Steel Constrn., Am. Arbitration Assn., Indpls. Sci. and Engring. Found. (pres. 1992-93), Am. Legion, Lions, Masons, Shriners. Mem. Christian Ch. Home: 3024 Gorham Ct Carmel IN 46033-3280 Office: Monical Assocs 3024 Gorham Ct Carmel IN 46033-3280

MONISMITH, CARL LEROY, civil engineering educator; b. Harrisburg, Pa., Oct. 23, 1926; s. Carl Samuel and Camilla Frances (Geidt) M. BSCE, U. Calif., Berkeley, 1950, MSCE, 1954. Registered Civil Engr., Calif. From instr. to prof. of civil engring. dept. civil engring. U. Calif., Berkeley, 1951—; 1986—; Henry M. Shaw lectr. in civil engring. N.C. State U., 1993; cons. Chevron Rsch. Co., Richmond, Calif., 1957-93, U.S. Army CE Waterways Expt. Sta., Vicksburg, Miss., 1968—; B.A. Valierga, Inc., Oakland, Calif., 1980—, ARE, Austin, Tex. and Scotts Valley, Calif., 1978-92; cons. Bechtel Corp., San Francisco, 1982-86. Contbr. numerous articles to profl. jours.

Served to 2d lt. U.S. Army Corps Engrs., 1945-47. Scholar Fulbright St. U. New South Wales, 1971; recipient Rupert Myers medal U. New South Wales, 1976; Henry M. Shaw Lectr. in Civil Engring., N.C. State U., 1993. Fellow ASCE (hon., pres. San Francisco sect. 1979-80, edn. activities com. 1989-91, State of the Art award 1977, James Laurie prize 1988), AAAS; mem. Assn. Asphalt Paving Technologists (hon., pres. 1968, W.J. Emms award 1961, 65, 85), Transp. Rsch. Bd. (assoc., chmn. pavement design sect. 1973-79, K. B. Woods award 1972, 1st Disting. Lectureship 1992), Am. Soc. Engring. Edn., ASTM, NAE, Internat. Soc. for Asphalt Pavements (chmn. bd. dirs. 1988-90), The Asphalt Inst. (roll of honor 1990), Sigma Xi, Tau Beta Pi, Xi Epsilon. Avocations: swimming, stamp collecting. Office: U Calif Dept Civil Engring 115 McLaughlin Hall Berkeley CA 94720

MONIZ, ERNEST JEFFREY, physics educator; b. Fall River, Mass., Dec. 22, 1944; s. Ernest Perry and Georgina (Pavao) M.; m. Naomi Hoki, June 9, 1973; 1 child, Katya. B.S., Boston Coll., 1966; Ph.D., Stanford U., 1971. Prof. physics MIT, Cambridge, Mass., 1973—; dir. Bates Linear Accelerator Ctr. MIT, Middleton, Mass., 1983-91, head physics dept., 1991—; Cons. Los Alamos Nat. Lab., 1975—. Contbr. numerous articles to profl. jours. Office: MIT Dept Physics 6-113 77 Massachusetts Ave Cambridge MA 02139-4307

MONJO, JOHN CAMERON, ambassador; b. Stamford, Conn., July 17, 1931; s. Ferdinand Nicolas, Jr. and Mayme (Holden Bahin) M.; m. Sirkka Orvokki Kortelainen, Feb. 28, 1964; children: Christina Cameron, Rolf Kortelainen. B.S., U. Pa., 1953. Joined Fgn. Service, Dept. State, 1957; fgn. service officer Phnom Penh, Cambodia, 1958-61; with econ.-comml. sect. Dept. State, Tokyo, 1961-64; with econ.-comml. sect. Dept. State, Washington, 1967-71, country dir. Philippines, 1978-79, dep. asst. sec., 1983-87; detail to U.S. Army, Naha, Okinawa, Japan, 1963-67; polit. officer U.S. Embassy, Jakarta, Indonesia, 1971-76, dep. chief of mission, 1982-83; prin. officer U.S. Consulate Gen., Casablanca, Morocco, 1976-78; dep. chief of mission U.S. Embassy, Seoul, South Korea, 1979-82; prin. dep. asst. sec. East Asia Bur. Dept. State, 1983-87; U.S. amb. to Malaysia Kuala Lumpur, 1987-89; U.S. amb. to Indonesia Jakarta, 1989-92; U.S. amb. to Pakistan Islamabad, 1992—. Served to lt. USN, 1953-56. Home and Office: Am Embassy Jakarta PO Box 1 APO AP 96520

MONK, ALBERT C., III, manufacturing executive; b. 1939. With A.C. Monk & Co., 1961—; pres., CEO Monk & Austin, Farmville, N.C., 1990—. Office: Monk Austin Inc 1200 W Marlboro Rd Farmville NC 27828

MONK, ALLAN JAMES, baritone; b. Mission City, B.C., Can., Aug. 19, 1942; m. Marlene Folk; 3 children. Student, Elgar Higgin and Boris Goldovsky. Operatic debut in Old Maid and the Thief San Francisco, 1967; joined touring co., later main co. San Francisco Opera; appeared with Tulsa Opera, Pitts. Opera, Edmonton Opera, Vancouver Opera, So. Alta. Opera, Chgo. Opera, Balt. Opera, Miami Opera, Colo. Opera, Mont real Opera, Hawaii Opera Theatre, Portland Opera; 1976. Met. Opera debut as Schaunard in La Boheme, 1976, sang title role in Wozzeck, Wolfram in Tannheuser, Dr. Malatesta in Don Pasquale, Rodrigo in Don Carlo, Sharpless in Madame Butterfly, Herald in Lohengrin; sang with Can. Opera Co. as Abelard in Heloise and Abelard, Macbeth, Rigoletto, Belcore in L'Elisir D'Amoure, Jago in Otello, as Ford in Falstaff, four villains in Les Contes d'Hoffman; with Nat. Arts Ctr. Opera Festival, Ottawa, Ont., Can., title role in Don Giovanni, Almaviva in Le Nozze Di Figaro, gulielmo in Cossi Fan Tutti, Tomsky in Pique Dame, Marcello in La Boheme; Carnegie Hall debut as Vladislav in Dalibor, 1977; European debut as Wozzeck, 1980; solo recitalist; toured with Nat. Arts Ctr. Orch. in USSR, Poland, Italy, 1973; movie debut as Baron Douphol in La Traviata, 1983. Named Artist of Yr. Can. Music Council, 1983, laureat Order of Can., 1985. Office: 97 Woodpark Close SW, Calgary, AB Canada T2W 6HI

MONK, ART, football player; b. White Plains, N.Y., Dec. 5, 1957. Student, Syracuse U. With Washington Redskins, 1980-94, N.Y. Jets, 1994-95. Named to Pro Bowl team, 1984-86, Sporting News All-Pro team, 1984, 85. Set record for most consecutive games with a reception (178), 1994; holds record for most career receptions. *

MONK, DEBRA, actress. Stage appearances include (Broadway) Nick & Nora, Prelude to a Kiss, Pump Boys and Dinettes (also co-author), Redwood Curtain (Tony award featured actress in a play 1993), Picnic (Tony nomination featured actress 1994), (off Broadway) Death Defying Acts, 3 Hotels (Helen Hayes award leading actress 1994), Assassins, Man in His Underwear, The Innocent's Crusade, Molière in Spite of Himself, Oil City Symphony (co-author, Drama Desk award best ensemble 1988); TV apprearances include Women and Wallace, The Becky Bell Story, Law and Order, Redwood Curtain; film appearances include Prelude to a Kiss, For Love or Money, 1993, Fearless, 1993, Quiz Show, 1993, Jeffry, 1994, The Bridges of Madison County, 1994, Amelia and the Book of Plants, Reckless. Office: Gage Group 315 W 57th St Apt 4H New York NY 10019-3147

MONK, GREGORY BRITTAIN, artist, business owner; b. San Francisco, Dec. 28, 1942; s. John Clarkson and Barbara (Brittain) M.; m. Yvonne Adele Jones, Mar. 30, 1974 (div. Jan. 1987). AA, City Coll., San Francisco, 1963; BA in Econs., San Francisco State U., 1965. Freelance actor and extra various media Calif. and Hawaii, 1961—; salesman, mgr. San Francisco Luggage Co., 1961-65; computer programmer Western Union, Mahwah, N.J., 1966-73; owner Gregory Monk - Wood and Glass, Sausalito, Calif., 1973-74, G. Brittain M. Co., Haleiwa, Hawaii, 1975-80, Greg Monk Stained Glass, Aiea, Hawaii, 1981—. Artist (stained glass designs) Maka Koa, 1981 (1st prize 1982), Flowing, 1984; glass artist (TV show) Portraits of Paradise, 1988. Sgt. USMC, 1966-68. Mem. SAG, Assn. Hawaii Artists, Stained Glass Assn. Hawaii (co-founder 1979, pres. 1979-81, treas. 1982-83), Glass Art Soc., Arts Coun. Hawaii, Hawaii Craftsmen, Pacific Handcrafters, Honolulu Acad. Arts, The Contemporary Mus., Profl. Stained Glass Guild, Art Glass Suppliers Assn., Internat. Platform Assn., San Francisco State U. Alumni Assn. Democrat. Avocations: photography, walking, skiing, model trains, old movies. Office: Greg Monk Stained Glass 98-027 Hekaha St Aiea HI 96701-4910

MONK, MEREDITH JANE, artistic director, composer, choreographer, film maker, director; b. N.Y.C., Nov. 20, 1942; d. Theodore G. and Audrey Lois (Zellman) M. BA, Sarah Lawrence Coll., 1964; ArtsD (hon.), Bard Coll., 1988, U. of the Arts, 1989. Artistic dir., founder House Found. for Arts, N.Y.C., 1968—. Prin. works include Vessel, 1971, Quarry, 1976, Turtle Dreams, 1983, Recent Ruins, 1979, The Games, 1983, Book of Days, 1988, Facing North, 1990, Atlas, 1991, Three Heavens and Hells, 1992, Volcano Songs, 1994, American Archeology, 1994. Recipient Obie award Village Voice, 1972, 76, 85, Creative Arts award Brandeis U., 1974, Deutches Kritiker Preis for best record 1981, 86, Brandeis award N.Y. Dance and Performance awards, 1985, Nat. Music Theatre award, 1986, Dance Mag. award, 1992; Guggenheim fellow, 1972, 86, Norton Stevens fellow, 1993-94, MacArthur fellow, 1995. Fellow MacDowell Colony (Sigma Phi Omega award 1987); mem. ASCAP. Office: House Found for Arts 131 Varick St New York NY 10013-1410*

MONK, RICHARD FRANCIS, air force officer, health care administrator; b. Washington, Feb. 9, 1947; s. Leslie G. and Doris Coleman (White) M.; m. Rhonda Lee Wise, Mar. 24, 1978; children: Ryan Michael, Robyn Lynn. BA in Chemistry, N.C. Wesleyan Coll., 1969; postgrad., Med. Coll. Va., 1969-72; MS, Trinity U., San Antonio, 1975. Assoc. adminstr. French Hosp., San Francisco, 1977-78; adminstr. Mono Gen. Hosp., Bridgeport, Calif., 1978-79, Polk Cmty. Hosp., Dallas, Oreg., 1979-80, San Cruval, Green Valley, Ariz., 1980; commd. officer USAF, 1981, advanced through grades to maj.; CFO, March Regional Hosp., Riverside, Calif., 1981-85; asst. prof. Uniformed Svcs. U. Health Scs., Bethesda, Md., 1985-88; squadron comdr. 15th Med. Group, Honolulu, 1988-91; hosp. comdr. Homestead AFB, Homestead, Fla., 1992; assoc. adminstr. 355th Med. Group, Tucson, 1992-94; ops. officer 355th Med. Support Squadron, Tucson, 1994—. 1st counselor LDS Ch., Tucson, 1994—. Fellow Am. Coll. Health Care Execs.; mem. Internat. Brotherhood Magicians (v.p. ring 1972). Libertarian. Avocations: magic, hiking, weight training, high end stereo equipment. Home: 7345 E Shorewand Loop Tucson AZ 85715-3455 Office: 355th Med Support Squadron SGSO 4175 S Alamo Ave Davis Monthan AFB AZ 85707

MONK, RICHARD HUNLEY, JR., textile company executive; b. Anniston, Ala., Aug. 25, 1939; s. Richard Hunley and Marjorie Louise (Schneider) M.; m. H. Ann McDougald, June 24, 1961; children: Jennifer L. Borden, Richard H. III. AB, Emory U., 1961, LLB, 1963. Pvt. practice Atlanta, 1963-65; legal counsel WestPoint Pepperell, West Point, Ga., 1965-74, asst. sec., 1967-90, sec., 1970-83, v.p., 1973-90, gen. counsel, 1977-83, pres. internat. div., 1983-90; exec. v.p. Avondale Mills, Inc., Sylacauga, Ala., 1990, pres., 1990-94, bd. dirs., 1990—; chief adminstrv. officer, sec., 1994—; bd. dirs. First Nat. Bank and First Nat. Bankshares, West Point, Lantor Internat., Manchester, Eng., chmn. Arthur Sanderson & Sons Ltd., Uxbridge, Eng., 1985-90; bd. dirs., pres. Arthur Sanderson & Sons (N.Am.) Ltd., 1985—; sec. West Point-Pepperell Found., 1971-83, vice chmn., 1976-83. Bd. dirs. Chattahoochee-Lee Jr. Achievement, Lanett, Ala., 1978-82; commr. West Point Housing Authority, 1968-74; trustee Chattahoochee Valley Ednl. Found., 1969-86, v.p., 1980-81, pres., 1981-83; past pres. Chattahoochee Valley Hist. Soc., West Point; mem. exec. bd. G.H. Lanier coun. Boy Scouts Am., 1981-88, fin. chmn., 1981-83, v.p., 1982-83, pres., 1983-85; Chmn. Sylacauga Remembers Committee(World War II 50th Anniversary Commemoration) 1992-95; mem. bd. visitors Presbyn. coll., Clinton, S.C., 1981-84, vice chmn. bd. visitors, 1982-83, chmn. bd. visitors, 1983-84; trustee Presbyn. Coll., 1987—; bd. dirs. Valley United Fund, West Point, 1967-73, 76-81, v.p., 1977-78, pres., 1978-79; Sylacauga City Sch. Fedn., 1992—; Coosa Valley Med. Ctr. Fedn., 1992—; chmn. Sylacauga Remembers com., 1992-95; fin. chmn. Troup County YMCA of Ga., 1983-90. Mem. ABA, Ga. Textile Mfrs. Assn. (bd. dirs. 1977-80, 81-83, 86-88, treas. 1983-84, v.p. 1984-85, pres. 1985-86), Am. Textile Mfrs. Inst., Soc. Internat. Bus. Fellows, State Bar Ga. (sec. antitrust sect. 1970-72, vice chmn. 1972-73, chmn. 1973-74, co-chmn. corp. counsel com. 1981-82, ex-officio dir. 1988—), Sylacauga C. of C. (bd. dirs. 1995—), Am. Yarn Spinners Assn. (2nd v.p. 1991-92, 1st. v.p. 1992-93, pres. 1993-94, bd. dirs. 1991-94), Coosa Valley Country Club (Sylacauga, Ala.). Office: Avondale Mills Inc 900 Avondale Ave Sylacauga AL 35150

MONKE, EDWIN JOHN, agricultural engineering educator; b. Harvel, Ill., June 7, 1925; s. Edwin Herman and Emma Lillian (Prange) M.; m. Marian Mildred Hubb, Aug. 24, 1963; children: Karen Ruth, Sarah Elizabeth, Dianne Mildred. B.S., U. Ill., 1950, M.S., 1953, Ph.D., 1959. Registered profl. engr., Ind. Instr. agrl. engring. U. Ill., Urbana, 1951-58; asst. prof. agrl. engring. Purdue U., West Lafayette, Ind., 1958-62, assoc. prof., 1962-67, prof., 1967—; dir. Third Internat. Seminar for Hydrology Profs., 1971. Editor: Biological Effects in the Hydrological Cycle, 1971. Served with U.S. Army, 1944-46. Fellow Am. Soc. Agrl. Engrs. (chmn. soil and water div. 1978-79); mem. Soil and Water Conservation Soc. Am., Am. Geophys. Union, Nat. Soc. Profl. Engrs., Am. Soc. Engring. Edn., Nat. Soc. Profl. Engrs. (pres. A.A. Potter chpt. 1971-72, state dir. 1972-73), Sigma Xi, Tau Beta Pi, Alpha Zeta, Alpha Epsilon, Gamma Sigma Delta. Lutheran. Club: Optimists (West Lafayette) (pres. 1979-80). Home: 2501 Newman Rd West Lafayette IN 47906-4537 Office: Purdue U Agrl Engring West Lafayette IN 47907

MONKEWITZ, PETER ALEXIS, mechanical and aerospace engineer, educator; b. Berne, Switzerland, Nov. 9, 1943; came to U.S., 1977; s. Kurt and Marie M. (Krähenbühl) M.; m. Annelise Heidy Sturzenegger, Jan. 15, 1972; children: Serge M., Florence S., Cyril P. Diploma Physics, Fed. Inst. Tech., Zurich, 1967, D of Natural Scis., 1977. Software cons. Sperry Rand UNIVAC, Zurich, 1968; teaching asst. Fed. Inst. Tech., Zurich, 1969-77; rsch. assoc. U. So. Calif. L.A., 1977-80; asst. prof. UCLA, 1980-85, assoc. prof., 1985-91, prof., 1991—. Co-editor Jour. Applied Math. and Physics, 1991—; contbr. articles to Jour. Fluid Mechanics, Physics of Fluids, Ann. Revs. Fluid Mechanics, others. Recipient U.S. Sr. Scientist award Humboldt Found., Germany, 1988. Fellow Am. Phys. Soc.; mem. AIAA. Achievements include rsch. on self-excited oscillations and their control with regard to altering mixing rates or the drag of a body. Office: UCLA MANE Dept 405 Hilgard Ave Los Angeles CA 90024-1301

MONKS, DONALD RICHARD, banker; b. Orange, N.J., May 5, 1948; s. Frank J. and Helen (Walker) M.; m. Margaret Wallace, June 13, 1970; children—Daniel, Jonathan, Laura. B.S. in Bus. Adminstrn., Rider Coll., 1970; M.A. in Econs., U. Del., 1974. With Irving Trust Co., N.Y.C., 1972—; sr. v.p. Irving Trust Co., 1982-84, exec. v.p., 1984—; former vice chmn. fin. services industry standards Am. Nat. Standards Com., 1983. Served to capt. USAR. Mem. Am. Bankers Assn. (chmn. exec. com. ops. and automation div., past chmn. wholesale ops. com.). Home: 3 Allerton Ct Florham Park NJ 07932-1606

MONMONIER, MARK, graphics educator, geographer; b. Balt., Feb. 2, 1943; s. John Carroll and Martha Elizabeth (Mason) M.; m. Margaret Janet Kollner, Sept. 4, 1965; 1 child, Jo Kerry. BA, Johns Hopkins U., 1964; MS, Pa. State U., 1967, PhD, 1969. Asst. prof. U. Rhode Island, Kingston, 1969-70, SUNY, Albany, 1970-73; assoc. prof Syracuse U., N.Y., 1973-79, prof., 1979—; cons. N.Y. State, Albany, 1974-93, Nat. Geog. Soc., 1987, Microsoft Corp., 1993—; rsch. geographer U.S. Geol. Survey, Reston, Va., 1979-84; dep. dir. N.Y. Ctr. for Geographic Info. and Analysis, 1989-90; Robinson vis. fellow George Mason U., 1985; Ida Beam Disting. vis. prof. U. Iowa, 1985; mem. adv. bd. GIS Law and Policy Inst. Author: Maps, Distortion and Meaning, 1977, Computer-assisted Cartography, 1982, Technological Transition in Cartography, 1985, Maps with the News, 1989, How to Lie with Maps, 1991, Mapping It Out, 1993, Drawing the Line, 1995; co-author: The Study of Population: Elements, Patterns, Processes, 1982, Map Appreciation, 1988; editor: The American Cartographer, Falls Church, Va., 1977-82; assoc. editor Mapping Scis. and Remote Sensing, 1987—; contbg. editor Cartographica, 1984—. Statistician, Police Dept., Syracuse, 1978-80. Fellow John Simon Guggenheim Meml. Found., 1984; recipient Chancellor's citation for Disting. Acad. Achievement, 1993. Mem. Assn. Am. Geographers, Am. Cartographic Assn. (pres. 1983-84), Can. Cartographic Assn., N. Am. Cartographic Info. Soc., Pa. Acad. Sci. (editorial bd. 1979—), Soc. for History of Soc., Sigma Xi, Pi Tau Sigma, Tau Beta Pi. Home: 302 Waldorf Pky Syracuse NY 13224-2240 Office: Syracuse U Dept Of Geography Syracuse NY 13244

MONNIG, DONNA SUE, librarian; b. Cin., Mar. 28, 1944; d. Richard Kirker and Rose June (Liming) Stoms; m. William Bernard Monnig, July 8, 1967; children: Aaron William, Thomas Richard. BA, U. Cin., 1966; MA, Rosary Coll., 1970. Tchr. Finneytown (Ohio) H.S., 1966-69; head lit. dept. Pub. Libr. of Cin. and Hamilton County, 1970—; ref. libr., 1970-83, dept. head, 1983—, chair book selection policy com., 1993-94. Pres. Hope Cottage Guild, Covington, Ky., 1978; sec. Literacy Network of Greater Cin., 1990, mem. awards com., 1992-93. Mem. Ohioana Libr. Assn., Beta Phi Mu. Republican. Roman Catholic. Office: Pub Libr Cin & Hamilton Co Lit Dept 800 Vine St Cincinnati OH 45202

MONRAD, ERNEST EJNER, trust company executive; b. Little Falls, N.Y., May 30, 1930; s. Karl J. and Augusta (Olsen) M.; m. Elizabeth Ann Haffenreffer, June 15, 1951; children: Ernest Scott, Elizabeth, Bruce H. AB in Econs, Harvard U., 1951; LLB, U. Va., 1954. Bar: Mass. 1956. Asso. firm Herrick & Smith, Boston, 1956-59; treas. H.P. Nichols, Inc., Boston, 1960-64; v.p. Alsace Corp., Boston, 1964-67; trustee Northeast Investors Trust, Boston, 1960-69, chmn. trustees, 1969—; v.p., bd. dirs., clk. Furman Lumber Co., Inc., Boston, 1971—; trustee, corporator Boston 5 Cent Savs. Bank, 1972—, mem. bd. investment, 1976—; trustee Century Shares Trust, 1976—, Ostrander High Income Res. fund, 1988-90; bd. dirs. New Am. High Income Fund, Inc. Trustee Simmons Coll., acting chmn., 1991-92; trustee Harvard Coll. Fund, chmn. 1987-89; pres. bd. trustees Fessenden Sch., West Newton, Mass., 1971-78; mem. com. on univ. resources Harvard U., 1978; corporator Mass. Gen. Hosp., Boston, 1980-90; bd. overseer Mus. Fine Arts, 1990—; commr. trust fund Town of Weston, Mass., 1975. 2d lt. U.S. Army, 1951-53. Mem. Boston Security Analysts Soc. (dir. 1973-75). Home: 91 Dean Rd Weston MA 02193-2709 Office: Northeast Investors Trust 50 Congress St Boston MA 02109-4002

MONRO, JAMES ALEXANDER, JR., retail executive; b. Eastlake, Ohio, Sept. 6, 1949; s. James Alexander and Shirley (Geer) M.; m. Susan A. Allison, May 19, 1978; children—Jason Alexander, Jessica Allison. B.A., Bob Jones U., 1972. Buyer, May Co., Cleve., 1971-75, Rike Kumler, Dayton, Ohio, 1975-77; asst. store mgr. Joseph Horne Co., Pitts., 1977-78; div. mdse. mgr. Gold Circle Co., Worthington, Ohio, 1978-79; div. mdse. mgr.

Winkelman Stores, Detroit, 1979-80, v.p.; div. mdse. mgr., 1980-81, sr. v.p., 1981-83, exec. v.p., 1983-84, pres., 1984—; also dir.; pres., exec. v.p Fabri-Ctrs. Am. Inc., Beachwood, Ohio, 1986—; dir. Win Spot Ltd. Co., Hong Kong. Mem. Nat. Retail Mchts. Assn., Am. Mgmt. Assn., Mgmt. Horizons. Republican. Presbyterian. Clubs: Renaissance, Detroit, Detroit Athletic (Detroit). Home: 32655 Wintergreen Dr Cleveland OH 44139-1392 Office: Fabri- Ctrs Am Inc 5555 Darrow Rd Hudson OH 44236-4011

MONROE, BROOKS, investment banker; b. Greenville, S.C., July 24, 1925; s. Clarence Jenningsand Edith Cabot (Johnson) M.; m. Hilda Marie Meredith, June 30, 1956. B.S. in Commerce, U. Va., 1948, J.D., 1951; grad. Inst. Investment Banking, U. Pa., 1959. Dir. pub. relations Scott, Horner & Co., Lynchburg, Va., 1951-53; sales mgr. Scott, Horner & Co. Richmond, Va., 1953-56; v.p., gen. sales mgr. Scott, Horner & Co., Lynchburg, 1956-59; sales mgr. nat. and underwriting Francis I. duPont & Co., N.Y.C., 1959-61; gen. partner Francis I. duPont & Co., 1961-66, Paine, Webber, Jackson & Curtis, N.Y.C., 1966-69; pres., chief exec. officer Brooks Monroe & Co., Inc., N.Y.C., 1969—; chmn. HHM Corp., Wilmington and Beverly Hills, Calif., 1969—, Bargeland Corp., Phila., 1970—, IGAS Corp., Pitts., 1975—; chmn. PPM Internat., Inc., Spartanburg; S.C.founder, chmn. Execs. Guardian Co., N.Y.C., 1971—; Tchr. U. Va., 1949-51; asso. mem. A.N.Y. stock exchanges, 1961-72; mem. Pacific Stock Exchange, 1962-66, Chgo. Bd. Trade, 1962-66. Bd. dirs. McIntire Sch. Commerce U. Va. Served with USAAF, 1943-46, PTO. Mem. U. Va. Alumni Assn. (N.Y. pres. 1978-81), Sigma Chi, Delta Sigma Rho, Pi Delta Epsilon, Omicron Delta Kappa, Delta Theta Pi. Republican. Presbyterian. (trustee). Clubs: Boar's Head Sport, (Charlottesville, Va.), Farmington Country (Charlottesville); Bond, City Midday, Union League (N.Y.C.); Quogue (N.Y.) Field, Quogue Beach; Clan Munro (Scotland and U.S.). Home: Ednam Forest Charlottesville VA 22903 Office: PO Box 5246 2 Boars Head Pl Charlottesville VA 22905

MONROE, HASKELL M., JR., university educator; b. Dallas, Mar. 18, 1931; s. Haskell M. and Myrtle Marie (Jackson) M.; m. Margaret Joan Phillips, June 15, 1957; children: Stephen, Melanie, Mark, John. B.A., Austin (Tex.) Coll., 1952, M.A., 1954; Ph.D., Rice U., Houston, 1961. From instr. to prof. Tex. A&M U., 1959-80; asst. dean Tex. A&M U. (Grad. Sch.), 1965-68, asst. v.p. acad. affairs, 1972-74, dean faculties, 1974-80, assoc. v.p. acad. affairs, 1977-80; pres. U. Tex., El Paso, 1980-87; chancellor U. Mo., Columbia, 1987-91; prof. history U. Mo., 1987—; instr. Schreiner Inst., Kerrville, Tex., summer 1959; vis. lectr. Emory U., summers 1967, 72; faculty lectr. Tex. A&M U., 1972; alumni lectr. Austin Coll., 1980; bd. dirs. Southwestern Bell Corp., Boone County Nat. Bank. Contbr. articles, revs.; editor: Papers of Jefferson Davis, 1964-69; adv. editor: Texana, 1964-71; bd. editorial advisers: Booker T. Washington Papers, 1965-85 . Bd. dirs. Brazos Valley Rehab. Center, 1975-77, Salvation Army, El Paso, 1984-87, Columbia, Mo., 1988—, Crime Stoppers of El Paso, United Way Columbia, 1988-94; trustee Bryan Hosp., 1976-79, chmn., 1979; bd. ch. visitors Austin Coll., 1977-78; deacon First Presbyn. Ch., Bryan, 1961-63, elder, 1965-67, 69-71, 73-74, clk. of session, 1973-74, chmn. pulpit nominating com., 1971-72; mem. presbytery's council Presbytery of Brazos, 1969-71, mem. resources for the 80s steering com., 1978-80; elder 1st Presbyn. Ch., El Paso, 1984-87, 1st Presbyn. Ch., Columbia, 1994—; mem. exec. bd. Great Rivers coun. Boy Scouts of Am., 1990—; mem. Pres. Coun. NCAA, 1986-87. Served with USNR, 1954-56. Recipient Citation of Appreciation, LULAC, 1982, also numerous achievement awards; grantee Social Sci. Rsch. Coun., Tex. A&M U., Huntington Libr. Mem. Am. Hist. Assn., Orgn. Am. Historians, So. Hist. Assn. Hist. Found. Presbyn. and Reformed Chs. (pres. 1970-72), Coll. Football Assn. (chmn. bd. 1989-90, bd. dirs.), Truman Scholarship Panel, So. Conf. Deans Faculties and Acad. V.P.s (pres. 1978), Rotary (El Paso, hon. Columbia, Mo.). Home: 3200 Westcreek Cir Columbia MO 65203-0904 Office: U Mo 306 Reynolds Ctr Columbia MO 65211

MONROE, HELEN LEOLA, nurse, consultant, educator; b. Alma, Ga., Jan. 30, 1931; d. Silas Leo Monroe and Thelma (Fussell) Smith; 1 child, Reavena M. M. Oliver. BS, Fla. A&M U., 1954; MS, St. John's U., L.I., N.Y., 1959. Staff nurse Vis. Nurse Assn. Duval County, Jacksonville, Fla., 1954-55; instr. sch. nursing Fla. A&M U., Tallahassee, 1955-57, asst. prof., 1959-64; dir. nursing edn. Mississippi Valley State Coll., Itta Bena. Miss., 1964-67; asst. prof. Norfolk State Coll. Va., 1967-68; asst. prof., dir. nursing edn. Lincoln U., Jefferson City, Mo., 1968-80; pvt. practice nursing Jefferson City, 1981-85; pvt. practice achievement cons. Jacksonville, 1987—; cons. nursing William Woods Coll., Fulton, Mo., 1972-73. Sec. Jefferson City chpt. NAACP, 1971-73; chmn. edn. com. Cancer Soc. Cole County, Jefferson City, 1972-74; v.p. Cole County Mental Health Assn., 1973; mem. fin. com. United Way Cole County, 1975. Recipient Outstanding Achievement award Citizens' Com. of Jefferson City, 1970, Woman of Achievement award AAUW, 1974, Permanent Royal Patronage from Principality of the Hutt River Province, 1994. Avocations: gardening, sewing, reading, bicycling, bowling. Home: 5436 Mays Dr Jacksonville FL 32209-2926

MONROE, JAMES WALTER, organization executive; b. Fairfax, S.D., Feb. 13, 1936; s. Sherman William and Frances (Burnett) M.; m. Dorothy Lou Gillette, Apr. 1, 1961; children—Steven James, David Walter, Melody Anne, Andrew Scott. Student, Huron (S.D.) Coll., 1954-56, U. Nebr., 1956-57; B.A., Nebr. Wesleyan U., 1960. Mgr. Belleville (Kans.) C. of C., 1960-61, Concordia (Kans.) C. of C., 1961-62; asst. chief Div. Nebr. Resources, 1962-65; dir. S.D. Indsl. Devel. Expansion Agy., 1965-67, Nebr. Dept. Econ. Devel., 1967-71; sec. Nebr. Resources Found., 1967-71; exec. dir. Omaha Econ. Devel. Council, 1971-76; pres. Kansas City (Mo.-Kans.) Area Devel. Council, 1976-90; pres., chief exec. officer New Orleans and the River Region C. of C., 1990—. Metrovision Found., Econ. Devel. Coun. Metro, New Orleans; mem. Am. Indsl. Devel. Council, 1965—, chmn. certification bd., 1981-82; sec. labor mgmt. council Greater Kansas City, 1979-90; mem. exec. com. Gov.'s Econ. Devel. Adv. Council, 1979-81. Bd. dirs. Am. Econ. Devel. Coun., 1992—. Served with AUS, 1957-59. Mem. Nat. Assn. Corporate Real Estate Execs. (pres. econ. devel. council 1986-88). Republican. Presbyterian. Home: Park VII 170 Walnut St # 3C New Orleans LA 70118-4836 Office: New Orleans & River Reg 301 Camp St New Orleans LA 70130-2825

MONROE, KENDYL KURTH, lawyer; b. Clayton, N.Mex., Sept. 6, 1936; s. Dottis Donald and Helen (Kurth) M.; m. Barbara Sayre, Sept. 12, 1956; children: Sidney, Dean, Loren. AB, Stanford U., 1958, LLB, 1960. Bar: N.Y. 1961, Calif. 1961. Assoc. Sullivan & Cromwell, N.Y.C., 1960-67, ptnr., 1968-94; chmn. TEB Charter Svcs., Inc., Teterboro, N.J.; bd. dirs. No Minerals Co., Keesville, N.Y. Chmn. Lambs Theatre, N.Y.C., Pub. Health Rsch. Inst., N.Y.C.; bd. dirs Greenwich Village Soc. Historic Preservation, N.Y.C., N.Y. Chamber Soloists, N.Y.C., Seamen's Ch. Inst., N.Y.C. Mem. ABA (tax sect.), N.Y. State Bar Assn. (past chmn. various coms., tax sect.), Calif. State Bar Assn., Assn. Bar City N.Y. (mem. taxation coun.), Met. Club (N.Y.C.). Home: Kenton Rte Seneca NM 88437

MONROE, L. A. J., oil well drilling company executive; b. Springhill, Ark., Nov. 8, 1919; s. Eugene and Alma Edna (Collins) M.; m. Elizabeth Kirkland Moore, Apr. 18, 1942; children: Jamison, Mark Kirkland. B.S., Tex. Christian U., 1942. With Nat. Supply Co., 1945-65; regional mgr. Nat. Supply Co. (Gulf Coast), 1960-62, gen. mgr. sales, domestic and Can. cos., 1962-65; with Dixilyn-Field Drilling Co., Houston, 1965-83; pres., chief exec. officer Dixilyn-Field Drilling Co., 1971-83, chmn. bd., 1978-83; ptnr. Monroe & Bruner, Inc., 1983-92, chmn., 1983-92; chmn. Monroe & Monroe, Inc., Houston, 1992—; dir. First City Bank of Highland Village. Trustee Tex. Christian U.; adminstrv. bd. Chapelwood United Meth. Ch., Houston. Served with U.S. Navy, 1942-45. Named Most Valuable Alumnus Tex. Christian U., 1974, named to Hall of Fame Tex. Christian U., 1991. Mem. Internat. Assn. Drilling Contractors, Nat. Ocean Industry Assn., Mid-Continent Oil and Gas Assn. Republican. Baptist. Clubs: River Oaks Country, Ramada, Petroleum (past dir.), Houston; Les Ambassador (London). Office: Monroe & Monroe Inc 415 Brown Saddle Rd Houston TX 77057

MONROE, MURRAY SHIPLEY, lawyer; b. Cin. Sept. 25, 1925; s. James and Martha (Shipley) M.; m. Sally Longstreth, May 11, 1963; children: Tracy, Murray, Courtney, David. BE, Yale U., 1946, BS, 1947; LLB, U. Pa., 1950. Bar: Ohio 1950, U.S. Dist. Ct. (so. dist.) Ohio 1954, U.S. Dist. Ct. (mid. dist.) Tenn. 1981, US. Dist. Ct. (mid. dist.) N.C. 1974, U.S. Dist. Ct. (mid. dist.) Pa. 1986, U.S. Dist. (ea. dist.) Pa. 1960, U.S. Dist. Ct. (we. dist.) Mo. 1974, U.S. Dist. Ct. Mass. 1978, U.S. Dist. Ct. (ea. dist.) La. 1979,

U.S. Dist. Ct. (no. dist.) Ill. 1980, U.S. Ct. Appeals (4th cir.) 1984, U.S. Ct. Appeals (6th cir.) 1969, U.S. Supreme Ct. 1977, U.S.C. Ct. Appeals (3d cir.) 1990. Assoc. Taft, Stettinus & Hollister, Cin., 1950-58, ptnr., 1958—; mem. lawyers com. Nat. Ctr. for State Cts., 1985—; faculty Ohio Legal Ctr. Inst., 1970-93. Contbr. articles to profl. jours. Trustee, treas. The Coll. Prep. Sch., 1972-76; trustee The Seven Hills Schs., 1982-88, chmn. bd., 1982-85. 2d lt. USNR, 1943-46. Recipient award Seven Hills Schs., 1985. Fellow Ohio Bar Found.; mem. ABA (speaker symposiums), Ohio Bar Assn. (coun. dels. 1977-82, bd. govs. antitrust sect. 1960—, chmn. bd. govs. 1973-75, Merit award 1976, speaker symposiums), Bankers Club (Cin.), Cin. Country Club, Tau Beta Pi. Republican. Episcopalian. Avocations: sailing, tennis. Office: 425 Walnut St Cincinnati OH 45202-3957

MONROE, ROBERT RAWSON, engineering construction executive; b. Oakland, Calif., Sept. 25, 1927; s. Robert Ansley and Muriel Estelle (Burnham) M.; m. Charlotte Boies Anderson, Oct. 16, 1951; children: Robert Anderson, Nancy Lynn Monroe Sims, Susan Leslie Monroe Gordon. BS in Naval Sci., U.S. Naval Acad., 1950; MA in Internat. Rels., Stanford U., 1962. Commd. ensign USN, 1950, advanced through grades to vice-admiral, 1977; dir. Navy Systems Analysis, 1972-73, comdr. South Atlantic Force, 1973-74; comdr. Operational Test and Evaluation Force USN, 1974-77; dir. Def. Nuclear Agy., 1977-80, dir. Navy Rsch., Devel., Test and Evaluation, 1980-83, ret., 1983; joined Bechtel Nat., Inc., San Francisco, 1984, mgr. def. and space, 1984-89, v.p., 1985, sr. v.p., ptnr., 1987, mgr. mktg. and govt. ops., 1989-91, mgr. spl. projects, 1992-93; mgr. govt. ops. Bechtel Nat., Inc., Washington, 1993—; mem. nat. security adv. bd. Los Alamos (N.Mex.) Nat. Lab., 1983-88; mem. tech. evaluation panel U.S. Dept. Energy, 1983-88; mem. engring. adv. com. Oak Ridge (Tenn.) Nat. Lab., 1986-89, Rensselaer Poly Inst., 1990-91; mem. bd. advisors Office Tech. Assessment, Washington, 1987-89, Nat. Contract Mgmt. Assn., 1986-91; mem. task forces Def. Sci. Bd., Washington, 1983-89; corp. mem. Charles Stark Draper Lab., Cambridge, Mass., 1983—; affiliate mem. Ctr. for Internat. Security and Arms Control, Stanford U., 1989-93. Decorated Def. D.S.M., USN D.S.M., Legion of Merit, Bronze Star medal with combat device, Joint Svcs. Commendation medal, USN Commendation medal with combat device; Legion of Honor (France). Mem. AIAA, Nat. Security Indsl. Assn., Soc. Am. Mil. Engrs., Am. Def. Preparedness Assn., U.S. Naval Inst. Avocations: tennis, golf, hiking, reading. Home: 2313 Sawdust Rd Vienna VA 22181 Office: Bechtel Nat Inc 1015 15th St NW Ste 700 Washington DC 20005-2605

MONROE, RUSSELL RONALD, psychiatrist, educator; b. Des Moines, June 7, 1920; s. Ronald Russell and Mildred (Schmidt) M.; m. Lillian Constance Brooks, June 23, 1945; children—Constance Ellen Monroe Teevan, Nancy Brooks Monroe Amoss, Russell Ronald Jr. B.S., Yale U. 1942, M.D., 1944; cert. in psychoanalysis, Columbia U., 1950. Intern New Haven Hosp., 1944-45; resident Rockland State Hosp., Orangeburg, N.Y. 1947-50; from asst. to assoc. prof. psychiatry Tulane U. Sch. Med., New Orleans, 1950-60; prof. U. Md. Sch. Med., Balt., 1960—; chmn. dept. U. Md. Sch. Med., 1976-85; dir. Inst. Psychiatry and Human Behavior U. Md., 1976-85; vis. prof. Am. U., Beirut, Lebanon, 1966-67; mem. adv. commm. Nat. Inst. Law Enforcement and Criminal Justice, 1977-80. Author: Episodic Behavioral Disorders, 1970, Brain Dysfunction in Aggressive Criminals, 1978, Creative Brainstorms, 1992. Served to capt. AUS, 1945-47. Commonwealth fellow, 1966-67, NIMH fellow, 1966-67; grantee NIMH. Fellow Am. Psychiat. Assn., Am. Coll. Psychiatrists; mem. Am. Acad. Psychoanalysis (charter). Clubs: Hamilton St., So. Yacht. Home: 236 W Lafayette Ave Baltimore MD 21217-4210 Office: U Md Sch Medicine 645 W Redwood St Baltimore MD 21201-1549

MONROE, THOMAS EDWARD, industrial corporation executive; b. Ironton, MO., Nov. 19, 1947; s. Donald Edward and Edwina Frances (Carr) M.; children: Thomas Edward II, Katherine Jenna. B.A., Drury Coll., 1969; postgrad., Washington U. Sch. Bus. Adminstrn., St. Louis, 1970. Acctg. mgr., asst. controller Am. Transit Corp., St. Louis, 1970-74; mgr. corp. devel., asst. treas. Chromalloy Am. Corp., St. Louis, 1974-77, v.p. fin., 1977-78, exec. v.p., 1978-82; dir. Chromalloy Fin. Corp., 1976-82, Am. Universal Ins. Co., 1978-82; chmn. Capital Assocs. Corp., 1982—, Fed. Air Ambulance, The Safe Deposit Co., CompuVault, Inc., James Flying Svc., Inc., Lindbergh Leasing, Inc. Mem. St. Louis Club, Algonquin Club. Presbyterian. Office: Capital Assocs Corp 515 S Lindbergh Blvd Saint Louis MO 63131-2731

MONROE, VERNON EARL, JR. (THE PEARL MONROE), former professional basketball player; b. Phila., Nov. 21, 1944; s. Vernon Earl and Rose (Smith) M. B.S. in Edn., Winston-Salem State U., 1967. Basketball player Balt. Bullets, 1967-71, N.Y. Knickerbockers, N.Y.C., 1971-80; capt. N.Y. Knickerbockers, 1976-79; pres. Electra Pretty Pearl Records, Pretty Pearl, Inc. Recipient Big Apple award Jr. Achievement N.Y., 1977, Global award Mt. Calvary Ch., 1977, Daily News Front Page award, 1986; named Rookie of Yr., NBA, 1969; named to Sporting News All-Am. 1st Team, 1966, NBA All-Rookie Team, 1968, NAIA Basketball Hall of Fame, 1975, Central Intercollegiate Athletic Assn. Hall of Fame, 1977; inductee Naismith Meml Basketball Hall of Fame, 1989. Mem. Groove Phi Groove. Republican. Reached 15,000 points, 1977; mem. NCAA Coll. Divsn. championship team, 1967, NBA championship team, 1973. Office: 1775 Broadway New York NY 10019-1903*

MONROE, WALTER HARRIS, III, lawyer; b. Montgomery, Ala., Feb. 28, 1944; s. Walter Harris Jr. and Clara (Tatum) M.; m. Peggy McLean, Sept. 3, 1966; children: Margaret McLean, Walter Harris. BA, U. Ala., 1966; JD, Samford U., 1971. Bar: Ala. 1971, U.S. Ct. Claims 1983, U.S. Supreme Ct. 1979. Asst. gen. counsel Daniel Internat. Corp., Greenville, S.C., 1971-73; v.p., gen. counsel Rust Internat. Corp., Birmingham, 1973-83; ptnr. Bradley, Arant, Rose & White, Birmingham, 1983—; adj. profl. of law Samford U., 1978-83; counsel to dirs. Sherman Internat. Corp., 1978—; mem. planning com. Southeastern Corp. Law Inst., U. Ala., 1981—. Mem. Metro. Devel. Bd., Birmingham, 1982. 1st lt U.S. Army, 1966-68, Vietnam. Mem. ABA (div. 5 steering com. forum on constrn. industry 1988—), Ala. Bar. Assn., Jefferson County Bar Assn., Am. Arbitration Assn. (mem. panel of arbitrators), Phi Delta Phi (past pres., named Outstanding Student 1971), Alpha Tau Omega (Alumni Advisor 1984-87). Presbyterian. Lodge: Rotary. Avocations: golf, fishing. Office: Bradley Arant Rose & White 2001 Park Pl Birmingham AL 35203-2709

MONROE, WILLIAM LEWIS, human resources executive; b. Detroit, May 11, 1941; s. Lewis Stewart and Ada Jeanette (Williams) Monroe; m. Sharon Lynne Kahal, June 30, 1967; children: Andrea C., William J. BA, Western Mich. U., 1963, MA, 1964. Rsch. analyst Chrysler Corp., Detroit, 1965-72, labor economist, 1972-77, mgr. retirement, savs. and unemployment benefit plans, 1977-81; dir. employee benefits W. R. Grace & Co., N.Y.C., 1981-87, v.p. human resources, 1987—; bd. trustee, v.p. coun. on employee benefits, 1989—; pres. coun. on employee benefits W. R. Grace & Co., N.Y.C., 1995—; corp. bd. dirs. Internat. Found. Employee Benefits, 1986-88; mem. bus. rsch. adv. coun. to U.S. Dept. Labor/Bur. Labor Stats., 1987—; mem. Human Resources Policy Inst. Boston U., 1993—. Co-chmn. closing com. PTSA Sch., Birmingham, Mich., 1977; chmn. personnel com. Wilton Presbyn. Ch., Wilton, Conn., 1982-86; officer, bd. dirs. Forest Hills Property Owners Assn. Birmingham, 1974-80; mem. exec. bd. Gulf Stream coun. Boy Scouts Am., 1993—. Served with USAF, 1954-56. Mem. Soc. for Human Resources & Mgmt., Boca Raton (Fla.) Resort and Club, Princeton Club N.Y.C. Republican. Presbyterian. Avocations: tennis, golf. Office: W R Grace & Co 1 Town Center Rd Boca Raton FL 33486-1010

MONROE, WILLIAM SMITH, mandolin player, singer; b. Rosine, Ky., Sept. 13, 1911; s. James Buchanan and Malissa (Vandiver) M.; m. Carolyn Brown, 1935 (div.); children: James, Melissa. Worked in oil refinery; mem. WSN Grand Ole Opry, 1939—. Played on, WLS Barn Dance, East Chicago, Ind., 1929-34, formed group, The Monroe Brothers, 1934-38, playing on radio stas. in N.C. and S.C.; formed group, The Blue Grass Boys, 1938—, nationwide concert and festival appearances; recorded for, Victor Records, 1940-41, Columbia Records, 1945-49, Decca (now MCA), 1950—; songs recorded include My Little Georgia Rose; albums include In The Pines, 1988, Live at The Opry, 1989, The Country Music Hall of Fame, 1991, The Essential Bill Monroe and His Bluegrass Boys (1945-49),1992, Mule Skinner Blues, 1991, The Music of Bill Monroe 1936-1994, 1994. Elected to County Music Hall of Fame, 1970. Originated term bluegrass and defined its style.

Office: care Buddy Lee Attractions 38 Music Sq E Ste 300 Nashville TN 37203-4396*

MONROY, GLADYS H., lawyer; b. N.Y., Aug. 29, 1937; d. Henry B. and Leonora E. (Low) Chu; m. Jaime L. G. Monroy (div.); m. C. Lawrence Marks, Nov. 29, 1980. BA, Hunter Coll., N.Y., 1957; MS, NYU, 1968, PhD, 1973; JD, U. San Francisco, 1986. Bar: Calif. Lab. technician Sloan-Kettering Inst., N.Y., 1957-60; lab. technician Pub. Health Rsch. Inst., N.Y., 1960-63, rsch. asst., 1963-68; post doctoral fellow Albert Einstein Coll. Medicine, Bronx, N.Y., 1973-77; asst. prof. N.Y. Med. Coll., Valhalla, 1977-79; acquisitions editor Acad. Press, Inc., 1979-81; reseach assoc. U. Calif., San Francisco, 1981-83; atty. Irell & Manella, Menlo Park, Calif., 1986-90, ptnr., 1990-91; ptnr. Morrison & Foerster, Palo Alto, Calif., 1991—. Contbr. articles to profl. jours. Bd. dirs. Project Hogar De Los Ninos, Menlo Park, Calif., 1987, Child Advocates Santa Clara & San Mateo Counties, Calif., 1995—; mem. Profl. Women's Network, San Francisco, 1988--. Mem. ABA, Am. Intellectual Property Law Assn., Am. Soc. Human Genetics, Am. Chem. Soc., Calif. Bar Assn., San Francisco Intellectual Property Law Assn. (chair patent com. 1992-94), Peninsula Patent Law Assn. (program chair 1993-94, treas. 1994-95), Am. Soc. Microbiology, Phi Alpha Delta. Avocations: swimming, bicyle riding, skiing, reading, opera. Office: Morrison & Foerster 755 Page Mill Rd 545 Middlefield Rd Palo Alto CA 94304-1018

MONSEES, JAMES EUGENE, engineering executive, consultant; b. Sedalia, Mo., Mar. 27, 1937; s. Olen Owen and Ruth Caroline (Weiffenbach) M.; m. Leda L. Hoehns, Oct. 8, 1961; children: Brenda G., Mark E. BSCE, U. Mo., 1960, MSCE, 1961; PhDCE, U. Ill., 1970. Registered profl. engr., Ill., Md., Washington, Ohio, Calif., Wash., Colo. Grad. asst. U. Mo., Columbia, 1958-61; project mgr. USAF Spl. Weapons Ctr., Albuquerque, 1961-64; engr. Exxon, Baton Rouge, 1964-66; rsch. assoc. U. Ill., Champaign, 1967-69; sr. v.p. A.A. Mathews, CRS Engrs., Arcadia, Calif. and Rockville, Md., 1969-80; dept. mgr. Battelle Meml. Inst., Columbus, Ohio, 1980-82; v.p.-engr. Lachel L. Hanson & Assocs., Golden, Colo., 1982-83; chief tunnel engr. Metro Rail Transit Couns., L.A., 1983-1990; project mgr. Collider/SSC The PB/MK Team, Dallas, 1990-94; v.p., tech. dir., prin. profl. assoc. Parsons Brinckerhoff, N.Y.C.; mem. Seismic Lifeline Com., San Francisco, 1987—; mem. exec. com. Rapid Excavation/Tunnel Conf., Denver, 1989—. Author: (with others) Guidelines for Tunnel Lining Design, 1984, Mining Handbook, 1992, Tunnel Engineering, 1994. Mem. U.S. Nat. Com. for Rock Mechanics, Wash., D.C., 1983-86, 88-94, Internat. Soc. for Rock Mechanics, 1983—. 1st Lt. USAF, 1961-64. Recipient Mo. Honor award U. Mo., 1992. Fellow ASCE; mem. NAE, Am. Underground Space Assn. (bd. dirs. 1995—), The Moles, Underground Tech. Rsch. Coun. Republican. Avocations: shooting, biking, tennis, reading, dog training. Home: 834 Mill Creek Cir Lancaster TX 75146-2839 Office: Parsons Brinckerhoff Ste 200 7220 S Westmoreland Rd Dallas TX 75237-2984

MONSEN, ELAINE RANKER, nutritionist, educator, editor; b. Oakland, Calif., June 6, 1935; d. Emery R. and Irene Stewart (Thorley) Ranker; m. Raymond Joseph Monsen, Jr., Jan. 21, 1959; 1 dau., Maren Ranker. B.A., U. Utah, 1956; M.S. (Mead Johnson grad. scholar), U. Calif., Berkeley, 1959, Ph.D. (NSF fellow), 1961; postgrad. NSF sci. faculty fellow, Harvard U., 1968-69. Dietetic intern Mass. Gen. Hosp., Boston, 1956-57; asst. prof. nutrition, lectr. biochemistry Brigham Young U., Provo, Utah, 1960-63; mem. faculty U. Wash., 1963—, prof. nutrition and medicine, 1984—, prof. nutrition, adj. prof. medicine, 1976-84, chmn. div. human nutrition, dietetics and foods, 1977-82, dir. grad. nutritional scis. program, 1994—, mem. Council of Coll. Arts and Scis., 1974-78, mem. U. Wash. Press com., 1981—; chmn. Nutrition Studies Commn., 1969-83; vis. scholar Stanford U., 1971-72; mem. sci. adv. com. food fortification Pan-Am. Health Orgn., São Paulo, Brazil, 1972; tng. grant coordinator NIH, 1976—. Editor Jour. Am. Dietetic Assn., 1983—; mem. editorial bd. Coun. Biology Editors, 1992—; author research papers on lipid metabolism, iron absorption. Bd. dirs. A Contemporary Theatre, Seattle, 1969-72; trustee, bd. dirs. Seattle Found. 1978—, vice chmn., 1987-91, chmn., 1991-93; pres. Seattle bd. Santa Fe Chamber Music Festival, 1984-85. Grantee Nutrition Found., 1965-68, Agrl. Rsch. Svc., 1969—; recipient Disting. Alumnus award U. Utah, F. Fischer Meml. Nutrition Lectr. award, 1988, L.F. Cooper Meml. Lectr. award, 1991, L. Hatch Meml. Lectr. award, 1992. Mem. Am. Inst. Nutrition, Am. Soc. Clin. Nutrition (sec. 1987-90), Am. Dietetic Assn., Soc. Nutrition Edn., Am. Soc. Parenteral and Enteral Nutrition, Wash. Heart Assn. (nutrition council 1973-76), Phi Beta Kappa, Phi Kappa Phi. Office: U Wash Dept Human Nutrition DL-10 Seattle WA 98195

MONSEN, RAYMOND JOSEPH, JR., economist, educator, art patron; b. Payson, Utah, Mar. 13, 1931; s. Raymond Joseph and Lucile (Monsen) m. Elaine Ranker, Jan. 21, 1959; 1 dau., Maren Ranker. B.S. U. Utah, 1953; M.A., Stanford U., 1954; Ph.D., U. Calif. at Berkeley, 1960. Asst. prof. econs. Brigham Young U., 1960-63; cons. to govt. and banking industry, 1962-63; assoc. prof. Coll. of Bus. U. Wash., Seattle, 1963-65; prof. U. Wash., 1966-63, prof. dept. mgmt., 1986, chmn. dept. bus., govt. and society, 1966, 73-81, prof. emeritus, 1986—; dir. research Coll. of Bus., U. Wash. (Grad. Sch. Bus.), 1966-68; Guggenheim fellow, dept. econs. Harvard U., 1968-69; vis. prof. Grad. Sch. Bus., Stanford U., 1971-73; vis. prof. U. Calif., Berkeley, Spring 1985. Author: Modern American Capitalism: Ideologies and Issues, 1963, (with Mark Cannon) American Power Groups and Their Ideologies, 1965, Business and the Changing Environment, 1973, (with others) Management, Systems, and Society, 1976, (with K. Walters) Nationalized Companies: Capitalism Challenged, 1983; Editor: (with B. Saxberg) The Business World, 1967; contbr. over 50 articles to profl. jours.; photographic and ceramic works exhibited at Portland Crafts Ctr., 1968, U. Wash. Art Gallery, 1969, 79, 86, San Francisco Art Mus., 1973, Seattle Art Mus., 1974, 76, Portland Art Mus., 1977, La Jolla (Calif.) Mus., 1989, U. Wash. Art Gallery, 1994-95, San Francisco: Friends of Photography, 1995. Past pres. contemporary art coun. Seattle Art Mus., 1967, trustee, 1968-85; mem. vis. com. U. Pugent Sound Law Sch., 1981-88; mem. vis. com. Met. Mus. Art, N.Y.C., 1992—; founder-trustee Seattle Opera Assn., Henry Art Gallery Assn., U. Wash.; past trustee Salt Lake Art Ctr., Pacific N.W. Art Assn.; established Monsen Photography collection U. Wash. Art Mus., 1978. Mem. Am. Econs. Assn., Acad. of Mgmt., Seattle Tennis Club. Avocation: art patron.

MONSKY, JOHN BERTRAND, investment banking executive; b. Montgomery, Ala., May 17, 1930; s. Harry and Belle (Golding) M.; m. Joan Gilbert, June 8, 1952; children: Leslie Joy, John Richard, Harry Robert. B.A., Yale, 1952; M.B.A., Harvard, 1954. Sec. Devoe & Raynolds Co., Inc., Louisville, Ky., 1956-65; v.p., dir. Universal Marion Corp., Jacksonville, Fla., 1965-69, pres., chmn. bd., chief exec. officer, 1969-71, cons., 1971—; vice chmn. ServAmerica, Inc., Jacksonville, 1972-74, co-chmn. bd. dirs., 1974-80, chmn. bd. dirs., 1992—, pres., chmn. bd. dirs. First Fla. Capital Corp., 1985—; dir. Fla. Wire & Cable Co., Jacksonville, 1975-82. Past pres. bd. trustees Jacksonville Country Day Sch.; bd. dirs. Jacksonville Art Mus.; trustee Bolles Sch., Jacksonville, Jacksonville Symphony Assn. Served with USAF, 1954-56. Mem. Jacksonville Area C. of C. (com. of 100), Jackson Coun. Citizen Involvement Clubs, Harvard Bus. Sch. Club of Ky. (exec. com. 1964-65), Phillips Acad. Andover Alumni Club of Ky. (pres. 1963-64), Epping Forest Community Master Assn. (bd. dirs. 1987—), Yale Club of N.E. Fla. (dir. bus. 1987—), Yale Club of N.Y.C., Harvard Club (Jacksonville), River Club, Ponte Vedra Club, Epping Forest Yacht Club. Home: Epping Forest 7015 Gaines Ct Jacksonville FL 32217-2672 Office: 2050 Art Museum Dr Jacksonville FL 32207-2595

MONSMA, MARVIN EUGENE, library director; b. Prairie City, Iowa, May 14, 1933; s. John and Johanna Hester (Branderhorst) M.; m. Elaine Gross, Aug. 2, 1963; children: Kristy Lynne Monsma De Vos, Kimberly Sue Monsma Rottschafer, Michelle Eileen Monsma Haan. AB, Calvin Coll., 1957; AM in Secondary Edn., Mich. State U., 1961; AMLS in Librarianship, U. Mich., 1967. English tchr. Muskegon (Mich.) Christian Sch., 1957-60, Grand Rapids (Mich.) Christian H.S., 1960-63, Unity Christian H.S., Hudsonville, Mich., 1963-65; asst. libr. Calvin Coll. & Sem., Grand Rapids, 1965-67, head gen. svcs., 1967-68, asst. libr. dir., 1968-69, acting libr. dir., 1969-70, libr. dir., 1970—. Christian Reformed. Avocations: classical music, gardening, nature. Office: Calvin Coll and Sem Libr 3207 Burton St SE Grand Rapids MI 49546

MONSON, ARCH, JR., fire alarm manufacturing company executive; b. Thorntown, Ind., Nov. 10, 1913; s. Arch and Mabel (Miller) M.; m. June Hammersmith, Jan. 10, 1959; children—Eminel, Arch III, Dwight, Jay. Grad. high sch. Pres. Monson-Pacific Inc., San Francisco, 1935—; pres. Monson Electric Co. div. Monson-Pacific Inc., San Francisco, 1935—; West coast mgr. Autocall div. Fed. Signal Corp., Blue Island, Ill., 1945—; owner, operator St. George Ranch, Geyserville, Calif., 1959—; dir. Ampex Corp., Redwood City, Calif., Signal Cos. Inc., Beverly Hills, Calif. Chmn. Nat. Jamboree Boy Scouts Am., 1973, v.p. nat. exec. bd., 1973-74, pres., 1975-77; Trustee Pacific Med. Center, San Francisco, 1964—. mem. exec. com., 1969—; trustee Golden Gate U., YMCA of San Francisco, Salvation Army. Recipient Silver Beaver award Boy Scouts Am., 1968, Silver Antelope award, 1968, Silver Buffalo award, 1971. Mem. San Francisco Electric Club, Pacific Coast Elec. Assn., Nat. Elec. Contractors Assn., San Francisco Conv. and Visitors Bur., Internat. Assn. Fire Chiefs, Internat. Municipal Signal Assn. Republican. Presbyn. (elder). Clubs: Mason (Shriner, 33 deg.), Rotarian, Bohemian (pres. 1962, 63), Olympic, The Family. Home: 2825 Broadway St San Francisco CA 94115-1060

MONSON, DAVID CARL, farmer, state legislator; b. Langdon, N.D., July 30, 1950; s. Carl Arthur and Shirley Jean (Klai) M.; m. Mary Kathryn Greutman, July 8, 1972; children: Cordell Carl, Cale David, Jared Arthur. Cert. tchr., N.D. Sci. tchr. Hankinson (N.D.) Pub. Sch., 1972-75; tchr. Nekoma (N.D.) Pub. Sch., 1975-76; tchr., prin. NeKoma (N.D.) Pub. Sch., 1976-79; tchr., supt. Nekoma (N.D.) Pub. Sch., 1979-80; tchr., prin. Milton (N.D.)-Osnabrock High Sch., 1981-84; supt. Adams (N.D.) Pub. Schs., 1984-88; ins. agt. N.Y. Life, Fargo, N.D., 1988—; farmer Osnabrock, 1975—; state rep. N.D. State Legis., Bismarck, 1993—; bd. dirs. No. Canola Growers, Rugby, N.D. Mem. sch. bd. dirs. Osnabrock Sch. Bd., 1989—; leader Bobcats 4-H Club, 1988—. Mem. N.D. Farm Bur., Nat. Assn. Life Underwriting (Quality award 1992, 93, 94) Eagles, Knights of Pythias of N.D. and Sask. (grand sec. 1985-93, award 1990). Republican. Lutheran. Avocations: skiing, gardening, hunting, coin collecting.

MONSON, DAVID SMITH, accountant, former congressman; b. Salt Lake City, June 20, 1945; s. Smith Weston and Dorothy (Brammer) M.; m. Julianne Johnson, Feb. 4, 1971; children: David Johnson, Traci Lyn, Marianne, Kari, Smith Douglas. BS in Acctg., U. Utah, 1970. C.P.A., Utah. Acct. Elmer Fox and Co., Salt Lake City, 1970-72; auditor State of Utah, Salt Lake City, 1973-76; lt. gov. State of Utah, 1977-84; mem. 99th Congress, 1985-87; v.p. I Corp., 1987-91; bus. cons. and acct., 1992—; mem. exec. com. Nat. Conf. Lt. Govs., 1978-84 mem. State Bd. Regents, 1981-84. Bd. dirs. Utah Soc. to Prevent Blindness, 1976-83; chmn. Utah Cancer Crusade, 1979-80, chmn. Bd. Salt Lake County Am. Cancer Soc., 1980-81; govt. group chmn. United Way, 1979, assoc. campaign chmn., 1981, campaign chmn. 1982; treas. Utah Reps., 1975-76; trustee Ballet West, 1977-81, Travis Found., 1977-84, bd. dirs. Osmond Found., 1982-84, Utah Opportunities Industrialization Ctrs., Inc., 1988-91; sec. bd. dirs. Utah Sports Found., Inc., 1988-91. Recipient Outstanding Young Man Am. award, 1977, 81; named One of 3 Outstanding Young Men Utah Jaycees, 1980-81. Mem. Council State Govts. (v.p. Western conf. 1974-75). Republican. Mem. Ch. Jesus Christ Latter Day Saints. Home: 792 Northview Dr Salt Lake City UT 84103-4027 *Two principles have been the overriding factors in motivating the actions I have taken throughout my life—a strong desire to be the successful leader and provider of a stable family unit and a faith in and a desire to follow the teachings of a loving God.*

MONSON, DIANNE LYNN, literacy educator; b. Minot, N.D., Nov. 24, 1934; d. Albert Rachie and Iona Cordelia (Kirk) M. B.S., U. Minn., 1956, M.A., 1962, Ph.D., 1966. Tchr. Rochester Pub. Schs. (Minn.), 1966-59, U.S. Dept. Def., Schweinfurt, W.Ger., 1959-61, St. Louis Park Schs. (Minn.) 1961-62; instr. U. Minn., Mpls., 1962-66; prof. U. Wash., Seattle, 1966-82; prof. literacy edn. U. Minn., Mpls., 1982—; chmn. Curriculum and Instrn., 1986-89. Co-author: New Horizons in the Language Arts, 1972; Children and Books, 6th edit., 1981; Experiencing Children's Literature, 1984; (monograph) Research in Children's Literature, 1976; Language Arts: Teaching and Learning Effective Use of Language, 1988; Reading Together: Helping Children Get A Good Start With Reading, 1991. Recipient Outstanding Educator award U. Minn. Alumni Assn., 1983, Alumni Faculty award, 1991. Fellow Nat. Conf. Rsch. in English (pres. 1990-91); mem. Nat. Coun. Tchrs. of English (exec. com. 1979-81), Internat. Reading Assn. (dir. 1980-83, Arbuthnot award 1993), ALA, U.S. Bd. Books for Young People (pres. 1988-90). Lutheran. Home: 740 River Dr Saint Paul MN 55116-1009 Office: U Minn 350 Peik Hall Minneapolis MN 55455

MONSON, FORREST TRUMAN, shop owner, clergyman; b. Climax, Minn., May 1, 1915; s. Edwin George and Pauline Marie (Moen) M.; m. Thelma J. Sydnes, Sept. 5, 1940; children—Paul, Michael, Lois. A.B., Augsburg Coll., Mpls., 1937; C.T., B.Th., Augsburg Theol. Sem., 1940. Ordained to ministry Luth. ch., 1940; pastor First Ch., Richmond Beach, Wash., 1940-42; Calvert Ch. Everett, 1942-45, Sharon Ch., Grand Forks, N.D., 1945-53; pres. West Coast dist. Luth. Free Ch., 1943-45, mem. bd. parish edn., 1947-55, chmn. bd., 1951-55, ch. sec., 1949-59, dir. stewardship and exec. sec. stewardship bd., 1953-63; dir. resident counseling service Am. Luth. Ch., Mpls., 1963-80; adminstrv. asst. Office Communication and Mission Support, 1974-80; propr. Forest Enterprises 1980-87; dir. FTM Assos., 1980-87; chaplain Casa de las Campanas, San Diego; pres. dir. Luth. seminar U. N.D., 1946-53. Trustee Oak Grove Luth. High Sch., Fargo, N.D., 1947-53. Mem. Luth. Welfare Soc. N.D. (dir. 1946-50), Nat. Luth. Council subs., Luth. World Action (ch. dir. 1955-63, youth bd. 1956-63). Office: 17621 Cumana Ter San Diego CA 92128-1813

MONSON, JAMES EDWARD, electrical engineer, educator; b. Oakland, Calif., June 20, 1932; s. George Edward and Frances Eleanor (Fouche) M.; m. Julie Elizabeth Conzelman, June 25, 1954; children—John, Jamie, Jennifer. BSEE, Stanford U., 1954, MSEE, 1955, PhD in Elec. Engring., 1961. Mem. tech. staff Bell Telephone Labs., Murray Hill, N.J., 1955-56; devel. engr. Hewlett-Packard Co., Palo Alto, Calif., 1956-61; Robert C. Sabini prof. engring. Harvey Mudd Coll., 1961—. Mem. governing bd. Claremont Unified Sch. Dist., 1966-71, pres., 1969-70; pres. Claremont Civic Assn., 1974-75; bd. dirs. Claremont YMCA, 1978-82. NSF fellow, 1954-55; Fulbright research grantee, 1975-76; Fulbright sr. lectr., 1980; Japan Soc. Promotion of Sci. fellow, 1984. Mem. AAUP, IEEE, Magnetics Soc. Japan, Phi Beta Kappa, Sigma Xi, Tau Beta Pi. Home: 353 W 11th St Claremont CA 91711-3806 Office: Harvey Mudd Coll 301 E 12th St Claremont CA 91711-5994

MONSON, JOHN RUDOLPH, lawyer; b. Chgo., Feb. 4, 1941; s. Rudolph Agaton and Ellen Louise (Loeffler) M.; m. Susan Lee Brown, May 22, 1965; children: Elizabeth Louisa, Christina Lee, Donald Rudolph. BA with honors, Northwestern U., 1963; JD with distinction, U. Mich., 1966. Bar: Ill. 1966, N.H. 1970, Mass. 1985. Atty. assoc. Chapman & Cutler, Chgo., 1966-68, Levenfeld, Kanter, Baskes & Lippitz, Chgo., 1968-70, Nighswander, Martin & Mitchell, Laconia, N.H., 1970-71; ptnr. Wiggin & Nourie, P.A., Manchester, N.H., 1972—; pres. Wiggin & Nourie, P.A., Manchester, 1991-94. Mem. Fish & Game Commn., State of N.H., Concord, 1980-94, chmn. 1983-93; sr. bd. dirs. Brown-Monson Found., 1991—; incorporator Optima Health, Manchester, 1989-94, Optima Health, 1994—. Fellow Am. Coll. Trust and Estate Counsel. Republican. Avocations: skiing, hunting, running. Home: 24 Wellesley Dr Bedford NH 03110-4531 Office: Wiggin & Nourie PA 20 Market St Manchester NH 03101

MONSON, THOMAS SPENCER, church official, publishing company executive; b. Salt Lake City, Aug. 21, 1927; s. George Spencer and Gladys (Condie) M.; m. Frances Beverly Johnson, Oct. 7, 1948; children—Thomas L., Ann Frances, Clark Spencer. BS with honors in mktg, U. Utah, 1948; MBA, Brigham Young U., 1974, LLD (hon.), 1981. With Deseret News Press, Salt Lake City, 1948-64; mgr. Deseret News Press, 1962-64; mem. Council Twelve Apostles, Ch. of Jesus Christ of Latter Day Saints, 1963-85, mem. first presidency, 1985—; bishop, 1950-55; pres. Canadian Mission, 1959-62; chmn. bd. Deseret News Pub. Co., 1977—; dir. Deseret Mgmt. Corp.; pres. Printing Industry Utah, 1958; bd. dirs. Printing Industry Am., 1958-64; mem. Utah nat. bd. U.S. West Communications. Mem. Utah Bd. Regents; mem. nat. exec. bd. Boy Scouts Am.; trustee Brigham Young U.. With USNR, 1945-46. Recipient Recognition award, 1964, Disting. Alumnus award U. Utah, 1966; Silver Beaver award Boy Scouts Am., 1971; Silver Buffalo award, 1978; Bronze Wolf award World Orgn. of the Scout

Movement, 1993. Mem. Utah Assn. Sales Execs., U. Utah Alumni Assn. (dir.), Salt Lake Advt. Club, Alpha Kappa Psi. Club: Exchange (Salt Lake City). Office: LDS Ch 47 E South Temple Salt Lake City UT 84150 also: Deseret News Pub Co PO Box 1257 30 E 1st St Salt Lake City UT 84110

MONTAG, JOHN JOSEPH, II, librarian; b. Omaha, Jan. 8, 1948; s. John Joseph and Ruth Helen (Johnston) M.; m. Linda Kay Lubanski, Apr. 8, 1971; children: Nicole Elizabeth, Megan Kristine. BA, Midland Luth. Coll., 1970, postgrad., Wash. State U., 1970-74; MA, U. Iowa, 1976; postgrad., U. Nebr., 1982-84. English tchr. pub. schs., Nebr., Iowa, 1972-75; reference librarian Concordia Coll., Moorhead, Minn., 1976-81; asst. prof. library sci. U. Nebr., Lincoln, 1981-84; dir. Office of Info. State Library Iowa, Des Moines, 1984-86, state librarian, 1986-87; dir. Thomas Library Wittenberg U., 1987—; trustee Bibliog. Ctr. for Research, Denver, 1986-87; adv. bd. No. Lights Library Network, Detroit Lakes, Minn., 1980-81; chair Southwest Ohio Consortium Higher Edn. Libr. Coun. Contbr. articles to profl. jours. Univ. Found. library improvement grantee, U. Nebr., 1983; Challenge grantee NEH, 1992. Mem. ALA, Assn. Coll. and Research Libraries. Office: Wittenberg U Thomas Libr PO Box 720 Springfield OH 45501-0720

MONTAGU, ASHLEY, anthropologist, social biologist; b. London, June 28, 1905; came to U.S., 1927, 30; naturalized, 1940; s. Charles Ehrenberg and Mary (Plotnick) M.; m. Helen Marjorie Peakes, Sept. 18, 1931; children: Audrey, Barbara, Geoffrey. Spl./student, U. London, 1922-25; student, U. Florence, 1928-29; Ph.D., Columbia U., 1937; D.Sc. (hon.), Grinnell Coll., 1967, U. N.C., 1987; D.Litt. (hon.), Ursinus Coll., 1972. Research asso. Brit. Mus. Natural History, London, 1926-27; curator phys. anthropology Wellcome Hist. Med. Mus., 1929-30; asst. prof. anatomy N.Y. U., 1931-38; asso. prof. anatomy Hahnemann Med. Coll. and Hosp., Phila., 1938-49; chmn. dept. anthropology Rutgers U., 1949-55; vis. lectr. dept. social sci. Harvard, 1945; sr. lectr. VA Postgrad. Tng. Program Psychiatry and Neurology, 1946—; lectr. New Sch. Social Research, 1931-59; vis. prof. U. Del., 1955; Regents prof., U. Calif., Santa Barbara, 1962; lectr. Princeton U., 1978-83; dir. Natural Philosophy, 1979-81; fellow Stevenson Hall, Princeton U., 1978—; dir. rsch. N.J. com. phys. devel. and health, 1953-57; family affairs editor, anthrop. adv. NBC-TV, 1954; chmn. Anisfield-Wolf Award Com., 1954—, co-chmn. Attach, 1992—; responsible for drafting statement on race for UNESCO, 1949-50, cons., 1949; a drafter NSF Bill, 1946-47, co-drafter constn. Am. Assn. Human Genetics, 1949; Hon. cor. mem. anthrop. socs. Paris and Florence. Produced, financed, wrote and directed: film One World or None for, Nat. Commn. on Atomic Info. and Am. Fedn. Sci. Workers, 1946; Author: Coming into Being Among the Australian Aborigines, 1937, 2d edit., 1974, Man's Most Dangerous Myth: The Fallacy of Race, 1942, 5th edit., 1974, Edward Tyson, M.D., F.R.S., (1650-1708): and the rise of human and comparative anatomy in England, 1943, Introduction to Physical Anthropology, 1945, 3d edit., 1960, Adolescent Sterility, 1946, On Being Human, 1950, 2d edit., 1966, On Being Intelligent, 1951, Statement on Race, 1952, 3d edit., 1972, Darwin, Competition and Cooperation, 1952, The Natural Superiority of Women, 1953, 3d edit., 1992, The Direction of Human Development, 1955, 2d edit., 1970, Immortality, 1955, Biosocial Nature of Man, 1956, Anthropology And Human Nature, 1957, Man: His First Million Years, 1957, The Reproductive Development of the Female, 1957, 3d edit., 1979, Education and Human Relations, 1958, The Cultured Man, 1958, Human Heredity, 1959, 2d edit., 1963, Handbook of Anthropometry, 1960, Man in Process, 1961, Prenatal Influences, 1962, The Humanization of Man, 1962, Race, Science, and Humanity, 1963, The Dolphin in History, 1963, Life Before Birth, 1964, 2d edit., 1978, The Science of Man, 1964, (with E. Steen) Anatomy and Physiology, 1959, 2d edit., 1983, (with C.L. Brace) Man's Evolution, 1965, The Idea of Race, 1965, (with C.L. Brace) The Human Revolution, 1965, 2nd edit., 1977, Up the Ivy, 1966, The American Way of Life, 1967, The Anatomy of Swearing, 1967, (with E. Darling) The Prevalance of Nonsense, 1967, Man Observed, 1968, Man, His First Two Million Years, 1957, 2d edit., 1969, Sex, Man, and Society, 1969, (with E. Darling) The Ignorance of Certainty, 1970, Immortality, Religion, and Morals, 1955, 2nd edit., 1971, Touching, 1971, 3d edit., 1986, (with M. Levitan) Textbook of Human Genetics, 1971, 2d edit., 1977, The Elephant Man, 1971, 2d edit., 1979, America As I See It, 1971, (with S.S. Snyder) Man and the Computer, 1972, The Endangered Environment, 1974, The Nature of Human Aggression, 1976, (with C.L. Brace) Human Evolution, 1977, (with Floyd Matson) The Human Connection, 1979, (with Floyd Matson) The Dehumanization of Man, 1983, Growing Young, 1981, The Peace of the World, 1986, Living and Loving, 1986, Humanity Speaking to Humankind, 1986, The World of Humanity, 1986, Times Change-Do People?, 1986, What We Know About Race, 1987, Coming into Being, 1988, the Story of People, 1988; editor Nat. Hist. Soc. Series, Classics of Anthropology; adv. editor Sci., Tech. and Humanitiesanthropology editor Isis, 1936-56, publs. editor, 1937-45. Guardsman with Welsh Guards, 1919. Recipient 1st prize Morris Chaim prize Centenary 2d Dist. Dental Soc., 1936, Chgo. Forum Lit. contest, 1943, Rollo May award Saybrook Inst. Humanistic Studies, 1991, Verney award Pre-Perinatal Psychol. Assn. N.Am., 1993; recipient Disting. Svc. award Assn. Childbirth at Home Internat., 1970, Am. Anthrop. Assn., 1984, Phi Beta Kappa, 1985, Inst. Human Behavior, 1986, Nat. Assn. Parents and Profls. Safe Alternatives in Childbirth, 1986. Fellow AAAS; mem. Internat. Soc. Study of Race Rels., Internat. Assn. Human Biologists, Am. Assn. Anatomists, Am. Soc. Study of Child Growth and Devel., Am. Assn. Maternal and Child Health, Am. Assn. Phys. Anthropologists (Charles Darwin Lifetime Achievement award 1994), Sigma Xi. Expert forensic problems witness on legal, sci. problems relating to race and anthrop. matters, 1930. Home: 321 Cherry Hill Rd Princeton NJ 08540-7617 *To be kind, to be, to do, and to depart gracefully.*

MONTAGU, JEAN IVAN, electro-optic company executive; b. Courberoie, France, July 9, 1933; came to U.S., 1952, naturalized 1958; s. Leonide Petrovich and Jenny (Spalenice) K.; m. Kyra Lockhart Gordon, Apr. 1, 1961; children—Sasha, Dominic. B.S. in Mech. Engring., MIT, 1955, M.S. in Mech. Engring., 1956. Asst. prof. Cath. U., Rio de Janeiro, Brazil, 1967-68; engr. Honeywell, Boston, 1958; v.p., founder Mechanics for Electronics, Salem, N.H., 1959-67; chmn., chief exec. officer Gen. Scanning, Inc., Watertown, Mass., 1968—; dir. Can. Corp. Mgmt., Toronto, 1981-86, Ctr. for Blood Research Lab., Boston, 1980-83; instr. Northeastern U., Boston, 1968. Inventor in thermodynamics and electromagnetics. Contbr. section to book, articles to profl. jours. Office: Gen Scanning Inc 500 Arsenal St Watertown MA 02172-2888

MONTAGUE, BRIAN JOHN, consulting company executive; b. Washington, Oct. 9, 1951; s. H.C. and Dorothy (Brand) M.; m. Kathryn Valente, Oct. 2, 1993. B.A., Bridgewater Coll., 1973; student, St. Mary's (Md.) Coll., 1975, George Washington U., 1980, Miss. State U., 1981. Toxicology technician Hazelton Labs., Vienna, Va., 1973-74; asst. mgr. Chesapeake Sea Farms, Ridge, Md., 1974-76; tng. instr., program coord. Natural Resources Dept., Annapolis, Md., 1976-77; fishery biologist Nat. Aquarium, U.S. Fish and Wildlife Svc., Washington, 1977-82, curator aquarium, 1982-88; pres. Aquatic Images, Annapolis, 1989—; lectr. local interest groups. Office: Aquatic Images 740 Red Cedar Rd Annapolis MD 21401-6000

MONTAGUE, DROGO K., urologist; b. Alpena, Mich., Dec. 11, 1942; s. Frank Wright and Susan Alice (Kidder) M.; m. Prudence Buck (separated); children: Mark Andrew, Lisa Joy. Student, U. Mich., 1963, MD cum laude, 1968. Diplomate Am. Bd. Urology. Intern Cleve. Clinic Hosp., 1968-69, resident in gen. surgery, 1969-70, resident in urology, 1970-73; assoc. staff urologist Cleve. Clinic Found., 1973-75, staff urologist, 1975—, head sect. prosthetic surgery, 1981—, urology residence program dir., 1985—, dir. Ctr. for Sexual Function, 1987—; prof. surgery Ohio State U. Coll. Medicine, 1992—; trainee cardiovascular rsch. tng. program NIH, 1962-68; trustee Am. Bd. Urology, 1989-95, mem. examination com., 1975-80, examiner cert. exam., 1980-88, rep. to Am. Bd. Med. Specialties, 1989-95. Reviewer various publs. in field; contbr. numerous articles to profl. publs., chpts. to books; editor: Disorders of Male Sexual Function, 1988, Surgical Treatment of Erectile Dysfunction, 1993; author audiovisual tapes in field. James B. Angell scholar, 1961, 62, Nat. Found. scholar, 1963-68; recipient Russell and Mary Hugh Scott Edn. award, 1989, Iowa Rsch. award, 1967. Fellow ACS; mem. Am. Urolog. Assn. (examination com. North Ctrl. sect. 1977, mem. residency edn. com. 1979-83, vice chmn. audio visual com. 1989—, mem. ad hoc impotence adv. com. 1988-92, mem. lithotripsy tng. site rev. com. 1987-92, mem. practice parameters stds. and guidelines for impotence com. 1990—, editorial Video Digest 1988-92), Am. Assn. Genitourinary

Surgeons, Am. Assn. Clin. Urologists, Cleve. Urolog. Soc. (sec.-treas. 1978-80, v.p. 1980-81, pres. 1981-82). Office: Cleve Clinic Found Dept Urology 9500 Euclid Ave Cleveland OH 44195

MONTAGUE, EDGAR BURWELL (MONTY), III, industrial designer; b. Charlotte, N.C., Aug. 6, 1958; s. Edgar B. Jr. and Mary Sue (Calhoun) M.; m. Nancy Oliver Stallworth, Feb. 25, 1984; children: Nancy Lea, Edgar Eubank. B Environ. Design cum laude, N.C. State U., 1980. Indsl. design Design/Joe Sonderman, Inc., Charlotte, 1980-85; design prin. Machen Montague, Inc., Charlotte, 1985-93, BOLT, Charlotte, 1994—. Holder 7 design patents; work published in Product Design 1-6, Design for Humanity. Designer corp. identity program Habitat for Humanity, Charlotte, 1987 (logo design now used throughout world). Recipient Am. design award Internat. Design mag., 1988-93, ID-40 ID Mag., 1994. Mem. Indsl. Designer Soc. Am. (co-founder Carolina chpt., program chmn. 1981-83, vice chmn. 1984, 93, Kudo award for chpt. svc. 1982, Indsl. Design Excellence awards 1989-94). Avocations: travel, art, time with family. Office: BOLT 2221 Edge Lake Dr Ste 100 Charlotte NC 28217-4509

MONTAGUE, JOEL GEDNEY, public health consultant; b. N.Y.C., July 6, 1932; s. William Pepperrell and Jean Lois (Gedney) M.; m. Shahnaz Emami-Nikou, Dec. 16, 1963; children: Jahan, Maryam. BA, Oberlin Coll., 1956; MA, Johns Hopkins U., 1960; MS in Pub. Health, U. N.C., 1970; postgrad., U. Tehran, 1961. Field rep. mission chief CARE, Iran, Egypt, Tunisia, 1961-68; regional dir. CARE, N.Y.C., 1968-69, The Population Coun., N.Y.C., 1971-76; dep. dir. Project for Strengthening Health Delivery Systems in Ctrl. and West Africa, Boston, also Ivory Coast, 1976-79; regional dir. Mgmt. Scis. for Health, Boston, 1979-80; head health and hosps. Secretariat of His Highness The Aga Khan, Aiglemont, France, 1980-85; v.p. John Snow Pub. Health, Boston, 1985-89; pub. health cons. Wellesley, Mass., 1990—. Contbr. articles to profl. jours. Bd. dirs. Nat. Coun. for Internat. Health, 1993—, Am .Coun. for Nationalities Svcs., 1992—, U.S. Com. for Refugees, 1991-94. With signal corps U.S. Army, 1956-58. Decorated Medal of Honor, Iranian Red Cross, Tehran, 1964; order of the Republic (Tunisia) Fund; Fulbright grantee, 1961; Ford Found. fellow, 1970-71; Aspen Fund grantee, 1993. Fellow Royal Soc. Tropical Medicine and Hygiene. Home: 24 Maugus Ave Wellesley MA 02181

MONTAGUE, KENNETH CHARLES, congressman; b. Balt., Aug. 25, 1942; s. Kenneth Charles and Mary DeBar (Ferron) M.; m. Mary Louise Osweiler, Jan. 30, 1970 (div. 1993); children: Kenneth Charles III, Kyle Trevor. Grad., Morgan State Coll., 1967; JD, U. Md., 1977. Vol. U.S. Peace Corps, Lesotho, South Africa, 1961-71; community organizer Sinai Druid Pediatric Ctr., Balt., 1971-73; mem. faculty univ. without walls Morgan State U., Balt., 1973-83; lobbyist Mayor's Task Force for Liaison with Gen. Assembly, Balt., 1983-86; del. Md. Gen. Assembly, Annapolis, 1987—; ptnr. Needle, Montague & Frank, Balt., 1988—; mem. Ho. Judiciary Com., Annapolis, 1987—; mem. spl. com. on drug and alcohol abuse Md. Gen. Assembly, 1987—, chair joint com. on legis. ethics, 1990—; apptd. to Atty. Gen's Adv. Coun. on Family Legal Needs of Low Income People, co-chair subcom. on family ct., 1991-92, gov.'s coun. on adolescent pregnancy, 1989-92, gov.'s employment and tng. coun., 1988-91. Chair Md. com. UNICEF, 1988—; treas. Md. Citizen Action Coalition, 1991—, chair personnel com., 1988—; bd. dirs. House of Ruth, 1989—, Harford-Bel Air Community Mental Health Ctr., 1988—; vice chair Chesapeake AIDS Found., 1987—; bd. dirs. Theatre Project, 1988-93; vice chair Internat. Visitors Ctr., 1987-89; bd. dirs. Family and Childrens Svcs. Ctrl. Md., 1987-92; pres., bd. dirs. Balt. Neighborhoods, Inc., 1983-87; bd. dirs. Citizens Labor and Energy Coalition; many others. Recipient Award for Outstanding Svc. MARFY, 1994, Md. Food Com., 1993, Award for Disting. Svc. on Behalf of Family Dept. Human Resources, 1992, MARFY, 1992. Mem. Md. State Bar Assn., Engring. Soc. Md., Nat. Conf. State Legislatures (vice chair state fed. assembly), Nat. Abortion Rights Action League (mem. exec. com. 1991—, asst. treas. 1991—, various coms.), Nat. Abortion Rights Action League Polit. Action Com. (bd. dirs. 1991—), Citizens Fund/Citizen Action (vice chair for polit. affairs 1991—), Nat. Ctr. for Policy Alternatives (bd. dirs., leader policy alternatives 1990—). Democrat. Roman Catholic. Avocations: gardening, home brewing, golf, cooking, canning. Home: 513 E 39th St Baltimore MD 21218-1902 Office: 310 House Office Bldg Annapolis MD 21401

MONTAGUE, MARY ELLEN, secondary school educator; b. Georgetown, Ohio, Aug. 12, 1933; d. Carrol Russel and Martha Gail (Lucas) Martin; m. Patrick E. Montague, Feb. 14, 1958; children: Catherine, Michael. BS, Fla. State U., 1955; MS, West Ga. Coll., 1989. Cert. tchr., Ga., Fla., N.C. Tchr. Duval County Schs., Jacksonville, Fla., 1955-59, InterLangue, Paris, 1971-74, Jackson County Schs., Jylva, N.C., 1976-79, Fulton County Schs., Atlanta, 1959-71, 80—, Creekside High Sch., Fairburn, Ga. Author various curriculum guides, 1980—. Hostess Tour of Homes, Fairburn, Ga., 1989, 90, 91; vestry person St. Andrews Ch., Peachtree City, Ga., 1989-92. Fellow Smithsonian Instn.; mem. Nat. Coun. Social Studies, Delta Kappa Gamma (1st v.p. 1990-91, pres. 1991-94, dist. treas. 1994—). Home: PO Box 738 Fairburn GA 30213 also: Freeze House 7 Sylvan Ct Sylva NC 28779

MONTALBAN, RICARDO, actor; b. Mexico City, Nov. 25, 1920; s. Jenaro and Ricarda M.; m. Georgiana Young; children: Mark, Victor, Laura, Anita. Appeared in Mexican motion pictures, 1942-46; appeared in numerous films in U.S. including, Fiesta, 1947, Kissing Bandit, 1949, Neptune's Daughter, 1949, Battleground, 1950, Sombrero, 1953, Latin Lovers, 1954, Sayonara, 1957, Let No Man Write My Epitaph, 1960, Cheyenne Autumn, 1964, The Money Trap, 1965, Madame X, 1966, Sweet Charity, 1968, Escape From the Planet of the Apes, 1971, Conquest of the Planet of the Apes, 1972, The Train Robbers, 1972, Joe Panther, 1976, Won Ton Ton, The Dog Who Saved Hollywood, 1976, Star Trek II: The Wrath of Khan, 1982, Cannonball Run II, 1984, The Naked Gun, 1988; TV films include The Pigeon, 1969, The Aquarians, 1970, Fireball Forward, 1972, The Mark of Zorro, 1974, McNaughton's Daughter, 1976, Fantasy Island, Return to Fantasy Island, 1978; TV advertisements Chrysler, 1973—; TV appearances include Columbo, Star Trek, Return to Fantasy Island; starred in: ltd. series McNaughton's Daughter, 1976; TV series Fantasy Island, 1978-84 (Recipient Emmy award 1978), The Colbys, 1986-87. Mem. Acad. Motion Picture Arts and Scis. Office: William Morris Agency 151 El Camino Beverly Hills CA 90212*

MONTALI, DENNIS, judge; b. San Francisco, May 20, 1940; s. Ralph H. and Eleanor F. (Moore) M.; m. Mary A. Concannon, June 20, 1964; children—Lisa, Amy, Julie. B.A., U. Notre Dame, 1961; J.D., U. Calif.-Berkeley, 1968. Bar: Calif. 1969. Assoc. Rothschild, Phelan & Montali and predecessor Rothschild & Phelan, San Francisco, 1968-72, ptnr., 1973-80; ptnr. Dinkelspiel, Pelavin, Steefel & Levitt, San Francisco, 1980; ptnr. Pillsbury, Madison & Sutro, San Francisco, 1981-93; U.S. bankruptcy judge No. Dist. of Calif., 1993—; frequent lectr. Practising Law Inst., Calif. Continuing Edn. of Bar; instr. Lone Mountain Coll., 1975. Served to lt. USN, 1961-65, with Res. Mem. Nat. Bankruptcy Conf., ABA (sec. bus. bankruptcy com.), Am. Coll. of Bankruptcy, Bar Assn. San Francisco (chmn. comml. law and bankruptcy sect.), State Bar Calif. Author: Collier Bankruptcy Practice Guide, 1982; contbg. author to numerous course books for Practising Law Inst. and Continuing Edn. of the Bar. Office: 235 Pine St San Francisco CA 94104-2701

MONTANA, JOSEPH C., JR., former professional football player; b. New Eagle, Pa., June 11, 1956; s. Joseph C. Montana, Sr., and Theresa M.; m. 1st, Kim Monses, 1975 (div.); m. 2nd, Cass Castillo (div. 1983); m. 3rd, Jennifer Wallace, 1984; 2 children, Alexandra, Elizabeth. B.B.A. in Mktg., U. Notre Dame, 1978. Quarterback San Francisco 49ers, 1979—. Named Super Bowl Championship Team, 1982, 85, 90; named to Pro Bowl, 1981, 83, 84, 85, 87, 89, 90, 93; quarterback Kansas City Chiefs, 1993-95. Author (with Alan Steinberg): Cool Under Fire, 1989. Named MVP at Super Bowl, 1982, 85, MVP at NFL, 1989, Player of Yr., The Sporting News, 1989, Man of Yr., The Sporting News, 1989; named to Pro Bowl 1981, 83-85, 87, 89, 90, 93. Holds NFL career records for highest completion percentage (63.67), highest passer rating (93.5), NFL single-season record for highest passer rating (112.4), 1989, NFL record for most consecutive games with 300 or more yards passing (5), 1982, most consecutive passes completed (22), 1987. Office: care Internat Management Group 1 Erieview Plz Ste 1300 Cleveland OH 44114*

MONTANA, PATRICK JOSEPH, management educator; b. N.Y.C.; s. Joseph Paul and Constance (Frezza) M. B.S. cum laude, L.I. U., M.S. cum laude; Ph.D., N.Y. U., 1966; M.B.A., U. Cin., 1974. Asst. dean, asso. prof., dir. placement, chmn. mgmt. L.I. U., Bklyn., 1960-66; asso. prof. Drexel U. Phila., 1966-67; asst. dean N.Y. U. Grad. Sch. Bus. Adminstrn., N.Y.C., 1967-69; asst. v.p., dir. planning and manpower devel. Sperry & Hutchinson Co. (trading stamps and subsidiaries), N.Y.C., 1969-74; U.S. presdl. interchange exec., 1973; pres. Profl. Inst., Am. Mgmt. Assn., N.Y.C., 1974-76, Nat. Center Career Life Planning, 1975-80, 80—; prof. mgmt. Hofstra U. Sch. Bus.; corp. cons. New Choices mag.; adj. prof. mgmt. and mktg. Fordham U. Grad. Sch. Bus., N.Y.C., 1969-79; curriculum cons. U. P.R., 1968; guest lectr. Congress for Internat. Progress in Mgmt., 1965, IBM Corp. Mgmt. Sch., 1964-65, 76-77; mediator Pub. Employee Relations Bd., 1969; bd. dirs. Ednl. Systems and Publs., 1970-75. Author: The Marketing Executive of the Future, 1967, You Can Change Your Future, 1976, Managing Nonprofit Organizations, 1977, Marketing in Nonprofit Organizations, 1978, Career Life Planning for Americans, 1978, Overcoming Mid and Late Career Crises, 1978, Successful Teamwork—How Managers and Secretaries Achieve It, 1979, Managing Terrorism, 1982; Retirement Programs: How to Develop and Implement Them, 1985; Work Force Management in the Arabian Peninsula, 1986, Management, 1987, Preretirement Planning, 1988, Stepping Out, Starting Over, 1992, Managing Public and Nonprofit Organizations, 1994; contbr. numerous articles to profl. publs. Recipient achievement award Wall Street Jour., 1959-60; U.S. Sec. Labor's Recognition award, 1974; Ford Found. fellow, 1963-64. Mem. Am. Assembly Collegiate Schs. Bus. (accreditation com. 1970-72, standards com. 1973-75, govt. relations com. 1976-78), Am. Mktg. Assn. (awards com., continuing edn. com.), Beta Gamma Sigma, Eta Mu Pi. Office: Hofstra U Sch Bus Hempstead NY 11550

MONTANA, PATSY See ROSE, RUBYE BLEVINS

MONTCALM, NORMAN JOSEPH, lawyer; b. Trois-Rivieres, Que., Can., July 8, 1945; s. Aimé and Alida (Filion) M.; m. Marie Lanctôt, July 28, 1973; children: Julie, Valérie, Jean-François. BA, Collège des Trois-Rivières, 1967; BCL, McGill U., 1971. Bar: Que. 1972. Legal counsel Hydro-Que., Montreal, 1972-79; v.p. legal affairs, sec. Civitas Corp., Montreal, 1979-83; legal counsel Imasco Ltd., Montreal, 1983-88, sec., legal counsel, 1988-89; ptnr. Legault Longtin Laurin Halpin, Montreal, 1992—. Mem. St. Justine Hosp. Found., Montreal, 1986—, Order of Que. Olympic Games, Montreal, 1988—. Mem. Can. Bar Assn., Que. and Montreal bar assns. (various coms.), Montreal C. of C. Roman Catholic. Home: 221 Carlyle, Mount Royal, PQ Canada H3R 1T1 Office: Legault Longtin Laurin Halpin, 630 Blvd René-Lévesque W # 1800, Montreal, PQ Canada H3B 1S6

MONTE, BONNIE J., performing company executive; b. Stamford, Ct., Nov. 27, 1954; d. Eugene N. and Ruth M. (Thompson) M. BA, Bethany Coll., 1976; diploma, Hartman Conservatory, Stamford, 1978. Assoc. artistic dir. Williamstown (Mass.) Theatre Festival, 1981-89; casting dir. Manhattan Theatre Club, N.Y.C., 1989-90; artistic dir. N.J. Shakespeare Festival, Madison, 1990—; mem. faculty Drew U., Madison, 1991—. Grantee Lotte Crabtree Found., Boston, 1977. Democrat. Avocations: equerry, cycling, archery, writing, travel. Office: NJ Shakespeare Festival c/o Drew U 36 Madison Ave Madison NJ 07940-1434*

MONTECEL, MARIA ROBLEDO (CUCA ROBLEDO MONTECEL), educational association administrator; b. Laredo, Tex., Jan. 14, 1953; d. Ismael and Paula (Benavides) Robledo; m. Lucas Montecel, Aug. 18, 1979; children: Ismael Gervino, Xavier Mario. BSSW magna cum laude, Our Lady of Lake U., 1972; MEd, Antioch U., 1975; PhD in Urban Edn., U. Wis., 1985. Rsch. asst. D.C. Devel. Assocs., Inc., San Antonio, 1973-75; test designer Dissemination and Assessment Ctr. for Bilingual Edn. U. Tex., San Antonio, 1975-76; grad. rsch. asst. office rsch. Sch. Edn. U. Wis., Milw., 1980-81, program dir. Midwest NODAC dept. cultural founds. Sch. Edn., 1985; evaluator Ctr. for Mgmt. Innovation in Multicultural Edn. Intercultural Devel. Rsch. Assn., San Antonio, 1976-77, dir. bilingual edn. cost analysis project, 1977-78, dir. divsn. rsch., devel. and evaluation, 1978-80, rsch. specialist, 1982-85, dir. Ctr. for Prevention and Recovery Dropouts, 1985-88, 90-92, dir. tng. and tech. assistance, 1988-89, dir. valued youth program, 1988-90, dep. dir., 1992, exec. dir., 1992—; trustee Our Lady of Lake U. Mem. editorial bd. Tex. Rschr.; contbr. articles to profl. jours. Vol. advocate Alamo Area Rape Crisis Ctr.; mem. rsch. com. Hispanas Unidas; participant Leadership Tex. '85; invited mem. Tex. State Task Force Dropout Prevention; chmn. lifelong learning coun. San Antonio 2000; cons. edn. and immigrant students Mellon Found.; bd. dirs. Mex.-Am. Solidarity Found.; founding bd. dirs. CIVICUS World Alliance Citizen Participation; bd. dirs. community edn. leadership program Mott Found.; mem. nat. adv. coun. Race and Ethnic Studies Inst., Tex. A & M; mem. ednl. review bd. Tex. Ctr. Ednl. Rsch.; mem. nat. adv. bd. ERIC/CRESS, 1994. Recipient High Achievement Commendation, Antioch Coll., 1975, Peter F. Drucker award Coca-Cola Valued Youth Program; Women and Minority Rsch. fellow Nat. Inst. Edn., 1979, Title VII Doctoral fellow U. Wis., 1980-82. Mem. Am. Edn. Rsch. Assn., Nat. Assn. Bilingual Edn., Nat. Dropout Prevention Network (charter), Alphi Chi. Roman Catholic. Avocations: reading, writing, fishing, golf. Office: Intercultural Devel Rsch Assn 5835 Callaghan Rd Ste 350 San Antonio TX 78228

MONTEFERRANTE, JUDITH CATHERINE, cardiologist; b. N.Y., Jan. 27, 1949; d. Stanley and Monica (Vinckus) Sosaris; m. Roger E. Salisbury, Mar. 3, 1990. BS, Adelphi U., Garden City, 1970; MS, SUNY, Buffalo, 1973; MD, Mt. Sinai, N.Y.C., 1978. Attending N.Y. Med. Coll., Valhalla, N.Y., 1983-84; pvt. practice White Plains, N.Y., 1984—; pres. Am. Heart Assn., 1984-86, bd. dirs. Westchester, N.Y., 1987—. Contbr. articles to profl. jours. fellow Am. Colls. of Cardiology, Am. Coll. of Physicians. fellow Council on Clinical Cardiology of AHA, N.Y. Cardiological Soc.; mem. AMA, FACC, FACP, Soc. of Critical Care Medicine. Office: 222 Westchester Ave # 405 White Plains NY 10604-2906

MONTEIRO, GEORGE, English educator, writer; b. Cumberland, R.I., May 23, 1932; s. Francisco José and Augusta (Temudo) M.; m. Lois Ann Hodgins, Aug. 14, 1958 (div. 1992); children: Katherine, Stephen, Emily; m. Brenda Murphy, Mar. 25, 1995. AB, Brown U., 1954; AM, Columbia U., 1956; PhD, Brown U., 1964; DHL honoris caus, U. Mass., Dartmouth, 1993. Instr., asst. prof., then assoc. prof. Brown U., Providence, 1961-72, prof. English, 1972—; vis. prof. Providence Coll., 1967-68; Fulbright prof. Am. lit. U. Sao Paulo, 1969-71. Author: Henry James and John Hay: The Record of a Friendship, 1965, The Coffee Exchange: Poems, 1982, Robert Frost and the New England Renaissance, 1988; editor: The Man Who Never Was: Essays on Fernando Pessoa, 1982, The Correspondence of Henry James and Henry Adams, 1877-1914, 1992; translator: In Crete With the Minotaur and Other Poems, 1980, Fernando Pessoa: Self Awareness and Thirty Other Poems, 1988, A Man Smiles at Death with Half a Face, 1991. Decorated Order of Prince Henry the Navigator, govt. of Portugal, 1989. Office: Brown U Dept English Providence RI 02912

MONTEIRO, LOIS ANN, medical science educator; b. Central Falls, R.I., Mar. 22, 1934; d. William Henry and Martha Mae (Leach) Hodgins; m. George Monteiro, Aug. 14, 1958 (div. Feb. 1992); children: Katherine, Stephen, Emily. RN, Roger Williams Hosp., Providence, 1954; BA, Brown U., k1958, PhD, 1970; MS, Boston U., 1960. Asst. prof. Boston U., 1960-65; asst. prof. Brown U., Providence, R.I., 1971-77, assoc. prof., 1978-82, prof., 1983—, chmn. dept., 1985—, assoc. dean medicine, 1991—; vis. prof. U. Va., 1990; bd. dirs. Harvard Community Health Plan, 1990—. Author: Monitoring Health Status, 1976k Cardiac Rehabilitation, 1980; contbr. articles to profl. jours. Me. Commn. State of R.I., Providence, 1989—. NSF grantee, 1969, Robert W. Johnson Found. grantee, Princeton, N.J., 1983, NIH grantee, 1987; Bunting Inst. fellow, Cambridge, Mass., 1981. Mem. Am. Sociol. Assn., R.I. State Nurses Assn. (pres. 1974-76), Women in Medicine/Assn. Am. Med. Colls. Democrat. Presbyterian. Avocation: collecting books on nursing history. Office: Brown U Dept Med Sci Box G-A413 Providence RI 02912

MONTEITH, LARRY KING, university chancellor; b. Bryson City, N.C., Aug. 17, 1933; s. Earl and Essie (King) M.; m. Nancy Alexander, Apr. 19, 1952; children: Larry, Carol, Steve. BSEE, N.C. State U., 1960; MSEE,

Duke U., 1962, PhDEE, 1965. Registered profl. engr., N.C. Mem. tech. staff Bell Telephone Labs., Burlington, N.C., 1960-62; mem. tech. staff Resch. Triangle Inst., Raleigh, 1962-66, group leader rsch. sect., 1966-68; adj. asst. prof. elec. engring. N.C. State U., Raleigh, 1965-68, assoc. prof., 1968-72, prof., 1972—, head dept. elec. engring., 1974-78, dean of engring., 1978-89, interim chancellor, 1989-90, chancellor, 1990—; bd. dirs. Microelectronics Ctr. N.C., Rsch. Triangle Inst. Contbr. articles to profl. jours. Trustee Nat. Tech. Univ., Triangle Univ. Ctr. Advanced Studies, Inc.; corp. mem. Underwriters Labs., Inc.; bd. visitors Air U. With USN, 1952-55. Recipient Disting. Engring. Alumnus award Duke U., 1984, Outstanding Engring. Achievement award N.C. Soc. Engrs., 1990. Fellow IEEE, Am. Soc. for Engring. Edn.; mem. NSPE (edn. adv. group), Raleigh C. of C. (bd. dirs.), Rotary Internat. (Paul Harris fellow Rotary Found. 1991), Phi Beta Kappa, Sigma Xi, Sigma Iota Rho, Phi Kappa Phi, Eta Kappa Nu, Tau Beta Pi. Home: 1903 Hillsborough St Raleigh NC 27607-7348 Office: NC State U Pullen Rd Raleigh NC 27695

MONTEITH, WALTER HENRY, JR., utility company executive; b. Framingham, Mass., Sept. 9, 1930; s. Walter H. and Ann (Sullivan) M.; m. Jane Marceau, Aug. 14, 1954; children: Deborah, Diane, Karen. B.A., Amherst Coll., 1952. With So. Eng. Telephone Co., New Haven, 1954—, asst. comptr., 1966-68, asst. v.p., div. ops. mgr., 1968-70, v.p. staff, 1970-79, exec. v.p. adminstrn. and fin., 1979-82, pres., 1982-84, pres., chief exec. officer, 1984—, chmn., 1985—; now also chmn., pres., chief exec. officer So. New Eng. Telecommunications, New Haven; bd. dirs. Conn. Nat. Bank, Hartford, Kaman Corp., Bloomfield, Conn. Bd. dirs. Long Wharf Theater, New Haven, 1978, Yale New Haven Hosp., 1985. Mem. Conn. World Trade Assn. (bd. dirs. 1987—). Clubs: New Haven Country, Quinnipiack (New Haven). Office: So New England Tel Co 15th Fl 227 Church St New Haven CT 06510-1801

MONTELONGO, MICHAEL, career officer; b. N.Y.C.; m. Debra Tenison; 1 child, Amanda. BS in Nat. Security and Pub. Affairs, U.S. Military Acad.; MBA in Corp. Strategy and Fin., Harvard U., 1988; grad., Command and Gen. Staff Coll., 1992. Commd. 2d lt. U.S. Army, 1977, advanced through grades to lt. col., platoon leader, 1980, staff officer, 1982, ops. officer, company comdr., 1986; admissions officer U.S. Military Acad., West Point, N.Y., 1991, asst. prof. social scis. dept., 1991; rsch. analyst office economic and manpower analysis U.S. Army, 1991; adviser, spl. asst. Comdr.-in-Chief U.S. Southern Command, 1991; bat. exec. officer, bat. and brigade ops. officer U.S. Army, 1993; special asst. to U.S. Army chief of staff U.S. Army, Washington, 1994—; sec. supervisory com. Ft. Bliss Fed. Credit Union; ch. music minister, 1969—. Sec. Nat. Soc. Hispanic MBA, 1995; Mex.-Am. Legal Def. and Ednl. Fund Advanced Leadership Program, 1993; trustee Unite El Paso, 1993. U.S. Army Advanced Civil Schooling fellow, 1986, Inter-Univ. Seminar on Armed Forces and Soc. fellow, 1990, Congrl. Hispanic Caucus Inst. fellow, 1992, Leadership El Paso fellow, 1993. Home: 5589 Anne Peake Dr Fairfax VA 22032 Office: HQDA OCSA ATTN DACS-ZAA 200 Army Pentagon Washington DC 20310-0200

MONTEMAYOR, JESUS SAMSON, physician; b. La Carlota City, The Philippines, May 17, 1939; came to U.S., 1972; s. Jesus Cavada and Elena Poticar (Samson) M.; m. Catalina Abellana, Sept. 26, 1971; children: Grace, Gail, Jennifer, Jessica. AA, U. San Carlos, Cebu City, The Philippines, 1958; MD, Southwestern U., Cebu City, Philippines, 1969. Adj. physician C.L. Montelibano Meml. Hosp., Bacolod City, The Philippines, 1969-70; resident physician Drs. Hosp., Bacolod City, 1970-72; resident in pathology Wyckoff Heights Hosp., Bklyn., 1975-80, emergency rm. physician, 1984-88; fellow in medicine NYU Med. Ctr.-Goldwater Meml. Hosp., Roosevelt Island, 1980-84, attending physician, 1984-94; emergency rm. physician Astoria (N.Y.) Hosp., 1983-84. Fellow Am. Coll. Internat. Physicians; mem. AAAS, Am. Geriatric Soc., Assn. Philippine Physicians in Am., Am. Acad. Home Care Physicians, Am. Med. Dirs. Assn., N.Y. Acad. Scis. Republican. Roman Catholic. Achievements include research in electromagnetic energy in medicine. Home: 1073 Hart St Brooklyn NY 11237-3405 Office: 647 W 207 St Ste 13 New York NY 10034

MONTERO, DARREL MARTIN, sociologist, social worker, educator; b. Sacramento, Mar. 4, 1946; s. Frank and Ann Naake; m. Tara Kathleen McLaughlin, July 6, 1975; children: David Paul, Lynn Elizabeth, Laura Ann, Emily Kathryn. AB, Calif. State U., 1970; MA, UCLA, 1972, PhD, 1974. Postgrad. researcher Japanese-Am. Research Project UCLA, 1971-73, dir. research, 1973-75; assoc. head Program on Comparative Ethnic Studies, Survey Research Ctr. UCLA, 1973-75; asst. prof. sociology Case Western Res. U., Cleve., 1975-76; asst. prof. urban studies, research sociologist Pub. Opinion Survey, dir. urban ethnic research program U. Md., College Park, 1976-79; assoc. prof. Ariz. State U., Tempe, 1979—; cons. rsch. sect. Viewer Sponsored TV Found., Los Angeles, Berrien E. Moore Law Office, Inc., Gardena, Calif., 1973, Bur. for Social Sci. Research, Inc., Washington, Friends of the Family, Ltd., Nat. Sci. Found. Author: Japanese Americans: Changing Patterns of Ethnic Affiliation Over Three Generations, 1980, Urban Studies, 1978, Vietnamese Americans: Patterns of Resettlement and Socioeconomic Adaptation in the United States, 1979, Social Problems, 1988; mem. editorial bd. Humanity and Society, 1978-80; contbr. articles to profl. jours. Served with U.S. Army, 1966-72. Mem. Am. Sociol. Assn., Am. Assn. Pub. Opinion Research (exec. council, standards com.), Am. Ednl. Research Assn., Council on Social Work Edn., Soc. Study of Social Problems, D.C. Sociol. Soc., Am. Soc. Pub. Adminstrn., Nat. Assn. Social Workers, Pacific Sociol. Assn. Office: Sch Social Work Ariz State U Tempe AZ 85281

MONTERO, FERNAN GONZALO, advertising executive; b. Buenos Aires, May 22, 1948; came to U.S., 1952; s. Adolfo and Donne (Strang) M.; m. Cheryl Bowman, Dec. 30, 1976. BBA, U. Wis., 1971; M. Journalism in Advt., Northwestern U., 1972. With Young & Rubicam Inc., 1972-82; pres. Young & Rubicam Argentina, Buenos Aires, 1982-85; dep. area mgr. Young & Rubicam Latin Am., Sao Paulo, Brazil, 1985-87; sr. v.p., dir. bus. devel. Young & Rubicam Inc., N.Y.C., 1987-91, chmn., CEO Latin Am., 1991-92, chmn., CEO Europe Young & Rubicam Inc., London, 1993—. Office: Young & Rubicam, Greater London House, Hampstead Rd London NW1, England

MONTFORD, JOHN THOMAS, lawyer, state legislator; b. Ft. Worth, June 28, 1943; s. Thomas L. and Jewell F. (Coursey) M.; m. Pamela Jacobs, June 3, 1966 (div.); 1 child, Melinda; m. Debra Kay Mears, Dec. 24, 1975; children: Melonie, John Ross. BA, U. Tex.-Austin, 1965, JD, 1968; LLD (hon.), Lubbock (Tex.) Christian U., 1989. Bar: Tex. 1968. Pvt. practice law, Lubbock, Tex., 1971-78; criminal dist. atty. Lubbock County, Tex., 1979-82; state senator Dist. 28, Lubbock, 1983—. Trustee S. Park Hosp., Lubbock, 1981-82; bd. dirs., trustee Tex. Boys Ranch, Lubbock, 1982—; chmn. profl. div. United Way, Lubbock, 1980; energy com. So. Legis. Conf., 1983; senate appointee So. Growth Policies Bd., 1983; chmn. adv. coun. Lubbock Substance Abuse Prevention Partnership; mem. bd. govs. West Tex. Chpt. Multiple Sclerosis. Mem. dean's roundtable U. Tex. Sch. Law, 1988. Maj. USMC, 1968-71. Recipient Outstanding Young Man of Lubbock award Jaycees, 1973, Headliner of Yr. award Greater Lubbock Press Club, 1979, Man of Yr./Law Enforcement award Lubbock Optimist Club, 1979, Boss of Yr. award Legal Secs. Assn., 1980, Exec. of Yr., Lubbock Sales Exec. Assn., 1981; named Finest Freshman, Tex. Bus. Mag., 1983, Outstanding State Senator Tex. Youth Commn., 1988, Legislator of Yr. Tex. Pub. Health Assn., 1988, Legislator of Yr. Tex. Pub. Employees Assn. and State Employees, 1989, Outstanding Tex. Leader award John Ben Shepperd Pub. Leadership Forum, 1989, Best New Legislator award Tex. Monthly mag., 1983, Disting. Alumni, L.D. Bell High Sch., 1984, Lubbock's Man of the Yr. League of Women Voters and Am. Diabetes Assn., 1987, Disting. Svc. award Tex. C. of C., 1989, Outstanding Legislator in State of Tex. Epsilon Sigma Phi, 1989, Legislator of Yr. award Tex. Soc. Profl. Surveyors, 1989, Legislator of Yr. award 71st Legislature, Tex. Mcpl. League, 1989, Tree of Life award Jewish Nat. Fund, 1989; named one of the Ten Best Legislators 71st Legislature, Tex. Monthly, 1989, 72d Legislature, 1991, Tex. Monthly, 1989, 91, Outstanding Legislator Epsilon Sigma Phi, 1989, Legislator of Yr. 71st Legislature Tex. Soc. Profl. Surveyors, 1989, Tex. Mcpl. League, 1989; recipient Outstanding Svc. award Tex. Electric Coops., 1989, Pub. Ofcl. award Tex. Pub. Power Assn., 1990, George Woods award in politics NAAACP, 1990, Legislative Leadership award 72d Legislator Tex. C. of C., 1992, One of the Seven Best Legislators 73d Legislature

Dallas Morning News, 1993, One of the Ten Best Legislators 73d Legislature Tex. Monthly, 1993, Legislator of the Yr. Tex. Public Employees Assn., 1993, Bowie award Tex. State Guard Assn., 1993. Mem. State Bar Tex. (com. admissions), Tex. Criminal Def. Lawyers Assn., Tex. Dist. and County Attys. Assn. (legis. com.), Western States Water Council, Tex. Assn. Community Schs. (hon. life), Tex. Heart Inst. (nat. adv. coun. 1991), Order of Coif (hon.), Omicron Delta Kappa, Delta Theta Phi. Club: Jaycees (v.p. 1974), Met. Rotary, Lubbock Lions. Home: 10901 Wintergreen Hl Austin TX 78750-3453 Office: PO Box 1709 Lubbock TX 79408-1709

MONTGOMERY, BETTY D., state official, former state legislator. BA, Bowling Green State U.; JD, U. Toledo, 1976. Former criminal clk. Lucas County Common Pleas Ct.; asst. pros. atty. County of Wood, Ohio, pros. atty., 1980-88; asst. pros. atty. City of Perrysburg, Ohio; mem. Ohio Senate, 1989-94; attorney general State of Ohio, Columbus, 1995—. Mem. Nat. Dist. Atty. Assn., Ohio Bar Assn., Toledo Bar Assn., Wood County Bar Assn. Address: 11145 Riverbend Ct W Perrysburg OH 43551-3678 also: Attorney Generals Office State Offical Tower 30 E Broad St Columbus OH 43266

MONTGOMERY, CHARLES BARRY, lawyer; b. Latrobe, Pa., Apr. 17, 1937. BA cum laude Muskingum Coll., 1959; JD U. Mich., 1962. Bar: Ill. 1962, U.S. Dist. Ct. (no. dist.) Ill., 1982, U.S. Supreme Ct. 1971. Atty. Jacobs & McKenna, 1962-67; founder, ptnr. Jacobs, Williams and Montgomery, Ltd., 1967-85; sr. ptnr. Williams and Montgomery, Ltd., Chgo., 1985—; instr. advocacy inst. U. Mich., Ann Arbor, 1985, advanced program Nat. Inst. Trial Advocacy, 1986, trial acad. Internat. Assn. Def. Counsel, 1987, law inst. program Def. Rsch. Inst; pub. speaker ins. litigation; contbr. articles to profl. jours. Fellow Internat. Acad. Trial Lawyers; mem. ABA (vice-chair medicine and law com. 1989-90), Am. Arbitration Assn., Chgo. Bar Assn., Def. Rsch. Inst., Ill. Assn. Def. Trial Counsel, Ill. Assn. Hosp. Attys., Ill. State Bar Assn., Internat. Assn. Def. Counsel, Nat. Assn. R.R. Trial Counsel, Soc. Trial Lawyers, Legal Club of Chgo., Trial Lawyers Club of Chgo. Office: Williams and Montgomery Ltd 20 N Wacker Dr Chicago IL 60606-2806

MONTGOMERY, CHARLES HOWARD, retired bank executive; b. Bloomington, Ill., Mar. 23, 1930; s. Dewey H. and Madeline (Wonderlin) M.; m. Diane Dickerson Cohen, Aug. 30, 1978; children: Alison, Douglas. A.B., Ill. Wesleyan U., 1951; M.S., U. Ill., 1960. CPA, Ill. Auditor Lybrand Ross Bros. & Montgomery, Rockford, Ill., 1955-59; with Abbott Labs., North Chicago, Ill., 1959-67; controller Abbott Labs., 1965-67; v.p. finance Anchor Coupling Co., Libertyville, 1967-69; v.p., comptroller First Nat. Bank Chgo., 1969-73, sr. v.p., 1973-75, exec. v.p., 1976-88, comptroller, 1973-88; comptroller First Chgo. Corp.; ret.; past chmn. Inter-Assn. Com. Bank Acctg. Served with AUS, 1952-53. Mem. Fin. Execs. Inst., AICPA, Ill. Soc. CPAs, Tau Kappa Epsilon, Phi Kappa Phi, Univ. Club (Chgo.). Home: 5490 S South Shore Dr Chicago IL 60615-5984

MONTGOMERY, DAVID BRUCE, marketing educator; b. Fargo, N.D., Apr. 30, 1938; s. David William and Iva Bernice (Trask) M.; m. Toby Marie Franks, June 11, 1960; children: David Richard, Scott Bradford, Pamela Marie. BSEE, Stanford U., 1960, MBA, 1962, MS in Stats., 1964, PhD in Mgmt. Sci., 1966. Asst. prof. mgmt. MIT, 1966-69, assoc. prof., 1969-70; assoc. prof. mktg. and mgmt. sci. Stanford U. 1970-73, prof., 1973-78, Robert A. Magowan prof. mktg., 1978-92, Sebastian S. Kregge prof. mktg. strategy, 1992—; prin. The MAC Group Inc., 1969-91; mem. adv. bd. LEK Partnership, London; mem. sci. adv. bd. Univ. Connection, Bonn, Germany; acad. trustee Mktg. Sci. Inst., 1994—, exec. dir., 1995—. Author: (with Glen L. Urban) Management Science in Marketing, 1969, (with Massy and Morrison) Stochastic Models of Buying Behavior, 1970, (with Day et al) Planning: Cases in Computer and Model Assisted Marketing, 1973, (with others) Consumer Behavior: Theoretical Sources, 1973, (with G. J. Eskin) Data Analysis, 1975; editor 4 books; contbr. over 70 articles and tech. reports. Trustee Family Service Assn. of Mid Peninsula, 1972-73. Recipient citation for outstanding contbns. to use of computers in mgmt. edn. Hewlett Packard, 1977. Fellow Royal Statis. Soc.; mem. Inst. Mgmt. Scis., Am. Mktg. Assn., Econometric Soc., Am. Inst. Decision Scis., Tau Beta Pi. Republican. Congregational. Home: 960 Wing Pl Stanford CA 94305 Office: Stanford U Grad Sch Bus Stanford CA 94305

MONTGOMERY, DAVID CAMPBELL, physicist, educator; b. Milan, Mo., Mar. 5, 1936; s. Merrill Edward and Ruth E. (Campbell) M.; m. Shirley Arlene Imig, July 20, 1957; children: Kathleen Montgomery Sutton, Elizabeth. Student, U. Mo., 1953-55; B.S., U. Wis., 1956; M.A., Princeton, 1958, Ph.D., 1959. Research assoc. Princeton U., 1959-60; instr. U. Wis., 1961-62; asst. prof. U. Md., 1962-65; assoc. prof. U. Iowa, Iowa City, 1965-70; prof. U. Iowa, 1970-77; prof. physics Coll. William and Mary, Williamsburg, Va., 1977-84; prof. Dartmouth Coll., Hanover, N.H., 1984-88, Eleanor and A. Kelvin Smith prof. physics, 1988—; vis. prof., researcher U. Colo., 1966, U. Alaska, 1968, U. Calif.-Berkeley, 1969-79, Bell Labs., 1971, U. Wis., 1989; lectr. Internat. Summer Sch. Theoretical Physics, Les Houches, France, 1972, U. Wis., Madison, 1973; vis. prof. Hunter Campus, CUNY, 1973-74, U. Nagoya (Japan), 1983, Columbia U., N.Y.C., 1985, Tech. U., Eindhoven, Netherlands, spring 1992; vis. scientist Nat. Center Atmospheric Research, Boulder, Colo., summers 1975, 76, 79, 87; cons. NASA Hdqrs., Washington, 1977-82, JET Joint Undertaking, Culham, U.K., fall 1991; vis. rsch. prof. U. Md., 1977-84; mem. vis. staff Los Alamos Sci. Lab., summers 1977, 78, 79, 80, 81, 86, 91, 92, 94; former cons. Oak Ridge Nat. Lab., Los Alamos Sci. Lab., NASA; vis. researcher Los Alamos Nat. Lab., 1987-88. Former assoc. editor: Physics of Fluids, Internat. Jour. Engring. Sci.; contbr. more than 150 rsch. articles to profl. publs.; also monographs. Fellow Am. Phys. Soc.; mem. N.Y. Acad. Scis., Phi Beta Kappa, Sigma Xi, Pi Mu Epsilon, Phi Mu Alpha. Achievements include introduction of modern fluid turbulence methods into space and controlled fusion theory; developed maximum entropy, or "most probable" states, method of describing coherent structures achieved as a product of turbulent relaxation. Home: 46 River Rd Hanover NH 03755-6612 Office: Dartmouth College Physics Dept Hanover NH 03755

MONTGOMERY, DAVID PAUL, professional baseball team executive; b. Phila.; m. Lyn Sagendorph. BA in History, U. Pa., 1968; MBA, Wharton Sch., U. Pa., 1970. With Phila. Phillies, 1971—, successively mem. sales dept., dir. mktg., dir. sales, exec. v.p., COO. Office: Phila Phillies PO Box 7575 Philadelphia PA 19101-7575

MONTGOMERY, DONALD JOSEPH, physicist, educator; b. Cin., June 11, 1917; s. Robert John and Stella (Steffen) M.; m. Mary Miller, July 27, 1951; children—Denis Broyles, Malcolm David, Steven Michael, Laurence Matthew. Chem.E., U. Cin., 1939, Ph.D., 1945; postgrad., Cornell U., 1941-42. Instr. elec. engring. U. Cin., 1942-44; physicist Flight Propulsion Lab., NACA, Cleve., 1944-45; research assoc. physics, asst. prof. Princeton, 1945-46; sci. liaison officer Office Naval Research, London, Eng., 1947-48; research fellow physics U. Manchester, Eng., 1947-48; chief spl. problems br. Interior Ballistics Lab., Ballistic Research Lab., Aberdeen Proving Ground, Md., 1948-50; head gen. physics sect. Textile Research Inst., Princeton, N.J., 1950-53; asso. prof. physics Mich. State U., East Lansing, 1953-56; prof. Mich. State U., 1956-61, research director physics, prof. engring. research, 1961-66, prof. physics, chmn. dept. metallurgy, mechanics and material sci., 1966-71, research prof. engring. sci., 1971-88, prof. emeritus, 1988; Cons. Chemstrand Research Center, Durham, N.C., 1958-66, Owens-Ill., 1966-88; spl. asst. to dir. Office Grants and Research Contracts, NASA, 1964-65; vis. research physicist Space Sci. Lab., U. Calif.-Berkeley, 1965-66; vis. scholar dept. polit. sci. U. Ill., 1984-87. Author: Cosmic Ray Physics, 1949; also chpts. in books, articles, revs. Recipient Distinguished Faculty award Mich. State U., 1961, Distinguished Alumnus award U. Cin., 1969; Fulbright lectr. in physics Guggenheim fellow U. Grenoble, France, 1959-60; Fulbright researcher in engring., econs. U. Augsburg, Germany; asso. Internat. Inst. Empirical Socioecons., Leitershofen-Augsburg, 1974-75. Fellow Am. Phys. Soc.; mem. AAAS, Am. Nuclear Soc. (charter), Am. Assn. Physics Tchrs., Biophys. Soc., Am. Acad. Mechanics, Textile Rsch. Inst., Am. Soc. Engring. Edn., Internat. Assn. Impact Assessment, Internat. Soc. Tech. Assessment, Am. Acad. Polit. & Social Sci., Policy Studies Assn., Acad. Polit. Sci., Coun. Applied Social Rsch., Fulbright Alumni Assn., Mich. Acad. Art, Letters & Sci., N.Y. Acad. Scis., Soc. Social Studies of Sci., Sigma Xi, Tau Beta Pi, Phi Kappa Phi, Omicron Delta Kappa. Achievements include development of practical formula for predicting charge transfer in static electrification of solids, of scheme for sociotechnical assessment of consequences of public policy measures as an aid to decision making; research on materials science. Home: 2391 Shawnee Trl Okemos MI 48864-2529 Office: Mich State U Coll Engring East Lansing MI 48824-1226

MONTGOMERY, DONALD RUSSELL, labor consulting firm executive; b. Canora, Sask., June 8, 1920; s. Milton Templeton and Margaret Genva (Culbert) M.; m. Lu Eirene Huggard, May 20, 1954; children—Charmeine, Donald Kirk. Student, Turner Bus. Coll. With United Steelworkers of Am., 1940—; steelworkers area supr. Toronto-Barrie area, 1953-74; sec.-treas. Toronto and Lakeshore Labour Coun., 1953-64, pres., 1964-74; sec.-treas. Can. Labour Congress, 1974-84; cons. union adminstrn., indsl. rels., Ottawa and Toronto; pres., chief exec. officer MertoLabour Cons. Inc., Toronto, 1989—; founding mem. Labor Coun. Devel. Found.; former mem. Export Trade Devel. Bd., adv. com. Aviation Unions; bd. dirs. GSW Ltd. (formerly Gen. Steel Wares Ltd.); cons. in field to labor unions, govts. and employers. Contbr. numerous papers on unions, labor edn. to profl. jours. Mem. Assn. Comml. and Tech. Employees. Home: 19 Bay Point Rd, Toronto, ON Canada M6S 2E8 Office: MetroLabour Cons Inc, PO Box 98546, 873 Jane St, Toronto, ON Canada M6N 5N6

MONTGOMERY, EDWARD ALEMBERT, JR., not-for-profit developer; b. Pitts., July 2, 1934; s. Edward Alembert and Marian (Elder) M.; m. Susan Oliver, June 18, 1938; children—Martha Oliver, Margaret Elder. B.A., Trinity Coll., Conn., 1956; postgrad., Harvard Bus. Sch., Cambridge, 1959. Vice pres. in charge N.Y.C. div. Mellon, N.Y.C., 1970-74; v.p., mgr. Mellon, London, Eng., 1974-77; sr. v.p. Mellon Bank N.A., Pitts., 1977-85; chmn., chief exec. officer Mellon Bank East, Phila., 1985-88, ret., 1988; vice chmn. Mellon Bank Corp., Pitts., 1985-89, also bd. dirs.; v.p resource devel. United Way Southeastern Pa., Phila., 1990—; bd. dirs. Fisher Sci. Internat. Inc. Trustee emeritus Trinity Coll., Hartford, 1978—; bd. dirs. Acad. Natural Scis., Phila., 1985—, Phila. OIC, 1985—; chmn. emeritas Am. Music Theater Festival; v.p resource devel. United Way S.E. Pa. Sgt. U.S Army, 1956-58. Mem. Pvt. Industry Coun. Phila. (bd. dirs.), Greater Phila. C. of C. Republican. Presbyterian. Avocations: golf; skiing; reading. Office: United Way Southeastern Pa 7 Benjamin Franklin Pky Philadelphia PA 19103-1208

MONTGOMERY, EDWARD BENJAMIN, physicist, retired educator; b. Louisville, June 15, 1915; s. Thomas Edward and Mary (Nofsinger) M.; m. Mary Louise Lynch, May 30, 1942; children—Mary Patterson Montgomery Cleary, Susan Ellen Montgomery Gartner, Thomas Edward, Margaret Aquin. A.B., U. Louisville, 1942. Ballistic physicist Ind. Ordnance Works, E.I. duPont de Nemours & Co., Inc., 1941-42; research asst. Manhattan project. U. Chgo., 1943-44; reactor physicist Hanford Works, 1944-46; with Gen. Electric Co., 1947-63, head spl. irradiations program, 1948-49, group head experimental physics, 1949-51, sect. chief reactor physics and engring., 1951-52, physicist advanced tech., 1953-54, data processing specialist, 1954-56, mgr. computer applications, 1956-57, cons. product planning, 1957-59; cons. physicist sci. applications computer dept. Gen. Electric Co., Phoenix, 1956-61; project engr. eldel. tech. Gen. Electric Co., Syracuse, N.Y., 1961-63; research cons. info. systems Syracuse U., 1963-65; prof., dean Syracuse U. (Sch. Library Sci.), 1965-68; prof. Health Sci. Center, U. Tex., Dallas, 1968-82, also; coordinator council of pres.'s U. Tex. components in North Tex.; Cons. in field, 1965—. Mem. Gov. Ariz., Com. Arid Lands, 1959-60; Trustee Richland (Wash.) Pub. Library, 1953-55, chmn. bd., 1955. Mem. Am. Phys. Soc., IEEE, AAAS. Home: 6720 Greenwich Ln Dallas TX 75230-2844

MONTGOMERY, GEORGE CRANWELL, lawyer, former ambassador; b. Chattanooga, Aug. 24, 1944; s. George Donaldson and Mary Elizabeth (Cranwell) M.; m. Carol Lanfear, 1 child, Erynn Elizabeth. BA, U. Va., 1966; JD, Vanderbilt U., 1975. Bar: U.S. Ct. Appeals (D.C. cir.) 1976. Mem. legis. staff Senator Howard Baker, Washington, 1975-80; spl. counsel Senate Majority Leader, Washington, 1980-85; U.S. amb. to Oman, 1985-89; ptnr. Baker, Donelson, Bearman and Caldwell, Washington, 1989—; bd. dirs. Vinnell Corp.; mem. bd. visitors Georgetown U. Sch. of Bus. Mem. Coun. on Fgn. Rels. With USN, 1966-72, capt. Res. Mem. ABA, D.C. Bar Assn., Sigma Chi. Office: Baker Donelson Bearman & Caldwell 801 Pennsylvania Ave NW Ste 800 Washington DC 20004-2615

MONTGOMERY, GEORGE FRANKLIN, electrical engineer, consultant; b. Oakmont, Pa., May 1, 1921; s. George Mason and Marie Naomi (Sanner) M.; m. Joan Elizabeth Hartman, Dec. 2, 1967; 1 child, Christopher Mason. BSEE, Purdue U., 1941. Registered profl. engr., D.C. Radio engr. Naval Rsch. Lab., Washington, 1941-44; electronics engr. Nat. Bur. of Standards, Washington, 1946-78; pvt. practice, 1978—. Invention reviewer Nat. Inst. Standards and Tech., 1978—; patentee in field. Master sgt. U.S. Army, 1944-46. Fellow IEEE; mem. Audio Engring. Soc. (cons. tech. editor jour.). Avocation: licensed radio amateur. Home and Office: 2806 Kanawha St NW Washington DC 20015-1244

MONTGOMERY, GILLESPIE V. (SONNY MONTGOMERY), congressman; b. Meridian, Miss., Aug. 5, 1920; s. Gillespie M. and Emily (Jones) M. B.S., Miss. State U. Mem. Miss. Senate, 1956-66, 90th-104th Congresses from 3rd Miss. Dist., 1967—; chmn. vets. affairs com. 1981-94; mem. vets. affairs com., chmn. spl. com. on S.E. Asia 90th-102d Congresses, 1978—; ranking minority mem., 1994—; mem. armed services. com. 90th-103d Congresses, chmn. select com. on missing persons in southeast Asia, 1975—; mem. vets. affairs com.; mem. Woodcock Commn., 1977. Pres. Miss. N.G. Assn., 1959; pres. Miss. Heart Assn., 1967-68. Served with AUS, World War II, Korea, ret. maj. gen. Miss N.G. Decorated Bronze Star medal, Combat Inf. Badge; recipient Miss. Magnolia award, 1966, Lifetime Achievement award Mil. Educators & Counselors Assn., 1992. Mem. VFW, Am. Legion 40 and 8, Congl. Prayer Breakfast Group (pres. 1970). Episcopalian. Lodges: Masons; Shriners; Scottish Rite. Office: US Ho Reps Office of Postmaster Washington DC 20510

MONTGOMERY, GRETCHEN GOLZÉ, secondary educator; b. Washington, Sept. 16, 1941; d. Alfred Rudolph and Marjorie (Lodge) Golzé; m. Charles Williams, Jan. 25, 1963 (div. Oct. 1975); children: Rebecca, Matthew; m. Jerry L. Montgomery, May 14, 1977. BA, Marietta Coll., 1963. Cert. tchr., Ohio. Tchr. Warren Local Sch. Dist., Vincent, Ohio, 1963-67; dir. Betsey Mills Club, Marietta, Ohio, 1975-80; tchr. Wolf Creek Sch. Dist., Waterford, Ohio, 1980—; mem. lang. arts course of study com. Washington County, Marietta, 1985—, mem. competency based edn. testing com., 1985—; mem. ednl. planning com. Wolf Creek Edn., Waterford, 1988-91, mem. testing com., 1988—, mem. textbook com., 1989-90; mentor tchr. Washington County, 1991—, mentor tchr. trainer, 1994—. Jennings scholar Martha Holden Jennings Found., 1982. Mem. NEA, Nat. Coun. Tchrs. English, Ohio Coun. Tchrs. English Lang. Arts, Wolf Creek Local Tchrs. Assn. (sec. 1985—), Ohio Edn. Assn., Ohio Tchr. Leader Network. Avocations: reading, gardening, spectator sports, theater. Home: 105 Rathbone Ter Marietta OH 45750 Office: Wolf Creek Schs Box 45 Waterford OH 45786

MONTGOMERY, HENRY IRVING, financial planner; b. Decorah, Iowa, Dec. 18, 1924; s. Harry Biggs and Martha Grace (Wilkinson) M.; m. Barbara Louise Hook, Aug. 14, 1948; children: Michael Henry, Kelly Ann, Andrew Stuart. Student U. Iowa, 1942-43, 47-48; B.B.A., Tulane U., 1952, postgrad., 1952; postgrad. U. Minn., 1976. Cert. fin. planner, Colo. Field agt. OSS, SSU, CIG, CIA, Central Europe, 1945-47; pres. Nehi Bottling Co., Decorah, Iowa, 1952-64; prin. Montgomery Assocs., Mktg. Cons., Trieste, Italy and Iowa, 1965-72; pres. Montgomery Internat. Mgmt., 1992—; author: Race Toward Berlin, 1945. Served with U.S. Army, 1943-46; ETO. Mem. Inst. Cert. Fin. Planners (bd. dirs. 1977-82, pres. 1980-81, chmn. 1981-82, Cert. Fin. Planner of Yr. 1984, chmn. Fin. Products Standards Bd. 1984-88), Nat. Assn. Securities Dealers (mem. dist. 8 com. 1988-91, vice chmn. 1990), Internat. Assn. Fin. Planning (internat. dir. 1976-81), Mpls. Estate Planning Coun., Met. Twin Planning Group (pres. 1984-87), Twin City Fin. Planners (pres. 1976-78), Twin Cities Soc. of Inst. Cert. Fin. Planners, Am. Legion, Elks (Decorah), Beta Gamma Sigma. Avocations: Italian and German langs. Office: Planners Fin Svcs Inc 7710 Computer Ave Ste 100 Minneapolis MN 55435-5417

MONTGOMERY, JAMES FISCHER, savings and loan association executive; b. Topeka, Nov. 30, 1934; s. James Maurice and Frieda Ellen (Fischer) M.; m. Diane Dealey; children: Michael James, Jeffrey Allen, Andrew Steven, John Gregory. BA in Acctg., UCLA, 1957. With Price, Waterhouse & Co., C.P.A.'s, Los Angeles, 1957-60; controller Conejo Valley Devel. Co., Thousand Oaks, Calif., 1960; asst. to pres. Gt. Western Fin. Corp., Beverly Hills, Calif., 1960-64; pres. United Financial Corp of Calif., Los Angeles, 1964-75; pres., c.e.o. Great Western Financial Corp., Chatsworth, Calif., 1975—; fin. v.p., treas. United Fin. Corp., Los Angeles, 1964-69, exec. v.p., 1969-74, pres., 1975; pres. Citizens Savs. & Loan Assn. Los Angeles, 1970-75. Served with AUS, 1958-60. Office: Gt Western Fin Corp 9200 Oakdale Ave Chatsworth CA 91311-6519*

MONTGOMERY, JAMES MORTON, public relations, marketing executive, association executive; b. Birmingham, Ala., July 4, 1931; s. Hugh Nelson and Sidney Tazewell (Morton) M.; m. Helen Patton Martin, June 12, 1954 (div. Oct. 1987); children: Louis Martin, Caroline Montgomery Brown, Helen Montgomery DeBevoise, Fleta Montgomery Edwards; m. Helen Preston Tapp, Jan. 29, 1994. AB, U. Ala., 1953, MBA, 1958. Mktg. instr. U. Ala., Tuscaloosa, 1953-54, 56-57; dir. publs. Gulf States Paper Corp., Tuscaloosa, 1957-60, advt. dir., 1963-66, dir. mgr., 1963-71, corp. communications mgr., 1971-76; v.p. pub. info. Am. Forest Inst., Washington, 1976-77; v.p. regions Am. Forest Inst., Atlanta, 1980-86; exec. v.p. So. Forest Inst., Atlanta, 1977-86; pres. Montgomery & Assocs., pub. rels. and mktg., Atlanta, 1986—; strategic ptnr. ABOA (Shandwick) Pub. Rels., 1992—; communications cons., Atlanta, 1973-86; guest, adj. lectr. various univs. in Ala. and Ga., 1965—; keynote speaker ann. meeting Forest Hist. Soc., 1989; coord. Advt. Coun. Smokey Bear, N.Y.C., 1970-76. Contbr. articles, essays, revs. to profl. jours. Mem. adv. bd. Metro Atlanta Salvation Army, 1993—; v.p. U. Ala. Nat. Alumni Assn., 1974-75; mem. State Rep. Exec. Com., Ala., 1962-70. 1st lt. USAF, 1954-56. Recipient 1st Pl. award Am. Bus. Communicators, 1969, Addy awards Am. Advt. Fedn., 1969, 71, Silver medal, 1971, Silver Bell award Advt. Coun., 1975; named to Ga. Pub. Rels. Hall of Fame, Order of the Phoenix. Fellow Pub. Rels. Soc. Am. (accredited, chpt. pres. 1972, nat. assembly 1973-76, 80-81); mem. Counselor's Acad., Clan Montgomery Soc. Internat. (pres. 1993—), Phoenix Soc. (trustee 1984-85), Burns Club Atlanta (pres. 1990-91), Kiwanis Internat. (pres. Tuscaloosa Club 1972-73), Atlanta Club, Soc. Profl. Journalists, Beta Gamma Sigma, Omicron Delta Kappa, Delta Tau Delta. Presbyterian. Office: Ten West Ferry Ct NE Atlanta GA 30319

MONTGOMERY, JEFFREY THOMAS, professional baseball player; b. Wellston, Ohio, Jan. 7, 1962. BS Computer Sci., Marshall Coll., 1984. With Cin. Reds, 1983-88, Kansas City Royals, 1988—; mem. Am. League All-Star Team, 1992-93. Names Am. League Fireman of Yr., Sporting News, 1993. Office: Kansas City Royals PO Box 419969 Kansas City MO 64141-6969*

MONTGOMERY, JOHN ATTERBURY, research chemist, consultant; b. Greenville, Miss., Mar. 29, 1924; s. Daniel Cameron and Ruth (Atterbury) M.; m. Jean Kirkman, July 19, 1947; children: John Jr., Elaine Porter, Kirkman, Ruth Adrianne. AB cum laude, Vanderbilt U., 1946, MS in Organic Chemistry, 1947; PhD in Organic Chemistry, U. N.C., Chapel Hill 1951. Research chemist So. Research Inst., Birmingham, Ala., 1952-56; dir. organic chemistry So. Research Inst., 1956-74, v.p., 1974-81, sr. v.p., dir. Kettering Meyer Lab., 1981-90, disting. scientist rsch., 1990—; exec. v.p., dir. rsch., chief exec. officer Biocryst, 1990—; adj. prof. Birmingham So. Coll., 1957-62; adj. sr. scientist U. Ala., Birmingham, 1978—; bd. dirs. Am. Assn. Cancer Research, Assn. Am. Cancer Insts.; mem. Pres. Reagan's Cancer Panel. Author over 600 rsch. papers; editor profl. books; mem. editl. bd. numerous profl. jours. Recipient T.O. Soine Meml. award U. Minn., 1979. Fellow N.Y. Acad. Scis.; mem. Am. Chem. Soc. (councilor 1971-86, recipient Herty medal 1974, So. Chemist award 1980, Burger award 1986, Edward E. Smissman Bristol-Myers Squibb Award, 1995), Am. Assn. Cancer Research (Cain Meml. award 1982), Am. Soc. Pharmacology and Exptl. Therapeutics, Internat. Soc. Heterocyclic Chemistry (adv. bd. 1982-83), Sigma Xi, Alpha Chi Sigma. Republican. Episcopalian. Clubs: Country of Birmingham, The Club (Birmingham) Lodge: Rotary. Home: 3596 Springhill Rd Birmingham AL 35223-2032 Office: So Research Inst PO Box 55305 Birmingham AL 35255-5305 also: BioCryst Pharmaceuticals 2190 Parkway Lake Dr Birmingham AL 35244

MONTGOMERY, JOHN DICKEY, political science educator; b. Evanston, Ill., Feb. 15, 1920; s. Charles William and Lora Kathryn (Dickey) M.; m. Jane Ireland, Dec. 19, 1954; children—Faith, Patience, John. A.B., Kalamazoo Coll., 1941, A.M., 1942, LL.D., 1962; A.M., Harvard, 1948, Ph.D., 1951. Dir. devel. research center African studies program Boston U., 1961-63; prof. pub. adminstrn. Harvard U., 1963-86, Ford Found. prof. internat. studies, 1986—, chmn. dept. govt., 1980-84; dir. Pacific Basin Rsch. Ctr. Soka U. Am., L.A., 1991—. Author: The Purge in Occupied Japan, 1953, Forced to be Free, 1957, The Politics of Foreign Aid, 1962, Foreign Aid in International Politics, 1967, Technology and Civic Life, 1974, Aftermath, Tarnished Outcomes of American Foreign Policy, 1986, Bureaucrats and People, 1988; co-editor (with Dennis Rardinelli): Great Policies, Strategic Innovations in Asia and the Pacific, 1995. Home: 36 Hyde Ave Newton MA 02158-2311 Office: Harvard U 79 John F Kennedy St Cambridge MA 02138-5800

MONTGOMERY, JOHN E., federal medical association administrator; b. Chgo., Jan. 30, 1946; m. Susan Maree Smith, June 6, 1969; children: Marcus John, Matthew Glenn, Anne Maree, Berkley Diane, Joseph Young. BA in Physics cum laude with honors, Brigham Young U., 1970; M in Hosp. Adminstrn., U. Minn., 1972; PhD in Engring. Sci., U. Calif., Berkeley, 1981; grad., Marine Corps Command and Staff Coll., 1982. Commd. ensign USN, 1972, advanced through grades to capt., 1989; asst. to adminstrv. officer Naval Hosp., San Diego, 1972-73; rsch. assoc. Naval Sch. Health Care Adminstrn., Bethesda, Md., 1973-74; ops. rsch. analyst sys. engring. br., bur. medicine and surgery Dept. Navy, Washington, 1977-78; asst. dir. rsch. dept. Naval Sch. Health Scis., Bethesda, 1978-81; exec. officer 1st med. bn. 1st Force Svc. Support Group, Camp Pendleton, Calif., 1982-84; dir. for adminstrn. Naval Hosp., Camp Pendleton, Calif., 1984-85; spl. asst. to dir. Office of Civilian Health and Med. Program of Uniformed Svcs., Aurora, Colo., 1985-89; exec. officer Naval Hosp., Bremerton, Wash., 1989-91; head health care planning and devel. dept. Naval Hosp., San Diego, 1991-93; dir. managed care support office Office of Civilian Health and Med. Program of Uniformed Svcs., 1993—; instr. Va. Commonwealth U., Washington, 1973-74, Ctrl. Mich. U., Washington, 1979-81; adj. asst. prof. George Washington U., Washington, 1978-81. Contbr. articles to profl. jours. Decorated Commendation medal; recipient Award for Excellence in Health Care Adminstrn., McGaw Found.; scholar McGaw Found. Mem. Am. Coll. Healthcare Execs. (affiliate), Inst. Ops. Rsch. and Mgmt. Scis. Avocations: running, reading, poetry, golfing. Office: Dept Def CHAMPUS Aurora CO 80045*

MONTGOMERY, JOHN RICHARD, pediatrician, educator; b. Burnsville, Miss., Oct. 24, 1934; s. Guy Austin and Harriet Pauline (Owens) M.; m. Dottye Ann Newell, June 26, 1965; children: John Newell, Michelle Elizabeth. BS, U. Ala., 1955, MD, 1958. Intern U. Miss., Jackson, 1958-59, resident in pediatrics, 1959-60; resident in pediatrics Baylor Coll. Medicine, Houston, 1960-61, 63-64, fellow in pediatric infectious diseases and immunology, 1964-66, asst. prof. pediatrics, 1966-70, assoc. prof. pediatrics, 1970-75; chief pediatric programs U. Ala. Sch. Medicine, Huntsville, 1975—. Served with AUS, 1961-62; Korea. Mem. Soc. Pediatric Rsch., Am. Assn. Immunologists, Infectious Diseases Soc. Am., N.Y. Acad. Scis., Am. Acad. Pediatrics (pres. Ala. chpt. 1991-93), Sigma Xi, Phi Beta Kappa. Contbr. articles to profl. jours.; assisted in devel. of germ-free environ. bubble to protect patient with no natural immunity (patient later subject of movie The Boy in The Bubble).

MONTGOMERY, JOHNNY LESTER, physician, radiologist; b. Conroe, Tex., Mar. 1, 1934; s. Henry Lester and Mary Frances (Welch) M.; m. Alma Clanton, June 8, 1956; children: Michelle, Mark, Andrew. B.S., Baylor U., 1955; M.D., U. Tex. Med. Br., Galveston, 1958. Diplomate: Am. Bd. Radiology. Intern Meml. Hosp., Corpus Christi, Tex., 1959; resident Tripler Gen. Hosp., Honolulu and Walter Reed Hosp., Washington, 1966-69; fellow angiography Walter Reed Hosp., 1969-70, chmn. angiography, 1970-71, chmn. diagnostic radiology, 1971-72; chmn. dept. radiology Scott and White

Hosp., Temple, Tex., 1974—; bd. dirs. Clinic, 1978—; chmn. dept. radiology Tex. A&M U. Coll. Medicine, College Station, 1977—; pres. Scott & White Clinic, 1992—. Served to lt. col. U.S. Army, 1966-72. Mem. AMA, Tex. Med. Assn., Bell County Med., Soc., Am. Coll. Radiology, Tex. Radiol. Soc. Home: PO Box 1027 Salado TX 76571-1027 Office: 2401 S 31st St Temple TX 76508-0001

MONTGOMERY, JON B., museum administrator. Supt. Appomattox Court House Nat. Hist. Park, Appomattox, Va. Office: Appomattox Court House Nat His Park PO Box 218 Appomattox VA 24522-0218

MONTGOMERY, KEITH NORRIS, SR., insurance executive, state legislator; b. Natchez, Miss., Sept. 22, 1951; s. Charles Norris Jr. and Miriam (Marron) M.; m. Joan Marie Bishop; children: Keith Jr., Mason, Brenton. BBA, U. Miss., 1974. Sales rep. Boyle-Midway, Monroe, La., 1975-77, Am. Nat. Ins., Jackson, Miss., 1977-79; owner Exec. Benefits, Clinton, Miss., 1979—; state rep. Miss. Ho. of Reps., Jackson, 1993—. City councilman City of Clinton, 1985-93. Master sgt. USAR, 1972—. Mem. Am. Legis. Exch. Coun., Miss. Econ. Coun., Jackson Assn. Health Underwriters (bd. dirs. 1992-94), Clinton C of C. Republican. Methodist. Home: 104 Countrywood Cir Clinton MS 39056-5717 Office: PO Box 2204 Clinton MS 39060-2204

MONTGOMERY, LESLIE DAVID, biomedical engineer, cardiovascular physiologist; b. Otterbein, Ind., Sept. 4, 1939; s. Gerald Wesley and Doris Elnora (Sosbe) M.; m. Patricia Ann Trigg, Aug. 25, 1971; children: Gerald Wesley, Nathaniel Brendon, David Patrick. BA, Monmouth Coll., 1962; MS in Engring., Iowa State U., 1963; PhD in Engring., UCLA, 1972. Rsch. engr. N.Am./Rockwell, L.A., 1963-73; owner LDM Assocs., San Jose, Calif., 1973—; rsch. engr. SRI Internat., San Mateo, Calif., 1980-85; dir. rsch. Ctr. for Neurodiagnostic Study, Inc., 1987-91; author presentations on physiology and biomed. engring. Contbr. articles to profl. jours. NRC postdoctoral fellow NASA-Ames, Calif., 1973-75; NRC sr. postdoctoral fellow Wright Patterson AFB, Ohio, 1986-88, NASA-Ames Rsch. Ctr., 1992-94; sr. rsch. engr. Bionetics, Inc., 1994—. Fellow Aerospace Med. Assn. (assoc.); mem. Biomed. Engring. Soc. Republican. Presbyterian. Avocations: woodwork, computer programming. Home and Office: 1764 Emory St San Jose CA 95126-1910

MONTGOMERY, MICHAEL DAVIS, advanced technology consultant, hotelier; b. San Luis Obispo, Calif., June 4, 1936; s. Herold Ray and Elva Dee (Davis) M.; m. Rita Martin, Dec. 28, 1957 (div. Sept. 1975); children: Jeanne, Gwen, Michele. MSEE, Stanford U., 1959; PhD, U. N.Mex., 1967. Group leader Max Planck Inst. for Astrophysics, Munich, 1974-76; group leader advanced concepts Los Alamos (N.Mex.) Nat. Labs., 1976-83; program mgr. for simulation Maxwell Labs. Inc., San Diego, 1983-84, dep. for DNA programs, 1984-85, v.p. rsch. and devel., 1986-91, sr. staff applied tech., 1991-92; sr. cons., 1993—; owner Casa Del Mar Inn, Santa Barbara, Calif., 1991—. Assoc. editor Jour. Geophys. Research; contbr. articles to sci. jours. Served to lt. comdr. USN, 1959-62. Recipient Sr. Scientist award Alexander Von Humboldt Found., 1972. Mem. AAAS, Am. Phys. Soc., Phi Beta Kappa, Sigma Xi, Tau Beta Pi. Avocations: amateur radio. Home: 18 Bath St Santa Barbara CA 93101-3805 Office: Casa Del Mar Inn 18 Bath St Santa Barbara CA 93101-3803

MONTGOMERY, PARKER GILBERT, investment banker; b. Norwood, Mass., July 30, 1928; s. Spencer Bishop and Eleanor Carrie (Gilbert) M.; children: Parker Jr., Carol, John B., William W., Kathryn. A.B., Harvard U., 1949, LL.B., 1953. Bar: Mass. 1953, N.Y. 1956. Assoc. Heminway & Barnes, Boston, 1953; assoc. Dewey, Ballantine, Bushby, Palmer & Wood, N.Y.C., 1956; with Baker, Weeks & Co., investment bankers, N.Y.C., 1957; founder Cooper Labs., Inc., Palo Alto, Calif., 1958; chmn. bd., pres. Cooper Devel. Co., Mountain View, Calif.; pres. Montgomery Group Inc., N.Y.C.; spl. Asst. to Sec. of State Dept. State, 1959-61, vice chmn. Task Force on Internat. Pvt. Enterprise, 1983-84; mem. Investment Policy Adv. Com. U.S. Trade Rep., 1990—; alt. U.S. rep. 47th Session Gen. Assembly U.N., 1992-93. Councilman Town of Bedford, 1971-75; bd. dirs. Santa Barbara Med. Found. Clinic. Lt. USNR, 1945-46, 54-55. Mem. Coun. Fgn. Rels. (N.Y.C.), Econ. Club (N.Y.), Harvard Club (N.Y.C.), Pacific Union Club, Metro Club, River Club (N.Y.C.), Royal Thames Yacht Club (London), Bedford Golf and Tennis Club, The Valley Club of Montecito, Coral Casino Club of Santa Barbara.

MONTGOMERY, PATRICIA ALINE, family physician; b. Williamsport, Pa., Jan. 6, 1954; d. George Leroy and Pauline (Ritter) M. BS in Chemistry, Dickinson Coll., 1975; MD, U. Pa., 1979. Diplomate Am. Bd. Family Practice. Resident in family medicine Abington (Pa.) Meml. Hosp., 1979-82; pvt. practice medicine specializing in family practice Media, Pa., 1982-85, Drexel Hill, Pa., 1985—. Mem. AMA, Pa. Med. Soc., Delaware County Med. Soc., Am. Acad. Family Practice, Pa. Acad. Family Practice, Delaware County Assn. Family Practice (sec.). Democrat. Lutheran. Avocations: reading, gardening. Office: Delaware County Family Practice Assocs 800 Derwyn Rd Drexel Hill PA 19026-1523

MONTGOMERY, PAULA KAY, school editor, publishing executive; b. Omaha, Sept. 23, 1946; d. Floyd Woodrow and Adelyn Ann (Peterson) M. BA in English, Fla. State U., 1967, MLS in Libr. Sci., 1968; PhD in Reading Edn., 1989. Sch. libr. Montgomery County Pub. Sch., Rockville, Md., 1969-72, libr. specialist, 1972-79; chief sch. libr. Md. State Dept. Edn., Balt., 1979-88; pub. Sch. Libr. Media Activities Monthly, Balt., 1984—; del. Gov.'s Conf. on Librs., Balt., 1990. Author: Teaching Library Media Skills, 1983, Thematic Approaches to Literature, 1991, Subject Approaches to Literature, 1991; editor: (book series) Library Media Skills, 1982—. Mem. ALA, Nat. Assn. State Ednl. Media Profls. (pres. 1987), Assn. Edn. Communication and Tech. Lutheran. Office: 17 E Henrietta St Baltimore MD 21230-3910

MONTGOMERY, REX, biochemist, educator; b. Halesowen, Eng., Sept. 4, 1923; came to U.S., 1948, naturalized, 1963; s. Fred and Jane (Holloway) M.; m. Barbara Winifred Price, Aug. 9, 1948 (dec.); children: Ian, David, Jennifer, Christopher. BSc, U. Birmingham, Eng., 1943, PhD, 1946, DSc, 1963. Rsch. assoc. U. Minn., 1951-55; mem. faculty U. Iowa, Iowa City, 1955—; prof. biochemistry U. Iowa, 1963—, assoc. dean U. Iowa Coll. Medicine, 1974-95, v.p. rsch., 1989-90; vis. prof. Nat. Australian U., 1969-70; mem. physiol. chemistry study sect. NIH, 1968-72; mem. drug devel. contract rev. com., 1975-87; chmn. com. biol. chemistry NAS, 1961-64; pesticide and fertilizer adv. bd. Iowa Dept. Agr., 1990-91; bd. dirs. Wallace Tech Transfer Found., 1989-93; chmn. bd. dirs. Neurotron Inc., 1990-95; cons. in field. Author: Chemical Production of Lactic Acid, 1949, Chemistry of Plant Gums and Mucilages, 1959, Quantitative Problems in Biochemical Sciences, 2d edit., 1976, Biochemistry—A Case-Orientated Approach, 5th edit., 1990; mem. editorial adv. bd. Carbohydrate Rsch., 1968-80; mem. editorial bd. Molecular Biotherapy, 1988-92; also articles. Postdoctoral fellow Ohio State U., 1948-49; fellow Sugar Research Found., Dept. Agr., 1949-51. Home: 701 Oaknoll Dr Iowa City IA 52246-5168 Office: U Iowa Coll Medicine Dept Biochemistry Iowa City IA 52242

MONTGOMERY, RICHARD ALAN, sales executive; b. Arlington Heights, Ill., Sept. 5, 1949; s. Charles Gaylord and Luva (Snider) M. BS in Communications, U. Tenn., 1974. Account exec. John M. Rose Advt., Knoxville, Tenn., 1974-75, Metcalfe-Cook & Smith Advt., Nashville, 1975-77, Sta. WTVF-TV, Nashville, 1977-78; div. mgr. Showbiz, Inc., Nashville, 1978-81; sales supr. Multimedia Program Prodns., Nashville, 1981-83; v.p., western regional mgr. Paramount TV, Los Angeles, 1983—. Served with USNG, 1970-78. Mem. Nat. Assn. TV Program Execs., Jr. C. of C. Republican. Methodist. Avocations: golf, yachting, scuba diving, tennis, skiing.

MONTGOMERY, ROBERT F., state legislator, retired surgeon, cattle rancher; b. Ogden, Utah, May 13, 1933; s. William Floyd and Adrianna (Van Zweden) M.; m. Jelean Skeen, June 24, 1953; children: Lance, Dana, Kristen, Keri, Tanya. AS, Weber State U., 1953; BS, Brigham Young U., 1957; MD, U. Utah, 1961. Pvt. practice Anaheim, Calif., 1966-88; senator Utah State Senate, 1992—; chief surgery Anaheim Gen. Hosp., 1970, Anaheim Meml. Hosp., 1972-74. Rep. chmn. Weber County, Utah, 1991-93;

pres. Am. Cancer Soc., Salt Lake City, 1992—. Sgt. U.S. Army, 1953-55, Korea. Mem. Rotary, Utah Elephant Club, Travelor's Century Club. Mormon. Avocations: traveling, reading, hunting, fishing, golfing. Home: 1825 Mountain Rd Ogden UT 84414-2903

MONTGOMERY, ROBERT HUMPHREY, JR., lawyer; b. Boston, Apr. 1, 1923; s. Robert Humphrey and Mary (Murray) M.; m. Henriette de Sieyes, 1952; children: Margaret, Anne (dec.), Samuel Bishop. AB, Harvard U., 1947; LLB, Columbia U., 1950. Bar: N.Y. 1953, D.C. 1978. Ptnr. Paul, Weiss, Rifkind, Wharton & Garrison, N.Y.C., 1950-93, of counsel, 1994—. Chmn. Alliance for the Arts, N.Y.C., 1985—; bd. dirs. Arts Connection, N.Y.C., 1985—; trustee Vassar Coll. Sgt. U.S. Army, 1943-46. Mem. Century Assn., Groucho Club (London). Democrat. Home: 31 E 79th St New York NY 10021-0124 Office: Paul Weiss Rifkind Wharton & Garrison 1285 Ave of the Americas New York NY 10019-6028

MONTGOMERY, ROBERT MOREL, JR., lawyer; b. Birmingham, Ala., June 9, 1930; s. Robert Morel and Ella Bernice (Smith) M.; m. Mary Lemerle McKenzie, Mar. 6, 1953; 1 child, Courtnay Elizabeth. B.S., U. Ala., 1952; LL.B., U. Fla., 1957. Bar: Fla. 1957; diplomate Acad. Fla. Trial Lawyers. With Howell & Kirby Attys at Law, Jacksonville, Fla., 1957-59; ptnr. Howell, Kirby, Montgomery, Sands & D'Aiuto, Jacksonville, Fla., 1959-66, Howell, Kirby, Montgomery, D'Aiuto, Dean & Hallowes, West Palm Beach, Fla., 1966-75, Montgomery, Lytal, Reiter, Denny & Searcy, West Palm Beach, Fla., 1976-85, Montgomery Searcy & Denny, West Palm Beach, Fla., 1986-89; sr. ptnr. Montgomery & Larmoyeux, West Palm Beach, Fla., 1989—; civil trial adv. Nat. Bd. Trial Advocacy. Chmn. Palm Beach Opera; vice chmn. Kravis Ctr., Palm Beach Cultural Coun. 1st lt. AUS, 1952-54. Mem. ABA, Fla. Bar Assn. (lectr. continuing edn.), Palm Beach County Bar Assn., Fla. Trial Lawyers Assn. Am., Inner Circle Advs. Home: 1800 S Ocean Blvd Palm Beach FL 33480-5104 Office: PO Box 3086 West Palm Beach FL 33402-3086

MONTGOMERY, ROGER, dean; b. N.Y.C., May 28, 1925; s. Graham Livingston and Ann Katharine (Cook) M.; m. Mary Elizabeth Hoyt, Apr. 23, 1949 (dec. Feb. 1980); children: Richard W., Thomas V., John L., Peter G. Student, Oberlin Coll., 1942-44, 47, N.C. State U., 1953-55; MArch, Harvard U., 1957. Architect Zeller & Hunter, Springfield, Ohio, 1948-53; assoc. prof. architecture Washington U., St. Louis, 1957-64, prof. architecture, 1964-67; architect, planner Anselevicius & Montgomery, St. Louis, 1957-70; prof. U. Calif., Berkeley, 1967—, assoc. dean environ. design, 1976-79, 81-84, acting dean, 1988-89, dean, 1989—; pres. Calif. Council on Archtl. Edn., 1986, bd. dirs., 1983-87. Co-author: Architecture in State of Washington, 1980; co-editor: Housing in America, 1979, Housing Policy for the 1980's; contbr. articles to profl. jours. mem. Redevel. Commn., Berkeley, 1978-80, pres. 1980. Served with U.S. Army, 1945-47. Mem. AIA, Am. Planning Assn., Urban Land Inst., Planners Network. Office: U Calif 230 Wurster Hall Berkeley CA 94720-1820

MONTGOMERY, RONALD EUGENE, chemist, research and development director; b. Rural Valley, Pa., Feb. 17, 1937; s. Harry Noble amd Wilda Ruth (Bleakney) M.; m. Judith Ann Cyphert, June 3, 1961; children: Cheryl Joy, Sharon Lynn, Wendlene Kay, David Wesley. BS, Waynesburg Coll., 1959; MA, Duke U., 1961, PhD, 1963. Rsch. chemist FMC Corp., Middletport, N.Y., 1964-70, mgr. Organic Synthesis, 1970-76, mgr. Discovery, 1976-80; mgr. process rsch. & engring. FMC Corp., Princeton, N.J., 1980-82, dir. process rsch. & engring., 1982-88, dir. devel. chemistry, 1988-90, dir. rsch. & devel., 1990—. Mem. sch. bd. Royalton-Hartland Ctrl. Sch. Dist., Middleport, N.Y., 1972-76, Five-Mile Woods, Yardley, Pa., 1982—. Avocations: botany, geology, birding, canoeing, geneology. Office: FMC Corp Agrl Chem Group PO Box 8 Princeton NJ 08543

MONTGOMERY, ROY DELBERT, retired gas utility company executive; b. Indpls., Apr. 24, 1926; s. Lloyd Sipes and Nona Mae (Brummett) M.; m. Barbara Ann Reno, Apr. 21, 1946; children: Stephanie, Rebecca, Jeffrey, Laura. Student, Purdue U. 1950-51; M.E., Internat. Corr. Schs., 1953; A.S. in mgmt. and Adminstrn., Ind. U., 1973. Registered profl. engr. Ind. Engr. Citizens Gas & Coke Utility, Indpls., 1952-59, supt., 1959-60, dir., 1960-73, exec. dir., 1973-78, v.p., 1978-82, sr. v.p., 1982-86, cons., 1986-88. Contbr. articles to profl. jours. Vice pres. exploring Crossroads of Am. Council Boy Scouts Am., Ind., 1978; corp. rep. Jr. Achievement Ind., 1970-82. Recipient Bronze Big Horn award Boy Scouts Am. Explorer Div., Ind., 1978. Mem. Am. Gas Assn. (merit award 1966), Ind. Gas Assn., Scientec Club Ind., Kiwanis. Republican. Avocations: oil painting, boating, golf, genealogy.

MONTGOMERY, RUTH SHICK, author; b. Sumner, Ill.; d. Ira Whitmer and Bertha (Judy) Shick; m. Robert H. Montgomery, Dec. 26, 1935 (dec. 1993). Student, Baylor U. and Purdue U.; LL.D., Baylor U., 1956, Ashland Coll., 1958. Former news reporter Waco (Tex.) News-Tribune; women's editor Louisville Herald-Post; feature writer St. Louis Post-Dispatch, Indpls. Star; news reporter Detroit Times, Detroit News, Chgo. Tribune; Washington corr. N.Y. Daily News, 1944-55; Jpn. corr. S.Am., Europe, Far and Middle East, intermittently 1946-68; spl. Washington corr. Internat. News Service, 1956-58; syndicated columnist Capital Letter King Features, Hearst Headline Service, 1958-68. Author: Once There Was a Nun, 1962, Mrs. LBJ, 1964, A Gift of Prophecy, 1965, A Search for the Truth, 1966, Flowers at the White House, 1967, Here and Hereafter, 1968, Hail to the Chiefs, 1970, A World Beyond, 1971, Born to Heal, 1973, Companions Along The Way, 1974, The World Before, 1976, Strangers Among Us, 1979, Threshold to Tomorrow, 1983, Aliens Among Us, 1985; subject of book Ruth Montgomery: Herald of the New Age, 1986. Recipient Pall Mall Journalism award, 1947; Front Page award Indpls. Press Club, 1957; George Holmes Journalism award, 1957; best non-fiction award Ind. U., 1966; Most Valuable Alumna award Baylor U., 1967; inducted into Journalism Hall of Fame (Ind.), 1993. Mem. White House Corrs. Assn., State Dept. Corrs. Assn., Theta Sigma Phi (Woman of Year award 1964), Alpha Chi Omega, Kappa Kappa Kappa. Clubs: Nat. Press (pres. 1950-51, gov. 1951-54). Only woman selected to cover Pres. Roosevelt's funeral, 1945. Home: 3115 Gulf Shore Blvd N Penthouse 2 Naples FL 33940

MONTGOMERY, SETH DAVID, retired state supreme court chief justice; b. Santa Fe, Feb. 16, 1937; s. Andrew Kaye and Ruth (Champion) M.; m. Margaret Cook, Oct. 29, 1960; children: Andrew Seth, Charles Hope, David Lewis. AB, Princeton U., 1959; LLB, Stanford U., 1965. Bar: N.M. 1965. Ptnr. Montgomery & Andrews, P.A., Santa Fe, 1965-89, of counsel, 1994—; justice N.Mex. Supreme Ct., 1989-94, chief justice, 1994; adj. prof. U. N.Mex. Sch. Law, Albuquerque, 1970-71; chmn. N.Mex. adv. coun. Legal Svcs. Corp., Santa Fe 1976-89. Bd. visitors Stanford U. Sch. Law, 1967-70, 82-85; pres., chmn. Santa Fe Opera, 1981-86; pres. Santa Fe Opera Found., 1986-89; chmn., vice chmn. Sch. Am. Rsch., Santa Fe, 1985-89; bd. dirs. New Vistas, Santa Fe, 1986-89, First Interstate Bank of Santa Fe, 1977-89, Old Cienega Village Mus., 1980-89. Lt. (j.g.) USN, 1959-62. Named Citizen of Yr., Santa Fe C. of C. 1986, Sunwest Bank of Santa Fe, 1994; recipient Disting. Cmty. Svc. award Anti-Defamation League, 1991, Western Area Outstanding Achievement award Nat. Multiple Sclerosis Soc., 1992, award for advancement of law N.Mex. Trial Lawyers, 1994, Award for Outstanding Judge Albuquerque Bar Assn., 1994. Fellow Am. Coll. Trial Lawyers, Am. Coll. Trust and Estate Counsel, Am. Bar Endowment, N.Mex. Bar Assn. (bd. bar commrs. 1986-89, sec., treas. 1988-89, Professionalism award 1993); mem. ABA, Am. Judicature Soc. Democrat.

MONTGOMERY, TERRY GRAY, textiles researcher; b. Ft. Knox, Ky., Aug. 25, 1953; s. Bobby Gray Montgomery and Shirley Mitchell Sutphin; m. Linda Stoltz, May 18, 1973; 1 child, Matthew Gray. BS, N.C. State U., 1974, PhD, 1980; MBA, Winthrop U., 1991. Asst. prof. of textile scis. Southeastern Mass. U., Dartmouth, Mass., 1979-81; product devel. mgr. Milliken & Co., Spartanburg, S.C., 1981-85; mgr. new bus. devel. Burlington Industries, Inc., Greensboro, N.C., 1985-87; product design mgr. Springs Industries, Inc., Ft. Mill, S.C., 1987-88, dir. R & D, 1988—; bd. dirs. Armor Techs., Houston. Author: (rsch. pub.) Textile Rsch. Jour., 1982-84; mem. adv. bd. (mag.) Safety & Protective Fabrics, 1992—. Mem. Am. Textile Mfg. Inst. (flammability com. 1992—, consumer affairs com. 1992—), Fiber Soc., Phi Kappa Phi, Beta Gamma Sigma, SAMPE. Republican. Moravian. Achievements include 3 U.S. patents. Home: Springs Industries Inc 220 Rose Arbor Ln Matthews NC 28105 Office: Springs Industries Inc 123 N White St Fort Mill SC 29715-1652

MONTGOMERY, THEODORE ASHTON, physician; b. Los Angeles, Oct. 27, 1923; s. Wayne A. and Hazel (Osmer) M. M.D., U. So. Calif., 1946; M.P.H. cum laude, Harvard U., 1955. Diplomate: Am. Bd. Preventive Medicine, Am. Bd. Pediatrics. Intern Los Angeles County Gen. Hosp., 1946-48; intern Los Angeles Children's Hosp., 1948; resident Los Angeles Childrens' Hosp., 1950-51, St. Louis Childrens' Hosp., 1951-52; asst. in pediatrics Washington U., St. Louis, 1951-52; instr. pediatrics U. So. Calif., 1952-55; practice medicine specializing in pediatrics Los Angeles, 1952-54; lectr. pub. health U. Calif., Berkeley, 1960-83; cons. child health Calif. Dept. Pub. Health, 1954-60, chief maternal and perinatal health, 1960-61, acting chief bur. maternal and child health, 1961-63, asst. chief div. preventive med. services, 1963-66, chief, 1966-68, chief preventive medicine program, 1968-69, dep. dir. of Dept., 1969-73; chief div. disease control Alameda County Health Care Services Agy., 1973-74; cons. maternal and child health Calif. Dept. Health, Berkeley, 1974-78; chief maternal and child health br. No. Calif. Regional Office, Calif. Dept. Health Services, 1978-83; WHO fellow med. care adminstrn., Europe, 1966; co-chmn. Calif. Inter-agy. Council on Tb, 1966-72; vice chmn. Calif. Drug Research Adv. Panel, 1969-70;; White House Conf. Mental Retardation, 1963; Gov's. chmn. Calif. Regional Hemodialysis Rev. Com., 1968-73; exec. sec. Gov.'s Population Study Commn., 1966; mem. com. on Tb, Calif. Lung Assn., 1973-74. Author: (with others) Standards and Recommendations for Public Prenatal Care, 1960, Guide to Hearing Testing of School Children, 1961; contbr. articles to med. jours. Bd. dirs. Calif. Interagy. Coun. on Family Planning, 1970-73; chmn. Calif. State Interdepartmental Com. on Food and Nutrition, 1977-79, pres. Clan Montgomery Soc. Internat., 1981-84, regional commr., 1985-91. With M.C. AUS, 1948-50. Fellow Am. Acad. Pediatrics (chmn. Calif. com. Indian health 1973-76, mem. nat. com. on Indian Health 1963-79, vice chmn. 1977-79), Am. Pub. Health Assn. (chmn. task force on population policy 1971-72); mem. Clan Montgomery Soc. N.Am. (founding pres. 1980-83, Calif. regional commr. 1984-90), Alpha Epsilon Delta, Delta Omega. Home: 85 Wildwood Gdns Piedmont CA 94611-3831

MONTGOMERY, VELMANETTE, state senator; b. Tex. M.Ed., NYU; student U. Ghana; LLD (hon.) St. Joseph's Coll., 1991. Mem. N.Y.C. Dist. 13 Sch. Bd., 1977-80, pres., from 1977; former co-dir. advocacy group Child Care Inc.; mem. N.Y. Senate, 1984—, mem. child care, consumer protection, health, fin. and housing, mental hygiene coms. State of N.Y. Fellow Inst. Ednl. Leadership, 1981, Revson Found., 1984. Democrat. Office: 70 Lafayette Ave Brooklyn NY 11217-1520 also: N.Y. State Senate Albany NY 12224

MONTGOMERY, WALTER GEORGE, communications executive, consultant; b. Elmira, N.Y., Aug. 24, 1945; s. Elwood Herbert Montgomery and Eleanor Leila (Manchester) Spiegel; m. Pamela Sue Shaw, June 11, 1966 (div. Oct. 1976); children: Caleb Manchester, Kirsten Shaw; m. Marian Amy Gruber, Sept. 18, 1977; children: Abigail Lynn, Samuel Edwin, Rebecca Eleanor. AB, Syracuse U., 1967; MA, Brown U., 1976, PhD, 1979. Lectr. Keene (N.H.) State Coll., 1976-79, asst. prof., 1979; assoc. Kekst & Co., N.Y.C., 1979-82, ptnr., 1983; v.p. Am. Express Co., N.Y.C., 1983-85, sr. v.p., 1985-87; ptnr., vice chmn. Robinson, Lake, Lerer & Montgomery, N.Y.C., 1987—. With U.S. Army, 1970-72. Office: Robinson Lake Lerer & Montgomery Sawyer Miller Group 75 Rockefeller Plz New York NY 10019-6908

MONTGOMERY, WILLIAM ADAM, lawyer; b. Chgo., May 22, 1933; s. John Rogerson and Helen (Fyke) M.; m. Jane Fauver, July 28, 1956 (div. Dec. 1967); children: Elizabeth, William, Virginia; m. Deborah Stephens, July 29, 1972; children: Alex, Katherine. AB, Williams Coll., 1955; LLB, Harvard U., 1958. Bar: D.C. 1958, Ill. 1959, U.S. Ct. Appeals (7th cir.) 1959, U.S. Supreme Ct. 1977. Atty. civil div., appellate sect. Dept. Justice, Washington, 1958-60; assoc. Schiff Hardin & Waite, Chgo., 1960-68, ptnr., 1968-93; v.p., gen. counsel State Farm Ins. Cos., Bloomington, Ill., 1994—. Author: (39 corp. practice series) Tying Arrangements, 1984, also articles. Fellow Am. Coll. Trial Lawyers; mem. ABA (coun. antitrust sect. 1989-92), Ill. Bar Assn., Chgo. Bar Assn., Seventh Cir. Bar Assn. (pres. 1988-89), Legal Club Chgo., Law Club Chgo., Econ. Club Chgo. Avocations: skiing, tennis, woodturning. Office: State Farm Ins Cos 1 State Farm Plz Bloomington IL 61710-0002

MONTGOMERY, WILLIAM D., United States ambassador; b. Carthage, Mo., Nov. 8, 1945; m. Lynne Germaine Montgomery; 3 children. BA, Bucknell U.; MA, George Washington U.; student, Nat. War Coll., 1986-87. With Fgn. Svc., 1974; econ. officer Fgn. Svc., Belgrade, Yugoslavia, 1975-78; comml. then polit. officer Fgn. Svc., Moscow, 1979-81; line officer, secretariat staff then exec. asst. to under sec. polit. affairs Dept. State, 1981-84, exec. asst. to dep. sec., 1991-93; dep. chief mission Dar es Salaam, Tanzania, 1984-85, Sofia, Bulgaria, 1988-91; U.S. ambassador Bulgaria, 1993—. Decorated Bronze Star; recipient Order of the Horseman of the Madara, Bulgaria. Mem. Am. Fgn. Svc. Assn. Office: Am Embassy-Sofia Unit 1335 APO AE 09213-1335

MONTGOMERY, WILLIAM J., finance company executive; b. 1930; married. BA, Dartmouth Coll., 1952. Sales rep. IBM Corp., 1954-59; div. mgr. Security Leasing Co., 1959-62; v.p. US Leasing Corp., 1962-68; pres. Computer Property Corp., 1968-70, Singer Leasing Corp., 1970-74, Chase Manhattan Leasing Corp., 1974-79; chmn., chief exec. officer, dir. Xerox Credit Corp., Stamford, Conn., 1979-91; chmn., CEO Am. Fin. Group, Boston, 1991-93; pres. The Alta Group, Hanover, N.H., 1993—. Office: The Alta Group 11 Berrill Farms Ln Hanover NH 03755-3206

MONTGOMERY, WILLIAM WAYNE, surgeon; b. Proctor, Vt., Aug. 20, 1923; s. Charles Lynn and Ann (Jones) M. AB, Middlebury (Vt.) Coll., 1944; MD, U. Vt., 1947. Diplomate: Am. Bd. Otolaryngology. Intern Mary Fletcher Hosp., Burlington, Vt., 1947-48; gen. practice medicine W. Rutland, Vt., 1948-50; resident otolaryngology Mass. Eye and Ear Infirmary, 1952-55, mem. staff, 1956—, sr. surgeon in otolaryngology, 1966—; mem. staff Mass. Gen. Hosp., 1956—; surgeon otolaryngology, 1966-86; prof. Harvard Med. Sch., 1986-94, John W. Merriam prof. otology and laryngology, 1994—; med. dir. voice lab., 1993. Author: Surgery of the Upper Respiratory System, Vol. I-II; Contbr. med. jours. Served as battalion surgeon USMCR, 1950-52, Korea. Decorated Purple Heart, Bronze Star, Commendation medal; recipient Disting. Alumni award U. Vt. Med. Sch., 1968, Alumni Achievement award Middleburg Coll., 1985. Fellow ACS; mem. AMA, Am. Acad. Ophthalmology and Otolaryngology (instr. 1963-67), Am. Broncho-Esophagological Assn., Am. Laryngol. Assn. (James E. Newcomb award 1990), Am. Otologic Soc., Am. Laryngol., Rhinol. and Otol. Soc. (Cert. of merit 1990), Pan Am. Med. Assn., Mass. Med. Soc. (program chmn. 1966—), Suffolk Med. Soc., Am. Triological Soc. (Mosher award 1963, v.p. 1987), New Eng. Otolaryngol. Soc. (pres. 1977-78), Am. Soc. Head and Neck Surgery, Am. Acad. Facial Plastic and Reconstructive Surgery. Spl. research paranasal sinuses and laryngeal surgery. Home: 20 Hilltop Rd Chestnut Hill MA 02167-1846 Office: 243 Charles St Boston MA 02114-3004

MONTLE, PAUL JOSEPH, entrepreneur; b. Medford, Mass., Aug. 28, 1947; s. Joseph Frederick and Frances Elizabeth (Fogarty) M.; m. Elizabeth Anne Rusch, Mar. 3, 1973; children: Alexis Elizabeth, Daphne Caroline. BA in Econs., Tufts U., 1969; postgrad., Boston U., 1969-70. Pres., chief exec. officer Killebrew, Montle Internat. Inc., Boston, 1971-73; v.p. Burgess & Leith, Boston, 1973-75, Hawthorne Securities Corp., 1975-76; founder, pres. First New Eng. Securities Corp., Boston, 1976-80, chmn., 1980-83; founder, pres. The Yankee Cos. Inc., Boston, 1977-88, chmn., chief exec. officer, 1988-89; founder, pres. Montle Internat., Boston, Houston, Hong Kong, London, 1987—, Am. Pacific Properties, Inc., Houston, 1990-92, Glenville Properties Inc., Houston, 1990—; chmn., CEO Teleconcepts Inc., 1992-93, founder, chmn., CEO Lone Star Casino Corp. 1992—; founder, gen. ptnr. Travis Ptnrs. G.P., 1991—, Great So. Capital Ptnrs. G.P., 1994—; also bd. dirs., pres. Viral Testing Systems Corp., 1992-94, also bd. dirs., Motion Media Techs. Corp., 1991-92, also bd. dirs.; chmn., CEO 1st Response Med. Inc., 1993; trustee, treas. Derby Acad., Hingham, Mass., 1985-90; bd. dirs. South Shore Playhouse Assn., Cohasset, Mass., 1987-90. Mem. Algonquin Club, Woods Hole Golf Club, Falcon Point Club, Houston Racquet Club. Avocations: sailing, golf, tennis. Office: Lone Star Casino Corp 1 Riverway Ste 2550 Houston TX 77056

MONTO, ARNOLD S., epidemiology educator; b. Bklyn., Mar. 22, 1933; s. Jacob and Mildred (Kaplan) M.; m. Ellyne Gay Polsky, June 15, 1958; children: Sarah D. Monto Maniaci, Jane E., Richard L., Stephan A. BA in Zoology, Cornell U. Ithaca, N.Y., 1954; MD, Cornell U., N.Y.C., 1958. Intern, asst. resident in medicine Vanderbilt U. Hosp., Nashville, 1958-60; USPHS postdoctoral fellow in infectious disease Stanford U. Med. Ctr., Palo Alto, Calif., 1960-62; mem. staff virus diseases sect. mid. Am. rsch. unit Nat. Inst. Allergy and Infectious Disease, Panama Canal Zone, 1962-65; asst. prof., assoc. prof. epidemiology U. Mich. Sch. Pub. Health, Ann Arbor, from 1965, prof., chmn. dept. population planning and internat. health, 1993—; dir. Ctr. for Population Planning, 1993—; vis. scientist Clin. Rsch. Ctr., Northwick Park Hosp., Harrow, Eng., 1976; scholar-in-residence bd. on sci. and tech. for internat. devel. NAS and Inst. Medicine, Washington, 1983-84; vis. scientist div. communicable diseases WHO, Geneva, 1986-87; mem. pulmonary diseases adv. com. Nat. Heart, Lung and Blood Inst., Bethesda, Md., 1979-83; mem. nat. adv. coun. Nat. Inst. Allergy and Infectious Diseases, Bethesda, 1989-93,. Contbr. articles to med. jours. Recipient career devel. award NIH. Fellow Am. Coll. Epidemiology, Infectious Diseases Soc. Am.; mem. APHA (governing coun. 1978-80), Am. Epidemiol. Soc. Achievements include research on respiratory viral infections in the community; demonstration of effectiveness of influenza vaccine in severe disease in the elderly; prevention of spread of influenza virus and treatment of illness, occurrence and causes of common cold. Office: U Mich Sch Pub Health 109 S Observatory Ann Arbor MI 48109

MONTORIO, JOHN ANGELO, magazine editor; b. Montclair, N.J., June 26, 1948; s. John Daniel and Lorraine (DiVita) M.; m. Lois Ann Marco, May 15, 1977; children—John Nicholas, Nicholas Ross. B.A. cum laude in English, Seton Hall U., 1970; M.A. in English, U. Va., 1972. Sr. editor Gralla Pubs., N.Y.C., 1972-74; assoc. editor Lebhar-Friedman Pubs., N.Y.C., 1974-76; asst. editor Fairchild Pubs., N.Y.C., 1976-77; Sunday mag. editor Washington Star, 1977-81; asst. bus.-fin. editor, dep. home editor N.Y. Times, N.Y.C., 1981-83; Sunday mag. editor Newsday, L.I., N.Y., 1983—. Recipient pubs. award Newsday Inc., 1984. Democrat. Roman Catholic. Office: The NY Times Co 229 W 43rd St New York NY 10036-3913

MONTOYA, REGINA T., lawyer, television and radio commentator; b. Tucumcari, N.Mex., Dec. 25, 1953; d Fred and Rosa (Meraz) M.; m. Paul E. Coggins, June 12, 1976; 1 child, Jessica. BA, Wellesley Coll., 1975; JD, Harvard U., 1979. Bar: Tex. 1979. Law clk. to U.S. Dist. Judge Sarah T. Hughes Dallas, 1979-80; ptnr. Akin, Gump, Strauss, Hauer & Feld, Dallas, 1980-90; shareholder Godwin, Carlton & Maxwell, Dallas, 1990-93; asst. to pres., dir. Office of Intergovernmental Affairs, Washington D.C., 1993—; v.p. Westcott Comm., 1994—; panelist Between the Lines KERA-TV, 1994—; Bd. dirs. The Trammell Crow Co., Dallas Urban League, La Voz del Anciano. Trustee Wellesley Coll., 1990—; bd. dirs. Sci. Place, 1987—, Girls, Inc., 1991—. Mem. Student Loan Mktg. Assn. (bd. dirs. 1994—). Democrat. Roman Catholic. Home: 3302 Oakhurst St Dallas TX 75214-3117

MONTOYA THOMPSON, VELMA, federal agency administrator; b. L.A., Apr. 9, 1938; d. Jose Gutierrez and Consuelo (Cavazos) Montoya; m. Earl A. Thompson; 1 child, Bret L. Thompson. BA in Diplomacy and World Affairs, Occidental Coll., 1959; MA in Internat. Rels., Fletcher Sch. of Law and Diplomacy, 1960; MS in Econs., Stanford U., 1965; PhD in Econs., U. Calif., L.A., 1977. Asst. prof. Econs. Calif. State U., L.A., 1965-68; vis. assoc. prof. U. So. Calif., 1979; instr. U. Calif., L.A., 1981-82; staff economist The Rand Corp., Santa Monica, Calif., 1973-82; asst. dir. for strategy, White House Office of Policy Devel. Exec. Office of the Pres., 1982-83; expert economist, Office of Regulatory Analysis, Occupational Safety and Health Adminstrn. U.S. Dept. of Labor, 1983-85; dir. of Studies in Pub. Policy and Social Policy, Sch. of Political Economy, Sch. of Bus. Mgmt. Chapman Coll., 1985-87; adj. prof., Sch. of Bus. Mgmt. Pepperdine Univ., 1987-88; pres. Hispanic-Am. Pub. Policy Inst., 1984-90; assoc. prof. of Fin., Sch. of Bus. Adminstrn. Calif. State Polytechnic Univ., Pomona, 1988-90; commr. Occupational Safety and Health Review Commn., 1990—; cons. Urban Inst., 1974, Mexican-Am. Study Project UCLA, 1966, Graduate and Profl. Fellowships to the Office of Post Secondary Education, U.S. Dept. of Edn.; editorial referee Contemporary Policy Issues, Economic Inquiry, Policy Analysis, The Journal of Economic Literature; reader Kaplan lecture ser. Univ. Calif., 1994; mem. adv. com. U.S. Senate Rep. Conf. Task Force on Hispanic Affairs, 1991—. Named One of the 100 U.S. Hispanic Influentials Hispanic Bus. Mag., 1982, 90, Woman of the Yr. Mex.-Am. Opportunity Found., 1983, The East L.A. Com. Union, 1979, Marshall scholar, Fulbright scholar; recipient Freedom Found. at Valley Forge Honor Econ. Edn. Excellence Cert., 1986, fellow Stanford Univ., Internat. Rels. fellow Calif. PTA, John Hay Whitney Opportunity fellow; Calif. State Univ. Found. Faculty Rsch. grantee. Mem. ASTM (com. on rsch. and tech. planning 1985-87), Am. Econ. Assn. (session chair ann. meetings 1995), Nat. Coun. of Hispanic Women, State Bar of Calif. (disciplinary bd. 1986-89), Calif. State Bar Ct. (exec. com. 1987-89), Western Econ. Assn., Indsl. Rsch. Inst. for Pacific Nations (adv. bd. 1988-89), Salesian Boys and Girls Club (bd. dirs 1989—), Vets. in Com. Svc. (adv. com. 1989-94), Phi Beta Kappa, Omicron Delta Epsilon, Phi Alpha Theta. Home: 6970 Los Tilos Rd Los Angeles CA 90068

MONTRONE, PAUL MICHAEL, scientific instruments company executive; b. Scranton, Pa., May 8, 1941; s. Angelo H. and Beatrice M. (Giancini) M.; m. Sandra R. Gaudenzi, May 30, 1963; children: Michele Marie Cogan, Angelo Henry, Jerome Lawrence. B.S. in Accounting magna cum laude, U. Scranton, 1962; Ph.D. in Fin., Econs. and Ops. Research, Columbia U., 1965. Ops. analyst Office Sec. Def., Washington, 1965-67; exec. v.p., chief fin. officer Wheelabrator-Frye Inc., Hampton, N.H., 1970-83; exec. v.p. Signal Cos., Inc., La Jolla, Calif., 1983-85; pres. Engineered Products Group Signal Cos., Inc., Hampton, N.H., 1983-85; exec. v.p. fin. and adminstrn. AlliedSignal Inc., Morristown, N.J., 1985-86; chmn., CEO Wheelabrator Techs. Inc., Hampton, N.H., 1986-92, bd. dirs.; chmn., CEO Wheelabrator Techs. Inc., Hampton, N.H., 1987-90; pres., co-owner The Gen. Chem. Group Inc., 1989-94, chmn. bd., 1994—; pres., CEO, bd. dirs. Fisher Sci. Internat., Inc., Hampton, 1991—; vice chmn. Abex Inc., Hampton, 1992—; bd. dirs. Wheelabrator Techs.; adv. bd. ICI, Inc., Zeneca Inc., Sintokagio, Ltd. Mng. dir. Met. Opera Assn.; mem. dean's adv. coun. The Bus. Roundtable, Bus. Sch. Columbia U., N.Y.C. Capt. U.S. Army, 1965-67. Roman Catholic. Clubs: Brook, University (N.Y.C.); Bald Peak Colony (Melvin Village, N.H.); Lyford Cay (Nassau, Bahamas). Office: Fisher Sci Internat Inc Liberty Ln Hampton NH 03842-1808*

MONTROSE, DONALD W., bishop; b. Denver, May 13, 1923. Student, St. John's Sem., Calif. Ordained priest Roman Cath. Ch., 1949. Aux. bishop Roman Cath. Ch., Los Angeles, 1983; bishop Diocese of Stockton, Calif., 1985—. Office: Diocese of Stockton PO Box 4237 1105 N Lincoln St Stockton CA 95203-2410*

MONTROSS, ALBERT EDWARD, electronics company executive; b. Albany, N.Y., Sept. 5, 1936; s. Albert John and Anna Marie (Schurtleff) M.; Nancy Ann Madelin, Aug. 8, 1957 (div. 1982); children: Candace, Kirk, Scott; m. Susana Sam Sturkey, Mar. 4, 1984; children: Rachel, Christopher. BS in Econs. St. Bernadine of Siena Coll., Loudenville, N.Y., 1960. Mgmt. trainee GE Schenectady, N.Y., 1960-61, sales exec. computer div., 1968-70; sales rep. bus. forms div. Moore Corp., Albany, 1961-64, dist. sales mgr. bus. forms div., 1965-67; mgr. staff ops. ea. div hdqrs. Moore Corp., Niagara Falls, N.Y., 1971-76; dir. mktg. nat. hdqrs. Moore Corp., Glenview, Ill., 1977-79; v.p. sales and mktg. Moore Bus. Systems, Dallas, 1979-80; founder, pres. Compco Computer Ctrs., Dallas, 1981-85; pres. Erintec Mgmt. Co., Toronto, Ont., Can., 1986-89; pres., chief oper. officer Inacomp Computer Ctrs. Troy, Mich., 1990-91; pres., gen. mgr. Inacomp div. of Inacom, Troy, Mich., 1991-92; founder, pres. CEO Degas Internat. Ltd.,

1992—; bd. dirs. Inacomp/Centel, Reston, Va.; Erintec Mgmt. Corp.; mem. IBM Dealer Adv. Cound., N.Y.C., 1980—, Toshiba Am., Irvine, Calif. 1989—. With USN, 1955-57. Named Merchandiser of Yr., Computer Merchandising Mag., 1983. Republican. Avocations: blue water sailing, skiing, woodworking, racquetball. Home: 620 Guinda St Palo Alto CA 94301-2140 Office: Inacomp Computer Ctrs Inc 1800 E Maple Rd Troy MI 48083-4240

MONTY, CHARLES EMBERT, utility company executive; b. Plainfield, Conn., Mar. 9, 1927; s. Arthur Ovila and Mary Louise (Bromley) M.; children: Charles E., Mary, Janice, Nathan, Marcia. BSEE, Northeastern U., 1950; MBA, U. Maine, 1969. Registered profl. engr., Maine. Chmn. bd. dirs. Maine Yankee Atomic Power Co., 1988-92; chief oper. officer Cen. Maine Power Co., 1984-89; also bd. dirs.; energy cons., 1989—; mem. mgmt. com. New Eng. Power Pool, 1982-86. Mem. IEEE, Maine Assn. Engrs. Republican. Mem. United Chs. of Christ.

MONTY, GLORIA, television producer; b. Union City, N.J.; d. Joseph and Concetta M. (Mango) Montemuro; m. Robert Thomas O'Byrne, Jan. 8, 1952. BA, NYU; MA, Columbia U. Dir. New Sch. Rsch., N.Y.C., 1952-53; dir. Old Towne Theatres, Smithtown, N.Y., 1952-56, Abbey Theatre Workshop, N.Y.C., 1952-56; cons. ABC. Dir. numerous TV programs, including Secret Storm, 1956-72, Bright Promise, numerous episodes ABC Wide World Entertainment; exec. prodr. General Hospital, 1977-86, 90-92, The Hamptons, 1983-85; made-for-TV movies, including Confessions of a Married Man, 1982, The Imposter, 1984; exec. prodr. in devel. for primetime TV 20th Century Fox, 1987-90; head cons. daytime TV ABC, 1987-90; prin. Gloria Monty Prodns. for new ABC daytime drama devel.; developer (with Grosso-Jacobson) movie for NBC, 1992-93. Recipient Emmy awards, 1982, 84, Am. Soc. Lighting Dirs. award, 1979, Most Successful TV Show in History of TV award ABC, 1982, Spl. Editors award Soap Opera Digest, numerous others; named Woman of Yr., Paulist Choristers So. Calif., 1986. Mem. Women in Film, Dirs. Guild Am. (mem. exec. com.), Stuntman's Assn. (hon.), Thunderbird Country Club (Rancho Mirage, Calif.), Bel Air Country Club (Calif.).

MONTY, JEAN CLAUDE, telecommunications company executive; b. Montreal, Que., Can., June 26, 1947; s. Jean R. Monty; m. Jocelyne Belanger, May 17, 1969; children—Jean Sebastien, Pierre-Paul. BA, College Sainte-Marie, Montreal, 1967; MA in Econs., U. Western Ont., London, Ont. Can., 1969; MBA, U. Chgo., 1970. Vice pres. Merrill Lynch Can., Montreal, 1973-74; asst. v.p. Bell Can., Montreal, 1974-82; v.p. Bell Can., 1982-85, exec. v.p., from 1985, pres., 1989—, chief exec. officer, 1993-95; exec. v.p. BCE Inc., 1987-89; ceo Northern Telecom Ltd., 1993—; pres. Bell Can. Mgmt. Corp. chmn. Bell Cellular; dir. Mut. Life Can., Rostland Corp., Bimcor, BN Ins., Internat. Bus. Council Can. Bd. dirs., v.p. Maison des Sciences et des Techniques, Montreal, 1985; bd. dirs. Fondation sur la Recherche des Maladies Mentales, Montreal, 1984-85, l'Institut de Cardiologie de Montreal. Home: 1437 Mt Royal Blvd, Outremont, PQ Canada H2V 2J5 Office: Bell Can, 1050 Beaver Hall Hill, Montreal, PQ Canada H2Z 1S4 Also: No Telecom Ltd, PO Box 458 Sta A, Mississauga, ON Canada L5A 3A2

MONTZ, FLORENCE STOLTE, church official; b. Lowden, Iowa, June 7, 1924; d. Emil L. and Emma Marie (Meier) Stolte; m. C. R. Montz, June 15, 1947; children: Jennifer Montz Rechlin, Fredrick John. BS, RN, U. Iowa, 1947; LLD (hon.), Concordia Coll., Bronxville, N.Y., 1984; LHD (hon.), Concordia Coll., St. Paul, 1988. RN, Iowa. V.p., then pres. N.D. dist. Luth. Women's Missionary, Luth. Ch.-Mo. Synod, Bismarck, 1960-68, 1st v.p. internat., 1967-71, pres., 1971-75; editor Better Health mag. Luth. Ch.-Mo. Synod, Bismarck, 1983—, also bd. dirs. Mem. Sigma Theta Tau. Home: PO Box 1293 Bismarck ND 58502-1293

MOODY, CURTIS JEROME, architect; b. Columbus, Ohio, Dec. 28, 1950; s. William Gernale and Jessie (Lindsay) M.; m. Frances Marie Baker, 1975 (div. 1978); m. Elaine Sutfield Moody, Apr. 12, 1980; children: Curtis Jerome, David, Jonathan. BS in Architecture, Ohio State U., 1973. Registered architect. v. Draftsman W.G.K. Architects, Columbus, Ohio, 1972-73, design architect, 1975-77; draftsman Brubaker/Brandt Architects, Columbus, 1973-75, asst. mktg. dir., 1981-82; design architect Coke Harpham Architects, Columbus, 1977-79, Trott & Bean Architects, Columbus, 1979-81; pres., chief exec. officer Moody & Assocs., Columbus, 1982-84, Moody, Nolan Ltd. Architects, Engrs., Columbus, 1984—; instr. Columbus Tech. Inst.; cons. Columbus Minority Bus.; bd. dirs. Soc. Bank, Columbus. Contbr. articles to profl. jours. Mem. exec. com. New World Ctr., 1986-87. Recipient Community Service award Plaque, Ohio State U. Coll. Nursing, 1985, Key Note Speaker award Council Black Students in Adminstrn., Ohio State U., 1986, Franklin County Minority Bus. award, 1986, City Beautiful award, 1987, Preservation Merit award Ohio Hist. Soc., 1987, Ohio Masonry Design award, 1988, Minority Bus. of Yr. award, State of Ohio, 1986, James B. Recchie Urban Design award, 1987, Ohio Arts Council Urban Design award, 1987. Mem. AIA (architects honor award Columbus shpt. 1987), Ohio Soc. Architects, Ohio Assn. Minority Architects/Engrs., Nat. Council Archtl. Registration Bds., Columbus Area C. of C. (bd. dirs. 1987—), Ohio State U. Alumni Assn., Ohio State U. Varsity O Alumni Assn. Avocations: basketball, church, fishing, hunting. Home: 3887 Sudbury Rd Columbus OH 43219-3054 Office: Moody Nolan Ltd Architects Engrs 1776 E Broad St Columbus OH 43203-2013

MOODY, FLORENCE ELIZABETH, education educator, retired college dean; b. Penn Yan, N.Y., Sept. 29, 1932; d. James William Southby and Rebecca (Worrall) M.; B.S., SUNY, Geneseo, 1954; M.S., Syracuse (N.Y.) U., 1961; Ed.D. (NDEA fellow), U. Rochester (N.Y.), 1969. Elem. sch. tchr., N.Y. State, 1954-64, 66-68; coord. profl. devel. Eastern Regional Inst. Edn., Syracuse, 1969-71; mem. faculty SUNY, Oswego, 1971-92, prof. elem. edn., 1978-92, assoc. dean profl. studies, 1980-85, dean, 1985-92; mem. N.Y. State Tchr. Edn. Cert. and Practice Bd., 1983-89; mem. Tchr. Edn. Conf. Bd., 1982-84. Nat. sec. Nat. Women's Party, 1974-76; bd. dirs. Oswego County Extension Service, 1974-76. Danforth asso., 1978—. Mem. A.A. Assn. Colls. Tchr. Edn. (pres. N.Y. State chpt. 1983-84), Assn. Tchr. Educators, Assn. Supervision and Curriculum Devel., Am. Ednl. Research Assn., N.Y. State Assn. Tchr. Educators (sec., exec. bd. 1976-78), Kappa Delta Pi, Pi Lambda Theta, Phi Delta Kappa, Delta Kappa Gamma. Presbyterian. Club: Order Eastern Star. Author reports, curriculum materials in field. Home: 5143 Franklin Ave Oswego NY 13126-1711

MOODY, FREDERICK JEROME, mechanical engineer, consultant thermal hydraulics; b. Aurora, Ill., Apr. 2, 1935; s. Frederick J. and Ruth K. (King) M.; m. Phyllis Arlene Ivemeyer, Aug. 27, 1955; children: David, John, Paul, Daniel. B.S. in Mech. Engring., U. Colo., 1958; M.S. in Mech. Engring., Stanford U., 1965, Ph.D. in Mech. Engring., 1971. Engr., GE, San Jose, Calif., 1958-78, prin. engr., 1978-81, cons. engr., 1981—; adj. prof. San Jose State U., 1971—; model developer, GE, 1958—. Author: Introduction to Unsteady Thermofluid Mechanics, 1990; co-author: The Thermal-Hydraulics of a Boiling Water Nuclear Reactor, 1977, 2nd edit., 1993. Sunday Sch. tchr. Calvary Baptist Ch., Los Gatos, Calif., 1960—; chmn. bd. dirs. Med. Inst. Chaplains, San Jose, 1984. Fellow ASME (George Westinghouse Gold Medal 1980). Republican. Home: 2265 Sunrise Dr San Jose CA 95124-2640 Office: Gen Electric Co Mail Code 747 175 Curtner Ave San Jose CA 95125-1014

MOODY, GENE BYRON, engineering executive, small business owner; b. Calhoun, Ga., Aug. 29, 1933; s. Denzel Elwood and Mary Edna (Hughes) M.; m. Willie Earline Chauncey, Sept. 1, 1955; children: Byron Eugene, Iva Marie Levy. BSCE, U. Tenn., 1956. Registered profl. engr., Ala., Ark., Ga., La., Miss., Tex. V.p.c S.I.P. Engring. Corp., Baton Rouge, 1968-70; project engr. J.E.T., Inc., Houston, 1970-73; dir. of engring. Jacus Assoc., Mpls., 1972-73; dir. of civil engring. Barnard & Burk, Baton Rouge, 1973-79; project mgr. Process Svcs., Baton Rouge, 1979-80, Salmon & Assoc., Baton Rouge, 1980-81; chief engr. Minton & Assoc., Lafayette, La., 1982; mgr. Assoc. Engr. Cons., Baton Rouge, 1982-86; owner Gene B. Moody, P.E., Baton Rouge, 1986—. Author: Good Homemakers, 1988, Deliverance Manual, 1989; contbr. articles to profl. jours. Deacon South Side Bapt. Ch., Baton Rouge, 1974; tchr. Hamilton Bible Camp, Hot Springs, Ark., 1981-91;

trustee Manna Bapt. Ch., Baton Rouge, 1989-91. With U.S. Army, 1957. U. Chattanooga scholar, 1951, U. Tenn. scholar, 1953. Fellow ASCE; mem. Am. Soc. Safety Engrs., La. Soc. Profl. Surveyors, Soc. Automotive Engrs., Inst. Transp. Engrs., La. Engring. Soc., Transp. Res. Rsch. Bd. Mem. Christian Ch. (minister). Home and Office: 9852 Hillyard Ave Baton Rouge LA 70809-3109

MOODY, GRAHAM BLAIR, lawyer; b. Roswell, N. Mex., July 20, 1925; s. Graham Blair and Vinnie Charlotte (Burton) M.; m. Linda Alden Swanson, Apr. 11, 1970; children: Graham Blair, III, Stuart, Katherine, Charlotte, Douglas, Margaret. BA, Yale U., 1947; MBA, Harvard U., 1947; LLB, U. Calif., Berkeley, 1955. Bar: Calif. 1956, U.S. Dist. Ct. (no. dist.) Calif. 1956, U.S. Ct. Appeals (9th cir.) 1956, U.S. Supreme Ct. 1963. Asst. to dist. mgr. producing dept. Standard Oil of Calif., L.A., 1948-52; head law clk. to chief justice U.S. Supreme Ct., Washington, 1955-56; assoc. McCutchen, Doyle, Brown & Enersen, San Francisco, 1956-64; ptnr. McCutchen, Doyle, Brown & Enersen, 1964-85, of counsel, 1985-86; ptnr. Moody & Moody, 1987-94. Vestryman St. Clement's Episc. Ch., then All Souls Episc. Ch., 1960-68, Ch. of Our Savior, 1988-90; bd. dirs., 1st pres. Eugene O'Neill Found., Tao House, Danville, Calif., 1975-76; bd. dirs. League to Save Lake Tahoe, 1978—, pres., 1980-82, 88-90, mem. exec. com., 1980-93; bd. dirs. Trauma Found., 1988—, Point Reyes Bird Obs., Stinson Beach, Calif., 1991—, Calif. Kidney Cancer Found., 1994—, Henry Ohloff House, San Francisco, 1994—, Friends of Redwoods, Mill Valley, Calif., 1991-92. Supply officer USN. Mem. ABA, Am. Law Inst. (life), Pacific-Union Club, Yale Club (past pres. local club).

MOODY, JAMES L., JR., retail food distribution company executive; b. Manchester, N.H., 1931; married. AB, Bates Coll., 1953. With Gen. Electric Co., 1955-59; with Hannaford Bros. Co., Scarborough, Maine, 1959—; treas. Hannaford Bros. Co., 1961-69, pres., 1969-84, chief exec. officer, 1973-92, chmn., 1992—, also bd. dirs.; dir. Penobscot Shoe Co., UNUM Corp., Sobey's Stores Ltd., Can., Hills Dept. Stores, Mass., Colonial Group of Funds, Mass. Served with U.S. Army, 1953-55. Office: Hannaford Bros Co 145 Pleasant Hill Rd Scarborough ME 04074-8768*

MOODY, JOHN STEPHEN, real estate executive; b. Houston, Nov. 11, 1948; s. Dan McMillan and Florence (Hendrick) M.; m. Eileen Arnold, Apr. 10, 1971; children: John, Joe, Dan. BS, Stanford U., 1970; JD, U. Tex., 1973. Ptnr. Wood, Campbell, Moody & Gibbs, Houston, 1973-83; pres. Moody Corp., Houston, 1984-86; 1st v.p. Rotan Mosle, Houston, 1987—; pres., chief exec. officer Paine Webber Properties, N.Y.C., 1987—; dir. Geodyne Resources, Inc., Paine Webber, Inc., Paine Webber Properties, Inc. Home: 15 Beechcroft Rd Greenwich CT 06830-3911 Office: Paine Webber Properties 1290 Avenue Of The Americas New York NY 10104-0012

MOODY, LAMON LAMAR, JR., retired civil engineer; b. Bogalusa, La., Nov. 8, 1924; s. Lamar Lamon and Vida (Seal) M.; BS in Civil Engring., U. Southwestern La., 1951; m. Eve Thibodeaux, Sept. 22, 1954 (div. 1991); children: Lamon Lamar III, Jennifer Eve, Jeffrey Matthew. Engr., Tex. Co. N.Y.C., 1951-52; project engr. African Petroleum Terminals, West Africa, 1952-56; chief engr. Kaiser Aluminum & Chem. Corp., Baton Rouge, 1956-63; pres., owner Dyer & Moody, Inc., Cons. Engrs., Baker, La., 1963-94, also chmn. bd., dir.; ret., 1994. Chmn., Baker Planning Commn., 1961-63. Trustee La. Coun. on Econ. Edn., 1987-93. Served with USMCR, 1943-46. Decorated Purple Heart; registered profl. engr., La., Ark., Miss., Tex.; registered profl. land surveyor, La., Tex. Fellow ASCE, Am. Congress Surveying and Mapping (award for excellency 1972); mem. La. Engring. Soc. (dir., v.p. 1980-81, pres. 1982-83, Charles M. Kerr award for public relations 1971, A.B. Patterson medal 1981, Odom award for disting. svc. to engring. profession, 1986), Profl. Engrs. in Pvt. Practice (state chmn. 1969-70), La. Land Surveyors Assn. (pres. 1968-69, Land Surveyor of Yr. award 1975), Cons. Engrs. Coun., Pub. Affairs Rsch. Coun. of La. (exec. com., trustee 1983—), Good Roads and Transp. Assn. (bd. dirs. 1984—), Baker C. of C. (pres. 1977, Bus. Leader of Yr. award 1975), NSPE (nat. dir. 1982-83), Blue Key. Republican. Baptist. Clubs: Masons (32 deg., K.C.C.H. 1986), Kiwanis (dir. 1964-65). Home: 451 Ray Weiland Dr Baker LA 70714-3353 Office: 2845 Ray Weiland Dr Baker LA 70714-3247

MOODY, LIZABETH ANN, law educator; b. Johnson City, Tenn., July 11, 1934; d. Robert Alexander and Clara Pauline (Fine) M.; m. Alan Paul Buchmann, Sept. 5, 1959. AB, Columbia U., 1956; LLB, Yale U., 1959. Bar: Conn. 1959, Ohio 1960, U.S. Dist. Ct. Conn. 1960, U.S. Supreme Ct. 1977, U.S. Dist. Ct. (no. dist.) Ohio 1961. Assoc. Goldstein & Peck, Bridgeport, Conn., 1959-60, Slough & Slough, Cleve., 1960-61, 63-66, Ginsberg, Guren & Meritt, Cleve., 1962; ptnr. Metzenbaum, Gaines, Finley & Stern, Cleve., 1967-71; assoc. prof. Cleve. State U., 1970-73, prof., 1973—, interim dean and prof., 1987-88; vis. prof. U. Toledo, Ohio, 1976-77; rev. authority on civil rights HEW, Washington, 1973-79; vis. prof. Nat. Law Ctr. George Washington U., 1981-82, U. Hawaii, Honolulu, 1988. Author: (books) Smith's Review of Corps, 1987, Smith's Review of Estates, 1987; contbr. articles to profl. jours. Pres. Cuyahoga County Econ. and Community Devel., Cleve., 1984-88, Task Force on Violent Crime, Cleve., 1987-88; chmn. audit com. Law Sch. Admission Coun., Newton, Pa., 1988-89; bd. trustees Law Sch. Admission Svc., 1989—, exec. dir., 1991-93, pres. Law Sch. Admission Svc., 1991-93; commr. Ohio Ethics Commn., Columbus, Ohio, 1988-91, Ohio Pub. Defender Commn.; v.p., trustee Gt. Lakes Theatre Festival, Cleve., 1972-90; dir. Cleve. Growth Assn., 1987-88. Recipient New Frontier award Ams. for Dem. Action, 1977, YWCA Women of Distinction award, 1988, Josephine Irwin award, 1990. Mem. ABA (chair non-profit corp. com. 1987-91), Ohio State Bar Assn. (coun. of dels. 1981-91, Ohio Bar medal 1992), Cleve. Bar Assn. (pres. 1987-88, meritorious svc. award 1987), Assn. Univ. Profs., Univ. Club, English Speaking Union (trustee 1988-89). Office: Cleve State U Coll Law Cleveland OH 44115

MOODY, RHEA PHENON, banking executive; b. Portland, Ind., Oct. 6, 1930; d. George D.C. and Mollie (Evans) M.; m. Phillip L. Bond, Sept. 5, 1974 (div. Dec. 1979). BS in Acctg., Ind. U., 1959. Mgr., teller First Nat. Bank, East Chgo., 1959-66; credit officer Lasalle Nat. Bank, Chgo., 1966-73; asst. v.p. State Nat. Bank, Evanston, Ill., 1973-77; v.p. Lakeview Bank, Chgo., 1977-81, W.N. Lane Interfinancial, Northbrook, Ill., 1981-83, Uni Banc Trust, Chgo., 1983-85, Republic Bank, Lubbock, Tex., 1985-86, Sun-belt Savings, FSB, Dallas, 1986-91, Home Fed. Bank, San Diego, 1991—. Cpl. WAC, 1952-55. Home: 7264 Shoreline Dr Apt 127 San Diego CA 92122 Office: Home Fed Bank 707 Broadway Ste 900 San Diego CA 92121

MOODY, ROBERT ADAMS, neurosurgeon; b. nil. Swampscott, Mass., Oct. 1, 1934; s. George F. and Florence P. M.; m. Claudia; children: Robert Adams, II, Cathy, Paul, Lisa, Sherri. B.A., U. Chgo., 1955, B.S., 1956, M.D., 1960. Intern Royal Victoria Hosp., Montreal, Que., Can., 1960-61; resident in neurosurgery U. Vt. Affiliated Hosps., 1961-66; fellow Lahey Clinic, Boston, 1963-64; asst. prof. neurol. surgery U. Chgo. Med. Sch., 1966-71; sr. clin. instr., then asst. clin. prof. Tufts U. Med. Sch., 1972-74; prof. neurosurgery Abraham Lincoln Med. Sch., U. Ill., Chgo., 1975-81; chmn. div. neurosurgery Cook County Hosp., Chgo., 1974-81; assoc. chmn. dept. surgery Cook County Hosp., 1976-81; chmn. neurosurgery Guthrie Clinic, Sayre, Pa., 1981—; clin. prof. neurosurgery SUNY-Binghamton, 1983—; chmn. neurosurgery Guthrie Clinic, Sayre, Pa., 1981-95; ret., 1995. Contbr. articles med. jours. USPHS fellow, 1957-58. Mem. ACS, Am. Assn. Neurol. Surgeons, Pa. Neurosurg. Soc. (councillor 1986-87, pres.-elect 1988, pres. 1989), Mid-Atlantic Neurosurg. Soc., Ctrl. Neurosurg. Soc. (pres. 1978-79), Alumni Assn. Lahey Clinic Found., Sigma Xi. Office: Guthrie Clinic Guthrie Sq Sayre PA 18840

MOODY, ROBERT M., bishop; b. Balt., July 23, 1939; m. Lance Baty Martin; children: Leanne Moody Stoufer, Sharon, Christian, Elizabeth. Grad., Rice Univ., 1962; postgrad. in law, U. Tex.; MDiv, Va. Theol. Seminary, 1966, DD, 1988. Rector St. James Ch., Riverton, Wyo., 1970-75, Grace Ch., Alexandria, Va., 1975-88; elected Bishop Coadjutor Diocese Okla., Oklahoma City, 1988-89, 4th diocesan bishop, 1989—. Office: 924 N Robinson Oklahoma City OK 73102

MOODY, ROBERT VAUGHAN, mathematician, educator; b. Hornchurch, Essex, Eng., Nov. 28, 1941; s. Norman Frank and Joan Catherine (Start) M.; m. Marian Hart, Aug. 12, 1965; children—Lisa, David, Collin. B.A., U. Sask., Can., 1962; M.A., U. Toronto, Can., 1964, Ph.D., 1966. Prof. math.

U. Sask., Saskatoon, Can., 1966-89, U. Alta., Edmonton, 1989—; vis. prof. Centre de Recherche de Mathematiques, Montreal, 1983-84, Concordia U., Montreal, 1984-85. Co-founder: Theory of Affine and Kac-Moody Lie Algebras, 1967. Research grantee, 1966—, including Royal Soc. Can., 1981, Japan Soc. Promotion of Sci., 1981. Mem. Am. Math. Soc., Canadian Math. Soc. (v.p. 1983-85). Office: U Alta, Dept Math, Edmonton, AB Canada T6G 2G1

MOODY, ROLAND HERBERT, retired librarian; b. Manchester, N.H., July 17, 1916; s. Louis and Alice (Heath) M.; m. Ethel Corwin, Aug. 20, 1939; children—Jonathan Corwin, Ellen Jane. A.B., Dartmouth, 1938; B.S. in L.S, Columbia, 1941. Asst. ref. desk Dartmouth Library, 1938-39; asst. reference and circulation librarian Middlebury (Vt.) Coll. Library, 1939-40; gen. asst. Harvard Coll. Library, 1941-43, keeper collections, 1946-48; circulation librarian Lamont Library, 1948-53; dir. Northeastern U. Library, 1953-83, dean libraries and learning resources, 1975-83. Served with inf. AUS, 1943-45, ETO. Decorated Bronze Star. Mem. Am., Mass. library assns., Am. Assn. U. Profs. Conglist. (deacon).

MOODY, STANLEY ALTON, entrepreneur, financial consultant; b. Portland, Maine, Oct. 16, 1939; s. Alton Elwood and Mary Gwendolyn (Young) M.; m. Jo-Ann Newton Vercoe, Dec. 15, 1975 (dec. Apr. 1992); children: Karen Elizabeth, Kirt Edward, Leslie Ann; m. Barbara Marie Katkus, June 28, 1992; 1 child, Jonathan Edwards. BSEE, U. Maine, 1962; postgrad., George Washington U., 1963-66; MA in Theol. Studies, Gordon-Conwell Theol. Sem., 1994; postgrad., Trinity Theological Sem., 1995—. Various positions Eastman Kodak Co., Kelsey-Hayes Co., Components, Inc., 1962-73; prin. Stan Moody Assoc., Augusta, Maine, 1973—; pres. Newton and Moody, Inc., Portland, Maine, 1980-84, Family Bookstores of New Eng., Portland, 1973—; dir. bus. cons. Maine Devel. Found., 1984-86. Author: No Turning Back, 1989, I Will Walk Again, 1993. Candidate for Gov. Maine, 1978; pastor North Manchester Meeting House, 1994—. Sgt. USAF, 1957-62. Mem. Safari Club Internat. Maine (v.p. 1993, pres. elect 1994). Republican. Avocations: hunting, fly fishing, writing. Home: PO Box 240 Manchester ME 04351 Office: Stan Moody Assoc 7 N Chestnut St Augusta ME 04330

MOODY, W. JARVIS, think-tank executive. Chmn. Inst. for Defense Analyses, Alexandria, Va. Office: Inst Def Analyses 1801 N Beauregard St Alexandria VA 22311-1733

MOOERS, CHRISTOPHER NORTHRUP KENNARD, physical oceanographer, educator; b. Hagerstown, Md., Nov. 11, 1935; s. Frank Burt and Helen (Miner) M.; m. Elizabeth Eva Fauntleroy, June 11, 1960; children: Blaine Hanson MacFee, Randall Walden Lincoln. BS, U.S. Naval Acad., 1957; MS, U. Conn., 1964; PhD, Oreg. State U., 1969. Postdoctoral fellow U. Liverpool (Eng.), 1969-70; asst. prof. U. Miami (Fla.), 1970-72, assoc. prof., 1972-76; assoc. prof. U. Del., Newark, 1976-78, prof., 1978-79; prof., chmn. dept. oceanography Naval Postgrad. Sch., Monterey, Calif., 1979-86; dir. Inst. Naval Oceanography, Stennis Space Ctr., Miss., 1986-89; sci. advisor to dir. Inst. for Naval Oceanography, 1989; rsch. prof. U. N.H., Durham, 1989-91; prof., chmn. div. applied marine physics U. Miami, Fla., 1991-93, dir. Ocean Pollution Rsch. Ctr., 1992—; coord. Coastal Ocean Scis. program, 1991—. Editor Jour. Phys. Oceanography, 1991—; mng. editor Coastal and Estuarine Studies, 1978—. Served with USN, 1957-64. NSF fellow, 1964-67; NATO fellow, 1969-70; Sr. Queen Elizabeth fellow, 1980. Mem. AAAS, The Oceanography Soc. (interim councilor 1987-88), Am. Geophys. Union (pres. ocean sci. 1982-84), Ea. Pacific Oceanic Conf. (chmn. 1979-86), U.S. Nat. Com./Internat. Union Geodesy and Geophysics, Univ. Nat. Oceanographic Lab. Sys./Fleet Improvement Com. (chair 1994—), Am. Meteorol. Soc., Marine Tech. Soc., Acoustical Soc. Am., Estuarine Rsch. Fedn., Sigma Xi, Phi Beta Delta. Achievements include pioneering direct observation of transient coastal ocean currents and fronts plus mesoscale and coastal ocean prediction rsch. Home: 2521 Inagua Ave Coconut Grove FL 33133-3811 Office: U Miami Div Applied Marine Physics RSMAS 4600 Rickenbacker Causeway Miami FL 33149-1098 *My central goal is to understand the ocean as a physical system by combining the interpretation of observations with dynamical theory and numerical models. Special emphasis has been on the dynamics of coastal oceans (continental shelf regions), now the scientific basis for practical mesoscale ocean prediction.*

MOOERS, DANIEL WILLIAM, lawyer; b. Belfast, Maine, Mar. 11, 1943; s. Darrell Linwood and Dorothy (Whitcomb) M.; m. Sarah Shaw, Sept. 1, 1962 (div. Sept. 1980); 1 child, Daniel W. Jr.; m. Shirley Aldrich, Dec. 31, 1986. BS, Am. U., Washington, 1965; JD, U. Maine, 1968. Bar: Maine 1968, U.S. Dist. Ct. Maine 1968, U.S. Ct. Appeals (1st cir.) 1969, U.S. Ct. Internat. Trade 1985. Assoc. atty. Bennett, Swarz & Reef, Portland, Maine, 1968-69; legal advisor, atty. Office of Gov., Augusta, Maine, 1970; ptnr. Reef & Mooers, Portland, 1969-86; pvt. practice Portland, 1986—. Bd. dirs. Susan B. Curtis Found., Augusta, Maine, 1970-78; trustee Samantha Smith Found., 1987—; mem. Urban Renewal Authority, South Portland, 1972-74, Civil Svc. Commn., South Portland, 1974-79. Mem. ABA, Assn. Trial Lawyers Am. (chmn. young lawyers 1970-71), Maine Bar Assn., Rotary Internat. (bd. govs. 1990-91, internat. bd. dirs. 1994-96, recipient citation for meritorious svc. 1990). Democrat. Office: 111 Commercial St Portland ME 04101-4719

MOOMAW, RONALD LEE, economics educator; b. Orkney Springs, Va., Aug. 1, 1943; s. Leo V. and Vivian (Fansler) M.; m. Juliana Pendleton, Dec. 27, 1971; children: Sara Christina, Kate Winston. BS with highest distinction, U. Va., 1966; PhD, Princeton (N.J.) U., 1976. Vis. asst. prof. U. Va., Charlottesville, 1968-72; asst. prof., assoc. prof. econs. Okla. State U., Stillwater, 1972-83, prof., 1983—, head dept., 1987-93; vis. rsch. assoc. Urban Inst., Washington, 1980-81; vis. assoc. prof. U. B.C., Vancouver, Can., 1983-84; prof. bus. adminstrn. CBA Assocs., 1994—. Co-author: Profile of Oklahoma, 1977, Economics and Contemporary Issues, 1994; asst. editor Jour. of Econs., 1991—, Jour. of Regional Sci., 1994—; contbr. articles to profl. jours. Vestryman St. Andrew's Episcopal Ch., Stillwater, 1979-80, treas., 1990—; mem. budget com. Diocese of Okla., 1994—. Woodrow Wilson fellow, 1964, NSF fellow, 1964-66. Mem. Am. Econ. Assn., So. Econ. Assn. (bd. trustees 1989-91), Regional Sci. Assn., So. Regional Sci. Assn. (exec. com. 1985-87), Missouri Valley Econ. Assn. (v.p. 1993-95, pres.-elect 1995-96). Office: Coll Bus Okla State U Stillwater OK 74078

MOON, HARLEY WILLIAM, veterinarian; b. Tracy, Minn., Mar. 1, 1936; s. Harley Andrew Moon and Catherine Mary (Engesser) Lien; m. Irene Jeannette Casper, June 9, 1956; children: Michael J., Joseph E. Anne E. Teresa J. BS, U. Minn., 1958, DVM, 1960, PhD, 1965. Diplomate Am. Bd. Veterinary Pathologists. Instr. Coll. Vet. Medicine U. Minn., St. Paul, 1960-62, NIH postdoctoral fellow, 1963-65; vis. scientist Brookhaven Nat. Lab., Upton, N.Y., 1965-66; assoc. prof. Coll. Vet. Medicine U. Sask., Saskatoon, Can., 1966-68; rsch. vet. Nat. Animal Disease Ctr. Agrl. Rsch. Svc., USDA, Ames, Iowa, 1968-88, ctr. dir., 1988—; assoc. prof. Iowa State U., Ames, 1970-73, prof. 1973-74; cons. U. N.C., Chapel Hill, 1985-92, Pioneer Hy-Bred Internat., Johnson, Iowa, 1986-92. Contbr. articles reporting rsch. on animal diseases. Recipient Superior Svc. award USDA. Mem. NAS, Am. Coll. Vet. Pathologists, AVMA, Am. Soc. Microbiologists, AAAS, NAS, Sigma Xi, Phi Zeta. Avocation: farming. Home: 800 Shagbark Dr Nevada IA 50201-2702 Office: USDA ARS Nat Animal Disease Ctr PO Box 70 2300 Dayton Ave Ames IA 50010-9679

MOON, HAROLD WARREN, JR., professional football player; b. L.A., Nov. 18, 1956; m. Felicia Hendricks; children: Joshua, Jeffrey, Chelsea, Blair. Degree in comm., U. Wash., 1978. With Edmonton Eskimos, 1978-84, Houston Oilers, 1984-94, Minnesota Vikings, 1994—. Named to Pro Bowl, 1988-93, Sporting News NFL All-Pro team, 1990. AFC Passing Leader, 1992; holds NFL single-season records for most passes attempted-665, 1991; most passes completed-404, 1991; sheares NFL single game record for most times sacked-12, 1985; shares NFL single season records for most games with 300 or more yards passing-9, 1990, most fumbles-18, 1990; Played in Grey Cup CFL Championship Game 1978-82. Address: Minnesota Vikings 9520 Viking Dr Eden Prairie MN 55344*

MOON, JOHN HENRY, SR., banker; b. Van Buren, Ark., Aug. 19, 1937; s. B.R. and Alma (Witte) M.; m. Agnes Rose Dickens, Aug. 16, 1958;

children: John Henry, Randall Allen. AA, Delmar Coll., Corpus Christi, 1956; BBA cum laude, Tex. A&M Univ., Kingsville, 1958. Sr. acct. Tex. Eastern Transp. Co. and subs., 1958-63; exec. v.p., dir. Houston Research Inst., 1963-68; sr. v.p., asst. to chmn. bd. Main Bank, 1968; vice chmn. bd., dir. N.E. Bank, 1969; CEO, chmn. bd., dir. Pasadena (Tex.) Nat. Bank, 1970-81; gen. ptnr. Moon and Assocs., Ltd., 1977—; chmn. bd., pres. Inter-service Life Ins. Corp., Phoenix, Cmty. Bank, Houston, 1975-81; Interstate Bank, Houston, 1977-81; chmn. bd., pres. Cmty. Capital Corp., Pasadena, 1975—; Peoples Bank, Houston, 1983-93; chmn. bd. Cmty. Nat. Bank, Friendswood, Tex., 1981-93; chmn. bd. Peoples Nat. Bank, Pasadena, Tex., 1984-93; dir. San Jacinto River Authority, 1991-93; chmn., pres. Sam Houston Pky. Transp. Corp., 1991—; bd. dirs. Pro Tech. Inc. Past bd. dirs. Pasadena Heart Assn., Salvation Army, Tex. Assn. Prevention of Blindness; past chmn. City of Pasadena Bd. Devel.; past chmn. adv. bd. Pasadena Civic Ctr.; past dir. S.E. Econ. Devel., Inc. Named Outstanding Young Man of Yr., Pasadena Jr. C. of C., 1973; named to Pasadena Hall of Fame, 1988. Mem. AICPA, Pasadena C. of C. (bd. dirs. Southeast Econ. Devel., Citizen of Yr. 1994), Tex. Soc. CPAs, Tex. Bankers Assn., Ind. Bankers Assn., Rotary. Home: 3914 Peru Cir Pasadena TX 77504-2320 Office: PO Box 910 Pasadena TX 77501-0910

MOON, WAYNE, health facility administrator. With Kaiser Foundation Hospital, Oakland, Calif., 1969—, v. pres., regional manager, 1978-85, pres., coo, 1988—. Office: Kaiser Foundation Health of NW 1 Kaiser Plz Oakland CA 94612

MOONEY, CHARLES WILLIAM, JR., law educator; b. Shawnee, Okla., Aug. 13, 1947; s. Charles W. and Mary Jane (Jones) M.; m. Christina Eager Anderson, Dec. 31, 1973; children: Mia Elizabeth, Natasha Lea. BA with high honors, U. Okla., 1969; JD cum laude, Harvard U., 1972. Bar: Okla. 1972, Pa. 1988, U.S. Dist. Ct. (we. dist.) Okla. 1972, N.Y. 1982, U.S. Ct. Appeals (10th cir.) 1973. Assoc. Crowe & Dunlevy, Oklahoma City, 1972-77, ptnr., 1977-81; ptnr. Shearman & Sterling, N.Y.C., 1981-86; assoc. prof. law U. Pa., Phila., 1986—; assoc. bar examiner Okla. Bd. Examiners, Oklahoma City, 1977-81; del. U.S. Dept. State Internat. Inst. for Unification of Pvt. Internat. Law, Conv. on Internat. Fin. Leasing, Rome, 1986-87, Ottawa, 1988—; visiting scholar Bank of Japan, 1988. Contbr. articles to profl. jours. Mem. ABA (mem. council bus. law sect. 1987—, chmn. on uniform comml. code bus. law sect. 1982-87), Okla. Bar Assn., N.Y. State Bar Assn., assn. of Bar of City of N.Y., Am. Law Inst. (advisor to permanent edit. bd. for uniform comml. code 1987—, Article 2 study com. 1988—), Phi Beta Kappa. Republican. Office: U Pa Law Sch 3400 Chestnut St Philadelphia PA 19104-6204

MOONEY, DONALD JAMES, JR., lawyer; b. Albany, N.Y., Nov. 14, 1950; s. Donald James and Marguerite (Walsh) M.; m. Ann Marie Tracey, June 16, 1972 (div. 1993); children: Ryan, Maureen; m. Jennifer Mooney, July 17, 1993; children: Caroline, Nora Esther. BA, U. Notre Dame, 1972; JD, U. Cin., 1975. Bar: Ohio 1975, U.S. Ct. Appeals (6th cir.) 1976, U.S. Dist. Ct. (so. dist.) Ohio 1976. Staff atty. U.S. Ct. Appeals (6th cir.), Cin., 1975-76; assoc., ptnr. Paxton and Seasongood, Cin., 1977-88; ptnr. Benesch, Friedlander, Coplan & Aronoff, Cin., 1988—. Chmn., mem. Cin. Planning Commn., 1983—; bd. dirs. Vol. Lawyers for the Poor Found., Cin., 1988—; mem. Cin. Human Rels. Commn., 1976-80; del. Dem. Nat. Convs., 1980, 84, 88. Mem. ABA, Fed. Bar Assn., Ohio Bar Assn., Cin. Bar Assn., Cincinnatus Assn. (com. chair 1989-92). Democrat. Roman Catholic. Office: Benesch Friedlander Coplan & Aronoff 600 Vine St Cincinnati OH 45202-2400

MOONEY, EDWARD JOSEPH, JR., chemical company executive; b. Omar, W.Va., May 19, 1941; s. Edward Joseph Sr. and Johnny Mae (Kidd) M.; m. Mary Martha May, Aug. 22, 1964; children—Elizabeth Anne, Edward Joseph III. BS in Chem. Engring., U. Tex., 1964, JD, 1967; Sr. Exec. Program, MIT, 1979. Bar: Tex. 1967, Ill. 1973. Corp. counsel Howe-Baker Corp., Tyler, Tex., 1969-70; gen. counsel Nalco Chem. Co., Oak Brook, Ill., 1970-80, group gen. mgr., 1980-82, v.p. 1982-84, sr. v.p. 1985; group v.p. Nalco Chem. Co., Sugarland, Tex., from 1985; pres. Nalco Chem. Co., Naperville, Ill., 1990—. Mem. Ill. Bar Assn., State Bar Tex., Am. Patent Law Assn. Office: Nalco Chem Co 1 Nalco Ctr Naperville IL 60563-0130

MOONEY, HAROLD ALFRED, plant ecologist; b. Santa Rosa, Calif., June 1, 1932; s. Harold Walter and Sylvia Anita Stefany; m. Sherry Lynn Gulmon, Aug. 15, 1974; children—Adria, Alyssa, Arica. AB, U. Calif., Santa Barbara, 1957; MA, Duke U., 1958, PhD, 1960. From instr. to assoc. prof. UCLA, 1960-68; assoc. prof. Stanford U., 1968-73, prof. biology, 1975—, Paul S. Achilles prof. environ. biology, 1976—; adviser NRC, Dept. Energy, NSF, Electric Power Research Inst., Ford Found. Author: Mediterranean-type Ecosystems, 1973, Convergent Evolution in Chile and California, 1977, Components of Productivity of Mediterranean Climate Regions, 1981; Disturbance in Ecosystems, 1983, Physiological of Plants in the Wet Tropics, 1984, Physiological Ecology of North American Plant Communities, 1985, Ecology of Biological Invasions of North America and Hawaii, 1986, Biological Invasions, A Global Perspective, 1989. Served with AUS, 1953-55. Recipient Humboldt award, 1989, Max Planck Forscungs Preis award Alexander von Humboldt Soc., 1992; Guggenheim fellow, 1974; Nat. Acad. Scis. fellow, 1982. Fellow AAAS; mem. Ecol. Soc. Am. (Mercer award 1961), Brit. Ecol. Soc. Home: 2625 Ramona St Palo Alto CA 94306-2315 Office: Stanford U Dept of Biol Sci 459 Herrin Lab Stanford CA 94305

MOONEY, JAMES HUGH, newspaper editor; b. Pitts., Aug. 18, 1929; s. James H. and Kathryn A. (Hall) M.; m. Eileen Jane Casey, July 30, 1960; children: Mark Hall, Sean Francis, Annina Marie, James Matthew, Lorelei Jane, Paul Adam, Kathryn Celeste. B.A. in Journalism, Duquesne U., Pitts., 1957. With advt. dept., then editorial dept. Pitts. Post-Gazette, 1953-61; writer-editor Nat. Observer, 1961-77, Nat. Geographic, 1977-79; editor Found. News mag., Washington, 1979-81; press sec. Congressman Mickey Edwards of Okla., Washington, 1982; asst. nat. editor Washington Times, 1982-83; editor Status Report, 1983-92; dir. info. resources Ins. Inst. for Hwy. Safety, 1992-93; editor Western Pa. Medicine, Johnstown, 1993—. Mem. editorial adv. bd. Nat. Study Ctr. Trauma and Emergency Med. Systems. Served with AUS, 1951-53. Mem. European Assn. Sci. Editors, Washington Automotive Press Assn., Nat. Press Club. Home: 13820 N Gate Dr Silver Spring MD 20906-2215

MOONEY, JOHN BRADFORD, JR., oceanographer, engineer, consultant; b. Portsmouth, N.H., Mar. 26, 1931; s. John Bradford and Margaret Theodora (Akers) M.; m. Martha Ann Huntley, Dec. 25, 1953 (dec. May 1990); children: Melinda Jean, Pamela Ann, Jennifer Joan; m. Jennie Marie Duca, Nov. 24, 1990. BS, U.S. Naval Acad., 1953; postgrad., George Washington U., 1970, 71, 76; grad. nat. and internat. security program, Harvard U., 1980. Commd. ens. USN, 1953, advanced through grades to rear adm., 1979; chief staff officer Submarine Devel. Group 1, 1971-73; commdr. Bathyscaphe Trieste II, 1964-66, Submarine Menhaden, 1966-68; comdg. officer Naval Sta., Charleston, S.C., 1973-75; dep. dir. Deep Submergence Systems Div., Office Chief Naval Ops., Washington, 1975-77; comdr. Naval Tng. Ctr., Orlando, Fla., 1977-78; dir. Total Force Planning Div., Office Chief Naval Ops., Washington, 1978-81; oceanographer USN, 1981-83, chief naval rsch., 1983-87, ret., 1987; pres. Harbor Br. Oceanographic Instn., Inc., Ft. Pierce, Fla., 1988-92, marine bd., 1991-94; bd. dirs. Coltec Industries, 1992—; mem. marine programs adv. coun. U.R.I., Narragansett, 1989—. At controls of Trieste II when hull of Thresher was found on floor of Atlantic, 1964; coordinated deep search and recovery of hydrogen bomb lost off coast of Spain, 1966; condr. recovery operation from depth of 16,400 feet in Mid-Pacific, 1972. Decorated Legion of Merit with 1 gold star; recipient spl. citation Armed Forces Recreation Assn., 1975. Mem. Marine Tech. Soc. (pres. 1991-93), Nat. Acad. Engring., U.S. Naval Inst., Nat. Geog. Soc., Smithsonian Assocs., Masons, Shriners, Order of DeMolay. Avocations: racquetball, sailing. Home and Office: 807 N Howard St # 424 Alexandria VA 22304

MOONEY, MARILYN, lawyer; b. Pitts., July 29, 1952; d. James Russell and Mary Elizabeth (Cartwright) M. BA summa cum laude, U. Pa., 1973, JD, 1976. Bar: Mass. 1977, D.C. 1985, Pa. 1990, U.S. Dist. Ct. D.C. 1985, U.S. Ct. Appeals (D.C. cir.) 1985, U.S. Supreme Ct. 1986. Atty. E. I. du Pont de Nemours & Co., Wilmington, Del., 1976-84, Washington, 1985; with Fulbright & Jaworski L.L.P., Washington, 1985-90, ptnr., 1990—. Contbr.

articles to profl. jours. Active Greater Washington Bd. Trade, D.C. Pub. Affairs Coun., 1992—. Mem. ABA, Fed. Regulation of Securities Com. (subcom. registration statements-1933 Act 1986—), Internat. Bar Assn. Office: Fulbright & Jaworski LLP 801 Pennsylvania Ave NW Washington DC 20004-2615

MOONEY, MICHAEL EDWARD, lawyer; b. Beloit, Wis., Jan. 21, 1945; s. William C. and Edith (Slothower) M. BA in Econs., St. Norbert Coll., 1966; JD, Boston Coll., 1969. Bar: Mass. 1969, Maine 1969, U.S. Tax Ct. 1975, U.S. Ct. Internat. Trade 1986. Assoc. Nutter, McClennen & Fish, Boston, 1969-77, sr. ptnr., 1978—; bd. dirs. Lincoln and Therese Filene Found., Boston; mem. exec. com. Fedn. Tax Inst. of New Eng., 1987—, mem. artery bus. com., 1994—; spkr., lectr. numerous seminars. Co-editor: Considerations in Buying or Selling a Business, 1985; mem. bd. editors Accounting for Law Firms, 1988—. Bd. dirs. Alliance Francaise of Boston, 1987—, Internat. Bus. Ctr. of New Eng., 1986-89. Mem. Boston Tax Forum, Boston Bar Assn. (chmn. tax highlights com. 1986—, mem. fin. com. 1990-92), Boston Ptnrs. in Edn. (lawyer's fund com.). Office: Nutter McClennen & Fish 1 International Pl Boston MA 02110-2699

MOONEY, MICHAEL JOSEPH, academic administrator, philosopher; b. Evansville, Ind., Dec. 15, 1942; s. Joseph Thomas and Marie Louise (DeJean) M.; m. Hannelore Karasek, Dec. 27, 1969; children: Susanne, Julia. AB summa cum laude, St. Meinard Coll., 1964; STL magna cum laude, Univ. Innsbruck, Austria, 1968; M in Philosophy, Columbia U., 1973, PhD, 1982. Lectr. dept. religious studies, St. Mary's U., Halifax, N.S., Can., 1968-70, Union Theol. Sem., N.Y.C., 1972-74; project coord. Columbia U., N.Y.C., 1973-74, preceptor dept. religion, 1975-76; spl. asst. to exec. v.p. for acad. affairs, 1976-77, asst. provost, 1977-79, assoc. provost, 1979-82, dep. provost, 1982-89; pres. Lewis and Clark Coll., Portland, Oreg., 1989—; summer visitor Inst. for Advanced Study, Princeton, N.J., 1984; trustee Joun. of Philosophy, 1982—. Author: Vico in the Tradition of Rhetoric, 1985 (Gottschalk prize Am. Soc. 18th Century Studies 1985); editor: Renaissance Thought and Its Sources, 1979; co-editor: Toward a Theology of Christian Faith: Readings in Theology, 1968, Vico and Contemporary Thought, 1976, Small Comforts for Hard Times: Humanists on Public Policy, 1977. Dir Reid Hall, Inc., N.Y.C. and Paris, 1977-89, v.p., 1983-89; dir. Roothbert Fund, 1980-92, Portland Opera Assn., 1992-93; trustee Scuola d'Italia, N.Y.C., 1986-90, World Affairs Coun., 1992—, Oreg. Ballet Theatre, 1992—; mem. adv. com. chamber Music N.W., 1990—; mem. Commn. on Internat. Edn., Am. Coun. on Edn. Recipient Rome prize Am. Acad. in Rome, 1989; Roothbert Fund fellow, 1972, Kent fellow Danforth Found., 1972, Woodrow Wilson fellow, 1972, Presdl. fellow Columbia U., 1972, F.J.E. Woodbridge Disting. fellow Columbia U., 1973; NEH grantee, 1984; Cavaliere Ufficiale, Order Merit, Republic of Italy, 1991. Fellow Italian Acad. for Advanced Studies in Am. (sr.); mem. Soc. for Values in Higher Edn., Am. Soc. for Eighteenth-Century Studies, Internat. Soc. for History of Rhetoric, Renaissance Soc. Am., Am. Acad. Religion, Am. Philos. Assn. Office: Lewis & Clark Coll Office of Pres 0615 SW Palatine Hill Rd Portland OR 97219

MOONEY, RICHARD E., editorial writer; b. Plainfield, N.J., Mar. 31, 1927; s. Wandell M. and Alice (Joy) M.; m. Elizabeth B. Coleman, Oct. 30, 1954; children: James C., Stephen E., John B. B.A., Yale U., 1947; postgrad. (Nieman fellow), Harvard U., 1955-56. Writer United Press, N.Y.C., 1948-51; econ. reporter United Press, Washington, 1951-56, N.Y. Times, Washington, 1957-63; European econ. correspondent N.Y. Times, Paris, 1963-67; econ. reporter N.Y. Times, N.Y.C., 1967; asst. to exec. editor N.Y. Times, 1968, asst. to mng. editor, 1969, dep. fgn. editor, 1970-72, asst. fin. editor, 1972-76, mem. editl. bd., 1982-95; contbg. editor, 1995—; v.p. Hartford Courant, 1976-81, exec. editor, 1976-81, dir., 1977-81. Author: (with Edwin L. Dale, Jr.) Inflation and Recession, 1959. Trustee Hartford Courant Found., 1977-81. Served with USNR, 1944-48. Mem. Yale Club (N.Y.). Home: 130 E 67th St New York NY 10021-6136 Office: NY Times 229 W 43rd St New York NY 10036-3913

MOONEY, THOMAS T., association executive; Pres. Rochester (N.Y.) Area C. of C. Office: St Paul St Rochester Area C of C care Pub Relations Dept 55 Rochester NY 14604

MOONEY, TIMOTHY M., retail executive. With Coopers & Lybrand, Cin., 1969-88; sr. v-pres., cfo Hook-Super X Inc., Cin., 1988—. Office: Hook-Superx Inc 175 Tri County Pky Cincinnati OH 45246

MOONEY, WILLIAM PIATT, actor; b. Bernie, Mo., May 2, 1936; s. Lowell E. and Louise S. M.; m. Valorie Shaw Goodall, Jan. 13, 1962; children: Sean Goodall, William Norvell. Student Am. theater wing, U. Colo. pres. William Mooney Assocs., cons. to industry for exec. presentations. Appeared in continuing role of Paul Martin on TV series All My Children, 1972—; one-man show Half Horse, Half Alligator & Damn Everything But the Circus; stage appearances: Brownsville Raid, We, A Man for All Seasons, Lolita; films: The Next Man, Network, A Flash of Green, Beer, Second Sight, C.A.T. Squad; author/star mus. play Banjo Reb and the Blue Ghost; co-author: ASAP-The Fastest Way to Create a Memorable Speech, 1992, Ready-to-Tell Tales, 1994, A Storyteller's Guide, 1995. Dir. jazz mus. Jam. Address: 8 Brookside Ct East Brunswick NJ 08816

MOONEY, YVETTE MIGDALIA, health facility administrator; b. Santurce, P.R., Nov. 7, 1944; d. Jose Octavio and Olga Iris (Lopez) Jimenez; m. Michael Gerald Mooney, Oct. 2, 1968; children: Yvette Christina, Marissa Gabrielle, Kelly Aileen. BSN, SUNY, 1965; MS in Community Health Adminstrn., L.I. U., 1977. CNAA. Asst. dir. II Albert Einstein Coll. of Medicine Hosp., Bronx, N.Y., 1971-77; assoc. DON South Nassau Communities Hosp., Oceanside, N.Y., 1977-82, DON, 1982—. Mem. ANA, AONE, Nassau-Suffolk Dirs. Roman Catholic. Avocations: dancing, swimming, biking. Office: S Nassau Communities Hosp 2445 Oceanside Rd Oceanside NY 11572

MOONEYHAN, ESTHER LOUISE, retired nurse, educator; b. Wabash, Ind., Oct. 2, 1920; d. Edward Lamont and Ina Louretta (Adams) Smithee; children: William Cecil, Mary Kathleen, Stephen Alan. Student (scholar), Ind. Wesleyan U., 1938-40; diploma (scholar), Meth. Hosp. Sch. Nursing, Indpls., 1943; BS in Gen. Nursing, Ind. U., 1964, MS in Nursing Edn., 1965, Ed. D. (fellow), 1973. Staff nurse Putnam County (Ind.) Hosp., 1943-44, Meth. Hosp., Indpls., 1951; pvt. duty nurse Ind. U. Med. Ctr., Indpls., 1953-60; staff nurse, assoc. supr., ednl. dir. Bur. Pub. Health Nursing Health & Hosp. Corp., Indpls. and Marion County, Ind., 1960-67; nurse adviser AID, Haile Selassie I U. Coll. Pub. Health, Ethiopia, 1967-69; asst. prof. nursing Tex. Woman's U., Denton, 1972-73; assoc. prof. nursing Fla. Internat. U. Miami, 1973-79, chmn., 1974-76; prof., adminstr. Ind. U. Sch. Nursing, South Bend, Ind., 1979-88; prof. Ind. U. Sch. Nursing, Indpls., 1989-91; community health nurse Manatee County Pub. Health unit State of Fla. Health and Rehab. Svc., Bradenton, Fla., 1992-95; ret., 1995; vis. prof. U. South Fla. Coll. Nursing, 1988-89, U. Ctrl. Fla., Orlando, 1991-92; charter mem. Nursing Rsch. Consortium North Ctrl. Ind.; speaker state workshops and nat. convs.; cons. in field. Contbr. articles to profl. jours. Recipient Outstanding Achievement award Ind. Wesleyan U. Alumni Assn., 1992. Mem. Am. Nurses Assn., Coun. Nurse Researchers, Fla. Nurses Assn. Dist. 4 , Nat. League Nursing, Am. Pub. Health Assn., Internat. Health Soc. (bd. dirs. 1977-79), Nat. Coun. Internat. Health, Am. Assn. for World Health, Pi Lambda Theta, Sigma Theta Tau. Baptist. Achievements include research in nursing curricula, international development, international health, international nursing, and family/community health.

MOONIE, CLYDE WICKLIFFE, financial consultant; b. San Francisco, May 23, 1918; s. William B. and Vivienne (Selby) M.; m. Liana Maria Gabrielli, June 18, 1949; children: Gregory James, Barbara Marie. M.B.A., U. Chgo., 1941. C.P.A., Calif. C.P.A., N.Y. Mgr. Arthur Andersen & Co., C.P.A.s, 1941-58; adminstrv. mgr. Marcona Mining Co. S.A., 1958-62; controller Minerals & Chems. Philipp Corp., 1962-67; v.p., controller Engelhard Minerals & Chems. Corp, N.Y.C.; (merger Minerals & Chems. Philipp Corp. and Englehard Industries, Inc.), 1967-73, sr. v.p., 1973-76, exec. v.p., 1976-80; exec. v.p. Phibro-Salomon Inc. (formerly Engelhard Minerals & Chems. Corp.), 1981-82; exec. dir. Fin. Acctg. Standards Adv. Council, 1983-86; fin. cons., 1982—; mem. panel arbitrators Am. Arbitration Assn. Served to capt. AUS, 1942-45. Recipient Forbes gold medal Calif. C.P.A. Soc., 1945. Mem.

Am. Inst. C.P.A.s, Fin. Execs. Inst. Home and Office: 10 Baldwin Farms South Greenwich CT 06831

MOONVES, LESLIE, television company executive; b. N.Y.C., Oct. 6, 1949; s. Herman and Josephine (Schleifer) M.; m. Nancy Wiesenfeld, Dec. 17, 1978; children: Adam, Sara, Michael. Ba, Bucknell U., 1971. Devel. exec. Catalina Prodns., Burbank, Calif., 1980-81; v.p. devel. Saul Ilson Prodns. Columbia Pictures TV, Burbank, 1981-82; v.p. movies and mini-series 20th Century Fox, L.A., 1982-85, Lorimar, Inc., Culver City, Calif., 1985-87; exec. v.p. creative affairs Lorimar-Telepictures, Culver City, 1987-90; pres. Lorimar TV, Burbank, 1990-93, Warner Bros. TV, Burbank, 1993—. Developer, producer TV series including Dallas, Dark Justice, Guns of Paradise, Knots Landing, Midnight Caller, Sisters, Family Matters, Full House, Perfect Strangers, Family Man, I'll Fly Away, Reasonable Doubts, Step by Step, Hangin' with Mr. Cooper, the Jackie Thomas Show, Crossroads, Homefront, Going to Extremes, Shaky Ground, It Had to Be You, Time Trax, Against the Grain, Lois & Clark: The Adventures of Superman, Cafe Americain, How'd They Do That, Living Single, Family Album, Getting By. Bd. dirs. L.A. Free Clinic. Mem. Acad. TV Arts and Scis. (exec. com.), Hollywood Radio & TV Soc. (bd. dirs. 1988-91, pres. 1991). Democrat. Jewish. Office: Warner Bros TV 300 Television Plz Burbank CA 91505-4365*

MOOR, MANLY EUGENE, JR., retired banker; b. Birmingham, Ala., Apr. 28, 1923; s. Manly Eugene and Nell (Pulliam) M.; m. Anne Simms Beddow, Oct. 10, 1944; children: Manly Eugene III, William Tillman, Anne Beddow, John Matthew Bolling. B.S., Auburn U., 1947; grad. Sch. Banking, La. State U., 1956. With Am South Bank N.A. (formerly First Nat. Bank), Birmingham, 1950—, asst. cashier, 1953-57, mgr. comml. loan dept., 1953-54, mgr. Southside br., 1954-57, asst. v.p. Southside br., 1957-59, v.p. Southside br., 1959-67, sr. v.p. Southside br., 1967-68, exec. v.p. Southside br., 1968-72; pres. Am South Bank N.A., Birmingham, 1972-77, vice chmn. bd., 1977-88; vice chmn. bd. Am South Bank of Fla., Birmingham, 1988-92; ret. Am South Bank of Fla., 1992; dir. Matthews Electric Supply Co., Birmingham, AmSouth Fin. Corp., Engel Mortgage Co., Am South Bank Internat. Crusade chmn. Am. Cancer Soc., 1959, Girls Club Birmingham, 1968—, Jefferson County chpt. Am. Cancer Soc., 1962—; mem. adv. bd. Salvation Army, Birmingham, 1963—; gen. treas. YMCA, 1968—; co-chmn. United Appeal, 1966, gen. chmn., 1969; Bd. dirs. Boy Scouts Am., 1960—, Birmingham Downtown Improvement Assn., 1963—; bd. dirs. Blue Cross-Blue Shield of Ala., 1964—, chmn., 1969—. Served with USAAF, 1942-45. Presbyterian. Club: Mountain Brook, Downtown (bd. dirs. 1963—), Redstone (Birmingham); Shoal Creek (pres.). Office: AmSouth Bank PO Box 11007 Birmingham AL 35288

MOOR, ROY EDWARD, finance educator; b. Riverside, Calif., Oct. 11, 1924; s. Hugh Erin and Clara Viola Moor; m. Beverly A. Colbroth, Aug. 29, 1959; children—Cynthia Ann, Sheryl Lynn. B.A., UCLA, 1949; Ph.D., Harvard U., 1958. Vice pres., chief economist Fidelity Bank, Phila., 1965-68; vice pres., chief economist Drexel Firestone, Phila., 1968-71, Warburg Paribas Becker, N.Y.C., 1971-81; sr. v.p., chief economist First Chgo. Corp., 1981-86; prof. fin. Ill. Inst. Tech., Chgo., 1986—; dir. Nat. Bur. Econ. Research, Cambridge, Mass. Author: Federal Budget as an Economic Document, 1962. Fellow Nat. Assn. Bus. Economists (pres. 1973). Home: 1013 Woodrush Ct Westmont IL 60559-8823 Office: Ill Inst Tech 10 W 31st St Chicago IL 60616

MOORCROFT, JUDY, costume designer. Costume designer: (films) Who Is Killing the Great Chefs of Europe?, 1978, Crossed Swords, 1978, The Europeans, 1979 (Academy award nomination best costume design 1979), Murder By Decree, 1979, Silver Dream Racer, 1980, Sphinx, 1981, Yentl, 1983, French Lesson, 1984, The Killing Fields, 1984, A Passage to India, 1984 (Academy award nomination best costume design 1984), Shanghai Surprise, 1986, Clockwise, 1986, Without a Clue, 1988, City of Joy, 1992. Office: care Costume Designer's Guild 13949 Ventura Blvd Ste 309 Sherman Oaks CA 91423*

MOORE, ACEL, journalist; b. Phila., Oct. 5, 1940; s. Jerry A. and Hura Mae (Harrington) Acel M.; m. Carolyn Weaver, June 1964 (div. 1974); 1 child, Acel; m. Linda Wright Avery, Aug. 6, 1988. Student, Settlement Music Sch., 1958, Charles Morris Price Sch., 1966-67. Copyboy Phila. Inquirer, 1962-64, editorial clk., 1964-68, staff reporter, 1968-80, editorial writer/columnist, 1980-81, asso. editor, 1981—; also mem. edit. bd.; co-producer Black Perspective on the News (Nat. PBS weekly news program), 1972-78. Served with U.S. Army, 1959-62. Recipient Pulitzer prize, 1977, Robert F. Kennedy Journalism prize, 1977, Heywood Broun prize, 1977, Pa. Prison Soc. award, 1977, Humanitarian award House of Umoja, 1977, Community Service award Youth Devel. Center, 1976, Journalism award Phila. Party, 1977, Phila. Bar Assn. award, 1970, Ann. Paul Robeson award, 1977, Clarion award, 1977, Media award Mental Health Assn., 1977; Nieman fellow Harvard U., 1979-80. Mem. Nat. Assn. Black Journalists, Phila. Assn. Black Journalists (pres.), Am. Soc. Newspaper Editors, Sigma Delta Chi (Phila. chpt. Pub. Service awards 1972, 77, Reporting award 1977). Office: Phila Inquirer 400 N Broad St Philadelphia PA 19130-4099

MOORE, ALBERT CUNNINGHAM, lawyer, insurance company executive; b. Miami, Fla., May 31, 1931; s. Elias Richard and Virginia Adelaide (Thompson) M.; m. Anne Cambreleng Bonynge, Aug. 24, 1957; children: Emily Robinson French, Barbara Raffield Walton, Catherine Anne Bonynge. A.B., U. N.C., 1953; J.D., U. Va., 1959. Bar: N.Y. 1960. Atty. White & Case, N.Y.C., 1959-69; corporate sec. Studebaker-Worthington, Inc., N.Y.C., 1969-72; sr. v.p., gen. counsel Crum & Forster, 1973-87. Former trustee N.J. Shakespeare Festival; former bd. dirs. DeBordieu Property Owners Assn., Debordieu Arch. Rev. Bd. With USNR, 1953-56. Mem. ABA, Wilton Ctr. Tennis Club (N.H.), DeBordieu Club (S.C.), Phi Alpha Delta, Chi Phi. Home: 29 Lafayette Blvd DeBordieu Colony Georgetown SC 29440

MOORE, ALDERINE BERNICE JENNINGS (MRS. JAMES F. MOORE), association and organization administrator; Sacramento, Apr. 17, 1915; d. James Joseph and Elise (Thomas) Jennings; BA, U. Wash., 1941; m. James Francis Moore, Aug. 14, 1945. Sec. to div. Plant supr. Pacific Tel. & Tel. Co., Sacramento, 1937-39; exec. sec. Sacramento Community Chest Fund Raising Dr., 1941; sec. USAAF, Mather Field, Sacramento, 1942; statistician Calif. Western States Life Ins. Co., 1943; treas. Women's Aux. Stranger's Hosp., Rio de Janeiro, Brazil, 1964-65. Vice pres. Douglaston (N.Y.) Women's Club, 1955; mem. Douglaston Garden Club, 1955-55; pres. Nina Opland chpt. Women's Cancer Assn. U. Miami, 1960-61; corr. sec. Coral Gables (Fla.) Garden Club, 1966-62; pres. Miami Alumnae Club of Pi Beta Phi, 1961-62; mem. Putnam Hill chpt. D.A.R., Greenwich Conn., 1967-75, Palm Beach chpt., 1978—; mem. Woman's Club, Greenwich, Conn., 1967-75; mem. Women's Panhellenic Assn., Miami, 1961-62; internat. treas. Ikebana Internat., Tokyo, Japan, 1966-67, parliamentarian Tokyo chpt., 1966-67, N.Y. chpt., 1968-69; mem. Coll. Women Assn. Japan, 1965-66; mem. Tchrs. Assn. Sogetsu Sch. Japanese Flower Arranging, 1966—; Atlantis Golf Club. Served to 1st.lt. WAVES, 1943-45. Mem. Internat. Platform Assn., AAUW, Pi Beta Phi (local v.p. alumnae club 1969-71). Baptist. Club: Steamboat Investment (pres. 1972-73) Home: 316 Fairway Ct Lake Worth FL 33462-1212

MOORE, ALFRED ANSON, corporate executive; b. Muttontown, N.Y., Oct. 1, 1925; s. Benjamin Moore and Alexandra (Emery) McKay; m. Sarah Carolyn Rush, July, 1954 (div. 1973); m. Betty Ruth Teipel, July 19, 1974; children: Jeremiah, Alexandra, Nicholas. BA, Yale U., 1946; postgrad., Harvard U., 1946-47. Reporter, re-writer Bergen Evening Record, Hackensack, N.J., 1948-49; v.p. Emery Kunston, Cin., 1961-62; pres. Profl. Realty Service, Cin., 1967, Emery Realty, Cin., 1969; dir. Thomas Emery's Sons, Inc., Cin., 1949—; pres. Chelsea Moore Corp., N.Y. and Cin., 1953-91, chmn. bd., 1979—; trustee various personal trusts, Ohio, Maine, Pa., 1969—, ptnr. various real property devels., Ohio, S.C., Colo., 1964—; executor Estate of Alexandra E. McKay, Monticello, Fla., 1983-89; co-chmn. Emery Air Corp., 1987—. Chmn. bd. Contemporary Arts Ctr., Cin., 1977-80, trustee, 1972—; chmn. Save the Terminal, Cin., 1972-73; trustee, sec. Community Improvement Corp., Cin., 1975—; trustee Am. Farm Sch., Thessaloniki, Greece, 1980-83, Seven Hills Sch. 1987-92, Nat. Dropout Prevention Fund. 1988-90; trustee, v.p. Miami Purchase Assn., Cin., 1962-67, 87-90. Lt. (j.g.)

USNR, 1943-46, ETO, PTO. Named Benefactor, City Mgr., Cin., 1968. Mem. Soc. Colonial Wars, Camargo Club, Racquet Club, Mason. Republican. Avocations: squash, shooting, fishing. Office: 2300 Carew Tower 441 Vine St Cincinnati OH 45202-2800

MOORE, ANDREA S., state legislator; b. Libertyville, Ill., Sept. 2, 1944. Attended, Drake U. m. William Moore; 3 children. Mem. Ill. Ho. of Reps., 1993—; mem. com. on elections and state govt., mem. com. on aging, mem. labor and villages com., mem. environ. and energy com., mem. labor and commerce com. Republican. Home: 234 W Cook Ave Libertyville IL 60048 Office: Ill Ho of Reps State Capitol Springfield IL 62706 also: 2014-H Stratton Bldg Springfield IL 62706 also: 733 N Milwaukee Libertyville IL 60048

MOORE, ANDREW GIVEN TOBIAS, II, investment banker, educator; b. New Orleans, Nov. 25, 1935; m. Ann Elizabeth Dawson, June 5, 1965; children—Cecily Elizabeth, Marianne Dawson. B.B.A., Tulane U., 1958, J.D., 1960. Bar: La. 1960, Del. 1963. Law clk. to chief justice Del. Dover, 1963; assoc. firm Killoran & Van Brunt, Wilmington, Del., 1964-70; partner Killoran & Van Brunt, 1971-76; partner firm Connolly, Bove & Lodge, Wilmington, 1976-82; justice Del. Supreme Ct., Wilmington, 1982-94; sr. mng. dir. Wasserstein Perella & Co., Inc., N.Y.C., 1994—; mem. Del. Bd. Accountancy, 1965-72, Del. Bd. Bar Examiners, 1975-82, Del. Jud. Selection Commn., 1977-82; mem. Del. Gen. Corp. law com., 1969-83; chmn. joint com. Del. Bar Assn.-Del. Bankers Assn., 1978-79; chmn. Del. Jud. Proprieties Com., 1983—, Del. Bench and Bar Conf., 1988-94; trustee Del. Bar Found., 1984-94; faculty Tulane Inst. European Legal Studies, Paris Inst. 1990—; adj. prof. law Georgetown U. Law Ctr., Widener U. Sch. Law, U. Iowa Coll. of Law; guest lectr. law Tulane U., U. Toronto, Can., U. Tex., Villanova U., Washington U., St. Louis, U. Iowa, Geo. Mason U., DeVrije U. van Brussel, Cath. U. Louvain La Neuve; mem. pres's. coun. Tulane U., 1990—; chmn. Tulane Corp. Law Inst., 1988—; Lehmann disting. vis. prof. law Washington U., St. Louis, 1994; Mason Ladd Disting. vis. prof. of Law U of Iowa, 1995. Trustee Del. Home and Hosp. for Chronically Ill, Smyrna, 1966-70, chmn., 1966-69; mem. New Castle County Hist. Rev. Bd., Wilmington, 1974-82; mem. Del. Cts. Planning Com., 1982-94; dean's coun. Tulane U. Law Sch., 1988—; bd. visitors Walter F. George Sch. Law, Mercer U., 1985-91, chmn., 1988-90. With JAGC, USAF, 1960-63. Mem. ABA, La. Bar Assn., Del. Bar Assn. (v.p. 1976-77, exec. com. 1982-83), Am Judicature Soc. (bd. dirs. 1982-86), Order Barristers, Phi Delta Phi, Delta Theta Phi (hon.), Omicron Delta Kappa. Democrat. Presbyterian. Office: Wasserstein Perella & Co 31 W 52d St New York NY 10019

MOORE, ANDREW TAYLOR, JR., banker; b. Tarboro, N.C., June 17, 1940; s. Andrew Taylor and Mary Dare (Allsbrook) M. BA in History, Duke U., 1962; LLB, U.Va., Charlottesville, 1965. Asst. sec. Signet Banking Corp., Richmond, 1965-71; asst. v.p., corporate sec., 1971-75, v.p., corporate sec., 1975-82, sr. v.p., corporate sec., 1982-94. Bd. dirs. Theatre IV, Richmond, Va., 1981—, Va. State YMCA adv. coun., Lynchburg, 1988—, trustee 1994—; trustee Hist. Richmond Found., 1993—. With U.S. Army, 1967. Mem. Am. Banking Inst., Am. Soc. Corp. Secs. (pub. practices com.), Assn. Bank Holdings Cos. (govt. rels. com. 1979—), Am. Bankers Assn. (legis. liaison adv. com. 1979-94), Va. Bankers Assn. (state legis. com. 1981-94), conf. State Bank Suprs. (legis. panel 1993—), Met. Richmond C. of C. (legis. affairs com.), Commonwealth Club. Presbyterian. Avocations: jogging; gardening; travel. Home: 2011 Hanover Ave Richmond VA 23220-3539

MOORE, ANNE FRANCES, museum director; b. Jan. 6, 1946; d. William Clifton and Frances Woods M.; m. Michael P. Mezzatesta, Mar. 14, 1970 (div. 1987); children: Philip Moore, Alexander Woods, Marya Frances. BA in Art History, Columbia U., 1969, MA, 1971, MEd in Fine Arts, 1971, MA in Art History, 1982. Tchr. Manassas (Va.) High Sch., 1971-72, Poly. Prep. Country Day Sch., Bklyn., 1972-74; intern Kimbell Art Mus., Ft. Worth, 1980-83, rsch. assoc., lectr., 1983; assoc. mus. educator, outreach dir. Dallas Mus. Art, 1986-88; curator of edn., lectr. dept. art Oberlin (Ohio) Coll., 1988-90, curator acad. programs, lectr. dept. art 1991-92; acting dir. The Allen Meml. Art Mus. at Oberlin Coll., 1991-92, dir., 1992—. Bd. trustees Intermus. Conservation Assn. Mem. Assn. Art Mus. Dirs., Assn. Coll. and Univ. Mus. and Galleries, Am. Assn. Mus. (edn. com.), Ohio Mus. Assn., Coll. Art Assn. Office: Allen Memorial Art Museum Oberlin College Oberlin OH 44074

MOORE, ANTHONY R., lawyer; b. Cleve., Feb. 19, 1950. AB, Harvard U., 1972; JD, U. Va., 1975. Bar: Ohio 1975. Ptnr. Jones, Day, Reavis & Pogue, Cleve. Office: Jones Day Reavis & Pogue North Point 901 Lakeside Ave Cleveland OH 44114

MOORE, ARTHUR COTTON, architect; b. Washington, Apr. 12, 1935; s. C. Godwin and Beatrice (McLean) M.; m. Patricia Stefan, June 10, 1966. BA cum laude, Princeton, 1958, MFA in Architecture, 1960. With firm Satterlee & Smith, Washington, 1960-61; Asso. firm Chloethiel Woodard Smith & Assocs., Washington, 1961-65; owner firm Arthur Cotton Moore/Assocs., Washington, 1965—; Profl. adviser Com. Against Nat. Airport, 1966; mem. planning project Nat. Airport, 1967; architect N.W. One Urban Renewal Community, 1970; treas., mem. exec. com. Georgetown Planning Council, Washington, 1970; chmn. subcom. on airports Com. of 100 on Federal City, 1973; mem. design adv. panel Balt. Dept. Housing and Community Devel. Author foreword Historic Buildings of Washington D.C, 1973; contbg. editor on urban affairs: Washingtonian, 1965-68; contbr. articles to profl. jours; designer: Canal Square, Washington, 1968, Madeira Sch. bldg., Bedford-Stuyvesant Comml. Ctr., 1978, pvt. houses, Old Post Office, 1983, Washington Harbour, 1986, The Portals, The Phillips Collection, 1989, Libr. of Congress Restoration, 1990; exhibited in group shows at Cooper-Hewitt Mus., N.Y.C., 1981, Columbia U., 1983, Libr. of Congress, 1985; painter & furniture designer Indsl. Baroque, N.Y.C., 1990, Facades, Chgo., 1991, Urban Stories, Paris, 1993, Visions of the Future, Prague, Wroclaw, and Berlin, 1995. Mem. Washington Bicentennial Program, 1973, Bicentennial Assembly of D.C., 1973. Served with AUS. Recipient numerous nat. archtl. awards. Fellow AIA (nat. Honor award 1977); mem. Nat. Trust for Hist. Preservation, Soc. Archtl. Historians, Met. Washington Planning and Housing Assn. Democrat. Clubs: Chevy Chase (Md.); Metropolitan (Washington), Princeton (Washin.N.Y.C.). Office: Arthur Cotton Moore Assocs PC Washington Harbour 3050 K St NW Washington DC 20007-5108

MOORE, ARTHUR JAMES, editor; b. San Antonio, May 7, 1922; s. Arthur James and Martha (MacDonald) M. B.A., Emory U., 1947. With N.Y. Daily News, 1947-50; editorial asst. Musical Am., 1950; editor, contbr. encys. other reference books Columbia U. Press, 1951-53; with Methodist Bd. of Global Ministries (formerly Bd. Missions), 1953-87; editor World Outlook, 1964-70; editor New World Outlook, 1970-87, dir. editorial dept. Edn. and Cultivation Div., 1980-87; cons. in field, 1987—; mem. press staff World Council Chs. assembly, Evanston, Ill., 1954, New Delhi, India, 1961; spl. corr. Religious News Service, Vatican Council, 1965, World Conf. Ch. and Soc., 1966. Mem. editorial bd. Christianity and Crisis, 1967-72, bd. dirs., 1971-82, contbg. editor, 1974-93; contbg. author: Religion and Peace, 1966, Ethics in the Present Tense, 1991; contbr. to various nat. mags. Served with USNR, 1942-45. Recipient Citation of Honor Associated Ch. Press, 1990; named to United Meth. Assn. of Communicators Hall of Fame, 1988. Mem. Alpha Tau Omega. Methodist. Home: 252 Henry St Brooklyn NY 11201-4651

MOORE, BEA, religious organization executive. Pres. The Woman's Home and Foreign Mission Society, Loudon, N.H.; nat. pres. The Woman's Home and Foreign Mission Society, Charlotte, N.C. Office: Woman's Home & Foreign Mission 845 Loudon Ridge Rd Loudon NH 03301

MOORE, BENJAMIN, theatrical producer; b. Boston, Oct. 25, 1945; s. Charles Frederick and Adeline Reeves (Nichols) M.; m. Mary Bradford Paine, May 31, 1969 (div. Jan. 1982); children: Alexandra Paine, Brendan Adams; m. Barbara Ann Dirickson, June 25, 1983; children: Lillian, Richard Braden. BA, Dartmouth U., 1967; MFA, Yale U., 1970. Asst. mng. dir. Yale Repertory Theatre, New Haven, 1969-70; gen. mgr. Westport (Conn.) Country Playhouse, 1970; prodn. dir. Am. Conservatory Theatre, San Francisco, 1970-79, gen. mgr., 1979-81, mng. dir., 1981-85; mng. dir., bd.

dirs. Seattle Repertory Theatre, 1985—. Active Seattle Arts Commn., 1986-90, chair, 1989. Mem. Wash. State Arts Alliance (bd. dirs. 1985—), League Resident Theatres (mem. exec. com. 1986—), Rainier Club. Office: Seattle Repertory Theatre 155 Mercer St Seattle WA 98109-4639

MOORE, BETTY JEAN, retired education educator; b. L.A., Apr. 4, 1927; d. Ralph Gard and Dora Mae (Shinn) Bowman; m. James H. Moore, Nov. 25, 1944 (div. 1968); children: Barbara, Suzanne, Sandra; m. George W. Nichols, Oct. 15, 1983. BA, Pasadena Coll., 1957; MA, U. Nev., 1963; PhD, U. Ill., 1973. Tchr. Calif. pub. schs., 1953-63, sec. tchr., 1963-68; asst. prof. Ea. Ill. U., Charleston, 1968-71; grad. teaching asst. U. Ill., Champaign, 1971-73; asst. prof. to assoc. prof. S.W. Tex. State U., San Marcos, 1973-83; prof. edn. S.W. Tex. State U., 1983-89, ret., 1989; sch. evaluator; cons. in field; reading clinic dir. S.W. Tex. State U., 1974-85; cons. Min. Edn., Rep. of Singapore, 1980. Contbr. articles to profl. jours.; author: Teaching Reading, 1984; producer/dir. 5 ednl. videos. Active fund raising various charitable orgns. Mem. Internat. Reading Assn. (chpt. pres. 1964-65), Nat. Council Tchrs. English, AAUP. Presbyterian. Avocations: reading, writing, swimming, cooking. Office: Southwest Tex State U C & I Dept San Marcos TX 78666

MOORE, BEVERLY COOPER, lawyer; b. Greensboro, N.C., Dec. 1, 1909; s. Adolphus Greene and Georgia (Cooper) M.; m. Irene Warren Mitchell, July 10, 1943; children: Beverly Cooper Jr., Irene Warren Moore Miller. AB, U. N.C., 1931; JD, Yale U., 1934. Bar: N.C. 1934, U.S. Dist. Ct. N.C. 1934, U.S. Ct. Appeals (4th cir.) 1954, U.S. Supreme Ct. 1945. Practice law Greensboro, 1934—; ptnr., then counsel Smith, Helms Mulliss & Moore (and predecessors), 1946-94; solo practice, 1994—; mem. N.C. Gen. Assembly, 1941-42. Contbr. to legal publs. Trustee Consol. U. N.C., 1967-72; chmn. bd. trustees U. N.C.-Greensboro, 1972-75. Served with USAAF, 1942-45. Fellow Am. Bar Found.; mem. ABA (ho. of dels. 1962-68, 73-75, 76-80, bd. govs. 1970-73), N.C. Bar Assn. (pres. 1958-59), Greensboro Bar Assn. (pres. 1949-50), assn. of Bar of City of N.Y., Internat. Bar sssn., Am. Coll. Trial Lawyers, Practising Law Inst. (trustee 1965-72), Am. Judicature Soc. (bd. dirs. 1964-67), Am. Law Inst., Fed. Jud. Conf., Am. Counsel Assn. (pres. 1970-71), Inst. Jud. Administrn., Nat. Center Adminstrv. Justice (dir. 1979-81, chmn. 1981-82), Southeastern Legal Found. (chmn. legal adv. bd. 1979-87), SAR, Phi Beta Kappa, Selden Soc. (London). Episcopalian. Clubs: Sedgefield Country, Greensboro City, Greensboro Country. Home: 906 Country Club Dr Greensboro NC 27408-5602

MOORE, BOB STAHLY, communications executive; b. Pasadena, Calif., July 3, 1936; s. Norman Hastings and Mary Augusta (Stahly) M. Student, U. Mo., 1954-58, MIT, 1958-62. News dir. WPEO, Peoria, Ill., 1958-60, KSST, Davenport, Iowa, 1960-62, WIRE, Indpls., 1962-64, WCFL, Chgo., 1964-67; White House corr. Metromedia, Inc., Washington, 1967-71; news dir. Gateway Communications, Altoona, Pa., 1972-74; Washington Bur. chief MBS, 1974-76; v.p. news MBS, Arlington, Va., 1976-78; White House corr. MBS, 1978-81; dir. communications Fed. Home Loan Bank Bd., Washington, 1981-85; spl. asst. to bd. govs. Fed. Res. System, Washington, 1985—. Active ARC. Served with USAF, 1961-63. Recipient profl. awards Ind. News Broadcasters, 1963, Ill. News Broadcasters, 1965, UPI, 1960, 63, 65, AP, 1956, 58, 61, 65, 67, Mo. News Broadcasters, 1956, 61. Mem. Radio and Television News Dirs. Assn. (Profl. award), White House Corrs. Assn., State Dept. Corrs. Assn., Radio-Television Corrs. Gallery (U.S. Capitol), Chgo. Council on Fgn. Relations, Pub. Relations Soc. Am., Nat., Washington, Chgo. press clubs, U.S. Jr., Mo., Ill. chambers commerce, Sigma Delta Chi. Presbyterian. Home: 817 Crescent Dr Alexandria VA 22302-2214 Office: 20th and Constitution NW Washington DC 20551

MOORE, BOBBY See RASHAD, AHMAD

MOORE, BRIAN, writer; b. Belfast, No. Ireland, Aug. 25, 1921; came to U.S., 1960; s. James Bernard and Eileen (McFadden) M.; m. Jean Denney, Oct. 1967; 1 son, Michael. Author: The Lonely Passion of Judith Hearne, 1955, The Feast of Lupercal, 1957, The Luck of Ginger Coffey, 1960, An Answer From Limbo, 1962, The Emperor of Ice-Cream, 1965, I Am Mary Dunne, 1968, Fergus, 1970, The Revolution Script, 1971, Catholics, 1972, The Great Victorian Collection, 1975, The Doctor's Wife, 1976, The Mangan Inheritance, 1979, The Temptation of Eileen Hughes, 1981, Cold Heaven, 1983, Black Robe, 1985, The Color of Blood, 1987, Lies of Silence, 1990, No Other Life, 1993. Recipient Que. Lit. prize, 1958, U.S. Nat. Arts and Letters award, 1961, Fiction award Gov.-Gen. Can., 1961, 75, W.H. Smith award, 1973, James Tait Black Meml. award, 1975, Heinemann award Royal Soc. Lit., 1986, Sunday Express Book of Yr. award, 1987, Lifetime Achievement award L.A. Times, 1994; Guggenheim fellow, 1959; Can Coun. sr. fellow, 1962, 76; Scottish Arts Coun. Internat. fellow, 1983. Office: care Curtis Brown 10 Astor Pl New York NY 10003

MOORE, BROOKE NOEL, philosophy educator; b. Palo Alto, Calif., Dec. 2, 1943; s. Ralph Joseph and Dorothy Louise (Noll) M.; m. Linda Ely; children: Sherry, Bill. BA, Antioch Coll., 1966; PhD, U. Cin., 1973. Asst. prof. Calif. State U., Chico, 1970-74, assoc. prof., 1974-79, prof., 1980—. Author: Philosophical Possibilities Beyond Death, 1981; co-author: Critical Thinking, 1987, 4th edit., 1993, The Power of Ideas, 1990, 2d edit., 1992, The Cosmos, God and Philosophy, 1992, Moral Philosophy, 1993, The Power of Ideas: A Brief Edition, 1995, Making Yout Case, 1995; mem. editl. bd. Tchg. Philosophy, 1972. Mem. Am. Philos. Assn. Office: Calif State U Chico Dept of Philosophy Chico CA 95929

MOORE, C. BRADLEY, chemistry educator; b. Boston, Dec. 7, 1939; s. Charles Walden and Dorothy (Lutz) M.; m. Penelope Williamson Percival, Aug. 27, 1960; children—Megan Bradley, Scott Woodward. B.A. magna cum laude, Harvard U., 1960; Ph.D., U. Calif., Berkeley, 1963. Predoctoral fellow NSF, 1960-63; asst. prof. chemistry U. Calif., Berkeley, 1963-68, assoc. prof., 1968-72, prof., 1972—, vice chmn. dept., 1971-75, chmn. dept. chemistry, 1982-86, dean Coll. Chemistry, 1988-94; professeur associé Faculté des Scis. Paris, 1970, 75; vis. prof. Inst. for Molecular Sci., Okazaki, Japan, 1979, Fudan U., Shanghai, Peoples Republic China, 1979, adv. prof., 1988—; vis. fellow Joint Inst. for Lab. Astrophysics, U. Colo., Boulder, 1981-82; mem. editorial bd. Jour. Chemical Physics, 1973-75, Chemical Physics Letters, 1980-85, Jour. Physical Chem., 1981-87, Laser Chemistry, 1982—. Editor: Chemical and Biochemical Applications of Lasers; assoc. editor Annual Review of Physical Chemistry, 1985-90; contbr. articles to profl. jours. Recipient Coblentz award, 1973, E.O. Lawrence Meml. award U.S. Dept. Energy, 1986, Lippincott award, 1987, 1st award Inter-Am. Photochem. Soc., 1988; nat. scholar Harvard U., 1958-60; fellow Alfred P. Sloan Found., 1968, Guggenheim fellow, 1969, Humboldt Rsch. award for Sr. U.S. Scientists, 1994. Fellow AAAS, Am. Phys. Soc. (Plyler award 1994); mem. NAS (chmn. com. undergrad. sci. edn.), Am. Chem. Soc. (past chmn. div. phys. chemistry, Calif. sect. award 1977), Indsl. Rsch. Inst. (acad. adv. com.). Avocation: cycling. Home: 936 Oxford St Berkeley CA 94707-2435 Office: U Calif Dept Chemistry 211 Lewis Hall Berkeley CA 94720

MOORE, CALVIN C., mathematics educator, administrator; b. N.Y.C., Nov. 2, 1936; s. Robert A. and Ruth (Miller) M.; m. Doris Lienhard, Sept. 14, 1974. A.B. summa cum laude, Harvard U., 1958, M.A., 1959, Ph.D. in Math., 1960. Research instr. U. Chgo., 1960-61; asst. prof. U. Calif. at Berkeley, 1961-65, assoc. prof., 1965-66, prof. math., 1966—, dean phys. scis., 1971-76; dir. Center Pure and Applied Math 1977-80; dep. dir. Math. Scis. Research Inst., 1981-85; asst. v.p. acad. planning and personnel U. Calif. Systemwide Adminstrn., 1985-86, assoc. v.p. acad. affairs, 1986-94; mem. Inst. for Advanced Study, 1964-65; mem. at large NRC, 1971-73; mem. pres.'s com. on Nat. Medal Sci., 1979-81. Chmn. bd. govs. Pacific Jour. Math., 1972-76; editor: Mathematische Zeitschrift, Ill. Jour. Math, Pacific Jour. Math.; exec. editor research announcements; mng. editor: Bull. Am. Math. Soc.; contbg. editor: Advances in Mathematics; contbr. articles to profl. jours. Fellow Am. Acad. Arts and Scis.; mem. Am. Math. Soc. (exec. com., council mem. at large, v.p., chmn. bd. trustees). Home: 1408 Eagle Point Ct Lafayette CA 94549-2328

MOORE, CARL GORDON, chemist, educator; b. Zanesville, Ohio, Feb. 7, 1922; s. Henry Carl and Hilda Marie (Oberfield) M.; m. Sheila Marie O'Toole, Nov. 2, 1951; children: Carl, Patrick, Martina, Michael, Maureen, Regina, Madeleine, Terence. BS in Chem. Engring., Ga. Inst. Tech., 1947; MS in Chem. Engring., Carnegie Mellon U., 1948, postgrad., 1948-51; prof.

grad., U. Newark, Del., 1973-74. Cert. tchr., Pa., Del. Chemist Manhattan Project, Oak Ridge, Tenn., 1944-46; chem. engr. Koppers Co., Pitts., 1946-47; rsch. chemist E.I. DuPont de Nemours & Co., Wilmington, Del., 1951-73; tchr. Chester (Pa.)-Upland Sch., 1974-78; tutor Del. Tutoring, Wilmington, 1981-88; instr. Del. Tech. and Community Coll., Wilmington, 1982-90, U. Del., Newark, 1984—. Author tech. reports on hydrogen over voltage of titanium and zirconium. Adult leader Wilmington area Boy Scouts Am., 1953-73; tchr. Sunday sch., Wilmington, 1962-67; group leader U.S. Census Bur., 1980. Sgt. U.S. Army, 1943-46. Mem. Am. Chem. Soc., Sigma Xi. Achievements include 13 patents, production of TiO2 Rutile by chloride process, 100% oxygen oxidation of TiCl4, 100% anatase by chloride process. Home: 1913 Oak Lane Rd Wilmington DE 19803-5237

MOORE, CAROLE IRENE, librarian; b. Berkeley, Calif., Aug. 15, 1944. AB, Stanford U., 1966; MLS, Columbia U., 1967. Reference libr. Columbia U., N.Y.C., 1967-68; reference libr. U. Toronto, Can., 1968-80, head cataloguing, 1980-85, assoc. libr., 1985-86, chief libr., 1986—; mem. nat. adv. bd. Nat. Libr. Can., Ottawa, 1991-94; bd. dirs. Rsch. Librs. Group. 1994—, U. Toronto Press, 1994—. Recipient Disting. Alumni award Columbia U., 1989. Mem. ALA, Can. Libr. Assn., Can. Assn. Rsch. Librs. (pres. 1989-91). Avocation: gardening. Office: U Toronto Libr, 130 Saint George St, Toronto, ON Canada M5S 1A5

MOORE, CAROLYN LANNIN, video specialist; b. Hammond, Ind., Aug. 14, 1945; d. William Wren and Julia Audrey (Mathews) Lannin; m. F. David Moore, Oct. 21, 1967; children: Jillian Winter, Douglas Mathew, Owen Glen. BA, Ind. U., 1967; MA, Purdue U., 1991. Stockholders corr. Sears Roebuck and Co., Chgo., 1967-68; caseworker Lake County Dept. of Pub. Welfare, Hammond, Ind., 1968-71; field dir. Campfire Girls Inc., Highland, Ind., 1975-77; project dir. Northwest Ind. Pub. Broadcasting, Highland, 1984-85, interim exec. dir., 1985-87; cons. Telecommunications and Grant Writing, Munster, Ind., 1981-85; prin. Carolyn Moore and Assocs.-Laughing Cat Prodns., Munster, Ind., 1987—; instr. Purdue U.-Calumet, Ind., 1989; instr. Valparaiso (Ind.) U., 1990-91; lectr. in field. Producer tv series Visclosky Viewpoint, 1985-87; video producer A Kid's Eye View of the Symphony, 1987; co-host This Week in Munster. Mem. Munster Cable TV Commn., 1984—; bd. dirs., pres. N.W. Ind. Literacy Coalition, Inc.; mem. Lake County Master Gardeners. Mem. AAUW, NAFE, Alliance for Community Media, Assn. Ind. Video and Filmmakers Inc., Munster C. of C., Communicators N.W. Ind. (treas. 1995), Ind. U. Alumni Assn., Scherwood Ladies Golf Leagues, Wicker Park Ladies Golf League. Democrat. Catholic. Avocations: golf, reading, sailing. Home and Office: Carolyn Moore & Assocs Laughing Cat Prodns 9604 Cypress Ave Hammond IN 46321-3418

MOORE, CHARLES AUGUST, JR., psychologist; b. Medford, Oreg., Feb. 22, 1944; s. Charles August and Bernadine (Newlun) M. BS, Lewis and Clark Coll., 1965; MA, U. Colo., 1967, PhD, 1972. Lic. psychologist, Calif., Oreg. Teaching asst. U. Colo., Boulder, 1965-66, 70-71, rsch. asst., counselor, practicum supr., 1966-67, 71-72; asst. psychologist State Home and Tng. Sch., Grand Junction, Colo., 1967; intern in psychology Camarillo (Calif.) State Hosp., 1968-69; psychology assoc., program psychologist Camarillo Drug Abuse Program (The Family), 1969-70; intern in psychology Oxnard (Calif.) Mental Health Ctr., 1969; clin. psychologist, dir. intern tng. Rural Clinics, Reno, 1972; clin. psychologist Kern County Mental Health Svcs., Bakersfield, Calif., 1972-74; clin., cons. psychologist San Diego County Mental Health Svcs., 1974-88; pvt. practice La Jolla (Calif.) Clinic, 1976-78; August Ctr., Chula Vista, Calif., 1978-85; staff psychologist Dept. Vet.'s Affairs Domiciliary, White City, Oreg., 1988—; guest lectr. Calif. State Coll., Bakersfield, 1973-74; mem. Health Systems Agy. Mental Health Task Force, 1979; mem. doctoral dissertation com. U.S. Internat. U., 1975-76; mem. mental health task force San Diego County Bd. Suprs., 1979. Contbr. articles to profl. jours. Mem. Univ. City Community Coun., San Diego, 1976-78; bd. dirs. Pub. Employees Assn., 1976-77. Recipient Experiment in Internat. Living European Study award Lewis and Clark Coll., 1962; USPHS fellow, 1967-68; U. Colo. Grad. Sch. Rsch. grantee, 1971; recipient Hands and Heart award Dept. Vets. Affairs, 1989-90, Domiciliary Spl. Contbn. and Outstanding Performance awards, 1990, 91. Mem. APA, Am. Psychology and Law Soc., Calif. Psychol. Assn., Western Psychol. Assn., San Diego County Psychol. Assn., Assn. County Clin. Psychologists San Diego, San Diego Psychology and Law Soc., San Diego Soc. Clin. Psychologists. Office: Dept VA Domiciliary Psychology Svc 8495 Crater Lake Hwy White City OR 97503-3011

MOORE, CHARLES HEWES, JR., industrial and engineered products executive; b. Coatesville, Pa., Aug. 12, 1929; s. Charles Hewes and Jane Richards (Scott) M.; m. Judith L. McClellan, June 23, 1971; children: Charles Hewes III, James, David, Susan, Kevin, Christopher, Margery, Brian, Amanda. BME, Cornell U., 1952. With Lenape Forge Co. div. Gulf & Western Industries, West Chester, Pa., 1952-73; pres. Lapp div. Interpace Corp., Le Roy, N.Y., 1973-77; pres., chief exec. officer Allied Thermal Corp. subs. Interpace, 1978-79; sr. v.p., dir. Interpace, 1979-80; exec. v.p., dir. Interpace Corp., Parsippany, N.J., 1980-81; pres., chief exec. officer, dir. Clevepak Corp., 1981-83, 84-86, chief exec. officer, vice chmn. bd., dir., 1983-84; mng. dir. Peers & Co., 1987-88; chief exec. officer Peers Mgmt. Resources, Inc., 1987-88; pres., chief exec. officer Ransburg Corp., Indpls., 1988-92; pres. ITW Finishing Systems and Products, Indpls., 1990-92; exec. v.p. Ill. Tool Works Inc., Glenview, 1991-92; vice-chmn. Advisory Capital Ptnrs., Inc., Greenwich, Conn., 1993-94; CEO, chmn. bd. dirs. Xpander Pak Inc., 1995—; athletic dir. Cornell U., 1994—; bd. dirs. Turner Corp., Elcotel, Inc. Mem. mgmt. policy coun., mem. adv. bd. Fundamental Mgmt.; chmn. audit com., pub. sector dir. U.S. Olympic Com. Recipient Gold medal in 400 meter hurdles, 1952 Olympics, Herbert Adams Meml. award for advancement of Am. sculpture, Nat. Sculpture Soc., 1985. Mem. Pine Valley Golf Club (N.J.), Royal and Ancient Golf Club St. Andrews (Scotland). Republican. Episcopalian. Office: Cornell U Teagle Hall Campus Rd Ithaca NY 14853-6501

MOORE, CHRISTOPHER HUGH, writer; b. Stoke-on-Trent, Eng., June 9, 1950; arrived in Can., 1954; s. M. Vincent and Kathleen A. (Lennox) M.; m. Louise A. Brophy, May 7, 1977; children: Elizabeth, Kate. BA with honors, U. B.C., Vancouver, 1971; MA, U. Ottawa, Ont., Can., 1977. Staff historian Nat. Historic Pks. Svc., Louisbourg, N.S., Can., 1972-75; sec. to bd. Heritage Can. Found., Ottawa, 1977-78; writer, historian Toronto, Ont., 1979—. Author: Louisbourg Portraits, 1982, The Loyalists, 1984, 94; co-author: Illustrated History of Canada, 1987, The Story of Canada, 1992. Recipient Gov. Gen.'s Lit. award Can., 1983, Sec. of State Prize Govt. Can., Ottawa, 1985, Mr. Christie's Prize Christie-Brown Ltd., Toronto, 1993. Mem. Writers' Union of Can. (chair contracts com. 1990-94), Can. Hist. Assn. Office: 396 Pacific Ave # 202, Toronto, ON Canada M6P 2R1

MOORE, DALTON, JR., petroleum engineer, scientist, geologist; b. Snyder, Tex., Mar. 25, 1918; s. Dalton and Anne (Yonge) M. Grad., Tarleton State U., 1938; BS, Tex. Agrl. and Mech. U., 1942; diploma, U.S. Army Command and Gen. Staff Sch., 1945. Field engr. Gulf Oil Corp., 1946; dist. engr. Chgo. Corp., 1947-48; chief reservoir engr. 1949; mgr. Burdell Oil Corp. N.Y.C. and Snyder, Tex., 1950-52; mgr. Wimberly Field Unit, 1953-55; profl. petroleum cons. Abilene, Tex., 1956—; pres. Dalton Moore Engring. Co., 1957-67, First Oil Co., 1960-64; Second Oil Co., 1960-72, Petroleum Engrs. Operating Co., 1967-90, Evaluation Engr. for Investment Bankers Corp., 1968-89, Investment Bankers Oil Corp., Inc. 1968-89. Pres. Sweetwater (Tex.) Jr. C. of C., 1938; precinct chmn. Taylor County Dem. Com., 1956-76; bd. dirs. Taylor County chpt. ARC, 1956-62. Served to maj., AUS, 1940-46. Named Eagle Scout, Boy Scouts Am.; mem. Mus. Natural History. Mem. AIME (chmn. West Cen. Tex. sect. 1954), NRA (charter, Golden Eagle), Nat. Audubon Soc., Tex. Nat. Arbor Day Found., Nature Conservancy, Soc. Petroleum Engrs. (mem. legion of hon. 1989—), Abilene Geol. Soc., Smithsonian Assocs., Am. Mus. Natural History, The Highlander Club, Bass Anglers Sportsman Soc., N.Am. Hunting Club, VFW, KP. Address: 326 N Turner Ave Moore OK 73160-5944

MOORE, DAN TYLER, writer; b. Washington, Feb. 1, 1908; s. Dan T. and Luvean Jones (Butler) M.; m. Elizabeth Valley Oakes, Mar. 12, 1932; children: Luvean O. (Mrs. Owens), Elizabeth Oakes (Mrs. Thornton), Harriet (Mrs. Lester Ballard), Dan Tyler III. BS, Yale, 1931. Chief counter-intelligence OSS, Middle East, 1943-44; pres. Middle East Co., Cleve., 1946-48,

China Co., Cleve., 1946-48; asst. to pres. Intercontinental Hotels Corp., Istanbul, Turkey, 1948-50; freelance writer Cleveland Heights, Ohio, 1950—. Author: The Terrible Game, 1957, Cloak and Cipher, 1962, Wolves, Widows and Orphans, 1966, Lecturing For Profit, 1967, (movie) Gymkata 1988; contbr. articles and stories to popular mags. Pres. Greater Cleve. Muscular Dystrophy Assn., 1952-65; mem. exec. com. Cuyahoga County Dem. Party, 1951-70, mem. state exec. com., 1962-65; commr. Ohio Fed. Jury, 1961-68; trustee, bd. dirs. Cleve. Mus. Natural History; bd. dirs. Near East Coll. Assn., Karamu Theatre, Cleve. Served with AUS, 1942-44. Mem. Internat. Platform Assn. (chmn. bd., dir. gen.). Clubs: Met. (Washington, D.C.); Yale (N.Y.C.); Union, Tavern, Skating and Rowfant (Cleve.). Home: 2564 Berkshire Rd Cleveland OH 44106-3365

MOORE, DANIEL CHARLES, physician; b. Cin., Sept. 9, 1918; s. Daniel Clark and May (Strebel) M.; m. Betty Maxine Tobias, Aug. 5, 1945 (div. 1988); children: Barbara, Nancy, Daniel, Susan. Grad., Amherst (Mass.) Coll., 1940; M.D., Northwestern U., 1944. Diplomate: Am. Bd. Anesthesiologists. Intern Wesley Meml. Hosp., Chgo., 1944; resident Wesley Meml. Hosp., 1945-47; dir. anesthesia Va. Mason Hosp., Seattle, 1947-72; anesthesiologist (Mason Clinic), 1947-72, sr. cons. in anesthesia, 1972-83; clin. prof. U. Wash. Sch. Medicine, 1963—. Author: Regional Block, 1953, Stellate Ganglion Block, 1954, Complications of Regional Anesthesia, 1955, Anesthetic Techniques for Obstetrical Anesthesia and Analgesia, 1964, also papers. Served as capt. M.C. AUS, 1945-47. Recipient Ralph M. Waters award Ill. Soc. Anesthesiologists, Carl Koller Gold medal European Soc. Regional Anaesthesia, 1995. Mem. Am. Soc. Anesthesiologists (1st v.p. 1953-54, 2d v.p. 1954-55, pres. 1958-59, distinguished service award 1976), AMA (sec. anesthesiology sect. 1956-58), Am. Acad. Anesthesiology, Am. Soc. Regional Anesthesia (adv. bd., Gaston Labat award 1977), Wash. Soc. Anesthesiologists (pres. 1949-50), Wash. Med. Soc., King County Med. Soc., Faculty Anaesthetists Royal Coll. Surgeons (hon.), Northwest Forum, Beta Theta Pi, Nu Sigma Nu. Home: Madison Park Pl # 103 2000 43rd Ave E Seattle WA 98112-2759 Office: PO Box 900 Seattle WA 98111-0900

MOORE, DANIEL L., architect; b. Chgo., Oct. 1, 1953; s. James Edward and Rosemary (Anderson) M.; m. Jeanne Marie Starshak, Dec. 2, 1978; children: Elisabeth Anne, Anne Rose. AAS, S.W. Jr. Coll., Chgo., 1974. Registered architect, Va., Ill., N.Y., Del., Pa., Md., D.C. Draftsman Rebar Detailing, Burbank, Ill., 1974, Sargeant & Lundy Engring., Chgo., 1974-78, Chris Stefanos & Assocs., Oak Lawn, Ill., 1978-79; staff architect Hansen Lind Meyer, Chgo., 1979-90; architect, mng. prin. Hansen Lind Meyer, Reston, Va., 1990-94, Hansen Lind Meyer Inc., McLean, Va., 1994—. Mem. AIA (nat. and Va. chpt.). Democrat. Roman Catholic. Home: 13631 Dornock Ct Herndon VA 22071-3376 Office: Hansen Lind Meyer Inc 1420 Beverly Rd Mc Lean VA 22101

MOORE, DAVID GRAHAM, sociologist, educator; b. Norwich, Conn., May 9, 1918; s. Royal Tolman and Alta Gladys (Jenkin) M.; children by previous marriage: Barbara E., Linda C. Turbyville; m. Margaret Louise Rider, Dec. 2, 1950; children: David G., Kathryn R. (Mrs. T.J. Miller). B.A., U. Ill., 1940, M.A., 1943; Ph.D., U. Chgo., 1954. Personnel research Western Electric Co., 1940-41; mem. personnel staff Sears, Roebuck and Co., 1941-43, 46-50; personnel dir. Am. Flange & Mfg. Co., 1943-46; asst. prof. sociology, indsl. relations U. Chgo., 1950-55, asso. prof. bus. adminstrn., sociology, dir. exec. program, 1955-56; prof. mgmt. Mich. State U., 1956-58, head dept. personnel and prodn. adminstrn., 1958-61, prof. mgmt., sociology, 1961-63; dean N.Y. State Sch. Indsl. and Labor Relations, Cornell U., 1963-71; sr. v.p. Conf. Bd., N.Y.C., 1971-73; exec. v.p. Conf. Bd., 1973-79; prof., chmn. dept. bus. adminstrn. U. North Fla., 1979-86, prof. bus. adminstrn., 1986-89, asst. to pres., 1983-84; vis. Ford Found. prof. behavioral scis. U. Wis., fall 1962. Co-author: Human Relations in Industry, 4th edit, 1964, SRA Employee Inventory, 1951, The Enterprising Man, 1964. Mem. Am. Sociol. Assn., Soc. Applied Anthropology, Acad. Mgmt., Indsl. Relations Research Assn. Home: 91 San Juan Dr Apt D-1 Ponte Vedra Beach FL 32082-2304 Office: U North Fla PO Box 17074 Jacksonville FL 32245-7074

MOORE, DAVID LOWELL, dentist; b. Hartshorne, Okla., Apr. 3, 1930; s. David Lee and Zula (Winslow) M.; m. Mary Janell Stewart, Sept. 7, 1962; children—David Lee, Andrew Stewart. B.S., Okla. State U., 1949; M.S., M.A., U. Mo., 1964, D.D.S., 1955. Asst. prof. dentistry U. Mo. Dental Sch., Kansas City, 1958-61; teaching fellow U. Mo. Dental Sch., 1961-63, assoc. prof., 1963-64, prof., chmn. dept. restorative dentistry, 1964—; cons. VA hosps., Leavenworth, Kans., Topeka, Kansas City and Columbia, Mo.; mem. faculty VA Physician and Dentist in Residence Program; mem. test constrn. com. Nat. Bd. Dental Exams. Author articles in field, chpt. in textbook; editorial rev. bd. Jour. Prosthetic Dentistry. Deacon Nall Ave. Baptist Ch., Shawnee, Kans., 1970—. Served with USAF, 1955-58. Recipient Univ. Alumni Achievement award; trustees faculty fellow. Mem. ADA, Omicron Kappa Upsilon, Omicron Delta Kappa, Psi Omega. Home: 10705 W 52nd Cir Shawnee KS 66203-1817 Office: U Mo Dental Sch 650 E 25th St Kansas City MO 64108-2716

MOORE, DAVID SUMNER, forensic document examiner; b. Natick, Mass., Aug. 29, 1939; s. Sumner Lucian and Lillian Rose (Kirman) M.; m. Betty Edwina Morris, Feb. 3, 1962 (div. 1982); children: Ronald Anthony, Michael David; m. Beverly Ann Holt, Apr. 23, 1982; 1 child, Rachel Rene. BS in Law Enforcement and Corrections, U. Nebr., 1972; MEd in Adult Edn., Ga. So. Coll., 1976. Diplomate Am. Bd. Forensic Document Examiners. Enlisted pvt. U.S. Army, 1959, advanced through grades to CW4, chief questioned document sect., ret., 1979; sr. questioned document analyst U.S. Postal So. Region Crime Lab., Memphis, Tenn., 1980-82; sr. questioned document examiner Las Vegas (Nev.) Met. Crime Lab., 1982-84; sr. questioned document examiner II Calif. Dept. Justice, Sacramento, 1984—. Editorial staff: Southwestern Examiner, 1992; contbr. articles to Jour. Forensic Scis., Forensic Sci. Internat. Decorated Legion of Merit. Fellow Am. Acad. Forensic Scis.; m. Southwestern Assn. Forensic Document Examiners, So. Assn. Forensic Scientists, No. Calif. Laser Study Group, Phi Kappa Phi. Home: 9010 Barrhill Way Fair Oaks CA 95628 Office: Calif Dept Justice Bur Forensic Svcs Questioned Doc Sect 4949 Broadway Sacramento CA 95820

MOORE, DEMI (DEMI GUYNES), actress; b. Roswell, N.Mex., Nov. 11, 1962; d. Danny and Virginia Guynes; m. Bruce Willis, Nov. 21, 1987; 2 daughters: Rumer Glenn, Scout LaRue. Studies with Zina Provendie. Actress: (feature films) Choices, 1981, Parasite, 1981, Young Doctors in Love, 1982, Blame it on Rio, 1984, No Small Affair, 1984, St. Elmo's Fire, 1985, About Last Night..., 1986, Wisdom, 1986, One Crazy Summer, 1987, The Seventh Sign, 1988, We're No Angels, 1989, Ghost, 1990, Mortal Thoughts, 1991 (also co-producer), The Butcher's Wife, 1991, Nothing But Trouble, 1991, A Few Good Men, 1992, Indecent Proposal, 1993, Disclosure, 1994, The Scarlet Letter, 1995; (TV series) General Hospital, 1982-83. Office: Creative Artists Agy Inc 9830 Wilshire Blvd Beverly Hills CA 90212*

MOORE, DIANNE J. HALL, insurance claims administrator; b. Wadsworth, Ohio, June 9, 1936; d. Glenn Mackey and Dorothy Laverne (Broomall) Hall; widowed; children: Christine M. Gardner Fiocca, Jon R. Gardner. BA in Speech, Heidelberg Coll., Tiffin, Ohio, 1958. Receptionist Buckeye Union Ins. Co., Akron, Ohio, 1966-67; adjuster Liberty Mut. Ins. Co., Akron, 1967-69; claims liaison Ostrov Agy., Akron, 1969-70; underwriter Clark Agy., Wadsworth, 1971-72; adjuster Celina Group, Wadsworth, 1972-73, Nationwide, Canton, Ohio, 1973-77; asst. claim mgr. Motorist Mut. Ins. Co., Akron, 1977-87; claim rep. Ohio Casualty Ins. Co., San Diego, 1987-88; claims adminstr. Riser Foods, Inc. Risk Mgmt., Bedford Heights, Ohio, 1989—. Mem. Ohio Hist. Soc., Friends of Gettysburg. Mem. Ohio State Claims Assn., Akron Claims Assn. (pres. 1985), Canton Claims Assn. Avocations: Civil War history, genealogical research, reading, painting, boating. Office: Riser Foods Inc 5300 Richmond Rd Bedford Heights OH 44146-1335

MOORE, DOLORES J., nursing executive; b. Martin, Tenn., Apr. 7, 1931; d. Robert James and Ruby Mae (Dowdy) Jones; m. Perry Moore Jr., Jan. 2, 1949; children: David Moore, Margaret Pfaff. AA in Nursing, Union U., 1964; B.S.N., U. Ill., 1975; MS in Edn., Ill. State U., 1978. Staff nurse Jackson-Madison County Gen. Hosp., Jackson, Tenn., 1964-66; supr. nursing Jackson-Madison County Gen. Hosp., 1966-69; asst. dir. nursing Deaconess Hosp., St. Louis, 1969-70; dir. nursing svcs. Mennonite Hosp., Bloomington, Ill., 1971-78; dir. med./surgical svcs. Meml. Hosp. Gulfport, Gulfport, Miss., 1978-81; v.p. nursing Jackson-Madison County Gen. Hosp., Jackson, 1981—; chmn. Tenn. Bd. Nursing, Nashville, 1985—; mem. adv. bd. Jackson Area Vocat. Tech. Sch., paramedics program Jackson State Community Coll., Sch. Practical Nursing, Jackson; adj. faculty mem. Union U. Sch. Nursing, Jacskon. Mem. Tenn. Orgn. Nurse Execs., Am. Orgn. Nurse Execs., Nat. League Nursing, Tenn. Hosp. Assn. (nursing coun.), Nat. Honor Soc., Rotary. Avocations: quilt-making, remodeling old homes. Office: Jackson Madison County Gen Hosp 708 W Forest Ave Jackson TN 38301-3901

MOORE, DONALD EUGENE, retired botanical garden administrator, communications executive; b. Topeka, June 17, 1928; s. Carl H. and Janet (Whitten) M.; m. Susan Elizabeth Taylor, May 29, 1950; children: Stephen Carl, Leslie Ann. AB in English, Washburn U., 1951. Ptnr. MDG Communications, N.Y.C., 1959-68; pres. Downtown Bklyn. Devel. Assn., 1968-78, N.Y. C. of C. and Industry, 1978-80; pres. Bklyn. Bot. Garden, 1980-90, ret., 1990. Mem. N.Y.C. Art Commn., 1976-79. Cpl. USMC, 1946-48. Mem. Internat. Downtown Execs. Assn. (pres. 1974-75), Bklyn. C. of C. (pres. 1975-78). Republican. Lutheran.

MOORE, DONALD FRANCIS, lawyer; b. N.Y.C., Dec. 14, 1937; s. John F. and Helen A. (McLoughlin) M.; m. Alice L. Kalmar; children: Christina M., Marianne, Karen L., Alison A. AB, Fordham U., 1959; JD, St. John's U., Bklyn., N.Y., 1962. Bar: N.Y. 1962, D.C. 1970. Assoc. Paul, Weiss, Rifkind, Wharton & Garrison, N.Y.C., 1962-70, ptnr., 1970—. Editor in chief St. John's U. Law Rev., 1962. Served to 1st lt. U.S. Army, 1962-64. Mem. N.Y. State Bar Assn., Assn. of Bar of City of N.Y. Roman Catholic. Avocation: fishing. Home: 7 Wedgewood Ct Glen Head NY 11545-2229 Office: Paul Weiss Rifkind Wharton & Garrison 1285 Ave Of The Americas New York NY 10019-6028

MOORE, DONALD PAUL, retired electrical engineer; b. Dayton, Ohio, Aug. 14, 1926; s. Walter Jennings and Dora (Hill) M.; m. Elizabeth Gerretje Derksen, Dec. 18, 1949; children: Anne, Donald, Dora, Peter, William, Richard, Norman, Emily. BEE, Ohio State U., 1954; B in Indsl. Mgmt., Franklin U., 1969, B in Real Estate, 1981; M in Indsl. Mgmt., Cen. Mich. U., 1974. Profl. elec. engr., Ohio; lic. steam engr., radio operator. Nuclear rsch. tech. Ohio State U., Columbus, 1949-54; microwave antenna engr. Ohio State U. Rsch. Found., Columbus, 1954-58; prof. electronics and computers Franklin U., Columbus, 1958-78, plant engr., 1978-88; tech. writer Liebert Corp., Columbus, 1991; chief engr. City of Columbus, 1991-92; cons. x-ray instrumentation Riverside Meth. Hosp., Columbus, 1971; cons. computer instrn. Western Electric Co., Columbus, 1969; cons. engr. Halmar Electronics, Columbus, 1959-64. Sci. judge Ohio Jr. Acad. Sci., Columbus, 1960-70; vol. instr. Columbus Met. Libr., 1978; rsch. chmn. Franklin County Geneal. Soc., Columbus, 1992. With USN, 1944-46. Rsch. grantee NSF, 1948. Mem. IEEE (editor 1984-87), Ohio Soc. Profl. Engrs. (editor 1991-92), Engrs. Club Columbus, Nat. Mgmt. Assn., Eta Kappa Nu. Presbyterian. Avocations: genealogy, computers, science, invention. Home: 1300 Fairview Ave Columbus OH 43212-3309

MOORE, DORSEY JEROME, dentistry educator, maxillofacial prosthetist; b. Boonville, Mo., Feb. 8, 1935; s. Lloyd Elliott Moore and Mary Elizabeth (Day) Katemann; m. Mary Louise Foote, May 2, 1959; children: Elizabeth L., David J. DDS, U. Mo., Kansas City, 1959. Diplomate Am. Bd. Prosthodontics. Commd. ensign USN, 1955, advanced through grades to capt., 1973; gen. practice dentistry various naval stas., 1959-63; resident in prosthodontics USS Proteus AS-19, 1963-66; resident in prosthodontics and maxillofacial prosthetics Naval Dental Sch., Bethesda, Md., 1966-69, chief maxillofacial prosthetics div., 1969-70; sr. dental advisor Naval Adv. Group, Comdr. Naval Forces, Saigon, Vietnam, 1970-71; chief maxillofacial prosthetics div. Nat. Naval Dental Ctr., 1971-76; chief maxillofacial prosthetics br. Naval Regional Med. Ctr., Great Lakes, Ill., 1976-79, ret., 1979; vis. lectr. U. Mo. Sch. Dentistry, Kansas City, 1976-79, H.G.B. Robinson prof., chmn. dept. removable prosthodontics, 1979—; assoc. prof. U. Saigon Sch. Dentistry, 1970-71; advisor to Min. of Health, Saigon, 1970-71; profl. lectr. George Washington U., Washington, 1971-76; clin. assoc. prof. surgery U. Kans. Sch. Medicine, 1987—; cons. maxillofacial prosthetics NIH Treatment Ctr., 1973—, Nat. Cancer Inst., 1973—, VA Hosp., North Chicago, Ill., 1976—, ADA Couns. Dental Edn., Hosp. Dental Svc. and Commn. on Accreditation, 1978—; vice chancellor Devel. Adv. Com., 1983—; examiner Mo. Specialty Bd. Prosthodontics, 1982—; internat. cir. course lectr. Am. Prosthetics Soc., Indonesia, 1974, Guatelmala, 1975, N.Z., 1976, S.Africa, 1981; nat. cons. U.S. Naval Dental Sch., Bethesda, 1991—. Author: Practical Oral Rehabilitation of the Edentulous Patient, 8th edit., 1995; mem. editorial bd. Cancer of the Head and Neck: A Comprehensive Review of the Literature, 1982—; contbr. over 40 articles and abstracts to profl. jours. Mem. adminstrv. ch. bd. Cen. Methodist Ch., 1981-88, pres. official ch. bd., 1983-85; bd. dirs. Ednl. Rsch. Found. Prosthodontics, 1982—, chmn. 1988—; bd. dirs. Penn Valley Fitness Trail Assn., 1982—. Decorated Legion of Merit with combat V, other awards; Navy Cross of Gallantry with palm (Republic of Vietnam). Fellow Am. Acad. Maxillofacial Prosthetics (bd. dirs. 1972-75, mem. exec. coun. 1973-76, pres. 1978-79, mem. exec. coun. 1979-82), Am. Coll. Prosthodontics (charter), Acad. Denture Prosthetics, Internat. Coll. Dentist, Midwest Acad. Prosthodontics; mem. ADA. Avocations: jazz musician, string bassist. Office: U Mo-Kans City Sch Dentistry 650 E 25th St Kansas City MO 64108-2716

MOORE, DUDLEY STUART JOHN, actor, musician; b. Dagenham, Essex, Eng., Apr. 19, 1935; s. John and Ada Francis (Hughes) M.; m. Suzy Kendall, 1966 (div.); m. Tuesday Weld, 1975 (div.); 1 child: Patrick; m. Brogan Lane (Denise Brogan), Feb. 21, 1988 (div.); m. Nicole Rothschild, April 16, 1994. Student, Guildhall Sch. Music; BA, Oxford (Eng.) U., 1957, MusB, 1958. Author: Dud and Pete: The Dagenham Dialogues, 1971; stage debut with Oxford U. Drama Soc., 1955; other stage appearances include Beyond the Fringe, London, 1960-62, Broadway, 1962-64, Play It Again Sam, 1970, Good Evening, 1973-75; appeared with Vic Lewis, John Dankworth Jazz Band, 1959-60; composed incidental music Royal Ct. Theatre, 1958-60; appeared in own BBC-TV series with Peter Cook Not only...but also, 1964, 66, 70; Royal Command Performance, ITV, 1965, Goodbye Again, ITV, 1968; appeared on BBC-TV series It's Lulu, not to mention Dudley Moore, 1972, Dudley, 1993, Daddy's Girls, 1994—; toured U.S., 1975; appeared on various TV and radio shows with jazz piano trio; actor (films) The Wrong Box, 30 is a Dangerous Age, Cynthia, Alice in Wonderland, Those Daring Young Men in their Jaunty Jalopies, Bedazzled, The Bed Sitting Room, The Hound of the Baskervilles, Foul Play, 10, Wholly Moses, Arthur (Golden Globe award 1983, Acad. award nomination 1983), Six Weeks, Lovesick, Romantic Comedy, Unfaithfully Yours, Best Defense, Mickey & Maude (Golden Globe award 1985), Santa Claus The Movie, Like Father, Like Son, Arthur on the Rocks, (voice over) The Adventures of Milo and Otis, 1989, Crazy People, 1990, Blame it on the Bellboy, 1991; also various TV shows; composer (film music) 30 is a Dangerous Age, Cynthia, Inadmissible Evidence, The Staircase, Six Weeks; rec. artist (albums) The Other Side of Dudley Moore, Today, Genuine Dud, Derek and Clive - Live, Beyond the Fringe and All That Jazz, Dudley Moore Trio - Down Under, Bedazzled, Songs Without Words, 1992, others. Named Male Star of Yr. N.A.T.O., 1983; Organ scholar Oxford U., 1958. Mem. St. James's Club, Annabel's Club, Harry's Bar, Tramp Club. Office: care Mr Lou Pitt 8942 Wilshire Blvd Beverly Hills CA 90210 also: Dennis Selinger I.C.M., Oxford House 76 Oxford St, W1R 1RB London England

MOORE, DUNCAN, healthcare executive; b. Nashville, June 23, 1941; married. B, Fla. State U., 1963; MHA, U. Iowa, 1965. Adminstrv. extern Washington Hosp. Ctr., 1964; adminstrv. resident Vanderbilt U. Hosp. & Clinic, Nashville, 1965-66, asst. dir, 1967, adminstrv. asst., 1966-67; asst. adminstr. Sparks Regional Med. Ctr., Ft. Smith, Ark., 1967-71; adminstr. Imperial Point Med. Ctr., Ft. Lauderdale, Fla., 1971-74; pres. Trinity Regional Hosp., Ft. Dodge, Iowa, 1974-80; adminstr. Phoebe Putney Meml. Hosp., Albany, Ga., 1982-88; pres., chief exec. officer Tallahassee (Fla.) Meml. Regional Med. Ctr., 1988—. Mem. Am. Coll. Healthcare Execs., SEHC (bd. dirs.), Ga. Hosp. Assn. (former chmn.), Iowa Hosp. Assn. (treas.). Office: Tallahassee Meml Regional Med Ctr Miccosukee Rd & Magnolia Dr Tallahassee FL 32308

MOORE, DUNCAN THOMAS, optics educator; b. Biddeford, Maine, Dec. 7, 1946; s. Thomas Fogg Moore and Virginia Robinson Wing; m. Susan Marie Rocheleau, June 14, 1969 (div. Aug. 1986); 1 child, Matthew. BA in Physics, U. Maine, 1969; MS in Optics, U. Rochester, 1970, PhD in Optics, 1974. Asst. prof. U. Rochester, N.Y., 1974-79, assoc. prof., 1979-86, prof., 1986-95, Kingslake prof. optics, 1993—, dean engring. and applied sci., 1995—; pres., founder Gradient Lens Corp., Rochester, 1980; dir. Ctr. Advanced Optical Tech., Rochester, 1987-94, Inst. Optics, Rochester, 1987-93; vis. sci. Nippon Schlumberger, Tokyo, 1983; Congl. fellow Am. Phys. Soc., Washington, 1993—; sci. adviser to Sen. John D. Rockefeller IV, W.Va.; bd. dirs. Sm. Precision Optical Mfrs. Assn., N.Y. State Photonics, Rome, N.Y. Contbr. 70 articles to profl. jours.; patentee in field. Chmn. Hubble Independent Review Panel, 1991-92; mem. adv. bd. high tech. Rochester C. of C., 1987—. Recipient Disting. Inventor of Yr. award Intellectual Property Law Assn., 1993, Grin Optics award Japanese Soc. Applied Physics, 1993, Sci. and Tech. award Greater Rochester C. of C., 1992. Mem. IEEE Lasers and Electro-Optics Soc., Am. Ceramic Soc., Am. Soc. Precision Engring., Optical Soc. Am. (editor Applied Optics 1989-92, bd. dirs. 1987-90, 92-93, v.p. 1994, pres. 1996), Am. Assn. Engring. Soc., Nat. Rsch. Coun., Internat. Soc. Optical Engring. (bd. govs. SPIE 1986-88), Materials Rsch. Soc. Home: 4 Claret Dr Fairport NY 14450 Office: U Rochester Inst Optics 509 Wilmot Bldg Rochester NY 14627

MOORE, E. HARRIS, bishop. Bishop Western Mo. Ch. of God in Christ, Kansas City.

MOORE, EDWARD FORREST, computer scientist, mathematician, former educator; b. Balt., Nov. 23, 1925; s. James Bernard and Edith (Thorn) M.; m. Elinor Constance Martin, July 30, 1950; children—Nancy, Shirley, Martha. BS in Chemistry, Va. Poly. Inst., 1947; MS in Math., Brown U., 1949, PhD in Math., 1950. Asst. prof. math. U. Ill., 1950-51; mem. tech. staff Bell Tel. Labs., Murray Hill, N.J., 1951-61, 62-66; vis. prof. elec. engring. Mass. Inst. Tech., 1961-62; vis. lectr. applied math. Harvard, 1961-62; prof. computer scis. math. U. Wis.-Madison, 1966-85; now ret. Author: Sequential Machines, 1964. Membership chmn. Fair Housing Com. of Chathams, N.J., 1964; treas. Francis Wayland Found., 1970-73; bd. dirs. Madison Campus Ministry, 1970-75. Served with USNR, 1944-46. Mem. AAAS, Nat. Speleological Soc. Wis. Speleological Soc., Am. Math. Soc., Soc. Indsl. and Applied Math., Math. Assn. Am., Bat Conservation Internat., N.Y. Acad. Scis., State Hist. Soc. Wis., Sigma Xi, Phi Kappa Phi, Phi Lambda Upsilon. Baptist. Home: 4337 Keating Ter Madison WI 53711-1563

MOORE, ELLIS OGLESBY, retired public affairs consultant; b. N.Y.C., May 12, 1924; s. Francis Lee and Gertrude (Ellis) M.; m. Peggy Sorrells, June 21, 1944; children: Ellis Oglesby, Jane Elizabeth Avallone, Kathleen Arnett, John Francis, Michael William. Student, Washington and Lee U., 1941-43. Reporter Pine Bluff (Ark.) Coml., 1946-47, Memphis Comml. Appeal, 1947-52; writer, exec. press and publicity NBC, N.Y.C., 1952-63; pub. relations exec. Standard Oil Co. (N.J.), N.Y.C., 1963-66, Am. Broadcasting Cos. Inc., N.Y.C., 1966-85; v.p. pub. relations Am. Broadcasting Cos. Inc., 1972-79, v.p. corp. relations, 1979-82, v.p. pub. affairs, 1982-85; pub. affairs cons., 1985-90. Served with AUS, 1943-46. Recipient Nat. Headliners award, 1950. Home: 984 Esplanade Pelham NY 10803-2904

MOORE, ELVI, performing company executive. Mem. faculty U. Chgo.; dir. corp. and found. devel. Nat. Symphony Orch.; with Washington Ballet, 1983—, gen. dir.; bd. dirs. Dance/USA; adv. panels Nat. Endowment for Arts, D.C. Commn. Arts and Humanities. Dancer, choreographer, prodr. numerous dance festivals. Office: The Washington Ballet 3515 Wisconsin Ave NW Washington DC 20016-3010

MOORE, EMMETT BURRIS, JR., physical chemist; b. Bozeman, Mont., June 14, 1929; s. Emmett Burris and Iris Marie (Brown) M.; m. Diane Elizabeth Girling, Oct. 1, 1960; children: Karen Elizabeth, Robin Diane. B.S. in Chemistry, Wash. State U., 1951; Ph.D. in Phys. Chemistry (Shell fellow), U. Minn., 1956. Teaching asst. U. Minn., Mpls., 1951-55; asst. prof. chemistry U. Minn., Duluth, 1957-59; mem. staff Boeing Sci. Research Labs., Seattle, 1959-73; lectr. chemistry Seattle U., 1973; dir. power plant siting Minn. Environ. Quality Bd., St. Paul, 1973-76; gen. mgr. Richland (Wash.) Divsn. Olympic Engring. Corp., 1976-78; mem. staff Pacific N.W. Lab., 1978—; mem. environ. engring. rev. panel EPA, 1989—; adj. prof. environ. sci. Wash. State U., 1990—. Contbr. articles to profl. jours. Trustee Mid-Columbia Symphony Soc., 1978-85, v.p., 1980-81, pres., 1981-83; trustee Richland Light Opera Co., 1984-88, bus. mgr., 1984-88. Fellow AAAS; mem. Am. Phys. Soc., Am. Chem. Soc. (chmn. Pauling award com. 1971, sec. Puget Sound sect. 1971-73, mem. energy panel of com. on chemistry and pub. affairs 1983-86), Am. Assn. Physics Tchrs. (v.p. Wash. sect. 1965-66, pres. 1966-67), N.W. Sci. Assn., Phi Beta Kappa, Phi Kappa Phi, Phi Eta Sigma, Alpha Chi Sigma, Phi Lambda Upsilon, Sigma Alpha Epsilon (v.p. province 1972-73). Episcopalian (vestryman 1967-69, 76-79, 91, sr. warden 1969, del. diocesan conv. 1969-72). Home: 2323 Greenbrook Blvd Richland WA 99352-8427 Office: PO Box 999 Richland WA 99352-0999

MOORE, ERNEST EUGENE, JR., surgeon, educator; b. Pitts., June 18, 1946; s. Ernest Eugene Sr. and Mary Ann (Burroughs) M.; m. Sarah Van Duzer, Sept. 2, 1978; children: Hunter Burroughs, Peter Kitrick. BS in Chemistry, Allegheny Coll., 1968; MD, U. Pitts., 1972. Surg. resident U. Vt., Burlington, 1972-76; chief of trauma Denver Gen. Hosp., 1976—; chief dept. surgery, 1984—; chief div. of emergency med. svcs. U. Colo., Denver, 1984—, prof. surgery, vice chmn. dept., 1985—; dir. rsch. Colo. Trauma Inst., Denver, 1984—. Editor: Critical Decisions in Tauma, 1987, Trauma, 1988, rev. edits., 1990, 91, 94, Early Care of the Injured, 1989; assoc. editor Jour. Trauma, Am. Jour. Surgery, Surgery-Problem Solving Approach, 2d edit., 1994, others; patentee retrohepatic vena cava shunt. Fellow ACS (com. on trauma, vice chair 1990), Soc. Univ. Surgeons (pres. 1989), Am. Assn. Surgery of Trauma (pres. 1993), Pan Am. Trauma Assn. (pres. 1991), Southwestern Surgical Congress (recorder 1986-91), Western Trauma Assn. (pres. 1989). Republican. Avocations: skiing, hockey, hunting, running, fishing, camping. Home: 2909 E 7th Ave Denver CO 80206 Office: Denver Gen Hosp Dept Surgery Denver CO 80204

MOORE, F. RICHARD, music educator; b. Uniontown, Pa., Sept. 4, 1944; s. Franklin L. and Anna Jane (White) M.; children: Amanda, Dariel, Marick. BFA in Music Composition, BFA Music Performance, Carnegie-Mellon U., 1966; postgrad., U. Ill., 1966-67; MSEE, Stanford U., 1975, PhD, 1977. Acoustics researcher AT&T Bell Labs., Murray Hill, N.J., 1967-79; music prof. U. Calif.-San Diego, La Jolla, 1979—, dir. comuter audio research lab., 1979—, dir. ctr. for music experiment, 1982-92; percussionist Pitts. Symphony, 1964-66. Author: Programming in C with a Bit of UNIX, 1985, Elements of Computer Music, 1990; contbr. articles to profl. jours. Grantee for computer music research System Devel. Found., 1982-88, NEA, 1979—, Rockefeller Found., 1978, Ford Found., 1982. Mem. IEEE, Am. Engring. Soc., Acoustical Soc. Am. Avocations: aviation, amateur radio, skiing. Office: U Calif San Diego Dept Music La Jolla CA 92093-0037

MOORE, FLETCHER BROOKS, engineering company executive; b. Heiberger, Ala., June 15, 1926; s. Amzi Wallace and Mary Elizabeth (May) M.; m. Margaret Marian Foreman, Sept. 5, 1954; children—Larry Brooks, Ronald Howell. BS in Electronic Engring, Auburn U., 1948; M.S. in Electronic Engring, Ga. Inst. Tech., 1949. With U.S. Navy Mine Counter-Measures Sta., Panama City, Fla., 1949-52, Army Ballistic Missile Redstone Arsenal, Ala., 1952-60; with Marshall Space Flight Ctr., NASA, Huntsville, Ala., 1960-81; dir. Astrionics Lab. NASA Marshall Space Flight Ctr., 1968-81; chief missile system Teledyne Brown Engring., Huntsville, 1981-83; v.p. Control Dynamics Co., Huntsville, 1983-91; pres. Logicon Control Dynamics, Inc., Huntsville, 1991-94; divsn. mgr. Control Dynamics, a Divsn. of Bd. Systems, Huntsville, 1994—. Past chmn. alumni engring. coun. Auburn U.; mem. Auburn U. rsch. coun.; mem. Ala. Indsl. Coun. on Engring. Ednl.; mem. adminstrv. sci. adv. coun. U. Ala., Huntsville. Mem. AIAA, Inst. of Navigation, NASA Alumni League (pres. Marshall Space Flight Ctr. chpt.). Home: 119 Sherwood Dr SE Huntsville AL 35802-2430

MOORE, FRANCIS DANIELS, retired surgeon, educator, consultant, editor; b. Evanston, Ill., Aug. 17, 1913; s. Philip W. and Caroline Seymour

(Daniels) M.; m. Laura Benton Bartlett, June 24, 1935 (dec. July 1988); children: Nancy, Peter, Sarah, Caroline, Francis Daniels; m. Katharyn Watson Saltonstall, May 13, 1990. AB, Harvard U., 1935, MD, 1939, DSc (hon.), 1982; M Surgery (hon.), Nat. U. Ireland, 1961; LLD (hon.), U. Glasgow, Scotland, 1965; ScD (hon.), Suffolk U., 1966; MD (hon.), U. Goteborg, Sweden, 1975; U. Edinburgh, Scotland, 1976, U. Paris, 1976, U. Copenhagen, 1979. Diplomate Am. Bd. Surgery. Surg. intern, asst. resident and resident Mass. Gen. Hosp., Boston, 1939-43; instr. surgery Harvard Med. Sch., 1934-46, assoc. in surgery, 1946-47, asst. prof., 1947-48, Moseley prof. surgery, 1948-76, Elliott Carr Cutler prof. surgery, 1976-80, Moseley prof. emeritus, 1980—; surgeon in chief Peter Bent Brigham Hosp., Boston, 1948-76, surgeon in chief emeritus, 1980—; cons. emeritus div. surg. oncology Dana-Farber Cancer Inst., 1980—; pres. Mass. Health Data Consortium, Inc., Waltham, 1981-87; cons. to surgeon gen., 1952; cons. NIH, chmn. surgical study sect., 1956-59; cons. life scis. NASA, 1970-92; mem. numerous adv. panels, bd. trustees, others. Contbr. surg. and investigative articles on transdiaphragmatic resection of vagus nerves for peptic ulcer, determination of total body water and solids with isotopes, transplantation of liver, metabolic balance studies in surg. patients, studies on surg. manpower and care distbn., and econs. and pub. policy; mem. editorial bd. Annals of Surgery, Jour. of Enteral and Parenteral Nutrition; editor book rev. sect. New Eng. Jour. Medicine, 1980-91. Mem. Gov.'s Task Force on Organ Transplantation, Boston, 1984-85; del. Basic Biomed. Rsch., Washington, 1978-86; trustee New Eng. Conservatory Music, 1977—; bd. regents Uniformed Svcs. Univ. for Health Scis., 1976-83. Recipient Alvarenga award Phila. Acad. Physicians, Blakeslee award Am. Herat Assn., 1968, Gold Headed Cane award U. Calif., 1970, Bigelow medal Boston Surg. Soc., 1974, Cutler medal, 1975, Lister medal Royal Coll. Surgeons of Eng., 1978, Ellen Browning Scripps medal, La Jolla, Calif., 1982, others. Hon. fellow Royal Coll. Surgeons of: Eng., Edinburgh, Ottawa, Dublin, Glasgow; hon. mem. Polish Acad. Scis., Assn. Surgeons Gt. Britain and Ireland, Swedish Surg. Assn.; mem. NAS, Am. Acad. Arts. and Scis., NAS/NRC Com. on Space Station, 1992—, Am. Surg. Assn. (Samuel D. Gross medal 1978), Inst. Medicine, Soc. Clin. Surgery, Soc. Univ. Surgeons, New Eng. Surg. Soc., Surg. Biology Club, Soc. Clin. Investigation, Inst. Medicine, Internat. Soc. Surgery (Silver medal 1959), other profl. orgns., Century Assn., Beverly Yacht Club, The Country Club, Tavern Club, Saturday Club, Tihonet Club, Phi Beta Kappa. Avocations: musical composition, piano, sailing, writing, gardening. Home: 10 Longwood Dr # 264 Westwood MA 02090 Office: Countway Libr Medicine HMS 10 Longwood Dr # 264 Boston MA 02115-6011

MOORE, FREDERICK C., manufacturing executive; b. 1933; married. BA, Amherst Coll., 1955; MBA, Lehigh U., 1963. Various positions Gen. Crushed Stone Co., 1954-70, exec. v.p., 1972-77, pres., 1977-81, corp. v.p., asst. to pres. Road Materials Group, 1981-83, v.p., mgr. ea. region, from 1983; with Beazer Materials & Svcs. Inc. (formerly Koppers Co. Inc.), Pitts., 1970—, pres., chief exec. officer, 1988—, also chmn. bd. dirs.; pres., chief exec. officer Beazer East, Inc., 1989—. Office: Beazer Materials & Svcs Inc 437 7th Ave Pittsburgh PA 15219-1910

MOORE, GARY ALAN, economist; b. Indianola, Iowa, Jan. 23, 1946; s. Robert Lincoln and Ruby Marie Moore; B.S., Nebr. Wesleyan U., 1968; M.A. (grad. teaching asst. 1971-74), U. Nebr., Lincoln, 1973, Ph.D., 1974; 1 son, Adrian David. Secondary sch. tchr., Nebr., 1968-70; prof. bus. and econs. SUNY, Geneseo, 1985—; mediator, factfinder N.Y. Public Employment Relations Bd., Albany, 1977—; mediator, arbitrator N.Y. Bd. Mediation, Albany, 1980—. Served with USAR, 1970. Grantee SUNY, N.Y. Com. Work Environment and Productivity. Mem. Am. Econ. Assn., Indsl. Relations Research Assn., Am. Bus. Law Assn., Midwest Econ. Assn., Blue Key, Omicron Delta Epsilon, Pi Gamma Mu. Author: (with R. Elkin) Labor and the Economy, 1983, (with A. Magaldi and J. Gray) Legal Environment of Business, 1987; contbr. research papers to profl. jours. Office: Sch Bus SUNY Geneseo NY 14454

MOORE, GEOFFREY HOYT, economist; b. Pequannock, N.J., Feb. 28, 1914; s. Edward H. and Marian (Leman) M.; m. Ella C. Goldschmid, July 12, 1938 (dec. June 2, 1975); children: Stephen, Peter, Kathleen, Pamela; m. Melita H. Riley, Sept. 28, 1975. BS, Rutgers U., 1933, MS, 1937; PhD, Harvard, 1947. Assoc. prof. econs. NYU, 1947-48; assoc. dir. Nat. Bur. Econs. Rsch., N.Y.C., 1948-64, dir. rsch., 1965-67, v.p. rsch., 1968, 73-75, dir. bus. cycle rsch., 1975-79; commr. labor stats. Dept. Labor, 1969-73; dir. Ctr. for Internat. Bus. Cycle Rsch., Columbia U., N.Y.C., 1979—; instr. agrl. econs. Rutgers U., 1936-42; sr. rsch. fellow Hoover Instn., Stanford U., 1973-78; adj. scholar Am. Enterprise Inst., 1975-80; vis. lectr. Columbia U. 1953-54, sr. rsch. scholar, 1983—. Author: (with W. A. Wallis) A Significance Test for Time Series, 1941, Production of Industrial Materials in World Wars I and II, 1944, Statistical Indicators of Cyclical Revivals and Recessions, 1950, The Diffusion of Business Cycles, 1955, Measuring Recessions, 1958, Business Cycle Indicators, 1961, Tested Knowledge of Business Cycles, 1962, (with J. Shiskin) Indicators of Business Expansions and Contractions, 1966, (with P. Klein) The Quality of Consumer Instalment Credit, 1967, The Anatomy of Inflation, 1969, The Cyclical Behavior of Prices, 1971, How Full is Full Employment, 1973, Slowdowns, Recessions and Inflation, 1975, An Inflation Chronology, 1977, Business Cycles, Inflation and Forecasting, 1983, (with P. Klein) Monitoring Growth Cycles in Market-Oriented Countries, 1985, (with M. Moore) International Economic Indicators: A Sourcebook, 1985, The Service Industries and the Business Cycle, 1987, Leading Indicators for the 1990's, 1989, (with K. Lahiri) Leading Economic Indicators, 1991, (with E. Boehm and A. Banerji) Using Economic Indicators to Reduce Risk in Stock Market Investments, 1992. Mem. N.Y. State Coun. Econ. Advisers, 1973-74. Subject of book edited by Philip A. Klein, Analyzing Modern Business Cycles: Essays Honoring Geoffrey H. Moore, 1990. Fellow Am. Statis. Assn. (pres. 1968), Nat. Assn. Bus. Economists, Am. Econs. Assn. (disting. fellow); mem. Nat. Economists Club, Forecasters Club N.Y., Cosmos Club, Phi Beta Kappa, Alpha Zeta. Home: 1171 Valley Rd New Canaan CT 06840-2428 Office: Columbia U Ctr Internat Bus Cycle Rsch Uris Hall New York NY 10027

MOORE, GEORGE CRAWFORD JACKSON, lawyer. BA, U. Fla., 1963; PhB in Soviet Law, U. St. Andrews, Scotland, 1966; MA in English Law with honors, Cambridge U., Eng., 1968, LLM in Internat. Law, 1969. Bar: Eng. (Barrister, Inner Temple) 1970, Jamaica 1971, Fla. 1973, Turks & Caicos Islands 1974, Antigua and Barbuda, Brit. V.I., Grenada, Montserrat, St. Lucia 1977; U.S. Supreme Ct. 1976. Legis. asst. to U.S. sen. Washington, 1970-72; asst. pub. defender Palm Beach County, Fla., 1973; pvt. practice West Palm Beach, Fla., 1973—; chmn. Fla. Export Coun. of U.S. Dept. Commerce, 1991-92; chmn. Fla. Coun. Internat. Devel., 1983-84, chmn. emeritus, 1990—; chmn. Fla. Gov.'s Conf. on World Trade and Investment, 1989; founding pres. World Trade Coun. of Palm Beach County, 1981—. Editor spl. issues Fla. Bar Jour., 1982, 87, chmn. editorial bd., 1988-89; mem. editorial bd. The Internat. Lawyer jour. of ABA, 1979-84; contbr. articles to profl. jours. Chmn. Fla. Econ. Growth and Internat. Devel. Commn., 1989-90. Fellow Soc. Internat. Bus. Fellows; mem. ABA, Fla. Bar (chmn. internat. law sect. 1994—). Office: 105 S Narcissus Ave Ste 812 West Palm Beach FL 33401-5530

MOORE, GEORGE EMERSON, JR., geologist, educator; b. Lebanon, Mo., Jan. 2, 1914; s. George Emerson and Dorothea Louisa (Niewohner) M.; m. Wilma Corrine Leonard, May 20, 1939; children: George E. III, Dana Corinne, Craig G. A.B., U. Mo., 1936, M.A., 1938; Ph.D., Harvard U., 1947. Instr. U. Mo. 1938-39; teaching asst. Harvard U. 1940-42, 1946-47; geologist A.P. Green Fire Brick Co., Mexico, Mo., 1942-46; instr. Ohio State U. at Columbus, 1947-48, asst. prof., 1948-57, assoc. prof., 1957-64, prof., 1964-84, prof. emeritus, 1984—; geologist U.S. Geol. Survey, 1952-83. Fellow Geol. Soc. Am.; mem. Phi Beta Kappa, Sigma Xi. Home: 58 Mulberry Dr Wakefield RI 02879-1416

MOORE, GEORGE EUGENE, surgeon; b. Minn., Feb. 22, 1920; s. Jesse and Elizabeth (MacRae) M.; m. Lorraine Hammell, Feb. 22, 1945; children—Allan, Laurie, Linda, Cathy, Donald. B.A., U. Minn., 1942, M.A., 1943, B.S., 1944, B.M., 1946, M.D., 1947, Ph.D. in Surgery, 1950. Intern surgery U. Minn. Hosps., 1946-47; med. fellow gen. surgery, 1947, dir. tumor clinic, 1951-53; sr. research fellow USPHS, 1947-48; faculty U. Minn. Med. Sch., 1948-53, cancer coordinator, 1951-53; chief surgery Roswell Park Meml. Inst., Buffalo, 1953-72; dir. Roswell Park Meml. Inst., 1953-67; dir.

pub. health research N.Y. State Health Dept., Albany, 1967-73; clin. prof. surgery State U. N.Y. at Buffalo, 1962-73, also prof. research biology, 1955-69; dir. surg. oncology Denver Gen. Hosp., 1973—; prof. surgery U. Colo., 1973—. Author: Diagnosis and Localization of Brain Tumors, 1950, Cancerous Diseases, 1970; contbr. 660 articles to profl. jours. Recipient Outstanding Citizen award Buffalo Evening News, 1958, Outstanding Sci. Achievement award, 1959, Disting. Achievement award Modern Medicine mag., 1962, Chancellor's medal U. Buffalo, 1963, Charles Evans Hughes award pub. administn. Albany, 1963, Bronfman prize Am. Pub. Health Assn., 1964, Tchr. of Yr. award Dept. Surgery, U. Colo., 1977, Disting. Svc. award U. Colo., 1990, Meritorious Svc. Regents award U. Colo., 1990. Mem. Soc. U. Surgs., Halsted Soc., Am. Surg. Assn., Colo. Oncology Found. (pres.). Home: 12048 S Blackhawk Dr Conifer CO 80433-7110 Office: Denver Gen Hosp 645 Bannock St PO Box 1806 Denver CO 80204 Individuals are miraculous temporal genetic patterns whose accomplishments will always transcend those of any committee, consensual group, or political assembly; society must provide special early educational opportunities for creative youngsters and those with genius. I hope to see the practical development of cell therapy for the infectious and cancerous diseases and genetic corrections of inherited disorders.

MOORE, GORDON E., electronics company executive; b. San Francisco, Jan. 3, 1929; s. Walter Harold and Florence Almira (Williamson) M.; m. Betty I. Whittaker, Sept. 9, 1950; children: Kenneth, Steven. BS in Chemistry, U. Calif., 1950; PhD in Chemistry and Physics, Calif. Inst. Tech., 1954. Mem. tech. staff Shockley Semicondr. Lab., 1956-57; mgr. engring. Fairchild Camera & Instrument Corp., 1957-59, dir. research and devel., 1959-68; exec. v.p. Intel Corp., Santa Clara, Calif., 1968-75; pres., chief exec. officer Intel Corp., 1975-79, chmn., chief exec. officer, 1979-87, chmn., 1987—; bd. dirs. Varian Assocs. Inc., Transamerica Corp. Fellow IEEE; mem. Nat. Acad. Engring., Am. Phys. Soc. Office: Intel Corp 2200 Mission College Blvd Santa Clara CA 95054-1537

MOORE, HAL G., mathematician, educator; b. Vernal, Utah, Aug. 14, 1929; s. Lewis Henry and Nora (Gillman) M.; m. D'On Empey, July 20, 1956; children: David, Nora (Mrs. Bret C. Hess), Alison (Mrs. Samuel M. Smith). BS, U. Utah, 1952, MS, 1957; PhD, U. Calif., Santa Barbara, 1967. Tchr. Salt Lake City Public Schs., 1952-53; instr. math. Carbon Jr. Coll., also Carbon High Sch., Price, Utah, 1953-55, Purdue U., Lafayette, Ind., 1957-61; administrv. asst. dept. math Purdue U., 1960-61; from asst. prof. math. to assoc. prof. math. Brigham Young U., Provo, 1961-71, prof., 1971-95; prof. emeritus, 1995—; assoc. chmn. dept. Math. Brigham Young U., 1986-89. Author: Precalculus Mathematics, 2d edit, 1977, (with Adil Yaqub) Elementary Linear Algebra With Applications, 1980, College Algebra and Trigonometry, 1983, A First Course in Linear Algebra, 1992; contbr. articles to profl. jours. Mem. High Coun., Ch. of Jesus Christ of Latter Day Saints, 1985-91, MTC br. pres., 1991-94, Bishop, 1958-61, 78-82. NSF faculty fellow U. Calif., Santa Barbara, 1964-66. Mem. Am. Math Soc., Math Assn. Am. (bd. govs. 1989-92), Utah State Math. Coalition (planning dir. 1990, bd. dirs. 1991-92), Sigma Xi (State 1974-80, 82-85, com. chmn. 1982-90), Phi Kappa Phi. Home: 631 W 650 S Orem UT 84058-6027 Office: Brigham Young U Box 26530 316 TMCB Provo UT 84602-6530

MOORE, HENRY ROGERS, consulting engineer, retired railroad executive; b. Chatham, Va., Jan. 15, 1916; s. Charles Anderson and Lillian (Moon) M.; m. Billie Henslee, Mar. 26, 1949; 1 child, Mary James Moore Quillen. BSCE with honors, Va. Poly. and State U., 1940. Various positions So. Ry., southeastern U.S., 1939-52, div. supt., 1952-56; asst. chief engr. Washington, and chief engr. MWS, So. Ry., Charlotte, N.C., 1956-64; gen. supt. transp. Atlanta, 1965-68, gen. mgr., 1968-82; cons. AMTRAK, 1983-86; exec. v.p., chief oper. officer AMTRAK, Washington, 1986-88; pres. R.R. Transp. Cons. Inc., Atlanta, 1982—. Baptist. Club: Atlanta Athletic. Home and Office: PO Box 98208 Atlanta GA 30359-1908

MOORE, J. JAMISON, consulting firm executive, economist; b. Boston, Aug. 10, 1928; s. Joseph Jamison and Winifred (Currier) M.; children—Cathleen, Colleen, Christiene, Karen, Stacey, Jamison. B.A., UCLA, 1946; postgrad. U. Oreg., 1946 to 1948; M.A., CORO Found., San Francisco, 1950; Ph.D., Caux-Sur-Moutreaux, Switzerland, 1954; postgrad. Loyola Law School, Los Angeles, 1954-56. Asst. to pres. Ralph M Parsons Co., Los Angeles, 1954-56; assoc. McKinsey & Co., Los Angeles, 1956-57; exec. dir. Modern Mgmt., Beverly Hills, Calif., 1958; chief exec. officer Atlantis, Inc., Beverly Hills, Calif., 1967—; instr. U. So. Calif., UCLA and various Calif. colls., 1965-69; commr. Calif. Dept. Navigation & Ocean Devel., 1969, Calif. Com. on Marine & Coastal Resources, 1968, Calif. Com. on Ocean Resources, 1967, Calif. Task Force on Transportation, 1967. Contbr. numerous articles to profl. jours. Gov.'s rep. to Pacific Basin Community, Calif. Mem. Los Angeles Cons. Council (founder and chmn.), Los Angeles C. of C. (past chmn, chmn. com. on Ocean Industries and Marine Activities), Am. Arbitration Assn., Am. Mktg. Assn., Marine Tech Assn. (v.p. econs. and resource utilization). Republican. Episcopalian. Clubs: Jonathan. Home: 1258 N Clark St West Hollywood CA 90069-2018 Office: Atlantis Inc PO Box 10777 Beverly Hills CA 90213

MOORE, JACKSON WATTS, corporate executive; b. Birmingham, Ala., Nov. 2, 1948; s. Joseph Watts and Shellye Louise (Jackson) M.; m. Elizabeth Wilson, June 12, 1971; children: Jackson Jr., Wilson, Shellye. BS, U. Ala., 1970; JD, Vanderbilt U., 1973. Assoc. Martin, Tate, Morrow and Marston, Memphis, 1973-77; mng. ptnr. Wildman, Harrold, Allen, Dixon and McDonnell, Memphis, 1977-89; pres. Union Planters Corp., Memphis, 1989—, also bd. dirs.; bd. dirs. Union Planters Nat. Bank, Biotherapeutics, Inc., Franklin, Tenn., KW Bancshares, Inc., Memphis, PSB Bancshares, Clanton, Ala. Bd. dirs. Boy Scouts Am., Ch. Health Ctr., Memphis, Memphis Emmaus Community. Capt. U.S. Army, 1973. Mem. ABA, Tenn. Bar Assn., Memphis Country Club, Memphis Hunt and Polo Club. Republican. Methodist. Avocations: golf, tennis, reading. Home: 6486 May Creek Cv Memphis TN 38119-6529 Office: Union Planters Corp 67 Madison Ave Memphis TN 38103-2147

MOORE, JAMES ALFRED, ski company executive, lawyer; b. Madisonville, Ky., Oct. 20, 1915; s. Virgil Yandell and Dorothy Ina (Price) M.; m. Lucile Carpenter, June 29, 1970; children by previous marriage: Marjorie M. Eickel, James Kelly, Kathleen M. Marozzi. A.B., U. Ky., 1936; LL.B., Harvard U., 1939. Bar: Pa. 1940, D.C. 1969, Va. 1978. Assoc. firm Pepper, Hamilton & Scheetz, Phila., 1940-51; partner Pepper, Hamilton & Scheetz 1951-69; partner firm Pepper, Hamilton & Scheetz, Washington, 1969-77; pres. Camelback Ski Corp., Tannersville, Pa., 1963-86, chmn., bd. dirs., 1986-93, chmn. emeritus, 1993—. Contbr. articles to various law revs. Bd. dirs. Phila. Soc. for Crippled Children and Adults, 1959-69. Served from ensign to lt. comdr. USNR, 1942-45. Mem. Am. Bar Assn., Am. Law Inst. Republican. Methodist. Club: Merion Cricket (Haverford, Pa.). Home: PO Box 1241 Front Royal VA 22630-1241 Office: Camelback Ski Corp PO Box 168 Tannersville PA 18372-0168

MOORE, JAMES ALLAN, agricultural engineering educator; b. Fresno, Calif., Mar. 11, 1939; s. E. Dale and Anne Moore; m. Janet Rae Robles, Dec. 19, 1960; children: Catherine, Kimberly, Donald, Dennis, Korinna. BSAE, Calif. State Poly. U., 1962; MSAE, U. Ariz., 1964; PhD in Agrl. Engring., U. Minn., 1975. Registered profl. engr., Oreg. Research engr. agrl. engring. dept. U. Calif., Davis, 1964-68; from instr. to asst. prof. agrl. engring. U. Minn., Mpls./St. Paul, 1968-79; assoc. prof. agrl. engring. Oreg. State U., Corvallis, 1979-85, prof., 1985—, acting head dept. agrl. engring., 1983-84; forward planning com. Dept. Agrl. Engring., 1973, instruction com., 1973, 75. chmn. recruiting com. 1973-79, chmn. student activities, 1974-75; mem. steering com. Experiment Station Waste Mgmt., 1975-79, grad. com. 1979; mem. Midwest Plan Service Com. on Waste Mgmt., 1975-78; bd. dirs. Oreg. State U. Water Resources Research Inst., 1983-85, 89-91. Contbr. numerous articles to profl. jours. Recipient Superior State award USDA, 1985. Fellow Am. Soc. Agrl. Engrs. (tech. dir. 1979-81, various editorial positions, Blue Ribbon award 1983, 84, G.B. Gunlogson Countryside Engring. award, 1985), mem. Soil Conservation Soc. Am., AM. Soc. Agrl. Engrs., Council for Agrl. Sci. and Tech., Sigma Xi, Gamma Sigma Delta, Alpha Epsilon. Avocations: hunting, fishing.

MOORE, JAMES COLLINS, museum director; b. Topeka, Kans., Oct. 12, 1941; s. Albert Ora and Alice Winifred (Collins) M.; m. Margaret Ruth

Vasquez, Jan. 30, 1965; children—Daniela Ruth, Evan Albert. BFA, U. N.Mex., 1966; MA, Ind. U., 1968, PhD, 1974. Asst. prof. art history Wichita State U., Kans., 1970-77; chmn. dept. art history Wichita State U., 1975-77; coordinator art history Toledo Mus. Art, Ohio, 1977-79; dir. Albuquerque Mus., 1979—; adj. curator Wichita Art Mus., Kans., 1970-77, trustee, 1975-77; adj. assoc. prof. U. Toledo, Ohio, 1977-79, U. N.Mex., Albuquerque, 1980—. Author: Harry Sternberg, 1975; also articles in field. Bd. dirs. The Albuquerque Conservation Assn., 1979-81, Albuquerque Arts Alliance, 1985. Served to sgt. Air N.G., 1963-69. Woodrow Wilson Found. fellow, 1966-67; Samuel H. Kress Found. fellow, 1968-69, 1969-70, grantee, 1971. Mem. Am. Assn. Mus. Lodge: Rotary. Office: Albuquerque Mus PO Box 1293 Albuquerque NM 87103-1293

MOORE, JAMES L., JR., beverage company executive; b. 1942. BA, Davidson Coll., 1964; MBA, Univ. N.C., 1968. Dist. mgr. Pepsi-Cola Co., 1972-74, mgr. market planning Pepsi-Cola Bottling group, 1974-75, v.p., area mgr. Houston, 1975-76; v.p., gen. mgr. Atlantic Soft Drink, Knoxville, Tenn., 1977-82, v.p. mktg., 1982-83, pres., chief exec. officer, 1983-87; pres., chief exec. officer Coca-Cola Bottling Co. Consolidated, 1987—, also dir. 1st lt. U.S. Army, 1972-76. Office: Coca-Cola Bottling Co 1900 Rexford Rd Charlotte NC 28211-3440*

MOORE, JAMES MENDON, industrial engineering educator, consultant; b. Winchester, Mass., Apr. 25, 1925; s. Mendon Preston and Fannie Judith (Merrill) M.; m. Lenna Mary Maguire, June 10, 1950; children: Thomas P., Richard M., Terry R., Alan M. B.S., Rensselaer Poly. Inst., 1950; M.S., Cornell U., 1956; Ph.D., Stanford U., 1964. Instr. Cornell, Ithaca, N.Y., 1952-56; asst. prof. mech. engring. Clarkson Coll. Tech., Potsdam, N.Y., 1956-59; instr. Stanford U., 1959-60; prof., chmn. indsl. engring. dept. Northeastern U., Boston, 1961-73; head dept. indsl. engring. and ops. research Va. Poly. Inst. and State U., Blacksburg, 1973-75, prof., 1976-90; pres. Moore Productivity Software, Blacksburg, 1976—; Lucas vis. prof. engring. prodn. U. Birmingham, Eng., 1975-76; sr. Fulbright lectr. Tech. U. Finland, Helsinki, 1968-69; dir. rsch. Hefei U., China, 1988, County Bd. Suprs., 1990—; chmn. bd. Internat. Found. Prodn. Rsch., 1991-93. Author: Plant Layout and Design, 1962; Co-author: Computer Aided Layout: A User's Guide, 1978, Applications of Graph Theory Algorithms, 1979, An Engineer's Guide to Spreadsheets, Word Processors & Data Base Managers, 1986; co-editor: The Production System: An Efficient Integration of Resources; asso. editor: Internat. Jour. Prodn. Research, 1973-1983. Served with AUS, 1943-45. Decorated Bronze Star, Purple Heart. Fellow Am. Inst. Indsl. Engrs. (pres. chpt. 1963-64), Royal Soc. Home: 1607 Greenwood Dr Blacksburg VA 24060-5937

MOORE, JAMES R., lawyer; b. Longview, Wash., Sept. 14, 1944; s. James Carlton and Virginia (Rice) M.; m. Patricia Riley, Aug. 25, 1967 (div. 1978); 1 child, Katherine M.; m. Christine M. Monkman, July 14, 1979; children: Amy McKenna, John McKenna, Zia Sunseri (foster child). BA, Whitman Coll., 1966; JD, Duke U., 1969. Bar: Wash. 1970, U.S. Ct. Appeals (4th cir.) 1972, U.S. Supreme Ct. 1973, U.S. Ct. Appeals (9th cir.) 1974. Law clk. to Hon. J. Barnes U.S. Ct. Appeals (9th cir.), L.A., 1969-70; trial atty. pollution control, land and natural resources U.S. Dept. Justice, Washington, 1970-74; asst. U.S. atty. U.S. Atty.'s Office, Seattle, 1974-82; regional counsel U.S. EPA Region 10, Seattle, 1982-87; counsel Perkins Coie, Seattle, 1987-88, ptnr., 1989—; trainer, speaker on environ. litigation, negotiation and law. Contbr. articles to profl. jours. Bd. dirs. Environ. Law Inst., Our Lady of the Lake, Seattle, 1990-94, religious edn. bd. Mem. ABA (sect. natural resources 1987—), Wash. State Bar Assn. (environ. and land use sect. 1974—, spl. dist. coun. 1988—). Democrat. Office: Perkins Coie 1201 3rd Ave Ste 4100 Seattle WA 98101-3099 also: 607 14th NW Washington DC 20005-2011

MOORE, JAMES ROBERT, geological oceanographer; b. Temple, Tex., May 18, 1925; s. James Robert and Mary Louise (Petty) M. B.S. with honors, U. Houston, 1951; M.A., Harvard U., 1954; Ph.D., U. Wales, 1964. Research geologist Standard Oil, Ohio, 1951-52; sr. scientist Texaco Research, 1956-66; chief marine geologist U.K.-Irish Sea Project, 1962-64; prof. U. Wis., Madison, 1966-77; also dir. marine lab.; prof., dir. Marine Sci. Inst., U. Alaska, 1977-79; prof. marine studies U. Tex., Austin, 1979—; cons. in marine mining to internat. cos. and consortia. Editor: Marine Mining, 1976—; editor-in-chief: Marine Series, 1978—; Contbr. articles to profl. jours. Served with USNR, 1943-46. Recipient Career Achievement award Underwater Mining Inst., 1989, Outstanding Rsch. award Internat. Mariner Mining Soc., 1989. Mem. Assn. Marine Mining (v.p.), Am. Assn. Petroleum Geologists, Soc. Econ. Mineralogists, Geochem. Soc., Challenger Soc. Oceanography, AAAS, Internat. Assn. Sedimentologists, Sigma Xi. Home: 13000 Grubstake Austin TX 78736 Office: U Tex Dept Marine Sci Austin TX 78712

MOORE, JAMES TERRENCE, II, industrial distribution company executive; b. Detroit, June 16, 1948; s. James Terrence Sr. and Marion Grace (Gleason) M.; m. Lizabeth Clair Kinsey; children: Ryan Barry, Bryce Ward, Kevan Patrick. BA, Olivet Coll., 1970. Salesman, administr. SKF Industries, Inc., Phila., 1970-73; asst. v.p. Detroit Ball Bearing Co., 1973-78; pres., COO Moore Bearing Co., Denver, 1978—, Am. Bearing & Power Transmissions, Charlotte, N.C., 1985—; former exec. v.p. Invetech, Detroit, also bd. dirs., now pres., COO; bd. dirs. Power Transmission Distbr. Assn.; past chmn. Young Execs. Bearing Specialist Assn., 1985. Mem. Rep. Senatorial Inner Circle, Washington, 1980—; bd. dirs. Manresa Jesuit Retreat House, Bloomfield Hills, Mich., 1986—; chmn. Catholic Services Appeal, Birmingham, Mich., 1986-87; rep. St. Regis Parish Council, Birmingham, Mich., 1986-87. Mem. Am. Mgmt. Assn., Profit Sharing Council Am. Roman Catholic. Clubs: Pine Lake Country; Detroit Athletic; Renaissance. Avocations: reading, hiking. Office: Invetech Co 1400 Howard St Detroit MI 48216-1917*

MOORE, JANE ROSS, librarian; b. Phila., Apr. 24, 1929; d. John William and Mary (McClure) Ross; m. Cyril Howard Moore, Jr., June 1, 1956 (div. Mar. 1967). A.B., Smith Coll., 1951; M.S. in L.S. Drexel U., 1952; postgrad., Columbia U.; M.B.A. with distinction, NYU, 1965; Ph.D.; Case Western Res. U., 1974. Cataloguer, Yale U. Library, 1952-54; chief tech. processes librarian Lederle Labs., Am. Cyanamid Co., Pearl River, N.Y., 1954-58; chief serials catalog librarian Bklyn. Coll. Library, 1958-65, asst. prof., chief catalog div., 1965-70, asso. prof., chief catalog div., 1971-73, asso. prof. asso. librarian administrv. services, 1973-74; prof., chief librarian Mina Rees Libr., Grad. Sch. and Univ. Center, CUNY, 1976-91, prof. chief libr. emerita, 1991—; lectr. Syracuse U. Grad. Sch. Libr. Sci., summer 1967, 69, Queens Coll. Grad. Sch. Libr. and Info. Studies, 1967-69; adj. assoc. prof. 1974-76, adj. prof., 1977-86; HEW Title IIB fellow Case Western Res. U. Sch. Library Sci., 1970-72; trustee N.Y. Met. Reference and Rsch. Libr. Agy., 1984-93, 2d v.p., 1985-88, v.p., 1988-90, treas. 1991-93; mem. chancellor's task force on librs. CUNY, 1979-81. Bd. dirs. Vis. Nurse Assn. of Bklyn., 1984—, mem. exec. com., 1987—; elder, clk. of session, pres. of corp. Presbyn. Ch. Mem. N.Y. Library Assn. (pres. 1979-80, pres. resources and tech. services sect. 1966-67, councilor 1966-67, 75-76, 78-81, sec.-treas. acad. and spl. libraries sect. 1973-75), ALA (membership com. 1967-71, chmn. council regional groups, resources and tech. services div. 1968-69, div. 1968-70, 75-76, chmn. div. cataloging and classification sect. 1975-76), N.Y. Tech. Services Librarians (pres. 1963-64, award 1976), Assn. Coll. and Research Libraries (chmn. univ. libraries sect. 1983-84), N.Y. Library Club (sec. 1964-66, pres. 1980-81, council 1966-70, 73-79, 79-82), OCLC Users Council (SUNY del. 1981-85), AAUP, AAUW, Am. Printing History Assn., Am. Soc. Info. Sci., Archons of Colophon, Library Assn. of Great Brit., Spl. Libraries Assn., The Typophiles, NYU Grad. Sch. Bus. Adminstrn. Alumni Assn. (rec. sec. 1967-69, dir. 1969-70, 75-79), Smith Coll. Club Bklyn. (pres. 1966-67, 67-68, class treas. 1976-81), Smith Coll. Club N.Y., Princeton Club N.Y., Phi Kappa Phi. Home: 35 Schermerhorn St Brooklyn NY 11201-4826 Office: CUNY Mina Rees Libr Grad Sch & U Ctr 33 W 42nd St New York NY 10036-8099

MOORE, JERRY, religious organization administrator. Exec. sec. Home Mission Bd. of the Nat. Baptist Convention, USA, Washington, D.C. Office: Home Mission Bd 1612 Buchanan St NW Washington DC 20011

MOORE, JOAN ELIZABETH, human resources executive, lawyer; b. Valleyfield, Que., Can., Apr. 29, 1951. BS in Social Scis., Mich. State U., 1973;

JD, Case Western Res. U., 1976. Bar: Ohio 1977; cert. sr. profl. in human resources. Pers. exec. Ford Motor Co., Dearborn, Mich., 1976-80; cons. James Lash & Co., Southfield, Mich., 1980-83; pres., owner The Arbor Cons. Group, Inc., Plymouth, Mich., 1983—; owner Integrated Pers. Systems Inc., Plymouth, 1986—. V.p., bd. dirs. Pvt. Industry Coun., Wayne County, Mich., 1985-87; grad. Leadership Detroit VII, 1986, active alumni bd.; mem. computer subcom. Mich. Tech. Coun., 1986—; bd. dirs. Am. Cancer Soc. Mem. ABA, Ohio Bar Assn. Soc. for Human Resources Mgmt., Leadership Detroit Alumni, Ann Arbor Art Assn. (bd. dirs.), Children's Aid Soc. (pers. advisor). Office: The Arbor Cons Group 711 W Ann Arbor Trl Plymouth MI 48170-1677

MOORE, JOANNE IWEITA, pharmacologist, educator; b. Greenville, Ohio, July 23, 1928; d. Clarence Jacob and Mary Edna (Klepinger) M. A.B., U. Cin., 1950; Ph.D., U. Mich., 1959. Rsch. asst. Christ Hosp. Inst. Med. Rsch., Cin., 1950-55; rsch. asst. U. Mich., Ann Arbor, 1955-57, teaching fellow, 1957-59; postdoctoral fellow in pharmacology Emory U., Atlanta, 1959-61; asst. prof. pharmacology U. Okla. Coll. Medicine, Oklahoma City, 1961-66, assoc. prof., 1966-71, acting chmn., 1969-71, prof., interim chmn., 1971-73, prof., chmn. dept., 1973—; David Ross Boyd prof., chair, 1993; mem. gen. rsch. support rev. com. NIH, 1975-79, mem. biomed. scis. study sect., 1986-90; mem. adv. bd. Fogarty Internat. Ctr., 1992-94. Contbr. articles to profl. jours. USPHS grantee, 1963-69, 72-74, 79-87. Mem. AAAS, Am. Soc. Pharmacology and Exptl. Therapeutics, Assn. Med. Sch. Pharmacology, Am. Heart Assn. (bd. dirs. Okla. affiliate 1973-88, pres. 1979-80, chmn. bd. 1983-85, bd. dirs. Oklahoma City div. 1988-91, pres. 1989-90), Sigma Xi. Office: U Okla Coll Medicine Dept Pharmacology 753 BMSB OUHSC Oklahoma City OK 73190

MOORE, JOHN ALEXANDER, biologist; b. Charles Town, W.Va., June 27, 1915; s. George Douglas and Louise Hammond (Blume) M.; m. Anna Betty Clark, 1938; 1 child. Student, Columbia Coll. Columbia U. Asst. zoology dept. Columbia U., N.Y.C., 1936-39, chair zoology dept., 1949-52, prof., 1954-68; tutor in biology Bklyn. Coll., 1939-41; instr. Queens Coll., 1941-43; asst. prof. zoology Barnard Coll., 1943-47, assoc. prof., 1947-50, prof., 1950-68, chair zoology dept., 1948-54, 60-66; rsch. assoc. Am. Mus. Natural History, 1942—; prof. biology U. Calif., Riverside, 1969-82, prof. emeritus, 1982—; mem. com. on human resources NRC, 1979-82, mem. coord. coun. for edn., 1991—, mem. com. on undergrad. sci. edn., 1992—; Walker Ames prof. U. Wash., 1966; mem. Biol. Scis. Curriculum Study, 1959-76; mem. Commn. on Sci. Edn., 1967-73, chair, 1971-73; mem. Nat. Sci. Resource Ctr., 1994. Author: Principles of Zoology, 1957, Heredity and Development, 1963, 2d edit., 1972, A Guide Book to Washington, 1963, Biological Science: An Inquiry into Life, 19673, 3d edit., 1973, (with others) Interaction of Man and the Biosphere, 1970, 3d edit., 1979, Science for Society: A Bibliography, 1970, 2d edit., 1971, Readings in Heredity and Development, 1972, Science as a Way of Knowing - Evolutionary Biology, 1984, Science as a Way of Knowing - Human Ecology, 1985, Science as a Way of Knowing - Genetics, 1986, Science as a Way of Knowing - Form and Function, 1988, Science: A Conceptual Framework for Biology, Part I, 1989, Part II, 1990, Part III, 1991, Science as a Way of Knowing: The Foundations of Modern Biology, 1993; editor: Physiology of the Amphibia, 1964, Ideas in Modern Biology, 1965, Ideas in Evolution and Behavior, 1970, Dobzhansky's Genetics of Natural Populations, 1981; supr.: Biological Science: An Inquiry into Life, 1963, ed edit., 1973. Fulbright rsch. scholar, Australia, 1952-53; Guggenheim fellow, 1959. Mem NAS, AAAS (mem. project 2061 1985-89), Genetics Soc. Am., Am. Soc. Zoologists (pres. 1974), Am. Soc. Naturalists (pres. 1972), Soc. for Study Evolution (pres. 1963), Am. Acad. Arts and Scis. Avocations: photography, history of American science, history of illumination. Home: 11522 Tulane Ave Riverside CA 92507-6649 Office: U Calif Dept Biology Riverside CA 92521-0427

MOORE, JOHN ASHTON, zoo director; b. Inglewood, Calif., May 23, 1940; s. Ashton Edward and Maddie Ruth (Eaves) M.; m. Edna Louise Hotchkiss, June 25, 1959; children—Linda Marie, Theresa Ruth. Student, Mt. San Antonio Coll., 1960-61; grad., Jessup A.I. Tech. Sch., 1961. Mgr. Movieland Animal Park, Bloomington, Calif., 1964-65; curator birds Balt. Zoo, 1965-67, asst. dir., 1967-71; dir. Salisbury (Md.) Zoo, 1971-72, Audubon Park, New Orleans, 1972-77; dir. Rio Grande Zool. Park, Albuquerque, 1977—; cons. wildlife research, zoos. King, Crew of Tucks, New Orleans; Mem. part time faculty Johns Hopkins U., Balt., 1968-71, research assoc., 1971-78; pioneer in hand rearing of Kagu; first western hemisphere captive breeding of Kagu. Contbr. articles to profl. jours. National avicultural achievement award Peter Scott, Slimbridge, Eng., 1971. Fellow Am. Assn. Zool. Parks and Aquariums (profl. fellow); mem. La. Fedn. Zoos (past pres.), Internat. Crane Found. (hon. life). Club: Exchange. Office: Rio Grande Zoological Park 903 10th St SW Albuquerque NM 87102-4098

MOORE, JOHN DENNIS, publisher; b. Mexico, Mo., Mar. 2, 1931; s. Dennis Talmage and Vona Mae (Vance) M.; m. Lydia Benz Ahern, Aug. 15, 1959; children: Alison Ahern, Lydia Benz, John Talmage, Maude Ahern, Meredith Coleman. Student, Princeton U., 1948-51, U.S. Naval Acad., 1951-53; B.A., U. Mo., Columbia, 1953; postgrad., Harvard Law Sch., 1955-56. Coll. traveler The Dryden Press, Inc., N.Y.C., 1957-59; coll. traveler The Macmillan Co., N.Y.C., 1959-60; editor The Macmillan Co., 1960-67, Columbia U. Press, N.Y.C., 1968-74; editor in chief Columbia U. Press, 1974-80, pres., bd. dirs., 1980—; bd. dirs., pres. Columbia U. Music Press; bd. dirs. Univ. Presses of Calif., Columbia and Princeton, Chichester, West Sussex, Eng., 1979—, chmn., 1981-83, 85-87; trustee Composer's Recordings, Inc., 1984—. Bd. dirs. Greenwich Health Assn., Conn., 1970-75; bd. dirs. assoc. The Family Center, Greenwich, 1975—; trustee Princeton Library in N.Y.C., 1984—. Served with U.S. Army, 1953-55. Bd. dirs. Greenwich Health Assn., Conn., 1970-75; bd. dirs. assoc. The Family Ctr., Greenwich, 1975—; trustee Princeton Libr. in N.Y.C., 1984—; mem. vestry St. Baruobas Ch., Greenwich, Mich., 1995—. Episcopalian. Clubs: Publishers Lunch (N.Y.C.), Princeton (N.Y.C.), Faculty House Columbia U. (N.Y.C.), Century Assn. (N.Y.C.); Nassau (Princeton, N.J.), the Book Table (N.Y.C.). Office: Columbia U Press 562 W 113th St New York NY 10025-8099

MOORE, JOHN EDWIN, JR., college president; b. Aurora, Mo., Nov. 7, 1942; s. John Edwin and Emma Lou (Harback) M.; m. Louise R. Watkins, June 4, 1966; children: John E. III, Catherine Porter. BA cum laude, Yale U., 1964, MA in Teaching, 1965; EdD, Harvard U., 1971. Tchr. N.C. Advancement Sch., Winston-Salem, 1965-66; rsch. asst. Tech. Edn. Rsch. Ctr., Cambridge, Mass., 1969-70; adminstrv. asst., treas. Kirkwood Sch. Dist. R-VII, St. Louis, 1970-73, asst. supt., treas., 1973-74; adj. prof. U. Mo., St. Louis, 1973-74; v.p. Athens (Greece) Coll., 1974-75; asst. commr. edn. Dept. Elem. and Secondary Edn., Jefferson City, Mo., 1975-83; pres. Drury Coll., Springfield, Mo., 1983—; part-time instr. Far-East div. U. Md., 1967-68. Bd. dirs. United Way Ozarks, campaign chmn., 1988; bd. dirs. Mo. Colls. Fund, chmn., 1988-89; bd. dirs. Make-A-Wish Found. With U.S. Army, 1966-68. Recipient Vincent Conroy Meml. award Harvard Grad. Sch. Edn., 1971; named one of Outstanding Young Men Am., 1973. Mem. Springfield Area C. of C. (v.p. 1988, bd. dirs. Springfieldian of Yr. 1989), Nat. Assn. Intercollegiate Athletics (coun. pres.'s), Rotary (pres. Springfield chpt. 1988-89). Presbyterian (elder). Avocations: hunting, fishing, gardening, conservation. Home: 1234 N Benton Ave Springfield MO 65802-1902 Office: Drury Coll 900 N Benton Ave Springfield MO 65802-3791

MOORE, JOHN GEORGE, JR., medical educator; b. Berkeley, Calif., Sept. 17, 1917; s. John George and Mercedes (Sullivan) M.; m. Mary Louise Laffer, Feb. 8, 1946; children: Barbara Ann, Douglas Terence, Bruce MacDonald, Martha Christine. B.A., U. Calif., Berkeley, 1939, M.D., U. Calif., San Francisco, 1942. Diplomate: Am. Bd. Ob-Gyn (pres. 1974-78, chmn. 1978-82). Asst. prof. U. Iowa, 1950-51; asso. prof. UCLA, 1951-65, prof., chmn. dept. ob-gyn, 1968-88; prof., chmn. dept. ob-gyn Columbia U. Coll. Physicians and Surgeons, 1965-68; chief of gynecology VA Hosp., Sepulveda, Calif., 1988-94. Contbr. articles to profl. jours. Served to maj. M.C. U.S. Army, 1942-46. Decorated Silver Star, Bronze Star, Purple Heart; NIH grantee U. Copenhagen; Royal Postgrad. Sch. Medicine, London. Mem. ACS, ACOG, Soc. Gynecol. Investigation (pres. 1967), Assn. Profs. Gynecology and Obstetrics (pres. 1975), Western Assn. Gynecol. Oncologists (pres. 1976), Am. Gynecol. Soc., Pacific Coast Ob-Gyn. Soc., L.A. Ob-Gyn. Soc., Pepperdine U. Assocs. Home: Tamarron Unit 843 PO Box #3131 Durango CO 81302-3131

MOORE, JOHN HAMPTON, academic administrator; b. Grand Forks, N.D., Apr. 19, 1935; s. Charles Harold and Marie (Lindberg) M.; m. Barbara Sue Corbett, Feb. 23, 1963; children: John Randolph, Matthew Corbett. BS in Engring., U. Mich., 1958, MBA, 1959; PhD in Econs., U. Va., Charlottesville, 1966. Rsch. chemist Procter & Gamble Co., 1959-63; asst. prof. econs. U. Va., Charlottesville, 1966-70, assoc. prof. econs., 1970-77; assoc. dir., rsch. prof. Law and Econs. Ctr. U. Miami, Fla., 1977-80; assoc dir., prof. econs. Law and Econs. Ctr. Emory U., Atlanta, 1981; assoc. dir., sr. fellow Hoover Instn. Stanford U., Calif., 1981-85, acting dep. dir. Hoover Instn., 1983-84; dep. dir. NSF, Washington, 1985-89; dir. internat. inst. George Mason U., Washington, 1990—; sr. assoc. mem. St. Antony's Coll. Oxford U., Eng., 1973; mem. Nat. Sci. Bd., Washington, 1982-85. Author: Growth With Self-Management: Yugoslav Industrialization, 1952-75, 80; co-translator, co-editor: Stalinist Planning for Economic Growth, 1933-52, 1980; editor: To Promote Prosperity, 1984, Legacies of the Collapse of Marxism, 1994; contbr. articles to profl. jours. Bd. dirs. Thomas Jefferson Ctr. Found., 1972-85; chmn. standing fin. com. Internat. Coun. Sci. Unions, 1992—; trustee Earhart Found., 1993—. NASA fellow, 1963-66, Hoover Instn., Stanford U. fellow, 1975-76. Mem. AAAS, Am. Econ. Assn., Mont Pelerin Soc. (bd. dirs. 1992—, v.p. 1994—), Raven Soc., So. Econ. Assn., Phila. Soc., Sigma Xi (chmn. internat. com. 1991—), Phi Eta Sigma, Tau Beta Pi, Omicron Delta Kappa. Home: 6516 Bradley Blvd Bethesda MD 20817-3248 Office: George Mason U 4001 Fairfax Dr Arlington VA 22203-1616

MOORE, JOHN HEBRON, history educator; b. Greenville, Miss., Feb. 26, 1920; s. John Pressley and Cora (Hebron) M.; m. Margaret Burr DesChamps, Dec. 20, 1955; 1 child, John Hebron Jr. BS in Aero-engring., Miss. State U., 1946; MA in History, U. Miss. Oxford, 1951; PhD, Emory U., 1955. Asst. prof. Delta State U., Cleveland, Miss., 1955-56; asst. prof. U. Miss., Oxford, 1956-57, assoc. prof., 1957-62, prof., 1962-70, chmn. history dept., 1966-69; prof. Fla. State U., Tallahassee, 1970-93, chmn. history dept., 1975-80; prof. emeritus, 1993—. Author: Agriculture in Antebellum Mississippi, 1958, Andrew Brown and Cypress Lumbering in the Old Southwest, 1967, The Emergence of the Cottom Kingdom in the Old Southwest: Mississippi, 1770-1860, 1988. With U.S. Army, 1941-43, USAAF, 1943-45, ETO, PTO. Mem. Agrl. History Soc. (pres. 1985), So. Hist. Assn., Miss. Hist. Soc. Presbyterian. Home: 2529 Blarney Dr Tallahassee FL 32308-3152

MOORE, JOHN HENRY, II, federal judge; b. Atlantic City, Aug. 5, 1929; s. Harry Cordery and Gertrude (Wasleski) M.; m. Joan Claire Kraft, Dec. 29, 1951; children—Deborah Joan, Katherine Louise. Student, Cornell U., 1947; BS, Syracuse U., 1952; JD, U. Fla., 1961. Bar: Fla. 1961. Assoc. Fisher & Phillips, Atlanta, 1961; ptnr. Flemming O'Bryan & Fleming, Fort Lauderdale, Fla., 1961-67, Turner, Shaw & Moore, Fort Lauderdale, Fla., 1967; judge 17th Jud. Circuit, Fort Lauderdale, Fla., 1967-77, U.S. Dist. Ct. Appeals for 4th Cir., West Palm Beach, Fla., 1977-81; judge, now chief judge U.S. Dist. for Mid. Dist. Fla., Jacksonville, 1981—; mem. Fla. Constitution Revision Com., 1977-78; chmn. Fla. Jud. Qualifications Commn., 1977-81. Bd. dirs. Community Service Council, Fort Lauderdale, 1970-75; pres. Broward County Assn. for Retarded Children, Fort Lauderdale, 1962; hon. bd. trustees Broward Community Coll., Fort Lauderdale, 1970. Served to comdr. USNR, 1948-71, Korea. Named hon. Alumnus Nova U., 1977; recipient cert. of good govt. Gov. of Fla., 1967. Mem. ABA, Fla. Bar Assn. Fed. Bar Assn., Jacksonville Bar Assn., Fla. Conf. Circuit Judges (chmn.-elect 1977), Fla. Blue Key (hon.), U.S. Navy League, Naval Res. Assn., Ret. Officers Assn. Republican. Presbyterian. Clubs: Timuquana Country, Jacksonville Quarterback, Seminole (Jacksonville). Lodge: Rotary. Avocations: golf, tennis, boating. Office: US Dist Ct PO Box 53137 Jacksonville FL 32201-3137

MOORE, JOHN JOSEPH, lawyer; b. West New York, N.J., Jan. 24, 1933; s. George Thomas and Dorothy (Zimmer) M.; m. Carmela Macrini, Mar. 10, 1957; children: Christine, John Joseph. B.S., Jersey City State Coll., 1956; LL.B., N.Y. Law Sch., 1961; LL.M., NYU, 1970. Bar: N.Y. 1961. Since practiced in N.Y.C.; assoc. with firm Dwyer & Lawler, after 1961; then mem. firm Reid, Devlin, Grubbs & Moore (now Alio & McDonough); chmn. bd. Leber Inc., 1983-93; mem. Barry McTiernan and Moore, 1970—; guest lectr. disclosure Fordham U.; tchr. social studies pub. schs., Union City, N.J.; Sponsor, coach local Biddy Basketball Team, 1972—. Author: Discovery and Inspection, 1969, Legal Significance, 1975; editor: Defendant, 1969-73, 1987-92. Trustee devel. fund Jersey City State Tchrs. Coll., 1973-81; trustee Jersey City State Coll., 1982, vice chmn. bd. trustees, 1983-87, chmn., 1989—; chmn. governing bds. Assn. State Colls. N.J., 1985-87; chair Civilian Rev. Complaint Bd., Teaneck, N.J., 1992—; mem. Bd. Higher Edn. State N.J., 1985-87, Coun. N.J. State Colls., 1984-85; mem. governing bds. Assn. State Colls. N.J., 1985-89. With AUS, 1956-58. Mem. ABA, Am. Arbitration Assn. (arbiter 1968—), N.Y. State Bar Assn., N.Y. County Bar Assn., Def. Assn. N.Y. (pres. 1973-74, chmn. bd. 1974-75), Assn. State Colls. N.Y. (gov. bd. 1985-93), Cath. Ins. Guild (pres. 1972-73, chmn. bd. 1973-74), Def. Rsch. Inst. (regional v.p. 1983-86), Downtown Athletic Club (N.Y.C.), Manhattan Club, Oritani Field Club (Hackensack, N.J.), Hackensack Golf Club. Roman Catholic (dir. mus. group). Home: 573 Standish Rd Teaneck NJ 07666-2605 Office: 25 Broadway New York NY 10004-1010

MOORE, JOHN LEO, JR., journalist, writer, editor; b. Providence, R.I., June 24, 1927; s. John Leo and Annabelle Cecilia (Eastwood) M.; m. Dorothy Dolores Drankwicz, 1952; children: John Leo III, Christopher, Meredith Margaret Moore Poffenberger. AB, Brown U., 1950. Reporter Pawtucket (R.I.) Times, 1950-66, Providence (R.I.) Jour.-Bulletin, 1966; correspondent Carpenter News Svc., Washington, 1966-69; assoc. editor Nat. Jour., Washington, 1969-74; asst. mng. editor Congl. Quarterly, Washington, 1974-78, asst. dir. books, 1978-90; freelance writer, editor Washington, 1990—; cons. World Bank Internat. Monetary Fund, Washington, 1990—. Editor: (Books) Guide to U.S. Elections, 2nd edit. 1985, 3rd rev. edit. 1994, CQ's Washington Guidebook, 1990, Congressional Ethics, 1992; author: Speaking of Washington, 1993. Committeeman Boy Scouts Am. Troop 15, Pawtucket, 1946-50, Troop 12, 1964-66; pres. Local 185 Newspaper Guild, Pawtucket, 1964-66; v.p. Community Assn., Severna Forest, Md., 1976-78. Named Eagle Scout, 1943; recipient salute Pawtucket C. of C., 1965, resolution of praise Pawtucket City Coun., 1966; cited for disting. reporting pub. affairs Am. Polit. Sci. Assn., 1961. Mem. Soc. Profl. Journalists. Roman Catholic. Avocations: photography, home improvement, lawn and garden work, reading, walking. Home and Office: 807 Cottonwood Dr Severna Park MD 21146-2813

MOORE, JOHN NEWTON, retired natural science educator; b. Columbus, Ohio, Apr. 2, 1920; s. Lawrence Newton and Grace C. (Jones) M.; m. Wilma Marie Proctor, Aug. 30, 1941; children—Douglas Warren, Donald Norman. A.B., Denison U., Granville, Ohio, 1941; M.S., Mich. State U., E. Lansing, 1943, Ed.D., 1952. Grad. asst. botany Mich. State U., 1941-43, instr. math., 1943-44, mem. faculty, 1946-82, prof. natural sci., 1970-82, prof. emeritus, 1982—; vis. prof. edn. Tenn. Temple Coll., summer 1974; bd. dirs. Creation Research Soc., 1963-86. Author: Questions and Answers on Creation/Evolution, 1976, How to Teach Origins, 1983, co-editor: Biology: A Search for Order in Complexity, rev. edit, 1974; mng. editor: Creation Research Soc. Quar, 1965-77; author chpts. in books. Served to lt. (j.g.) USNR, 1944-46. Fellow Creation Research Soc.; mem. Lambda Chi Alpha, Beta Beta Beta. Address: 119 Edward Ave Lehigh Acres FL 33936-5411

MOORE, JOHN NORTON, lawyer, diplomat, educator; b. N.Y.C., June 12, 1937; s. William Thomas and Lorena (Norton) M.; m. Barbara Schneider, Dec. 12, 1981; children: Victoria Norton, Elizabeth Norton. AB in Econs., Drew U., 1959; LLB with honors, Duke U., 1962; LLM, U. Ill., 1965; postgrad., Yale U., 1965-66. Bar: Fla. 1962, Ill. 1963, Va. 1969, D.C. 1972, U.S. Supreme Ct. 1972. Walter L. Brown prof. law, dir. Ctr. Oceans Law and Policy Ctr. for Nat. Security Law, U. Va., 1965-72, 76—; counselor on internat. law Dept. State, Washington, 1972-73; chmn. Nat. Security Coun. Task Force on Law of Sea and dep. spl. rep. of Pres. and amb. Law of Sea Conf., 1973-76; fellow Woodrow Wilson Internat. Ctr. for Scholars, Washington, 1976; adj. prof. Georgetown Law Ctr., 1978—; mem. Nat. Adv. Com. on Oceans and Atmosphere, 1984-85; mem. U.S. del. Conf. Security and Coop. in Europe, 1984; spl. counsel for U.S. to World Ct.; former cons. to the Pres.'s Intelligence Oversight Bd., Arms Control and Disarmament Agy., U.S. Info. Agy.; chmn. bd. dirs. U.S. Inst. Peace; co-chmn. with the U.S. dep. atty. gen. Moscow Seminar on the Rule of Law, 1990; legal advisor during Gulf crisis for Kuwait's Amb. to U.S., including legal adviser to the Kuwait Rep. to UN Boundary Commn., 1991-94. Author: Law and the Indo-China War, 1972 (Phi Beta Kappa award); editor: Law and Civil War in the Modern World, 1976, Readings in International Law, 1979, The Arab-Israeli Conflict, 3 vols., 1976, 4th vol., 1991, Nat. Security Law, 1990, Crisis in the Gulf, 1992, Nat. Security Law Documents, 1995; contbr. articles on oceans policy, nat. security, internat. law, congl.-exec. rels. in fgn. policy and democracy-building to profl. jours. Sesquicentennial assoc. Ctr. Advanced Studies, U. Va., 1971-72; mem. adv. bd. on law of sea State Dept., 1977-80, mem. adv. bd. on internat. law, 1982; chmn. bd. U.S. Inst. Peace, 1986-89, 89-91; chmn. oceans policy com. Rep. Nat. Com.; mem. Consortium on Intelligence. Recipient Alumni award in arts Drew U., 1976; Compass Disting. Achievement award for significant contbns. to art and sci. of oceanography and marine tech., 1994; NIH fellow Yale U., 1965-66. Mem. ABA (past vice-chmn. sect. internat. law and past 5-term chmn. com. on law and nat. security), Am. Law Inst., Am. Oceanic Orgn. (exec. coun.), Marine Tech. Soc. (exec. coun.), Coun. Fgn. Rels., Order of Coif, Cosmos Club, N.Y. Yacht Club, Freedom House (bd. dirs.), Phi Beta Kappa. Republican. Episcopalian. Home: 824 Flordon Dr Charlottesville VA 22901-7810 Office: U Va Sch Law North Grounds Charlottesville VA 22901 *Life offers opportunity to pursue many worthwhile interests. In selecting among them it has seemed most useful to focus on those issues of sufficiently broad general significance as to justify the efforts of a lifetime. For me that has meant focus on improving the functioning of government, controlling and reducing international conflict, and the policy choices of the ocean frontier.*

MOORE, JOHN PORFILIO, federal judge; b. Denver, Oct. 14, 1934; s. Edward Alphonso Porfilio and Caroline (Carbone) Moore; m. Joan West, Aug. 1, 1959 (div. 1983); children—Edward Miles, Joseph Arthur, Jeanne Kathrine; m. Theresa Louise Berger, Dec. 28, 1983; 1 stepchild, Katrina Ann Smith. Student, Stanford U., 1952-54; BA, U. Denver, 1956, LLB, 1959. Bar: Colo. 1959, U.S. Supreme Ct. 1965. Asst. atty. gen. State of Colo., Denver, 1962-68, dep. atty. gen., 1968-72, atty. gen., 1972-74; U.S. bankruptcy judge Dist. of Colo., Denver, 1975-82; judge U.S. Dist. Ct. Colo., Denver, 1982-85, U.S. Ct. Appeals (10th cir.), Denver, 1985—; instr. Colo. Law Enforcement Acad., Denver, 1965-70, State Patrol Acad., Denver, 1968-70; guest lectr. U. Denver Coll. Law, 1978. Committeeman Arapahoe County Republican Com., Aurora, Colo., 1968; mgr. Dunbar for Atty. Gen., Denver, 1970. Mem. ABA. Roman Catholic. Office: US Ct Appeals Byron White US Courthouse 1823 Stout St Denver CO 80257-9999

MOORE, JOHN RONALD, manufacturing executive; b. Pueblo, Colo., July 12, 1935; s. John E. and Anna (Yesberger) M.; m. Judith Russelyn Bauman, Sept. 5, 1959; children: Leland, Roni, Timothy, Elaine. BS, U. Colo., 1959; grad. advanced mgmt. program, Harvard Grad. Sch. Bus., 1981. Mgmt. trainee Montgomery Ward & Co., Denver, 1960-65; distbn. mgr. Midas Internat. Corp., Chgo., 1965-71; v.p. gen. mgr. Midas, Can., Toronto, Ont., 1972-75; pres. Auto Group Midas Internat. Corp., Chgo., 1976-82, pres., chief exec. officer, 1982—; also bd. dirs.; bd. dirs. Midas Australia Pty. Ltd., Melbourne. Served with U.S. Army, 1953-55. Mem. Ill. Mfr.'s Assn., Motor Equipment Mfrs. Assn. (pres.'s council 1982—), Internat. Franchising Assn., Econ. Club of Chgo., Comml. Club Chgo., Harvard Bus. Sch. Alumni Assn., U. Colo. Alumni Assn. Republican. Office: Midas Internat Corp 225 N Michigan Ave Chicago IL 60601-7601 *There is very little we accomplish in our lifetime that results from effort we alone expend. All of us should have the wisdom to express our appreciation to our families and associates who have helped us attain our goals and accomplishments—for failure to do so tarnishes our successes and breeds selfishness.*

MOORE, JOHN RUNYAN, agricultural and resource economics educator; b. Columbus, Ohio, Sept. 30, 1929; s. Lawrence Levi and Hazel Marie (Runyan) M.; m. Marjorie Ann Coy, June 14, 1953; children: Lee, Andrew. BSc in Agriculture, Ohio State U., 1951; MSc in Agrl. Econs., Cornell U., 1955; PhD in Agrl. Econs., U. Wis., Madison, 1959. County 4-H Club agt. Ohio Coop. Extension Svc., Stuebenville, 1951; grad. rsch. asst. Cornell U., Ithaca, N.Y., 1953-55, U. Wis., Madison, 1955-58; asst. prof. Mich. State U., East Lansing, 1958-62; mktg. specialist, econ. cons. Ford Found., New Delhi, 1968-70; assoc. prof. U. Md., College Park, 1962-68, prof. in world food situation and food mktg., 1968—, asst. dean internat. program, 1979-94; econ. cons. FTC, Washington 1963-64, World Bank, India and Nigeria, 1971-74, U.S. AID, Indonesia, Malawi, Haiti, Liberia and Egypt, various dates, FAO, Beijing, 1990. Co-author: (book) Market Structure of Agriculture Industries, 1964, U.S. Investment In Latin American Food Processing, 1966, Indian Food Grain Market, 1972. Trustee S.E. Consortium for Internat. Devel., 1978—. Lt. (j.g.) USNR, 1951-53. Recipient Internat. Honor award USDA, Washington, 1985, Cert. of Appreciation, 1986. Mem. Am. Agrl. Econ. Assn. (Thesis award 1960), Am. Econ. Assn., Internat. Agrl. Econ. Assn., S.E. Consortium for Internat. Devel. (trustee), Rotary. Avocations: photography, travel, gardening, golf.

MOORE, JOHN STERLING, JR., minister; b. Memphis, Aug. 25, 1918; s. John Sterling and Lorena (Bounds) M.; m. Martha Louise Paulette, July 6, 1944; children: Sterling Hale, John Marshall, Carolyn Paulette. Student, Auburn U., 1936-37; AB, Samford U., 1940; ThM, So. Bapt. Theol. Sem., 1944. Ordained to ministry So. Bapt. Conv., 1942. Pastor chs. Pamplin, Va., 1944-48, Amherst, Va., 1949-57; pastor emeritus, 1984—; mem. Hist. Commn., So. Bapt. Conv., 1968-75; pres. Va. Bapt. Pastor's Conf., 1963. Author: History of Broad Run Baptist Church, 1762-1987, 1987; co-author: Meaningful Moments in Virginia Baptist Life, 1715-1972, 1973; editor Va. Bapt. Register, 1972—; contbr. articles to profl. jours. Chmn. Lexington Mayor's Com. on Race Rels., 1962-65; bd. dirs. Stonewall Jackson Hosp., 1967-72, pres., 1969-71; treas. Rockbridge Mental Health Clinic, 1971-84. Recipient Disting. Svc. award Hist. Commn., So. Bapt. Conv., 1988. Mem. Am. Soc. Ch. History, So. Bapt. Hist. Soc. (bd. dirs. 1972-91, pres. 1975-76, sec. 1977-85), Va. Bapt. Hist. Soc. (exec. com. 1963—, pres. 1984-85), Va. Hist. Soc., Masons. Home: 8709 Gayton Rd Richmond VA 23229-6331

MOORE, JOHN W., academic administrator. Pres. Ind. State U., Terre Haute. Office: Indiana State U Office of President Terre Haute IN 47809

MOORE, JOHN W., lawyer; b. Atlanta, Apr. 26, 1947; s. John Wilbur Moore and Marjory ELizabeth (Davis) Johnston; m. Phyllis Arue Norris, Jan. 16, 1982; 1 child, Ashley Alillian. BA, Emory U., 1968, JD, 1974. Bar: Ga. 1974. Assoc. Troutman Sanders, Lockerman & Ashmore, Atlanta, 1974-79; ptnr. Troutman Sanders, Atlanta, 1982—; assoc. counsel Cousins Properties Inc., Atlanta, 1980-81. Bd. dirs. Am. Cancer Soc., Atlanta, 1984. With U.S. Army, 1969-71, Vietnam. Mem. State Bar Ga., Atlanta Bar Assn., Phi Beta Kappa. Republican. Presbyterian. Avocations: hiking, fishing, bicycling, golf. Office: Troutman Sanders 600 Peachtree St Ste 5200 Atlanta GA 30308-2216

MOORE, JOHN WARD, chemistry educator; b. Lancaster, Pa., July 17, 1939; s. Joseph D. and Lillian B. M.; m. Elizabeth Augustin, Aug. 26, 1961. AB, Franklin & Marshall Coll., 1961; PhD, Northwestern U., 1965. Asst. prof. Ind. U., Bloomington, 1965-71; assoc. prof. Eastern Mich. U., Ypsilanti, 1971-76, prof., 1976-89; prof. U. Wis., Madison, 1989—; cos. Ecology Ctr. of Ann Arbor, 1979-81; vis. prof. U. Wis., Madison, 1981-82; vis. assoc. prof. U. Nice, France, 1987—; dir. Project SERAPHIM, 1982—. Inst. for Chem. Edn., 1989—. Editor Jour. Chem. Edn.: Software, 1988—; contbr. articles to profl. jours. Recipient Disting. Faculty award for Rsch. Publ. and Svc., Ea. Mich. U., 1977, Sci. Faculty Profl. Devel. award NSF, 1979, Disting. Faculty award Mich. Assn. of Governing Bds., 1982, Catalyst award Chem. Mfg., 1982, Silver medal CASE Prof. Yr., 1986, George C. Pimentel award in chem. edn. Am. Chem. Soc., 1991. Home: 3995 Shawn Trl Middleton WI 53562-3521 Office: U Wis Dept Chemistry 1101 University Ave Madison WI 53706-1396

MOORE, JOHN WILLIAM, university administrator; b. Bayonne, N.J., Aug. 1, 1939; s. Frederick A. and Marian R. (Faser) M.; m. Nancy Baumann, Aug. 10, 1968; children: Matthew, Sarah, David. BS in Social Sci. and Edn., Rutgers U., 1961; MS in Counseling and Student Pers. Svcs., Ind. U., 1963; EdD, Pa. State U., College Station, 1970. Asst. to dean Coll. Edn. Pa. State U., University Park, 1968-70; asst. to dean students U. Vt., Burlington, 1970-71, asst. prof. edn. adminstrn., 1973-76, asst. v.p. acad.

affairs, 1973-76, assoc. v.p. acad. affairs, 1976-77; v.p. policy and planning Old Dominion U., Norfolk, Va., 1977-78, exec. v.p.; 1982-85; pres. Calif. State U., Stanislaus, Turlock, 1985-92, Ind. State U., 1992—. Author: (with others) The Changing Composition of the Work Force: Implications for Future Research and Its Application, 1982, also articles, papers presented at profl. meetings. Pres. United Way, Modesto, Calif., 1989; bd. dirs. Pvt. Industry Coun., Modesto, 1989, Union Hosp., Swope Mus.; bd. dirs., exec. com. Alliance for Growth and Progress, Terre Haute, Ind., 1992—, Terre Haute of C., Wabash Valley United Way. Recipient Disting. Svc. award Old Dominion U. Alumni Assn., 1985, Hispanic C. of C., 1992; recipient Community Svc. award Norfolk Commn. Edn., 1985, Leadership award United Way,1 986, Svc. award Pvt. Industry Coun., 1989; Alumni fellow Pa. State U., 1990. Mem. Am. Assn. State Colls. and Univs. (rep. Calif. chpt. 1988-92, bd. dirs. 1994—), Gould Med. Found. (bd. dirs. 1988-92, trustee 1988-92), Modesto Symphony Orch. Assn. (bd. dirs. 1990-92), Am. Coun. Edn., Commn. on Women in Higher Edn., Turlock C. of C. (bd. dirs. 1988-92), Rotary. Methodist. Avocations: fitness training, skiing, coaching youth sports. Office: Ind State Univ Condit House Cherry St Terre Haute IN 47803

MOORE, JOHN WILSON, neurophysiologist, educator; b. Winston-Salem, N.C., Nov. 1, 1920; s. John Watson and Marjorie (MacAlpine) M.; m. Natalie Bayless, May 6, 1944 (div. 1977); children: John Reid, Marjorie Lee, Stephen Wilson; m. Ann E. Stuart, Apr. 2, 1978; 1 son, Jonathan Watson Stuart-Moore. B.S. in Physics, Davidson (N.C.) Coll., 1941; M.S., U. Va., 1942, Ph.D. in Physics, 1945. Asst. prof. physics Med. Coll. Va., 1946-50; biophysicist Naval Med. Research Inst., 1950-54, Lab. of Biophysics, Nat. Inst. Nervous Diseases and Blindness, NIH, 1954-61; mem. faculty Duke U., 1961—, prof. physiology and pharmacology, 1965-88, prof. neurobiology, 1988—; vis. prof. dept. neurobiology Harvard U. Med. Sch., 1978-79. Trustee, mem. exec. com. Marine Biol. Lab., Woods Hole, Mass. DuPont fellow, 1941-46; Nat. Neurol. Research Found. scientist, 1961-66. Mem. IEEE, AAAS, Am. Physiol. Soc., Biophys. Soc. (coun., Cole award 1981), Soc. Neuroscience, Marine Biol. Lab. Corp., Soc. Gen. Physiologists, Phi Beta Kappa, Omicron Delta Kappa. Office: Duke Univ Dept Neurobiology PO Box 3209 Duke Univ Med Ctr Durham NC 27710-0001

MOORE, JONATHAN, diplomat, policy analyst, advisor; b. N.Y.C., Sept. 10, 1932; s. Charles Frederick and Adeline Reeves (Nichols) M.; m. Katherine Weeks Andres, June 15, 1957; children: Joan Brooke, Jennifer, Jocelyn Andres, Charles Frederick IV. AB cum laude, Dartmouth Coll., 1954; MPA, Harvard U., 1957; LLD (hon.), World Coll. West, 1992. Staff asst. Newmyer Assos., Washington, 1956-57; pub. affairs asst. USIA, Bombay, India, and Monrovia, Liberia, 1957-59; legis. asst. to Senator Leverett Saltonstall Mass., 1959-61; spl. asst. to asst. sec. def. for internat. security affairs Dept. Def., 1961-64; spl. asst. to asst. sec. state for Far East Dept. State, 1964-66; resident fellow Kennedy Inst., Cambridge, Mass., 1966-67, 68; fgn. affairs adviser Romney nat. presdl. campaign, 1967-68, Rockefeller nat. presdl. campaign, 1968; exec. asst. under sec. state Dept. State, Washington, 1969; dep. asst. sec. state for East Asia Dept. State, 1969-70; counselor HEW, 1970-72; spl. asst. to sec. def. Dept. Def., 1973; assoc. atty. gen. Justice Dept., 1973; dir. Inst. of Politics; lectr. public policy John F. Kennedy Sch. of Govt. Harvard U., 1974-86; U.S. coord. and amb.-at-large Refugee Affairs, 1986-89; dir. bur. refugee program U.S. Dept. State, 1987-89; U.S. amb. to UN for spl. polit. affairs N.Y.C., 1989-90, U.S. amb. to UN for econ. and social affairs, 1990-92; sr. assoc. Carnegie Endowment for Internat. Peace, Washington, 1992-94; fellow Ctr. Naval Analyses, Alexandria, Va., 1994—; sr. adv. to adminstr. UN Devel. Programme, 1994—. Mem. sr. adv. com. Barone Press-Politics Ctr., Harvard U., 1988—; bd. dirs., chmn. nat. program polit. com. PBS, 1989—; mem. internat. com. Red Cross Consultative Group Internat. Experts, 1992—; past chmn. editl. bd. Channel 5, Boston; past bd. dirs. Nat. Med. Care, Inc., IU Internat., Inc.; past pres. Mass. Cultural Alliance; past mem. exec. com., trustee Washington Theol. Consortium. Recipient Disting. Svc. award HEW, Rockefeller Disting. Pub. Svc. award, Presdl. medal Dartmouth Coll. Mem. Council Fgn. Relations, Phi Beta Kappa (alumni). Home: 955 26th St NW Apt 303 Washington DC 20037-2039 Office: 4401 Ford Ave PO Box 16268 Alexandria VA 22302

MOORE, JULIA ALICE, non-profit executive; b. Jersey City, N.J., Sept. 10, 1950; d. John Richard and Jean (Alexander) M.; mm. Harry C. Blaney III, Feb. 14, 1976. BS in Fgn. Svc., Georgetown U., Washington, 1972. Analyst Washington Analysis Corp., Washington, 1972-73; assoc. dir. Joseph S. White & Assoc., Washington, 1973-75; dep. dir. Arms Control Assn., Washington, 1982-84; legis. & pub. affairs officer U.S. Dept. of State, Washington, 1975-86; v.p. communications World Wildlife Fund, Washington, 1986-90; sr. assoc. Ogilvy & Mather Pub. Affairs, Washington, 1990-91; exec. dir. Physicians for Social Responsibility, Washington, 1991—; bd. dirs Scoville Fellowships, Washington. Author: OP-EDS. Mem. Coun. on Fgn. Rels. Named Rusk Fellow, Georgetown U., 1985. Mem. Nat. Press Club, Internat. Inst. for Strategic Studies, Arms Control Assn. (mem. alliance to end childhood lead poisoning). Roman Catholic. Home: 4700 Connecticut Ave NW Washington DC 20008-5629 Office: Physicians for Social Responsibility 1101 14th St NW # 700 Washington DC 20005

MOORE, JULIANNE, actress; m. John Gould Rubin. BA, Boston Univ. With The Guthrie Theater, 1988-89. Actress: (theatre) Serious Money, 1987, Bone-the-Fish, 1988, Ice Cream with Hot Fudge, 1990, Uncle Vanya, (TV soap operas) As the World Turns (Emmy award outstanding ingenue in daytime drama series 1988), The Edge of Night, (TV movies) Money, Power, Murder, 1989, Lovecraft, 1991, (feature films) The Hand That Rocks the Cradle, 1992, The Gun in Betty Lou's Handbag, 1992, Body of Evidence, 1993, Benny & Joon, 1993, The Fugitive, 1993, Short Cuts, 1993, Vanya on 42nd Street, 1994, Roommates, 1995, Nine Months, 1995, Safe, 1995. Office: CAA 9830 Wilshire Blvd Beverly Hills CA 90212*

MOORE, KATHLEEN, dancer; b. Chgo.. Student with Sonia Arova, Thor Sutowski, Ala. Sch. Fine Arts; student, Sch. Am. Ballet, Am. Ballet Theatre Sch. Joined ABT II, 1980; mem. corps de ballet Am. Ballet Theatre, N.Y.C. 1982-88, soloist, 1988-91, prin. dancer, 1991—. Repertoire includes Dark Elegies, Don Quixote (Kitri's Wedding), Fall River Legend, Fancy Free, Giselle, Rodeo, Romeo and Juliet, The Leaves Are Fading, Nine Sinatra Songs, Everlast, Enough Said, Gaite Parisienne, The Rite of Spring, Pillar of Fire, The Informer, Brief Fling, Duets, Sinfonietta, Sunset, Les Liasons Dangereuses, Manon, Undertow, others; created roles in Agnes de Mille's The Informer, Mark Morris' Drink to Me Only With Thine Eyes. Office: Am Ballet Theatre 890 Broadway New York NY 10003-1211*

MOORE, KENNETH CAMERON, lawyer; b. Chgo., Oct. 25, 1947; s. Kenneth Edwards and Margaret Elizabeth (Cameron) M.; m. Karen M. Nelson, June 22, 1974; children: Roger Cameron, Kenneth Nelson, Kristin Karen. BA summa cum laude, Hiram Coll., 1969; JD cum laude, Harvard U., 1973. Bar: Ohio 1973, U.S. Dist. Ct. Md. 1974, U.S. Ct. Appeals (9th cir.) 1974, D.C. 1975, U.S. Dist. Ct. (no. dist.) Ohio 1976, U.S. Ct. Appeals (6th cir.) 1977, U.S. Ct. Appeals (D.C. cir.) 1979, U.S. Supreme Ct. 1980. Law clk. to judge Harrison L. Winter, U.S. Ct. Appeals, 4th Cir., Balt., 1973-74; assoc. Squire, Sanders & Dempsey, Washington, 1974-75, Cleve., 1975-82, ptnr., 1982—; mem. fin. com., 1990—. Chmn. Ohio Fin. Com. for Jimmy Carter presdl. campaign, 1976; del. Dem. Nat. Conv., 1976; chief legal counsel Ohio Carter-Mondale Campaign, 1976; mem. Cleve. com., Cleve. Coun. World Affairs; mem. bd. advisors The Environ. Counselor; dir. environ. law Environ. Resource Inst. Served with AUS, 1970-76. Mem. ABA, Fed. Bar Assn., Ohio Bar Assn., Greater Cleve. Bar Assn., Cleve. City Club. Home: 15602 Edgewater Dr Cleveland OH 44107-1212 Office: Squire Sanders & Dempsey 4900 Society Ctr 127 Public Sq Cleveland OH 44114-1304

MOORE, KENNETH EDWIN, pharmacology educator; b. Edmonton, Alta., Can., Aug. 8, 1933; came to U.S., 1957, naturalized, 1966; s. Jack and Emily Elizabeth (Tarbox) M.; m. Barbara Anne Stafford, Sept. 19, 1953; children—Grant Kenneth, Sandra Anne, Lynn Susan. B.S., U. Alta., 1955, M.S., 1957; Ph.D., U. Mich. 1960. Instr. pharmacology Dartmouth Med. Sch., Hanover, N.H., 1960-61; asst. prof. Dartmouth Med. Sch., 1962-66; assoc. prof. pharmacology Mich. State U., East Lansing, 1966-70; prof. Mich. State U., 1970—, chmn. dept. pharmacology and toxicology, 1987—; vis. scholar Cambridge (Eng.) U., 1974; instr. Lansing Community Coll., 1975-81; cons. NIH, also pharm. industry. Author 1 book; contbr. articles

to profl. jours. Fellow Am. Coll. Neuropsychopharmacology; mem. Am. Soc. Pharmacology and Exptl. Therapeutics (chmn. bd. publs. trustees 1992—), Soc. Exptl. Biology and Medicine, Soc. Neuroscis. Home: 4790 Arapaho Trl Okemos MI 48864-1402 Office: Dept Pharmacology Mich State U East Lansing MI 48824

MOORE, KENNETH JAMES, agronomy educator; b. Phoenix, June 6, 1957; s. George Taylor and Barbara Joyce (Amy) M.; m. Gina Marie McCarthy Aug. 11, 1979; children: Ellyn Elizabeth, David Taylor, Mark Daniel. BS in Agr., Ariz. State U., 1979; MS in Agronomy, Purdue U., 1981, PhD in Agronomy, 1983. Asst. prof. agronomy U. Ill., Urbana, 1983-87; assoc. prof. N.Mex. State U., Las Cruces, 1988-89; rsch. agronomist Agrl. Rsch. Svc., USDA, Lincoln, Nebr., 1989-93; prof. Iowa State U., Ames, 1993—; adj. assoc. prof. U. Nebr. Lincoln, 1989-93, prof., 1993—. Author: Crop Science Laboratory Manual, 1988, assoc. editor Agronomy Jour., 1989-93, tech. editor, 1994—; assoc. editor Crop Sci., 1994; contbr. chpts. to books. Bd. dirs. Lincoln Children's Mus., 1991-93; mem. mgmt. com. N.E. YMCA, Lincoln, 1991-93; mem. youth policy forum Lincoln YMCA, 1991-92. Recipient Point of Light award USDA, 1991. Mem. Am. Soc. Agronomy, Crop Sci. Soc. Am. (div. chmn. 1990-92, Young Crop Scientist award 1993), Am. Forage and Grassland Coun. (Outstanding Young Scientist award 1982, merit award 1991), Am. Soc. Animal Sci., Am. Dairy Sci. Assn. Republican. Presbyterian. Avocations: swimming, fishing, music. Office: Iowa State U Agronomy Dept 1567 Agronomy Hall Ames IA 50011

MOORE, KEVIN MICHAEL, federal judge; b. 1951. BA, Fla. State U.; JD, Fordham U. Bar: Fla. 1976. U.S. atty. no. dist. State of Fla., Tallahassee, 1987-89; dir. U.S. Marshals Svc., Arlington, Va., 1989-92; judge US. Dist. Ct. So. Dist. Fla., Miami, 1992—. Office: US Dist Ct Federal Justice Bldg 99 NE 4th St Rm 1168 Miami FL 33132-2139

MOORE, LAURENCE JOHN, business educator; b. Greeley, Colo., May 7, 1938; s. John Harold and Ruth Anderson M.; m. Nancy Kay Hibbert, Aug. 31, 1963; children: Rebecca Ann, John Andrew, Stefani Ruth. B.A. in Econs, Monmouth Coll., Ill., 1962; M.S. in Econs, Ariz. State U., 1965, D.B.A. in Mgmt. Sci, 1970. Dist. mktg. rep. Standard Oil Co. (Ind.), Chgo., 1962-63; sr. analyst long range and capital planning, 1964-66; head quantitative studies Continental Ill. Bank, Chgo., 1966-67; mem. faculty dept. mgmt. sci. Coll. Bus. Va. Poly. Inst. and State U., Blacksburg, 1970—; prof. Coll. Bus. Va. Poly. Inst. and State U., 1977-85, C&P Disting. prof. bus., 1985—, head dept. Coll. Bus., 1976-83, dir. univ. fin. planning and analysis, 1983-84; dir. univ. planning Va. Poly. Inst. and State U., Blacksburg, 1988-89; cons. in field. Author: (with S.M. Lee, B.W. Taylor) Management Science, 1981, 4th edit., 1993, (with S.M. Lee) Introduction to Decision Sciences, 1975, (with E.R. Clayton) GERT Modeling and Simulation: Fundamentals and Applications, 1976. Served with U.S. Army, 1957-59. Recipient Disting. Service award SE region Am. Inst. Decision Scis., 1977. Fellow Am. Inst. Decision Scis. (pres. 1983-84, Disting. Service award 1986); mem. Inst. Mgmt. Sci. (Disting. Service award SE region), Ops. Research Soc. Am., Inst. Indsl. Engrs., Alpha Iota Delta, Beta Gamma Sigma, Omicron Delta Epsilon, Sigma Iota Epsilon. Presbyterian. Home: 6109 Tall Oaks Dr Blacksburg VA 24060-8189 Office: Va Poly Inst and State U Dept Mgmt Sci 1007 Pamplin Hall Blacksburg VA 24061-5102

MOORE, LAWRENCE JACK, oil company executive, lawyer; b. Brownwood, Tex., Jan. 24, 1926; s. Lawrence Houston and Lena Emily (Grantham) M.; m. Eloise Camille Dickinson, May 24, 1947; children: John L., James D. Jane E. Moore Horner. Student Howard Payne U., 1946-47, Tarleton State U., 1942-43; LLB, U. Tex., 1949. Bar: Tex. 1949, N.Y. 1980. Pvt. practice, 1949-57; city atty., Ballinger, Tex., 1950, 55-57; county atty. Runnels County, Tex., 1951-54; atty. Texaco Inc., 1957-70, assoc. gen. counsel, 1970-79; v.p., gen. counsel Caltex Petroleum Corp., Dallas, 1979-89; mem. Johnson & Gibbs, P.C., Dallas, Houston, Austin, Tex., Washington, 1989-91; pvt. practice, 1992—; adv. bd. Internat. and Comparative Law Ctr., Internat. Oil and Gas Ctr. of Southwestern Legal Found.; mem. devel. bd. U. Tex., Dallas, 1986-91; dir. Nat. Fgn. Trade Coun., N.Y., 1985-93. Served to cpl. AUS, 1944-46. Mem. ABA, State Bar Tex., University Club (N.Y.C.), Country Club of Darien (Conn.), Petroleum Club (Dallas), Horseshoe Bay Country Club, Barton Creek Country Club (Lakeside), Masons. Republican. Methodist. Office: PO Box 8510 Horseshoe Bay TX 78654

MOORE, LOIS JEAN, health science facility administrator; married; 1 child. Grad., Prairie View (Tex.) Sch. Nursing, 1957; BS in Nursing, Tex. Woman's U., 1970; MS in Edn., Tex. So. U., 1974. Nurse Harris County (Tex.) Hosp. Dist., 1957—; pres., chief exec. officer Harris County Hosp.; adminstr. Jefferson Davis Hosp., Houston, 1977-88, exec. v.p., chief ops. officer, 1988—; mem. adv. bd. Tex. Pub. Hosp. Assn. Contbr. articles to profl. jours. Mem. Mental Health Needs Council Houston and Harris County, Congressman Mickey Leland's Infant Mortality Task Force, Houston Crack-down Com., Gov.'s task force on health care policy, 1991; chairperson Tex. Assn. Pub. and Nonprofit Hosps., 1991, subcom. of Gov.'s task force to identify essential health care svc., 1992; bd. dirs. ARC, 1991—, Greater Houston Hosp. Coun., March of Dimes, United Way. Recipient Pacesetter award North-East C. of C., 1991; named Nurse of Yr. Houston Area League Nursing, 1976-77, Outstanding Black Achiever YMCA Century Club, 1974, Outstanding Women in Medicine YWCA, 1989. Mem. Am. Coll. Hosp. Adminstrs., Tex. Hosp. Assn. (chmn. pub. hosp. com.), Young Hosp. Adminstrs., Nat. Assn. Pub. Hosps. (bd. dirs., mem. exec. com. Tex. assn.), License Vocat. Nurses Assn., sigma Theta Tau. Home: 3837 Wichita St Houston TX 77004-6536 Office: Harris County Hosp Dist PO Box 66769 Houston TX 77266-6769

MOORE, LORETTA WESTBROOK, banker; b. Cameron, Tex., Jan. 2, 1938; d. Merrill Holman and Gladys Evangeline (Strelsky) Westbrook; m. Joe Gregg Moore Jr., Sept. 22, 1956; children: Terri Lynn, Joe Gregg III. Grad. high sch., Hearne, Tex. With Planters & Merchants State Bank, Hearne, Tex., 1956—; v.p., cashier, 1980—; also bd. dirs.; group pres. Nat. Assn. Bank Women (now Fin. Women Internat.), Waco, Tex., 1980-81. Mem. adv. coun. Hearne Pub. Schs., 1984—. Named Hon. Chpt. Farmer Future Farmers Am., 1984, Notable Women of Tex., 1984. Mem. Bank Adminstrn. Instn. (pres. Brazos Valley chpt. 1983-84), Am. Inst. Banking (bd. dirs. Brazos Valley chpt., charter), Order Eastern Star (past matron). Methodist. Avocations: travel, ranching with husband, grandchildren. Home: RR 1 Box 395 Hearne TX 77859-9617 Office: Planters & Mchts State Bank 122 4th St Hearne TX 77859

MOORE, LOUIS LEE, medical instrumentation company executive; b. Cambridge, Md., Mar. 1, 1939; s. Louis Lee and Doris Elizabeth (Kramer) M.; m. Deanna Lynn Whited, Oct. 6, 1979; children: Amy, Laura. BSEE Swarthmore Coll., 1962; MBA, Harvard U., 1965. Mktg. dir. Harris Intertype, Cleve., 1969-71; exec. v.p. Ohio Nuclear Co., Cleve., 1971-79; pres. Technicare Diagnostic Products Co., Cleve., 1979-82, Johnson & Johnson Ultrasound Co., Independence, Ohio, 1982-87, Moore & Assocs., Cleve., Ohio, 1987—; bd. dirs. Advanced Biomed. Co., Cleve., Prototest Electronics, Chardon, Ohio, Interior Steel Equipment Co. Co-author: Automating Newspaper Composition, 1965. Pres. Windward Bound, Cleve., 1987; chmn. svc. com., bd. dirs. No. Ohio Multiple Sclerosis Soc., Cleve., 1985—, Ohio Gov.'s Tech. Task Force, 1982. Mem. Ohio Venture Assn., Edison Biotech. Ctr., Assn. Corp. Growth, Greater Cleve. Growth Assn., Harvard Bus. Sch. Club, Edgewater Yacht Club, Vermilion Yacht Club. Methodist. Home: 23230 Sheppards Pt Cleveland OH 44140-2973 Office: Moore & Assocs 1991 Crocker Rd Ste 600 Cleveland OH 44145-1962

MOORE, MALCOLM ANDREW STEPHEN, cancer researcher; b. Edinburgh, Scotland, Jan. 18, 1944; came to U.S., 1974; m. Francine Zuckerman, May 30, 1989; children: Julian Alexander Stephen, Andrew Stephen. MB, U. Oxford, 1963, BA in Human Physiology 1st class honors, 1964, DPhil, 1967, MA, 1970. Prize fellow Magdalen Coll. U. Oxford, 1965-70; head lab. devel. biology Walter and Eliza Hall Inst. Med. Rsch., 1970-74; prof. biology Cornell U. Grad. Sch. Med. Sci., 1974—, head James Ewing Lab. Devel. Hematopoiesis, 1974—, Enid A Haupt chair cell biology, 1989—; attending biologist div. med. oncology Meml. Sloan-Kettering Cancer Ctr., 1987—. Contbr. over 350 articles to profl. jours. Mem. sci. adv. bd. Cancer Rsch. Inst., 1988, N.Y. Blood Ctr., 1989. Co-recipient Armand Hammer Cancer prize, 1987; recipient David Syme prize U.

Melbourne, 1973, numerous others. Mem. Leukemia Soc. Am. (Trustee, Kenny award 1987), Am. Assn. Immunologists, Am. Assn. Cancer Rsch. (Rhoads Meml. award 1980), Am. Soc. Hematology (Henry Stratton lectr. 1990), Leukocyte Biol. Soc., Harvey Soc. Office: Meml Sloan-Kettering Cancer Ctr R717 1275 York Ave New York NY 10021-6007

MOORE, MALCOLM ARTHUR, lawyer; b. Paterson, N.J., Feb. 10, 1937; s. Harold Henry and Mary Letitia (Northrop) M.; m. Phoebe Ann King, Aug. 18, 1962; children: Malcolm Read, Rebecca Cabell, George Northrop. A.B., Princeton U., 1959; LL.B., Harvard U., 1962. Bar: N.Y. 1963, Wash. 1966. Assoc. Hughes, Hubbard, Blair and Reed, N.Y.C., 1962-65; ptnr. Davis Wright Tremaine, Seattle, 1965—. Trustee Lakeside Sch., Seattle, 1974-88. Mem. ABA (chmn. sect. of real property, probate and trust law 1982-83), Wash. Bar Assn., Seattle-King County Bar Assn., Am. Coll. Trust and Estate Coun. (pres. 1988-89), Am. Coll. Tax Counsel, Am. Law Inst., Internat. Acad. Estate and Trust Law. Clubs: Seattle Tennis, Men's Univ., Columbia Tower. Home: 645 NW 137th St Seattle WA 98177-3932 Office: Davis Wright Tremaine 1501 4th Ave 2600 Century Sq Seattle WA 98101-1688

MOORE, MARC ANTHONY, university administrator, writer, retired military officer; b. Dallas, July 15, 1928; s. Edward Clark and Mary Cathrine (Spake) M.; m. Mary Joan Donahue, Sept. 5, 1953; children—Daniel, Mary Ellen, Virginia, Andria. B.A., So. Meth. U., 1951; M.A., George Washington U., 1970; grad., Amphibious Warfare Sch., 1960, Nat. War Coll., 1974; LHD (hon.), Philippine Women's U., 1987. Served as enlisted man U.S. Marine Corps, 1946-48, commd. 2d lt., 1951, advanced through grades to maj. gen., 1978; regtl. comdr. Camp Pendleton, Calif., 1971; regtl. exec. officer Vietnam, 1970; with Joint Chief Staff Ops., Washington, 1977-78; asst. dir. Marine Command and Staff Coll., 1972-73; dir. div. English and history U.S. Naval Acad., 1974-76; comdg. gen. 4th Marine Div., New Orleans, 1978-80; chief of staff U.S. Forces, Japan, from 1980, now ret.; former chancellor San Diego campus, v.p. for devel. Nat. U., 1990-91; teaching asst. dept. psychology George Washington U., 1974; instr. dept. behavioral sci. U.S. Naval Acad., 1975-76; adj. faculty Nat. U., 1983. Cofounder Leadership 2000; mem. coun. advisors Calif. State U., San Marcos, 1993—; mem. bd. advisors Marine Mil. Acad., 1983-95; founder, chmn. bd. advisors Command Mus. and Warfare Leadership Ctr., Marine Recruit Depot, San Diego, 1984—. Decorated Legion of Merit, Bronze Star with oak leaf cluster, Air medal, D.S.H., Order Sacred Treasure (Japan); recipient Disting. Alumni award So. Meth. U., 1981, Superior Svc. medal, Dept. Def., Meritorious Svc. medal Dept. Def. Mem. Marine Corps Assn., Phi Delta Theta. Roman Catholic. Home: 3611 Lago Sereno Escondido CA 92029-7902

MOORE, MARIANNA GAY, law librarian, consultant; b. La Grange, Ga., Sept. 12, 1939; d. James Henry and Avanelle (Gay) M. AB in French, English, U. Ga., 1961; MLS, Emory U., 1964; postgrad., U. Ga., 1965-66, U. Ill., 1967-68. Asst. law libr. U. Ga., Athens, 1964-66; asst. libr. Yavapai Coll. Libr., Prescott, Ariz., 1969-72; libr. U. Ill. Law Libr., Urbana, 1966-68; law libr. Leva, Hawes, Symington, Washington, 1972-75; libr. project coord. Wash. Occupational Info. Svc., Olympia, 1976-80, Wash. State Health Facilities Assn., Olympia, 1981-82; mgr. Wash. State Ret. Tchrs. Assn., Olympia, 1982-83, exec. dir., 1984-89; exec. dir. Wash. State Retired Tchrs. Found., Olympia, 1986-89; law libr. Solano County Law Libr., Fairfield, Calif., 1989—; libr. LIBRARY/USA N.Y. World's Fair, N.Y.C., 1965; consulting law libr. Dobbins, Weir, Thompson & Stephenson, Vacaville, Calif., 1989—; law libr. cons. Coconino County Law Libr., Flagstaff, Ariz., 1968-70. Author: Guide to Fin. Aid for Wash. State Students, 1979; tng. package to introduce librs. to Wash. State Info. Svc., 1980. Bd. dirs. Thurston County Sr. Ctr., Olympia, 1976-84, Thurston-Mason Nutrition Program, Olympia, 1977-79, Wash. Soc. Assn. Execs., Edmonds, 1987-89. Mem. Am. Assn. Law Librs., No. Calif. Assn. Law Librs., Calif. Coun. of County Law Librs., Wash. Soc. Assn. Execs. Avocations: reading, tatting, travel, music, calligraphy. Office: Solano County Law Libr Hall of Justice 600 Union Ave Fairfield CA 94533-6321

MOORE, MARK HARRISON, criminal justice, public policy educator; b. Oak Park, Ill., Mar. 19, 1947; s. Charles Eugene and Jean (McFeely) M.; m. Martha Mansfield Church, June 15, 1968; children—Phoebe Sylvina, Tobias McFeely, Gaylen Williams. Student, Phillips Acad., 1962-65; B.A., Yale U., 1969; M.Public Policy, Harvard U., 1971, Ph.D., 1973. Teaching fellow, instr. public policy J.F. Kennedy Sch. Govt., Harvard U., Boston, 1971-73; asst. prof. J.F. Kennedy Sch. Govt., Harvard U., 1973-74, 75-76, assoc. prof., 1976-79, Guggenheim prof. criminal justice policy and mgmt., 1979—; spl. asst. to adminstr., chief planning officer Drug Enforcement Adminstrn., U.S. Dept. Justice, Washington, 1974-75; cons. U.S. Dept. Justice, 1975-76, 81. Author: Buy and Bust: The Effective Regulation of an Illicit Market in Heroin, 1977, (with others) Dangerous Offenders, 1985, From Children to Citizens: Vol. 1, The Mandate for Juvenile Justice, 1987 (with Malcolm K. Sparrow) Ethics in Government, 1990, (with Malcolm K. Sparrow and David Kennedy) Beyond 911: A New Era for Policing, 1991; editor (with Joel Fleishman and Lance Leibman) Public Duties, 1980, (with Dean Gerstein) Alcohol and Public Policy, 1981. Mem. Assn. Sch. Public Policy and Mgmt., Phi Beta Kappa. Home: 331 Waverley St Belmont MA 02178-2418 Office: JF Kennedy Sch Govt Harvard U 79 John F Kennedy St Cambridge MA 02138-5800

MOORE, MARY, advertising agency executive. Formerly sr. v.p. Humphrey Browning MacDougall Inc. (now Arnold, Fortuna, Lawner, and Cabot Inc., Boston, exec. v.p., creative dir., then pres. creative dir.; vice-chmn., chief creative officer Wells Rich Greene BDDP, N.Y.C., 1988—. Office: Wells Rich Greene BDDP 9 W 57th St New York NY 10019

MOORE, MARY ANN, health care administrator; b. Potlatch, Idaho, Feb. 11, 1940; d. Verona Witt; m. Gary Moore, July 19, 1963; children: Kimberly, Gregory, Christina, Matthew. BS, Columbia Pacific U., 1980, MS in Healthcare Adminstrn., 1981; MPH, U. Minn., 1982. RN, Wash. Assoc. exec. dir. Alaska Hosp. & Med. Ctr., Anchorage, 1976-81; ind. cons. Denver, 1981-82; assoc. adminstr. Va. Mason Med. Ctr., Seattle, 1983—; presenter in field. Contbr. articles to profl. jours. Kellogg fellow. Mem. Med. Group Mgmt. Assn., Am. Acad. Ambulatory Nursing Adminstrn. (bd. dirs. 1986-89, chmn. nat. networking com. 1987-88, chmn. nat. edn. rsch. standards and program coms. pres. 1990-91), Wash. Orgn. Nurse Execs. (membership com. 1986-87, task force on organizational change, strategic planning com., chmn. fin. com. 1988, bd. dirs. 1988-89), Am. Pub. Health Assn., Am. Orgn. Nurse Execs., Am. Coll. Healthcare Execs., Sigma Theta Tau. Avocations: reading, skiing, boating. Office: Va Mason Med Ctr 1100 9th Ave Seattle WA 98101-2756

MOORE, MARY TYLER, actress; b. Bklyn., Dec. 29, 1936; d. George and Marjorie Moore; m. Richard Meeker; 1 child, Richard (dec.); m. Grant Tinker, 1963 (div. 1981); m. Robert Levine, 1983. Chmn. bd. MTM Enterprises, Inc., Studio City, Calif. Appeared in TV series Richard Diamond, Private Eye, 1957-59, Dick Van Dyke Show, 1961-66, Mary Tyler Moore Show, 1970-77, Mary, 1978, Mary Tyler Moore Hour, 1979, Mary, 1985, Annie McGuire, 1988, miniseries Gore Vidal's Lincoln, 1988; in TV movies Love American Style, 1969, Run a Crooked Mile, 1969, First You Cry, 1978, Heartsounds, 1984, Finnegan Begin Again, 1984, The Last Best Year, 1990, Thanksgiving Day, 1990, Stolen Babies, 1993 (Emmy award, Outstanding Supporting Actress in a Miniseries or Special, 1993); films: X-15, 1961, Thoroughly Modern Millie, 1967, Don't Just Stand There, 1968, What's So Bad About Feeling Good?, 1968, Change of Habit, 1969, Ordinary People, 1980 (Acad. Award nominee for best actress 1981), Six Weeks, 1982, Just Between Friends, 1986; appeared on Broadway in Whose Life Is It Anyway?, 1980, Sweet Sue, 1987; in TV spl. How to Survive the Seventies, 1978, How To Raise a Drug Free Child. Recipient Emmy award Nat. Acad. TV Arts and Scis. 1964-65, 73-74, 76, Golden Globe award 1965, 81; named to TV Hall of Fame, 1985. Office: MTM Enterprises 4024 Radford Ave Studio City CA 91604*

MOORE, MCPHERSON DORSETT, lawyer; b. Pine Bluff, Ark., Mar. 1, 1947; s. Arl Van and Jesse (Dorsett) M. BS, U. Miss., 1970; JD, U. Ark., 1974. Bar: Ark. 1974, Mo. 1975, U.S. Patent and Trademark Office 1977, U.S. Dist. Ct. (ea. dist.) Mo. 1977, U.S. Ct. Appeals (8th, 10th and Fed. cirs.). Design engr. Tenneco, Newport News, Va., 1970-71; assoc. Rogers,

Eilers & Howell, St. Louis, 1974-80; ptnr. Rogers, Howell, Moore & Haferkamp, St. Louis, 1981-89; ptnr. Armstrong, Teasdale, Schlafly & Davis, St. Louis, 1989-95; ptnr. Polster, Lieder, Woodruff & Lucchesi, 1995—. Bd. dirs. Legal Services of Eastern Mo., 1984—. With USAR, 1970-76. Mem. ABA, Bar Assn. Met. St. Louis (chmn. young lawyers sect. 1981-82, sec. 1984-85, v.p. 1985-86, chmn. trial sect. 1986-87, pres. 1988-89), Ark. Bar Assn., St. Louis Bar Found. (sec. 1984-85, v.p. 1988-89, pres. 1989-90), The Mo. Bar (chmn. patent, trademark and copyright law com. 1992-94, cochmn. 1994—), St. Louis County Bar Assn., Women Lawyers Assn., Am. Intellectual Property Law Assn., Moond City Bar Assn., Phi Delta Theta Alumni (treas. St. Louis chpt. 1987-88, sec. 1988-89, v.p. 1989-90). Episcopalian. Club: Univ. (St. Louis). Home: 33 Deerfield Rd Saint Louis MO 63124-1412 Office: Armstrong Teasdale Schlafly & Davis 1 Metropolitan Sq Ste 2600 Saint Louis MO 63102-2740

MOORE, MECHLIN DONGAN, business consultant; b. N.Y.C., May 21, 1930; s. Albere Ethier and Pamela (Robinson) M.; m. Elizabeth Ann Tonkin, Feb. 11, 1956 (dec. 1992); children: Lansing, Pamela; m. Valery Ann Shields, July 14, 1995. A.B., Harvard U., 1952. Reporter Washington Post, 1955-59; dir. build Am. better com. Nat. Assn. Real Estate Bds., D.C., 1960-64; dir. info. Urban Land Inst., D.C., 1964-66; exec. v.p. Central Assn. Seattle, 1966-70; asst. to pres. United Airlines, Inc., Chgo., 1971-72; sr. v.p. external affairs, 1972-74, group v.p. mktg., 1975-76, sr. v.p. pub. affairs, 1976-79; pres. Ins. Info. Inst., N.Y.C., 1979-91; pvt. practice cons. Eagles Mere, Pa., 1991—, Naples, Fla., 1991—; pres. Eagles Mere Water Co., 1993—; bd. dirs. Internat. Inst. Coun., Automobile Protection Corp.; bd. electors Ins. Hall of Fame; bd. govs. Internat. Ins. Seminars. Contbg. author publs. Nat. Assn. Real Estate Bds.; assoc. editor Jour. Property Mgmt. Bd. dirs. Nat. Commn. Against Drunk Driving; adv. bd. Traffic Inst. Northwestern U.; bd. mgrs. Seaman's Ch. Inst.; past mem. St. George's Vestry, N.Y.C. 1st lt. U.S. Army, 1952-54. Recipient Disting. Service award Central Assn. Seattle, 1972. Mem. Univ. Club, Eagles Mere Country Club. Republican. Episcopalian. Home: 532 Bay Villas Ln Naples FL 33963

MOORE, MELVIN G., school system administrator; b. Snow, Okla., Jan. 14, 1944; s. Manuel G. and Millie K. (Crownover) M.; m. Merlene S. Klinge, Feb. 24, 1962; (div. Dec. 1979); children: Torri Lynn Moore Wilson, Michael Trevor; m. Christine B. Levak, June 21, 1982; 1 child, Lyndsey Laura Victoria. BS, Oreg. Coll of Edn., Monmouth, 1967, MS, 1971; PhD, U. N.C., Chapel Hill, 1977. Cert. tchr., adminstr. Tchr Dallas Pub. Schs., Dallas, Oreg., 1968-70; instr., teaching research div. OSSHE, Monmonth, 1971-72; asst. to dir., tech. assistance devel. systems U N.C., Chapel Hill, 1972-74; adminstrv. intern, bur. of edn. for handicapped U.S. Office of Edn., Washington, 1974-75; research asst. U. N.C., Chapel Hill, 1975-76; asst. research prof. to assoc. research prof. OSSHE, Monmouth, 1976-79; dir. clin. svcs. Ea. Oreg. Hosp. & Tng. Ctr., Pendleton, 1980; dir. special edn. Hillsboro Union High Sch. Dist., 1980-92, Washington County Edn. Svc. Dist., Portland, Oreg., 1992—; program dir. Marion County Mental Health Div., Salem, Oreg., 1977-79; asst. dir. WESTAR, U. Wash., Seattle, 1977-78, dir. 1979-80. Contbr. articles to profl. jours. Bd. dirs. Coalition in Oreg. for Parent Edn., Salem, 1986—; legis. com. Confederation of Oreg. Sch. Adminstrs., Salem, 1987—; adv. bd. Oreg. Adv. Coun. for Handicapped Children, Salem, 1988—; Tualatin Valley Mental Health Dept., Portland, 1984—, Oreg. Early Childhood Spl. Edn. Interagency Adv. Com., 1993—. Recipient Exemplary Service award, Coalition in Oreg. for Parent Edn., Salem, 1988, Recognition of Service award, Portland Tech. Edn. Consortium, 1988. Mem. Coun. of Exceptional Children (gov. 1970-71), Assn. for Retarded Citizens, Confederation of Oreg. Sch. Adminstrs. (pres. 1986-87), Assn. for Supervision and Curriculum Devel. Democrat. Avocations: sailing, fly fishing, reading. Home: 5205 SW 49th Dr Portland OR 97221-1803 Office: Washington County ESD 17705 NW Springville Rd Portland OR 97229-7998

MOORE, MICHAEL, film director. Films include Roger and Me, 1989; creator, host TV Nation, 1994. Office: ICM 8942 Wilshire Blvd Beverly Hills CA 90211-1908*

MOORE, MICHAEL C., retail executive. Sr.v.p. Hook-Super X Inc., Cin. Office: Hook-SuperX Inc 175 Tri County Pky Cincinnati OH 45246

MOORE, MICHAEL T., lawyer; b. Mullins, S.C., Feb. 21, 1948; s. Claude Richard and Melinda Doris (Stone) M.; m. Leslie Jean Lott, Nov. 12, 1978; children: Michael T. Jr., Emmett Russell Lott. BA, U. Fla., 1970, JD, 1974. Assoc. Burlingham, Underwood & Lord, N.Y.C., 1974-77, Hassan, Mahassni, Burlington, Underwood & Lord, Jeddah, Saudi Arabia, 1977-79; ptnr. Holland & Knight, Miami, Fla., 1982—; bd. dirs. Holland & Knight, Miami, 1986—, adminstrv. ptnr., 1988—; bd. dirs. Marine Arbitration Bd., Inc., Miami, 1985—; pres. The Marine Coun., 1989-90. Editor-in-chief Southern District Digest, 1980-82; contbr. articles to profl. jours. Dir. United Way Greater Miami, 1994—; mem. Miami River Coordinating Com. 1987-89; bd. dirs. U.S. Sailing Ctr.; trustee St. Stephens Sch.; mem. Coral Gables (Fla.) Youth Adv. Bd. Fellow ABA; mem. Maritime Law Assn. U.S., Fla. Bar Assn., Dade County Bar Assn. (bd. dirs. 1981—, outstanding young lawyer award 1981-82). Republican. Home: 3515 Anderson Rd Miami FL 33134-7050 Office: Holland & Knight 701 Brickell Ave PO Box 15441 Miami FL 33101

MOORE, MICHAEL THOMAS, mining executive; b. Bklyn., Oct. 10, 1934; s. Michael Joseph and Lucille M. (Wild) M.; m. Beatrice Lorraine Quinto, Sept. 10, 1960; children: Teresa, Stephanie, Jennifer, Elisabeth. BS in Bus., Indiana U. of Pa., 1956; postgrad., U. Pitts. 1959-63, Am. U., 1963-64, NYU, 1964-66. Fin. analyst, supr. U.S. Steel Corp., Duquesne, Pa., 1956-63; plant controller Am.-Standard, Balt., 1963-64; sr. fin. analyst Celanese Corp., N.Y.C., 1964-66; asst. controller to controller Cleve.-Cliffs Inc., 1966-72, v.p. controller, 1972-75, sr. v.p., 1975-83, exec. v.p., chief fin. officer, 1983-86, pres., dir., 1986, pres., dir., chief exec. officer, 1987, pres., chief exec. officer, 1987—, chmn., chief exec. officer, 1988—; bd. dirs. KeyCorp, LTV Corp. Bd. dirs. Cleve. Tomorrow, 1987—; trustee Magnificat High Sch., Rocky River, Ohio, 1983—, Health Cleve., 1990—; dir. Capital Am. Fin. Corp. 1992. Served with U.S. Army, 1957-58. Named Outstanding Alumnus Indiana U. of Pa., 1981. Mem. Am. Iron and Steel Inst. (bd. dirs. 1987—), Am. Mining Congress (bd. dirs. 1987—), Bus. Roundtable, Am. Iron Ore Assn. (bd. dirs. 1987—), Greater Cleve. Growth Assn. (bd. dirs. 1989—), Union Club, The Fifty Club, Westwood Country Club, Pepper Pike Club, Rolling Rock Club, Quail Creek Country Club, Laurel Valley Golf Club. Roman Catholic. Office: Cleveland Cliffs Inc 1100 Superior Ave E Cleveland OH 44114-2589

MOORE, MIKE, state attorney general; m. Tisha Moore; 1 child, Kyle. Grad., Jackson County Jr. Coll., 1972; BA, U. Miss., 1974, JD, 1976. Asst. dist. atty. State of Miss., 1977-78, dist. atty., 1979, atty. gen., 1988—. Mem. ABA, Miss. State Bar Assn. Office: Office of Atty Gen PO Box 220 Jackson MS 39205-0220

MOORE, MILO ANDERSON, banker; b. Orange, N.J., Aug. 26, 1942; s. Milo H. and Helen (Wiley) M.; m. Judith J. Colosimo, May 4, 1968; children: Milo Robert, Matthew Wiley, Marykate Bartlett. BS, Ithaca Coll., 1964; MBA, Rutgers U., 1971. Traffic supt. N.Y. Tel. Co., N.Y.C., 1964-71; trust officer Midlantic Nat. Bank, Newark, 1971-76; v.p. Shearson Loeb Rhoades, N.Y.C., 1976-80; sr. v.p. Donaldson Lufkin & Jenrette, N.Y.C., 1980-85; sr. mng. dir. Bear, Stearns & Co., 1985-92; v.p. Princeton Bank and Trust Co., Morristown, N.J., 1992—. Advisor Jr. Achievement, Bronx, N.Y., 1967-68; pres. Chatham Jaycees, N.J., 1974; big bros. Morris County Big Bros., Morristown, 1971-81; pres. Stanley Congl. Ch., Chatham, N.J., 1995—; trustee SAGE Inc., 1994—. Mem. Securities Industry Assn. (ca shelter com. 1982-85), Glenburnie Club (pres. 1989—), Canoe Brook Country Club (Summit, N.J.), Beta Gamma Sigma. Office: Princeton Bank and Trust 67 Summit Ave Summit NJ 07901

MOORE, NORMAN SLAWSON, physician; b. Ithaca, N.Y., Apr. 17, 1901; s. Veranus A. and Mary Louise (Slawson) M.; m. Bernice A. Barkee, June 28, 1932. A.B., Cornell, 1923, M.D., 1926. Diplomate: Am. Bd. Internal Medicine. Intern Bellevue Hosp., 1926-28; asst. resident Rockefeller Inst., 1928-29; instr. anatomy Cornell Med. Coll., 1929-31, head dept. clin. and preventive medicine, 1943-67; emeritus prof. clin. medicine Cornell U. Sch. Nutrition; clin. dir. Sage Hosp.-Gannett Clinic, 1943-67; pvt. practice internal medicine Ithaca, 1929-40; cons. physician Tompkins County Meml. Hosp., 1940-72, hon., 1973; Dir., chmn. emeritus Ithaca Savs. and Loan Assn.; Responsible investigator at Cornell for OSRD, 1942-45; mem. nurse adv. council N.Y. State Dept. Edn., 1946-54; mem. Pub. Health Council N.Y. State, 1954-80, chmn., 1969-80; mem. Temporary Health Ins. Bd. N.Y. State, 1956-59; pres. Empire State Med., Sci. and Ednl. Found., 1961-70, dir., 1960-74; chmn. N.Y. State Hosp. Rev. and Planning Council, 1961-70; mem. N.Y. State Health Resources Commn., 1967-74; mem. adv. council N.Y. State Health Planning Commn., 1968-72; mem. N.Y. State Mental Hygiene Council, 1970-75, N.Y. State Commn. on Acupuncture, 1973. Contbr. articles med. publs. Fellow A.C.P., N.Y. Acad. Medicine; mem. Am. Coll. Health Assn. (pres. 1954), Med. Soc. State N.Y. (past v.p., past pres. 6th dist. br., council 1955-65, chmn. com. pub. health and edn. 1957-60, pres. 1960-61, trustee 1961-65, dir. sci. activities 1967-74), AMA (del. 1956-70, chmn. council vol. health agys. 1967-70), Tompkins County Med. Soc. (past pres.), Sigma Xi, Phi Sigma Kappa, Omega Alpha Omega, Nu Sigma Nu. Home and Office: 128 Pleasant Grove Rd Ithaca NY 14850-2602

MOORE, OLIVER SEMON, III, publishing executive, consultant; b. Jersey City, July 26, 1942; s. Oliver S. and Ann Loy (Spies) M.; m. Dina Downing DuBois, Feb. 23, 1961 (div. 1974); 1 child, Deborah; m. Christine Laine Meyers, May 12, 1990; 1 child, Kathryn Laine. BA, U. Va., 1964. Chief bur. Richmond (Va.) Times-Dispatch, 1964-66; corr. Time mag., N.Y.C., 1966-67, contbg. editor, 1967-68; assoc. editor Newsweek, N.Y.C., 1969-71; freelance writer, 1972-75; mng. editor Motor Boating and Sailing, N.Y.C., 1976-78, editor, 1980-82; exec. editor US Mag., N.Y. Times Co. 1978-80; dep. editor Town & Country Mag., N.Y.C., 1982-84; editor Sci. Digest Mag., N.Y.C., 1984-86; pub. dir. Yachting Mag., N.Y.C., 1986—; editorial dir. Outdoor Life, N.Y.C., 1993-95; v.p. The Outdoor Co., N.Y.C., 1994-95; pres. Alamo Pub. Svcs., Inc., Detroit, 1995—. Author: (poems) Voices International, 1969. Recipient Merit award Art Dirs. Club, 1981, award of merit Soc. Publ. Designers, 1981, Excellence in Media award Nat. Arbor Day Found., 1985. Mem. Nat. Marine Mfrs. Assn., Am. Soc. Mag. Editors, Mag. Pubs. Assn., N.Y. Yacht Club, Grosse Pointe (Mich.) Club, Bayview (Mich.) Yacht Club, Mashomac Fish and Game Preserve. Republican. Episcopalian. Avocations: sailing, antique cars. Office: Alamo Pub Svcs Inc 3645 Crooks Rd Troy MI 48084

MOORE, OMAR KHAYYAM, experimental sociologist; b. Helper, Utah, Feb. 11, 1920; s. John Gustav and Mary Jo (Crowley) M.; m. Ruth Garnand, Nov. 19, 1942; 1 child, Venn. BA, Doane Coll., 1942; MA, Washington U., St. Louis, 1946, PhD, 1949. Instr. Washington U., St. Louis, 1949-52; teaching assoc. Northwestern U., Evanston, Ill., 1950-51; rsch. asst., prof. sociology Tufts Coll., Medford, Mass., 1952-53; researcher Naval Rsch. Lab., Washington, 1953-54; asst. prof. sociology Yale U., New Haven, 1954-57, assoc. prof. sociology, 1957-63; prof. psychology Rutgers U., New Brunswick, N.J., 1963-65; prof. social psychology, sociology U. Pitts., 1965-71, prof. sociology, 1971-89, prof. emeritus, 1989—; scholar-in-residence Nat. Learning Ctr.'s Capital Children's Mus., Washington, 1989-90; pres. Responsive Environ. Found., Inc., Estes Park, Colo., 1962—; assessor of rsch. projects The Social Scis. and Humanities Rsch. Coun. Can., 1982—; adj. prof. U. Colo., Boulder, 1992—. Contbg. editor Educational Technology; contbr. numerous articles to profl. jours.; patentee in field; motion picture producer and director. Recipient Award The Nat. Soc. for Programmed Instruction, 1965, Award Doane Coll Builder Award, 1967, Ednl. Award Urban Youth Action, Inc., 1969, Award House of Culture, 1975, Cert. of Appreciation, 1986, Cert. of Appreciation D.C. Pub. Schs., 1987, da Vinci Award Inst. for the Achievement of Human Potential, 1988, Cert. of Appreciation Capital Children's Museum, 1988, award Jack & Jill of America Found., 1988, Cert. of Appreciation U.S. Dept. of Edn., 1988, Cert. of Appreciation D.C. Pub. Schs., 1990, Person of Yr. in Ednl. Tech. award Ednl. Tech. mag., 1990. Mem. AAAS, Am. Math. Soc., Am. Psychol. Assn., Internat. Sociol. Assn., Am. Sociol. Assn., Assn. for Symbolic Logic, Assn. for Anthrop. Study of Play, Philosophy Sci. Assn., Psychonomics Soc., Soc. for Applied Sociology, Soc. for Exact Philosophy, Math. Assn. Am. Republican. Avocation: mountaineering. Home and Office: 2341 Upper High Dr PO Box 1673 Estes Park CO 80517

MOORE, PAT HOWARD, engineering and construction company executive; b. Laredo, Tex., Sept. 16, 1930; s. Howard Warren and Odette Evelyn (Bunn) M.; m. Elsie Mae Crossman, Mar. 23, 1954; children: Linda Marie Ford, Margaret Ann, Andrew Patrick. BA, Rice U., 1952, BS in Civil Engring., 1953; postgrad., Tulane U., 1956-58. Registered profl. engr., Tex., La. Spl. investigator Army Counter Intelligence Corps, Houston, 1954-56; div. engr. McDermott Inc., Morgan City, La., 1956-58; pres., dir. Navasota Tel. Co., Tex., 1958-63; project mgr. Brown & Root, Inc., Houston, 1963-67, exec. v.p., chief fin. officer, dir., 1990—; pres., dir. Fluor Ocean Svcs., Houston, 1968-80; sr. v.p. Raymond Internat., Inc., Houston, 1980-86; pres. dir. Martin Moore Inc., Bellaire, Tex., 1986-90; dir. Charter Builders, Inc., Dallas, 1988-90; bd. dirs. Tex. Commerce Bank-Richmond-Sage, Houston. Bd. govs. Rice U., 1984-88. With U.S. Army, 1954-56. Fellow ASCE. Lodge: Kiwanis (pres. 1960). Home: 5251 Birdwood Rd Houston TX 77096-2503 Office: Brown & Root Inc PO Box 3 Houston TX 77001-0003

MOORE, PAUL, JR., bishop; b. Morristown, N.J., Nov. 15, 1919; s. Paul and Fanny Weber (Hanna) M.; m. Jenny McKean, Nov. 26, 1944 (dec.); children: Honor, Paul III, Adelia, Rosemary, George Mead, Marian Shaw, Daniel Sargent, Susanna McKean, Patience; m. Brenda Hughes Eagle, May 16, 1975. Grad., St. Paul's Sch., Concord, N.H., 1937; B.A., Yale U., 1941; S.T.B., Gen. Theol. Sem., N.Y.C., 1949, S.T.D. (hon.), 1960; D.D. (hon.), Va. Theol. Sem., 1964, Berkeley Divinity Sch., 1971; PhD (hon.), City Coll. N.Y. Ordained to ministry Protestant Episcopal Ch., 1949; mem. team ministry Grace Ch., Jersey City, 1949-57; dean Christ Ch. Cathedral, Indpls., 1957-64; suffragan bishop Washington, 1964-70; bishop coadjutor Diocese, N.Y., 1970-72; bishop Diocese, 1972-89; lectr. St. Augustine's Coll., Canterbury, Eng., 1960; chmn. commnn. Delta ministry Nat. Coun. Chgs., 1964-67; mem. urban divsn., nat. exec. coun. Episcopal Ch., 1952-68; dep. to Gen. Conv., 1961, Anglican Congress, 1963; chmn. com. 100; legal def. fund NAACP. Author: The Church Reclaims the City, 2d edit, 1970, Take A Bishop Like Me, 1979. Trustee Bard Coll.; former trustee Gen. Theol. Sem., Trinity Sch., Bereeley Div. Sch. at Yale U., N.Y.C.; mem. Fund for Free Expression; mem. adv. coun. Gov.'s Com. on AIDS, 1983-87; chmn. The Timor Project, Project on Religion and Human Rights. Capt. USMCR, 1941-45, PTO. Decorated Navy Cross, Silver Star, Purple Heart.; recipient Margaret Sanger award Planned Parenthood, 1984, Frederick Douglas award North Star Fund, 1989, Freedom of Worship medal Franklin and Eleanor Roosevelt Inst., 1991; Yale Corp. sr. fellow, 1987-90. Club: Century (N.Y.C.). Home and Office: 55 Bank St New York NY 10014-2146

MOORE, PAUL BRIAN, geophysical sciences educator; b. Stamford, Conn., Nov. 24, 1940; s. George Joseph and Bessie Mina (Biddick) M. BS, Mich. Tech. U., Houghton, 1962; SM, U. Chgo., 1964, PhD, 1965. Instr. U. Chgo., 1966-67, asst. prof., 1967-69, assoc. prof., 1969-71, prof. geophys. sci., 1971-73; cons. to approximately 20 industries, 1966-92. Co-editor: The Phosphate Minerals, 1983; sr. author over 200 profl. papers, 1966-92. Recipient award Sloan Found., 1969-71; Dreyfus Found. grantee, 1973-74. Fellow Mineral. Soc. Am. (life, councillor 1975-78, award 1974); mem. Am. Chem. Soc., Mineral. Soc. Gt. Britain, N.Y. Acad. Scis., Lepidopterist's Soc. Explorer's Club. Lutheran. Avocations: butterflies, beetles, baroque and romantic organ music. Home: 5559 S Blackstone Ave # 3 Chicago IL 60637-1833 Office: U Chgo Geophys Scis Dept 5734 S Ellis Ave Chicago IL 60637-1434

MOORE, PEARL B., nurse; b. Pitts., Aug. 25, 1936; d. Hyman and Ethel (Antis) Friedman; diploma Liliane S. Kaufmann Sch. Nursing, 1956; BS in Nursing, U. Pitts., 1968, M. Nursing, 1974; 1 child, Cheryl. Staff nurse Allegheny Gen. Hosp., Pitts., 1957-60; instr. Liliane S. Kaufman Sch. Nursing, Pitts., 1960-70, asst. dir., 1970, dir., 1970-72; cancer nurse specialist Montefiore Hosp., Pitts., 1974-75; coordinator Brain Tumor Study Group, Pitts., 1975-83; adj. asst. prof. U. Pitts. 1983—. Fellow Am. Acad. Nursing; mem. Am. Nurses Assn., Oncology Nursing Soc. (exec. dir. 1983—), Disting. Svc. award 1995), Am. Soc. Clin. Oncology, Am. Soc. Assn. Execs., Nurses Alumnae U. Pitts., Sigma Theta Tau. Contbr. articles in field to profl. publs. Home: 4221 Winterburn Ave Pittsburgh PA 15207-1101 Office: 501 Holiday Dr Pittsburgh PA 15220-2749

MOORE, PETER BARTLETT, biochemist, educator; b. Boston, Oct. 15, 1939; s. Francis Daniels and Laura Benton (Bartlett) M.; m. Margaret Sue Murphy, Jan. 30, 1966; children: Catherine, Philip. BS, Yale U., 1961, MA (hon.); PhD, Harvard U., 1966. Postdoctoral fellow U. Geneva, 1966-67, MRC Lab. of Molecular Biology, Cambridge, Eng., 1967-69; asst. prof., then assoc. prof. dept. molecular biophysics Yale U., New Haven, 1969-76, assoc. prof. dept. of chemistry, 1976-79, prof., 1979—, chmn. dept. chemistry, 1987-90. Contbr. numerous articles to profl. publs. Guggenheim Found. fellow, 1979-80. Mem. Am. Chem. Soc., Am. Soc. Biol. Chemists and Molecular Biologists, Biophys. Soc. Office: Yale U Dept of Chemistry 225 Prospect Ave New Haven CT 06520-8118

MOORE, PETER MELVILLE, foundation adminstrator; b. Kansas City, Mo., Dec. 1, 1939; s. Robert Milo and Ruth Elizabeth (Williams) M. BA, U. of the South, Sewanee, Tenn., 1963. Adminstr. dept. ob-gyn U. Tex. Med. Br., Galveston, 1967-72, dir. devel., 1972-73, adminstr. dept. psychiatry, 1973-77; program officer The Moody Found., Galveston, 1977-82, grants adminstr., 1982—; speaker Funding Info. Ctr., San Antonio, 1985—. Bd. mem. Am. Paralysis Assn. N.J., 1983-86; bd. mem., officer Grand 1894 Opera House, Galveston, 1985-88; mem. adv. bd. Galveston Hist. Found., 1986—; bd. mem., officer Animal Shelter and Adoption Ctr., Galveston, 1985-87; mem. adv. bd. Grand 1894 Opera House, Galveston, 1988—. Republican. Episcopalian. Avocations: antique hunting, hiking, cultural acitvities. Home: 702 N Holiday Dr Galveston TX 77550-3006

MOORE, PHILIP WALSH, appraisal company executive; b. Burmont, Pa., Aug. 1, 1920; s. Louise J.F. and Florence (Walsh) M.; m. Katherine Shean, Dec. 26, 1967 (div.); children: Jourdan, Thomas, Philip, Edward; m. Marya Phaedra Cocalis; children: Stuart, Kristina. AB, Princeton U., 1942; MBA, NYU, 1950. Security analyst First Boston Corp., N.Y.C., 1946-48, v.p. gen. adminstrn., 1967-70; asst. to pres. Schroder Rockefeller and Co., N.Y.C., 1948-50; pres. First Research Co., Miami, Fla., 1950-67, chmn., chief exec. officer, 1971-84; pres. J&W Seligman Valuations Corp., N.Y.C., 1984—; founder, then bd. dirs. Flagship Banks (now Sun Trust Banks), Miami, 1964. Author: Florida Real Estate, 1960, Branch Banking Strategy, 1964, National Image of Economic South, 1976, Valuation Revisited, 1987; author, editor: Internat. Banking Services, 1981. Trustee Ransom Everglades Sch., Miami, 1956-82; mem. adminstrv. com. Lincoln Ctr. Performing Arts, N.Y.C., 1969-75; mem. devel. council U. Hosp. Jacksonville, Fla., 1985—. Served to lt. USN, 1942-46, ETO, PTO. Mem. Inst. Bus. Appraiser, Nat. Assn. Bus. Economists, Am. Soc. Appraisers, Investment Assn. N.Y.C. (pres. 1948-50), So. Assn. Sci. and Industry (trustee, chmn. 1955-72), Overseas Mgmt. Internat. (bd. dirs. 1972-80), Phi Beta Kappa. Republican. Roman Catholic. Clubs: Down Town (N.Y.C.); River (Jacksonville); Ponte Vedra (Fla.). Avocations: tennis, gardening, reading. Home: 78 San Juan Dr Ponte Vedra Beach FL 32082-1330

MOORE, POWELL ALLEN, former government official, consultant; b. Milledgeville, Ga., San. 5, 1938; s. Jere N. and Sarah (Allen) M.; m. Katherine Southward, Oct. 14, 1961; children: Frances Moore Preston, Powell Allen Jr. B.A. in Jounalism, U. Ga., 1959. Press sec. to Richard Russell, U.S. Senate, Washington, 1966-71; dep. dir. pub. info. Dept. Justice, Washington, 1971-72; dep. asst. to Pres. for legis. affairs The White House, Washington, 1973-75, dep. asst. to Pres. for legis. affairs, 1981-82; cons. pub. affairs Washington, 1975-81; asst. sec. for congl. rels. Dept. State, Washington, 1982-83; v.p. legis. affairs Lockheed Corp., Washington, 1983-85, Ginn, Edington, Moore and Wade, Washington, 1985-90; pres. ASL Internat., Washington, 1990-93; sr. prin., mng. dir. Capitoline, MS&L, Washington, 1993—. Dir. press Com. to Re-elect the Pres., Washington, 1972; cons. Pres. Ford Com., 1976, Reagan-Bush Com., 1980. Served to capt., inf. U.S. Army, 1959-62. Mem. Belle Haven Country Club, Capitol Hill Club, Met. Club. Republican. Episcopalian.

MOORE, RAYBURN SABATZKY, American literature educator; b. Helena, Ark., May 26, 1920; s. Max Sabatzky and Sammie Lou (Rayburn) M.; m. Margaret Elizabeth Bear, Aug. 30, 1947; children: Margaret Elizabeth, Robert Rayburn. A.B., Vanderbilt U., 1942, M.A., 1947; Ph.D., Duke U., 1956. Script writer King Biscuit Time, Interstate Grocer Co., KFFA, 1947-50; Vice pres. Interstate Grocer Co., Helena, 1947-50; research grad. asst. Duke U., 1952-54; asst. prof. English, Hendrix Coll., Conway, Ark., 1954-55; asso. prof. Hendrix Coll., 1955-58, prof., 1958-59; asso. prof. U. Ga., Athens, 1959-65; prof. U. Ga., 1965-90, prof. emeritus, 1990—, chmn. Am. studies program, 1968-90, chmn. dir. lang and lit., 1975-90; vis. scholar Duke U., 1958, 64. Author: Constance Fenimore Woolson, 1963, For the Major and Selected Short Stories of Constance Fenimore Woolson, 1967, Paul Hamilton Hayne, 1972, A Man of Letters in the Nineteenth-Century South: Selected Letters of Paul Hamilton Hayne, 1982; sr. editor: History of Southern Literature, 1985, Selected Letters of Henry James to Edmund Gosse (1882-1915): A Literary Friendship, 1988, The Correspondence of Henry James and the House of Macmillan, 1877-1914: All the Links in the Chain, 1993; mem. editorial bd. U. Ga. Press, 1972-74, Ga. Rev., 1974-82, chmn., 1980-82; contbr. articles, revs. to profl. jours. Mem. troop com. Boy Scouts Am., Athens, 1973-75; deacon, elder Presbyterian Ch., 1962—; mem. Lamar Meml. Lectures com. Mercer U., 1984-91. Served to capt. U.S. Army, 1942-46, PTO. Mem. MLA (exec. com. Gen. Topics VI 1972-75), Soc. Study So. Lit. (exec. com. 1968, 74-79, 85-88, 91-94, v.p. 1981-82, pres. 1983-84), South Atlantic Grad. English Coop. Group (exec. com. 1969-79, chmn. 1971-72), South Atlantic Modern Lang. Assn. (exec. com. 1975-77, nominating com. 1985-87), William Gilmore Simms Soc. (exec. com. 1993—, pres.-elect 1993—), Blue Key, Phi Beta Kappa, Sigma Chi. Office: U Ga Dept English Park Hall Athens GA 30602

MOORE, RAYMOND A., agricultural educator; b. Britton, S.D., Nov. 16, 1927; s. Arthur L. and Anna (Schuur) M.; m. Marlys Schiefelbein, Jun 17, 1951; children: Craig, Jay, Kent, Jeff. BA in Agrl. Edn. and Econs., S.D. State U., 1951, MS in Agronomy, 1958; PhD in Crop Physiology and Ecology, Purdue U., 1963. Instr. vocat. agriculture Bennett County H.S. Martin, S.D., 1951-56; instr., prof., adminstr. S.D. State U., Brookings, 1956-94, dir. emeritus agrl. sta., 1994—; cons. Coop. States Rsch. Svcs. U.S. Dept. Agriculture, Washington, Renewable Resources Rsch. Inst., St. Paul. Contbr. chpts. to books, articles to profl. jours. With USN, 1945-47. Nat. Sci. Faculty fellow forage & pasture mgmt. CSRS/U.S. Dept. Agriculture, 1965; Citizens Ambassador Program People to People Internat. travel grantee, U.S. Dept. Agriculture travel grantee. Mem. Am. Soc. Agronomy, Kiwanis Internat., Sigma Xi, Gamma Sigma Delta. Avocations: hunting, fishing, gardening, farming. Home: 207 17th Ave Brookings SD 57006-2609 Office: South Dakota State Univ PO Box 2207 Brookings SD 57007

MOORE, RICHARD, public relations executive. Grad., Marietta, Ohio. Grad., Ohio State U., 1980. Account exec. Haverhill Mass. Gazette, 1980-82, Northwest Pub. Power Assn., 1982-83; account exec. Miller Comm., 1983-85, account supr., 1985-87, gen. mgr., 1988; v.p. gen. mgr. Miller Comm., Mountain View, Calif., 1988; ptnr. Copithorne & Bellows, San Francisco, 1988—. Office: Copithorne & Bellows 131 Steuart St Ste 220 San Francisco CA 94105-1291*

MOORE, RICHARD ALAN, landscape architect; b. St. Louis, Jan. 17, 1930; s. Ira Mack and Helen Adoline (Fakes) M.; m. Patricia Ruth Burke, Mar. 15, 1952 (div. 1967); children: Sheryl Louise, Richard Dennis, Sara Lynn, Sandra Lee. BS, U. Mo., 1951; MLA, U. Oreg., 1957. Registered landscape architect, Calif., Hawaii. Asst. prof., head dept. landscape architecture Calif. State Poly. Coll., Pomona, 1957-61; assoc. prof., head dept. landscape architecture N.C. State U., Raleigh, 1962-67; pvt. practice landscape architecture Pomona, Calif., 1957-61; dir. land devel. and planning Oceanic Properties Inc., Honolulu, 1967-69; pvt. practice Honolulu, 1969-70, 79—; dir. ops. Eckbo, Dean, Austin & Williams, Honolulu, 1970-71, v.p. ops., 1971-73; pres. EDAW, Inc., San Francisco, 1973-76, chmn. bd., 1976-78; prof. landscape architecture Tex. A&M U., Bryan, 1977-79. Prin. works include Whispering Pines Motor Lodge, N.C., 1964 (award of merit N.C. chpt. AIA 1964), North Shore Devel. Plan, Kauai, Hawaii, 1973, Comprehensive Zoning Ordinance, County of Kauai, 1973 (Am. Soc. Landscape Architects honor award 1973, HUD honor award 1974), Lihue Devel. Plan, Kauai, 1975, Koloa, Poipu, Kalaheo Devel. Plan, Kauai, 1978, Gen. Plan

Update, Kauai, 1982, Mililani Town Devel. Plan, 1967-69 (Am. Soc. Landscape Architects merit award 1970), Lanai Land Mgmt. and Devel. Study, 1969 (Am. Soc. Landscape Architects merit award 1970), Wailea Master Devel. Plan, 1971, Kukuiula Devel. Plan, 1983, Lanai Project Dist. Master Plan, 1983-89, Maliu Ridge Devel. Plan, North Kohala, 1985, Mililani Mauka Devel. Plan, 1988, Devel. Plan, Lanai City Comml. Dist., 1990, Dandan Golf Course, Guam, 1991. 1st lt. U.S. Army, 1951-53, Korea. Fellow Am. Soc. Landscape Architects; mem. Masons. Avocations: sports, drawing, painting.

MOORE, RICHARD ALLAN, mathematics educator; b. Mansfield, Ohio, Jan. 11, 1924; s. Robert Allan and Ruth (Miller) M.; m. Ruth Marguerite Neuhoff, July 30, 1949; children—Peter Allan, Susan Rebecca Moore McJunkin, Sarah Marguerite. A.B., Washington U., St. Louis, 1948, M.A. in math, 1950, Ph.D., 1953. Instr. math. U. Nebr., 1953-54, Yale, 1954-56; mem. faculty Carnegie-Mellon U., Pitts., 1956-87; prof. math. Carnegie-Mellon U., 1967-87, prof. emeritus, 1987—, assoc. head dept., 1965-71, 75-85, chmn. dept., 1971-75; vis. lectr. Pa. Dept. Pub. Instrn., 1968-70; cons. in field, 1967—. Author. Mem. sch. bd. Churchill Area Schs., 1963-71; sch. bd. Eastern Area Spl. Schs., 1964-69. Served with AUS, 1943-45. Recipient Ryan Teaching award, 1969. Mem. Am. Math. Soc., Math. Assn. Am., Math. Coun. Western Pa. (bd. dirs. 1962-70), Pa. Coun. Tchrs. Math. (bd. dirs. 1966-68), Sigma Xi, Phi Kappa Phi. Episcopalian. Research papers, textbook ordinary differential equations. Home: 165 Fieldcrest Dr Pittsburgh PA 15221-3742

MOORE, RICHARD ANTHONY, diplomat, lawyer; b. Albany, N.Y., Jan. 23, 1914; s. John Denis and Julia Frances (Leader) M.; m. Jane Gertrude Swift, Mar. 27, 1943 (dec. Nov. 1985); children: Richard Anthony Jr., Matthew, Joseph, Kate, Samuel; m. Esther Horstkotte Jantzen, Dec. 29, 1986. BA, Yale U., 1936, LLB, 1939. Bar: N.Y. 1939, D.C. 1976. Atty. Breed, Abbott & Morgan, N.Y.C., 1939-41, Cravath Swaine & Moore, N.Y.C., 1942; asst., gen. counsel ABC, 1946-48; dir. TV, gen. mgr. ABC Western Div., L.A., 1948-51; pres., chief exec. officer Times Mirror Broadcasting Co., L.A., 1951-62; also bd. dirs. Times Mirror Co., L.A. 1956-62; pres., part owner Southwestern Cable Co., other cable systems, L.A., 1962-70; spl. asst. Atty. Gen. of U.S., Washington, 1970-71; spl. counsel Pres. of U.S., Washington, 1971-74; counsel Wilner & Scheiner, Washington, 1975-89; founder, assoc. producer The McLaughlin Group, Washington, 1981-89; amb. to Ireland Dept. State, Dublin, 1989-92; co-founder, chmn. TV Bur. Advt., N.Y.C., 1955-60; pres. TV Broadcasters of So. Calif., L.A., 1953-55, vice chmn. Nat. Cable TV Assn., 1967-68. Bd. dirs. L.A. Community Chest, 1955-60, L.A. C. of C., 1957-63, Hollywood Bowl, 1952-58; mem. L.A. Mayor's Com. on Human Rights, 1952-56. Pres. Eisenhower's Com. on Nat. Goals, 1955-56; pres. Friendly Sons St. Patrick, L.A., 1965; campaign adviser Sen. George Murphy, L.A., 1964, Lt. Gov. Robert Finch., L.A. 1966, Pres. Nixon, 1968, Pres. Bush, 1980-88. Capt. USAAF, 1942-46. Decorated Legion of Merit; recipient Emmy award TV Acad., 1984. Mem. N.Y. Bar Assn., D.C. Bar Assn., Metropolitan Club, Chgo. Club, Cypress Point Club (Pebble Beach), Sunset Club (L.A.), Portmarnock Golf Club (Ireland), Stephen's Green Club (Dublin), Yale Club of N.Y. Home and Office: 1801 Kalorama Sq NW Washington DC 20008-4021

MOORE, RICHARD EARL, communications creative director; b. Pontiac, Mich., Nov. 3, 1940; s. Earl Russel and Dorothy Grace (Daubenspeck) M.; m. Noriko Negishi, Feb. 1, 1966. B.F.A., Art Ctr. Coll. Design, Los Angeles, 1968. Sr. designer Lippincott & Margulies, N.Y.C., 1969-71; prin. Richard Moore Assocs., N.Y.C., 1972-76; vice chmn., co-founder Muir Cornelius Moore, N.Y.C., 1976-90; prin. Richard Moore Assocs., N.Y.C., 1990—; juror frequent nat. advt. competitions. Recipient numerous creative awards. Mem. Am. Inst. Graphic Art, Art Directors Club, Type Directors Club. Avocations: mountaineering; wilderness photography, scuba diving, skiing.

MOORE, RICHARD HARLAN, biology educator, university official; b. Houston, Sept. 16, 1945; s. Russell Lewis and Hazel Dean (Harlan) M; m. M. Robin Morris, May 14, 1977; 1 child, Merlin R. Morris. BA in Gen Biology, Vanderbilt U., 1967; MA in Zoology, U. Tex., 1970, PhD in Marine Zoology, 1973. Staff scientist Environment Cons. Inc., Dallas, 1973-74; asst. prof. biology Coastal Carolina U., Conway, 1974-77, assoc., 1977-86, chmn. sci. div., 1978-79, dean Sch. Sci., 1979-87, prof., 1986—, asst. vice chancellor for rsch., 1987-93, asst. v.p., 1993—; rsch. assoc. Belle W. Baruch Inst. for Marine Biology and Coastal Rsch., Columbia, S.C., 1974—. Author: (with H.D. Hoese) Fishes of the Gulf of Mexico, 1971, 94; contbr. articles to profl. jours. Leader Boy Scouts Am., Port Aransas, Tex., 1980-82; com. mem. S.C. Crawfish Festival Assn., Pawleys Island, 1980—. Recipient NSF grants 1975, 77. Mem. Am. Soc. Ichthyologists and Herpetologists, Am. Fisheries Soc., Ecological Soc. Am., Southeastern and Gulf Estuarine Rsch. Socs., Southeastern Fishes Coun. Office: Coastal Carolina U PO Box 1954 Conway SC 29526-1954

MOORE, RICHARD KERR, electrical engineering educator; b. St. Louis, Nov. 13, 1923; s. Louis D. and Nina (Megown) M.; m. Wilma Lois Schallau, Dec. 10, 1944; children: John Richard, Daniel Charles. B.S., Washington U. at St. Louis, 1943; Ph.D., Cornell U., 1951. Test equipment engr. RCA, Camden, N.J., 1943-44; instr. and research engr. Washington U., St. Louis 1947-49; research assoc. Cornell U., 1949-51; research engr., sect. supr. Sandia Corp., Albuquerque, 1951-55; prof., chmn. elec. engring. dept. U. N.Mex., 1955-62; Black and Veatch prof. U. Kans., Lawrence, 1962-94; prof. emeritus, 1994—; dir. remote sensing lab U. Kans., 1964-74, 84-93; pres. Cadre Corp., Lawrence, 1968-87; cons. cos., govt. agys. Author: Traveling Wave Engineering, 1960; co-author: (with Ulaby and Fung) Microwave Remote Sensing, Vol. I, 1981, Vol. II, 1982, Vol. III, 1986; contbr. to profl. jours. and handbooks. Served to lt. (j.g.) USNR, 1944-46. Recipient Achievement award Washington U. Engring. Alumni Assn., 1978, Outstanding Tech. Achievement award Geosci. and Remote Sensing Soc., 1982, Louise E. Byrd Grad. Educator award U. Kans., 1984, Irving Youngberg Rsch. award U. Kans., 1989. Fellow AAAS, IEEE (sect. chmn. 1960-61, Outstanding Tech. Achievement award coun. oceanic engring. 1978, Australia prize 1995); mem., NAE, AAUP, Am. Soc. Engring. Edn., Am. Geophys. Union, Internat. Sci. Radio Union (chmn. U.S. commn. F 1984-87, internat. vice chmn. commn. F 1990-93, chmn. 1993), Kiwanis, Sigma Xi, Tau Beta Pi. Presbyterian (past elder). Achievements include research in submarine communications, radar altimetry, radar as a remote sensor, radar oceanography; patent for polypanchromatic radar. Home: 1620 Indiana St Lawrence KS 66044-4046 Office: U Kans R S & Remote Sensing Lab 2291 Irving Rd Lawrence KS 66044-7541

MOORE, RICHARD LAWRENCE, structural engineer, consultant; b. Rocky Ford, Colo., Feb. 7, 1934; s. Lawrence and Margaret Kathryn (Bolling) M.; m. Donna St. Clair, Mar. 26, 1972 (div. 1983); 1 child, Andrew Trousdale; m. Margaret Ann Guthrie, May 4, 1984. BSCE, U. Colo., 1957; MS, Princeton U., 1963; PhD, Calif. Western U., Santa Ana, 1975. Registered profl. engr., Mass., Maine, Colo., Pa., Iowa, Nebr., N.Mex., Wyo., Ill., Ark., Mo., N.D., Mich., Okla., Mont. Structural engr. Cameron Engrs., Denver, 1964-66; v.p. Moore Internat., Jeddah, Saudi Arabia, 1978-87; asst. to pres. C.H. Guernsey Co., Oklahoma City, 1979-82; pres. R.L. Moore Co., Boston, 1983—; v.p. dir. Isolink Ing., Basel, Switzerland, 1990—; nat. chmn. Roof Cons. Inst., Raleigh, N.C., 1988-92; prof. Episcopal Sch. Theology, Denver, 1967-71. Patentee in field. Member Mound City (Mo.) Libr. Bd., 1963-64; pres. Dist. Rep. Party, Boston, 1988—; sr. warden St. John Chrysostom Epis. Ch., Denver, 1966-71. Danforth Found. scholar, 1962. Mem. ASCE, NSPE, Am. Concrete Inst., Nat. Forensic Club. Avocations: golf, travel, antique pocket watch collecting. Home and Office: RL Moore Co 534 E Broadway Boston MA 02127-4407

MOORE, RICHARD THOMAS, federal agency administrator; b. Milford, Mass., Aug. 7, 1943; s. Thomas James and Helen Eliza (Andrew) M.; m. Joanne Bednarz, May 26, 1979. BA in History, Clark U., 1966; MA in Student Pers., Colgate U., 1967; postgrad., Clark U., 1967-70, U Mass., 1981-85. Cert. tchr. secondary level social studies. Assoc. dean students Assumption Coll., Worcester, Mass., 1967-69; asst. to pres. Bentley Coll., Waltham, Mass., 1969-77; mem. Mass. Ho. of Reps., Boston, 1977-94; assoc. dir. mitigation Fed. Emergency Mgmt. Agy., Washington, 1994—; chmn. Mass. Selectmen's Assn., Boston, 1975-76; chmn. House Com. on Election Laws, Boston, 1992-94, House Com. on Taxation, Boston, 1983-85, House Com. on State Adminstrn., Boston, 1983. Chmn. Blackstone Nat. Heritage Corridor Commn., Uxbridge, Md., 1988-90; presdl. elector Mass. Electoral Coll., Boston, 1992; chmn. Mass. Dem. Leadership Coun., Boston, 1990-93. Named Outstanding Legislator Mass. Town Clks., Boston, 1993, New Dem. of Yr. Mass. Dem. Leadership Coun., Boston, 1994. Mem. Am. Soc. Pub. Adminstrn. (mem. bd. Mass. chpt. 1981-85), Nat. Emergency Mgmt. Assn. Roman Catholic. Avocations: politics, collecting political items. Home: 700 7th St SW Apt 215 Washington DC 20024

MOORE, ROBERT CLAY, petroleum industry executive, lawyer; b. McCamey, Tex., Mar. 22, 1934; s. Leon and Margret Lucille (Gamble) M.; m. Dorothy Anne Engh, Oct. 4, 1959; children: Robert Clay, Holly Anne, Helen Gamble, Kelsey Suzanne. B.B.A., Tex. Tech. U., 1956; J.D., U. Tex. 1962. Bar: Tex. 1962, Ill. 1964. Atty. Argonne Nat. Lab. U.S. AEC, Chgo., 1962-63, Humble Oil & Refining Co., Houston, 1963-65; v.p., gen. counsel, sec. Tex. Industries, Inc., Dallas, 1965-74; sr. v.p. affiliated ops. Geosource, Inc., Houston, 1974—; dir. Tex. Commerce Bank-Richmond-Sage, Houston, LBL Oil Corp., Houston, GH Transport Ltd., Al-Khobar, Saudi Arabia, Geosource-SBS Communications, Inc., Houston. Served to lt. (j.g.) USN, 1956-59. Mem. AM. Soc. Corp. Sec., ABA, Ill. Bar Assn., Tex. Bar. Assn., Houston Bar Assn., Am. Corp. Counsel Assn., East Tex. C. of C., Am. Petroleum Inst., Sudan-U.S. Bus. council. Republican. Presbyterian. Clubs: University (Houston), Forum (Houston); Economic (Chgo.). Office: Tex Industries Inc 8100 Carpenter Fwy Dallas TX 75247

MOORE, ROBERT CONDIT, civil engineer; b. Newark, July 27, 1921; s. Ira Condit and Mildred A. (Gill) M.; m. Betty Aierstock, Sept. 21, 1946; children—Robert Condit, Patricia, Margaret. B.S. in Civil Engring. with honors, Lehigh U., 1943. Registered profl. engr., N.J., Mass., Pa., Conn., Vt. Jr. engr. Dravo Corp., Pitts., 1943; with Elson T. Killam Assos., Inc., 1946-80; exec. v.p., sec. Elson T. Killam Assos., Inc., Millburn, N.J., 1970-75; sr. v.p. Elson T. Killam Assos., Inc., 1976-80; cons. environ. engr., 1980-90, ret., 1990. Contbr. articles to profl. jours. Chmn. Bd. Adjustment Madison, N.J., 1972-75; mem. Meml. Ctr. for Women, West Orange, N.J., 1974-92; elder First Presbyn. and Trinity Ch., South Orange, N.J. With U.S. Army, 1943-46. Fellow ASCE (Samuel A. Greeley award 1971), Am. Cons. Engrs. Coun. (nat. v.p. 1981-82); mem. ASTM (chmn. com. on asbestos cement products 1980-86), Am. Water Works Assn., Water Pollution Control Fedn., Am. Acad. Environ. Engrs. (diplomate), Cons. Engrs. Coun. of N.J. (pres. 1975, nat. dir. 1976-78), Rock Spring Club, Rotary, Kappa Alpha. Home: 75 Silver Springs Rd Short Hills NJ 07078-3120 also: Landmark, Southampton Bermuda SB-04

MOORE, ROBERT EDWARD, electronics executive; b. Winsted, Conn., July 29, 1923; s. Alfred Edward and Elizabeth (Clark) M.; m. Georgiana Muriel Moore, Dec. 22, 1946; children—Kathleen Moore Roberson, Brian Robert, John Craig. B.S. in Mech. Engring, U. Wis., 1948. Registered profl. engr., D.C. Chief insp. Rockwell-Standard Corp., Newark, Ohio, 1948-51; sec.-treas. A.E. Moore Co., Oshkosh, Wis., 1951-53; v.p. John I. Thompson & Co., Washington, 1953-65; founder, chmn., pres. Potomac Rsch., Inc. (merged with Electronic Data Systems Corp. 1979), Alexandria, Va., 1965-79, cons., 1979-81; chmn. Potomac Rsch. Internat., Fairfax, Va., 1981—. Served with U.S. Army, 1943-46. Mem. ASME. Episcopalian. Home: 11171 Crest Hill Rd Marshall VA 22115-9801 Office: Potomac Rsch Internat 11320 Random Hills Rd Fairfax VA 22030

MOORE, ROBERT LOWELL, JR. (ROBIN MOORE), author; b. Boston, Oct. 31, 1925; s. Robert Lowell Sr. and Eleanor (Turner) M.; m. Joan Friedman, Sept. 15, 1952 (div. 1955); 1 child, Margo Joan; m. Mary Olga Troshkin, Feb. 17, 1973. AB, Harvard U., 1949. European corr. Boston Globe, 1947; ind. TV producer N.Y.C., 1949-52; dir. pub. relations Sheraton Corp. Am., Boston, 1952- 54, dir. advt. and pub. relations, 1954-56, bd. dirs., 1954-62. Author: Pitchman, 1956, The Devil to Pay, 1961, The Green Berets, 1965, The Country Team, 1967, Fiedler, 1968, The French Connection, 1969, Court Martial, 1970, The Khaki Mafia, 1971, The Fifth Estate, 1974, Compulsion, 1982; (with Xaviera Hollander) The Happy Hooker, 1972, The Treasure Hunter, 1975, Dubai, 1976, Mafia Wife, 1977, The Banksters, 1977, Rhodesia, 1978, The Big Paddle, 1978, Search and Destroy, 1978, The Washington Connection, 1979; (with Milt Machlin) The Family Man, 1985, Force Nine, 1987, The Man Who Made It Snow, 1990, The White Tribe, 1991, The Moscow Connection, 1994; screenwriter: The Green Berets, 1967, The French Connection, 1971, The Happy Hooker, 1973, Inchon, 1979, Hoffa. Served as staff sgt. USAAF, 1944-46, ETO. Decorated Air medal with two bronze oak leaf clusters. Mem. Met. Club (N.Y.C.). Developed pvt. TV closed circuit network for hotels. Home: 179 Nashawtuc Rd Concord MA 01742-1634

MOORE, ROBERT MADISON, food industry executive, lawyer; b. New Orleans, June 21, 1925; s. Clarence Greer and Anna Omega (Odendahl) M.; m. Evelyn Eileen Varva, Apr. 11, 1953; children: Eileen Alexandria Moore Wynne, John Greer. B.B.A., Tulane U., 1943; J.D., U. Va., 1952; LL.M. (Food Law Inst. fellow), NYU, 1953. Bar: La. 1956, Calif. 1972. Asst. to pres., gen. counsel Underwear Inst., N.Y.C., 1953-55; pvt. practice law New Orleans, 1955-56; asst. gen. atty., dir. Legal services, sec. and gen. atty. Standard Fruit & Steamship Co., New Orleans, 1957-72; v.p., gen. counsel Castle & Cooke Foods, 1972-81; v.p., gen. counsel Castle & Cooke, Inc., 1973-81, sr. v.p. law and govt., 1981-82; pres. Internat. Banana Assn., 1983—; dir. Ferson Optics of Del., Inc., 1958-69, Baltime Securities Corp., Pan American Devel. Found. Asst. atty. gen., La., 1958-63. Served with AUS, 1943-46. Mem. ABA, Calif. Bar Assn., La. Bar Assn., SAR (sec. 1960-61), Essex Club, Cosmos Club, Phi Delta Phi, Alpha Tau Omega. Democrat. Roman Catholic. Home: 3323 R St NW Washington DC 20007-2310 Office: 1929 39th St NW Washington DC 20007-2110

MOORE, ROBERT STUART, furniture company executive; b. Filbert, W.Va., Mar. 28, 1924; s. Robert Harless and Anna Ethel (Fowler) M. Student, Va. Poly. Inst., 1942-43; BBA, So. Meth. U., 1948; MBA, Harvard U., 1950. Trainee, The Lane Co., Inc., Altavista, Va., 1953-54; asst. to v.p. and gen. mgr. The Lane Co., Inc., 1955-58, sec., dir., 1959—, exec. v.p., 1969-81, pres., 1981-86, pres., chief exec. officer, 1986-88, chmn., chief exec. officer, 1989—; v.p. Interco, Inc., 1986—, also bd. dirs.; dir. CRESTAR; 1st Nat. Bank of Lynchburg, Va. So. Furniture Market Ctr., High Point, N.C. Pres. Piedmont Area coun. Boy Scouts Am., 1965-67; trustee Ferrum Coll. (Va.), 1970-73, 83-90. Served to sgt. C.E. AUS, 1973-46; to 2d lt. USAF, 1951-52. Mem. Phi Delta Theta, Delta Sigma Pi. Republican. Methodist. Clubs: James River (Lynchburg). Home: PO Box 678 Lynchburg VA 24505-0678 Office: Lane Co Inc E Franklin Ave Altavista VA 24517

MOORE, ROBERT WILLIAM, professional organization executive; b. Claysburg, Pa., June 4, 1924; s. Frank B. and Sarah A. (Edelbute) M.; m. Helen Lingenfelter, July 17, 1948; children: Thomas R., Priscilla Jane. B.A., Pa. State U., 1948. With Price Waterhouse & Co., Pitts., 1948-62; mgr. Price Waterhouse & Co., 1955-62; asst. contr. Con-Gas Svc. Corp., Pitts., 1962-65, Consol. Natural Gas Svc. Co., Inc., Pitts., 1966-72; contr. Consol. Natural Gas Svc. Co., Inc., 1972-78, Consol. Natural Gas Co., Pitts., 1972-78; pres. Fin. Execs. Inst., Morristown, N.J., 1978-89, pres. emeritus, 1989—; mem. Fin. Acctg. Standards Adv. Coun., 1978-89. Bd. dirs. Central Blood Bank, Pitts., 1960-78, treas. chpt., 1960-78; mem. finance com., 1962-68, chmn. bd., 1969-72; mem. exec. bd. Pa. State U. Alumni Council, 1975-83; mem. exec. com. Campaign for Pa. State U., bd. vis.; pres. Pa. State Coll. Bus. Adminstrn. Soc., 1981-83. Served with AUS, 1943-45. Mem. Am., Pa. insts. C.P.A.s, Nat. Assn. Accountants, Fin. Execs. Inst., Pa. State U. Alumni Assn., Pa. Soc., Beta Alpha Psi (nat. forum), Delta Tau Delta. Episcopalian. Clubs: University (Pitts. 1975-76), Valley Brook Country (dir. 1968-70, v.p. bd. 1970), Duquesne (Pitts.), University, St. Clair Country, Morris County Golf, Morristown (N.J.).

MOORE, ROBERT YATES, neuroscience educator; b. Harvey, Ill., Dec. 5, 1931; s. Raymon Erwin and Marie Louise (Fischer) M.; children: Elizabeth Allen, Matthew McCormick, Joshua Gilbert, Thomas Douglas. BA magna cum laude, Lawrence U., 1953; MD with honors, U. Chgo., 1957, PhD, 1962; MD (hon.), Lund (Sweden) U., 1974. Diplomate: Am. Bd. Psychiatry and Neurology. Intern Univ. Hosp., Ann Arbor, Mich., 1958-59; resident U. Chgo., 1959-64, asst. prof. neurology and anatomy, 1964-66, assoc. prof., 1966-70, prof., 1970-74; prof. neurosci. U. Calif., San Diego, 1974-79; prof., chmn. dept. neurology SUNY, Stony Brook, 1979-90; dir. Ctr. for Neurosci., prof. psychiatry, neurology and behavirol neurosci. U. Pitts., 1990—; cons. Contbr. numerous articles to profl. jours. Recipient numerous grants. Fellow Am. Acad. Neurology; mem. Am. Neurol. Assn., Soc. Neurosci., Internat. Brain Research Orgn., Am. Assn. Anatomists. Office: U Pitts Ctr for Neurosci Biomed Sci Tower W 1656 Pittsburgh PA 15261

MOORE, ROGER GEORGE, actor; b. London, Oct. 14, 1927; s. George and Lily (Pope) M.; m. Luisa Mattioli, Apr. 11, 1968; children: Deborah, Geoffrey, Christian. Student, Royal Acad. Dramatic Arts, London, 1944-54. Theatrical performances London, 1944-54, N.Y.C., 1953—. Star: (TV series) The Alaskans, 1960-61, Ivanhoe, 1957-58, Maverick, 1961, The Saint, 1962-68, The Persuaders, 1971-72, The Muppet Show, 1981; actor: (films) including The Last Time I Saw Paris, 1954, Interrupted Melody, 1955, The King's Thief, 1955, Diane, 1956, The Miracle, 1959, Rape of the Sabines, 1961, Gold of the Seven Saints, 1961, Rachel Cade, 1961, No Man's Land, 1961, Crossplot, 1969, The Man Who Haunted Himself, 1970, Live and Let Die, 1973, Gold, 1974, The Man With The Golden Gun, 1974, Lucky Touch, 1975, Shout at the Devil, 1975, Street People, 1975, Sherlock Holmes in New York, 1976, The Spy Who Loved Me, 1977, The Wild Geese, 1977, Escape to Athena, 1978, Moonraker, 1978, North Sea Ransom, 1979, The Sea Wolves, 1981, Sunday Lovers, 1981, The Cannonball Run, 1981, For Your Eyes Only, 1981, Octopussy, 1982, The Naked Face, 1984, A View to a Kill, 1984, Bullseye, 1990, Bed and Breakfast, 1992, The Quest, 1995; author: James Bond Diary, 1973. Chmn. Stars Orgn. for Spastics, 1973-75, v.p., 1976-77. Served to capt. Brit. Army, 1945-48. Clubs: St. James's, Garrick (London). Address: Chalet Fenil, Grund BEI, Staad Switzerland*

MOORE, RONALD L., bank executive. Chmn. Affiliated Bankshares of Colo., Inc., Denver, also bd. dirs. Office: Banc One Colo Corp 1125 17th St Ste 1500 Denver CO 80202

MOORE, RONALD QUENTIN, minister; b. Langley, S.C., Aug. 12, 1939; s. George Quentin and Jennie Evelyn (Workman) M.; m. Doris Lorene Jones, July 5, 1959; children: David Quentin, Timothy Ray, Phillip Edward. BTh, Holmes Theol. Sem., Greenville, S.C., 1960; BA, Central (S.C.) Wesleyan Coll., 1969; MEd, Clemson U., 1975; postgrad., Columbia (S.C.) Bible Sem., Fuller Theol. Sem.; DD (hon.), Holmes Coll. of the Bible, Greenville, S.C., 1991; M in Min., Southwestern Coll. of Christian Min. Ordained to ministry Pentecostal Holiness Ch., 1959. Founder, pastor Pentecostal Holiness Ch., Belvedere, S.C., 1961-64; pastor Pentecostal Holiness Ch., Easley, S.C., 1965-70, Taylor Meml. Pentecostal Holiness Ch., Anderson, S.C., 1970-75; asst. dir. world missions dept. Pentecostal Holiness Ch., Okla., 1975-90; pres. Southwestern Coll. Christian Ministries, Oklahoma City, 1990—; chmn. Pastoral Care Dept. Internat. Pentecostal Holiness Ch., Oklahoma City, 1989—. Assoc. editor (mag.) Worldorama, 1975-90; exec. editor INSIGHT, Southwestern Alumni Assn., 1990—; contbr. articles to Advocate Pentecostal Holiness Ch. Office: Southwestern Coll Christian Ministries 7210 NW 39th Expy Bethany OK 73008-2321

MOORE, ROY DEAN, judge; b. Chickasha, Okla., Jan. 15, 1940; s. Frank B. and Delia Pauline (Morgan) M.; m. Carolyn Kaye Wood, Aug. 10, 1962; children—Darla Kaye, Jared Dean, Amy Darise. B.A., Central State U., 1962, M. Teaching, 1966; J.D., Oklahoma City U., 1970; grad., Nat. Coll. State Trial Judges, 1972. Bar: Okla. 1970. Coach debate, instr. dramatics Kingfisher (Okla.) High Sch., 1962-67; instr. English and journalism, head dept. lang. arts. Jarman Jr. High Sch., Midwest City, Okla., 1967-70; pros. atty. City of Lawton, Okla., 1970; spl. dist. judge 5th Jud. Dist. Okla., 1971-72; pvt. practice law Lawton, 1973-90; dist. judge 5th Jud. Dist. Okla., 1990—. Pres. Swinney PTA, 1975-76; Editor: Problems in Teaching in the Secondary School, 1966. Pres. Comanche County Mental Health Assn., 1973-74, bd. dirs., 1972-76; co-chmn. Kingfisher County Reps. for Congressman James V. Smith, 1966; mem. state exec. com. Okla. Republican Com., 1973-74, chmn. auditing com., 1977-78; del. Rep. Nat. Conv., 1976; chmn. cts. com. Assn. South Central Okla. Govts. Crime Commn.; chmn. Comanche County Reps. for Reagan for Pres., 1973-83; mem. adv. bd. Jim Taliferro Mental Health Center, 1977-78; del. Nat. Mental Health Assn. Conv., 1975; bd. dirs. Lawton Campfire Girls; elder N.W. Ch. of Christ, 1977—; dir. Back to Bible Campaigns, 1976—. Mem. Am., Okla., Comanche County bar assns., Okla. Trial Lawyers Assn., Lawton Antique Auto Club, Ford Retractible Club Am., Alpha Psi Omega, Delta Theta Phi. Republican. Mem. Ch. of Christ (elder). Clubs: Fraternal Order of Police, Lion. Home: 2114 NW Atlanta Ave Lawton OK 73505-3923

MOORE, RUTH JOHNSTON, medical center official; b. Washington, Pa., Mar. 25, 1939; d. Warren and Wilma Bell (McDaid) Johnston; 1 child, Dean Jason. BS in Nursing, Fla. Internat. U., 1978; MEd, Fla. Atlantic U., 1980, EdS, 1986, EdD, 1987. Adj. faculty health svcs. Broward Community Coll., Ft. Lauderdale, Fla., 1978-80, div. chmn. continuing edn. and health-related professions, 1980-89; v.p. Boca Raton Community Hosp, Boca Raton, FL, 1989-92; prin. Moore Cons., 1992; corp. dir. profl. practice and devel. Charleston (W.Va.) Area Med. Ctr., 1992—; cons. in field. Mem. ANA (edn. com., mem. instr. nursing practice 1993—), Am. Orgn. Nurse Execs., Am. Assn. Deans & Dirs. Nursing Edn., Nat. League Nursing, W.Va. Nurses Assn. (bd. dirs. 1994—), W.Va. Health & Human Resources (task force subcom.), W.Va. Congress on Nursing Practice (chair 1994), Phi Kappa Phi, Sigma Theta Tau. Methodist. Avocations: exercise physiology, tennis, biking, basket weaving, skiing. Office: Charleston Area Med Ctr 3101 MacCorkle Ave SE Charleston WV 25304

MOORE, SALLY FALK, anthropology educator; b. N.Y.C., Jan. 18, 1924; d. Henry Charles and Mildred (Hymanson) Falk; m. Cresap Moore, July 14, 1951; children: Penelope, Nicola. B.A., Barnard Coll., 1943; LL.B., Columbia U., 1945, Ph.D., 1957. Asst. prof. U. So. Calif., Los Angeles, 1963-65, assoc. prof., 1965-70, prof., 1970-77; prof. anthropology Harvard U., Cambridge, Mass., 1981—, Victor Thomas prof. anthropology, 1991—, dean Grad. Sch. Arts and Scis., 1985-89. Author: Power and Property in Inca Peru, (Ansley Prize 1957), 1958, Law as Process, 1978, Social Facts and Fabrications, 1986, Moralizing States, 1993, Anthropology and Africa, 1994. Trustee Barnard Coll., Columbia U. 1991-92; master Dunster House, 1984-89. Rsch. grantee Social Sci. Rsch. Coun., 1968-69, NSF, 1972-75, 79-80, Wenner Gren Found., 1983; Guggenheim fellow, 1995—. Fellow Am. Acad. Arts & Scis., Am. Anthrop. Assn., Royal Anthrop. Inst.; mem. Assn. Polit. and Legal Anthropology (pres. 1983), Am. Ethnological Soc. (pres. 1987-88). Democrat. Office: Harvard U 348 William James Hall Cambridge MA 02138

MOORE, SANDRA M., director of admissions. BA in English Lit. cum laude, Mt. Holyoke Coll., 1973; MA in Student Personnel Adminstrn., Columbia U., 1977. Coord. student activities, residence dir. Bennett Coll., Millbrook, N.Y., 1973-75; coord. admissions and devel. Poughkeepsie (N.Y.) Day Sch., 1976-78; asst. and acting dir. admissions Sarah Lawrence Coll., Bronxville, N.Y., 1978-83; dir. admissions Eugene Lang Coll., New Sch. for Social Rsch., N.Y.C., 1983-86, The Masters Sch., Dobbs Ferry, N.Y., 1986—; guest lectr. NYU, 1981; leader workshop ACE/NIP Conf., Westchester, Rockland, 1982. Avocations: children, travel, fiber arts, architecture. Office: Masters Sch 49 Clinton Ave Dobbs Ferry NY 10522-2200

MOORE, SCOTT, state official; b. York, Nebr., 1960; m. Danene Tushar, 1989. BA in Polit Sci., U. Nebr. Legis. aide Nebr. Legislature, 1981-86, mem., 1986-94, chair appropriations com.; sec. of state State of Nebr., 1995—; with Moore & Sons. Office: State Capitol # 2300 PO Box 94608 Lincoln NE 68509-4608 Address: 440 E Pinewood Ave Seward NE 68434-1178 also: State Legislature State Capital Lincoln NE 68516*

MOORE, SEAN, pathologist, educator; b. Belfast, No. Ireland, Nov. 24, 1926; arrived in Can. 1951; s. James Bernard and Eileen (McFadden) M.; m. Cynthia Balch, Oct. 1957; children: John Brian, Martha Ailish, Patrick Balch. MB, BChir, Queen's U., Belfast, 1950. From asst. to assoc. pathologist Montreal Gen. Hosp., Que., Can., 1958-69; pathologist-in-chief Jewish Gen. Hosp., Montreal, 1969-71; chmn. dept. pathology McMaster U., Hamilton, Ont., Can., 1972-78, dir. labs. med. cen., 1972-84; pathologist-in-chief Royal Victoria Hosp., Montreal, 1984-94; chmn. dept. pathology, Strathcona prof. pathology McGill U., Montreal, 1984-94. Editor: Injury Mechanisms in Atherosclerosis, 1981; mng. editor: Experimental and

Molecular Pathology; contbr. articles to profl. jours. Fellow Royal Coll. Physicians & Surgeons (Can.). Home: 522 Clarke Ave, Montreal, PQ Canada H3Y 3C9 Office: McGill U Dept Pathology, 3775 University St, Montreal, PQ Canada H3A 2B4

MOORE, STANLEY RAY, lawyer; b. Dallas, July 20, 1946; s. Elzey and Heloise (Dillon) M.; children—Natalie, William. B.S.M.E., So. Meth. U., 1969, J.D., 1973. Bar: Tex. 1973; U.S. Dist. Ct. (no. dist.) Tex. 1974. Assoc. Clegg, Cantrell, Crisman, Dallas, 1973-75; ptnr. Crisman & Moore, Dallas, 1975-80, Schley Cantrell & Moore, Dallas, 1980-83, Schley, Cantrell, Kice & Moore, Dallas, 1983-87, Johnson & Wortley, P.C., 1987-94, Jenkews & Gilchrist, 1995—. Patentee in field. Foster parent Hope Cottage, Dallas, 1982-90; fund raiser Am. Heart Assn., Republican Party. Recipient Outstanding Leadership commendation ASME, 1969. Mem. Dallas Bar Assn., ABA, Am. Patent Law Assn. Baptist. Home: 1 Victoria Cir Rowlett TX 75088 Office: Jenkews & Gilchrist 1445 Ross Ave Ste 3200 Dallas TX 75202

MOORE, SUSANNA, writer; b. Bryn Mawr, Pa., Dec. 9, 1948; d. Richard Dixon and Anne (Shields) M.; 1 child, Lulu Linnane Sylbert. Author: My Old Sweetheart, 1982 (Am. Book award nomination for best first novel 1983, Sue Kaufman prize for first fiction Am. Acad. Inst. Arts and Letters 1983), Whiteness of Bones, 1989, Sleeping Beauties, 1993. Recipient Literary Lion award N.Y. Pub. Libr., 1993. Office: Wallace & Sheil Agy Inc 177 East 70th St New York NY 10021*

MOORE, THOMAS A., consumer products company executive; b. Cambridge, Mass., Jan. 28, 1951; s. Leo B. and Christine (Banios) M.; m. Avril Barton, Nov. 8, 1975; children: Thomas, Diana, Juliet. BA in History, Princeton U., 1973. Brand asst. Procter & Gamble Co., Cin., 1973-84, advt. mgr. Beauty Care, 1984-86; gen. mgr. Vidal Sassoon Procter & Gamble Co., L.A., 1986-88; v.p. Health Care Procter & Gamble Co., Cin., 1988-91; pres. Procter & Gamble Can., Toronto, Ont., Can., 1991-92; pres. Health Care Procter & Gamble USA, Cin., 1992—; group v.p. Procter & Gamble Co., Cin., 1992—. Treas. Alliance Drug Free Care., Toronto, 1991, 92; chmn. Cin. Ballet Co., 1986-91; bd. dirs. Am. Health Found., N.Y.C., 1989—, Mercy Hosp., Anderson, Ohio, 1993—. Mem. Non Prescription Drug Mfrs. Assn. (vice chmn. 1992—), Princeton Club. Avocations: fly fishing, wine collecting, consumption. Home: 750 Old Ludlow Ave Cincinnati OH 45220 Office: Procter & Gamble Co 1 Procter & Gamble Plz Cincinnati OH 45220

MOORE, THOMAS CARROL, botanist, educator; b. Sanger, Tex., Sept. 22, 1936; s. Thomas M. and Willie Mae M.; m. Arvida Inmon DePriest, Sept. 1, 1956; children—Cynthia, Linda, Alan. B.A. in Biology, U. N. Tex., Denton, 1956; M.A. in Botany, U. Colo., 1958, Ph.D. (Outstanding Grad. Student in Biology award 1960, USPHS predoctoral fellow 1960-61), 1961. Instr. biology, then part-time instr. U. Colo., 1958-60; asst. prof. Ariz. State Coll., Flagstaff, 1961-63; mem. faculty Oreg. State U., Corvallis, 1963-93, prof. botany, 1971-93, prof. emeritus, 1993—, chmn. dept. botany and plant pathology, 1973-86, asst. to v.p. for rsch. and grad. studies, 1972-73; vis. prof. Colo. State Coll., 1963. Mem. editorial bd. Plant Physiology, 1981-86; editor in chief Jour. Plant Growth Regulation; contbr. articles to profl. jours. Recipient Mosser award outstanding undergrad. teaching Oreg. State U., 1966. Mem. Am. Soc. Plant Physiologists, Bot. Soc. Am., Am. Phytopathol. Soc., Internat. Plant Growth Substances Assn., Plant Growth Regulator Soc. Am., Sigma Xi. Democrat. Lodge: Elks. Home: 560 NW Merrie Dr Corvallis OR 97330-6524 Office: 2082 Cordley Hall Oreg State Univ Corvallis OR 97331

MOORE, THOMAS DAVID, academic administrator; b. Rochester, N.Y., July 26, 1937; s. Robert Franklin and Hilda (Kennedy) M.; m. Virginia Muller, June 13, 1959; children: Kathleen Mary, Michael David, Thomas David. BSS, St. John Fisher Coll., 1959; MS, SUNY, Brockport, 1962; EdD, Rutgers U., 1966. Tchr. Rochester City Schs., 1959-62; grad. asst. Rutgers U., New Brunswick, N.J., 1963-65; from asst. to full prof. Kent (Ohio) State U., 1965-93, asst. v.p. acad. affairs, 1976-83, v.p. faculty affairs and personnel, 1984-86, provost, v.p. acad. and student affairs, 1987-91; provost, v.p. acad. affairs Ctrl. Washington U., 1993—. Roman Catholic. Avocations: sports, film, public affairs, music. Office: Ctrl Wash U Ellensburg WA 98926

MOORE, THOMAS E., biology educator, museum director; b. Champaign, Ill.; s. Gerald E. and Velma (Lewis) M.; m. E. Eleanor Sifferd, Feb. 4, 1951; children: Deborah S., Melinda S. BS, U. Ill., 1951, MS, 1952, PhD, 1956. Tech. asst. Ill. Natural History Survey, Urbana, 1950-56; instr. zoology U. Mich., Ann Arbor, 1956-59, asst. prof. zoology, 1959-63, assoc. prof. zoology, 1963-66, prof. biology, 1966—, curator insects, 1956—, dir. exhibit mus., 1988-93; vis. prof. Orgn. for Tropical Studies, San Jose, Costa Rica, 1970, 72; bd. dirs. Orgn. Tropical Studies, San Jose, 1968-79; mem. steering com. tropical biome U.S. Internat. Biol. Program, 1969-72; mem. conf. planning com. Nat. Inst. for Environment, 1991-92; mem. steering com. Univ. Colloquium on Environ. Rsch. and Edn., 1991-93. Co-editor: Lectures on Science Education, 1991-1992, 1993; Cricket Behavior and Neurobiology, 1989; author movie 17-Year Cicadas, 1975. County rep. Huron River Watershed Coun., Ann Arbor, 1987-95; mem. Mich. H.S. Accreditation Adv. Com., Ann Arbor, 1988-92; mem. U. Mich. Senate Adv. Com. on Univ. Affairs, 1993—, vice chair, 1995-96; bd. mem. U. Mich. Acad. Freedom Lecture Fund, 1995—, treas., 1995-96; cons. NSF Visual Tech. in Environ. Curricula, 1994—. Rsch. grantee NSF, 1963-66, 66-69, rsch. equipment grantee, 1984-86. Fellow AAAS, Royal Entomol. Soc. London, Linnaen Soc. London; mem. Assn. Tropical Biology (pres. 1973-75), Sigma Xi (pres. U. Mich. chpt. 1994-96, coun. 1993—). Home: 4243 N Delhi Rd Ann Arbor MI 48103-9485 Office: Mus of Zoology U Mich Ann Arbor MI 48109-1079

MOORE, THOMAS GALE, economist, educator; b. Washington, Nov. 6, 1930; s. Charles Godwin and Beatrice (McLean) M.; m. Cassandra Chrones, Dec. 28, 1958; children: Charles G., Antonia L. B.A., Geroge Washington U., 1957; M.A., U. Chgo., 1959, Ph.D., 1961. Fgn. research analyst Chase Manhattan Bank, N.Y.C., 1960-61; asst. prof. econs. Carnegie Inst. Tech., 1961-65; assoc. prof., then prof. econs. Mich. State U., East Lansing, 1965-74; sr. staff economist Council Econ. Advisers, 1968-70; hon. research fellow Univ. Coll., London, 1973-74; adj. scholar Am. Enterprise Inst., 1971—; CATO Inst., 1982—; sr. fellow Hoover Inst. on War, Revolution and Peace-Stanford U., 1974—; dir. domestic studies program, 1974-85; mem. Council Econ. Advisers, Washington, 1985-89; mem. Nat. Critical Materials Council, 1985-89; mem. econ. adv. bd. Dept. Commerce, 1971-73; mem. adv. com. RANN, 1975-77, NSF, 1975-77; cons. Dept. Transp., 1973-74, 81-83; mem. adv. panel Synthetic Fuels Corp., 1982; mem. adv. bd. Reason Found., 1982—; dir. Stanford Savs. & Loan, 1979-82, chmn., 1982. Author: The Economics of American Theater, 1968, Freight Transportation Regulation, 1972, Trucking Regulation: Lessons from Europe, 1976, Uranium Enrichment and Public Policy, 1978; co-author: Public Claims on U.S. Output, 1973; contbr. articles to profl. jours. Served with USN, 1951-55, Korea. Fellow Earhart Found., 1958-59; fellow Walgreen Found., 1959-60, Hoover Instn., 1973-74. Mem. Am. Econ. Assn., Mont. Pelerin Soc., Chevy Chase Club. Home: 3766 La Donna Ave Palo Alto CA 94306-3150 Office: Stanford U Hoover Instn Stanford CA 94305

MOORE, THOMAS JOSEPH, financial company executive; b. Kalamazoo, Jan. 5, 1943; s. John Joseph and Bernita (Ryan) M.; m. Laura Leigh Johnson, Aug. 1, 1975; children: Ryan Michael, Janelle Marie, Darcie Kathleen. BBA, Western Mich. U., 1965; MBA, So. Meth. U., 1990. Various sales and mktg. positions IBM Corp., Southfield, Mich., 1968-79; exec. v.p., owner Carsonville (Mich.) Metal Products Corp., 1976-79; assoc. prof. Oakland Coll., Farmington Hills, Mich., 1977-78; group mgr. industry mktg. Recognition Equipment Inc., Dallas, 1979-81; mgmt. cons. APC Skills div. Alexander Proudfoot Co., Palm Beach, Fla., 1982-83; pres., chief exec. officer Lumentech of Am., Inc., Dallas, 1983-85; v.p., prin. Capital Alliance Corp., Dallas, 1985—; chmn., CEO, Laura Leigh Stores, Inc., Plano, Tex.; vis. lectr. Baylor U., Waco, Tex., 1986-89, sponsor, CEO roundtable, 1989-93. Pres. Bent Tree Homeowners Assn., Dallas, 1987-93; co-chair Jesuit Coll. Prep. Sch. Challenge Dr., 1992-94; chair car raffle Ursuline Acad. of Dallas, 1993-94, chmn. maj. donor campaign, 1994-95. Mem. M&A Internat., So. Meth. U. Exec. MBA Alumni Assn. (bd. dirs.). Republican. Roman Catholic. Avocations: running, reading, racquetball. Home: 4402 Cobblers Ln Dallas TX 75287-6732 Office: Capital Alliance Corp 2777 N Stemmons Fwy Ste 1220 Dallas TX 75207-2271

MOORE, THOMAS KAIL, chief judge; b. Idaho Falls, Idaho, Jan. 15, 1938; s. Burton L. and Clara E. (Kail) Moore; m. Judith Diane Gilman, July 30, 1966; children: David T., Jonathan G. AB in Phys. Scis., Harvard U., 1961; JD, Georgetown U., 1967. Bar: D.C., V.I., Va. Law clk. to Hon. John A. Danaher U.S. Ct. Appeals (D.C. Cir.), 1967-68; staff atty. Office Gen. Coun., Office Sec. Dept. Transp., Washington, 1968-69; assoc. Stanford, Reed & Gelenian, Washington, 1969-70; asst. U.S. Atty. U.S. Attys. Office, Washington, 1970-71; asst. U.S. Atty. U.S. Attys. Office (ea. dist.), Va., 1971-76, prin. asst. Alexandria office, 1974-76; asst. U.S. Atty. U.S. Attys. Office (V.I. dist.), 1976-78; pvt. practive St. Thomas, V.I., 1978-81; shareholder Hoffman & Moore, P.C., St. Thomas, 1981-87; ptnr. Grunert, Stout, Moore & Bruch, St. Thomas, 1987-92; chief judge U.S. Dist. Ct. (V.I. dist.), 1992—. Editor-in-chief Georgetown Law Journal, 1966-67. Scoutmaster Antilles Sch. Troop; trustee V.I. Montessori Sch. Capt. USAF, 1961-64, USAFR. Mem. ABA, V.I. Bar Assn. (mem. St. Thomas subcom. of grievance com.), V.I. C. of C., St. Thomas Yacht Club. Avocations: tennis, swimming, sailing. Office: Dist Ct of VI Ste 310 5500 Veterans Dr Ste 310 Charlotte Amalie VI 00802-6424

MOORE, THOMAS LLOYD, librarian; b. Springfield, Ill., Oct. 4, 1942; s. Edward Joseph and Dorothy A. (Menezes) M.; m. Ann Mary Walsh, Aug. 29, 1971; children: Sean Christopher, Martin Thomas, Kathleen Adele. AA, Springfield Coll., 1963; BA, Cardinal Glennon Coll., St. Louis, 1968; MA in Library Sci., Rosary Coll., 1973. Tchr. Little Flower Grade Sch., Springfield, 1963-66; head of adult services Elk Grove Village (Ill.) Pub. Library, 1973-74; dir. Northlake (Ill.) Pub. Library Dist., 1974-75, Danville (Ill.) Pub. Library, 1975-78; adminstrv. librarian Palatine (Ill.) Pub. Library Dist., 1978-81; dir. Wake County Dept. of the Pub. Library, Raleigh, N.C., 1981—. Bd. dirs. Commit to a Healthier Raleigh, 1991-93, Planned Parenthood of the Capital & Coast, 1993—, sec., 1994—; bd. dirs. Pirates Cove Homeowners Assn., 1992, v.p., 1993-94, pres., 1995—; mem. Libr. Power Adv. Com., 1993—; mem. ASSIST Wake to Health Coalition, 1992-94. Mem. ALA, N.C. Library Assn. Democrat. Roman Catholic. Office: Wake County Pub Libr 4020 Carya Dr Raleigh NC 27610-2900

MOORE, THOMAS PAUL, broadcast executive; b. Danville, Ill., Feb. 29, 1928; s. Lester Rufus and Mabel Ellen (Jackson) M.; m. Jean LaVonne Sather, Aug. 31, 1952; children: Randyl Ellen, Patricia Kay, Gregory Sather. BA, North Cen. Coll., Naperville, Ill., 1952; postgrad., Denver U., 1952-53. Newscaster Sta. KFEL-AM-FM-TV, Denver, 1952-54; sales rep. Sta. KGMC, Englewood, Colo., 1954-56; sales mgr. Sta. KDEN-AM-FM, Denver, 1956-62; pres. Stas. WBCO, WQEL, Bucyrus, Ohio, 1962—; bd. dirs. First Fed. Savings and Loan, Bucyrus, 1990—. Lay leader, mem. program council Ohio Sandusky Conf., United Methodist Ch., 1966-69 (pres. gen. laity bd. and laymen's found. 1968-72); mem. Gen Council on Ministries, 1980-84, N.W. Ohio Water Devel. Adv. Com., 1967-69, Sandusky River Basin Water Pollution Study Com., 1968-69; v.p., bd. mgrs. EUB Men, Evang. United Brethren Ch., 1958-68; pres. Rocky Mountain Conf., 1957-61; mem. gen. bd. Nat. Council Christian Chs. Am., 1968-72; charter pres. Bucyrus Bratwurst Festival, Inc., 1968; adv. bd. Bucyrus Salvation Army, 1964-68; mem. planning com. East Ohio Conf., 1972-76 (chmn. commn. on minimum salaries, 1968-72, lay leader, 1972-76); vice chmn. council ministries, mem. episcopal com., 1972-76, head. del. to gen. conf., Portland, Oreg., 1976, Balt., 1984; head del. to Jurisdictional Conf., Sioux Falls, 1976, Duluth, Minn., 1984; pres. United Meth. Communications, 1972-76, mem. gen. council fin. and adminstrn., 1976-80; mem. communications commn. Nat. Council Chs., 1972-76; mem. communications con. Ohio Council Chs.; mem. Episc. com., chmn. New Vision Task Group, both East Ohio Conf., North Cen. Jurisdiction, United Meth. Ch.; mem. exec. com. Council on Ministries, 1980-86; mem. World Meth. Council, 1986-91; trustee United Theol. Sem., 1972-80; trustee Ohio Northern U., 1986—, mem. exec. com., 1991—, vice chair student affairs com., 1991—; mem. exec. com. East Ohio del. to United Meth. Gen. Conf. and Jurisdictional Conf., 1987-91; v.p. Community Improvement Corp., Bucyrus, 1989-91; mem. Overall Econ. Devel. Com. of Crawford County; chmn. Crawford County Traffic Safety Council, 1979-89; pres. Crawford County Econ. Devel. Adv. Coun., 1992-94; mem. Crawford County Devel. Bd., Inc.; mem. exec. com. of del. to 1988 Gen. Conf. United Meth. Ch., St. Louis; bd. dirs. Bucyrus Community Hosp., 1992—, mem. fin. com., 1993—, chair nominating com., 1993—, campaign dir., chair fundraising com., 1993—, v.p. bd. dirs., 1994—. Served with USN, 1946-48, PTO. Named a Civic Leader of Am., 1968. Mem. Bucyrus Area C. of C. (chmn. airport study com. 1967-68, bd. dirs. 1964-67, pres. 1989-91), Ohio Assn. Broadcasters (pres. 1982-85), Nat. Assn. Broadcasters (legis. liaison 1984-91, mem. small market radio com.), North Cen. Ohio Broadcasters Assn. (pres. 1983-84, v.p. 1985—), Rotary Club (pres. Bucyrus chpt. 1992-93). Office: SA-MOR Stas 403 E Rensselaer St Bucyrus OH 44820-0789

MOORE, THOMAS RONALD, lawyer; b. Duluth, Minn., Mar. 27, 1932; s. Ralph Henry and Estelle Marguerite (Hero) M.; m. Margaret C. King, Sept. 10, 1955; children: Willard S., Clarissa, Charles R.H. BA magna cum laude, Yale U., 1954; JD, Harvard U., 1957. Bar: N.Y. 1958, U.S. Supreme Ct. 1958. Instr. Internat. Program in Taxation Harvard Law Sch., 1956-57; assoc. Dewey Ballantine, N.Y.C.; ptnr. Breed, Abbott & Morgan, N.Y.C., Finley Kumble & Wagner, N.Y.C., Hawkins, Delafield & Wood, N.Y.C.; prin. Law Offices Thomas R. Moore, N.Y.C.; lectr. on law Cornell Law Sch., NYU Inst. Fed. Taxation, So. Fed. Tax Inst., U. Hartford Tax Inst., Practising Law Inst., N.Y.C., Las Vegas, New Orleans; lectr. N.Y.C., San Antonio, Tampa, Fla., L.A., Moscow, Charlottesville, Va., Washington, Kansas City. Author: Plantagenet Descent, 31 Generations from William the Conqueror to Today, 1995; co-author: Estate Planning and the Close Corporation; editor-in-chief Gastronome; bd. editors: The Tax Lawyer; contbr. articles to profl jours., popular press and TV commentaries. Bd. dirs. exec. com. Citymeals on Wheels; pres. bd. dirs. Nat. Soc. to Prevent Blindness, 1973-81, chmn. 1981-83, now hon. pres.; sec.-treas., trustee A.D. Henderson Found., Del.; trustee, Fla.; bd. dirs. Phoenix Theatre Inc., Inst. Aegean Prehistory, Found. Future of Man, Am. and Internat. Friends of Victoria and Albert Mus., London; conservator N.Y. Pub. Libr.; trustee Found. for Renaissance of St. Petersburg (Russia), Lawrence W. Levine Fedn. Awarded Arms by Queen Elizabeth II; decorated comdr. Most Venerable Order of the Hosp. of St. John of Jerusalem, Order of the Crown of Charlemagne, Magna Charta Barons; honoree Thomas R. Moore Disting. Pub. Servant award Nat. Soc. to Prevent Blindness; recipient Key to Kansas City by Mayor of Kansas City, Mo., 1989; Yale Scholar of the House, 1954. Mem. ABA, N.Y. State Bar Assn. (exec. com. sector on taxation), Assn. of Bar of City of N.Y., Confrerie de la Chaine des Rotisseurs (nat. pres., dir., exec. com., world coun. Paris), Chevalier du Tastevin, Nat. Wine Coalition (bd. dirs. 1989—), Downtown Assn., Univ. Club, Church Club, Pilgrims, Delta Sigma Rho. Republican. Episcopalian. Office: 730 Fifth Ave Ste 900 New York NY 10019-4105

MOORE, THURSTON ROACH, lawyer; b. Memphis, Dec. 10, 1946; s. Richard Charlton Moore and Halcyon Hall (Roach) Lynn; m. Grace Branch, Nov. 8, 1969. BA with distinction, U. Va., 1968, JD, 1974. Bar: Va. 1974. Rsch. analyst Scudder, Stevens & Clark, N.Y.C., 1968-71; ptnr. Hunton & Williams, Richmond, Va., 1974—; bd. dirs. Exec. Info. Systems, Inc., Darien, Conn., Sealey Optical Corp., Inc., Richmond, Advantages Corp., Richmond. Bd. dirs. Met. Bus. Found., Richmond, 1990—, Mary Morton Parsons Found., Charlottesville, Va., 1992—; bd. dirs., vice chmn. Va. chpt. The Nature Conservancy, Charlottesville, 1991—; trustee Va. Aerospace Bus. Roundtable, Hampton, Va., 1989—. Mem. ABA (bus. law sect., chmn. ptnrs. com., mem. fed. regulation security com.), Va. Bar Assn., Va. State Bar. Office: Hunton & Williams 951 E Byrd St Richmond VA 23219-4040

MOORE, TOM, film and theater director; b. Meridian, Miss., Aug. 6, 1943; s. Heustis T. and Maryanne (Moody) M. B.A., Purdue U., 1965; M.F.A., Yale U., 1968. Tchr. Am. Dramatic Inst., U. London, 1968; guest dir. SUNY-Buffalo, 1968, Brandeis U., Boston, 1968; artistic dir. Peterborough Players (N.H.), 1971; lectr. Seminar Am. Studies, Salzburg, Austria, 1974. Dir. Broadway plays: Grease (one of the longest-running shows in history of Broadway), 1972-80, Over Here, 1974-75, Once in a Lifetime, 1978, Division Street, 1980, Frankenstein, 1981, 'night Mother, 1983 (Pulitzer Prize) (dir. film by same name 1986), The Octette Bridge Club, 1985, A Little Hotel on the Side, Nat. Actors Theatre, 1992; off-Broadway play: Welcome to Andromeda, 1973; plays Am. Conservatory Theatre, San Francisco, 1977-81, Williamstown (Mass.) Theatre Festival, 1976, 79, 93, Mark Taper Forum,

Los Angeles, 1980, 82, 83, 84, 86, 91, Tyrone Guthrie Theatre, Mpls., 1975, Arena Stage, Washington, 1975, Old Globe Theatre Festival, San Diego, 1982, 85, Ahmanson Theatre, Los Angeles, 1983, Am. Repertory Theatre, Cambridge, Mass., 1982, 84, La Jolla (Calif.) Playhouse, 1990; film Journey, 1972; co-dir. Fridays, ABC-TV; dir. thirtysomething, ABC-TV, LA Law, NBC-TV (Emmy nominee 1991), Almost Grown, CBS-TV, Wonder Years, ABC-TV (Humanitas prize for Square Dance episode, 1990), Cheers, NBC-TV, Northern Exposure, CBS-TV, Picket Fences, CBS-TV, Civil Wars, ABC-TV, Class of '96, Fox TV, Mad About You, NBC-TV; TV movies Maybe, Baby, and Fine Things, NBC, 1990; TV pilots The Flamingo Kid, 50 Minute Man. Recipient Tony award nomination 1974, 83, Golden Knight award Malta Film Festival, 1973, Cine Golden Eagle award, 1973, 6 Dramalogue awards, 1981-86. Fellow Am. Film Inst. *

MOORE, VERNON LEE, agricultural consultant, retired food products company executive; b. Creston, Iowa, Mar. 29, 1928; s. Newton and Eulalia Pearl (Lewis) M.; m. Lorene Shirley Moore, Jan. 29, 1949; children: Dianne, Nancy, Jack. BS in Agr., Iowa State U., 1951. Instr. vocat. agrl. Gowrie (Iowa) Sch. Dist., 1951-55; with Land O'Lakes, Inc., Mpls., 1955-88, sr. v.p., 1988, ret., 1988; pvt. practice agrl. cons., 1989—. Bd. dirs. exec. com. Agrl. Coop. Devel. Internat., Washington, 1972-89, Am. Inst. Coop., Washington, 1975-88, Minn. 4-H Found., Washington, 1980-91; bd. dirs. Vols. in Overseas Coop. Devel., Washington, 1980-88, The Coop. Found., St. Paul, 1978-88; commr. Civil Svc. Commn., Columbia Hts., Minn., 1974—; mem. U. Minn. Adv. Com., St. Paul, 1984-91; various leadership positions Fridley United Meth. Ch., Minn., 1971—; Minn. dir. Chs. United in Global Mission Russian Farms Projects, 1992—. Recipient Internat. Coop. award Coop. Coordinating Group, 1987. Lodges: Rotary, Masons, Shriners. Avocations: photography, woodworking, gardening.

MOORE, WALTER BRUCE, career officer; b. Big Spring, Tex., Mar. 4, 1940; s. Walter C. and Mildred A. (Foytik) M.; m. Janice Louise Wolff, June 19, 1982 (div. June 1991); children: Robert, Leslie, Kelly, Richard. BS in Animal Husbandry, Tex. A&M U., 1962; MPA, Auburn U., 1974. Commd. 2d lt. U.S. Army, 1962, advanced through grades to maj. gen., 1991; student U.S. Army Inf. Sch., Ft. Benning, Ga., 1962; asst. S-3 Student Brigade, Ft. Benning, Ga., 1962; platoon leader Co. C, 1st Bn., 46th Inf. 1st Armored Div., Ft. Hood, Tex., 1962-63; student U.S. Army Primary Helicopter Sch. Ft. Wolters, Tex., 1963; rotary wing aviator 25th Aviation Bn, 25th Inf. Div., Hawaii, 1963-65; aviator 173d Aviation Co., Hawaii, 1965-66, Vietnam, 1966; asst. S-4 11th Combat Aviation Bn., Vietnam, 1966-67; student U.S. Army Aviation Sch., Ft. Stewart, Ga., 1967; gunnery instr., aviation. pilot, flight commdr. U.S. Army Aviation Sch., Ft. Rucker, Ala., 1967-69; student U.S. Army Inf. Sch., Ft. Benning, 1969-70; flight standardization office 1st Aviation Brigade, Vietnam, 1970, comdr. 162d Aviation Co., 1970-71; pers. mgmt. officer Office Pers. Ops., Washington, 1971-73; stidemt U.S. Army Inf. Sch., Ft. Benning, 1973, Air Command and Staff Coll., Maxwell AFB, Ala., 1973-74; exec. officer, sec. gen. staff 9th Inf. Div., Ft. Lewis, Wash., 1974-77, cmdr. 2d Bn, 2d Inf., 1977-79, chief Bn. Tng. Mgmt. System, 1979; student U.S. Army War Coll., Carlisle Barracks, Pa., 1979-80; asst. chief of staff G-3, Berlin Brigade U.S. Command, Berlin, 1980-82; comdr. 3d Brigade 101st Airborne Div., Ft. Campbell, Ky., 1982-84, chief of staff, 1985-86; asst. div. comdr 3d Inf. Div. (Mech.) U.S. Army Europe, 1986-88; chief of staff XVIII Airborne Corps and Ft. Bragg, Ft. Bragg, N.C., 1988-89; asst. chief staff UN Command/Combined Forces Command, Korea, 1989-91. Decorated Legion of Merit with two oak leaf clusters, Def. Supr. Svc. medal, D.F.C. with oak leaf cluster, Bronze Star with oak leaf cluster, Meritorious Svc. medal with two oak leaf clusters, Air Medal with 35 oak leaf clusters, Army Commendation medal with V device and two oak leaf clusters, Expert Infantryman badge, Master Army Aviator badge, Sr. Parachutist badge, Air Assault badge, Ranger tab. Home: 23030 Whisper Cyn San Antonio TX 78258-3210 Office: Department of the Army Chief of Public Affairs Office Washington DC 20310

MOORE, WALTER PARKER, JR., civil engineering company executive; b. Houston, May 6, 1937; s. Walter Parker Sr. and Zoe Alma (McBride) M.; m. Mary Ann Dillingham, Aug. 19, 1992; children: Walter P. III, Melissa Moore Magee, Matthew Dillingham. BA in Civil Engring., Rice U., 1959, BS in Civil Engring., 1960; MS in Civil Engring., U. Ill., 1962, PhD in Civil Engring., 1964. Registered profl. engr., Ark., Ariz., Colo., Fla., Ga., Idaho, Ill., Ind., Kans., Maine, Md., Mich., Minn., Mo., Nev., N.H., N.Mex., N.Y., N.C., Okla., Oreg., Pa., R.I., Tex., Utah, Wash., Wis., Wyo. Rsch. asst. U. Ill., Urbana, 1960-64; design engr. Walter P. Moore & Assocs., Inc., Houston, 1966-70, sec., 1970-75, exec. v.p. 1975-83, pres., chmn., 1983—, chmn., 1993—; engring. adv. coun. Rice U., 1970-74, adj. prof. architecture, 1975-82, archtl. adv. com., 1988—; pres. Rice U. Alumni Assn., 1975; civil engring. vis. com. U. Tex. Austin, 1975-77; adv. com. effects of earthquake motions on reinforced concrete bldgs. U. Ill. Adv. Com., 1980; pres. Rice U. Engring. Alumni Assn., 1983; vis. lectr. Cornell U., 1986; mem. sesquicentennial com. State of Tex. Bus. and Fin. Com., 1986; vis. lectr. U. Ill., 1988, 89; engring. adv. coun. Tex. A&M U., 1990—; Thomas A. Bullock Endowed Chair Leadership and Innovation Coll. Arch., Dept. Civil Engring. Texas A&M U., 1994—; dir. Ctr. Bldg. Design and Constrn., dir. Ctr. Constrn. Edn. Group editor (monograph) Tall Building Systems and Concepts; mem. editorial adv. bd. Constrn. Bus. Rev., 1992—. Bd. dirs. Kiwanis Club Houston, 1974-76, Rice Design Alliance, 1976-79, Rice Ctr. for Community Design and Rsch., 1977-82, Harris County Heritage Soc., 1984-86, River Oaks Bank, 1983-91, Compass Bank, 1991-92; bd. dirs., v.p. The Forest Club, 1976-78; chmn. architects and engrs. United Way, 1985; mem. exec. com. River Oaks Bank, 1984-91. Capt. U.S. Army, 1964-66. Recipient Disting. Alumnus award Rice U., 1995. Fellow Am. Concrete Inst., mem. AIA (hon. Houston chpt.), NAE, NSPE, ASCE (activities chmn. 1968-69, sec. structures group Tex. sect. 1976-77, vice-chmn. 1977-78, structural standards divsn., exec. com. 1989—, chmn. A7 com. 1988—), keynote speaker nat. conv. New Orleans 1986), Am. Cons. Engrs. Coun. (bd. dirs. CEC-T 1981-83, v.p. 1990-92), Internat. Assn. Bridge and Structural Engrs., Am. Concrete Inst. (mem. com. # 318, bd. direction 1989-91, Alfred E. Lindau award 1992), Soc. Am. Mil. Engrs., Coun. on Tall Bldgs. and Urban Habitat (mem. steering group 1971—, editor Com. 3 1975—, chmn. final plenary session Hong Kong Fourth World Congress, 1990, Hong Kong Forth World Congress, 1990, internat. and regional conference 1990—), Consulting Engrs. Coun. Tex. (bd. dirs. 1974-76, v.p. 1976-77, pres. 1977-78), Tex. Soc. Profl. Engrs. (Young Engr. of Yr. 1969-70, region IV Engr. of Yr., 1985), Post Tensioning Inst. (juror nat. awards 1983—), Structural Engrs. Assn. Tex. Episcopalian. Office: 2d Fl 3131 Eastside Houston TX 77098 also: Tex A&M U Dept Civil Engring CE/TTI Bldg Rm 710F College Station TX 77843-3136

MOORE, WARD WILFRED, medical educator; b. Cowden, Ill., Feb. 12, 1924; s. Cecil Leverett and Velma Leona (Frye) M.; m. Frances Laura Campbell, Jan. 29, 1947; children—Scott Thomas, Ann Gail, Brian Dean, Kevin Lee. A.B., U. Ill., 1948, M.S., 1951, Ph.D., 1952. Instr., rsch. assoc. U. Ill., 1952-54; asst. prof. Okla. State U., Stillwater, 1954-55, Ind. U., Bloomington, 1955-59; assoc. prof. Ind. U., 1959-66, prof. physiology, 1966-89, prof. physiology and biophysics emeritus, 1989—, acting chmn. dept. anatomy, 1971-73, assoc. dean basic med. scis., 1971-89, assoc. dean, dir. med. scis. program, 1976-89; vis. prof. postgrad. Med. Center, Karachi, Pakistan, 1963-64; staff mem. Rockefeller Found., 1968-71; vis. prof., chmn. dept. physiology, faculty sci. Mahidol U., Bangkok, Thailand, 1968-71. Served with U.S. Army, 1943-46. Mem. Am. Physiol. Soc., Endocrine Soc., Am. Soc. Nephrology, Soc. Study Reproduction, Am. Assn. Anatomists, Soc. Exptl. Biology and Medicine, Am. Assn. Med. Colls., AAAS, Am. Inst. Biol. Scis., AAUP, Ind. Acad. Sci., Ind. Hist. Soc., Sigma Xi, Phi Sigma. Home: 3421 E Latimer Rd Bloomington IN 47401-4219 Office: Ind U Myers Hall # 203 Bloomington IN 47405

MOORE, WAYNE V., pediatrician, educator, endocrinologist; b. Wichita, Kans., May 3, 1942. BA, Friends U., 1964; PhD, U. Minn., 1969, MD, 1970. Diplomate Am. Bd. Pediatrics, Am. Bd. Pediatric Endocrine; lic. physician, Kans., Minn. Fellow in biochemistry U. Minn., Mpls., 1969-70, intern in pediatrics, 1970-71, resident in pediatrics, 1971-72; clin. assoc. NIH, Bethesda, Md., 1972-74; asst. prof. pediatrics U. Kans. Med. Ctr., Kansas City, 1974-78, assoc. prof., 1978-82, prof., 1982—; head. sect. pediatric endocrinology and metabolism U. Kans. Med. Ctr., 1974—, attending physician pediatric inpatient svc., 1976—, elected mem. grad. sch. faculty in biochemistry, 1977, departmental reviewer dept. diatetics and nutrition, 1974-75, acad. com. student promotions subcom., 1975—, physiology chmn.

search com., 1975-76, ad-hoc com. for devel. tenure guidelines, 1976-77, faculty coord. for pediatric grand rounds, 1975-81, pediatric rsch. com., 1976-79, adminstrn. PKU and congenital hypothyroid follow-up clinic, 1976—, ad-hoc com. for rev. Nat. Intensive Care Unit, 1976-77, ENT chmn. search com., 1978, chmn. CRC adv. com., 1978-79, utilization rev. com., 1979-80, promotion and tenure com. dept. pediatrics, 1979-82, acting chmn. pediatrics, 1981-83, instn. promotion and tenure com., 1984-86, dean search com., 1985, departmental awards com., 1986-87, dept. promotion and tenure com., 1987-88, chmn., 1988—, coll. promotion and tenure com., 1988-89, 89-91, telethon com., pediatric dept. rsch. com., 1988—; vis. prof. U. Okla-Tulsa, 1979, U. S.D., 1979, U. Minn., 1980, European Soc. for Pediatric Endocrinology, 1986; mem. Nat. Pituitary Agy., 1978-85, chmn. growth hormone subcom., 1984-89. Reviewer Jour. AMA, Endocrinology, Jour. Pediatrics, Diabetes, Jour. Clin. Endocrinology and Metabolism; contbr. over 150 articles and abstracts to profl. and sci. jours., chpt. to book. Am. Cancer Soc. scholar, 1970; grantee Nat. Pituitary Agy., 1975-85, State Dept. Child and Maternal Health, 1976—, NIH, 1980-85, 81-84, 87-90, Muscular Dystrophy Assn., 1980-82, Carey Endorsement, 1983—, Genetech, 1985—, Astrowe Found., 1986-87, 87-88, Juvenile Diabetes Found., 1986-88, Amoco Found., 1986—, Cosmopolitan Club, 1987—, Am. Heart Assn., 1987-89, 89-90, Ctr. for Disease Control., 1987-90, Mother Mary Ann Found., 1991—. Mem. Am. Acad. Pediatrics (v.p. Kans. chpt. 1988, pres. Kans. chpt. 1991), Am. Pediatric Soc., Am. Diabetes Assn. (grantee 1986-87), Endocrine Soc., Pediatric Endorcine Soc. (chmn. com. on future use of polypeptide hormones 1986-88), Human Growth Found., Soc. for Pediatric Rsch., Southwest Pediatric Soc., Kans. Med. Soc., Kans. Diabetes Assn., Greater Kansas City Diabetes Assn. (invited lectr. 1979—), Kansas City Endocrine Roundtable, Lawson Wilkins Pediatric Endocrine Soc., Sigma Xi, Alpha Omega Alpha. Achievements include research in mechanism of active growth hormones, early detection and treatment of chronic complications associated with diabetes, Islet transplantation, treatment of prediabetes with nicotinamide, role of intrathymic transplantation in development of tolerance, isolation and characterization of antigen presenting cells, early detection of vascular dysfunction in type 1 diabetes, treatment of short stature growth hormone, development of an implantable glucose sensor. Office: U Kansas Pediactric Endocrine Dept 3901 Rainbow Blvd Kansas City KS 66160-0001

MOORE, WILLIAM GOWER INNES, biochemist; b. Phillipsburg, N.J., Dec. 18, 1951; s. Ralph Gower Davies and Joan Elizabeth Innes (Read) M.; m. Nancy Leo Moore, June 8, 1985. BA, SUNY, Binghamton, 1973; PhD, Purdue U., 1981; MS in Pub. Health, U. Ala., Birmingham, 1988. Asst. prof. Keuka Coll., 1981-83; visiting asst. prof. Birmingham-Southern Coll., 1983-84; research fellow U. Ala., Birmingham, 1984-88, rsch. asst. prof., 1988-94; database mgr., 1994—. Recipient Regents Scholarship SUNY, 1969. Mem. Am. Chem. Soc., AAAS, N.Y. Acad. of Scis., Sigma Chi (assoc.). Democrat. Episcopalian. Avocation: music performance. Office: 1719 Clinic 908 S 20th St Birmingham AL 35294-2050

MOORE, WILLIAM GROVER, JR., consultant, former air freight executive, former air force officer; b. Waco, Tex., May 18; s. William Grover and Annie Elizabeth (Pickens) M.; student Kilgore (Tex.) Coll., 1937-39, Sacramento State Coll., 1951, George Washington U., 1962; grad. Air War Coll., Air U., 1957, Nat. War Coll., 1962; m. Marjorie Y. Gardella, Jan. 18, 1943; 1 dau., Allyson. Enlisted U.S. Army Air Force, 1940, commd. 2d lt., 1941, advanced through grades to gen., 1977; comdr. 777th Squadron, 15th AF, Italy, 1944-45, 3535th Maintenance and Supply Group, Mather AFB, Calif., 1951, 3d Bomb Group, Korea, 1952; chief bases and units div. Hdqrs. USAF, 1952-56; asst. dep. chief of staff ops. Hdqrs. USAF Europe, 1957-61; comdr. 314th Troop Carrier Wing, Sewart AFB, Tenn., 1962-63, 839th Air Div., 1963-65; asst. J3 U.S. Strike Command, 1965-66; comdr. 834th Air Div., Vietnam, 1966-67; dir. operational requirements Hdqrs. USAF, 1967-70; comdr. 22d AF, 1970-73, 13th AF, 1973; chief of staff Pacific Command, 1973-76; asst. vice chief of staff Hdqrs. USAF, 1976-77; comdr. in chief Mil. Air Lift Command, 1977-79; ret., 1979; pres., chief operating officer Emery Air Freight Corp., Wilton, Conn., 1981-83; bus. cons., 1983—. Decorated Def. D.S.M., Air Force D.S.M. with 2 oak leaf clusters, Legion of Merit with 4 oak leaf clusters, Silver Star, D.F.C. with oak leaf cluster, Air medal with 9 oak leaf clusters, AF Commendation medal with 10 oak leaf clusters (U.S.); Croix de Guerre with palm (France); Armed Forces Honor medal 1st class (Vietnam); Republic of China Cloud and Banner; Legion of Honor (Republic of Philippines); recipient L. Mendel Rivers award of excellence; Jimmy Doolittle fellow in aerospace edn., 1978; named to Minuteman Hall of Fame, 1979. Mem. Air Force Assn., Nat. Def. Transp. Assn., Am. Ordnance Assn. Home: 932 W Main St Franklin TN 37064-2730 Office: Nashville Internat Airport 1 Terminal Dr Ste 501 Nashville TN 37214-4110

MOORE, WILLIAM JASON, museum director; b. Asheboro, N.C., Aug. 4, 1938; s. Lonnie James and Pauline (Hamilton) M.; m. Jane Beane, Dec. 16, 1962; 1 son, William David. B.B.A., High Point Coll., 1960. Asst. to archeologist Town Creek Indian Mound, Mt. Gilead, N.C., 1959; dir. Greensboro Mus., N.C., 1963—; assessor Am. Assn. Mus., Washington, 1976—. Mem. N.C. Mus. Council (award 1976; pres. 1973-74), Am. Assn. Mus., Am. Assn. State and Local History. Episcopalian. Lodge: Rotary.

MOORE, WILLIAM JOHN MYLES, electrical engineer, researcher; b. Edinburgh, Scotland, May 3, 1924; arrived in Can., 1928; s. William Harold and Doris Kate (Paddon) M.; m. Ruth Elizabeth Duffy, Aug. 21, 1948; children: Roberta Louise, Marilyn Elizabeth. B in Applied Sci., U. B.C., Can., 1946; postgrad., NRC, Ottawa, Can., summer 1947; M in Engring., McGill U., 1948. Rsch. officer NRC Can., Ottawa, Ont., 1948-51, 55-88, sect. head power engring sect. elec. engring. div., 1988-90, ret., 1990; rsch. officer Can. Armament R&D Establishment, Valcartier, Que., 1951-52, head analysis sect., 1952-54, group leader analysis, control and simulation sects., 1954-55; cons. prof. Huazhong U. Sci. and Tech., Wuhan, Peoples Republic of China., 1988. Author: The Current Comparator, 1987; holder 10 patents. Fellow IEEE (chmn. Ottawa sect. 1966-67, chmn. Elec. and Electronic Measurement and Test Instrumentation Conf. and Instrumentation and Measurement Symposium 1969, pres. Group on Instrumentation and Measurement 1974, chmn. power systems instrumentation and measurement com. Power Engring. Soc. 1981-82, Morris E. Leeds award, 1987, Centennial medal 1984, A.G.L. McNaughton medal 1991), Assn. Prof. Engrs. Ont. Avocations: downhill skiing, personal computing. Home: 797 Dunloe Ave, Ottawa, ON Canada K1K 0K3

MOORE, WILLIAM LEROY, JR., career officer, physician; b. Savannah, Ga., June 1, 1934; s. William Leroy Sr. and Helen Louise (Robbins) M.; m. Anna Elizabeth Ballard, Mar. 15, 1958; children: William L., Christopher A., Mary Beth. Student, Ga. Inst. Tech., 1951-52; AB, Emory U., 1955; MD, Med. Coll. Ga., 1959; postgrad. mil. tng. courses, 1962-94. Diplomate Am. Bd. Internal Medicine, Am. Bd. Infectious Diseases. Commd. capt. U.S. Army, 1962, advanced through grades to maj. gen., 1991; intern Floyd Hosp., Rome, Ga., 1959-60; pvt. practice Rome, 1960-61; resident in internal medicine Brooke Gen. Hosp., Ft. Sam Houston, Tex., 1965-68; rsch. fellow in infectious diseases U. Tex. Southwestern Med. Sch., Dallas, 1968-70; resident in internal medicine Parkland Meml. Hosp., Dallas, 1968-70; gen. med. officer Martin Army Hosp., Ft. Benning, Ga., 1962, 5th Spl. Forces Group, Spl. Warfare Ctr., Ft. Bragg, N.C., 1962-63; gen. internist, group surgeon, commdg. officer 1st Spl. Forces Group, Spl. Action Force, Okinawa, Japan, 1965-63; asst. chief to chief infectious disease svc. Brooke Gen. Hosp.; Ft. Sam Houston, Tex., 1970-74; chief internal medicine svc., chief dept. medicine, chief profl. svcs. Eisenhower Army Med. Ctr., Ft. Gordon, Ga., 1978-83; comdr. Frankfurt (Germany) Army Regional Med. Ct., 97th Gen. Hosp., 1983-86; project mgr. Office of Surgeon Gen., Washington, 1986-88; adj. faculty Nat. Def. U., Ft. Lesley J. McNair, Washington, 1986-88; vice comdr. Joint Mil. Med. Command, Randolph AFB, Tex., 1988-91; comdr. Brooke Army Med. Ctr., Ft. Sam Houston, Tex., 1988-91, U.S. Army Med. Dept. Ctr. & Sch., Ft. Sam Houston, Tex., 1991-94; clin. assoc. in medicine U. Tex. Southwestern Med. Sch., 1969-70; clin. assoc. prof. medicine, U. Tex. Med. Sch., 1970-74; chief. sect. of infectious diseases, Med. Coll. Ga., 1974-75, assoc. prof., 1974-78, clin. prof., 1978-83; prin. investigator infectious disease rsch. VA Hosp., Augusta, Ga., 1974-78, asst. chief med. svc., 1974-75, dir. clin : microbiology lab., 1974-78, epidemiologist, 1974-78; head intenal medicine infectious disease 97th gen. Hosp., Frankfurt, 1983-86, Walter Reed Army Med. Ctr., 1986-88; clin. prof. medicine U. Tex. Health Sci. Ctr., San Antonio, 1989-94; mem. ref. panel on Am. Hosp. Formulary Svc. of Am. Soc. Hosp. Pharmacists, 1974-78; faculty

Advisor Lane-Walker AMSA Free Clinic, Augusta, 1975-78; mem. various coms. and bds., VA Hosp., Augusta, 1974-78. Contbr. articles to profl. jours. Mem. Army Comty. Coun. San Antonio, 1988-94; dir., bd. dirs. Army Med. Dept. Mus. Found. Inc. 1989-94; bd. dirs. San Antonio Area chpt. ARC, 1989. Decorated Army Commendation medal, Meritorious Svc. medal (3), Legion of Merit with three oak leaf clusters, Disting. Svc. medal Army Med. Dept. Regiment, 1994, Order of Mil. Med. Merit; recipient Scholastic Excellence award C.V. Mosby Co., 1959, Dirs. Commendation VA Hosp., Augusta, 1978, Surgeon Gen.'s A Profl. Designer fr Internal Med., 1982. Fellow ACP, Infectious Diseases Soc. Am.; mem. AMA, NAS (nat. rsch. coun. 1995-96), Assn. Mil. Surgeons U.S. (mem.-at-large exec. coun. Alamo chpt. 1989), Am. Soc. for Microbiology, Am. Soc. for Tropcial Medicine and Hygiene, Soc. Med. Cons. to Armed Forces (chmn. com. on cons. activities 1977-79), Am. Heart Assn. (bd. dirs. San Antonio divsn. 1988-89), San Antonio Rsch. Club (sec., pres. 1970-74), Alpha Omega Alpha.

MOORE, WILLIAM VINCENT, political science educator; b. Columbia, Mo., Apr. 13, 1944; s. Willis and Mabelle (Rogers) M.; m. Suzanne Shelton, July 14, 1967 (div. Feb. 1984); children: Mark, Laura. BA, So. Ill. U., 1966, MA, 1968; PhD, Tulane U., 1975. Instr. Fla. Meml. Coll., Miami, 1968-69, Xavier U., New Orleans, 1970-72; asst. prof. to assoc. prof. polit. sci. Coll. of Charleston, S.C., 1972-83, prof., 1983—, scholar-in-residence, 1976, dir. summer sessions, 1984-87, chmn. dept., 1987-93, dir., masters in pub. adminstrn. dept., 1993—; chmn. S.C. Interagy. Merit Coun., Columbia, 1987—. Author: Political Extremism in the U.S.A., 1983; co-author: Politics and Government in South Carolina, 1994; contbr. articles to profl. jours. Recipient Disting. Teaching award Coll. of Charleston, 1981; grantee U. N.C., 1980; rsch. fellow U. S.C., 1983. Mem. Am. Polit. Sci. Assn., So. Polit. Sci. Assn., S.C. Polit. Sci. Assn. (pres. 1983-84), Phi Kappa Phi (chpt. pres. 1982-84), Pi Sigma Alpha (chpt. pres. 1987-93). Avocations: tennis, racquetball. Home: 1555 N Pinebark Ln Charleston SC 29407-3513 Office: Coll of Charleston Polit Sci Dept Charleston SC 29424

MOORE, WILLSON CARR, JR., lawyer; b. Honolulu, Nov. 24, 1928; s. Willson Carr and Jenna Vee (McMillan) C.; m. Sally Churchill, Apr. 25, 1952; children: Willson C. III, Brian C., Sharon Moore Fink. BA, U. Calif., Berkeley, 1950; JD, U. Calif., San Francisco, 1953. Law elk. to Hon. Jon Wiig U.S. Dist. Ct., Honolulu, 1953-54; dep. atty. gen. State of Hawaii, 1955-59; pvt. practice Moore & Moore, Honolulu, 1959-64; with Rush, Moore, Craven, Sutton, Morry & Beh, Honolulu, 1965—; bd. dirs. Hawaii Def. Lawyers, 1990-94, Def. Rsch. Inst., 1989-93. Col. USAR, 1950-81. Fellow Am. Coll. Trial Lawyers; mem. ABA, Am. Bd. Trial Lawyers (adv.), Am. Judacature Soc., Assn. Def. Trial Attys. (pres. 1989-90, mem. exec. coun. 1983-91), Phi Alpha Delta. Office: Rush Moore Craven Sutton Morry & Beh 745 Fort Street Mall Ste 2000 Honolulu HI 96813-3820

MOOREFIELD, JAMES LEE, retired insurance executive, lawyer; b. Beckley, W.Va., June 12, 1922; s. Terrence Clyde and Judith (Shepherd) M.; m. Joyce Ward, Dec. 9, 1944; children: Nancy Jo, James Stewart, David Lee. BS, Concord Coll., Athens, W.Va., 1947; LLB, U. Va., 1953. Bar: Mass. 1954, U.S. Supreme Ct. 1964. Tchr. high sch., coach Raleigh County (W.Va.) Bd. Edn., 1947-48; with Paul Revere Life Ins. Co., Worcester, Mass., 1953-80; v.p., gen. counsel Paul Revere Life Ins. Co., 1968-76, sec., 1970-74, v.p., 1974-80; pres. Health Ins. Assn. Am., Washington, 1980-87; bd. dirs. Guaranty Bank & Trust Co., Conifer Group, Inc., Bank of New Eng., Worcester, John Alden Corp.; moderator Town of West Boylston, Mass., 1959-74, NHC; coordinator campaign of Elliot Richardson for lt. gov. and atty. gov., Mass., 1964—; mem. HHS Organ Transplant T.F., 1985-86, Pvt. Pub. Sector Adv. Com. on Catastrophic Ill., 1986; mem. Nat. ARC Adv. com. on AIDS, 1985-87; mem. Dunlop Group of Six, 1981-87. Contbr. legal, and ins. articles to profl. jours. Bd. dirs. Worcester chpt. ARC, chmn., 1974, 75; bd. dirs. treas Worcester Meml. Hosp.; bd. dirs. Worcester City Missionary Soc., 1967-72; corporator Holden Dist. Hosp., 1967-72. Served with AUS, 1943-46, 50-52. Mem. ABA, Ins. Econ. Soc. (exec. com 1968-80), Mass. Bar Assn., Worcester County Assns., Assn. Life Ins. Counsel. Republican. Congregationalist. Lodges: Masons, Rotary. Home: Apt 307 41 High Point Cir S Naples FL 33940

MOORE MOIF, FLORIAN HOWARD, electronics engineer; b. Shelby, Ohio, Aug. 23, 1929; s. Carl Leslie and Mona Pearl (Dearth) M.; m. Dorothy Elizabeth Morse, Dec. 19, 1950. AA, Harvard U., 1974. Cert. indsl. maint. electrician. With Diebold Inc., Boston, 1955-56; electronics R&D staff Radio Corp. Am., Burlington, Mass., 1956-59; electronics/mech. R&D staff MIT, Cambridge, 1974-79; electricity/electronics/electromech. R & D Charles Stark Draper Labs., Cambridge, 1974-76; tchr. indsl. electronics Ashland County Joint Vocat. Sch., Ashland, Ohio, 1974-78; buyer Autocall div. Fed. Signal Corp., Shelby, Ohio, 1978-79; journeyman electrician Excel Wire & Cable div. United Tech., Tiffin, Ohio, 1980-86; tchr. indsl. electricity Madison Comprehensive High Sch., Mansfield, Ohio, 1986-88; pres., CEO Florian H. Moore & Assocs., Shelby, Ohio, 1988—. Vol. Ohio Geneal. Libr., Mansfield. With USAF, 1948-52. Mem. Ohio Geneal Soc. (v.p. Richland-Shelby gen. chpt. 1993-95), 10th Foot Royal Lincolnshire Regtl. Assn. (life), DAV (life), Order Internat. Fellowship (charter, U.S. rep. 1995), Masons (32d degree), Kappa Delta Phi (life). Avocations: history, snow skiing, sky diving, computer programming. Home and Office: 6234 State Route 61 N Shelby OH 44875-9575

MOORER, MICHAEL, professional boxer; b. Detroit, Mich., 1968; m. Bobbie; s. Michael, Jr. Champion World Boxing Assn., light heavyweight title, Pittburgh, Pa., 1990, World Boxing Assn. and Internat. Boxing Federation, heavyweight title, Las Vegas, Nev., 1994. Office: Internat Boxing Fedn 134 Evergreen Pl 9th Fl East Orange NJ 07018*

MOORER, THOMAS HINMAN, retired naval officer; b. Mt. Willing, Ala., Feb. 9, 1912; s. Richard Randolph and Hulda (Hill) M.; m. Carrie Ellen Foy, Nov. 28, 1935; children: Thomas Randolph, Mary Ellen, Richard Foy, Robert Hill. B.S., U.S. Naval Acad., 1933; grad., Naval War Coll., 1953; LL.D. (hon.), Sanford U., Auburn U., Troy U., The Citadel. Commd. ensign U.S. Navy, 1933, advanced through grades to adm., 1957; held several fleet commands at sea; chief naval ops., 1967-70, chmn. joint chiefs of staff, 1970-74, ret., 1974; dir. Blount Inc., Montgomery, Ala., 1974—; dir. U.S. Life Ins. Corp., Arlington, Va., CACI, Arlington; adviser Center Strategic and Internat. Studies, The Citadel. Co-author: U.S. Overseas Bases: Problems of Projecting American Military Power Abroad, 1977, Sea Power and Strategy in the Indian Ocean, 1981. Chmn. Naval Aviation Mus. Found., Inc. Decorated Def. Dept. D.S.M. with oak leaf cluster, Navy D.S.M. with 4 stars, Army D.S.M., Air Force D.S.M., Silver Star, Legion of Merit, D.F.C., Purple Heart, others; recipient Forrestal award, 1975; named to Nat. Aviation Hall of Fame, 1987, Naval Aviation Hall of Honor, 1988. Mem. U.S. Naval Acad. Alumni Assn., U.S. Naval Inst., Ret. Officers Assn., Assn. Naval Aviation (chmn. 1974—). Republican. Baptist. Clubs: Chevy Chase, Army-Navy, Internat. Brook. Home: 6901 Lupine Ln Mc Lean VA 22101-1518 Office: 1800 K St NW Washington DC 20006-2202

MOORHEAD, CARLOS J., congressman; b. Long Beach, Calif., May 6, 1922; s. Carlos Arthur and Florence (Gravers) M.; m. Valery Joan Tyler, July 19, 1969; children: Theresa, Catharine, Steven, Teri, Paul. BA, UCLA, 1943; JD, U. So. Calif., 1949. Bar: Calif. 1949, U.S. Supreme Ct. 1973. Pvt. practice law Glendale, Calif., 1949-72; dir. Lawyers Reference Service, Glendale, 1950-66; mem. 93d-104th Congresses from 22d (now 27th) Dist. Calif., 1973—; mem. judiciary com. Judiciary Com.; chmn. subcom. on cts. and intellectual property; vice chmn. Energy and Commerce Com. Energy and Commerce Com.; dean Calif. Congl. Rep. Delegation; apptd. to Fed. Cts. Study Com. Pres. Glendale Hi-Twelve Club; mem. Verdugo Hills council Boy Scouts Am.; mem. Calif. Assembly, 1967-72; mem. Calif. Law Revision Commn. 1971-72; pres. 43d Dist. Republican Assembly, Glendale Young Republicans; mem. Los Angeles County Rep. Central Com., Calif. Rep. Central Com.; pres. Glendale La Crescenta Camp Fire Girls, Inc. Served to lt. col. AUS, 1942-46. Recipient Man of Yr. award USO, 1979. Mem. Calif. Bar Assn. L.A. County Bar Assn., Glendale Bar Assn. (past pres.), Glendale C. of C., Masons, Shriners, Lions, Moose, VFW. Presbyterian. Office: US House of Representatives 2346 Rayburn House Office Bldg Washington DC 20515

MOORHEAD, GERALD LEE, architect; b. Davenport, Iowa, Feb. 18, 1947; s. Wayne Lee and Marilou (George) M. BA, Rice U., 1969, BArch, 1971. Architect Middleton & Statton, El Paso, Tex., 1967, MA Floyd Assos., Houston, 1968, CRS Design Inc., Houston, 1969-70, Phillips & Peterson AIA, Houston, 1969-73; architect, v.p. Charles Tapley Assos., Houston, 1973-83; propr. Lloyd Jones Fillpot Assocs., 1986-87, Gerald Moorhead, Architect, 1983— Photography exhibited in group shows Galveston Arts Coun., Tex., 1976, Jewish Community Center, Houston, 1977, Cronin Gallery, Houston, 1977; one-man photog. exhbns. include Autry House Gallery, Houston, 1979; contbg. editor Tex. Architect; regional corr. Archtl. Record; contbr. articles on architecture to profl. publs. Treas. Houston Ctr. for Photography, 1985-87. Recipient Spl. award Houston AIA/Houston Home & Garden, 1979, Honor award Houston AIA, 1979, Young Architect award Houston AIA, 1985, Internat. prize Union Architects of Kazahkstan, 1991; named Architect Laureate of Kazahkstan, 1992. Fellow AIA; mem. Archtl. Historians, Nat. Trust for Hist. Preservation, Tex. Soc. Architects (1st Honor award 1976, Interiors award 1986), Rice Design Alliance. Home: 1842 Marshall St Houston TX 77098-2639

MOORHEAD, JOHN B., lawyer; b. Riverside, Calif., Sept. 22, 1945. BA cum laude, U. Pacific, 1967; JD, U. Calif., 1970. Bar: Colo. 1970. Ptnr. Baker & Hostetler, Denver. Editor Hastings Law Jour. 1969-70. Mem. ABA, Colo. Bar Assn., Denver Bar Assn., Order of Coif, Blue Key, Thurston Soc. Office: Baker & Hostetler Ste 1100 303 E 17th Ave Denver CO 80203-1264

MOORHEAD, PAUL SIDNEY, geneticist; b. El Dorado, Ark., Apr. 18, 1924; s. Earle William and Ethel (Martin) M.; m. Betty Blanton Belk, June 8, 1949 (dec. 1989); children: Ann, Emily, Mary; m. Rebecca Otter, 1992. A.B., U. N.C., 1948, M.A. in Zoology, 1950; Ph.D., U. Tex., 1954. Research assoc. U. Tex. Med. Sch., Galveston, 1954-56, U. Pitts. Med. Sch., 1956-58; assoc. mem. Wistar Inst. Anatomy and Biology, Phila., 1959-69; assoc. prof. genetics and pediatrics U. Pa. Sch. Medicine, 1969-85, emeritus, 1985—; mem. rsch. staff Children's Hosp., Phila., 1974-85, mem. rsch. staff emeritus, 1985—. Contbr. numerous articles on genetics and cytology to sci. jours. Served to ensign USNR, 1942-46. Fellow AAAS; mem. Am. Soc. Human Genetics, AAUP, Environ. Mutagenesis Soc., Tissue Culture Assn. (pres. 1980-82), N.Y. Acad. Scis., Sigma Xi. Home and Office: PO Box 4 Claiborne MD 21624

MOORHEAD, SYLVESTER ANDREW, education educator retired; b. Denver, Feb. 23, 1920; s. Ray Rodney and Cora Margaret (Payne) M.; m. Katherine May Schlessman, July 21, 1945; children: Rodney A., Sylvia Kay, Kent A., Pamela Ann. B.A., U. No. Colo., 1942; Ph.D., Stanford U., 1950. Tchr. secondary sch. Redwood City, Calif., 1947-48, Sunnyvale, Calif., 1948-49; mem. faculty U. Miss., 1949—, prof. edn., 1955—, dean U. Sch. Edn., 1961-85, dean emeritus, 1985—. Contbr. articles profl. jours. Served with USAAF, 1942-45. Mem. NEA (life), Kappa Delta Pi, Phi Delta Kappa. Baptist. Lodge: Rotary. Home: 211 Vivian St Oxford MS 38655

MOORHEAD, THOMAS BURCH, lawyer, pharmaceutical company executive; b. Evanston, Ill., May 3, 1934; s. John William and Jane (Hendrich) M.; m. Christie Barnard, Dec. 31, 1966 (div. June 1992); children: Merrell Hendrich, Hannah Christie, Rachel McGill. BA, Yale U., 1956; postgrad., The Hague Acad. Internat. Law, 1958; JD, U. Pa., 1959; LLM, NYU, 1964. Bar: N.Y. 1960, Conn. 1971. Assoc. Milbank, Tweed, Hadley & McCloy, N.Y.C., 1959-63; assoc. counsel, asst. sec. Hooker Chem. Corp., N.Y.C., 1963-68, dir. indsl. rels., 1968-69, v.p. indsl. rels., 1969-72; v.p. employee rels. Champion Internat. Corp., N.Y.C., 1972-74; v.p. adminstrn. Beker Industries Corp., Greenwich, Conn., 1974-76; v.p. corp. affairs Estée Lauder, Inc., N.Y.C., 1976-84, sr. v.p., 1984-87; v.p. human resources Carter-Wallace, Inc., N.Y.C., 1987—; bd. dirs., vice chmn. Transaction Billing Resources, Inc., 1991—; elected mem. Corp. Culinary Inst. of Am., 1993—. Mem. New Canaan (Conn.) Rep. Town Com., 1980-85; elected mem. New Canaan Town Coun., 1985—, vice chmn., 1989—; bd. dirs. Employment Policy Found., 1993—, Les Amis d'Escoffion Soc., 1990—, Les Amis d'Escoffion Found., 1990—, Yale U. Alumni Fund, 1987-92, Nat. Choral Coun., 1988-93, United Way Tri-State, Inc., 1986-89, United Way New Canaan, 1983-89, pres., 1986-87; mem. Conn. Oversight Commn., Metro-North Commuter R.R., 1985-89; U.S. del. ILO, 1985, 93, 94, head U.S. employer del., 1994. Mem. ABA, Assn. of Bar of City of N.Y., Am. Soc. Internat. Law, Met. Club, New Canaan Country Club, Gridiron Club of New Canaan (pres. 1990—), Yale Club. Home: 148 Ramhorne Rd New Canaan CT 06840-3007 Office: 1345 Ave of the Americas New York NY 10105-0099

MOORHOUSE, LINDA VIRGINIA, symphony orchestra administrator; b. Lancaster, Pa., June 26, 1945; d. William James and Mary Virginia (Wild) M. BA, Pa. State U., 1967. Sec. San Antonio Symphony, Tex., 1970-71, adminstrv. asst., 1971-75, asst. mgr., 1975-76; exec. dir. Canton (Ohio) Symphony, 1977—. Mem. Ohio Arts Coun. Music Panel, 1980-82, 87-89, Mich. Arts Coun. Music Panel, 1986; bd. dirs. Stark County unit Arthritis Fedn., 1986-92, treas., 1989-91. Bd. dirs. Canton Palace Theatre Assn., treas. 1994—; active Cen. Stark County United Way Allocations Panel, 1991—. Mem. Met. Orch. Mgrs. Assn. (pres. 1983-85), Orgn. Ohio Orchs. (pres. 1985-86), Am. Symphony Orch. League (bd. dirs. 1983-85), Stark County Women's Hall of Fame (charter inductee), Soroptimist (Canton, Ohio, Women of Distinction 1992). Office: Canton Symphony Orch 1001 Market Ave N Canton OH 44702-1024

MOORMAN, JOHN A., librarian; b. Humboldt, Nebr., Sept. 15, 1947; m. Ileen Mary Geiger, Dec. 20, 1968; children: Johanna, Jessica, John A. AB, Guilford Coll., Greensboro, N.C., 1969; MSLS, U. N.C., 1972; postgrad., U. N.C., Greensboro, 1974-75, U. Ill., 1994—. Pub. svcs. and circulation libr. Guilford Coll., 1972-75; dir. Elbert Ivey Meml. Libr., Hickory, N.C., 1975-80, Brazoria County Libr. System, Angleton, Tex., 1980-86, Oak Lawn (Ill.) Pub. Libr., 1986-88; exec. dir. Cumberland Trail Libr. System, Flora, Ill., 1989-92; city libr. Decatur (Ill.) Pub. Libr. 1992—. Author: Managing Small Library Collections in Businesses and Community Organizations: Advice for Non-Librarians, 1989. Mem. Econ. Devel. Coord. Com.; mem. exec. com. bd. dirs. Downtown Decatur Coun.; grad. Decatur Leadership Inst. 1993. Mem. ALA, Ill. Libr. Assn. (chmn. pub. policy com. 1993), Nat. Soc. Fund Raising Execs., Decatur C. of C. (small bus. coun. seminar com.), Decatur Civil War Round Table, Decatur Rotary Club. Quaker. Avocations: travel, reading, woodworking, sports. Home: 315 Hackberry Pl Decatur IL 62521-5503 Office: Decatur Pub Libr 247 E North St Decatur IL 62523-1128

MOORSTEIN, MARK ALAN, lawyer; b. Ann Arbor, Mich., June 27, 1949; s. Benjamin and Barbara Sue Moorstein; m. Georgia Sue Boyle, Apr. 29, 1978; children: Timothy Brandon, Kathryn Elizabeth. AB cum laude, Princeton U., 1971; JD, Temple U., 1974. Bar: Ohio 1974, U.S. Dist. Ct. (no. dist.) Ohio 1975, Ohio 1975, U.S. Ct. Appeals (6th cir.) 1975, U.S. Supreme Ct. 1977, D.C. 1980, Va. 1981, U.S. Dist. Ct. (ea. dist.) Va. 1982, U.S. Ct. Appeals (D.C. cir.) 1982, U.S. Ct. Appeals (4th cir.) 1984, U.S. Tax Ct. 1984. Assoc. Roetzel & Andress, Akron, Ohio, 1974-76; atty. HUD, Cleve. and Washington, 1976-80; v.p. Walker & Dunlop, Washington, 1980-84; ptnr. Dixon & Smith, Fairfax, Va., 1984-86, Watt, Tieder, Killian & Hoffar, McLean, Va., 1986—; bd. dirs. Raven Corp., Washington. Mem. Editorial Columnist, Jour. Messenger; contbr. articles to profl. jours. Chmn. Coles Rep. Party, Prince William County, Va., 1985—; founder Mid-County Civic Assn., 1985; active Prince William Little Theatre, Manassas, Va. Recipient Silver Bird award No. Va. Soc. Newspaper Columnists, 1986. Mem. ABA, Va. State Bar Assn., Fed. Bar Assn., Fairfax Bar Assn., Aircraft Owners and Pilots Assn. (panelist 1984). Avocations: writing, musical compositions, flying, swimming, cycling. Office: Watt Tieder Killian & Hoffar 7929 W Peacock Dr Mc Lean VA 22102

MOOS, EUGENE, federal agency administrator. BS Argrl. Chemistry, Wash. State U. Adv. to House Majority leader Tom Foley; former Congl staff mem., dir. Wheat, Soybeans, Feed Grains subcom., House agrl. com., sr. staff profl. Ho. Reps.; pres. Gene Moos & Assocs. cons., Washington; under sec. agr. for farm and fgn. agrl. svcs. Dept. Agr., Washington, 1993; owner family farm, 1967—; adv. to U.S. Delegation Multilateral Trade Negotiations, Geneval 1st pres., founding mem. East West Trade Coun. Mem. Nat. Assn. Wheat Growers (internat. trade adv.), Nat. Assn. Wheat

Growers (pres.). Office: Dept Agr Farm and Fgn Agrl Svcs 14th & Independence Ave SW Washington DC 20250

MOOS, H. WARREN, physicist, astronomer, educator, administrator; b. N.Y.C., Mar. 26, 1936; s. Henry H. and Dorothy E. (Warren) M.; m. Doris Elaine McClure, July 13, 1957; children: Janet, Paul, Daniel, David. BS, Brown U., 1957; MA, U. Mich., 1959, PhD, 1962. Rsch. assoc. Stanford (Calif.) U., 1961-63; acting asst. prof. Johns Hopkins U., Balt., 1963-64, asst. prof., 1964-68, assoc. prof., 1968-71, prof., 1971—; dir. Ctr. for Astrophys. Scis., 1988-93, chmn. Physics & Astronomy, 1993—; cons. in field; mem. com. on planetary and lunar exploration NRC/Nat. Acad. Sci., Washington, 1982-86; mem. space and earth sci. adv. com. NASA, Washington, 1984-87; vis. fellow Joint Inst. for Lab. Astrophysics, 1972-73, 80-81. Editor: Optical Properties of Ions in Crystals, 1967; contbr. over 250 articles to profl. jours. Sloan Found. fellow, 1965-69. Fellow Am. Phys. Soc.; mem. Am. Astron. Soc., Internat. Astron. Union. Achievements include prin. investigatorof far ultraviolet spectroscopic explorer; co-investigator of Apollo 17 ultraviolet spectrometer, of Hopkins Ultraviolet Telescope, of Voyager ultraviolet spectrometer, of space telescope imaging spectograph; research on ultraviolet astronomy of fusion plasma diagnostics. Home: 804 Post Boy Ct Baltimore MD 21286 Office: Johns Hopkins U 34th & Charles Sts Baltimore MD 21218

MOOSE, CHARLES A., state official; b. Aug. 11, 1953. BA in U.S. History, U. N.C., 1975; MA in Pub. Adminstrn., Portland State U., 1984, PhD in Urban Studies and Criminology, 1993; grad., FBI Nat. Acad. Patrol officer Portland Police Dept., 1975-81, sergeant, 1981-84, lieutenant, 1984-91, capt. of No. Precinct, 1991-92, dep. chief of Ops. Branch, 1992-93, chief of police, 1993—. Bd. dirs. Boys and Girls Club of Portland, Comprehensive Options for Drug Abusers; mem. funding allocation com. Black United Fund Oreg.; mem. Multnomah County Cmty. Action Commn., Police Exec. Rsch. Forum, Bd. Pub. Safety Standards and Tng., Gov.'s Drug and Violent Crime Policy Bd., Gov.'s Juvenile Justice Task Force; bd. dirs. Portland State U. Mem. Am. Soc. Criminology, Nat. Orgn. of Black Law Enforcement Execs., Soc. of Police Futurists Internat., Internat. Assn. Chiefs of Police. Address: Police Bureau 1111 SW 2nd Ave Portland OR 97204-3232

MOOSE, GEORGE E., government official; b. N.Y.C., June 23, 1944; s. Robert and Ellen Amanda Lane (Jones) M.; m. Judith Roberta Kaufmann, Jan. 3, 1981. BA, Grinnell Coll., 1966, LLD (hon.), 1990; postgrad., Syracuse U., 1967. Spl. asst. to under sec. for polit. affairs Dept. of State, Washington, 1977-78, dep. dir. for South Africa, 1978-79; internat. affairs fellow Coun. Fgn. Rels., N.Y.C., 1979-80; dep. polit. counselor U.S. Mission to UN Dept. of State, 1980-83; U.S. ambassador to Benin Dept. of State, Washington, 1983-86, U.S. ambassador to Senegal, 1988-91; U.S. alt. rep. UN Security Coun., 1991-92; dep. dir. mgmt. ops. Dept. of State, Washington, 1986-87, dir. mgmt. ops., 1987-88; diplomat in residence, Howard U., 1991-92; asst. sec. African Affairs Dept. of State, 1993—. Recipient Superior Honor award Dept. of State, Grenada, 1974, 79, Meritorious Honor award, Washington, 1975, Presdl. Performance award, 1989, 94. Mem. Am. Fgn. Service Assn. Office: Bureau African Affairs Dept Of State Washington DC 20520

MOOSE, RICHARD M., federal official; b. Little Rock, Feb. 27, 1932; m. Margaret Davis; 2 children. BA, Hendrix Coll.; MA, Columbia U. Joined Fgn. Svc., 1956; assigned Fgn. Svc., Mexico City, 1957-59, Yaounde, Cameroon, 1957-69; from exec. secretariat Dept. State to Congl. fellow Am. Polit. Sci. Assn., 1962-66; spl. asst. to Walt W. Rostow Nat. Security Coun., 1966-67; conducted study nat. security decision-making Ford Found., 1968-69; staff sec. Nat. Security Coun., 1969; sr. staff mem. Senate Com. on Fgn. Rels., 1969-74, staff dir. sub. com. on fgn. assistance, 1974-76; dep. under sec. mgmt. Dept. State, 1977, asst. sec. African Affairs, 1977-80; sr. advisor Lehman Bros., Kuhn Loeb, N.Y.C., 1981-83; London, 1983-85; mng. dir. Shearson Lehman, 1985-88; v.p. internat. and govt. affairs Am. Express Co., 1988-93; under sec. for mgmt. Dept. State, Washington, 1993—. Editor 2 books; contbr. articles to N.Y. Times. Mem. Coun. Fgn. Rels. With U.S. Army, 1954-56. Office: Under Secy Mgmt Dept State 2201 C St NW Washington DC 20520-7207

MOOSER, STEPHEN, author; b. Fresno, Calif., July 4, 1941; s. Joseph Nathan and Lillian Ruth (Davidson) M.; m. Etta Karlovec, Dec. 29, 1972 (div. Dec. 1994); children: Chelsea, Bryn. BA, UCLA, 1963, MA in Journalism, 1968. Reporter Dodge Svcs., L.A., 1964-66; freelance film maker Utah, 1966-68; author children's books SWRL, L.A., 1969-75; freelance author children's books L.A. and N.Y.C., 1975—. Author: New York Kids Book, 1979, 101 Black Cats, 1979, Elvis Is Back and He's in the Sixth Grade, 1994, many others. With U.S. Army, 1963-68. Mem. Soc. Childrens Book Writers and Illustrators (co-founder, pres. 1971—). Home and office: 8 Arata Dr Bar Harbor ME 04609

MOOSSA, A. R., surgery educator; b. Port Louis, Mauritius, Oct. 10, 1939; s. Yacoob and Maude (Rochecoute) M.; m. Denise Willoughby, Dec. 28, 1973; children: Pierre, Noel, Claude, Valentine. BS, U. Liverpool, Eng., 1962, MD (hon.), 1965; postgrad., Johns Hopkins U., 1972-73, U. Chgo., 1973-74. Intern Liverpool Royal Infirmary, 1965-66; resident United Liverpool Hosps. and Alder Hey Children's Hosp., 1966-72; from asst. prof. surgery to assoc. prof. U. Chgo., 1975-77, prof., dir. surg. rsch., chief gen. surgery svc., vice chmn. dept., 1977-83; chmn. dept. surgery U. Calif.-San Diego Med. Ctr., 1983—; Litchfield lectr. U., Oxford, Eng.; 1978; praelector in surgery U. Dundee, Scotland, 1979; Hampson Trust vis. prof. U. Liverpool, Eng., 1992, G.B. Ong. vis. prof. U. Hong Kong, 1993, Philip Sandblon vis. prof. U. Lund, Sweden. Editor: Tumors of the Pancreas, 1982, Essential Surgical Practice, 1989, 2d edit., 1989, Comprehensive Textbook of Oncology, 1985, 2d edit., 1991, Gastrointestinal Emergencies, 1985, Problems in General Surgery, 1989, Operative Colorectal Surgery, 1993. Fellow Royal Coll. Surgeons (Hunterian prof. 1977); mem. ACS, Am. Surg. Assn., Soc. Univ. Surgeons, Soc. Surg. Clin. Oncology. Office: U Calif San Diego Med Ctr 200 W Arbor Dr San Diego CA 92103-1910

MOOSSY, JOHN, neuropathologist, neurologist, consultant; b. Shreveport, La., Aug. 24, 1925; s. John Yazbeck and Rose (Ferris) M.; m. Yvonne Reese, Mar. 15, 1951; children: John Jefferson, Joan Marie. MD, Tulane U., 1950. Intern Charity Hosp. of New Orleans, 1950-51, neurology resident, 1951-53; neuropathology fellow Columbia U. Coll. of Physicians and Surgeons, N.Y.C., 1953-54; assoc., lectr. in neuropathology Tulane U. Sch. Medicine, New Orleans, 1954-57; asst. to prof. in pathology, neurology La. State U., New Orleans, 1957-65; prof. pathology, grad. faculty U. Pitts., 1965-67; prof. pathology neuropathology Bowman Gray Sch. of Medicine, Winston-Salem, N.C., 1967-72, prof. pathology and neurology, dir. div. neuropathology, 1972-93; dir. Cerebrovascular Disease Study, World Fedn. of Neurology, Antwerp, Belgium, 1960-61; cons. Armed Forces Inst. of Pathology, Washington, 1977—, mem. sci. adv. bd., Washington, 1984-86. Editor: Cerebral Vascular Disease Seventh Conference, 1970, Cerebrovascular Diseases 12th Research Conference, 1981; editor-in-chief Jour. Neuropathology and Exptl. Neurology, 1981-91; mem. editorial bd. Archives Neurology, 1982-92. Recipient Excellence in Teaching award U. Pitts. Sch. of Medicine, 1987-88; named Commencement Speaker U. Pitts. Sch. of Medicine, 1989. Mem. Am. Acad. Neurology (sec.-treas. 1963-655), Am. Neurol. Assn. (v.p. 1977-78), Am. Assn. Neuropathologists (pres. 1974-75, Neuropathology award 1992), Internat. Soc. Neuropathology, Coun. Biology Editors.

MOOTE, A. LLOYD, history educator; b. Hamilton, Ont., Can., Mar. 22, 1931; s. Stanley Alanson and Esther Grace (Wood) M.; m. Barbara Brown, Dec. 27, 1956 (div. 1982); children: Karen, Peter, Daphne, Robert; m. Dorothy Carter May, May 30, 1986. B.A., U. Toronto, 1954; M.A., U. Minn., Mpls., 1956, Ph.D., 1958. Teaching asst. U. Minn., Mpls., 1955-58; lectr. U. Toronto, 1958-61; asst. prof. U. Cin., 1961-62, U. So. Calif., L.A., 1962-65; assoc. prof. U. So. Calif., Los Angeles, 1965-71, prof. dept. history, 1971-92; prof emeritus U. So. Calif., 1993—; vis. prof. Queen's U., Kingston, Ont., 1955-66; chmn. gen. edn. program U. So. Calif., 1978-81; mem. Inst. Advanced Study, Princeton, 1988-89; affiliated prof. Rutgers U., 1994—. Author: The Seventeenth Century, 1970, The Revolt of the Judges, 1971, The World of Europe: The Seventeenth Century, 1973, 2d edit., 1979, Louis XIII: The Just, 1989, paperback edit., 1991; mem. editorial bd. French Hist. Studies, 1971-74; internat. adv. bd. European History Quar., 1983—. Recipient William Koren prize Soc. French Hist. Studies, 1962, Creative

Scholarship award U. So. Calif. Assocs., 1973, Faculty Book award Phi Kappa Phi U. So. Calif., 1990; Younger scholar NEH, 1969; grantee Am. Philol. Soc., 1962, Haynes Found., 1973, Wellcome Inst. for History of Medicine, 1993-94; Guggenheim fellow, 1976; fellow U. Essex, Eng., 1993-94, Rutgers Ctr. for Hist. Analysis, 1995-96. Mem. Am. Hist. Assn., Past and Present Soc., Soc. French Hist. Studies (pres. 1984-85), Western Soc. for French History, Soc. for Study French History (U.K.), Sixteenth-Century Studies Conf. Home: 149 Meadowbrook Dr Princeton NJ 08540

MOOTY, JOHN WILLIAM, lawyer; b. Adrian, Minn., Nov. 27, 1922; s. John Wilson and Genevieve (Brown) M.; m. Virginia Nelson, June 6, 1952 (dec. 1964); children: David N., Bruce W., Charles W.; m. Jane Nelson, Jan. 15, 1972. B.S.L., U. Minn., 1943, LL.B., 1944. Bar: Minn. 1944. Ptnr. Gray, Plant, Mooty & Bennett, Mpls., 1945—; chmn. bd. Internat. Dairy Queen, Inc.; bd. dirs. Bur. of Engraving, Inc., Riverway Co. and subs., Rio Verde Svcs., Inc., Ariz., Turnquist, Inc. Author: (with others) Minnesota Practice Methods, 1956. Chmn. Gov.'s Task Force on Edn., 1981; pres. Citizens League Mpls.; 1970; acting chmn. Republican Party of Minn., 1958. Mem. ABA, Minn. Bar Assn., Hennepin County Bar Assn., U. Minn. Alumni Assn. (pres. 1982). Clubs: Interlachen (Mpls.), Lafayette (Mpls.), Minikahda (Mpls.), Mpls. (Mpls.). Home: 6601 Dovre Dr Minneapolis MN 55436-1711 Office: 3400 City Ctr 33 S 6th St Minneapolis MN 55402-3601

MORA, ABRAHAM MARTIN, lawyer; b. Trenton, N.J., Jan. 15, 1954; s. Morris and Greta (Winograd) M.; m. Pamela Barbara Fitch, July 6, 1990; 1 child, Pamela Fitch. BA, U. Pa., 1975; JD, Stanford U., 1978. Bar: Pa. 1978, Fla. 1982. Assoc. Blank, Rome, Comisky & McCauley, Phila., 1978-86; ptnr. Blank, Rome, Comisky & McCauley, West Palm Beach, Fla., 1986—. Author, co-author, lectr. in field. Mem. Phila. Bar Assn., Palm Beach County Bar Assn., Fla. Bar (real property, probate and trust law sect., probate litigation com.). Office: Blank Rome Comisky & McCauley 1401 Forum Way Ste 700 West Palm Beach FL 33401-2353

MORA, FEDERICO, neurosurgeon; b. Guatemala, Guatemala, Jan. 11, 1926; came to the U.S., 1945; s. Carlos Federico and Rosa (Castaneda) M.; m. Natalie Virginia Ramin, June 30, 1951; children: Federico, Clara Luz, Ana Maria, Claudia Inez, Juan Rafael. Student, Harvard Coll., 1945-46, MD, 1950. Diplomate Am. Bd. Neurol. Surgery. Pvt. practice neurol. surgery Guatemala and Albuquerque, 1958—; asst. prof. surgery and anatomy U. N.Mex. Sch. Medicine, Albuquerque, 1969-70. Capt. USAFR, 1954-56. Mem. Alpha Omega Alpha. Democrat. Avocations: scuba diving, nature studies. Home: 1809 Avenida Altures NE Albuquerque NM 87110 Office: Albuquerque Neurosurg Group Ste 301 715 Grand NE Albuquerque NM 87102

MORA, FRANCISCO, artist, printmaker; b. Uruapan, Mexico, May 7, 1922; s. Jose Maria and Clotilde (Perez) M.; m. Elizabeth Catlett, Oct. 31, 1946; children: Francisco, Juan, David. Student, Escuela de Pintura y Escultura La Esmeralda, 1941-46. Tchr. drawing Sch. Pub. Edn. Mexico, 1949-54; art adviser Mexican Acad. Edn., 1956—. Exhibited one-man shows Nitra, Prague, Czechoslovakia, 1971, Cite International de l'universite, Paris, 1972, Saxon Princes Palace, Dresden, 1973, Green Room Nat. Fine Arts Museum, Mexico, 1974-75, New Visions Gallery, San Diego, 1981, Atlanta, 1988, Salon de la Plastica, Mexico City, 1983, Tougaloo, Miss., 1986, U. Ariz. Mus., 1987, Kenkeleba Gallery, N.Y.C., 1988, In Faust Gallery, Hamburg, 1989, Miss. Mus. Art W. Catlett, 1990, Montgomery (Ala.) Mus. Art, 1991, Polk Mus. Art, Lakeland, Fla., 1991-92, Mus. African Am. Art, Detroit, 1992, Malcol Brown Gallery, Shaker Heights, Ohio, 1993, Isobel Neal Gallery, Chgo., 1994, Jame Lewis Mus., Balt., 1994-95, I-Space; illustrator books, pamphlets, mags. Mem. Salon de la Plastica Mexicana (founding mem.), Mexican Acad. Edn. (founding mem.). Home: Apartado Postal 694, 62000 Cuernavaca Morelos, Mexico

MORA, JAMES ERNEST, professional football coach, professional sports team executive; b. Glendale, Calif., May 24, 1935; s. Mario Joseph and Helen Laverne (Thompson) M.; m. Connie Beatrice Saunders, Dec. 18, 1959; children—James L., Michael J., Stephen P. B.S., Occidental Coll., 1957; M.A., U. So. Calif., 1967. Asst. coach U. Washington, Seattle, WA, 1975-78, Seattle Seahawks, Seattle, WA, 1978-82, New England Patriots, Foxboro, MA, 1982-83; head coach Philadelphia Stars (name changed to Baltimore Stars), Baltimore, MD, 1983-86, New Orleans Saints, New Orleans, LA, 1986—; head coach, v.p. New Orleans Saints, L.A., 1994—. Served to capt. USMCR, 1957-60. Mem. Am. Football Coaches Assn. Republican. Lutheran. Avocations: working out; golf; skiing; reading; biking. Office: care New Orleans Saints 6928 Saints Dr Metairie LA 70003-5151*

MORABITO, BRUNO PAUL, machinery manufacturing executive; b. Motticella, Italy, Feb. 10, 1922; s. Paul and Maria Antoinetta (Tedesco) M.; m. Therese Riccelli, June 29, 1946; 1 dau., Paula. B.C.E., Syracuse U., 1945. Application engr. Machinery and Systems div. Carrier Corp., Syracuse, N.Y., 1945-55; engring. mgr. Carrier Corp., 1955-66, mgr. centrifugal sales, 1966-69, mgr. machinery mktg., 1970-73, mgr. mktg., 1973-81; group v.p., gen. mgr. Environ. Systems Group Aeronca, Inc., Pineville, N.C., 1981-84; cons. Syracuse/Onondaga County Planning Agy., 1985—; pres. BPM Planning and Cons., 1988—. Chmn. sewage disposal dist. com. and street lighting dist. com. of Syracuse Gardens Tract, 1951-52. Recipient ASHRAE Wolverine Diamond Key award, 1961, Silver Knight of Mgmt. award Nat. Mgmt. Assn., 1978. Fellow ASHRAE (bd. dirs. 1970-78, v.p. 1974-76, pres. 1977-78); mem. Beaver Meadows Golf and Recreational Club (bd. dirs. 1973-80, 84-89). Roman Catholic. Home and Office: 302 Saltmakers Rd Liverpool NY 13088-6229

MORACZEWSKI, ROBERT LEO, publisher; b. Saint Paul, Nebr., May 13, 1942; s. Leo and Florence May (Wadas) M.; m. Virginia Kay Rohman, July 26, 1960; children—Mark, Matthew, Monika, Michael. BS in Agrl. Journalism, U. Nebr., 1964. Assoc. editor Farmer Mag. Webb Co., St. Paul, 1964-72; minor editor Farm Industry News Webb Co., St. Paul, 1972-74; editor Big Farmer Mag., Chgo., 1974-75; editorial dir. Webb Agrl. Services, St. Paul, 1976; editor The Farmer, The Dakota Farmer Webb Co., St. Paul, 1983-89; group pub. Webb Co., St. Paul, 1989-90; v.p., 1990—; exec. dir. Minn. Agri-Growth Coun. Contbr. articles to profl. jours. Recipient numerous media awards. Mem. Am. Agrl. Editors Assn., Nat. Agrl. Mktg. Assn., Investigative Reporters and Editors Assn. Roman Catholic. Home: 26589 Everton Cir N Wyoming MN 55092-9008 Office: Webb Div Intertec Pub 7900 Internat Dr Minneapolis MN 55425

MORAFF, HOWARD, science foundation program director; b. N.Y.C., Feb. 5, 1936; s. Frank and Sylvia Moraff; m. Connie J. McClure, Oct. 4, 1975; children: Kenneth, Judith, Steve. AB, Columbia U., 1956, BSEE, 1957, MSEE, 1958; PhD in Neurophysiology, Cornell U., 1967. Dir. vet. med. computing resources Cornell U., Ithaca, N.Y., 1967-82; dir. computing resources Merck Sharp & Dohme Rsch. Labs., Rahway, N.J., 1982-84; program dir. NSF, Washington, 1984—. Co-author: Electronics for Neurobiologists, 1973, Electronics for the Modern Scientist, 1982; contbr. articles to profl. jours. Capt. USAF, 1958-61. Mem. IEEE (sr.), IEEE Robotics and Automation Soc. (adminstrv. com. 1993-95), Am. Assn. Artificial Intelligence, N.Y. Acad. Scis., Sigma Xi, Tau Beta Pi, Eta Kappa Nu, Phi Kappa Phi. Achievements include patent for transistor circuit; research in on-line laboratory computing and end-user computing. Office: NSF 4201 Wilson Blvd Arlington VA 22230

MORAHAN, MATTHEW JOSEPH, investment banker; b. Newark, N.J., Sept. 30, 1949; s. Matthew Joseph and Monica (Maguire) M.; m. Elaine Barrington Roach. children: Erin, Megan, Matthew, Caitlin. BS, Villanova U., 1970. Vice president Hornblower Weeks, Hemphill Noyes, N.Y.C., 1971-76; mng. dir. Wertheim Schroder & Co., Inc., N.Y.C., 1976—. Mem. Corp. Bond Traders Club N.Y., Bond Club N.Y., Treasury Securities Luncheon Club, Villanova Fin. Alumni Club. Roman Catholic. Club: Canoe Brook Country (Summit, N.J.). Office: Wertheim Schroder & Co Inc 787 7th Ave New York NY 10019-6018

MORAHAN, PAGE S., microbiologist, educator; b. Newport News, Jan. 7, 1940; d. Robert Bruce and Margaret (Coleman) S. BA, Agnes Scott Coll., Decatur, Ga., 1961; MA, Hunter Coll., N.Y.C., 1964; PhD, Marquette U., Milw., 1969. Asst. prof. microbiology Med. Coll. of Va., Richmond, 1971-

74, assoc. prof., 1974-81, prof., 1981-82; prof. and chmn. dept. microbiology Med. Coll. Pa., Phila., 1982-93; assoc. dean faculty affairs, 1993—; adv. com. NCI Cancer Ctr. Rev. Com., Washington, 1986-90, mem. manpower rev. com., 1977-81; lectr. in field; conductor seminars in field. Editor Jour. of Reticuloendothelial Soc., 1982-88, Infection and Immunity, 1982-85; contbr. over 100 articles to profl. jours., chpts. to books. Sec., Spring Garden Historic Dist. Civic Assn., 1984-85, bd. dirs., 1985-86; mem.-at-large adminstrn. bd. First United Meth. Ch. of Germantown, 1990—. Recipient rsch. career devel. award NIH, 1974-79, Lindback award, 1988; grantee NIMH, 1989—, Nat. Inst. Arthritis and Infectious Disease, 1987—, Nat. Cancer Inst., 1989—; fellow Am. Coun. Edn., 1992-93; also others. Mem. AAAS, Am. Acad. Microbiology, Am. Assn. Immunologists, Am. Assn. for Cancer Rsch., Soc. for Exptl. Biology and Medicine, Soc. Virus Rsch., Reticuloendothelial Soc. (councilor 1981, chmn. membership com. 1984), Am. Soc. Microbiology (med. microbiology and immunology com. of pub. affairs bd. 1989-92), Assn. Med. Microbiology (pres. 1989, dir. 2d ednl. workshop 1988, adv. com. 3d, 4th, 5th ednl. workshops 1990, 92, 94), Phi Beta Kappa, Sigma Xi. Methodist. Office: Med Coll Pa Dept Microbiology 2900 W Queen Ln Philadelphia PA 19129-1033

MORAIN, WILLIAM DOUGLAS, surgeon, educator; b. Jefferson, Iowa, June 17, 1942; s. Frederick Elwyn and Lois (Garver) M.; m. Dagmar Ristic, Sept. 6, 1969; children: Anne, Peter William. AA, Graceland Coll., 1962; BA, Grinnell Coll., 1964; MD, Harvard, 1968. Diplomate Am. Bd. Plastic Surgery (bd. dirs. 1992—, sec.-treas. 1994—). Intern, resident in surgery Peter Bent Brigham and Children's Hosp., Boston, 1968-71; resident, chief resident in plastic surgery Stanford Med. Ctr., Calif., 1973-76; prof. surgery Dartmouth Med. Sch., Hanover, N.H., 1987—; staff surgeon Dartmouth-Hitchcock Med. Ctr., Hanover, 1976—; chief plastic surgery VA Hosp., White River Junction, Vt., 1976—; pres. Plastic Surgery Ednl. Found., 1991. Author: The Cutaneous Arteries of the Human Body (Webster Soc. prize 1982), 1983. Assoc. editor: Advances in Plastic Surgery, 1983—; editor-in-chief Annals of Plastic Surgery, 1992—; Medical Heritage, 1985—; Dartmouth Medical Alumni Bulletin, 1984-93. Assoc. producer EF Teleplast, 1984-87. Producer videoteleconf. series, 1985. Contbr. articles to profl. jours. Bd. dirs. Bel Canto Chamber Singers, Hanover, 1984. Served to maj. U.S. Army, 1971-73. Recipient Disting. Service award Plastic Surgery Ednl. Found., 1985. Fellow ACS (v.p. N.H. chpt. 1985-87, pres. 1987-89); mem. Am. Soc. Plastic and Reconstructive Surgeons (bd. dirs. 1984-91, Presdl. Appreciation award 1981), Am. Assn. Plastic Surgeons, Northeastern Soc. Plastic Surgeons (pres. 1992), Soc. Head and Neck Surgeons, New Eng. Surg. Soc. Mem. United Ch. of Christ. Avocations: singing; antiquarian book collecting. Home: 6 Wheelock Wood Hanover NH 03755 Office: Dartmouth-Hitchcock Med Ctr One Medical Center Dr Lebanon NH 03756

MORAKINYO, AKINBOLA OLUWOLE, mechanical, energy engineer; b. Ibadan, Oyo, Nigeria, Aug. 9, 1944; s. Samuel Akinkunmi and Emily Ibirinade (Adeniyi) M.; m. Olayinka Anike Fagbemi, July 25, 1970; children: Omolayo, Olufunmilola, Abosede, Olubolanle. BME, CUNY, 1975; MSME, Poly. U. Bklyn., 1976; PHD in Mech. and Energy Engnring., Pacific Western U., 1992. Reg. profl. engr. Machine design engr. Hamburg Machine Co., Bklyn., 1975-77; rsch. test engr. Purolator Filters Co., Rahway, N.J., 1976-77; pvt. practice mech. engr., 1976-80; dir. physical plants U. Ife, Nigeria, 1983-90; mech./energy engr. U. Mich., Ann Arbor, 1990—; energy cons. Bolmor Assocs., Inc., Ann Arbor, 1991—; adj. prof. Dept Mech. Engring. U. Ife, Nigeria 1977-90. Author tech. papers in field. Mem. ASME, Am. Soc. Automotive Engrs., Nigerian Soc. Engrs., Am. Assn. Energy Engrs. (sr., cert. energy mgr.), Nigerian Indust. Com. Achievements include development of models for evaluating energy conservation. Home: 2722 Golfside Dr Apt 916 Ann Arbor MI 48108-1462

MORALES, DAN, state attorney general. Grad. with honors, Trinity U., 1978; JD, Harvard U., 1981. Asst. dist. atty. Bexar County, 1983-85; former mem. Ho. of Reps. Tex.; atty. gen. State of Tex., Austin, 1991—. Bd. dirs. NCCJ, World Affairs Coun.; trustee So. Meth. U., Schreiner Coll., Kerrville; elder First Presbyn. Ch. Named one of Seven Best Legislators Dallas Morning News, Politician of Yr. San Antonio Express News; recipient Outstanding Svc. award Ind. Colls. and Univs., Outstanding Leadership award Texan's War on Drugs,. Mem. Tex. Lyceum Assn. Office: Office of Atty Gen PO Box 12548 Austin TX 78711-2548

MORALES, DIANE K., government official; b. Houston, July 11, 1946; d. Arthur Clement and Helen Mary (Araiza) M. B.A., U. Tex.-Austin, 1968. Account exec. Goodwin, Dannenbaum, Littman & Wingfield, Houston, 1968-70; pub. relations rep. Gittings, Inc., Dallas, 1970-71; asst. buyer, mgr. Neiman-Marcus, Dallas, 1971-80; sr. assoc., mktg. mgr. 3/D Internat., Houston, 1980-81; dep. asst. sec. policy U.S. Dept. Interior, Washington, 1981-83; bd. dirs. CAB, Washington, 1983-86; v.p. Earth Tech. Corp., Washington, 1986-88; pvt. practice cons. Washington, 1988-90; dep. asst. sec. def. for logistics Dep. Def., Washington, 1990—; mem. Def. Depot Maintenance Coun.; chmn. Def. Material Mgmt. Bd, Def Transp. Polic Coun., Def. Energy Policy Coun. Pres. Downtown Rep. Women's Club, Dallas, 1979-80, bd. dirs. Dallas County Men's Rep. Club, 1980, Dallas County Women's Rep. Club, 1980; mem. Rep. Women's Fed. Forum, Rep. Nat. Hispanic Assembly. Presbyterian.

MORALES, PABLO, Olympic athlete, swimmer. Olympic swimmer Barcelona, Spain, 1992. Recipient 100m Butterfly Gold medal Olympics, Barcelona, 1992. World record holder for 100 meter butterfly 52.84 seconds, set June 23, 1986, Orlando, Fla. Office: US Olympic Com 1750 E Boulder St Colorado Springs CO 80909-5746*

MORAN, BARBARA BURNS, librarian, educator; b. Columbus, Miss., July 8, 1944; d. Robert Theron and Joan (Brown) Burns; m. Joseph J. Moran, Sept. 4, 1965; children: Joseph Michael, Brian Matthew. AB, Mount Holyoke Coll., S. Hadley, Mass., 1966; M.Librarianship, Emory U., Atlanta, 1973; PhD, SUNY, Buffalo, 1982. Head libr. The Park Sch. of Buffalo, Snyder, N.Y., 1974-78; prof. Sch. Info. and Libr. Sci. U. N.C., Chapel Hill, 1981—, asst. dean, 1987-90; dean Sch. Info. and Libr. Sci., U. N.C., Chapel Hill, 1990—; participant various seminars; evaluator various edn. progs.; cons. in field. Author: Academic Libraries, 1984; co-author: (with Robert D. Stueart) Library Management, 4th edit., 1993; contbr. articles to profl. jours., chpts. to books; editl. bd. Jour. Acad. Librarianship, 1992-94. Coun. Libr. Resources grantee, 1985, Univ. Rsch. Coun. grantee, 1983, 89, others. Mem. ALA, Assn. for Libr. and Info. Sci. Edn., Popular Culture Assn., N.C. Libr. Assn., Beta Phi Mu. Home: 1307 Leclair St Chapel Hill NC 27514-3034 Office: Univ NC Sch Info & Libr Sci Chapel Hill NC 27599-3360

MORAN, CHARLES A., securities executive; b. Chgo., Feb. 7, 1943; s. Charles W. and Rose B. (Sutcher) M.; m. Donna L. Orbach, Sept. 3, 1967; children: Scott Alan, Erin Lizabeth. AB, Princeton U., 1964; JD, U. Mich., 1967; postgrad. advanced mgmt., Harvard U., 1982. CFP. With Chase Manhattan Bank, N.Y.C., 1967-70; pension trust officer, adminstrv. officer, officer in charge new bus. devel., pension div. Mfrs. Hanover Trust Co. N.Y.C., 1970-87, sr. v.p., officer-in-charge employee benefit trust div., 1979-80; chmn. bd., pres. MH/Edie Investment Counsel (formerly Lionel D. Edie & Co.), N.Y.C., 1980-82, officer-in-charge corp. trust div., 1982-83, officer in charge-global securities group, 1983-87; pres. Govt. Securities Clearing Corp., N.Y.C., 1987—; bd. dirs. Mfrs. Hanover Trust Co. Calif., Mfrs. Hanover Data Svcs. Corp., Mortgage Backed Securities Clearance Corp., Nat. Securities Clearance Corp.; chmn. bd. dirs. Inform, Inc.; former lectr. bus. and econs. Bloomfield Coll.; former lectr. sociology and fin. employee benefits C.W. Post Coll., L.I. U.; cons. Urban Vol. Cons. Group, Inc.; mem. adv. coun. Dept. Labor; mem. adv. bd. BNA Pension Reporter; mem. Employees Retirement Income Security Act of 1974 Roundtable; mem. industry adv. com. Future Electronic Funds Payments svcs. Fed. Res. Contbr. articles to profl. jours. Mem. AAUP, Am. Inst. Banking, Am. Pension Conf. (treas. 1976-79), N.Y. State Bankers Assn. (employees trust com.), Assn. Pvt. Pension and Welfare Plans (dir., mem. exec. com.), ERISA Industry Com. (pres., dir. mem. exec. com., treas.), Am. Bankers Assn. (chmn. employee benefit trust com. 1977-82), Internat. Found. Pension and Welfare Plans, Bank Adminstrn. Inst. (mem. tech. commn.), N.Y. C. of C. (task force on pub. pensions), Princeton Club. Office: Govt Securities Clearing Corp 55 Water St Fl 22D New York NY 10041-0001

MORAN, DANIEL AUSTIN, mathematician; b. Chgo., Feb. 17, 1936; s. Austin Thomas and Violet Lillian (Johnson) M.; m. Karen Krull, Sept. 14, 1963; children: Alexander, Claudia. B.S. summa cum laude, St. Mary's of Tex., 1957; M.S., U. Ill., 1958, Ph.D., 1962. Research instr. U. Chgo., 1962-64; asst. prof. Mich. State U., 1964-68, assoc. prof., 1968-76, prof. math., 1976—; vis. scholar U. Cambridge, 1970-71, U. North Wales, 1978. Contbr. articles to profl. jours. Mem. Math. Assn. Am., Sigma Xi, Pi Mu Epsilon, Delta Epsilon Sigma, Kappa Mu Alpha. Roman Catholic. Home: 2633 Roseland Ave East Lansing MI 48823-3870 Office: Dept Math Michigan State Univ East Lansing MI 48824

MORAN, DORIS ANN, educational consultant, mathematics educator; b. English, W.Va., Oct. 19, 1944; d. William and Margaret (Pruitt) Vinson; m. John L. Moran, Mar. 17, 1973; children: Geoffrey Patrick, Lauren Kathleen, Randy Allen. BS in Edn., Southwestern U., Georgetown, Tex., 1986. Cert. Elem. Edn., Math. Social worker W.Va. Dept. Welfare, Beckley, 1963-68; dir. pub. rels. Meml. Med. Ctr., Corpus Christi, Tex., 1969-75; exec. dir. Kidney Found. Tex. Coastal Bend, Corpus Christi, Tex., 1975-76; tchr. math. Killeen (Tex.) Ind. Sch. Dist., 1986-94; ednl. cons. Creative Edn. Inst., Waco, Tex., 1994—; curriculum writer, 1989— Killeen Ind. Sch. Dist., mem. dist. testbook adoption task force, 1990-91, pre-algebra math module trainer, 1991—, mentor, 1991-94, dept. chmn., 1991-94; sponsor Yearbook Smith MS, Fort Hood, Tex., 1987-93; trainer Reaching the Hard to Teach, 1993—. Bd. mem., chmn. pub. rels. United Way Coastal Bend, Corpus Christi, Tex., 1976, Mental Health Assn., Corpus Christi, Tex., 1972-75; pub. rels. chmn. City of Corpus Christi Ambulance Steering Com., 1972; conf. chmn. Tex. Hosp. Pub. Rels. Assn., Corpus Christi, Tex., 1972. Named fellow Tex. Alternative Blueprint for Curriculum Devel., 1992; recipient Outstanding Tchr. award Killeen (Tex.) Jr. League, 1994. Mem. ASCD, Tex. ASCD, Tex. Computer Educators Assn., Nat. Coun. Tchrs. Math., Grace Episcopal Ch., Tex. Coun. Tchrs. Math. Episcopalian. Avocations: sewing, gardening, reading, computers, travel. Home: 116 Oaktree Dr Rockport TX 78382 Office: Creative Edn Inst 5000 Lakewood Dr Waco TX 76710

MORAN, FRANK SULLIVAN, accounting executive; b. Detroit, Oct. 11, 1918; s. Thomas and Lucy (Sullivan) M.; m. Georgene Stritch, Jan. 4, 1941; children: Frank Jr., Midge Vandenberg, George, Elaine Kelly. AB in Philosophy, U. Detroit, 1940. Ptnr. Plante & Moran, Southfield, Mich., 1950—, mng. ptnr., 1955-82, chmn., 1982—. Office: Plante & Moran CPAs 27400 Northwestern Southfield MI 48037-0307

MORAN, GERALD DWIGHT, academic librarian; b. Arthur Dale, W.Va., Aug. 25, 1944; s. Bruce Gerald and Colleen (Riggleman) M.; m. Emily Jeanne Wilson, Aug. 7, 1965; children: Gretchen, Laura, Geralyn. AB in Edn., Fairmont (W.Va.) State Coll., 1965; MLS, Vanderbilt U., 1968; PhD, U. Pitts., 1985. Tchr. Wood County Sch., Parkersburg, W.Va., 1965-68; tech. service librarian Alderson Braddus Coll., Phillippi, W.Va., 1968-75; librarian Geneva Coll., Beaver Falls, Pa., 1975—. Author: Normative Library Standards, 1985. Trustee Eastern Nazarene Coll., Quincy, Mass., 1986—; bd. dirs. Big Beaver Falls Sch. Bd., 1986—; mem. com. Beaver County Vocat. Tech. Sch., Monaca, Pa., 1987—. Mem. Am. Library Assn., Assn. of Coll. and Research Libraries, Pa. Library Assn. Democrat. Mem. Ch. of Nazarene. Avocations: interior designing, reading, speaking. Home: 702 35th St Beaver Falls PA 15010-3548 Office: Geneva Coll McCartney Beaver Falls PA 15010

MORAN, JAMES BYRON, federal judge; b. Evanston, Ill., June 20, 1930; s. James Edward and Kathryn (Horton) M.; children: John, Jennifer, Sarah, Polly; stepchildren: Katie, Cynthia, Laura, Michael. AB, U. Mich., 1952; LLB magna cum laude, Harvard U., 1957. Bar: Ill. 1958. Law clk. to judge U.S. Ct. of Appeals (2d cir.), 1957-58; assoc. Bell, Boyd, Lloyd, Haddad & Burns, Chgo, 1958-66, ptnr., 1966-79; judge U.S. Dist. Ct. (no. dist.) Ill., Chgo., 1979—. Dir. Gamco on Ill. Govt., 1968-70, chmn., 1968-70; vice chmn., sec. Ill. Dangerous Drug Adv. Coun., 1967-74; dir. Gateway Found., 1969—; mem. Ill. Ho. of Reps., 1965-67; mem. Evanston City Council, 1971-75. Served with AUS, 1952-54. Mem. Chgo. Bar Assn., Chgo. Council Lawyers, Phi Beta Kappa. Clubs: Law, Legal. Home: 117 Kedzie St Evanston IL 60202-2509 Office: US Dist Ct 219 S Dearborn St Chicago IL 60604-1702

MORAN, JAMES J., JR., lawyer; s. James J. and Marilyn A. (Sullivan) M.; m. Mary Therese Stevens, Oct. 6, 1979; children: Sean M., James E., Matthew S. AB cum laude, Boston Coll., 1975, JD, 1978. Bar: Mass. 1978, U.S. Ct. Appeals (1st cir.) 1979, U.S. Dist Ct. Mass. 1979, U.S. Tax Ct. 1979, U.S. Supreme Ct. 1982; CPCU. Assoc. Haussermann, Davison & Shattuck, Boston, 1978-84; assoc. Morrison, Mahoney & Miller, Boston, 1984-87, ptnr., 1988—; legal com. Commonwealth Automobile Reinsurers, 1988; CLU/CPCU adv. com. Mass. Divsn. Ins., 1988-89; v.p., gen. counsel Ind. Property-Casualty Insurers Inc., 1991—; counsel Profl. Ind. Ins. Agts. of Mass., Inc., 1985—; ins. broker, Mass.; New Gne. regional regulatory counsel Alliance of Am. Insurers, 1994—; spkr. in field. Contbr. articles to profl. jours. Bd. dirs. (gubernatorial appointee) Mass. Pollution Liability Reinsurance Corp., 1988-90. Mem. ABA (Tort and Ins. practice sect.), Internat. Assn. Def. Coun., Mass. Bar Assn., CPCU Soc. (pres. Boston chpt. 1993-94), Fedn. Regulatory Coun., Ins. Libr. Assn. Boston (trustee 1983—, pres. 1989-90). Democrat. Roman Catholic. Office: Morrison Mahoney & Miller 250 Summer St Boston MA 02210

MORAN, JAMES M., automotive sales executive; b. 1918; married. Owner Courtesy Motor Sales Inc. (formerly Hudson Motor Franchise Inc.), Chgo., 1947-68; chmn. JM Family Enterprises Inc., Deerfield Beach, Fla., 1969—. Office: JM Family Enterprises 100 NW 12th Ave Deerfield Beach FL 33442-1702

MORAN, JAMES MICHAEL, JR., astronomer, educator; b. Plainfield, N.J., Jan. 3, 1943; s. James Michael and Martha (Algermissen) M.; m. Barbara Putney Smith, Nov. 30, 1974; children: Susan Harrison, Michael Putney. BS, U. Notre Dame, 1963; SM, MIT, 1965, PhD, 1968. Mem. staff MIT Lincoln Lab., Lexington, 1968-70; sr. radio astronomer Smithsonian Astrophys. Obs., Cambridge, Mass., 1970—; prof. practice of astronomy Harvard U., Cambridge, 1979-89, prof. astronomy, 1989—; trustee N.E. Radio Obs. Corp., Cambridge, 1983—. Contbr. numerous articles on radio astronomy to profl. publs. Co-recipient Rumford prize Am. Acad. Arts and Scis., 1971; recipient Sr. award Alexander von Humboldt Soc., 1993. Fellow AAAS; mem. IEEE (sr.), Am. Astron. Soc. (Pierce prize 1978), Explorers Club. Avocations: photography, flying, hiking. Achievements include development of technique of very long baseline interferometry. Home: 93 Anson Rd Concord MA 01742-5704 Office: Harvard-Smithsonian Center for Astrophysics 60 Garden St Cambridge MA 02138-1596

MORAN, JAMES PATRICK, JR., congressman, stockbroker; b. Buffalo, N.Y., May 16, 1945; s. James Patrick and Dorothy (Dwyer) M.; m. Mary Craig, Dec. 27, 1967 (div. 1974); children: Jimmy, Mary; m. Mary Howard; children: Michael, Patrick, Dorothy. BA in Econs., Coll. of Holy Cross, Worcester, Mass., 1967; postgrad., CUNY, 1967-68; MA in Pub. Adminstrn., U. Pitts., 1970. Budget analyst HEW, Washington, 1969-74; budget and fiscal policy specialist, Congl. rsch. Libr. of Congress, Washington, 1974-76; sr. staff appropriations com. U.S. Senate, Washington, 1976-79; city councilman Alexandria, Va., 1979-91, vice-mayor, 1982-84, mayor, 1985-91; investment broker A.G. Edwards & Sons, Alexandria, Va., 1979—; mem. 102nd-103rd Congresses from 8th Va. dist., Washington, D.C. 1991—; mem. govt. reform & oversight coms.; ranking minority mem. civil svcs. subcom.; mem. internat. rels. on internat. ops. & human rights coms. Councilman, City of Alexandria 1979-82, vice-mayor, 1982-84, mayor, 1985—; chmn. No. Va. Transportation Bd., 1988—, United Way, 1977-79; vice chmn. Mental Health Retard and Substance Abuse Bd., 1976-78, vice chmn. D.E.O., 1976-78;dir., Met. Area Council Govts., dir. No. Va. Transp. Commn., 1985—. Recipient Outstanding Citizenship award YMCA, 1963. Mem. C. of C. (dir. 1985-86). Democrat. Roman Catholic. Home: 205 Uhler Ter Alexandria VA 22301-1551 Office: US Ho of Reps 405 Cannon HOB Washington DC 20515

MORAN, JOHN, religious organization administrator; b. Oct. 4, 1935; m. Retha Jean Patrick; children: John II, James, Helen. Missionary Nigeria, 1963-68; pastor, 1969-87; pres. The Missionary Ch., Fort Wayne, Ind., 1987—. Mem. Nat. Assn. Evang. (mem. exec. bd. 1987—), vice dist. supt.

1977-81, mem. Nat. Assn. Evang./Nat. Black Evang. Assn. com. on racial reconciliation 1995—). Office: Missionary Ch PO Box 9127 3811 Vanguard Dr Fort Wayne IN 46899-9127

MORAN, JOHN A., investment company executive; b. L.A., Mar. 22, 1932; s. Benjamin Edward and Louise (Chisholm) M.; m. Mary Darlene Whittaker, Aug. 14, 1954 (div. Oct. 1984); children—Kelli, Marisa, Elizabeth. B.S., U. Utah, 1954; postgrad., NYU, 1958-59, U. So. Calif., 1959-60. Assoc. Blyth & Co., Inc, N.Y.C. and Los Angeles, 1958-64; v.p. Blyth & Co, Inc, Los Angeles, 1964-67; v.p. Dyson-Kissner Corp., N.Y.C., 1967-74, exec. v.p., 1974-75, pres., 1975-84, chmn., 1984-90; chmn. exec. com. Dyson-Kissner-Moran, N.Y.C., 1990—; bd. dirs. Fortune Bank Corp., Bessemer Securities. Chmn. Rep. Nat. Fin. Com.; bd. dirs. World Pres. Orgn.; chmn. nat. adv. bd. U. Utah. Lt. USNR, 1955-58. Mem. Chief Execs. Orgn. Republican. Roman Catholic. Clubs: Metropolitan, Racquet and Tennis (N.Y.C.); Larchmont Yacht (N.Y.); Winged Foot Golf, (Mamaroneck, N.Y.). also: Dyson-Kissner-Moran 230 Park Ave Ste 659 New York NY 10169

MORAN, JOHN BERNARD, government official; b. Saginaw, Mich., Nov. 26, 1936; s. Leo Lewis and Marie Katherine (Langley) M.; m. Diann Marie Markey, May 20, 1963 (div.); m. Barbara Jane Livingston, Aug. 18, 1978; children—Leslie Marie, Leanne Rene, Jeffrey John. B.S. in Metall. Engring., Ill. Inst. Tech., 1959. Sr. automotive specialist Dow Chem. Co., Midland, Mich., 1962-71; program dir. research EPA, Research Triangle Park, N.C., 1971-75; dir. monitoring tech. div. EPA, Washington, 1975-76; dir. div. safety research Nat. Inst. for Occupational Safety and Health, Ctrs. for Disease Control, USPHS, HHS, Morgantown, W.Va., 1976-77, 83-88; dir. research and devel. safety products div. Am. Optical Corp., Southbridge, Mass., 1977-80; v.p., dir. ops. Geomet, Inc., Rockville, Md., 1980-83; program dir. Hartford Engring. Tech., Inc., Windsor, Conn., 1988; assoc. dir. health and safety laborers Associated Gen. Contractors, 1988-89; dir. safety and health Laborers Health and Safety Fund, 1989-95; spl. asst. to dep. asst. sec. Worker Health and Safety U.S. Dept. Energy, Washington, 1995—; mem. Nat. Mine Health Rsch. Adv. Com., Atlanta, 1980-84; govt. del. ILO, Geneva, 1985; mem. Nat. Adv. Com. on Constrn. Safety and Health, 1985-88, Bur. Labor Stats. Rsch., 1991-95, hazardous material transp. info. com. NAS, 1991-93, Hazardous Materials Control Rsch. Inst.; chmn. lead subcom. Bldg. Constrn. Trades Dept., 1991-95; adj. asst. prof. mech. engring. W.Va. U., 1985-88; vis. ext. prof. U. Conn., Storrs, 1988-90; mem. Fed. Facilities Environ. Restoration Com., constrn. com. A 10 Am. Nat. Stds. Inst.; co-chair EPA-Labor Superfund Task Force, 1990-95; mem. nat. lead task force HUD, 1993-95; cons., expert witness. Patentee; contbr. articles to profl. jours, chpts. to books. Mem. Task Force on Hazardous Materials, Rockville, Md., 1983. chmn. Nat. Inst. Environ. Health Sci., 1990. Served to capt. USMC, 1959-65. Recipient Bronze medal for commendable service EPA, 1974, Commitment to Life award Nat. Safe Workplace Inst., 1988. Mem. Internat. Soc. Respiratory Protection (pres. 1985-87, bd. dirs. 1987-89), Am. Conf. Govtl. Indsl. Hygienists. Roman Catholic. Home: 1605 Savannah Hwy North SC 29112-9625

MORAN, JOHN HENRY, JR., retired electrical engineer, consultant; b. Phila., Sept. 22, 1923; s. John Henry and Mary Joseph (Sheehan) M.; m. Jane Miriam Daly, June 29, 1946; children—Terrence, Kathleen, Michael, Patrick. B.S.E.E., Case Western Res. U., 1947. Profl. engr., N.Y., Ohio. Devel. engr. Allis-Chalmers, West Allis, Wis., 1947-55; engr. Lapp Insulator, LeRoy, N.Y., 1955-63, chief elec. engr., 1963-86, mgr. bushing engring., 1977-86; prin. cons., 1986—. Author: High Voltage Bushings, 1989; co-author: Electrostatics and Its Applications, 1973; author tech. papers; patentee. Active Genesee Boy Scouts Am., 1936-88. Served with USN, 1942-46, U.S., ETO. Fellow IEEE (life); mem. Electrostatic Soc. Am. (founding, v.p. 1978-82). Republican. Roman Catholic. Home and Office: 9053 Roanoke Rd Stafford NY 14143-9524

MORAN, JOHN PATRICK, JR., publishing executive, marketing consultant; b. N.Y.C., June 6, 1943; s. John Patrick and Evelyn (Dowdy) M.; m. Mary Ann Sheehan, Feb. 2, 1994; children from previous marriage: John P. III, Sarah Alice. BSBA, Boston U., 1969. Sales rep., key account mgr. Datagraphix, N.Y.C. and Los Angeles, 1969-73; nat. sales rep. Sta. NBC-TV, N.Y.C., 1973-75; consumer account rep. Wall Street Jour., N.Y.C., 1975-77; sr. account rep. U.S. News and World Report, N.Y.C., 1977-79; category mgr. Time, Inc., N.Y.C., 1979-82; assoc. pub. CDM Communications, N.Y.C., 1982-84; exec. v.p., assoc. publ., 1984-85; pres., chief exec. officer, group pub. CDM Communications, N.Y.C.; exec. v.p., pub. CDM Communications/CDM Publs., N.Y.C., 1983-85; pres. chief exec. officer Group Pubs. CDM Communications/CDM Publs., 1986—; pres., CEO CDM Group, 1989—; founder Land and Marine Products, Inc., Rowayton, Conn., 1993—; chmn. C.O.M. Mfrs. Assocs., N.Y.C., 1971-72; mktg. cons. 21 Brands, Inc., N.Y.C., 1980—, Bell Atlantic/Ketchum Advt., 1986-87. Publ., founder America's Cup Challenge Mag., 1986, Performance Sailing Mag., 1987, America's Cup Defense Mag., 1987. Com. U.S. Olympic Sailing Team, Greenwich, Conn., 1986, chmn., 1987-88, 89-90; chmn. C.O.M. Mfrs. Assn., 1971-72. With USNR, 1962-64. Mem. U.S. Yacht Racing Union (industry rels. com. L.I. chpt., 1977—, Spl. Achievement award 1978), N.Y. Yacht Club, Am. Yacht Club, Storm Trysail Club, Block Island Raceweek Com., 1983, 85, 87, 89, Ft. Worth Boat, Royal Hawaiian Ocean Racing Club, Antigua Yacht Club. Republican. Presbyterian. Avocations: sailing, skiing, tennis, squash, exercise. Office: Land and Marine Products Inc 102 Highland Ave Rowayton CT 06820

MORAN, JOHN THOMAS, JR., lawyer; b. Oak Park, Ill., Mar. 15, 1943; s. John T. and Corinne Louise (Dire) M.; m. Catherine Casey Pyne, May 16, 1981; 1 child, Sean Michael Pyne-Moran. AB cum laude, U. Notre Dame, 1965; JD, Georgetown U., 1968. Bar: Ill. 1969, Colo. 1976, U.S. Supreme Ct. 1973. Chief appeals div. Pub. Defender Cook County, Ill., 1970-82; gen. counsel Pub. Defender Cook County, Chgo., 1984-86; chief litigation atty. Frank & Flaherty, Chgo., 1982; cons. ABA, Chgo., 1982-83; sole practice Chgo., 1986-93; founder Law Offices of John Thomas Moran; assoc. Thomas A. Daley, Chgo., 1993—. Editor: Gideon Revisited, 1983. Bd. dirs. Lawyers for the Creative Arts, 1973—. Ford Found. grantee Internat. Common Law Colloquium, London, 1976, NEH grantee, Harvard Law Sch., 1977. Mem. ABA, Ill. State Bar Assn., Appellate Lawyers Assn., Nat. Legal Aid and Defenders Assn., Am. Soc. Internat. Law, Georgetown U. Law Ctr. Alumni Soc. Avocation: sailing. Home: 930 Oakwood Ave Wilmette IL 60091-3320 Office: The Delaware Bldg 36 W Randolph St Ste 800 Chicago IL 60601

MORAN, JOSEPH MILBERT, retired banker; b. Dentsville, Md., July 23, 1929; s. Thomas Roger and May Marianne (Montgomery) M.; m. Jacqueline V. Kines, Sept. 5, 1955; children: Susanne, Stacey, Siobain, Meaghan. Ph.B., Loyola Coll., Balt., 1950; LL.B., U. Md., 1959. Bar: Md. 1959. Copy boy Balt. News Post, 1950-51; with INA, Balt., 1955-56; with aerospace div. Martin Marietta Co., Balt., 1956-59, with nuclear div., 1959-64; with Wilmington Trust Co., Del., 1964-91; sr. v.p. Wilmington Trust Co., 1972-91, sec., dir., 1979-91; legis. agent Wilmington Trust Co., Dover, Del., 1991—; mem. Govs. Council on Banking, 1982—. Bd. visitors Weidner Law Sch., 1985-91. Capt. USNR, 1951-73. Mem. ABA, Del. Bar Assn., Md. Bar, Navy League, Naval Res. Assn., Am. Banker's Assn. (legis. council 1979-82, leadership del. 1985-86), Del. Banker's Assn. (chmn. legis. com. 1966-91). Democrat. Roman Catholic. Home: 14 Yorkridge Trl Hockessin DE 19707-9633 Office: Wilmington Trust Co 139 S State St Dover DE 19901-7394

MORAN, JULIETTE M., management consultant; b. N.Y.C., June 12, 1917; d. James Joseph and Louise M. B.S., Columbia U., 1938; M.S., NYU, 1948. Research asst. Columbia U., 1941; jr. engr. Signal Corps Lab., U.S. Army, 1942-43; with GAF Corp. (formerly Gen. Aniline & Film Corp.), 1943-82; successively jr. chemist process devel. dept., tech. asst. to N.Y. process devel. dept., tech. asst. to dir. Central Research Lab., tech. asst. to dir GAF Corp., 1953-55, supr. tech. service comml. devel. dept., 1955-59, sr. devel. specialist, 1959-60, mgr. planning, 1961, asst. to the pres., 1962-67, v.p., 1967-71, sr. v.p. 1971-74, exec. v.p., dir. 1974-83, vice chmn., 1980-82, cons., 1982—. Bd. dirs. N.Y. State Sci. and Tech. Found. Recipient Greater N.Y. Advt. award for excellence in communications N.Y. chpt. Assn. Indsl. Advertisers, 1972, Alumni Achievement award N.Y. U. Grad. Sch. Arts and Scis., 1977. Fellow AAAS, Am. Inst. Chemists; mem. Am. Chem. Soc., Comml. Devel. Assn. Home: 10 W 66th St New York NY 10023

MORAN, M. MARCUS, JR., retail executive; b. Fitchburg, Mass., Apr. 19, 1943; s. M. Marcus Sr. and Claire Paulette (Aubuchon) M.; m. Tonia Francavilla, July 29, 1966; children: Marcus III, Coutney L., Justin M. BBA, Nichols Coll., 1966; MBA, Babson Coll., 1967. Prof. North Shore Community Coll., Beverly, Mass., 1967-70; pres., treas., v.p. W. E. Aubuchon Co., Inc., Westminster, Mass., 1970—, pres., treas., 1993—, also bd. dirs.; bd. dirs. chmn. investment com. I-C Fed. Credit Union, Fitchburg, Mass., 1987—; past instr. acctg. and fin. Fitchburg State Coll., Boston U., North Shore Community Coll., Mt. Wachusett Community Coll. Author: Business Mathematics, 1969. Pres., bd. dirs. United Way, Fitchburg, 1984-88; trustee Fitchburg State Coll./FTC Found., 1978—; past trustee Nichols Coll., Notre Dame Acad., Worcester, Mass.; bd. dirs. Julie Country Day Sch., Leominster, Mass., 1980, Cushing Acad., Ashburnham, Mass., 1989—; chmn. bus. edn. fund, Monty Tech. Vocation Sch. Recipient Key to City-Life Saving, City of Fitchburg, 1965, Community Leadership award Fitchburg State Coll., 1991, Disting. Citizen award Boy Scouts Am., 1993. Mem. Fay Club (past dir., pres. 1970—), Beta Gamma, Zeta Alpha Phi. Republican. Roman Catholic. Avocation: education. Home: Round Meadow Pond Westminster MA 01473 Office: W E Aubuchon Co Inc 95 Aubuchon Dr Westminster MA 01473

MORAN, MARTIN JOSEPH, fundraising company executive; b. Bklyn., Nov. 3, 1930; s. Dominick and Mary (Lydon) M.; m. Mary Therese Schofield, June 5, 1954; children: Martin Joseph, John P., Maureen M., Thomas S., Robert P., William M., Maria M. BA, St. John's U., 1952. Profl. fundraising cons., 1956—; founder Martin J. Moran Co., Inc., N.Y.C., 1964, pres., 1964-74, chmn. bd., 1974—. Mem. Cardinal's Com. for Edn., N.Y.C., 1970-79, Cardinal's Com for Laity Archdiocese N.Y., 1979—, Am. Revolution Bicentennial Commn., Oyster Bay, N.Y.; mem. Massapequa Park (N.Y.) Bd. Zoning Appeals, 1972-84, chmn., 1978-84; mem. Massapequa Park Ethics Commn., 1969-72; trustee Notre Dame Coll., S.I., 1969-72, La Salle Acad., N.Y.C., 1971-87; mem. pres.'s council Cath. U.P.R., Ponce, 1966-71. Served as aviator USNR, 1952-56. Decorated knight Order Holy Sepulchre, Pope Paul VI, 1968, Knight of Malta, Pope Paul VI, 1973; recipient Pietas medal St. John's U., N.Y., 1988; bd. councilors, sec., treas. Equestrian Order Holy Sepulchre of Jerusalem, 1990—, sec.-treas. 1990-93, pres., 1993—. Mem. Navy League, Navy Hist. Assn., St. John's U. Alumni Assn. (pres. 1987-94), Am. Assn. Fund Raising Counsel (bd. dirs. 1970—), Nassau County Hist. Soc., Friendly Sons of St. Patrick. Roman Catholic. Club: Madison Square Garden (N.Y.C.); Lost Tree Club (North Palm Beach, Fla.), Old Port Yacht Club. Lodge: KC. Home: 1300 Lakeshore Dr Massapequa Park NY 11762-1764 also: 677 Village Rd No Palm Beach FL 33408-3329 Office: Martin J Moran Co 1 Penn Plz New York NY 10119

MORAN, PATRICIA GENEVIEVE, corporate executive; b. Evanston, Ill., July 26, 1945; d. James M.; children: Christine Coyle, Thomas Beddia, Donald Beddia. Attended. Marquette U. Pers. mgr. Sesco, 1983-84, dir. corp. transp., assoc. rels. dir., 1984-85, v.p. assoc. rels., 1985-88; group v.p. sales Southeast Toyota, Deerfield Beach, Fla., 1988-89, pres., 1989-94; v.p. H.R. JM Family Enterprises, Inc., Deerfield Beach, pres., 1989-94. Dir. Beacon Coun., Miami, Fla., 1992—, Broward Econ. Devel., Ft. Lauderdale, Fla., 1991—, Youth Automotive Tng. Ctr., Hollywood, Fla., 1985—. Named Top 50 Working Women by Working Woman's Mag. Mem. Ft. Lauderdale C. of C. (dir. 1991—), Tower Club, The Haven (adv. bd. 1994-95). Office: JM Family Enterprises 100 NW 12th Ave Deerfield Beach FL 33442-1702

MORAN, PAUL JAMES, journalist, columnist; b. Buffalo, July 20, 1947; s. Paul James and Frances (Sciortino) M.; m. Kim Maldiner, Mar. 17, 1975 (div. July 1979); m. Colette Stass (separated); 1 child, Heather. Student, SUNY, Buffalo, 1965-67, Millard Fillmore Coll., 1971-73. Sports editor Tonawanda News, North Tonawanda, N.Y., 1972-75; writer/columnist Fort Lauderdale (Fla.) News/Sun Sentinel, 1975-85, N.Y. Newsday, Melville, 1985—; cons. Green Country Racing Assn., Tulsa, 1983-85. Contbr. articles to mags. and newspapers. Sgt. USAF, 1967-71. Recipient Eclipse award Thoroughbred Racing Assn., 1985, 90, Disting. Writing award Am. Soc. Newspaper Editors, 1990, Deadline Writing award Soc. Silurians, 1990, Deadline Reporting award L.I. Press Club, 1991, Disting. Sports Writing award N.Y. Newspaper Pubs. Assn., 1992, (with others) Journalism collection Best Newspaper Writing 1991—. Mem. N.Y. Turf Writers' Assn. (pres. 1990-92, sec.-treas. 1992-94), Nat. Turf Writers' Assn. (bd. dirs. 1987-90). Republican. Avocations: photography, art collecting, body building. Home: 270 Jericho Park Floral Park NY 11001 Office: NY Newsday 235 Pinelawn Rd Melville NY 11747-4226

MORAN, PHILIP DAVID, lawyer; b. Lynn, Mass., June 3, 1937; s. J. Francis and Margaret M. (Shanahan) M.; m. Carole A. Regan, May 12, 1962; children: Maura F., Philip David. A.B., Holy Cross Coll., 1958; Ed.M., Salem State Coll., 1961; J.D., Suffolk U., 1968. Bar: Mass. 1968, U.S. Dist. Ct. Mass., 1972, U.S. Supreme Ct., 1988, U.S. Ct. Appeals (1st cir.), 1993. House counsel Viatron Computer Systems Corp., Burlington, Mass., 1968-71; ptnr. Kane & Moran, Lynn, Mass., 1972-78; pvt. practice law Salem, Mass., 1978—; asst. dist. atty. Essex County (Mass.), 1974-78. Bd. dirs. Nat. Right to Life Inc., 1977-83, 87—, treas., 1981-83; Contbg. author: Encyclopedia of Biomedical Policy, 1995. Bd. dir. Mass. Citizens for Life, 1973—, pres. 1979-80, chmn. 1991-93. mem. Salem Conservation Commn., 1980-89, chmn., 1982-89; mem. pres.'s coun. Holy Cross Coll., 1985—; mem. Nat. Inst. Trial Advocacy U. Colo., 1973; gen. chmn bicentenary com. MayNooth Coll., Boston, 1994-95. With U.S. Army, 1960-66. Recipient Ignatius O'Connor Pro Life award, 1994. Mem. Mass. Bar Assn., Salem Bar Assn., Lynn Bar Assn., Am. Trial Lawyers Assn., Nat. Acad. Elder Law Attys., Murray Inn of Ct. Roman Catholic. Avocations: swimming, reading, gardening, boating. Home: 415 Lafayette St Salem MA 01970-5337 Office: 265 Essex St Salem MA 01970-3447

MORAN, RACHEL, lawyer, educator; b. Kansas City, Mo., June 27, 1956; d. Thomas Albert and Josephine (Portillo) M. AB, Stanford U., 1978; JD, Yale U., 1981. Bar: Calif. 1984. Assoc Heller, Ehrman, White & McAuliffe, San Francisco, 1982-83; prof. law U. Calif., Berkeley, 1984—; vis. prof. UCLA Sch. Law, 1988, Stanford (Calif.) U. Law Sch., 1989; ann. civil rights lectr. Creighton U. Sch. Law, Omaha, 1989; Pirsig lectr. William Mitchell Coll. St. Paul, 1989, others; mem. steering com. Nat. Resource Ctr., Berkeley, 1988-89; chair Chicano/Latino Policy Project, 1993—. Contbr. numerous articles to profl. jours. Grantee Joseph and Polly Harris Trust Inst. Govtl. Studies, Berkeley, 1987-89, Faculty Devel. U. Calif. Berkeley, 1985-86. Mem. ABA, AAUP, Calif. Bar Assn., Phi Beta Kappa. Democrat. Unitarian. Avocations: jogging, aerobics, reading, listening to music. Office: U Calif Sch Law Boalt Hall Berkeley CA 94720

MORAN, RICARDO JULIO, economist; b. Havana, Cuba, Sept. 4, 1939; came to U.S., 1960; s. Jose Ricardo and Maria Luisa (Forcade) M.; m. Mayra Buvinic, Dec. 24, 1973 (div. 1981); m. Mary Louise Fox, Apr. 25, 1987. BA, Tulane U., 1963; MA in Econs., U. Calif., Berkeley, 1966, postgrad., 1968. Prof., sr. rsch. assoc. Universidad Catolica de Chile, Santiago, 1967-70; pvt. practice Washington, 1970-73; v.p. Moran Equities, Inc., Miami, Fla., 1973; economist The World Bank, Washington, 1973-90; prin. Moran Internat., Washington, 1990-92; sr. economist Interam. Devel. Bank, Washington, 1992—. Co-author: Declining Births in Chile, 1972, Brazil, 1981; contbr. articles to profl. jours. Fellow Latin Am. Teaching Program Tufts U., 1957, Ford Found., 1965, OAS, 1963-65. Mem. Am. Econ. Assn. Avocation: literature, music, travel, tennis. Home: 2910 Cortland Pl NW Washington DC 20008-3429 Office: Interam Devel Bank Washington DC 20577

MORAN, ROBERT FRANCIS, JR., library director; b. Cleve., May 3, 1938; s. Robert Francis Sr. and Jeanette (Mulholland) M.; m. Judith Mary Pacér, Dec. 28, 1968; children: Mary Jeanette, Catherine, Margaret. BA, Cath. U. Am., Washington, 1961, MLS, 1965; MBA, U. Chgo., 1976. Head librarian St. Patrick's Sem., Menlo Park, Calif., 1965-69; coordinator and reference librarian U. Chgo., 1969-72; serials librarian U. Ill. Chgo., 1972-78, acquisitions librarian, 1977-80; dir. library services Ind. U. Northwest, Gary, 1980—; asst. vice chancellor tech., 1991—; v.p., sec., treas. Northwest Ind. Area Library Services Authority, Merrillville, 1982-91. Contbr. articles to profl. jours. Mem. ALA, Libr. Adminstrn. and Mgmt. Assn. (com. chmn. 1981-86, sect. chmn. 1986-88, chmn. program com. 1988-91, chair nominating com. 1991-92, networked info. discussion group 1994—).

Democrat. Roman Catholic. Office: Ind Univ NW Library 3400 Broadway Gary IN 46408-1197

MORAN, THOMAS FRANCIS, chemistry educator; b. Manchester, N.H., Dec. 11, 1936; s. Francis Leo and Mamie Marie (Morin) M.; m. Joan Elinor Belliveau, June 25, 1960; children: Dorothy, Michael, Linda, Mary. BA, St. Anselm's Coll., 1958; PhD, Notre Dame U., 1962. Teaching and rsch. fellow Notre Dame U., South Bend, Ind., 1958-62; USAEC postdoctoral fellow Brookhaven Nat. Lab., Upton, N.Y., 1962-64; staff scientist Brookhaven Nat. Lab., 1964-66; asst. prof. Ga. Inst. Tech., Atlanta, 1966-68; assoc. prof. Ga. Inst. Tech., 1968-72; prof. chemistry dept., 1972—. Contbr. articles to profl. jours. Danforth fellow Danforth Found. Mem. Am. Chem. Soc., Am. Physical Soc., Am. Soc. Mass Spectrometry, AAAS, Sigma Xi (award). Home: 2324 Annapolis Ct NE Atlanta GA 30345-3803 Office: Chemistry Dept Ga Inst Tech Atlanta GA 30332

MORAN, W. DENNIS, engineering consulting executive; b. Springfield, Mass., Jan. 13, 1940; s. Walter Louis and Laura Kathryn (Ostiguy) M.; m. Kathleen Marie Boulet, Nov. 5, 1966; children: Molly Michelle, Julie Kathryn. BCE, Union Coll. Schenectady, N.Y., 1964; MBA, U. Pa., 1982. Registered profl. engr., N.Y., Queensland, Australia. Project engr. O'Brien & Gere Engrs., Syracuse, N.Y., 1964-67, data processing mgr., 1967-70; sr. engr. Camp Dresser & McKee Internat. Inc., Bangkok, 1970-74; asst. to pres. Camp Dresser & McKee Inc., Boston, 1974-76, v.p., 1976-78; sr. v.p., 1978—, also bd. dirs.; pres. Camp Dresser & McKee Internat. Inc., Boston, 1983—; chmn. CDM Devel. Corp., Boston, 1986—; bd. dirs. Camp Scott Furphy, Melbourne, Australia, Am. Brit. Cons., London and Cairo, Scottsdale (Ariz.) Water Svc. Co., CDM Pte Ltd., Singapore. Mem. adv. bd. Wurster Ctr., Wharton Sch., U. Pa.; bd. dirs. Syracuse Jaycees, 1964-70. Mem. ASCE, Water Pollution Control Assn., Am. Water Works Assn. Treas. Club Boston, Blue Water Sailing Club (commodore 1987, bd. govs. 1984—), Scituate Harbor Yacht Club, Tau Beta Pi. Roman Catholic. Avocation: offshore racing and cruising. Home: 52 Hollett St Scituate MA 02066-1432 Office: Camp Dresser & McKee Internat Inc One Cambridge Ctr Cambridge MA 02142

MORAND, BLAISE E., bishop; b. Tecumseh, Ont., Can., Sept. 12, 1932. Ordained priest Roman Cath. Ch., 1958. Ordained coadjutor bishop Diocese of Prince Albert, Sask., Can., 1981, bishop, 1983—. Office: Diocese of Prince Albert, 1415 4th Ave W, Prince Albert, SK Canada S6V 5H1

MORAND, PETER, research agency executive; b. Montreal, Que., Can., Feb. 11, 1935; s. Frank and Rose Alice (Fortier) M.; m. Dawn McKell, Oct. 10, 1957; children: Clifford, Tanya. BSc with honors, Bishop's U., Lennoxville, Que., 1956, DCL (hon.), 1991; PhD, McGill U., Montreal, 1959. NATO postdoctoral fellow Imperial Coll., London, 1959-61; sr. rsch. chemist Ayerst Labs., Montreal, 1961-63; asst. prof. chemistry U. Ottawa, Can., 1963-67, acad. asst. vice rector, 1968-71, dean sci.and engring., 1976-81, prof. chemistry, dir. rsch. svcs., 1981-87, vice rector univ. R&D, 1987-90; pres. Natural Scis. and Engring. Rsch. Coun., Ottawa, 1990—; bd. dirs. Ottawa-Carleton Econ. Devel. Corp., Can., Royal Ottawa Hosp. Contbr. articles to profl. jours.; patentee in field. Trustee B.C. Applied Systems Inst., Vancouver, Can., 1990—; bd. dirs. Ottawa Life Scis. Tech. Park. Natural Scis. and Engring. Rsch. Coun. grantee, 1964-90. Fellow Chem. Inst. Can.; mem. Soc. of Rsch. Adminstrs., Rideau Club, Cercle Univ. Office: Natural Scis & Engrng Rsch Coun Can, 350 Albert St 13th Fl #1302, Ottawa, ON Canada K1A 1H5

MORANIS, RICK, actor; b. Toronto, Ont., Can., Apr. 18, 1954. Appeared in films Ghostbusters, 1984, Streets of Fire, 1984, The Wild Life, 1984, Brewster's Millions, 1985, Head Office, 1985, Club Paradise, 1986, Little Shop of Horrors, 1986, Spaceballs, 1987, Ghostbusters II, 1989, Honey, I Shrunk the Kids, 1989, Parenthood, 1989, My Blue Heaven, 1990, L.A. Story, 1991, Honey, I Blew Up the Kid, 1992, Splitting Heirs, 1993, The Flintstones, 1994, Little Giants, 1994, Big Bully, 1995; actor, co-writer, co-dir.: (films) Strange Brew, 1983; actor, writer: (TV) Second City TV, 1980-81, SCTV Network 90, 1981-82 (Emmy award 1982), (with Dave Thomas) A Funny Thing Happened on the Way to the Olympics, 1988; albums include (with Dave Thomas) Great White North, 1981, Strange Brew, 1983. Office: CAA 9830 Wilshire Blvd Beverly Hills CA 90212*

MORANT, RICARDO BERNARDINO, psychology educator; b. New Britain, Conn., Feb. 13, 1926; s. J. Ramon and Rosario (Ciscar) M.; m. G. Francisca Giner, Dec. 26, 1955; children—Ramon, Francisca, Dolores, Ricardo. A.B., Harvard, 1948; postgrad., Wesleyan Coll., Middletown, Conn., 1948-49; M.A., Clark U., 1950, Ph.D., 1952. Faculty Brandeis U., Waltham, Mass., 1952—; prof. psychology Brandeis U., 1965—, Fierman prof. psychology, 1968—, chmn. dept., 1962-73, chmn. Sch. Social Scis., 1982-86, chmn. Latin Am. Studies, 1984-91; Prin. investigator NIMH, Spencer Found., Rothman Found. 1960—; spl. research space perception, body orientation. Bd. dirs. Council for Pub. Schs., 1970-73; mem. steering com. Sensory Aid Eval. and Devel. Ctr., MIT, 1963-67; chmn. bd. trustees Hiatt Ednl. Programs, 1982—. Served with USNR, 1946-48. Fellow Am. Psychol. Assn.; mem. Eastern, New Eng., Mass psychol. assn., Psychonomic Soc. Home: 35 Cliff Rd Wellesley MA 02181-3001 Office: Brandeis Univ Waltham MA 02154

MORARI, MANFRED, chemical engineer, educator; b. Graz, Austria, May 13, 1951; came to U.S., 1975; s. Manfred and Hilde (Florian) M.; m. Marina Korchynsky, May 12, 1984. Diploma Chem. Engring., Eidgenoessische Technische Hochschule, Zurich, Switzerland, 1974; PhD in Chem. Engring., U. Minn., 1977. Asst. prof. U. Wis., Madison, 1977-81, assoc. prof., 1981-83; prof. chem. engring. Calif. Inst. Tech., Pasadena, 1983—, McCollum-Corcoran prof., 1991—, exec. officer, 1990-93, prof. control and dynamical sys., 1993—; exec. officer, 1993—; Gulf vis. prof. chem. engring. Carnegie Mellon U., 1987. Contbr. articles to profl. jours. Recipient D.P. Eckman award Am. Automatic Control Coun., 1980. Mem. IEEE (George S. Axelby Outstanding Paper award 1990), Am. Soc. for Engring. Edn. (Curtis W. McGraw rsch. award 1989), Am. Inst. Chem. Engrs. (A.P. Colburn award 1984), Nat. Acad. Engring., Am. Chem. Soc. Home: 2735 Ardmore Rd San Marino CA 91108-1768 Office: Calif Inst Tech Chem Engring 210 # 41 Pasadena CA 91125

MORATH, INGE, photographer; b. Graz, Austria, May 27, 1923; d. Edgar Eugen and Mathilde (Wiesler) M.; m. Arthur Miller, Feb. 1962; 1 child, Rebecca Augusta. BA, U. Berlin; DFA (hon.), U. Hartford, 1984. Formerly translator and editor ISB Feature Sect., Salzburg and Vienna, Austria; later editor lit. monthly Der Optmist, Vienna and Austrian editor Heute Mag.; former free-lance writer for mags. and Red White Red Radio Network; with Magnum Photos, Paris and N.Y.C., 1952—; mem. Magnum Photos, 1953—; tchr. photography course Cooper Union, 2 years; lectr. at various univs. including U. Miami, U. Mich. Exhibited photographs one-woman shows Wuehrle Gallery, Vienna, 1956, Leitz Gallery, N.Y.C., 1958, N.Y. Overseas Press Club, 1959, Chgo. Art Inst., 1964, Oliver Woolcott Meml. Library, Litchfield, Conn., 1969, Art Mus., Andover, Mass., 1971, U. Miami, 1972, U. Mich., 1973, Carlton Gallery, N.Y.C., 1976, Neikrug Galleries, N.Y.C., 1976, 79, Grand Rapids (Mich.) Art Mus., 1979, Mus. Modern Art, Vienna, 1980, Kunsthaus, Zurich, Switzerland, 1980, Burden Gallery Aperture Inc., N.Y.C., 1987, Moscow Ctr. Photojournalists, 1988, Sala del Canal, Madrid, 1988, Cathedral, Norwich, Eng. 1989, Am. Cultural Ctr., Brussels, 1989, Kolbe Mus., Berlin, 1991, Mus. Rupertinum, Salzburg, 1991; retrospective Neue Galerie, Linz, Austria, Amerika House, Berlin, 1993, Hradčini, Prague, 1993, Royal Photographic Soc., Bath, Eng., 1994, Mus. Contemporary Art, Madrid, 1995, Book Fair, Frankfurt, 1995; numerous group shows include Photokina, Cologne, Ger., World's Fair, Montreal, Que., Can.; represented in permanent collections Met. Mus. Art, Boston Mus. Art, Art Inst. Chgo., Bibliothèque Nationale, Paris, Kunsthaus, Zurich, Prague (Czechoslovakia) Art Mus., Rupertinum Mus., Salzburg, Austria; photographer for books Guerreà la Tristesse (Dominique Aubier), 1956, Venice Observed (Mary McCarthy), 1956, (with Yul Brynner) Bring Forth the Children (Yul Brynner), 1960, From Persia to Iran (Edouard Sablier), 1961, Tunisia (Claude Roy, Paul Sebag), 1961, Le Masque (drawings by Saul Steinberg), 1967, In Russia (Arthur Miller), 1969, East West Exercises (Ruth Bluestone Simon), 1973, Boris Pasternak: My Sister Life (O. Carlisle, translator), 1976, In the Country (Arthur Miller), 1977, Chinese Encounters (Arthur Miller), 1979, Salesman in Beijing (Arthur Miller), 1984,

Images of Vienna (Barbara Frischmuth, Pavel Kohout, Andre Heller, Arthur Miller), 1981, Inge Morath: Portraits, 1987, In Our Time, 1990, Russian Journal (E. Yevtushenko, A. Voznesensky, O. Andreyev Carlisle), 1991, Inge Morath: Fotografien 1952-92, Inge Morath: Spain in the 50s, 1994; editor, co-photographer books Paris/Magnum, Aperture Inc., biography Grosse Photographen unserer Zeit, 1975; contbr. numerous photographs to European, U.S., S. Am., Japanese mags., and to numerous anthologies including Life series on photography and photographic yearbooks. Recipient Great Austrian State Prize for photography, 1991, various citations for shows. Mem. Am. Soc. Mag. Photographers. Home: Tophet Rd PO Box 232 Roxbury CT 06783 Office: Magnum Photos 151 W 25th St New York NY 10001-7204

MORATH, JULIANNE MOLLIE, nursing administrator; b. Marquette, Mich., Oct. 23, 1947; d. Gilbert O. and Frances (Layne) M.; m. Donald R. Morath; children: Mollie, Alexandra, Christopher, Todd. BS in Nursing, U. Mich, 1969; MS, U. Calif., San Francisco, 1971; postgrad., U. Cin. Clin. nurse U. Mich. Hosp., Ann Arbor, 1967-69, Denver Gen. Hosp., 1970-71; assoc. dir. Meml. Med. Ctr., Savannah, Ga., 1971-77; assoc. v.p. Jewish Hosp., Cin., 1977-80; asst. adminstr. U. Cin. Hosp., 1980-86; pres. Malone Morath, P.C., Cin., 1986—; v.p. patient care, chief nursing Roger Williams Med. Ctr., 1986-90; asst. prof. U. Cin., 1981; lectr. in field. Contbr. articles to profl. jours. NIHM grantee, 1975, 80. Mem. ANA, AONE, Nat. League for Nursing, Sigma Theta Tau. Office: Abbott-Northwestern Hosp 800 E 28th St Minneapolis MN 55407-3723

MORATH, MAX EDWARD, entertainer, composer; b. Colorado Springs, Colo., Oct. 1, 1926; s. Frederic Palmer and Gladys Hester Nancy (Ramsell) M.; m. Norma Loy Tackitt, Oct. 23, 1953 (div. 1992); children: Kathryn, Christine, Frederic; m. Diane Fay Skomars, May 24, 1993. BA in English, Colo. Coll., 1948; postgrad., Stanford NBC-Radio-TV Inst., Palo Alto, Calif., 1951. Mem. adv. bd. Keyboard mag. Composer One For Amelia, 1964, Golden Hours, 1966, One For the Road, 1982, Cripple Creek: A Ragtime Suite for Piano, 1986; editor: Best of Ragtime, 1964; radio debut Sta. KVOR, Colorado Springs, 1944-48; actor, announcer, dir. radio and television, Colo., Tex., Ariz., Fla., 1949-59, also summer stock and nightclubs; performer, writer (TV series) The Ragtime Era and Turn of the Century, NET, 1959-61; New York nightclub debut at Blue Angel, 1963; off-Broadway debut in Max Morath at the Turn of the Century, 1969; also nat. tours, 1969-73; nat. tour The Ragtime Years, 1973-78, Living a Ragtime Life, 1978-84, Pop Goes the Music with Max Morath Quintet, 1984-87; off-Broadway Ragtime Life, 1986, tour, 1987—; rec. artist Epic, RCA, Vanguard, SoloArt, Omega. Mem. Broadcast Music, Inc., Am. Fedn. Musicians, AFTRA, Screen Actors Guild, Actors Equity Assn.

MORAVA, CAROL, lawyer; b. Pasadena, Calif., Oct. 5, 1937; d. Dean Howell and Jeanne Elizabeth (Briggs) Sheldon; m. Emmett Morava, May, 1959; children: Michelle, Leslie. BA, Pomona Coll., 1954; JD, Loyola U., L.A., 1981. Data ctr. assoc. IBM, L.A., 1959-62; assoc. sys. engr. IBM, Pitts., 1962-65, L.A., 1966-67; programmer, analyst MIS Thrifty Corp., L.A., 1967-81, corp. counsel, 1981—. Pres., dir. Huntington Palisades Homeowners Assn., L.A., 1984-87; mem. pres. coun. Planned Parenthood, L.A., 1992—; bd. dirs. Angeles Girl Scout Coun., L.A., 1994—. Recipient Cert. Achievement from YWCA of L.A., Mayor's cert. Mayor of L.A., 1987. Mem. Calif. Women Lawyers, Wilshire Bar Assn., L.A. Area C. of C. (pres. coun. 1986-87). Avocations: tennis, gardening, reading, travel. Home: 744 Ocampo Dr Pacific Palisades CA 90272 Office: Thrifty Co 3424 Wilshire Blvd Los Angeles CA 90010

MORAVCSIK, JULIUS MATTHEW, philosophy educator; b. Budapest, Hungary, Apr. 26, 1931; came to U.S., 1949; s. Julius and Edith (Fleissig) M.; m. Marguerite Germain Truninger, Sept. 14, 1954; children: Adrian Clay, Peter Matthew. BA, Harvard U., 1953, PhD, 1959. Asst. prof. U. Mich., Ann Arbor, 1960-66, assoc. prof., 1966-68; prof. Stanford (Calif.) U., 1968—. Author: Understanding Language, 1975, Thought and Language, 1990, Plato and Platonism, 1992. Recipient Sr. Humanist prize Humboldt Found., 1983; fellow Ctr. Advanced Studies Behavioral Scis., 1986-87, Inst. Advanced Studies, 1988. Mem. Am. Philos. Assn. (pres. Pacific divsn. 1987-88), Am. Soc. Aesthetics (trustee 1988-92), Soc. Ancient Greek Philosophy (pres. 1989-91). Avocations: golf, tennis. Office: Stanford U Dept Of Philosophy Stanford CA 94305

MORAWETZ, CATHLEEN SYNGE, mathematician; b. Toronto, May 5, 1923; came to U.S., 1945, naturalized, 1950; d. John Lighton and Elizabeth Eleanor Mabel (Allen) Synge; m. Herbert Morawetz, Oct. 27, 1945; children: Pegeen Morawetz Rubinstein, John Synge, Lida Morawetz Jeck, Nancy. BA, U. Toronto, 1945; SM, MIT, 1946; PhD, NYU, 1951; hon. degree, Eastern Mich. U., 1980, Smith Coll., 1982, Brown U., 1982 Princeton U., 1986, Duke U., 1988, N.J. Inst. Tech., 1988, U. Waterloo, 1993. Research assoc. Courant Inst., NYU, 1952-57, asst. prof. math., 1957-60, assoc. prof., 1960-65, prof., 1965—, assoc. dir., 1978-84, dir., 1984-88. Editor Jour. Math. Analysis and Applications, Comms. in PDE; author articles in applications of partial differential equations, especially transonic flow and scattering theory. Trustee Princeton U., 1973-78, Sloan Found., 1980—. Guggenheim fellow, 1967, 79; Office Naval Rsch. grantee, until 1990. Fellow AAAS; mem. NAS, Am. Math. Soc. (term trustee 1975-85, pres. 1995—), Am. Acad. Arts and Scis., Soc. Indsl. and Applied Math. Office: 251 Mercer St New York NY 10012-1185

MORAWETZ, HERBERT, chemistry educator; b. Prague, Czechoslovakia, Oct. 16, 1915; came to U.S., 1945, naturalized, 1951; s. Richard and Frida (Glaser) M.; m. Cathleen Synge, Oct. 28, 1945; children: Pegeen Morawetz Rubinstein, John S., Lida Morawetz Jeck, Nancy B. B.A. Sci., U. Toronto, 1943, M.A. Sci., 1944; Ph.D., Poly Inst. Bklyn., 1951. With Bakelite Co., 1945-49; mem. faculty Poly. U. (formerly Poly. Inst. Bklyn.), 1951-81, prof. polymer chemistry, dir. Inst. Polymer Research, 1971-81; Inst. prof., 1981-86, Inst. prof. emeritus, 1986—; mem. materials research adv. com. NSF, 1977-80. Author: Macromolecules in Solution, 1965, rev. edit., 1975; Polymers: The Origins and Growth of a Science, 1985; mem. editorial bd. Jour. Polymer Sci., 1969-89; contbr. articles to profl. jours. Recipient Heyrovsky medal Czechoslovakia Acad. Sci., 1990; Case Centenary scholar, 1980; Whitby Meml. lectr. U. Akron, 1984. Fellow AAAS; mem. Am. Chem. Soc. (award in polymer chemistry 1986, assoc. editor Macromolecules 1991—). Home: 246 W 12th St New York NY 10014-1912 Office: 333 Jay St Brooklyn NY 11201-2907

MORBY, JACQUELINE, venture capitalist; b. Sacramento, June 19, 1937; d. Junior Jennings and Bertha (Backer) Collins; m. Jeffrey L. Morby, June 21, 1959; children: Andrew Jennings, Michelle Lorraine. BA in Psychology, Stanford U., 1959; M in Mgmt., Simmons Grad. Mgmt. Sch., Boston, 1978. Assoc. TA Assocs., Boston, 1978-81, gen. ptnr., 1982-89, mng. dir., 1989—; bd. dirs. Ontract Computer Sys., Mpls., Raxco, Inc., Rockville, Md., Software 2000, Hyannis Mass., Q-Star Techs. Inc., Rockville, Ansys, Inc., Houston, Pa. Trustee Chatham Coll.; mem. Mass. Gov.'s Coun. on Growth and Tech. Mem. Nat. Venture Capital Orgn., New England Venture Capital Assn. (bd. dirs.). Avocations: theatre, reading, art, skiing, travel. Office: TA Assocs 125 High St Boston MA 02110

MORBY, JEFFREY LEWIS, banker, investment banker; b. Reno, Aug. 4, 1937; s. Andrew E. and Velda (Warren) M.; m. Jacqueline Collins, June 21, 1959; children: Andrew J., Michelle L. BS in Engring., Stanford U., 1959; MBA, Harvard U., 1961. Gen. mgr. Argentina/Brazil divs. Bank of Boston, Buenos Aires, Sao Paulo, 1969-75; sr. v.p. Latin Am. Bank of Boston, Boston, 1975-78; sr. v.p. loan rev. div., 1978-80, sr. v.p. N.E. div., 1980-81, sr. v.p. strategic planning, 1981-83, group exec. v.p. investment banking, 1983-84; vice chair, bd. dirs. Crocker Nat. Corp., San Francisco, 1984-86; vice chair, dir. Am. Express Bank, Ltd. N.Y.C., 1986-88; vice chmn. Mellon Bank Corp., Pitts., 1990—; chmn. Mellon Bank Europe, 1993—; bd. dirs. Boston Co., Boston Safe Deposit and Trust Co. Founder, pres. Bank of Boston Found., Buenos Aires, 1982; founder Argentine Sch. Exports, Buenos Aires, 1982; bd. dirs. New Eng. Coun., Boston, 1984, Pitts. Office Promotion, 1990, Pitts. Cultural Trust, Duquesne U. Recipient Congressman's medal U.S. Congress, 1954; Howard Hughes fellow Hughes Aircraft Co., 1959-61. Mem. Internat. Fin. (del. 1991), Internat. Monetary Conf. (alt. del. 1990-94), Bankers Roundtable, Duquesne Club, Laurel Valley Club, Al-

legheny Club. Avocations: sports, reading, travel. Office: Mellon Bank Corp 1 Mellon Bank Ctr Pittsburgh PA 15258-0001

MORCOTT, SOUTHWOOD J., automotive parts manufacturing company executive; b. 1939; married. Student, Davidson Coll.; MBA, U. Mich. Pres. Dana Corp., Toledo, 1963—; sales engineer, plant mgr. Dana Corp., Tyston, Ind., 1963-75; pres. Dana World Trade Corp., 1969; v.p. ops. Hayes Dana Ltd. Dana Corp., 1975-77, exec. v.p., gen. mgr., 1977-78, pres. Hayes-Dana Ltd., 1978-80, group v.p. Dana svc. parts group, 1980-84, pres. N.Am. ops., 1984-86, pres., chief operating officer, 1986—, chief exec. officer, 1989—, also chmn., dir., 1990—. Office: Dana Corp PO Box 1000 Toledo OH 43697-1000*

MORDECAI, BENJAMIN, theatrical producer, drama educator; b. N.Y.C., Dec. 10, 1944; s. Allen Lewis Mordecai and Florence Doris (Goldman) Holl; m. Sherry Lynn Morley, July 20, 1974; 1 child, Rachel Elizabeth. BA, Buena Vista Coll., 1967; MA, Eastern Mich. U., 1968; postgrad., Ind. U., 1968-70. Founder, producing dir. Ind. Repertory Theatre, Indpls., 1971-82; mng. dir. Yale Repertory Theatre, New Haven, 1982-93; assoc. dean Yale Sch. Drama, New Haven, 1992—; mng. ptnr. Benjamin Mordecai and Assocs., New York, 1992—; cons. Found. for the Extension and Devel. of the Am. Profl. Theatre, N.Y.C., 1974; adj. prof. Yale Sch. of Drama, 1982—; ind. cons., New Haven, 1984—. Dir.: (plays) Fables Here and Then, 1972, Dracula, 1973, Bird in the Hand, 1975; assoc. prodr.: (plays) Fences, 1987 (Tony award 1987), Joe Turner's Come & Gone, 1988 (N.Y. Drama Critics Circle award 1988), A Walk in the Woods, 1988; gen. mgr.: (play) A Walk in the Woods (USSR), 1989; exec. prodr.: (play) The Piano Lesson, 1990 (N.Y. Drama Critics Circle award 1990, Drama Desk award 1990), Two Trains Running, 1992, Angels in America (N.Y. Drama Critics award 1993, Tony award 1993, 94); prodr.: Redwood Curtain, 1993, Twilight: Los Angeles, 1992, 94; assoc. prodr.: The Kentucky Cycle, 1993; prodr.: Gate of Heaven (U.S. Holocaust Mus.), 1995. Recipient Disting. Svc. award Indpls. Jaycees, Indpls., 1979, spl. commendation City-County Coun., Inpls., 1982, Robert Whitehead award, 1993; named Outstanding Young Alumnus, Buena Vista Coll., 1987. Mem. League of Resident Theatres (exec. com. 1982-91), Assn. Arts Adminstrn. Educators (sec.-treas. 1984-88), Am./Soviet Theatre Initiative (bd. dirs. 1987—, pres. 1994—), Writers Theatre (bd. advisors 1983—), Stage Dirs. and Choreographers Found. (bd. dirs. 1990—), League Am. Theatres & Prodrs., Nat. Theatre Conf.

MORDEN, JOHN REID, Canadian government corporation administrator; b. Hamilton, Ont., Can., June 17, 1941; s. Warren Wilbert and Isabelle Gemmell (Reid) M.; m. Margaret Elizabeth Keens, June 27, 1964; children: Michael, Geoffrey. BA, Dalhousie U., Halifax, N.S., Can., 1962. Min., dep., permanent rep. Can. Mission UN, N.Y.C., 1980-82; counsellor Can. Embassy, Tokyo, 1975-78; dir. gen. Dept. External Affairs, Ottawa, Ont., 1982-84, asst. dep. min. trade policy, 1985-86; asst. dep. min. native claims Dept. Indian and No. Affairs, Ottawa, 1984-85; asst. sec. to cabinet Privy Coun. Office, Ottawa, 1986-87; dir. Can. Security Intelligence Svc., Ottawa, 1987-91; dep. min. of fgn. affairs, 1991-94; pres., CEO Atomic Energy Can. Ltd., Ottawa, 1994—; mem. internat. adv. bd. York U. Sch. Bus.; alt. gov. European Bank for Reconstrn. and Devel., 1991-94; bd. dirs. Can. Energy Coun., Red Cross Fractionation Corp. Mem. Can. Nuclear Assn. (bd. dirs.), Nuclear Project Mgrs. (bd. dirs.), Order St. Lazarus of Jerusalem, Rideau Club, Five Lakes Club. Avocations: reading, music, ballet.. Office: Atomic Energy Can Ltd, 244 Slater St, Ottawa, ON Canada K1A 0G2

MORDINI, MARILYN HEUER, physical education educator; b. Waukegan, Ill., Aug. 23, 1936; d. Lester and Evelyn (Scott) Heuer; m. Robert D. Mordini, Feb. 24, 1962; children: Robert Jr., Bruce, Beth. BS in Phys. Edn., Ill. State U., 1958; MS in Phys. Edn., Chgo. State U., 1994; MS in Adminstrn., Northeastern Ill. U., 1994. Tchr. phys. edn. Libertyville (Ill.) Pub. Schs., 1958-63, Highland Park (Ill.) Pub. Schs., 1978-81; tchr. phys. edn. North Chicago (Ill.) Sch. Dist. 187, 1981—, dir. intramural sports, 1985-92; tchr. phys. edn. Highland Park Summer Migrant Program, 1981-90; adv. bd. Park Dist. Highland Park, 1982-84. Rep. United Way, North Chicago, 1990-92; bd. dirs. Lake County divsn. Am. Heart Assn., 1992—, chmn. Highland Park/Highwood br. Lake County divsn., 1995—. Mem. AAHPERD, Ill. Assn. Health, Phys. Edn., Recreation and Dance (Elem. Phys. Educator of Yr. 1991, pres. northeastern dist. 1995—), Am. Fedn. Tchrs. Home: 2035 Grange Ave Highland Park IL 60035-1719

MORDO, JEAN HENRI, financial executive; b. Cairo, Arab Republic of Egypt, Feb. 2, 1945; came to U.S., 1970; s. Henri and Ameé (Arditi) M. m. Nicole Setton, 1966 (div. 1984); children: Candice, Nathaniel; m. Barbara Van Buren, Mar. 31, 1985; 1 child, Janelle. MS in Engring., Ecole Poly., Paris, 1966, MS in Stats., 1969; MBA, Stanford U., 1972. Cons. McKinsey & Co., N.Y.C., 1972-78; dir. planning Otis Elevator Co., West Palm Beach, Fla., 1978-80, dir. fin., 1980-82; v.p. fin. planning Otis Elevator Co., Farmington, Conn., 1982-84, v.p., contr., 1984-85, v.p. fin., 1985-89, 1989—, pres. Latin Am. ops., 1989-92; sr. v.p. fin. Pratt and Whitney, Hartford, Conn., 1992—. Home: 50 Woodford Hills Dr Avon CT 06001-3923 Office: Pratt & Whitney 400 Main St M/S 133-50 East Hartford CT 06108

MORDY, JAMES CALVIN, lawyer; b. Ashland, Kans., Jan. 3, 1927; s. Thomas Robson and Ruth (Floyd) M.; m. Marjory Ellen Nelson, Nov. 17, 1951; children: Jean Claire Mordy Jongeling, Rebecca Jane Mordy King, James Nelson. AB in Chemistry, U. Kans., 1947; JD, U. Mich., 1950; postgrad., George Washington U., 1950-51. Bar: Kans. 1950, Mo. 1950. Assoc. Morrison, Hecker, Buck, Cozad & Rogers, Kansas City, Mo., 1950-59; ptnr. Morrison & Hecker, Kansas City, 1959—; Bar: Kans. 1950, Mo. 1950; cert. in bus. bankruptcy Am. Bankruptcy Bd. Cert. Contbg. author: Missouri Bar Insurance Handbook, 1968, Missouri Bar Bankruptcy Handbook, 1991, 2d edit., 1995; contbr. articles to profl. jours. Chmn. bd. Broadway United Meth. Ch., Kansas City, 1964-70, chmn. bd. trustees, chmn. fin. com., 1988-90, 94; bd. dirs., exec. com. Dalla C. Lamb Neighborhood House, Kansas City, 1973-80; coun. mem. St. Paul Sch. Theology, Kansas City, 1986-95. Comdr. USNR, 1945-46, 51-53. Summerfield scholar, 1943-47; recipient Shepherd of the Lamb award Della C. Lamb Neighborhood House, 1980. Fellow Am. Bar Found. (life); mem. ABA, Am. Judicature Soc., Am. Bankruptcy Inst., Mo. Bar Assn., Kans. Bar Assn., Kansas City Met. Bar Assn., Lawyers Assn. Kansas City, Workout Profls. Assn. Kansas City, Univ. Club (v.p., bd. dirs. 1983, 86), Barristers Soc., Phi Beta Kappa, Delta Tau Delta (pres. Kansas City alumni chpt. 1965-72, pres. U. Kans. House Corp. 1966-72), Alpha Chi Sigma, Phi Alpha Delta. Avocations: travel, geography (maps), history, music, theology. Home: 8741 Ensley Ln Leawood KS 66206-1615 Office: Morrison & Hecker 2600 Grand Blvd Kansas City MO 64108-4606

MORE, DOUGLAS MCLOCHLAN, lawyer; b. N.Y.C., Apr. 21, 1926; s. Morgan Berkeley and Lucinda (Bateson) M.; m. Pamela Bennett Marr, Aug. 6, 1954; children—Robin Maclachlan More Eddy, Alison Marr More Davies. Grad., Phillips Exeter Acad., 1943; B.A., Harvard U., 1947; LL.B., Columbia U., 1950. Bar: N.Y. State bar 1950, Conn. bar 1981, Fla. bar 1983. With N.Y. Trust Co., 1950-51; assoc. firm Bigham, Englar, Jones & Houston, N.Y.C., 1951-53; fin. analyst Johns-Manville Corp., 1953-54; assoc. firm Kissam & Halpin, N.Y.C., 1954-59; assoc. counsel Hooker Chem. Corp., 1959-63, gen. counsel, 1963-72, v.p. 1967-72; v.p. law Airco Inc., 1972-75; gen. counsel Beker Industries Corp., 1975-81, v.p., 1975-78, sr. v.p., 1978-81; ptnr. firm More Phillips & Duncan, P.C., Greenwich, Conn., 1981-88, of counsel, 1988—. Served to lt. (j.g.) USNR, 1943-46. Mem. ABA, Conn. Bar Assn., Greenwich Bar Assn., Phi Delta Phi, Phoenix S-K Club, Hasty Pudding Inst. 1770 (Harvard). Home and Office: 27 Skylark Rd Greenwich CT 06830-4624

MOREHART, DONALD HADLEY, food products executive; b. Little Rock, Nov. 6, 1938; s. Homer H. and Golda (Welton) M.; m. Maribeth Hornsby, July 8, 1961; children: Barry, Linley. BA, DePaul U.; BBA, U. of Ark., 1960. Various positions Anderson Clayton Foods, Dallas, 1960-77; v.p. refined oil Central Soya Co. Inc., Ft. Wayne, Ind., 1977—; comm. adv. com. Inst. Shortening & Edible Oils, Washington, 1985—. Treas. YMCA (Ft. Wayne), 1987—; mem. Leadership Ft. Wayne, Class of 1988. Republican. Methodist. Office: Central Soya Co Inc PO Box 2507 Fort Wayne IN 46801-2507

MOREHEAD, CHARLES RICHARD, insurance company executive; b. Independence, Mo., Jan. 25, 1947; s. Robert E. and Ruth Elizabeth (Taylor) M.; m. Donna Joyce Shores, Feb. 17, 1968 children: Grant, Blaine. BSBA, U. Mo., 1971. CPA, Fla. Mem. staff Peat, Marwick, Mitchell & Co., Kansas City, Mo., 1972-75; audit mgr. Peat, Marwick, Mitchell & Co., Jacksonville, Fla., 1976-83, audit ptnr., 1983-86; treas., CFO Standard Havens, Inc., Kansas City, 1975-76; sr. v.p., treas. Am. Heritage Life Ins. Co., Jacksonville, Fla., 1986-94, exec. v.p., CFO, 1994—, also bd. dirs. Mem. AICPA, Fla. Soc. CPA's. Home: 4050 Chicora Wood Pl Jacksonville FL 32224 Office: Am Heritage Life Ins Co 1776 Am Heritage Life Dr Jacksonville FL 32224

MOREHEAD, JAMES CADDALL, JR., architect, educator; b. Bradenton, Fla., Oct. 29, 1913; s. James Caddall and Jeannette Dandridge (White) M.; m. Martha Petty Netting, Aug. 27, 1940; children: James Caddall, III, Naomi Willson, Kenneth Fielding. B.A., Princeton U., 1935; B.Arch., Carnegie Mellon U., 1939. Instr. math. Carnegie Mellon U., 1936-40; architecture, 1938-40; instr. architecture Rice U., 1940-42, 46, asst. prof., 1946-48, assoc. prof., 1948-51, prof., 1951-79, prof. emeritus, 1979—, head dept., 1953-61; registrar, 1964-79; asso. Wilson, Morris & Crain, Houston, 1951-55; past partner Morehead and Ransom (Architects); pvt. practice of architecture, 1960—; dir. of permits City of Piney Point Village, Tex., 1954-81, 86—. Author: (with J.C. Morehead, Sr.) Handbook of Perspective Drawing, 1952, Perspective and Projective Geometries, A Comparison, 1955, Elementary Structures, 2 vols, Intermediate Structures, ACSA Learning Packages, 1974, 75, A Walking Tour of Rice U., 1984, 2d edit., 1990. Dir. San Jacinto Girl Scouts, 1954-61; Mem. Study Commn. on Archtl. Edn. in South, So. Regional Edn. Bd., 1953, chmn. planning and zoning commn., Piney Point Village, Tex., 1954-81. Served as lt. col. F.A. AUS, 1942-46. Decorated Bronze Star with oak leaf cluster; recipient Alpha Rho Chi Medal in Architecture Carnegie Inst. Tech., 1939; Award of Merit Houston chpt. AIA, 1953. Fellow AIA (treas. Houston chpt. 1950-51); mem. Houston Philos. Soc. Scarab. Home: 354 Piney Point Rd Houston TX 77024-6506

MOREHOUSE, DAVID C., military lawyer. Judge advocate gen. Dept. Air Force. Office: USAF Judge Advocate Gen The Pentagon Washington DC 20330

MOREHOUSE, DAVID FRANK, geologist; b. Charles City, Iowa, Dec. 8, 1943; s. Neal Francis and Florence E. (Schwendener) M. BS in Gen. Scis., State U. Iowa, 1967; MS in Geology, Iowa State U., 1970; postgrad., Pa. State U., 1970-74. Staff geologist Nat. Gas Survey and Planning and Spl. Projects Div., FPC, Washington, 1974-78; dir. Info. Processing and Interpretation and Analysis Divs. Oil and Gas Info. System, Energy Info. Adminstrn., Washington, 1978-80, sr. supervisory geologist, 1980—; advisor petroleum data sys. U. Okla., Norman, 1975-86; Energy Info. Adminstrn. rep. Am. Gas Assn. Com. on Natural Gas Res., Washington, 1991-95, Potential Gas Com., Boulder, Colo., 1991—. V.p. Iowa Jr. Acad. Sci., 1961. Recipient awards for outstanding performance Fed. Govt., Washington, 1974-95. Fellow Nat. Speleological Soc.; mem. AAAS, AIME, Internat. Assn. Math. Geology, N.Y. Acad. Scis., AGI, Internat. Platform Assn. Congregationalist. Achievements include first evidence that sulfuric acid can be important to speleogenesis; exercising the prin. responsibility for design and establishment of fed. govts. domestic oil and gas reserves estimation and analysis program. Office: Energy Info Adminstrn EI443 1000 Independence Ave SW Washington DC 20585-0001

MOREHOUSE, DOROTHY VAN WINKLE, museum director; b. Paterson, N.J., Oct. 1, 1928; d. John Shaw and Verna Kuett VanWinkle; m. Curtis Bradley Morehouse, Oct. 8, 1950; children—Susan B., Charles Schuyler, Elizabeth Curtis. B.A., Cornell U., 1949. Docent, Cin. Art Mus., 1961-63; trustee Monmouth Mus., Lincroft, N.J., 1964-67, 70-78, dir., 1978—; ednl. coordinator Stanford U. Art Mus. (Calif.), 1967-70; reader Inst. Mus., 1980, 81. Mem. bd. edn. Rumson Sch. Dist., 1979-83, pres., 1981-83. Mem. Monmouth County Hist. Assn., N.J. Assn. Mus. Club: Jr. League Monmouth County. Editor: New Jersey, A Heritage for Now and Tomorrow, 1976. Office: Monmouth Mus Newman Springs Rd PO Box 359 Lincroft NJ 07738-0359

MOREHOUSE, LAWRENCE GLEN, veterinarian, educational administrator; b. Manchester, Kans., July 21, 1925; s. Edwy O. and Ethel (Glenn) M.; m. GeorgiaAnn Lewis, Oct. 6, 1956; children: Timothy, Glenn Ellen. BS in Biol. Scis. Kans. State U., 1952, DVM, 1952; MS in Animal Pathology, Purdue U., 1956, PhD, 1960. Veterinarian County Vet. Hosp., St. Louis, 1952-53; supr. Brucellosis labs. Purdue U., Lafayette, Ind., 1953-60; staff veterinarian lab. svcs. USDA, Washington, 1960-61; discipline leader in pathology and toxicology, animal health div. USDA Nat. Animal Disease Lab., Ames, Iowa, 1962-64; prof., chmn. dept. veterinary pathology Coll. Vet. Medicine U. Mo., Columbia, 1964-67, 84-86; dir. Vet. Med. Diagnostic Lab., 1968-88; prof. emeritus Coll. Vet. Medicine U. Mo., Columbia, 1986—; cons. to U.S. Dept Agr., Surgeon Gen. U.S. Army, Am. Inst. Biol. Scis. Nat. Acad. Sci., Miss. State U., St. Louis Zoo Residency Tng. Program, Miss. Vet. Med. Assn., Okla State Univ., Pa. State Dept. Agriculture, Ohio State Dept. Agriculture; adv. com. med. rsch. and devel. U.S. Army. Co-editor: Mycotoxic Fungi, Mycotoxins, Mycotoxicoses: An Encyclopedic Handbook, 3 vols., 1977; contbr. numerous articles on diseases of animals to profl. jours. With USN, 1943-46, U.S. Army, 1952-56. Recipient Outstanding Svc. award U.S. Dept Agr., 1959, Merit Cert., 1963, 64, Disting. Svc. award Coll. Vet. Medicine U. Mo., 1987. Fellow Royal Soc. Health London; mem. Am. Vet. Med. Assn., Mo. Vet. Med. Assn., Nat. Assn. Vet. Lab. Diagnosticians (E.P. Pope award 1976, chmn. lab. accreditation bd. 1972-79, 87-90), World Assn. Vet. Lab. Diagnosticians (bd. dirs. 1983—), N.Y. Acad. Sci., U.S. Animal Health Assn., Am. Assn. Lab. Animal Sci., Mo. Soc. Microbiology, Am. Assn. Avian Pathologists. Presbyterian. Home: 916 Danforth Dr Columbia MO 65201-6164 Office: U Mo Vet Med Diagnostic Lab PO Box 6023 Columbia MO 65201

MOREIRA, MARCIO MARTINS, advertising executive; b. Sao Paulo, Brazil, Nov. 20, 1947; came to U.S. 1980; naturalized, 1990; s. Guido Martins and Maria Rosa (Macrine) M.; children from previous marriage: Joaquim Pedro Rezende Martins Moreira; m. Maria Auxiliadora Godinho, Oct. 18, 1981; children: Eliana Maria Godinho Martins Moreira. Ed., U. Sao Paulo, Brazil, 1970. TV producer-copywriter McCann-Erickson, Sao Paulo, Brazil, 1967-71; creative dir. McCann-Erickson, Sao Paulo, 1974-77; group creative dir. McCann-Erickson, London, Lisbon and Frankfurt, 1971-74; executive creative dir. McCann-Erickson, Latin America, 1977-80; internat. creative dir. McCann-Erickson, N.Y.C., 1980-88; vice chmn., chief creative officer McCann Erickson Worldwide, N.Y.C., 1988—; exec. v.p., regional dir. Asia-Pacific McCann-Erickson Worldwide, N.Y.C., 1995—; lectr. various univs. Author: Terraplenagem, 1968 Liquidacao, 1979; lyricist, 1968—; contbr. articles to profl. jours. U.S. judge, pres. jury Cannes Film Festival, 1989; chmn. bd. judges The New York Festivals. Recipient 5 Clio awards, 1976-89, Gold Lion, Silver Lion, Bronze Lion awards, Cannes, France, H.K. McCann award, Brazil, 1977, Paul Foley award Interpub. Group of Cos., 1983, Terence Cardinal Cooke medal for Disting. Svc. in Health Care, N.Y. Med. Coll., 1994. Mem. Brazilian-Am. C. of C. (bd. dir.). Republican. Roman Catholic. Avocations: cinema, songwriting, cars, swimming. Office: McCann-Erickson Worldwide 750 3rd Ave New York NY 10017-2701

MOREIRA, MARTHA, critical care nurse; b. N.Y.C., Mar. 1, 1951; d. Miguel and Georgina (Caraballosa) M.; children: Dennis, Rebeca, Aimee, Amanda. AAS, Middlesex County Coll., 1973. RN, N.J. Charge nurse, staff nurse Robert Wood Johnson Med. Ctr., New Brunswick, N.J.; critical care relief nurse Favorite Nurses, Union, N.J.; charge nurse telemetry Muhlenberg Regional Med. Ctr., Plainfield, N.J., nurse mgr. Mem. Am. Assn. Critical Care Nurses.

MOREL, FRANÇOIS MARIE MICHEL, environmental geology educator; b. Versailles, France, Oct. 11, 1944; came to U.S. 1967; s. André M.J. Morel and Elizabeth Penicaud; m. Nicole M.L. Laurens, July 8, 1967; children: Sébastien, Chantal. License-ès-Scis. in Math. Appliquées, U. Grenoble, France, 1966, diplôme d'Ingénieur Hydraulicien, 1967; MS in Civil Engring., Calif. Inst. Tech., 1968, PhD in Engring. Scis., 1971. Rsch. fellow in environ. engring. scis. Calif. Inst. Tech., Pasadena, 1971-73; asst. prof. to assoc. prof. to prof. MIT, Cambridge, 1973-94; prof. geology Princeton (N.J.) U., 1994—; vis. scientist Woods Hole Oceanographic Instn., 1982—; assoc. dir. for rsch. Ecole des Mines de Paris, 1986; vis. prof. Ecole Normale Supérieure, Paris, 1987—; panel on marine mineral tech. Nat. Rsch. Coun., 1976-77, com. on ocean waste transp., 1982-84, com. on irrigation-induced water quality problems, 1985-88; participant workshops Nat. Oceanic and Atmospheric Adminstrn., 1977, 78, 79, tech. reviewer, cons.; panel on ocean mining Nat. Adv. Com. for Oceans and Atmosphere, 1981-82; participant workshops, cons. EPA, Bur. Land Mgmt., Nat. Aerospace Adminstrn., Internat. Joint Commn.; environ. cons. Institut Nat. de l'Environnement Indsl. et des Risques, Environ. Def. Fund, Nashua Corp., Water Purification Assocs., Mass. Exec. Office Environ. Affairs, Procter and Gamble, Nat. Oceanic and Atmospheric Adminstrn., Ocean Mining Co., Pelican Pipe Co., Nat. Highway Adminstrn., Homestake Mining Co., Tetra Tech, MITRE Corp., Ciba-Geigy, Alcoa, Gradient Corp., AMOCO, other private and pub. interest groups. Author: Principles of Aquatic Chemistry, 1983, (with D.A. Dzombak) Surface Complexation Modeling: Hydrous Ferric Oxide, 1990, (with J.G. Hering) Principles and Applications of Aquatic Chemistry, 2d edit., 1993; co-editor vol. 36, No. 8 of Limnology & Oceanography, 1991; contbr. numerous chpts. to books including Ocean Margin Processes in Global Change, Aquatic Chemical Kinetics, Chemical Processes in Lakes, also articles to jours. including Limnol. and Oceanography, Environ. Sci. and Tech., Deep-Sea Rsch., Biol. Oceanography, Water Rsch. Named Doherty prof. in ocean utilization, 1974-77; Govt. Ministry of Fgn. Affairs scholar, 1967, Fulbright Internat. travel scholar, 1967. Mem. AAAS, Am. Chem. Soc. (adv. bd. Environ. Sci. & Tech. 1978-83, assoc. editor Environ. Sci. & Tech. 1980), Am. Soc. of Limnology and Oceanography (organizer of symposium 1978, mem. editorial bd. Limnology & Oceanography 1980-83, editor spl. issue Limnology & Oceanography 1990), New Eng. Aquarium (sci. coun. 1988-90), Assn. of Environ. Engring. Profs., Am. Geophys. Union, Biogeochemistry (cons. editor 1991—). Achievements include research in theoretical and experimental studies on fate and effects of chemical pollutants; computer modeling of chemical characteristics of natural and polluted waters; coordination chemistry, surface chemistry, and photochemistry of trace metals in natural waters; interactions between the chemistry and microbiota in aquatic systems; trace metal nutrition and toxicity in phytoplankton. Home: 210 Constitution Dr Princeton NJ 08540 Office: Princeton U Dept Geology Guyot Hall Princeton NJ 08540

MORELAN, PAULA KAY, choreographer; b. Lafayette, Ind., Nov. 24, 1949; d. Dickie Booth and Marian Maxine (Fetterhoff) M.; m. Kerim Sayan, Aug. 10, 1974. Student U. Utah, 1968-69; BFA, Tex. Christian U., 1972; postgrad., El Centro Coll., 1969-70. Tchr., Rosello Sch. Ballet, Dallas, 1972-74; mgr., tchr. Ballet Arts Ctr., Dallas, 1974-76; owner, tchr. Ballet Classique, Garland, Tex., 1976-87, Garland Ballet Acad., 1977-87; asst. to Mythra Rosello, Tex. Civic Ballet, Dallas, 1972-74; assoc. artistic dir. Dance Repertory Theatre Dallas, 1974-75; artistic dir. Dance Repertory Theatre Dallas, 1975-76, Garland (Tex.) Ballet Assn., 1977-90, Classical Ballet Acad., Performing Arts Sch., 1987-90; resident choreographer Garland Civic Theatre, 1988—.

MORELAND, ALVIN FRANKLIN, veterinarian; b. Morven, Ga., Sept. 5, 1931; s. Robert Hamilton and Laura Eloise (Edenfield) M.; m. Mary Ellen Hardee, Feb. 12, 1955; children: Ellen, Frank, Clyde. BS in Edn., Ga. Tchrs. Coll., 1951; MSEd, Ga., 1952, DVM, 1960. Diplomate Am. Coll. Lab. Animal Medicine. Asst. prof. U. Fla. Coll. Vet. Medicine, Charlottesville, 1962-63; asst. prof. to prof. U. Fla. Coll. Vet. Medicine, Gainesville, 1963—; cons. vet. NASA, Kennedy Space Ctr., Fla., Bionetics Corp., 1983—. Contbr. articles to profl. jours. Served to lt. USNR, 1952-56. Mem. AVMA, Am. Assn. Lab. Animal Sci., Fla. Vet. Med. Assn. (Gold Star award 1976), Alachua Vet. Med. Assn., Internat. Assn. Aquatic Animal Medicine. Methodist.

MORELAND, DONALD EDWIN, plant physiologist; b. Enfield, Conn., Oct. 12, 1919; s. Albert Sinclair and Ruth (Cowan) M.; m. Verdie Brown Stallings, Nov. 6, 1954; 1 child, Donna Faye; stepchildren: Frank C., Paul Ziglar. BS in Forestry, N.C. State U., 1949, MS in Plant Physiology, 1950, PhD in Plant Physiology, 1953. Plant physiologist SUNY Coll. Forestry, Syracuse, 1952-53; plant physiologist USDA-Agrl. Rsch. Svc., Raleigh, N.C., 1953-71, rsch. leader, 1972-78, sr. exec., 1979—; asst. prof. to prof. N.C. State U., Raleigh, 1953—; mem. toxicology study sect. NIH, USPHS, Bethesda, Md., 1963-67. Editor: Biochemical Responses Induced by Herbicides, 1982; mem. editorial bd. Pesticide Biochemistry and Physiology, 1971—, Pesticide Sci., 1987—; contbr. articles to profl. jours. 1st lt. U.S. Army, 1941-46. AEC predoctoral fellow, 1950-52. Fellow AAAS, Weed Sci. Soc. Am. (outstanding rsch. award 1973); mem. Am. Chem. Soc., Plant Growth Regulator Soc. Am., Am. Soc. Plant Physiologists, So. Weed Sci. Soc., Sigma Xi. Avocations: woodworking, surf fishing, square dancing. Home: 1508 Pineview Dr Raleigh NC 27606-2562 Office: USDA-Agrl Rsch Svc NC State U Crop Sci Dept 4123 Williams Hall Raleigh NC 27695

MORELAND, ERNEST FERMAN, dean; b. Hiawassee, Ga., Aug. 22, 1934; s. Dean and Dora Bell (Dayton) M.; m. Helen Burch, Apr. 14, 1955; children: Michael Ernest, Rhonda. BS in Edn., U. Ga., 1960; MA in Edn. Western Carolina U., 1962; EdD, Ind. U., 1967. Tchr. Monroe (Ga.) Area High Sch., 1962-64; dir. edn. media N.E. La. U., Monroe, 1967-69; dir. edn. media U. Md. Dental Sch., Balt., 1969-74, assoc. dean acad., 1974-91; v.p. acad. affairs U. Md., Balt., 1991—; cons. Pan Am. Health Orgn., Washington, 1972-81, ADA, Chgo., 1978, 88-91, VA Perry Point, Md., 1976-91. Author: Manual for Chairside Dental Assisting in Dental Offices, 1976; editor: Balt. Coll. Dental Surgery Jour., 1979-80; (manuals and films) Dental Assisting Tng. Program, 1974. Chmn. admonist. Columbia Bapt. Fellowship, Columbia, Md., 1983-85, trustee, 1986-89. Devel. fellow Ind. U., 1965, 66. Mem. Am. Assn. Dental Schs. (also learning resources sect.). Home: 5151 Darting Bird Ln Columbia MD 21044-1503 Office: U Md Office Acad Affairs 520 W Lombard St Baltimore MD 21201-1627

MORELAND, RONALD WILLIAM, insurance company executive; b. Decatur, Ill., Dec. 14, 1940; s. John William and Susan Irene (Daniels) M.; m. Jean Ann Cloyd, June 15, 1963 (div. 1976); children: Michael, Susan; m. Randi Elaine Thompson, June 3, 1984; 1 child, Lindsey. BEd, Eastern Ill. U., 1962, MEd, U. Ill., 1963. CLU. Group mgr. Prudential Ins. Co., Chgo., 1963-68; regional mgr. Prudential Ins. Co., San Francisco, 1968-71; dir. group ins. Prudential Ins. Co., Newark, 1971-73, N.Y.C., 1973-78; v.p. group ins. Prudential Ins. Co., Los Angeles, 1983-88; exec. v.p. Transamerica Occidental Life Ins. Co., Los Angeles, 1983-88; pres. Western Ops. Equicor, Los Angeles, 1988—. Mem. Wilshire County Club. Clubs: Jonathan (Los Angeles); Beverly Hills Country (Cheviot Hills, Calif.). Avocations: tennis, golf, scuba, jogging.

MORELLA, CONSTANCE ALBANESE, congresswoman; b. Somerville, Mass., Feb. 12, 1931; d. Salvatore and Mary Christine (Fallette) Albanese; m. Anthony C. Morella, Aug. 21, 1954; children: Paul, Mark, Laura; guardians of: Christine, Catherine, Louise, Rachel, Paul, Ursula. AA, Boston U., 1950, AB, 1954; MA, Am. U., 1967, D of Pub. Svc. (hon.), 1988; D of Pub. Svc. (hon.), Norwich U. and Dickinson Coll., 1989. Tchr. Montgomery County (Md.) Pub. Schs., 1956-60; instr. Am. U., 1968-70; prof. Montgomery Coll., Rockville, Md., 1970-86; mem. Md. Ho. Dels., Annapolis, 1979-86, 100th-103rd Congresses from 8th Md. dist., 1987—; adv. bd. Am. Univ., Washington; trustee Capitol Coll. Laurel, Md. Trustee Capitol Coll, Laurel, Md., 1977—; chair Sci. Com. Tech. Subcom., Basic Rsch. Subcom., coun. mem. Montgomery County United Way; adv. coun. Montgomery County Hospice Soc.; hon. bd. mem. Nat. Kidney Found; active Human Rights Caucus, co-chair Congressional Women's Caucus, Black Caucus; chair Gov. Reform and Oversight Com. Avocations: theatre, tennis, reading. Office: US Ho of Reps 106 Cannon House Office Bu Washington DC 20515 also: 51 Monroe St Rockville MD 20850-2417

MORELLI, WILLIAM ANNIBALE, SR., aerospace manufacturing company executive; b. Cin., July 2, 1938; s. Annibale and Angiolina (DiPietro) M.; m. Velma Lois Hammond, May 12, 1962 (div. Sept. 1974); children: Paula Anne, Cathi Susan, Melissa Anne; m. Beverly Ann Bulmer, Feb. 14, 1975 (div. 1995); 1 child, William A. Jr.; stepchild, Stacey Dawn Watson. BBA, U. Cin., 1960. Fin. analyst Federated Dept. Stores, Cin., 1961-66; mfrs. rep. Hyde Corp., Cin., 1966-75; sales mgr. Clipper Industries, Roseville, Mich., 1975-76, Bachan Aerospace Corp., Madison Heights, Mich., 1976-83; pres. Caratron Industries Inc., Warren, Mich., 1983—, Norwood Precision Products, 1991—; v.p. TKO Sports Prodn. Ltd., 1992—; pres. Caratron RDM, L.C., 1994—, TKO Sports Prodn. Ltd., 1991-93. Apptd. to Gov.'s Entrepreneurial and Small Bus. Commn., 1988-91, bd. dirs. Macomb-St. Clair Pvt. Industry Coun. Ill.; chmn. bd. Mich. Found., Inc. Mem. Am. Gear Mfrs. Assn., Warren C. of C. (bd. dirs., chmn. 1988-90), Italian Am. C. of C., Phoenix Cir. Club (bd. dirs., treas. 1988-89, v.p. 1990-91), Masons, Shriners. Office: Caratron Industries Inc 27955 College Park Dr Warren MI 48093-4877

MORELLO, JOSEPH ALBERT, musician, educator; b. Springfield, Mass., July 17, 1928; s. Joseph Charles and Lilia (LaPalme) M.; m. Jean Ann Mehnert. Grad. high sch., Springfield. Ind. drummer Springfield, 1945-49; drummer Gil Melé, Stan Kenton, Tal Farlow, Johnny Smith, N.Y.C., 1953-55, Dave Brubeck Quartet, touring worldwide, 1955-68; clinician Selmer Ludwig Drum Co., Elkhart, Ind., 1957-92; leader Joe Morello Quartet, 1979—; clinician DW Drums, Oxnard, Calif., 1993—; rec. artist Digital Music Products Inc., 1993—. Rec. artist Savoy, Capitol, Norgran, Blue Note, Columbia, RCA labels; innovator finger control in jazz drumming; author: Joe Morello Drum Method, The Natural Approach to Technique, 1993, Joe Morello Drum Method 2, 1994, also New Directions in Rhythm, Rudimental Jazz, Off the Record, Master Studies; releases include (with Joe Morello Quartet) Going Places, 1993, Morello's Standard Time, 1994. Recipient New Star award Downbeat mag., 1955, Melody Maker mag. award, 1963-67, Jazz mag. award, 1964-67, Thomas A. Edison lifetime achievement award, 1990, record, CD and tape release RCA Bluebird Label, 1989, CD Joe Morello Quartet Going Places release DMP Label, 1990; poll winner Downbeat mag., 1963-65, Playboy mag., 1963-67; named to Hall of Fame, Modern Drummer mag., 1988, Percussive Arts Soc. Hall of Fame, 1993. Avocation: photography.

MORELOCK, JAMES CRUTCHFIELD, mathematician; b. Martin, Tenn., Feb. 7, 1920; s. Joseph Fletcher and Laura Martha (Crutchfield) M.; student Bethel Coll., McKenzie, Tenn., 1937-39; B.S., Memphis State Coll., 1941; M.A., U. Mo., 1948; Ph.D., U. Fla., 1952; m. Eugenia Scott Browne, Apr. 29, 1945 (dec.); children: Elinor Morelock Smith, Constance Morelock Grear (dec.), Diana Morelock Brown. Instr. astronomy and math. U. Fla., Gainesville, 1949-52; asst. prof. math. Auburn (Ala.) U., 1952-56; head math. dept. King Coll., Bristol, Tenn., 1956-60; mathematician U.S. Naval Computation Lab., Dahlgren, Va., 1960-61; mem. staff Computation Ctr. Gen. Electric, Huntsville, Ala., 1961-63; mathematician computation lab. Marshall Space Flight Center, Huntsville, Ala., 1963-78, ret., 1978. Instl. rep. to Boy Scouts, Civitan Club, Auburn, 1952-56; v.p. Huntsville Concert Band, 1963—; mem. Internat. Platform Assn. Served with USAAF, 1941-45; PTO. Recipient U.S. Treasury award, 1968, NASA 10 year Achievement award, 1969, NASA Apollo Achievement award, 1969; Manning scholar, 1940-41, U. Fla. fellow, 1952. Mem. Am. Math. Soc., Math. Assn. Am., Assn. Computing Machinery, Bristol Astronomy Soc. (pres. 1956-60), Internal Platform Assn. Methodist. Club: Pistol. Home: 2515 Oak View Dr Mobile AL 36606-1830

MOREN, NICHOLAS CHARLES, investment and holding company executive; b. Hampton, Va., Sept. 12, 1946; s. Stephen A. and Mary Jane (Dederich) M.; divorced; children: Emily Jane, Alix Evelyn, Benjamin Charles; m. Margaret-Ann Howie, May 14, 1988. B.A., Brown U., 1968; M.B.A., Wharton Sch., 1972. With Trans World Airlines, N.Y.C., 1972-79; asst. controller Transworld Corp., N.Y.C., 1979-81, asst. treas., 1982-83, treas., 1983-85; v.p., treas. TW Services, Inc. (formerly Transworld Corp.), N.Y.C., 1986—. Club: Springdale Golf (Princeton, N.J.). Home: 138 Poe Rd Princeton NJ 08540-4122 Office: Loral Infrared Imaging Systems 2 Forbes Rd Lexington MA 02173 also: Canteen Corp 1430 Merchandise Mart Chicago IL 60654

MORENA, JOHN JOSEPH, manufacturing engineer, executive; b. Rockaway Beach, N.Y., Dec. 6, 1937; s. John Michael and Theresa (Verdoni) M.; children from a previous marriage: John Joseph, Stephen Scott, Todd Theodore; m. Diane Pizo, Feb. 9, 1990. Student, NYU, 1956-65, SUNY, 1956-65, FAU, Boca Raton, Fla., 1988-91. Cert. mfg. engr. With AIL, Melville, N.Y., 1962-66, Maxson Electronics, Great River, N.Y., 1966-70, Airtron/Litton Inc., Morris Plains, N.J., 1970-72, Microlab/FXR, Livingston, N.J., 1972-74; v.p. Fibes Drums Inc., Farmingdale, N.Y., 1974-77; pres. Meam Inc., Farmingdale, 1977-79, GSU Inc., Farmingdale, 1976-80, Am. Composites Edn. Inc., Stuart, Fla., 1980—; rsch. dir. Am. Composites Mfg. Learning Ctr., Stuart, Fla., 1983—; primary tech. advanced materials advisor Superconducting Super Collider, Dallas, 1988-94; exec. dir. Am. Maglev Star Orgn., Stuart, 1991—. Author: Advanced Composite Mold Making, 1988, World Composites Encyclopedia, 1992, Advanced Composites World Reference Dictionary, 1995; contbr. articles to profl. jours.; patentee in field. Avocations: instrumental music, painting, boating, sports, writing. Home: 4540 Sandpebble Trace # 104 Stuart FL 34996 Office: Am Composites Edn Inc Am Composites Bldg 425 California Ave Stuart FL 34994

MORENCY, PAULA J., lawyer; b. Oak Park, Ill., Mar. 13, 1955. AB magna cum laude, Princeton U., 1977; JD, U. Va., 1980. Bar: Ill. 1980, U.S. Dist. Ct. (no. dist.) Ill. 1980, U.S. Ct. Appeals (7th cir.) 1981, U.S. Ct. Appeals (5th cir.) 1990. Assoc. Mayer, Brown & Platt, Chgo., 1980-86, ptnr., 1987-94; ptnr. Schiff Hardin & Waite, Chgo., 1994—. Contbr. author: Federal Litigation Guide Vol. 3, 1985. Mem. ABA, Chgo. Coun. of Lawyers (bd. govs. 1989-93). Office: Schiff Hardin & Waite 7200 Sears Tower Chicago IL 60606

MORENO, FEDERICO ANTONIO, federal judge; b. Caracas, Venezuela, Apr. 10, 1952; came to U.S., 1963; s. Francisco Jose and Rejane Genevieve (Nogues) M.; m. M. Cristina Man Morales-Gomez, May 31, 1977; children: Cristi, Ricky, Victoria. AB cum laude, U. Notre Dame, 1974; JD, U. Miami, 1974. Bar: Fla. 1978, U.S. Dist. Ct. (so. dist.) 1978, (mid. dist.) 1986, U.S. Ct. Appeals (5th cir.) 1979, (11th cir.) 1981, U.S. Supreme Ct. 1981. Ptnr. Thornton, Rothman & Moreno, Miami, 1982-86; judge Dade County Cir. Ct., Miami, 1986-90; dist. judge U.S. Dist. Ct. (so. dist.) Fla., Miami, 1990—. Recipient People Helping People award United Way, 1980, Pro Bono award Pub. Interest Law Bank, 1985. Mem. ABA, Fed. Bar Assn., Fla. Bar Assn., Dade County Bar Assn., Trial Lawyer's Assn. Roman Catholic. Office: US Courthouse 301 N Miami Ave Miami FL 33128-7701

MORENO, GLEN RICHARD, banker; b. San Jose, Calif., July 24, 1943; s. John and Ellen (Oberg) M.; m. Cheryl Lynne Eschbach, Mar. 26, 1966. B.A. with distinction, Stanford U., 1965; J.D., Harvard U., 1969. Group exec. Citicorp, N.Y.C., 1969-87; dir. Fidelity Internat. Ltd., Bermuda, 1987—; chmn. Indonesian Capital Fund Ltd., 1987—, chmn., bd. dirs. Latin Am. Fund; dir. ED&F Man Group PLC; bd. dirs. India Fund., Rea Bros. PLC. Bd. govs. Ditchley Found., Oxford, Eng., 1983—. Mem. Bucks Club. Home: "Neala" Rt 1 Box 73 Madison VA 22727 also: 3 Whitehall Ct Flat 124A, London SW1A 2EL, England Office: Fidelity Investments, 25 Lovat Ln, London EC3, England

MORENO, MANUEL D., bishop; Educator U. of Calif., L.A., St. John's Sem., Camarillo, Calif. Ordained priest Roman Cath. church, 1961. Ordained aux. bishop of Los Angeles, titular bishop of Tanagra, 1977; installed as bishop of Tucson, 1982—. Office: PO Box 31 192 S Stone Ave Tucson AZ 85702*

MORENO, RITA, actress; b. Humacao, P.R., Dec. 11, 1931; m. Leonard I. Gordon, June 18, 1965; 1 child, Fernanda Luisa. Spanish dancer since childhood, night club entertainer; appeared on Broadway in The Sign in Sidney Brustein's Window, 1964-65, Gantry, 1969-70, The Last of the Red Hot Lovers, 1970-71, The National Health, 1974, The Ritz, 1975, Wally's Cafe, 1981, The Odd Couple, 1985; motion picture debut, 1950; appeared in numerous films including West Side Story, Carnal Knowledge, The King and I, Singing in the Rain, The Four Seasons, I Like it Like That, 1994. Recipient Acad. Award for best supporting actress, 1962; Grammy award for best rec., 1973; Antoinette Perry award for best supporting actress Broadway play, 1975; Emmy award, 1977, 78. In Guinness Book of World Records as only person to win Acad., Grammy, Tony and Emmy awards. Address: care Agency for Performing Arts 9000 W Sunset Blvd Los Angeles CA 90069-1843

MOREST, DONALD KENT, neuroscience educator; b. Kansas City, Mo., Oct. 4, 1934; s. F. Stanley and Clara Josephine (Riley) M.; m. Rosemary Richtmyer, July 13, 1963; children: Lydia, Claude. BA, U. Chgo., 1955; MD, Yale U., 1960. Sr. asst. surgeon USPHS, Bethesda, Md., 1960-63; asst. prof. U. Chgo., Ill., 1963-65; asst. to assoc. prof. Harvard Med. Sch., Boston, 1965-77; prof., dir. Ctr. for Neurol. Scis. U. Conn. Health Ctr., Farmington, 1977—; cons. NIH, Bethesda, 1975—, mem. adv. bd. Nat. Deafness and Other Communication Disorders. Contbr. articles to profl. jours. and books. Recipient Loeser award U. Conn. Health Ctr., Farmington, 1982; Career Devel. awardee NIH, 1971; named Javits neurosci. investigator NIH, 1984, Claude Pepper awardee, 1990. Mem. Am. Assn. Anatomists (C.Judson Herrick award 1966), Soc. for Neurosci., Assn. for Rsch. in Otolaryngology, Conn. Acad. Sci. & Engring. (elected), Cajal Club (pres. 1980). Avocations: flute, badminton. Home: 18 Shady Ln West Simsbury CT 06092-2232

MORET, MARC, chemicals executive; b. Ménières, Switzerland, Nov. 15, 1923; married; 3 children. D Pub. Econs., U. Fribourg and Sorbonne, Paris, 1948. With practical indsl. tng. and assignments Swissair, Sulzer Bros., Nestlé S.A.; gen. mgr. Guigoz Internat.; from head of agro sales, to head agro and nutrition divsns. Sandoz Ltd., 1968, head finance dept., 1976, bd. dirs., CEO, 1977—, vice chmn. bd. dirs., 1980-85, chmn. bd. dirs., 1985—. Office: Sandoz Ltd. Lichtstrasse 35, CH 4002 Basel Switzerland also: Sandoz Inc 608 Fifth Ave New York NY 10020-2303

MORETTI, AUGUST JOSEPH, lawyer; b. Elmira, N.Y., Aug. 18, 1950; s. John Anthony and Dorothy M. (De Blasio) M.; m. Audrey B. Kavka, Nov. 8, 1981; children: David Anthony, Matthew Alexander. BA magna cum laude, Princeton U., 1972; JD cum laude, Harvard U., 1975. Assoc. Heller, Ehrman, White and McAuliffe, San Francisco, 1976-82, ptnr., 1982—; lectr. bus. adminstrn. U. Calif. Berkeley, 1977-79. Bd. dirs. Ann Martin Children's Ctr.; advisor, and adv. panel U. Calif. Berkeley Entrepreneur Program. Mem. ABA. Office: Heller Ehrman White & McAuliffe 525 University Ave Palo Alto CA 94301-1903

MOREY, CARL REGINALD, musicologist, academic administrator; b. Toronto, Ont., Can., July 14, 1934; s. Reginald Donald and Julia Beatrice (Mabey) M.; m. Lorna Ann Dalton, June 2, 1960 (dec.); 1 child, Rachel Adriana. Mus.B., U. Toronto, 1957; Mus.M., Ind. U., 1961, Ph.D., 1965. Asst. prof. Wayne State U., Detroit, 1962-63; assoc. prof. U. Windsor, Ont., Can., 1964-70; prof. music U. Toronto, 1970—, dean faculty of music, 1984-90, Jean A. Chalmers prof., dir. Inst. for Can. Music, 1991—. Avocation: swimming. Home: 540 Palmerston Blvd, Toronto, ON Canada M6G 2P5 Office: U Toronto, Faculty of Music, Toronto, ON Canada M5S 1A1

MOREY, CHARLES LEONARD, III, theatrical director; b. Oakland, Calif., June 23, 1947; s. Charles Leonard Jr. and Mozelle Kathleen (Milliken) M.; m. Mary Carolyn Donnet, June 10, 1973 (div. 1975); m. Joyce Miriam Schilke, May 29, 1982; 1 child, William. AB, Dartmouth Coll., 1969; MFA, Columbia U., 1971. Artistic dir. Peterborough (N.H.) Players, 1977-88, Pioneer Theatre Co., Salt Lake City, 1984—; adj. asst. prof. theatre U. Utah, Salt Lake City, 1984—. Actor: N.Y. Shakespeare Festival, Playwrights Horizons, New Dramatists, ARK Theatre Co., Ensemble Studio Theatre, Cubiculo, Folger Theatre, Syracuse Repertory Theatre, Theatre by Sea, others; over 150 plays acted in or directed; guest dir. Ensemble Studio Theatre, ArK Theatre, Am. Stage Festivel, McCarter Theatre, Pioneer Theatre Co., PCPA Theatrefest, The Repertory Theater of St. Louis, Meadow Brook Theatre; author new adaptations Alexander Dumas' The Three Musketeers, Bram Stoker's Dracula, Charles Dickens' A Tale of Two Cities, Victor Hugo's The Hunchback of Notre Dame; TV appearances include: Young Maverick, Edge of Night, World Apart, Our Town. Trustee Utah Arts Endowment, Inc. Mem. Soc. Stage Dirs. and Choreographers, AEA, SAG, AFTRA, Salt Lake City C. of C. (Honors in the Arts award 1991), Utah Assn. Gifted Children (Community Svc. award 1991), Peterborough Players (Edith Bond Stearns award 1990). Democrat. Episcopalian. Home: 1803 Yale Ave Salt Lake City UT 84108-1837 Office: Pioneer Theatre Co U Utah Salt Lake City UT 84112

MOREY, JAMES NEWMAN, advertising executive; b. N.Y.C., Nov. 13, 1933; s. Ira and Mary Ernestine (Newman) M.; m. Frances Mae Rogers, Aug. 23, 1958 (div. 1978); children: Allison, David Newman, John Rogers; m. Marsha Ann Rogler, Nov. 8, 1980; 1 son, Stephen Rogler. B.A., Ohio U., 1955; M.A., Columbia U., 1956; postgrad., Duke U., 1958-59. Advt. copywriter Maxon Inc., 1957; copywriter, TV producer, creative dir. Howard Marks, Inc., Cleve., 1960-61; copywriter Marshalk dir. Interpublic, Cleve., 1961; creative dir. Wyse Advt., Cleve., 1962-63; sr. copywriter Hutchins Advt. Co., Rochester, N.Y., 1964-66, creative dir., exec. v.p., 1967-68, pres., 1969-70; pres. Hutchins-Darcy, Inc., Rochester, N.Y., 1971-76; pres., chief operating officer Hutchins/Young & Rubicam, Rochester, N.Y., 1977-79, pres., chief exec. officer, 1980-91, chmn., 1991—; exec. v.p., mem. exec. com. Cato Johnson USA div. Young & Rubicam Inc., Rochester, 1991-93; bd. dirs. Cato Johnson Worldwide. Advt. cons. Monroe County Republican Party, Rochester, N.Y., 1967-72; mem. adv. bd. Human Rels. Commn., Rochester, 1968-73; pres. Friends of Child Welfare, 1966-67; mem. coun. Empire State Coll. SUNY, Saratoga Springs, 1972-82; coord. Upstate N.Y. for Media-Advertising Partnership for Drug Free America, 1987-88; mem. adv. bd. Communications Magnet Program Franklin High Sch., 1988-91; mem. bd. edn. Wyo. Cen. Sch., 1989-91; mem. communications com. coalition goals for a greater Rochester, 1990-91; mem. comm. com. Mayor's Com. on Violence, 1992-93; mem. strategic planning com. Wyo. Ctrl. Sch., 1993—; leader shared decision-making planning com. Wyo. Ctrl. Sch., 1993-94; baseball coach Warsaw Kiwanis Little League, 1993-95; mem. bd. trustees Wyo. Free Libr., 1994-95, pres. bd. trustees 1995—. Mem. Am. Assn. Advt. Agys. (treas. N.Y. State coun. 1985-86, chmn. 1987-88, bd. govs. 1988-91), Rochester Advt. Coun. (dir. 1979-80, Lantern award for pub. svc. 1988, City of Rochester Volunteerism award 1991), Sigma Chi, Omicron Delta Kappa. Republican. Episcopalian. Home: 1061 Tower Rd Wyoming NY 14591-9557 Office: Hutchins/Young Rubicam Inc 400 Midtown Tower Rochester NY 14604-2001

MOREY, PHILIP STOCKTON, JR., mathematics educator; b. Houston, July 11, 1937; s. Philip Stockton and Helen Holmes (Wolcott) M.; m. Jeri Lynn Snyder, Sept. 5, 1964; children: William Philip, Christopher Jerome. BA, U. Tex., 1959, Ma, 1961, PhD, 1967. Asst. prof. math. U. Nebr., Omaha, 1967-68; assoc. prof. Tex. A&I U. Kingsville, 1968-76; prof. Tex. A&M U. Kingsville, 1976—; lectr. U. Tokyo, 1976, U. Hokkaido, 1977, 88. Contbr. articles to Tensor N.S., Internat. Jour. Engring. Sci, Tex. Jour. Sci. Recipient Researcher of Yr. awrd Tex. A&I Alumni Assn., 1985. Mem. Tex. Acad. Sci. (chmn. math. sect. 1982, '85), Am. Math. Soc., Tensor Soc. (Japan). Achievements include research in extensor analysis, tensor analysis, differential geometry, mathematical physics. Home: 1514 Lackey St Kingsville TX 78363-3199 Office: Tex A&M Univ Kingsville TX 78362

MOREY, SHARON LYNN, psychotherapist, mediator; b. Cherokee, Iowa, Apr. 8, 1948; d. Joseph Glenn and Annie (Bush) M.; m. Edward Devere Beck, July 23, 1988; stepchildren: Mark Edward, Bruce David. Cert. in bus., Mpls. Bus. Coll., 1968; BA in Psychology, Adminstrn., Met. State U., 1988; PhD in Clin. Psychology, The Union Inst., 1992. Exec. dir. Iowa Lakes Regional Orgn., Spirit Lake, 1982-86; peer acad. advisor Met. State U., St. Paul, 1986-88; appointed to multip. task force Minn. State U. System, St. Paul, 1987-88; crisis phone counselor Lovelines Counseling Ctr., Mpls., 1987-88; mediator North Hennepin Mediation Project, Brooklyn Center, Minn., 1988-93; pvt. practice St. Anthony Mental Health Ctr., Mendota Heights, Minn., 1988-93; intern in clin. psychology Richfield (Minn.) High Sch., 1990-91; psychotherapist, mediator St. Anthony Mental Health Clinic, St. Paul, 1990-93; cons. Iowa Lakes Regional Orgn., Spirit Lake, 1986-90; group facilitator Toughlove Orgn., Eagan, Minn., 1987-90. Mem. Okoboji Area After 5 Christian Bus. Women, Spirit Lake, 1978-82, Okoboji Lakes Bible and Missionary Conf., Spirit Lake, 1978—; Grad. Sch. of Union Inst. Exec. Learner Coun., Cin., 1990-92; bd. dirs. N.W. Iowa Singles Weekend Conf., Spirit Lake, 1978. Met. State U. scholar, 1987, Highland Park Bus. and Profl. Women scholar, 1987; grantee Dept. Vocat. Rehab., 1986-87, Alliss Edn. Foun., 1986, Pell, 1986-87. Mem. APA, N.Am. Soc. Adlerian Psychologists, Minn. Coun. Mediators (interim v.p. 1990-91), Minn. Psychol. Assn., Grad. Sch. of Union Inst. Alumni Assn., Met. State U. Alumni Assn., Minority and Women Doctoral Directory, Soc. Profls. in Dispute Resolu-

tion, Assn. Family and Conciliation Cts. Mem. Christian Ch. Avocations: tennis, golf, walking, singing.

MORFORD, JAMES WARREN, international health care executive; b. Duluth, Minn., Feb. 22, 1945; s. James Andrew and Christine (Warner) M.; m. Pamela Ann Carlson, July 20, 1974; children: James Warren II, Melissa Lynn. AA, U. Minn., 1965; BS, U. Ariz., 1969. Asst. account exec. Tathum, Laird and Kudner Advt., Chgo., 1969; salesman Guest Pac Corp., Mt. Vernon, N.Y., 1970; v.p. Student Service Directory, Mt. Vernon, 1970-71; dir. mktg. Doctors Diagnostic Labs., Mpls., 1971-76, pres., 1976-78; pres., CEO Lab. Cons. Internat., Mpls., 1977-80; COO Morford Clin., Ltd., Mpls., 1980-88; pres. Morford Properties, Inc., Mpls. and Tucson, 1980—; COO Foothills Women's Ctr., Tucson, 1988—; pres., chmn., bd. dirs. Sistemas de Salud Panamericanos, S.A., Centro Panamericano de Diagnostico pro Imagenes, S.A., Mexico City, 1991—. Mem. Med. Group Mgmt. Assn., Ariz. Med.Group Mgmt. Assn., Minn. Med. Group Mgmt. Assn., Aircraft Owners and Pilots Assn., Chi Phi. Republican. Methodist. Avocations: flying (pilot with advanced ratings). Home: 5081 N Camino Sumo Tucson AZ 85718-6053 Office: PanAm Health Sys 5081 N Camino Tucson AZ 85718

MORFORD-BURG, JOANN, state senator, investment company executive; b. Miller, S.D., Nov. 26, 1956; d. Darrell Keith Morford and Eleanor May (Fawcett) Morford-Steptoe; m. Quinten Leo Burg, Nov. 12, 1983. BS in Agrl.-Bus., Comml. Econs., S.D. State U., 1979; cert. in personal fin. planning, Am. Coll., 1992. Agrl. loan officer 1st Bank System, Presho, S.D., 1980-82, Wessington Springs, S.D., 1982-86; agrl. loan officer Am. State Bank, Wessington Springs, 1986; registered investment rep. SBM Fin. Svcs. Inc., Wessington Springs, 1986—; mem. S.D. State Senate, Wessington Springs, 1990—, majority whip, 1993-94, minority whip, 1994—; mem. senate appropriations com. 1993—; chair senate ops. and audit com. 1993, 94; mem. ops. and audit com., 1995—; active Nat. Conf. State Legislators' Assembly of Fed. Issues Environ. Com., 1995—. Mem. Midwestern-Can. task force Midwest Conf., 1990-94; mem. transp. com., commerce com., taxation com. S.D. State Senate, Pierre, 1990-92; treas. twp. bd. Wessington Springs, 1990-92; mem. Wessington Springs Sch. Improvement Coun. Mem. Future Farmers Am. (adv. bd. Wessington Springs chpt.), S.D. State U. 4-H Alumni Assn., Nat. Life Underwriters Assn. (Huron chpt.), Order Ea. Star (various offices 1980—). Democrat. Methodist. Home and Office: 38678 SD Hwy 34 Wessington Springs SD 57382-5806

MORGA BELLIZZI, CELESTE, editor; b. N.Y.C., Mar. 8, 1921; d. Louis and Emma (Macari) Morga; m. John J. Bellizzi, Sept. 1, 1942; children: John J., Robert F. Student, Columbia U., 1940-41, SUNY, Albany, 1970. Cert. med. lab. technician. Medical lab. technician USMC Hosp., N.Y.C., 1942, Woman's Hosp., N.Y.C., 1942-52; spl. investigator N.Y. State Atty. Gen.'s Office, Albany, 1958-65; editor Internat. Drug Report publ., The Narc Officer publ. internat. Narcotic Enforcement Officers Assn., Albany, 1965—. Dir. Albany Inst. History and Art, 1988-90, N.Y. State Press Women, Albany, 1987; advisor UN Non-govtl. Orgns. Drug Com., N.Y.C., 1980-90, White House Conf. Drug Free Am., Washington, 1987; mem. com. Bethlehem Drug Prevention Program, Delmar, N.Y., 1987-90, Action Commn. Narc Edn., Delmar, 1984-90; v.p. Women's Rep. Party Albany, 1972. Recipient Pres.'s award INEOA, 1982, Disting. Svc. award Houston Police Dept., 1981. Mem. Nat. Fedn. Press Women, Nat. Press Club, Univ. Club, Albany Country Club, Aberdeen Country Club. Avocations: painting, golf, tennis. Office: Internat Narcotic Enforcement Officers Assn 112 State St Albany NY 12207-2005

MORGADO, ROBERT, music company executive; m. Sec. to the governor State of N.Y.; with Warner Commns. Inc., 1982—; exec. v.p. Warner Commns., N.Y.C.; with Warner Music Group, N.Y.C., 1985—, now chmn., 1990—. Office: Warner Communications Inc 75 Rockefeller Plz New York NY 10019*

MORGAN, ALAN D., state education official. State supt. education State of N.Mex. Office: N Mex Edn Dept Edn Bldg 300 Don Gaspar Ave Santa Fe NM 87501-2786

MORGAN, ALAN VIVIAN, geologist, educator; b. Barry, Glamorgan, Wales, Jan. 29, 1943; emigrated to Can., 1964, naturalized, 1977; s. George Vivian Williams and Sylvia Nesta (Atkinson) M.; m. Marion Anne Medhurst, June 14, 1966; children: Siân Kristina, Alexis John. B.Sc. with honors in Geology and Geography, U. Leicester, Eng., 1964; M.Sc. in Geography, U. Alta., Calgary, Can., 1966; Ph.D. in Geology, U. Birmingham, Eng., 1970. Postdoctoral fellow U. Western Ont. and U. Waterloo, Ont., Can., 1970-71; asst. prof. earth scis. and man-environ. studies U. Waterloo, 1971-78, assoc. prof. earth scis., 1978-85, prof., 1985—; mem. Brit. Schs. Exploring Soc. Ctrl. Iceland Expn., 1960; rep. Can. Geosci. Coun., 1977-83, exec. dir., 1988-94; mem. com. on global change Royal Soc. Can., 1988-91, com. on pub. awareness of sci., 1989-94; coord. global change Geol. Survey Can., 1990-92; assoc. dir. Quaternary Scis. Inst., U. Waterloo, 1992—. Author 6 field guides; editor newsletter OYEZ, 1990-94; contbr. articles to numerous profl. publs.; dir., prodr. documentary film The Heimaey Eruption, 1974. Recipient award for MS thesis Can. Assn. Petroleum Geologists, 1967, Bancroft award Royal Soc. Can., 1994—, John A. Moss award Nat. Assn. Geology Tchrs., 1995; Charles Lapworth scholar, 1970; Nat. Scis. and Engring. Rsch. Coun. Can. grantee, 1971—. Fellow Geol. Assn. Can. (sec.-treas. 1975-83), Geol. Soc. Am.; mem. Am. Quaternary Assn. (pres. 1990-92), Can. Quaternary Assn. (pres. 1987-89), Brit. Quaternary Research Assn., Internat. Union Quaternary Research (sec. gen. XII congress 1983-87). Office: U Waterloo, Dept Earth Scis, Waterloo, ON Canada N2L 3G1

MORGAN, ALFRED V., . Pres. Morgan Bus. Assocs., Inc., Montecito and Santa Barbara, Calif. Office: Morgan Bus Assocs Inc 1676 E Valley Rd Santa Barbara CA 93108-2150

MORGAN, ANDREW WESLEY, artist, educator; b. Cleve., July 29, 1922; s. John B. and Bertha (Amersbach) M.; m. Dahlia Kaplow, May 18, 1973; children from previous marriage—Alexander, Vincent, Nicholas. B.A., Kenyon Coll., 1948; M.F.A., U. N.C., 1952; postgrad., N.Y.U., 1955-57; L.H.D. (hon.), Tarkio Coll. Head art dept. Greenwich (Conn.) Country Day Sch., 1952-59; chmn. dept. art, dir. gallery U. Miss., 1959-60; pres. Kansas City (Mo.) Art Inst., 1960-70; prof., chmn. art dept. U. Miami, Fla., 1970-87; adv. bd. Vt. Studio Ctr., Johnson, 1987—; Commr. Municipal Art Commn., Kansas City, 1965-70; co-chmn. Mid-Am. Urban Design Conf., 1966. One-man shows include Stanford (Conn.) Mus., 1958, Pietrantonio Gallery, N.Y.C., 1960, Lowe Mus., 1980, Viscaya Mus., Miami, Fla., 1984, Leedy-Voulkos Art Ctr., Kansas City, Mo., 1990, Polk Mus., Lakeland, Fla., 1991, New World Sch. for Arts Gallery, Miami, 1992, U. Miami, 1993, Art Mus. No. Ariz. U., 1993-94; one-person show Ctr. for Visual Comm., Coral Gables, Fla., 1995; groups shows include Boston Arts Festival, 1960, Mid-South Annual, Memphis, 1961, Roko Gallery, N.Y.C., 1960, U. Miss., 1959, N.E. Ann. (Jury award oil prize), Silver Mine, Conn., 1958, Ctr. for Contemporary Art, 1989, Six Miami Painters, 1st Ave. Gallery, 1993, Fla. Landscape, 1994. Active Com. Econ. Devel., Kans., 1965-70; bd. dirs. Kansas City Regional Coun. Higher Edn.; pres. bd. dirs. Union Ind. Colls. Art, 1967-70; mem. visual arts bd. Nat. Found. for Arts, Miami, 1988; adv. bd. Vt. Studio Ctr., Johnson, 1989. With AUS, 1942-46. Mem. Nat. Assn. Schs. Art (dir.), Coll. Art. Assn. Home: 10331 SW 59th Ave Miami FL 33156-4114

MORGAN, ANNETTE N., state legislator; b. Kennett, Mo., Aug. 31, 1938; m. William P. Morgan, 1961; children: John, Catherine. BA, U. Mo., MA. Tchr. adult edn.; mem. Mo. Ho. of Reps. Mem. Adult Edn. Assn. Democrat. Presbyterian. Home: 639 W 57th Ter Kansas City MO 64113-1168 Office: Mo Ho of Reps State Capitol Jefferson City MO 65101

MORGAN, ARLENE NOTORO, newspaper editor, reporter, recruiter; b. Phila., July 27, 1945; d. James Vincent and Mary Rose (Actis-Grande) Notoro; m. David J. Morgan, Mar. 3, 1948; children: Elizabeth, Lauren. BS in Journalism, Temple U., 1967. Reporter Delaware County Daily Times, Chester, Pa., 1967-69; reporter Philadelphia Inquirer, 1969—, dep. metro. editor, 1990-91, sr. editor, 1991—. Bd. dirs. Friends Hosp., Phila., 1978—. Recipient Community Service award Phila. chpt. VFW, 1983, Rafters Chari-

ties, Phila., 1982, Phila. Newspapers Inc. Employee Recognition award, 1987. Mem. Soc. Profl. Journalists. Roman Catholic. Avocations: ballet, travel, opera and art appreciation, advocate to the mentally ill. Office: Phila Inquirer 400 N Broad St Philadelphia PA 19130-4099*

MORGAN, ARTHUR EDWARD, technology company executive; b. Milw., July 3, 1929; s. Burchell Earl and Irene Clara (Schneiberg) M.; children by previous marriage: Sandra Morgan Harter, Nancy Morgan Wetzel; m. Karen Charlene Binder, Sept. 4, 1982. BBA, U. Wis., 1951, MBA, 1960. Div. controller Cutler Hammer Inc., Milw., 1960-70, gen. mgr., v.p., 1970-78, group v.p., 1979; group pres. Eaton Corp., Cleve., 1979-82; pres., chief exec. officer Cybernetics Tech. Inc., Mpls., 1983-84; gen. mgr. BBC Brown Boveri, 1985-87; pres., chief exec. officer R. Scan Corp., Mpls., 1988-91, also bd. dirs., 1988-91; pres. Sussex Assocs., Mpls., 1991—; bd. dirs. Filcon Corp. St. Paul. Served with USN, 1952-65. Mem. IEEE, Assn. Oldcrows. Republican. Home: 8108 Telegraph Rd Minneapolis MN 55438-1182 Office: Sussex Assocs 8108 Telegraph Rd Minneapolis MN 55438-1182

MORGAN, BEVERLY CARVER, physician, educator; b. N.Y.C., May 29, 1927; d. Jay and Florence (Newkamp) Carver; children—Nancy, Thomas E. III, John E. M.D. cum laude (Mosby Scholar), Duke U., 1955. Diplomate Am. Bd. Pediatrics (oral examiner 1984-90, mem. written examination com. 1990—), Nat. Bd. Med. Examiners. Intern, asst. resident Stanford U. Hosp., San Francisco, 1955-56; clin. fellow pediatrics, trainee pediatric cardiology Babies Hosp.-Columbia Presbyn. Med. Center, N.Y.C., 1956-59; research fellow cardiovascular diagnostic lab. Columbia-Presbyn. Med. Center, N.Y.C., 1959-60; instr. pediatrics Coll. Physicians and Surgeons, Columbia U., 1960; dir. heart sta. Robert B. Green Meml. Hosp., San Antonio, 1960-62; lectr. pediatrics U. Tex., 1960-62; spl. research fellow in pediatric cardiology Sch. Medicine, U. Wash., Seattle, 1962-64; from instr. to prof. pediatrics Sch. Medicine, U. Wash., 1962-73, chmn. dept. pediatrics, 1973-80; mem. staff U. Wash. Hosp., chief of staff, 1975-77; mem. staff Harborview Med. Ctr.; mem. staff Children's Orthopedic Hosp. and Med. Ctr., dir. dept. medicine, 1974-80; prof., chmn. dept. pediatrics U. Calif., Irvine, 1980-88; pediatrician in chief Children's Hosp. Orange County, 1988; mem. pulmonary acad. awards panel Nat. Heart and Lung Inst., 1972-75; mem. grad. med. edn. nat. advisory com. to sec. HEW, 1977-80; mem. Coun. on Pediatric Practice; chmn. Task Force on Opportunities for Women in Pediatrics, 1982; mem. nursing rev. com. NIH, 1987-88. Contbr. articles to profl. jours.; mem. editorial bd. Clin. Pediatrics, Am. Jour. Diseases of Children, Jour. of Orange County Pediatric Soc., Jour. Am. Acad. Pediatrics, Los Angeles Pediatric Soc. Recipient Women of Achievement award Matrix Table, Seattle, 1974; Disinguished Alumnus award Duke U. Med. Sch., 1974; Ann. award Nat. Bd. Med. Coll. Pa., 1977; USPHS career devel. awardee, 1966-71. Mem. Am. Acad. Pediatrics (chmn. com. on pediatric manpower 1984-86), Am. Coll. Cardiology, Soc. for Pediatric Research, Am. Fedn. Clin. Research, Am. Pediatric Soc., Assn. Med. Sch. Pediatrics Dept. Chairmen (sec.-treas. 1981-87), Western Soc. for Pediatric Research, N. Pacific, Puget Sound. pediatrics socs., Am., Wash. State heart assns., Wash. State Med. Soc., King County Med. Soc., Alpha Omega Alpha. Home: 601 Lido Park Dr Newport Beach CA 92663-4411 Office: U Calif Irvine Med Ctr Dept Pediatrics 101 City Blvd W Orange CA 92668-2901

MORGAN, BRUCE RAY, international consultant; b. Los Angeles, Oct. 28, 1932; s. Francis Raymond and Rose Hall (Black) M.; m. Bette Jeanne Moore, Oct. 7, 1957; children: Michael John, Brian Leo, Jeanne Ann. A.A., Sacramento Jr. Coll., 1952; B.S., U. Calif.-Berkeley, 1954, LL.B., 1957. Bar: Calif. 1957. Judge adv. USAF, Saudi Arabia and Morocco, 1958-61; atty. firm Thelen, Marrin, Johnson & Bridges, San Francisco, 1961-67; dep. dir. Peace Corps, Nepal, 1967-68, dir, 1968-70; exec. dir. Center Research and Edn., Denver, 1971-75; dir. U.S. representation to Saudi Arabia-U.S. Joint Commn. on Econ. Coop., Riyadh, 1975-76; pres. Bruce Morgan Assocs., Inc., Washington, 1976—. Editor: Calif. State Bar Jour. Legis. Rev, 1957. Served with USAF, 1958-61. Mem. U.S. Calif. Bar. Office: Bruce Morgan Assocs 1010 N Glebe Rd Ste 500 Arlington VA 22201-5704

MORGAN, CAROL MIRÓ, marketing executive; b. Ancon, Republic of Panama, Jan. 31, 1942; d. Morton A. and Dora (Rebolledo) Blum; m. Edward J. Morgan, July 24, 1963 (div. Jan. 1972); children: Edward M., John G.; m. Doran J. Levy, Oct. 3, 1986. BS, Spring Hill Coll., 1962, Met. State U., 1986; MA, Kans. State U., 1966. Cert. tchr., La. Instr. Ohio State U., Columbus, 1966-67; staff writer Palm Beach (Fla.) Daily News, 1967-70; tchr. Isidore Newman Sch., New Orleans, 1972-77; dir. pub. rels. Hennepin County Med. Ctr., Mpls., 1977-79; mgr. pub. rels. Peavey Co., Mpls., 1979-81; owner, pres. Carol Morgan Assocs., Inc., Mpls., 1981-92, Strategic Directions Group, Inc., Mpls., 1992—. Home: 1029 Lombard Ave Saint Paul MN 55105-3256 Office: Strategic Directions Group Inc 119 N 4th St Ste 311 Minneapolis MN 55401-1787

MORGAN, CAROLYN F., lawyer; b. Gadsden, Ala., Nov. 23, 1945; d. Sephes Jonah and Garnet Sylvia (Watson) M.; m. Galen Kennah, Dec. 16, 1967 (div. Nov. 1979); children: Jason, Jennifer. BS, Jacksonville State U., 1970; JD, Cumberland Sch. of Law, 1983. Bar: Ala., U.S. Dist. Ct. (no. dist.) Ala., U.S. Ct. Appeals (11th cir.), U.S. Supreme Ct. Social worker II State of Ala., Gadsden, Birmingham, 1969-80; asst. city atty. City of Gadsden, 1983-84; asst. dist. atty. State of Ala., Anniston, 1984-90; corp. counsel BE & K, Inc., Birmingham, 1990—. Office: BE&K Inc 2000 Internat Park Dr Birmingham AL 35243

MORGAN, CHARLES DONALD, JR., manufacturing executive; b. Ft. Smith, Ark., Feb. 4, 1943; s. Charles Donald Sr. and Betty (Speer) M; m. Jane Dills Morgan, Aug. 20, 1966; children: Caroline Speer, Charles Robert. ME, U. Ark., 1966. Systems engr. IBM, Little Rock, Ark., 1966-71; v.p. Acxiom Corp. (formerly CCX Network, Inc.), Conway, Ark., 1972-75; pres. CCX, Conway, Ark., 1976-82, chief exec. officer, 1983—, also chmn. bd. dirs. bd. dirs. First State Bank & Trust, Conway. Trustee Hendrix Coll., Conway, 1985—; chmn. bd. dirs. Jobs for Ark. Future, 1986-87, mem. commn. 1988—; mem. Southern Growth Policies Bd., N.C., 1986, Ark. Bus. Council, 1987—. Mem. Third Class Mailers Assn., Pub. Chief Exec. Officers Council. Episcopalian. Avocation: auto racing. Office: Acxiom Corp 301 Industrial Blvd Conway AR 72032-7168

MORGAN, DAVID ERNEST, computer and communications research executive; b. Terre Haute, Ind., Mar. 22, 1942; s. George Ernest and Barbara Marguerite (Lutz) M.; m. Judith Johanna Clement, July 2, 1966; children: Heidi Elizabeth, Gwendolen Anne. BS in Math, Rose Poly. Inst., 1964; MS in Math., U. Mich., 1965; PhD in Computer Sci., U. Waterloo, Can., 1971. Reporter, photographer WTHI Radio and TV, Terre Haute, 1961-64; mem. tech. staff Bell Telephone Labs., Holmdel, N.J., 1964-70; asst. prof. computer sci. U. Waterloo, 1970-80, dir. networks rsch. lab., 1972-80; v.p. Telecom Network Tech., Toronto, Ont., 1975-80; mgr. arch. and tech. Digital Equipment Corp., Maynard, Mass., 1977-78, 80-84; dir. computer and networks lab. indsl. Tech. Inst., Ann Arbor, Mich., 1984-86; v.p. rsch. Motorola Inc., Schaumburg, Ill., 1986—; pres. Mordata Inc., Waterloo, 1973-86; dir. advisor bd. Co. of Open Systems, McLean, Va., 1986-94; vice chmn., adv. bd. Microelectronics and Computer Corp., Austin, Tex., 1992-93; mem. Ill. Gov.'s Task Force Comm., 1992-93; bd. dirs. Computer-Based Patient Record Inst., Chgo., 1992—; speaker numerous confs. and seminars. Contbr. articles to profl. jours.; patentee/inventor in field. Weston-Wabash scholarship Westin-Wabash Found., 1960; fellowship IBM, 1970, grad. study fellowship Bell Labs., 1965. Mem. IEEE, SME, Am. Nat. Stds. Inst. (mem. X3 com. 1984-87, TI com. 1988-), Tau Beta Pi. Avocations: vocal music, photography, travel. Office: Motorola Inc Ste MI 50 E Commerce Dr Schaumburg IL 60173

MORGAN, DONALD CRANE, lawyer; b. Detroit, Sept. 17, 1940; s. Donald Nye and Nancy (Crane) M.; m. Judith Munro, June 23, 1962; children: Wendy, Donald. BA, Ohio Wesleyan U., 1962; JD, U. Mich., 1965. Bar: Mich. 1966, U.S. Dist. Ct. (ea. dist.) Mich. 1966, U.S. Ct. Appeals (6th cir.) 1967, U.S. Supreme Ct. 1971. Ptnr. Kerr, Russell and Weber, Detroit, 1965-87; of counsel Draugelis & Ashton, Plymouth, Mich., 1988-93; pvt. practice, pvt. practice, Plymouth, Mich., 1993—; twp. atty. Plymouth Twp., 1970-85, Northville Twp., 1972-85; mediator Wayne County Mediation Tribunal, Detroit, 1981—, Oakland County Mediation Tribunal, Pontiac, Mich., 1992—; hearing panelist Mich. Atty. Discipline Bd., 1981—; city atty. City of Plymouth, 1995—. Chmn. Wayne County II congl. Dist.

Rep. Party, 1979-81; ruling elder 1st Presbyn. Ch., Plymouth, 1976-79, 90-93; twp. atty. Plymouth Twp., 1970-85, Northville Twp., 1972-85; city atty. City of Plymouth, 1995—; bd. dirs. Growth Works, Inc., treas., 1992—. Paul Harris fellow, 1980. Mem. ABA, Mich. Def. Trial Counsel, State Bar of Mich. (rep. assembly 1979-85, 92—), Detroit Assn. Def. Trial Counsel, Plymouth Rotary (pres. 1985-86), Phi Alpha Delta, Sigma Alpha Epsilon. Republican. Presbyterian. Avocations: reading, travel, sports. Home: 1440 Woodland Pl Plymouth MI 48170-1535 Office: 134 N Main St Plymouth MI 48170-1637

MORGAN, E. A., church administrator. Chaplain Ch. of the Living God Exec. Bd. Office: Church of the Living God 735 S Oakland Dr Decatur IL 62522

MORGAN, EDMUND SEARS, history educator; b. Mpls., Jan. 17, 1916; s. Edmund Morris and Elsie Sears (Smith) M.; m. Helen Theresa Mayer, June 7, 1939; children: Penelope, Pamela.; m. Marie Caskey, June 22, 1983. A.B., Harvard U., 1937, Ph.D., 1942. Instrument maker Radiation Lab., Mass. Inst. Tech., 1942-45; instr. U. Chgo., 1945-46; asst. prof. Brown U., 1946-49, asso. prof., 1949-51, prof., 1951-55, acting dean grad. sch., 1951-52; prof. Yale U., 1955-65, Sterling prof., 1965-86, prof. emeritus, 1986—; Research fellow Huntington Library, 1952-53; Johnson research prof. U. Wis., 1968-69. Author: The Puritan Family, 1944, Virginians at Home, 1953, (with Helen M. Morgan) The Stamp Act Crisis, 1953, The Birth of the Republic, 1956, The Puritan Dilemma, 1958, The Gentle Puritan, 1962, Visible Saints, 1963, Roger Williams, 1967, So What About History, 1969, American Slavery American Freedom, 1975, The Challenge of the American Revolution, 1976, The Meaning of Independence, 1976, The Genius of George Washington, 1980, Inventing the People, 1988; Mem. editorial bd.: N.E. Quar; Contbr. articles and revs. to hist. jours. Trustee Smith Coll., 1984-89. Mem. Organ. Am. Historianss (pres. 1971-72), Colonial Soc. Mass., Mass. Hist. Soc., Am. Antiquarian Soc., Am. Philos. Soc., Am. Acad. Arts and Scis., Conn. Acad. Arts and Scis., Brit. Acad., Royal Hist. Soc.

MORGAN, ELIZABETH, plastic and reconstructive surgeon; b. Washington, July 9, 1947; d. William James and Antonia (Bell) M.; children: 1 dau., Ellen. BA magna cum laude, Harvard U., 1967; postgrad. (fellow), Oxford U., Somerville Coll., 1967, 70; MD, Yale U., 1971; law student, Georgetown U., 1986-87; PhD in Psychology, U. Canterbury, Christchurch, New Zealand, 1995. Diplomate Am. Bd. Surgery, Am. Bd. Plastic Surgery. Intern Yale-New Haven Hosp., 1971-72, resident, 1972-73, 76-77; resident Tufts-New Eng. Med. Center, Boston, 1973-76, Harvard-Cambridge (Mass.) Hosp., 1977-78; columnist Cosmopolitan mag., 1973-80; practice medicine specializing in plastic and reconstructive surgery Washington, 1978-86, McLean, Va., 1978-86. Author: The Making of a Woman Surgeon, 1980, Solo Practice, 1982, Custody, A True Story, 1986, The Complete Book of Cosmetic Surgery for Men, Women and Teens, 1988. Trustee Kent (Conn.) Sch. Fellow ACS, Am. Soc. Plastic and Reconstructive Surgeons; mem. New Zealand Postgrad. Med. Soc., Internat. Soc. for Study Multiple Personality and Dissociation. Episcopalian.

MORGAN, ELMO RICH, former university official; b. Liberty, Idaho, Apr. 25, 1913; s. John S. and Ethel (Rich) M.; m. Frances Bennion, June 19, 1937; children: Kent B., Anthony W., Nancy. B.S. in Civil Engring. Utah State U., 1935; D.Sc. (hon.), U. Utah, 1983. Research asst. Utah Agrl. Expt. Sta., 1932-34, field engr., 1934-35; asst. engr. Utah Engineer's Office, 1935-40; mgr. Zia Co., Los Alamos, 1946-47; asst. mgr. AEC, Los Alamos, 1947-51; coordinator coop. research U. Utah, 1951-53, v.p., 1953-58; dir. hwys. State of Utah, 1958-60; v.p. phys. planning and constrn. U. Calif. at Berkeley, 1960-70, dir. facilities, 1974-77; pres. Elmo R. Morgan and Assos., cons., 1977—; sr. v.p. John Carl Warnecke and Assos., architects, 1970-74; dep. asst. sec. interior for water pollution control, 1967-68; cons. State Dept. and Ford Found., Am. univs. abroad; mem. adv. panel, space analysis manual western Interstate Comm. Higher Edn.; chmn. facilities and planning and mgmt. com. Nat. Assn. Coll. and Univ. Bus. Officers; mem. Energy Task Force U.S. Higher Edn.; mem. tech. council Nat. Conf. States on Bldg. Codes and Standards, Inc. Trustee emeritus Pierce Coll., Athens, Greece. Served to lt. col. C.E. AUS, 1940-46. Fellow ASCE; mem. Am. Soc. Pub. Adminstrs., Am. Council Edn. (chmn. commn. adminstrv. affairs). Home: 1928 Ptarmigan Dr # 1 Walnut Creek CA 94595-3505

MORGAN, EVAN, chemist; b. Spokane, Wash., Feb. 26, 1930; s. Evan and Emma Anne (Klobucher) M.; m. Johnnie Lu Dickson, Feb. 14, 1959; 1 child, James. BS, Gonzaga U., 1952; MS, U. Wash., 1954, PhD, 1956. Staff chemist IBM Corp., Poughkeepsie, N.Y., 1956-60; group supr. Olin Mathieson Co., New Haven, 1960-64; assoc. prof. chemistry High Point (N.C.) Coll., 1964-65; sr. rsch. chemist Reynolds Metals Co., Richmond, Va., 1965-72; prin. chemist Babcock & Wilcox, Lynchburg, Va., 1972—. Mem. Am. Chem. Soc., Cen. Va. Air Pollution Control Com. Home: 5128 Wedgewood Rd Lynchburg VA 24503-4208 Office: Babcock & Wilcox Corp PO Box 11165 Lynchburg VA 24506-1165

MORGAN, FRANK, mathematician. BS, MIT, 1974; PhD, Princeton U., 1977. Asst. prof. to assoc. prof., chmn. dept. math. MIT, 1977-87; prof. and chmn. dept. math. Williams Coll., Williamstown, Mass., 1987—; vis. prof. Rice U., Houston, 1982-83, Stanford U., 1986-87; mem. Inst. Adv. Study, Princeton. Author: Geometric Measure Theory, 1988. Baker Teaching award, MIT. Office: Williams College Dept of Mathematics Williamstown MA 01267 Home: 61 Moorland St Williamstown MA 01267

MORGAN, FRANK BROWN WEBB, JR., journalist, consultant; b. San Antonio, Aug. 26, 1935; s. Frank Brown Webb and Annie Kathleen (Harman) M.; m. Janice Dorine Schlittenhardt, Aug. 19, 1961; children: Roxanne, John Harman. BA in English, U. Kans., 1961. Bur. chief, reporter UPI, Santa Fe, 1961-64; staff corr. Wall St. Jour., Dallas, L.A., 1964-67; bur. chief, reporter Newsweek mag., L.A., Boston, 1967-73; founder, pres. Morgan Assocs., Boston, 1973-74; pub., owner Pittsfield/Farmington, N.H. Press, Pittsfield, 1973-74; v.p. The Boston Co., 1974-76, 1st Nat. Stores, Boston, 1976-78; founding editor INC. mag., Boston, 1978-79; pres. Miller Communications Inc., Boston, 1979-91; bd. dirs. Boston Computer Soc.; editor The Common, Metro-Boston, 1973-76. Bd. dirs. Fund for Arts in Newton, Mass., 1982, The Copley Soc. Boston. With U.S. Army, 1957-59. Recipient Hancock Ins. Co. bus. writing award Newsweek mag., 1971. Mem. Mass. Hist. Soc., Donald Ross Soc., St. Botolph Club (bd. dirs 1975—), The Atheaneaum, Brae Burn Country Club (Newton, Mass.). Avocations: golf, travel, reading, sports. Office: Miller Comm Four Copley Pl Boston MA 02116

MORGAN, FRANK EDWARD, II, lawyer; b. Burlington, Vt., May 16, 1952; s. Robert Griggs and Ruth (Jepson) M. First Class Cert. Merit, U. Edinburgh, Scotland, 1973; A.B. with honors, Brown U., 1974; LL.M., Cambridge U., Eng., 1976; J.D., U. Va., 1978. Bar: Mass. 1978, N.Y. 1990. Assoc. Gaston & Snow, Boston, 1978-82; v.p., gen. counsel Madison Fund, Inc. and Adobe Resources Corp., N.Y.C., 1982-87; ptnr. Gaston & Snow, N.Y.C., 1987-91; Mayer, Brown & Platt, N.Y.C., 1991—. Mem. ABA, N.Y. State Bar Assn., Am. Soc. Internat. Law. Republican. Congregationalist. Home: 400 E 70th St New York NY 10021-5387 Office: Mayer Brown & Platt 1675 Broadway New York NY 10019-5820

MORGAN, (GEORGE) FREDERICK, poet, editor; b. N.Y.C., Apr. 25, 1922; s. John Williams and Marion Haviland (Burt) M.; m. Constance Canfield, Dec. 20, 1942 (div. Aug. 1957); children: Gaylen, Veronica, George F.; m. Rose Fillmore, Aug. 14, 1957 (div. Aug. 1969); m. Paula Deitz, Nov. 30, 1969. A.B. magna cum laude, Princeton U., 1943. Founder The Hudson Rev., N.Y.C., 1947, editor, pres., 1947—; mem. adv. council dept. Romance langs. and lits. Princeton U., N.J., 1973-91. Author: A Book of Change, 1972, Poems of the Two Worlds, 1977, The Tarot of Cornelius Agrippa, 1978, Death Mother and Other Poems, 1979, The River, 1980, Refractions, 1981, Northbook, 1982, Eleven Poems, 1983, The Fountain and Other Fables, 1985, Poems: New and Selected, 1987, Poems for Paula, 1995. Served with U.S. Army, 1943-45. Decorated chevalier de l'Ordre des Arts et des Lettres, Govt. of France, 1984. Clubs: Knickerbocker (N.Y.C.) (gov. 1981-89), University (N.Y.C.), Somerset (Boston). Office: The Hudson Review 684 Park Ave New York NY 10021-5043

MORGAN, FREEMAN LOUIS, JR., engineer, consultant; b. Farrell, Miss., Aug. 23, 1931; s. Freeman Louis Sr. and Florence (McCloud) M.; m. Billie Delores Mason, June 20, 1954; children: Deborah Lee, Randall Douglas. BS, La. State U., Baton Rouge, 1954. Registered profl. engr., Tex., La. Process supr. Humble Oil and Refining Co., Houston, 1956-65; pvt. practice cons. engr. Houston, Chandler, Tyler, Tex., 1965—. Contbr. articles to profl. jours. Served to lt. U.S. Army, 1954-56. Republican. Avocation: golf. Home and Office: 3310 Greenoak Pl Tyler TX 75701

MORGAN, GAYLIN F., public realtions executive; b. Cedar Falls, Iowa, Nov. 3, 1938. BS in Journ., Bus., Iowa State U., 1962. Creative dir. Reiman Assocs., 1965-75; pres. Morgan & Myers, Jefferson, Wis., 1976—. Office: Morgan & Meyers 146 E Milwaukee St Jefferson WI 53549-1696*

MORGAN, GEOFFREY RICHARD, lawyer; b. Glendale, Calif., July 17, 1954; s. Wesley K. and Evelyn M. (Callaway) M.; m. Lisa Marie Pedersen, Nov. 9, 1989; children: Christopher, Alexander. BA with distinction, U. Ky., 1977, JD, 1980. Assoc. Lord Bissell & Brook, Chgo., 1980-84; ptnr. Schiff Hardin & Waite, Chgo., 1984-92, Michael Best & Friedrich, Milw., 1992—. Contbr. articles to legal jours. Mem. Univ. Club of Milw., Phi Beta Kappa. Home: Michael Best & Friedrich 6009 North Shore Dr Whitefish Bay WI 53217

MORGAN, GEORGE CARL, retired newspaper editor; b. Toronto, Ont., Can., Nov. 12, 1931; s. Thomas and Christine (Genier) M.; m. Gloria Plexman, July 14, 1956; children—Jocelyn, Scott, Julianne. Jr. reporter Courier Advocate, Trenton, Ont., Can., 1950-52; reporter Sudbury Star, Ont., Can., 1952-55; reporter, then copy editor Windsor (Ont.) Star, Can., 1955-62, 63-68, city editor, 1968-73, gen. news editor, 1973-77, editor, 1977-92; pub. rels. rep. Union Gas Co., Chatham, Ont., 1992-93. Author: Early Woodenware in Canada, 1977, Birth of a City, 1991. Mem. Windsor Media Coun., 1970, Ont. Press Coun., 1971. Office: Windsor Star, 167 Ferry St, Windsor, ON Canada N9A 4M5

MORGAN, GEORGE JEFFERSON, interior designer; b. Montgomery, Ala., June 21, 1908; s. Platte Jefferson and Margaret Louise (Wagner) M.; m. Frances E. Fitz, Feb. 7, 1937; children—Pamela Fitz Marvin, Leslie Platte Van Der Zee. B.S., Auburn U., 1930. Dir. interior design Mayfair, Inc., Albany, N.Y., 1934—; cons. various historic restorations. Important works include interior, Ten Broeck Mansion. Fellow Am. Soc. Interior Designers, Inst. Profl. Designers (Gt. Britain); mem. Albany Inst. History and Art, Albany County Hist. Assn., Albany Historic Found. Democrat. Presbyterian. Clubs: University, Albany Country. Home and Office: 66 Chestnut St Albany NY 12210-1902

MORGAN, GLEN D., superintendent. Supt. Ind. Sch. Dist. #1, Lewiston, Idaho. Recipient State Finalist for Nat. Supt. of Yr. award, 1993. Office: Ind Sch Dist # 1 3317 12th St Lewiston ID 83501

MORGAN, HENRY COKE, JR., judge; b. Norfolk, Va., Feb. 8, 1935; s. Henry Coke and Dorothy Lea (Pebworth) M.; m. Margaret John McGrail, Aug. 18, 1965; 1 stepchild, A. Robertson Hanckel Jr.; children: Catherine Morgan Stockwell, Mrogan Stewart Coke. BS, Washington and Lee U., 1957, JD, 1960. Bar: Va. 1960, U.S. Dist. Ct. (ea. dist.) Va. 1961, U.S. Ct. Appeals (4th cir.) 1964. Asst. city atty. City of Norfolk (Va.), 1960-63; ptnr., chief exec. officer Pender & Coward, Virginia Beach, Va., 1963-92; vice chmn., gen. counsel Princess Anne Bank, 1986-92; judge U.S. Dist. Ct. (ea. dist.) Va. 1992—. Served with U.S. Army, 1958-59. Episcopalian. Office: US Dist Ct Walter E. Hoffman U.S. Courthouse 600 Granby St Norfolk VA 23510-1915

MORGAN, HOWARD CAMPBELL, banker; b. Phila., June 14, 1935; s. Howard Moody and Margaret (Lyon) M.; m. Patricia H. Morgan (dec.); children: Pamela Ann, Kimberly Joy, Jennifer Lee; m. Judith P. Sanderson. BA in History, Lafayette Coll., Easton, Pa., 1957; postgrad., Harvard U., 1967. Comml. banker Citicorp, N.Y.C., 1957-79, sr. v.p., 1979-80; midwest sr. exec. Citicorp, Chgo., 1981—; mem. Govt. Commn. Fin. Insts., Chgo., 1984. Mem. Govt. Commn. Fin. Insts., Chgo., 1984; councilman Borough of Waldwick, N.J., 1964-68; trustee St. Ignatius Coll. Prep., Chgo., 1986-88, Lyric Opera Co., Chgo., 1987—; chmn. Lincoln Pk. Zool. Soc., Chgo., 1987-90, bd. dirs., 1984—; bd. dirs. Roosevelt U.; bd. dirs. Exec. Svc. Corps, Chgo. Mem. Chgo. Econ. Club, Chgo. Club. Avocations: painting, gardening. Home: 5727 Kenwood Ave Chicago IL 60637 Office: Citicorp 500 W Madison St Chicago IL 60661

MORGAN, HOWARD EDWIN, physiologist; b. Bloomington, Ill., Oct. 8, 1927; s. Lyle V. and Ethel E. (Bailey) M. Student, Ill. Wesleyan U., 1944-45; M.D., Johns Hopkins U., 1949. Intern Vanderbilt U., Nashville, 1949-51; resident in ob-gyn Vanderbilt U., 1951-53, instr., 1953-55, instr. physiology, 1957-59, asst. prof. physiology, 1959-62, assoc. prof., 1962-65, prof. physiology, 1965-67; Evan Pugh prof., chmn. physiology Pa. State U., Hershey, 1967-87; sr. v.p. research Geisinger Clinic, Danville, Pa., 1987—; v.p. research Am. Heart Assn., 1977-79; mem. Nat. Heart, Lung and Blood Adv. Council, 1979-83. Editor: Physiol. Revs, 1973-79, Am. Jour. Physiology: Cell Physiology, 1981-84. Served with U.S. Army, 1955-57. Recipient award of Merit Am. Heart Assn., 1979, Carl Wiggers award, 1984; Howard Hughes scholar, 1982. Mem. Am. Physiol. Soc. (pres., Daggs award 1992), Am. Heart Assn. (pres., Disting. Achievement award 1988, Gold Heart award 1994), Am. Soc. Biol. Chemists, Biochem. Soc., Biophysic. Soc., Internat. Soc. Heart Rsch. (pres.), Inst. Medicine NAS. Office: Geisinger Clinic Weis Ctr for Rsch Danville PA 17822

MORGAN, HUGH JACKSON, JR., bank executive; b. Nashville, Aug. 10, 1928; s. Hugh Jackson and Robert Ray (Porter) M.; m. Ann Moulton Ward, Aug. 28, 1954; children—Ann, Grace, Caroline, Hugh. A.B., Princeton U., N.J., 1950; LL.B., Vanderbilt U., Nashville, 1956; A.M.P., Harvard Bus. Sch., 1976. Bar: Tenn. 1956. Practice law Miller & Martin, Chattanooga, 1956-60; atty. So. Natural Gas Co., Birmingham, Ala., 1961-65, gen. atty., 1966-70, v.p. 1971-78, pres., 1982-84, chmn. bd., 1984-87; v.p. Sonat Inc., Birmingham, Ala., 1973-78, sr. v.p. 1979-84, exec. v.p. 1984, vice chmn. bd., 1984-87; vice chmn. Nat. Bank of Commerce, Birmingham, Ala., 1987-90; chmn. Nat. Bank Commerce, Birmingham, Ala., 1990—, also bd. dirs.; bd. dirs. AlaTenn Resources, Inc., Ala.-Tenn. Nat. Gas Co., Blue Cross-Blue Shield Ala. Chmn. Birmingham Airport Authority, 1986—; trustee Episcopal High Sch., Alexandria, Va., Children's Hosp. Ala., Birmingham, 1974—. Served to lt. (j.g.) USN, 1950-53. Recipient Bennett Douglas Bell Meml. prize Vanderbilt Law Sch., 1956. Mem. Order of the Coif. Clubs: Mountain Brook (pres. 1972), Redstone, (Birmingham); Belle Meade (Nashville); Linville Golf (N.C.). Lodge: Rotary. Home: 3121 Brookwood Rd Birmingham AL 35223-2016 Office: Nat Bank of Commerce 1927 First Ave N Birmingham AL 35203

MORGAN, JACQUI, illustrator, painter, educator; b. N.Y.C., Feb. 22, 1939; d. Henry and Emily (Cook) Morganstern; m. Onnig Kalfayan, Apr. 23, 1967 (div. 1972); m. Tomás Gonda, Jan. 1983 (dec. 1988). B.F.A. with honors, Pratt Inst., Bklyn., 1960; M.A., Hunter Coll., CCNY, 1978. Textile designer M. Lowenstein & Sons, N.Y.C., 1961-62, Fruit of the Loom, N.Y.C., 1962; stylist-design dir. Au Courant, Inc., N.Y.C., 1966—; assoc. prof. Pratt Inst., Bklyn., 1977—; guest lectr. U. Que., Syracuse U., Warsaw TV & Radio, Poland, NYU, Parsons Sch. Design, N.Y., Sch. Visual Arts, N.Y.C., Va. Commonwealth U., others; mem. profl. juries; condt. workshops. One-person shows include Soc. Illustrators, N.Y.C., 1977, Art Dirs. Club, N.Y.C., 1978, Gallerie Nowe Miasto, Warsaw, 1978, Gallerie Baumeister, Munich, W.Ger., 1978, Hansen-Feuerman Gallery, N.Y.C., 1980; group shows include Mus. Contemporary Crafts, N.Y.C., 1975, Smithsonian Instns., Washington, 1976, Mus. Warsaw, 1976, 78, Mus. Tokyo, 1979, Nat. Watercolor Soc., 1989, Salmagundi Club, 1990, New Eng. Watercolor Soc. Open, 1990, Miss. Watercolor Grand Nat., 1990, Illustration West 29, 1990, Adirondack Nat., 1990, Die Veriassenen Schuhe, 1994; represented in permanent collections: Smithsonian Instn., Mus. Warsaw; author-illustrator: Watercolor for Illustration; produced three of seven instrnl. watercolor videos; series of prints pub., 1995; series of plates pub., 1995; contbr. articles to profl. jours. Recipient more than 150 awards from various orgns. including Soc. Illustrators, Fed. Design Coun., Comm. Arts Mag., Am. Inst. Graphic Arts, N.Y. Art Dirs. Club, Print Design Ann. Mem. Graphic

Artists Guild (dir. 1975-79), Soc. Illustrators, Women Artists of the West, Pa. Watercolor Soc. Studio: 692 Greenwich St New York NY 10014-2876

MORGAN, JAMES A., rubber products company executive. Bar: N.C. 1962, Ohio 1966. Asst. sec. B.F. Goodrich, 1965-74, asst. sec., counsel, 1974-77, v.p., sec., counsel, 1979-82; v.p., sec., counsel Rubbermaid, Inc., Wooster, Ohio, 1983-88, sr. v.p., gen. counsel, 1988—. Office: Rubbermaid Inc 1147 Akron Rd Wooster OH 44691-2501

MORGAN, JAMES C., electronics executive; b. 1938. BSME, Cornell U., MBA. With Textron Inc., 1963-72, West Ven Mgmt., San Francisco, 1972-76; chmn. bd., pres., CEO Applied Materials, Inc., Santa Clara, Calif., 1976-87, chmn. bd., CEO, 1987—. Office: Applied Materials Inc 3050 Bowers Ave Santa Clara CA 95054-3201*

MORGAN, JAMES DURWARD, computer company executive; b. N.Y.C., Sept. 10, 1936; s. Durward Field and Harriet (Airey) M.; m. Ruth Ann Dobson, Jan. 14, 1967; children: Jennifer, Andrew. BEE, Yale U., 1961, MEE, 1962. Systems engr. Calspan Corp., Buffalo, 1962-68; v.p. Comptek Rsch. Inc., Buffalo, 1968-83, 90—, also bd. dirs.; v.p. Barrister Info. Systems Corp., Buffalo, 1983-90; also bd. dirs. Barrister Info. Systems Corp., 1983—. Mem. adv. coun. Erie C.C., Amherst, N.Y., 1985—, past chmn.; bd. dirs. Yale Alumni Bd., Buffalo, 1987—. Served with USN, 1959-61. Mem. IEEE, ACM (past chmn. local chpt.). Home: 34 Ironwood Ct East Amherst NY 14051-1628 Office: Comptek Telecomm Inc 140 Mid County Dr Orchard Park NY 14127

MORGAN, JAMES EARL, librarian, administrator; b. Wheeling, W.Va., June 30, 1941; s. James H. L. and Ethel Irene (Goodwin) M.; m. Carman H. Head, Dec. 23, 1966; 1 child, Scott Andrew. BS in Edn., Ariz. State Coll., 1965; M.S.L.S., Fla. State U., 1966. Reference asst. social scis. Fla. State U., Tallahassee, 1965-66; head pub. services Ga. Coll., Milledgeville, 1967-69; dir. pub. services U. Tex. Med. Br., Galveston, 1969-73; dir. libraries U. Conn. Health Ctr., Farmington, 1973-76, Oreg. Health Sci. U., Portland, 1976—. Contbr. articles to profl. jours. Grantee Nat. Library Medicine, 1974-76, 78-81. Mem. ALA (life), Med. Library Assn. (chmn. Pacific NW chpt. 1981), Oreg. Health Scis. Libraries Assn., Pacific NW Library Assn., Spl. Library Assn., Oreg. Library Assn., Portland Area Spl. Librarians Assn., Assn. Coll. and Research Libraries. Democrat. Office: Oreg Health Scis Univ Library Biomedical Info Comm Ctr 3181 SW Sam Jackson Park Rd Portland OR 97101-3098

MORGAN, JAMES GILMOR, insurance executive; b. Balt., May 8, 1939; s. James G. Morgan and Frances Kell Morgan Hartley; m. Bernice Kenney; children: Catharine, Kimberly, Joseph, Thomas. BS in Mktg., U. Balt. CLU; registered health underwriter. Sales mgr. Aetna Life & Casualty, Balt., 1964-69; CEO, agy. head Lincoln Nat./Morgan Fin., Balt., 1969—; lectr. in field. Contbr. articles to profl. jours.; speaker in field. Bd. dirs. Jemicy Sch., Owings Mills, Md., 1975—, Calvert Hall Coll., Balt., 1984-93; bd. dirs., pres. Greater Balt. chpt. Football Hall of Fame, 1975-76; pres. Eastern Football Ofcls., Balt., 1984-85. With U.S. Army, 1961-63. Named to Alumni Hall of Fame, Calvert Hall Coll., 1986. Mem. Am. Soc. CLU/ChFC (pres. Balt. chpt. 1995—), Balt. Gen. Agts. and Mgrs. Assn. (pres. 1981-82, 91-92), Balt. Life Underwriters (pres. 1986-87), Md. Assn. Health Underwriters (pres. 1975-76), Nat. Orton Soc. (bd. dirs. 1983-87), Gen. Agts. and Mgrs. Assn. (treas. nat. bd.). Republican. Roman Catholic. Avocations: golf, skiing, running. Office: Morgan Fin Group 1300 York Rd Lutherville MD 21093

MORGAN, JAMES JOHN, environmental engineering educator; b. N.Y.C., June 23, 1932; s. James and Anna (Treanor) M.; m. Jean Laurie McIntosh, June 15, 1957; children—Jenny, Johanna, Eve, Michael, Martha, Sarah. B.C.E., Manhattan Coll., 1954; M.S.C.E., U. Mich., 1956; postgrad., U. Ill., 1956-60; Ph.D., Harvard U., 1964; Sc.D. (hon.), Manhattan Coll., 1989. Instr. civil engring. U. Ill., Urbana, 1956-60; assoc. prof. U. Fla., Gainesville, 1963-65; assoc. prof. Calif. Inst. Tech., Pasadena, 1965-69, prof. environ. engring., 1969-87, Marvin L. Goldberger prof. environ. engring. sci., 1987—, dean of students, 1972-75, dean grad. studies, 1981-84, v.p. student affairs, 1980-89; exec. officer environ. engring. sci., 1993—; assoc. officer environ. engring. studies bd., NRC, 1974-80, 93—; chmn. Acid Deposition Sci. Adv. Com., Calif., 1983-92; chmn. Gordon Rsch. Conf. on Environ. Sci.; Water, 1970. Author: (with Werner Stumm) Aquatic Chemistry, 1970, 2d edit., 1981, 3rd edit. 1995; editor Environ. Sci. and Tech., 1966-74; contbr. articles to profl. jours. Mem. Am. Chem. Soc. (award 1980), AAAS, Am. Soc. Limnology and Oceanography (editorial bd. 1977-80), Nat. Acad. Engring. Assn. Environ. Engring. Profs. (award 1981, 83, 94), Am. Water Works Assn. (award 1963), Sigma Xi, Chi Epsilon. Democrat. Roman Catholic. Club: Athenaeum. Avocations: tennis; folk music.

MORGAN, JAMES NEWTON, research economist, educator; b. Corydon, Ind., Mar. 1, 1918; s. John Jacob Brooke and Rose Ann (Davis) M.; m. Gladys Lucille Hassler, May 12, 1945; children—Kenneth, Timothy, Salim, Janet. BA, Northwestern U., 1939; PhD, Harvard U., 1947. Asst. prof. econs. Brown U., Providence, 1947-49; Carnegie research fellow U. Mich., Ann Arbor, 1949-51; asst. prof. econ., asst. program dir. Inst. for Social Research, U. Mich., Ann Arbor; asst. prof. econs., assoc. program dir. Inst. Social Research for Advanced Study in Behavior Sci., Palo Alto, Calif., 1955-56; prof. econs., program dir. Inst. Social Research U. Mich., Ann Arbor, 1956-88, prof. emeritus, 1988—; bd. dirs. Consumers Union, Mt. Vernon, N.Y., 1972-83; com. on sci. and pub. policy NAS, 1983-86, report rev. com., 1987-91; com. on basic rsch. in behavior and social sci. NRC, Washington, panel on census requirements, 1992-95. Fellow Am. Statis. Assn., Am. Acad. Arts and Scis., Gerontol. Soc. Am., Wissenschaftskolleg zu Berlin; mem. Nat. Acad. Scis., Am. Econ. Assn. Methodist. Avocations: swimming; gardening. Home: 1217 Bydding Rd Ann Arbor MI 48103-3103 Office: Inst Social Research Thompson St Ann Arbor MI 48104

MORGAN, JAMES PHILIP, pharmacologist, cardiologist, educator; b. Cin., Jan. 13, 1948; s. James Weldon and Dorcas Adele (Meyer) M.; m. Kathleen Greive, Dec. 22, 1973; children: James Patrick, Jonathan Michael. BS, U. Cin., 1970, PhD, 1974, MD, 1976. Diplomate Am. Bd. Internal Medicine and Subspecialty Cardiovascular Disease. Fellow in internal medicine Mayo Clinic, Rochester, Minn., 1976-79, fellow in cardiovascular disease, 1979-83; asst. in medicine, Beth Israel Hosp., Boston, 1983—; instr. pharmacology U. Cin., 1975-76; asst. prof. pharmacology, instr. medicine, Mayo Clinic, 1981-83; asst. prof. medicine, Harvard U., Boston, 1983, assoc. prof., 1988—; affiliate faculty, dept. pharmacology, Harvard Med. Sch., 1986—; chief and prgram dir. cardiovascular divsn. Beth Israel Hosp., 1994—. Contbr. articles to profl. jours. Recipient Young Investigators award Am. Coll. Cardiology, 1982; Balfour award Mayo Clinic, 1983, Advanced Cardiac Life Support Spl Recognition award Mayo Clinic, 1983, Research Career Devel. award NIH, 1985-90. Mem. AMA, Am. Heart Assn., Biophys. Soc. Am. Soc. Pharmacology and Exptl. Therapeutics, Masons. Avocation: philatelics. Office: Beth Israel Hosp Cardiovascular Div 330 Brookline Ave Boston MA 02215-5400

MORGAN, JANE HALE, retired library director; b. Dines, Wyo., May 11, 1926; d. Arthur Hale and Billie (Wood) Hale; m. Joseph Charles Morgan, Aug. 12, 1955; children: Joseph Hale, Jane Frances, Ann Michele. BA, Howard U., 1947; MA, U. Denver, 1954. Mem. staff Detroit Pub. Library, 1954-87, exec. asst. dir., 1973-75, dep. dir., 1975-78, dir. 1978-87; mem. Mich. Libr. Consortium Bd.; exec. bd. Southeastern Mich. Regional Film Libr.; vis. prof. Wayne State U., 1989—. Trustee New Detroit, Inc., Delta Dental Plan of Mich., Delta Dental Plan of Ohio; v.p. United Southwestern Mich.; pres. Univ.-Cultural Center Assn.; bd. dirs. Rehab. Inst., YWCA, Met. Affairs Corp., Literacy Vols. Am., Detroit, Mich. Ctr. for the Book, Interfaith Coun.; bd. dirs., v.p. United Community Svcs. Met. Detroit; chmn. Detroiters for Adult Reading Excellence; chmn. adv. coun. libr. sci. U. Mich.; mem. adv. coun. libr. sci. Wayne State U.; dir. Met. Detroit Youth Found.; chmn. Mich. LSCA adv. coun.; mem. UWA Literacy Com., Attys. Grievance Com., Women's Commn., Mich. Civil Svc. Rev. Com.; vice chair Mich. Coun. for Humanities; mem. Commn. for the Greening of Detroit; adv. com. Headstart; mem. Detroit Women's Com., Detroit Women's Forum, Detroit Exec. Svc. Corps. Recipient Anthony Wayne award Wayne State U., 1981, Summit award Greater Detroit C. of C.; named Detroit Howardite of Year, 1983. Mem. ALA, Mich. Library Assn., Women's Nat.

Book Assn., Assn. Mcpl. Profl. Women, NAACP, LWV, Women's Economic Club, Alpha Kappa Alpha. Democrat. Episcopalian.

MORGAN, JOE LEONARD, investment company executive, former professional baseball player; b. Bonham, Tex., Sept. 19, 1943. Student, Oakland City (Ind.) Coll., Calif. State U.-Hayward. Infielder Houston Astros, 1962-71, 2d baseman, 1980-81; 2d baseman Cin. Reds, 1971-80, San Francisco Giants, 1981-82, Phila. Phillies, 1982-83, Oakland A's, 1983-84; pres. Joe Morgan Investments Inc, Oakland, 1984—; player World Series, 1972, 75-76, 83. Named Most Valuable Player Tex. League, 1964; Rookie of Yr. in Nat. League Sporting News, 1965; Most Valuable Player Nat. League, 1975, 76; Maj. League Player of Year. Sporting News, 1975, 76; named to Nat. League All-Star Team, 1970, 72-79, Nat. League Comeback Player of the Year Sporting News, 1982, Nat. League Player of the Year Sporting News, 1975, Nat. League All Star Team Sporting News, 1972, 73-77; recipient Silver Slugger award Sporting News, 1982; elected to Baseball Hall of Fame, 1990. Office: Joe Morgan Investments Inc 3650 Hayman St Hayward CA 94544*

MORGAN, JOHN BRUCE, hospital care consultant; b. Youngstown, Ohio, Oct. 25, 1919; s. John Benjamin and Ida May (Lane) M.; m. Marian Frampton, July 11, 1969; children: John B., Carolyn, Leonard, Suzanne (dec.). B.S., Miami U., 1941; M.B.A., Harvard U., 1946. Field rep. Gen. Motors Acceptance Corp., Youngstown, 1941; pres. Assoc. Hosp. Service, Inc., Youngstown, 1947-74; pres. Hosp. Care Corp. (Blue Cross), Cin., 1974-83, cons., 1983—; pres. Health Maintenance Plan, Cin., 1974-83, Health Care Mutual, Cin., 1974-83; chmn. bd. govs., chmn. exec. com. Blue Cross Assn., Chgo., 1981-82; chmn. bd. Community Life Ins. Co., Worthington, Ohio, 1979-83; mem. joint exec. com. Blue Cross-Blue Shield Assns., mem. joint bds., Chgo.; mem. bus. adv. com. Miami U., Oxford, Ohio. Gen. chmn. United Fund campaign, Youngstown, 1965; pres. Cancer Soc., 1965. Served with AUS, 1942-46. Mem. Am.Hosp. Assn. (Justin Ford Kimball award 1983), Ohio Hosp. Assn., Ohio C of C. (bd. dirs.), Youngstown Area C. of C. (pres. 1966-67), Delray Beach, Fla. C of C., Youngstown Country Club, Delray Dunes Golf and Country Club (bd. dirs., v.p.), Rotary (bd. dirs. Delray Beach club, pres. 1992, Paul Harris fellow), Masons, Elks, Sigma Alpha Epsilon, Delta Sigma Pi. Mem. United Ch. of Christ. Home: 9 Slash Pine Dr Boynton Beach FL 33436-5524 Office: 1351 William Howard Taft Rd Cincinnati OH 45206-1721

MORGAN, JOHN DAVIS, government official; b. Newark, Feb. 14, 1921; s. John Davis and Caroline Frommel (Schaller) M.; m. Leta Maude Bretzinger, June 27, 1953; children: John Davis III, Bret Zinger. BS., Pa. State U., 1942, M.S., 1947, Ph.D., 1948, E.M., 1950; grad. extension course, Indsl. Coll. of Armed Forces, Washington, 1953. Asst. for materials and stockpile policies Nat. Security Resources Bd., Washington, 1948-51; dir. materials rev. div. DPA, Washington, 1951-53; materials expert ODM, Washington, 1953-56; mem. staff President's Cabinet Com. on Mineral Policy, 1953-54; cons. bus. and def. problems in metals, minerals and fuels Washington, from 1956; mem. nat. def. exec. res. for ODM, 1956-58, OCDM, 1958-61, Office Emergency Planning, 1961-71, Emergency Minerals Adminstrn., 1972—; mem. spl. stockpile advisory com. to ODM, 1957-58; com. on scope and conduct of materials research NAS, 1959-60, then, mem. com. on mineral sci. and tech., 1966-70; mem. Interagy. Adv. Com. on Mining and Mineral Research, 1977—; head dept. sci. and math. Daytona Beach Community Coll., Fla., 1961-71; asst. dir. mineral position analysis U.S. Bur. Mines, Dept. Interior, Washington, 1971-74, acting dir. bur., 1973-74, 77-78, assoc. dir. mineral and materials supply/demand analysis, 1974-79, chief staff officer, 1979—; Interior Dept. liaison to Council Internat. Econ. Policy Staff, 1973-77, to Econ. Policy Bd. Staff, 1974-77, to Dept. Def. Materials Steering Group, 1975—, to FPA-FEMA Stockpile Com., 1975-88, to Winter Energy Emergency Planning Group of Dept. of Energy, 1977—; alt. Interior rep. Trade Policy Rev. Group, 1975-81; chmn. minerals rev. com. Non-Fuel Minerals Policy Study, 1978; chmn. materials supply task force NSC Stockpile Study, 1983-87; liaison To Dept. Def. Stockpile Com., 1988—; mem. Defense Logistics Agy. Market Impact Com., 1988—; mem. Def. Dept. Adv. Com. Operation and Modernization of Stockpile, 1993—; U.S. rep. UN Sci. Com. on Resources, 1949; lectr. numerous univs. including Nat. Def. U., War Coll., Indsl. Coll., Def. Intelligence Coll., 1949—; hon. prof. Indsl. Coll., 1983; invited speaker nat. meetings sci. and engring. socs., 1949—. Author: Domestic Mining Industry of the U.S. in World War II, 1949; also numerous tech. articles; Corr.: Mining Ann. Rev, London, 1958—. Served from 2d lt. to maj. Corps Engrs. AUS, 1942-46. Decorated Bronze Star; recipient Distinguished Service gold medal Interior Dept., 1976; named Meritorious Exec. Sr. Exec. Service, 1983. Fellow Soc. Am. Mil. Engrs.; mem. Sci. Research Soc. Am., Soc. Mining Engrs. (Disting. mem.), AIME (nat. Krumb lectr. 1973, Legion of Honor 1989), Mining and Metall. Soc. Am., Am. Def. Preparedness Assn., Sigma Xi, Tau Beta Pi, Sigma Tau, Pi Mu Epsilon, Phi Lambda Upsilon, Phi Kappa Phi, Phi Eta Sigma, Sigma Gamma Epsilon. Club: Cosmos (Washington). Home: 5013 Worthington Dr Bethesda MD 20816-2748 Office: US Bur Mines 810 7th St NW Washington DC 20241-0002

MORGAN, JOHN DERALD, electrical engineer; b. Hays, Kans., Mar. 15, 1939; s. John Baber and Avis Ruth (Wolf) M.; m. Elizabeth June McKneely, June 23, 1962; children: Laura Elizabeth, Kimberly Ann, Rebecca Ruth, John Derald. BSEE, La. Tech. U., 1962; MS, U. Mo., Rolla, 1965, Degree in Elec. Engring. (hon.), 1987; PhD, Ariz. State U., 1968. Registered profl. engr., forensic engr., Mo., N.Mex. Elec. engr. Tex. Eastman div. Eastman Kodak Co., 1962-63; instr. U. Mo., Rolla, 1963-65, Ariz. State U., 1965-68; asso. prof. elec. engring. U. Mo., Rolla, 1968-72; Alcoa Found. prof. elec. engring. U. Mo., 1972-75, chmn. elec. engring., 1978-85, assoc. dir. Ctr. Internat. Programs, 1970-78, Emerson Electric prof., 1975-85; dean engring. N.Mex. State U., 1985—; cons. to industry. Author: Power Apparatus Testing Techniques, 1969, Computer Monitoring and Control of Electric Utility Systems, 1972, Control and Distribution of Megawatts Through Man-Machine Interaction, 1973, Electromechanical and Electromagnetic Machines and Devices, 1986; also articles. Pres. bd. trustees First Meth. Ch., Rolla, 1971-73; pres. adminstrv. bd. First United Meth. Ch. Rolla, 1978-79; v.p., mem. bd. adminstrn. People to People, 1976; bd. dirs., cubmaster Ozarks dist. Boy Scouts Am., 1968-79, asst. dist. commr., 1971-73, cubmaster Yucca coun., 1989-90, coun. commr., 1989-90, asst. scout master, 1990—, dist. com. Sushine Dist.; dist. chmn. Meramec dist., 1978-80; bd. dirs. Mo. Partners of the Americas. Recipient Scouters Key award and Scouter Tng. award Ozarks coun., Boy Scouts Am., 1971, Dist. award of merit 1977, Silver Beaver award, 1982, Cub Leader award, Webelos Leader award, Sunshine Dist. Yucca coun.; T.H. Harris scholar, 1959-61; John H. Horton scholar, 1961-62. Fellow IEEE (chmn. internat. practices subcom. 1972-79, sec. PSE com., vice chmn., chmn. 1979-85, chmn. ednl. resources subcom. 1973-78, selected award of Merit St. Louis sect., Educators award St. Louis sect., honor award St. Louis sect., Centennial award 1984), Nat. Acad. Forensic Engrs., ASTM; mem. NSPE (bd. govs., nat. dir., vice chmn., S.W. chmn. Profl. Engrs. in Edn., v.p.), N.Mex. Soc. Profl. Engrs. (N.Mex. Engr. of Yr. 1993), Am. Soc. Engring. Edn., Sigma Xi, Tau Beta Pi, Eta Kappa Nu, Omicron Delta Kappa, Phi Kappa Phi, Kappa Sigma (faculty and alumni advisor), Epsilon Gamma (grand master, grand procurator, PSI exec. of yr. 1993). Home: 2425 Janet Ann Ln Las Cruces NM 88005-5119 Office: NMex State U Main Campus Coll Engring PO Box 30001 Las Cruces NM 88003-8001

MORGAN, JOHN STEPHEN, state representative, materials science researcher; b. Washington, Dec. 23, 1963; s. James Donald and Virginia Louise (Hendrickson) M. BS, Loyola Coll., Balt., 1984; MS in Engring., Johns Hopkins U., 1988, PhD, 1990. Rsch. assoc. Johns Hopkins U., Balt., 1986-90; sr. engr. Johns Hopkins U., Laurel, Md., 1990—; mem. commerce and govt. matters com. Md. Gen. Assembly, Annapolis, 1991—. Chmn. adv. com. Bd. Edn. Howard County, Md., 1989-90. Recipient Charles Miller award Howard County Rep. Party, 1988. Mem. Am. Phys. Soc. (Congl. Sci. fellow 1994-95), Materials Rsch. Soc., Kiwanis. Lutheran. Home: 7920 Ashford Blvd Laurel MD 20707 Office: Md Gen Assembly Lowe House Office Bldg Annapolis MD 21401

MORGAN, JOYCE ELIZABETH, elementary school educator; b. Pitts., June 8, 1940; d. Richard Gailbreth and Pauline (Wasil) Cunningham; m. John F. Morgan; children: Janet Lynn, Jennifer Ann, Joy Ellyn, Jamie Elizabeth. BS, Calif. State U., 1962. Elem. tchr. Chartiers Valley Sch. Dist.,

Pitts., 1971—; mem. Tchrs. & Adminstrs. for Better Schs. Com., 1993-94. Facilitator Our Lady of Grace Bible Sch., Scott Twp., 1975-78, CCD tchr., 1978-82, mem. choir, 1982-85, mem. folk group choir, 1990-93, tchr. children's liturgy, 1993-94. Republican. Roman Catholic. Avocations: reading, landscaping, plants. Office: Washington Sch Dewey Ave Bridgeville PA 15107

MORGAN, KATHRYN LAWSON, historian, educator; 1 child, Susan Morgan Crooks. M.A., Howard U., 1952, U. Pa., 1967; Ph.D., U. Pa., 1970. Asst. prof. U. Del., Newark, 1970-71; lectr. Swarthmore Coll., Pa., spring 1970, prof. history and folklore, 1972—; vis. assoc. prof. Bryn Mawr Coll., 1972-75, Haverford Coll., 1972-74, U. Calif.-Berkeley, winter 1975; cons. Research for Better Schs., Phila., 1968-69, Black History Mus., Phila., 1966-76, Smithsonian Instn., 1974-76, Ednl. Film Service, 1977. Author: Children of Strangers; Stories of a Black Family, 1980, Books Across the Seas, Selected for Youth, 1981; contbr. articles to profl. jours., mags. Danforth Found. fellow, 1968-70; Smithsonian Instn.-Am. Philos. Soc. grantee, 1983. Avocations: traveling; storytelling; theatre; music. Office: Swarthmore Coll Swarthmore PA 19081

MORGAN, LARRY RONALD, minister; b. Springhill, La., Mar. 12, 1936; s. Woodrow Wilson Morgan and Alma Elizabeth (Dunn) Burch; m. Elizabeth Dianne Baker, May 24, 1958; children: Elizabeth Denise Morgan Davis, Dennis Kevin. ADiv, Bapt. Missionary Assn. Theol. Sem., Jacksonville, Tex., 1990. Ordained to ministry Bapt. Ch., 1971. Clk., carrier U.S. P.O., Springhill, La., 1956-71; assoc. pastor Webb Chapel Bapt. Ch., Dallas, 1971-72, pastor, 1972—; clk., trustee Bapt. Missionary Assn. Sem., Jacksonville, 1983-86; chmn. bd. trustees Bapt. Progress, Dallas, 1984-87. Pres. PTA Browning Elem. Sch., Springhill, 1969-70. With USAR, 1959-66. Mem. Bapt. Missionary Assn. Am. (v.p. hdqrs. Little Rock 1985-86, pres. 1986-88), Dallas County Bapt. Assn. (moderator 1982-84). Home: 14517 Heartside Dr Dallas TX 75234-2152

MORGAN, LAWRENCE ALLISON, headmaster, educational administrator; b. Norman, Okla., June 12, 1935; s. Lawrence Nelson and Catherine (Edwards) Morgan; m. Nancy Catherine Somogyi, July 3, 1960; children: Michael Lawrence, Katherine Elizabeth, Thomas Leverett. AB, Harvard U., 1957; MA, Washington U.-St. Louis, 1969, Webster U., 1977. Faculty, Thomas Jefferson Sch., St. Louis, 1957-66, trustee, 1959—, dir. admissions, 1966-80, v.p. bd. trustees, 1966-80, headmaster, pres., 1980—; trustee Riverways Sch., 1986-87. Bd. dirs. Jefferson Twp., Dem. Club, 1971-72. Episcopalian. Clubs: Harvard Club (St. Louis, Boston, N.Y.C.). Avocations: travel; photography; camping; cycling; hiking. Home: 9112 Pardee Spur Saint Louis MO 63126 Office: Thomas Jefferson Sch 4100 S Lindbergh Blvd Saint Louis MO 63127-1698

MORGAN, LEON ALFORD, retired utility executive; b. Washington, Dec. 29, 1934; s. Albert Lewis and Alice Viets (Alford) M.; children: David Richard, Sherry Alice; m. Jacqueline Jamieson, Feb. 14, 1993. BSEE, Worcester (Mass.) Poly. Inst., 1957. Registered profl. engr., Conn. With United Illuminating Co., New Haven, 1957-94; gen. ops. mgr., then v.p. ops. United Illuminating Co., 1973-76, exec. v.p., 1976-83, sr. v.p. fin., 1984-94. Mem. Quinnipiack Club (New Haven). Republican. Episcopalian. Home: 43 Forest Brook Rd Guilford CT 06437-2245

MORGAN, LEWIS B., counseling education educator; b. Fountain Springs, Pa., May 23, 1934; s. Burgess S. and Marion R. (Lewis) M.; m. Irene L. Morgan, Dec. 30, 1960; children: Jennifer, David. BS in Edn., Kutztown State Coll., 1960; EdM in Counseling, Rutgers U., 1963; PhD in Counseling, U. Conn., 1970. Lic. psychologist, N.J. Tchr. Triton Regional High Sch., Runnemede, N.J., 1960-61; tchr., counselor Overbrook Regional High Sch., Clementon, N.J., 1961-63; counselor Pennsauken (N.J.) High Sch., 1963-64; registrar Kutztown (Pa.) State Coll., 1964-66; guidance dir. Bolton (Conn.) Pub. Schs., 1966-70; prof. counselor edn. Villanova (Pa.) U., 1970—; pvt. practice counselor, 1970—; cons. local sch. dists., 1970—. Author: A Casebook for School Counselors, 1974; contbr. articles on counseling to profl. publs. Mem. NEA, AACD, Am. Psychol. Assn., Assn. Specialists in Group Work, Phi Kappa Phi, Kappa Delta Pi. Democrat. Episcopalian. Avocations: running, travel, jazz. Office: Villanova U Dept Edn And Svcs Villanova PA 19085

MORGAN, LEWIS RENDER, federal judge; b. LaGrange, Ga., July 14, 1913; s. William Ellington and Bettie (Render) M.; m. Sue Phillips, July 29, 1944; children: Parks Healy, Sue Ann. Student, U. Mich., 1930-32; LLB, U. Ga., 1935; LLB (hon.), Atlanta Law Sch., 1963, La Grange Coll., 1977. Bar: Ga. 1935. Mem. Wyatt & Morgan, LaGrange, 1935-61; judge U.S. Dist. Ct. (no. dist.) Ga., 1961-68, chief judge, 1965-68; judge U.S. Cir. Ct. Appeals (5th and 11th cirs.), Newnan, Ga., 1968—, now sr. justice; Mem. budget com. U.S. Courts, 1967—; Mem. Gen. Assembly Ga., 1937-39; exec. sec. A Sidney Camp (congressman) 1939-42; Mem. visitors com. U. Ga. Law Sch., 1970-73; mem. spl. div. U.S. Ct. Appeals for D.C., 1978—; mem. Temporary Emergency Ct. Appeals, 1979—. Mem. Phi, Phi Delta Phi. Presbyn. Home: Cameron Mill Rd La Grange GA 30240 Office: US Ct Appeals 11th Cir PO Box 759 Newnan GA 30264-0759

MORGAN, LORRIE (LORETTA LYNN MORGAN), country singer; b. Nashville, May 9, 1959; d. George Morgan; divorced; m. Keith Whitley (dec. 1989); children: Morgan, Jesse. Rec. artist RCA, 1989—. Albums: Leave the Light On, 1989, Something in Red, 1991, Tell Me I'm Dreaming, 1992, Watch Me, 1992, Trainwreck of Emotion, 1993, (with Sammy Kershaw) War Paint, 1994; # 1 gold single Something in Red, 1991; TV movies include: Proudheart, 1993. Office: RCA Records 1 Music Circle Nashville TN 37203*

MORGAN, LUCY W., journalist; b. Memphis, Oct. 11, 1940; d. Thomas Allin and Lucile (Sanders) Keen; m. Alton F. Ware, June 26, 1958 (div. Sept. 1967); children—Mary Kathleen, Andrew Allin; m. Richard Alan Morgan, Aug. 9, 1968; children—Lynn Elwell, Kent Morgan. A.A., Pasco Hernando Community Coll., New Port Richey, Fla., 1975; student, U. South Fla., 1976-80. Reporter Ocala Star Banner, Fla., 1965-68; reporter St. Petersburg Times, Fla., 1967-86, capitol bur. chief, 1986—; assoc. editor and bd. dirs. Times Pub. Co. Recipient Paul Hansel award Fla. Soc. Newspaper Editors, 1981, First in Pub. Service award Fla. Soc. Newspaper Editors, 1982, First Place award in pub. service Fla. Press Club, 1982, Pulitzer award for investigative reporting Columbia U., 1985, First Place award in investigative reporting Sigma Delta Chi, 1985; named to Kappa Tau Alpha Hall of Fame, 1992. Home: 1727 Brookside Blvd Tallahassee FL 32301-6769 Office: St Petersburg Times 336 E College Ave Tallahassee FL 32301-1551

MORGAN, LYNDA M., state legislator; d. Tommy and Grace (Arviso) Murphy; married; children: Kelly, Russell, Jacob. AA in Elem. Edn., U. N.Mex., Gallup, 1985; BS in Pub. Adminstrn., No. Ariz. U., 1987. Adminstrv. asst. Navajo Skill Ctr. Inc., Crownpoint, N.Mex., 1979-81, acting exec. dir., 1981-83, tng. instr., 1983-84; program mgr. Dept. Youth Svcs., Crownpoint Agy., The Navajo Nation, Crownpoint, N.Mex., 1987-89; mem. N.Mex. Ho. of Reps. Chairwoman Health, Phys., Edn. & Recreation Program Adv. Com., Gallup, N.Mex., 1988—. Home: PO Box 705 Crownpoint NM 87313-0705 Office: N Mex Ho of Reps State Capitol New Mexico State Capitol NM 87503

MORGAN, MADEL JACOBS, retired archives and library administrator; b. Rosedale, Miss., Apr. 26, 1918; d. Charles Clark and Vera (Joest) Jacobs; m. Adlia Morgan, June 11, 1940 (dec. Dec. 1984); 1 child, Susan Miller Griffith; m. Murray Davis Stringer, Apr. 26, 1988 (dec. Feb. 1990). B.A., Miss. U. for Women, Columbus, 1939; library cert., Miss. Coll., 1960. Libr. St. Andrews Sch., Jackson, 1955-68; spl. programs cons. Miss. Libr. Commn., Jackson, 1968-79; dir. archives and libr. div. Miss. Dept. Archives and History, Jackson, 1979-88, ret., 1988; mem. Miss. Hist. Records Adv. Bd., 1981-89. Geneal. editor Jour. Miss. History, 1953-94. Trustee Pub. Libr. Sys. Madison County, 1993—; v.p. Miss. Hist. Soc., 1993, pres. 1994-95. Mem. ALA (coun. 1971-75), Miss. Libr. Assn. (pres. 1979), Nat. Assn. Govt. Archives and Records Adminstrs. (bd. dirs. 1985-86), Libr. Svcs. and Constrn. Act (adv. coun. 1981-87), Friends of Miss. Librs., Inc. (treas. 1992-94), Nat. Soc. Colonial Dames Am., Order of the First Families of Miss.,

Miss. Geneal. Soc. (pres. 1991-92). Democrat. Episcopalian. Home: 592 Rice Rd Ridgeland MS 39157-2905

MORGAN, MARABEL, author; b. Crestline, Ohio, June 25, 1937; d. Howard and Delsa (Smith) Hawk; m. Charles O. Morgan, Jr., June 25, 1964; children—Laura Lynn, Michelle Rene. Ed., Ohio State U. Pres. Total Woman, Inc., Miami, Fla., 1970—; pub. speaker. Author: The Total Woman, 1973, Total Joy, 1976, The Total Woman Cookbook, 1980, The Electric Woman, 1985. Office: care Total Woman Inc 1300 NW 167th St Miami FL 33169-5738

MORGAN, MARILYN, federal judge; b. 1947; 1 child, Terrence M. Adamson. BA, Emory U., 1969, JD, 1976. Bar: Ga. 1976, Calif. 1977. Ptnr. Morgan & Towery, San Jose, Calif., 1979-88; bankruptcy judge U.S. Bankruptcy Ct. (no. dist.) Calif., 1988—; mem. bankruptcy adv. com. U.S. Dist. Ct., 1984-88; law rep. 9th Cir. Jud. Conf., 1987-88. Mem. adv. bd. Downtown YMCA, 1984-88; dir. The Women's Fund, 1987-88. Mem. Santa Clara County Bar Assn. (chmn. debtor and creditor and insolvency com. 1979, 81, treas. 1982, pres. 1985-86), Santa Clara County Bar Assn. Law Found. (trustee 1982, 86-88, pres. 1985, law related edn. trustee 1986-88), Nat. Assn. Bankruptcy Trustees (founding mem., v.p., sec. 1981-88), Rotary Club San Jose (bd. dirs. 1992—), Nat. Assn. Bankruptcy Trustees (founder). Office: US Bankruptcy Ct 280 S 1st St Rm 3035 San Jose CA 95113-3010

MORGAN, MARY ANNE, secondary education educator; b. Camden, N.J., Sept. 15, 1943; d. Anthony Warren and Eleanor Elizabeth (Frederick) Mackara; children: Elizabeth Anne, James Frederick. Student, Moore Coll. Art, Phila., 1961; BFA, Temple U., 1965; MEd, Rutgers U., 1984. Cert. elem. and secondary tchr., N.J. Tchr. art Sterling High Sch., Somerdale, N.J., 1965-68, head fine arts dept., advisor, coach, 1976—. Advisor Teen Inst. of the Garden State, N.J., 1991-92. Named Outstanding Young Woman of Am., 1976; state poster chairperson N.J. Dept. Vocat. Edn., 1979. Mem. NEA, N.J. Edn. Assn., Art Educators N.J. (cons., resources speaker 1982—), Nat. Art Edn. Assn., Citizens Community Bd., Mcpl. Alliance, Order Ea. Star, Delta Kappa Pi, Delta Kappa Gamma. Avocations: golf, music. Home: 535 Beech Ave Laurel Spgs NJ 08021-3003 Office: Warwick Rd Somerdale NJ 08083

MORGAN, MELANIE KARYN, lawyer; b. Kans. City, Mo., July 29, 1962; married; 2 children. BA in Philosophy, Coll. of William and Mary, 1984, JD, 1987. Bar: Tex. 1987. Assoc. atty. Geary, Stahl & Spencer, Dallas, 1987-89; atty. PepsiCo, Inc.-Frito-Lay, Inc., Dallas, 1989-91; sr. atty., 1991-94, of counsel, 1994—. Mem. ABA, Dallas Bar Assn., Dallas Assn. Young Lawyers, Collin County Bar Assn., Promotion Mktg. Assn. of Am. (legal com.).

MORGAN, MONROE, retired savings and loan executive; b. Long Beach, Calif., Sept. 4, 1921; s. Karle Barett and Ethel (Monroe) M.; m. Ann Betts, Sept. 30, 1949; children: Sarah Nell, Daniel, Margaret Jane. BA, Pomona Coll., 1942. Cert. vol. counselor Health Ins. Counseling and Advocacy Program, Calif. Acctg. exec. Coast Fed. Savs. and Loan Assn., Los Angeles, 1945-50; sec., treas. Am. Savs. and Loan Assn., Whittier, Calif., 1954-56; sr. v.p. Gt. Western Fin. Corp., Beverly Hills, Calif., 1956-87; also officer subs. savs. and loan assns.; trustee Depositors Investment Trust, 1984-85; mem. investment mgmt. com. Internat. Found. Employees Plans, 1970-76; chmn. Thrift Industry Acctg. Com., 1976-78. Active Los Angeles County Art Mus.; chmn. Ethnic Arts Coun., 1977-80; dir. non-profit food distbn. orgn. Love Is Feeding Everyone, 1986-90, treas., 1981-94; bd. dirs. Amberjack, Ltd., Bloomington, Ill., 1985; mem. alumni coun. Pomona Coll., 1989-92, chmn. edn. com., 1992-94. Maj. USMCR, 1942-45, 50-51. Mem. Savs. and Loan Instns. (bd. govs. 1957-62), Fin. Mgrs. Soc. for Savs. Instns., Calif. Savs. and Loan League, Savs. Assns. Fin. Execs. (pres. 1968-75), Fin. Analysts Fedn. Home: 922 San Vicente Blvd Santa Monica CA 90402-2004

MORGAN, NEIL, author, newspaper editor, lecturer, columnist; b. Smithfield, N.C., Feb. 27, 1924; s. Samuel Lewis and Isabelle (Robeson) M.; m. Caryl Lawrence, 1945 (div. 1954); m. Katharine Starkey, 1955 (div. 1962); m. Judith Blakely, 1964; 1 child, Jill. AB, Wake Forest Coll., 1943. Columnist San Diego Daily Jour., 1946-50; columnist San Diego Evening Tribune, 1950-92, assoc. editor, 1977-81, editor, 1981-92; assoc. editor, sr. columnist San Diego Union-Tribune, 1992—; syndicated columnist Morgan Jour., Copley News Service, 1958—; lectr.; cons. on Calif. affairs Bank of Am., Sunset mag. Author: My San Diego, 1951, It Began With a Roar, 1953, Know Your Doctor, 1954, Crosstown, 1955, My San Diego 1960, 1959, Westward Tilt, 1963, Neil Morgan's San Diego, 1964, The Pacific States, 1967, The California Syndrome, 1969, (with Robert Witty) Marines of Margarita, 1970, The Unconventional City, 1972, (with Tom Blair) Yesterday's San Diego, 1976, This Great Land, 1983, Above San Diego, 1990, (with Judith Morgan) Dr. Seuss & Mr. Geisel, 1995; contbr. non-fiction articles to Nat. Geog., Esquire, Redbook, Reader's Digest, Holiday, Harper's, Travel and Leisure, Ency. Brittanica. Served to lt. USNR, 1943-46. Recipient Ernie Pyle Meml. award, 1957, Bill Corum Meml. award, 1961, Disting. Svc. citation Wake Forest U., 1966, grand award for travel writing Pacific Area Travel Assn., 1972, 78, Fourth Estate award San Diego State U., 1988, The Morgan award Leadership Edn. Awareness Devel. San Diego, 1993; co-recipient Ellen and Roger Revelle award, 1986; named Outstanding Young Man of Yr. San Diego, 1959. Mem. Authors Guild, Am. Soc. Newspaper Editors, Soc. Profl. Journalists, Explorers Club, Soc. of Am. Travel Writers, Bohemian Club, Phi Beta Kappa, Omicron Delta Kappa. Home: 7930 Prospect Pl La Jolla CA 92037-3721 Office: PO Box 191 San Diego CA 92112-4106

MORGAN, PETER F., English educator, philosophy educator; b. Stafford, Eng., Sept. 1, 1930; s. Frederick John and Kathleen (May) M.; m. Eleanor Thompson, 1958 (div. 1983); children: Peter, Martin, Alison, Katy. BA, U. Birmingham, U.K., 1951; MA, U. London, 1955, PhD, 1957. Lectr. Victoria Coll., B.C., 1959-60; lectr. U. Toronto, 1960-64, asst. prof., 1964-68, assoc. prof., 1968-74, prof., 1974—; chmn. panel symposium on visual rhetoric Scarborough Coll., 1991, mem. panel on futurism, 1991. Author: Literary Critics and Reviewers in Early Nineteenth-Century Britain, 1983, Poetic and Pictorial Elements, 1992; editor: The Letters of Thomas Hood, 1973, Jeffrey's Criticism, 1983; co-editor Victorian Periodicals Rev., 1973-78, also adv. editor, 1979—, Ultimate Reality and Meaning, 1989—; cons. editor Jour. Mental Imagery, 1986—; contbr. articles to profl. jours. Mem. Soc. Study of Ultimate Reality and Meaning (pres. 1992—). Office: Int'l Society Study Human Ideas, University of Toronto, Toronto, ON Canada M5S 1A1*

MORGAN, RALEIGH, JR., linguistics educator; b. Nashville, Nov. 12, 1916; s. Raleigh and Adrien Louise (Beasley) M.; m. Virginia Carol Moss, Dec. 25, 1941(dec. 1993); children: Carol Ann (Mrs. Donald Russell), Jill Virginia (Mrs. Stanton Burrows), Phyllis Adrien. (dec.). A.B., Fisk U., 1938; A.M., U. Mich., 1939, Ph.D., 1952. Tchr. French Sumner High Sch., St. Louis, 1940-42; head dept. French N.C. Coll., Durham, 1944-49, 51-56; dir. U.S. Cultural Ctr., Cologne, Germany, 1956-57; dep. chief cultural operations embassy Bonn, Germany, 1957-59; asso. dir. Ctr. Applied Linguistics, Modern Lang. Assn., 1959-61; prof. Romance langs., head dept. Howard U., 1961-65; prof. Romance linguistics U. Mich., Ann Arbor, 1965-87, prof. emeritus Romance linguistics, 1987—, faculty assoc. Ctr. Afro-Am. and African Studies, 1982—; vis. prof. linguistics Cornell U., 1973; lectr. linguistics Dept. State, Georgetown U.; visiting prof. linguistics U. Maryland, 1962; 63, 65; cons. linguist Audio Lingual Materials French, 1962; mem. adv. com. Ctr. Applied Linguistics, 1961-62; mem. overseas com. Germanic langs. and lits. of bd. overseers Harvard Coll., 1972-80; mem. assembly behavioral and social scis. NRC, 1971—. Author: The Regional French of County Beauce, Quebec, 1975; contbr. articles to profl. jours. Chmn. Mich. Council for Humanities, 1974-77; vice chmn. Ann Arbor Historic Dist. Commn., 1977-82; mem. exec. bd. Rackham Sch. Grad. Studies U. Mich., 1983-86. Grantee Carnegie Faculty, 1952; Grantee Am. Council Learned Socs., 1953, 55; Fulbright-Hayes sr. research scholar in France, 1974. Mem. MLA, Linguistic Soc. Am., Internat. Linguistic Assn., Soc. Caribbean Linguistics, Société de Linguistique Romane, Phi Beta Kappa, Kappa Alpha Psi. Roman Catholic. Home: 3157 Bluett Rd Ann Arbor MI 48105-1425

MORGAN, RAYMOND F., plastic surgeon; b. Pitts., Apr. 24, 1948; s. Edwin J. and Alberta (Hirt) M.; m. Sue Ann Malone, Oct. 3, 1951; children: Ryan Frederic, Alexander Evan, Elizabeth Anne. BS, U. Pitts., 1969, MEd, 1972, DMD, 1972; MD, W.Va. U., 1976. Diplomate Am. Bd. Plastic Surgery, Am. Bd. Hand Surgery. Intern Johns Hopkins U. Hosp., Balt., 1976-77, resident surgery, 1977-80, resident plastic surgery, 1980-82; resident hand surgery Union Meml. Hosp., Balt.; staff U. Va. Health Scis. Ctr., Charlottesville, prof., chmn. dept. plastic surgery, 1988—. Mem. ACS, Soc. Univ. Surgeons, So. Surg. Assn., Am. Soc. for Surgery of Hand, Soc. of Head and Neck Surgeons. Office: U of Va Dept of Plastic Surgery Charlottesville VA 22908*

MORGAN, RAYMOND VICTOR, JR., university administrator, mathematics educator; b. Brownwood, Tex., May 10, 1942; s. Raymond Victor and Lovey Lucille (Tate) M.; m. Mary Jane Folks, Aug. 13, 1967; children: Jason Wesley, Jeremy Victor. BA, Howard Payne U., 1965; MA, Vanderbilt U., 1966; PhD, U. Mo., 1969. Asst. prof. So. Meth. U., Dallas, 1969-75; assoc. prof. Sul Ross State U. Alpine, Tex., 1975-82, math. dept. chmn., 1976-85, prof., 1982—, dean of scis., 1979-86, exec. asst. pres., 1985-90, pres., 1990—; bd. dirs. Tex. Internat. Edn. Consortium; bd. dirs. Southwestern Livestock Exposition, 1993—. Author textbook: Agricultural Mathematics, 1978; author articles. Founder, regional commr. Alpine Soccer League, 1984; v.p., coach Alpine Baseball League, 1983; pres. Alpine PTA, 1982-83; founder, pres. So. Meth. U. Faculty Club, 1973-75; mem. exec. com. Tex. Assn. Coll. and Univ. Student Personnel Adminstrs., 1990-92. NSF grantee, 1979. Mem. Am. Assn. Higher Edn., Tex. Assn. Coll. Tchrs. (chpt. v.p. 1978-79), Math. Assn. Am. (chmn. Tex. sect. 1985-86). Republican. Mem. Ch. of Christ. Clubs: Lions (pres. 1979-80, Lion of Yr. 1980, 83), Alpine Country. Avocations: motorcycling, golf, shooting. Home: PO Box 1341 Alpine TX 79831-1341 Office: Sul Ross State U E Highway 90 PO Box C114 Alpine TX 79831-0114

MORGAN, RICHARD ERNEST, political scientist, educator; b. Centre County, Pa., May 17, 1937; s. James Ernest and Helen Estelle (Hogge) M. A.B., Bowdoin Coll., Brunswick, Maine, 1959; A.M., Columbia U., 1961, Ph.D., 1967. Instr. in govt. Columbia U., 1962-63, 65-67, asst. prof. govt., 1967-68; assoc. prof. govt. Bowdoin Coll., 1969-75, William Nelson Cromwell prof. constl. law and govt., 1975—; fellow in law and govt. Harvard U. Law Sch., 1968-69; research dir. Twentieth Century Fund Project on Polit. Surveillance in Am., 1975-79. Author: The Politics of Religious Conflict, 1968, The Supreme Court and Religion, 1972, (with others) American Politics: Directions of Change, Dynamics of Choice, 1979, Domestic Intelligence: Monitoring Dissent in America, 1980, Disabling America: The Rights Industry in Our Time, 1984, People, Power and Politics, 1994; contbr. articles to profl. publs.; editor: (with James E. Connor) The American Political System: Introductory Readings, 1971. Chmn. Spl. Commn. on Legis. Compensation, State of Maine, 1973-74; chmn. Maine adv. com. U.S. Commn. on Civil Rights, 1985-87. Served to 1st lt. U.S. Army, 1963-65. Mem. Am. Polit. Sci. Assn., New. Eng. Polit. Sci. Assn. (pres. 1988-89). Republican. Episcopalian. Home: RR 2 South Harpswell ME 04079-9802 Office: Bowdoin Coll Brunswick ME 04011

MORGAN, RICHARD THOMAS, publishing executive; b. Herkimer, N.Y., May 19, 1937; s. Roland F. and Eva J. (Butcher) M.; m. Eileen A. Bumbly, Nov. 21, 1966; children: Richard Joseph, Susan Eileen. AB, Hope Coll., 1959; MA, SUNY, Albany, 1960; EdD, Columbia U., 1968. Asst. prof. SUC at Fredonia, N.Y., 1961-64, Fla. Atlantic U., Boca Raton, Fla., 1966-68; sr. v.p., editor in chief Ginn & Co., Lexington, Mass., 1968-79; exec. v.p. Macmillan, Inc., N.Y.C., 1979-83; pres., chief exec. officer Scott, Foresman and Co., Glenview, Ill., 1984-88, Macmillan/McGraw-Hill, Lake Forest, Ill., 1989-92, Harcourt Brace and Co., Orlando, Fla., 1992—. Mem. Conway Farms Golf Club. Democrat. Catholic. Avocations: running, golf. Office: 6277 Sea Harbor Dr Orlando FL 32887

MORGAN, ROBERT ARTHUR, accountant; b. Decatur, Ill., Oct. 23, 1918; s. Robert Howard and Katherine (Massey) M.; m. Julia Ann Franklin, June 28, 1941; children: Robert A., Susan Ruth. BS, U. Ill., 1941. Acct. Pure Oil Co., 1941; acct. Caterpillar Tractor Co., Peoria, Ill., 1945-56, controller, 1956-78; mem. Fin. Acct. Standards Bd., Stamford, Conn., 1978-82; cons. Morton, Ill., 1982—. Contbr. articles to acctg. periodicals. Past mem. fin. acctg. standards adv. coun. Fin. Acctg. Found.; pres. bd. edn. Morton Twp. High Sch., 1960-61. Civilian auditor AUS, 1942-44. Mem. Nat. Assn. Accts. (nat. dir., nat. v.p. 1965-66, chmn. mng. practices 1974-75), Machinery and Allied Products Inst. (fin. coun. II 1956-78), Fin. Execs. Inst. (mem. com. corp. reporting 1977-78), Internat. Fedn. Accts. (chmn. com. fin. and mgmt. acctg. 1983).

MORGAN, ROBERT B., insurance company executive; b. 1934. AB, Eastern Ky. U., 1954. Tchr. Ind. Sch. System, 1954-56; casualty underwriter Ins. Co. of N.Am., Phila., 1960-66; asst. casualty mgr. Cin. Ins. Co., Inc., 1966-69, asst. v.p., 1969-71, v.p., gen. mgr., 1972-75, exec. v.p., gen. mgr., 1975, pres., 1976, pres., chief exec. officer, 1986—; pres. Cin. Fin. Corp., 1981, pres., chief exec. officer, 1991—. Capt. AUS, 1956-68. Office: Cin Fin Corp PO Box 145496 6200 S Gilmore Rd Cincinnati OH 45250

MORGAN, ROBERT DALE, federal judge; b. Peoria, Ill., May 27, 1912; s. Harry Dale and Eleanor (Ellis) M.; m. Betty Louise Harbers, Oct. 14, 1939; children—Thomas Dale, James Robert. A.B., Bradley U., 1934; J.D., U. Chgo., 1937. Bar: Ill. 1937. Practice in Peoria, 1937-42, 46-67, Chgo., 1946-50; partner firm Morgan, Pendarvis & Morgan, Peoria, 1946-57, Davis, Morgan & Witherell, Peoria, 1957-67; U.S. judge So. Dist Ill. (became Central Dist. 1979), Peoria, 1967—, sr. status U.S. judge, 1982. Contbr. articles to law revs. Mayor, Peoria 1953-57; Bd. dirs. YMCA, Peoria, 1940-72, pres., 1947-53; Trustee Bradley U. Served from 1st lt. to maj. AUS, 1942-46. Mem. ABA, Am. Judicature Soc., Ill. Bar Assn., Peoria County Bar Assn. Presbyterian. Clubs: Creve Couer (Peoria), Rotary (Peoria) (pres. 1962-63), Country (Peoria). Office: US Dist Ct 228 Fed Bldg 100 NE Monroe Peoria IL 61602

MORGAN, ROBERT EDWARD, state supreme court justice; b. Mitchell, S.D., Aug. 13, 1924; s. Chester Lawrence and Phyllis Mae (Saterlie) M.; m. Mary Doyle, Oct. 28, 1950; children: Mary Alice, Michael Chester, Thomas Wayne, Margaret Jane; m. Mary Ann Ver Meulen, June 1, 1974; 1 child, Daniel James. Student, Creighton U., 1942, 46-47, 48; J.D., U. S.D., 1950. Bar: S.D. 1950. Mem. firm Mitchell & Chamberlain, S.D., 1950-76; justice S.D. Supreme Ct., Pierre, 1977-90, ret., 1991. Served with USAAF, 1943-45. Mem. S.D. Bar Assn.

MORGAN, ROBERT MARION, educational research educator; b. Ponca City, Okla., Feb. 5, 1930; s. Perry Harrison and Velma Beatrice (Stowe) M.; m. Constance Louise Claus, Jan. 3, 1963; children—Stephen, Melayne. B.S., Okla. State U., 1955, M.S., 1956; Ph.D., Ohio State U., 1958; LL.D., Dongah U., Pusan, Korea. Asst. prof. U. N.M., 1958-62; pres. Gen. Programmed Teaching Corp., Palo Alto, Calif., 1961-64; v.p. Ranchers Corp., Albuquerque, 1962-64; dir. ednl. systems Litton Industries, College Park, Md., 1964-66; dep. dir. div. vocational research U.S. Office Edn. Washington, 1966-68; prof., head dept. ednl. research Fla. State U., Tallahassee, 1968-74; dir. Center for Ednl. Tech., 1968-75, Learning Systems Inst., 1975—; Lectr. Catholic U. Am., 1966-68, Seoul (Korea) Nat. U., 1970-71; cons. AID, Republic of Brazil, Korea, Italian Air Force, Navy Dept., U.S. Naval Acad.; Chmn. Fla. Research and Devel. Council, 1969—; mem. sch. bd. U. Sch., Tallahassee, 1969-74. Author: Programmed Instruction—A Concept of Learning, 1963, An Educational Systems Analysis for the Republic of Korea, 1970; also articles. Bd. dirs. U.S. Coalition for Edn. for All, 1992—; trustee Aerospace Ednl. Found. With AUS, 1949-52. Fellow Royal Soc. Arts; mem. Am. Ednl. Research Assn., Am. Psychol. Assn., Nat. Soc. for Programmed Instrn., Am. Mgmt. Assn., Sigma Xi. Republican. Presbyterian. Avocation: flying. Home: 3322 Remington Run Tallahassee FL 32312-1308 Office: Fla State Univ 205 Dodd Hall Tallahassee FL 32306

MORGAN, ROBERT P., music theorist; educator; b. Nashville, July 28, 1934; s. Hugh J. and Robert (Porter) M.; m. Carole Ann Montgomery, June 12, 1965. BA, Princeton U., 1956, MFA, 1960, PhD, 1969; MA, U. Calif., 1958. Instr. U. Houston, 1963-67; asst. prof. Temple U., Phila., 1967-70, assoc. prof., 1970-75, prof., 1975-79; prof. U. Chgo., 1979-89, Yale U., New Haven, 1989—; vis. prof. U. Pa., Phila., 1976-78, Yale U., 1987; adv. bd.

Fromm Music Found., Chgo., 1984-89. Author: Twentieth Century Music, 1991; mem. editorial bd. Critical Inquiry, 1980—, Studies in the Criticism and Theory of Music, 1981—, Composers of the Twentieth Century; composer orch., chamber ensemble, voice and piano works; articles in field. Grantee German Govt., 1960-62; Woodrow Wilson fellow, 1956-57, NEH sr. fellow, 1983-84. Mem. Am. Musicol. Soc. (council mem. 1982-85), Soc. for Music Theory (bd. dirs. 1985—), Coll. Music Soc., Yale Club (N.Y.C.). Democrat. Avocations: tennis, skiing. Home: 232 Bradley St East Haven CT 06512-1471 Office: Yale Univ Dept Of Music New Haven CT 06520

MORGAN, ROBERT PETER, engineering educator; b. Bklyn., Feb. 26, 1934; s. Jack and Minna (Cohen) M.; m. Nancy Beverly Hutchins, Dec. 20, 1958; children: Thomas Albert, Jonathan Andrew. B.Ch.E., Cooper Union, 1956; S.M., MIT, 1959, Nucl.E., 1961; Ph.D., Rensselaer Poly. Inst., 1965. Asst. dir. MIT Practice Sch., Oak Ridge, 1958-59; instr. chem. engring. Rensselaer Poly. Inst., 1960-64; assoc. prof. nuclear and chem. engring. U. Mo., 1964-68; assoc. prof. engring. Washington U., St. Louis, 1968-74, prof. tech. and human affairs, 1974-87, Elvera and William Stuckenberg prof. tech. and human affairs, 1987—; dir. Ctr. for Tech. Assessment and Policy, 1968—, chmn. dept. tech. and human affairs, 1976-83; sci. and pub. policy fellow Brookings Instn., 1982-83; council mem. Vols. in Tech. Assistance; chmn. adv. subcom. NASA Tech. Transfer Program, 1978-80; mem. nat. adv. bd. program on ethics and values in sci. and tech. NSF, 1977-79; mem. com. on research grants NRC, 1983-86; Sigma Xi nat. lectr., 1981-83; vis. sr. analyst Office of Tech. Assessment of U.S. Congress, 1989-90. Author: The Role of U.S. Universities in Science and Technology for Development, 1979, Renewable Resource Utilization for Development, 1981; Science and Technology for International Development: An Assessment of U.S. Policies and Programs, 1984; contbr. numerous articles to profl. publs.; mem. editorial bd. Telecommunications Policy, 1976-80, Sci., Tech. and Human Values, 1977-79, 81-88. Recipient Disting. Faculty award Washington U., 1989; AEC fellow, 1959-60. Fellow AAAS (com. on sci., engring. and pub. policy 1977-80, program com. 1992—); mem. AAUP, Fedn. Am. Scientists, Am. Soc. Engring. Edn. (Chester F. Carlson award 1978), Tau Beta Pi. Office: Washington U Campus Box 1106 Saint Louis MO 63130

MORGAN, ROBIN EVONNE, poet, author, journalist, activist, editor; b. Lake Worth, Fla., Jan. 29, 1941; 1 child, Blake Ariel. Grad. with honors, The Wetter Sch., 1956; student, pvt. tutors, 1956-59, Columbia U.; DHL (hon.), U. Conn., 1992. Free-lance book editor, 1961-69; editor Grove Press, 1967-70; editor, columnist World column Ms. Mag., N.Y.C., 1974-87, editor in chief, 1989-93, internat. cons. editor, 1993—; vis. chair and guest prof. women's studies New Coll., Sarasota, Fla., 1973; disting. vis. scholar, lectr. Ctr. Critical Analysis of Contemporary Culture, Rutgers U., 1987; invited spl. cons. UN com. UN Conv. to End All Forms Discrimination Against Women, Sao Paulo and Brasilia, Brazil, 1987; mem. adv. bd. ISIS (internat. network women's internat. cross-cultural exch.); spl. advisor gen. assembly conf. on Gender UN Internat. Sch., 1985-86; free-lance journalist, lectr. cons., editor, 1969—; invited speaker numerous confs., orgns., acad. meetings, U.S. and abroad. Author, compiler, editor: Sisterhood Is Powerful: An Anthology of Writings from the Women's Liberation Movement, 1970, Swedish edit., 1972, Sisterhood Is Global: The International Women's Movement Anthology, 1984, U.K. edit., 1985, Spanish edit., 1994; author: (nonfiction) Going Too Far: The Personal Chronicle of a Feminist, 1978, German edit., 1978, The Anatomy of Freedom: Feminism, Physics and Global Politics, 1982, 2d edit., 1994, fgn. edits. U.K., 1984, Germany, 1985, Argentina, 1986, Brazil, 1992, The Demon Lover: On the Sexuality of Terrorism, 1989, U.K. edit., 1989, Japanese edit., 1992, The Word of a Woman: Feminist Dispatches 1968-91, 1992, 2d edit., 1994, U.K. edit., 1992, Chinese edit., 1995 (diction) Dry Your Smile: A Novel, 1987, U.K. edit., 1988, The Mer-Child: A New Legend, 1991, German edit., 1995 (poetry) Monster: Poems, 1972, Lady of the Beasts: Poems, 1976, Death Benefits: Poems, 1981, Depth Perception: New Poems and a Masque, 1982, Upstairs in the Garden: Selected and New poems, 1968-88, 1990, (plays) In Another Country, 1960, The Duel, 1979; co-editor: (with Bunch and Weeks) The Woman: Anthology, 1969; contbr. numerous articles, essays, book revs., peoms to various publs.; presenter poetry readings, univs., poetry ctrs., radio, TV, others, 1970—. Mem. 1st women's liberation caucus CORE, 1965, Student Nonviolent Coordinating Com., 1966; organizer 1st feminist demonstration against Miss Am. Pageant, 1968; founder, pres. The Sisterhood Fund 1970; founder, pres. N.Y. Women's Law Ctr., 1970; founder N.Y. Women's Ctr., 1969; co-founder, bd. dirs. Feminist Women's Health Network, Nat. Battered Women's Refuge Network, Nat. Network Rape Crisis Ctrs.; bd. dirs. Women's Fgn. Policy Coun.; adv. trustee Nat. Women's Inst. for Freedom of Press; founding mem. Nat. Mus. Women in Arts; co-founder Sisterhood is Global Inst. (internat. think-tank), 1984, officer, 1989—; co-organizer, U.S. mem. official visit Coalition of Philippines Women's Movement, 1988; chair N.Y. state com. Hands Across Am. Com. for Justice and Empowerment, 1988; mem. adv. bd. Global Fund for Women. Recipient Front Page award for disting. journalism, Wonder Woman award for internat. peace and understanding, 1982, Feminist of Yr. award Fund for Feminist majority, 1990; writer-in-residence grantee Yaddo, 1980; grantee Nat. Endowment for Arts, 1979-80, Ford Found., 1982, 83, 84. Mem. Feminist Writers' Guild, Media Women, N.Am. Feminist Coalition, Pan Arab Feminist Solidarity Assn. (hon.), Israeli Feminists Against Occupation (hon.). Office: Ms Mag 230 Park Ave New York NY 10169-0005

MORGAN, RUTH PROUSE, academic administrator, educator; b. Berkeley, Calif., Mar. 30, 1934; d. Ervin Joseph and Thelma Ruth (Prcesang) Prouse; m. Vernon Edward Morgan, June 3, 1956; children: Glenn Edward, Renée Ruth. BA summa cum laude, U. Tex., 1956; MA, La. State U., 1961, PhD, 1966. Asst. prof. Am. govt., politics and theory So. Meth. U., Dallas, 1966-70, assoc. prof., 1970-74, prof., 1974—; asst. provost, 1978-82, assoc. provost, 1982-86, provost ad interim, 1986-87, provost, 1987-93, provost emerita, 1993—; pres. RPM Assocs., 1993—; Tex. state polit. analyst ABC, N.Y.C., 1972-84. Author: The President and Civil Rights, 1970; mem. editorial bd. Jour. of Politics, 1975-82, Presdl. Studies Quar., 1980—; contbr. articles to profl. jours. Active Internat. Women's Forum, 1987—; trustee Hockaday Sch., 1988-94; bd. dirs. United Way Met. Dallas, 1993—; trustee Kilby Awards Found.; mem. adv. com. U.S Army Command and Gen. Staff Coll., 1994—. Mem. Am. Polit. Sci. Assn., So. Polit. Sci. Assn. (mem. exec. coun. 1979-84), Southwestern Polit. Sci. Assn. (pres. 1982-83, mem. exec. coun. 1981-84), Charter 100 Club (pres. 1991-92), Dallas Summit Club (pres. 1992-93), Phi Beta Kappa, Pi Sigma Alpha, Phi Kappa Phi, Theta Sigma Phi. Avocations: photography, travel.

MORGAN, SAMUEL P(OPE), physicist, applied mathematician; b. San Diego, July 14, 1923; s. Samuel Pope and Beatrice Marie (Summers) M.; m. Mary Caroline Annin, Jan. 23, 1948; children: Caroline Gail, Lesley Anne, Alison Lee, Diane Elizabeth. B.S., Calif. Inst. Tech., 1943, M.S., 1944, Ph.D. in Physics, 1947. Mem. tech. staff AT&T Bell Labs., Murray Hill, N.J., 1947-59; head dept. math. physics AT&T Bell Labs., 1959-67, dir. computing tech., 1969-70, dir. computing sci. research center, 1967-82, disting. mem. tech. staff, 1982—. Research, publs. on electromagnetic theory, applied math., queueing theory; patentee in field. Fellow IEEE: mem. AAAS, Am. Phys. Soc., Sigma Xi. Home: 9 Raleigh Ct Morristown NJ 07960-2535 Office: AT&T Bell Labs Murray Hill NJ 07974-0636

MORGAN, SCOTT ELLINGWOOD, publisher, lawyer; b. Kansas City, Kans., June 29, 1957; s. Ray Ellingwood and Mary Grace (Burkhardt) M.; m. Kathleen O'Leary, Oct. 8, 1983; children: Kelly, Calvin. BS in Journalism, U. Kans., 1979, JD, 1983. Bar: Kans. Mem. staff Senator Nancy Kassebaum, Washington, 1979-80; staff atty. U.S. Customs, Washington, 1983; staff counsel U.S Senate Judiciary Com., Washington, 1983-86; rep. Fed. Election Com., Washington, 1986-87; chief counsel Bob Dole for Pres., Washington 1987-88, Office of Gov., Topeka, Kans., 1988-91; atty. Schleicher, Latz, P.C., Kansas City, 1991-92; pres. Morgan Quitno Press, Lawrence, 1989—. Editor: State Rankings 1990—, Health Care State Rankings, 1993—, Crime State Rankings, 1994—, City Crime Rankings, 1995—. Nominee U.S. Congress 2nd Dist. Kans., 1990; Rep. chmn. 2nd Dist. Kans., 1991. Congregationalist. Office: Morgan Quitno Press PO Box 1656 Lawrence KS 66044

MORGAN, STEPHEN CHARLES, academic administrator; b. Upland, Calif., June 2, 1946; s. Thomas Andrew and Ruth Elizabeth (Miller) M.; m. Ann Marie McMurray, Sept. 6, 1969; 1 child, Kesley Suzanne. BA, U. La

Verne, 1968; MS, U. So. Calif., 1971; EdD, U. No. Colo., 1979. Devel. officer U. La Verne, Calif., 1968-71, asst. to pres., 1971-73, dir. devel., 1973-75, v.p. devel., 1975-76, pres., 1985—; dir. devel. U. So. Calif., L.A., 1976-79; exec. dir. Ind. Colls. No. Calif., San Francisco, 1979-85; dir. Ind. Colls. So. Calif., L.A., 1985—. Bd. dirs. Mt. Baldy United Way, Ontario, Calif., 1988—, McKinley Home for Boys, San Dimas, Calif., 1989—; chair nat. com. on higher edn. Ch. of Brethren, Elgin, Ill., 1988-90; dir. Pomona Valley Hosp. Med. Ctr., Inter Valley Health Plan, 1992—. Mem. Assn. Ind. Calif. Colls. and Univs. (exec. com. 1989—), L.A. County Fair Assn., Western Coll. Assn. (exec. com. 1992—), Pi Gamma Mu. Avocations: orchid culture, fly fishing, golf. Home: 2518 N Mountain Ave Claremont CA 91711-1579 Office: U of LaVerne Office of Pres 1950 3rd St La Verne CA 91750-4401

MORGAN, STEVEN MICHAEL, lawyer; b. Cleve., May 19, 1954; s. Harry David and Lilyan (Schwartz) M.; m. Cynthia Lough, Aug. 17, 1983; children: Alyssa Patrice, Rachel Elizabeth. BA, Northwestern U., 1976; JD, Vanderbilt U., 1979. Bar: Pa., Tex. Atty. Aluminum Co. of Am., Pitts., 1979-84; environ. counsel Tex. Instruments, Dallas, 1984-87; chmn. environ. health & safety sect. Arter Hadden & Witts, Dallas; now ptnr. Akin, Gump, Strauss, Hauer & Feld, Dallas; lectr. U.Tex., Arlington, 1988—, Tex. A&M U., Coll. Sta., 1988—. Mem. ABA (natural resources sect.), State Bar of Texas (environ. sect.), Dallas Bar Assn. (environ. law sect.), Air Pollution Control Assn., Richardson C. of C. (chmn. environ. com., recipient leadership award 1988-89). Avocations: wine collecting, travel, sports. Office: Akin Gump Strauss et al 4100 First City Center 1700 Pacific Ave Dallas TX 75201-4617

MORGAN, THOMAS BRUCE, public affairs executive, author, editor; b. Springfield, Ill., July 24, 1926; s. David Edward and Mabel Ariel (Wolfe) M.; m. Joan T. Zuckerman, Oct. 3, 1950 (div. 1972); children: Katherine Tarlow, Nicholas David; m. Mary Clark Rockefeller, May 4, 1974 (div. 1988); stepchildren: Geoffrey, Michael, Sabrina Strawbridge; m. Hadassah Teitz Brooks, Aug. 19, 1990; stepchildren: Shoshana Goldhill, Benjamin Brooks. BA, Carleton Coll., 1949. Assoc. editor Esquire Mag., N.Y.C., 1949-53; sr. editor Look Mag., N.Y.C., 1953-58; freelance writer N.Y.C., 1958-69; press sec. Mayor John V. Lindsay, N.Y.C., 1969-73; sr. editor New York Mag., 1974-75; editor The Village Voice, N.Y.C., 1975-76; publisher Politicks mag., N.Y.C., 1976-79; novelist, freelance writer, 1979-89; pres. WNYC Comm. Group, N.Y.C., 1990-94; pres., CEO UN Assn. of U.S.A., Inc., N.Y.C., 1994—; press sec. Stevenson for Pres., 1960, McCarthy for Pres., 1968. Author: Friends and Fellow Students, 1956, Self Creations, 1965, (novel) This Blessed Shore, 1966, Among the Anti-Americans, 1967, (novel) Snyder's Walk, 1987; screenwriter documentary feature film Albert Schweitzer, 1957 (Acad. award); contbr. numerous articles to nat. mags. Trustee Carleton Coll., Northfield, Minn., 1975-79, 80—. With AC, U.S. Army, 1945. Mem. PEN, Authors Guild, Century Assn. Democrat. Jewish. Home: 1155 Park Ave New York NY 10128 Office: UN Assn of USA 485 Fifth Ave New York NY 10017

MORGAN, THOMAS OLIVER, bishop; b. Jan. 20, 1941; s. Charles Edwin and Amy Amelia (Hoyes) M.; m. Lillian Marie Textor, 1963; three children. BA, U. Sask., Can., 1962; BD, King's Coll., London, 1965; DD (hon.), Coll. of Emmanuel and St. Chad, Sask., 1986. Curate Ch. of the Saviour, Blackburn, Lancashire, Eng., 1966-69; rector Ch. of the Good Shepherd, Porcupine Plain, Sask., Can., 1969-73; rector Ch. of the Saviour, Kinistino, 1973-77, Shellbrook, 1977-83; Archdeacon Sask., 1983-85; bishop Diocese of Sask., Prince Albert, 1985-93, Diocese of Saskatoon, Sask., 1993—. Office: Diocese of Saskatoon, PO Box 1965, Saskatoon, SK Canada S7K 3S5

MORGAN, THOMAS ROWLAND, retired marine corps officer; b. Allentown, Pa., Jan. 6, 1930; s. Harry Campbell and Olwen (Pierce) M.; m. Barbara A. Croze, June 29, 1957; children—Lynn A., Susan E., Beth E. B.A. in History, Colgate U., 1952; student, Marine Corps Command and Staff Coll., 1965-66; M.A. in Edn., U. Va., 1973. Commd. 2d lt. USMC, 1952, advanced through grades to gen., 1986; naval aviator Naval Air Sta., Pensacola, Fla., 1953-54; asst. maintenance officer 3d Marine Aircraft Wing, El Toro, Calif., 1954-55; personnel officer Marine Aircraft Group Western Pacific, 1954-55; dep. comdr. Fleet Marine Force, aide to comdg. gen. 1st Marine Aircraft Wing, Pacific, 1955; asst. ops. officer Marine Aircraft Group, Kaneohe Bay, Hawaii, 1956-57; squadron pilot, ground tng. officer Marine Attack Squadron, Hawaii, 1957-59; flight instr. Naval Air Sta., Olathe, Kans., 1959; personnel officer, aircraft maintenance officer Marine Fighter Squadron, Beaufort, S.C., 1959-61; exec. officer Hdqrs. and Maintenance Squadron, Atsugi, Japan, 1961-62; fleet liaison officer Marine Corps Air Sta., Yuma, Ariz., 1962-65; comdr. Marine Fighter Attack Squadron, Beaufort, 1966-67; group ops. officer, officer-in-charge DaNang DASC, Vietnam, 1968-69; exec. officer Marine Corps Air Sta., Quantico, Va., 1969-71; exec. officer Naval ROTC unit U. Va., 1971-73; chief war plans br. J-5 U.S. European Command Hdqrs., Stuttgart, Fed. Republic Germany, 1973-76; asst. to dep. chief of staff requirements and programs Hdqrs. U.S. Marine Corps, Washington, 1976-77; asst. div. comdr. 3d Marine Div., Okinawa, Japan, 1977-78; asst. chief of staff C-5 Combined Forces Command, Seoul, 1978-80; dep. comdr. FMF Pacific, Camp Smith, Hawaii, 1980-81; dep. chief of staff for requirements and programs Hdqrs. Marine Corps, Washington, 1981-85, dep. chief staff for plans, policies and ops., acting Chief of Staff, 1985-86, asst. commandant, 1986-88, ret. Decorated D.S.M., Def. Superior Service medal, Legion of Merit, Bronze Star medal, Meritorious Service medal, Air medal; Order of Nat. Security medal, Cheonsu medal (Korea). Mem. Am. Legion. Avocations: golf, skiing, water sports.

MORGAN, TODD MICHAEL, investment advisor; b. St. Paul, June 28, 1947; s. Alfred Blair and Evelyn (Sachs) M.; m. Cheri Rappaport, Sept. 3, 1969; children: Tammy, Joshua. BS, U. Minn., 1969. V.p. Piper Jaffray & Hopwood, Mpls., 1969-77; ptnr. Goldman Sachs & Co., N.Y.C., 1977-91. Bd. advisors N.Y. Hosp., N.Y.C., 1989-91; vice chmn. Coalition to Free Soviet Jews, 1989-91; bd. govs., mem. fin. com. Cedars Sinai Hosp., L.A., 1991; bd. dirs. Big Bros. Greater L.A. Office: Goldman Sachs & Co 333 S Grand Ave Los Angeles CA 90071-1504

MORGAN, VIRGINIA, magistrate judge; b. 1946. BS, Univ. of Mich., 1968; JD, Univ. of Toledo, 1975. Bar: Mich. 1975, Federal 1975, U.S. Ct. Appeals (6th cir.) 1979. Tchr. Dept. of Interior, Bur. of Indian Affairs, 1968-70, San Diego Unified Schs., 1970-72, Oregon, Ohio, 1972-74; asst. prosecutor Washtenaw County Prosecutor's Office, 1976-79; asst. U.S. atty. Detroit, 1979-85; magistrate judge U.S. Dist. Ct. (Mich ea. dist.) 6th circuit, Detroit, 1985—. Recipient Spl. Achievement award Dept. of Justice, Disting. Alumni award U. Toledo, 1993. Fellow Mich. State Bar Found.; mem. Nat. Assn. Women Judges, Mich. Bar Assn., Fed. Magistrate Judges Assn. (pres. 1995—), Fed. Bar Assn. (chpt. pres.-elect 1995—). Office: US Courthouse 231 W Lafayette Blvd Detroit MI 48226-2719

MORGAN, WALTER, retired poultry science educator; b. Ledyard, Conn., Dec. 22, 1921; s. Walter Clifford and Margaret (Allyn) M.; m. Marcella Hodge, Dec. 28, 1948 (div. 1960); children: Nancy, Peggy, Beth; m. Helen Naden, May 14, 1966. BSc, U. Conn., 1946; MS, George Washington U., 1949, PhD, 1953. Animal husbandman Nat. Cancer Inst., NIH, Bethesda, Md., 1946-49; rsch. assoc. Nevis Rsch. Sta., Columbia U., Irvington-on-Hudson, N.Y., 1950-53; asst. prof. U. Tenn., Knoxville, 1953-54; assoc. prof., prof. S.D. State U., Brookings, 1954-85; ret., 1985; fgn. expert on English and genetics People's Republic China, 1991; researcher biology div. Nuclear Energy Ctr., Mol, Belgium, 1968-69, genetics div. Commonwealth Sci. and Indsl. Rsch. Orgn., Sydney, Australia, 1975-76; cons., Kuala Lumpur, Malaysia, 1988. Author: (poetry) Now and Then, 1982, Down Under, 1983, Hitchin' Around, 1985, Here and There, 1990, What's Good About China, 1992; contbr. over 100 articles to profl. jours. Former scoutmaster Boy Scouts Am., Brookings; pres. Men's Brotherhood, Brookings, 1974, U.S. Friends Fgn. Students, Brookings, 1986-88. Sgt. USAAF, 1942-45, ETO. Fellow AAAS; mem. Am. Genetics Assn., World Poultry Assn., N.Y. Acad. Scis., S.D. Acad. Sci. (pres.). Home: 1610 1st St Brookings SD 57006-2617

MORGAN, WALTER EDWARD, management consultant; b. Hempstead, N.Y., Nov. 19, 1940; s. Edward A. and Anne (Wright) M.; m. Lorraine Roberson, June 1, 1962; children: Walter Edward Jr., Gary L., Cheryl E. BA magna cum laude in polit. sci., Morgan State Coll., 1962; MA magna cum laude in govt. and politics, U. Md., 1969; postgrad., U. So. Calif., 1974-78, George Washington U., 1979-88; PhD in Bus. Mgmt., LaSalle U., 1993. Adminstrv. specialist Social Security Adminstrn., Balt., 1966-68; dir. tng. Skills Upgrading, Inc., Balt., 1968-69; sr. assoc. Al Nellum & Assocs., Washington, 1969-71; v.p. Pagan & Morgan Assocs., Balt., 1971-74; pres., chief exec. officer Morgan Mgmt. Systems, Inc., Columbia, Md., 1974—. Vice pres. United Way Cen. Md., Balt., 1974; commr. Howard County Compensation Commn., Md., 1986; mem. Judicial Nominating Com., Howard, Md., 1983. 1st lt. U.S. Army, 1962-66. Mem. NAACP, Inst. Mgmt. Consultants, Pi Alpha Alpha, Alpha Kappa Mu. Office: Morgan Mgmt Systems Inc 5401 White Mane Columbia MD 21045-2407

MORGAN, WAYNE PHILIP, art and popular culture exhibition producer; b. Dunnville, Ont., Can., Apr. 1, 1942. Cert., Sch. Art, Regina Coll., 1963; BA, U. Sask., Can., 1966; student, Emma Lake Artists Workshop, Sask., 1964-68, McGill U., Montreal, 1968, Art and Mass Culture Banff Ctr. for Arts, 1991. Community resident artist Weyburn (Sask.) Arts Council, 1967-70; dir., curator Dunlop Art Gallery, Regina (Sask.) Public Library, 1970-84; head curatorial services div. Winnipeg Art Gallery, Man., Can., 1984-85; ind. exhbn. prodr. specializing in popular culture, 1985—; mem. explorations jury Can. Coun., 1977-79; mem. secretariat Regina Arts Commn., 1979—; chmn. visual arts subcom. Ottawa-Carleton Adv. Com. for Arts. Mem. Western Can. Art Assn. (founding), Sask. Mus. Assn. (bd. dirs. 1978-80, pres. 1982-84), Sask. Craft Coun. (founding), Can. Mus. Assn. (bd. dirs. 1984-86, chmn. profl. devel. stds. com. 1985-86), Can. Ephermera Soc., Am. Ephermera Soc., Popular Culture Assn., Am. Culture Assn., Am. Game Collectors Assn., N.Y. State Hist. Assn. Address: 75 Markham St # 2, Toronto, ON Canada M6J 2G4

MORGAN, WILLIAM BRUCE, naval architect; b. Fairfield, Iowa, Dec. 20, 1926; s. Orville Burns and Mary Verle (Balderson) M.; m. Mary Maxine Gillam, June 21, 1950; children: Margaret Ann, Ann Elise. BS in Marine Engring., U.S. Mcht. Marine Acad., 1950; MS in Hydraulic Engring., U. Iowa, 1951; DEng in Naval Architecture, U. Calif., 1961. Hydraulic engr. David Taylor Model Basin, Bethesda, Md., 1951-52, naval architect, 1952-58, naval architect supr., 1958-62; head propeller br. David Taylor Model Basin, Bethesda, 1962-70; head hydromechanics div. David Taylor Naval Ship Research & Devel. Ctr. (formerly David Taylor Model Basin), Bethesda, Md., 1970-79; head hydromechanics directorate David Taylor Model Basin, Bethesda, Md., 1979—; chmn. exec. com. Am. Towing Tank Conf., 1983-86; mem. exec. com. Internat. Towing Tank Conf., 1984-90. Co-inventor ventilated propeller, supercavitating propeller with air ventilation; contbr. articles to profl. jours. Recipient Navy Superior Civilian USN, 1974, Meritorious Exec. award Office of Pres., 1987, William Froude medal Royal Instn. Naval Architects, 1989, Capt. Robert Dexter Conrad award USN, 1993. Fellow Soc. Naval Architects and Marine Engrs. (hon. life; exec. com. 1985—, Davidson medal 1986), ASME (chmn. fluids engring. div. 1981-82); mem. NAE, Schiffbautechnische Gesellschaft, Am. Soc. Naval Engrs. (Gold Medal award 1993), Chinese Soc. Naval Architects and Marine Engrs. (hon.), Sigma Xi. Mem. Ch. of the Brethen. Home: 110 Upton St Rockville MD 20850-1836 Office: David Taylor Model Bas Bethesda MD 20084-5000

MORGAN, WILLIAM DOUGLASS, diplomat; b. Rochester, N.Y., Nov. 10, 1925; s. Richard Douglass and Jeanette (Harned) M.; m. Nancy Gardner, July 30, 1949; children: Patricia L., Thomas G. B.A., U. Rochester, 1949; M.F.S., U. Paris, 1950. Second sec. U.S Delegation NATO, Paris, 1956-58; consul Birmingham, Eng., 1958-60; Russian lang. and area studies, 1960-62; second sec. Am. Embassy, Moscow, 1962-64; consul Am. Embassy, Beirut, 1968-73; insp. State Dept., Washington, 1974-76; dep. dir. visa office State Dept., 1976-78; U.S. consul gen. Am. Embassy, Paris, 1978-81, Montreal, 1981-85; dir. employee relations State Dept., 1985-87, ret. Served to pfc. U.S. Army, 1943-46, ETO. Mem. U.S. Fgn. Service Assn., Diplomatic & Consular Officers Ret.

MORGAN, WILLIAM J., accounting firm executive; b. Bklyn., Jan. 12, 1947; s. William J. and Emma T. (Kraft) M.; m. Patricia A. Maltz, Mar. 23, 1968; children: Michele, Jennifer. BS St. John's U., 1968. CPA, N.Y., Conn., N.J. Ptnr. in charge Metro. N.Y. Area, manufacturing, retailing and distbn. practice, audit staff KPMG Peat Marwick, N.Y.C., 1968-72, audit supr., 1972-74, audit mgr., 1974-77, ptnr.-in-charge pvt. bus. adv. service, N.Y.C., 1977-79, exec. office, ptnr.-in-charge recruiting, 1982-91, ptnr. comml. health care practice, Short Hills, 1982-91; ptnr.-in-charge N.J. audit practice, 1989-91, mng. ptnr. Fairfield/Westchester counties, 1991-94; mem. Bus. Unit Planning Task Force, 1987-90, mem. compensation com., 1990-91, bd. dirs., 1991—, chmn. profit distbn. com., 1991—, mem. future direction com., 1991-93, pension task force, 1991-92; mem. acctg. adv. bd. Grad. Sch. Bus. Fordham U., 1979-82, mem. standardization com. Nat. Retail Mchts. Assn., 1979; bd. dirs.N.Y. chpt. small bus. fund drive ARC, 1978; trustee Tri County Scholarship Fund, 1984-91; chmn. Blackberry Hill Property Owners Assoc., 1986-87; v.p., exec. com., adv. bd. Fairfield coun. Boy Scouts Am., 1993-95; chmn. Fairfield County Info. Exchange, 1992-94; bd. dirs. S.W. Area Commerce and Industry Assn., 1994—, Inroads Fairfield and Westchester County chpt., 1992-95; mem. Bus. Execs. for Nat. Security, Ambs. Roundtable. Mem. Am. Inst. CPA's (small bus. devel. com. 1979-81, acctg. lit. awards com. 1983-86), N.J. Soc. CPA's (chmn. acctg. and auditing stds. com. 1988-90, trustee 1990-92, mem. pub. rels. task force, 1987, subcom. health care acctg. 1983-86), N.Y. State Soc. CPA's (retail acctg. com. 1975-78, com. on edn. in coll. and univs. 1978-82), Nat. Assn. Accts. (dir. manuscripts 1975-77, v.p. N.Y. chpt. 1977-81, pres. N.Y. chpt. 1982-84, nat. pubis. com. 1982-83, com. acad. relations 1983-84, dir. 1983-86, Disting. Service award 1975), Health Care Fin. Mgmt. Assn. (N.J. chpt. chmn. auditing com. 1982-83, legis. task force com. 1985-86, chmn. joint ventures com., 1987-88). Club: Fairmount Country (bd. govs., treas. 1987-90), Woodway Country, Conn. Golf, Landmark Club. Roman Catholic. Home: 14 Talmadge Hill Rd Darien CT 06820 Office: KPMG Peat Marwick 3001 Summer St Stamford CT 06905

MORGAN, WILLIAM LIONEL, JR., physician, educator; b. Honolulu, Nov. 18, 1927; s. William Lionel and Lucy Salisbury (Grimes) M.; m. Joan Brunjes, Apr. 10, 1954; children: Nancy Salisbury, Linda Pittman. B.A. cum laude, Yale U., 1948; M.D. magna cum laude, Harvard U., 1952. Diplomate: Am. Bd. Internal Medicine. (mem. bd. 1973-80, mem. residency review com. 1975-80, chmn. residency rev. com. 1979-80). Intern Mass. Gen. Hosp., Boston, 1952-53; resident in medicine Mass. Gen. Hosp., 1953-54, 56-57, fellow in cardiology, 1957-58; asso. physician div. cardiovascular disease Henry Ford Hosp., Detroit, 1958-62; asso. prof. medicine U. Rochester (N.Y.) Sch. Medicine and Dentistry, 1962-65, prof., 1966-89, prof. medicine emeritus, 1989—, asso. chmn. dept. medicine, 1966-89. Author: (with G.L. Engel) The Clinical Approach to the Patient, 1969. Served with USPHS, 1954-56. Mem. ACP (Master), Am. Clin. and Climatol. Assn., Phi Beta Kappa, Alpha Omega Alpha. Home: 160 Collingsworth Dr Rochester NY 14625-2024 Office: Dept Medicine Strong Meml Hosp 601 Elmwood Ave Rochester NY 14642

MORGAN, WILLIAM NEWTON, architect, educator; b. Jacksonville, Fla., Dec. 14, 1930; s. Thomas and Kathleen (Fiske) M.; m. Bernice E. Leimback, July 31, 1954; children: William Newton, Dylan Thomas. AB magna cum laude, Harvard Coll., 1952, MArch Grad. Sch. of Design, 1958. Pres. William Morgan Architects, P.A., Jacksonville, Fla., 1961—; critic various archtl. schs.; lectr. in field. Prin. works include Fla. State Mus., Jacksonville Police Meml. Bldg., Pyramid Condominium, Ocean City, Fed. Cts. and Offices, Ft. Lauderdale, Fla., Westinghouse World Hdqs., Orlando, Fla., Neiman-Marcus store, Ft. Lauderdale, 1st Dist. Ct. Appeal, Tallahassee, Fla., Conf. Ctr., Tallahassee, U.S. Embassy, Khartoum, Sudan; author: Prehistoric Architecture in the Eastern United States, 1980, Prehistoric Architecture in Micronesia, 1988, Ancient Architecture of the Southwest, 1994. Subject of The Architecture of William Morgan (Paul Spreiregen) 1987; Fulbright grantee, 1958-59; grantee Graham Found. Advanced Studies Arts; Lehman fellow Harvard U., 1957, Wheelwright fellow, fellow NEA, 1991; Sam Gibbons Eminent scholar Fla. A&M U. and U. South Fla. Fellow AIA (past chmn. com. design). Office: William Morgan Architects 220 E Forsyth St Jacksonville FL 32202-3364

MORGAN, WILLIAM ROBERT, lawyer; b. Arkansas City, Kans., Jan. 6, 1924; s. Louis and Betty (Starner) M.; m. Willa June Hall, Mar. 11, 1945; children: Marilyn, Robert. A.A., Arkansas City Jr. Coll., 1942; postgrad.,

U. Okla., 1942-43, Susquehanna U., 1943; B.A., Stanford U., 1948, LL.B., 1949. Bar: Calif. 1949, U.S. Supreme Ct. 1953. Assoc. Johnson, Morgan, Thorne, Speed & Bamford, San Jose, Calif., 1949-52; founder, ptnr. Morgan, Beauzay, Hammer, Ezgar, Bledsoe & Rucka (and predecessors), San Jose, 1952-78; sr. ptnr. Morgan & Assocs., San Jose, 1978—; pres., chmn. bd. Triton Corp.; owner, operator Stas. KRAD-AM and KJKF-FM, Perry, Okla. Author: Chairman Mao's Big Red Book, 1976, Justin Morgan, Founder of the Breed, 1987, Morgan Horse of the West, 1985, The Perfect Horse, 1989; editor Labor Code Annotated, 1960—. Chmn. San Jose Fine Arts Commn., 1960-63; chmn., bd. dirs. Triton Mus. Art, 1963; mem. cen. com. Santa Clara County Dem. Com., 1958-60, campaign mgr. numerous Calif. Dems.; mem. San Martin Planning Commn., 1981, Calif. Jud. Coun., 1980-83; Gideon elder Presbyn. Ch.; appointee Regents Selection Adv. Com. State of Calif. With U.S. Army, 1943-46. W. Robert Morgan day proclaimed on March 14, 1972 by resolution of Calif. Senate. Mem. ABA (Bus. Frauds and Their Complexities 1986), Calif. Bar Assn. (bd. govs. 1977-80), Santa Clara County Bar Assn. (pres.), Santa Clara County Bar Assn. (pres. sr. lawyers club 1986-87), Calif. State Bar (v.p. 1979-80, exec. bd. law office mgmt. sect. 1980—), Assn. Trial Lawyers Am. (jud. coun.), Internat. Acad. Trial Lawyers (past pres., past sec., Am. nat. dir.-at-large, editor Twenty-Four Dramatic Cases 1974), Am. Law Inst., Am. Bd. Profl. Liability Attys., Am. Law Inst., No. Calif. Morgan Horse Clubs, Geranium Soc., Lloyd's of London. Presbyterian (elder). Clubs: Masons, Shriners (v.p. club), Eastern Star, Rotary, Kiwanis. Home: 9500 New Ave PO Box 1507 Gilroy CA 95020 Office: Morgan & Assocs 1501 The Alameda San Jose CA 95126 *Whatever success I have had as a lawyer and a businessman has come from my identification with my friends and clients. The empathy I have for others who have sincere problems is a very real one. I firmly believe in the old adages concerning hard work, honesty and the importance of human service.*

MORGANROTH, FRED, lawyer; b. Detroit, Mar. 26, 1938; s. Ben and Grace (Greenfield) M.; m. Janice Marilyn Cohn, June 23, 1963; children: Greg, Candi, Erik. BA, Wayne State U., 1959, JD with distinction, 1961. Bar: Mich. 1961, U.S. Dist. Ct. (ea. dist.) Mich. 1961, U.S. Supreme Ct. 1966, U.S. Ct. Claims 1967. Ptnr. Greenbaum, Greenbaum & Morganroth, Detroit, 1963-68, Lebenbom, Handler, Brody & Morganroth, Detroit, 1968-70, Lebenbom, Morganroth & Stern, Southfield, Mich., 1971-78; sole practice Southfield, 1979-83; ptnr. Morganroth & Morganroth P.C., Southfield, 1983-94, Morganroth, Morganroth, Alexander & Nye, P.C., Southfield, 1994—. Mem. ABA (family law sect. 1987—), Mich. Bar Assn. (hearing panelist grievance bd. 1975—), Oakland County family law com. 1988—, vice-chmn. 1992-93, chair 1993—), State Bar of Mich. (hearing law coun. of family law sect. 1990—, treas. 1993-94, chmn.-elect 1994-95, chmn. 1995-96), Detroit Bar Assn., Oakland Bar Assn. (cir. ct. mediator 1983—, dist. ct. mediator 1984—), Am. Arbitration Assn. (Oakland County family law com. 1985—, vice-chmn. 1992-93, chmn. 1993-94), Detroit Tennis Club (Farmington, Mich.) (pres. 1978-82), Admirals Club (N.Y.), Skyline Club. Jewish. Avocations: comml. pilot, tennis. Home: 30920 Woodcrest Ct Franklin MI 48025-1435 Office: 4000 Town Ctr Ste 555 Southfield MI 48075-1406

MORGANROTH, MAYER, lawyer; b. Detroit, Mar. 20, 1931; s. Maurice Jack Morganroth and Sophie (Reisman) Blum; m. Sheila Rubinstein, Aug. 16, 1958; children: Lauri, Jeffrey, Cherie. JD, Detroit Coll. Law, 1954. Bar: Mich. 1955, U.S. Dist. Ct. Mich. 1955, Ohio 1958, U.S. Dist. Ct. (no. dist.) Ohio 1958, U.S. Ct. Appeals (6th cir.) 1968, U.S. Supreme Ct. 1971, N.Y. 1983, U.S. Dist. Ct. N.Y. 1985, U.S. Tax Ct. 1985, U.S. Ct. Appeals (4th cir.) 1985, U.S. Ct. Claims 1986, U.S. Ct. Appeals (2d cir.) 1986, U.S. Ct. Appeals (fed. cir.), U.S. Ct. Appeals (8th cir.) 1994. Sole practice Detroit, 1955—, N.Y.C., 1983—; ptnr. Morganroth & Morganroth, 1989—; cons. to lending instns.; lectr. on real estate NYU, 1980—, bus. entities and structures Wayne State U., 1981—; trial atty. in fed. and state jurisdictions, nationwide. Served with USN, 1948-50. Mem. ABA, FBA, N.Y. State Bar Assn., Southfield Bar Assn., Oakland Bar Assn., Assn. Trial Lawyers Am., Assn. Trial Lawyers Mich. Am. Judicature Soc., U.S. Supreme Ct. Hist. Soc., Nat. Criminal Def. Assn., West Bloomfield (Mich.) Club, Fairlane Club (Dearborn, Mich.), Knollwood Country Club, Edgewood Athletic Club (pres. 1963-65). Democrat. Jewish. Office: 2000 Town Ctr Ste 2000 Southfield MI 48075-1153 also: 444 Madison Ave Ste 2801 New York NY 10022-6903

MORGEN, LYNN, public relations executive. Grad., CCNY. Former rep. Gruntal & Co., First Manhattan Co.; assoc. ECOM Cons. 1978-79, v.p. investor rels., 1979-82; ptnr. Morgen-Walke Assocs., 1982—. Office: Morgen-Walke Assocs Inc 380 Lexington Ave New York NY 10168-0001

MORGENSEN, JERRY LYNN, construction company executive; b. Lubbock, Tex., July 9, 1942; s. J.J. and Zelline (Butler) M.; m. Linda Dee Austin, Apr. 17, 1965; children: Angela, Nicole. BCE, Tex. Tech U., 1965. Area engr. E.I. Dupont Co., Orange, Tex., 1965-67; div. engr. E.I. Dupont Co., La Place, La., 1967-73; project mgr. Hensel Phelps Constrn. Co., Greeley, Colo., 1973-78, area mgr., 1978-80, v.p., 1980-85, pres., 1985—. Office: Hensel Phelps Constrn Co 420 Sixth Ave PO Box O Greeley CO 80632

MORGENSTEIN, WILLIAM, shoe company executive; b. Bklyn., Jan. 11, 1933; s. Samuel and Jeanne Marie (Mittentag) M.; m. Sylvia Dove, June 8, 1952; children: Lee Brian, David Barry. BS in Fin., U. Ala., 1955. Salesman Greenwald Shoe Co., Birmingham, Ala., 1954-56; sr. buyer Melville Shoe Corp., N.Y.C., 1958-67; pres. Kitty Kelly Shoe Co., 1967-70; exec. v.p. A.S. Beck Shoes, N.Y.C., 1970-71, Sandia Internat., Englewood Cliffs, N.J., 1971-75; pres., chief exec. officer Marquesa Internat. Corp., Englewood, N.J., 1975—; internat. cons. footwear exporting, 1965—. Served with U.S. Army, 1956-58. Mem. Footwear Distbrs. and Retailers Am. (vice chmn., bd. dirs., exec. com.), Internat. Footwear Assn. (chmn. 1989—, vice chmn. 1986—, exec. com.), 210 Assn. (Pres.' Circle 1987), Toastmasters (past pres. Teaneck, N.J. chpt.). Republican. Jewish. Avocations: history, golf.

MORGENSTERN, DAN MICHAEL, jazz historian, educator, editor; b. Munich, Germany, Oct. 24, 1929; came to U.S., 1947; s. Soma and Ingeborg Henrietta (von Klenau) M.; m. Elsa Schocket, Mar. 31, 1974; children: Adam Oran, Joshua Louis. Student, Brandeis U., 1953-56. Editorial asst. N.Y. Post, 1957-58; N.Y. corr. Jazz Jour., London, 1958-61; assoc. editor, then editor in chief Metronome mag., 1961; editor Jazz mag., 1962-64; assoc. editor Down Beat mag., 1964-67, editor, 1967-73; lectr. jazz history Peabody Instn., Balt., 1978-80; vis. prof., sr. research fellow in Am. Music, Bklyn. Coll., 1979; dir. Inst. Jazz Studies, Rutgers U., 1976—; bd. dirs. Jazz Inst. Chgo., N.Y. Jazz Mus. Producer ann. 10-concert series Jazz in the Garden, Museum Modern Art, N.Y.C., 1961-66; co-producer concert series Jazz on Broadway, 1963, Just Jazz; 10 program TV series, Public Broadcasting Service, 1971; author: The Jazz Story: An Outline History, 1973, Jazz People, 1976; translator, editor: (Joachim E. Berendt) The New Jazz Book, 1962, rev. edit., 1975; co-editor Ann. Rev. Jazz Studies, 1982—. Served with U.S. Army, 1951-53. Recipient Deems Taylor award ASCAP, 1977, Grammy award for best album notes 1973, 74, 76, 81, 91. Mem. NARAS (gov. 1971—, trustee 1976-79, 81-84, 85-89, 91—, v.p. 1979-83, 1st v.p. 1983-85), Nat. Endowment for Arts (chmn. jazz adv. panel 1971-73, cons. music programs 1973-80), Music Critics Assn., PEN, Authors Guild. Home: 365 W End Ave Apt 603 New York NY 10024-6563 Office: Rutgers U Inst Jazz Studies Newark NJ 07102*

MORGENSTERN, LEON, surgeon; b. Pitts., July 14, 1919; s. Max Samuel and Sarah (Master) M.; m. Laurie Mattlin, Nov. 27, 1967; 1 son, David Ethan. Student, CCNY, 1936-37; B.A. magna cum laude, Bklyn. Coll., 1940; M.D., N.Y. U., 1943. Diplomate: Am. Bd. Surgery. Intern Queens Gen. Hosp., Jamaica, N.Y., 1943-44; fellow, asst. resident in pathology Queens Gen. Hosp., 1947-48, resident in surgery, 1948-52; practice medicine, specializing in surgery Los Angeles, 1953-59, 60—, Bronx, N.Y., 1959-60; dir. surgery Cedars of Lebanon Hosp., Los Angeles, 1960-73; dir. surgery Cedars-Sinai Med. Center, Los Angeles, 1973-88, emeritus dir. surgery, 1989—; clin. prof. surgery UCLA Sch. Medicine, 1973-85, prof. in residence 1985—; asst. prof. surgery Albert Einstein Coll. Medicine, N.Y.C., 1959-60. Assoc. editor Mount Sinai Jour. Medicine, 1984-88; contbr. articles to profl. pubis. Served to capt. M.C. U.S. Army, 1944-46. Mem. Soc. for Surgery Alimentary Tract, Soc. Am. Gastrointestinal Endoscopic Surgeons (hon.),

Am. Gastroent. Assn., L.A. Surg. Soc. (pres. 1977), ACS (sec.-treas. 1976-77, pres. 1978, bd. dirs. So. Calif. chpt. 1976-78, gov.-at-large), Internat. Soc. Surgery, Western Surg. Assn.. Pacific Coast Surg. Assn., AMA, Calif. Med. Assns., Los Angeles County Med. Assn., Am. Surg. Assn., others. Home: 5694 Calpine Dr Malibu CA 90265

MORGENSTERN, NORBERT RUBIN, civil engineering educator; b. Toronto, Ont., Can., May 25, 1935; s. Joel and Bella (Skornik) M.; m. Patricia Elizabeth Gooderham, Dec. 28, 1960; children: Sarah Alexandra, Katherine Victoria, David Michael Gooderham. BASc, U. Toronto, 1956, DEng h.c., 1983; DIC, Imperial Coll. Sci., 1964; PhD, U. London, 1964; DSc h.c., Queen's U., 1989. Research asst., lectr. civil engring. Imperial Coll. Sci. and Tech., London, 1958-68; prof. civil engring. U. Alta., Edmonton, Can., 1968-83, Univ. prof., 1983—, chair dept. civil engring., 1994—; cons. engr., 1961—. Contbr. articles to profl. jours. Bd. dirs. Young Naturalists Found., 1977-82, Edmonton Symphony Soc., 1978-85. Athlone fellow, 1956; recipient prize Brit. Geotech. Soc., 1961, 66, Huber prize ASCE, 1971, Legget award Can. Geotech. Soc., 1979, Alta. order of Excellence, 1991. Fellow Royal Soc. Can., Can. Acad. Engring.; mem. U.S. Nat. Acad. Engring. (fgn. assoc.), Cancian Geosci. Coun. (pres. 1983), Can. Geotechnical Soc. (pres. 1989-91), Internat. Soc. for Soil Mechanics and Found. Engring. (pres. 1989-94), Royal Glenora Club, Athenaeum (London), various other profl. assns. Home: 106 Laurier Dr, Edmonton, AB Canada T5R 5P6 Office: U Alta, Edmonton, AB Canada T6G 2G7

MORGENSTERN, SHELDON JON, symphony orchestra conductor; b. Cleve., July 1, 1939; s. Irwin Arthur and Harriet Sue Morgenstern; m. Patricia Lou Bradshaw; 1 child, Sali Sharpe Hagan. BMus, Northwestern U., 1961; MMus, New Eng. Conservatory, 1966; DMA (hon.), Greensboro (N.C.) Coll., 1986. Mem. conducting staff New Eng. Conservatory, 1966-67; music dir. Greensboro Symphony Orch., 1967-74; prin. guest conductor Betica Philharmonic, Seville, Spain, 1978-82, Polish Radio Orch., Warsaw, Poland, 1990—; music dir. Ea. Music Festival, Greensboro, 1962—; music advisor Miss. Symphony Orch., 1985-86; bd. mem. Istanbul (Turkey) Internat. Festival, 1975—; Company for Televised Theatre; mus. cons. U.S. Dept. Interior for Wolf Trap Farm Park, 1972; mem. adv. bd. Avery Fisher Award, 1978—. Recipient O'Henry award City of Greensboro, 1980, Long Leaf Pine award State N.C., 1989, Nat. Alumni award Northwestern U., 1990. Home: 26 ch des Clochettes, 1206 Geneva Switzerland Office: Ea Music Festival PO Box 22026 Greensboro NC 27420

MORGENTALER, ABRAHAM, urologist, researcher; b. Montreal, Quebec, Can., May 14, 1956; came to U.S., 1974; s. Henry Morgentaler and Chawa Rosenfarb; m. Susan Deborah Edbril, June 12, 1982; children: Maya Edbril, Hannah Edbril. AB, Harvard U., 1978, MD, 1982. Diplomate Am. Bd. Urology. Intern Harvard Surg. Svc.-N.E. Deaconess Hosp., Boston, 1982-83; resident Harvard Program in Urology, Boston, 1984-88; instr. surgery Harvard Med. Sch., Boston, 1988-92, asst. prof. surgery (urology), 1993—; staff urologist, dir. male infertility program and impotency Beth Israel Hosp., Boston, 1988—; dir. andrology lab. Beth Israel Hosp., 1990—. Author: The Male Body, 1993. Mem. AMA, Am. Urologic Assn., Am. Fertility Soc., Am. Soc. Andrology, Boston Fertility Soc., Am. Assn. Clin. Urologists. Achievements include detection of protein abnormalities in infertile sperm, detection of temperature dependent protein expression in rat testis, use of investigational stents for treatment of benign prostatic hypertrophy. Office: Beth Israel Hosp 330 Brookline Ave Boston MA 02215-5400

MORGENTHALER, FREDERIC RICHARD, physics educator; b. Cleve., Mar. 12, 1933; s. Frederick H. and Anna (Welke) M.; m. Barbara Pullen, May 17, 1958; children—Ann Welke, Janet Nason. S.B., S.M., MIT, 1956, Ph.D., 1960. Asst. prof. elec. engring. MIT, Cambridge, 1960-65; Ford Found. postdoctoral fellow in engring. MIT, 1962-63, asso. prof., 1965-68, prof., 1968—; Cecil H. Green prof., 1984-86; prof. div. health scis. and tech. Harvard U.-MIT, 1978—; grad. officer dept. EECS MIT, Cambridge, 1993—; research fellow applied physics Harvard U., 1960, vis. lectr. on applied physics, 1960-61; cons. microwave solid state physics and electronics, med. ultrasonics. Contbr. articles to profl. jours. Served to 1st lt. USAF, 1957-59. Recipient Air Force Cambridge Research Labs. award, 1960. Fellow IEEE (chmn. Boston sect. Microwave Theory and Techniques Profl. Group 1970-71); mem. Am. Inst. Physics, AAAS, Sigma Xi, Tau Beta Pi, Eta Kappa Nu. Patentee in field. Office: Center Materials Sci and Engring Mass Inst Tech Cambridge MA 02139

MORGENTHAU, ROBERT MORRIS, lawyer; b. N.Y.C., July 31, 1919; s. Henry Jr. and Elinor (Fatman) M.; m. Martha Pattridge (dec.); children: Joan, Anne, Elinor, Robert P., Barbara; m. Lucinda Franks, Nov. 19, 1977; children: Joshua, Amy. Grad., Deerfield (Mass.) Acad., 1937; BA, Amherst Coll., 1941, LLD (hon.), 1966; LLB, Yale U., 1948; LLD (hon.), N.Y. Law Sch., 1968, Syracuse Law Sch., 1976, Albany Law Sch., 1982, Colgate U., 1988. Bar: N.Y. 1949. Assoc. firm Patterson Belknap & Webb, N.Y.C., 1948-53; ptnr. Patterson Belknap & Webb, 1954-61; U.S. atty. So. Dist. N.Y., 1961-62, 62-70; dist. atty. New York County, 1975—; former pres. N.Y. State Dist. Attys. Assn. Pres. Police Athletic League; Dem. candidate for Gov. of N.Y., 1962; bd. dirs. P.R. Legal Def. and Edn. Fund; trustee Baron de Hirsch Fund, Federated Jewish Philanthropies, Temple Emanu-El, N.Y.C.; co-chair N.Y. Holocaust Meml. Commn.; chmn. Gov.'s Adv. Com. on Sentencing, 1979; counsel N.Y. State Law Enforcement Coun.; mem. N.Y. exec. com. State of Israel Bonds. Served on destroyers USN, 1941-45. Recipient Emory Buckner award Fed. Bar Coun., 1983, Yale Citation of Merit, 1982, Fordham-Stein prize, 1988, Thomas Jefferson award in law U. Va., 1991. Fellow Am. Bar Found.; mem. ABA, N.Y. State Bar Assn., Assn. of the Bar of the City of N.Y., N.Y. County Lawyers Assn. (Disting. Pub. Svc. award 1993), Phi Beta Kappa. Office: Office Dist Atty One Hogan Pl New York NY 10013

MORGERA, SALVATORE DOMENIC, electrical engineering educator, researcher; b. Providence, Aug. 5, 1946; s. Salvatore and Blanche (Bono) M.; m. Mischa Atrzadeh, May 21, 1983; 1 child, Eric Alexander. ScB in Physics with honors, Brown U., 1968, MSEE, 1970, PhDEE, 1975. Sr. scientist, prin. investigator, tech. dir. Raytheon Co., Portsmouth, R.I., 1968-78; prof. Concordia U., Montreal, Que., Can., 1978-85, adj. prof., 1985—; responsible adminstr. Concordia U., Montreal, Que., 1980-85; prof. elec. engring., area rep. McGill U., Montreal, 1985—, dir. Info. Networks and Systems Lab., 1985—; vis. expert Bell Can., Ottawa, Ont., 1990; vis. scientist Nat. Rsch. Coun., Ottawa, 1991—; rsch. fellow, major project leader, project leader Can. Inst. for Telecom. Rsch., Montreal, 1990—, mem. program com., 1991-93; cons. Nat. Security Indsl. Assn., Washington, 1979-78; pres. program grant com., mem. program com. Que. Rsch. Coun., St. Foy, 1988-90; pres. SRC, cons., Montreal and Ottawa, 1985—; chmn. tech. sessions and mem. tech. program com. over 25 internat. symposia, 1978—. Author: Digital Signal Processing Applications to Communications and Algebraic Coding Theories, 1989; mem. editorial bd. Jour. Orgnl. Behaviour and Stats., 1980—; contbr. over 130 articles to sci. jours. and symposia, chpts. to books. Rsch. grantee Natural Scis. and Engring. Rsch. Coun., 1978—, Que. Rsch. Coun., 1978—; fellow Concordia U. Sci. Coll., 1980—. Fellow IEEE (citation 1990), IEEE Comm. Soc. (chmn. Montreal sect. 1988—, Disting. Lectr. award 1993); mem. Can. Soc. Elec. Engring., Soc. Indsl. and Applied Math. Statis. Soc. Can., Am. Statis. Assn., European Soc. for Signal Processing, Inst. for Math. Stats., N.Y. Acad. Scis., Sigma Xi, Tau Beta Pi, Zeta Psi. Avocations: astronomy, amateur radio, languages, classical music. Office: McGill U Dept Elec Engring, 3480 University St, Montreal, PQ Canada H3A 2A7

MORGESE, JAMES N., broadcast executive; b. Bronx, N.Y., Jan. 5, 1951; s. George N. and Tina C. (Papa) M.; m. Zoe A. Larsen, July 11, 1976; children: Mila, Lane. BA in Mass Comm., U. Denver, 1973, MA in Pub. Comm., 1979. Prodn. asst. NBC, N.Y.C., 1971-74; mem. creative staff Prodns. Unltd., Denver, 1974-75; prodn. asst. Sta. KOA-TV, Denver, 1975-79; prodn. mgr. WKYU-TV, Bowling Green, Ky., 1980-82; mgr. prodn. ops. Sta. KUID-TV, Moscow, Idaho, 1982-85; local program mgr. Sta. WUFT-TV, Gainsville, Fla., 1985-86, sta. mgr., 1986-90; sta. mgr. KRMA-TV, Denver, 1990-93, pres., gen. mgr., 1993—. Chmn. Borah Symposium, Moscow, 1980; adv. bd. Alachua County Cable T.V., Fla., 1989-90; exec. in charge prodn. And Learning For All, Denver, 1992-93, A Place to Call Home, Denver, 1992-93. Mem. adv. commn. U. Denver Alumni, 1991-92. Mem. NATAS, Colo. Hispanic Media Assn., Denver Advertising Fedn.,

Urban League Met. Denver. Office: Station KRMA-TV 1089 Bannock St Denver CO 80204-4036

MORGNANESI, LANNY M., journalist; b. Trenton, N.J., Sept. 21, 1951; s. Orlando John and Kathryn Theresa (Mercurio) M.; m. Lucille Heu, Nov. 27, 1987; 1 child, Dante Michael. BA in Liberal Arts, Millersville U., 1973; MA in Journalism, U. Mo., 1975. Reporter Bucke County Courier Times, Levittown, Pa., 1975-80, editl. page writer, 1980, assoc. editor, 1980-84; copy editor, advisor New China News Agy., Beijing, 1984-85; asst. city editor The Fla. Times-Union, Jacksonville, Fla., 1986-90, zoned editions editor, 1990-92, city editor, 1992-93; exec. editor The Intelligencer/Record, Doylestown, Pa., 1993—; exec. prodr., host cable TV show The Intelligencer Monthly, Suburban Cmty. TV, Doylestown, 1994—. Bd. dirs. Ctrl. Bucks Family YMCA, Doylestown, 1993—. Mem. Am. Soc. Newspaper Editors, Pa. Soc. Newspaper Editors, Pa. Newspaper Pubs. Assn. Office: The Intelligencer/Record 333 N Broad St Doylestown PA 18901

MORGNER, AURELIUS, economist, educator; b. N.Y.C., May 23, 1917; s. Oscar A. and Anna G. (Hoffmeister) M. B.S. in Bus. Adminstrn., U. Mo., 1938, M.A. in Econs., 1940; Ph.D., U. Minn., 1955. Investigator Dept. Labor, 1941; project dir. Employment Stblzn. Research Inst., 1941-42; instr. bus. adminstrn. U. Minn., 1942-46; lectr. Northwestern U., 1946-47; assoc. prof. Tex. A&M U., 1947-56, prof., 1956-58; vis. prof. U. São Paulo, Brazil, 1958-60; dir. grad. social studies U. São Paulo, 1959-60; prof. econs. U. So. Calif., L.A., 1960—; chmn. dept. U. So. Calif., 1962-69; prof. internat. econs. Sch. Internat. Relations, 1960—; Pub. panel mem. Chgo. Regional War Labor Bd., 1943-45; pub. rep. minimum wage com. Dept. Labor, 1942,43; cons. Govt. Ecuador, 1965-68, Govt. Guyana, 1968, state Nev., 1970, Philippines, 1971-72, Yemen Arab Republic, 1974-75; U.S. State Dept. vis. lectr., Brazil, summer 1966. Co-author: Local Labor Markets, 1948, Problems in Economic Analysis, 1948, Problems in the Theory of Price, 1954 (trans. Spanish 1965, Portuguese 1967). Ford faculty fellow Columbia U. 1954-55. Mem. So. Calif. Econ. Assn. (pres. 1965-66), Am. Econs. Assn., Western Econ. Assn., Am. Arbitration Assn., Internat. Studies Assn. Office: U So Calif Dept Econs Los Angeles CA 90089

MORGRIDGE, HOWARD HENRY, architect; b. Pasadena, Calif., May 29, 1919; s. George Burton and Hazel (Hill) M.; m. Alice C. Best, Feb. 1, 1947; children: Sarah, Susan, Shan. BArch, U. So. Calif., 1942. Registered architect, Calif. Ptnr. Marsh, Smith & Powell, Los Angeles, 1947-55, Smith, Powell & Morgridge, Los Angeles, 1955-65; pres. Powell, Morgridge, Richards & Coghlan, Inc., Los Angeles, 1965-72, Morgridge, Bader, Richards & Coghlan, Inc. Los Angeles and Newport Beach, Calif., 1972-78; pres. Howard H. Morgridge FAIA & Assoc., Inc., Tustin, Calif., 1978-86, Balboa, Calif., 1987—; pres. Calif. State Bd. Archtl. Examiners, Sacramento, 1975. Paintings exhibited Stary-Sheets Fine Arts Galleries, Irvine, Calif. Bd. dirs. Pasadena Beautiful, 1965-71; bd. dirs. Planning and Conservation League, San Francisco, 1968-70; mem. art commn. City of Newport Beach, Calif., 1975-77; chmn., exec. com. Nat. Council Archtl. Regulatory Bds. Western States, 1975-76. Served with U.S. Army, 1944-46, PTO. Artist watercolor landscape permanent collection displayed City of Newport Beach Art Festival, Purchase award, 1985, 86. Fellow AIA (pres. so. Calif. chpt. 1963, pres. Calif. council 1967, 1st Honor award 1949, 54). Republican. Congregationalist. Clubs: Newport Harbor, Yacht (Newport Beach). Office: Howard H Morgridge & Assocs 1 Bay Is Newport Beach CA 92661-1124

MORI, HANAE, fashion designer; b. Muikaichi, Shimane, Japan, 1926; m. Ken Mori, May 1947; children: Akira, Kei. BA in Lit., Tokyo Women's Christian Coll., 1947. Pres., founder, designer Hanae Mori Group, N.Y.C., 1951—; uniform designer Japan Airlines, Tokyo, 1967, 70, 73; costume designer Monaco Ballet, 1976, Paris Opera Ballet, 1986, (opera) Madame Butterfly at La Scala, Milan, 1985. Author: Designing for Tomorrow, 1978, A Glass Butterfly, 1984, Hanae Mori 1960-1989, 1989. Adviser Ministry of Cultural Affairs, Tokyo; mem. overseas bd. Boston Symphony Orch.; mem. various cultural coms., Tokyo. Recipient Neiman Marcus award, 1973, Purple Ribbon, Govt. of Japan, 1988, La Croix Chevalier des Arts et Lettres, Govt. of France, 1984, Legion of Honor, 1989. Mem. Chambre Syndicale de Haute Couture Parisienne. Avocations: opera, theater. Office: Hanae Mori New York Inc 27 E 79th St New York NY 10021-0101

MORI, JUN, lawyer; b. San Francisco, Dec. 13, 1929; s. Isamu Arthur and Hide (Nakae) M.; m. May Tsutsumoto, Apr. 25, 1954; children: Jean Kikuko, Richard Isamu, Ken Arthur. B.A., UCLA, 1955; LL.B., Waseda U., Tokyo, Japan, 1951; J.D., U. So. Calif., 1958. Bar: Calif. 1959, U.S. Supreme Ct. 1971, D.C. 1979. Dep. commr. of corp. State of Calif., 1959-60; sr. ptnr. firm Mori & Ota, Los Angeles, 1960-84, Kelly Drye & Warren, L.A., N.Y.C., Washington and Tokyo, 1984—; dir. Yamaha Internat. Corp., Buena Park, Calif.; legal adviser Sumitomo Bank of Calif., Los Angeles, 1962—. Chmn. Los Angeles-Nagoya Sister City Affiliation, 1966-67; trustee UCLA Found.; mem. com. on Pacific Basin studies UCLA; pres. Bd. Harbor Commrs., City of Los Angeles, 1980-82, 86-88, 89; mem. adv. bd. Office Internat. Trade, Calif. Dept. Econ. and Bus. Devel.; mem. President's Export Coun., 1976-80. Mem. Am. Bar Assn., Am. Judicature Soc., Japanese Am. Jr. C. of C. (pres. 1962-63), Japan Am. Soc. So. Calif., Los Angeles World Affairs Council. Home: 2219 Cheswic Ln Los Angeles CA 90027-1134 Office: Kelley Drye & Warren 515 S Flower St Los Angeles CA 90071-2201 also: 101 Park Ave New York NY 10178-0001

MORIAL, MARC H., mayor; b. New Orleans, 1958; s. Ernest and Sybil M.; divorced; 1 child, Kemah. Bar: La. Legis. intern U.S. Sen. Russell Long, Washington, 1979; dir. U. Pa. Office of Supportive Svcs., Phila., 1979-80; summer assoc. U.S. Atty. U.S. Dist. Ct. (so. dist.) N.Y., 1982; legis. asst. U.S. Rep. George T. Leland, Washington, 1983; atty. Barham & Churchill, New Orleans, 1983-85; pvt. practice New Orleans, 1985—; mem. La. Senate, Baton Rouge, 1991-93, mem. revenue and fiscal affairs com., commerce com., labor and indsl. rels. com., select com. crime & drugs, intergovtl. rels. com., Pres. Clinton's action com. on crime & drugs, senate select com. on econ. devel.; mayor City of New Orleans, 1993—; adj. prof. law, polit. sci. Xavier U. La., New Orleans, 1988-90. Del. Nat. Rainbow Coalition Conv., 1986, La. State Dem. Conv., 1986, Dem. Nat. Conv., Atlanta, 1988; cooperating atty. NAACP Legal Def. Fund, mem. nat., New Orleans br.; gen. counsel La. Assn. Minority and Women Owned Businesses, Inc., La. Voter Registration/Edn. Crusade; cooperating atty. Minority Bus. Enterprise Legal Def. and Edn. Fund; divestment coord.; legal advisor New Orleans Anti-Apartheid Coalition, 1983—; bd. dirs. La. ACLU, La. Spl. Olympics, Milne Boys Home; mem. project steering com. Voting Rights Law Reporter; mem. Young Leadership Coun., Friend of New Orleans Ctr. for Creative Arts. Recipient Chmns. award Congl. Black Caucus, 1989, Outstanding Svc. award Lutcher (La.) H.S., 1990, La. NAACP Cmty. Svc. award, 1989; named Legis. Rookie of Yr. Baton Rouge Bus. Report, 1992, All Rookie Team by polit. columnist John Maginnis, 1993, Legis. Newcome of Yr., 1992. Mem. ABA (standing com. on world order under law 1982-83), Nat. Bar Assn., La. State Bar Assn. (Pro Bono Pub. award 1988), La. Assn. Criminal Def. Attys., Nat. Conf. Black Lawyers, Amnesty Internat. USA, Transafrica, Louis A. Martinet Legal Soc. New Orleans, La. Trial Lawyers Assn. (pres. adv. coun.), Nat. Black Law Students Assn. (nat. bd. dirs. 1981-83), Alpha Phi Alpha. Office: Office of the Mayor City Hall Rm 2E10 1300 Perdido St New Orleans LA 70112*

MORIARTY, CATHY, actress; b. Bronx, N.Y., Nov. 29, 1960; d. John and Catherine M.; m. Carmine Dana, 1981. Actress: (films) Raging Bull, 1980 (Academy award nomination best supporting actress 1980), Neighbors, 1981, White of the Eye, 1987, Burndown, 1990, Kindergarten Cop, 1990, Soapdish, 1991, The Mambo Kings, 1992, The Gun in Betty Lou's Handbag, 1992, Matinee, 1993, Another Stakeout, 1993, Corrina, Corrina, 1994, Pontiac Moon, 1994, Forget Paris, 1995, Casper, 1995, (TV series) Tales from the Crypt (CableACE award). Office: ICM 8942 Wilshire Blvd Beverly Hills CA 90211*

MORIARTY, DONALD WILLIAM, JR., banker; b. Amarillo, Tex., Sept. 15, 1939; s. Donald William and Lorraine Julia (Walck) M.; m. Rita Ann Giller, Nov. 28, 1964; children: Mary Kathleen, Jennifer Ann, Anne Marie, Kerry Lee, Erin Teresa. Student, St. Benedict's Coll., 1957-59, 60-61; B.Sc., Washington U., 1962; M.Sc., St. Louis U., 1965, Ph.D., 1970. Cost acct. Emerson Electric, St. Louis, 1959-63; grad. fellow in econs. St. Louis U., 1963-65, instr., 1965-68; asst. prof. U. Mo., St. Louis, 1968-70; with Fed. Res. Bank of St. Louis, 1968-83, v.p., 1971-74, sr. v.p., controller, 1974-77, 1st v.p., 1977-83; sr. v.p. Gen. Bancsharp Corp., 1983-86; exec. v.p. Commerce Bancshares, Inc., 1986-87; bank cons., 1987-89; pres., CEO, bd. dirs. Duchesne Bank, St. Peters, Mo., 1989—; bd. dirs. Mid-Am. Payments Exchange, Duchesne Bank; vis. instr. Webster Coll., 1975-82; adviser City of Des Peres (Mo.), chmn. fin. com., 1976-78, chmn. mgmt. com., 1978-81, mem. personnel commn., 1978-81, mem. planning and zoning com., 1981-83. Trustee, vice chmn. St. Joseph Hosp., 1982-93; mem. adv. bd. St. Joseph Acad., 1982-86; mem. pres.'s coun. St. Louis U., 1983—; bd. dirs. ea. Mo. region NCCJ, 1987-93; dist. chmn. Boy Scouts Am., 1991-93, vice chmn. 1994—. Recipient Alumni Merit award St. Louis U., 1979. Mem. Am. Econ. Assn., Am. Fin. Assn., Am. Mgmt. Assn., St. Peters C. of C., St. Charles C. of C., Beta Gamma Sigma, Alpha Kappa Psi. Club: Media.

MORIARTY, GEORGE MARSHALL, lawyer; b. Youngstown, Ohio, Sept. 16, 1942; s. George Albert Moriarty and Caroline (Jones) Bass; m. Elizabeth Bradley Moore, Sept. 11, 1965 (div. 1986); children: Bradley Marshall, Caroline Walden, Sarah Cameron. BA magna cum laude, Harvard U., 1964, LLB magna cum laude, 1968. Bar: Mass. 1969, U.S. Dist. Ct. Mass. 1973, U.S. Ct. Appeals (1st cir.) 1976, U.S. Ct. Appeals (D.C. cir.) 1984, U.S. Claims Ct. 1983, U.S. Supreme Ct. 1976. Law clk. to Hon. Bailey Aldrich U.S. Ct. Appeals (1st cir.), Boston, 1968-69; law clk. to Hon. Warren Burger, Hon. Hugo Black, Hon. Potter Stewart, Hon. Byron White U.S. Supreme Ct., Washington, 1969-70; spl. asst. to Hon. Elliot L. Richardson, Dept. Health, Edn. & Welfare, Washington, 1970-71, exec. asst., 1971-72; assoc. Ropes & Gray, Boston, 1972-77, ptnr., 1977—. Trustee Boston Athenaeum, Brigham & Women's Hosp., Ptnrs. Health Care Sys. Inc.; warden Trinity Ch. in City of Boston, vestryman. Mem. ABA, Am. Law Inst., Boston Bar Assn., Somerset Club, Tavern Club, Met. Club. Office: Ropes & Gray 1 Internat Pl Boston MA 02110

MORIARTY, JEANNE MARIE, medical center administrator; b. Muncy, Pa., Oct. 30, 1944; d. James T. and Ruth Kimble (Turner) M. BSN, St. Joseph Coll., Emmitsburg, Md., 1966; M. in Health Adminstrn., Med. Coll. Va., 1979. V.p. West Nebr. Gen. Hosp., Scottsbluff, Theda Clark Regional Med. Ctr., Neenah, Wis., Immanuel Med. Ctr., Omaha. Wharton fellow 1990. Fellow Am. Coll. Health Execs.; mem. ANA, Nebr. Nurses Assn., Am. Orgn. Nurse Execs., Nebr. Orgn. Nurse Execs., Sigma Theta Tau. Office: Immanuel Med Ctr 6901 N 72nd St Omaha NE 68122

MORIARTY, JOHN, opera administrator, artistic director; b. Fall River, Mass., Sept. 30, 1930; s. John J. and Fabiola Marie (Ripeau) M. MusB summa cum laude, New Eng. Conservatory, 1952; D.M. New England Conservatory, 1992. Artistic adminstr. Opera Soc. of Washington, 1960-62, Santa Fe Opera, N.Mex., 1962-65; dir. Wolf Trap Co., Vienna, Va., 1972-77; chmn. opera dept. Boston Conservatory, 1973-89; chmn. opera dept. New Eng. Conservatory, 1989—; prin. condr. Central City Opera, Denver, 1978—; artistic dir., 1982—; panelist Nat. Inst. Music Theater, 1985, 86, 87, Conn. Arts Council, 1982, 84; adjudicator various contests including Met. Opera auditions, 1965—. Author: Diction, 1975. Trustee Boston Concert Opera. Recipient Frank Huntington Beebe award, Boston, 1954, Disting. Alumni award New Eng. Conservatory Alumni Assn., 1982, Gold Chair award Cen. City Opera House Assn., 1988. Mem. Nat. Opera Assn., Sigma Alpha Iota, Delta Omicron, Pi Kappa Lambda. Office: New Eng Conservatory 290 Huntington Ave Boston MA 02115-5000 also: Cen City Opera House Assn 621 17th St Ste 1601 Denver CO 80293-1601

MORIARTY, JUDITH KAY SPRY, state official; b. Fairfield, Mo., Feb. 2, 1942; d. Earl Price and Blanche May (McDavitt) Spry; children: Derek David, Michael Price, Timothy John. Student Central Mo. State U., State Fair C.C.; tng. cert. Elections and County Clks. Assn., Mo., 1985. Motor Vehicle agt. Sedalia Motor Vehicle Registration, Mo., 1977-81; county clk. Pettis County, Sedalia, 1982-93; sec. of state State of Mo., 1993—. Vice regent Daus. Isabella, Sedalia, 1985-86; del. Mo. Dem. Conv., 1980, 84; active Women's Dem. Club Pettis County, Sacred Heart Cath. Ch., Mo. Coun. Econ. Edn., Mo. Hist. Recs. Preservation Bd., Friends of Archives, Local Recs. Bd., State Recs. Commn., Literacy Investment for Tomorrow; bd. dirs. Salvation Army, Sedalia, 1978—, Am. Cancer Soc., Sedalia, 1982—; Sedalia Area Council for Arts, 1980-84. Named Outstanding Young Woman Sedalia, Sedalia Jaycees, 1959. Mem. LWV, Bus. and Profl. Women (legis. chmn. 1984-86), Sedalia Area C. of C. (v.p., bd. dirs. 1982-85), Women's Aglow. Avocations: reading; physical fitness; walking; pen and ink sketching; baking. Office: Office Sec of State PO Box 778 Jefferson City MO 65102*

MORIARTY, MICHAEL, actor; b. Detroit, Apr. 5, 1941; s. George and Eleanor (Paul) M.; m. Françoise Martinet, June 1966 (div.); 1 son, Matthew; m. Anne Hamilton Martin. B.A., Dartmouth Coll., 1963; postgrad. (Fulbright fellow), London Acad. Music and Dramatic Arts; D.F.A. (hon.), Fairleigh Dickinson U. Profl. debut with N.Y. Shakespeare Festival as Octavius Caesar in Antony and Cleopatra, Delacorte Theatre, N.Y.C., 1963, also Florizel in The Winter's Tale, 1963; stage appearances include Love's Labour Lost, 1965, Troilus and Cressida, 1965, Major Barbara, 1966, Henry IV, 1968, The House of Atreus, 1968, The Resistible Rise of Arturo Ui, 1968, Mourning Becomes Electra, 1969, The Alchemist, 1970, In the Jungle of Cities, 1970, Peanut Butter and Jelly, 1970, The Night Thoreau Spent in Jail, 1971, The Trial of the Catonsville Nine, 1971, Find Your Way Home, 1974 (Tony award for best actor 1974), King Richard III, 1974, Long Day's Journey into Night, 1983, Caine Mutiny-Court Martial, Richard III, My Fair Lady, 1994; films include Glory Boy, 1971, Hickey & Boggs, 1972, Bang the Drum Slowly, 1973, The Last Detail, 1974, Report to the Commissioner, 1975, Shoot It, 1976, Who'll Stop the Rain, 1978, Too Far to Go, 1979 (San Sebastian Internat. Film Festival award), Reborn, 1982, Q, 1982, The Stuff, 1985, Pale Rider, 1985, Troll, 1986, The Hanoi Hilton, 1987, It's Alive III: Island of the Alive, 1987, Return to Salem's Lot, 1987, Full Fathom Five, 1990; TV appearances include The Glass Menagerie, 1973 (Emmy award for best supporting actor in drama 1974), Holocaust, 1978 (Emmy award), The Deadliest Season, 1979, The Equalizer (Emmy nomination for best guest lead performance 1989), NBC Movie of the Week Born Too Soon, 1992; TV series: Law & Order, 1990-94 (Emmy nominations for best lead actor 1991, 92, 94); HBO movie Tailspin; writer: Flight to the Fatherland; writer, star: Ballad of Dexter Creed; composer score: The 15th Time; albums include Reaching Out, 1990, The Michael Moriarty Jazz Trio, 1991. Recipient Outstanding Creative Versatility award Yeshiva U., Emmy nomination lead actor Law and Order, 1993, Golden Globe nomination lead actor, 1993. Office: Lasher Mgmt PO Box 247 Flushing NY 11353-0001*

MORIARTY, RICHARD WILLIAM, pediatrician; b. Pitts., Oct. 4, 1939; s. Edwin Joseph and Catherine Bernadine (Binnie) M. BS, U. Pitts., 1961, MD, 1966. Chief pediatric resident Children's Hosp. Pitts., 1970-71; asst. prof. pediatrics U. Pitts. Sch. Medicine, 1971-77, assoc. prof., 1977—; assoc. dir. dept. pediatrics St. Francis Med. Ctr., 1987—; dir. Pitts. Poison Ctr., Children's Hosp. Pitts., 1971-87, Nat. Poison Ctr. Network, 1971-87; mem. adv. com. on hazardous chemicals, 1974-87; mem. tech. adv. com. poison prevention packaging Consumer Product Safety Commn., 1975-77; bd. dirs. Comprehensive Health Planning Com. Southwestern Pa., 1974-76; commr. Health Edn. Ctr., 1977-87. Named Man of Yr. in Medicine, 1977. Mem. Am. Acad. Pediatrics, Am. Assn. Poison Control Centers, Am. Acad. Clin. Toxicology, Am. Coll. Emergency Physicians (toxicology com. 1980-87), PGH Acad. of Medicine (pres. 1987-92). Democrat. Club: University

(Pitts.). Office: St Francis Med Office Bldg 4221 Penn Ave Ste 402 Pittsburgh PA 15224-1389

MORIARTY, ROBERT BRIAN, lawyer; b. N.Y.C., Oct. 14, 1940; s. Robert Lewis and Mary Ellen (Gard) M.; m. Margaret Elizabeth Edwards, Dec. 21, 1974; children: Kathleen, Matthew, Thomas. BA, Canisius Coll., 1962; JD, SUNY, Buffalo, 1968. Bar: N.Y. 1968, U.S. Dist. Ct. (we. dist.) N.Y. 1969, U.S. Supreme Ct. 1969. Assoc. Cox, Barrell & Walsh, Buffalo, 1968-70; pvt. practice Buffalo, 1970-72, 80-84; ptnr. Carnahan, DiGiulio, LaFalce, Moriarty & Hill, Buffalo, 1972-77, Moriarty, Allen, Lippes & Hoffman, Buffalo, 1977-79; sr. ptnr. Moriarty & Condon, Buffalo, 1984—; confidential sec. to justice N.Y. Supreme Ct., 1970-75; bd. advisors N.Y. Domestic Rels. Reporter, 1990—. Co-author: New York Domestic Relations Guide, 3 vols., 1988; contbr. articles to legal publs. Mem. exec. com. pres.'s coun. Canisius Coll., Buffalo, 1984—. Recipient Disting. Svc. award Parents Without Ptnrs., 1981. Fellow Am. Acad. Matrimonial Lawyers; mem. ABA (chmn. continuing legal edn. com. family law sect. 1987-89, coun. family law sect. 1989—, publs. bd. sect. 1989—, contbr. to ann. compendium), N.Y. State Bar Assn., Erie County Bar Assn., SUNY-Buffalo Sch. Law Alumni Assn. (bd. dirs. 1987—), Saturn Club (bd. dirs. 1987—), Cherry Hill Golf Club. Republican. Roman Catholic. Avocations: reading, travel, fishing, golf. Office: 1109 Delaware Ave Buffalo NY 14209-1699

MORICE, JAMES L., public relations executive; b. St. Louis, Mo., Aug. 30, 1948. BA in History, Ind. U., 1970; MS in Journalism, U. Mo., 1973. Gen. assignment and labor reporter St. Louis-Globe Democrat, 1973-77; investigative reporter Milw. Sentinel, 1977-78; counselor Fleishman-Hillard, 1978-82, v.p., sr. ptnr., 1982-84, exec. v.p., sr. ptnr. 1984—. Office: Fleishman-Hillard Inc 200 N Broadway Saint Louis MO 63102-2730

MORICE, JOSEPH RICHARD, history educator; b. Phila., Apr. 2, 1923; s. Joseph and Anna (Seary) M.; m. Josephine Tumminello, May 31, 1958; children—Ann Marie, Jacqueline. B.A., LaSalle Coll., 1947; M.A., Fordham U., 1951; M.Litt., U. Pitts., 1953, Ph.D., 1962. Mem. faculty Duquesne U., Pitts., 1948-89; prof. history Duquesne U., 1963-89, chmn. dept., 1965-69, dir. debate, 1955-89, emeritus prof. history, 1990—; mng. editor Duquesne Rev., 1956-73. Vol. Pub. acct. office, 1991—. Served with AUS, 1943-45. Mem. Orgn. Am. Historians, Phi Kappa Phi, Phi Alpha Theta. Home: 1632 Worcester Dr Pittsburgh PA 15243-1534

MORIKAWA, DENNIS J., lawyer; b. Feb. 14, 1946. BA, Dennison U., 1968; JD, Syracuse U., 1974. Bar: Pa. 1974, U.S. Supreme Ct. 1983. Ptnr. Morgan, Lewis & Bockius, Phila. Mem. ABA (mgmt. co-chair occupational safety and health law com. 1989-92). Office: Morgan Lewis & Bockius 2000 One Logan Sq Philadelphia PA 19103

MORIMOTO, CARL NOBORU, computer system engineer, crystallographer; b. Hiroshima, Japan, Mar. 31, 1942; came to U.S., 1957, naturalized, 1965; s. Toshiyuki and Teruko (Hirano) M.; m. Helen Kiyomi Yoshizaki, June 28, 1969; children: Matthew Ken, Justin Ray. BA, U. Hawaii, 1965; PhD, U. Wash., 1970. Research assoc. dept. chemistry Mich. State U., East Lansing, 1970-72; postdoctoral fellow dept. biochemistry and biophysics Tex. A&M U., College Station, 1972-75; sr. sci. programmer Syntex Analytical Instruments Inc., Cupertino, Calif., 1975-78; prin. programmer analyst, software engring. mgr. Control Data Corp., Sunnyvale, Calif., 1978-83; mem. profl. staff GE Aerospace, San Jose, Calif., 1983-93; prin. engr. GE Nuclear Energy, San Jose, 1993—. Mem. Am. Crytallographic Assn., Assn. Computing Machinery, Am. Chem. Soc., Sigma Xi. Am. Baptist. Home: 4003 Hamilton Park Dr San Jose CA 95130-1223

MORIN, CARLTON PAUL, private investments executive; b. Ashland, Maine, July 10, 1932; s. Leo Joseph and Leona (Nadeau) M.; children: Catherine Lee, Cynthia Ann, Bruce Carlton. AB, U. Maine, 1954; LLB, Seton Hall U., 1964. Tax acct. Internat. Nickel Co., Inc., N.Y.C., 1956-62; tax mgr. Abex Corp., N.Y.C., 1962-67; asst. to contr. Toad Shipyards Corp., N.Y.C., 1967-68; asst. treas. Interlake, Inc., Chgo., 1968-75, Congoleum Corp., Milw., 1975-77; treas. Congoleum Corp., 1977-79, v.p., treas., 1979-80, v.p. treasury and adminstrn., 1980-83, v.p. corp. devel., 1983-86; pvt. practice pvt. investor Portsmouth, 1986-92; chmn. Piscataqua Savs. Bank, 1991-92; bd. dirs. Kinderworks Corp., Casco Bay Gear and Apparel. With USMC, 1954-56. Office: PO Box 6676 Portsmouth NH 03802-6676

MORIN, PATRICK JOYCE, advertising executive; b. Manila, Philippines, June 10, 1938; (parents Am. citizens); s. Martin Joseph and Janet (Westwater) M.; m. Deborah E. O'Brien, Apr. 7, 1993; children: Martin, Sarah. B.A., Ohio State U., 1961, J.D., 1964. Account exec. J. Walter Thompson Co., N.Y.C., 1964-66, Chgo., 1966-69; pres. Ky. Roast Beef div. Ky. Fried Chicken Inc., Louisville, 1969-71; v.p., account dir. Grey Advt. Co., Detroit, 1971-75; pres. Griswold Eshleman Inc., N.Y.C., 1976-79; pres., CEO Griswold Eshleman, Cleve., 1979—; bd. dirs. Nat. Advt. Rev. Bd. With U.S. Army, 1956. Mem. Am. Mass. Assn. Advt. Agys. (Cleve. coun., past pres.), N.E. Ohio Squash Racquet Assn. (bd. dirs.), Ohio State U. Alumni Assn. (former mem. adv. coun.), Ohio State U. Pres.'s Club, Cleve. Advt. Club (pres. 1986-87), Hermit Club, Shorery Club, Muirfield Village Club. Home: 13 Shoreby Dr Bratenahl OH 44108 Office: Griswold Eshleman 101 Prospect Ave W Cleveland OH 44115-1027

MORIN, PIERRE JEAN, retired management consultant; b. Quebec City, Que., Can., Aug. 5, 1931; s. Augustin Norbert and Yvonne (Gaudry) M.; m. Colette Poulin, Apr. 3, 1954; children: Anne, Gilles, Louis. B.S., Concordia U., Montreal, 1964; M.S., Laval U., 1969; M.S., Que., 1970, D.Sc., 1973. Quality control technician Dow Brevery, Montreal, Que., 1952-56; research assoc. Royal Victoria Hosp., Montreal, 1957-67; coordinator of research Que. Heart Inst., 1967-73; dir. research labs. Laval Hosp., Que., 1973-80, lectr. dept. medicine, 1973-77; dir. gen. Community Service Ctr., 1980-88; mgmt. cons., 1988-91, ret., 1991; cons. Que. Minister of Environ., 1975-84. Contbr. articles to profl. jours. and news media. Bd. dirs. St. mary's Hosp., Three Rivers, Que. Schering Travelling fellow, 1971. Mem. AAAS. Roman Catholic. Home: 336 Rg Castor, Leclercville, PQ Canada G0S 2K0

MORIN, WILLIAM J., management consultant; b. Kankakee, Ill., Aug. 5, 1939; s. Carl Wesley and Viola Grace (Seaberle) M.; children: Mark, Timothy, Jason. BS, So. Ill. U., 1961; MS. Pres. Drake, Beam, Morin, N.Y.C., 1977-79, chmn., chief exec. officer, 1979—. Author: Successful Termination, Outplacement Techniques, Parting Company. Mem. Assn. Outplacement Cons. Firms (standards com.). Office: Drake Beam Morin 100 Park Ave New York NY 10017-5516

MORIN, WILLIAM RAYMOND, bookstore chain executive; b. Escanaba, Mich., Apr. 19, 1949; s. Raymond Louis and Naomi Rita (Flynn) M.; m. Yvonne Catherine Singleton, Aug. 7, 1971; children: Timothy Raymond, Kathryn Naomi. BS in Bus. summa cum laude, No. Mich. U., 1974; MBA, Mich. State U., 1979. Grad. teaching assoc. Mich. State U., East Lansing, 1977-79; instr. U. Wash., Seattle, 1979-80; regional franchise rep. Taco John's, Cheyenne, Wyo., 1981-87; dir. franchising Dawn Donut Systems, Inc., Flint, 1987-91; sr. rep. leasing and rsch. Family Bookstores, Grand Rapids, Mich., 1991-93, dir. real estate and legal, 1993—. Contbr.: (book) Principles of Modern Management, 1980. Staff sgt. U.S. Army, 1967-70. Home: 1207 Fallingbrook SE Kentwood MI 49508 Office: 5300 Patterson Ave SE Grand Rapids MI 49530

MORIN, YVES-CHARLES, linguistics educator, researcher; b. St. Germain, Yvelines, France, Nov. 7, 1944; arrived in Can. 1972; s. Georges and Denise (Montaudouin) M.; 1 child, Yannig. Lic., U. Paris, 1967; Diploma in Engring., Ecole Centrale, 1967; M.A. in Linguistics, U. Mich., 1970, Ph.D. in Linguistics U. 1971. Engr. Mil. Radar Estab., Pontoise, France, 1971-72; asst. prof. U. Montreal, Montreal, Que., Can. 1972-76, assoc. prof., 1967-82, prof., 1982—, mem. exec. com. Faculty of Arts and Scis., 1984-86; invited prof. Bourguiba Inst., Tunis, Tunisia, 1977; mem. cons. bd. Humanities and Social Scis. Research Council of Canada, Ottawa, 1980-83; vis. scholar Centre d'Etudes Metriques de Nantes (France), 1994. Contbr. articles to profl. jours. Served to lt. Logistics-Radar, 1971-72 France. Harkness fellow Commonwealth Fund, 1967. Mem. Linguistic Soc. Am., Can. Linguistic Soc., Can. Jour. Linguistics, Société Asiatique, Sigma

Xi, Phi Kappa Phi. Office: Univ Montreal, Dept Linguistics, CP 6128, Montreal, PQ Canada H3C 3J7

MORING, JOHN FREDERICK, lawyer; b. Farmville, Va., Oct. 30, 1935; s. Scott O'Ferrall and Margaret Macon (Mitchell) M.; m. Margaret Ann Clarke, Mar. 30, 1959; children: Martha, Elizabeth, Scott, Lee. BS, Va. Poly. Inst., 1957; JD, George Washington U., 1961. Bar: Va. 1961, D.C. 1962, U.S. Supreme Ct. 1964. Assoc. Morgan, Lewis & Bockius, Washington, 1961-68, ptnr., 1969-78; ptnr. Jones, Day, Reavis & Pogue, Washington, 1978-79, Crowell & Moring, Washington and London, 1979—. Local gas utility columnist Nat. Gas Jour., 1989—; mem. editl. bd. Natural Gas Contracts, 1994—. Pres. Sterling Citizens Assn., Alexandria, Va., 1971-77; Rep. candidate 23d Dist./Va. Gen. Assembly, Alexandria, 1973; chmn. Alexandria Rep. Com. on Candidate Recruitment, 1974; bd. govs. St. Stephen's and St. Agnes Sch., Alexandria, 1989—; pres. St. Stephen's Found., Inc., 1990-93; sr. warden Immanuel Ch. of the Hill, Alexandria, 1988, 89. 2d lt. U.S. Army, 1958. Mem. ABA (natural resources law sect. 1982-86, coun.), Fed. Energy Bar Assn. (sec. 1963-66, pres. 1982-83), Belle Haven Country Club. Episcopalian. Avocations: golf, fishing, canoeing. Home: 509 Canterbury Ln Alexandria VA 22314-4747 Office: Crowell & Moring 1001 Pennsylvania Ave NW Washington DC 20004-2505 also: 2010 Main St Irvine CA 92714-7203 also: 180 Fleet St, London EC4 A2HD, England

MORING, REBECCA OWEN, university official; b. Louisville, Miss., Mar. 17, 1939; d. Boyd Franklin Owen and Lora Jewell (Hancock) Freeman; m. H. Adrian Moring, July 29, 1955; children: Susanne Moring Jeffcoat, Sharyn Moring Kirk. Student, Faulkner Jr. Coll., Fairhope, Ala., 1981-83, Springhill Coll., Mobile, Ala., 1985-88. Acct. Teledyne-Continental Motors, Mobile, 1968-70; exec. sec. U. South Ala., Mobile, 1970-80, dept. mgr., 1980-88, bus. mgr. Coll. Medicine, 1988—; cons. Assn. Pathology Chmn., 1995, program chair, 1994. Bd. dirs. March of Dimes, Mobile, 1975-84; treas. Edn. for Democracy, Inc., USA, Mobile, 1990—. Mem. NAFE, Med. Group Mgmt. Assn. (coun. mem. 1992-95, Acad. Practice Assembly, pres. Pathology Mgmt. Assembly 1993-94), Clin. Lab. Mgmt. Assn., Southeastern Path. Bus. Mgrs. (program chmn. 1989, 95), Med. Group Mgmt. Assn. Ala. (state membership chmn.), Assn. Pathology Chmn. (cons. practice com. 1995—). Office: U South Ala 241 Fillingim St Mobile AL 36617

MORIS, LAMBERTO GIULIANO, architect; b. Siena, Tuscany, Italy, Mar. 29, 1944; came to U.S., 1972; s. Gualtiero Luigi and Giovanna (Avanzati) M.; m. Tracy P. Schilling, 1970 (div. 1985); children: Giacomo, Stefano; m. Beverly Chiang, Mar. 28, 1986; 1 child, Christopher. MA in Arch., U. Florence, Italy, 1970. Assoc. Marquis Assocs., San Francisco, 1972-78, prin., 1978-85; prin. Simon Martin-Vegue Winkelstein Moris, San Francisco, 1985—; tchr. San Francisco City Coll.; juror DuPont Antron Design Awards, 1989; mem. adv. com. Acad. of Art-Coll., San Francisco, 1991—. Mem. San Francisco Opera Guild. Fellow AIA (mem. Coll. of Fellows, mem. Interior Arch.); mem. Italingua Inst. (bd. dirs.), The Engrs. Club, Il Cenacola Club. Roman Catholic. Avocations: coin collecting, skiing, travel. Office: Simon Martin-Vegue Winkelstein Moris 501 2nd St Ste 701 San Francisco CA 94107-1447

MORISATO, SUSAN CAY, actuary; b. Chgo., Feb. 11, 1955; d. George and Jessie (Fujita) M.; m. Thomas Michael Remec, Mar. 6, 1981. BS, U. Ill., 1975, MS, 1977. Actuarial student Aetna Life & Casualty, Hartford, Conn., 1977-79; actuarial asst. Bankers Life & Casualty, Chgo., 1979-80, asst. actuary, 1980-83, assoc. actuary, 1983-85, health product actuary, 1985-86, v.p., 1986—; participant institutional forum Health Ins. Assn. Am., 1983; spkr. health forum Life Ins. Mgmt. Rsch. Assn., 1992, long-term care conf. Sharing the Burden, 1994. Mem. adv. panel on long term care financing Brookings' Inst. Fellow Soc. Actuaries (conf. speaker 1988, 94, workshop leader 1990, 93, news editor health sect. news 1988-90); mem. Am. Acad. Actuaries, Health Ins. Assn. Am. (long term care task force 1988—, chair 1993—, conf. speaker 1990, tech. adv. com. 1991-93, mem. health care reform strategy com. 1993—), Nat. Assn. Ins. Commrs. (ad hoc actuarial working group for long term care nonforfeiture benefits 1992), Chgo. Actuarial Assn. (sec. 1983-85, program com. 1987-89), Phi Beta Kappa, Kappa Delta Pi, Phi Kappa Phi. Office: Bankers Life & Casualty Co 222 Merchandise Mart Plaza Chicago IL 60654

MORISHITA, AKIHIKO, trading company executive; b. Osaka, Japan, Oct. 14, 1941; came to U.S., 1981; s. Sueyoshi and Toshiko Morishita; m. Fumiko Okamura; children: Shizuko, Kumiko, Okamura. BA in Econs., Wakayama U., Wakayama, Japan, 1965. Mgr. Hanwa & Co. Ltd., Osaka, 1965-80; coin. oil dept. Pacific Southwest Trading Co., San Diego, 1981-82; exec. Pacific Marine Bunkering, Inc., L.A., 1982—. Mem. L.A. Oilmen's Club, Woodland Hills Country Club. Home: 4610 Don Pio Dr Woodland Hills CA 91364-4205

MORISON, JOHN HOPKINS, casting manufacturing company executive; b. Milw., June 29, 1913; s. George Abbot and Amelia (Elmore) M. m. Olga de Souza Dantas, July 29, 1944; children: Maria de Souza Dantas, John Hopkins III. AB, Harvard U., 1935; LLD, New Eng. Coll., 1973. Various positions Bucyrus-Erie Co., South Milwaukee, Wis., U.S. and Latin Am., 1935-49; pres., dir. Hitchiner Mfg. Co., Inc., Milford, N.H., 1949-93, chmn. bd., 1973-93, chmn. emeritus, 1994—; pres., treas. Upland Farm Inc., Peterborough, N.H.; chmn. RiverMead Retirement Community, Peterborough, N.H., 1991—; bd. dirs. Markem Corp., Keene, N.H. Munters Corp. USA, Ft. Myers, Fla. Commr. N.H. Commn. on Arts, 1967-77; mem. regional exec. com. Boy Scouts Am., Framingham, Mass., 1970-76; mem. exec. com., pres. N.H. Coun. on World Affairs, 1955-76; trustee Canterbury Shaker Village, 1982—; trustee Land Use Found. N.H., 1970-75, World Peace Found., 1962-90, Currier Gallery Art; pres. bd. dirs. Matthew Thornton Health Plan, 1972-82; bd. dirs. Forum on N.H.'s Future, 1991-; pres., distbg. dir. N.H. Charitable Fund., 1968-79; mem. corp. MacDowell Colony; v.p. bd. govs. N.H. Public TV, 1979-89. Lt. (j.g.) USNR, 1943-46. Recipient Lifetime Achievement award N.H. Bus. and Industry Assn., 1993, Granite State award U. N.H., 1994. Mem. Somerset Club. Unitarian. Home: RR 1 Box 326 Lyndeborough NH 03082-9734

MORITA, (NORIYUKI) PAT, actor, comedian; b. Isleton, Calif., 1932; m. Yuki Morita, 1970; children: Tia, Aly. Grad. high sch., Fairfield, Calif. Ind. nightclub comedian, actor Los Angeles, 1964—. Regular mem. cast: (TV series) Sanford and Son, 1974-75, (as Arnold) Happy Days, 1975-76, 82-83; starring roles: (TV series) Mr. T and Tina, 1976, Blansky's Beauties, 1977, Ohara, 1987; TV films include The Vegas Strip War, Amos, Return to Manzanar, Greyhounds; feature films: Thoroughly Modern Millie, 1967, Midway, 1976, When Time Ran Out, 1980, Savannah Smiles, 1982, Jimmy the Kid, 1983, The Karate Kid, 1984 (Acad. award nomination 1985), The Karate Kid Part II, 1986, Collision Course, 1987, The Karate Kid Part III, 1989, Do or Die, 1991, Honeymoon in Vegas, 1992, Even Cowgirls Get the Blues, 1994, The Next Karate Kid, 1994, American Ninja 5, 1995. Recipient Lifetime Achievement award Assn. Asian/Pacific Am. Artists, 1987. *

MORITA, RICHARD YUKIO, microbiology and oceanography educator; b. Pasadena, Calif., Mar. 27, 1923; s. Jiro and Reiko (Yamamoto) M.; m. Toshiko Nishihara, May 29, 1926; children—Sally Jean, Ellen Jane, Peter Wayne. B.S., U. Nebr., 1947; M.S., U. So. Calif., 1949; Ph.D., U. Calif., 1954. Microbiologist Mid-Pacific Expdn., 1950, Danish Galathea Deep-Sea Expdn., 1952, Trans-Pacific Expdn.; Postdoctoral fellow U. Calif., Scripps Inst. Oceanography, 1954-55; asst. prof. U. Houston, 1955-58; asst. prof., assoc. prof. U. Nebr., 1958-62; prof. microbiology and oceanography Oreg. State U., Corvallis, 1962—; prog. dir. biochemistry NSF, 1968-69; Disting. vis. prof. Kyoto Univ.; cons. NIH, 1968-70; researcher in field. Contbr. articles to sci. lit. Patentee in field. Served with U.S. Army, 1944-46. Grantee NSF, 1962—, NIH, 1960-68, NASA, 1967-72, Office Naval Research, 1966-70, Dept. Interior, 1968-72, NOAA, 1975-82, Bur. Land Mgmt., 1982, EPA, 1986—; recipient awards including King Fredericus IX Medal and Ribbon, 1954, Sr. Queen Elizabeth II Fellowship, 1973-74, Hotpack lectr. and award Can. Soc. Fellow Japan Soc. for Promotion Sci.; mem. Am. Soc. Microbiology (Fisher award). Office: Oreg State U Dept Microbiology Corvallis OR 97331

MORITSUGU, KENNETH PAUL, physician, government official; b. Honolulu, Mar. 5, 1945; s. Richard Yutaka nd Hisayo Joan (Nishikawa) M.;

children: Erika Lizabeth, Vikki Lianne; m. Donna Jones (dec. 1992). Student, Chaminade Coll. Honolulu, 1963-65; BA in Classical Langs. with honors, U. Hawaii, 1967; MD, George Washington U., 1971; MPH, U. Calif., Berkeley, 1975; DSc (hon.), Coll. Osteopathic Medicine, U. New Eng., 1988, Midwestern U., 1993; D Pub. Svc. (hon.), U. North Tex., 1994. Diplomate Am. Bd. Preventive Medicine (fellow); cert. correctional health profl. Intern USPHS Hosp., San Francisco, 1971-72, resident, 1972-75; commd. USPHS, 1968, advanced through grades to med. dir., 1979; promoted to rank of rear adm., asst. surgeon gen., 1988; staff med. officer USPHS Hosp., San Francisco, 1972-73; regional cons. med. manpower planning and devel. HEW, San Francisco, 1976-78; chief internat. edn. programs br. HEW, Washington, 1978; dep. dir. div. medicine HEW, 1978; dir. Bur. Health Professions, div. medicine HHS, Rockville, Md., 1978-83, dir. Nat. Health Service Corps, 1983-87, dep. dir. Bur. Health Professions, 1987; med. dir. Fed. Bur. Prisons Dept. Justice, Washington, 1987—. Decorated D.S.M.; recipient Commendation medal, Meritorious Svc. medal, Outstanding Svc. medal, Surgeon Gen.'s medallion, Surgeon Gen.'s medal, others. Fellow Am. Coll. Preventive Medicine, Royal Soc. Health; mem. APHA, Assn. Tchrs. Preventive Medicine, Assn. Mil. Surgeons U.S., Res. Officers Assn., Mensa, Am. Guild Organists. Home: 726 Sonata Way Silver Spring MD 20901-5063 Office: US Dept Justice Fed Bur Prisons 320 1st St NW Ste 1000 Washington DC 20534-0002

MORITZ, CHARLES FREDRIC, book editor; b. Cleve., Jan. 23, 1917; s. Frederic and Alberta (Hartwig) M. B.A., Ohio State U., 1942; student, Harvard U., 1946-47, Columbia U., 1947-48; B.S. in L.S. Middlebury (Vt.) Coll., 1948, M.A., 1950. Asst. librarian rare book room and reference dept. Yale Library, 1948-50; mem. staff N.Y. Pub. Library, 1950-52; asst. prof. Grad. Sch. Library Service, Rutgers U., 1955-58; editor of Current Biography, 1958-92. Contbr. book revs. for Booklist, 1952-55; also articles. Served with AUS, 1942-45. Mem. ALA, Bibliog. Soc. Am. Democrat. Lutheran. Home: 518 W 232nd St Bronx NY 10463-3509 Office: Current Biography 950 University Ave Bronx NY 10452-4224

MORITZ, CHARLES WORTHINGTON, business information and services company executive; b. Washington, Aug. 22, 1936; s. Sidney Jr. and Ruth Whitman (Smith) M.; m. Susan Prescott Tracy, June 14, 1958; children: Peter W., Tracy W., Margaret Anne. BA, Yale U., 1958. With R.H. Donnelley Corp., 1960-76, v.p., gen. mgr. mktg. div.; 1972-74, sr. v.p., 1974-76, dir., 1975-85; exec. v.p. Dun & Bradstreet Corp., N.Y.C., 1976-78; vice chmn. Dun & Bradstreet Corp., 1979-81, dir., 1979—, pres., chief operating officer, 1981-84, chmn., chief exec. officer, 1985-93, chmn., 1994—. Served to lt. (j.g.) USNR, 1958-60. Mem. Direct Mktg. Assn. (dir. 1973-76), Am. Mgmt. Assn., Econ. Club N.Y., Bus. Roundtable, Pine Valley (N.J.) Club, Wee Burn Country Club, Nat. Golf Links Am. Club, John's Island Club, Blind Brook Club, Links Club, Zeta Psi. Republican. Episcopalian. *

MORITZ, DONALD BROOKS, mechanical engineer, consultant; b. Mpls., June 17, 1927; s. Donald B. and Frances W. (Whalen) M.; m. Joan Claire Betzenderfer, June 17, 1950; children: Craig, Pamela, Brian. B.S. in Mech. Engring., U. Minn., 1950; postgrad., Western Res. U., 1956-58. Registered profl. engr., Ill. Minn., Ohio. V.p., gen. mgr. Waco Scaffold Shoring Co., Addison, Ill., 1950-72; group v.p. Bliss and Laughlin Industries, Oak Brook, Ill., 1972-83; sr. v.p. AXIA Inc. (formerly Bliss and Laughlin Industries, Oak Brook, 1983-84, exec. v.p., chief operating officer, 1984-88; cons. Exec. Svc. Corps Chgo., 1988—; pres. Image-A-Nation, Unltd., 1988—; bd. dirs. Am. Photographic Acad. Patentee in field. Served with USN, 1945-46. Mem. ASME, Scaffold and Shoring Inst. (founder, past pres.), Mensa, Meadow Club. Office: Moritz and Assocs PO Box 305 Clarendon Hills IL 60514-0305

MORITZ, DONALD I., energy company executive; b. McKeesport, Pa., Oct. 23, 1927; s. Maurice Louis and Rose (Klein) M.; m. Janet Papernick, Nov. 9, 1952; children: Paula, Laurie, J. Kenneth. B.S., U. Pitts., 1948, J.D. 1951. Bar: Pa. 1952. With Equitable Resources, Inc. (and subsidiaries), 1952—; asst. to pres. Equitable Gas Co. (and subsidiaries), 1967-72; exec. v.p. Equitable Gas Co. (and subsidiaries), Pitts., 1972-77; pres. Equitable Gas Co. (and subsidiaries), 1977—, chief exec. officer, 1978—, also dir.; bd. dirs. subsidiaries Ky-W.Va. Gas Co., Ashland, Ky., Equitable Resources Energy Co., Equitable Resources Mktg. Co., Equitrans, Inc., Nora Transmission Co., Andex Energy, Inc., Fin. Corp., PNC Bank. Trustee Seton Hill Coll., Penn.'s S.W. Assn., Pitts. Cultura Trust; bd. dirs. Presbyn. Univ. Hosp.; past pres. bd. Riverview Ctr. for Jewish Srs.; pres. Pitts. Symphony Soc.; exec. com. Allegheny Conf. on County Devel. Mem. Nat. Petroleum Coun., Am. Gas Assn., Pa. Gas Assn. (past pres.), Pa. Bar Assn., Allegheny County Bar Assn., PItts. C of C., Pitts. Law Alumni Assn., Duquesne Club (past bd. dirs.), Westmoreland Country Club, Concordia Club, Rivers Club, Order of the Coif, Pi Eta Sigma, Beta Gamma Sigma. Republican. Jewish. Office: Equitable Resources Inc 420 Blvd Of The Allies Pittsburgh PA 15219-1393

MORITZ, EDWARD, historian, educator; b. Columbia, S.C., Jan. 24, 1920; s. Edward and Edith (Jumper) M.; m. Betty Gene Reid, Apr. 8, 1946; children—Stephen Edward, John Reid, Richard Douglas, Sarah Anne. B.A., Miami U., Oxford, Ohio, 1949; M.A. (Taft scholar), U. Cin., 1950; Ph.D. (Knapp scholar), U. Wis., 1953. Instr. U. Wis., Madison, 1953-55; mem. faculty Kalamazoo (Mich.) Coll., 1955—, prof. history, 1963—, chmn. dept., 1965-88, prof. emeritus, 1988—; vis. prof. Oxford, Eng., 1971-72. Author: Winston Churchill, Parliamentary Career, 1908-12. Served with USAAF, 1942-46. Kellog fellow, 1971. Mem. Am. Hist. Assn., Conf. Brit. Studies, AAUP, Phi Beta Kappa, Phi Eta Sigma. Home: 420 Edgemoor Ave Kalamazoo MI 49001-4207

MORITZ, JAMES R., financial executive; b. Balt., Nov. 18, 1945; s. Francis Xavier and Eleanor (Dougherty) M.; m. Nancy Theresa Amesse, Oct. 12, 1945; children: Kathleen Teresa, Carolyn Marie. BS in Econs., Loyola Coll., Balt., 1967; MBA in Fin., U. Pitts., 1968. With Ford Motor Co., Livonia, Mich., 1968-75; mgr. fin. planning Baxter Travenol Labs., Deerfield, Ill., 1975-78; controller Hyland div. Baxter Labs., Deerfield, 1978-80; dir. fin. control Gen. Mills, Inc., Mpls., 1980-81; v.p., controller The Talbots div. Gen. Mills, Hingham, Mass., 1981-85; v.p. fin., chief fin. officer Popular Svcs., Inc., Garfield, N.J., 1985-87; sr. v.p. fin. Medco Containment Svcs., Inc., Montvale, N.J., 1987—. Avocations: tennis, golf, skiing, reading. Office: Medco Containment Svcs 100 Summit Ave Montvale NJ 07645-1712

MORITZ, MICHAEL EVERETT, lawyer; b. Marion, Ohio, Mar. 30, 1933; s. Charles Raymond and Elisabeth Bovie (Morgan) M.; m. Lou Ann Yardley, Sept. 12, 1959; children: Ann Gibson, Jeffrey Connor, Molly Elisabeth, Catharine Morgan. BS, Ohio State U., 1958, JD summa cum laude, 1961. Bar: Ohio 1961, U.S. Tax Ct. 1970. Assoc. Dunbar, Kienzle & Murphey, Columbus, Ohio, 1961-65, ptnr., 1966-72; ptnr. Moritz, McClure, Hughes & Kerscher, Columbus, 1972-80, Baker & Hostetler, Columbus, 1980—; adj. prof. Capital U. Law Sch., Columbus, 1969-70; lectr. Ohio Legal Ctr. Inst., Columbus, 1967; bd. dirs. Cardinal Distbn., Inc., Columbus; chmn. legal div. United Appeal Franklin County, Columbus, 1964; pres. Capital City Young Rep. Club, Columbus, 1966; mem. Franklin County Rep. Exec. Com., Columbus, 1966—; mem. bd. dirs. The Ohio State U. Found., Ohio State U. Coll. Bus. Pacesetters Club; trustee Kenyon Festival Theatre, 1981-86, Players Theatre Columbus, 1986-88; commr. Ohio Elections Commn., 1993—. With USN, 1954-56. Recipient Disting. Service award Columbus Jaycees, 1966. Mem. ABA, Ohio Bar Assn., Columbus Bar Assn., Am. Judicature Soc., Ohio State U. Faculty Club, Order of Coif, Phi Gamma Delta, Beta Gamma Sigma. Clubs: Muirfield Village Golf Club, Scioto Country, Capital, Columbus, Ohio State U. President's, Wedgewood Golf & Country Club, Columbus Athletic Club, The Club at Seabrook Island. Office: Baker & Hostetler 65 E State St Columbus OH 43215-4213

MORITZ, MILTON EDWARD, security consultant; b. Reading, Pa., Sept. 5, 1931; s. Edward Raymond and Anna May M.; m. Elizabeth Ann Walls, June 6, 1952; children: Betsy Ann Moritz Koppenhaver, Stephen Edward, Sandra E. Student, U. Md., 1950-51, Fla. State U., 1959-60. Enlisted U.S. Army, 1949, chief warrant officer 3, 1968, spl. agt. M.I.; ret., 1970; safety and security dir. Harrisburg (Pa.) Hosp., 1970-72; security mgr. Sprint, Carlisle, Pa., 1972-94; prin. Moritz Assocs., Harrisburg, 1994—; lectr., instr. Harrisburg Area Community Coll.; mem. Indsl. Security Adv. Coun. Pres. Greater Harrisburg Crime Clinic, 1974. Decorated Bronze Star with oak leaf

cluster. Mem. Am. Soc. Indsl. Security (past pres., chmn. bd. dirs.), Assn. Former Intelligence Officers, Internat. Narcotic Enforcement Officers Assn., Pa. Crime Prevention Assn. (bd. dirs.). Republican. Lutheran. Home and Office: 7723 Avondale Terr Harrisburg PA 17112-3805

MORIYAMA, RAYMOND, architect; b. Vancouver, B.C., Can., Oct. 11, 1929; s. John and Nobuko (Sejima) M.; m. Sachiko Miyauchi, Sept. 17, 1954; children: Mark-Michi, Murina-Lei, Selena-Midori, Jason-Jun, Adrian-Keiju. B.Arch., U. Toronto, 1954; M.Arch., McGill U., 1957; LL.D. (hon.), York U., 1973, Brock U., 1973, Trent U., 1981; D.Eng. (hon.), Tech. U. N.S., 1980; fellow, Ryerson Poly. Coll., 1980; LLD (hon.), U. Sask., Can., 1987; DSc (hon.), McGill U., 1993; LLD (hon.), U. Toronto, 1994. Practice architecture, 1958—; propr. Raymond Moriyama (Architects and Planners), Toronto, 1958-79; partner Moriyama & Teshima Architects, Toronto, 1979—; design tutor U. Toronto; mem. council Ont. Coll. Art; pres. Group One Ltd.; dir. Multilingual TV Ltd.; chmn. Ecol. Research Ltd. Prin. works include Can. Embassy, Tokyo, Ont. Sci. Centre, Toronto, Met. Toronto Library, Scarborough Civic Centre, Meewasin Valley 100 Yr. Conceptual Plan, Sask., South Beach Urban Design, Miami Beach, St. Charles Place, New Orleans, Science North, Sudbury, Sci. Ctr. study, Amsterdam, The Netherlands, Ont.'s Niagara Pks.: Planning the Second 100 Yrs., Bank of Montreal, Waterfront Ctr. (top honors). Decorated officer Order of Can., Order of Ont.; recipient Massey medal for architecture, 1961, 76, Scarborough Citizens award, 1974, Gov. Gen.'s medal for archiecture, 1982, 90, 91, civic award City of Toronto, 1980, CSLA Regional honours, 1989, citation, 1989, nat. award 1989, Progressive Architecture award, 1990, Toronto Lifetime Achievement Arts award, 1990, Gov. Gen.'s award, 1991, Waterfront Top honor, Wash., 1991, Archtl. Conservation award of excellence, Ottawa, 1991, Excellence award and highest recognition Scarborough Urban Design, 1993, North York design award, 1993, Ont. Energy Efficiency award of excellence, 1993, award Agnes Etherington Art Ctr. Design Competition, 1994, Seneca Coll. at York U. Design Competition, 1994. Fellow Royal Archtl. Inst. Can., Royal Soc. Arts (Eng.); mem. Can. Inst. Archs. (award of excellence for Centennial Bapt. Ch. 1968, for Meewasin Valley project plan 1979), Royal Can. Inst. (councillor), Ont. Assn. Archs. (25 Yr. award of excellence 1991, 95-96, Archtl. Excellence award 1995-96). Office: 32 Davenport Rd, Toronto, ON Canada M5R 1H3

MORKOÇ, HADIS, electrical engineer, educator; b. Senkaya, Erzurum, Turkey, Oct. 2, 1947; came to U.S., 1971; s. Mustafa and Saadet (Metin) M.; m. Amy C. Ahlberg, Sept. 5, 1975; 1 child, Erol Taner. MS, Tech. U., Istanbul, 1969; PhD, Cornell U., 1975. Postdoctoral fellow Cornell U., Ithaca, N.Y., 1975-76; mem. tech. staff Varian Assocs., Palo Alto, Calif., 1976-78; prof. elec. engring. U. Ill., Urbana, 1978—; disting. vis. scientist Calif. Inst. Tech., Pasadena, 1987-88; bd. advisers Kopin Corp., Tounton, Mass., 1985—; cons. Motorola, IBM, AT&T, others. Author: Principles and Technology of Modfets, 1991; contbr. chpts. to 2 books, 700 articles to profl. jours. Fellow IEEE, AAAS, Am. Phys. Soc.; mem. Math. Rsch. Soc., Optical Soc. Am., Sigma Xi, Eta Kappa Nu. Achievements include invention of fastest transistor in world. Home: 1803 Golfview Dr Urbana IL 61801 Office: Univ IOll 104 S Goodwin St Urbana IL 61801

MORLAND, JOHN KENNETH, sociology and anthropology educator; b. Huntsville, Ala., July 4, 1916; s. Howard Cannon and Ethel Mae (Cowan) M.; m. Margaret Louise Ward, Feb. 26, 1949; children: Carol, Katherine, Evelyn. B.S., Birmingham So. Coll., 1938; B.D., Yale U., 1943; Ph.D., U. N.C., 1950. Instr. Yale in China Middle Sch., Changsha, Hunan, 1943-46; exec. sec. Yale in China Assn., New Haven, 1946-47; asst. prof. Coll. William and Mary, Williamsburg, Pa., 1949-53; Charles A. Dana prof., chmn. dept. sociology and anthropology Randolph Macon Woman's Coll., Lynchburg, Va., 1953-87; rsch. analyst City of Lynchburg, 1989-94; cons. U.S. Dept. Edn., Dept. Commerce, NEH, So. Regional Council NSF. Author: Social Problems in the United States, 1975, Millways of Kent, 1958, (with John Williams) Race, Color and the Young Child, 1976, (with Jack Balswick) Social Problems: A Christian Understanding and Response, 1990; contbr., editor: The Not So Solid South, 1971. Pres. bd. nat. ministries Am. Bapt. Chs., USA, 1973-79. Named Eminent Laureate of Va., 1981; recipient Disting. Alumnus award Birmingham-So. Coll., 1985, Nat. Conf. Christians and Jews Humanitarian award, 1994; Fulbright scholar Chinese U., Hong Kong, 1966-67; grantee NSF, Taiwan, 1975, U.S. Dept. Edn., 1972. Fellow Am. Anthropol. Assn.; mem. Am. Sociol. Assn., So. Sociol. Soc., Va. Social Sci. Assn. (pres. 1963), AAUP (pres. 1962). Home: 1619 Dogwood Ln Lynchburg VA 24503-1923 Office: Randolph Macon Womans Coll PO Box 477 Lynchburg VA 24503

MORLAND, RICHARD BOYD, retired educator; b. Huntsville, Ala., June 27, 1919; s. Howard Cannon and Ethel May (Cowan) M.; A.B., Birmingham-So. Coll., 1940; M.Ed., Springfield Coll., 1947; Ph.D. (So. Fellowships Fund fellow 1957-58), N.Y. U. 1958; m. Jessie May Parrish, Mar. 17, 1949; 1 child, Laura. Phys. dir. YMCA, Frankfort, Ky., 1940-41; dir. athletics, head basketball coach Fla. So. Coll., 1947-50; lectr. in edn. N.Y. U., 1950-51; chmn. dept. phy. edn., Stetson U., Deland, Fla., 1952-60, head basketball coach, 1952-57, assoc. prof., 1958-63, prof. philosophy of edn. 1963-89, J. Ollie Edmunds prof., 1982-85, sr. active prof., 1989-90, chmn. grad. coun., 1962-69, chmn. dept. edn., 1969-75. Contbr. articles to profl. jours. Lt. USNR, 1941-45. Decorated 11 battle stars, USS Lexington. Named to Stetson U. Sports Hall of Fame; recipient McEniry award for Excellence in teaching, 1983; Richard B. Morland Distinguished Alumni award named in his honor; Bronze bust by Harry Messersmith dedicated, 1992. Mem. Philosophy of Edn. Soc. (pres. region 1963-64), Fla. Coun. Deans and Dirs. Tchr. Edn. (pres. 1974-75), Am. Ednl. Rsch. Assn., Am. Edn. Studies Assn., Soc. Profs. Edn., Fla. Founds. Edn. and Policy Studies Soc. (exec. bd. 1987-90), Univ. Profs. for Acad. Order, DeLand Country Club, Omicron Delta Kappa, Phi Alpha Theta, Kappa Delta Pi, Phi Delta Kappa (pres. region 1977-78, editorial bd. Phi Delta Kappan 1978-83, named Regional Educator of Yr. 1991), panel gallup poll on edn., 1995, Kappa Alpha. Democrat. Methodist. Home: 524 N Mcdonald Ave Deland FL 32724-3643

MORLEY, GEORGE WILLIAM, gynecologist; b. Toledo, June 6, 1923; s. Francis Wayland and Florence (Sneider) M.; m. Constance J. Morley, July 27, 1946 (dec. 1960); children: Beverly, Kathryn, George W. Jr.; m. Marcheta F. Morley, June 14, 1963. BS, U. Mich, 1944, MD, 1949, MS, 1955; cert. in Gynecologic Oncology. Am. Bd. Ob-Gyn, 1974. Diplomate, Am. Bd. Ob-Gyn. Intern U. Mich. Hosp., 1949-50, asst. resident, 1950-51, resident, 1951-52, jr. clin. instr., 1952-53, sr. clin. instr., 1953-54; mem. faculty Sch. Medicine U. Mich., Ann Arbor, 1963-93, dir. gynecology svc., 1973-85, dir. gynecologic oncology svc., 1986, Norman F. Miller prof. dept. ob.-gyn., 1987—, assoc. chmn., 1987-91; Chmn. Mich. Jud. Commn., Lansing, 1987-88. Contbr. to med. publs. Fellow, ACS (bd. govs. 1986-91), Am. Coll. Ob.-Gyn. (pres. 1987); mem. Rotary. Republican. Presbyterian. Avocations: golf, music. Home: 1120 Chestnut St Ann Arbor MI 48104-2826 Office: U Mich Med Ctr 1500 E Medical Center Dr Ann Arbor MI 48109-0718

MORLEY, HARRY THOMAS, JR., real estate executive; b. St. Louis, Aug. 13, 1930; s. Harry Thomas and Celeste Elizabeth (Davies) M.; m. Nelda Lee Mulholland, Sept. 3, 1960; children: Lisa, Mark, Marci. BA, U. Mo., 1955; MA, U. Denver, 1959. Dir. men's student activities Iowa State Tchrs. Coll., 1955-57; dir. student housing U. Denver, 1957-60; pvt. practice psychol. consulting St. Louis, 1960-63; dir. admintrn. County of St. Louis, Mo., 1963-70; regional dir. HUD, Kansas City, Mo., 1970-71; asst. sec. adminstrn. HUD, 1971-73; pres. St. Louis Regional Commerce and Growth Assn., 1973-78, Taylor, Morley, Inc., St. Louis, 1978—; teaching cons.-lectr. Washington U., St. Louis, 1962-70. Bd. dirs., mem. exec. com. St. Louis Coll. Pharmacy; past chmn. Better Bus. Bur.; chmn. Mo. Indsl. Devel. Bd., Mo. State Hwy. Commn.; dir. St. Luke's Hosps., St. Johns Hosp., Downtown St. Louis, Inc., Laclede's Landing Redevel. Corp. Served with USN, 1951-53. Mem. Am. C of C. Execs., Nat. Assn. Homebuilders, St. Louis Homebuilders Assn. (pres.), St. Louis Advt. Club, Mo. Athletic Club, St. Louis Club, Noonday Club, Castle Oak Country Club, Round Table Club, Sunset Country Club. Republican. Methodist. Home: 14238 Forest Crest Dr Chesterfield MO 63017-2818 Office: 1224 Fern Ridge Pky Saint Louis MO 63141-4451

MORLEY, JOHN C., electronic equipment company executive; b. 1931. BA, Yale U., 1954; MBA, U. Mich., 1958. Mng. dir. Esso Pappas Chem. Ae., Greece, 1969-70; pres. Esso Eastern Chems. Inc., N.Y., 1970-71; exec. v.p. Enjay Chem. Co., 1971-74; pres. Exxon Chem. Co. U.S.A., Houston, 1974-78; sr. v.p., 1978-80; pres., chief exec. officer Reliance Electric Co. Inc., Cleve., 1980-94; vice chmn. Gen. Signal Corp., Stamford, Conn., 1994—; also bd. dirs. Reliance Electric Co. Inc., Cleve. Served to lt. (j.g.) USNR, 1954-56. Office: Gen Signal Corp PO Box 10010 High Ridge Park Stamford CT 06904

MORLEY, LAWRENCE WHITAKER, geophysicist, remote sensing consultant; b. Toronto, Feb. 19, 1920; s. George Whitaker and Mary Olive (Boyd) M.; divorced; children; Lawrence, Patricia, Chris, David; m. Beverly Anne Beckworth; step-children: Sandra Wellman, Stephen Burdett, Richard Burdett. BA, U. Toronto, 1946, MA, 1949, PhD, 1952; DSc (hon.), York U., Toronto, 1974. Dir. geophysics div. Geol. Survey Can., Ottawa, 1952-71; dir. gen. Can. Centre for Remote Sensing, Ottawa, 1971-80; exec. dir. Inst. for Space and Terrestrial Sci., Toronto, 1987-91; pres. Teledetection Internat., 1991—. Lt. Can. Navy, 1941-45. Fellow Royal Soc. Can.; mem. Can. Soc. Remote Sensing (founding pres. 1971-74), Am. Geophys. Union, Am. Soc. Phototogrammetry and Remote Sensing, Soc. Exploration Geophysicists, Can. Geophys. Union, Can. Geomatics Inst. Home and Office: 767 2d Ave W, Owen Sound, ON Canada N4K 4M2

MORLEY, LLOYD ALBERT, mining engineering educator; b. Provo, Utah, Oct. 28, 1940; s. John Jr. and Dorothea (Nielsen) M.; m. Jo Ann Bryant, Feb. 22, 1975; 1 child, Paul Loring. BS in Mining Engring., U. Utah, 1968, PhD in Mining Engring., 1972. Teaching asst., rsch. assoc. U. Utah, Salt Lake City, 1968-71; asst. prof. mining engring. Pa. State U., University Park, 1971-75, assoc. prof., 1975-80, prof., 1980-85; prof., head dept. mineral engring. U. Ala., Tuscaloosa, 1985-93, endowed chair mining engring., 1993—; cons. Jim Walter Resources, Inc., Brookwood, Ala., 1987—, Pitts. and Midway Coal Mining Co., Englewood, Colo., 1990—, Drummond Co., Inc., Birmingham, Ala., 1991—; engr. in tng., Utah. Author: Mine Power Systems, 1990; contbr. articles to profl. jours. Staff sgt. USNG, 1958-66. Recipient Wilson Outstanding Teaching award Pa. State U., 1980; Outstanding Rsch. Report awards U.S. Bur. Mines, 1983-84, grantee, 1991-87. Fellow IEEE (bd. dirs. 1991-92, 94, v.p. pubs. 1994); mem. Industry Applications Soc. IEEE (Mining Best Paper awards 1985, 88, 90, pres. 1988, Disting. lectr. 1991—), Soc. for Mining, Metallurgy and Exploration AIME, Soc. Petroleum Engrs., Masons. Republican. Episcopalian. Avocations: high-fidelity systems, classic sports cars, rose growing, music. Office: U Ala Dept Mineral Engring PO Box 870207 Tuscaloosa AL 35487-0207

MORLEY, MALCOLM A., artist; b. London, 1931. Student, Royal Coll. Art, London, 1954-57. Tchr. Royal Coll. Art, London, from 1956; mem. faculty Ohio State U., Columbus, 1965-66, Sch. Visual Arts, N.Y.C., 1967-69, SUNY, Stony Brook, 1972; Asso. Royal Coll. Art. London. Exhibited in one-man shows Kornblee Gallery, N.Y.C., 1964, 67, 69, Xavier Fourcade, N.Y.C., 1986, Temerance Hall Gallery, Bellport, N.Y., 1988, Pace Gallery, N.Y.C., 1988, 89, Anthony D'Offay Gallery, London, 1990, Pace Gallery, N.Y.C., 1991; group shows include Bienal de Sao Paulo, Brazil, 1957-67, Guggenheim Museum, N.Y.C., 1966, Am. Fedn. Arts, N.Y.C., 1968, Milw. Art Center, 1969, Whitney Mus. Am. Art, 1970, 72, Kunst des 20 Jahrhunderts, Stadtische, Kunsthalle, Dusseldorf, 1970, Documenta V, Kassel, Germany, 1972, Projekt 74, Cologne, Germany, 1974, Xavier Fourcade, N.Y.C., 1982, 83/84, 86, Akron Art Mus. (Ohio), 1982, Tate Gallery, London, 1983, 84, Mus. Modern Art, N.Y.C., 1984, 88, Museo Rufino Tamayo, Mexico City, 1984, Fabian Carlsson Gallery, London, 1985, Pace Prints, N.Y.C., 1986, Mus. Contemporary Art, L.A., 1989; touring retrospective show Basel Kunsthalle, 1983, Rotterdam Mus., 1983, White Chapel, London, 1983, Corcoran Mus. Art, Washington, 1983, Mus. Contemporary Art, Chgo., 1983-84, Bklyn. Mus., 1984, Bonnefanten Mus. Maastricht, 1991, Kunshalle Basel, 1991, Mus. de Marseille, 1991, The Tate Gallery, Liverpool, 1992, Parish Art Mus., Southampton, N.Y., 1992; represented in numerous pub. collections. First recipient Turner prize, London, 1984.

MORLEY, MICHAEL, pubic relations executive. Dir. Harris & Hunter Pub., 1960-67; mng. dir. Daniel J. Edelman/London, 1967-73; chmn. Daniel J. Edelman/Europe, 1973-80; pres. Edelman Internat. Corp., 1980-88; dep. chmn. Edelman PR Worldwide, 1988—. Office: Edelman PR Worldwide 1500 Broadway New York NY 10036*

MORLEY, MICHAEL B., public relations executive; b. Madras, India, Nov. 18, 1935; s. Gordon and Violet M.; m. Ingrid Hellman, Aug. 20, 1957; children: Andrew, Helen, Ann. Attended, Eastbourne Coll. Dir. Harris & Hunter Pub. Rels., 1960-67; mng. dir. Daniel J. Edelman, 1967; pres. Edelman Internat., 1970; dep. chmn. Edelman Worldwide, 1992—; pres. Edelman N.Y., 1994—. Comms. Advt. and Mktg. Edn. Found. fellow, 1981; decorated Knight of First Class, Order of Lion, Rep. Finland, 1978. Mem. Internat. Pub. Rels. Assn., Internat. Pub. Rels., Brit. C. of C., Japan Soc., Bus. Coun. Internat. Understanding, Inc., Korea Soc. Home: 1 Devon Pl Cresskill NJ 07626 Office: Edelman Pub Rels Worldwide 1500 Broadway New York NY 10036-4015

MORLEY, RICHARD E., manufacturing engineer. Recipient SME Albert M. Sargent Progrss award Soc.of Mfg. Engr., 1994. Office: Flavors Technology Inc 3 Northern Blvd # 1C Amherst NH 03031-2329*

MORLOCK, CARL GRISMORE, physician, medical educator; b. Crediton, Ont., Can., Sept. 11, 1906; came to U.S., 1934, naturalized, 1939; s. Charles Edward and Emma (Grismore) M.; m. Katherine Ruth Mercer, Sept. 18, 1937; children: Anne Louise, William Edward. B.A., U. Western Ont., 1929, M.D., 1932; fellow internal medicine, Mayo Found., Grad. Sch. U. Minn., 1934-37; M.S. in Medicine, U. Minn., 1937. Intern Victoria Hosp., London, Ont., 1932-33; resident Victoria Hosp., 1933-34; practice medicine specializing in internal medicine and gastroenterology Rochester, Minn., 1934—; assoc.prof. internal medicine Mayo Found., 1949-62, prof. clin. medicine, 1962-72; prof. medicine Mayo Med. Sch., 1972—. Contbr. articles on gastrointestinal subjects to med. jours. Fellow ACP; mem. Am., Minn. med. assns., Osler Med. Soc., Am. Gastroent. Assn., Gideons Internat. Sigma Xi, Alpha Omega Alpha. Baptist. Home: Apt 1303 211 NW 2nd St Rochester MN 55901 Office: Mayo Clinic 200 1st St SW Rochester MN 55905-0001

MORLOK, EDWARD KARL, engineering educator, consultant; b. Phila., Nov. 3, 1940; s. Edward Karl and Anna Marie (Kurtz) M.; m. Ottilia Angela Husz, Dec. 14, 1968 (div. July 1983); 1 child, Jessica Angela; m. Patricia Campbell Conboy, Mar. 23, 1991. BE, Yale U., 1962; PhD, Northwestern U., 1967; MA (hon.), U. Pa., 1973. Civil engr. transp. U.S. Dept. Commerce, Washington, 1966-67; from asst. prof. civil engring. to assoc. prof. Northwestern U., Evanston, Ill., 1967-73, asst. dir. rsch., transp. ctr., 1969-73; 1907 Found. assoc. prof. U. Pa., Phila., 1973-75, chmn., transp. grad. group, 1983-86, 91—, UPS found. prof. transp., 1975—, chair systems grad. program, 1988-91; cons. nat. transp. policy study commn., Washington, 1978-79. Author: Analysis Transportation Technology and Network Structure, 1969, Introduction to Transportation Engineering and Planning, 1978; assoc. editor Transp. Rsch. Jour., 1975—; consulting editor series in transp. for McGraw-Hill Publ. Co., 1980—; contbr. more than 60 articles to profl. jours. Mem. Nat. Assembly Engring. panel on innovation in transp., Washington, 1979-80, panel on hazardous material transp., Washington, 1980-81. Recipient U.S. Sr. Scientist award Alexander von Humboldt Found., 1980-81; rsch. grantee Commonwealth of Pa., Consol. Rail Corp., U.S. Dept. Transp., NASA, NSF. Mem. Ops. Rsch. Soc. Am., Transp. Rsch. Forum (v.p. 1974-75, pres. 1975-76, bd. dirs. disting. mems. 1983—), Transp. Rsch. Bd. (rev. com. of coun. of univ. transp. ctrs. 1985-88, coun. mem. 1988-90, chair freight transp. planning and mktg. com. 1994—). Lutheran. Office: U Pa Dept Systems Engring 220 S 33d St Philadelphia PA 19104

MORNING, JOHN, graphic designer; b. Cleve., Jan. 8, 1932; s. John Frew and Juanita Kathryn (Brannan) M.; m. Carole Ann Coleman, Jan. 24, 1964 (div. July 1984); children: Ann Juanita, John Floyd. BFA, Pratt Inst., 1955. Art dir. McCann-Erickson, Inc., N.Y.C., 1958-60; pvt. practice design N.Y.C., 1960—; bd. dirs. Dime Savings Bank N.Y. Bd. dirs. Repertory Theater Lincoln Ctr., 1970-73, N.Y. Landmarks Conservancy, Charles E.

Culpepper Found., 1990—, Henry St. Settlement, chmn., 1979-86, Bklyn. Acad. Music, 1993, Lincoln Ctr. Inst., 1993; trustee Wilberforce U., com. on edn. Mus. Modern Art; chmn. bd. trustees Pratt Inst., Bklyn., 1988-92; bd. dirs. Mus. for African Art, N.Y.C., co-chair, 1991-94; vice chmn. N.Y.C. Cultural Affairs Adv. Commn., 1994—. With U.S. Army, 1956-58. Recipient Alumni medal Pratt Inst., 1972, Presdl. Recognition award Pres. of U.S., 1984, Lillian D. Wald Humanitarian award, 1992. Mem. Am. Inst. Graphic Arts, Am. Acad. Dramatic Arts (trustee 1988-95), Assn. Governing Bds. Colls. and Univs. (bd. dirs.). Republican.

MOROSANI, JOHN WARRINGTON, brokerage house executive; b. N.Y.C., Mar. 19, 1953; s. Remy Edmund and C. Virginia (Warrington) M.; m. Joan Clark Devine, Nov. 8, 1980; children: Daniel H.C., Allegra. AB, Middlebury Coll., 1974; MBA, Amos Tuck Sch., Dartmouth Coll., 1979. Area sales mgr. Cessna Aircraft Co., Wichita, Kans., 1976-77; account exec. Smith Barney, N.Y.C., 1977-81; instl. sales CJ. Lawrence, N.Y.C., 1981-87; instl. sales S.G. Warburg & Co., N.Y.C., 1987-88, brokerage mgmt., 1988—. Mem. Racquet and Tennis Club. Republican. Episcopalian. Office: S G Warburg & Co Inc Equitable Tower 26th Fl 787 7th Ave New York NY 10019-6018

MOROSKY, ROBERT HARRY, private investor, operator; b. Erie, Pa., Apr. 24, 1941; m. Dianne Dombrowski, Sept. 21, 1963; children: Elaina, Rebecca, Michael. Student, Pa. State U., 1959-60; B.S., Gannon Coll., 1963; M.B.A. with honors, U. Cin., 1964; postgrad., Case Western Res. U., 1964-65; LLD (hon.), Gannon U. C.P.A. Carter Andersen & Co., Cleve. and Columbus, Ohio, 1964-72; vice chmn. Limited Inc., 1972-87; pres. Allied Store/ Federated Dept. Stores, N.Y.C., 1987-88, also bd. dirs.; bd. dirs., chmn. Safelite Glass Corp., Columbus, Drug Emporium; ltd. ptnr. Forstmann-Little. Chmn. Cath. Found. of Columbus; chmn., founder Nat. Soc. Cath. Founds.; active Nat. Cath. Stewardship Coun. Recipient Gannon U. Disting. Alumnae award; decorated Knight of Malta, Knight of St. Gregory the Great, Knight of Holy Sepulchre. Mem. Internat. Game Fishing Assn. Clubs: Athletic of Columbus; Ocean Reef; Bimini Big Game; Cat Cay; Treasure Cay, Murfield Village Golf.

MOROWITZ, HAROLD JOSEPH, biophysicist, educator; b. Poughkeepsie, N.Y., Dec. 4, 1927; s. Philip Frand and Anna (Levine) M.; m. Lucille Rita Stein, Jan. 30, 1949; children: Joanna Lynn, Eli David, Joshua Alan, Zachary Adam, Noah Daniel. B.S., Yale U., 1947, M.S., 1950, Ph.D., 1951. Physicist Nat. Bur. Standards, 1951-53, Nat. Heart Inst., Bethesda, Md., 1953-55; mem. faculty Yale, 1955—, assoc. prof. biophysics, 1960-68, prof. molecular biophysics and biochemistry 1968-88, master Pierson Coll., 1981-86; faculty George Mason U., Fairfax, Va., 1988—, Robinson prof. biology and natural philosophy, 1988—; dir. Krasnow Inst. for Advanced Study, 1993—; chmn. com. on models for biomed. rsch. NRC, 1983-85, mem. bd. on basic biology, 1986-92. Author: Life and the Physical Sciences, 1964, (with Waterman) Theoretical and Mathematical Biology, 1965, Energy Flow in Biology, 1968, Entropy for Biologists, 1970, (with Lucille Morowitz) Life On The Planet Earth, 1974, Ego Niches, 1977, Foundations of Bioenergetics, 1978, The Wine of Life, 1979, Mayonnaise and the Origin of Life, 1985, Cosmic Joy and Local Pain, 1987, The Thermodynamics of Pizza, 1991, Beginnings of Cellular Life, 1992, (with James Trefil) The Facts of Life, 1992, Entropy and the Magic Flute, 1993; editor Complexity, 1994—; contbr. articles to profl. jours. Mem. sci. adv. bd. Santa Fe Inst., 1984—. Mem. Biophys. Soc. (mem. exec. com. 1965), Nat. Ctr. for Rsch. Resources (mem. coun. 1987-92). Office: George Mason Univ 207 E Bldg Fairfax VA 22030

MORPHESIS, JAMES GEORGE, artist; b. Phila., Aug. 26, 1948; s. George Spiros and Bettie (Sarikianos) M.; m. Melody Ann Poltroneri, May 26, 1988. BFA, Temple U., 1970; MFA, Calif. Inst. Arts., Valencia, 1972. Instr. Otis/Parsons Inst., Los Angeles, 1977-83, Immaculate Heart Coll., Los Angeles, 1974-76, Los Angeles City Coll., Los Angeles, 1974-80; dept. chmn. Calif. Bapt. Coll., Riverside, 1977-78; instr. Los Angeles Pierce Coll., Woodland Hills, Calif., 1978-79, 82, Calif. State U. Northridge, Calif., 1979-80; freelance artist, 1983—; art dir. Master Graphics, Inc., Phila., 1966-68. One man shows include Los Angeles County Mus. Art, 1987, Tortue Gallery, Santa Monica, Calif, 1987, Marianne Deson Gallery, Chgo., 1987, Freidus/ Ordover Gallery, N.Y.C., 1983; exhibited in group shows at Abstract Expressionism and After, San Francisco Mus. Modern Art, 1987, Security Pacific Nat. Bank's Gallery at the Plaza, 1985, Emanuel Walker/Atholl McBean Galleries, San Francisco Art Inst., 1985, L.A: County Mus. Art, 1987. Recipient Biennial grant Louis Comfort Tiffany Found., N.Y.C., 1986, Young Talent Purchase award Los Angeles County Mus. Art, 1983, Calif. Small Images Exhibition award Calif. State U., 1971, Nathan Margolis Meml. Painting award, Temple U., Phila., 1970. Mem. Coll. Art Assn. Am. Democrat. Greek Orthodox. Home: 118 S Hobart Blvd Los Angeles CA 90004-5206

MORPHY, JOHN, manufacturing company executive; b. Rochester, N.Y., Aug. 14, 1947; s. John and Mary (Kelleher) M.; m. Marcia Price, June 5, 1971; children: Jaime, Matthew. BS in Acctg., Le Moyne Coll., Syracuse, N.Y., 1969, CPA, N.Y. Mgr. Arthur Andersen & Co., Rochester, 1969-76; v.p., controller Computer Consoles Inc., Rochester, 1976-85; v.p., chief fin. officer Goulds Pumps Inc., Seneca Falls, N.Y., 1985; group vice pres. Goulds Pump Inc., 1992—. Office: Goulds Pumps Inc 240 Fall St Seneca Falls NY 13148-1590

MORR, CHARLES VERNON, food science educator; b. Ashland, Ohio, Oct. 7, 1927; s. Perry Allen and Helen Lucile (Hoag) M.; m. Dorothy Dela Bowers, Sept. 8, 1951; children: Douglas Charles, Debra Jean. BS, Ohio State U., 1952, MS, 1955, PhD in Dairy Tech., 1959. Rsch. assoc. Carnation Rsch. Lab., Calif., 1959-61; asst. prof. Ohio State U., Columbus, 1961-64; prof. U. Minn., St. Paul, 1964-73; rsch. dir. Ralston Purina Co., 1973-76; prof., chmn. dept. Tex. Tech U., Lubbock, 1976-78; Stender prof. food sci. Clemson U., S.C., 1978—. Contbr. chpts. to books, articles to profl. jours. Served with USN, 1945-47. Recipient Dairy Rsch. Found. award Am. Dairy Sci. Assn., 1973, Advancement Application Agrl. & Food Chemistry award ACS, 1993. Fellow Inst. Food Technologists; mem. Am. Dairy Sci. Assn. (bd. dirs. 1981-84), Am. Chem. Soc. (coordinator agr. food chemistry div. S.E. sect. 1984—), Am. Oil Chemists Soc. Republican. Lutheran. Home: 390 Ridgecrest Dr Clemson SC 29631-1849 Office: Clemson U Dept Food Sci Clemson SC 29631*

MORRA, BERNADETTE, newspaper editor, journalist; b. Toronto, Ont., Can., Jan. 22, 1961; d. John Anthony and Josephine Lucia (Slobodzian) Morra; m. James Molloy, June 20, 1993. BA, U. Toronto, 1983. Fashion writer Toronto Star, 1988-94, fashion editor, 1994—; pub. speaker fashion various TV and radio shows, Toronto chpt. Fashion Group Internat., 1988—; judge various student and profl. design competitions. Contbr. articles to profl. jours. Recipient Merit award Art Dirs. Club Toronto, 1990. Mem. Southern Ont. Newspaper Guild. Office: Toronto Star Newspapers Ltd, 1 Yonge St, Toronto, ON Canada M5E 1E6

MORRAL, FRANK ROLF, English educator, psychologist; b. Vanersborg, Sweden, Apr. 7, 1937; came to U.S., 1937; s. Facundo Rolf and Lillie (Westberg) M.; m. Linda Jane Backus, Oct. 7, 1961; children: Andrew, Tobit, Holly, Elena, Asa. BA, Whitman Coll., 1959; MA, Columbia U. 1960, PhD, 1965; MA, Coll. of St. Thomas, 1980. Lic. psychologist, Minn. Instr. Whitman Coll., Walla Walla, Wash., 1962-64; instr. Carleton Coll., Northfield, Minn., 1964-65, asst. prof. English, 1965-71, assoc. prof. English, 1976—; part-time therapist Ctr. for Human Resources, Northfield, 1982—. Home: 28 Fareway Dr Northfield MN 55057-2611 Office: Carleton Coll Dept Of English Northfield MN 55057

MORREL, WILLIAM GRIFFIN, JR., banker; b. Lynchburg, Va., Aug 25, 1933; s. William Griffin and Virginia Louise (Baldwin) M.; m. Sandra Virginia Coats, Jan. 31, 1959; children: William Griffin, John Coats, Elisabeth White, Jane Coleman. BS, Yale U., 1955; postgrad. Rutgers U., 1965-67. With Md. Nat. Bank, Balt., 1955-84, asstl. v.p., 1959, v.p., 1964, sr. v.p., 1975-84, mgmt. com. 1979-84, chmn. three lending coms., others; pres., bd. dirs. Md. Nat. Overseas Investment Corp.; chmn. bd. London Interstate Bank Ltd.; chmn. bd. dirs. Md. Internat. Bank; sr. v.p., chief operating officer Abu Dhabi Internat. Bank, Inc., 1984-86, pres., chief exec. officer Heritage Internat. Bank, 1986-89; dir., pres., CEO Madison Fin. Group,

1989—; chief exec. officer, chmn. The Valley Fin. Group, Balt., 1989—; pres., chief exec. officer Summit Bancorp, Balt., 1990-92; consul of the Netherlands at Balt., 1978-84. Mem. Balt. Consular Corps, 1978-84; chmn. Md. World Trade Efforts Commn., 1983-84; mem. Md. Trade Policy Council, 1985-88; vice chmn. Dist. Export Council, 1983—. Contbr. articles to profl. jours. Sr. fellow Ctr. for Internat. Banking Studies, Darden Grad. Bus. Sch. U. Va., 1978-91. Served with U.S. Army, 1956-58. Mem. Bankers Assn. for Fgn. Trade (bd. dirs. 1975-78), Robert Morris Assocs. (nat. bd. dirs. 1984-88), Internat. Lending Council (bd. dirs., chmn., 1978-80), Md. Hist. Soc. (trustee), Balt. Council Fgn. Relations (trustee), Econ. Devel. Council. Republican. Presbyterian. Clubs: Yale, Farmington Country, Elkridge, Md. Club. Home: 6 Beechdale Rd Baltimore MD 21210 Office: The Madison Fin Group Inc PO Box 16265 Baltimore MD 21210

MORRELL, ARTHUR ANTHONY, lawyer, state legislator; b. New Orleans, Mar. 22, 1943; s. Reynard and Mildred (Gray) M.; m. Cynthia Hedge; children: Todd, Matthew, Jean-Paul, Nicholas. BA, So. U., 1970, JD, 1978. Bar: La. 1978, all state and fed. cts. In-flight exec. Ea. Airlines, Chgo., 1969-70, ticket agt., 1970-73, passenger svc. agt., 1973-74; fed. voters examiner Civil Svcs. Dept., New Orleans, 1975-78; pres., owner ACTMP Enterprises, New Orleans, 1978-85; pvt. practice New Orleans, 1978—; owner, breeder, trainer La. Horsemen, New Orleans, 1985—; state rep. La. Ho. of Reps., New Orleans, 1984—. Mem. Very Spl. Arts; bd. dirs Total Cmty. Action. With Spl. Forces, U.S. Army, 1963-66. Mem. ABA, La. Trial Lawyers Assn., Assn. for Effective Govt., Am. Legion (Post 395), Delta Theta Pi. Democrat. Roman Catholic. Office: Ste 107-108 3200 St Bernard Ave New Orleans LA 70119-1922

MORRELL, GENE PAUL, liquid terminal company executive; b. Ardmore, Okla., Oct. 4, 1932; s. Paul T. and Etta L. (Weaver) M.; m. Jan A. Foster, Aug. 20, 1954; children: Jeffrey T., Kelly Ann, Rob Redman. BS in Geology, U. Okla., 1954, LLB, 1962. Bar: Okla. 1962, D.C. 1973. Geologist Gilmer Oil Co., Ardmore, Okla., 1957-59, atty.-geologist, 1962-63; sole practice, Ardmore, 1963-69; ofcl. Dept. Interior, Washington, 1969-72; v.p. Lone Star Gas Co., Washington, 1972-76; sr. v.p. United Energy Resources, Inc., Houston, 1976-86; vice chmn. Petro United Terminals, Inc., Houston, 1986—. Contbr. articles to profl. jours. Commr. City of Ardmore, 1967-69, vice-mayor, 1968. Mem. ABA, Okla. Bar Assn., D.C. Bar Assn., Am. Assn. Petroleum Geologists, Coun. Fgn. Rels., Phi Alpha Delta, Sigma Alpha Epsilon. Episcopalian. Clubs: City Tavern (Washington), Ramada-Tejas, Houston Artillery, Galveston Country, The Yacht Club (Galveston).

MORRELL, JAMES WILSON, consulting company executive; b. Kalamazoo, Feb. 13, 1931; s. Wilson and Evelyn Jewel (Anderson) M.; m. Marylyn J. Eck, June 21, 1952; children—Martha Jo Morrell-Trinkaus, David James. BA, Kalamazoo Coll., 1953. Foodservice mgr. for Kalamazoo Coll. Saga Corp., Kalamazoo, 1955-57, dist. mgr. edn. div., 1958-61; regional v.p. edn. div. Saga Corp., Kalamazoo, Mich., 1962-66, v.p. adminstrn., 1966-68, exec. v.p. adminstrn., 1968-70; pres. SCOPE, 1970-71; pres. Saga Enterprise, 1972-78, exec. v.p., chief oper. officer, 1978-82, exec. v.p., mem. Office of Pres., 1983-85, vice chmn., 1985-86; owner J.W. Morrell & Assocs., Atherton, Calif., 1986—; pres., CEO Telesensory Corp., Mountain View, Calif., 1988—; bd. dirs. Muffins-Muffins, Telesensory Corp., Schwab Trust Co., Fabri-Kal Corp, Foster Farms Corp. Chmn. Resource Ctr. for Women, Palo Alto, Calif., 1976-77, March of Dimes, San Mateo County, Calif., 1983-85; co-chmn. modernization project Stanford U. Hosp., 1985; bd. dirs. Foodservice Ctr., NYU, 1980-86; chmn. World Bus. Forum, San Francisco, 1981-82 ; bd. dirs., trustee Kalamazoo Coll., 1985—, vice chmn., 1990—; bd. dirs. World Bus. Coun., 1990—. With U.S. Army, 1953-55. Mem. Sharon Heights Country Club, Menlo Park Circus club. Republican. Presbyterian. Avocations: golf, photography, opera. Home and Office: 2 Mesa Ct Menlo Park CA 94027-6418 also: Telesensory PO Box 7455 Mountain View CA 94043

MORRELL, MICHAEL PRESTON, utility executive; b. Camilla, Ga., Oct. 16, 1948; s. Ennis Monroe and Mattie Lou (Watts) M.; m. Rochelle Martha Lebous, May 25, 1975; children: Ashlea, Brett. BS in Oceanography, U.S. Naval Acad., 1971; MBA in Fin. and Econs., Fairleigh Dickinson, 1980. Registered profl. nuclear engr., Pa. Commd. lt. USN, 1971, resigned, 1976; nuclear engr. Burns & Roe, Inc., Oradell, N.J., 1976-77; systems engr. Gen. Pub. Utilities, Parsippany, N.J., 1977-79, spl. projects mgr., 1979-80, fin. projects mgr., 1980-81, mgr. treasury ops., 1981-84, asst. treas., 1984-86, v.p., treas. 1986-93; v.p. materials, svcs., regulatory affairs Jersey Ctrl. Power & Light, 1993—. Trustee, sec. Vis. Nurses Assn. Morris County, Morristown, N.J., 1987; trustee Bus. and Edn. Found. Morris County, 1991. Republican. Roman Catholic. Office: Gen Pub Utilities Corp 100 Interpace Pky Parsippany NJ 07054-1113

MORRELL, WAYNE BEAM, JR., artist; b. Clementon, N.J., Dec. 24, 1923; s. Wayne Beam and Martha L. (Plack) M.; student Drexel Inst., Phila. Sch. Indsl. Art.; grad. Famous Artist Sch., Westport, Conn.; m. Lillian Eunice Major, July 14, 1952 (dec. 1994); children: David Wayne (dec.), Lisa Anne. Exhibited one-man show Washington County Art Mus., Hagerstown, Md., 1973; exhibited nat. group shows including NAD, Conn. Acad. Fine Arts, Butler Inst. Am. Art, Am. Artists Profl. League, Knickerbocker Artists, N.Y.C., Newman Gallery, Phila., Houston, Palm Beach, Fla., Carmel, Calif., Guild Boston Artists, Wadsworth Atheneum, Addison Gallery Am. Art, Mus. Fine Arts, Columbus, Ga., New Britain Mus., Smithsonian Inst., Expn. Intercontinental, Monaco, France, Gateway Art Gallery, Palm Beach, Fla., Bleich Galleries, Carmel, Calif., Mus., Bombay, India, 1967, City Hall, Hong Kong, 1975-76; indsl. exhibitor, designer John Oldham Studios, 1955-58, art dir., 1958-61; designer Paris and Brussells Worlds Fairs, other maj. exhibits; designer cover Reader's Digest, 1967, Yankee mag. 1980. Served with AUS, 1949-52. Recipient Louis Seley purchase award; Gold medal Rockport Art Assn., 1969; Gold medal Jordan Marsh, Boston; award Council Am. Art Socs., 1971; Canelli Gold Medal award Academic Artists Assn., 1974; others. Mem. Allied Artists Am. (Jane Peterson award 1969, 74), Am. Artists Profl. League, Am. Vet. Soc. Artists, Springfield Acad. Artists (past council), Rockport Art Assn. (William Mariboe award, Harriet Mattson award, award for Winter Marshes 1980, Meyerowitz Meml. award 1989, William Meyerwith award 1989), North Shore Art Assn., Americana Gallery, Golden Web, Santa Fe, Montcrest Gallery, Chattanooga (Tenn.), 210 Gallery, Grand Central Art Galleries, Newman Galleries Phila. and Bryn Mawr, Pa., Dassin Gallery, L.A., Salmagundi Club (Louis Seley Purchase award 1969, Gwynne Lennon prize 1971, Phillip J. Ross award 1971, 1st hon. mention 1971). Home and Office: 1 Squam Holw Rockport MA 01966-2164

MORRILL, RICHARD LELAND, geographer, educator; b. L.A., Feb. 15, 1934; s. Robert W. and Lillian M. (Riffo) M.; m. Joanne L. Cooper, 1965; children: Lee, Andrew, Jean. B.A., Dartmouth Coll., 1955, M.A., U. Wash., 1957, Ph.D., 1959. Asst. prof. geography Northwestern U., 1959-60; NSF research fellow U. Lund, Sweden, 1960-61; assoc. prof. U. Wash., Seattle, 1961-65; assoc. prof. U. Wash., 1965-69, prof., 1969—, chmn. dept. geography, 1974-83, assoc. dir. environ. studies, 1974—; chmn. urban planning PhD program, 1992—; vis. assoc. prof. U. Chgo., dir. Chgo. Regional Hosp. Study, 1966-67; cons. population, regional and urban planning. Author: Geography of Poverty, 1970, Spatial Organization of Society, 1973, Political Redistricting and Geographic Theory, 1981, Spatial Diffusion, 1987. Mem. King County Boundary Rev. Bd. Guggenheim fellow, 1983-84. Mem. Assn. Am. Geographers (Meritorious Contbn. award 1970, mem. coun. 1970-73, sec. 1979-81, pres. 1981-82), Regional Sci. Assn., Wash. Regional Sci. Assn. (pres. 1993-94), Population Assn. Am., Lambda Alpha. Office: Dept Geography U Wash Seattle WA 98195

MORRILL, RICHARD LESLIE, university administrator; b. Weymouth, Mass., June 4, 1939; s. Duncan Russel and Violet Erma (Gibson) M.; m. Martha Leahy, June 24, 1964; children: Katie, Amy. A.B in History magna cum laude, Brown U., 1961; B.D. in Religious Thought, Yale U., 1964; Ph.D. in Religion, Duke U., 1968. Instr. Wells Coll., Aurora, N.Y., 1967-68; asst. prof. Chatham Coll., Pitts., 1968-74, assoc. prof., 1974-77, assoc. provost and asst. to pres., 1973-77; assoc. provost Pa. State U., University Park, 1977-79; pres. Salem Coll. and Acad., Winston-Salem, N.C., 1979-82, Centre Coll., Danville, Ky., 1982-88; U. Richmond, Va., 1988—. Author: Teaching Values in College, 1980; contbr. articles to profl. jours. Bd. dirs. Southeastern Ctr. for Contemporary Art, Winston-Salem, 1981-84, Higher

Edn. Retirement Annuity Assn., 1987—, Nat. Assn. of Ind. Colls. and Univs., 1988—; mem. adv. com. for Liberal Edn., 1986—. Woodrow Wilson fellow, 1961-62; James B. Duke fellow Duke U., 1964-67. Mem. Soc. for Values in Higher Edn. (dir. 1981-84), Am. Acad. Religion, Am. Soc. for Christian Ethics, Am. Assn. Higher Edn., So. Assn. Colls. and Schs. (commr. 1985—), Coll. Athletic Conf. (chmn. 1985-87), Council Ind. K. Colls. and Univs. (exec. com. 1984-86, v.p. 1986-88, exec. com. 1984-86), Assn. Presbyn. Colls. and Univs. (exec. com. 1984-86), Phi Beta Kappa. Club: University. Lodge: Rotary. Home: 7000 River Rd Richmond VA 23229-8532 Office: U Richmond Richmond VA 23173-1903

MORRILL, THOMAS CLYDE, insurance company executive; b. Chgo., July 1, 1909; s. Walter and Lena Elpha (Haney) M.; m. Hazel Janet Thompson, Oct. 18, 1930; children: Dorothy Mae (Mrs. Gerald L. Kelly), Charles T. Student, Cen. Coll. Arts and Scis., Chgo., 1928-29, Northwestern U., 1929-30. With Alfred M. Best Co., Inc., 1929-45, assoc. editor, 1940-45; with N.Y. State Ins. Dept., 1945-50, dep. supt. ins., 1947-50; with State Farm Mut. Automobile Ins. Co., Bloomington, Ill., 1950-77, v.p., 1952-77; chmn. bd. State Farm Fire and Casualty Co., Bloomington, 1970-86, State Farm Gen. Ins. Co., Bloomington, 1970-91; cons. State Farm Ins. Cos., Bloomington, 1991—; founder, chmn., dir. Ins. Inst. for Highway Safety. Chmn. exec. subcom. Nat. Hwy. Safety Adv. Com., 1971-73; chmn. tech. com. on transp. White House Conf. on Aging, 1971; mem. Pres.'s Task Force on Hwy. Safety. Clubs: Union League (Chgo.); Union Hills Country, Lakes (Sun City, Ariz.).

MORRILL, WILLIAM ASHLEY, research executive; b. Bronxville, N.Y., Apr. 23, 1930; s. Ashley B. and Katharine A. (Anderson) M.; m. Lois Birrell, Dec. 27, 1953 (div. 1978); children: Margaret, Carolyn, Elizabeth, Janet; m. Nancy Porter, Aug. 26, 1978. B.A., Wesleyan U., 1952; M.P.A., Syracuse U., 1953. Mgmt. analyst, acting chief plans and policy Directorate of Manpower and Orgn., USAF, 1953-62; asst. div. chief AEC unit Bur. of Budget, Washington, 1962-65, Mil. Divsn. Bur. Budget, 1965-67; dep. dir. Nat. Security Programs div. Office of Mgmt. and Budget, 1967-71; dep. county exec. Fairfax County, Va., 1971-72; asst. dir. Office Mgmt. and Budget, Washington, 1972-73; asst. sec. for planning/evaluation HEW, 1973-77; mem. Energy Policy and Planning Office, White House, 1977; sr. fellow Mathematica Policy Research, Princeton, N.J., 1977-79, sr. v.p., 1979-80, pres., 1980-86; pres. Mathtech, Inc., 1985-95, chmn., 1995—; mem. com. on child devel. rsch. and pub. policy NRC, 1978-87, chmn., 1983-87, com. on nat. stats., 1989-92, mem. Commn. on Behavioral and Social Scis. and Edn., 1990—. Chmn. No. Va. Planning Dist. Commn., 1965-70, 1986-89, William A. Jump Meml. Found. Recipient Meritorious award William A. Jump Meml. Found., 1966, Citizen of Yr. award for Fairfax County, Washington Star, 1970, Disting. Alumni award Maxwell Sch., Syracuse U., 1974, Disting. Svc. award Nat. Conf. on Social Welfare, 1976. Mem. Assn. Pub. Policy Analysis & Mgmt. (pres. 1982-83, mem. policy coun.), Nat. Acad. Pub. Adminstrn. (trustee 1984-93, vice-chmn. 1991-93), Coun. for Excellence in Govt. (chmn. bd. trustees 1986-89). Home: PO Box 38 New Hope PA 18938-0038 Office: Mathtech Inc 202 Carnegie Ctr Ste 111 Princeton NJ 08540-6233

MORRIN, PETER PATRICK, museum director; b. St. Louis, Oct. 31, 1945; s. Kevin Charles and Helen Louise (Clanton) M.; m. Carolyn Brooks, Oct. 5, 1974; children: Matthew, Rebecca. AB, Harvard U., 1968; MFA, Princeton U., 1972. Asst. prof., dir. art gallery Vassar Coll., Poughkeepsie, N.Y., 1974-78; curator 20th century art High Mus. Art, Atlanta, 1979-86; dir. J.B. Speed Art Mus., Louisville, 1986—; panelist Nat. Endowment Arts. Contbr. articles to profl. publs. Served with USAR, 1968-74. Office: JB Speed Art Mus PO Box 2600 Louisville KY 40201-2600

MORRIN, THOMAS HARVEY, engineering research company executive; b. Woodland, Calif., Nov. 24, 1914; s. Thomas E. and Florence J. (Hill) M.; m. Frances M. Von Ahn, Feb. 1, 1941; children: Thomas H., Diane, Linda, Denise. BS, U. Calif., 1937; grad., U.S. Navy Grad. Sch., Annapolis, Md., 1941. Student engr. Westinghouse Electric Mfg. Co., Emeryville, Calif., 1937; elec. engr. Pacific Gas & Electric Co., 1938-41; head microwave engring. div. Raytheon Co., Waltham, Mass., 1947-48; chmn. elec. engring. dept. Stanford Research Inst., 1948-52, dir. engring., research, 1952-60, gen. mgr. engring., 1960-64, vice pres. engring., sci., 1964-68; pres. University City Sci. Inst., Phila., 1968-69; pres., chmn. bd. Morrin Assos., Inc., Wenatchee, Wash., 1968-72. Trustee Am. Acad. Transp. Served as officer USNR, 1938-58, comdr. USN, 1945-48. Decorated Bronze Star; recipient Bank Am. award for automation of banking during 1950's, 1992. Fellow IEEE, AAAS; mem. Sci. Research Soc. Am., U.S. Naval Inst., Navy League, Marine Meml. Club (San Francisco). Address: 654 23rd Ave San Francisco CA 94121-3709

MORRIONE, PAOLO, polypropylene company executive. Pres., CEO Himont Inc., Wilmington, Del. Office: Himont Inc Box 15439 2801 Centerville Rd Wilmington DE 19850

MORRIS, ALBERT JEROME, pest control company executive; b. N.Y.C., Jan. 3, 1919; s. Peter and Minnie (Miller) M.; Barbara McLeod, Feb 6, 1943; children: Peter A., Lee Ellen Morris Guenther, Lisa Ann Morris Rasche. BS in Electronics, U. Calif., Berkeley, 1941; MS in Electronics, Stanford U., 1948, Degree of Engr., 1950. Registered profl. engr., Calif. Sr. v.p., co-founder Levinthal Elec. Products, Palo Alto, Calif., 1953-60; pres., dir. Radiation at Stanford, Palo Alto, 1960-63; pres., chief exec. officer Energy Systems Inc., Palo Alto, 1963-66, Genesys Systems Inc., Palo Alto, 1967-84; pres., chief exec. officer Biosys, Palo Alto, 1983-88, chmn. bd., 1989; also chmn. bd. TurboEnergy Systems, Phoenix, 1989-90; chmn. bd., chief exec. officer Neural Systems Corp., Palo Alto, 1991—; cons. to schs. of engring., Stanford U. and 18 other major univs.; chmn. San Francisco coun. Western Electronics Mfrs. Assn., 1965; chmn. bd. Western Electronics Show and Conv., Calif., 1961. Author over 50 papers on spin stabilization, high power electronics, med. electronics and continuing edn. Recipient Best Paper award IEEE/ASEE Frontiers in Edn. Conf., 1978. Fellow IEEE, Sigma Chi Iota; mem. AAAS. Avocation: tennis.

MORRIS, ARLENE MYERS, marketing professional; b. Washington, Pa., Dec. 29, 1951; d. Frank Hayes Myers and Lula Irene (Slusser) Kolcan; m. John L. Sullivan, Feb. 17, 1971 (div July 1982); m. David Wellons Morris, July 27, 1984. BA, Carlow Coll., 1974; postgrad., Western New England Coll., 1981-82. Sales rep. Syntex Labs., Inc., Palo Alto, Calif., 1974-77; profl. sales rep. McNeil Pharm., Spring House, Pa., 1977-78, mental health rep., 1978-80, asst. product dir., 1981-82, dist. mgr., 1982-85, new product dir., 1985-87, exec. dir. new bus. devel., 1987-89, v.p. bus. devel., 1989-93; v.p. bus. devel. Scios Nova IMC, Mountain View, Calif., 1993—. Mem. Found. of Ind. Colls., Phila., 1989. Mem. Pharm. Advt. Coun., Am. Diabetes Assn., Am. Acad. Sci., Healthcare Bus. Womens Assn., Lic. Execs. Soc. Home: 11701 Winding Way Los Altos CA 94024-6331 Office: Scios Nova IMC 2450 Bayshore Pky Mountain View CA 94043-1107

MORRIS, BEVAN HOWELL, university official; b. Adelaide, South Australia, Australia, Mar. 3, 1949; came to U.S., 1979; s. Gronwy Lewis and Dulcie Edna M. BA, Cambridge U., Eng., 1975, MA, 1979; DSCI, Maharishi European Research U., Switzerland, 1979. Internat. coordinator Maharishi European Research U., Seelisberg, Switzerland, 1975-79; pres. and bd. trustees Maharishi Internat. U., Fairfield, Iowa, 1980—; chmn. Maharishi Coun. of Supreme Intelligence of Age of Enlightenment, Maharishi Nagar, India, 1987—; chmn. bd. Maharishi Sch. of Age of Enlightenment, Fairfield; internat. pres. Maharishi Vedic U., 1992—

MORRIS, C. ROBERT, law educator; b. Denver, June 29, 1928; s. Clarence and Lillian (Eppstein) M.; m. Sandra Mueller, Sept. 1, 1970. BA, St. John's Coll., Annapolis, Md., 1948; JD, Yale U., 1951. Bar: Tex. 1951, Minn. 1974. Asst. prof. law Rutgers U., Camden, N.J., 1954-57; assoc. prof. law Rutgers U., 1957-60, prof. law, 1960-64; prof. law Univ. Minn., Mpls., 1964—. 1st lt. USAF, 1951-53. Office: U Minn Sch Law 229 19th Ave S Minneapolis MN 55455-0400

MORRIS, (WILLIAM) CARLOSS, lawyer, insurance company executive; b. Galveston, Tex., June 7, 1915; s. William Carloss and Willie (Stewart) M.; m. Doris Poole, Dec. 2, 1939; children: Marietta (Mrs. Morgan Maxfield),

William Carloss III, Malcolm Stewart, Melinda Louise (Mrs. Glen Ginter). BA with distinction, Rice Inst., 1936; JD with highest honors, U. Tex., 1939. Bar: Tex. 1938. With Stewart Title Guaranty Co., Houston, 1939—, pres., 1951-75, chmn. bd. dirs., chief exec. officer, 1975-91; chmn. bd. dirs., co-chief exec. officer Stewart Info. Services Inc., 1975—; bd. dirs. Morris, Lendais, Hollrah and Brown, Houston. Chmn. Interdisciplinary Commn. on Housing and Urban Growth, 1974-77; chmn. Star Hope Mission, 1951-90, hon.; mem.—; pres. Tex. Safety Assn., 1950-51; bd. dirs. Goodwill Industries; bd. dirs., mem. exec. com. Billy Graham Evangelistic Assn.; chmn. Baylor Coll. Medicine, 1968, trustee, 1952—; trustee, deacon 1st Bapt. Ch., Houston, chmn. bd. deacons, 1987-89; trustee Baylor U., 1952-72, past vice chmn. bd. dirs.; trustee Oldham Little Ch. Found., B.M. Woltman Found. Fellow Am. Bar Found., State Bar Tex. Found.; mem. ABA (past chmn. younger lawyers sect.), Tex. Bar Assn., Tex. Young Lawyers Assn. (past pres.), Chancellors, Order of Coif, Phi Delta Phi, Alpha Tau Omega. Clubs: River Oaks Country, University. Lodge: Kiwanis. Office: 1980 Post Oak Blvd Ste 800 Houston TX 77056

MORRIS, CAROL ANN, nursing educator; b. Quapaw, Okla., July 31, 1935; d. Grover Cleveland and Sylvia Veota (McBee) Bingham; m. Ernest Guye Morris, Nov. 21, 1955; children—Kimberly Diane Jacobs, Timothy Duane Morris. Diploma Nursing, St. John's Sch., Joplin, Mo., 1956; B.S. Nursing, Pittsburg State U., Kans., 1973, M.S., 1975; M.Nursing, U. Kans., 1982; Ed.D., Okla. State U., 1985. Head nurse Bapt. Regional Health Ctr., Miami, Okla., 1956-67; nursing instr. Northeastern Okla. A&M Coll., Miami, 1967-82, dir. dept. nursing, 1983—. Contbr. articles to profl. publs. Mem. Am. Nurses Assn., Okla. Tech. Soc., Midwest Nursing Research Soc., N.Am. Nursing Diagnosis Assn., DAR (vice regent local chpt.). Republican. Mem. Disciple of Christ Ch. Avocations: reading; needlework.

MORRIS, CHARLES ELLIOT, neurologist; b. Denver, Mar. 30, 1929; s. Jacob M. and Lillian Y. M.; m. Naomi Carolyn Minner, June 28, 1951; children: Jonathan E., David C. B.A., U. Denver, 1950, M.A. in Biochemistry, 1951; M.D., U. Colo., 1955. Diplomate: Am. Bd. Psychiatry and Neurology. Intern Los Angeles County Gen. Hosp., 1955-56; resident in neurology, teaching fellow neurology Harvard U. Med. Sch.-Boston City Hosp., 1956-59; mem. faculty U. N.C. Med. Sch., Chapel Hill, 1961-77; prof. neurology and medicine U. N.C. Med. Sch., 1976-77; attending neurologist Guam Meml. Hosp., Tamuning, also neurologist in charge Nat. Inst. Neurol. and Communicative Disorders and Stroke Rsch. Ctr., Agana, 1970-71; prof. neurology, 1976—, chmn. dept. Finch U. Health Scis. Chgo. Med. Sch., acting chief neurology svc. VA Med. Ctr., North Chgo., 1976-91; prof. dept. cell biology and anatomy, 1991-94; prof. neurosci., 1994—; vis. lectr. dept. neurology Rush Med. Coll., 1994—. Contbr. articles to profl. jours., chpts. to books. Served to lt. comdr. M.C., USNR, 1959-61. Mem. Am. Acad. Neurology, Assn. Rsch. in Nervous and Mental Diseases, AMA, AAAS, Am. Epilepsy Soc., So. Soc. Clin. Investigation, Ill. Med. Soc., Lake County Med. Soc., Sigma Xi, Alpha Omega Alpha, Phi Lambda Upsilon. Office: Dept Neurology UHS/Chgo Med Sch 3333 Green Bay Rd North Chicago IL 60064

MORRIS, CLAYTON LESLIE, priest; b. Eugene, Oreg., June 23, 1946; s. Joseph William Morris and Betty Fern (Rasmussen) Morris Darby; m. Mary Susan Pacquer, Dec. 30, 1968; children: Andrea Christine, Jonathan William. B Music, Willamette U., 1968; MA in Theology, Grad. Theol. Union, 1971, PhD in Theology, 1986; MDiv, Ch. Div. Sch., 1971. Ordained priest Episcopal Ch., 1971. Assoc. priest St. Andrew's Ch., Saratoga, Calif., 1971-74; rector St. Mark's Ch., King City, Calif., 1974-79; organist, choirmaster St. Paul's Ch., Oakland, Calif., 1979-80; teaching fellow, instr. Ch. Div. Sch., Berkeley, 1979-86; dir. music All Souls Ch., Berkeley, Calif., 1980-86; assoc. rector St. Mark's Ch., Palo Alto, Calif., 1986-91; staff officer liturgy and music Episc. Ch. Ctr., N.Y., 1991—. Mem. N.Am. Acad. Liturgy, Assn. Anglican Musicians, Assn. Diocesan Liturgy and Music Commns., Consultation on Common Texts, Associated Parishes Coun. Office: Episcopal Church Ctr 815 Second Ave New York NY 10017

MORRIS, DANIEL, osteopath. Pvt. practice Pinellas Park, Fla. Recipient Robert C. Erwin award Am. Coll. Osteo. Surgeons, 1993. Office: 7800-66th St N Ste 204 Pinellas Park FL 34665*

MORRIS, DANIEL KEARNS, journalist; b. Youngstown, Ohio, Jan. 14, 1954; s. John Mackey and Nancy Todd (Kearns) M.; m. Lisa Rachel Herrick, Aug. 25, 1984; children: Sarah Herrick, Nicholas Herrick. Student, Boston U., 1972-73; AB, U. Mich., 1978. VISTA vol. Winnebago (Nebr.) Indian Reservation, 1977-78; editor Pierian Press, Ann Arbor, Mich., 1979-81; pub., editor Alternative Rev. of Lit. and Politics mag., Ann Arbor, 1981-82; press sec. Richard Fellman for U.S. Congress campaign, Omaha, 1982; producer, editor Nat. Pub. Radio, Washington, 1983-88; producer CBS News, Washington, 1988-91; ABC News Nightline, Washington, 1991—. Field organizer McGovern for President, Washington, 1972. Recipient Robert F. Kennedy Journalism award RFK Found., 1988. Home: 6208 31st St NW Washington DC 20015-1518 Office: ABC News 1717 Desales St NW Washington DC 20036-4407

MORRIS, DAVID HUGH, manufacturing and marketing executive; b. Trail, B.C., Can., Sept. 21, 1941; came to U.S., 1974; s. Joseph and Gladys Dorothy (Mawdsley) M.; m. Erika Meisl; children: Christian David, Caroline Erika. B of Commerce, U. B.C., Vancouver, 1965. Internat. contr. Toro Co., Mpls., 1979-81, gen. contr., 1981, dir. internat. mktg., 1981-83, mng. dir. internat., 1983-84, v.p., gen. mgr. internat., 1984-85, v.p., gen. mgr. irrigation div., 1985, pres., chief oper. officer, 1988—. Mem. B.C. Inst. Chartered Accts. Office: Toro Co 8111 Lyndale Ave S Minneapolis MN 55420-1196

MORRIS, DESMOND, author; m. Ramona Morris; 1 son. Author: Biology of Art, 1962, Apes and Monkeys, 1965, Big Cats, 1965, Mammals: A Guide to the Living Species, 1966, The Naked Ape, 1968, The Human Zoo, 1969, Patterns of Reproductive Behavior, 1971, Intimate Behavior, 1971, Manwatching: A Field Guide to Human Behavior, 1977, The Soccer Tribe, 1981, The Book of Ages, 1983, The Art of Ancient Cyprus, 1985, Bodywatching: A Field Guide to the Human Species, 1985, The Illustrated Naked Ape, 1986, Catwatching, 1986, Dogwatching, 1986, The Secret Surrealist, 1987, Catlore, 1987, The Animals Roadshow, 1988, The Human Nestbuilders, 1988, Horsewatching, 1988, The Animal Contract, 1990, Animalwatching, 1990, Babywatching, 1991, Christmas Watching, 1992, The World of Animals, 1993, The Human Animal, 1994, Body Talk, A World Guide to Gestures, 1994, The Naked Ape Trilogy, 1994, Illustrated Cat Watching, 1994; co-author: (with Ramona Morris) Men and Snakes, 1965, Men and Apes, 1966, Men and Pandas, 1966, The Giant Panda, 1981, Gestures: Their Origins and Distribution, 1979; autobiography Animal Days, 1979; editor: Primate Ethology, 1969, (fiction) Inrock, 1983. Address: care Jonathan Cape, 20 Vauxhall Bridge Rd, London SWIV 2SA, England

MORRIS, DEWEY BLANTON, lawyer; b. Richmond, Va., Sept. 15, 1938; s. Thomas Cecil and Mary Katherine (Rowlett) M.; m. Nancy Edmunds, Aug. 27, 1960; children: Sally Pendleton, Katherine Archer. BA, U. Va., 1960, LLB, 1965. Bar: Md. 1965, Va. 1968, D.C. 1991, U.S. Dist. Ct. Md. 1965, U.S. Dist. Ct. (ea. dist.) Va. 1968, U.S.C. t. Appeals (4th cir.) 1966. Assoc. Piper & Marbury, Balt., 1965-67; ptnr. Hunton & Williams, Richmond, 1967—. Served to 1st lt., USMC, 1960-62. Mem. ABA (bus. law sect.), Va. Bar Assn. (bus. law sect.), Richmond Bar Assn., Raven Soc., Commonwealth Club, Country Club Va. (Richmond), Army & Navy Club (Washington), Kiwanis, Phi Alpha Delta, Omicron Delta Kappa. Presbyterian. Clubs: Commonwealth, Country Club Va. (Richmond). Lodge: Kiwanis. Avocations: golf, tennis, skiing, photography. Home: 302 Locke Ln S Richmond VA 23226-1714 Office: Hunton & Williams Riverfront Plaza East Tower 951 East Byrd St Richmond VA 23219

MORRIS, DONALD ARTHUR ADAMS, college president; b. Detroit, Aug. 31, 1934; s. Robert Park and Margaret Lymburn (Adams) M.; m. Zella Mae Stormer, June 21, 1958; children: Dwight Joseph, Julie Adams. B.A., Wayne State U., 1961; M.P.A., U. Mich., 1966, Ph.D., 1970; LLD (hon.), Olivet Coll., 1987. Copy boy Detroit Times, 1952-55, reporter, 1955-57, edn. writer, 1957-60; adminstrv. asst. Wayne State U., Detroit, 1960-62, mgr. editor news service U. Mich., 1962-64, mgr. spl. programs, 1964-68; mgr. Met. Detroit Devel. Program, 1968-71; v.p. for devel. Hobart and William

Smith Colls., Geneva, N.Y., 1971-76; exec. v.p. Hobart and William Smith Colls., 1976-77; pres., prof. polit. sci. Olivet (Mich.) Coll., Mich., 1977-92; pres. emeritus Olivet Coll., Mich., 1992—; cons., 1992-93; chmn. Mich. Intercollegiate Athletic Assn., 1978-79, 85-86, 90-91; cons. evaluator North Ctrl. Assn. Colls. and Schs., 1986-92; mem. Jud. Tenure Commn., 1991-94. Contbr. articles to profl. jours. Trustee Olivet Coll., 1977-92, Mich. Coll. Found., 1977-92, exec. com., 1989-92; mem. Mich. Higher Edn. Assistance and Student Loan Authorities, 1986—, chair, 1989-94; pres. Planned Parenthood of Finger Lakes, N.Y., 1973-77, pres. 75-77; bd. dirs., treas. Genesee Regional Family Planning Program N.Y., 1975-77; trustee Coun. Higher Edn., United Ch. of Christ, 1977-92, mem. exec. com., 1982-92, chair, 1986-88; trustee Glen Lake Cmty. Libr. Bd., 1993—, pres., 1994—; mem. Sleeping Bear Noontiders, 1993—, sec. 1995—. South Manitou Meml. Soc., 1980—. Mem. Am. Assn. for Higher Edn., Sigma Delta Chi, Omicron Delta Kappa, Alpha Lambda Epsilon, Kappa Sigma Alpha, Gamma Iota Sigma, Alpha Mu Gamma, Phi Mu Alpha Sinfonia, Rotary (local pres. 1987-88, Paul Harris fellow). Congregationalist. Home: 8330 S Dunn's Farm Rd Maple City MI 49664-9614 also: 6551 E Dorado Blvd Tucson AZ 85715-4705

MORRIS, DOUGLAS PETER, recording company executive; b. Far Rockaway, N.Y., Nov. 23, 1938; s. Walter and Mary (Lerner) M.; m. Monique Jequel, Mar. 20, 1964; children: Walter, Peter. B.A., Columbia Coll., 1960. Gen. mgr. Robert Mellin, Inc., N.Y.C., 1964-65; v.p., gen. mgr. Laurie Records, Inc., N.Y.C., 1965-69; owner Big Tree Records, N.Y.C., 1969-79; pres. Atlantic Records, N.Y.C., 1980—, chief oper. officer, 1989-94; chmn. CEO, COO, pres. Warner Music-U.S., 1994—; cons. Ampex Records, 1968. Composer: songs Sweet Talkin Guys, 1968, Smoking in the Boys' Room, 1970. Served with U.S. Army, 1962-64. Recipient scholarship Paragon Oil, 1954, scholarship Columbia Coll., 1960; named Man of Yr. in Record Industry United Jewish Appeal, 1981. Mem. ASCAP. Office: Atlantic Rec Co 75 Rockefeller Plz New York NY 10019-6907

MORRIS, EDWIN ALEXANDER, retired apparel manufacturing company executive; b. Concord, N.C., Aug. 13, 1903; s. William Lee M. and Martha Margaret (Ervin) M.; m. Mary Ella Cannon, Nov. 1, 1933; children: Joseph E., Mary Lou (dec.). BS in Commerce, Washington and Lee U., 1926. Joined Blue Bell, Inc., Greensboro, N.C., 1937; pres., chief exec. officer Blue Bell, Inc., 1948-66, chmn. bd., chief exec. officer, 1966-74, chmn. bd., 1974-81, dir., 1940-81. Bd. dirs. emeritus N.C. Citizens Assn.; trustee emeritus Wesley Long Hosp., Greensboro, 1958-83; bd. dirs. Nat. Taxpayers Union, Washington, Washington and Lee U. Planning and Devel. Com., The Jesse Helms Ctr. Found., Wingate Coll., N.C., 1989-91, Students for Am., Raleigh, N.C., 1990-94, The John Locke Found., Raleigh, 1992-94, N.C. Taxpayers United, Raleigh; bd. overseers Duke Comprehensive Cancer Ctr., Durham, 1985—. Presbyterian. Clubs: Greensboro Country, Greensboro City. Office: 400 W Market St Ste 408 Greensboro NC 27401-2241

MORRIS, EDWIN THADDEUS, construction consultant; b. N.Y.C., Jan. 13, 1912; s. Edwin T. and Helen (Hughes) M.; m. Winifred Walsh, Apr. 23, 1938; children—Edwin Thaddeus, Joan M., David M., Patrick J. Student, Manhattan Coll., 1928-30. Field engr. Madigan Hyland Cons. Engrs., 1936-37; supt. Raymond Concrete Pile Co., 1937-43; project engr., gen. supt., officer subsidary Raymond Internat. Companies, 1946-58; v.p. Raymond Internat., Inc. (and subsidiaries), 1958-60, sr. v.p. overseas heavy constrn. div., 1960-66; pres., dir. Balt. Contractors, Inc., 1966-76; pres. Edwin T. Morris Constrn. Consultants, Inc., Towson, Md., 1976—. Served to lt., C.E. USNR, 1943-46. Mem. Engring. Soc. of Balt. Clubs: Explorers (N.Y.C.), Moles (N.Y.C.). Home: 7927 Ruxway Rd Baltimore MD 21204-3515

MORRIS, ERROL M., filmmaker; b. Hewlett, N.Y., Feb. 5, 1948; s. Abner and Cinnabelle (Burzinsky) M.; m. Julia Bynum Sheehan; 1 child, Nathaniel Hamilton. BA, U. Wis., 1969; student, Princeton U., U. Calif., Berkeley. Pres. Fourth Floor Prodns., Inc., Cambridge, Mass. Dir., producer Gates of Heaven, 1978, The Thin Blue Line, 1987, A Brief History of Time, 1991. Guggenheim fellow, 1990, MacArthur fellow, 1990-94. Office: Fourth Floor Prodns 678 Mass Ave Cambridge MA 02139

MORRIS, EUGENE JEROME, lawyer; b. N.Y.C., Oct. 14, 1910; s. Max and Regina (Cohn) M.; m. Terry Lesser, Mar. 28, 1934 (dec. Sept. 1993); 1 child, Richard S.; m. Blanche Bier Finke, June 22, 1994. B.S.S., CCNY, 1931; LL.B., St. John's U., 1934. Bar: N.Y. 1935. Practiced N.Y.C., 1935—; sr. and founding partner firm Demov, Morris & Hammerling, 1946-87; v.p., sr. counsel Ea. region Am. Title Ins. Co., N.Y.C., 1990-93; of counsel Spector Scher and Feldman, 1991—; adj. prof. land use regulation NYU Grad. Sch. Pub. Arminstrn., 1978-81; adj. prof. legal issues in real estate, Real Estate Inst. NYU, 1988—; spl. master Supreme Ct. State of N.Y., 1979—; arbitrator Civil Ct. N.Y., 1994—. Editor weekly column N.Y. Law Jour., 1965-87, It's the Law, Real Estate Forum, 1982-87; editor-in-chief N.Y. Practice Guide: Real Estate, 4 vols., 1986, Real Estate Development, 4 vols., 1987; contbr. articles to profl. jours. Mem. N.Y. State Tax Revision Commn., 1977-80, N.Y.C. Rent Guidelines Bd., 1983-85. Served with AUS, 1943-45. Mem. ABA (chmn. spl. com. housing and urban devel. 1970-73, council sect. real property, probate and trust law 1971-74, assoc. editor Real Property Probate and Trust Jour. 1979-86, editor Real Property, Probate and Property mag., articles editor 1986-94), Am. Judges Assn., Assn. of Bar of City of N.Y. (chmn. com. housing and urban devel. 1971-74, chmn. com. on lectures and continuing edn. 1980-83), Coun. on Jud. Adminstrn. 1989-92, N.Y. State Bar Assn. (exec. com. 1980—, chmn. com. meetings and lectures 1982-92, continuing legal edn. com. 1984-90, ho. of dels. 1986—, del. ho. of dels. 1992—), Citizens Union (dir.), Lambda Alpha Internat. (bd. dirs. 1990—, pres. N.Y. chpt. 1990-93, sect. Lambda Alpha Delta), Nat. Housing Conf. Home: 200 Central Park S New York NY 10019-1415

MORRIS, FRANK EUGENE, banker; b. Detroit, Dec. 30, 1923; s. Frank and Beatrice (Perkins) M.; m. Geraldine Elizabeth Coltharp, Dec. 22, 1944; children—Susan, Lisa, Betsy. B.A., Wayne U., 1948; M.A., U. Mich., 1949, Ph.D. in Econs., 1955. Research dir. Investment Bankers Assn., Washington, 1955-61; asst. to sec. debt mgmt. Treasury Dept., 1961-63; v.p. Loomis Sayles and Co., Boston, 1963-68; pres. Fed. Res. Bank Boston, 1968-88; Peter Drucker prof. mgmt. Boston Coll., 1989-94; tchg. fellow U. Mich., 1949-51; bd. dirs. Thermo Electron Corp., Thermo Remediation Corp.; trustee SEI Mut. Funds. Served to 1st lt. USAAF, 1943-45.

MORRIS, G. RONALD, automotive executive; b. East St. Louis, Ill., Aug. 30, 1936; s. George H. and Mildred C. M.; m. Margaret Heino, June 20, 1959; children: David, Michele, James. B.S. in Metall. Engring. U. Ill., 1959. Metall. engr. Delco-Remy div. Gen. Motors Corp., 1959-60; factory metallurgist Dubuque Tractor Works, John Deere Co., Iowa, 1960-66; with Fed.-Mogul Corp., 1966-79, v.p., group mgr. ball and roller bearing group, 1979; pres. Tenneco Automotive div. Tenneco, Inc., Deerfield, Ill., 1979-82; pres., chief exec. officer PT Components, Inc., Indpls., 1982-88; vice-chmn. Rexnord Corp., Indpls., 1988-89; chmn., pres., chief exec. officer CTP Holdings Inc., 1986-88; chmn. Integrated Technologies, Inc., Indpls., 1990-92, also bd. dirs.; chmn., pres., chief exec. officer Western Industries, Inc., Milw., 1991—, also bd. dirs.; bd. dirs. Mulligan & Assocs., Chgo., Ky. Railworks, Inc., NN Ball & Roller, Inc., Erwin, Tenn.; corp. bd. dirs. Milw. Sch. of Engring. Mem. Pres.'s Coun., U. Ill.; corp. bd. dirs. Milw. Sch. of Engring. Mem. ASM, SAE, Meridian Hills Country Club (Indpls.), Exmoor Country Club (Highland Park, Ill.), Marshwood Country Club (Savannah, Ga.), Blue Mound Golf and Country Club (Wauwatosa, Wis.), Elks, Masons. Republican. Presbyterian. Office: Western Industries Inc 1215 N 62nd St Milwaukee WI 53213-2915

MORRIS, GARRETT, actor, singer; b. New Orleans, Feb. 1, 1937. Student, Tanglewood, Juilliard Sch. Music, Manhattan Sch. Music.; BA, Dillard U. Debut as singer and music arranger with Harry Belafonte folk singers; Broadway stage appearances include What The Wine Sellers Buy; Broadway stage appearances include Hallelujah Baby, Showboat, Porgy and Bess, I'm Solomon, Ain't Supposed to Die A Natural Death, The Great White Hope; other stage appearances in I'm Not Rappaport, 1990; appeared in films Where's Poppa?, 1970, The Anderson Tapes, 1971, Cooley High, 1975, Car Wash, 1976, How to Beat the High Cost of Living, 1980, The Census Taker, 1984, The Stuff, 1985, Critical Condition, 1987, The Underachievers, 1988, Dance to Win, 1989, Husbands, Wives, Money, and Murder,

1989 ; television series: Roll Out!, 1973-74, NBC's Saturday Night Live, 1975-80, It's Your Move, 1984-85, Hunter, 1986-90, Roc, 1990-91, Martin, 1992—; TV film The Invisible Woman, 1983, Maid For Each Other, 1992; author: play The Secret Place, 1969, Daddy Picou and Marie Le Veau, 1981. Mem. AFTRA, SAG, Equity. Office: Stone Maunfurs Talent Agy 8091 Selma Ave Los Angeles CA 90046*

MORRIS, GEORGE NORTON, insurance company executive; b. Bklyn., May 23, 1930; s. George L. and Karolyn E. (Bamberger) M.; BA, Wesleyan U., 1952; MBA, Harvard U., 1956; m. Ann E. Smith, May 22, 1954; children—George L., Elizabeth D., Emily H. Security analyst New Eng. Mut. Life Ins. Co., Boston, 1956-58, Hornblower & Weeks, Hemphill, Noyes, N.Y.C., 1958-63, ptnr., 1963-72, exec. v.p., 1972; v.p. Dillon, Read & Co., N.Y.C., 1972-74; exec. v.p., chmn. investment policy com. Gen. Accident Group, Phila., 1975-85; vice-chmn. 1985—; bd. dirs. Gen. Accident plc, Perth, Scotland, Gen. Accident Ins. Co. Am., Gen. Accident P.R., San Juan, Pa. Gen. Ins. Co., Camden Fire Assn., Potomac Ins. Co. Ill., Chgo., Pilot Ins. Co., Toronto. With USNR, 1952-54. Mem. Union League. Republican. Episcopalian. Home: 2829 N Providence Rd Media PA 19063-1816 Office: 434 Walnut St Philadelphia PA 19106-3703

MORRIS, GERALD DOUGLAS, newspaper editor; b. Boston, May 7, 1937; s. George Christopher and Lucy Bell (MacPhee) M.; m. Elaine Louise Owen, Nov. 13, 1964 (div. 1976); children: Laura Louise, Douglas Owen; m. Mary Elizabeth Simpson Stevens, Apr. 15, 1977; children: Jeffrey David Stevens Morris, Wendy Elizabeth Stevens Morris. Student, Boston U., 1959. Reporter Patriot Ledger, Quincy, Mass., 1961-66; copy editor Boston Globe, 1966—, travel editor, 1989—; syndicated columnist Globe-Trotting, 1970—. Author: Boston Globe Guide to Boston, 1989, New England under Sail, 1993. Chmn. Canton (Mass.) Cable Adv. Bd., 1990-92. With U.S. Army, 1959-61. Mem. Soc. Am. Travel Writers, Skal Club Boston, Lions (pres. Canton 1969-70, 80-81). Avocations: photography, travel. Home: 78 Cheney St Orange MA 01364-1603 Office: Globe Newspaper Co 135 Morrissey Blvd Boston MA 02125

MORRIS, GERALD FRANCIS, manufacturing company executive; b. Fall River, Mass., Sept. 29, 1943; s. Alfred Francis and Beatrice (Pontes) M.; m. Madeleine Anne Lacroix, July 2, 1966; children: Maureen Anne, Allison Jeanne, Alfred Jason. B.S. in Mech. Engring., Worcester Poly. Inst., Mass., 1965; M.B.A., Harvard U., 1970. Mfg. engr. Eastman Kodak Co., Rochester, N.Y., 1954; div. traffic supr. N.Y. Telephone, Albany, N.Y., 1965-68; corp. asst. treas. Textron Inc., Providence, 1970-80, asst. v.p., dir. planning, 1980-81; v.p., treas., chief fin. officer The Foxboro (Mass.) Co., 1981—; dir. Rubison Systems Inc., Maitland, Fla., 1982—; South Shore Bank, Quincy, Mass., 1983—; instr. Babson Coll. Grad. Sch., Wellesley, Mass., 1970-72, Bryant Coll. Grad. Sch., Smithfield, R.I., 1970-80. Chmn. sch. sect. Swansea (Mass.) Fin. Bd., 1974-80; treas. Bayview Acad., Riverside, R.I. 1983—. Served with USCGR, 1966-72. Gen. Motors scholar, 1965. Mem. Machinery and Allied Inst. (mem. fin. council 1981—), Fin. Execs. Inst., Treasurers Club Boston, Pi Tau Sigma, Phi Kappa Theta. Clubs: Coles River (dir. 1976-78); Cedar Cove (Swansea) (dir. 1974-80). Home: 6683 Militia Hill St NW Canton OH 44718-3769 Office: The Foxboro Co Bristol Pk 38 Neponset Ave Foxboro MA 02035-2098

MORRIS, GRANT HAROLD, legal educator; b. Syracuse, N.Y., Dec. 10, 1940; s. Benjamin and Caroline Grace (Judelson) M.; m. Phyllis Silberstein, July 4, 1967; children: Joshua, Sara. A.B., Syracuse U. (N.Y.), 1962, J.D., 1964; LL.M., Harvard U., 1971. Bar: N.Y. 1964. Atty. N.Y. Mental Hygiene Law Recodification Project, Inst. Public Adminstrn., N.Y.C., 1964-66; mem. faculty Wayne State U. Law Sch., 1967-73, prof. law, 1970-73, dean acad. affairs, 1971-73; prof. law U. San Diego Law Sch., 1973—, acting dean, 1977-78, 88-89, assoc. dean grad. legal edn., 1978-81; prof. law in psychiatry Wayne State U. Med. Sch., 1974-73; adj. prof. U. Calif. San Diego Med. Sch., 1974-84, clinical prof., 1984—; legal counsel Mich. Legis. Com. to Revise Mental Health Statutes, 1970-73; organizer law and psychiatry sect. Assn. Am. Law Schs., 1973, chmn., 1973-74; patients advocate, San Diego County, 1978-78; cons. Criminal Code Commn., Ariz. Legis., 1974; reporter task force on guidelines governing roles of mental health profls. in criminal process Am. Bar Assn. standing com. on assn. standards for criminal justice, 1981-84; cert. rev. hearing officer San Diego Superior Ct., 1984-90, ct. commr./judge pro tem, 1990-92, mental health hearing officer, 1992—; hearing officer San Diego Housing Commn., 1988-92; mem. exec. com. sect. law and mental disability Assn. Am. Law Schs., 1990—. Author: The Insanity Defense: A Blueprint for Legislative Reform, 1975; co-author: Mental Disorder in the Criminal Process: Stan Stress and the Vietnam/ Sports Conspiracy, 1993; editor, contbr.: The Mentally Ill and the Right to Treatment, 1970. Mem. Phi Alpha Delta (faculty adv. 1970-73, 75—). Home: 8515 Nottingham Pl La Jolla CA 92037-2125 Office: U San Diego Law Sch 5998 Alcala Park San Diego CA 92110-2492

MORRIS, HENRY ALLEN, JR., publisher; b. Moncks Corner, S.C., Feb. 9, 1940; s. Henry Allen Sr. and Edith Luther (Wall) M.; divorced; 1 child, Anthony Duane Allen. A in Acctg., Palmer Jr. Coll., Charleston, S.C. 1959; BA in English cum laude, Belmont Abbey Coll., N.C., 1974. Office mgr. Gas Engine and Electric Co., Charleston, 1959; cargo coord. S.C. State Ports Authority, Charleston, 1959-70; headmaster St. Stephen Acad., S.C., 1973-77; gen. mgr. The Berkeley Democrat, Moncks Corner, 1977-86, owner, 1989—; pub., editor Berkeley Ind., Moncks Corner, 1987—; pres. Berkeley Pub. Inc., Moncks Corner, 1987—. Author: (short story) The Easter Gift, 1973. Bd. dirs. Council of Govts. Regional Forum, Charleston, 1987, Winthrop Coll., 1983, Moncks Corner Downtown, Inc., 1986-87; mem. Moncks Corner City Council, 1983-88; mayor pro tem, 1986-88; commr. S.C. Vocat. Rehab. Agy.; treas. bd. dirs. Berkeley County YMCA. Recipient Pres. award Berkeley Arts Council, 1985, Charleston Jaycees, 1971, Friend of Edn. award Berkeley County Sch. System, 1991; named Handicapped Man of Yr., Moncks Corner's Mayor's Com., 1990. Mem. Low County Soc. Profl. Journalists (pres.), S.C. Mcpl. Assn. (lesis. com.), Trident United Way (mem. exec. bd. 1983-91), Trident C. of C. (bd. dirs.), Charleston Opera Club (founder), Rotary (past pres.). Episcopalian. Avocations: reading, painting, collecting art. Home: 117 Merrimack Dr Moncks Corner SC 29461-3580

MORRIS, HENRY MADISON, JR., education educator; b. Dallas, Oct. 6, 1918; s. Henry Madison and Ida (Hunter) M.; m. Mary Louise Beach, Jan. 24, 1940; children: Henry Madison III, Kathleen Louise, John David, Andrew Hunter, Mary Ruth, Rebecca Jean. BS with distinction, Rice Inst., 1939; MS, U. Minn., 1948, PhD, 1950; LLD, Bob Jones U., 1966; LittD, Liberty U., 1989. Registered profl. engr., Tex. Jr. engr. Tex. Hwy. Dept., 1938-39; from jr. engr. to asst. engr. Internat. Boundary Commn., El Paso, 1939-42; instr. civil engring. Rice Inst., 1942-46; from instr. to asst. prof. U. Minn., Mpls., also research project leader St. Anthony Falls Hydraulics Lab., 1946-51; prof., head dept. civil engring. Southwestern La. Inst., Lafayette, 1951-57, Va. Poly. Inst., Blacksburg, 1957-70; v.p. acad. affairs Christian Heritage Coll., San Diego, 1970-78, pres., 1970-80; dir. Inst. for Creation Rsch., 1970-80, pres., 1980—. Author: (with Richard Stephens) Report on Rio Grande Water Conservation Investigation, 1942, That You Might Believe, 1946, 2d edit., 1978, (with Curtis Larson) Hydraulics of Flow in Culverts, 1948, The Bible and Modern Science, 1951, rev. edit., 1968, (with John C. Whitcomb) The Genesis Flood, 1961, Applied Hydraulics in Engineering, 1963, The Twilight of Evolution, 1964, Science, Scripture and Salvation, 1965, 2d edit., 1971, Studies in the Bible and Science, 1966, Evolution and the Modern Christian, 1967, Biblical Cosmology and Modern Science, 1970, The Bible has the Answer, 1971, Science and Creation: A Handbook for Teachers, 1971, (with J.M. Wiggert) Applied Hydraulics, 1972, A Biblical Manual on Science and Creation, 1972, The Remarkable Birth of Planet Earth, 1973, Many Infallible Proofs, 1974, Scientific Creationism, 1974, 2d edit., 1985, Troubled Waters of Evolution, 1975, The Genesis Record, 1976, Education for the Real World, 1977, 3d edit., 1991, The Scientific Case for Creation, 1977, The Beginning of the World, 1977, 2d edit., 1991, Sampling the Psalms, 1978, 2d edit., 1991, King of Creation, 1980, Men of Science, Men of God, 1982, 2d edit., 1988, Evolution in Turmoil, 1982, The Revelation Record, 1983, History of Modern Creationism, 1984, 2d edit. 1993, The Biblical Basis for Modern Science, 1984, Creation and the Modern Christian, 1985, Science and The Bible, 1986, Days of Praise, 1986, The God Who is Real, 1988, The Remarkable Record of Job, 1988; (with Martin Clark) The Bible Has The Answer, 2d edit., 1987; (with Gary E. Parker) What is Creation Science, 1982, 2d edit., 1988, The

Long War Against God, 1989, (with John D. Morris) Science, Scripture and the Young Earth, 1989, The Bible Science and Creation, 1991, Creation and the Second Coming, 1991, Biblical Creationism, 1993, The Defender's Bible, 1995; research bulls., tech. articles, reports and booklets. Fellow AAAS, ASCE, Am. Sci. Affiliation; mem. Am. Soc. Engring. Edn. (sec.-editor civil engring. divsn. 1967-70), Trans-Nat. Assn. Christian Schs. (pres. 1983-95), Creation Rsch. Soc. (pres. 1967-73), Am. Geophys. Union, Geol. Soc. Am., Am. Assn. Petroleum Geologists, Geochem. Soc., Gideons (pres. La. 1954-56), Phi Beta Kappa, Sigma Xi, Chi Epsilon, Tau Beta Pi. Baptist. Home: 6733 El Banquero Pl San Diego CA 92119-1129 *The Bible is the inerrant word of God and thus should be believed and obeyed in all things.*

MORRIS, HERBERT, lawyer, educator; b. N.Y.C., July 28, 1928; s. Peter and Minnie (Miller) M.; m. Virginia Ann Grenier, Apr.3, 1956 (div. Nov. 1977); children: Jacob Jeremy, Benjamin John.; m. Margery Ruth Maslon, June 8, 1980. A.B., UCLA, 1951; LL.B., Yale, 1954; D. Phil., Oxford (Eng.) U., 1956. Bar: Calif. 1958. Mem. faculty UCLA, 1956—, prof. philosophy and law, 1962—, dean div. humanities, 1983-92, interim provost Coll. Letters and Sci., 1992-94; rsch. clin. assoc. So. Calif. Psychoanalytic Inst., 1992-93. Editor: Freedom and Responsibility, 1961, The Masked Citadel, 1968, Guilt and Shame, 1971, On Guilt and Innocence, 1976. Home: 233 S Medio Dr Los Angeles CA 90049-3911 Office: UCLA Sch Law 405 Hilgard Ave Los Angeles CA 90024-1301

MORRIS, JAMES ALOYSIUS, economist, educator; b. Lawrence, Mass., May 25, 1918; s. George Thomas and Elizabeth (Reardon) M.; m. Marjorie Leila Frampton, May 30, 1942 (dec. Jan. 1993); children: Stephen Frampton, Elizabeth Harvey; m. Frances Harvey Chalk, Sept. 24, 1994. B.A. with high honors, Northeastern U., 1942, LL.D., 1968; A.M., Harvard U., 1947, Ph.D., 1951; Litt.D. Coll. Charleston, 1970; L.H.D., Lander Coll., 1971, Francis Marion Coll., 1982. Adj. prof. U. S.C. economics, dir. Econ. Rsch. Bur., 1956-61, dean Sch. Bus. Adminstrn., 1961-66, v.p. advanced studies and research, dean Grad. Sch., 1966-68, chmn. faculty com. on admissions and athletics, Disting. prof., 1972-77; econ. cons., 1977—; commr. S.C. Commn. on Higher Edn., 1968-72, Edn. Commn. of the States, 1968-72, So. Regional Edn. Bd.; past chmn. bd. dirs., exec. com. S.C. Blue Cross-Blue Shield; past vice chmn. Gov.'s Productivity Coun.; past chmn. Charlotte br. Fed. Res. Bank, Rep. Nat. Bank; labor arbitrator Fed. Mediation Svcs., Am. Arbitration Assn., 1948—; vis. rsch. prof. Nuffield Coll., Oxford U., 1953-54; cons. to dir. ICA, 1955; spl. econ. adviser to dir. USOM, Turkey, 1956-57; past chmn. S.C. Regional Export Expansion Coun.; past mem. Nat. Export Expansion Coun.; past mem. Gov.'s Task Force on the Economy, Gov.'s Adv. Group on Health Planning; past chmn. Gov.'s Adv. Group on Mental Health Planning; past chmn. bd. S.C. Bd. Econ. Advisers, S.C. Law Inst.; adv. bd. dirs. Egyptian Studies Assn., Earth Sci. Inst., Heathwood Hall Episc. Sch.; pres. Carolina Econ. Assocs. Inc., 1979—. Author: Woolen and Worsted Manufacturing in the Southern Piedmont, 1952; contbr. articles and revs. to profl. jours. Bd. dirs. United Community Svcs., S.C. Coun. Econs. Edn., 1988—; pres. emeritus U. S.C. Ednl. Found.; past chmn. bd. dirs. Nat. Lab. Higher Edn.; past mem. corp. Northeastern U.; trustee Episc. Div. Upper S.C., 1988—; mem. adv. bd. Still Hopes Episcopal Home. Lt. col. U.S. Army, 1940-41, 42-46. Mem. Am. Econ. Assn., So. Econ. Assn., Nat. Assn. Bus. Economists, Am. Arbitration Assn., Forum Club, Forest Lake Country Club, Palmetto Club, Rotary. Episcopalian. Home: 1829 Senate St Columbia SC 29201 Office: U SC Columbia SC 29208

MORRIS, JAMES CARL, architect; b. Richmond, Va., Sept. 2, 1930; s. James Carl and Florence Virginia (Hey) M.; m. Frances Parrott Wooten, June 9, 1952; children: James Carl Jr., David Palmer. Student, N.C. State U., 1948-50; BS in Bldg. Constrn., Va. Polytechnic Inst., 1952. Cert. Nat. Coun. Archtl. Registration Bds. Archtl. draftsman Va. Electric & Power Co., Richmond, Va., 1955-56, Marcellus, Wright & Son, Richmond, 1956-57; architect C.W. Huff, Jr., Richmond, 1957; ptnr. to prin./owner Huff-Morris Architects, Richmond, 1966—; pres. Point of Rocks Devel. Corp., Chesterfield, Va., 1986—; ptnr. Rivermont Assocs., Chesterfield, 1987—, JCM Partnership, Chesterfield, 1988—. Contbr. articles to profl. jours. Bd. dirs. Chesterfield Preservation Commn.; deacon Branch's Ch., Richmond, 1986-90; chmn. Va. Bapt. Extension Bd., Richmond, 1991—. With U.S. Army, 1953-54. Recipient award of Merit S.S. Bd. of So. Bapt., Nashville, Excellence in Masonry Design award Va. Masonry Coun., Richmond. Mem. AIA (past pres. Richmond chpt.), Interfaith Forum on Religion, Art & Architecture, Commonwealth Club of Va. Avocations: woodworking, fishing, hunting. Office: Huff-Morris Architecture PC 10100 Ironbridge Rd Chesterfield VA 23832

MORRIS, JAMES MATTHEW, history educator; b. Reed City, Mich., July 13, 1935; s. Fred Michael and Florence C. (Weiland) M.; m. Nancy Christina Becker, Aug. 23, 1958; children: Patrick J., Anne C., Michael J., John E., Joseph A., Mary Jane. BA, Aquinas Coll., 1957; MA, Central Mich. U., 1962; Phd, U. of Cin., 1969. High sch. tchr. Mich., 1957-1962; instr.history Coll. Steubenville, Ohio, 1962-64; asst. prof. Providence Coll., R.I., 1967-71; prof. Christopher Newport U., Newport News, Va., 1971—; host radio series Sta. WGH-FM, Hampton, Va., 1978-83; prodr., host Crossroads TV series Centex TV Network, Williamsburg, Va., 1982-83; orientation speaker Nat. Com. on U.S.-China Rels., Coll. William and Mary, Williamsburg, 1987-92. Author: Our Maritime Heritage, 1979, History of the U.S. Navy, 1984, History of the U.S. Army, 1986, America's Armed Forces: A History, 1991; sr. editor: America's Maritime Legacy, 1979. Recipient edn. award U.S. Dept. Edn., Washington, 1985, disting. prof. award, Alpha Chi, Zeta Chpt., Newport News, Va., 1985. Mem. Nat. Assn. Scholars, U.S. Naval Inst., N.Am. Soc. for Oceanic Historians, Soc. for Mil. History. Roman Catholic. Home: 303 Woodroof Rd Newport News VA 23606-2211 Office: Christopher Newport U 50 Shoe Ln Newport News VA 23606-2998

MORRIS, JAMES PEPPLER, bass; b. Balt., Jan. 10, 1947; s. James Deal and Geraldine (Peppler) M.; m. Joanne Frances Vitali, Nov. 15, 1971; 1 dau., Heather Frances; remarried Susan Louise Quittmeyer, Jan. 3, 1987. Student, U. Md., 1965-66, Peabody Conservatory, 1966-68, Acad. Vocal Arts, 1968-70. Recorded with Angel Records div. EMI and Deutche Grammophone, Sony, Phillips. Debut at. Met. Opera, N.Y.C., 1970; singer, 1970—, opera and concert singer, throughout U.S., Can., S.Am. Europe, Australia, Japan, 1970—; recs. include Wotan in the New Ring Cycles. Recipient Grammy award for rec. of Wagner's Ring Cycle. Mem. Actors Equity (Can.), Am. Guild Mus. Artists. Office: care Colbert Artists Mgmt Inc 111 W 57th St New York NY 10019-2211*

MORRIS, JANE ELIZABETH, home economics educator; b. Marietta, Ohio, Nov. 28, 1940; d. Harold Watson and LaRue (Graham) M. Student, U. Ky., 1960; BS, Marietta Coll., 1962, postgrad., 1963; MA, Kent State U., 1970, postgrad., 1985-87; postgrad., Coll. Mt. St. Joseph, 1984-86, John Carroll U., 1986, Ashland Coll., 1987. Cert. high sch. tchr., Ohio. Tchr. home econs. Chagrin Falls (Ohio) Mid. and High Sch., 1963-95; head cheerleading advisor Chagrin Falls High Sch., 1970-80, freshman class advisor, 1981-82, head fine and practical arts dept., 1982-84, sophomore class advisor, 1982-85, 87-89, mem. prin.'s cabinet, 1987-88, tchr. adminstr. adv. coun., 1990—. Vice chmn. The Elec. Women's Round Table, Inc., Cleve., 1968, chmn., 1969-71; treas. Trees Condominium Assn., 1981-83, pres., 1991-94; active Chagrin Falls chpt. Am. Heart Assn., Am. Cancer Soc., Geauga County Humane Soc. Mem. NEA, Career Edn. Assn., Ohio Edn. Assn., N.E. Ohio Edn. Assn., Chagrin Falls Edn. Assn. (bldg. rep. 1986-95, negotiating team 1990, negotiating com. 1993, election chmn., 1995), Alpha Xi Delta. Methodist. Avocations: swimming, interior design, sewing, gourmet cooking. Office: Chagrin Falls Schs 77 E Washington St Chagrin Falls OH 44022-3001

MORRIS, JASON, Olympic athlete. Mem. Olympic team Seoul, Korea, 1988; judo Barcelona, Spain, 1992. Recipient 172 lbs. Class Pan Am. Games champ, 1987, 91, 172 lbs. Class Judo Silver medal Olympics, Barcelona, 1992. Office: US Olympic Com 1750 E Boulder St Colorado Springs CO 80909-5746*

MORRIS, JERRY DEAN, academic administrator; b. Gassville, Ark., May 11, 1935; s. James Henry and Maud Idella (Taylor) M.; m. Marylin Jo Pitman, June 11, 1955; children: Joseph, Neil, Laura, Kara. BS, U. Ark., 1960, MEd, 1964, EdD, 1971. Cert. sch. adminstr., Ark. High sch. tchr. Cotter (Ark.) Pub. Schs., 1959-60, high sch. prin., 1960-63; jr. high prin. Mountain Home (Ark.) Pub. Schs., 1963-66, high sch. prin., 1966-67, asst. supt., 1967-69; editor Ark. Sch. Bds. Newsletter, U. Ark., Fayetteville, 1969-70; dir. placement services East Tex. State U., Commerce, 1970-71, dean admissions & records, 1971-73, dean grad. sch., 1973-81, v.p. acad. affairs, 1982-86, pres., 1987—; cons. Ark. Basic Edn., 1970, U. Cen. Ark., Conway, 1972, coordinating bd. Tex. Colls. & Univs., Austin, 1981. Pres. Commerce C. of C., 1975; bd. dirs. Commerce Lions Club, 1977; chmn. Commerce United Way, 1978; mem. Commerce Indsl. Devel. Assn., 1974—. Named an Outstanding Young Man in Edn., Ark. Jaycees, 1966, Outstanding Young Man in Am., 1967. Mem. Tex. Assn. Coll. Tchrs., Assn. Tex. Grad. Schs. (pres. 1978-79), Coun. of So. Grad. Schs. (bd. dirs. 1976-79), Coun. of Grad. Schs. in U.S., Coun. of Pub. U. Pres. and Chancellors (exec. com. 1989-90), Assn. of Tex. Colls. and Univs. (exec. com. 1989-90), Phi Delta Kappa. Methodist. Avocations: jogging, gardening, reading, singing, travel. Home: ET Sta PO Box 3001 Commerce TX 75429-3001 Office: East Tex State U ET Station Commerce TX 75429

MORRIS, JOHN, composer, conductor, arranger; b. Elizabeth, N.J., Oct. 18, 1926; s. Thomas Arthur and Helen (Sherratt) M.; m. Francesca Bosetti; children: Evan Bosetti, Bronwen Helen. Student, Julliard Sch. Music, 1946-48, U. Wash., 1947, New Sch. Social Research, 1946-49. Composer mus. scores for (films) The Producers, The Twelve Chairs, The Gamblers, Blazing Saddles (nominated Acad. award 1976), The Bank Shot, Young Frankenstein, Sherlock Holmes Smarter Brother, Silent Movie, The Last Remake of Beau Geste, The In-Laws, The World's Greatest Lover, In God We Trust, High Anxiety, The Elephant Man (nominated Acad. award 1981), Table for Five, History of the World Part I, Yellowbeard, The Doctor and the Devils, Clue, To Be or Not To Be, Woman in Red, Johnny Dangerously, Haunted Honeymoon, Dirty Dancing, Spaceballs, Ironweed, The Wash, Stella, Life Stinks, (Broadway stage plays) My Mother, My Father and Me, Doll's House, Camino Real, (mus.) A Time for Singing, (off-Broadway) Take One Step, Young Andy Jackson, 15 scores for N.Y. Shakespeare Festival, Am. Shakespeare Festival, Stratford, Conn., (TV shows) Fresno, Katherine Anne Porter, Ghost Dancing, The Firm, The Mating Season, Splendor in the Grass, The Electric Grandmother, The Scarlet Letter, The Adams Chronicles, Georgia O'Keeffe, The Franken Project, The Tap Dance Kid (Emmy award 1986), Make Believe Marriage, ABC After Sch. Spl. Theme, Making Things Grow Theme, The French Chef Theme, The Desperate Hours, The Skirts of Happy Chance, Infancy and Childhood, The Fig Tree, The Little Match Girl, Our Sons, The Last to Go, The Last Best Year, The Sunset Gang, Coach Theme, Favorite Son, Journey Into Genius, When Lions Roar, Scarlett Mini Series, several documentary films; mus. supr., conductor, arranger numerous TV spls., Broadway and off-Broadway shows and recordings including Anne Bancroft Spl. #1 (Emmy award), 'S Lemmon 'S Gershwin 'S Wonderful (Emmy award), Hallmark Christmas Spls., (Broadway) Mack and Mabel, Much Ado About Nothing, Bells Are Ringing, (off-Broadway) Hair, (records) Wildcat, All-American, Bells Are Ringing, First Impressions, Bye-Bye Birdie, Kwamina, Baker Street, Rodgers and Hart, George Gershwin vols. I and II, Jerome Kern, Lyrics of Ira Gershwin, Cole Porter, others. Mem. ASCAP, Acad. Motion Picture Arts and Scis., Am. Fedn. Musicians. Avocations: computers, humorous poetry, cooking. Office: Alan Stein 270 Madison Ave New York NY 10016

MORRIS, JOHN E., lawyer; b. N.Y.C., Sept. 30, 1916; s. John and Honora C. (Long) M.; m. Patricia E. Grojean. A.B., CCNY; A.M., Columbia U.; J.D., Harvard U. Bar: N.Y. 1942, U.S. Dist. Ct. (so. and ea. dists.) N.Y. Trial lawyer Clarke & Reilly, 1946-50; ptnr. Morris & Duffy, N.Y.C., 1950—. Served to lt. USCG, 1942-46; ETO. Mem. ABA, N.Y. State Bar Assn., N.Y. County Lawyers Assn. (mem. judiciary com.), Airplane Owners & Pilots Assn., Internat. Assn. Ins. Counsel, USCG Combat Vets. Assn., Harvard Club, N.Y. Athletic Club (N.Y.C.), Great Dane Club Am. (bd. dirs.). Roman Catholic. Office: 170 Broadway Fl 7 New York NY 10038-4103

MORRIS, JOHN HITE, chemical industry executive; b. Pitts., Jan. 12, 1942; s. John and Margaret Lane (Geisey) M.; m. Susan Heimert, June 20, 1964; children: Scott, Kirk. B.S., W.Va. U.-Morgantown, 1964; M.B.A., Case Western Res. U., Cleve., 1983. With Armstrong Cork Co., Lancaster, Pa., 1967-73, ADS, Columbus, Ohio, 1974-75, Gen. Tire Co., Akron, Ohio, 1975-77; exec. v.p. RPM, Inc., Medina, Ohio, 1977—, dir. Capt. U.S. Armed Forces, 1964-67. Office: RPM Inc 2628 Pearl Rd Medina OH 44256-7623

MORRIS, JOHN LUNDEN, international transportation executive; b. Wilmington, Del., Feb. 26, 1943; s. Arthur Lunden and Carolyn Wilson (Bickell) M.; m. Sally Carolyn Wheeler, Mar. 9, 1967; children: Christopher Wheeler, Kevin Arthur. BA, U. Del., 1965; postgrad., Rutgers U., 1968-71. Ocean container specialist E.I. DuPont de Nemours & Co., Inc., N.Y.C., 1968-72; mgr. pricing U.S. gulf Seatrain Lines, Inc., Weehauken, N.J., 1972-73; dir. pricing Europe Seatrain Lines, Inc., Rotterdam, Holland, 1973-75; dir. market planning, advt. Seatrain Lines, Inc., Weehauken, 1975-76; dir. pricing Seatrain Agys., Inc., N.Y.C., 1976-80; dir. mktg. Prudential Lines, Inc., N.Y.C., 1980-85; dir. mktg. and rsch. Trans Atlantic Associated Freight Confs., N.Y.C., 1985-87; exec. dir. U.S Atlantic and Gulf Venezuela Conf., Jersey City, 1987-91; chief exec. officer Inter-Am. Freight Conf., Jersey City, 1987-94; pres. Inwood Assocs. Transp. Cons., Upper Montclair, N.J., 1985-94, INTRANSCO, Internat. Transp. Solutions, Inc., Montclair, N.J., 1994—; authorized lead agt. MCI Telecomm. Inc., 1994—; mem. U.S. Commerce Fgn. Trade Data Users Group, Washington, 1986—; electronic systems adv. com. U.S. Customs Svc., Washington, 1988—; study com. Fed. Maritime Commn., Washington, 1989-91, expert witness, also Fed. Cts. Boston, N.Y.C.; spkr.; presenter N.Y./N.J. Port Authority, World Trade Seminar. Mem. adv. com. Ward 1 Montclair, Upper Montclair, N.J., 1982-90; mem. Twp. Transp. Adv. Com., Montclair, 1982-85; chmn. Upper Montclair troop 7 Boy Scouts Am., 1982-88. Mem. Assn. Corp. Computing Tech. Profls., Assn. Banyan Users Internat., Christian Bus. Men's Club (N.Y.C.), Transp. Rsch. Forum, Assn. for Corp. Computing Tech. Profl., Montclair YMCA. Presbyterian. Avocations: bicycling, golf, touring, art and architectural history. Office: INTRANSCO Internat Transp Solutions 24-26 Church St Montclair NJ 07042

MORRIS, JOHN SELWYN, philosophy educator, college president emeritus; b. Tonypandy, Wales, July 2, 1925; came to U.S., 1954, naturalized, 1993; s. Jenkin and Hannah M. (Williams) M.; m. Enid Elry Walters, Apr. 10, 1954; 1 child, Paul John. B.A., Univ. Coll. South Wales and Monmouthshire, 1951; M.A., Cambridge (Eng.) U., 1953; student, Union

Theol. Sem., 1957-60; M.A., Colgate U., 1961; Ph.D., Columbia U., 1961; LL.D. (hon.), Hartwick Coll., 1979; LHD (hon.), Elmyra Coll., 1990; DLitt, Skidmore Coll., 1991. Ordained to ministry Presbyterian Ch., 1954; minister Vernon (N.Y.) and Vernon Center Presbyn. chs., 1954-57; instr. Colgate U., Hamilton, N.Y., 1960-63; asst. prof. Colgate U., 1963-66, asso. prof., 1966-70, prof. philosophy and religion, 1970-79, dir. div. humanities, 1970-72, dir. div. univ. studies, 1972-73, provost, dean of faculty, 1973-79, acting pres., 1977; prof. philosophy Union Coll., Schenectady, 1979-90, pres., chancellor Union U., 1979-90, pres. emeritus, 1990—. prof. philosophy, 1990—; Leverhulme vis. fellow U. Exeter, Eng., 1968-69; chmn. Commn. Ind. Colls. and Univs., 1984-86; bd. dirs. Trustco N.Y. Bd. dirs. Schenectady Found.; trustee Skidmore Coll. With RAF, 1943-47. Recipient Disting. Svc. award Colgate U. Alumni Corp., 1978, Schenectady Patroon award, 1989. Mem. AAUP, Am. Philos. Assn., Am. Acad. Religion, Royal Inst. Philosophy, Soc. for Study Theology, Nat. Welsh Am. Found. (bd. advisors). Office: Union Coll Humanities Ctr Schenectady NY 12308

MORRIS, JOHN WOODLAND, businessman, former army officer; b. Princess Anne, Md., Sept. 10, 1921; s. John Earl and Allice (Cropper) M.; m. Geraldine Moore King, May 12, 1947; children: Susan K., John Woodland III. BS, U.S. Mil. Acad., 1943; MS, U. Iowa, 1947; postgrad., Army War Coll., 1961-62, U. Pitts., 1966. Commd. 2d lt. U.S. Army, 1943, advanced through grades to lt. gen., 1971; dep. dist. engr. Savannah, Ga., 1952-54; resident engr. Goose Bay, Labrador, 1955-57; staff officer Office Chief Engrs., 1957-60; comdg. officer 8th Engr. Bn., Korea, 1960-61; dist. engr. Tulsa, 1962-65; dep. comdt. U.S. Mil. Acad., 1965-67; dep. chief legis. liaison Office Sec. Army, Washington, 1967-69; comdg. gen. 18th Engr. Brigade, Vietnam, 1969-70; div. engr. Missouri River Div., Omaha, 1970-72; dir. civil works Office C.E., Washington, 1972-75; dep. chief engr. U.S. Army, 1975-76, chief engr., 1976-80; ret., 1980; exec. dir. Royal Volker Stevin, 1980-84; pres. J.W. Morris Ltd., 1981—; prof. U. Md., 1983-86; chmn. bd., chief exec. officer PRC Engring., 1986-88, cons.; cons., engr. advisor Zorc, Rissetto, Weaver & Rosen, 1988-92, engr. advisor Seltzer & Rosen, 1992—. Councilman Indian Nations coun. Boy Scouts Am., 1962-65; chmn. Water Resources Congress, 1988-90; bd. dirs. Metcalf and Eddy Cos. Inc., 1988-92, Air Water Tech., 1992—, Morganti Constrn. Co., 1991—; trustee U.S. Mil. Acad. Assn. of Grads., 1986—; advisor dean English/Math., U. Vt., 1990—. Decorated Legion of Merit with three oak leaf clusters, Army D.S.M., Def. D.S.M.; recipient Merit award Am. Cons. Engrs. Council; Palladium medal Audubon Soc. Fellow ASCE; mem. AIA (hon.), Internat. Navigation Congress (v.p.), U.S. Soc. Mil. Engrs. (pres.), Nat. Acad. Engrs., U.S. Com. on Large Dams (past chmn. environ. effect com., named Constrn. Man of Yr. 1977, Navigation Hall of Fame 1990, Golden Beaver award for engring. 1995). Episcopalian. Home: 1329 N Lynnbrook Dr Arlington VA 22201-4918 Office: 3800 N Fairfax Dr Suite 7 Arlington VA 22203

MORRIS, JORDEN WALTER, dancer, educator; b. Banff, Alta., Can., Aug. 19, 1967; s. Walter Edgard Morris and Penny Ann (Stenton) Tillenius. Tchr./coach Royal Winnipeg Ballet, Can., 1985, 88—; mem. corps de ballet, 1987-89, soloist, 1989-92, prin. dancer, 1992—; asst. chorepgrapher Les Ballet Jazz De Montreal, Que., 1979; guest artist Banff (Alta.) Centre Sch. Fine Arts, 1984. Repertoire includes lead roles in Rodeo, Giselle, Romeo and Juliet, Four Last Songs, Lilac Garden, The Nutcracker, Swan Lake, Symphony in D, Stoolgame, Myth, Pas des Déeses, Dark Elegies, La Princesse et le Soldat; gala performer Canadian AIDS Benefit, Toronto, Ont., 1990. Coach Little League Baseball, Canmore, Alta., 1986. Recipient Alan Hooper scholarship Banff Centre Fine Arts, 1981, Larry MCkinnon scholarship Royal Winnipeg Ballet, 1984. Mem. Canadian Actors Equity Assn. (adv. com. 1990). Avocations: carpentry, guitars, mountain climbing, horse ranching. Home: 3H-440 Assiniboine Ave, Winnipeg, MB Canada Office: Royal Winnipeg Ballet, 380 Graham Ave, Winnipeg, MB Canada R3C 4K2*

MORRIS, JUSTIN ROY, food scientist, enologist, consultant; b. Nashville, Ark., Feb. 20, 1937; s. Roy Morris; m. Ruby Lee Blackwood, Sept. 5, 1956; children: Linda Lee, Michael Justin. BS, U. Ark., 1957, MS, 1961; PhD, Rutgers U., 1964. Rsch. asst. Rutgers U., New Brunswick, N.J., 1957-61, instr., 1961-64; extension horticulturist U. Ark., Fayetteville, 1964-67, from asst. to assoc. prof., 1967-75, prof., 1975-85; univ. prof., 1985—; cons. viticulture sci. program Fla. A&M U., Tallahassee, 1979-81; cons. viticulture and enology program Grayson City Coll., Denison, Tex., 1987—; cons. J. M. Smucker Co., Orrville, Ohio, 1982-91. Co-author: Small Fruit Crop Management, 1990, Quality and Preservation of Fruits, 1991, Modern Fruit Science Text Book, 1995; assoc. editor: Am. Jour. Enology and Viticulture, 1985; contbr. more than 300 articles to sci. jours. Recipient rsch. award Nat. Food Processors Assn., 1982. Fellow Am. Soc. for Hort. Sci. (assoc. editor 1985, Gourley award 1979, Outstanding Rsch. award 1983); mem. Ozark Food Processors Assn. (exec. v.p 1988—), Coun. for Agrl. Sci. and Tech. (bd. dirs. 1987-93, chmn. nat. concerns 1987-91, pres.-elect 1993, pres. 1994, 95), Inst. Food Technologists (co-organizer fruit and vegetable divsn. 1987—), Gamma Sigma Delta (Outstanding Rsch. award 1982, Faculty Achievement award for rsch. & svc. 1993). Achievements include development of mechanical cane fruit harvester, of mechanical strawberry harvester, of modified grape harvester for wine grapes, of mechanical shoot positioner for grapes; development of systems for the production, harvesting, handling, utilization, and marketing of grape juice and wine. Office: U Ark Dept Food Sci 272 Young Ave Fayetteville AR 72703-5584

MORRIS, KENNETH BAKER, mergers, acquisition and real estate executive; b. Bklyn., Feb. 12, 1922; s. Clarence E. and Mabel (Baker) M.; m. Dorothy E. Kohler, Sept. 3, 1960; children: Laura Susan, Sandra Lee. Student bus. adminstrn., Manhattan Coll. 1940-43, B.C.E., 1949; postgrad., Inst. Design, 1959-62, U. Nebr., 1970. Registered profl. engr. N.Y., N.J., Conn., Pa., Mass., Ga., Can. licensed profl. planner, also real estate broker. Asst. to pres., chief engr. Kretzer Constrn. Corp., N.Y.C., 1956-58; cons. engr. Kenneth B. Morris (P.E.), N.Y.C., Augusta, Ga., 1958-61; dir. plant and properties N.Y. U., 1961-66, bus. mgr., 1966-68; v.p. Cooper Union U., N.Y.C., 1968-74; v.p charge gen. svcs. East River Savs. Bank, N.Y.C., 1974-79; sr. ptnr. cons. Morris Real Estate Co., N.Y.C., 1979—; adj. prof. Pace U., NYU, Fordham U.; Pres, bd. dirs. Grammercy Greenwich Corp., N.Y.C.; bd. dirs. Washington Sq. S.E.; adv. com. Poly. Inst. N.Y.; devel. and fin. adv. com. Cabrini Med. Center. Contbr. articles to mags. and newspapers. Mem. adv. bd., chmn. edn. com. Salvation Army. Served with USAAF, 1943-45. Mem. N.Y. Savs. Bank Assn. (chmn. security com.), Nat. Assn. Real Estate Execs., N.Y. State Real Estate Bd. (city planning com., edn. com., internat. real estate com., taxes and assessments com.), N.Y. State Soc. Real Estate Appraisers, A.I.M., N.Y.C. East Side C of C. (past pres. and chmn. bd.), Am. Soc. Appraisers (sr. mem.), N.Y. State C. of C. (edn. com.), Lion (1st v.p. club), Am. Arbitration Assn. (nat. panel arbitrators, arbitrator for Am. Stock Exch., City Real Estate Bd.), Inst. Nat. Social Scis., Highlands Country Club. Home: 388 Cedar Dr W Briarcliff Manor NY 10510-2621 Office: Morris Real Estate 280 Madison Ave New York NY 10016-0801

MORRIS, KENNETH DONALD, lawyer; b. Montclair, N.J., Apr. 5, 1946; s. Thomas Almerin and Katherine Louise (Jacobs) M.; m. Susan Sauer, May 1, 1976; children: Ian, Jennifer. BA, Ohio Wesleyan U., 1968; MBA, George Washington U., 1971, JD, 1972. Bar: Pa. 1973, N.J. 1975, D.C. 1989. Atty. Westinghouse Electric, Pitts., 1972-74, Tenneco Chems., Inc., N.J., 1974-76; asst. corp. counsel Ronson Corp., Bound Brook, N.J., 1976-78; assoc. Walder, Sondak, Berkley & Brogan, Newark, 1978-81; sec., gen. counsel, mem. mgmt. com. NOR-AM Chem. Co. subs. Schering AG, Wilmington, Del., 1981-94, environ. com., 1987—, mem. fiduciary com., 1988—; sec., gen. counsel AgrEvo USA Co., Wilmington, 1994—. Incorporator, pres. Charter Oaks Assn.; mem. Gov.'s Internat. Trade Coun., Del. Wolcott Found. scholar, 1969. Mem. ABA (antitrust sect., tort and ins. sect., corp. counsel com., banking and bus. law sect., multinational corps. subcom.), Am. Arbitration Assn. (panel arbitrators), Del. Bar Assn., Am. Corp. Counsel Assn. (dir. Delvacca chpt.), Def. Rsch. Inst. (corp. counsel com.), George Washington U. Sch. Govt. and Bus. Adminstrn. Alumni Assn. (Phila. chpt.), George Washington U. Nat. Law Ctr. Alumni Assn., European-Am. Gen. Counsel Assn., Fed. Bar Assn. (corp. counsel com.), Nat. Agrl. Chem. Assn. (vice chmn. law com.). Republican. Presbyterian. Avocations: classical music, running, sailing, tennis. Office: NOR-AM Chem Co 2711 Centerville Rd Wilmington DE 19808

MORRIS, L. DANIEL, JR., lawyer; b. Jacksonville, Fla., Nov. 21, 1939; s. L. Daniel and Cladine (Mumaw) M.; m. Melanie Monk, June 5, 1965; children: Melanie Michele, Leigh Danielle. BCE, Auburn U., 1961; JD, Georgetown U., 1968. Bar: Ill. 1969, U.S. Patent Office 1969, Ala. 1970. Patent examiner U.S. Patent Office, Washington, 1966-68; assoc. Wolfe, Hubbard, Voit & Ossan, Rockford, Ill., 1968-69; gen. atty., asst. sec. Vulcan Materials Co., Birmingham, Ala., 1970-81; sr. v.p., gen. counsel Brookwood Health Svcs., Birmingham, 1981; dir. legal svcs. Blount, Inc., Montgomery, Ala., 1981-88, v.p. legal svcs., 1988—; chmn. Blount Employees PAC, 1982—, Southeastern Corp. Law Inst., 1989-90; bd. dirs. Brownell Travel Bur., Inc., Birmingham, 1985-89. Pres. Friends of Carver Creative & Performing Arts Ctr., Montgomery, 1989-91; sec. C. Eugene Ireland Found., Birmingham, 1978—; mem. Civil Engring. Industry Liaison Coun., Auburn U., 1987—. Lt. USAR, 1963-69. Mem. ABA, Ala. Bar Assn., Ala. Corp. Counsel Assn. (bd. dirs. 1983-87), Montgomery Bar Assn., Montgomery Country Club. Republican. Episcopalian. Avocations: tennis, reading. Home: 3155 Highfield Dr Montgomery AL 36111-1737 Office: Blount Inc 4520 Executive Park Dr Montgomery AL 36116-1602

MORRIS, LARRY GARNER, transportation company executive; b. New Kensington, Pa., Apr. 1, 1938; s. Fred Chester and Mary Elizabeth (Robinson) M.; m. Janet Louise Moon; children: Blake, Colleen, Kent. BS, Pa. State U., 1960; MBA, U. Pitts. 1964; cert. program for mgmt. devel., Harvard U., 1974. Controller telecommunications ops. Gen. Cable Corp., Greenwich, Conn., 1970-74, v.p. corp. planning, 1974-77, v.p., gen. mgr. power cable, 1977-78; v.p. adminstrn. G.K. Techs., Greenwich, 1978-81; sr. v.p. adminstrn. Penn Cen. Corp. and G.K. Techs., Greenwich, 1981-83; sr. v.p. fin. and adminstrn. electronics telecommunications and def. group Penn Cen., Greenwich, 1983-85; sr. v.p., chief fin. officer Tiger Internat. and Flying Tiger Line, Los Angeles, 1986—. Served to lt. (j.g.) USN, 1960-62. Mem. Fin. Execs. Inst. Assn. Republican. Baptist. Home: 116 Northstar Mall Marina Dl Rey CA 90292-6794 Office: Tiger Internat 7401 World Way W Los Angeles CA 90045-5836 Office: Advo-System Inc One Univac Lane Windsor CT 06095

MORRIS, LEIGH EDWARD, hospital executive officer; b. Hartford City, Ind., Dec. 26, 1934; s. Fredus Orlando and Martha (Malott) M.; m. Marcia Renee Meredith, Oct. 7, 1967; children: Meredith Anne, Curtis Paul. BS in Commerce, Internat. Coll., 1954; BSBA, Ball State U., 1958; M in Health Adminstrn., U. Minn., 1972. Mem. labor relations staff Borg-Warner Corp., Muncie, Ind., 1961-64; various positions then personnel mgr. Internat. Harvester Co., Ft. Wayne, Ind., 1964-70; pres. Huntington (Ind.) Meml. Hosp., 1972-78, La Porte (Ind.) Hosp., 1978—; bd. dirs. First of Am. Bank, N.W. Ind. Am. Hosp. Svcs., Inc., Soc. for Healthcare Planning and Mktg.; chmn., bd. dirs. Am. Hosp. Pub. Co. Chmn. La Porte Devel. Corp., 1980-81, La Porte chpt. ARC, 1984-86. Served with U.S. Army, 1958-60. Recipient Disting. Alumni award U. Minn., Mpls., 1972. Fellow Am. Coll. Healthcare Adminstrn., Health Care Fin. Mgmt. Assn.; mem. Am. Hosp. Assn. (trustee, regional chmn. 1985-89), Am. Pub. Health Assn., Ind. Hosp. Assn. (chmn. 1980-81), La Porte C. of C. (chmn. 1981-82), Constantian Soc. Republican. Presbyterian. Lodge: Mason. Avocations: classic cars, civic affairs. Home: 1519 Indiana Ave La Porte IN 46350-5105 Office: La Porte Hosp Inc PO Box 250 La Porte IN 46352-0250

MORRIS, LOIS LAWSON, education educator; b. Antoine, Ark., Nov. 27, 1914; d. Oscar Moran and Dona Alice (Ward) Lawson; m. William D. Morris, July 2, 1932 (dec.); 1 child, Lavonne Morris Howell. B.A., Henderson U., 1948; M.S., U. Ark., 1951, M.A., 1966; postgrad. U. Colo., 1954, Am. U., 1958, U. N.C., 1968. History tchr. Delight High Sch., Ark., 1942-47; counselor Huntsville Vocat. Sch., 1947-48; guidance dir. Russellville Pub. Sch. System, Ark., 1948-55; asst. prof. edn. U. Ark., Fayetteville, 1955-82, prof. emeritus, 1982—; ednl. cons. Ark. Pub. Schs., 1965-78. Mem. Commn. on Needs for Women, 1976-78, Hist. Preservation Alliance Ark.; pres. Washington County Hist. Soc., 1983-85; pres. Pope County Hist. Assn.; mem. Ark. Symphony Guild; charter mem. Nat. Mus. in Arts; bd. dirs. Potts Inn Mus. Found. Named Ark. Coll. Tchr. of Year, 1972; recipient Plaque for outstanding svcs. to Washington County Hist. Soc., 1984. Contbr. articles to jours. Mem. LWV, AAUW, Ark. Coun. Social Studies (sec.-treas.), Washington County Hist. Soc. (exec. bd. 1977-80), NEA, Nat. Coun. Social Studies, Ark. Edn. Assn., Ark. Hist. Assn., Pope County Hist. Assn. (pres. 1991-92), The So. Hist. Assn., U. Ark. Alumni Assn., Sierra Club, Nature Conservancy, So. Hist. Assn., Ark. River Valley Arts Assn., Phi Delta Kappa, Kappa Delta Pi, Phi Alpha Theta. Democrat. Episcopalian. Address: 1601 W 3d St Russellville AR 72801

MORRIS, MAC GLENN, advertising bureau executive; b. Bessemer City, N.C., Jan. 24, 1922; s. Manly T. and Erin C. (Cline) M.; m. Janelle Convevey, July 27, 1946; children—Robert S., Janelle C., Patricia A., John Logan. A.B., Davidson Coll., 1942. Space salesman Progressive Farmer mag., N.Y.C., 1946-52; exec. v.p., advt. dir. This Week mag., 1952-68; pres. Newspaper One, N.Y.C., 1968-71; sr. v.p. nat. sales Newspaper Advt. Bur., N.Y.C., 1972-87; proprietor MGM Assocs., Princeton, N.J., 1987—; dir. Princeton Bank & Trust Co. (div. Chem. Bank N.J., N.A., owned by Chem. Bank, N.Y.C.). Served to 1st lt., pilot USMCR, World War II. Decorated D.F.C. (2), Air medal (7). Mem. Newcomen Soc. in N. Am., Pi Kappa Phi. Presbyn. (deacon). Club: Springdale Golf (Princeton, N.J.) (bd. govs.). Home and Office: 417 Herrontown Rd Princeton NJ 08540-2932

MORRIS, MALCOLM STEWART, lawyer; b. Houston, May 8, 1946; s. William Carloss and Doris Eletta (Poole) M.; m. Rebecca Ann Simmons, June 14, 1969; children: Matthew William, Andrew James. BBA, So. Meth. U., 1968; JD, U. Tex., 1970, MBA, 1972. Bar: Tex. 1970. Legis. aid State of Tex., Sen. Charles Wilson, Austin, 1969-70; examiner Stewart Title Austin Inc., 1970-71; trainee Bank of the S.W., Houston, 1973-74; bus. mgr. Richard Hogue Evangelism, Inc., Houston, 1974-75; v.p. ops. Stewart Title Guaranty Co., Houston, 1975-87; sr. exec. v.p., asst. chmn. Stewart Title Guaranty Co., 1987—; now lawyer Morris, Lendais, Hollrah, et al., Houston; bd. dirs. Tex. Land Title Assn., Austin, Stewart Title Co. of Memphis, Stewart Title Dallas, Inc., Morris, Tinsley & Snowden, Houston, Stewart Title, Houston; chmn. bd. Stewart Title Ins. Co., N.Y.C. Deacon, First Bapt. Ch. of Houston, 1982—. Fellow Am. Bar Found., Houston Bar Assn.; mem. ABA, Am. Land Title Assn. (exec. com. underwriter's sect. 1988—), Phi Delta Phi. Baptist. Office: Morris Lendais Hollrah et al 1980 Post Oak Blvd Ste 700 Houston TX 77026-6852*

MORRIS, MARJORIE HALE, artist, writer, photgrapher, retail executive, appraiser; b. Chattanooga, Aug. 4, 1940; d. Laurie Everett and Marjorie (Hunt) H.; 2 children. Student El Camino Jr. Coll., 1958-60. Stewardess Am. Airlines, 1960-62, mem. staff nat. advt. and publicity, 1961-62; mgr. Viking Ski Shop, Pacific Palisades, Calif., 1963-64; Pepsi Cola Corp. rep. to Republican Nat. Conv., 1964; co-owner, mgr. Ready Room Restaurant, L.A., 1967; architects adv., restaurant devel. and design, Honolulu, Dallas, Atlanta, L.A., 1967-73; mgr., buyer Great Things, Honolulu, 1972-74; mgr. Braille Inst. Thrift Shop, L.A., 1975-78, dir. 1978—, devel. officer, 1980-86; account exec. Alexanders Moving & Storage, Atlas Van Lines, 1981-86, interstate truckdriver, 1986-87; U.S. promotional cons. Kids Only Market, Granville Island, Vancouver, B.C., Can., 1985; owner Marjorie Morris, appraisers; freelance writer and photographer, 1974—; designer floats Pacific Palisades Parade, 1965, TransPace Race Com., Honolulu, 1972. Team mother Pacific Palisades Little League, 1974-76. Mem. Beverly Hills C. of C. (Outstanding Svc. to Cmty. awards 1976, 77). Originator, dir. Christmas Tree Project, Beverly Hills; cover editor Calif. Yacht Club Mag., 1976; founder, editor Waterlines, newsletter of Flotilla 12-7, USCG Aux., 1979. Mem. Am. Soc. Appraisers (panel speaker nat. conv. 1983). Address: PO Box 2651 Mc Kinleyville CA 95521

MORRIS, MARK RONALD, advertising agency executive; b. N.Y.C., July 11, 1941; s. John H. and Louise (Edwards) M.; m. Elena Kusa, Nov. 24, 1963; children: Eric, Nicole. B.A., St. Lawrence U. 1963. Account exec. Ted Bates Advt., N.Y.C., 1968-71; mng. dir. Ted Bates Advt. Milan, Italy, 1971-74; v.p., account dir. Ted Bates Advt., N.Y.C., 1974-77, sr. v.p., mgmt. rep, 1977-83, exec. v.p., 1983-87; exec. v.p. acctg. mgmt., chmn. ops. bd. Backer Spielvogel Bates, N.Y.C., 1987-94; dir. Ted Bates U.S.A., 1994—. Bd. dirs. 140 East Assn., N.Y.C., 1974-76, Palisades Free Libr., 1983-87. Capt. U.S. Army, 1963-67. Decorated Bronze Star, Air medal with four oak

leaf clusters, Army Commendation medal; Vietnamese Cross Gallantry. Mem. Assn. Non-Prescription Drug Mfrs. , Am. Assn. Advt. Agys. Home: Snedens Landing Palisades NY 10964 Office: Bates USA Chrysler Bldg 405 Lexington Ave New York NY 10174-0002

MORRIS, MARK WILLIAM, choreographer; b. Seattle, Wash., Aug. 29, 1956; s. William and Maxine (Crittenden) M. Studied with, Verla Flowers and Perry Brunson. Artistic dir. Mark Morris Dance Group, N.Y.C., 1980—, Théâtre Royal de la Monnaie, Brussels, 1988—; choreographer White Oaks Dance Project, 1990; performed with Lar Lubovitch Dance Co., Hannah Kahn Dance Co., Laura Dean Dancers and Musicians, Eliot Feld Ballet, Koleda Balkan Dance Ensemble. Choreographer for Mark Morris Dance Group: Mythologies, 1986, L'Allegro, il Penseroso ed il Moderato, 1988, Dido and Aeneas, 1989, The Nutcracker, 1991, Lucky Charms, 1994, Rondo, 1994, The Office, 1994, others; choreographer: Mort Subite, Boston Ballet, 1986, Esteemed Guests, Joffrey Ballet, 1986, Drink to Me Only With Thine Eyes, Am. Ballet Theatre, 1988, Ein Herz, Paris Opera Ballet, 1990, Nixon in China, Houston Grand Opera, 1987, Orfée et Euridice, Seattle Opera, 1988, The Death of Klinghoffer, Théâtre de la Monnaie, 1991; (television) Great Performances/Dance in America: The Hard Nut, 1992; dir: Die Fledermaus, Seattle Opera, 1988. Recipient N.Y. Dance and Performance award, 1984, 90; Guggenheim fellow, 1986. Office: Mark Morris Dance Group 225 Lafayette Ste 504 New York NY 10012-4015*

MORRIS, M(ARY) ROSALIND, cytogeneticist, educator; b. Ruthin, Wales, May 8, 1920; came to U.S., 1942, naturalized, 1954; d. Aneurin Edmund and Celia Charles (Evans) M. BS in Horticulture, Univ. Agrl. Coll., Guelph, Can., 1942; PhD in Plant Breeding and Genetics, Cornell U., 1947. Mem. faculty U. Nebr., Lincoln, 1947—, prof. agronomy, 1958-90, prof. emeritus, 1990—. Contbr. chpts. to textbooks, articles to sci. jours. U. Nebr. Johnson Faculty fellow, Calif. Inst. Tech., Pasadena, 1949-50; John Simon Guggenheim Found. fellow, Sweden and Eng., 1956-57. Fellow AAAS, Am. Soc. Agronomy, Crop Sci. Soc. Am.; mem. AAUW, Genetics Soc. Can., Nebr. Acad. Sci., Nebr. Ornithologists' Union (editor The Nebr. Bird Rev. 1992—), Lincoln Camera Club, Sigma Xi, Gamma Sigma Delta, Sigma Delta Epsilon. Avocations: bird watching, photography, writing. Office: U Nebr Dept Agronomy Lincoln NE 68583-0915

MORRIS, MAX F., lawyer; b. Yuba City, Calif., Dec. 24, 1943. BAE, U. Fla., 1965, JD, 1968. Bar: Fla. 1968. Law clk. to judge U.S. Ct. Appeals (5th cir.), 1968-70; ptnr. Baker & Hostetler, Orlando, Fla. Mem. ABA, Am. Resort Devel. Assn. (bd. dirs.), Orange County Bar Assn., Fla. Bar (mem. real property, corp. and bus. law sect.). Office: Baker & Hostetler SunBank Ctr 200 S Orange Ave Ste 2300 Orlando FL 32801-3439

MORRIS, MICHAEL HOWARD, public relations executive; b. Detroit, July 4, 1938; s. Robert and Cele (Scabnick) M.; m. Marcia H. Kirschenbaum, Sept. 16, 1962 (dec. 1991); children: Steven, Leslie; m. Wendy Burnham, Dec. 5, 1993. BS in Econs., Hofstra U., 1959. From account exec. to exec. v.p. Burson-Marsteller, N.Y.C., 1962—. Mem. Pub. Rels. Soc. Am. (Silver Anvil award 1970, 72, 74, 78, internat. com.), U.S. China Coun. (bd. dirs.), Bus. Coun. of Understanding Internat. (bd. dirs.), Global Pub. Affairs Inst. (bd. dirs.), Asia Soc. Office: Burson Marsteller 230 Park Ave S New York NY 10003-1513

MORRIS, MICHAEL J., book publishing executive. With Mike Morris Ltd., London, England, 1963-73; chmn. ICBP, London, England, 1973-83, Joshua Morris Pub. Inc., Wilton, Conn. Office: Joshua Morris Pub Inc 221 Danbury Rd Wilton CT 06897

MORRIS, NORVAL, criminologist, educator; b. Auckland, New Zealand, Oct. 1, 1923; s. Louis and Vera (Burke) M.; m. Elaine Richardson, Mar. 18, 1947; children: Gareth, Malcolm, Christoper. LLB, U. Melbourne, Australia, 1946, LLM, 1947; PhD in Criminology (Hutchinson Silver medal 1950), London Sch. Econs., 1949. Bar: called to Australian bar 1953. Asst. lectr. London Sch. Econs., 1949-50; sr. lectr. law U. Melbourne, 1950-58, prof. criminology, 1955-58; Ezra Ripley Thayer teaching fellow Harvard Law Sch., 1955-56, vis. prof., 1961-62; Boynthon prof., dean faculty law U. Adelaide, Australia, 1958-62; dir. UN Inst. Prevention Crime and Treatment of Offenders, Tokyo, Japan, 1962-64; Julius Kreeger prof. law and criminology U. Chgo., 1964—, dean Law Sch., 1975-79; chmn. Commn. Inquiry Capital Punishment in Ceylon, 1958-59; mem. Social Sci. Rsch. Coun. Australia, 1958-59; Australian del. confs. div. human rights and sect. social def. UN, 1955-66; mem. standing adv. com. experts prevention crime and treatment offenders. Author: The Habitual Criminal, 1951, Report of the Commission of Inquiry on Capital Punishment, 1959, (with W. Morison and R. Sharwood) Cases in Torts, 1962, (with Colin Howard) Studies in Criminal Law, 1964, (with G. Hawkins) The Honest Politicians Guide to Crime Control, 1970, The Future of Imprisonment, 1974, Letter to the President on Crime Control, 1977, Madness and the Criminal Law, 1983, Between Prison and Probation, 1990, The Brothel Boy and Other Parables of the Law, 1992. Served with Australian Army, World War II, PTO. Decorated Japanese Order Sacred Treasure 3d Class. Fellow Am. Acad. Arts and Scis. Home: 1207 E 50th St Chicago IL 60615-2908 Office: U Chgo Law Sch 1111 E 60th St Chicago IL 60637-2702

MORRIS, OWEN GLENN, engineering corporation executive; b. Shawnee, Okla., Feb. 3, 1927; s. Vestus and Myrtle (Lindsey) M.; m. Joyce Gast; children: Deborah Moree, Janine Inez. B.S. in Mech. Engring. U. Okla. 1947, M.Aero. Engring., 1948; postgrad., U. Va., 1952-53, Va. Poly. Inst. 1955-56, Coll. William and Mary, 1957-58. Aero., research scientist NASA, Langley Field, Va., 1948-61; mgr. mission engring. NASA (Apollo), Houston, 1961-64; mgr. reliability and quality assurance NASA (Apollo), 1964-66, chief project engr. lunar module, 1966-69, mgr. lunar module, 1969-72; mgr. NASA (Apollo Spacecraft Program), 1972-73; dep. mgr. NASA (Space Shuttle Sorbiter), 1973-80; mgr. systems integration NASA (Space Shuttle), 1974-80; pres. Eagle Engring., 1980-86; pres., chief exec. officer Eagle Aerospace, Houston, 1987-90, chmn., chief exec. officer, 1990-93, chmn. bd., 1992—. Mem. Tex. Water Control Improvement Dist. Bd., 1969-76. Served with USNR, 1943-46. Recipient U.S. Medal of Freedom, 1972, NASA Distinguished Service medal, 1973, NASA Exceptional Service medal, 1969. Asso. fellow Am. Inst. Aeros. and Astronautics; mem. Am. Asronautical Soc., Am. Aviation Hist. Soc., Acad. Model Aeros., Tau Beta Pi, Tau Omega. Presbyterian (elder 1964—). Club: Rotary. Home: 14914 Timberland Ct Houston TX 77062-2922 Office: Eagle Aerospace 910 Gemini Houston TX 77058

MORRIS, PATRICIA SMITH, media specialist, author, educator; b. Franklin, N.J., Jan. 31, 1940; d. Joseph P. and Pauline C. (Lasinski) Smith; m. Carl W. Morris; children: Margaret, Sarah, Maureen. BA, Paterson State Coll.; MLS, Rutgers U. Media specialist East Hanover (N.J.) Bd. Edn. Author: Stepping into Research!, 1990; 6 Vols. of Young Adult Reading Activities Library, 1993. Asst. exec. dir. N.J. Connection. Recipient N.J. Gov's. Tchr. Recognition award, 1989; named Outstanding Ednl. Media Specialist of N.J. 1990. Mem. ALA, NEA, Am. Assn. Sch. Libr., N.J. Edn. Assn., N.J. Connection (asst. exec. dir.), Morris County Sch. Media Assn. (past pres.), Ednl. Media Assn. N.J. (exec. bd.). Office: E Hanover Mid Sch 477 Ridgedale Ave East Hanover NJ 07936-3022

MORRIS, PHILIP JOHN, aerospace engineering educator; b. Llandudno, Wales, Apr. 21, 1946; came to U.S. 1973; s. William Garnet and Dora (Butterworth) M.; m. Brenda Mary English, Aug. 24, 1968; children: Nicola Carol, Karen Elizabeth, Anthony Richard. BSc with honors, Southampton (Eng.) U., 1967, MSc, 1969, PhD, 1972. Rsch. assoc. U. Toronto, Ont., 1971-73; rsch. engr. Lockheed-Ga. Co., Marietta, 1973-77; asst. prof. Pa. State U., University Park, 1977-80; assoc. prof. Pa. State U., 1980-86, prof., dir. computational fluid dynamic studies, 1986—; Boeing prof. aerospace engring., 1990—; cons. Lockheed Ga. Co., 1977-88. Contbr. to tech. publs. Mem. AIAA (aeroacoustics tech. com. 1981-84, 89-95, chmn. 1993-95). Avocations: soccer, running. Office: Pa State U 233 P Hammond Bldg University Park PA 16802

MORRIS, PHYLLIS SUTTON, philosophy educator; b. Quincy, Ill., Jan. 25, 1931; d. John Guice and Helen Elizabeth (Provis) Sutton; m. John Martin Morris, Feb. 4, 1950; children: William Robert, Katherine

Jill. Student, U. Mich., 1948-51; AB, U. Calif., 1953; MA, Colo. Coll., 1963; PhD, U. Mich., 1969. Instr. humanities Mich. State U., East Lansing, 1968-69; from lectr. to assoc. prof. Kirkland Coll., Clinton, N.Y., 1969-78; assoc. prof. Hamilton Coll., Clinton, 1978-83; adj. assoc. prof. LeMoyne Coll., Syracuse, N.Y., 1983-85; rsch. assoc. in philosophy Oberlin (Ohio) Coll., 1995—. Author: Sartre's Concept of a Person, 1976; revs. editor Sartre Studies Internat. jour., 1995; contbr. articles to profl. jours. Travel grantee Am. Coun. Learned Socs., 1988, Summer Seminar grantee NEH, 1974, 82. Mem. Am. Philos. Assn., Sartre Cir., Sartre Soc. N.Am. (cofounder 1985, exec. com. 1985-91), Soc. for Phenomenology and Existential Philosophy, Soc. for Women in Philosophy. Democrat. Avocations: reading, walking, film watching. Home: 2116 Runnymede Blvd Ann Arbor MI 48103

MORRIS, RALPH WILLIAM, chronopharmacologist; b. Cleveland Heights, Ohio, July 30, 1928; s. Earl Douglas and Viola Minnie (Mau) M.; m. Carmen R. Mueller; children: Christopher Lynn, Kirk Stephen, Timothy Allen and Todd Andrew (twins), Melissa Mary. BA, Ohio U., Athens, 1950, MS, 1953; PhD, U. Iowa, 1955; postgrad., Seabury-Western Theol. Sem., 1979-81, McHenry County Coll., 1986-88. Research fellow in pharmacology, then teaching fellow U. Iowa, 1952-55; instr. dept. pharmacology Coll. Medicine, 1955-56; asst. prof. dept. pharmacognosy and pharmacology Coll. Pharmacy, 1956-62, assoc. prof., 1962-69; prof. pharmacology Med. Center, U. Ill., 1969—; adj. prof. edn. Coll. Edn. U. Ill. at Chgo., 1976-85; vis. scientist San Jose State U., Calif., 1982-83; mem. adv. com. 1st aid and safety Midwest chpt. ARC, 1972-83; cons. in drug edn. to Dangerous Drug Commn., Ill. Dept. Pub. Aid, Chgo., Ill. Dept. Profl. Regulataions, Ill. Dept. Corrections and suburban sch. dists. Referee and contbr. articles to profl. and sci. jours., lay mags., radio and TV appearances. Trustee Palatine (Ill.) Pub. Libr., 1967-72, pres., 1969-70; trustee N. Suburban Libr. System, 1968-72, pres. 1970-72, mem. long-range planning com., 1975-81; chmn. Ill. Libr. Trustees, 1970-72, intellectual freedom com.; mem. Title XX Ill. Citizens Adv. Coun., 1981-83; trustee McHenry (Ill.) Pub. Libr. Dist., 1987-89, pres., 1987-89; trustee St. Gregory's Abbey, Three Rivers, Mich., 1989—; bd. dirs. United Campus Ministry U. Ill. at Chgo., 1983-87. Recipient Golden Apple Teaching award U. Ill. Coll. Pharmacy, 1966; cert. of merit Town of Palatine, 1972. Mem. AAAS, Am. Assn. Coll. Pharmacists, Am. Pharm. Assn., Ill. Pharm. Assn., Internat. Soc. Chronobiology, European Soc. Chronbiology, Am. Soc. Pharmacology and Exptl. Therapeutics, Am. Library Trustee Assn., Ill. Library Trustee Assn. (v.p. 1970-72, dir. 1969-72), Sigma Xi, Rho Chi, Gamma Alpha. Episcopalian. Home: 584 Shoreline Dr Barrington IL 60010-3883 Office: U Ill MC 865 833 S Wood St Chicago IL 60612-7229

MORRIS, RANDALL ELLIS, immunologist, university program director; b. San Mateo, Calif., May 9, 1948; s. Walter King and Janet (McClanahan) M.; m. Kay Goenne, July 12, 1975; children: Christine Kay, Robert Randall. AB, Stanford U., 1970, MD, 1976. Intern Stanford (Calif.) U. Med. Ctr., 1976-77; resident in surgery U. Wis. Health Sci. Ctr., Madison, 1977-79, 81-82, rsch. fellow in immunology dept. pediatrics, 1979-81, rsch. fellow in immunology dept. surgery, 1982-83; dir. lab. for transplant immunology dept. cardiovascular Stanford (Calif.) U. Med. Ctr., 1983—; cons. Syntex Pharms., Palo Alto, Calif., 1987—, Genentech, Inc., South San Francisco, 1988—, Wyeth-Ayerst Pharms., Princeton, N.J., 1988—. Editorial adv. bd.: Reviews in Contemporary Pharmcotherapy, 1990—; contbr. more than 50 articles to profl. jours. Recipient Shearing award ACS, 1980. Mem. Internat. Transplantation Soc., Internat. Soc. for Heart Transplantation, European Soc. for Organ Transplantation, Internat. Soc. for Immunopharmacology. Office: Stanford U Med Ctr Dept Cardiovascular Surgery 300 Pasteur Dr Palo Alto CA 94304-2299

MORRIS, REBECCA ROBINSON, lawyer; b. McKinney, Tex., July 27, 1945; d. Leland Howell and Grace Laverne (Stinson) Robinson; m. Jesse Eugene Morris, July 18, 1964; children: Jesse III, Susan, John. BBA in Acctg., So. Meth. U., 1974, JD, 1978. Bar: Tex. 1979, U.S. Dist. Ct. (no. dist.) Tex. Acct. Electronic Data Systems Corp., Dallas, 1975; assoc. atty. Dresser Industries, Inc., Dallas, 1978-83, staff atty., 1981-83, corp. atty. 1983-86, asst. sec., 1984-90, sr. atty. corp. adminstrn., 1986-87, corp. counsel, 1987—, sec., 1990—, v.p., 1994—. Trustee Plano (Tex.) Ind. Sch. Dist., 1979-91, 93-94, pres., 1980-85, sec., 1986-91; bd. dirs. Plano Futures Found., Inc., 1992—, pres., 1992-93. Mem. ABA, AICPA, Tex. State Bar, Dallas Bar Assn., Tex. Soc. CPAs, Am. Soc. Corp. Secs. (mem. securities law com. 1988—, proxy system com. 1990-93, exec. steering com. 1993-94, budget com. 1993—, bd. dirs. 1991-94, chmn. mem. com. Dallas chpt. 1986, treas. 1987, v.p. 1988, pres. 1989), Am. Corp. Counsel Assn. (corp. and securities law com. 1991—). Methodist. Home: 1718 14th Pl Plano TX 75074-6404 Office: Dresser Industries Inc 2001 Ross Ave Box 718 Dallas TX 75221-3610

MORRIS, RICHARD HERBERT, physicist, educator; b. Oakland, Calif., Nov. 22, 1928; s. William H. and Blandine (Franklin) M.; m. Barbara J. Norris, Jan. 21, 1956; children—Katherine E., William Henry II. A.B., U. Calif. at Berkeley, 1950, Ph.D., 1957. Physicist Radiation Lab., U. Calif. at Berkeley, 1953-56; instr. physics Sacramento State Coll., 1956-57; faculty San Diego State U., 1957—, prof. physics, 1966—; Invited lectr. NSF Summer Inst., U. Calif. at Berkeley, 1960-66; cons. Naval Electronics Lab. San Diego, 1962-63; judge Greater San Diego Sci. Fair, 1964—; mem. Calif. Natural Scis. Liaison Com., 1976-78. Recipient Distinguished Teaching award Calif. Legislature, 1968, TRW Excellence Teaching award, 1987-88. Mem. Am. Inst. Physics, Am. Assn. Physics Tchrs., Am. Phys. Soc., Optical Soc. Am., Sci. Rsch. Soc., Phi Beta Kappa, Sigma Xi, Phi Kappa Phi. Home: 1775 Granite Hills Dr El Cajon CA 92019-2603 Office: San Diego State U San Diego CA 92182

MORRIS, RICHARD WARD, nonprofit organization administrator, author; b. Milw., June 16, 1939; s. Alvin Harry and Dorothy Lydia (Wissmueller) M. BS, U. Nev., 1962, PhD, 1968; MS, U. N.Mex., 1964. Exec. dir. COSMEP, Inc., San Francisco, 1968—. Author: Poetry Is a Kind of Writing, 1975, Light, 1979, The End of the World, 1980, The Fate of the Universe, 1982, Evolution and Human Nature, 1983, Dismantling the Universe, 1983, Time's Arrows, 1985, The Nature of Reality, 1987, The Edges of Science, 1990, Assyrians, 1991, (with others) The Word and Beyond, 1982, Cosmic Questions, 1993. Office: COSMEP Inc PO Box 420703 San Francisco CA 94142-0703

MORRIS, ROBERT, artist; b. Kansas City, Mo., Feb. 9, 1931. Student, Kansas City Jr. Coll., Kansas City Art Inst., 1948-50, U. Kansas City, Calif. Sch. Fine Arts, San Francisco, Reed Coll., 1954-55; MA, Hunter Coll., 1966. Instr. art Hunter Coll., N.Y.C., 1964-75, prof. art., 1975—. One man shows include, Corcoran Gallery Art, Washington, 1969, Whitney Mus. Am. Art, N.Y.C., 1970, Leo Castelli Gallery, N.Y.C., 1972, 76, Max Protetech Gallery, Washington, 1973, Stedelijk Mus., Amsterdam, 1977, Florence Wilcox Art Gallery, Swarthmore (Pa.) Coll., 1978, Whitney Mus. Am. Art, 1972, 73, 75, 76, Ind. U. Art Mus., 1972, Art in Evolution, Xerox Sq. Exhbn. Center, Rochester, N.Y., 1973, Princeton U. Art Mus., 1974, Art Inst. Chgo., 1974, 76, 77, Ponderosa Collection, 74, Contemporary Arts Center, Cin., Some Recent Am. Art (traveling exhbn. Australia, New Zealand), Mus. Modern Art, N.Y.C., 1974, Galerie Ricke, Cologne, W. Ger., 1974, Beaubourg Centre Nat. d'Art Contemporain, Paris, 1974, Phila. Coll. Art, 1975, Portland Art Mus., 1975, Sculpture Am. Directions 1945-1975, Nat. Collection Fine Arts, Smithsonian Inst., Washington, 1975, Mus. Contemporary Art, Chgo., 1975, 77, High Mus. Art, Atlanta, N.Y. State Mus., Albany, 1977, Madison (Wis.) Art Center, 1977, New Gallery Contemporary Art, Cleve., 1977, Kansas City Art Inst., 1978, Mus. Contemporary Art, La Jolla, 1978, Inst. Contemporary Art, Boston, 1982, Sonnabend Gallery, 1992; group exhbns. include, Guggenheim Internat., Solomon R. Guggenheim Mus., N.Y.C., 1967, Minimal Art, The Hague, 1968, The Art of the Real, Mus. Modern Art, 1968, Phila. Mus. Art, 1968, High Mus. Art, Atlanta, 1982, Stedelijk Mus., Amsterdam, 1982, Sonnabend Gallery, 1985, Mus. Contemporary Art, Chgo., 1986, Dessins d'Ameriques, Frac Picardie, Amiens France, 1992, others; represented in permanent collections, Nat. Gallery of Victoria, Melbourne, Australia, Dallas Mus. Fine Arts, Whitney Mus. Am. Art, Tate Gallery, London, Modern Museet, Stockholm, commd. works include, Earth Project Nat. Planning Commn., Ottawa, Ont., Can., Steam Piece, Western Wash. U., Bellingham, 1969, Grand Rapids Project, City of Grand Rapids, Mich., 1974, Observatory, Sonbeek Unlimited, Oost-Elevo-

land, Netherlands, 1977. Served with U.S. Army, 1951-52. Recipient prize Walker Art Center, Mpls., 1966; 1st prize Internat. Inst., Torcuato di Tella, Buenos Aires, Argentina, 1967; sculpture award Soc. Four Arts, 1975; Guggenheim fellow, 1969. Home: 109 N Mountain Rd Gardiner NY 12525 Office: Dept Studio Art Hunter Coll 695 Park Ave New York NY 10021-5024 also: Castelli Gallery 4 E 77th St New York NY 10021-1727

MORRIS, ROBERT, lawyer, writer; b. Jersey City, Sept. 30, 1915; s. John Henry and Sarah (Williams) M.; m. Joan Russell Byles, Dec. 27, 1951; children: Robert, Paul E., Roger, Joan Byles Barry, William E., John Henry II, Geoffrey. A.B., St. Peters Coll., Jersey City, 1936; J.D., Fordham U., 1939; L.L.D. St. Francis Coll., Bklyn., 1954, U. Plano, 1976; L.H.D., Fujen U., Taipei, 1971. Bar: N.Y. 1939, Tex. 1962, U.S. Supreme Ct. 1952. Newspaper reporter, 1934-36; tchr. Greek, Latin and govt. St. Peters Prep. Sch., Jersey City, 1936-39; with firm Hines, Rearick, Dorr & Hammond, N.Y.C., 1939-40; asst. counsel N.Y. State Investigating Com., 1940-41; sec. to Congressman F. R. Coudert, Jr., 1946-50; sec.-treas. Monrovia Port Mgmt. Co., Africa, 1947-49; with firm Hochwald, Morris & Richmond, N.Y.C., 1946-52; spl. counsel U.S. Senate Internal Security Subcom., 1951-53, chief counsel, 1953, 56-58; judge Municipal Ct., N.Y.C., 1954-56; counsel to U.S. senators Hickenlooper and Lodge on U.S. Senate Fgn. Relations Com., 1950; adviser U.S. Senate Rules Com., 1955; pres. U. Dallas, 1960-62, U. Plano, Tex., 1964-71, 73-77; chancellor U. Plano, 1971-72; observer Zimbabwean parliamentary elections, 1979. Author: No Wonder We Are Losing, 1958, Disarmament, Weapon of Conquest, 1963, What Is Developmental Education?, 1967, Self-Destruct, 1979, Our Globe Under Siege, 1982, vol. II, 1985, vol. III, 1988, also nat. column; contbr. articles to profls. Candidate for Rep. nomination to U.S. Senate from N.J., 1958, 60, 84, from Tex., 1964, 70; chmn. Nat. Com. to Restore Internal Security, 1979—; bd. dirs. Insts. for achievement Human Potential, 1977-89, bd. govs., 1989—; bd. dirs. Univ. Profs. for Acad. Order, 1988-91, U.S. Coun. World Freedom, 1981-91, Am.'s Future, 1985—, chmn. bd. and pres., 1989—. Served to lt. comdr. USNR, 1941-46, comdr. Ret. Mem. ABA (internat law sect.), Am. Zimbabwean Assn. (chmn. 1978-87), Mil. Order World Wars (comdr. Monmouth chpt. 1984—), Phi Delta Phi. Clubs: Univ. (N.Y.C.); Mantoloking Yacht; Shanghai-Tiffin; Circumnavigators; Army-Navy (Washington); Admirals. Home: 1237 Ocean Ave Mantoloking NJ 08738-1613 Office: PO Box 234 Mantoloking NJ 08738-0234

MORRIS, ROBERT ALAN, aerospace industry executive; b. North Platte, Nebr., Sept. 9, 1934; s. Robert A. and Freda (Zediker) M.; m. Joyce D. Rigg, Dec. 5, 1959; children: Linda K., Laura D., Robert A. BBA, McCook (Nebr.) Jr. Coll., 1954; BS in Journalism, Northwestern U., 1956, MS in Journalism, 1957. Reporter, editor Chgo. Tribune, 1958-60; dir. pub. relations BOAC, Chgo., 1960-64; dir. communications IBM Corp., N.Y.C., 1964-77; v.p. communications Borg-Warner, Chgo., 1977-86, Gen. Dynamics Corp., St. Louis, 1986—; mem. Pub. Rels. Seminar, 1978—, Golden Workshop, N.Y.C., 1981—. Bd. dirs. Family Personal Svc. Ctr. St. Louis, 1986—, Jr. Achievement, Hazelwood, Mo. 1986—, St. Louis Regional Commerce and Growth Assn., 1988—. With USAR, 1957-63. Mem. Aerospace Industries Assn. Am. (communications council 1987—), Pub. Affairs Council (bd. dirs. 1982—), St. Louis Press Club, St. Louis Club, Sigma Delta Chi. Republican. Presbyterian. Office: Gen Dynamics Corp 3190 Fairview Park Dr Falls Church VA 22042-4524

MORRIS, ROBERT C., historian, archivist, educator; b. Alexandria, Va., Aug. 6, 1942; s. Chester O. and Mary Louise (Eisele) M.; m. Darlene K. Kerstetter, Sept. 19, 1964. BA, U. N.Mex., 1964; AM, U. Chgo., 1965, PhD, 1976. Instr. U. Md., College Park, 1968-69; instr. Rutgers U., Newark, 1970-71, vis. prof. history, 1983, 85-87; manuscripts curator N.J. Hist. Soc., Newark, 1972-74, library dir., 1974-79; head spl. collections, assoc. prof. history and edn. Tchrs. Coll., Columbia U., N.Y.C., 1979-82; spl. collections adminstr. Schomburg Ctr. Research in Black Culture, N.Y.C., 1982-87, mem. selection com. Scholars-in-Residence program, 1987—; dir. Nat. Archives N.E. Region, 1987—; mem. N.J. Hist. Records Adv. Bd., Trenton, 1976-79, 88—; mem. com. on scholarly programs, higher edn. and libraries, N.J. Hist. Commn., Trenton, 1976-87; mem. N.J. planning com. White House Conf. on Libraries, 1979; cons. exec. com. Hist. Soc. U.S. Dist. Ct. for Dist. N.J., N.Y. Fed. Exec. Bd., Fed. Exec. Bd. Met. No. N.J.; cons. CARE, Inc., N.Y.C., 1985-88. Author: Reading, 'Riting, and Reconstruction: The Education of Freedmen in the South 1861-1870, 1981 (nominated for Pulitzer prize in history), Freedmen's Schools and Textbooks: Black Education in the South, 1861-1870, 1980, "Educational Reconstruction" in the Facts of Reconstruction: Essays in Honor of John Hope Franklin, 1991; contbr. numerous articles to profl. publs. Mem. Mid-Atlantic Regional Archives Conf. (chmn. 1985-87), Orgn. Am. Historians, Am. Hist. Assn., Assn. for Study of Afro Life and History, Soc. Am. Archivists, Archivists Round Table Met. N.Y., Phi Beta Kappa. Democrat. Presbyterian. Avocations: archaeology, art, theater, tennis, biking. Office: Nat Archives NE Region 201 Varick St New York NY 10014

MORRIS, ROBERT CHRISTIAN, education educator; b. Anderson, Ind., Mar. 1, 1948; s. Robert Childs and Velma Jane (Vogley) M.; m. Linda Marie Butkus, Jan. 14, 1989. AB, Duke U., 1970; MS, Ind. State U., 1971, PhD, 1977. Cert. tchr.; lic. prin., supt. Profl. football player Houston Oilers, 1970; tchr. social studies Roanoke (Va.) Schs., 1970-71, 74-76; profl. football player New Orleans Saints, 1971-73; asst. prof. edn. Auburn (Ala.) U., 1976-81; assoc. prof. edn. U. S.C., Columbia, 1981-84, No. Ill. U., DeKalb, 1984-87; prof., head dept. edn., leadership, tech. and rsch. Ga. So. U., Statesboro, 1987-91; dean. sch. edn. U. Indpls., 1991-93; prof. edn. West Ga. Coll., Carrollton, 1993—; cons. Mt. Morris (Ill.) Pub. Schs., Dixon Pub. Sch., 1986; cons., evaluator bi-lingual programs Dixon (Ill.) Pub. Schs. Author: A Resource Guide for Working with Youth-At-Risk, 1992, (pamphlet) A Field Practicum for Tchrs. of Gifted Children, 1982—; editor: Vantil on Education, 1978, Youth at Risk: A Resource Guide, 1991, Solving the Problems of Youth-At-Risk, 1992, Using What We Know About At-Risk Youth: Lessons From the Field, 1994; contbr. over 100 articles to profl. jours. Sponsor Sigma Nu Auburn U., 1977-81, Phi Kappa Sigma No. Ill. U., 1984-88, Alpha Tau Omega West Ga. Coll., 1993—; regional co-dir. Auburn Spl. Olympics, Auburn, 1977-81; games dir. S.C. Spl. Olympics, Columbia, 1982-84. Mem. ASCD, VFW, Am. Assn. Colls. for Tchrs. Edn., Am. Ednl. Rsch. Assn., John Dewey Soc. (exec. sec.-treas. 1982—), Profs. of Curriculum, Soc. Profs. of Edn., Phi Delta Kappa (former v.p. local chpt.), Phi Kappa Sigma (sponsor/advisor local chpt.), Kappa Delta Pi (sec.-treas.), Civitan. Avocations: weightlifting, travel, painting. Home: 628-E Cedar Villas Cedar St Carrollton GA 30117 Office: West Ga Coll Dept Secondary Edn Carrollton GA 30118

MORRIS, ROBERT G(EMMILL), retired foreign service officer; b. Des Moines, July 20, 1929; s. Robert William and Eva May (Gemmill) M.; m. Beverly Schupfer, July 3, 1955; children: Robert William II, John Schupfer, Richard Edward. BS, Iowa State U., 1951; postgrad., Charles Francis U. Graz, 1951-52; MS, Calif. Inst. Tech., 1954; PhD, Iowa State U., 1957. Asst. prof. S.D. Sch. Mines and Tech., Rapid City, 1958-59, assoc. prof., 1959-62, prof., head dept. physics, 1962-68; phys. sci. officer Office of Naval Research, Washington, 1968-73, dir. electronics program, 1973-74; U.S. fgn. service officer U.S. Dept. State, Washington, 1974-78; counselor for sci. and technol. affairs U.S. Mission to OECD, Paris, 1978-82, U.S. Embassy, Bonn, Fed. Republic Germany, 1982-85; dep. asst. sec. of state for sci. and tech. affairs Washington, 1985-87; fgn. svc. officer U.S. Embassy, Buenos Aires, 1987-90, Madrid, 1990-92. Contbr. articles to profl. jours. Fulbright scholar, Austria, 1951; Swiss govt. fellow, Zurich, 1957. Fellow APS; mem. IEEE, Am. Fgn. Service Assn.

MORRIS, ROBERT JULIAN, JR., art gallery owner; b. Decatur, Ill., Jan. 12, 1932; s. Robert J. and M. Letitia (Ross) M.; m. J. Jean Nelson Morris, June 6, 1952; children: R. Thomas, Debora L., Charles A., Sandra J. BS in Chemistry, U. Ill., 1954; MS in Chemistry, Marshall U., 1961. Analytical chemist Union Carbide Chemicals, South Charleston, W.Va., 1954-61; sr. research chemist U.S. Gypsum Co., Des Plaines, Ill., 1961-63; research mgr. MacAndrews and Forbes Co., Camden, N.J., 1963-66; tech. dir. Nat. Can Corp., Chgo., 1966-73; v.p. corp. engring. Coachmen Industries Inc., Middlebury, Ind., 1973-74; pres. Coachmen Homes Corp., 1974-76; chmn. bd., chief exec. officer Medallion Plastics Inc., Elkhart, Ind., 1976-93; owner Robert Morris Gallery, Goshen, Ind., 1993—. Contbr. articles to profl. jours. Bd. dirs. Career Ctr., Elkhart, 1983-89, Ind. Voc. Tech. Coll., Plastics

R&D Ctr. Ball State U., 1987-94. Mem. Rotary. Republican. Methodist. Avocations: fine art black and white photographic silver prints, camping. Home: 510 Skyview Dr PO Box 730 Middlebury IN 46540 Office: Robert Morris Gallery 1100 N Chicago Ave Goshen IN 46526-1941

MORRIS, ROBERT LEE, gallery administrator, jewelry designer; b. Nurnberg, Federal Republic Germany, July 7, 1947; came to U.S., 1947; s. Jack Bret and Sara Ellen (Holloway) M. BA, Beloit Coll., 1969. Owner, pres. Robert Lee Morris, N.Y.C., 1977—, Artwear, 1977-94. Trustee Beloit (Wis.) Coll., 1989—. Recipient Coty award N.Y.C., 1981, Coun. Fashion Designers Am. award, 1985, M Spl. award Internat. Gold, N.Y.C., 1986, Disting. Svc. award Beloit Coll. Alumni Assn., 1988, Woodmark award, 1992, FAAB award, 1992, Coun. Fashion Designers Am. award, 1994. Office: 161 6th Ave Fl 14 New York NY 10013-1205

MORRIS, ROBERT LOUIS, management consultant; b. Phila., Aug. 24, 1932; s. Joseph Aloysius and Philomena Mary Ellen (Clauser) M.; BS, Drexel U., 1955; MS, U. Pa., 1957; postgrad. U. Cin., 1965-66, U. Chgo., 1969-71; m. Elizabeth Marie Smyth, Sept. 10, 1955; children—Robert L., Thomas J., Lawrence F., Elizabeth M., Mary Ellen, Richard B. Group leader Procter & Gamble Co., Miami Valley Labs., 1958-68; dir. computing services research and devel. div. Kraft, Inc., Glenview, Ill., 1968-71; dir. research and process devel. Continental Baking Co., Rye, N.Y. and St. Louis, 1971-77, v.p. tech. affairs, 1978-92; tech. dir. food and chem. products ITT Inc., N.Y.C., 1977-78; pres., Managing Tech., Inc., Williamsburg, Va., 1992—. Bd. dirs. Fundacion Chile, Santiago, 1978-79, 83-85; mem. Greenwich Rep. Town Meeting, 1977. Served with AUS, 1957. NSF fellow, 1955-56; Wilson S. Yerger fellow, 1956-57. Fellow Am. Inst. Chem. Engrs.; mem. Assn. Rsch. Dirs., Indsl. Rsch. Inst. (bd. dirs. 1988-91), Am. Chem. Soc., Am. Assn. Cereal Chemists, Inst. Food Techs. Roman Catholic. Clubs: Ford's Colony Golf. Patentee in field. Office: Managing Tech Inc PO Box 679 Lightfoot VA 23090-0679

MORRIS, RUSTY LEE, administrative executive; b. Glenwood Springs, Colo., Nov. 28, 1940. Student, York Christian Coll., 1974-75, U. Nebr., 1975-76, Mesa State Coll., 1992-95, Colo. Christian U., 1995—. Specialist comm. security Martin-Marietta Corp., Larson AFB, 1962-63; communications security specialist classified def. project Boeing Aerospace Div., Larson AFB, Wash., 1963-64; with F.W. Sickles div. Gen. Instrument Corp., Chicopee, Mass., 1965-68; adminstr. judicial affairs J. Arthur Hickerson, Judge, Springfield, Mass., 1969-71; researcher Mont. United Indian Assn., Helena, 1970-72; adminstrv. asst. Vanderbilt U. Hosp., Nashville, 1980-82; paid bus. supr. Sears Svc. Ctr., Grand Junction, Colo., 1987-89; founder, chief exec. officer Vast Spl. Svcs., Grand Junction, 1988—; courier U.S. Census Bur., Grand Junction, 1990; spl. program coord. Colo. Dept. Parks and Recreation, Ridgway, 1990-91; acad. athletic program founder/coord. Mesa State Coll., 1992-93, math. and sci. rep., student govt., 1992—, athletic coun., 1993—, student health ctr. com., 1993—, faculty search com., 1993; founder, chief exec. officer Rolling Spokes Assn. Vol. Easter Seals Soc., 1964-67, vol. instr. Adult Literacy Program, 1984-87; vol. T.V. host Muscular Dystrophy Assn. Am., 1975-94; bd. dirs. Independent Living Ctr. 1985-87, Handicap Awareness Week, 1989; trails com. Colo. State Parks and Outdoor Recreation, 1988—; condr. seminars Ams. With Disabilites Act, 1989—; cons. Bur. Reclamation, 1988—, Bur. Land Mgmt., 1989—; staff trainer Breckenridge Outdoor Recreation Ctr., 1989-90; emergency svcs. officer Colo. Civil Air Patrol, Thunder Mountain Squadron, 1989—; bd. dirs. Handicap Awareness, 1989; dir. com. Colo. State Trails Commn. 1989-90; mem. Dem. Nat. Com., 1991—; dist. com. Grand Junction Sch. Dist., 1992—; mem. Restore the Com., Avalon, 1993—; bd. dirs., presenter No. Colo. chpt. Colo. Orgn. of Victim Assistance; with victim assistance Mesa County Sheriff's Dept., 1993—. Recipient Hometown Hero award, 1993. Mem. Handicap Scholarship Assn. (bd. dirs. 1994, award 1993), Nat. Orgn. Victim Assistance (presenter 1988—), Nat. Coun. Alcoholism and Drug Abuse (vol. 1987—), Mother's Against Drunk Driver's (bd. dirs. Mesa County chpt., v.p. 1985—), Concerns of Police Survivors, Club 20 of Western Colo. (mem. com. status), Great Outdoor Colo., Grand Junction C. of C., Grand Junction Symphony, Mus. Western Colo., Mesa State Coll. Geology Club, Toastmasters (Able Toastmaster, winner speech contests 1985-87). Home and Office: Vast Spl Svcs 612 N 15th St Grand Junction CO 81501-4422

MORRIS, SANDRA JOAN, lawyer; b. Chgo., Oct. 13, 1944; d. Bernard and Helene (Davies) Aronson; m. Richard William Morris, May 30, 1965 (div. Jan. 1974); children: Tracy Michelle, Bretton Todd; m. William Mark Bandt, July 12, 1981; 1 child, Victoria Elizabeth. BA, U. Ariz., 1965; JD, Calif. Western U., 1969. Bar: Calif. 1970, U.S. Dist. Ct. (so. dist.) Calif. 1970; diplomate Am. Coll. Family Trial Lawyers. Ptnr. Morris & Morris, APC, San Diego, 1970-74; sole practice San Diego, 1974—; mem. Adv. Commn. on Family Law, Calif. Senate, 1978-79. Contbr. articles to profl. jours. Pres. San Diego Community Child Abuse Coordinating Coun., 1977; mem. human rsch. rev. bd. Children's Hosp., San Diego, 1977-92. Fellow Am. Acad. Matrimonial Lawyers (chpt. pres. 1987-88, nat. bd. govs. 1987-89, 93-94, parliamentarian 1989-91, treas. 1994—), Internat. Acad. Matrimonial Lawyers; mem. ABA (exec. com. family law sect. 1982-83, 87-93), State Bar Calif. (cert. family law specialist 1980—), Lawyers Club San Diego (bd. dirs. 1973). Republican. Jewish. Avocations: skiing, travel. Office: 2121 5th Ave San Diego CA 92101-2101

MORRIS, SETH IRWIN, architect; b. Madisonville, Tex., Sept. 1, 1914; s. Seth Irwin and Carrie (Holleman) M.; m. Suzanne Kibler, Dec. 29, 1945; children: Mark Peter, Maria, David Kibler, Laura Houston, John Hampson. B.A., Rice Inst., 1935. Practice architecture Houston, 1935-87; ptnr. Wilson & Morris, 1938-47, Wilson, Morris & Crain, 1946-87, Wilson, Morris, Crain & Anderson, 1954-87; ptnr. S.I. Morris Assocs., 1972-87, cons., 1988—; ptnr. Morris/Aubry Architects, 1980-85, Morris Architects, 1986-87; cons. Jackson & Ryan, 1989—. Prin. works include Harris County Domed Stadium (Astrodome), 1965, Houston Pub. Library, 1975, S.W. Home Office Texaco Inc., 1975, Prudential Ins. Co., 1977, One Houston Center, 1977, Brown and Root, Inc. hdqrs, 1978, Alfred C. Glassell, Jr. Sch. Art, 1979, 1st City Bank Tower, 1981, Wortham Theater Ctr., 1985. Chmn. bd. trustees Houston Mus. Fine Arts, 1961-63, 67-68, pres., 1967-68; chmn. bd. trustees Contemporary Arts Mus., 1988-89; bd. govs. Rice U., Houston.; bd. dirs. ARC Harris County. Served to comdr. USNR, 1942-46. Decorated Legion of Merit; Order Cloud and Banner China; recipient numerous archtl. honor awards Tex. Soc. Architects, numerous archtl. honor awards Houston chpt. AIA; nat. awards AIA, Gold medal Assn. Rice U. Alumni, 1991; named Disting. Alumnus Rice U., 1981. Fellow AIA; mem. Tex. Soc. Architects (Llewellen Pitts award 1992), Assn. Gen. Contractors (master builder awrd 1994), Houston C. of C. (dir. 1964-86). Presbyterian (elder). Home: 2 Waverly Ct Houston TX 77005-1842 Office: 2370 Rice Blvd Ste 210 Houston TX 77005-2644

MORRIS, STANLEY E., federal official; b. Hayward, Calif., Feb. 17, 1942; s. Richard Ellsworth and Lavila (Gibson) M.; m. Judith Rosenblum, 1968; 1 child, Courtney. BA, San Jose State Coll., 1963; MA, Columbia U., 1967. Intern mgmt. HEW, Washington, 1968-71; dir. operational planning HEW, 1971-73; dep. assoc. dir. Office Mgmt. and Budget, Washington, 1973-79; sr. fellow, lectr. U. Md., College Park, 1980-81; assoc. dep. atty. gen. U.S. Dept. Justice, Washington, 1981-83; dir. U.S. Marshals Svc., Washington, 1983-89; dep. dir. Office of Nat. Drug Control Policy, Exec. Office of the Pres., Washington, 1989—. Recipient Sec.'s Spl. Citation HEW, 1973, Presdl. Meritorious Exec. award, 1983, Pres.'s award Nat. Sheriffs Assn., 1988, Spl. Achievement award Assn. Fed. Investigators, 1988. Mem. Assn. Fed. Investigators (pres. 1991—). Office: Office Nat Drug Control Policy Exec Office of the Pres Washington DC 20500

MORRIS, STEPHEN BURRITT, marketing information executive; b. Morristown, N.J., Aug. 13, 1943; s. Grinnell and Cornelia Rogers (Kellogg) M. m. Victoria Ann French, Feb. 18, 1967; children: Christopher Jackson, Robin Taylor. BA, Yale U., 1965; MBA, Harvard U., 1969. With product mgmt. Gen. Foods Corp., White Plains, N.Y., 1969-83, gen. mgr. Maxwell House Coffee div., 1983-85; v.p. Gen. Foods Corp., 1983-87, pres. Maxwell House div., 1986-87; founder, dir. Spectra Mktg. Systems Inc., Chgo., 1987-90; pres., CEO Vid Code Inc., Waltham, Mass., 1990-92; pres. The Arbitron Co., N.Y.C., 1992—; bd. dirs. John B. Stetson Co., 1991—. Served to 2nd lt. USMCR, 1965-66. Avocations: tennis; skiing; gardening. Home: 300 Mt

Holly Rd Katonah NY 10536 Office: The Arbitron Co 142 W 57th St New York NY 10019-3300

MORRIS, STEPHEN JAMES MICHAEL, lawyer; b. Los Angeles, Aug. 22, 1934; s. Thomas Ambrose and Kathryn Adele Brown M.; m. Ann Austin Moseley, Aug. 31, 1956 (div.); children: Brook Barrett, Clea Alden; m. Anne Sturdy Abbott, June 30, 1990. B.A., Pomona Coll., 1956; LL.B., U. Calif. at Berkeley, 1961. Bar: Calif. 1962. Since practiced in Los Angeles; law clk. for Judge Albert Lee Stephens, U.S. Ct. Appeals 9th Circuit, 1961, Judge Albert Lee Stephens Jr., U.S. Dist. Ct., Central Dist. Calif., 1962; asso. firm Walker, Wright, Tyler & Ward (attys.), Los Angeles, 1962-66; founding partner Dietsch, Gates, Morris & Merrell (and predecessor firm), Los Angeles, 1966-78; ptnr. Hahn Cazier & Smaltz, Los Angeles, 1978-87, Morgan, Lewis & Bockius, 1987—. Bd. dirs. Pasadena Symphony Assn., 1985—, sec., 1988-90, pres., 1990-94; bd. dirs. Calif. Symphony Orchs., 1994—. Served to 1st. lt. Armored Corps AUS, 1956-58. Mem. ABA, State Bar Calif. (del. 1973-76), Los Angeles County Bar Assn. (exec. com. bus. and corp. law sect. 1973-75), Calif. Club (dir. 1992—), Valley Hunt Club (dir. 1977-83, treas. 1979-81, v.p. 1981-82, pres. 1982-83), Chancery Club, Sigma Tau, Phi Alpha Delta. Home: 270 S Arroyo Blvd Pasadena CA 91105-1507 Office: Morgan Lewis & Bockius 801 S Grand Ave Los Angeles CA 90017-4613

MORRIS, STEVLAND See WONDER, STEVIE

MORRIS, STEWART, JR., title insurance company executive; b. Houston, Oct. 14, 1948; s. Stewart Sr. and Joella (Mitchel) M. BA, Rice U., 1971; MBA, U. Tex., 1973. V.p. Stewart Title Co., Houston, 1975-87, sr. exec. v.p., asst. to pres., 1987—; bd. dirs. Southern Nat. Bank, Houston. Bd. dirs. Houston chpt. Cystic Fibrosis Found., 1985—. Mem. Am. Land Title Assn., Am. Driving Soc. (bd. dirs. 1984—), Houston Area Carriage Assn. (pres. 1985—), Carriage Assn. Am. Office: 2200 West Loop S Houston TX 77027-3502

MORRIS, THOMAS BATEMAN, JR., lawyer; b. Columbus, Ohio, Aug. 11, 1936; s. Thomas Bateman and Margaret (O'Shaughnessy) M.; m. Ann Peirce, Feb. 23, 1963; children: Lauren, Thomas III, Richard. AB, Princeton U., 1958; JD, Harvard U., 1962. Bar: Pa. 1962. Ptnr. Dechert Price & Rhoads, Phila., 1962—, chmn., 1990—; bd. dirs. PNC Bank N.A., Phila., Berwind Corp., Phila., Asten, Inc., Charleston, S.C., Envirite Corp., Plymouth Meeting, Pa., Peirce-Phelps, Inc., Phila., Harmac Med. Products, Inc., Buffalo. Co-chmn. Greater Phila. Internat. Network, 1978—; trustee Princeton U., 1975-80; bd. trustees Thomas Jefferson U., 1989—. Hon. Consul King of Belgium, Phila., 1974-89. Mem. ABA, Pa. Bar Assn., Phila. Bar Assn. (chmn. city tax policy com.), Internat. Bar Assn. (chmn. com. on structure and ethics of law practice), Phila. Club, Phila. Cricket Club, Princeton Club, Sunnybrook Golf Club, Pine Valley Golf Club. Home: 8320 Seminole Ave Philadelphia PA 19118-3932 Office: Dechert Price & Rhoads Bell Atlantic Tower 1717 Arch St Philadelphia PA 19103-2793

MORRIS, THOMAS QUINLAN, hospital administrator, physician; b. Yonkers, N.Y., Jan. 3, 1933; s. William Thomas and Mary Berenice (Quinlan) M.; m. Jacqueline Ingram, Sept. 12, 1959; children: Thomas, Amy, MaryAnne. BS, U. Notre Dame, 1954; MD, Columbia U., 1958. Diplomate Am. Bd. Internal Medicine. From instr. to assoc. prof. clin. medicine Coll. Physicians and Surgeons, Columbia U., N.Y.C., 1964-79, prof., 1979—, acting chmn. dept. medicine, 1978-82, assoc. dean academic affairs, 1979-82, vice dean faculty of medicine, 1982-84, vice chmn. dept. medicine, 1993-94, sr. assoc. v.p. for health scis., vice dean faculty medicine, 1994—; acting dir. Med. Services, Presbyn. Hosp., N.Y.C., 1978-82, pres., 1985-90; v.p. for programs N.Y. Acad. Medicine, 1990-94, active 1994—. Med. editor Complete Home Medical Guide, 1985. Trustee Mary Imogene Bassett Hosp., Cooperstown, N.Y., 1980—, chmn. 1994—; trustee Am. Univ. of Beirut, N.Y.C., 1985—. Served to capt. USAF, 1962-64. Fellow ACP; mem. Greater N.Y. Hosp. Assn. (bd. govs. 1985-90), League of Voluntary Hosps. and Homes (chmn. bd. dirs. 1985-89). Clubs: The Century, Harvey Soc. (N.Y.C.). Office: Coll Physicians and Surgeons 630 W 168th St New York NY 10032-3702 also: New York Acad Medicine 2 E 103rd St New York NY 10029

MORRIS, THOMAS ROBBINS, political science educator; b. Roanoke, Va., July 28, 1944; s. Robert Vaughan and Ethel (Robbins) M.; children from previous marriage: Sheila Dawn, Tabbitha Lyn, Sharon Robbins, Rosalyn Vaughan. B.A. in History, Va. Mil. Inst., 1966; M.A., U. Va., 1969, Ph.D. in Govt., 1973; postgrad. Princeton Theol. Sem., 1966-67. Asst. prof. U. Richmond, Va., 1971-78, assoc. prof. polit. sci., 1978-87, prof., 1987—, chair dept., 1981-84; polit. analyst WTVR-Channel 6 TV, Richmond, 1981—; vis. scholar U. Utah, 1986-87. Author: The Virginia Supreme Court: An Institutional and Political Analysis, 1975, Virginia Government and Politics: Readings and Comments, 2d edit., 1984. Bd. dirs. Housing Opportunities Made Equal, Richmond, Va., 1982—. Liberal arts fellow Harvard Law Sch., Cambridge, Mass., 1976-77, NEH fellow U. Wis.-Madison, 1979-80; named Disting. Educator, U. Richmond, Va., 1982. Mem. Am. Polit. Sci. Assn., Omicron Delta Kappa. Methodist. Home: 3216 Noble Ave Richmond VA 23222-2530 Office: Dept Polit Sci U Richmond Richmond VA 23173

MORRIS, THOMAS WILLIAM, symphony orchestra administrator; b. Rochester, N.Y., Feb. 7, 1944; s. William H. and Eleanor E. M.; m. Jane Allison, Aug. 7, 1965; children: Elisa L., Charles A., William H. A.B., Princeton U., 1965; M.B.A., Wharton Sch. U. Pa., 1969. Adminstrv. asst., Ford Found. fellow for adminstrv. interns in arts Cin. Symphony, 1965-67; payroll clk. bus. office Boston Symphony Orch., 1969-71, asst. mgr. bus. affairs, 1971-73, mgr., 1973-78, gen. mgr., 1978-86, v.p. spl. projects and planning, 1986; pres. Thomas W. Morris and Co., Inc., Boston, 1986-87; exec. dir. Cleve. Orch., 1987—; chmn. policy com. Maj. Orch. Mgrs., 1977-79; chmn. orch. panel Nat. Endowment for Arts, 1979—. Chmn. Cleve. Cultural Coalition, 1992-95; mem. Cleve. Bicentennial Commn., 1993—. Mem. Am. Symphony Orch. League (dir. 1977-79). Office: Cleve Orch Severance Hall Cleveland OH 44106

MORRIS, VICTOR FRANKLIN, JR., meteorology educator; b. Hyannis, Mass., Mar. 1, 1947; s. Victor Franklin and Florence Muriel (Rund) M. Student, MIT, 1965-66; BS in Atmospheric Scis., U. Wash., 1969; MS in Meteorology, U. Hawaii, 1975; MA in Environ. Geography, San Diego State U., 1979. Cert. community coll. instr. earth scis., Calif.; cert. advanced and instrument ground instr. FAA. Rsch. asst. U. Hawaii, Honolulu, 1973-75; teaching asst., lectr. San Diego State U., 1976-80; instr. San Diego Community Colls., 1976-80; prof. aero. sci. in meteorology Embry-Riddle Aero. U., Daytona Beach, Fla., 1981-94; pres. Caribbean Weather Svc., Rincon, Puerto Rico, 1994—; cons. meteorologist Surf Publs., Dana Point, Calif., 1980—; chief East Coast meteorologist Surf Line, Huntington Beach, Calif., 1987—. Author: The Weather Survival Kit, 1977, Meteorology: A Study Guide, 1985; writer monthly newsletter Sea Watch, 1980—; contbr. articles to profl. jours. and mags. Lt. USN, 1970-72. Mem. Am. Meteorol. Soc., Phi Kappa Phi. Avocations: surfing, distance running, gardening, beachcombing, amateur radio. Home: PO Box 909 Rincon PR 00677-0909

MORRIS, WALTER SCOTT, investment company executive; b. Paterson, N.J., Mar. 7, 1912; s. Edwin Royle and Katherine Dorothy (Landau) M; m. Vera G. Curie, Jan. 31, 1941 (dec. 1966); children: Hugh C., Gordon S.; m. Dorothy L. Geeteh, July 15, 1988. Student, Coll. City N.Y., 1932-36, N.Y. Inst. Fin., 1936-39. Various positions stock brokerage firms, 1928-43; with Argus Rsch., 1946-48; pres. Fund Mgmt. Inc., 1948-52; v.p. treas. Model, Roland & Co., N.Y.C., 1952-74, also bd. dirs., 1952-74; v.p. Shields, Model, Roland Inc., N.Y.C., 1974-77; assoc. Bache, Halsey Stuart Shields, 1977-80; bd. dirs. Blue Ridge Real Estate, 1967-75; instr. investment subjects N.Y. Inst. Fin., 1940-50. Pres., bd. dirs. Camp Nejeda Found., 1965-68, Morris Found., Inc., 1960—; bd. dirs., treas., mem. exec. com. Heifer Project Inc., 1968-77, Am. Diabetes Assn., 1969-75; bd. dirs., mem. exec. com. Reinhold Niebuhr Award, 1971-75; sec. bd. dirs. Hospice of Ark., 1978-80. With AUS, 1943-45, ETO. Mem. Inst. Chartered Fin. Analysts, N.Y. Soc. Security Analysts, Lawyers Club (N.Y.C.), Union League Club (N.Y.C. and Chgo.), Little Rock Club. Office: 700 E 9th St Little Rock AR 72202-3978

MORRIS, WILLIAM, lawyer; b. Lakewood, N.J., Sept. 2, 1941; s. Saul and Beatrice Morris; m. Susan Wolfbein, Feb. 13, 1965; children: David, Jonathan. AB, Rutgers U., 1963; JD, Georgetown U., 1966, LLM in Taxation, 1971. Bar: Va. 1966, D.C. 1981. Trial atty. IRS, Washington, 1966-70; atty.-advisor U.S. Tax Ct., Washington, 1970-72; gen. counsel U.S. Senate Fin. Com., Washington, 1972-80; with Reid & Priest, Washington, 1981-83, Rogers & Wells, Washington, 1984—; mem. IRS Commr.'s Adv. Group, 1985-86. Mem. ABA (sect. taxation), D.C. Bar Assn. (tax com.), Fed. Bar Assn. (sect. taxation), Nat. Coun. Aging (vice-chmn. nat. inst. fin. issues and svcs. for elders). Office: Rogers & Wells 607 14th St NW Washington DC 20005-2011

MORRIS, WILLIAM CHARLES, investor; b. St. Louis, Apr. 15, 1938; s. Barney Lockhart and Kathryn (Evers) M.; m. Susan VanAvery Follett, Aug. 26, 1961; children: Edward F., David L., Kenneth V. SB in Chem. Engring., MIT, 1960; MBA, Harvard Bus. Sch., 1963. Assoc. Mobil Chem. Co., N.Y.C., 1963-66, Lehman Bros., N.Y.C., 1967-72; mng. dir. Lehman Bros. Kuhn Loeb Inc. (and predecessor), N.Y.C., 1973-84; sr. advisor Shearson Lehman Bros., N.Y.C., 1985-87; chmn. Carbo Ceramics Inc., Dallas, 1987—; chmn., pres. J&W Seligman & Co., Inc., N.Y.C., 1988—; chmn. Tri-Continental Corp., N.Y.C., 1988—, The Seligman Group of Investment Cos., N.Y.C., 1988—; bd. dirs. Kerr McGee Corp., Oklahoma City, 1977—, Daniel Industries, Houston, 1969—. Trustee Sarah Lawrence Coll., 1991—. Served as ensign USCG, 1961. Home: 5 Hampshire Cir Bronxville NY 10708-5803 Office: J & W Seligman & Co Inc 100 Park Ave 8th Fl New York NY 10017

MORRIS, WILLIAM JOSEPH, paleontologist, educator; b. Balt., Oct. 14, 1923; s. Benjamin Moss and Aida (Ruble) M.; m. Ann Bates, Aug. 11, 1945; children—Lynn Ann (Mrs. Thomas W. Nadal), Carol Florence. B.A., Syracuse U., 1947; M.A., Princeton, 1948, Ph.D., 1950. Asst. prof. to asso. prof. geology Tex. A. and M. U., 1950-55; asso. prof. to prof. geology Occidental Coll., 1955—; also research asso. in vertebrate paleontology Los Angeles County Mus. Natural History, 1957—; mem. Nat. Geog. Soc. expdn. to Baja, Calif., 1968-73. Contbr. articles profl. jours. Served with AUS, 1942-45. Recipient Arnold Guyot award Nat. Geog. Soc., 1968. Fellow Geol. Soc. Am., So. Calif. Acad. Scis. (pres. 1969-70, dir. 1958-70); mem. AAAS, Soc. Vertebrate Paleontologists, Soc. Study Evolution, Sigma Xi. Club: Explorers (N.Y.C.). Home: 707 S 3d Ave Battle Ground WA 98604 *I maintain that a commitment to intellectual and personal integrity is necessary for spiritual well-being. My rules are not complex. Honesty and an undeviating sense of responsibility to those who have offered opportunities and placed their trust in me are a part of my life. Intelligence appears necessary in order to contribute significantly to our society, but often lacking in those with adequate mental status is perseverance. One must be firm in belief and determination, and have a mature skepticism that can lead to invention.*

MORRIS, WILLIAM OTIS, JR., lawyer, educator, author; b. Fairmont, W.Va., Dec. 2, 1922; s. William Otis and Flora Helois (Preston) M.; m. Hazel Irene Kolbus, May 28, 1948; children: Barbara Ann, Melinda Lou. Student, Fairmont State Coll., 1940-41; AB, Coll. William and Mary, 1944; LLB, U. Ill., 1946, JD, 1968; LLD (hon.), Nicolaus Copernicus U., Torun, Poland, 1992; DHC, Nicholas Copernicus U., Torun, Poland, 1992. Bar: Va. 1945, Ill. 1946, U.S. Supreme Ct. 1949. Prof. bus. law U. Ill., 1947-55; assoc. prof. law Stetson U., 1955-58; prof. law W.Va. U., Morgantown, 1958-94, prof. emeritus, 1994—; vis. U. Vienna, Austria, Nat. U. Singapore, Nat. U., Seoul, Korea, U. Sydney, Australia, East China Inst. of Law and Politics, U. Thessaloniki, Greece. Author: Dental Litigation, 1972, 2d edit., 1977, The Law of Domestic Relations in West Virginia, 1975, Veterinarian in Litigation, 1976, Revocation of Professional License, 1985, Handbook of Dental Law, 1994, The Dentist's Legal Advisor, 1994; mem. bd. editors Jour. Law and Ethics in Dentistry, Med. Malpractice Prevention, Clin. Jour.; contbr. articles to profl. jours. Decorated Merit medal (Poland); recipient Spl. award Nat. U. Seoul, Old Guard Medallion Coll. William and Mary, 1994, Lifetime Achievement award Loyola U. Coll. Dentistry, 1994. Fellow Cleve. Clinic Med. Inst.; mem. Va. Bar, Ill. Bar, Am. Trial Lawyers Assn., W.Va. Trial Lawyers Assn., Order of Coif, Order of White Jackets. Republican. Lutheran. Home: 644 Bellaire Dr Morgantown WV 26505-2421 Office: WVa U 117 Law Ctr Morgantown WV 26506

MORRIS, WILLIAM SHIVERS III, newspaper executive; b. Augusta, Ga., Oct. 3, 1934; s. William Shivers Jr. and Florence (Hill) M.; m. Mary Sue Ellis, Jan. 18, 1958; children: William Shivers IV, John Tyler, Susie Blackmar. A.B. in Journalism, U.Ga., 1956. Asst. to pres., pub. Southeastern Newspapers and Augusta Newspapers, 1956-60; v.p., dir. Savannah Newspapers, Inc. and Savannah News-Press, Inc., Ga., 1960-63; v.p., dir. Southeastern Newspapers Corp., 1963-65, chmn. bd., chief exec. officer; chmn. bd., chief exec. officer Bannor-Herald Pub. Co., Athens, Ga., 1965, Morris Communications Corp., Augusta, Southwestern Newspapers Corp., N. Am. Pubs., Inc., Fla. Pub. Co., Jacksonville; chmn. bd., chief exec. officer, pub. Augusta Chronicle, Athens Star and Augusta Herald, Ga., 1966-94, Augusta Chronicle and Athens Star, Ga., 1966—; pub. Juneau Empire; dir. Ga. Power Co., Atlanta, So. Co., Atlanta, Associated Press. Trustee Augusta Coll. Found.; bd. regents Univ. System Ga., 1967-73. Served to capt. USAF, 1956-58. Hon. mem. Golden Quill Soc., 1960. Mem. Am. Newspaper Pubs. Assn., Southeastern Newspaper Pubs. Assn. (dir. 1966—), So. Newspaper Pubs. Assn. Internat. Press Inst. Presbyterian (elder). Clubs: Pinnacle (Augusta) (pres.); University (N.Y.C.); Oglethorpe (Savannah); Commerce (Atlanta). Office: Fla Pub Co PO Box 1949 1 Riverside Ave Jacksonville FL 32202-4904 also: Morris Communications Corp PO Box 936 Augusta GA 30903-0936 also: Amarillo Globe-News Div PO Box 2091 Amarillo TX 79166*

MORRIS, WILLIE, author, editor; b. Jackson, Miss., Nov. 29, 1934; s. Henry Rae and Marion (Weaks) M.; m. Celia Ann Buchan, Aug. 30, 1958 (divorced 1969); 1 child, David Rae; m. JoAnne Shirley Prichard, Sept. 14, 1991. BA, U. Tex., 1956; BA (Rhodes scholar 1956), New Coll., Oxford (Eng.) U., 1959, M.A., 1960; Ph.D. (hon.), Grinnell Coll., 1967, Gettysburg Coll., 1968. Assoc. editor Tex. Observer, Austin, 1960; editor in chief Tex. Observer, 1960-62; assoc. editor Harper's mag., 1963-65, exec. editor, 1965-67, editor in chief, 1967-71; v.p. Harper's Mag., Inc., 1967-71; writer-in-residence U. Miss. 1980-91; hon. fellow Silliman Coll., Yale. Author: The South Today, 100 Years After Appomattox, 1965, (autobiography) North Toward Home (Carr P. Collins nonfiction award, Houghton-Mifflin lit. award 1967), Yazoo: Integration in a Deep Southern Town, 1971, (children's fiction) Good Old Boy, 1971, (novel) The Last of the Southern Girls, 1973, (memoir) James Jones: A Friendship, 1978, (essays) Terrains of the Heart and Other Essays, 1981, (nonfiction) The Courting of Marcus Dupree, 1983 (Christopher medal), (essays), Always Stand in Against the Curve, 1983, Homecomings, 1989, Miss. Disting. Book award), (children's fiction) Good Old Boy and the Witch of Yazoo, 1989, Faulkner's Mississippi, 1990, (stories) After All, It's Only a Game, 1992, (autobiography) New York Days, 1993 (Gov.'s artistic achievement award 1994, Best Book of 1993 Miss. award Miss. Inst. Arts and Letters), My Dog Skip, 1995; contbr. to mags. and jours. Mem. P.E.N. Club, Soc. Rhodes Scholars, ACLU, Phi Beta Kappa, Phi Eta Sigma, Sigma Delta Chi, Delta Tau Delta.

MORRIS, WRIGHT, novelist, critic; b. Central City, Nebr., Jan. 6, 1910; s. William H. and Grace (Osborn) M.; m. Mary E. Finfrock, 1934 (div. 1961); m. Josephine Kantor, 1961. Student, Pomona Coll., 1930-33; hon. degrees, Westminster Coll, U. Nebr., Pomona Coll. Prof. San Francisco State U., 1962-75. Author: My Uncle Dudley, 1942, The Man Who Was There, 1945, The Inhabitants, 1946, The Home Place, 1948, The World in the Attic, 1949, Man and Boy, 1951, The Works of Love, 1952, The Deep Sleep, 1953, The Huge Season, 1954, The Field of Vision, 1956 (Nat. Book award 1957), Love Among the Cannibals, 1957, The Territory Ahead, 1958, Ceremony in Lone Tree, 1960, The Mississippi River Reader, 1961, What a Way to Go, 1962, Cause for Wonder, 1963, One Day, 1965, In Orbit, 1967, A Bill of Rites, a Bill of Wrongs, a Bill of Goods, 1968, God's Country and My People, 1968, Wright Morris: A Reader, 1970, Fire Sermon, 1971, War Games, 1971, Love Affair: A Venetian Journal, 1972, Here is Einbaum, 1973, A Life, 1973, About Fiction, 1975, Real Losses, Imaginary Gains, 1976, The Fork River Space Project, 1977, Earthly Delights, Unearthly Adornments: The American Writer as Image Maker, 1978, Plains Song, 1980 (Am. Book award 1981), Will's Boy, 1981, Photographs and Words, 1982, Solo: An American

Dreamer in Europe, 1933-34, 1983, A Cloak of Light, 1985, Collected Stories, 1986, Time Pieces: Word and Image, 1989, Writing My Life: An Autobiography, 1992, Three Easy Pieces, 1993, Two for the Road, 1994. Recipient Robert Kirsch award for body of work, 1981, Life Achievement award Nat. Endowment for Arts, 1986; Guggenheim fellow, 1942, 46, 54. Mem. Nat. Inst. Arts and Letters, Am. Acad. Arts and Scis. (Whiting award 1982). Office: care Harper & Row Pubs 10 E 53d St New York NY 10022*

MORRISETT, LLOYD N., foundation executive; b. Oklahoma City, Nov. 2, 1929; s. Lloyd N. and Jessie Ruth (Watson) M.; m. Mary Frances Pierre, June 10, 1952; children: Sarah, Julie. B.A., Oberlin Coll., 1951, L.H.D. 1971; postgrad., U. Calif., 1951-53; Ph.D. (NSF fellow) Yale U., 1956. Instr. U. Calif., 1956-57, asst. prof., 1957-58; staff mem. Social Sci. Research Council, 1958-59; exec. asst. Carnegie Corp. of N.Y., 1959-61, exec. assoc., 1961-63, exec. assoc. and asst. to pres., 1963-65, v.p., 1965-69; v.p. Carnegie Found. for Advancement Teaching, 1965-69; pres. Markle Found., 1969—; trustee Sys. Devel. Found., 1978-80; trustee N.Y. Rand Inst., 1969-75, chmn. bd., 1972-75; trustee Riverside Rsch. Inst., 1971-74, Research Triangle Inst., 1970-79, Edul. Testing Svc., 1983-87; trustee Oberlin Coll., 1972-88, chmn. bd., 1975-81; trustee Rand Corp., 1973-83, 85-95, chmn., bd., 1986-95; chmn. bd. trustees Children's TV Workshop, 1970—; bd. dirs. The Multi Media Corp., 1990—, Classroom, Inc., 1992—, Infonautics Corp.; mem. adv. bd. Walt Whitman Ctr., Rutgers U., 1993—; mem. bd. overseers Dartmouth Sch. Medicine, 1995—; active NRC. Mem. Council on Fgn. Relations, 1968—; mem. N.Y. State Commn. on Quality, Cost and Financing Elementary and Secondary Edn., 1969-72; bd. dirs. System Devel. Corp., 1966-70; mem. vis. com. Office for Info. Tech., Harvard, 1974-80; mem. Am. Council on Germany, 1975-79, The Cleve. Conf., 1972—; bd. dirs. Haskins Labs., 1976—; mem. MultiMedia Corp., 1990—; mem. Classroom, Inc., 1992—; adv. bd. mem. Rutgers U.-W. Whitman Ctr, 1993—; mem. Infonautics Corp., 1994; Steering Com. mem. Nat. Rsch. Coun., 1994—; bd overseers mem. Dartmouth Sch. of Medicine, 1995—. Fellow Am. Psychol. Assn., AAAS; mem. N.Y. Acad. Scis. (bd. govs. 1989—), Sigma Xi. Home: 12 Castle Rd Irvington NY 10533-2017 Office: The Markle Found 75 Rockefeller Plz Ste 1800 New York NY 10019

MORRISEY, MARENA GRANT, art museum administrator; b. Newport News, Va., May 28, 1945. BFA in Interior Design, Va. Commonwealth U., 1967, MA Art History, 1970. With Orlando (Fla.) Mus. Art, 1970—, exec. dir., 1976—; trustee Am. Fedn. Arts, former v.p., chmn. mus. svcs. com., mem. ad hoc com. on collections sharing and long range planning com., past chmn. exhbns. and edn. com.; former mem. nat. adv. coun. George Washington U. Clearinghouse on Mus. Edn.; former mem. accreditation com. Nat. Found. for Interior Design Edn. Rsch. Former mem. strategic planning adv. coun. Orange County Sch. Dist.; former mem. advt. rev. bd. BBB; former mem. Orlando Pub. Art Adv. Bd., Orlando Leadership Coun., Orlando Hist. Bldg. Commn.; former chmn. art selection com. Orlando Internat. Airport; former mem. bd. dirs. Sta. WMFE-TV. Named Orlando's Outstanding Woman of Yr. in Field of Art; recipient Fla. State of Arts award. Mem. Am. Assn. Mus. (governing bd., accreditation commnr., profl. standards and practices com., internat. com. on mus.), Assn. Art Mus. Dirs., Southeastern Mus. Conf. (past pres.), Fla. Art Mus. Dirs. Assn. (past pres.), Fla. Assn. Mus. (former bd. dirs.), Greater Orlando C. of C. (past mem. steering com. Leadership Orlando, former mem. Project 2000), Jr. League Orlando-Winter Park, Rotary Club Orlando (program com. Orlando, membership com., chmn. found. com., Paul Harris fellow). Office: Orlando Museum of Art 2416 North Mills Ave Orlando FL 32803

MORRISH, ALLAN HENRY, electrical engineering educator; b. Winnipeg, Man., Can., Apr. 18, 1924; s. Stanley and Agnes (Payne) M.; children: John Stanley, Allan Richard. B.Sc. with Honors, U. Man., 1943; M.A., U. Toronto, 1946; Ph.D., U. Chgo., 1949. Mem. faculty U. B.C., Vancouver, Can., 1949-52; research asst. Radiation Lab., McGill U., Montreal, Que., Can., 1952-53; with dept. elec. engring. U. Minn., Mpls., 1953-64; prof. dept. elec. engring. U. Minn., 1959-64; prof. U. Man., Winnipeg, 1964—; head dept. physics U. Man., 1966-87, disting. prof., 1984—; vis. prof. Monash U., Clayton, Victoria, Australia, 1971-72, U. Calif., Davis, 1978, Ariz. State U., Tempe, 1984, U. Wash., Seattle, 1984, Tex. A&M U., College Station, 1989, Iowa State U., Ames, 1991; cons. Honeywell, Inc., Hopkins, Minn., 1956-57, 59-63. Author: The Physical Principles of Magnetism, 1965, Canted Antiferromagnetism: Hematite, 1994; also articles. NRC Can. postdoctoral fellow U. Bristol, Eng., 1950-51; Guggenheim fellow U. Oxford, Eng., 1957-58. Fellow Royal Soc. Can.; inst. of Physics (Eng.); mem. Am. Phys. Soc., Can. Assn. Physicists (pres. 1974-75, medal for achievement in physics 1977), Sigma Xi. Research on magnetic materials using superconducting solenoids. Home: 71 Agassiz Dr, Winnipeg, MB Canada R3T 2K9

MORRISH, THOMAS JAY, golf course architect; b. Grand Junction, Colo., July 6, 1936; s. Wilbur Merle and Margaret Beula (Cronk) M.; m. Louise Ann Dunn, Apr. 2, 1965; children: Carter J., Kimberly L. Coder. AA, Mesa Coll., Grand Junction, 1956; BS in Landscape and Nursery Mgmt., Colo. State U., 1964. Golf course arch. Robert Trent Jones, Montclaire, N.J., 1964-67, George Fazio, Jupiter, Fla., 1967-69, Desmond Muirhead, Newport Beach, Calif., 1969-72, Jack Nicklaus, North Palm Beach, Fla., 1972-83; prin. Jay Morrish & Assocs. Ltd., Flower Mound, Tex., 1983—. Prin. golf course designs include: Troon Golf & Country Club, Scottsdale, Ariz., Las Colinas Sports Club, Irving, Tex., Mira Vista, Ft. Worth, Foothills Golf Course, Phoenix, Forest Highlands, Flagstaff, Ariz. (One of 100 Top Golf Courses in World, Golf mag., Golf Digest), Bentwater on Lake Conroe, Houston, Shadow Glen Golf Club, Olathe, Kans. (Best New Private Course, Golf Digest 1989), Troon North Golf & Country Club, Scottsdale (One of 100 Top Courses in U.S., Golf mag.), Harbor Club on Lake Oconee, Greensboro, Ga., Loch Lomond, Scotland, The Country Club of St. Albans, Mo., Broken Top, Bend, Oreg., numerous others. Edn. grantee State of Colo., 1961-64; Truman-Miss. golf scholar, 1962-64. Mem. Am. Soc. Golf Course Archs., Nat. Golf Found., Safari Club Internat., Dallas Safari Club. Republican. Avocation: hunting. Office: 3700 Forums Dr Ste 207 Flower Mound TX 75028-1840

MORRISON, ANGUS CURRAN, aviation executive; b. Toronto, Ont., Can., Apr. 22, 1919; s. Gordon Fraser and Mabel Ethel (Chalcraft) M.; m. Carlotta Townsend Munoz, Mar. 1, 1947; children—Sandra, James, Christian, Mark. Student, Upper Can. Coll., Bishop's Coll. Sch. Pres. Atlas Aviation, Ltd., Ottawa, Ont., 1946-51; sec. Air Industries and Transport Assn. Can., Ottawa, 1951-62; pres., chief exec. officer Air Transport Assn. Can., 1962-85; ret., 1985—; v.p., dir. Munoz Corp., Montclair, N.J., 1969-73. Councillor Town of Almonte, Ont., 1960-65. Served with Royal Can. Armoured Corps, 1939-46. Recipient Diplome Paul Tissandier Fedn. Aeronautique Internationale, 1977, Casi C.D. Howe award, 1987, Companion of Order of Flight, 1989; named to Can.'s Aviation Hall of Fame, 1989. Assoc. fellow Can. Aeronautics and Space Inst.; mem. Internat. N.W. Aviation Coun., Chartered Inst. Transport. Anglican. Clubs: Rideau, Wings. Home: Burnside, PO Box 609, Almonte, ON Canada K0A 1A0

MORRISON, ASHTON BYROM, pathologist, medical school official; b. Northern Ireland, Oct. 13, 1922; came to U.S. 1955; s. Samuel and Henrietta (Good) M.; m. Claire Morris, M.D.; 1 dau., Mary Claire. MB, Queen's U., Belfast, No. Ireland, 1946; PhD, Queens U., Belfast, No. Ireland, 1950, MD (hon.), 1988; MD, Duke U., 1946. Asst. lectr. Queens U., 1947-52; registrar dept. exptl. medicine Cambridge U., 1952-55, dir. med. studies Corpus Christi Coll., 1954-55; assoc. Duke U., N.C., 1955-58; Intern Royal Victoria Hosp., Belfast, Ireland; asst. prof. pathology U. Pa. Sch. Medicine, 1958-61; assoc. prof. U. Rochester Sch. Medicine, 1961-65; prof. pathology, chmn. dept. Rutgers U. Med. Sch., 1965-80; v.p. acad. affairs Eastern Va. Med. Authority, 1980-83; dean Eastern Va. Med. Sch., 1980-83; prof. pathology Robert Wood Johnson Med. Sch.-U. Medicine and Dentistry N.J., Camden, 1983-93; assoc. dean in charge Robert Wood Johnson Med Sch.-U. Medicine and Dentistry N.J., Camden, 1983-89, prof. pathology emeritus, 1994—. Recipient Disting. Alumnus award Duke U. Med. Sch., 1987. Mem. Am. Assn. Investigative Pathologists (emeritus), Am. Physiol. Soc. (emeritus), Soc. Exptl. Biology and Medicine (emeritus), Am. Soc. Nephrology (emeritus). Home: 615 Shirley Ave Norfolk VA 23517 Office: Robert Wood Johnson Med Sch U Medicine & Dentistry NJ 401 Haddon Ave Camden NJ 08103-1505

MORRISON, CLINTON, banker; b. Mpls., Mar. 26, 1915; s. Angus Washburn and Helen (Truesdale) M.; m. Mary K. Morrison. B.A., Yale U., 1937; M.B.A., Harvard U., 1939. With Shell Oil Co., N.Y.C., St. Louis, 1939-41; with Vassar Co., Chgo., 1946-48, Holding Co., Mpls., 1948, First Nat. Bank, Mpls., 1955-80; former vice chmn. bd., chmn. trust com. First Nat. Bank; former dir. Gt. No. Ins. Co., Minn. Title Fin Corp., Munsingwear, Inc.; Dep. regional dir. Far East Fgn. Operations Adminstrn. for U.S. Govt., 1953- 55; mem. Internat. Pvt. Investment Adv. Council to AID, Dept. State, 1967-68, Nat. Adv. Council on Minority Bus. Enterprise, 1968-72. Life trustee Mpls. Art Inst., Mpls. Coll. Art and Design; former trustee Lakewood Cemetery Assn. Served to maj. Q.M.C. AUS, 1942-46. Mem. U.S. C. of C. (chmn. 1975-76), Bankers Assn. (exec. com. trust div. 1969-72), Twin Cities Soc. Security Analysts, Mpls. Econ. Roundtable. Home: 2400 Cedar Point Dr Wayzata MN 55391-2618 Office: First Bank Pl Ste 4940 601 Second Ave S Minneapolis MN 55402

MORRISON, DARREL GENE, landscape architecture educator; b. Orient, Iowa, June 20, 1937; s. Raymond Delbert and Rosy Christina (Mensing) M.; m. Dawna Lee Hauptman, June 29, 1963 (div. Sept. 1987); children: Jon David, Scott Darrel. B.S.L.A., Iowa State U., 1959; M.S.L.A., U. Wis., 1969. Landscape architect Md. Nat. Capital Park and Plan Commn., Silver Spring, 1962-64, T.D. Donovan & Assocs., Silver Spring, Md., 1964-66, City Washington, 1966-67; research asst. U. Wis., Madison, 1967-69, mem. faculty, 1969-83; John Bascom prof. U. Wis., 1978; dean environ. design U. Ga., Athens, 1983-92, prof. environ. design, 1992—. Co-editor: Landscape Jour., 1981-88. Served with U.S. Army, 1960-62. Recipient Disting. Teaching award U. Wis., 1976; named Outstanding Educator Council Educators in Landscape Architecture, 1977. Fellow Am. Soc. Landscape Architects (v.p. 1987-89). Office: U Ga Sch Environ Design Denmark Hall Athens GA 30602

MORRISON, DAVID, science administrator; b. Danville, Ill., June 26, 1940; s. Donald Harlan Morrison and Alice Lee (Douglass) Guin; m. Nancy Dunlap, June 19, 1966 (div. 1977); m. Janet L. Irick, Aug. 23, 1981. BA, U. Ill., 1962; PhD, Harvard U., 1969. Prof. astronomy U. Hawaii, Honolulu, 1969-88, vice chancellor rsch., 1983-85, dir. IRTF telescope, 1985-88; dep. assoc. adminstr. NASA OFfice Space Sci., Washington, 1981; chief space sci. div. NASA Ames Rsch. Ctr., Moffett Field, Calif., 1988—; pres. Astron. Soc. of the Pacific, San Francisco, 1982-84; chmn. Divsn. for Planetary Scis., Washington, 1980-81; councillor Am. Astron. Soc., Washington, 1982-85; pres. Internat. Astron. Union Commn. on Planets, 1991-94. Author: Exploration of the Universe, 1987, 91, The Planetary System, 1988, Cosmic Catastrophes, 1989, Exploring Planetary Worlds, 1993; editor: Satellites of Jupiter, 1982; contbr. articles to profl. jour. Fellow AAAS, 1982, Com. for Sci. Investigation of Claims of Paranormal, 1983, Calif. Acad. Sci. Mem. Cosmos Club. Achievements include advanced research for Voyager and Galileo planetary exploration missions. Home: 14460 Fieldstone Saratoga CA 95070 Office: NASA Ames Rsch Ctr # N245-1 Moffett Field CA 94035

MORRISON, DAVID CAMPBELL, immunology educator; b. Stoneham, Mass., Sept. 1, 1941; s. Walter Howard and Grace Falkner (May) M.; m. Pamela Wentworth, May 9, 1981; children: Michael Lawrence, Jenilee Angelica. BS magna cum laude, U. Mass., 1963; PhD, Yale U., 1969. Assoc. NIH, Bethesda, Md., 1969-71; assoc. Research Inst. Scripps Clinic, La Jolla, Calif., 1971-74, asst. prof., 1974-78, assoc. prof., 1978-80; assoc. prof. Emory U., Atlanta, 1980-81, prof., 1981-85; prof., chmn. dept. microbiology Med. Ctr. Kans. U. Kansas City, 1985-91, assoc. dir. Cancer Ctr., 1991—; cons. EPA, Washington, 1976-80, NIH bacteriology and mycology study sect., Bethesda, 1986-90; vis. scientist Max Planck Inst., Freiburg, Fed. Republic Germany, 1975. Editor Immunology Letters, 1991—, Infection and Immunity, 1992-94, Jour. Endotoxin Rsch., 1993—. Recipient Rsch. Career Devel. award NIH, 1975, Merit award, 1990. Fellow Infectious Disease Soc. Am.; mem. Am. Assn. Immunologists, Am. Soc. Exptl. Pathology, Am. Soc. Microbiology, Reticuloendothelial Soc., Am. Soc. Biochemistry and Molecular Biology. Avocations: gardening, banjo. Home: 6235 Mission Dr Mission Hills KS 66208-1252 Office: U Kans Med Ctr Cancer Ctr Kansas City KS 66160

MORRISON, DAVID FRED, freight company executive; b. Columbus, Ohio, Aug. 15, 1953; s. Fred Liew and Sophie Ann (Snider) M.; 1 child, Ian. BA, Stanford U., 1975; MBA, U. So. Calif., 1978. Sr. corp. planning analyst Tiger Internat., L.A., 1978-80, mgr. new bus. devel., 1980-81; dir. planning and controls Hall's Motor Transit Co., Mechanicsburg, Pa., 1981-82; mng. dir., gen. mgr. Consol. Freightways Export-Import Svc., San Francisco, 1984-86; asst. treas. McKesson Corp., San Francisco, 1987-90, treas., 1990-91; dir. strategic planning Consol. Freightways, Inc., Palo Alto, Calif., 1982-84, 86-87, v.p., treas., 1991—. Bd. dirs. Am. Sports Inst., Mill Valley, Calif., 1992—. Fellow State of Calif., 1977, Commerce Assocs., 1977. Mem. Nat. Assn. Corp. Treas., Fin. Execs. Inst. (silver medal 1978), Turnaround Mgmt. Assn. Avocations: tennis, rugby, nordic skiing. Office: Consol Freightways Inc 3240 Hillview Ave Palo Alto CA 94304-1201

MORRISON, DAVID LEE, chemist, research institute executive; b. Butler, Pa., Jan. 25, 1933; s. Charles R. and Mildred (McFadden) M.; m. Carole J. White, July 31, 1954; children: Scott, Karyn. B.S., Grove City Coll., 1954; M.S., Carnegie Mellon U., 1960, Ph.D, 1961. Chemist Callery Chem. Co., Pa., 1954; with Battelle Meml. Inst., Columbus, Ohio, 1961-77; mgr. environ. systems and processes sect. Battelle Meml. Inst., 1970-74, mgr. energy and environ. programs office, 1974-75, assoc. dir., 1975-77; pres. IIT Research Inst., Chgo., 1977-90; tech. dir. MITRE Corp., Mc Lean, Va., 1990-95; dir. nuc. regulatory tech. U.S. Nuc. Regulatory Commn., Washington, 1995—; mem. Energy Engring. Bd., 1990-94; chmn. nuclear safety rsch. rev. com. Nuclear Regulatory Commn., 1990-94. Contbr. articles to profl. jours. Served with USAF, 1954-57. Mem. Am. Nuclear Soc., Am. Chem. Soc., AAAS, Sigma Xi, Omicron Delta Kappa. Office: US Nuc Regulatory Commn Washington DC 20555

MORRISON, DAVID LEE, librarian, educator; b. New London, Conn., Aug. 28, 1948; s. Samuel and Beatrice (Kinslinger) M. BA in Classics with highest honors, U. Calif., Santa Barbara, 1979; MLS, U. Ariz., 1986. Documents libr. Marriott Libr., U. Utah, Salt Lake City, 1987—, instr. libr. literacy course, 1990—; workshop presenter in field; guest lectr. U. Ariz. Grad. Libr. Sch., fall 1988-94; participant confs. in field. Fay and Lawrence Clark Powell scholar U. Ariz., 1983. Mem. ALA (Govt. Docs. Round Table info. tech. com. 1987-89), Utah Libr. Assn. (GODORT bylaws com. 1987-88, 91-92, chmn. nominating com. 1987-88, mem. continuing edn. com. 1987-89, vice chmn., chmn.-elect 1992-93, chmn GODORT 1993), Patent and Trademark Depository Libr. Assn. (fin. com. 1988-95, sec.-treas. 1989-90, 92-95), Patent Documentation Soc. Home: 859 So Blair St Salt Lake City UT 84111 Office: U Utah Documents Div Marriott Libr Salt Lake City UT 84112

MORRISON, DEBORAH JEAN, lawyer; b. Johnstown, Pa., Feb. 18, 1955; d. Ralph Wesley and Norma Jean (Kinsey) Morrison; m. Ricardo Daniel Kamenetzky, Sept. 6, 1978 (div. Nov. 1991); children: Elena Raquel, Julia Rebecca. BA in Polit. Sci., Chatham Coll., 1977; postgrad., U. Miami, Fla., 1977-78; JD, U. Pitts., 1981. Bar: Pa. 1981, Ill. 1985. Legal asst. Klein Y Mairal, Buenos Aires, Argentina, 1978-79; legal intern Neighborhood Legal Svcs., Aliquippa, Pa., 1980-81; law clk. Pa. Superior Ct., Pitts., 1981-84; atty. John Deere Credit Co., Moline, Ill., 1985-89; sr. atty. Deere & Co., Moline, Ill., 1989—. Mem. ABA, Pa. Bar Assn., Phi Beta Kappa, Order of the Coif. Democrat. Mem. United Methodist. Office: Deere & Co John Deere Rd Moline IL 61265

MORRISON, DONALD FRANKLIN, statistician, educator; b. Stoneham, Mass., Feb. 10, 1931; s. Daniel Norman and Agnes Beatrice (Packard) M.; m. Phyllis Ann Hazen, Aug. 19, 1967; children: Norman Hazen, Stephen Donald. B.S. in Bus. Adminstrn, Boston U., 1953, A.M., 1954; M.S., U. N.C., 1957; Ph.D., Va. Poly. Inst. and State U., 1960; M.A. (hon.), U. Pa. 1971. Mem. staff Lincoln Lab., M.I.T., 1956; cons. math. statistician NIMH, Bethesda, Md., 1956-63; mem. tech. staff Bell Labs., Holmdel, N.J., 1967; mem. faculty, dept. stats. Wharton Sch., U. Pa., 1963—, prof. stats., 1973—, chmn. dept., 1978-85. Author: Multivariate Statistical Methods, 3d edit., 1990, Applied Linear Statistical Methods, 1983; editor: The American Statistician, 1972-75; assoc. editor: Biometrics, 1972-74; contbr. articles to profl. jours. Served with USPHS, 1956-58. NSF grantee, 1966. Fellow Am.

Statis. Assn., Inst. Math. Stats.; mem. AAAS, Internat. Statis. Inst., Biometric Soc., Royal Statis. Soc., Psychometric Soc., B&M R.R. Hist. Soc., Nat. R.R. Hist. Soc. Democrat. Home: 118 E Brookhaven Rd Wallingford PA 19086-6327 Office: U Pa Wharton Sch Philadelphia PA 19104-6302

MORRISON, DONALD GRAHAM, business educator, consultant; b. Detroit, Feb. 26, 1939; s. Roderick and Ethelyne (Murray) M.; m. Sherie Leaver, Sept. 12, 1964; children—Heather Margaret, Tracey Michelle. B.S.M.E., MIT, 1961; Ph.D. in Ops. Research, Stanford U., 1965. Instr. Stanford U., Calif., 1965-66, vis. prof., 1982; mem. faculty Columbia U., N.Y.C., 1966-87, prof., 1973-87, Armand G. Erpf prof. bus., 1985-87; William E. Leonard prof. Anderson Grad. Sch. Mgmt., UCLA, 1987—; vis. prof. U. Calif., Berkeley, 1970-71; cons. in field. Editor in chief Mgmt. Sci., 1983-90; founding editor Mktg. Sci., 1980-82. Elder Hitchcock Presbyn. Ch.; Scarsdale, N.Y., 1978-84, Westwood Presbyn. Ch., L.A., 1991-94; treas. Scarsdale Jr. High Sch. PTA, 1977-78; acad. trustee Mktg. Sci. Inst., 1986-92; mem. Decision, Risk and Mgmt. Sci. rev. bd. NSF, 1989-91. Mem. Inst. Mgmt. Sci. (pres. 1990-92), Ops. Rsch. Soc. Am., Am. Statis. Assn. Presbyterian. Avocations: golf; jogging; bridge. Office: Anderson Grad Sch Mgmt UCLA 405 Hilgard Ave Los Angeles CA 90024-1481

MORRISON, DONALD WILLIAM, lawyer; b. Portland, Oreg., Mar. 31, 1926; s. Robert Angus and Laura Calista (Hodgson) M.; m. Elizabeth Margaret Perry, July 25, 1953; children: Elizabeth Laura, Carol Margaret. B.S.E.E., U. Wash., 1946; LL.B., Stanford U., 1950. Bar: Oreg. 1950, Calif. 1950, N.Y. 1967, Ill. 1968, Ohio 1974. Assoc. Pendergrass, Spackman, Bullivant & Wright, Portland, 1950-57; ptnr. Pendergrass, Spackman, Bullivant & Wright, 1957-60; gen. atty. Pacific N.W. Bell, Portland, 1960-66; atty. AT&T, N.Y.C., 1966-68; counsel Ill. Bell Telephone Co., Chgo., 1968-74; v.p., gen. counsel Ohio Bell Telephone Co., Cleve., 1974-91; of counsel Arter & Hadden, Cleve., 1991—. Trustee Citizens League Rsch. Inst., Health Trustees Inst., Cleve.; vice chair, mem. exec. com. Cleve. Coun. on World Affairs; mem. adv. com. Cleve. Play House; adv. com. Cleve. Bot. Garden; mem. vis. com. Cleve. State U. Law Sch. With USN, 1943-50. Recipient various bar and civic appreciation awards. Mem. ABA, Ohio State Bar Assn., Bar Assn. Greater Cleve., Oreg. State Bar Assn., Calif. Bar Assn. The Country Club, Rowfant Club. Office: Arter & Hadden 1100 Huntington Bldg Cleveland OH 44115

MORRISON, FRANCIS HENRY, lawyer; b. Springfield, Mass., July 3, 1947; s. Frank Henry Jr. and Rita Jean (Conley) M.; m. Sally Murphy, Sept. 26, 1970; children: Brian Conley, Matthew J. A.B., Coll. of Holy Cross, 1969; J.D. with distinction, Duke U., 1975. Bar: Conn. 1975, U.S. Dist. Ct. Conn. 1975, U.S. Dist. Cts. (so. and ea. dists.) N.Y. 1975, U.S. Ct. Appeals (2d cir.) 1976. Assoc. Day, Berry & Howard, Hartford, Conn., 1975-81, ptnr., 1981—; corp. counsel Town of West Hartford, Conn., 1983-85; spl. master U.S. Dist. Ct. Conn., 1983—; med. malpractice cons. various hosps., Con., 1983-85. pres. parish council Ch. of St. Helena, West Hartford, 1987—. Served to lt. USNR, 1969-72. Note and comments editor Duke Law Jour., 1974-75. Fellow Am. Coll. Trial Lawyers; mem. Am. Bd. Trial Advocates (charter Conn. chpt., cert. as a Civil Trial Specialist by Nat. Bd. Trial Advocacy 1991), ABA, Hartford County Bar Assn., Def. Rsch. Inst., Fed. Insurance and Corp. Counsel, Conn. Def. Lawyers Assn. (pres. 1991-92). Democrat. Roman Catholic. Avocations: travel, golf. Home: 57 Pheasant Hill Dr West Hartford CT 06107-3328 Office: Day Berry & Howard Cityplace Hartford CT 06103

MORRISON, FRANCIS MARTIN, real estate broker; b. Phila., Nov. 14, 1936; s. Francis Joseph and Beatrice (Solimeo) M.; m. Janice Norlyn Busk, June 30, 1956 (div. Mar. 1978); children: Bruce, Rebecca Randolph, Valerie; m. Shirley Leone Sink, Mar. 31, 1978; stepchildren: John, Jeffrey. Student, various colls., 1954-80. Commd. U.S. Army, advanced through grades, chief warrant officer; shipping and receiving mgr. Sears Roebuck & Co., Sierra Vista, Ariz., 1977-78; real estate salesman Sierra Vista Realty, Century 21, El Dorado, Sierra Vista, 1978-85; real estate broker Realty World, Andy Anderson Realty, Sierra Vista, 1985—. Contbr. articles to profl. jours. Precinct committeeman Ariz. Rep. Party, Sierra Vista, 1979—, area chmn., 1981-88, state alt. del., Phoenix, 1988; dep. registrar Cochise County, Ariz., 1979—; v.p. Ariz. State Bowling Assn. Mem. Ariz. Assn. Realtors (dir. 1987—, exec. com. 1988-89, regional v.p. 1989—, Hon. Soc. 1987), Nat. Assn. Realtors, Cochise Bd. Realtors (pres. 1988-89, dir. 1980—), 82d Airborne Div. Assn., Vietnam Helicopter Pilots Assn., Elks (com. chmn. 1988—). Republican. Roman Catholic. Avocations: bowling, golf, reading, flying, parachuting. Home: 5137 E Calle Virada Sierra Vista AZ 85635-3955 Office: Realty World 1723 S Hwy 92 Sierra Vista AZ 85635-4621

MORRISON, FRANCIS SECREST, physician; b. Chgo., July 29, 1931; s. Clifton B. and Marie B. (LaPierre) M.; m. Dorothy Daniels, Nov. 29, 1957; children: Francis, Thomas, Kenneth. Student, U. Ill., Chgo., 1949-51; B.S. with honors, Miss. State U., 1954; M.D., U. Miss., 1959. Diplomate: Am. Bd. Internal Medicine. Intern Hosp. of U. Pa., Phila., 1959-60; resident in internal medicine Hosp. of U. Pa., 1960-62; trainee in hematology Blood Research Lab., Tufts-New Eng. Med. Center, Boston, 1962-64; research fellow Blood Research Lab., Tufts-New Eng. Med. Center, 1964-65; vis. investigator St. Mary's Hosp., London, 1966; attending physician, dir. div. hematology and oncology Univ. Hosp., Jackson, Miss., 1969-80; dir. div. hematology Univ. Hosp., 1980-92, dir. blood transfusion service, 1974-92, chief of staff, 1986; cons. in hematology Miss. Meth. Rehab. Ctr., Jackson, 1976; asst. prof. medicine U. Miss., Jackson, 1969-70, dir. div. hematology, 1969-92, assoc. prof., 1970-76, prof., 1976-95, prof. emeritus medicine, 1995—, med. dir. MetraHealth Gov. Programs, 1995—; mem. faculty U. Miss. Grad. Sch. Medicine, 1971-80; profl. adv. Jackson Community Blood Bank, Inc., 1973-75; dir. regional cancer program, also regional blood program Miss. Regional Med. Program, 1971-75; exec. dir. Miss. Regional Blood Ctr., 1975-79; mem. adv. bd. Jackson-Hinds Comprehensive Health Ctr., 1973-78; rsch. cons. Alcorn A. and M. Coll., 1973-74; med. dir. Travelers Medicare Miss. 1994-95; guest lectr. various health orgns. and TV programs; mem., chmn. hemophilia adv. bd. Miss. Bd. Health, 1974-90; chmn. task force on regionalization Am. Nat. Blood Commn., 1978-80; mem. Miss. Gov.'s Council on Aging, 1976-88; bd. dirs. Lake Lorman Corp., 1983-87, pres., 1987-88; commr. Lake Lorman Utility Dist., 1983-90, sec., treas., 1984-89, pres., 1989-91. Contbr. numerous articles on hematology and oncology to med. jours. Pres. parish coun. St. Peter's Cathedral, Jackson, 1972-74; chmn. Natchez-Jackson Diocesan Com. Community Svcs., 1972-76l bd. dirs. Miss. Opera Assn., 1973-78, Miss. Found. for Med. Care, 1993—; pres. bd. St. Joseph High Sch., 1974-75; bd. dirs. Med. Alumni of U. Miss., 1987—, mem. exec. com., 1990—, pres., 1992, mem dean's med. alumni adv com., 1987—. Served to comdr. M.C., USN. Fellow ACP; mem. Am. Assn. Blood Banks (sci. workshop com. 1975-78, Component Therapy com. 1987-90, sci. program com. 1988-90, extracorporeal therapy com. 1989-93, S. Cen. dist. adv. group 1985-93), Internat. Soc. Blood Transfusion, Am., Internat. socs. hematology, Jackson Acad. Medicine (pres. 1976), Am. Coll. Nuclear Medicine (alt. del. Miss. 1975), Am. Assn. Cancer Edn. (exec. com. 1978-81), Am. Assn. Cancer Rsch., N.Y. Acad. Scis., Miss. Acad. Scis., World Fedn. Hemophilia, Internat. Soc. Thrombosis and Haemostasis, Can. Med. Soc., So. Med. Assn., So. Assn. Oncology (founding mem. 1988), Miss. Med Assn (com. on blood transfusion 1976-77, ho. of dels. 1985-94, fin. com. 1985-90), Am. Soc. Nuclear Medicine, Am. Soc. Clin. Oncology, S.W. Oncology Group (prin. investigator), Soc. Cryobiology, Am. Cancer Soc. (dir. 1971-82, pres. Miss. div. 1977, chmn. exec. com. 1978, nat. del. 1981-82), South Central Assn. Blood Banks (hon. life, bd. dirs. 1974-89, program chmn. 1975, v.p. 1977-79, pres. 1987-88, pres. found. 1992-94), So. Blood Club (pres. 1977), Council Community Blood Centers (trustee 1975-79), Am. Soc. for Apheresis (bd. dirs. 1987-93, sec. treas, 1987-88, v.p. 1988-89, pres. 1990, program com., fin. com., internat. affairs com. 1990—, chmn. 1992—), World Apheresis Assn (bd. dirs. 1990-91, sec.-elect 1993, pres. 1994), Internat. Platform Assn., Chain des Rotisseurs (founding Jackson bailli 1994), Sigma Xi, Phi Kappa Phi, Omicron Delta Kappa. Home: 173 Lakeshore Dr Jackson MS 39213-9473 Office: Metrahealth 775 Woodlands Pky Ridgeland MS 39157

MORRISON, FRED BEVERLY, real estate consultant; b. Gt. Neck, N.Y., May 21, 1927; s. Fred B. and Beverly (Fitzgerald) M.; m. Janet Thornton Johnson, May 22, 1948; children—Jane, Susan, Martha, James, Ann, David. BA, Columbia U., 1948, LLB, 1951. Bar: D.C. 1952. Asst. gen. counsel ARC, Washington, 1951-54; nat. exec. sec., voluntary home mort-

gage program Housing and Home Fin. Agy., Washington, 1954-57; investment v.p. mortgages Met. Life Ins. Co., N.Y.C., 1957-67; pres. Lomas & Nettleton Co., Dallas, 1967-76; pres., CEO Western Mortgage Corp., L.A., 1976-78; exec. v.p. real estate industries div. Crocker Nat. Bank, L.A., 1978-84; pres. Pearce, Urstadt, Mayer & Greer, N.Y.C., 1984-89; real estate cons., 1989—; bd. dirs. Guardian Life Ins. Co., MetLife Internat. Real Estate Equity Shares; chmn. Fed. Nat. Mortgage Assn. Adv. Com., 1981. Mem. Mortgage Bankers Assn. Am. (gov. 1979-84). Club: Union League (N.Y.C.). Home: 947 Post Rd Wakefield RI 02879-7521

MORRISON, FRED LAMONT, law educator; b. Salina, Kans., Dec. 12, 1939; s. Earl F. and Madge Louise (Glass) M.; m. Charlotte Foot, Dec. 27, 1971; children: Theodore, George, David. AB, U. Kans. 1961; BA, Oxford (Eng.) U., 1963, MA, 1968; PhD, Princeton U., 1967; JD, U. Chgo. 1967. Bar: Minn. 1973. Asst. prof. law U. Minn., 1967-69; assoc. prof. law U. Minn., 1969-73, prof. law, 1973-90, prof., 1990—, acting dean, 1994-95; prof. Oppenheimer Wolff and Donnelly, Mpls., 1990—; counselor on internat. law U.S. State Dept., Washington, 1982-83; of counsel Popham, Haik, Schnobrich & Kaufman, Mpls., 1983—. mem. adv. com. on internat. law U.S. Dept. State, Washington, 1987-89; mem. internat. adv. bd. Inst. on Internat. Law, Kiel, Fed. Republic of Germany, 1989—. Home: 1412 W 47th St Minneapolis MN 55409-2204 Office: U Minn Law Sch 229 19th Ave S Minneapolis MN 55455-0400

MORRISON, GARY BRENT, hospital administrator; b. Anamosa, Iowa, Aug. 30, 1952; s. Kenneth Dale and Norma Elizabeth (Higgens) M.; children: Daniel, Lindsay. BA Polit. Sci., U. Mich., Dearborn, 1975; M Health Svc. Adminstrn., U. Mich., 1978. With Univ. Hosp. Univ. Mich., Ann Arbor, 1975-78, Robert Packer Hosp., Sayre, Pa., 1978-88; assoc. adminstr. St. Mary's Hosp., Rochester, Minn., 1988-90, adminstr., 1990-93; exec. v.p., COO Scott & White Meml. Hosp., Temple, Tex., 1993—. Dir. Tex. State Tech. Coll. Mem. Am. Coll. Healthcare Execs. (diplomate), Tex. Assn. Pub. and Not-for-Profit Hosps. (bd. dirs.). Office: Scott & White Meml Hosp 2401 S 31st St Temple TX 76508

MORRISON, GEORGE HAROLD, chemist, educator; b. N.Y.C., Aug. 24, 1921; s. Joseph and Beatrice (Morel) M.; m. Annie Foldes, Oct. 19, 1952; children—Stephen, Katherine, Althea. B.A., Bklyn. Coll., 1942; Ph.D., Princeton, 1948. Instr. chemistry Rutgers U., 1948-50; research chemist AEC, 1949-51; head inorganic and analytical chemistry Gen. Tel. & Electronic Labs., 1951-61; prof. chemistry Cornell U., 1961—; chmn. com. analytical chemistry NAS-NRC, 1965-77; Internat. Francqui chair U. Antwerp, Belgium, 1989. Editor Analytical Chemistry, 1980-91; contbr. articles to profl. jours. Served with AUS, 1943-46. Recipient Benedett-Pichler award Am. Microchem. Soc., 1977, Ea. Analytical Symposium Jubilee award, 1986, Pitts. Analytical Chemistry award Soc. for Analytical Chemists of Pitts., 1990; NSF sr. fellow, U. Calif. San Diego, 1967-68, Guggenheim fellow, U. Paris, Orsay, 1974-75, NIH sr. fellow, Harvard Med. Sch., 1982-83. Mem. Am. Chem. Soc. (award analytical chemistry 1971), Soc. Applied Spectroscopy (award 1975), Sigma Xi. Office: Cornell Univ Baker Lab Chemistry Ithaca NY 14853

MORRISON, GILBERT CAFFALL, psychiatrist; b. Beaumont, Tex., Feb. 28, 1931; s. Frank William and Ardis Emma (Caffall) M.; m. Betty Joyce Neville, June 28, 1952; children: Kay Morrison Mammen, Keith Neville, Kimberly Sue Morrison Pelz, Christopher Gilbert. Student, Southwestern U., 1948-50; B.S., Tulane U., 1952, M.D., 1957; Ph.D., So. Calif. Psychoanalytic Inst., 1978. Intern Touro Infirmary, New Orleans, 1957-58; resident in psychiatry Cin. Gen. Hosp. U. Cin., 1958-60; fellow in child psychiatry Children's Psychiat. Center, U. Cin., 1960-62, asst. prof. child psychiatry, 1964-68; with So. Calif. Psychoanalytic Inst., 1968-73; clin. prof. psychiatry and child psychiatry dept. psychiatry and human behavior U. Calif., Irvine, 1968—; practice medicine specializing in psychiatry, child psychiatry, psychoanalysis and family psychiatry Newport Beach, Irvine, Calif., 1973—; supervising and tng. psychoanalyst So. Calif. Psychoanalytic Inst., Los Angeles, 1978. Author, editor: Emergencies in Child Psychiatry, 1975. Served to lt. comdr. M.C. USNR, 1962-64. Fellow Am. Psychiat. Assn. (life), Am. Orthopsychiat. Assn., Am. Acad. Child Psychiatry, Am. Psychoanalytic Assn.; mem. Orange County Coun. Child Psychiatry (pres. 1975-76). Home: 22382 Valdemosa Mission Viejo CA 92692 Office: 7700 Irvine Ctr Dr Ste 210 Irvine CA 92718

MORRISON, GORDON MACKAY, JR., investment company executive; b. Boston, Jan. 18, 1930; s. Gordon Mackay and Alice (Blodgett) M.; m. Barbara J. Lee, June 15, 1954; children: Lee, Leighton, Faith. AB, Harvard U., 1952, MBA, 1954. Regional mgr. Bankers Leasing Corp., Boston, 1965-68; portfolio mgr. Sayles and Co., Boston, 1969-71; sr. v.p. Ft. Hill Investors Mgmt., Boston, 1972-75; chmn. bd. Bradford Gordon, Inc., Boston, 1976—; trustee East Boston Savs. Bank, 1962-91, Meridian Mut. Holding Co., 1991—. Bd. dirs. The New Eng. Hosp., 1961—. Republican. Congl. Club: Harvard. Lodge: Masons. Home: 32 Old Orchard Rd Sherborn MA 01770-1037 Office: Bradford Gordon Inc 50 Congress St Boston MA 02109-4002

MORRISON, HARRY, chemistry educator, university dean; b. Bklyn., Apr. 25, 1937; s. Edward and Pauline (Sommers) M.; m. Harriet Thurman, Aug. 23, 1958; children—Howard, David, Daniel. B.A., Brandeis U., 1957; Ph.D., Harvard U., 1961. NATO-NSF postdoctoral fellow Swiss Fed. Inst., Zurich, 1961-62; research assoc. U. Wis., Madison, 1962-63; asst. prof. chemistry Purdue U., West Lafayette, Ind., 1963-69, assoc. prof., 1969-76, prof., 1976—, dept. head, 1987-92, dean Sch. Sci., 1992—; mem. acad. adv. com. Indsl. Rsch. Inst., 1993—. Contbr. numerous articles to profl. jours. Bd. fellows Brandeis U. Mem. Am. Chem. Soc., Am. Soc. Photobiology, Interam. Photochem. Soc., Coun. for Chem. Rsch. (chmn.-elect 1993—), Phi Beta Kappa, Sigma Xi. Office: Purdue U Sci Adminstrn Math Bldg West Lafayette IN 47907

MORRISON, JAMES FREDERICK, flavor and fragrance company administrator; b. Evanston, Ill., Aug. 12, 1933; s. Paul Leslie and Carolyn Lola (Rosemeier) M.; m. Myra Val Wokoun, June 22, 1957; children: Myra Hollie Morrison Nielsen, Cynthia Leslie Morrison Karlsson. BA, Northwestern U., 1955, MBA, 1958. CPA, Wis. Accounting mgr. Froedtert Malt Corp., Milw., 1958-61; asst. controller, asst. v.p. Northwestern Nat. Ins. Co., Milw., 1961-65; controller Eutectic Welding Alloys Corp., Flushing, N.Y., 1965-68; internal auditor Sterling Drug, N.Y.C., 1968-69; controller Internat. Flavors and Fragrances, N.Y.C., 1970-76; mng. dir., v.p. Europe Internat. Flavors and Fragrances, London, 1977-80; v.p. new bus. group U.S. Internat. Flavors and Fragrances, N.Y.C., 1981-84; v.p. export and communications U.S. Internat. Flavors and Fragrances, Hazlet, N.J., 1984—. Mem. Manhasset (N.Y.) Bd. Edn., 1970-75, v.p., 1975; bd. dirs. United Way Monmouth County, 1991—, chmn. priorities com., 1992, 93. 1st lt. USAF, 1955-57. Mem. AICPA, Fin. Execs. Inst. (pres. L.I. chpt. 1975-76), Internat. Trade Facilitation Coun. (vice-chmn. 1991—), Wis. Soc. CPA's, Internat. Commerce Club N.J., Systems and Procedures Assn. (pres. Milw. chpt. 1965), Eastern Sr. Golf Assn. (treas. 1994—), Beta Gamma Sigma. Presbyterian. Avocation: golf. Home: 14 Circle Dr Rumson NJ 07760-1112 Office: Internat Flavor & Fragrances 600 State Hwy 36 Hazlet NJ 07730

MORRISON, JAMES IAN, research institute executive; b. Irvine, Scotland, Dec. 22, 1952; came to U.S., 1985; s. James Morrison and Janet Miller (McCondach) Munro; m. Nora Cadham, Dec. 6, 1980; children: David, Caitlin. BPhil, U. Newcastle-upon-Tyne, Eng., 1976; MA, U. Edinburgh, Scotland, 1974; PhD, U. B.C., Can., 1985. Isntr. B.C. Inst. Tech. Vancouver, 1980-85; rsch. assoc. U. B.C., Vancouver, 1980-85; rsch. fellow Inst. for the Future, Menlo Park, Calif., 1985-86, dir. health care rsch. program, 1986—, pres., 1990—; bd. dirs. Interim Svcs., Ft. Lauderdale, Fla.; mem. corp. adv. bd. Bristol-Myers Squibb, Princeton, N.J., 1992—; mem. UNIS Press Adv. Bd., 1990—. Co-author: Looking Ahead at American Health Care, 1988, Directing the Clinical Laboratory, 1990, System in Crisis: The Case for Health Care Reform, 1991, Reforming the System: Containing Health Care Costs in an Era of Universal Coverage, 1992, Future Tense: The Business Realities of the Next Ten Years, 1994; contbr. articles to profl. jours. Mem. environ. scanning com. United Way of Am., 1990—. Social Sci. Rsch. Coun. scholar U. Newcatle-upon-Tyne, 1974-76. Avocation: golf. Office: Inst for the Future 2744 Sand Hill Rd Menlo Park CA 94025-7020

MORRISON, JAMES R., retired banker; b. Duluth, Minn., May 1, 1924; s. Earl Angus and Jessie (McLean) M.; m. Clarice Mae Wolf, June 5, 1949; children—Kenneth, Alan, Jane, Richard. M.B.A., U. Chgo., 1976. Br. mgr. Parkersburg State Bank, Iowa, 1947-49; asst. cashier Bank of Sparta, Wis., 1949-50; cashier Tobacco Exchange Bank, Edgerton, Wis., 1950-53; sr. v.p. Fed. Res. Bank Chgo., 1953-89, ret.; chmn. subcom. on credits and discounts Fed. Res. System, Chgo., 1984-86; mem. Mt. Prospect Fin. Commn., 1989—; dir. Chgo. Tokyo Bank. Served with U.S. Army, 1943-46, ETO.

MORRISON, JAMES WILLIAM, JR., lobbyist and government relations consultant; b. Bluefield, W.Va., Jan. 14, 1936; s. James William and Winnie Ella (Hendricks) M.; B.A., W.Va. State Coll., 1957; M.P.A., U. Dayton (Ohio), 1970; m. Marva Elizabeth Tillman, Aug. 8, 1957 (div.); children: Traquita Renee, James William, III. Inventory mgr. Dayton Air Force Depot/Def. Electronics Supply Center, 1959-63; mgmt. specialist Air Force Logistics Command, Dayton, 1963-72; exec. asst. to dir. mgmt. systems NASA, Washington, 1972-74; sr. mgmt. asso. Exec. Office of Pres., Office Mgmt. and Budget, 1974-79; asst. dir. econ. and govt. U.S. Office Personnel Mgmt., 1979, dir. congressional relations, 1979-81, assoc. dir. compensation, 1981-87; sr. mgr. CNA Ins. Co., 1987-88; pres. Morrison Assocs., 1988—; vis. lectr. pub. exec. project State U. N.Y., Albany, 1974-76. Mem. adv. com. Dayton Bd. Edn., 1971. Served to 1st lt. U.S. Army, 1957-59. Recipient Sustained Superior Performance award Def. Supply Agy., 1963; Exceptional Service award Exec. Office Pres., Office Mgmt. and Budget, 1977; Disting. Service award U.S. CSC, 1978; Presdl. cert. of Appreciation, 1979; award for meritorious service Office of Personnel Mgmt., 1980; Presdl. rank award meritorious exec., 1983; award for disting. service Office Personnel Mgmt., 1984; Presdl. Rank award-Disting. Exec., 1985. Mem. Alpha Phi Alpha, Pi Delta Phi, Pi Alpha Alpha. Democrat. Presbyterian. Contbr. articles to profl. jours. Home: 5225 Pooks Hill Rd Apt 1710 N Bethesda MD 20814-2052 Office: 1000 Potomac St NW Ste 401 Washington DC 20007

MORRISON, JEANETTE HELEN See LEIGH, JANET

MORRISON, JENNIFER ANN, lawyer, oil company executive; b. Providence, Feb. 22, 1956; d. John Stephen McKnight and Mary Morrison. BA in Polit. Sci., Oakland U., 1976; JD, U. Okla., 1980. Bar: Okla. 1980, Tex. 1988, U.S. Ct. Appeals (5th, 10th, 11th and D.C. cirs.) 1981, U.S. Supreme Ct 1983, U.S. Ct. Appeals (8th cir.) 1985, U.S. Dist. Ct. (no. dist.) Okla. 1986, U.S. Dist. Ct. (so. dist.) Tex. 1994. Atty. Phillips Petroleum Co., Bartlesville, Okla., 1980-88; counsel BP Exploration Inc., Houston, 1988-90; v.p., gen. counsel, sec. Tex./Con Oil & Gas Co., Houston, 1990-92, Plains Mktg. and Transp., Inc., Houston, 1992-93; pvt. practice Houston, 1993—; apptd. by gov. to Commn. on Oil and Gas Practices, 1990-91; mem. legal subcom. Offshore Operators, 1983-87. Editor U. Okla. Law Rev., 1978-80. Pres., adv. council Retired Sr. Vol. Program, Bartlesville, 1982-88; bd. dirs. Bluestem Girl Scout Council, Bartlesville, 1982-88, SunFest, Inc., Bartlesville, 1984-88. Mem. ABA (royalty task force 1983), Houston Bar Assn. (com. law and the arts 1995—), Okla. Bar Assn., Fed. Energy Bar Assn. (commn. on devel. of fed. lands 1989-90, sec. Houston 1991-92, pres. Houston chpt. 1992-93, vice chair environ. com. 1992-93), Am. Petroleum Inst. (royalty task force 1983-88), Intl. Petroleum Assn. Am. (natural gas com. 1990-93), Tex. Ind. Petroleum Assn., Natural Gas Supply Assn. (legal subcom. 1988-92), Tex. Mid-Continent Oil and Gas Assn. (legal subcom. 1990-92), Am. Corp. Counsel Assn. (chair Houston chpt. oil and gas com. 1992-93), asst. chair litigation com. 1991-92), Nat. Assn. Women Bus. Owners (sec. Houston chpt. 1995—), Houston Bus. Coun., Pilot Internat. (coord. 1985-88), Phi Alpha Delta. Avocations: golf, French, art history, tennis, weaving. Office: 8705 Katy Freeway Ste 105 Houston TX 77024

MORRISON, JOEL LYNN, cartographer, geographer; b. Johnsville, Ohio, July 19, 1940; s. James Everett Morrison and Janet Maxine Rogers Rumpf; m. Carolyn Lee Coffman McVey, June 23, 1962 (div. May 1972); Ashley Scott, Anja Lynne; m. Beverly Sargent, Dec. 14, 1974; stepchildren: Anne Marie Hudson, Jane Elizabeth Hudson. BA cum laude, Miami U., Oxford, Ohio, 1962; MS, U. Wis., 1964, PhD, 1968. From instr. to assoc. prof. U. Wis., Madison, 1968-83, chmn. dept. geography, 1977-80; sr. sci. advisor for geography Nat. Mapping div. U.S. Geol. Survey, Reston, Va., 1983-86, asst. div. chief for rsch., 1986-95; adj. prof. U. Md., College Park, 1983-87; fellow Newberry Libr., 1974; adv. editor Rand McNally Corp., 1971—; vice chmn. U.S. Bd. on Geog. Names, 1993—; mem. bd. direction Internat. Union Surveying and Mapping, 1985-87, Nat. Ctr. for Geog. Info. and Analysis, 1990-94; mem. U.S. nat. com. for internat. geog. union NAS, NRC, 1985-92; pres. Am. Congress on Surveying and Mapping, 1981-82, speaker and presenter in field. Sr. author: Elements of Cartography, 6th edit., 1995; chief editorial com. Atlas of North America, 1985; editor-in-chief Mapping Scis. and Remote Sensing, 1984—; editor Rand McNally Co., Chgo.; contbr. chpts. to books, numerous articles to profl. jours. NDEA Title IV fellow, 1962-65. Mem. URISA, Internat. Cartographic Assn. (pres. 1984-87), Assn. Am. Geographers, Am. Congress on Surveying and Mapping, Am. Soc. for Photogrammetry and Remote Sensing, Nat. Computer Graphics Assn., AM/ FM Internat., Cosmos Club, Phi Beta Kappa, Omicron Delta Kappa, Phi Eta Sigma, Pi Mu Epsilon. Home: 2022 Turtle Pond Dr Reston VA 22091 Office: US Bur Census Churchton MD 20733-7400

MORRISON, JOHN HADDOW, JR., engineering company executive; b. Bozeman, Mont., Aug. 24, 1933; s. John Haddow Sr. and Rosalie (Lehrkind) M.; m. Shirley Easbey, Sept. 11, 1954; children: Robert, Richard. BS, Mont. State U., 1955. Registered profl. engr., Mont., Nev., Utah, Ariz., Oreg., Calif.; registered land surveyor, Mont. Project engr. Morrison-Maierle Inc., Helena, Mont., 1957-64, chief airport design, 1967-73, chief exec. officer, 1973-88, chmn., 1988—, also bd. dirs. Bd. dirs. Mont. State U. Found., Inc., 1983—; chmn. 1992-94; sec.-treas. Helena YMCA, 1977-80. With U.S. Army 1955-57. Mem. ASCE, NSPE (pres. Helena chpt. 1968-69, Outstanding Young Engr., Helena chpt. 1965), Cons. Engrs. Council Mont. (past sec., past v.p., pres. 1986-87). Methodist. Lodges: Optimists (pres. 1976); Masons. Avocations: golf, photography. Home: 201 N Hannaford St Helena MT 59601-4725 Office: Morrison Maierle Inc 910 Helena Ave PO Box 6147 Helena MT 59604

MORRISON, JOHN HORTON, lawyer; b. St. Paul, Sept. 15, 1933. BBA, U. N.Mex., 1955; BA, U. Oxford, 1957, MA, 1961; JD, Harvard U., 1962. Bar: Ill. 1962, U.S. Supreme Ct. 1966. Assoc., Kirkland & Ellis, Chgo., 1962-67, ptnr., 1968—. Named Officer Most Excellent Order Brit. Empire, 1994; Rhodes scholar. Mem. ABA, Ill. Bar Assn., Internat. Bar Assn., Chgo. Bar Assn. Home: 2717 Lincoln St Evanston IL 60201-2042 Office: Kirkland & Ellis 200 E Randolph Dr Chicago IL 60601

MORRISON, JOHN LEWIS, former food company executive, investor; b. Mpls., Apr. 6, 1945; s. John Washburn and Charlotte (Lewis) M.; m. Christine Anderson, June 23, 1967; children—Kelly, John. B.A., Yale U., 1967; M.B.A., Harvard U., 1971. V.p. Kidder, Peabody & Co., Inc., N.Y.C., 1971-76; asst. treas. Pillsbury Co. Mpls., 1976-79; gen. mgr. Pillsbury-Mex., Mex. City, Mex., 1979-81; group v.p. Pillsbury Internat., Mpls., 1981-84; pres. Pillsbury Internat. Group, Mpls., 1984-87; exec. v.p., chmn. consumer food group Pillsbury Internat. Group; mng. dir. Goldner Hawn Johnson & Morrison Inc., Mpls., 1989—; bd. dirs. Diamond Brands Internat., Human Capital Corp. Bd. dirs. Abbott-Northwestern Hosp., Mpls., 1978—, Mpls. Inst. Arts, 1985—. Recipient All-Am. award in Hockey, NCAA, 1967; participant U.S. Olympic Hockey Team, Grenoble, France, 1968; Mallory award Yale U., New Haven, 1967. Republican. Presbyterian. Clubs: Woodhill Country (Mpls. 1984—), Mpls. (bd. dirs. 1987—), Links (N.Y.C.), Mill Reef (Antigua). Avocation: sports. Office: By Holding Inc 7171 France Ave S Minneapolis MN 55435

MORRISON, JOHN WASHBURN, banker; b. Mpls., June 1, 1922; s. Angus W. and Helen (Truesdale) M.; m. Charlotte Lewis, Dec. 28, 1942; children: John Lewis, Helen; m. Jane McMillen Hayes, Feb. 13, 1988. B.A., Yale U., 1944; M.B.A., Harvard U., 1948. With Honeywell, Inc., Mpls., 1948-76, dir. fin. internat. ops., 1965-67, v.p. internat. div., 1967-68, treas., 1968, v.p., treas., chief fin. officer, dir., 1968-76; chmn. bd., chief exec. officer Northwest Nat. Bank Mpls., 1976-81; vice chmn. Northwest Corp., 1981, chmn. bd., chief exec. officer, 1981-85. Served with USAAF, 1943-46. Clubs: Woodhill Country (Wayzata); Minneapolis; Riomar, John's Island, The Honors Course (Chattanooga, Tenn.), Bent Pine (Vero Beach, Fla.).

MORRISON, KARL FREDERICK, history educator; b. Birmingham, Ala., Nov. 3, 1936; s. Karl and Gladys (McConatha) M.; m. Anne Blunt, Aug. 29, 1964; children—Andrew, Sarah. B.A., U. Miss., 1956; M.A., Cornell U., 1957, Ph.D., 1961. Acting instr. history Stanford U., 1960-61; instr. U. Minn., 1961-62, asst. prof., 1962-64; asst. prof. Harvard U., 1964-65; assoc. prof. U. Chgo., 1965-68, prof., 1968-84, chmn. dept. history, 1970-76; Ahmanson-Murphy disting. prof. Medieval and Renaissance history U. Kans., Lawrence, 1984-88; Lessing prof. history and poetics Rutgers U., New Brunswick, N.J., 1988—; vis. asst. prof. Columbia U., N.Y.C., summer 1963; vis. prof. Princeton U., 1992; mem. faculty selection com. U. Cyprus, 1991—; vis. mem. Inst. for Advanced Study, 1966-67, 76-77; v.p. Midwest Medieval Conf., 1975-76, pres., 1976-77. Author: The Two Kingdoms, 1964, Rome and the City of God, 1964, Carolingian Coinage, 1967, Tradition and Authority in the Western Church, 1969, Europe's Middle Ages, 1970, The Mimetic Tradition of Reform in the West, 1982, I am You: The Hermeneutics of Empathy in Western Literature, Theology and Art, 1988, History as a Visual Art in the Twelfth-Century Renaissance, 1990, Understanding Conversion, 1992, Conversion and Text, 1992; contbr. articles to Speculum, other jours. in field. Bd. trustees Princeton Cmty. Housing Inc., 1994—. Recipient award in humanities McKnight Found., 1963; Guggenheim fellow, 1987. Fellow Medieval Acad. Am. (counsellor 1972-75, Haskins medal 1994); mem. Am. Hist. Assn., Medieval Assn. Midwest (pres. 1977-78), Medieval Assn. Mid-Am. (pres. 1988-89), Internat. Mus. Surg. Scis. and Hall of Fame (bd. dirs. 1982-84). Office: Rutgers U Dept History 5059 New Brunswick NJ 08903

MORRISON, KENNETH DOUGLAS, newspaper columnist; b. Mpls., Apr. 1, 1918; s. Kenneth Mortimore and Florence Myrtle (Sutton) M.; m. Helen Curtis, Feb. 25, 1943; children: Kenneth D., Sally, Steven C., Mary. A.B., Carleton Coll., 1940; grad. study, U. Miami, 1940-41, U. Minn., 1941. Free lance writer Mpls., 1941; editor publs. Minn. Dept. Conservation, 1942-47; Minn. rep. to Nat. Audubon Soc., 1947-49, dir. pub relations, editor Audubon mag., 1949-56, v.p., 1955-56; dir. Mountain Lake Sanctuary and Singing Tower Am. Found., 1956-80, dir. environ. concerns, 1980-82, fellow, 1982-83; syndicated nature-conservation newspaper columnist 4 papers, 1985—; Audubon tour lectr., 1958-63; interviewer naturalists Wildlife Unltd., TV sta. WOR-TV, N.Y.C., 1951- 52; Mem. Minn. Bird Commn., 1951-54; trustee emeritus Fla. Nature Conservancy; trustee Fla. Conservation Found.; v.p., trustee Conservation 70's; mem. Gov. Fla. Natural Resources Com., State Parks Adv. Council, 1971-79. Author: Favorite Birds of America, 1951, Favorite Animals of America, 1951, Mountain Lake Almanac, 1984; Compiler: (with Mrs. M. E. Herz) Where to Find Birds In Minnesota, 1950. Bd. dirs. Defenders Wildlife; adv. bd. Webber Coll., 1969—. Recipient Gov. Fla. Wildlife Conservation award, 1960, Gulf Oil Conservation award, 1982, Feinstone Environ. award SUNY, 1987. Mem. Wilson Ornithol. Soc., Wilderness Soc., Cornell U. Ornithol. Lab., Fla. Audubon Soc. (pres., Award of Merit 1964, Cruickshank Conservation award 1993), Hawk Mountain Sanctuary Assn. (bd. sponsors), Nature Conservancy, Sierra Club, Friends of Earth, Pi Delta Epsilon. Methodist. Home: 1351 Hollister Rd Babson Park FL 33827-9631 *We ought to keep in mind that we are mammals and that we need to renew regularly our contact with the basic, simple life of soil, sun, water, animals and trees.*

MORRISON, LINDA L., women's health nurse, medical/surgical nurse; b. Rocester, N.H., Aug. 23, 1949; m. Roy L. Morrison, Nov. 23, 1969; children: Aaron, Gina. AS magna cum laude, Lake City Community Coll., 1987. RN, Fla. Office nurse for pvt. physician Lake City, Fla.

MORRISON, LIONEL B., architect. BA, U. Tex., 1972; MArch, U. Tex., Arlington, 1978. Prin. Morrison-Seifert, 1981—; vis. critic grad. design program sch. architecture and design U. Tex., Arlington, lectr.; juror various archtl. design competitions. Prin. works include Morrison-Seifert Residence (Merit award Dallas chpt. AIA 1986, Honor award Tex. Soc. Architects 1988), 2811 McKinney Ave. (Merit award Dallas chpt. AIA 1986, Honor award Tex. Soc. Architects 1986), Roberdeau Residence (Honor award Dallas chpt. AIA 1987, Honor award Tex. Soc. Architects 1987), Levine Residence (Honor award Dallas chpt. AIA 1988), Travis St. Condominiums (Citation award Dallas chpt. AIA 1989, Honor award Tex. Soc. Architects 1989), Fujitsu Am. (Citation award Dallas chpt. AIA 1991), Fidelity Bank Interiors (Merit award Dallas chpt. AIA 1993), Lebowitz Town Hos. (Honor award Dallas chpt. AIA 1993). Fellow AIA (commr. design and environment Dallas chpt., Citation award disting. architect exhbn. Dallas chpt. 1990); mem. Tex. Soc. Architects (mem. design awards com.). Office: Omniplan Inc 400 S Record St # 900 Dallas TX 75202

MORRISON, MABLE JOHNSON, business technology educator; b. Carthage, Miss., July 13, 1930; d. Horace Lawrence and Mable (Barnette) Johnson; married; children: Lisa Susan Stone, Rayburn Holmes Bates, Jr. BS in Commerce, U. Miss., 1952; MEd, Miss. State U., 1976. Cert. tchr. bus. edn., mktg. Bus. tchr. Clinton (Miss.) Pub. Schs., 1952-53; sec. Jackson (Miss.) Pub. Schs., 1954-64, tchr. bus., 1964-69, tchr., coordr. mktg., 1971-78; instr. bus. Jones County Jr. Coll., Ellisvile, Miss., 1978-84; instr. bus. tech. Miss. Gulf Coast C.C., Gautier, 1984-92. Mem. Am. Vocational Assn., Delta Kappa Gamma, Phi Beta Lambda (adviser, Outstanding Adviser 1991). Episcopalian. Avocations: gardening, horses, vol. work. Home: 3100 Phil Davis Dr Ocean Springs MS 39564

MORRISON, MANLEY GLENN, real estate investor, former army officer; b. Weston, W.Va., July 29, 1915; s. Henry Frank and Alice (Riffle) M.; m. Ida Lerlene Johnson, Dec. 12, 1942 (dec. 1982); children: Manley James (dec.), Richard Glenn, Sandra Lynn.; m. Samma Annette Muffley, July 30, 1983. B.S. U. Md., 1958; M.A., Am. U., 1960; postgrad., U. Pitts., 1961, Ind. U., 1968; grad., Command and Gen. Staff Coll., Ft. Leavenworth, Kans., 1956, Army War Coll., Carlisle Barracks, Pa., 1960, DeVry Inst. Tech., 1974; D.H.L., Mass. Coll. Optometry, 1973. Table waiter Mills Cafeteria, Columbus, Ohio, 1935-36; mgr. Speer's Cafe, Twin Falls, Idaho, 1937-38; exec. chef steward U.P. R.R., Sun Valley, Idaho, 1939-42; commd. 2d lt. U.S. Army, 1942, advanced through grades to brig. gen., 1969; chief statis. analysis Hdqrs. EUCOM and USAREUR, Berlin, Nurnberg, Heidelberg, 1948-52; chief Manpower Div., Office Surgeon Gen., Washington, 1952-55; comptroller Walter Reed Army Med. Center, Washington, 1956-59; dir. adminstrn. and asst. exec. officer Office Surgeon Gen., Washington, 1960-62; chief of systems analysis Office of Mgmt., dep. chief of staff for logistics Dept. Army Gen. Staff, Washington, 1962-64; exec. officer, dir. personnel and adminstrn. Office of Surgeon, Hdqrs. U.S. Army Europe, Heidelberg, 1964-67; exec. officer Office of Comptroller, Office Army Surgeon Gen., Washington, 1967-69; chief of Army Med. Service Corps, Washington, 1969-73; ret., 1973, self-employed as real estate investor, 1973—. Community Scout leader, Heidelberg, 1948-52; bd. dirs. Teen Clubs, Am. Youth Assocs., Heidelberg, 1967; chmn. Residents' Coun. Freedom Pla., Peoria, Ariz. Decorated D.S.M., Legion of Merit, Bronze Star, Commendation medal with oak leaf cluster. Mem. Assn. Mil. Surgeons U.S., Alumni Assn. Army War Coll., Fed. Health Care Execs. Inst. Alumni Assn., Baylor U. Alumni Assn., Phi Kappa Phi, Pi Sigma Alpha. Republican. Club: Union Hills Country (Sun City, Ariz.) (bd. dirs. 1985-86, pres.). Lodge: Masons. Home: 13373 N Plaza Del Rio Blvd #7764 Peoria AZ 85381-4874 *I have sincerely tried to assess each problem and challenge in a positive manner. Once the decision has been made and an objective plan established, I have attempted to achieve the objectives while avoiding what I consider the most Common Mistakes of Man: (1) the delusion that individual advancement is made by crushing others, (2) the tendency to worry about things that cannot be changed or corrected, (3) insisting that a thing is impossible because we cannot accomplish it, (4) neglecting development and refinement of the mind and not acquiring the habit of reading and studying, (5) refusing to set aside trivial preference, (6) attempting to compel other persons to believe and live as we do, (7) attempting to quantify in mathematical terms the depth of human experience.*

MORRISON, MARCY, state legislator; b. Watertown, N.Y., Aug. 9, 1935; m. Howard Morrison; children: Liane, Brenda. BA, Queens Coll., 1957; student, Colo. Coll., U. Colo. Mem. Colo. Ho. of Reps., ward, 1992—; mem. judiciary, health, environ., welfare and instns. coms. Mem. Manitou Springs (Colo.) Sch. Bd., 1973-83, pres., 1980-82, County Park Bd., 1976-83, State Bd. Health, 1985-93, pres., 1988-90, Mountain Scar Commn., 1989, Future Pub. Health, 1989-90, Health Policy Commn., 1990-92; commr. El Paso County, 1985-92, chmn. 1987-89; active Citizens Goals, United Way. Named Outstanding Sch. Bd. Mem., Pikes Peak Tchrs. Assn., 1978, Woman of Spirit, Penrose-St. Francis Hosp. Sys., 1991. Mem. LWV, Health Assn. Pikes Peake Area, Women's Edn. Assn., El Paso Mental Health Assn. Republican. Jewish. Home: 302 Sutherland Pl Manitou Springs CO 80829 Office: Colo Ho of Reps State Capitol Denver CO 80203

MORRISON, MARTIN EARL, computer systems analyst; b. Oakland, Calif., Mar. 28, 1947; s. Raymond Earl and June (Cabral) M. AB with distinction, U. Calif., Berkeley, 1967, MA, 1969, postgrad., 1969-73. Certified (life) nat. tournament dir.; cert. jr./community coll. tchr. (life), Calif. Instr. classics and English composition U. Calif. at Berkeley, 1967-73; instr. legal argument Boalt Hall Law Sch., 1972; with exec. office CF Air Freight, Inc., 1979-83, asst. to traffic mgr. for spl. projects, 1982-83, computer systems mgr., 1982-83; computer systems analyst Qantel Bus. Computers, 1983-86, sr. computer systems analyst, 1986-92; sr. tech. writer Shared Med. Systems, 1992—. Author: Writing Argument, 1972, USCF Yearbooks, 1974-76, Official Rules of Chess, 1975, 77, Chess Competitor's Handbook, 1980, Transparent Language, 1992-93; editor: Chess Voice, 1968-73, Keeping Ancient Rome Alive, 1987-89; chess editor: Oakland Tribune, 1965-66; columnist Via Lorenzo, 1987-88, Metric Today, 1985—; pub., bus. mgr. Chess Life & Rev., 1977-78. Asst. concertmaster Berkeley Community Chorus and Orch., 1980-83; concertmaster Oakland Philharm., 1987-90, bd. dirs., corp. sec., 1988-90; 1st violin Albany Trio, 1987—; vol. staff Chabot Sci. Ctr., 1981-84, chmn. computer system mgmt. staff; sec., treas. AstroSoft, 1983-87. Schola Gregoriana San Francisco, 1989—, Schola Cantemus, 1992—. Fellow U.S. Metric Assn. (chmn. consumer edn. com. 1984—), Spl. Citation 1986, cert. advanced metrication specialist 1987); mem. Am. Philol. Assn., Am. Classical League, Eastbay Astron. Soc. (bd. dirs. 1981-84, v.p. 1983-84), Internat. Assn. Chess Press (v.p. 1973-77), Chess Journalists Assn. (pres. 1972-75), World Chess Fedn. (internat. life arbiter, mem. rules com. 1973-78, chmn. 1976-78), U.S. Chess Fedn. (bd. dels. 1968-78, 1st v.p. Pacific Region 1972-73, nat. sec. 1972-75, tech. dir. 1973-76, exec. dir. 1976-78, state and nat. committeeman and chmn. 1971-78, Spl. Svc. award 1985), Calif. Alumni Assn. (life, scholarship com., chmn. 1987-93, Disting. Chmn. award 1990), San Lorenzo Garden Homes Assn. (v.p./sec/ 1985-86, pres. 1986-92), Phi Beta Kappa. Home: 136 Loma Verde Dr San Lorenzo CA 94580-1782

MORRISON, MICHAEL GORDON, university president, clergyman, history educator; b. Green Bay, Wis., Mar. 9, 1937; s. Gordon John and Gertrude (Crilly) M. A.B., St. Louis U., 1960, M.A., 1965, Ph.L., 1965, S.T.L., 1969; Ph.D., U. Wis., 1971. Ordained priest Roman Catholic Ch., 1968. Joined S.J., 1955; asst. v.p. acad. affairs Marquette U., Milw., 1974-77; v.p. acad. affairs Creighton U., Omaha, 1977-81, acting pres., 1981, pres., 1981—; dir.; mem. governing bd. Creighton Prep. Sch., 1993—. Bd. dirs. Health Future Found., 1983—, Xavier U., 1992—, Omaha 100 Inc., 1991—; mem. cons. com. SAC, 1988—; mem. adv. bd. Salvation Army, 1992—; trustee Duchesne Acad. of Sacred Heart, 1995—. Recipient Human Rights award Anti-Defamation League, 1982, Humanitarian award Nat. Conf. Christians and Jews, 1989. Mem. Assn. Jesuit Colls. and Univs. (bd. dirs.), Assn. Ind. Colls. and Univs. Nebr. (bd. dirs. 1981—), Nat. Assn. Ind. Colls. and Univs. (bd. dirs. 1993—), Greater Omaha C. of C. (bd. dirs. 1993—), Rotary Internat., Alpha Sigma Nu, Beta Alpha Psi. Office: Creighton U 2500 California Plz Omaha NE 68178-0002

MORRISON, MICHAEL IAN DONALD, insurance company executive; b. Floriana, Malta, Dec. 22, 1929; came to U.S., 1959; s. Donald Carter and Mabel Margaret (Campbell) M.; m. Eileen Betty Park, July 15, 1963; children: Penelope, Heather, Andrew. Student pvt. schs., Toronto, Ont., Can. and Taunton, Eng. Lloyd's broker Thomas Stephens & Sons Ltd., London, 1953-56; underwriter St. Helens Ins. Co., London, 1956-59; broker N.Y.C., 1959-63; sr. v.p. Am. Internat. Group, N.Y.C., 1964-89; vice chmn.; dir. Am. Home Assurance Co., N.Y.C., 1964—; exec. v.p., dir. Nat. Union Fire Ins. Co., 1964—, Birmingham Fire Ins. Co., 1964—, Ins. Co. State of Pa., 1964—; dir. Commerce & Industry Ins. Co., Commerce & Industry Ins. Co. Can. Served to capt. Brit. Army, 1948-50. Office: Am Home Assurance Co 70 Pine St New York NY 10270-0001

MORRISON, MICHAEL P., lawyer; b. Hinsdale, Ill., Feb. 21, 1944. BA with honors, Mich. State U., 1967; JD, U. Tex., 1972. Bar: Ill. 1972. Ptnr. Hopkins & Sutter, Chgo. Mem. ABA, Ill. State Bar Assn., Chgo. Bar Assn. Office: Hopkins & Sutter 3 1st Nat Plz Chicago IL 60602

MORRISON, PATRICE B., lawyer; b. St. Louis, July 8, 1948; d. Frank J. and Loretta (S.) Burgert; m. William Brian Morrison, Aug. 12, 1969; 1 child, W. Brett. AB, U. Miami, 1971, MA, 1972; JD, Am. U., 1975; LLM in Taxation, Georgetown U., 1978. Bar: Fla. 1975, D.C. 1977, N.Y. 1983. Atty. U.S. Dept. Treas., Washington, 1975-79; atty., ptnr. Nixon Hargrave Devans & Doyle, Palm Beach County, Fla., 1980-89, Rochester, N.Y., 1989—. Author: (jour.) The Practical Lawyer, 1986, 91. Bd. dirs. Linden Knoll, Inc., Rochester, 1991—, Alzheimer's Assn., Rochester, 1990—, Nat. Women's Hall of Fame, 1990-92; mem. Rochester Women's Network; mem. exec. com. Estate Planning Coun. Rochester, 1992—. Mem. Am. Immigration Lawyers Assn. Republican. Office: Nixon Hargrave Devans & Doyle PO Box 1051 Clinton Sq Rochester NY 14603

MORRISON, PERRY DAVID, librarian, educator; b. Mpls., Nov. 30, 1919; s. Arthur D. and Vera Mae (Perry) M.; m. Catherine Jean Gushwa, Apr. 22, 1946 (dec. Oct. 1991). A.A., Pasadena City Coll., 1940; A.B., Whittier Coll., 1942, M.A., 1947; B.L.S., U. Calif. Berkeley, 1949, D.L.S., 1961. Asst. Huntington Library, San Marino, Calif., 1947-48; asst. univ. librarian, head social sci. librarian U. Oreg., Eugene, 1949-63; prof. Sch. Librarianship U. Oreg., 1967-82, prof. emeritus, 1982—; dean Sch. Librarianship, 1970-73, coordinator library research, univ. library, 1978-82, parttime reference librarian, 1982-89, acting asst. univ. librarian, 1979-80; coll. librarian, dir. library sci. program Sacramento State Coll., 1963-65; assoc. prof. U. Nash. Sch. Librarianship, 1965-67; cons. Monash U. Library, Australia, 1975-76, Central Oreg. Community Coll., 1977, Victoria State Coll., Toorak, Melbourne St. Coll., Kevin Grove St. Coll., Australia, 1980, Portland Community Coll., 1981, Treaty Oak Ednl. Dist., Oreg., 1983; dir. various Office Edn. Insts., 1968-75; mem. grant award appraisal panels Office Edn., Washington, 1972-74. Author: Career of the Academic Librarian, 1969; contbr. numerous articles, revs. to profl. jours.; editorial bd. Serials Libr., 1978-92, Social and Behavioral Scis. Libr., 1978-92; issue editor: Libr. Trends, 1981; compiler: A Journey Through Time: The Oregon Library Association, 1940-90. Mem. adv. bd. Lane County Law Libr., 1986-92; treas. Residents Assn. Cascade Manor, Eugene, Oreg., 1993-95; active U. Oreg. Learning in Retirement Program Com., 1993-94. Capt. U.S. Army, 1942-46. Mem. ALA (life), Spl. Librs. Assn. (hon. life, pres. Oreg. chpt. 1974-75), Oreg. Libr. Assn. (hon. life, pres. 1961-62), Pacific N.W. Libr. Assn. (editor and bus. mgr. jour. 1967-71), Assn. Coll. and Rsch. Librs. Assn. (coms.), Lane County Assn. Oreg. Pub. Employees Retirement System (pres. 1985-86), U. Oreg. Ret. Profs. Assn., Faculty Club U. Oreg. (treas. 1981-82). Democrat. Mem. United Ch. of Christ. Home: 65 W 30th Ave Apt 416 Eugene OR 97405-3361 Office: Library U Oreg Eugene OR 97403

MORRISON, PORTIA OWEN, lawyer; b. Charlotte, N.C., Apr. 1, 1944; d. Robert Hall Jr. and Josephine Currier (Hutchison) M.; m. Alan Peter Richmond, June 19, 1976; 1 child, Anne Morrison. BA in English, Agnes Scott Coll., 1966; MA, U. Wis., 1967; JD, U. Chgo., 1978. Bar: Ill. 1978. Ptnr. Rudnick & Wolfe, Chgo., 1978—, also chmn. real estate dept., mem. governing policy com.; lectr. in field. Mem. ABA, Am. Coll. Real Estate Lawyers, Chgo. Bar Assn. (real property com., subcom. real property fin., alliance for women), Pension Real Estate Assn., Chgo. Fin. Exch. Office: Rudnick & Wolfe 203 N La Salle St Ste 1800 Chicago IL 60601-1210

MORRISON, ROBERT LEWIN, lawyer; b. Waukegan, Ill., Feb. 26, 1947; s. Robert L. Morrison; m. Nancy Gaye; children: Robert, Patrick. BS in Econs., Wharton U., 1969; JD, U. Mich., 1972. Bar: Calif. 1972. Joined Pillsbury, Madison & Sutro L.A., 1972, ptnr., 1977—; faculty lender liability litigation PLI, 1989; speaker, lectr. in field. Assoc. editor U. Mich. Law Rev. Mem. State Bar Calif., L.A. County Bar, L.A. Jr. C. of C., Fin. Lawyers Conf., Phi Beta Kappa, Omicron Delta Epsilon (hon.), Order of Coif. Office: Pillsbury Madison & Sutro Citicorp Plz 725 S Figueroa St Ste 1200 Los Angeles CA 90017-5413

MORRISON, ROBERT SCHECK, food processing company executive; b. Flushing, L.I., N.Y., Apr. 4, 1942; s. Forrest John Morrison and Grayce Morrison (Scheck) Hopkins; m. Susan E. Brennan, Oct. 1988; children: R. Scott, Stephen L., Emily E., Catherine A. BS in English, Coll. Holy Cross, 1963; MBA, U. Pa., 1969. Asst. brand mgr. Procter & Gamble, Cin., 1969-72, brand mgr., 1972-75, assoc. advt. mgr., 1975-81, div. mgr., 1981-83; v.p. mktg. Kraft Co., Glenview, Ill., 1983-85, group v.p., pres. refrigerated products group, 1985-89; pres. Kraft Gen. Foods Can., Toronto, Ont., 1989-91, Gen. Foods U.S.A., White Plains, N.Y., 1991-95; chmn., CEO, Kraft Foods, Inc., Northfield, Ill., 1995—. Capt. USMC, 1963-67, Vietnam. Decorated Silver Star, Purple Heart. Clubs: Glen View (Golf, Ill.), Stanwich (Greenwich, Conn.). Avocations: golf, tennis, skiing. Office: Kraft Foods Inc Three Lakes Dr Northfield IL 60093-2753

MORRISON, ROGER BARRON, geologist; b. Madison, Wis., Mar. 26, 1914; s. Frank Barron and Elsie Rhea (Bullard) M.; BA, Cornell U., 1933, MS, 1934; postgrad. U. Calif., Berkeley, 1934-35, Stanford U., 1935-38; PhD, U. Nev., 1964; m. Harriet Louise Williams, Apr. 7, 1941 (deceased Feb. 1991); children: John Christopher, Peter Hallock and Craig Brewster (twins). Registered profl. geologist, Wyo. Geologist U.S. Geol. Survey, 1939-76; vis. adj. prof. dept. geoscis. U. Ariz., 1976-81, Mackay Sch. Mines, U. Nev., Reno, 1984-86; cons. geologist; pres. Morrison and Assocs., Ltd., 1978—; prin. investigator 2 Landsat-1 and 2 Skylab earth resources investigation projects NASA, 1972-75. Fellow Geol. Soc. Am.; mem. AAAS, Internat. Union Quaternary Rsch. (mem. Holocene and paleopedology commns., chmn. work group on pedostratigraphy), Am. Soc. Photogrammetry, Am. Soc. Agronomy, Soil Sci. Soc. Am., Internat. Soil Sci. Soc., Am. Quaternary Assn., Am. Water Resources Assn., Colo. Sci. Soc., Sigma Xi, Colorado Mountain Club. Author 2 books, co-author one book, co-editor 2 books; editor Quaternary Nonglacial Geology, Conterminous U.S., Geol. Soc. Am. Centennial Series, vol. K-2, 1991; mem. editorial bd. Catena, 1973-88; contbr. over 150 articles to profl. jours. Research includes Quaternary geology and geomorphology, hydrogeology, environ. geology, neotectonics, remote sensing of Earth resources, paleoclimatology, pedostratigraphy. Office: 13150 W 9th Ave Golden CO 80401-4201

MORRISON, ROY DENNIS, II, philosophy, religion and science educator emeritus; b. Marshall, Tex., Dec. 30, 1926; s. Roy Dennis and Louise (Smith) M.; m. Margaret Cornelia Johnson, July 18, 1959; 1 child, Sylvia Louise. BA, Howard U., 1947; BD, North Bapt. Theol. Seminar, Chgo., 1950; MA, U. Chgo., 1969, PhD with distinction, 1972. Asst. prof. New Collegiate Div., U. Chgo., 1970-73, Divinity Sch., U. Chgo., 1970-73; prof. philosophy, epistemology, religion and sci. Wesley Theol. Sem., Washington, 1973-93; retired, 1993; chmn. Master of Theol. Studies degree program Wesley Theol Sem. Author: Science, Theology and the Transcendental Horizon: Einstein, Kant and Tillich, 1994; contbr. articles to profl. jours. Mem. Am. Acad. Religion, N.Am. Paul Tillich Soc. (pres. 1985), Inst. on Religion in Age of Sci. (acad. fellow 1991), Psi Chi. Unitarian Universalist. Avocations: H.O. scale model railroading, photography, high fidelity radio, high technology computing systems, metal machining. Home: 2611 Evans Dr Silver Spring MD 20902-4932

MORRISON, SAMUEL FERRIS, secondary school educator; b. Glasgow, Scotland, Oct. 7, 1941; came to U.S., 1949; s. Thomas Green and Susan (McCaskill) M.; m. Kathryn Emily Schnaible, Aug. 14, 1971; 1 child, Ian James. BA, U. Wyo., 1968, MEd, 1985. Tchr. social studies Platte County Sch. Dist. 1, Wheatland, Wyo., 1968—, athletic dir., 1987—. With U.S. Army, 1963-65. Mem. NEA, Wyo. Edn. Assn., Platte County Edn. Assn. (pres. 1972-73). Democrat. Presbyterian. Avocations: golf, woodworking, photography. Home: 200 Front Rd Wheatland WY 82201-9158 Office: Wheatland Jr High Sch 13 And Oak St Wheatland WY 82201

MORRISON, SHELLEY, actress; b. N.Y.C., Oct. 26, 1936; d. Maurice Nissim and Hortense (Alcouloumre) Mitrani; m. Walter R. Dominguez, Aug. 11, 1973. Student, L.A. City Coll., 1954-56. Actress: (films) Interns, 1962, The Greatest Story Ever Told, 1964, Castle of Evil, 1965, Divorce, American Style, 1965, How to Save a Marriage, 1966, Funny Girl, 1967, Three Guns for Texas, 1969, Man & Boy, 1971, Blume in Love, 1972, McKenna's Gold, 1967, Breezy, 1973, People Toys, 1973, Rabbit Test, 1975, Max Dugan Returns, 1982, Troop Beverly Hills, 1988, (TV movies) Three's a Crowd, 1969, Once an Eagle, 1974, The Night That Panicked America, 1975, Kids Don't Tell, 1984Cries From the Heart, 1994, (TV series) Laredo, 1965-67, The Flying Nun, 1966-70, First and Ten, 1987, I'm Home, 1990, The Fanelli Boys, 1990, Love, Lies and Murder, 1990, Playhouse 90, Dr. Kildare, The Fugitive, Gunsmoke, Marcus Welby, and many others, 1960-70, Man of the People, Sisters, 1991, 92, Murder She Wrote, 1992, Johnny Bago, 1993, Columbo, 1993, L.A. Law, 1994, numerous others, (stage prodns.) Pal Joey, 1956, Bus Stop, 1956, Only in America, 1960, Orpheus Descending, 1960, Spring's Awakening, 1962, over 65 other prodns., 1956-1970; prodr., writer live shorts, 1975—. Condr. seminars (with husband Walter Dominquez) about Native Americans to keep traditions and ceremonies flourishing. Honored (with husband Walter Dominguez) for work with homeless City of L.A., 1985, for work during L.A. riots, 1992. Mem. SAG, AFTRA, Actors Equity Assn. Democrat.

MORRISON, TONI (CHLOE ANTHONY MORRISON), novelist; b. Lorain, Ohio, Feb. 18, 1931; d. George and Ella Ramah (Willis) Wofford; m. Harold Morrison, 1958 (div. 1964); children: Harold Ford, Slade Kevin. B.A., Howard U., 1953; M.A., Cornell U., 1955. Tchr. English and humanities Tex. So. U., 1955-57, Howard U., 1957-64; editor Random House, N.Y.C., 1965—; assoc. prof. English SUNY, Purchase, NY, 1971-72; Schweitzer Prof. of the Humanities SUNY, Albany, NY, 1984-89; Robert F. Goheen Prof. of the Humanities Princeton Univ., Princeton, NJ, 1989—; Visiting prof., Yale Univ., 1976-77, Bard Coll., 1986-88. Author: The Bluest Eye, 1969, Sula, 1973 (National Book award nomination 1975, Ohioana Book award 1975), Song of Solomon, 1977 (National Book Critics Circle award 1977, American Acad. and Inst. of Arts and Letters award 1977), Tar Baby, 1981, (play) Dreaming Emmett, 1986, Beloved, 1987 (Pulitzer Prize for fiction 1988, Robert F. Kennedy Book award 1988, Melcher Book award Unitarian Universalist Assn. 1988, National Book award nomination 1987, National Book Critics Circle award nomination 1987), Jazz, 1992, Playing in the Dark: Whiteness and the Literary Imagination, 1992, Nobel Prize Speech, 1994; editor: The Black Book, 1974, Race-ing Justice, En-Gendering Power: Essays on Anita Hill, Clarence Thomas, and the Construction of Social Reality, 1992; lyricist: Honey and Rue, 1992. Recipient New York State Governor's Art award, 1986; Washington College Literary award, 1987; Elizabeth Cady Stanton award National Organization for Women; Nobel prize in Literature Nobel Foundation, 1993. Mem. Author's Guild (council). Office: Princeton U Dept Creative Writing 185 Nassau St Princeton NJ 08544-2095 also: care Suzanne Gluck Internat Creative Mgmt 40 W 57th St New York NY 10019*

MORRISON, VAN, musician, songwriter; b. Belfast, Ireland, Aug. 31, 1945; s. George and Violet Morrison; 1 child, Shana. Founder, lead singer rock group Them, 1964-67, albums include Them, 1965, Them Again, 1966, Them featuring Van Morrison, 1972; solo career, 1967—; albums include Blowin' Your Mind, 1967, Astral Weeks, 1968, Moondance, 1968, Best of Van Morrison, 1970, His Band and Street Choir, 1970, Tupelo Honey, 1971, St. Dominic's Preview, 1972, Hard Nose the Highway, 1973, It's Too Late To Stop Now, 1974, TB Sheets, 1974, Veedon Fleece, 1974, This Is Where I Came In, 1977, A Period of Transition, 1977, Wavelength, 1978, Into the Music, 1979, Common One, 1980, Beautiful Vision, 1982, Inarticulate Speech of the Heart, 1983, Live at the Grand Opera House Belfast, 1984, A Sense of Wonder, 1985, No Guru, No Method, No Teacher, 1986, Poetic Champions Compose, 1987, (with The Chieftains) Irish Heartbeat, 1988, Live for Ireland, 1988, Avalon Sunset, 1989, Enlightenment, 1990, The Best of Van Morrison, 1990, Hymns to the Silence, 1991, Bang Masters, 1991, The Best of Van Morrison, 1993, Too Long in Exile, 1993, A Night in San Francisco, 1994, Days Like This, 1995; composer numerous hit singles including Gloria, 1965, Brown Eyed Girl, 1967, Moondance, 1968, Domino, 1970, Wild Night, 1971. *

MORRISON, WALTON STEPHEN, lawyer; b. Big Spring, Tex., June 16, 1907; s. Matthew Harmon and Ethel (Jackson) M.; m. Mary Lyon Bell, Dec. 19, 1932. Student Tex. A&M U., 1926-28; J.D., U. Tex., 1932. Bar: Tex. 1932. Asso. Morrison & Morrison, Big Spring, 1932-36, ptnr., 1939, 46;

atty. County of Howard, 1937-39, judge, 1941-42, 47-48; atty. City of Big Spring, 1949-58; sole practice, Big Spring, 1953—; lectr. Am. Inst. Banking. Served with USAF, 1942-46. Fellow Tex. Bar Found., Am. Coll. Probate Counsel; mem. Tex. City Attys. Assn. (pres. 1955-56), Am. Judicature Soc., Tex. Bar Assn., ABA. Baptist. Clubs: Rotary (pres. 1949), Masons, Shriner. Home: 1501 E 11th Pl Big Spring TX 79720-4903 Office: PO Box 792 113 E 2nd St Big Spring TX 79720-2502

MORRISON, WILLIAM DAVID, lawyer; b. Phila., Aug. 19, 1940; s. Maxey Neal and Mary Fuller (Chase) M.; m. Barbara Heath, Aug. 25, 1962 (div.); children—David Conrow, Stephen Munro, John Pomeroy; m. Sandra Elizabeth Butter, Mar. 16, 1983; children: Charles, Nicholas, Sophie Natasha. BA, Princeton U., 1962; LLB, Yale U., 1965. Bar: N.Y. 1966, Calif. 1975. Assoc. Winthrop, Stimson, Putnam & Robert, N.Y.C., 1965-74; ptnr. Erickson & Morrison, and predecessor firms, Los Angeles, 1974-78, LeBoeuf, Lamb, Leiby & Macrae, N.Y.C., 1978-88, Bryan & Cave, St. Louis, 1988—; lectr. on Saudi Arabian law. Active Internat. Inst. for Strategic Studies. Mem. ABA, Assn. Bar City of N.Y., Calif. Bar Assn., Internat. Bar Assn., The Pilgrims, Brooks Club, Marks Club, Whites Club, Annabel's Club, RAC Club (London), Princeton Club (N.Y.C.). Author chpt. in Saudi Arabia: Keys to Business Success, 1981; contbr. articles to profl jours. Home: 34 Norland Sq, London England Office: Bryan & Cave, 29 Queen Anne's Gate, London SW1H 9BU, England

MORRISON, WILLIAM FOWLER, JR., health care consultant; b. Wilmington, N.C., June 26, 1928; s. William Fowler and Gladys (Polvogt) M.; m. Patricia Biggs; children: William Stephen, Janet Elizabeth, Nancy Elise. A.B. in Biology, Johns Hopkins, 1949; hosp. adminstrv. residency, Rex Hosp., Raleigh, N.C., 1949-51. Asst. dir. Ch. Home and Hosp., Balt., 1953-55; dir. Ch. Home and Hosp., 1955-65; dir. coll. hosps. Med. Coll. Va., 1965-69; pres. New Hanover Regional Med. Ctr., Wilmington, N.C., 1969-90; mem. faculty Sch. Hosp. Adminstrn., Med. Coll. Va., 1965-90; cons. in field. Author articles. Bd. dirs. Blue Cross Va., 1968-69, Va. Hosp. Assn., 1968-69, Md., D.C., Del. Hosp. Assn., 1964-65, N.C. Hosp. Assn., 1975-77, 79-82, Health Scis. Found., 1975-90; mem. N.C. State Health Coordinating Coun., 1979-86. Served with USAF, 1951-53. Mem. Am. Coll. Health Care Execs. (life), Sigma Phi Epsilon. Lutheran. Home: 8740 Bald Eagle Ln Wilmington NC 28405-9317

MORRISS, FRANK, film editor. Editors: (TV movies) Duel, 1971, The Law, 1974, The Execution of Joe Slovik, 1974, (films) Charley Varrick, 1973, Ode to Billy Joe, 1976, First Love, 1977, I Wanna Hold Your Hand, 1978, Youngblood, 1978, Hometown, U.S.A., 1979, Inside Moves, 1980, Whose Life Is It, Anyway?, 1981, The Earthling, 1981, (with Edward Abroms) Blue Thunder, 1983 (Academy award nomination best film editing 1983), (with Donn Cambern) Romancing the Stone, 1984 (Academy award nomination best film editing 1984), American Flyer, 1985, Short Circuit, 1986, Hot to Trot, 1988, (with Dallas Puett) Disorganized Crime, 1989, (with Puett) Bird on a Wire, 1990, Short Time, 1990, (with Tony Lombardo) The Hard Way, 1991, Point of No Return, 1993, Another Stakeout, 1993. Office: care Motion Picture Editors 7715 Sunset Blvd #220 Los Angeles CA 90046*

MORRISS, FRANK HOWARD, JR., pediatrics educator; b. Birmingham, Ala., Apr. 20, 1940; s. Frank Howard Sr. and Rochelle (Snow) M.; m. Mary J. Hagan, June 29, 1968; children: John Hagan, Matthew Snow. BA, U. Va., 1962; MD, Duke U., 1966. Diplomate Am. Bd. Pediatrics, Am. Bd. Perinatal and Neonatal Medicine. Intern Duke U. Med. Ctr., Durham, N.C., 1966-67, resident in pediatrics, 1967-68, fellow in neonatology, 1970-71; fellow in neonatology U. Colo., Denver, 1971-73; asst. prof. to prof. U. Tex. Med. Sch., Houston, 1973-86; prof. U. Iowa Coll. Medicine, Iowa City, 1987—, chmn. dept., 1987—. Editor: Role of Human Milk in Infant Nutrition and Health, 1986; contbr. numerous articles to profl. jours, chpts. to books. Lt. comdr. USN, 1968-70. NIH grantee, 77-87, 90—. Mem. Am. Pediatric Soc., Soc. Pediatric Rsch., Am. Acad. Pediatrics, Soc. Gynecol. Investigation, Midwest Soc. Pediatric Rsch., Assn. Med. Sch. Pediatric Dept. Chmn. Methodist. Avocation: tennis. Office: U Iowa Hosps & Clinics Dept Pediatrics Iowa City IA 52242

MORRISS, GEORGE W., banking executive; b. Detroit, Sept. 24, 1947; s. George Albert and Marietta (Wyman) M.; m. Susan Williams, Jan. 3, 1970; children—Kelly, Gregg, Keith. B.A. in Polit. Sci., U. Pa., 1969; M.B.A. in Fin., Temple U., 1975. Vice pres. Girard Bank, Phila., 1970-79; v.p., sr. trust investment officer Conn. Nat. Bank, Bridgeport, 1979-82; sr. v.p. People's Bank, Bridgeport, 1982—. Vice chmn. econ. devel. Town of Guilford, Conn., 1980—; asst. treas., chmn. investment com. Family Services-Woodfield Bridgeport, Conn., 1981—; mem. Republican Town Com., Guilford, 1982—; mem. investment com. YMCA Greater Bridgeport, 1982—. Served with USMC, 1969. Fellow fin. Analysts Fedn. Episcopalian. Office: Peoples Bank Whitney Grove Square Two Whitney Ave New Haven CT 06510

MORRISSETTE, BRUCE ARCHER, Romance languages educator; b. Richmond, Va., Apr. 26, 1911; s. James Archer and Mary (Bell) M.; m. Dorothy Behrens, Oct. 12, 1940; 1 child, James. B.A., U. Richmond, 1931, Litt.D., 1975; Docteur d'Université, Clermont-Ferrand, France, 1933; Ph.D., Johns Hopkins U., 1938. Jr. instr. French Johns Hopkins U., 1934-38; from asst. prof. to prof. Romance langs. Washington U., St. Louis, 1938-62; vis. prof. U. Wis., 1962; prof. French lit. U. Chgo., 1962—, mem. bd. publs., 1963-66, chmn. dept. Romance langs. and lits., 1967-70, 73-76, Bernard E. and Ellen C. Sunny Disting. Service prof., 1974—; vis. prof. U. Ill. at Urbana, 1967-68, U. Calif. at Los Angeles, 1969; Fulbright lectr. U. Western Australia, 1969; lectr. colls., univs. Author: L'Esthétique symboliste, 1933, Life and Works of Mlle Desjardins, 1947, The Great Rimbaud Forgery, 1956, La Bataille Rimbaud, 1959, Les Romans de Robbe-Grillet, 1963, Alain Robbe-Grillet, 1966, The Novels of Robbe-Grillet, 1975, Intertextual Assemblage from Topology to the Golden Triangle, 1979, Novel and Film: Essays in Two Genres, 1985; also numerous articles; assoc. editor: French Rev. and Symposium, 1963-69, Modern Philology, 1974-79, Critical Inquiry, 1976—. Mem. Christian Gauss Prize Award Com., 1967-69. Decorated chevalier Ordre des Palmes Academiques, France, 1962; chevalier Ordre du Mérite National France, 1980. Mem. Modern Lang. Assn. Am. (exec. council 1962-66), AAUP, Am. Assn. Tchrs. French, Soc. des Professeurs Francais, Assn. Internat. des Etudes Francaises, Soc. des Rosettes et Rubans de France. Address: PO Box 167 Harbert MI 49115-0167

MORRISSEY, CHARLES THOMAS, historian, educator; b. Newton, Mass., Nov. 11, 1933; s. Leonard Eugene and Margaret (McCarthy) M. AB, Dartmouth Coll., 1956; MA, U. Calif., Berkeley, 1957. Instr. Dartmouth Coll., Hanover, N.H., 1961-62; oral historian Harry S. Truman Library, Independence, Mo., 1962-64; chief John F. Kennedy Libr. Oral History Project, Washington, 1965-66; dir. Vt. Hist. Soc., Montpelier, 1966-71, 73-75; adj. prof. history U. Vt., Burlington, 1969-73, 75-85; oral history cons. Oral History Inst., Montpelier, 1975—; dir. Oral History and Archives Office, Baylor Coll. Medicine, Houston, 1985—; bd. advisors Who's Who in the East; lectr. in field. Author: Vermont: A Bicentennial History, 1981, (with others) Vermont, 1985; editor: Oral History Assn. Newsletter, 1968-71, Vermont History, 1966-71, 73-76, Internat. Jour. Oral History, 1985-89; contbg. editor: Vermont Life mag., 1969-81, editor, 1982-83; also articles. Recipient Harvey Kantor award New England Assn. Oral Historians, 1980. Fellow Ctr. for Research on Vt.; mem. Soc. Am. Archivists, Acad. Cert. Archivists, Oral History Assn. (pres. 1971-72), Am. Assn. for History of Medicine, Pub. History Assn. (coun. 1980-82), Sharpshooters Club (North Fayston, Vt.), Cosmos Club (Washington)

MORRISSEY, DOLORES JOSEPHINE, insurance executive; b. N.Y.C., July 22; d. Joseph Lawrence and Madeleine Catherine (Curran) M. B.S., NYU, 1963, M.B.A., 1968. Sr. v.p., treas. Bowery Savs. Bank, N.Y.C., 1958-87; exec. v.p. Mut. of Am., N.Y.C., 1987-94; pres., CEO Mut. of Am. Capital Mgmt., N.Y.C., 1994—; bd. dirs. Mut. of Am., N.Y.C., 1972-85; pres. Mut. of Am. Investment Corp., 1989—; mem. adv. commn. N.Y. State Comptroller Investment Adv. Com., N.Y.C., 1979-87. Dir. Yorkville Christian-Jewish Coun., N.Y.C., 1978—; past pres. Soroptimist Internat. of N.Y., N.Y.C. Mem. Money Marketeers of NYU, NYU Bus. Forum, Women's Bond Club, Women's Econ. Round Table, Alpha Kappa Delta. Roman Catholic. Avocations: travelling; photography; opera. Home: 180 E End Ave New York NY 10128-7763 Office: Mutual of America 666 Fifth Ave New York NY 10103-0001

MORRISSEY, EDMOND JOSEPH, classical philologist; b. N.Y.C., June 5, 1943; s. William J. and Anne K. (Gaffney) M.; m. Patricia M. Hanlon, Oct. 11, 1967; children: William, Edmond, Kathleen, Jennifer, Lisa, Paula. A.B. summa cum laude, Boston Coll., 1965; B.A., U. Oxford, 1967, M.A., 1971; M.A., Harvard U., 1969, Ph.D., 1974. Seminarian Pope John XXIII Nat. Sem., Weston, Mass., 1974-77; collaborator prof. Sterling Dow Harvard U., Cambridge, Mass., 1977-95; cons. in pub. and photoreprodn. Author: Studies in Inscriptions Listing the Agonistic Festivals, 1974, A Quinquagesimal History of the Church of St. Bernadette, 1987; contbr. articles to profl. jours. Pres., chmn. adminstrn. fin., St. Bernadette's Ch. Archdiocese of Boston, 1980—; founding dir. Theol. Lectures Series, Randolph, Mass., 1978—, Randolph Hist. Commn., 1988—; staff vol. Cardinal Medeiros Program for Handicapped, 1980-82; treas., bd. dirs. Randolph Community Food Pantry, 1994—. Marshall scholar, 1965-67; Wilson scholar, 1965—; Gen. Motors scholar, 1962-65; Ford Found. fellow, 1967-69; Harvard U. fellow, 1969-71. Mem. Am. Inst. Archaeology, Am. Philol. Assn., Alumni Assn. Harvard, Oxford U. Alumni Assn., Boston Coll. Alumni Assn. Democrat. Roman Catholic. Home: 4 Bennington St Randolph MA 02368-2106

MORRISSEY, FRANCIS DANIEL, lawyer; b. Chgo., June 28, 1930; m. Corinne Seither, 1989; children: Francis, Mary. A.B., St. Mary of the Lake U., 1952; J.D., Loyola U., Chgo., 1958. Bar: Ill. 1958, U.S. Dist. Ct. (no. dist.) Ill. 1958, U.S. Ct. Appeals (7th cir.) 1963, U.S. Ct. Appeals (D.C. cir.) 1978, U.S. Ct. Appeals (2d cir.) 1969, U.S. Ct. Appeals (5th cir.) 1972, U.S. Supreme Ct. 1962. Assoc. Baker & McKenzie, Chgo., 1958-62, ptnr., 1962—. Contbr. articles to legal jours. Recipient Francis J. Rooney St. Thomas More Loyola U., 1977, Medal of Excellence Loyola U. Chgo., 1988. Fellow Am. Coll. Trial Lawyers, Am. Bar Found.; mem. Nat. Conf. Bar Examiners (past chmn., pres.), Bd. Law Examiners Ill. (past pres.), Chgo. Bar Assn. (bd. mgrs.), Ill. Appellate Lawyers Assn. (past pres.), Ill. Trial Lawyers Assn. Office: Baker & McKenzie 1 Prudential Plz 130 E Randolph Chicago IL 60601

MORRISSEY, JOHN CARROLL, lawyer; b. N.Y.C., Sept. 2, 1914; s. Edward Joseph and Estelle (Caine) M.; m. Eileen Colligan, Oct. 14, 1950; children: Jonathan Edward, Ellen (Mrs. James A. Jenkins), Katherine, John, Patricia, Richard, Brian, Peter. BA magna cum laude, Yale U., 1937, LLB, 1940; JSD, N.Y. U., 1951; grad., Command and Gen. Staff Sch., 1944. Bar: N.Y. State 1940, D.C. 1953, Calif. 1954, U.S. Supreme Ct. 1944. Asso. firm Dorsey and Adams, 1940-41, Dorsey, Adams and Walker, 1946-50; counsel Office of Sec. of Def., Dept. Def., Washington, 1950-52; acting gen. counsel def. Electric Power Adminstrn., 1952-53; atty. Pacific Gas and Electric Co., San Francisco, 1953-70; assoc. gen. counsel Pacific Gas and Electric Co., 1970-74, v.p., gen. counsel, 1975-80; individual practice law San Francisco, 1980—; dir. Gas Lines, Inc. Bd. dirs. Legal Aid Soc. San Francisco; chmn. Golden Gate dist. Boy Scouts Am., 1973-75; commr. Human Rights Commn. of San Francisco, 1976-89, chmn., 1980-82; chmn. Cath. Social Svc. of San Francisco, 1966-68; adv. com. Archdiocesan Legal Affairs, 1991—; regent Archdiocesan Sch. of Theology St. Patrick's Seminary, 1994—. Served to Col. F.A., U.S. Army, 1941-46. Decorated Bronze star, Army Commendation medal. Mem. NAS, AAAS, ABA, Calif. State Bar Assn., Fed. Power Bar Assn., N.Y. Acad. Scis., Calif. Conf. Pub. Utility Counsel, Pacific Coast Electric Assn., Pacific Coast Gas Assn., Econ. Round Table of San Francisco, World Affairs Council, San Francisco C. of C., Calif. State C. of C., Harold Brunn Soc. Med. Rsch., Electric Club, Serra Club, Commonwealth Club, Yale Club of San Francisco (pres. 1989-90), Pacific-Union Club, Sometimes Tuesday Club, Sovereign Mil. Order Malta, Phi Beta Kappa. Roman Catholic. Home: 2030 Jackson St San Francisco CA 94109-2840 Office: PO Box 77000 1 California St Ste 3125 San Francisco CA 94111-5432

MORRISSEY, JOHN EDWARD, wholesale grocery company executive; b. N.Y.C., Apr. 21, 1930; s. John Edward and Marilyn Beatrice (Macalis) M.; m. Marilyn Beatrice Macalis, June 6, 1953; children—Michelle, John Edward, Melissa, Dennis. B.S. in Chem. Engring., Villanova U., 1953; M.S. in Nuclear Engring., N.C. State U., 1958; M.B.A., Stanford U., 1969. Asst. dir. Nat. Aero and Space Council Exec. Office of Pres. U.S., Washington, 1969-72, exec. dir. nat. commn. on productivity, 1973-74; sr. v.p. Super Valu Stores, Mpls., 1974—; dir. Malt-o-Meal Corp., Mpls., Ultimap Corp.; Bd. advisers Stanford U. Grad. Sch. Bus., 1983-85. Contbr. articles on productivity in transp. and food distbn. to profl. publs. Served to lt. USNR, 1953-57. Republican. Roman Catholic. Avocations: tennis; gardening. Home: 6616 Dovre Dr Minneapolis MN 55436-1712 Office: Super Valu Stores Inc 11840 Valley View Rd Eden Prairie MN 55344-3691

MORRISSEY, PETER A., public relations executive; b. Boston, Jan. 15, 1953; s. Edward William and Margaret Francis (L'Heureaux) M.; m. Carey S. Sherman; children: Halley, Jack, Cara. BS, Boston U., 1987; cert. in mgmt. program, Harvard U., 1990. Account exec. Prudential Ins. Co. Am., Boston, 1977-78; account exec. Clarke and Co., Boston, 1978-82; v.p., 1982-84, pres., chief exec. officer, 1984—; mng. ptnr. WORLDCOM. editor, pub.: The Boston Marathon, 1980-82. Dir. Multiple Sclerosis Soc., Morgan Meml. Goodwill Industries. Named one of Ten Outstanding Young Leaders Boston Jaycees, 1985. Mem. Pub. Rels. Soc. Am. (counselors acad.), Boston C. of C. (bd. dirs.), Publicity Club Boston. Roman Catholic. Office: Clarke & Co Pub Rels 535 Boylston St Boston MA 02116-3720

MORRISSEY, ROBERT JOHN, communications executive; b. Manchester, Conn., Apr. 21, 1944; s. Thomas J. and Lillian F. (Bischoff) M. BA, Fairfield U., 1966; postgrad., U. Mo., 1966-67. Mgr. pub. rels. United Techs. Rsch. Ctr., East Hartford, Conn., 1975-77; various pub. rels. positions United Techs. Corp., Conn., 1967-75; dir. employee communications United Techs. Corp., Hartford, Conn., 1977-82, dir. corp. communication svcs., 1982-86, corp. cons., ombudsman, 1986-88, corp. ombudsman, 1988-92, dir. communications planning, 1992—; bd. dirs. Conn. Radio Info. Sys., 1995. Mem. exec. com. Downtown Coun. Hartford, 1995. Mem. Pub. Rels. Soc. Am., Internat. Assn. Bus. Comm., Comm. Roundtable, Soc. for Preservation and Encouragement Barbershop Quartet Singing in Am. (past pres. Manchester). Avocations: reading, barbershop quartet singing. Office: United Techs Corp United Techs Bldg 1 Financial Plz Hartford CT 06103-2601

MORRISSEY, THOMAS JEROME, investment banker; b. Racine, Wis.; s. Patrick William and Lillian (Mitchell) M.; PhB, U. Wis., 1940; postgrad. U. Ill., 1942, U.S. Naval Acad., 1942; m. Clovene Marie Nogel, Feb. 21, 1957. Merchandising trainee Vick Chem. div. Richardson-Merrill, Inc., N.Y.C., 1940-41, sales promotion asst., 1941-42, mgr. mil. sales, 1942; pvt. practice mktg. and fin. cons., N.Y.C., 1952-54; dir. mktg. rsch. Pharmacraft Labs. div. Seagrams Distillers, Inc., N.Y.C., 1946-48, mgr. sales promotion, 1948-49, gen. sales mgr., 1949-52; asst. to pres. Turner-Smith Drug Co., N.Y.C., 1954-55, sales mgr., Smithtown, L.I., N.Y., 1955-57; mgr. advt. and sales Denver Chem. Mfg. Co., Stamford, Conn., 1957-58, N.Y.C., 1958-59; v.p., dir. mktg., account exec. Ralph Allum Advt. Agy., N.Y.C., 1959-67; v.p. Community Sci., Inc., 1959-67; account exec. Walston & Co., Inc., N.Y.C., 1967-74, Harris, Upham & Co., Inc., 1974-76; sr. account exec., v.p. Smith Barney Harris Upham & Co., 1976—. Lt. USNR, 1942-46. Decorated Silver Star; knighted Knight of Grace Soverign Orthodox Order of St. John of Jerusalem, Knights Hospitaller. Mem. The Marketeers (pres. 1963-67), Astoria Park Tennis Assn. (pres. 1967-70), Ea. Lawn Tennis Assn. (del. 1967-69), Met. Badminton Assn. (del. 1968-4), Vet. Corps of Artillery of State of N.Y. (commd. major 1989) Mil. Order of Foreign Wars (bd. govs.), St. George's Soc., New Eng. Soc., Sigma Chi. Clubs: Dutch Treat (chmn. 1960-61), Army and Navy (pres.), Cen. Badminton (pres. 1971-83), Badminton Club of City of N.Y. (sec. 1985-94), West Side Tennis (Forest Hills), Princeton U. Club, St. George's Soc., New England Soc. Rsch. in field. Home: 865 United Nations Plz New York NY 10017-1812 Office: c/o Smith Barney Inc 40 W 57th St Fl 19 New York NY 10019-4001

MORRONE, EDWARD PATRICK, state senator, insurance and real estate company executive; b. Westerly, R.I., Mar. 17, 1950; s. Anthony Joseph and Elizabeth E. (Herres) M.; m. Deborah A. Chappell, Sept. 18, 1971; children: Darrell E., Kerri Lynn, Courtney Beth. BA, U.R.I., 1972. State rep. Dist. 51, Westerly-New Shoreham, 1980-84; state senator Dist. 26, Westerly-New Shoreham, 1988—; pres. Capalbo & Morrone Agy. Ins. & Real Estate Inc., Westerly, 1975—. Pres. Westerly-Pawcatuck C. of C., 1986. Mem. Westerly

Lions, Fraternal Order Police. Home: 16 Pasadena Ave Westerly RI 02891 Office: 90 High St PO Box 526 Westerly RI 02891

MORRONE, FRANK, electronic manufacturing executive; b. Marano Marchesato, Cosenza, Italy, May 13, 1949; s. Luigi and Emma (Molinaro) M.; m. Katherine Ann Kuehn, Feb. 1, 1975; children: Louis H., Cecilia E., Joseph V. BSEE, U. Wis., 1972; M in Mgmt., Northwestern U., 1993. Project engr. 3M Co., St. Paul, 1972-73; product engr. Mayer Eaton Corp., Kenosha, Wis., 1973-79; chief elec. engr. Tree Machine Tool, Racine, Wis., 1979-80; v.p. engring. MacPower divsn. Manu-Tronics, Inc., Kenosha, 1980-84, exec. v.p., 1984—, bd. dirs., sec., 1988—. Mem. exec. bd. southeast coun. Boy Scouts Am., Racine, 1987—; bd. dirs. Kenosha Libr., 1987—. Mem. IEEE. Office: Manu-Tronics Inc 8701 100th St Kenosha WI 53142

MORROW, ANDREW NESBIT, interior designer, business owner; b. Fremont, Nebr., Feb. 22, 1929; s. Hamilton N. and May (Oberg) M.; m. Margaret M. Stoltinberg; children: Megan Beth, Molly Jean, Andrew C. BFA, U. Nebr., 1950. Interior designer Hardy Furniture, Lincoln, Nebr., 1950-61, Morrow Interiors, Lincoln, 1961—; bd. visitors Found. for Interior Design Edn. and Rsch., 1976-84; mem. standards com. Found. for Interior Design Edn. and Research, N.Y.C. Exhibitor Fremont Art Gallery, 1986, Haymarket Art Gallery, 1984. Pres. First Luth. Ch., Lincoln, 1976-80; v.p. Found. Nebr. Women's Commn., Lincoln, 1987-90; bd. dirs. Lincoln Symphony, 1988-91, Nebr. Republicans for Choice, 1992, Luth Family Svcs. of Nebr., 1995—; treas. NCID, 1992—. Fellow Am. Soc. Interior Designers (bd. dirs. Nebr.-Iowa chpt. 1974-78, pres. 1986-88); mem. Interior Design Educators Council (hon.). Republican. Avocations: gardening, horseback riding, cross-country skiing. Home: 1531 Kingston Rd Lincoln NE 68506-1524 Office: Morrow Interiors Inc 1010 K St Lincoln NE 68508-2851

MORROW, BARRY NELSON, screenwriter, producer; b. Austin, Minn., June 12, 1948; s. Robert Clayton and Rose Nell (Nelson) M.; m. Beverly Lee McKenzie, Mar. 3, 1969; children: Clayton McKenzie, ZoeAnna Rachel. BA, St. Olaf Coll., 1970; DHL (hon.), U. La Verne, Calif., 1990. Media specialist U. Iowa, Iowa City, 1974-81; freelance screenwriter Los Angeles, 1989-90; pres. Morrow-Heus Prodns., 1990—. Storywriter (TV film) Bill, 1981 (Emmy award 1982); screenwriter: (TV films) Bill: On His Own, 1983, Conspiracy of Love, 1987, Silent Victory, 1988, The Karen Carpenter Story, 1989, (feature film) Rain Man, 1988 (co-recipient Acad. award Best Original Screenplay 1989); screenwriter, exec. prodr.: Christmas on Division Street, 1991; exec. prodr.: Switched at Birth, 1991 (Emmy nomination), Gospa, 1995; monologist: Bill for Short, 1992. Recipient Pres.'s award Am. Acad. for Cerebral Palsy and Devel. Medicine, 1978, Outstanding Contbn. award Mid-Am. Congress on Aging, 1983, SI award NASW, 1991, Pope John XXIII award Viterbo Coll., 1992. Mem. Writers Guild Am. West, Acad. TV Arts and Scis., Acad. Motion Picture Arts and Scis. Democrat.

MORROW, CHARLES TABOR, aerospace consulting engineer; b. Gloucester, Mass., May 3, 1917; s. Charles Harvey and Melissa Luella (Tabor) M.; m. Julia Buxton Brown, June 4, 1949; children: Hope Elizabeth, Anne Barbara. AB, Harvard U., 1937, SM, 1938, SD, 1946. Sr. project engr. Sperry Gyroscope Co., Great Neck, N.Y., 1946-51; research physicist Hughes Aircraft Co., L.A., 1951-55; mgr. sci. and engring. relations Ramo Wooldridge Co., L.A., 1955-60; mgr. tech. relations Aerospace Corp., L.A., 1960-67; staff scientist LTV Research Ctr., Anaheim, Calif. and Dallas, 1967-76; cons. in field., Dallas and Encinitas (Calif.), 1977—. Author: Shock and Vibration Engineering, 1963; also numerous articles to profl. jours. Pres. Covey Aux. San Diego Mus. Natural History, 1983-85. Fellow Acoustical Soc. Am., Inst Environ. Scis. (Vigness award 1971), AIAA (assoc.); mem. IEEE (life), Inst. Noise Control Engring. (founding), Am. Soc. Engring. Edn., Sigma Xi. Avocations: music, photography, natural history, travelling. Home and Office: 1345 Cherrytree Ct Encinitas CA 92024-4011

MORROW, DAVID AUSTIN, III, veterinary medical educator; b. Arch Spring, Pa., Jan. 14, 1935; s. David Austin and Mary Harnish (Burket) M.; m. Sarah Linda MacDonough, Aug. 28, 1965; children: David Austin IV, Laurie Elizabeth, Melanie MacDonough. BS, Pa. State U., 1956; DVM, Cornell U., 1960, PhD, 1967. Postdoctoral fellow Cornell U., Ithaca, N.Y., 1965-68; assoc. prof. Mich. State U., East Lansing, 1968-81, prof. Coll. Vet. Medicine, 1981-90, prof. emeritus, 1990—; vet. cons., 1990—; vis. scientist Colo. State U., Ft. Collins, 1975-76. Editor: Current Therapy in Theriogenology, 1980, 2d edit., 1986. Elder Presbyn. Ch.; trustee Pa. State U., 1987—, chmn. bd. trustees phys. plant com., 1994—. Recipient Norden Disting. Teaching award Mich. State U., 1975, Outstanding Teaching award, 1979, 80, 84, 85, 86, Dairy Sci. Disting. Alumnus award Pa. State U., 1992, Hon. Lion Ambassador award Pa. State U., 1993, Hon. Alumnus award Mich. State U. Coll. Veterinary Medicine, 1993. Mem. AVMA (Borden award 1980, Am. Feed Mfg. award 1992), Am. Coll. Theriogenologists (charter diplomate), Pa. State U. Coll. Agr. Alumni Soc. (pres.-elect 1985-86, pres. 1987-89, past pres. 1989-91), Pa. State U. Alumni Coun. (exec. bd. 1983-95, pres.-elect 1989-91, pres. 1991-93, past pres. 1993-95), Phi Zeta (pres. 1977-79), Phi Kappa Phi (exec. bd.), Golden Key (hon.). Republican. Avocations: skiing; gardening. Home and Office: 1060 Haymaker Rd State College PA 16801-6900

MORROW, E. FREDERIC, financial consultant, retired banker; b. Hackensack, N.J., Apr. 20, 1909; s. John Eugene and Mary Ann (Hayes) M.; m. Catherine Gordon, Sept. 18, 1957. Student, Bowdoin Coll., 1926-30, LL.D., 1970, J.D., Rutgers U., 1948. Field sec. NAACP, N.Y.C., 1937-45; writer pub. affairs CBS-TV, N.Y.C., 1945-52; exec. asst. Eisenhower, Washington, 1953-61; v.p. African-Am. Inst., N.Y.C., 1962-64, Bank of Am., N.Y.C., 1964-75; exec. assoc. Ednl. Testing Service, Princeton, N.J., 1975—; dir. JRB Assos., Inc. Author: Black Man in the White House, 1963, Way Down South Up North, 1973, Forty Years a Guinea Pig, 1980. Trustee Phelps-Stokes Fund.; spl. ambassador, leader Am. del. to Liberian Sesquicentennial, 1972. Served to maj. AUS, 1942-46. Mem. United Nations Assn., Alpha Phi Alpha, Sigma Pi Phi. Republican. Methodist. Home: 1270 Fifth Ave New York NY 10029-3417

MORROW, ELIZABETH, business owner, sculptress, museum association administrator, educator; b. Sibley, Mo., Feb. 28, 1947; d. Elman A. and Lorine (Hostetter) Morrow; married, 1970 (div. 1979); children: Jan Pawel, Lorentz Arthur. Student, William Jewell Coll., 1958-59, Colo. Coll., 1959-60, U. Okla., 1960-62; BFA, U. Kans., 1964, MFA, 1967; postgrad., U. Minn., 1965, U. Kans., 1968. Pres. E. Morrow Co., Kansas City, Mo., 1966-67; head dept. art U. Hawaii, Honolulu, 1968-69, Tarkio (Mo.) Coll., 1970-74; exec. dir. Pensacola (Fla.) Mus. Art, 1974-76; pres., owner Blair-Murrah Exhbns., Sibley, Mo., 1980—; pres. bd. trustees, chief exec. officer Blair-Murrah, Inc., 1991—; sec.-treas. Coun. for Cultural Resources, 1995—. Del. White House Conf. on Small Bus., 1986. Lew Wentz scholar U. Okla., 1960-62. Mem. AAUW, Internat. Coun. of Mus., Internat. Coun. Exhbn. Exch., Internat. Soc. Appraisers, Am. Assn. Mus., Nat. Orgn. of Women Bus. Owners, Nat. Assn. Mus. Exhibitions, Ft. Osage Hist. Soc., Friends Art, Internat. Com. Fine Arts, Internat. Com. Conservation, Internat. Sculpture Ctr., DAR, Delta Phi Delta. Republican. Avocations: historical and cultural activities, antique cars, midwest farm auctions. Home: Vintage Hill Orch Sibley MO 64088 Office: Blair-Murrah Vintage Hill Orch Sibley MO 64088 also: 7 rue Muzy, PO Box Nr 554, 1211 Geneva 6 Switzerland

MORROW, GEORGE LESTER, retired oil and gas executive; b. New Haven, Apr. 27, 1922; s. Lester W.W. and Esther (Morrow) M.; m. Mary L. Evenburg, Dec. 28, 1946; children: Susan Morrow Donaldson, William, John, Thomas. B.S., Rutgers U., 1943; M.B.A., U. Chgo., 1954. Registered profl. engr., Ill. With Peoples Gas Light and Coke Co., Chgo, 1947-77; v.p. ops. Peoples Gas Light and Coke Co., 1966-71, pres., 1971-77; also dir.; pres. Natural Gas Pipeline Co. Am., 1977-83; vice chmn., dir. Midcon Corp., 1983-87. Capt. AUS, 1943-46. Mem. Am. Gas Assn., Sarasota Yacht Club, Lake Zurich Golf Club. Presbyterian.

MORROW, GRANT, III, geneticist; b. Pitts., Mar. 18, 1933; married, 1960; 2 children. BA, Haverford Coll., 1955; MD, U. Pa., 1959. Intern U. Colo., 1959-60; resident in pediatrics U. Pa., 1960-62, fellow neonatology, 1962-63, assoc. prof., 1964-65, assoc. prof. metabolic disease, 1965-71; from assoc. prof. to prof. neonatology and metabolism U. Ariz., 1972-78, assoc. chmn. dept., 1976-78; med. dir. Columbus (Ohio) Children's Hosp., 1978-94; prof.

neonatology and metabolism, chmn. dept. Ohio State U., 1978-94. Mem. Am. Pediatric Soc., Am. Soc. Clin. Nutrition, Soc. Pediatric Rsch. Achievements include research on children suffering inborn errors of metabolism, mainly amino and organic acids, patients on total parental nutrition. Office: Children's Hosp Rsch Found 700 Childrens Dr Columbus OH 43205

MORROW, JAMES BENJAMIN, retired sea products company executive; b. Halifax, N.S., Can., 1926. Grad., Dalhousie U., 1948, Tech. U. N.S., 1950; doctoral degree (hon.), Tech. U. N.S., 1978. Exec. v.p. Nat. Sea Products Ltd., Halifax; past pres. Assoc. Prof. Engrs. of Novascotia; pres. Lunenburg Mutual Ins. Co., Lunenburg Mutual Relief Assn., Laubach Literacy of Can.; hon. dir. Sea Food Producers Assn. Nat. Sea Products Ltd. Past pres. Fishermen's Meml. Hosp., Lunenburg, N.S. Mem. Lunenburg Yacht Club (past commodore). Home: PO Box 339, Lunenburg, NS Canada B0J 2C0

MORROW, JAMES FRANKLIN, lawyer; b. Shenandoah, Iowa, Oct. 23, 1944; s. Warren Ralph and Margaret Glee (Palm) M. BS, Kans. State U., 1967; JD, U. Ariz., 1973. Bar: Ariz. 1973, U.S. Dist. Ct. Ariz. 1973. Ptnr. Bilby, Shoenhair, Warnock & Dolph, Tucson, 1973-83, Streich Lang, P.A., Tucson, 1984—. Mng. editor U. Ariz. Law Rev., 1972-73. Past chmn. bd. trustees Palo Verde Mental Health Svcs.; past pres. U. Ariz. Alumni Assn.; past chmn. bd. Palo Verde Hosp., Ariz. Tech. Devel. Corp.; past pres. U. Ariz. Alumni Assn.; past chmn. bd. Palo Verde Hosp., Ariz. Tech. Devel. Corp.; past pres. bd. Cath. Community Svcs.; exec. com. chmn. bd. dirs. U. Ariz. Found. Capt. U.S. Army, 1967-70. Mem. Am. Coll. Real Estate Lawyers, Am. Coll. Mortgage Attys., State Bar Ariz. (cert. real estate specialist, adv. commn. real esatate specialists, past chmn. real estate property sect.), Pima County Bar Assn. Calif. Bar Assn. Democrat. Roman Catholic. Avocation: golf. Office: Streich Lang PA Ste 1700 One South Church Ave Tucson AZ 85701

MORROW, JOHN ELLSWORTH, lawyer; b. Los Angeles, Mar. 17, 1943; s. Charles Henry and Lillian (Harmon) M.; m. Sue C. Taylor, June 28, 1989. BS, U. Southern Calif., 1965; JD, U. Chgo., 1968; postgrad. U. Munich (Germany), 1969. Bar: Calif. 1969, Ill. 1971. Law clk. to judge U.S. Dist. Ct. (cen. dist.) Calif., 1969-70; ptnr. Baker & McKenzie, Chgo., 1970-73, 75-76, 83—; Zurich, Switzerland, 1974-75, Hong Kong, 1976-82. Mem. ABA (subcom. on internat. bus. law com. of corp. sect.). Office: Baker & McKenzie 1 Prudential Plz 130 E Randolph Dr Fl 36 Chicago IL 60601-6206

MORROW, JON STANLEY, pathology educator, medical scientist; b. Ft. Wayne, Ind., BS, Ind. U., 1969, PhD, 1974; MD, Yale U., 1976. Prof. pathology Yale Med. Sch., New Haven, Conn., 1989—; chmn. pathology dept. Yale Med. Sch., New Haven, 1990—; chief pathology Yale-New Haven (Conn.) Hosp., 1990—. Office: Yale U Sch Medicine Dept Pathology 333 Cedar St New Haven CT 06510-3218

MORROW, LANCE, writer; b. Phila., Penn., 1939. Grad., Harvard U. Began career as reporter Washington Star, 1964-65; with Time mag., 1965—, now sr. writer, contributing mainly to magazine's Essay section. Author: The Chief: A Memoir of Fathers and Sons, 1984, America: A Rediscovery, 1987, (essays) Fishing in the Tiber, 1988, Safari, 1992. Recipient Nat. Mag. Award for Time essays, 1981. Office: Time Magazine Time & Life Bldg Rockefeller Ctr New York NY 10020

MORROW, LAURA ANNETTE, marketing professional; b. Tulsa, Okla., Nov. 14, 1958; d. William Lane and Betty (Whaley) Storey; m. James A. Morrow, May 5, 1984; children: Patrick, Anna, Katherine. BFA, U. Tulsa, 1980; MA, U. Okla., 1983. Commml. designer A2 Inc., Tulsa, Okla., 1980-81; grad. rsch. asst. U. Okla., Norman, Okla., 1981-82; v.p. Profl. Systems Svcs., Tulsa, 1982-83; dir. of mktg. Commn. & Research MCC Ctr. Line, Tulsa, 1983-84; coll. instr. Tulsa Jr. Coll., 1982-88; reg. mktg. dir. Century HealthCare Corp., Tulsa, 1984-88; corp. mktg. dir. Cent. HealthCare Corp., Tulsa, 1988-89; regional mktg. dir. Psychiatric Insts. Am., Washington, 1989-90; v.p. mktg. and devel. Children's Med. Ctr., Tulsa, 1990—. Author: presentation, Effective Advt. Strategies 1987-88. Recipient audio projects award Nat. Assn. Pvt. Psychiat. Hosps., 1986, 88, internat. newsletters award, feature articles award, spl. purpose pub. award, 1987, gold medal award, 1987-88, internat. newsletters award, pub. rels. campaign, 4-color brochures award, 1986, Pub. Rels. Soc. Am. Silver Link merit awards, 1987, Gold Ring merit awards Bus. and Profl. Advt. Assn., 1986, 88, Addy and citations Tulsa Advt. Fedn., 1989, gold award, Addy and citations Healthcare ADvt. Review award, 1992. Mem. Am. Mktg. Assn. (competition judge 1986; Health Svcs. Mktg. Award 1987-88). Office: Childrens Med Ctr 5300 E Skelly Dr Tulsa OK 74135-6599

MORROW, PATRICE ANN, biology educator; b. Glendale, Calif., Jan. 11, 1945; d. James Winton and Virginia Mae (Logan) M. BA in Botany, U. Calif., Santa Barbara, 1966; MS in Botany, U. Calif., L.A., 1968; PhD in Biology, Stanford U., 1971. Rsch. fellow Australian Nat. U., Canberra, 1971-76; asst. prof. biology U. Minn., Mpls., 1976-80, assoc. prof., 1980-84, prof., 1984-94, head, 1994—. Fellow Fulbright Found., 1971, J. S. Guggenheim Found., 1983. Fellow AAAS; mem. Assn. Women in Sci., Ecol. Soc. Am., Ecol. Soc. Australia, Soc. Study Evolution. Office: U Minn Dept Ecology Evolution and Behavior 1987 Upper Buford Cir Saint Paul MN 55108-1051

MORROW, PAUL EDWARD, toxicology educator; b. Fairmont, W.Va., Dec. 27, 1922; s. Paul Reed and Imogene (Tench) M.; m. Anne Kelly, June 14, 1947; children—Robert Randolph, William David. BS in Chemistry, U. Ga., 1942, MS in Chemistry, 1947; PhD in Pharmacology, U. Rochester, N.Y., 1951. Diplomate Am. Bd. Indsl. Hygiene. Indsl. hygienist Tenn. Eastman Corp., Kingsport, 1942-43; instr. pharmacology and toxicology U. Rochester, 1952-56, asst. prof. radiation biology and pharmacology, 1956-60, assoc. prof. radiation biology and pharmacology, 1960-66, prof. radiation biology and pharmacology, 1967-85, assoc. prof. pharmacology and toxicology, 1967-69, prof. pharmacology and toxicology, 1969-85, emeritus prof. toxicology, 1985—, acting chmn. dept. radiation biology and biophysics, 1975-77; NIH-USPHS fellow U. Göttingen, Germany, 1959-60, U. Zurich, Switzerland, 1960-61; mem. Internat. Commn. for Radiol. Protection Com., 1967-77; space sci. bd. Nat. Acad. Scis., 1977-80; adv. com. NRC, 1968, toxicology info. program com., 1979-82; mem. Nat. Coun. for Radiation Protection, 1977-87. Contbg. author: Inhalation Carcinogenesis, 1970, Environmental Factors in Respiratory Disease, 1972, Respiratory Defense Mechanisms, 1978, Pulmonary Diseases and Disorders, 1978; editor: Assessment of Airborne Particles, 1972, Polluted Rain, 1980, Occupational and Industrial Medicine: Concepts and Methods, 1984, Aerosols in Medicine, 1985, 93, others; contbr. numerous articles to profl. jours. Advisor particulate matter control criteria Nat. Air Pollution Control Adminstrn., Nat. Acad. Scis. Health Effects of Fossil Fuel Combustion Products, 1968-69; cons. Comitato Nazionale Per L'Energia Nucleare, Cascacia Center, Rome, Italy, 1968-69; mem. temporary staff Med. Research Council, Carshalton, Eng., 1968-69; chmn. com. air pollution Rochester Com. Sci. Info., 1972—; chmn. com. environ. health planning Genesee Region Health Planning Council, 1970-74. Served with USNR, 1943-45. Recipient Aerosol Rsch. award Internat. Soc. Aerosols Med., 1988, Founders award Chem. Industry Inst. Toxicology, 1989. Fellow AAAS, N.Y. Acad. Scis., Acad. Toxicology Scis.; mem. Am. Indsl. Hygiene Assn., Am. Inst. Biol. Scis., Radiation Research Soc., Am. Coll. Toxicology, Health Physics Soc., Soc. Toxicology (Inhalation Toxicology Speciality Sect. Achievement award 1985), Am. Thoracic Soc., Am. Assn. Aerosol Research, Gesellschaft für Aerosolforschung, Soc. of Leukocyte Biology, Internat. Soc. Aerosols in Med., Am. Acad. Hygiene. Home: 200 Laney Rd Rochester NY 14620-3018 Office: U Rochester Dept Biophysics Box EHSC Rochester NY 14642

MORROW, RALPH ERNEST, historian, educator; b. Marshall County, Ind., Sept. 16, 1920; s. Ralph E. and Myrtle (Parrish) M.; m. Vera Cummings, June 4, 1949; children: Jason Drew, Leslie Ellen. B.S., Manchester (Ind.) Coll., 1943; A.M., Ind. U., 1948, Ph.D., 1953. Instr. Ind. U., 1948-50, Mich. State U., 1953-55; mem. faculty Washington U., St. Louis, 1955—; prof. history Washington U., 1963—, chmn. dept., 1960-65, from 1967, dean Grad. Sch., 1967-79, dean Faculty Arts and Scis., 1979-84, provost, 1984-86, prof. emeritus, historian of the univ., 1986—; cons. on call Danforth Found.

Author: Northern Methodism and Reconstruction, 1956. Served to lt. (j.g.) USNR, 1943-46, PTO. Guggenheim fellow, 1959-60. Mem. Am. Hist. Assn. (chmn. com. coll. and univ. teaching from 1967), Orgn. Am. Historians. Presbyterian. Office: Washington Univ 1 Brookings Dr # 1133 Saint Louis MO 63130-4862

MORROW, RICHARD MARTIN, retired oil company executive; b. Wheeling, W.Va., Feb. 27, 1926; married. B.M.E., Ohio State U., 1948. With Amoco Corp., 1948-91; v.p. Amoco Prodn. Co., 1964-66; exec. v.p. Amoco Internat. Oil Co., 1966-70; exec. v.p. Amoco Chem. Corp., 1970-74, pres., 1974-78; pres. Amoco Corp., 1978-83, chmn. chief exec. officer, 1983-91; ret., 1991; bd. dirs. 1st Chgo. Corp., 1st Nat. Bank of Chgo., Westinghouse Electric Corp., R.R. Donnelly & Sons Co., Potlatch Corp., Marsh & McLennan Cos., Inc., Seagull Energy Corp. Trustee U. Chgo. and Rush-Presbyn. St. Luke's Med. Ctr. Office: Amoco Corp 200 E Randolph Dr Ste 7909 Chicago IL 60601-6401

MORROW, RICHARD TOWSON, lawyer; b. Glendale, Calif., Aug. 3, 1926; s. Ray Leslie and Marion Elizabeth (Towson) M.; m. Virginia Alice Kaspar, June 28, 1947; children: Kathleen Ann, Randall Ray, Nancy Lynn. Student, Occidental Coll., 1944-45; BA, UCLA, 1947; LLB, U. So. Calif., 1950. Assoc. Musick & Burrell, Los Angeles, 1950-53; lawyer Walt Disney Prodns., Burbank, Calif., 1953-64, v.p., 1964-69, v.p., gen. counsel, 1969-85, dir., 1971-84; ptnr. Hufstedler, Kaus & Beardsley, Los Angeles, 1985-90, of counsel, 1990-91; ret., 1991; trustee Roy Disney Family Found., Burbank. Former pres., bd. dirs. Glendale YMCA, Calif.; former mem. adv. bd. Glendale Salvation Army; former trustee Glendale Cmty. Found., 1991-94. Served to lt. (j.g.) USNR, 1944-46. Mem. ABA (chmn. corp. law dept. com. 1982-84, coun. bus. law sect. 1984-88), Calif. Bar Assn. (chair 1973-74, trustee 1969-85, Outstanding Corp. Counsel award), L.A. County Bar Assn., Glendale Bar Assn., Am. Law Inst., Calif. Club, Chancery Club (L.A.) Lakeside Golf Club (North Hollywood, Calif.), Alisal Men's Golf Club (Solvang). Republican. Presbyterian. Avocation: golf. Home: 665 Hillside Dr Solvang CA 93463

MORROW, ROB, actor; b. New Rochelle, N.Y., Sept. 21, 1962; s. Murray and Diane Francis (Markowitz) M. mem. Ensemble Studio Theatre. Stage appearances include Escape from Riverdale, 1984, The Return of Pinnochio, 1988, The Chosen, 1987-88, The Substance of Fire, 1990; TV series Tattingers, 1988, Northern Exposure, 1990-94 (Lead Actor in TV Drama Emmy award nominee 1991, 92, 93, Lead Actor in TV Drama Golden Globe nominee 1991, 92, 93); films: Private Resort, 1985, Quiz Show, 1994, Last Dance, 1995. Mem. Naked Angels (co-founder). Jewish.

MORROW, WALTER EDWIN, JR., electrical engineer, university laboratory administrator; b. Springfield, Mass., July 24, 1928; s. Walter Edwin and Mary Elizabeth (Ganley) M.; m. Janice Lila Lombard, Feb. 25, 1951; children—Clifford E., Gregory A., Carolyn F. S.B., M.I.T., 1949, S.M., 1951. Mem. staff Lincoln Lab., MIT, Lexington, Mass., 1951-55, group leader, 1956-65; head div. communications MIT Lincoln Lab., 1966-68, asst. dir., 1968-71, assoc. dir., 1972-77, dir., 1977—. Contbr. articles to profl. publs. Recipient award for outstanding achievement Pres. M.I.T., 1963, Edwin Howard Armstrong Achievement award IEEE Communications Soc., 1976. Fellow IEEE, Nat. Acad. Engring. Achievements include patent for synchronous satellite, electric power plant using electrolytic cell-fuel cell combination. Office: MIT Lincoln Lab 244 Wood St PO Box 73 Lexington MA 02173

MORROW, WILLIAM CLARENCE, lawyer; b. Austin, Tex., Aug. 9, 1935; s. Theodore Faulkner and Gladys Lee (Ames) M.; 1 stepchild, Shana Lynn Barbee; m. Sandra Jean Scott, Jan. 19, 1959 (div. Feb. 1971); m. Sheila Beth Pfost, June 29, 1973. children: Scott Fitzgerald Morrow, Elizabeth Ann Rettig. BA, Baylor U., 1957; JD, So. Meth. U., 1962. Bar: Tex., 1962. Trial atty. SEC, Ft. Worth, 1963-65; former ptnr. Turpin, Smith, Dyer & Hardie, Midland, Tex., Stubbeman, McRae, Sealy, Laughlin & Browder, Midland, Cotton, Bledsoe, Tighe, Morrow & Dawson, Midland; exec. v.p. Magnatex Corp., Midland, 1980-86; v.p., gen. counsel and sec. Elcor Corp., Midland, 1986-88; shareholder Lynch Chappell & Alsup, Midland, 1988—. Mem. Midland City Coun., 1992—, mayor pro tem, 1994-95; former vice chmn. Tex. Rehab. Commn.; pres. Found. Mental Health and Mental Retardation Permian Basin; pres. United Way of Midland, 1985, Indsl. Found. Midland, 1987; trustee Midland Community Theatre, 1980—, chmn. 1995—; elder 1st Presbyn. Ch., Midland. Mem. Tex. Bar Assn., Midland County Bar Assn., Midland C. of C. (past v.p.), Petroleum Club of Midland (past bd. dirs.), Phi Delta Phi. Home: 3110 Gulf Ave Midland TX 79705-8205 Office: Lynch Chappell & Alsup 300 N Marienfeld St Ste 700 Midland TX 79701-4393

MORROW, WINSTON VAUGHAN, financial executive; b. Grand Rapids, Mich., Mar. 22, 1924; s. Winston V. and Selma (von Egloffstein) M.; m. Margaret Ellen Staples, June 25, 1948 (div.); children: Thomas Christopher, Mark Staples; m. Edith Burrows Ulrich, Mar. 2, 1990. AB cum laude, Williams Coll., 1947; JD, Harvard U., 1950. Bar: R.I. 1950. Assoc. atty. Edwards & Angell, Providence, 1950-57; exec. v.p., asst. treas., gen. counsel bd. dirs. Avis, Inc. and subs., 1957-61; v.p., gen. mgr. Rent A Car div. Avis, Inc., 1962-64, pres., bd. dirs., 1964-75; chmn., chief exec. officer, bd. dirs. Avis, Inc. and Avis Rent A Car System, Inc., 1965-77; chmn., pres., bd. dirs. Teleflorists Inc. and subs., 1978-80; pres. Westwood Equities Corp., L.A., 1981—, chief exec. officer, 1984—, also bd. dirs. New TC Holding Corp.; chmn., pres., chief exec. officer Ticor Title Ins. Co., 1982-91, also bd. dirs.; chmn. TRTS Data Svcs. Inc., 1985-91; bd. dirs. AECOM Tech. Corp., L.A., 1990—; dir. William & Scott, Inc., 1994—; mem. Pres.'s Industry and Govt. Spl. Travel Task Force, 1968, travel adv. bd. U.S. Travel Svcs., 1968-76, L.A. City-wide Airport Adv. Com., 1983-85; co-chmn. L.A. Transp. Coalition, 1985-91. Mem. juvenile delinquency task force Nat. Coun. Crime and Delinquency, 1985-86, L.A. Mayor's Bus. Coun., 1983-86, Housing Roundtable, Washington, 1983-85; chmn., pres. Spring St. Found., 1991—; bd. dirs. Police Found., Washington, 1983-91; trustee Com. for Econ. Devel., Washington, 1987-91. Decorated Stella Della Solidarieta Italy, Gold Tourism medal Austria). Mem. Fed. Bar Assn., R.I. Bar Assn., Car and Truck Rental and Leasing Assn. (nat. pres. 1961-63), Am. Land Title Assn. (bd. govs. 1989-90), L.A. Area C. of C. (bd. dirs. 1983-90), The Huntington (fellow), Bald Peak Colony Club, Williams Club, L.A. Tennis Club, Phi Beta Kappa, Kappa Alpha. Home: 4056 Farmouth Dr Los Angeles CA 90027-1314 also: Meadowview Farm Cushing Corners Rd Freedom NH 03836-0221

MORSCH, THOMAS HARVEY, lawyer; b. Oak Park, Ill., Sept. 5, 1931; s. Harvey William and Gwenodyne (Maun) M.; m. Jacquelyn Casey, Dec. 27, 1954; children: Thomas H. Jr., Margaret, Mary Susan, James, Kathryn, Julia. BA, Notre Dame U., 1953; B.S.L., Northwestern U., 1953, J.D., 1955. Bar: Ill. 1955, D.C. 1955. Assoc. Crowell & Leibman, Chgo., 1955-62; ptnr. Leibman, Williams, Bennett, Baird & Minow, Chgo., IL, 1962-72, Sidley & Austin, Chgo., 1972—; bd. dirs. Chgo. Lawyers Com. for Civil Rights Under Law, chmn., 1982-83; bd. dirs. Pub. Interest Law Initiative, pres., 1993-95; mem. adv. bd. Legal Svcs. Inst., 1982-85, No. Dist. Ill. Civil Justice Reform Com., 1991-95; mem. vis. com. Northwestern U. Law Sch., 1989-90. Pres. Republican Workshops of Ill., 1970; gen. counsel Ill. Com. to Re-elect the Pres., 1972; mem. LaGrange Plan Commn., Ill., 1972-80, LaGrange Fire and Police Commn., 1968-72; trustee LaGrange Meml. Hosp., 1983-89; adv. bd. Catholic Charities of Chgo., 1985—. Fellow Am. Coll. Trial Lawyers; mem. ABA, Ill. State Bar Assn., Chgo. Bar Assn. (bd. mgrs. 1979-81), D.C. Bar Assn., Northwestern Law Sch. Alumni Assn. (pres. 1988-89), Chgo. Bar Found. (bd. dirs., 1st v.p. 1993—). Roman Catholic. Clubs: Legal, Univ. (Chgo.), Mid Day (Chgo.); LaGrange Country, Palisades Park Country (Mich.), Point O'Woods Country (Mich.). Home: 301 S Edgewood Ave La Grange IL 60525-2153 Office: Sidley & Austin 1 First Nat Plz Chicago IL 60603

MORSE, DANIEL E., biochemistry educator, science administrator; b. N.Y.C., May 20, 1941. BA, Harvard U., 1963; PhD in Molecular Biology, Albert Einstein Coll. Medicine, 1967. Fellow in molecular genetics Stanford U., 1967-69; from Silas Arnold Houston asst. prof. to Silas Arnold Houston assoc. prof. med. sch. Harvard U., 1969-73; prof. molecular genetics and biochemistry U. Calif., Santa Barbara, 1973—, chmn. sect. molecular biology and biochemistry dept. biol. sci., 1981-85, chmn. Marie Biotechnology Ctr.,

1986—; mem. NRC, U.S. Nat. Com. Internat. Union Biol. Sci., 1986—; chmn. task force biotechnology in ocean sci. NSF, 1987—. Fellow AAAS; mem. Am. Soc. Molecular Biology and Biochemistry, Am. Soc. Limnology and Oceanography, Am. Soc. Microbiology, Am. Soc. Zoology, N.Y. Acad. Sci., Internat. Soc. Chem. Ecology. Achievements include research on molecular mechanisms controlling reproduction, larval metamorphosis, development and gene expression; signal molecules, receptors, and transducers; molecular marine biology; molecular neurobiology; molecular chemosensory mechanisms. Office: U Calif Marine Biotech Ctr Dept Biology Santa Barbara CA 93106*

MORSE, EDMOND NORTHROP, investment management executive; b. Balt., Dec. 31, 1922; s. Edmond Harris and Ethel (Dannenberg) M.; m. Sidney Harvey Phillips, June 5, 1948; children: Edmond H., David F., Judith B., Anne S., John B. BA, Brown U., 1944; M.B.A., Harvard, 1947. With Smith, Barney & Co. (investment bankers), N.Y.C., 1947-81; gen. partner Smith, Barney & Co. (investment bankers), 1961-64, v.p., dir., 1964-68, sr. v.p., dir., 1968-70, exec. v.p., dir., 1970-76; exec. v.p., dir. Smith Barney, Harris Upham, 1976-81; exec. v.p. First Manhattan Co., 1981-89; gen. ptnr. Morse Equity Ptnrs., Darien, Conn., 1989—; dir. First Century Ptnrs.; dir., vice chmn. Lockwood Mathews Mansion Mus., Norwalk, Conn. Bd. dirs. Easter Seal Rehab. Ctr., Stamford, Conn. 1st lt. USMCR, 1943-46. Mem. Wee Burn Country Club. Home: Ridge Acres Darien CT 06820 Office: 36 Old King S Hwy Darien CT 06820

MORSE, EDWARD J., automotive executive; b. 1949. Pres. Morse Ops., Ft. Lauderdale, 1970—, Ed Morse Chevrolet, Inc., Ft. Lauderdale, Fla., 1979—. Office: Morse Operations Inc 6363 NW 6th Way 400 Fort Lauderdale FL 33309

MORSE, GARLAN, JR., real estate investment counseling officer; b. Salem, Mass., Dec. 2, 1947; s. Garlan and Priscilla (Slee) M.; m. Jody Neilson, Nov. 17, 1973; children: Margot Appleton, Joanna Baldwin, Samuel Mackenzie. A.B. in English, Princeton U., 1969. Mem. faculty Middlesex Sch., Concord, Mass., 1969-72; mgmt. trainee Bank of Boston, 1972-74, loan officer, 1974-79, v.p., 1979-81, 1st v.p. 1981-83, sr. v.p., 1983-90; founding dir. Morris & Morse Co., Inc., Boston, 1990—. Mem. Am. Soc. Real Estate Counselors, Internat. Coun. Shopping Ctrs., Real Estate Fin. Assn./Greater Boston Real Estate Bd. (pres.), Urban Land Inst. Clubs: Manchester Yacht, Essex County. Office: Morris & Morse Co Inc 399 Boylston St Boston MA 02116

MORSE, JACK HATTON, utilities consultant; b. San Diego, June 4, 1923; s. John Henderson and Alberta (Peterson) M.; m. Kathleen Clark (div.); children: David Eugene, Steven Allen; m. Jean Larson. BA, San Diego State U., 1956, M in Bus. Sci., 1971. Exec. San Diego Gas & Electric, 1947-89; cons. Pub., contbr. Sea Power mag., 1987-89. Pres. Cystic Fibrosis Found., San Diego, 1980-83, Project Handclasp, 1991—, Oceans Found., 1992-94. Comdr. USNR, 1943-46, 52-54. Recipient Dr. Frederick Patterson award United Negro Coll. Fund, San Diego, 1989. Mem. IEEE, Pacific Coast Elec. Assn., Pacific Coast Gas Assn. (Silver medal 1981), Navy League U.S. (nat. pres., chmn. adv. com. 1987-89, Disting. Svc. award 1979, 88, 89), La Jolla Beach and Tennis Club, Masons. Republican. Mem. LDS Ch. Avocation: traveling. Home and Office: 6125 Terryhill Dr La Jolla CA 92037-6837

MORSE, JAMES L., state supreme court justice; b. N.Y.C., Sept. 11, 1940; m. Gretchen B, June 19, 1965; children: Rebecca Penfield, Rachel Lasell. AB, Dartmouth Coll., 1962; JD magna cum laude, Boston U., 1969. Bar: Vt. 1970, U.S. Dist Ct. Vt. 1970, U.S. Ct. Appeals (2d cir.) 1970, U.S. Supreme Ct. 1973. Law clk. to Judge Sterry R. Waterman U.S. Ct. Appeals (2nd cir.), 1969-70; pvt. practice Burlington, Vt., 1970-73, 75-76; asst. atty. gen. State of Vt., Montpelier, 1973-75, defender gen., 1976-81; judge Vt. Superior Ct., Montpelier, 1981-88; justice Vt. Supreme Ct., Montpelier, 1988—. Editor in chief Boston U. Law Rev., 1967-69. Lt. USNR, 1963-66. Mem. Vt. Bar Assn. Office: Vt Supreme Ct 109 State St Montpelier VT 05609-0001

MORSE, JOHN HARLEIGH, lawyer; b. Estherville, Iowa, Sept. 22, 1910; s. James W. and Winifred E. (Williams) M.; m. Marie A. Forrest, Nov. 11, 1936 (div. June 1962); children: James W. II, Bruce F.; m. Ann U. Stanton, May 23, 1964. B.A., State U. Iowa, 1930; M.B.A., Harvard U., 1932; JD, Yale U., 1935. Bar: N.Y. 1936. Since practiced in N.Y.C.; with firm Carter, Ledyard & Milburn, 1935; with firm Cravath, Swaine & Moore, 1936-76, ptnr., 1946-76. Pres. Forest Property Owners Assn., 1992-94. Mem. ABA (chmn. labor relations law sect. 1961-62), Forest Country Club, Phi Beta Kappa, Phi Gamma Delta. Home and Office: 16301 Fairway Woods Dr Fort Myers FL 33908-5306

MORSE, JOHN M., book publishing executive. Exec. editor, v.p. Merriam-Webster Inc., Springfield, Mass. Office: Merriam Webster Inc 47 Federal St Springfield MA 01105-3805

MORSE, JOHN MOORE, architect, planner; b. Brookline, Mass., Aug. 23, 1911; s. Arthur Moore and Helen (Stearns) M.; m. Emily Hall (dec. 1989); children: David Hall, Catherine Morse Wikkerink; m. Helen Taverniti, Aug. 5, 1989. AB, Harvard U., 1934, MArch, 1940. Registered architect, Wash. Tchr. Loomis Sch., Windsor, Conn., 1934-36; ptnr. Bassetti & Morse, Seattle, 1947-62; prin. John Morse & Assocs., Seattle, 1962-78; ptnr. Morse Stafford Ptnrship., Seattle, 1978-85; prin. John Morse Architect & Planner, Seattle, 1985—. Mem. King County (Wash.) Planning Commn., 1965-70, Design Rev. Bd., Mill Creek, Wash., 1987-89; chmn. Seattle Urban Design Bd., 1966; bd. dirs. Cornish Coll. Arts, Seattle, 1974-80. Fellow AIA (pres. Seattle chpt. 1969, various local and nat. awards). Democrat. Office: 1402 3d Ave Ste 1020 Seattle WA 98101-2118

MORSE, JOSHUA MARION, III, lawyer, educator; b. Poplarville, Miss., Mar. 7, 1923; s. Joshua Marion and Eva (Triplett) M.; m. Mary Nell Hartzog, May 26, 1946; children: Joshua Stanford, Anne Elizabeth, Mary Jeanne. J.D., U. Miss., 1948; postgrad., Yale U. Law Sch. Bar: Miss. 1948, U.S. Ct. Appeals (5th cir.) 1954, U.S. Supreme Ct. 1966, U.S. Ct. Appeals (11th cir.) 1984. Ptnr. Morse & Morse, Poplarville, 1948-61, Morse & Smith, Poplarville, 1961-63; assoc. prof. law U Miss., 1962-63; dean U. Miss. (Sch. Law), 1963-69; dean, prof. Fla. State U. Coll. Law, 1969-81, prof., 1981—; of counsel Fowler, White, Gilley, Boggs, & Villereal, Tampa, Fla., 1981—; bd. dirs. Micronesian Legal Service; mem. Fla. Law Revision Commn.; commr. Nat. Conf. Commrs. on Uniform State Laws, 1963—, v.p. exec. commn., 1981-83. Served with AUS, 1942-46; capt. Judge Adv. Gen. Corps., USNR, ret. Mem. ABA, Maritime Law Assn., Assn. Am. Law Schs. Home: 504 Plantation Rd Tallahassee FL 32303-4208 Office: PO Box 11240 Tallahassee FL 32302-3240 also: Ste 1040 Allen Morris Bldg 101 N Monroe St Tallahassee FL 32301

MORSE, JUDY, science foundation administrator. Ceo Arboretum Foundation, Los Angeles County Arboreta and Botanic Gardens, Arcadia, Calif. Office: Los Angeles County Arboretum Found 301 N Baldwin Ave Arcadia CA 91007

MORSE, KAREN WILLIAMS, academic administrator; b. Monroe, Mich., May 8, 1940; m. Joseph G. Morse; children: Robert G., Geoffrey E. BS, Denison U., 1962; MS, U. Mich., 1964, PhD, 1967; DSc (hon.), Denison U., 1990. Rsch. chemist Ballistic Rsch. Lab., Aberdeen Proving Ground, Md., 1966-68; lectr. chemistry dept. Utah State U., Logan, 1968-69, from asst. to assoc. prof. chemistry, 1969-83, prof. chemistry dept., 1983-93, dept. head Coll. Sci., 1981-88, dean Coll. Sci., 1988-89, univ. provost, 1989-93; pres. Western Wash. U., Bellingham, 1993—; mem. chair Grad. Record Exam in chemistry com., Princeton, N.J., 1980-89, Gov.'s Sci. Coun., Salt Lake City, 1986-93, Gov.'s Coun. on Fusion, 1989-91, ACS Com. on Profl. Tng., 1984-92; cons. 1993. Contbr. articles to profl. jours.; patentee in field. Mem. Cache County Sch. Dist. Found., Cache Valley, Logan, 1988-93; swim coach, soccer coach; trustee First United Presbyn. Ch., Logan, 1979-81, 82-85; adv. bd. Sci. Discovery Ctr., Logan, 1993; mem. bd. dirs. United Way, Whatcom County, 1993—; exec. com. Fourth Corners Econ. Devel. Bd., 1993—; mem. policies and procedures com. AASCU, 1993—. Recipient Disting. Alumni in Residence award U. Mich., 1989. Fellow AAAS; mem. Am. Chem. Soc. (Utah award Salt Lake City and Cen. dists. 1988), Bus. and Profl. Women

Club (pres. 1984-85), Philanthropic Edn. Orgn., Phi Beta Kappa, Sigma Xi, Phi Beta Kappa Assocs., Phi Kappa Phi, Beta Gamma Sigma. Avocations: skiing, biking, photography. Office: Western Washington Univ Office of Pres Bellingham WA 98225-9000

MORSE, KENNETH PRATT, manufacturing executive; b. Cambridge, Mass., Mar. 9, 1905; s. Clifford E. and Jessie C. (Barr) M.; m. Florence Stillwell, June 20, 1931; children—Kenneth P., Peter S. Student, MIT, 1922-26. Asst. chief engr. Lanston Monotype Machine Co., Phila., 1926-37; devel. engr. Standard Register Co., Dayton, 1937, chief engr., 1938, chief engr., works supt., 1938-42, asst. gen. mgr., 1942-45, exec. v.p., gen. mgr., 1945-64, pres., 1964-70, chmn. bd., 1970-71, chmn. emeritus, 1971—; v.p., dir. Office Equipment Mfg. Inst., 1953-54, pres., dir., 1955-57; pres., dir. Huebner Co., Dayton, 1951-58; dir. emeritus 3d Nat. Bank & Trust Co., Dayton; Mem. Industry adv. com. continuous forms and adv. com. office equipment U.S. Dept. Commerce and U.S. Dept. Labor Manpower Commn., 1951—. Mem. budget com. Community Chest, 1948-54; chmn. com. financing devel. Dayton area Mass. Inst. Tech., 1949—; adv. bd. Salvation Army, 1953-60; Bd. dirs. Goodwill Industries, Dayton, 1957-66, pres., 1960-64; bd. dirs. Community Chest, 1958—, chmn. campaign, 1961; Trustee Miami Valley Hosp., Dayton, 1958-77, U. Dayton, 1970-75. Recipient Inland Printer award, 1958, Disting. Corp. Leadership award MIT, 1987. Mem. Edn. Council of Graphic Arts (dir. 1959-66, pres. 1964-66), U.S. C of C., Dayton C of C. (pres. 1957-59), Printing Industry Am., Inc. (sec. 1952-53, dir. 1952-54), Dayton Printing Industry Assn. (pres. 1950-53, dir. 1950—), Graphic Arts Research and Engring. Council (planning com. 1953). Presbyterian. Lodges: Masons, Shriners. Home: 10 Wilmington Ave Apt W-221 Dayton OH 45420-1882

MORSE, LEON WILLIAM, traffic, physical distribution and transportation management executive, consultant; b. N.Y.C., Nov. 13, 1912; s. Benjamin and Leah (Shapiro) M.; m. Goldie Kohn, Mar. 30, 1941; children: Jeffrey W., Saul J. BS, NYU, 1935; grad. Acad. Advanced Traffic, 1937, 1954; DBA, Columbia Pacific U., 1979. Registered practitioner ICC, Fed. Maritime Commn. Individual bus., traffic mgmt. cons., Phila., 1950-58; gen. traffic mgr. W.H. Rorer, Inc., Ft. Washington, Pa., 1958-78; adj. prof. econs. of transp., logistics Pa. State U., Ogontz campus, 1960-82; owner Morse Assocs.; course leader seminars in freight traffic mgmt., phys. distbn. mgmt., transp. contract negotiations and freight claims for univs. in the U.S.; bd. dirs. Sr. Security Assocs., Inc.; treas., exec. com. Temple B'rith Shalom. Author: Practical Handbook of Industrial Traffic Management, 1980, 87, (manuals) Job of the Traffic Manager, Effective Traffic Management, Fundamentals of Traffic Management, Transportation Contract Negotiations and Freight Claims. Capt. transp. corps, AUS, World War II. Recipient Del. Valley Traffic Mgr. of Yr. award, 1963. Mem. Traffic and Transp. Club of Phila., Traffic Club of Phila., Traffic Club of Norristown, Am. Soc. Internat. Execs. (past pres., bd. dirs., sec., cert.), Assn. Transp. Practitioners, Am. Soc. Transp. and Logistics (emeritus), Council Logistics Mgmt., Transp. Research Forum, Health & Personal Care Distribution Conf. (pres. 1973-75, chmn. bd. 1975-77), Sr. Security Assn., Inc. (bd. dirs.), Delta Nu Alpha Transp. Fraternity, Mason, Shriner.

MORSE, LOWELL WESLEY, banking and real estate executive; b. West Palm Beach, Fla., May 1, 1937; s. Alton and Blanche (Yelverton) M.; B.S., U. Santa Clara, 1968; grad. Def. Lang. Inst., Monterey, Calif., 1959; m. Vera Giacalone, June 22, 1958; children: Lowell Wesley, Stephen D., Michael S. Russian linguist U.S. Army Security Agy., 1957-60; asst. city mgr. City of Pacific Grove (Calif.), 1961-66; city mgr. Town of Los Altos Hills (Calif.), 1967-69; chmn. Morse & Assos., Inc., Portland, Oreg., 1972—; founder, dir. Comerica Bank Calif., San Jose, 1979—; chmn. Cypress Ventures Inc., Portland, The Bagel Basket, Inc.; bd. trustees Regent U. Served with U.S. Army, 1957-60. Home: 21042 SW Wyndham Hill Ct Tualatin OR 97062-7711 Office: 5335 SW Meadows Rd # 365 Lake Oswego OR 97035

MORSE, MARVIN HENRY, judge; b. Mt. Vernon, N.Y., July 19, 1929; s. Frank Irving and Lillian (Seeger) M.; m. Betty Anne Hess, Dec. 27, 1953; children: Martin Albert, Michael Howard, Lee Anne. AB, Colgate U., 1949; LLB, Yale U., 1952. Bar: N.Y. 1952, Ky. 1956, Md. 1964, U.S. Supreme Ct. 1960, U.S. Ct. Appeals (6th cir.), U.S. Dist. Ct. (we. dist.) Ky., U.S. Ct. Mil. Appeals, U.S. Ct. Claims, U.S. Ct. Appeals (D.C. cir.), U.S. Ct. Appeals (fed. cir.), U.S. Dist. Ct. (no. dist.) Tex., U.S. Dist. Ct. Hawaii. Pvt. practice Louisville, 1956-62; asst. counsel Office of Gen. Counsel Dept. Navy, Washington, 1962-65, Office of Gen. Counsel Office Sec. Def., Washington, 1965-68; asst. gen. counsel GSA, Washington, 1968-70, U.S. Postal Svc., Washington, 1970-73; adminstrv. law judge Fed. Energy Regulatory Commn., Washington, 1973-75, Postal Rate Commn., Washington, 1975-77, CAB, Washington, 1977-80; dir. adminstrv. law judges Office Pers. Mgmt., Washington, 1980-82; chief adminstrv. law judge SBA, Washington, 1982-87, asst. adminstr. office of hearings and appeals, 1986-87; adminstrv. law judge Exec. Office of Immigration Rev. Dept. Justice, Washington, 1987—; mem. Adminstrv. Conf. of U.S., 1980-84, govt. mem., 1985-86, 87—, liaison mem.; faculty and faculty coord. The Nat. Jud. Coll., 1977, 79-80. Author: (with S. Groner) ABA Handbook chpt. on adminstrv. law, 1981. Trustee Washington area chpt. Am. Digestive Disease Soc., 1976-87. With JAGC, USAF, 1952-56, to col. USAFR, ret. 1979. Decorated USAF Legion of Merit; recipient Disting. Svc. award Am. Digestive Disease Soc., 1980. Mem. ABA (exec. com. 1977-82, 84-87, chmn. 1980-81, conf. adminstrv. law judges , del. ho. of dels. 1984-87, lawyers in govt. com. 1985-86, jud. selection, tenure and compensation com. 1987-93), Fed. Bar Assn. (nat. coun. 1976—, chmn. career svc. sect. 1983-86, chmn. judiciary sect. 1986-88, sect. coord. 1988-90, sec. 1991, del. to ABA ho. of dels. 1992-93, v.p. 1993-94, pres.-elect 1994-95, pres. 1995—), Am. Law Inst., Fed. Adminstrv. Law Judges Conf. (exec. com. 1975-77, 82—), Nat. Assn. Adminstrv. Law Judges (hon.), Fed. Am. Inn of Ct. (coun. 1990-92, pres. 1992-94). Home: 8027 Cindy Ln Bethesda MD 20817-6912 Office: US Dept Justice 5107 Leesburg Pike Falls Church VA 22041-3234

MORSE, PETER HODGES, ophthalmologist, educator; b. Chgo., Mar. 1, 1935; s. Emerson Glover and Carol Elizabeth (Rolph) M. AB, Harvard U., 1957; MD, U. Chgo., 1963. Diplomate: Am. Bd. Ophthalmology. Intern U. Chgo. Hosp., 1963-64; resident Wilmer Inst. Johns Hopkins Hosp., Balt., 1966-69; fellow, retina service Mass. Eye and Ear Infirmary, Boston, 1969-70; asst. prof. ophthalmology, chief retina service U. Pa., 1971-75, assoc. prof., 1975; assoc. prof. U. Chgo., 1975-77; prof. ophthalmology, 1979-93, sec. dept. ophthalmology, 1976-77, chief retina service, prof., 1979-93; clin. prof. ophthalmology U.S.D. Sch. Medicine, Sioux Falls, 1993—; prof. La. State U., 1978; chmn. dept. ophthalmology, chief retina service Ochsner Clinic and Found. Hosp., New Orleans, 1977-78; clin. prof. Tulane U., 1978. Author: Vitreoretinal Disease: A Manual for Diagnosis and Treatment, 1979, 2d edit., 1989, Practical Management of Diabetic Retinopathy, 1985; co-editor: Disorders of the Vitreous, Retina, and Choroid; bd. editors Perspectives in Ophthalmology, 1976—, Retina, 1980—; contbr. articles to profl. jours. Served with USNR, 1964-66. Fellow ACS, Coll. Ophthalmologists Eng., Am. Acad. Ophthalmology, Royal Soc. Health (Eng.), Royal Coll. Ophthalmologists (Eng.); mem. AMA, La. Med. Soc., Orleans Parrish Med. Soc., New Orleans Acad. Ophthalmology, La. Ophthalmol. and Otolaryngol. Soc., Miss. Ophthalmol. and Otolaryngol. Soc., Assn. Rsch. Vision and Ophthalmology, Retina Soc., Soc. Heed Fellows, Ophthalmol. Soc. U.K., Pan Am. Assn. Ophthalmology, Oxford Ophthalmol. Congress, All-India Ophthalmol. Soc., Soc. Eye Surgeons, Vitreoretinal Soc. (India), Sigma Xi. Republican. Episcopalian. Home: 1307 S Holly Dr Sioux Falls SD 57105-0221 Office: Central Plains Clinic Ltd Dept Ophthalmology 1100 E 21st St Sioux Falls SD 57105-1020

MORSE, RICHARD, social scientist; b. Boston, Oct. 12, 1922; s. Stearns and Helen Ward (Field) M.; m. Romola Thomas Chowdhry, June 23, 1949; children: Ashok Daniel, Martha Sunita Keily. A.B., Dartmouth Coll., 1946; postgrad., Banaras Hindu U., Aligarh Muslim U., Gokhale Inst. Politics and Econs., India, 1947, Columbia, 1950; A.M., ABD, Harvard, 1958. Edn. officer ECA, Burma, 1950-53; asst. rep. Ford Found., Burma, 1954-56; sr. internat. economist Stanford Research Inst., Menlo Park, Calif., 1958-64, 66-69; cons. Ford Found., India, 1964-66; indsl. devel. cons. Andover, Mass., 1969-74; rsch. assoc., sr. fellow, co-coord. Participatory Devel. Group East West Ctr., Honolulu, 1974-94; sr. fellow emeritus East West Ctr., Honolulu, 1994—; study dir. Nat. Acad. Sci. and Nat. Acad. Engring. Internat. Panel on Internat. Industrialization Inst., 1972-73; chmn. bd. govs. Inst. Current

World Affairs, 1972-74, trustee, 1988-91; bd. dirs. Inst. World Affairs, 1988-91, mem. adv. coun., 1992—; co-founder, dir. Hawaii Entrepreneurship Tng. and Devel. Inst., 1977—; mem. adv. com. Immigrant Ctr. Enterprise Project, Honolulu, 1992—. Co-author: Modern Small Industry for Developing Countries, 1965; (with Eugene Staley) Village Voices in Rural Development and Energy Planning, 1987; co-editor: Grassroot Horizons: Connecting Participatory Development Initiatives East and West, 1995. Served with AUS, 1942-45. Fellow Inst. Current World Affairs, 1946-49; recipient certificate of honor Hawaii Ho. of Reps., 1994. Mem. Am. Econ. Assn., Am. Agrl. Econs. Assn., Am. Assn. Asian Studies, Economists Allied for Arms Reduction, Nitrogen Fixing Tree Assn., Soc. for Internat. Devel. Home: 1621 Halekoa Dr Honolulu HI 96821-1126 Office: 1777 E West Rd Honolulu HI 96848-0001

MORSE, RICHARD JAY, human resources and organizational development consultant, manufacturers' representative company executive; b. Detroit, Aug. 2, 1933; s. Maurice and Belle Rosalyn (Jacobson) M. BA, U. Va., 1955; MA in Clin. Psychology, Calif. State U., L.A., 1967. Area pers. adminstr. Gen. Tel. Co. of Calif., Santa Monica, 1957-67; sr. v.p. human resources The Bekins Co., Glendale, Calif., 1967-83; pvt. cons. human resources and orgn. devel. Glendale, 1983—. Contbr. articles to profl. jours. Fund raiser various orgns., So. Calif., 1970—. Mem. Nat. Soc. Performance and Instrn. (founding mem. 1958—). Republican. Jewish. Avocations: travel, tennis, walking, swimming. Home and Office: 6410 Cambria Pines Rd Cambria CA 93428-2009

MORSE, RICHARD MCGEE, historian; b. Summit, N.J., June 26, 1922; s. William Otis and Marie (Zimmerman) M.; m. Emerante de Pradines, Dec. 30, 1954; children—Marise, Richard. Grad., Hotchkiss Sch., 1939; B.A. magna cum laude, Princeton U., 1943; M.A., Columbia U., 1947, Ph.D., 1952; M.A. (hon.), Yale U., 1963. Successively lectr., instr., asst. prof. history Columbia, 1949-58; dir. Inst. Caribbean Studies, U. P.R., 1958-61; vis. lectr. history Harvard U., 1960; prof. history, chmn. dept. SUNY-L.I., 1961-62; assoc. prof. history Yale U., 1962-63, prof., 1963-78, chmn. Council Latin Am. Studies, 1963-64, 65-70; William H. Bonsall prof. history Stanford U., Calif., 1978-84; sec. Latin Am. Program, Wilson Ctr., Washington, 1984-89; advisor U. Nuevo León Mex., 1958-60; L.Am. cons. to Ford Found., 1958-64, 73-75; vis. prof. El Colegio de Mex., 1981; sec. Interam. Found. Arts, 1963-68; disting. lectr. U. Guyana, 1975; Charles Phelps Taft Meml. lectr. history U. Cin., 1978; disting. Fulbright lectr. U. Rio de Janeiro, 1983; mem. selection com. Guggenheim Found., 1969-88, chmn. 1978-88; vis. scholar Getty Ctr., 1994. Author: From Community to Metropolis, A Biography of São Paulo, Brazil, 1958, The Bandeirantes, 1965, (with others) The Founding of New Societies, 1964, La Investigación urbana latino americana, 1971, Las Ciudades Latinoamericanas, 1973, Lima en 1900, 1973; play The Narrowest Street, 1945; El Espejo de Próspero, 1982, New World Soundings, 1989; also numerous articles; co-editor: Columbia Volumes on Contemporary Civilization, 1954-55; bd. editors Hispanic Am. Hist. Rev, 1960-65, 74-79; adv. editor Caribbean Studies, 1961-89, Jour. Urban History, 1973-90, Cuadernos Americanos, 1986—, Wilson Quarterly, 1989-92. Served to lt. USNR, 1943-46, PTO. Recipient Nat. Theatre Conf. prize play award, 1945, Conf. Latin Am. History prize essay award, 1962; Woodrow Wilson fellow, 1946-47; State Dept. fellow, 1947-48; Guggenheim fellow, 1964-65; Social Sci. Research Council fellow, 1964-65; fellow Center Advanced Studies Behavioral Scis., 1970-71; Stanford Humanities Ctr. fellow, 1983-84, Inst. Advanced Studies U. São Paulo, 1987; recipient medal of merit Getulio Vargas Found., 1975, medal of honor U. São Paulo, 1988, Casa Rui Barbosa medal, 1992, Brazilian Order Cruzeiro do Sul, 1993. Mem. Conf. Latin Am. History (chmn. 1969), Phi Beta Kappa. Home: 4412 Volta Pl NW Washington DC 20007-2019

MORSE, ROBERT ALAN, actor; b. Newton, Mass., May 18, 1931; s. Charles and May (Silver) M.; children: Andrea, Robin, Hillary; m. Elizabeth Roberts, 1989; 1 child, Allyn. Motion pictures include The Cardinal, 1963, The Loved One, 1965, How to Succeed in Business without Really Trying, 1967, Oh Dad, Poor Dad, Mama's Hung You In The Closet And I'm Feelin' So Sad, 1967, Where Were You When the Lights Went Out?, 1968, The Boatniks, 1970, Hunk, 1987, The Emperor's New Clothes, 1987; actor in many plays including The Matchmaker, 1955, Say Darling, 1957, Take Me Along, 1959, How to Succeed in Business without Really Trying, 1960 (Tony award 1961), Sugar, 1972, So Long 174th St., Tru, 1990 (Tony award best actor, 1990, Drama League N.Y. Distinguished Performance award, 1990, Emmy award Outstanding Leading Actor in a Miniseries or Special, 1993), Show Boat, 1993; star TV series That's Life, 1968-69, miniseries Wild Palms, 1993. With USN, 1950-54. Office: 13830 Davana Ter Sherman Oaks CA 91423

MORSE, ROBERT WARREN, research administrator; b. Boston, May 25, 1921; s. Walter L. and Ethel (Prince) M.; m. Alice Muriel Cooper, Jan. 25, 1943; children—Robert Warren, Pamela Morse Donati, James Prince. B.S., Bowdoin Coll., 1943, D.Sc. (hon.), 1966; Sc.M., Brown U., 1947, Ph.D., 1949. Mem. faculty Brown U., 1946-64, prof. physics 1958-64, chmn. dept., 1960-62, dean coll., 1962-64; asst. sec. of navy, research and devel. Washington, 1964-66; pres. Case Inst. Tech., 1966-67, Case Western Res. U., Cleve., 1967-71; dir. research Woods Hole (Mass.) Oceanographic Instn., 1971-73, sr. scientist, 1973-83, scientist emeritus, 1983—, asso. dir., dean grad. studies, 1973-79; dir. PPG Industries, Research Corp. Tech.; Howard Found. fellow Royal Soc. Mond Lab., Cambridge (Eng.) U., 1954-55; mem. com. undersea warfare Nat. Acad. Scis., 1957-64, chmn., 1962-64; vis. lectr. U. Oslo, 1962; chmn. interagy. com. oceanography Fed. Council Sci. and Tech., 1964-66; chmn. bd. on marine resources Nat. Acad. Scis., 1970-74, chmn. ocean affairs bd., 1971-76; vis. scientist Scripps Instn. Oceanography, La Jolla, Calif., 1982. Author articles on ultrasonics, superconductivity, properties metals, underwater acoustics. Overseer Bowdoin Coll., 1971-87. Served to lt. (s.g.) USNR, 1943-46. Recipient Navy Distinguished Pub. Service medal, 1966. Fellow Am. Phys. Soc. (chmn. divsn. solid state physics 1963-64), Acoustical Soc. Am. (pres. 1965-66), Am. Acad. Arts and Scis.; mem. Woods Hole Golf Club, Sigma Xi. Home: 95 Wild Harbor Rd North Falmouth MA 02556-2308

MORSE, STEPHEN J., law educator; b. 1945. AB, Tufts U., 1966, EdM, 1970, JD, 1970; PhD, Harvard U., 1973. Bar: Mass. 1972. Teaching fellow Social Rels. Dept. Harvard U., 1969-73; prin. investigator Ctr. for Law and Health Scis., Boston U., 1973-74; asst. prof. psychology Ctr. for Law and Health Scis., 1973-74; asst. prof. So. Calif. U., 1974-76, assoc. prof., 1976-79, assoc. dean, 1979-80, prof., 1979-82, Orrin B. Evans prof. law. psychology and behavior scis., 1982-88; Ferdinand Wakeman Hubbell prof. U. Pa., 1988—; cons. Ctr. for Law and Health Scis. Boston U., 1974-76. Author: (with R.I. Watson Jr.) Psychotherapies: A Comparative Casebook, 1977. Cons. MacArthur Found. Program on Mental Health and the Law, 1988—. Mem. Am. Psychol.-Law Soc. (pres. 1981-82, bd. dirs. 1977), Am. Psychol. Assn. (div. 41, pres. 1986-87). Office: U Pa Law Sch 3400 Chestnut St Philadelphia PA 19104-6204

MORSE, SUSAN E., film editor. Editor: (films) Manhattan, 1979, Stardust Memories, 1980, Arthur, 1981, A Midsummer Night's Sex Comedy, 1982, Zelig, 1983, Broadway Danny Rose, 1984, The Purple Rose of Cairo, 1985, Hannah and Her Sisters, 1986 (Academy award nomination best film editing 1986), September, 1987, Radio Days, 1987, Another Woman, 1988, New York Stories ("Oedipus Wrecks"), 1989, Crimes and Misdemeanors, 1989, Alice, 1990, Shadows and Fog, 1992, Husbands and Wives, 1992, Manhattan Murder Mystery, 1993, Bullets Over Broadway, 1994. Office: care Motion Picture Editors 7715 Sunset Blvd #220 Los Angeles CA 90046*

MORSE, TRUE DELBERT, business and agricultural consultant, former undersecretary of agriculture; b. Carthage, Mo., Jan. 21, 1896; s. Delbert Lewis and Olive (Lawrence) M.; m. Mary Louise Hopkins, Nov. 20, 1927; 1 son, James Buckner. B.S. in Agr., U. Mo., 1924; LL.B., LaSalle Extension U., 1932. Bar: Mo. 1932. Exec. sec. Mo. Fed. Co-op Livestock Shipping Assn., Columbia, 1920; part-time extension asst. in livestock marketing U. Mo., 1922-24, extension specialist agrl. econs., 1924-25; farm mgr., appraiser and head research Doane Agrl. Service, Inc., St. Louis, 1925-43, pres., 1943-52, chmn. bd., 1952-53; editor (originator) Doane Agrl. Digest, St. Louis, 1938-53; head farm mgr. and rural appraiser schs. Am. Soc. Farm Mgrs. and Rural Appraisers, 1945-46; faculty mem. Sch. Banking, U. Wis.; dir. Mut. Savs. Life Ins. Co.; under sec. agr., also pres. CCC, Washington, 1953-61;

bus. and agrl. cons., asst. to pres. Alton Box Board Co., 1961-72; pres. U.S. Commodity Credit Corp., 1953-61; dir., spl. cons. Pet Inc., 1962-71; spl. cons. Farm Jour., Inc., 1961-70; chmn. bd. Man Exec., Inc., 1972—; mem. Pres.'s Adv. Bd. Econ. Growth and Stability, Presdl. Task Force for Rural Devel.; mem. Pres. Nixon's task force for Rural Devel., 1969-70; head U.S. delegations Internat. Wheat Agreement and Internat. Sugar Agreement; trustee, sec. Nat. Council Community Improvement; dir. Found. Am. Agr.; trustee, exec. dir. Agrl. Inst.; chmn. nat. com. rural devel. program, dir. Council Chs. Nat. Capital area. Author appraisal and farm loan handbooks and univ. bulls.; Contbr. farming pubs. Trustee Nat. Benevolent Assn. Christian Chs.; b. dirs. Nat. City Christian Ch. Corp., Christian Bd. Pubns.; adv. council Nat. Capital area council Boy Scouts Am.; mem. bd. Community Planning and Research Council. Named Churchman of Yr. Washington Area, 1958; recipient Animal Agr. award Am. Meat Inst., 1960. Mem. Am. Soc. Farm Mgrs. and Rural Appraisers (pres. 1941), Am. Farm Econs. Assn. (past v.p.), Alpha Gamma Rho, Alpha Zeta, Alpha Pi Zeta, Gamma Sigma Delta. Republican. Mem. Disciples Christ Ch. (pres. St. Louis Christian Missionary Soc. 1935-40, v.p. Mo. Christian Chs. 1943, pres. local ch., 1941-43, trustee Mo. Bible Coll., an organizer Sun City ch). Clubs: Rotary, Lakes. Address: 10330 W Thunderbird Blvd El Dorado B-314 Sun City AZ 85351

MORSHEAD, RICHARD WILLIAMS, philosophy of education educator; b. Saginaw, Mich., Mar. 30, 1931; s. Philip Spencer and Elma Sophie (Niemi) M.; m. Mary Martha Saros, June 25, 1955; children—Lisa, Diana. B.S., Wayne State U., 1954, M.Ed., 1956, Ed.D. 1963. Assoc. prof. div edn. U. Mich., Dearborn, 1967-74, chmn. dept., 1969-74, prof., assoc. dean, 1974-82, dean div. edn., 1982-86, dean sch. edn., 1986-89; prof., 1972—. Author: Patterns of Educational Practice: Theories of Curriculum, 1995. Mem. Detroit Regional Bd. Edn., 1971-73; exec. dir. Mich. Colls. Consortium for Faculty Devel., 1985-94; v.p. Grosse Pointe (Mich.) Unitarian Ch., 1980-81, pres., 1989-91, past pres., 1991-92. Recipient Outstanding Svc. award Mich. Colls. Consortium for Faculty Devel., 1993. Mem. Philosophy of Edn. Soc., John Dewey Soc., Assn. for Supervision and Curriculum Devel., Nat. Coun. for Accreditation of Tchr. Edn., Mich. Assn. Coll. Tchrs. of Edn. (pres. 1987-89), Phi Delta Kappa. Home: 941 N Oxford Rd Grosse Pointe MI 48236-1859 Office: U Mich Sch Edn Dearborn MI 48128

MORSS, LESTER ROBERT, chemist; b. Boston, Apr. 6, 1940; s. Sumner M. and Sylvia F. (Woolf) M.; m. Helaine Sue Gubin, June 19, 1966; children: Sydney, Benjamin, Rebecca, Alisa. B.A., Harvard U., 1961; Ph.D, U. Calif., Berkeley, 1969. Postdoctoral rsch. assoc. Purdue U., West Lafayette, Ind., 1969-71; from asst. prof. to assoc. prof. Rutgers U., New Brunswick, N.J., 1971-80; chemist, sr. chemist Argonne (Ill.) Nat. Lab., 1980—; vis. prof. U. Liège, Belgium, 1978-79, U. Paris, Orsay, 1993. Author, co-editor: The Chemistry of the Actinide Elements, 1986, Syntheses of Lanthanide and Actinide Compounds, 1991; editor procs. Rare Earth Rsch. Conf., 1986—. Lt. USN, 1961-65, Atlantic and Mediterranean. Recipient Sr. Scientist award Alexander von Humboldt Found., 1992. Fellow AAAS; mem. Am. Chem. Soc. (sec. div. nuclear chemistry and tech. 1990-92), Am. Nuclear Soc., Sigma Xi (pres. Argonne chpt. 1988-89). Jewish. Home: 1s680 Verdun Dr Winfield IL 60190-1716 Office: Argonne Nat Lab Chem Dv Bldg 200 Argonne IL 60439

MORTENSEN, ARVID LEGRANDE, lawyer; b. Bremerton, Wash., July 11, 1941; s. George Andrew and Mary Louise (Myers) M.; m. Elaine Marie Mains, Aug. 2, 1968; children: Marie Louise, Anne Catherine, Joseph Duncan. BS in English and Psychology, Brigham Young U., 1965, MBA in Mktg. and Fin., 1967; JD cum laude, Ind. U., 1980. Bar: Ind. 1980, U.S. Supreme Ct. 1983, Mo. 1985, D.C. 1985, FCC lic. amateur radio operator, 1994—; CLU. Agt. Conn. Mut. Life Ins. Co., Salt Lake City, 1967-68, agt. and br. mgr., Idaho Falls, Idaho, 1968-74; with Rsch. and Rev. Svc. Am., Inc./Newkirk Assocs., Inc., Indpls., 1974-83, sr. editor, 1975-79, mgr. advanced products and seminars, 1979-80, sr. mktg. exec., 1980-83; tax and fin. planner, Indpls., 1980-85, St. Louis and Chesterfield, Mo., 1985-90, Tampa Bay, Fla., 1990-91, Orange County, Calif., 1991—. mem. sr. mgmt. com., v.p. Allied Fidelity Corp., 1983-85, Allied Fidelity Ins. Co., 1983-85, Tex. Fire and Casualty Ins. Co., 1983-85; v.p., bd. dirs. Gen. Am. Ins. Co., St. Louis, 1985-86; v.p. Gen. Am. Life Ins. Co., St. Louis, 1985-90; pvt. practice law, Indpls., 1980-85, St. Louis, Chesterfield and Bridgeton, Mo., 1985-90, Tampa Bay, 1990-91, Orange County, 1991—; active with Ch. Jesus Christ of Latter-day Saints, Denver, Idaho Falls, Idaho, Indpls., St. Louis, Chesterfield, Tampa Bay Area and Orange County, 1980—, Profl. Assn. Diving Instrs. cert. Divemaster, 1989—. Mem. Assn. Advanced Life Underwriting, Mo. Bar Assn., Bar Assn. Met. St. Louis, D.C. Bar Assn., Ind. Bar Assn., Am. Soc. CLU's, Nat. Assn. Life Underwriters, Orange County,. Author: Employee Stock Ownership Plans, 1975, Fundamentals of Corporate Qualified Retirement Plans, 1975, 78, 80, Buy-Sell Agreements, 1988, The Key Executive Sale, 1989, (with Norman H. Tarver) The IRA Manual, 1975-87 edits., (with Norman H. Tarver) The Keogh Manual, 1975, 77, 78, 80 edits., (with Norman H. Tarver) The Section 403 (b) Manual, 1975, 77, 78, 80, 84, 85, 87 edits., sole author 1991,93, 94, edit., (with Leo C. Hodges) The Life Insurance Trust Handbook, 1980; contbr. articles to profl. jours.; editor-in-chief various tax and fin. planning courses; bd. editors Ind. Law Rev., 1977-78. Avocation: lic. amateur radio operator. Office: 620 Newport Ctr Dr Ste 1100 Newport Beach CA 92660 Also: PO Drawer 6362 Laguna Niguel CA 92607

MORTENSEN, AUDREY R., church administrator. Lay leader, chair steering com. commn. for women Evang. Luth. Ch. in Am., Chgo., Ill. Office: Evangelical Lutheran Church Am 8765 W Higgins Rd Chicago IL 60631

MORTENSEN, EUGENE PHILLIPS, hospital administrator; b. N.Y.C., Mar. 28, 1941; s. Eugene Phillips and Mary (Hogarty) M.; m. Ellen Louise McDavitt, Aug. 8, 1964; children: Jeffrey Phillips, Jennifer-Kristine McDavitt. BA, Seton Hall U., 1963; MS in Mgmt., Frostburg State U., 1974; M in Profl. Studies, Cornell U., 1976. Commd. 2d lt. U.S. Army, 1963, advanced through grades to col., 1987; ret., 1994; med. budget advisor Office Army Surgeon Gen., Cholon, Vietnam, 1968-69; chief materials mgmt. br. and test and standards Office of Compt., Office Surgeon Gen., Washington, 1969-71; chief systems div. and health care system br. U.S. Army Health Svcs. Data Systems Agy., Ft. Detrick, Md., 1971-74, resigned, 1974; asst. adminstr. for gen. svcs. St. Joseph's Hosp. and Med. Ctr., Paterson, N.J., 1976-79, for clin. svcs., 1979-83, v.p. clin. svcs., 1983-89, exec. v.p., chief operating officer, 1989-92; sr. v.p. for operation, chief oper. officer Jersey City Med. Ctr., 1992—; chief op. officer Liberty Home Care Agency, 1994—. mem. editorial bd. Perinatal Newsletter, 1984-92. Coach Upper Saddle River (N.J.) Soccer Assn., 1986—; webelos den leader cub scouts, Boy Scouts Am., Upper Saddle River, 1986-90, asst. scoutmaster, 1990—; trustee N.J. Vis. Health Svcs., Totawa, 1988-92; trustee, mem. adv. bd. Passaic Valley Hospice, Totawa, 1986-92; bd. trustees Hudson County Occupational Ctr., 1993—. Decorated Bronze Star. Fellow Am. Coll. Healthcare Execs. (coun. regents); mem. Am. Hosp. Assn., N.J. Hosp. Assn. (coun. on govt. rels. 1992-94), Paterson C. of C. (bd. dirs. 1989-92). Republican. Roman Catholic. Home: 8 Iron Latch Ct U Saddle Riv NJ 07458-2005 Office: Jersey City Med Ctr 50 Baldwin Ave Jersey City NJ 07304-3154

MORTENSEN, GORDON LOUIS, artist, printmaker; b. Arnegard, N.D., Apr. 27, 1938; s. Gunner and Otillia Ernestine (Reiner) M.; m. Phoebe Hollis Hansen, Apr. 10, 1965 (div. 1968); m. Linda Johanna Sisson, Dec. 7, 1969. B.F.A., Mpls. Coll. Art and Design, 1964; postgrad., U. Minn., 1969-72. Exhibited one-man shows, Minn. Mus., St. Paul, 1967, Sioux City Art Ctr., Iowa, 1968, Plains Art Mus., Moorhead, Minn., 1976, 78, 80, 82, 83, Assoc. Am. Artists, Phila., 1979, Mary Ryan Gallery, N.Y.C., 1983, Concept Art Gallery Pitts., 1981, 83, 85, 87, 89, 91, 93, Louis Newman Gallery, Beverly Hills, 1983, C.G. Rein Galleries, Mpls., 1978, 80, 85, 89, 91; group shows, Miami U. Oxford, Ohio (1st place award 1977), Phila. Print Club (George Bunker award 1977), 12th Nat. Silvermine Guild Print Exhbn., New Canaan, Conn., 1976, 78, 80, 83, 86, 94 (Hearsh Mag. award 1978, Purchase award 1983, 86), 4th Miami Internat. Print Biennial (4th place award 1980), Rockford Internat. Print, 1981, 85 (Juror's award 1981), Mpls. Inst. Arts Biennial, 1963, 67, Bklyn. Mus., 1976, Boston Printmakers Nat. Exhbn., 1977, 79, 80, 81, 83 (purchase award 1977, 79, 83); represented permanent collections, Achenbach Foun. Graphic Arts at Palace of Legion of Honor, San Francisco, Bklyn. Mus., Phila. Mus. Art, Library of Congress, Minn. Mus.

Art, Met. Mus. and Art Ctr., Miami, Fla., Mus. Am. Art, Washington, Art Inst. Chgo., Mus. Art at Carnegie-Mellon Inst., Pitts., Walker Art Ctr., Mpls., Dulin Gallery Art, Knoxville, Tenn., numerous corp. collections; profiled in numerous art jours. Served with USMC, 1957-60. Mem. Boston Printmakers, Phila. Print Club, Artists Equity, Albany Print Club. Home and Office: 4153 Crest Rd Pebble Beach CA 93953-3052

MORTENSEN, JAMES E., management consultant; b. Brayton, Iowa, Mar. 15, 1925; s. Axel C. and Mabel (Ide) M.; m. Genevieve Edsall, Nov. 8, 1946; 1 son, Arthur C. Student, U. Denver, 1946-48, Columbia Exec. Program, 1965. Gen. mgr. dog food div. Cargill, Inc., Mpls., 1949-56; exec. v.p. Battle Creek Dog Food Co., Mich., 1956-57; dir., vice chmn. bd., chief fin. officer pres. affiliates Young & Rubicam, Inc., N.Y.C., 1957-81; now ind. cons.; pres. Asbury Terrace, Inc., 1965-69; mem. adv. bd. NPD Group Inc., Port Washington, N.Y.; pub. Digital Jour. Trustee Caramoor Ctr. Music and Art, Katonah, N.Y. With paratroops AUS, 1943-45. Decorated Bronze Star, Purple Heart. Mem. Am. Radio Relay League, Am. Digital Radio Soc. Republican (pres. Irvington, N.Y. 1961-62). Home: PO Box 328 Indian Rocks Beach FL 34635-0328

MORTENSEN, PETER, banker; b. Ellwood City, Pa., Dec. 4, 1935; s. Norman Peter and Mary Letitia (Brown) M.; m. Collette; children: Linda V. Haning, Kelly J. Hebble, Nancy Sarah Patton, Karen Sue Harris. B.A., Coll. of Wooster, Ohio, 1956. With First Nat. Bank of Pa., Hermitage, Pa., 1959—; pres., chief exec. officer F.N.B. Corp., Hermitage, Pa., 1973—, chmn., 1987—. Mem. United Church of Christ. Avocation: hunting.

MORTENSEN, RICHARD EDGAR, engineering educator; b. Denver, Sept. 29, 1935; s. Edgar Steele and Frieda Amalie (Boecker) M.; m. Sarah Jean Raulston, Oct. 12, 1974 (div. 1978). BSEE, MIT, 1958, MSEE, 1958, PhD, U. Calif., Berkeley, 1966. Co-op. engr. GE Co., Schenectady, N.Y., 1955-57; mem. tech. staff Space Tech. Labs., L.A., 1958-61; rsch. asst. U. Calif., Berkeley, 1961-65; prof. engring. UCLA, 1965-91, prof. emeritus, 1991—; cons. TRW, Inc., Redondo Beach, Calif., 1966-70, Aerojet-Gen. Corp., Azusa, Calif., 1970-72, Applied Sci. Analytics, Inc., Canoga Park, Calif., 1980-82; guest lectr. Indian Inst. Sci., Bangalore, India, 1991. Author: Random Signals and Systems, 1987; contbr. to profl. publs. Team mem. Beyond War, Topanga, Calif., 1986-89; alcoholism counselor. Grantee NSF, 1987-90. Mem. IEEE, Soc. Indsl. and Applied Math., Sigma Xi, Tau Beta Pi, Eta Kappa Nu. Avocations: hiking, yoga. Office: Dept Elec Engring 405 Hilgard Ave Los Angeles CA 90095-1594

MORTENSEN, ROBERT HENRY, landscape architect; b. Jackson, Mich., June 9, 1939; s. Henry and Charlotte Marie (Brown) M.; divorced; children: Phillip, Paul, Susan, Julia; m. Mate Jane Harriet Blakely, Nov. 1975; stepchildren: Laura, Kathryn. B Landscape Architecture, Ohio State U., 1961; M Landscape Architecture, U. Mich., 1965. Registered landscape architect, Ohio, Fla., Va., Md., Ohio. Landscape architect various firms, Louisville, 1960, 61-63; with Ohio Div. Parks, Columbus, 1960-61; landscape architect various firms, Toledo, 1963, 65-67; pvt. practice Ann Arbor, Mich., 1963-65; ptnr. firms Toledo, 1967-78; pres. Harvey Jones and Assocs., Clearwater, Fla., 1979-81; owner Mortensen Assocs., Toledo and Falls Church, Va., 1979-85; prin. Mortensen, Lewis & Scully, Inc., Vienna, Va., 1985-93; owner Mortensen Assocs., Vienna, Va., 1993—; assoc. prof. U. Mich. Grad. Sch., 1973; vis. lectr. Ohio State U., 1965—, Bowling Green (Ohio) State U., 1969—, U. Mich., 1971, Purdue U., 1971, Mich. State U., 1973—; mem. archtl. environ. rev. com. Ohio Arts Coun., 1974-78; adj. prof. Dept. Landscape Architecture, U. Md., 1973—. Editor: Handbook of Professional Practice, 1972, Marketing Landscape Architectural Services to the Federal Government, 1974. Mem. Ohio Bd. Unreclaimed Strip Mined Lands, 1973-76; mem. Lucas County facilities rev. com. Health Planning Assn. N.W. Ohio, 1972-76, chmn. maternal and child health subcom., 1972-74; bd. dirs. No. Va. Cmty. Appearance Alliance, 1988—, chair, 1991, pres., 1994. Recipient Disting. Svc. award Health Planning Assn. N.W. Ohio, 1973, Disting. Alumni award U. Mich. Sch. Natural Resources, 1985, Disting. Alumnus award Ohio State U. Coll. Engring., 1985. Fellow Am. Soc. Landscape Architects (trustee 1977-82, v.p. 1982-83, pres.-elect 1983-84, nat. pres. 1984-85, del. to Internat. Fedn. Landscape Architects 1987—); mem. Ohio Soc. Landscape Architects (pres. 1969-74), Am. Soc. Planning Ofcls., Toledo C. of C. (chmn. sts. and hwys. transit com. 1972-73), Washington Golf and Country Club, Sigma Phi Epsilon. Home: 6843 Churchill Rd Mc Lean VA 22101-2822 Office: Mortensen Assocs 2787 Hartland Rd Falls Falls Church VA 22043 One of the best continuing educational experiences for a practising professional is to teach students what you have learned. They respond in a critical and ever-so-fresh "so what" atmosphere, and demand more of you sometimes than you demand of yourself. Thus, there is learning on both sides of the lectern.

MORTENSEN, WILLIAM S., banking executive; b. 1932. Chmn. bd., pres., CEO 1st Fed. Bank Calif., 1955—. Office: 1st Fed Bank Calif 401 Wilshire Blvd Santa Monica CA 90401-1416

MORTENSEN-SAY, MARLYS (MRS. JOHN THEODORE SAY), school system administrator; b. Yankton, S.D., Mar. 11, 1924; d. Melvin A. and Edith L. (Fargo) Mortensen; BA, U. Colo., 1949, MEd, 1953; adminstrv. specialist U. Nebr., 1973; m. John Theodore Say, June 21, 1951; children: Mary Louise, James Kenneth, John Melvin, Margaret Ann. Tchr. Huron (S.D.) Jr. High Sch., 1944-48, Lamar (Colo.) Jr. High Sch., 1950-52, Norfolk Pub. Sch., 1962-63; sch. supt. Madison County, Madison, Nebr., 1963—. Mem. NEA (life), AAUW, Am. Assn. Sch. Adminstrs., Dept. Rural Edn., Nebr. Assn. County Supts., N.E. Nebr. County Supts. Assn., Assn. Sch. Bus. Ofcls., Nat. Orgn. Legal Problems in Edn., Assn. Supervision and Curriculum Devel., Nebr. Edn. Assn., Nebr. Sch. Adminstrs. Assn. Republican. Methodist. Home: 4805 S 13th St Norfolk NE 68701-6627 Office: Courthouse Madison NE 68748

MORTENSON, M. A., JR., construction executive. Chmn., pres., ceo M. A. Mortenson Co., Mpls., 1960—. Office: M A Mortenson Co 700 Meadow Ln N Ste 710 Minneapolis MN 55422-4817

MORTHAM, SANDRA BARRINGER, state official; b. Erie, Pa., Jan. 4, 1951; d. Norman Lyell and Ruth (Harer) Barringer; m. Allen Mortham, Aug. 21, 1950; children: Allen Jr., Jeffrey. AS, St. Petersburg Jr. Coll., 1971; BA, Eckerd Coll. Cons. Capital Formation Counselors, Inc., Bellair Bluffs, Fla., 1972—; commr. City of Largo, Fla., 1982-86, vice mayor, 1985-86; mem. Fla. Ho. of Reps., 1986-94, Rep. leader pro tempore, 1990-94, minority leader, 1994; Sec. of State State of Fla., 1995—. Bd. dirs. Performing Arts Ctr. & Theatre, Clearwater, Fla.; exec. com. Pinellas County Rep. Com., Rep. Nat. Com. Named Citizen of Yr., 1990; recipient numerous outstanding legislator awards, achievement among women awards from civic and profl. orgns. Mem. Am. Legis. Exch. Coun., Nat. Rep. Legislators Assn., Largo C. of C. (bd. dirs. 1987—, pres.), Largo Jr. Woman's Club (pres., Woman of Yr. award 1979), Suncoast Community Woman's Club (pres., Outstanding Svc. award 1981, Woman of Yr. award 1986), Suncoast Tiger Bay, Greater Largo Rep., Belleair Rep. Woman's, Clearwater Rep. Woman's. Presbyterian. Home: 2860 Vernon Ter Largo FL 34640-4224 Office: Secretary of State State Capitol Rm 2 Tallahassee FL 32399

MORTIMER, DOYLE MOSS, business consultant, state legislator, business owner; b. Idaho Falls, Idaho, Dec. 8, 1954; s. Don and Clara Wanda (Moss) M.; m. Kitty Jean Pearson, Aug. 5, 1976; children: Anna Louise, Suzanne, Daniel Doyle, Julie Jean, Caroline, Sarah Katherine. AA, Ricks Coll., 1977; BS in Sociology, Brigham Young U., 1981. Owner, pres. Randall Book Co., Orem, Utah, 1982-87; cons. IBM, Provo, Utah, 1988-93; owner Mortimer & Assoc., Orem, 1988-93; with Alexander's Print Shop, Orem; state legislator Utah State Legislature, 1993-94, 94-95. Developer (game) Cues and Clues; editor in field. Rep. county treas., Utan County, 1979-81; Rep. 3d Congl. vice chmn., Utah, 1983-85; pres. LDS Booksellers Assn., 1985; bd. dirs. Latter-day Found. Arts, Salt Lake City, 1990—. Recipient Exemplary Svc. award Utah Co. Rep. Party, 1991. Mem. Rotary. Avocations: music, fishing, public speaking, sports, biking.

MORTIMER, GARTH EUGENE, mathematics educator; b. South Williamsport, Pa., July 7, 1941; s. Eugene Lewellyn and Margaret Lucinda

(Fisher) M.; m. Ann Charlotte Bensley, Nov. 27, 1965; children: Julianne, Timothy Scott, Melissa. BS in Edn., Mansfield U., 1963; MS in Edn., Elmira (N.Y.) Coll., 1970; postgrad., Alfred (N.Y.) U., 1964-65, U. Maine, summer 1966. Cert. tchr. N.Y. Tchr. Campbell (N.Y.) Cen. Sch., 1963-67; tchr. math. Horseheads (N.Y.) Cen. Sch., 1967—, chmn. dept. math., 1972-78; chief negotiator Horseheads Tchrs. Assn., 1978-89. Contbg. editor: 11th Year Mathematics, 1984. Coach Cinderella Softball, Little League, Soccer, Horseheads, 1978-87. Named Female Team Coach of Year Elmira Kiwanis, 1991 for undefeated girl's basketball. Mem. Assn. Math. Tchrs. of N.Y. State, Elks. Methodist. Avocations: computers, baseball card collecting, coin collecting, sports. Home: 754 Cayuga Dr Horseheads NY 14845-1009 Office: Horseheads Cen Sch One Raider Ln Horseheads NY 14845

MORTIMER, HENRY TILFORD, JR., financial assurance executive; b. N.Y.C., Aug. 12, 1942; s. Henry Tilford and Marie Elise (Duggan); m. Susan E. Lewis, Dec. 28, 1989; children: Henry Tilford III, Caroline Elise; stepchildren: Richard Bierbaum, Caroline Bierbaum. B.A., Harvard U., 1964, M.B.A., 1969. First v.p. Blyth Eastman Dillon, Paris, 1969-79; pres. Blyth Eastman Dillon Internat., 1972-79; sr. v.p. E.F. Hutton & Co. Inc., N.Y.C., 1979-85; pres. Am. Internat. Adv. Group, N.Y.C., 1985—; mng. dir. Fin. Security Assurance Co., N.Y.C., 1985—; bd. dirs. Tipiak, S.A., Nantes, France, Danskin, Inc. 1st lt. U.S. Army, 1965-67. Republican. Episcopalian. Home: 485 Park Ave New York City NY 10022 Office: Fin Security Assurance 350 Park Ave New York NY 10022-6022

MORTIMER, J. THOMAS, biomedical engineering educator; b. Las Vegas, Oct. 12, 1939; s. John Thomas and Frances Harriet (Sample) M.; m. Sarah Van Gorder Watterson, Oct. 28, 1967; children—Elizabeth Van Gorder, Katherine Sample, Anne Watterson. B.S. in Elec. Engring., Tex. Tech Coll., Lubbock, 1964; M.S. in Engring., Case Inst. Tech., Cleve., 1965; Ph.D. in Engring., Case-Western Res. U., Cleve. 1968. Mem. faculty Case-Western Res. U., Cleve., 1969—; prof. biomed. engring. Case-Western Res. U., 1981—, dean engring., 1985-86, chmn. computer engring. and sci., 1986-88; vis. prof. U. Karlsruhe, Fed. Republic Germany, 1977-78; cons. Medtronic, Inc., Mpls., 1974—, NIH, Bethesda, Md., 1975-77, VA, Washington, 1979—, LaJolla Tech, Inc., Calif., 1983-84. Recipient numerous grants, NIH, VA. Mem. Biomed. Engring. Soc., Soc. Neuroscis., N.Y. Acad. Scis., Am. Assn. Engring. Edn. Office: Case Western Reserve U Univ Cir Dept Bio-Engining 10900 Euclid Ave Cleveland OH 44106-1749*

MORTIMER, PETER MICHAEL, lawyer; b. Detroit, May 20, 1943; s. Robert J. and Harriet C. (Evenson) M.; m. Sharon M. Olson, Aug. 20, 1966; children: Katherine, Trever, Peter. AB magna cum laude, Cornell U., 1965; JD cum laude, Harvard U., 1968. Bar: D.C. 1968, N.Y. 1970. Atty. Office Legal Adviser, U.S. Dept. State, Washington, 1968; assoc. Milbank, Tweed, Hadley & McCloy, N.Y.C., 1969-76, ptnr., 1977—; mem. compensation com., 1992—, co-practice group leader banking and institutional investment group, 1995—; resident ptnr. Milbank, Tweed, Hadley & McCloy, Hong Kong, 1977-79, London, 1983-88. Fellow Frick Collection, N.Y.C., 1981—; Pierpont Morgan Libr., N.Y.C., 1980—, mem. coun., 1981-83. Decorated Order of Francisco de Miranda 1st class (Venezuela). Mem. D.C. Bar, Assn. Bar City N.Y., Century Assn., Down Town Assn., Grolier Club (admissions com. 1991—), Short Hills Club, Baltusrol Golf Club, Phi Beta Kappa. Address: 57 Jefferson Ave Short Hills NJ 07078 Office: Milbank Tweed Hadley & McCloy 1 Chase Manhattan Plz New York NY 10005-1401

MORTIMER, WENDELL REED, JR., lawyer; b. Alhambra, Calif., Apr. 7, 1937; s. Wendell Reed and Blanche (Wilson) M.; m. Cecilia Vick, Aug. 11, 1962; children: Michelle Dawn, Kimberly Grace. AB, Occidental Coll. 1958; JD, U. So. Calif., L.A., 1965. Bar: Calif. 1966. Trail atty. Legal div. State of Calif., L.A., 1965-73; assoc. Thelen, Marrin, Johnson & Bridges, L.A., 1973-76, ptnr., 1976-93; pvt. practice law San Marino, Calif., 1994—; judge pro tem L.A. Superior Ct., settlement officer. Active San Marino Community Ch. With U.S. Army, 1960-62. Mem. ABA (litigation sect.), Am. Arbitration Assn. (arbitrator), State Bar Calif., L.A. County Bar Assn. (jud. appointments com. 1990-92), Pasadena Bar Assn., Legion Lex., U. So. Calif. Alumni Assn., San Marino City Club. Home and office: 1420 San Marino Ave San Marino CA 91108-2042

MORTIMER, WILLIAM JAMES, newspaper publisher; b. Provo, Utah, June 26, 1932; s. William Earl and Margaret (Johnson) M.; m. Paula Ann Deline, Sept. 17, 1956; children: Jeffrey, David, Gregory, Bradley, Judy, William James II, Jennifer. BS, Utah State U., 1954; MS, Columbia U., 1957. Reporter Deseret News, Salt Lake City, 1957-59, pres., pub., 1985—; sales mgr. Deseret News Press, Salt Lake City, 1959-63; gen. mgr. Deseret News Press, 1979-80, Deseret Book Co., Salt Lake City, 1966-79; sr. account exec. Wheelwright Lithographing, Salt Lake City, 1963-66; dir. LSD Ch. Printing Svcs., Salt Lake City, 1980-85; v.p., dir. Newspaper Agy. Corp., Salt Lake City, 1985—; pres. Printing Industries of Utah, 1964-65, Utah Retail Mchts. Assn., Salt Lake City, 1977-79. Author: How Beautiful Upon the Mountains, 1963. Campaign chmn. Salt Lake Area United Way, 1987; hon. col. Utah N.G.; chmn. Utah Partnership Ednl. and Econ. Devel.; mem. exec. com. Salt Lake Conv. and Visitors Bur.; chmn. bd. Pioneer State Theatre, 1990-93; pres. Utah Arts Endowment; bd. dirs. Utah Symphony. 1st lt. U.S. Army, 1954-56, Korea. Named Alumnus of Yr. Utah State U., Logan, 1985. Mem. Utah-Idaho-Spokane AP Assn. (pres. 1993-94), Utah Press Assn. (pres. 1994-95), Salt Lake Area C. of C. (chmn. bd. 1988-89), Alta Club. Mem. LDS Ch. Avocations: music, reading, family activities. Home: 8763 Kings Hill Dr Salt Lake City UT 84121-6135 Office: Deseret News Pub Co PO Box 1257 Salt Lake City UT 84110-1257

MORTLOCK, ROBERT PAUL, microbiologist, educator; b. Bronxville, N.Y., May 12, 1931; s. Donald Robert and Florance Mary (Bellaby) M.; m. Florita Mary Welling, Sept. 1954; children—Florita M., Jeffrey R., Douglas P. B.S., Rensselaer Poly. Inst., N.Y., 1953; Ph.D., U. Ill., Urbana, 1958. Asst. prof. microbiology U. Mass., Amherst, 1963-68, assoc. prof. microbiology, 1968-73, prof. microbiology, 1973-78; prof. microbiology Cornell U., Ithaca, N.Y., 1978—. Editor: Microorganisms as Model Systems for Studying Evolution, 1984, The Evolution of Metabolic Function, 1992. Served to 1st lt. U.S. Army, 1959-61. Fellow Am. Acad. Microbiology; mem. AAAS, Am. Soc. Microbiology, Northeastern Microbiologists, Physiology, Ecology and Taxonomy (pres. 1984-91). Office: Cornell U Sect Microbiology Wing Hall Ithaca NY 14852

MORTOLA, EDWARD JOSEPH, emeritus university chancellor; b. N.Y.C., Feb. 5, 1917; s. John and Letitia (Pellarano) M.; m. Doris Slater, May 3, 1941; children: Doreen Mortola LeMoult, Elaine Mortola Clark. B.A., Fordham U., 1938, M.A., 1941, Ph.D., 1946, L.H.D. (hon.), 1964; postgrad., Columbia U., 1946; L.H.D. (hon.), Medaille Coll., 1980; LL.D. (hon.), Bryant Coll., 1965, Syracuse U., 1967, N.Y. Law Sch., 1968; Litt.D. (hon.), Manhattan Coll., 1967, Coll. St. Rose, 1971; LL.D. (hon.), Western State U., 1985; L.H.D. (hon.), Pace U., 1987. Grad. fellow, sch. edn. Fordham U., 1938-39, asst. registrar, 1939-41, asst. registrar, city hall div., lectr. grad. faculty, sch. edn., 1946-47; instr. math. Cooper Union and Townsend Harris High Sch., N.Y.C., 1941-42; mem. faculty St. Peter's Coll., Jersey City, part time 1946-47; with Pace U., N.Y.C., 1947—; asst. dean Pace U., 1947-49, dean, 1949-50, provost, 1950-54, v.p., 1954-60, pres., 1960-84, chancellor, 1984-90, chancellor emeritus, 1990—; mem. Community Planning Bd. 1, Borough Manhattan, 1954-66, chmn., 1956-64; mem. legis. com. Assn. Colls. and Univs. State N.Y., v.p., 1965-66, pres., 1967-68; mem. adv. council on higher edn. State Edn. Dept.; trustee, past pres. Com. on Ind. Colls. and Univs.; mem. Middle States Assn. Colls. and Schs., N.Y. Gov.'s Commn. on Quality, Cost and Finance of N.Y. State Elementary and Secondary Edn., 1969-71, Westchester Planning Commn., 1966-73, Westchester County Assn., N.Y.C. Council on Econ. Edn., Commn. on Ind. Colls. and Univs. State N.Y., chmn. 1961-63; mem. council Fordham U.; mem. Mayor's Com. on Long-Term Fin. of N.Y.C.; former mem. adv. bd. Elizabeth Seton Coll.; past dir. and sec. Greater N.Y. Council Fgn. Students; chmn. bd. govs. Fordham U Alumni Fedn., 1958-60; formerly trustee Rosemont Coll., St. Joseph's Sem., Yonkers, N.Y.; co-chmn. N.Y. State Edn. Dept. Task Force on Teaching Profession, 1987-88; chmn. Lincoln Ctr. Inst., 1987; bd. dirs. Lincoln Ctr., 1987—; hon. dir. N.Y.C. Partnership 1987—. Bd. govs. New Rochelle Hosp.; hon. bd. govs. White Plains Hosp.; Downtown-Lower Manhattan Assn., Econ. Devel. Council; former trustee Instructional TV. Served with USNR, 1942-46; lt. comdr. Res. Decorated cavaliere, commendatore dell'Ordine Al Merito Republic of Italy., Knight of

Malta; recipient Ann. Achievement award in edn. Fordham Coll., 1960, William O'Brien award Cardinal Newman Found., 1964, Ednl. and Youth Advancement award Westchester chpt. Am. Com. Italian-Immigration, 1969, James E. Allen Jr. Meml. award Disting. Svc. to Edn. Bd. Regents N.Y. State, 1977, Leadership in Edn. award Assn. Colls. and Univs. State of N.Y., 1986, Outstanding Achievement award 100 Yr. Assn. of N.Y., 1983, Big Bros. of N.Y. Achievement award, 1987, Distinguished Alumni award Fordham U. Sch. Edn. Alumni Assn., 1970, Outstanding Achievement award One Hundred Yr. Assn., 1983, Achievement award in edn. Big Bros. N.Y., 1987, Starr award Good Counsel Acad., 1991; named Man of Yr. B'nai B'rith Youth Services, 1975. Mem. N.Y. Acad. Pub. Edn. (pres. 1962-64, dir.), N.Y. C. of C. (chmn. edn. com. 1966-68, mem. exec. com.), Nat. Office Mgmt. Assn., NEA, N.Y. Adult Edn. Coun., Knights of Malta. Clubs: Metropolitan (N.Y.C.), Univ. (N.Y.C.); Larchmont Yacht Club, Old Port Yacht Club.

MORTON, BRIAN, writer, editor, educator; b. N.Y.C., July 8, 1955; s. Richard Paul and Tasha (Brisman) M. BA, Sarah Lawrence Coll., 1978. Tchr. grad. dept. English NYU, N.Y.C., 1992—; tchr. 92d St. Y, N.Y.C., 1993—. Author: The Dylanist, 1991; contbr. articles to profl. publs. including Dissent, The Nation, The New Leader, Lingua Franca; book rev. editor Dissent Mag., 1988—. Office: Dissent 521 5th Ave New York NY 10175-0001

MORTON, BRUCE A., news correspondent; b. Norwalk, Conn., Oct. 28, 1930; s. Alexander X. and Jeanette Mae (Cook) M.; divorced; children: Sarah J., Alexander J. AB, Harvard U., 1952. Corr. ABC News, London, 1962-64, CBS News, Washington, 1964-93; nat. corr. CNN, Washington, 1993—. Contbr. The Picture Man, 1993. With U.S. Army, 1952-55. Recipient Emmy awards (6) TV Acad., Peabody award U. Ga., Polk award Overseas Press Club. Mem. Soc. Profl. Journalists. Avocations: reading, tennis.

MORTON, CLIFFORD A., holding company executive; b. Glasgow, Scotland, May 8, 1936; came to U.S., 1954; s. John Rufus and Jane Dickens (Bowie) M.; m. Katherine Carla; children: Wyant, Stephanie, Christopher. BS, Queen Elizabeth's U., Bristol, Eng., 1952; postgrad. in banking with honors, So. Meth. U., 1968; MBA, Golden Gate U., 1972. V.p. Security Pacific Nat. Bank, Los Angeles, 1954-68; sr. v.p. Bank Calif. N.A., San Francisco, 1968-74; dir. SBA, San Francisco, 1974-75; dir., chmn. audit com. Siliconix Inc., Santa Clara, Calif., 1975-76; sr. v.p. info. services, pres. Clearfield Ins. Boise (Idaho) Cascade, 1976-86; sr. v.p., chief fin. officer Portland (Oreg.) Gen. Corp., 1986—; assoc. prof. Golden Gate U., 1973-74; guest lectr. Stanford U., 1975. Author: Managing Operations in Emerging Companies, 1984. Exec. v.p. Idaho Soccer Assn., 1973-84. Club: Economic (N.Y.). Lodge: Rotary. Office: Portland Gen Corp 121 SW Salmon St Portland OR 97204

MORTON, DONALD CHARLES, astronomer; b. Kapuskasing, Ont., Can., June 12, 1933; s. Charles Orr and Irene Mary (Wightman) M.; m. Winifred May Austin, Dec. 12, 1970; children: Keith James, Christine Elizabeth. BA, U. Toronto, 1956; PhD, Princeton U., 1959. Astronomer U.S. Naval Rsch. Lab., Washington, 1959-61; from rsch. assoc. to sr. rsch. astronomer with rank of prof. Princeton (N.J.) U., 1961-76; dir. Anglo-Australian Obs., Epping and Coonabarabran, Australia, 1976-86; dir. gen. Herzberg Inst. Astrophysics, NRC of Can., Ottawa, Victoria, Ont./B.C., Ottawa, Victoria & Penticton, 1986—; dir. gen. Herzberg Inst. Astrophysics NRC of Can. Victoria and Penticton, B.C., 1986—. Contbr. numerous articles to profl. jours. Fellow Australian Acad. Sci.; mem. Internat. Astron. Union, Royal Astron. Soc. (assoc. 1980), Astron. Soc. Australia (pres. 1981-83, hon. mem. 1986), Royal Astron. Soc. Can., Am. Astron. Soc. (councilor 1970-73), Can. Astron. Soc. Australian Inst. Physics (Pawsey Meml. lectr. 1985), Can. Assn. Physicists, U.K. Alpine Club, Am. Alpine Club, Alpine Can. Club. Avocations: mountaineering, rock climbing, ice climbing, marathon running. Office: Herzberg Inst Astrophysics, NRC Can 5071 W Saanich Rd, Victoria, BC Canada V8X 4M6

MORTON, DONALD JOHN, librarian; b. Bklyn., Jan. 11, 1931; s. Ellwood Stokes and Gladys (Hassler) M.; m. Ann Mayo Tilden, Aug. 16, 1958; children—Saundra Kay, Donald John, Mary Ann. BS, U. Del., 1952; MS, La. State U., 1954; PhD, U. Calif. at Berkeley, 1958; MS in Libr. Sci., Simmons Coll., 1969, Dr. Arts in Library Sci., 1976. Asst. prof. botany N.M. State U., Las Cruces, 1957-58; asst. prof. plant pathology N.D. State U., Fargo, 1959-61; plant industry Agr. Dept., Tifton, Ga., 1961-65; asso. prof. plant pathology U. Del., Newark, 1965-68; librarian Northeastern U., Boston, 1968-70; head librarian, asst. prof. history of medicine U. Mass. Med. Sch., Worcester, 1970-74; dir. libr., assoc. prof. libr. sci. U. Mass. Med. Sch., 1974-94, libr. cons., 1994—; cons. in field; mem. adv. com. med. librarianship Simmons Coll., 1972-94; mem. task force com. New Eng. Regional Libr. Svc., 1971-94; mem. cooperating staff Worcester Found. Exptl. Biology, 1972-94; chmn. Coun. Developing Med. Librs., 1974; pres. North Atlantic Health Scis. Librs., 1974-75, Worcester Area Coop. Librs., 1974-75. Contbr. articles to profl. jours. Mem. Oliver Wendell Holmes endowment com. Boston Med. Libr., 1973-74, U. Mass. Bicentennial Com., 1973-75. Mem. Am. Assn. Univ. Adminstrs., Simmons Coll. Libr. Sch. Alumni Assn. (pres. 1975-76), Worcester Art Mus., Worcester Hist. Soc., Northboro Hist. Soc., Am. Soc. Info. Sci., ALA, Mass. Libr. Assn., Med. Libr. Assn. (chmn. New Eng. group 1974-75), Mycol. Soc. Am., Spl. Librs. Assn., New Eng. Coll. Librarians, Sigma Xi, Phi Kappa Phi, Phi Sigma, Delta Tau Delta. Home: 314 High St Hampton NH 03842-4004

MORTON, EDWARD JAMES, insurance company executive; b. Ft. Wayne, Ind., Nov. 8, 1926; s. Clifford Leroy and Clara Marie (Merklein) M.; m. Jean Ann McClernon, Apr. 30, 1949; children: Marcia Lynn, Anne; m. Matthild Schneider, Sept. 19, 1986; 1 child, Katharine. BA, Yale U., 1949. With John Hancock Mut. Life Ins. Co., Boston, 1949—, v.p., then sr. v.p., 1967-74, exec. v.p., 1974-82, pres., chief operating officer, 1982-86, chmn., chief exec. officer, 1987-92, also bd. dirs.; bd. dirs. John Hancock Mutual Life Ins. Co., M/A-COM, Inc. Trustee Gettysburg Coll.; bd. dirs. Eisenhower World Affairs Inst., 1995; vis. com. Mus. Fine Arts, Boston, dept. Ancient Egyptian, Nubian and Near Ea. Art; hon. life overseer Children's Hosp.; chmn. 1991 Boston Geog. Savs. Bond Campaign. Fellow Soc. Actuaries; mem. Nat. Assn. Security Dealers (prin.), Actuaries Club Boston, Comml. Club of Boston, Algonquin Club of Boston, Phi Beta Kappa. Office: John Hancock Mut Life Ins Co PO Box 111 Boston MA 02117-0111

MORTON, FREDERIC, author; b. Vienna, Austria, Oct. 5, 1924; s. Frank and Rose (Ungvary) M.; m. Marcia Colman, Mar. 28, 1957; 1 dau., Rebecca. B.S., Coll. City N.Y., 1947; M.A., New Sch. Social Research, 1949. Author: novels The Hound, 1947, The Darkness Below, 1949, Asphalt and Desire, 1952, The Witching Ship, 1960, The Schatten Affair, 1965, Snow Gods, 1969, An Unknown Woman, 1976, The Forever Street, 1984, Crosstown Sabbath, 1987; biography The Rothschilds, 1962 (nominated for Nat. Book award), A Nervous Splendor—Vienna 1888/9, 1979 (nominated for Nat. Book award), Thunder at Twilight—Vienna 1913/14, 1989; books transl. into 14 langs.; contbr. to: publs. including Martha Foley's Best Am. Short Stories; other anthologies, N.Y. Times, Harper's mag., Atlantic mag., Nation, Playboy, Esquire, N.Y. Mag., Hudson Rev., others; columnist: Village Voice, Conde-Nast Traveler. Recipient Author of Year award Nat. Anti-Defamation League, B'nai B'rith; Hon. Professorship award Republic of Austria, 1980, Tom Osborne Disting. lectureship U. Nebr., 1989; Dodd, Mead Intercollegiate Lit. fellow, 1947; Yaddo residence fellow, 1948, 50; Breadloaf Writers' Conf. fellow, 1947; Columbia U. fellow, 1953; recipient Golden Merit award City of Vienna, 1986. Mem. Author's Guild (exec. council), P.E.N. Home: 110 Riverside Dr New York NY 10024 Office: The Lantz Office 888 7th Ave New York NY 10106-0001 As a writer I'm trying to tell the truth interestingly.

MORTON, HERBERT CHARLES, editor, economist; b. Mpls., July 19, 1921. B.A., U. Minn., 1942, M.A., 1950, Ph.D., 1964. Info. specialist War Assets Adminstrn., 1946-47; staff writer, telegraph news editor St. Paul Pioneer Press & Dispatch, 1947-53; rsch. editor, asst. prof. Amos Tuck Sch., Dartmouth Coll., 1953-56; dir. publs. Brookings Instn., Washington, 1956-68; dir. Public Publs. U.S. Bur. Labor Stats., 1968-70, assoc. commr., 1971-75; dir. pub. affairs Resources for Future, Washington, 1975-80; sr. fellow Resources for Future, 1981-82; cons. Russell Sage Found., 1980-84; dir.

Office Scholarly Communication, Am. Coun. Learned Socs., 1984-87; cons. Ford Found., 1964-65, Internat. Inst. Applied Systems Analysis, 1978, Nat. Commn. on Unemployment Stats., 1978, Nat. Enquiry into Scholarly Communication, 1978-79, vis. lectr. Amos Tuck Sch., 1966, Am. U., 1970. Author: Public Contracts and Private Wages, 1965, The Story of Webster's Third, 1994; co-author: An Introduction to Economic Reasoning, 1956, 5th edit., 1979, Scholarly Communication: The Report of the National Enquiry, 1979, Energy Today and Tomorrow, 1983, The ACLS Survey of Scholars, 1989; editor: Brookings papers on Public Policy, 1965; co-editor: The American Business Corporation, 1972, Writings on Scholarly Communication, 1988; cons. editor Scholarly Publishing, 1984-92; mem. editorial bd. Book Research Quarterly, 1985—; contbr. articles to profl. jours. Trustee Joint Coun. Econ. Edn., 1960-68; bd. dirs. Am. U. Press Svcs. Inc., 1966-68. Served with Signal Corps AUS, 1942-46. NEH fellow, 1989. Mem. Soc. Scholarly Pub. (bd. dirs. 1988-92), Dictionary Soc. N.Am., Am. Dialect Soc. Home: 7106 Laverock Ln Bethesda MD 20817-4734

MORTON, JAMES CARNES, JR., public relations executive; b. Duncan, Okla., May 8, 1945; s. James Carnes and Syble Lyda (Looney) M.; m. Susan Phillips, May 25, 1968; children: James III, Terrissa Anne, Scott Thomas. BA, Westminster Coll., 1967; JD, U. Mo., 1972. Bar: Mo. 1972. Tax acct. Arthur Andersen Co., St. Louis, 1972-74; tax atty. Gen. Dynamics Corp., St. Louis, 1974-76; asst. gen. counsel Michelin Tire Corp., Greenville, S.C., 1976-86; gen. counsel Michelin Tire Corp. and Michelin Tires (Can.) Ltd., Greenville, S.C., 1990-92; dir. pub. rels. and govt. affairs Michelin Tire Corp., Greenville, S.C., 1986-92; exec. dir. external rels. Michelin N.Am., Greenville, S.C., 1992—. Bd. dirs. Greenville Symphony Orch., 1986-89, United Way Greenville, 1987-88, Greenville YMCA, 1988-89; mem. S.C. State Reorgn. Commn., 1987—. Capt. U.S. Army, 1967-72, Vietnam. Mem. Rubber Mfrs. Assn. (tire div. exec. com., govt. affairs com., pub. rels. com., tire mgmt. com., tire industry safety coun.), Mo. Bar Assn., S.C. C. of C. (bd. dirs., pres. 1993-94, chmn. 1994-95, exec. com. 1981-84, 1986-95, Svc. recognition award 1982), Greater Greenville C. of C. (chmn. govt. affairs com. 1990, bd. dirs. 1990-93), Greenville Country Club, Commerce Club, Faculty House Club. Presbyterian. Avocations: tennis, golf. Office: Michelin NAm PO Box 19001 Greenville SC 29602-9001

MORTON, JAMES DAVIS, lawyer; b. Pitts., Jan. 30, 1928; s. Roy S. and Magdeline M. (Meeder) M.; m. Ann Medved, Sept. 7, 1957; children: Timothy, Ann, Gary. BS in Bus. Administrn., U. Pitts., 1951, Dr. of Laws, 1954. Bar: Pa. 1955, Fla. 1979. Assoc. Brown, Critchlow, Flick, Peckham & Miller, Pitts., 1954-55; shareholder Buchanan Ingersoll, P.C. (and predecessor firms), Pitts., 1955—; dir. Indsl. Sci. Corp., Pitts. Dir. Civic Light Opera, Pitts., 1985—; del. Pa. Constl. Conv., Harrisburg, 1967-68. Fellow Am. Coll. Trial Lawyers; mem. Acad. Trial Lawyers Allegheny County (past pres.), U.S. Dist. Ct. West Dist. Pa. (com. mem. civil justice adv. group), Edgewood Country Club (past pres.). Republican. Episcopalian. Office: Buchanan Ingersoll PC USX Tower 600 Grant St Ste 57 Pittsburgh PA 15219-2703

MORTON, JAMES IRWIN, hospital administrator; b. Chulumani, Sud Yungas, Bolivia, Feb. 28, 1935; came to U.S., 1952; s. Harrison Cecil and Flossie Mae (Irwin) M.; m. Beverly Jean Nash, June 9, 1957; c1 child, Linda Kathleen. BA, Andrews U., 1957; MHA, U. Mich., 1959. Commd. 2nd lt. USAF, 1959, advanced through grades to col., 1988.; adminstr. Whitfield (Miss.) Med. Surg. Hosp., 1988—; pres. coun. Jackson-Vicksburg Hosp., 1992-93; cons. to surgeon gen. USAF, Washington, 1980-88. Bd. dirs., treas. The Miss. Chorus, 1990-93. Decorated Legion of Merit. Fellow Am. Coll. Healthcare Execs. (pres. Miss. affiliates 1991-92, Miss. Regent 1994-98). Avocations: singing, computers, photography, reading. Office: Whitfield Med Surg Hosp Whitfield MS 39193

MORTON, JEFFREY BRUCE, aerospace engineering educator; b. Chgo., Apr. 25, 1941; s. Max E. and Tillie (Forman) M.; m. Judy Gail Moss, June 14, 1964; children: Jonathan, Amy, Michael. BS, Mass. Inst. Tech., 1963; PhD, Johns Hopkins U., 1967. Sr. scientist U. Va., Charlottesville, 1967-68, asst. prof., 1968-72, assoc. prof., 1972-80, prof., 1980—; lectr. U. Va., 1967-68; pres. M.J. Systems Inc., Charlottesville, 1976—. Contbr. articles to profl. jours. Assoc. Fellow AIAA; mem. Am. Soc. Engring. Edn. (southeast sect. rsch. award 1981), Am. Physical Soc., Sigma Xi. Office: U Va Dept Mech Aerospace Engring Charlottesville VA 22901

MORTON, JOHN, engineering educator, researcher; b. Gateshead, U.K., Dec. 11, 1949; came to U.S., 1987; m. Maria Rosario Larrarte, Aug. 18, 1977; children: John, Christopher. BA, Cambridge U., 1968-71; DPhil, Oxford U., 1971-74; MA, Cambridge U., 1975. Chartered Engr. Rsch. assoc. Oxford U., U.K., 1974-79; lectr. Imperial Coll., London, 1979-86; prof. Va. Tech. Coll., Blacksburg, 1987—; dir. ctr. Composite Materials and Structures Va. Tech. Coll., 1991-94. Editor: Structural Impact and Crash Worthiness, 1984; co-editor: European Conference on Composite Materials, 1987; contbr. articles to profl. jours. Recipient William Sweet Smith prize I. Mech. E., London, 1990, Donald Julian Groen prize, London, 1991. Office: VA Polytechnic Inst CCMS Ctr Composite Materials & Struct 201 Hancock Hall Blacksburg VA 24061-0257*

MORTON, JOHN, III, banker; b. Orange, N.J., Nov. 8, 1943; s. John and Elizabeth (Brice) M.; m. Marion Louis Harvey, June 10, 1967; children: Caroline Dunlap, Tiffany Brice, John Tilghman. BS in Nuclear Sci., U.S. Naval Acad., 1967; MBA in Fin., Harvard U., 1973. Accts./Current mgr. nat. div. Md. Nat. Bank, Balt., 1973-76; v.p. nat. div. Ea. region, 1976-79, v.p. internat. div. Latin Am. group, 1979-81, regional v.p. Montgomery County, Rockville, 1981-83, sr. v.p. Washington suburban banking, Greenbelt, 1983-85, exec. v.p. exec. dept., Balt.; now CEO Farm & Home Fin. Corp., Kansas City; bd. dirs. ERC Internat., Fairfax, Va., RJO Enterprises, Lanham, Md. Vice-chmn., trustee Severn Sch., Severna Park, Md., 1982-88, trustee Balt. Mus. Art, 1987—; trustee, treas. Greater Washington Rsch. Ctr., 1987—; treas. fin. com. Washington Opera, 1988-89. Lt. USN, 1967-71. Mem. Am. Bankers Assn., Md. Bankers Assn., Harvard Club (N.Y.C.), Maryland Club, Annapolis Yacht Club, Center Club. Republican. Episcopalian. Avocations: squash, golf, skiing. Office: Farm & Home Fin Corp 221 W Cherry St Nevada MO 64772

MORTON, JOHN H., surgeon, educator; b. New Haven, Jan. 15, 1923; s. John J. and Nancy Barnard M.; m. Ruth Mitchell Halm, Oct. 15, 1949; children: John I., Nancy L., Peter S., Bruce J. BA, Amherst Coll., 1945; MD, Yale U., 1946. Diplomate Am. Bd. Surgery. Instr. surgery Sch. Medicine U. Rochester, N.Y., 1953-57, asst. prof. surgery, 1957-62, assoc. prof. surgery, 1962-67, prof., 1967—; pres. N.Y. State Med. Examiners, 1970-71, 72-73, bd. dirs., 1967-77; pres. Fedn. State Med. Bds. U.S., Ft. Worth, 1976-77, bd. dirs., 1971-78; vice chmn. Nat. Bd. Med. Examiners, Phila., 1975-79, mem. exec. com., 1974-83. Contbr. articles to profl. jours. Bd. dirs. Neighborhood Health Ctrs. Monroe County, Rochester, N.Y., 1969-73, Med. Scholarship Fund Med. Soc. County Monroe, 1969—; pres. Monroe Plan for Med. Care, Rochester, 1971-73; elder Third Presbyn. Ch., Rochester, 1958-61, 67-69, 80-83. Lt. (j.g.) USN, 1947-49. Recipient Edward Mott Moore award Med. Soc. County Monroe, 1975, Merit award Rochester Acad. Medicine, 1977, Disting. Svc. award Nat. Bd. Med. Examiners, 1983, Disting. Svc. award Fed. State Med. Bds. U.S., 1989, Henry I. Fineberg award Med. Soc. State N.Y., 1990. Mem. Am. Coll. Surgeons (gov. 1984-90), Am. Surg. Assn., Ctrl. Surg. Assn. Avocations: hiking, birdwatching, travelling. Home: 179 Maybrooke Rd Rochester NY 14618-1719 Office: U Rochester Sch Medicine 601 Elmwood Ave Rochester NY 14642-0001

MORTON, LELAND CLURE, judge; b. Knoxville, Tenn., Feb. 20, 1916; s. George W. and Birdie (Myers) M.; m. Marjorie J. Hernandez, Sept. 13, 1945 (dec. 1993). BA, U. Tenn., 1934, JD, 1936. Bar: Tenn. 1937. Pvt. practice law, Knoxville, 1937-41, 46-70; spl. agt. FBI, Washington, 1941-42, Cen. and S.Am., 1942-46; judge U.S. Dist. Ct. (mid. dist.) Tenn., Nashville, 1970-77, chief judge, 1977-84, sr. judge, 1984—; trustee, V. Tenn.; co-founder Vol. State Bank, Knoxville, 1964. Counselor East Tenn. council Boy Scouts Am., 1937-40; bd. dirs. Cerebral Palsy Found., Boys Club, Boys of Tenn. Mem. Tenn. Bar Assn., Nashville Bar Assn., S.R., Phi Kappa Phi. Republican. Methodist. Office: PO Box 459 Cookeville TN 38503-0459

MORTON, MARILYN MILLER, genealogy and history educator, lecturer, researcher, travel executive, director; b. Water Valley, Miss., Dec. 2, 1929; d. Julius Brunner and Irma Faye (Magee) Miller; m. Perry Wilkes Morton Jr., July 2, 1958; children: Dent Miller Morton, Nancy Marilyn Morton Driggers, E. Perian Morton Ethridge. BA in English, Miss. U. for Women, 1952; MS in History, Miss. State U., 1955. Cert. secondary tchr. Tchr. English, speech and history Starkville (Miss.) H.S., 1952-58; part-time instr. Miss. State U., 1953-55; mem. spl. collection staff Samford U. Libr., Birmingham, Ala., 1984-92; lectr. genealogy and history, instr. Inst. Genealogy & Hist. Rsch., Samford U., Birmingham, 1985-93, assoc. dir., 1985-88, exec. dir., 1988-93; founding dir. SU British and Irish Inst. Genealogy & Hist. Rsch. Samford U., Birmingham and British Isles, 1986-93; owner, dir. Marilyn Miller Morton Brit-Ire-U.S. Genealogy, Birmingham, 1994—; instr. genealogy classes Samford U. Metro Coll., 1989-94; lectr. nat. conf. Fedn. of Geneal. Socs. Contbr. articles and book revs. to profl. jours. Active Birmingham chpt. Salvation Army Aux., 1982—. Inducted into Miss. U. for Women Hall of Fame, 1952. Fellow Irish Geneal. Rsch. Soc. London; mem. Internat. Soc. Brit. Genealogy and Family History, Nat. Geneal. Soc. (mem. nat. program com. 1988—, lectr. nat. meetings), Assn. Profl. Genealogists, Soc. Genealogists London, Antiquarian Soc. Birmingham (sec., 2d v.p. 1982-84), DAR (regent Cheaha chpt. 1977-78), Dau. Am. Colonists (regent Edward Waters chpt. 1978-79), Phi Kappa Phi (charter mem. Samford U. chpt. 1972). Avocations: reading, travel, walking, public speaking, chess. Home and Office: 3508 Clayton Pl Birmingham AL 35216-3810

MORTON, MARSHALL NAY, financial executive; b. Chgo., Oct. 3, 1945; s. Frederick Samuel and Margaret Elizabeth (Burke) M.; m. Caroline Sanders, Sept. 13, 1969; children—Marshall Burke, Margaret Elizabeth. BA, U. Va., 1970, MBA, 1972. Fin. analyst West Point Pepperell Inc., Ga., 1972-73, budget dir., 1973-74, fin. mgr., 1974-75, asst. treas., 1975-81, treas., 1981-86, v.p., controller, 1986—, sr. v.p., CFO, Media Gen., Inc., Richmond, Va., 1989—. Pres., Valley United Fund, West Point, 1982, Am. Cancer Soc., West Point chpt., 1985-87; v.p. fin. Lanier Council Boys Scouts Am., 1986-87; former bd. dirs. Commonwealth Girl Scout Coun. of Va., also pres.; pres. The Robert E. Lee Coun. Boys Scouts Am. Served with USN, 1966-68, Vietnam. Episcopalian. Mem. Richmond Metro C. of C. (former bd. dirs.), Union League Club (N.Y.C.), Country Club of Va., The Commonwealth Club. Avocations: tennis, sailing. Office: Media Gen Inc 333 E Grace St Richmond VA 23293-1000

MORTON, MICHAEL RADER, career and technology education director; b. W.Va., Feb. 27, 1942; s. Shirley and Ruth Morton; m. Kathleen Morton; children: Matthew, Mark; 1 stepchild, Kelly Wechsler. BS in Edn., W.Va. U., 1964, MEd, 1966. Tchr. Fairfax (Va.) County Pub. Schs., 1964-70, Va. State, Richmond and Hampton, Va., 1968-70; supr. Frederick (Md.) County Pub. Schs., 1970-73; exec. dir. Md. Coun. on Vocat.-Tech. Edn., Annapolis, 1973-93; co-chair, founder Md. Ctr. Values Edn., Balt.; bd. advisors Md. Ctr. for Quality and Productivity, U. Md., College Park; mem. Nat. Assessment of Vocat. Edn., Md. Commn. on Funding of Pub. Edn.; mem. program improvement panel Nat. Ctr. for Rsch. in Vocat. Edn., U. Calif., Berkeley, 1993—; co-developer SETN Career Devel. Collaborative, 1995. Contbr. articles to profl. jours. Mem. Nat. Coun. Local Adminstrs., Nat. Assn. State Couns. on Vocat. Edn., Am. Vocat. Assn., Md. Soc. Assn. Execs., Iota Lambda Sigma. Avocation: tennis. Home: 7442 Twinbrook Chattanooga TN 37421 Office: Chattanooga Pub Schs 1161 W 40th St Chattanooga TN 37409-1317

MORTON, STEPHEN DANA, chemist; b. Madison, Wis., Sept. 7, 1932; s. Walter Albert and Rosalie (Amlie) M.; B.S., U. Wis., 1954, Ph.D., 1962. Asst. prof. chemistry Otterbein Coll., Westerville, Ohio, 1962-66; postdoctoral fellow water chemistry, pollution control U. Wis., Madison, 1966-67; water pollution research chemist WARF Inst., Madison, 1967-73; head environ. quality dept., 1973-76; mgr. quality assurance Raltech Sci. Services, 1977-82; pres. SDM Cons., 1982—. Served to 1st lt. Chem. Corps, AUS, 1954-56. Mem. Am. Chem. Soc., Am. Water Works Assn., Am. Soc. Limnology and Oceanography, Water Pollution Control Fedn., AAAS. Author: Water Pollution—Causes and Cures, 1976. Home: 1126 Sherman Ave Madison WI 53703-1620

MORTON, WILLIAM GILBERT, banker; b. Fulton, N.Y., Oct. 1, 1906; s. Albert I. and Martha (Gilbert) M.; m. Barbara Link, Jan. 22, 1936; children—William Gilbert, Linda Morton Cote, Albert Harry. MCS, Amos Tuck Sch., 1929. Rep. bond dept. Bankers Trust Co., N.Y.C., 1929-33, L. F. Rothschild & Co., 1933-34; with Onondaga Savs. Bank, Syracuse, N.Y., 1934-79; successively asst. to pres., asst. treas., treas., v.p. Onondaga Savs. Bank, 1934-53, exec. v.p., 1954- 58, pres., 1958-73, chmn., 1973-79, also trustee, 1947-81; Mem. N.Y. State Banking Bd., 1973-76. Mem. alumni council Dartmouth, 1948-52, 55-57, chmn. alumni fund campaign, 1956-58; bd. dirs. Met. Devel. Corp., 1962-86 , pres., 1970; adminstrv. bd. Lab. Ornithology, Cornell U., 1972-78. Mem. Savs. Bank Assn. N.Y. (council adminstrn. 1956-62, 64-68, 70-76, 1st v-p. 1970, pres. 1971), Phi Sigma Kappa. Republican. Clubs: Century, Univ., Onondaga Golf and Country, Royal Poinciana Golf (Naples, Fla.); Dartmouth; Club of S.W. Fla. Office: Boston Stock Exch 30 W Cottage Rd Jamesville NY 13078

MORTON, WILLIAM GILBERT, JR., stock exchange executive; b. Syracuse, N.Y., Mar. 13, 1937; s. William Gilbert and Barbara (Link) M.; m. Margaret Halleron, Nov. 26, 1982; children: Andrew Baker, William Gilbert III, Sarah Ellsworth, Kate Spencer. BA, Dartmouth Coll., 1959; MBA, NYU, 1965. Asst. v.p. Discount Corp. N.Y., 1960-67; co-mgr. trading, sr. v.p., dir. Mitchell Hutchins Inc., 1967-79; mng. stock exch. floors, sr. v.p. dir. Dean Witter Reynolds Inc., 1979-85; chmn., chief exec. officer Boston Stock Exch. Inc., 1985—; chmn. allocation com. N.Y. Stock Exch., floor ofcl., 1976-81, various working coms., 1970-85; bd. dirs. Tandy Corp., Ft. Worth, Investment Funds, Morgan Stanley Asset Mgmt. Inc., N.Y. Bd. dirs. Vt. Acad., Saxton's River, Bostonian Soc., Nat. Football Found. and Coll. Hall of Fame, N.Y.; trustee search com. Dartmouth Alumni Coun., 1988-91. With USMC, 1959-65. Mem. Economic Club (Mass. bus. roundtable), Algonquin Club (Boston), Racquet and Tennis Club N.Y.C., Stratton Mt. Country Club (Vt.), Colo. Arlberg Club (Winter Park), Brae Burn Country Club (Newton), Ekwanok Country Club (Vt.), Theta Delta Chi. Republican. Presbyterian. Office: Boston Stock Exch 1 Boston Pl Boston MA 02108-4401

MORTVEDT, JOHN JACOB, soil scientist; b. Dell Rapids, S.D., Jan. 25, 1932; s. Ernest R. and Clara (Halvorson) M.; m. Marlene L. Fodness, Jan. 23, 1955; children: Sheryl Mortvedt Jarrett, Lori Mortvedt Klopf, Julie Mortvedt Stride. BS, S.D. State U., 1953, MS, 1959; PhD, U. Wis., 1962. Soil chemist TVA, Muscle Shoals, Ala., 1962-87, sr. scientist, 1987-92, regional mgr. field programs dept., 1992-93; extension soils specialist Colo. State U., Ft. Collins, 1994—. Editor: Micronutrients in Agriculture, 1972, 2d edit., 1991; contbr. articles to profl. jours. 1st lt. U.S. Army, 1953-57. Fellow AAAS, Soil Sci. Soc. Am. (pres. 1988-89, editor-in-chief 1982-87, Profl. Svc. award 1991), Am. Soc. Agronomy (exec. com. 1987-90); mem. Internat. Soil Sci., Colombian Soil Sci. Soc. (hon.), Exch. Club (pres. Florence, Ala. chpt. 1987-88), Toastmasters (pres. Florence chpt. 1964-65), Phi Kappa Phi. Avocations: photography, golf. Office: Colo State U Dept Soil and Crop Scis Fort Collins CO 80523

MORUD, ROLLIE D., school system administrator. Supt. Dickinson (N.D.) Pub. Schs. Recipient Nat. Superintendent of the Yr. awd., North Dakota, Am. Assn. of School Administrators, 1993. Office: Dickinson Pub Schs 444 4th St W Dickinson ND 58602

MORWAY, RICHARD A., newspaper publishing executive; m. Vincenza Morway; children: Andrea, Cynthia. BBA, Cleve. State U.; MBA, Lake Erie Coll., 1994. From gen. acctg. clk. to asst. treas./asst. contr. Plain Dealer Pub. Co., Cleve., 1969-92, treas., 1992—; sec., treas. Plain Dealer Charities, Inc.; treas. Delcom, Inc. Mem. fin. support rev. com. Greater Cleve. Growth Assn.; active Blue Cross/Blue Shield Adv. Coun.; bd. dirs. Project Learn. Mem. Internat. Newspaper Fin. Execs. Office: Plain Dealer Pub Co 1801 Superior Ave E Cleveland OH 44114-2107

MORWOOD, BETTY JO, psychiatrist, physician; b. Burlington, Vt., Nov. 8, 1948; d. Nicholas Abraham and Alice (Thamer) M.; 1 child, Sophia Ruth. BA, U. Vt., 1970, MD, 1974, fellow, 1978-80. Diplomate Am. Bd.

Psychiatry and Neurology. Resident Stanford (Calif.) U., 1976-77; fellow U. Vt., Burl, 1978-80; med. dir. Cath. Social Services, San Jose, Calif., 1977-78; sr. staff psychiatrist Santa Clara County, San Jose, 1977-78; practice medicine specializing in psychiatry Burlington, 1980—; staff physician Med. Ctr. Vt. Mem. Am. Psychiatry Assn., Vt. Psychiatry Assn.

MOSBACHER, MARTIN BRUCE, public relations executive; b. N.Y.C., Nov. 4, 1951; s. Walter and Grete (Wolffs) M.; m. Andrea Dow, Jan. 25, 1980; children: Sarah Mariel, Rachel Helene. BA in Polit. Sci., CCNY, 1972, MS in Urban Planning, 1975. Spl. asst. to speaker N.Y. State Assembly, Albany, 1976-78; mgr. pub. rels. Sea-Land Corp., Menlo Park, N.J., 1979-83; dir. pub. rels. Commodity Exch., Inc., N.Y.C., 1983-86; prin. NYCOM Assocs., N.Y.C., 1986-88; chmn. Trimedia Inc., N.Y.C., 1988—. Del. Dem. Nat. Conv., Miami, Fla., 1972. Mem. Internat. Assn. Bus. Communicators, Futures Industry Assn., Pub. Rels. Soc. Am. Office: Trimedia Inc 425 Madison Ave Ste 600 New York NY 10017-1110

MOSBACHER, ROBERT ADAM, oil and gas industry executive, political organization executive; b. Mt. Vernon, N.Y., Mar. 11, 1927; s. Emil and Gertrude (Schwartz) M.; m. Georgette Paulsin; children—Diane, Robert, Kathryn, Lisa Mosbacher Mears. BS, Washington and Lee U., 1947, LLD (hon.), 1984. Independent oil and gas producer, 1948-89; former sec. Dept. of Commerce, Washington, from 1989; gen. chmn. Pres. Bush's re-election campaign, 1992; now gen. chmn. finance Rep. Nat. Com., Washington, 1992—; former chmn., chief exec. officer Mosbacher Energy Co., Houston; dir. Tex. Commerce Bancshares, Houston, N.Y. Life Ins. Co. Bd. dirs. Choate Sch., Wallingford, Conn.; dir. Aspen Inst., Center for Strategic and Internat. Studies; chmn. bd. visitors M.D. Anderson Hosp.; nat. fin. chmn. George Bush for Pres.; chmn. Pres. Ford Fin. Com.; co-chmn. Republican Nat. Fin. Com.; dir. Tex. Heart Inst. Mem. Am. Petroleum Inst. (dir., exec. com.), Nat. Petroleum Coun. (past chmn.), All Am. Wildcatters Assn. (past chmn.), Am. Assn. Petroleum Landmen (past pres.). Presbyterian. Address: 712 Main St Ste 2200 Houston TX 77002

MOSBY, JOHN DAVENPORT, III, investment banking executive; b. Jackson, Miss., Jan. 24, 1956; s. John Davenport and Normastel (Ford) M.; m. Macie Glenn Bush, June 30, 1979; children: Matthew, Laura, Anna. BA, Vanderbilt U., 1978; MBA, Harvard U., 1982. V.p. Raymond James & Assocs., Inc., St. Petersburg, Fla., 1982-85, sr. v.p., 1985-88, mng. dir., 1988—, mem., spokesman investment policy com., 1987—; mem. Fin. Products Standards Bd., Denver, 1985-88. Bd. dirs. Samaritan Counseling Ctr., Clearwater, Fla., 1988-90; mem., chmn. bus. rels. com. St. Anthony's Health Care Found., St. Petersburg, 1990—; trustee Shorecrest Prep. Sch., St. Petersburg, 1991—, treas., 1993—. Mem. Securities Industry Assn. (direct investment com. 1991—), Nat. Assn. Securities Dealers (direct participation programs com. 1993—). Republican. Episcopalian. Office: Raymond James & Assoc Inc 880 Carillon Pky Saint Petersburg FL 33716

MOSCA, ANTHONY JOHN, substance abuse professional; b. Cambridge, Mass., June 28, 1944; s. Anthony Mosca and Margaret Mary Kelleher; m. Sheryl Lyn Everett, July 12, 1986. BA in Psychology, U. N.H., 1978; MA in Psychology, Assumption Coll., Worcester, Mass., 1984; postgrad., Rivier Coll., Nashua, N.H., 1990. Lic. mental health counselor, Mass.; cert. addictions specialist, Am. Acad. Health Care Providers in the Addictive Disorders. Psychiat. counselor, milieu coord. New England Meml. Hosp., Stoneham, Mass., 1979-80; alcoholism counselor Nor Cap Lodge, Foxboro, Mass., 1980-82; alcohol and drug counselor Bournwood Hosp., Brookline, Mass., 1982-83; coord. of vocat. evaluation unit Project Hire, Norwood, Mass., 1983-85; rehab. counselor Driving Under the Influence program, Tewksbury, Mass., 1985-86; clin. dir./substance abuse counselor New Beginnings Counseling, Inc., Lowell, Mass., 1986-88; substance abuse specialist Human Resource Inst., Lowell, Mass., 1986-94; coord. Structured Outpatient Addictions Program Behavioral Health Consortium No. Mass. Lawrence, 1994—; pvt. practice A.S.M. Counseling, Dracut, Mass., 1988—; guest speaker Sharsheen Vocat. Tech. High Sch., Billerica, Mass., 1986. Campaign cons., Seabrook, N.H., 1975; handicap access advocate, Lowell, Dracut, 1990—; guest speaker disabled students group, Middlesex C.C., Lowell, 1993, Ctr. Ind. Living, Lawrence, 1995. Recipient letter of commendation from Nancy Reagan. Mem. Internat. Assn. of Addictions and Offender Counselors, Am. Counseling Assn., Am. Acad. of Health Care Providers in the Addictive Disorders, Am. Mental Health Counselors Assn., Mass. Mental Health Counselors Assn. Avocations: keeping current on material regarding the addictions field, fantasy football leagues. Home: 59 Mill St Unit 106 Dracut MA 01826-3248 Office: Behavioral Health Consortium No Mass 30 General St Lawrence MA 01841

MOSCARINO, GEORGE J., lawyer; b. Cleve., May 30, 1934. AB, Ohio U., 1955; JD, Case Western Res. U., 1958. Bar: Ohio 1958. Asst. atty. gen. U.S. Attys. Office, Cleve., 1960; asst. pros. atty. U.S. Attys. Office, Cuyahoga County, Ohio, 1961-70; ptnr. Jones, Day, Reavis & Pogue, Cleve. Fellow Am. Coll. Trial Lawyers; mem. ABA (mem. grand jury com. 1983-86, spl. advisor gran jury com. 1986—, mem. sect. coun. 1984-88, mem. criminal justice sect.). Office: Jones Day Reavis & Pogue North Point 901 Lakeside Ave E Cleveland OH 44114-1190

MOSCATO, ANTHONY CHARLES, federal official; b. N.Y.C., Sept. 4, 1945; s. Charles Joseph and Anne (Antreassian) M.; m. Deborah Louise (Stackawitz), Feb. 10, 1973; children: Charles Joseph, Emily Clair. BA, Columbia U., 1967; JD, George Washington U., 1970. Trial atty. tax div. U.S. Dept. Justice, Washington, 1976-77, spl. asst. to asst. atty. gen. justice mgmt. div., 1977-79, dir. property mgmt. and procurement staff justice mgmt. div., 1979-81, dir. evaluation staff justice mgmt.div., 1981-84, dir. fin. staff justice mgmt. div., 1984, counselor to asst. atty. gen. justice mgmt. div., 1984-87, dep. asst. atty. gen., administrn. justice mgmt. div., 1987-89, acting insp. gen. Office of Insp. Gen., 1989-90, dep. asst. atty. gen., adminstrn., justice mgmt. div., 1990-92, dir. exec. office U.S. attys., 1992-94; dir. exec. office Immigration Rev., 1994—. Recipient Atty. Gen.'s award for Disting. Svc., 1988, Atty. Gen's. Medallion, 1990, Presdl. Meritorious Exec. Rank award, 1991, Edmund Randolph award, 1993. Office: Exec Office US Attys 10th & Constitution Ave NW Washington DC 20530-0001

MOSCHELLA, SAMUEL L., dermatology educator; b. East Boston, Mass., Apr. 22, 1921. BS, Tufts U., 1943, MD cum laude, 1946. Diplomate Am. Bd. Dermatology. Intern in medicine Boston City Hosp., 1946-47; resident in dermatology U.S. Naval Hosp., Phila., 1948, St. Albans, 1951; postgrad. in skin and cancer Bellevue Hosp., N.Y.C., 1952-53; chief dermatology U.S. Naval Hosp., Phila., 1953-54, chief dermatology, asst. chief medicine, Guantanamo Bay, Cuba, 1948-51, chief dermatology, Chelsea, Mass., 1956-62, chmn. dept. dermatology, Phila., 1962-67; chmn. dept. dermatology Lahey Clinic Med. Ctr., Burlington, Mass., 1969-82; clin. prof. dermatology Harvard U. Med. Sch., Boston, 1980-91, prof. emeritus, 1991—; cons. U.S. Pub. Health Leprosarium, Carville, La., 1968—, U.S. Naval Hosp., Phila., 1967-72, Bethesda, Md., 1976—; guest lectr. U. Pa. Grad. Sch., 1962-67, Harvard Sch. Tropical Medicine, 1975—. Author/editor: (with otherw) Dermatology, 3d edit., 1992; contbr. articles to profl. jours.; also papers, book chpts. Fellow ACP; mem. AMA, Am. Acad. Dermatology, Am. Dermatol. Assn., Am. Soc. Dermapathology, Internat. Leprosy Assn., Internat. Soc. Dermatology, New Eng. Dermatologic Soc., Mass. Acad. Dermatology, Boston Dermatology Soc., Mass. Med. Soc., soc. Investigative Dermatology. Home: 887 Commonwealth Ave Newton MA 02159-1036 Office: Lahey Clinic Med Ctr 41 Mall Rd Box 541 Burlington MA 01805

MOSCHIN, SUSAN KAMIN, school board executive; b. Chgo., May 28, 1945; d. Samuel F. and Josephine M. (Roth) Kamin; m. Arnold Moschin, Aug. 15, 1971; children: Adam Lee, Amy Lynn. BS in Elem. Edn., U. Ill., Champaign, 1967; MA in Elem. Edn., Northeastern Ill. U., Chgo., 1971. Tchr. Glenview (Ill.) Pub. Schs., 1967-69, Skokie (Ill.) Sch. Dist. 69, 1969-71; administr., sec.-treas. 'Contractor Indsl. Supply, Northbrook, Ill., 1976-91; founder Handi Wear, 1992; pres., bd. mem. Highland Park (Ill.) Dist. 108 Sch. Bd., 1983-93; mem. Lake County Fin. com., 1990-93. Mem. State of Ill. Guardianship and Advocacy, Human Rights Authority Commn., 1991—, Lake County Race Bd., Michael Jordan/Ronald McDonald Golf Outing Com.; chmn. budget & fin. Nile's Township Jewish Congregation, religious edn. bd.; past mem. Skokie Youth Commn. Recipient awards Dist. 108 High Park Sch. Bd., 1982. Mem. ASCD, Ill. Assn. Sch. Bds. (Leadership

award 1992, 93). Jewish. Avocations: walking, reading, voluteering. Home: 1933 Burr Oak Ln Highland Park IL 60035-4201

MOSCONA, ARON ARTHUR, biology educator, scientist; b. Israel, July 4, 1922; came to U.S., 1955, naturalized, 1965; s. David DeAbravanel and Lola (Krochmaal) M.; m. Malka Kempinsky, July 6, 1954; 1 child, Anne. M.Sc., Hebrew U., Jerusalem, 1947, Ph.D., 1950. Postgrad. fellow Strangeways Research Lab., Cambridge, Eng., 1950-52; vis. investigator Rockefeller Inst., N.Y.C., 1955-57; prof. biology U. Chgo., 1958—, Louis Block prof. biol. scis., 1972-92, Louis Block prof. emeritus, 1992—; chmn. Com. on Devel. Biology, 1969-76; vis. prof. Stanford U., 1959, U. Montreal, 1960, U. Palermo, Italy, 1966, Hebrew U., Jerusalem, 1972, Tel-Aviv (Israel) U., 1977, 79, Kyoto U., Japan, 1980. Author: (with A. Monroy) Introductory Concepts in Developmental Biology, 1979; founder, editor: Current Topics in Developmental Biology, 1965; past mem. editorial bd. Jour. Molecular Neurosci., New Biologist, Mechanisms of Aging and Development, Cell Differentiation, Cancer Research, Devel. Neurosci, Experimental Cell Research; contbr. 260 articles to profl. jours. Recipient Claude Bernard medal in exptl. medicine, 1962, Alcon prize in visual sci., 1990, Gold medal Azabu Univ., Japan, 1991. Fellow AAAS, Am. Acad. Arts and Scis., Lombardo Inst. (Milan), N.Y. Acad. Scis.; mem. NAS, Internat. Soc. Devel. Biology (pres. 1977-81), Am. Soc. Devel. Biology, Internat. Soc. Cell Biology, Am. Soc. Zoology, Sigma Xi.

MOSCOWITZ, ALBERT JOSEPH, chemist, educator; b. Manchester, N.H., Aug. 20, 1929; s. Mark and Sarah (Kavesh) M. B.S., City Coll. N.Y., 1950; M.A., Harvard, 1954, Ph.D., 1957. NRC-Am. Chem. Soc.-Petroleum Research Fund postdoctoral fellow Harvard, 1957-58, Washington, 1958-59; mem. faculty U. Minn., 1959—, prof. chemistry, 1965—; vis. prof. U. Copenhagen, Denmark, 1961-62, 67-68, 76; Seydel-Woolley vis. prof. Ga. Inst. Tech., 1966; cons. to industry, 1960—, Chmn. nat. screening com. Fulbright-Hays awards for Scandinavia and Iceland, 1966; vice chmn. Gordon Conf. in Theoretical Chemistry, 1968, chmn., 1970. Adv. editorial bd.: Chem. Physics Letters, 1967-80; assoc. editor: Jour. Chem. Physics, 1970-73; Contbr. profl. jours. Fulbright lectr., 1961; Sloan fellow, 1962-66. Fellow AAAS, Am. Phys. Soc., N.Y. Acad. Scis.; mem. Am. Chem. Soc., Faraday Soc., Royal Soc. Chemistry (Eng.), Royal Danish Acad. Scis. and Letters (fgn. mem.), Harvard Club Minn., Skylight Club, Sigma Xi, Phi Beta Kappa. Home: The Towers 19 S 1st St Minneapolis MN 55401-1839 Office: U Minn Dept Chem Minneapolis MN 55455

MOSEBAR, DONALD HOWARD, professional football player; b. Yakima, Wash., Sept. 11, 1961. Student, U. So. Calif. Center L.A. Raiders, 1983—. Named NFL All-Pro team center, The Sporting News, 1991, Played in Super Bowl XVIII, 1983. Played in Pro Bowl, 1990-91. Office: L.A. Raiders 332 Center St El Segundo CA 90245-4047*

MOSEBY, LEBARON CLARENCE, JR., mathematics and computer science educator; b. Phila., Oct. 8, 1944; s. LeBaron Clarence and Louise (Walker) M. BA in math., Harvard U., 1966, MA in math., 1967, D in edn. 1972. Asst. dean admissions and studies Harvard Grad. Sch. Edn., 1971-73; faculty Nat. Sci. Found. Project Simmons Coll., Boston, 1974; asst. prof. edn. and dir. student teaching Simmons Coll., Boston, 1973-76; acting chmn. edn. dept. Trinity Coll., Hartford, 1977-78, asst. prof. edn. and dir. student teaching, 1976-81; dir. social context teaching and learning program U. Tex., Austin, 1981-83; asst. prof. math. and computer sci. South West Tex. State U., 1983-86; tech. edn. con. and tech. edn. specialist Wang Labs., Lowell, Mass., 1987—; cons., writer Southern Assn. Colls. and Schs., 1968-69; dir., coord. Miles Coll., 1968-69. Contbr. articles to profl. jours. Cons. Capitol Region Edn. Coun., Hartford, 1979, Nat. Inst. Edn., Washington, 1979-83, Hartford Pub. Schs., 1980, New Eng. Ctr. Urban Rsch., Hartford, 1978-80, Ct. State Dept. Edn., 1980; reviewer Am. Edn. Rsch. Assn., 1979-83. Fellow in edn. Harvard U., 1970-71. Mem. IEEE, Math. Assn. Am., Phi Delta Kappa. Home: 89 Union Park St Apt 407 Boston MA 02118-2470

MOSELEY, CARLOS DUPRE, former music executive, musician; b. Laurens, S.C., Sept. 21, 1914; s. Carlos Roland and Helen Allston (DuPre) M. BA magna cum laude, Duke, 1935; postgrad., Phila. Conservatory Music, 1941-44; student piano with Harold Morris, Olga Samaroff, Sophia Rosoff; LHD (hon.), Wofford Coll., 1966, Duke U., 1985; MusD (hon.), Converse Coll., 1971; DFA (hon.), U. S.C., 1989; LHD (hon.), The Juilliard Sch., 1995. Head fgn. information research div. OWI, N.Y.C., 1944-45; chief music sect. State Dept., Washington, 1946-48; music officer Office Mil. Govt. for Bavaria, Munich, Germany, 1948-49; chief fine arts and exhibits sect. reorientation br. Army Dept., N.Y.C., 1949-50; dir. N.Y. Sch. Music; prof. music U. Okla., 1950-55; dir. press and pub. relations N.Y. Philharmonic Symphony Soc., N.Y.C., 1955-59; assoc. mng. dir. N.Y. Philharmonic Symphony Soc., 1959-61, mng. dir., 1961-70, pres., 1970-78, vice chmn., 1978-83, chmn., 1983-85, chmn. emeritus, 1985—; U.S. del. to UNESCO Music Conf., Paris, 1948; U.S. del Internat. Music Coun., Paris, 1953; mem. music panel Nat. Endowment for Arts, 1967-69, N.Y. State Coun. on Arts, 1973-77, Nat. Coun. on Arts, 1985-91. Soloist, N.Y. Philharmonic Orch., N.Y.C. Symphony, Berkshire Music Center Orch., San Diego Symphony, Portuguese Nat. Symphony, Lisbon, Vt. Symphony, others. Trustee Fan Fox and Leslie R. Samuels Found., Eleanor Naylor Dana Charitable Trust, Charles A. Dana Found. Converse Coll.; mem. Lincoln Center coun., Lincoln Center Performing Arts, 1961-78; chmn. performing arts adv. com. Asia Soc., 1970-91; mem. Metro. Opera Assn. Winner MacDowell Nat. Young Artists Competition, 1939; Woodrow Wilson vis. fellow, 1979-80, 80-81; recipient N.Y.C. Mayor's Medal of Honor for Arts and Culture, 1978, Disting. Svc. citation U. Okla., 1989, Order of the Palmetto State of S.C. nat. citation Nat. Fedn. of Music Clubs, 1991. Mem. Met. Opera Assn., Century Assn. (N.Y.C.), Piedmont Club (S.C.), Phi Beta Kappa, Mu Phi Epsilon, Pi Kappa Lambda, Phi Eta Sigma. Office: care Dana Charitable Trust 375 Park Ave New York NY 10152-0001

MOSELEY, FREDERICK STRONG, III, investment banker; b. N.Y.C., May 4, 1928; s. Frederick S. Jr. and Jane Hamilton (Brady) M.; m. Elizabeth Hall Perkins, June 12, 1952; children: Frederick Strong IV, Elizabeth Howland Edwards, Cassandra Hamilton Berry. Ed., Harvard U., 1951. With F.S. Moseley & Co., Boston, 1955—; gen. partner F.S. Moseley & Co., 1959-69, mng. partner, 1970-73; pres., chief exec. officer, dir. F.S. Moseley, Estabrook Inc., 1973-75; chmn., chief exec. officer Moseley, Hallgarten & Estabrook Holding Corp., 1976-79; chmn., co-chief exec. officer Moseley, Hallgarten, Estabrook & Weeden Holding Corp., 1979-82, chmn., 1982-88; sr. v.p. Gruntal and Co., Inc., Boston, 1988-90; mng. dir. Seaward Mgmt. Corp., Boston, 1990—; gov., mem. exec. com. Assn. Stock Exchange Firms, 1966-71; gov. Am. Stock Exchange, 1970-72; mem. regional firms adv. com. N.Y. Stock Exchange, 1973-76; bd. dirs. Fifty Assocs., Boston, Gloucester Bank & Trust Co. Mem. corp. Mass. Gen. Hosp.; trustee Humane Soc. of Commonwealth Mass., Que. Labrador Mission Found.; mem. corp. Trustees of Reservations; trustee, v.p. Mass. Soc. for Promoting Agr. Served to 1st lt. AUS, 1953-55. Mem. Securities Industry Assn. (dir., governing council 1972), Asso. Harvard Alumni (dir. 1977-78, v.p. 1980). Clubs: Somerset (Boston), Myopia Hunt (Hamilton, Mass.), Midocean (Bermuda), Augusta Nat. (Ga.), Tarratine (Islesboro, Maine). Office: Seaward Mgmt Corp 10 Post Office Sq Boston MA 02109-4603

MOSELEY, FURMAN C., timber company executive; b. 1935. With Simpson Paper Co., 1960—, formerly exec. v.p., now chmn. bd., also dir.; pres. Simpson Investment Co., Seattle. Served USMC, 1956-59. Office: Simpson Paper Co 8140 Ward Pky Kansas City MO 64114-2006 also: Simpson Paper Co 1 Post St San Francisco CA 94104-5201

MOSELEY, JACK EDWIN, newspaper editor; b. Jefferson, Tex., Dec. 2, 1936; s. Alexander Augustus and Ethel (Clayton) M.; m. Margaret Dawson, Mar. 22, 1963; children: Dixie Lee, Charlotte Anne. BJ, U. Tex., 1959, grad. fellow, 1967-68. Reporter Scripps Howard Newspapers, Ft. Worth, 1959-68, asst. city editor, 1968-70, city editor, 1970-72, mng. editor, 1972-75; editor Southwest Times Record, Ft. Smith, Ark., 1975—. Author: Life, Luck & : 30-, 1980. Served as sgt. U.S. Army, 1961-62. Recipient approximately 60 nat. and regional writing/journalism awards. Mem. Soc. Profl. Journalists, Am. Soc. Newspaper Editors (edn. com.). Office: SW Times Record 920 Rogers Ave PO Box 1359 Fort Smith AR 72902-1359

MOSELEY, JAMES FRANCIS, lawyer; b. Charleston, S.C., Dec. 6, 1936; s. John Olin and Kathryn (Moran) M.; m. Anne McGehee, June 10, 1961; children: James Francis Jr., John McGehee. AB, The Citadel, 1958; JD, U. Fla., 1961. Bar: Fla. 1961, U.S. Supreme Ct. 1970. Pres. Taylor, Moseley & Joyner, Jacksonville, Fla., 1963—; chmn. jud. nominating com. 4th Jud. Cir., 1978-80. Assoc. editor: American Maritime Cases; contbr. articles on admiralty, transp. and ins. law to legal jours. Pres. Jacksonville United Way, 1979; chmn. bd. dirs. United Way Fla., 1992-93, S.E. regional coun. United Way, 1992—; trustee Jacksonville Cmty. Found.; chmn. bd. trustees Jacksonville Pub. Libr.; trustee Libr. Found., sec., 1987-91; trustee CMI Am. Found.; chmn. Jacksonville Human Svcs. Coun., 1989-91. Fellow Am. Coll. Trial Lawyers, Am. Bar Found.; mem. Jacksonville Bar Assn. (pres. 1975), Fla. Coun. Bar Pres. (chmn. 1979), Maritime Law Assn. U.S. (exec. com. 1978-81, chmn. navigation com. 1981-88, 1st v.p. 1992—), Comm. Maritime Internat. (titulary), Com. on Collision (Lisbon Rules), Fed. Ins. Corp. Counsel (chmn. maritime law sect.), Internat. Assn. Def. Counsel (chmn. maritime com. 1989-91), Am. Inns of Ct. (master of bench), Assn. of Citadel Men (bd. mem. 1989-93, exec. com. 1994, Man Yr. award, 1992), Citadel Inn of Ct. (sr. bencher), Deerwood Club, River Club, Downtown Athletic Club (N.Y.C.), India House (N.Y.C.), Army Navy Club (Washington), St. John's Dinner Club (pres. 1988). Home: 7780 Hollyridge Rd Jacksonville FL 32256-7134 Office: Taylor Moseley & Joyner 1887 Bldg 501 W Bay St Jacksonville FL 32202

MOSELEY, JOHN TRAVIS, university administrator, research physicist; b. New Orleans, Feb. 26, 1942; s. Fred Baker and Lily Gay (Lord) M.; m. Belva McCall Hudson, Aug. 11 1964 (div. June 1979); m. Susan Diane Callow, Aug. 6, 1979; children: Melanie Lord, John Mark, Stephanie Marie, Shannon Eleanor. BS in Physics, Ga. Inst. Tech., 1964, MS in Physics, 1966, PhD in Physics, 1969. Asst. prof. physics U. West Fla., Pensacola, 1968-69; sr. physicist SRI Internat., Menlo Park, Calif., 1969-75, program mgr., 1976-79; vis. prof. U. Paris, 1975-76; assoc. prof. U. Oreg., Eugene, 1979-81, dir. chem. physics inst., 1980-84, prof. physics, 1984—, head physics dept., 1984-85, v.p. rsch., 1985-94, v.p. acad. affairs, provost, 1994—; bd. dirs. Oreg. Resource and Tech., Portland; mem. com. on Atomic and Molecular Sci., 1983-85. Contbr. numerous articles to profl. jours. Mem. So. Willamette Rsch. Corridor, Eugene, 1985—, Lane Econ. Devel. Com., Eugene, 1988—; bd. dirs. Eugene/Springfield Metro Partnership, 1985—; Oreg. Bach Festival, Eugene, 1987-94. Recipient Doctoral Thesis award Sigma Xi, 1969; Fulbright fellow, 1975; numerous rsch. grants, 1969—. Fellow Am. Physical Soc.; mem. Am. Chem. Soc., Am. Assn. for Advancement Sci., Am. Assn. Univ. Prof. Avocations: skiing, backpacking. Home: 2140 Essex Ln Eugene OR 97403 Office: U Oreg Office of VP Acad Affairs and Provost Eugene OR 97403-1226

MOSELEY, MARK DEWAYNE, retired professional football player; b. Lanesville, Tex., Mar. 12, 1948; m. Sharon Allison; children: Megan Allison, Lindsay, Mark DeWayne, Michelle, Ellen. Student, Tex. A&M U., Stephen F. Austin Coll. Kicker Phila. Eagles, NFL, 1970, Houston Oilers, NFL, 1971-72, Washington Redskins, NFL, 1974-86; player NFL Pro Bowl, 1980, 83, NFL Championship Game, 1983, 84, Cleve. Browns, 1986-87; retired, 1987. Named Most Valuable Player of NFL, 1982 (the only placekicker in history of NFL to be named MVP). Address: PO Box 3 Haymarket VA 22069-0003

MOSELEY-BRAUN, CAROL, senator; b. Chgo., Aug. 16, 1947; d. Joseph J. and Edna A. (Davie) Mosley; m. Michael Braun, 1973 (div. 1986); 1 child, Matthew. BA, U. Ill., Chgo., 1969; JD, U. Chgo., 1972. Asst. U.S. atty. U.S. Dist. Ct. (no. dist.) Ill., 1973-77; mem. Ill. Ho. of Reps., 1978-88; recorder of deeds Cook County, Ill., 1988-92; U.S. senator from Ill. Washington, 1993—; mem. fin. com., subcom. on social security and family policy, subcom. on medicare, long-term care and health ins., mem. com. on banking, housing and urban affairs, subcom. on HUD oversight and structure, subcom. on internat. fin. and monetary policy, subcom. on fin. instns. and regulatory relief. Office: US Senate 320 Hart Senate Bldg Washington DC 20510

MOSELY, LINDA HAYS, surgeon; b. New Orleans, Feb. 20, 1941; d. Charles Hodge Mosely and Florence (Morley) Mosely Williams. Student Emory U., 1959-61; BS, La. State U., 1963, MD, 1967. Diplomate Am. Bd. Surgery, Am. Bd. Plastic Surgery; lic. physician, Va., D.C., La. Rotating intern Charity Hosp., New Orleans, 1967-68, med. resident, 1968-69, gen. surgery resident, 1970-72; surgery resident Mt. Sinai Hosp., N.Y.C., 1969-70; hand surgery fellow Dr. Harold Kleinert, Louisville, 1972, 74; clin. surg. fellow U. Louisville Med. Ctr., 1972, gen. surgery resident, 1973; rsch. fellow Yale Med. Ctr., New Haven, 1975, plastic surgery resident, 1975-77; tutor specialist Middlemore Hosp., Auckland, N.Z., 1977-78; practice aesthetic surgery Clinica Planas, Barcelona, Spain, 1978-79; cons. plastic surgery John Fitzgerald Kennedy Hosp., Monrovia, Liberia, 1979; clin. and rsch. fellow Toronto Gen. Hosp., Ont., Can., 1979-80; pvt. practice medicine specializing in hand and plastic surgery, Alexandria, Va., 1980—. Mem. People to People Citizen Amb. Program-Soviet Union-Orthopedic Del., 1991. Contbr. articles to med. jours. Mem. ACS, Am. Soc. for Plastic and Reconstructive Surgeons, Am. Soc. for Surgery of Hand, Met. Washington D.C. Soc. for Surgery of Hand, D.C. Met. Plastic Surgery Soc., Med. Soc. Va., Alexandria Med. Soc., Tysons Corner, Va., Georgetown Club, Washington. Home: 5318 Echols Ave Alexandria VA 22311-1309 Office: 2500 N Van Dorn St Apt 128 Alexandria VA 22302-1601

MOSEMANN, LLOYD KENNETH, II, government official; b. Lancaster, Pa., May 16, 1936; s. Lloyd Kreider and Beatrice Elizabeth (Frey) M.; m. Arlene K. White, Sept. 5, 1957; children—Gigi Renee Mosemann Falke, Lloyd Kenneth III, Douglas Lamar, Holly Joy. A.B. in Social Sci., U. Chgo., 1957, A.M. in Internat. Relations, 1959. Gen. supply officer Navy Electronics Supply Office, Great Lakes, Ill., 1958-62; inventory mgmt. specialist Def. Electronics Supply Ctr., Dayton, Ohio, 1962-63; head integrated-retail supply and support br. Naval Supply Systems Command, Washington, 1963-69; dep. chief logistics support analysis office Def. Logistics Agy., Alexandria, Va., 1969-71; dep. for supply and maintenance Office Sec. of Air Force, Washington, 1971-74; dep. asst. sec. for logistics and communications Dept. Air Force, Washington, 1974-91, dep. asst. sec. for comm., computers and logistics, 1991-93, dep. asst. sec. for comm., computers and support systems, 1993—; mem. Air Force Exec. resources Bd., 1981—. Decorated D.S.M.; recipient Meritorious Svc. medal Sec. Air Force, 1977, Exceptional Civilian Svc. medal sec. Air Force, 1979, 81, 82, 87, Meritorious Sr. Exec. award Pres. of U.S., 1982, 87, Def. Meritorious Civilian Svc. medal, 1985. Mem. Soc. Logistics Engrs. (bd. advisers 1983—, Founders medal 1983), Am. Def. Preparedness Assn. (bd. dirs. 1974-83). Home: 2918 Melanie Ln Oakton VA 22124-1811 Office: Dept Air Force Safaqk Washington DC 20330

MOSENA, DAVID R., aviation commissioner. M in City Planning, U. Tenn. Dir. rsch. Am. Planning Assn., Chgo.; mem. staff City of Chgo., 1984-89, planning commr., 1989-91, chief of staff, 1991-92, aviation commr., 1992—. Chmn. bd. dirs. U.S. Chgo. Lab. Schs. Office: Chgo O'Hare Internat Airport PO Box 66142 Chicago IL 60666*

MOSER, DONALD BRUCE, magazine editor; b. Cleve., Oct. 19, 1932; s. Donald Lyman and Kathryn (McHugh) M.; m. Penny Lee Ward, Dec. 20, 1975. B.A., Ohio U., 1957; postgrad., Stanford U., 1975-58, U. Sydney, 1959-60. With Life mag., 1961-72, West Coast bur. chief, 1964-65, Far East bur. chief, 1966-69, asst. mng. editor, 1970-72; free-lance writer, 1972-77; exec. editor Smithsonian mag., Washington, 1977-80; editor Smithsonian mag., 1981—. Author: The Peninsula, 1962, The Snake River Country, 1974, A Heart to the Hawks, 1975, Central American Jungles, 1976, China-Burma-India, 1978; contbr. articles to numerous mags., jours. Served with U.S. Army, 1953-55. Stegner fellow, 1957-58; Fulbright scholar, 1959-60. Mem. Phi Beta Kappa. Office: Smithsonian Mag Arts & Indsl Bldg 900 Jefferson Dr SW Washington DC 20560-0003

MOSER, ELIZABETH MARIE, lawyer; b. Teaneck, N.J., Nov. 14, 1957; d. Joseph Edward and Rose (Lebeda) M. BA magna cum laude, Montclair (N.J.) State Coll., 1979-79; JD, New England Sch. Law, 1979-82. Bar: N.J. 1983. Atty.-at-law Woolson, Guterl, Sutphen & Anderson, Somerville, N.J., 1984-86; corp. atty. Foster Wheeler Corp., Clinton, N.J., 1986—. Active

Glen Gardner (N.J) Planning Bd., 1988-89. Office: Foster Wheeler Corp Perryville Corp Park Clinton NJ 08809

MOSER, HAROLD DEAN, historian; b. Kannapolis, N.C., Oct. 31, 1938; s. Walter Glenn and Angie Elizabeth (Allen) M.; m. Carolyn Irene French, Mar. 28, 1964; children: Andrew Paul, Anna Elizabeth. A.A., Wingate Coll., 1959; B.A. cum laude, Wake Forest U., 1961, M.A. Univ. fellow, 1963; Ph.D. Ford fellow, U. Wis., 1977. Tchr. Robert B. Glenn High Sch., Winston-Salem, N.C., 1961-62; instr. history Chowan Coll., Murfreesboro, N.C., 1963-65; teaching asst dept. history U. Wis., Madison, 1967-69; Nat. Hist. Publ. commn. fellow The Papers of Daniel Webster (Dartmouth Coll.), Hanover, N.H., 1971-72, asst. editor, 1972-73; assoc. editor The Papers of Daniel Webster (Danmouth Coll.), Hanover, N.H., 1973-76; co-editor The Papers of Daniel Webster (Dartmouth Coll.), Hanover, N.H., 1976-77, editor corr. series, 1978-79; editor dir. The Papers of Andrew Jackson, 1979—; adv. bd. The Papers of Albert Gallatin, Baruch Coll., CCNY, 1987—; rsch. prof. history U. Tenn., Knoxville, 1987—. Contbr. articles to profl. jours. Mem. Am. Hist. Assn., So. Hist. Assn., Orgn. Am. Historians, Soc. Historians of Early Am. Republic, Assn. for Documentary Editing, Tenn. Hist. Soc., Phi Alpha Theta, Eta Sigma Phi, Phi Theta Kappa. Democrat. Episcopalian. Home: 9605 Tallahassee Ln Knoxville TN 37923-2737 Office: U Tenn Hoskins Library Knoxville TN 37996

MOSER, HUGO WOLFGANG, physician; b. Switzerland, Oct. 4, 1924; came to U.S., 1940, naturalized, 1943; s. Hugo L. and Maria (Werner) M.; m. Ann Boody, Dec. 28, 1963; children—Tracey, Peter, Karen, Lauren. M.D., Columbia U., 1948; A.M. in Med. Sci, Harvard U., 1956. Intern Columbia-Presbyn. Med. Center, N.Y.C., 1948-50; asst. in medicine Peter Bent Brigham Hosp., Boston, 1950-52; research fellow dept. biol. chemistry Harvard U., 1955-57; asst. resident, resident in neurology Mass. Gen. Hosp., 1957-59, asst. neurologist, 1960-67, assoc. neurologist, 1967-69, neurologist, 1969-76; teaching fellow neuropathology Harvard Med. Sch., 1959-60, instr. neurology 1960-64, assoc. in neurology, 1964-67, asst. prof., 1967-69, assoc. prof., 1969-72, prof., 1972-76; dir. research and tng. Walter E. Fernald State Sch., 1963-68, asst. supt., 1968-73, acting supt., 1973-74, supt., 1974-76; dir. Center for Research on Mental Retardation and Related Aspects of Human Devel., dir. univ. affiliated facilities for mentally retarded, 1965-74; co-dir. Eunice Kennedy Shriver Center for Mental Retardation, Inc., 1969-74; pres. John F. Kennedy Inst., Balt., 1976-88; prof. neurology and pediatrics Johns Hopkins U., 1976—. Author: (with others) Mental Retardation: An Atlas of Diseases with Associated Physical Abnormalities, 1972; Contbr. (with others) articles to med. jours. Served with AUS, 1943-44; to capt. U.S. Army, 1952-54. Recipient Hower award Child Neurology Soc., 1994. Mem. Am. Acad. Neurology, Am. Assn. Mental Deficiency, Am. Assn. Neuropathologists, Am. Neurol. Assn., Internat. Soc. Neurochemistry, Am. Pediatrics Soc., Sigma Xi, Alpha Omega Alpha. Home: 100 Beechdale Rd Baltimore MD 21210-2209 Office: Kennedy Inst Inc 707 N Broadway Baltimore MD 21205-1832

MOSER, KENNETH MILES, physician; b. Balt., Apr. 12, 1929; s. Simon and Helene Joyce M.; m. Sara Falk, June 17, 1951; children—Gregory, Kathleen, Margot, Diana. B.A., Haverford Coll., 1950; M.D., Johns Hopkins U., 1954. Diplomate: Am. Bd. Internal Medicine. Intern, resident in medicine D.C. Gen. Hosp., Georgetown Hosp., 1954-59; chief pulmonary and infectious disease service Nat. Naval Med. Center, Bethesda, Md., 1959-61; dir. pulmonary div. Georgetown U. Med. Center, Washington, 1961-68; prof. medicine, dir. pulmonary and critical care med. div. U. Calif., San Diego Sch. Medicine, 1968—; dir. Specialized Ctr. Rsch. U. Calif.-San Diego/Nat. Heart Lund and Blood Inst., 1978—. Author 10 books in field of pulmonary medicine and thrombosis; Contbr. articles to med. jours. Bd. dirs. Am. Lung Assn. of San Diego and Imperial Counties, 1969-76, Am. Lung Assn. of Calif., 1976-80; mem. manpower com. Nat. Heart, Lung and Blood Inst., bd. dirs. 1978—. Served with U.S. Navy, 1959-61. Fellow ACP, AAAS, Am. Coll. Chest Physicians; mem. Am. Thoracic Soc. (exec. bd., pres. 1985-86), Am. Heart Assn. Coun. on Thrombosis, Am. Physiol. Soc. Office: U Calif San Diego Med Ctr 200 W Arbor Dr San Diego CA 92103 *Participating in academic medicine and research is like being a member of a relay team engaged in a race of infinite length. Two forces keep one running through the often difficult terrain: the goal of improving health; and the privilege of passing the baton to many others who will seek that same goal.*

MOSER, M(ARTIN) PETER, lawyer; b. Balt., Jan. 16, 1928; s. Herman and Henrietta (Lehmayer) M.; m. Elizabeth Kohn, June 14, 1949; children—Mike, Moriah, Jeremy. A.B., The Citadel, Charleston, S.C., 1947; LL.B., Harvard U., 1950. Bar: Md. 1950, U.S. Supreme Ct., U.S. Ct. Appeals (4th cir.), U.S. Dist. Ct. Md. Asst. states atty. City of Balt., 1951, 53-54; assoc. Blades Rosenfeld, Balt., 1950, 53-54; ptnr. Frank, Bernstein, Conaway & Goldman and predecessor firms, Balt., 1955-90, co-chmn. firm, 1983-86; counsel, 1991-92; of counsel Piper & Marbury, 1992—; instr. U. Balt. Law Sch., 1954-56, 86, U. Md. Law Sch., 1986-87. Contbr. articles to profl. jours. Del., chmn. local govt. com. Md. Constl. Conv., 1967-68; mem. Balt. City Planning Commn., 1961-66, Balt. Regional Planning Council, 1963-66, Md. Commn. to Study Narcotics Laws, 1965-67, Mayor's Task Force on EEO, 1966-67, Met. Transit Authority Adv. Council, 1962, Com. to Revise Balt. City Planning Laws, 1962, Com. to Revise Balt. City Charter Provision on Conflicts of Interest, 1969-70; mem. Citizens Adv. Com. on Dist. Ct., chmn., 1971, Dist. Adv. Bd. for Pub. Defender System for Dist. 1, 1973-85; mem. Atty. Grievance Commn. of Md., 1975-78, chmn. 82-86; chmn. Md. State Ethics Commn., 1987-89; bd. dirs. Sinai Hosp., 1983—, Ct. of Appeals Comm. to Study the Model Rules, 1983-86. Served with JAGC, U.S. Army, 1951-53. Fellow Am. Bar Found., Md. Bar Found; mem. ABA (ho. of dels 1978—, treas. 1993—, bd. govs. 1984-87, 1992—, ethics com. 1981-84, 87-90, chmn. 1981-82, 87-90, scope and cor. com. 1987-92, chmn. 1990-91), Md. State Bar Assn. (pres. 1979-80), Balt. Bar Assn. (pres. 1971-72), Assn. Trial Lawyers Am., Fed. Bar Assn., Am. Law Inst. Democrat. Jewish. Clubs: Wednesday Law, Lawyers' Round Table, Hamilton St. Office: Piper & Marbury 36 S Charles St 8th Fl Baltimore MD 21201

MOSER, MARVIN, physician, educator, author; b. Newark, Jan. 24, 1924; s. Sol and Sophia (Markowitz) M.; m. Joy Diane Lipez, July 1, 1954; children: Jill, Stephen, John. A.B., Cornell U., 1943; M.D., Downstate Coll. Medicine, N.Y.C., 1947. Diplomate: Am. Bd. Internal Medicine, subbd. cardiovascular disease. Intern univ. div. Kings County Hosp., N.Y.C., 1947-48; resident in medicine Kings County Hosp., 1948-49, Montefiore Hosp., N.Y.C., 1949-50; Nat. Heart Assn. fellow Mt. Sinai Hosp., N.Y.C., 1950-51; charge vascular service Walter Reed Army Hosp. Med. Centre, Washington, 1951-53; practice medicine specializing in cardiology White Plains, N.Y., 1953-95; assoc. physician cardiology Montefiore Hosp., 1953-75, in charge hypertension sect., 1960-71; attending physician cardiology White Plains Hosp., 1968-95, chief cardiology, 1969-78; adj. physician in cardiology Grasslands Hosp., Valhalla, N.Y., 1953-60; attending physician in medicine in charge Hypertension Clinic, Westchester County Med. Center, Valhalla, 1974-84; asst. clin. prof. medicine Albert Einstein Coll. Medicine, 1965-75; clin. prof. medicine N.Y. Med. Coll., 1974-84, Yale U. Sch. Medicine, 1984—; sr. med. cons. nat. high blood pressure program NIH, 1975—, mem. nat. high blood pressure coordinating com., 1976—; chmn. Joint Nat. Com. Hypertension, 1975-76, vice-chmn., 1979, mem., 1984-88, 92; mem. exec. com. Nat. Citizens for Treatment High Blood Pressure, 1976-78, vice chmn., 1978-88; mem. N.Y. State Adv. Com. on Hypertension, 1977-84; chmn. Nat. Conf. on High Blood Pressure Control, 1979; mem. select panel on hypertension in Am. Congl. Subcom. on Aging, 1978-79; cons. cardiology N.Y. State Dept. Health, Gen. Hosp., Saranac Lake, N.Y., 1980-90; med. dir. Westchester County Hypertension Program, N.Y., 1979-88. Author: (with A.M. Master, M. Moser, H. Jaffee) Cardiac Emergencies and Heart Failure, 2d edit., 1955, (with A. Goldman) Hypertensive Vascular Disease, 1967, Hypertension, A Practical Approach, 1975, Lower Your Blood Pressure and Live Longer, 1989; co-editor, contbr. Yale University School of Medicine Heart Book, 1992, Weekly by Week to a Strong Heart, 1992; assoc. editor: Angiology, 1976-85; bd. editors Primary Cardiology, 1975-78, assoc. editor-in-chief 1978—, Jour. Cardiovas. Risk Factors, Jour. Geriatric Cardiology. Chmn. Narcotics Guidance Coun., Scarsdale, 1968-72; trustee Scarsdale Bd. Edn., 1970-73, Trudeau Inst., 1992—; Third Ave. Value Fund, 1994—. Served U.S. Army, 1941-46; capt. M.C. USAF, 1951-53. Nat. Heart Inst. grantee, 1958-62; recipient Achievement award for contbns. to hypertension control Nat. High Blood Pressure Edn. Program, 1985. Fellow ACP, Am. Coll. Cardiology; mem. Am. Heart Assn. (fellow coun. clin.

cardiology, coun. high blood pressure rsch. 1974—, coun. geriatric cardiology 1988—, v.p. 1994—, chmn. N.Y. State com. on hypertension 1974-75), N.Y. Cardiol. Soc. Century Country Club. Home and Office: 13 Murray Hill Rd Scarsdale NY 10583-2829

MOSER, ROBERT HARLAN, physician, educator, writer; b. Trenton, N.J., June 16, 1923; s. Simon and Helena (Silvers) M.; m. Linda Mae Salsinger, Mar. 18, 1989; children from previous marriage: Steven Michael, Jonathan Evan. BS, Loyola U., Balt., 1944; MD, Georgetown U., 1948. Diplomate Am. Bd. Internal Medicine. Commd. 1st lt. U.S. Army, 1948, advanced through grades to col., 1966, intern D.C. Gen. Hosp., 1948-49, fellow pulmonary disease D.C. Gen. Hosp., 1949-50; bn. surgeon U.S. Army, Korea, 1950-51; asst. resident Georgetown U. Hosp., 1951-52; chief resident Georgetown U. Hosp. U.S. Army, 1952-53; chief med. service U.S. Army Hosp. U.S. Army, Salzburg, Austria, 1953-55, Wurzburg, Fed. Republic Germany, 1955-56; resident in cardiology Brooke Gen. Hosp. U.S. Army, 1956-57, asst. chief dept. medicine Brooke Gen. Hosp., 1957-59, chief Brooke Gen. Hosp., 1967-68, fellow hematology U. Utah Coll. Medicine, 1959-60, asst. chief U.S. Army Tripler Gen. Hosp., 1960-64, chief William Beaumont Gen. Hosp., 1965-67, chief Walter Reed Gen. Hosp., 1968-69, ret., 1969; chief of staff Maui (Hawaii) Meml. Hosp., 1969-73, chief dept. medicine, 1975-77; exec. v.p. Am. Coll. Physicians, Phila., 1977-86; v.p. med. affairs The NutraSweet Co., Deerfield, Ill., 1986-91; assoc. prof. medicine Baylor U., 1958-59; clin. prof. medicine Hawaii U., 1969-77, Washington U., 1970-77, Abraham Lincoln Sch. Medicine, 1974-75; adj. prof. medicine U. Pa., 1977-86, Northwestern U., 1987-91; adj. prof. Uniformed Services U. Health Scis., 1979—; clin. prof. medicine U. N.Mex. Coll. Medicine, 1992—; flight controller Project Mercury, 1959-62; cons. mem. med. evaluation team Project Gemini, 1962-66; cons. Project Apollo, 1967-73, Tripler Gen. Hosp., 1970-77, Walter Reed Army Med. Ctr., 1974-86; mem. cardiovascular and renal adv. com. FDA, 1978-82; bd. dirs. Pub. Service Satellite Commn., 1980-86; chmn. life scis. adv. com. NASA, 1984-87, mem. NASA adv. coun., 1983-88, chmn. gen. med. panel Hosp. Satellite Network, 1984-86; mem. adv. com. NASA Space Sta., 1988-93; mem. Dept. Def. Com. on Grad. Med. Edn., 1986-87; mem. Life Scis. Strategic Planning Study Group, 1986-88; mem. space studies bd. NRC, 1988-93, space exploration initiation study, 1990, NASA Space Sta. Commn., 1992-93. Author: Diseases of Medical Progress, 1955, rev. edit., 1969, House Officer Training, 1970; co-author: Adventures in Medical Writing, 1970, Decade of Decision, 1992; editor, chief div. sci. publs. Jour. AMA, Chgo., 1973-75; contbg. editor Med. Opinion and Rev., 1966-75; chmn. editorial bd. Diagnosis mag., 1986-89; mem. editorial bd. Hawaii Med. Jour., Family Physicians, Archives of Internal Medicine, 1967-73, Western Jour. Medicine, 1975-87, Chest, 1975-80, Med. Times, 1977-84, Quality Rev. Bull., 1979-91, The Pharos, 1991—, Emergency Med., 1993—, Travel Medicine, 1994—; contbr. over 200 articles to med. sci. jours and med. books. Master Am. Coll. Physicians (exec. v.p. 1977-86). Fellow Am. Coll. Cardiology, Royal Coll. Physicians and Surgeons Can. (hon.), Am. Clin. and Climatol. Assn.; mem. Am. Med. Writers Assn., Am. Therapeutic Soc., Am. Osler Soc., Inst. Med., AMA (adv. panel registry of adverse drug reactions 1960-67, council on drugs 1967-73), Chgo. Soc. Internal Medicine, Coll. Physicians Phila., Soc. Med. Cons. to Armed Forces, Alpha Sigma Nu, Alpha Omega Alpha. Democrat. Jewish. Avocations: hiking, backpacking, white water rafting. Home and Office: Canones Rd # 616 Chama NM 87520

MOSER, ROBERT LAWRENCE, pathologist, health facility administrator; b. Passaic, N.J., Mar. 22, 1952; s. Robert George and Marjorie Ann (Frankenberger) M.; m. Rosemarie Scolaro, June 16, 1978; children: Rachel Ann, Alexander Robert. BA in Biology magna cum laude, Lafayette Coll., 1974; MD in Microbiology and Internal Medicine with honors, Hahnemann Med. Coll., 1978. Diplomate Am. Bd. Pathology, Am. Bd. Anatomic Pathology, Am. Bd. Clin. Pathology. Intern, fellow dept. Pathology The Johns Hopkins Hosp., Balt., 1978-79, resident, fellow dept. Pathology, 1979-81, chief resident, fellow dept. Pathology, 1981-82, resident, fellow dept. Lab. Medicine, 1982-84; cons. pathologist Perry Point (Md.) VA Med. Ctr., 1983-84; pathologist Helene Fuld Med. Ctr., Trenton, N.J., 1984-88; dir. Pathology St Francis Med. Ctr., Trenton, 1988—; pres. Pathology Assocs., Lawrenceville, N.J., 1981—. Contbr. articles to profl. jours. Fellow Coll. Am. Pathologists, Coll. Physicians of Phila.; mem. Am. Med. Informatics Assn., Med. Soc. N.J., Mercer County Med. Soc. (mem. edit. bd., cancer com., pub. health com.), Ctrl. Jersey Ind. Physician Assn. (v.p. 1994), Phi Beta Kappa. Avocations: golf, gardening, skiing. Office: Pathology Assocs 3131 Princeton Pike # 5-202 Lawrenceville NJ 08648

MOSER, ROYCE, JR., physician, medical educator; b. Versailles, Mo., Aug. 21, 1935; s. Royce and Russie Frances (Stringer) M.; m. Lois Anne Hunter, June 14, 1958; children: Beth Anne Moser McLean, Donald Royce. BA, Harvard U., 1957, MD, 1961; MPH, Harvard Sch. Pub. Health, Boston, 1965. Diplomate Am. Bd. Preventive Medicine (trustee), Am. Bd. Family Practice. Commd. officer USAF, 1962, advanced through grades to col., 1974; resident in aerospace medicine USAF Sch. Aerospace Medicine, Brooks AFB, Tex., 1965-67; chief aerospace medicine service Def. Command, Colorado Springs, Colo., 1967-70; comdr. 35th USAF Dispensary Phan Rang, Vietnam, 1970-71; chief aerospace medicine br. USAF Sch. Aerospace Medicine, Brooks AFB, 1971-77; comdr. USAF Hosp., Tyndall AFB, Fla., 1977-79; chief clin. scis. div. USAF Sch. Aerospace Medicine, Brooks AFB, 1979-81, chief edn. div., 1981-83, sch. comdr., 1983-85; ret., 1985; prof., vice chmn. Dept. Family and Preventive Medicine U. Utah Sch. Medicine, Salt Lake City, 1985—, dir. Rocky Mountain Ctr. for Occupational and Environ. Health, 1987—; cons. in occupational, environ. and aerospace medicine, Salt Lake City, 1985—; presenter nat. and internat. med. meetings. Author: Effective Management of Occupational and Environmental Health and Safety Programs, 1992; contbr. book chpts. and articles to profl. jours. Mem., past pres. 1st Bapt. Ch. Found., Salt Lake City, 1987-89; mem., chmn. numerous univ. coms., Salt Lake City, 1985—; bd. dirs. Hanford Environ. Health Found., 1990-92; mem. preventive medicine residency rev. com. Accreditation Coun. Grad. Med. Edn., 1991—; mem. ednl. adv. bd. USAF Human Systems Ctr., 1991—; chmn. long-range planning commn. Am. Bd. Preventive Medicine, 1992—. Decorated Legion of Merit (2). Fellow Aerospace Med. Assn. (pres. 1989-90, chair fellows group 1994—, Harry G. Mosely award 1981, Theodore C. Lyster award 1988), Am. Coll. Preventive Medicine (regent 1981-82), Am. Coll. Occupational and Environ. Medicine, Am. Acad. Family Physicians; mem. Internat. Acad. Aviation and Space Medicine (selector 1989-94, chancellor 1994—), Soc. of USAF Flight Surgeons (pres. 1978-79, George E. Schafer award 1982), Phi Beta Kappa. Avocations: photography, fishing. Home: 664 Aloha Rd Salt Lake City UT 84103-3329 Office: Dept Family & Preventive Med 50 N Medical Dr Salt Lake City UT 84132-0001

MOSER, WILLIAM OSCAR JULES, mathematics educator; b. Winnipeg, Can., Sept. 5, 1927; s. Robert and Laura (Fenson) M.; m. Beryl Rita Pearlman, Sept. 2, 1953; children—Marla, Lionel, Paula. B.Sc., U. Man., 1949; M.A., U. Minn., 1951; Ph.D., U. Toronto, 1957. Lectr. U. Sask., 1955-57, asst. prof., 1957-59; assoc. prof. U. Man., 1959-64, prof. McGill U., 1964-66, prof., 1966—. Author: (with H.S.M. Coxeter) Generators and Relations for Discrete Groups, 1957, 4th edit., 1980; also research papers.; Editor Can. Math. Bull., 1962-70, Can. Jour. Math., 1982-85. NRC fellow, 1951-53; Can. Council leave fellow, 1971. Mem. Am. Math. Soc., Can. Math. Soc. (pres. 1975-77), Math. Assn. Am. Office: McGill U Dept Math, 805 Sherbrooke St W, Montreal, PQ Canada H3A 2K6

MOSES, ABE JOSEPH, international financial consultant; b. Springfield, Mass., July 15, 1931; s. Mohammed Mustapha and Fatima (Merriam) M.; m. Donna C. Moses (dec.); children: James Douglas, John C., Peter J. BA, Amherst Coll., 1955; MA in Internat. Affairs, Johns Hopkins U., 1957. Legis. aide Sen. J.F. Kennedy, 1955-57; fgn. service officer Dept. State, 1960-65; v.p., gen. mgr. Libyan Desert Oil Co., Texfel Petroleum Corp., Tripoli, Libya, 1965-67; v.p. adminstrn., fin Occidental Petroleum Corp., Libya, 1967-70; v.p. fin., dir. Northrop Corp., 1970-74; chmn. Transworld Trade Ltd., Washington, 1971—; v.p., mng. dir. world adv. group Chase Manhattan Bank, 1974-80; pres. Gradiari Internat., Inc., Danbury, Conn., 1980-82; chief exec. officer, dir. Galadari Bros., Dubai, United Arab Emirates, 1982-86; internat. bus. and fin. cons. Traxol, Dubai, 1986—; fin. cons. Govt. Costa Rica, 1986-89; chmn. Aviation Systems Corp., Arlington, Va., 1974, Dillon Internat., Akron, Ohio, 1986—; mng. dir. Sheraton Suites Akron, Cuyahoga Falls, Ohio, 1990—; owner's rep. Monarch Sheraton Hotel, Springfield, Mass., 1993—; bd. dirs., v.p. Morgan Freeport Co.,

Hudson, Ohio; bd. dirs. Seeds of Peace, Washington. Pres., bd. dirs. Riverside Community Urban Redevel. Corp.; mem. exec. com., bd. dirs. Near East Found., N.Y.C., 1978—; pres. Riverfront Ctr. Assn., Cuyahoga Falls, 1992—. Capt. USAF, 1957-60. Ford Found. fellow Johns Hopkins U., 1955, Barr Found. fellow, 1955-57. Mem. Mid. East Inst. Democrat. Home: 15 Bagburn Rd Monroe CT 06468-1432 Office: Riverside CURC 1989 Front St Cuyahoga Falls OH 44221-3811 also: Falcon Hotel Mgmt Corp 1 Monarch Pl Springfield MA 01144-1001

MOSES, ALFRED HENRY, lawyer; b. Balt., July 24, 1929; s. Leslie William and Helene Amelia (Lobe) M.; m. Carol Whitehill, Nov. 24, 1955; Barbara, Jennifer, David, Amalie. BA, Dartmouth, 1951; student, Woodrow Wilson Sch., Princeton U., 1951-52; JD, Georgetown U., 1956. Bar: D.C. 1956. Assoc. Covington & Burling, Washington, 1956-65, ptnr., 1965-94; spl. advisor, spl. counsel Pres. Jimmy Carter, Washington, 1980-81; amb. to Romania U.S. Dept. State, Bucharest, 1994—; legal advisor minority rights Dem. Nat. Com., Washington, 1969, DC Commision on Urban Renewal, 1972; lectr. Am. Law Inst., ABA , New Orleans, 1970, Am. Inst. CPAs, ABA, Washington, 1969, Georgetown U. Law Ctr., 1971, Tax Exec. Inst., Washington, 1967-68, Tulane Tax Inst., New Orleans, 1971; commr. Pub. Housing, Fairfax County, Va., 1971-72. Contbr. articles, commentaries to jours. Co-chmn. legal div. United Givers Fund, Washington, 1975-76; mem. Coun. Fgn. Rels., N.Y.C. 1977—; bd. dirs. Paralysis Cure Rsch. Found., 1978-81; trustee Phelps Stokes Fund, N.Y.C., 1978-84; pres. Nat. Children's Island, Washington, 1975-76; pres. Golda Meir Assn., 1986-88, nat. chmn., 1988-93; trustee Jewish Publ. Soc., 1989-94, Haifa U., 1988-90; pres. Am. Jewish Com., 1991-94; mem. bd. regents Georgetown U., 1986-92. Mem. ABA, D.C. Bar Assn., Met. Club. Democrat. Jewish. Home: PO Box 7566 Washington DC 20044 Office: Am Embassy, Bucharest Romania

MOSES, BETH HERMAN, psychiatric-mental health nurse, nursing educator; b. Phila., Oct. 15, 1955; d. Ellis and Charlotte (Hoffman) Herman; m. Fredric Moses, July 7, 1984. BSN, U. Pa., 1978, MSN, 1984. RN, Pa. Clin. intern VA Mental Health Clinic, Phila., 1983-84; asst. prof. nursing East Stroudsburg (Pa.) U., 1984-86, now guest lectr., facilitator support group on eating disorders Women's Ctr., 1990; psychotherapist in pvt. practice Family Treatment Assocs., Stroudsburg, Pa., 1984—; clin. instr. nursing Northampton C.C, Bethlehem, Pa., 1990-92; mem. Monroe County HIV/AIDS Task Force, health and treatment com., 1990-94; cons. Fitzmaurice Resdl. Svcs., Stroudsburg, 1990—; cons. Vis. Nurses Assn., Stroudsburg, 1994—; conf. facilitator Pocono Med. Ctr. Nursing Mgrs., 1985. Dir., bd. dirs. Women's Resource Ctr. Monroe County, Inc., 1985-86, co-facilitator support group for adult women victims of incest, 1985; guest lectr. Pocono Med. Ctr., Pocono Mountain H.C., East Stroudsburg H.S., also other cmty. instns.; facilitator breast cancer support group Am. Cancer Soc., 1994, vol. reach to recovery program, 1994—. Named Rehab. Specialist of Yr., Intracorp., 1983. Mem. ANA (cert. clin. specialist in adult psychiat.-mental health nursing), Pa. Nurses Assn.

MOSES, BRUCE HADLEY, manufacturing company executive; b. Oak Park, Ill., Apr. 20, 1933; s. Donald Phillip and Althea (Hadley) M.; m. Joan Abel, June 30, 1956 (div. 1983); children: Leslie, Mary, Pamela, John, Amy; m. Marilyn Parker, May 31, 1986. BA in Psychology, U. Rochester, 1955. With UARCO Inc., 1955—; sales writer Chgo., 1955-57; sales rep. Tulsa, 1957-63, dist. sales mgr., 1963-65; dist. sales mgr. Kansas City, Mo., 1965-71; region sales mgr. Hartford, Conn., 1971-77, N.Y.C., 1977-81; v.p. sales Barrington, Ill., 1981-86, pres., chief operating officer, 1986—. Trustee coun. U. Rochester, N.Y., 1987—; bd. dirs. Internat. Bus. Forms Industries Inc., 1989—, Internat. Bus. Forms Industries, Inc. Club: Meadow (Rolling Meadows, Ill.). Avocations: tennis, antiques. Home: PO Box 996 Williams Bay WI 53191-0996 Office: UARCO Inc W County Line Rd Barrington IL 60010

MOSES, CHARLES E., superintendent. Supt. Milford (Del.) Sch. Dist. Recipient State Finalist for Nat. Supt. of Yr. award, 1993. Office: Milford Sch Dist 906 Lakeview Ave Milford DE 19963-1732

MOSES, EDWARD CROSBY, artist; b. Long Beach, Calif.; s. Alfonsus Lemuel and Olivia (Branco) M.; m. Avilda Peters, Aug. 11, 1959; children: Cedd, Andrew. BA, U. Calif., Long Beach, 1954, MA, 1956. lectr. painting, drawing UCLA, 1961, 75-76, U. Calif., Irvine, 1968-72, Bakersfield Coll., Calif., 1977; guest lectr. Oberlin Coll., Wichita Art Mus., Cranbrook Inst. Numerous one-man shows, 1958—, latest include Andre Emmerich Gallery, N.Y.C., 1974-75, L.A. County Mus. Art, 1976, Tex. Gallery, Houston, 1979, High Mus. Art, Atlanta, 1980, Janus Gallery, L.A., 1982, Dorothy Rosenthal Gallery, Chgo., 1982—, L.A. Louver Gallery, Venice, 1985—, Louver Gallery, N.Y.C., 1989-93, Galerie Georges Lavrov, Paris; exhibited numerous group shows, 1958—, latest include Corcoran Gallery Art, Washington, 1979, High Mus., 1980, San Francisco Mus., 1980, San Francisco Art Inst., 1981, Mus. Modern Art, Paris, 1982, L.A. Mcpl. Gallery, 1982, Mus. Contemporary Art, L.A., 1983, 86, Nat. Gallery Art, Washington, 1984, Nat. Gallery of Modern Art, 1988, Smithsonian Instn., 1986, Galerie Koltontorvet, Copenhagen, Mus. Contemporary Art, L.A., 1986, Whitney Mus., 1991; represented in permanent collections U. Calif. Art Mus., Berkeley, Santa Barbara, San Francisco Art Mus., Mus. Modern Art, N.Y.C., San Francisco Art Inst., Chgo. Art Inst., Hirshhorn Mus., Phila., Akron Art Inst., Ohio, Harvard U., Cambridge, Mass., Yale U., New Haven, Walker Art Mus., Mpls., Corcoran Gallery Art, Whitney Mus. Am. Art, N.Y.C., Mus. Modern Art, N.Y.C., Los Angeles County Mus. Art, Nat. Mus. Am. Art at Smithsonian Inst., Washington, Phila. Mus. Art. Served with USN, 1944-46. Recipient Tamarind fellowship in lithography, 1968, Art in Pub. Places award Calif. Arts Coun., 1987; NEA grantee, 1976; Guggenheim fellow, 1980.

MOSES, EDWIN, former track and field athlete; b. Dayton, Ohio, 1955; m. Myrella Moses. Student, Morehouse Coll. Olympian hurdler; Worlds Top Ranked Intermediate Hurdler, 1976—. Chmn. USOC Substance Abuse Com., 1989—. Holder world record 400 meter hurdle; Olympic gold medalist, 1976, 84; 1st U.S. athlete to be voted delegate to Internat. Amateur Athletic Fedn.; named Sportsman of the Yr. U.S. Olympic Com. Office: Hurdler US Olympic Com 1750 E Boulder St Colorado Springs CO 80909-5746*

MOSES, FRANKLIN MAXWELL, retired chemical marketing executive; b. Kansas, Ohio, Oct. 17, 1918; s. Otto Franklin and Edith Mary (Diller) M.; m. Elizabeth Fleming, Feb. 27, 1948; children: Steven F., Gregory F., Christopher R. (dec.), Elizabeth Ann. B.S., Ohio State U., 1941; postgrad., U. Pitts., 1941-42. Indsl. engr. U.S. Steel Corp., Pitts., 1941-42; pilot Pan Am. World Airways, San Francisco, 1946-53; exec. v.p. Wilson & Geo Meyer & Co., South San Francisco, Calif., 1954-84; pvt. practice mktg. cons. Portola Valley, CA, 1984-94; ret., 1994; dir. Portola Ranch Assn., WGM Hydro, San Francisco. Served to capt. USMCR, 1942-46. Decorated with two Distinguished Flying Crosses, seven Air Medals. Mem. Calif. Acad. Scis., Marine Corps Aviation Soc., Assn. Naval Aviation, Tailhook Assn., Calif. Hist. Soc., Am. Inst. Wine and Food, Ohio State U. Alumni Assn. (life), St. Francis Yacht Club (San Francisco), California Club (L.A.), Portola Valley Polo Club, Los Altos Hunt Club, World Trade Club, Family Club, Shack Riders, Frontier Boys, Marines Meml. Club (San Francisco). Republican. Episcopalian. Home: 4 Coal Mine Vw Portola Valley CA 94028

MOSES, GILBERT, film and theatre director; b. Cleve., Aug. 20, 1942; s. Gilbert and Bertha Mae (Jones) M. Student, Oberlin (Ohio) Coll., 1960-63, Sorbonne, Paris, 1963, NYU Sch. Arts, 1966-67. Copy boy N.Y. Post, 1964; mem. staff Free Press, Jackson, Miss., 1963-64; editor Free Press, 1964; co-founder, artistic dir. Free So. Theatre, Jackson, 1963—; bd. dirs. Free So. Theatre, 1966—; stage dir. Arena Stage, 1982-83. Mem. Second City, Chgo., 1967, guitarist, composer, Nick Gravenitis Group, 1967, The Street Choir, 1968; dir.: Slaveship, 1969 (Obie award 1970), The Taking of Miss Janie (Obie award 1977), N.Y. Drama Critics Circle award 1977, N.Y. Drama Critics award 1977), Ain't Supposed to Die a Natural Death, 1973 (Tony nomination), 1600 Pennsylvania Avenue, 1976, The Duplex, 1972, Don't Let it Go To Your Head, 1973, Every Night When the Sun Goes Down, 1975, all in N.Y.C., Bloodknot in San Francisco, 1970, No Place to Be Somebody, 1971, Mother Courage, 1971, all in Washington, Buried Child, Arena Stage Co., all in Washington, Rigoletto at San Francisco Opera House, 1972; dir., composer: music and lyrics for film Willie Dynamite, 1975, The Fish That

Saved Pittsburgh; dir.: TV films including Roots (2 segments) (Humanitas award 1977, Emmy nominee 1977), The Greatest Thing That Almost Happened, 1977, The Wiz (prior to Broadway opening), 1976; multicamera episodes Benson, 1985, M.O.W., Fight for Jenny, 1986, The Day They Came to Arrest the Book, 1987 (Humanitas award 1987), Runaway, 1989; dir. episodes TV series: Call to Glory, Paper Chase, Maximum Security (HBO), 1994; producer, dir. Daddy Can't Read, ABC; producer PBS-TV prodn. The Ossie and Ruby Series, 1988. Office: Shapiro Lichtman Agy 8827 Beverly Blvd Los Angeles CA 90048*

MOSES, GREGORY ALLEN, engineering educator; b. Kalamazoo, Mich., Apr. 7, 1950; s. John Stuart and Blanche (Marousek) M.; m. Sharon Louise Hallquist, Apr. 16, 1983; children: Laurel Erin, Lindsey Elizabeth. BS in Engring., U. Mich., 1972, PhD, 1976. Asst. prof. U. Wis., Madison, 1976-80, assoc. prof., 1980-84, prof. of engring., 1984-89, assoc. dean rsch., 1989—. Co-author: Inertial Confinement Fusion, 1982; author: Engineering Applications Software Development, 1989; contbr. over 50 articles to profl. jours. Mem. Am. Nuclear Soc., Am. Phys. Soc. Lutheran. Home: 5 Mt Rainier Ln Madison WI 53705-2453 Office: U Wis Engring Expt Sta 1500 Johnson Dr Madison WI 53706-1687

MOSES, IRVING BYRON, architect; b. Chgo., Aug. 5, 1925; s. Morris and Dorothy (Berns) M.; m. Toby June Kornfeld, June 29, 1947; children: Barbara Moses Tarr, Jack Robert, Carol Lynn. BS in Architecture Design, U. Ill., 1950. Time, motion and material research Small Homes Council of Ill., 1947-48; archtl. designer Holsman, Holsman, Klekamp & Taylor, Chgo., 1950-51; architect, ptnr. Comm, Comm & Moses, AIA, Chgo., 1951-62; prin. I. Moses Assocs., AIA, Chgo., 1962-78, Moses Assocs., AIA, Chgo., 1978—; cons. architect A. Epstein & Sons, Chgo., 1974-75, Globe Engring. Co., Chgo., 1975-77, Slip & Fall Litigation, 1980—; judge, arbitrator, Am. Arbitration Assn., 1976—. Author: Chicago School Architecture, 1982, Doors, 1984. Chmn. Appearance Review Commn., Highland Park, Ill., 1976-86; commr. Zoning Bd. Appeals, Highland Park, 1987—. Served with USN, 1943-46. Mem. AIA (chmn. membership commn. 1984-86, Bldg. award, 1965, 70, 75, 85), Am. Registered Architects, Ill. Soc. Architects. Club: Cliffdwellers (Chgo.). Avocations: art, running. Home: 145 Blackhawk Rd Highland Park IL 60035-5266 Office: Moses Assocs AIA 225 W Ohio St Chicago IL 60610-4119

MOSES, JOEL, computer scientist, educator; b. Petach Tikvah, Israel, Nov. 25, 1941; came to U.S., 1954, naturalized, 1960; s. Bernhard and Golda (Losner) M.; m. Margaret A. Garvey, Dec. 27, 1970; children: Jesse, David. B.A., Columbia U., 1962, M.A., 1963; Ph.D., M.I.T., 1967. Asst. prof. dept. elec. engring. and computer sci. M.I.T., 1967-71, assoc. prof., 1971-77, prof., 1977—, assoc. dir. Lab for Computer Sci., 1974-78, assoc. head computer sci. and engring., dept. elec. engring. and computer sci., 1978-81, head dept., 1981-89, dir. Dept. D.C. Jackson prof., 1989—, dean Sch. Engring., 1991—; vis. prof. Harvard Grad. Sch. Bus. Adminstrn., 1989-90; bd. dirs. Analog Devices, Inc., Coltec Industries Inc. Editor: The Computer Age: A Twenty Year View, 1979. Recipient Achievement award MIT Lab. for Computer Sci., 1985. Fellow IEEE, AAAS; mem. NAE, Assn. for Computing Machinery, Am. Soc. for Engring. Edn. (centennial certificate, vice chmn. engring. deans coun.). Office: MIT 1-206 Cambridge MA 02139

MOSES, LEON NATHAN, economist, educator; b. N.Y.C., Oct. 27, 1924; s. Charles and Jean (Gibbell) M.; m. Clare Baum, Dec. 25, 1949 (div. 1972); children: Jonathan David, Richard Allen, Jared Daniel; m. Rae Arlene Stallcupp, May 30, 1936; 1 child, Megan. BA with highest distinction, Ohio State U., 1945; MA, Harvard U., 1951, PhD, 1955. Rsch. assoc. Harvard U., Cambridge, Mass., 1951-57, asst. prof., 1956-57; assoc. prof. Northwestern U., Evanston, Ill., 1957-59, prof., 1960—, dir. Transp. Ctr., 1975-80, Robert and Emily King Prof. Bus. Insts. Endowed Chair, 1993—. Author, editor: Safety in an Era of Economic Deregulation, 1990, The Transportation of Hazardous Materials, 1993. With U.S. Army, 1942-43. Mem. Am. Econ. Assn. Avocations: hiking, gardening, sailing. Home: 114 4th St Wilmette IL 60091-3410 Office: Northwestern U Econ Dept 633 Clark St Evanston IL 60208-0001

MOSES, LINCOLN E., statistician, educator; b. Kansas City, Mo., Dec. 21, 1921; s. Edward Walter and Virginia (Holmes) M.; m. Jean Runnels, Dec. 26, 1942; children—Katherine, James O'D., William C., Margaret, Elizabeth; m. Mary Louise Coale, 1968. A.B., Stanford, 1941, Ph.D., 1950. Asst. prof. edn. Columbia Tchrs. Coll., 1950-52; faculty Stanford U., 1952—, prof. stats., 1959—, exec. head dept., 1964-68; assoc. dean Stanford U. (Sch. Humanities and Scis.), 1965-68, 85-86, dean grad. studies, 1969-75; faculty Stanford U. (Med. Sch.), 1952—; adminstr. Energy Info. Adminstrn., Dept. of Energy, 1978-80; L.L. Thurstone disting. fellow U. N.C., 1968-69; com. mem. Am. Friends Svc. Com., intermittently 1954—, chmn. No. Calif. chpt., 1972-76, 84-88. Guggenheim fellow, 1960-61; fellow Ctr. for Advanced Study in Behavioral Scis., 1975. Fellow Am. Acad. Arts and Scis., Inst. Math. Statistics (council 1969-72); mem. Inst. of Medicine of Nat. Acad. Scis., Am. Statis. Assn. (council 1966-67), Biometric Soc. (pres. Western N. Am. region 1969), Internat. Statis. Inst. Office: Stanford U Dept Stats Stanford CA 94305

MOSES, PAUL DAVIS, career officer; b. Quincy, Fla., Jan. 7, 1938; s. Lonnie Paul and Mary Virginia Moses; m. Mary Charles Davis, June 22, 1961; children: Paul Davis Jr., Daniel Charles. BS, U.S. Naval Acad., 1961; MS, George Washington U., 1971. Command. ensign USN, 1961, advanced through grades to rear adm., 1987; force readiness and tng. officer Naval Surface Force, Pacific Fleet, 1976-78; surface ops. and readiness officer Carrier Group 1, 1978-80; instr. Tactical Tng. Group Pacific, 1980-82; comdg. officer USS Halsey (CG-23), 1983-85; dir. surface and gen. unrestricted line officer distbn. div. Naval Mil. Pers. Command, 1985-87; comdr. Combat Logistics Group 2, 1987-88; dep. dir. plans and policy Hdqrs. U.S. European Command, 1988-91; chief staff Supreme Allied Comdr. Atlantic, Norfolk, Va., 1991-94; comdr. Norfolk (Va.) Naval Base, 1994—. Decorated Legion of Merit with two oak leaf clusters, Bronze Star. Mem. U.S. Naval Inst. Democrat. Office: Norfolk Naval Base 1530 Gilbert St Ste 200 Norfolk VA 23511-2797

MOSES, RAPHAEL JACOB, lawyer; b. Girard, Ala., Nov. 6, 1913; s. William Moultrie and Anna (Green) M.; m. Marian Eva Beck, Aug. 22, 1938 (dec. Feb. 1976); 1 child, Marcia (Mrs. William S. Johnson); m. Fletcher Lee Westgaard, Jan. 20, 1979. A.B., U. Colo., 1935, LL.B., 1937. Bar: Colo. 1938. Practiced in Alamosa, 1938-62, Boulder, 1962—; pres. Moses, Wittemyer, Harrison & Woodruff (P.C.), from 1970, now of counsel; spl. asst. atty. gen. Rio Grande Compact, 1957-58; mem. Colo. Water Conservation Bd., 1952-58, chmn., counsel, 1958-76, cons., 1976-77; research asso., faculty law U. Colo., 1962-66, vis. lectr., 1966-76, resident counsel, 1964-66, regent, 1973-74; grad. faculty Colo. State U., 1963-67; mem. Western States Water Council, 1965-77, chmn., 1966-70. Trustee Rocky Mountain Mineral Law Inst., 1964-66; bd. dirs. U. Colo. Found., 1977—, chmn., 1977-79, mem. chancellor's adv. coun., 1981—; bd. dirs. Colo. Open Lands, 1983-91, U. Colo. Improvement Corp., 1980-90, Colo. Endowment for Humanities, 1986-89; mem. adv. bd. Natural Resources Ctr., U. Colo. Sch. Law, 1983-92, chmn., 1986-88. Served to lt. (s.g.) USNR, 1942-45. Recipient William E. Knous award U. Colo. Sch. Law, 1971, Norlin award U. Colo. 1972; Raphael J. Moses Disting. Natural Resources professorship established U. Colo., 1994. Fellow Am. Bar Found. (life), Colo. Bar Found. (trustee 1977-90), Am. Coll. Trial Lawyers; mem. ABA (chmn. water rights com. sect. natural resources 1959-60), Colo. Bar Assn. (pres. 1959-60, Award of Merit 1972), San Luis Valley Bar Assn. (pres. 1942), Am. Counsel Assn., Order of Coif (hon.). Presbyterian (elder). Clubs: Univ. (Denver) Boulder Country; Garden of the Gods (Colorado Springs). Home: 7060 Roaring Fork Trl Boulder CO 80301-3635

MOSES, ROBERT DAVIS, retired diversified industry executive; b. Hartford, Conn., Jan. 4, 1919; s. Eli Morris and Ida (Lublin) M.; m. Greta Westerfeld, Aug. 22, 1942; m. Renee J. Wolfson, Nov. 28, 1992; children: Linda Joan (Mrs. Paul Litwin) Dana Elaine, Elliot Davis. B.S. in Mech. Engring. Mich. State U., 1940; M.B.A., U. Hartford, 1975. Structure design engr. McDonnell Aircraft Corp., 1940-44; chief structures Piasecki Helicopter, Springfield, Pa., 1946-50; with Kaman Aerospace Corp., Bloomfield, Conn., 1950-72; exec. v.p. Kaman Aerospace Corp., 1969-72; v.p. Kaman Corp., Bloomfield, 1972-84; pres. Airkaman Inc., Airkaman Jack-

sonville Inc., Airkaman Omaha Inc., Danelin Enterprise Inc.; dir. Gerber Systems Tech., Inc.; ret. Mem. Conn. Gov.'s Select Com. on Airport Noise Abatement; trustee Ward Sch., U. Hartford.; pres. Friendship Forces Conn.; state ombudsman Nat. Guard and Res. Forces. Served with AUS, 1944-46. Mem. Am. Helicopter Soc., Mfg. Assn. Conn. (dir.), Greater Hartford C. of C. (dir. policies com., aviation com., energy com.), Conn. C. of C. (dir.), Mich. State U. Alumni Assn. (pres. Conn. 1964).

MOSES, ROBERT EDWARD, lawyer; b. Syracuse, N.Y., Feb. 23, 1936; s. Robert Henry and Kathryn Anne (Schoeneck) M.; m. Virginia Joan Speno, July 23, 1970; children: Robert, Kathryn, Hope, Frank. Student, U. Fribourg, Switzerland, 1957; BS, Georgetown U., 1958, JD, 1960. Bar: N.Y. 1961, U.S. Ct. Appeals (2d cir.) 1966, U.S. Supreme Ct. 1967. Assoc. Bond, Schoeneck & King, Syracuse, 1960-70, mem., 1970-74, ptnr., 1974—. Bd. dirs. George Jr. Republic Assn., Inc., Freeville, N.Y., 1976-88; bd. govs. Georgetown U., Washington, 1983-89; bd. regents LeMoyne Coll., Syracuse, 1985—; mem. adv. bd., spl. counsel Nat. Sports Acad., Lake Placid, N.Y., 1990-93. Lt. (j.g.) USCG, 1961-66. Mem. ABA, N.Y. State Bar Assn. (chmn. young lawyers sect. 1971-72, mem. exec. com. 1971-72, ho. of dels. 1972-75), Onondaga County Bar Assn.. Onondaga County Bar Found. (bd. dirs. 1978—, pres. 1988-89), Am. Judicature Soc., Am. Arbitration Assn. (panel arbitrators 1969—), N.Y. State Econ. Devel. Coun. (mem. state legis. com. 1983—, chmn. 1983), Century Club, Ft. Orange Club, Skaneateles Country Club. Republican. Roman Catholic. Home: West Lake Rd Otisco Lake Marietta NY 13110 Office: Bond Schoeneck & King 1 Lincoln Ctr Fl 18 Syracuse NY 13202-1324

MOSES, RONALD ELLIOT, retired toiletries products executive; b. Chelsea, Mass., Dec. 29, 1930; s. Isadore Philip and Ida (Finstein) M.; m. Eleanor Antoinette Vitale, June 22, 1952; children: Judith Jeanne, Thomas Charles. AB, Harvard U., 1952; MS in Chemistry, Northeastern U., Boston, 1959. Chemist Gen. Foods Corp., Woburn, Mass., 1954-60; sr. chemist Gillette Safety Razor Co., Boston, 1960-65, project chemist toiletries div., 1965-70, sr. mgr. rsch. toiletries div., 1970-73, dir. product devel. toiletries div., 1973-78, dir. product devel. personal care div., 1978-83, v.p. R&D personal care div., 1983-87; v.p. R&D personal care group Gillette North Atlantic, Boston, 1987-90, dir. R&D shaving and personal care group, 1990-91, v.p. R & D Toiletries Techs. Lab., 1991-93. Co-patentee gelatin fining and preparation, shaving product composition, hair conditioning composition. Lt. (j.g.) USN, 1952. Fellow Am. Inst. Chemists; mem. Am. Chem. Soc., Soc. Cosmetic Chemists, Winthrop Golf Club. Jewish. Avocations: classical music, reading, golf, model ships, computer programming. Home: 1039 Shirley St Winthrop MA 02152-1442

MOSETTIG, MICHAEL DAVID, television producer, writer; b. Washington, July 21, 1942; s. Erich and Ann (Nelson) M.; m. Anne L. Groer. Student, Ind. U., 1960-61; BA in Polit. Sci., George Washington U., 1964; MA in European History, Georgetown U., 1968. Reporter Leslie E. Carpenter News Bur., Washington, 1961-65, Newhouse Nat. News Svc., Washington, 1965-69, UPI, London and Brussels, 1969-70; editor, reporter Nat. Jour., Washington, 1970-71; producer NBC News, Washington and N.Y.C., 1971-79; assoc. Grad. Sch. Journalism Columbia U., N.Y.C., 1979-83; producer MacNeil/Lehrer News Hour, 1983-85, sr. producer fgn. affairs and def., 1985—; mem. internat. inst. for Strategic Studies, London, Coun. Fgn. Rels., N.Y. Author: DeGaulle and His Anglo-Saxon Allies, 1968, (with Ronald Müller) Revitalizing America, 1980. With USCGR, 1966-68, USNR, 1968-78. Herman Lowe Meml. scholar Washington chpt. Sigma Delta Chi; Joan Barone award Radio-TV Corrs. Assn. Mem. Overseas Writers, Cosmos Club. Home: 3340 Northampton St NW Washington DC 20015-1653

MOSHER, DONALD RAYMOND, chemical engineer, consultant; b. Mpls., Jan. 7, 1930; s. Cleveland Bert and Rose (Alkofer) M.; m. Jane Lucille Ryan, June 20, 1954 (div. Dec. 1989); children: Leslie Renee Mosher Goode, Lee David, Laura Ann Mosher Flanders, Jennifer Lynn Mosher Konzen, Jill Teresa, Jody Lavonne; m. Lurlie Elizabeth Amsler, Dec. 19, 1992. BSChemE, U. Minn., 1953, MS, 1954. Prodn. area engr. U.S. Chem. Corps., Edgewood, Md., 1955-57; mng. engr. Union Carbide Corp., South Charleston, W.Va., 1957-68; cons. in new ventures Union Carbide Linde Div., Tanawhonda, N.Y., 1968-69; chief engr. design Hess Oil Corp., Woodbridge, N.J., 1969-70; plant mgr. Stearns Roger Ops., Rapid City, S.D., 1970-72; mgr. engring. sect. Stearns Roger Corp., Denver, 1972-82; mgr. gas process and environ. Allis Chalmers Coal Gas Corp., Milw., 1982-88; cons. Ralston Internat. Trading Assn. Inc., Kingsport, Tenn., 1988—, EG & G Analytical Svcs. Inc., Morgantown, W.Va., 1989—. Author conf. reports; contbr. articles to profl. jours. Chmn. South Hills Community Assn., Charleston, 1967; mem. sponsor's com. So. Ill. U., 1986. With U.S. Army, 1955-57. Univ. and AEC scholar, 1952-54. Mem. Am. Inst. Chem. Engrs. (treas. local sect. 1963), Am. Chem. Soc., Assn. Cons. Chemists and Chem. Engrs. (cons. 1989—), Police Star Found. Tex., Rotary, Phi Kappa (v.p. 1952-54), Phi Beta Epsilon. Republican. Roman Catholic. Achievements include patent for oxidation of butane; invention of system for conserving energy while cleaning dirty gas, of system for removing oil and tar from water with no discharge. Office: D R Mosher Corp PO Box 820295 Houston TX 77282-0295

MOSHER, GEORGE ALLAN, distribution company executive; b. Detroit, June 21, 1939; s. Carroll Leonard and Susan (Harris) M.; m. Julie Zaber, Dec. 31, 1966; children: Karen, Holly, Robert. AB, Harvard U., 1961, MBA, 1963. With sales promotion dept. Look mag., 1963-65; pres. Bus. & Instl. Furniture Co., Milw., 1965-75, Nat. Bus. Furniture Co., Milw., 1975—; chmn. Bus. Mailers, 1976; pres. Alfax Mfg. Co., N.Y.C., 1984—; Office Furniture Ctr., Boston, 1986—, Dallas Midwest, 1990—. Bd. dirs. Milw. Pub. Affairs Coun., 1975-84, v.p., 1982-83; bd. dirs. Future Milw., 1979-82, Vol. Ctr., 1988-91, Communique, 1986-90, Nat. Hospitality Supply, 1990—, Milw. Bus. Forum, 1975—, Capital Commerce Bancorp, 1994—. Mem. Wis. Direct Mktg. (founder, pres. 1987-88. Marketer of Yr. award 1991), Univ. Club, River Tennis Club (treas. 1983-86), Harvard Bus. Sch. Club (pres. 1973), Rotary, Harvard Club (Milw., N.Y.C.). Home: 4706 N Wilshire Rd Milwaukee WI 53211-1262 Office: 222 E Michigan St Milwaukee WI 53202-4910

MOSHER, GILES EDMUND, JR., banker; b. Boston, Jan. 1, 1933; s. Giles Edmund and Mary (Downs) M.; m. Thelma Ann Doyle, Sept. 22, 1956; children: Mary Beth, Susan, Michelle, Giles Edmund III, Alison, Caitlyn. BSBA, Boston Coll., 1955; postgrad., Northwestern U. Sch. Fin. Pub. Rels., 1963, Stonier Sch. Banking Rutgers U., 1975. With Newton-Waltham Bank & Trust Co., Waltham, Mass., 1959—; mgr. credit dept. Newton-Waltham Bank & Trust Co., 1959-60, asst. treas., 1960-62, asst. v.p., 1962-64, v.p., 1964-65, sr. v.p., 1965-68, exec. v.p., 1968-70, pres., 1970-79; pres., chmn. bd. BayBank Middlesex, Burlington, Mass., 1979—; chmn. Baybank Fin. and Leasing Corp.; dir. Mass. Bus. Devel. Corp.; Mem. fin. and adminstrn. adv. com. Archdiocese of Boston. Trustee Inner City Fund, Newton-Wellesley Hosp.; trustee, adminstrn. and finance com., corp. com., exec. com. St. Elizabeth's Hosp., Brighton, Mass.; bd. dirs. Mass. Taxpayers Found.; bd. dirs. northeastern div. NCCJ; trustee (assoc.) Boston Coll., 1973, former mem. endowment investment com.; mem. Mass. Gov.'s Com. on Criminal Justice, 1979—; treas. Equestrian Order of the Holy Sepulchre of Jerusalem. Named Man of Year City of Newton, 1960; recipient Bronze medallion Boys Clubs Am., 1964; Named One of Ten Outstanding Young Men of Greater Boston Jr. C. of C., 1964, One of Four Outstanding Young Men of Mass., 1965, One of Five Outstanding Young Men of New Eng. 1966; recipient Brandeis U. Disting. Community Service award, 1975, Disting. Citizen's award Minuteman Council Boy Scouts Am., 1980. Mem. Newton Taxpayers Assn. (dir.), Newton Bankers Assn. (pres.), Am. Banking Assn. (bd. govs. Boston chpt.), Newton C. of C. (pres. 1967), Boston Coll. Alumni Assn. (pres. 1970), Alpha Gamma Sigma. (hon. mem. award 1967). Club: Brae Burn Country (West Newton, Mass.) (chmn. fin. com.). Home: 227 Windsor Rd Newton MA 02168-1119 Office: 7 New Eng Exec Park Burlington MA 01803

MOSHER, HOWARD IRA, automotive executive; b. Boston, Nov. 29, 1946; s. Howard I. and Carolyn Hamilton M.; m. Cynthia Potter Eames, Apr. 18, 1966; children: Mark, Christopher. AB, Colby Coll. 1968; MBA, Boston U., 1971. Mktg. mgr. Atlantic Richfield Co., New Haven, 1968-69; zone mgr., dir. mktg., dir. sales ops. Am. Motors Corp., Detroit, Southfield,

Mich., 1971-84; v.p mktg. Rolls-Royce Motor Cars Inc., Lyndhurst, N.J., 1984-86, pres., chief exec. officer, 1988-94; v.p. retail ops. Land Rover N.Am., Lanham, Md., 1994—; dir. product planning Rolls-Royce Motor Cars Ltd., Crewe, Eng., 1986-88; pres. Cantieri Riva Inc., Lyndhurst, 1990-94. Brit. Am. Ch. Commerce bd. dirs. Madison Sq. Boys and Girls Club, N.Y.C., 1986-95. Mem. Brit. Automobile Mfrs. Assn. N.Am. (pres. 1990-94), Automotive Golf Soc. (U.K.), Ridgewood (N.J.) Country Club, Royal Liverpool Golf Club (West Kirby, Eng.). Republican. Presbyterian. Office: Rolls-Royce Motor Cars Inc 120 Chubb Ave Lyndhurst NJ 07071

MOSHER, LAWRENCE FORSYTH, journalist; b. L.A., July 12, 1929; s. Jack Marsh and Alice (Forsyth) M.; m. Constance Bauerlein, 1963 (div. 1980); children: Kirsten Louise, Honor Forsyth. BA, Stanford U., 1952; B Fgn. Trade, Am. Grad. Sch. Internat. Mgmt., 1956. Reporter Bergen Record, Hackensack, N.J., 1958-59, N.Y. World-Telegram & Sun, N.Y.C., 1959-62; staff writer, then Beirut bur. chief Copley News Svc., San Diego, 1962-67; staff corr. The Nat. Observer, Silver Spring, Md., 1967-77; staff writer, then contbg. editor Nat. Jour., Washington, 1979-88; editor The Water Reporter, Washington, 1984-90; resident journalist Environ. Health Ctr., Washington, 1988-89; mng. editor Middle East Insight, Washington, 1989-90; editor High Country News, Paonia, Colo., 1990-91; Rocky Mountain corr. The Economist, 1991—; news dir. Sta. KVNF pub. radio Paonia, Colo., 1992-93; writer-in-residence Fgn. Svc. Sch. Georgetown U., Washington, 1977-79, Ctr for Contemporary Arab Studies. Contbr. chpts. to America's Wild and Scenic Rivers, 1983, Bordering on Trouble: Resources and Politics in Latin America, 1986, World Resources, 1987-89. Lt. (j.g.) USNR, 1952-54, Korea. Named Communicator of Yr., Nat. Wildlife Fedn. 1982. Mem. Nat. Press Club, Potomac Rowing Club. Democrat. Avocations: choral music, sailing, sculling, horseback riding, skiing. Home and Office: 323 4200 Dr Crawford CO 81415

MOSHER, PAUL H., research library administrator, author, consultant; b. Portland, Oreg., Jan. 3, 1936; s. Harold Clarke and Leona (Hostetler) M.; m. Judith Johnston, 1958 (div. 1969); 1 child, Colin; m. Jennie Nicolayev, Feb. 23, 1981 (div. 1989); 1 child, Katherine Alexandra. BA, Portland State U., 1961; MA, U. Calif., Berkeley, 1962, PhD, 1969. Mgmt. analyst Legis. Counsel Com., Salem, Oreg., 1958-60; dir. Upward Bound Program U. Wash., Seattle, 1962-63, asst. prof. history, 1966-75; asst. dir. collection devel. Stanford U. Libraries, Calif., 1975-79, assoc. dir. collection devel., 1979-84, dir. research services, 1984-85, dep. dir. libraries, 1985-88; vice provost, dir. librs., adj. prof. history U. Pa., Phila., 1988—; vis. prof. Trinity Coll. of Hartford, Conn. in Rome, 1971, 72, 73; cons. U. Chgo., 1978, Lilly Endowment, 1979, U. Minn. Library, Mpls., 1980, U. Alaska and Alaska State Library, Fairbanks and Juneau, 1982-84, U. Alaska, Juneau, 1983-84, Swedish Del. for Sci. and Tech. Info., Uppsala, Stockholm, Umeå, Goteborg, Lund, Linkoping, Sweden, 1984, U. of Pacific, 1984, Oreg. State U., Corvallis, 1985, N.Y. Pub. Library, 1985, 86, Fred Meyer Charitable Trust, 1986, 89, Oreg. State Library Found., 1986, N.Mex. State U., 1988, U. So. Calif., 1989, Chgo. Pub. Library, 1989, Mich. State U., 1991, U. de Montreal, Can., 1991, McGill U., 1992; cons. external rev. of library Calif. State U.-Long Beach, 1981; Rsch. Librs. Group vice chmn. collection mgmt. and devel. com., 1979-85, bd. dirs., 1988-91, mem. exec. com., 1990-91; chmn. Research Libraries Group Task Force on the RLG Conspectus, 1982-85, bd. govs. 1982-88, bd. dirs., 1988-91; chair bd. 1992—, mem. Assn. Rsch. Librs. adv. com. to N.Am. collections inventory project, 1983-86, com. on rsch. collections, 1989-91, com. on preservation, 1992-93, access to res. cons. com., 1993—; instr. Sch. Library and Info. Sci., U. Calif.-Berkeley, 1980; vis. scholar U. Nebr., Lincoln, 1987; Contbr. articles to profl. jours. Mem. univ. libr. com. Brown U., 1989-92; adv. coun. Drexel U. Coll. of Info. Studies, 1989-94. Recipient Blackwell N.Am. award, 1983; Italian-Am. traveling fellow U. Calif.-Berkeley, 1965-66, Fulbright-Hays sr. research scholar, Italy, 1971; sr. fellow Council on Library Resources, UCLA Grad. Sch. Library and Info. Sci., 1983-84. Fellow Royal Soc. Arts, Manufacture Commerce; mem. ALA (mem. resources and tech. services div., chmn., chief collection devel. officers of large research libraries 1978-79, chmn. resources sect. 1980-81, chmn. nominating com. 1983-84, councillor, bd. dirs. 1986-87, chmn. pubs. com. 1987-88, assn. councillor-at-large 1988-92, mem. planning com. 1987-89, 90-92, self-study steering com., 1992—), Assn. Coll. and Research Libraries (standards and accreditation com. 1981-83, planning com. western European specialists sect. 1980-84), Medieval Assn. Pacific (councillor 1977-80), Balch Inst. for Ethics Studies (bd. dirs. 1988-92). Clubs: Cosmos (Washington), Grolier (N.Y.C.). Avocations: book and wine collecting; reading; running; swimming; photography. Home: 2033 Pine St Philadelphia PA 19103-6522 Office: Van Pelt Library U Pa 3420 Walnut St Philadelphia PA 19104

MOSHMAN, JACK, statistical consultant; b. Richmond Hill, N.Y., Aug. 12, 1924; s. Morris and Sadye (Pomper) M.; m. Annette Gordon, Aug. 10, 1947; children: Gordon, Marc, Sherri, Ira. BA, NYU, 1946; MA, Columbia U., 1947; PhD, U. Tenn., 1953. Instr. Queens Coll., Flushing, N.Y., 1946-47, U. Tenn., Knoxville, 1947-53; statistician U.S. AEC, Oak Ridge, Tenn., 1948-50; sr. statistician Oak Ridge Nat. Labs., Oak Ridge, 1950-54; mem. tech. staff Bell Tel. Labs., Murray Hill, N.J., 1954-57; v.p. C-E-I-R Inc., Washington, 1957-66; mng. dir. EBS Mgmt. Cons., Washington, 1966-68; sr. v.p. Leasco Systems & Rsch., Bethesda, Md., 1968-69; pres. Moshman assocs. Inc., Bethesda, Md., 1970—; adj. prof. Rutgers U., 1963-66; professorial lectr. George Washington U., 1959-62; chmn. Inst. for Safety Analysis, Rockville, Md., 1975-89. Editor: Faith, Hope & Parity, 1967; author Ency. sect. Computers & Politics, 1985, 90, 93; contbr. articles to profl. jours. Trustee Babbage Found., St. Paul, 1983-87. With U.S.Army, 1943-46, ETO. Fellow Am. Statis. Assn. (coun. 1956, 58); mem. Am. Fedn. Info. Processing Soc. Am. (bd. dirs. pres. 1986-87), Assn. for Computing Machinery (sec. 1956-64, v.p 1964), Inst. for Math. Stats., Inst. for Mgmt. Scis., Ops. Rsch. Soc. Am., Biometrics Soc. Avocation: psephology. Office: Moshman Assocs Inc 7315 Wisconsin Ave # 410-N Bethesda MD 20814

MOSICH, ANELIS NICK, accountant, author, educator, consultant; b. Yugoslavia, Aug. 30, 1928; came to U.S., 1939, naturalized 1951; s. Dinko and Josephine (Ursich) M.; m. Dorothy V. Rasich, June 15, 1958; children: Lori, Lisa, Jeffrey. BS, UCLA, 1951, MBA, 1953, PhD (fellow), 1963. CPA, Calif. Mem. faculty UCLA, 1955-63, Calif. State U., Northridge, 1963-64; examiner for Calif. State Bd. Accountancy, 1964-70; prof. acctg. U. So. Calif., Los Angeles, 1964-74; William C. Hallett prof. acctg. U. So. Calif., 1974-81, Ernst & Young prof., 1981-90, chmn. acctg. dept., 1970-74, 77-78, prof. emeritus, 1993; cons. various bus. orgns., 1953—; expert witness; bd. dirs. Western Waste Industries; guest speaker various profl. and bus. groups in Calif., Oreg., N.Y., Tex., Fla., and Hawaii, 1963-93. Author: Intermediate Accounting, rev. 6th edit., 1989, Financial Accounting, 1970, 75, Accounting: A Basis for Business Decision, 1972, Modern Advanced Accounting, 4th edit., 1988, The CPA Examination: Text, Problems and Solutions, 1978; editor: Education column Calif. CPA Quar., 1965-66; contbg. editor: Education and Professional Training column Jour. Accountancy, 1971-77; contbr. numerous articles to jours. and acctg. Served with U.S. Army, 1953-55. Recipient Dean's award Sch. Bus. Adminstrn., U. So. Calif., 1973, 78, Fred B. Olds Support Group award U. So. Calif., 1994. Mem. AICPA, Calif. Soc. CPAs. Office: U So Calif Sch Acctg University Park Los Angeles CA 90007

MOSIER, ARVIN RAY, chemist, researcher; b. Olney Springs, Colo., June 11, 1945; s. Isaac James Ellen Rena (Ross) M.; m. Susan Minnick, Dec. 30, 1965; children: Andrew, Katherine. BS, Colo. State U., 1967, MS, 1967-68, PhD, 1974. Chemist agr. research services USDA, Ft. Collins, 1967—; Contbr. papers and book chpt. to profl. publ. Mem. AAAS, Am. Soc. Agronomy, Soil Sci. Soc. Am., Internat. Soil Sci. Sco., Council Agrl. Sci. Tech., Phi Kappa Phi, Sigma XI, Gamma Sigma Delta. Republican. Methodist. Club: Aresnal Competitive Soccer. Avocations: tennis, soccer. Home: 903 Hilldale Dr Fort Collins CO 80526-4345 Office: USDA Agrl Rsch Svc PO Box E Fort Collins CO 80522-0470

MOSIER, HARRY DAVID, JR., physician, educator; b. Topeka, May 22, 1925; s. Harry David and Josephine Morrow (Johnson) M.; m. Nadine Oclea Merialtt, Aug. 24, 1949; children: Carolyn Josephine Mosier Polhlmeyer, William David, Daniel Thomas, Christine Elizabeth Mosier Mahoney; m. Marjorie Knight Armstrong, Sept. 26, 1963. B.S. magna cum laude, U. Notre Dame, 1948; M.D., Johns Hopkins U., 1952. Diplomate Am. Bd. Pediatrics, Am. Bd. Pediatric Endocrinology. Intern Johns Hopkins Hosp., Balt., 1952-53; resident in pediatrics Los Angeles Children's Hosp., 1953-54, resident pediatric pathology, 1954-55; fellow pediatric endocrinology Johns Hopkins U., 1955-57; asst. prof. pediatrics UCLA, 1957-61, assoc. prof., 1961-63; dir. research Ill. State Pediatric Inst., Chgo., 1963-67; assoc. prof. U. Ill., 1963-67; prof. pediatrics, head div. pediatric endocrinology U. Calif.-Irvine, 1967—; staff Children's Hosp. Med. Center, Long Beach, Calif., 1970—, U. Calif. Irvine Med. Center, Orange, 1979—. Contbr. articles to med. jours. With AUS, 1943-46, col. U.S. Army Med. Corps, 1990-91, Persian Gulf War. USAR Med. Corps. 1952-62, 83-93 (ret.). Office: U Calif Dept Pediatrics Irvine CA 92717

MOSIG, GISELA, molecular biology educator; b. Schmorkau, Fed. Republic of Germany, Nov. 29, 1930; d. Hilde (Pilz) M. PhD, U. Köln, Fed. Republic of Germany. Postdoctoral rsch. fellow Carnegie Inst. Washington, Cold Spring Harbor, N.Y., 1962-65; postdoctoral rsch. fellow Vanderbilt U., Nashville, 1959-62, from asst. prof. molecular biology, 1965-67, assoc. prof., 1967-71, prof., 1971—; mem. adv. com. on microbiology and virology Am. Cancer Soc., Atlanta, 1987-91; mem. study sect. on microbial chemistry NIH, Bethesda, Md., 1977-81. Recipient Humboldt (Found.) Sr. Scientist award, Fed. Republic of Germany, 1976. Mem. AAAS, Am. Soc. for Microbiology (chairperson div. MII 1983), Am. Soc. Plant Physiologists, Genetics Soc. Am. (assoc. editor Genetics 1976-90), Am. Acad. Microbiology. Home: 1923 18th Ave S Nashville TN 37212-3803 Office: Vanderbilt Univ PO Box 1820 Nashville TN 37235-1820

MOSK, RICHARD MITCHELL, lawyer; b. L.A., May 18, 1939; s. Stanley and Edna M.; m. Sandra Lee Budnitz, Mar. 21, 1964; children: Julie, Matthew. AB with great distinction, Stanford U., 1960; JD cum laude, Harvard U., 1963. Bar: Calif. 1964, U.S. Supreme Ct. 1970, U.S. Ct. Mil. Appeals 1970, U.S. Dist. Ct. (no., so., ea., and cen. dists.) Calif 1964, U.S. Ct. Appeals (9th cir.) 1964. Mem. staff Pres.'s Commn. on Assassination Pres. Kennedy, 1964; research clk. Calif. Supreme Ct., 1964-65; ptnr. Mitchell, Silberberg & Knupp, L.A., 1965-87; prin. Sanders, Barnet, Goldman, Simons & Mosk, P.C., L.A., 1987—; spl. dep. Fed. Pub. Defender, L.A., 1975-76; instr. U. So. Calif. Law Sch., 1978; arbitrator Iran-U.S. Claims Tribunal, 1981-84, substitute arbitrator 1984—; mem. Los Angeles County Jud. Procedures Commn., 1973-82, chmn., 1978; bd. dirs. Internat. Arbitration Commn.; mem. adv. coun. Asia/Pacific Ctr. for Resolution Internat. Trade Disputes, 1986—; chmn. Motion Picture Assn. Classification and Rating Adminstrn., 1994—. Contbr. articles to profl. jours. Mem. L.A. City-County Inquiry on Brush Firs, 1970; bd. dirs. Calif. Mus. Sci. and Industry, 1979-82, Vista Del Mar Child Ctr., 1979-82; trustee L.A. County Law Libr., 1985-86; bd. govs. Town Hall Calif., 1986-91; mem. Christopher Commn. on L.A. Police Dept., 1991; mem. Stanford U. Athletic Bd., 1991—. Served with USNR, 1964-75. Hon. Woodrow Wilson fellow, 1960; recipient Roscoe Pound prize, 1961. Fellow Am. Bar Found.; mem. ABA (coun. internat. law sect. 1986-90), FBA (pres. L.A. chpt. 1972), L.A. County Bar Assn., Beverly Hills Bar Assn., L.A. Assn. Bus. Trial Lawyers, Internat. Bar Assn., Am. Arbitration Assn. (comml. panel, large complex case panel, Asia/Pacific panel), Hong Kong Internat. Arbitration Ctr. (mem. panel 1986—), Am. Film Mktg. Assn. (arbitration panel), L.A. Ctr. Internat. Comml. Arbitration, B.C. Internat. Arbitration Ctr. (mem. panel), World Intellectual Property Orgn. (mem. arbitration panel), Ctr. Pub. Resources (mem. arbitration panel), Phi Beta Kappa. Office: Sanders Barnet Goldman Simons & Mosk 1901 Avenue Of The Stars Los Angeles CA 90067-6078

MOSK, STANLEY, state supreme court justice; b. San Antonio, Sept. 4, 1912; s. Paul and Minna (Perl) M.; m. Edna Mitchell, Sept. 27, 1937 (dec.); 1 child, Richard Mitchell; m. Susan Hines, Aug. 27, 1982 (div.); m. Kaygey Kash, Jan. 15, 1995. Student, U. Tex., 1931; Ph.B., U. Chgo., 1933; postgrad., U. Chgo. Law Sch., 1934; JD, Southwestern U., 1935; postgrad., Hague Acad. Internat. Law, 1970, U. Pacific, 1970; LLD, U. San Diego, 1971, U. Santa Clara, 1976, Calif. Western U., 1984, Southwestern U., 1987, Whittier Coll. Law, 1993; postgrad., Pepperdine U., 1995. Bar: Calif. 1935, U.S. Supreme Ct. 1956. Practiced in Los Angeles, until 1939; exec. sec. to gov. Calif., 1939-42; judge Superior Ct. Los Angeles County, 1943-58; pro tem justice Dist. Ct. Appeal, Calif., 1954; atty. gen. Calif., also head state dept., justice, 1959-64; justice Supreme Ct. Calif., 1964—; mem. Jud. Council Calif., 1973-75, Internat. Commn. Jurists. Chmn. San Francisco Internat. Film Festival, 1967; mem. Dem. Nat. Com., Calif., 1960-64; bd. regents U. Calif., 1940; pres. Vista Del Mar Child Care Service, 1954-58; bd. dirs. San Francisco Law Sch., 1971-73, San Francisco Regional Cancer Found., 1980-83. Served with AUS, World War II. Recipient Disting. Alumnus award U. Chgo., 1958, 93. Mem. ABA, Nat. Assn. Attys. Gen. (exec. bd. 1964), Western Assn. Attys. Gen. (pres. 1963), Calif. Bar Assn., L.A. Bar Assn., San Francisco Bar Assn., Am. Legion, Manuscript Soc., Calif. Hist. Soc., Am. Judicature Soc., Internat. Jud. Adminstrn., U. Chgo. Alumni Assn. No. Calif. (pres. 1957-58, 67), Order of Coif, B'nai B'rith, Hillcrest Country Club (L.A.), Commonwealth Club, Golden Gateway Tennis Club (San Francisco), Beverly Hills Tennis Club. Office: Supreme Ct Calif 303 2nd St San Francisco CA 94107-1366

MOSKAL, ROBERT M., bishop; b. Carnegie, Pa., Oct. 24, 1937; s. William and Jean (Popivchak) M. BA, St. Basil Coll. Sem., Stamford, Conn., 1959; lic. sacred theology, Cath. U. Am., 1963; student, Phila. Mus. Acad. and Conservatory of Mus., 1963-66. Ordained priest Ukrainian Cath. Ch. 1963. Founder, pastor St. Anne's Ukrainian Cath. Ch., Warrington, Pa., 1963-72; sec. Archbishop's Chancery, Phila., 1963-67; apptd. vice-chancellor Archeparchy of Phila., 1967-74; pastor Annunciation Ukrainian Cath. Ch., Melrose Park, Phila., 1972-74; named monsignor, 1974; chancellor archidiocese, pastor Ukrainian Cath. Cathedral of the Immaculate Conception, Phila., 1974-84; apptd. bishop, 1981; Ordained titular bishop of Agathopolis and aux. bishop Ukrainian-Rite Archeparchy of Phila., 1981-83; first bishop Diocese of St. Josaphat, Parma, Ohio, 1983—; pro-synodal judge Archidiocean Tribunal, Phila., 1965-67; founder Ukrainian Cath. Hour: God is with Us, Sta. WIBF-FM, Phila, 1972-77; Christ Among Us, Sat. WTEL, 1975—; mem. Ukrainian Cath. Ch. Liturgical Subcommn., 1980; host to His Holiness Pope John Paul II. Bd. dirs. Ascension Manor, Inc., Phila., 1964-84, sec.-treas., 1964-78, exec. v.p., 1977-84. Office: PO Box 347180 5720 State Rd Parma OH 44134-2500*

MOSKIN, JOHN ROBERT, editor, writer; b. N.Y.C., May 9, 1923; s. Morris and Irma (Rosenfeld) M.; m. Doris Marianne Bloch, Oct. 7, 1948 (div. 1978); children: Mark Douglas, David Scott, Nancy Irma; m. Lynn Carole Goldberg, Apr. 10, 1986. Grad., Horace Mann Sch., 1940; B.S., Harvard U., 1944; M.A., Columbia U., 1947. Reporter Boston Post, 1941-42, Newark News, 1947-48; asst. to gen. mgr. N.Y. Star, 1948-49; editor Westport (Conn.) Town Crier, 1949; med. editor Look mag., N.Y.C., 1950-51; articles editor Look mag., 1951-53, sr. editor, 1956-66, fgn. editor, 1966-71; mng. editor Woman's Home Companion, 1953-56; sr. editor Collier's, 1956; editor at large Saturday Rev., 1972-75; sr. editor World Press Rev., 1976-87, contbg. editor, 1987-93; editorial dir. Aspen Inst. Humanistic Studies, 1977-83; editorial dir. Commonwealth Fund, 1984-87, sr. editorial advisor, 1987-93. Author: (with others) The Decline of the American Male, 1958, Morality in America, 1966, Turncoat, 1968, The U.S. Marine Corps Story, 1977, 82, 87, 92, Among Lions, 1982, (with Julia Vitullo-Martin) The Executive's Book of Quotations, 1994; mem. editorial adv. com. Dimensions mag, 1970-71, Present Tense, 1973-90. Trustee Scarsdale Adult Sch., 1965-72, chmn., 1969-70; mem. Dana Reed Prize com. Harvard, 1947—; mem. com. Class of 1944, 1943—; mem. communications screening com. Council Internat. Exchange of Scholars, 1974-77, President's Coun. Heritage Coll., 1995—; bd. dirs. SIECUS, 1972-80, Jerusalem Found., 1977—, Marine Corps Hist. Found., 1979-82, 89—, Faculty for Continuing Med. Edn., 1983-86. Served with AUS, 1943-46. Recipient Benjamin Franklin gold medal for pub. service Woman's Home Companion, 1955, Page One award Newspaper Guild N.Y., 1965, Sidney Hillman Found. award, 1965; National Headliners award, 1967; Overseas Press Club award, 1969; citation for excellence, 1971; Disting. Service award Marine Corps Combat Corrs. Assn., 1978; Nat. Jewish Book award, 1983. Mem. Am. Hist. Assn., Authors Guild, Fgn. Editors Group (chmn. 1970-71), Nat. Press Club (Washington), Overseas Press Club (gov. 1975-79), Century Club, Harvard Club (N.Y.C.), Lotos Club, (bd. dirs. 1988-90, 94— pres. 1991-94), Sigma Delta Chi (mem. nat. freedom of info. com. 1964, 71). Home: 945 Fifth Ave New York NY 10021-2655 also: 157 Jerusalem Rd Tyringham MA 01264

MOSKIN, MORTON, lawyer; b. N.Y.C., Mar. 28, 1927; s. Barnett and Sonia (Burr) M.; m. Rita Lee Goldberg, June 15, 1952; children: Tina, Ilene,

Jonathan. B.A., Pa. State Coll., 1947; LL.B., Cornell U., 1950. Assoc. White & Case, N.Y.C., 1950-61, ptnr., 1962-94, cons., 1995—; chmn. exec. com. Mallinckrodt Group (formerly IMCERA, previously Internat. Minerals & Chem. Corp.), St. Louis, 1988-91, chmn. corp. governance com., 1993—, also bd. dirs.; sec. BT Mortgage Investors, Garden City, N.J., 1975-82. Bd. dirs. Fedn. Employment and Guidance Svcs.; bd. dirs., pres. Henry M. Blackmer Found., N.Y.C., Achievement Found., to 1994, Stamford, Conn.; bd. dirs. Jewish Cmty. Svcs. L.I., 1974-93, pres., 1984-87. Fellow Am. Bar Found.; mem. ABA, N.Y. State Bar Assn., N.Y. County Lawyers Assn. (dir. 1981-86), Am. Judicature Soc. Clubs: Norfolk Country (Conn.). Home: 1160 Park Ave Apt 15B New York NY 10128-1212 Office: White & Case 1155 Ave of the Americas New York NY 10036-2711

MOSKOS, CHARLES C., sociology educator; b. Chgo., May 20, 1934; s. Charles and Rita (Shukas) M.; m. Ilca Hohn, July 3, 1966; children—Andrew, Peter. B.A. cum laude, Princeton, 1956; M.A., UCLA, 1961, Ph.D., 1963; L.H.D. (hon.), Norwich U., 1992. Asst. prof. U. Mich., Ann Arbor, 1964-66; assoc. prof. sociology Northwestern U., Evanston, Ill., 1966-70, prof., 1970—; fellow Progressive Policy Inst., 1992—; mem. Presdl. Commn. on Women in the Mil., 1992. Author: The Sociology of Political Independence, 1967, The American Enlisted Man, 1970, Public Opinion and the Military Establishment, 1971, Peace Soldiers, 1976, Fuerzas Armadas y Sociedad, 1984, The Military--More Than Just a Job?, 1988, A Call to Civic Service, 1988, Greek Americans, 1989, Soldiers and Sociology, 1989, New Directions in Greek American Studies, 1991, The New Conscientious Objection, 1993. Mem. bd. advisors Dem. Leadership Coun., 1989—; chmn. Theodore Saloutos Meml. Fund; mem. Archdiocesean Commn. Third Millenium, 1982-88. Served with AUS, 1956-58. Decorated D.S.M., Fondation pour les Etudes de Def. Nat. (France), S.M.K. (The Netherlands); named to Marshall rsch. chair ARI, 1987-88; Ford Found. faculty fellow, 1969-70; fellow Wilson Ctr., 1980-81, guest scholar, 1991; fellow Rockefeller Found. Humanities, 1983-84, Guggenheim fellow, 1992-93, fellow Annenberg Washington Program, 1995; grantee 20th Century Fund, 1983-87, 92-94, Ford Found., 1989-90. Mem. Praesidium Russia Assn. Armed Forces and Soc. Am. Sociol. Assn., Internat. Sociol. Assn. (pres. rsch. com on armed forces and conflict resolution 1982-86), Am. Polit. Sci. Assn., Inter-Univ. Seminar on Armed Forces and Soc. (chmn. 1987—). Greek Orthodox. Home: 2440 Asbury Ave Evanston IL 60201-2307

MOSKOW, MICHAEL H., federal official; b. Paterson, N.J., Jan. 7, 1938; s. Jacob and Sylvia (Edelstein) M.; m. Constance Bain, Dec. 18, 1966; children: Robert Bain, Eliot Marc, Lisa Danielle. AB, Lafayette Coll., Easton, Pa., 1959; MA in Econs., U. Pa., 1962, PhD, 1965. Instr. econs. Lafayette Coll., 1964-65; asst. prof. mgmt. Drexel Inst. Tech., Phila., 1963-64, 65-67; assoc. prof. econs., dir. Bus. Econ. and Bus. Research, Temple U. Phila., 1967-69; sr. staff economist Council Econ. Advisers, Washington, 1969-70; exec. dir. Constrn. Industry Collective Bargaining Commn., 1970-71; dep. under sec. U.S. Dept. Labor, 1971-72, asst. sec. for policy, evaluation and research, 1972-73; asst. sec. for policy devel. and research HUD, 1973-75; dir. Council on Wage and Price Stability, 1975-76; under-sec. labor U.S. Dept. Labor, 1976-77; cons. Com. for Econ. Devel., 1977; dir. corp. devel. and planning Esmark, Inc., 1977-78, v.p. corp. devel. and planning, 1978-80; exec. v.p. Estronics, Inc. div. Esmark, Inc., 1980-82; v.p. Velsicol Chem. Corp. div. N.W. Industries, Inc., Chgo., 1982-84; v.p. corp. devel. Dart & Kraft, Inc., Northbrook, Ill., 1985-86; v.p. strategy and bus. devel. Premark Internat. Inc. (spinoff from Dart & Kraft), Deerfield, 1986-90; amb. Washington, 1991-93; prof. strategy and internat mgmt. Northwestern U. Kellogg Grad. Sch. Mgmt., Evanston, Ill., 1993-94; pres. Fed. Reserve Bank Chgo., 1994—; pres. Fed. Reserve Bank Chgo., 1994—; bd. dirs. Conrail, Inc., 1994. Author: Teachers and Unions, 1966, Labor Relations in the Performing Arts: An Introductory Survey, 1970; co-author: Collective Negotiations for Teachers, 1966, Collective Bargaining in Public Employment, 1970, Strategic Planning in Business and Government, 1978; co-editor: Readings on Collective Negotiations in Public Education, 1967, Employment Relations in Higher Education, 1969, Women and Work, 1987; contbr. articles to profl. jours. Bd. trustees U. Chgo. Hosp., 1980-90. 1st lt. AUS, 1959-60. Mem. Indsl. Rels. Rsch. Assn. (pres. 1987), Nat. Bur. Econ. Rsch. (bd. dirs., exec. com.), Comml. Club Chgo. (civic com.), Econs. Club Chgo. Home: 400 Sheridan Rd Winnetka IL 60093-2628 Office: Fed Reserve Bank Chgo 230 S LaSalle St Chicago IL 60604-1413

MOSKOWITZ, ARNOLD X., strategist, economist, educator; b. N.Y.C., Jan. 27, 1944; s. Morris and Millie (Kozichovsky) M.; children: Dara, Alex, Nicole. B.S. in Elec. Engring., CCNY, 1966; M.S. in Indsl. Mgmt., Poly. Inst. N.Y., 1970; M.Phil., NYU, 1979, Ph.D. in Econs. and Fin., 1985. Analyst Grumman Corp., N.Y.C., 1968-70; assoc. economist Dean Witter Reynolds, Inc., N.Y.C., 1970-74, first v.p., economist, 1975-82, sr. v.p., economist, 1983-89; sr. v.p., dir. investment strategy County NatWest U.S.A., N.Y.C., 1989-90; chmn. Moskowitz Capital Cons. Inc., N.Y.C., 1990—; lectr. New Sch. Social Research, 1978—; adj. assoc. prof. fin. Pace U., N.Y.C., 1980-82; pres. Money Marketers NYU, 1988-89. Contbr. articles to profl. jours.; chpts. to books, including Security Selection and Active Portfolio Management; contbr. to Ency. of Economics, How to Beat Wall Street. Mem. Am. Econ. Assn., Nat. Econ. Club, Nat. Assn. Bus. Economists, Atlantic Soc., Beta Gamma Sigma. Jewish. Office: Moskowitz Capital Cons Inc 135 W 50th St Ste 1830 New York NY 10020-1201

MOSKOWITZ, HERBERT, management educator; b. Paterson, NJ, May 26, 1935; s. David and Ruth (Abrams) M.; m. Heather Mary Lesgnier, Feb. 25, 1968; children: Tobias, Rebecca, Jonas. BS in Mech. Engring., Newark Coll. Engring., 1966; MBA, U.S. Internat. U. 1964; PhD, UCLA, 1970. Rsch. engr. GE, 1956-60; systems design engr. Gen. Dynamics Convair, San Diego, 1960-65; asst. prof. Purdue U., West Lafayette, Ind., 1970-75, assoc. prof., 1975-79, prof., 1979-85, Disting. prof., 1985-87, James B. Henderson Disting. prof., 1987-91, Lewis B. Cullman Dist. prof. mfg. mgmt., 1991—; dir. ctr. mgmt. mfg. enterprises; cons. AT&T, Inland Steel Co., Abbott Labs., others; adv. panelist NSF, 1990—. Author: Management Science and Statistics Texts, 1975-90; assoc. editor Decision Scis. Jour., 1984-90, Jour. Behavioral Decision Making, 1986-90; contbr. articles to jours. in field. Bd. dirs. Sons of Abraham Synagogue, Lafayette, Ind., 1970—; mem. Lafayette Klezmorem, 1973—. Capt. USAF, 1956-60. Recipient Disting. Doctoral Student award UCLA Alumni Assn., 1969-70; Fulbright Rsch. scholar, 1985-86. Fellow Decision Scis. Inst. (sec. 1985-87, v.p. 1978-80); mem. Ops. Rsch. Soc. Am./Inst. Mgmt. Sci. (liaison officer 1977—, mem. adv. com., advisor NSF and Fulbright Scholar program 1993—), Tau Beta Pi, Pi Tau Sigma. Jewish. Avocations: Jewish music, tennis. Home: 1430 N Salisbury St West Lafayette IN 47906-2180 Office: Purdue U Krannert Grad Sch Mgmt Ctr Mgmt Mfg ENterprises West Lafayette IN 47907-1310

MOSKOWITZ, JAY, public health sciences educator; b. N.Y.C., Jan. 9, 1943; s. Murray and Helene Moskowitz; m. Joanne Cathy Schindelheim, Dec. 27, 1970; children: Michael Bradley, Andrew Cory. B.S., Queens Coll. 1964; postgrad., CUNY, 1965; Ph.D., Brown U., 1969. Research assoc. in pharmacology NIH, 1969-71, grants assoc. div. research grants, 1971-72, acting chief spl. programs br., div. lung diseases, 1972-74; assoc. dir. program planning and evaluation Nat. Heart, Lung and Blood Inst., 1979-80, assoc. dir. sci. program ops, 1980-86, dir. office of program planning and evaluation, 1976-86; assoc. dir. for program planning and evaluation NIH, 1986-88, dir. Office Program Planning and Evaluation, Office of Dir., 1986-88, assoc. dir. for sci. policy and legislation, 1988-90; dep. dir. for sci. policy & tech. transfer, prin. dep. dir. NIH, 1993; dep. dir. Nat. Inst. on Deafness and Other Communication Disorders, 1993-95; sr. assoc. dean for rsch. devel., prof. pub. health scis. Wake Forest U. Bowman Gray Sch. Medicine, Winston-Salem, N.C., 1995—. Contbr. articles to profl. jours. Served to lt. comdr. USPHS. Recipient Meritorious award William A. Jump Meml. Found., 1977, Dir.'s award NIH, 1978, Superior Svc. award USPHS, 1980, performance awards Sr. Exec. Svc., Presdl. Meritorious Exch. Rank award 1989, Disting. Svc. award HHS, 1991, Disting. Svc. award Nat. Inst. on Deafness and Other Comm. Disorders, 1994. Mem. Soc. Exptl. Biology and Medicine, AAAS. Jewish. Home: 20130 Darlington Dr Gaithersburg MD 20879-1008 Office: Wake Forest U Bowman Gray Sch Medicine Office Rsch Devel Winston Salem NC 27104

MOSKOWITZ, JOEL STEVEN, lawyer; b. N.Y.C., Jan. 14, 1947; s. Jack I. and Myra (Shor) M.; children: David, Michael, Ellen. BA, UCLA, 1967,

JD, 1970. Bar: Calif. 1971, U.S. Ct. Appeals (9th cir.) 1971, U.S. Ct. Appeals (D.C. cir.) 1975, U.S. Supreme Ct. 1975, U.S. Ct. Appeals (2d cir.) 1979. Dep. atty. gen. Calif. Dept. Justice, Sacramento, 1970-83; dep. dir. Calif. Dept. Health Svcs., Sacramento, 1983-85; of counsel Gibson, Dunn & Crutcher, L.A., 1985-88, ptnr., 1988—. Author: Environmental Liability in Real Property Transactions, 1989; contbr. articles to legal publs. Mem. Phi Beta Kappa. Office: Gibson Dunn & Crutcher 333 S Grand Ave Ste 4963 Los Angeles CA 90071

MOSKOWITZ, MICHAEL ARTHUR, neuroscientist, neurologist; b. N.Y.C., May 26, 1942; s. Irving Lawrence and Clara (Dranoff) M.; m. Mary Henderson, May 18, 1991; 1 child, Jenna Rachel. AB, Johns Hopkins U., 1964; MD, Tufts U., 1968. Diplomate Am. Bd. Psychiatry and Neurology, Am. Bd. Internal Medicine. Intern Yale U. Dept. Medicine, 1968-69, resident, 1969-71; resident in neurology Peter Bent Brigham Children Hosp., 1971-74; asst. prof. Med. Sch. Harvard U., Boston, 1975-79, assoc. prof. 1979-92, prof., 1992—; established investigator Am. Heart Assn., 1980-85; assoc. neurophysiologist and neurologist Mass. Gen. Hosp., Boston, 1981—; H.J. Barnett lectr. Canadian Heart Assn., Queens U., Kingston, Ont., 1993—, Witter lectr. U. Calif., San Francisco, 1994—, Barraquer-LaFora lectr. Spanish Neurol. Soc., Barcelona, Spain, 1994—. Contbr. over 200 articles to profl. jours. MIT postdoctoral fellow 1974-76, Alfred Sloan Found. fellow, 1978-80; recipient Enrico Greppi award Italian Neurology Soc., 1986, 88, Tchr.-Investigator award Nat. Inst. of Neurol. Disease and Stroke, 1975-80; rsch. grantee Bristol-Myers Squibb, 1993—, MGH Interdepartmental Stroke Ctr. Mem. Am. Heart Assn. (nat. rsch. com. 1991—, exec. com. stroke coun. 1991—), Am. Neurol. Assn., Am. Acad. Neurology (Decade of the Brain lecture 1995), Am. Pain Soc., Soc. Neurosci., Internat. Soc. for Cerebral Blood Flow and Metabolism (bd. dirs.). Achievements include research in neuroscientific, neurology literature. Office: Mass Gen Hosp 149 13th St Charleston Navy Yard Charlestown MA 02129

MOSKOWITZ, RONALD, electronics executive; b. N.Y.C., Feb. 15, 1939; m. Phyllis Lenes, June 30, 1957; 4 children. BEE, CUNY, 1961; MSEE, Rutgers U., 1963, PhD in Engring., 1966. Registered profl. engr., Mass. Prin. investigator RCA Labs. and Astroelectronics div., 1961-67; instr. elec. engring. Rutgers U., 1965-67; prof. elec. engring. U. Miss., 1967; sr. cons. engr., programs mgr. Avco. Corp., 1967-68; founder, chmn. bd., chief exec. officer Ferrofluidics Corp., Nashua, N.H., 1968—; adj. faculty Lowell Tech. Inst., 1967. Contbr. articles to profl. jours.; patentee in field. RCA fellow MIT, 1963, AEC fellow Princeton U., 1964, NSF fellow Rutgers U., 1964-65. Mem. IEEE, AAAS, Am. Vacuum Soc., Tech. Assn. Graphic Arts, ASME, Am. Soc. Lubrication Engrs., Sigma Xi, Eta Kappa Nu. Office: Ferrofluidics Corp 40 Simon St Nashua NH 03060-3027

MOSKOWITZ, SAM (SAM MARTIN), author, editor, publisher; b. Newark, June 30, 1920; s. Harry and Rose (Gerber) M.; m. Christine Elizabeth Haycock, July 6, 1958. Partner Taurasi & Moskowitz (lit. agts.), N.Y.C., 1941-42; sales mgr. Hazel Specialty Co., Newark, 1944-52; mng. editor Gernsback Publishers, N.Y.C., 1952-54, Frosted Food Field, 1954-55; editor, asso. pub. Quick Frozen Foods, N.Y.C., 1955-72; editor, co-pub. Quick Frozen Foods, 1974-80; asso. pub. Quick Frozen Foods Internat., 1980-85; pub. Private Label, 1981-85; editor Beverage Industry, 1972-74; instr. creative writing City Coll. N.Y., 1953-55; spl. cons. frozen foods, sci. fiction; sci. fiction historian and anthologist. Author: 60 books on sci. fiction, including The Immortal Storm, 1954, Explorers of the Infinite, 1963, Seekers of Tomorrow, 1966, Science Fiction by Gaslight, 1968, Under the Moons of Mars, 1970, The Man Who Called Himself Poe, 1969, The Crystal Man, 1973, Out of the Storm, 1975, Strange Horizons, 1976, Far Future Calling, 1979, Science Fiction in Old San Francisco, 1980, A Merritt: Reflections in the Moon Pool, 1985, H.P. Lovecraft and Nils H. Frome, 1989, After All These Years (autobiography), 1991, The Haunted Pampero, 1992, Terrors of the Sea, 1994; editor Hyperion Press Science Fiction Classics, 1974. Served with AUS, 1942-43. Guest of honor 13th World Sci. Fiction conv., Cleve., 1955; recipient Big Heart award Pitts. World Sci. Fiction conv., 1960; Author's award for sci. fiction N.J. Assn. English Tchrs., 1966; Sci. Fiction Hall of Fame award, 1974; named Lit. Luminary of N.J. N.J. Inst. Tech., 1977; named to N.J. Lit. Hall of Fame, 1979. Mem. Eastern Frosted Foods Assn. (dir. 1962-72), Eastern Sci. Fiction Assn. (pres. 1945-50, 80-87), Sci. Fiction Writers Assn., Mystery Writers Am., Fantasy Amatuer Press Assn., First Fandom. Home: 361 Roseville Ave Newark NJ 07107-1721 Attracted to science fiction in my youth by its suggested answers to provocative mysteries of time and space, I have devoted much of my life to revealing and illuminating its fascinating development, which has reflected mankind's most far-reaching aspirations and sometimes replaced, in modern tense, the voices of the ancient prophets.

MOSKOWITZ, STANLEY ALAN, financial executive; b. N.Y.C., June 8, 1956; s. Sol and Kate (Mermelstein) M.; m. Eve Kronenberger, Sept. 20, 1981; children: Alana, Kate. BA, Queens Coll., 1978; MBA in Fin., St. John's U., 1980. Sr. credit analyst Mfrs. Hanover Leasing Corp., N.Y.C., 1979-81; gen. ptnr. Exec. Leasing Co., N.Y.C., 1981-83; pres. Execulease Corp., Elmont, N.Y., 1983—. Mem. Ea. Assn. Equipment Lessors (chmn. pub. rels. 1985-90, bd. dirs. 1988-92, Meretorious Svc. award 1986-87, chmn. ethics com. 1991-92), Omicron Delta Epsilon. Republican. Jewish. Avocations: reading, cycling. Office: Execulease Corp 1975 Linden Blvd Floral Park NY 11003

MOSLER, JOHN, retired financial planner; b. N.Y.C., Sept. 24, 1922; s. Edwin H. and Irma M.; children: Bruce Elliot, John Edwin, Michele Andree. Student, Philips Exeter Acad., 1938-41, Princeton U., 1941-43; L.H.D., Fordham U., 1965; D.C.S., Duquesne U., 1968. With Mosler Safe Co., 1945-67, exec. v.p., 1948-61, pres., 1961-66, chmn., 1966-67; pres., dir. Mosler Lock Co., 1953-67, Mosler de Mexico S.A., 1953-67; exec. v.p., dir. Mosler Research Products, Inc., 1956-67; dir. 1st Caribbean Mainland Capital Co., Inc., 1962-68, chmn. bd., 1963-68, pres., 1963-68; v.p., dir. Am. Standard Inc., 1967-68; chmn. bd., dir., chief exec. officer Holmes Protection, Inc., 1968-73, Holmes Protection Services Corp., 1968-73; chmn. bd. Hidromex, S.A. de C.V., Mex., 1968—, Mosler N.V., Europe, 1973—; chmn. bd. Internat. Controls Corp., 1973-87, resigned, 1987; past chmn. bd. Royal Bus. Funds Inc.; pres. Mosler Investments. Mem. Mayor's Com. on Judiciary; pres. Am.-Romanian Flood Relief Com.; past dir. Jr. Achievement N.Y.; spl. U.S. amb. to Mauritius, to Zambia's Independence ceremony; vice-chmn. N.Y. Rep. County Com.; trustee, dir. Nat. Urban League; trustee Appeal of Conscience Found., Linden Hall Sch. for Girls, Lititz, Pa.; hon. trustee, past pres. N.Y. Urban League; founder Harlem Prep. Sch. With CIC, AUS, 1943-46. Decorated knight comdr. Ordo Supremus Militaris A. Lilio Regni Navarrae; Sovereign Order Hospitallers St. John of Jerusalem, Knights of Malta; comdr. L'Ordre Senegal; recipient Man of Conscience award Appeal of Conscience Found., 1994. Mem. Young Pres.' Orgn. (past pres.), U.S. C. of C., N.Y. World Bus. Council. Clubs: Bankers of Mexico (Mexico); Princeton; University (N.Y.); Confrerie des Chevaliers du Tastevin, Manhattan; Real Nautico de Barcelona (Spain); Sag Harbor Yacht.

MOSLEY, ELAINE CHRISTIAN SAVAGE, principal, chief education officer, consultant; b. St. Louis, Mar. 4, 1941; d. John W. Savage and Mabel (Mahone) Christian; m. Melvin Ronell Mosley, Aug. 7, 1966; children: Dawn Edith, Melanie Denise, Dana Jean, John Melvin. BS, Lincoln U., 1964, MEd, 1973; EdD, Okla. State U. 1982. Tchr. St. Louis Pub. Sch. System, 1964-70, Immaculate Conception Sch., Jefferson City, 1970-73; counselor Bartlesville (Okla.) Sch. System, 1973-75, elem. prin., 1975-83; elem. prin. Bartlesville Pub. Sch. System, 1983-85, Oak Park (Ill.) Pub. Sch. System, 1985-87; founder, prin., chief edn. officer Corp. Community Schs. of Am., Chgo., 1987—; adj. instr. Langston U. Urban Ctr., Tulsa, Okla., 1983; edn. cons. pub. speaking, workshops, seminars, nat., 1985—; bd. regents Rogers State Coll., Okla., 1978-85; adv. bd. First Nat. Bank, Okla, 1982-85; nat. edn. adv. bd. Channel One, Whittle Communications, 1989-91. Freelance writer in field. Active Westside Assn. Community Action, Chgo., mem. nat. adv. bd. Marwen Found., mem. early childhood adv. bd. North Ctrl. Regional Ednl. Lab. Named Citizen of the Day for contbns. to edn. Bartlesville Area C. of C., 1976; numerous other awards, citations. Mem. League of Black Women (Black Rose award for Edn. 1990), Assn. Supervision and Curriculum Devel., Nat. Assn. Edn. Young Children, Nat. Black Child Devel. Inst., Delta Sigma Theta (West Suburban chpt.), Jack & Jill of Am., Inc. (West Suburban chpt.). Democrat. Baptist. Avocations: writing, poetry reading (oral), singing, traveling, cooking. Home: 5666 Cascade Dr Lisle IL 60532-2047 Office: Corp Community Schs of Am 751 S Sacramento Blvd Chicago IL 60612-3365

MOSLEY, MARY MAC, retired librarian; b. Rome, Ga., Nov. 11, 1926; d. William McKinley and Mary (Caldwell) H.; m. Samuel A. Mosley, June 12, 1946 (div. 1964); children: Samuel A. Jr., Pamela Ann, James Irwin. Student, Ga. State Coll. for Women, 1943-45; BS, Auburn U., 1947; cert. in teaching, Athens Coll., 1963; M in Library, Emory U., 1968. Tchr. sci. Rome City Schs., 1964-66; extension libr. Tri-County Regional Libr., 1966-67; libr. Shorter Coll., 1967-68, assoc. prof. libr. sci., 1968-76, dir. libr. svcs., 1968-93. Corr. sec. Rome Symphony Women's Guild; pres. Christian Women's Fellowship, 1st Christian Ch., 1992-94. Mem. ALA, AAUW (pres. Rome br.), N. Ga. Assn. Librs., Ga. Libr. Assn., Christian Women's Fellowship, Delta Kappa Gamma. Democrat. Mem. Christian Ch. Avocations: piano, knitting, reading, gardening. Home: 24 Rockwood Pl Rome GA 30165-1728

MOSLEY, WALTER, writer; b. L.A., 1952; m. Joy Kellman. Student, Goddard Coll., City Coll., CUNY; grad., Johnson State Coll. Author: Devil in a Blue Dress, 1990 (Shamus award Private Eye Writers Am. 1990, Edgar award nomination Mystery Writers Am. 1990), A Red Death, 1991, White Butterfly, 1992, Black Betty, 1994, RL's Dream, 1995. Office: care W W Norton 500 Fifth Ave New York NY 10110*

MOSLEY, ZACK TERRELL, cartoonist; b. Hickory, Okla., Dec. 12, 1906; s. Zack Taylor and Irah Corinna (Aycock) M.; m. Betty Adcock, May 31, 1945; 1 dau., Jill M. Grad., Shawnee (Okla.) High Sch., 1925; student, Chgo. Acad. Fine Arts, 1926-27, Chgo. Art Inst., 1927-28. Worked in restaurants in Chgo. while studying art, began flying lessons, 1932; flown over U.S., parts of Can., Mex. and S.Am., Alaska, Europe.; col. Civil Air Patrol on active duty with coastal anti-sub patrol units.; now ret. col. CAP. Created: Smilin' Jack, 1933; selling it to, Chgo. Tribune and N.Y. News Syndicate (nationally syndicated), discontinued, 1973, free lance writer and artist; Author: Brave Coward Zack, 1976, The Hot Rock Glide, 1979, De-Icers Galore, 1980. Awarded Air Medal by Air Forces for Anti-submarine patrol flying during World War II; named to Civil Air Patrol Hall Fame, 1976. Mem. Aviation Writers Assn., Aircraft Owners and Pilots Assn. (Sharples trophy for promoting gen. aviation), Nat. Cartoonists Soc., Quiet Birdmen. Episcopalian. Club: Elk. *

MOSS, AMBLER HOLMES, JR., academic administrator, lawyer, former ambassador; b. Balt., Sept. 1, 1937; s. Ambler Holmes and Dorothea Dandridge (Williams) M.; m. Serena Welles, May 6, 1972; children: Ambler H., Benjamin Sumner, Serena Montserrat, Nicholas George Oliver. B.A., Yale U., 1960; J.D., George Washington U., 1970. Bar: D.C., Fla. Joined Fgn. Service Dept. State, 1964; vice consul Barcelona, 1964-66; adviser U.S. del. to OAS, 1966-69; Spanish desk officer, 1968-70; assoc. firm Coudert Bros., Washington, 1971-73; resident atty. Coudert Bros., Brussels, Belgium, 1973-76; mem. U.S. Negotiating Team for Panama Canal treaties, 1977; dep. asst. Sec. of State, Washington, 1977-78; ambassador to Panama, 1978-82; of counsel Greenberg, Traurig, Askew, Hoffman, Lipoff, Quentel, Wolff P.A., 1982-87, 95—; prof., dir. N.S. Ctr. and former dean Grad. Sch. Internat. Studies U. Miami, Fla. Served with USN, 1960-64. Mem. Am. Soc. Internat. Law, Am. Fgn. Svc. Assn., Coun. Fgn. Rels., Am. Legion, Navy League, Greater Miami C. of C. (gov. 1983-86), Royal Inst. Internat. Affairs (London), Internat. Inst. Strategic Studies (London), Army and Navy Club. Address: 5711 San Vicente St Coral Gables FL 33146

MOSS, ARTHUR HENSHEY, lawyer; b. Reading, Pa., July 26, 1930; s. John Arthur and Christine Bracken (Henshey) M.; m. E. Leslie Fritz, Feb. 1982; 1 child by previous marriage, John Arthur. AB, Williams Coll., 1952; JD, U. Pa., 1955. Bar: Pa. 1956. Assoc. Montgomery, McCracken, Walker & Rhoads, Phila., 1960-69, ptnr., 1969—. editor U. Pa. Law Review, 1953-55; chmn. Radnor-Haverford-Marple Sewer Authority, 1968-83: pres. Wayne Civic Assn., 1964-65; steward, deacon Wayne Presbyn. Ch., 1963-66, ruling elder, 1966-72, 79-84, 86-95, clk. of session, 1971, 78-89, trustee, 1987-93; commr. Gen. Assembly Presbyn. Ch. (U.S.A.), 1983; dir. John Bartram Assn., 1987—, treas. 1989—; trustee Presbytery of Phila., 1984, 94—. Lt. USN, 1955-60. Mem. ABA, Pa. Bar Assn., Phila. Bar Assn., Radnor Hist. Soc. (dir., sec. 1978-90), The Athenaeum of Phila., Broadacre Trouting Assn., Merion Golf Club, Edgemere Club. Editor: U. Pa. Law Rev., 1954-55. Contbr. articles to profl. jours. Home: 200 Walnut Ave Wayne PA 19087-3423 Office: Montgomery McCracken Walker & Rhoads 3 Parkway 20th Fl Philadelphia PA 19102

MOSS, ARTHUR JAY, physician; b. White Plains, N.Y., June 21, 1931; s. Abraham Loeb and Ida (Bank) M.; m. Joy Folkman, June 23, 1957; children: Katherine, Deborah, David. BA, Yale U., 1953; MD, Harvard U., 1957. Resident Mass. Gen. Hosp., 1957-58, 60-61; fellow in cardiology med. ctr. U. Rochester, N.Y., 1961-65, from asst. to assoc. prof. sch. medicine and dentistry, 1966-71, clin. assoc. prof., 1971-82, clin. prof., 1982-91, prof. medicine, 1991—, dir. heart rsch. follow-up program med. ctr., 1971—; mem. cardiology adv. com. Nat. Heart, Lung, and Blood Inst., NIH, 1980-82, chmn., 1982-84. Author: Antiarrhythmic Agents, 1977; editor: Clinical Aspects of Life-threatening Arrhythmias, 1984, QT Prolongation and Ventricular Arrhythmias, 1992, Noninvasive Electrocardiology, 1995; mem. editl. bd. Am. Jour. Cardiology, 1988—. Lt. USN, 1958-60. Mem. Alpha Omega Alpha. Home: 581 Claybourne Rd Rochester NY 14618 Office: Univ Rochester Med Ctr Box 653 Rochester NY 14642

MOSS, BEN FRANK, III, art educator, painter; b. Phila., Feb. 28, 1936; s. B. Frank Jr. and Helen Charlotte (Figge) M.; m. Jean Marilyn Russel, Aug. 26, 1960; children: Jennifer Kathleen, Benjamin Franklin IV. BA, Whitworth Coll., 1959; postgrad., Princeton Theol. Seminary, 1959-60; MFA, Boston U., 1963; MA (hon.), Dartmouth Coll., 1993; studied with Walter Murch, Karl Fortess and Herman Keys. Instr. Gonzaga U., Spokane, Wash., 1964-65; assoc. prof., dir. MFA and vis. artist program Fort Wright Coll., Spokane, 1965-72; acting dean, co-founder Spokane Studio Sch., 1972-74; prof. painting and drawing Sch. Art and Art History U. Iowa, Iowa City, 1975-88; George Frederick Jewett prof. art., chmn. studio art dept. Dartmouth Coll., Hanover, N.H., 1988—, Vt. Studio Ctr., Johnson, 1990; area head printing U. Iowa, 1985; artist-in-residence Queens Coll., U. Melbourne, Australia, 1993—; vis. artist, lectr. in field. Represented in permanent collections Kraushaar Galleries, N.Y.C., Susan Conway Galleries, Washington, Gallery 68, Belfast, Maine; one-man shows include Susan Conway Galleries, 1990, Dartmouth Coll.; 1989, Kraushaar Galleries, 1981, 83, 87, Swarthmore Coll., Pa., 1984, Stony Brook (N.Y.) Sch., 1982, Saint-Gaudens, Picture Gallery, Cornish, N.H., 1981, Kans. State U., 1980, Francine Seders Gallery, Seattle, 1979, 82, Hudson D. Walker Gallery, Fine Arts Work Ctr., Provincetown, Mass., 1978, Arnot Art Mus., Elmira, N.Y., 1977, Kirkland Coll., Clinton, N.Y., 1977, Juniper Tree Gallery, Spokane, 1975, Middlebury (Vt.) Coll., 1971, Seligman Gallery, Seattle, 1967, 69, Cheney Cowels Meml. Mus., Spokane, 1967; exhibited in group shows at Susan Conway Galleries, 1993, Chase Gallery City Hall, Spokane, 1993, Colby-Sawyer Coll., New London, N.H., 1992, Idaho State U., Pocatello, 1972, Francine Seders Gallery, 1972, Kraushaar Galleries, 1978—, Susan Conway Galleries, 1989—, Middlebury Coll. Mus. Art, Babcock Galleries, N.Y.C., Albany Inst. History and Art, Owensboro (Ky.) Mus. Fine Art, Corcoran Gallery Art, Washington, 1993—, Gallery 68, 1992, Vt. Studio Ctr. Visiting Critics, Vergennes, 1992, 79th Ann. Maier Mus. Art, Randolph, Macon Women's Coll., Lynchburg, Va., 1990, Del. Ctr. Contemporary Arts, Wilmington, 1988, U. Iowa, 1976, 78, 80, 82, 84, 86, 88, Bladen Meml. Mus., Fort Dodge, Iowa, 1987, Phila. Mus. Art, 1986, Union League Club, N.Y.C., 1986, Blackfish Gallery, Portland, 1986, Columbia (S.C.) Mus. Art, 1985, Columbus Mus. Art, 1982-86, Paine Art Ctr., Oshkosh, Wis., 1985, Burpee Art Ctr., Rockford, Ill., 1985, Ill. State U., Normal, 1985, Wilkes Coll., Wilkes-Barre, Pa., 1985, Albright-Knox Mus., Buffalo, N.Y., 1984, Ark. Art Ctr., Little Rock, 1984, Millersville (Pa.) U., 1983, Fairfield (Conn.) U., 1983, Marion Koogler McKay Inst., San Antonio, 1983, Boston City Hall Gallery, 1983, Cedar Rapids (Iowa) Mus. Art, 1982, Montclair (N.J.) Jr. League, 1981, Iowa Arts Coun., Des Moines, 1980-81, numerous others. Sr. Faculty fellow Dartmouth Coll., 1993, MacDowell Colony, 1992, Devel. grant U. Iowa, 1980, 86; Summer fellowship U. Iowa, 1979, Rsch. and Travel grantee Ford Found., 1979-80, Yaddo Found., 1965, 72, Travel grantee U. Iowa Found., 1986; recipient Disting.

Alumni award Boston U., 1988. Mem. Coll. Art Assn. Independent. Presbyterian. Avocations: music, poetry, travel, tennis. Office: Dartmouth Coll Hb 6081 Studio Art Hanover NH 03755

MOSS, BERNARD, virologist, researcher; b. N.Y.C., July 26, 1937; s. Jack and Goldie (Altman) M.; m. Toby Frima Lieberman, Dec. 25, 1960; children: Robert, Jennifer, David. BA, NYU, 1957, MD, 1961; PhD, MIT, 1966. Diplomate Am. Bd. Medical Examiners. Intern Children's Hosp., Boston, 1961-62; investigator, sect. head NIH, Bethesda, Md., 1966—, lab. chief, 1984—; mem. adv. bd. Virus Res., 1984—, Current Opinion Biotech., 1989—. Assoc. editor Virology Jour., 1976-92, editor., 1992—; mem. editorial bd. Jour. of Virology, 1972—, Antimicrobial Agts. and Chemotherapy, 1973-79, Jour. Biol. Chemistry, 1982-87; AIDS rsch. Human Retroviruses, 1989—; contbr. more than 400 articles to profl. jours. Mem. adv. com. Am. Cancer Soc., N.Y.C., 1983-86; bd. dirs. Found. Advanced Edn. in Scis., Bethesda, 1989—. Served as med. dir. USPHS, 1966—. Named one of 100 Most Innovative Scientists of 1986, Sci. Digest; recipient Solomon A. Berson Alumni Achievement award Sch. Medicine, NYU, Meritorious Svc. medal USPHS, Disting. Svc. medal USPHS, Dickson prize in medicine, Invitrogen award for eukaryotic gene expression, ICN Internat. prize in Virology. Mem. AAAS, Am. Soc. for Biochemistry and Molecular Biology, Am. Soc. Microbiology, Am. Soc. Virology (pres. 1995—), Nat. Acad. Sci., Phi Beta Kappa, Sigma Xi, Alpha Omega Alpha. Office: NIH 9000 Rockville Pike Rm 229A Bethesda MD 20892

MOSS, CHARLES, advertising agency executive; b. Bklyn., Sept. 7, 1938; s. Samuel and Celia (Liebes) Moskowitz; m. Margo Jean Schekman, July 3, 1963 (div.); 1 child, Robert Evan; m. Susan Dukes Calhoun, Mar. 18, 1977; children: Mary Calhoun, Samuel Calhoun. BA cum laude, Ithaca Coll. 1961. Copywriter Doyle, Dane, Bernbach, N.Y.C., 1962-65; group copy supr. J. Tinker & Partners, N.Y.C., 1965-66; creative dir. Wells, Rich, Greene, Inc., N.Y.C., 1968-74; pres., chief operating officer Wells, Rich, Greene, Inc., 1971-76, vice chmn., corp. creative dir., 1976—, also bd. dirs.; now chmn. Moss/Dragoti (ptnr. co. Wells, Rich, Greene/BDDP), N.Y.C. Author (with Stan Dragoti): film Dirty Little Billy, 1971. Mem. adv. bd. NYU Sch. Continuing Edn.; mem. creative rev. bd. Com. for Drug Free Am. Served with AUS, 1962-68. Recipient Gold Key Copy Club, 1968, 1st prize Clio award, 1968, 1st prize Art Dirs. Club, 1968; Andy award N.Y. Advt. Club, 1968, spl. Tony award, Golden Apple award for I Love New York advt. campaign 1978, Clio Classic Hall of Fame award 1983, 86. Mem. Writers Guild Am., Screen Authors Guild, Vertical Club. Avocations: tennis, jogging. Office: Moss Dragoti 9 W 57th St New York NY 10019-2600

MOSS, CRUSE WATSON, automobile company executive; b. Kent, Ohio, Apr. 7, 1926; s. Cruse Watson and Lucile (Shafer) M.; m. Virginia Ann Patton, Dec. 22, 1949; children: Stephen, Carol Susan, Michael. BS in Indsl. Engring., Ohio U., 1948, LLD (hon.), 1985. Pres. Kaiser Jeep Automotive div., also exec. v.p. Kaiser Jeep Corp., 1960-70; group v.p. Am. Motors Corp., 1970; pres., dir. AM Gen. Corp., Detroit, 1970-79; chmn., chief exec. officer, dir. White Motor Corp., Farmington Hills, Mich., 1979-81; chmn. bd., chief exec. officer Gen. Automotive Corp., Ann Arbor, Mich., 1981—; chmn. bd. dirs., chief exec. officer The Flxible Corp., Delaware, Ohio; bd. dirs. The Burnham Fund Inc., N.Y.C. Mem. founders soc. Detroit Inst. Arts; dir. The Burnham Fund, Inc., N.Y.C. With USNR, 1944-46. Mem. Soc. Automotive Engrs., Confrerie des Chevaliers du Tastevin, Chief Execs. Orgn., Beta Theta Pi, Tau Beta Pi. Presbyterian. Clubs: Circumnavigators, Barton Hills Country, Detroit Athletic, Travis Pointe Country. Office: Gen Automotive Corp 2015 Washtenaw Ave Ann Arbor MI 48104-3600

MOSS, ERIC OWEN, architect; b. L.A., July 25, 1943. BA, UCLA, 1965; MArch with honors, U. Calif., Berkeley, 1968, Harvard U., 1972. Prof. design So. Calif. Inst. Architecture, 1974—; prin. Eric Owen Moss Archs., Culver City, Calif., 1975—; Eliot Noyes chair Harvard U., Cambridge, Mass., 1990; Eero Saarinen chair Yale U., New Haven, 1991; lectr. Hirshhorn Mus. Symposium, Washington, 1990, Nat. AIA Conv., 1990, Mus. Contemporary Art, L.A., 1991, N.Y. Archtl. League, 1991, Archtl. Assn. Ireland, Dublin, Archtl. Assn., London, 1991, Royal Coll. Art, London, 1991, Smithsonian Inst., Washington, 1992, U. Calif., Berkeley, 1992, Osterreichiaches Mus. fur Angewandte Kunst, Vienna, Austria, 1992, UCLA, 1992, Royal Danish Acad. Fine Arts, Copenhagen, 1993, U. Lund, Sweden, 1993, Mus. Finnish Architecture, Helsinki, 1993, Royal Acad. Arts, London, 1993, U. Pa., Phila., 1994, others; tchr. U. Tex., Austin, 1983, Wash. U., St. Louis, 1984, U. Ill. Chgo., 1985, Tulane U., New Orleans, 1985, U. Minn., Mpls., 1985, Columbia U., N.Y.C., 1986, Rice U., Houston, 1988; participant various confs. Exhbns. of work include World Biennial of Architecture, Sofia, Bulgaria, 1989, Salle des Tirages du Credit Foncier de France, Paris, 1990, Bartlett Sch. Architecture and Urban Design, London, 1991, Gallery of Functional Art, Santa Monica, Calif., 1992, GA Gallery, Tokyo, 1992, Mus. fur Gestaltung Zurich, Switzerland, 1993, Santa Monica (Calif.) Mus. Art, 1993, Fonds Regional D'Art Contemporain du Centre, 1993, Aspen (Colo.) Art Mus., 1993, Centro de Arte y Comunicacion, Buenos Aires, 1993, Contemporary Arts Ctr., Cin., 1993, Philippe Uzzan Galerie, Paris, 1993, Contemporary Arts Ctr., Tours, France, 1993, Internat. Exhbn. Contemporary Architecture, Havana, Cuba, 1994, others. Recipient Progressive Architecture Design award, 1978, 92, Winning Interior Archtl. Record award, 1984, Interiors Design award, 1991. Fellow AIA (L.A. awards 1977, 79, 83, 88, 90, Calif. Coun. awards 1981, 86, 88, L.A. Honor awards 1991, Nat. Honor awards 88, 89, Calif. Coun. Urban Design/Adaptive Re-Use awards 1991, Nat. Interior Design awards 1992, 94, L.A. Design awards 1992, 93). Subject of monographs and numerous articles in mags. and jours. Office: 8557 Higuera St Culver City CA 90232

MOSS, GARY CURTIS, lawyer; b. Taylorville, Ill., Feb. 17, 1944; s. William Clary and Sophronia Irene (McClellan) M.; m. Judith K. Jones, April 14, 1945; children—Gary Curtis, Kristin Suzanne. B.A., U. Ill.-Champaign, 1966; J.D., U. Iowa-Iowa City, 1969. Bar: Iowa 1969, Calif. 1970, U.S. Dist. Ct. (cen. dist.) Calif. 1972, Nev. 1991, U.S. Ct. Appeals (9th cir.) 1974, U.S. Dist. Ct. (so. and no. dists.) Calif. 1976, U.S. Dist Ct. Nev. 1991. Assoc., O'Melveny & Myers, Los Angeles, 1969-75; assoc. Seyfarth, Shaw, Fairweather & Geraldson, Los Angeles, 1975-78, ptnr., 1978-87; judge pro tem West Los Angeles Mcpl. Ct., 1981-83, Pasadena Mcpl. Ct., 1983—. Mem. ABA, State Bar Calif. (hearing referee, arbitrator mandatory fee arbitrations), State Bar Iowa, Los Angeles County Bar Assn. Republican. Club: Athletic (Los Angeles). Home: 3055 Westwind Rd Las Vegas NV 89102 Office: Morgan Lewis & Bockius 801 S Grand Ave Los Angeles CA 90017 also: 3800 Howard Hughes Pky Ste 600 Las Vegas NV 89109

MOSS, GERALD S., dean, medical educator; b. Cleve., Mar. 4, 1935; s. Harry and Lillian (Alter) M.; m. Wilma Jaback, Sept. 1, 1957; children: William Alan, Robert Daniel, Sharon Lynn. BA, Ohio State U., 1956, MD cum laude, 1960. Diplomate Am. Bd. Surgery (apptd. assoc. examiner com. 1989); lic. Ill. Intern Mass. Gen. Hosp., Boston, 1960-61, resident, 1961-65; from asst. prof. to assoc. prof. dept. surgery Coll. Medicine U. Ill., Chgo., 1968-72, prof., 1973-77, 89—, head dept. surgery, 1989, dean, 1989—; prof. dept. surgery Pritzker Sch. Medicine U. Chgo., 1977-89; prof. dept. surgery U. Ill., Coll. of Medicine, 1989—; tutor in surgery Manchester (Eng.) Royal Infirmary, 1964; asst. chief surgical svcs. VA West Side Hosp., Chgo., 1968-70; attending surgeon dept. surgery Cook County Hosp., Chgo. 1970-72, chmn. 1972-77; dir. surgical rsch. Hektoen Inst. for Med. Rsch., Cook County Hosp., 1972-77, Micheal Reese Hosp. and Med. Ctr., Chgo., 1977-89, chmn. dept. surgery, 1977-89, chief svc. 1989, trustee, 1981, and numerou coms.; appointed to Nat. Rsch. Coun., NAS, 1966-68, Ad Hoc Subcom., NAE, 1970, Ad Hoc Study Sect., 1970, del. to Third Joint U.S-USSR Symposium, 1983, Blood Diseases and Resources Adv. Com., 1984-88, Planning Com. for discussing key blood problems, Nat. Heart and Lung Inst., 1987, chmn. Plasma and Plasma Products Com., 1979, bd. dirs., 1983, v.p., 1985, Ad Hoc Transition Com., Am. Blood Comm., 1989, Panel on Rsch. Opportunities, Office Naval Rsch. Program, 1987, exec. com., coord. com., Nat. Blood Edn. Program, 1988, Tech. Adv. Task Force Am. Hosp. Assn., 1988, chmn. review panel contract proposals, NIH, 1975, program project site visit, 1976, chmn. site-visit review group, 1977, adv. com. Blood Resources Work group, 1978, Planning Com. for Consensus, 1987, Small Bus. Innovation Rsch., 1988, Med. Rsch. Scv. Merit Review Bd. VA, 1978-81, Liaison Com. Graduate Med. Edn. AMA, 1979, and numerous other

coms. for various med. organizations; cons. Nat. Heart and Lung Inst., Transfusion Medicine Acad. Awardees Program; vis. prof. Montefiore Med. Ctr. Bronx, N.Y., 1986, Ohio State U., 1988, U. N.Mex., Albuquerque, 1989, Seton Med. Ctr., Austin, Tex., 1990, U. Ill. Coll. Medicine, Peoria, 1991; guest lectr., participant numerous meetings, symposiums; cons. in field. Contbr. numerous articles to profl. jours., chpts. to books. With U.S. Army, 1965-68, Vietnam. Teaching fellow Harvard Med. Sch., 1962; receipient Stitt Lectr. award Assn. Mil. Surgeons U.S.A., 1981; grantee U.S. Navy, 1969-84, U.S. Army, 1971-74, 75-78, NIH, 1969, 83-84, Dept. Pub. Health, 1973, HEW, 1974-77, UpJohn, 1974, Northfield Labs. 1985-89. Fellow ACS (pre and postoperative care com. 1975-83, rep. Am. blood commn. 1977—, mem. various coms., speaker various symposiums), Am. Soc. Surgery Trauma; mem. Am. Surgical Assn. (rep. Nat. Soc. Med. Rsch. 1984-88), Am. Trauma Soc., Am. Physicians Fellowship (rep. Israel Med. Assn.), Assn. Acad. Surgery (chmn. membership selection com. 1973-75, pres. elect 1974-75, pres. 1975-76, exec. coun. 1977-79), Soc. Univ. Surgeons (rep. Nat. Soc. Med. Rsch. 1973-77, com. Surgical Edn. 1979-81), Ctrl. Surgical Soc. (rep. Nat. Soc. Med. Rsch. 1973-77), Shock Soc. (chmn. planning com. 1986, chmn. program com. 1986, pres. elect 1986-87, pres. 1987-88), Soc. for Surgery Alimentary Tract (mem. com. west north ctrl. region 1978-82), Internat. Soc. Blood Transfusion, SurgicalBiology Club II, Nat. Soc. for Med. Rsch., Collegium Internationale Chirugiae Digestivae, Societe Internationale de Chirugie, Sigma XI, Alpha Omega Alpha (faculty advisor 1972-73). Office: U Ill Coll Medicine 1853 W Polk St M/C 784 Chicago IL 60612

MOSS, GUY B., lawyer; b. N.Y.C., Aug. 22, 1944; s. Tobias and Florence (Press) M.; m. Joyce Ann Green, Dec. 25, 1969; children: Jason, David. BA, Yale U., 1966; JD, Harvard Law Sch., 1969. Bar: Mass. 1969, U.S. Dist. Ct. Mass. 1970, U.S. Ct. Appeals (1st cir.) 1973, U.S. Supreme Ct. 1973. Instr. Suffolk U. Law Sch., Boston, 1969-70; law clk. Mass. Superior Ct., Boston, 1970-71; assoc. Lappin, Rosen, et al., Boston, 1972-73, Friedman & Atherton, Boston, 1973-74; ptnr. Widett, Slater & Goldman, Boston, 1974-90, Bingham, Dana & Gould, Boston, 1990—. Author: (audio cassettes) MCLE Legal Update, 1988-94, Enforcing Security Interests in Personal Property, 1992. Mem. ABA, Mass. Bar Assn., Boston Bar Assn., Comml. Law League Am., Am. Bankruptcy Inst. Home: 229 Franklin St Newton MA 02158-2324 Office: Bingham Dana & Gould 150 Federal St Boston MA 02110-1726

MOSS, JAMES TAYLOR, hospital administrator; b. New Iberia, La., July 19, 1947; married. B, U. Southwestern La., 1973; MHA, U. Ala., 1975. Adminstrv. resident Baptist Med. Ctr., Montgomery, Ala., 1974-75; dir. profl. svcs. Lake Charles (La.) Meml. Hosp., 1975-81; assoc. adminstr. Jackson-Madison County (Tenn.) Gen. Hosp., 1981-85, exec. v.p., chief oper. officer, 1985-86, pres., 1986—. Mem. Tenn. Hosp. Assn. Home: 163 Windemere Jackson TN 38305 Office: Jackson-Madison County Gen Hosp 708 W Forest Ave Jackson TN 38301

MOSS, JOE FRANCIS, sculptor, painter; b. Kincheloe, W.Va., Jan. 26, 1933; s. Thomas R. and Audra (Frazier) M.; m. Jean Elizabeth Marcrum, July 1, 1952 (dec.); children: Joe Marcum, Jon Eric, Jay Keith; m. Daphne Brauner, 1992. BA in Art, W.Va. U., 1955, MA in Art, 1960. Tchr. art Morgantown (W.Va.) High Sch., 1956-60; assoc. prof. art W.Va. U., Morgantown, 1960-70; prof. art U. Del., Newark, 1970—. One-man shows of sculpture Washington Gallery Modern Art, 1967, Russell Mus., Great Falls, Mont., 1973, Sculpture Now Gallery, N.Y.C., 1975, CUNY Grad. Center, 1975, J.B. Speed Mus., Louisville, 1977, Madison Sq. Park, N.Y.C., 1980, Marian Locks Gallery and Marian Locks East, Phila., 1981, Fine Arts Gallery U.M.B.C., Balt., 1986; 20-yr. retrospective Edison Fine Arts Gallery, Ft. Myers, Fla., 1985; exhibited in numerous group shows including, Mus. Modern Art, N.Y.C., 1966, Fischbach Gallery, N.Y.C., 1966, Fellows of the Center Exhbn., M.I.T., 1978, Sculpture Now, N.Y.C., 1979, Laumeier Sculpture Park, St. Louis, 1979, Neuberger Mus., Purchase, N.Y., 1981, Kunsthalle, Hamburg, Fed. Republic Germany, 1985, Robert Moses Plaza, N.Y.C., 1985-86, MIT, 1986 Lights Orot, Yeshiva U., N.Y.C., 1988-89, St. Mary's Coll., South Bend, Inc., 1989—, Hist. and Fine Arts Mus., Anchorage, 1987, Montreal, Can. 1988; traveling exhibits include Multiple Interaction, MIT, also Phila., N.Y.C., L.A., Sculpture 75 Exhbn., Phila., 1975, invitational exhibit, U. Tenn., Chattanooga, 1971; represented in permanent collections Arts and Humanities Council Huntington (W.va.) Galleries, Polaroid Corp., Cambridge, Mass., Martin Fine Villa, Miami, Fla., Cedarcrest Coll., Allentown, Pa., Johnson Mus., Ithaca, N.Y., Urban Am., Washington, Bloomsburg (Pa.) State Coll., St. Louis Art Mus., Del. Art Mus., others, also pvt. collections; one-man shows of paintings Pa. State U., 1965, Pitts. Playhouse Gallery, 1965, W.Va. U., 1965; exhibited in group shows, Fifty Artists Fifty States, Burpee Mus., Rockford, Ill., 1965, Am. Fedn. Art, 1966-68, Bocour Collection, Keene (N.H.) State Coll., 1974, others, interviews, WTOP-TV, Washington, 1967, Voice of Am, 1967; speaker Internat. Sculpture Conf. Kans. U., Lawrence, 1974; feature CNN including Sci. Week in Rev. Grantee W.Va. U., 1963, 67, 68, U. Del. Research Found., 1971, 72, Dimer Found., 1976-77; vis. research fellow Ctr. for Advanced Visual Studies MIT, Cambridge, 1973, Nat. Endowment for Arts fellow, 1980-81, Del. State Arts Council fellow, 1980-81; recipient 1st prize Nat. Show Huntington Galleries Mus., 1963, Environmental Sculpture award Three Rivers Exhbn., 1968, sculpture award Appalachian Corridors Exhibit, 1968. Home: 801 Valley Rd Newark DE 19711-2585

MOSS, JOHN EMERSON, banker, former congressman; b. Carbon County, Utah, Apr. 13, 1915; s. John Emerson and Della Orta (Mower) M.; m. Jean Kueny, Sept. 15, 1935; children: Jennifer, Allison. In retail bus., 1938-43, real estate broker, 1945-85; mem. 83d-95th congresses 3d Dist Calif., mem. govt. ops., interstate and fgn. commerce comms., chmn. select com. on govt. info., 1955-68; also chmn. oversight and investigation subcom.; dep. majority whip 2d session 87th-91st congresses; mem. 93d-94th congresses Democratic Policy and Steering Com.; chmn. bd. 1st Comml. Bank, Sacramento, 1979-85; chmn. Capitol Hist. Preservation Soc., 1985-92; Mem. Calif. Assembly, 9th Dist., 1948-52. Served with USNR, 1943-45. Mem. Laguna Hts. Coop. Corp. (v.p. 1993, pres. bd. dirs.), C. of C., Am. Legion, DAV. Club: Commonwealth of Calif.

MOSS, KATE, model; b. Croydon, England, Jan. 16, 1974. With Storm Agy., England, Women Model Mgmt., N.Y.; model Calvin Klein Jeans. Office: Women Model Mgt 107 Greene St Fl 2 New York NY 10012-3803

MOSS, LAWRENCE KENNETH, composer, educator; b. L.A., Nov. 18, 1927; s. Oscar and Sadye (Jacobs) M.; m. Graydon Hindley, Mar. 29, 1958; children: Pamela Ann, Claramarie, Jonathan, Ruth. Student, Pomona Coll., 1945-47; AB, UCLA, 1949; AM, Eastman Sch. Music, 1950; PhD, U. So. Calif., 1957. Prin. studies with Leon Kirchner, 1951-53; asst. prof. music theory Yale U., 1960-65, asso. prof. music theory, 1965-69; prof. music composition U. Md., 1969—. Composer: String Quartet, 1958, Sonata for Violin and Piano, 1959; 1 act comic opera The Brute, 1960; Four Scenes for Piano, 1961; Fromm commn., Scenes for Small Orchestra, 1961; women's chorus and piano In Spring, 1962; brass quintet Music for Five, 1963; soprano and piano Three Rilke Songs, 1963; chamber ensemble Remembrances, 1964; 2 act opera The Queen and the Rebels, 1965, rev. for chamber ensemble, 1989; piano for 4 hands Omaggio, 1966; flute, clarinet, doublebass Windows; flute, clarinet, viola, piano Patterns, 1967; wood-winds brass, percussion Exchanges, 1968; (New Haven Symphony commn.) soprano and orch. Ariel; 2 violins and viola Elegy, 1970; violin, piano, percussion Timepiece, 1970; (U. Chgo. Symphony commn.) orch. Paths, 1970; woodwind quintet and tape Auditions, 1971; alto saxophone and tape Evocation and Song, 1972; Fantasy for Piano, 1973; chorus and tape Exercise, 1973; soprano, oboe, tape, slides, lights Unseen Leaves, 1975; String Quartet, 1975; oboe, percussion Toot-Sweet, 1976; trombone, piano B.P., A Melodrama, 1976; Symphonies for Brass Quintet and Chamber Orchestra, 1977; piano and tape Omaggio II, 1977; oboe, harpsichord Little Suite, 1978; soprano, flute, clarinet, violin, percussion, dancer, slides, tape Nightscape, 1978; piano Ballad, 1979; piano, tape Hands Across the C, 1979; brass quintet Flight, 1979; tuba and bass-baritone Toshua, 1979; dancer, tape, slides and lights Dreamscape, 1980; Flute choir Chanson, 1980; (Kindler Found. Commn.) string quartet String Quartet No. 3, 1980; cello solo Espressivo, 1981; clarinet, tape, dancer Images, 1981; soprano, flute, guitar Somewhere Inside Me, 1981; conductor soprano, flute, clarinet, viola, harp, piano, Loves, 1982 (NEA Consortium commn.); conductor, flute, clarinet, percussion, violin, cello, piano Music of Changes, 1986; tape, slides, lights, dancers, Rites, 1983; soprano, tape, Darkharbor, 1983; flute, percussion Aprèsludes, 1983; soprano, tape, piano At Night, 1984; dancer, tape Song to the Floor, 1984; piano A Musical Trip, 1984; piano, tenor Portals, 1984; movie Installation — Lament, 1984; tape, dance That Gong-Tormented Sea, 1985; tenor, flute, clarinet, cello, percussion, violin, viola Voyages, 1985, Videotape Ephemeral Art, 1985; singer, tape, dancer Lesbia's Sparrow, 1985; dancer, percussion Incidental Music, 1986; flute, clarinet, violin, cello, percussion, piano Music of Changes, 1986; baritone, piano Drumtaps, 1986; clarinet solo Nature Studies, 1987; viola, tape Violaria, 1988; clarinet, mime/dancer, tape Blackbird, 1987; woodwind quintet Various Birds, 1987; chorus and piano Grand Is the Seen, 1988; 2 flutes, trumpet, harp, percussion, string quintet Clouds, 1989; soprano, tape Summer Night on the Youghiheny River, 1989, baritone, harp Lovesongs, 1990, soprano, violin, clarinet piano 4-hands Songs of the Earth and Air, Piano 4-hands Hommage, 1991, flute, clarinet, double bass, Through A Window..., 1992, Quartet for flute, cello, percussion and piano, chorus and piano, alto saxophone and tape Saxpressivo, The Gate, 1992; soprano, piano 2 songs to poems by Emily Dickinson, 1993; tenor, harp, oboe 10 Miracles, 1993; alto saxophone, piano 6 Short Pieces, 1993; China for tape alone, 1994. Served with AUS, 1954-56. Fulbright scholar Vienna, 1953-54; Guggenheim fellow Florence, 1959-60, 68-69; Morse fellow Yale U., to Rome, 1964-65; Nat. Endowment Humanities grantee, 1975, 77, 80; U. Md. Disting. Scholar/Tchr. award, 1982-83; composer-in-residence Rockefeller Cultural Ctr., Bellagio, Italy, 1986. Mem. ASCAP. Home: 220 Mowbray Rd Silver Spring MD 20904-1221 Office: U Md Dept Music College Park MD 20740

MOSS, LESLIE OTHA, court administrator; b. Detroit, Mar. 8, 1952; s. Lonnie and Emma (Robinson) M. BA, U. Mich., 1982, postgrad., 1990—. Technician oper. rm. Sinai Hosp., Detroit, 1972-75; nurses' technician Detroit Osteo. Hosp., 1976-83; supr. Southfield (Mich.) Placement Ctr., 1983-85; rsch. asst. Wayne County Commr.'s Office, Detroit, 1985-86; fin. aid counselor Wayne State U., 1986-87; probation officer Dept. Corrections State of Mich., 1988—; exec. asst. Human Rights Dept., City of Detroit; rsch. asst. Law Dept. City of Detroit, 1990; asst. pers. mgr. Detroit Osteo. Hosp., 1991-93, Highland Pk. P.C.C., 1991-93; mental health worker Mich. Health Ctr.-Adult Mental Health and New Ctr. Hosp., Detroit, 1992-94; legal technician Ptnrs. Against Crime, Detroit, 1994; social work technician, 1994; sgt. of arms Detroit Police Res., 1987—; intern, assoc. prodr. local TV sta., Detroit, 1993; mem. bd. advisors, mem. bd. govs. Am. Biog. Rsch. Inst., dep. gov., 1994; exec. cons. in field., 1993—; asst. pers. mgr., 1993—. Bd. advisors Am. Biog. Inst., 1994; active re-election com. Mayor Coleman A. Young, Detroit, 1989-93; patient care counselor; adv. various causes, including industrialized Am., higher edn., automotive quality. Recipient Twentieth Century Achievement award Biog. Centre, 1994, Spl. Recognition award Detroit Pub. Sch. Sys., 1992, Internat. Man of Yr. award, 1992-93, award for mass media svc. participation Barden Cable Vision, Detroit, 1991; named Most Admired Man of Decade, 1994. Mem. NAFE, NAACP (advisor 1989), Internat. Order of Merit, Am. Pre-Med Students (cons. 1988—), Assn. Psychologists, Am. Biog. Rsch. Inst. Assn. (mem. bd. govs. 1993, dep. gov.), Internat. Platform Assn., U. Mich. Alumni Assn., Golden Key (life), Kappa Alpha Psi. Home: 1581 Kendall Detroit MI 48238 Office: Ptnrs Against Crime 163 Madison Ave Ste 120 Detroit MI 48226

MOSS, LYNDA BOURQUE, museum director; b. Torrington, Wyo., Mar. 15, 1950; d. Leroy Alfred and Mary (Halley) Bourque; m. Thomas Charles Moss, Jan. 31, 1970; children: Heather, Christopher Eric. BFA, U. Nebr., Omaha, 1977; MA, U. No. Iowa, 1979; MFA, Mont. State U., 1984. Guest lectr. U. Nebr., Omaha, 1977-78; program developer Children's Mus., Omaha, 1977-78; gallery asst. U. No. Iowa, Cedar Falls, 1978-79; curator edn. Western Heritage Ctr., Billings, Mont., 1979-83, dir., 1986—; adj. prof. Ea. Mont. Coll., Billings, 1985-87; curator Mont. Art Gallery Dirs., Kalispell, 1986-87. Represented in pub. and pvt. collections, Am. Northwest. Art scholar Washington U., St. Louis, 1968-70. Mem. Internat. Coun. Mus., Am. Assn. Mus., Mont. Art Assn. Democrat. Home: 2540 Hoover Ave Billings MT 59102-1658 Office: Western Heritage Ctr 2822 Montana Ave Billings MT 59101-2305

MOSS, MADISON SCOTT, editor; b. Charlotte, N.C., May 23, 1948; s. James Madison and Nellie Lee (Jenkins) M. BA in English, U. N.C., 1970. Editorial aide NASW, Inc., Washington, 1974, promotions specialist, 1974-79, assoc. editor, 1979-80, editor, 1980-90, mng. editor, 1990—. Creator numerous videos. Campaign coord. Eugene McCarthy for Pres., Rutherford County, N.C., 1968. Recipient award for Pub. Excellence Comms. Concepts, 1993, 94. Mem. ACLU, Am. Found. AIDS Rsch. Democrat. Avocations: video producing, studying digital multimedia technology, reading. Office: NASW Inc 750 1st St NE # 700 Washington DC 20002

MOSS, MELVIN LIONEL, anatomist; b. N.Y.C., Jan. 3, 1923; s. Maurice and Ethel (Lander) M.; m. Letty Salentijn, Apr. 1970; children (by previous marriage)—Noel Morrow, James Andrew. A.B., N.Y. U., 1942; D.D.S., Columbia, 1946, Ph.D., 1954. Mem. faculty Columbia, 1954—, prof., 1967-93; prof. emeritus, 1993; also dean Columbia (Sch. Dental and Oral Surgery.). Recipient Lederle Med. Faculty award, 1954-56. Fellow AAAS, Royal Anthrop. Soc. Gt. Britain; mem. Am. Assn. Anatomists, Am. Assn. Phys. Anthropologists, Internat. Assn. Dental Research (craniofacial biology award), Am. Soc. Zoologists, Sigma Xi, Omicron Kappa Upsilon. Research, numerous publs. on skeletal growth and application of computer-assisted methods of numerical and graphic analysis of growth. Home: 560 Riverside Dr New York NY 10027-3202

MOSS, MICHAEL ERIC, museum director; b. Columbus, Ohio, June 21, 1947; s. Harrison Peter and Francenia (Bolenbaugh) M.; m. Jane Ellen Wright, Nov. 25, 1972; 1 child, Charles Andrew. BA, Ohio State U., 1970; MA in History of Art, Case Western Res. U., 1977. Curatorial asst. Toledo Mus. Art, 1970-73, Case Western Res. U., Cleve., 1974-75; curator of art West Point (N.Y.) Mus., U.S. Mil. Acad., 1975-85, dir., 1985—. Author: Posters for Victory, 1978, (with others) Guide to West Point Museum Collections, 1987; editor: Robert W. Weir of West Point, Illustrator, Teacher and Poet, 1976. Office: US Mil Acad Bldg 2110 West Point Mus West Point NY 10996

MOSS, MITCHELL LAWRENCE, urban planning educator; b. N.Y.C., Nov. 21, 1948; s. Irving and Belle (Koven) M.; m. Candace Greene, Nov. 16, 1976; 1 child, Alexandra Helen. BA, Northwestern U., 1969; MA, U. Wash., 1970; PhD, U. So. Calif., 1975. Asst. prof. NYU, 1973-76, assoc. prof., 1977-86, prof. planning, 1987—; dir. Urban Rsch. Ctr., 1987—; cons., Port Authority N.Y. and N.J., 1981-82, State of N.Y., 1988-89; Nynex, White Plains, N.Y., 1988-89; dep. to chmn., N.Y. Coun. Fiscal and Econ. Priorities, Albany, 1983—. Editor: Telecommunications and Productivity, 1981; contbr. articles to various publs. Mem. rsch. com., United Way N.Y., 1987—; mem. com. on N.Y.C., Mcpl. Art Soc. N.Y., 1988—; mem. commil. devel. com., N.Y. Partnership, 1988—. Grantee, NSF, 1975-77, Corp. Pub. Broadcasting, 1981-82, Benton Found., 1981-82. Mem. Am. Soc. Pub. Adminstrn., Am. Planning Assn., Urban Affairs Assn. Democrat. Jewish. Home: 110 Bleecker St New York NY 10012-2101 Office: NYU Urban Rsch Ctr 4 Washington Sq N New York NY 10003-6671

MOSS, MYRA ELLEN (MYRA MOSS ROLLE), philosophy educator; b. L.A., Mar. 22, 1937; m. Andrew Frank Rolle, Nov. 5, 1983. BA, Pomona Coll., 1958; PhD, The Johns Hopkins U., 1965. Asst. prof. Santa Clara (Calif.) U., 1968-74; prof. Claremont McKenna Coll., 1975—, chmn. Dept. of Philosophy, 1992-95; assoc. dir. Gould Ctr. for Humanities, Claremont, Calif., 1993-94; adv. coun. Milton S. Eisenhower Libr./Johns Hopkins U., 1994—. Author: Benedetto Croce Reconsidered, 1987; translator Benedetto Croce's Essays on Literature & Literary Criticism, 1990; assoc. editor Special Issues; Symposia Journal of Value Inquiry, 1991, 92, 93 (Honorable Mention, Phoenix award). Dir. Flintridge (Calif.) Riding Club, 1991. Mem. Am. Philosophical Assn., Am. and Internat. Socs. for Value Inquiry, Am. Soc. for Aesthetics, Phi Beta Kappa (hon.). Avocations: gardening, horseback riding. Office: Claremont McKenna Coll 890 Columbia Ave Claremont CA 91711-6400

MOSS, ROBERT DREXLER, lawyer; b. Cleve., June 12, 1909; s. Morris and Rosa (Goldman) M.; m. Ruth K. Rivitz, Dec. 28, 1939; children: Kenneth H., Suzanne R. A.B., Case Western Res. U., 1931, LL.B., 1933, J.D.,

1969. Bar: Ohio bar 1933, U.S. Supreme Ct 1960. Practice in Barberton, Ohio and Summit County, Ohio, 1937—; past chmn. Ohio Legal Services Fund. Pres. Barberton chpt. ARC, 1966-67;life mem. adv. bd. Salvation Army, Barberton Corps . Served to maj. USAAF, 1942-46. Decorated Bronze Star; recipient Outstanding Law Alumnus award Case Western Res. U., 1976, Sir Thomas More award Bishop Gilbert Sheldon, Vicar of Akron, Bishop for so. region of Cleve. diocese, 1990. Fellow Am. Bar Found. (life mem.); mem. ABA, Ohio State Bar Assn. (pres. 1968-69, Ohio Bar medal 1978), Akron Bar Assn. (pres. 1956-57), Ohio State Bar Assn. Found. (life), Summit County Legal Aid Soc. (pres. 1955). Jewish (past pres. temple). Clubs: Rotary (Barberton), Elks (Barberton), Masons (Akron) (32 deg.), Shriners (Akron), Akron City (Akron), Rosemont Country (Akron) (past pres.); Play House (Cleve.). Home: 1006 Bunker Dr Apt 301 Akron OH 44333-3079 Office: 102 First National Bank Bldg PO Box 307 Barberton OH 44203

MOSS, STANLEY, poet; b. N.Y.C., June 21, 1925; s. Samuel and Margaret M.; m. Ana Maria Vandellos Nicholson, 1953 (div. 1960); m. Jane Zech, 1967. BA, Trinity Coll., Hartford, Conn.; MA, Yale U. Pres. Stanely Moss and Co. Art Dealers, N.Y.C., 1959—; chief editor, pub. Sheep Meadow Press, N.Y.C., 1977—. Author: (poetry) The Wrong Angel, 1966, Skull of Adam, 1979, The Intelligence of Clouds, 1989; various books published by Anvil Press, London and Harcourt Brace Jovanovich Pubs., Macmillan; editor: The Art of Poetry: Interviews with Stanley Kunitz, 1989, The Sheep Meadow Press Anthology, 1993. Rockefeller grantee, 1967. Office: care The Sheep Meadow Press PO Box 1345 Riverdale NY 10471*

MOSS, STEPHEN B., lawyer; b. Jacksonville, Fla., July 14, 1943; s. Rudy and Betty (Sobel) M.; m. Rhoda Goodman, Nov. 24, 1984; children: Kurt, Shannon. BA, Tulane U., 1964; JD, Samford U., 1968. Bar: Fla. 1968, U.S. Dist. Ct. (so. dist.) Fla., U.S. Tax Ct. From assoc. to ptnr. Heiman & Crary, Miami, Fla., 1971-74; pvt. practice law So. Miami, Fla., 1974-75; ptnr. Glass, Schultz, Weinstein & Moss P.A., Coral Gables, Fla., 1975-78, Ft. Lauderdale, Fla., 1978-80; ptnr. Holland & Knight, Ft. Lauderdale, 1980—; gen. counsel Greater Ft. Lauderdale C. of C., 1991-92. Capt. U.S. Army, 1968-70, Vietnam. Named Outstanding Kiwanian, Miami, 1974. Fellow ABA, Fla. Bar Found.; mem. Fla. Bar Assn., Greater Ft. Lauderdale C. of C. (chmn. bd. dirs., bd. govs., Chmn.'s award 1991), Tower Club, Tower Forum (pres. 1993-94). Democrat. Jewish. Avocations: running, softball, hiking, family activities. Office: Holland & Knight Ste 1300 1 E Broward Blvd 13th Fl Fort Lauderdale FL 33301

MOSS, SUSAN LINDA, nurse; b. Charlotte, N.C., Sept. 29, 1948; d. Edward and Rose (Goldstein) M. BS in Nursing, U. Fla., 1971; MS in Health Care Adminstrn., U. South Fla., 1977. RN. Fla. Nurse Shands Teaching Hosp., Gainesville, Fla., 1971; head nurse Walston Army Hosp., Ft. Dix, N.J., 1971-72; nurse Bay Pines (Fla.) VA Med. Ctr., 1973-74, 75-77, Gainesville VA Med. Ctr., 1974-75; instr. Bay Pines VA Med. Ctr., 1977-78, supr., 1978-81; asst. chief nursing service Shreveport (La.) VA Med. Ctr., 1981-83, Jerry L. Pettis Meml. VA Hosp., Loma Linda, Calif., 1983-85, Durham (N.C.) VA Med. Ctr., 1985-87; chief nursing service Jerry L. Pettis Meml. VA Hosp., Loma Linda, Calif., 1987—; bd. dirs. Desert Area Wellness Network, Palm Springs, Calif. 1984-85; pres. Triangle chpt. Mission Air, Durham 1987—; chmn. task force Identify Health Care Needs Female Vets., 1985; instr., organizer Regional Edn. Program 1982; mem. hosp. couns. So. Calif. Patient Care Svcs. Com., Inland Area Coun. Nurse Execs. Organizer Spl. Olympics, St. Petersburg, Fla., 1979-80. Named Citizen Yr., Kiwanis Club St. Petersburg, 1979. Mem. Sigma Theta Tau (mem. selection com. 1986-87). Avocations: reading, creative needlework, tennis, water sports. Home: 355 Highlander Dr Riverside CA 92507-3128 Office: Jerry L Pettis Meml VA Hosp Benton St Loma Linda CA 92357-0002

MOSS, THOMAS HENRY, university dean, physicist; b. Cleve., June 27, 1939; s. Joseph Harold and Elsa Margaret (Lemkau) M.; m. Kathleen Goddard, May 31, 1965; children: Ellen, Joseph, Cheryl, David. AB, Harvard U., 1961; PhD, Cornell U., 1965. Cons. analyst govtl. sci. policy U.S. Govt. Office Mgmt. and Budget, Washington, 1963-67; research physicist IBM Corp., Yorktown, N.Y., 1967-74, 75-76; staff dir., sci. advisor Office of Congressman George E. Brown, Washington, 1976-79; staff dir. subcom. sci., research and tech. Ho. of Reps., Washington, 1979-82; prof. physics, dean grad. studies and research Case Western Res. U., Cleve., 1982—; adj. prof. physics Columbia U., N.Y.C., 1966-76; mem. nat rev. com. Office of Nuclear Waste Isolation, Columbus, 1983—; bd. dirs. Univ. Tech. Inc., Cleve.; bd. dirs. Ctr. Great Lakes, Chgo., 1985—; v.p. Edison Poymer Innovation Corp., Independence, Ohio, 1986-90. Editor: The Three Mile Island Nuclear Accident-Lessons, 1981; asst. editor Environ. Profl. mag.; cons. editor Sci, Tech. and Human Values Environ. mag.; contbr. articles to profl. jours. Treas. Lake Barcroft Community Assn., Falls Church, Va., 1980; mem. adv. bd. Small Bus. SBIR Program, Cleve., 1983-85; mem. Shaker Heights (Ohio) Bd. Edn., 1989—; chmn. N.E. Region Ohio Systemic Statewide Initiative in Sci. and Math. Edn., 1992—. NSF fellow Nobel Instn., 1966-67. Fellow Am. Phys. Soc. (chmn. panel pub. affairs 1985-86, chmn. forum on physics and soc. 1990—), Nat. Council Univ. Research Adminstrs. (Nat. Innovative Program award 1987), Scientists Inst. Pub. Info. (Disting. Service award Harlem Prep. Sch. 1971); chmn. AAAS (com. on sci., engring. and pub. policy 1989—). Avocations: gardening, camping. Office: Case Western Res U Sch Grad Stds & Rsch Adelbert 4 Office Of The Dean Cleveland OH 44106

MOSS, WILLIAM JOHN, lawyer; b. Duluth, Minn., Aug. 31, 1921; s. John Hugh and Mary (Quinn) M.; m. Kathryn Casale, June 14, 1947; children: Mary Appleton, Catherine Warner, Elizabeth Bradley, Amy Moss Brown, John, Gerard, Hugh, Patricia Moss Sheng, Susan Moss Homola, Barbara. A.B., Harvard U., 1947, LL.B., 1950. Bar: N.Y. 1950. Assoc. firm Cadwalader, Wickersham & Taft, N.Y.C., 1949-58, ptnr., 1959—. Served to maj. AUS, 1942-45. Republican. Roman Catholic. Home: RR 9 # D Garrison NY 10524 Office: Cadwalader Wickersham & Taft 100 Maiden Ln New York NY 10038-4892

MOSSAWIR, HARVE H., JR., lawyer; b. Morton, Miss., Aug. 9, 1942; s. Harve H. and Madeline (Price) M.; children: Anna Christine, Karen Elyse; m. Judy S. Bardugo, Aug. 5, 1985; 1 child, Leigh Sarah. BA with honors, U. Ala., 1964; MA in Econs., U. Manchester, 1965; JD with honors, U. Chgo., 1968. Bar: Calif. 1970. Asst. prof. U. Ala. Law Sch., Tuscaloosa, 1968-69; assoc. Irell & Manella, L.A., 1969-74, ptnr., 1974-94, of counsel, 1995—. Mem. bd. editors U. Chgo. Law Rev., 1966-68; contbr. articles to profl. jours. Fulbright scholar 1964-65, Floyd Russell Mecham scholar, 1965-68. Mem. Calif. Bar Assn. Republican. Office: Irell & Manella 1800 Ave Of The Stars Ste 900 Los Angeles CA 90067

MOSSBRUCKER, TOM, dancer; b. Tacoma. Scholarship student, The Joffrey Ballet Sch., 1975-77. Dancer Joffrey II Dancers, N.Y.C., 1978-80, The Joffrey Ballet, N.Y.C., 1980—. Office: The Joffrey Ballet 130 W 56th St New York NY 10019-3818*

MOSSE, GEORGE LACHMANN, history educator, author; b. Berlin, Sept. 20, 1918; came to U.S., 1939, naturalized, 1945; s. Hans Lachmann-Mosse and Felicia M. Student, Cambridge (Eng.) U., 1937-39; B.S., Haverford Coll., 1941; Ph.D., Harvard U., 1946; D.Litt., Carthage Coll., 1973; D.H.L., Hebrew Union Coll., 1987; laurea honoris causa, U. Camerino, Italy, 1995. From instr. to assoc. prof. State U. Iowa, 1944-55; from assoc. prof. to prof. U. Wis., 1955-89, Bascom prof. history, 1964-83, Bascom-Weinstein prof. Jewish studies, 1983-89, prof. emeritus, 1989—; fellow Inst. for Advanced Studies Hebrew U., 1987; vis. prof. Stanford U., 1963-64, Hebrew U., 1969-70, 72, 74, 76, 78, Koebner prof., 1979-86, emeritus, 1986—, U. Munich, Germany, 1982-83, École des Hautes Études, Paris, 1986; fellow Inst Contemporary Jewry, Hebrew U., 1974—; vis. prof. Jewish Theol. Sem. Am. 1977; sr. fellow Australian Nat. U., 1972, 79; Kaplan vis. prof. Jewish studies U. Cape Town (South Africa), 1980; vis. prof. U. Amsterdam, 1988, U. Tel Aviv, 1989, Pembroke Coll. Cambridge U., 1990, 91, 94, Cornell U., 1989, 92, A.D. White prof., 1993—, U. San Marino, 1992, Shapiro Sr. Scholar in residence, U.S. Holocaust Meml. Mus., 1994-95. Author: The Struggle for Sovereignty in England, 1950, The Holy Pretence, 1957, The Reformation, 1953, 2d edit., 1963, The Crisis of German Ideology, 1964, The Culture of Western Europe, 1961, 3d edit., 1988, Nazi Culture, 1966, (with H. Koenigsberger) Europe in the Sixteenth Century, 1968, 2d

edit., 1989, Germans and Jews, 1970, The Nationalisation of the Masses, Political Symbols and Mass Movements in Germany, 1975, Nazism, 1978, Towards the Final Solution: A History of European Racism, 1978, Masses and Men. Nationalist and Fascist Perceptions of Reality, 1980, German Jews Beyond Judaism, 1985, Nationalism and Sexuality: Respectability and Abnormal Sexuality in Modern Europe, 1985, Fallen Soldiers: Reshaping the Memory of the World Wars, 1990, Ebrei in Gerhania Fra Assimilazione i antisemitismo, 1991, Ich Bleibe Emigrant: Gespräche, 1991, Confronting the Nation: Jewish and Western Nationalism, 1993; editor: Police Forces in History, 1975, International Facism, 1979; co-editor: Europe in Review, 1957, Jour. Contemporary History, 1966—, (with Bella Vago) Jews and Non-Jews in Eastern Europe, 1975 (with Jehuda Reinharz) The Impact of Western Nationalisms, 1992; contbr. New Cambridge Modern History. Bd. dirs. Wiener Library, London, 1974-92, Leo Baeck Inst., N.Y.C., 1978—; bd. overseers Tauber Inst., Brandeis U., 1980—. Recipient Premio Storia Aqui, 1975, Premio Prezzolini, Florence, 1985, Goethe Medallie, Goethe Inst., 1988. Mem. AAUP (chmn. Iowa conf. 1954-55), Am. Soc. Reformation Research (pres. 1962), Am. Soc. Ch. History (council 1969-73), Am. Hist. Assn., Am. Acad. Arts and Scis., Phi Beta Kappa, Phi Eta Sigma (hon.). Home: 36 Glenway St Madison WI 53705-5206

MOSSE, PETER JOHN CHARLES, financial services executive; b. Mtarfa, Malta, Sept. 8, 1947; came to U.S., 1977; s. John Herbert Charles and Barbara Haworth (Holden) M.; m. Christine Marielle St. Preux, Oct. 17, 1994. BA, Oxford U., 1969; MBA, U. Pa., 1971; MA, Oxford U., 1989. Bank officer N.M. Rothschild & Sons Ltd., London, 1971-76; spl. projects officer banking Bumiputra Mcht. Bankers Berhad, Kuala Lumpur, Malaysia, 1976-77; v.p.; treas., sec. NMR Metals Incorp., N.Y.C., 1977-79, exec. v.p., 1979-83; sr. v.p. Rothschild, Inc., N.Y.C., 1983-90; v.p., CFO, The Arista Group Inc., N.Y.C., 1991-93; U.S. rep. Travelex Fin. Svcs. Ltd., London, 1994-95; ptnr. Creelman Fine Arts, N.Y.C., 1995—. Mem. Pilgrims of the U.S., St. George's Soc. N.Y. (life), Oxford U. Alumni Soc. (exec. com. 1994—), The Gold Inst. (co. rep. bd. dirs. 1985-90), The Silver Inst. 9co. rep., bd. dirs. 1989-90), The Copper Club, Commodity Exch., Inc. (cop. rep. 1979-90). Episcopalian. Avocations: international travel, railroads. Home and Office: 353 E 72d St Ste 330 New York NY 10021

MOSSEL, PATRICIA FLEISCHER, opera executive; b. N.Y.C., Nov. 19, 1933; d. Burnet Thomas and Martha Camille (Leigh) Kraut; m. Allan A. Fleischer, Dec. 30, 1956 (div. 1987); children: Hillary Lee, Jason Allan. BA, U. Rochester, 1955; MA, Yale U., 1956. Cert. fund raising exec. Tchr. Colby Coll., New London, N.H., 1956-57; editor Far Eastern Pub.-Yale U., New Haven, 1957-60; dir. devel. San Francisco Opera, 1979-84; dir. devel., mktg. and pub. relations The Wash. Opera, 1984-95, exec. dir., 1995—; mem. bd. San Francisco Symphony and Opera; bd. chmn., exec. dir. Mt. Diablo Rehabilitation Ctr.; co-founder Medi-Physics, Inc.; cons. D.C. Humanities Council, 1989—. Editor: Western Lit. on China, 1959. Mem. adv. council Fund Raising Sch., Indpls.; v.p. Nat. Soc. Fund Raising Exec. Found. bd. dirs., Washington, 1985-87. Mem. Nat. Soc. Fund Raising Execs. (named Fund Raising Exec. of Yr. 1986), Assocs. of Yale Alumni (del. 1988-91), Yale Club, Phi Beta Kappa. Republican. Episcopalian. Avocations: painting, writing, piano. Office: Washington Opera Kennedy Center Washington DC 20566-0012*

MOSSINGHOFF, GERALD JOSEPH, lawyer, association executive; b. St. Louis, Sept. 30, 1935; m. Jeanne Carole Jack, Dec. 29, 1958; children: Pamela Ann Jennings, Gregory Joseph, Melissa M. Ronayne. BSEE, St. Louis U., 1957; JD with honors, George Washington U., 1961. Bar: Mo. 1961, D.C. 1965, Va. 1981. Dir. congl. liaison NASA, Washington, 1967-73, dep. gen. counsel, 1976-81; asst. Sec. Commerce, commr. patents and trademarks U.S. Patent Office, 1981-85; pres. Pharm. Rsch. & Mfrs. Am., Washington, 1985—; adj. prof. prof. U. Washington Coll. Law; ambassodor Paris Conv. Diplomatic Conf. Recipient Exceptional Svc. medal NASA, 1971, Disting. Svc. medal, 1980, Outstanding Leadership medal, 1981; granted presdl. rank of meritorious exec., 1980; Disting. Pub. Svc. award Sec. of Commerce, 1983. Fellow Am. Acad. Pub. Adminstrn.; mem. Reagan Alumni Assn. (bd. dirs.), Internat. Fedn. Pharm. Mfrs. Assn. (bd. dirs.), Cosmos Club, Knights of Malta, Order of Coif, Eta Kappa Nu, Pi Mu Epsilon. Home: Apt PH 28 1530 Key Blvd Arlington VA 22209-1532 Office: Pharm Rsch and Mfrs Am 1100 15th St NW Washington DC 20005-1707

MOSSMAN, THOMAS MELLISH, JR., television manager; b. Honolulu, Nov. 20, 1938; s. Thomas Mellish and Marian (Ledwith) M.; children: Thomas Mellish III, James Michael; m. Jan Carla MacAlister, Dec. 31, 1989. Student, U. Hawaii, 1954-57; BA, U. Denver, 1958, MA, 1965. Producer-dir. KRMA-TV, Denver, 1960-64, KCET-TV, L.A., 1964-72; pres. Mosaic Films, L.A., 1972-73; prodn. and operations dir. KLCS-TV, L.A., 1973-78, station mgr., 1978-87; dept. dir. Archdiocese of L.A., 1987—; instr. Calif. State U., Northridge, 1981—; chairperson, founder L.A. Community TV, 1987-95. Chmn. exec. bd. Regional Ednl. TV Adv. Coun., 1989-93; chmn., founding mem. Alliance for Distance Edn. in Calif., 1991-95; pres. Cath. TV Network, 1993—. Mem. NATAS, Dirs. Guild Am., Alliance for Community Media. Episcopalian. Office: Archdiocese Los Angeles 1530 W 9th St Los Angeles CA 90015-1111

MOSSO, DAVID, accountant; b. Pasadena, Calif., Aug. 13, 1926; s. Joseph Ernest and Marian (Ure) M.; m. Lee McVoy Pierce, June 11, 1955; children: Janet, Andrew, Jocelyn. B.B.A. magna cum laude, Washburn U., 1950, D.Commerce, 1982; M.A. in Econs., U. Minn., 1951. CPA, Va. With Santa Fe Ry., 1942-44; instr. econs. and acctg. Washburn U., 1954-55; with U.S. Treasury Dept., 1955-77, commr. accounts, 1971-73, dep. asst. sec. treasury, 1973-75, asst. sec., 1975-77; mem. Fin. Acctg. Standards Bd., 1978-87, vice chmn., 1986-87, asst. dir. rsch., 1988—. Contbr. articles to profl. jours. Mem. Comptr. Gen's Acctg. Stds. Adv. Coun., 1987—; mem. charter revision commn. City of Stamford, 1986-87, Internat. Adv. Group on Fed. Reporting, 1984-86; alt. trustee Nat. Gallery Art, 1975-77; dir. Stamford Emergency Med. Svc., 1993-94. 1st lt. AUS, 1944-46, 51-53. Recipient Alexander Hamilton award Treasury Dept., 1977. Mem. AICPA (Elijah Watt Sells award 1962), Va. Soc. CPAs (Gold medal 1962), Assn. Govt Accts. (fed. fin. mgmt. standards bd. 1971-77, dir. Washington chpt. 1972-73, Disting. Leadership award 1977, Elmer Staats award 1990), Treasury Hist. Assn. (pres. 1978), TauDelta Pi, Pi Gamma Mu, Phi Kappa Phi. Home: 111 Saddle Hill Rd Stamford CT 06903-2307 Office: 401 Merritt 7 Norwalk CT 06856

MOSSOP, GRANT DILWORTH, geological institute director; b. Calgary, Alta., Can., Apr. 15, 1948; s. Cyril S. and Freida E. (Dilworth) M.; m. Ruth Shaver, May 24, 1969; children: Jenny, Jonathan, David. BSc in Geology, U. Calgary, 1970, MSc in Geology, 1971; PhD, DIC in Geology, Imperial Coll., U. London, 1973. Postdoctoral fellow U. Calgary, Alta., Can., 1974; asst. rsch. officer Alta. Rsch. Coun., Edmonton, 1975-77, assoc. rsch. officer, 1977-80, head geol. survey dept., 1980-84, sr. rsch. officer, 1985-91; dir. Geol. Survey of Can., Calgary, 1991—; acad. visitor dept. earth sci. Oxford (Eng.) U., 1984-85. Project mgr., editor Geol. Atlas of Western Canada Sedimentary Basin. Fellow Geol. Assn. Can. (pres. 1986-87); mem. Can. Soc. Petroleum Geologists. Home: 68 Colleen Cres SW, Calgary, AB Canada T2V 2R3 Office: Inst Sedimentary & Petroleum Geology, 3303-33d St NW, Calgary, AB Canada T2L 2A7

MOSS-SALENTIJN, LETTY (ALEIDA MOSS-SALENTIJN), anatomist; b. Amsterdam, The Netherlands, Apr. 14, 1943; came to U.S.; 1968; d. Ewoud and Johanna Maria (Schoonhoven) Salentijn; m. Melvin Lionel Moss, Apr. 17, 1970. DDS, State U. Utrecht, The Netherlands, 1967, PhD, 1976. Asst. prof. histology, State U., Utrecht, 1967-68; asst. prof. Columbia U., 1968-74, assoc. prof., 1974-86, prof., 1986—; dir. dental radiology, 1980-86, dir. grad. program dental sci., 1986—; dir. postdoctoral affairs, 1987-90, asst. dean postdoctoral programs, 1990-94, acting dean academic affairs, 1994-95, assoc. dean acad. affairs, 1995—. Author: Orofacial Histology & Embryology, 1972; Dental and Oral Tissues, 1980, 2d edit., 1984, 3d edit. 1990. Contbr. chpts. to books, articles to profl. jours. Fellow Royal Microscopical Soc.; mem. Am. Assn. Anatomists, Internat. Assn. Dental Research, Am. Soc. Biomechanics, Sigma Xi. (chpt. sec. 1980-87, pres. 1987-89), Omicron Kappa Upsilon (pres. local chpt. 1987). Avocation: stained glass art. Home: 560 Riverside Dr Apt 20K New York NY 10027-3242 Office: Columbia U Assoc Dean Academic Affairs 630 W 168th St New York NY 10032-3702

MOST, JACK LAWRENCE, lawyer, consultant; b. N.Y.C., Sept. 24, 1935; s. Meyer Milton and Henrietta (Meyer) M.; children: Jeffrey, Peter; m. Irma Freedman Robbins, Aug. 8, 1968; children: Ann, Jane. BA cum laude, Syracuse U., 1956; JD, Columbia U., 1960. Bar: N.Y. 1960, U.S. Dist. Ct. (so. and ea. dists.) N.Y. 1963. Assoc. Hale, Grant, Meyerson and O'Brien, N.Y.C., 1960-66; dep. assoc. dir. OEO, Exec. Office of The Pres., Washington, 1965-67; asst. to gen. counsel C.I.T. Fin. Corp., N.Y.C., 1968-70; corp. counsel PepsiCo, Inc., Purchase, N.Y., 1970-71; v.p. legal affairs Revlon, Inc., N.Y.C., 1971-76; asst. gen. counsel Norton Simon, Inc., N.Y.C., 1976-79; ptnr. Rogers Hoge and Hills, N.Y.C., 1979-86; ptnr. Finkelstein Bruckman Wohl Most & Rothman, N.Y.C., 1986—; mng. ptnr., 1990-93; corp. sec. Requa, Inc., Flowery Beauty Products, Inc., 1987—. Contbr. articles to profl. jour. and mags. Bd. dirs. Haym Salomon Home for Aged, 1978-91, pres., 1981-92; bd. dirs. The Jaffa Inst. for Advancement of Edn., 1994—, Haym Salomon Geriatric Found., 1992—, pres. 1992—; bd. advisors Touro Coll. Health Scis., 1989-90. Mem. ABA (fed. regulation of securities com., food, drug and cosmetic law com., trademark and unfair competition com.), N.Y. State Bar Assn. (food, drug and cosmetics sect.), Am. Soc. Pharmacy Law, YRH Owners Corp. (bd. dirs., pres. 1989-92), Lords Valley Country Club (bd. govs. 1984-90, 1st v.p. 1987-88, 2d v.p. 1988-90), Zeta Beta Tau, Omicron (trustee Syracuse chpt. 1988-91). Jewish. Home: 429 E 52d St New York NY 10022-6478 Office: Finkelstein Bruckman Wohl Most & Rothman 575 Lexington Ave New York NY 10022-6102

MOST, NATHAN, securities exchange executive; b. Los Angeles, Mar. 22, 1914; s. Bernard and Bertha (Saltzman) M.; m. Evelyn Rosenthal, July 10, 1964; children—Stephen, John, Robert, Barbara. B.A., U. Calif. at Los Angeles, 1935. Vice v.p. Getz Bros. & Co., San Francisco, 1945-60; pres. Carad Corp., Palo Alto, Calif., 1961-64; exec. v.p. James S. Baker Co., San Francisco, 1964-65, Pacific Vegetable Oil Corp., San Francisco, 1965-70, Am. Import Co., San Francisco, 1970-74; pres. Pacific Commodities Exchange, San Francisco, 1974-76; spl. asst. to chmn. Commodity Futures Trading Commn., Washington, May-Dec. 1976; pres. Amex Commodities Exch., N.Y.C., 1977-80; v.p. new products devel. Am. Stock Exch., 1980-91, sr. v.p., 1991—; pres. Amex Commodities Corp. Inc., N.Y.C., 1982—; v.p. Calif. Council Internat. Trade, 1966-67; pres. Commodity Club San Francisco, 1970—; bd. dirs. San Francisco-Pacific Commodity Exch., 1970—, San Francisco World Trade Assn., 1970—, World Affairs Council No. Calif., 1953-65; pres. San Francisco World Trade Assn., 1956-58. Councilman Atherton, Calif., 1959-64. Mem. Export Mgmt. Assn. No. Calif. (pres. 1972—), San Francisco Commodity Club (dir.). Home: 415 Pinehill Rd Hillsborough CA 94010 Office: American Stock Exchange 86 Trinity Pl New York NY 10006-1818

MOSTELLER, FREDERICK, mathematical statistician, educator; b. Clarksburg, W.Va., Dec. 24, 1916; s. William Roy and Helen (Kelley) M.; m. Virginia Gilroy, May 17, 1941; children: William, Gale. ScB, Carnegie Inst. Tech. (now Carnegie-Mellon U.), 1938, MSc, 1939, DSc (hon.), 1974; AM, Princeton U., 1942, PhD, 1946; DSc (hon.), U. Chgo., 1973, Wesleyan U., 1983; D. of Social Scis. (hon.), Yale U., 1981; LLD (hon.), Harvard U., 1991. Instr. math. Princeton U., 1942-44; research assoc. Office Pub. Opinion Research, 1942-44; spl. cons. research br. War Dept., 1942-43; research mathematician Statis. Research Group, Princeton, applied math. panel Nat. Devel. and Research Council, 1944-46; mem. faculty Harvard U., 1946—, prof. math. stats., 1951-87, Roger I. Lee prof., 1978-87, prof. emeritus, 1987—, chmn. dept. stats., 1957-69, 75-77, chmn. dept. biostats., 1977-81, chmn. dept. health policy and mgmt., 1981-87; dir. Tech. Assessment Group, 1987—; dir. Ctr. for Evaluation Am. Acad. Arts and Scis., 1994—; vice chmn. Pres.'s Commn. on Fed. Stats., 1970-71; mem. Nat. Adv. Council Equality of Ednl. Opportunity, 1973-78, Nat. Sci. Bd. Commn. on Pre-coll. Edn. in Math., Sci. and Tech., 1982-83; Fund for Advancement of Edn. fellow, 1954-55; nat. tchr. NBC's Continental Class-room TV course in probability and stats., 1960-61; fellow Center Advanced Study Behavioral Sciences, 1962-63, bd. dirs., 1980-86; Guggenheim fellow, 1969-70; Miller research prof. U. Calif. at Berkeley, 1974-75; Hitchcock Found. lectr. U. Calif., 1985. Co-author: Gauging Public Opinion (editor Hadley Cantril), 1944, Sampling Inspection, 1948, The Pre-election Polls, 1948, 49, Stochastic Models for Learning, 1955, Probability with Statistical Applications, 1961, Inference and Disputed Authorship, The Federalist, 1964, The National Halothane Study, 1969, Statistics: A Guide to the Unknown, 3d edit., 1988, On Equality of Educational Opportunity, 1972, Sturdy Statistics, 1973, Statistics By Example, 1973, Cost, Risks and Benefits of Surgery, 1977, Data Analysis and Regression, 1977, Statistics and Public Policy, 1977, Data for Decisions, 1982, Understanding Robust and Exploratory Data Analysis, 1983, Biostatistics in Clinical Medicine, 1983, 3d edit., 1994, Beginning Statistics with Data Analysis, 1983, Exploring Data Tables, Trends and Shapes, 1985, Medical Uses of Statistics, 1986, 2d edit., 1992, Quality of Life and Technology Assessment, 1989, Fundamentals of Exploratory Analysis of Variance, 1992, Meta-analysis for Explanation, 1992, Doing More Good Than Harm, 1993, Medicine Worth Paying For, 1995; author articles in field. Trustee Russell Sage Found.; mem. bd. Nat. Opinion Research Center, 1962-66. Recipient Outstanding Statistician award Chgo. chpt. Am. Statis. Assn., 1971, Boston chpt., 1989, Myrdal prize Evaluation Research Soc., 1978, Paul F. Lazarsfeld prize Council Applied Social Research, 1979, R.A. Fisher award Com. of Pres.'s of Statis. Socs., 1987, Medallion of Ctrs. for Disease Control, 1988. Fellow AAAS (chmn. sect. U 1973, dir. 1974-78, pres. 1980, chmn. bd. 1981), Inst. Math. Statistics (pres. 1974-75), Am. Statis. Assn. (v.p. 1962-64, pres. 1967, Samuel S. Wilks medal 1986), Social Sci. Research Council (chmn. bd. dirs. 1966-68), Math. Social Sci. Bd. (acad. governing bd. 1962-67), Am. Acad. Arts and Scis. (council 1986-88), Royal Statis. Soc. (hon.), Am. Philos. Soc. (council 1986-88), Internat. Statis. Inst. (v.p. 1986-88, pres.-elect 1989, pres. 1991-93), Math. Assn. Am., Psychometric Soc. (pres. 1957-58), Inst. Medicine of Nat. Acad. Scis. (council 1978), Nat. Acad. Scis., Biometric Soc. Office: 1 Oxford St Cambridge MA 02138-2901

MOSTELLER, ROBERT P., law educator; b. 1948. BA, U. N.C., 1970; MA, Harvard U., 1975; JD, Yale U., 1975. Bar: N.C. 1975, D.C. 1976. Law clk. to Hon. Braxton Craven U.S. Ct. Appeals (4th cir.), Asheville, N.C., 1975-76; atty., chmn. trial div., reg. dir. D.C. Pub. Defender Svc., 1976-83; assoc. prof. Duke U., 1983-87, prof., 1987—; sr. assoc. dean, 1989-91. Mem. Phi Beta Kappa (pres. 1969-70). Office: Sch Law Duke U Durham NC 27708

MOSTEN, FORREST STEVEN, lawyer, educator; b. Detroit, Apr. 18, 1947; s. Jack Lewis and Shelia Loretta (Rader) M.; 1 child, Jordana Lynne. Student, U. Birmingham, Eng., 1969; BA, U. Calif., Riverside, 1969; JD, UCLA, 1972. Cert. family law specialist. Co-founder, ptnr. Meyers, Jacoby & Mosten, L.A., 1972-76; asst. regional dir. for consumer protection FTC, L.A., 1978-79; sr. ptnr. Mosten & Wasserstrom, L.A., 1979—; dir. clin. edn., asst. law Mercer U. Sch. Law, 1976-78; cons. advisor in personalized tng. and supervision in mediation and arbitration; vol. mediator in family law L.A. Superior Ct.; arbitrator, mediator Am. Arbitration Assn.; arbitrator in atty. fee disputes L.A. County Bar; settlement officer for mandatory settlement confs. Family Law Dept., L.A. Superior Ct., West Dist.; adj. prof. Pepperdine U. Sch. Law, Inst. for Dispute Resolution, 1989—; dir. clin. edn., asst. prof. law Mercer U. Sch. Law, 1976-78. Contbr. to legal publs. Mem. ABA (standing com. on delivery of legal svcs.), Assn. Cert. Family Law Specialists (dir. South sect.). Avocations: tennis, golf, travel, guitar, classical music. Office: Mosten & Wasserstrom 10990 Wilshire Blvd Ste 940 Los Angeles CA 90024-3924

MOSTERT, PAUL STALLINGS, mathematician, educator; b. Morrilton, Ark., Nov. 27, 1927; s. Johannes F.T. and Lucy (Stallings) M.; m. Barbara Bond; children: Paul Theodore, Richard Stallings, Kathleen, Kristina. A.B. Rhodes Coll., 1950; M.S., U. Chgo., 1951; Ph.D., Purdue U., 1953. Mem. faculty Tulane U., 1953-70, prof. math., 1962-70, chmn. dept., 1968-70; prof. math. U. Kans., 1970-91, prof. emeritus math., 1991—, chmn. dept., 1970-73; vis. prof. U. Tubingen, Germany, 1962-63; vis. prof. math. U. Ky. 1984-85; mem. Inst. Advanced Study, Princeton, 1967-68; chmn. Rhodes Coll. Sci. Initiative Task Force, 1989-90; pres. Equix, Inc., 1984-85, Pennfield Biomechanics Corp., Inc., 1985-89, Equix Biomechanics, 1989—. Co-author: Elements of Compact Semigroups, 1966, The Cohomology Ring of Finite and Compact Abelian Groups, 1974; Editor: Proc. Conf. Transformation Groups at New Orleans, 1969, Questiones Mathematicae; co-founder, exec. editor: Semigroup Forum, 1970-85, mng. editor, 1967-85, editor, 1985-88.

Mem. Ky. Statewide Exptl. Program to Stimulate Competeive Rsch. Com., 1994—. With USNR, 1945-46. NSF sr. postdoctoral fellow, 1967-68. Mem. Am. Math. Soc. (mem. at large coun. 1972-75, chmn. com. on acad. freedom, tenure and employment security 1973-76), Assn. Mems. of Inst. for Advanced Studies, Soc. Indsl. and Applied Math., Internat. Soc. for Optical Engring., Internat. Soc. for Neural Networks. Office: Equix Biomechanics 870 Enterprise Dr Lexington KY 40503-5416

MOSTILLO, RALPH, medical association executive; b. Newark, Apr. 11, 1944; s. Joseph and Antoinette (Cipriano) M. BA in Chemistry magna cum laude, Rutgers U., Newark, 1972; MA in Biochemistry, Princeton U., 1974, PhD in Biochemistry, 1978. NIH rsch. fellow Princeton (N.J.) U., 1972-78; sr. scientist drug regulatory affairs Hoffmann-La Roche, Inc., Nutley, N.J., 1979-85; founder, chmn., chief exec. officer Am. Cancer Assn., Nutley, 1986—. Assoc. editor U.S. Pharmacopoeia XX-Nat. Formulary XV, 1980-85. With USN, 1962-66, Vietnam. Mem. Am. Chem. Soc., Am. Mgmt. Assn., Am. Mktg. Assn., N.Y. Acad. Scis., Am. Legion, Vietnam Vets. of Am., Phi Beta Kappa. Achievements include research on molecular transport systems in E. coli as general models for drug delivery into cells. Home: PO Box 505 Nutley NJ 07110-0505 Office: Am Cancer Assn PO Box 87 Nutley NJ 07110-0087

MOSTOFF, ALLAN SAMUEL, lawyer, consultant; b. N.Y.C., Oct. 19, 1932; s. Morris and Ida (Goldman) M.; m. Alice Tamara Popelowsky, July 31, 1955; children: Peter Alexander, Nina Valerie. BS, Cornell U., 1953; MBA, N.Y.U., 1954; LLB, N.Y. Law Sch., 1957. Bar: N.Y. 1957, D.C. 1964. Assoc. Olwine Connelly Chase O'Donnell & Weyher, N.Y.C., 1958-61; atty. SEC, Washington, 1962-66, asst. dir. 1966-69, assoc. dir. 1969-72, dir. div. investment mgmt. regulation, 1972-76; ptnr. Dechert Price & Rhoads, Washington, 1976—; adj. prof. Georgetown U. Law Ctr., 1972-82; mem. Fin. Acctg. Standards Adv. Bd., 1983-87; mem. adv. bd. Investment Lawyer. Mem. ABA (chmn. internat. devel. sub-com., com. on devels. in investment svcs.), Assn. of Bar of City of N.Y., Fed. Bar Assn. (chmn. exec. coun. securities regulation com. 1990-92), Am. Law Inst. Home: 6417 Waterway Dr Falls Church VA 22044-1325 Office: Dechert Price & Rhoads 1500 K St NW Washington DC 20005-1209

MOSTOV, KEITH ELLIOT, cell biologist, educator; b. N.Y.C., Mar. 6, 1956; s. Philip M. and Frances (Landau) M.; m. Emily Leah Silverman, Apr. 9, 1989. BA, U. Chgo., 1976; postgrad., Oxford (Eng.) U., 1976-77; PhD, Rockefeller U., 1983; MD, Cornell U., 1984. Whitehead fellow Whitehead Inst. Biomed. Rsch., Cambridge, Mass., 1984-89; asst. prof. cell biology U. Calif., San Francisco, 1989-92, assoc. prof., 1992—. Editorial bd. Internat. Rev. Cytology, 1986—; guest editor Saunders Press series Seminars in Cell Biology, 1990—; contbr. numerous sci. papers to profl. publs. Rhodes scholar Rhodes Trust, 1976; recipient Investigator award Hood Found. Med. Rsch., Boston, 1985, Cancer Rsch. Investigator award Cancer Rsch. Inst., N.Y.C., 1990, Med. scholarship Charles Culpeper Found., 1992, Med. scholar Edward Mallnokrodt Found., 1992, Established Investigator award Am. Heart Assn., 1993; Searle scholar Searle Family Trust, Chgo., 1989. Mem. AAAS, Am. Soc. Cell Biology, Soc. Murosal Immunology. Democrat. Jewish. Office: U Calif San Francisco Sch Med 513 Parnassus Ave San Francisco CA 94143-6513

MOSTOVOY, MARC SANDERS, conductor, music director; b. Phila., July 1, 1942; s. Ira and Floretta (Schiff)M. MusB, Temple U., 1963; postgrad. musicology U. Pa., 1964-66; pvt. study in U.S.A., France, 1950-66; MusD (hon.), Combs Coll. of Music, 1980; diploma, Academie di Musique, Nice, France. Conductor, music dir. Concerto Soloists of Phila., 1964—; also dir., 1964—; cultural advisor to gov., Commonwealth of Pa., Harrisburg, 1971-77; music dir. Mozart on the Square, Phila., 1980-91, also dir., 1980-91; music advisor Walnut St. Theater, Phila., 1970—; editor various music compositions. Mem. adv. com. arts and cultural council Greater Phila. C. of C., 1984-88; mem. program adv. com. Nat. Mus. Am. Jewish History, 1985-86; bd. dirs. Citizens for the Arts in Pa., 1984-86; Condr. numerous nat. and internat. concert tours with Concerto Soloists Chamber Orch. of Phila.; artistic dir. Laurel Festival of the Arts, Jim Thorpe, Pa., 1990—; mem. music adv. panel Pa. Coun. on the Arts, 1991-92. Recipient Orpheus Club award, 1958; Gov.'s citation, Commonwealth of Pa., 1976; Mayor's citation City of Phila., 1984; Temple U. scholar, 1960-63. Mem. Mus. Fund Soc. of Phila., Greater Phila. C. of C. Jewish. Office: Concerto Soloists Chamber Orch care Walnut St Theatre 9th & Walnut Sts Philadelphia PA 19107

MOSTOW, GEORGE DANIEL, mathematics educator; b. Boston, July 4, 1923; m. Isaac J. and Ida (Rotman) M.; m. Evelyn Davidoff, Sept. 1, 1947; children: Mark Alan, David Jechiel, Carol Held, Jonathan Carl. B.A., Harvard U., 1943, M.A., 1946, Ph.D., 1948; DSc (hon.), U. Ill., Chgo., 1989. Instr. math. Princeton U., 1947-48; mem. Inst. Advanced Study, 1947-49, 56-57, 75, trustee, 1982-92; asst. prof. Syracuse U., 1949-52; asst. prof. math. Johns Hopkins U., 1952-53, assoc. prof., 1954-56, prof., 1957-61; prof. math. Yale U., 1961-66, James E. English prof. math., 1966-81, Henry Ford II prof. math., 1981—, chmn., 1971-74; vis. prof. Conselho Nat. des Pesquisas, Inst. de Matematica, Rio de Janiero, Brazil, 1953-54, VI, U. Paris, 1966-67, Hebrew U., Jerusalem, 1967, Tata Inst. Fundamental Rsch., Bombay, 1970, Inst. des Hautes Etudes Scientifiques, Bures-Sur-Yvette, 1966, 71, 75, Japan Soc. for Promotion of Sci., 1985, Eidgenossische Technische Hochschule, Switzerland, 1986; chmn. U.S. Nat. Com. for Math , 1971-73, 83-85, Office Math. Scis., NRC, 1975-78; mem. sci. adv. coun. Math. Scis. Rsch. Inst., Berkeley, Calif., 1988-91, Weizmann Inst., Israel, Tel Aviv U.; mem. vis. com. dept. math. Harvard U., 1975-81, MIT, 1981-94; Ritt lectr. Columbia U., 1982, Bergman lectr. Stanford U., 1983, Sachar lectr. Tel Aviv U., 1985, Karcher lectr. U. Okla., 1986, Markert lectr. Pa. State U., 1993. Assoc. editor Annals of Math, 1957-64, Trans. Am. Math. Soc., 1965-70; assoc. editor Jour. D'Analyse, 1994—; editor Am. Jour. Math, 1965-69; assoc. editor, 1969-79; author rsch. articles. Fulbright rsch. scholar, Utrecht U., The Netherlands; Guggenheim fellow, 1957-58. Mem. AAAS, NAS (chmn. sect. math. 1982-84), Am. Math. Soc. (pres. 1987-88, Steele prize 1993, 94), Internat. Math. Union (chmn. U.S. del. to gen. assembly Warsaw 1982, mem. exec. com. 1983-86), Phi Beta Kappa, Sigma Xi. Home: 25 Beechwood Rd Woodbridge CT 06525-1331 Office: Yale Univ Dept Mathematics New Haven CT 06520

MOSZKOWSKI, LENA IGGERS, secondary school educator; b. Hamburg, Mar. 8, 1930; d. Alfred G. and Lizzie (Minden) m. m Steven Alexander, Aug. 29, 1952 (div. Oct. 1977); children: Benjamin Charles, Richard David, Ronald Bertram. BS, U. Richmond, 1948; MS, U. Chgo., 1953; postgrad., UCLA, 1958. Tchr. Lab. asst. U. Chgo. Ben May Cancer Research Lab., Chgo., 1951-53; biology, sci. tchrs. Bishop Conaty High Sch., Los Angeles, 1967-68; chemistry, sci. tchr. St. Paul High Sch., Santa Fe Springs, Calif., 1968-69; chemistry, human ecology tchr. Marlborough Sch., Los Angeles, 1969-71; tchr. biology and sci. ecology L.A. Unified Sch. Dist., 1971—. Author: Termite Taxonomy Cryptotermes Haviland and C. Krybi, Madagascar, 1955, Ecology and Man, 1971, Parallels in Human and Biological Ecology, 1977, American Public Education, An Inside Journey, 1991-92. Founder, adminstr. com. mem. UCLA Student (and Practical Assistance Cooperative Furniture), Los Angeles, 1963-67; active participant UCLA Earth Day Program, Los Angeles, 1970. Recipient Va. Sci. Talent Search Winner Va. Acad. of Sci., 1946; Push Vol. Tchr. award John C. Fremont High Sch., Los Angeles, 1978. Mem. NEA, Calif. Tchrs. Assn., United Tchrs. L.A., Sierra Club. Democrat. Jewish. Avocations: civil rights, workers rights, redirecting public education, photography, animals. Home: 3301 Shelburne Rd Baltimore MD 21208

MOTAYED, ASOK K., engineering company executive. MS, Rutgers U., 1974. Pres. Sheladia Assoc., Inc., Rockville, Md., 1979—. Office: Sheladia Assoc Inc 15825 Shady Grove Rd Rockville MD 20850*

MOTE, CLAYTON DANIEL, JR., mechanical engineer, educator, administrator; b. San Francisco, Feb. 5, 1937; s. Clayton Daniel and Eugenia (Isnardi) M.; m. Patricia Jane Lewis, Aug. 18, 1962; children: Melissa Michelle, Adam Jonathan. BSc, U. Calif., Berkeley, 1959, MS, 1960, PhD, 1963. Registered prof. engr. Calif. Asst. specialist U. Calif. Forest Products Labs., 1961-62; asst. mech. engr., 1962-63; lectr. mech. engring. U. Calif., Berkeley, 1962-63, asst. prof., 1967-69, asst. research engr., 1968-69, assoc. prof., assoc. research engr., 1969-73, prof., 1973—, vice chmn. mech. engring. dept., 1976-80, 83-86, chmn. mech. engring. dept., 1987-91, vice

chancellor univ. rels., FANUC chair mech. systems, 1991—; research fellow U. Birmingham, Eng., 1963-64; asst. prof. Carnegie Inst. Tech., 1964-67; vis. prof. Norwegian Inst. Wood Tech., 1972-73, vis. sr. scientist, 1976, 78, 80, 84, 85; cons. in engring. design and analysis; sr. scientist Alexander Von Humboldt Found., Fed. Republic Germany, 1988, Japan Soc. for Promotion of Sci., 1991; mem. adv. bd. for mech. engring. Ga. Inst. Tech., Carnegie Mellon U.; pres. U. Calif. Berkeley Found.; trustee Behring-Hofmann Ednl. Inst. Mem. editorial bd. Soma, Jour. Sound and Vibration; contbr. articles to profl. jours.; patentee in field. NSF fellow, 1963-64; recipient Disting. Teaching award, U. Calif., 1971, Pi Tau Sigma Excellence in Teaching award, U. Calif., 1975, Humboldt Prize, Fed. Republic Germany, 1988, Frederick W. Taylor Rsch. medal. Soc. Mfg. Engrs., 1991, Hetenyi award Soc. Exptl. Mechanics, 1992. Fellow NAE, AAAS, ASME (Blackall award 1975, v.p. environ. and transp. 1986-90, nat. chmn. noise control and acoustics 1978-79, Disting. Svc. award 1991, Charles Russ Richards award 1994, Rayleigh lectr. 1994), Internat. Acad. Wood Sci., Acoustical Soc. Am.; mem. ASTM (com. on snow skiing F-27 1984-87, chmn. new projects subcom.), Am. Acad. Mechanics, Am. Soc. Biomechanics, Orthopaedic Rsch. Soc., Internat. Soc. Skiing Safety (v.p., sec. 1977-85, bd. dirs. 1977—, chmn. com. 1985—), Sigma Xi, Pi Tau Sigma, Tau Beta Pi. Office: U Calif 2440 Bancroft Way Berkeley CA 94704-1609

MOTHERWAY, JOSEPH EDWARD, mechanical engineer, educator; b. Providence, Jan. 28, 1930; s. Edward John and Josephine Dorothea (Conway) M.; m. Sally Alicia Doherty, June 11, 1955; children: Carmel A., Suzanne M., Joseph Edward, Mavis E., Melita A., Megan L., William D., Edward J., Mara A. Sc.B., Brown U., 1955; M.S., U. Conn., 1961; postgrad., Columbia U., 1965-67; Ph.D., U. Conn., 1970. Mech. engr. Standard Oil (N.J.), Bayway, 1955-56; design engr. Electric Boat div. Gen. Dynamic Corp., Groton, Conn., 1956-58; design group leader Electric Boat div. Gen. Dynamic Corp., 1958-59; sr. project engr. Remington Rand Univac Lab., South Norwalk, Conn., 1959-60; chief engr. C.H.I. div. Textron, Inc., Warwick, R.I., 1960-64; lectr. Brown U., Providence, 1962-64; asst. prof. mech. engring. U. Bridgeport, Conn., 1964-65; assoc. prof. U. Bridgeport, 1965-70, Bullard prof. engring. design, 1970-82, head dept. mech. engring., 1971-75; prof. mech. engring. U. Mass., 1982—; pres. Alpha Engring. Co., 1975—; Cons. U.S. Navy, 1965-69, Dorr-Oliver Inc., Consol. Controls Corp., Energy Research Corp., Malcolm Pirnie Engrs. Assoc. editor: Jour. Mech. Design, 1978-80; contbr. articles to profl. jours. Served with USMC, 1949-53. Recipient Engring. Service award Brown Engring. Assn., 1962; NSF Sci. Faculty fellow, 1968-69. Mem. ASME, Soc. Exptl. Mechanics, Am. Soc. Engring. Edn., Brown Engring. Assn. (pres. 1968-69), Sigma Xi, Tau Beta Pi. Home: 360 Earle Dr North Kingstown RI 02852-6245 Office: Dept Mech Engring U Mass Amherst MA 01003

MOTIN, REVELL JUDITH, data processing executive; b. Bayonne, N.J., July 24, 1941; d. Charles and Belle (Laks) Motin; children from a previous marriage: Laura Mantell, Deborah Mantell. BS in Psychology cum laude, Bklyn. Coll., CUNY, 1969. Systems analyst Univac div. Sperry Corp., N.Y.C., 1961-66; programmer, analyst J.C. Penney Co., N.Y.C., 1966-67; systems and programming cons. Automated Concepts, Inc., N.Y.C., 1968-72; ind. systems and programming cons. N.Y.C., 1972-76; mgr. systems and programming Citibank, NA, N.Y.C., 1976-83; v.p. data processing Columbia Savs. Bank S.L.A., Fair Lawn, N.J., 1983—. Mem. Fin. Mgrs. Soc., Mensa. Jewish. Home: 3 Jockey Ln New City NY 10956-6608 Office: Columbia Savs Bank SLA 25-00 Broadway Fair Lawn NJ 07410-3830

MOTLEY, CONSTANCE BAKER (MRS. JOEL WILSON MOTLEY), federal judge, former city official; b. New Haven, Sept. 14, 1921; d. Willoughby Alva and Rachel (Huggins) Baker; m. Joel Wilson Motley, Aug. 18, 1946; 1 son, Joel Wilson III. A.B., N.Y. U., 1943; LL.B., Columbia U., 1946. Bar: N.Y. bar 1948. Mem. Legal Def. and Ednl. Fund, NAACP, 1945-65; mem. N.Y. State Senate, 1964-65; pres. Manhattan Borough, 1965-66; U.S. dist. judge So. Dist. N.Y., 1966-82, chief judge, 1982-86, sr. judge, 1986—. Mem. N.Y. State Adv. Council Employment and Unemployment Ins., 1958-64. Mem. Assn. Bar City N.Y. Office: US Dist Ct US Courthouse Foley Sq New York NY 10007-1501

MOTLEY, JOHN PAUL, psychiatrist, consultant; b. Carbondale, Pa., July 5, 1927; s. Joseph Adrian and Lillian (McCormick) M.; BS, Georgetown U., 1951; MD, Hahnemann Med. Coll., Phila., 1955; m. Barbara Bennett Mitchell, Feb. 1, 1958 (div.); children: Marianne, Patricia, Kathleen, John Paul, Elizabeth, Joseph A. III, Grace, Michael. Intern, Hahnemann Med. Coll. Hosp., Phila., 1955-56; resident in psychiatry Inst. of Living, Hartford, Conn., 1956-59; practice medicine specializing in psychiatry, Point Pleasant, N.J., 1961—; mem. staff Jersey Shore Med. Ctr., 1961-72; chief of psychiatry, 1970-72; mem. staff Point Pleasant Hosp., 1961—, chief of psychiatry, 1961—; sec. Key Edn. Co., Shrewsbury, N.J., 1981—; cons. in forensic psychiatry to various cts. and agys. Served with U.S. Army, 1944-46, ETO. Diplomate Am. Bd. Psychiatry and Neurology. Fellow Am. Psychiat. Assn.; mem. AMA, Royal Coll. Psychiatry, Am. Coll. Psychiatry, N.J. Psychiat. Assn. (past pres.). Clubs: Springlake Golf. Republican. Roman Catholic. Office: 3822 River Rd Point Pleasant Beach NJ 08742-2067

MOTLEY, THOMAS, JR., lawyer; b. Boston, Feb. 7, 1942; s. Thomas and Barbara (Chandler) M.; divorced; children: Thomas III, Sarah, Elisabeth. BA cum laude, Harvard Coll., 1963; LLB, Columbia U., 1966. Bar: N.Y. 1966, Mass. 1973. Assoc. Davis Polk & Wardwell, N.Y.C., 1966-69, 71-72, Paris, 1969-71; assoc. Gaston & Snow, Boston, 1972-73, ptnr., 1973—. Editor: Business in Massachusetts: A Guide for Foreign Investors, 1979. mem. Boston Bar Assn., Harvard Club Boston, Marshall St. Hist. Soc. Office: Gaston & Snow One Federal St Boston MA 02110-2099

MOTT, STEWART RAWLINGS, business executive, political activist; b. Flint, Mich., Dec. 4, 1937; s. Charles Stewart and Ruth (Rawlings) M.; m. Kappy Wells, Oct. 13, 1979; 1 child, Samuel Apple Axle. Grad., Deerfield (Mass.) Acad., 1955; B.S. in Bus. Adminstrn, Columbia, 1961, B.A. in Comparative Lit. 1961, postgrad. English lit., 1961-62. Exec. trainee various cos., 1956-63; English instr. Eastern Mich. U., 1963-64; corp. dir. U.S. Sugar Corp., Clewiston, Fla., 1965—; investor various diversified cos., 1968—. Founder Flint Community Planned Parenthood, 1963; pres., founder Spectemur Agendo (merged with S.R. Mott Charitable Trust 1989), N.Y.C. and Flint, 1965—; bd. dirs. Fund For Peace, N.Y.C., 1967—, S.R. Mott Charitable Trust, 1968—, Nat. Com. for Effective Congress, N.Y.C., 1968-Planned Parenthood Fedn. Am. 1964-81, Am. Commn. on U.S.-Soviet Rels., 1977-92, Citizens Research Found., 1977—, Ams. for Dem. Action, 1978-90, Friends of Family Planning, 1979-84, Voters for Choice, 1979-89; bd. dirs. founder Fund Constl. Govt., 1974—; bd. dirs. Population Action Council, 1978-82; maj. donor McCarthy, McGovern, Anderson campaigns. Mem. Phi Beta Kappa. *At age 18 I realized that two problems confront planet earth that dwarf and aggravate all conventional problems: namely the threat of nuclear war and the continuing worldwide population explosion. Coming to grips with these realities, I decided to dedicate my life to help find solutions to these two problems through public service in philanthropy and politics.*

MOTT, VINCENT VALMON, publisher, author; b. Washington, La., Sept. 18, 1916; s. Lucius and Marie (LeDoux) M.; m. Margaret McDonald, June 19, 1948; children: Vincent Valmon, Helene Virginia, John Michael. AB, Xavier U., 1938; MA, Fordham U., 1947, PhD, 1956. Instr. social sci. U. Scranton, Pa., 1947-51; instr. econs. Seton Hall U., South Orange, N.J., 1952-53; asst. prof. Seton Hall U., 1954-58, assoc. prof., 1958-66, prof. mktg., 1966—; adj. asso. prof. sociology St. Peters Coll., Jersey City, 1955-60; Pres. Florham Park Press, Florham Park, N.J., 1957—; pres., principal stockholder V.V.R.&D., Inc. Author: The American Consumer, 1972, (with N. Chirovsky) Philosophy in Economic Thought, 1972, Philosophical Foundations of Economic Doctrines, 1978, The Creole, 1991, Academia Revisited, 1994; editor: Jour. Bus., Seton Hall U., 1963-64. Mem. bd. advisers Scranton Inst. Indsl. Relations, 1949-50. Served with AUS, 1940-45. Home and Office: 12 Leslie Ave Florham Park NJ 07932-2165

MOTT, WILLIAM CHAMBERLAIN, lawyer, retired naval officer; b. Maplewood, N.J., Sept. 7, 1911; s. Raymond Louis and Helen (Chamberlain) M.; m. Rosemary Blake, Sept. 17, 1938 (div. 1947); children: Adam S., Janie B.; m. Edith Grace, Nov. 13, 1947; children: Diane B., Lucy A., Sarah G., William Chamberlain. B.S., U.S. Naval Acad., 1933; LL.D., George Washington U., 1940; LL.D., John Marshall Law Sch., 1961, Rhode Island Coll.,

1964. Bar: D.C. 1940. Patent examiner Washington, 1936-40; commd. lt. (j.g.) U.S. Navy, 1939, advanced through grades to rear adm., 1960; asst. naval aide to Pres. Roosevelt, 1942-43; assigned (Amphibious Forces Pacific), 1944-45; liaison (UN and Dept. of State), 1946-48; legal adviser comdr. in chief (Pacific Area Command), 1948-50; comdg. officer (Sch. Naval Justice), 1950-53; spl. asst., chmn. (Joint Chiefs Staff), 1954-58; dep. judge adv. gen. (Office Judge Adv. Gen., Dept. of Navy), 1958-60, judge adv. gen., 1960-64; exec. dir. (Council on Econs. and Nat. Security). Exec. v.p. U.S. Ind. Telephone Assn., 1964-77; pres. Capital Legal Found.; chmn. adv. com. Nat. Strategic Materials and Minerals Program. Decorated Legion of Merit. Fellow Am. Bar Found.; mem. Am. Soc. Internat. Law, Am. Bar Assn., Fed. Bar Assn. Episcopalian. Clubs: Army and Navy, Farmington, Chevy Chase. Home: 9 N Dogwood Ln Charlottesville VA 22901-1907

MOTTALE, MOIS, oil industry executive. With Fallek Chemical Internat., Milan, Italy, 1974-80; pres., ceo. Aectra Refining and Marketing, Houston, 1980—. Office: Aectra Refining & Marketing 3 Riverway Ste 800 Houston TX 77056-1909

MOTTET, NORMAN KARLE, pathologist, educator; b. Renton, Wash., Jan. 8, 1924; s. Louis John and Amalia (Lentzner) M.; m. Nancy Noble, June 21, 1952; children: Gretchen, Kurt, Mark. BS summa cum laude, Wash. State U., 1947; MD, Yale U., 1952. Diplomate: Am. bd. Pathology. Postdoctoral fellow Strangeways Research Lab., Cambridge, Eng., 1952-53, vis. scientist, 1969-70; rotating intern, then intern in pathology Yale Med. Ctr., 1953-55, resident in pathology, 1955-56, mem. faculty Med. Sch., 1951-52, 55-59; pathologist, dir. labs. Griffin Hosp., Derby, Conn., 1955-59; mem. faculty U. Wash. Med. Sch., Seattle, 1959—, prof. pathology, 1966—; dir. hosp. pathology Univ. Hosp. U. Wash. Med. Sch., Seattle, 1959-74; mem. extramural program council Fred Hutchinson Carcer Research Ctr., 1975. Contbr. articles to med. jours.; mem. editorial bds. Served with AUS, 1942-45. James Hudson Brown fellow, from Conn. for Found. Infantile Paralysis, 1952-53; recipient Keese prize Yale U., 1952; trainee fellowship USPHS, 1954-55; spl. rsch. fellow USPHS, 1969-70. Fellow Am. Soc. Clin. Pathology; mem. AAAS, Am. Soc. Pathology, Tetatology Soc., Internat. Soc. Trace Element Research, Internat. Com. Occupational Health, Internat. Com. Trace Metals, Sigma Xi, Alpha Omega Alpha. Home: E 360 Old Olson Rd Shelton WA 98584 Office: U Wash Sch Medicine Dept Path Seattle WA 98195

MOTTL, RONALD M., state legislator, lawyer; b. Cleve., Feb. 6, 1934; s. Milton and Anna Huml; m. Debra Budan; children: Ronald Jr., Ronda, Ron Michael, Amanda L. BS, Notre Dame U., 1956, LLB, 1957. Asst. law dir. City of Cleve., 1958-60; councilman Ward 2 City Coun., Parma, Ohio, 1960-61; pres. Parma City Coun., 1961-66; mem. Ohio Ho. of Reps., Columbus, 1967-68, 87—, Ohio State Senate, Columbus, 1969-74, U.S. Ho. of Reps., Washington, 1975-82; pres. Parma Sch. Bd., 1985; ptnr. Cassidy & Mottl, Cleve. State rep. Ohio House of Reps., 1986—. With U.S. Army, 1957. Mem. ABA, Ohio Bar Assn., Cuyahoga Bar Assb., Cleve. Bar Assn., Parma Bar Assn. Roman Catholic. Home: 10626 Stone Hinge N Royalton OH 44133-1997 Office: Cassidy & Mottl 6285 Pearl Rd Cleveland OH 44130-3069

MOTTO, JEROME ARTHUR, psychiatry educator; b. Kansas City, Mo., Oct. 16, 1921. MD, U. Calif., San Francisco, 1951. Diplomate Am. Bd. Neurology and Psychiatry. Intern San Francisco Gen. Hosp., 1951-52; resident Johns Hopkins Hosp., Balt., 1952-55; sr. resident U. Calif., San Francisco, 1955-56, from asst. prof. to prof. emeritus., 1956—. Contbr. articles to profl. jours. With AUS, 1942-46; ETO. Fellow Am. Psychiatric Assn. (life).

MOTTOLA, GARY F., lawyer; b. Englewood, N.J., May 2, 1947; s. Ross F. and Marie (Richards) M.; m. Irene Mottola, Apr. 19, 1981; 1 child, Alexandra. AB, Harvard U., 1969; JD, U. Calif., Berkeley, 1972. Bar: N.Y. 1973, N.J. 1977. Ptnr. Simpson Thacher & Bartlett, N.Y.C.; prof. law Vt. Law Sch. Office: Simpson Thacher & Bartlett 425 Lexington Ave New York NY 10017-3954

MOTTRAM-DOSS, RENÉE, corporate executive; b. Erie, Pa., Apr. 7, 1939; d. Robert Harlan and Anita Gray; m. Arden Doss Jr., Mar. 7, 1986; children from previous marriage: Lisa Marie Mottram, Jeffrey Scott Mottram. Student, Barry U., 1968-70, Vt. State Coll., 1975-76. Various positions D.W.G. Corp., Royal Crown Cola, Arby's, Victor Posner Affiliated Cos., Miami Beach, Fla., 1972-90, sr. v.p., 1989—; chmn. Renar Devel. Co. St. Lucie West, Fla., 1990—. Bd. dirs. Coconut Grove Playhouse, Miami, Barry U., Miami. Recipient Twin award YWCA, 1984; named Outstanding Woman of Yr. Dade County Fla., 1983. Office: 401 SW Fairway Lndg Port Saint Lucie FL 34986-2124

MOTULSKY, ARNO GUNTHER, geneticist, physician, educator; b. Fischhausen, Germany, July 5, 1923; came to U.S., 1941; s. Herman and Rena (Sass) Molton; m. Gretel C. Stern, Mar. 22, 1945; children: Judy, Harvey, Arlene. Student, Cen. YMCA Coll., Chgo., 1941-43, Yale U., 1943-44; BS, U. Ill., 1945, MD, 1947, DSc (hon.), 1982, MD (hon.), 1991. Diplomate Am. Bd. Internal Medicine, Am. Bd. Med. Genetics. Intern, fellow, resident Michael Reese Hosp., Chgo., 1947-51; staff mem. charge clin. investigation dept. hematology Army Med. Service Grad. Sch., Walter Reed Army Med. Ctr., Washington, 1952-53; research assoc. internal medicine George Washington U. Sch. Medicine, 1952-53; from instr. to assoc. prof. dept. medicine U. Wash. Sch. Medicine, Seattle, 1953-61, prof. medicine, prof. genetics, 1961—; head div. med. genetics, dir. genetics clinic Univ. Hosp., Seattle, 1959-89; dir. Ctr. for Inherited Diseases, Seattle, 1972-90; attending physician Univ. Hosp., Seattle; cons. Pres.'s Commn. for Study of Ethical Problems in Medicine and Biomed. and Behavioral Research, 1979-83; cons. various coms. NRC, NIH, WHO, others. Editor Am. Jour. Human Genetics, 1969-75, Human Genetics, 1969—, Commonwealth Fund fellow in human genetics Univ. Coll., London, 1957-58; John and Mary Markle scholar in med. sci., 1957-62; fellow Ctr. Advanced Study in Behavioral Scis., Stanford U., 1976-77, Inst. Advanced Study, Berlin, 1984. Fellow ACP, AAAS; mem. NAS, Internat. Soc. Hematology, Am. Fedn. Clin. Research, Genetics Soc. Am., Western Soc. Clin. Research, Am. Soc. Human Genetics, Am. Soc. Clin. Investigation, Am. Assn. Physicians, Inst. of Medicine, Am. Acad. Arts and Scis. Home: 4347 53d Ave NE Seattle WA 98105 Office: U Wash Div Med Genetics RG-25 Seattle WA 98195

MOTZ, DIANA GRIBBON, judge; b. Washington, July 15, 1943; d. Daniel McNamara and Jane (Retzler) Gribbon; m. John Frederick Motz, Sept. 20, 1968; children: Catherine Jane, Daniel Gribbon. BA, Vassar Coll., 1965, LLB, U. Va., 1968. Bar: U.S. Dist. Ct. Md. 1969, U.S. Ct. Appeals (4th cir.) 1969, U.S. Supreme Ct. 1980. Assoc. Piper & Marbury, Balt., 1968-71; asst. atty. gen. State of Md., Balt., 1972-81, chief of litigation 1981-86; ptnr. Frank, Bernstein, Conaway & Goldman, Balt., 1986-91; judge Md. Ct. of Special Appeals, Md., 1991-94, U.S. Ct. Appeals (4th Cir.), 1994—. Mem. ABA, Md. Bar Assn., Balt. Bar Assn. (exec. com. 1988), Am. Law Inst., Am. Bar Found., Md. Bar Found., Lawyers Round Table, Fed. Cts. Study Com., Wranglers Law Club. Roman Catholic. Office: Ste 920 101 Lombard St Baltimore MD 21201

MOTZ, JOHN FREDERICK, federal judge; b. Balt., Dec. 30, 1942; s. John Eldered and Catherine (Grauel) M.; m. Diana Jane Gribbon, Sept. 20, 1968; children: Catherine Jane, Daniel Gribbon. AB, Wesleyan U., Conn., 1964; LLB, U. Va., 1967. Bar: Md. 1967, U.S. Ct. Appeals (4th cir.) 1968, U.S. Dist. Ct. Md. 1968. Law clk. to Hon. Harrison L. Winter U.S. Ct. Appeals (4th cir.), 1967-68; Assoc. Venable, Baetjer & Howard, Balt., 1968-69; asst. U.S. atty. U.S. Atty's. Office, Balt., 1969-71; assoc. Venable, Baetjer & Howard, Balt., 1971-75, ptnr., 1976-81; U.S. atty. U.S. Atty's Office, Balt., 1981-85; judge U.S. Dist. Ct. Md., Balt., 1985—. Trustees Friends Sch. Balt., 1970-77, 1981-88, Sheppard Pratt Hosp., 1987—. Mem. ABA, Md. State Bar Assn., Balt. Bar Assn., Am. Bar Found., Am. Law Inst., Am. Coll. Trial Lawyers. Republican. Mem. Soc. of Friends. Office: US Dist Ct 101 W Lombard St Rm 510 Baltimore MD 21201-2607

MOTZ, KENNETH LEE, former farm organization official; b. Grand Junction, Colo., Mar. 6, 1922; s. Harold I. and Acquila (Ulmer) M.; m. Margaret Florence Mitchell, Oct. 9, 1948; children: Gwendolyn Ann,

Stephen Mitchell. AA, Mesa Jr. Coll., 1942; BS, Denver U., 1947. Bookkeeper Farmers Union Mktg. Assn., Denver, 1942-43; asst. sec. Nat. Farmers Union, Denver, 1947-50, 59-66, sec.-treas., 1966-72, 85-86, treas., asst. sec., 1972-85, retired, 1987; treas. Green Thumb, Inc., 1980-85, sec.-treas., 1985-86, retired, 1987; ins. acct. Nat. Farmers Union Ins. Cos., Denver, 1952-59. sec. uniform pension com. Nat. Farmers Union, 1959-93; Dem. precinct committeeman, 1960-68; elder Calvary Presbyn. Ch. Maj. USMCR, ret. 1982. Mem. Masons, Delta Sigma Pi. Home: 11186 E Baltic Dr Aurora CO 80014-1070

MOUCH, FRANK MESSMAN, college president, priest. BA, Pontifical Coll.; MEd, U. Fla.; STL, Angelicum U., Rome. Ordained priest Roman Cath. Ch., 1958. Pres. Cardinal Mooney High Sch., Sarasota, Fla., 1966-68; suptd. edn. Diocese of St. Petersburg, Fla., 1968-74; trustee St. Leo (Fla.) Coll., 1970-74, pres., 1987—; rector Pontifical Coll. Josephinum, 1974-84; dir. planning, devel., communications and bldg. Diocese of Venice, Fla., 1984-86; bd. dirs. Fla. Cath., 1985-87; trustee St. Vincent de Paul Sem., Boynton Beach, Fla., 1985-87, Acad. of Holy Names of Fla., 1992—; chaplain Cath. students U. Fla., 1964-66; asst. chancellor Diocese of St. Augustine, Fla., 1963-64; pastor Holy Redeemer Ch., Jacksonville, Fla., St. Martha Ch., Sarasota, others. Mem. Pontifical Coll. Alumni Assn. (Outstanding Alumni of Yr. 1987). Office: St Leo Coll Office of Pres 33701 State Rd 52W Saint Leo FL 33574-9999

MOUCHLY-WEISS, HARRIET, business executive; b. N.Y.C., Aug. 12, 1942; d. Robert and Anita (Shawmut) Berg; m. Charles Weiss, Sept. 13, 1975; children: Noa, Yoav. BA, Muhlenberg Coll., 1960; MA in Clin. Psychology, Hebrew U., 1964; 1993—. Clin. psychologist Hadassah Hosp., Israel, 1962-65; chmn. Ruder & Finn, Israel, 1968-80; sr. v.p. Ruder Finn & Rotman, N.Y.C., 1980-86; pres. GCI Internat., N.Y.C., 1986-92; mng. dir. Strategy XXI Group, Ltd., N.Y.C., 1993—. Bd. dirs. N.Y. State Gov.'s World Trade Coun., Com. for Econ. Growth Israel; bd. dirs. U. Haifa, Capital Circle, Com. for Econ. Growth of Israel, Israel Policy Forum; trustee Internat. Ctr. for Peace in the Mid. East; state of the world forum adv. Friends of the U.N., The Chinese Found. of Culture and Arts for Children. Recipient cert. of appreciation, HUD. Mem. Women in Commns., Pub. Rels. Soc. Am., Internat. Pub. Rels. Assn., Com. of 200 (N.E. chair), Friends of UN. Avocations: art, art history, politics. Office: Strategy XXI Group Ltd 515 Madison Ave 34th Fl New York NY 10022

MOUDON, ANNE VERNEZ, urban design educator; b. Yverdon, Vaud, Switzerland, Dec. 24, 1945; came to U.S., 1966; d. Ernest Edouard and Mauricette Lina (Duc) M.; m. Dimitrios Constantine Seferis, Dec. 30, 1982; children: Louisa Moudon, Constantine Thomas. BArch with honors, U. Calif., Berkeley, 1969; DSc, Ecole Poly. Fed., Lausanne, Switzerland, 1987. Fed. Register of Swiss Architects. Rsch. assoc. Bldg. Systems Devel., Inc., San Francisco, 1969-70; sr. project planner J. C. Warnecke and Assocs., N.Y.C., 1973-74; archtl. cons. McCue, Boone & Tomsick, San Francisco, 1974-76; asst. to assoc. prof. architecture MIT, Cambridge, Mass., 1975-81, Ford internat. career chair, 1977-79; assoc. prof. urban design U. Wash., Seattle, 1981-87, prof. architecture, landscape architecture, urban design and planning, 1987—, dir. urban design program, 1987-93, assoc. dean acad. affairs Coll. Arch. & Urban Planning, 1992-95; dir. Cascadia Cmty. and Environ. Inst., Seattle, 1993—; lectr. in architecture U. Calif., Berkeley, 1973-75; sec. Assn. Collegiate Schs. of Architecture, 1978-80; sr. rschr. Kungl Tekniska Hogskolan, Sch. of Architecture, Stockholm, 1989. Author: Built for Change, 1986; editor: Public Streets for Public Use, 1987, 91, (monograph) Master-Planned Communities, 1990; contbr. articles to profl. jours. Recipient seven rsch. grants Nat. Endowment for the Arts, Washington, 1976-89, individual fellowship, 1986-87, Applied Rsch. award Progressive Architecture, 1983, two rsch. grants Wash. State Dept. Transp., Seattle, 1991-92. Fellow Inst. for Urban Design; mem. Internat. Assn. for the Study of People in Their Phys. Surroundings, Orgn. Women Architects, Tau Sigma Delta. Avocations: walking, gardening, skiing. Home: 3310 E Laurelhurst Dr NE Seattle WA 98105-5336 Office: U Wash Urban Design Gould Hall JO-40 Gould Hall Seattle WA 98195

MOUDRIANAKIS, EVANGELOS N., cell biology and biochemistry educator, biomedical researcher; b. Chania, Greece, Feb. 12, 1939; came to U.S., 1960; s. Nikolaos M. and Eudokia S. (Katzourakis) M. B.Sc., U. Athens, Greece, 1959; diploma, Greek Atomic Energy Commn., Athens, 1960; M.A., Johns Hopkins U., 1963, Ph.D., 1964. Instr. genetics lab. U. Athens., Greece, 1959-60; research assoc. Johns Hopkins U., Balt., 1964-65, asst. prof., 1965-68, assoc. prof., 1968-73, prof. cell biology and biochemistry, 1973—, prof. biophysics, 1986—; cons. NSF, 1975-78, dir. NSF biochemistry program, 1980-81. Mem. editorial bd.: Jour. Bioenergetics, 1977-83, Biophys. Jour., 1977-80, Gene Analysis Techniques, 1983—. Recipient Disting. Young Scientist of Yr. award Md. Acad. Sci., 1970. Mem. Am. Soc. Biol. Chemists, Am. Soc. Cell Biology, Soc. Devel. Biology, Biophys. Soc., Am. Chem. Soc., Am. Soc. Photobiology. Office: Dept Biology Johns Hopkins U Charles Street St Baltimore MD 21201

MOUL, MAXINE BURNETT, state official; b. Oakland, Nebr., Jan. 26, 1947; d. Einer and Eva (Jacobson) Burnett; m. Francis Moul, Apr. 20, 1972; 1 child, Jeff. BS in Journalism, U. Nebr., 1969; DHL (hon.), Peru State Coll., 1993. Sunday feature writer, photographer Sioux City Iowa Jour., 1969-71; reporter, photographer, editor Maverick Media, Inc., Syracuse, Nebr., 1971-73, editor, pub., 1974-83, pres., 1983-90; grant writer, asst. coord. Nebr. Regional Med. Program, Lincoln, 1973-74; lt. gov. State of Nebr., Lincoln, 1991-93; dir. Dept. Econ. Devel., Lincoln, 1993—. Mem. Dem. Nat. Com., Washington, 1988-92, Nebr. Dem. State Ctrl. Com., Lincoln, 1974-88; del. Dem. Nat. Conf., 1972, 88, 92; mem. exec. com. Nebr. Dem. Party, Lincoln, 1988-93. Recipient Margaret Sanger award Planned Parenthood, Lincoln, 1991, Champion of Small Bus. award Nebr. Bus. Devel. Ctr., Omaha, 1991, Toll fellowship Coun. State Govts., Lexington, Ky., 1992. Mem. Bus. and Profl. Womem, Nebr. Mgmt. Assn. (Silver Knight award 1992), Nat. Conf. Lt. Govs. (bd. dirs. 1991-93), Nebr. Press Women, Women Execs. in State Govt., Cmty. Devel. Soc., U. Nebr.-Lincoln Journalism Alumni. Democrat. Avocations: reading, gardening. Office: State of Nebr PO Box 94666 Lincoln NE 68509-4666

MOUL, WILLIAM CHARLES, lawyer; b. Columbus, Ohio, Jan. 12, 1940; s. Charles Emerson and Lillian Ann (Mackenbach) M.; m. Margine Ann Tessendorf, June 10, 1962; children—Gregory, Geoffrey. B.A., Miami U., Oxford, Ohio, 1961; J.D., Ohio State U., 1964. Bar: Ohio 1964, U.S. dist. Ct. (so. dist.) Ohio 1965, U.S. Ct. Appeals (2d cir.) 1982, U.S. Ct. Appeals (6th cir.) 1984, U.S. Ct. Appeals (3d cir.) 1985. Assoc., ptnr. George, Greek, King, McMahon & McConnaughey, Columbus, Ohio, 1964-79; ptnr. McConnaughey, Stradley, Mone & Moul, Columbus, 1979-81; ptnr.-in-charge Thompson, Hine & Flory, Columbus, 1981—. Chmn. Upper Arlington Civil Service Commn., Ohio, 1981-86. Mem. ABA, Ohio State Bar Assn. (labor sect. bd. 1983—), Columbus Bar Assn. (chmn. ethics com. 1980-82), Lawyers Club Columbus (pres. 1976-77), Athletic Club, Scioto Country Club, Wedgewood Country Club, Masons. Lutheran. Home: 2512 Danvers Ct Columbus OH 43220-2822 Office: Thompson Hine & Flory 10 W Broad St Ste 700 Columbus OH 43215-3673

MOULDER, WILLIAM H., chief of police; b. Kansas City, Mo., Feb. 19, 1938; s. Roscoe B. and Charleen M. (Flye) M.; m. Louise M. Pollaro, Aug. 2, 1957; children: Deborah, Ralph, Robert. BA, U. Mo., Kansas City, 1971, MA, 1976. Cert. police officer, Mo., Iowa. From police officer to maj. Kansas City (Mo.) Police Dept., 1959-84; chief of police City of Des Moines, 1984—. Mem. Internat. Assn. Chiefs of Police, Police Exec. Rsch. Forum, Iowa Police Exec. Forum. Avocations: racquetball, travel. Office: Office of Police Chief 25 E 1st St Des Moines IA 50309-4800

MOULDS, JOHN F., federal judge; m. Elizabeth Fry, Aug. 29, 1964; children: Donald B., Gerald B. Student, Stanford U., 1955-58; BA with honors, Calif. State U., Sacramento, 1960; JD, U. Calif, Berkeley, 1963. Bar: U.S. Supreme Ct., U.S. Dist. Ct. (no. dist.) Calif., U.S. Ct. Appeals (9th cir.) 1967, Calif. Rsch. analyst Calif. State Senate Fact-Finding Com. on Ed. Revenue, 1960-61; administrv. asst. Senator Albert S. Rodda, Calif., 1961-63; staff atty. Calif. Rural Legal Assistance, Marysville, 1966-68; dir. atty. Marysville field office and Sacramento legis. adv. office Calif. Rural Legal Assistance, 1968-69; staff atty. Sacramento Legal Aid, 1968-69; ptnr. Blackmon, Isenberg & Moulds,

1969-85, Isenberg, Moulds & Hemmer, 1985; judge U.S. Dist. Ct. (ea. dist.) Calif., 1985-88, chief judge, 1988—; moot ct. and trial practice judge U. Calif. Davis Law Sch., 1975—, U. of Pacific McGeorge Coll. Law, 1985—; part-time U.S. magistrate judge U.S. Dist. Ct. (ea. dist.) Calif., 1983-85; mem. 9th Cir. Capital Case Com., 1992—, U.S. Jud. Conf. Com. on the Magistrate Judge Sys., 1992—, Adv. Com. to the Magistrate Judges' Divsn. Adminstv. Office of U.S. Jud. Conf., 1989—. Author: (with others) Review of California Code Legislation, 1965, Welfare Recipients' Handbook, 1967; editor: Ninth Circuit Capital Punishment Handbook, 1991. Atty. Sacramento Singlemen's Self-Help Ctr., 1969-74; active Sacramento Human Relations Commn., 1969-75, chair, 1974-75; active community support orgn. U. Calif. at Davis Law Sch., 1971—; mem., atty. Sacramento Community Coalition for Media Change, 1972-75; bd. dirs. Sacramento Country Day Sch., 1982-90, Sacramento Pub. Libr. Found., 1985-87; active various polit. orgns. and campaigns, 1960-82. Mem. ABA, Fed. Bar Assn., Nat. Coun. Magistrates (cir. dir. 1986-88, treas. 1988-89, 2d v.p. 1989-90, 1st v.p. 1990-91), Fed. Magistrate Judges Assn. (pres.-elect 1991, pres. 1992-93), Calif. State-Fed. Jud. Coun. Conf. (panelist capital habeas corpus litigation 1992), Fed. Jud. Ctr. Training Conf. for U.S. Magistrate Judges (panel leader 1993), Milton L. Schwartz Inns of Ct. Office: 5054 US Courthouse 650 Capitol Mall Sacramento CA 95814-4708

MOULTHROP, EDWARD ALLEN, architect, artist; b. Rochester, N.Y., May 22, 1916; s. Ray Josiah and Jetta (McDonald) M.; m. Mae Elizabeth Crotser, Jan 31, 1942; children: Mark, Philip, Samuel, Timothy. B.Arch., Western Res. U., 1939; M.F.A., Princeton, 1941. Asst. prof. architecture Ga. Inst. Tech., 1943-46, asst. prof. physics, 1944-46; chief designer Robert and Co. Asso. Architects and Engrs., Atlanta, 1948-72; prin. Edward Allen Moulthrop (architect and cons.), Atlanta, 1972—; 1st chmn. Ga. Art Commn., 1954-65. Exhibited in, Watercolor U.S.A., 1962, USIA traveling show to Russia, crafts, 1970, Wichita Nat. Decorative Arts and Ceramics Exhbn., 1972, Ga. artists exhibit, High Mus. Art, Atlanta, 1971, 72, 74, Vatican Mus., Italy, 1978; represented in permanent collections, Mus. Modern Art, N.Y.C., Boston Mus. Fine Arts, Met. Mus. Art, N.Y.C. (Recipient Nat. Design award Am. Inst. Steel Constrn. 1959, 67, 1st Purchase award for crafts Atlanta Arts Festival 1963, 64, 67, 72, 74, 77, 78, Craftsman U.S. award of merit 1966, Judges Choice award Western Colo. Center for Arts 1973, purchase award 1975, prize Marietta Coll. Crafts Nat. 1974, 76, Craftwork prize Am. Crafts Council 1976, 78, Ga. Gov.'s Award in Arts 1981), USIA traveling show to Europe, crafts, 1990-93, The Art of Woodturning, 1993—, Permanent Collection of the White House, 1993. Fellow AIA (pres. Ga. chpt. 1953), Am. Craft Coun.; mem. Ga. Engring. Soc. (pres. 1958, spl. hon. mem. 1969), Am. Craftsmens Coun. (Ga. rep. 1973-75), Ga. Designer Craftsmen (pres. 1975-76). Home and Office: 4260 Carmain Dr NE Atlanta GA 30342-3504

MOULTHROP, JAMES SYLVESTER, research engineer, consultant; b. DuBois, Pa., Feb. 24, 1939; s. John Oliver Jr. and Pauline Margaret (Allen) M.; m. Martha Sue Mulloy, Sept. 14, 1963; children: James S. Jr., Margaret Winn, Mary Mulloy. BA, St. Joseph's Coll., Rensselaer, Ind., 1960; MS, Kans. state U., 1963. Registered profl. engr., Pa. Soils engr. Pa. Dept. Transp., Franklin and Harrisburg, 1963-72; materials engr. Pa. Dept. Transp., Harrisbvurg, 1972-81, dir. maintenance, 1981-83; regional engr. Chemkrete Techs., Inc., Wyckliff, Ohio, 1983-85; sr. applications engr. Exxon Chem. Co., Houston, 1985-87; rsch. engr. U. Tex., Austin, 1987-93; co-founder, sr. ptnr. Asphalt R & D Internat., Austin, 1993—; pres. Moulthrop Techs. Inc., Austin, 1994—; mem. Trasnp. Rsch. Bd., Washington, 1970—. Co-author manual: Statistical Quality Control of Highway Construction in Pennsylvania, 1975, Practical Applications of Statistical Quality Control in Highway Construction, 1979. With U.S. Army, 1963. Recipient Creativity award Nat. Univ. Extension Assn. Mem. ASTM (subcom. chair 1987—), Assn. Asphalt Paving Tech., Am. Soc. Hwy. Engrs. (sr.), Am. Concrete Inst. Achievements include chairing committee responsible for implementation of roadway management system in Pennsylvania, directing technical program for $50 million strategic highway research program in asphalt. Home: 7400 Anaqua Dr Austin TX 78750 Office: Moulthrop Techs Inc 8240 N Mopac Ste 280 Austin TX 78759

MOULTON, DAVID AUBIN, library director; b. Portsmouth, N.H., Nov. 20, 1952; s. Howard Turner and Dorothy Margaret (McLaughlin) M. BA in History, U. New Hampshire, 1974; MLS, Simmons Coll., 1976. Asst. libr. Strayer Coll., Washington, 1976-83; dir. LRC Strayer Coll., Arlington, Va., 1983-86; dir. lbrs. Strayer Coll., Washington, 1987—; chair library networking com. Consortium for Continuing Higher Edn. in No. Va., 1987. Mem. covenants com. Parc East Condominium, Alexandria, Va, 1987-90. Mem. ALA, Dist. of Columbia Libr. Assn., Va. Libr. Assn., Phi Delta Kappa. Avocation: collecting childrens and boy's books, 1820-1940. Office: Strayer Coll 1025 15th St NW Washington DC 20005-2603

MOULTON, EDWARD QUENTIN, civil engineer, educator; b. Kalamazoo, Nov. 16, 1926; s. Burt Frederick and Esther (Fairchild) M.; m. Joy Wade, Jan. 2, 1951; children: Jennifer Fairchild, Charles Wade, David Frederick II, Alison Joy. B.S., Mich. State U., 1947; M.S., La. State U., 1948; Ph.D., U. Calif.-Berkeley, 1956; D.Sc. (hon.), Wittenberg U., 1980; LL.D. (hon.), Xavier U., 1983, Wilmington Coll., 1983. Registered profl. engr., Ohio. Instr. civil engring Mich. State U., 1947; hydraulic engring. fellow La. State U., 1947-48; engr. U.S Waterways Expt. Sta., C.E., Vicksburg, Miss., 1948; research fellow U. Wis., 1948-49; asst. prof. civil engring. Auburn U., 1949-50; lectr. civil engring. U. Calif.-Berkeley, 1950-54; asst. prof. civil engring. Ohio State U., 1954-58, assoc. prof., 1958-64; asst. dean Ohio State U. (Grad. Sch.), 1958-62, assoc. dean Grad. Sch., Coll. Arts and Scis., chmn. geodetic sci., 1962-64, dean off-campus edn., asso. dean faculties for personnel budget, prof. engring. mechanics, 1964-66; dir. Coll. Sci. and Engring. Dayton campus Miami U.-Ohio State U., 1963-66; pres. U. S.D., 1966-68; exec. asst. to pres. Ohio State U., 1968-69, sec. trustees, 1968-79, prof. civil engring., 1968-79, v.p. adminstrv. ops., 1969-70, exec. v.p. adminstrv. ops., 1970-71, exec. v.p. 1971-73, v.p. bus. and adminstrn., 1973-79, v.p. sec. emeritus, 1984—; chancellor Ohio Bd. Regents, 1979-83, chancellor emeritus, 1984—; exec. v.p. Cranston Securities Co., 1983-84; pres. Lake Erie Coll., 1985-86; pres., gen. mgr. Columbus Symphony Orchestra, 1986-88; cons. civil engring. 1954—. Author articles, reports, bulls. on environ. engring. and edn. Trustee Blue Cross Central Ohio, 1971-77, 80-82; mem. nat. adv. council for small bus. to U.S. Sec. Treasury, 1975-76; mem. steering com. Devel. Com. Greater Columbus, 1970-80, chmn., 1978-79; mem. nat. adv. council SBA, 1973-76; bd. dirs. Columbus Safety Council, 1970-79, Greater Columbus Arts Council, 1970-78, Mid-Ohio Health Planning Commn., 1973-74, Am. Univs. for Research in Astronomy, 1972-79, Ohio Transp. Research Center, 1979-83; trustee Columbus Symphony Orch., 1980-85; trustee Riverside Meth. Hosp., 1979—, chmn. fin. and assets com., 1983-94, treas. 1988-94, vice chmn., 1994—; vice chmn. Ohio Higher Edn. Facilities Commn., 1979-83; mem. Ohio Sch. and Coll. Bd. Registration, 1979-83, Ohio Ednl. TV Commn., 1979-83; chmn. Columbus Symphony Grand Ball, 1983; chmn. judging Internat. Sci. and Engring. Fair, 1984; mem. Midwest Edn. Commn., 1979-83. With USN, 1945-46. Fellow ASCE; mem. Ohio Hist. Soc. (bd. dirs. 1979-83), State Higher Edn. Exec. Officers (exec. com. 1981-83), Ohio Commodore, Scioto Country Club, Faculty Club (Columbus), Sigma Xi, Tau Beta Pi, Pi Mu Epsilon, Chi Epsilon, Delta Omega, Romophos, Sigma Alpha Epsilon. Congregationalist. Home: 1303 London Dr Columbus OH 43221-1541

MOULTON, GRACE CHARBONNET, physics educator; b. New Orleans, Nov. 1, 1923; d. Wilfred J. and Louise A. (Hellmers) Charbonnet; m. William Gates Moulton, June 1, 1947; children: Paul Charbonnet Moulton, Nancy Gates Moulton. BA, Tulane U., 1944; MS, U. Ill., 1948; PhD, U. Ala., 1962. Asst. prof. physics U. Ala., Tuscaloosa, 1962-65; asst. prof. physics Fla. State U., Tallahassee, 1965-74, assoc. prof. physics, 1974-80, prof. physics, 1980—; cons. State Bd. Regents, Fla., 1984-85, Fla. Univ. System, 1989-90. Referee jour. articles Jour. Chem. Physics, Radiation Rsch.; contbr. many sci. rsch. articles to profl. jours. Four Yr. Undergrad. scholar Tulane U., scholar U. Ill.; rsch. grantee NIH. Mem. Am. Phys. Soc. (mem. coun. southeastern sect. 1988—). Avocations: gardening, music (classical and folk), snorkeling. Office: Fla State U Dept Physics Tallahassee FL 32304

MOULTON, HUGH GEOFFREY, lawyer, business executive; b. Boston, Sept. 18, 1933; s. Robert Selden and Florence (Bracq) M.; m. Catherine

Anne Clark, Mar. 24, 1956; children: H. Geoffrey, Cynthia C. Moulton Bassett. B.A., Amherst Coll., 1955; LL.B., Yale U., 1958; postgrad. Advanced Mgmt. Program, Harvard U., 1984. Bar: Pa. 1959. Assoc. Montgomery, McCracken, Walker-Rhoads, Phila., 1958-66, ptnr., 1967-69; v.p., counsel Dolly Madison Industries, Inc., Phila., 1969-70; sec. Alco Std. Corp., Valley Forge, Pa., 1970-72, v.p. law, 1973-79, v.p., sec., gen. counsel, 1979-83, sr. v.p., gen. counsel, 1983-92, exec. v.p., chief adminstrv. officer, gen. counsel, 1992-94, exec. v.p., 1994—. Pres. Wissahickon Valley Watershed Assn., Ambler, Pa., 1975-78, treas., 1978—; mem. Pa. Coun. for Econ. Edn., bd. dirs. 1985—; bd. trustees Beaver Coll., 1991—. Mem. ABA, Pa. Bar Assn., Phila. Bar Assn., Am. Corp. Counsel Assn. (bd. dirs. Delaware Valley chpt. 1984-88, pres. 1986-87), Nature Conservancy (trustee Pa. chpt. 1991—, chmn. 1993—), Sunnybrook Golf Club (Plymouth Meeting, Pa.). Home: 300 Williams Rd Fort Washington PA 19034-2015 Office: Alco Standard Corp PO Box 834 Valley Forge PA 19482-0834

MOULTON, WILBUR WRIGHT, JR., lawyer; b. Pensacola, Fla., Dec. 3, 1935; s. Wilbur Wright and Evelyn (Nobles) M.; m. Ann Arnow, Nov. 10, 1978; 1 child, Kelly Arnow. BA, Duke U., 1957; LLB, U. Va., 1959; LLM in Taxation, NYU, 1964. Bar: Fla. 1959; cert. tax lawyer, Fla. Assoc. Beggs & Lane, Pensacola, 1964-69; gen. counsel The Moulton Trust, Pensacola, 1970-74; pvt. practice, Pensacola, 1974-83; ptnr. Carlton, Fields, Ward, Emmanuel, Smith & Cutler, P.A., Pensacola, 1983—, also bd. dirs. Pres. Pensacola Heritage Found., 1971-72, Lakeview Ctr., Inc., Pensacola, 1975-77, dir. emeritus, 1984; chmn. bd. Lakeview Found., Inc., Pensacola. Lt. USNR, 1960-64. Mem. ABA, Fla. Bar Assn., Estate Planning Coun. N.W. Fla. (pres. 1978), Escambia-Santa Rosa Bar Assn. (pres. 1988-89), Rotary, Pensacola Country Club. Democrat. Episcopalian. Avocations: reading, running, traveling. Office: Carlton Fields Ward Emmanuel Smith & Cutler PA 25 W Cedar St Pensacola FL 32501-5951

MOULTRIE, FRED, geneticist; b. Albertville, Ala., Apr. 18, 1923; s. Walter Louis and Minnie Alma (Bodine) M.; m. Frances Grace Aldridge, May 28, 1947; children: Marilyn R. Moultrie Phillips, Elizabeth Anne Moultrie Becker, Janet Carol Moultrie Gauger. B.S., Auburn U., 1948, M.S., 1949; Ph.D. in Genetics, Kan State U., 1953. Asso. prof. Auburn U., 1951-55, prof., 1955-56; geneticist Arbor Acres Farm, Inc., Glastonbury, Conn., 1956-59; research coordinator Arbor Acres Farm, Inc., 1959-62, v.p., dir. research, 1962-64, exec. v.p., 1964-72, pres. domestic div., 1972-73; pres. Corbett Breeders, Westover, Md., 1973-81; v.p., dir. research Corbett Enterprises, Inc., 1973-81, Kennebec Internat., 1981-84; geneticist Perdue Farms, Salisbury, Md., 1984-88; genetics cons., 1988—. Served with USCGR, 1942-46. Mem. World's Poultry Sci. Assn., Am. Poultry Sci. Assn., Poultry Breeders Am. (pres. 1967-68), Sigma Xi, Phi Kappa Phi, Alpha Zeta, Gamma Sigma Delta. Club: Masons. Home and Office: 4360 Coulbourn Mill Rd Salisbury MD 21801-9268

MOUNT, DAVID ALLEN, video specialist; b. Jersey City, June 11, 1943; s. Ernest O. and Dorothy (Nattress) M.; m. Sheri Jorgensen Mar. 20, 1965; children: Susan, David Jr. BA, U. Nebr., 1967; MBA, Pepperdine U., 1980. Br. mgr. Pickwick Internat., North Hollywood, Calif., 1964-77; v.p. sales Warner Atlantic Corp., Burbank, Calif., 1977-84, Warner Home Video, Burbank, 1984-88; pres., chief exec. officer LIVE Home Video, Van Nuys, Calif., 1988—. Office: Live Home Video 15400 Sherman Way Van Nuys CA 91406-4211

MOUNT, KARL A., manufacturing executive; b. Trenton, N.J., Feb. 15, 1945. BS in Commerce, Rider Coll., 1967. Sr. auditor S. D. Leidesdorf and Co., N.Y.C., 1967-75; contr. Alpha Metals Inc., Jersey City, N.J., 1975-83, v.p. fin., 1983-84, exec. v.p., 1984-87, pres., 1987-90; v.p. fin. Cookson Am. Inc., Providence, 1990-92; cons. J.F. Krahnert Assn., Edison, N.J., 1993-95; CFO Micro Ctrl., Inc., Old Bridge, N.J., 1995—. Office: 8998 Rte 18 N PO Box 1009 Old Bridge NJ 08857

MOUNT, THOMAS H(ENDERSON), independent film producer; b. Durham, N.C., May 26, 1948; s. Lillard H. and Bonnie M. Student, Bard Coll., 1968-70; MFA in Film, Art, Calif. Inst. Arts, 1973. Prodn. exec. Universal Studios, Universal City, Calif., 1975-79, pres. for prodn., 1976-84, ind. film producer, 1984—; ind. film producer Burbank, Calif., 1984—. Producer: (films) Roman Polanski's Pirates, 1985, Can't Buy Me Love, 1987, Frantic, 1987, Bull Durham, 1988, Stealing Home, 1988, Tequila Sunrise, 1988, Frankenstein Unbound, 1989, The Indian Runner, 1990, Death and the Maiden, 1994, (TV) Open Admissions, 1986, Son of the Morning Star, 1990, (stage) Coconuts and Suicide, 1987, Death and the Maiden, 1991. Trustee Bard Coll., 1979-94.

MOUNT, WILLIE LANDRY, mayor; b. Lake Charles, La., Aug. 25, 1949; d. Lee Robert and Willia Veatrice (McCullor) Landry; m. Benjamin Wakefield Mount, Aug. 19, 1976. BS, McNeese State U., 1971. Geophys. asst. Lousiana Land and Exploration, Lake Charles, La., 1971-76; pharm. rep. Lederle, Lake Charles, 1976-80; realtor Mary Kay Hopkins, Lake Charles, 1976-87; co-owner Paper Place, Lake Charles, 1991—; mayor City of Lake Charles, 1993—; mem. met. planning orgn. policy bd. IMCAL, Lake Charles, 1993—; active Gov. Violent Crime & Homicide Task Force, Baton Rouge, 1993—. Guest condr. Lake Charles Symphony, 1992; parish chmn. dist. D La. Mcpl. Assn. Grass Roots Lobbying Network, Baton Rouge, 1993-94; pres. Jr. League of Lake Charles; mem. adv. bd. S.W. La. Literacy Coalition; active First United Meth. Ch., La. Meth. Conf., McNeese State U. Found., United Way, Children's Miracle Network. Recipient Spiritual Aims award Kiwanis Club, 1991, Dorthea Combre award NAACP, 1994; named Woman of Yr., Quota Club, 1991, Citizen of Yr., Women's Com. SW La., 1992, Women of Yr., Pub. Official of Yr. Msgr. Cramers KC. Mem. LWV, SW La. Mayors Assn. (chmn. 1993-94). Home: 205 Shell Beach Dr Lake Charles LA 70601 Office: Office of Mayor PO Box 900 Lake Charles LA 70602

MOUNTAIN, CLIFTON FLETCHER, surgeon, educator; b. Toledo, Apr. 15, 1924; s. Ira Fletcher and Mary (Stone) M.; m. Marilyn Isabelle Tapper, Feb. 28, 1945; children: Karen Lockerby, Clifton Fletcher, Jeffrey Richardson. AB, Harvard U., 1947; MD, Boston U., 1954. Diplomate Am. Bd. Surgery. Dir. dept. statis. rsch. Boston U., 1947-50; cons. rsch. analyst Mass. Dept. Pub. Health, 1951-53; intern U. Chgo. Clinics, 1954, resident, 1955-58, instr. surgery, 1958-59; sr. fellow thoracic surgery Houston, 1959; mem. staff M.D. Anderson Hosp. and Tumor Rsch.; asst. prof. thoracic surgery U. Tex., 1960-63, assoc. prof. surgery, 1963-76, prof., 1976—, chief sect. thoracic surgery, 1970-79, chmn. thoracic oncology, 1979-84, chmn. dept. thoracic surgery, 1980-85, chmn. program in biomath and computer sci., 1962-64, Mike Hogg vis. lectr. in S.Am., 1967; mem. sci. mission on cancer USSR, 1970-78, and Japan, 1976-84; mem. com. health, rsch. and edn. facilities Houston Community Coun., 1964-78; cons. Am. Joint Com. on Cancer Staging and End Result Reporting, 1974-74, mem. Am. Joint Com. on Cancer, 1974-86, chmn. lung and esophagus task force; mem. working party on lung cancer and chmn. com. on surgery, Nat. Clin. Trials Lung Cancer Study Group, NIH, 1971-76; mem. plans and scope com. cancer therapy Nat. Cancer Inst., 1972-75, mem. lung cancer study group, 1977-89, chmn. steering com., 1973-75, mem. bd. sci. counselors div. cancer treatment, 1972-75; hon. cons. Shanghai Chest Hosp. and Lung Cancer Ctr., Nat. Cancer Inst. of Brazil. Editor The New Physician, 1955-59; mem. editorial bd. Yearbook of Cancer, 1960-88, Internat. Trends in Gen. Thoracic Surgery, 1984-91; contbr. articles to profl. jours., chpts. to textbooks. Chmn. profl. adv. com. Harris County Mental Health Assn.; bd. dirs. Harris County chpt. Am. Cancer Soc. Lt. USNR, 1942-46. Recipient award Soviet Acad. Sci., 1977, Garcia Meml. medal Philippine Coll. Surgeons, 1982, Disting. Alumni award Boston U., 1988, Disting. Achievement U. Tex. M.D. Anderson Cancer Ctr., 1990, Disting. Svc. award Internat. Assn. for the Study of Lung Cancer, 1991, Disting. Alumnus award U. Sch. of Medicine, 1992. Fellow ACS, Am. Coll. Chest Physicians (chmn. com. cancer 1967-75), Am. Assn. Thoracic Surgery, Inst. Environ. Scis., N.Y. Acad. Sci., Assn. Thoracic and Cardiovascular Surgeons of Asia (hon.), Hellenic Cancer Soc. (hon.), Chilean Soc. Respiratory Diseases (hon., hon. pres. 1982); mem. AAAS, Am. Assn. Carcer Rsch., AMA, So. Med. Assn., Am. Thoracic Soc., Soc. Thoracic Surgeons, Soc. Biomed. Computing, Am. Fedn. Clin. Rsch., Internat. Assn. Study Lung Cancer (pres. 1976-78), Am. Radium Soc., Pan-Am. Med. Assn., Houston Surg. Soc., Soc. Surg. Oncology, James Ewing Soc., Sigma Xi. Achievements include conception and development of program for application of mathematics and computers to the life sciences, of

resource for experimental designs, applied statistics and computational support; first clinical use of physiologic adhesives in thoracic surgery; demonstration of clinical behavior of undifferentiated small cell lung cancer; first laser resection of lung tissue at thoracotomy; development of international system for staging of lung cancer. Home: 1612 South Blvd Houston TX 77006-6338 Office: 6624 Fannin Ste 200 Houston TX 77030-2312

MOUNTCASTLE, KATHARINE BABCOCK, foundation executive; b. Phila., Feb. 2, 1931; d. Charles H. and Mary (Reynolds) Babcock; m. Kenneth Franklin Mountcastle, Sept. 1, 1951; children: Mary Babcock, Laura Lewis, Kenneth Franklin, Katharine Reynolds. B.A., Sweet Briar (Va.) Coll., 1952. Dir., Internat. Social Service, N.Y.C., 1960-68; dir. Mary R. Babcock Found., Winston-Salem, N.C., 1954—; pres. Mary R. Babcock Found., Winston-Salem, 1981—; bd. dirs. Inform, N.Y.C., The Giraffe Project Friends of Thirteen, Bus. Execs. for Nat. Security. Served with U.S. Army, 1950-52. Republican. Presbyterian. Address: 37 Oenoke Ln New Canaan CT 06840-4516

MOUNTCASTLE, KENNETH FRANKLIN, JR., stockbroker; b. Winston-Salem, N.C., Oct. 8, 1928; s. Kenneth Franklin and May M.; B.S. in Commerce, U. N.C., Chapel Hill, 1950; m. Mary Katharine Babcock, Sept. 1, 1951; children: Mary Babcock, Laura Lewis, Kenneth Franklin, Katharine Reynolds. With Mountcastle Knitting Co., Lexington, N.C., 1952-55, Reynolds & Co., N.Y.C., 1955-71; with Reynolds Securities Inc. (co. name changed to Dean Witter Reynolds 1978), N.Y.C., 1971—, sr. v.p., 1974—. Trustee, New Canaan (Conn.) Country Sch., 1962-68, Ethel Walker Sch., Simsbury, Conn., 1973-85; trustee Coro Found., 1980—, nat. chmn., 1986-89; bd. dirs., past pres. Mary Reynolds Babcock Found., Winston-Salem, N.C.; bd. visitors U. N.C., Chapel Hill; bd. dirs. Inform, N.Y.C., Fresh Air Fund, N.Y.C., The Giraffe Project Friends of Thirteen, Bus. Execs. for Nat. Security. Served with U.S. Army, 1950-52. Republican. Presbyterian. Clubs: Country of New Canaan; Wee Burn Country (Darien, Conn.); Old Town (Winston-Salem, N.C.); Racquet and Tennis, City Midday, Hampton (St. Simons Island, Ga.), Pine Valley Golf, Bond, Stock Exchange Luncheon. Home: 37 Oenoke Ln New Canaan CT 06840-4516 Office: Dean Witter Reynolds 2 World Trade Ctr 17th Fl New York NY 10048

MOUNTCASTLE, VERNON BENJAMIN, neurophysiologist; b. Shelbyville, Ky., July 15, 1918; s. Vernon Mountcastle and Anne-Francis Marguerite (Waugh) M.; m. Nancy Clayton Pierpont, Sept. 6, 1945; children: Vernon Benjamin III, Anne Clayton, George Earle Pierpont. B.S. in Chemistry, Roanoke Coll., Salem, Va., 1938, D.Sc. (hon.), 1968; M.D., Johns Hopkins U., 1942; D.Sc. (hon.), U. Pa., 1976, Northwestern U., 1985; M.D. (hon.), U. Zurich, 1983, U. Siena, 1984, U. Santiago, Spain, 1990. House officer surgery Johns Hopkins Hosp., 1942-43; mem. faculty Johns Hopkins Sch. Medicine, 1946—, prof. physiology, 1959, dir. dept., 1964-80, Univ. prof. neurosci., 1980-92, prof. emeritus, 1992—; dir. Neurosci. Research Program, Rockefeller U., 1981-84; dir. Bard Labs. Neurophysiology Johns Hopkins U., Balt., 1981-91; pres. Neurosci. Research Found., 1981-85; spl. research physiology brain; chmn. physiology study sect., mem. physiology tng. com. NIH, 1958-61; adv. council Nat. Eye Inst., 1971-74; mem. sci. adv. bd. USAF, 1969-71; vis. com. dept. psychology Mass. Inst. Tech., 1966-75; bd. biology and medicine NSF, 1970-73; mem. commn. on neurophysiology Internat. Union Physiol. Sci. Editor-in-chief: Jour. Neurophysiology, 1961-64; assoc. editor: Bull. Johns Hopkins Hosp, 1954-62; editorial bd.: Physiol. Revs, 1957-59, Exptl. Brain Research, 1966-85; editor, contbr.: Med. Physiology, 12th edit, 1968, 13th edit., 1974, 14th edit., 1980, (with G.M. Edelman) The Mindful Brain, 1978; author articles in field. Served to lt. (s.g.) M.C. USNR, 1943-46. Recipient Lashley prize Am. Philos. Soc., 1974, F.O. Schmitt prize and medal MIT, 1975, Sherrington prize and gold medal Royal Acad. Medicine, London, 1977, Horowitz prize Columbia U., 1978, Fyssen Internat. prize, Paris, 1983, Lasker award, 1983, Helmholtz prize, 1982, Nat. Medal Sci., 1986, McGovern prize and medal AAAS, 1990, award in neurosci. Fidia Fedn., 1990, Australia prize, 1993. Mem. Am. Physiol. Soc., Am. Acad. Arts and Scis., Nat. Acad. Sci. (chmn. sect. physiology 1971-74), Harvey Cushing Soc., Am. Neurol. Assn. (Bennett lectr. 1978, hon. mem.), AAAS, Soc. Neurosci. (pres. 1970-72, Gerard Prize 1980), Am. Philos. Soc. (councillor 1979-82), Nat. Inst. Medicine; hon. mem. Physiol. Soc. (London); fgn. mem. Acad. des Scis. (France); Phi Beta Kappa, Sigma Chi, Alpha Omega Alpha, Phi Chi. Home: 15601 Carroll Rd Monkton MD 21111-2009

MOUNTCASTLE, WILLIAM WALLACE, JR., philosophy and religion educator; b. Hanover, N.H., July 10, 1925; s. William Wallace and Grace Elizabeth (Zottarelli) M.; m. Ila M. Warner (div.); children: Christine, Susan, Gregory, Eric; m. Barbara Kaye Griffin, Oct. 19, 1979; 1 child, Cathleena; stepdaughter, Dasha. BA, Whittier Coll., 1951; STB, Boston U., 1954, PhD, 1958. Ordained to ministry United Meth. Ch. Asst. prof. philosophy and religion High Point (N.C.) Coll., 1958-60; mem. So. Calif. Ann. Conf. United Meth. Ch., 1954-60; assoc. prof., head dept. philosophy Nebr. Wesleyan U., Lincoln, 1960-63, prof., head dept. philosophy, 1963-67; mem. Nebr. Ann. Conf. United Meth. Ch., 1960—; prof. philosophy Fla. So. Coll., Lakeland, 1967-69; assoc. prof. philosophy and religion U. W. Fla., Pensacola, 1969-79, prof. philosophy and religion, 1979-84, M.L. Tipton prof. philosophy and religion, 1980—. Author: Religion in Planetary Perspective, 1979; contbr. articles to jours. in field. 1st lt. USAAF, 1942-49, PTO. Mem. NEA/ United Faculty Fla., Am. Assn. Religion, Am. Philos. Assn.. Democrat. Home: 4549 Sabine Dr Gulf Breeze FL 32561-9253 Office: Dept Philos & Religious Studies U West Fla Pensacola FL 32561

MOUNTZ, LOUISE CARSON SMITH, retired librarian; b. Fond Du Lac, Wis., Oct. 20, 1911; d. Roy Carson and Charlotte Louise (Scheurs) Smith; m. George Edward Mountz, May 4, 1935 (dec. Oct. 3 1951); children: Peter Carson, Pamela Teeters Mountz McDonald. Student, Western Coll., 1929-31; AB, The Ohio State U., 1933; MA, Ball State U., 1962; postgrad., Manchester Coll., 1954, Ind. U., 1960-61. Cert. tchr., Ind. Tchr. Monroeville (Ind.) High Sch., 1953-54, Riverdale High Sch., St. Joe, Ind., 1954-55; libr. High Sch., Avilla, Ind., 1955-58; head libr. Penn High Sch., Mishawaka, Ind., 1958-67, Northwood Jr. High Sch., Ft. Wayne, Ind., 1967-69, McIntosh Jr. High Sch., Auburn, Ind., 1969-74; dir. Media Ctr. DeKalb Jr. High Sch., Auburn, Ind., 1974-78; ret., 1978; cons. media ctr. planning Penn-Harris-Madison Sch. Corp., Mishawaka, 1966-67. Author: Biographies for Junior High Schools and Correlated Audio-Visual Materials, 1970; contbr. articles to profl. jours. Bd. dirs. DeKalb County chpt. ARC, 1938-42, 51-53, DeKalb County Heart Assn., 1946-52, DeKalb County Community Concert Assn., 1946-58, Am. Field Svc. Mishawaka chpt., 1960-67; active Ft. Wayne Philharmonic Orch. Assn., Ft. Wayne Art Mus., Ft. Wayne Hist. Soc., Preservation of Dekalb County Assn., DeKalb Meml. Hosp. Womens Guild, also life mem. Mem. AAUW, ALA, NEA, World Confedn. Orgns. Teaching Professions, Nat. Coun. Tchrs. English, Ind. Sch. Librarians Assn. (dir. 1963-67), Internat. Assn. Sch. Librarianship, Ind. Assn. Ednl. Communication and Tech., Assn. Ind. Media Educators, Nat. Ret. Tchrs. Assns., Nat. Trust Hist. Preservation, Hist. Landmarks Found. Ind., Delta Kappa Gamma (charter mem., Beta Beta chpt.), Kappa Kappa Kappa (pr. officer 1941-45, pres. Alpha Chi chpt. 1938-40, Garrett Assoc. chpt. 1971-73), Delta Delta Delta (house pres.). Methodist. Lodge: Order Ea. Star. Clubs: Greenhurst Country, Ft. Wayne Women's, Athena Lit. (hon. mem.), Ladies Lit. of Auburn. Home: 19 Castle Ct Auburn IN 46706-1439

MOUNTZ, WADE, retired health service management executive; b. Winona, Ohio, Nov. 19, 1924; s. Lowell J. and Ethel M. (Coppock) M.; m. Betty G. Wilson, June 3, 1946; children: David John, Timothy Wilson. BA, Baldwin-Wallace Coll., 1948; MHA, U. Minn., 1951; LHD (hon.), Ky. Wesleyan Coll., 1991. With Norton Meml. Infirmary, Louisville, 1951-69; adminstr. Norton Meml. Infirmary, 1958-69; pres. Norton-Children's Hosps., Inc., Louisville, 1969-81, NKC Inc., Louisville, 1981-85; vice chmn. NKC Inc., 1985-87, pres. emeritus, 1987—. Vice chmn. Comprehensive Health Planning Council Ky., 1968-73, chmn., 1973-79; bd. dirs. Louisville chpt. ARC, 1961-74; trustee Blue Cross Hosp. Plan, 1959-72; trustee Am. Hosp. Assn., 1971-76, chmn. bd., 1975. Served with A.C., USNR, 1943-45. Recipient Disting. Service award Ky. Hosp. Assn.; Disting. Layman award Ky. Med. Assn. Fellow Am. Coll. Hosp. Healthcare Execs. (gold medal). Masons. Home: 9 Muirfield Pl Louisville KY 40222-5074 Office: 4350 Brownsboro Rd Ste 110 Louisville KY 40207

MOURA, JOSÉ MANUEL FONSECA, electrical engineering and computer science educator; b. Beira, Mozambique, Portugal, Jan. 9, 1946; s. José Saraiva and Maria José (Fonseca) M.; m. Maria Tereza Fernandes, 1969 (div. 1981); 1 child, Barbara Fernandes; m. Maria Manuela Veloso, 1982; children: André Veloso, Pedro Veloso. Engenheiro Electrotecnico, Instituto Superior Tecnico, Lisbon, 1969; M.S. in Elec. Engring., MIT, 1973, Sc. D. in Elec. Engring. and Computer Sci., 1975. Prof. auxiliar Instituto Superior Técnico, Lisbon, 1975-78, prof. aggregado, 1978, prof. catedrático, 1979-86; prof. Carnegie Mellon U., Pitts., 1986—; vis. assoc. prof. elec. engring. and computer sci. MIT, Cambridge, 1984-86; vis. scholar U. So. Calif., Los Angeles, summers 1978, 79, 80, 81. Editor: (with others) Nonlinear Stochastic Problems, 1983, Acoustic Signal Processing for Ocean Exploration, 1993. Contbr. articles to profl. jours. Fellow IEEE; mem. NAS Portugal (corr. mem.), Am. Math. Soc., Soc. Indsl. and Applied Math., Ordem dos Engenheiros. Home: 6645 Woodwell St Pittsburgh PA 15217-1320 Office: Carnegie-Mellon U Dept Elec & Computer Engring 5000 Forbes Ave Pittsburgh PA 15213-3816

MOUREK, JOSEPH EDWARD, musician; b. Chgo., Jan. 5, 1910; s. Anton Peter and Anna (Prucha) M.; m. Jean Katherine Masek, Sept. 1, 1934. Pupil, Bruno Jaenicke, Pellegrino Lecce, Thorwold Otterstrom. Tchr. Interlochen (Mich.) Music Acad., 1929-31. French hornist, Chgo. Symphony Orch., 1929—, other appearances with opera, mus. comedies, also on radio, TV and films; rec. artist for, RCA, Columbia, Mercury, Angel, London, Decca records. Served with AUS, World War II. Recipient certificate of merit Mayor Daley of Chgo., 1971, Chgo. certificate of merit, 1971; named Chicagoan of Year Chgo. Press Club, 1971. Home: 6594 29th St Berwyn IL 60402-2942 Office: Orch Hall 220 S Michigan Ave Chicago IL 60604-2508

MOURELATOS, ALEXANDER PHOEBUS DIONYSIOU, humanities educator; b. Athens, Greece, July 19, 1936; came to U.S., 1955, naturalized, 1968; s. Dionysius Alexandrou and Elia Constantinou (Voutsara) M.; m. Linda Jean Oppen, June 12, 1962. BA, Yale, 1958, MA, 1961, PhD, 1964; PhD (hon.), U. Athens, 1994. Instr. philosophy Yale, New Haven, 1962-64; jr. fellow Inst. for Research in Humanities, U. Wis., Madison, 1964-65; asst. prof. U. Tex., Austin, 1965-67; assoc. prof., 1967-71; prof. U. Tex., 1971—; mem. Inst. for Advanced Study, Princeton, N.J., 1967-68; vis. fellow Australian Nat. U., Canberra, 1978, 91; vis. prof. Carleton Coll., 1994. Author: The Route of Parmenides, 1970; editor: The Pre-Socratics, 1974, 2d edit., 1993. Nat. Endowment for Humanities fellow, 1968, 1982-83; Am. Council Learned Socs. and Center for Hellenic Studies fellow, 1973-74; Guggenheim fellow, 1988-89. Mem. Am. Philol. Assn., Am. Philos. Assn., Soc. Ancient Greek Philosophy. Home: 3705 Eastledge Dr Austin TX 78731-5813 Office: U Tex Dept Philosophy Austin TX 78712-1180

MOURNING, ALONZO, professional basketball player; b. Chesapeake, Va., Feb. 8, 1970. Student, Georgetown U. Center Charlotte Hornets, 1992—; player All-Star Game, 1994. Named to NBA All-Rookie First Team, 1993, Dream Team II, 1994. Office: Charlotte Hornets Hive Drive Charlotte NC 28217*

MOURTON, J. GARY, communications executive; b. Mena, Ark., Jan. 22, 1947; s. Malvin G. and Helen J. (Eckhardt) M.; m. J. Gayle Lay, June 29, 1968; children: Jennifer, Lindsay, Kimberly, Natalie. B.S.B.A., U. Ark., 1969. C.P.A., Okla. Audit mgr. Arthur Andersen & Co., Tulsa, 1969-80; fin. officer T/SF Comm. Corp. (formerly Swab-Fox Cos. and Midwest Energy Corp.), Tulsa, 1980—. Mem. Am. Inst. C.P.A.s, Okla. Soc. C.P.A.s, Fin. Execs. Inst. Republican. Office: T/SF Comm Corp 2407 E Skelly Dr Tulsa OK 74105-6006

MOUSTAFA, FIKRY SAYED, accountant; b. Cairo, Egypt, June 27, 1944; came to U.S., 1969; s. Sayed Moustafa and Taheya Elkoumy; m. Tahani Soliman, July 9, 1970; 1 child, Nora. BS in Acctg., Ain Shams U., Cairo, 1967. CPA, Md. Clk. to sr. staff Bank of Alexandria, Cairo, 1960-69; acct. to mgr. reports and consolidations records divsn. CBS Inc., N.Y.C., 1970-79; mgr. acctg. Polygram Records, Inc., N.Y.C., 1980-83; assoc. dir. acctg. Sony Music Inc., N.Y.C., 1983-93, dir. credit and collection, 1993—. Mem. Md. Assn. CPAs, N.Y. State Soc. CPAs, Nat. Soc. Tax Profls., AICPA. Avocations: travel, photography, reading. Home: 15 Gail Ct Robbinsville NJ 08691-1337

MOUTOUSSAMY, JOHN WARREN, architect; b. Chgo., Jan. 5, 1922; s. Jean Marie and Julia Nettie (Walker) M.; m. Elizabeth Rose Hunt, Mar. 15, 1942; children: John Jr. (dec.), Claude Louis, Jeanne Marie. BSArch, Ill. Inst. Tech., 1948; LLD (hon.), Loyola U., Chgo., 1982. Lic. architect, Ill. Draftsman Schmidt, Garden & Erikson Architects, Chgo., 1950-56; architect PACE Assocs., Chgo., 1956-65; ptnr. Dubin, Dubin and Moutoussamy, Chgo., 1966-83, mng. ptnr., 1983—; cons. architect Metro. Pier and Exhbn. Authority, Chgo., 1975—. Trustee Art Inst. Chgo., 1973—, Loyola U., 1972-81; bd. govs. Sch. Art Inst., 1980-93; vice chmn. Chgo. Plan Commn., 1979-81. Fellow AIA; mem. Wayfarers' Club. Roman Catholic. Office: Dubin Dubin & Moutoussamy 455 E Illinois St 672 Chicago IL 60611-4305

MOVSHOVITZ, HOWARD PAUL, film critic, educator; b. Trenton, N.J., Dec. 30, 1944; s. Abraham H. and Helen (Peskin) M.; m. Janis Hallowell, Dec. 23, 1989; 1 child, Zoe. BA, U. Pa., 1966; PhD, U. Colo., 1977. Film critic Colo. Pub. Radio, Denver, 1976—; asst. prof. U. Colo., Denver, 1978-90; asst. adj. prof. U. Colo., Denver, 1978—; reporter Nat. Pub. Radio, Washington, 1986—. Mem. ACLU (bd. dirs. 1986-87). Office: Denver Post 1560 Broadway Denver CO 80202-5133

MOW, DOUGLAS FARRIS, former naval officer, consultant; b. Carbondale, Colo., Nov. 10, 1928; s. James Leroy and Marie (Gerkin) M.; m. Rosalie Stearns Johnson, June 16, 1951; children: Douglas Farris, Deborah, Laura, Nancy. B.S., US Naval Acad., 1951; M.S. in Physics, U.S. Naval Postgrad. Sch., 1958; student, Armed Forces Staff Coll., 1964-65. Commd. ensign USN, 1951, advanced through grades to rear adm., 1977; night attack pilot San Diego, 1953-56; served with research and devel. div. (Def. Nuclear Agy.), Albuquerque, 1958-60; nuclear weapons employment officer (Carrier Air Wing 11), Naval Air Sta. Miramar, San Diego, 1960-62; pilot, ops. officer (Light Attack Squadron), Naval Air Sta. Lemoore, Calif., 1962-64; assigned to atomic energy div. (Office Chief of Naval Ops.), Washington, 1965-66; comdg. officer squadron Vietnam War, 1967-68; staff comdr. (7th Fleet), 1969; comdr. (Carrier Airwing 19), 1970-71, (Light Attack Wing One), Jacksonville, Fla., 1971-73; exec. asst./naval aide to Sec. Navy Washington, 1973-77; VSTOL program coordinator, 1977-80; comdr. (Tactical Wings Atlantic), Virginia Beach, Va., 1980-81; cons., 1982—. Decorated D.S.M., Silver Star, D.F.C. with 2 oak leaf clusters, Legion of Merit with 2 oak leaf clusters, Bronze Star with 2 oak leaf clusters, Air medal with 4 oak leaf clusters, Navy Commendation medal with 2 oak leaf clusters. Mem. U.S. Naval Inst. Republican. Episcopalian.

MOW, ROBERT HENRY, JR., lawyer; b. Cape Girardeau, Mo., Dec. 10, 1938; s. Robert H., Sr. and Ann Elise (Beck) M.; m. Jody K. Boggs, Aug. 29, 1987; children: Robert M., Brynn A., W.Brett, Rebecca M., W. Kirk, Allison M. Student, Westminster Coll., 1956-57; A.B. with distinction, U. of Mo., 1960; LL.B. magna cum laude, So. Meth. U., 1963. Bar: Tex. 1963, U.S. Dist. Ct. (no. dist.) Tex. 1965, U.S. Dist. Ct. (so. dist.) Tex. 1969, U.S. Dist Ct. (ea. dist.) Tex. 1976, U.S. Dist. Ct. (we. dist.) Tex. 1976, U.S. Ct. Claims 1973, U.S. Ct. Appeals (5th cir. 1972, U.S. Ct. Appeals (11th cir.) 1981, U.S. Ct. Appeals (Fed. cir.), 1994, U.S. Supreme Ct. 1978. Assoc. Carrington, Johnson & Stephens, Dallas, 1963-69; ptnr. Carrington, Coleman, Sloman, & Blumenthal, Dallas, 1970-85; Hughes & Luce, L.L.P., Dallas, 1985—. Editor-in-chief Southwestern Law Jour., 1962-63. Served to 1st lt. U.S. Army, 1963-65. Fellow Am. Coll. of Trial Lawyers, mem. Dallas Jr. Bar Assn. (pres. 1968), Dallas Assn. of Def. Counsel (chmn. 1976-77), Tex. Assn. of Def. Counsel (v.p. 1981-82), Am. Bd. of Trial Advocates (pres. Dallas chpt. 1983-84). Republican. Baptist. Office: Hughes & Luce LLP 1717 Main St Ste 2800 Dallas TX 75201

MOW, VAN C., engineering educator, researcher; b. Chengdu, China, Jan. 10, 1939. B. Aero. Engring., Rensselaer Poly. Inst. 1962, Ph.D. 1966. Mem. tech. staff Bell Telephone Labs., Whippany, N.J., 1968-69; assoc. prof. mechanics Rensselaer Poly. Inst., Troy, N.Y., 1969-76, prof. mechanics and biomed. engring., 1976-82, John A. Clark and Edward T. Crossan prof. engring., 1982-86; prof. mechanical engring. and orthopedic bioengring. Columbia U., N.Y.C., 1986—; dir. Orthopedic Research Lab., Columbia-Presbyn. Med. Ctr., N.Y.C., 1986—; vis. mem. Courant Inst. Math. Sci., NYU, 1967-68; vis. prof. Harvard U., Boston, 1976-77; chmn. orthopaedics and musculoskeletal study sect. NIH, Bethesda, Md., 1982-84; hon. prof. Chengdu U. Sci. Tech., 1981, Shanghai Jiao Tong U., 1987; mem. grants rev. bd. Orthopaedic Rsch. Edn. Found., 1992-96; bd. dirs. Hoar Rsch. Found., 1993—; cons. in field. Assoc. editor Jour. Biomechanics, 1981—, Jour. Biomech. Engring., 1979-86; chmn. editorial adv. bd. Jour. Orthopedic Rsch., 1983-90; adv. editor Clin. Orthopedic Rel. Rsch., 1993—; contbr. numerous articles to profl. jours. Founder Gordon Research Conf. on Bioengring. and Orthopedic Sci., 1980. NATO sr. fellow, 1978; recipient William H. Wiley Disting. Faculty award Rensselaer Poly. Inst., 1981; Japan Soc. for Promotion Sci. Fellow, 1986, Fogarty Sr. Internat. fellow, 1987; Alza disting. lectr. Biomed. Engring. Soc., 1987; H.R. Lissner award ASME, 1987, Kappa Delta award AAOS, 1980, Giovani Borelli award, 1991. Fellow ASME (chmn. biomechanics divsn. 1984-85, Melville medal 1982), Am. Inst. Med. Biol. Engring.; mem. NAE, Orthopaedic Rsch. Soc. (pres. 1982-83), Am. Soc. Biomechanics (founding), Internat. Soc. Biorheology, U.S. Nat. Com. on Biomechanics (sec.-treas. 1985-90, chmn. 1991-94). Office: Columbia-Presbyn Med Ctr BB-1412 630 W 168th St New York NY 10032

MOW, WILLIAM, apparel executive; b. 1936. PhD, Purdue U., 1967. With Honeywell Inc., Boston, 1963-65; program mgr. Litton Industries, L.A., 1967-69; founder, pres., chmn. bd. MacroData Corp., L.A., 1969-76; sci. advisor Cutler Hammer, L.A., 1976-77; with Bugle Boy Industries, Inc., Simi Valley, Calif., 1977—, now chmn., CEO. Office: Bugle Boy 2900 N Madera Rd Simi Valley CA 93065-6236

MOWAT, FARLEY MCGILL, writer; b. Belleville, Ont., Can., May 12, 1921; s. Angus McGill and Helen (Thomson) M.; m. Frances Elizabeth Thornhill, Dec. 21, 1947; children: Robert Alexander, David Peter; m. Claire Angel Wheeler, 1965. BA, U. Toronto, 1949, LLD, 1973; DLitt (hon.), Laurentian U., 1970; LLD, U. Lethbridge, Alta., 1973, U. P.E.I., 1979; DLitt, U. Victoria, B.C., 1982, Lakehead U., Thunder Bay, Ont. 1986; LHD (hon.), McMaster U., Hamilton, Ont., 1994; LLD (hon.), Queen's Univ., Kingston, Ont., 1995. Arctic exploration, sci. work, 1947-48, writer, 1950—. Author: People of the Deer, 1952, The Regiment, 1955, Lost in the Barrens, 1956, The Dog Who Wouldn't Be, 1957, Coppermine Journey, 1958, The Grey Seas Under, 1958, The Desperate People, 1959, Ordeal By Ice, 1960, Owls in the Family, 1961, The Serpent's Coil, 1961, The Black Joke, 1962, Never Cry Wolf, 1963, Westviking, 1965, The Curse of the Viking Grave, 1966, Canada North, 1967, The Polar Passion, 1967 (with John de Visser) This Rock Within the Sea, 1968, The Boat Who Wouldn't Float, 1969, The Siberians, 1971, A Whale for the Killing, 1972, Tundra, 1973, (with David Blackwood) Wake of the Great Sealers, 1973, The Snow Walker, 1975, Canada North Now, 1976, and No Birds Sang, 1979, The World of Farley Mowat, 1980, Sea of Slaughter, 1984, My Discovery of America, 1985, Woman in the Mist, 1987, The New Found Land, 1989, Rescue the Earth, 1990, My Father's Son, 1992, Born Naked, 1993, A Traveller's Tale, 1995; author documentary script The New North (Gemini award 1989); film Sea of Slaughter (Conservation Film of Yr. award 1990, ACE award finalist 1990, award of Excellence Atlantic Film Festival 1990). Served to capt. inf. Canadian Army, 1939-45. Recipient Pres. Medal Univ. Western Ont., 1952, Anisfield Wolfe award, 1954, Gov. Gen.'s medal, 1957, Book of Yr. Medal Can. Library Assn., 1958, Hans Christian Anderson Internat. award, 1958, 65, Can. Women's Clubs award, 1958, Boys Clubs Am. award, 1962, Nat. Assn. Ind. Schs. award, 1963, Can. Centennial medal, 1967, Stephen Leacock medal for humor, 1970, Leacock Medal for Humour, 1970, Vicky Metcalf award, 1970, Mark Twain award, 1971, Book of Yr. award, 1976, Curran award, 1977, Queen Elizabeth II Jubilee medal, 1978, Knight of Mark Twain, 1980, Can. Author's award, 1981, 85, Can. Author of Year award, 1988, Can. Book of Yr. award, 1988, Torgi Can. Talking Book of Yr. award, 1989, Can. Achievers award Toshiba Can., 1990, Take Back the Nation award Coun. Cans., 1991, Authors award, Author of Yr. Found. for Advancement of Can. Letters, 1993; decorated officer Order of Can., 1981, L'Etoile de la Mer, 1972. Office: care Writers Union Can, 24 Ryerson Ave, Toronto, ON Canada M4T 2P3

MOWDAY, RICHARD THOMAS, management educator; b. Oakland, Calif., Sept. 4, 1947; s. Richard Walter and Jessie Elizabeth (Steet) M.; m. Mary Nelson; children: Graham Thomas, Garrett Nelson. BS in Manpower Adminstrn., San Jose State U., 1970; MS in Adminstrn., U. Calif., Irvine, 1972, PhD in Adminstrn., 1975. Asst. prof. U. Nebr., Lincoln, 1975-77; asst. prof. U. Oreg., Eugene, 1977-81, assoc. prof., 1981-86, prof. mgmt., 1986—, Holden Affilate prof. mgmt., 1988, Gerald B. Bashaw disting. prof. mgmt., 1990, assoc. dean, 1994—; vis. scholar Tuck Sch. Mgmt. Dartmouth Coll., Hanover, N.H., 1983-84; Hanson vis. prof. U. Washington, 1991—. Co-author: Employee-Organization Linkages, 1982, Managing Effective Organizations, 1985; co-editor: Research in Organizations, 1979; editor Acad. Mgmt. Jour., 1988-90, cons. editor, 1984-87; internat. cons. editor Jour. Occupational Psychology, 1983-91; editorial rev. bd. Jour. Vocat. Behavior, Jour. Mgmt., Adminstrv. Sci. Quarterly. Fellow Acad. Mgmt. (div. chmn. 1984-85, bd. govs., v.p., program chmn., pres.-elect, best rsch. paper award orgnl. behavior div. 1986), APA, Am. Psychol. Soc.; mem. Western Acad. Mgmt., Soc. Orgnl. Behavior. Congregationalist. Avocations: cross country skiing, bicycling, running. Home: 5225 Miramar St Eugene OR 97405-4842 Office: U Oreg Coll Bus Adminstrn Eugene OR 97403

MOWE, GREGORY ROBERT, lawyer; b. Aberdeen, Wash., Feb. 23, 1946; s. Robert Eden and Jeannette Effie (Deyoung) M.; m. Rebecca Louise Nobles, June 14, 1969; children: Emily, Tom. BA, U. Oreg., 1968, MA, 1969; JD magna cum laude, Harvard Law Sch., 1974. Bar: Oreg. 1974, U.S. Dist. Ct. Oreg. 1974, U.S. Ct. Appeals (9th cir.) 1974. Assoc. atty. Stoel Rives Boley Jones & Grey, Portland, Oreg., 1974-79; ptnr. Stoel Rivis Boley Jones & Grey, Portland, 1979—. Pres. bd. dirs. Planned Parenthood of Columbia/Willamette, Portland, 1989-90. 1st lt. U.S. Army, 1969-71, Vietnam. Mem. ABA, Phi Beta Kappa. Office: Stoel Rives Boley Jones & Grey 900 SW Fifth Ave Ste 2300 Portland OR 97204

MOWER, ERIC ANDREW, communications and marketing executive; b. N.Y.C., Oct. 10, 1944; s. Jack Henry Mower and Doris (Bernfeld) Schecter; m. Judith Ann Cotey, May 28, 1967; 1 child, Hillary Beth. BA, Syracuse (N.Y.) U., 1966, MA, 1968. Prin. Eric Mower and Assocs., Syracuse, 1968—. Pres. Health Sci. Ctr. Found., SUNY Syracuse, 1983-88; pres., bd. dirs. Syracuse Symphony Orch., 1988-90; chmn. Cen. N.Y. chpt. Nat. Kidney Found., 1987-88, Cen. N.Y. Regional Market Task Force, 1988-90, Partnership for Arts; bd. dirs. Met. Devel. Assn., Everson Mus., Nat. Advt. Rev. Bd.; past bd. dirs. Everson Mus., Syracuse Stage, Jr. Achievement, Cen. N.Y. coun. Boy Scouts Am., Sta. WCNY-TV/FM; trustee Syracuse U. Mem. Am. Assn. Advt. Agys. (chmn. N.Y. state coun. 1986, chmn. bd. govs. ea. region 1988-89, nat. bd. govs. 1990—, sec.-treas. 1993-94, dir.-at-large), Greater Syracuse C. of C. (chmn. bd. dirs. 1992-93), Univ. Club (N.Y.C.), Friars Club, Century Club. Office: Eric Mower and Assocs Inc 500 Plum St Syracuse NY 13204-1401 also: Eric Mower and Assocs/Buffalo Inc 360 Delaware Ave Buffalo NY 14202-1610 also: Eric Mower and Assocs 350 Linden Oaks Dr Rochester NY 14625

MOWERY, ANNA RENSHAW, state legislator; b. Decatur, Tex., Jan. 4, 1931; d. Lafayette William and Early Virginia (Bobo) Renshaw; m. Wesley Harold Mowery, June 2, 1951; children: Jeanette Mowery Heffernan, Mark William, Timothy Dean, Marianne Mowery Fichera. BA, Baylor U., 1951; MA, Ctrl. State U., 1967. Tchr. Ft. Hood (Tex.) Pub. Schs., 1951-52; petroleum landman Ft. Worth, 1979-82; dist. dir. U.S. Congl. Dist. 6 Joe Barton, Ft. Worth, 1985-86; polit. cons., pres. Trinity Assocs., Ft. Worth, 1987-88; state rep. Tex. House Reps., Ft. Worth, 1988—. Chmn. Tarrant County (Tex.) Rep. Party, 1975-77; mem. Tex. Rep. Exec. Com., Ft. Worth, 1980-84, Greater Ft. Worth Literacy Coun., 1990—; mem. adv. bd. Sr. Citizen Svcs./Tarrant County, Ft. Worth, 1988—. Recipient 4-H Clubs Am. Alumni award 1990; nominee Newsmaker of Yr. Ft. Worth Press Club, 1974-76. Mem. Southwest Rep. Club, Tex. Women's Alliance, Ft. Worth Rep. Women (v.p. 1991-92), Women's Policy Forum. Baptist. Home: 4108 Hildring Dr W Fort Worth TX 76109-4722 District Office: Ste 534 Twr II

4100 International Plz Fort Worth TX 76109 Office: Tex House of Reps State Capitol Austin TX 78768-2910

MOWERY, BOB LEE, librarian; b. Charlotte, N.C., June 22, 1920; s. Kerr Lee and Ella (Holman) M.; m. Peggy Setzer, Sept. 9, 1945; children: Margaret Mowery Paul, Mary, Robert, John. BA, Catawba Coll., 1941; BS in L.S., U. Chgo., 1947, MA, 1951. Catalogue libr. Dickinson Coll., Pa., 1947-50; libr., head dept. libr. sci. Murray State Coll., 1951-53; libr. McNeese State Coll., 1953-58, Stetson U., 1958-64; dir. librs. Wittenberg U., 1964-83, prof., dir. librs. emeritus, 1983—; cons., acting dir. libr. Davis & Elkins Coll., 1986-87. Chmn. com. parish edn. Fla. synod Luth. Ch. Am., 1962-64, chmn. com. local arrangements constituting conv., 1962; mem. hist. work com. N.C. Synod., Evang.-Luth. Ch. Am., 1983-92; chmn. com. libr. resources Regional Coun. Internat. Edn.; del. Seminar Current Trends Edn., Yugoslavia, Aug. 1966. Editor La. Libr. Bull., 1955-58; contbr. articles to profl. jours. Trustee DeLand (Fla.) Pub. Library, Newberry Coll., 1962-64, Springfield Art Center, 1976-81; bd. dirs., treas. Ohio Coll. Libr. Ctr., 1969-74; bd. dirs. Ohionet, 1978-83; pres. Friends of the Henderson County Pub. Library, 1984-86; bd. dirs. Friends of N.C. Pub. Libraries, 1987-93, pres. 1989-91; chmn. Saluda Med. Ctr., 1989-93; bd. dirs. Polk County chpt. ARC, 1992—. Served with AUS, 1942-46; maj., ret. Nat. Def. Fgn. Lang. fellow, 1967. Fellow Am. Coun. Learned Socs.; mem. Am. Libr. Assn., N.C. Libr. Assn., Bibliog. Soc., Bibliog. Soc. Am., Arthur Machen Soc. (Am.) (pres. 1965-83), Arthur Machen Soc. (Eng., hon. life mem.), Assn. Coll. and Rsch. Librs. (pres. Tri-state chpt. 1974-75), Acad. Libr. Assn. Ohio (pres. 1975-76), , Rotary. bd. dirs. Deland club 1961-63), Univ. Club (Springfield), Hendersonville Club. Democrat. Address: PO Box 218 Saluda NC 28773-0218

MOWRY, ROBERT DEAN, art museum curator, educator; b. Quinter, Kans., Sept. 27, 1945; s. Eugene Adrian and Pearl Helen (Kreft) M. BA with honors, U. Kans., 1967, MA with honors, 1974, MPhil. with honors, 1975. Curatorial asst. and translator Nat. Palace Mus., Taipei, Taiwan, 1975-77; asst. curator Oriental art Fogg Art Mus., Harvard U., Cambridge, Mass., 1977-80; curator Mr. and Mrs. John D. Rockefeller 3d collection Asia Soc., N.Y.C., 1980-86; curator Asian Art Harvard U. Art Mus., Cambridge, 1986-92; curator Chinese art and head dept. Asian art Harvard U. Art Mus., 1992—; lectr. dept. fine arts Harvard U., Cambridge, 1987-94; sr. lectr. Chinese and Korean art dept. fine arts Harvard U., 1994—; contbg. editor Art and Auction, N.Y., 1982-86; lectr. grad. program Cooper-Hewitt Mus., N.Y.C. 1983-86, Inst. Asian Studies, N.Y.C., 1982—. Author: Handbook of the Mr. and Mrs. John D. Rockefeller 3d Collection, 1981, The Chinese Scholar's Studio: Artistic Life in the Late Ming Period, 1987, China's Renaissance in Bronze: The Robert H. Clague Collection of Later Chinese Bronzes 1100-1900, 1993, Ancient China, Modern Clay: Chinese Influences on Five Ceramic Artists, 1994; contbr. articles to profl. jours. Vol. U.S. Peace Corps, Seoul Nat. U., Republic of Korea, 1967-69. Hackney scholar Freer Gallery Art, Washington, 1975-76; fellow U. Kans., Lawrence, 1971-75, J.D. Rockefeller 3d Fund, N.Y.C., 1976-77, Samuel Kress Found., N.Y.C., 1975. Mem. Coll. Art Assn. Am., Assn. for Asian Studies, Am. Com. for South Asian Art, Am. Assn. Mus., Nat. Trust for Hist. Preservation. Avocations: movies, reading, theatre, dance, opera, concerts. Office: Harvard U Art Mus Asian Dept 485 Broadway Cambridge MA 02138-3802

MOWRY, ROBERT WILBUR, pathologist, educator; b. Griffin, Ga., Jan. 10, 1923; s. Roy Burnell and Mary Frances (Swilling) M.; m. Margaret Neilson Black, June 11, 1949; children: Janet Lee, Robert Gordon, Barbara Ann. B.S., Birmingham So. Coll., 1944; M.D., Johns Hopkins U., 1946. Rotating intern U. Ala. Med. Coll., 1946-47, resident pathology, 1947-48; sr. asst. surgeon USPHS-NIH, Bethesda, Md., 1948-52; fellow pathology Boston City Hosp., 1949-50; asst. prof. pathology Washington U., St. Louis, 1952-53; asst. prof. pathology U. Ala. Med. Ctr., Birmingham, 1953-54, assoc. prof. pathology, 1954-57; prof. U. Ala. Med. Center, Birmingham, 1958-89, prof. emeritus, 1989—, prof. health svcs. adminstrn., 1976-84, dir. Anat. Pathology Lab., 1960-64, dir. grad. programs in pathology, 1964-72; sr. scientist U. Ala. Inst. Dental Research, 1967-72, dir. autopsy services, 1975-79; vis. scholar dept. pathology U. Cambridge, Eng., 1972-73; cons. FDA, 1975-81. Author: (with J.F.A. McManus) Staining Methods: Histologic and Histochemical, 1960; mem. editorial bd. Jour. Histochemistry and Cytochemistry, 1960-75, Stain Tech., 1965-90, AMA Archives of Pathology, 1967-76, Biotechnics and Histochemistry, 1991—. Served with USPHS, 1948-52. Mem. Am. Soc. Investigative Pathology, Internat. Acad. Pathology, Biol. Stain Commn. (v.p. 1974-76, pres. 1976-81, trustee 1966—), Soc. for Glycobiology, Am. Assn. Univ. Profs. Pathology, Phi Beta Kappa, Sigma Xi, Delta Sigma Phi, Alpha Kappa Kappa. Presbyterian. Achievements include perfection of staining methods for complex carbohydrates (Alcian blue and colloidal iron) and insulin (Alcian blue-aldehyde fuchsin); showed the utility of these in diagnostic histopathology. Home: 4165 Sharpsburg Dr Birmingham AL 35213-3234

MOXLEY, JOHN HOWARD, III, physician; b. Elizabeth, N.J., Jan. 10, 1935; s. John Howard, Jr. and Cleopatra (Mundy) M.; m. Doris Banchik; children: John Howard IV, Brook. BA, Williams Coll., 1957; MD, U. Colo., 1961; DSc (hon.), Sch. Medicine Hannemann U. Bar: Diplomate Am. Bd. Internal Medicine. Intern Peter Bent Brigham Hosp., Boston, 1961-62, resident in internal medicine, 1962-66; with Nat. Cancer Inst., USPHS, 1963-65; asst. to dean, instr. medicine Harvard Med. Sch., Boston, 1966-69; dean Sch. Medicine, U. Md., 1969-73; vice chancellor health scis., dean Med. Sch., U. Calif.-San Diego, 1973-79; assoc. sec. for health affairs Dept. Def., Washington, 1979-81; sr. v.p. Am. Med. Internat., Beverly Hills, Calif., 1981-87; pres. MetaMed. Inc., Playa Del Rey, Calif., 1987-89; mgr. dir. Korn/Ferry Internat., L.A., 1989—; cons. FDA, NIH; dir. Nat. Fund for Med. Edn., 1986—, chmn., 1993—; dir. Henry M. Jackson Found. for Adv. Mil. Medicine. Contbr. articles to profl. jours. Dir. Polyclinic Health Svcs. Games of XXIII Olympiad. Recipient gold and silver award U. Colo. Med. Sch., 1974, commr.'s citation for outstanding svc. to over-the-counter drug study FDA, 1977, sgl. achievement citation Am. Hosp. Assn., 1983, Sec. of Def. medal for disting. pub. svc., 1981. Fellow ACP, Am. Coll. Physicians Execs. (Disting.); mem. Inst. Medicine NAS, AMA (chmn. coun. sci. affairs 1985), Calif. Med. Assn. (chmn. sci. bd. 1978-83, councilor), San Diego C. of C., Soc. Med. Adminstrs., Am. Hosp. Assn. (trustee 1979-81), Alpha Omega Alpha. Rotary. Office: Korn/Ferry Internat 1800 Century Park E Ste 900 Los Angeles CA 90067-1512

MOY, RICHARD HENRY, academic dean, educator; b. Chgo., Feb. 2, 1931; s. Henry B. and Gladys (Pope) M.; m. Caryl L. Towsley, Aug. 21, 1954; children: Philip B., Eric R. BA in Pre-Medicine with gen. honors, U. Chgo., 1953, BS in Pre-Medicine, 1954, MD in Pathology with honors, 1957. Diplomate Am. Bd. Internal Medicine. Intern U. Chgo. Hosps. and Clinics, 1957-58, resident, 1960-63; clin. assoc. Nat. Cancer Inst. NIH, Bethesda, Md., 1958-60; instr. dept. internal medicine U. Chgo., 1962-63, rsch. assoc., asst. prof., 1964-68, assoc. prof., 1968-70; prof. internal medicine, dean Sch. Medicine So. Ill. U., Springfield, 1970-93, dean emeritus, 1974-93, 1993—; mem. health care program com. Health Care Svc. Corp., 1978-79, 82—; exec. com., 1979-80, 82-83, 84-86, 88—; fin. com., 1981-82, bd. orgn. and nominating com., 1984—, ad hoc com. for long range planning, 1982-83, bd. dirs., 1971—; mem. ad hoc rev. group for start-up assistance grants HEW, 1976; del. People-to-People Med. Edn. Trip to Africa, 1982; mem. med. determination bd. Ill. Dept. Pub. Health, 1980-85, adv. com. family practice residency, 1978, health svc. corps task force, 1980-93; mem. task force on future of mental health in Ill., 1986-87; panelist, lectr., cons. S.C. Commn. on Higher Edn., 1990, other orgns. Contbr. articles to profl. jours. Mem. adv. bd. Ill. Emergency Svcs. and Disaster Agy., 1984-93, Ill. Geriatric Edn. Ctr., 1989-93; chair emergency med. care com. Gov.'s Task Force on Earthquake Preparedness, 1989-90; bd. dirs. Am. Heart Assn. Ill., 1982-84; mem. planning com. St. John's Hosp., 1976-93, Meml. Med. Ctr., 1991-93; mem. VA med. assistance rev. com., 1974-78; chmn. citizens' task force to pass tax referendum Springfield Pub. Sch. Dist. 186, 1984; mem. site visit team Marshall U., 1974, 82, Duke U., 1978, Creighton U., 1980, UCLA, 1981, U. Okla., 1985, Temple U., 1988, Vanderbilt U. Sch. Medicine, 1992; chmn. site visit team U. Calif. Sch. Medicine, 1975, East Tenn. U., 1990, Med. Coll. Pa., 1991, Mich. State U., 1992, Loma Linda U. Med. Sch., 1994. Recipient Disting. Svc. award Med. Alumni Assn. U. Chgo., 1979, Recognition award Soc. Tchrs. of Family Medicine, 1981, Pub. Svc. award So. Ill. U. Carbondale Alumni Assn., 1984, Golden Achievement award Nat. Sch. Pub. Rels. Assn., 1985, Gold Medallion for Humanitarian Svc., Am. Lung Assn.,

1993; named rector for medicine and sci. Lincoln Acad. Ill., 1991. Fellow ACP; mem. Assn. Am. Med. Colls. (various coms. and offices), AMA (sect. med. schs. 1977-93), Am. Bd. Med. Spltys. (rep. Assn. Med. Colls. 1986-91), Ill. Coun. Med. Deans (pres. 1978-79), Ill. Hosp. Assn. (ad hoc study group funding med. edn.), Ill. State Med. Soc., Nat. Bd. Med. Examiners (chair composite com. for U.S. med. licensing examination 1990-92, comprehensive part I and part II coms. 1986-92, John F. Hubbard award com. 1987, mem. ednl. adv. com. Nat. Fund for Med. Edn. 1988-90, chmn. 1988), Sangamon County Med. Soc., Springfield Med. Club, Cen. Ill. Consortium for Health Manpower Edn. (pres. 1976-77), Ill. State Acad. Sci. (hon.), Alpha Omega Alpha, Sigma Xi. Presbyterian. Avocations: med. history, fishing, reading. Office: So Ill U Sch Medicine 801 N Rutledge PO Box 19230 Springfield IL 62794-9230

MOYA, PATRICK ROBERT, lawyer; b. Belen, N.Mex., Nov. 7, 1944; s. Adelicio E. and Eva (Sanchez) M.; m. Sara Dreier, May 30, 1966; children: Jeremy Brill, Joshua Dreier. AB, Princeton U., 1966; JD, Stanford U., 1969. Bar: Calif. 1970, Ariz. 1970, D.C. 1970, U.S. Dist. Ct. (no. dist.) Calif. 1970, U.S. Ct. Claims 1970, U.S. Tax Ct. 1970, U.S.C. Appeals (D.C. cir.) 1970, U.S. Supreme Ct. 1973. Assoc. Lewis and Roca, Phoenix, 1969-73, ptnr., 1973-83; sr. ptnr. Moya, Bailey, Bowers & Jones, P.C., Phoenix, 1983-84; ptnr., mem. nat. exec. com. Gaston & Snow, Phoenix, 1985-91; ptnr., Ariz. legal practice coord. Quarles & Brady, Phoenix, 1991—; instr. sch. of law Ariz. State U., 1972; bd. dir. Bobby McGee's U.S.A., Inc., 1982-86. Mem. Paradise Valley Bd. Adjustment, 1976-80, chmn., 1978-80; mem. Paradise Valley Town Coun., 1980-82; bd. dirs. Phoenix Men's Arts Coun., 1973-81, pres., 1979-80; bd. dirs. The Silent Witness, Inc., 1978-84, pres., 1981-83; bd. dirs. Enterprise Network, Inc., 1989-94, pres., 1991-92; bd. dirs. Phoenix Little Theatre, 1973-75, Interfaith Counseling Svc., 1973-75; precinct committeeman Phoenix Rep. Com., 1975-77; dep. voter registrar Maricopa County, 1975-76; mem. exec. bd. dirs. Gov.'s Strategic Partnership for Econ. Devel.; pres. GSPED, Inc.; mem. of Steering Com. for Sonora Ariz. Joint Econ. Plan; mem. Gov.'s Adv. Com., Ariz. and Mex., Ariz. Corp. Commn. Stock Exch. Adv. Coun., Ariz. Town Hall. Mem. ABA, Nat. Hispanic Bar Assn., Los Abogados Hispanic Lawyers Assn., Nat. Assn. Bond Lawyers, Ariz. Bar Assn., Maricopa County Bar Assn., Paradise Valley Country Club, Univ. Club. Office: Quarles & Brady 1 E Camelback Rd Ste 400 Phoenix AZ 85012-1649

MOYARS-JOHNSON, MARY ANNIS, university administrator; b. Lafayette, Ind., July 19, 1938; d. Edward Raymond and Veronica Marie (Quigg) Moyars; m. Raymond Leon Mother, Aug. 1, 1959 (div. 1970); children: Marilyn Eileen Molter Davis, William Raymond, Ann Marie; m. Thomas Elmer Johnson, May 25, 1973 (div. 1989); children: Thomas Edward, John Alan, Barbara Suzanne. BS, Purdue U., 1960; MA, Purdue U., West Lafayette, Ind., 1991, postgrad., 1985—. Grader great issues Purdue U., West Lafayette, 1960-63, writer ednl. films, 1962-65, publicity dir. convocations and lectures, 1969-74, devel. officer Sch. Humanities, 1978-88, asst. to dir. Optoelectronics Rsch. Ctr., 1989-90, mgr. indsl. rels. Sch. Elec. Engring., 1990—; tchr. English and math. Benton Community Schs., Fowler, Ind., 1966-69; pub. rels. dir. Sycamore Girl Scout Coun., Lafayette, Ind., 1974-78; dir. pub. info. Ind. Senate, Majority Caucus, Indpls., 1977-78; sr. script writer Walters & Steinberg, Lafayette, 1988-89. Author: Colonial Potpourri, 1975; co-author: Historic Colonial French Dress, 1982; contbr. articles to profl. jours. Bd. govs. Tippecanoe County Hist. Assn., Lafayette, 1981—. Mem. Women in Communications, Inc. (v.p. program, Pres. award 1983), Ctr. for French Colonial Rsch. (dir. 1986-89, editor 1988-89), Am. Hist. Assn., Germanna Found., Palatines to Am., Ind. History Assn., Ind. Hist. Soc., Minitrista Coun. for Great Lakes Native Am. Studies, French Colonial Hist. Soc. Roman Catholic. Avocations: history, genealogy, embroidery. Home: 924 Elm Dr West Lafayette IN 47906-2246 Office: Sch Electrical Engring Purdue U West Lafayette IN 47907

MOYE, CHARLES ALLEN, JR., federal judge; b. Atlanta, July 13, 1918; s. Charles Allen and Annie Luther (Williamson) M.; m. Sarah Ellen Johnston, Mar. 9, 1945; children: Henry Allen, Lucy Ellen. A.B., Emory U., 1939, J.D., 1943. Bar: Ga. 1943. Since practiced in Atlanta; partner firm Gambrell, Russell, Moye & Killorin (and predecessors), 1955-70; chief judge U.S. Dist. Ct. (no. dist.) Ga., 1979-87, judge, 1970-87, sr. judge, 1986—. Chmn. DeKalb County Republican Exec. Com., 1952-56; chmn. Rep. Exec. Com. 5th Congl. Dist. Ga., 1956-64; mem. Ga. Rep. Central Com., 1952-64; Rep. candidate for Congress, 1954; del. Rep. Nat. Conv., 1956, 60, 64; chmn. Rep. Exec. Com. 4th Congl. Dist., 1964, Rep. presdl. elector, 1964. Mem. ABA, Fed. Bar Assn., Atlanta Bar Assn., State Bar Ga., Lawyers Club Atlanta, Am. Judicature Soc., Am. Bar Found., Am. Law Inst., Atlanta Athletic Club, Delta Tau Delta. Congregationalist. Home: 1317 Council Bluff Dr NE Atlanta GA 30345-4131 Office: US Dist Ct 2342 US Courthouse 75 Spring St SW Atlanta GA 30335-3361

MOYE, JOHN EDWARD, lawyer; b. Deadwood, S.D., Aug. 15, 1944; s. Francis Joseph and Margaret C. (Roberts) M.; children: Kelly M., Mary S., Megan J. BBA, U. Notre Dame, 1965; JD with distinction, Cornell U., 1968. Bar: N.Y. 1968, Colo. 1971. Prof. law U. Denver, 1972-78, assoc. dean Coll. Law, 1974-78; prof. law So. Meth. U., Dallas, 1973; ptnr. Moye, Giles, O'Keefe, Vermeire & Gorrell, Denver, 1976—; lectr. Harcourt Brace Jovanovich, Chgo., 1972—, Profl. Edn. Group, Minnetonka, Minn., 1982—; chmn. Bd. Law Examiners, Denver, 1988-92. lectr. Harcourt Brace Jovanovich, Chgo., 1972-95, Profl. Edn. Group, Minnetonka, Minn., 1982-95, West Bar Rev., 1995—; chmn. Bd. Law Examiners, Denver, 1988-92. Chmn. Denver Urban Renewal Authority, 1988-93, Colo. Hist. Found.; Denver, 1987—; pres. Downtown Denver, Inc., 1986-88; mem. Consumer Credit Commn., 1985—. Named Prof. of Yr., U. Denver, 1972-74, 76-78, Outstanding Faculty Mem., 1975. Fellow Am. Bar Found.; mem. ABA, Colo. Bar Assn. (chmn. corp., banking and bus. sect. 1982-84, Young Lawyer of Yr. award 1980), N.Y. State Bar Assn., Denver Bar Assn. (Young Lawyer of Yr. award 1980), Law Club (pres. 1982-84). Republican. Roman Catholic. Office: 1225 17th St Denver CO 80202-5501

MOYER, ALAN DEAN, retired newspaper editor; b. Galva, Iowa, Sept. 4, 1928; s. Clifford Lee and Harriet (Jacques) M.; m. Patricia Helen Krecker, July 15, 1950; children: Virginia, Stanley, Glenn. BS in Journalism, U. Iowa, 1950. Reporter, copy editor Wis. State Jour., Madison, 1950-53; reporter, photographer Bartlesville (Okla.) Examiner-Enterprise, 1953; telegraph editor Abilene (Tex.) Reporter-News, 1954-55; makeup editor Cleve. Plain Dealer, 1955-63; mng. editor Wichita (Kans.) Eagle, 1963-70; exec. editor Wichita Eagle and Beacon, 1970-73; mng. editor Phoenix Gazette, 1973-82, Ariz. Republic, 1982-89; ret., 1989; pres., dir. Wichita Profl. Baseball, Inc., 1969-75; mem. jury Pulitzer Prizes, 1973-74, 85, 86, 88. Mem. AP Mng. Editors Assn. (dir. 1973-78), Am. Soc. Newspaper Editors, Wichita Area C. of C. (dir. 1970-72), Sigma Delta Chi. Office: Phoenix Newspaper Inc 120 E Van Buren St Phoenix AZ 85004-2227

MOYER, ALBERT J., company executive, financial analyst; b. Pitts., Dec. 8, 1943; s. C. Joseph and Mary Moyer; m. Jean E. Moyer, Mar.18, 1977; children: Bret, Adam, Ryan. BBA, Dusquene U., 1965. Controller, officer Nat. Semiconductor Corp., Santa Clara, Calif., 1977-79, v.p., chief fin. officer, 1981-83; recy. v.p. Nat. Advanced Systems, Mountain View, Calif., 1979-81; pres., chief exec. officer Enhansys Inc., Cupertino, Calif., 1983-86; v.p. fin., chief fin. officer Western Digital Corp., Irvine, Calif., 1986—. Bd. dirs., treas. Nat. Commn. Indsl. Innovation, Los Angeles, 1983. Mem. Fin. Execs. Inst., Sports Car Club of Am. Republican. Roman Catholic. Home: 29882 Hillside Ter San Juan Capistrano CA 92675-1534 Office: Western Digital Corp PO Box 19665 2445 Mccabe Way Irvine CA 92714-6244

MOYER, DAVID LEE, veterinarian; b. Reading, Pa., May 7, 1940; s. Robert Bretz and Helen Verna (Lutz) M.; m. Ann Marie DeGarmo, Aug. 8, 1964 (div. Sept. 1979). BS, Pa. State U., 1962; postgrad., Temple U., 1967; VMD, U. Pa., 1968; psychology, Kutztown U., 1980. Lic. doctor vet. medicine, Pa. Veterinarian Antietam Valley Animal Hosp., Reading, 1969-76, Kutztown Animal Hosp., Dryville, Pa., 1976-83; meat and poultry inspection supr., vet. med. officer U.S. Dept. Agr., Food Safety and Inspection Svc., Fredericksburg, Pa., 1983-88; veterinarian Exeter Animal Hosp./Cat Clinic/Pet Care Ctr., Birdsboro, Pa., 1983—; veterinarian Reading Police Dept. K-9 Corps, City of Reading, 1969-80, Humane Soc. Berks County, Reading, 1970-72, Animal Rescue League SPCA, Reading, 1970—. Advisor Boy Scouts Am., Reading, 1969-74. Mem. Am. Vet. Med. Assn., Am.

Animal Hosp. Assn., Am. Acad. Vet. Dermatology, Pa. Vet. Med. Assn., Keystone Vet. Med. Assn., Schulykill Vet. Med. Assn., Lehigh Vet. Med. Assn., Western Vet. Conf., Vet. Orthopedic Soc., Am. Soc. Vet. Ophthalmology, Am. Assn. Feline Practitioners (charter), Cornell Feline Health Ctr., Acad. Feline Medicine, Internat. Vet. Ophthalmology, Am. Soc. Vet. Nutrition, Am. Assn. Food Hygiene, Am. Assn. Avian Pathologists, Vet. Cardiology Soc. (pres. 1983), Am. Vet. Dental Soc., Acad. Vet. Dermatology, Toastmasters (pres. 1983). Democrat. Lutheran. Avocations: skiing, gardening, fine dining, travel. Home and Office: 6800 Daniel Boone Rd Birdsboro PA 19508

MOYER, F. STANTON, financial executive, advisor; b. Phila., June 7, 1929; s. Edward T. and Beatrice (Stanton) M.; m. Ann P. Stovell, May 16, 1953; 1 child, Alice E. B.S. in Econs., U. Pa., 1951. Registered rep. Smith, Barney & Co., Phila., 1951-54, Kidder, Peabody & Co., Phila., 1954-60; mgr. corp. dept. Blyth Eastman Dillon & Co., Inc. (formerly Eastman Dillon, Union Securities & Co.), Phila., 1960-65; instl. sales mgr. Blyth Eastman Dillon & Co., Inc. (formerly Eastman Dillon, Union Securities & Co.), 1965-67, gen. partner, 1967-71, 1st v.p., 1971-74, sr. v.p., 1974-80; v.p., resident officer Kidder, Peabody & Co. Inc., Phila., 1980-86; chmn. Pa. Mcht. Group Ltd., Radnor, 1987-88; exec. v.p. Rorer Asset Mgmt., Phila., 1990-92; chmn. Mercer Capital Mgmt., 1992-93, Global Mgmt. Group, Inc., 1993-95; mng. dir. Avonwood Capital Corp., 1995—. Trustee U. Pa., 1978-83, Hosp. of U. Pa., 1978-87; bd. dirs. Atwater Kent Mus., Phila., 1983—. Mem. Delta Psi. Republican. Episcopalian. Clubs: Racquet (Phila.), St. Anthony (Phila.); Merion Cricket (Haverford, Pa.); Gulph Mills Golf (King of Prussia, Pa.). Home: 445 Caversham Rd Bryn Mawr PA 19010

MOYER, JOHN ARTHUR, obstetrician/gynecologist, state senator; b. Glendive, Mont., Feb. 25, 1922; s. Arthur Boeman Moyer and Nora Elizabeth Moore; m. Caroline Louise Atkinson, Dec. 31, 1947 (dec. 1982); children: Nora, John Jr., David, Julia, Mary Janci, Tim, Jim, Elizabeth, Chris, Susan; m. Joanne Halsted, Jan. 5, 1987. BS, N.D. State U., 1941; MD, U. Ill., 1947. Intern Garfield Park Community Hosp., Chgo., 1947-49; resident Cook County Hosp., Chgo., 1951-53; pvt. practice Spokane, Wash., 1955-85; chief of staff St. Lukes Hosp., Spokane, 1958; cons., clin. rschr. Group Health N.W., Spokane, 1985; state rep. Wash. State Legislature, Olympia, 1986-92, state senator, 1993; clin. prof. ob-gyn. U. Wash. Med. Sch., Seattle, 1990—; adj. prof. East Wash. U., Spokane, 1987; ob-gyn. cons. Community Clinic, Othello, Wash., 1990—. Dir. Eastern Wash. Hist. Soc., Spokane, 1990—. Capt. M.C., 1953-55. Fellow Am. Coll. Ob-Gyn. Mem. Wash. State Med. Assn. (pres. 1978), Spokane County Med. Soc. (pres. 1958-59), Spokane Ob-Gyn. Soc. (pres. 1976). Republican. Roman Catholic. Avocations: woodworking, saxophone music. Home: 1405 W 9th Ave Spokane WA 99204-3338

MOYER, KENNETH EVAN, psychologist, educator; b. Chippewa Falls, Wis., Nov. 19, 1919; s. John Evan and Margaret (Lashway) M.; m. Doris Virginia Johnson, May 29, 1943; children: Robert Stephen, Cathy Lita. A.B. with honors, Park Coll., 1943; M.A., Washington U., St. Louis, 1948, Ph.D., 1951. Mem. faculty Carnegie-Mellon U., Pitts., 1949—; prof. psychology Carnegie-Mellon U., 1961—; cons. on higher edn. Gov. Norway, 1954; mem. research adv. com. Pa. Commonwealth Mental Health Found., 1956—. Author: The Physiology of Hostility, 1971, You and Your Child: A Primer for Parents, 1974, The Psychobiology of Aggression, 1976, Physiology of Aggression and Implications for Control, 1976, A Reader's Guide to Aggressive Behavior, 1977, Neuroanatomy, 1980, Bibliography of Aggressive Behavior: A Reader's Guide to the Literature, Vol. II, Violence and Aggression, 1987. Recipient Carnegie Found. award for excellence in teaching, 1954. Fellow AAAS, Am. Psychol. Assn.; mem. Psychonomic Soc., So. Soc. Philosophy and Psychology, Pitts. Psychol. Assn. (past dir.), Sigma Xi, Theta Kappa Theta. Research, publs. endocrinology emotion, startle response avoidance behavior, physiology aggression; demonstrated young children have capacity for prolonged attention spans if proper toys are used, that adrenal glands are not essential for effects electroconvulsive shock on behavior; devel. physiol. theory aggressive behavior. Home: 1211 Ridgewood DR Lillian AL 36549-5329

MOYER, ROBERT THEODORE, newspaper editor; b. Lincoln, Nebr., Dec. 31, 1948; s. Jean Lee and Anna Elizabeth (Hoff) M.; m. Candyce Kaye Epp, Dec. 23, 1972; children: Scott Theodore, Ann Kathleen. BA, U. Nebr., 1975, MBA, 1986. Reporter/copy editor Lincoln Journal, 1968-77, asst. sports editor, 1977-82, regional editor, 1982-85, news editor, 1985-87, mng. editor, 1987—. Bd. dirs. Lincoln Family Service Assn., 1987—; fellow Leadership Lincoln, 1987-88, bd. dirs. Alumni Assn., 1988-89; active StarVenture Action Com. for Lincoln's Future, 1987—. Mem. Am. Soc. Newspaper Editors. Republican. Methodist. Home: 3142 Ryons St Lincoln NE 68502-4140 Office: Jour-Star Printing Co PO Box 81689 926 P St Lincoln NE 68508-3615

MOYER, THOMAS J., state supreme court chief justice; b. Sandusky, Ohio, Apr. 18, 1939; s. Clarence and Idamae (Hessler) M.; m. Mary Francis Moyer, Dec. 15, 1984; 1 child, Drew; stepchildren: Anne, Jack, Alaine, Elizabeth. BA, Ohio State U., 1961, JD, 1964. Asst. atty. gen. State of Ohio, Columbus, 1964-66; pvt. practice law Columbus, 1966-69; dep. asst. Office Gov. State of Ohio, Columbus, 1969-71, exec. asst., 1975-79; assoc. Crabbe, Brown, Jones, Potts & Schmidt, Columbus, 1972-75; judge U.S. Ct. Appeals (10th cir.), Columbus, 1979-86; chief justice Ohio Supreme Ct., Columbus, 1987—. Sec. bd. trustees Franklin U., Columbus, 1986-87, trustee Univ. Club, Columbus, 1986; mem. nat. council adv. com. Ohio State U. Coll. Law, Columbus. Recipient Award of Merit, Ohio Legal Ctr. Inst.; named Outstanding Young Man of Columbus, Columbus Jaycees, 1969. Mem. Ohio State Bar Assn. (exec. com., council dels.), Columbus Bar Assn. (pres. 1980-81), Critchon Club, Columbus Maennerchor Club. Republican. Avocations: sailing, tennis. Office: Ohio Supreme Ct 30 E Broad St 3d Fl Columbus OH 43266-0419

MOYERS, BILL D., journalist; b. Hugo, Okla., June 5, 1934; s. John Henry and Ruby (Johnson) M.; m. Judith Davidson, Dec. 18, 1954; children: William Cope, Suzanne, John. BJ with honors, U. Tex., 1956; grad. student, U. Edinburgh, Scotland, 1956-57; MTh with honors, Southwestern Baptist Theol. Sem., 1959; hon. doctorate, Am. Film Inst. Personal asst. to Senator Lyndon B. Johnson, 1960; assoc. dir. Peace Corps, 1961-62, dept. dir., 1963; spl. asst. to Pres. Johnson, 1963-67, press sec., 1965-67; pub. Newsday, Garden City, N.Y., 1967-70; editor-in-chief Bill Moyers Jour. (weekly pub. affairs program on pub. TV), 1971-76, 78-81; chief corr. CBS Reports, CBS-TV, 1976-78; sr. news analyst CBS News, CBS-TV, 1981-86; exec. editor Pub. Affairs TV, Inc., 1987—; news analyst NBC News, 1995—. Author: Listening to America, 1971, Report from Philadelphia, 1987, The Secret Government, 1988, Joseph Cmapbell and the Power of Myth, 1988, A World of Ideas, 1989, 2d edit., 1990., Healing and the Mind, 1993. Recipient Emmy awards (more than 30); Ralph Lowell medal for contbn. to Pub. TV; George Peabody award, 1976, 80, 85-86, 88-90; DuPont/Columbia Silver Baton award, 1979, 86, 88, Gold Baton award, 1991; George Polk award, 1981, 86; Career Achievement award Internat. Documentary Assn. Fellow Am. Acad. Arts and Scis. Office: Pub Affairs TV Inc 356 W 58th St New York NY 10019-1804

MOYLAN, JOHN L., secondary school principal. Prin. DeMatha Cath. High Sch., Hyattsville, Md. Recipient Blue Ribbon Sch. award U.S. Dept. Edn., 1983-84, 90-91, Disting. Prin. award Archdiocese of Washington, 1991, Sch. Adminstr. award Md. Music Educators Assn., 1992, Disting. Ednl. Leadership award Washington Post, 1993. Office: DeMatha Cath High Sch 4313 Madison St Hyattsville MD 20781-1692

MOYLE, PETER BRIGGS, fisheries and biology educator; b. Mpls., May 29, 1942; s. John Briggs and Evelyn (Wood) M.; m. Marilyn Arneson, June 11, 1966; children—Petrea Ruth, John Noah. B.A., U. Minn., 1964; M.S., Cornell U., 1966; Ph.D., U. Minn., 1969. Asst. prof. Calif. State U. Fresno, 1969-72; from asst. prof. to prof. U. Calif., Davis, 1972—; chmn. dept. wildlife and fisheries, 1982-87; head, Delta Native Fishes Recovery Team, 1993-94. Author: Inland Fishes of California, 1976; Fishes: An Introduction to Ichthyology, 2d edit., 1988; Distribution and Ecology of Stream Fishes of Sacramento San Joaquin Drainage, 1982, Fish: An Enthusiast's Guide, 1993. Fellow Calif. Acad. Sci.; mem. Am. Fisheries Soc. (life, award of excellence West div. 1991), Ecol. Soc. Am., Am. Soc. Ichthyologists and Herpetologists,

Soc. Conservation Biology., Natural Heritage Inst. (v.p. 1994—). Home: 612 Eisenhower St Davis CA 95616-3031 Office: Dept Wildlife & Fisheries U Calif Davis Davis CA 95616

MOYNAHAN, JOHN DANIEL, JR., insurance executive; b. Chgo., Dec. 10, 1935; s. John Daniel and Helen (Hurley) M.; m. Virginia Thomas, Oct. 10, 1959; children: Laura, Mark, Tricia, Kate. B.A. cum laude, U. Notre Dame, 1957. With Met. Life Ins. Co., N.Y.C. 1957—; regional v.p. Met. Life Ins. Co., from 1971, with nat. div. group nat. accounts, 1979-80, sr. v.p. group life and health ops., 1980-86, exec. v.p., 1986—. Office: Met Life Ins Co 1 Madison Ave New York NY 10010

MOYNAHAN, JULIAN LANE, English language educator, author; b. Cambridge, Mass., May 21, 1925; s. Joseph Leo and Mary (Shea) M.; m. Elizabeth Rose Reilly, Aug. 6, 1945; children: Catherine (dec.), Brigid, Mary Ellen. A.B., Harvard U., 1946, A.M., 1951, Ph.D., 1957. Cataloguer, rare books asst. Boston Pub. Library, 1948-49, 51; teaching fellow Harvard U., 1951-53; instr. English Amherst Coll., 1953-55; instr., asst. prof. English Princeton, 1955-63; Fulbright lectr. Am. and English lit. Univ. Coll., Dublin, 1963-64; assoc. prof. English Rutgers U., 1964-66, prof., 1966-93, disting. prof., 1976-93, prof. emeritus, 1993—; vis. prof. U. Wyo., summer 1965, Harvard U., summer 1967, Bread Loaf Sch., 1969; NEH vis. prof. Manhattanville Coll., 1972; Gauss lectr. Princeton U., 1975; vis. scholar English dept. U. Utah, spring 1980. Author: Sisters and Brothers, 1960, The Deed of Life, A Critical Study of D.H. Lawrence, 1963, Pairing Off, 1969, Vladimir Nabokov, 1971, Garden State, 1973, Where the Land and Water Meet, 1979, Anglo-Irish: The Literary Imagination in a Hyphenated Culture, 1994; editor: (D.H. Lawrence) Sons and Lovers: Text, Criticism, Backgrounds, 1968, 77, The Viking Portable Thomas Hardy, 1977; Contbr. revs. and criticism to N.Y. Times Book Rev., New Republic, T.L.S., Washington Post Book World, N.Y. Rev. Books, London Observer. Bicentennial preceptorship Princeton, 1960-63, grants-in-aid Am. Council Learned Socs., Am. Philos. Soc.; mem. Pulitzer Book Prize Fiction Jury, 1981, chmn., 1987. Served with AUS, 1943-44. 7500 creative writing award Nat. Found. Arts, 1966; Ingram-Merrill award, 1967; NEH fellow, 1975; Guggenheim fellow, 1983-84. Mem. MLA, AAUP, PEN, Harvard Club of Princeton. Democrat. Home: 3439 Lawrenceville Rd Princeton NJ 08540-4717 also: 405 W 23rd St Apt 9B New York NY 10011-1412

MOYNE, JOHN ABEL, computer scientist, linguist, educator; b. Yezd, Iran, July 6, 1920; s. Abul Kasim and Sogra (Afshar) M.; came to U.S., 1956, naturalized, 1965; BA, Georgetown U., 1959, MA, 1960; PhD, Harvard U., 1970; m. Claudia Wienert, July 4, 1963; children: David, Nicholas, Parvin. With Brit. Govt., Iran and India, 1943-52, market research officer, Tehran, 1952; linguist U.S. Govt., Cyprus, 1953-56; rsch. assoc. Georgetown U., Washington, 1960-63; mgr. applied linguistics dept. IBM Corp., Cambridge, Mass., 1963-71; prof., chmn. computer sci. dept. Queens Coll., CUNY, Flushing, 1971-81, chmn. div. math. and natural scis., 1978-81, chmn. univ. faculty for Ph.D. in Computer Sci., 1978-82, exec. officer Grad. Sch. Ph.D. Program in Linguistics, 1983-88; prof. linguistics and computer sci. CUNY, 1971-91, prof. emeritus linguistics and computer sci., 1991—. Grantee, EURATOM, AEC, NSF, City U. N.Y. Mem. Linguistic Soc. Am., Assn. Computational Linguistics, Brit. Inst. Engring. Technology. Democrat. Episcopalian. Author: Hafiz of Shiraz, 1946; Life in India, 1949; Open Secret, 1984; Understanding Language: Man or Machine, 1985; Unseen Rain, 1986, Rumi: These Branching Moments, 1988; This Longing: Poetry, Teaching Stories, and Letters of Rumi, 1988, LISP: A First Language for Computing, 1991, Say I Am You, 1994; contbr. articles to profl. jours., chpts. to books. Home: 40 Prospect Ave Sea Cliff NY 11579-1029 Office: CUNY PhD Program Linguistics Grad Ctr 33 W 42d St New York NY 10036-8099

MOYNIHAN, DANIEL PATRICK, senator, educator; b. Tulsa, Mar. 16, 1927; s. John Henry and Margaret Ann (Phipps) M.; m. Elizabeth Therese Brennan, May 29, 1955; children: Timothy Patrick, Maura Russell, John McCloskey. Student, CCNY, 1943; BA cum laude, Tufts U., 1948; MA, Fletcher Sch. Law and Diplomacy, 1949, PhD, 1961, LLD (hon.), 1968; Fulbright fellow, London (Eng.) Sch. Econs. and Polit. Sci., 1950-51; AM (hon.), Harvard U., 1966; LLD (hon.), Cath. U. Am., 1968, New Sch. Social Rsch., 1968, U. Notre Dame, 1969, Fordham U., 1970; St. Bonaventure U., 1972, Boston Coll., 1976, Yeshiva U., 1978, Rensselaer Polytech. Inst., 1983, Syracuse U. Sch. Law, 1984, Columbia U., 1987, U. Rochester, 1994; D in Pub. Adminstrn. (hon.), Hamilton Coll., 1968; DSI (hon.), Defense Intelligence Coll., 1984; numerous other hon. degrees. With Internat. Rescue Com., 1954; successively asst. to sec., asst. sec., acting sec. to gov. State of N.Y., 1955-58, mem. tenure commn., 1959-60, dir. Syracuse U. govt. rsch. project, 1959-61, spl. asst. to sec. labor, 1961-62, exec. asst. to sec., 1962-63, asst. sec. labor, 1963-65; dir. Joint Ctr. for Urban Studies MIT and Harvard U., 1966-69; prof. edn. and urban politics Kennedy Sch. Govt., Harvard U., 1966-73, sr. mem., 1966-77, prof. govt., 1973-77; asst. for urban affairs to Pres. U.S., 1969-70; counsellor to Pres. U.S., mem. Cabinet, 1969-70, cons. to Pres. U.S., 1971-73; mem. U.S. del. 26th Gen. Assembly, UN, 1971, Pres.'s Sci. Adv. Com., 1971-73; ambassador to India New Delhi, 1973-75; U.S. permanent rep. to UN, N.Y.C., 1975-76; U.S. senator from N.Y., 1977—, chmn. senate fin. com., 1993—; mem. senate fgn. rels. com., rules com. , environ., and pub. works com., joint com. on taxation, libr.; vice chmn. Pres.'s Temp. Commn. on Pennsylvania Avenue, 1964-73; chmn. adv. com. traffic safety dept. HEW; fellow Ctr. Advanced Studies, Wesleyan U., 1965-66; hon. fellow London Sch. Econs. and Polit. Sci., 1970—; sec. pub. affairs com. N.Y. State Dem. Com., 1958-60; alt. del. Dem. Nat. Conv., 1960, 76. Author: Maximum Feasible Misunderstanding, 1969, The Politics of a Guaranteed Income, 1973, Coping: On the Practice of Government, 1974, A Dangerous Place, 1978, Counting Our Blessings, 1980, Loyalties, 1984, Family and Nation, 1986, Came the Revolution: Argument in the Reagan Era, 1988, On the Law of Nations, 1990, Pandaemonium: Ethnicity in International Politics, 1993; co-author: Beyond the Melting Pot, 1963; editor: The Defenses of Freedom, 1966, On Understanding Poverty, 1969, Ethnicity: Theory and Experience, 1975, others; editorial bd. Pub. Interest; contbr. articles to profl. jours. Vice chmn. Woodrow Wilson Internat. Ctr. for Scholars, 1971-76; chmn. bd. trustees Joseph H. Hirshhorn Mus. and Sculpture Garden, 1971-85; mem. bd. regents Smithsonian Instn., 1987—. With USN, 1944-47. Recipient Meritorious Svc. award U.S. Dept. Labor, 1965, Centennial medal Syracuse U., 1969, Internat. League for Human Rights award, 1975, John LaFarge award for Interracial Justice, 1980, Medallion SUNY Albany, 1984, Henry medal Smithsonian Instn., 1985, SEAL Medallion, CIA, 1986, Meml. Sloan-Kettering Cancer Ctr. medal, 1986, Britannica award, 1986, Notre Dame U. Laetare medal, 1992, Thomas Jefferson award AIA, 1993. Mem. AAAS (vice chmn. 1971, dir. 1972-73), Am. Philos. Soc. (Hubert Humphrey award 1983, Thomas Jefferson medal 1993), Nat. Acad. Pub. Adminstrn., Am. Acad. Arts and Scis. (chmn. seminar on poverty), Century Club, Harvard Club. Office: US Senate 464 Russell Senate Bldg Washington DC 20510-3201

MOYNIHAN, MICHAEL J., artistic and producing director, writer; b. New Berlin, Wis., July 23, 1946; s. John F. and Irene A. (Gautier) M.; m. Melinda Boyd; children: Margaret, Emily. Co-founder Friends Mime Theatre, Milw., 1973-91; artistic/producing dir. Milw. Pub. Theatre, 1991—; dir. Digital Theatrics, Milw., 1992—. Prodr. (play) Into the Water, 1993, The Snow Queen, 1991, Amber in Wasteland, 1992, (multi-media) Mondo Lingo, 1992 (WAB award 1992). Mem. Walkers Point Artists Assn., Dave-Click MUG, MKE ANRCHY, Ltd. Office: Milw Pub Theatre PO Box 07147 Milwaukee WI 53207-0147

MOYNIHAN, WILLIAM J., museum executive; b. Little Falls, N.Y., Apr. 8, 1942; s. Bernard J. and Mary A. (Flynn) M.; m. Irene A. Sheilds, July 2, 1966; children: Patricia, Erin, Sean. BA, SUNY, Binghamton, 1966; MA, Colgate U., 1966; PhD, Syracuse U., 1973. From asst. to assoc. prof. Colgate U., Hamilton, N.Y., 1973-77; from asst. to assoc. dean faculty, 1977-80, dean students, 1980-83, dean coll., 1983-88; v.p.m dir. Am. Mus. Natural History, N.Y.C., 1988-95; pres., CEO Milw. Pub. Mus., 1995—; bd. dirs. N.Y. State Mus.; adv. com. arts and culture Congressman J. Nadler, N.Y.C., 1993-95. Adv. editor Curator jour., 1991-95. Mem. Am. Museum Assn. Home: 203 W Coventry Ct Glendale WI 53217 Office: Milw Pub Mus 800 W Wells St Milwaukee WI 53233

MOYSE, HERMANN, JR., banker; b. Baton Rouge, Aug. 3, 1921; s. Hermann and Rosalie (Gottlieb) M.; m. Marie Louise Levy, June 4, 1942; children—Lewis Arthur, Hermann III, Marie Rosalie. B.A., La. State U., 1942. With City Nat. Bank of Baton Rouge, 1946—, v.p., 1962-70, exec. v.p., 1970-72, pres., 1972-81, chmn., 1981-94, chmn. emeritus, 1995—, also dir.; pres., dir. Bistineau-Webster Oil Co.; sec., dir. Baton Rouge Realty Co., Ltd., Lottie Land & Devel. Co., Inc., Melrose Devel. Corp.; chmn. bd. First Commerce Corp., 1992—; bd. dirs. Pan Am. Life Ins. Co., Bank of Zachary, 1971-93. Pres. Capital Area United Givers Fund, 1966-67; mem. exec. com. Pub. Affairs Research Council, 1968-70; exec. com. Perkins Radiation Center. Served to maj. F.A. AUS, 1942-46. Decorated Bronze Star. Mem. Am. Bankers Assn. (governing coun. 1975-77), La. Bankers Assn. (pres. 1967-68, Baton Rouge Country Club, City Club of Baton Rouge. Office: City Nat Bank PO Box 1231 Baton Rouge LA 70821-1231

MOZIAN, GERARD PAUL, real estate company executive, business consultant; b. N.Y.C., Jan. 16, 1945; s. Gerard and Virginia (Chadik) M.; m. Mary Susan McKelvey, July 26, 1969. BMechE, Manhattan Coll., 1966; MBA, U. Pitts., 1967. Fin. administr. Philco-Ford Corp., Tehran, Iran, 1969-71; fin. analyst Gen. Waterworks Corp., Phila., 1971-73; regional contr. Gen. Waterworks Corp., Miami, Fla., 1973-75; v.p. fin. Gen. Devel. Utilities, Miami, 1975-78, sr. v.p. fin. and adminstrn., 1978-81, exec. v.p. ops., 1981-82, pres., 1982-87; sr. v.p. planning and fin. Gen. Devel. Corp., Miami, 1983-87; sr. v.p., chief fin. officer Gen. Devel. Corp., 1988-89; pres. Sugarmill Woods Inc., 1990-92; v.p., chief fin. officer Montenay Internat. Corp., MIami, 1992—. Home: 7521 SW 113th St Miami FL 33156-4548 Office: 3225 Aviation Ave Miami FL 33133-4741

MOZLEY, PAUL DAVID, obstetrics and gynecology educator; b. Decatur, Ala., Oct. 27, 1928; s. James Howard and Ruth Dianne (Brindely) M.; m. Mary Dale Goss, Aug. 30, 1983; children from previous marriage: Susan Ruth, Paul David Jr., Sally Robin. BA, U. Ala., 1950; MD, Med. Coll. Ala., 1955. Diplomate Am. Bd. Ob-Gyn, Am. Bd. Psychiatry and Neurology. Commd. lt. USN, 1955; advanced through grades to capt., 1970, resident ob-gyn, Corona (Calif.) and San Diego Naval Hosp., 1956-59; resident in psychiatry Bethesda, Md., 1964-66, Phila. Naval Hosp., 1969-70; staff gynecologist U.S. Naval Hosp., Yokosuku, Japan, 1959-62; chief gynecologist U.S. Naval Hosp., Memphis, 1962-64; dir. med. services U.S. Naval Hosp., Naples, Italy, 1966-68, comdg. officer, 1969; chmn. neuropsychiatry Naval Regional Med. Ctr., Portsmouth, Va., 1970-75; ret., 1975; assoc. prof. psychiatry Eastern Va. Med. Sch., Norfolk, 1975-77, prof., interim chmn. dept., 1977-78, vice chmn. psychiatry, 1978-79; prof., dir. undergrad. edn. Dept. Ob-Gyn Sch. Medicine, East Carolina U., Greenville, 1979-84; prof. ob-gyn, chmn. dept., Coll. Community Health Scis. U. Ala., Tuscaloosa, 1984—; prof. ob-gyn, assoc. chmn. dept., Sch. Medicine, 1984—; dir. psychiat. services Norfolk Gen. Hosp., 1975-79; chmn. dept. ob-gyn DCH Regional Med. Ctr., Tuscaloosa, 1986—; cons. med. liability law legal firms., Ala., Tenn., 1980—. Contbr. numerous articles to profl. jours. Mem. Regional Perinatal Adv. Council, Montgomery, Ala., 1986-87; sponsor Tuscaloosa Symphony Assn. Recipient Meritorious Service medal Pres. U.S., 1975, Surgeon Gen.'s Merit award, 1975, Attending of Yr. award Residents in Psychiatry, 1979, Clin. Sci. Course award Dept. Ob-Gyn grad. class, 1982, Eastern Va. Sch. Medicine; named one of Outstanding Young Men in Am., Jaycees, 1964. Fellow ACS, Am. Coll. Ob-Gyn (chmn. various programs 1974, 76, 77, Chmn.'s award clin. research 1969), Am. Psychiat. Assn. (Continuing Med. Edn. Standards award 1977); mem. AMA (Physician's Recognition award 1986), Am. Soc. Psychosomatic Ob-Gyn (founding mem., pres. 1979-80, chmn. nominating com. 1981, permanent steering com. 1982), Va. Ob-Gyn Soc., Assn. Acad. Psychiatry, Va. Med. Soc., N.C. Neuropsychiat. Assn., Pitt County Med. Soc., Med. Assn. Ala., Ala. Psychiat. Assn., LWV, Alpha Epsilon Delta. Democrat. Mem. Ch. of Christ. Club: Torch (Portsmouth). Avocations: cabinetry, goldsmithing. Home: 21 Beech Hls Tuscaloosa AL 35404-4959 Office: The Univ of Ala Dept of Ob-Gyn PO Box 870376 Tuscaloosa AL 35487-0376

MRAZ, ALANA L., elementary school principal. Prin. Rockland Sch., Libertyville, Ill. Recipient Elem. Sch. Recognition award U.S. Dept. Edn., 1989-90. Office: Rockland Sch 160 W Rockland Rd Libertyville IL 60048

MRKONIC, GEORGE RALPH, JR., retail executive; b. Lawrence, Kans., July 13, 1952; s. George Ralph and Ruth (Clayton) M.; m. Barbara Machmer, June 22, 1974; children: Matthew George, John William, Kelsey Margaret. BA and MA in Econs., Stanford U., 1975; MBA, Harvard U., 1978. Fin. analyst WR Grace/Retail Group, N.Y.C., 1978-79, group mgr., 1979-80, dir. fin. planning, 1980-81, v.p., chief fin. officer, 1981; v.p., chief fin. officer Herman's Sporting Goods Inc., Carteret, N.J., 1981-85, sr. v.p., chief fin. officer, 1985-87; exec. v.p., dep. chief exec. officer Herman's Sporting Goods Inc., Carteret, 1986-87, pres., chief exec. officer, 1987; pres. Eyelab, Inc, River Edge, N.J., 1987-90; exec. v.p. splty. retailing K Mart Corp., Troy, Mich., 1990-94; pres. and vice chmn. Borders Group, Inc., Ann Arbor, Mich., 1994—.

MRKONICH, DOROTHY EVANSON, nursing educator; b. Echo, Minn., July 10, 1938; d. August Alfred and Tilda (Sollom) Evanson; m. Thomas Mrkonich, Aug. 15, 1959; children: Jana Kaye Balfany, Kristen DeAnn, Jon Thomas. BS in Nursing, St. Olaf Coll., 1960; MEd, U. Minn., 1961, PhD in Ednl. Adminstrn., 1982. Mem. faculty dept. nursing Coll. of St. Catherine, St. Paul, 1961-62; mem. faculty dept. nursing St. Olaf Coll., Northfield, Minn., 1970—, prof., 1986—, chmn. dept. nursing, 1979-86; mem. Minn. Bd. Nursing, 1981—, pres., 1984-85; bd. dirs. Minn. Intercollegiate Nursing Consortium; incorporating trustee Neuman Systems Model Group, 1988—. Mem. ANA, Minn. Nurses Assn., Am. Assn. Colls. Nursing (bd. dirs.), Minn. Bd. Nursing, Nat. League Nursing Accreditation (site vistor 1985—), Nat. League for Nursing (bd. mem.), Sigma Theta Tau, Phi Lambda Theta. Office: 2004 Randolph Ave Saint Paul MN 55105-1750

MRKVICKA, EDWARD FRANCIS, JR., financial writer, publisher, consultant; b. Aurora, Ill., Oct. 17, 1944; s. Edward Francis Sr. and Ruth Caroline (Phillips) M.; m. Madelyn Helen Atmnac, July 1, 1972; children: Edward Francis III, Kelly Helen. Cert. comml. pilot, U. Ill., 1965; diploma, Dept. Def., 1967, Bank Mktg. Assn., 1972; grad. cert., Bank Mktg. Assn., 1973. Mktg. officer Downers Grove (Ill.) Nat. Bank, 1964-72; asst. v.p. and mktg. officer Bank of Westmont, Ill., 1972-73; v.p. and cashier 1st State Bank Hanover Park, Ill., 1973-76; pres. 1st Nat. Bank Marengo, Ill., 1976-81, Reliance Enterprises, Inc., Fin. News Syndicate, Omni, Fin. Group, Eagle Publishing, Marengo, 1981—; adv. coun. Am. Monetary Found., Fullerton, Calif., 1987; mem. panel of experts Boardroom Reports, 1990—. Pub.: (newsletter) Money Insider; author: Battle Your Bank - And Win!, 1984, Moving Up, 1985; (with others) The Complete Book of Personal Finance, 1987, The Bank Book, 1989, 1,037 Ways to Make or Save Up to $100,000 This Year Alone, 1991, The Rational Investor, 1992; contbr. numerous articles to profl. jours. and newspapers. Bd. dirs. DuPage County Lung Assn., Downers Grove, Ill., 1970; mem. bd. Western Suburbs Combined Com. Appeal, Downers Grove, 1971; bd. dirs. McHenry County Easter Seals Clinic, Woodstock, Ill., 1979; v.p., treas. Marengo/Union Chamber, 1980; Am. rep. Cans. for Constitutional Money, 1990—. Sgt. USAF, 1965-69. Mem. Nat. Writers Union. Republican. Avocations: bowling, fishing. Office: Reliance Enterprises Inc PO Box 413 Marengo IL 60152-0413

MROZ, JOHN EDWIN, political scientist; b. Lowell, Mass., May 1, 1948; s. Edwin T. and Margaret Mary (Little) M.; m. Karen Linehan, June 17, 1972; children: Jonathan E.R., Jessica, Jeffrey. BA, cert. Soviet and East European studies, U. Notre Dame, 1970; M.A., Northeastern U., 1972; M.A., M.A.L.D., Tufts U., 1974. Exec. sec. UN Assn. Greater Boston, 1971-73; exec. v.p., dir. Middle East Studies, Internat. Peace Acad., Inc., N.Y.C., 1976-81; pres. Inst. East West Studies, N.Y.C., 1981—; cons. U.S. govt. intermediary in Middle East, U.S. Dept. State, 1981-82; cons. Fgn. Svc. Inst., Dept. State, 1977-81; cons. Coun. of Europe, Strasbourg, Fed. Republic Germany, 1989—, East European govts., 1990—. Author: Beyond Security: Private Perceptions Among Arabs and Israelis, 1980. Contbr. articles to profl. jours. Teaching fellow NSF, 1971-72. Decorated Officer's Cross of Order of Merit Fed. Republic of Germany, 1991. Mem. Coun. on Fgn. Rels., Internat. Inst. Strategic Studies. Republican. Avocations: travel, falconry. Office: Inst East West Studies 360 Lexington Ave New York NY 10017-6502

MROZEK, DONALD L., lawyer; b. Chgo., Mar. 17, 1947. BSE, Northwestern U., 1969; JD with honor, DePaul U., 1973. Bar: Ill. 1973, U.S. Dist. Ct. (no. dist.) Ill. 1973, U.S. Dist. Ct. (no. dist. trial bar) Ill. 1973, U.S. Ct. Appeals (7th cir.) 1982, U.S. Supreme Ct. 1981. Ptnr. Hinshaw & Culbertson, Chgo. Mem. ABA, Ill. State Bar, Chgo. Bar Assn., Internat. Assn. Defense Counsel, Defense Rsch. Inst., Trial Lawyers Club Chgo. Office: Hinshaw Culbertson 222 N LaSalle St Ste 300 Chicago IL 60601-1081

MTEWA, MEKKI, foundation administrator; b. Sungo, Mangochi, Malawi, Apr. 13, 1946; 1 child, Natasha. BA, Chapman Coll., 1974; MA in Polit. Sci., Calif. State U., Fullerton, 1975; postgrad., Miami U., Oxford, Ohio, 1975-76; diploma in exec. law and leadership studies, LaSalle Extension U., Chgo., 1977; PhD in Pub. Adminstrn. and Pub. Policy, Claremont Grad. Sch., 1979; postdoctoral in legal studies, Vrije U., Brussels, 1985-86. Regional adminstrv. sec. Agrl. Devel. and Mktg. Corp., Limbe, Malawi, 1964-66; adminstrv. sec. United Transport (Malawi) Ltd., Blantyre, 1966-67; legal asst. Lilley, Wills & Co., Limbe, 1968-70; exec. dir., founder Assn. for Advancement Policy, Research and Devel. in the Third World, 1981—; exec. v.p., dep. dir. POS Inst., Washington, 1982—; chmn., chief exec. officer Internat. Devel. Found. Inc., 1984—; chmn. Malawi Inst. Internat. Affairs, 1987—; sec.-gen. AFORD Alliance for Democracy, 1993; research asst. Calif. State U., Fullerton, 1974-75, adj. prof., spring 1978-79; research asst. Polit. Sci. Dept Miami U., Oxford, Ohio, 1975-76; adj. asst. prof. polit. sci. and mgmt. U. D.C., 1982-85; asst. prof. polit. sci. Howard U., Washington, 1979-85; cons. in field; lectr. in field. Author: Public Policy and Development Politics: The Politics of Technical Expertise in Africa, 1980, The Consultant Connexion: Evaluation of the Federal Consulting Service, 1981, Malawi Democratic Theory and Public Policy: A Preface, 1986; editor: Science Technology and Development: Options and Policies, 1982, Perspectives in International Development, 1986, Contemporary Issues in African Adminstration and Development Politics, 1987, International Development and Alternative Futures: The Coming Challenges, 1988, Internat. Science and Technology: Theory, Philosophy and Policy, 1990; contbr. articles to profl. jours., chpts. to books; mem. adv. bd. CHANGE: The Internat. Tech. newspaper; guest editor Jour. Ea. African Research and Devel.; various TV and radio appearances; subject of articles. Dep. br. sec. Malawi Congress party, 1965-66; com. chair S.W. Scholarship Fund, S.S. Neighborhood Assembly, Washington; chair election com. Rosemary Coop. Housing project; sec.-gen. Alliance for Democracy in Malawi, 1993; parliamentary candidate Mangochi Centre Constituency in Malawi, 1994. Grantee Sci. and Tech. in So. Africa Devel. Coordination Conf., 1982, Peace Corps Coll. project, 1982; fellow Midwestern U. Consortium, Miami U., Alpha Assn. Phi Beta Kappa Alumni in So. Calif.; recipient Seminar award Fgn. Student Council. Mem. Internat. Services Assn. (bd. dirs.), Sci. Soc. Chile (bd. dirs.), Lions, Phi Sigma Alpha. Avocation: travel. Office: Internat Devel Found PO Box 70257 Washington DC 20024-0257

MUCHIN, ALLAN B., lawyer; b. Manitowoc, Wis., Jan. 10, 1936; s. Jacob and Dorothy (Biberfeld) M.; m. Elaine Cort, Jan. 28, 1960; children: Andrea Muchin Leon, Karen, Margery Muchin Goldblatt. BBA, U. Wis., Manitowoc, 1958, JD, 1961. Gen. counsel IRS, Chgo., 1961-65; assoc. Altman, Kurlander & Weiss, Chgo., 1965-68, ptnr., 1968-74; co-mng. ptnr. Katten Muchin & Zavis, Chgo., 1974—; bd. dirs. Adrco, Inc., Chgo., Chgo. Bulls, Chgo. White Sox, Sportmart, Inc., Niles, Ill., Globe Glass & Mirror, Chgo. Trustee Ravinia Music Festival, Highland Park, Ill., 1992—, Lyric Opera Chgo., 1993—; mem. adv. com. Loyola Family Bus. Ctr., Chgo., 1991—; co-com. chmn. Am. Com. for Weizmann Inst. of Sci., Chgo., 1991—. Mem. Econ. Club Chgo., Econ. Devel. Commn. (com. mem.), Comml. Club Chgo. Avocations: travel, tennis, reading. Office: Katten Muchin & Zavis 525 W Monroe St Ste 1600 Chicago IL 66661-3693

MUCHIN, ARDEN ARCHIE, lawyer, director; b. Manitowoc, Wis., Dec. 9, 1920; s. Alfred and Ida (Golden) M.; m. Bettie Lou Barenbaum, Dec. 19, 1948; children: Ann L., Efrem B., Jay Z. BA, U. Wis., 1942, JD, 1947; IA, Harvard U. Grad. Sch. Bus. Adminstrn., 1943. Bar: Wis. 1947, U.S. Dist. Ct. (ea. dist.) Wis. 1948, U.S. Tax Ct. 1965. Pres. Muchin, Muchin & Bruce, S.C. and predecessors, Manitowoc, 1947-92; ptnr. Nash, Spindler, Dean & Grimstad, 1993—; sec. and/or dir. Foster Needle Co., Inc., Manitowoc, Foster Needle Ltd. (Eng.), Sorenson Industries, Inc., Manitowoc; sec., dir. WaterCare Corp., Kaysun Plastics Inc., Water Svcs. Corp.; sec. Schwartz Mfg. Co., Heresite Protective Coatings, Inc.; sec., v.p. CUB Radio, Inc., Manitowoc; gov. State Bar Wis., 1976-80. Bd. dirs. Manitowoc United Way Inc., 1968-92; mem. Wis. adv. com. U.S. Commn. Civil Rights, 1985-89. Mem. ABA, Manitowoc County Bar Assn. (pres. 1972-73), B'nai Brith (nat. commn. anti-defamation league). Home: 1426 Arden Ln Manitowoc WI 54220-2517 Office: Nash Spindler Dean & Grimstad 201 E Waldo Blvd Manitowoc WI 54220-2992

MUCHMORE, CHARLES J., lawyer; b. Delaware, Ohio, Jan. 5, 1950. BA cum laude, N.Mex. Highlands U., 1972; JD, U. N.Mex., 1976. Bar: Ariz. 1976. Ptnr. Muchmore & Wallwork, P.C., Phoenix; judge pro tem Maricopa County Superior Ct., 1986—. Fellow Ariz. Bar Found. (founder); mem. ABA (litigation sect., natural resourcess sect., energy and environ. law sect., tort and ins. practice sect.), Maricopa County Bar Assn., State Bar Ariz. (trial practice sect.), Ariz. Assn. Def. Coun., Def. Rsch. Inst., Internat. Assn. Def. Counsel (toxic and hazardous substances litigation com.), Am. Bd. Trial Advocates, Phi Kappa Phi. Office: Muchmore & Wallwork PC 2700 North Central Ave Ste 1225 Phoenix AZ 85004-1165

MUCHMORE, DON MONCRIEF, museum, foundation, educational, financial fund raising and public opinion consulting firm administrator; b. Wichita, Kans., Dec. 26, 1922; s. Floyd Stephen and Ivy Fay (Campbell) M.; m. Virginia Gunn, June 18, 1949 (div. Dec. 1978); children—Melinda, Marcia. BA., Occidental Coll., Los Angeles, 1945; postgrad., U. So. Calif. Law Sch., 1945; postgrad. polit. sci., UCLA. Intern Nat. Inst. Pub. Affairs, Washington, 1944; exec. asst. to congressman Washington, 1946-48; teaching asst. UCLA, 1949-50; mem. faculty San Diego State U., 1950-51; asst. prof., adminstr. Calif. State U., Long Beach, 1951-56; pres., chief exec. officer The Campbell Found., L.A., 1956—; spl. asst. to supt. pub. instrn. Calif. Dept. Edn., Sacramento, 1956-57; exec. mus. dir. Calif. Mus. Sci. and Industry, L.A., 1957-62, 82-88; exec. v.p., chief exec. officer Calif. Mus. Found., L.A., 1957-62, 82-89; dep. dir. (on loan from mus.) Calif. Dept. Fin., Sacramento, 1960; exec. vice chancellor Calif. State Colls. and Univs. System, Long Beach, 1962-64; first exec. asst. to chmn. and chief exec. officer Calif. Fed. Savs. and Loan Assn., L.A., 1964-66; sr. v.p. Calif. Fed. Savs. and Loan Assn, L.A., 1966-82; pres., CEO PE Conservation Svcs., Inc., 1990-94; chmn. bd. dirs., CEO Opinion Rsch. of Calif., Opinion Surveyors, The State Poll & Market Surveys, Inc., Long Beach, 1948-71, syndicated by L.A. Times, 1961-70, also M-R Assocs. campaigns; cons. in pub. opinion mus. mgmt. and fund raising, 1948-71; chmn. CEO, cons. DMM & Assocs., Long Beach, 1961—; sec., treas. EVENUP Am. Mus., 1994—; mem. Inst. Mus. Svcs., 1983-88. Contbr. chpts. to books. Participant in pub. opinion work Dem. and Rep. campaigns, 1954-72; mem., chmn. 4 presdl. commns., 1970-82, Just Say No Internat., 1989-91, Reading is Fundamental, 1989—, The Buckley Sch., 1989-90; cons. overseas traveling sci. exhibit, planning mus., 1984—, sr. adminstrn., advisor Gas Caps Youth Work Orgn., 1991-93; lead cons. New Solution to Homeless, 1993—, prin. officer Peruvians Cultural Exhibit, 1988—; prin. cons. cultural exhibit Wonders of World, Queensway Bay, Long Beach, Calif., 1992—. Recipient Highest Mus. Edn. award Sigma Alpha Epsilon, 1992, Citizen of Yr. award and numerous other awards from nat., state and local groups; named Pollster of Yr. Washington Post, 1962; Elks Nat. scholar. Mem. Am. Assn. Mus., Calif. Mus. Assn. (pres. 1960, bd. dirs. 1982-88), Assn. Sci. and Tech. Ctrs. (bd. dirs. 1982-88), Am. Assn. Pub. Opinion Rsch., Am. Polit. Sci. Assn., AAAS. Home: 4225 N Virginia Vis Long Beach CA 90807-3122 Office: The Campbell Found 4225 N Virginia Vis Long Beach CA 90807-3122

MUCHMORE, ROBERT BOYER, engineering consultant executive; b. Augusta, Kans., July 8, 1917; s. Ray Boyer and Charlotte (McPherron) M.; m. Betty Vaughan, Jan. 29, 1944; children: Vaughan Vaughan, Douglas Boyer. BS, U. Calif., Berkeley, 1939; degree in Elec. Engineering., Stanford U., 1942. Project engr. Sperry Gyroscope Co., Garden City, N.Y., 1942-46; sr. mem. tech. staff Hughes Aircraft, Culver City, Calif., 1946-54; v.p., chief scientist TRW Systems, Redondo Beach, Calif., 1954-73; cons. TRW Systems, Sonoma, Calif., 1973—; lectr. in engring. UCLA, 1954-58. Author: Essentials of Microwaves, 1952. Fellow IEEE; mem. AAAS, Assn. Computing Machinery, Sierra Club. Home: 4311 Grove St Sonoma CA 95476-6046

MUCHMORE, WILLIAM BREULEUX, zoologist, educator; b. Cin., July 7, 1920; s. Oliver Charles and Ruby (Breuleux) M.; m. Marjorie Murrin, Aug. 15, 1943; children—Susan Jane, Patricia Ann. B.A., Oberlin Coll. 1942; Ph.D. in Zoology, Washington U., St. Louis, 1950. Instr. biology U. Rochester, N.Y., 1950-52; asst. prof. U. Rochester, 1952-58, assoc. prof., 1958-70, prof., 1970-85, prof. emeritus, 1985—, asst. chmn. dept. biology, 1964-66, assoc. chmn., 1974-78; vis. prof. U. Hull, Eng., 1963-64; research assoc. Fla. State Collection Arthpods, 1974—. Contbr. articles to profl. jours. Served with U.S. Army, 1943-46. NSF grantee, 1958-69, 73-76; Fulbright travel grantee, 1963-64; Office Naval Research grantee, 1979-81. Fellow Rochester Acad. Sci., Nat. Speleological Soc.; mem. Am. Arachnological Soc., Am. Micro. Soc., Brit. Arachnological Soc., Centre Internat. de Documentation Arachnologique. Office: Dept Biology Univ of Rochester Rochester NY 14627

MUCK, GEORGE ARTHUR, food products executive; b. Filmore, Ill., Sept. 28, 1937; s. George O. and Edna M. (Funderburk) M.; m. E. Joanne Inness, June 6, 1959; children: Jane, Dale, Nancy, Lori, Lynn. BS, U. Ill., 1959, MS, 1961, PhD, 1962. With research dept. Dean Foods Co., Rockford, Ill., 1962-67; dir. research Dean Foods Co., Rockford, 1967-70, v.p. research and devel., 1970—. Contbr. articles to profl. jours. Patentee in field. Mem. Am. Dairy Sci. Assn. (pres. 1979-80), Am. Cultured Dairy Products Assn. (pres. 1976). Office: Dean Foods Co 1126 Kilburn Ave Rockford IL 61101-5996

MUCKENFUSS, CANTWELL FAULKNER, III, lawyer; b. Montgomery, Ala., Apr. 25, 1945; s. Cantwell F. and Dorothy (Dauphine) M.; m. A. Angela Lancaster, June 25, 1978; children: Alice Paran Lancaster, Cantwell F. IV. BA, Vanderbilt U., 1967; JD, Yale U., 1971. Bar: N.Y. 1973, D.C. 1976. Law clk. to presiding justice U.S. Ct. Appeals (6th cir.), 1971-72; atty., project developer Bedford Stuyvesant D and S Corp., Bklyn., 1972-73; spl. asst. to the dir. FDIC, Washington, 1974-77, counsel to the chmn., 1977-78; sr. dep. comptroller for policy Office of the Comptroller of the Currency, Washington, 1978-81; ptnr. Gibson, Dunn & Crutcher, Washington, 1981—; mem. editorial adv. bd. Issues in Bank Regulation, Rolling Meadows, Ill., 1977-91; mem. bd. advisors Rev. Fin. Regulation, N.Y.C., 1985—; bd. dis. Fair Tax Edn. Fund, Washington, 1987-90. Served with USNG, 1968-70, USAR, 1970-74. Recipient Spl. Achievement award U.S. Dept. Treasury, 1979, Presdl. Rank award U.S. Govt., 1980. Mem. ABA, Fed. Bar Assn. Democrat. Episcopalian. Clubs: Kenwood Country (Bethesda, Md.); Yale (N.Y.C.). Office: Gibson Dunn & Crutcher 1050 Connecticut Ave NW Ste 900 Washington DC 20036-5306

MUCKENHOUPT, BENJAMIN, retired mathematics educator; b. Newton, Mass., Dec. 22, 1933; s. Carl Frederick and Sarah Joanna (Boell) M.; m. Mary Kathryn Heath, Aug. 29, 1964; children: Margaret, Carl Edward. A.B., Harvard U., 1954; M.S., U. Chgo., 1955, Ph.D., 1958. Instr. DePaul U., Chgo., 1958-59; asst. prof. math. DePaul U., 1959-60; faculty Rutgers U., New Brunswick, N.J., 1960-91; prof. math. Rutgers U., 1970-91; vis. assoc. prof. Mt. Holyoke Coll., 1963-65; visitor Inst. Advanced Study, Princeton, N.J., 1968-69, 75-76; vis. prof. SUNY-Albany, 1970-71. Contbr. articles to profl. jours. NSF rsch. grantee, 1965-88; Rutgers Rsch. Coun. fellow, 1968-69. Mem. Am. Math. Soc., Math. Assn. Am., Phi Beta Kappa, Sigma Xi. Home: 196 Woodfern Rd Neshanic Station NJ 08853-4054

MUCKERMAN, NORMAN JAMES, priest, writer; b. Webster Groves, Mo., Feb. 1, 1917; s. Oliver Christopher and Edna Gertrude (Hartman) M. B.A., Immaculate Conception Coll., 1940, M. in Religious Edn., 1942. Ordained priest Roman Catholic Ch., 1942. Missionary Redemptorist Missions, Amazonas, Para, Brazil, 1943-53; procurator missions Redemptorist Missions, St. Louis, 1953-58; pastor, administr. St. Alphonsus Ch., Chgo. 1958-67, St. Gerard, Kirkwood, Mo., 1967-71; mktg. mgr. circulation Liguori Pubs., Liguori, Mo., 1971-76; editor Liguorian Mag., Liguori, Mo., 1977-89. Author: How to Face Death Without Fear, 1976, Redemptorists on the Amazon, 1992; compiling. editor Liguorian, 1989—. Recipient Nota Dez award Caixa Fed. Do Para, Brazil, 1958. Mem. Catholic Press Assn. (cons. 1971—, bd. dirs. 1976-85, pres. 1981-84, St. Francis De Sales award 1985), St. Louis Press Club, Crystal Hills Golf Club. Avocations: golf; travel; reading.

MUCKLER, JOHN, professional hockey coach, professional team executive; b. Midland, Ont., Can.; married; 5 children. Profl. hockey player, Ea. Hockey League, Baltimore, also Long Island Ducks; coach, gen. mgr. Long Island Ducks; 1st pres. N.Y. Jr. Met. League; coach, gen. dir. player pers., mgr. New York Rangers affiliate team, Am. Hockey League, Providence, R.I.; formerly head coach Minnesota North Stars; with Edmonton Oilers, 1981—, formerly co-coach; head coach Edmonton Oilers, 1989-1991; head coach Buffalo Sabres, 1991—, gen. mgr., 1994—. Office: Buffalo Sabres Meml Auditorium 140 Main St Buffalo NY 14202*

MUCKLOW, NEALE HARMON, philosophy educator; b. Albany, N.Y., Aug. 21, 1929; s. Lucian Howe and Marion Eaton (Blakeslee) M.; m. Barbara Jean DeSmidt, Aug. 16, 1951; children: David Hamilton, Roxanne, Nadine M. Cornett. AB, Hamilton Coll., Clinton, N.Y., 1951; PhD, Cornell U., Ithaca, N.Y., 1963. Instr. Hamilton Coll., Clinton, 1953-54; asst. prof. Lycoming Coll., Williamsport, Pa., 1957-64, chmn. dept. philosophy, 1964-69, assoc. prof., 1964-70; assoc. prof. U. Richmond, Va., 1970-74, prof. philosophy, 1974-92, prof. emeritus, 1992—. Founding mem. Blvd. Civic Assn., Richmond, 1979. Mem. Am. Philos. Assn., South Atlantic Philosophy of Edn. Soc. Presbyterian.

MUDD, ANNE CHESTNEY, small business owner, mathematics educator, real estate agent; b. Macon, Ga., June 30, 1944; d. Bard Sherman Chestney and Betty (Bartow) Houston; children: Charles Lee Jr., Richard Chestney, Robert Jason. BA, U. Louisville, 1966, MA, 1976; 1986-90, 1989-92. Math statistican U.S. Bur. Census, Jeffersonville, Ind., 1966-70; instr. math. U. Louisville, 1975-77, Coll. DuPage, Glen Ellyn, Ill., 1978-85, 92; tchr. math and substitute tchr. Lyons Twp. High Sch., La Grange, Ill., 1986-91; realtor First United Realtors, Western Springs, Ill., 1989-92; owner, mgr. retail bus., 1992—; math tutor Louisville 1969-77, Western Springs, Ill. 1977—. editor: Mathematics Textbook, 1991-92. Mem. steering com. Village Western Springs, 1986-87. Mem. NAFE, Children's Theater Western Springs (bd. dirs. 1987-91), LWV (pres. 1983-85, bd. dirs.), Lyons Twp. High Sch. Com. Student Discipline, Western Springs Hist. Soc., Nat. Coun. Tchrs. Math., Western Springs Hist. Soc., Cmty. Family Svc. and Mental Health Assn. Avocations: local govt., theater, gardening. Home: 3958 Hampton Ave Western Springs IL 60558-1011

MUDD, JOHN PHILIP, lawyer; b. Washington, Aug. 22, 1932; s. Thomas Paul and Frances Mary (Finotti) M.; m. Barbara Eve Sweeney, Aug. 10, 1957; children: Laura, Ellen, Philip, Clare, David. BSS, Georgetown U., 1954; JD, Georgetown Law Center, 1956. Bar: Md. 1956, D.C. 1963, Fla. 1964, Calif. 1973. Pvt. practice Upper Marlboro, Md., 1956-66; v.p., sr. gen. counsel Deltona Corp., Miami, Fla., 1966-72; gen. counsel Nat. Community Builders, San Diego, 1972-73; gen. counsel Continental Advisers (adviser to Continental Mortgage Investors), 1973-75, sr. v.p., gen. counsel, 1975-80; sr. v.p., gen. counsel Am. Hosp. Mgmt. Corp., Miami, 1980-89; legal coord. Amerifirst Bank, Miami, 1989-92; v.p., legal counsel Cartaret Savs. Bank, Morristown, N.J., 1991-93, cons., 1991-92; gen. counsel Golden Glades Hosp., Miami, 1992-93, Bank of N.Am., Miami, 1994—; gen. counsel Golden Glades Hosp., Miami, 1992-93; cons. FSLIC, 1988-89, J.E. Robert Cos., Alexandria, Va., 1988-89, Real Estate Recovery, Inc., Boca Raton, Fla., 1991-92, Bank N.Am., Ft. Lauderdale, Fla., 1992; dir. Unitower Mortgage Corp., Miami, Fla.; dir. Unitower Mortgage Corp., Miami; pres. Marquette Realty Corp., Miami. Former mem. Land Devel. Adv. Com. N.Y. State; chmn. student interview com. Georgetown U.; bd. dirs. Lasalle High Sch., Miami; corp. counsel Com. of Dade County, Fla.; trustee Golden Glades Gen. Hosp., Miami, Fla., 1992—; gen. counsel, 1991—, Bank of North Am., Miami, 1992—. Mem. Fla. Bar Assn., Calif. Bar Assn., Md. Bar Assn., D.C. Bar Assn. Fla. State Bar (exec. com. on corp. counsel com.). Democrat. Roman Catholic. Home: 411 Alhambra Cir Miami FL 33134-7044 Office: Bank of North Am Golden Glades Med Plz 8701 SW 137th Ave Ste 301 Miami FL 33183

MUDD, ROGER HARRISON, news broadcaster, educator; b. Washington, Feb. 9, 1928; s. Kostka and Irma Iris (Harrison) M.; m. Emma Jeanne Spears, Oct. 28, 1957; children: Daniel H., Maria M., Jonathan, Matthew M. A.B., Washington and Lee U., 1950; M.A., U. N.C., 1953. Tchr. Darlington Sch., Rome, Ga., 1951-52; reporter Richmond News Leader, Va., 1953; news dir. Sta. WRNL, Richmond, 1953-56; reporter radio and TV Sta. WTOP, Washington, 1956-61; corr. CBS, 1961-80; chief Washington corr. NBC, 1980-87; Congl. corr. MacNeil/Lehrer News Hour, 1987-92, spl. corr., 1993—; prof. journalism Princeton U., 1992-94, Washington & Lee U., 1995—. Host The History Channel, 1995. Trustee Randolph-Macon Women's Coll., Lynchburg, Va., 1971-78, Robert F. Kennedy Journalism Awards Com., 1971-78, Blue Ridge Sch., Dyke, Va., 1978-84; bd. dirs. Fund for Investigative Journalism, PEN/Faulkner, 1985-92, Va. Found. for Humanities, Va. Hist. Soc., 1988-94; mem. adv. com. Mt. Vernon Ladies Assoc. With AUS, 1945-47. Mem. Radio-TV Corr. Assn. (chmn. exec. com. 1969-70).

MUDD, SIDNEY PETER, former beverage company executive; b. St. Louis, Jan. 21, 1917; s. Urban Sidney and Hallie Newell (Perry) M.; m. Ada Marie Herbermann, Oct. 22, 1942; children: Sidney Peter, Ada Marie, Peter, Michael, Mary, Elizabeth, Catherine. A.B. magna cum laude, St. Louis U., 1938; L.H.D., Coll. New Rochelle, N.Y., 1974; LHD, Iona Coll., 1985. Distr. Joyce Seven-Up, Chgo., 1938; sales mgr. Joyce Seven-Up, 1939; coordinator N.Y. ops. Joyce Seven-Up, New Rochelle, 1941; v.p. charge ops. Joyce Seven-Up, 1949-51; exec. v.p. N.Y. Seven-Up Bottling Co., Inc., New Rochelle, 1951-63; pres. N.Y. Seven-Up Bottling Co., Inc., 1963-73, dir., 1952-84, chmn. bd., 1973-84; pres. Joyce Beverages, Inc. (Joyce Advt.), 1973-84; past chmn. bd. Joyce Beverages/N.Y., N.J., Conn., Ill., Wis.; past dir. Joyce Beverages Inc., Joyce Advt., Joyce Beverages/N.Y., N.J., Conn., Chgo., Washington, Wis., Ill., Joyce Assocs.; dir., vice-chmn. Westchester Fed. Savs. Bank; bd. dirs. Marine Midland Bank Regional Bd., chmn. 1987-88. Past pres., bd. trustees St. Joseph's Hosp., N.Y.C., St. Francis Hosp.; chmn. Westchester County Assn.; past bd. lay advisers St. Agnes Hosp., White Plains; past chmn. bd. trustees Coll. of New Rochelle; past bd. dirs. U.S. Cath. Hist. Soc.; former trustee St. Louis U.; bd. dirs., v.p. John M. and Mary A. Joyce Found.; chmn. N.Y. Industry-Labor Com. for Resource Recovery; bd. dirs. Am. Alliance Resource Recovery Interests; pres. New Rochelle Devel. Council; bd. dirs. Keep Am. Beautiful, Inc.; chmn. Westchester 2000, 1984-85. Served with USNR. Decorated Knight of Malta, knight Equestrian Order of Holy Sepulchre; recipient St. Louis U. Alumni award, 1967, Dr. Martin Luther King, Jr. award New Rochelle Community Action Agy., 1978, New Rochelle K.C. Civic award, 1978, Outstanding Citizen award New Rochelle YMCA, 1979, Disting. Service award Westchester region NCCJ, 1980, Medallion award Westchester Community Coll. Found., 1981; honoring resolution N.Y. State Senate, 1982; honoring resolution N.Y. State Assembly, 1982; honoring proclamation County of Westchester, City of Yonkers, City of White Plains, 1982; ARC award of excellence, 1983, Man of Yr. award Beverage Industry, 1974, Disting. Service award Sr. Personnel Employment Council, 1986, Disting. Achievement award Mental Health Assn., 1987, Disting. Citizen award New Rochelle Hosp. Med. Ctr., 1990; named to St. Louis U. Sports Hall of Fame, 1976, Beverage World Hall of Fame, 1984. Mem. Nat. Soft Drink Assn. (dir., pres. 1974-76, Disting. Achievement award 1980), N.Y. State Soft Drink Assn. (pres. 1966-67, Disting. Service award 1985, 86), Theta Kappa Phi, Crown and Anchor Soc. (St. Louis U.). Clubs: Winged Foot Golf (Westchester) (founder, past v.p., dir.); Sales and Mktg. Execs.

MUDGE, LEWIS SEYMOUR, theologian, educator, university dean; b. Phila., Oct. 22, 1929; s. Lewis Seymour and Anne Evelyn (Bolton) M.; m. Jean Bruce McClure, June 15, 1957; children: Robert Seymour, William McClure, Anne Evelyn. B.A., Princeton, 1951, M. Div., 1955, Ph.D. (Kent fellow), 1961; B.A. with honors in Theology, Oxford (Eng.) U., 1954, M.A. (Rhodes scholar), 1958. Ordained to ministry Presbyn. Ch., 1955. Presbyn. univ. pastor Princeton, 1955-56; sec. dept. theology World Alliance Ref. Chs., Geneva, 1957-62; minister to coll. Amherst Coll., 1962-68, asst. prof. philosophy and religion, 1962-64, assoc. prof., 1964-70, prof. philosophy and religion, 1970-76, chmn. dept. philosophy and religion, 1968-69, 75-76; dean faculty, prof. theology McCormick Theol. Sem., Chgo., 1976-87, San Francisco Theol. Sem., 1987—; prof. Grad. Theol. Union, Berkeley, Calif., 1987—; dir. Ctr. for Hermeneutical Studies, Grad. Theol. Union/U. Calif., Berkeley, 1990—; Stuart prof. theology Grad. Theol. Union, Berkeley, Calif., 1995—; mem. commn. on faith and order Nat. Council Chs., 1965-70; sec. spl. com. on confession faith United Presbyn Ch., 1965-67, chmn. spl. com. on theology of the call, 1968-71; chmn. theol. commn. U.S. Consultation on Ch. Union, 1977-89; co-chmn. Internat. Ref.-Roman Cath. Dialogue Commn., 1983-90; observer Extraordinary Synod Bishops, 1985. Author: One Church: Catholic and Reformed, 1963, Is God Alive?, 1983, Why is the Church in the World?, 1967, The Crumbling Walls, 1970, The Sense of a People: Toward a Church for the Human Future, 1992; also numerous articles and revs.; editor: Essays on Biblical Interpretation (Paul Ricoeur), 1980, (with James Poling) Formation and Reflection: the Promise of Practical Theology, 1987. Pres. Westminster Found. in New Eng., 1963-67; chmn. bd. Nat. Vocation Agy., 1972-75; mem. com. selection Rhodes Scholars, Wis., 1983-85, Iowa, 1986. Mem. Phi Beta Kappa. Democrat. Home: 130 Bolinas Ave San Anselmo CA 94960-2902 Office: San Francisco Theol Sem 2 Kensington Rd San Anselmo CA 94960-2997

MUECKE, CHARLES ANDREW (CARL MUECKE), federal judge; b. N.Y.C., Feb. 20, 1918; s. Charles and Wally (Roeder) M.; m. Claire E. Vasse; children by previous marriage: Carl Marshall, Alfred Jackson, Catherine Calvert. B.A., Coll. William and Mary, 1941; LL.B., U. Ariz., 1953. Bar: Ariz. 1953. Rep. AFL, 1947-50; reporter Ariz. Times, Phoenix, 1947-48; since practiced in Phoenix; with firm Parker & Muecke, 1953-59, Muecke, Dushoff & Sacks, 1960-61; U.S. atty. Dist. Ariz., 1961-64, U.S. dist. judge, 1964—, now sr. judge; mem. 9th cir. Jud. Coun. com. review local dist. Ct. Rules. Mem. Phoenix Planning Commn., 1955-61, chmn., 1960; chmn. Maricopa County Dem. Party, 1961-62; trustee U. San Diego Coll. Law. Maj. USMC, 1942-45, USMCR, 1945-60. Mem. Fed. Bar Assn., Ariz. Bar Assn., Maricopa Bar Assn., Am. Trial Lawyers Assn., Dist. Judges Assn. Ninth Circuit, Phi Beta Kappa, Phi Alpha Delta, Omicron Delta Kappa. Office: US Dist Ct US Courthouse & Fed Bldg 230 N 1st Ave Ste 7015 Phoenix AZ 85025-0007

MUEDEKING, GEORGE HERBERT, editor; b. Arcadia, Wis., Aug. 19, 1915; s. George Fredrick and Rosalie Carolina (Brodt) M.; m. Harriet Laura Rollwagen, June 26, 1941; children—Miriam Harriet (Mrs. W. Ron Heyer), George David. B.A., Capital U., 1936, D.D. (hon.), 1955; M.A., Ind. U., 1938; B.D., Evang. Lutheran Theol. Sem., 1941; Ph.D., U. Calif., Berkeley, 1961. Ordained to ministry Luth. Ch., 1941; pastor Luth. Ch. of Holy Trinity, Long Beach, Calif., 1941-47, First Luth. Ch., Fullerton, Calif., 1947-51, Christ Luth. Ch., El Cerrito, Calif., 1951-59; instr. Pacific Luth. Theol. Sem., Berkeley, 1953-55, asst. prof., 1960-64, prof., 1965-66; editor Luth. Standard, Mpls., 1967-78, roving editor, 1978-80; lectr. Australian Luth. Tchrs. Coll., 1981-82; sr. mentor Calif. Luth. U., 1984, 87; resident faculty Luth. Bible Inst. Calif., 1993; v.p. Calif. dist. Am. Luth. Ch.; mem. com. on interpretation Am. sect. World Coun. Chs.; pres. Luth Editors Assn.; bd. dirs. Assn. ch. Press, Luths. for Life. Author: Emotional Problems and the Bible, 1956; editor FOCL-Point, 1991—; contbr. articles to religious publs. Mem. Assn. for Profl. Edn. for Ministry, Nat. Council on Family Relations, Minn. Press Club, Am. Acad. Religion and Mental Health, Am. Acad. Polit. and Social Sci., Phi Beta Kappa. Republican. Home and Office: 4414 Springwood Dr Napa CA 94558-1724

MUEHLBAUER, JAMES HERMAN, manufacturing executive; b. Evansville, Ind., Nov. 13, 1940; s. Herman Joseph and Anna Louise (Overfield) M.; m. Mary Kay Koch, June 26, 1965; children: Stacey, Brad, Glen, Beth, Katy. BSME, Purdue U., 1963, MS Indsl. Adminstrn., 1964. Registered profl. engr., Ind. Engr. George Koch Sons, Inc., Evansville, 1966-67; chief estimator George Koch Sons, Inc., 1968-72, chief engr., 1973-74, v.p., 1975-81, dir., 1978—, v.p., mng. v.p., 1982—; v.p., bd. dirs. Brake Supply Co., Evansville; bd. dirs. Citizens Nat. Bank, Evansville, Page-Koch (Europe) Ltd., Lichfield, Eng.; v.p., bd. dirs. Gibbs Die Casting Corp., Henderson, Ky., Uniseal, Inc., Evansville. Co-author: Tool & Manufacturing Engineering

Handbook, 1976; patentee in paint finishing equipment. Bd. dirs., past pres. Evansville Indsl. Found., 1980—; bd. dirs., past pres., past campaign chmn. United Way S.W. Ind., Evansville, 1983—; bd. dirs., past vice-chmn. Univ. So. Ind. Found., Evansville, 1988—, Deaconess Hosp., Evansville, 1986—, treas., 1991—. Named Engr. of Yr. S.W. chapt. Ind. Soc. Profl. Engrs., 1983; recipient Tech. Achievement award Tri-State Coun. for Sci. & Engring., Evansville, 1984. Mem. Soc. Mfg. Engrs. (nat. chmn. finishing & coating tech. div.), ASME, NSPE, Evansville Country Club, Evansville Petroleum Club, Evansville Kennel Club. Republican. Roman Catholic. Home: 2300 E Gum St Evansville IN 47714-2338 Office: George Koch Sons Inc 10 S 11th Ave Evansville IN 47744-0001

MUEHLEISEN, GENE SYLVESTER, retired law enforcement officer, state official; b. San Diego, Dec. 28, 1915; s. Adolph and Vesta C. (Gates) M.; m. Elsie Jane Conover, Sept. 14, 1940; 1 son, John Robert. Student, San Diego State Coll., 1935-39, San Diego Jr. Coll., 1957. U.S. park ranger Yosemite Nat. Park, summers 1936-39, 79-84; with San Diego Police Dept., 1940-60, dir. tng., 1957-59, comdg. officer patrol div., capt., 1958-60; exec. dir. Commn. on Peace Officer Standards and Tng., Calif. Dept. Justice, Sacramento, 1960-65, 67-76; assoc. dir. Pres.'s Commn. on Law Enforcement and Adminstrn. of Justice, Nat. Crime Commn., 1965-67; chmn. police sci. adv. com. San Diego Jr. Coll., 1957-60, police sci. faculty, 1957-60; staff instr. San Diego Police Acad., 1954-60; guest instr. police adminstrn. Sacramento State Coll., 1964; grad. FBI Nat. Acad. 51st Session, 1953, pres. of class, guest faculty, 1963-66; cons. Ford Found. Internat. Assn. Chiefs of Police Project, 1964-67; cons. U.S. Nat. Park Svc., 1965-84, spl. asst. to regional dir. Western region, 1977-79; adviser Royal Can. Mounted Police, 1961—; guest lectr., 1960—. Mem. tng. com. Internat. Assn. Chiefs of Police, 1963—; mem. adv. com. on police tng. Ford Found., 1964—; U.S. rep. Interpol Symposium on Police Edn. and Tng., Paris, 1965; chmn. Atty. Gen.'s Com. on Law Enforcement Standards, 1957-59; vice chmn. Calif. Commn. Peace Officer Standards and Tng., 1959-60; chmn. police services task force Calif. Council Criminal Justice, 1968-78 ; mem. Atty. Gen.'s Commn. Police-Community Relations, 1971—; mem. adv. com. FBI, 1972—; mem. Gov.'s Pub. Safety Planning Council, 1974—; Pres. San Diego Police Officers Assn., San Diego Police and Fire Retirement System; bd. dirs. San Diego Hist. Soc. Served to capt. USNR, World War II. The Gene Muehleisen Nature Area, Valley Oak Park, Sacramento dedicated, 1992. Mem. Nat. Conf. Police Assns. (com. chmn.), Calif. Peace Officers Assn. (com. chmn.), Peace Officers Research Assn. Calif. (pres. 1959-60, com. chmn.), Am. Soc. Pub. Adminstrn. (dir. San Diego County chpt.), Nat. Assn. State Dirs. Law Enforcement Tng. (pres. 1972-73), Am. Corrections Assn., Calif. Assn. Adminstrn. of Justice Educators, Park Rangers Assn. of Calif., Internat. Police Assn. (life, v.p. region 29 USA), Internat. Assn. Chiefs of Police (life), Calif. Parks and Recreation Soc. (Citizen of Yr. 1992), Sacramento Tree Found. (tech. adv. com. 1983—). Clubs: Kiwanis, San Diego Ski (pres.). Home and Office: 4221 Corona Way Sacramento CA 95864-5301

MUEHLNER, SUANNE WILSON, library director; b. Rochester, Minn., June 29, 1943; d. George T. and Rhoda (Westin) Wilson. Student Smith Coll., 1961-63; A.B., U. Calif.-Berkeley, 1965; M.L.S., Simmons Coll., 1968; M.B.A., Northeastern U., Boston, 1979. Librarian Technische Univ. Berlin, Germany, 1970-71; earth and planetary scis. librarian MIT Libraries, Cambridge, 1968-70, 1971-73; personnel librarian, 1973-74, asst. dir. personnel services, 1974-76, asst. dir. pub. services, 1976-81; dir. libraries Colby Coll., Waterville, Maine, 1981—. Mem. ALA, New Eng. Assn. Coll. and Research Librarians (sec.-treas. 1983-85, pres. 1986-87), Maine Libr. Assn. (chmn. intellectual freedom com. 1984-88, OCLC Users Coun., 1988—), Nelinet (bd. dirs. 1985-91, chair 1989-91). Office: Colby Coll Miller Libr Waterville ME 04901

MUELLER, BETTY JEANNE, social work educator; b. Wichita, Kans., July 7, 1925; d. Bert C. and Clara A. (Pelton) Judkins; children—Michael J., Madelynn J. M.S.S.W., U. Wis., Madison, 1964, Ph.D. (E.B. Fred fellow, Nat. Inst. Child Health and Human Devel. fellow), 1969. Asst. prof. U. Wis., Madison, 1969-71; vis. assoc. prof. Bryn Mawr (Pa.) Coll., 1971-72; asso. prof., dir. social work Cornell U., Ithaca, N.Y., 1972-78, prof. human services studies, 1978—; nat. cons. Head Start, Follow Through, Appalachian Regional Commn., N.Y. State Office Planning Services, N.Y. State Dept. Social Services, N.Y. State Div. Mental Hygiene, Nat. Congress PTA, ILO. Author: (with H. Morgan) Social Services in Early Education, 1974, (with R. Reinoehl) Computers in Human Service Education, 1989; contbr. articles to profl. jours. Grantee HEW, 1974-76, 79-80, State of N.Y., 1975—, Israeli Jewish Agy., 1985-87, Israeli Nat. Council for Research, 1986-87; Fulbright Research award, 1990. Mem. Am. Sociol. Assn., Internat. Conf. Social Welfare, Nat. Assn. Social Workers, Council Social Work Edn., Chi Omega. Democrat. Unitarian. Home: 11 Forest Ln Ithaca NY 14850-8736 Office: Cornell U Human Services Studies N139MVR Hall Ithaca NY 14853

MUELLER, CARL GUSTAV, JR., lawyer; b. Houston, June 30, 1929; s. Carl G. and Louise (Young) M.; m. Joanne Youngblood, Aug. 2, 1950; children—Carl Clinton, Craig Steven, Robert Loyd. B.B.A. U. Tex., 1951, JD, 1953. Cert. in estate planning and probate law, comml. real estate law, residential real estate law, farm and ranch real estate law, Tex. Mem., tchr. Hines Baker Bible Class; former chmn. adminstrv. bd., former chmn.bd. trustees St. Luke's Meth. Ch.; dir., sec. Retina Rsch. Found.; bd. dirs Student Aid Found. Fellow Am. Coll. Trust and Estate Counsel; mem. ABA, Tex. Bar Assn., Houston Bar Assn., Am. Coll. Real Estate Lawyers, Am. Coll. Mortgage Attys., Tex. Acad. Probate and Trust Lawyers, Tex. Acad. Real Estate Lawyers, Houston Estate and Fin. Forum (past pres.), Houston Real Estate Lawyers Counsel. Avocations: fishing, hunting, walking, travel. Office: 17 S Briar Hollow Ste 204 Houston TX 77027

MUELLER, CARL RICHARD, theater arts educator, author; b. St. Louis, Oct. 7, 1931; s. Anton John and Bonita Blanche (Lacy) M. BS, Northwestern U., 1954; MA, UCLA, 1960, PhD, 1967; cert., Freie U., Berlin, 1961. Prof. theater dept. Sch. Theater, Film and Television UCLA, 1967—; dramaturg New Theatre, Inc., Los Angeles, 1975—; cons. U. Calif. Press, Berkeley, 1972—. Translator plays published include Buechner: Complete Plays, 1963, Brecht: The Visions of Simone Machard, 1965, Brecht: The Measures Taken, 1977, Hauptmann: The Weavers, 1965, Hebbel: Maria Magdalena, 1962, Strindberg: A Dream Play and the Ghost Sonata, 1966, Schnitzler: La Ronde and Game of Love, 1964, Hofmannsthal: Electra, 1964, Wedekind: The Marquis of Keith, 1964, Wedekind: The Lulu Plays, 1967, Zuckmayer: The Captain of Koepenick, 1972; translator plays produced include Anon: The Puppet Play of Dr. Johannes Faustus, Hauptmann: The Beaver Coat, Schnitzler: Dr. Bernhardi, Schnitzler: Anatol, Schnitzler: The Underpants, Brecht: Mother Courage, Brecht: Caucasian Chalk Circle, Brecht: The Trial of Joan of Arc, Brecht: In the Jungle of Cities, Brecht: Man is Man, Brecht: He Who Says Yes, Brecht: He Who Says No, Brecht: Schweyk in the Second World War, Kleist: The Broken Jug, 1992, Lessing: Nathan the Wise, 1993, Toller, The Blind Goddess, 1993, Sophokles, Elektra, 1994, Zweig, Volpone, 1995; gen. editor Visual Resources, Inc., 1976—; theater editor Mankind mag., 1975-82; editor New Theater/Teatro Nuevo, 1985-87; author catalogue and slides A Visual History of European Theater Arts, 1978, A Visual History of European Experimental Theater, 1983, Greek and Roman Classical Theatre Structures and Performance Iconography, 1991, Medieval Theater and Performance Iconography, 1991, The Theater of Meyerhold, 1992, Stanislavsky and the Moscow Art Theater, 1992, The Commedia dell'Arte, 1992, Russian Scene and Costume Design, vols. 1 and 2, 1993, The Baroque Stage, 1993, 18th and 19th Cen. European Theater Structures, Performance Iconography and Costume Designes, 1994, Renaissance Theater Structures, Performance Iconography and Costume Designs, 1994; dir.: (plays) Spring's Awakening, Endangered Species, Hedda Gabler, My Body, Frankly Yours, Hamlet, Macbeth. Served with U.S. Army, 1954-56. Recipient Samuel Goldwyn Creative Writing award Goldwyn Found., 1959; Fulbright exchange grantee Berlin, 1960-61. Mem. Internat. Arthur Schnitzler Research Assn., UCLA Center for Medieval and Renaissance Studies (mem. adv. com. 1980-83). Office: UCLA Dept Theater Sch Theater Film and TV 102 E Melnitz Box 951622 Los Angeles CA 90095-1622 *Communication has always been the primary goal of my life. The challenge of passing on to generations of new students the life sustaining ideas of human culture is formidable; the joy of searching out new*

ideas and methods of thought and action is a privilege of which far too few of us take proper advantage.

MUELLER, CHARLES BARBER, surgeon, educator; b. Carlinville, Ill., Jan. 22, 1917; s. Gustav Henry and Myrtle May (Barber) M.; m. Jean Mahaffey, Sept. 7, 1940; children: Frances Ann, John Barber, Richard Carl, William Gustav. A.B., U. Ill., 1938; M.D., Washington U., St. Louis, 1942; LHD (honoris causa), Blackburn Coll., 1984. Intern, then resident in surgery Barnes Hosp., St. Louis, 1942-43, 46-51; asst. prof. Washington U. Med. Sch., 1951-56; prof. surgery, chmn. dept. State U. N.Y. Med. Sch., Syracuse, 1956-67; prof. surgery McMaster U. Med. Sch., Hamilton, Ont., Can., 1967—; chmn. dept. McMaster U. Med. Sch., 1967-72. Contbr. articles to med. jours. Served with USNR, 1943-46. Decorated Purple Heart with 2 oak leaf clusters, Bronze Star; Jackson Johnson fellow, 1938-42; Rockefeller postwar asst., 1946-49; Markle scholar, 1949-54; recipient Alumni Achievement award Washington U., 1987. Mem. ACS (v.p. 1987-88, Disting. Svc. award 1984), Am. Surg. Assn., Ctrl. Surg. Assn., Soc. Univ. Surgeons, Assn. Acad. Surgery, Royal Coll. Physicians and Surgeons (Duncan Graham Disting. Svc. award 1992), Phi Beta Kappa, Sigma Xi, Alpha Omega Alpha, Phi Kappa Phi. Home: 139 Dalewood Crescent, Hamilton, ON Canada L8S 4B8 Office: 1200 Main St W, McMaster U, Hamilton, ON Canada L8N 3Z5

MUELLER, CHARLES WILLIAM, electric utility executive; b. Belleville, Ill., Nov. 29, 1938; s. Charles A. and Clara R. (Jorn) M.; m. Janet Therese Vernier, July 9, 1960; children: Charles R., Michael G., Craig J. BSEE, St. Louis U., 1961, MBA, 1966. Registered profl. engr., Mo., Ill. Engr. Union Electric Co., St. Louis, 1961-75, supervisory engr., 1975-77, asst. dir. corp. planning, 1977-78, treas., 1978-83, v.p. fin., 1983-88, sr. v.p. adminstrv. svcs., 1988-93; pres., CEO, 1994—; bd. dirs. Union Colliery Co., St. Louis Electric Energy Inc., Regional Commerce and Growth Assn., Edison Electric Inst.; dir. The Boatmen's Nat. Bank of St. Louis, Assn. of Edison Illuminating Cos., St. Louis Children's Hosp., St. Louis Sci. Ctr., Civic Progress, The Mcpl. Theatre Assn. Trustee Webster U. Mem. IEEE, Mo. Athletic Club, Oak Hill Tennis Club, St. Clair Country Club, The Bogey Club, Saint Louis Club. Avocations: tennis, boating, travel. Office: Union Electric Co 1901 Chouteau Ave Saint Louis MO 63103

MUELLER, DAVID BRIAN, accountant, chief financial officer; b. St. Louis, June 30, 1953; s. David H. and Laverne (Benne) M.; m. Elizabeth A. Eardley, July 21, 1979; children: Robert Brian, Caroline Ashley, William Christopher, Elizabeth Michelle. BSBA, U. Mo., 1974. CPA, Mo. Sr. mgr. Arthur Andersen, St. Louis, 1974-81; corp. controller, dir. tax and data processing Apex Oil Co., St. Louis, 1981-88; v.p., chief fin. officer Spartech Corp., Clayton, Mo., 1988-91; sec., 1994, also bd. dirs. Mem. Am. Inst. CPA's, Mo. Soc. CPA's. Office: Spartech Corp 7733 Forsyth Blvd # 1450 Saint Louis MO 63105-1817

MUELLER, DONALD DEAN, food company executive; b. Columbus, Nebr., Sept. 12, 1937; s. Emil J. and Hulda M. (Cattau) M.; m. JoAnn Ferris, Aug. 17, 1963; children: Bradford Paul, Bartley Brandon. Student U. Nebr., 1956-58, 62-63; BBA, U. Denver, 1965. CPA, Colo. Acct., Ernst & Ernst, Denver, 1965-69; treas. Monfort of Colo., Greeley, 1969-72; v.p. fin. Spencer Foods, Iowa, 1972-79; group v.p. fin. svcs. Monfort, Inc., 1979-83, group v.p. fin. svcs. and lamb ops., 1983-89; exec. v.p. fin. and adminstrn. ConAgra Red Meats, 1989-92, pres. Mapelli Food Distbn. Co., 1990-94; exec. v.p. ConAgra Red Meats, 1994—; bd. dirs. 1st Nat. Bank Greeley, 1989—, Purdue Valley Bank, Ft. Collins, Colo., 1993—, Weld Broadcasting Co., 1992—. Bd. dirs. Econ. Devel. Action Partnership, Greeley, Weld County, 1984-92, pvt. industry coun., Greeley, 1985-90, chmn. EDAP, 1990, bd. trustees N.C. Med. Ctr., 1992—; pres., 1993-94, bd. dirs., 1993—. Mem. AICPA, Nat. Assn. Accts., Colo. Soc. CPAs, Greeley Country Club. Republican. Lutheran. Avocations: church activities, singing, sports. Office: ConAgra Red Meats PO Box Q Greeley CO 80632-0350

MUELLER, EDWARD ALBERT, transportation engineer executive; b. Madison, Wis., May 12, 1923; s. Edward F. and Lulu (Wittl) M.; m. Margaret Wetzel, Sept. 12, 1953; children: Lynn, Karen. Student, U. Wis., 1941-43; B.C.E., Notre Dame U., 1947; cert. in traffic, Yale U., 1953; postgrad., Fla. State U., 1955-62; M.C.E. Catholic U. Am., 1967. Registered profl. engr., Fla. Project engr. Carl C. Crane, Inc., 1947-50; engr. Ammann & Whitney, Inc., Milw., 1950-52; asst. dir., dir. traffic and planning div. Fla. State Rd. Dept., Tallahassee, 1955-63; engr. traffic and ops. Hwy. Research Bd., Washington, 1963-70; sec. Fla. Dept. Transp., Tallahassee, 1970-72; exec. dir. Jacksonville (Fla.) Transp. Authority, 1972-80; mgr. transp. div. Reynolds, Smith & Hills, 1980-83; v.p. Morales and Shumer Engrs., Inc., 1983—; occasional lectr. U. Fla., 1971-76, U. N.Fla., 1974-76. Author: Steamboating on the St. Johns, 1979, Ocklawaha River Steamboats, 1983, St. Johns River Steamboats, 1986, Perilous Journeys, 1990, Upper Mississippi River Ratting Steamboats, 1995; contbr. engring. articles to profl. jours. Mem. Fla. Com. of 100, 1970-72; bd. dirs. Luth. Social Svcs., Jacksonville, 1982-94; v.p., 1981-91; regional v.p. Fla.-Ga. dist. Luth. Laymen's League, 1982-92; curator Jacksonville Maritime Mus., 1990—, mem. exec. com., 1989—, pres., 1993—. Recipient Disting. Service award Coll. Engring., U. Fla., 1975; named one of top 10 pub. works ofcls. in U.S., 1978. Mem. Southeastern Assn. State Hwy. Ofcls. (pres., v.p. 1971-72), Engrs. in Govt. (chmn., vice chmn., sec.), Fla. Engring. Soc. (pres. Northeast chpt. 1982-83, Engr. of Year, Tallahassee chpt. 1972, Jacksonville chpt. 1974, award for outstanding tech. achievement 1976, Outstanding Svc. to Engring. Profession, 1989), Inst. Transp. Engrs. (pres. 1977, Disting. Service award Fla. sect. 1976), Fla. Transit Assn. (pres. 1974, 75), Fla. Engring. Found. (sec. 1986—). Lutheran. Home: 4734 Empire Ave Jacksonville FL 32207-2136 Office: 4811 Atlantic Blvd Jacksonville FL 32207-2129

MUELLER, FREDERICK, principal. Prin. La Salle Acad., Providence. Recipient Blue Ribbon award U.S. Dept. Edn., 1990-91. Office: La Salle Acad 612 Academy Ave Providence RI 02908-2725

MUELLER, GERD DIETER, financial and administrative executive; b. Hannover, Germany, Nov. 12, 1936. Student, U. Munich, 1957-59; LLB, U. Cologne, Germany, 1961; LLM, Nordrhein-Westfalen, Duesseldorf, Germany, 1965. Mgr. fin. Bayer AG Leverkusen, Germany, 1965-72; sr. v.p. fin. svcs. Rhinechem Corp., N.Y.C., 1972-74; treas. Mobay Chem. Corp., Pitts., 1974-77; v.p. and treas. Mobay Corp., Pitts., 1977-83; exec. v.p. fin. Miles, Inc., Elkhart, Ind., 1983-86; exec. v.p. adminstrn. and fin. Mobay Corp., Pitts., 1986-88; exec. v.p. and CFO former holding co. Bayer USA Inc., Pitts., 1988-91; exec. v.p., chief adminstrv. and fin. officer Bayer Corp., Pitts., 1992—; pres. CDS Internat., N.Y.C. Mem. NAM. Office: Bayer Corp 1 Mellon Ctr 500 Grant St Pittsburgh PA 15219-2507

MUELLER, GERHARD G(OTTLOB), accounting educator; b. Eineborn, Germany, Dec. 4, 1930; came to U.S., 1952, naturalized, 1957; s. Gottlob Karl and Elisabeth Charlotte (Hossack) M.; m. Coralie George, June 7, 1958; children: Kent, Elisabeth, Jeffrey. AA, Coll. of Sequoias, 1954; BS with honors, U. Calif.-Berkeley, 1956, MBA, 1957, PhD, 1962; D Econs. (hon.), Swedish Sch. Econs. and Bus. Adminstrn., 1994. CPA, Wash. Staff accountant FMC Corp., San Jose, Calif., 1957-58; faculty dept. accounting U. Wash., Seattle, 1960—; asst. prof. U. Wash., 1963-67, prof., 1967—; chmn. dept., 1969-78, dir. grad. profl. accig. program, 1979-90, sr. assoc. dean, 1990-95, acting dean, 1994; dir. Seattle Menu Specialists, Inc., U. Wash. Acctg. Devel. Fund, Overlake Hosp. Med. Ctr., Bellevue, chmn. bd. trustees, 1991-93; cons. internat. tax matters U.S. Treasury Dept., 1963-68; cons. Internat. Acctg. Rsch., 1964—; vis. prof. Cranfield Sch. Mgmt., Eng., 1973-74, U. Zurich, Switzerland, 1973-74; lectr. in field. Author: International Accounting, 1967; co-author: Introductory Financial Accounting, 3d edit., 1991, A Brief Introduction to Managerial and Social Uses of Accounting, 1975, International Accounting 1978, 2nd edit., 1992, Accounting: An International Perspective, 1987, 3rd edit., 1994; editor: Readings in International Accounting, 1969, Accounting-A Book of Readings, 2d edit., 1976, A New Introduction to Accounting, 1971, A Bibliography of International Accounting, 3d edit., 1973, Essentials of Multinational Accounting—An Anthology, 1979, Frontiers of International Accounting, 1986, AACSB Curriculum Internationalization Resource Guide, 1988; contbr. numerous articles to profl. jours. Expert legal witness, IRS, 1991-93. Recipient U. Wash. Disting. Teaching award, 1983, Disting. Service award,

1984; Price Waterhouse internat. accounting research fellow, 1962-64; Ford Found. fellow, 1958-59. Fellow Acad. Internat. Bus.; mem. AICPA (internat. practice exec. com. 1972-75, exec. coun. 1987-89), Am. Acctg. Assn. (pres. 1988-89, acad. v.p 1970-71, chmn. adv. bd internat. acctg. sect. 1977-79, Wildman medal 1986, Nat. Outstanding Educator 1982, Disting. Internat. Lectr. in Black Africa 1987, Outstanding Internat. Acctg. Educator 1991), Fin. Execs. Inst., Wash. Soc. CPAs (pres. 1988-89, Outstanding Educator award 1985, Pub. Svc. award 1995), Acctg. Edn. Change Commn. (chair 1994—), Beta Alpha Psi (Acad. Acct. of Yr. 1987), Beta Gamma Sigma (Disting. scholar 1978-79), Alpha Gamma Sigma. Home: 9660 NE 34th St Bellevue WA 98004-1827 Office: U Washington Mackenzie Hall Dj # 10 Seattle WA 98195 *It has always been important to me to associate with people and tangible and intangible things of the highest quality. I make it a practice to set clear goals and then pursue them actively. A broad world view on all aspects of life engenders more success and happiness than special interest perspectives. I welcome change in professional matters, but seek constancy in personal and family affairs. Fate has played a role in my successes. I believe in God, Protestant ethics, and the merits of classical academic scholarship.*

MUELLER, GREGORY M., museum curator, botanist, researcher; b. East St. Louis, Ill., June 22, 1953; s. Raymond A. and Helen A. (Zillen) M.; m. Betty A. Strack, June 4, 1977. BA in Botany, So. Ill. U., 1976, MS in Botany, 1979; PhD in Botany, U. Tenn., 1982. Vis. scientist with Prof. Nils Fries Inst. Physiological Botany Uppsala U., Sweden, 1982-83; postdoctoral fellow Mountain Lake Biol. Sta., Pembroke, Va., 1983; postdoctoral rsch. asst. U. Tenn., Knoxville, 1983; postdoctoral rsch. assoc. with Dr. Joseph Ammirati, dept. botany U. Wash., Seattle, 1984-85; asst. curator Mycology, Dept. Botany, Field Mus. Natural Hist., Chgo., 1985-92, assoc. curator, head cryptogams, 1993—; lectr. com. evolutionary biology U. Chgo., 1994—. Cons. Regional Poison Control Ctr., Rush Presbyn.-St. Luke's Med. Ctr., other Chgo. area hosps., on call for mushroom poisoning cases, 1985—. Ill. State scholar, 1971-76; postdoctoral fellow Mountain Lake Biol. Sta., Pembroke, Va., 1983; Puget Sound Mycological Soc. scholar 1984; grant-in aid rsch. Sigma Xi, 1977, 79, 81; rsch. grant Highlands (N.C.) Biol. Sta., 1979, 80, 83; NSF grantee 1982-83, 84-87, 86-90, 93—; teaching grant NSF 1988-91; grantee MacArthur Found., 1989-92, others. Mem. AAAS, Mycological Soc. Am. (grad. rsch. award 1981, 1st prize paper 1981, Alexopoulos prize 1992, chmn. com. liaison Mycological Soc. Am. and amateur mycological socs., 1987-91, liaison conservation cultural resources 1991—, counselor systematics/evolution 1993—), N.Am. Mycological Assn. (com. inter-soc. liaison 1991—, edit. com. 1990—, chmn. edit. com. 1991—), Sociedad Mexicana de Micología, Ill. Acad. Sci., Ill. Mycological Assn. (sci. advisor 1985—), Botanical Soc. Am., Am. Soc. Plant Taxonomists, Assn. Tropical Biol., Soc. Systematic Biologists. Office: Field Mus of Natural History Dept Botany Chicago IL 60605-2496

MUELLER, JAMES BERNHARD, anesthesiologist, pain managememt consultant; b. Milw., Sept. 5, 1952; s. Bernhard Oscar and Perl Elizabeth (Benda) M.; m. Reba Marie Tisdale, Dec. 18, 1982; children: James Preston, Catherine Elizabeth. BS in Chemistry, Coll. Charleston, 1978; MD, Med. U. S.C., 1983. Diplomate Am. Bd. Anesthesiology, Am. Bd. Pain Medicine; added qualifications in pain mgmt. Commd. lt. USN, 1983, advanced through grades to lt. comdr., 1990; intern Naval Hosp., Portsmouth, Va., 1983-84, resident, 1986-87; fellow Naval Hosp./Med. Coll. Va., Richmond, 1986-87; staff anesthesiologist Naval Hosp., Richmond, 1987-89; resigned USN, 1991; staff anesthesiologist Julius Snyder and Assocs., Norfolk, Va., 1989-92; pvt. practice anesthesiology and pain mgmt. Irving, Tex., 1992-93, Dallas, 1993—; asst. prof. clin. anesthesiology Med. Coll. Hampton Rds., Norfolk, 1988-92, Med. Coll. Va., Richmond, 1989-92; lectr. Nurse Anesthesia Faculty Assocs., Richmond, 1989-92; med. cons. Janssen Pharmaceutica, N.J., 1989—. Contbr. book chpts. Mem. Operation Smile, The Philippines, 1988, Norfolk, 1989. Mem. Am. Soc. Anesthesiologists, Internat. Assn. for Study Pain, Soc. for Regional Anesthesia, Internat. Anesthesial Rsch. Assn., Va. Soc. Anesthesiologists (bd. dirs. 1990-92), Tex. Soc. Anesthesiologists, Tex. Med. Assn., Dallas County Med. Soc. Episcopalian. Office: 1454 Cottonwood Valley Ct Irving TX 75038-6100

MUELLER, JAMES E., agricultural products executive; b. 1931. BS, U. Louisville, 1958. With Dairymen, Inc., Louisville, 1957—, sr. v.p., CEO, 1992—. Office: Flav-O-Rich 10140 Linn Station Rd Louisville KY 40223-3813

MUELLER, JOHN C., lawyer; b. L.A., Sept. 19, 1952. AB, Stanford U., 1974; JD, U. So. Calif., 1977. Bar: Calif. 1977. Ptnr. Baker & Hostetler, L.A. Mem. ABA, L.A. County Bar Assn., State Calif. Bar. Office: Baker & Hostetler 600 Wilshire Blvd Los Angeles CA 90017

MUELLER, JOHN D., electric company executive; b. Mahoning, Pa., June 11, 1934; s. Frank C. and Kathryn (Ziegenfus) M.; m. Donna Dean Klann, Sept. 8, 1956; children—John H., Stephen H., Kathryn A. B.S. in Chem. Engring., MIT, 1956, M.S. in Mgmt., 1957. Gen. mgr. Alberto Culver, Melrose Park, Ill., 1968-72; v.p. Maremont, Chgo., 1972-76; v.p. Motorola, Schaumburg, Ill., 1976-77; pres. G & W Electric Co., Blue Island, Ill., 1977—; dir. First Nat. Bank, Blue Island, Midtown Brake, Chgo. Served to 1st lt. U.S. Army, 1957-58. Republican. Presbyterian. Clubs: Onwentsia, Mid-Am. Home: 1291 3 Blue Rd Lake Forest IL 60045 Office: G & W Electric Co 3500 127th St Blue Island IL 60406-1872

MUELLER, JOHN ERNEST, political science educator, dance critic and historian; b. St. Paul, June 21, 1937; s. Ernst A. and Elsie E. (Schleh) M.; m. Judy A. Reader, Sept. 6, 1960; children—Karl, Karen, Susan. A.B., U. Chgo., 1960; M.A., UCLA, 1963, Ph.D., 1965. Asst. prof. polit. sci. U. Rochester, N.Y., 1965-69, assoc. prof., 1969-72, prof., 1972—; prof. film studies, 1973—, founder, dir. Dance Film Archive, 1973—; lectr. on dance in U.S., Europe, Australia, 1973—; OP-ED columnist Wall St. Jour., 1984—, L.A., Times, 1988—, N.Y. Times, 1990—; mem. dance panel NEA, 1983-85; columnist Dance Mag., 1974-82; dance critic Rochester Dem. and Chronicle, 1974-82; mem. adv. bd. Dance in Am., PBS, 1975. Author: War, Presidents and Public Opinion, 1972, Dance Film Directory, 1979, Astaire Dancing: The Musical Films, 1985 (de la Torre Bueno prize 1983), Retreat From Doomsday: The Obsolescence of Major War, 1989, Policy and Opinion in the Gulf War, 1994, Quiet Cataclysm: Reflections on the Recent Transformation of World Politics, 1995; co-author: Trends in Public Opinion: A Compendium of Survey Data, 1989; editor: Approaches to Measurement, 1969; co-editor Jour. Policy Analysis and Mgmt., 1985-89; mem. editl. bd. Pub. Opinion Quar., 1988-91; producer 12 dance films; recorded commentator on 2d soundtrack of laser disc edit. Swing Time, 1986. Grantee NSF, 1967-70, 74-75, NEH, 1972-73, 74-75, 77-78, 79-81; Guggenheim fellow, 1988. Mem. Am. Acad. Arts and Scis., Am. Polit. Sci. Assn., Dance Critics Assn. (bd. dirs. 1983-85), Am. Assn. for Public Policy and Mgmt. (editorial bd. 1985-89). Home: 246 Roslyn St Rochester NY 14619-1812 Office: U Rochester Polit Sci Dept Rochester NY 14627

MUELLER, MARK CHRISTOPHER, lawyer; b. Dallas, June 19, 1945; s. Herman August and Hazel Deane (Hatzenbuehler) M.; m. Linda Jane Reed. BA in Econs., So. Meth. U., 1967, MBA in Acctg., 1969, JD, 1971. Bar: Tex. 1971, U.S. Dist. Ct. (no. dist.) Tex. 1974, U.S. Tax Ct. 1974. Acct. Arthur Young & Co., Dallas, 1967-68, A.E. Krutilek, Dallas, 1968-71; pvt. practice law, Dallas, 1971—; assoc. L. Vance Stanton, Dallas, 1971-72; instr. legal writing and rsch. So. Meth. U., Dallas, 1970-71, instr. legal acctg., 1975. Leading articles editor Southwestern Law Jour., 1970-71. Mem. NRA, SAR, Tex. Bar Assn., Tex. Soc. CPA's, Dallas Bar Assn., Sons of Am. Revolution, Sons Republic Tex., Sons of Union Vets. of Civil War, Sons Confederate Vets., Mil. Order Stars and Bars, Order of Coif, Beta Alpha Psi, Phi Delta Phi, Sigma Chi. Club: Rock Creek Barbeque. Lodges: Masons (32 degree), Shriners, Grotto, KCCH. Home: 7310 Brennans Dr Dallas TX 75214-2804 Office: Ste 410 9401 Lyndon B Johnson Fwy Dallas TX 75243-4540

MUELLER, MARNIE WAGSTAFF, insurance company executive, economist; b. Ft. Worth, Feb. 2, 1937; d. Robert McAlpine and Texas (Orms) W.; m. Robert Ernest Mueller; children: Sarah, Paul, Emily. BA in Econs., Wellesley Coll., 1959; MA in Econs., Yale U., 1961, PhD in Econs., 1965. CLU. Instr. Washington U., St. Louis, 1966-67; assoc. prof. Wesleyan U., Middletown, Conn., 1972-77, vis. prof., 1994-95; various positions in rsch., planning and mktg. to sr. vp. corp. resources Conn. Mut. Life Ins. Co.,

Hartford, 1977-93. Fellow Ford Found., 1963-64, 75-76, sr. fellow Am. Leadership. Mem. Am. Econs. Assn. Episcopalian. Home: 102 N Beacon St Hartford CT 06105-2513

MUELLER, NANCY SCHNEIDER, retired biology educator; b. Wooster, Ohio, Mar. 8, 1933; d. Gilbert Daniel and Winifred (Porter) Schneider; m. Helmut Charles Mueller, Jan. 27, 1959; 1 child, Karl Gilbert. AB in Biology, Coll. of Wooster, 1955; MS in Zoology, U. Wis., 1957, PhD in Zoology, 1962. Instr. zoology U. Wis., Madison, 1966; asst. prof. poultry sci. and zoology N.C. State U., Raleigh, 1968-71; vis. prof. biology N.C. Ctrl. U., Durham, 1971-73, assoc. prof., 1973-79, prof., 1979-93; ret., 1993; vis. scientist U. Vienna, Austria, 1975. Contbr. articles, abstracts to profl. publs. Mem. Am. Soc. Zoologists, Am. Ornithologists Union, Cooper Ornithol. Soc., Wilson Ornithol. Soc., Wis. Acad. Sci., Arts and Letters, N.C. Acad. Sci., LWV (bd. dirs. 1988—, natural resources com. 1988—), Sigma Xi. Avocations: bird migration, conservation and environmental issues. Home: 409 Moonridge Rd Chapel Hill NC 27516-9385

MUELLER, PAUL HENRY, retired banker; b. N.Y.C., June 24, 1917; s. Paul Herbert and Helen (Cantwell) M.; m. Jean Bonnel Vreeland, Sept. 10, 1949; 1 child, Donald Vreeland. BS, NYU, 1940; AB, Princeton U., 1941; LittD (hon.), Heriot-Watt U., Edinburgh, Scotland, 1981; LHD (hon.), Bloomfield Coll., 1991. Page Citibank N.A., 1934; on leave, 1939-46, asst. cashier, 1947-52, asst. v.p., 1952-58, v.p., 1958-65, sr. v.p., 1965-74, chmn. credit policy com., 1974-82; chmn. Saab-Scania Am. Inc., 1982-90, Atlas Copco N.Am. Inc., 1975-93; dir. Atlas Copco AB, Stockholm, 1982-91, Skandinaviska Enskilda Banken Corp., 1983-93, Ericson N.Am., Inc., 1986-91; entered U.S. Fgn. Svc., served in Panama, Cairo, Washington, 1941-43; asst. adminstry. sec. UN Monetary and Fin. Conf., Bretton Woods, N.H., 1944; divisional asst. Dept. State, 1946; sec. West Indian Conf., 2d session, St. Thomas, V.I., 1946; vis. lectr. U. Va., 1980—; founding chmn., sr. fellow Ctr. Internat. Banking Studies, 1977-91. Contbg. author: Offshore Lending by U.S. Commercial Banks, 1975, 81, Bank Credit, 1981, Classics in Commercial Bank Lending, 1981, Vol. II, 1985, Loan Portfolio Management, 1988, Credit Culture, 1994; author: (with Leif H. Olsen) Credit and the Business Cycle, 1979, Learning from Lending, 1979, Credit Doctrine for Lending Officers, 1976, 81, Credit Endpapers, 1982, Perspective on Credit Risk, 1988; contbr. articles to profl. jours. Trustee Bloomfield Coll., N.J., 1983-91, vice chmn., 1987-88, chmn., 1988-91, trustee emeritus; treas. Marcus Wallenberg Found. (U.S.), 1984—. Served from 2d lt. to capt. USMCR, 1944-45. Decorated Royal Order Polar Star (Sweden); recipient Alumni award Grad. Sch. Credit and Fin. Mgmt., Dartmouth Coll., Disting. Svc. award Robert Morris Assocs., award for journalistic excellence, 1991. Mem. Bankers Assn. Fgn. Trade (hon., v.p. 1976), Pilgrims, SAR, Swedish-Am. C. of C. U.S. (chmn. 1989-90, hon. dir.), Royal Econ. Soc. (U.K.), Univ. Club (N.Y.C.), Beta Gamma Sigma. Republican. Presbyterian. Home: 75 Rotary Dr Summit NJ 07901-3131

MUELLER, PETER STERLING, psychiatrist, educator; b. N.Y.C., Dec. 28, 1930; s. Reginald Sterling and Edith Louise (Welleck) M.; m. Ruth Antonia Shipman, Aug. 9, 1958; children: Anne Louise, Peter Sterling, Paul Shipman, Elizabeth Ruth. A.B., Princeton U., 1952; M.D., U. Rochester, 1956. Am. Cancer Soc. student fellow Francis Delafield Hosp., N.Y.C., summer 1955; intern Bellevue Hosp., Columbia U., N.Y.C., 1956-57; asst. resident in psychiatry Henry Phipps Psychiat. Clinic, Johns Hopkins Hosp., Balt., 1963-66; asst. prof. psychiatry St. Medicine, Yale U., New Haven, 1966-72; asso. prof. psychiatry Coll. Medicine and Dentistry of N.J., Rutgers Med. Sch., Piscataway, 1972-76; clin. prof. psychiatry Coll. Medicine and Dentistry of N.J., Rutgers Med. Sch., 1976-82; cons. for Rehab. Unit and Center for Indsl. Human Resources, Community Mental Health Center, 1973—; mem. courtesy staff dept. psychiatry Princeton Med. Center, 1976—; cons. in psychotherapy Conn. Valley Hosp., Middletown, 1966-72; cons. in psychiatry Carrier Clinic, Belle Mead, N.J., 1973—; VA Hosp., Lyons, N.J., 1975-78. Contbr. writings in field to profl. publs. U.S. and Brit., papers to profl. confs. on the use patents in U.S. and fgn. countries for direct dopamine agonists in the treatment of tobacco addiction. Served with USPHS, 1957-63. Recipient Exemplary Psychiatrist award Nat. Alliance for the Mentally Ill, 1994. Mem. Am. Psychosomatic Soc., Am. Psychiat. Assn., AAAS, Amyotrophic Lateral Sclerosis Found. (adv. bd.), Sigma Xi. Episcopalian. Home: 182 Snowden Ln Princeton NJ 08540-3915 Office: 601 Ewing St Princeton NJ 08540-2757 *For some, a hyperactive learning disorder is a curse that hobbles them throughout life; but for others, including myself, this disorder has become a somewhat uncomfortable and bewildering spur for lifelong compulsive puzzle-solving. This bittersweet mandate has produced the original, serendipitous, and occasionally disconcerting ideas which have marked my life.*

MUELLER, RICHARD WALTER, foreign service officer; b. Washington, Dec. 1, 1944; s. Walter Julius and Eleanor (Maack) M.; m. Claire McCormick, Mar. 15, 1975; children: Jonathan R., Eric R. AB, Coll. William and Mary, 1966. Joined Fgn. Svc., Dept. State, 1966; assigned Am. Embassy, Canberra, Australia, 1967-68; polit. officer Am. Embassy, Saigon, Vietnam, 1969-71; staff officer Office Sec. State, Washington, 1971-74; econ. officer U.S. Liaison Office, Beijing, Peoples Republic China, 1976-78; dep. dir. Office East-West Trade Dept. State, Washington, 1978-81, dep. dir. Office Chinese Affairs, 1981-83; chief econ. sect. Am. Consulate Gen., Hong Kong, 1983-86; dep. exec. sec. Office Sec. of State Dept. State, Washington, 1986-89, dep. asst. sec. Office Legis. Affairs, 1989-92; charge d'affaires Am. Embassy, Hong Kong; consul gen. Am. Consulate Gen., Hong Kong, 1993—. Office: Am Consulate General, 26 Garden Rd, Hong Kong Hong Kong

MUELLER, ROBERT KIRK, management consulting company executive; b. St. Louis, July 25, 1913; s. Edward Robert Otto and Lucille M. (Flaugher) M.; m. Jane Elizabeth Konesko, Dec. 27, 1939; children: Lucy Alison, Patricia Kirk, James Arno. BS, Washington U., St. Louis, 1934; MS, U. Mich., 1935; grad., Advanced Mgmt. Program, Harvard U., 1950. Chemist Sinclair Refining Co., East Chicago, Ind., 1935; with Monsanto Co., 1935-68, gen. mgr. plastic div., 1952-61, v.p., dir., exec. com. co., 1963-68; prodn. supt. Shawinigan Resins Corp., Springfield, 1938-40, pres., dir., 1952-61, chmn. bd., dir., 1961-63; supt. Longhorn Ordnance Works, 1942-44, plant mgr., 1944-46; indsl. research, cons., corp. exec. Arthur D. Little, Inc., 1968-88, v.p., 1973-77, chmn. bd., 1977-89; bd. dirs. Decision Resources, Inc., Waltham, Mass., Interneuron Pharms. Inc., Lexington, Mass., Arthur D. Little, Ltd., London, Bus. Ethics Found., Brookline, Mass.; chmn. faculty, lectr. Salzburg (Austria) Seminar in Am. Studies, 1970, bd. dirs., mem. exec. com., 1972-85. Author: Effective Management Through Probability Controls, 1950, Risk, Survival, and Power, 1970, The Innovation Ethic, 1971, Board Life, Realities of Being a Corporate Director, 1974, Buzzwords, A Guide to the Language of Leadership, 1974, Metadevelopment, Beyond the Bottom Line, 1977, New Directions for Directors, Behind the Bylaws, 1977, Career Conflict, Management's Inelegant Dysfunction, 1978, Board Compass, What a Director Needs to Know in a Changing World, 1979, The Incompleat Board, The Unfolding of Corporate Governance, 1981, Behind the Boardroom Door, 1984, Corporate Networking: Building Channels of Information and Influence, 1986, Director's and Officers Guide to Advisory Boards, 1990, Boardworthiness: From a President's and Director's Perspective, 1992, Building A Power Partnership: The CEO and the Board of Directors, 1993. Trustee Cheswick Ctr., 1968—, Colby Sawyer Coll., N.H., 1972-91, Am. Austrian Found., 1988-94. Recipient Disting. Alumnus Achievement award Washington U., 1963. Fellow AAAS, N.Y. Acad. Scis., Inst. Dirs. (London), Internat. Acad. Mgmt.; mem. AIChE, Am. Chem. Soc., Am. Mgmt. Assn. (life, mem. internat. coun.), Soc. Chem. Industry, Nat. Assn. Corp. Dirs. (bd. dirs.), Algonquin Club (Boston), Ommegang Club (Brussels). Office: Arthur D Little Inc 25 Acorn Park Cambridge MA 02140-2201

MUELLER, ROBERT LOUIS, business executive; b. Denver, Aug. 25, 1927; s. George Winchester and Ruth Mabel (Cole) M.; m. Sue McCoy, July 3, 1949; children: Robert, Richard, Edward, Mark; m. Susan Galbraith, June 23, 1985. BSMechE, Yale U., 1948. Chief computer Western Geophys. Co., Mont., Wyo., Colo., Tex., 1949-50; dist. mgr. Armco Steel Corp., Colo., Ohio, N.Y., 1950-63, L.B. Foster Co., N.Y.C., 1963-66; v.p. Wheeling Pitts. Steel Co., W.Va. and Pa., 1966-75; chmn., pres., chief exec. officer Connors Steel Co., Ala., 1975-82; pres., chief exec. officer Judson Steel Co., Calif., 1982-87; pres., COO Proler Internat., Houston, 1987-94, also bd. dirs., cons.,

1994—. Co-author: Handbook of Drainage and Construction Products, 1954. With USN, 1945-46. Mem. ASCE, Assn. Iron and Steel Engrs., Duquesne Club (Pitts.), Houston City Club, Sedona Racquet Club.

MUELLER, ROBERT SWAN, III, lawyer, former federal official; b. N.Y.C., Aug. 7, 1944; s. Robert Swan Jr. and Alice (Truesdale) M.; m. Ann Standish, Sept. 3, 1966; children: Cynthia, Melissa. BA, Princeton U., 1966; MA, NYU, 1967; JD, U. Va., 1973. Bar: Mass., U.S. Dist. Ct. Mass., U.S. Ct. Appeals (1st cir.), Calif., U.S. Dist. Ct. (no. dist.) Calif., U.S. Ct Appeals (9th cir.). Assoc. Pillsbury, Madison & Sutro, San Francisco, 1973-76; asst. U.S. atty. U.S. Atty.'s Office, No. Dist. Calif., San Francisco, 1976-80; chief unit spl. prosecutions, Calif. no. dist. U.S. Atty.'s Office, San Francisco, 1980-81, chief criminal div., 1981-82; chief criminal div. Mass. dist. U.S. Atty.'s Office, Boston, 1982-85, 1st asst. U.S. atty. in Boston, 1985, U.S. atty. for Mass. dist., 1986-87, dep. U.S. atty. for Mass. dist., 1987-88; ptnr. Hill and Barlow, Boston, 1988-89; asst. to atty. gen. for criminal matters U.S. Dept. Justice, Washington, 1989-90, asst. atty. gen. for criminal div., 1990-93; lawyer Hale & Dorr, Washington, 1993—. Capt. USMC, 1967-70; Vietnam. Decorated Bronze Star, Purple Heart, Vietnamese Cross of Gallantry. Office: Hale and Dorr Ste 600 1455 Pennsylvania Ave NW Washington DC 20004-1008

MUELLER, RONALD RAYMOND, public relations executive; b. Sioux City, Iowa, Apr. 1, 1947; s. Clare Robert and Betty Louise (Abker) M.; m. Virginia Lee Ramsburg, July 18, 1982; children: Jeffrey Ryan, Christina Kelly. BS, U.S. Naval Acad., 1969; MA, U. Okla., 1982. Commd. ensign USN, Annapolis, Md., 1969; pub. affairs officer Dept. of Def., Washington, 1969-77; counselor Carl Byoir and Assocs., Boston, 1977-78; v.p. Carl Byoir and Assocs., Washington, 1978-82; sr. v.p. Fraser/Assocs., Washington, 1982-83; pres. Mueller/Assocs., Balt., 1983-84, Earle Palmer Brown Pub. Relations, Washington, 1984-87; exec. v.p. Ketchum Pub. Relations, Washington, 1987-91; exec. v.p. Burson-Marsteller, Chgo., 1991-92, Washington, 1992—; assoc. prof., lectr. George Washington U., 1978—; bd. dirs. Washington Sch. Psychiatry. Pres. Norfolk (Va.) Jaycees, 1970; bd. dirs. Child-Savers, 1992—. Capt. USNR, 1989—. Mem. Pub. Relations Soc. Am. (pres. Washington chpt. 1982), Pub. Relations Counselors Acad. Republican. Presbyterian. Office: Burson-Marsteller 1850 M St NW Washington DC 20036

MUELLER, STEPHAN, geophysicist, educator; b. Marktredwitz, Ger., July 30, 1930; s. Hermann Friedrich and Johanna Antonie Fanny (Leuze) M.; m. Doris Luise Pfleiderer, July 31, 1959; children: Johannes Christoph, Tobias Ulrich. Dipl.-Phys., Inst. Tech. Stuttgart, 1957; M.Sc. in Elec. Engring., Columbia U., 1959; Dr.rer.nat., U. Stuttgart, 1962. Lectr. geophysics U. Stuttgart, 1962-64; vis. prof. S.W. Center Advanced Studies, Richardson, Tex., 1964-65; prof. geophysics U. Karlsruhe, 1964-71, dean Faculty Natural Scis., 1968-69; vis. prof. U. Tex., Dallas, 1969-70; prof. Swiss Fed. Inst. Tech., 1971—, U. Zurich, 1977—; dean Sch. Natural Scis., Swiss Fed. Inst. Tech., 1978-80; dir. Swiss Earthquake Service, 1971—; pres. Swiss Geophys. Commn., 1972-93, hon. pres. 1994; pres. European Seismol. Commn., 1972-76, Internat. Commn. Controlled Source Seismology, 1975-83; chmn. governing council Internat. Seismol. Centre, 1975-85; chmn. European-Mediterranean Seismol. Centre, 1976-82; chmn. Swiss Specialist Group of Geophysics, 1993—. German Acad. Interchange scholar, 1954-55. Fellow Royal Astron. Soc. (hon. fgn. assoc.), Am. Geophys. Union, Geol. Soc. London (hon.); mem. Internat. Assn. Seismology and Physics of Earth's Interior (pres. 1987-91), European Geophys. Soc. (pres. 1978-80, hon. mem.), European Union Geoscis. (Alfred Wegener medal 1993), German Geophys. Soc., Soc. Exploration Geophysicists, European Assn. Geoscientists and Engrs., Seismol. Soc. Am., Seismol. Soc. Japan, Acoustical Soc. Am., Swiss Geophys. Soc. (pres. 1977-80), Swiss Acad. Scis., Academia Europaea (founding mem.), German Acad. Leopoldina Researchers in Natural Scis., Internat. Assn. Geodesy (hon. assoc.), Swiss Fed. Comm. Geology, Sigma Xi. Co-editor Pure and Applied Geophysics, 1974-83; editor-in-chief Annales Geophysicae, 1982-87; editorial bd. Jour. Geophysics, 1969-87, Tectonophysics, 1971-77, 84—, Bolletino di Geofisica Teorica ed Applicata, 1978—, Jour. Geodynamics, 1983—, Tectonics, 1988—; Recipient Medaille de l'Ordre Grand-Ducal Luxembourgois de la Couronne de Chene, 1994, Gustav Steinmann medal, 1995. Office: ETH, Geophysics, CH-8093 Zurich Switzerland

MUELLER, ULRICH, literature educator; b. Goeppingen, Germany, Dec. 19, 1940; arrived in Austria, 1976; s. Rudolf and Julie (Bayer) M.; m. Ursula Speiser, Oct. 6, 1967; children: Michaela, Felix. PhD, U. Tuebingen, Fed. Republic Germany, 1967; PhD Habil., U. Stuttgart, Fed. Republic Germany, 1971. Asst. U. Tuebingen, 1967-68; asst. U. Stuttgart, 1968-71, lectr., 1972-76; prof. medieval lit. U. Salzburg (Austria), 1976—. Author books on medieval and modern lit. and music; contbr. articles and essays to profl. publs. Recipient Grimm prize, 1984. Mem. Oswald-von-Wolkenstein-Gesellschaft (pres.), Gesellschaft für Interkulturelle Germanistik (pres.). Avocations: photography, performing arts. Home: Niederalm 247, A-5081 Anif Austria Office: U Salzburg, Akademiestrasse 20, A-5020 Salzburg Austria

MUELLER, WAYNE DENNIS, pastor, administrator, educator; b. Winona, Minn., Jan. 6, 1945; s. Alfred William and Elsie Adele (Janssen) M.; m. Barbara Ruth Meier, Aug. 31, 1969; children: Adam, Melissa, Molly, Aaron, Andrew, Mara, Megan. BA, Northwestern U., Watertown, Wis., 1966; MDiv, Wis. Luth. Sem., 1970. Ordained parish pastor. Parish pastor Chgo., 1970-77, Waukesha, Wis., 1977-84; chmn. Chgo. Area Mission Effort, 1974-76; preacher Message from the Master, 1983—; prof. theology Wis. Luth. Sem., Mequon, 1984-90; adminstr. for parish svcs. Wis. Evang. Luth. Synod, Milw., 1990—; prof. theology Wis. Luth. Coll., 1992—; vice chmn., bd. regents Wis. Luth. Coll., 1977-83; nat. bd. chmn. WELS Lutherans for Life, 1986-92; program dir. Luth. Radio Ch. Svc., 1986—. Author: Correlated Studies, 1976, 100 Lessons, 1979, Jesus on Stewardship, 1986, Contemporary Moral Issues, 1991, The Bible and Bioethics, 1992, (video) Visitation Ministry, 1984, (periodical series) The Northwestern Lutheran, 1989-90; editor: WELS Ministry Compendium, TCM Ch. and Ministry, 1993, The Lutheran Leadership Series, 1994; gen. editor: (periodical) Parish Leadership, 1992—. Avocations: woodworking, model railroading. Home: W1554 North Side Dr Oconomowoc WI 53066 Office: Wis Evan Luthern Synod 2929 N Mayfair Rd Milwaukee WI 53222

MUELLER, WILLARD FRITZ, economics educator; b. Ortonville, Minn., Jan. 23, 1925; s. Fritz and Adele C. (Thormaehlen) M.; m. Shirley I. Liesch, June 26, 1948; children: Keith, Scott, Kay. B.S., U. Wis., 1950, M.S., 1951; Ph.D., Vanderbilt U., 1955. Asst. prof. U. Calif., Davis, 1954-57; prof. U. Wis., 1957-61; chief economist small bus. com. U.S. Ho. of Reps., 1961; chief economist, dir. bur. econs. FTC, 1961-68; exec. dir. President's Cabinet Com. Price Stability, 1968-69; faculty mem. U. Wis., Madison, 1969—, William F. Vilas rsch. prof. agrl. econs. emeritus, 1969—; pres. Argus Econ. Svcs. Served with USN, 1943-46. Recipient Distinguished Service award FTC, 1969. Fellow Am. Agrl. Econs. Assn.; mem. AAAS, Am. Econ. Assn., Am. Agr. Assn., Assn. Evolutionary Econs. (pres. 1974-75), Indsl. Orgn. Soc. (pres. 1989-90). Unitarian. Home: 121 Bascom Pl Madison WI 53705-3975 Office: U Wis 427 Lorch St Madison WI 53706-1503

MUELLER, WILLIAM MARTIN, former academic administrator, metallurgical engineering educator; b. Denver, Jan. 14, 1917; s. Charles Franklin M. and Nydia (Hough) Mueller; m. Kathryn C. Connor, Nov. 3, 1942; children: Kathryn Irene Ingram, Joann Elaine Goss. Met.E., Colo. Sch. Mines, 1940, M.S., 1949, D.Sc., 1952. Registered profl. engr., Colo. Metallurgist ALCOA, New Kensington, Pa., 1940-45; engr. Gates Rubber Co., 1945-47; instr. Colo. Sch. Mines, Golden, 1947-52; prof. metall. engring., dept. head Colo. Sch. Mines, 1974-79, v.p., 1979-83; staff metallurgist Dow Chem. Co., Rocky Flats, Colo., 1952-57; div. head Denver Research Inst., 1957-65; dir. refin. Am. Soc. Metals, Metals Park, Ohio, 1965-74; cons. Western Forge Corp., Colorado Springs, Colo., 1975-83; invited lectr. Beijing U., 1980; del. leader for People to People to China, 1984, to S.E. Asia, 1986, to USSR, 1990, to Russia, 1993. Author: (with Blackledge and Libowitz) Metal Hydrides, 1968, (with McCall) Microstructural Analysis, 1973; editor: Energetics in Metallurgical Phenomena, 4 vols., 1965-68, (with McCall) Metallographic Specimen Preparation, 1974; sr. editor: Advances in X-Ray Analysis, 1960-66. Recipient Waltman award Colo. Sch. Mines, 1940, Disting. Achievement award, 1972, Halliburton award, 1983. Fellow Am. Soc. Metals (life, trustee 1964-65); mem. ASTM (dir. 1980-83), AIME (life, com.

chmn. 1980-83), Am. Soc. Engring. Edn., Mining and Metall. Soc. Am. Home: 14430 W Ellsworth Ave Golden CO 80401-5322 Office: Colo Sch Mines Hill Hall Golden CO 80401

MUELLER-HEUBACH, EBERHARD AUGUST, medical educator, obstetrician-gynecologist; b. Berlin, Feb. 24, 1942; U.S., 1968; s. Heinrich G. and Elisabeth (Heubach) Mueller; m. Cornelia R. Uffmann, Feb. 6, 1968; 1 child, Oliver Maximilian. Abitur, Lichtenbergschule, Darmstadt, W.Ger., 1961; M.D., U. Cologne (W.Ger.), 1966. Diplomate Am. Bd. Ob-Gyn. Intern U. Cologne, 1967-68, Middlesex Gen. Hosp., New Brunswick, N.J., 1968-69; rsch. fellow Columbia U., N.Y.C., 1969-71; resident and chief resident Sloane Hosp. for Women, N.Y.C., 1971-75; asst. prof. U. Pitts. Sch. Medicine/Magee-Women's Hosp., 1975-81, assoc. prof., 1981-89; prof., chmn. dept. Ob-Gyn., Bowman Gray Sch. Medicine, Wake Forest U., Winston-Salem, N.C., 1989—. Reviewer Am. Jour. Ob-Gyn, 1978—, Obstetrics and Gynecology, 1979—; contbr. chpts. to books, articles to profl. jours. Fellow Am. Coll. Obstetricians and Gynecologists (Hoechst award 1972); mem. Tri-State Perinatal Orgn. (v.p. 1981), Pa. Perinatal Assn. (pres.-elect 1982-84, pres. 1984-86), Soc. Gynecologic Investigation, So. Perinatal Obstetricians, Am. Fedn. Clin. Rsch., Pitts. Ob-Gyn. Soc. (v.p. 1985-86, pres. 1986-87), Am. Gynecol. and Obstet. Soc., Perinatal Rsch. Soc., Coun. Univ. Chairs Obstetrics and Gynecology (sec.-treas. 1995—). Research on animal studies in fetal and maternal physiology; diabetes mellitus in pregnancy, high risk obstetrics. Office: Bowman Gray Sch Med Dept Ob-Gyn Medical Center Blvd Winston Salem NC 27157

MUENCH, JOHN E., lawyer; b. Evanston, Ill., July 21, 1948. AB, Coll. Holy Cross, 1970; JD, Northwestern U., 1976. Bar: Ill. 1976, U.S. Dist. Ct. (no. dist.) Ill. 1976. Law clk. to Hon. Robert A. Sprecher U.S. Ct. Appeals (7th cir.), 1976-77; law clk. to Hon. John Paul Stevens U.S. Supreme Ct., Washington, 1977-78; asst. prof. law U. Ill., 1978-83; ptnr. Mayer, Brown & Platt, Chgo. Editor-in-chief Northwestern U. Law Rev., 1975. Mem. Ill. State Bar Assn. Office: Mayer Brown & Platt 190 S La Salle St Chicago IL 60603-3410

MUESING ELLWOOD, EDITH ELIZABETH, writer, researcher, publisher, editor; b. N.Y.C., Sept. 18, 1947; d. Carl Earl and Elsbeth (Bushbeck) Muesing; m. William Adonis Ellwood, Sept. 15, 1980; children: Jeanie, Colin, Caroline. BA, Fordham U., 1969; MA, NYU, 1971. Adminstrv. asst. The English Speaking Union, N.Y.C., 1979; freelance writer, researcher The Acad. Rsch. Group, Rutherford, N.J., 1975-78, 80-82; pres. Colin-Press, Bklyn., 1984-88; editor Ellwood Editing Svc., 1990-93; writer, editor Bushkill, Pa., 1993—. Author: U.S. Democracy: Myth vs. Reality, 1985, The Alternative to Technological Culture, 1986; contbr. haiku poems and sketches to mags., newsletters and anthologies, 1979—; contbr. articles to jours., mags., tabloids and newsletters; mem. panel experts Freelance Writers Report, monthly issue. Active Nat. Trust for Hist. Preservation, Washington, 1980—, South St. Seaport Mus., N.Y.C., 1974-83, 90-93; founding mem. Nat. Mus. Women in Arts, Washington, 1985-88; mem. Environ. Def. Fund, 1973—, Nature Conservancy, 1986-93, Nat. Chronic Pain Outreach Assn., 1991—; contbg. mem. Dem. Nat. Com., 1991—; founding patron Katharine Houghton Hepburn Fund, 1992, Planned Parenthood, 1989—. Mem. Nat. Writers Club, Internat. Women's Writing Guild, Women in Scholarly Pub. (editor column in newsletter 1990), Am. Acad. Poets (contbr.), Interstitial Cystitis Assn., Nat. Writers Union, Nat. Trust Historic Preservation. Democrat. Roman Catholic. Avocations: water colors, sketching, music, guitar, collecting country furnishing antiques. Home and Office: 792 Saw Creek Est Bushkill PA 18324-9455

MUETH, JOSEPH EDWARD, lawyer; b. St. Louis, Aug. 8, 1935; s. Joseph and Marie Clare (Reher) M.; m. Ellen Agnes O'Heron, Dec. 24, 1973; children: Erin R., Patricia A. B.Chem. Engring., U. Dayton, 1957; LL.B., Georgetown U., 1960, LL.M., 1961. Bar: Calif. 1964. Practice law L.A.; ptnr. Wills, Green & Mueth, L.A., 1974-83; pvt. practice law, 1983—; adj. prof. law U. Calif. Hastings Coll. Law, San Francisco, 1972-75; lectr. Claremont Grad. Sch., 1982—. Author: Copyrights Patents and Trademarks, 1974. Chmn. bd. Rio Hondo council Camp Fire Girls Inc., 1967-72. Mem. AAAS, Am., Los Angeles County bar assns., State Bar Calif., N.Y. Acad. Scis., L.A. Athletic Club. Home: 1217 Seal Way Seal Beach CA 90740-6419

MUFSON, MAURICE ALBERT, physician, educator; b. N.Y.C., July 7, 1932; s. Max and Faye M.; m. Diane Cecile Weiss, Apr. 1, 1962; children: Michael Jeffrey, Karen Andrea, Pamela Beth. A.B., Bucknell U., 1953; M.D., NYU, 1957. Intern Bellevue Hosp., N.Y.C., 1957-58; resident Bellevue Hosp., 1958-59; chief resident Cook County Hosp., Chgo., 1965-66; sr. surgeon USPHS Lab. Infectious Diseases, NIH, 1961-65; asst. prof. medicine U. Ill., 1965-69, assoc. prof., 1969-73, prof., 1973-76; prof., chmn. dept. medicine Marshall U., 1976—; vis. scientist Karolinska Inst., 1984-85. Contbr. articles to profl. jours. Served with U.S. Navy, 1959-61. WHO grantee, 1967; recipient Meet-the-Scholar award Marshall U., 1986, REsearcher of Yr. award Sigmz Xi, Marshall U., 1989; co-recipient Louis Weinstein award Jour. Clin. Infectious Diseases, 1994. Fellow ACP (traveling scholar 1987, Laureate award W.va. chpt.), Infectious Diseases Soc. Am.; mem. AMA, Soc. Exptl. Biology and Medicine, Ctrl. Soc. Clin. Rsch., So. Soc. Clin. Investigation, W.va. State Med. Assn., Assn. Profs. Medicine (counselor 1992-95, pres.-elect 1995—), Alpha Omega Alpha. Office: Dept Medicine Marshall U Sch Medicine Huntington WV 25701

MUGGERIDGE, DEREK BRIAN, dean, engineering consultant; b. Godalming, Surrey, U.K., Oct. 10, 1943; arrived in Can., 1956; s. Donald William and Vera Elvina (Jackson) M.; m. Hanny Meta Buurman, Dec. 4, 1965; children: Karen Julie, Michael Brent. BS in Aero. Engring., Calif. State Polytech. U., 1965; MASc in Aerospace Engring., U. Toronto, 1966, PhD in Aerospace Engring., 1970. Spl. lectr. U. Toronto, Ont., Can., 1971; indsl. post-doctoral fellow Fleet Mfg. Co., Fort Erie, Ont., 1970-72; from asst. prof. to prof. Meml. U. of Nfld., St. John's, 1972-93, univ. rsch. prof., 1990-93; dean Okanagan U. Coll., Kelowna, B.C., Can., 1993—; pres. Offshore Design Assocs. Ltd., Portugal Cove, Nfld., 1980—; sec., ptnr. Nfld. Ocean Cons., St. John's, 1981-93; ptnr. LNF Joint Venture Ltd., St. John's, 1984-90; vis. prof. U. Victoria, B.C., 1988-89. Co-author: Ice Interaction with Offshore Structures, 1988; contbr. articles to profl. jours.; contbr. conf. articles, reports. U. Toronto Grad. fellow, 1965, Nat. Rsch. Coun. Can. Grad. fellow U. Toronto, 1966-70. Mem. Assn. Profl. Engrs. & Geoscis. of Province of B.C., Marine Tech. Soc., Soc. Naval Archs. and Marine Engrs. Avocations: windsurfing, sailing, skiing. Home: 16438 Carr's Landing Rd, Winfield, BC Canada V4V 1C3 Office: Okanagan Univ Coll, 3333 College Way, Kelowna, BC Canada V1V 1V7

MUHLBERGER, RICHARD CHARLES, former museum administrator, writer; b. Engelwood, N.J., Jan. 20, 1938; s. George Albert and Margaret Bertha (Heins) M. A.A., Calif. Concordia Coll., 1958; B.A., Wayne State U., 1964; M.A. in Art History, Johns Hopkins U., 1967. Curator mus. edn. Worcester Art Mus., Mass., 1966-72; chmn. edn. Detroit Inst. Arts, 1972-75; dir. Mus. Fine Arts and George Walter Vincent Smith Art Mus., Springfield, Mass., 1976-87; vice dir. for edn. Met. Mus. Art, N.Y.C., 1987-89; dir. Knoxville (Tenn.) Mus. Art, 1990-91; mem. adv. panel NEH, 1976-78, Mass. Council on Arts and Humanities, 1979-81; mem. policy panel, mus. program Nat. Endowment Arts, 1981-83. Author: The Bible in Art, The New Testament, 1990, The Bible in Art, The Old Testament, 1990, The Christmas Story, 1990, What Makes a Raphael a Raphael, 1993, What Make a Bruegel a Bruegel, 1993, What Makes a Rembrandt a Rembrandt, 1993, What Makes a Monet a Monet, 1993, What Makes a Degas a Degas, 1993, What Make a Van Gogh a Van Gogh, 1993, What Makes a Leonardo a Leonardo, 1994, What Makes a Goya a Goya, 1994, What Makes a Cassatt a Cassatt, 1994, What Make a Picasso a Picasso, 1994; Woodrow Wilson fellow, 1965-66; recipient Outstanding Young Man award Greater Worcester Jaycees, 1970. Mem. Am. Assn. Museums (chmn. com. on edn. 1974-76, councilor 1988-91), New Eng. Mus. Assn. (pres. 1985-87). Home: 41 Smithfield Ct Springfield MA 01108-3129

MUHLEBACH, RICHARD FRANK, management and development company executive; b. San Francisco, July 16, 1943; s. Frank Joseph and Flora Delores (Laurin) M.; m. Maria Delia Rivera, Nov., 1966; children: Kathy, Eric. BA, San Francisco State U., 1968; AA, Golden West Coll., 1972. Cert. property mgr., shopping ctr. mgr., real property adminstr. Caseworker

Alameda County Welfare Dept., Oakland, Calif., 1968-69; v.p. The Lusk Co., Irvine, Calif., 1969-76, Tishman West Mng. Corp., Orange, Calif., 1976-80; pres. TRF Mgmt. Corp., Bellevue, Wash., 1980—; v.p. The Rainier Fund, Inc., Bellevue, 1984—; instr. Orange Coast Coll., Costa Mesa, Calif., 1976-80, Internat. Coun. Shopping Ctrs., N.Y.C., 1980—, N.W. Ctr. for Profl. Edn., Bellevue, 1980—. Contbr. articles to profl. jours. With USNG, 1965-71. Mem. Inst. Real Estate Mgmt (instr. 1980—, r.v.p. 1987-88), Real Estate Educators Assn. (pres. 1989, v.p. 1988), Internat. Real Estate Mgmt. (v.p. western Wash. chpt. 1984, pres. 1985). Avocations: family activities, reading, teaching, lecturing. Home: 17910 NE 125th St Redmond WA 98052-2265 Office: TRF Mgmt Corp 12400 SE 38th St Bellevue WA 98006-1298

MUHLENBRUCH, CARL W., civil engineer; b. Decatur, Ill., Nov. 21, 1915; s. Carl William and Clara (Theobald) M.; m. Agnes M. Kringel, Nov. 22, 1939; children: Phyllis Elaine (Mrs. Richard H. Wallace), Joan Carol (Mrs. Frederick W. Wenk). BCE, U. Ill., 1937, CE, 1945; MCE, Carnegie Inst. Tech., 1943; LLD (hon.), Concordia U., River Forest, Ill., 1995. Research engineer Aluminum Research Labs., Pitts., 1937-39; cons. engring., 1939-50; mem. faculty Carnegie Inst. Tech., 1939-48; assoc. prof. civil engring. Northwestern U., 1948-54; pres. TEC-SEARCH, Inc. (formerly Ednl. and Tech. Consultants Inc.), 1954-67, chmn. bd., 1967—; Pres. Profl. Centers Bldg. Corp., 1961-77. Author: Experimental Mechanics and Properties of Materials; Contbr. articles engring. publs. Treas., bd. dirs. Concordia Coll. Found.; dir. Mo. Lutheran Synod, 1965-77, vice chmn. 1977-79. Recipient Stanford E. Thompson award, 1945. Mem. Am. Econ. Devel. Coun. (cert. econ. developer), Am. Soc. Engring. Edn. (editor Ednl. Aids in Engring.), NSPE, ASCE, Sigma Xi, Tau Beta Pi, Omicron Delta Kappa. Club: University (Evanston). Lodge: Rotary (dist. gov. 1980-81, dir. service projects Ghana and the Bahamas). Home: 4071 Fairway Dr Wilmette IL 60091-1005

MUILENBURG, ROBERT HENRY, hospital administrator; b. Orange City, Iowa, Apr. 29, 1941; s. Henry W. and Anna (Vander Zwaag) M.; m. Judith Ann Gebauer, Jan. 1, 1959; children: Ronald, Eric, Matthew. B.A., U. Iowa, 1964, M.A., 1966. Administrv. asst. Ill. Masonic Med. Ctr., Chgo., Ill., 1966-67; asst. administr. Ill. Masonic Med. Ctr., Chgo., Ill, 1967-68; assoc. administr. Ill. Masonic Med. Ctr., Chgo., Ill., 1968-71; assoc. administr. U. Utah Hosp., Salt Lake City, 1971-75, administr., 1975-78; administr. U. Wash. Med. Ctr., Seattle, 1978-84; clin. assoc. prof. health services adminstrn. and planning U. Wash., Seattle, 1978—; exec. dir. U. Wash. Med. Ctr., 1984—. USPHS trainee, 1966. Fellow Am. Coll. Hosp. Adminstrs.; mem. Am. Hosp. Assn. (del. 1984-88, chmn. metro. hosp. sect. 1987, bd. dirs. 1992-94), Wash. State Hosp. Assn. (bd. dirs. 1982-84, 89-94), Seattle Area Hosp. Coun. (pres. 1983). Home: 10019 49th Ave NE Seattle WA 98125-8131 Office: U Wash Med Ctr RC-35 1959 NE Pacific St Seattle WA 98195

MUIR, J. DAPRAY, lawyer; b. Washington, Nov. 9, 1936; s. Brockett and Helen Cassin (Dapray) M.; m. Louise Rutherfurd Pierrepont, July 16, 1966. A.B., Williams Coll., 1958; J.D., U. Va., 1964. Bar: MD., Va., D.C. 1964, U.S. Supreme Ct. 1967. Legal advisor for econ. and bus. affairs U.S. Dept. State, 1971-73; pvt. practice law, 1974—; mem. U.S. del. to Joint U.S./USSR Comml. Commn., 1972; chmn. D.C. Securities Adv. Com., 1981-84, mem. 1985-88. Bd. editors Va. Law Rev, 1963-64; contbr. articles to profl. jours. Mem. bd. dirs. Internat. Fedn. of Insts. for Advanced Study, 1992—. Lt. (j.g.) USNR, 1958-61. Mem. D.C. Bar (chmn. internat. div. 1977-78, chmn. environ., energy and natural resources div. 1979-81), Washington Fgn. Law Soc. (pres. 1982-83). Clubs: Metropolitan (Washington); Union (N.Y.C.); Chevy Chase (Md.). Home: 3104 Q St NW Washington DC 20007-3027 Office: Ste 300 1919 Pennsylvania Ave NW Washington DC 20006-3400

MUIR, MALCOLM, federal judge; b. Englewood, N.J., Oct. 20, 1914; s. John Merton and Sarah Elizabeth (Stabler) M.; m. Alma M. Brohard, Sept. 6, 1940 (dec. 1985); children: Malcolm, Thomas, Ann Muir Weinberg, Barbara (dec.), David Clay. B.A., Lehigh U., 1935; LL.B., Harvard U., 1938. Sole practice Williamsport, Pa., 1938-42, 45-49; mem. firm Williamsport, 1949-70; judge U.S. Dist. Ct. (mid. dist.) Pa., 1970—. Active charitable orgns., Williamsport, 1939-70. Mem. ABA, Pa. Bar Assn. (pres.-elect 1970). Avocation: reading. Office: US Dist Ct PO Box 608 Williamsport PA 17703-0608

MUIR, WARREN R., chemist, toxic substances specialist; b. N.Y., 1945; s. Ernest Roger and Phyllis (Stirn) M.; m. Jo-Ann McNally; children: Amy, Douglas, Michael, Gregory, Daniel. AB in Chemistry cum laude, Amherst Coll., 1967; MS in Chemistry, Northwestern U., Evanston, Ill., 1968, PhD in Chemistry, 1971; postgrad. in epidemiology, Johns Hopkins U., 1975-77. Sr. staff mem. environ. health Council on Environ. Quality, EPA, Washington, 1971-78; dir. Office of Toxic Substances, EPA, 1978-81; pres. Hampshire Rsch. Assocs., Inc., 1981—, Hampshire Rsch. Inst., 1987—; assoc. environ. health scis. Johns Hopkins U., 1981—; rsch. prof. biology Am. U., 1985; sr. fellow INFORM, 1982-95; mem. Nat. Conf. Lawyers and Scientists, 1987-89. Contbr. articles on environ. quality to profl. jours. Bd. dirs. clean air coordinating com. Tb Inst., Chgo., 1970-71; mem., chair several Nat. Rsch. Coun. coms.; local coord. Children's Friendship Project for No. Ireland, 1993—. Recipient NSF Acad. award, 1966, Howard Waters Doughty prize Amherst Coll., 1967, Forris Jewett Moore fellow, 1967, NIH predoctoral fellow, 1971; knighted assoc. officer brother Most Venerable Order of St. John, 1992; co-recipient Adminstrs.' award U.S. EPA, 1992. Mem. AAAS, Am. Chem. Soc. (Student award Conn. Valley sect. 1967), Soc. Risk Analysis, Soc. Epidemiol. Rsch., Am. Chem. Soc., Sigma Xi, Phi Lamda Upsilon. Home: 9426 Forest Haven Dr Alexandria VA 22309-3151

MUIR, WILLIAM KER, JR., political science educator; b. Detroit, Oct. 30, 1931; s. William Ker and Florence Taylor (Bodman) M.; m. Paulette Irene Wauters, Jan. 16, 1960; children: Kerry Macaire, Harriet Bodman. Student, Clifton Coll., Bristol, Eng., 1949-50; B.A., Yale U., 1954, Ph.D., 1965; J.D., U. Mich., 1958. Bar: N.Y. 1960, Conn. 1965. Asst. U. Mich. Law Sch., 1958-59; assoc. firm Davis Polk & Wardwell, N.Y.C., 1959-60; lectr. in polit. sci. Yale U., 1960-64, 65-67; from assoc. to ptnr. Tyler Cooper Grant Bowerman & Keefe, New Haven, 1964-68; prof. polit. sci. U. Calif.-Berkeley, 1968—, dept. chmn., 1980-83; speechwriter v.p. U.S., 1983-85; columnist Oakland (Calif.) Tribune, 1992-93; writer Gov. of Calif., Sacramento, 1994; sr. cons. Calif. State Assembly, Sacramento, 1975-76; cons. Oakland (Calif.) Police Dept., 1970-72; vis. prof. polit. sci. Harvard U., summers 1976, 79. Author: Prayer in the Public Schools, 1967, later republished as Law and Attitude Change, 1974, Police: Streetcorner Politicians, 1977, Legislature: California's School for Politics, 1982, The Bully Pulpit: The Presidential Leadership of Ronald Reagan, 1993. Mem. Berkeley (Calif.) Police Rev. Commn., 1981-83; chmn. New Haven Civil Liberties Coun., 1965-68. Recipient Hadley B. Cantril Meml. award, 1979, Disting. teaching award U. Calif., Berkeley, 1974, Phi Beta Kappa No. Calif. Assoc. Excellence In Teaching award, 1994. Mem. Am. Polit. Sci. Assn. (Edward S. Corwin award 1966). Republican. Presbyterian. Home: 59 Parkside Dr Berkeley CA 94705-2409 Office: Dept Polit Sci U Calif Berkeley CA 94720

MUIRHEAD, VINCENT URIEL, aerospace engineer; b. Dresden, Kans., Feb. 6, 1919; s. John Hadsell and Lily Irene (McKinney) M.; m. Bobby Jo Thompson, Nov. 5, 1943; children: Rosalind, Jean, Juleigh. B.S., U.S. Naval Acad., 1941; B.S. in Aero. Engring, U.S. Naval Postgrad. Sch., 1948; Aero. Engr., Calif. Inst. Tech., 1949; postgrad., U. Ariz., 1962, 64, Okla. State U., 1963. Midshipman U.S. Navy, 1937, commd. ensign, 1941, advanced through grades to comdr.; 1951; nav. officer U.S.S. White Plains, 1945-46; comdr. Fleet Aircraft Service Squad, 1951-52; with Bur. Aeros., Ft. Worth, 1953-54; comdr. Helicopter Utility Squadron 1, Pacific Fleet, 1955-56; chief staff officer Comdr. Fleet Air, Philippines, 1956-58; exec. officer Naval Air Tng. Center, Memphis, 1958-61; ret., 1961; asst. prof. U. Kans., Lawrence 1961-63; assoc. prof. aerospace engring. U. Kans., 1964-76, prof., 1976-89, prof. emeritus, 1989—, chmn. dept., 1976-88; cons. Black & Veatch (cons. engrs.), Kansas City, Mo., 1964—. Author: Introduction to Aerospace, 1972, 5th edit., 1994, Thunderstorms, Tornadoes and Building Damage, 1975. Decorated Air Medal. Fellow AIAA (assoc.); mem. Am. Acad. Mechanics, Am. Soc. Engring. Edn., Tau Beta Pi, Sigma Gamma Tau. Mem. Ch. of Christ (elder). Research on aircraft, tornado vortices, shock

tubes and waves. Home: 503 Park Hill Ter Lawrence KS 66046-4841 Office: Dept Aerospace Engring Univ Kans Lawrence KS 66045

MUJICA, BARBARA LOUISE, foreign language educator, author; b. Altoona, Pa., Dec. 25, 1943; d. Louis and Carol Freida (Kline) Kaminar; A.B., UCLA, 1964; M.A., Middlebury Coll., 1965; Ph.D., N.Y. U., 1974; m. Mauro E. Mujica, Dec. 26, 1966; children: Lillian Louise, Mariana Ximena, Mauro Eduardo Ignacio. Tchr. French, UCLA, 1963-64; assoc. editor modern langs. Harcourt Brace Jovanovich, N.Y.C., 1966-73; instr., asst. prof. Romance langs. CUNY, 1973-74; assoc. prof. Spanish, Georgetown U., Washington, 1974—. Penfield fellow, 1971; NEH summer Inst. faculty, 1980, Spanish Govt. grantee, 1987. Dir. El Retablo, Spanish lang. theater. Mem. Writers Center, Brazilian Am. Cultural Inst., Am. Assn. Tchrs. Spanish and Portuguese, MLA, Women's Caucus MLA, South Atlantic MLA, N.E. MLA, AAUP, Annual Symposium on Spanish Golden Age Drama (editor Proceedings, 1987, 88), Philological Assn. Pacific Coast, Assn. Tchrs. Spanish Classical Drama. Author: A-LM Spanish, Levels I-IV, 1969-74; Readings in Spanish Literature, 1975; Calderon's Characters: An Existential Point of View, 1980; Pasaporte, 1980, rev. edit., 1984; Aquí y ahora, 1979; Entrevista, 1982; Iberian Pastoral Characters, 1986; editor, pub. Verbena: Bilingual Rev. of the Arts, 1979-85; sr. assoc. editor, bd. dirs. Washington Rev.; contbr. articles to profl. jours., newspapers, lit. mags. Home: 8807 Fox Hills Trl Rockville MD 20854-4212 Office: Georgetown U Dept Spanish Washington DC 20057

MUJICA, MAURO E., architect; b. Antofagasta, Chile, Apr. 20, 1941; came to U.S., 1965, naturalized, 1970; s. Mauro Raul and Graciela (Parodi-Blayfus) M.; m. Barbara Louise Kaminar, Dec. 26, 1966; children: Lillian Louise, Mariana Ximena, Mauro Eduardo Ignacio III. MArch, Columbia U., 1971. Head designer Columbia U. Office Archtl. Planning, N.Y.C., 1966-71; project mgr. Walker, Sander, Ford & Kerr, Architects, Princeton, N.J., 1971-72; prin. Mauro E. Mujica, Architect, N.Y.C., 1972-74; dir. internat. div. Greenhorne & O'Mara, Inc., Riverdale, Md., 1974-78; prin. Mujica & Reddy Architects, Washington, 1978-80; prin. Mauro E. Mujica, Architect, Washington, 1980-81; ptnr. Mujica & Berlin Investment Bankers, Washington, 1982-85, Mujica Keppie Henderson Internat., Washington and Glasgow, Scotland, 1981-83, Mujica-Seifert Architects, Washington and London, 1983-87; pres., chief exec. officer The Pace Group, Washington, 1987-91; ptnr. PACE/WALSHE Internat., London and Washington. Chmn. bd. and CEO U.S. English Found., Washington, 1993—. Prin. works include: Tennis Clubhouse, Columbia U., Nat. Hosp., Puerto Barrios, Guatemala, Plaza Hotel interiors, La Paz, Bolivia. Fellow Inst. Dirs. (London); mem. AIA, Columbia U. Archtl. Alumni Assn, Capitol Hill Club, Bethesda Country Club. Republican. Home: 7601 Quintana Ct Bethesda MD 20817-2042

MUJUMDAR, VILAS SITARAM, structural engineer, management executive; b. Indore, India, June 26, 1941; s. Sitaram and Kamala (Kulkarni) M.; m. Ingrid M. Dietrich, Mar. 1, 1969. BScin Civil Engring., Vikram U., India, 1961; MS, U. Roorkee, India, 1962; MBA, U. Santa Clara, Calif., 1980. Registered profl. engr., U.S., Can., U.K.; registered structural engr., Calif. Design engr. U.S.D. & Co., India, 1962-65, Donovan H. Lee & Ptnrs., London, 1965-66; asst. chief engr. Francon & Spancrete Ltd., Montreal, Can., 1966-68; gen. mgr., dir. engring. Modular Constructors, Woburn, Mass., 1968-70; sr. project engr., tech. mgr. LeMessurier Assocs., Cambridge, Mass., 1970-74; v.p. Precast Systems Cons., Woburn, Mass., 1974-77; prin. structural engr. Ecodyne Corp., Santa Rosa, Calif., 1977-79; v.p. Foster Engring., Inc., San Francisco, 1979-81, 3D/Internat. Inc., Houston, 1981-85; pres. VSM Assocs., Santa Rosa, Calif., 1986-88; v.p. BSHA, Inc., San Diego, 1988-90; pres. McNamara, Salvia, Mujumdar, Inc., San Diego, 1990-92; chief office of regulation svcs. Div. State Architect Dept. Gen. Svcs., Calif., 1992—; tchr. concrete course Calif. State U., Long Beach. Author: Concrete Design Manual, Structural Engineer Review Course; inventor pre-cast concrete bldg. systems; contbr. articles to profl. jours. Merit scholar Govt. India, 1957-62, Gold medal; recipient numerous awards. Fellow ASCE, Inst. Structural Engrs., Am. Concrete Inst.; mem. Prestressed Concrete Inst. (chmn. several Earthquake Engring. coms.), Structural Engrs. Assn. Calif. (chmn. seismology com. 1992-93), Beta Gamma Sigma (hon. bus. soc.). Home: 2120 Parrish Dr Santa Rosa CA 95404-2323 Office: 1300 I St Ste 800 Sacramento CA 95814

MUKASEY, MICHAEL B., federal judge; b. 1941. AB, Columbia U., 1963; LLB, Yale U., 1967. Assoc. Webster Sheffield Fleischmann Hithcock & Brookfield, 1967-72, Patterson, Belknap, Webb & Tyler, 1976-88; asst. U.S. atty. U.S. Dist. Ct. (so. dist.) N.Y., 1972-76, chief judge, 1988—. Contbr. articles to profl. jours. Mem. Assn. of Bar of City of N.Y. (fed. cts. com. 1979-82, communications law com. 1983-86). Office: US Dist Ct US Courthouse Foley Sq New York NY 10007-1581

MUKERJEE, PASUPATI, chemistry educator; b. Calcutta, India, Feb. 13, 1932; s. Nani Gopal and Probhabati (Ghosal) M.; m. Lalita Sarkar, Feb. 29, 1964. B.Sc., Calcutta U., 1949, M.Sc., 1951; Ph.D., U. So. Calif., 1957. Lectr., vis. asst. prof. U. So. Calif., 1956-57; research assoc. Brookhaven Nat. Lab., L.I., 1957-59; reader in phys. chemistry Indian Assn. Cultivation of Sci., Calcutta, 1959-64; guest scientist U. Utrecht, Holland, 1964; sr. scientist chemistry dept. U. So. Calif., 1964-66; vis. assoc. prof. U. Wis., Madison, 1966-67, prof. Sch. Pharmacy, 1967-94, emeritus prof., 1994—; vis. prof. Indian Inst. Tech., Kharagpur, 1971-72; mem. commn. on colloid and surface chemistry Internat. Union Pure and Applied Chemistry. Contbr. articles to profl. jours.; editorial bd. Jour. Colloid and Interface Sci., 1978-80, Asian Jour. Pharm. Scis., 1978-85, Colloids and Surfaces, 1980-86. Grantee USPHS, NSF, Nat. Bur. Standards, Petroleum Research Fund. Fellow AAAS, Acad. Pharm. Scis., Am. Inst. Chemistry; mem. Am. Chem. Soc. (editorial bd. Langmuir 1985-86), Am. Pharm. Assn., Acad. Pharm. Scis., Rho Chi. Home: 5526 Varsity Hl Madison WI 53705-4652 Office: 425 N Charter St Madison WI 53706-1515

MUKHERJEE, AMIYA K, metallurgy and materials science educator. PhD, Oxford (Eng.) U., 1962. Prof. U. Calif., Davis. Recipient Alexander von Humboldt award, 1988, Albert Easton White Disting. Tchr. award, 1992, Pfeiland prize Inst. of Materials, Eng., 1993, U. Calif. prize and citation, 1993. Office: U Calif Davis Dept Chem Engring & Material Sci Davis CA 95616

MUKHERJEE, KALINATH, materials science and engineering educator, researcher; b. Calcutta, India, Feb. 19, 1932; naturalized U.S. citizen, 1966; s. Ramkrisna and Saraju Mukherjee; m. Patricia Stapleton, Aug. 20, 1959; children: Joia S., Maia S., Janam S. B in Engring., Calcutta U., 1956; BS in Engring., U. Ill., Urbana, 1959, PhD, 1963. Metallurgist Indian Iron and Steel Co., 1956-57; rsch. asst. U. Ill., Urbana, 1957-63, rsch. assoc., instr., 1963-64; asst. prof. SUNY, Stony Brook, 1964-67; assoc. prof. Poly. Inst. Bklyn., 1967-72, prof., 1972-80; head dept. metallurgy Poly. Inst. N.Y., 1974-80; prof. Mich. State U., East Lansing, 1980—, chmn. dept., 1985—. Co-editor: Lasers in Metallurgy, 1982, Laser Processing of Materials, 1985, Laser Materials Processing III, 1989, Laser Materials Processing IV, 1994; eidtor: Metall./Materials Sci. Edn. yearbook, 1974—; contbr. numerous articles to profl. jours. Recipient Alumnus award Bengal Engring. Coll., India, 1989. Fellow AAAS, Am. Soc. Metals (Edn. award N.Y. chpt. 1976); mem. AIME, Am. Phys. Soc., Am. Soc. Engring. Edn., Metal Soc. N.Y., Minerals, Metals and Materials Soc. (bd. dirs. 1991-94, dir. structural materials divsn. 1991-94), Sigma Xi, Alpha Sigma Nu. Democrat. Office: Mich State U Dept Metallurgy Mech & Material Sci East Lansing MI 48824

MUKOYAMA, JAMES HIDEFUMI, JR., securities executive; b. Chgo., Aug. 3, 1944; s. Hidefumi James and Miye (Maruyama) M.; m. Kyung Ja Woo, June 20, 1971; children: Sumi Martha, Jae Thomas. BA in English, U. Ill., 1965, MA in Social Studies, 1966; honor grad. U.S. Army Inf. Sch., 1966; grad. U.S. Army Command and Gen. Staff Coll., 1979, U.S. Army War Coll., 1984. Registered prin., sr. registered options prin. Nat. Assn. Securities Dealers. Commd. 2nd. lt. U.S. Army, 1965-70; with USAR, 1970—, brig. gen., 1987-90, maj. gen., 1990-95; asst. dept. mgr. Mitsui & Co. (USA), Inc., Chgo., 1971-74; mem. Chgo. Bd. Options Exchange, 1974-75; v.p. 1st Omaha Securities, Chgo., 1975-76, Heartland Securities, Chgo., 1976-90; aliment mem. N.Y. Stock Exchange, 1982-84; v.p. Lefta Advt., Chgo., 1976-90; v.p. Fleet Brokerage, Chgo., 1990-95, exec. v.p. and chief op officer Regal Discount Securities, 1995—. Mem. exec. bd. Hillside Free Meth. Ch.,

Evanston, Ill., 1982-93; dir. chgo. coun. Boy Scouts of America, 1993—; trustee Nat. Japenese Am. Meml. Found., 1995—. Decorated Silver Star, Legion of Merit, Purple Heart, 3 Bronze Stars; Vietnamese Army Cross of Gallantry; Japanese Army Parachutist badge; recipient cert. of merit Korean Army, others. Mem. U. Ill. Alumni Assn. (life), Assn. U.S. Army, U.S. Army War Coll. Alumni Assn. (life), Vets. of Fgn. Wars (life), Army Res. Assn. (pres., founder 1992—), Mil. Order Purple Heart (life), Am. Legion, Res. Officers Assn. (life), Sr. Army Res. Commdrs. Assn. Home: 4009 Tracey Ct Glenview IL 60025-2468 Office: 209 W Jackson Blvd 4th Fl Chicago IL 60606

MULARZ, THEODORE LEONARD, architect; b. Chgo., Nov. 6, 1933; s. Stanley A. and Frances (Baycar) M.; m. Ruth L. Larson, Nov. 9, 1963; children: Anne Catherine, Mark Andrew. BArch, U. Ill., 1959. Registered architect Colo., Calif., Oreg. Prin. Theodore L. Mularz, AIA Architects, Aspen, 1963-77; v.p. Benedict-Mularz Assocs. Inc., 1978-81; prin. Theodore L. Mularz & Assocs., Aspen, 1981-90; pvt. practice, Ashland, Oreg., 1990—. Designer numerous archtl. projects including commercial, indsl., religious, recreational, residential and historic restoration. Vice-chmn. Pitkin County Bd. Appeals, 1972-90, City of Aspen Bd. Appeals, 1985-90; City of Aspen Planning/Building Dept. adv. com., 1988-89; planning dir. search. com. City of Aspen, Pitkin County, 1989; mem. Colo. Bd. Examiners of Architects, 1975-85, pres., 1976-80, v.p. 1978; bd. dirs. Rogue Valley Symphony, Ashland, 1990-92, treas., 1991-92, chmn. fin. com., 1991-92. Served with USCGR, 1953-55. Fellow AIA (chair Southern Oreg. program com. 1994-95); mem. Nat. Council Archtl. Registration Bds. (profl. conduct com. 1977-78, procedures and documents com. 1978-82, chmn. edn. com. 1982-83, chmn. procedures and documents com. 1983-84, dir. 1982-84, pres. 1985-86, internat. rels. com. 1984-89, exec. com. 1984-87, mem. interprofl. council on registration 1984-85, pres., 1985, internat. oral exam. com. 1984-89), Colo. Soc. Architects (Community Service award 1975), Aspen Architects Collaborative (chmn. 1973-74), Aspen C. of C. (past dir., past pres., past v.p.), Aspen Hist. Soc. (com. chmn. 1963-64), Rotary (bull. editor Ashland Lithia Springs 1994—). Roman Catholic. Home: 793 Elkader St Ashland OR 97520-3307 Office: 585 A St Ste # 2 Ashland OR 97520-2069

MULCAHEY, SISTER PATRICIA, school system administrator. Supt. schs. Archdiocese of Omaha. Office: Office Schs Supt 3212 N 60th St Omaha NE 68104-3421

MULCAHY, J. PATRICK, food company executive. Chmn., chief exec. officer Eveready Battery Co., St. Louis; v.p. adminstrn. Ralston Purina Co., St. Louis; chmn., chief exec. officer Ralston Purina Internat., St. Louis. Office: Ralston Purina Co Checkerboard Sq Saint Louis MO 63164

MULCAHY, JOHN J., bishop; b. Dorchester, Mass., June 26, 1922. Student, St. John's Sem., Mass. Ordained priest, Roman Catholic Ch. 1947. Rector Pope John XXIII Sem. for Delayed Vocations, 1969-73; ordained titular bishop of Penafiel and aux. bishop Diocese of Boston, 1975—. Office: Archdiocese Boston 58 Blaney St Swampscott MA 01907-2559

MULCAHY, ROBERT EDWARD, management consultant; b. Cambridge, Mass., Mar. 2, 1932; s. George Frances and Hazel (Douglas) M.; m. Ethel Walworth, Nov. 14, 1953; children: Linda, Scott, Steven, Susan. B.S., Lowell Textile Inst., 1953. With Allied Chem. Corp., Morristown, N.J., 1953—; from engr. to mktg. mgr. Nat. Aniline div. Allied Corp., 1953-63, from dir. indsl. mktg. to v.p.-mktg. Fibers div., 1963-69, asst. to group v.p., corporate office, 1969, v.p. and gen. mgr.-consumer group Fabricated Products div., 1969-71, pres. Fibers div., 1971-74, group v.p., 1974-75, pres., dir., 1975-79, asst. to chmn. and dir., 1979-80; sr. assoc. The Corp. Dir., Inc., N.Y.C., 1981-83; pres. Counselors to Mgmt. Inc., 1984—.

MULCAHY, ROBERT WILLIAM, lawyer; b. Milw., Jan. 11, 1951; s. T. Larry and Mary Margaret (Chambers) M.; m. Mary M. Andrews, Aug. 3, 1974; children: Molly, Kathleen, Margaret, Michael. BS, Marquette U., 1973, JD, 1976. Staff atty. NLRB, Milw., 1976-79; ptnr. Mulcahy & Wherry, S.C., Milw., 1979-90, Michael, Best & Friedrich, Milw., 1990—; bd. dirs. WERC Coun. on Mcpl. Collective Bargaining, 1990-93. Co-author: Comparable Worth: A Negotiator's Guide, Public Sector Labor Relations in Wisconsin, Strike Prevention and Control Handbook. Bd. dirs. Milw. Repertory Theater, 1993—, Charles Allis/Villa Terrace, 1991—; chmn. St. Monica Parish Coun., 1992—; mem. Whitefish Bay Police and Fire Commn.; divsn. chmn. United Performing Arts Fund, 1993-94. Mem. ABA, State Bar Wis. (chair labor sect. 1986-87), Milw. Bar Assn. (co-chair labor sect. 1988—), Nat. Assn. Counties, Nat. Pub. Employers Labor Rels. Assn., Wis. Counties Assn., Indsl. Rels. Rsch. Assn., Mgmt. Resources Assn., Milw. Area Mcpl. Employers Assn. Office: Michael Best & Friedrich 100 E Wisconsin Ave Milwaukee WI 53202-4108

MULCKHUYSE, JACOB JOHN, energy conservation and environmental consultant; b. Utrecht, The Netherlands, July 21, 1922; came to U.S., 1982; s. Lambertus D. and Aagje (Van Geyn) M.; m. Cornelia Jacoba Wentink, Jan. 17, 1953; children: Jacobien, Hans, Dieuwke, Linda, Marlies. MSc, U. Amsterdam (the Netherlands), 1952, PhD, 1960. Dir. Chemisch-Farmaceutische Fabriek Hamu, the Netherlands, 1951-57; tech. asst. mgr. Polak & Schwarz (now IFF), the Netherlands, 1957-60; asst. tech. mgr. Albatros Superphosphate Fabrieken, the Netherlands, 1960-61; tech. mgr. for overseas subsidiaries Verenigde Kunstmestfabrieken, the Netherlands, 1961-64, gen. mgr. process engring. dept., 1964-70; dept. head process engring. dept. Unie van Kunstmestfabrieken, the Netherlands, 1970-82; sr. chem. engr. World Bank, Washington, 1982-83, sr. cons. chem. engr., 1983-87; ind. cons. environ. engring. World Bank and several cons. firms, 1987—. Author: (with Heath and Venkataraman) The Potential for Energy Efficiency in the Fertilizer Industry, 1985, (with Gamba and Caplin) Industrial Energy Rationalization in Developing Countries and Constraints in Energy Conservation, 1990, Process Safety Analysis: Incentive for the Identification of Inherent Process Hazards, 1992, Energy Efficiency and Conservation in the Developing World, 1992; editor: Environmental Balance of the Netherlands, 1972. Mem. AICE, Royal Dutch Chem. Soc., Fertilizer Soc. (pres. 1969-70), Internat. Inst. for Energy Conservation (bd. dirs. 1990-93), Rotary. Avocations: philosophy, tennis, advising developing countries. Home: 53 Ponderosa Ln Palmyra VA 22963-2405

MULDAUR, DIANA CHARLTON, actress; b. N.Y.C., Aug. 19, 1938; d. Charles Edward Arrowsmith and Alice Patricia (Jones) M.; m. James Mitchell Vickery, July 26, 1969 (dec. 1979); m. Robert J. Dozier, Oct. 11, 1981. B.A., Sweet Briar Coll., 1960. Actress appearing in: Off-Broadway theatrical prodns., summer stock, Broadway plays including A Very Rich Woman, 1963-68; guest appearances on TV in maj. dramatic shows; appeared on: TV series Survivors, 1970-71, McCloud, 1971-73, Tony Randall Show, 1976, Black Beauty, 1978; star: TV series Born Free, 1974, Hizzoner, 1979, Fitz & Bones, 1980, Star Trek: The Next Generation, 1988-89; NBC miniseries and TV series A Year in the Life, 1986; TV movie Murder in Three Acts, The Return of Sam McCloud, 1989; TV series L.A. Law, 1989-91; motion picture credits include McQ, The Lawyer, The Other, One More Train to Rob, Mati, etc. Bd. dirs. Los Angeles chpt. Asthma and Allergy Found. Am.; bd. advisors Nat. Ctr. Film and Video Preservation, John F. Kennedy Ctr. Performing Arts, 1986. Recipient 13th Ann. Commendation award Am. Women in Radio and TV, 1988, Disting. Alumnae award Sweet Briar Coll., 1988. Mem. Acad. Motion Picture Arts and Scis., Screen Actors Guild (dir. 1978), Acad. TV Arts and Scis. (exec. bd., pres. 1983-85), Conservation Soc. Martha's Vineyard Island. Office: The Artists Group Ltd 1930 Century Park W Ste 403 Los Angeles CA 90067-6803

MULDER, DAVID S., cardiovascular surgeon; b. Eston, Sask., Can., July 28, 1938; s. Peter and Laura (Lovie) M.; m. Norma D. Johnston, Aug. 19, 1961; children—Scott D., Lizabeth J. John C. M.D., U. Sask., 1962; M.Sc. McGill U., 1964. Intern, resident in surgery Montreal Gen. Hosp., McGill U., 1963-67; resident in cardiac surgery U. Iowa, 1967-69; surgeon-in-chief Montreal Gen. Hosp., 1977—; prof. surgery McGill U., 1979—; chmn. dept. surgery, 1993—. Contbr. articles to med. jours. Fellow Royal Coll. Surgeons Can., ACS; mem. Univ. Surgeons, Am. Assn. Surgery of Trauma, Am. Assn. Thoracic Surgery, Soc. Thoracic Surgeons. Conservative. Home: 76 Sunnyside Ave, Westmount, PQ Canada H34 1C2 Office: Montreal Gen Hosp, Room D-6-136, Montreal, PQ Canada H3G 1A4

MULDER, DENNIS MARLIN, religious organization executive; b. Renville, Minn., Feb. 15, 1943; s. Lambert and Ruby (Gerdes) M.; m. Sharon Kaye Meyer, Aug. 16, 1963; children: Michael Glen, Kendall James, Eric Scott. BA, Calvin Coll., Grand Rapids, Mich., 1965; BDiv, Calvin Sem., 1969. Missionary Christian Ref. Bd. World Missions,, Republic of China, 1969-76; dir. Asian ministries The Bible League, South Holland, Ill. 1976-85, chief exec. officer, 1985—. Office: The Bible League 16801 Van Dam Rd South Holland IL 60473-2658

MULDER, DONALD GERRIT, surgeon, educator; b. Hospers, Iowa, 1924. M.D., Johns Hopkins U., 1952. Diplomate Am. Bd. Surgery, Am. Bd. Thoracic Surgery (chmn. 1983-85). Intern Johns Hopkins Hosp., Balt., 1952-53, resident 1953-55; resident Calif. Med. Ctr., Los Angeles, 1955-57; instr. surgery U. Calif, Los Angeles, 1957-58, asst. prof., 1958-64, assoc. prof., 1964-69, prof., 1969—. Fellow ACS; mem. AMA. Office: Univ Calif Sch Medicine Los Angeles CA 90024

MULDER, DONALD WILLIAM, physician, educator; b. Rehobath, N.Mex., June 30, 1917; s. Jacob D. and Gertrude (Hofstra) M.; m. Gertrude Ellens, Feb. 22, 1943. B.A., Calvin Coll., 1940; M.D., Marquette U., 1943; M.S., U. Mich., 1946. Intern Butterworth Hosp., Grand Rapids, Mich. 1943-44; resident U. Hosp., Ann Arbor, Mich., 1944-46, Denver, 1947-49; asst. prof. medicine in neurology U. Colo., 1949-50; prof. neurology Mayo Found. Faculty, 1964—, Mayo Med. Sch., 1973—; cons. neurology Mayo Clinic, Rochester, Minn., 1950—; gov. Mayo Clinic, 1950—, chmn. dept. neurology, 1966-71, pres. staff, 1971—, Andersen prof. neurology, 1977-83, prof. emeritus, 1983—; sci. advisor ALS. Contbr. articles on neuromuscular disease to sci. jours. Ret. capt. USNR. Recipient Disting. Alumni award Calvin Coll., 1992. Fellow A.C.P., Am. Acad. Neurology; mem. Am. Neurol. Assn. (hon.). Home: 331 75th St NW Rochester MN 55901-8868 Office: 200 1st St SW Rochester MN 55905-0001

MULDER, EDWIN GEORGE, minister, church official; b. Raymond, Minn., Mar. 25, 1929; s. Gerrit and Etta (Dresselhuis) M.; m. Luella Rozeboom, June 14, 1952; children: Timothy, Mary, Mark, Elizabeth. BA, Cen. Coll., Pella, Iowa, 1951, DD (hon.), 1979; BD, Western Theol. Sem., Holland, Mich., 1954. Ordained to ministry Ref. Ch. in Am., 1954. Pastor Reformed Ch. in Am., 1954-83, v.p. particular N.J. Synod, 1975-76, pres. particular N.J. Synod, 1976-77, v.p., then pres. Gen. Synod, 1978-80, gen. sec., 1983-94; chmn. bd. dirs. Religion in Am. Life, 1995—; chair U.S. Ch. Leaders, 1989-94; mem. exec. com. World Alliance Reformed Chs., 1990—, Nat. Coun. Chs., 1991; mem. cen. com. World Coun. Chs., 1991-94. Trustee Cen. Coll., 1968-94. Office: Ref Ch in Am 475 Riverside Dr New York NY 10115-0001

MULDER, ELDON PAUL, state legislator, real estate agent; b. Sioux Center, Iowa, Aug. 28, 1957; s. Theron John and Marcia Arlene (Schut) M.; m. Wendy Anne Chamberlain, Aug. 1, 1985; children: Corey Anne, Mackenzie Anne. BA, Ctrl. Coll., Pella, Iowa, 1980; MA, U. Colo., 1982. Lic. real estate agt., Alaska. Campaign mgr. Rep. Congl. Campaign from 6th Dist., Sioux Center, 1983-84; legis. aide Alaska State Senate, Juneau, 1985-92; owner Mulder gfmt. Svcs., Anchorage, Alaska, 1989—; real estate agt. Penco Devel., Anchorage, 1993-94; mem. Alaska Ho. of Reps., Juneau, 1993—; appraiser trainee Appraisal Co. Alaska, 1994—. Bd. dirs. Armed Svcs. YMCA, Anchorage, 1992—, Alaska Spl. Olympics, Anchorage, 1993—. Mem. NRA, Anchorage Sports Assn., Assn. U.S. Army, Nat. Rep. Legis. Assn., Alaska Golf Assn., Kenai River Sportfish Assn. Avocations: golf, fishing, basketball, home remodeling, antiques. Home: PO Box 140711 Anchorage AK 99514 Office: Alaska State Ho of Reps State Capitol Rm 116 Juneau AK 99801

MULDER, GARY, religious publisher. Office: CRC Publ 2850 Kalamazoo Ave SE Grand Rapids MI 49560

MULDER, PATRICIA MARIE, educator; b. South Bend, Ind., Dec. 28, 1944; d. Ervin James and Carmen Virginia (Sheeley) Anderson; m. James R. Mulder, Dec. 27, 1964; children: Todd Alan, Scott Robert. BA, Western Mich. U., 1967. Freelance writer, photographer Berrien Springs, Mich., 1980—; tchr. Eau Claire (Mich.) Pub. Schs., 1969-70; staff writer, sales rep. Jour. Era, Berrien Springs, 1979-81; sales rep. Berrien County Record, Buchana, Mich., 1981-82; account exec. WHFB Radio Palladium Pub. Co., St. Joseph, Mich., 1982-86; substitute tchr. Berrien County Intermediate Dist., 1986-89; instr. Southwestern Mich. Coll., Dowagiac, 1989—. Editor The Positive Image newsletter, 1980—, The F Stop, 1982-90; author: Poetry Anthologies, 1989—; staff writer Decision Point, 1988-89; newsletter editor Fernwood Nature Photographers, 1980—. Named Emerging Artist Ind. Coun. for the Arts, 1989, Honor award Southwestern Coun. of Camera Clubs, 1988, Photographer of the Yr. Berrien County Photographic Artists, 1987, 90. Mem. Nat. Authors Registry, Southwestern Mich. Coun. Cambera Clubs, Berrien Springs Camera Club (v.p 1980—), Meth. Profl. Women (sec. 1990—), Berrien County Artists (v.p 1986), Berrien County Photographic Artists (v.p. 1984). Methodist. Avocations: writing, photography, oil painting, watercolor painting. Home: 10252 Castner Dr Berrien Springs MI 49103-9602 Office: Southwestern Mich Coll 58900 Cherry Grove Rd # 316L Dowagiac MI 49047-9793

MULDER, ROBERT UDO, nuclear engineering educator, researcher; b. Sao Paulo, Brazil, Jan. 23, 1952; came to U.S., 1962; s. Walter Johan Jacob and Annemarie Gerda (Hendel) M.; m. Nailda Xavier Secundo, Aug. 10, 1973; children: Luival Xavier, Derrick Jason. ME in Nuclear Engring., U. Va., 1976, PhD in Nuclear Engring., 1981. Group mgr. Comissao Nacional Energia Nuclear, Rio, Brazil, 1981-83; resident asst. prof. nuclear engring., reactor dir. U. Va., Charlottesville, 1984—; Cons. S.A.I.C., 1991. Contbr. articles to Nuclear Tech. Jour., Nuclear Sci. and Engring. Jour. Mem. Am. Nuclear Soc., Am. Soc. for Engring. Edn. Lutheran. Office: U Va Dept Nuclear Engring Nuclear Reactor Facility Charlottesville VA 22903

MULDOON, BRIAN, lawyer; b. Phila., Oct. 7, 1947; s. Joseph Patrick and Isabella K. (O'Flynn) M.; m. Andrea K. Bloom, Apr. 1, 1984; 1 child, Lily Bloom. BA, Lafayette Coll., 1969; postgrad., U. Pa., 1969; JD, Temple U. 1978. Bar: Colo. 1978, U.S. Dist. Ct. Colo. 1978, U.S. Ct. Appeals (10th cir.) 1978. Law clk. to justice Colo. Supreme Ct., Denver, 1978-79; assoc. Holland & Hart, Denver, 1979-84, ptnr., 1984—; mem. Colo. Grievance Hearing Bd., 1983—. Contbg. author: Bloom, Lender Liability, Practice and Prevention, 1989. Mem. ABA, Assn. Trial Lawyers Am., Colo. Bar Assn., Colo. Trial Lawyers Assn., Denver Bar Assn. (chmn. subcom. on alternative dispute resolution 1985). Avocations: basketball, cycling, mountain climbing. Home: 337 Emerson St Denver CO 80218-3705 Office: Holland & Hart 555 17th St Ste 2900 Denver CO 80202-3979

MULDOON, FRANCIS CREIGHTON, Canadian federal judge; b. Winnipeg, Manitoba, Canada, Aug. 3, 1930; s. William John and Laura Grace (Meredith) M.; m. M. Lucille Shirtliff, Aug. 6, 1955; 2 children. BA, U. Manitoba, 1952, LLB, 1956. Cert. barrister, solicitor, notary pub. Lawyer Monnin, Grafton, Deniset & Co., Winnipeg, Man., 1956-70; chmn. Manitoba Law Reform Commn., Winnipeg, 1970-77; v.p. Law Reform Commn. Can., Ottawa, 1977-78, pres., 1978-83; judge Fed. Ct. Can., Ottawa, 1983—; Ct. Martial Appeal Ct., Ottawa, 1983—; Bencher Law Soc. Manitoba, Winnipeg, 1968-71. Contbr. articles to profl. jours. President Children Aid Soc. Winnipeg, 1969-70, Manitoba Medico-Legal Soc., Winnipeg, 1973-77. Lt. Can. Army, 1952-60. Disting. Svc. Manitoba Bar Assn., 1987; hon. mem. Bar U.S. Ct. Milit. Appeals, 1991. Mem. Med. Legal Soc. Ottawa-Carleton (co-founder), St. Paul's Coll. (hon.). Roman Catholic. Avocations: reading, bicycling, public speaking. Office: Fed Ct Can, Kent & Wellington Sts, Ottawa, ON Canada K1A 0H9

MULDOON, ROBERT JOSEPH, JR., lawyer; b. Somerville, Mass., Nov. 16, 1936; s. Robert Joseph and Catherine Eileen (Hurley) M.; m. Barbara Joyce Mooney, Aug. 24, 1968; children: Andrew Robert, Catherine Lane, Timothy John. A.B., Boston Coll., 1960, MA, 1961, LL.B., 1965. Bar: Mass. 1965, U.S. Tax Ct 1966, U.S. Supreme Ct 1970. Law clk. Supreme Jud. Ct. Mass., 1965-66; assoc. Withington, Cross, Park & Groden, Boston, 1966-71; ptnr. Withington, Cross, Park & Groden, 1972-82, Sherin and Lodgen, Boston, 1982—; mem. Bd. Bar Examiners Mass.; chmn. Nat. Conf.

Bar Examiners, 1985-86; prs. Mass. Continuing Legal Edn., Inc., 1992-94. Trustee Boston Coll. High Sch., 1990—. Fellow Am. Coll. Trial Lawyers; mem. ABA, Am. Law Inst., Boston Bar Assn., Curtis Club. Office: Sherin & Lodgen 100 Summer St Boston MA 02110-2109

MULDOON, THOMAS LYMAN, writer; b. Sioux Falls, S.D., Apr. 23, 1945; s. Lyman Thomas and Margaret Mary (Wallace) M.; m. Kathryn Lee Harmon, June 30, 1973; m. Kathryn Muldoon. B in Polit. Sci., Merrimack Coll., 1967; MS in Mass. Comm., Fla. State U., 1973, MA in English, 1994. Bur. chief Palm Beach Post, 1970; gen. reporter Daytona Beach News-Jour., 1973; contract editor Frankfurt, Germany, 1973-74; reporter North Dade County bur. Miami Herald, 1977-78; journalist Nat. Enquirer, 1978-89; travel editor Petite Mag., 1992; tchr. journalism, TV journalism, cinema, TV prodn. Fla. State U., 1971-73. Contract writer: Football Little Big Leaguers, 1990, More Baseball Little Big Leagues, 1991; freelance writer newspapers and mags.; appearances on local TV shows; interviewee nat. programs; producer TV programs for local ednl. TV; scriptwriter Future Shock; screenwriter 4 movie scripts. Polit. press sec. Mayor Kevin White, Boston, 1974-75; pub. affairs dir. Boston Community Sch., 1975; campaign pres sec. State Rep. Joseph Timilty 1975; pub. affairs dir. Barry U., Miami, 1976-77; sports info. dir. Quantico Marines football and basketball programs, 1968. With USMC, 1968-70, Vietnam.

MULFORD, DAVID CAMPBELL, finance company executive; b. Rockford, Ill., June 27, 1937; s. Robert Lewis Mulford and Theodora Henie Countryman; m. Jeannie Louise Simmons, Oct. 19, 1985; children: Robert Ian, Edward Maitland. BA Econs., Lawrence U., 1959; postgrad., U. Cape Town, South Africa, 1960; MBA Polit. Sci., Boston U., 1962; PhD, Oxford U., 1965; LLD (hon.), Lawrence U., 1984. White House fellow Dept. Treas., Washington, 1965-66, under asst. sec. internat. affairs, 1984-89; dir. White Weld & Co., N.Y.C. and London, 1966-74; sr. investment advisor Saudi Arabian Monetary Agy., Riyadh, 1974-84; asst. sec. internat. affairs Dept. of Treas., 1984-89; under sec. treasury internat. affairs U.S. Treas. Dept., Washington, 1989-92; vice chmn. First Boston Corp., N.Y.C., 1992-93; chmn., CEO Credit Suisse First Boston, London, 1993—. Author: Northern Rhodesia General Election, 1962, Zambia: The Politics of Independence, 1967. Trustee Lawrence U., 1986—. Decorated Legion d'Honneur, 1990; recipient Order of May Merit Pres. Argentina, 1993; Rotary Internat. fellow Oxford U., U. Cape Town, 1961-62, Woodrow Wilson fellow Boston U., Oxford U., 1962, Ford Found. fellow St. Anthony's Coll., Oxford, 1963-65; named Disting. Alumni Boston U., 1992; Disting. scholar Ctr. Strategic and Internat. Studies, Washington, 1993—. Mem. Coun. Fgn. Rels., White House Fellows Assn., Metropolis Club (Washington). Republican. Home: 301 S St Asaph St Alexandria VA 22314-3745 Office: Credit Suisse First Boston Ltd, 1 Cabot Square, London E14 4QJ, England

MULGREW, KATHERINE KIERNAN, actress; b. Dubuque, Iowa, Apr. 29, 1955; d. Thomas James and Joan Virginia (Kiernan) M.; m. Robert Harry Egan; children: Ian Thomas, Alexander James. Student, Northwestern U., U. Iowa; AA, NYU, 1976; studies with Stella Adler; trained at, Tyrone Guthrie Theater, Mpls. Formerly waitress and model. Played role of Emily in, Am. Shakespeare Festival's prodn. of Our Town; other stage appearances include Othello, Hartman Theatre, Stamford, Conn., Three Sisters, N.Y.C. Center, The Plow and the Stars, Irish Rebel Theatre, Orpheus Descending, Circle in the Square, Another Part of the Forest, Major Barbara, The Ballad of Soapy Smith and The Misanthrope, Seattle Repertory Theatre, Cat on a Hot Tin Roof, Syracuse Stage, Measure for Measure and Hedda Gabler, Mark Taper Forum, White Liars & Black Comedy, Roundabout Theatre Company; in films Lovespell, Remo Williams: The Adventure Begins, Lovespell, A Stranger is Watching, 1982, Throw Momma from the Train, 1987; former regular on daytime TV serial Ryan's Hope; appeared in TV mini-series The Word, Manions of America; in TV film Jennifer: A Woman's Story; star TV series Kate Loves a Mystery (formerly Mrs. Columbo), 1979, Heart Beat, Star Trek: Voyager, 1995—; TV spl. A Time for Miracles, 1980, Carly Mills; guest appearances on TV series Cheers, St. Elsewhere; actress TV shows Mother Seaton, Roses Are For the Rich, Roots: The Gift. Address: care Stan Rosenfield Pub Rels 9595 Wilshire Blvd Ste 911 Beverly Hills CA 90212-2511

MULHERN, JOHN DAVID, former academic dean, educator; b. Milton, Mass., Dec. 11, 1928; s. John Henry and Mary Cecilia (Lehan) M.; m. Margaret Jane Gilligan, Jan. 24, 1959; children: Helen E., Mary T., John L., Thomas P., Margaret J. A.B., Boston Coll., 1950; M.Ed., State Coll., Bridgewater, Mass., 1955; Ph.D., U. Wis., 1960. Asst. prof. U. Wis. Madison, 1960-61, Boston Coll., Chestnut Hill, Mass., 1961-62, Okla. State U., Stillwater, 1962-63; dir. student teaching Marquette U., Milw., 1963-67; assoc. dean profl. studies SUNY Coll., Buffalo, 1967-76; dean Coll. Edn. Eastern Mich. U., Ypsilanti, 1976-80; dean Coll. U. S.C., Columbia, 1980-87, prof. ednl. adminstrn. and policies, 1987-93; prof. ednl. adminstrn. U. Tex.-Pan. Am., Edinburg, 1993-95; team leader Asian devel. Bank Lower Secondary Edn. Project, Jakarta, Indonesia, 1995—; evaluation bd. mem. Nat. Council Accreditation Tchr. Edn., Washington, 1972-77. Author (with others) Educational Psychology workbook, 1967; contbr. articles to profl. jours. Served with USAF, 1950-54. Mem. Internat. Coun. Edn. Tchrs., Am. Assn. Coll. Tchrs. Edn., Am. Ednl. Rsch. Assn., Assn. Tchrs. Educators. Roman Catholic. Office: c/o EDC 1250 24th St NW Ste 300 Washington DC 20037

MULHERN, JOSEPH PATRICK, lawyer; b. Chgo., Sept. 18, 1921; s. Joseph P. Sr. and Catherine C. (O'Brien) M.; m. Mary McGrath, June 28, 1947; children: Joseph P., Brian J. BE, Chgo. Tchr.'s Coll., 1946; JD cum laude, DePaul U., 1951. Bar: Ill. 1951. Assoc. McDermott, Will & Emery, Chgo., 1952-56, ptnr., 1956-89. Served with U.S. Army, 1942-46. Decorated Bronze Star. Mem. ABA. Republican. Roman Catholic. Clubs: Union League (Chgo.); Hinsdale (Ill.) Golf. Avocations: gardening, golfing. Home: 123 N Bruner St Hinsdale IL 60521-3022 also: 56 Grey Wing Pt Naples FL 33962-8405

MULHOLLAN, PAIGE ELLIOTT, university president emeritus; b. Ft. Smith, Ark., Dec. 10, 1934; s. Paige Elwood and Ruth Dickinson (Berry) M.; m. Mary Bess Flack, July 8, 1956; children: Paige E. Jr., Kelly V. BBA, U. Ark., 1956, MA in History, 1962; PhD in History, U. Tex., 1966. From asst. to assoc. prof. history U. Ark., Fayetteville, 1963-70; assoc. dean arts and scis. Kans. State U., Manhattan, 1970-73; dean arts and scis. U. Okla., Norman, 1973-78; provost, v.p. acad. affairs Ariz. State U., Tempe, 1978-81, exec. v.p. 1981-85; pres. Wright State U. Dayton, Ohio, 1985-94; ret., 1994; cons. examiner North Ctrl. Assn., Chgo., 1972-94; chair Interuniv. Coun. Ohio, 1993-94. Mem. Okla. Humanities Coun., 1974-77, chmn., 1975-77; bd. dirs. Pub. Sta. WPTD-TV, Dayton Art Inst., Miami Valley Rsch. Found.; mem. adv. com. Air Force ROTC, 1989-93. 1st lt. U.S. Army, 1956-57. Mem. nat. Assn. State Univs. and Land Grant Colls. (commn. on arts and scis. 1973-78, chmn. 1974-76), Am. Assn. State Colls. and Univs. (bd. dirs. 1991-92), Coun. Colls. Arts and Scis. (bd. dirs. 1976-78, sec.-treas. 1977-78), Dayton Area C. of C., Ohio Coll. Assn. (pres. 1989). Avocations: jogging, sailing, birdwatching. Home: 24 Big Woods Dr Hilton Head Island SC 29926

MULHOLLAND, JOHN HENRY, physician, educator; b. Charlottesville, Va., May 24, 1932; s. Henry B. and Elizabeth (Brown) M.; m. Anne P.C., Sept. 1, 1956; children: Anne Randol, David Bearden, Jeffrey Bolton. BA, U. Va., 1955; MD, Johns Hopkins U., 1959. Diplomate Am. Bd. Internal Medicine; lic. physician, N.C., Md. Asst. prof. medicine Johns Hopkins U., Balt., 1966—; co-dir. nurse clin. assoc. program Union Meml. Hosp., Balt., 1972-90, gen. med. attending, 1968—, infections disease cons., 1968—; asst. prof. medicine U. Md., Balt., 1976-85, clin. assoc. prof. medicine, 1985—. Author: Bugs and Drugs-Antibiotic Guidelines, 1970; contbr. numerous articles to profl. jours. Fellow ACP (chmn. arrangements com. 1975—, nat. chmn. group ins. programs sbcomm. 1986-87, membership policy com. 1986-87, postgrad. courses subcom. 1990); mem. AMA, Am. Clin. and Climatological Assn. (v.p. 1990), Md. Soc. Internal Medicine (mem. coun. 1976-78, 82-86), Md. Hosp. Edn. Inst. (mem. steering com. quality assurance/risk mgmt. project 1980—, mem. quality assurance/risk mgmt. tech. adv. com. 1985—), Balt. City Med. Soc. (nominating com. 1984—, chmn. liaison com. 1991—), Infectious Disease Soc. Am., Home: 1317 Walnut Hill Ln Baltimore MD 21204

MULHOLLAND, KENNETH LEO, JR., health care facility administrator; b. Chgo., July 16, 1943; s. Kenneth Leo Sr. and Virginia May (Groble) M.; m. Betty Lou Bledsoe, Feb. 18, 1978; children: Arthur G. Pope, Michelle Rae Pope. BS, Loyola U., 1969; M in Mgmt., Northwestern U., 1974. RN. Nurse VA Med. Ctr., Chgo., 1970-72, health care adminstr. tng., 1972-74; assoc. dir. tng VA Med. Ctr., Lexington, Ky., 1976-77; assoc. dir. VA Med. Ctr., Muskogee, Okla., 1977-79; assoc. dir. VA Med. Ctr., Knoxville, Iowa, 1979-81, acting dir., 1981; assoc. dir. VA Med. Ctr., Richmond, Va., 1981-83; dir. VA Med. Ctr., Bronx, N.Y., 1983-85, Memphis, 1985—. Pres. Memphis Area Fed. Exec. Assn., 1988—; bd. dirs. Memphis chpt. ARC, 1985—, Health Systems Agy., Memphis, 1985-87. Recipient Presdl. Rank award for meritorious executive, 1989. Mem. Memphis Area Fedl. Exec. Assn. Lodge: Rotary. Home: 2024 Thorncroft Dr Germantown TN 38138-4017 Office: VA Med Ctr 1030 Jefferson Ave Memphis TN 38104-2127

MULHOLLAND, ROBERT EDGE, broadcasting company executive; b. Hartford, Conn., Sept. 27, 1933; s. Hugh Andrew and Gertrude (Edge) M.; 1 child, Todd Andrew. B.S. in Journalism, Northwestern U., 1955, M.S., 1956. News writer, producer Sta. WGN, Chgo., 1958-61; news writer NBC, Chgo., 1961-64; producer Huntley-Brinkley News, NBC, Washington, 1964-67; dir. news Sta. KNBC, Los Angeles, 1967-71; exec. producer NBC Nightly News, N.Y.C., 1971-74; exec. v.p. NBC News, N.Y.C., 1974-77; pres. NBC TV Network, 1977-81; pres., chief operating officer NBC, 1981-84, broadcast cons., 1984-86, dir. TV info. office, 1986-88; prof. journalism Northwestern U., Evanston, Ill., 1988-93. Served with AUS, 1956-58. Mem. TV Acad. Arts and Scis. Presbyterian.

MULHOLLAND, S. GRANT, urologist; b. Springfield, Ohio, Sept. 1, 1936; s. Stanford Wallace and Florence Kathryn (Grant) M.; m. Ruth Fritz, Aug. 21, 1961; children: David, Michael, Mark, John. BS, Dickinson Coll., Carlisle, Pa., 1958; MD, Temple U., 1962; MS, U. Va., 1966. Intern Reading (Pa.) Hosp., 1962-63; resident in surgery Tampa (Fla.) Gen. Hosp., 1963-64; resident in urology U. Va., Charlottesville, 1964-68; urologist U.S. Naval Hosp., St. Albans, N.Y., 1968-70; epidemiologist Grad. Hosp. of U. Pa., Phila., 1971-74; asst. urologist, 1970-77; chief urologist Phila. Gen. Hosp., 1972-77; asst. surgeon Children's Hosp. Phila., 1974-77; urologist Hosp. U. Pa., Phila., 1974-77; chmn. dept. urology Thomas Jefferson U. Hosp., Phila., 1977—; cons. VA Ctr., Phila., 1974-77; cons. urologist Lankenau Hosp., Bryn Mawr Hosp., VA Hosp., Wilmington, Del., 1977—. Author: Urinary Tract Infection, 1990, Bladder Infections, 1991, (with others) Prostate Cancer, 1992. Lt. comdr. USN, 1968-70. Grantee NIH, Jefferson U., 1989. Fellow ACS; mem. Am. Urol. Assn. (pres. 1988-89), Phila. Urol. Assn. (pres. 1988-89), Internat. Soc. Urology, AMA, Phila. Country Club (Gladwyne, Pa.). Republican. Avocations: golf, fishing, skiing. Home: 1050 Sentry Ln Gladwyne PA 19035-1009 Office: Jefferson Med Coll 1025 Walnut St # 1112 Philadelphia PA 19107

MULHOLLAND, TERENCE JOHN (TERRY MULHOLLAND), professional baseball player; b. Uniontown, Pa., Mar. 9, 1963. Student, Marietta Coll. Pitcher San Francisco Giants, 1984-89, Phila. Phillies, 1989-94, N.Y. Yankees, 1994—; mem. Nat. League All-Star Team, 1993. Pitched no-hit victory, Aug. 15, 1990. Office: NY Yankees Yankee Stadium E 161st St and River Ave Bronx NY 10451*

MULICH, STEVE FRANCIS, safety engineer; b. Kansas City, Mo., Apr. 23, 1934; s. Stephen Francis and Mary Margret (Mish) M.; m. m. Apr. 5, 1974 (div.); children: Michael Francis, Mischelle Marie, Merko Mathew, Cherie Regina, Michael Klaus, Gary John, Josette Marie. BS in Gen. Sci., U. Notre Dame, 1956. Phys. chemist high altitude combustion Army Rocket and Guided Missile Agy., Huntsville, Ala., 1957-59; ballistics facility mgr. Aerojet Gen. Corp., Sacramento, 1960-65; chief engr. minute man penetration aids MB Assoc., Bollinger Canyon, Calif., 1968-72; lab mgr. hazardous materials and ballistics Martin Marietta, Waterton, Colo., 1966-75; plant mgr. smog sampler collectors mfg. Gen. Tex. Corp., Santa Clara, Calif., 1976-77; chief engr. auto airbag plant mgr. Talley Industries, Mesa, Ariz., 1978-84; prin. engr. engring. unit mgr. high energy test labs. FMC Corp., Mpls., 1984-95; v.p. engring. NEI Corp., Rock Island, Ill., 1995—. Author: Solid Rocket Technology, 1967; inventor stun gun, combustion augemented plasma gun, semiconductor initiator. With U.S. Army, 1957-59. Recipient Acad. Achievement award Bausch & Lomb, Kenosha, Wis., 1952. Mem. IEEE, AIAA (assoc.), Am. Def. Preparedness Assn., Navy League. Avocations: skiing, sailing, climbing, camping, hiking. Home: 1325 104th Pl NE Minneapolis MN 55434-3620 Office: NEI Corp Rock Island IL 61204

MULICK, EDWARD JAMES, orthodontist; b. Missoula, Mont., June 2, 1938; s. Edward Claude Mulick and Neta I. (McFadden) Marolich; m. Jeanne Mae Christison, Aug. 13, 1960; children: Edward Michael, Susan Marie, Michelle Ann, Michael John, Patrick Sean. BS, Gonzaga U., 1960; DDS, Creighton U., 1963; MS, U. Nebr., 1970. Gen. practice dentistry Priest River, Idaho, 1963-68; practice dentistry specializing in orthodontics Boise, Idaho, 1970—; cons. Boise State U. Vocat. Sch., 1978—, Am. Inst. Health, Boise, 1986—. Fellow Internat. Coll. Dentists; mem. ADA, Am. Assn. Orthodontists, Idaho Dental Assn. (pres. 1986), SW Idaho Dist. Dental Assn. (pres. 1982-83), Idaho State Orthodontic Assn. Republican. Roman Catholic. Lodge: Kiwanis (pres. 1976). Avocations: fly fishing, hunting, golf, skiing. Home: 4001 Delmonte Dr Boise ID 83704-3514 Office: Boise Orthodontic Assocs 7373 Emerald St Boise ID 83704-8624

MULKEY, JACK CLARENDON, library director; b. Shreveport, La., Oct. 31, 1939; s. Jack Youmans and Hilda Lillian (Beatty) M.; m. Mary Lynn Shepherd, Jan. 30, 1971; 1 child, Mary Clarendon. B.A., Centenary Coll., 1961; postgrad (Rotary scholar), U. Dijon, France, 1961-62, Duke U. Law Sch., 1962-63; M.S., La. State U., 1969. Jr. exec. Lykes Bros. S.S. Co., 1964-66; asst. dir. admissions Centenary Coll. of La., 1966-67; head reference services and acquisitions Shreveport Pub. Library, 1968-71; dir. Green Gold Library System of N.W. La., 1971-73; mgmt. cons. Miss. Library Commn., 1973-74, asst. dir., 1974-76, dir., 1976-78; dir. Jackson Met. Library System, 1978-85; assoc. dir. Ark. State Library, 1986—; adj. prof. U. So. Miss. Grad. Sch. Library Sci., 1979—; treas., bd. dirs. Southeastern Library Network (SOLINET), 1985-86; cons. in field; mem. White House Conf. Taskforce on Libraries and Info. Services, 1980—. Mem. Miss. Govs. Conf. on Libraries, 1979; chmn. Miss. delegation White House Conf. on Libraries, 1979; hon. del. White House Conf. on Librs., 1991. Served with USAF, 1963-64. Mem. ALA (chmn. state libr. agy. sect. 1995-97), Southeastern Libr. Assn., Miss. Libr. Assn. (pres. 1981-82), Ark. Libr. Assn. (exec. bd. 1994-96), Chief Officers of State Libr. Agys., Phi Alpha Delta, Beta Phi Mu, Omicron Delta Kappa, Phi Kappa Phi. Episcopalian. Home: 1805 Martha Dr Little Rock AR 72212-3840 Office: 1 Capitol Mall Little Rock AR 72201

MULL, GALE W., lawyer; b. Hillsdale, Mich., Sept. 8, 1945; s. Wayne E. and Vivien M. (Bavin) M.; m. Holly Ann Allen, Aug. 2, 1969 (div. Nov. 1983); 1 child, Carter B.; m. Jeanne Anne Haughey, Aug. 18, 1985. BA, Mich. State U., 1967; MA in Sociology, Ind. U., 1969; JD, Emory U., 1972. Bar: Ga. 1972, U.S. Dist. Ct. (no. dist.) Ga. 1972, U.S. Ct. Appeals (5th cir.) 1973, U.S. Ct. Appeals (11th cir.) 1981. Instr. sociology Clemson (S.C.) U., 1968-69, Spelman Coll., Atlanta, 1969-70; pvt. practice, Atlanta, 1972-75; ptnr. Mull & Sweet, Atlanta, 1975-81; pres. Gale W. Mull, P.C., Atlanta, 1981—; bd. dirs. BOND Community Fed. Credit Union, Atlanta, 1975-81; directing atty. Emory Student Legal Services, Atlanta, 1975-91; Sociology instr. Clemson U., Clemson, S.C., 1968-69, Spelman Coll., Atlanta, Ga., 1969-70. Pres. Inman Park Restoration, Inc., Atlanta, 1972-74, BASS Orgn. for Neighborhood Devel., Inc., 1974-78; mem. Housing Appeals Bd. Atlanta, 1982-88; mem. Mayor's Task Force on Prostitution, 1984-86; bd. dirs. ACLU Ga., 1981-92, sec. bd. dirs., 1983-85, cooperating atty., 1972—; vestry St. John's Episcopal Ch., 1991—; bd. dirs. St. John's Episcopal Day Sch., 1992—. Mem. ABA, Ga. Bar Assn., Atlanta Bar Assn., Lawyers Club Atlanta. Clubs: East Lake Country; Quail Unltd. (bd. dirs., sec. 1984-86). Office: 990 Edgewood Ave NE Atlanta GA 30307-2531

MULL, MARTIN, comedian, singer; b. Chgo., 1943; m. Sandra Baker. Grad., R.I. Sch. Design. Nightclub singer and comedian; recorded albums including Sex and Violins; appeared in TV series Soundstage, Domestic Life, Mary Hartman, Mary Hartman, 1976-77, His & Hers, 1990, Roseanne, (TV movies) The Day My Parents Ran Away, 1993, How the West Was Fun, 1994; star TV series Fernwood Tonight, 1977; guest on TV talk shows; appeared in movies FM, 1977, My Bodyguard, 1980, Serial, 1980, Take This

Job and Shove It, 1981, Mr. Mom, Private School, 1983, Lots of Luck, Clue, 1987, O.C. amd Stiggs, 1987, Home is Where The Heart Is, 1987, Rented Lips, 1988, Cutting Class, 1989, Ski Patrol, 1990, Far Out Man, 1990, Think Big, 1990, Ted & Venus, 1991, Mrs. Doubtfire, 1994; writer cable TV documentary The History of White People in America, also co-author book, 1986; co-writer, host video The History of White People in America: Volume II, 1987; other TV work includes writer, prod., star Candid Camera Christmas Special, 1987, Portrait of a White Marriage. Office: care Agy Performing Arts 9000 W Sunset Blvd Ste 1200 West Hollywood CA 90069-5894*

MULLALEY, ROBERT CHARLES, manufacturing company executive; b. Marion, Iowa, Dec. 31, 1926; s. Harold C. and Blanche A. (McGuire) M.; m. Josephine E. Fiala, Apr. 23, 1949; children: Maureen, Kathleen, Mary, Daniel, Michael, Susan. BA, U. Iowa, 1949, JD, 1951. Bar: Iowa 1951, Tex. 1976. With Collins Radio Co., Richardson, Tex., 1951-75; v.p. adminstrn. Collins Radio Co., 1970-71, sr. v.p., 1971-75; also adv. dir.; v.p. Avantek, Inc., Santa Clara, Calif., 1976-82; bd. dirs. Celeritek, Inc. Author: History of the Mullaleys: A Twelve Hundred Year Journey from County Galway to Iowa, 1993. With USNR, 1945-46. Mem. Tex. Bar Assn., Phi Kappa Theta. Home: 710 Rose Ln Los Altos CA 94024-4146

MULLAN, DONALD WILLIAM, bishop; b. Galt, Ont., Apr. 26, 1937; s. William James and Lillian Maude (Sachs) M.; m. Cathy Templeman. Presiding bishop Christ Cath. Ch. Internat.; pastor Cathedral of St. Luke, Niagara Falls, Ont. Editor (mag.) The St. Luke Mag. Trustee Bd. Edn., Preston, Ont., 1962-68, Waterloo County, Ont., 1969-70, Wellington County, Ont., 1971-72. Mem. Order of Noble Companions of the Swan (prelate), Moose. Office: Cathedral of St Luke, 5965 Palmer Ave, Niagara Falls, ON Canada L2E 3T9

MULLAN, JOHN FRANCIS (SEAN MULLAN), neurosurgeon, educator; b. County Derry, Northern Ireland, May 17, 1925; came to U.S., 1955; naturalized, 1962; s. John and Mary Catharine Ann (Gilmartin) M.; m. Vivian C. Dunn, June 3, 1959; children: Joan Claire, John Charles, Brian Francis. MB, BCh, BAO, Queen's U., Belfast, Northern Ireland, 1947, DSc (hon.), 1976; postgrad., McGill U., 1953-55. Diplomate Am. Bd. Neurol. Surgery. Trainee gen. surgery Royal Victoria Hosp., Belfast, 1947-50, trainee in neurosurgery, 1951-53; trainee gen. surgery Guy's Hosp. and Middlesex Hosp., London, 1950-51, Montreal Neurosurg. Inst., Que., Can., 1955; asst. prof. neurol. surgery U. Chgo., 1955-61, assoc. prof., 1961-63, prof., 1963—; John Harper Seeley prof., chmn. dept., 1967—; dir. Brain Rsch. Inst., 1970-84. Author: Neurosurgery for Students, 1961; contbr. over 150 articles to profl. jours.; mem. editorial bd. Jour. Neurosurgery, 1974-84, Archives of Neurology, 1976-87. Recipient Olivecrona medal Karolinska Inst., 1976, Wilder Penfield medal Can. Neurosurg. Soc., 1979, Jamieson medal Australian and New Zealand Neurosurg. Soc., 1980. Fellow ACS, Royal Coll. Surgeons; mem. Soc. Neurol. Surgeons (past pres.), Acad. Neurol. Surgery, Am. Assn. Neurol. Surgeons, Am. Neurol. Assn., Cen. Neurosurg. Soc., Chgo. Neurol. Soc., World Fedn. of Neurosurg. Socs. (sec. 1989-93, hon. pres. 1993—). Roman Catholic. Conductor of research on vascular diseases of the brain, pain, head injury. Avocations: walnut tree farming, gardening. Office: U Chgo Med Ctr 5841 S Maryland Ave Chicago IL 60637-1470

MULLANE, DENIS FRANCIS, insurance executive; b. Astoria, N.Y., Aug. 28, 1930; s. Patrick F. and Margaret (O'Neill) M.; m. Kathryn Mullman, June 28, 1952; children: Gerard, Kevin, Denise. BS in Mil. Engring, U.S. Mil. Acad., 1952; LHD (hon.), U. Conn., 1988, St. Joseph's Coll., 1990; LLD (hon.), U. Hartford, 1993, Trinity Coll., Hartford, Conn., 1995. C.L.U. With Conn. Mut. Life Ins. Co., Hartford, 1956—, v.p., 1969-72, sr. v.p., 1972-74, exec. v.p., 1974-76, pres., 1977—, chief exec. officer, 1983-85, chmn., chief exec. officer, 1985-90; chief exec. officer, pres. Conn. Mut. Life Ins. Co., 1990-93, chmn. bd. dirs., 1993-94; bd. dirs. Conn. Natural Gas Co.; chmn. The Am. Coll., Bryn Maur, Pa., 1993—. Dir. U.S. Chamber, 1991-95. 1st lt. C.E. U.S. Army, 1952-56. Recipient John Newton Russell award, 1987, Knight of St. Gregory award. Mem. Am. Soc. Corp. Execs., Nat. Assn. Life Underwriters, Assn. Grads. U.S. Mil. Acad. (pres. 1989-93). Republican. Roman Catholic. Office: Mullane Enterprises 29 S Main St West Hartford CT 06107

MULLANE, DONALD A., banker; b. Los Angeles, May 24, 1938; s. William Paul and Petra Hilda (DeVilla Fuerte) M.; m. Dorothy Ann Sarosy, July 2, 1960; children—Deborah, Donna, David, Donald, Douglas. Student, U. So. Calif., Los Angeles; participant Stanford exec. program, Stanford U.; cert., Am. Inst. Banking. Asst. cashier Bank of Am., So. Calif., 1958-69, asst. v.p., 1969-72, v.p., 1972-81, sr. v.p., 1981-85; exec. v.p. Bank of Am., Los Angeles and San Francisco, 1985—; chmn. bd. Bank of Am. State Bank; chmn. social policy com. Bank Am. Foun., Skid Row Housing Corp., 1991. Bd. dirs. Las Familias, L.A., 1985—, A.P. Giannini Found., 1986—, Maryvale Inc., L.A. Sports Coun., St. Vincents Hosp.; bd. dirs. Calif. Community Reinvestment Corp., chmn., 1990—; chmn. Jr. Achievement So. Calif., L.A., 1985-90; co-chmn. Community Reinvestment Inst.; chmn. bd. Pacific Coast Sch. Banking, U. Wash., 1989—; bd. councilors Sch. Urban Planning, Sch. of Pub. Adminstrn., U. So. Calif.; chmn. L.A. Community Reinvestment Com. Recipient Disting. Achievement award Am. Heart Assn., L.A., 1985, Social Responsibility award Mex. Am. Legal Def. and Edn. Fund, 1992; named Outstanding Mgr., Bank of Am., 1979, 80; honoree Nat. Ctr. for Am. Indians, 1991. Mem. Retail Bank Am. (chmn. retail banking conf. 1986), L.A. C. of C., Calif. Bankers Assn. (bd. dirs. 1986—, pres. 1990-91), Hacienda Golf Club (La Habra, Calif.), City Club on Bunker Hill, Bankers Club San Francisco. Office: Bank of America 555 S Flower St Los Angeles CA 90071

MULLANE, JOHN FRANCIS, pharmaceutical company executive; b. N.Y.C., Mar. 10, 1937; s. John Gerard and Rita Ann (Hoben) M.; m. Ruth Ann Cecka, Nov. 17, 1962; children—Rosemarie, Michael, Kathleen, Therese, Thomas. M.D., SUNY, 1963, Ph.D., 1968; J.D., Fordham U., 1977. Bar: N.Y. 1978, D.C. 1979. Assoc. med. dir. Ayerst Labs. div. Am. Home Products Corp., N.Y.C., 1973-75, dir. clin. research, 1975-76, v.p. clin., 1977, v.p. sci., 1978-82, sr. v.p., 1982, exec. v.p., 1983-88; pres. Mullane Health Care Cons., N.Y.C., 1989—; dir. drug devel. DuPont Med. Products, Wilmington, Del., 1990; sr. v.p. DuPont-Merck, Wilmington, 1991-94; exec. v.p. Amylin Pharms., 1994—. Contbr. articles to profl. jours. Served to lt. col. U.S. Army, 1970-73. Recipient Upjohn Achievement award, 1970; N.Y. Heart Assn. Crawford-Maynard fellow, 1966-68. Fellow Am. Coll. Clin. Pharmacology; mem. ABA, Am. Soc. Nephrology, Am. Soc. Clin. Pharmacology and Therapeutics, Am. Assn. Study of Liver Diseases, Pelham Country Club, DuPont Country Club, Tara Golf and Country Club. Roman Catholic. Avocation: golf. Home: 1860 Rossini Dr Cardiff CA 92007-1671 Office: Amylin Pharms 9373 Towne Centre Dr San Diego CA 92121

MULLANEY, JOSEPH E., lawyer; b. Fall River, Mass., Mar. 22, 1933; s. Joseph E. and Beatrice (Hancock) M.; m. Rosemary Woodman, June 22, 1957; children—Joseph E. III, Brian, Sean, Evan. A.B. magna cum laude, Coll. Holy Cross, Worcester, Mass., 1955; LL.B. magna cum laude, Harvard U., 1958. Bar: Ohio bar, D.C. bar, Mass. bar. Ptnr. Jones, Day, Cockley & Reavis, Cleve., 1960-70; gen. counsel Office Spl. Rep. Trade Negotiations, Exec. Office Pres., Washington, 1970-71, Cost of Living Council, 1971-72; assoc. gen. counsel Gillette Co., Boston, 1972-77, sr. v.p., gen. counsel, 1977-90, vice chmn. bd., 1990—; dir. Park St. Corp., Greater Boston Legal Services Corp.; mem., dir. Boston Mcpl. Research Bur. Bd. dirs. New Eng. Legal Found. Office: Gillette Co Prudential Towers Bldg Boston MA 02199

MULLARE, T(HOMAS) KENWOOD, JR., lawyer; b. Milton, Mass., Jan. 19, 1939; s. Thomas Kenwood and Catherine Marie (Leonard) M.; m. Joan Marie O'Donnell, May 27, 1967; children: Jennifer M., Tracy K., Jill M. Joyce M. AB, Holy Cross Coll., 1961; LLB, Boston Coll., 1964. Bar: Mass. 1964. Atty. New Eng. Electric System, 1964-71; v.p., gen. counsel, sec. AVX Corp., N.Y.C., 1971-73; v.p., gen. counsel, clk. Tyco Labs., Inc., Exeter, N.H., 1974-77; v.p., gen. counsel, sec. SCA Svcs., Inc., Boston, 1977-84; spl. counsel Houghton, Mifflin Co., Boston, 1984-85, v.p., dir. bus. softwaRe divsn., 1985-89; pres. North River Capital Inc., Norwell, Mass., 1990—; also bd. dirs. Broadcast Info. Tech., Norwell, Mass.; bd. dirs. North River Capital Co., Inc. Bd. dirs. Barque Hill Assn., Norwell, 1980-84, pres., 1981-82; pres. Ch. Hillers, Norwell, 1983-84; vice chmn. South Shore Assn. for Retarded Citizens, Weymouth, Mass., Agape Inn Respite Care Ctr.,

---

Holbrook, Mass. Mem. ABA, Mass. Bar Assn., Boston Bar Assn. Home: 31 Barque Hill Dr Norwell MA 02061-2815 Office: 6A Grove St Ste 271 PO Box 9105 Norwell MA 02061-9105

MULLARKEY, MARY J., state supreme court justice; b. New London, Wis., Sept. 28, 1943; d. John Clifford and Isabelle A. (Steffes) M.; m. Thomas E. Korson, July 24, 1971; 1 child, Andrew Steffes Korson. BA, St. Norbert Coll., 1965; LLB, Harvard U., 1968; LLD (hon.), St. Norbert Coll., 1989. Bar: Wis. 1968, Colo. 1974. Atty.-advisor U.S. Dept. Interior, Washington, 1968-73; asst. regional atty. EEOC, Denver, 1973-75; 1st atty. gen. Colo. Dept. Law, Denver, 1975-79, solicitor gen., 1979-82; legal advisor to Gov. Lamm State of Colo., Denver, 1982-85; ptnr. Mullarkey & Seymour, Denver, 1985-87; justice Colo. Supreme Ct., Denver, 1987—. Recipient Alumni award St. Norbert Coll., De Pere, Wis., 1980, Alma Mater award, 1993. Fellow ABA Found.; mem. ABA, Colo. Bar Found. (mem. bd. dirs.), Colo. Women's Bar Assn. (recognition award 1986), Denver Bar Assn., Thompson G. Marsh Inn of Ct. (pres. 1993-94). Office: Supreme Ct Colo 2 E 14th Ave Denver CO 80203-2116

MULLEN, DANIEL ROBERT, finance company executive; b. Swedesboro, N.J., Apr. 17, 1941; s. Harold Legrand and Gladys (DeVault) M.; m. Elizabeth A. Willers, Dec. 17, 1977. BS in Fin., Ariz. State U., 1966, postgrad., 1966-67. Appraiser Ariz. Dept. Revenue, Phoenix, 1966-68; financial analyst Amerco, Inc., Phoenix, 1968-70; treas., CFO Amerco, Inc., 1970-82; pres., dir. Continental Leasing Co., 1980—; v.p. Southwest Pipe and Supply Co., 1982; treas. Talley Industries, Inc., 1982—; v.p. Talley Industries, Inc., Phoenix, 1993—. Del. Ariz. Presdl. Dem. Conv., 1972; bd. dirs. Big Sisters of Ariz., 1975, Found. for Blind Children, 1984-90, Phoenix Little Theatre, 1985-91, Kachina Country Day Sch., 1988-94, New Way Sch., 1994—. With U.S. Army, 1959-62. Ariz. Soc. CPAs grantee, 1964-65. Mem. Fin. Execs. Inst. Home: 3627 E Medlock Dr Phoenix AZ 85018-1505 Office: 2702 N 44th St Phoenix AZ 85008-1583

MULLEN, EDWARD JOHN, JR., Spanish language educator; b. Hackensack, N.J., July 12, 1942; s. Edward J. and Elsie (Powell) M.; m. Helen Cloe Braley, Apr. 2, 1971; children: Kathleen, Julie Ann. B.A., W.Va. Wesleyan Coll., 1964; M.A., Northwestern U., 1965, Ph.D., 1968. Asst. prof. modern langs. Purdue U., West Lafayette, Ind., 1967-71; assoc. prof. Spanish U. Mo., Columbia, 1971-78, prof. Spanish, 1978—. Author: La Revista Contemporáneos, 1972, Carlos Pellicer, 1977, Langston Hughes in the Hispanic World and Haiti, 1977, The Life and Poems of a Cuban Slave: Juan Francisco Manzano 1797-1854, 1981, Critical Essays on Langston Hughes, 1986, Sendas Literarias: Hispanomerica, 1988, El cuento hispánico, 1994; co-editor Afro-Hispanic Rev., 1987—. Recipient Diploma de Honor Instituto de Cultura Hispánica, 1964; Woodrow Wilson fellow, 1964-65; Northwestern U. fellow, 1965-67; summer research grantee U. Mo., 1972, 76; grantee Am. Council Learned Socs., 1979. Mem. MLA, Am. Assn. Tchrs. Spanish and Portuguese, Assn. of Depts. Fgn. Langs. (mem. exec. com.). Home: 207 Edgewood Ave Columbia MO 65203-3413 Office: U Mo Dept Romance Langs 143 Arts and Sci Bldg Columbia MO 65211

MULLEN, EILEEN ANNE, staff training and development executive; b. Phila., Feb. 14, 1943; d. Joseph Gregory and Helen Rita (Kane) M. BS in English, St. Joseph U., 1967; MA in English, Villanova U., 1978. Cert. tchr., Pa. Tchr.; St. Anastasia Sch., Newtown Square, 1960-67, West Cath. Girls High Sch., 1967-74; mgr. staff tng. and devel. ASTM, Phila., 1974—; instr. lit., speech and communications Widener U. Weekend Coll., Chester, Pa. and Wilmington, Del. Author: Speech Command, 1995; contbg. author articles on communications tng. programs; contbr. articles to profl. publs. Mem. ASTD (pres. Phila./Delaware Valley chpt. 1980-81, award for outstanding leadership as pres. 1981), Am. Soc. Tng. Assn. Execs. (Delaware Valley chpt.). Democrat. Roman Catholic. Office: ASTM 100 Bar Harbour Dr Conshohocken PA 19428

MULLEN, FRANK ALBERT, university official, clergyman; b. Lafayette, Ind., Apr. 7, 1931; s. Albert Edwin and Bernice Elizabeth (Weidlich) M.; m. Ruth Charlotte Ackerman, May 28, 1960 (dec. Oct. 1969). BA, Wabash Coll., Crawfordsville, Ind., 1953; MDiv, Yale U., 1956; DD (hon.), Berkeley Div. Sch., New Haven, 1988. Ordained to ministry Christian Ch. (Disciples of Christ), 1956. Exec. dir. YMCA of Wilmington, Del., 1956-60, YMCA of Greater N.Y., N.Y.C., 1960-74; pastor St Marks United Ch. of Christ, Ridgewood, N.Y., 1973—; assoc. dir. Campaign for Yale, Yale U., N.Y.C., 1975-79; min. Cmty. Ch. of Elmhurst, 1974—; div. exec. Bapt. Med. Ctr., N.Y.C., 1980-83; dir. devel. Div. Sch. Yale U., New Haven, 1984—; dir. planned giving Guideposts, Inc., Carmel, N.Y., 1983-84. Trustee Park Avenue Christian Ch., N.Y.C., 1970—. Recipient Liberty Bell award Queens County Bar Assn., 1969, Alumni award of merit Wabash Coll., 1970; Wright fellow Yale U., 1955, fellow Trumbull Coll., 1985—. Mem. Assn. Theol. Schs., Coun. for Advancement in Secondary Edn., Wellness Assn., Travelers' Century Club. Home: 178-33 Croydon Rd Jamaica Estates NY 11432-2203 Office: Yale U 409 Prospect St New Haven CT 06511-2167 Live for others. It is the only true way to find happiness.

MULLEN, GRAHAM C., federal judge; b. 1940. BA, Duke U., 1962, JD, 1969. Bar: N.C. 1969. Ptnr. Mullen, Holland, Cooper, Morrow, Wilder & Sumner, 1969-90; judge U.S. Dist. Ct. (we. dist.) N.C., Charlotte, 1990—. Lt. USN, 1962-66. Mem. N.C. Bar Assn. (bd. govs. 1983-88), Mecklenburg County Bar Assn. Office: US Courthouse 401 W Trade St Charlotte NC 28202-1619

MULLEN, J. THOMAS, lawyer; b. Evanston, Ill., Aug. 27, 1940. BSE, Princeton U., 1963; JD cum laude, U. Mich., 1967. Bar: Ill. 1967. Ptnr. Mayer, Brown & Platt, Chgo. Bd. dirs. Legal Assistance Found. Chgo., 1979-85. Mem. ABA, Ill. State Bar Assn., Chgo. Bar Assn., Chgo. Coun. Lawyers. Office: Mayer Brown & Platt 190 S La Salle St Chicago IL 60603-3410

MULLEN, JAMES GENTRY, physics educator; b. St. Louis, Sept. 17, 1933; s. James and Lillian A. (Nelms) M.; children by previous marriage: Anne Lynette, Barbara Gaye, James Gentry, Laura Marie; m. Sara Jane; children: Carol Melissa, Erin Joy, Elizabeth Nancy Jane, Kevin Alexander. B.S., U. Mo., 1955; M.S., U. Ill., 1957, Ph.D., 1960. Asst. physicist Argonne Nat. Lab., 1960-63, assoc. physicist, 1963-64; mem. faculty Purdue U., 1964—, asst. prof., 1964-66, assoc. prof., 1966-75, prof. physics, 1975—; pres. Word Technologies, Inc., West Lafayette, Ind., 1981-85; mem. organizing com., program chmn. Internat. Conf. for Applications of Mössbauer Effect, 1993. Contbr. to profl. jours. Fundamenteel Onderzoek Materie fellow, 1979-80. Mem. Am. Phys. Soc., Am. Assn. Physics Tchrs., AAUP, Sigma Xi, Phi Kappa Phi, Tau Beta Pi. Home: 3212 Elkhart St West Lafayette IN 47906-1151 Office: Purdue U Dept Physics West Lafayette IN 47907

MULLEN, JOSEPH PATRICK, professional hockey player; b. N.Y.C., Feb. 26, 1957. Student, Boston Coll. With St. Louis Blues, 1979-86, Calgary Flames, 1986-90; right wing Pitts. Penguins, 1990—; player NCAA All-Am. East Game, 1977-78, 78-79, NHL All-Star Game, 1989, 90, 94, Stanley Cup Championship Game, 1989, 91, 92. Recipient Ken McKenzie trophy, 1979-80, Lady Byng Meml. trophy, 1986-87, 88-89; named MVP, 1974-75. Office: Pitts Penguins Civic Arena Gate 9 Pittsburgh PA 15219*

MULLEN, PETER P., lawyer; b. N.Y.C., Apr. 8, 1928. A.B., Georgetown U., 1948; LL.B., Columbia U., 1951. Bar: N.Y. 1951. Assoc. firm Dewey Ballantine Bushby Palmer & Wood, N.Y.C., 1951-61; partner firm Skadden Arps Slate Meagher & Flom, N.Y.C., 1961—, exec. ptnr., 1982-94. Bd. dirs. Lawrence Hosp., Bronxville, N.Y., 1984-89, Project Orbis, Georgetown U., Washington, 1982—, chmn., 1985-92; mem. Bd. Edn. Bronxville, N.Y., 1976-81, pres., 1979-81, chmn. Gregorian U. Found., 1989—. Mem. Am. Bar Assn., N.Y. State Bar Assn. (com. securities regulation 1963-68), Assn. Bar City N.Y. (com. corp. law 1964-67, com. admissions 1965-68, com. securities regulation 1970-73). Office: Skadden Arps Slate et al 919 Third Ave New York NY 10022-3903

MULLEN, REGINA MARIE, lawyer; b. Cambridge, Mass., Apr. 22, 1948; d. Robert G. and Elizabeth R. (McHugh) M. BA, Newton Coll. Sacred Heart, 1970; JD, U. Va., 1973. Bar: Pa., Del., U.S. Dist. Ct. Del., U.S. Ct.

Appeals (3d cir.), U.S. Supreme Ct. Dep. atty. gen. State Del. Dept. Justice, Wilmington, 1973-79, state solicitor, 1979-83, chief fin. unit, 1983-88; v.p., counsel MBNA Am. Bank, N.A., Newark, Del., 1988-91, 1st v.p., sr. v.p., counsel, 1991—; Mem. bd. Bar Examiners, State Del., 1979-89; bd. dirs. Del. Cmty. Investment Corp., Wilmington, 1994—, Wilmington Music Festival, 1992—. Mem. fin. com. Chesapeake Bay Girl Scout coun., Wilmington, 1985-94, bd. dirs., 1988-94, v.p., 1990-94, mem. fund devel. com., 1994—; bd. dirs. Comty. Legal Aid Soc., 1994—. Mem. ABA, Del. State Bar Assn. (chair adminstrv. law sect. 1983-85). Democrat. Roman Catholic. Office: 400 Christiana Rd Newark DE 19713-4217

MULLEN, ROBERT CHARLES, school system administrator; b. Muskogee, Okla., Nov. 13, 1944; s. Charles W. and Kathryn B. (Hunt) M.; m. Celesta Rose Schmidt, June 25, 1966; children: Charles, Robert, Michael, Kevin. BS, Minot (N.D.) State U., 1966, MS, 1967; EdD, U. No. Colo., Greeley, 1981. Speech pathologist Benton-Tama-Iowa-Poweshiek Dept. Spl. Edn., Toledo, Iowa, 1967-68, hearing clinician, 1968-69, coord. speech and hearing, 1969-73; dir. ACCA Speech and Hearing Ctr., Fairbanks, Alaska, 1973-75; asst. dir. Alaska Treatment Ctr., Anchorage, 1975-76, exec. dir., 1976-79; dir. Reno County Ein. Coop. USD #610, Hutchinson, Kans., 1981-85, Rio Blanco Bd. Endl. Svcs., Rangely, Colo., 1985-89; supt. Rangely Pub. Schs. RE-4, 1989—; co bd. dirs. Horizon Inc., Steamboat, Colo.; pres. Vocat. Edn. Adv. Bd., Colo. No. Community Coll., Rangely, 1988. Commr. Mayor's Health Commn., Anchorage, 1976-79; Alaska rep. Nat. Conf. on Aging, WAshington; bd. mem. Spl. Edn. Adv. Bd., U. No. Colo., 1988; state com. mem. Colo. Parent/Profl. Partnership, Denver, 1988-90; mem. planning com. White house Conf. on Handicapped. U.S. Office Edn. grantee, Greeley, Colo., 1980, 81. Mem. Am. Assn. Sch. Adminstrs., Coun. Exceptional Children, Colo. Assn. Sch. Execs. Roman Catholic. Avocations: fishing, swimming, writing, geneology. Office: Rangely Pub Schs 402 W Main St Rangely CO 81648-2408

MULLEN, RON, insurance company executive; b. Tex., Aug. 8, 1939; s. Durward Lacy and Blanche V. (Coulson) M.; m. Carole King, Dec, 29, 1959; children: Lacy Lynne Holcomb, Misty Kay. Student, Abilene Christian Coll., 1957-58, San Antonio Coll., 1958-59; BBA, S.W. Tex. State U., 1965. C.L.U., Chartered Fin. Cons. City council mem. City of Austin, 1977-83, mayor, 1983-85; mgr. Prin. Fin. Group, Austin, 1965—; pres., prin. Fin. Group, Ron Mullen & Assocs. Inc., Austin, 1966—; chmn. TML Ins. Trust Fund Com., 1983—; mem. Gov.'s Task Force on State Employees Health Ins. Benefits, Austin, 1984. Chmn. Austin Transp. Study com., Austin, 1983—, Greater Austin-San Antonio Corridor Council, 1984—, Social Policy Adv. com., Austin, 1979-80, March of Dimes campaign, Austin, 1974-75; co-chmn. Consumers United for Rail Equity, Austin, 1983—; v.p. Austin Symphony Orchestra, 1974-75; mem. exec. com. Capital Area Planning Council, Austin, 1976—, exec. bd. Tex. Mcpl. League, Austin, 1983—, Gov.'s Task Force on Indigent Health Care, Austin, 1984, Tex. Adv. Commn. on Intergovtl. Relations, Austin, 1981—; chmn. Infant Parent Tng. Ctr., 1985-93; bd. dirs., chmn. South MoPac Transp. Com., 1986-87; life mem. Austin Jaycees, bd. dirs. 1974-75; vice chmn. mental health Mental Retardation Bd.; vice chmn. South Tex. Audio Reader Svc. Recipient Road Hand award Tex. Dept. Hwys. and Transp., 1985, award for regional statesmanship Greater Austin-San Antonio Corridor Commn.; named Boss of Yr., Treaty Oaks chpt. Am. Bus. Women's Assn., 1978, Nat. Mgr. of Yr., Bankers Life Ins. Co., 1977, 82, 84-85, Alumnus of Yr. Austin Jaycees, 1988-90. Mem. Am. Coll. Life Underwriters (pres. 1974-75), Austin Assn. Life Underwriters (regional dir.), Austin Assn. Life Underwriters (pres. 1974-75), Austin Gen. Agents and Mgrs. Assn. (pres. 1975-76), Tex. Gen. Agents and Mgrs. Assn. (pres. 1978-80), Sales and Mktg. Execs. of Austin (pres. 1972-73), Rotary (pres. elect.). Baptist. Home: 6902 Mesa Rd #B Austin TX 78703-2009

MULLEN, RUSSELL E., agricultural studies educator. Prof. agronomy Iowa State U., Ames. Recipient Ensminger Interstate Disting. Tchr. award Nat. Assn. Colls. Tchrs. Agriculture, 1992. Office: Iowa State U Dept Agronomy 1126 Agronomy Hall Ames IA 50011

MULLEN, THOMAS EDGAR, real estate consultant; b. Hackensack, N.J., Feb. 10, 1936; s. Luke B. and Jean (Edgar) M.; m. Sarah Lee Huff, Aug. 17, 1984. BS in Engring., Va. Poly. Tech., 1954; grad mgmt. program, Harvard U., 1964. Cons. in field. Mgr. mktg. Eastern Airlines, N.Y.C., 1954-69; pres. Profl. Sprits Mktg., N.Y.C., 1969-72, Shelter Devel. Corp. Am., N.Y.C., 1972-79; supr. ops. Gen. Mills, Orlando, Fla., 1980-86; cons., exec., realtor A.H.M. Graves Co. Inc., Indpls., 1986-92; pres. Pegasus Assocs. Ltd., 1992—. Inventor TV Guider Holder, patent, 1971. Fundraiser Am. Cancer Soc., Miami, 1967-70, Westchester Hosp., N.Y.C., 1967-70; pres. Brighton Found. Mem. Met. Bd. Realtors, Builders Assn. Greater Indpls. (bd. dirs.), Ind. Builders Assn. (bd. dirs.), Nat. Assn. Realtors, Inst. Residential Mktg. (pres. sales & mktg. coun., bd. dirs.). Republican. Roman Catholic. Avocations: tennis, recreational pilot. Home: 6251 Behner Way Indianapolis IN 46250-1494

MULLEN, WILLIAM JOSEPH, III, military analyst, retired army officer; b. Plattsburg, N.Y., Dec. 26, 1937; s. William Joseph Jr. and Georgia (Cook) M.; m. Norma Sturgeon, Aug. 6, 1962; 1 child, William Joseph IV. BS, U.S. Mil. Acad., West Point, N.Y., 1959; MS in Internat. Affairs, George Washington U., 1971. Commd. 2d lt. U.S. Army, 1959, advanced through grades to brig. gen., 1987; various assignments in U.S., Vietnam, Korea, Panama, Germany, Saudi Arabia, 1959-92; mem. staff, faculty U.S. Mil. Acad., West Point, 1967-70; comdr. 1st Brigade, 1st Inf. Div., Ft. Riley, Kans., 1983-86; asst. div. comdr. 5th Inf. Div., Ft. Polk, La., 1986-87; comdg. gen. U.S. Army Combined Arms Tng. Activity, Ft. Leavenworth, Kans., 1987-89, 1st Inf. Div. (Forward), Germany, 1989-91; dep. dir. ops. J3 Forces Command, Ft. McPherson, Ga., 1991-92; dir. mil. tng. sys. BDM Fed., Inc., Monterey, Calif., 1992—. Co-author: Changing an Army, An Oral History of Gen. W.E. DePuy, 1979; contbr. articles, book revs. to Mil. Rev. Decorated D.S.C., D.S.M. Mem. Assn. U.S. Army, Soc. of 1st Div. (chpt. officer 1968, assoc. 1989-93, trustee found. 1989-93, bd. dirs.), Legion of Valor. Avocations: sports, reading. When in doubt, I have always found direction from the guidance explicit in the 1st Infantry Division's motto, "Duty first!".

MULLENDORE, WALTER EDWARD, economist; b. Harrah, Okla., Apr. 22, 1940; s. Newton and Ida Minnie (Lohmann) M.; m. Edra Janell Havenstrite, July 4, 1963; children—Matthew Edward, Karen Kay, Mark Andrew. BS, Okla. State U., 1961, MS, 1963; PhD in Econs, Iowa State U., 1968. Grad. asst. Okla. State U., 1961-63; instr. Iowa State U., 1965-67; mem. faculty dept. econs. U. Tex., Arlington, 1968—, prof., 1975—, dean Coll. of Bus., 1980-93. Contbr. articles to profl. jours. Served with U.S. Army, 1963-65. Mem. Mo. Valley Econ. Assn. (v.p. 1980-81, pres. 1982-83), Atlantic Econ. Soc., Regional Sci. Assn., Western Regional Sci. Assn., Gt. S.W. Rotary (pres. 1989-90), Omicron Delta Epsilon. Methodist. Home: 8003 John T White Rd Fort Worth TX 76120-3611 Office: U Tex Coll Bus Arlington TX 76019

MULLENIX, LINDA SUSAN, lawyer, educator; b. N.Y.C., Oct. 16, 1950; d. Andrew Michael and Roslyn (Rosenthal) Marasco; children: Robert Bartholomew, John Theodore, William Joseph. B.A., CCNY, 1971; M. Philosophy, Columbia U., 1974, Ph.D. (Pres.'s fellow), 1977; J.D., Georgetown U., 1980. Bar: D.C. 1981, U.S. Dist Ct. D.C. 1981, U.S. Supreme Ct. 1986. U.S. Ct. Appeals (D.C. cir.) 1991. Tex. 1991. Assoc. prof., lectr. George Washington U., Washington, 1977-80; asst. prof. Am. U., Washington, 1979; clin. prof. Loyola U. Law Sch., Los Angeles, 1981-82, vis. asst. prof., 1982-83; vis. asst. prof. Catholic U. Law Sch., Washington, 1983-84, asst. prof., chmn. acad. personnel, 1986-90, prof., 1990; Jud. Fellow U.S. Supreme Ct. and Fed. Jud. Ctr., 1989-90; Bernard J. Ward Centennial prof. U. Tex., 1991—; Vinson & Elkins chair, U. Tex., 1993; vis. prof. Harvard Law Sch., 1994-95; assoc. Pierson, Ball & Dowd, Washington, 1980-81; adj. instr. Fordham U., N.Y.C., 1975-76, adj. asst. prof. 1977; adj. asst. prof. CCNY, 1977; adj. instr. adj. asst. prof. Cooper Union Advancement Sci. Art, N.Y.C., 1977; instr. N.Y. Inst. Tech., N.Y.C., 1976, U. Md. European div., Ramstein, Germany, 1974. Author: (with others) Moore's Fed. Practice and Procedure, 1991; editor bibliographies Polit. Theory, A Jour. Polit. Philosophy, 1972-74, The Tax Lawyer Jour., 1979-80; contbg. editor Preview of U.S. Supreme Ct. Cases, Pub. Edn. Div. ABA, 1988—; co-reporter Report and Plan of Civil Justice Reform Act Adv. Group, S.D., Tex. 1991, Restatement of the Law Governing Lawyers; contbr. articles to profl. publs. Alt. del. Va. Democratic State Conv., 1980. Fellow NDEA, 1971-74, Georgetown U. Law Sch., 1978; N.Y. State Regents scholar, 1967-71. Mem. ABA, Am. Law Inst., D.C. Bar Assn. (com. on ethics, CLE and the Model Rules 1987), Am. Assn. Law Schs. (exec. com. sect. on civil proc. 1987-88, exec. com. sec. on conflicts of law 1991-92, chair prof. devel. com. 1991-93), Phi Beta Kappa, Phi Alpha Delta. Home: 722 Crystal Creek Dr Austin TX 78746-4730 Office: U Tex Sch Law 727 E 26th St Austin TX 78705-3224

MULLENIX, TRAVIS H., food products company executive; b. 1931. BA, Univ. of Texas, 1956. With Ralston-Purina Co., 1956-84, group v.p.; with Tri-Valley Growers, 1984—, exec. v.p., chief operating officer, then pres., 1985—. Office: Tri/Valley Growers Inc 1255 Battery St San Francisco CA 94111-1174

MULLENS, WILLIAM REESE, retired insurance company executive; b. Franklin, Tenn., Sept. 12, 1921; s. William Pope and Elizabeth (Reese) M.; m. Katherine Ann Jones, Nov. 24, 1945; children: Jo Ann Mullens Sanditz, Carol Ann Mullens Slegers. B.A., Vanderbilt U., 1942. With Bus. Men's Assurance Co., Kansas City, Mo., 1947-75; exec. v.p., dir. Bus. Men's Assurance Co., 1969-75; pres., dir. J.C. Penney Life Ins. Co., 1975-82; pres. Gt. Am. Res. Ins. Co., 1975-84, dir., 1975-89; dir. Nat. Fidelity Life Ins. Co., 1986-89. Served to lt. comdr. USNR, 1943-46. Fellow Soc. Actuaries; mem. Phi Beta Kappa, Alpha Tau Omega. Presbyterian. Home: 2502 N Broken Circle Rd Flagstaff AZ 86004

MULLER, CHARLOTTE FELDMAN, economist, educator; b. N.Y.C., Feb. 19, 1921; d. Louis and Lillian (Drogin) Feldman; m. Jonas N. Muller, 1942 (dec.); m. Carl Schoenberg, 1970; children: Jeremy Lewis Muller, Sara Linda Muller. A.B., Vassar Coll., 1941; A.M., Columbia U., 1942, Ph.D. in Econs., 1946. Instr. econs. Bklyn. Coll., 1943; lectr. Barnard Coll., 1943-46; asst. prof. Occidental Coll., 1947; asst. study dir. Survey Rsch. Ctr., U. Mich., 1948; rsch. assoc. U. Calif., Berkeley, 1948-50; lectr. Yale U. Sch. Pub. Health, 1952-53; asst. prof. Columbia U. Sch. Pub. Health, 1957-67; assoc. dir. Ctr. for Social Rsch. CUNY, 1967-86, prof. econs., 1978-91, prof. emerita, 1991—, prof. sociology, 1982-91, prof. urban studies Ctr. for Social Rsch., 1967-78; v.p. CUNY Acad. for Humanities and Scis., 1985-88; prof. health econs. Mt. Sinai Sch. Medicine, 1986-91, prof. emerita, 1991—, dir. div. health econs. 1988-91, prof. dept. geriatrics, 1990-91; assoc. dir. Internat. Longevity Ctr., HHS, 1991—; cons. Health Care Financing Adminstrn., U.S. VA; disting. alumna speaker Vassar Centennial, 1971. Author: Health Care and Gender, 1990; mem. editorial bd. Am. Jour. Pub. Health, 1980-84, Women and Health, Rsch. on Aging; contbr. numerous articles on health econs. to profl. publs. Mem. N.Y.C. Mayor's Com. on Prescription Drug Abuse, 1970-73; bd. dirs. Alan Guttmacher Inst., 1972-81, CUNY Rsch. Found., 1985-91; vice chmn. Med. and Health Rsch. Assn., N.Y.C.; mem. health care tech. study sect. Nat. Ctr. Health Svcs. Rsch., 1976-79; mem. commn. on nat. policy Am. Jewish Congress, 1980-91. Ford/Rockefeller Founds. grantee, 1972-73, 75-76; Russell Sage Found. grantee, 1985-90. Mem. APHA, NOW, Am. Econ. Assn. Jewish. Office: Mt Sinai Sch Medicine Box 1070 1 Gustave L Levy Pl New York NY 10029-6504

MULLER, DIETRICH ALFRED HELMUT, physicist, educator; b. Leipzig, Germany, Sept. 14, 1936; came to U.S., 1968; s. Herbert and Johanna (Potzger) M.; m. Renate Runkel, Mar. 23, 1968; children: Georg, Michael, Agnes. Student, U. Leipzig, German Dem. Republic; diploma in physics, U. Bonn, Fed. Republic Germany, 1961, PhD in Physics, 1964. Rsch. assoc. U. Bonn, 1965-68; rsch. assoc. U. Chgo., 1968-70, asst. prof., 1970-77, assoc. prof., 1977-84, prof. physics, 1985—, dir. Enrico Fermi Inst., 1986-92; prin. investigator on rsch. in high energy astrophysics using baloons and spacecraft, NASA; rsch. in exptl. physics and particle physics. Contbr. numerous articles to profl. jours. Fellow Am. Phys. Soc.; mem. AAAS, Am. Astron. Soc. Office: U Chgo Enrico Fermi Inst 933 E 56th St Chicago IL 60637-1460

MULLER, DONALD BRUCE, chemical executive; b. Long Beach, Calif., Sept. 19, 1947; s. Howard Eugene and Deloris June (Holthus) M.; m. Mary Louise Morris, Sept. 11, 1971; children: Bret David, Carolyn Adele, Susan Christine. BSChemE, Va. Poly. Inst., 1970. Mktg. research rep. DuPont Co., Wilmington, Del., 1973-79; v.p., gen. mgr. Mid-State Plastics, Seagrove, N.C., 1979-84; v.p., gen. mgr. Morganite, Inc., Dunn, N.C., 1984-85, pres., 1985—, also bd. dirs.; bd. dirs. Morganite-U.K., Morriston, Wales and Wandsworth, Eng. Mem. Am. Mgmt. Assn., Soc. of Plastic Engrs. Republican. Episcopalian. Avocations: tennis, antique refinishing. Home: 3018 Eton Rd Raleigh NC 27608-1112 Office: Morganite Inc 1 Morganite Dr Dunn NC 28334-3699

MULLER, EDWARD ROBERT, lawyer; b. Elmira, Mar. 26, 1952; s. Rudolph E. and Elizabeth (Steiner) M.; m. Patricia Eileen Bauer, Sept. 27, 1980; children: Margaret Anne, John Frederick. AB summa cum laude, Dartmouth Coll., 1973; JD, Yale U., 1976. Assoc. Leva, Hawes, Symington, Martin & Oppenheimer, Washington, 1977-83; dir. legal affairs Life Scis. group Whittaker Corp., Arlington, Va., 1983-84; v.p. Whittaker Health Svcs., Arlington, Va., 1984-85; v.p., gen. counsel, sec. Whittaker Corp., L.A., 1985-93, chief adminstrv. officer, 1988-92, CFO, 1992-93, bd. dirs., 1993—; v.p., gen. counsel, sec. BioWhittaker, Inc., 1991-93; pres., CEO, bd. dirs. Mission Energy Co., Irvine, Calif., 1993—; mem. Brookings Task Force on Civil Justice Reform, 1988-89. Trustee Exceptional Children's Found., L.A., 1988-94, treas., 1988-93; co-chair Internat. Energy Devel. Coun., Washington, 1993—. Office: Mission Energy Co 18101 Von Karmen Ave Ste 1700 Irvine CA 92715

MULLER, ERNEST H., geology educator; b. Tabriz, Iran, Mar. 4, 1923; (parents U.S. citizens); s. Hugo Arthur and Laura Barnett (McComb) M.; m. Wanda Custis, Apr. 7, 1951; children: Ruth Anne, David Stewart, Katherine Lee. BA, Wooster Coll., 1947; MS, U. Ill., 1949, PhD, 1952. Geologist U.S. Geol. Survey, Washington, 1947-54; asst. prof. geology Cornell U., Ithaca, N.Y., 1954-59; assoc. prof. Syracuse U., N.Y., 1959-63, prof., 1963-89, interim chmn. dept. geology, 1970-71, 79-81, prof. emeritus, 1989—; seasonal geologist N.Y. Geol. Survey, 1956-76; geologist Am. Geog. Soc., Chile, 1959; rsch. assoc. Natural History Mus., Rejkjavik, Iceland, 1968-69; vis. prof. Alaska Pacific U., Anchorage, 1979; Erskine vis. prof. U. Canterbury, Christchurch, New Zealand, 1974; mem. Bering Glacier (Alaska) Rsch. Group, 1988—; N.Y. Pleistocene Stratigraphy. Author: Geology of Chautauqua County, New York, 1964, Seaway Trail Rocks and Landscapes, 1987. 1st lt. USAAF, 1943-46. Fellow Geol. Soc. Am. (geomorphology panel 1962-64, 66-68, 75-77), AAAS; mem. Am. Quaternary Assn. (counselor 1982-86), Glaciological Soc., Nat. Assn. Geology Tchrs., Sigma Xi. Home: 874 Livingston Ave Syracuse NY 13210-2936 Office: Syracuse U 204 Heroy Geology Lab Syracuse NY 13244-1070

MULLER, FRANK B., advertising executive; b. Copenhagen, Denmark, Nov. 25, 1926; came to U.S., 1927; s. Herman B. and Johanne M. (Ammentorp) M.; m. Judith Hunter, Apr. 14, 1956; children: Mark W., Hunter J., Frank B. Student, Harvard U., 1944; BNS in Naval Sci., Tufts Coll., 1946; BS in Mech. Engring., Tufts U., 1948. Account supr. advt. dept. GE, 1948-55; exec. v.p. Muller Jordan Weiss Inc., N.Y.C., 1955-90; pres. MultiMedia Unltd., Inc., N.Y.C., 1990—. Lt. (j.g.) USNR, 1944-47. Mem. ASME. Republican. Congregationalist. Clubs: N.Y. Yacht (N.Y.C.); Saugatuck Harbor Yacht (Westport, Conn.) (bd. govs. 1965-75, 79-80, commodore 1970-71). Home: 46 Marion Rd Westport CT 06880-2923 Office: MultiMedia Unltd Inc 280 Madison Ave New York NY 10016

MULLER, FREDERICA DANIELA, psychology educator; d. Leopold and Elena; m. Dr. L. Muller; children: Daniela, Adrian. Grad. Med. Inst. Radiology, Romania, 1962; PsyD in Clin. Psychology, 1965, M in Internat. Law and Bus., 1966; postgrad. in psychodrama, Vienna, 1969; grad. rsch. specialization, Instituto Dermatologica, Rome, 1970; postgrad., Miami Inst. Psychology, 1987. Lic. psychologist, Fla., psychotherapist, Fla. Prof. Sch. Continuing Edn. Barry U., North Miami, Fla.; instr. advanced courses in psychology, psychodrama, med. ethics, social manners Colloqué Internat., Bucharest, Romania, 1989-93; guest lectr. U. Arboga, Sweden 1968-72; founder Internat. Studies for Biopsychosocial Issues, 1991; cons. dept. of marriage, family and child devel. systemic studies, Nova U., 1992; founder Euro Am. Exch. Co., 1980; with Santé Internat., Switzerland, 1982-85. Conducted rsch. on stress and aging with Dr. Anna Aslan, world renowned author; developed 45 minute stress reduction program for use in the work place. Author: The Management of Occupational Stress and Its Linkage to

Social Pressures; contbr. articles to profl. jours. Mem. Medicins du Monde (hon.), Am. Soc. Group Psychotherapy and Psychodrama, Soc. Psychol. Studies Social Issues, World Fedn. for Mental Health.

MULLER, GEORGE T., automotive executive; b. 1949. CPA. Acct. Arthur Andersen & Co., 1972-78; with Auto Parts Distbn., 1978-79; with Subaru of Am., Inc., Cherry Hill, N.J., 1979—, pres., COO. Office: Subaru of Am Inc 2235 Route 70 W Cherry Hill NJ 08002-3308 Office: PO Box 6000 Cherry Hill NJ 08034-6000

MULLER, HENRY JAMES, journalist, magazine editor; b. Garmisch-Partenkirchen, Germany, Feb. 10, 1947; came to U.S., 1953; s. Henri Jacques and Helga (Mensch) M.; m. Maggie McComas, June 19, 1968. BA, Stanford U., 1968. Tchr. U.S. Peace Corps, Ethiopia, 1968-70; chief Vancouver (B.C., Can.) bur. Time mag., 1971-73; European econ. corr. Time mag., Brussels, 1973-77; chief Paris bur. Time mag., 1977-81; world editor Time mag., N.Y.C., 1982-85, chief of corrs., 1986-87, mng. editor, 1987-93; editorial dir. Time Inc., 1993—; faculty mem. profl. pub. course Stanford (Calif.) U., 1989—. Trustee Stanford U., 1991—, Carnegie Corp., 1992—, Overseas Press Club, 1993—. Recipient David Brower Environ. Journalism award Sierra Club, 1990, Gerald Loeb award for disting. bus. and fin. journalism, 1992. Mem. Am. Soc. Mag. Editors (bd. dirs. 1991-95), Coun. of Fgn. Rels. Avocations: hiking, reading, skiing. Office: Time Inc Time & Life Bldg Rockefeller Ctr New York NY 10020

MULLER, HENRY JOHN, real estate developer; b. N.Y.C., July 27, 1919; s. Henry and Anne (Wulf) M.; m. Cecelia M. Ziffer, May 19, 1943; children: Richard, Robert, Ceil Anne, Roger. BS, Bklyn. Poly. Inst., 1949. Engr. GE Co., Bloomfield, N.J., 1948-49, Prudential Ins. Co., Newark, 1949-56; dep. dir. Harvard U., 1956-64; sr. v.p. 1st Nat. City Bank, N.Y.C., 1964-71; chmn. Citicorp. Realty, N.Y.C., 1971-72; sr. v.p. Allied Maintenance Corp., N.Y.C., 1972-74; exec. v.p. Moorings Devel. Co., Vero Beach, Fla., 1974-77; pres. Muller & Assocs. Inc., Vero Beach, 1977-89, Criterion Svcs. Corp., Vero Beach, 1988—. With AUS, 1941-46. Mem. Tau Beta Pi, Lambda Chi Alpha. Home: 5954 River Run Dr Sebastian FL 32958-4709 Office: Criterion Svcs Corp 8730 US 1 Micco FL 32976

MULLER, H(ENRY) NICHOLAS, III, historical society director; b. Pitts., Nov. 18, 1938; s. Henry N. Jr. and Harriet (Kerschner) M.; m. Nancy Clagett, June 20, 1959 (div. 1985); children: Charles T., Brook W.; m. Carol A. Cook, Jan. 4, 1986. BA, Dartmouth Coll., 1960; PhD, U. Rochester, 1968. Instr. Dartmouth Coll., Hanover, N.H., 1964; lectr. Mt. Allison U., Sackville, N.B., Can., 1964-66; asst. prof. history U. Vt., Burlington, 1966-69; assoc. prof. history, 1970-73; prof. history U. Vt., Burlington, 1974-78, asst. dean Coll. Arts and Scis., 1969-70, assoc. dean Coll. Arts and Scis., 1970-73, dir. Living/Learning Ctr., 1973-78; pres. Colby-Sawayer Coll., New London, N.H., 1978-85; dir. State Hist. Soc. Wis., Madison, 1985—; chmn. State Hist. Records Adv. Bd., 1985—, Wis. Burial Sites Bd., 1988—; bd. dirs. Wis. Submerged Cultural Resources, Standex Internat. Corp., Salem, N.H., Nat. Trust for Hist. Preservation; mem. Gov. Coun. on Tourism, 1987—. Co-author: An Anxious Democracy, 1982; co-editor: Science, Technology and Culture, 1974, In a State of Nature, 1982; sr. editor Vt. Life mag., 1975-87; editor Vt. History, 1977-85. Chmn. Bicentennial Com., Burlington, 1976, Vt. Coun. Hist. Preservation, 1975-78; fin. chmn. Vt. Bicentennial Commn., 1970-77; mem. N.H. Postsecondary Edn. Commn., 1983-85; trustee Vt. Hist. Soc., 1972-85, v.p., 1975-82; bd. dirs. USS Wisconsin, 1989-93, Wis. Preservation Fund Inc., 1989—; trustee, vice chmn. Taliesin Preservation Commn., 1990—. Fellow Ctr. for Nat. on Vt.; mem. Nat. Coun. on Pub. History (bd. dirs. 1988-90), Am. Assn. State and Local History (councillor 1988-91), Vt. Archaeol. Soc. (pres. 1971-74), Madison Club, Rotary. Office: State Hist Soc Wis 816 State St Madison WI 53706-1482

MULLER, JENNIFER, choreographer, dancer; b. Yonkers, N.Y., Oct. 16, 1944; d. Don Medford and Lynette (Heldman) Muller. BS, Juilliard Sch. Music, 1967. instr. in dance H.S. Performing Arts, 1967-72, Sarah Lawrence Coll., 1968-72, The Juilliard Sch., 1969-70, Nederlands Dans Theater, 1971-76, U. Utah, 1973-74, Alvin Ailey Am. Dance Theatre, N.Y.C., 1977-85, Festival d'Avignon, France, 1980, Aterballetto, 1988, Ballet Stagium, 1991, Dansgroep Krisztina de Chatel, 1992, Tanz-Forum der Opera Stadtkoln Sachsische Staatopera-Dresden, ARTSCAPE-Balt., 1991, 95, Aterballetto, Italy, 1993, Les Ballet Jazz de Montreal, 1994, Ballet du Nord, France, 1995, Bat Dor Dance Co., Israel, Nederlands Dans Theatre III, Ballet Contemporaneo, Argentina; cons. Met. Mus. Art, 1971-72. Mem. Pearl Lang Dance Co., N.Y.C, 1959-63, prin. dance, Jose Limon Dance Co., N.Y.C., 1963-71, assoc. dir., choreographer, prin. dancer, Louis Falco Dance Co., N.Y.C., 1968-74; founder, dir. choreographer: Jennifer Muller/The Works, N.Y.C., 1974—; choreographic works include: Nostalgia, 1971, Rust, 1971, Cantata, 1972, Tub, 1973, An American Beauty Rose, 1974, Biography, 1974, Speeds, 1974, Winter Pieces, 1974, Clown, 1974, Four Chairs, 1974, Wyeth, 1974, White, 1975, Strangers, 1975, Beach, 1976, Crossword, 1977, Predicaments for Five, 1977, Mondrian, 1977, Lovers, 1978, Solo, 1979, Conversations, 1979, Chant, 1980, Terrain, 1981, Shed, 1982, Kite, 1983, Souls, 1984, The Enigma, 1985, Fields, 1985, Darkness and Light, 1986, Interrupted River, 1987, Occasional Encounters, 1988, City, 1988, The Flight of a Predatory Bird, 1989, Refracted Light, 1990, Righteous About Passing (on the Left), 1990, Woman with Visitors at 3 am, 1991, Regards, 1991, arm in arm in arm..., 1991, Thesaurus, 1991, Glass Houses, 1991, 2-1=1/Attic, 1992, Momentary Gathering, 1992, The Waiting Room, 1993, The Politician/Peeling the Onion, 1993, Orbs, Spheres and Other Circular Bodies, 1993, Human/Nature A Response to the Longhouse Gardens, 1993, Pierrot, 1993, Desire-That DNA Urge, 1994, Point of View (A Case of Persimmons and Picasso), 1994, The Spotted Owl, 1995; commissions include Lyon Opera Ballet, 1984; choreographer for theatrical prodns.: Frimbo, 1980, The Death of von Richthofen..., 1982, Fame, The Musical, 1988, Up Against It, 1989, The Seven Deadly Sins, 1990, Signature, 1990, Esther, 1993. Recipient Best Performance award Berlin Festival, 1977, Acad. award Juilliard Sch. Music, 1967, Carbonell award, 1989; grantee Nat. Endowment for Arts, 1971-77, 80-85, 86-87, 87-88, Creative Artists Pub. Svc., 1976-77, N.Y. State Coun. on Arts, 1976-77, 78-79, 85-93, N.Y.C. Dept. Cultural Affairs, 1978-79, 94. Mem. Am. Guild Mus. Artists, Soc. Stage Dirs. and Choreographers. Home and Office: The Muller/Works Found Inc 131 W 24th St New York NY 10011-1942

MULLER, JEROME KENNETH, editor, photographer; b. Amityville, N.Y., July 18, 1934; s. Alphons and Helen (Haberl) M.; m. Nora Marie Nestor, Dec. 21, 1974. BS, Marquette U., 1961; postgrad., Calif. State U., Fullerton, 1985-86; MA, Nat. U., San Diego, 1988; postgrad., Newport Psychoanalytic Inst., 1988-90. Comml. and editorial photographer N.Y.C., 1952-55; mng. editor Country Beautiful mag., Milw., 1961-62, Reprodns. Rev. mag., N.Y.C., 1967-68; editor, art dir. Orange County (Calif.) Illustrated, Newport Beach, 1962-67, art editor, 1970-79, exec. editor, art dir. 1968-69; owner, CEO Creative Svcs. Advt. Agy., Newport Beach, 1969-79; founder, CEO Mus. Graphics, Costa Mesa, Calif., 1978—; tchr. photography Lindenhurst (N.Y.) High Sch., 1952-54; tchr. comic art U. Calif., Irvine, 1979; guest curator 50th Anniversary Exhbn. Mickey Mouse, 1928-78, The Bowers Mus., Santa Ana, Calif., 1978; organized Moving Image Exhbn. Mus. Sci. and Industry, Chgo., Cooper-Hewitt Mus., N.Y.C., William Rockhill Nelson Gallery, Kansas City, 1981; collector original works outstanding Am. cartoonists at major mus. One-man shows include Souk Gallery, Newport Beach, 1970, Gallery 2, Santa Ana, Calif., 1972, Cannery Gallery, Newport Beach, 1974, Mus. Graphics Gallery, 1993; Author: Rex Brandt, 1972; contbr. photographs and articles to mags. Served with USAF, 1956-57. Recipient two silver medals 20th Ann. Exhbn. Advt. and Editorial Art in West, 1965. Mem. APA, Am. Assn. Mus. Profl. Hypnotherapists, Newport Harbor Art Mus., Mus. Modern Art (N.Y.C.), Met. Mus. Art, Art Mus. Assn. Am., Laguna Beach Mus. Art, L.A. Press Club, Newport Beach Tennis Club, Alpha Sigma Nu. Home: 2438 Bowdoin Pl Costa Mesa CA 92626-6304 Office: PO Box 10743 Costa Mesa CA 92627-0234

MULLER, JOHN BARTLETT, university president; b. Port Jefferson, N.Y., Nov. 8, 1940; s. Frederick Henry and Estelle May (Reeve) M.; m. Barbara Ann Schmidt, May 30, 1964 (dec. 1972); m. Lynn Anne Spongberg, Oct. 10, 1987. AB in Polit. Sci., U. Rochester, 1962; postgrad. in apologetics, Westminster Sem., Phila., 1962-63; MS in Psychology, Purdue U., 1968, PhD in Psychology, 1975. Asst. prof. psychology Roberts Wesleyan

Coll., Rochester, N.Y., 1964-66, acting chmn. div. behavioral sci., dir. instl. research, 1967-70; vis. asst. prof. psychology Wabash Coll., Crawfordsville, Ind., 1970-71; research assoc. Ind. U.-Purdue U., Indpls., 1971-72; prof. psychology, v.p. for acad. affairs Hillsdale (Mich.) Coll., 1972-85; pres. BMW Assocs., Osseo, Mich., 1984-85, Bellevue (Nebr.) U., 1985—; bd. dirs. Nebr. Ind. Coll. Found., Omaha, Assn. Ind. Colls. Nebr., Lincoln; bd. advisors Norwest Bank of Bellevue, Applied Systems Tech., Inc. Contbr. articles to profl. jours. and textbooks. Bd. dirs. Midlands Community Hosp., 1989—, Boys Club of Omaha. Nat. Inst. Mental Health fellowship Purdue U., 1963, Nat. Tchg. fellowship Fed. Govt., 1967, Townsend fellowship U. Rochester, 1962. Mem. APA, Bellevue C. of C. (bd. dirs. 1989—), Phi Beta Kappa, Phi Kappa Phi. Republican. Home: 404 Ridgewood Dr Bellevue NE 68005-4745 Office: Bellevue U Office of the Pres 1000 Galvin Rd S Bellevue NE 68005-3098

MULLER, LYLE DEAN, religious organization administrator; b. Owatonna, Minn., Mar. 9, 1935; s. Robert John and Esther Ida (Eaker) M.; m. Marlene K. Kliemek, Sept. 7, 1957; children: Mark, Susan. BA, Valparaiso U., 1956; MDiv, Concordia Sem., 1961. Ordained to ministry Luth. Ch.-Mo. Synod. Pastor Emmanuel Luth. Ch., Ft. Wayne, Ind., 1961-63, Trinity Luth. Ch., Danville, Ill., 1963-69, St. Luke Luth. Ch., Itasca, Ill., 1969-79; exec. evangelism and missions no. Ill. Dist. Luth. Ch.-Mo. Synod, Hillsdale, 1979-90; exec. dir. evangelism svcs. Luth. Ch.-Mo. Synod, St. Louis, 1990—. Author: (manuals) Good News Day, 1982, Witness Workshop, 1983, Ministry to Inactives, 1987, Assimilation, 1988. Office: Luth Ch Mo Synod 1333 S Kirkwood Rd Saint Louis MO 63122-7226

MULLER, MARCEL W(ETTSTEIN), electrical engineering educator; b. Vienna, Austria, Nov. 1, 1922; came to U.S., 1940; s. Georg and Josephine (David) M.; m. Esther Ruth Hagler, Feb. 2, 1947; children: Susan, George, Janet. BSEE, Columbia U., 1949, AM in Physics, 1952; PhD, Stanford U., 1957. Sr. scientist Varian Assocs., Palo Alto, Calif., 1952-66; prof. elec. engring. Washington U., St. Louis, 1966-91, prof. emeritus, rsch. prof., 1991—; vis. lectr. U. Zurich, Switzerland, 1962-63; vis. prof. U. Colo., Boulder, summer 1969; vis. scientist Max Planck Inst., Stuttgart, Fed. Republic of Germany, 1976-77; cons. Hewlett-Packard Labs., Palo Alto, 1985-89, SRI Internat., Menlo Park, Calif., 1986—. Sgt. U.S. Army, 1943-46. Recipient Humboldt prize Alexander von Humboldt Soc., 1976; Fulbright grantee, 1977, grantee NSF, 1967—. Fellow IEEE, Am. Physical Soc. Achievements include development of Maser quantum noise theory; developments in micromagnetism; contributions to magnetic information storage. Home: 4954 Lindell Blvd Saint Louis MO 63108-1500 Office: Washington Univ Campus Box 1127 1 Brookings Dr Saint Louis MO 63130-4862

MULLER, MERVIN EDGAR, information systems educator, consultant; b. Hollywood, Calif., June 1, 1928; s. Emanuel and Bertha (Zimmerman) M.; m. Barbara McAdam, July 13, 1963; children: Jeffrey McAdam, Stephen McAdam, Todd McAdam. AB, UCLA, 1949, MA, 1951, PhD, 1954. Instr. in math. Cornell U., 1954-56; rsch. assoc. in math. Princeton U., 1956-59; sr. statistician, dept. mgr. IBM, N.Y.C., White Plains, 1956-64; sr. scientist statis. and elec. engring. Princeton U., 1968-69; prof. computer sci. and stats. U. Wis., 1964-71; prof. computer sci. George Mason U., 1985; dept. dir. World Bank, Washington, 1971-81, sr. advisor, 1981-85; Robert M. Critchfield prof. computer info. sci. Ohio State U., 1985—, dept. chair, 1985-94; chair sci. and tech. info. bd. NRC, NAS; bd. dirs. Advanced Info. Tech. Ctr., Columbus, Ohio. Contbr. numerous articles to profl. jours. Bd. trustees First Unitarian Ch., Bethesda, Md., 1975-79. NSF grantee AT&T, Columbus, Ohio, 1987. Fellow Am. Statis. Assn.; mem. Internat. Statis. Inst. (steering com. Internat. Rsch. Ctr., 1987-89), Internat. Assn. for Statis. Computing (sci. sec. 1979-83, pres. 1977-79). Avocations: reading, jogging, walking. Home: 4171 Clairmont Rd Columbus OH 43220-4501 Office: Ohio State U Dept Computer Info Sci 2015 Neil Ave Columbus OH 43210-1226

MULLER, NICHOLAS GUTHRIE, lawyer, business executive; b. Porterville, Calif., Nov. 27, 1942; s. Francis J. and Jane Ellen (Guthrie) M.; m. Sally Anne Diggles, June 10, 1964; children: Thomas, Amy. A.B. in English, U. Notre Dame, 1964; J.D., U. Calif., Berkeley, 1967. Bar: Colo. 1968. Lic. real estate broker, Colo. Summer intern Solicitor's Office, Dept. Interior, Washington, 1966; assoc. Gorsuch, Kirgis, Campbell, Walker & Grover, Denver, 1967-69; legal counsel Gates Aviation Corp., Denver, 1970-71; corp. sec., gen. counsel Gates Learjet Corp., Denver, 1971-72; legal counsel Samsonite Corp., Denver, 1972-75, gen. counsel, 1975-85, v.p.; 1978-85; gen. counsel Gates Corp. and Gates Rubber Co., 1985-87; mem. mgmt. com., gen. counsel Colo. Power Ptnrs., Denver, 1987—; exec. dir. Colo. Ind. Energy Assn., Denver. Formerly bd. dirs. Presbyn./St. Luke's Med. Ctr.; bd. dirs. Mt. Med. Affiliates, Leadership Denver. Mem. ABA, Colo. Bar Assn. (bd. dirs., bd. govs.), Denver Bar Assn., Am. Corp. Counsel (dir. nat. assn. and Colo. chpt.), U.S.C. of C., Denver C. of C., Notre Dame Club of Denver, Rotary. Home: 25931 Village Cir Golden CO 80401-7228 Office: Colorado Power Ptnrs 1675 Broadway Ste 2350 Denver CO 80202-4620

MULLER, PETER, lawyer, entertainment company executive, retail company executive, consultant; b. Teplitz-Sanov, Czechoslovakia, Mar. 4, 1947; came to U.S., 1949; s. Alexander and Elizabeth Rudolpha (Weingarten) M.; m. Irene Smolarski, Nov. 18, 1971 (div. 1973); children: Chloe, Aurora; m. Esther Unterman Meisler, Jan. 4, 1987 (div. 1995). BA, NYU, 1968, JD cum laude. Entertainment editor Ambience mag., N.Y.C., 1978-79, Women's Life mag., N.Y.C., 1980-81; sole practice N.Y.C., 1984—; chief exec. officer Producers Releasing Corp., N.Y. and Nev., 1987-88, pres. entertainment div., 1987-88; pres., founder Muller Entertainment Group, N.Y.C. and Calif., 1988—; pres., chief oper. officer ACA Joe, Inc., San Francisco and N.Y.C., 1989-90; also bd. dirs. ACA Joe Inc., San Francisco and N.Y.C.; expert tech. adv. svc. for attys., Pa., 1987—; lectr. entertainment and communication bus. to various orgns.; adj. prof. York U.; founder Peter Muller Essentialism, 1995. Author: Show Business Law, 1991, The Music Business: A Legal Perspective, 1994. Mem. Vol. Lawyers for the Arts, N.Y.C., 1987—. Mem. ABA (forum on entertainment and sports industries, forum on copyright, trademark and patent law), N.Y. State Bar Assn., NYU Alumni Assn. (bd. dirs. 1987—, v.p. bd. dirs, coun.), NYU Alumni Coun., Assn. of Am. Mgmt. Assn. (pres.). Avocations: sports, swimming, car enthusiast, writing, travel. Office: 100 S Doheny Dr Los Angeles CA 90048

MULLER, PRISCILLA ELKOW, curator; b. N.Y.C., Feb. 15, 1930; d. John and Katherine (Bulka) Elkow; m. C. Robert Muller, Feb. 15, 1950. BA, Bklyn. Coll., 1951; MA, NYU, 1959, PhD, 1963. Asst. curator Hispanic Soc. Am., N.Y.C., 1964-68; curator Hispanic Soc. Am., 1968—; lectr. Bklyn. Coll., 1966; cons. in field. Author: The Drawings of Antonio del Castillo y Saavedra, 1964, Jewels in Spain, 1972, Goya's Black Paintings, 1984, Sorolla: An 80th Anniversary Exhibition; contbr. articles to profl. jours. NEA fellow, 1977. Mem. Author's Guild, Coll. Art Assn. Am., Internat. Coun. Mus. (internat. com. fine arts), Am. Soc. Hispanic Art Hist. Studies, Internat. Found. Art Rsch. (adv. coun.), Internat. Inst. Spain, The Soc. for Jewelry Historians. Avocation: distance running. Office: Hispanic Soc Am Broadway 155th St New York NY 10032

MULLER, RALPH W., hospital administrator; b. 1945. With FCC, Washington, 1967, Harvard U., Boston, 1967-68, 69-70, Orgn. Social and Tech. Info., Cambridge, Mass., 1969-70, Suffolk U., Boston, 1969-72, Commonwealth of Mass., Boston, 1972-74, U. Chgo., 1974-80; pres. U. Chgo. Hosp., 1980—. Office: U Chicago Hosps 5841 S Maryland Ave Chicago IL 60637-1463

MULLER, RICHARD AUGUST, physicist, author; b. N.Y.C., Jan. 6, 1944; s. August Joseph and Catherine (Harabin) M.; m. Rosemary Findley, Sept. 3, 1966; children: Betsy, Melinda. AB, Columbia U., N.Y.C., 1964; PhD, U. Calif., Berkeley, 1969; LHD, Am. U., Switzerland. Leysin, 1989. Rsch. physicist U. Calif., Berkeley, 1969-78, assoc. prof. physics, 1978-80, prof. physics, 1980—; Jason cons. U.S. Dept. Def., Washington, 1980—; mem. arms control com. U.S. Nat. Acad. Scis., Washington, 1984-87; mem. adv. bd. Inst. Theoretical Physics, Santa Barbara, Calif., 1982-86; fellow Com. for Sci. Investigation Claims of Paranormal; author: Nemesis, 1988. Recipient Founder's prize Tex. Instruments Found., 1977, Alan T. Waterman award NSF, 1978; MacArthur Found. fellow, 1982. Fellow AAAS, Am. Phys. Soc.; mem. Am. Geophys. Union, Fedn. Am. Scientists (sponsor), Bohemian Club. Avocations: skiing, backpacking.

Home: 2831 Garber St Berkeley CA 94705-1347 Office: Lawrence Berkeley Lab 50-232 Lbl Berkeley CA 94720 *Learning is the second greatest joy in life.*

MULLER, RICHARD STEPHEN, electrical engineer, educator; b. Weehawken, N.J., May 5, 1933; s. Irving Ernest and Marie Victoria Muller; m. Joyce E. Regal, June 29, 1957; children: Paul Stephen, Thomas Richard. ME, Stevens Inst. Tech., Hoboken, N.J., 1955; MSEE, Calif. Inst. Tech., 1957, PhD in Elect. Engring. and Physics, 1962. Engr.-in-tng., 1955. Test engr. Wright Aero/Curtiss Wright, Woodridge, N.J., 1953-54; mem. tech. staff Hughes Aircraft Co., Culver City, Calif., 1955-61; instr. U. So. Calif., L.A., 1960-61; asst. prof., then assoc. prof. U. Calif., Berkeley, 1962-72, prof., 1973—; guest prof. Swiss Fed. Inst. Tech., 1993; dir. Berkeley Sensor and Actuator Ctr., 1985—. Co-author: Device Electronics for Integrated Circuits, 1977, 2d rev. edit., 1986, Microsensors, 1990; contbr. more than 200 articles to profl. jours. Pres. Kensington (Calif.) Mcpl. Adv. Coun. Fellow Hughes Aircraft Co. 1955-57, NSF 1959-62, NATO postdoctoral 1968-69, Fulbright 1982-83, Alexander von Humboldt prize 1993, Tech. U., Berlin, 1994. Fellow IEEE (press bd.); mem. NAE, Nat. Materials (adv. bd. 1994—), Electron Devices Soc. (adv. com. 1984—), Internat. Sensor and Actuator Meeting (chmn. steering com.). Achievements include 15 U.S. and foreign construction of first operating micrmotor. Office: U Calif Dept EECS 401 Cory Hall Berkeley CA 94720-1770

MULLER, RICHARD W. (WILHELM GUSTAV MULLER), importer architectural textiles, consultant on fabrics, designer, writer, former operatic baritone; b. Cologne, Germany, Aug. 15, 1909; came to U.S., 1926; s. Richard Otto Andreas and Magda Maria (Fassbinder) Muller; m. Marjorie Kathryn Alcorn, Aug. 15, 1936; children—Richard L., Marshall K. Tchr.'s cert. Am. Conservatory of Music, Chgo., 1929; B.A., Sherwood Music Sch., 1934; postgrad engring. and writing, Northwestern U., 1940. Sec. Sherwood Music Sch., Chgo., 1930-31; maintenance supr. Sinclair Refining Co., Chgo., 1931-40; spl. tng. apprentice Stroock's Woolen Mills, Newburgh, N.Y., 1926-27; test engr., asst. shift supt. Buick div. Gen. Motors, Melrose Park, Ill., 1940-45; pres., prin. Richard W. Muller & Assocs., Chgo., 1946—; witness com. on trade, Ways and Means Com., U.S. Ho. of Reps., 1981. Designer Lyric Opera entries Venetian Nights, 1982 (1st place award 1982, 83, 1st place overall 1983); asst. Frank Lloyd Wright, Keland Home, Racine, Wis., 1958; boy soprano Cologne Cathedral, 1918-19. Mem. German Am. Nat. Congress; sustaining mem. Republican Nat. Com., 1979—. Club: Chgo. Corinthian Yacht. Home: 700 Americana Dr Apt 52 Annapolis MD 21403-3180

MÜLLER, ROBBY, cinematographer; b. The Netherlands, Apr. 4, 1940. Cinematographer: (films) Summer in the City, 1970, The Goalie's Anxiety at the Penalty Kick, 1972, The Scarlet Letter, 1973, Alice in the Cities, 1974, The Wrong Move, 1975, Kings of the Road, 1976, The American Friend, 1977, Mysteries, 1979, Saint Jack, 1979, They All Laughed, 1981, The Glass Cell, 1981, Paris, Texas, 1984, Repo Man, 1984, Body Rock, 1984, Class Enemy, 1984, To Live and Die in L.A., 1985, The Longshot, 1986, Down By Law, 1986, Barfly, 1987, The Believers, 1987, Il Piccolo Diavolo, 1988, Mystery Train, 1989, Until the End of the World, 1991, Korczak, 1991, Mad Dog and Glory, 1993, (TV movies) Finnegan Begin Again, 1985. Office: Smith Gosnell Nicholson & Assocs PO Box 1166 1515 Palisades Dr Pacific Palisades CA 90272*

MULLER, ROBERT JOSEPH, JR., manufacturing company executive; b. Yonkers, N.Y., Oct. 29, 1946; s. Robert and Frances (Ritko) M.; m. Mary Elizabeth DeRoberts, Nov. 28, 1968; children: Robert, Jeffrey, Jennifer. B-SchemE, Manhattan Coll., 1968; MSChemE, U. Mass., 1969; MBA, U. Del., 1973. V.p. corp. devel. Vickers Petro div. Esmark, Wichita, Kans., 1978-81; pres. RTZ Ore Sorters div. RioTinto Zinc, Atlanta, 1981-84; v.p. merchandising systems Crane Internat., St. Louis, 1984-85, pres. merchandising systems, 1985-87; pres. engineered materials and merchandising systems Crane Co., N.Y.C., 1987-88, exec. v.p., 1988—. Lt. USN, 1969-74. Mem. Nat. Automatic Merchandising Assn. (bd. dirs. 1985—). Republican. Roman Catholic. Avocations: tennis, racquetball, hunting, gardening, travel. Office: Crane Co 711 Fifth Ave New York NY 10022-3109

MULLER, SCOTT WILLIAM, lawyer; b. Stamford, Conn., Feb. 15, 1950; s. Robert Sielke and Patricia (Harris) M.; m. Caroline Severance Adams, June 24, 1972; children: Christopher Adams, Robin McPherson, Peter Severance. BA, Princeton U., 1971; JD, Georgetown U., 1975. Bar: N.Y. 1976, U.S. Dist. Ct. (so. dist.) N.Y. 1977, U.S. Ct. Appeals (2d. cir.) 1978, U.S. Supreme Ct. 1978, U.S. Tax Ct. 1984, D.C. 1986. Law clk. to presiding justice U.S. Ct. Appeals (3d cir.), Phila., 1975-76; assoc. Davis, Polk & Wardwell, Washington, 1976-78, 82-84, ptnr., 1985—; asst. atty. criminal div. U.S. Atty's Office, N.Y.C., 1978-82. Served with NG, 1971-72. Mem. ABA, N.Y. State Bar Assn., Fed. Bar Assn., Assn. of Bar of City of N.Y. Republican. Episcopalian. Office: Davis Polk & Wardwell 1300 I St NW Washington DC 20005-3314

MULLER, SIGFRID AUGUSTINE, dermatologist, educator; b. Panama City, Panama, Feb. 20, 1930; came to U.S., 1932, naturalized, 1967; s. Louis and Marciana (Espino) M.; m. Jane Barbara Zierden, Dec. 28, 1964; children—Sigfrid Augustine, Stephen, Scott, Maria. A.B., Pepperdine U., 1949; M.D., St. Louis U., 1953; M.S., Mayo Grad. Sch. Medicine, 1958. Intern Gorgas Hosp., C.Z., 1953-54; resident Indpls. Hosp., 1954-55, Mayo Grad. Sch. Medicine, 1955-58; practice medicine specializing dermatology Rochester, Minn., 1961—; cons. dermatology Mayo Clinic, 1961—; asst. prof. dermatology U. Panama, 1958-60; prof. dermatology Mayo Clinic, 1972—, Robert H. Kieckhefer prof. dermatology, 1983—, chmn. dept., 1983-94, dir. dermatology residency tng., 1983-94, dir. dermatopathology lab., 1983-94; dir. task force for genetics Nat. Program for Genetics, 1969; bd. dirs., treas. Found. for Internat. Dermatol. Edn., 1976-85, pres., 1985—. Contbr. articles to profl. jours. Asst. chief editor: Archives of Dermatology, 1974—, Medicins Cutanea, 1968—, Internat. Bull. Psoriasis, 1973—. Recipient Pres.'s award Pepperdine U., 1973, condecoracion Order of Vasco Nunez de Balboa, Panama, 1994. Fellow ACP; mem. Am. Dermatol. Assn., Am. Acad. Dermatology, Soc. Investigative Dermatology, Am. Soc. Dermatopathology, AAAS, AMA, Am. Fedn. Clin. Rsch., Minn. Dermatol. Soc. (pres. 1972-73), Soc. Dermatol. Genetics (pres. 1972-73), Noah Worcester Dermatol. Soc. (pres. 1972-73), Internat. Soc. Dermatology (v.p., sec.-gen. 1979-89, pres. 1989—), Found. for Internat. Dermatol. Edn. (sec./treas. 1975-84, pres. 1985—). Home: 1237 Skyline Dr SW Rochester MN 55902-0940 Office: 200 1st St SW Rochester MN 55905-0001 *I have never felt like a foreigner in this wonderful land of opportunity. Rather, I perceived at an early age that achievement is within almost everyone's abilities. Ultimately, my success will not be determined by honors or recognition but by love: love of God, love of family, and love of my fellow man.*

MULLER, WILLARD C(HESTER), writer; b. Havre, Mont., May 7, 1916; s. Chester Rudolph and Clara (Hansen) M.; m. Carolyn Elfrid Bue, Jan. 27, 1945; children: Marolyn Jean, Barbara Anne, Nancy Eleanor. BA, Stanford U., 1941; MPA, Maxwell Grad. Sch. Govt. Adminstrn., 1943; student, Nat. War Coll., 1961-62. Newspaper reporter, short story writer Bremerton (Wash.) Daily Searchlight, 1934-36; White House corr. Bremerton Daily Searchlight and Port Angeles Evening News, Washington, 1941; mgmt. analyst USDA, 1942, 46-47; mem. staff for food, agr. and forestry U.S. Dept. Army and U.S. High Commr. for Germany, Munich and Frankfurt, Fed. Republic Germany, 1948-50; dist. adminstr., Am. consul U.S. Trust Territory of Pacific Islands, Truk, Caroline Islands, 1951-55; dep. dir. ICA, U.S. Ops. Mission to Nepal, Kathmandu, 1956-58; dir. U.S. Ops. to Somali Republic, 1958-61, Office East and Southern African Affairs, AID, Dept. State, Washington, 1962-65, AID, Kampala, Uganda, 1965-70; assoc. dir. for land reform AID, Saigon, Republic of Vietnam, 1970-73; ret. AID, 1973, cons., 1974-81; free lance writer, 1973—. Author various short stories; contbr. artcles to profl. jours. Chmn. steering com. 4-state program dialogue on peace Pacific NW dist. Am. Luth. Ch., Seattle, 1983-85; mem. Clallam br. Wash. State Centennial Commn., 1986-89; mem. Food Bank Bd., Port Angeles, Wash., 1986-90. Lt. USNR, 1943-45, PTO. Mem. Am. Soc. Pub. Adminstrn., Am. Forestry Assn., Am. Fgn. Service Assn., Pacific N.W. Morgan Horse Assn. Lodge: Kiwanis. Avocations: horseback riding, backpacking, world travel. Home: 3624 S Mt Angeles Rd Port Angeles WA 98362-9347 Office: 3624 S Mount Angeles Rd Port Angeles WA 98362-8910

MULLER, WILLIAM HENRY, JR., surgeon, educator; b. Dillon, S.C., Aug. 19, 1919; s. William Henry and Octavia Elizabeth (Bethea) M.; m. Hildwin Clare Headly, Mar. 23, 1946; children: William Henry III, Marietta John Lewis. BS, The Citadel, 1940, DS (hon.), 1972; MD, Duke U., 1943; DHL (hon.), Med. U. S.C., 1977. Diplomate Am. Bd. Thoracic Surgery, Am. Bd. Surgery (rep. conf. com. grad. tng. in surgery). Intern Johns Hopkins Hosp., Balt., 1944, asst. surgery, asst. resident, 1944-46, resident gen. surgery, instr. surgery, 1948-49, resident cardiovascular surgery, 1949; practice gen. surgery Dillon, 1947-48; asst. prof. surgery UCLA, 1949-53, assoc. prof. Sch. Medicine, 1953-54; attending specialist thoracic surgery Wadsworth VA Hosp., Los Angeles; chief sect. cardiovascular surgery Los Angeles County-Harbor Gen. Hosp., Torrance, Calif.; cons. surgery St. John's, Santa Monica Hosps., 1949-54; cons. cardiovascular surgery U.S. Naval Hosp., San Diego, 1953-54; Stephen H. Watts prof. surgery, chmn. dept. U. Va. Sch. Medicine, 1954-82, v.p. health affairs, 1976-88, univ. prof. surgery and health policy, 1988-90, S. Hurt Watts prof. surgery emeritus, 1990—, v.p. for health affairs emeritus; surgeon-in-chief U. Va. Hosp., 1954-82; chmn. S.E. Surg. Congress; mem. Pres.'s Panel on Heart Disease, 1972; past chmn. surgery study sect. NIH; mem. exec. com., div. med. scis. NRC. Mem. editorial bd.: Am. Jour Surgery, Annals of Surgery, Am. Surgeon; contbr. articles to med jours. Trustee, mem. exec. com. Duke U. Served as capt. M.C. AUS, 1946-47. Named One of 10 Outstanding Young Men of Yr. U.S. Jr. C. of C., Calif. Jr. C. of C., 1952; recipient Disting. Alumni award (1st award) Duke U. Med. Ctr., 1969; Thomas Jefferson award U. Va., 1982; McCallie Sch. Alumni Achievement award, 1986; Paul Harris fellow Nat. Rotary Found., 1988. Fellow ACS (past chmn., forum com. fundamental surg. problems, regent 1971—, chmn. bd. regents 1976-78, pres.-elect 1979); mem. Internat. Soc. Surgery, Internat. Cardiovascular Soc. (past v.p.), AMA, Am. Surg. Assn. (pres. 1974-75), So. Surg. Assn. (pres. 1975), Pacific Coast Surg. Assn., Am. Assn. Thoracic Surgery, Soc. Univ. Surgeons (past pres.), Soc. Surgery Alimentary Tract, Assn. Acad. Surgeons, James IV Assn. Surgeons (v.p. U.S.), Med. Soc. Va., Albemarle County Med. Soc., Soc. Vascular Surgery (past pres.), Am. Heart Assn. (chmn. surgery research study com., mem. central research com.), Va. Surg. Soc, Halsted Soc., Johns Hopkins Soc. Scholars, Raven Soc., Sigma Xi, Alpha Omega Alpha, Phi Chi. Office: U Va Health Sci Ctr PO Box 470 Charlottesville VA 22902-0470

MÜLLER-EBERHARD, HANS JOACHIM, medical research scientist, administrator; b. Magdeburg, Germany, May 5, 1927; came to U.S., 1959, naturalized, 1973; s. G. Adolf and Emma (Jenrich) Müller-E.; m. Irma Gigli, June 29, 1985. M.D., U. Göttingen, Fed. Republic Germany, 1953; M.D.Sc., U. Uppsala, Sweden, 1961; D. Medicinae h.c., Ruhr U., Bochum, W.Ger., 1982. Asst. physician dept. medicine U. Göttingen, 1953-54; asst., also asst. physician hosp. Rockefeller Inst., 1954-57; fellow Swedish Med. Research Council, 1957-59; asst. prof., then assoc. prof., also hosp. physician Rockefeller U., 1959-63; mem. dept. exptl. pathology Scripps Clinic and Research Found., La Jolla, Calif., 1963-74, chmn. dept. molecular immunology, 1974-82, chmn. dept. immunology, 1982-85, head div. molecular immunology, 1985-87; assoc. dir. Scripps Clinic and Research Found. (Research Inst.), 1978-86; dir. Bernhard Nocht Inst. for Tropical Medicine, Hamburg, Fed. Republic Germany, 1988—; Cecil H. and Ida M. Green investigator med. rsch., 1972-86; lectr. immunochemistry U. Uppsala, 1961—; Harvey lectr., 1970; adj. prof. pathology U. Calif. Med. Sch., La Jolla, 1968—; prof. U. Hamburg, 1990—; vis. prof. internal medicine U. Tex. Med. Sch., Houston, 1991—. Co-editor: Textbook of Immunopathology, 1976, Springer Seminars in Immunopathology, 1978-87; author numerous sci. articles; adv. editor: Jour. Exptl. Medicine, 1963—; mem. jour. editorial bds. Recipient Squibb award Infectious Diseases Soc. Am., 1970; T. Duckett Jones Meml. award Helen Hay Whitney Found., 1971; Distinguished Achievement award Modern Medicine mag., 1974; Karl Landsteiner Meml. award Am. Assn. Blood Banks, 1974; ann. Internat. award Gairdner Found., Can., 1974; Mayo H. Soley award Western Soc. Clin. Research, 1975; Emil von Behring prize Philipps U., Marburg, Ger., 1977; Caballero de la Orden de San Carlos (Colombia), 1984, Robert Koch Medal in Gold, 1987, Rous-Whipple award Am. Assn. Pathologists, 1988, Philip Levine award Am. Soc. of Clin. Pathologists, 1988. Fellow AAAS; mem. NAS, Am. Soc. Exptl. Pathology (Parke, Davis award 1966), Assn. Am. Physicians, Western Assn. Physicians, Am. Soc. Clin. Investigation, Am. Assn. Immunologists, Am. Acad. Allergy, Am. Soc. Biochemistry and Molecular Biology, Sigma Xi. Office: Bernhard Nocht Inst for Tropical Medicine, Bernhard-Nocht-Strasse 74, 20359 Hamburg Germany

MULLIGAN, ELINOR PATTERSON, lawyer; b. Bay City, Mich., Apr. 20, 1929; d. Frank Clark and Agnes (Murphy) P.; m. John C. O'Connor, Oct. 28, 1950; children: Christine Fulena, Valerie Clark, Amy O'Connor, Christopher Criffan O'Connor; m. William G. Mulligan, Dec. 6, 1975. BA, U. Mich. 1950; JD, Seton Hall U., 1970. Bar: N.J., 1970. Assoc. Springfield and Newark, 1970-72; pvt. practice, Hackettstown, N.J., 1972; ptnr. Mulligan & Jacobson, N.Y.C., 1973-91, Mulligan & Mulligan, Hackettstown, 1976—; atty. Hackettstown Planning Bd., 1973-86, Blairstown Bd. Adjustment, 1973—; sec. Warren County Ethics Com., 1976-78, sec. Dist. X and XIII Fee Arbitration Com., 1979-87, mem. and chair., 1987-91, mem. dist. ethics com. XIII, 1992—; mem. spl. com. on atty. disciplinary structure N.J. Supreme Ct., 1981—; lectr. Nat. Assn. Women Judges, 1979. Contbr. articles to profl. jours. Named Vol. of Yr. Attys. Vols. in Parole Program, 1978. Fellow Am. Acad. Matrimonial Lawyers (pres. N.J. chpt. 1995—); mem. ABA, Warren County Bar Assn. (pres. 1987-88), N.J. State Bar Assn., Am. Mensa Soc., Kappa Alpha Theta, Union League Club (N.Y.C.), Baltusrol Golf Club (Springfield, N.J.), Panther Valley Golf and Country Club (Allamuchy, N.J.). Republican. Home: 12 Goldfinch Way Panther Valley Hackettstown NJ 07840 Office: 480 Hwy 517 PO Box 211 Hackettstown NJ 07840-0211

MULLIGAN, GERALD JOSEPH (GERRY MULLIGAN), composer, arranger, musician, songwriter; b. N.Y.C., Apr. 6, 1927; s. George V.R. and Louise (Shannon) M.; m. Contessa Franca Rota; 1 son, Reed Brown. Studied with Sam Correnti (saxophone), Johnny Warrington, Gil Evans, Charlie Parker, Duke Ellington (arranging and composition). Arranger, Johnny Warrington, Elliot Lawrence, Sta. WCAU, Phila., Tommy Tucker, Gene Krupa, Claude Thornhill, Kai Winding, Miles Davis; leader Gerry Mulligan Quartet, 1951—, Concert Jazz Band, 1957—; artist-in-residence U. Miami, 1974; rec. artist A&M Records, Columbia, Verve, Phillips, World Pacific, Concord, Atlantic, DRG, GRP; solo appearances N.Y. Philharm., London Symphony Orch., La Fenice, Venice, CBC Symphony, Toronto, Can., others; albums include Birth of the Cool, Gerry Mulligan Quartet, The Age of Steam, Litle Big Horn, Walk on Water (Grammy award 1981), Lonesome Boulevard, Mulligan Meets Monk, Mulligan Meets Webster, etc.; orchestral works rec. Symphonic Dreams (Houston Symphony), New American Music, Vol. 1 (The Sea Cliff Chamber Players), What is There To Say, 1994, Re-Birth of the Coop, 1992, Paraiso-Jazz Brazil, 1993, Live In Stockholm, 1995, Jazz 'Round Midnight, 1992, Dream a Little Dream with Ted Rosenthal et al, 1994, Verve Jazz Masters 36, 1994. Recipient numerous awards as baritone saxophonist including Down Beat new star award, Hall of Fame award Phila. Music Found., 1990, Viotti Gold medal, Italy, Grammy award Best Big Band performance for Walk on the Water, 1981; Duke Ellington fellow Yale U.; named to Down Beat Hall of Fame, 1993. Mem. ASCAP. Office: care Klaus Kolmar Touring Artists Group 1560 Broadway New York NY 10036-1525*

MULLIGAN, GERALD THOMAS, banker; b. Quincy, Mass., Dec. 13, 1945; s. Joseph I. and Louise (O'Callaghan) M.; m. Caroline Chambers, Sept. 22, 1979; children: Brian T., Elizabeth L., Timothy W. AB, Coll. of Holy Cross, Worcester, Mass., 1967; JD, Georgetown U., 1970; MBA, Harvard U., 1977. Bar: Mass. 1970, R.I. 1971, D.C. 1972. Law clk. to chief presiding justice U.S. Supreme Ct., Providence, 1970-71; staff atty. R.I. Legal Services, Inc., Boston, 1971-72; assoc. Gadsby & Hannah, Boston, 1972-73; staff atty. Bd. Govs. of Fed. Res. System, Washington, 1974-76; corp. lender 1st Nat. Bank Boston, 1977-79; commr. of banks Commonwealth of Mass., Boston, 1979-83; pres. 1st Mut. Boston, 1983—; bd. dirs. Mass. Higher Edn. Assistance Corp., Boston; MIL Electronics, Inc., Waltham, Mass., Fed. Home Loan Bank Boston, Mass. Thrift Insts. Fund for Econ. Devel. Treas., bd. dirs. Park St. Corp., Boston; bd. dirs. Cath. Charitable Bur. of Boston, Boston Housing Ptnrship., Inc., The New England Banking Inst.; corporator Mass. Gen. Hosp. Club: Bus. Assocs. (Boston). Office: 1st Mut Boston 800 Boylston St Boston MA 02199-8001

MULLIGAN, HUGH AUGUSTINE, journalist; b. N.Y.C., Mar. 23, 1925; s. John Joseph and Jeanette (Wilton) M.; m. Brigid Mary Murphy, Jan. 14, 1948. B.A. summa cum laude, Marlboro Coll., 1948, L.H.D. (hon.), 1973; M.A. in English Lit, Harvard U., 1951; M.S. in Journalism, Boston U., 1951. With AP, 1952—; feature writer AP, N.Y.C., 1956-65; fgn. corr. AP, Vietnam, 1965-68; fgn. corr. Biafra, Middle East, Paris Peace Talks, 1968-69, Cambodia, Laos, 1971, No. Ireland, Nigeria, Mid. East, China, Russia, Persian Gulf, Iceland, 1971-75, The Sahel, Angola, Ulster, Svalbard, Iran, 1975-77; columnist Biafra, Middle East, Paris Peace Talks, N.Y.C., 1977—; spl. corr. Biafra, Middle East, Paris Peace Talks, 1966—; as fgn. corr. covered wars in Vietnam, Middle East, Oman, Biafra-Nigeria, Cambodia, Upper Volta-Mali, No. Ireland, Vietnam, Middle East, Biafra-Nigeria, Oman, Upper Volta-Mali, No. Irel; as spl corr. covered papal journeys (Pope John Paul II) Mex., Poland, Ireland, U.S., Africa, Cen. Am., Brit. Isles, Can., 1979-87. Author: The Torch is Passed, 1963, No Place to Die, The Agony of Vietnam, 1967, (with Sid Moody, John Barbour) Lightning Out of Israel, 1967, anthologies How I Got That Story, 1967, Reporting, Writing from Front Row Seats, 1971, Best Sports Stories, 1980, 82, The Family Book of Humor, The Best of Irish Wit an Wisdom, 1987, The Annotated Night Before Christmas, 1991, (with Sid Moody) The 50th Anniversary: Pearl Harbor, 1991; editor: anthologies The World in 1964, 1965; now A.P. sr. feature writer and roving reporter. Served with U.S. Army, 1944-46. Recipient Gold medal Am. Newspaper Pubs. Assn., 1951, award for feature writing Nat. Headliners, 1963, award for fgn. coverage, 1967, award for internat. reporting Overseas Press Club, 1967, award for fgn. corr. Sigma Delta Chi, 1970, Mng. Editor's award for top reportial performance AP, 1972, 78, Disting. Alumni award Boston U. Sch. Pub. Communication, 1983, Yankee Quill award Acad. New Eng. Journalists, 1993; Eugene Pulliam lectureship Ball State U., 1985. Mem. Overseas Press Club, Sigma Delta Chi. Roman Catholic. Home: 50 Crest Rd Ridgefield CT 06877-2115 Office: 50 Rockefeller Plz New York NY 10020 *"Life is too short to read good books—read the best." This advice from a high school English teacher has given a golden glow to my leisure hours that TV's dreadful dross can never outsparkle.*

MULLIGAN, JAMES FRANCIS, retired business executive, lawyer; b. Attleboro, Mass., Aug. 27, 1925; s. Henry D. and Eleanor R. (Carey) M.; m. Mary Alice Mangels, Aug. 28, 1948; 1 child, Christopher. AB, Tufts U., 1947; JD, Columbia U., 1950. Bar: N.Y. 1950, Pa. 1968, U.S. Supreme Ct. 1986. Gen. atty. Erie-Lackawanna R.R., Cleve. and N.Y.C., 1950-61; gen. counsel Monroe Internat. div. Litton Industries, Orange, N.J., 1961-67; v.p., sec., gen. counsel Lukens Steel Co., Coatesville, Pa., 1967-83; v.p. law and corp. affairs, sec. Lukens, Inc., Coatesville, Pa., 1983-88; ret. Lukens, Inc., Coatesville, 1988. Pres. United War Chest County, West Chester, Pa., 1980-81. Lt. (j.g.) USNR, 1943-46. Mem. Radley Run Country Club, Springhaven Country Club, Mariner Sands Country Club. Avocations: running, golf. Home: PO Box 213 Pocopson PA 19366-0213 Home (winter): 5623 Foxcross Pl Stuart FL 34997

MULLIGAN, JAMES KENNETH, government official; b. Pawtucket, R.I., Aug. 31, 1911; s. James Alexander and Margaret (Fitzsimmons) M.; m. Louise Wring Lane, June 3, 1932; children—Kathryn Lane, Martha Louise, Jean Margaret. Ph.B., U. Chgo., 1934, M.A., 1937. Personnel adminstr. Chgo. Park Dist., 1938-40; dir. youth personnel Chgo. Nat. Youth Adminstrn., 1941-42; manpower analyst HEW, 1942-43; chief wage classification New Eng., Atlantic and Mediterranean area Dept. Navy, Boston, 1946-56; with U.S. CSC, Washington, 1956-71; exec. vice chmn. inter-agy. adv. group U.S. CSC, 1957-58; dir. Bur. Tng., 1959-71; cons. AID, State Dept., Nat. Civil Service League, WHO, 1971-79, Fed. Energy Adminstrn., UN, 1974-76; chmn. task force Presdl. Commn. on Exec., Legis. and Jud. Salaries, July-Dec. 1976; adj. instr. Boston U., 1955. Bgt. Agr. Grad. Sch., 1958. Chmn. Personnel Bd. Wakefield, Mass., 1954-56; mem. adv. bd. Washington Tech. Inst., 1969-70, George Washington U., 1970—; mem. governing bd. Washington Interns in Edn., 1966-68. Served to lt. USNR, 1944-46. Recipient Commr.'s award CSC, 1968, founder's award Federal Exec. Inst., 1993. Mem. Conf. Continuing Edn. for Public Adminstrn. (chmn. 1970). Address: 4615 Hunt Ave Chevy Chase MD 20815-5424

MULLIGAN, JOSEPH FRANCIS, physics educator; b. N.Y.C., Dec. 12, 1920; s. Joseph Lawrence and Mary (Collins) M.; m. Eleanor L. Wells 1984. Student, Fordham Coll., 1938-39, 41-43; A.B., Boston Coll., 1945, M.A., 1946; Ph.D. in Physics, Cath. U. Am., 1951. Instr. physics St. Peter's Coll., Jersey City, 1946-47; faculty Fordham U., 1955-68, assoc. prof. physics, 1963-68, chmn. dept., 1956-64, dean Grad. Sch. Arts and Scis., dean liberal arts faculty, 1964-67; prof. physics U. Md., Baltimore County, 1968-89, prof. emeritus, 1989—, dean for grad. studies and rsch., 1968-82. Mem. adv. com. grad. fellowship program NDEA, 1960-63. Author: Practical Physics: The Production and Conservation of Energy, 1980, Introductory College Physics, 2d edit., 1990, translated into 3-vol. Italian edit., Fisica, 1993; editor: Heinrich Rudolf Hertz (1857-1894); A Collection of Articles and Addresses, 1994; contbr. articles to profl. jours. NSF fellow U. Calif. at La Jolla, 1961-62. Mem. Am. Phys. Soc., Am. Assn. Physics Tchrs., History of Sci. Soc., AAAS, Sigma Xi. Home: 228 Canal Park Dr Salisbury MD 21801 Office: U Md 5401 Wilkens Ave Baltimore MD 21228-5329

MULLIGAN, MARTIN FREDERICK, clothing executive, professional tennis player; b. Sydney, Australia, Oct. 18, 1940; s. Frederick William and Marie Louise (Tome) M.; m. Rossella Rita Labella, Sept. 19, 1969 (div. Mar. 1980); children: Monica, Martin Thomas. Winner Tennis Singles Championships of Australia, 1952, 53, 55, 56, 57, 58; mem. Davis Cup team Australia, 1959, 60; winner Australian Hard Court Singles and Doubles tournaments, 1960, 64; finalist Wimbledon Singles tournaments, 1962; winner Italian Open Singles tournaments, 1963, 65, 67, German Open Singles tournament, 1963; winner singles and doubles titles Monte Carlo Championships, 1964; coach Italian Davis Cup team, 1966-76; winner, Davis Cup tournament, 1976; winner Spanish Open tournament, 1966, 67, Swedish Open tournament, 1966, 67, Austrian Open tournament, 1966, 67, Champion Cup tournament, 1966, 67; promotional cons. Alpina Australian Mfg. Co., 1973-74; cons. and internat. promotion mgr. Diadora Co., 1973-78; internat. promotion mgr. FILA U.S.A. Inc. subs. FILA-Italy Sportswear, Hunt Valley, Md., 1979-90, v.p. internat. promotion and pub. rels., 1979—; co-promotor, tournament dir. Italian Open Tennis Championships, 1972, 73; negotiator contracts between FILA and various sports profls. and celebrities. Ranked Number 3 in World in Tennis, 1967, ranked 5 times in world's top 10 tennis players. Avocation: stamp collecting. Office: FILA USA Inc 11350 Mccormick Rd Hunt Valley MD 21031-1016

MULLIGAN, MICHAEL DENNIS, lawyer; b. St. Louis, Mar. 9, 1947; s. Leo Virgil and Elizabeth (Leyse) M.; m. Theresa Baker, Aug. 7, 1971; children—Brennan, Colin. B.A. in Biology, Amherst Coll., 1968; J.D., Columbia U., 1971. Bar: Mo. 1971, U.S. Dist. Ct. (ea. dist.) Mo. 1972, U.S. Ct. Appeals (8th cir.) 1982, U.S. Tax Ct. 1985. Law clk. to judge U.S. Dist. Ct. (ea. dist.) Mo., 1971-72; assoc. Lewis & Rice, St. Louis, 1972-80, ptnr., 1980—. Served as cpl. USMC, 1968-70. Fellow Am. Coll. Probate Counsel; mem. ABA (mem. real property, probate and trust, and taxation sects.), Mo. Bar Assn. (mem. probate and trust, taxation sects.). Contbr. numerous articles to profl. jours. Mem. editorial bd. Estate Planning Mag., 1985—. Office: Lewis Rice & Fingersh 500 N Broadway Ste 2000 Saint Louis MO 63102-2130

MULLIGAN, RICHARD M., actor, writer; b. Bronx, N.Y., Nov. 13, 1932; s. Robert Edward and Ann-Elizabeth (Gingell) M.; m. Lenore Mulligan, June 25, 1978 (div.); 1 son, James. Regular on TV series The Hero, 1966, 67, Diana, 1973-74, Soap, 1977-80 (Emmy award 1980), Reggie, 1983, Empty Nest, NBC, 1988-95 (Emmy award 1989); numerous other TV appearances include Kate McShane, Charlie's Angels, Medical Story, Dog & Cat, Doctor's Hospital, Knowledge, Little House on the Prairie, Love Boat, Switch, Kingston, Mike Douglas Show, Merv Griffin Show, Dinah Shore Show, Hollywood Squares; TV movies include Jealousy, Malibu, Harvey, The Pueblo Incident, Having Babies III; films include One Potato, Two Potato, 1964, The Group, 1966, Little Big Man, 1970, A Change in the Wind, 1972, The Big Bus, 1976, S.O.B, 1981, Trail of the Pink Panther, 1982, Summertime, 1983, Mickey and Maude, 1984, Meatballs II, 1984, Teachers, 1984, The Heavenly Kid, 1985, A Fine Mess, 1986, Quicksilver, 1986, (voice) Oliver and Company, 1988; Broadway debut in All the Way Home, 1960; other Broadway plays include Special Occasions; other stage appearances include Mating Dance (Theatre World award), The Crucible, Luv, Other People, Pound on Demand, Nobody Loves an Albatross, Hogan's Goat (Theatre World award), Beyond the Horizon, Glass Menagerie, The Great God Brown; playwright: Never Too Late. Mem. Actors Equity Assn., AFTRA, Screen Actor's Guild. Que sais-je? (Montaigne).

MULLIGAN, ROBERT J., retail store executive, accountant; b. Bklyn., Oct. 24, 1938; s. William and Alice (Skelly) M.; m. Eileen Chrystal, Oct. 14, 1961; children: Brian, Peter. BBA in Acctg., St. John's U., N.Y.C. 1960. With Peat, Marwick, Mitchell & Co., 1960-65; sr. v.p. fin. and ops. Bonwit Teller, N.Y.C., 1965-71; sr. v.p., treas. Gimbels, N.Y.C., 1971-76; vice chair, chief adminstrv. officer, bd. dirs. Woodward & Lothrop Inc., Washington, 1976—; bd. dirs., asst. treas. Met. Washington Bd. of Trade, 1980—; bd. dirs. Nations Bank of Md., Bethesda. Bd. dirs. Sovereigh Mil. Order of Malta, Washington, 1984-87; trustee, vice chair Holy Cross Hosp., Silver Spring, Md., 1988-91; chmn. bd. trustees Georgetown Prep. Sch., Washington, 1986-89. Recipient Pres.'s award St. John's U., 1985. Mem. St. John's U. D.C. Area Alumni Assn. (pres. 1982-87), Soc. of Friendly Sons of St. Patrick of Washington (pres.). Roman Catholic. Clubs: Congl. (Bethesda); City, Met. (Washington), Econ. (Washington), Georgetown (Washington). Avocation: tennis. Office: Woodward & Lothrop Inc 1025 F St NW Washington DC 20004*

MULLIGAN, ROBERT PATRICK, film director, producer; b. N.Y.C., Nov. 13, 1932; s. Robert Edward and Elizabeth (Gingell) M. Grad., Fordham U. Dir.: TV prodns. including Philco Playhouse, Suspense, Playhouse 90; film producer/dir.: films The Jimmy Piersol Story, Come September, The Spiral Road, To Kill a Mockingbird, Love with the Proper Stranger, Inside Daisy Clover, Summer of '42, Bloodbrothers, Same Time Next Year, The Other, Kiss Me Goodbye, Nickel Ride, Stalking Moon, Baby the Rain Must Fall, Pursuit of Happiness, Up the Down Staircase, Clara's Heart, The Man in the Moon. Office: United Talent Agy 9560 Wilshire Blvd 5th fl Beverly Hills CA 90212*

MULLIGAN, ROBERT WILLIAM, university official, clergyman; b. Chgo., Oct. 11, 1916; s. John Sexton and Esther Mary (Cordesman) M. A.B., Loyola U., 1937; M.A., U. Detroit, 1946; Ph.D., Louvain U., Belgium, 1953; LL.D., U. Cin., 1976. Ordained priest Roman Cath. Ch., 1949; chmn. dept. philosophy Loyola U., 1953-59, trustee, 1958-71, v.p., dean faculties, 1959-69; provost Xavier U., Cin., 1971-72; pres. Xavier U., 1972-82; sec. St. Louis U., 1982-89; acad. v.p. St. Joseph's U., Phila., 1989—; cons. Grolier Soc., 1959-65; mem. vis. faculty Oxford U., Eng., 1970-71. Mem. adv. com. Bd. Higher Edn., Luth. Ch. Mo. Synod, 1966-67; chmn. bd. Greater Cin. Consortium Colls. and Univs., 1973; bd. dirs. Cin. chpt. ARC, Campion Hall, Oxford U., 1976—. Decorated chevalier Legion of Honor France; recipient Blue Key award, 1959; key City Cin., 1972. Mem. Am. Ednl. Assn., Am. Philos. Assn., Am. Cath. Philos. Assn. (chmn. Midwest chpt. 1956), Ill. Philos. Assn., No. Ill. Philos. Assn., Metaphys. Soc., Phi Sigma Tau (nat. pres. 1962—). Home: Saint Louis Univ Saint Louis MO 63103

MULLIGAN, WILLIAM G(OECKEL), machinery manufacturing company executive; b. Kingston, Pa., Aug. 5, 1930; s. Eugene W. and Marion (Goeckel) M. BS in Mining Engring., Lafayette Coll., 1952. With Ingersoll-Rand Co., Woodcliff Lake, N.J., 1952—; gen. mgr. constrn. and mining group, 1971-73, v.p., 1973-76, exec. v.p., from 1976. Office: Ingersoll Rand Co 200 Chestnut Ridge Rd Westwood NJ 07675-7703

MULLIGAN, WILLIAM HUGHES, lawyer, former federal judge; b. N.Y.C., Mar. 5, 1918; s. Stephen Hughes and Jane (Donahue) M.; m. Roseanna Connelly, Oct. 20, 1945; children: Anne O'Boyle Mulligan Hartmere, William Hughes, Stephen Edward. A.B. cum laude, Fordham U., 1939, LL.B. cum laude, 1942, LL.D., 1975; LL.D., St. Peter's Coll., Jersey City, 1966, Bklyn. Law Sch., 1972, Iona Coll., 1972, Villanova U., 1974, Pace U., 1979, Suffolk U., 1987; L.H.D., Siena Coll., 1967. Lectr. law Fordham U., 1946-52, assoc. prof., 1953-54, asst. dean. prof. law., 1954-56; dean Fordham U. (Law Sch.), 1956-71, Wilkinson prof. law, 1961-71; judge U.S. Ct. Appeals, 2d circuit, 1971-81; ptnr. firm Skadden, Arps, Slate, Meagher & Flom, N.Y.C., 1981-91; Mem. Law Revision Commn. State N.Y., 1958-71; chmn. exam. bd. Manhattan and Bronx Surface Transit Operating Authority, 1964-71; mem. N.Y. State Commn. on Constl. Conv., 1965; mem. adv. council Labor and Mgmt. Improper Practices Act, 1968-71; mem. state Commn. Rev. Legislative and Jud. Salaries, 1970-71; mem. Com. Adminstrn. Cts., 1970-71; bd. dirs. Fed. Jud. Center, 1979-81; internat. arbitrator; legal cons. counsel various state and local coms.; chmn. Citizens Com. of Reapportionment Gov. Rockefeller, 1964; assoc. chmn. N.Y. State Com. on Sentencing Guidelines, 1984-86. Contbr. articles to profl. publs. Gen. counsel Republican delegation N.Y. Constl. Conv., 1967; trustee St. Patrick's Cathedral, 1981-91; trustee Fordham U., 1982-88, trustee emeritus, 1989—; trustee Cath. Charities, Archdiocese of N.Y., 1985-91; mem. N.Y.C. Bd. Ethics, 1986-87. Served as spl. agt. CIC AUS, 1942-46. Recipient St. John de La Salle medal Manhattan Coll., 1967, Learned Hand award Am. Jewish Com., 1986; Encaenia medal Fordham Coll., 1966; Fordham Law Alumni medal, 1971; Gold medal N.Y. State Bar Assn., 1982. Mem. Fed. Judges Assn., Am. Judicature Soc. (bd. dirs. 1988-92), Rep. Lawyers Assn. (hon. nat. chmn. 1987—), Friendly Sons of St. Patrick (pres. 1983-85), Knights of Malta, Merchants Club. Roman Catholic.

MULLIKIN, HARRY COPELAND, mathematics educator; b. Flintville, Tenn., July 10, 1940; s. Houston Yost and Daisy (Copeland) M.; m. Gary W. Parker. Student, U. Paris, France, 1960-61; B.A., U. of the South, Sewanee, Tenn., 1963; M.A., U. Wis., Madison, 1964, Ph.D., 1968. Asst. prof. math. Pomona Coll., Claremont, Calif., 1968-74, assoc. prof. math., 1974-82, prof. math., 1982—, chmn. dept. math., 1979-85, William Polk Russell prof. math., 1984—, acting assoc. dean of students, 1982. Bd. dirs. Calif. br. Humane Soc. U.S., Long Beach, 1974-78; bd. dirs. Golden State Humane Soc., Garden Grove, Calif., 1974-82, sec., 1978-82. Woodrow Wilson fellow, 1963-64; recipient Disting. Prof. award Pomona Coll., 1972, 76, 80, 90. Mem. Am. Math. Soc., Math. Soc. Am., Assn. Computing Machinery, So. Calif. Phi Beta Kappa Alumni Assn. (treas. 1990-94), Phi Beta Kappa (chpt. pres. 1973-74, sec.-treas. 1979-80, 82-83). Democrat. Episcopalian. Home: 4433 N Glen Way Claremont CA 91711-2122 Office: Dept Math Pomona Coll Claremont CA 91711

MULLIKIN, THOMAS WILSON, mathematics educator; b. Flintville, Tenn., Jan. 9, 1928; s. Houston Yost and Daisy (Copeland) M.; m. Mildred Virginia Sugg, June 14, 1952; children—Sarah Virginia, Thomas Wilson, James Copeland. Student, U. South, 1946-47; A.B., U. Tenn., 1950; postgrad., Iowa State U., 1952-53; A.M., Harvard, 1954, Ph.D., 1958. Mathematician Rand Corp., Santa Monica, Calif., 1957-64; prof. math. Purdue U., 1964-93, interim v.p., dean grad. sch., 1991-93, dean grad. sch., prof. math emeritus, 1993—. Served with USNR, 1950-52. Mem. Am. Math. Soc., Soc. for Indsl. and Applied Math., AAAS, Sigma Xi. Home: Cape Carteret 104 Club Ct Swansboro NC 28584

MULLIKIN, VERNON EUGENE, aerospace executive; b. Windsor, Ill., July 16, 1935; s. Charles Austin and Oma Leah (Gilbreath) M.; m. Mary Lou Walker (div.); children: Michael, Mark; m. Joan Marie Boes, Aug. 1, 1986. BS in Aero. Engring., U. Ill., 1957; MBA, So. Ill. U., Edwardsville, 1977. Aero. engr. Northrup Aircraft Co., Hawthorne, Calif., 1957-60; group engr. Douglas Missile & Space Systems, Santa Monica, Calif., 1960-63; chief engr. McDonnell Douglas Astronautics Co., St. Louis, 1963-87; program dir. Convair div. Gen. Dynamics Corp., San Diego, 1987-92; sr. sci. engr. Hughes Missile Systems Co., Tucson, 1992—. Mem. AIAA (cert. recognition 1987), Phi Eta Sigma, Sigma Gamma Tau, Tau Beta Pi, Beta Gamma Sigma. Office: GM Hughes Missile Systems PO Box 11337 Mail Zone 847-B3 Tucson AZ 85734

MULLIN, CHRIS(TOPHER) PAUL, professional basketball player; b. N.Y.C., July 30, 1963. Student, St. John's U., 1981-85. Basketball player Golden State Warriors, 1985—; mem. U.S. Olympic Team (received Gold medal), 1984, 92. Recipient Wooden award, 1985; named to Sporting News All-Am. First Team, 1985, NBA All-Star team, 1989-93, NBA First Team, 1992—. Office: Golden State Warriors Oakland Coliseum Arena 7000 Coliseum Way Oakland CA 94621-1918*

MULLIN, J(ACK) SHAN, lawyer; b. Bellingham, Wash., Mar. 9, 1934; s. Jack D. and Naomi (Smith) M.; m. Lora Jane Fraser, Aug. 9, 1957; children: Barbara, Stephen, John, Anne. BS in Bus., U. Wash., 1956, JD, 1958. Bar: Wash. 1958, U.S. Supreme Ct. 1963. Assoc. Perkins Coie, Seattle, 1958-66, ptnr., 1967—; speaker various nat. and internat. sems. Co-author Legal Compliance Manual chpts. on internat. transactions, rev. edit., 1994. Mem. adv. bd. Pvt. Initiatives in Pub. Edn., Seattle, 1986-93, co-founder, 1980-81; co-founder Leadership Tomorrow, Seattle, 1982-83, bd. chmn., 1991; pres. Mcpl. League Seattle-King County, Seattle, 1976-78; trustee Law Sch. Found. U. Wash., Seattle, 1983-86, 90—, The Seattle Found., 1983-92; bd. dirs., exec. com. United Way King County, 1978-90, chmn. bd. dirs. 1987-88; co-founder, vice chmn. Seattle Alliance for Edn., 1990—; bd. dirs. United for Wash., Seattle, 1985-94, Blue Cross Wash. and Alaska, Seattle, 1981-84, Wash. State China Rels. Coun., Seattle, 1983-85; pres., bd. mgrs. The Archibald Found., 1991—; mem. bd. dirs. Am. Red Cross (King County chpt. 1994—), mem. bd. dirs. Fred Hutchinson Cancer Rsch. Ctr., 1994—. Capt. USAR, 1958-65. Mem. ABA (internat. law and corp. banking and bus. law sects.), Wash. State Bar Assn. (chmn. young lawyers sect. 1963-64, internat. law, corp. banking and bus. law, tax, and intellectual and indsl. property sects.), Seattle-King County Bar Assn. (internat. law sect.), Internat. Bar Assn. (bus. law sect.), Seattle Internat. Tax Roundtable, Greater Seattle C. of C. (gen. counsel 1980-82), Rainier Club, Seattle Tennis Club, Brorchmon Golf Club, Rotary, Beta Gamma Sigma, Phi Gamma Delta, Phi Delta Phi. Clubs: Rainier, Seattle Tennis, Broadmoor Golf. Lodge: Rotary. Office: Perkins Coie 1201 3rd Ave Fl 40 Seattle WA 98101-3000

MULLIN, LENORE MARIE RESTIFO, computer scientist, researcher; b. Albany, N.Y., Dec. 18, 1947; d. Salvatore Joseph and Mary Madeline (Gadomski) Restifo; widowed; children: Lisa Marie, Craig Benjamin, Sara Townsend. BS, SUNY, New Paltz, 1974; MS, Syracuse U., 1978, PhD, 1988. Sci. programmer IBM, Fishkill, N.Y., 1974-76; rsch. programmer IBM, Yorktown Heights, N.Y., 1976-78, mem. rsch. tech. staff, 1978-81, 82-84; vis. lectr. math. and computer sci. Vassar Coll., Poughkeepsie, N.Y., 1981-82; grad. asst. Syracuse (N.Y.) U., 1984-85, rsch. asst. elec. and computer engring., 1985-86; rsch. assoc., prin. investigator Computer Applications in Software Engring. Ctr., Syracuse, 1986-89; sr. rschr. Computer Sci. Rsch. Inst. of Montreal, 1989-90; vis. prof. dept. computer scis. and elec. engring. U. Vt., Burlington, 1990-92; assoc. prof. dept. computer scis. U. Mo., Rolla, 1992-95, SUNY, Albany, 1995—. Leader LaLeche League, 1970—. Presdl. Faculty fellow NSF, 1993. Mem. IEEE, Soc. Indsl. and Applied Mechanics, Assn. for Computing Machines. Avocations: glass art, skiing, biking, physics. Office: SUNY Albany NY 12222

MULLIN, LEO FRANCIS, banker; b. Concord, Mass., Jan. 26, 1943; s. Leo F. and Alice L. (Fearns) M.; m. Leah J. Malmberg, Sept. 10, 1966; children: Jessica, Matthew. AB, Harvard U., 1964, MS, 1965, MBA, 1967. Assoc. McKinsey & Co., Washington, 1967-73, prin., 1973-76; sr. v.p. strategic planning Consol. Rail Corp., Phila., 1976-78; sr. v.p. 1st Chgo. Corp., 1981-84, exec. v.p., 1984-91; chmn. Am. Nat. Bank and Trust Co. Chgo. subs. 1st Chgo., Chgo., 1991—; pres., COO 1st Chgo. Corp., Chgo., 1993—. Vice chmn. Chgo. Urgan League, 1993—; chmn. bd. trustees Field Mus. Natural History, 1994—; bd. dirs. Chgo. chpt. Juvenile Diabetes Found., 1985—; bd. dirs. Met. Planning Coun., 1983—; bd. dirs. Children's Meml. Hosp., Chgo., 1989—; mem. Chgo. Econ. Devel. Commn., 1992—; trustee Northwestern U., 1992—; bd. dirs. Chgo. Coun. Fgn. Rels., 1994—. Mem. The Bankers Roundtable, Chgo. Club, Harvard Club of Chgo., Econ. Club of Chgo. Office: 1st Chgo Corp Ste 0830 9th Fl 1 First National Plz Chicago IL 60670

MULLIN, MARK HILL, headmaster; b. Chgo., July 6, 1940; s. F. Joseph and Alma Grey (Hill) M.; m. Martha Jane Leamy, July 23, 1966; children: Cara, Sean, Kevin. BA, Harvard U., 1962, Oxford U., 1964; MA, Oxford U., 1968; MDiv, Gen. Theol. Seminary, N.Y.C., 1968. Chaplain Choate Sch., Wallingford, Conn., 1968-73; dean Choate-Rosemary Hall, Wallingford, 1973-76; asst. head master Blue Ridge Sch., Dyke, Va., 1976-77; head master St. Albans Sch., Washington, 1977—. Author: Educating for the 21st Century, 1991; contbr. chpts. to books and articles to publs. Pres., Inter-State Athletic Conf., Washington, 1986-87. Pvt. AUS, 1965. Named to Hall of Fame, Harvard Varsity Club, 1988. Mem. Country Day Schs. Headmasters Assn., Cosmos Club. Episcopalian. Office: St Albans Sch Mt St Alban Washington DC 20016

MULLIN, ROGER WILLIAM, JR., lawyer, former truck manufacturing company executive; b. Bklyn., June 2, 1914; s. Roger William and Blanche (Kirchner) M.; m. Mary Louise Moran, June 2, 1943. A.B. Bklyn. Coll., 1935; LL.B., Fordham U., 1938; LL.M., George Washington U., 1952; LL.D., Allentown Coll., 1977. Bar: N.Y. 1939. Atty. Am. Bankers Assn., 1940-41; staff atty. N.Y. State Jud. Council, 1941-42, 46-48; atty. firm Gordon, Brady, Caffrey & Keller, N.Y.C., 1948-50; counsel chem. div. NPA, 1950-53; corp. counsel, sec. Curtis-Wright Corp., 1953-61; v.p., gen. counsel, sec. Mack Trucks, Inc., 1962-64, v.p. adminstrn. and legal affairs, 1964-67, exec. v.p. adminstrn., 1967-74, vice chmn., 1974-76, chmn. bd., 1976-79; chmn. bd. Coplay Cement Co., 1980-89; bd. dirs., mem. exec. com. Merchants Nat. Bank, Allentown, 1970-85. Editor in chief Fordham Law Rev., 1937-38. Past bd. dirs. Allentown Art Mus., Pa. Stage Co.; past treas., bd. dirs. Allentown and Sacred Heart Hosp. Ctr. Inc.; past pres., bd. dirs. Sacred Heart Hosp., Allentown; past trustee Allentown Coll., Cedar Crest Coll.; bd. dirs. Allentown Pub. Libr., 1983—; Allentown Comml. and Indsl. Devel. Authority, 1983—; bd. dirs., mem. exec. com. Allentown Econ. Devel. Corp., 1985-86. Served to 1st lt. AUS, 1942-46. Decorated knight of St. Gregory. Mem. Allentown-Lehigh County C. of C. Clubs: Lehigh Country (Allentown), Livingston, Contemporary. Lodge: Rotary. To get anything worthwhile accomplished requires two basic personal attributes—persistence and flexibility. And anyone can develop them.

MULLINAX, OTTO B., lawyer; b. Clearwater, Tex., June 28, 1912; s. Claxton Napoleon and Essie Ruth (Shelby) M.; m. Ernestine Maxey, July 20, 1941; 1 child, Michael Lewis. B.A., U. Tex., 1937, LL.B., 1937. Bar: Tex. 1937, U.S. Ct. Mil. Appeals 1957, U.S. Supreme Ct. 1958. Assoc. firm Mandell & Combs, Houston, 1938-40; sr. ptnr. Mullinax, Wells, Morris & Mauzy (named changed to Mullinax, Wells, Baab & Cloutman, 1980). Author: Some Mullinax Roots: South Carolina to Texas, 1982, Thus Spake Idion, 1983, Sam Adams: Freedom Fighter, 1991, Gods, Prophets and Slaves, 1994. Pres. Dallas UN Assn., 1971-72; Bd. dirs. Ams. for Democratic Action, 1952-71. Served to maj. AUS, 1941-46; lt. col. JAG Corps, Res. 1954-57. Fellow Am. Law-Sci. Acad.; mem. Dallas Trial Lawyers Assn. (pres. 1956), Tex. Trial Lawyers Assn. (dir.), Nat. Assn. Compensation Claimants Attys. (asso. editor jour. 1952-65). Home and Office: 11806 Cheswick St Dallas TX 75218-1803

MULLINEAUX, DONAL RAY, geologist; b. Weed, Calif., Feb. 16, 1925; s. Lester Ray and Mary Lorene (Drew) M.; m. Diana Suzanne Charais, Nov. 21, 1951; children: Peter, Lauren, Keith. Student, U. Wash., 1942, BS in Math, 1947, BS in Geology, 1949, MS in Geology, 1950, PhD in Geology, 1961. Drilling insp. U.S. Army C.E., 1948; geologist U.S. Geol. Survey, 1950-86; contracting geologist, 1987-90; scientist emeritus U.S. Geol. Survey, 1990—. Author articles on volcanic activity and hazards, Mt. St. Helens, other Cascade Range volcanoes, stratigraphy and engring. geology of Puget Sound lowland, Wash. With USNR, 1943-54, active duty, 1943-46, 51-53. Rsch. fellow Engring. Expt. Sta. U. Wash., 1949-50. Fellow Geol. Soc. Am. (E.B. Burwell Jr. award 1983); mem. Colo. Sci. Soc. Unitarian. Home: 14155 W 54th Ave Arvada CO 80002-1513 Office: PO Box 25046 Denver CO 80225-0046

MULLINS, ANNA CARROLLE, hospital administrator; b. Wings, Ky., Oct. 29, 1945; d. Louis and Opal (Rowland) M. AD in Nursing, Paducah Community Coll, 1968; BSN, U. Calif, San Francisco, 1969; MSN, U. Calif, 1971, Dr. Nursing Sci, 1975. Reg. profl. nurse. Head nurse Mayfield (Ky.) Hosp., 1968; charge nurse Unity Hosp., San Francisco, 1971-74; clin. nurse IV U. Calif. Hosps., San Francisco, 1974-77; assoc. dir. rsch. and mem. U. Calif. Hosps., 1977-79, dir. nursing, 1978-81; asst. administr. nursing Children's Hosp., San Francisco, 1981-83; asst. v.p., 1983-86, chief ops. officer, 1986; chief ops. officer Seton Med. Ctr. and St. Catherine Hosp., Daly City and Half Moon Bay, Calif., 1989-86; chief exec. officer Ctr. St. Catherine Hosp., Daly City & Half Moon Bay, Calif., 1989—; clin. prof., U. Calif. Sch. Nursing 1977—; adj. prof. nursing, San Francisco State U. 1977—. Contbr.

Instl. Rev. Bds., 1981; contbr. articles to profl. jours. Mem. Aldersgate United Meth. Ch., San Rafael, 1985-87; Christian edn. com., Mill Valley, Calif., 1978-79; vol. Marin Co. Heart Assn. Crusade, San Rafael, 1977-83. Named Tchr. of Yr. Adminstr., U. Calif., San Francisco, 1985-86. Mem. Calif. League Nursing (chmn. nominating com. 1983-85), Calif. Soc. Nursing Svc. Adminstrs. Democrat. Avocations: music, golf, gardening, crafts, needlework. Home: 125 Holmes Ave San Rafael CA 94903-2813 Office: Seton Med Ctr 1900 Sullivan Ave Daly City CA 94015-2200

MULLINS, BETTY JOHNSON, realtor; b. Killen, Ala., Dec. 29, 1925; d. James E. and Vernie (Muse) Johnson; m. Charles Harvey Mullins, Nov. 18, 1944; children: Charles Harvey Jr., Susan. BS, U. North Ala., 1945. Tchr. Biloxi (Miss.) City Schs., 1945-46, Elizabeth City County Schs., Buckroe Beach, Va., 1946-47, Sheffield (Ala.) City Schs., 1949-58; with family automobile bus., 1958-86; real estate assoc. Neese Real Estate, Inc., Florence, Ala., 1986—. Pres. Project Courtview, Florence, 1980, Heritage Found., Florence, 1994—; mem. Tenn. Valley Art Guild, Tuscumbia, Tenn. Valley Art Ctr., Tuscumbia, Concert Guild, Florence, pres., 1994, Friends of Kennedy Douglas Art Ctr., Florence; v.p. Salvation Army Aux., 1991-92; mem., past pres. United Meth. Women, First Meth. Ch., Florence, mem. adminstrv. bds.; bd. dirs. Friends of the Libr., Florence, 1993—; mem., past pres. Lauderdale-Colbert-Franklin Foster Grandparent Adv. Bd., Russellville, Ala., Retired Sr. Vol. Program Adv. Bd.; past pres.; mem. Pres. Cabinet U. North Ala.; trustee United Way, Shoals, 1992—; mem. Found. Bd. Univ. North Ala., 1994. Recipient Shoals Area Citizen of Yr., 1984, Shoals Area Top Prodr. Muscle Shoals Area Bd. Realtors, 1991, 92, 93, 94, Cmty. Svc. award U. North Ala., 1994; named Woman of Yr. Bus. and Profl. Women, 1980. Mem. LWV, Shoals-AAUW (pres. 1990-91), Nat. Bd. Realtors, U. North Ala. Alumni Assn. (past pres., bd. dirs., Alumni of Yr. award 1985, Cmty. Svc. award 1994, Found. Bd. 1994), Internat. Fertilizer Devel. Ctr. Century Club (past pres. Muscle Shoals, Ala. chpt.), Shoals C. of C. (past bd. dirs.), Tenn. Valley Hist. Assn., U. North Ala. Sportsman Club, Muscle Shoals Bd. Realtors, Ala. Bd. Realtors. Republican. Methodist. Avocation: family. Home and Office: PO Box 70 Florence AL 35631-0070

MULLINS, CHARLES BROWN, physician, academic administrator; b. Rochester, Ind., July 29, 1934; s. Charles E. and Mary Ruth B. (Bamberger) M.; B.A., N. Tex. State U., 1954; M.D., U. Tex., 1958; m. Stella Churchill, Dec. 27, 1955; children—Holly, David. Intern, U. Colo. Med. Center, Denver, 1958-59; resident medicine Parkland Meml. Hosp., Dallas, 1962-64; USPHS rsch. fellow U. Tex. Southwestern Med. Sch., Dallas, 1964-65; chief resident medicine Parkland Meml. Hosp., 1965-66; USPHS spl. rsch. fellow cardiology br. Nat. Heart Inst., Bethesda, Md., 1967-68; practice medicine specializing in cardiology, Dallas, 1966—; mem. sr. attending staff Parkland Meml. Hosp., dir. med. affairs, 1977-79; mem. cons. staff Presbyn. Hosp., VA Hosp.; asst. prof. medicine U. Tex. Southwestern Med. Sch., Dallas, 1968-71, asso. prof., 1971-75, dir. clin. cardiology, 1971-77, prof., 1975-79, clin. prof. medicine, 1979-81, prof., 1981—; prof. medicine U. Tex. Health Sci. Center, Dallas, 1979-81; exec. vice-chancellor health affairs U. Tex. System, 1981—; chief exec. officer Dallas County Hosp. Dist., 1979-81. Served with M.C., USAF, 1959-62. Diplomate Am. Bd. Internal Medicine. Fellow ACP, Am. Coll. Cardiology (Tex. gov. 1974-77, chmn. bd. govs. 1976), Am. Heart Assn. Council on Clin. Cardiology; mem. Am. Fedn. Clin. Rsch., Assn. Acad. Health Ctrs., Assn. Univ. Cardiologists, Laennec Soc., AMA, Alpha Omega Alpha. Contbr. articles on cardiology to med. jours. Office: 601 Colorado St Austin TX 78701-2904

MULLINS, JAMES I., virologist, educator; b. Miami, May 25, 1952; s. James I. Mullins and Evelyn Lelia (Bailey) Meier; m. Barbara J. Sina, Aug. 8, 1978 (div. Feb. 1984). BA, U. So. Fla., 1974; PhD, U. Minn., 1978. Postdoctoral fellow Calif. Inst. Technology, Pasadena, 1978-82; asst. prof. Harvard U., Sch. Pub. Health, Boston, 1982-86; assoc. prof. Harvard U., Dept. Cancer Biology, Boston, 1987-89, adj. prof., 1989—; acting prof. Stanford (Calif.) U. Sch. Medicine, 1989-90; prof. Stanford U., Dept. Immunology, 1990—, prof., chmn., 1991—; cons. in field. Contbr. over 60 articles to profl. jours. Recipient Gov.'s Recognition award for AIDS Rsch., 1986. Office: Stanford U Sch of Medicine 300 Pasteur Dr Stanford CA 94305

MULLINS, JAMES LEE, library director; b. Perry, Iowa, Nov. 29, 1949; s. Kenneth Wiley and Lorene (Gift) M.; m. Kathleen Stiso, May 10, 1986; 1 stepchild, Michael Stiso. BA, U. Iowa, 1972, MA, 1973; PhD, Ind. U., 1984. Instr. Ga. So. U., Statesboro, 1973-74; assoc. law librarian Ind. U., Bloomington, 1974-78; dir. library Ind. U., South Bend, 1978—. Contbr. articles to profl. publs. Mem. exec. com. South Bend Art Ctr., 1984-89; mem. Mayor's Task Force Redevel., South Bend, 1986; pres. Fischoff Nat. Chamber Music Assn., 1989-91, Gov. Conf. on Libr. Planning Com., 1989-91, Mich. Freenet bd., 1993—, Ind. Coop. Libr. Svcs. Athority, 1993-94. Mem. ALA, Ind. Library Assn., Assn. Coll. and Research Libraries, Ind. Lib. Endowment Bd. (pres. 1988-91). Lodge: Rotary. Avocations: reading, gardening, cross-country skiing, historic preservation. Home: 1005 W Washington St South Bend IN 46601-1434 Office: Ind Univ Library 1700 Mishawaka Ave PO Box 7111 South Bend IN 46634

MULLINS, JEROME JOSEPH, real estate developer, consulting engineer; b. Reedsville, Wis., June 3, 1925; s. James Raymond and Anna (Wilhelm) M.; m. Carol M. Fessler, Sept. 12, 1949; children: Maureen, Brian, Mallory, Bradley, Jerome J. Jr. BSCE, U. Wis., 1950. Registered profl. engr., land surveyor, Wis.; lic. real estate broker and appraiser, Wis. Engr. Gen. Engring. Co., Baraboo, Wis., 1950-51; engring. mgr. George Nelson & Sons, Inc., Madison, Wis., 1951-56, Weiler & Strang Architects/Engrs., Madison, 1956-64; pres. Sample-Mullins Architects/Engrs., Madison, 1964-69; chief exec. officer J.J. Mullins & Assocs., Inc., Madison, 1969—. Pres. Bayview Found., Madison, 1968-72, Greater Madison Conv. and Visitors Bur., 1976-78; bd. dirs. Downtown Madison, Inc., 1976—, Madison Conv. and Visitors Bur., 1986-90; mem. Madison Taxicab Com., 1977-78. Officer USN, 1943-46. PTO. Recipient award Capital Community Citizens, 1974, appreciation award Madison Conv. and Visitors Bur., 1976-79, 87-89, U. Wis. Athletics 1983, Employer of Yr. award Goodwill Industries South Cen. Wis., 1981, award Downtown Madison, Inc., 1986, award for support Badger State Games, 1989. Mem. NSPE, AIA (assoc.), Nat. Bd. Realtors, Nat. Constrn. Specifications Instr., Wis. Soc. Profl. Engrs., Profl. Engrs. in Pvt. Practice, Wis. Soc. Registered Land Surveyors. Avocations: boating, hunting, reading. Office: 401 N Carroll St Madison WI 53703-1803

MULLINS, RICHARD AUSTIN, chemical engineer; b. Seelyville, Ind., Apr. 22, 1918; s. Fred A. and Ethel (Zenor) M.; B.S. in Chem. Engring., Rose Poly. Inst., 1940; postgrad. Yale, 1942-43; m. Margaret Ann Dellacca, Nov. 27, 1946 (dec. Nov. 1982); children—Scott Alan, Mark Earl. Chemist, Ayrshire Collieries Corp., Brazil, Ind., 1940-49; chief chemist Fairview Collieries Corp., Danville, Ill., 1949-54; preparations mgr. Enos Coal Mining Co., Oakland City, Ind., 1954-72, Enoco Collieries, Inc., Bruceville, Ind., 1954-62; mining engr. Kings Station Coal Corp.; mgr. analytical procedures Old Ben Coal Corp., 1973-84; ret., 1984. Am. Mining Congress cons. to Am. Standards Assn. and Internat. Orgn. for Standards, 1960-74; mem. indsl. cons. com. Ind. Geol. Survey, 1958-72; mem. organizing com. 5th Internat. Coal Preparation Congress, Pittsburgh, 1966. Mem. exec. bd. Buffalo Trace council Boy Scouts Am., also mem. speakers bur. Bd. dirs. Princeton Boys Club. Served with AUS, 1942-46; ETO. Decorated Medaille de la France Liberee (France); recipient Eagle Scout award; Boy Scouts Am., 1935, Silver Beaver award, 1962, Wood Badge Beads award, 1960; Outstanding Community Svc. award Princeton Civitan Club, 1964; Engr. of Year award S.W. chpt. Ind. Soc. Profl. Engrs., 1965; Prince of Princeton award Princeton C. of C., 1981, Sagamore of the Wabash award Ind. gov. R.D. Orr, 1984. Registered profl. engr., Ind., Ill. Mem. AIME (life mem.), ASTM (sr. mem., R.A. Glenn award 1985), Am. Chem. Soc., Nat. Soc. Profl. Engrs. (life mem.), Ind., Ill. mining insts., Ind. Coal Soc. (pres. 1958-59), Am. Mining Congress (chmn. com. coal preparation 1964-68), Am. Legion (past commn. chmn.), VFW (40 & 8 coms.), Ind. Soc. Profl. Land Surveyors, Rose Tech. Alumni Assn. (pres. 1976-77, Honor Alumnus 1980), Order of Ring, Sigma Nu. Methodist (lay speaker). Mason, Elk. Contbr. articles to profl. jours. Home: RR 4 Box 310 Princeton IN 47670-9412

MULLINS, RUTH GLADYS, nurse; b. Westville, N.S., Can., Aug. 25, 1943; d. William G. and Gladys H.; came to U.S., 1949, naturalized, 1955; student Tex. Womans U., 1961-64; BS in Nursing, Calif. State U.-Long

Beach, 1966; MNursing, UCLA, 1973; m. Leonard E. Mullins, Aug. 27, 1963; children: Deborah R., Catherine M., Leonard III. Pub. health nurse, L.A. County Health Dept., 1967-68; nurse Meml. Hosp. Med. Center, Long Beach, 1968-72; dir. pediatric nurse practitioner program Calif. State U., Long Beach, 1973—, asst. prof., 1975-80, assoc. prof., 1980-85, prof., 1985—; health svc. credential coord. Sch. Nursing Calif. State U., Long Beach, Calif., chmn., 1979-81, coord. grad. programs, 1985-92; mem. Calif. Maternal, Child and Adolescent Health Bd., 1977-84; vice chair Long Beach/Orange County Health Consortium Divsn. Nursing, 1984-85, chair 1985-86. Tng. grantee HHS, Calif. Dept. Health; cert. pediatric nurse practitioner. Fellow Nat. Assn. Pediatric Nurse Assocs. and Practitioners (exec. bd., past pres.), Nat. Fedn. Nursing Specialty Orgns. (sec. 1991-93); mem. Am. Pub. Health Assn., Nat. Alliance Nurse Practitioners (governing body 1990-92), Assn. Faculties Pediatric Nurse Practitioner Programs, L.A. and Orange County Assn. Pediatric Nurse Practitioners and Assocs., Am. Assn. U. Faculty, Ambulatory Pediatric Assn. Democrat. Methodist. Author: (with B. Nelms) Growth and Development: A Primary Health Care Approach; contbg. author: Quick Reference to Pediatric Nursing, 1984; asst. editor Jour. Pediatric Health Care. Home: 6382 Heil Ave Huntington Beach CA 92647-4232 Office: Calif State U Dept Nursing 1250 N Bellflower Blvd Long Beach CA 90840-0004

MULLIS, KARY BANKS, biochemist; b. Lenoir, N.C., Dec. 28, 1944; s. Cecil Banks Mullis and Bernice Alberta (Barker) Fredericks; children: Christopher, Jeremy, Louise. BS in Chemistry, Ga. Inst. Tech, 1966; PhD in Biochemistry, U. Calif., Berkeley, 1973. Lectr. biochemistry U. Calif., Berkeley, 1972; postdoctoral fellow U. Calif., San Francisco, 1977-79, U. Kans. Med. Sch., Kansas City, 1973-76; scientist Cetus Corp., Emeryville, Calif., 1979-86; dir. molecular biology Xytronyx, Inc., San Diego, 1986-88; cons. Specialty Labs, Inc., Amersham, Inc., Chiron Inc. and various others, Calif., 1988—; chmn. StarGene, Inc., San Rafael, Calif. Contbr. articles to profl. jours.; patentee in field. Recipient Preis Biochemische Analytik award German Soc. Clin. Chem., 1990, Allan award Am. Soc. of Human Genetics, 1990, award Gairdner Found. Internat., 1991, Nat. Biotech. award, 1991, Robert Koch award, 1992, Chiron Corp. Biotechnology Rsch. award Am. Soc. Microbiology, 1992, Japan prize Sci. and Tech. Found. Japan, 1993, Nobel Prize in Chemistry, Nobel Foundation, 1993; named Calif. Scientist of Yr., 1992, Scientist of Yr., R&D Mag., 1991. Mem. Am. Chem. Soc., Am. Acad. Achievement, Inst. Further Study (dir. 1983—). Achievements include invention of Polymerase Chain Reaction (PCR). Office: 6767 Neptune Pl Apt 5 La Jolla CA 92037-5924

MULLONEY, PETER BLACK, steel, oil and gas executive; b. Boston, Oct. 24, 1932; s. Daniel Clifford and Mabel (Black) M.; m. Marie Weprich. BA, Yale U., 1954. V.p. mktg. U.S. Steel Corp., Pitts., 1978-81; v.p., asst. to chmn. USX Corp., Pitts., 1981—; bd. dirs. Pitts. Vintage Grand Prix. Mem. adv. bd., sec. Salvation Army, Pitts.; vice chmn. World Affairs Coun. Pitts.; mem. bd. trustees La Roche Coll. Mem. Am. Iron and Steel Inst. (active com. on internat. trade, Washington, chmn. com. 1983-85), Internat. Iron and Steel Inst. (active com. on econ. studies, Brussels, chmn. com. 1983-85). Roman Catholic. Clubs: Duquesne (Pitts.), Harvard-Yale-Princeton, Pitts., Army and Navy (Washington), Pitts. Athletic Assn. Avocations: reading, walking. Home: 213 Grandview Ave Pittsburgh PA 15211-1525 Office: USX Corp 600 Grant St Pittsburgh PA 15219-4776

MULREANY, ROBERT HENRY, retired lawyer; b. Bklyn., Aug. 5, 1915; s. John Robert and Elfriede (Hartman) M.; m. Dorothy E. Muens, Sept. 7, 1940; children: Doreen Elizabeth (Mrs. John J. Harris), Carol Ann (Mrs. Thomas D. Henwood). LL.B., NYU, 1940. Bar: N.Y. 1940. Law clk. DeForest, Cullom & Elder, N.Y.C., 1933-39; mng. clk., atty. Neil F. Cullom, N.Y.C., 1939-42; since practiced in N.Y.C.; mem. DeForest & Elder, 1942-47, ptnr., 1947-49; ptnr. DeForest, Elder & Mulreany, 1949-69, sr. ptnr., 1954-69; ptnr. DeForest & Duer, 1969-87, of counsel, 1988-91; pres. Provident Loan Soc. N.Y., 1955-89, trustee, 1989—. Mem. adv. council Sch. Social Work Columbia, 1960-64; mayor, Westfield, 1965-68; pres. Bd. Edn. Westfield, N.J., 1959-62; chmn. N.Y.C. Adv. Com. Pub. Welfare, 1963-67; chmn. bd. trustees Community Service Soc. of N.Y., 1959-72; trustee Overlook Hosp., 1970-78, chmn., 1976-78; trustee John A. Hartford Found.; former trustee Westfield YMCA, Westfield Found., Tuskegee Inst.; trustee, pres. Overlook Hosp. Found., 1978-84, trustee, 1993—; trustee Smith Richardson Found. Served as lt. (j.g.) USNR, 1944-46. Mem. ABA, Bar Assn. City N.Y. Presbyterian. Clubs: Downtown Assn. (N.Y.C.), Echo Lake Country (Westfield, N.J.), Bay Head Yacht (N.J.). Home: 11 Euclid Ave Apt 4B Summit NJ 07901-2167

MULRONEY, (MARTIN) BRIAN, former prime minister of Canada; b. Mar. 20, 1939; s. Benedict and Irene (O'Shea) M.; m. Mila Pivnicki, 1973; 4 children. B.A., St. Francis Xavier U., LL.D. (hon.), 1979; LL.L., U. Laval, Que.; LL.D. (hon.), Meml. U., 1980; LLD honoris causa, U. W.I., 1993, Tel Aviv U., 1994, Cen. Conn. State U., 1994. Ptnr. Ogilvy Renault, Montreal, Que., 1965-76; pres. Iron Ore Co. of Can., Montreal, Que., 1976-83, 1976-83; mem. Parliament Can. from Central Nova, Nova Scotia, Ottawa, Ont., 1983-84; mem. Parliament Can. from Manicouagan, 1984-88, mem. Parliament Can. from Charlevoix, 1988-93, leader of Her Majesty's Loyal Opposition, 1983-84; prime minister Can., 1984-93; royal commr. Cliche Commn. investigating violence in Que. constrn. industry, 1974; sr. ptnr. Ogilvy Renault, Montreal, 1993—; chmn. internat. adv. bd., bd. dirs. Barrick Gold Corp., bd. dirs.; bd. dirs. Power Corp., Chem. Bank of N.Y., Archer Daniels Midland Co., Horsham Corp., Petrofina, S.A.; trustee Freedom Forum; mem. internat. adv. coun. Inst. Internat. Studies. Author: Where I Stand, 1983. Office: Ogilvy Renault, 1981 McGill College Ave Ste 1100, Montreal, PQ Canada H3A 3C1

MULRONEY, JOHN PATRICK, chemical company executive; b. Phila., 1935; married. BS, U. Pa., 1957, MS, 1959. With Rohm and Haas Co., Phila., 1958—; group leader engring. dept. Rohm & Haas Co., Phila., 1962-64, dept. head, 1964-67, asst. dir. rsch., 1967-71, pres., chief oper. officer, 1986—; asst. gen. mgr. Rohm and Haas Italy, Milan, 1971-73, gen. mgr., 1973-75; bus. mgr. AG Chem., Europe, 1975-77, regional dir. Europe, 1977-78; v.p. polymers, resins, monomers Indsl. Chem., 1978-80, v.p. tech., 1980-82, v.p. corp. bus., from 1982, also bd. dirs., 1982—; bd. dirs. Aluminum Co., Am. Teradyne Inc. Mem. Am. Inst. Chem. Engrs., Am. Chem. Soc. Office: Rohm and Haas Co 100 Independence Mall West Philadelphia PA 19106

MULRONEY, MICHAEL, lawyer, law educator, graduate program director; b. Chgo., Feb. 26, 1932; s. Alphonsus James and Genevieve (Moran) M.; m. Ellen Goen Mulroney, Dec. 28, 1959; children: Sean, Conor, Dermot, Kieran, Moira. BSC in Econ., State U. Iowa, 1954; JD, Harvard Law Sch., 1959. Bar: Iowa 1959, D.C. 1960, U.S. Supreme Ct., U.S. Ct. Appeals (2nd, 3rd, 4th, 5th, 6th, 7th, 8th, 9th and D.C. cirs.), U.S. Tax Ct., U.S. Dist. Ct. D.C., D.C. Ct. Appeals, D.C. Superior Ct. Atty. adv. U.S. Tax Ct., Washington; 1959-61; appellate atty. Tax Div. U.S. Dept. Justice, Washington, 1961-65; assoc. Lee, Toomey & Kent, Washington, 1965-68, ptnr., 1969-87, counsel, 1987-88; prof., dir. Grad. Tax Program Villanova (Pa.) Law Sch., 1988—; adjunct prof. Grad. Tax Program Georgetown Law Sch., Washington, 1986—. Author: Federal Tax Examinations Manual, 1988, Foreign Taxation, 1992; mng. editor: The Tax Lawyer, 1989—; contbr. articles to profl. jours. With U.S. Army, 1954-56. Mem. ABA (taxation sect., chmn. tax lawyer com., mem. ct. procedure com., standards of practice com., teaching taxation com.; legal edn. and admissions to the bar sect.), D.C. Bar (tax sect.), Fed. Bar Assn. (tax sect.), Iowa Bar Assn. (tax sect.), J. Edgar Murdock Am. Inn. of Ct. (founding master), Internat. Fiscal Assn. (U.S. br. coun. mem.), Internat. Fiscal Rsch. Inst. (mem. coun. experts), Wash. Tax Lawyers' Study Group, Phila. Tax Conf. (mem. exec. coun.), Am. Assn. Law Schs. (tax sect.). Roman Catholic. Avocation: sports car racing. Office: Villanova Law Sch Villanova PA 19085

MULROW, PATRICK JOSEPH, medical educator; s. Patrick J. and Delia (O'Keefe) M.; m. Jacquelyn Pinover, Aug. 8, 1953; children—Deborah, Nancy, Robert, Catherine. AB, Colgate U., 1947; MD, Cornell U., 1951; MSc (hon.), Yale U., 1969. Intern N.Y. Hosp., 1951-52, resident, 1952-54; instr. physiology Med. Coll. Cornell U., 1954-55; research fellow Stanford U., 1955-57; instr. medicine Yale U., 1957-60, asst. prof., 1960-66, assoc. prof., 1966-69, prof. medicine, 1969-75; chmn. dept. medicine Med. Coll. Ohio, Toledo, 1975-95, prof. medicine, 1975—; chmn. ednl. com. Council for high blood pressure rsch. Am. Heart Assn., 1968-70, mem. exec. com., 1986—, vice-chmn. of coun., 1990-92, chmn. 1992-94, past chmn., 1995—; mem. study sect. NIH, 1970-74. Editorial bd. Jour. Clin. Endocrinology and Metabolism, 1966-70, 75-79, Endocrine Rsch., 1974—, Jour. Exptl. Biology and Medicine, Hypertension, 1994—; contbr. articles to profl. jours. With USNR, 1944-46. Mem. ACP, Am. Soc. Clin. Investigation, Am. Assn. Physicians, Am. Physiol. Soc., endocrine Soc., Am. Fedn. Clin. Rsch., Am. Clin. and Climatol. Assn., Am. Heart Assn. (nat. rsch. com., chmn. cardiovascular regulation rsch. study com. 1986-91), Assn. Profs. Medicine, Assn. Program Dirs. in Internal Medicine, Cen. Soc. Clin. Rsch., Internat. Soc. Hypertension, Inter-Am. Soc. Hypertension, Sigma Xi (pres. Yale chpt. 1965-66), Alpha Omega Alpha. Home: 9526 Carnoustie Rd Perrysburg OH 43551-3501 Office: Med Coll of Ohio Dept of Medicine PO Box 10008 Toledo OH 43699-0008

MULROY, THOMAS MICHAEL, lawyer; b. Pitts., Oct. 16, 1948; s. Michael Francis and Della L. (O'Dea) M.; married; children: Cindy, Michael. AB, John Carroll U., 1970; JD, Notre Dame U., 1973. Bar: U.S. Dist. Ct. (we. dist.) Pa., U.S. Ct. Appeals (3d cir.) 1973. Assoc. Wick, Vuono & Lavelle, Pitts., 1973-75; sole practice Pitts., 1975-78; ptnr. Pillar & Mulroy, Pitts., 1978—. Pres. Children's Council West Pa., Pitts., 1987—; treas. Pitts. New Music Ensemble, 1985-87; dir. Pitts. Opera Inc., 1988—. Mem. ABA (family law sect. 1980—), Assn. Trial Lawyers Am., Pa. Bar Assn. (family law sect. 1980—), Allegheny County Bar Assn. (family law council 1988—). Democrat. Office: Pillar & Mulroy PC 312 Blvd Of The Allies Ste 700 Pittsburgh PA 15222

MULRYAN, HENRY TRIST, mineral company executive, consultant; b. Palo Alto, Calif., Jan. 6, 1927; s. Henry and Marian Abigail (Trist) M.; m. Lenore Hoag, Aug. 25, 1948; children: James W., Carol. Student, Yale U., 1945-46; AB in Econs. Stanford U., 1948; postgrad., Am. Grad. Sch. Internat. Bus., 1949, Columbia U., 1983. V.p. mktg. Sierra Talc Co., South Pasadena, Calif., 1955-65; v.p. mktg. United Sierra, Trenton, N.J., 1965-67, v.p., gen. mgr., 1967-70, pres., 1970-77; v.p. Cyprus Mines Corp., Los Angeles, 1978-80; sr. v.p. ops. Cyprus indsl. minerals div. Amoco Minerals Co., Englewood, Colo., 1980-85; pres. Cyprus Indls. Minerals Co., Englewood, 1985-87; v.p. Cyprus Minerals Co., Englewood, 1985-87, sr. v.p. mktg., corp. adminstr., 1987-89; pres. Mineral Econs. Internat., 1989—. Served with U.S. Army, 1944-46. Clubs: Jonathan (Los Angeles). Lodge: Rotary (pres. South Pasadena club 1964-65) (bd. dirs. Princeton, N.J. club 1969-75). Office: 15237 Sunset Blvd # 72 Pacific Palisades CA 90272-2500

MULVA, JAMES JOSEPH, oil company executive; b. Oshkosh, Wis., June 19, 1946; m. Miriam Mulva; 2 children. BBA in Fin., U. Tex., 1968, MBA in Fin., 1969. Mgmt. trainee, treas. Phillips Petroleum Co., Bartlesville, Okla., 1973; asst. treas. Phillips Petroleum Co., London, 1974; mgr. fgn. exch. and investment Phillips Petroleum Co., Bartlesville, 1976; v.p., treas. Europe/Africa div. Phillips Petroleum Co., London, 1980; mgr. corp. and planning Phillips Petroleum Co., Bartlesville, 1984, asst. treas., 1985, treas., 1986, v.p., treas., 1988-90, chief fin. officer, 1990—. With USN, 1969-73. Roman Catholic. Office: Phillips Petroleum Co 1250 Adams Bldg Bartlesville OK 74003

MULVANEY, JAMES FRANCIS, lawyer; b. Chgo., Nov. 2, 1922; m. Mary Ruth Rinderer, 1945; 7 children. BS, Loyola U., Chgo., 1942, JD, 1948. Atty. Chgo., 1948-55, San Diego, Calif., 1956-62; exec. v.p. U.S. Nat. Bank, 1963-72, pres., CEO, 1972-73; pres. San Diego Baseball Co., 1955-68; v.p., gen. counsel San Diego Padres Nat. League, 1968-73; ptnr. Mulvaney, Kahan & Barry, San Diego, 1973—; bd. dirs., chmn. Calif. Higher Edn. Loan Authority, 1983—. Bd. vis. U. San Diego Sch. Law; chmn. United Way Internat., 1991-94, mem. exec. com., United Way Am., 1987-93, various officers; co-chmn. San Diego Organizing Project, 1983—; bd. dirs. World SHARE, Inc., 1986-92, Old Globe Theatre London, Del mar Charites, 1985—; numerous other civic activities. Officer USN, WWII; lt. comdr. USNR, Korea. Recipient Mr. San Diego award, 1991, First Annual Spirit of Charity award Cath. Community Svcs., 1984, Brotherhood award Nat. Conf. Christians and Jews, Inc., 1983, Citizen of Yr. award Jr. C. of C. and The City Club, 1983, numerous others. Mem. San Diego County Bar Found. (treas., Outstanding Svc. award 1988), ABA, Calif. State Bar Assn., Ill. State Bar Assn., San Diego C. of C., San Diego Coun. on World Affairs, The City Club of San Diego, Navy League. Office: Mulvaney Kahan & Barry 401 W A St Fl 17 San Diego CA 92101-7901

MULVANEY, MARY JEAN, physical education educator; b. Omaha, Jan. 6, 1927; d. Marion Fowler and Blanche Gibons (McKee) M. BS, U. Nebr., 1948; MS, Wellesley Coll., 1951; LHD (hon.), U. Nebr., 1986. Instr. Kans. State U., Manhattan, 1948-50; instr. U. Nebr., Lincoln, 1951-57, asst. prof. 1957-62; asst. prof. U. Kans., Lawrence, 1962-66; assoc. prof. U. Chgo., 1966-76, prof., 1976-90, prof. emeritus, 1990—, chmn. women's divsn., 1966-76, chmn. dept. phys. edn. and athletics, 1976-90; mem. vis. com. on athletics MIT, 1978-81, Wellesley Coll., 1978-79. Recipient Honor award Nebr. Assn. Health, Phys. Edn. and Recreation, 1962. Mem. AAHPERD, Nat. Collegiate Athletic Assn. (mem. coun. 1983-87), Collegiate Coun. Women Athletic Adminstrs., Midwest Assn. Intercollegiate Athletics for Women (chmn. 1979-81), Nat. Assn. Collegiate Dirs. of Athletics (mem. exec. com. 1976-80, Hall of Fame 1990), Ill. Assn. Intercollegiate Athletics for Women (chmn. 1978-80), Univ. Athletic Assn. (exec. com. mem. exec. com. 1986-90, mem. dels. com., chmn. athletic adminstr.'s com. 1986-88), Mortar Bd., Alpha Chi Omega. Home: 12 Skyline Dr Ogden Dunes IN 46368-1024

MULVEE, ROBERT EDWARD, bishop; b. Boston, Feb. 15, 1930; s. John F. and Jennie T. (Bath) M. B.A., U. Sem. Ottawa, 1953, Ph.B., 1953; M.R.E., Am. Coll., Louvain, Belgium, 1957; D. Canon Law, Lateran U., Rome, 1964; D.D. (hon.), Rivier Coll., Nashua, N.H., 1979. Ordained priest Roman Catholic Ch., 1957; asst. chancellor of diocese, 1964-72, named monsignor, 1966, elevated to domestic prelate, 1970, named chancellor, 1972; aux. bishop Roman Catholic Diocese of Manchester, N.H., 1977-85; bishop of Wilmington, 1985—. Trustee Nat. Shrine Immaculate Conception, Washington D.C. 1987. Mem. Nat. Conf. Cath. Bishops (campaign for human devel. com. 1985, joint com. Orthodox and Roman Cath. Bishops 1986, chmn. bd. bishops Am. Coll. of Louvain, Belgium, 1986, Cath. Relief Services bd., 1987); Nat. Conf. Cath. Bishops/ U.S. Cath. Conf. (adminstrv. com. and bd. dirs. 1986, com. on personnel and adminstrv. services 1987). Office: 1 Cathedral Sq Providence RI 02903

MULVEY, HELEN FRANCES, emeritus history educator; b. Providence, Feb. 22, 1913; d. William James and Anna (Nelson) M. A.B., Pembroke Coll., 1933; A.M., Columbia U., 1934; A.M., Radcliffe Coll., 1942; Ph.D., Harvard U., 1949. Instr. history Russell Sage Coll., Troy, N.Y., 1944-46; asst. prof. to prof. history, Conn. Coll., New London, 1946-83, prof. emeritus, 1983—, Brigida Pacchiana Ardenghi chair, 1975-78; vis. prof. Brit. history, U. Wis., Madison, 1971-72; vis. lectr. Yale U., 1974-83; lectr. Irish history, Pfizer Adult Edn., Groton, Conn., 1983-84; vis. scholar Phi Beta Kappa, Washington, 1982-83. Author articles, essays Irish and Brit. history; co-editor bibliog. vol. in A New History of Ireland, 9 vols. Anne Crosby Emery fellow, Brown U., 1933. Mem. Am. Hist. Assn., Am. Conf. for Irish Studies, North Am. Conf. on Brit. Studies, AAUP (chpt. pres. 1962-64), Phi Beta Kappa. Clubs: Harvard. Office: Conn Coll PO Box 5508 New London CT 06320

MULVEY, MARY C., adult education administrator, gerontologist; b. Bangor, Maine, Aug. 17, 1909; d. Michael J. and Ann Loretta (Higgins) Crowley; m. Gordon F. Mulvey, Jan. 25, 1940. BA, U. Maine, 1930; MA, Brown U., 1953; EdD, Harvard U., 1951; LHD (hon.), U. Maine, 1991. Dir. Adminstrn. on Aging, Providence, 1960-63; co-founder Nat. Coun. Sr. Citizens, 1961, 1st v.p., 1976—; guidance counselor Providence Sch. Dept., 1963-65; dir. adult edn. City of Providence Sch. Dept., 1965-79; reg. prop. rep. Title V, Older Ams. Act, Nat. Coun. Sr. Citizens, Washington, 1980-94; co-founder Nat. Coun. Sr. Citizens, 1961, 1st v.p., 1976—; pres. Nat. Sr. Citizens Edn. and Rsch. Ctr., Washington, 1970—; cons. Fed. Housing for the Aging, Washington, 1963-65; tech. rev. com. Title IV, Older Americans Act, 1966-70; del./adv. com. White House Conf. on Aging, 1961, 71, 81, 95; major role in enactment of Medicare and Older Americans Act, 50's-65; appt. by Pres. Carter to Fed. Coun. Aging, 1979; charter mem., adv. bd. Coll. Arts/Humanities, U. Maine, 1992—; pres. R.I. State Coun. Sr. Citizens, 1982—; instr. preparing retirement, developer women's program U. R.I.,

1963-80; various coms. state and nat. level. Publs. and contbr. articles to profl. jours. Numerous hons. including Soroptimists fellow award for rsch. in gerontology, Harvard U., 1955, 57, 59, Cert. of Award as Project Dir. of Sr. AIDES Employment Program, 1968-79, Medicare award, R.I. State Coun. Sr. Citizens and Nat. Coun. Sr. Citizens, 1985, Disting. Achievement award U. Maine, 1980, Disting. Achievement award Berwick Acad., 1981, Justice for All award R.I. Bar Assn., 1981, Woman of Yr. award Nat. Sr. Pageant, 1982, R.I. Women First R.I. Sec. of State, 1991, citation Syracuse U., 1991, R.I. Dept. Elderly Affairs, 1993, 25th Anniversary Title V Sr. Employment award Nat. Coun. Sr. Citizens, 1993, Lifetime Achievement award Nat. Coun. Sr. Citizens, 1994; inducted into R.I. Heritage Hall of Fame, 1993; recipient co-founder and continuing bd. mem. award Nat. Coun. Sr. Citizens, 1995, Improvement of Lives of Sr. Citizens award Nat. Coun. Sr. Citizens, 1995. Fellow Gerontol. Soc.; mem. ACA, AAUW, Am. Assn. Adult and Continuing Edn., Harvard U. Alumni Assn. (Alumni award R.I. chpt. 1986), U. Maine Alumni Assn., Brown U. Alumni Assn., Pi Lambda Theta, Delta Delta Delta. Home: 95 Plymouth Rd East Providence RI 02914-1943

MULVIHILL, JAMES EDWARD, periodontist, university administrator, educator, health care executive; b. Cleve., Sept. 24, 1940; s. John F. and Teresa J. (Carlos) M.; m. May Jane Forino, 1963; children—Karen, Kristen, Jason. B.A., Coll. of Holy Cross, 1962; D.M.D., Harvard U., 1966. Asst. dean for student affairs, coordinator Harvard-VA continuing edn. program Harvard Sch. Dental Medicine, Boston, 1970-71; dean clin. campus L.I. Jewish-Hillside Med. Ctr., Queens Hosp. Ctr. Affiliation, Jewish Inst. for Geriatric Care, Health Scis. Ctr. SUNY-Stony Brook, 1971-80; v.p. for edn. and research L.I. Jewish-Hillside Med. Ctr., New Hyde Park, N.Y., 1975-80; v.p., provost for health affairs, exec. dir. Health Ctr., prof. periodontics U. Conn., Farmington, 1980-92; attending periodontist John Dempsey Hosp., U. Conn. Health Ctr., Farmington, 1982-92; pres. John Dempsey Fin. Corp., Farmington, 1988-92; sr. v.p. for health policy The Travelers Corp., Hartford, Conn., 1992-94; chmn. bd. The Travelers Health Co., Hartford, 1992-93; sr. fellow in health policy Assn. of Acad. Health Ctrs., 1994; pres., CEO Managed Health, Inc., 1994, Comty. Health Plan of Queens/Nassau, New Hyde Park, N.Y., 1994—; cons. in field. Author: (with others) Guide to Foreign Medical Schools, 1975, Editorial Instructions for Dental Authors, 1979-80, 1979, Human Subjects Research: The Operational Handbook for IRB's, 1982, 2d edit., 1984, Japanese edit., 1987; also articles, chpt. in book. Bd. dirs. and chair Nat. Fund for Med. Edn. Recipient Disting. Alumnus award Harvard Sch. Dental Medicine, 1982, Disting. alumnus award Holy Cross Coll., 1991. Fellow ADA, AAAS; mem. Am. Acad. Peridontology, Am. Assn. Dental Schs., Conn. State Dental Assn., Harvard Dental Alumni Assn., Harvard Odontological Soc., internat. Assn. for Dental Rsch., Alpha Sigma Nu, Sigma Psi. Avocations: golf; gardening. Home: 2 Muls Hill St Andrews Dr Farmington CT 06032 Office: CHP-Medical Group 410 Lakeville Rd New Hyde Park NY 11042

MULVIHILL, JOHN GARY, information services administrator; b. Mpls., Mar. 3, 1933; s. Jack Albert and Aurelia Dolores (Voelker) M.; m. Anna Marie Stubenrauch, Aug. 24, 1959; children: Lawrence, Daniel. BA, U. St. Thomas, Houston, 1955; MA, Rice U., 1958; MLS, U. Tex., 1959. Assoc. libr. St. Benedicts Coll., Atchison, Kans., 1960-62; libr. Astra Pharm. Products, Worcester, Mass., 1962-64; indexer, asst. to mgr. Am. Petroleum Inst., N.Y.C., 1964-74; dir. GeoRef Information System, Am. Geol. Inst., Alexandria, Va., 1974—. Mem. Geoscience Info. Soc. (pres. 1977), Spl. Librs assn. Democrat. Roman Catholic. Avocation: woodworking. Home: 9516 Rockport Rd Vienna VA 22180-3446 Office: Am Geol Inst 4220 King St Alexandria VA 22302-1507

MULVIHILL, ROGER DENIS, lawyer; b. Pitts., June 28, 1936; s. Dennis and Mary (Scheib) M.; m. Mary Brennan, Sept. 25, 1971; children: Christopher, Kerry, Suzanne. BS, Georgetown U., 1958; LLB, Yale U., 1961; LLM, NYU, 1965. Bar: N.Y. 1963. Ptnr. Olwine, Connelly, Chase, O'Donnell and Weyher, N.Y.C., 1969-91, Dechert Price & Rhoads, N.Y.C. 1991—; counsel Planning Bd. Bronxville, Westchester, N.Y., 1984-91. Author: (with others) Handbook for Raising Capital, 1987; contbr. numerous articles to profl. jours. Active Land Use Commn., Bronxville, N.Y.; dir. Religion in Am. Life, N.Y.C., 1986—. With U.S. Army, 1961-63. Mem. ABA, N.Y. State Bar Assn., Assn. of Bar of City of N.Y., Yale Club, Meadow Club, Bronxville Field Club. Roman Catholic. Avocations: tennis, skiing. Office: Dechert Price & Rhoads 477 Madison Ave New York NY 10022-5802

MULVIHILL, TERENCE JOSEPH, investment banking executive; b. Omaha, Feb. 4, 1931; children: Mary Louise, Patricia, Kathleen (dec.), Joan, Carol, Nancy. BS in Econs., Georgetown U., 1952. Sec., treas. Mulvihill Co., Streator, Ill., 1955-64; instl. salesman Goldman, Sachs & Co., Chgo., 1964-71, v.p., 1971-80, asst. regional mgr., 1972-74, regional sales mgr., 1974-92, ptnr., 1980-92, COO, 1988-92, limited ptnr., 1992—. Pres. St. Francis Xavier Sch. Bd., Wilmette, Ill., 1971, Regina Dominican H.S. Parents Assn., 1973; bd. dirs. Glenkirk Assn. for Retarded, Glenview, Ill., 1980-82, St. Joseph's Carondelet Child Ctr., Chgo., 1980-86; trustee Univ. of Chgo. Coun. Grad. Sch. of Bus., 1980—, Regina Dominican H.S. Charitable Trust, Wilmette, 1992, Marmion Military Acad., 1990—, Children's Meml. Hosp., Chgo., 1992—; mem. adv. com. Treas's Office of City of Chgo., 1990—; mem. Govs. Task Force Human Svcs. Reform, 1992—; governing mem. Orchestral Assn. Chgo. Symphony Orch., 1992—. 1st lt. U.S Army, 1952-54. Mem. Chgo. Coun. Fgn. Rels., Met. Club, Carlton Club, Bond Club of Chgo. (dir. 1981-82). Office: Goldman Sachs & Co 4900 Sears Tower Chicago IL 60606

MULVOY, MARK, journalist; b. 1942. BA, Boston Coll., 1964. Began career as sports writer Boston Globe, 1964-65; former reporter, writer, sr. editor Sports Illustrated mag.; now mng. editor Sports Illustrated mag., N.Y.C. Office: Sports Illustrated 1271 Ave Of The Americas New York NY 10020-1300

MULVOY, THOMAS F., JR., newspaper editor, journalist; b. Boston, Feb. 4, 1943; s. Thomas Francis and Julia Frances (Harrington) M.; m. Anastasia Vakina Coulianos, June 1, 1985; children: Stephen Tasso, Michael Thomas, Nicholas Ramirez. AB in Philosophy, Boston Coll., 1964. News dir. Sta. WPLM AM/FM, Plymouth, Mass., 1965-66; copy editor The Boston Globe, 1967-74, asst. sports editor, 1974-76, news editor, 1976-79, asst. mng. editor, 1979-83, dep. mng. editor, 1983-86, mng. editor, 1986—. Stanford U. fellow, 1983. Roman Catholic. Avocations: reading, writing, golfing, walking. Office: The Boston Globe PO Box 2378 Boston MA 02107-2378

MUMAW, JAMES WEBSTER, lawyer; b. Youngstown, Ohio, Apr. 11, 1920; s. Daniel W. and Helen (James) M.; m. Lois M. Baird, May 28, 1948; children: Thomas, Daniel, William. A.B., Coll. of Wooster, 1941; J.D., U. Cin., 1948. Bar: Ohio 1949. Since practiced in Youngstown; partner Luckhart, Mumaw, Morrison & Zellers and predecessor firm, 1959-66; mem. firm Luckhart, Mumaw, Zellers & Robinson, 1966—; Dir. Ohio Bar Title Ins. Co., 1955-91, Western Res. Bank of Ohio, 1963-95. Mem. Youngstown City Bd. Edn., 1972-75; pres. Christ Mission Kindergarten Assn., Goodwill Industries, 1967-69; trustee Ohio Land Title Assn., 1975-79, v.p., 1981, pres., 1982-83, Penn Ohio Coll., 1989—. Served with AUS, 1943-46. Mem. Ohio State Bar Found. (life), ABA, Ohio State Bar Assn. (exec. com. 1978-81), Mahoning County Bar Assn. (pres. 1963-64), Am. Judicature Soc., Phi Alpha Delta. Presbyterian (elder, trustee). Club: Kiwanian. Home: 3315 Glenwood Ave Youngstown OH 44511-3165 Office: Legal Arts Center Youngstown OH 44503

MUMFORD, CHRISTOPHER GREENE, corporate financial executive; b. Washington, Oct. 21, 1945; s. Milton C. and Dorothea L. (Greene) M.; B.A., Stanford U., 1968, M.B.A., 1975. Cons. Internat. Tech. Resources Inc., 1974; asst. v.p. Wells Fargo Bank, San Francisco, 1975-78; v.p., treas. Arcata Corp., San Francisco 1978-82. v.p.fin. 1982-87, exec. v.p.fin. 1987-94. gen. ptnr. Scarff, Sears & Assocs., San Francisco, 1986-95, v.p. bd. dirs. Triangle Pacific Corp., Dallas, 1986-88, Norton Enterprises Inc., Salt Lake City, 1988-90; bd. dirs. Community Home Med. Enterprises, Inc., Grass Valley, Calif., Crown Pacific Ltd., Portland, Oreg., Union Security Mortgage, Inc., Santa Ana, Calif., 1993-94. Office: Arcata Corp 601 California St Ste 1800 San Francisco CA 94108-2823

MUMFORD, DAVID BRYANT, mathematics educator; b. Worth, Sussex, Eng., June 11, 1937; came to U.S., 1940; s. William Bryant and Grace (Schiott) M.; m. Erika Jentsch, June 27, 1959 (dec. July 30, 1988); children: Stephen, Peter, Jeremy, Suchitra; m. Jenifer Moore, Dec. 29, 1989. B.A., Harvard U., 1957, Ph.D., 1961; D.Sc. (hon.), U. Warwick, 1983. Jr. fellow Harvard U., 1958-61, asso. prof., 1962-66, prof. math., 1966-77, Higgins prof., 1977—, chmn. dept. math, 1981-84; v.p. Internat. Math. Union, 1990-94, pres., 1995—. Author: Geometric Invariant Theory, 1965, Abelian Varieties, 1970, Introduction to Algebraic Geometry, 1976. Recipient Fields medal Internat. Congress Mathematicians, 1974; MacArthur Found. fellow, 1987-92. Fellow Tata Inst. (hon.); mem. Accad. Nazionale dei Lincei, Nat. Acad. Scis., Am. Acad. Arts and Scis. Home: 26 Gray St Cambridge MA 02138-1510 Office: Harvard U 1 Oxford St Cambridge MA 02138-2901

MUMFORD, GEORGE SALTONSTALL, JR., former university dean, astronomy educator; b. Milton, Mass., Nov. 13, 1928; s. George S. and Alice (Herrick) M.; m. Nancy Carey, Dec. 22, 1949; children: Barbara, Elizabeth, Robert, George. A.B., Harvard U., 1950; M.A., Ind. U., 1952; Ph.D., U. Va., 1955. Mem. faculty Randolph-Macon Woman's Coll., 1952-53; mem. faculty Tufts U., Medford, Mass., 1955—; prof. astronomy Tufts U., 1968—, dean Coll. Liberal Arts, 1969-79, dean research and instl. programs, dean Grad. Sch. Arts and Scis., 1979-84; acting dir. Dudley Wright Ctr. for Innovation in Sci. Teaching, 1991-92; vis. astronomer Kitt Peak Nat. Obs., Tucson, 1962-82; cons. NSF, 1967-68; vis. astronomer Cerro Tololo Inter-Am. Obs., La Serena, Chile, 1969-72; dir. Wyman-Gordon Inc., Worcester, Mass. Corp; bd. dirs. Coun. of Grad. Schs. in U.S., 1979-83; mem. space sci. rev. panel NAS, 1989-95; mem. planetarium adv. com. Mus. Sci., Boston. Mem. AAAS, Am. Astron. Soc., Astron. Soc. Pacific, Am. Phys. Soc., Internat. Astron. Union, Am. Assn. Physics Tchrs., Royal Astron. Soc. Can., Royal Astron. Soc., N.E. Assn. Grad. Schs. (pres. 1981-82), Sigma Xi. Research in photometric studies of cataclysmic variables and related objects, early Am. astronomy, software for astronomy education. Home: Pegan Ln Dover MA 02030 Office: Tufts U Dept Physics And Astro Medford MA 02155

MUMFORD, MANLY WHITMAN, lawyer; b. Evanston, Ill., Feb. 25, 1925; s. Manly Stearns and Helen (Whitman) M.; m. Luigi Thorne Horne, July 1, 1961; children—Shaw, Dodge. A.B., Harvard U., 1947; J.D., Northwestern U, Chgo., 1950. Bar: Ill. 1950, U.S. Supreme Ct. 1969. Assoc. Chapman and Cutler, Chgo., 1950-62, ptnr., 1963-90. Contbr. articles to profl. jours. Served with USNR, 1942-46. Mem. Nat. Assn. Bond Lawyers (Bernard P. Friel medal 1987). Democrat. Clubs: Cliff Dwellers, University, Chgo. Literary. Avocation: computers. Home: 399 W Fullerton Pky Chicago IL 60614-9904 Office: 22 W Monroe St Ste 1503 Chicago IL 60603-2505

MUMFORD, PATRICIA RAE, religious organization administrator; b. Oklahoma City, Feb. 25, 1932; d. Raymond William and Mildred Louise (Wisdom) Gallagher; m. Donald Earl Mumford, April 6, 1951; children: Raymond Scott, Kenneth Earl, Robert Paul. Columnist The Sapulpan, Sapulpa, Okla., 1949-51; continuity writer Sta. KRMG, Tulsa, 1951-52; with continuity and production TV stas., Phoenix, Las Vegas, Denver, 1953-57; continuity and traffic radio stas. KPOI and KKUA, Honolulu, 1965-71; part-time program asst. Hawaii Council of Chs., Honolulu, 1972-80, assoc. dir., acting dir., 1980-85, exec. coordinator, 1986-87; exec. dir. Hawaii Council of Chs., Kailua, Hawaii, 1987-94, ret., 1994. Contrib. articles to newspapers, newsletters and mags. Bd. dirs. UNA-Hawaii, Meml. Soc. of Hawaii, Vol. Leadership Devel. program, Hawaii Pub. Broadcasting Authority Adv. Bd., Honolulu, 1978-82; mem. Hawaii State Commn. on Martin Luther King Jr. Holiday, 1988—. Named Outstanding Woman of Yr., City and County of Honolulu, 1982. Mem. Nat. Assn. Ecumenical Staff (svc. award 1987, 92), Ch. Women United (local and state pres., mem. nat. coun. 1965-72). Democrat. Mem. Christian Ch., United Presbyn. Ch.

MUMFORD, WILLIAM PORTER, II, lawyer; b. Kewanee, Ill., July 13, 1920; s. Harold E. and Mary K. (Harry) M.; m. Jean N. Hagemann, Nov. 22, 1951; children—William Porter III, James F., Michael E. B.S. in Accounting, U. Ill., 1943, J.D., 1949. Bar: Ill. bar 1949, Oreg. bar 1955; C.P.A., Ill., Oreg. Jr. accountant Price Waterhouse & Co., Chgo., 1949-51; practiced in Chgo., 1951-54, Grants Pass, Ore., 1955-57, Eugene, Oreg., 1957—; mem. firm McAdams & Kirby, 1951-55; sr. accountant B.K. Herndon & Co., 1955-57; partner Thompson, Mumford, Anderson & Fisher, 1957-86, ret., 1986. Eugene campaign mgr. Hatfield for Gov., 1960-62; chmn. bd. trustees Oreg. State Library. Served to capt., inf. AUS, 1943-46. Mem. Am. Legion, Pi Kappa Alpha, Phi Alpha Delta. Republican. Club: Elk. Home: 1960 Alder St Eugene OR 97405-2938

MUMMA, ALBERT G., retired naval officer, manufacturing company executive, management consultant; b. Findlay, Ohio, June 2, 1906; grad. U.S. Naval Acad., 1926; D.Eng. (hon.) N.J. Inst. Tech.; m. Carmen Braley, 1927; children—Albert G. Jr., John S., David B. Commd. ensign USN, 1926, advanced through grades to rear adm.; head tech. intelligence div. Naval Forces Europe, World War II; comdr. David Taylor Model Basin, Mare Island Naval Shipyard, also chief Bur. Ships, U.S. Navy, 1955-59; builder nuclear high speed submarines, U.S.S. Enterprise, Long Beach, Bainbridge and Polaris submarines; ret., 1959; v.p., group exec. Worthington Corp., 1964, exec. v.p., dir. in charge all domestic ops., 1967, pres., chief operating officer, 1967, chmn. bd., 1967-71; chmn. Am. Shipbldg. Commn., 1971-73. Trustee emeritus Drew U., Madison, N.J. Recipient Adm. Jerry Land Gold medal; awarded Knight Grand Officer of Orange Nassau by the Queen of the Netherlands. Fellow Soc. Naval Architects and Marine Engrs. (hon.; past pres.); mem. Am. Soc. Naval Engrs. (hon.; past pres.), Nat. Acad. Scis. (past mem. research council; past chmn. numerous coms.), Nat. Acad. Engring. (life). Clubs: Army and Navy, Army and Navy Country (Washington), Baltusrol Golf (Springfield, N.J.); Mountain Lake (Lake Wales, Fla.). Home: 69 Mountain Lk Lake Wales FL 33859 summer: 1400 Waverly Rd # 25 Gladwyne PA 19035-1253

MUMMA, ALBERT GIRARD, JR., architect; b. Long Beach, Calif., July 2, 1928; s. Albert Girard and Carmen (Ramey) M.; m. Janeal Thomas Woolf, Dec. 24, 1973; children: Eugenia M. Villagra, Albert Girard III, Peter Brennaman. B.Arch., U. Va., 1951. Designer McLeod & Ferrara, Architects, Washington, 1951-56; assoc. Deigert & Yerkes, Architects, 1956-62; prin. Mumma & Assocs., Washington, 1962—; archtl. designer hotel div. Marriott Corp., 1980-82. Prin. archtl. works include Nat. Arboretum Hdqrs. Bldg, 1961, Finnmark Sq. Silver Spring, Md., 1964, Inverness townhouses, Potomac, Md., 1971, Post Office and Fed. Bldg., Elkins, W.Va., 1971, U.S. Trade Fairs in Spain, Finland, Japan, El Salvador, Poland 1963-72, Fallswood housing project, Falls Church, Va., 1972, Bristow Village townhouses, Annandale, Va., 1972-73, Marriott Hotel, Dayton, Ohio, 1982, Plaza Venetia, Biscayne Bay, Miami, Fla., 1983, Houston Med. Ctr. Hotel, Newark Airport Hotel, 1984, pvt. residences, subdivision and townhouse projects, Washington, Md., Va., Pa., 1962—. Served with USMC, 1945-47. Recipient Design award Washington Bd. Trade, 1964; winner Newark Airport Hotel Competition, 1981. Mem. AIA (medal 1951), Rappahannock River Yacht Club.

MUMMA, GORDON, composer, educator, author; b. Framingham, Mass., Mar. 30, 1935; s. Colgan Thomas and Adamae (McCoy) M.; children: Christopher, Jonathan. Student, U. Mich., 1952-53. Guest lectr. Brandeis U., 1966, 67; composer, musician Merce Cunningham Dance Co., 1966-74, Sonic Arts Union, from 1966; guest lectr. U. Ill., 1969-70, Ferienkurse für Neue Musik, Darmstadt, Fed. Republic Germany, 1974; mem. faculty Cursos Latinoamericanos de Música Contemporánea, Montevideo, 1975, Buenos Aires, 1977, Dominican Republic, 1981; prof. music U. Calif., Santa Cruz, 1975-94; prof. emeritus U. Calif., 1994—; Darius Milhaud prof. Mills Coll., 1981; co-founder ONCE Festivals of Contemporary Music, Ann Arbor, Mich., 1961-66, Cybersonics, Ann Arbor, 1963; electronic designer Pepsi Pavilion, Expo 70, Osaka, Japan; tech. dir. Intermedia Inst., N.Y.C., 1970; founder Tao Chem. Co., performance-arts prodn. co., N.Y.C., 1976; vis. prof. U. Calif.-San Diego, 1985, 87; vis. disting. composer Mills Coll., 1989. Commd. works, recs. and performances include music for Venezia Space Theatre, Venice, Italy, 1963, Megaton for William Burroughs, Ann Arbor, 1964, Mesa, St. Paul de Vence, France, 1966, Hornpipe, Boston, 1967, Beam, Tokyo, 1969, Cybersonic Cantilevers, Syracuse, 1973, Some Voltage Drop, Paris, 1974, Passenger Pigeon, Albany, N.Y., 1976, (with

David Cotter, Jann McCauley, Tom Robbins), Ear Heart, Portland, Oreg., 1977, (with Jann McCauley, Henk Pander, Peter West), Echo, Portland, 1978, Pontpoint, 1980, (with William Winant) Than Particle, 1985, (with Tandy Beal Dance Co.), Orait, 1988, (with Abel-Steinberg-Winant Trio) Ménages à Deux, 1990; author: (with James Klosty) Merce Cunningham, 1975, (with Jon Appleton) Development and Practice of Electronic Music, 1975. N.Y. State Council on Arts grantee; Nat. Endowment Arts grantee, 1977-78; Oreg. Arts Council grantee, 1977-78. Mem. Broadcast Music Inc., Internat. Horn Soc., Soc. Ethnomusicology. Office: Univ Calif Dept Music Santa Cruz CA 95064

MUMMA, MICHAEL JON, physicist; b. Lancaster, Pa., Dec. 3, 1941; s. John Henry and Violet Lyndell (Baxter) M.; m. Sage Bailey Tower, Aug. 20, 1966; children: Peter Robb, Amy Elizabeth. A.B. in Physics with honors, Franklin and Marshall Coll., 1963; Ph.D. in Physics, U. Pitts., 1970. Grad. research asst. U. Pitts., 1963-70; astrophysicist NASA Goddard Space Flight Center, Greenbelt, Md., 1970-76; head br. Infrared and Radio Astronomy NASA Goddard Space Flight Center, 1976-84, assoc. chief Lab. Extraterrestrial Physics, 1984-85, head Planetary Systems br., 1985-90, chief scientist Lab. Extraterrestrial Physics, 1990—; adj. research assoc. in physics Pa. State U., 1978-81, prof. physics, 1981-88; mem. numerous working groups and adv. coms. NASA, Nat. Bur. Standards, NSF, Nat. Acad. Scis., 1973—; lectr. in field. Contbr. numerous articles to profl. publs., 1970—; editor: The Study of Comets, Vols. 1, 2, 1976, Vibrational-Rotational Spectroscopy for Planetary Atmospheres, vols. 1, 2, 1982, Astrophysics from the Moon, 1990. Recipient NASA medal for Exceptional Sci. Achievement, 1986; Kershner award for physics, 1962; Coll. Trustee's scholar Franklin and Marshall Coll., 1963. Fellow Am. Phys. Soc., Washington Acad. Sci.; mem. AAAS, Am. Astron. Soc., Am. Geophys. Union, Internat. Astron. Union, Sigma Pi Sigma. Achievements include discovery of natural lasers in atmospheres of Mars, Venus, and Jupiter; first detection of water vapor, formaldehyde and methanol in comets; first definitive measurements of deuterium and hydrogen on Mars and Venus; first absolute wind measurements on Venus and Mars; invention of tunable diode laser heterodyne spectrometer and other advanced instruments; development of Doppler-limited infrared spectroscopy for laboratory and astrophysical applications, of absolute calibration procedures in vacuum ultraviolet, of molecular branching ratio technique for intensity calibration in vacuum ultraviolet; measurement of many absolute cross sections in vacuum ultraviolet; research on atomic and molecular physics and chemistry, on comets, on planetary atmospheres, on infrared astronomy, on high-resolution spectroscopy, and in the field of dissociative excitation of molecules. Office: Code 690 Goddard Space Flight Ctr Greenbelt MD 20771

MUMZHIU, ALEXANDER, optical and imaging processing engineer, researcher; b. St. Petersburg, Russia, June 6, 1937; came to U.S., 1979; s. Mikhail and Henrietta (Rosenblum) M.; m. Natalya Takjas, Sept. 22, 1967; children: Jennifer, Daniel. Enginizing diploma, Leningrad Tech. Inst., 1959. Engr. Petzochemical Inst., St. Petersburg, Russia, 1959-65; sr. engr. optical dept. Mendeleev Inst. Metrology, St. Petersburg, Russia, 1965-79; prin. engr. Mid-West Instr., Troy, Mich., 1980-83; electro-optical engr. Perceptron Co., Farm Hills, Mich., 1983-84; cons. Arthur D. Little Co., Washington, 1984-85; sr. rsch. scientist Hunterlab., Reston, Va., 1985—. Contbr. articles to profl. jours. Recipient awards Moscow Indsl. Show. Mem. IEEE, OSA. Achievements include development of fundamental principles of imaging colotimetry; 2 U.S. patents for fiber optic sensor of rotation; desing of first scanning spectrophotometer, automatic lensmeter, thermoelectric flowmeter. Office: Hunterlab Inc 11491 Sunset Hills Rd Reston VA 22090

MUNASINGHE, MOHAN, development economist; b. Colombo, Sri Lanka, July 25, 1945; s. Peter Munasinghe and Flower Wickramasinghe; m. Sria Gooneratne, May 8, 1970; children: Anusha, Ranjiva. BA with honors, Cambridge (Eng.) U., 1967, MA, 1968; SM, MIT, 1969, EE, 1970; PhD in EE, McGill U., Montreal, Can., 1973; MA in Econs., Concordia U., 1975. Rsch. officer Ceylon Inst. Sci. and Indsl. Rsch., Colombo, 1968-70; asst. dir. Internat. Inst. Quantitative Econs., Montreal, 1973-75; div. chief World Bank, Washington, 1975—; vis. prof. Am. U., Washington, 1977-81, Inst. Tech. Policy in Devel., SUNY, 1982-88, Energy Ctr. U. Pa., Phila., 1988-94, Decision Scis. Ctr., 1992—, Beijer Inst., Stockholm, 1993—; disting. vis. prof. of environ. mgmt. Colo. U., Sri Lanka, 1995—; sr. advisor to pres. Office of Pres. of Sri Lanka, Colombo, 1982-87, chmn. computer and info. tech. coun., 1983-86; sr. rsch. fellow Ctr. Internat. Devel. and Conflict Mgmt. U. Md., College Park, 1987-90; pres.-emeritus Sri Lanka Energy Mgmt. Assn., Colombo, 1985—, pres. 1983-85. Author: 51 books including Economics of Power System Reliability and Planning, 1979, Energy Economics, Demand Management and Pricing, 1983, Rural Electrification for Development, 1987, Integrated National Energy Planning and Management, 1988, Computers and Informatics in Developing Countries, 1989, Energy Analysis and Policy, 1990, Electric Power Economics, 1990, Water Supply and Environmental Management, 1992, Energy Modelling and Policy, 1992, Environmental Economics & Sustainable Development, 1993, Economywide Policies and the Environment, 1994, Protected Area Economics & Policy, 1994, Defining & Measuring Sustainability, 1995, Natural Disasters & Environment, 1995, Property Rights in Social and Ecological Context, 1995; author over 200 tech. papers. Recipient Prize for Outstanding Achievement Latin Am. and Caribbean Energy Conf., 1988, Exceptional Contbns. award Internat. Assn. Energy Econs., 1987, Outstanding Scientists Gold medal Lions Internat., 1985; Grass fellow MIT, 1968, fellow Beijer Inst.-Royal Swedish Acad. Scis. Fellow NAS (Sri Lanka), Third World Acad. Scis. (Italy), Royal Soc. Arts, U.K. Inst. Elec. Engrs. (Beauchamp prize 1967), Inst. Engrs. (Sri Lanka); mem. IEEE, Am. Econ. Assn., Am. Phys. Soc., Sri Lanka Assn. Adv. Sci., Sri Lanka Econ. Assn. Home: 4201 E West Hwy Bethesda MD 20815-5910 Office: World Bank 1818 H St NW Washington DC 20433-0002

MUNCH, DAVID EDWARD, newspaper executive; b. Racine, Wis., Apr. 4, 1948; s. Hans Ernest and Ruth Eleanor (Fazen) M.; m. Christine Barbara Nemtuda; children: Hans Jakob, David Ernest. BA, Purdue U., 1970; MSBA, Ind. U., Gary, Ind., 1978. Mktg. research mgr. Post-Tribune, Gary, Ind., 1973-77; suburban circulation mgr. Post-Tribune, Gary, 1978-80; circulation mktg. mgr. Detroit Free Press, 1980-82, sales devel. mgr., 1982-84, mktg. svcs. dir., 1984-86, advt. dir., 1986-87, v.p. advt., 1987-90; v.p. advt. Phila. Inquirer and Daily News, Phila., 1991—; cons. in field. Scout leader Cub Scouts, Detroit Council, 1989. Sgt. U.S. Army, 1971-73. Mem. Adcraft Club of Detroit. Republican. Roman Catholic. Avocations: tennis, music, scout leadership, golf. Home: 454 Montgomery Ave Merion Station PA 19066-1220 Office: Phila Inquirer and Daily News 400 N Broad St Philadelphia PA 19101

MUNCH, DOUGLAS FRANCIS, pharmaceutical and health industry consultant; b. Bronx, N.Y., Mar. 15, 1947; s. Robert Joseph and Isabel (Fiordelisi) M.; m. Janice Ann Davis, Apr. 3, 1976: children: Sarah Christine, Eric Christopher. BSChemE, Villanova U., 1969; MS, U. Calif., Santa Barbara, 1974; PhD, Johns Hopkins U., 1978. Project engr. Grumman Aerospace Corp., Bethpage, N.Y., 1969-73; postdoctoral fellow U. South Ala., 1978-80; program mgr. Travenol Labs., Round Lake, Ill., 1980-82; dir. Kimberly Clark Corp., Atlanta, 1982-86; pres. Biomed. Products Group Inc., Roswell, Ga., 1986-87; cons., pres. D.F. Munch & Assocs., Roswell, 1986-88; pres., dir. Sphinx Pharmaceuticals, Inc., Durham, N.C., 1988-89; v.p., dir. Orthopharm Corp.-Advanced Care Products, Johnson & Johnson, Raritan, N.J., 1989-92; pres. D.F. Munch, Ltd., Basking Ridge, N.J., 1992—. Author: Cardiovascular Pharmacology, 1981; contbr. articles to profl. jours. Pres. Hollyberry Civic Assn., Roswell, 1980-87, Roswell Neighborhood Network, 1987, Basking Ridge (N.J.) Little League, 1992—; elder Basking Ridge Presbyn. Ch., 1992-95. Recipient Apollo Achievement award NASA, 1969; Profl. Achievement award Villanova U., 1987; NIH fellow, 1974-78. Fellow Royal Soc. Medicine; mem. Am. Physiol. Soc., Biomed. Engring. Soc., Johns Hopkins Med. and Surg. Assn. Avocations: woodworking, music, camping, cycling, swimming. Home: 41 Fieldstone Dr Basking Ridge NJ 07920-1605

MUNCK, ALLAN ULF, physiologist, educator; b. Buenos Aires, Argentina, July 4, 1925; came to U.S., 1945, naturalized, 1959; s. Carl and Elisabeth (Schmidt) M.; m. Claire Brosi, Oct. 5, 1957; children—Alexander Charles, Ingrid Claire, Kirsten Tanya. B.S. in Chem. Engring, Mass. Inst. Tech., 1948, M.S., 1949, Ph.D. in Biophysics, 1956. Chem. engr. Ducilo, Buenos Aires, 1949-50; mem. staff Huntington Lab. Mass. Gen. Hosp., Boston,

1956-57, Worcester Found. Exptl. Biology, Shrewsbury, Mass., 1957-59; mem. faculty Dartmouth Coll. Med. Sch., 1957—; prof. physiology Dartmouth Med. Sch., 1967—. Assoc. editor: Jour. Steroid Biochemistry; editorial bd.: Jour. Biol. Chemistry. Served with Argentine Army, 1949. Mem. Physiol. Soc., Endocrine Soc., Am. Soc. Biochemistry and Molecular Biology. Home: PO Box 114 Norwich VT 05055-0114 Office: Dartmouth Med Sch Dept Physiology Lebanon NH 03756

MUNCY, ESTLE PERSHING, physician; b. Tazewell, Tenn., Apr. 9, 1918; s. William Loyd and Flora Media (Monday) M.; m. Dorothy Davis, Dec. 31, 1946 (div. Apr. 1980); children: Robert H., Teresa A., Dorothy J., Estle II, James; m. Jean Marie Hayter, Mar. 19, 1985. AB, Lincoln Meml. U., 1939; MD, U. Tenn., 1943. Resident Dallas Meth. Hosp., 1948; tchg. resident Tufts Med. Sch., Boston, 1949-50; physician Jefferson City, Tenn. Author: The Muncys in the New World, 1988, People and Places in Jefferson County, Tennessee, 1994. Alderman Jefferson City, 1974-77; chmn. Jefferson City Planning Commn., 1976-79. Capt. M.C., U.S. Army, 1944-46. Mem. Tenn. Heart Assn. (pres. 1966-67), Hamblen County Med. Soc. (pres. 1960-61), Jefferson County Hist. Soc. (pres. 1993-94). Republican. Baptist. Avocations: photography, gardening. Home: 1428 Russell Ave Jefferson City TN 37760-2529

MUND, GERALDINE, bankruptcy judge; b. L.A., July 7, 1943; d. Charles J. and Pearl (London) M. BA, Brandeis U., 1965; MS, Smith Coll., 1967; JD, Loyola U., 1977. Bar: Calif. 1977. Bankruptcy judge U.S. Cen. Dist. Calif., 1984—. Past pres. Temple Israel, Hollywood, Calif. Mem. ABA, L.A. County Bar Assn. Office: Roybal Bldg 255 E Temple St Los Angeles CA 90012

MUND, RICHARD GORDON, foundation executive; b. Balt., Feb. 11, 1942; s. Allan Winfield and Irma Louetta (Kaufman) M.; m. Joan Ann Dennis, June 24, 1967; children: Mary Jean, John Winfield, Elizabeth Anne. Student, Johns Hopkins U., 1960-63; BA, Ill. Wesleyan U., 1965; M.A., U. Denver, 1967, Ph.D., 1970. Asst. dir. admissions Marshall U., Huntington, W.Va., 1970, dir. fin. aid, 1971, v.p. student affairs, 1971-77; coll. rels. coord. Mobil Oil Corp., N.Y.C., 1977-79; asst. sec. Mobil Found., Inc., N.Y.C., 1979, sec., exec. dir., 1980—; mem. contbns. coun. Conf. Bd., N.Y.C., 1980—, chmn., 1985. Trustee Huntington (W.Va.) Galleries, 1975-77, Coun. for the Advancement and Support of Edn., 1987-89, Fairfax County Pub. Schs. Edn. Found., 1991—; adv. coun. ARC, BBB, Nat. Ctr. Non-Profit Bds., United Way Am. Mem. Kappa Delta Pi, Kappa Alpha Order, Phi Delta Kappa. Office: Mobil Found Inc 3325 Gallows Rd Fairfax VA 22037

MUNDEL, MARVIN EVERETT, industrial engineer; b. N.Y.C., Apr. 20, 1916; s. Maxwell Herbert and Aimee (Baer) M. B.S.M.E., NYU, 1936; M.S. in Indsl. Engring., State U. Iowa, Iowa City, 1938, Ph.D. in Indsl. Engring., 1939. Registered profl. engr., Ind., Wis. Prof. Purdue U., West Lafayette, Ind., 1942-52; dir. U.S. Army Mgmt. Tng., Rock Island, Ill., 1952-53; staff officer U.S. Bur. Budget, Washington, 1963-65; prin. M.E. Mundel & Assocs., Silver Spring, Md., 1953-63, 65—. Author texts: Motion and Time Study, 7th edit., 1994, (with David L. Danner) Improving Productivity and Effectiveness, 1983. Recipient Gold medal Asian Productivity Orgn., Tokyo, 1980; named Engr. of Yr., Washington Council Engrs., 1980. Fellow Inst. Indsl. Engrs. (pres. 1979-80, Frank and Lillian Gilbreth award 1982), World Acad. Productivity Sci. Home and Office: 821 Loxford Ter Silver Spring MD 20901-1131

MUNDELL, DAVID EDWARD, leasing company executive; b. Montreal, Que., Can., Dec. 27, 1931; s. Charles D.T. and Elise Warden (Dunton) M.; m. Willa Price McReynolds, July 25, 1969; children: David Edward (dec.), Elise Mundell. BSc, Royal Mil. Coll. Can., 1953; B Engring., McGill U., 1954; MBA, Harvard, 1957. With DuPont of Can., 1957-59; pres. Can.-Dominion Leasing Corp., Ltd., Toronto, 1959-65; exec. v.p. U.S. Leasing Corp., 1965-68; pres. U.S. Leasing Internat. Inc., San Francisco, 1976-89, chief exec. officer, 1976-90; chmn. Orix USA Corp. N.Y., San Francisco; bd. dirs. Blazer Homes Inc., Commodity Corp. N.J., San Francisco Varian Assocs., Inc., Palo Alto. Mem. Pacific-Union Club, Toronto Golf Club. Office: Orix USA 1 Bush St Ste 68 San Francisco CA 94104-4406

MUNDELL, ROBERT ALEXANDER, economics educator; b. Kingston, Ont., Can., Oct. 24, 1932; s. William C. and Lila (Knifton) M.; m. Barbara Sheff, Oct. 14, 1957 (div. 1972); children: Paul Alexander, William Andrew, Robin Leslie. BA, U. B.C., Can., 1953; postgrad., U. Wash., 1953-54, London Sch. Econs. and Polit. Sci., 1955-56; PhD, MIT, 1956; postgrad., U. Chgo., 1956-57. Instr. econs. U. B.C., Vancouver, Can., 1957-58; acting asst. prof. econs. Stanford U., Calif., 1958-59; vis. prof. econs. Sch. Advanced Internat. Studies, Johns Hopkins U. Ctr., Bologna, Italy, 1959-61; sr. economist research dept. IMF, Washington, 1961-63; vis. prof. econs. McGill U., Montreal, Que., Can., 1973-74; Rockefeller vis. research prof. internat. econs. Brookings Instn., Washington, 1964-65; prof. Grad. Inst. Internat. Studies, Geneva, summers 1965—; Ford Found. vis. research prof. econs. U. Chgo., 1965-66, prof., 1966-71; prof. econs., chmn. dept. U. Waterloo, Ont., Can., 1972-74; prof. econs. Columbia U., N.Y.C., 1974—; economist Can. Royal Commn. on Price Spreads on Food Products, summer 1957; mem. joint fiscal mission to Puru OAS and Inter-Am. Devel. Bank, summer 1964; cons. FRS, IBRD, 1966—, U.S. Treasury Dept., 1969-74, EEC, 1970-73, UN, Govt. Panama; organizer, participant internat. confs., lectr. numerous univs. and profl. orgn. meetings. Author: The International Monetary System—Conflict and Reform, 1965, Man and Economics, 1968, International Economics, 1968, Monetary Theory—Interest, Inflation and Growth in the World Economy, 1971; contbr. sects. to books, encys.; U.S. Congl. Hearings; numerous articles to profl. jours.; co-editor, contbr.: Monetary Problems of the International Economy, 1969, Trade, Balance of Payments and Growth, 1971; co-editor: The New International Monetary System, 1977; editor: Jour. Polit. Economy, 1966-70. NSF research grantee, 1967-70; Guggenheim fellow, 1970-71. Mem. Can. Polit. Sci. Assn. (exec. council 1963-64), Can. Econ. Assn., Am. Acad. Polit. and Social Sci., Acad. Polit. Sci., Am. Econ. Assn., Econometric Soc., Royal Econ. Soc. Office: Dept Econs Columbia U 1031 Internat Affairs 118th St & Amsterdam Ave New York NY 10027

MUNDEN, ROBIN GHEZZI, lawyer; b. Rome, May 22, 1947; (parents Am. citizens); s. Kenneth White and Lia (Ghezzi) M.; m. Gail J. Schoch, June 2, 1973. BA in Polit. Sci., U. Denver, 1970; JD cum laude, Northwestern U., 1973. Bar: Ill. 1973, U.S. Dist. Ct. (no. dist.) Ill. 1973. Litigation assoc. McDermott, Will & Emery, Chgo., 1973-79; gen. counsel King-Seeley Thermos Co., Prospect Heights, Ill., 1979-82; v.p., gen. counsel, sec. Household Mfg. Inc., Prospect Heights, Ill., 1982-89; ptnr. Trizna, Lepri & Munden, Chgo., 1990-93; v.p., gen. counsel DSC Logistics, Inc., Des Plaines, Ill., 1993—. Mem. editorial bd. Northwestern Univ. Law Review, 1971-73. Mem. Sheffield Neighbors, Chgo. Mem. ABA, Ill. Bar Assn., Chgo. Bar Assn., Burnham Pk. Yacht Club (Chgo.), Royal Ocean Racing Club (U.K.). Democrat. Avocation: sailing. Home: 2140 N Bissell St Chicago IL 60614-4202 Office: DSC Logistics Inc 1750 S Wolf Rd Des Plaines IL 60018

MUNDHEIM, ROBERT HARRY, legal educator; b. Hamburg, Germany, Feb. 24, 1933; m. Guna Smitchens; children—Susan, Peter. B.A., Harvard U., 1954, LL.B., 1957; M.A. (hon.), U. Pa., 1971. Bar: N.Y. 1958, Pa. 1979. Assoc. Shearman & Sterling, N.Y.C., 1958-61; spl. counsel to SEC, Washington, 1962-63; vis. prof. Duke Law Sch., Durham, N.C., 1964; prof. law U. Pa., Phila., 1965—, Univ. prof. law and fin., 1980-93, dean, 1982-89, Bernard G. Segal prof. law, 1987-89—; co-chmn. Fried, Frank, Harris, Shriver & Jacobson, N.Y.C., 1990-92; exec. v.p., gen. counsel Salomon Inc.; gen. counsel U.S. Dept. Treasury, Washington, 1977-80; dir. Ctr. for Study of Fin. Instns., U. Pa.; dir. Corestates Bank N.A., Commerce Clearing House; gen. counsel Chrysler Loan Guarantee Bd., 1980; exec. v.p., gen. counsel Salomon, Inc., 1992—; mng. dir., mem. exec. com. Salomon Bros. Inc., N.Y.C., 1992—. Served with USAF, 1961-62. Recipient Alexander Hamilton award U.S. Dept. Treasury, 1980, Harold P. Seligson award Practicing Law Inst., 1988, Francis J. Rawle award, ABA-ALI, 1992. Mem. Am. Law Inst. (council, mem. exec. com.), Nat. Assn. Securities Dealers (gov.-at-large, vice-chmn.), San Diego Securities Regulation Inst. (chmn.). Author: Outside Director of the Publicly Held Corporation, 1976; American Attitudes Toward Foreign Direct Investment in the United States, 1979; Conflict of Interest and the Former Government Employee: Re-thinking the

Revolving Door, 1981. Office: Salomon Brothers Inc 7 World Trade Ctr New York NY 10048-1100

MUNDINGER, DONALD CHARLES, college president retired; b. Chgo., Sept. 2, 1929; s. George Edward and Bertha (Trelkenberg) M.; m. June Myrtle Grubbe, June 17, 1951; children: Debra Sue, Donald William, Mary Ruth (dec.). Student, U. Ill., 1947-48; BA, Concordia Coll., River Forest, Ill., 1951, LLD (hon.), 1982; MA, Northwestern U., 1952; PhD, Washington U., St. Louis, 1956; DH (hon.), MacMurray Coll. Jacksonville, Ill., 1984, Ritsumeikan U., Kyoto, Japan, 1992; LLD (hon.), Ill. Coll., Jacksonville, 1993; postdoctoral study, Cambridge U. (Eng.), 1967-68. Asst. prof. polit. sci., chmn. dept. Augustana Coll., Sioux Falls, S.D., 1956-58; asst. prof. govt. Valparaiso (Ind.) U., 1958-61, assoc. prof., 1961-65, prof., 1965-73; dean Valparaiso (Ind.) U. (Coll. Arts and Scis.), 1965-67; dir. Overseas Center, Cambridge, Eng., 1967-68; v.p. acad. affairs Overseas Center, 1968-73; pres. Ill. Coll., Jacksonville, 1973-93; chmn. Fedn. Ind. Ill. Colls. and Univs., 1975-78; chmn. non-public adv. com. Ill. Bd. Higher Edn., 1988-91; postdoctoral fellow Center Study Higher Edn., U. Mich., 1964-65; chmn. bd. Council Ind. Colls., 1988-90. Contbr. articles to profl. jours. Mem. Ill. State Bar Assn. (com. on fed. judicial and related appointments 1983-89), Nat. Assn. Ind. Colls. and Univs. (commn. on new initiatives, 1988-90), Pi Sigma Alpha, Phi Eta Sigma. Home: 3803 Pheasant Walk Valparaiso IN 46383

MUNDLAK, YAIR, agriculture and economics educator; b. Pinsk, Poland, June 6, 1927; arrived in Israel, 1927; s. Lipa and Batia (Bodankin) M.; m. Yaffa Mundlak; children: Tal, Yaelle, Guy. BS in Agrl. Econs. with highest honors, U. Calif., Davis, 1953; MS in Stats., U. Calif., Berkeley, 1956, PhD in Agrl. Econs., 1957. Prof. agrl. econs. Hebrew U., Jerusalem, 1956-85, head dept. agrl. econs., 1965-73, dir. research Ctr. for Agrl. Econs. Research, 1968-85, dean faculty agriculture, 1972-74; vis. prof. econs. U. Chgo., 1966-67, 78-85, F.H. Prince prof. econs., 1978—; vis. prof. agrl. econs. U. Calif., Berkeley, 1961-63; vis. prof. econs. Harvard U., Cambridge, Mass., 1974-76; research fellow Internat. Food Policy Research Inst., Washington, 1976—; vis. fellow CORE, Louvain, Belgium, 1973; vis. rsch. fellow World Bank, 1990-91; cons. Ministry Agriculture, Devel. Research Ctr. The World Bank, Washington, 1972; mem. research coms. Nat. Council for Research and Devel., 1964-74. Co-author (with Ben-Shahar, Berglas and Sadan) The West Bank and Gaza Strip—Economic Structure and Development Prospects, 1971; editor: Research in Agricultural Economics, 1976, (with F. Singer) Arid Zone Management, 1977; contbr. articles to profl. jours.; assoc. editor Jour. Econometrics, 1973-77. Pres. bd. trustees Israel Found., 1977-88. Recipient Bareli prize, 1965, Rothschild prize, 1972, Quality of Research Discovery award Am. Agrl. Econ. Assn., 1980, 82; Ford Found. research fellowship, 1966-67. Fellow Econometric Soc.; mem. Phi Beta Kappa. Office: Univ of Chgo Dept Econs 1127 E 59th St Chicago IL 60637 also: Faculty Agriculture, PO Box 12, Rehovot 76100, Israel

MUNDT, BARRY MAYNARD, management consultant; b. San Francisco, June 28, 1936; s. Kenneth Francis and Janet (Doughty) M.; m. Sally Hanscom, June 13, 1960; children: Kevin Warren, Trevor Stevens, Stacey Corbin. BS in Indsl. Engring., Stanford U., 1959; MBA, U. Santa Clara, 1964. Registered indsl. engr., Calif. Statistician Aerojet-Gen., Sacramento, 1957-58; reliability engr. Lockheed Missiles, Sunnyvale, Calif., 1959-61; mgmt. engr. C-E-I-R, Inc., Los Altos, Calif., 1961-65; sr. cons. Peat, Marwick, Livingston & Co., Los Angeles, 1965-68; mgr., prin. Peat, Marwick, Mitchell & Co., Atlanta, 1968-84; ptnr.-in-charge, ops. mgmt. cons. KPMG Peat Marwick Main & Co., N.Y.C., 1984-88; internat. mgmt. cons. ptnr. KPMG Internat., N.Y.C. and Amsterdam, The Netherlands, 1988-92; mgmt. cons., ptnr. KPMG Peat Marwick U.S., Montvale, N.J., 1992-95; prin. The Strategy Facilitation Group, Darien, Conn., 1995—. Author-editor: Managing Public Resources, 1982; co-author II Manager Pubblico (Italy) 1986; contbr. articles to profl. jours. Mem. ann. campaign Atlanta Symphony Orch., 1974-82, Atlanta Arts Alliance, 1976-81; del. to assembly United Way of Met. Atlanta, 1974-84; bd. chmn., mem. Brandon Hall Sch., Atlanta, 1980—. Fellow Inst. Indsl. Engrs. (treas. 1976-81, prse. 1982-83, asst. treas. 1985-92). Episcopalian. Avocations: golf; residential remodeling. Home and Office: 26 Searles Rd Darien CT 06820-6222

MUNDT, RAY B., diversified industry executive; b. Appleton, Wis., Aug. 10, 1928; s. Benjamin J. and Jessie V. (Toft) M.; m. Ruth C. Stanchik, June 15, 1953; children: R. Scott, William C., Robert J., Mary Ruth. BS, U. Wis., Stevens Point, 1953; postgrad., Harvard U., 1969, Syracuse U. Salesman to v.p., gen. sales mgr. Kimberly-Clark Corp., Neenah, Wis., 1953-70; pres Unisource Corp. (subsidiary Alco Standard Corp.), Valley Forge, Pa., 1970-73; exec. v.p. Alco Standard Corp., Valley Forge, 1973-74; chief operating officer Alco Standard Corp., 1973-80, pres., 1974-87, CEF, 1980-93, chmn., 1986—, also bd. dirs. Served with USNR, 1945-49. Clubs: Union League, Phila. Country, Harvard Bus. Sch. of Phila. Lodge: Masons. Office: Alco Std Corp 1255 Drummers Ln # 200 Wayne PA 19087-1565*

MUNDY, CARL EPTING, JR., commandant of the marine corps; b. Atlanta, July 16, 1935; s. Carl Epting Sr. and Anne Louise (Dunn) M.; m. Linda Stringfield Sloan, Nov. 28, 1957; children: Elizabeth Anne, Carl Epting III, Timothy Sloan. BS, Auburn U., 1957; MS, Naval War Coll., 1977. 2d lt. USMC, 1957, advanced through grades to gen.; apptd. comdt. USMC, Washington, 1991—. Decorated Legion of Merit, Bronze Star, Purple Heart, Navy Commendation medal. Mem. Phi Kappa Tau. Office: USMC Office of the Commandant Hdqrs Marine Corps Washington DC 20380-1775

MUNDY, JOHN HINE, history educator; b. London, Dec. 29, 1917; s. John and Clytie; m. Charlotte Fisher Williams, Sept. 3, 1942; children—Martha W., John W. B.A., Columbia, 1940, M.A., 1941, Ph.D., 1950. Mem. faculty Columbia U., N.Y.C., 1947-88, prof. history, 1962-88, prof. emeritus, 1988—, chmn. dept., 1967-70; vis. prof. Brown U., Providence, 1990-91; mem. Inst. Advanced Study, Princeton, 1963-64, 70-71. Author: Liberty and Political Power in Toulouse, 1954, The Medieval Town, 1958, Europe in the High Middle Ages, 1150-1309, 2d edit., 1990, The Repression of Catharism at Toulouse, the Royal Diploma of 1279, 1985, Men and Women at Toulouse in the Age of the Cathars, 1990, also articles. Served with AUS, 1943-46. Fulbright fellow, 1958-59; Am. Council Learned Socs. fellow, 1958-59; Guggenheim fellow, 1965, 77-78; Nat. Endowment Humanities fellow, 1970-71. Fellow Medieval Acad. Am. (2d v.p. 1986, 1st v.p. 1987, pres. 1988), Am. Acad. Arts and Scis. Home: 29 Claremont Ave New York NY 10027-6822

MUNDY, MARK JAMES, hospital administrator; b. N.Y.C., July 8, 1942. BS in History and Bus. Adminstrn., Murray State U., 1966; MS in Hosp. Adminstrn., Columbia U., 1970. Lic. nursing home adminstr., N.Y. Asst. dir. St. Vincent's Hosp., N.Y.C., 1970-73; assoc. adminstr. Winthrop Univ. Hosp., Mineola, N.Y., 1973-81; exec. dir. N.Y. Downtown Hosp., N.Y.C., 1981-83; chief exec. officer Quincy (Mass.) Hosp., 1983-90; pres., chief exec. officer N.Y. Meth. Hosp., Bklyn., 1990—; guest lectr., residency preceptor Columbia U., N.Y.C.; bd. dirs. N.Y. Hosp. Care Network Inc., N.Y. Health Plan Inc., Combined Coordinating Coun. Ins. Co.; mem. N.Y. health adv. bd. to speaker N.Y. Assembly, 1994; mem. N.Y. State Coun. on Grad. Med. Edn., 1994. Bd. dirs. Cancer Inst. Bklyn.; bd. trustees, mem. exec. com. League Voluntary Hosps. Capt. U.S. Army Med. Svc. Corps, 1966-68. Named Top 25 Turnaround Execs., Healthweek, 1989. Fellow Am. Coll. Health Care Execs.; mem. Am. Hosp. Assn. (at-large del., mem. regional policy bd. 1989-90), Met. Health Adminstrs. Assn. (pres. 1972-73), Greater N.Y. Hosp. Assn. (bd. govs., exec. com., officer 1992—), Healthcare Assn. N.Y. State (bd. trustees, strategic planning com.), Bklyn. C. of C. (bd. dirs.), Columbia U. Sch. Pub. Health Alumni Assn. (pres. 1976-77), Hosp. Adminstrs. Club N.Y. (pres. 1993-94). Office: NY Meth Hosp 506 6th St Brooklyn NY 11215-3609

MUNECHIKA, KEN KENJI, research center administrator; b. Waimea, Kauai, Hawaii, June 18, 1935; s. Masao (Yasutake) Munechika; m. Grace Shizue Wakayama, June 10, 1958; children: Curtis K., Stacy M., Kenny K. BS, U. Hawaii, 1958; MS, U. So. Calif., 1976, PhD, 1979. Commd. 2d lt. USAF, 1958, advanced through grades to col., 1980, ret., 1989; exec. dir. State of Hawaii, Honolulu, 1992-93; dir. Ames Rsch. Ctr. NASA, Mountain View, Calif., 1994—. Mem. AIAA, Air Force Assn. Baptist. Avocations:

golf, jogging, fishing. Home: 318 Casitas Bulevar Los Gatos CA 95030 Office: NASA Ames Rsch Ctr Mail Stop 200-1 Moffett Field CA 94035

MUNERA, GERARD EMMANUEL, manufacturing company executive; b. Algiers, Algeria, Dec. 2, 1935; s. Gabriel and Laure (Labrousse) M.; m. Paule A. Ramos, July 28, 1959; children: Catherine, Philippe, Emmanuelle, Jean-Marie. M in Math., M in Physics, M in Chemistry, Ecole Polytechnique, Paris, 1956; CE, Ecole des Ponts et Chaussees, Paris, 1959. Chief county engr. Dept. Rds. and Bridges, South Algiers, 1959-62; cons. French Ministry Fgn. Affairs, Argentina, 1962-66; sr. v.p. fin. Camea Group Pechiney Ugine Kuhlmann, Buenos Aires, 1966-70, chmn. bd., chief exec. officer, 1976-77; exec. v.p. Howmet Aluminum Corp., Greenwich, Conn., 1976-77, pres., chief operating officer, 1977-79, pres., chief exec. officer, 1980-83; corporate v.p. nuclear fuels Pechiney, Brussels, 1983-85; vice chmn., chief exec. officer Union Minière, Brussels, 1985-89; head corp. planning and devel. RTZ, London, 1989-90; pres., CEO Minorco USA, Englewood, Colo., 1990-94, also bd. dirs.; chmn. and CEO Latin Am. Gold, Inc., N.Y.C., 1994—; bd. dirs. Arcadia Inc., Synergex Inc., Scaltech Inc. Patentee low-income housing system. Served with French Air Force, 1956-57. Decorated Legion of Honor. Roman Catholic. Office: Latin Am Gold Inc 245 Park Ave New York NY 10167-0002

MUNFORD, LUTHER TOWNSEND, lawyer; b. Jackson, Miss., Dec. 14, 1949; m. Virginia Thompson, Aug. 18, 1979; children: Charles S., Margaret T., Mary R. AB, Princeton (N.J.) U., 1971; BA, Oxford U., 1973; JD, U. Va., 1976. Clk. to Paul H. Roney U.S. Ct. Appeals (5th cir.), 1976-78; clk. to Harry A. Blackmun U.S. Supreme Ct., Jackson, Miss., 1978-79; assoc. to ptnr. Butler, Snow, O'Hara, Stevens and Cannada, Jackson, 1979-86; assoc. prof. Miss. Coll. Sch. of Law, Jackson, 1986-89; ptnr. Phelps Dunbar, Jackson, 1989—; mem. lawyer adv. com. U.S. Ct. Appeals (5th cir.); adj. prof. Miss. Coll. Sch. of Law, 1989—. Author: Mississippi Supreme Court Practice, 1987; (with others) Appellate Practice Manual, 1992. Adminstrv. bd. Galloway United Meth. Ch., Jackson, 1984—. Mem. ABA (chmn. fed. and local rules subcom. litigation sect.), Am. Inn of Ct. (bencher), Am. Law Inst., Am. Acad. of Appellate Lawyers (bd. dirs. 1992). Democrat. Methodist. Office: Phelps Dunbar 2829 Lakeland Dr Jackson MS 39208-9798

MUNGAN, NECMETTIN, petroleum consultant; b. Mardin, Turkey, Mar. 1, 1934; came to U.S., 1953, came to Can., 1966; s. Kerim and Saide M.; m. Gunilla Ersman, May 19, 1962; children—Carl Edward, Christina Deniz, Nils Kerim, Tanya Katerina. BS Petroleum Engring., U. Tex., 1956, BA Math., 1957, MS Petroleum Engring., 1958, PhD Petroleum Engring., 1961. Head rsch. Sinclair Research, Tulsa, 1961-66; chief research officer Petroleum Recovery Inst., Calgary, Alta., Can., 1966-78; pres. Mungan Petroleum Cons., Ltd., Calgary, 1978-86; chief tech. advisor AEC Oil and Gas Co. Calgary, 1986—. Contbr. numerous articles to profl. publs. Named hon. citizen State of Tex., 1956, hon. prof. chem. and petroleum engring. U. Calgary, 1993; recipient Excellence in Presentation of Tech. Paper award Am. Inst. Chem. Engrs., 1966. Mem. Soc. Petroleum Engrs. (Uren Award, 1990), AIME (C.K. Ferguson award 1966, Disting. lectr 1969-70, Disting. Svc. award 1992), Petroleum Soc., Assn. Profl. Engrs., Geologists and Geophysicists Alta., Sigma Xi, Tau Beta Pi, Sigma Gamma Epsilon, Pi Epsilon Tau, Kappa Mu Epsilon. Office: AEC Oil and Gas Co, 3900 421-7 Ave SW, Calgary, AB Canada T2P 4K9

MUNGER, BENSON SCOTT, association executive; b. St. Johns, Mich., Jan. 21, 1942; s. Kenneth L. and Doris (Benson) M.; m. Bette Louise Johnson, June 15, 1963; children: Heidi Lynn, Chad Benson. BA, Mich. State U., 1965, PhD, 1969. Tchr. Grand Ledge Pub. Schs., Mich., 1965-66; mem. staff Southwest Regional Lab, Los Angeles, 1969-70; dir. negotiations Mich. Edn. Assn., East Lansing, 1970-75; vis. asst.prof. Indsl. Relations Ctr., U. Minn., Mpls., 1975-76; dep. exec. dir. Am. Coll. Emergency Physicians, 1976-80; exec. dir. Am. Bd. Emergency Medicine, East Lansing, Mich., 1980—, chmn. com. bd. assocs., 1991—; commr. City of Johns, 1983—; cons. in field. Contbr. articles in field. Mich. State U. fellow, 1966-69. Mem. Am. Soc. Assn. Execs., Am. Assn. Med. Soc. Execs. Office: Am Bd Emergency Med 3000 Coolidge Rd East Lansing MI 48823-6319*

MUNGER, BRYCE L., physician, educator; b. Everett, Wash., May 20, 1933; s. Leon C. and Lina (Eaton) M.; m. Donna Grace Bingham, July 20, 1957; children: Ailene, D'Arcy, Gareth Torrey, Bryce Kirtley. Student, U. Wash., 1951-54; M.D. magna cum laude, Wash. U., 1958. Intern in pathology Johns Hopkins U., 1958-59; asst. prof. anatomy Washington U., St. Louis, 1961-65; asso. prof. U. Chgo., 1965-66; prof. Milton S. Hershey Med. Center, Pa. State U., Hershey, 1966-91, chmn. dept. anatomy, 1966-87; prof., head dept. anatomy U. Tasmania, Hobart, 1992—. Bd. dirs. Pa. Spl. Olympics Inc. Served with MC USAF, 1959-61. Mem. AAAS, Am. Assn. Anatomists, Am. Soc. Cell Biology, Phi Beta Kappa, Sigma Xi, Alpha Omega Alpha. Office: U Tasmania, Dept Anatomy, Hobart Tasmania 7001, Australia

MUNGER, CHARLES T., diversified company executive; b. 1924; married. Ptnr. Wheeler Munger & Co., 1961-76; chmn., chief exec. officer Blue Chip Stamps, 1976-78; vice chmn. Berkshire Hathaway, Inc., Omaha, Nebr., 1978—. Office: Berkshire Hathaway Inc 1440 Kiewit Plz Omaha NE 68131-3302

MUNGER, EDWIN STANTON, political geography educator; b. LaGrange, Ill., Nov. 19, 1921; s. Royal Freeman and Mia (Stanton) M.; m. Ann Boyer, May 2, 1970; 1 child, Elizabeth Stanton Gibson. B.Sc., U. Chgo., 1948, M.Sc., 1949, Ph.D., 1951. Fulbright fellow Makerere U., 1949-50; research fellow U. Chgo.; field assoc. Am. Univs. Field Staff, 1950-60; faculty Calif. Inst. Tech., Pasadena, 1961—; prof. polit. geography Calif. Inst. Tech., 1960—; research fellow Stellenbosch U., 1955-56; vis. prof. U. Warsaw, 1973. Author books including Afrikaner and African Nationalism, 1968, The Afrikaners, 1979, Touched by Africa: An Autobiography, 1983, Ethnic Chess Sets, 1992; editor books including Munger Africana Library Notes, 1969-82; contbr. numerous articles to profl. jours., chpts. to books. Evaluator Peace Corps, Uganda, 1966, Botswana, 1967; chmn. State Dept. Evaluation Team South Africa, 1971; trustee African-Am. Inst., 1956-62; acting pres. Pasadena Playhouse, 1966; chmn. bd. trustees Crane Rogers Found., 1979-82, fellow 1950-54; mem. exec. com. NAACP, Pasadena, 1979—, nat. del., 1984, 85; trustee Leakey Found., 1968—, pres., 1971-84; pres. Cape of Good Hope Found., 1985—; pres. Internat. Vis. Coun., L.A., 1991-93, bd. dirs., 1979-93. Recipient Alumni Citation award for pub. svc. U. Chgo., 1993. Fellow South African Royal Soc., Royal Soc. Arts, African Studies Assn. (founding bd. dirs. 1956-66); mem. PEN USA West (v.p.), Coun. Fgn. Rels.; Cosmos Club, Athenaeum Club, Twilight Club. Office: Calif Inst Tech Div Humanities and Social Scis 1201 E California Blvd Pasadena CA 91125-0001

MUNGER, ELMER LEWIS, civil engineer, educator; b. Manhattan, Kans., Jan. 4, 1915; s. Harold Hawley and Jane (Green) M.; m. Vivian Marie Bloomfield, Dec. 28, 1939; children: John Thomas, Harold Hawley II, Jane Marie. B.S., Kans. State U., 1936, M.S., 1938; Ph.D., Iowa State U., 1957. Registered profl. engr., Nebr., Kans., Iowa, Vt. Rodman St. Louis-Southwestern Ry., Ark., Mo., 1937-38; engr. U.S. Engr. Dept., Ohio, Nebr., 1938-46; missionary engr. Philippine Episcopal Ch., 1946-48; engr. Wilson & Co., Salina, Kans., 1948; tchr. Iowa State U., 1948-51, 54-58; engr. C.E., U.S. Army, Alaska, 1951-54; from tchr. to dean Norwich U., Northfield, Vt., 1958-69; prof. gen. engring. U. P.R., Mayagüez, 1969-75; prof. civil engring. Mich. Tech. U., 1975-80; ret.; mem. spl. com. on engring. Inter-Am. Devel. Bank, U. W.I., 1971. Author: (with Clarence J. Douglas) Construction Management, 1970. Fellow ASCE; mem. Am. Mil. Engrs. (mil. engr. mem.), NSPE, Vt. Soc. Profl. Engrs., Am. Soc. Engring. Edn., Phi Kappa Phi, Sigma Tau, Tau Beta Pi, Chi Epsilon. Episcopalian. Clubs: Masons, Shriners. Home: 21260 Brinson Ave # 311 Port Charlotte FL 33952-5005

MUNGER, PAUL R., civil engineering educator; b. Hannibal, Mo., Jan. 14, 1932; s. Paul Oettle and Jane Lucille (Williams) Munger; m. Frieda Ann Mette, Nov. 26, 1954; children: Amelia Ann, Paul David, Mark James, Martha Jane Munger Cox. BSCE, Mo. Sch. Mines and Metallurgy, 1958, MSCE, 1961; PhD in Engring. Sci., U. Ark., 1972. Registered profl. engr., Mo., Ill., Ark. Instr. civil engring Mo. Sch. Mines and Metallurgy, Rolla, 1958-61, asst. prof., 1961-65; assoc. prof. U. Mo., Rolla, 1965-73, prof.,

1973—; dir. Inst. River Studies, U. Mo., Rolla, 1976—; exec. dir. Internat. Inst. River and Lake Systems, U. Mo., Rolla, 1984—. Mem. Nat. Soc. Profl. Engrs., Mo. Soc. Profl. Engrs., Am. Soc. Engring. Edn., ASCE, Nat. Coun. Engring. Examiners (pres. 1983-84), Mo. Bd. Architects, Profl. Engrs. and Land Surveyors (chmn. 1978-84). Office: U Mo Inst River Studies 111 Civil Engring Rolla MO 65401*

MUNGER, SHARON, market research firm executive; M. Robert Munger; 3 children: Shawn, Shane, Blair. Grad. Vanderbilt U. Sec., data processor, acct. exec. M/A/R/C, Inc., Irving, Tex., from 1973; now pres., chief operating officer Irving, Tex. Office: M-A-R-C Inc 7850 N Belt Line Rd Irving TX 75063-6064

MUNHALL, EDGAR, curator, art history educator; b. Pittsburgh, Mar. 14, 1933; s. Walter and Anna (Burns) M.; life ptnr. Richard Barsam. BA, Yale U., 1955, PhD, 1959; MA, NYU, 1957. Instr. art history Yale U., New Haven, 1959-64, asst. prof., 1964-65; curator The Frick Collection, N.Y.C., 1965—; adj. prof. Columbia U., 1979, 81—. Decorated chevalier Ordre des Arts et des Lettres. Office: The Frick Collection 1 E 70th St New York NY 10021-4907

MUNISTERI, JOSEPH GEORGE, construction executive; b. Rome, Sept. 24, 1930; s. Peter P. and Inez Gertrude (Ziniti) M.; m. Theresa Grasso, June 7, 1952; children: Joanne, Robert, Laura, Stephen, James, Richard. BE, Yale U., 1952. With Bechtel Corp., San Francisco, 1952-59; with The Lummus Co., N.Y.C., London and Houston, 1959-67, gen. mgr., 1964-67; sr. v.p. sales Brown & Root, Inc., Houston, 1967-75, group v.p. power div., 1975-80, group v.p. corp. devel., 1980-81, also bd. dirs.; pres. Enserch Engrs. & Constructors, Inc., Houston, 1981-85; exec. v.p. Ford, Bacon & Davis, Inc., Dallas, 1985-87; chmn., pres., CEO Comstock Group, Inc., Danbury, Conn., 1987-88; pres. Joseph G. Munisteri Co., Houston, 1989—; former chmn. bd. Pine-O-Pine. Former mem. Bd. dirs. Atomic Indsl. Forum; Bd. dirs. Am. Nuclear Energy Council. Mem. Atomic Indsl. Forum, Am. Inst. Chem. Engrs., Am. Nuclear Soc., Atomic Indsl. Forum, ASTM, Council Engring. Law, ASCE, Assn. Iron and Steel Engring., Assoc. Builders and Contractors (dir.). Clubs: Yale of N.Y., Yale S.E.T., Houston.

MUNITZ, BARRY, chief university administrator, English literature educator, business consultant; b. Bklyn., July 26, 1941; s. Raymond J. and Vivian L. (LeVoff) M.; m. Anne Tomfohrde, Dec. 15, 1987. BA, Bklyn. Coll., 1963; MA, Princeton U., 1965, PhD, 1968; cert., U. Leiden, Netherlands, 1962. Asst. prof. lit. and drama U. Calif, Berkeley, 1966-68; staff assoc. Carnegie Commn. Higher Edn., 1968-70; mem. presdl. staff, then assoc. provost U. Ill. System, 1970-72, acad. v.p., 1972-76; v.p., dean faculties Central campus U. Houston, 1976-77, chancellor, 1977-82, chmn. coordinating bd. faculty workload, 1976-80; chmn. Tex. Long Range Planning, 1980-82; pres., chief oper. officer Federated Devel. Co., 1982-91; vice chmn. Maxxam Inc., L.A., 1982-91; chancellor Calif. State U. System, Long Beach, Calif., 1991—; prof. English lit. Calif. State U., L.A., 1991—; bd. dirs. Sta. KCET-TV, Am. Coun. on Edn., Calif. Econ. Devel. Corp., SunAmerica Inc., SallieMae; cons. in presdl. evaluation and univ. goverance. Author: The Assessment of Institutional Leadership, 1977, also articles, monographs. Mem. task force NSF. Recipient Disting. Alumnus award Bklyn. Coll., 1979, U. Houston Alumni Pres.'s medal, 1981; Woodrow Wilson fellow, 1963. Mem. Young Pres. Orgn., Heritage Club, Phi Beta Kappa. Office: Calif State U System Office of Chancellor 400 Golden Shore Long Beach CA 90802-4275

MUNITZ, GERALD F., lawyer; b. Jersey City, Aug. 3, 1933. AB, U. Mich., 1955; JD, U. Chgo., 1960. Bar: Ill. 1960. Ptnr. Winston & Strawn, Chgo.; conferee Nat. Bankruptcy Conf., 1971—. Contbg. editor: Collier Bankruptcy Guide, 1981, 84, Prentice Hall Law and Business, Bankruptcy Litigation Manual, 1990. Fellow Am. Coll. Bankruptcy; mem. ABA, Ill. State Bar Assn., Chgo. Bar Assn. (chmn. bankruptcy and reorganization com. 1967-68, mem. com. character and fitness 1973-85), Legal Club Chgo., Law Club Chgo. Office: Winston & Strawn 35 W Wacker Dr Chicago IL 60601-1614

MUNIZZI, PAM, state senator; b. Evergreen Park, Ill., June 16, 1954; d. Anthony Joseph and Pauline Mary (Krstulovich) M. BA, U. Ill., Chgo., 1976; postgrad., Ill. Inst. Tech., 1992—. Adminstrv. asst. Chgo. City Coun., 1983-87; legis. asst. Ill. State Gen. Assembly, Chgo., 1987-88, state rep., 1989-92, state senator, 1992—; supr. Cook County Office of States Atty., Chgo., 1988-89; dir. intergovtl. affairs Chgo. Pk. Dist., 1992—. Mem. 11th Ward Dem. Orgn., Chgo., 1974—; bd. dirs. Valentine Boys and Girls Club, 1989—, Mercy Hosp. Women's Bd., 1989—, Benton Community Settlement, 1989—. Recipient Mil. Baton award U.S. Army Parachute Team, 1992. Roman Catholic. Avocations: golf, sports, baseball. Home: 2934 S Parnell Ave Chicago IL 60616-3128 Office: 3659 S Halsted St Chicago IL 60609-1642

MUNK, PETER, oil industry executive; b. 1950. Self-employed Toronto, Ont., Can., 1964-86; officer Horsham Corp., Toronto, 1986—, AOC Holding, Inc., St. Louis, 1988—, Clark Oil & Refining Corp., St. Louis, 1992—. Office: Clark Oil & Refining Corp 8182 Maryland Ave Saint Louis MO 63105-3786

MUNK, PETER, mining executive; b. Budapest, Hungary, Nov. 8, 1927; arrived in Can., 1948; s. Louis L. and Katherine (Adler) M.; m. Linda Gutterson; children: Anthony, Nina; m. Melanie Jane Bosanquet, 1973; children: Natalie, Cheyne, Marc David. BASc in Elec. Engring., U. Toronto, Ont., Can., 91953; LLD, Upsala Coll., N.J., 1991. Chmn., chief exec. officer So. Pacific Hotel Corp., Sydney, Australia 1969-81; chmn. Barrick Resources, Toronto, 1981-83, Am. Barrick Resources Corp., Toronto, 1983—; The Horsham Corp., Toronto, 1987—; chmn., bd. dirs. Clark Oil & Refining Corp., St. Louis, Trizec Corp. Ltd.; bd. dirs. World Gold Coun., Geneva, Hollinger Inc., Toronto. Trustee Toronto Hosp.; bd. dirs. U. Toronto Found. Decorated officer Order of Can. Office: Am Barrick Resources Corp, 27th Fl S Tower, 200 Bay St, Toronto, ON Canada M5J 2J3

MUNK, WALTER HEINRICH, geophysics educator; b. Vienna, Austria, Oct. 19, 1917; came to U.S., 1933; m. Edith Kendall Horton, June 20, 1953; children: Edith, Kendall. BS, Calif. Inst. Tech., 1939, MS, 1940; PhD in Oceanography, U. Calif., 1947; DhD (hon.), U. Bergen, Norway, 1975, Cambridge (Eng.) U., 1986. Asst. prof. geophysics Scripps Inst. Oceanography, U. Calif., San Diego, 1947-54, prof., 1954—; dir. Inst. Geophysics and Planetary Physics, U. Calif., La Jolla, 1960-82; prof. geophysics, dir. heard island expt. Scripps Inst., U. Calif. Author (with Mac Donald) The Rotation of the Earth: A Geophysical Discussion, 1960, (with Worcester and Wunsch) Ocean Acoustic Tomography, 1995; contbr. over 200 articles to profl. jours. Recipient Albatross award Am. Misc. Soc., 1959, gold medal Royal Astron. Soc., 1968, Nat. Medal Sci., 1985, award Marine Tech. Soc., 1969, Capt. Robert Dexter Conrad award Dept. Navy, 1978, G. Unger VVetlesen prize Columbia U., 1993, Presdl. award N.Y. Acad. Scis., 1993; named Calif. Scientist of Yr., Calif. Mus. Sci. and Industry, 1969; fellow Gugenheim Found., 1948, 55, 62, Overseas Found., 1962, 81-82, Fulbright Found., 1981-82, sr. Queen's fellow, 1978. Fellow Am. Geophys. Union (Maurice Ewing medal 1976, William Bowie medal 1989), AAAS, Am. Meteorol. Soc. (Sverdrup Gold medal 1966), Acoustical Soc. Am., Marine Tech. Soc. (Compass award 1991); mem. Nat. Acad. Scis. (Agassiz medal 1976, chmn. ocean studies bd. 1985-88), Am. Philos. Soc., Royal Soc. London (fgn. mem.), Russian Acad. of Sci., Deutsche Akademie der Naturforscher Leopoldina, Am. Acad. Arts and Scis. (Arthur L. Day medal 1965), Am. Geol. Soc., NY Acad. of Scis. (Presdl. Awd., 1994). Office: U Calif San Diego Scripps Inst Oceanography 0225 La Jolla CA 92093

MUNN, CECIL EDWIN, lawyer; b. Enid, Okla., Aug. 8, 1923; s. Cecil Edwin and Margaret (Kittrell) M.; m. Carolyn Taylor Culver, May 8, 1948; children: Franklin Culver, Charlotte Munn Cummings. BA, U. Okla., 1947; JD cum laude, Harvard U., 1947. Bar: Okla. 1947, Tex. 1955. Practice in Enid, 1947-54, Ft. Worth, 1954—; partner firm Cantey & Hanger, Ft. Worth, 1960-91, of counsel, 1992—; with Champlin Petroleum Co., 1954-60, v.p., atty., 1958-60, dir., 1962-75. Fellow Am. Coll. Trial Lawyers, Am. Bar Found.; mem. ABA (chmn. natural resources law sect. 1970-71), Southwestern Legal Found. (past dir.), Tex. Bar Found., Phi Delta Theta, Phi Delta Phi. Presbyterian. Home: 42 Valley Ridge Rd Fort Worth TX 76107-3108 Office: 2100 Burnett Plz 801 Cherry St Fort Worth TX 76102-3108

MUNN, JANET TERESA, lawyer; b. De Funiak, Fla., Nov. 7, 1952; d. Willard Ernest and Olive Pauline (Wilkinson) M.; m. Michael E. Fass, Sept. 27, 1975. BA in Anthropology, Fla. State U., 1975, MA in Social Scis., 1977; JD with high honors, Nova U., 1985. Bar: Fla. 1985, U.S. Dist. Ct. (so. dist.) Fla. 1986, U.S. Dist. Ct. (mid. dist.) Fla. 1988, U.S. Ct. Appeals (11th cir.) 1989, U.S. Supreme Ct. 1990. Jud. clerk for Judge Jose A. Gonzalez Jr. U.S. Dist. Ct. (so. dist.) Fla., Ft. Lauderdale, 1985-87; litigation assoc. Steel Hector & Davis, Miami, Fla., 1987-91, litigation ptnr., 1992—. Editor: Southern District Digest, 1987-88. Leo S. Goodwin fellow Nova U., 1983-84. Mem. ABA (co-chmn. intellectual properties litigation com. litigation sect. 1991-92, chmn. trade regulation/intellectual property com. gen. practice sect. 1990-91, vice chmn. 1989-90), Fed. Bar Assn., Fla. Bar (Pro Bono award 1988), Dade County Bar Assn., Phi Kappa Phi. Office: 200 S Biscayne Blvd Ste 4000 Miami FL 33131-2398

MUNN, STEPHEN P., manufacturing company executive. Pres., chief exec. officer Carlisle Cos. Inc., Cin., also bd. dirs.; bd. dirs. Carrier Corp. N.Y. Office: Carlisle Cos Inc 250 E 5th St Cincinnati OH 45202-4103

MUNNEKE, GARY ARTHUR, law educator, consultant; b. Cedar Rapids, Iowa, Dec. 29, 1947; s. Leslie Earl and Margaret Frances (Fortsch) M.; children—Richard Arthur, Matthew Frederick. B.A. in Psychology, U. Tex. 1970; J.D., 1973. Bar: Tex. 1973. Asst. dean, dir. placement U. Tex., Austin, 1978-80; asst. prof., asst. dean Del. Law Sch., Widener U., Wilmington, 1980-84, assoc. prof., 1984-87; pres. Legal Info. Systems, 1987-92; assoc. dean, assoc. prof. Sch. Law Pace U., 1988—. Contbr. articles to profl. jours. Mem. ABA (chmn. standing com. on profl. utilization and career devel. 1981—, chmn. law practice mgmt. sect. pub. bd., articles editor Legal Econs. mag. 1984—), State Bar Tex. Presbyterian. Office: Pace U Sch Law 78 N Broadway White Plains NY 10603-3710

MUNNELL, ALICIA HAYDOCK, economist; b. N.Y.C., Dec. 6, 1942; d. Walter Howe Haydock and Alicia (Wildman) Haydock Roux; m. Thomas Clark Munnell (div.); children: Thomas Clark Jr., Hamilton Haydock; m. Henry Scanlon Healy, Feb. 2, 1980. BA in Econs., Wellesley, 1964; MA in Econs., Boston U., 1966; PhD in Econs., Harvard U., 1973. Staff asst. bus. rsch. div. New Eng. Tel. Co., Boston, 1964-65; teaching fellow econs. dept. Boston U., 1965-66; rsch. asst. for dir. econ. studies program Brookings Instn., Washington, 1966-68; teaching fellow Harvard U., Cambridge, Mass., 1971-73; asst. prof. econs. Wellesley Coll., Mass., 1974; economist Fed. Res. Bank Boston, 1973-76, asst. v.p., economist, 1976-78, v.p., economist, 1979-84, sr. v.p., dir. rsch., 1984-93; asst. sec. for econ. policy Dept. Treasury, Washington, 1993—; mem. Gov.'s Task Force on Unemployment Compensation, Mass., 1975; mem. spl. funding adv. com. for Mass. pensions, 1976; mem. Mass. Retirement Law Commn., 1976-82; staff dir. joint com. on pub. pensions Nat. Planning Assn., 1978; mem. adv. com. for urban inst. HUD grant on state-local pensions, 1978-81; mem. pension rsch. council Wharton Sch. Fin. and Commerce, U. Pa., 1979—; mem. adv. group Nat. Commn. for Employment Policy, 1980-81; mem. adv. bd. Nat. Aging Policy Ctr. in Income Maintenance, Brandeis U., 1980-84; participant pvt. sector retirement security and U.S. tax policy roundtable discussions Govt. Rsch. Corp., 1984; mem. supervisory panel Forum Inst. of Villers Found., 1984; mem. Medicare working group, div. of health policy rsch. and edn. Harvard U., 1984-87; mem. Commn. on Coll. Retirement, 1984-86; mem. com. to plan major study of nat. long term care policies Inst. Medicine, Nat. Acad. Scis., 1984-87; mem. steering com. Am. Assn. Ret. Persons, 1987—; mem. adv. council Am. Enterprise Inst., 1987—; com. mem. Inst. Medicine, Nat. Acad. Scis. Human Rights Com., 1987—; co-founder, pres. Nat. Acad. Social Ins., 1986—; bd. dirs. Pension Rights Ctr.; mem. program rev. com. Brigham and Women's Hosp., 1988—; mem. Commn. to Rev. Mass. Anti-Takeover Laws, 1988-89, econs. vis. com. MIT, 1989—. Author: The Impact of Social Security on Personal Saving, 1974, Future of Social Security, 1977 (various awards), Pensions for Public Employees, 1979, The Economics of Private Pensions, 1982; co-author: Options for Fiscal Structure Reform in Massachusetts, 1975; editor: Lessons from the Income Maintenance Experiments, 1987, Is There a Shortfall in Public Capital Investment?, 1991, (conf. proc.) Retirement and Public Policy, 1991, Pensions and the Economy: Sources, Uses, and Limitations of Data, 1992, co-editor: Pensions and the Economy: Sources, Uses, and Limitations of Data; contbr. articles to profl. jours., chpts. to books. Mem. Inst. Medicine of NAS, Nat. Acad. Pub. Adminstrn. Office: US Treasury Dept Office of Econ Policy 1500 Pennsylvania Ave NW Washington DC 20220

MUÑOZ, CARLOS RAMÓN, bank executive; b. N.Y.C., Dec. 8, 1935; s. Alejandro and Gladys Helena (Judah) M.; m. Wilhelmina Elaine North, June 8, 1957 (div. 1993); children: Carla Christine, Kyle Alexander. BA, Columbia U., 1957, MA, 1961. Insp., ofcl. asst. Citibank, N.A., N.Y.C., 1959-64, asst. mgr., then mgr. in Dominican Republic and P.R., 1965-70, asst. v.p., N.Y.C., 1971-72, v.p., dept. head, 1972-78, sr. v.p., regional mgr. and dir. Citicorp. USA, San Francisco, 1978-81, sr. v.p., mem. Credit Policy Com., 1982-85; chief credit officer Dime Savings Bank, N.Y.C., 1995—. Bd. dirs. Episcopal Mission Soc., N.Y.C., 1974—, chmn. exec. com., 1990-93; bd. dirs. Inner City Scholarship Fund, 1984—, Corp. for Relief Widows and Orphans of Protestant Episcopal Clergymen in State N.Y., 1974-79. Served as 1st lt. USAR, 1968-74. Recipient Productivity award State Senator Diane Watson, Los Angeles, 1981; named Fairfield County Alumnus of Yr., 1989-90. Mem. Columbia Coll. Alumni Assn. (bd. dirs. 1983—, treas. 1988-92, v.p. 1992-93, 1st v.p. 1994—). Republican.

MUNOZ, JOHN JOAQUIN, research microbiologist; b. Guatemala City, Guatemala, Dec. 23, 1918; came to U.S., 1938, naturalized, 1954; s. Juan Muñoz and Carmen Valdés; m. Margaret Allen, June 21, 1947; children: William Allen, Maureen Carmen, John Richard, Michael Raymond. Grad. Escuela Preparatoria, Guatemala City, 1938; B.S., La. State U., 1942; M.S., U. Ky., 1945; Ph.D., U. Wis., 1947. Asst. prof. U. Ill. Med. Sch., 1947-51; rsch. assoc. Merck-Sharp & Dohme Rsch. Labs., 1951-57; prof. bacteriology, dir. Stella Duncan Meml. Fund rsch. U. Mont., 1957-61, staff affiliate, 1968—; rsch. microbiologist Inst. Allergy and Infectious Diseases, NIH, Rochy Mountain Lab., 1961—, head allergy-immunology sect., 1968-79, head pertussis sect., 1979-82, acting head immunopathology sect., 1985-88, scientist emeritus, 1989—; spl. assignment Pasteur Inst., Paris, 1966-67, Walter and Eliza Hall Inst. Med. Rsch., Melbourne, Australia, 1982-83. Author: (with R.K. Bergman) Bordetella pertussis—immunological and other biological activities, 1977; Contbr. articles to profl. jours. Fellow Am. Acad. Microbiology (emeritus); mem. Am. Soc. Microbiology, Am. Assn. Immunologists, Soc. Exptl. Biology and Medicine, Reticuloendothelial Soc. Internat. Endotoxin Soc., Sigma Xi, Phi Sigma. Home: 199 Meadowlark Ln Hamilton MT 59840-9111 Office: NIH Rocky Mountain Lab 903 S 4th St Hamilton MT 59840-2932

MUNOZ, MICHAEL ANTHONY, professional football player; b. Ontario, Calif., Aug. 19, 1958; m. Dede Munoz; children: Michael Anthony, Michelle. BS in Pub. Adminstrn., U. So. Calif., 1980. Offensive tackle Cin. Bengals, 1980-93; with Tampa Bay Buccaneers, 1993-94. Appeared in films: The Border Line, 1980, The Right Stuff, 1983. Player Pro Bowl, 1981, 83-91; NFL All-Star team, The Sporting News, 1981, player NFL Championship Game, 1982; named Lineman of Yr., 1981, NFL Alumni, NFLPA and Cin. Bengals, Best Offensive Lineman, NFL, 1986; recipient Sports award Seagrams Seven Crown, 1982; named to 1985 All NFL Team. *

MUÑOZ-SOLÁ, HAYDEÉ SOCORRO, library administrator; b. Caguas, P.R., Dec. 27, 1943; d. Gilberto Muñoz and Carmen Haydée (Solá) de Muñoz; m. Juan M. Masini-Soler, Jan. 8, 1966 (div. 1979); children: Juan Martín Masini-Muñoz, Haydée Milagros Masini-Muñoz. BA in Psychology, U. P.R., Río Piedras, 1965; MLS, U. P.R., Río Piedras, 1970; D in Libr. Sci., Columbia U., 1985. Asst. libr. U. P.R., Río Piedras, 1964-67; dir. libr. Interam. U., Aguadilla, P.R., 1974-75; head svcs. to pub. U. P.R., Aguadilla, 1975-76; cataloguer Cath. U. Ponce, P.R., 1976-79; cataloguer U. P.R., Río Piedras, 1982-84, head libr. and info. sci. libr., 1984-85, prof. grad. libr. sch., 1986, dir. libr. sys., 1986-93; coord. external resources libr. sys. U. P.R., mem. Seminar for the Acquisitions of Latin Am. Libr. Materials, Miami, Fla., 1982—; dir. P.R. Newspaper Project, Rio Piedras, 1986-90; mem. Adv.

Com. on Pub. Libra., San Juan, 1987-93; proposal reviewer NEH, 1990—; chmn. Puerto Rican Del. to Nat. White House Conf. on Libr. and Info. Svcs., 1991. Author: La Información y la Documentación Educativa/ Informe Sobre la Situación Actual en Puerto Rico, 1991, Memorias: Segunda Pre-Conferencia de Casa Blanca Sobre Bibliotecas y Servicios de Información en Puerto Rico, 1991; contbr. articles to profl. jours. Mem. Ponce Sport Club, 1976-83, ARC, Ponce, 1978. Recipient plaque White House Pre-Conf. on Libr. and Info. Scis., 1990; French Alps Study Tour scholar Assn. Caribbean Univ. Rsch. and Instl. Librs., 1989, Germany Study Tour scholar Fgn. Rels. Office, Germany, 1991. Mem. ALA, Am. Mgmt. Assn., Grad. Sch. Libr. and Info. Sci. Alumni Assn. (pres. 1988-90), Iberoamerican Nat. Librs. Assn. (pres. 1992-93), Puerto Rican Librs. Soc. (coord. So. area 1974, Lauro award 1989), Assn. Caribbean U. Rsch. and Instnl. Librs. (Parchment award 1988), Asoc. para las Comunicaciones y Tecnología Educativa, Mid. States Assn. Colls. and Schs. (collaborator), Am. Women Assn., Phi Delta Kappa (pres. P.R. com. 1988-90, Kappan of Yr. 1990), Eta Gamma Delta. Roman Catholic. Avocations: reading, crewel work, embroidery, knitting, movies. Office: U of PR Library System PO Box 23302 University Sta San Juan PR 00931-3302

MUNRO, ALICE, author; b. Wingham, Ont., Can., July 10, 1931; d. Robert Eric and Anne Clarke (Chamney) Laidlaw; m. James Armstrong Munro, 1951 (div. 1976); children: Sheila, Jenny, Andrea; m. Gerald Fremlin, 1976. BA, U. Western Ont., 1952, DLitt (hon.), 1976. Author: (short stories) Dance of the Happy Shades, 1968 (Gov.-Gen.'s Lit. award 1969), A Place for Everything, 1970, Lives of Girls and Women, 1971 (Can. Booksellers award, 1972), (short stories) Something I've Been Meaning To Tell You, 1974, Who Do You Think You Are?, 1979 (pub. in U.S. as Beggar Maid: Stories of Flo and Rose, 1984, Gov.-Gen.'s Lit. award 1978), The Moons of Jupiter, 1982, The Progress of Love, 1986 (Gov. Gens. Lit. award 1987), Friend of My Youth, 1990, (short stories) Open Secrets, 1994, A Wilderness Station, 1994; TV scripts: A Trip to the Coast, 1973, Thanks For The Ride, 1973, How I Met My Husband, 1974, 1847: The Irish, 1978. Recipient Can.-Australia Lit. Prize 1994, Marian Engel award, 1986. Home: PO Box 1133, Clinton, Ont. Canada N0M 1L0 Office: care Alfred A Knopf Inc 201 E 50th St New York NY 10022-7703*

MUNRO, BARBARA HAZARD, nursing educator, researcher; b. Wakefield, R.I., Nov. 28, 1938; d. Robert J. and Honore (Egan) Hazard; m. Bruce Munro, June 1, 1961; children: Karen Aimee, Craig Michael, Stephanie Anne. BS, MS, U. R.I., Kingston; PhD, U. Conn. RN, Conn. Asst. prof. U. of R.I. Coll. of Nursing, Kingston; assoc. prof., chmn. program in nursing rsch. Yale U., New Haven, Conn.; assoc. prof., asst. dir. Ctr. for Nursing Rsch. U. Pa., Phila.; dean, prof. Boston Coll. Sch. Nursing, 1990—; presenter and workshop leader various nursing confs. and seminars in U.S. Contbr. articles and rsch. to profl. pubs. Recipient Nat. Rsch. Svc. award. Fellow Am. Acad. Nursing; mem. ANA, Nat. League for Nursing, Sigma Theta Tau, Pi Lambda Theta, Phi Kappa Phi.

MUNRO, CRISTINA STIRLING, artistic director; b. London, May 22, 1940; m. Richard Munro (div. 1986); children: Alexandra, Nicholas. Attended various artistic schs., London. Mem. ballet corps Sadlers Wells Opera Ballet, London, 1960-62, Het Nederlands Ballet, The Hague, Holland, 1962-63; soloist London Festival Ballet, 1963-72; prin. soloist Eliot Feld Ballet, N.Y.C., 1972-75; prin. dancer, artistic dir. Old Dominion U., Norfolk, Va., 1975; artistic dir. Louisville Ballet Co., 1975-79; ballet mistress Houston Ballet, 1979-85; dir. Munro Ballet Studios, Corpus Christi, Tex., 1985—; artistic dir. Corpus Christi Ballet, 1985—; guest artist and choreographer numerous cos. in U.S. Recipient Giovanni Martini award Louisville, 1978. Mem. Imperial Soc. Tchrs. of Dance, Royal Acad. Dancing, Brit. Actors Equity Assn., Am. Guild Mus. Artists. Office: Munro Ballet Studios/ Corpus Christi Ballet 5610 Everhart Rd Corpus Christi TX 78411-4905

MUNRO, DONALD JACQUES, philosopher, educator; b. New Brunswick, N.J., Mar. 5, 1931; s. Thomas B. and Lucile (Nadler) M.; m. Ann Maples Patterson, Mar. 3, 1956; 1 child, Sarah de la Roche. A.B., Harvard U., 1953; Ph.D. (Ford Found. fellow), Columbia U., 1964. Asst. prof. philosophy U. Mich., 1964-68, asso. prof., 1968-73, prof. philosophy, 1973—; prof. philosophy and Asian langs., 1990—, chmn. dept. Asian langs. and cultures, 1993—; vis. research philosopher Center for Chinese Studies, U. Calif., Berkeley, 1969-70; asso. Center for Chinese Studies, U. Mich., 1964—; chmn. com. on studies of Chinese civilization Am. Council Learned Socs., 1979-81; mem. Com. on Scholarly Communication with People's Republic China, 1978-82, China Council of Asia Soc., 1977-80, Com. on Advanced Study in China, 1978-82, Nat. Com. on U.S.-China Rels., Nat. Faculty of Humanities, Arts and Scis., 1986—; Evans-Wentz lectr. Stanford U., 1970; Fritz lectr. U. Wash., 1980; Gilbert Ryle lectr. Trent U., Ont., 1983; John Dewey lectr. U. Vermont, 1989; vis. rsch.scholar Chinese Acad. Social Scis. Inst. Philosophy, Beijing, 1983, dept. philosophy Beijing U., 1990. Author: The Concept of Man in Early China, 1969, the Concept of Man in Contemporary China, 1977; editor: Individualism and Holism, 1985, Images of Human Nature: A Sung Portrait, 1988. Mem. exec. com. Coll. Literature, Sci. and The Arts U. Mich., 1986-89. Served to lt. (j.g.) USNR, 1953-57. Recipient letter of commendation Chief Naval Ops.; Disting. Svc. award U. Mich., 1968, Excellence in Edn. award, 1992; Rice Humanities award, 1993-94; Nat. Humanities faculty fellow, 1971-72; John Simon Guggenheim Found. fellow, 1978-79; grantee Social Sci. Rsch. Coun., 1965-66, Am. Coun. Learned Socs., 1982-83, China com. grantee NAS, 1990. Mem. Assn. for Asian Studies (China and Inner Asia Council 1970-72), Soc. for Asian and Comparative Philosophy. Club: Ann Arbor Racquet. Home: 14 Ridgeway St Ann Arbor MI 48109-0001 Office: Dept Philosophy U Mich Ann Arbor MI 48104 *I believe that much knowledge is interrelated and that academic disciplinary boundaries are transitory conveniences. The human significance of any research task I undertake should be obvious to those inside and outside my professional group (a goal I seek but do not always achieve).*

MUNRO, J. RICHARD, publishing company executive; b. 1931; married. B.A., Colgate U., 1957; postgrad., Columbia U., NYU; Litt. D. (hon.), Richmond U., 1983. With Time Inc. (now Time Warner Inc.), 1957—; pres. Pioneer Press Inc., subs. Time, 1969; pub. Sports Illus., 1969-71; v.p. Time Inc., 1971-75, group v.p. for video, 1975-79, exec. v.p., 1979-80, pres., 1980-86; chief exec. officer Time Inc. (name changed to Time Warner Inc.), 1980-90, chmn., 1986-90, chmn. exec. com., 1990—, also bd. dirs.; dir. IBM Corp. Mem. Pres.' Council on Phys. Fitness and Sport; trustee Experiment in Internat. Living, Brattleboro, Vt., Northfield Mount Hermon Sch., Colgate U.; bd. dirs. Urban League of Southwestern Fairfield County (Conn.), Jr. Achievement, United Negro Coll. Fund; bd. dirs., chmn. edn. com. N.Y.C. Partnership. Served with USMCR., Korea. Decorated Purple Heart with 2 clusters. Clubs: Country of New Canaan (Conn.), River, Winter of New Canaan. Office: Time Warner Inc 75 Rockefeller Plz New York NY 10019-6907*

MUNRO, JOHN HENRY ALEXANDER, economics educator, writer; b. Vancouver, B.C., Can., Mar. 14, 1938; s. Hector Gordon and Blanche (Almond) M.; m. Jeanette Roberta James, May 25, 1968; children: Robert Ryder, Valerie Marlene. B.A. with honors, U. B.C., Vancouver, 1960; M.A. in History, Yale U., 1961. Ph.D. in History, 1965. Instr. in history U. B.C., 1964-65, asst. prof. history and econs., 1965-68; assoc. prof. econs. U. Toronto, 1968-73, prof., 1973—; assoc. dir. Centre for Medieval Studies, U. Toronto, 1975-78; cons. on coinage to pub. U. Toronto Press, 1973—. Author: Wool, Cloth, and Gold, 1973, Bullion Flows and Monetary Policies in England and the Low Countries, 1350-1500, 1992, Textiles, Towns and Trade: Essays in the Economic History of Late-Medieval England and the Low Countries, 1994; contbr. articles to profl. jours., essays to books; editl. bd. Textile History, 1980—. Named Can. Coun. leave fellow, Belgium, 1970-71, Social Scis. and Humanities Rsch. Coun. Can. fellow, Eng. and Holland, 1979-80, Belgium, 1986-87, Eng. and Belgium, 1993—, Connaught Rsch. fellow, 1993-94. Mem. Can. Econ. Assn., Econ. History Assn. (U.S.), Econ. History Soc. (U.K.), Medieval Acad. Am. (economic 1992-93). Presbyterian. Home: 9 Woodmere Ct, Islington, ON Canada M9A 3J1 Office: Dept Econs U Toronto, 150 Saint George St, Toronto, ON Canada M5S 1A1

MUNRO, MEREDITH VANCE, lawyer; b. Natick, Mass., Aug. 4, 1938; s. George Lawrence and Florence Estella (Murphy) M.; m. Gail Wittekind, June 10, 1960 (div. 1974); children: Susan Heidi, Elizabeth Holly, Meredith Heather. AB, Princeton U., 1960; JD, Harvard U., 1963. Bar: Mass. 1963.

Assoc. atty. Gaston Snow & Ely Barlett, Boston, 1963-71, ptnr., 1971—; bd. dirs. Heath Cons. Inc., Stoughton, Mass., 1974—. Trustee The Tabor Acad., Marion, Mass., 1975—. Mem. Mass. Bar Assn., Boston Bar Assn. Avocations: antiques, gardening, cooking. Home: 5 Patricia Rd Framingham MA 01701-3931 Office: Gaston & Snow 1 Federal St Boston MA 02110-2003

MUNRO, MICHAEL DONALD, entertainment and hospital consultant, professional voice talent; b. Kindley AFB, Bermuda, May 6, 1953; (parents Am. citizens); s. Donald M. and Marilyn Barbara (Ravenelle) M. AAS in Criminology, U. Md., 1978; BA in Sociology, SUNY, Plattsburg, 1981; MA in Mgmt., Embry-Riddle U., 1986. Commd. 2d lt. USAF, 1976, advanced through grades to capt., 1985; chief security adminstr. Plattsburg AFB, N.Y., 1979-81; ICBM launch officer Grands Forks AFB, N.D., 1981-83, ICBM flight comdr., 1984-86; satellite officer Colorado Springs, Colo., 1986-87; chief satellite officer U.S. Space Command, Colorado Springs, 1987; chief U.S. Space Def. Ops. Ctr., Colorado Springs, 1988-91; ret., 1991, profl. voice talent, broadcaster, 1991—; cons. 1980 Winter Olympics, Lake Placid, N.Y., 1979-80; dir. Grand Forks City Govt., 1986. Contbr. articles to profl. jours. Mem. Pike's Peak Rodeo Com., Colorado Springs, 1987. Recipient Scholastic Achievement award Boeing Aerospace, 1988; named Outstanding Young Man Grand Forks County, 1985. Mem. Profl. Rodeo Cowboys Assn. (judge 1987-88, announcer, broadcaster 1989—), Assn. Govt. Execs., Crewmembers Assn. (pres. 1985-86), Grand Forks C. of C., Wild Horse Futurity Assn. (bd. dirs. 1992-94). Republican. Roman Catholic. Avocations: profl. rodeo, hunting, fishing, horseback riding. Home: PO Box 49266 Colorado Springs CO 80949

MUNRO, RALPH DAVIES, state government official; b. Bainbridge Island, Wash., June 25, 1943; s. George Alexander and Elizabeth (Troll) M.; m. Karen Hansen, Feb. 17, 1973; 1 son, George Alexander. BA in History and Edn. (scholar), Western Wash. U. Successively indsl. engr. Boeing Co.; sales mgr. Continental Host, Inc.; asst. dep. dir. ACTION Agy.; spl. asst. to gov. of Wash.; gen. mgr. Tillicum Enterprises & Food Services Co.; dir. Found. for Handicapped; pres. Northwest Highlands Tree Farm; now sec. of state State of Wash. Chmn. community service com. Seattle Rotary Club 4; founder 1st pres. Rotary Youth Job Employment Center, Seattle. Named Man of Yr. Assn. Retarded Citizens, Seattle, 1970. Mem. Nat. Assn. Secs. State (pres.), Nat. Assn. Retarded Children, Wash. Historic Mus. (dir.), Wash. Trust Historic Preservation (founder), Nature Conservancy. Republican. Lutheran. Office: Sec of State Legislative Bldg PO Box 40220 Olympia WA 98504-0220

MUNROE, GEORGE BARBER, former metals company executive; b. Joliet, Ill., Jan. 5, 1922; s. George Muller and Ruth (Barber) M.; m. Elinor Bunin, May 30, 1968; children by previous marriage: George Taylor, Ralph W. Taylor. AB, Dartmouth Coll., 1943; LLB, Harvard U., 1949; BA (Rhodes scholar), Christ Church, Oxford (Eng.) U., 1951, MA, 1956; DHL (hon.), No. Ariz. U., 1981; LLD (hon.), Dartmouth Coll., 1993. Bar: N.Y. 1949. Assoc. Cravath, Swaine & Moore, N.Y.C., 1949; atty. Office Gen. Counsel U.S. High Commn. Germany, Frankfurt and Bonn, 1951-53; justice U.S. Ct. Restitution Appeals Allied High Commn. Germany, Nuremberg, 1953-54; assoc. Debevoise, Plimpton & McLean, N.Y.C., 1954-58; with Phelps Dodge Corp., 1958-90, v.p., 1962-66, pres., 1966-75, 80-82, chief exec. officer, 1969-87, chmn. bd., 1975-87, chmn. fin. com., cons., 1987-90; bd. dirs. N.Y. Times Co., Sante Fe Pacific Gold Corp. Trustee, chmn. fin. com. Met. Mus. Art; vice chmn., bd. dirs. N.Y. Internat. Festival of Arts, Acad. Polit. Sci. Lt. (j.g.) USNR, 1943-46. Mem. Mining and Metall. Soc. Am., Coun. Fgn. Rels., Century Assn., River Club, Sky Club, Univ. Club (N.Y.C.), Bridgehampton Club. Office: Phelps Dodge Corp 399 Park Ave 29th Fl New York NY 10022-4614

MUNROE, PAT, retired newsman; b. Quincy, Fla., Nov. 3, 1916; s. Mark Welch and Mary Frances (Gray) M.; m. Mary Johnson Norris, Dec. 6, 1952; children: Anne Logan, Katherine Gray. B.S. in Indsl. Mgmt., Ga. Inst. Tech., 1939; M.S., Columbia Sch. Journalism, 1941. Reporter Atlanta Jour., 1939-40, Washington Post, 1946-47; former propr. Munroe News Bur., Washington, rep. book pubs. and newspapers, 1947-83; covered maj. polit. convs., presdl. campaigns, 1948—, (Vice Pres. Nixon's trip to Russia), 1959; chmn. standing com. corrs. U.S. Senate-House Press Galleries, 1955-56; bd. govs. Nat. Press Club, 1955-56. Bd. govs. Nat. Cathedral Sch., Washington; trustee Webb Sch., Bell Buckle, Tenn.; former trustee James Monroe Meml. Found., Fredericksburg, Va. Served to lt. comdr. USNR, 1941-45. Recipient Raymond Clapper Meml. award and cert. Columbia Sch. Journalism, 1957. Mem. White House Corrs. Assn., Sigma Delta Chi (pres. Washington 1964-65). Republican. Episcopalian. Clubs: Chevy Chase; University (N.Y.C.); Metropolitan, Nat. Press (bd. govs. 1957-59). Home: 9025 Bronson Dr Potomac MD 20854-4607

MUNSAT, STANLEY MORRIS, philosopher, educator; b. Rutland, Vt., Apr. 12, 1939; s. Leo and Ethel (Geron) M.; m. Rosemary S.; children—Steven, Tobin. A.B., Cornell U., 1960; M.A., U. Mich., 1962, Ph.D. 1965. Asst. prof. U. Calgary, Alta., Can., 1963-66; asst. prof. philosophy U. Calif., Irvine, 1966-68; assoc. prof. U. Calif., 1968-71, prof., 1971-72; prof. philosophy U. N.C., Chapel Hill, 1972—. Author: The Concept of Memory, 1967; Editor: The Analytic Synthetic Distinction, 1971; gen. editor: (with A.I. Melden) Wadsworth Basic Problems in Philosophy Series; contbr. articles to profl. jours. Mem. Am. Philos. Assn. Home: 837 Shadylawn Rd Chapel Hill NC 27514-2007 Office: Univ NC Dept Philosophy Chapel Hill NC 27514

MUNSAT, THEODORE L., neurologist, researcher; b. Rutland, Vt., Aug. 6, 1930; s. Leo and Ethel (Garon) M.; m. Carla Anne Hoffman, May 31, 1959; children: Amy, Peter. BS in Chemistry, U. Mich., 1952; MD, U. Vt., 1957; DSc (hon.), U. Marseille, France, 1987. Diplomate Am. Bd. Neurology and Psychiatry (examiner). Rsch. asst. pharmacology Cornell U. Med. Coll., 1955-56; intern Mt. Sinai Hosp., N.Y.C., 1957-58; resident in neurology Neurol. Inst., N.Y.C., Columbia Presbyn. Med. Ctr., 1958-60; chief resident in neurology UCLA Ctr. Health Scis., 1960-61, asst. prof. medicine, neurology dept., 1963-70, dir. Myasthenia Gravis Clinic, 1963-70, dir. UCLA Ctr. Health Scis., 1970-76; assoc. prof. neurology U. So. Calif. Sch. Medicine, 1970-73, prof., 1973—; dir. Muscle Disorder Clinic. 1970-76; prof., chmn. dept. neurology Tufts U. Sch. Medicine, 1976-83, prof. pharmacology, 1989—; dir. Neuromuscular Rsch. Unit Tufts-New Eng. Med. Ctr., 1976—; attending physician in neurology Wadsworth VA Hosp., 1963-70; staff neurologist L.A. County/U. So. Calif. Med. Ctr., 1970-76; neurologist in chief New Eng. Med. Ctr., 1976-83, co-dir. Muscular Dystrophy Clinic, 1976—, neuromuscular pathology lab., 1976—; program chmn. Congress Asian and Oceanic Neurologic Socs., 1983; 10th Carrell-Krusen lectr. Tex. Scottish Rite Hosp., Southwestern Med. Sch., Dallas, 1988, 1st Ann. Baird Med. Sci. Ctr. lectr. SUNY at Buffalo, 1988; cons. U.S. Naval Hosp., San Diego, Fresno County Gen. Hosp., Calif., State Calif. Vocat. Rehab. Svcs., Crippled Children Svcs., NIH, Serano Corp., Johns Hopkins Applied Physics Lab., others; adv. bd. Nat. Com. for Rsch. in Neurol. Diseases, Blindness and Stroke.; nat. adv. coun. Am. Fedn. for Aging Rsch. Contbr. numerous articles to profl. publs.; mem. editorial bd. Muscle and Nerve, Jour. Neurol. Rehabilitation, Bull. L.A. Neurol. Socs.; reviewer New Eng. Jour. Medicine, Neurology, Muscle and Nerve, Science. Trustee Easter Seal Rsch. Found.; bd. dirs., vice chmn. Nat. Coalition for Rsch. in Neurologic Diseases; bd. dirs. Nat. Found. for Rsch. in Neurologic Disorders. Lt. comdr. M.C., USN, 1961-63. Recipient Teaching Excellence award Tufts U. Sch. Medicine, 1982. Mem. Am. Acad. Neurology (pres. 1987-89, councillor, exec. com., chmn. continuing edn. com.), Am. Neurologic Assn., Soc. Neurosci., AAAS, Assn. Am. Colls., Am. Pub. Health Assn., Assn. Rsch. in Nervous and Mental Diseases, Soc. Clin. Neurologists, Muscular Dystrophy Assn. Am. Inc. (chmn. med. adv. bd. L.A. County chpt.), Pan Am. Med. Assn., L.A. Soc. Neurology and Psychiatry, Mass. Neurologic Assn., Boston Soc. Neurology and Psychiatry, Greater Boston Post-Polio Assn. (hon. dir.), Societe Francaise de Neurologie, Phi Lambda Upsilon. Office: Tufts-New Eng Med Ctr Dept Neurology 750 Washington St Boston MA 02111-1526

MUNSCH, MARTHA HARTLE, lawyer; b. Meyersdale, Pa., Oct. 31, 1948. BA, U. Pitts., 1970; JD, Yale U., 1973. Bar: Pa. 1973. Ptnr. Reed Smith Shaw & McClay, Pitts.; asst. prof. law U. Pitts. 1976-78. Office: Reed Smith Shaw & McClay James H Reed Bldg 435 6th Ave Pittsburgh PA 15219-1886

MUNSELL, ELSIE LOUISE, lawyer; b. N.Y.C., Feb. 15, 1939; d. Elmer Stanley and Eleanor Harriet (Dickinson) M.; m. George P. Williams, July 14, 1979. AB, Marietta Coll., 1960; JD, Marshall-Wythe Coll. William and Mary, 1972. Bar: Va. 1972, U.S. Dist. Ct. (ea. dist.) Va. 1974, U.S. Ct. Appeals (4th cir.) 1976, U.S. Supreme Ct. 1980. Tchr. Norview High Sch., Norfolk, Va., 1964-69; asst. Commonwealth atty. Commonwealth Atty.'s Office, Alexandria, Va., 1972-73; asst. U.S. atty. Alexandria, 1974-79; U.S. magistrate U.S. Dist. Ct. (ea. dist.) Va., Alexandria, 1979-81; U.S. atty. Dept. Justice, Alexandria, 1981-86; sr. trial atty. Office of Gen. Counsel, Dept. Navy, Washington, 1986-89, asst. gen. counsel installations and environ. law, 1989-91; dep. asst. environ. and safety Sec. Navy, 1991—. Active Va. Commn. on Status of Women, 1966-74; bd. vistors Coll. William and Mary, 1972-76; active Atty. Gen.'s Adv. Com. U.S. Attys., 1981-83; bd. dirs. Carpenter's Shelter, Inc., 1990-93. Mem. Environ. Law Inst. (assoc.), Sr. Execs. Assn. Episcopalian. Office: Dept Navy 1000 Navy Pentagon Washington DC 20350-1000

MUNSEY, VIRDELL EVERARD, JR., utility executive; b. Washington, Sept. 25, 1933; s. Virdell Everard and Mildred Lovenia (Wood) M.; m. Bernice Ann Wilson, Sept. 20, 1956; children: Wanda Louise, Allan Coll, Andrew Everard, Carolyn Jane. B.A. magna cum laude, Yale U., 1955; M.P.A., Harvard U., 1967. Reporter Washington Post, 1957-63; legis. asst. Rep. Henry S. Reuss, Washington, 1963-68; info. dir. United Democrats for Humphrey, Washington, 1968; asst. dir. public affairs Dem. Nat. Com., 1968; with Nat. Planning Assn., Washington, 1969-77; exec. v.p. Nat. Planning Assn., 1974-76; dep. asst. sec. for public affairs Dept. Treasury, Washington, 1977-81; cons. World Bank, 1981; with Va. Electric and Power Co., 1981-86, mgr. corp. communications, 1982-83, exec. dir. public policy, 1983-86, v.p. pub. policy, 1986; v.p. pub. policy Dominion Resources Inc., 1986—; mem. Va. Coal and Energy Commn., 1983—. Chmn. Arlington County Dem. Party, 1967-69; mem. Arlington County Bd., 1972-75, chmn., 1973; vice chmn. No. Va. Transp. Commn., 1973, chmn., 1974; bd. dirs. Washington Met. Area Transit Authority, 1975; mem. transp. planning bd. Met. Washington Coun. Govts., 1973-75; treas. Competitive Power Policy Forum, 1990—. Served with U.S. Army, 1955-57. Am. Polit. Sci. Assn. fellow, 1966-67. Mem. United Ch. Christ. Office: 901 E Byrd St Richmond VA 23219-4069

MUNSON, ALEX ROBERT, judge; b. L.A., Sept. 25, 1941; s. Robert Alexander and Lillian Agnus (Hamel) M.; m. Kathleen Rae Abernathey, June 29, 1968. BA, Long Beach (Calif.) State Coll., 1964, MA, 1965; EdD, U. So. Calif., L.A., 1970; JD, Loyola U., L.A., 1975. Atty. Kirtland and Packard, L.A., 1978-82; chief justice High Ct. of The Trust Terr. of The Pacific Islands, Saipan, Commonwealth of the No. Mariana Islands, 1982-88; chief judge U.S. Dist. Ct. of No. Mariana Islands, Saipan, Commonwealth of the No. Mariana Islands, 1988—. Mem. ABA, Calif. Bar Assn. Republican. Home: Box 5356 CHRB, Saipan MP Office: US Dist Ct PO Box 687 Saipan MP 96950-0687

MUNSON, DEE TAYLOR ALLISON, food marketing executive; b. Geneva, Ill., Nov. 17, 1936; d. R. Wayne and S. Dorothy (Locke) Allison; m. William Walfred Munson, Aug. 20, 1960 (dec. Jan. 1976); children: Daniel Stewart, Katherine Allison. BS in Food and Nutrition, Purdue U., 1958. Asst. food editor Better Homes & Gardens mag., Des Moines, 1958-60; home economist Calif. Foods Rsch. Inst., San Francisco, 1960-61; food editor Institutions mag., Chgo., 1961-62; ind. food cons. Chgo., 1962-70, 72-75; dir. home econs. Wheat Flour Inst., Chgo., 1970-72; v.p. advt. and consumer edn. Am. Egg Bd., Chgo., 1975-82; v.p. Cole & Weber Advt., Seattle, 1982-85; prin., cons. Food Profls., Vashon, Wash., 1985-88; mng. dir. Evans food group Evans Group, Seattle, 1988-94; sr. ptnr. EMB Ptnrs., Inc., Seattle, 1994—. Author: Miracle Blender Cook Book, 1965, Culinary Arts Nutrition Cook Book, 1974, 1974, Crepes Cook Book, 1975, Consumer Guide Food Processor Cook Book, 1975. Named Outstanding Alumnae, Purdue U., 1993. Mem. Am. Home Economists Assn., Pub. Rels. Soc. Am. (one of Top 100 Pub. Rels. Profls. 1989), Home Economists in Bus. (program chmn. 1983, nat. chmn.-elect 1986-87, nat. chmn. 1987-89, Outstanding Bus. Home Economist 1992). Baha'i. Avocations: needlework, gardening. Home: PO Box 1326 Vashon WA 98070-1326

MUNSON, ERIC BRUCE, hospital administrator; b. Elmhurst, Ill., Mar. 11, 1943; married. B, Wabash Coll., 1965; MHA, U. Chgo., 1967. Asst. to adminstr. Swedish Covenant Hosp., Chgo., 1966-67, asst. adminstr. U. Chgo. Hosps., 1970-73; assoc. adminstr. U. Hosp., Denver, 1973-77, adminstr., 1977-80; exec. dir. U. Hosp., Chapel Hill, 1980—. Home: 119 Black Oak Pl Chapel Hill NC 27514-6502 Office: Univ N C Hosps 101 Manning Dr Chapel Hill NC 27514-4335

MUNSON, HAROLD LEWIS, education educator; b. Windham, N.Y., Aug. 2, 1923; s. Esmond Lewis and Gladys (Disbrow) M.; m. Evelyn Claire Moore, Sept. 8, 1946; children: Michael Lewis, Jeffrey Charles. A.B. Hobart Coll., 1947; M.A, SUNY, Albany, 1948; Ed.D., NYU, 1961. Tchr. social studies, counselor Cairo (N.Y.) Central Sch., 1948-50; dir. guidance Williamson (N.Y.) Central Sch., 1950-54; supr. guidance N.Y. State Edn. Dept., Albany, 1954-59; prof. edn., chmn. Center for Counseling, Family and Worklife Studies, U. Rochester, N.Y., 1959-85; prof. emeritus Center for Counseling, Family and Worklife Studies, U. Rochester, 1985—; prof. edn. Overseas Program, Boston U., 1985-87; pres. Munson Assocs., 1988—; vocat. cons. Social Security Adminstrn., HEW, 1962-79. Author: (with H.W. Houghton) Organizing Orientation Activities, 1956, My Educational Plans, 1959, 70, Guidance Activities for Teachers of English, Social Studies, Science, Mathematics and Foreign Languages, 1965, (with Gilbert Gockley) Career Insights and Self Awareness Games, 1973; contbg. author: Ency. of Careers, 1967, Elementary School Guidance: Concepts, Dimensions and Practice, 1970, The Foundations of Developmental Guidance, 1971, Career Education for Deaf Students: An Inservice Leader's Guide, 1975. Served with USNR, 1944-46. Mem. Am. Counseling Assn., Nat. Career Devel. Assn., Am. Sch. Counselor Assn., Phi Delta Kappa. Home: 745 Thayer Rd Fairport NY 14450-9514 Office: U Rochester Warner Grad Sch Edn and Human Devel Rochester NY 14627 *Success is whatever you want it to be. By defining it in such personal terms, everyone should be able to experience some degree of success. For me, it has been being able to feel a measure of personal fulfillment through my accomplishments in helping others to define and examine their own existence.*

MUNSON, HOWARD G., federal judge; b. Claremont, N.H., July 26, 1924; s. Walter N. and Helena (O'Halloran) M.; m. Ruth Jaynes, Sept. 17, 1949; children: Walter N., Richard J., Pamela A. B.S. in Economics, U. Pa., 1948; LL.B., Syracuse U., 1952. Bar: N.Y. With Employers' Assurance Corp., Ltd., White Plains, N.Y., 1949-50; mem. firm Hiscock, Lee, Rogers, Henley & Barclay, Syracuse, N.Y., 1952-76; judge U.S. Dist. Ct. No. Dist. N.Y., Syracuse, 1976—. Mem., pres. Syracuse Bd. Edn.; bd. dirs. Sta. WCNY-TV; chmn. ethics com. Onondaga County Legislature. Served with U.S. Army, 1943-45, ETO. Decorated Bronze Star, Purple Heart. Mem. Am. Coll. Trial Lawyers, Nat. Assn. R.R. Trial Counsel, Am. Arbitration Assn., Justinian Soc., Alpha Tau Omega, Phi Delta Phi. Office: US Dist Ct 349 US Courthouse P O Box 7376 Syracuse NY 13261-7376

MUNSON, JAMES CALFEE, lawyer; b. Asheville, N.C., May 17, 1944; s. James B. and Margaret (Calfee) M.; children: Garrett Calfee, Ingrid Grove, James Birger, Elizabeth Tippet; m. Melinda Tippet, Sept. 14, 1985. BA, Yale U., 1966; JD, U. Wis., 1969. Bar: Wis. 1970, Ill. 1971. Law clk. to presiding justice U.S. Dist. Ct., Milw., 1969-70; assoc. Kirkland & Ellis, Chgo., 1970-75, ptnr., 1975—. Bd. dirs. Ronald Knox Montessori Sch., Wilmette, Ill., 1975-78, Trevian Youth Soccer Club, Wilmette, 1984-88. Mem. ABA, Chgo. Bar, Indian Hill Club. Office: Kirkland & Ellis 200 E Randolph Dr Chicago IL 60601-6401

MUNSON, JOHN BACKUS, computer systems consultant, retired engineering company executive; b. Chgo., May 1, 1933; s. Mark Frame and Catherine Louise (Cherry) M.; m. Anne Lorraine Cooper, July 6, 1957; children: David B., Sharon A. BA, Knox Coll., 1955. With Unisys Corp., McLean, Va., 1957-93, v.p. corp. software engring., 1977-81, v.p. tech. ops., 1981-84, v.p., gen. mgr. space transp. systems, 1984-89, 89-93; v.p., gen. mgr. Space Systems div., 1989-94, retired, 1994; mem. sci. adv. bd. USAF, 1981-86, mem. USN panel on F14D issues, 1987-88. Recipient Exceptional Civilian Service award USAF, 1986, Superior Pub. Svc. award USN, 1988,

cert. of appreciation NATO, 1984. Mem. bd. advisors U. Houston, Clear Lake, 1988-93, chmn. 1990-92; bd. dirs. Bay Area YMCA, 1988-93, chmn. 1992, Clear Lake Am. Heart Assn., 1989-93; co-chmn. Bay Area United Way, 1988—, chmn., 1992; Disting. visitor IEEE Computer Soc., 1981-94. Capt. U.S. Army, 1955-57. Named to Nat. Mgmt. Assn. Hall of Fame, 1994. Fellow IEEE (editor Trans. on Software Engring. 1982-84, bd. dirs. tech com. software engring. 1982—); mem. AIA, Am. Astronautical Soc. (bd. dirs. Southwest sect. 1989-94), Aerospace Industries Assn. (space com. 1989-94), U.S. Army Assn., Nat. Security Indsl. Assn., Armed Forces Communication Electronics Assn. (pres. Houston chpt. 1987-90), S.W. Regional Coun. Corp. CEOs. Home: 1018 Westcreek Ln Westlake Village CA 91362 Office: 595 Gemini St Houston TX 77058-2753

MUNSON, JOHN CHRISTIAN, acoustician; b. Clinton, Iowa, Oct. 9, 1926; s. Arthur J. and Frances (Christian) M.; m. Elaine Hendershot, Sept. 2, 1950; children: John Christian, Holly Elizabeth. BS, Iowa State Coll. 1949; MS, U. Md., 1952, PhD, 1962; Navy Dept. scholar, MIT, 1956. Electronic scientist Naval Ordnance Lab., Washington, 1949-66; tech. dir. navy portion Practice Nine, Naval Air Systems Command, 1967; supt. acoustics divsn. Naval Rsch. Lab., 1983-85; v.p. Engring. & Sci. Assocs., 1983-94; chmn. bd. dirs., 1994; ret.; asst. extension prof. elec. engring. U. Md., 1964-66; mem. Underwater Sound Adv. Group, 1969-75, U.S. Sonar Team, 1971-85, Mobile Sonar Tech. Com., 1972-85; cons., 1985—. Editor U.S. Navy Jour. Underwater Acoustics, 1983-91; patentee in field. Mem. exec. bd. D.C. Bapt. Conv., 1973—, chmn. fin. com., 1973; trustee Midwestern Bapt. Theol. Sem., 1970-80; trustee Bapt. Sr. Adult Ministries of Washington Met. Area, 1976-91, 92—, CEO, 1991-92; mem. Gen. Bd. Am. Bapt. Chs. U.S.A., 1994—; dir., pres. Allied Silver Spring Interfaith Svcs. to Srs. Today, 1994—. Fellow IEEE, Acoustics, Speech and Signal Processing Soc. (mem. adminstrv. com. 1974-76, chmn. underwater acoustics com. 1973-76), Acoustical Soc. Am.; mem. Sigma Xi. Home: 119 Marine Ter Silver Spring MD 20905-5925 *I have a positive joy for life, and I am an incurable optimist: my basic attitude is that things will work out for the best—but only if we do our very best. Each of us has a responsibility to grow to our maximum capacity and to be of reasonable service to mankind. The proper balance among family, job, service to God, service to others, and attention to yourself is essential. Whatever you are doing, do it from the right motivation and with enthusiasm.*

MUNSON, LAWRENCE SHIPLEY, management consultant; b. N.Y.C., Jan. 10, 1920; s. Lawrence J. and Anna (Lee) M.; m. Gretchen Thannhauser, May 24, 1947; children: Catherine Anne, Shipley John. A.B., Harvard U., 1942, JD, 1948. Bar: N.Y. 1948. Assoc. Willkie, Owen, Farr, Gallagher & Walton, N.Y.C., 1948-51; assoc., then partner McKinsey & Co., Inc., N.Y.C., 1953-67; pres. Loral Corp., Scarsdale, N.Y., 1967-69; v.p. Allegheny Power System, Inc., N.Y.C., 1969-72; v.p., mng. prin. Louis Allen Assocs., Inc., 1972—. Author: How To Conduct Training Seminars, 1984, 2d edit., 1992. Chmn. bd. Planned Parenthood N.Y.C., 1966-70; mem. bd. Planned Parenthood Manhattan and Bronx, 1960-66, Planned Parenthood World Population, 1967-70; bd. dirs. Greater N.Y. Fund, 1966-88, chmn. mgmt. assistance com., 1970-75; pres. East Hampton Village Preservation Soc., 1982-87, trustee, 1982—, chmn., 1993—; bd. dirs. United Way N.Y.C., 1988-89. Served to maj. USAAF, 1942-46; with USAF, 1951-53. Mem. Am. Soc. Tng. and Devel. (pres. N.Y. met. chpt. 1988-89, chmn. bd. dirs. 1990-93), Maidstone Club (East Hampton), Harvard Club (N.Y.C.). Home: 25 Dayton Ln East Hampton NY 11937-2415

MUNSON, NANCY KAY, lawyer; b. Huntington, N.Y., June 22, 1936; d. Howard H. and Edna M. (Keenan) Munson. Student, Hofstra U., 1959-62; JD, Bklyn. Law Sch., 1965. Bar: N.Y. 1966, U.S. Supreme Ct. 1970, U.S. Ct. Appeals (2d cir.) 1971, U.S. Dist. Ct. (ea. and so. dists.) N.Y. 1968. Law clk. to E. Merritt Weidner Huntington, 1959-66, sole practice, 1966—; mem. legal adv. bd. Chgo. Title Ins. Co., Riverhead, N.Y., 1981—; bd. dirs., legal officer Thomas Munson Found. Trustee Huntington Fire Dept. Death Benefit Fund; pres., trustee, chmn. bd. Bklyn. Home Aged Men Found.; bd. dirs. Elderly Day Svcs. on the Sound. Mem. ABA, N.Y. State Bar Assn., Suffolk County Bar Assn., Bklyn. Bar Assn., NRA, DAR, Soroptimists (past pres.). Republican. Christian Scientist. Office: 197 New York Ave Huntington NY 11743-2711

MUNSON, PAUL LEWIS, pharmacologist; b. Washta, Iowa, Aug. 21, 1910; s. Lewis Sylvester and Alice E. (Orser) M.; m. Aileen Geisinger, Mar. 7, 1931 (div. 1948); 1 dau., Abigail (Mrs. Mark Krumel); m. Mary Ellen Jones, Aug. 15, 1948 (div. 1971); children: Ethan Vincent, Catherine Laura; m. Yu Chen, Feb. 27, 1987; 1 stepchild, Ming An Chen. B.A., Antioch Coll., 1933; M.A., U. Wis., 1937; Ph.D., U. Chgo., 1942; M.A. (hon.), Harvard, 1955. Fellow, asst. biochemistry U. Chgo., 1939-42; research biochemist William S. Merrell Co., Cin., 1942-43; research biochemist, head endocrinology research Armour Labs., Chgo., 1943-48; research asst., then research asso. Yale Sch. Medicine, 1948-50; asst. prof., asso. prof. pharmacology, then prof. Harvard Sch. Dental Medicine, 1950-65; prof. pharmacology, chmn. dept. U. N.C. Sch. Medicine, 1965-77, Sarah Graham Kenan prof., 1970—; Mem. U.S. Pharmacopeia Panel on Corticotropin, 1951-55; mem. pharmacology test com. Nat. Bd. Med. Examiners, 1966-71; mem. gen. medicine B study section NIH, 1966-70, chmn., 1969-70, mem. pharmacology-toxicology rev. com., 1972-76. Author numerous articles on hormones; co-editor: Vitamins and Hormones, 1968-82; editl. bd. Endocrinology, 1957-63, Jour. Pharmacology and Exptl. Therapeutics, 1959-65, Jour. Dental Rsch., 1962-64, Biochem. Medicine, 1967-84, Am. Jour. Chinese Medicine, 1973-79, Pharmacol. Revs., 1967-70, editor-in-chief, 1977-81; editor-in-chief: Principles of Pharmacology, 1981-94. Fellow AAAS, Am. Acad. Arts and Scis.; mem. Am. Soc. Pharmacology and Exptl. Therapeutics (council 1970-73, sec.-treas. 1971-72), Am. Soc. Biol. Chemists, Endocrine Soc. (council 1963-65, Fred Conrad Koch award 1976), Am. Soc. Bone and Mineral Research (William F. Neuman award 1982), Am. Chem. Soc., Biometrics Soc., Internat. Assn. Dental Research (councillor 1957-59), AAUP, ACLU (mem. internat. com. on calcium regulating hormones, Elsevier Sci. Pubs. award 1989), Assn. Med. Sch. Pharmacology (council 1971-73, sec. 1972-73, pres. 1974-76), Am. Thyroid Assn. (nominating com. 1973), Sigma Xi. Dem. Socialist. Unitarian. Home and office: 1520 Taylor Ave Parkville MD 21234

MUNSON, RICHARD HOWARD, horticulturist; b. Toledo, Dec. 20, 1948; s. Stanley Warren and Margaret Rose (Winter) M.; m. Joy Ellen Smith, July 8, 1972; children: Sarah Joy, David Remington. BS, Ohio State U., 1971; MS, Cornell U., 1973, PhD, 1981. Plant propagator The Holden Arboretum, Mentor, Ohio, 1973-76; asst. prof. Agrl. Tech. Inst., Wooster, Ohio, 1976-78, Tex. Tech U., Lubbock, 1981-84; dir. botanic garden Smith Coll., Northampton, Mass., 1984—; v.p. Childs Park Found., Northampton, Mass., 1985—. Lt. col. USAR. Mem. Internat. Plant Propagators Soc., Am. Soc. for Hort. Sci., Am. Assn. Bot. Gardens and Arboreta (com. chmn. 1987-92), Am. Assn. Nurserymen, Internat. Soc. Arboriculture, Sigma Xi, Pi Alpha Xi, Gamma Sigma Delta. Republican. Methodist. Avocations: fishing, golf, woodworking, gardening. Office: Bot Garden of Smith College Lyman Plant House College Lane Northampton MA 01063

MUNSON, RICHARD JAY, congressional coalition policy analyst; b. Hollywood, Calif., Aug. 10, 1950; s. Jay S. and Grace P. (Palmer) M.; m. Diane MacEachern; children: Daniel, Dana. BA, U. Calif., Santa Barbara, 1971; MA, U. Mich., 1973. Instr. U. Mich., Ann Arbor, 1973-75; coord. Environ. Action Found., Washington, 1975-77, Solar Action, Washington, 1977-78; exec. dir. Solar Lobby, Washington, 1978-83, N.E.-Midwest Congl. Coalition, Washington, 1985—. Author: The Cardinals of Capitol Hil, 1993, The Power Makers, 1985, Cousteau, 1988. Recipient Award for Exceptional Pub. Svc., U.S. Dept. Energy, 1978. Office: NE Midwest Inst 218 D St SE Washington DC 20003

MUNSON, WILLIAM LESLIE, insurance company executive; b. Chgo., Apr. 28, 1941; s. David Curtiss and Leona Ruth (Anderson) M.; m. Marian Lee Blanton, July 16, 1966; children: Katherine, Sandra, Deborah. Student, U. Md., 1959-62; BBA cum laude, Coll. of Ins., 1968. CPCU, 1967. Asst. mgr. N.Y. Fire Ins. Rating Orgn., N.Y.C., 1959-69; br. mgr. CNA Ins. Co., N.Y.C., 1969-75; pres., dir. Commerce & Industry Ins. Co., N.Y.C., 1975-83; pres. Commerce & Industry of Can., 1983-87; sr. v.p., chief underwriting officer Am. Internat. Underwriters, 1983-87; exec. v.p. Home Ins. Co., 1987-93; pres., chief exec. officer Home Indemnity Ins. Co., 1987-93, also bd. dirs.;

chmn. City Internat. Ins. Co. Ltd., 1991-93; pres., COO Merc. and Gen. Reins. Co. Am., 1993—; chmn., pres., CEO Toa-Re-Ins. Co. Am., 1993—; trustee Coll. of Ins., 1985—; bd. dirs. Nat. Coun. Compensation Ins., 1989-92, ISO Comml. Risk Svcs., 1993; mem. comml. lines com Ins. Svcs. Office, 1989-92. Pres. Wyckoff (N.J.) Bd. Edn., 1979-82; chmn. bd. lay leaders Grace United Meth. Ch., Wyckoff, 1989-92. Mem. Soc. CPCUs (bd. dirs. N.Y. chpt.), Conf. Spl. Risk Underwriters, Reinsurance Assn. Am. (bd. dirs.), Brokers Reinsurance Markets Assn. (bd. dirs.). Republican. Club: John St. (N.Y.C.). Home: 762 Albemarle St Wyckoff NJ 07481-1005 Office: Merc and Gen Reins 177 Madison Ave Morristown NJ 07960-7331

MUNSTER, ANDREW MICHAEL, medical educator, surgeon; b. Budapest, Hungary, Dec. 10, 1935; came to U.S., 1965; s. Leopold S. and Marianne (Barcza) M.; m. Joy O'Sullivan, Dec. 7, 1963; children: Andrea, Tara, Alexandra. MD, U. Sydney (Australia), 1959. Diplomate Am. Bd. Surgery. Research fellow Harvard U. Med. Sch., Boston, 1966-67; asst. prof. surgery U. Tex.-San Antonio, 1968-71, assoc. prof. surgery Med. U. S.C., Charleston, 1971-76; assoc. prof. Johns Hopkins U., Balt., 1976-85, prof. surgery, 1985—; dir. burn ctr. Balt. City Hosp., 1976—; v.p. Chesapeake Physicians, Balt., 1978-84. Author: Surgical Anatomy, 1971; Surgical Immunology, 1976; Burn Care for House Officers, 1980; contbr. numerous articles to med. jours. Pres., Chesapeake Ednl. Research Trust, Balt., 1980-84, Charleston Symphony, 1974-75, Charleston TriCounty Arts Council, 1975-76. Served to lt. col. U.S. Army, 1968-71. Recipient John Hunter prize U. Sydney, 1959; named Hunterian prof. Royal Coll. Surgeons, 1974. Fellow Royal Coll. Surgeons of Eng., Royal Coll. Surgeons of Edinburgh (Scotland), Am. Assn. Surgeons of Trauma, Colombian Coll. Surgeons (hon.); mem. Am. Burn Assn. (sec. 1990-93, 1st v.p. 1993-94, pres.-elect 1994-95, pres. 1995), Soc. Surg. Assn., Soc. Univ. Surgeons, Am. Surg. Assn. Office: Am Burn Assn 4940 Eastern Ave Baltimore MD 21224-2780

MUNTZ, ERIC PHILLIP, aerospace engineering and radiology educator, consultant; b. Hamilton, Ont., Can., May 18, 1934; came to U.S., 1961, naturalized, 1985; s. Eric Percival and Marjorie Louise (Weller) M.; m. Janice Margaret Furey, Oct. 21, 1964; children: Sabrina Weller, Eric Phillip. B.A.Sc., U. Toronto, 1956, M.A.Sc., 1957, Ph.D., 1961. Halfback Toronto Argonauts, 1957-60; group leader Gen. Electric, Valley Forge, Pa., 1961-69; assoc. prof. aerospace engring. and radiology U. So. Calif., Los Angeles, 1969-71, prof., 1971-87, chmn. aerospace engring., 1987—; cons. to aerospace and med. device cos., 1967—; mem. rev. of physics (plasma and fluids) panel NRC, Washington, 1983-85. Contbr. numerous articles in gas dynamics and med. diagnostics to profl. publs., 1961—; patentee med. imaging, isotope separation, nondestructive testing, net shape mfg., transient energy release micromachine. Mem. Citizens Environ. Avc. Coun., Pasadena, Calif., 1972-76. Pilot RCAF, 1955-60. U.S. Air Force grantee, 1961-74, 82—; NSF grantee, 1970-76, 87—; FDA grantee, 1980-86. Fellow AIAA (aerospace Contbn. to Soc. award 1987), Am. Phys. Soc.; mem. NAE. Epsicopalian. Home: 1560 E California Blvd Pasadena CA 91106-4104 Office: U So Calif Univ Pk Los Angeles CA 90089-1191

MUNTZ, ERNEST GORDON, historian, educator; b. Buffalo, Nov. 15, 1923; s. J. Palmer and Laura Estelle (Wedekindt) M.; m. Marjorie Corinne Wilson, June 29, 1948; children—Carolyn Odell, Deborah Lynn, Howard Gordon. A.B., Wheaton (Ill.) Coll., 1948; Ph.D., U. Rochester, N.Y., 1960. Asst. prof. social sci. Blue Mountain (Miss.) Coll., 1954-56; from asst. prof. to prof. history Union U., Jackson, Tenn., 1956-61; assoc. faculty U. Cin., 1961-91, prof. history, 1969-91, prof. emeritus, 1991—; dean Raymond Walters Coll., Cin., 1969-90, dean emeritus, 1991—; cons.-evaluator North Central Assn. Colls. and Schs., 1974-91, mem. Commn. on Instns. of Higher Edn., 1983-87. Served as officer USAAF, 1943-46. So. Fellowships Fund fellow, 1955. Mem. Am. Hist. Assn., Am. Assn. Community and Jr. Colls. (bd. dirs. coun. 2 yr. colls. of 4 yr. instns. 1988-90), Cincinnatus Assn., Phi Alpha Theta, Pi Gamma Mu. Presbyterian. Clubs: Cin. Literary, University. Home: 7950 Indian Hill Rd Cincinnati OH 45243-3906

MUNTZING, L(EWIS) MANNING, lawyer; b. Harrisonburg, Va., June 24, 1934; s. H. Gus and Virginia (Manning) M.; m. Nancy Snyder, June 20, 1959; children: Catherine Muntzing Boyden, Elizabeth Muntzing McKaig, Nancy Muntzing Seward, Kimberly Stuart. AB, U. N.C., 1956; postgrad., Woodrow Wilson Sch. Public and Internat. Affairs, Princeton U., 1956-57; LLB, Harvard U., 1960. Bar: D.C. 1960, Md. 1960, W.Va. 1960. Atty. Chesapeake & Potomac Telephone Cos., Washington, 1960-71; dir. of regulation Atomic Energy Commn., Washington, 1971-75; pvt. practice Washington, 1975-79; ptnr. Doub & Muntzing, Chartered, Washington, 1979-88, Doub, Muntzing & Glasgow, Washington, 1988-91, Newman & Holtzinger, Washington, 1991-94; spl. counsel Morgan, Lewis & Bockius, Washington, 1994—; pres. Adtechs Corp., 1992—; co-chmn. Pacific Basin Nuclear Cooperation Com., 1985-89. Editor: International Instruments for Nuclear Technology Transfer, 1978; mem. editorial adv. bd. Progress in Nuclear Energy Internat. Rev. Jour., 1976—. Trustee Bridgewater Coll., 1984—; mem. vis. com. MIT Nuclear Engring. Dept., 1985-90. Recipient Arthur S. Fleming Disting. Service award Atomic Energy Commn., 1974, Disting. Service award U.S. Atomic Energy Commn., 1974. Mem. Coun. of Sci. Soc. Pres. (exec. com. 1984-88, chmn. 1987, legal advisor, 1988—), Am. Nuclear Soc. (pres. 1982-83, v.p. 1981-82, bd. dirs. 1977-80), Am. Assn. of Engring. Socs. (sec./treas. 1985), Am. Standards of Testing Materials (chmn. rsch.and tech. planning com.), Nat. Acad. Scis. (con. on internat. coop. in magnetic fusion 1983-84), ABA, Fed. Bar Assn. (chmn. atomic energy com 1975-76, coun. on sci. tech. and the law sect. 1976-78, Internat. Nuclear Socs. Coun. (vice chmn. 1991-92, chmn. 1993-94), D.C Bar Assn., Md. Bar Assn., W.Va. Bar Assn., Russian Order of St. John, Knights of Malta, Phi Beta Kappa. Republican. Presbyterian. Clubs: Harvard of Washington, Internat., Capitol Hill, Princeton. Home: 10805 Pleasant Hill Dr Rockville MD 20854-1512 Office: Morgan Lewis & Bockius 1800 M St NW Washington DC 20036

MUNYER, EDWARD A., zoologist, museum adminstrator; b. Chgo., May 8, 1936; s. G. and M. (Carlson) M.; m. Marianna J. Munyer, Dec. 12, 1981; children: Robert, William, Richard, Laura, Cheryl. BS, Ill. State U., 1958, MS, 1962. Biology tchr. MDR High Sch., Minonk, Ill., 1961-63; instr. Ill. State U., Normal, 1963-64; curator zoology Ill. State Mus., Springfield, 1964-67, asst. dir., 1981—; assoc. prof. Vincennes (Ind.) U., 1967-70; dir. Vincennes U. Mus., 1968-70; assoc. curator Fla. Mus. Natural History, Gainesville, 1970-81; mem. Mus. Accreditation Vis. Com. Roster, 1976—. Contbr. articles to profl. jours. Mem. Am. Assn. Mus. (bd. dirs. 1992-95), Midwest Mus. Conf. (pres. 1990-92), Ill. Assn. Mus. (bd. dirs. 1981-86), Wilson Ornithol. Soc. (life). Office: Ill State Mus Spring & Edward Sts Springfield IL 62706

MUNZER, CYNTHIA BROWN, mezzo-soprano; b. Clarksburg, W.Va., Sept. 30, 1948; d. Ralph Emerson and Doris Marguerite (Dixon) Brown; 1 dau., Christina Marie. Student, U. Kans., 1965-69. Adj. prof. U. So. Calif.; adj. prof. voice U. So. Calif. Debut, Oxford (Eng.) Opera, 1969, Met. Opera debut, N.Y.C., 1973; performed 1973-95 with: Met. Opera, Phila. Opera, Wolftrap Festival, Washington Opera, Goldovsky Opera, Washington Civic Opera, St. Petersburg Opera, Dallas Opera, Met. Opera-Japan, Boston Concert Opera, Dayton Opera, Chgo. Opera Theatre, Mich. Opera, Kansas City Opera, New Orleans Opera, Houston Grand Opera, Ft. Worth Opera, Florentine Opera-Milw., Minn. Opera, Central City Opera, Aspen Festival, Opera Colo., Boston Festival Orch., Ontario Opera, Salt Lake City Opera, Nev. Opera, Cleve. Opera, Opera Pacific, Des Moines Opera, Ky. Opera, Mobile Opera, Internat. Artist Series in Kuala Lumpur, Penang, Jakarta; Hong Kong Philharmonic, Shanghai Symphony, Singapore Symphony, Philippine Philharmonic, N.Y.C. Ballet, Am. Symphony, Nat. Symphony, Charleston Symphony, Phila. Orch., New Haven Symphony, Houston Symphony, Ft. Wayne Symphony, El Paso Symphony, San Antonio Symphony, Amarillo Symphony, Wichita Symphony, Milw. Symphony, Minn. Orch., Denver Symphony, Phoenix Symphony, Oreg. Bach. Festival, San Francisco Symphony, L.A. Philharm., Louisville Symphony, Rochester Philharmonic, Binghamton Symphony, Rhode Island Symphony, Carmel Bach Festival, Anchorage Symphony, L'Opera de Montreal, Colo. Opera Festival, New York Mozart Bicentennial Festival, Brattleboro Festival, Knoxville Opera, Gold Coast Opera, Hawaii Opera, Augusta Opera, Berkshire Opera, Madison Opera, Chattanooga Symphony. Recipient Frederick K. Weyerhaeuser award, Gramma Fisher Found. award, Goeran Gentele award, Sullivan Found. award, Geraldine Farrar award. Office: PO Box 77332 Los Angeles CA 90007

MUNZER, STEPHEN R., law educator; b. 1944. BA, U. Kans., 1966; BPhil, Oxford U., Eng., 1969; JD, Yale U., 1972. Assoc. Covington & Burling, Washington, 1972-73; staff atty. Columbia U., N.Y.C., 1973-74; asst. prof. philosophy Rutgers U., New Brunswick, N.J., 1974-77; assoc. prof. U. Minn., Mpls., 1977-80, prof., 1980-81; prof. UCLA, 1981—. NEH fellow, 1991. Office: UCLA Sch Law 405 Hilgard Ave Los Angeles CA 90024-1476

MURA, TOSHIO, civil engineering educator; b. Kanazawa, Ishikawa, Japan, Dec. 7, 1925; came to U.S., 1958; s. Shinzo and Chie (Miyamoto) Fujii; m. Sawa Ozaki, May 3, 1952; children: Miyako, Nanako. B.S., U. Tokyo, 1949, Ph.D., 1954. Asst. prof. Meiji U., Tokyo, 1954-58; asst. prof. Northwestern U., Evanston, Ill., 1961-63, assoc. prof., 1963-66, prof. dept. civil engring., 1966—, Walter P. Murphy disting. prof. civil engring., mech. engring., applied math., theoretical and applied math., 1986—; cons. Argonne Nat. Lab., Ill., 1956-58, 73, Nat. Bur. Standards, Washington, 1969-70, Atomic Energy Research Establishment, Harwell, Eng., 1973, Inst. Space and Astronautical Sci., Tokyo, 1983. Author: Micromechanics of Defects in Solids, 1982, Variational Methods in Mechanics, 1992; editor: Mathematical Theory of Dislocations, 1969, Mechanics of Fatigue, 1981. Grantee Japanese Govt., 1950-54; grantee NSF, 1961—, Dept. Energy, 1971-73, Army Research Office, 1978—. Fellow ASME, Am. Acad. Mechanics; mem. NAE, Japan Inst. Metals (hon.). Home: 2727 Orchard Ln Wilmette IL 60091-2141 Office: Dept Civil & Mech Engring Northwestern U Evanston IL 60201

MURABAYASHI, HARRIS NOZOMU, retired management analyst; b. Kaneohe, Hawaii, May 10, 1928; s. Junichi and Kaneko (Kodama) M.; widowed' children: Dona Sachie Murabayashi Kang, Fern Miyoko. BA, U. Hawaii, 1950. Jr. acct. Hideo Kajikawa, CPA, Honolulu, 1950; bookkeeping machine operator Dillingham Bros. Ltd., Honolulu, 1950-51; budget analyst Budget and Fin. Dept., State of Hawaii, 1955-59, Planning Dept., City of Honolulu, 1959-64; capital improvement programming analyst Planning and Econ. Devel. Dept., State of Hawaii, 1964-71; chief fiscal analyst Office of Coun. Svcs., City Coun., Honolulu, 1971-91, mgmt. analyst, 1991-93, ret., 1993; owner, operator McCully Apts., Honolulu, 1976—. Home: 1925 Nehoa Pl Honolulu HI 96822-3069

MURAD, FERID, physician; b. Whiting, Ind., Sept. 14, 1936; s. John and Josephine (Bowman) M.; m. Carol Ann Leopold, June 21, 1958; children: Christine, Marianne, Carrie, Julie, Joseph. BA, DePauw U., 1958; MD, Case Western Res. U., 1965, PhD, 1965. Diplomate Nat. Bd. Med. Examiners. Intern and resident Mass. Gen. Hosp., Boston, 1965-67; clin. assoc. NIH, Bethesda, Md., 1967-70; from assoc. prof. to prof. U. Va., Charlottesville, 1970-81, dir. clin. research ctr., 1971-81, dir. clin. pharmacology, 1973-81; prof. Stanford (Calif.) U., 1981-88, assoc. chmn. dept. medicine, 1984-88; chief of medicine VA Med. Ctr., Palo Alto, Calif., 1981-88; v.p. pharm. div. Abbott Labs., 1988-92, CEO, pres. molecular geriatrics, 1993—. Co-editor The Pharmacological Basis of Therapeutics, 7th edit., 1985; patentee in field; contbr articles to profl. jours. Recipient numerous awards for accomplishments in field. Mem. Am. Fedn. Clin. Research, Am. Soc. for Pharmacology and Exptl. Therapeutics, Endocrine Soc., NIH Alumni Assn. (mem. task force Evaluation of Research Needs in Endocrinology and Metabolic Diseases 1978-79, ad hoc mem. Molecular Cytology study sect. 1979, Pathology study sect. 1979, Endocrinology Tng. Grant study sect. 1980, Pharmacology study sect. 1980, 84), Am. Cancer Soc. (ad hoc rev. and site vis. 1979, sci. councillor NIDDK 1990-94, chmn. 1993-94), Am. Soc. Biol. Chemi st s, Am. Soc. Clin. Investigation, Assn. Am. Physicians, Western Assn. Physicians, NSF (ad hoc rev. 1982). Home: 1421 Lake Rd Lake Forest IL 60045-1425

MURAD, JOHN LOUIS, clinical microbiology educator; b. Tyler, Tex., Dec. 15, 1932; s. Louis George and Ruby (Sawyer) M.; m. Sameera Hamra; children: John Nichols, Philip Louis, David Clay, Richard Andrew. BA, Austin Coll., 1956; MS, North Tex. State U., 1958; PhD, Tex. A&M U., 1965. Instr. biology Stephen F. Austin State U., Nacogdoches, 1959-61, Tex. A&M U., College Station, 1961-65; mem. faculty La. Tech. U., Ruston, 1965-88, asso. prof. zoology, 1967-70, prof., 1970-88, dir. rsch. and grad. studies, Coll. Life Scis., 1971-88, ret., 1988; prof. med. lab. scis. U. Tex. Southwestern Med. Ctr., Dallas, 1991—; safety mgmt. cons. Author: Laboratory Exercises in Zoology, 1967, The Laboratory in Biology, 1968, Zoology, 1971, Workbook in Zoology, 1975, Explorations in Zoology, 1980, 2d edit., 1984, Adventures in Zoology, 1989; contbr. articles to profl. jours. Served with M.C. AUS, 1953-55, Korea. U. Tex. Med. Br. rsch. fellow Galveston, 1958-59; NSF travel grantee, 1972; NATO regional sci. participant Germany, 1972; Sci. Info. Exch. fellow Gt. Britain, 1974. Mem. AAAS, ASTM, AAUP, Am. Inst. Biol. Scis., Am. Soc. Microbiology, southwestern Soc. Microbiology, La. Acad. Sci., Tex. Acad. Sci., N.Y. Acad. Sci., Helminthological Soc. Washington, Soc. Nematologists, European Soc. Nematology, Masons, Shriners, Kiwanis, Sigma Xi. Presbyterian (elder). Home: 5724 Melshire Dr Dallas TX 75230-2116

MURADIAN, VAZGEN, composer, viola d'amore player; b. Ashtarak, Armenia, Oct. 17, 1921; came to U.S., 1950, naturalized, 1956; s. Grigor and Arusiak (Vardanian) M.; m. Arpi Kirkyasharian, Aug. 29, 1964; children: Vardges, Armen. Grad., Benedetto Marcello State Conservatory Music, Venice, 1948; studied composition with, Gabriele Bianchi; studied violin with, Luigi Ferro. Tchr. violin, solfeggio and theory of music Collegio Armeno, Venice, Italy, 1945-50; pvt. tchr. viola d'amore. Composer numerous works including 36 symphonies, 64 concertos for all classical instruments and many concertos for rare instruments, 8 suites for orch., 4 moto perpetuos for violin and orch., 7 sonatas for solo violin, 6 sonatas for violin and piano, 2 sonatas for piano, sonata for viola d'amore, 2 quartets, 2 trios for violin, violoncello and piano, 56 songs with orch. and 8 songs for chorus and orch. on works of Shakespeare, Goethe, Dante, Hugo, others; author articles in field; debut, N.Y. Lincoln Center, 1972; violist with various U.S. orchs. including New Orleans Philharmonic, Wagner Opera Co.; appeared as viola d'amore soloist, U.S. and abroad, compositions performed throughout Europe and Am. Recipient Tekeyan prize, 1962. Mem. ASCAP, Viola D'amore Soc. Achievements include being the only composer in history of music who wrote concerti for all classical instruments and many for lesser known instruments, so far 64 concerti for 35 different instruments. All major compositions written in Sonata form. Home: 269 W 72nd St New York NY 10023-2713

MURANE, WILLIAM EDWARD, lawyer; b. Denver, Mar. 4, 1933; s. Edward E. and Theodora (Wilson) M.; m. Rosemarie Palmerone, Mar. 26, 1960; children: Edward Wheelock, Peter Davenport, Alexander Phelps. AB, Dartmouth Coll., 1954; LLB, Stanford U., 1957. Bar: Wyo. 1957, Colo. 1958, Calif. 1958, D.C. 1978, U.S. Supreme Ct. 1977. Assoc. then ptnr. Holland & Hart, Denver, 1961-69; dep. gen. counsel U.S. Dept. Commerce, Washington, 1969-71; gen. counsel FDIC, Washington, 1971-72; ptnr. Holland & Hart, Denver, 1972—, chmn. litigation dept., 1986-90; pub. mem. Adminstrv. Conf. of the US, Washington, 1978-81. Bd. dirs. Ctr. for Law and Rsch., Denver, 1973-76, Acad. in the Wilderness, Denver, 1986—, Colo. Symphony Assn., 1994—; mem. bd. visitors Stanford U. Law Sch. Capt. USAF, 1958-61. Fellow Am. Coll. Trial Lawyers; mem. ABA (ho of dels. 1991—), U. Club, Cactus Club. Republican. Avocations: fishing, classical music. Office: Holland & Hart 555 17th St Ste 2900 Denver CO 80202-3979

MURASE, JIRO, lawyer; b. N.Y.C., May 16, 1928. B.B.A., CCNY, 1955; J.D., Georgetown U., 1958, LL.D. (hon.), 1982. Bar: D.C. 1958, N.Y. 1959. Sr. ptnr. Marks & Murase, N.Y.C., 1971—; legal counsel Consulate Gen. of Japan; mem. Pres.'s Adv. Com. Trade Negotiations, 1980-82; mem. Trilateral Commn., 1985—; apptd. mem. World Trade Coun., 1984-94; adv. com. on internat. investment, tech. and devel. Dept. State, 1975. Editorial bd.: Law and Policy in Internat. Bus. Trustee Asia Found., 1979-83, Japan Center Internat. Exchange, Japanese Ednl. Inst. N.Y.; bd. dirs. Japan Soc., Japanese C. of C. in N.Y., Inc.; bd. regents Georgetown U.; adv. council Pace U., Internat. House Japan. Recipient N.Y. Gov.'s citation for contbns. to internat. trade, 1982; named to Second Order of Sacred Treasure (Japan), 1989. Mem. ABA, Assn. of Bar of City of N.Y., N.Y. State Bar Assn., N.Y. County Lawyers Assn., Maritime Law Assn., Consular Law Soc., Fed. Bar Council, Am. Soc. Internat. Law, World Assn. Lawyers, Japanese-Am. Soc. Legal Studies, Am. Arbitration Assn., Lic. Execs. Soc., U.S. C. of C. Clubs:

Nippon (dir.); Ardsley Country; N.Y. Athletic; Mid-Ocean (Bermuda). Office: Marks & Murase 399 Park Ave New York NY 10022-4689

MURASHIGE, ALLEN, defense analysis executive; b. Lihue, Hawaii, Mar. 20, 1946; s. Fred A. and Evelyn Y.T. M.; m. Rae Ann Sears, June 7, 1981; children: Lance, Danielle. BS in Aero. Engring., U. Washington, 1968; MS in Statistics/Ops. Rsch., U. Denver, 1973; postgrad. Program for Execs. in Nat. Security, Harvard U., 1989; postgrad., Fed. Exec. Inst. 1993. Aero. engr. Air Force Western Test Range, Vandenberg AFB, Calif., 1968-70; aero. engr. Space & Missile Test Ctr., Vandenberg AFB, 1970-73, ops. analyst, 1973-77; ops. analyst Hdqrs. USAF in Europe, Ramstein AFB, Germany, 1977-84; chief current ops. div. Hdqrs. USAF in Europe, Ramstein AFB, 1985-87; sci. tech. advisor Air Force Studies and Analysis, Washington, 1987-95; U.S. rep. and com. chmn. NATO Adv. Group for Aero Rsch. & Devel., Paris, 1987—; mem. NATO Sci. and Tech. Coordinating Commn., 1994—; chief scientist air force modelling, simulation and analysis, 1995—; mem. Joint Tech. Coord. Group Sr. Adv. Bd., 1989—; mem. Dept. of Def. Simulation Validation Sr. Steering Com., 1990—, Joint Test & Evaluation Tech. Adv. Bd., 1995—; bd. dirs. Air Force Incentive Awards Bd., Pentagon, Washington, 1987—; rep. Dept. of Def. C3I Test and Evaluation Steering Com., Pentagon, 1989-91, Dept. of Def. Modeling and Simulation Policy Group, 1990-92; sr. civilian rep. Air Force Sci. Adv. Bd., 1992-94. Author tech. reports in field. Nominee Dept. of Def. Disting, Civilian Svc. award, 1986; fellow Grad. Study in Ops. Rsch., 1972. Mem. AIAA, Mil. Ops. Rsch. Soc., Air Force Assn., Am. Def. Preparedness Assn., Internat. Platform Assn., Porsche Club of Am. Avocations: pvt. pilot, tennis, skiing. Office: USAF Modelling Simulation & Analysis Pentagon Washington DC 20330

MURASUGI, KUNIO, mathematician, educator; b. Tokyo, Mar. 25, 1929; s. Kiyoshi and Torae (Nakatani) M.; m. Yasue Kuwahara, Oct. 30, 1955; children—Chieko, Kumiko, Sachiho. B.Sc., Tokyo U. Edn., 1952, D.Sc., 1961. Research asso. Princeton (N.J.) U., 1962-64; asst. prof. U. Toronto, Ont., Can., 1964-66; asso. prof. U. Toronto, 1966-69, prof. dept. math., 1969—. Editor: Can. Jour. Math, 1969-71; assoc. editor: Jour. Knot Theory and its Ramification, 1992—; contbr. articles to profl. jours. Fellow Royal Soc. Can.; mem. Am. Math. Soc., Japanese Math. Soc. (Fall prize 1993). Anglican. Home: 611 Cummer Ave, Willowdale, ON Canada M2K 2M5 Office: 100 Saint George St, Toronto, ON Canada M5S 1A1

MURATA, AKIRA, manufacturing executive; b. Mar. 25, 1921; m. Shizue Murata. Ed. pub. schs., Kyoto, Japan. Founder Murata Mfg. Co., Ltd., 1944; pres. Fukui Murata Mfg Co. Ltd., 1950-55; pres. Murata Mfg. Co. Ltd., from 1955, now chmn.; chmn. Murata Erie NA div. Murata Mfg. Co. Ltd., Smyrna, Ga. Decorated Medal of Honor with Blue Ribbon, 1980. Avocation: photography. Home: 15 Maruyama, Muko, Kamiueno-cho, Kyoto Japan Office: Murata Erie NA Inc 2200 Lake Park Dr Smyrna GA 30080-7643 also: Murata Mfg Co Ltd, 26-10 Tenjin 2-chome, Nagaokakyoshi, Kyoto 617, Japan

MURATA, JUNICHI, electronics company executive; b. 1935. With parent co. of Murata Automated Sys., Inc., 1957—; now CEO, pres. Murata Automated Sys., Inc., Charlotte, N.C. Office: Murata Automated Systems Inc 2120 S Interstate 85 Serv Charlotte NC 28208

MURATA, RYOHEI, diplomat; b. Kyoto, Japan, Nov. 2, 1929; s. Tahei and Yoshiko (Tada) M.; m. Reiko Akama, Jan. 23, 1958. B of Law, Kyoto U., 1952. A.E. and P. to the United Arab Emirates, 1978-80; dir.-gen. Middle Ea.-African Affairs Bur. Ministry Fgn. Affairs, Tokyo, 1980-82; dir.-gen. Econ. Affairs Bur., Tokyo, 1982-84; A.E. and P. to Austria, 1985-87; vice-minister for fgn. affairs Tokyo, 1987-89; ambassador to Washington, 1989—. Author (with others): Between Friends, 1985. Recipient Grand Decoration Province of Salzburg, Austria, 1987, First Class Commander's Cross Order of Merit City of Vienna, Austria, 1987. Home: 37-15 Eifuku 2-chome, Suginami-ku, Tokyo 168, Japan Office: Embassy of Japan 2520 Massachusetts Ave NW Washington DC 20008-2822

MURATA, TADAO, engineering and computer science educator; b. Takayama, Gifu, Japan, June 26, 1938; came to U.S., 1962; s. Yonosuke and Ryu (Aomame) M.; m. Nellie Kit-Ha Shin, 1964; children: Patricia Emi, Theresa Terumi. B.S.E.E., Tokai U., 1962; M.S.E.E., U. Ill., 1964, Ph.D. in Elec. Engring., 1966. Research asst. U. Ill., Urbana, 1962-66; asst. prof. U. Ill. at Chgo., 1966-68, assoc. prof., 1970-76, prof., 1977—; assoc. prof. Tokai U., Tokyo, Japan, 1968-70; vis. prof. U. Calif., Berkeley, 1976-77; cons. Nat. Bur. Stds., Gaithersburg, Md., 9184-85; panel mem. NAS, Washington, 1981-82, 83-85; vis. scientist Nat. Ctr. For Sci. Rsch, France, 1981; guest rschr. Gesellschaft für Mathematik und Datenvearbeitung, Germany, 1979; Hitachi-Honored prof. Osaka (Japan) U., 1993-94. Editor IEEE Trans. on Software Engring., 1986-92; assoc. editor Jour. of Cirs., Sysems and Computers, 1990—; contbr. articles to sci. and engring. jours. Recipient Sr. Univ. Scholar award U. Ill., 1990; dNSF grantee, 1978—, U.S.-Spain coop. research grantee, 1985-87. Fellow IEEE (mem. IEEE Computer Soc., Donald G. Fink Prize award 1991); mem. Assn. Computing Machinery, Info. Processing Soc. Japan, European Assn. for Theoretical Computer Sci., Upsilon Pi Epsilon (hon.). Avocations: golf; travel. Office: U Ill Dept Elec Engring & Comp Sci 851 S Morgan St Chicago IL 60607-7053

MURATORE, PETER FREDERICK, securities executive; b. Bklyn., Mar. 18, 1932; s. Fred John and Rose Mary (Muscatello) M.; m. Patricia Margaret Feerick, Jan. 21, 1956; children: John, Robert, Catherine. B.S. in Social Sci., Georgetown U., 1953. Owner, operator St. George Men's Shop, Bklyn., 1955-65; exec. v.p. E.F. Hutton & Co., Inc., N.Y.C., 1965-88; dir. E.F. Hutton & Co., Inc., N.Y.C.; mem. exec. com. N.Y. dist. S.I.A.; guest lectr. Wharton Grad. Sch. Bus. U. Pa., Phila., 1979—; ofcl. Am. Stock Exchange, N.Y.C., 1981-87; sr. exec. v.p. Shearson Lehman Hutton, N.Y.C., 1988-89; pres. Quest For Value Distributive, N.Y.C., 1989—; chmn., Hutton Equipment Mgmt. Co., Hutton Asset Recovery Fund; dir. New Energy Co. Ind., Hutton Aircraft Mgmt., Inc., Employees Pension Service Corp., New Energy Co., Ind. Bd. advisors Fin. Services Rev., 1982. Served to lt. j.g. USNR, 1953-55. Founder Bklyn. Prep. N.Y.C., 1964. Mem. Securities Industry Assn. (chmn. mktg. com. 1979-81), Bond Club. Roman Catholic. Clubs: N.Y. Athletic. Home: Post House Rd Morristown NJ 07960 Office: Quest For Value Distributive Oppenheimer Tower World Fin Ctr New York NY 10281

MURATORE, ROBERT PETER, advertising executive; b. Bklyn., Oct. 31, 1957; s. Peter Fredrick and Patricia Margret (Feerick) M. BS, Lehigh U., 1979. Analyst client svc. IMS Am. Ltd., Wayne, N.J., 1979-81; sales analyst E.R. Squibb and Sons, Lawrenceville, N.J., 1981, supr. sales analysis, 1982; account exec. Thomas G. Ferguson Assocs., Inc., Parsippany, N.J., 1982-83, account supr., 1983-85, v.p., 1984-88, account group supr., 1985-87, mgmt. supr., 1987-90, sr. v.p., 1988-92, pres. Ferguson 2000 divsn., 1995, pres. Ferguson dir. divsn., 1995—. Mem. Am. Profl. Platform Tennis Assn., Morris Country Golf Club, Delta Chi. Avocations: skiing, tennis, golf, platform tennis. Office: Thomas G Ferguson Assocs 30 Lanidex Plz W Parsippany NJ 07054-2717

MURAYAMA, MAKIO, biochemist; b. San Francisco, Aug. 10, 1912; s. Hakuyo and Namiye (Miyasaka) M.; children: Gibbs Soga, Alice Myra. B.A., U. Calif., Berkeley, 1938, M.A., 1940; Ph.D. (NIH fellow), U. Mich., 1953; ScD honoris causa, Open Internat. U., Sri Lanka, 1994. Rsch. biochemist Bellevue Hosp., N.Y.C., 1943-45, Children's Hosp. of Mich., Detroit, 1943, 45-48, Bellevue Hosp., N.Y.C., 1943-45; Research biochemist Harper Hosp., Detroit, 1949-54; research fellow in chemistry Calif. Inst. Tech., Pasadena, 1954-56; research asso. in biochemistry Grad. Sch. Medicine, U. Pa., Phila., 1956-58; spl. research fellow Nat. Cancer Inst. at Cavendish Lab., Cambridge, Eng., 1958; research biochemist NIH, Bethesda, Md., 1958-93. Author: (with Robert M. Nalbandian) Sickle Cell Hemoglobin, 1973; discovered DIPA (decompression-inducible platelet aggregation, 1975; discovered DIPA causes vascular occlusion in both acute mountain sickness and diver's syndrome. Fellow Am. Inst. Chemists; mem. AAAS, Am. Chem. Soc., Am. Soc. Biol. Chemists, Am. Clin. Scientists, Undersea and Hyperbaric Med. Soc., Aerospace Med. Assn., Internat. Platform Assn., West African Soc. Pharmacology (hon.), N.Y. Acad. Sci., Sigma Xi. Achievements include patent for automatic amperometric titration

apparatus; development of molecular mechanism of human red cell sickling and prevention of sickle cell crisis by oral prophylactic carbamide; discovery that simulation of diving in frogs and mice indicated that diver's disease could be alleviated by piracetam and thymol, antiplatelet agents. Home: 5010 Benton Ave Bethesda MD 20814-2804

MURCH, WALTER SCOTT, director, writer, film editor, sound designer; b. N.Y.C., July 12, 1943; s. Walter Tandy and Katherine (Scott) M.; m. Muriel Ann Slater, Aug. 6, 1965; children: Walter, Beatrice, Carrie, Connie. BA, Johns Hopkins U., 1965. Ind. film editor, sound designer, 1969—. Sound recorder, supr. re-rec., film editor: (films) The Rainpeople, 1969, THX-1138, 1971, The Godfather, 1971, American Graffiti, 1973, The Conversation, 1974 (Best Sound award Brit. Acad. 1974, Best Editing award Brit. Acad. 1974, Acad. award nomination 1974), The Godfather Part II, 1974, Julia, 1977 (Acad. award nomination 1977), Apocalypse Now, 1979 (Acad. Award 1979, Brit. Acad. award nomination), Dragonslayer, 1981, The Right Stuff, 1984, (writer, dir.) Return to Oz, 1985, Captain Eo, 1986, The Unbearable Lightness of Being, 1988, Ghost (Acad. Award nomination), 1990, The Godfather Part III (Acad. Award nomination), 1990, The Godfather Trilogy, 1991, House of Cards, 1993, Romeo is Bleeding, 1994; writer Black Stallion, THX 1138, Return to Oz, 1985. Mem. Writers Guild Am., Dirs. Guild Am., Acad. Motion Picture Arts and Scis. Home: 77 Bolinas Rd Bolinas CA 94924*

MURCHAKE, JOHN, publishing executive; b. Washington, July 30, 1922; s. John Sr. and Mary Ann (Keretzman) M.; m. Mary Evelyn Graninger, June 15, 1944 (dec. Sept. 1989); children: Evelyn Ann, Stephen John. BA, George Washington U., 1961, MA, 1964. CPA, Md. Office mgr. Army Times Pub. Co., Washington, 1940-43, 46-47; subscription mgr. Kiplinger Washington Editors Inc., Washington, 1947-82; pres., CEO Co-Op New Issue Svc., Stuart, Fla., 1966—; pres. Jonev Orchids, Stuart, Fla., 1980—, J.M. and Assocs., Stuart, Fla., 1982—; pres., CEO Nat. Postal Forum, Washington, 1990-93; also bd. dirs.; adv. bd. mem. Smithsonian Postal History Mus.; chmn. founder Met. Washington Postal Customer Coun., 1972-74, Treasure Coast Fla. Postal Customers Coun., 1994; industry chmn. Mailers Tech. Adv. Com., 1978-80. Editor, founder: (newsletter) The Postal Counselor, 1974, Information, 1981, Port St. Lucie Orchid, 1993-94. Pres. Martin County Orchid Soc., Stuart, 1985-86; mem. adv. bd. Smithsonian Postal History Mus., 1993—. 1st lt. USAF, 1943-46, ETO. Decorated Air medal with 4 clusters; recipient of 2 Disting. Service awards U.S. Postal Service, Washington, 1980. Mem. Dir. Mktg. Assn. (pres., founder 1979, Profl. of Yr. 1980, Disting. Svc. award 1980, chmn. Max Sackheim awards com. Fla. chpt. 1987), Fulfillment Mgmt. Assn. (Lee C. Williams award 1980, pres., founder Washington chpt. 1977-78, founder Fla. chpt. 1987, Hall of Fame award 1989). Republican. Methodist. Avocations: stamp collecting, raising orchids, public speaking. Home: 974 NW Pine Lake Dr Stuart FL 34994-9427 Office: JM & Assocs PO Box 83 Stuart FL 34995-0083

MURCHIE, EDWARD MICHAEL, accountant; b. N.Y.C., Apr. 21, 1947; s. Edward Thomas and Dorothy (Busk) M.; m. Karen M. Raftery, Aug. 26, 1967; children: David, Maureen, Carolyn. B.S., Fordham U., Bronx, N.Y., 1968. C.P.A., N.Y. Staff acct. Price Waterhouse, N.Y.C., 1968-71, sr. auditor, 1971-74, audit mgr., 1974-75; dir. internal audit Eltra Corp., N.Y.C., 1975-78, asst. controller, 1978-79; v.p.fin. Eltra Corp., Morristown, N.J., 1981-82, Converse Rubber, Wilmington, Mass., 1979-80, Allied Corp: Allied Electronic Components Co., Morristown, 1982-84; sr. v.p., chief fin. officer Emery Air Freight Corp., Wilton, Conn., 1984-87; sr. v.p., chief fin. officer Fairchild Industries, Inc., Chantilly, Va., 1987-88, pres., chief operating officer, 1989; pres., COO Vernitron Corp., N.Y.C., 1989—. Chmn., South Brunswick Rank Levelling Bd., N.J., 1977-78; bd. dirs. Norwalk/ Wilton chpt. ARC, 1985. Mem. AICPA. Republican. Roman Catholic. Office: Vernitron Corp 645 Madison Ave New York NY 10022-1010

MURCHISON, DAVID RODERICK, lawyer; b. Washington, May 28, 1948; s. David Claudius and June Margaret (Guilfoyle) M.; m. Kathy Ann Kohn, Mar. 15, 1981; children: David Christopher, Benjamin Michael. BA cum laude, Princeton U., 1970; JD, Georgetown U., 1975. Bar: D.C. 1975, Fla. 1993. Legal asst. to vice chmn. CAB, Washington, 1975-76, enforcement atty., 1976-77; sr. atty. Air Transport Assn., Washington, 1977-80, asst. v.p., sec., 1981-85; sr. assoc. Zuckert, Scoutt and Rasenberger, Washington, 1980-81; v.p., asst. gen. counsel Piedmont Aviation, Inc., Winston-Salem, N.C., 1985-88; v.p., gen. counsel, sec. Braniff, Inc., Dallas, 1988-89; chief exec. officer Braniff, Inc., Orlando, 1990-94; fed. adminstrv. law judge Office of Hearings and Appeals, Charleston, W.Va., 1994—; lectr. continuing legal edn. program Wake Forest U., Winston-Salem, 1988. Contbr. articles to legal jours. Lt. USNR, 1970-72. Mem. ABA, Met. Club Washington. Republican. Roman Catholic. Home: 1428 Virginia St E Charleston WV 25301 Office: Office Hearings and Appeals 2 Monongalia St Charleston WV 25302

MURDOCH, BERNARD CONSTANTINE, psychology educator; b. Greensboro, N.C., Dec. 5, 1917; s. Homer Odell and Hilma Caroline (Lang) M.; m. Martha Grace Hood, June 29, 1946; children: Norma, Constance, Joyce, Diana. B.S., Appalachian State Tchrs. Coll., 1938; Ed.M., U. of Cincinnati, 1939; Ph.D., Duke, 1942; postgrad., N.Y. U., 1942-43. Licensed applied psychologist, Ga. Math. critic tchr. Appalachian State Tchrs. Coll. demonstration sch. 1938; math. and sci. tchr. Lexington (N.C.) High Sch., 1939-40; sci. tchr. Harding High Sch., Charlotte, N.C., 1945-46; also dir. Guidance and Testing Bur., Vets. Info. Center, Charlotte; prof. edn. and psychology Presbyn. Coll., Clinton, S.C., 1946-48; acad. dean Presbyn. Coll., 1947-48; also extension prof. edn. U.S.C., 1946-48; mem. research staff Am. Council on Edn., Office of Naval Rsch., Washington, 1948-50; dean Muskingum Coll., New Concord, Ohio, 1950-54; prof., head psychology dept. Wesleyan Coll., Macon, Ga., 1954-82, prof. emeritus, 1982—; chmn. dept. behavioral scis. Wesleyan Coll., 1973-82, also dir. testing.; pres. Fore(In)Sight Found. Inc., 1991—. Author: Consistency of Test Responses, 1942, Love and Problems of Living, 1992; co-author: The Production of Doctorates in the Sciences, 1936-48; contbr. to sci., ednl. and religious publs. Served to capt. USAAF, 1942-45. Fellow AAAS; mem. Am. Psychol. Assn. (life), Southeastern Psychol. Assn., Ga. Psychol. Assn. (dir., pres. 1969-70), Ga. Mental Health Assn. (dir.), NEA, Ga. Mental Health Council (psychology rep. 1973-74), Ga. State Bd. Examiners Psychologists (pres. 1974-75), Am. Ednl. Research Assn., Phi Kappa Phi (past pres.), Phi Delta Kappa, Kappa Delta Pi, Pi Gamma Mu. Presbyn. Club: Mason. Home: 1241 Adams St Macon GA 31201-1568 *Opportunities vary widely, and the necessary perception to capitalize on such also is a distinct variable. Those of us who have achieved a measure of "success" in vocational or other ways must feel very humble as we recognize our good fortune. We have not only had opportunities come before us, but we were able to perceive them in such a way as to accomplish whatever recognition has been ours. Millions have not been so fortunate.*

MURDOCH, DAVID ARMOR, lawyer; b. Pitts., May 30, 1942; s. Armor M. and N. Edna (Jones) M.; m. Joan Wilkie, Mar. 9, 1974; children: Christina, Timothy, Deborah. AB magna cum laude, Harvard U., 1964, LLB, 1967. Bar: Pa. 1967, U.S. Dist. Ct. (we. dist.) Pa. 1967, U.S. Ct. Mil. Appeals 1968, U.S. Supreme Ct. 1990, U.S. Ct. Appeals (3d cir.) 1991. Assoc. Kirkpatrick & Lockhart, Pitts. 1971-78, ptnr., 1978—. Co-author: Business Workouts Manual. Vice pres., bd. dirs. Avonworth Sch. Dist., 1977-83; chmn. bd. dirs. Pitts. Expt., 1980-82, mem. 1988-93, chmn., 1989-90; mem. Pa. Housing Fin. Agy., 1981-88, vice chmn., 1983-87; alt. del. Rep. Nat. Conv., 1980; elder The Presbyn. Ch. of Sewickley, 1986-92; past pres. Harvard Law Sch. Assn. W. Pa.; bd. advisors Geneva Coll., 1993—, trustee, 1994—; trustee Sewickley Pub. Libr., 1994—; dir. Allegheny County Libr. Assn., 1994—. Capt. U.S. Army, 1968-71. Fellow Am. Coll. Bankruptcy, Am. Bar Found.; mem. ABA (mem. bus. bankruptcy com., chmn. subcom. on bankruptcy coms., trust indentures and claims trading 1991—), Pa. Bar Assn., Allegheny County Bar Assn., Am. Law Inst., Nat. Soc. SAR, World Affairs Coun. Pitts., St. Andrews Soc. Pitts., Clan Donald USA, Duquesne Club, Harvard-Yale-Princeton Club, Edgeworth Club. Republican. Office: Kirkpatrick & Lockhart 1500 Oliver Bldg Pittsburgh PA 15222-2404

MURDOCH, (JEAN) IRIS, author; b. Dublin, Ireland, July 15, 1919; d. Wills John Hughes and Irene Alice (Richardson) M.; m. John Oliver Bayley, 1956. Student, Froebel Ednl. Inst., London; Badminton Sch., Bristol, Eng.; Somerville Coll., Oxford, Eng. Read Literae Humaniores (1st class)

Somerville Coll., 1938-42; asst. prin. Treasury, 1942-44; adminstrv. officer UNRRA, London, Belgium, Austria, 1944-46; Sarah Smithson studentship philosophy Newnham Coll., Cambridge (Eng.) U., 1947-48; fellow, univ. lectr. philosophy St. Anne's Coll., Oxford U., 1948-63, hon. fellow, 1963; lectr. Royal Coll. Arts, London, 1963-67. Author: Sartre Romantic Rationalist, 1953, Under the Net, 1954, The Flight From the Enchanter, 1955, The Sandcastle, 1957, The Bell, 1958, A Severed Head, 1961, (writer stage prodn. with J.B. Priestley), 1964, An Unofficial Rose, 1962, The Unicorn, 1963, The Italian Girl, 1964, play, 1967; The Red and The Green, 1965, The Time of the Angels, 1966, The Nice and the Good, 1968, Bruno's Dream, 1969, A Fairly Honourable Defeat, 1970, The Sovereignty of Good, 1970, An Accidental Man, 1971, The Black Prince, 1973 (James Tait Black Meml. prize), The Sacred and Profane Love Machine, 1974, A Word Child, 1975, Henry and Cato, 1976, The Fire and the Sun, 1977, The Sea, The Sea, 1978 (Booker prize), Nuns and Soldiers, 1980, The Philosopher's Pupil, 1983, The Good Apprentice, 1985, Acastos, Two Platonic Dialogues, 1986, The Book and the Brotherhood, 1987, The Message to the Planet, 1989, Metaphysics as a Guide to Morals, The Green Knight, 1993; plays The Servants and the Snow, 1970, The Three Arrows, 1972, The Black Prince, 1989; contbr. papers to profl. meetings. Recipient Black Meml. prize, 1974, Whitbread Lit. award, 1974, Booker prize, 198's; decorated Dame Comdr. Order Brit. Empire. Hon. mem. AAAL, Am. Acad. Arts and Scis.; mem. Irish Acad.

MURDOCH, LAWRENCE CORLIES, JR., retired banker, economist; b. Phila., June 3, 1926; s. Lawrence C. and Barbara (Boyd) M.; children: Lawrence C. III, Anne G.; m. 2d Eleanor M. Egan, June 16, 1970. B.S. Wharton Sch., U. Pa. in Econs., 1948; M.B.A., Wharton Sch., U. Pa., 1956. With Fed. Res. Bank Phila., 1954-92; ret., 1992; bd. dirs. Cliveden Inc. 1981. Contbr. articles to consumer and monetary publs.; producer documentary films; spokesman (radio and TV). Lt. (j.g.) USN, 1948-54. Mem. Soc. Cin. (pres. 1990—), Little Egg Harbor Yacht Club (Beach Haven, N.J.), Beta Gamma Sigma, Zeta Psi. Home: 115 Hilltop Rd Philadelphia PA 19118-3737

MURDOCH, ROBERT WAUGH, cement and construction materials company executive; b. 1942. Pres. LaFarge Corp., Reston, Va., 1987-92, COO, until 1989, CEO, 1989-92. Office: Lafarge Corp 11130 Sunrise Valley Dr Reston VA 22091-4329 Office: 600 Cathcart Ste 900, Montreal, PQ Canada H3B 1L7

MURDOCH, (KEITH) RUPERT, publisher; b. Melbourne, Australia, Mar. 11, 1931; came to U.S., 1974, naturalized, 1985; s. Keith and Elisabeth Joy (Greene) M.; m. Anna Maria Torv, Apr. 28, 1967; children: Prudence, Elisabeth, Lachlan, James. M.A., Worcester Coll., Oxford, Eng., 1953. Chmn. News Am. Pub. Inc. (pub. London Times), 1974—, News Internat. Ltd. Group, London; mng. dir. News Ltd. Group & Associated Cos., Australia; chmn. 20th Century Fox Prodns., 1985—, William Collins PLC Glasgow, 1989—; owner, pub. numerous newspapers, mags. and TV stas. in U.S.A., Australia, U.K., Asia, 1983—; Chmn., CEO, News Corp. Ltd., Sydney, Australia, 1991—. Office: The News Corp Limited, 2 Holt St, Surry Hills Sydney NSW 2010, Australia*

MURDOCK, CHARLES WILLIAM, lawyer, educator; b. Chgo., Feb. 10, 1935; s. Charles C. and Lucille Marie (Tracy) M.; m. Mary Margaret Hennessy, May 25, 1963; children: Kathleen, Michael, Kevin, Sean. BSChemE, Ill. Inst. Tech., 1956; JD cum laude, Loyola U., Chgo., 1963. Bar: Ill. 1963, Ind. 1971. Asst. prof. law DePaul U., 1968-69; assoc. prof. law U. Notre Dame, 1969-75; prof., dean Law Sch. Loyola U., Chgo., 1975-83, 86—; dep. atty. gen. State of Ill., Chgo., 1983-86; of counsel Chadwell & Kayser, Ltd., 1986-89; vis. prof. U. Calif., 1974; cons. Pay Bd., summer 1972, SEC, summer 1973; co-founder Loyola U. Family Bus. Program; arbitrator Chgo. Bd. Options Exch., Nat. Assn. Securities Dealers, N.Y. Stock Exch., Am. Arbitration Assn.; co-founder, mem. exec. com. Loyola Family Bus. Ctr., 1990—. Editor: Illinois Business Corporation Act Annotated, 2 vols., 1975; tech. editor The Business Lawyer, 1989-90. Chmn. St. Joseph County (Ind.) Air Pollution Control Bd., 1971; bd. dirs. Nat. Center for Law and the Handicapped, 1973-75, Minority Venture Capital Inc., 1973-75. Capt. USMCR. Mem. ABA, Ill. Bar Assn. (cert. of award for continuing legal edn.), Chgo. Bar Assn. (cert. of award for continuing legal edn., bd. mgrs. 1976-78), Ill. Inst. Continuing Legal Edn. (adv. com). Roman Catholic. Home: 655 W Irving Park Rd Apt 3501 Chicago IL 60613 Office: Loyola U Sch Law 1 E Pearson St Chicago IL 60611

MURDOCK, DAVID H., diversified company executive; b. Kansas City, Apr. 10, 1923; m. Maria Ferrer, Apr., 1992. LLD (hon.), Pepperdine U., 1978; LHD (hon.), U. Nebr., 1984, Hawaii Loa Coll., 1989. Sole proprietor, chmn., chief exec. officer Pacific Holding Co., L.A.; chmn., chief exec. officer Dole Food Co. (formerly Castle & Cooke, Inc.), L.A., 1985—, also bd. dirs. Trustee Asia Soc., N.Y.C., L.A.; founder, bd. dirs. Found. for Advanced Brain Studies, L.A.; bd. visitors UCLA Grad. Sch. Mgmt.;bd. govs. Performing Arts Coun. of Music Ctr., L.A.; bd. govs. East-West Ctr., L.A.; patron Met. Opera, N.Y.C. With USAAC, 1943-45. Mem. Regency Club (founder, pres.) Bel-Air Bay Country Club, Sherwood Country Club (founder, pres.), Met. Club (N.Y.C.). Office: Dole Food Co Inc 31355 Oak Crest Westlake Village CA 91361 also: Pacific Holding Co 10900 Wilshire Blvd Ste 1600 Los Angeles CA 90024*

MURDOCK, EUGENE CONVERSE, retired history educator; b. Lakewood, Ohio, Apr. 30, 1921; s. Stanley Howard and Elizabeth Kathryn (Carter) M.; m. Margaret Bowes McColl, Oct. 7, 1950; children: Gordon Graham, Kathryn Carter. B.A., Wooster (Ohio) Coll., 1943; M.A., Columbia U., 1948, Ph.D., 1951. Prof. social sci. Rio Grande (Ohio) Coll. 1952-56, asst. dean, 1953-56; mem. faculty Marietta (Ohio) Coll., 1956-86, prof. history, 1963-86, chmn. dept., 1972-86; mem. adv. bd. historians Ohio Civil War Centennial Com., 1960-65. Author: Ohio's Bounty System in the Civil War, 1963, Patriotism Limited, 1967, One Million Men, 1971, Ben Johnson, 1982, Mighty Casey, 1984, The Civil War in the North: A Selective Annotated Bibliography, 1987, Buckeye Empire: An Illustrated History of Ohio Enterprise, 1988, Bernard P. McDonough: The Man and His Work, 1989, Baseball Players and Their Times: Oral Histories of the Game, 1920-1940, 1991, Tom Johnson of Cleveland, 1992, A History of the People's Banking and Trust Co., 1991; Baseball Between the Wars: Memories of the Game by the Men Who Played It, 1992; co-author: Fenton Glass, 3 vols., 1978, 80, 89; contbg. author: Choice, 1964-67, America: History and Life, 1964-77, Ency. So. History, 1979, Insider's Baseball, 1983, Biographical Dictionary American Sport, 1987, Dictionary of American Biography, 8th supplement, 1988, Ohio's Western Reserve: A Regional Reader, 1988; contbr. articles to profl. jours.; mem. editorial bd. Ohio History, 1964-74, Pro Football Digest, 1967-69, Jour. Sport History, 1974-78. Served with AUS, 1943-46. Recipient Disting. Svc. award M-Team of Marietta Coll., 1991. Mem. Ohio Acad. History (exec. coun. 1970-73, pres. 1984-85, Disting. Svc. award 1991), Soc. Am. Baseball Rsch. (pres. 1976-78), N.Am. Soc. Sport History. Home: 7640 NW Folkstone Way Lawton OK 73505-4107 Office: Marietta Coll Marietta OH 45750

MURDOCK, MARY-ELIZABETH, history educator; b. Boston, Jan. 4, 1930; d. Lester Joseph and Elizabeth Rowe (Collingwood) M. A.B., Tufts U., 1952; A.M., Boston U., 1958; Ph.D., Brown U., 1962; S.M., Simmons Coll., 1970; cert. mgmt. inst. women in higher edn., Wellesley Coll., 1985; cert. master gardener, U. Mass., 1988. Tchr. Nat. Cathedral Sch., Washington, 1954-57; assoc. prof. Trenton State Coll., N.J., 1962-66, U. R.I., Kingston, 1966-69; archivist, dir. Sophia Smith collection Smith Coll., Northampton, Mass., 1970-84, lectr. history, 1973-86, instr. Southeast Asian ESL program, 1986-88; guest lectr. colls. and univs.; cons. N.Y.C. YWCA, 1974-75, NEH, 1978-86, Greenfield Community Coll., Mass., 1983-86, Ednl. Testing Svc., Princeton, N.J., 1985—, Nat. Evaluation Systems, Amherst, Mass., 1984-92; bd. reviewers Hist. Jour. Mass., 1985-88; adv. bd. Ctr. Am. Studies, Concord, Mass., 1985-88; indexer Liberty Party newspaper (1845-48). Author articles, monographs, analytical catalogs. Mem. Am. Studies Assn., New Eng. Am. Studies Assn., Orgn. Am. Historians (state membership chmn. 1980-88), Am. Assn. State and Local History, Hist. Deerfield Inc., Hist. Northampton, Nat. Trust for Hist. Preservation, Northampton Hist. Commn. (officer), Phi Alpha Theta. Avocations: choral singing, piano, painting, photography, gardening.

MURDOCK, MICKEY LANE, insurance company executive; b. Enterprise, Ala., Aug. 3, 1942. BS, U. Ala., Tuscaloosa, 1964. CPA, Ala. Acct. Hill & Flurry, CPAs, Montgomery, Ala., 1968-70; sr. v.p., CFO Nat. Security Group, Elba, Ala., 1970—; officer, dir. Nat. Security Ins. Co., Elba, 1975—, Nat. Security Fire & Casualty, Elba, 1975—, NASCO, Elba, 1975—, NATSCO, 1985—. Chair Water and Electric Bd., Elba, 1988-94, indsl. Devel. Bd., Elba, 1990—. Capt. USAF, 1964-68. Mem. Rotary (past pres., treas., dir.).

MURDOCK, ROBERT MEAD, art consultant, curator; b. N.Y.C., Dec. 18, 1941; s. Robert Davidson and Elizabeth Brundage (Mead) M.; m. Ellen Rebecca Olson, Apr. 22, 1967 (div.); children: Alison Mead, Anne Davidson. B.A., Trinity Coll., Conn., 1963; M.A., Yale U., 1965; student, Mus. Mgmt. Inst., U. Calif., Berkeley, 1980. Ford Found. intern Walker Art Center, Mpls., 1965-67; curator Albright-Knox Art Gallery, Buffalo, 1967-70; curator contemporary art Dallas Mus. Fine Arts, 1970-78; dir. Grand Rapids (Mich.) Art Mus., 1978-83; chief curator Walker Art Ctr., Mpls., 1983-85; program dir. IBM Gallery of Sci. and Art, N.Y.C., 1985-87, 90-93; dir. exhbns. Am. Fedn. Arts, N.Y.C., 1987-88; panelist/cons. Nat. Endowment for Arts, 1974—. Author: (with others) Tyler Graphics: The Extended Image, 1987; articles on David Novros, William Conlon, 1985, on Bill Freeland, 1989, on Nassos Daphnis, 1990; exhbn. catalogues Early 20th Century Art from Midwestern Museums, 1981, Berlin/Hanover: The 1920's, 1977. Nat. Endowment for Arts fellow, 1973. Home: 202 1st Ave #14 New York NY 10009-3726

MURDOCK, STUART LAIRD, banker, investment adviser; b. Hackensack, N.J., July 18, 1926; s. Charles Watson and Mary-Evelyn (Mehrhof) M.; m. Lois Maura Anderson, Aug. 12, 1950; 1 dau., Susan Lynn. AB, Yale U., 1949; MBA, STanford U., 1951. Security analyst Bank of N.Y., 1952-53; portfolio mgr. Brown Bros. Harriman & Co., N.Y., 1954-56; trust investment officer United Mo. Bank Kansas City N/A, 1957-62, v.p., 1963-66, sr. v.p., sr. trust investment officer, 1967-70, exec. v.p., sr. trust investment officer, 1971-94. Retired marshal City of Countryside, Kans., 1968-93; past mem. fin. adv. com. to bd. trustees Pub. Sch. Retirement System Kansas City; adv. dir., past pres. Friends of the Zoo; bd. dirs. Youth Symphony of Kansas City. With U.S. Army, 1945-46. Mem. Kansas City Soc. Fin. Analysts (past pres.), Inst. Chartered Fin. Analysts, Fin. Analysts Fedn., C. of C., Yale Club (past pres.), Saddle and Sirloin Club (past pres.), Mercury Club, Desert Caballeros, Shriners. Home: 4613 W 113th Ter Leawood KS 66211-1728 Office: United Mo Bank Kans City N/A 1010 Grand Ave Kansas City MO 64106-2220

MURDOCK, WILLIAM JOHN, librarian; b. N.Y.C., Nov. 19, 1942; s. William and Catherine T. (Ryan) M.; m. Barbara Tyra, Nov. 24, 1968. BS, Manhattan Coll., 1964; MLS, Pratt Inst., 1966; MA, NYU, 1972. Librarian N.Y. Pub. Libr., N.Y.C., 1964-67; serials librarian Manhattan Coll., Riverdale, N.Y., 1967-70; asst. prof. CUNY-Lehman Coll., Bronx, 1970-77, chief circulation libr., 1970-77; dir. librs. Pace U., Pleasantville, N.Y., 1977-94, univ. libr., 1994—; chmn. Coun. of Librarians, N.Y.C., 1988-89. Contbr. articles to profl. jours. Candidate for bd. trustees Mt. Kisco, N.Y., 1991; mem. Republican Com., 1989—; mem. Cath. Big Bros., Westchester, 1983—. Mem. ALA, N.Y. Libr. Assn., Westchester Libr. Assn. (treas. 1981-83), Westchester Assn. Libr. Dirs. (sec. 1986-87), AAUP, Assn. Coll. and Rsch. Librarians, Am. Legion. Avocations: travel, baseball, skydiving, auto cross racing. Office: Pace U 861 Bedford Rd Pleasantville NY 10570-2700

MURDY, JAMES L., petroleum company executive; Exec. v.p. Gulf Corp. and Gulf Oil Corp., Pitts. Office: Allegheny Ludlum Corp 1000 6th Ppg Pl Pittsburgh PA 15222

MURDY, WAYNE WILLIAM, mining company executive, financial officer; b. Los Angeles, July 4, 1944; s. Lee Robert and Louise Marie (Kleinemas) M.; m. Diana Yvonne DeCruse, Nov. 23, 1968; children: Dawn Marie, Christopher John, Joseph William, Elizabeth Anne. A.A., El Camino Coll., 1966; B.S., Calif. State U. Long Beach, 1968. C.P.A., Calif. With Atlantic Richfield Co., Los Angeles, 1969-78; gen. auditor Getty Oil Co., Los Angeles, 1978-81; group v.p. Texaco Trading & Transp. Inc., Denver, 1981-87; sr. v.p., chief fin. officer Apache Corp., Denver, 1987-92, Newmont Mining Corp. and Newmont Gold Co., Denver, 1993—. Mem. Am. Inst. C.P.A.s. Roman Catholic. Clubs: University (Denver); Village (Cherry Hills Village, Colo.). Office: Newmont Mining Corp 1 Norwest Ctr 1700 Lincoln St Denver CO 80203

MUREN, DENNIS E., visual effects director; b. Glendale, Calif., Nov. 1, 1946; s. Elmer Ernest and Charline Louise (Clayton) M.; m. Zara Pinfold, Aug. 29, 1981; children: Gregory, Gwendolen. AA, Pasadena (Calif.) City Coll., 1966; student, Calif. State U., LA. Freelance spl. effects expert, 1968-75; camera operator Cascade of Calif., Hollywood, 1975-76; visual effects dir. photography Indsl. Light & Magic, San Rafael, Calif., 1976-80, visual effects dir., 1980—; guest speaker Berlin Film Festival, UCLA, Film Dept., U. Calif. Berkeley Film Series, Liverpool (Eng.) U. Film Program, Mill Valley Film Festival Program, Siggraph '86, Siggraph '87, Am. Film Inst., Portland Creative Conf. '89. Cameraman, photographer various films including Star Wars, 1977, Close Encounters of the Third Kind, 1977, Battlestar Galactica, 1978, The Empire Strikes Back, 1980 (Oscar award); visual effects supr. films include Dragonslayer, 1981 (Oscar nomination), ET: The Extraterrestrial, 1982 (Oscar award), Return of the Jedi, 1983 (Oscar award, Brit. Acad. of Film and TV award), Indiana Jones and the Temple of Doom, 1984 (Oscar award, Brit. Acad. of Film and TV award), Young Sherlock Holmes, 1985 (Oscar nomination), Captain Eo, 1986, Star Tours, 1986, Innerspace, 1987 (Oscar award), Empire of the Sun, 1987, Willow, 1988 (Oscar nomination), Ghostbusters II, 1989, The Abyss, 1989 (Oscar award), Terminator 2, 1991 (Oscar award, Brit. Film and TV award), Jurassic Park, 1993 (Oscar award, Brit. Film and TV award), Casper, 1995; visual effects supr. (TV program) Caravan of Courage (Emmy award). Academy Scientific/Technical Award for the development of a Motion Picture Figure Mover for animation photography, 1981. Mem. Am. Soc. Cinematographers, Acad. Motion Picture Arts and Scis.

MURFIN, DONALD LEON, investment company executive; b. Akron, Ohio, May 24, 1943; s. Leon C. and Ellen (Dabney) M.; m. Karen L. Donaldson, Dec. 18, 1965; children: Cherie S., Erin K., Anne E. BS in Chemistry, U. Iowa, 1965. Rsch. chemist The Lubrizol Corp., Wickliffe, Ohio, 1965-72, project mgr. rsch. and devel., 1972-74, asst. to v.p. adminstrn., 1974-76, asst. sec., 1976-77, sec., 1977-78, asst. to chief exec. officer, 1978-79, v.p., 1985-88; pres. Lubrizol Enterprises Inc., Wickliffe, Ohio, 1979-88; mng. ptnr. Trident Capital Fund, Cleve., 1988-89; gen. ptnr. Chems. and Materials Enterprise Assocs., Cleve., 1989—; bd. dirs. Genentech Inc., South San Francisco, Corvita Corp. Miami; bd. trustees Edison BioTech. Ctr., Cleve. Trustee Parmadale Childrens Village, Parma, Ohio, 1986; bd. dirs. Lake Cath. High Sch. Endowment Trust, 1988-93. Mem. Nat. Venture Capital Assn. Office: Chems and Materials Enterprise 1 Cleveland Ctr Ste 2700 Cleveland OH 44114

MURFIN, ROSS C, university dean, English educator; b. Richmond, Ind., Nov. 14, 1948; s. Mark and Elizabeth (Crawford) M.; m. Pamela Kay Martin, Jan. 23, 1971; children: Audrey Dean, Justin Riley. AB in English cum laude, Princeton U., 1971; MA in English, U. Va., 1972, PhD with distinction, 1974. Asst. prof. English Yale U., New Haven, 1974-81, assoc. prof., 1981-82; dir. grad. studies in English U. Miami, Coral Gables, 1982-83; dir. program in honors, 1984-85, master Hecht Residential Coll., 1983-87, assoc. dean Coll. Arts and Scis., 1985-89, vice provost for undergrad. affairs, 1989-91, dean Coll. Arts and Scis., 1991—. Author: Swinburne, Hardy, Lawrence and the Burden of Belief, 1978, The Poetry of D.H. Lawrence, 1983, Sons and Lovers, A Novel of Division and Desire, 1987, Lord Jim: After the Truth, 1992; editor: Conrad Revisited: Essays for the Eighties, 1986, Heart of Darkness: A Case Study of Contemporary Criticism, 1989, The Scarlet Letter: A Case Study in Contemporary Criticism, 1991. Recipient Prof. of Yr. award Honors Students Assn., 1982-83, Panhellenic Prof. of Yr. award U. Miami, 1984-85; Am. Coun. Learned Socs. fellow, 1978-79, Summer fellow NEH, 1982. Mem. AAUP, MLA (chmn. 20th Century English session 1990), South Atlantic Modern Lang. Assn. (chmn. Modern Brit. div. 1985-86), The Victorians Inst. Democrat. Congregationalist. Avocations: tennis, fishing, gardening. Home: 4550 Alhambra Cir

Miami FL 33146-1061 Office: U Miami 227 Ashe Bldg Coral Gables FL 33124

MURIAN, RICHARD MILLER, book company executive; b. East St. Louis, Ill., Sept. 17, 1937; s. Richard Miller Jr. and Margaret Keyes (Gregory) M.; m. Judith Lee, Aug. 11, 1961 (dec. Apr. 1992); 1 child, Jennifer Ann. BA, U. Calif., Davis, 1969; MLS, U. Calif., Berkeley, 1972; MA, Calif. State U., Sacramento, 1975; MDiv, Trinity Evang., 1977. Cert. history instr., libr. sci. instr., Calif. History reader Calif. State U., Sacramento, 1965-66; history reader U. Calif., Davis, 1966-68, philosophy researcher, 1968-69; bibliographer Argus Books, Sacramento, 1970-71; rsch. dir. Nat. Judical Coll., Reno, 1971-72; libr. Calif. State U., Sacramento, 1972-76; tv talk show host Richard Murian Show, L.A., 1979-80; pres. Alcuin Books, Ltd., Phoenix, 1981—; bd. mem. Guild of Ariz. Antiquarian Books; pres. East Valley Assn. Evangs., Mesa, Ariz., 1984-86; cons. Ariz. Hist. Soc., 1993—. Contbr. articles to profl. jours. Active U. Calif. Riverside Libr., 1981-83, KAET (PBS), 1988—, Ariz. State U., 1989—, Am. Asian Mus., Ariz. Preservation Found., Grand Canyon Nature Assn.; cons. Ariz. Hist. Soc. Recipient Sidney B. Mitchell fellowship U. Calif., Berkeley, 1971. Mem. Am. Assn. Museums, Ariz. Preservation Found., Grand Canyon Nature Assn., Internat. Platform Assn., Phi Kappa Phi. Democrat. Presbyterian. Avocations: fgn. films, jazz. Office: Alcuin Books Ltd 115 W Camelback Rd Phoenix AZ 85013-2519

MURILLO, VELDA JEAN, social worker, counselor; b. Miller, S.D., Dec. 8, 1943; d. Royal Gerald and Marion Elizabeth (Porter) Matson; m. Daniel John Murillo, June 25, 1967 (div. Dec. 1987); 1 child, Damon Michael. BS, S.D. State U., 1965; MA, Calif. State U., Bakersfield, 1980. Cert. marriage, family and child counselor. Social worker adult svcs. Kern County Dept. Welfare, Bakersfield, 1965-78, social worker child protective svcs., 1978-84; asst. coord. sexual abuse program Kern County Dist. Atty., Bakersfield, 1985-91, coord. sexual abuse program, 1991—; Mem. Calif. Sexual Assault Investigators, 1982-84, Kern Child Abuse Prevention Coun., Bakersfield, 1982-84; co-developer, presenter Children's Self Help Project, Bakersfield, 1982-87; cons. mem. Sexual Assault Adv. Com., Bakersfield, 1991—. Mem. Soroptimist Internat. Democrat. Avocations: traveling, metaphysical pursuits. Office: Kern County Dist Atty 1215 Truxtun Ave Bakersfield CA 93301

MURILLO-ROHDE, ILDAURA MARIA, marriage and family therapist, consultant, educator, dean; b. Garachine, Panama; came to U.S. 1945; d. Amalio Murillo and Ana E. (Diaz) de Murillo; m. Erling Rohde, Sept. 19, 1959. BS, Columbia U., 1951, MA, 1953, MEd, 1969; PhD, NYU, 1971; hon. diploma, Escuela Nat. de Enfermeria, Guatemala, 1964. RN; lic. marriage and family therapist, N.J.; cert. mental health-psychiat. nursing, ANA; lic. sex. therapist, N.J. Instr., supr. Bellevue Psychiat. Hosp., N.Y.C., 1950-54; asst. dir. psychiat. div. Wayne County Gen. Hosp., Eloise, Mich., 1954-56; chief nurse psychiat. div. Elmhurst Gen. Hosp., Queens, N.Y., 1956-58, Met. Hosp. Med. Ctr., N.Y.C., 1961-63; psychiat. cons. to govt. World Health Orgns., UN, Guatemala, Guatemala, 1963-64; assoc. prof., chmn. psychiat. dept. N.Y. Med. Coll. Grad. Sch. Nursing, N.Y.C., 1964-69; dir. mental health-psychiatry, asst. prof. NYU, N.Y.C., 1970-72; assoc. prof. Hostos Coll., CUNY, N.Y.C., 1972-76; assoc. dean. acad. affairs U. Wash., Seattle, 1976-81; prof., dean Coll. of Nursing SUNY, Downstate Med. Ctr., Bklyn., 1981-85; dean and prof. emeritus SUNY, Bklyn., 1985—; bd. dirs. Puerto Rican Family Inst., N.Y.C., 1983—; dir. Latin Am. Oncological Nurses Fuld Fellowships, 1989-90; psychiat. cons. Sch. Nursing, U. Antioquia, Medellin, Colombia, 1972-73, WHO; psychiat./rsch. cons. for master program Sch. Nursing, U. Panama, Project Hope, 1986. Editor: National Directory of Hispanic Nurses, 1981, 3d edit., 1994; contbr. numerous articles to profl. nat. and internat. jours., chpts. in books in field. Mem. Wash. State adv. com. U.S. Commn. on Civil Rights, Seattle, 1971-81; nat. adv. com. White House Conf. on Families, Washington, 1979-81; pres. King County Health Planning Council, Seattle, 1979-81; exec. com. Puget Sound Health Systems Agy., Seattle, 1979-81. Univ. Honors scholar NYU, 1972; named Citizen of the Day, Radio Sta. KIXI and N.W. Airlines, Seattle, 1979, disting. lectr. Sigma Theta Tau, 1988-89, Woman of Yr. N.Y. Gotham Club Bus. and Profl. Women, 1989; recipient 1st Nat. Intercultural Nursing award Coun. of Intercultural Nursing, ANA, New Orleans, 1984, Women's Honors in Pub. Svc. award Minority Fellowship Programs and Cabinet Human Rights, ANA, 1986, Disting. Alumna award Divsn. Nursing, NYU Alumni Assn., 1989, 1st Nat. Dr. Hildegard Peplau award Las Vegas conv. ANA, 1992. Fellow Am. Assn. Marriage and Family Therapy; mem. ANA (affirmative action task force 1974-84, commn. human rights, cabinet human rights, rep. at ICN Cong. Tokyo 1977, spokesperson Nat. Health Ins., conceived and designed Coun. Intercultural Nursing), Am. Orthopsychiatric Assn. (bd. dirs. 1976-79, treas. 1986-89), N.Y. Assn. Marriage and Family Therapy (pres. 1973-76), Nat. Assn. Hispanic Nurses (founder, 1st pres. 1976-80), Internat. Fedn. Bus. and Profl. Women (UN rep. to UNICEF, London 1987—, del. to World UN Summit for Children, N.Y.C. 1990), UN N.Y. Com. for Internat. Yr. of Family, 1994, Am. Rsch. Inst. (dep. gov. 1987). Democrat. Clubs: NYU, Gotham Bus. & Profl. Women (N.Y.C.). Avocations: travel, reading, music, stamp collecting, skiing. Home: 300 W 108th St Apt 12A New York NY 10025-2704 Office: SUNY Bklyn Coll Nursing Box 22 450 Clarkson Ave Brooklyn NY 11203-2012

MURIS, TIMOTHY JOSEPH, law educator; b. Massillon, Ohio, Nov. 18, 1949; s. George William and Louise (Hood) M.; m. Susan Sexton, Aug. 10, 1974; children—Matthew Allen, Paul Austin. B.A., San Diego State U., 1971; J.D., UCLA, 1974. Bar: Calif. 1974, U.S. Supreme Ct. 1983. Asst. to dir. policy planning and evaluation FTC, Washington, 1974-76, dir. Bur. Consumer Protection, 1981-83, dir. Bur. Competition, 1983-85; exec. assoc. dir. Office Mgmt. and Budget, Washington, 1985-88, cons., 1988-89; law and econs. fellow U. Chgo. Law Sch., 1979-80; asst. prof. antitrust and consumer law U. Miami Law Sch. and Law Econs. Ctr., Fla., 1976-79, assoc. prof., 1979-81, prof., 1981-83; Found. prof. law George Mason U., Va., 1988—; dep. counsel Presdl. Task Force on Regulatory Relief, Washington, 1981; cons. Coun. on Wage and Price Stability, Washington, 1981; mem. Nat. Issues Forum, Brookings Inst., 1986-88; mem. adv. bd. Anti-Trust and Trade Regulation Report, 1990—. Editor: The Federal Trade Commission Since 1970: Regulation and Bureaucratic Behavior, 1981. Mem. Reagan-Bush transition team for FTC, Washington, 1980; sr. advisor Bush-Quayle transition team, 1988-89. Am. Bar Found. affiliated scholar, 1979. Mem. ABA (antitrust law spl. com. to study role of FTC 1988-89), Calif. Bar Assn., Order of Coif. Office: George Mason U Sch Law 3401 Fairfax Dr Arlington VA 22201-4498

MURKISON, EUGENE COX, business educator; b. Donalsonville, Ga., July 2, 1936; s. Jeff and Ollie Mae (Shores) M.; m. Marilyn Louise Adams, July 3, 1965; children: James, David, Jennifer. BSA, U. Ga., 1959; MBA, U. Rochester, 1970; PhD, U. Mo., 1986. Surveyor U.S. Dept. Agri., Donalsonville, Ga., 1956-59; commd. 2d lt. U.S. Army, 1959, advanced through grades to lt. col., 1974, retired, 1981; infantry platoon leader U.S. Army, Vietnam, 1961-73; prof. leadership & psychology West Point, N.Y., 1970-73; instr. U. Mo., Columbia, 1981-84; asst. prof. Ga. So. U., Stateboro, 1984-89, assoc. prof., 1989-94, prof., 1995—; vis. prof. mgmt. and bus. U. Tirgoviste, Romania, 1994, 95. Contbr. articles to profl. jours. Membership chmn. U. Optimist Club, 1992, dir., 1993, v.p. 1994—; trustee Pittman Park Meth. Ch., Statesboro, 1992—, chmn., trustee 1995—. Recipient Bronze Star medal with oak leaf cluster, Devel. award Ga. So. U., 1990, Teaching award U. Mo., 1983, Albert Burke Rsch. award, 1992; grantee IREX, 1994, SOROS, 1995. Mem. Am. Statis. Assn., Inst. Mgmt. Sci., Southern Mgmt. Assn., Internat. Acad. Bus. (program chair 1994, 95), Acad. Mgmt., Inst. Mgmt. Sci., Bus. History Conf., Newcomen Soc., Blue Key, Scabbard & Blade, Beta Gamma Sigma, Alpha Zeta. Avocations: bus. history, mil history, tomato prodn., hiking, boating. Office: Ga So U Coll Bus Adminstrn Statesboro GA 30460-8152

MURKOWSKI, FRANK HUGHES, senator; b. Seattle, Mar. 28, 1933; s. Frank Michael and Helen (Hughes) M.; m. Nancy R. Gore, Aug. 28, 1954; children: Carol Victoria Murkowski Sturgulewski, Lisa Ann Murkowski Martell, Frank Michael, Eileen Marie Murkowski Van Wyhe, Mary Catherine Murkowski Judson, Brian Patrick. Student, Santa Clara U., 1952-53; BA in Econs, Seattle U., 1955. With Pacific Nat. Bank, 1957-58, Nat. Bank of Alaska, Anchorage, 1959-67; asst. v.p., mgr. Nat. Bank of Alaska (Wrangell br.), 1963-66; v.p. charge bus. devel. Nat. Bank of Alaska,

Anchorage, 1966-67; commr. dept. econ. devel. State of Alaska, Juneau, 1967-70; pres. Alaska Nat. Bank, Fairbanks, 1971-80; mem. U.S. Senate from Alaska, Washington, Alaska, 1981—; chmn. Com. on Energy and Natural Resources; mem. Com. on Fin., Vets Affairs Com., Indian Affairs Com., Japan-US Friendship Com.; senate amb. UN Gen. Assembly, 1994-95; Rep. nominee for U.S. Congress from Alaska, 1970. Former v.p. B.C. and Alaska Bd. Trade. Served with U.S. Coast Guard, 1955-57. Mem. Am. Legion, Polish Legion Am. Vets., AMVETS, Ducks Unltd., NRA, Res. Officer's Assn., Pioneers of Alaska, Shilla Club, Internat. Alaska Nippon Kai, Capital Hill Club, Alaska Geographic Soc., Army Athletic Club, Alaska World Affairs Coun., Congl. Staff Club, AAA, Fairbanks Hist. Preservation Found., Coalition Am. Vets., Alaska Native Brotherhood, Diamond Athletic Club, Nat. Wildlife Fedn., Nat. Mining Hall of Fame, Naval Athletic Assn., Am. Bankers Assn, Alaska Bankers Assn. (pres. 1973), Young Pres.'s Orgn., Young Pres.'s Club, Washington Athletic Club, Alaska C. of C. (pres. 1977), Anchorage C. of C. (dir. 1966), B.C. C. of C., Fairbanks C. of C. (dir. 1973-78). Clubs: Elks, Lions, Washington Athletic. Office: US Senate 706 Hart Senate Bldg Washington DC 20510

MURMAN, EARLL M., aeronautics and astronautics educator. BEE, Princeton U., 1963, MA, 1965, PhD, 1967. Prof. aeronautics and astronautics, head dept. MIT, Cambridge, Mass. Fellow AIAA; mem. NAE, Phi Beta Kappa. Office: MIT Dept Aeronautics & Astronautics Cambridge MA 02139

MURNAGHAN, FRANCIS DOMINIC, JR., federal judge; b. Baltimore, Md., June 20, 1920; m. Diana Edwards; children: Sheila H., George A., Janet E. B.A., Johns Hopkins U., 1941; LL.B., Harvard U., 1948. Bar: Md. 1949. Asso. firm Barnes Dechert Price Smith & Clark, Phila., 1948-50; staff atty. Office of Gen. Counsel, U.S. High Commr. for Ger., 1950-52; asst. atty. gen. State of Md., 1952-54; asso. firm Venable Baetjer & Howard, Balt., 1952-57; partner Venable Baetjer & Howard, 1957-79; judge U.S. Ct. Appeals for 4th Circuit Balt., 1979—. Chmn. Balt. Charter Rev. Commn., 1963-64; trustee Walters Art Gallery, 1961, v.p. 1961-63, pres. 1963-80, chmn 1983-85, chmn. emeritus, 1985—; pres. Balt. Sch. Bd., 1967-70; trustee Johns Hopkins U., 1976—. Lt. USNR, 1942-46. Mem. ABA, Am. Coll. Trial Lawyers. Office: US Ct Appeals 4th Cir 101 W Lombard St Baltimore MD 21201

MURNANE, MARGARET MARY, physics educator; b. Limerick, Ireland, Jan. 23, 1959; d. Matthew and Helen (Bourke) M.; m. Henry Cornelius Kapteyn, Mar. 26, 1987. MSc, U. Coll. Cork, Ireland, 1983; PhD, U. Calif., Berkeley, 1989. Postdoctoral researcher U. Calif., Berkeley, 1990; asst. prof. Wash. State U., Pullman, 1990—. Presdl. Young Investigator awardee NSF, 1991, Sloan Found. fellow, 1992, Presdl. faculty fellow NSF, 1993. Mem. Am. Phys. Soc. (Simon Ramo award 1990), Optical Soc. Am., Soc. Photo-Optical Instrumentation Engrs., Assn. for Women in Sci. Office: Wash State Univ Dept Physics Pullman WA 99164

MURNANE, THOMAS GEORGE, JR., public health veterinarian, military; b. Dallas, May 5, 1926; s. Thomas George and Ellecia Catherine (Donohue) M.; m. Constance Marie Pollock, June 17, 1954; children: Mary Loretta, Constance Marie, Thomas George, Ellecia Catherine, Margaret Georgianna. DVM, Tex. A&M U., 1947. Diplomate Am. Coll. Vet. Preventive Medicine. Pvt. practice Brenham, Tex., 1947-48; field vet. U.S./Mex. Commn. for Eradication of Foot and Mouth Disease, Mex., 1948-49; 1st lt. Vet. Corps, U.S. Army, 1949, advanced through grades to brig. gen., 1976; chief U.S. Army Vet. Corps, 1976-80; regional vet. InterAm. Inst. for Cooperation in Agr., Mex., Cen. Am., Panama, 1980-83; pub. health vet. Tex. Dept. Health, Arlington, 1983-93; cons. in vet. pub. health to Surgeon Gen., U.S. Army, Washington, 1973-76; chmn. ad hoc com. on fgn. animal diseases, NRC, NAS, 1983-84; adj. prof. Coll. Vet. Medicine, Tex. A&M U., 1988—.Vet. Editor: Foreign Animal Disease Handbook, 1975; co-editor: Health Hazards in Veterinary Practice, 1989; contbr. chpts. to books, articles to profl. jours. Pres. Ridgle Country Club Homeowners Assn., Ft. Worth, 1985, pastoral coun. Holy Family Ch., Ft. Worth, 1989-92. Decorated D.S.M., Bronze Star, Legion of Merit, Meritorious Svc. medal; recipient Disting. Alumnus award Coll. Vet. Medicine, Tex. A&M U., 1989-90. Mem. AMVA (ho. of dels. 1974-80, ho. adv. com. 1976-81, co-chmn. regulatory sect. sci. program com. 1986-92, adv. com. vet. spltys. 1986-92, Pub. Svc. award 1990), Tex. Vet. Med. Assn. (chmn. pub. health sect. 1989-92, Disting. Achievement award 1994), Am. Coll. Vet. Preventive Medicine (pres. 1991-92, Helwig-Jennings award), U.S. Animal Health Assn. (chmn. fgn. animal diseases 1974-80). Republican. Roman Catholic. Avocation: swimming. Home: 6804 Benito Ct Fort Worth TX 76126

MURNICK, DANIEL ELY, physicist, educator; b. N.Y.C., May 5, 1941; s. Jacob Michael and Lena (Tishman) M.; m. Janet Barbara George, Oct. 26, 1969; children: Jonathan, Carolyn. AB in Physics and Math., Hofstra U., 1962; PhD, MIT, 1966. Physics instr. MIT, Cambridge, 1966-67; mem. tech. staff Bell Labs, Murray Hill, N.J., 1967-88; prof., chmn. physics Rutgers U., Newark, 1988—; cons. High Voltage Engring., Burlington, Mass., 1965-67, Diagnostics and Devices, Morristown, N.J., 1986—, Am. Std., Piscataway, 1990—; mem. sci. adv. bd. Surgilase, Warwick, R.I., 1984—. Contbr. more than 100 articles to profl. jours.; inventor method and apparatus for stable isotope analysis and for localized surface glazing. Recipient Humboldt award, Rep. of Germany, 1984. Fellow Am. Phys. Soc.; mem. IEEE, Am. Assn. Physics Tchrs., Sigma Xi. Office: Rutgers U Dept Physics 101 Warren St Newark NJ 07102-1811

MURO, ROY ALFRED, independent media service corporation executive; b. N.Y.C., Sept. 22, 1942; s. Angelo Dominick and Virginia (Guangi) M.; m. Lorraine D. Friedman, July 5, 1966; children: Bradley, Jessica. BS, Bklyn. Coll., 1964; MBA, N.Y. Grad. Sch. Bus., 1966. CPA, N.Y. Sr. acct. Price Waterhouse & Co., N.Y.C., 1966-71; comptr. Vitt Media Internat. Inc., N.Y.C., 1971-82, chmn., COO, 1982-91, chmn., 1991-94, CEO, 1991—; lectr. in field. Mem. AICPA, N.Y. State Soc. CPA's, Advt. Agy. Fin. Mgmt. Group, Nat. Agrimktg. Assn., Internat. Radio and TV Soc., N.Y. Credit and Fin. Mgmt. Assn. (lectr.),Am. Travel Mktg. Execs. Home: 8 Irene Ct East Brunswick NJ 08816-2223 Office: Vitt Media Internat Inc 1114 Ave of the Americas New York NY 10036-7701

MUROFF, LAWRENCE ROSS, nuclear medicine physician; b. Phila., Dec. 26, 1942; s. John M. and Carolyn (Kramer) M.; m. Carol R. Savoy, July 12, 1969; children: Michael Bruce, Julie Anne. AB cum laude, Dartmouth Coll., 1964, B of Med. Sci., 1965; MD cum laude, Harvard U., 1967. Diplomate Am. Bd. Radiology, Am. Bd. Nuclear Medicine. Intern Boston City Hosp., Harvard, 1968; resident in radiology Columbia Presbyn. Med. Ctr., N.Y.C., 1970-73, chief resident, 1973; instr. dept. radiology, asst. radiologist Columbia U. Med. Ctr., N.Y.C., 1973-74; dir. dept. nuclear medicine, computed tomography and magnetic resonance imaging Univ. Community Hosp., Tampa, Fla., 1974-94; pres. Imaging Cons. Inc., Tampa, 1994—; clin. asst. prof. radiology U. South Fla., 1974-78, clin. assoc. prof., 1978-82, clin. prof., 1982—; clin. prof. U. Fla., 1988—. Contbr. articles to profl. jours. Pres. Ednl. Symposia, Inc., 1975—. Lt. comdr. USPHS, 1968-70. Fellow Am. Coll. Nuclear Medicine (disting. fellow,, Fla. del.), Am. Coll. Nuclear Physicians (regents 1976-78m pres.-elect 1978, pres. 1979, fellow 1980), Am. Coll. Radiology (councilor 1979-80, 91—, chancellor 1981-87, chmn. commn. on nuclear medicine 1981-87, fellow 1981); mem. Am. Assn. Acad. Chief Residents Radiology (chmn. 1973), AMA, Boylston Soc., Fla. Assn. Nuclear Physicians (pres. 1976), Fla. Med. Assn., Hillsborough County Med. Assn., Radiol. Soc. N.Am., Nuclear Medicine (coun. 1975-90, trustee 1980-84, 86-89, pres. Southeastern chpt. 1983, vice chmn. correlative imaging coun. 1983), Fla. Radiol. Soc. (exec. com. 1976-91, treas. 1984, sec. 1985, v.p. 1986, pres. elect 1987, pres. 1988-89, gold medal 1995), West Coast Radiol. Soc., Soc. Mag. Resonance Imaging (bd. dirs. 1988-91, chmn. ednl. program 1989, chmn. membership com. 1989-93), Phi Beta Kappa, Alpha Omega Alpha. Office: 1527 S Dale Mabry Hwy Tampa FL 33629-5808

MURPHEY, ARTHUR GAGE, JR., law educator; b. Macon, Miss., June 16, 1927; s. Arthur Gage and Elizabeth (Crutcher) M.; m. Linda Chaney, May 17, 1975; children by previous marriage—Mason Alexander, Arthur Nesbit; 1 stepchild, Leslie Jo (Mrs. Thomas) Pafford. Student, Vanderbilt U., 1947-48; AB, U.N.C, 1951; JD, U. Miss., 1953; postgrad., London Sch. Econs., U. London, 1953-54; LLM, Yale U., 1962. Assoc. Satterfield, Ewing Williams and Shell, Jackson, Miss., 1953; asst. prof. U. Ga., Athens, 1956-58, Emory U., Atlanta, 1958-61; asst. prof. U. Akron, 1962-63, assoc. prof.,

1963-67; prof. U. Ark., Little Rock, 1967—, asst. dean Sch. Law, 1970-73; vis. lectr. Case Western Res. U., Cleve., 1966; vis. prof. U. Miss., 1977. Faculty editor: Jour. Public Law, 1958-61; faculty adv.: Ga. Bar Jour., 1958-61; contbr. articles to profl. jours. Served with USAAF, 1945-47. Fulbright scholar, 1953-54; Stirling fellow, 1961-62; Ford Found. grantee, 1964. Mem. ABA, Ark. Bar. Assn, Phi Delta Phi, Beta Theta Pi, Phi Beta Kappa. Mem. Anglican Ch. Home: 1918 Old Forge Dr Little Rock AR 72227 Office: U Ark Sch Law 1201 McAlmont Little Rock AR 72202

MURPHEY, MICHAEL MARTIN, country western singer, songwriter; b. Tex., Mar. 14, 1945; married; children: Ryan, Brennan, Laura Lynn. Attended, UCLA. Profl. musician, 1962—; with Lewis & Clark Expedition, 1966-70. Songwriter for Monkees, Kenny Rogers, Nitty Gritty Dirt Band; pop hit Wildfire, 1975, What's forever for, Carolina in the Pines, Love Affairs, Still Taken Chances; founder Westfest annual celebration; albums: Geronimo's Cadillac, 1971, Blue Sky Night Thunder, 1981, The Best of Michael Martin Murphey, 1981, The Heart Never Lies, 1986, Tonight We Ride, 1986, Americana, 1987, River of Time, 1988, Land of Enchantment, 1989, Best of Country Michael Martin Murphey, 1990, Cowboy Songs, 1990, Cowboy Christmas: Cowboy Songs II, 1991, Cowboy Songs III, 1993. Named Best New Artist, Country Music Assn., Acad. Country Music; recipient Grammy nomination for a Face in the Crowd, Nat. Am. Video award for What She Wants, award Cowboy Hall of Fame (3), 1990-92. Office: PO Box FFF Taos NM 87571

MURPHEY, MURRAY GRIFFIN, history educator; b. Colorado Springs, Colo., Feb. 22, 1928; s. Bradford James and Margaret Winifred (Griffin) M.; children—Kathleen Rachel, Christopher Bradford, Jessica Lenoir. A.B., Harvard U., 1949; Ph.D., Yale U., 1954. Asst. prof. U. Pa., Phila., 1956-61, assoc. prof., 1961-66, prof., 1966—, chmn. dept. Am. civilization, 1969-81, 87-94. Author: Development of Peirce's Philosophy, 1961, Our Knowledge of the Historical Past, 1973, (with E. Flower) A History of Philosophy in America, 1977, Philosophical Foundations of Historical Knowledge, 1994. Democrat. Home: 200 Rhyle Ln Bala Cynwyd PA 19004-2324 Office: U Pa 3440 Market St Fl 400 Philadelphia PA 19104-3338

MURPHEY, RHOADS, history educator; b. Phila., Aug. 13, 1919; s. William Rhoads and Emily (Hawkins) M.; m. Katherine Elizabeth Quinn, Nov. 26, 1942 (dec. July 1950); children: Katherine Ann, Rhoads; m. Eleanor Taylor Albertson, Jan. 12, 1952; children: David, Ellen. A.B., Harvard U., 1941, M.A., 1942, Ph.D., 1950. Asst. prof. geography Ohio State U., 1950-51; from asst. prof. geography to prof. U. Wash., also Far Eastern Inst., 1952-64; prof. Asian studies and history U. Mich., Ann Arbor, 1964—; dir. Center Chinese Studies U. Mich., 1969-76, dir. Asian studies, 1975—, dir. South and S.E. Asian studies, 1987-90. Author: Shanghai-Key to Modern China, 1953, An Introduction to Geography, 4th edit., 1978, (with others) A New China Policy, 1965, The Scope of Geography, 1969, 73, 3d rev. edit., 1982, The Treaty Ports and China's Modernization, 1970, China Meets the West, 1975, (with others) The Mozartian Historian, 1976, The Outsiders, 1977, The Fading of the Maoist Vision, 1980, (with others) The Chinese, 1986, 2nd edit., 1991; (with others) Civilizations of the World, 1990, 3d edit., 1995; A History of Asia, 1992, 2d edit., 1995; co-editor: (with others) Approaches to Modern Chinese History, 1967; asst. editor, then editor: Jour. Asian Studies, 1959-65; regional editor Asia: (with others) Ency. Brit. 1953-61; editor: Mich. papers in Chinese Studies, 1967-77, Assn. Asian Studies Monographs, 1992—; contbr. articles to profl. jours. Social Sci. Research Council fellow, 1948-50; Ford Found. fellow, 1955-56; Guggenheim fellow, 1966-67; Nat. Endowment Humanities fellow, 1972-73, JSPS fellow, 1978-79. Mem. Assn. Am. Geographers (council 1963-66, Honors award 1980), Assn. Asian Studies (dir., exec. sec. 1976-83, v.p. 1985, pres. 1987-88). Home: 2012 Washtenaw Ave Ann Arbor MI 48104-3639

MURPHEY, ROBERT STAFFORD, pharmaceutical company executive; b. Littleton, N.C., Oct. 29, 1921; married; 2 children. B.S., U. Richmond, 1942; M.S., U. Va., 1947, Ph.D. in Organic Chemistry, 1949. Research chemist in medicinal chemistry A.H. Robins & Co. Inc., Richmond, Va., 1948-53, dir. chemistry research, 1953-55, assoc. dir., 1955-57, dir. research, 1957-60, dir. internat. research, 1960-66, dir. sci. devel., 1966-82, asst. v.p., 1967-73, dir. sci. devel., v.p., 1973-82, v.p. sci. affairs and corp. devel., 1982-83, sr. v.p. sci. affairs and corp. devel., 1983-87, sr. v.p., dir. new bus. devel., 1983-90; sr. v.p., dir. bus. devel. E.C. Robins Internat., Inc., Glen Allen, Va., 1990—. Mem. AAAS, Am. Chem. Soc. Office: E C Robins Internat Inc 11064 Staples Mill Rd Glen Allen VA 23060-2404

MURPHREE, HENRY BERNARD SCOTT, psychiatry educator, consultant; b. Decatur, Ala., Aug. 11, 1927; s. Henry Bernard and Nancy Mae (Burrus) M.; m. Dorothy Elaine Simmons, Nov. 14, 1953 (dec.); children: Julie Elizabeth, Susan Louise, Jefferson Van; m. Dorothy Elizabeth Olson, Sept. 23, 1993. Student, MIT, 1944-45; BA, Yale U., 1950; MD, Emory U., 1959. Intern internal medicine, fellow clin. pharmacology, instr. Emory U., 1959-61; resident psychiatry Med. Sch. Rutgers U., 1972-76, mem. grad. faculty psychology, 1972—; rsch. asst. Johns Hopkins U., Balt., 1950; asst. chief neuropharmacology Bur. Rsch., Princeton, N.J., 1961-68; from assoc prof. to prof. Univ. of Medicine and Dentistry Robert Wood Johnson Med. Sch., Piscataway, N.J., 1968—, assoc. dean acad. affairs Univ. Medicine and Dentistry, 1977-81, chmn. psychiatry Univ. Medicine and Dentistry, 1977-91; cons. medicinal chemistry and pharmacology FMC Chem. R&D Ctr., Princeton, N.J., 1962-68, Hoffman-LaRoche, Nutley and Verona, N.J., 1968-77. Contbr. articles to profl. jours. Founding mem. Somerset Coun. Alcoholism, Somerville, N.J., 1974-77; mem. Sci. Adv. Com., State of N.J., 1981—; bd. trustees Carrier Found., Belle Mead, N.J., 1981—, vice chmn. bd., chmn. exec. com., 1989—. Lt. USN, 1951-55. Mem. Am. Soc. for Pharmacology and Exptl. Therapeutics, Am. Psychiat. Assn., Soc. Biol. Psychiatry, Am. Coll. Neuropsychopharmacology, Sigma Xi, Alpha Omega Alpha. Avocations: music, electronics. Home: 757 Route 518 Skillman NJ 08558-2513 Office: U Med & Dentistry NJ Robert Wood Johnson Med Sch 675 Hoes Ln Piscataway NJ 08854-5635

MURPHREE, TAMMY MARIE, hospital administrator; b. Jackson, Tenn., May 1, 1964; d. Talmage Herman and Hazel Marie (Morris) Evans; m. Paul Michael Murphree, Dec. 22, 1984; children: Mitzi Marie, Andrew Taylor. RN, Meth. Hosp., Memphis, 1988; BSN, Union U., Jackson, Tenn., 1989. Staff nurse med./surg. floor Jackson-Madison County Gen. Hosp., 1985-88; asst. head nurse med./surg. floor Jackson-Madison County Gen. Hosp., Jackson, 1988-89; 1st surg. asst. Jackson Clinic, 1989-93; clin. mgr. med. fl. Jackson-Madison County Gen. Hosp., 1993—. Mem. Assn. Oper. Rm. Nurses, Sigma Theta Tau, Alpha Chi, Pi Epsilon Iota (treas. 1983-84).

MURPHY, ALVIN LEO, educational administrator; b. New Orleans, July 19, 1934; s. James J. and Marie Adele (Perret) M.; m. Celeste Marie Ferry, Nov. 24, 1956; children: Angelle, Alice, Emily, Claire. BS in Secondary Edn., Loyola U., New Orleans, 1956; MEd, Loyola U., 1967. Tchr. De La Salle High Sch., New Orleans, 1958-67; asst. prin. De La Salle High Sch., 1967-72; asst. supt. Archdiocese of New Orleans, 1972-74, assoc. supt., 1974-83; prin. Archbishop Chapelle High Sch., Metairie, La., 1983-89; pres. Archbishop Chapelle High Sch., 1989—. Contbr. articles to profl. jours. Mem. Kenner Bus. Assn., 1989—, Metairie chpt. Am. Heart Assn., 1990—. 1st lt. U.S. Army, 1956-58. Recipient Blue Ribbon Sch. Excellence award U.S. Dept. Edn., 1987, 91, One to Watch in '79 award New Orleans Mag., 1979, Presdl. award Nat. Cath. Ednl. Assn., 1984, St. Louis medal Archdiocese of New Orleans, 1983; named Outstanding Educator La. Libr. Assn., 1994. Mem. Nat. Cath. Edn. Assn. (Nat. Outstanding Contbn. award 1980, reg. assoc. 1988—), Cath. Secondary Prins. Assn. (treas. 1985-87), Nat. Chief Adminstrs. of Cath. Edn., Am. Mgmt. Assn., Nat. Assn. Secondary Sch. Prins. Roman Catholic. Avocations: reading, sports, computers, photography. Office: Archbishop Chapelle High 8800 Veterans Memorial Blvd Metairie LA 70003-5235

MURPHY, ANDREW J., JR., newspaper editor. Now mng. editor, news editor Columbus (Ohio) Dispatch. Office: Columbus Dispatch 34 S 3rd St Columbus OH 43215-4241*

MURPHY, ANN BURKE, insurance company executive, computer engineer; b. Portland, Maine, Dec. 7, 1938; d. James Hudner and Mary Theresa (Monahan) Burke; m. John B. Murphy, Aug. 20, 1960 (div. Jan. 3, 1979); children: Kim Murphy Francis, Suzanne Murphy Farrell. BA in

Math., U. Maine, 1960. Rsch. analyst United Tech. Corp., East Hartford, Conn., 1960-61, Travelers Ins. Co., Hartford, Conn., 1961-69; tennis profl., cons. East Hartford, 1969-82; adv. system analyst Phoenix Home Life, Hartford, 1982—; ofcl. linesperson Aetna Ins. Co. World Cup Tennis Tournament, Hartford, 1973-76; dir. Hartford Ins. Group City Tennis Open, 1978-80. Mem. New Eng. chpt. U.S. Tennis Assn. (bd. dirs. 1987-89, ranked #1 1972-93, hall of fame 1993, friendship cup capt.), Phi Beta Kappa, Phi Kappa Phi. Democrat. Roman Catholic. Home: 124 Bradley St East Hartford CT 06118 Office: Phoenix Home Life Ins 1 American Row Hartford CT 06115-2520

MURPHY, ANN PLESHETTE, magazine editor-in-chief. Editor-in-chief Parents mag., N.Y.C. Office: Parents Magazine 685 3rd Ave New York NY 10017*

MURPHY, ARTHUR THOMAS, systems engineer; b. Hartford, Conn., Feb. 15, 1929; s. Arthur T. and Mary (Beakey) M.; m. Jane M. Gamble, Aug. 16, 1952; children: Thomas, Patricia, Mary, John, Sheila, Jane, Joseph. BEE, Syracuse U., 1951; MS, Carnegie-Mellon U., 1952, PhD, 1957. Registered profl. engr., Kans. Instr. Carnegie-Mellon U., Pitts., 1952-56; asst., assoc. prof., head. elec. engring. Wichita State U., Kans., 1956-61; vis. assoc. prof. mech. engring. MIT, Cambridge, Mass., 1961-62; prof., dean engring. Widener U., Chester, Pa., 1962-71, v.p., acad. dean, 1971-75; Brown prof., head mech. engring. dept. Carnegie-Mellon U., Pitts., 1975-79; mgr. computer and automated systems, sr. research fellow Du Pont de Nemours Co., Camp Hill, Pa., 1979-87; Du Pont fellow Du Pont de Nemours Co., Wilmington, Del., 1987—; vis. rsch. fellow Sony Corp. Rsch. Ctr., Yokohama, Japan, 1991-92, Internat. Superconductivity Tech. Ctr., Tokyo, 1993; vis. prof. control engring. U. Manchester, Eng., 1968-69; cons. Boeing Co., Wichita and Morton, Pa., 1957-68; bd. dirs. Rumford Pub. Co., Chgo., 1975-90; lectr. Pa. State U., 1983-87. Author: Introduction to System Dynamics, 1967; contbr. articles to profl. jours.; editor Pergamon Press, 1966-75; patentee thick film filter connector, ceramic land grid array, superconducting active antenna array. Mem. adv. coun. Tex. A&M U., Swarthmore Coll. DuPont fellow, 1987—; recipient DuPont Spl Accomplishment award, 1988, Mktg. Excellence award DuPont Co., 1990. Fellow AAAS, IEEE (exec. com., treas. computer packaging); mem. ASME (exec. com. control div.), Am. Soc. Engring. Edn. (chmn. grad. studies awards com., Dupont rep.), Western Electric Fund award 1966). Avocations: hiking, photography. Home: 388 Spring Mill Rd Chadds Ford PA 19317 Office: Du Pont Co Exptl Sta PO Box 80174 Wilmington DE 19880

MURPHY, ARTHUR WILLIAM, lawyer, educator; b. Boston, Jan. 25, 1922; s. Arthur W. and Rose (Spillane) M.; m. Jane Marks, Dec. 21, 1948 (dec. Sept. 1951); 1 dau., Lois; m. Jean C. Marks, Sept. 30, 1954; children—Paul, Paul. A.B. cum laude, Harvard, 1943; LL.B., Columbia, 1948. Bar: N.Y. State bar 1949. Asso. in law Columbia Sch. Law, N.Y.C., 1948-49; asso. dir. Legislative Drafting Research Fund, 1956, prof. law, 1963—; trial atty. U.S. Dept. Justice, 1950-52; asso. firm Hughes, Hubbard, Blair & Reed, N.Y.C., 1953-56, 57-58; partner firm Baer, Marks, Friedman & Berliner, N.Y.C., 1959-63; mem. safety and licensing panel AEC, 1962-73; mem. spl. commn. on weather modification NSF, 1964-66; mem. Presdl. Commn. on Catastrophic Nuclear Accidents, 1988-90. Author: Financial Protection against Atomic Hazards, 1957, (with others) Cases on Gratuitous Transfers, 1968, 3d edit., 1985, The Nuclear Power Controversy, 1976. Served with AUS, 1943-46. Decorated Purple Heart. Mem. ABA, Assn. of Bar of City of N.Y. (spl. com. on sci. and law). Office: Columbia Sch of Law 435 W 116th St New York NY 10027-7201

MURPHY, AUSTIN DE LA SALLE, economist, educator, banker; b. N.Y.C., Nov. 20, 1917; s. Daniel Joseph and Marie Cornelia (Austin) M.; m. Mary Patricia Halpin, June 12, 1948 (dec. May 1974); children: Austin Joseph, Owen Gerard; m. Lee Chilton Romero, Dec. 14, 1974; stepchildren: Thomas Romero, Robert Romero. AB, St. Francis Coll., Bklyn., 1938; AM (Hayden fellow 1938-40), Fordham U., 1940, PhD, 1949. Instr. econs. Fordham U., 1938-41; Instr. econs. Georgetown U., 1941-42; asst. statistician, statis. controls Bd. Econ. Warfare, 1942; sr. econs. research editor N.Y. State Dept. Labor, 1947-50; lectr. econs. Fordham U. Sch. Edn., 1946-55; instr. N.Y. U. Sch. Commerce, 1949-51; dean sch. bus. adminstrn. Seton Hall U., South Orange, N.J., 1950-55; Albert O'Neill prof. Am. enterprise, dean sch. bus. adminstrn. Canisius Coll., Buffalo, 1955-62; dir. edn. dept. NAM, 1962-63; exec. v.p. Savs. Banks Assn. N.Y. State, 1963-70; chmn., pres. River Bank Am. (formerly East River Savs. Bank), 1970-89, vice chmn., dir., 1989—; charter trustee Savs. Bank Rockland County, 1965-70; dir. Bank of Charleston (S.C.), 1989-91; chmn. bd., trustee Savs. Bank Life Ins. Fund, 1983-87; chmn. dist. I, mem. adv. coun. Conf. State Bank Suprs., 1986-93; bd. dirs. MSB Fund, Inc. Author: (with Fleming Frasca, and Mannion) Social Studies Review Book, 1946, Leading Problems of New Jersey Manufacturing Industries, (with Bullock and Doerflinger), 1953, Reasons for Relocation, 1955, Forecast of Industrial Expansion in Buffalo and the Niagara Frontier, 1956, Metropolitan Buffalo Perspective, 1958; editor Handbook of New York Labor Statistics, 1950. Mem. Livingston (N.J.) Charter Commn., 1954-55; mem. capital expenditures com., City of Buffalo, 1957-63; trustee Fordham U., 1973-79, N.Y. Med. Coll., 1978-81; bd. dirs. N.Y. council Boy Scouts Am., 1974—, Jr. Achievement of Buffalo, 1958-63, Invest-in-Am. 1st lt. U.S. Army, 1942-46. Named Knight of Malta. Mem. NAM (chmn. ednl. aids com. 1958-63), Am. Fin. Assn., Def. Transp. Assn. (life), Nat. Assn. Mut. Savs. Banks (bd. dirs., treas. 1976-81), Friendly Sons St. Patrick (2d v.p.). DownTown Lower Manhattan Assn. (dir., vice chmn. 1982-93), Union League (pres. 1991-93), World Trade Club, Larchmont Yacht Club, KC, Alpha Kappa Psi, Pi Gamma Mu. Home: 1060 Bayhead Dr Mamaroneck NY 10543-4701 Office: River Bank Am 145 Huguenot St New Rochelle NY 10801-5216

MURPHY, BARRY AMES, lawyer; b. Summit, N.J., Mar. 3, 1938; s. Robert Joseph and Florence C. (Ames) M.; m. Leslie Lynn Smith, June 9, 1962; children—Karen Irene, Sean Patrick, Conor Brendan, Ilana Taraleigh. B.A. in English, Stanford U., 1960; M.B.A., Harvard U., 1963; J.D., U. So. Calif., 1972. Bar: Calif. bar 1973, U.S. Supreme Ct 1976, U.S. Tax Ct 1976. Fin. analyst Office of Sec. Def., 1963-65; pres. Tech. Industries Inc., Los Angeles, 1966-72; invidiual practice law San Mateo, Calif., 1972-74; corp. counsel Falstaff Brewing Co., San Francisco, 1974-77; sr. partner firm Levine & Murphy, San Francisco, 1978-81; v.p. Microvertics, Mountain View, Calif., 1981-86; pres. Murphy Law Corp., San Anselmo, 1987—. Mem. Am., Calif. bar assns., Calif. Trial Lawyers. Address: 28 Fern Ln San Anselmo CA 94960

MURPHY, BARRY JOHN, publishing executive; b. N.Y.C., Oct. 14, 1940; s. Joseph Bernard and Rita (Beneville) M.; m. Joanne Catherine Ruvo, Aug. 29, 1964; children: Kristen, Joseph. BS, Rutgers U., 1963; postgrad., U. Pa., 1980, Dartmouth Coll., 1984. Sales and real estate rep. Mobil Oil Corp., N.Y.C., 1964-69; nat. account mgr. Med. Econs., Oradell, N.J., 1970-79; pub. Hosp. Pubs., Inc., Secaucus, N.J., 1979-84, Argus Press, Secaucus, 1984-86; v.p. group pub. Argus, Secaucus, 1986-89, Reed Elsevier Med. Publ., Belle Mead, N.J., 1989—. With U.S. Army, 1963. Mem. Pharm ADvt. Coun., Midwest Pharm. Advt. Coun., Med. Mktg. Assn., Assn. Med. Pubs., Bloomfield Jaycees, Forest Hill Field Club (Bloomfield), Grenelefe Club (Fla.), Montclair Ski Club (bd. dirs.), Delta Kappa Epsilon. Republican. Roman Catholic. Avocations: golf, skiing, jogging, scuba diving, growing roses. Office: Cahners Pub Excerpta Medica 105 Raider Blvd Belle Mead NJ 08502

MURPHY, BARTH T., insurance company executive. Pres. Bankers Life & Casualty Co., Chgo., 1950—. Office: Bankers Life and Casualty Co 222 Merchandise Mart Plz Chicago IL 60654

MURPHY, BENJAMIN EDWARD, actor; b. Jonesboro, Ark., Mar. 6, 1942; s. Patrick Henry and Nadine (Steele) M. Student, Loras Coll., 1960-61, Loyola U., New Orleans, 1961-62, U. Americas, 1962-63, 64-65; B.A. in Polit. Sci., U. Ill., 1964; student, Pasadena Playhouse, 1965-67; B.A. in Theatre Arts, U. Soc. Calif., 1968. Appeared in: TV series Name of the Game, NBC, 1968-70, Alias Smith and Jones, ABC, 1971-73, Griff, 1973-74, Gemini Man, NBC, 1976, The Chisholms, CBS, 1979-80, The Winds of War, 1983, Lottery, 1983-84, Berrenger's, NBC, 1985, The Dirty Dozen, Fox Network, 1988.

MURPHY, BERNARD THOMAS, electronics executive, researcher, consultant; b. Hull, Yorkshire, Eng., May 30, 1932; came to U.S., 1959; s. Edward Thomas and Lily (Wilkinson) M.; m. Judith Angela Hart, Aug. 2, 1959; children: Steven Christopher, Lynne Helen, Claire Elaine. BS in Physics, Leeds U., Eng., 1953, PhD, 1959. Physicist Philips Rsch. Lab. Eng., 1956-59; supr. Westinghouse Electric Co., Youngwood, Pa., 1959-62; R&D dir. Siliconix Inc., Sunnyvale, Calif., 1962-63; mem. tech. staff Bell Labs., Murray Hill, N.J., 1963-68, supr., 1968-69; dept. head Bell Labs., Murray Hill, Pa., 1970-85; dir. Bell Labs., Reading, Pa., 1985-89; pres. E&P Techs., Mertztown, Pa., 1989—; program chmn. GaAs Mfg. Tech. Conf., 1988, chmn., 1989, chmn. awards com., 1992. Contbr. 40 papers in profl. jours.; 28 patents in field. Recipient Outstanding Paper award Internat. Solid State Cirs. Conf., 1968, Best Paper award European Solid State Circs. Conf., 1982. Fellow IEEE (chmn. confs. and coms., mem. editorial bd. Spectrum).

MURPHY, BETTY JANE SOUTHARD (MRS. CORNELIUS F. MURPHY), lawyer; b. East Orange, N.J.; d. Floyd Theodore and Thelma (Casto) Southard; m. Cornelius F. Murphy, May 1, 1965; children: Ann Southard, Cornelius Francis Jr. AB, Ohio State U.; student, Alliance Française and U. Sorbonne, Paris; JD, Am. U., 1958; LLD (hon.), Eastern Mich. U., 1975, Capital U., 1976, U. Puget Sound, 1986; LHD, Tusculum coll., 1987. Bar: D.C. 1958. Corr., free lance journalist Europe and Asia, UPI, Washington; pub. relations counsellor Capital Properties, Inc. of Columbus (Ohio), Washington; atty. Appellate Cts. br. NLRB, Washington, 1958-59; practiced in Washington, 1959-74; mem. firm McInnis, Wilson, Munson & Woods (and predecessor firm); dep. asst. sec., administr. Wage and Hour Divsn. Wage and Hour div. Dept. Labor, 1974-75; chmn. and mem. NLRB, 1975-79; ptnr. firm Baker & Hostetler, 1980—; adj. prof. law Am. U., 1972-80; mem. adv. com. on rights and responsibilities of women to Sec. HEW; mem. panel conciliators Internat. Ctr. Settlement Investment Disputes, 1974-85; mem. Adminstrv. Conf. U.S., 1976-80, Pub. Sec. Adv. Bd., 1976-79; mem. human resouces com. Nat. Ctr. for Productivity and Quality of Working Life, 1976-80; mem. Presdl. Commn. on Exec. Exch., 1981-85. Trustee Mary Baldwin Coll., 1977-85, Am. U., 1980—, George Mason U. Found., Inc., 1990—, George Mason U. Edn. Found., 1993—; nat. bd. dirs. Med. Coll. Pa., bd. corporators, 1976-85; bd. dirs. Ctr. for Women in Medicine, 1980-86; bd. govs. St. Agnes Sch., 1981-87; mem. exec. com. Commn. on Bicentennial of U.S. Constn., chmn. internat. adv. com., 1985-92; vice chmn. James Madison Meml. Fellowship Found., 1989—; bd. dirs. Meridian Internat. Ctr., 1992—, Friends of Congl. Law Libr., 1992—, Friends of Dept. of Labor. Recipient Ohio Gov.'s award, 1980, fellow award, 1981, Outstanding Pub. Service award U.S. Info. Service, 1987; named Disting. Fellow John Sherman Myers Soc., 1986. Mem. ABA (adminstrv. law sect., chmn. labor law com. 1980-83, chmn. internat. and comparative law adminstrv. law sect. 1983-88, chmn. customs, tariff and trade com. 1988-90, employment law sect. 1983-88, chmn. internat. com. dispute resolution sect. 1995—), Fed. Bar Assn., Inter-Am. Bar Assn. (editor newsletter 1960-69, Silver medal 1967, co-chmn. labor law com. 1975-83), Bar Assn. D.C., World Peace Through Law Ctr., Am. Arbitration Assn. (bd. dirs. 1985—, mem. editl. bd. 1992), Supreme Ct. Hist. Soc., Am. U. Alumni Assn. (bd. dirs. 1964-65, sec. law sch. 1965-66, pres. 1966-69, chmn. bd. govs. law sch. alumni 1969-73), Mortar Bd., Kappa Beta Pi. Republican. Office: Baker & Hostetler 1050 Connecticut Ave NW Washington DC 20036-5303

MURPHY, BEVERLEY ELAINE PEARSON, scientist, administrator, physician, educator; b. Toronto, Ont., Can., Mar. 15, 1929; d. Ernest Wallace and Edith (Johnson) Pearson; m. David Raymond Murphy, June 15, 1958; children: Madeleine, Catherine. B.A., U. Toronto, 1952, M.D., 1956; M.Sc., McGill U., Can., 1960, Ph.D., 1964. Cert. Med. Biochemistry, Endocrinology. Rotating interne Toronto Gen. Hosp., 1956-57; rsch. fellow Royal Victoria Hosp., Montreal, Que., Can., 1957-59, resident in medicine, 1959-61; rsch. fellow Queen Mary Vets. Hosp., Montreal, 1961-64, dir. endocrinology lab., 1964-78, cons. in endocrinology, 1970-73; asst., assoc. obstetrician & gynecologist Montreal Gen. Hosp., 1972-79; dir. reproductive physiology unit Montreal Gen. Hosp. Rsch. Inst., 1972—; sr. physician, sr. obstetrician and gynecologist Montreal Gen. Hosp., 1979—; med. scientist Royal Victoria Hosp., Montreal, 1981—; lectr., asst., assoc. prof. medicine McGill U., Montreal, 1964-74, prof., 1975—; prof. obstetrics and gynecology, 1979—, assoc. mem. dept. physiology, 1981—, prof. psychiatry, 1985—; lectr. in U.S., Fed. Republic of Germany, Eng., France, Mex., India, Italy, Switzerland, New Zealand, Can.; organizer Satellite Symposium, Internat. Congress Endocrinology, McGill U., 1982, Symposium on Psychoendocrinology, McGill U., 1989; reviewer grant applications for Med. Rsch. Coun. Can., Fonds de la recherche en Santé du Qué, March of Dimes, Ont. Mental Health Found., Can. Heart Found., Can. Liver Found., NSF, B.C. Health Scis; career investigator Med. Rsch. Coun. Can., 1968-94. Mem. editorial bd. Jour. Clin. Endocrinology Metabolism, 1975-79, Jour. Steroid Biochemistry, 1976-94, Jour. Immunoassay, 1979—; contbr. articles, abstracts to profl. jours.; patentee in field. Fellow Royal Soc. Can.; mem. ACP, Am. Soc. Clin. Investigation, Endocrine Soc., Can. Assn. Med. Biochemists, Can. Soc. Clin. Investigation, Can. Soc. Endocrinology and Metabolism (sec.-treas. 1984-89), Can. Investigators in Reproduction, Can. Biochem. Soc., Montreal Physiol. Soc. (pres. 1972-73, 73-74), Que. Assn. Lab. Physicians, Soc. Obstetricians and Gynecologists Can., Syndicat Professionel des Médecins Endocrinologues du Québec, Assn. Women in Sci. Avocations: art, music, jogging, skiing. Office: Montreal Gen Hosp, 1650 Cedar Ave, Montreal, PQ Canada H3G 1A4

MURPHY, CARYLE MARIE, foreign correspondent; b. Hartford, Conn., Nov. 16, 1946; d. Thomas Joseph and Muriel Kathryn (McCarthy) M. BA cum laude, Trinity Coll., 1968; M in Internat. Pub. Policy, Johns Hopkins U., 1987. Tchr. English, history St. Cecilia Tng. Coll., Nyeri, Kenya, 1968-71; reporter Brockton (Mass.) Enterprise, 1972-73; freelance corr. Washington Post, Newsweek, Sunday Times of London, et al, Luanda, Angola, 1974-76; reporter Fairfax County Washington Post, 1976-77, fgn. corr. in South Africa, 1977-82, reporter immigration issues, 1982-85, bur. chief Alexandria, Va., 1985-89; fgn. corr. Mid. East Washington Post, Cairo, 1989-94. Vol. ARC, Washington, 1984, Whitman-Walker Found., Washington, 1988-89. Recipient Courage in Journalism award Internat. Women's Media Found., 1990, George Polk award L.I. U., 1991, Edward Weintal Journalism award Sch. Fgn. Svc., Georgetown U., 1991, Pulitzer Prize for internat. reporting, 1991; Edward R. Murrow fellow Coun. on Fgn. Rels., N.Y., 1994-95. Roman Catholic. Avocations: fgn. langs., hiking. Office: Washington Post Fgn Desk 1150 15th St NW Washington DC 20071-0002

MURPHY, CATHERINE, painter; b. Cambridge, Mass., 1946. BFA, Pratt Inst., 1967; student, Skowhegan Sch. Painting and Sculpture, 1966. One-woman shows First Street Gallery, N.Y.C., 1972, Piper Gallery, Mass., 1972, Fourcade, Droll, Inc., N.Y.C., 1975, Phillips Collection, Washington, 1976, Xavier Fourcade, Inc., N.Y.C., 1979, 85, J. Rosenthal Fine Arts, Ltd., Chgo., 1988, Lennon, Weinberg, Inc., N.Y.C., 1989, 92; exhibited in group shows at Whitney Mus. Am. Art, N.Y.C., 1972, 73, Indpls. Mus., 1974, Inst. Contemporary Art, Boston, 1976, Mus. Contemporary Art, Chgo., 1977, Am. Acad. and Inst. Arts and Letters, N.Y.C., 1979, 87, 89, 90, 92, Xavier Fourcade, Inc., N.Y.C., 1977, 80, 83, 87, 93, (traveling exhbn.) San Francisco Mus. Modern Art, 1985, Daniel Weinberg Gallery, L.A., 1989, (traveling exhbn.) Cin. Art Mus., 1989, Lennon Weinberg, Inc., N.Y.C., 1989, 90, 91, 93, 94, (traveling exhbn.) Miyaqi Mus. Art, Sendai, Japan, 1991-92, Forum Gallery, N.Y.C., 1993, Koplin Gallery, Santa Monica, Calif., 1993, Tibor de Nagy Gallery, N.Y.C., 1994; permanent collections Chase Manhattan Bank, N.Y.C., Hirshhorn Mus. & Sculpture Garden, Washington, Met. Mus. Art, N.Y.C., Newark Mus., N.J. Art Mus., Trenton, Phillips Collection, Washington, Va. Mus. Fine Arts, Richmond, Weatherspoon Art Gallery, Greensboro, N.C., Whitney, Mus. Am. Art, N.Y.C. Grantee NEA, 1979, 89, Ingram Merrill Found., 1986; Guggenheim fellow, 1982; recipient AAIAL award, 1994. Office: care Lennon Weinberg Inc 580 Broadway Ste 204 New York NY 10012-3223

MURPHY, CHARLES FRANKLIN, agriculturist; b. Des Moines, Dec. 13, 1933; s. Hickman Charles and Greta Marion (Hanmer) M.; m. Carol Parker, Nov. 18, 1961; 1 child, Charles Reid. BS, Iowa State U., 1956, PhD, 1961; MS, Purdue U., 1957. Asst. prof. Dept. Crop Sci. N.C. State U., Raleigh, 1960-67, assoc. prof., 1967-78, prof., 1978-83; germplasm coord. USDA S&E, Beltsville, Md., 1981; nat. program leader/grain crops USDA Agrl. Rsch. Svc., Beltsville, 1983—; exec. sec. Nat. Plant Genetic Resources Bd.,

Washington, 1983-89; trustee Internat. Bd. on Plant Genetic Resources, Rome, 1987-92; bd. dirs. Genetic Resources Communications Systems, Inc., Washington; planner Nat. Plant Germplasm System. Author: (with others) Seeds and Soverignty, 1988; contbr. articles to profl. jours. Precinct chmn. Dem. Party, Raleigh, 1970-80. Named Man of Yr. Progressive Farmer, 1967; recipient Outstanding Young Alumnus award Iowa State U., 1968, Citation N.C. Gov., 1968. Fellow AAAS, Am. Soc. Agronomy (bd. dirs. 1989-92), Crop Sci. Soc. Am. (bd. dirs. 1989-92); mem. Delta Upsilon, Alpha Zeta. Achievements include development and release of 12 varieties of wheat, oats and barley; pioneering work on polygenic systems controlling yield traits in oats. Home: 616 Cobblestone Ct Silver Spring MD 20905-5806 Office: USDA Agrl Rsch Svc-NPS Bldg 005 BARC-W Beltsville MD 20705

MURPHY, CHARLES HAYWOOD, JR., petroleum company executive; b. El Dorado, Ark., Mar. 6, 1920; s. Charles Haywood and Bertie (Wilson) M.; m. Johnie Walker, Oct. 14, 1939; children: Michael Walker, Martha, Charles Haywood, III, Robert Madison. Ed. pub. schs., Ark.; LLD (hon.), U. Ark., 1966. Ind. oil producer, 1939-50; chmn., also bd. dirs. Murphy Oil Corp., El Dorado, Ark., 1972—; chmn. exec. com. 1st Comml. Corp., Little Rock. Bd. govs. Oschner Med. Found.; bd. adminstrs. Tulane U.; mem. nat. adv. bd. Smithsonian Instn.; past mem. Ark. Bd. Higher Edn. Served as infantryman World War II. Recipient citation for outstanding individual service in natural resource mgmt. Nat. Wildlife Fedn. Mem. Am. Petroleum Inst. (past exec. com., hon. bd. dirs.), Nat. Petroleum Council (past chmn.), 25 Yr. Club Petroleum Industry (past pres.). Office: Murphy Oil Corp 200 E Peach St El Dorado AR 71730-5850*

MURPHY, CHARLES JOSEPH, investment banker; b. N.Y.C., Sept. 18, 1947; s. Charles Joseph and Mary V. (Vaughan) M.; m. Karen Lyn Canevari, Aug. 18, 1973; 4 children. BEE, Manhattan Coll., 1969; MBA, NYU, 1974, APC, 1975. Chartered fin. analyst; cert. advance profl. Avionics engr. Sikorsky Aircraft, Stratford, Conn., 1969-70; engr., rate analyst Am. Electric Power Co., N.Y.C., 1970-76; equity analyst First Boston Corp., N.Y.C., 1976-78, v.p. capital markets, 1982-84, mng. dir. utilities and telecommunications fin., 1984-87, head investment banking group, 1988-92, head investment banking dept., 1992-94; co-head worldwide investment banking, 1994-95; head global equities First Boston Corp., N.Y.C., 1995—; mem. CS First Boston operating com., 1993—, exec. bd., 1995—, co-chmn. investment banking operating com., 1994-95. Mem. N.Y. Soc. Security Analysts (sr.). Roman Catholic. Avocations: jogging; racquet sports; winter sports. Office: CS First Boston Corp Pk Ave Plz 55 E 52nd St New York NY 10055-0001

MURPHY, CHRISTOPHER JOSEPH, III, financial executive; b. Washington, Apr. 24, 1946; s. Christopher Joseph Murphy Jr. and Jean Olive (Connelly) Murphy Vos; m. Carmen Morris Carmichael, Feb. 1, 1969; children: Christopher IV, Sean, Kelly, Kevin, Conor, Dillon. BA, U. Notre Dame, 1968; JD, U. Va., 1971; MBA with distinction, Harvard U., 1973. Bar: Va. 1971, U.S. Dist. Ct. 1971. V.p. Rsch. Group, Charlottesville, Va., 1969-72, Citicorp Mgmt. Services, Corp., St. Louis, 1973-77; officer, pres. 1st Source Corp., South Bend, Ind., 1977—; bd. dirs. Weldun Internat., Bridgman, Mich., 1981-89, Meml. Health Systems, South Bend, 1981-90, chmn., 1990-92, Omega Health Group, Inc., South Bend, 1984-90, Comair Inc., Cin., 1989—, Discover Re Insurance Inc., 1991-95, Trust Corp. Mortgage Inc., 1991—, Quality Dining, 1994—; cons. U.S. Ho. of Reps. House Com. on Edn. and Labor, 1967; adminstrv. asst. Comptroller of Currency's Office U.S. Treasury, 1965-67; adv. council Notre Dame Coll. Arts and Letters, 1981—, chmn., 1985-89; bd. dirs. South Bend C. of C., 1984—; bd. dirs. Meml. Hosp., South Bend, 1980-86, South Bend Symphony, 1981-83, chmn. Med. Edn. Found., South Bend, 1982—; chmn. United Way Campaign, St. Joseph County, Ind., 1980. Mem. ABA, Young Pres.'s Orgn. (internat. bd. dirs. 1993-95, exec. com.), Ind. Bar Assn., Va. Bar Assn., St. Joseph County Bar Assn., Nat. Assn. Bus. Economists (chpt. pres. 1980), Robert Morris Assocs., Nat. Assn. Publically Traded Cos. (bd. dirs. 1983—, chmn. 1986-87, 1990—), Nat. Assn. Security Dealers (corp. adv. bd. 1988-92), Am. Bankers Assn. (chmn. payment systems policy bd. 1984-85). Roman Catholic. Office: 1st Source Corp 100 N Michigan St PO Box 1602 South Bend IN 46634

MURPHY, DANIEL HAYES, II, lawyer; b. Hartford, Conn., Jan. 8, 1941; s. Robert Henry and Jane Granville (Cook) M.; m. Deann Ellison, June 30, 1962; children—Edward Ellison, Jessica Jane. B.A., Yale U., 1962; LL.B., Columbia U., 1965. Bar: N.Y. 1965, U.S. Dist. Ct. (so. and ea. dists.) N.Y. 1967, U.S. Ct. Appeals (2d cir.) 1968, Conn. 1978, Calif. 1984, Fla. 1986. Assoc. White & Case, N.Y.C., 1965-70; asst. U.S. atty. So. Dist. N.Y., N.Y.C., 1970-74; pvt. practice law N.Y.C., 1974-76, 85—; assoc. Mendes & Mount, N.Y.C., 1977-81, jr. ptnr., 1981-85; spl. master Supreme Ct. N.Y. County, 1981—. Chmn. planning commn., Groton Long Point, Conn., 1977-84. Mem. ABA, N.Y. State Bar Assn., N.Y. County Lawyers Assn., Assn. Bar City N.Y., Yale Club N.Y.C., Ocean Reef Key Largo, Fla. Roman Catholic. Office: 123 William St Ste 2301 New York NY 10038-3804

MURPHY, DENNIS F., retail executive; b. Jersey City, Mar. 21, 1937; m. Catherine T. McCann; children: Linda C., Michael D., Matthew C. BS, St. Peter's Coll., 1958. Corp. sec., dir. ins. Merc. Stores Co. Inc., Fairfield, Ohio, 1965—. Office: Merc Stores Co Inc 9450 Seward Rd Fairfield OH 45014-5412

MURPHY, DENNIS MICHAEL, state legislator; b. Springfield, Mass., Sept. 12, 1962; s. Maurice Francis and Kathleen (Doyle) M.; m. Kathleen L. Leahy, May 24, 1987; 1 child, Kelsey Lauren. BSBA, Am. Internat. Coll., Springfield, 1985. Exec. asst. to mayor City of Springfield, 1991-92; assoc. dir. United Cerebral Palsy, Springfield, 1992-93; legis. asst. Mass. Ho. of Reps., Boston, 1985-91, mem., 1993—. Chmn. Springfield Dem. Com., 1988-92; mem. North End Adv. Com., 1992—. Mem. John Boyle O'Rielly Club. Roman Catholic. Avocations: golf, skiing, basketball, travel, charitys. Address: 221 Atwater Rd Springfield MA 01107 Office: Mass Ho of Reps Beacon Hill Boston MA 02133

MURPHY, DIANA E., federal judge; b. Faribault, Minn., Jan. 4, 1934; d. Albert W. and Adleyne (Heiker) Kuske; m. Joseph Murphy, July 24, 1958; children: Michael, John E. BA magna cum laude, U. Minn., 1954, JD magna cum laude, 1974; postgrad., Johannes Gutenberg U., Mainz, Germany, 1954-55, U. Minn., 1955-58. Bar: Minn. 1974, U.S. Supreme Ct. 1980. Assoc. Lindquist & Vennum, 1974-76; mcpl. judge Hennepin County, 1976-78, Minn. State dist. judge, 1978-80; judge U.S. Dist. Ct. for Minn., Mpls., 1980-94, chief judge, 1992-94; judge U.S. Ct. of Appeals (8th cir.), Minneapolis, 1994—. Bd. editors: Minn. Law Rev., Georgetown U. Jour. on Cts., Health Scis. and the Law, 1989-92. Bd. dirs. Spring Hill Conf. Ctr., 1978-84; bd. dirs. Mpls. United Way, 1985—, treas., 1990-94; bd. dirs. Bush Found., 1982—, chmn. bd. dirs., 1986-91; bd. dirs. Amicus, 1976-80, also organizer, 1st chmn. adv. coun.; mem. Mpls. Charter Commn., 1973-76, chmn., 1976-78; bd. dirs. Ops. De Novo, 1971-76, chmn. bd. dirs., 1975-75; mem. Minn. Constl. Study Commn., chmn. bill of rights com., 1971-73; regent St. Johns U., 1978-87, 88—, vice chmn. bd., 1985-87, chmn. bd., 1995—; mem. Minn. Bicentennial Commn., 1987-88; trustee Twin Cities Pub. TV, 1985-94, chmn. bd., 1990-92; trustee U. Minn. Found., 1990—, treas., 1992—; bd. dirs. Sci. Mus. Minn., 1988-94, vice chmn., trustee U. St. Thomas, 1991—; dir. Nat. Assn. Pub. Interest Law Fellowships for Equal Justice, 1992—. Fulbright scholar; recipient Amicus Founders' award, Outstanding Achievement award U. Minn., Outstanding Achievement award YWCA. Fellow Am. Bar Found.; mem. ABA (mem. ethics and profl. responsibility judges adv. com. 1981-88, standing com. on jud. selection, tenure and compensation 1991-94, mem. standing com. on fed. jud. improvements 1994—), Minn. Bar Assn. (bd. govs. 1977-81), Hennepin County Bar Assn. (gov. coun. 1976-81), Am. Law Inst., Am. Judicature Soc. (bd. dirs. 1982-93, pres. 1985-88, treas. 1988-89, chmn. bd. 1989-91), Nat. Assn. Women Judges, Minn. Women Lawyers, U. Minn. Alumni Assn. (bd. dirs. 1975-83, pres. 1981-82), Fed. Judges Assn. (bd. dirs. 1982—, vice chmn. 1988-89, pres. 1989-91), Hist. Soc. for 8th Cir. (bd. dirs. 1988-91), Fed. Jud. Ctr. (bd. dirs. 1990-94, 8th cir. coun. 1992-94, mem. U.S. jud. conf. com. on ct. adminstrn. and case mgmt. 1994—), Order of Coif, Phi Beta Kappa. Office: US Dist Ct 684 Courthouse 110 S 4th St Minneapolis MN 55401-2216

MURPHY, DONN BRIAN, theater educator; b. San Antonio, July 21, 1930; s. Arthur Morton and Claire Frances (McCarthy) M. BA, Benedictine Coll., 1954; MFA, Catholic U., 1956; PhD, U. Wis., 1964. Prof. Georgetown U., Washington, 1954—; exec. dir. Nat. Theatre Corp. Washington, 1985—; tech. theater liaison The White House, Washington, 1961-65. Author: A Director's Guide to Good Theatre, 1968, Stage for a Nation, 1985, Helen Hayes: A Bio-Bibliography, 1993; (plays) Creation of the World, 1970, Something of a Sorceress, 1971, Tyger/Tyger, 1977; (with others) Eleanor: First Lady of the World, 1984. Cpl. U.S. Army, 1950-52. Recipient Outstanding Svc. award Am. Theatre Assn., 1984, Forrest Roberts award No. Mich. U., 1977; Ford Found. fellow, 1963; inducted Coll. Fellows of Am. Theatre, 1994. Democrat. Roman Catholic. Avocations: travel, motorcycling. Home: 2401 N Kenmore St Arlington VA 22207-4938

MURPHY, DONNA, actress. Stage appearances include: (regional theatre) Miss Julie, Pal Joey; (off-Broadway) Song of Singapore, Hey Love: The Songs of Mary Rodgers, Privates on Parade, Showing Off, Birds of Paradise, Little Shop of Horrors, A...My Name is Alice; (Broadway) Hello Again, Passion (Leading Actress in Musical Tony award 1994), They're Playing Our Song, The Mystery of Edwin Drood; TV appearences include Law & Order, All My Children, Another World. Office: Silver Massetti & Assocs 145 W 45th St Ste 1204 New York NY 10036

MURPHY, EDDIE, comedian, actor; b. Bklyn., Apr. 3, 1961; s. Vernon and Lillian Murphy Lynch; m. Nicole Mitchell, March 18, 1993; children: Bria, Myles. Student pub. schs., Bklyn. Began performing Richard M. Dixon's White House, L.I., N.Y.; performed at various N.Y.C. clubs, including The Comic Strip; with Saturday Night Live, N.Y.C., 1980-84; host 35th Ann. Emmy Awards, 1983. Starring roles in motion pictures include 48 Hours, 1982, Trading Places, 1983, Best Defense, 1984, Beverly Hills Cop, 1984, The Golden Child, 1986, Beverly Hills Cop II, 1987, Eddie Murphy Raw, 1987, Coming to America, 1988, Harlem Nights,1989, Another 48 Hours, 1990, Boomerang, 1992, The Distinguished Gentleman, 1992, Beverly Hills Cop III, 1994; one-man HBO spl., 1983; albums include Eddie Murphy, 1982, Eddie Murphy Comedian, 1983, How Could it Be, 1984, So Happy, 1989, Distinguished Gentleman, 1992, Love's Alright, 1993. Office: Eddie Murphy Prodns Inc 5555 Melrose Ave Los Angeles CA 90038-3149 also: Eddie Murphy Prodns Inc Carnegie Hall Tower 152 W 57th St New York NY 10019*

MURPHY, EDMUND MICHAEL, demographer; b. Steubenville, Ohio, Apr. 7, 1936; s. Edmund Bernard and Catherine Margaret (Allen) M.; m. Mary Elizabeth Jeske, Dec. 15, 1962; 1 child, Maureen Cecilia. BA, Miami U., Oxford, Ohio, 1959; MA, U. Chgo., 1963, PhD, 1965. Asst. prof. U. Chgo., 1965-68, U. Pa., Phila., 1968-70; statistician Statistics Can., Ottawa, Ont., 1970-73; dir. rsch. Manpower and Immigration Dept. Can., Ottawa, 1973-77; dir. gen. Dept. Health and Welfare Can., Ottawa, 1977-78, asst. dep. min. policy and planning, 1978-82, asst. dep. min. social svcs. programs, 1982-86, asst. dep. min., sec. rev. of demography and its implications for social and econ. policy, 1986-92; sr. demographer Statistics Canada, Ottawa, 1992-94; pres., CEO Global Demographics Inc., Ottawa, 1994—. Contbr. numerous articles to profl. jours. With Carleton Condominium Corp. # 43, Ottawa, 1983-93, pres., 1994—. With U.S. Army, 1960-62. NSF fellow, 1962-65. Mem. Population Assn. Am., Population Assn. Can. Roman Catholic. Home: 1133 Ambleside Dr, Ottawa, ON Canada K2B 8E2 Office: Global Demographics, 350 Sparks St Ste 1103, Ottawa, ON Canada K1R 7S8

MURPHY, EDWARD FRANCIS, sales executive; b. Chgo., July 30, 1947; s. Edward F. and Marjorie (Mooney) M.; m. Kay A. Worcester, Apr. 17, 1970; 1 child, Dean D. BA in Mktg., No. Ill. U., 1976. Dist. mgr. Midas Internat. Corp., Chgo., 1977-85; sales mgr. Raybestos, McHenry, Ill., 1985-89, Wagner Brakes, St. Louis, 1989—. Author: Vietnam Medal of Honor Heroes, 1987, Heroes of World War II, 1990, Korea's Heroes, 1990, Dak To, 1993; hist. cons. (book) Above and Beyond, 1985. Sgt. U.S. Army, 1965-68. Recipient Dist. Svc. award Congl. Medal of Honor Soc., 1989. Mem. Medal of Honor Hist. Soc. (founder, pres. 1975—). Republican. Avocations: writing, flying. Home: 2659 E Kael St Mesa AZ 85213

MURPHY, EDWARD J., school system administrator. Dist. supt. Suffolk County (BOCES III), Dix Hills, N.Y. Recipient Nat. Superintendent of the Yr. awd., New York, Am. Assn. of School Administrators, 1992. Office: Suffolk County 507 Deer Park Rd Dix Hills NY 11746

MURPHY, EDWARD PATRICK, JR., gas utility company executive; b. Syracuse, N.Y., Apr. 28, 1943; s. Edward Patrick and Rosemary Margaret (McCloskey) M.; m. Barbara Lynne Stibitz; children: E. Patrick III, Kevin C., Meghan L. BA in Acctg./Law, Clarkson U., 1965; exec. program, Columbia U., 1984. Mgmt. trainee The Bklyn. Union Gas Co., 1965, various staff and operating positions, 1966-75, budget dir., 1976-81, auditor, 1982-88, asst. v.p., 1988-89, v.p., 1990—. Vice chmn. bd. Bklyn. chpt. ARC, 1986-91, chmn., 1991-94; mem. adult com. ARC of Greater N.Y., 1987—, chmn., 1994—. Mem. Am. Gas Assn. (mem. internal auditing com. 1982-88, vice chmn. 1985-86, chmn. 1986-87; mem. budgeting and fin. forecasting com. 1974-81, vice chmn. 1977-78, chmn. 1978-79; Outstanding Svc. award 1987). Avocations: golf, cooking, fishing. Office: Bklyn Union Gas Co One MetroTech Ctr Brooklyn NY 11201-3851

MURPHY, ELLIS, association management executive; b. Lincoln, Nebr.; s. Ellis F. and Virgie (Olson) M.; m. Judy Neel, 1975; children by previous marriage—Sharon, Michael, Edward, Randall; stepchildren—Mary, Janet, Susan. B.S. in Agr, Purdue U., 1947; M.B.A., Northwestern U., 1957; postgrad., Ill. Inst. Tech., 1969-81, U. Wash., 1950-51, Mexico City Coll., 1947, U. Chgo., 1964. Assoc. editor Pacific Builder & Engr., Seattle, 1948-51; tech. editor Portland Cement Assn., 1953-55; dir. public relations Chgo. chpt. AIA, 1955-56; account exec. Carrier & Jobson, Inc., Chgo., 1956-57; pres. Ellis Murphy, Inc., Chgo., 1957-73, Murphy, Tashjian & Assocs., Chgo., 1973-78; v.p. Lurie/Murphy Assocs., Inc., Chgo., 1979-83; pres. Murphy & Murphy Inc., Chgo., 1984—; cons. mktg. communication to various bus. firms, 1970—; instr. (part-time) mktg. Ill. Inst. Tech., Chgo., 1977-79; instr. (part-time) assn. mgmt. DePaul U., Chgo., 1985—; cons. to various trade assns., 1970—. Mem. Bd. Edn., Thornton Fractional Dist., Ill., 1961-67; trustee First Meth. Ch., Lansing, Ill., 1959-65; chmn. dirs. fund Purdue Club, Chgo. Maj. USMC, 1943-46, 50-52. Mem. Public Relations Soc. Am. (citation 1963), Am. Mktg. Assn., Am. Soc. Assn. Execs., Chgo. Soc. Assn. Execs. (Disting. Service award 1986), Knights Templar, St. Bernard Commndery (past comdr.), Sigma Delta Chi. Club: Plaza. Home: 3100 N Sheridan Rd Chicago IL 60657-4954 Office: Murphy & Murphy Inc 43 E Ohio St Ste 1022 Chicago IL 60611-2744

MURPHY, EUGENE F., aerospace, communications and electronics executive; b. Flushing, N.Y., Feb. 24, 1936; s. Eugene P. and Delia M.; m. Mary Margaret Cullen, Feb. 20, 1960. BA, Queens Coll., 1956; JD, Fordham U., 1959; LLM, Georgetown U., 1964. Bar: N.Y. With RCA Global Communications Inc., N.Y.C., 1964-81, v.p. and gen. counsel, 1969-71, exec. v.p. ops., 1972-75, pres., chief operating officer, 1975-76, pres., chief exec. officer, 1976-81; chmn., chief exec. officer RCA Communications Inc., N.Y.C., 1981-86; sr. v.p. communications and info. svcs. GE, N.Y.C., 1986-91; pres., chief exec. officer GE Aerospace, King of Prussia, Pa., 1992-93; pres., CEO GE Aircraft Engines, Cin., 1993—; bd. dirs. Lockheed Martin Corp.; mem. Pres. Reagan's Nat. Secur. Telecommunications Adv. Com.; bd. govs. Aerospace Industries Assn. Bd. Served with USMCR, 1959-60. Mem. Armed Forces Comm. and Electronics Assn. (past nat. chmn.). Clubs: Marco Polo, Plandome Country, Plandome Field and Marine. Office: GE Aircraft Engines Maildrop 101 1 Neumann Way Cincinnati OH 45215-1915

MURPHY, EUGENE FRANCIS, consultant, retired government official; b. Syracuse, N.Y., May 31, 1913; s. Eugene Francis and Mary Grace (Thompson) M.; m. Helene M. Murphy, Dec. 31, 1955; children: Anne F., Thomas E. M.E., Cornell U. 1935; M.M.E., Syracuse U., 1937; Ph.D., Ill. Inst. Tech., 1948. Teaching asst. Syracuse U., 1935-36; engr. Ingersoll-Rand Co., Painted Post, N.Y., 1936-39; instr. Ill. Inst. Tech., 1939-41; from instr. to asst. prof. U. Calif., Berkeley, 1941-48; staff engr. Nat. Acad. Scis., Washington, 1945-48; adv. fellow Mellon Inst., Pitts., 1947-48; with VA, N.Y.C., 1948-83; chief research and devel. div. Prosthetic and Sensory Aids Service, 1948-73; dir. Research Center for Prosthetics, 1973-78; dir. Office of Tech.

Transfer, 1978-83, sci. advisor, 1983-85; mem. coun. Alliance for Engring. in Medicine and Biology, 1970-90; mem. adv. com. U. Wis., 1978-82, Case Western Res. U., 1981, Am. Found. for Blind, 1981-83; cons. disability and rehab. rsch., 1983—. Contbg. author: Human Limbs and their Substitutes, 1954, Orthopaedic Appliances Atlas, vol. 1, 1952, vol. 2, 1960, Human Factors in Technology, 1963, Biomedical Engineering Systems, 1970, Critical Revs. in Bioengring, 1971, CRC Handbook of Materials, Vol. III, 1975, Atlas of Orthotics, 1975, 2d edit., 1985, Therapeutic Medical Devices: Application and Design, 1982, McGraw-Hill Ency. Sci. and Tech. Yearbook, 1985; contbr. to Wiley Encyclopedia of Medical Devices and Instrumentation, 1988; editor Bull. Prosthetics Research, 1978-82; contbr. articles to profl. jours. Recipient Silver medal Paris, France, 1961; Meritorious Service award VA, 1971; Disting. Career award VA, 1983; Biomedical Engring. Leadership award Alliance for Engring. in Medicine and Biology, 1983; citation Outstanding Handicapped Fed. Employee, 1971; Profl. Achievement award Ill. Inst. Technology, 1983; Fulbright lectr. Soc. and Home for Cripples, Denmark, 1957-58. Fellow AAAS, ASME, Rehab. Engring. Soc. N.Am. (now RESNA), Internat. Soc. for Prosthetics and Orthotics, N.Y. Acad. Medicine; mem. NAE, ASTM, Soc. for Urology and Engring. (hon.), N.Y. Acad. Sci., Acoustical Soc. Am., Optical Soc. Am., Sigma Xi, Tau Beta Pi, Phi Kappa Phi. Home: 511 E 20th St MB New York NY 10010-7522

MURPHY, EVELYN FRANCES, healthcare administrator, former lieutenant governor; b. Panama Canal Zone, Panama Canal Zone, May 14, 1940; d. Clement Bernard and Dorothy Eloise (Jackson) M. AB, Duke U., 1961, PhD, 1965; MA, Columbia U., 1963; hon. degrees, Regis Coll., 1978, Curry Coll., Northeastern U., Simmons Coll., Wheaton Coll., Anna Maria Coll., Bridgewater State Coll., Salem State Coll., Emmanuel Coll.; hon. degree, Suffolk U. Pres. Ancon Assocs., Boston, 1971-72; ptnr. Llewelyn-Davies, Weeks, Forrester-Walker & Bor, London, 1973-74; sec. environ. affairs Commonwealth of Mass., Boston, 1975-79, sec. econ. affairs, 1983-86, lt. gov., 1987-91; mng. dir. Brown Rudnick Freed and Gesmer, Boston, 1991-93; exec. v.p. Blue Cross/Blue Shield of Mass., Boston, 1994—; also bd. dirs. Blue Cross Blue Shield Mass., Boston; vis. pub. policy scholar Radcliffe Coll., 1991; vice chmn./chmn. Nat. Adv. Com. on Oceans and Atmosphere (Presdl. apptd.), 1979-80; bd. dirs. Shawmut Bank of Conn., Shawmut Bank of Mass. Recipient Disting. Svc. award Nat. Sierra Club, 1978, Nat. Govs. Assn. 1978, Outstanding Citizen award Mass. Audubon Soc., 1978; Harvard U. fellow, 1979-80. Mem. Women Execs. in State Govt. (chair 1987). Democrat. Avocation: jogging. Office: Blue Cross Blue Shield Mass 100 Summer St Boston MA 02110-2190

MURPHY, EWELL EDWARD, JR., lawyer; b. Washington, Feb. 21, 1928; s. Ewell Edward and Lou (Phillips) M.; m. Patricia Bredell Purnell, June 26, 1954 (dec. 1964); children: Michaela, Megan Patricia, Harlan Ewell. B.A., U. Tex., 1946, LL.B., 1948; D.Phil., Oxford U., Eng., 1951. Bar: Tex. 1948. Assoc. Baker & Botts, Houston, 1954-63, ptnr., 1964-93, head internat. dept., 1972-89; pres. Houston World Trade Assn., 1972-74; trustee Southwestern Legal Found., 1978—; chmn. Houston Com. on Fgn. Rels., 1984-85, Inst. Transnat. Arbitration, 1985-89, Internat. and Comparative Law Ctr., 1986-87; mem. J. William Fulbright Fgn. Scholarship Bd., 1991—, vice chmn. 1992-93, chmn., 1993—; vis. prof. U. Tex. Law Sch., 1993—. Contbr. articles to profl. jours. Served to lt. USAF, 1952-54. Recipient Carl H. Fulda award U. Tex. Internat. Law Jour., 1980; Rhodes scholar, 1948-51. Mem. ABA (chmn. sect. internat. law 1970-71), Houston Bar Assn. (chmn. internat. law com. 1963-64, 70-71), Houston C. of C. (chmn. internat. bus. com. 1964, 65), Philos. Soc. Tex., Internat. Law Inst. (bd. dirs. 1994—). Home: 17 W Oak Dr Houston TX 77056-2117 Office: Baker & Botts 3000 One Shell Plz Houston TX 77002-4995

MURPHY, FRANCES LOUISE, II, newspaper publisher; b. Balt.; d. Carl James and L. Vashti (Turley) M.; m. James E. Wood (div.); children: Frances Murphy Wood Draper, James E. Jr., Susan Wood Barnes. BA, U. Wis., 1944; BS, Coppin State Coll., Balt., 1958; MEd, Johns Hopkins U., 1963. City editor Balt. Afro-Am., 1956-57; dir. News Bur., Morgan State Coll., Balt., 1964-71; chmn. bd. dirs. Afro-Am. Newspapers, Balt., 1971-74; assoc. prof. journalism SUNY, Buffalo, 1975-85, Howard U., Washington, 1985-91; editor Washington Afro-Am., 1951-56, pub., 1987—; bd. dirs. Afro-Am. Newspapers, Balt., 1985-87; mem. adv. bd. Partnership Inst., Washington, 1985-91; bd. trustees U. D.C.; treas. African Am. Civil War Meml. Freedom Found., African Am. Leadership Summit. Trustee State Colls. Md., 1971-76, U. D.C., 1993—; bd. dirs. Delta Rsch. and Ednl. Found., 1993-95; nat. bd. dirs. NACCP, 1971-76. Named One of 100 Most Influential Black Ams., Ebony mag., 1973, 74, Disting. Marylander, Gov. State of Md., 1975; recipient Ida B. Wells award Congl. Black Caucus, 1989, Public Svc. award African Methodist Episcopal Ch., 1991, Invaluable Svc. award Martin L. King Jr. Found., 1992, Black Women of Courage award Nat. Fedn. Black Women Bus. Owners, 1993, Black Awareness Ach. award Holy Redeemer Catholic Ch., 1993, Bus. of the Yr. award Bus. and Profl. Women's League, 1993, Oustanding Svc. award Capital Press Club, 1993, Black Conscious Com. trophy Unity Nation, 1993, Dedicated Cmty. Svc. award Ward I Cmty. and D.C. Pub. Schs., 1994, Women of Strength award Nat. Black Media Coalition, 1994, Outstanding Woman of Yr. award Alpha Gamma chpt. Iota Phi Lambda, 1994, Art Carter Excellence award Capital Press Club, 1994, Excellence in Comm. award Washington Inter-Alumni Coun. United Negro Coll. Fund, 1994. Mem. Nat. Newspaper Pubs. Assn. (editl. com. 1987—, Merit award 1987, 89-93), Soc. Profl. Journalists (Disting. Svc. award 1994), Links, Capital Press Club (exec. bd. 1987—, Outstanding Svc. award 1993), Delta Sigma Theta (Frances L. Murphy II Comm. award Fed. City Alumnae chpt. 1993, Fortitude Image award Prince George's County chpt. 1994), Kiwanis Club (first woman hon. 1995). Democrat. Episcopalian. Avocation: bridge. Home: 5709 1st St NW Washington DC 20011 Office: Washington Afro-Am 1612 14th St NW Washington DC 20009-4307

MURPHY, FRANCIS, English language educator; b. Springfield, Mass., Mar. 13, 1932; s. Frank Edward and Sarah (O'Connor) M. B.A., Am. Internat. Coll., 1953; M.A., U. Conn., 1955; Ph.D., Harvard U., 1960; LittD (hon.), Am. Internat. Coll., 1986. Mem. faculty English lang. and lit. Smith Coll., 1959—, assoc. prof., 1966-69, prof., 1970—; vis. curator Springfield Mus. Fine Arts, 1975-76, Hudson River Mus., 1983-84. Editor: The Diary of Edward Taylor, 1964, Major Am. Poets, 1967, Form and Structure in Poetry, 1964, Edwin Arlington Robinson, 1970, Walt Whitman, 1969, The Uncollected Essays of Yvor Winters, 1973, The Complete Poems of Walt Whitman, 1975, Of Plymouth Plantation (William Bradford), 1981; author: Willard Leroy Metcalf, 1976, (with Dean Flower) A Catalogue of American Paintings, Water Colors and Drawings (to 1923) in the G.W.V. Smith Museum, 1976, The Landscape Within: J. Francis Murphy, 1982, The Book of Nature: American Painters and the Natural Sublime, 1983; co-editor: Norton Anthology of American Literature, 1979—, Mass. Rev., 1966-67.

MURPHY, FRANCIS SEWARD, journalist; b. Portland, Oreg., Sept. 9, 1914; s. Francis H. and Blanche (Livesay) M.; BA, Reed Coll., 1936; m. Clare Eastham Cooke, Sept. 20, 1974. With The Oregonian, Portland, 1936-79, TV editor, Behind the Mike columnist, 1952-79. Recipient award Mayan ruins, Yucatan, Mex., 1950—, mem. Am. Quintana Roo Expdn., 1965, 66, 68. With AUS, 1942-46. Author: Dragon Mask Temples in Central Yucatan, 1988. Mem. Royal Asiatic Soc., City Club (bd. govs. 1950, 64-66), Explorers Club, Am. Club of Hong Kong, Oreg. Hist. Soc. Democrat. Congregationalist. Home: 4213 NE 32nd Ave Portland OR 97211

MURPHY, GEORGE, special effects expert. Computer graphics artist/ supervisor Industrial Light & Magic, San Rafael, CA. films include: Hook, 1991, Death Becomes Her, 1992, Jurassic Park, 1993, Forrest Gump, 1994 (Acad. award Best Visual Effects). Office: care ILM PO Box 2459 3160 Kerner Blvd San Rafael CA 94912*

MURPHY, GEORGE AUSTIN, justice; b. Bklyn., Mar. 16, 1923; s. Frank V. and Catherine L. (Milroy) M.; m. Teresa Marie Short, July 5, 1952; children: Michael, Timothy, Terence, Mary, James, Maureen, Christopher, Marjorie, Paul. LLB, St. John's U., N.Y.C., 1949; BS, Fordham U., 1951. Bar: N.Y. 1949, U.S. Dist. Ct. (so. and ea. dists.) N.Y. 1951, U.S. Supreme Ct. 1956. Sole practice, Freeport, N.Y., 1949-52, Kaelred N.Y., 1956-69; mem. Kelly, McDonald, Deeley & Murphy, Freeport, 1953-55, Sullivan, Rowley & Murphy, 1970-78; justice N.Y. State Supreme Ct. 10th Jud. Dist., Mineola, 1979—. Councilman, Town of Hempstead (N.Y.), 1963-71; mem. N.Y. State Senate, 1971-72, N.Y. State Assembly, 1973-78. Served to lt.

U.S. Army, 1943-46, ETO, CBI; maj. Res. ret. Mem. Nassau County Bar Assn., Nassau Lawyers Assn., Catholic Lawyers Assn., Am. Legion. Roman Catholic. Lodges: K.C., Elks. Office: Supreme Court Supreme Court Building Mineola NY 11501

MURPHY, GEORGE EARL, psychiatrist, educator; b. Portland, Oreg., Oct. 17, 1922; s. George Earl and Mary Ella (Wilcox) M.; m. Amanda Daniel, Mar. 24, 1976; children: Paul Douglas, Bruce Kevin. Student, U. Wash., 1940-42, U. Portland, 1946-47; BS, Oreg. State U., 1949; MD, Washington U., St. Louis, 1952. Diplomate Am. Bd. Psychiatry and Neurology. Intern Alameda County Hosp., Oakland, Calif., 1952-53, asst. resident in medicine, 1953-54; fellow in psychosomatic medicine Washington U., St. Louis, 1954-55; asst. resident in psychiatry Mass. Gen. Hosp., Boston, 1955-56, Washington U., St. Louis, 1956-57; instr. sch. of medicine Washington U., 1957-59, asst. prof. sch. of medicine, 1959-66, assoc. prof. sch. of medicine, 1966-69, prof. sch. of medicine, 1969-90, emeritus prof. psychiatry, 1990—; dir. psychiatry clinic Washington U., 1976-90, psychiat. student health, 1978-83, coursemaster human sexuality, 1978-90. Author: Suicide in Alcoholism, 1992; contbr. articles to profl. jours. Mem. University City (Mo.) Human Relations Commn., 1965-70, chmn., 1968-69; bd. dirs. Suicide Prevention, Inc., St. Louis, 1967-73. Served to 1st class petty officer USNR, 1942-45. Recipient Rsch. award for Advances in Suicide Prevention Am. Suicide Found., 1994; Louis I Dublin award Am. Assn. Suicidology, 1995. Fellow Am. Psychiat. Assn. (life); mem. Internat. Assn. for Suicide Prevention, Am. Psychopathological Assn., Royal Coll. Psychiatrists, Sigma Xi. Avocation: archaelogy of the bronze age. Office: Washington U Sch Medicine Dept Psychiatry 4940 Childrens Pl Saint Louis MO 63110-1002

MURPHY, GEORGE WILLIAM, insurance executive; b. Yonkers, N.Y., Sept. 27, 1941; s. George William and Virginia Rose (Byrne) M.; m. Catherine Anne Scully, Sept. 26, 1964; children: Peggy Anne, Timothy Patrick. BBA in Acctg., St. John's U., Jamaica, N.Y., 1964. CPA, N.Y. Sr. acct. Price Waterhouse, N.Y.C., 1965-69; treas. SwissRe Corp., N.Y.C., 1969; sr. v.p., treas. SwissRe Advisers, Inc., N.Y.C., 1969-89; treas. NARe Life Mgmt. Co., Inc., 1971-90, SwissRe Life Ins. Co., 1979-90, SR Geothermal, Inc., N.Y.C., 1981-90, Swiss-Am Reassurance Co., SwissRe Mgmt. Co., Swiss Reinsurance Co., Inc., N.Am. Reassurance Co., N.Am. Reinsurance Corp., 1981, Surety Support Svcs., Inc., Downers Grove, Ill., 1984; v.p. N.Am. Splty Ins. Co., Manchester, N.H., 1985; treas. SwissRe Svcs., Inc., Elmsford, N.Y., 1987, Western Atlantic Reinsurance Corp., Western Atlantic Mgmt. Corp., N.Y.C., 1988; exec. v.p., treas., COO SwissRe Holding(N.A.) Inc., N.Y.C., 1989-94; pres. SwissRe Leasing Inc., 1990, GT Holding Corp., 1990; treas. Alpine Life Ins. Co., Westport, Conn., 1991. Mem. AICPA, N.Y. State Soc. CPAs, Fin. Execs. Inst., Am.-Swiss Assn. (bd. dirs. 1991—). Roman Catholic. Avocation: jogging. Office: SwissRe Holding (NA) Inc 237 Park Ave New York NY 10017-3142

MURPHY, GERALD, government official; b. Washington, Aug. 25, 1938; s. Jeremiah T. and Jean (Curley) M.; m. Kathryn Beckman, Sept. 24, 1988; children by previous marriage: William Michael, Janet Marie, Kathleen Anne. B.C.S. with honors, Benjamin Franklin U., Washington, 1960, M.C.S., 1963. C.P.A., D.C. Dep. div. dir. Dept. Treasury, Washington, 1970-71, div. dir., 1971-74, asst. commr., 1974-75, dep. commr., 1975-79, dep. fiscal asst. sec., 1979-86; fiscal asst. sec. Dept. Treasury, 1986—; lectr. in acctg. Southeastern U., Washington, 1965-70, Dept. Agr. Grad. Sch., Washington, 1970-76; mem. Govt. Acctg. Standards Adv. Council, 1984-89; mem. Fed. Acctg. Standards Adv. Bd., 1991—. Served with U.S. Army, 1956. Recipient Meritorious Svc. award Dept. Treasury, 1972, Treasury Honor award, 1983, Pres.'s Rank award, 1992, Disting. Alumni award Benjamin Franklin U., Washington, 1976. Mem. Am. Inst. C.P.A.s, Assn. Govt. Accts. (nat. pres. 1977-78, Robert W. King award 1983), Sr. Execs. Assn., Fed. Exec. Inst. Alumni Assn. Roman Catholic. Office: Dept Treasury 15th & Pennsylvania Ave NW Washington DC 20220

MURPHY, GERALD D., food and agriculture chemicals manufacturing company executive; b. Ames, Iowa, 1928; BA Harvard U., 1952, MBA, 1954. Chmn., CEO Early Calif. Industries Inc.; chmn. Am. Rice, Inc. (bd. dirs.), Pinkertons Internat., Inc. Office: Erly Industries Inc 10990 Wilshire Blvd Los Angeles CA 90024-3913

MURPHY, GERALD PATRICK, urologist, educator; b. Harve, Mont., July 16, 1934; s. Francis J. and Margaret H. (Dolan) M.; m. Mary Bridget Cunningham, June 20, 1959; children: Anne Marie, Margaret, George, Maureen, Bridget, Gerald. B.Sc. summa cum laude, Seattle U., 1955; M.D., U. Wash., 1959; D.Sc., St. Thomas Inst., 1971, St. John's U., Jamaica, N.Y., 1979; LL.D., Niagara U., 1973; Litt.D., St. Bonaventure U., 1977; LLD (hon.), Daemon Coll., 1984, St. Thomas Inst., 1985. Diplomate Am. Bd. Urology. Buswell research fellow dept. urology U. Rochester, N.Y., 1959; intern in surgery Johns Hopkins Hosp., Balt., 1959-60; jr. asst. resident in urology Brady Urol. Inst., 1960-61, fellow in urology, 1964-65, sr. asst. resident in urology, 1964-65, chief resident, 1966-67, asst. prof. urology, 1968; asst. resident in surgery and urology Balt. City Hosp., 1961-62; research assoc., chief dept. surg. physiology Walter Reed Army Inst. Research, Washington, 1962-64; assoc. dir. clin. affairs Roswell Park Meml. Inst., Buffalo, 1968-70, chief dept urology, 1968-71, inst. dir., 1970-85, chief dept. exptl. surgery, 1968-85; assoc. prof. urology SUNY-Buffalo, 1968-70, prof., 1971-88, research prof. exptl. pathology Grad. Sch., 1972-88, 1st William J Staubitz vis. prof. urology, 1982; group v.p. med. afairs Am. Cancer Soc., Atlanta, 1988—; prof. biology Niagara U., 1968-88; mem. adv. council N.Y. State Coll. Vet. Medicine, 1975-81, from 1982; exec. dir. Health Research Council of N.Y. State, 1975-87; sec.-gen. Internat. Union against Cancer from 1974; mem. bd. sci. affairs Delta Regional Primate Research Ctr. (Tulane U.), 1979-81; also mem. various other profl. adv. bds.; cons. in field; trustee Damon Runyon-Walter Winchell Cancer Fund, 1979-88, v.p., bd. dirs., 1983; dir. nat. prostatic cancer project Nat. Cancer Inst., 1972-87; vis. prof. surgery U. Stellenbosch, Bellville, Cape Province, South Africa, 1967-68; dir.-at- large Am. Cancer Soc., 1972-88, pres., 1983, mem. exec. com. N.Y. State div, 1975-77, from 1978, pres. N.Y. State div, 1974-75, bd. dirs. N.Y. State div, 1978-88; mem. adv. council Gen. Motors Cancer Research Found., 1982—; mem. staff Ga. Bapt. Hosp., Atlanta; prof. urology Emory U., Atlanta; moderator Tumor Progression and Heterogeneity, 39th Ann. Gordon Conf. on Cancer, New London, N.H., 1985; mem. CALSPAN/UB Research Ctr., Buffalo, 1986; John Kline Meml. lectr. U. Soc. Calif. Med. Ctr., 1991. Mem. editorial bd. Yearbook of Cancer, 1968—, Jour. Medicine, Clin. and Exptl., 1971— Urol. Survey, 1972-89, Internat. Jour. Cancer, 1975-86, Cancer Bull. of M.D. Anderson Hosp., 1977-89, Current Surgery, 1978-84, Onkologie, 1978—, Oncology Times, 1980-90, Anticancer Research, 1980—, Neoplasia, 1983—, Current Opinion in Urology, 1991, Jour. Psychosocial Oncology, 1991—; editor in chief Jour. Surg. Oncology, 1979—, Seminars in Surgical Oncology, 1977—, The Prostate, 1979—, Ca-A Cancer Jour. for Clinicians, 1990—; mem. editorial adv. bd. Cancer, 1971—, Jour. Exptl. and Clin. Cancer Research, 1982—; cons. editor Urology, 1972—; editor Jour. Med. Primatology, 1973—, Oncology, 1975—; assoc. editor N.Y. State Jour. Medicine, 1973-85, Cancer jour., 1990—; corr. editor: Afican Jour. Medicine and Med. Sci., 1976; mem. internat. editorial rev. bd. King Faisal Specialist Hosp. Med. Jour., 1981-85; mem. internat. editorial adv. bd. Arab Jour. Medicine, 1982-85; mem. sci. rev. com. Florence Jour. Surgery, 1983—. V.p., bd. dirs. James Ewing Found., 1981-85. Served with M.C. U.S. Army, 1962-64. Recipient Schwentker award Johns Hopkins Hosp., 1962; recipient Heath Meml. award U. Tex. Cancer Ctr., M.D. Anderson Hosp. and Tumor Inst., 1978, cert. of appreciation for notable service in helping to save lives from cancer N.Y. State div. Am. Cancer Soc., 1982, Pro Pontifice et Ecclesia papal medal, 1982, silver medal Scientia Vincere Tenebras European Orgn. for Research and Treatment of Cancer, Brussels, 1982, Pub. Service award Alumni Assn. SUNY, 1984, Buffalonian of Yr. award, 1985, Disting. Alumnus award U. Wash. Sch. Med., 1985, Bronze Medal Nat. Hungarian Cancer Congress Com., 14th Internat. Cancer Congress, 1986, award in recognition contbns. to UB community for instn. new biotech. program CALSPAN/UB Research Ctr., 1986, Outstanding Alumnus award Seattle U., 1991, Isaac R. Lindley award Peruvian Cancer Soc., 1991. Mem. ACS (sr. mem. Commn. on Cancer 1978—), Am. Urol. Assn. (registry genito-urinary pathology 1975-85), Am. Cancer Soc. N.Y. State div. (hon. life), Assn. Am. Cancer Insts. (pres. 1979-80, chmn. bd. dirs. 1980-81), N.Y. State Cancer Program Assn. (pres. 1982-83), Soc. Surg. Oncology (pres. 1982-83, chmn. exec. council 1983-84, Lucy Wortham James Basic Rsch. award 1991), Johns Hopkins Med. and Surg. Assn., Am. Soc. Nephrology, Internat. Soc. Nephrology,

Soc. Univ. Urologists, Buffalo Urol. Soc. (ann. award for outstanding contbns. to urology 1983), Soc. Univ. Surgeons, Am. Fedn. Clin. Research, N.Y. Acad. Scis., Buffalo Acad. Medicine, Am. Assn. Cancer Research, AMA, Assn. Genito-Urinary Surgeons, N.Y. State Soc. Surgeons, N.E. Soc. Clin. Oncology, Am. Surg. Assn., Am. Soc. Clin. Oncology, Am. Radium Soc., Buffalo Urol. Soc. (hon. life), Alpha Omega Alpha (hon.). Home: 1134 23rd Ave E Seattle WA 98112-3521 Office: Am Cancer Soc 1599 Clifton Rd NE Atlanta GA 30329-4243*

MURPHY, GORDON JOHN, engineering educator; b. Milw., Feb. 16, 1927; s. Gordon M. and Cecelia A. (Knerr) M.; m. Dorothy F. Brautigam, June 26, 1948; children—Lynne, Craig. B.S., Milw. Sch. Engring., 1949; M.S., U. Wis., 1952; Ph.D., U. Minn., 1956. Asst. prof. elec. engring. Milw. Sch. Engring., 1949-51; systems engr. A C Spark Plug div. Gen. Motors Corp., 1951-52, cons., 1959-62; instr. U. Minn., 1952-56, asst. prof. elec. engring., 1956-57; faculty Northwestern U., Evanston, Ill., 1957—; prof. Northwestern U., 1960—, head dept. elec. engring., 1960-69, dir. Lab. for Design of Electronic Systems, 1987—; cons. numerous corps., 1959—; founder, 1st chmn. Mpls. chpt. Inst. Radio Engrs. Profl. Group on Automatic Control, 1956-57, Chgo. chpt., 1959-61. Author: Basic Automatic Control Theory, 1957, 2d edit., 1966, Control Engineering, 1959; contbr. articles, papers to profl. jours.; patentee TV, electronic timers, periodontal instruments and motion control systems. Mem. indsl. adv. com. Milw. Sch. Engring., 1971—. Served with USNR, 1945-46. Recipient ECE Centennial medal U. Wis., Outstanding Alumnus award Milw. Sch. Engring. Alumni Assn.; named One of Chgo.'s Ten Outstanding Young Men Chgo. Jr. C. of C. Fellow IEEE (for edn. and rsch. in automatic control); mem. feedback control systems com. 1960-68, discrete systems com. 1962-68, adminstrv. com. profl. group on automatic control 1966-69, chmn. membership and nominating coms. 1966-67); mem. Am. Automatic Control Coun. (edn. com. 1967-69), Engr.'s Coun. for Profl. Devel. (guidance com. 1967-69), Nat. Electronic Conf. (bd. dirs. 1983-85), Am. Electronics Assn. (exec. com. M.W. coun. 1993-95), Sigma Xi, Eta Kappa Nu, Tau Beta Pi. Home: 638 Garden Ct Glenview IL 60025 Office: Northwestern U Elec Engring Dept Evanston IL 60208

MURPHY, GORDON LAURENCE, insurance company executive; b. Stamford, Conn., Feb. 2, 1935; s. Dennis Joseph Sr. and Carolyn Gertrude (Fessenden) M.; m. Rosemary Elizabeth Engel; 1 child, Erin Maureen. BA with honors, Williams Coll., 1963; postgrad., Northwestern U., 1964. Group sales Conn. Gen. Life Ins. Co., Bloomfield, 1964-68, group administr., 1968-71, asst. sec. group underwriting, 1971-75, sec. corp. controllers, 1975-78; 2d v.p. field ops. Aetna Ins. Co., Hartford, Conn., 1978-82; sr. v.p. agy. div. INA/Aetna-CIGNA P&C Group, Phila., 1982-84; pres. Life Ins. Co. of N.A., Phila., 1984-92; chmn. bd. dirs. INA Life Ins. Co. N.Y., 1992—. Served to sgt. U.S. Army, 1954-59. Avocations: hiking, reading, duplicate bridge, white-water rafting, hunting. Home: PO Box 668 Wolfeboro NH 03894-0668

MURPHY, GREGORY GERARD, lawyer; b. Helena, Mont., Feb. 3, 1954; s. Michael Anthony and Elizabeth (Cooney) M.; m. Katherine Joan Koch, Dec. 30, 1977; children: Megan, Brian, Allison. BA, U. Mont., 1976; JD, U. Notre Dame, 1979. Bar: Oreg. 1979, U.S. Dist. Ct. Oreg. 1979, U.S. Ct. Appeals (9th cir.) 1979, Mont. 1980, U.S. Dist. Ct. Mont. 1980. Clk. to judge U.S. Ct. Appeals (9th cir.), Portland, 1979-80; assoc. Moulton, Bellingham, Longo & Mather P.C., Billings, Mont., 1980-84; shareholder Moulton, Bellingham, Longo & Mather, P.C., Billings, Mont., 1984—; trustee Mont. dist. U.S. Bankruptcy Ct., 1982-85; examiner Mont. Bd. Bar Examiners, 1985—; trustee Nat. Conf. Bar Examiners, 1990—, mem. multistate bar exam com., 1986-94, com. chmn., 1994—, chmn. legal affairs com., 1991-94, mem. test R & D com., 1990-94. Assoc. editor Notre Dame Law Rev., 1978-79. Bd. dirs. Billings Symphony Soc., 1982-91, French hornist, 1981—. Thomas and Alberta White scholar U. Notre Dame, 1978-79. Mem. Mont. Bar Assn., Oreg. Bar Assn., Am. Law Inst., Yellowstone County Bar Assn., Rotary. Roman Catholic. Avocations: french horn, golf, camping. Home: 5533 Gene Sarazen Dr Billings MT 59106 Office: Moulton Bellingham et al PO Box 2559 Billings MT 59103-2559

MURPHY, HAROLD LOYD, federal judge; b. Haralson County, Ga., Mar. 31, 1927; s. James Loyd and Georgia Gladys (McBrayer) M.; m. Jacqueline Marie Ferri, Dec. 20, 1958; children: Mark Harold, Paul Bailey. Student, West Ga. Coll., 1944-45, U. Miss., 1945-46; LL.B., U. Ga., 1949. Bar: Ga. 1949. Pvt. practice Buchanan, Ga., from 1949; ptnr. Howe & Murphy, Buchanan and Tallapoosa, Ga., 1958-71; judge Superior Cts., Tallapoosa Circuit, 1971-77; U.S. dist. judge No. Dist. of Ga., Rome, 1977—; rep. Gen. Assembly of Ga., 1951-61; asst. solicitor gen. Tallapoosa Jud. Circuit, 1956; mem. Jud. Qualifications Commn., State of Ga., 1977. With USNR, 1945-46. Fellow Am. Bar Found.; mem. ABA, Ga. Bar Assn., Dist. Judges Assn. for 11th Cir. Bar Assn., Am. Judicature Soc., Tallapoosa Cir. Bar Assn., Old War Horse Lawyers Club, Am. Inns Ct. (past pres. Joseph Henry Lumpkin sect.), Fed. Judges Assn. (exec. com.). Methodist. Home: 321 Georgia Hwy # 120 Tallapoosa GA 30176 Office: US Dist Ct PO Box 53 Rome GA 30162-0053

MURPHY, HELEN, recording industry executive; b. Glasgow, Scotland, Oct. 2, 1962; came to U.S., 1990; d. Francis and Kathleen (Gallagher) M.; m. Michael Christopher Luksha, Apr. 1, 1989. BA in Econs. with honors, U. Guelph, Can., 1982; MBA, U. Western Ontario, Can., 1984. CFA. Asst. mgr. securities rsch. Confederation Life, Toronto, Can., 1984-86; sr. analyst entertainment & merchandising Prudential Bache Securities, Toronto, Can., 1986-89; v.p. rsch. Richardson Greenshields Can., Toronto, 1989-90; v.p. investor rels. Polygram Records Inc., N.Y.C., 1990-91, v.p., treas., 1991-92, sr. v.p. corp. fin., treas., 1992—; lectr. U. Guelph, 1982-90. Fellow Nat. Investor Rels. Inst., N.Y. Soc. Security Analysts, N.Y. Treas. Group. Office: Polygram Records Inc 825 8th Ave New York NY 10019-7416

MURPHY, JAMES E., public relations and marketing executive. Degree in Journalism, U. Ill. Sr. corp. comms. officer Owens-Corning Fiberglas, Beatrice, Merrill Lynch; exec. v.p. Burson-Marsteller, vice chmn., 1990; chmn., CEO Burson-Marsteller, N.Y., 1991-93; pres. Murphy & Co., 1993—; mng. dir. mktg. and comms. Andersen Cons., 1993—. Trustee Inst. Pub. Rels. Rsch.; bd. advisors Medill Sch. Journalism, Northwestern U.; adv. bd. Coll. Bus. and Commerce, U. Ill., devel. bd. Coll. Comm. Mem. Sky Club, Union League Club, Belle Haven Club, Woodway Country Club, Palmetto Golf Club, Preston Mountain Club. Office: c/o Andersen Cons. 1345 Ave of the Americas New York NY 10105

MURPHY, JAMES LEE, college dean, economics educator; b. Detroit, Feb. 14, 1939; s. Philip E. and Julie T. M.; m. Linda J. Masson, July 31, 1965; children—Janel K., John R. B.S., Spring Hill Coll., 1961; M.S., Purdue U., 1963, Ph.D., 1964. Asst. prof. econs. U. N.C., Chapel Hill, 1964-67, assoc. prof., 1967-72, prof., 1972—, chmn. dept., 1975-85, dir. summer session, 1987-88, dean summer sch., 1988—; vis. prof. Thammasat U., Bangkok, Thailand, 1968-69, Econs. Inst., U. Colo., Boulder, 1979, U. New South Wales, Sydney, Australia, 1980, overseas program U. Utah, 1974; cons. in field, 1968—. Author: Introductory Econometrics, 1973, Introductory Statistical Analysis, 1975, 2d edit., 1980, Spanish lang. edit., 1987, Statistical Analysis for Business and Economics, 1985, Statistical Analysis, 1993. NDEA fellow, 1961-64; NSF grantee, 1969-71. Mem. Am. Econ. Assn., So. Econ. Assn., Assn. Univ. Summer Sessions, N.Am. Assn. Summer Sessions. Republican. Roman Catholic. Office: U NC Dept Econs Gardner Hall Campus Box 3305 Chapel Hill NC 27599-3305

MURPHY, JAMES PAUL, lawyer; b. Jackson, Tenn., Apr. 29, 1944; s. Paul Joseph and Marjorie Mary (Smyth) M.; m. Marcia Mae Gaughan, Sept. 5, 1975. B.A., U. Notre Dame, 1966; J.D., U. Mich., 1969. Bar: Ohio 1969, D.C. 1984, Md. 1984, U.S. Dist. Ct. (no. dist) Ohio 1970, U.S. Ct. Appeals (6th cir.) 1972, U.S. Supreme Ct. 1976, U.S. Dist. Ct. Md., 1984, U.S. Dist. Ct. D.C., 1984, U.S. Dist. Ct. of Appeals (4th cir., D.C. cir.) 1984. Vol. VISTA, 1969-70; assoc. Squire, Sanders & Dempsey, Cleve., 1970-79, ptnr., 1979—. Mem. ABA (litigation, antitrust sects.), Cleve. Bar Assn. (fed. ct. com.), Md. Bar Assn., D.C. Bar Assn., Ohio State Bar Assn. (antitrust sect.). Clubs: Westwood Country (Rocky River, Ohio), City (Washington). Home: 4512 Wetherill Rd Bethesda MD 20816-1837 Office: Squire Sanders & Dempsey PO Box 407 1201 Pennsylvania Ave NW Washington DC 20004-2401

MURPHY, JANET GORMAN, college president; b. Holyoke, Mass., Jan. 10, 1937; d. Edwin Daniel and Catherine Gertrude (Hennessey) Gorman. B.A., U. Mass., 1958, postgrad. 1960-61, Ed.D., 1974, LL.D. (hon.) 1984; M.Ed., Boston U., 1961. Tchr. English and history John J. Lynch Jr. High Sch., Holyoke, 1958-60; tchr. English, Chestnut Jr. High Sch., Springfield, Mass., 1961-63; instr. English and journalism Our Lady of Elms Coll., Chicopee, 1963-64; mem. staff Mass. State Coll., Lyndonville, Vt., 1977-83; pres. Mo. Western State Coll., St. Joseph, 1983—. Mem. campaign staff Robert F Kennedy Presdl. Campaign, 1967. Recipient John Gunther Tchr. award NEA, 1961, award Women's Opportunity Com., Boston Fed. Exec. Bd., 1963, Phi Delta Kappa Educator of Yr. award NAACP, 1992; named one of 10 Outstanding Young Leaders of Greater Boston Area, Boston Jr. C. of C., 1973. Office: Mo Western State Coll Office of the President 4525 Downs Dr Saint Joseph MO 64507-2294*

MURPHY, JILL, public relations executive; b. Fla., May 2, 1962. BA in Journalism, Ohio Wesleyan U., 1985. With Rand Pub. Rels., 1985-89; v.p. Shandwick N.Am., N.Y.C., 1990—. Office: Shandwick NAm Inc 666 3rd Ave New York NY 10017

MURPHY, JOHN ARTHUR, tobacco, food and brewing company executive; b. N.Y.C., Dec. 15, 1929; s. John A. and Mary J. (Touhy) M.; m. Carole Ann Paul, June 28, 1952; children: John A., Kevin P., Timothy M., Kellyann, Robert B., Kathleen. B.S., Villanova U., 1951; J.D., Columbia U., 1954. Bar: N.Y. 1954. Since practiced in N.Y.C.; ptnr. firm Conboy Hewitt O'Brien & Boardman, 1954-62; asst. gen. counsel Philip Morris Co. Inc., N.Y.C., 1962-66, v.p., 1967-76, exec. v.p., 1976-78, group exec. v.p., 1978-84, pres., 1984-91, vice chmn., 1991-92, also bd. dirs.; asst. to pres. Philip Morris Internat., 1966-67, exec. v.p., 1967-71; pres., chief exec. officer Miller Brewing Co., Milw., 1971-78, chmn. bd., chief exec. officer, 1978-84; bd. dirs. Nat. Westminster Bank USA. Trustee North Shore Univ. Hosp., Marquette U., 1973-91; mem. exec. com. Keep Am. Beautiful, Inc.; mem. bd. consultors Sch. Law Villanova U.; mem. bus. com. Met. Mus. Art. Decorated Knight of Malta. Mem. ABA, N.Y. State Bar Assn. Office: Philip Morris Cos Inc 100 Park Ave New York NY 10017-5516

MURPHY, JOHN CARTER, economics educator; b. Ft. Worth, July 17, 1921; s. Joe Preston and Rachel Elsie (Carter) M.; m. Dorothy Elise Haldi, May 1, 1949; children: Douglas C., Barbara E. Student, Tex. Christian U., 1939-41; BA, North Tex. State U., 1943, BS, 1944; AM, U. Chgo., 1949, PhD, 1955; postgrad., U. Copenhagen, 1952-53. Instr. Ill. Inst. Tech., 1947-50; instr. to assoc. prof. Washington U., St. Louis, 1950-62; vis. prof. So. Meth. U., Dallas, 1961, prof., 1962-90, prof. emeritus, 1990—, dir. grad. studies in econs., 1963-68, chmn. dept., 1968-71, faculty summer program in Oxford, 1982-91, dir., 1991, pres. faculty senate, 1988-89, co-dir. Insts. on Internat. Fin., 1982-87; vis. prof. Bologna (Italy) Ctr., 1983. Advanced Internat. Studies, Johns Hopkins U., 1961-62; UN tech. assistance expert, Egypt, 1964; vis. prof., spl. field staff Rockefeller Found., Thammasat U., Bangkok, 1966-67; sr. staff economist Coun. Econ. Advisers, 1971-72, U.S. dels. econ. policy com. and working party III OECD, 1971-72, U.S. del. 8th meeting Joint U.S.-Japan Econ. Com., 1971; cons. Washington U. Internat. Econs. Rsch. Project, 1950-53, U.S. Treasury, 1972, Fed. Res. Bank Dallas, 1994—; referee NSF; witness and referee congl. coms.; lectr. USIA Program, Germany, 1961-62, 84, Philippines, South Viet Nam, Thailand, 1972, France, Belgium, 1984; lectr. Southwestern and Midwestern Grad. Sch. Banking; adj. scholar Am. Enterprise Inst. for Pub. Policy Rsch., 1976—. Author: The International Monetary System: Beyond the First Stage of Reform, 1979; (with R.R. Rubottom) Spain and the U.S.: Since World War II, 1984; editor: Money in the International Order, 1964; contbr. articles to profl. books and jours. Chmn. rsch. com. on internat. conflict and peace Washington U., 1959-61; lectr. mgmt. tng. programs Southwestern Bell Telephone Co., 1961-66, St. Louis Coun. on Econ. Edn., 1958-61; mem. regional selection com. H.S. Truman Fellowships, 1976-89; pres. Dallas Economists, 1981, Town and Gown of Dallas, 1980-81; mem. Dallas Com. on Fgn. Rels. Lt. USNR, 1943-46. Decorated Silver Star; Fulbright scholar to Denmark, 1952-53; Ford Found. Faculty Research fellow, 1957-58; U.S.-Spanish Joint Com. for Cultural Affairs fellow, 1981; Sr. Fulbright lectr. Italy, 1961-62. Mem. Am. Econ. Assn., So. Econ. Assn. (bd. editors Jour. 1969-71), Midwest Econ. Assn., Am. Fin. Assn., Soc. Internat. Devel., Peace Rsch. Soc., Southwestern Social Sci. Assn. (pres. econs. sect. 1971-72), AAUP (chpt. pres. 1964-65). Home: 10530 Somerton Dr Dallas TX 75229-5323 Office: So Meth U Dept Econs Dallas TX 75275

MURPHY, JOHN CONDRON, JR., lawyer; b. Mpls., May 26, 1945; s. John Condron and Elaine Anne (Wentink) M.; m. Marie Antoinette Calcara, Aug. 17, 1968; children: Justin Peter, Jonathan Patrick. AB cum laude, Georgetown U., Washington, 1967; JD cum laude, U. Pa., 1972. Bar: Calif. 1972, D.C. 1978. Assoc. O'Melveny & Myers, L.A., 1972-75; spl. counsel U.S Securities & Exch. Commn., Washington, 1975-77; assoc. Cleary, Gottlieb, Steen & Hamilton, Washington, 1977-81, ptnr., 1982-84, 87—; gen. counsel Fed. Deposit Ins. Corp., Washington, 1984-87. Mem. bd. editors Banking Expansion Reporter, 1988— editorial adv. bd. Bank Atty., 1988—; contbr. articles to profl. jours. Lt. j.g. USN, 1968-69. Mem. ABA (subcom. chmn. banking law com., chmn. acquisitions and dispositions subcom. 1992-95), Fed. Bar Assn. (chmn. banking law com. 1992-94), Columbia Country Club (Chevy Chase, Md.). Republican. Roman Catholic. Home: 6 Newlands St Chevy Chase MD 20815-4202 Office: Cleary Gottlieb et al 1752 N St NW Washington DC 20036-2806

MURPHY, JOHN CULLEN, illustrator; b. N.Y.C., May 3, 1919; s. Robert Francis and Jane (Finn) M.; m. Katherine Joan Byrne, July 14, 1951; children: John Cullen, Mary Cullene, Katherine Siobhan, Joan Byrne, Robert Finn, Brendan Woods, Cait Naughton, Mairead Walsh. Student, Phoenix Art Inst., Chgo. Art Inst., Art Students League, N.Y.C. Illustrator: numerous mags. including Colliers, 1946-51; illustrator: comic strip King Features Syndicate, 1950-69, Prince Valiant, King Features Syndicate, 1970—; Illustrator numerous books. Served to maj. U.S Army, 1941-46. Decorated Bronze star. Recipient 6 Best Story Strip Artist awards Nat. Cartoonists Soc., 1988. Mem. Nat. Cartoonists Soc. (pres., Best Story Strip Cartoonist award (6), Segar award 1983), Soc. Illustrators, Artists and Writers Assn. Roman Catholic. Club: Dutch Treat. Office: care King Features Syndicate Inc 235 E 45th St New York NY 10017-3305

MURPHY, JOHN JOSEPH, manufacturing company executive; b. Olean, N.Y., Nov. 24, 1931; s. John Joseph and Mary M.; m. Louise John; children: Kathleen A. Murphy Bell, Karen L. Murphy Rochelli, Patricia L. Murphy Smith, Michael J. AAS in Mech. Engring., Rochester Inst. Tech., 1952; MBA, So. Meth. U. Engr. Clark div. Dresser Industries, Olean, 1952-67; gen. mgr. roots blower div. Dresser Industries, Connersville, Ind., 1967-69; pres. crane, hoist and tower div. Dresser Industries, Muskegon, Mich., 1969-70; pres. machinery group Dresser Industries, Houston, 1970-75; sr. v.p. ops. Dresser Industries, Dallas, 1980, exec. v.p., 1982, pres., 1982-92, chmn. bd., chief exec. officer, 1983—; bd. dirs. PepsiCo, Inc., NationsBank Corp., Kerr-McGee Corp.; mem. Bus. Roundtable, Bus. Coun.; bd. dirs. U.S.-Russia Bus. Coun.; chmn. Citizens Democracy Corps. Trustee St. Bonaventure (N.Y.) U., So. Meth. U. With U.S Army, 1954-56. Office: Dresser Industries Inc PO Box 718 2001 Ross Ave Dallas TX 75201-2911

MURPHY, JOHN JOSEPH, city official, retail executive; b. St. John's, Nfld., Can., Sept. 24, 1922; s. John and Gertrude (Wadden) M.; m. Marjorie Halley, June 4, 1951; children: Karen, Patricia, Paul, Jane; m. Sheilagh Guy, Oct. 4, 1994. Student, St. Bonaventure's Coll. Pres. Halley and Co. Ltd., St. Johns, Nfld., 1956—; Pres. John J. Murphy Ltd., St. Johns, Nfld., 1966—; mayor City of St. John's, 1981-90, 93—; dir. Lawton's Stores, Lawton's Drug Stores, Gt. Eastern Oil; mem. adv. bd. Royal Trust. Former pres., senator Jaycees; pres. Nfld. Bd. of Trade, Nfld. Cancer Soc.; campaign chmn., life mem. Can. Cancer Soc.; chmn. new bldg. fund Can. Nat. Inst. for Blind; mem. Royal Commn. on Edn., 1968-71; campaign chmn. new bldg. fund Salvation Army, St. John Ambulance; bd. regents Meml. U. Nfld. Decorated Order of Can., 1985. Can. medal, 1992, Order of St. John, 1994. Mem. Royal Nfld. Yacht. Avocations: sailing; archives. Home: 36 Smithville Crescent, Saint John's, NF Canada A1B 2V2 Office: City of St John's, PO Box 908, Saint John's, NF Canada A1C 5M2

MURPHY, JOHN NOLAN, mining executive, researcher, electrical engineer; b. Pitts., July 14, 1939; s. Maurice J. and Elizabeth (McVey) M.; m.

Catherine V. Schneider, Nov. 24, 1962; 1 child, Michael J. BSEE, U. Pitts. 1961; MBA, Duquesne U., 1967. With U.S. Bur. Mines, Pitts., 1961—, rsch. supr., 1971-78, rsch. dir., 1978—. Contbr. numerous articles to profl. jours. Asst. scoutmaster Boy Scouts Am., Bethel Park, Pa., 1987—. Recipient Brian Morgans Meml. Lecture award U.K., 1983, Disting. Svc. award, Gold medal Dept. Interior, 1985. Mem. IEEE (sr.), Soc. Mining, Metallurgy and Exptl. Engring. (chmn. Pitts. chpt. 1994). Nat. Mine Rescue Assn. (pres. 1990-91, bd. dirs. 1991—). Avocation: golf. Office: Pitts Rsch Ctr Cochrans Mill Rd PO Box 18070 Pittsburgh PA 15236-0070

MURPHY, JOSEPH EDWARD, JR., broadcast executive; b. Mpls., Mar. 13, 1930; s. Joseph Edward Murphy and Ann Hynes; m. Diana Kuske, July 24, 1958; children: Michael, John. BA, Princeton U., 1952; postgrad., U. Minn., 1956-60. Chartered fin. analyst. Teaching asst. dept. history U. Minn., Mpls., 1957-59; dir. investment rsch. and fin. analysis, corp. sec. Woodward-Elwood & Co., Mpls., 1961-67; lectr. fin. grad. bus. sch. U. Minn., Mpls., 1968; v.p. Northwestern Nat. Bank, Mpls., 1967-83; chmn. Midwest Communications, Inc., Mpls., 1990-92; ret.; dir. Midwest Communications, Inc., 1956-89, vice chmn., 1985-89, sec.; bd. dirs., v.p. Northwest Advisers, Inc., 1982-83. Author: Adventure Beyond the Clouds: How We Climbed China's Highest Mountain and Survived, 1986 (Friends Am. Writers award 1986), With Interest: How to Profit From Interest Rate Fluctuations, 1987, Stock Market Probability, 1988, revised edit., 1994, South to the Pole by Ski, 1990, The Random Character of Interest Rates, 1990. Vice chmn., rep. 5th cong. dist. Minn. Coun. on Quality Edn., 1971-77; trustee, vice chmn. fin. com. Mpls. Soc. Fine Arts, 1977-78; bd. dirs., chmn. fin. com., mem. exec. bd. Childrens Theater Co., 1975-80; trustee, chmn. various coms. Macalester Coll., St. Paul, 1973-87. 2d lt. U.S. Army, 1952-55. Mem. Explorers Club, Am. Alpine Club (life, v.p. and bd. dirs 1975-81), Himalayan Club (life), Mpls. Club. Avocations: mountaineering, exploration. Home: 2116 W Lake Isles Blvd Minneapolis MN 55405-2425

MURPHY, JOSEPH SAMSON, political science educator; b. Newark, Nov. 15, 1933; m. Susan Crile, 1984; children by previous marriage—Lisa, Susanne, Peter. Student, U. Colo., 1951-53; AB, Olivet Coll., Mich., 1955; Graham Kenan fellow, Woodrow Wilson fellow, U. N.C. at Chapel Hill, 1955-56; MA, Brandeis U., 1959, Ph.D., 1961, DHL (hon.), 1988; LLD (hon.), U. Wis., 1989. Teaching fellow, instr., asst. prof. Brandeis U., 1957-65; dir. V.I. Peace Corps Tng. Center, St. Croix, 1965-66; asst. Office Sec. HEW, Washington, 1966-67; assoc. dir. Job Corps, OEO, Washington, 1967-68; dir. U.S. Peace Corps, Ethiopia, 1968-70; vice chancellor for higher edn. State of N.J., 1970-71; pres. Queens Coll., prof. polit. sci. Grad. Faculty, CUNY, 1971-77; pres. Bennington (Vt.) Coll., 1977-82; chancellor CUNY, 1982-90; prof. CUNY Grad. Sch., N.Y.C., 1990—; cons. Constl. Commn., Addis Ababa, Ethiopia, 1993; bd. dirs. Yivo Inst. for Jewish Rsch., 1993—; UNESCO Global Project, 1992—; election observer The African Inst., Ethiopia, 1992. Author: The Theory of Universals in Eighteenth Century British Empiricism, 1961, Political Theory: A Conceptual Analysis, 1968; contbr. articles to profl. jours. Recipient Merit award U.S. Fgn. Service, 1965. Mem. AAAS, AAUP, Am. Philos. Assn., Am. Polit. Sci. Assn. Office: CUNY 450 W 41st St New York NY 10036-6807

MURPHY, JUDITH CHISHOLM, trust company executive; b. Chippewa Falls, Wis., Jan. 26, 1942; d. John David and Bernice A. (Hartman) Chisholm. BA, Manhattanville Coll., 1964; postgrad., New Sch. for Social Research, 1965-68, Nat. Grad. Trust Sch., 1975. Asst. portfolio mgr. Chase Manhattan Bank, N.A., N.Y.C., 1964-68; trust investment officer Marshall & Ilsley Bank, Milw., 1968-72; asst. v.p. Marshall & Ilsley Bank, 1972-74, v.p., 1974-75; v.p., treas. Marshall & Ilsley Invesment Mgmt. Corp., Milw., 1975-94; v.p. Marshall & Ilsley Trust Co., Phoenix, 1982—; Marshall & Ilsley Trust Co. Fla., Naples, 1985—; v.p., dir. instnl. sales Marshall & Ilsley Trust Co., Milw., 1994—; coun. mem. Am. Bankers Assn., Washington, 1984-86; govt. relations com. Wis. Bankers Assn., Madison, 1982-88. Contbr. articles to Trusts & Estates Mag., 1980, ABA Banking Jour., 1981, Maricopa Lawyer, 1983. Chmn. Milw. City Plan Commn., 1986—; commr. Milw. County Commn. on Handicapped, 1988-90; bd. dirs. Cardinal Stritch Coll., Milw., 1980-89, Children's Hosp. Wis., Milw., 1989—. Recipient Outstanding Achievement award YWCA Greater Milw., 1985, Sacajawea award Profl. Dimensions, Milw., 1988, Pro Urbe award Mt. Mary Coll., 1988, Vol. award Milw. Found., 1992; named Disting. Woman in Banking, Comml. West Mag., 1988. Mem. Milw. Analysts Soc. (sec. 1974-77, bd. dirs. 1977-80), Fin. Women Internat. (bd. dirs., v.p. 1976-80), Am. Inst. Banking (instr. 1975-78), TEMPO (charter), Profl. Dimensions (Inc.), University Club, Woman's Club Wis., Rotary. Democrat. Roman Catholic. Home: 1139 N Edison St Milwaukee WI 53202-3147 Office: Marshall & Ilsley Trust Co 1000 N Water St Milwaukee WI 53202-6025

MURPHY, JUNEANN WADSWORTH, microbiologist, educator; b. Chickasha, Okla., Mar. 13, 1937; d. Edward William and Ann (Adwan) Wadsworth; m. George W. Murphy, Sept. 2, 1967; children: Cynthia Ann Murphy-Erdosh, Sally E. Savino. BS, U. Okla., 1959, MS, 1961, 65, PhD, 1969. Asst. prof. microbiology U. Okla., Norman, 1970-81, dir. med. tech., 1978-82, assoc. prof. microbiology, 1981-86, prof. microbiology, 1986-88, GLC prof. microbiology, 1988-89, GLC prof. microbiology Health Sci. Ctr., 1989—; study section mem. NIH-Div. Rsch. Grants, Bethesda, Md., 1983-87, 92—; vis. asst. prof. U. Okla., Norman, 1969-70; vis. asst. prof. of clin. immunology U. Colo. Health Sci. Ctr., Denver, 1979. Mem. editl. bd. Infection and Immunity, Jour. Med. and Vet. Mycology. Mem. Am. Soc. Microbiology, Am. Assn. Immunologist, Med. Mycology Soc. of Ams., Internat. Soc. Human and Animal Mycology. Democrat. Methodist. Avocations: gardening, cooking. Home: 2328 Ashwood Ln Norman OK 73071-7416 Office: Univ Okla Health Sci Ctr PO Box 26901 Oklahoma City OK 73126-0901

MURPHY, KENNETH RAY, non-governmental organization executive; b. Lebanon, Ohio, Sept. 8, 1946; s. Raymond C. and Gloria J. (Machemehl) M.; m. Jennifer Pope, Aug. 15, 1969; children: Nicholas R., Samuel W. BA, Mich. State U., 1968; MA, Johns Hopkins U., 1971. Exec. dir. Environ. Resources Inc., Washington, 1970-72; reporter Bur. Nat. Affairs, Washington, 1973-75; editor Environ. Study Conf., U.S. Congress, Washington, 1975-79, staff dir., 1979-84; exec. Environ. and Energy Study Inst., Washington, 1984—. Mem. Sycamore Island Club. Office: Environ and Energy Study Inst 122 C St NW Ste 700 Washington DC 20001-2109

MURPHY, LAWRENCE THOMAS, professional hockey player; b. Scarborough, Ont., Can., Mar. 8, 1961. With L.A. Kings, 1980-83, Washington Capitals, 1983-89, Minn. North Stars, 1989-90; defenseman Pitts. Penguins, 1990—; player Cup All-Star Game, 1979-80, Stanley Cup Championships, 1991, 92, NHL All-Star Game, 1994. Recipient Max Kaminsky trophy, 1979-80. Holds NHL single-season record of 60 assists by rookie defenseman, 1980-81, record of 76 points by rookie defenseman, 1980-81. Office: Pitts Penguins Civic Arena Gate # 9 Pittsburgh PA 15219*

MURPHY, LEWIS CURTIS, lawyer, former mayor; b. N.Y.C., Nov. 2, 1933; s. Henry Waldo and Elizabeth Wilcox (Curtis) M.; m. Carol Carney, Mar. 10, 1957; children—Grey, Timothy, Elizabeth. B.S. in Bus. Adminstrn., U. Ariz., 1955, LL.B., 1961. Bar: Ariz. bar 1961. Individual practice law Tucson, 1961-66; trust officer So. Ariz. Bank & Trust Co., 1966-70; atty. City of Tucson, 1970-71; mayor, 1971-87, ret.; mem. law firm Schroeder & Murphy, Tucson, 1977-88; trustee U.S. Conf. Mayors, 1987-88, chmn. transp. com., 1984-87; mem. pub. safety steering com. Nat. League Cities, 1973-87, mem. transp. steering com., 1973-87; v.p. Ctrl. Ariz. Project Assn., 1978-87; bd. dirs. Ariz. Bank, Community Food Bank. Mem. adv. bd. Ariz. Cancer Ctr., 1988—; bd. dirs. United Way Greater Tucson, 1988—. Served with USAF, 1955-58. Mem. Ariz. Bar Assn., Pima County Bar Assn., Ariz. Acad. Republican. Presbyterian.

MURPHY, MARGARET HACKETT, federal bankruptcy judge; b. Salisbury, N.C., 1948. BA, Duke Coll., Charlotte, N.C., 1970; JD, U. N.C., Chapel Hill, 1973. Bar: Ga. 1973, U.S. Bankruptcy Ct. Assoc. Smith, Cohen, Ringel, Kohler and Martin, Atlanta, 1973-79; ptnr. Smith, Gambrell & Russell (formerly Smith, Cohen, Ringel, Kohler and Martin), Atlanta, 1980-87; U.S. bankruptcy judge U.S. Dist. Ct. (no. dist.) Ga., Atlanta, 1987—. Office: 1290 US Courthouse 75 Spring St SW Atlanta GA 30303-3367

MURPHY, MARTIN JOSEPH, JR., cancer research center executive; b. Colorado Springs, Dec. 29, 1942; s. Martin J. Sr. and Gertrude F. (Heffting) M.; m. Ann. A. Flesher, May 29, 1965; children: Siobhan, Deirdre, Martin III, Sean, Brendan. BS, Regis Coll., 1964; MS, N.Y.U., 1967, PhD, 1969. Vis. fellow Inst. de Pathologie Cellulaire, Paris, 1969-71, Christie Hosp., Manchester, Eng., 1971-72; visiting fellow John Curtin Sch. of Med. Rsch., Canberra, Australia, 1972-74; asst. prof. Sch. Medicine Cornell U., N.Y.C.; dir. Bob Hipple Lab for Cancer Rsch., N.Y.C., 1977-85; dir. hematology tng. program Sloan-Kettering Inst. for Cancer Rsch., N.Y.C., 1978-79; prof. Sch. of Medicine Wright State U., Dayton, 1984—; pres., chief exec. officer Hipple Cancer Rsch. Ctr., Dayton, 1985—; bd. chmn. AlphaMed Press, Inc., Dayton, 1983—; bd. dirs. Dayton Clin. Oncology Program. Editor: In Vitro Aspects of Erythropoiesis, 1978, Blood Cell Growth Factors: Their Biology and Clinical Applications, 1990, Blood Cell Growth Factors: Their Utility in Hematology and Oncology, 1991; editor-in-chief Internat. Jour. Cell Cloning, 1982-93, Stem Cells, 1993—; contbr. articles to profl. jours. NIH Postdoctoral fellow Nat. Inst. of Health, 1969-70, Damon Runyon fellow, 1970-71, Spl. fellow Leukemia Soc. Am., 1971-71, Pro America award, Dayton Exec. Club. mem. Assn of Am. Cancer Inst., Am. Soc. of Hematology, Am. Soc. of Oncology, Am. Assn. for Cancer Research, Internat. Soc. for Exptl. Hematology, Dayton Area Cancer Assn. (trustee). Avocation: photography. Office: Hipple Cancer Rsch Ctr 4100 Kettering Blvd Dayton OH 45439-2092

MURPHY, MARY C., state legislator. BA, Coll. St. Scholastica; postgrad. U. Minn., Macalester Coll., U. Wis.-Superior, Am. U., Indiana U. H.s tchr.; mem. Minn. Ho. of Reps., 1976—, mem. com. chair judiciary fin. com., tourism consumer affairs, labor-mgmt. relations coms.; active del. Duluth Central Labor Body AFL-CIO; mem. Minn. AFL-CIO; Rapahy's Parish; dir. State Democratic Farmer-Labor Party, 1972-74, chmn. 8th Dist. credentials com., 1974—, chmn. St. Louis County Legis. Delegation, 1985-86. Mem. Duluth Fedn. Tchrs. (1st v.p. 1976-77, various coms.), Minn. Fedn. Tchrs. (legis. com. 1972-75), Am. Fedn. Tchrs. (del. nat. convs.), Minn. Hist. Soc., Alpha Delta Kappa. Office: State Office Bldg Saint Paul MN 55155

MURPHY, MICHAEL CONLON, lawyer; b. N.Y.C., Nov. 14, 1937; s. Patrick and Bessie (Conlon) M. m. Mary Kay Connors, June 6, 1959; children—Holly Ann, Emily Louise, Patricia Marie. B.S., U.S. Air Force Acad., 1959; M.B.A., Ga. State Coll., 1964; J.D., Emory U., 1966. Bar: Ga. 1966, U.S. Dist. Ct. (no. dist.) Ga. 1966, U.S. Ct. Appeals (5th cir.) 1966, U.S. Ct. Appeals (11th cir.) 1971, U.S. Supreme Ct. 1973, U.S. Ct. Appeals (6th cir.) 1975, U.S. Ct. Appeals (3d cir.) 1977. Assoc., Wilson, Branch, Barwick & Wilcox, Atlanta, 1966-69, assoc. Troutman, Sams, Schroder & Lockerman, Atlanta, 1969-71; ptnr. Troutman, Sanders, Lockerman & Ashmore, Atlanta, 1972—; adj. prof. law Emory U., Atlanta, 1975-81. Mem. bd. mgmt. Ashford-Dunwoody YMCA, 1990—; trustee Phoenix Soc. Atlanta, 1981—; chmn. bd. mgmt. Downtown Atlanta YMCA, 1984—; bd. dirs. YMCA Met. Atlanta, 1985—. Served to capt. USAF, 1959-64, capt. USAFR, 1964-69. Mem. Atlanta Bar Assn., State Bar Ga., ABA, Lawyers Club Atlanta, Fed. Bar Assn., Atlanta Athletic Club. Roman Catholic. Contbr. articles in field to profl. jours. Office: Troutman Sanders 600 Peachtree St NE Atlanta GA 30308-2214

MURPHY, MICHAEL EMMETT, food company executive; b. Winchester, Mass., Oct. 16, 1936; s. Michael Cornelius and Bridie (Curran) M.; m. Adele Anne Kasupski, Sept. 12, 1959; children: Leslie Maura, Glenn Stephen, Christopher McNeil. B.S. in Bus. Adminstrn, Boston Coll., 1958; M.B.A., Harvard, 1962. Financial analyst Maxwell House div. Gen. Foods Corp., White Plains, N.Y., 1962-64; cost mgr. Maxwell House div. Gen. Foods Corp., San Leandro, Calif., 1964-65; controller Maxwell House div. Gen. Foods Corp., Jacksonville, Fla., 1965-67; controller Maxwell House div. Gen. Foods Corp., Hoboken, N.J., 1967-68, mgr. fin. planning and analysis, 1968-69; mgr. planning Hanes Corp., Winston-Salem, N.C., 1969-70, corp. controller, 1970—; v.p. administrn. Hanes Corp. (Hanes Knitwear), Winston-Salem, N.C., 1972-74; v.p. fin. Ryder System Inc., Miami, Fla., 1974-75, exec. v.p., 1975-79; exec. v.p., dir. Sara Lee Corp., Chgo., 1979-93, vice chmn., 1993—; bd. dirs. GATX Corp. Mgmt. adviser Jr. Achievement, 1965-66; mem. exec. com. Hudson County Tax Rsch. Coun., 1967-68; trustee Boston Coll., 1980-88; chmn. Civic Fedn. Chgo., 1984-86; bd. dirs. Jobs for Youth, Chgo., 1983-86, Lyric Opera, 1986—; bd. dirs. Northwestern Meml. Hosp., Chgo., Big Shoulders Fund. 1st lt. U.S. Army, 1958-60. Mem. NAM (bd. dirs. 1989—), dir. Big Shoulders Fund 1995—), Fin. Execs. Inst., Hoboken C. of C., Winson-Salem C. of C., Miami C. of C., Internat. Platform Assn., UN Assn., Ouimet Scholar Alumni Group, Beta Gamma Sigma. Roman Catholic. Home: 1242 N Lake Shore Dr Chicago IL 60610-2361 Office: Sara Lee Corp 3 First National Plz Chicago IL 60602

MURPHY, N. B. (NAP MURPHY), state congressman, automobile dealer; b. Rural Rte. Crescent, Ark., Sept. 16, 1921; s. Charles Ed and Isadee M.; m. Maxine James, Dec. 20, 1949; children: James N., Stephen E., Ila Sue Murphy Campbell. Grad., Crossett (Ark.) High Sch., 1941. With acctg. and traffic dept. AD&N Railroad, 1941-48; owner gas svc. station, 1948-53; owner Murphy Ford Co., Hamburg, Ark., 1953—; mem. Ark. Ho. of Reps., 1959—; pres. M&M Svcs. Corp., Murphy Farms. Mem. Nat. Automobile Assn., Masons (32nd degree). Democrat. Avocations: playing the fiddle, composing songs. Home and Office: S Main St PO Box 271 Hamburg AR 71646-0271

MURPHY, NEWTON JEROME, steel company executive, holding company executive; b. Spencer, Iowa, Nov. 22, 1928; s. Newton Hawley and Marian Rebecca (Livingston) M.; m. Shirley Anne Howard; children: Kathleen, Sarah (dec.), Michael Howard, Laura. BA, U. Iowa, 1952. Trainee Studebaker Corp., South Bend, Ind., 1952-53; car distbr. Studebaker Corp., Buffalo, 1953-54; trainee, sales rep. U.S. Steel Corp., Pitts., 1954-60; asst. to mgr. sales U.S. Steel Corp., Balt., 1960-65; v.p., gen. mgr. Feralloy Corp., Balt., 1965-68; v.p., gen. mgr. Feralloy Corp., Chgo., 1968-71, pres., chief exec. officer, dir., 1971—; pres., chief exec. officer Salzgitter Indsl. Corp., Chgo., 1975—, also bd. dirs.; chmn. owners com. Feralloy West Co., Chgo., 1984—; chmn. owners com. Feralloy Processing Co., Chgo., 1987—; bd. dirs. Salzgitter Machinery Inc., Chgo. Served with USN, 1946-48, PTO. Mem. Steel Service Ctr. Inst., Chgo. Execs. Club. Republican. Congregationalist. Club: Northshore Country (Glenview, Ill.). Avocations: golf, tennis. Office: Feralloy Corp 8755 W Higgins Rd Chicago IL 60631-2708

MURPHY, PATRICK JOSEPH, state representative; b. Dubuque, Iowa, Aug. 24, 1959; s. Lawrence John and Eileen (Heitz) M.; m. Therese Ann Gulick, Dec. 27, 1980; children: Jacob, John, Joey, Natalie. BA, Loras Coll., 1980. Transporter, security and safety officer, mental health technician Mercy Health Ctr., Dubuque, Iowa, 1975-88; documentation specialist software systems Cycare Systems Inc., Dubuque, 1988-90; state representative State of Iowa, Des Moines, 1989—. Adv. com. Iowa Birth Defects, 1995. Recipient Robert Tyson award Cmty. Action Assn., 1993, Pub. Svc. award Coalition for Family and Children's Svcs., 1994. Mem. NAACP, YMCA, Dubuque Mental Health Assn. (bd. dirs., Legis. of Yr.), Loras Club, FDR Club. Democrat. Roman Catholic. Avocations: weightlifting, jogging. Home: 1770 Hale St Dubuque IA 52001-6049 Office: Ho of Reps Des Moines IA 50319

MURPHY, PATRICK VINCENT, foundation executive; b. Bklyn, May 15, 1920; s. Patrick A. and Ellen (Jones) M.; m. Martha Elizabeth Cameron, June 2, 1945; children—Betty (Mrs. Thomas Kelley), Eileen (Mrs. Bernard Karam), Patrick, Anne T. (Mrs. Drew Zabriskie), Kevin, Gerard, Paul, Mark. B.A., St. John's U., 1954; M.P.A., City Coll. N.Y., 1960; LL.D. (hon.), U. Louisville. Patrolman N.Y. Police Dept., N.Y.C., 1945; dep. insp. N.Y. Police Dept., 1963; chief of police Syracuse, N.Y., 1963; deputy chief inspector N.Y. Police Dept., 1964; apptd. asst. dir. Office of Law Enforcement Assistance U.S. Dept. Justice, Washington, 1965-67; apptd. pub. safety dir. District of Columbia, 1967—; apptd. Adminstr. Law Enforcement Assistance Adminstrn. U.S. Dept. Justice, Washington, 1968-69; sr. staff Urban Inst., 1969—; apptd. commnr. Detroit Police Dept., 1970; commnr. N.Y. Police Dept., 1970-73; pres. Police Found., Washington, 1973—; dean police sci. City U. N.Y.; adv. Nat. Crime Commn. Cons. Nat. Adv. Commn. on Civil Disorders; mem. Nat. Conf. on Crime and Delinquency. Served with USNR, World War II. Mem. internat. Assn. Chiefs of Police, NCCJ, Beta Gamma Sigma. Office: Dept Transp Aviation & Internat Affairs 400 7th St SW Washington DC 20590

MURPHY, PAUL JAMES, high technology company executive; b. N.Y.C., Mar. 30, 1948; s. Edward Peter and Thelma (Samuels) M.; m. Marlene Louise Ritchie, May 15, 1993. BS in Acctg., Bklyn. Coll., 1973; MBA, Harvard U., 1975. CPA. Mgr. Price Waterhouse & Co., Boston, 1975-79; v.p. fin. Lexidata Corp., Billerica, Mass., 1979-85, Ztel, Inc., Wilmington, Mass., 1985-86, Xyplex, Inc., Boxboro, Mass., 1986—. Capt. U.S. Army, 1966-70, Vietnam. Decorated Bronze Star (5) U.S. Army; recipient Silver medal Mass. Soc. CPAs, 1978; fellow Mobile Oil, 1974. Mem. Pawley's Plantation Golf and Country Club, Sterling Country Club. Office: Xyplex Inc 330 Codman Hill Rd Boxboro MA 01719

MURPHY, PHILIP EDWARD, broadcast executive; b. Chgo., May 11, 1945; s. Edward Curtis and Mary Francis (D'Incecco) M.; m. Carol Jean Sefton, Mar. 11, 1967 (div. 1985); children: Mandy Jean, Patrick Jeffrey. BS, Ind. U., 1967. Prodn. mgr. Sta. WFIU-FM, Bloomington, Ind., 1968; news reporter, photographer, editor Sta. WTHR TV, Indpls., 1969, sr. account exec., 1970-80; account exec. Blair TV, L.A., 1980-81; pres. Am. Spot Cable Corp., Hollywood, Calif., 1981-82; v.p. tech. ops. for United Paramount Network, combined Viacom and Paramount TV markets Paramount Pictures TV, Hollywood, 1982—; spkr. film preservation, in field; advisor Libr. of Congress, Washington, Nat. Archives, Washington. Lighting designer Civic Theatre, Indpls., 1979; tech. dir. Footlite Mus., Indpls., 1970-78; bd. dirs. Cathedral Arts, Indpls., 1978-80. Mem. Internat. Platform Assn., Assn. Moving Image Archivists, Gay and Lesbian Alliance Against Defamation L.A., Hollywood Supports Assn., Soc. Motion Picture and TV Engrs., St. James' Club. Avocations: photography, videography, audio, theatre. Office: Paramount Pictures TV 5555 Melrose Ave Stage # 3/212 Los Angeles CA 90038-3197

MURPHY, PHILIP FRANCIS, bishop; b. Cumberland, Md., Mar. 25, 1933; s. Philip A.M. and Kathleen (Huth) M. Ed. St. Mary Sem., Balt., N.Am. Coll., Rome. Ordained priest Roman Catholic Ch., 1958; asst. pastor St. Bernardine Ch., Balt., 1959-61; asst. vice rector N.Am. Coll., Rome, 1961-65; sec. to Cardinal Archbishop, Balt., 1965-74, chancellor, 1975; ordained titular bishop of Tacarata and aux. of Balt., 1976—. Office: Archdiocese of Balt 320 Cathedral St Baltimore MD 21201-4421

MURPHY, RANDALL KENT, consultant; b. Laramie, Wyo., Nov. 8, 1943; s. Robert Joseph and Sally (McConnell) M.; student U. Wyo., 1961-65; MBA, So. Meth. U., 1983; m. Cynthia Laura Hillhouse, Dec. 29, 1978; children: Caroline, Scott, Emily. Dir. mktg. Wycoa, Inc., Denver, 1967-70; dir. Communications Resource Inst., Dallas, 1971-72; account exec. Xerox Learning Systems, Dallas, 1973-74; regional mgr. Systema Corp., Dallas, 1975; pres. Performance Assocs.; pres., dir. Acclivus Corp., Dallas, 1976—; founder, chmn. Acclivus Inst., 1982—. Active, Dallas Mus. Fine Arts, Dallas Hist. Soc., Dallas Symphony Assn.; vice chmn. bd. trustees The Winston Sch., 1994—. Served with AUS, 1968. Mem. Am. Soc. Tng. and Devel., Sales and Mktg. Execs. Internat., Inst. Mgmt. Scis., Soc. Applied Learning Tech., Nat. Soc. Performance and Instrn., Assn. Mgmt. Cons., Am. Assn. Higher Edn., World Future Soc., Soc. for Intercultural Edn., Tng. and Rsch., Internat. Fedn. Tng. and Devel. Orgns., Inst. Noetic Scis., Nat. Peace Inst., Amnesty Internat. The Acad. Pol. Sci., The Nature Conservancy, Children's Arts & Ideas Found., So. Meth. U. Alumni Assn. U. Wyo. Alumni Assn. Roman Catholic. Author: Performance Management of the Selling Process, 1979; Coaching and Counseling for Performance, 1980; Managing Development and Performance, 1982; Acclivus Performance Planning System, 1983; (with others) BASE for Sales Performance, 1983, Acclivus Coaching, 1984, Acclivus Sales Negotiation, 1985; BASE for Effective Presentations, 1987, BASE for Strategic Sales Presentations, 1988, The New BASE for Sales Excellence, 1988, Major Account Planning and Strategy, 1989, Strategic Management of the Selling Process, 1989, Building on the BASE, 1992; co-inventor The Randy-Band, multi-purpose apparel accessory, 1968. Home: 6540 Crestpoint Dr Dallas TX 75240-8615

MURPHY, REG, publishing executive; b. 1934. Reporter Macon (Ga.) Telegraph and News, 1953-60; polit. editor, editorial page editor Atlanta Constitution, 1961-74; pub., editor San Francisco Examiner, 1975-81; pub., pres. Balt. Sun, 1981-90, chmn., 1990-92; exec. v.p. Nat. Geographic Soc., Washington, 1993—. Office: Nat Geographic Soc 1145 17th St NW Washington DC 20036

MURPHY, RICHARD WILLIAM, retired foreign service officer, Middle East specialist, consultant; b. Boston, July 29, 1929; s. John Deneen Murphy and Jane (Diehl) Bonner; m. Anne Herrick Cook, Aug. 25, 1955; children: Katherine Anne, Elizabeth Drew, Richard McGill. Grad., Phillips Exeter Acad., 1947; AB, Harvard U., 1951, Cambridge (Eng.) U., 1953; postgrad. Arabic studies, U.S. Fgn. Service Inst., Beirut, 1959-60; LLD (hon.), New Eng. Coll., 1989, Hebrew U., 1992. Vice consul U.S. Consulate Gen., Salisbury, So. Rhodesia, 1955-58; consul Aleppo, Syria, 1960-63; polit. officer Am. Embassy, Jidda, Saudi Arabia, 1963-66, Amman, Jordan, 1966-68; pers. officer U.S. State Dept., Washington, 1968-69, dir. Office Arabian Peninsula Affairs, 1969-71, asst. sec. state for Near Ea. and South Asian affairs, 1983-89; U.S. amb. to Mauritania, 1971-74, Syria, 1974-78, The Philippines, 1978-81, Saudi Arabia, 1981-83; sr. fellow for Middle East Coun. Fgn. Rels., N.Y.C., 1989—; cons. Richard Murphy Assocs., N.Y.C., 1993—; chmn. Fgn. Students Svc. Coun., Washington, 1989-93; Middle East Inst., Washington, 1993—, Chatham House Found., 1993—; mem. bd. advisors Naval War Coll., 1991—; bd. dirs. MAXUS Energy, 1990-93, Harvard Med. Internat. Served with U.S. Army, 1953-55. Recipient Superior Honor award, U.S. Dept. State, 1969, Pres.'s Disting. Svc. award, 1986, 88, 89. Mem. Coun. Fgn. Rels., Fgn. Svc. Assn., Inst. of Diplomacy (Non-proliferation Coun.), Kissinger Assocs. Republican. Episcopalian. Avocations: tennis, scuba diving. Home: 16 Sutton Pl # 9A New York NY 10022-3057

MURPHY, ROBERT BLAIR, management consulting company executive; b. Phila., Jan. 19, 1931; s. William Beverly and Helen Marie (Brennan) M.; B.S., Yale, 1953; children: Stephen, Emily, Julia, David, Catherine. Indsl. engr. DuPont Corp., Aiken, S.C., 1953-55; mgr. sales can div. Reynolds Metals Co., Richmond, Va., 1955-69; gen. mgr. corrugated div. Continental Can Co., N.Y.C., 1969-73; v.p. and gen. mgr. beverage div. Am. Can Co., Greenwich, Conn., 1973-75; assoc. Heidrick & Struggles, Inc., N.Y.C., 1976-78, v.p., 1978; mng. dir. Stamford office Spencer Stuart & Assocs., 1978-84, ptnr., 1982-84; co-founder Sullivan-Murphy Assocs., 1984—. Clubs: Riverside Yacht (Greenwich); Yale (N.Y.C.); Merion Cricket (Haverford, Pa.). Home: 11 Indian Mill Rd Cos Cob CT 06807-1315 Office: 6 Landmark Sq Stamford CT 06901-2704

MURPHY, ROBERT BRADY LAWRENCE, lawyer; b. Madison, Wis., Dec. 5, 1905; s. Lawrence B. Murphy and Elizabeth M. Brady; m. Arabel Zenobia Alcott, Oct. 11, 1947. AB, U. Wis., 1929, AM, 1930, LLB, 1932, LLD (hon.), 1994. Bar: Wis. 1932. Mem. Murphy & Desmond, S.C. and predecessors, Madison, 1932—; lectr. U. Wis. Law Sch.; mem. Supreme Ct. Wis. Bd. Bar Examiners, 1981-86. Mem. Madison Police and Fire Commn., 1947-52; curator State Hist. Soc. Wis., 1948-90, pres., 1958-61; bd. dirs. Wis. History Found., 1958—, pres., 1960-90; bd. advisors Nat. Trust Hist. Preservation, 1967-73; bd. dirs. or advisor several founds.; bd. visitors U. Wis. Law Sch., 1975-81. Lt. USNR, 1943-46. Fellow Am. Bar Found.; mem. ABA, State Bar Wis., Am. Law Inst., Selden Soc. (Eng.), Bascom Hill Soc. (Wis.), Phi Beta Kappa Assocs., Phi Kappa Phi, Chi Phi, Phi Delta Phi. Republican. Roman Catholic. Clubs: Madison, Blackhawk Country. Home: 3423 Valley Creek Cir Middleton WI 53562 Office: Murphy & Desmond S C 2 E Mifflin St Madison WI 53703-2860

MURPHY, ROBERT C(HARLES), judge; b. Balt., Oct. 9, 1926; married; 3 children. JD, U. Md., 1951, LLD (hon.), 1973; LLD (hon.), U. Balt., 1981, Washington Coll., 1993. Bar: Md. 1952, D.C. 1952, U.S. Supreme Ct. 1957. Law clk. to Hon. William P. Cole Jr., assoc. judge U.S. Ct. Customs and Patent Appeals, Washington, 1951-53; gen. counsel U. Md., 1955-57; spl. asst. atty. gen. Balt., 1957-62, asst. atty. gen., then dep. atty. gen., 1962-66, atty. gen., 1966-67; chief judge Md. Ct. Spl. Appeals, Annapolis, 1967-72, Md. Ct. Appeals, Annapolis, 1972—; adminstrv. head Md. Jud. Br., 1972—; chmn. Constl. Commn. on Jud. Disabilities, 1971-73; hon. mem. Coun. State Govts., mem. governing bd., mem. exec. com., 1985; chmn. bd. dirs. Nat. Ctr. State Cts.; Williamsburg, Va., 1986-87; pres. J. Dudley Digges Am. Inn of Ct. With USN, 1944-46. Fellow Am. Bar Found.; mem. ABA, U. Md. Alumni Assn.-Internat. (chmn., trustee), Conf. Chief Justices (pres. 1986),

Md. State Bar Assn., Order of Coif. Office: Ct Appeals Md 361 Rowe Blvd Fl 4 Annapolis MD 21401-1672

MURPHY, ROBERT EARL, scientist, government agency administrator; b. Yakima, Wash., Sept. 24, 1941; s. William Barry and Caroline Norbeth (Boyd) M.; m. Nancy Jane Hybner, June 26, 1965; children: Kimberly Elizabeth, Mark Hybner. B.S. in Math, Worcester (Mass.) Poly. Inst., 1963; M.A. in Astronomy, Georgetown U., 1966; Ph.D., Case Western Res. U., 1969. Astronomer U.S. Army Map Service, 1965-66; asst. prof. astronomy Inst. Astronomy, U. Hawaii, 1969-73; exec. dir. Md. Acad. Scis., Balt., 1973-76; pres. Scientia Inc., Balt., 1976—; chief planetary atmospheres programs and program scientist Galileo project NASA, Washington, 1977-81; head earth resources br., project scientist heat capacity mapping mission Goddard Space Flight Center, Greenbelt, Md., 1981-84; chief land processes br. NASA Hdqrs., Washington, 1984-89, chief biochemistry, geophysics bur., 1989-92, sr. sci. advisor internat. programs, 1993—. Author curriculum materials, articles in field. Mem. AAAS, Am. Astron. Soc., Am. Geophys. Union. Republican. Baptist. Office: NASA Hdqrs Earth Sci Divsn Code YS Washington DC 20546

MURPHY, ROSEMARY, actress; b. Munich, Germany; came to U.S., 1939; d. Robert D. and Mildred (Taylor) M. Ed. in, Paris, France and Kansas City, Mo. Broadway appearances include Look Homeward Angel, 1958, Night of the Iguana, World premier at Spoleto (Italy) Festival of Two Worlds, 1959, Period of Adjustment, 1961, King Lear, 1963, Any Wednesday, 1964-66, Delicate Balance, 1966, Weekend, 1968, Butterflies Are Free, 1970, Lady Macbeth, Stratford, Conn., 1973, Ladies of the Alamo, 1977, John Gabriel Borkman, 1980, Learned Ladies, 1982, Coastal Disturbances, 1987, The Devil's Disciple, 1988; motion picture appearances include To Kill a Mockingbird, 1962, Any Wednesday, 1966, Ben, 1972, Walking Tall, 1972, You'll Like My Mother, 1972, Forty Carats, 1973, Julia, 1976, September, 1987, For The Boys, 1991, Lonely Hearts, 1991; TV appearance: Eleanor and Franklin, 1975 (Emmy award for best supporting actress 1976), George Washington, 1983 (Tony award nomination 1961, 64, 67, award Motion Picture Arts Club 1966). Recipient Variety Poll award, 1961, 67. Address: 220 E 73rd St New York NY 10021-4319

MURPHY, RUSSELL STEPHEN, theater company executive; b. North Canton, Ohio, Aug. 24, 1957; s. Allen Forest and Gene Selma (Russell) M. BA in Dance, Point Park Coll., 1984. Mem. stage crew, set constrn. Shenandoah Coll. & Conservatory of Music, Winchester, Va., 1977-78; student libr. Point Park Coll., Pitts., 1978-80; dancer, actor, costume constrn. and maintenance Fayette Heritage, Inc., Farmington, Pa., 1980; dancer, bookkeeper and tchr. Alloy Dance Ctr., asst. to dir. Pitts. Dance Alloy, 1981-84; asst. sales mgr., group leader, sponsor, host/cashier Macy's, Stamford, Conn., 1984-87; mgr., sales supr. Trans-Pacific Stores, Ltd. (Russell's), N.Y.C., 1987-88; box office mgr. Music Theatre Group, N.Y.C., 1987-89; gen. and bus. mgr., bus. assoc., office and box office mgr. Pan Asian Repertory Theatre, N.Y.C., 1987—. Deacon Met. Community Ch. of N.Y.C., 1989—; merchandise chmn. Heritage of Pride, N.Y.C., 1993-94. Democrat. Avocations: beach combing, fighting for civil and Gay-Lesbian rights. Home: 221 E 2d St Apt 2F New York NY 10009 Office: Pan Asian Repertory Theatre 97 Great Jones St New York NY 10012

MURPHY, SANDRA ROBISON, lawyer; b. Detroit, July 28, 1949; m. Richard Robin. BA, Northwestern U., 1971; JD, Loyola U., Chgo., 1976. Bar: U.S. Dist. Ct. (no. dist.) Ill. 1976. Assoc. Notz, Craven, Mead, Maloney & Price, Chgo., 1976-78; ptnr. McDermott, Will & Emery, Chgo., 1978—. Mem. ABA (family law sect.), Ill. Bar Assn. (chair sect. family law coun. 1987-88), Chgo. Bar Assn. (chair matrimonial law com. 1985-86), Am. Acad. Matrimonial Lawyers (sec. 1990-91, v.p. 1991-92, pres. Ill. chpt. 1992-93, pres.-elect. 1994-95), Legal Club Chgo.

MURPHY, SHARON MARGARET, university official, educator; b. Milw., Aug. 2, 1940; d. Adolph Leonard and Margaret Ann (Hirtz) Feyen; m. James Emmett Murphy, June 28, 1969 (dec. May 1983); children: Shannon Lynn, Erin Ann. BA, Marquette U., 1965; MA, U. Iowa, 1970, PhD, 1973. Cert. K-14 tchr., Iowa. Tchr. elem. and secondary schs., Wis., 1959-69; dir. publs. Kirkwood C.C., Cedar Rapids, Iowa, 1969-71; instr. journalism U. Iowa, Iowa City, 1971-73; asst. prof. U. Wis., Milw., 1973-79; assoc. prof. So. Ill. U., Carbondale, 1979-84; dean/prof. Marquette U., Milw., 1984-94; provost, v.p. acad. affairs, prof. Bradley U., Peoria, Ill., 1994—; pub. rels. dir., editor Worldwide mag., Milw., 1965-68; reporter Milw. Sentinel, 1967; Fulbright sr. lectr. U. Nigeria, Nsukka, 1977-78. Author: Other Voices: Black, Chicano & American Indian Press, 1971; (with Wigal) Screen Experience: An Approach to Film, 1968, (with Murphy) Let My People Know: American Indian Journalism, 1981, (with Schilpp) Great Women of the Press, 1983; editor: (book, with others) International Perspectives on News, 1982. Bd. dirs. Dow Jones Newspaper Fund, N.Y., 1986—. Recipient Medal of Merit, Journalism Edn. Assn., 1976, Amoco Award for Teaching Excellence, 1977, Outstanding Achievement award Greater Milw. YWCA, 1989; named Knight of Golden Quill, Milw. Press Club, 1977; Nat. headliner Women in Communication, Inc., 1985. Mem. Assn. Edn. in Journalism and Mass Comm. (pres. 1986-87), Internat. Comm. Assn., Tempo, Newspaper Assn. Am. Found. (mem. bd. trustees 1993—), Soc. Profl. Journalists, Nat. Press Club. Democrat. Roman Catholic. Office: Bradley U Office of Provost Peoria IL 61625

MURPHY, STEPHEN EDWARD, international media and finance consultant; b. Portland, Oreg., Mar. 20, 1944; s. Edward Alexander and Marian Elizabeth (Steigerwald) M. BA in Econs., U. Wash., 1966; MBA in Fin., Columbia U., 1972. V.p. multinat. div. First Nat. Bank Boston, 1972-83; v.p. CIC Video Internat. N.V. (div. Paramount Pictures and MCA Internat.), Rio de Janeiro, 1983-87; cons. S.E.M. Enterprises, Sao Paulo, Brazil, 1987-89; dir. TV and film svc. USIA, Washington, 1989-91; sr. adv. to dir. Voice of Am., 1992; internat. media and fin. cons. Miami Beach, Fla., 1993—; lectr. John F. Kennedy Sch. Govt. Harvard U., Cambridge, Mass., 1979, communications dept. Howard U., Washington, 1990-91. Founder Help for St. Kids, Rio de Janeiro, 1976-89; dir. Am. Soc. Rio de Janeiro, 1984-85; mentor Cities in Schs., 1993-95. Lt. USN, 1967-70. Mem. Wash. State Soc., Columbia U. Alumni Assn., Phi Kappa Psi. Republican. Roman Catholic. Office: 800 W Ave # 346 Miami FL 33139

MURPHY, STEPHEN P., lawyer; b. Milton, Mass., June 6, 1950. AB cum laude, Boston Coll., 1972; JD, Catholic U. Am., 1976. Bar: D.C. 1976. Ptnr. McDermott, Will & Emery, Washington. Mem. D.C. Bar, Defense Rsch. Inst. Office: McDermott Will & Emery 1850 K St NW Washington DC 20006-2296

MURPHY, STEPHEN P., corporate lawyer; b. 1926. Student, Mo. Valley U., 1948, U. Kans., 1949, Georgetown U., 1950. With Kansas City Star, 1951-56, Denver-Chgo. Truck Lines, Watson Wilson Transp. System, 1956-63; sr. v.p., sec. gen. counsel Yellow Freight System Inc., Overland Park, Kans., 1963—. Office: Yellow Freight System 10990 Roe Ave Overland Park KS 66211-1213

MURPHY, STEVEN LESLIE, state senator, utilities company official; b. San Francisco, Sept. 9, 1957; s. Russell Jr. and Helen Glendora (Black) M.; m. Robin Estelle Stelling, Feb. 9, 1979; children: Nikolaas Russell, Matthew Steven. AS in Bus. Mgmt., Red Wing (Minn.) Tech. Coll., 1992. Operator No. States Power, Red Wing, 1981—; senator Minn. State Senate, St. Paul, 1992—; steward Unit 47 Local 949 Internat. Brotherhood Elec. Workers, Red Wing, 1987—. Bd.dirs. CSAP Open/Charity Golf Tournament, Frontenac, Minn.; co-chair Fireman Caucus, Minn. Legislature, 1992—; vice-chair Vets. Com., Minn. Senate, 1992—. Served with USMC, 1976-80. Mem. Am. Legion, Marine Corps League. Mem. Democratic-Farmer Labor Party. Methodist. Avocations: hunting, fishing, youth activities coach. Home: 28421 Highway 61 Blvd Red Wing MN 55066-5531 Office: Minn State Senate State Capitol # 226 Saint Paul MN 55155-1002

MURPHY, S(USAN) (JANE MURPHY), small business owner; b. Williamsport, Pa., Dec. 26, 1950; d. Jack W. and Edythe J. (Grier) M.; m. Michael J. Sanchez, Dec. 30, 1979. BBA, Pa. State U., 1978. Gen. mgr. Murphy Swift Homes, Hummelstown, Pa., 1970-75; owner, operator Murphy's Home Ctr., Hummelstown, 1975-79, 85-91; mgr. Builder's

Emporium, San Diego, 1979-80; entrepreneur Castle in the Sand, San Diego, 1980-83; adminstr. Sohio Constrn., Prudhoe Bay, Alaska, 1983-85; fin. systems analyst Blue Shield, San Francisco, 1991-93; entrepreneur Pacific Bay Svcs., San Francisco, 1993—; owner, operator Murphy's Home Ctr., Hummelstown, Pa., 1994—; cons. in field; dealer Servistar Home Ctrs. Photographs displayed at San Diego Art Inst. Vol. Hershey (Pa.) Free Ch. Donald MacIntyre scholar, 1979, Class of 1920 scholar, 1979, Congressman Kunkel scholar, 1979. Mem. Pa. Hardware Assn., Hummelstown C. of C., Better Bus. Bur. Evangelical Christian. Avocations: sailing, scuba diving, photography. Office: Murphy's Home Ctr Hummelstown PA 17036

MURPHY, TERENCE MARTIN, biology educator; b. Seattle, July 1, 1942; s. Norman Walter and Dorothy Louise (Smith) M.; m Judith Baron, July 12, 1969; 1 child, Shannon Elaine. BS, Calif. Inst. Tech., 1964; PhD, U. Calif. San Diego, 1969. Sr. fellow dept. biochemistry U. Wash., Seattle, 1969-70; asst. prof. botany U. Calif., Davis, 1971-76, assoc. prof., 1976-82, prof. biology, 1982—, chmn. dept. botany, 1986-90. Author: Plant Molecular Development, 1988; N.Am. exec. editor, N.Am. office, Physiologia Plantarum, 1988—; contbr. articles to profl. jours. Mem. AAAS, Am. Soc. Plant Physiologists, Am. Soc. Photobiology, Scandinavian Soc. Plant Physiology. Home: 725 N Campus Way Davis CA 95616-3518 Office: U Calif Sect Plant Biology Davis CA 95616

MURPHY, TERENCE ROCHE, lawyer; b. Laurium, Mich., Oct. 20, 1937; s. M. Leonard and Alice Lenore (Roche) M.; m. Suzanne Kathryn Dupré, Oct. 14, 1967 (div. Apr. 1980); children: Braden Mathias, Fiona Elizabeth Dupré ; m. Patricia Ann Sherman, May 21, 1983. A.B., Harvard Coll., 1959; J.D. with distinction, U. Mich., 1966. Bar: D.C. 1967, U.S. Supreme Ct. 1971. Trial atty. Dept. Justice, Washington, 1966-68; assoc. Wald, Harkrader & Ross, Washington, 1968-72, ptnr., 1972-83; ptnr. McDermott, Will & Emery, Washington, 1983-84, Adams, Duque & Hazeltine, Washington, 1984-86; founding ptnr. Murphy & Weber (formerly Murphy & Malone), 1986—; bd. dirs. internat. corps., bus. assns.; author, lectr. on internat. trade, antitrust and administrv. law; founding chmn. Brit.-Am. Bus. Coun., 1989-90, legal counsel, 1993—; officer, bd. dirs Frankfurt Trade Fair (U.S. Subsidiary), Industry Coalition of Tech. Transfer. Co-editor: Coping With U.S. Export Controls, ann. edits., 1986, 87, 88; bd. advisor Internat. Fin. Law Rev., 1984—, Eurowatch, 1991—, The European Inst., 1993—; contbr. numerous articles to European and Am. legal publs. Mem. com. visitors U. Mich. Law Sch., 1975—; trustee Lawyer's Com. for Civil Rights Under Law, 1975-89. Lt. USN, 1959-63. Decorated U.S. Navy Commendation medal Cuban Missle Crisis, 1962, Hon. Officer Order Brit. Empire, 1993. Mem. ABA (coun. adminstrv. law sect 1980-83), Am. Law Inst., Am. Assn. Exporters and Importers (bd. dirs.), Internat. Bar Assn. (sec. antitrust and monopolies com. 1981-83), Am. Soc. Internat. Law, Brit.-Am. Bus. Assn. (Washington, founding dir. 1987—, chmn. 1989—, legal advisor 1992—), Royal Inst. Internat. Affairs (London), Am. Coun. on Germany, Deutsch-Amerikanische Juristen-Vereinigung (Bonn), Met. Club (Washington), Harvard Club (N.Y.C.). Home: 2710 Cathedral Ave NW Washington DC 20008-4120 Office: Murphy & Weber 818 Connecticut Ave NW Washington DC 20006

MURPHY, THOMAS ALLEN, government research administrator, scientist; b. Kewanee, Ill., Aug. 26, 1937; m. Arlene Louise (Lippert) M.; m. Ellen Diane McParland, Aug. 26, 1962; children: Alison Louise, Patrick Thomas, Andrew Gavin. AB, Knox Coll., 1959; cert., Glasgow U., 1960; MS, Yale U., 1962, PhD, 1964. Rsch. assoc. Cornell U., Ithaca, N.Y., 1966-67; biologist Fed. Water Pollution Control Adminstrn., Edison, N.J., 1967-70; rsch. program mgr. EPA, Washington, 1970-75, dep. asst. adminstr., 1975-79; rsch. lab. dir. EPA, Corvallis, Oreg., 1979—; mem. del. Nat. Acad. Sci., Malaysia, 1987, Romania, 1990; mem. pres.'s reorgn. project, Exec. Office of the Pres., Washington, 1978. Capt. U.S. Army, 1964-66, Vietnam. Recipient Meritorious Exec. award Pres. of U.S., 1987. Home: 31465 Bellfountain Rd Corvallis OR 97333 Office: EPA 200 SW 35th St Corvallis OR 97333-4902

MURPHY, THOMAS AQUINAS, former automobile manufacturing company executive; b. Hornell, N.Y., Dec. 10, 1915; s. John Joseph and Alma (O'Grady) M.; m. Catherine Rita Maquire, June 7, 1941; children: Catherine, Maureen, Thomas Aquinas. B.S., U. Ill., 1938. With Gen. Motors Corp., 1938-88; asst. treas. Gen. Motors Corp., N.Y.C., 1959; comptroller Gen. Motors Corp., Detroit, 1967; treas. Gen. Motors Corp., 1968, v.p. in charge car and truck group, 1970-72, vice chmn., 1972-74, chmn., chief exec. officer, 1974-80, dir., 1980-88. Bd. dirs. U. Ill. Found. Served with USNR, 1943-46. Mem. Fin. Execs. Inst., Bus. Council, Detroit Athletic Club, Bloomfield Hills (Mich.) Country Club, Delray Dunes (Fla.) Golf Club, Ocean Club (Fla.). Office: 3044 W Grand Blvd Detroit MI 48202-3091

MURPHY, THOMAS BAILEY, state legislator; b. Bremen, GA, Mar. 10, 1924; s. W.H. and Leita (Jones) M.; m. Agnes Bennett, July 22, 1946; children: Michael L., Martha L., Marjorie Lynn, Mary June. Grad., N.Ga. Coll., 1943; LL.B., U. Ga., 1949. Bar: Ga. bar 1949. Since practiced in Bremen as partner firm Murphy & Murphy; mem. Ga. Ho. of Reps., 1961—; adminstrv. floor leader for gov., 1969-70, speaker pro tem, 1971-74, speaker, 1974—. Mem. Ga. Bar Assn., Am. Legion, VFW, Gridiron Secret Soc.; hon. life mem. Ga. Peace Officers Assn.; hon. mem. Ga. Fraternal Order Police, Ga. Sheriffs Assn. Democrat. Baptist. Club: Moose. Office: Ho of Reps State Capitol SW Rm 332 Atlanta GA 30334-1160

MURPHY, THOMAS FRANCIS, federal judge; b. N.Y.C., Dec. 3, 1905; s. Thomas Michael and Susan Anne (White) M.; m. Katherine F. Hotaling, June 28, 1957. A.B., Georgetown U., 1927; LL.B., Fordham, 1930; LL.D., St. Joseph's Coll., 1950. Bar: N.Y. bar 1930. Asst. U.S. atty. So. Dist. N.Y., 1942-50; police commr. N.Y.C., 1950-51; U.S. dist. judge, 1951—. Decorated knight Equestrian Order of Holy Sepulchre of Jerusalem. Mem. Friendly Sons St. Patrick. Club: Sharon Country. Office: US Dist Ct PO Box 756 Sharon CT 06069-0756

MURPHY, THOMAS J., JR., mayor; m. Mona McMahon. BS in Biology and Chemistry, John Carroll U., 1967; MS in Urban Affairs/Planning summa cum laude, Hunter Coll., 1973. Vol. Peace Corps., Paraguay, 1970-72; exec. dir. Perry Hilltop Citizen's Coun., 1973-76; chem. sales rep. Alcoa, 1967-70; exec. dir. North Side Civic Devel. Coun., 1976-78; state rep. 20th Legis. Dist., 1979-94; mayor City of Pitts., 1994—. Democrat. Office: Office of the Mayor 512 City County Bldg 414 Grant St Pittsburgh PA 15219

MURPHY, THOMAS JOHN, publishing executive; b. Lockport, N.Y., Mar. 29, 1931; s. Matthew J. and Mary Frances (Tracy) M.; m. Maryann Elizabeth Stadnicki, Dec. 29, 1956; children: Kevin, Janine, Peter, Thomas. B.S., SUNY-Brockport, 1952; postgrad., Boston U., 1955-57, Northwestern U., 1976. Sales rep., asst. dir. advt., mgr. sales services, dir. tng., asst. dir. mktg., dir. mktg. McGraw-Hill Co., St. Louis, N.Y.C., 1954-73; v.p., gen. mgr. sch. dept. Holt, Rinehart & Winston pub. CBS, Inc., N.Y.C., 1973-78; sr. v.p. CBS Sch. Pub. 1978-80, pres., 1980-82 v.p. AICPA, 1982-88; ptnr. Profl. Pub. Svcs. Co., Westport, Conn., 1988—; pres. World Book Pubs., 1991. Contbr. articles to profl. jours. Bd. dirs. Brockport Found., 1977-83, Rec. for the Blind, 1980-89, Inter-Faith Housing Assn., 1991-94. Named to Heritage Hall of Fame, SUNY. Democrat. Roman Catholic. Home and Office: 4 Ivanhoe Ln Westport CT 06880-5038

MURPHY, THOMAS JOSEPH, strategic communications consultant; b. Jersey City, Sept. 26, 1945; m. Carol Elizabeth Murphy, Sept. 10, 1988. BS in Econs., Siena Coll., 1967; postgrad., SUNY, Albany, 1968-71. Sr. budget analyst N.Y. State Ways & Means Com., Albany, 1972-76; dir. program devel. N.Y. State Assembly, Albany, 1977-79, dir. ops., 1980-82; ptnr. Policy Econs. Group, Washington, 1983-86; owner Thomas J Murphy Assocs., Albany, 1987-91; ptnr. Decision Strategies Group, Albany, 1991—; chmn. Dormitory Authority of N.Y. State, 1995—; co-editor dir. Med. Waste Policy Com. 1988-89; mem. rev. panel Office of Tech. Assessment, Washington, 1990. Exec. dir. Rep. Assembly Campaign Com., Albany, 1982. Roman Catholic. Avocation: antique quilt collector. Home: 1 Fox Run Latham NY 12110-5035 Office: Decision Strategies Group 99 Washington Ave Albany NY 12210-2800

MURPHY, THOMAS JOSEPH, archbishop; b. Chgo., Oct. 3, 1932; s. Barthomew Thomas and Nellie M. AB, St. Mary of the Lake Sem., 1954, STB, 1956, MA, 1957, STL, 1958, STD, 1960. Ordained priest Roman Cath. Ch., 1958. Various positions with Archdiocese of Chgo.; bishop of Great Falls-Billings Mont., 1978-87; coadjutor archbishop of Seattle, 1987-91, archbishop of Seattle, 1991—. Office: Archdiocese of Seattle 910 Marion St Seattle WA 98104-1274*

MURPHY, THOMAS PATRICK, lawyer; b. Syracuse, N.Y., Feb. 12, 1952; s. George Edward and Sara Eileen (Murphy) M.; m. Susan Hollis Francher, Oct. 19, 1974 (div. Oct. 1992); m. Lise M. Adkins, Aug. 6, 1994; children: Casey Marie, Matthew Thomas. BS, Clarkson U., 1974; JD, Vermont Law Sch., 1978. Bar: N.Y. 1978, D.C. 1981, Md. 1988, Va. 1989. Asst. U.S. atty. U.S. Atty.'s Office, Washington, 1982-85; assoc. Highsaw & Mahoney, Washington, 1985-87, McGuire, Woods, Battle & Boothe, Washington, 1987-90; ptnr. Reed Smith Shaw & McClay, McLean, Va., 1990—. Contbr. articles to profl. jours. Chmn. bd. profl. responsibility D.C. Ct. Appeals. With USN, 1978-82, USNR 1978-90. Recipient Spl. Achievement Award U.S. Dept. Justice, 1984. Mem. ABA, Fed. Bar Assn., N.Y. State Bar Assn., D.C. Bar Assn. (chmn. pro se litigants com.), Md. Bar Assn., Asst. U.S. Attys., Bd. Profl. Responsibility D.C. Ct. Appeals (hearing com.). Office: Reed Smith Shaw & McClay 8251 Greensboro Dr Ste 1100 Mc Lean VA 22102

MURPHY, THOMAS S., media company executive; b. Bklyn., May 31, 1925; married. B.S., Cornell U., 1945; M.B.A., Harvard U., 1949. With Kenyon & Eckhardt, 1949-51; with Lever Bros. Co., 1951-54; with Capital Cities ABC Inc. (formerly Capital Cities Communications Inc.), N.Y.C., 1954—, exec. v.p., 1961-64, pres., 1964-72, chief exec. officer, 1966-90, chmn., 1966—, also bd. dirs.; dir. Gen. Housewares Corp., Texaco Inc., Johnson & Johnson, Internat. Bus. Machines Corp. Served with USN. Office: Capital Cities/ABC Inc 77 W 66th St New York NY 10023-6201*

MURPHY, WALTER FRANCIS, political science educator, author; b. Charleston, S.C., Nov. 21, 1929; s. Walter Francis and Ruth (Gaffney) M.; m. Mary Therese Dolan, June 28, 1952; children: Kelly Ann, Holly Ann. AB magna cum laude, U. Notre Dame, 1950; AM, George Washington U., 1954; PhD, U. Chgo., 1957; DLitt (hon.), Coll. Charleston, 1989. Fellow govtl. studies Brookings Instn., 1957-58; faculty Princeton, 1958—, prof. politics, 1965—; McCosh Faculty fellow Ford Research prof. govtl. affairs, 1965-66, chmn. dept. politics, 1966-69, McCormick prof. jurisprudence, 1968—; Fulbright lectr., 1981, 88, 89; mem. adv. com. on jud. conduct N.J. Supreme Ct., 1982—. Author: Congress and the Court, 1962, Elements of Judicial Strategy, 1964, Wiretapping on Trial, 1965, (with C.H. Pritchett and S.A. Barber) Courts, Judges and Politics, 5th edit., 1995, (with M. Danielson) American Democracy, 1969, (with J. Tanenhaus) The Study of Public Law, 1972, (with J. Tanenhaus, D. Kastner) Public Evaluations of Constitutional Courts, 1974, (with J. Tannenhaus) Comparative Constitutional Law, 1977, The Vicar of Christ, 1979, (with D. Lockard) Basic Cases in Constitutional Law, 3d edit., 1991, The Roman Enigma, 1981, (with J. Fleming and S.A. Barber) American Constitutional Interpretation, 1986, 2d edit., 1995, Upon This Rock, 1987; book rev. editor: World Politics, 1972-78; contbr. numerous articles to profl. jours. Mem. N.J. adv. com. U.S. Commn. Civil Rights, 1961-68, vice chmn., 1964-68; mem. N.J. Civil Rights Commn., 1968-70. Served to capt. USMC, 1950-55; col. Res., ret. Decorated D.S.C., Purple Heart; recipient Merriam-Cobb-Hughes award Am. Acad. Pub. Affairs, 1963, Chgo. Found. for Lit. award, 1980; Guggenheim fellow, 1973-74; Nat. Endowment for Humanities fellow, 1978-79. Fellow Am. Acad. Arts and Scis., Italian Acad. for Advanced Studies in Am.; mem. Am. Polit. Sci. Assn. (editl. bd. rev. 1966-72, Birkhead award 1958, sec. 1982-83, v.p. 1987-88), Pi Gamma Mu. Home: 240 Western Way Princeton NJ 08540-5306

MURPHY, WALTER YOUNG, college president, clergyman; b. Chester, S.C., Jan. 10, 1930; s. Samuel Fred and Iva (Simpson) M.; m. Marianne Perdue, Aug. 12, 1952; children—Mary Clarice, Julianne. AB, Emory U., 1950; MDiv, Candler Sch. Theology, 1953; LLD (hon.), Bethune Cookman Coll., 1975; DD (hon.), LaGrange Coll., Ga., 1980. Ordained to ministry, United Meth. Ch. Dir. religious life Oxford Coll., Emory U., Oxford, Ga., 1959-62; minister St. James United Meth. Ch., Athens, Ga., 1962-66; exec. v.p. Fla. So. Coll., Lakeland, 1972-76; pres. Andrew Coll., Cuthbert, Ga., 1976-80, La Grange (Ga.) Coll., 1980—; bd. dirs. Nations Bank, La Grange. Author: La Grange College: Georgia's Oldest Independent School, 1985. Bd. dirs. United Way, Lakeland, Fla., 1970-76, La Grange, 1980—, Ty Cobb Found., 1986—; pres. Chattahoocee coun. Boy Scouts Am., 1988-89; mem. Ga. State Scholarship Commn., 1986-94; trustee West Ga. Med. Ctr., 1990-93; mem. adv. com. Franklin D. Roosevelt Little White House Meml. Mem. La Grange C. of C., Rotary (gov. dist. 6900 1991-92), Nat. Assn. Schs., Colls. and Univs. of United Meth. Ch. (pres. 1990-91), The Commerce Club (Atlanta), Phi Beta Kappa, Omicron Delta Kappa, Sigma Chi. Democrat. Methodist. Home: 1102 Vernon St La Grange GA 30240-2940 Office: La Grange Coll 601 Broad St La Grange GA 30240-2999

MURPHY, WARREN BURTON, writer, screenwriter; b. Jersey City, Sept. 13, 1933; s. Joseph and Eleanore (Muller) M.; m. Dawn E. Walters, June 25, 1955 (div. 1974); children: Deirdre Lee, Megan Patricia, Warren Brian, Ardath Frances; m. Molly Cochran, Feb. 14, 1984; 1 child: Devin Miles. Reporter Hudson Dispatch, Union City, N.J., 1950-52, 1956-58, Jersey Jour., Jersey City, 1958-60; editor Kearny (N.J.) Observer, 1960-62; sec. to mayor Jersey City, 1963-68; novelist, screenwriter, 1972—; commr. N.J. Meadowlands, 1978-81; founding dir. Am. Crime Writers League. Author of more than 100 books including (novels) Razoni and Jackson series, 1974-76, Digger series, 1977-79, Trace series, 1983-87 (Mystery Writers of Am. Edgar award 1984); (with Richard Ben Sapir) The Destroyer series, 1971—, Dead End Street, 1973, One Night Stand, 1973, City in Heat, 1973, Down and Dirty, 1974, Lynch Town, 1974, On the Dead Run, 1975, Leonardo's Law, 1978, Atlantic City, 1979, The Assassin's Handbook, 1982, The Red Moon, (Gold Medal award West Coast Review of Books) 1984, The Ceiling of Hell (Shamus award Pvt. Eye Writers of Am. 1985) 1984, Remo Williams and the Secret of the Sinanju, 1985, Murder in Manhattan, 1986, The Sure Thing, 1988, The Hand of Lazarus, 1988, The Temple Dogs, 1988, The Forever King, 1992; (with Molly Cochran) Grandmaster, (Mystery Writers of Am. Edgar award 1985) 1984, High Priest, 1987; author screenplay The Eiger Sanction, 1976, (story) Lethal Weapon II, 1989; creator TV series Murphy's Law. Served to sgt. USAF, 1952-56. Recipient Citizenship award Freedoms Found., Valley Forge, Pa., 1955, Pub. Rels. award Nat. League of Cities, 1963. Mem. Private Eye Writers of Am., Mystery Writers of Am., Writers Guild of Am., Mensa. Republican. Methodist. Avocations: chess, math., opera. Home and Office: 2094 Cedar Ln Bethlehem PA 18015-9033

MURPHY, WARREN CHARLES, rector; b. Phila., May 6, 1944; s. Warren N. and Frances (Stanley) M.; m. Katharine Linde, June 24, 1977; children: Aaron, Malcolm. BA, Bridgewater Coll., 1967; MDiv, Episc. Grad. Sch., 1972; cert., St. George's Coll., Jerusalem, 1987. Community organizer VISTA, Buffalo and Lackawanna, N.Y., 1967-68; legis. asst. U.S. Sen. Birch Bayh, Washington, 1970-71; exec. dir., founder Compass House, Buffalo, 1972-75; dir. community rels. Cambridge (Mass.) Econ. and Opportunity Commn., 1975-76; rector Little Snake River Episc. Ch., Dixon, Wyo., 1977-82, Trinity Episc. Ch., Lander, Wyo., 1982-89, Christ Episc. Ch., Cody, Wyo., 1989—; rector, priest-in-charge Shoshone Episc. Ch., Ft. Washakie, Wyo., 1985-89; chmn. Wyo. Ch. Coalition, Laramie, 19988-92; dep. Gen. Convention Episc. Ch., Detroit, 1988, 91, 94. Contbr. articles to newspapers, mags.; author nature booklet Under the Firmament, 1989. Bd. dirs. Ring Lake Ranch, Dubois, Wyo., 1984-90; mem. nat. adv. bd., 1990—; organizer Orgn. of Orgns., Lackawanna, 1967-68; vol. Bayh for Pres., Boston, 1976; mem. Dixon Town Coun., 1979-82; mem. psychiat. adv. bd. Pine Ridge Hosp., Lander, 1984-88; bd. dirs. Crisis Intervention Ctr of Cody, 1991—, Wyo. Coun. for theHumanities, 1993—, pres. elect. 1995. Mem. Cody Ministerial Assn. Avocations: running, cross country skiing, hiking, nature studies, Western American history. Office: Christ Episc Ch 825 Simpson Ave # 1718 Cody WY 82414-4140

MURPHY, WILLIAM ALEXANDER, JR., diagnostic radiologist, educator; b. Pitts., Apr. 26, 1945; s. William Alexander and LaRue (Eshbaugh) M.; m. Judy Marie Lang, June 18, 1977; children: Abigail Norris, William Lawrence, Joseph Ryan. BS, U. Pitts., 1967; MD, Pa. State U., 1971. Diplomate Am. Bd. Radiology. Medicine intern Barnes Hosp., St. Louis, 1971-72, staff radiologist, 1975-93; radiology resident Washington U., St. Louis, 1972-75, prof. radiology, 1983-93; sect. chief Mallinckrodt Inst. Radiology, St. Louis, 1975-93; cons. Office Med. Examiner City and County St. Louis, 1977—; radiologist, prof. radiology, head divsn. diagnostic imaging, chmn. diagnostic radiology, John S. Dunn Sr. chair MD Anderson Cancer Ctr. U. Tex., 1993—. Contbr. numerous articles to profl. jours. and books. Fellow Am. Acad. Forensic Scis., Am. Coll. Radiology; mem. Radiol. Soc. N.Am., Am. Roentgen Ray Soc., Am. Soc. Bone and Mineral Research, Internat. Skeletal Soc., Assn. Univ. Radiologists. Methodist. Home: 4808 Bellview St Bellaire TX 77401-5306 Office: U Texas Anderson Cancer Ctr Div Dx Imaging 057 1515 Hollombe Blvd Houston TX 77030

MURPHY, WILLIAM JAMES, materials characterization company executive, metallurgical engineer; b. Lansing, Mich., Dec. 21, 1927; s. Leo Thomas and Kathryn (Wingeier) M.; m. Barbara Ann Byers, Oct. 16, 1976; children: Pamela, Cynthia D. Von Hofen, Carl W. B.S. in Metall. Engring., Wayne State U., 1949; M.S. in Metall. Engring., Lehigh U., 1951, Ph.D. in Metall. Engring., 1955. Metallurgist Gen. Electric Co., Lynn, Mass., 1951-52; asst. prof. Lehigh U., Bethlehem, Pa., 1952-57; div. chief U.S. Steel Research Lab., Monroeville, Pa., 1959-72, mgr. steel products, 1972-81, dir. corp. research, 1981-83; dir. contract research and tech. services USS Tech. Ctr., 1983-87; v.p. ops. RJ Lee Group, Monroeville, 1987-94; v.p., COO Advanced Tech. Sys., Monroeville, Pa., 1994-95. Fellow Am. Soc. Metals; mem. AIME, Metals Soc., Am. Welding Soc., Sigma Xi. Home: 5353 Beeler St Pittsburgh PA 15217-1062

MURPHY, WILLIAM MARK HICKEY, headmaster; b. Hartford, Conn., Dec. 7, 1944; s. William Mark Hickey II and Dorothy (MacVeagh) Hickey-Murphy; m. Grace Daniels, June 9, 1967; children: Christin, Jonathan, Kevin. BA, Norwich U., 1967; MA, U. Buffalo, 1969. History instr. Buffalo Sem., N.Y., 1969-72; investment officer Marine Midland Bank, Buffalo, 1972-76; asst. headmaster Park Sch. of Buffalo, 1976-79, headmaster, 1979-81, Keith Country Day Sch., Rockford, Ill., 1981-93; head of sch. Prairie Sch., Racine, Wis., 1993—. Mem. Greater Chgo. Assn. Ind. Schs., Coun. for Advancement and Support of Edn., Nat. Assn. Ind. Schs., Phi Alpha Theta. Avocations: golf, sailing, coaching ice hockey, skiing. Office: Prairie Sch 4050 Lighthouse Dr Racine WI 53402-3107

MURPHY, WILLIAM MICHAEL, literature educator, biographer; b. N.Y.C., Aug. 6, 1916; s. Timothy Francis and Florence Catherine (McDonald) M.; m. E. Harriet Doane, Sept. 2, 1939; children: David Timothy Michael, Susan Doane, Christopher Ten Broeck. B.A. magna cum laude, Harvard U., 1938, M.A., 1941, Ph.D., 1947. Instr. English Harvard U., 1938-40, 42-43, sec. univ. com. ednl. relations, 1940-42; asst. prof. English Union Coll., Schenectady, 1946-48, assoc. prof., 1948-60, prof., 1960-78, Thomas Lamont prof. ancient and modern lit., 1978-83, rsch. prof., 1983-94, prof. emeritus, 1995—; mem. adv. bd. Cornell Yeats Series, Ithaca, N.Y., 1978—; resident fellow Rockefeller Found. Study and Conf. Ctr., Bellagio, Italy, 1991. Author: David Worcester (1907-1947): A Memorial, 1953, The Yeats Family and the Pollexfens of Sligo, 1971, Prodigal Father: The Life of John Butler Yeats (1839-1922), 1978, Family Secrets: William Butler Yeats and His Relatives, 1995. Mem. N.Y. State com. U.S. Commn. on Civil Rights, 1962-74. Served to lt. USNR, 1943-46. Recipient Meritorious Service award United Negro Coll. Fund, 1967; fellow Am. Council Learned Soc., 1968; grantee Am. Philos. Soc., 1968, 75. Mem. MLA, AAUP, Am. Com. on Irish Studies, Can. Assn. Irish Studies, N.S. Bird Soc., Phi Beta Kappa (pres. Alpha chpt. 1954-56). Clubs: Harvard of Eastern N.Y. (pres. 1960-62); Fortnightly (Schenectady) (pres. 1966-67). Office: Humanities Bldg Union Coll Schenectady NY 12308

MURR, JAMES COLEMAN, federal government official; b. Lake Charles, La., Oct. 29, 1944; m. Connie Paige Chadwell, Sept. 21, 1968; children: Christopher David. Richard Reno. BA, Tex. Tech U., 1966; MPA, Am. U., 1974. With Sears, Roebuck & Co., Tex., 1971-72, Dept. Labor, Washington, 1972-74, U.S. Customs Svc., Treasury, Washington, 1975-76; legis. analyst Office Mgmt. and Budget, Washington, 1977-81, br. chief, 1982-89, assoc. dir. administrn., 1990-93, asst. dir. legis. reference, 1994—. Capt. USAF, 1967-70. Roman Catholic.

MURRA, JOHN VICTOR, anthropologist, educator; b. Odessa, Ukraine, Aug. 24, 1916; came to U.S., 1934, naturalized, 1950; B.A., U. Chgo., 1936, M.A., 1942, Ph.D., 1956; hon. doctorate, U. Barcelona, 1993. Instr. U. Chgo., 1943-47; asst. prof. U. P.R., 1947-49; from asst. prof. to prof. Vassar Coll., 1950-61; vis. prof. Yale, 1961-63; prin. investigator study Andes, NSF, 1963-66; vis. prof. U. San Marcos, Lima, Peru, 1958, 65-66; hon. prof. U. San Marcos, 1966; prof. anthropology Cornell U., 1968—; Lewis H. Morgan lectr. U. Rochester, 1969; area specialist UN Secretariat, 1951; founding mem. Inst. de Estudios Peruanos, Inst. Nacional de Antropologia e Historia of Ecuador; past mem. bd. Am. Com. Africa; mem. Inst. for Advanced Study, Princeton, 1974-75; directeur d'études associé Ecole des Hautes Etudes, Paris, 1975-76. Author: The Economic Organization of the Inka State, 1980. Served with Spanish Republican Army, 1937-39. Decorated Gran Cruz of Order of Sun (Perú); Guggenheim fellow, 1984-85. Mem. Am. Soc. Ethnohistory (pres. 1970-71), Am. Ethnol. Soc. (pres. 1972-73), Inst. Andean Research (pres. 1977—). Home: 515 Dryden Rd Ithaca NY 14850-4835

MURRAH, DAVID J., archivist, historian; b. Shattuck, Okla., Sept. 13, 1941; s. G. Leroy and M. Leila (Montgomery) M.; m. Sherry Edwards, Mar. 2, 1962 (div. 1966); 1 child, Jerel; m. Ann Lynskey, Dec. 29, 1973; children: Donna, Elaine, Gene. BA, Hardin-Simmons U., 1964; MA, Tex. Tech. U., 1970, PhD, 1979. Pub. sch. tchr. Springtown (Tex.) I.S.D., 1966-67, Morton (Tex.) I.S.D., 1967-71; asst. archivist S.W. Collection Tex. Tech U., Lubbock, 1971-76, asst. dir. S.W. Collection, 1976-77, dir. S.W. Collection, 1977-83, assoc. dir. librs., dir. S.W. Collection, 1983—; bd. dirs. Centercorp, Inc., Lubbock, 1990—. Author: C.C. Slaughter: Rancher, Banker, Baptist, 1981, Pitchfork Land and Cattle Co., 1983, Oil, Taxes and Cats, 1994; co-author: Lubbock & The South Plains, 1989. Bd. dirs. Broadway Festivals, Inc., Lubbock, 1990—. Recipient Disting. Svc. award Soc. Southwest Archivists, 1988. Mem. Soc. Am. Archivists, Tex. State Hist. Assn., West Tex. Hist. Assn. (pres. 1991-92). Democrat. Baptist. Office: Southwest Collection Tex Tech U PO Box 41041 Lubbock TX 79409-1041

MURRAY, ALAN STEWART, publishing executive; b. Akron, Ohio, Nov. 16, 1954; s. John and Catherine (Case) M.; m. Lori Esposito, Sept. 8, 1984; children: Lucy Ann, Amanda. BA in English, U. N.C.; MS in Econs, London Sch. Econs. Editor bus. and econs. Chattanooga Times, 1977-79; reporter Congrl. Quarterly, Washington, 1980-81, 82-83, Nihon Keizai Shimbun, Tokyo, 1981-82; reporter econs. Wall Street Jour., Washington, 1983-92, dep. bur. chief, 1992-93, bur. chief, 1993—. Co-author: Showdown At Gucci Gulch, 1987 (Carey McWilliams award 1988); panelist Sta. PBS, Washington in Rev.; commentary Sta. NBC, News at Sunrise. Bd. dirs. exec. com. Small Enterprise Assistance Fund, Washington, 1992—. Recipient Overseas Press Club award, 1991, Gerald Loeb award, 1992, Excellence in Bus./Fin. Journalism award John Hancock Fin. Svcs., 1992; John Motley Morehaed scholar; Luce fellow, Tokyo, 1981-82. Mem. U. N.C. Gen. Alumnus Assn. (bd. dirs. 1993—), Disting. Young Alumnus award), Gridiron Club, Phi Beta Kappa. Office: Wall St Jour 1025 Connecticut Ave NW Washington DC 20036

MURRAY, ALBERT L., writer, educator; b. Nokomis, Ala., May 12, 1916; s. John Lee and Sudie (Graham) Young; m. Mozelle Menefee, May 31, 1941; 1 child, Michele. B.S. in Edn., Tuskegee Inst., 1939; M.A. in English, NYU, 1948; postgrad., U. Mich., 1940, Northwestern U., 1941, U. Paris, 1950; Litt. D. (hon.), Colgate U., 1975. Tchr. undergrad. composition and lit. Tuskegee Inst., 1940-43, 46-51, also dir. Coll. Little Theatre, cons. on jazz; lectr. Grad. Sch. Journalism, Columbia U., N.Y.C., 1968; O'Connor prof. lit. Colgate U., 1970, O'Connor lectr., 1973, prof. humanities, 1982; vis. prof. lit. U. Mass., Boston, 1971; Paul Anthony Brick lectr. U. Mo., 1972; writer-in-residence Emory U., 1978; adj. assoc. prof. creative writing Barnard Coll., N.Y.C., 1981-83; lectr., participant symposia in field; duPont vis. scholar Washington and Lee U., 1993. Author: The Omni Americans, 1970, South to a Very Old Place, 1972, The Hero and the Blues, 1973, Train Whistle Guitar, 1974 (Lillian Smith award for fiction), Stomping the Blues, 1976 (ASCAP Deems Taylor award for music criticism), Good Morning Blues: The Autobiography of Count Basie as told to Albert Murray, 1985, TheSpyglass Tree, 1991; also numerous articles. Served to maj. USAAF, World War II; ret. USAAF. Woodrow Wilson fellow Drew U., 1983, Lincoln Ctr. Dirs. Emeriti award, 1991.

MURRAY, ALLEN EDWARD, oil company executive; b. N.Y.C., Mar. 5, 1929; s. Allen and Carla (Jones) M.; m. Patricia Ryan, July 28, 1951; children: Allen, Marilyn, Ellen, Eileen, Allison. B.S. in Bus. Adminstrn, NYU, 1956. Trainee Pub. Nat. Bank & Trust Co., N.Y.C., 1948-49; acct. Gulf Oil Corp., 1949-52; various fin. positions Socony-Vacuum Overseas Supply Co. (Mobil), 1952-56; with Mobil Oil Corp. (subs. Mobil Corp.), 1956—, v.p. planning N.Am. div., 1968-69, v.p. planning, supply and transp. N.Am. div., 1969-74, exec. v.p. N.Am. div., 1974, pres. U.S. mktg. and refining div., 1975-82, pres. worldwide mktg. and refining, 1979-82, corp. pres., 1983-84, COO, 1984-86, CEO, COO, chmn. exec. com., 1986—, chmn. bd., 1986—, also dir., 1976—; pres., chief operating officer Mobil Corp., N.Y.C., 1984-86, chmn., pres., chief exec. officer, 1986—, dir., 1977—; dir. Met. Life Ins. Co. Mem. adv. council Columbia U. Grad. Sch. Bus.; trustee Presbyn. Hosp., N.Y.C. Served with USNR, 1946-48. Mem. Nat. Fgn. Trade Council (dir.), Am. Petroleum Inst. (dir.), Council on Fgn. Relations. Club: Huntington Country. Office: Mobil Corp 3225 Gallows Rd Fairfax VA 22037

MURRAY, ANDREW, peace studies educator; b. Roanoka, Va., June 25, 1942; s. Max Andrew and Dorothy (Garst) M.; m. Teresa Kathleen Robinson, June 22, 1963; children: Kristin Alease, Kimberly Garst. AB, Bridgewater (Va.) Coll., 1964; MDiv, Bethany Theol. Sem., Oak Brook, Ill., 1968, DMin, 1980. Ordained to ministry Ch. of Brethren, 1968. Pastor Peace Ch. of Brethren, Portland, Oreg., 1968-71; campus min. Juniata Coll., Huntingdon, Pa., 1971-85, asst. prof. religion, 1973-85, prof. peace and conflict studies, 1986—, dir. peace and conflict studies, 1975—, dir. Baker Inst., 1986—; cons. to numerous colls. and univs. in U.S. and Can., 1975—; Staley disting. lectr. Staley Found., 1981, 88; vis. scholar Pa. State U., 1990; mem. Internat. Assn. Univ. Pres./UN Commn. on Arms Control, N.Y.C., 1991—; dir. UN Internat. Seminar on Arms Control and Disarmament, 1993—. Author: PACS as Applied Liberal Arts, 1984; writer, performer, producer rec. Just As I Am, 1991, also others. Mem. Pa. Commn. on Ministry in Higher Edn., 1979-86. Recipient Beechley award for disting. acad. svc. Juniata Coll., 1991. Mem. Nat. Peace Studies Assn. (charter, chmn. exec. com. 1988—), Nat. Pastors Assn. (pres. 1975). Democrat. Avocations: sailing, swimming, cooking, music, soaring. Home: 2110 Moore St Huntingdon PA 16652 Office: Juniata Coll Huntingdon PA 16652

MURRAY, ANNE, country singer; b. Springhill, N.S., Can., June 20, 1945; d. Carson and Marion (Burke) M.; m. William M. Langstroth, June 20, 1975; children: William Stewart, Dawn Joanne. B.Phys. Edn., U. N.B., 1966, D.Litt. (hon.), 1978; D.Litt. (hon.), St. Mary's U., 1982. Rec. artist for Arc Records, Can., 1968, Capitol Records, 1969—; appeared on series of TV spls., CBC, 1970-81, 88-93; star CBS spls., 1981-85; toured N. Am., Japan, England, Germany, Holland, Ireland, Sweden, Australia and New Zealand, 1977-82; released 31 albums including: A Little Good News, 1984, As I Am, 1988, Greatest Hits, vols. I, 1981, vol. II, 1989, Harmony, 1987, You Will, 1990, Yes I Do, 1991, Croonin', 1993, others. Hon. chmn. Can. Save the Children Fund, 1978-80. Recipient Juno awards as Can.'s top female vocalist, 1970-81; Can.'s Top Country Female Vocalist, 1970-86; Grammy award as top female vocalist-country, 1974; Grammy award as top female vocalist-pop, 1978; Grammy award as top female vocalist-country, 1980, 83; Country Music Assn. awards, 1983-84; named Female Rec. Artist of Decade, Can. Rec. Industry Assn., 1980, Top Female Vocalist 1970-86; star inserted in Hollywood Walkway of Stars, 1980; Country Music Hall of Fame Nashville; decorated companion Order of Can.; inducted Juno Hall of Fame, 1993. Mem. AFTRA, Assn. Canadian TV and Radio Artists, Am. Fedn. Musicians. Office: Balmur Ltd, 4950 Yonge St Madison Ctr 2400, Toronto, ON Canada M2N 6K1*

MURRAY, ARTHUR G., food products executive; b. 1945. Asst. corp. contr. Mickelberry Corp., Chgo., 1967-71; pres. Mama Cookie Bakeries Inc., Chgo., 1971-79; pres., CEO Salerno Magowen Biscuit Co., Chgo., 1979-84; exec. v.p. of ops. Sunshine Biscuits Inc., Woodbridge, N.J., 1984-88, pres., COO, 1988—. With U.S. Army, 1963-66. Office: Sunshine Biscuits Inc 100 Woodbridge Center Dr Woodbridge NJ 07095-1125

MURRAY, BILL, actor, writer; b. Evanston, Ill., Sept. 21, 1950; m. Margaret Kelly, 1980; children: Homer, Luke. Grad., Loyola Acad.; attended, Regis Coll., Denver; student, Second City Workshop, Chgo. Formerly with improvisational theater group Second City, Chgo.; writer/ performer off-broadway National Lampoon Radio Hour; regular on TV series Saturday Night Live, 1977-80, also writer; featured in 3 prodns. of, TVTV co.; played Johnny Storm, the Human Torch in radio series Marvel Comics' Fantastic Four; appeared in movies Meatballs, 1977, Mr. Mike's Mondo Video, 1979, Where the Buffalo Roam, 1980, Caddyshack, 1980, Stripes, 1981, Tootsie, 1982, Ghostbusters, 1984, The Razor's Edge, 1984, Nothing Lasts Forever, 1984, Little Shop of Horrors, 1986, Scrooged, 1988, Ghostbusters II, 1989, What About Bob?, 1991, Groundhog Day, 1993, Mad Dog and Glory, 1993, Ed Wood, 1994; co-producer, co-dir., actor film Quick Change, 1990; other TV appearances include Things We Did Last Summer. Recipient Emmy award for best writing for comedy series, 1977. Office: David Shapira & Assocs Inc 15301 Ventura Blvd Ste 345 Sherman Oaks CA 91403*

MURRAY, BILLY DWAYNE, SR., church administrator; b. Nash County, N.C., Apr. 8, 1930; m. Oma Lee Hensley; children: B. Dwayne, Jr., Susan Murray Duncan, Beth Murray Aukerman. Student, Kings Bus. Coll., Raleigh, N.C. Ordained to ministry, Ch. of God of Prophecy, 1950. Pastor Ch. God of Prophecy, Waynesville, N.C., 1950-51, Biltmore and Elk Mountain, N.C., 1951, Selma, N.C., 1954-58, Leaksville, N.C., 1958-61, Bethany, N.C., 1961-65, Greenville, S.C., 1965-66; served at N.C. state hdqs. Ch. God of Prophecy, 1951-54; gen. Sunday sch. sec. world hdqs. Ch. God of Prophecy, Cleveland, Tenn., 1966-72; state overseer Tenn. Ch. God of Prophecy, 1972-77; asst. editor White Wing Messenger, 1977-89; overseer Ill. Ch. God of Prophecy, 1989-90, gen. overseer, 1990—; chief usher Gen. Assembly, 1967-72; mem. questions and subjects com., mem. editorial com. ch. history, policy and doctrine, gen. properties com. Office: Church of God of Prophecy PO Box 2910 Cleveland TN 37320-2910

MURRAY, BRUCE C., planetary scientist, educator, administrator; b. N.Y.C., Nov. 30, 1931; married; 5 children. S.B., M.I.T., 1953, S.M., 1954; Ph.D. in Geology, M.I.T., 1955. Geologist California Co., La., 1955-58; geodesist Air Force Cambridge Research Labs., Mass., 1958-60; research fellow in planetary sci. Calif. Inst. Tech., 1960-63, asso. prof., 1963-68, prof., 1968—; dir. Jet Propulsion Lab., 1976-82; co-experimenter MAriner 4 TV expt., 1965, Mariner 6 and 7, 1969, Mariner 9, 1971-72; leader imaging team Mariner 10, 1973-75. Author: Navigating the Future, 1975, (with M. Daives) The View From Space, 1971, (with R. Greeley and M. Malin) Earthlike Planets, 1981, Journey Into Space, 1989; contbr. articles to profl. jours. Served with USAF, 1958-60. Achievement medal NASA, 1971, Disting. Public Svc. medal, 1974; Guggenheim fellow, 1975-76, 92—. Fellow Am. Geophys. Union (asso. editor Jour. Geophys. Research 1965-68, pres. planetology sect. 1974-75), Am. Acad. Arts and Scis. AAAS (bd. editors Sci. 1970-72, editorial adv. bd. Sci 80 1980—); mem. Am. Astron. Soc. Office: Calif Inst Tech Div Geol And Scis Pasadena CA 91125

MURRAY, BRYAN CLARENCE, professional sports team executive; b. Shawville, Que., Can., Dec. 5, 1942; came to U.S., 1980; s. Clarence Herbert and Rhoda (Schwartz) M.; m. Geraldine Frances Sutton, July 8, 1967; 1 dau., Heide Alicia. Grad., McGill U., 1964. Athletic dir. MacDonald Coll., Ste. Anne de Bellevue, Que., 1968-72; coach, tchr. Rockland Nat.-Pontiac High Sch., Rockland, Ont., 1974-76; coach Pembroke-Kings, Pembroke, Ont., 1976-79, Regina Pats, Sask., 1979-80, Hershey (Pa.) Bears, 1980-81; former coach Washington Capitals, Landover, Md., from 1981; coach, gen. mgr. Detroit Red Wings, 1990-94; gen. manager Florida Panthers, Fort Lauderdale, Flor., 1994—. Office: Florida Panthers 100 North East Third Ave 10th Fl Fort Lauderdale FL 33301

MURRAY, CAROLINE FISH, psychologist; b. Buenos Aires, Argentina, Mar. 28, 1920; came to U.S., 1924; d. Alfred Dupont and Caroline Johnston

(Ramsay) Chandler; m. Henry A. Murray, May 17, 1969; children by previous marriages: Caroline D. Janover, Alexander M. Davis, Ann Kelso D. MacLaughlin, Quita D. Palmer, Maude I. Fish. AB magna cum laude, Smith Coll., 1942; MEd, U. N.H., 1962; EdD, Boston U., 1967. Exec. sec. to dir. Alfred I. duPont Inst., Wilmington, Del., 1953-55; tchr. Kingston (N.H.) Pub. Schs., 1962-63; instr. Boston U., 1966-67, asst. prof. psychology, 1967-71, co-dir. psycho-educational clinic, 1966-70, coord. headstart evaluation and rsch. ctr., 1966-69, cons.; research asst. staff Mass. Mental Health Ctr., Boston, 1983-90; lectr. psychology dept. psychiatry Harvard Med. Sch., 1983-91; mem. profl. adv. com. Mass. Dept. Mental Health, 1983-85; cons. Indochinese Psychiatry Clinic, Brighton, Mass., 1987—, sch. consultation and treatment team Mass. Mental Health Ctr., 1987-90; mem. profl. adv. com. Mass. Dept. Mental Health, 1983-85, adolescent planning subcom., 1990—. Bd. dirs. Wediko Children's Svcs., 1975-85, Shaker Village, Hancock, Mass., Douglas A. Thom Clinic, Boston, 1974-77, pres., 1977; chmn. bd. Ariel Chamber Music, Cambridge, 1979, Mass. Children's Lobby, 1978-82, pres., 1979-81, Nantucket Edn. Trust, Friends of Nantucket Atheneum; chmn. statewide adv. council Office for Children, 1980-82. Mem. APA, Am. Assn. Advancement Psychology, Mass. Psychol. Assn., Eastern Psychol. Assn., N.Y. Acad. Scis., Fedn. Am. Sci., Jean Piaget Soc., Pi Lambda Theta. Democrat. Home: 11 Lincoln Ave Nantucket MA 02554-3412

MURRAY, CHARLES COURSEN, footwear manufacturing and retail company executive; b. Oak Park, Ill., Aug. 1, 1933; s. Charles Coursen Murray Sr. and Virginia McDowell (Fair) Hodgkins; m. Amanda Winter, Dec. 5, 1959; children: Marcelyn Amanda, Charles Coursen III, Christopher Winter. BA, Dartmouth Coll., 1956. Pres., chief exec. officer G.H. Bass & Co., Wilton, Maine, 1956-74, Murray Equipment Co., Farmington, Maine, 1975-79; v.p. mktg. Weinbrenner Shoe Co., Merrill, Wis., 1980-82; pres., chief exec. officer Ga. Boot Co., Franklin, Tenn., 1982-85; chmn., chief exec. officer Endicott (N.Y.) Johnson Corp., 1986—; mem. regional adv. bd. Chase-Lincoln 1st Bank, Binghamton, N.Y., 1986—. Mem. adv. com. SUNY Sch. Mgmt., Binghamton, 1986—; bd. dirs. United Way Broome County, Binghamton, 1987, Binghamton Symphony, 1986—. Mem. Footwear Industries Am. (chmn. bd. dirs. 1986—, named Exec. of Yr. 1985). Republican. Presbyterian. Clubs: Megantic Fish and Game (Eustis, Maine); Binghamton, Binghamton Country. Lodge: Masons (high priest 1959). Office: Endicott Johnson Corp 1100 E Main St Endicott NY 13760-5298

MURRAY, CHERRY ANN, physicist, researcher; b. Ft. Riley, Kans., Feb. 6, 1952; d. John Lewis and Cherry Mary (Roberts) M.; m. Dirk Joachim Muehlner, Feb. 18, 1977; children: James Joachim, Sara Hester. BS in Physics, MIT, 1973, PhD in Physics, 1978. Rsch. asst. physics dept. MIT, Cambridge, 1969-78; rsch. assoc. Bell Labs., Murray Hill, N.J., 1976-77; mem. tech. staff AT&T Bell Labs., Murray Hill, 1978-85, disting. mem. tech. staff, 1985-87, dept. head low-temperature and solid-state physics rsch., 1987-90, dept. head condensed matter physics rsch., 1990-93, dept. head semicond. physics rsch., 1993—; co-chair Gordon Rsch., Wolfeboro, N.H., 1982, chair, 1984. Contbr. numerous articles to profl. jours. and chpts. to books. NSF fellow, 1969; IBM fellow MIT, 1974-76. Fellow Am. Phys. Soc. (Maria Goeppart-Mayer award 1989), Sigma Xi. Office: AT&T Bell Labs Rm 1D 334 600 Mountain Ave Box 636 New Providence NJ 07974-0636

MURRAY, CHRISTOPHER CHARLES, III, architect; b. Bklyn., July 6, 1950; s. Christopher Charles and Gertrude Rose (Marr) M.; m. Ann Herring, Nov. 16, 1974. BArch, U. Notre Dame, 1973. Registered architect, N.Y., Md., D.C., Va., Ga. Project architect Hibner Architects, Garden City, N.Y., 1973-76; project mgr. BBM Architects, N.Y.C., 1976-79; project dir. Gensler & Assocs., N.Y.C., 1979-84, office dir., v.p., mem. nat. mgmt. com., 1984—. Prin. works include interior design Sidley & Austin Worldwide, Hewlett-Packard Regional HQ, Dept. Edn., First Am. Bankshares. Asst. scoutmaster Boy Scouts Am., also cubmaster, NCAC unit commr.; active Greater Washington Bd. Trade, 1986. Mem. AIA, N.Y. Soc. Architects, Md. Soc. Architects, Notre Dame Club, Club at Franklin Sq (bd. dirs.). Roman Catholic. Home: 12517 Knightsbridge Ct Rockville MD 20850-3732 Office: Gensler & Assocs 1101 17th St NW Washington DC 20036-4704

MURRAY, CONNEL LYLE, advertising and public relations executive, consultant; b. Lompoc, Calif., Feb. 22, 1928; s. Connel Victor and Mary Mandilla (Hostetler) M.; m. June Louise White, Jan. 9, 1954; children: Corinne Louise, Erin Lucille, Connel Raymond, Alison Reita. Student, Lewis and Clark Coll., 1944, 47; BA, San Francisco State Coll., 1954. Pub. relations account exec. Fred Gray & Assocs., San Francisco, 1954-55; v.p., owner Mitchell, Murray & Horn Pub. Relations, San Francisco, 1955-57; newswriter KRON-TV, San Francisco, 1957; account exec. various advt. cos., Calif., 1957-68; pres. Murray/Bradley Advt. and Pub. Relations, Anchorage, 1968-86, The Murray Group, Inc., Seattle, 1986—; cons. Bradley Advt., Anchorage, 1986—. Pres. YMCA, Anchorage, 1976; mem. found. bd. Evergreen State Coll., Olympia, Wash., 1987—. With USN, 1945-47. Recipient North Star award Alaska Visitors Assn., Juneau, 1976. Mem. Am. Assn. Advt. Agys. (Wash. chmn. 1986), Pub. Relations Soc. Am. (accredited, bd. govs. 1972—), Anchorage Yacht Club. Libertarian. Avocation: boating. Office: The Murray Group 3837 13th Ave W Ste 201 Seattle WA 98119-1359

MURRAY, CONSTANCE ANN, college dean; b. N.Y.C., Feb. 24, 1929; d. John Francis and Jeanne (Dur) M. B.S., Villanova U., 1959, M.A. in Secondary Edn., 1961; M.A. in English, Catholic U., 1969; Ph.D. in Higher Edn. Adminstrn, Syracuse U., 1976. Joined Sisters of the Holy Child Jesus; tchr. Oak Knoll Sch., Summit, N.J., 1957-58; prin., tchr. Sch. of the Holy Child, Rosemont, Pa., 1958-67; asst. prin., head English dept. Holy Child High Sch., Old Westbury, N.Y., 1967-69; resident adv. Syracuse U., 1969-71; adv., researcher Office Student Affairs, 1972-73, asst. to v.p. student affairs, 1973-74; student personnel intern Community Coll. of 213245 Lakes, Canandaigua, N.Y., 1971-72; asst. dean students Cornell U., 1974-76, assoc. dean, 1976-78; dean student services N.J. Inst. Tech., Newark, 1978-87 (on leave of absence), 89-90 (on leave of absence); faculty fellow, assoc. dir. project: Integrating the Scholarship on Gender, N.J. Dept. Social Scis. & Policy Studies; spl. lectr. Dept. Social Scis. and Policy Studies, N.J. Inst. Tech., 1993. Grantee Wharton Sch. Finance, 1978, faculty section Dept. Higher Edn. Mem. Am. Assn. Higher Edn., Am. Personnel and Guidance Assn., Nat. Assn. Women Deans, Adminstrs. and Counselors, Nat. Assn. Student Personnel Adminstrs., Nat. Womens Studies Assn., Assn. New Student Personnel Adminstrs. (charter), Student Personnel Assn. N.Y. State (charter). Roman Catholic. Home: 164 Brunswick St Jersey City NJ 07302-2331 Office: NJ Inst Tech Newark NJ 07102

MURRAY, DANIEL RICHARD, lawyer; b. Mar. 23, 1946; s. Alfred W. and Gloria D. Murray. AB, U. Notre Dame, 1967; JD, Harvard U., 1970. Bar: Ill. 1970, U.S. Dist. Ct. (no. dist.) Ill. 1970, U.S. Ct. Appeals (7th cir.) 1971, U.S. Supreme Ct. 1974. Ptnr. Jenner & Block, Chgo., 1970—; trustee Chgo. Mo. and Western Rlwy. Co., 1988—. Co-author: Illinois Code Comments, 1976, Secured Transactions, 1978. Bd. dirs. Big Shoulders Fund, Archdiocese of Chgo. Mem. Am. Bankruptcy Inst., Am. Law Inst., Am. Coll. Comml. Fin. Lawyers, Transp. Lawyers Assn., Assn. of Transp. Practitioners, Law Club, Legal Club. Roman Catholic. Home: 1307 N Sutton Pl Chicago IL 60610-2007 Office: Jenner & Block One IBM Plz Chicago IL 60611

MURRAY, DAVID, journalist, author; b. Boston, July 2, 1925; s. David and Jane (Davies) M.; m. Leda Feldman Hanson, July 12, 1990. A.B., Harvard, 1947. Student, Sorbonne, Paris, 1948. With Boston Herald-Traveler, 1946-48; European staff corr. U.P.I., 1948-52; asso. editor Newsweek mag., 1952-59; editor Fgn. News Service, N.Y.C., 1960-63; polit. reporter N.Y. Post, 1963-65, N.Y. Herald-Tribune, 1965-66; nat. polit. corr. Chgo. Sun-Times, 1966-77; press sec. to Gov. of N.Y. State, 1977-78; now working as publicist. Author: Charles Percy of Illinois, 1968; Contbr. articles to newspapers and periodicals. Home: Spring Hill New Lebanon NY 12125 Office: NY State Dept Transp Albany NY 12232

MURRAY, DAVID GEORGE, orthopaedic surgeon, educator; b. Ames, Iowa, July 1, 1930; s. William Gordon and Mildred (Furniss) M.; m. Lee McFarland, Dec. 27, 1952 (div. 1984); children: Christopher, Bruce, James; m. Judith M. Sayles, Aug. 4, 1984. Student, Cornell U., 1948-51; M.D., Washington U., St. Louis, 1955. Diplomate: Am. Bd. Orthopaedic Surgery.

Intern Vancouver (B.C., Can.) Gen. Hosp., 1955-56; asst. resident in surgery Upstate Med. Center, Syracuse, N.Y., 1958-59; resident in orthopedics State U. Iowa, Iowa City, 1959-62; asst. prof. orthopaedic surgery Upstate Med. Center, Syracuse, 1962-66; asso. prof. Upstate Med. Center, 1966-69, prof., 1969—, Disting. prof., 1990—, chmn. dept., 1966-86, 91—, acting chmn. dept., 1990-91; mem. staff State Univ. Hosp., Syracuse, 1962—, Crouse-Irving Meml. Hosp., Syracuse, 1962—, Syracuse VA Hosp., 1962—; cons. Community Gen. Hosp., Syracuse, 1965—; hon. staff Charles A. Wilson Meml. Hosp., Johnson City, N.Y., 1972—; med. dir. Muscular Dystrophy Assn. Clinic, 1962-67; mem. Task Force for Oral Exams., Nat. Bd. Med. Examiners; examiner Am. Bd. Orthopaedic Surgery. Bd. asso. editors: Jour. Bone and Joint Surgery, 1969-78, Clin. Orthopaedics, 1968-78, Jour. Surg. Research, 1972-82, Orthopaedic Surgery, 1978-79; contbr. articles to profl. jours.; trustee Am. Jour. Bone and Joint Surgery, 1984-90, treas., 1986-90. Bd. dirs. Planned Parenthood Ctr. of Syracuse; chmn. affiliate med. com. Planned parenthood Ctr. of Syracuse, 1976-82; trustee Orthopaedic Rsch. Edn. Found., 1986-92, pres., 1988-91, Martin Momoriac Found., 1988-92, chmn., 1990-92; mem. med. adv. com. Shirners Hosps., 1989-93. Served to lt. M.C. USNR, 1956-57. Mem. Am. Acad. Orthopaedic Surgeons (pres. 1982-83), AMA, Am. Orthopaedic Assn. (exec. com., chmn. program com. 1982), Assn. Acad. Surgery (sec.-treas., chmn. com. constn. and bylaws), N.Y. State Med. Soc., Onondaga County Med. Soc. (v.p. 1989-90, pres. 1992-93), ACS (vice chmn. 1992-93, chmn. bd. regents 1985-94, chmn. 1993-94), Am. Rheumatism Assn., AAAS, Orthopaedic Research Soc., Assn. Bone and Joint Surgeons, Continental Orthopaedic Soc., Knee Soc. (pres. 1989), N.Y. State Soc. Orthopaedic Surgeons, Assn. Orthopaedic Chmn., Phi Beta Kappa, Sigma Xi, Alpha Omega Alpha. Home: 5 Quaker Hill Rd Syracuse NY 13224-2011 Office: 750 E Adams St Syracuse NY 13210-2306

MURRAY, DAVID GEORGE, architect; b. Tulsa, Nov. 9, 1919; s. Lee Cloyd and Marion (Bennett) M.; m. Margaret Elizabeth Oldham, Sept. 23, 1944; children: Michael Allen, Lucy Margaret (Mrs. Norman Scheer), Patrick David. BArch, Okla. State U., 1942. Registered architect, Okla. Ptnr. Atkinson & Murray, Tulsa, 1949-52; prin. David G. Murray & Assocs., Tulsa, 1952-56; pres. Murray, Jones, Murray, Inc., Tulsa, 1957-85, chmn., 1986-89; chmn., bd. govs. Licensed Architects, Oklahoma City, 1964-74. Prin. works include Cities Service Technology Ctr., Broken Arrow, Okla., Terminal Bldg. Tulsa Internat. Airport, St. Patrick's Ch., Oklahoma City, Coll. of Osteopathic Medicine and Surgery, Tulsa, First Nat. Tower, Tulsa, Hillcrest Med. Ctr., Tulsa, Thomas Gilcrease Mus., Tulsa, Tulsa Civic Ctr. Bldgs. Chmn., dir. Goodwill Industries of Tulsa, 1966-87; chmn., exec. com. Downtown Tulsa Unltd., 1975-87; v.p. chmn., exec. com., dir. Met. Tulsa C. of C., 1979-85. Served to 1st lt. USAF, 1942-45. Named to Hall of Fame Coll. Engring. Okla. State U., 1969. Fellow AIA (pres. Tulsa chpt. 1964, mem. com. office practice 1983-87); mem. Southern Hills Country Club (dir. 1977-80). Republican. Methodist. Avocations: travel, golf.

MURRAY, DIANE ELIZABETH, librarian; b. Detroit, Oct. 15, 1942; d. Gordon Lisle and Dorothy Anne (Steketee) LaBoueff; m. Donald Edgar Murray, Apr. 22, 1968. AB, Hope Coll., 1964; MLS, Western Mich. U., 1968; MM, Aquinas Coll., 1982; postgrad., Mich. State U., East Lansing, 1964-66. Catalog libr., asst. head acquisitions sect. Mich. State U. Librs., East Lansing, 1968-77; libr. tech. and automated svcs. Hope Coll., Holland, Mich., 1977-88; dir. librs. DePauw U., Greencastle, Ind., 1988-91; acquisitions libr. Grand Valley State U., Allendale, Mich., 1991—; sec., vice chair, chairperson bd. trustees Mich. Libr. Consortium, Lansing, 1981-85. Vice pres. Humane Soc. of Putnam County, Greencastle, 1990-91. Mem. ALA. Methodist. Avocations: dog breeding and showing. Office: Grand Valley State U Zumberge Libr Allendale MI 49401

MURRAY, EDDIE CLARENCE, professional baseball player; b. L.A., Feb. 24, 1956. Student, Calif. State U., L.A. Player minor league teams Bluefield, Miami, Asheville, Charlotte, Rochester, 1973-76; player Balt. Orioles, 1973-88, L.A. Dodgers, 1988-91, N.Y. Mets, 1991-93, Cleveland Indians, 1993—. Named to All-Star Team, 1978, 81-86, 91; named Appalachian League Player of Yr., 1973, Am. League Rookie of Yr., Baseball Writers Assn. Am., 1977, First Baseman, Sporting News Am. League All-Star Team, 1983, 90; recipient Gold Glove award, 1982-84, Silver Slugger award, 1983-84, 90. Office: Cleve Indians 2401 Ontario St Cleveland OH 44115*

MURRAY, ELIZABETH, artist; b. Chgo., 1940; married; 1 child, Dakota Sunseri. B.F.A., Art Inst., Chgo., 1962; M.F.A., Mills Coll., Oakland, Calif., 1964. Vis. instr. Wayne State U., 1975, Calif. Inst. Arts, 1975-76, Chgo. Art Inst., 1975-76; instr. Bard Coll., Annandale on Hudson, N.Y., 1974-75, 76-77, Princeton U., 1977, Yale U., 1978-79. One-woman shows Jacobs Ladder Gallery, Washington, 1974, Paula Cooper Gallery, N.Y.C., 1975, 76, 78, 81, 83, 88, 89, Jared Sable Gallery, 1975, Ohio State U., Columbus, 1978, Phyllis Kind Gallery, Chgo., 1978, Galerie Mukai, Tokyo, 1980, Susanne Hilberry Gallery, Birmingham, Mich., 1980, Smith Coll. Art Gallery, Northampton, Mass., 1982, Daniel Weinberg Gallery, Los Angeles, 1982, Portland Ctr. Visual Arts, Oreg., 1983, Knight Gallery, Charlotte, N.C., 1984, Mayor Rowen Gallery, London, 1989, Barbara Krakow Gallery, Boston, 1990, Gallery Mukai, Tokyo, 1990, John Berggruen Gallery, San Francisco, 1990; group shows include, Whitney Mus. Am. Art, N.Y.C., 1972, 73, 77, 79, 81, 82, 84, John Doyle Gallery Cologne, Ger., 1974, Paula Cooper Gallery, 1974, 76, 77, 78, 79, 81, 82, 83, 84, Michael Walls Gallery, N.Y., 1975, Middlebury (Vt.) Coll., 1976, Gallery of July and August, Bradford, N.Y., 1976, Susanne Hilberry Gallery, Detroit, 1976, Guggenheim Mus., N.Y.C., 1977, Sarah Lawrence Coll. Gallery, Bronxville, N.Y., 1977, Lowe Art Gallery Syracuse U., 1977, Mus. Contemporary Art, Chgo., 1977, Inst. Contemporary Art, U. Pa., 1978, Tampa Bay Art Center, Fla., 1978, Phyllis Kind Gallery, Chgo., 1979, William Paterson Coll., Wayne, N.J., 1979, Susan Caldwell Gallery N.Y., 1979, U. N.C. Weatherspoon Art Gallery, Greensboro, 1979, Galerie Yvon Lambert, Paris, 1980, Bklyn. Mus., 1980, Dart Gallery, Chgo., 1981, Contemporary Arts Center, Cin., 1981, High Mus. Art, Atlanta, 1981, 82, Galerie Mukai, Tokyo, 1981, Va. Mus., Richmond, 1981, Boston Mus. Fine Arts, 1982, Milw. Art Mus., 1982, Art Inst. Chgo., 1982, Daniel Weinberg Gallery, Los Angeles and San Francisco, 1983, Hirshhorn Mus., Washington, 1983, Hobart and William Smith Colls., Geneva, N.Y., 1983, Mus. Art, Ft. Lauderdale, Fla., 1986, 40th Biennial Exhbn. Comtemp. Am. Paintings Corcoran Gallery of Art, 1988, numerous others; represented in permanent collections, Whitney Mus. Am. Art, N.Y.C., Guggenheim Mus., Hirshhorn Mus. and Sculpture Garden, Washington, H.H.K. Found., Milw., St. Louis Art Mus., Detroit Inst. Arts. Recipient Walter M. Campana award Art Inst. of Chgo., 1982, Skowhegan Prize Painting, 1986. mem. Am. Acad and Inst. of Arts and Letters, 1992. Office: care Paula Cooper Gallery 155 Wooster St New York NY 10012-3159

MURRAY, ELIZABETH DAVIS REID, writer, lecturer; b. Wadesboro, N.C., June 10, 1925; d. James Matheson and Mary Kennedy (Little) Davis; A.B. cum laude, Meredith Coll., Raleigh, N.C., 1946; postgrad. N.C. State U., 1967-68, 74-75; m. James William Reid, Feb. 7, 1948 (dec. June 1972); children: Michael Ernest, Nancy Kennedy Reid Baker, James William; m. Raymond L. Murray, May 12, 1979; stepchildren: Stephen, Ilah Murray Garton, Marshall. Continuity writer Sta. WPTF, Raleigh, 1946-47; program mgr., women's commentator Sta. WADE, Wadesboro, 1947-48; dir. news bur. Meredith Coll., 1948-51; state woman's news editor, columnist Raleigh News and Observer, 1951-52; exec. sec. Gov.'s Coordinating Com. on Aging, 1959-61; rsch. asst. to Dr. Clarence Poe, Raleigh, 1963-64; contbg. editor Raleigh Mag., 1969-72; local history corr. Raleigh Times, News and Observer, Spectator of Raleigh; lectr. art and local history; tchr. Wake history Wake Tech. Coll., Wake pub. schs. and librs.; rsch. cons. Wake County Pub. Libraries, Mordecai Historic Park, State Visitor Ctr., Exec. Mansion; resource person Wake Public Schs.; dir. Capital County Pub. Co.; writer; books include: From Raleigh's Past (cert. of commendation Am. Assn. State and Local History), 1965; Wake: Capital County of North Carolina, vol. 1, 1983 (W.P. Peace award for best book on N.C. history 1983); editor, compiler: North Carolina's Older Population: Opportunities and Challenges, 1960; editor, contbr. Wake County Hist. Soc. newsletter, 1965-69; History of Raleigh Fire Dept., 1970; guest editor Raleigh Mag. Wake County Bicentennial Issue, 1971; author, photographer filmstrip for Wake Pub. Schs., 1971; author sect. Windows of the Way, 1964; Am. arts slide lectures for pub. library; author instructional materials State Exec. Mansion and Mordecai Hist. Park docents; author monthly history page Raleigh Mag., 1969-72; contbr. biog. sketches Dictionary of North Carolina Biography, 1979; contbr. to newspapers and mags. Mem. Raleigh City Council, 1973;

pres. Jr. Woman's Club, 1956-57; organizing pres. Arts Council Raleigh, 1965; exec. com. N.C. Humanities Found., 1974-76; dir., officer North Carolinians for Better Libraries, 1965-69; mem. Meredith Bd. Assos., 1976-79; trustee Pub. Libraries, 1956-67, Meredith Coll., 1966-69; pres. Wake Meml. Hosp. Aux., 1962-63; mem. Raleigh Hist. Sites Commn., 1969-73; trustee Pullen Meml. Bapt. Ch., 1975-78, chmn., 1977-78, also deacon; chmn. Mayor's Com. to Preserve Hist. Objects, 1965—; mem. Tryon Palace Commn., 1967-78; adv. council WUNC-FM, 1976-80, N.C. Art Soc.; vis. lectr. N.C. Mus. History Assos., 1980; docent, lectr. N.C. Exec. Mansion, Mordecai Hist. Park, N.C. Mus. Art; bd. dirs. Raleigh-Wake County Symphony Orch. Devel. Assn. 1979-83, Estey Hall Found., 1980—, Friends of Meredith Library, 1980-83; mem. adv. bd. Raleigh City Mus., mem. task force on local history; bldg. adv. com. local history Wake County Pub. Libr.; com. 1000 to establish Children's Mus. About World. Recipient Outstanding Community Service award, 1952, best all-round Jr. Woman's Club mem., 1955, Disting. Alumna award Meredith Coll., 1970, recognition for service award Raleigh Hist. Sites Commn., 1973, Raleigh City Council, 1973; Community Service award Raleigh Bd. Realtors, 1983, Phi Beta Kappa award Wake County, 1985, Silver Bowl award N.C. Mus. of Art, 1987, Anthemion award Capital Area Preservation Inc., 1994. Mem. N. Caroliniana Soc., N.C. Soc. County and Local Historians (life), N.C. Lit. and Hist. Assn., Apex Hist. Soc. (charter), Yates Mill Assocs., Inc. (charter), N.C. Art Soc. (Disting. Service citation 1979), Docents N.C. Mus. Art (pres. 1980-81), Friends of N.C. State U. Library, Friends of Carlyle Campbell Library (charter, life), Wake County Hist. Soc. (Pres.'s Cup 1994), Wake County Genealogical Soc., N.C. African-Am. Genealogical and Hist. Soc., Friends of N.C. Archives (life), Kappa Nu Sigma. Democrat. Clubs: Carolina Country, Capital City (charter mem.). Home: 8701 Murray Hill Dr Raleigh NC 27615-2531

MURRAY, ERNEST DON, artist, educator; b. Asheville, N.C., Apr. 21, 1930; s. Ernest Burgin and Daisy Ann (Bishop) M. Student, Asheville-Biltmore Jr. Coll., 1950; A.A., B.A., U. Tenn., 1952; student, Art Students League, 1953; M.F.A., U. Fla., 1957, M.Ed., 1958. Instr. art Chipola Jr. Coll., Marianna, Fla., 1958; head div. humanities Chipola Jr. Coll., 1964-68; instr. humanities U. Fla., Gainesville, 1969-72; prof. humanities, asso. chmn. dept. humanities U. Fla., 1974-78, prof. fine art and humanities dept. fine art, 1978—; cons. Holt, Rinehart & Winston, Inc., N.Y.C., 1963-76, Harcourt Brace, Jovanovich, Inc., N.Y.C., 1964-76. One-man shows in Knoxville, Tex., 1952, N.Y.C., 1953, Gainesville, 1968, 71, 72, 75, 90, 93, Pub. Sculpture Commns., 1989, 90, 91, 93, 95, Fla. Mus. Natural History, Fla. State Fire Coll., Mathieson Hist. Ctr.; exhibited in group shows Asheville, 1949, Knoxville, 1951, 65, N.Y.C., 1953, 61, 67, Gainesville, Miami, Tallahassee, 1979—; represented in pvt. collections. With C.E. U.S. Army, 1954-56, USNR, 1949-54. Mem. So. Highlands Craftsman's Guild, Fla. Artists Assn., Phi Theta Kappa, Phi Kappa Phi, Phi Beta Kappa. Unitarian. Office: Univ of Florida 302C Architecture and Fine Arts Gainesville FL 32601

MURRAY, FLORENCE KERINS, state supreme court justice; b. Newport, R.I., Oct. 21, 1916; d. John X. and Florence (MacDonald) Kerins; m. Paul F. Murray, Oct. 21, 1943; 1 child, Paul F. AB, Syracuse U., 1938; LLB, Boston U., 1942; EdD, R.I. Coll. Edn., 1956; grad., Nat. Coll. State Trial Judges, 1966; LLD (hon.), Bryant Coll., 1956, U. R.I., 1963, Mt. St. Joseph Coll., 1972, Providence Coll., 1974, Roger Williams Coll., 1976, Salve Regina Coll., 1977, Johnson and Wales Coll., 1977, Suffolk U., 1981. Bar: Mass. 1942, R.I. 1947, U.S. Dist. Ct. 1948, U.S. Tax Ct. 1948, U.S. Supreme Ct. 1948. Sole practice Newport, 1947-52; mem. firm Murray & Murray, Newport, 1952-56; assoc. judge R.I. Superior Ct., 1956-78; presiding justice Superior Ct. R.I., 1978-79; assoc. justice R.I. Supreme Ct., 1979—; staff, faculty adv. Nat. Jud. Coll., Reno, Nev., 1971-72, dir., 1975-77, chmn., 1979-87, chair emeritus, 1990—; mem. com. Legal Edn. and Practice and Economy of New Eng., 1975—; former instr. Prudence Island Sch.; legal adv. R.I. Girl Scouts; sec. Commn. Jud. Tenure and Discipline, 1975-79; apptd. by Pres. Clinton to bd. dirs. State Justice Inst., 1994—; participant, leader various legal seminars. Mem. R.I. Senate, 1948-56; chmn. spl. legis. com.; mem. Newport Sch. Com., 1948-57, chmn., 1951-57; mem. Gov.'s Jud. Coun., 1950-60, White House Conf. Youth and Children, 1950, Ann. Essay Commn., 1952, Nat. Def. Adv. Com. on Women in Service, 1952-58, Gov.'s Adv. Com. Mental Health, 1954, R.I. Alcoholic Adv. Com., 1955-58, R.I. Com. Youth and Children, Gov.'s Adv. Com. on Revision Election Laws, Gov.'s Adv. Com. Social Welfare, Army Adv. Com. for 1st Army Area; mem. civil and polit. rights com. Pres.'s Commn. on Status of Women, 1960-63; mem. R.I. Com. Humanities, 1972—, chmn., 1972-77; mem. Family Ct. Study Com., R.I. com. Nat. Endowment Humanities; bd. dirs. Newport YMCA; sec. Bd. Physicians Service; bd. visitors Law Sch., Boston U.; bd. dirs. NCCJ; mem. edn. policy and devel. com. Roger Williams Jr. Coll.; trustee Syracuse U.; pres. Newport Girls Club, 1974-75, R.I. Supreme Ct. Hist. Soc., 1988—; chair Supreme Ct. Mandatory Continuing Legal Edn. Com., 1993—. Served to lt. col. WAC, World War II. Decorated Legion of Merit; recipient Arents Alumni award Syracuse U., 1956, Carroll award R.I. Inst. Instn., 1956, Brotherhood award NCCJ, 1983, Herbert Harley award Am. Judicature Soc., 1988, Melvin Eggers Sr. Alumni award Syracuse U., 1992, Merit award R.I. Bar Assn., 1994; named Judge of Yr. Nat. Assn. Women Judges, 1984, Outstanding Woman, Bus. and Profl. Women, 1972, Citizen of Yr. R.I. Trial Lawyers Assn.; Newport courthouse renamed in her honor, 1990. Mem. ABA (Chm. credentials com. nat. conf. state trial judges 1971-73, chair judges adv. com. on standing com. on ethics and profl. responsibility 1991—, joint com. on jud. discipline of standing com. on profl. discipline 1991-94), AAUW (chmn. state edn. com. 1954-56), Am. Arbitration Assn., Nat. Trial Judges Conf. (state chmn. membership com., sec. exec. com.), New Eng. Trial Judges Conf. (com. chmn. 1967), Boston U. Alumni Coun., Am. Legion (judge adv. post 7, mem. nat. exec. com.), Bus. and Profl. Women's Club (past state v.p., past pres. Newport chpt., past pres. Nat. legis. com.), Auota Club (past gov. internat., past pres. Newport chpt.), Alpha Omega, Kappa Beta Pi. Office: RI Supreme Ct 250 Benefit St Providence RI 02903

MURRAY, FRANCIS J., JR., energy executive. Chmn. bd. dirs. N.Y. State Energy Rsch., Albany, N.Y. Office: NY State Energy Rsch 2 Rockefeller Plz Albany NY 12223

MURRAY, FRED F., lawyer; b. Corpus Christi, Tex., Aug. 1, 1950; s. Marvin Frank and Suzanne Louise M.; m. Susan McKeen. BA, Rice U., 1972; JD, U. Tex., 1974. Bar: Tex. 1975, U.S. Dist. Ct. (so. dist.) Tex. 1976, U.S. Ct. Claims 1976, U.S. Tax Ct. 1976, U.S. Ct. Appeals (5th, D.C. and fed. cirs.) 1976, U.S. Supreme Ct. 1978, U.S. Ct. Internat. Trade 1985, N.Y. 1987, D.C. 1987, U.S. Dist. Ct. (ea. dist.) Tex. 1987; CPA, Tex. Ptnr. Chamberlain, Hrdlicka, White, Williams & Martin, P.C., Houston, 1985-92; spl. counsel (legislation) U.S. Dept. Treasury, IRS, Washington, 1992—; mem. Tax Law Adv. Commn., Tex. Bd. Legal Specialization, 1984—, vice chmn., 1987-92; mem. Commn. Tax Law Examiners, 1984—, vice chmn., 1987-92; adj. prof. U. Houston Law Ctr., 1984-92, U. Tex. Sch. Law, 1987; faculty lectr. Rice U. Jones Grad. Sch. Adminstrn., 1987-92; speaker various assns. and univs.; mem. bd. advisors Houston Jour. Internat. Law, 1986—, chmn., 1987-91. Author various publs. Del. Bishop's Diocesan Pastoral Coun., 1979-80; chmn. parish coun. Sacred Heart Cathedral, Cath. Diocese Galveston-Houston, 1979-81, 89, mem. Red Mass steering com., 1986-92; mem. exec. com., bd. dirs., 1987-91, chmn. deferred giving com. Houston Symphony Soc., 1987-88, chmn. govt. and pub. affairs com., 1988-91; co-trustee Houston Symphony Soc. Endowment Fund, 1987-91; mem. fund coun. Rice U., 1987—; exec. com. 1988-92, chmn. Major Gifts Com., 1988-92; gen. counsel, bd. dirs., com. on fin. and adminstrn. S.E. Tex. chpt. Nat. Multiple Sclerosis Soc.; mem. Red Mass com. Archdiocese Washington, 1993—. Fellow Am. Coll. Tax Counsel; mem. ABA (officer various coms.), Am. Arbitration Assn. (panels comml. and internat. arbitrators 1980—), Internat. Bar Assn., Houston Bar Assn., State Bar of Tex. (various coms.), N.Y. State Bar Assn., D.C. Bar Assn., AICPA, Tex. Soc. CPAs, Internat. Tax Forum of Houston (sec. 1981-84, pres. 1984-92), Internat. Fiscal Assn., Am. Soc. Internat. Law, Am. Fgn. Law Assn., Am. Law Inst. (tax adv. group 1990—), Fed. Bar Assn.

MURRAY, G(LENN) RICHARD, JR., lawyer; b. Cincinnati, Ohio, Feb. 5, 1930; s. Glenn Richard and Helen (Guminger) M.; m. Deborah Cruzen, Apr. 15, 1980. B.A., Yale U., 1951; LL.B. magna cum laude, Harvard, 1957. Bar: Calif. 1958. Assoc. McCutchen, Doyle, Brown & Enersen and predecessor firms, San Francisco, 1958-63, 65-66, pntr., 1966—. Editor Harvard Law Rev., 1957-58. Served to lt. USNR, 1951-54; Korea. Sheldon fellow Harvard U., 1957-58. Fellow Am. Coll. Trial Lawyers; mem. Am. Judicature Soc. Club: Pacific-Union (San Francisco). Avocations: sailing; hiking; gardening. Home: 27 Makin Grade PO Box 1172 Ross CA 94957-1172 Office: McCutchen Doyle Brown & Enerson 3 Embarcadero Ctr San Francisco CA 94111-4003

MURRAY, GREGORY S., lawyer; b. Phila., Apr. 19, 1949. AB, U. Notre Dame, 1971; JD, U. Va., 1974. Bar: Ill. 1974. Ptnr. Winston & Strawn, Chgo. Mem. ABA, Ill. State Bar Assn. Office: Winston & Strawn 35 W Wacker Dr Chicago IL 60601-1614

MURRAY, GROVER ELMER, geologist, educator; b. Maiden, N.C., Oct. 26, 1916; s. Grover Elmer and Lucy (Lore) M.; m. Nancy Beatrice Setzer, June 21, 1941 (dec. Sept. 1985); children: Martha Murray Poag, Barbara Elizabeth Baca; m. Sally Marie Sowell Williams, Oct. 26, 1986. B.S., U. N.C., 1937; M.S., La. State U., 1939, Ph.D., 1942. Rsch. geologist La. Geol. Survey, 1938-41; geologist Magnolia Petroleum Co., Jackson, Miss., 1941-48; prof. dept. geology La. State U., 1948-55, chmn. dept., 1950-53, Boyd prof. geology, 1955-66, cons. prof. geology, 1966—, v.p., dean acad. affairs, 1963-65; v.p. acad. affairs La. State U. System, 1965-66; pres. prof. geosci. Tex. Tech U., Lubbock, 1966-76; pres. Tex. Tech U. Sch. Medicine, 1969-76; Univ. prof., prof. geosci. Tex. Tech U. Complex, 1976-87; Univ. prof. emeritus and pres. emeritus Tex. Tech. U. and Tex. Tech. U. Sch. Medicine, 1988—; founder Ranching Heritage Ctr. Tex. Tech U., dir. Niger Agrl. Project, 1976-78; prof. La. State U. geology camp, Colo., 1949, 51, La., 1961; dir. U. Tex. geology camp, East Tex., 1949, 51; vis. lectr. Tex., 1958; dir. Global Exploration Inc.; bd. govs. Icasals, Inc., 1967-76; mem. Internat. Sub commn. on Stratigraphic Classification, 1955—; cons. geologist, 1988—; chmn. U.S. Nat. Com. on Geology, 1964-68; dir. NSF project for basic geologic studies in, Northeastern Mex., 1956-66; mem. Nat. Sci. Bd., 1968-80, vice chmn., 1978-80; mem. Tex. Natural Fibers and Food Protein Commn., 1966-76; U.S. del. Internat. Geol. Congresses, Mex., 1956, Scandinavia, 1960, India, 1964, Czechoslovakia, 1968, Can., 1972, U.S.A. 1989, hon. mem.; bd. dirs. Ashland Oil Inc., 1977-87, dir. emeritus, 1987—; Author: Geology of Atlantic and Gulf Coastal Province of North America, 1961; Contbr. articles to ednl., sci. jours. Bd. dirs. Africare, Inc., 1975-86, Tex. Ptnrs. with Peru. Recipient Disting. Alumnus award U. N.C., 1971, La. State U., 1988, Hollis D. Hedberg award in energy La. State U.-Inst. for Study of Earth and Man, So. Meth. U., 1986. Fellow Geol. Soc. Am. (chmn. symposium on sedimentary vols. in Coastal Plain, U.S. and Mex. 1952, commr. Am. Stratigraphic Commn. 1951-54, program chmn. New Orleans Meeting 1955, councilor 1961-64, gen. chmn. New Orleans meeting 1967, chmn. Southeastern sect. 1960); mem. Am. Assn. Petroleum Geologists (hon., chmn. com. geol. names and nomenclature 1952-54, Disting. lectr. 1954, editor 1959-63, pres. 1964-65, mem. Am. Stratigraphic Commn. 1957-63, hon. mem. 1972, Sidney Powers Meml. medal 1983), Soc. Econ. Paleontologists and Mineralogists (editor Jour. Paleontology 1952-54, chmn. rsch. com. 1958-59, pres. 1963-64, hon. mem. Gulf Coast sect. 1973, hon. mem. Permian Basin sect. 1992, hon. mem. nat. soc. 1981, mem. assn. found. 1986-89), Am. Geol. Soc. Am., Mineral Soc. Am., Am. Ceramic Soc. (v.p. 1974-75), Tech. Assn. Pulp and Paper Industry); mem. Clay Minerals Soc. (pres. 1965-66, Disting. mem. 1980), Soc. Mining Metallurgy and Exploration (dist. mem., pres. elect 1987, pres. 1988, Hal Williams Hardinge award 1976, found. bd. trustees 1993—), Internat. Clay Minerals Soc. (pres. 1993—), Am. Assn. Petroleum Geologists, Am. Inst. Profl. Geologists (pres.-elect 1990, pres. 1991), Am. Geol. Inst. Found. (dir. 1990—), Geol. Soc. Am. Fdn. Home: 3790 S Inverness Farm Rd Bloomington IN 47401-9110

MURRAY, HAYDN HERBERT, geology educator; b. Kewanee, Ill., Aug. 31, 1924; s. Herbert A. and Ardis M. (Adams) M.; m. Juanita A. Appenheimer, Dec. 16, 1944; children: Steven, Marilyn, Lisa. B.S., U. Ill., 1948, M.S., 1950, Ph.D., 1951. Asst. prof. geology Ind. U., 1951-53, assoc. prof., 1953-57, prof., chmn. dept. geology, 1973-84, prof. geology, 1984-94, prof. emeritus, 1994—; dir. research Georgia Kaolin Co., Elizabeth, N.J., 1957-60; mgr. ops. Georgia Kaolin Co., 1960-62, v.p. ops., 1962-64, exec. v.p., 1964-73; dir. Oil-Dri Corp. Am. Contbr. numerous articles to profl. jours.; patentee in field. Trustee Union Found., E.J. Grassmann Trust. Served with AUS, 1943-46. Recipient Disting. Svc. award Ind. U., 1993. Fellow Geol. Soc. Am., Mineral Soc. Am., Am. Ceramic Soc. (v.p. 1974-75), Tech. Assn. Pulp and Paper Industry; mem. Clay Minerals Soc. (pres. 1965-66, Disting. mem. 1980), Soc. Mining Metallurgy and Exploration (dist. mem., pres. elect 1987, pres. 1988, Hal Williams Hardinge award 1976, found. bd. trustees 1993—), Internat. Clay Minerals Soc. (pres. 1993—), Am. Assn. Petroleum Geologists, Am. Inst. Profl. Geologists (pres.-elect 1990, pres. 1991), Am. Geol. Inst. Found. (dir. 1990—), Geol. Soc. Am. Fdn. Home: 3790 S Inverness Farm Rd Bloomington IN 47401-9110

MURRAY, HENRY WILKE, physician, educator; b. Washington, Oct. 28, 1946; s. Albert Francis and Elizabeth (Wilke) M.; m. Diana Telling, June 14, 1969; children: Kathryn Elizabeth, John Henry. BA, Cornell U., 1968, MD, 1972. Diplomate Am. Bd. Internal Medicine, Am. Bd. Infectious Diseases. Intern, then resident N.Y. Hosp., N.Y.C., 1972-74, chief med. resident, 1976-77, attending physician, 1988—; resident Johns Hopkins Hosp., Balt., 1974-75; fellow Rockefeller U., N.Y.C., 1977-80; asst. prof. Cornell U. Med. Coll. N.Y.C., 1979-83, assoc. prof., 1983-87, chief infectious diseases, 1983—, prof. medicine, 1988—. Contbr. article to profl. jours. Trustee Nightingale-Bamford Sch., N.Y.C., 1989—. Recipient Tchr.-Scientist award Mellon Found., 1980, Career Devel. award, Rockefeller Found., 1981; NIH, WHO, Rockefeller Found. grantee, 1980—. Fellow Infectious Diseases Soc. Am. (Squibb award 1989); mem. Am. Soc. for Clin. Investigation, Am. Soc. for Microbiology. Office: Cornell U Med Coll 1300 York Ave New York NY 10021-4805

MURRAY, HERBERT FRAZIER, retired federal judge; b. Waltham, Mass., Dec. 29, 1923; s. Arnold Howatt and Hilda (Frazier) M.; m. Jane Ward, Sept. 4, 1948; 1 child, Douglas Frazier. B.A., Yale U., 1947; postgrad., Harvard U., 1947-48; LL.B., U. Md., 1951. Bar: Md. 1951. Law clk. to presiding judge U.S. Dist. Ct., 1951-52; assoc. Ober, Grimes & Stinson, Balt., 1952-54; asst. U.S. atty. for Md., 1954-56; from assoc. to ptnr. Smith, Somerville & Case, Balt., 1956-71; judge U.S. Dist. Ct. Md., 1971—. Past bd. dirs. Union Meml. Hosp., Legal Aid Bur., Inc. of Balt. Capt. USAAF, World War II, MTO. Decorated Air medal with 3 oak leaf clusters, D.F.C. Mem. ABA, Md. Bar Assn., Balt. Bar Assn., Fed Bar Assn. (hon.), Wednesday Law Club Balt., Nat. Lawyers Club of Washington (hon.).

MURRAY, J. ALEC G., manufacturing executive; b. 1936. With Coopers and Lybrand, Eng., 1957-69; with Standard Comml. Corp., London, 1969—, chief exec. officer, vice chmn. bd. dirs. Office: Standard Comml Co 2201 Miller Rd Wilson NC 27893

MURRAY, J. P. R., Canadian protective services official. Commr. Royal Can. Mounted Police, Ottawa, Ont., Can. Office: Royal Canadian Mounted Police, 1200 Vanier Pkwy, Ottawa, ON Canada K1A 0R2*

MURRAY, JAMES CUNNINGHAM, JR., lawyer; b. Chgo., Feb. 11, 1944; s. James Cunningham and Marie Rose (Grady) M.; m. Sandra Jean Isbella, Sept. 12, 1970; children: Caroline E., James Cunningham III. BA, U. Notre Dame, 1966; JD, Northwestern U., Chgo., 1969. Bar: Ill. 1969, U.S. Dist. Ct. (no. dist.) Ill. 1970, U.S. Ct. Appeals (7th cir.) 1971. Assoc. Carey Filter White, Chgo., 1969-70; atty. U.S. Dept. Justice, Chgo., 1970-73; assoc. Burditt & Calkins, Chgo., 1973-74; spl. asst. U.S. Atty. Dept. Justice, Chgo., 1974-75; ptnr. Katten, Murchin, Zavis, Chgo., 1975—; dir. Mental Health Assn. Greater Chgo., 1985-89. Mem. Chgo. Bar Assn. Office: Katten Muchin Zavis 525 W Monroe St Ste 1600 Chicago IL 60661-3629

MURRAY, JAMES DICKSON, mathematical biology educator; b. Moffat, Scotland, Jan. 2, 1931; s. Peter and Sarah Jane (Black) M.; m. Sheila Tough Campbell, Aug. Oct. 1959; children: Mark Newbole, Sarah Corrinne. BSc in Math. with 1st class honours, U. St. Andrews, Scotland, 1953, PhD in Applied Math., 1956; MA, U. Oxford, Eng., 1961, DSc in Math., 1968. Lectr. applied math. King's Coll. Durham U., Newcastle, Eng., 1955-56; Gordon

McKay lectr. and rsch. fellow Harvard U., Cambridge, Mass., 1956-59, rsch. assoc. engrng., applied physics, 1963-64; prof. engring. mechanics U. Mich., Ann Arbor, 1965-67; prof. math. NYU, N.Y.C., 1967-70; lectr. Univ. Coll., London, 1959-61; fellow in math. Hertford Coll. U. Oxford, 1961-63, reader, 1972-86, prof. math. biology, 1986—; dir. Ctr. for Math. Biology U. Oxford, 1983—; vis. prof. applied math. MIT, 1979, U. Utah, Salt Lake City, 1979, 85, Calif. Tech. U., 1983; vis. rsch. prof. Nat. Tsing Hua U., Republic of China, 1975, U. Florence, Italy, 1976, Winegard Guelph U., 1980; guest lectr. U. B.C., Vancouver, 1979; guest prof. U. Heidelberg, Fed. Republic Germany, 1980; disting. vis. prof., Scott Hawkins lectr. So. Meth. U., Dallas, 1984; ULAM scholar Los Alamos Nat. Lab., 1985; Robert F. Philip prof. U. Washington, 1988—; Lansdowne lectr. U. Victoria, 1990, Ostram lectr Washington State U. Author: Asymptotic Analysis, 1974, Nonlinear Differential Equation Models in Biology, 1977, Russian translation, 1983, Theories of Biological Pattern Formation, 1981, Modelling Patterns in Space and Time, 1983, Mathematical Biology, 1989; contbr. numerous articles to learned jours. Recipient Heineman Stiftung award NATO, 1980, Naylor prize for Applied Math. London Math. Soc. 1989; vis. fellow St. Catherine's Coll. U. Oxford, 1967, Guggenheim fellow, 1967-68. Fellow Royal Soc., Royal Soc. Edinburgh. Office: Applied Math FS-20 U Wash Seattle WA 98195

MURRAY, JAMES DOYLE, accountant; b. Rochester, N.Y., July 24, 1938; s. William Herbert and Mildred Frances (Becker) M.; m. Mary Louise Goodyear, June 22, 1962; children: William Doyle, Robert Goodyear. B.S., U. Rochester, 1961. CPA, N.Y. With Ernst & Whinney, Rochester, N.Y., 1963—, ptnr., 1977-86; pvt. practice Rochester, 1986—; mem. faculty Found. for Acctg. Edn., N.Y.C., 1979—. Contbr. articles to profl. jours. Treas. William Warfield Scholarship Fund, 1987—; active fund raising Boy Scouts Am., Rochester Philharm., Rochester Mus. and Sci. Ctr.; bd. dirs., treas. Downstairs Cabaret, 1985; mem. Eagle bd. of rev. Boy Scouts Am.; elder Presbyn Ch., 1987—; pres. Egypt Vol. Fire Dept., 1975. Lt. USN, 1961-63. Mem. AICPA, N.Y. State Soc. CPAs (pres. Rochester chpt. 1982-83), Nat. Assn. Accts. (bd. dirs. 1978-80). Republican. Presbyterian. Home: 42 Blackwatt Trl Fairport NY 14450-3702 Office: 349 W Commercial St Ste 3000 East Rochester NY 14445-2402

MURRAY, JAMES JOSEPH, III, association executive; b. Boston, Dec. 31, 1933; s. James Joseph Jr. and Anne Louise (Gurvin) M.; children: James Arthur, Paul, Douglas Joseph, Laura Anne. AB, Harvard U., 1955. Regional editor Prentice Hall, Inc., 1957-60, editor, 1960-64, exec. editor, 1964-69; pres. Winthrop Pubs., Inc. subs. Prentice Hall, Cambridge, Mass., 1969-82; also bd. dirs. Winthrop Pubs., Inc. subs. Prentice Hall; spl. mng. cons. Am. Coun. Edn., Washington, 1983-84, dir. external affairs, 1984—; chmn. N.J. Heart Fund; spl. cons. NEH, 1975—. Mem. editorial bd. Capitol Pub., 1992—. Mem. Dem. Nat. Com. from N.J., 1968; del. Dem. Nat. Conv., 1968. 1st lt. USMCR, 1955-57. Mem. Am. Polit. Sci. Assn., Assn. Physical Plant Administrs. (bd. dirs.), Harvard Club, Varsity Club, Pi Eta. Office: Ste 800 1 DuPont Circle Washington DC 20036

MURRAY, JAMES MICHAEL, librarian, law librarian, legal educator, lawyer; b. Seattle, Nov. 8, 1944; s. Clarence Nicholas and Della May (Snyder) M.; m. Linda Monthy Murray; MLaw Librarianship, U. Wash., 1978; JD, Gonzaga U., 1971. Bar: Wash., 1974. Reference/reserve librr. U. Tex. Law Libr. Austin, 1978-81; assoc. law libr. Washington U. Law Libr. St. Louis, 1981-84; law libr., asst. prof. Gonzaga U. Sch. Law, Spokane, 1984-91; librr. East Bonner County Libr., 1991—; cons. in field. Author: (with Gasaway and Johnson) Law Library Administration During Fiscal Austerity, 1992. Bd. dirs. ACLU, Spokane chpt., 1987-91; Wash. Vol. Lawyers for the Arts, 1976-78. Mem. ABA, Idaho Libr. Assn., Wash. State Bar Assn (law sch. liaison com., 1986-88). Mem. state advy. bd. National Reporter on Legal Ethics and Professional Responsibility, 1982-91; author: (with Reams and McDermott) American Legal Literature: Bibliography of Selected Legal Resources, 1985; editor Texas Bar Jour. (Books Appraisals Column), 1979-82; contbr. numerous articles and revs. to profl. jours., acknowledgements and bibliographies in field. Home: 921 W 29th Ave Spokane WA 99203-1318 Office: East Bonner County Libr 419 N 2nd Ave Sandpoint ID 83864-1501

MURRAY, JAMES PATRICK, newspaper columnist; b. Hartford, Conn., Dec. 29, 1919; s. James and Molly (O'Connell) M.; m. Geraldine Norma Brown, Oct. 20, 1945 (dec. Apr. 1984); children: Theodore, Anthony, Pamela, Eric (dec.). AB, Trinity Coll., Hartford, 1943, LittD honoris causa, 1981; LLD honoris causa, Pepperdine U., 1987. Mem. staff New Haven Register, 1943, Los Angeles Examiner, 1944-48, Time, Inc., 1948-61; sports columnist Los Angeles Times, 1961—. Author: The Best of Jim Murray, 1965, The Sporting World of Jim Murray, 1968, The Jim Murray Collection, 1988, Jim Murray: An Autobiography, 1993. Recipient Sportswriter of Yr. award Nat. Assn. Sportscasters and Sportswriters, 1964, 66-77, 79, Headliners Club award, 1965, 76, Alumni medal Trinity Coll., 1972, J.G. Taylor Spink award Baseball Hall of Fame, Cooperstown, N.Y., 1988, Pulitzer prize for disting. commentary, 1990. Mem. Time-Life Alumni Assn., L.A. Press Club (v.p. 1953), PGA West Club, Riviera Country Club, Bel Air Country Club. Office: Los Angeles Times Times Mirror Sq Los Angeles CA 90012*

MURRAY, SISTER JEAN CAROLYN, college president; b. Broadview, Ill., May 30, 1927. B.A., Rosary Coll., River Forest, Ill., 1949; Ph.D. in French Lang. and Lit., Fribourg, 1961. Instr. French Rosary Coll., 1961-66, asst. prof., 1966-68, assoc. prof., 1968—; pres. Rosary Coll., River Forest, Ill., 1981-94; bd. dirs Fenwick Prep. High Sch., St. Paul Fed. Bank for Savings. Editor: La genese Dialogues des Carmelites, 1963; editor, translator: Correspondance, choisie et presentee, Vol. I, Combat pour la verite Vol. II, Comban pour la liberte, 1971. Bd. dirs. Am. Heart Assn.; active Leadership Greater Chgo. Assocs. Mem. MLA, Am. Assn. Tchrs. French, Ill. Fgn. Lang. Tchrs. Assn., Associated Colls. Ill., Univ. Club Chgo., Chgo. Network, Econ. Club. Chgo., Oak Park Country Club, Fedn. Ind. Colls. and Univs. (chair). Home and Office: Rosary Coll 7900 W Division St River Forest IL 60305-1066

MURRAY, JEANNE See STAPLETON, JEAN

MURRAY, JEANNE MORRIS, scientist, educator, consultant; b. Fresno, Calif., July 6, 1925; d. Edward W. and Augusta R. (French) Morris; m. Thomas Harold Murray, June 19, 1964; children: Jeanne, Margaret, Barbara, Thomas, William. BS in Math., Morris Harvey Coll., 1957; MS in Info. and Computer Sci., Ga. Inst. Tech., 1966; PhD, in Pub. Adminstrn., Tech. Mgmt., Am. U., 1981, post doctoral student in internat. rels., 1993. Research scientist Ga. Inst. Tech., Atlanta, 1959-68; adj. prof. Am. U., Washington, 1968-73; computer scientist U.S. Dept. Def., Washington, 1968-69; staff scientist Delex Systems, Inc., Arlington, Va., 1969-70; mgmt. analyst GSA, Washington, 1971-74; assoc. prof. No. Va. Community Coll., 1975-76, U. Va., 1976—; guest lecturer, Computers and Soc., U. Md., 1986—, Govtl. Rels., Marymount U. Arlington Va., 1990; cons., TechDyn Systems, ABA Corp., OrKand Corp., 1978-80; pres. Sequoia Assocs., Arlington, Va., 1981—; panelist Inst. Agr., Akadamgorodok, Siberia, 1991. Nat. Nuclear Physics, 1991, M.Ulughbek Inst., Samarkand, Uzbekistan, 1991; chmn. confs. Future on Fin. Structure and Pvt. Industry for Uzbekistan, 1994; active U.S. Global Strategy Coun., 1993—. Author: Development and Testing of a System of Encoding Visual Information Based on Optimization of Neural Processing in Man—with Application to Pattern Recognition in the Computer, 1966, Cybernetics and the Management of the Research and Development Function in Society, 1971, Cybernetics as a Tool in the Control of Drug Abuse, 1972, Development of a General Computerized Forecasting Model, 1971, Political Humankind and the Future of Governance, 1974, The Doctrine of Management Planning, 1973, Policy Design, 1980, Computer Futures, 1982, A Search for Positive Response Level Indicators (PRLI's) Under Stress, 1987, Strategic Planning: Pathfinder to the Future, Beijing, 1988, Strategic Planning: A Systems Perspective, Shanghai PRC 1988, Electronic Control Systems for Railroads, Wuhan PRC 1988, Technology Forecasting Methodologies for Use on Personal Computers, 1989, Japan's Burgeoning Rates of Economic Expansion in the U.S. and other Western Countries, 1990, Technology Transfer and National Security, 1992, Privatization Mechanism for the Former Soviet Union and Central European Countries, 1992, Curriculum Development for Privatization Training of Entrepreneurs in Siberia, 1993, Development of Training Courses for Automated Acquisition Management Systems, 1994, Presentations on Methods of

Achieving More Effective, Less Costly Federal Government, 1994. Mem. Carter transition team, 1976-77, Arlington (Va.) Civil Def. Com., 1983—, Washington Met. Area Emergency Assistance Com., Arlington County Com. on Sci. and Tech. Mem. IEEE (sr. mem., vice chmn. Washington sect., chmn. panel on internat. mktg. high tech. in the persence of def. tech. controls 1983, nat. com. on a tech. transfer policy for the U.S. 1986, mem. land transp. com. Vehicular Tech. Soc. 1993-94), AAAS, N.Y. Acad. Scis., Assn. Computing Machinery, Washington Evolutionary Systems Soc., Inst. Noetic Scis., Soc. Gen. Rsch., Am. Soc. Pub. Adminstrn., World Future Soc., Better World Soc., Acad. Polit. Sci., Personality Assessment System Found., Soc. for the Advance of Socio-Econs.; Episcopalian. Home and Office: 2915 27th St N Arlington VA 22207-4922

MURRAY, JOHN A., orthopedic, medical association executive; b. Canton, Ohio, 1932. MD, U. Pitts., 1958. Diplomate Am. Bd. Orthop. Surgery. Intern Jefferson-Davis Hosp., Houston, 1958-59; resident in orthopedics Baylor Coll. Medicine, Houston, 1959-63; resident orthopedist M.D. Anderson Hosp., Houston, 1963—; prof., clin. orthopedics U. Tex. Med Sch., Houston, 1963—; pres. Am. Bd. Orthopedic Surgery. Office: MD Anderson Cancer Ctr Dept Surgery PO Box 106 1515 Holcombe Houston TX 77030-4009*

MURRAY, JOHN EDWARD, JR., lawyer, educator, university president; b. Phila., Dec. 20, 1932; s. John Edward and Mary Catherine (Small) M.; m. Isabelle A. Bogusevich, Apr. 11, 1955; children: Bruce, Susan, Timothy, Jacqueline. BS, LaSalle U., 1955; JD scholar, Cath. U., 1958; SJD fellow, U. Wis., 1959. Bar: Wis. 1959, Pa. 1986. Assoc. prof. Duquesne U. Sch. Law, Pitts., 1963-64, prof., 1965-67; prof. Villanova U. Sch. Law, 1964-65; prof. U. Pitts. Sch. Law, 1967-84, dean, 1977-84; dean Sch. Law Villanova U., 1984-86; disting. svc. prof. U. Pitts., 1986-88; pres. Duquesne U., Pitts., 1988—; cons. to law firms; chmn. Pa. Chief Justice's com. on comprehensive jud. and lawyer edn. Author: Murray on Contracts, 1974, 90, Murray, Commercial Transactions, 1975, Murray, Cases & Materials on Contracts, 1969, 76, 83, 91, Purchasing and the Law, 1978, Problems & Materials on Sales, 1982, Murray, Problems & Materials on Secured Transactions, 1987, Sales & Leases: Problems and Materials in National/International Transactions, 1993. Mayor Borough of Pleasant Hills, Pa., 1970-74. Mem. Assn. Am. Law Schs. (editor Jour. Legal Edn.). Democrat. Roman Catholic. Office: Duquesne U Pres Office Adminstrn Bldg Pittsburgh PA 15282

MURRAY, JOHN EINAR, lawyer, retired army officer, federal official; b. Clifton, N.J., Nov. 22, 1918; s. Joseph Michael and Maru Elizabeth (Liljeros) M.; m. Elaine Claire Riehlmann (dec. 1970); 1 dau., Valerie Ann; m. Phyllis Irene Harris (div. 1989). Student, St. Johns U., 1938-41; LLB, N.Y. Law Sch., 1949, LLD, 1975; MA, George Washington U., 1961. lectr. U.S. Marine Corps Nat. Def. U.; mem. sci. panel of White House Agent Orange Working Group, Def. Intelligence Agy. Task Force on POWS and MIAS; participant Georgetown U. Panel on Crisis Mgmt. Drafted pvt. U.S. Army, 1941, advanced through grades to maj. gen., 1972; comdr. truck group Europe Mil. Ports, Vietnam and maj. logistic units, 1968; dir. Army Transp., 1969-70; chief logistics Pacific Command, 1970-72, Mil. Assistance Command, Vietnam, 1972-73; def. attache Vietnam, 1973-74; ret., 1974; v.p. Assn. Am. Railroads, Washington, 1974-84; spl. consultant Am. Internat. Underwriters, 1985; prin. dep. asst. sec. of def. for spl. ops. and low intensity conflict, 1988-89; with Am. Internat. Group Cos., Washington, 1989; spl. counsel Snavely, King & Assocs., Inc. (econ. cons.), Washington, 1990—; adv. bd. U.S. Army Transp. Mus.; lectr. Nat. Def. U.; mem. sci. panel of White House Agent Orange Working Group, Def. Intelligence Agy. Task Force on POWs and MIAs; participant Georgetown U. Panel on Crisis Mgmt. Author: (with A.M. Chester) Orders and Directive, 1952, (with V.F. Caputo) Quick on the Vigor, 1966, The Myths of Business and the Business of Myths, 1975, The Third Curse of Moses, 1975, The Military Mind and the New Mindlessness, 1976, Lawyers, Computers and Power, 1977, Pothole Plague and Knothole Outlook, 1978, Railroads, Terrorism and the Pinkerton Legacy, 1978, Raising Corn and Beans and Hell, 1979, Remembering Who You Are, 1979, Running A Muck—The Folly of Coal Slurry, 1979, The Railroads and the Energy Crisis, 1980, U.S. Security Assistance—The Vietnam Experience, 1980, Hopeless Cause or Cause of Hope, 1980, War, Transport and Show Biz, 1981, Forget Everything You Ever Knew About the Japanese Railroads, 1981, Sweet Adversity: The U.S. Army-How It Motivates, 1982, Random Danger: The Railroad Response, 1983, Vietnam Logistics: An American Debacle, 1984, Dead Headheads and Warheads, 1987 ; Operation Desert Shield: The Smart Way to War, 1991; He Was There, 1992, The Logistics of Limited Wars, 1992, The United Nations: Sizing Up Consultant Prospects, 1992; contbr.: book revs. to Nat. Def. Transp. Mag., Time-Life books. Decorated D.S.M., Legion of Merit with 4 oak leaf clusters, Bronze Star medal, Italian War Cross, Joint Services Commendation medal with oak leaf cluster, Army Commendation medal with 2 oak leaf clusters, Sec. of Def. medal for Outstanding Pub. Svc., Italian Cross of War, Knight Order of Crown of Italy, Korean Chung Mu with gold star, Vietnamese Kim Khanh medal 1st class, Vietnamese Army Distinguished Service Order 1st class, Vietnamese Navy Distinguished Service Order 1st class, Vietnamese Air Force Distinguished Service Order 1st class, Vietnamese Gallantry Cross with palm. Mem. Spl. Forces Assn., Nat. Def. Transp. Assn., Army War Coll. Grad. Assn., Army and Navy Club. Home: 3823 Bosworth Ct Fairfax VA 22031-3807 Office: Mullenholz & Brimsek 1150 Connecticut Ave NW Washington DC 20036

MURRAY, JOHN FREDERIC, physician, educator; b. Mineola, N.Y., June 8, 1927; s. Frederic S. and Dorothy Murray; m. Diane Lain, Nov. 30, 1968; children—James R., Douglas S., Elizabeth. A.B., Stanford, 1949, M.D., 1953; D.Sc. (hon.), U. Paris, 1983. From instr. to asso. prof. medicine U. Calif. at Los Angeles, 1957-66; mem. sr. staff Cardiovascular Research Inst., U. Calif., San Francisco, 1966—; assoc. prof. medicine Cardiovascular Research Inst., U. Calif. (Sch. Medicine), 1966-69, 1969—; chief chest service San Francisco Gen. Hosp., 1966-89; Vis. prof. Brompton Inst. for Diseases of the Chest, London, 1972-73; Macy faculty scholar Inst. Nat. de la Santé et de la Recherche Medicale, Paris, 1979-80; mem. advl. council and pulmonary disease adv. com. Nat. Heart, Lung and Blood Inst.; mem. clin. studies panel NRC.; bd. govs. Am. Bd. Internal Medicine, Am. Bd. Emergency Medicine. Author: The Normal Lung, 1976, 2d edit., 1986; co-author: Diseases of the Chest, 5th edit., 1980; co-editor: Textbook of Respiratory Medicine, 1988, 2d edit., 1994; editor: Am. Rev. Respiratory Disease, 1973-79; contbr. articles to profl. jours. Chmn. Internat. Union Against Tb and Lung Disease. Served with USNR, 1945-46. Sr. Internat. fellow Fogarty Inst. Fellow Royal Coll. Physicians; mem. Assn. Am. Physicians, Am. Soc. Clin. Investigation, Am. Physiol. Soc., Western Soc. Clin. Research, Western Assn. Physicians, Am. Thoracic Soc. (pres. 1981-82), Académie Nationale de Médecine Francaise. Home: 24 Edith St San Francisco CA 94133-2913 Office: U Calif PO Box 0841 San Francisco CA 94143

MURRAY, JOHN PATRICK, psychologist, educator, researcher; b. Cleve., Sept. 14, 1943; s. John Augustine and Helen Marie (Lynch) M.; m. Ann Coke Dennison, Apr. 17, 1971; children—Jonathan Coke, Ian Patrick. PhD, Cath. U. Am., 1970. Rsch. dir. Office U.S. Surgeon Gen. NIMH, Bethesda, Md., 1969-72; assoc. prof. psychology Macquarie U., Sydney, Australia, 1973-79, U. Mich., Ann Arbor, 1979-80; dir. youth and family policy Boys Town Ctr., Boys Town, Nebr., 1980-85; prof., dir. Sch. Family Studies and Human Svcs. Kans. State U., Manhattan, 1985—. Author: Television and Youth: 25 Years of Research and Controversy, 1980, The Future of Children's TV, 1984, (with H.T. Rubin) Status Offenders: A Sourcebook, 1983, (with E.A. Rubenstein, G.A. Comstock) Television and Social Behavior, 3 vols., 1972, (with A. Huston and others) Big World, Small Screen: The Role of Television in American Society, 1992; contbr. articles to profl. jours. Mem. Nebr. Foster Care Rev. Bd., 1982-84 ; mem. Advocacy Office for Children and Youth, 1980-85 ; mem. Nat. Coun. Children and TV, 1982-87; trustee The Villages Children's Homes, 1986—. Fellow Am. Psychol. Assn. (pres. div. child youth and family svcs. 1990); mem. Am. Sociol. Assn., Soc. Rsch. in Child Devel. Clubs: Royal Commonwealth Soc. (London), Manhattan Country. Home: 1731 Humboldt St Manhattan KS 66502-4140 Office: Kans State U Sch Family Studies & Human Svcs Manhattan KS 66506-1403

MURRAY, JOHN PETER, insurance company executive; b. Jersey City, June 24, 1936; s. William Joseph and Mary Ellen (Conway) M.; m. Elaine

Marie Kelty, Apr. 25, 1959; children—John, Jane, Karen, Joseph. B.S. in Acctg., St. Peter's Coll. Auditing trainee Prudential Ins. Co. of Am., Newark, until 1967; assoc. auditor Prudential Ins. Co. of Am., Mpls., 1967-70; asst. comptroller Prudential Ins. Co. of Am., Newark, 1970-76; v.p. and asst. comptroller Prudential Ins. Co. of Am., Newark, 1976-80, v.p. and assoc. comptroller, 1980-84, sr. v.p., 1984—. Bd. dirs. Assn. for Retarded Citizens, Monmouth County, N.J., 1981; bd. regents St. Peter's Coll., Jersey City; bd. overseers N.J. Inst. Tech., Newark. Served with U.S. Army, 1958-64. Democrat. Roman Catholic. Avocations: reading; golf. Home: 8 Colonial Dr Matawan NJ 07747-2702 Office: The Prudential Ins Co of Am Prudential Plz Newark NJ 07101

MURRAY, JOHN RALPH, former college president; b. Alva, Okla., Apr. 17, 1916; s. John and Euna Vista (Young) M.; m. Fern Berniece Brauch, July 26, 1936; children: John Ralph III, Ann Elaine. A.B., Northwestern State U., 1937; A.M., U. So. Calif., 1939; Ph.D., U. Fla., 1952; L.H.D. (hon.), Elmira Coll., 1976. Prin., tchr. English Carrier and Gore high schs., Okla. 1936-38; teaching asst. U. So. Calif., 1939-41; instr. English U. Miami, Coral Gables, Fla., 1941; exec. asst. to pres. U. Miami, 1942, asst. prof. English, administrv. asst. dean, 1945, acting dean, dir. south campus, 1946-50, asst. to pres., assoc. prof. English, 1948-51; lectr., instr. English Ohio U., 1942-44; pres. Greenbrier Coll., Lewisburg, W.Va., 1952-54; pres. Elmira (N.Y.) Coll., 1954-72, chancellor, 1972-76, cons. to bd. trustees, 1976—; dir. Hardinge Bros.; Mem. N.Y. State Senate Adv. Com. on Higher Edn. Author: Secretary's Handbook, 1941; Editorial bd.: Learning Today; mem. pub. com.: The College and World Affairs; chmn. com. pub.: Non-Western Studies in Liberal Arts Colleges. Trustee Robert Packer Hosp., Coll. Center of Finger Lakes, Am. Center for Students and Artists, Paris; bd. mgrs. Arnot Ogden Hosp.; bd. regents Council on Tchr. Edn.; bd. dirs. Library Coll. Assocs.; mem. Pres.'s Task Force on Internat. Edn.; chmn. long range planning com. Friends of Weymouth; chmn. bd. dirs. Council on Internat. Ednl. Exchange; v.p. Given Meml. Library Bd.; chmn. dirs. Empire State Found., 1963-65, dir., mem. exec. com.; trustee Internat. Coll.; pres. World Golf Hall of Fame. Served as ensign USNR, 1944-45. Mem. Internat. Assn. U. Presidents, Assn. Am. Colls. (past chmn. com. on internat. understanding), Phi Sigma Pi, Kappa Delta Pi, Phi Kappa Phi, Epsilon Phi. Lodge: Rotary. Home: 6152 N Verde Tr Apt D 123 Boca Raton FL 33433

MURRAY, JOSEPH EDWARD, plastic surgeon; b. Milford, Mass., Apr. 1, 1919; s. William Andrew and Mary (DePasquale) M.; m. Virginia Link, June 2, 1945; children: Virginia, Margaret, Joseph Link, Katharine, Thomas, Richard. A.B., Holy Cross Coll., 1940, D.Sc., 1965; M.D., Harvard, 1943; D.Sc., Rockford (Ill.) Coll., 1966, Roger Williams Coll., 1986; hon. degree, Anna Marie Coll., 1993, SUNY, Albany, 1993, U. Suffolk, 1993. Diplomate: Am. Bd. Surgery, Am. Bd. Plastic Surgery (chmn. 1969). Chief plastic surgeon Peter Bent Brigham Hosp., Boston, 1951-86, chief plastic surgeon emeritus, 1986—; chief plastic surgeon Children's Hosp. Med. Center, Boston, 1972-85, emeritus, 1985; prof. surgery Harvard Med. Sch., 1970—. Served to maj. M.C. AUS, 1944-47. Recipient Gold medal Internat. Soc. Surgeons, 1963, hon. award Am. Acad. Arts and Sci., 1962, Nobel prize for medicine or physiology, 1990, Sabin award 1994. Fellow AAAS (hon.), AMA, Royal Australasian Coll. Surgeons, Royal Coll. Surgeons of Eng., Royal Coll. Surgeons Ireland, Royal Coll. Surgeons Edinburgh; mem. ACS (regent 1970-79, v.p. 1983), NAS, Am. Surg. Assn. (v.p. 1979), New Eng. Surg. Assn. (pres. 1986-87), Boston Surg. Soc. (pres. 1975), Soc. U. Surgeons, Am. Assn. Plastic Surgeons (hon. award 1969, pres. 1964-65), Am. Acad. Arts and Sci., Harvard Med. Sch. Alumni Coun. (pres. 1984), Alpha Omega Alpha. Clubs: Badminton and Tennis, Wellesley Country. Home: 108 Abbott Rd Wellesley MA 02181-6104

MURRAY, JOSEPH JAMES, JR., zoologist; b. Lexington, Va., Mar. 13, 1930; s. Joseph James and Jane Dickson (Vardell) M.; m. Elizabeth Hickson, Aug. 24, 1957; children—Joseph James III, Alison Joan, William Lister. B.S., Davidson Coll., 1951; B.A., Oxford U., Eng., 1954, M.A., 1957, D.Phil., 1962. Instr. biology Washington & Lee U., Lexington, Va., 1956-58; asst. prof. biology U. Va., Charlottesville, 1962-67, assoc. prof., 1967-73, prof., 1973-77, Samuel Miller prof. biology, 1977—, chmn. dept. biology, 1984-87; co-dir. Mountain Lake Biol. Sta., Pembroke, Va., 1963-91. Author: Genetic Diversity and Natural Selection, 1972; contbr. articles to profl. jours. Served with U.S. Army, 1955-56. Rhodes scholar, 1951-54. Fellow AAAS, Va. Acad. Sci.; mem. Am. Soc. Naturalists, Genetics Soc. Am., Soc. Study Evolution, Am. Soc. Ichthyologists and Herpetologists, Va. Acad. Sci. (pres. 1986-87), Va. Soc. Ornithology (pres. 1976-79). Avocations: walking; mountaineering; shooting. Office: U Va Dept Biology Gilmer Hall Charlottesville VA 22901

MURRAY, JOSEPH WILLIAM, banker; b. Alamosa, Colo., July 20, 1944; s. Joseph A. and Virginia (Wood) M.; m. Helen Hoberg, Jan. 20, 1970; children: Brian, Beth, Meghan. BS in Bus. with hon., U. Colo., 1966; MBA with hon., Northwestern U., 1967. Various positions with Continental Ill. Nat. Bank, Chgo., 1967-82; sr. v.p. First Nat. Bank, Balt., 1982—; faculty mem. U. N.C. Exec. Programs on Cash Mgmt., Chapel Hill, 1982—; lectr. cash mgmt.; mem. corp. svcs. commn. Bank Adminstrn. Inst., 1992-94. Assoc. editor: Essentials of Cash Management, 4th edit., 1992. Pres. Wakefield Improvement Assn., Timonium, Md., 1987, bd. dirs.; pres. Glen Ellyn (Ill.) Libr., 1978-82, trustee; pres. Glen Ellyn Tennis Assn., 1981, bd. dirs.; bd. trustees Ctr. Stage, 1987—. Mem. Treasury Mgmt. Assn., Mid-Atlantic Planning Assn., Beta Gamma Sigma. Club: L'Hirondelle (Ruxton, Md.). Avocations: tennis, jazz piano, reading, racewalking. Office: 1st Nat Bank Md PO Box 1596 Baltimore MD 21203-1596

MURRAY, LEONARD HUGH, railroad executive; b. Evanston, Ill., Sept. 26, 1913; s. Albert L. and Estelle A. (Matthews) M.; m. Virginia P. Dutcher, Aug. 23, 1940; children: Carole J., Linda P., John L. J.D., U. Minn., 1938. Bar: Minn. 1938. Legal sec. to justice Minn. Supreme Ct., 1938-40; pvt. practice law Mpls., 1940-42; chief price atty. dist. office OPA, Minn., 1942-44; pvt. practice law, specializing r.r. re-orgn. Mpls., 1944-54; asst. to pres. Duluth, S. Shore & Atlantic R.R., 1949-52, v.p. 1952-58, pres., dir., 1958-60; v.p., dir. Wis. Central R.R., 1954-60, v.p., gen. counsel, dir., 1958-60; counsel C.P. Ry. Co., 1958-60; pres., chief exec. officer, dir. Soo Line R.R. Co., 1961-78, chmn. bd., chief exec. officer, 1978-79, chmn. exec. com., 1980-83; former dir. First Bank System, Inc.; dir. Gt. No. Ins. Co., 1963-84; dir. emeritus 1st Nat. Bank Mpls. Pres. Jr. Achievement Mpls. 1964-66; former trustee Dunwoody Indsl. Inst., pres., 1966-67; bd. dirs. Minn. Council on Crime and Justice; pres. Correctional Service of Minn., 1976-79. Recipient Outstanding Achievement award U. Minn., 1971. Mem. Greater Mpls. C. of C. (pres. 1977-78), Beta Gamma Sigma. Republican. Episcopalian.

MURRAY, LOWELL, Canadian senator; b. New Waterford, N.S., Can., Sept. 26, 1936; s. Daniel and Evelyn (Young) M.; m. Colleen Elaine MacDonald; children: William, Colin. BA, St. Francis Xavier U., Antigonish, N.S., Can.; MA in Pub. Adminstrn., Queen's U. Kingston, Ont., Can. Chief of staff Minister of Justice and Minister of Pub. Works Can., Ottawa, Ont., Senator M. Wallace McCutcheon, Ottawa, Ont.; leader of opposition Can., Ottawa, Ont.; dep. minister Premier N.B. Can.; mem. Senate of Can., Ottawa, Ont., 1979—, co-chmn. joint Senate-House of Commons com. ofcl. langs., 1980-84; chmn. standing Senate com. on banking, trade and commerce Senate of Can., 1984-86; trustee Internat. Rsch. Pub. Policy, 1984-86, mem. Trilateral Commn., 1985-86. Nat. campaign chmn. gen. election Progressive Conservative Party Can., 1977-79, 81-83; sworn of the privy coun., appointed Leader of the Govt. in the Senate, 1986-94; Min. of the State Fed.-Provincial Rels., 1986-91; Min. Responsible for the actual Can. Opportunities Agy., 1987-88. Roman Catholic. Office: The Senate, Ottawa, ON Canada K1A 0A4

MURRAY, MICHAEL J., bank executive; b. Dubuque, Iowa, June 23, 1944; m. Christine Scribner; children: Sarah, David. BBA, U. Notre Dame, 1966; MBA, U. Wis., 1968. V.p in charge east coast regional offices Continental Bank, Chgo., 1981-84, v.p., 1981-84, sr. v.p., 1984-85, exec. v.p., 1985—. Mem. devel. bd. subcom. export fin. Ill. Dept. Commerce and Community Affairs, Chgo. 1984; chmn. employee campaign United Way Chgo.; 1986; bd. dirs. Chgo. Maternity Ctr., Northwestern Meml. Hosp. 1987—. Roman Catholic. Clubs: Chgo., Bankers of Chgo., Econ. of Chgo.; Sky (N.Y.C.). Office: Continental Ill Corp 231 S La Salle St Chicago IL 60604-1407

MURRAY, MICHAEL PETER, educator, economist; b. N.Y.C., Sept. 15, 1946; s. Thomas John and Marie Fitzgerald; m. Rosanne Ducey, June 21, 1969; children: Sarah, Anna, Adam, Ben, Seth, Peter. BA, U. Santa Clara, 1968; MS, Iowa State U., 1971, PhD, 1974. Acting asst. prof. U. Calif., San Diego, 1972-73; asst. prof. U. Va., Charlottesville, 1973-77; vis. asst. prof. U. Calif., Berkeley, 1977-78; assoc. prof. Duke U., Durham, N.C., 1978-80; prof. Claremont (Calif.) Grad. Sch., 1980-86; sr. economist The RAND Corp., Santa Monica, Calif., 1980-86; Charles Franklin Phillips prof. econs. Bates Coll., Lewiston, Maine, 1986—; cons. HUD, Washington, 1973, The World Bank, Washington, 1981—. Author: Subsidizing Industrial Location, 1988, Building Organizational Decision Support Systems, 1992; contbr. articles to profl. jours. NDEA fellow U. Calif., San Diego, 1971; vis. scholar HUD, Washington, 1979. Mem. Am. Econ. Assn., Western Econ. Assn., Order of Silver Spade. Democrat. Roman Catholic. Avocations: soccer, bridge, theater. Home: 342 College St Lewiston ME 04240-6001 Office: Bates Coll Dept Econs Lewiston ME 04240

MURRAY, PATRICK M., oilfield service company executive; b. New Malden, Surrey, Eng., Nov. 11, 1942; came to U.S., 1948; s. Thomas I. and Kathleen (McWeeney) M.; m. Mary Ann Pfaff, May 4, 1968; 1 child, Suzanne J. BS in Acctg., Seton Hall U., MBA. Project mgr. NL Industries, Inc., Hightstown, N.J., 1974-75, applications mgr., 1975-76; asst. controller NL Metals Corp., Hightstown, N.J., 1976-79, Shaffer div. NL Corp., Houston, 1980-81; controller Atlas Bradford div. NL Corp., Houston, 1981-82; pres. Sperry Sun Drilling Svcs., Houston, 1988—; bd. dirs. Russell Attitude Systems, Cheltonham, Eng. Served to 1st lt. U.S. Army, 1964-66. Roman Catholic. Avocations: tennis, golf, reading. Office: Sperry Sun Drilling Svcs PO Box 60070 Houston TX 77205-0070

MURRAY, PATTY, senator; b. Seattle, Wash., Oct. 11, 1950; d. David L. and Beverly A. (McLaughlin) Johns; m. Robert R. Murray, June 2, 1972; children: Randy P., Sara A. BA, Wash. State U. 1972. Sec. various cos., Seattle, 1972-76; citizen lobbyist various ednl. groups, Seattle, 1983-88; legis. lobbyist Orgn. for Parent Edn., Seattle, 1977-84; instr. Shoreline Community Coll., Seattle, 1984—; mem. Wash. State Senate, Seattle, 1989-92; U.S. senator from Washington, 1993—; ranking minority mem. Appropriations Legis. Branch; vice-chmn. Senate Dem. Policy Com.; mem. Com. on Banking, Housing, & Urban Affairs, Budget Com., Senate Dem. Tech. & Comms. Com. Mem. bd. Shoreline Sch., Seattle, 1985-89; mem. steering com. Demonstration for Edn., Seattle, 1987; founder, chmn. Orgn. for Parent Edn., Wash., 1981-85; 1st Congl. rep. Wash. Women United, 1983-85. Recipient Recognition of Svc. to Children award Shoreline PTA Coun., 1986, Golden Acorn Svc. award, 1989; Outstanding Svc. award Wash. Women United, 1986, Outstanding Svc. to Pub. Edn. award Citizens Ednl. Ctr. NW, Seattle, 1987. Democrat. Home: PO Box 7191 Arlington VA 22207-0191 Office: US Senate 111 Russell Senate Office Bldg Washington DC 20510-4704*

MURRAY, PAUL BRADY, lawyer, banker; b. Bklyn., Oct. 2, 1923; s. Thomas Edward and Marie (Brady) M.; m. Anne McVoy, Nov. 27, 1946; children—Paul, Joseph, Anne, John, Marie, Margot, Patricia, Marcia, Catherine, Elizabeth, Angelia. B.S., Georgetown U., 1943; LL.D., Fordham U., 1949. Bar: N.Y. 1949. Mem. firm Schmidt, Eagan, Murray, N.Y.C., 1949-52; v.p., treas. Murray Mfg. Corp. (elec. products), Bklyn., 1946-50; pres. Murray Mfg. Corp. (elec. products), 1950-69; exec. v.p. Arrow-Hart Inc., Hartford, Conn., from 1969; chmn. East N.Y. Sav. Bank, Bklyn. Lt. (j.g.) USNR, 1943-45. Office: East NY Sav Bank 350 Park Ave New York NY 10022

MURRAY, PETER, metallurgist, manufacturing company executive; b. Rotherham, Yorks, Eng., Mar. 13, 1920; came to U.S., 1967, naturalized, 1974; s. Michael and Ann (Hamstead) M.; m. Frances Josephine Glaisher, Sept. 8, 1947; children: Jane, Paul, Alexander. BSc in Chemistry with honors, Sheffield (Eng.) U., 1941, postgrad., 1946-49; PhD in Metallurgy, Brit. Iron and Steel Research Bursar, Sheffield, 1948. Research chemist Steetley Co., Ltd., Worksop, Notts, Eng., 1941-45; with Atomic Energy Research Establishment, Harwell, Eng., 1949-67; head div. metallurgy Atomic Energy Research Establishment, 1960-64, asst. dir., 1964-67; tech. dir., mgr. fuels and materials, advanced reactors div. Westinghouse Electric Corp., Madison, Pa., 1967-74; dir. research Westinghouse Electric Europe (S.A.), Brussels, 1974-75; chief scientist advanced power systems divs. Westinghouse Electric Corp., Madison, Pa., 1975-81; dir. nuclear programs Westinghouse Electric Corp., Washington, 1981-92; sr. cons. Nuclear Programs, 1992—; mem. divisional rev. coms. Argonne Nat. Lab., 1968-73; Mellor Meml. lectr. Inst. Ceramics, 1963. Contbr. numerous articles to profl. jours.; editorial adv. bd.: Jour. Less Common Metals, 1968—. Recipient Holland Meml. Research prize Sheffield U., 1949. Fellow Royal Inst. Chemistry (Newton Chambers Research prize 1954), Inst. Ceramics, Am. Nuclear Soc.; mem. Brit. Ceramics Soc. (pres. 1965), Am. Ceramic Soc., Nat. Acad. Engring. Roman Catholic. Home: 20308 Canby Ct Gaithersburg MD 20879-4014 Office: Westinghouse Electric Corp One Montrose Metro 11921 Rockville Pike Ste 450 Rockville MD 20852

MURRAY, PETER BRYANT, English language educator; b. N.Y.C., Oct. 6, 1927; s. Frederick James and Florence (Leech) M.; m. Frances N. Pearson, Apr. 24, 1954 (div. Apr. 1970); children: Jean P., Stephen F., Susan C., Christopher J.; m. Karen Louise Olson, Aug. 14, 1970. Student, Va. Mil. Inst., 1945-47; A.B., Swarthmore Coll., 1950; M.A., U. Pa., 1959, Ph.D., 1962. Research chemist Sun Oil Co., Marcus Hook, Pa., 1950-57; instr. English U. Pa., 1961-63, asst. prof., 1963-67; assoc. prof. English U. Del., 1967-68; prof. Macalester Coll., St. Paul, 1968—; chmn. dept. Macalester Coll., 1971-77; Vice pres. Spencer-Murray Corp., Swarthmore, Pa., 1961—. Author: A Study of Cyril Tourneur, 1964, A Study of John Webster, 1969, Thomas Kyd, 1969, Shakespeare's Imagined Persons: The Psychology of Role-Playing and Acting, 1995. Served with AUS, 1946-47. Mem. Modern Lang. Assn. Am., Modern Humanities Research Assn., Am. Assn. U. Profs. (past chpt. pres.), Shakespeare Assn. Am., Nat. Council Tchrs. English. Patentee in petroleum chemistry field, 1953-57, games entertainment field, 1962-66. Office: Macalester Coll Dept English Saint Paul MN 55105

MURRAY, PETER LOOS, lawyer, educator; b. Bethlehem, Pa., June 15, 1943; s. Samuel Elmer and Josephine Elizabeth (Loos) M.; m. Anita B. Jones, June 20, 1964 (div. 1976); children—Peter Marshall, Anne Lawrence; m. Deborah D. Clark, Nov. 18, 1989. A.B., Harvard U., 1964, LL.B., 1967. Bar: Maine 1967, Mass. 1967, U.S. Dist. Ct. Maine 1967, Mass. 1980, U.S. Ct. Appeals 1st circuit 1975, U.S. Supreme Ct. 1980, U.S. Fed. Ct. Appeals 1987. Law clk. Hon. Edward T. Gignoux, U.S. Dist. Ct., Dist. of Maine, 1967-68; assoc., then ptnr. Pierce, Atwood, Scribner, Allen & McKusick, Portland, Maine, 1968-73; ptnr. Murray, Plumb & Murray, Portland, 1973-93; Ezra Ripley Thayer Teaching fellow Harvard Law Sch., Cambridge, Mass., 1978-80, Edward R. Johnston lectr. law, 1980-87, 90-91, Edward J. Johnston lectr. law, 1993—; cons. Maine Adv. Com. on Rules of Evidence, 1973—; vis. prof. Harvard Law Sch., 1991—; vis. assoc. prof. U. Maine Sch. Law, 1992. Author: (with Richard H. Field) Maine Evidence, 1975, 2d edit., 1987, 3d edit., 1992, Basic Trial Advocacy, 1995; contbr. articles to profl. jours. Dist. rep. Portland West Model Cities Adv. Coun., 1970-71; trustee Greater Portland Landmarks, Inc., 1968-74, pres., 1972-74; trustee Home for Aged Women, 1973-78, pres., 1976-77; trustee Portland Soc. Art, 1970-76, Maine Opera Assn., 1983-85, Landing Sch. Boatbuilding, 1978—, Schooner Bowdoin Assn., 1984; trustee, pres. Spurwink Sch., 1983-85; exec. sec. Maine Jud. Coun., 1969-78; Rep. cand. Maine Ho. Reps., 1988. Mem. ABA, Maine Bar Assn., Mass. Bar Assn., Cumberland County Bar Assn., Fed. Bar Assn., Am. Law Inst. (asst. reporter, Article 3-4-8 com. 1979-84), Am. Law Inst., Harvard Club (N.Y.C.), Faculty Club (Cambridge). Republican. Home: 89 West St Portland ME 04102-3415 Office: 75 Pearl St Portland ME 04101-4168 also: Harvard Law Sch Griswold 307 Cambridge MA 02138

MURRAY, RAYMOND CARL, forensic geologist, educator; b. Fitchburg, Mass., July 2, 1929; s. Henry C. and Hattie (Mindt) M.; children: Robert, Martha; Maureen J. Fleming, Aug. 20, 1988. A.B., Tufts U., 1951; Ph.D., U. Wis., 1955. Head prodn. geol. research Shell Devel. Co., 1955-66; prof. geology U. N.Mex., 1966-67; prof. geology, head dept. Rutgers U., New Brunswick, N.J., 1967-77; v.p. research, dean Grad. Sch., U. Mont., Missoula, 1977—. Contbr. articles to books, profl. jours. Home: 106 Ironwood Pl Missoula MT 59803-2425 Office: U Mont Missoula MT 59812

MURRAY, RAYMOND HAROLD, physician; b. Cambridge, Mass., Aug. 17, 1925; s. Raymond Harold and Grace May (Dorr) M.; children—Maureen, Robert, Michael, Margaret, David, Elizabeth, Catherine, Anne. B.S., U. Notre Dame, 1946; M.D., Harvard U., 1948. Diplomate: Am. Bd. Internal Medicine, also Sub-bd. Cardiovascular Disease. Practice medicine Grand Rapids, Mich., 1955-62; asst. prof. to prof. medicine Ind. U. Sch. Medicine, 1962-77; prof. dept. medicine Mich. State U. Coll. Human Medicine, 1977—, chmn. dept. medicine, 1977-89; chmn. aeromed-bioscis panel Sci. Adv. Bd., USAF, 1977-81. Contbr. numerous articles to profl. publs. Served with USNR, 1942-45; Served with USPHS, 1950-53. Fellow ACP (gov. Mich. chpt. 1994—); mem. Am. Heart Assn. (fellow coun. clin. cardiology), Am. Fedn. Clin. Rsch. Office: Mich State U 210B Clinical Ctr East Lansing MI 48824-1313

MURRAY, RAYMOND LE ROY, nuclear engineering educator; b. Lincoln, Nebr., Feb. 14, 1920; s. Ray Annis and Bertha (Mann) M.; m. Ilah Mae Rengler, June 16, 1941; children: Stephen, Maureen, Michael; m. Quin Meyer, June 3, 1967; 1 stepdau., Tucker; m. Elizabeth Reid, May 12, 1979; stepchildren: Michael, Nancy, James. B.S., U. Nebr., 1940, M.S., 1941; Ph.D., U. Tenn., 1950; postgrad., U. Calif., Berkeley, 1941-43. Physicist U. Calif. Radiation Lab., Berkeley, 1942-43; asst. dept. supt. Tenn. Eastman Corp., Oak Ridge, 1943-47; research physicist Carbide & Carbon Chem. Co., Oak Ridge, 1947-50; prof. physics N.C. State U., 1950-57, Burlington prof. physics, 1957-80, prof. emeritus, 1980—, head dept. physics, 1960-63, head dept. nuclear engring., 1963-74; acting dir. Nuclear Reactor Project, 1956-57; cons. Oak Ridge Nat. Lab., 1950-68, Los Alamos Nat. Lab., 1988-92, also to industry and govt. Author: Introduction to Nuclear Engineering, 1954, 2d edit., 1961, Nuclear Reactor Physics, 1957, Physics: Concepts and Consequences, 1970, Nuclear Energy, 1975, 4th edit., 1993, Understanding Radioactive Waste, 1982, 4th edit., 1994; mem. edit. adv. bd., U.S. exec. editor Jour. Nuclear Energy, 1963-73; vis. editor Annals Nuclear Energy, 1973—; contbr. numerous articles to profl. jours. and encys. Mem. adv. com. on radiation N.C. Bd. Health, 1958-59; mem. Gov.'s Tech. Adv. Com. on Low Level Radioactive Waste, 1980-87; mem. N.C. Radiation Protection Commn., 1979-87, chmn., 1980-82; mem., vice chmn., chmn. N.C. Low Level Radioactive Waste Mgmt. Authority, 1987-93. Recipient O. Max Gardner award U. N.C., 1965; Arthur H. Compton award, 1970, Donald E. Fink award IEEE, 1988, Eugene P. Wigner Reactor Physicist award, 1994. Fellow Am. Phys. Soc., Am. Nuclear Soc. (chmn. edn. div. 1966-67, chmn. Eastern Carolinas sect. 1976-77, mem. nominating com. 1989); mem. Am. Soc. Engring. Edn. (chmn. com. on relationships with AEC 1967-68, chmn. nuclear engring. div. 1970-71, Glenn Murphy award 1976), N.C. Soc. Engrs. (Outstanding Engring. Achievement award 1975), Atomic Indsl. Forum (edn. coun. 1970-73), Inst. Nuclear Power Ops. (adv. coun. 1985-87, 89-94), Phi Beta Kappa, Sigma Xi, Pi Mu Epsilon, Phi Kappa Phi. Home: PO Box 5596 Raleigh NC 27650-5596

MURRAY, RAYMOND WILLIAM, JR., lawyer; b. Hartford, Conn., July 5, 1925; s. Raymond William and Alice (Swift) M.; m. Deborah Kassor, Feb. 19, 1949; children: David, Mark, Kevin, Matthew, Christopher, Peter. BA, Amherst Coll., 1948; JD, Harvard U., 1953. Bar: U.S. Ct. Appeals (1st cir.) 1975, U.S. Ct. Appeals (2d and 3d cirs.) 1980. Sr. ptnr. Bond, Schoeneck & King, Syracuse, N.Y., 1953—. 1st lt. USMCR, 1943-45, 50-52, ETO. Mem. ABA, N.Y. Bar Assn., Onondaga County Bar Assn., Century Club, Cazenovia Club. Republican. Roman Catholic. Avocations: fishing, tennis. Home: 812 S Manlius St Fayetteville NY 13066-2519 Office: Bond Schoeneck & King 1 Lincoln Ctr Syracuse NY 13202-1324

MURRAY, RICHARD BENNETT, physics educator; b. Marietta, Ga., Dec. 5, 1928; s. William Moore and Ruth (Mozley) M.; m. Clella Bay, Apr. 1, 1956; children: Ada, Annette. BA, Emory U., 1947; MS, Ohio State U., 1950; PhD, U. Tenn., 1955. Rsch. asst. Gaseous Diffusion Plant, Oak Ridge, 1947-48; rsch. physicist Oak Ridge Nat. Lab., 1955-66; vis. assoc. prof. physics U. Del., Newark, 1962-63, assoc. prof., 1966-69, prof., 1969—, acting chmn. dept. physics, 1975-76, univ. coord. for grad. studies, 1979-85, assoc. provost for grad. studies, 1986-88, acting provost and v.p. for acad. affairs, 1988-91, provost, 1993-94; lectr. physics U. Tenn., Knoxville, 1963-66; vis. rsch. physicist U.S. Naval Rsch. Lab., 1991-92; vis. scientist Clarendon Lab., Oxford U., 1992; cons. to industry, 1957-93; councillor Oak Ridge Associated Univs., 1979-88, bd. dirs., 1983-94, vice chmn. coun., 1983-85, chmn. coun., 1985-88; sec.-treas. NE Assn. Grad. Schs., 1982-84; dir. U. Del. Press, 1979-82. Contbr. numerous articles on exptl. nuclear and solid state physics to profl. publs., 1948—. Trustee Sanford Sch., Hockessin, Del., 1981-85; chmn. bd dirs. Oak Ridge Associated Univs. Found., 1989-94; bd. dirs. Del. Inst. for Med. Edn. and Rsch., 1989-91. Predoctoral fellow Oak Ridge Inst. Nuclear Studies, 1953-55; grantee AEC, NSF, Dept. Energy, 1967-84. Fellow AAAS, Am. Phys. Soc.; mem. Southeastern Univs. Rsch. Assn. (bd. dirs. 1989—), Phi Beta Kappa, Sigma Xi, Sigma Pi Sigma, Phi Kappa Phi. Home: 4 Bridlebrook Ln Newark DE 19711-2058 Office: U Del Dept Physics & Astronomy Newark DE 19716

MURRAY, RICHARD MAXIMILIAN, insurance executive; b. Vienna, Austria, Nov. 21, 1922; came to U.S., 1955, naturalized, 1961; s. and Elizabeth Helen Peiker. Grad. in world commerce studies, U. Vienna; postgrad., Columbia U. Asst. sec. Sterling Offices Ltd. (reins. intermediaries), London, Toronto, N.Y.C., 1951-59; v.p. Guy Carpenter, Inc. (reins. intermediaries), N.Y.C., 1959-68; v.p. Travelers Ins. Cos., 1968-87, ret., 1987; mng. dir. La Metropole Ins. Co., Brussels, ret., 1987; chmn. bd. Nippon Mgmt. Corp., N.Y.C., ret., 1991; chmn. bd. Travelers Marine Corp., ret., 1987; pres. Travelers Reins. Co. Bermuda Ltd., ret., 1987; pres. Travelers of Asia Ltd., Hong Kong, ret., 1987; vice-chmn. bd. La Prov Corp., N.U.C.; bd. electors Ins. Hall of Fame; bd. dirs. SCOR U.S. Corp., N.Y., SCOR Reins. Co., N.Y., Unity Fire and Gen. Ins. Co., N.Y.C., Gen. Security Ins. Corp. N.Y., Rockleigh Mgmt. Corp., N.Y.C., Preferred Life Ins. Co. N.Y., United Am. Ins. Co., United Am. Holdings Co., Inc.; mem. adv. bd. Firemark Global Ins. Fund, L.P. Contbr. articles to profl. publs. Decorated for promotion of pvt. ins. (Peru); Knight Order of St. John, Knights of Malta (ambassador at large). Mem. Internat. Ins. Coun. (chmn. 1979-81, award 1990), City Midday Club. Home: 60 Remsen St Brooklyn NY 11201-3453 Office: 80 Broad St Fl 35 New York NY 10004-2209

MURRAY, ROBERT BRUCE, theatre administrator; b. Evanston, Ill., Apr. 8, 1932; s. Robert Wolcott and Hazel (Clayton) M.; m. Erika Grob, Oct. 19, 1957 (dec. Feb. 1980); children: Christopher (dec.), Timothy, Molly, Gideon. BS, U. Wis., 1954; MFA, Yale U., 1961. Program dir. Aspen (Colo.) Inst. For Humanistic Studies, 1961-65; assoc. prof. dept. drama Emerson Coll., Boston, 1965-72; dir. cultural svcs. and bicentennial City of Salem (Mass.), 1972-78; dir. Aspen Community Sch., 1978-83; exec. dir. Wheeler Opera House, Aspen, 1983—; bd. dirs. League Hist. Am. Theatres, Washington, 1984—. Playwright: The Good Lieutenant, 1963 (PBS-TV award 1965), Donner, 1973 (Rockefeller Found. award 1975), Salem Chronicles, 1974 (U.S. Park Service award 1976). Mem. Hist. Salem Inc. 1970-76; bicentennial dir. City of Salem, 1973-77; pres. Aspen Hist. Soc., 1980-81; bd. mem. Mountain Valley Devel. Services, 1981—. Named Playwright in Residence Yale U., John Golden Found., 1963-65; recipient Bristol Myers Drama award, N.Y.C., 1963, Rockefeller Drama award Rockefeller Found., U. Calif. Davis, 1973. Office: Wheeler Opera House 320 E Hyman Ave Aspen CO 81611-1948

MURRAY, ROBERT EUGENE, coal company executive; b. Martins Ferry, Ohio, Jan. 13, 1940; s. Albert Edward and Mildred Etheline (Shepherd) M.; m. Brenda Lou Moore, Aug. 26, 1962; children: Sherri Sue (dec.), Robert Edward, Jonathan Robert, Ryan Michael. B in Engring., Ohio State U., 1962; postgrad. Case Western Res. U., 1968-70, Harvard U. Grad. Sch. Bus. Advanced Mgmt. Program, U. N.D., 1982-83. Registered profl. engr., Ohio. Asst. to mgr. indsl. engring. and coal preparation N.Am. Coal Corp., 1961-63, sect. foreman, plant foreman, gen. mine foreman, Ohio div., 1963-64, asst. supt., N.Am. Coal Corp., 1964-66, supt. 1966-68, asst. to v.p. operations, v.p. eastern div., 1969-74, pres. Western div., 1974-83; exec. v.p. and pres. coal ops. N.Am. Coal Corp., 1985-86, pres., chief operating officer, 1986-87, pres., chief exec. officer, 1987; pres. Coteau Properties Co., Falkirk Mining Co., Western Plains Mining Co., Mo. Valley Properties Co., N. Am. Constrn. and Reclamation Co.; v.p., bd. dirs. Nacco Mining Co.; bd. dirs. Sabine Mining Co. 1987-88; pres., chief exec. officer Ohio Valley Resources Inc., Coal Resources Inc., Am. Coal Sales Co., Ohio Valley Coal Co., Ohio Valley Transloading Co., 1988—; mining engring. departmental asst. Ohio

State U., 1960-62; past pres., chmn. bd. N.D. Lignite Council; bd. dirs. Energy Resources, Inc., Energy Transp., Inc. Exec. bd. Greater Cleve. and No. Lights council Boy Scouts Am.; past pres., bd. dirs. United Way of Bismarck; bd. regents U. Mary; trustee, lay speaker, tchr., lay leader Meth. Ch., bd. dirs. Mining Electro-Mech. Assn. (pres. Ohio Valley br. 1967-68), Pitts. Coal Mining Inst. Am., Soc. Mining Engrs. AIME (bd. dirs., exec. com., past chmn. coal div., pres.-elect, Howard N. Evenson award, Disting. Mem. award), Rocky Mountain Coal Mining Inst. (past pres., program chmn., chmn. adv. bd.), Nat. Coal Assn. (past bd. dirs., chmn. acctg. com., exec. com., low rank fuels com.), World Energy Conf., past chmn. ad hoc coalition on internat. electric power trade, research adv. com., generic mineral tech. ctr., Nat. Soc. Profl. Engrs. (pres. east Ohio chpt. 1966-67), Mining Hall Fame (dir.), Am. Mining Congress, Ohio Engrs. in Industry (mem. bd. govs. 1966-67). Republican. Lodges: Masons (32d degree), Shriners. Home: 32 Cotswold Ln Moreland Hills Chagrin Falls OH 44022 Office: Ohio Valley Resources Inc Coal Resources Inc 29525 Chagrin Blvd Suite 111 Pepper Pike OH 44122 also: N Am Coal Corp 13140 Coit Rd Dallas TX 75240-5755

MURRAY, ROBERT FULTON, JR., physician; b. Newburgh, N.Y., Oct. 19, 1931; s. Robert Fulton and Henrietta Frances (Judd) M.; m. Isobel Ann Parks, Aug. 26, 1956; children: Colin Charles (dec.), Robert Fulton III, Suzanne Frances, Dianne Akwe. B.S., Union Coll., Schenectady, 1953; M.D., U. Rochester, N.Y., 1958; M.S., U. Wash., Seattle, 1968. Diplomate Am. Bd. Internal Medicine, Am. Bd. Med. Genetics. Rotating intern Denver Gen. Hosp., 1958-59; resident in internal medicine U. Colo. Med. Center, 1959-62; staff investigator (service with USPHS) Nat. Inst. Arthritis and Metabolic Diseases, NIH, Bethesda, Md., 1962-65; NIH spl. fellow med. genetics U. Wash., 1965-67; mem. faculty Howard U. Coll. Medicine, Washington, 1967—; prof. pediatrics and medicine Howard U. Coll. Medicine, 1974—, grad. prof., 1976, prof. oncology, 1976, chief div. med. genetics, 1968—, chmn. dept. genetics and human genetics Grad. Sch., 1976—; nat. adv. gen. med. scis. coun. NIH, 1971-75, recombinant DNA adv. com., 1988-92; sci. adv. bd. Nat. Sickle Cell Anemia Found.; ethics adv. bd. to sec. HEW, 1978—; chmn. Washington Mayor's Adv. Com. on Metabolic Disorders, 1980-89; active Med. Com. Human Rights. Co-author: Genetic Variation and Disorders in Peoples of African Origin, 1990; co-editor: Genetic, Metabolic and Developmental Aspects of Mental Retardation, 1972, Genetic Counseling: Facts, Values and Norms, 1979; assoc. editor Am. Jour. Clin. Genetics, 1977-94; mem. editl. adv. bd. Jour. Clin. Ethics, 1990. Trustee Union Coll., 1972-80. Rotary Found. fellow, 1955-56; research grantee NIH, 1969-75. Fellow ACP, AAAS, Inst. Medicine (coun. mem. 1983-85), Inst. Soc., Ethics and Life Scis. (bd. dirs.), Am. Coll. Med. Genetics; mem. AAUP, Assn. Acad. Minority Physicians, Am. Soc. Human Genetics, Genetics Soc. Am., Acad. Medicine Washington, Neighbors Inc. D.C., Sigma Xi, Alpha Omega Alpha. Unitarian. Home: 510 Aspen St NW Washington DC 20012-2740 Office: Coll Medicine Box 75 Howard Univ Washington DC 20059

MURRAY, ROBERT GRAY, sculptor; b. Vancouver, B.C., Can., Mar. 2, 1936; s. John Gray and Vera (Meakin) M.; m. Cintra Wetherill Lofting, Jan. 23, 1971; children: Rebecca and Megan (twins), Claire, Hillary. Student, U. Sask., Can., 1956-58. One man shows Betty Parsons Gallery, N.Y.C., 1965, 66, 68, David Mirvish Gallery, Toronto, 1967, 68, 72, 73, 74, 75, Jewish Mus., N.Y.C., 1967, Hammarskjold Plaza, N.Y.C., 1971, Paula Cooper Gallery, N.Y.C., 1974, Janie Lee Gallery, Houston, 1977, Hamilton Gallery, N.Y.C., 1977, 79, 80, Klonaridis Inc., Toronto, 1979, 81, 82, Rice U., 1978, Dayton Mus., 1979, Columbus Mus., 1979, Lamont Gallery, Phillips Acad., Exeter, N.H., 1983, Art Gallery Greater Victoria, 1983, Gallery One, Toronto, 1985, Culturale Canadese Roma, 1985, Gallery 291, Atlanta, 1986, Richard Greene Gallery, N.Y.C.,1986, L.A., 1987, Del. Art Mus., Wilmington, 1990, Muhlenberg Coll., Allentown, Pa., 1992, Mira Godard Gallery, Toronto, Reading (Pa.) Pub. Mus., 1994, Andre Zarre Gallery, N.Y.C., 1994; exhibited in group shows at Whitney Mus. Am. Art, N.Y.C., 1964-66, Tibor de Nagy Gallery, N.Y.C., 1965, Musée cantonal des Beaux Arts, Lausanne, Switzerland, 1966, World House Gallery, N.Y.C., 1966, Betty Parsons Gallery, 1966, Sch. Visual Arts, N.Y.C., 1967, Los Angeles County Mus., 1967, Nat. Gallery Can., Toronto, 1967, Inst. Contemporary Art, Boston, 1967, U. Toronto, 1967, Guggenheim Mus., N.Y.C., 1967, Inst. Torcuato Di Tella, Buenos Aires, 1967, Musée d'Art Moderne, Paris, 1968, Whitney Mus., 1967, Walker Art Gallery, 1969, X Sao Paulo Biennial, Brazil, 1969, Boston City Hall, 1971, Artist and Fabricator, Amherst, Mass., 1975, Met. Mus., N.Y.C., 1983, Del. Art Mus., 1990, GrandRapids (Mich.) Mus., 1994; represented in permanent collections, Montreal Mus. Fine Arts, Nat. Gallery Can., Joseph Hirshhorn Collection, Art Gallery Ont., Larry Aldrich Mus., Ridgefield, Conn., New Brunswick Mus., Whitney Mus. Am. Art, Met. Mus., N.Y.C., Columbus Mus., Dayton Art Inst., Storm King Art Centre, Del. Art. Mus., Wilmington, Muhlenberg Coll., Allentown, Pa., others; major commns. include, Everson Mus., Syracuse, N.Y., Fredonia (N.Y.) State Coll., Canadian Dept. External Affairs, Ottawa, Ont., U. Mass., U. Toronto, Ont., State Ct. Bldg., Juneau, Alaska, Honeywell Corp., Mpls., also others.

MURRAY, ROBERT J., think-tank executive. Grad., Suffolk Coll., Harvard U. Under sec. Navy U.S. Govt., dep. asst. sec. defense, asst. to the sec., dep. sec. defense; pol. mil. attaché Am. Embassy, London; dean Naval War Coll., 1981-83; dir. Ctr. Naval Warfare Studies, 1981-83; mem. faculty, dir. nat. security program John F. Kennedy Sch. Govt. Harvard U., 1983-90 with CNA Corp., 1990—, pres., CEO, also trustee; pres. Ctr. Naval Analyses; mem. bd. advisors Naval War Coll., Nat. War Coll., Washington. Served USMC. Recipient numerous awards for pub. svc. Fellow Nat. Inst. Pub. Affairs; mem. Internat. Inst. Strategic Studies. Office: Center for Naval Analyses 4401 Ford Ave Alexandria VA 22302-9920

MURRAY, ROBERT J., consumer products company executive; b. Aug. 2, 1941; s. Andrew M.; m. Judith; children: Maura Murray Locke, Judith, Robert Jr., Jennifer, Caitlyn, Karyn. BS, BA, Boston Coll., 1962; MBA, Northeastern U., Boston, 1966; advanced mgmt. program, Harvard U., 1990. Product mgr., mktg. The Gillette Co.-Safety Razor Div., Boston, 1967-69; exec. asst. to pres. Gillette N.Am. Hdqrs., Boston, 1969-73; sales assignments Paper Mate Div., Boston, 1974-78; group gen. mgr. Braun U.K., London, 1978-80; group gen. mgr., Anglo Am. Braun AG, Germany, 1980-82; pres. Paper Mate Div., Boston, 1982-85; chmn. Braun AG, Germany, 1985-90; exec. v.p. Gillette North Atlantic, Boston, 1990—; bd. trustees Boston (Mass.) Coll., 1990—. Bd. of overseers Boston (Mass.) Symphony Orch., 1991. Mem. Scituate Yacht Club, Hatherly Country Club. Office: The Gillette Co Prudential Towers Bldg Boston MA 02199

MURRAY, ROBERT WALLACE, chemistry educator; b. Brockton, Mass., June 20, 1928; s. Wallace James and Rose Elizabeth (Harper) M.; m. Claire K. Murphy, June 10, 1951; children: Kathleen A., Lynn E., Robert Wallace, Elizabeth A., Daniel J., William M., Padraic O'D. AB, Brown U., 1951; MA, Wesleyan U., Middletown, Conn., 1956; PhD, Yale U., 1960. Mem. tech. staff Bell Labs., Murray Hill, N.J., 1959-68; prof. chemistry U. Mo., St. Louis, 1968-81; chmn. dept. U. Mo., 1975-80, curators' prof., 1981—; vis. prof. Engler-Bunte Inst. U. Karlsruhe, Fed. Republic Germany, 1982, dept. chemistry Univ. Coll., Cork, Ireland, 1989; cons. to govt. and industry. Co-editor: Singlet Oxygen, 1979; contbr. articles to profl. jours. Mem. Warren (N.J.) Twp. Com., 1962-63, mayor, 1963; mem. Planning Com. and Bd. Health, 1962-64, Bd. Edn., 1966-68. Served with USNR, 1951-54. Grantee EPA, NSF, NIH, Office of Naval Research. Fellow AAAS, Am. Inst. Chemists, N.Y. Acad. Scis.; mem. Am. Soc. Photobiology, Am. Chem. Soc., The Oxygen Soc., Sigma Xi. Home: 1810 Walnutway Dr Saint Louis MO 63146-3659 Office: Univ Mo Dept Chemistry Saint Louis MO 63121

MURRAY, ROBERT WILLIAM, diversified company executive; b. Cooma, New South Wales, Australia, Feb. 13, 1936; came to U.S., 1972; s. Robert Jack and Dulcie (Cavanough) M.; m. Susanne Roberta Green, Jan. 6, 1962; children: Stephen James, Richard Douglas. Charter in Acctg., Sydney Tech. Coll. (Australia). 1957. Chartered accts., Australia. Mgr. fin. Philip Morris Europe, Lausanne, Switzerland, 1970-71; v.p. fin. Philip Morris Internat., N.Y.C., 1972-74; pres. Benson & Hedges Can. Montreal, 1974-76. Philip Morris Europe, Lausanne, 1976-83, Philip Morris Internat., N.Y.C., 1983-87; vice chmn. Philip Morris Cos. Inc., 1987-94, chmn., 1994-95, also bd. dirs. Bd. dirs. Internat. Tennis Hall of Fame; trustee Poly. U., Bklyn., Alvin Ailey Am. Dance Theater, N.Y.C., Am. Mus. Natural History, N.Y.C. Mem. Inst.

Chartered Accts. in Australia. Office: Philip Morris Cos Inc 120 Park Ave New York NY 10017-5523*

MURRAY, ROGER FRANKLIN, economist, educator; b. N.Y.C., Oct. 11, 1911; s. Walter Fletcher and Mary (Van Horne) M.; m. Agnes M. McDede, Oct. 19, 1934; 1 child, Roger Franklin III. Grad., Phillips Andover, 1928; BA, Yale U., 1932; MBA, NYU, 1938, PhD, 1942; LLD, Hope Coll., Holland, Mich., 1960, Tulane U., 1992. Investment adminstr. Bankers Trust Co., N.Y.C., 1932-43, v.p.; 1946-56; assoc. dean Grad. Sch. Bus. Columbia U., N.Y.C., 1956-58, S. Sloan Colt prof. banking and fin., 1958-65, 71-77; v.p. Tchrs. Ins. and Annuity Assn. and Coll. Retirement Equities Fund, 1965-67, exec. v.p., 1967-70; bd. dirs. Alliance Group Mut. Funds, 1966-88, Chgo. Bd. Options Exch., Putnam Group of Mut. Funds; pres. Fund for Mut. Depositors, 1970-77, Investor Responsibility Rsch. Ctr., Inc.; trustee N.Y. Bank for Savs., 1947-77, Common Fund for Nonprofit Orgns., 1969-81. Pres. Phillips Andover Alumni Coun., 1973; mem. N.Y. State Coun. Econ. Advisers, 1973-74, Pension Rsch. Coun.; mem. investment policy panel Pension Benefit Guaranty Corp., 1975-84, Pres.'s Task Force on Aging, 1969-70; mem. investment adv. com. N.Y. State Tchrs. Retirement System, SEC Advisory Com. Corporate Disclosure; life trustee Collegiate Sch. (pres. 1968-72); trustee Smith Coll., 1969-79; trustee Mayhew Program, Wolfeboro Area Children's Ctr. Capt. USAAF, 1943-45. Decorated Legion of Merit. Mem. Am. Econ. Assn., Am. Fin. Assn. (pres. 1964), SR, Phi Beta Kappa, Beta Gamma Sigma. Mem. United Ch. Christ. Home: 32 Pleasant Valley Rd PO Box 669 Wolfeboro NH 03894-0669

MURRAY, ROYCE WILTON, chemistry educator; b. Birmingham, Ala., Jan. 9, 1937; s. Royce Leeroy and Justina Louisa (Herd) M.; m. Judith Studinka, 1957 (div.); children: Katherine, Stewart, Debra, Melissa, Marion; m. Mirtha X. Umana, Dec. 11, 1982. BS in Chemistry, Birmingham So. Coll., 1957; PhD in Analytical Chemistry, Northwestern U., 1960. Instr. U. N.C., Chapel Hill, 1960-61, asst. prof., 1961-66, assoc. prof., 1966-69, prof., 1969—, vice chmn., 1970-75, acting chair dept. chemistry, 1970-71, dir. undergrad. studies, 1978-80, dept. chmn. 1980-85, adj. prof curriculum of applied scis., 1987—, div. chmn., 1987-93, Kenan prof., 1980—. Contbr. articles to jours. in field. Recipient award Japanese Soc. for Promotion Sci., 1978, Electrochem. Group medal Royal Soc. Chemistry, 1989; Alfred P. Sloan fellow, 1969-72, Guggenheim fellow, 1980-82. Fellow AAAS, Am. Inst. Chemists, Am. Acad. Arts and Scis.; mem. NAS, Soc. for Electroanalytical Chemistry (bd. dirs., co-founder 1982-84, Charles N. Reilley award 1988, pres. 1991-93), Am. Chem. Soc. (Electrochemistry award 1990, Analytical Chemistry award 1991, editor in chief Jour. Analytical Chemistry 1991—), Electrochem. Soc. (hon. life, Carl Wagner Meml. award 1987). Presbyterian. Office: The Univ of NC Dept of Chemistry Chapel Hill NC 27599-3290

MURRAY, RUSSELL, II, aeronautical engineer, defense analyst, consultant; b. Woodmere, N.Y., Dec. 5, 1925; s. Herman Stump and Susanne Elizabeth (Warren) M.; m. Sally Tingue Gardiner, May 22, 1954; children: Ann Tingue, Prudence Warren, Alexandria Gardiner. BS in Aero. Engring., MIT, 1949, MS, 1950. Guided missile flight test engr. Grumman Aircraft Engring. Corp., Bethpage, N.Y., 1950-53, asst. chief operations analysis, 1953-62; prin. dep. asst. sec. of def. for systems analysis The Pentagon, Washington, 1962-69; dir. long range planning Pfizer Internat., N.Y.C., 1969-73; dir. review Center for Naval Analyses, Arlington, Va., 1973-77; asst. sec. of def. for program analysis and evaluation Dept. of Def., The Pentagon, Washington, 1977-81; prin. Systems Research & Applications Corp., Arlington, Va., 1981-85; prin. counsellor Com. on Armed Services U.S. Ho. of Reps., 1985-89, nat. security cons., 1989—. Served with USAAF, 1944-45. Recipient Sec. of Def. Medal for meritorious civilian service, 1968; Disting. Public Service medal Dept. Def., 1981. Home: 210 Wilkes St Alexandria VA 22314-3839

MURRAY, TERRENCE, banker; b. Woonsocket, R.I., July 11, 1939; s. Joseph W. and Florence (Blackburn) M.; m. Suzanne Young, Jan. 24, 1960; children: Colleen, Paula, Terrence, Christopher, Megan. B.A., Harvard U., 1962. With Fleet Nat. Bank, Providence, 1962—, pres., 1978-86; with Fleet Fin. Group Inc., Providence, 1969—, pres., 1978—, chmn., pres., chief exec. officer, 1982-88, pres., 1988, chmn., pres., chief exec. officer, 1988—; also bd. dirs.; bd. dirs. Fleet Nat. Bank, A.T. Cross Co., State Mut. Assurance Co. Am., Fed. Res. Bank Boston, Stop & Shop Cos. Inc. Trustee R.I. Sch. of Design, Brown U. Recipient Outstanding Bus. Leader award Northwood Inst., 1986, Humanitarian award Nat. Jewish Ctr. for Immunology and Respiratory Medicine, 1988, Never Again award Jewish Fedn., 1989, New Englander of Yr. award New England Coun., 1990, New England Businessperson of Yr. award New England Bus. Mag., 1991, Humanitarian award Fogarty Found., 1991. Mem. Am. Bankers Assn. (bd. dirs.), Assn. of Res. City Bankers (bd. dirs.), Harvard Alumni Assn. (bd. dirs.). Office: Fleet Fin Group Inc 50 Kennedy Plz Providence RI 02903-2393*

MURRAY, TERRY (TERENCE RODNEY MURRAY), professional hockey team coach; b. Shawville, Que., Can., July 20, 1950; m. Linda Murray; children: Megan, Lindsey. Hockey player Calif. Golden Seals, 1972-75, Phila. Flyers, 1975-77, 78-81, Detroit Red Wings, 1977; hockey player Washington Capitals, 1981-82, asst. coach, 1982-88, head coach, 1990-94; head coach Balt. Skipjacks, 1988-90, Philadelphia Flyers, 1994—. Named to 3 Am. Hockey League all-star teams; named most valuable defenseman Am. Hockey League, 1978, 79. Office: Philadelphia Flyers Pattison Pl Philadelphia PA 19148*

MURRAY, THOMAS FRANCIS, real estate executive; b. Oxford, Iowa, Oct. 27, 1910; s. Thomas F. and Fern (Hummer) M.; m. Margaret R. Regan, Nov. 11, 1939; children: William R., Robert C., James M. B.S. in Elec. Engring., U. Iowa, 1932. With United Light & Power Engring. and Constrn. Co., 1933-41; with Equitable Life Assurance Soc. U.S., 1946-75, exec. v.p., chief investment officer, chmn. finance com., mem. exec. com., 1973-75, also dir., 1971-75; trustee Franklin Savs. Bank, N.Y.C., 1965-82; trustee, chmn. Equitable Life Mortgage and Realty Investors, 1970-76; dir. Olentangy Mgmt. Co., 1977-82; chmn. Equico Securities, Inc., 1971-75, Equico Lessors, Inc., 1974-75; dir. The Bank of Tokyo Trust Co., 1978-81; dir. Am. Continental Properties, Inc., 1978—, pres., 1978-82, chmn., 1982—; dir. N.Y. Pub. Devel. Corp., 1973-80, chmn., 1977-79; dir. Allied Stores Corp., 1978-83, Rockefeller Ctr., Inc., 1976-82, PaineWebber Cash Fund, 1978—, PaineWebber Master Series Inc., 1987—, Search Am. Corp., 1982-86, Prudential Realty Trust, 1985—; trustee PaineWebber Tax Exempt Series, 1987—. Mem. exec. bd. Hutchinson River council Boy Scouts Am., 1960-73, pres., 1971-73; mem. exec. bd. Westchester-Putnam council, 1973-80, mem. adv. council, 1980—; trustee Urban Land Inst., 1969—, treas., 1970-73, 1st v.p., 1973-74, pres., 1975-77. Served to lt. col. C.E. AUS, 1941-46. Decorated Legion of Merit. Mem. Real Estate Bd. N.Y., N.Y. Soc. Security Analysts, Am. Soc. Real Estate Counselors, Newcomen Soc., C. of C. U.S.A. (dir. 1974-78). Clubs: University, Economic (N.Y.C.); Leewood Golf (Eastchester, N.Y.) (pres. 1965-67), The Country Club of Naples, Fla. Office: Am Continental Properties 400 Park Ave Ste 700 New York NY 10022-4406

MURRAY, THOMAS HENRY, bioethics educator, writer; b. Phila., July 30, 1946; s. Thomas Henry, Sr. and Colombia Rita (Lucci) M.; m. Sharon Marie Engelkraut, Jan. 1968 (div. Sept. 1975); children: Kathleen Elizabeth, Dominique Maria, Peter Albert; m. Cynthia Sarah Aberle, Apr. 1, 1978; 1 child, Emily Sarah Aberle. BA in Psychology, Temple U., 1968; PhD in Social Psychology, Princeton, 1976. Instr. New Coll., Sarasota, Fla., 1971-75; asst. prof. Interdisciplinary Studies Miami U., Oxford, Ohio, 1975-80, assoc. prof., 1980; assoc. social behavioral studies The Hastings Ctr., Hastings-on Hudson, N.Y., 1980-84; assoc. prof. Inst. Med. Humanities U. Tex Med. Br., Galveston, Tex., 1984-86, prof., 1986-87; prof., dir. Ctr. Biomed. Ethics Case We. Reserve U., Cleve., 1987—; mem. ethics working group Human Genome Project NIH/Dept. Energy, 1989-95. Founder, editor Medical Humanities Review; mem. editorial bd. Social Science and Medicine, Physician and Sportsmedicine, Human Gene Therapy. Mem. U.S. Olympic com., com. sports medicine. Fellow NEH, 1977-78, 1979-80, Aspen Inst., 1989. Fellow Soc. Values in Higher Edn., Hastings Ctr., Environ. Health Inst.; mem. APHA, Assn. Practical and Profl. Ethics. (exec. com.), Am. Soc. Law Medicine and Ethics (bd. dirs. 1993—), Assn. Integrative Studies (bd. dirs. 1980-87, pres. 1983), Soc. Health and Human Values (chair program dirs. sect. 1989-90, faculty assn. 1989-90, SHHV program com. 1990, pres.-

elect 1992-93, pres. 1993-94). Office: Case Western Res U Sch Medicine Ctr Biomed Ethics 10900 Euclid Ave Cleveland OH 44106-4976

MURRAY, THOMAS JOHN (JOCK MURRAY), medical humanities educator, medical researcher; b. Halifax, N.S., Can., May 30, 1938; m. Janet Kathleen Pottie; children: Shannon, Bruce, Suellen, Brian. Grad. pre-med, St. Francis Xavier U., 1958, LLD (hon.), 1989; MD, Dalhousie U., 1963; DSc (hon.), Acadia U., 1991. Family physician, Nashwaaksis, N.S., 1963-65; chief of medicine Camp Hill Hosp., Halifax, N.S., 1974-79; chief of neurology Dalhousie U., Halifax, 1979-85, dir. multiple sclerosis rsch. unit, 1980—, dean of medicine, 1985-92; prof. med. humanities, 1994—. Co-author: (textbook) Essential Neurology; author over 200 pub. works, including contbns. to 7 textbooks. Bd. dirs. St. Francis Xavier U., Pictou Acad. Found., Robert Pope Found., Nat. Coun. on Bioethics and Health Rsch. Decorated officer Order Can. Fellow Royal Coll. Physicians (Can.), ACP (gov. 1985-90, chmn. bd. govs. 1990-91, bd. regents, chmn. 1995—); mem. Can. Neurol. Soc. (pres. 1982-84), Am. Acad. Neurology (v.p. 1981-83), Can. Med. Forum (chair), Can. Med. Assn., N.S. Med. Soc., Assn. Can. Med. Colls. (pres. 1991-92), Can. Med. Forum (chmn. 1992-95). Avocations: medical history, marathon running, piano, windsurfing, beer-making. Home: 16 Bobolink St, Halifax, NS Canada B3M 1W3 Office: Dalhousie Med Sch, Clin Rsch Ctr, Halifax, NS Canada B3H 4H7

MURRAY, THOMAS JOSEPH, advertising executive; b. Bridgeport, Conn., Mar. 12, 1924; s. Thomas and Mary (Diskin) M.; m. Mary Elizabeth Cull, Feb. 22, 1945; children: Joshua Francis, Mary Elizabeth, Katherine Diskin. A.B., Dartmouth Coll., 1947. Instr., Dartmouth Coll., 1947-48; with Warwick & Legler, N.Y.C., 1948-68; sr. v.p. mgmt. account supr. Warwick & Legler, 1964-68; sr. v.p group supr. Gaynor & Ducas, Inc., 1968-74, exec. v.p., 1974—, chief fin. officer and gen. mgr., 1978-87; pres. TJM & Assn., 1987—. Pres., trustee Hillcrest Gen. Hosp., N.Y.; Westchester Inst. for Ing. in Psychoanalysis and Psychotherapy, Mt. Kisco, N.Y. Served as 1st lt. USAAF, 1942-45. Decorated D.F.C., Air medal with 4 oak leaf clusters. Mem. Nat. Wholesale Druggists Assn., Propriety Assn., Nat. Assn. Chain Drug Stores, Am. Mktg. Assn. Home & Office: 65 Norfield Rd Weston CT 06883-2213

MURRAY, THOMAS MICHAEL, civil engineering educator, consultant; b. Dubuque, Iowa, May 22, 1944; s. Raymond M. and Laura R. (Juergens) M.; m. Margaret Ann Schrodt, July 13, 1964 (div. 1995); children: Matthew R., Elizabeth A., Nicholas P. BSCE, Iowa State U., 1962; MSCE, Lehigh U., 1966; PhD in Engring. Mechanics, U. Kans., 1970. Registered profl. engr., Iowa, Okla. Engr. trainee Pitts. Des Moines (Iowa) Steel Co., 1962-64; instr. civil engring. U. Omaha, 1966-67, U. Kans., Lawrence, 1967-69; asst. prof., assoc. prof., prof. U. Okla. Sch. Civil Engring., Norman, 1970-86; Disting. vis. prof. USAF Acad., Colorado Springs, Colo., 1986-87; Montague-Betts prof. structural steel design Va. Poly. Inst. and State U., Blacksburg, 1987—; pres. Structural Engrs. Inc., Radford, Va., 1973—. Author: Design Guide for Connections, 1990; also numerous articles; patentee in field. Recipient various teaching awards U. Okla., 1979, 81, 84. Fellow ASCE (numerous offices 1970—); mem. Am. Inst. Steel Constrn. (T.R. Higgins lectr. 1991), Assn. for Engring. Edn., Structural Stability Rsch. Coun., also others. Republican. Roman Catholic. Avocations: skiing, spectator sports, railroads. Office: Va Poly Inst and State U Dept Civil Engring Blacksburg VA 24061

MURRAY, TY (THE KID), professional rodeo cowboy; s. Harold "Butch" and Joy M. Student, Odessa (Tex.) Coll. Five-time world all-around world champion Profl. Rodeo Circuit Assn., 1989-93; world champion bull rider, 1993. Named Nat. H.S. Rodeo All-Around Champion, 1987, PRCA Rookie of the Year Profl. Rodeo Cowboy Assn., 1988, Nat. Intercollegiate Rodeo All-Around Champion, 1988. Record for single season earnings, 1991. Office: Profl Rodeo Cowboy Assn 101 Pro Rodeo Drive Colorado Springs CO 80919*

MURRAY, WALLACE SHORDON, publisher, educator; b. Dorchester, Mass., May 9, 1921; s. Wallace Jennings and Ina (Shordon) M.; m. Eleanor Muriel Grandy, Oct. 30, 1948; children: Patricia Ann, William Howard. B.S., MIT, 1942; M.Ed., Boston U., 1949; Litt.D. (hon.), Western New Eng. Coll., 1965. Tchr. Bolles Sch., Jacksonville, Fla., 1945-46; head math. dept., asst. prin. Bolles Sch., 1946-49; headmaster Berwick Acad., South Berwick, Maine, 1949-50; sales rep. D.C. Heath & Co., Boston, 1950-52; editor D.C. Heath & Co., 1952-53, head elementary editorial dept., 1953-55, editor in chief, 1955-66, v.p., 1962-66, dir., 1956-66, sec. of corp., 1957-66; dir. Erica Corp., 1956-66; exec. v.p. Heath de Rochemont Corp., 1960-66, dir., 1960-66; editor-in-chief, mgr. materials devel. dept. Raytheon Edn. Co., 1966-68; v.p., editorial dir. domestic and internat. ops. Grolier Inc., 1968-80, dir., 1969-82, cons., 1980-82; dir. Grolier Edn. Corp., 1968-80, Scarecrow Press Inc., 1969-80; Chmn. elementary and high sch. research com. Am. Ednl. Pubs. Inst., 1966-68, chmn. elem. and high sch. sect., 1968-69. Lay leader Boston dist. Meth. Ch., 1952-56; mem. adv. bd. Boston U. Student Christian Assn., 1954-62, treas., 1957-59, chmn., 1959-61; mem. president's adv. council St. Joseph's Coll., North Windham, Maine, 1973-88; mem. corp. New Eng. Deaconess Assn., 1965—, exec. com., 1965-68; mem. corp. New Eng. Deaconess Hosp., 1967-93; dir. Japan America Soc. of Maine, 1981-91, pres., 1984-86; merit badge counselor Pine Tree Coun., Boy Scouts Am., 1984—; dir. Children's Mus. of Maine, 1987-89; dir. Leisure Ctr. for the Handicapped, Inc., Portland, Maine, 1987-93, treas. 1988-93; mem. adv. council So. Maine Retired Sr. Vol. Program, 1987-90, chmn. fin. com., 1987-89; mem. Foster Care Case Review Panel Maine Dept. Human Services, 1987-91; dir. Foreside Common Condominium Assn., Falmouth, Maine, 1986-89, 1991-92, pres., 1987-89; vol. staff mem. Vol. Lawyers Project of Maine, 1987-90; vol. math. mem. Adult Basic Learning Exchange, Portland, 1987-91. Served to capt. AUS, 1942-46, to maj. USAR. Mem. Newcomen Soc., World Affairs Council of Maine, Phi Delta Kappa. Republican. Methodist. Lodges: Masons, Shriners. Home: PO Box 17 Sebago Lake ME 04075-0017

MURRAY, WARREN JAMES, educator, philosopher; b. St. Paul, Dec. 3, 1936; s. James Bernard and Louise (Robertson) M.; m. Mary Ann McAulay, July 18, 1959; children: Mark, Anne, Kathleen. Student, St. Thomas Coll., 1954-55; B.A. in Chemistry, Wis. State Coll., River Falls, 1962; B.Ph. in Philosophy, Universite Laval, Que., Can., 1964, Ph.L., 1965, scolarite Ph.D., 1966. Analytical chemist 3M Co., St. Paul, 1957-61, research chemist, 1961-63; prof. philos. sci. U. Laval, Sainte-Foy, 1966—, vice dean, 1979—; invited prof. Faculte de philosophie Comparee, Paris, 1969, 72, Universite libre des sciences de l'homme, Paris, 1975—, Ecole des Hautes Etudes, Paris, 1976, Universidad Nacional de Tucuman, Argentina, 1991. fgn. exchange teaching grantee Province Que., 1969. Mem. Soc. Aristotelian Studies (pres.), Can. Soc. History and Philosophy Sci. Office: Faculte De Philosophie, Universite Laval, Sainte-Foy, PQ Canada G1K 7P4

MURRAY, WILLIAM, food products executive; b. 1936. Head internal audit divsn. UN Relief Works Agy, Lebanon, 1960-65; head budget divsn. Internat. Labor Orgn., Switzerland, 1965-70; with Philip Morris Inc., 1970—; pres. Benson & Hedges Ltd., Can., 1974; v.p. Philip Morris Internat. Divsn., 1976-78, exec. v.p., 1978-84, pres., CEO, 1984-87; vice chmn. bd. Philip Morris Cos., Inc., 1987-91, past pres., now chmn. bd., dir. Office: Philip Morris Cos Inc 120 Park Ave New York NY 10017-5523*

MURRELL, ESTELLE C., elementary school educator; b. Warren County, Ky., Feb. 13, 1931; d. James B. and Mary Ellen (Johnson) Clark; m. Allen Leslie Murrell, Mar. 14, 1953; children: Leslie Allen, Lisa Ellen. BS, Western Ky. U., 1956. Cert. tchr., Ky. 5th grade tchr. Bowling Green (Ky.) Ind. Bd. Edn.; 6th grade tchr. Warren County Bd. Edn., Bowling Green; 4th grade tchr. Hardin County Bd. Edn., Elizabethtown, Ky.; 4th, 6th and 7th grades tchr. lang. arts Bowling Green Bd. Edn.; tchr. Draughons Jr. Coll., Bowling Green, Ky. Named to Leader of Am. Elem. Edn. 1971, 73. Mem. NEA, Ky. Edn. Assn., Bowling Green Edn. Assn. (membership chair), Nat. Coun. Tchrs. of English, Ky. Coun. Tchrs. of English Lang. Arts, Internat. Reading Assn., Ky. Coun. Reading Assn. Home: 1404 Woodhurst St Bowling Green KY 42104-3322

MURRELL, THOMAS W., III, lawyer; b. Nov. 28, 1948. BA, Yale U., 1971; JD, U. Va., 1974. Bar: Pa. 1974. Ptnr. Morgan, Lewis & Bockius,

Phila. Office: Morgan Lewis & Bockius 2000 One Logan Sq Philadelphia PA 19103

MURRELL, WILLIAM IVAN, accountant; b. Bessemer, Ala., Dec. 28, 1923; s. Virgil Stewart Murrell and Mae (Rutledge) Ferguson; m. Virginia Byrd Reynolds, May 27, 1944; children: Melinda Ann, Barbara Kay, Shirley Sue. Student, Walton Sch. Commerce, 1941-46, Tex. Christian U., 1947-48, So. Meth. U., 1949-50. CPA. Bookkeeper Continental Oil Co., Ft. Worth, 1942-43; staff acct. Patterson & Leatherwood, Ft. Worth, 1946-48; sr. acct. Coopers & Lybrand, Dallas, 1949-51; sr. ptnr. Parish, Murrell & Co., Dallas, 1951-85; cons. Dallas, 1986—; bd. dirs. Rancho Oil Co., Dallas, Nat. Industries Corp., Dallas, Warehouse Properties Corp., Dallas. Author: World War II Love Letters, 1993, This Is It, Men, 1991, Murder for Profit or Loss, 1992. With U.S. Army, 1943-46. Mem. AICPA (life), Accts. Computer Users (Devoted Svc. award 1971), Tex. Soc. CPA (life, pres. 1968-69), Horatio Alger Soc. (Rags to Riches award 1990). Baptist. Avocations: travel, writing, music, oil painting, gardening. Home: 4321 W Lawther Dr Dallas TX 75214-2921

MURRET, EUGENE JOHN, SR., judicial administrator; b. New Orleans, Aug. 1, 1932; s. Charles Ferdinand and Lillian Sophie (Claverie) M.; m. Kathleen Teresa Corley, July 4, 1969; children: Patricia, Claire, Cecilia, Eugene Jr. AB, Loyola U., New Orleans, 1954, JD, 1959; MA, Spring Hill Coll., Mobile, Ala., 1964; LLM, NYU, 1969. Bar: La. 1959, U.S. Dist. Ct. (ea. dist.) La. 1959, U.S. Ct. Appeals (10th cir.) 1988. Exec. counsel to gov. State of La., Baton Rouge, 1969-71; jud. administr. Supreme Ct. La., New Orleans, 1971-87; cir. exec. U.S. Ct. Appeals (10th cir.), Denver, 1987—. With U.S. Army, 1954-56. Grantee Nat. Endowment for Humanities U. Va. Law Sch., 1979. Fellow Inst. for Ct. Mgmt.; mem. ABA (exec. com., lawyers conf., coun. of jud. adminstrn. div., budget officer), Assn. Jud. Disciplinary Counsel (bd. dirs., sec. 1982—), Nat. Ctr. for State Cts., Inst. Jud. Adminstrn., Am. Judicature Soc. Democrat. Roman Catholic. Avocations: golf, tennis, music, reading. Office: Circuit Exec Ste 1175 999 18th St Denver CO 80202

MURRIAN, ROBERT PHILLIP, federal judge, educator; b. Knoxville, Tenn., Apr. 1, 1945; s. Albert Kinzel and Mary Gilbert (Eppes) M.; m. Jerrilyn Sue Boone, Oct. 29, 1983; children—Kimberley Ann, Jennifer Rebecca, Albert Boone, Samuel Robert. B.S., U.S. Naval Acad., 1967; J.D., U. Tenn., 1974. Bar: Tenn. 1974, U.S. Dist. Ct. (ea. dist.) Tenn. 1975, U.S. Ct. Appeals (6th cir.) 1982. Law clk. to judge U.S. Dist. Ct. (ea. dist.) Tenn., 1974-76; assoc. Butler, Vines, Babb & Threadgill, Knoxville, 1976-78; magistrate judge U.S. Dist. Ct. (ea. dist.) Tenn., Knoxville, 1978—; adj. prof. U. Tenn. Coll. Law, 1990-93. Served to lt. USN, 1967-71. Green Scholar, 1973-74; Nat. Moot Ct. scholar, 1974. Fellow Tenn. Bar Found.; mem. ABA, Knoxville Bar Assn. (bd. govs. 1994), Tenn. Bar Assn., Order of Coif, Am. Inn of Ct. (master of the bench). Presbyterian. Office: 337 US Courthouse 501 Main Ave Knoxville TN 37902

MURRILL, PAUL WHITFIELD, former utility executive, former university administrator; b. St. Louis, July 10, 1934; s. Horace Williams and Grace (Whitfield) M.; m. Nancy Williams, May 17, 1959; children: Paul Whitfield, John Parham, William Britton. BS, U. Miss., 1956; MS, La. State U., 1962, PhD, 1963. Registered profl. engr., La. Instr. chem. engring. La. State U., 1961-62, spl. lectr. chem., mech., indsl. and aerospace engring., 1962-63, asst. prof., 1963-65, assoc. prof., 1965-67, assoc. prof., head dept. chem. engring., 1967-68, prof., head dept. chem. engring., 1968-69, prof., 1968-80, vice chancellor, dean acad. affairs, 1969-70, provost, 1970-74, chancellor, 1974-80, sr. v.p. Ethyl Corp., Richmond, Va., 1980-82; chmn. bd., chief exec. officer Gulf States Utilities Co., Beaumont, Tex., 1982-87, sr. v.p. advisor to chmn., 1987-90; pres. Monarch Internat. Corp., 1978—; chmn. FMOL Health System Inc., 1991-94; chmn. bd. dirs. Berden Found., 1992—, Piccadilly Cafeterias, 1994—; cons. in field; project mgr. Dept. Def. project THEMIS, 1967-72; bd. dirs. First Miss. Corp., Tidewater Inc., New Orleans, Gulf States Utilities Co., First Miss. Gold, Inc., Howell Corp. Piccadilly Cafeterias, Zygo, Inc., Entergy Corp., Pavilion Techs., Inc. Author: Automatic Control of Processes, 1967; co-author: Fortran IV Programming for Engineers and Scientists, 1968, The Development and Utilization of Mathematical Models, 1970, An Introduction to Fortran IV Programming: A General Approach, 1970, COBOL Programming, 1970, Basic Programming, 1970, PL/I Programming, 1973, Introduction to Computer Science, 1973, Fundamentals of Process Control, 1980, 2d edit., 1991, Application Concepts in Process Control, 1988; cons. editor: Chemical Engineering series, Internat. Textbook Co., 1966-72, Instrument Soc. Am., 1981—. Bd. dirs. local Boy Scouts Am., United Way; deacon Bapt. ch. Served to lt. comdr USNR, 1956-59. Recipient Faculty Service award Nat. U. Extension Assn., 1968, Halliburton Found. award for excellence in engring. teaching, 1966. Mem. La. Engring. Soc. (Tech. Accomplishment medal 1970, Andrew Lockett medal 1978), Am. Soc. Engring. Edn., Am. Inst. Chem. Engrs., Instrument Soc. Am. (Donald Eckman Nat. award 1976), Sigma Xi, Omicron Delta Kappa, Tau Beta Pi, Pi Kappa Pi, Phi Kappa Phi (Disting. Nat. medal 1976), Phi Eta Sigma, Phi Lambda Epsilon. Lodge: Rotary.

MURRIN, REGIS DOUBET, lawyer; b. Erie, Pa., June 2, 1930; s. John III and Gabrielle (Doubet) M.; m. Evelyn L. Alessio, Aug. 22, 1959; children: Catherine Shaw Murrin Hargenrader, Mary Murrin Smith, Elizabeth Murrin Tolatta, Rebecca Fielding Lamanna. BA, U. Notre Dame, 1952; JD, Harvard U., 1959; LLM, Temple U., 1968. Bar: Pa. 1959, U.S. Supreme Ct. 1971. Assoc. Murrin & Murrin, Butler, Pa., 1959-62; atty. Housing & Home Fin. Agy., Phila., 1962-64; ptnr. Baskin & Sears, Pitts., 1964-84; ptnr. Reed Smith Shaw & McClay, Pitts., 1985-95, of counsel, 1995—. Trustee Pitts. Oratory, 1976-93; chmn. Zoning Bd. Adjustment, City of Pitts., 1994—; bd. dirs. Ellis Sch., 1991—. Served as lt. USNR, 1952-55, Korea, Vietnam. Mem. Pa. Bar Assn. (real estate and common interest ownership coms.), Edwin Sorin Soc. Democrat. Roman Catholic. Office: Reed Smith Shaw & McClay 435 6th Ave Pittsburgh PA 15219-1886

MURRIN, THOMAS EDWARD, insurance company executive; b. Bklyn., Sept. 12, 1923; s. Maurice Joseph and Agnes (O'Brien) M.; m. Marguerite Judge, Aug. 23, 1947; children—Maureen, Thomas, Rosemary, Ann, Patricia, Elizabeth, James, Marguerite. B.S. magna cum laude, St. John's U., 1944. Actuary Nat. Bur. Casualty Underwriters, N.Y.C., 1946-61; v.p., actuary Am. Ins. Group, Newark, 1961-63, Fireman's Fund Am. Ins. Cos., San Francisco, 1963-68; sr. v.p., actuary Fireman's Fund Am. Ins. Cos., 1968-76, exec. v.p. ins. services office, 1976-83; exec. cons. Coopers & Lybrand, San Francisco, 1984—. Served to lt. (j.g.) USNR, 1944-46. Fellow Casualty Actuarial Soc. (past pres.); mem. Am. Acad. Actuaries (past pres.), Internat. Congress Actuaries. Home: 275 Calle de la Selva Novato CA 94949-6084 Office: 333 Market St San Francisco CA 94105-2102

MURRISH, CHARLES HOWARD, oil and gas exploration company executive, geologist; b. Rochester, Mich., Dec. 27, 1940; s. Richard John and Emily Louise (Marsh) M.; m. Brigitte Marie Furlotte, Oct. 23, 1965; children: Stephanie, Stephen, Brian. Student Mexico City Coll., 1962; BS, Mich. State U., 1963, MS, 1966. Exploration geologist and geophysicist Chevron, New Orleans, 1966-71; mgr. exploration Odeco, New Orleans, 1971-77; v.p. McMoRan Offshore Exploration Co., Metairie, La., 1977-79, sr. v.p., 1979-81; pres. McMoRan-Freeport Oil Co., New Orleans, 1981-83; pres. McMoRan Exploration Co., Metairie, 1983-86; exec. v.p. McMoRan Oil & Gas Co., 1986; sr. exec. v.p. McMoRan Oil & Gas Co., 1986-90; sr. exec. v.p. Freeport-McMoran Oil & Gas Co., 1990-92, also bd. dirs.; ptnr. CLK Co., 1992-94; pres., COO McMoRan Oil & Gas Co., 1994—. Chmn. bd. Hysell Ballet Arts, Inc., New Orleans, 1982-83; bd. dirs. Lenpac, Metairie, 1983. Mem. New Orleans Geol. Soc., Geol. Soc. Am., Am. Assn. Petroleum Geologists, Petroleum Club of New Orleans (bd. dirs. 1988, 89, 90), Houston Geol. Soc., La. Assn. Ind. Producers, Mid-Continent Oil and Gas Assn. Office: McMoRan Oil & Gas Co 1615 Poydras St New Orleans LA 70112-1254 also: PO Box 60004 New Orleans LA 70160

MURRY, CHARLES EMERSON, lawyer, official; b. Hope, N.D., June 23, 1924; s. Raymond Henry and Estelle Margarete (Skeim) M.; m. Donna Deane Kleve, June 20, 1948; children: Barbara, Karla, Susan, Bruce, Charles. B.S., U. N.D., 1948, J.D., 1950. Bar: N.D. 1950. Mem. firm Nelson and Heringer, Rugby, N.D., 1950-51; ptnr. N.D. Legis. Council, 1951-75; adj. gen. with rank of maj. gen. State of N.D., Bismarck, 1975-84; mgr. Garrison Diversion Conservancy Dist., 1985-93; cons. Council State Govts.;

mem. res. forces policy bd. Sec. of Def. Vice-pres. Mo. Slope Luth. Home of Bismarck, 1965-66. Served with AUS, 1942-45. Decorated D.S.M., Legion of Merit, Meritorious Service medal, Bronze Star, Army Commendation medal; Fourragere Belgium; Orange Lanyard Netherlands; recipient Sioux award U. N.D., 1970; Gov.'s award of excellence, 1971; Nat. Leadership award Bismarck C. of C., 1971. Mem. Adjs. Gen. Assn. (exec. com., sec. 1983-84), Nat. Legis. Conf. (past chmn.), N.G. Assn., Am. Bar Assn., N.D. Bar Assn., Commrs. Uniform State Laws. Lutheran. Lodges: Elks, Masons. Office: HC 9 5505 Ponderosa Ave Bismarck ND 58501-9159

MURRY, HAROLD DAVID, JR., lawyer; b. Holdenville, Okla., June 30, 1943; s. Harold David Sr. and Willie Elizabeth (Dees) M.; m. Ann Moore Earnhardt, Nov. 1, 1975; children: Elizabeth Ann, Sarah Bryant. BA, Okla. U., 1965, JD, 1968. Bar: Okla. 1968, D.C. 1974. Asst. to v.p. U. Okla., Norman, 1968-71; legal counsel Research Inst., 1969-71; atty. U.S. Dept. Justice, Washington, 1971-74; spl. asst. U.S. Atty., Washington, 1972; assoc. Clifford & Warnke, Washington, 1974-78, ptnr., 1978-91; ptnr. Howrey & Simon, Washington, 1991—. Mem. ABA, Okla. Bar Assn., D.C. Bar Assn., Fed. Bar Assn., Met. Club (Washington), Chevy Chase Club (Md.), Phi Alpha Delta. Democrat. Home: 8931 Bel Air Pl Potomac MD 20854-1606 Office: Howrey & Simon 1299 Pennsylvania Ave NW Washington DC 20004-2402

MURTAGH, JOHN EDWARD, chemist, alcohol production consultant; b. Wallington, Surrey, Eng., Sept. 12, 1936; came to U.S., 1982; s. Thomas Henry and Elsie (Kershaw Paterson) M.; m. Eithne Anne Fawsitt, July 18, 1959; children: Catherine, Rhoda, Sean, Aidan, Doreen. BSc, U. Wales, 1959, MSc, 1970, PhD, 1972. Rsch. council. House of Seagram, Long Pond, Jamaica, 1959-63; whisky distillery mgr. House of Seagram, Beaupre, Que., Can., 1963-64; rum distillery mgr. House of Seagram, Richibucto, N.B., Can., 1965-68; rsch. mgr. House of Seagram, Montreal, Que., 1968-70; alcohol prodn. cons. Murtagh & Assocs., Buttevant, Ireland, 1972-77, 79-82, Winchester, Va., 1982—; vodka distillery mgr. Iran Beverages, Tehran, 1977-79; ethanol tech. cons., adv. bd. Info. Resources, Inc., Washington, 1988—; lectr. Alltech Ann. Alcohol Sch., Lexington, Ky., 1982—. Author: Glossary of Fuel-Ethanol Terms, 1990; co-author, eidtor: The Alcohol Textbook, 1995; pub. Worldwide Directory of Distilleries, 1995; contbr. articles to profl. jours. Adv. bd. Byrd Sch. Bus., Shenandoah U., Winchester, Va., 1989—. Recipient Millers Mutual prize, U. Wales, 1959. Fellow Am. Inst. Chemists, Inst. Chemistry of Ireland, Inst. Food Sci. and Tech. of Ireland; mem. Royal Soc. Chemistry (chartered), Am. Arbitration Assn. (arbitrator nat. comml. panel 1990—). Achievements include development of proprietary process for production of ethanol from cheese whey and the design of whey-ethanol production plants. Home and Office: 160 Bay Ct Winchester VA 22602-4700

MURTAUGH, CHRISTOPHER DAVID, lawyer; b. Darby, Pa., Oct. 25, 1945; s. John Michael and Rita (Sullivan) M.; m. Nancy R. Hanauer, Nov. 30, 1968; children: Jason C., Colin M., Alison M. AB, U. Ill., 1967, JD, 1970. Bar: Ill. 1970, Fla. 1973, U.S. Dist. Ct. (no. dist.) Ill. 1975. Ptnr. Winston & Strawn, Chgo., 1974—, capital ptnr., 1987—. Mem. Glen Ellyn (Ill.) Capital Improvements Com., 1985-89; mem. Glen Ellyn Plan Com., 1989—. Lt. USNR 1971-74. Mem. ABA, Am. Coll. Real Estate Lawyers, Fla. Bar Assn., Ill. State Bar Assn., Chgo. Bar Assn., Order of Coif. Office: Winston & Strawn 35 W Wacker Dr Chicago IL 60601-1614

MURTAUGH, MICHAEL K., lawyer; b. Evanston, Ill., July 12, 1944. BA, Coll. of Holy Cross, 1966; JD, U. Ill., 1969. Bar: Ill. 1969. Ptnr. Baker & McKenzie, Chgo. Office: Baker & McKenzie 1 Prudential Plz 130 E Randolph Dr Chicago IL 60601-6206

MURTAUGH, RODGER W., oil company executive; b. Pitts., Feb. 15, 1938; s. Rodger W. and Ida Mae (Halstead) M.; m. Nancy Elizabeth Brown, June 26, 1965; children: Jennifer Jean, Elizabeth Lynn, Thomas Rodger, Michell Kathleen. BS, Northwestern U., 1961; MBA, Harvard U., 1963. Registered profl. engr. Ill. Various analyst positions Amoco Oil Co. (formerly Am. Oil Co.), Chgo., 1963-65, v.p. ops., planning and transp., 1987—; various analyst positions Amoco Corp. (formerly Standard Oil Co. Ind.), Chgo., 1965-69, gen. mgr. corp. divisification and analysis, 1977-81, v.p. planning, econs. and devel., 1985-87; various mng. positions Amoco Prodn. Co., Tulsa and Chgo., 1970-77; v.p. planning and adminstrn. Amoco Prodn. Co., Chgo., 1981-85. Poll watcher Rep. Com., Chgo., 1964; mem. Gov.'s Adv. Com., Chgo., 1968-72, Ill. Advisors to Minority Bus., Chgo., 1960's, City Council on Fgn. Relations, Chgo., 1979—, bus. adv. com. Northwestern U. Transp. Ctr., Evanston, Ill., 1987—. Mem. Am. Petroleum Inst., Nat. Petroleum Council (subcom. petroleum storage 1987-88). Presbyterian. Avocations: golf, sailing, skiing, music. Office: Amoco Oil Corp 200 E Randolph Dr Chicago IL 60601-6401

MURTHA, JOHN FRANCIS, priest, academic administrator, history educator; b. Mt. Pleasant, Pa., Mar. 28, 1930; s. Francis Regis and Margaret Ellen (Kearns) M. BA cum laude, St. Vincent Coll., 1953; MA, Columbia U., 1960; PhD, Cath. U. Am., 1965; M Div., St. Vincent Sem., 1985. Ordained priest Roman Cath. Ch., 1957. Assoc. prof. history St. Vincent Coll., Latrobe, Pa., 1977—, bd. dirs., 1977-81, pres., 1984—; prior St. Vincent Archabbey, Latrobe, 1980-85, mem. coun. srs., 1978-88. Editor: America 200, Essays in American History, 1976; contbr. articles to New Cath. Ency., 1963. Mem. Am. Benedictine Acad., Elks. Democrat. Office: St Vincent Coll Office of Pres Fraser Purchase Rd Latrobe PA 15650

MURTHA, JOHN PATRICK, congressman; b. New Martinsville, W.Va., June 17, 1932; s. John Patrick and Mary Edna (Ray) M.; m. Joyce Bell; three children. B.A. in Econs., U. Pitts., 1961; postgrad., Indiana U. of Pa., 1962-65; H.H.D. (hon.), Mt. Aloysius Jr. Coll. Mem. Pa. Ho. of Reps., 1969-73, 93rd-103rd Congresses from 12th Pa. dist., Washington, D.C., 1974—; mem. appropriations com. Served to lt. USMC, 1952-55, as maj. 1966-67, Vietnam; ret. col. Res. Decorated Bronze Star, Purple Heart (2); Cross of Gallantry Vietnam; Pa. Disting. Svc. award, 1978, Pa. Meritorious Svc. medal, numerous service awards for work during Johnstown flood, 1977, Iron Mike award Marine Corps League, 1988, Disting. Am. award Nation's Capital chpt. Air Force Assn., 1989, Outstanding Veteran award Vets. Caucus of Am. Acad. Physician Assts., 1989, Man of Steel award Cold Finished Steel Bar Inst., 1989; named Man of Yr. Johnstown Jaycees, 1978. Office: US Ho of Reps 2423 Rayburn Ho Office Bldg Washington DC 20515-3812*

MURTHA, JOHN STEPHEN, lawyer; b. Hartford, Conn., Apr. 30, 1913; s. John J. and Agnes E. (Hennessey) M.; m. Winifred Garvan, July 7, 1939; children—John Garvan, Leslie A., Brenda A. B.A., Yale, 1935, LL.B., 1938. Bar: Conn. bar 1938. Ptnr. Murtha, Cullina, Richter & Pinney, Hartford, 1946-88, of counsel, 1989—; asst. states atty., Hartford County, 1946-51; dir. Kaman Corp. Pres. Greater Hartford Community Chest, 1968-70, Oxford Sch., Hartford, 1960-62; chmn. distbn. com. Hartford Found. for Pub. Giving, 1983-86; bd. dirs. Blue Cross and Blue Shield Conn.; bd. dirs. emeritus Boys Clubs Hartford; trustee emeritus St. Joseph Coll., West Hartford, Conn., St. Thomas More Corp., New Haven, pres., 1962-64. Served to lt. (j.g.) USNR, 1943-46. Fellow Am. Coll. Trial Lawyers; mem. ABA, Greater Hartford C. of C., Conn. Bus. and Industry Assn., Hartford Golf Club (pres. 1961-63). Republican. Roman Catholic. Home: 6 Shibah Way Bloomfield CT 06002 Office: City Place Hartford CT 06103

MURTHY, SRINIVASA K., engineering corporation executive; b. Bangalore, Karnataka, India, June 12, 1949; came to U.S., 1979; s. Ramaswamy and Gowramma Kadur. BS in Physics, Bangalore U., India, 1967; MS in Physics, Bangalore U., 1969; MSEE, Mysore U., India, 1971. Mgr. project engring. Indian Space Rsch. Orgn., Bangalore, 1971-79; asst. prof. Calif. State U., Pomona, 1979-80, Fullerton, 1981-82; mgr. project Systems and Applied Scis. Corp., Anaheim, Calif., 1980-83; dir. div. IMR Systems Corp., Arlington, Va., 1983-84; mgr. systems engring. GE, Portsmouth, Va., 1984-85; bus. and program mgr. govt. rsch. programs AT&T Bell Labs, Homdel, N.J., 1985-94, Murray Hill, N.J., 1994—; bd. advisors IMR Sys. Corp., Roslyn, Va., 1988—; mem. editl. adv. bd. R&D Mag., Cahners Publs.; judge R&D 100 awards. Editorial adv. bd. Rsch. and Devel. Mag. Calvert Publs., Reed Publs. Group; contbr. articles to profl. jours. Recipient Disting. Achievement award Dept. Space, Indian Govt., 1975. Mem. IEEE (sr. mem., bd. govs. 1986—, standards bd. 1986—, bd. dirs. Electronics and

Aerospace Systems conf. 1983-84, editorial bd. dirs. Network Jour. 1986—, area activities bd. and tech. activities bd. 1988, Computer Soc. 1987—, lectr. India, Singapore, Australia 1989, South Am. 1990, inducted into Nat. Rsch. Coun., Advt. Rsch. Found. and Engring. Consortium, numerous other coms.), Engring. Mgmt. Soc. of IEEE (bd. govs. 1986—, v.p.). Home: 13 Willow Ave Somerset NJ 08873-1426 Office: AT&T Bell Labs 600 Mountain Ave Rm 38-329 Murray Hill NJ 07974-0636

MURTY, KORUKONDA LINGA, nuclear science educator. Prof. dept. nuclear engring. N.C. State U., Raleigh. Recipient Mishima award Am. Nuclear Soc., 1993. Office: North Carolina State U Box 7909 Dept Nuclear Engring Raleigh NC 27695*

MUSA, JOHN DAVIS, computer and infosystems executive, software reliability engineering researcher and expert; b. Amityville, N.Y., June 11, 1933; s. Khan Hussein and Ione Geraldine (Ryan) M.; m. Marilyn Laurene Allred, June 24, 1959. BA, Dartmouth Coll., 1954, MSEE, 1955. With AT&T Bell Labs., Murray Hill, N.J., 1958—, mem. tech. staff, 1958-63, supr. guidance program devel., 1963-68, supr. command and control program devel., 1968-69, supr. mgmt. control and new software tech., 1969-72, supr. human factors test, 1972-74, supr. computer graphics, 1974-80, supr. computer measurements, 1980-85, supr. software quality, 1985-90, tech. mgr. software reliability engring., 1991—; mem. N.J. Coun. R & D. Author: Software Reliability: Measurement, Prediction, Application, 1987; contbr. articles to profl. jours. and books. Lt. USN, 1955-58. Fellow IEEE; mem. IEEE Computer Soc. (2d v.p. 1986, v.p. publs. 1984-85, v.p. tech. activities 1986, chair tech. com. software engring. 1982-84, founding mem. editorial bd. IEEE Software Mag., Disting. lectr. 1980-83, Meritorious Svc. award 1984, 85, 87, founding officer subcom. on software reliability engring., mem. editorial bds. Spectrum mag. 1984-86, Proc. of the IEEE 1983-90, Technique et Science Informatiques jour., sr. editor Software Engring. Inst. book series, chair steering com. Internat. Conf. on Software Engring.), IEEE Reliability Soc., Assn. for Computing Machinery. Internat. leader in software engring. and in creation new tech. software reliability engring.; various presentations on software reliability engring. on video; developed concepts and practice of operational profile and software-reliability engineered testing. Avocations: French, opera, reading, wine tasting, travel. Office: AT&T Bell Labs PO Box 636 Rm 2C402 600 Mountain Ave Murray Hill NJ 07974-0636

MUSA, MAHMOUD NIMIR, psychiatry educator; b. Arraba, Jenin, Palestine, Mar. 22, 1943; came to U.S., 1964; s. Nimir A. and Zarifa (Haseeb) M.; m. Wafaa M. Arafat, Mar. 24, 1991. BS, Am. U. Beirut, 1964; MS, U. Wis., 1966, PhD, 1972; MD, Med. Coll. Wis., 1979. Diplomate Am. Bd. Psychiatry. Rsch. assoc. U. Wis., Madison, 1972-75; asst. prof. Idaho State U., Pocatello, 1975-76; resident Ill. State Psychiat. Inst., Chgo., 1979-83; assoc. prof. psychiatry Chgo. Med. Sch., North Chicago, Ill., 1987-90; prof. psychiatry Loyola U., Maywood, Ill., 1990—; cons. Mus. Sci. & Industry, CHgo., 1985-90. Editor: Pharmacikinetics and Monitoring Psychiatry Drugs, 1992. Cons. Kovler Ctr. for Treatment of Survivors of Torture, CHgo., 1989-92. Recipient Scientific Achievement award Ill. Psychiat. Soc., Chgo., 1982. Fellow Am. Coll. Clin. Pharmacology, Great Lakes Soc. Clin. Pharmacology (pres. 1991-92); mem. AAAS, Am. Psychiat. Assn. Avocations: reading, photography, theater. Home: 1115 S Plymouth #102 Chicago IL 60605

MUSA, SAMUEL ALBERT, electronics company executive; m. Judith Friedman; children: Gregory, Jeffrey. BA, Rutgers U., 1961, BSEE, 1961; MS in Applied Physics, Harvard U., 1962, PhD in Applied Physics, 1965. Rsch. scientist Gen. Precision Inc., Little Falls, N.J., 1965-66; asst. prof. elec. engring. U. Pa., Phila., 1966-71; project leader Inst. for Def. Analyses, Arlington, Va., 1971-78; dep. dir. Office of Under Sec. Def., Washington, 1978-83; dir. rsch. and advanced tech. E-Systems, Inc., Dallas, 1983-86, v.p. rsch. and advanced tech., 1986-95; cons. sci. adv. bd. USAF, 1987-91; mem. adv. bd. Def. Intelligence Agy. Contbr. articles to profl. jours. Fellow IEEE; mem. AIA (tech. and ops. coun. 1986-95, vice chmn. 1993, chmn. 1994), Sigma Xi, Tau Beta Pi, Pi Mu Epsilon.

MUSACCHIA, X(AVIER) J(OSEPH), physiology and biophysics educator; b. Bklyn., Feb. 11, 1923; s. Castrense and Orsolina (Mazzola) M.; m. Betty Cook, Nov. 23, 1950; children: Joseph, Mary, Thomas, Laura Ann. BS, St. Francis Coll., Bklyn., 1944; MS, Fordham U., 1947, PhD, 1949. Instr. biology Marymount (N.Y.) Coll., 1948-49; from instr. to prof. biology St. Louis U., 1949-65; prof. physiology U. Mo., Columbia, 1965-78; prof. physiology and biophysics U. Louisville, 1978-91, prof. emeritus, 1991—; dean Grad. Sch., 1978-89, assoc. provost for rsch., 1985-89; bd. dirs. Coun. Grad. Schs., 1986-89. Author: Depressed Metabolism, 1969, Regulation of Depressed Metabolism and Thermogenesis, 1976, Survival in Cold, 1981; also articles. Bd. govs. J. Graham Brown Cancer Ctr., Louisville, 1978-83; bd. dirs. Oak Ridge Associated Univs. Served with AUS, 1943-45. Research grantee NIH; Research grantee NASA. Fellow AAAS; mem. Am. Physiol. Soc., Am. Soc. Zoologists, Am. Soc. for Space and Gravitational Biology (v.p. 1988-89, pres. 1989-90), Soc. Exptl. Biology and Medicine, Corp. Marine Biol. Lab., Sigma Xi. (past chpt. pres.). Address: PO Box 5054 Bella Vista AR 72714

MUSANTE, TONY (ANTHONY PETER MUSANTE, JR.), actor; b. Bridgeport, Conn.; s. Anthony Peter and Natalie Anne (Salerno) M.; m. Jane Ashley Sparkes, June 2, 1962. B.A. (Baker scholar), Oberlin Coll., 1958; postgrad., Northwestern U., 1957; student, HB Studios, N.Y.C., 1961-65. Appearances include: (off Broadway prodns.) Borak, 1960, Zoo Story, Night of the Dunce, The Collection, Match-Play, Kiss Mama, L'Histoire du Soldat, A Gun Play, Falling Man, Cassatt, Grand Magic, The Big Knife, The Taming of the Shrew, Two Brothers, The Archbishop's Ceiling, Souvenir, A Streetcar Named Desire, Double Play, Dancing in the End Zone, Snow Orchid, Wait until Dark, Widows, Anthony Rose, Mount Allegro, Frankie and Johnny in the Clair de Lune, Breaking Legs, The Flip Side, Love Letters, (Broadway prodns.) PS Your Cat is Dead, 1975 (N.Y. Drama Desk nomination), Memory of Two Mondays, 27 Wagons Full of Cotton, The Lady from Dubuque; films: Once a Thief, 1964, The Incident (Best Actor award Mar del Plata Internat. Film Festival), 1967, The Detective, The Mercenary, One Night at Dinner, Bird with the Crystal Plumage, Grissom Gang, Anonymous Venetian, The Last Run, Pisciotta Case, Goodbye and Amen, Break-Up, Collector's Item, The Repenter, Devil's Hill, Appointment in Trieste, Nocturne, The Pope of Greenwich Village; TV appearances include Ride with Terror, 1963, star series Toma, 1973-74 (Photoplay Gold medal award 1974), scriptwriter several episodes; also starred in TV miniseries and movies: High Ice, Breaking Up is Hard to Do, The Baron, Legend of the Black Hand, The Story of Esther, My Husband is Missing, Nowhere to Hide, The Quality of Mercy (Emmy nominee 1975), Court Martial of Lt. William Calley, Night Heat, Rearview Mirror, Nutcracker: Money, Madness and Murder, American Playhouse: Weekend, Last Waltz on a Tightrope; daytime TV (guest star): Loving, ABC, 1993. Mem. SAG, AFTRA, ATAS, Actors Equity Assn., Writers Guild Am. West, Acad. Motion Picture Arts and Scis.

MUSBURGER, BRENT WOODY, sportscaster; b. Portland, Oreg., May 26, 1939; s. C.C. and Beryl Ruth (Woody) M.; m. Arlene Clare Sander, June 8, 1963; children: Blake, Scott. BJ, Northwestern U., 1962. Profl. umpire Midwest Baseball League, 1959; sports columnist Chgo. Am., 1962-68; dir. sports WBBM Radio and TV, Chgo., 1968-74; sportscaster CBS-TV, 1974-90; dir. sports Sta. KNXT, Los Angeles, 1979-81; host Sports Time, NCAA Today, Saturday/Sports Sunday, CBS, from 1981; host, mng. editor NFL Today; now with ABC-TV Sports, 1990—. Served with AUS, 1960. Named Ill. Sportscaster of Yr., Nat. Assn. Sportswriters and Sportscasters, 1971, 74. Hustle.*

MUSCATINE, CHARLES, English educator, author; b. Bklyn., Nov. 28, 1920; m. Doris Corn, July 21, 1945; children: Jeffrey, Alison. B.A., Yale U., 1941, M.A., 1942, Ph.D., 1948; L.H.D. (hon.), New Sch. for Social Research, 1982; Litt.D., SUNY, 1989, Rosary Coll., 1991. Mem. faculty dept. English U. Calif., Berkeley, 1948—; prof. U. Calif., 1960-91, prof. emeritus, 1991—; dir. Collegiate Seminar Program, 1974-80; vis. prof. Wesleyan U., 1951-53; Ward Phillips lectr. U. Notre Dame, 1969; mem. com. of selection J.S. Guggenheim Found., 1969-89, chmn. 1985-89. Author: Chaucer and the French Tradition, 1957, The Book of Geoffrey Chaucer, 1963, Poetry and Crisis in the Age of Chaucer, 1972, The Old French Fabliaux, 1986. Co-author, editor: Education at Berkeley, 1966, (with M. Griffith) The Borzoi

College Reader, 1966, 7th edit.; 1992, First Person Singular, 1973; co-editor Integrity in the Coll. Curriculum, 1985. Bd. dirs. No. Calif. chpt. ACLU, 1959-62, 63-66, Assn. Am. Colls., 1979-82, Ctr. for the Common Good, 1994—; bd. dirs. Fedn. State Humanities Couns., 1989-94, chair, 1991-93; mem. Commn. on Humanities, Rockefeller Found., 1978-79, Calif. Coun. Humanities, 1986-94. With USNR, 1942-45. Recipient Navy Commendation ribbon, 1945, Berkeley citation, 1991; Fulbright fellow, 1958, 62, ACLS Rsch. fellow, 1958, Guggenheim fellow, 1962, NEH Sr. fellow, 1968. Fellow Am. Acad. Arts and Scis., Medieval Acad. of Am.; mem. MLA, New Chaucer Soc. (pres. 1980-81), Aircraft Owners and Pilots Assn., Phi Beta Kappa. Club: Arts (Berkeley). Home: 2812 Buena Vista Way Berkeley CA 94708-2016

MUSCATO, ANDREW, lawyer; b. Newark, Aug. 28, 1953; s. Salvatore and Bertha (Kubilus) M.; m. Ann Marie Hughes, Aug. 19, 1978; children: Amy, Andrew Joseph, Amanda. AB magna cum laude, Brown U., 1975; JD, Seton Hall U., 1978. Bar: N.J. 1978, U.S. Dist. Ct. N.J. 1978, U.S. Ct. Appeals (3d cir.) 1981, N.Y. 1984, U.S. Dist. Ct. (so. and ea. dists.) N.Y. 1984. Law clk. to presiding judge, appellate div. N.J. Superior Ct., Somerville, 1978-79; staff atty. Adminstrv. Office of Cts., Trenton, N.J., 1979-80; assoc. Simon & Allen, Newark, 1980-86; ptnr. Kirsten & Simon, Newark, 1987-89, Whitman & Ransom, Newark, 1989-93, Whitman Breed Abbott & Morgan, Newark, 1993—; atty. Irvington (N.J.) Rent Leveling Bd., 1980—. Author: Executing on a Debtor's Interest in a Tenancy by the Entirety, 1986. Mem. ABA, Essex County Bar Assn., Trial Attys. N.J., N.J. Inst. Mcpl. Attys. Republican. Roman Catholic. Home: 66 Addison Dr Basking Ridge NJ 07920-2202 Office: Whitman Breed Abbott Et Al 1 Gateway Ctr Newark NJ 07102

MUSCHEL, LOUIS HENRY, immunologist, educator; b. N.Y.C., July 4, 1916; s. Maurice and Betty (Tobey) M.; m. Anne Orzel, Oct. 22, 1946; 1 child, Ruth Josephine. B.S., NYU, 1936; M.S., Yale U., 1951, Ph.D., 1953. Joined U.S. Army, 1941, advanced through grades to lt. col., 1961; chief dept. serology (Walter Reed Army Inst. Research), Washington, 1958-62; faculty U. Minn., Mpls., 1962-70; prof. microbiology U. Minn., 1964-70; with research dept. Am. Cancer Soc., 1970-88; adj. prof. microbiology Columbia U., 1977-83; adj. prof. pathology NYU, 1983—. Mem. Am. Assn. Immunologists, Brit. Soc. Immunology, N.Y. Acad. Scis., Am. Soc. Microbiology, Soc. Exptl. Biology and Medicine, Am. Assn. for Cancer Research, Phi Beta Kappa, Sigma Xi, Phi Lambda Upsilon. Research, publs. on bactericidal action of serum and its role in host defs., natural bactericidal and viral neutralizing antibodies, applications of complement fixation technique. Home: 3333 Henry Hudson Pky Apt 8A Bronx NY 10463-3233

MUSCHENHEIM, FREDERICK, pathologist; b. N.Y.C., July 9, 1932; s. Carl and Haroldine (Humphreys) M.; m. Linda Alexander, Mar. 29, 1958; children: Alexandra Lydia, Carl William, David Henry. AB, Harvard U., 1953; MDCM, McGill U., Montreal, Can., 1963. Intern Santa Clara County Hosp., San Jose, Calif., 1963-64; resident pathology U. Colo. Med. Ctr., Denver, 1964-68, chief resident clin. pathology, 1968-69; pathologist Freeman, Hanske, Munkittrick & Foley PA, Mpls., 1969-77; clin. pathologist Union-Truesdale Hosp., Fall River, Mass., 1977-78; chief pathologist St. Clare's Hosp., Denville, N.J., 1978-83, Oneida (N.Y.) City Hosps., 1984—; clin. asst. prof. SUNY Health Sci. Ctr., Syracuse, 1984-90, clin. assoc. prof., 1990—; chief med. staff Oneida City Hosps., 1991; pres. Sunderman Fund, Bermuda Biol. Sta. for Rsch., v.p. Madison County (N.Y.) bd. health, 1995. Mem. choir 1st Presbyn. Ch. of Cazenovia, N.Y., 1984—, trustee, 1985-89. Mem. Assn. Clin. Scientists (pres. 1990, Diploma of Honor 1991), Coll. Am. Pathologists (mem. govt. affairs com. 1994, nominating com. 1995), Med. Soc. State of N.Y. (mem. legis. com. 1991—), Med. Soc. Madison County (v.p. 1990-91, pres. 1991-93), N.Y. State Assn. Pub. Health Labs (v.p. 1992-93, pres. 1993-94, adn. chmn. 1994-95), N.Y. Soc. Pathologists (councilor2nd dist. 1991—). Home: 5257 Owera Point Rd Cazenovia NY 13035-9340 Office: Oneida City Hosps 321 Genesee St Oneida NY 13421-2611

MUSE, EWELL HENDERSON, III, gas company executive; b. Fort Worth, Dec. 25, 1938; s. Ewell Henderson and Mary Haydon (Tucker) M.; m. Ellen Estelle Cassin, June 23, 1962; children—Mary Ellen, Robert Cassin. B.S in Petroleum Engring., U. Tex., 1961; M.B.A. in Fin., U. So. Calif. 1963. Petroleum engr. Tenneco Oil E&P, Shreveport and Lafayette, La., 1963-69; mgr. econs. Tenn. Gas Transmission, Houston, 1969-74, dir. econs., 1974-77, v.p. 1977-80, sr. v.p., 1980-82, 1985—; v.p. Tenneco Inc., Houston, 1985—; pres. Tenneco Gas Latin Am., 1995—. Mem. Am. Petroleum Inst., Planning Execs. Inst., Nat. Soc. Profl. Engrs. Republican. Episcopalian. Clubs: Lakeside (Houston). Avocations: golf; fishing. Office: Tenn Gas PO Box 2511 1010 Milam St Houston TX 77002-5312

MUSE, MARTHA TWITCHELL, foundation executive; b. Dallas, Sept. 1, 1926; d. John Blackburn Muse and Kathryn (Poole) M. B.A., Barnard Coll., 1948; M.A., Columbia U., 1955; D.H.L., Georgetown U., 1981. Exec. dir. Tinker Found., N.Y.C., 1965-68, pres., 1968—, chmn., 1975—; bd. dirs. The Bank of N.Y. Co., Inc., Bank of N.Y., Trust & Investment Ct., Audit & Examining Ct., Community Reinvestment Act Ct.; bd. dirs. N.Y. Stock Exchange, mem. ct. for rev. and exec. coms., chmn. pub. policy ct. com. Bd. dirs. Am. Coun. Germany, Americas Found., Americas Soc. Inc., Coun. of the Ams.; trustee emeritus Columbia U., N.Y.C.; vice chmn., bd. dirs. Spanish Inst.; bd. visitors Edmund A. Walsh Sch. Fgn. Svc., Georgetown U., 1973—; bd. dir. Am. Portuguese Sc.; mem. Wilson coun. Woodrow Wilson Internat. Ctr. for Scholars; mem. coun. Internat. Exec. Svc. Corps; mem. adv. coun. Luso-Am. Devel. Found. Decorated Asscc. Dame Order St. John of Jerusalem, Gt. Britain; Lazo de Dama de la Orden del Merito Civil (Spain); comdr. Orden del Sol del Peru; comdr. Order of Bernardo O'Higgins (Chile); comdr. Orden de Mayo al Merito (Argentina); comdr. Ordem Nacional do Cruzeiro Do Sul (Brazil); recipient Alumni award for excellence Columbia U. Grad. Faculties, 1987. Mem. N.Y.C. Coun. Fgn. Relations, Huguenot Soc., Nat. Soc. Colonial Dames. Episcopalian. Clubs: Colony (N.Y.C.), Met (N.Y.C.). Home: 267 Westport Rd Wilton CT 06897-4724 Office: Tinker Found Inc 55 E 59th St New York NY 10022-1112

MUSE, WILLIAM VAN, university president; b. Marks, Miss., Apr. 7, 1939; s. Mose Lee and Mary Elizabeth (Hisaw) M.; m. Anna Marlene Munden, Aug. 22, 1964; children: Amy Marlene, Ellen Elizabeth, William Van. B.S. (T.H. Harris scholar), Northwestern La. State U., 1960; M.B.A. (Nat. Def. Grad. fellow), U. Ark., 1961, Ph.D. (Nat. Def. Grad. fellow), 1966. Instr. U. Ark., 1962-63; field supr. Tau Kappa Epsilon Fraternity, 1963-64; asst. prof. Ga. Tech., 1964-65; assoc. prof., chmn., dir. rsch. Ohio U., 1965-70; dean Coll. Bus. Appalachian State U., Boone, N.C., 1970-73; dean Coll. Bus. Adminstrn. U. Nebr., Omaha, 1973-79; dean Coll. Bus. Adminstrn. Tex. A&M U., College Station, 1979-82, vice chancellor, 1983-84; former pres. U. Akron, Ohio, 1984-92; now pres. Auburn U., Ala., 1992—. Author: Business and Economic Problems in Appalachia, 1969, Management Practices in Fraternities, 1965; Contbr. articles to profl. jours. Found. for Econ. Edn. fellow, 1967. Mem. Blue Key, Omicron Delta Kappa, Phi Kappa Phi, Delta Sigma Pi, Beta Gamma Sigma, Pi Omega Pi, Tau Kappa Epsilon. Club: Rotarian. Office: Auburn U Office of Pres Auburn AL 36849

MUSFELT, DUANE CLARK, lawyer; b. Stockton, Calif., Sept. 14, 1951; s. Robert H. and Doris E. (Roth) M.; m. Linh T. To, Sept. 6, 1980. Student, U. Calif., Davis, 1969-71; BA in Econs., U. Calif., Berkeley, 1973; JD, UCLA, 1976. Bar: Calif. 1976, U.S. Dist. Ct. (cen. dist.) Calif. 1977, U.S. Ct. Appeals (9th cir.) 1980, U.S. Dist. Ct. (no. dist.) Calif. 1982, U.S. Dist. Ct. (ea. and so. dists.) Calif. 1983, U.S. Supreme Ct. 1987. Assoc. Haight, Dickson, Brown & Bonesteel, L.A., 1976-77, Mori & Ota, L.A., 1977-79, Lewis, D'Amato, Brisbois & Bisgaard, L.A., 1979-82; ptnr. Lewis, D'Amato, Brisbois & Bisgaard, San Francisco, 1982—. Mem. State Bar Calif., No. Calif. Assn. Defense Counsel, Bar Assn. San Francisco, Defense Rsch. Inst. Democrat. Presbyterian. Avocations: tennis, skiing, bridge. Office: Lewis DAmato Brisbois & Bisgaard 601 California St Ste 1900 San Francisco CA 94108-2836

MUSGRAVE, CHARLES EDWARD, music director, correctional facility official; b. Alton, Ill., Nov. 17, 1932; s. Clay Everett and Fannie Adeline (Peek) M.; m. Barbara Jean Robertson, Aug. 11, 1952 (div. Feb. 1971); children: Michael David, Debra Ann; m. Toby Elaine Riley, Aug. 18,

1973. B in Mus. Edn., Shurtleff Coll., 1954; MS, U. Ill., 1957; postgrad., U. No. Colo., 1970. Cert. tchr., Ill., Ind. Tchr. music Alton (Ill.) Pub. Schs., 1953-67; v.p. Monticello Coll., Godfrey, Ill., 1967-69; asst. to v.p. U. No. Colo., Greeley, 1970; chmn. dept. music Duneland Sch. Corp., Chesterton, Ind., 1970-72; dir. devel. Interlochen (Mich.) Arts Acad., 1972-73; v.p. Musart Corp., Chgo., 1973-74; dir. music Ind. State Prison, Michigan City, 1974—; vice chmn. La Porter Fed. Credit Union, Michigan City, 1975—; facility coordinator adult continuing edn. Ind. U. Author: Fussell's Individual Technique Guide, 1973. Rep. committeeman, Chesterton, 1976—, del. to state conv., Ind., 1978—; mem. Porter County (Ind.) Planning Commn., 1984-85; chmn. govt. workers sect. United Way, Michigan City, 1981-90; mem. Ind. Gov.'s Adv. Com., 1983; minister of music 1st United Meth. Ch., Chesterton, 1978-91; bd. dirs. Five Lakes Conservation Club, Wolcottville, Inc., 1983-90; bd. dirs., v.p. Valparaiso Cmty. Concerts Assn., 1986—. Grantee Systems Mgmt. U. W. Va., U. Chgo., 1979. Mem. Correctional Edn. Assn. (Internat. Tchr. of Yr. 1981), Ind. Soc. Chgo., LaGrange Country Club, Masons, Shriners, Scottish Rite, Phi Delta Kappa. Avocations: sailing, golf, photography, computers. Home: 750 Graham Dr Chesterton IN 46304-1620 Office: Ind State Prison PO Box 41 Michigan City IN 46360-0041

MUSGRAVE, R. KENTON, federal judge; b. 1927. Student, Ga. Inst. Tech., 1945-46, U. Fla., 1946-47; BA, U. Wash., 1948; JD with distinction, Emory U., 1953. Asst. gen. counsel Lockheed Internat., 1953-62; v.p., gen. counsel Mattel, Inc., 1963-71; mem. firm Musgrave, Welbourn and Fertman, 1972-75; asst. gen. counsel Pacific Enterprises, 1975-81; v.p., gen. counsel Vivitar Corp, 1981-85; v.p., dir. Santa Barbara Applied Rsch., 1982-87; judge U.S. Ct. Internat. Trade, N.Y.C., 1987—. Trustee Morris Animal Found., The Dian Fossey Gorilla Fund, Dolphins of Sharks Bay (Australia); hon. trustee Pet Protection Svc.; mem. United Way, South Bay-Centinela Svc. Orgn., Save the Redwoods League; active LWV, Legal Aid, Palos Verdes Community Assn. Mem. ABA, Internat. Bar Assn., Pan Am. Bar Assn., State Bar Calif. (chmn. corp. law sect. 1965-66, del. 1966-67), L.A. County Bar Assn., State Bar Ga., Fng. Trade Assn. So. Calif. (bd. dirs.), Sierra Club. Office: US Ct Internat Trade 1 Federal Plz New York NY 10007

MUSGRAVE, RICHARD ABEL, economics educator; b. Königstein, Germany, Dec. 14, 1910; came to U.S., 1933, naturalized, 1940; s. Curt Abel and Charlotte (Pruefer) M.; m. Peggy Brewer Richman, May 7, 1964. Diploma, U. Heidelberg, 1933; MA, Harvard U., 1936, PhD, 1937; LLD (hon.), Allegheny Coll., 1980; Doktor der Wirtschaftswissenschaften honoris causa, U. Heidelberg, Fed. Republic Germany; Doctoris Oeconomiae honoris causa, Cath. U., Milan, 1989; LLD honoris causa, U. Mich., 1991. Tutor, instr. econs. Harvard, 1936-41; research economist Bd. Govs. Fed. Res. System, Washington, 1941-47; lectr. econs. Swarthmore Coll., 1947-48; prof. econs. U. Mich., 1950-59; prof. polit. economy Johns Hopkins, 1959-62; prof. econs. and pub. affairs Princeton, 1962-65; H.H. Burbank prof. polit. econ. Harvard U., faculty arts and scis. and Law Sch., 1965-81, prof. emeritus, 1981—; adj. prof. U. Calif., Santa Cruz, 1990—; chief economist Internat. Bank Mission to Columbia, 1949; chief ECA Fiscal Mission to Germany, 1951; pres. Colombian Tax Reform Commn., 1968-69; dir. Bolivian Fiscal Reform Mission, 1976-77; at various times cons. bd. govs. Fed. Res. System, Treasury Dept., Council Econ. Advisers, Commn. on Money and Credit. Author: Theory of Public Finance, 1959, Fiscal Systems, 1969, Public Finance in Theory and Practice, 1973; editor Quar. Jour. Econs., 1970-75, Public Finance in a Democratic Soc., 1986; contbr. profl. jours. Recipient Frank E. Seidman award in polit. economy, 1981. Fellow Am. Acad. Arts and Scis.; disting. fellow Am. Econ. Assn. (exec. com. 1956-59, v.p. 1962); hon. mem. Nat. Tax Assn.; mem. NAS, Internat. Seminar in Pub. econs., Internat. Inst. Pub. Fin. (hon. pres. 1978). Home: 760 Western Dr Santa Cruz CA 95060 Office: U Calif Social Sci 1 Santa Cruz CA 95064

MUSGRAVE, STORY, astronaut, surgeon, pilot, physiologist, educator; b. Boston, Aug. 19, 1935; children: Lorelei Lisa, Bradley Scott, Holly Kay, Christopher Todd, Jeffrey Paul, Lane Linwood. BS in Math. and Statis., Syracuse U., 1958; MBA, UCLA, 1959; BA in Chemistry, Marietta Coll., 1960; MD, Columbia U., 1964; MS in Biophysics, U. Ky., 1966; MA in Lit., U. Houston, 1987, MA in Humanities, 1989. Surg. intern U. Ky. Med. Ctr., Lexington, 1964-65; scientist-astronaut NASA, Houston, 1967—, backup sci.-pilot 1st Skylab mission, 1973, flew on first Challenger flight, STS-6, 1983, flew on Spacelab 2, 1985, flew on space shuttle mission STS-33, 1989, flew on STS-44, 1991; payload comdr. on STS-61 Hubble Telescope Repair Mission, Houston, 1993. Contbr. articles to profl. jours. With USMC, 1953-56. Recipient Reese AFB Comdr.'s trophy, 1969, NASA exceptional svc. medal, 1974, 83, 90, NASA disting. svc. medal, 1992, 94, NASA spaceflight medal, 1983, 85, 89, 91, 93; USAF postdoctoral fellow, 1965-66, Nat. Heart Inst. postdoctoral fellow, 1966-67. Mem. AAAS, AAS, AIAA, Flying Physicians Assn. (Airman of Yr. award 1974, 83), Civil Aviation Med. Assn., N.Y. Acad. Sci., Nat. Geog. Soc., Soaring Soc. Am., U.S. Parachute Assn., Marine Corps Assn., Alpha Kappa Psi, Phi Delta Theta, Omicron Delta Kappa, Beta Gamma Sigma. NASA Code CB Houston TX 77058 From subatomic particles, to the stardust from which I was created, from the forming galaxies, to the universes beyond our own, I live to participate physically and spiritually in every aspect of this cosmic creation and evolution.

MUSGRAVE, THEA, composer, conductor; b. Edinburgh, Scotland, May 27, 1928; m. Peter Mark, 1971. Ed., Edinburgh U., Paris Conservatory; Mus.D. (hon.). Composer: (opera) The Abbot of Drimock, 1955, The Decision, 1964-65, The Voice of Ariadne, 1972-73, Mary, Queen of Scots, 1975-77, A Christmas Carol, 1978-79 (first performed Va. Opera Assn., 1979), An Occurrence at Owl Creek Bridge, 1981, Harriet, The Woman Called Moses, 1981-84 (1st performed Va. Opera 1985), Simón Bolívar, (ballet) Beauty and the Beast, 1969, (symphony and orchestral music) Obliques, 1958, Noctures and Arias, 1966, Concerto for orch., 1967, Clarinet Concerto, 1968, Night Music, 1969, Scottish Dance Suite, 1969, Memento Vitae, 1969-70, Horn Concerto, 1971, Viola Concerto, 1973, Orfeo II, 1975, Soliloquy II and III, 1980, From One to Another, 1980, Peripeteia, 1981, The Seasons, 1988, (marimba concerto) Journey through a Japanese Landscape, (bass-clarinet concerto) Autumn Sonata, (chamber and instrumental music) String Quartet, 1958, Trio for flute, oboe and piano, 1960, Monologue, 1960, Serenade, 1961, Chamber Concerto No. 1, 1962, Chamber Concerto No. 2, 1966, Chamber Concerto No. 3, 1966, Music for horn and piano, 1967, Impromptu No. 1, 1967, Soliloquy I, 1969, Elegy, 1970, Impromptu No. 2, 1970, Space Play, 1974, Orfeo I, 1975, Fanfare, 1982, Pierrot, 1985, Narcissus, 1987, Niobe, 1987, (vocal and choral music) Two Songs, 1951, Four Madrigals, 1953, Six Songs: Two Early English Poems, 1953, A Suite O'Bairnsangs, 1953, Cantata for a Summer's Day, 1954, Song of the Burn, 1954, Five Love Songs, 1955, Four Portraits, 1956, A Song for Christmas, 1958, Triptych, 1959, Sir Patrick Spens, 1961, Make Ye Merry For Him That Is To Come, 1962, Two Christmas Carols in Traditional Style, 1963, John Cook, 1963, Five Ages of Man, 1963-64, Memento Creatoris, 1967, Primavera, 1971, Rorate Coeli, 1973, Monologues of Mary, Queen of Scots, 1977-86, O Caro M'e Il Sonno, 1978, The Last Twilight, 1980, Black Tambourine, 1985, For the Time Being, 1986, Echoes Through Time, 1988, Wild Winter for Viols & Voices, 1993. Office: VA Opera Assn PO Box 2580 Norfolk VA 23501

MUSGRAVES, ROBERT E., lawyer; b. Albuquerque, Feb. 15, 1955; s. Bobby E. and Betty J. (Sorrells) M.; m. Lynn E. Newkirk, May 9, 1976; children: J. David, Andrew M. BA, Rice U., 1976; JD, U. Tex., 1979. Bar: Colo. 1979, U.S. Dist. Ct. Colo. 1979, U.S. Ct. Appeals (10th cir.) 1981. Assoc. Gorusch, Kirgis, Campbell, Walker & Grover, Denver, 1979-81; assoc. Kirkland & Ellis, Denver, 1981-86, ptnr., 1986-90; v.p., sec., gen. coun. Titanium Metals Corp., Denver, 1990—. Author: (with others) American Law of Mining 2d edit., 1984, Mergers, Aquisitions and Leveraged Buyouts, 1989. Office: Titanium Metals Corp 1999 Broadway Ste 4300 Denver CO 80202-5743

MUSHER, DANIEL MICHAEL, physician; b. N.Y.C., Feb. 27, 1938; s. Sidney and Hadassah (Kaplan) M.; m. Karol Sue Katz, June 17, 1967; children: Rebecca Leah, Benjamin Leon, Deborah Ann. AB magna cum laude, Harvard Coll., 1959; MD, Columbia U., 1963; postgrad., MIT, 1969-70. Diplomate Am. Bd. Internal Medicine, specialty infectious diseases. Intern, jr. med. resident first med. divsn. Bellevue Hosp., 1963-65; sr. med. resident Tufts-New Eng. Med. Ctr. Hosps., 1967-68; NIH trainee in infec-

tious diseases New Eng. Med. Ctr. Hosps., 1968-71; instr. medicine Tufts U. Sch. Medicine, 1970-71; asst. prof. medicine, asst. prof. microbiology & immunology Baylor Coll. Medicine, Houston, 1971-73, assoc. prof., 1974-78, prof. microbiology and immunology, 1979—, prof. medicine, 1979—, chief infectious diseases, 1994—; chief infectious disease sect. VA Med. Ctr., Houston, 1971—; mem. Baylor House Staff Selection Com., 1973—; mem. infection control com. VA Med. Ctr., 1971—, chmn., 1971, mem. AIDS task force, 1987—; mem. Baylor Dept. Medicine Task Force, 1987—; mem. Baylor Dept. Medicine Exec. Faculty, 1992—. Mem. editorial bd. Sexually Transmitted Diseases, 1979-83; assoc. editor Jour. Infectious Diseases, 1983-88; contbr. articles to profl. jours. Chmn. edn. William Malev Schs. of Congregation Beth Yeshurun, Houston, 1993—; bd. mem., past pres. I. Weiner Jewish Secondary Sch., Houston, 1979—; bd. mem. Congregation Beth Yeshurun, Houston, 1975—; bd. mem., v.p. Houston Friends of Music, 1975—. With USAF, 1965-67. Recipient Physician's Recognition award AMA, 1991—, Dir.'s award for profl. leadership VA Med. Ctr., Houston, 1991. Fellow ACP; mem. AAAS, Am. Assn. Immunologists, Am. Fedn. Clin. Rsch., Am. Soc. Clin. Investigation, Am. Soc. Microbiology, Am. Thoracic Soc., Am. Venereal Disease Assn., Infectious Diseases Soc. Am., Med. Soc. for Study Venereal Diseases (Britain), So. Soc. Clin. Investigation, Soc. Exptl. Biology and Medicine, Sigma Xi. Avocations: music (string quartet playing), reading. Office: VA Hosp 2002 Holcomb Houston TX 77030

MUSHINSKY, MARY M., state legislator; b. New Haven; m. Martin J. Waters; children: Martin Waters, Edward Waters. Student, So. Conn. State U., Fla. Atlantic U., Wesleyan U. Mem. Conn. Ho. of Reps., 1985—, asst. majority leader, mem. environ., fin., revenue and bonding com., mem. planning and devel. com. Democrat. Home: 188 S Cherry St Wallingford CT 06492-4016 Office: Conn Senate State Capital Hartford CT 06106

MUSHKIN, LEONARD BARTON, podiatrist; b. Ft. Dodge, Iowa, Apr. 2, 1944; s. Jack and Bernice (Levin) M.; m. Susan Marie Hechtlinger, Aug. 14, 1966 (div. June 1982); children: Jeffrey Phillip, Lawrence Brandon; m. Karen Mildred Meyer, Sept. 27, 1984. BA, U. Calif., Berkeley, 1966; BS, Calif. Podiatry Coll., San Francisco, 1967; D.P.M., Calif. Coll. Podiatric Medicine, San Francisco, 1970. Diplomate Am. Coun. Cert. Podiatric Physicians and Surgeons; bd. cert. podiatric surgery and medicine. Preceptor Redwood Empire Podiatric Clinic, Santa Rosa, Calif., 1970-72; podiatrist Monterey (Calif.) Podiatry Group, Inc., 1973—; instr. Calif. Coll. Podiatric Medicine, San Francisco, 1984-86; cons. Productive Podiatry Practices, South San Francisco, 1992—. Recipient 1st place Am. Coll. Foot Roentgenologists, 1970. Fellow Acad. Ambulatory Foot Surgeons, Am. Acad. Podiatric Practice Mgmt.; mem. Am. Coll. Foot Surgeons (assoc.), Am. Coun. Cert. Podiatric Physicians and Surgeons, Am. Acad. Podiatric Sports Medicine (assoc.), Internat. Coll. Podiatric Laser Surgery (assoc.), Calif. Podiatric Med. Assn., Am. Podiatric Med. Assn. Avocations: walking, water skiing, boating, tennis, golf. Office: 1011 Cass St # 102 Monterey CA 93940-4518

MUSIAL, STAN(LEY) (FRANK MUSIAL), hotel and restaurant executive, former baseball team executive, former baseball player; b. Donora, Pa., Nov. 21, 1920; s. Lukasz M.; m. Lillian Labash, 1939; children: Richard, Geraldine, Janet, Jean. Ed. high sch., Donora. Baseball player St. Louis Cardinals Farm Team, 1938-41; 1st baseman, outfielder St. Louis Cardinals, Nat. League, 1941-63; sr. v.p. St. Louis Cardinals, 1963-91; pres. Stan Musial & Biggies, Inc., St. Louis. Author: Stan Musial: The Man's Own Story, 1964. Served with USNR, World War II. Voted Nat. League Rookie of Yr., 1943; named most valuable player Nat. League, 1943, 46, 48; mem. Nat. League All-Star Team, 1943-44, 46-63; voted most valuable player Baseball Writers Com., 1946; Maj. League Player of Year Sporting News, 1946, 51; Sid Mercer award N.Y. Baseball Writers, 1947; Kenesaw Mountain Landis Meml. plaque, 1948; Sports Illus. Sportsman of Yr., 1957; recipient Freedom Leadership medal, 1968; named to Baseball Hall of Fame, 1969; holder .331 lifetime batting average. Office: 12400 Olive St Ste 555 Saint Louis MO 63141*

MUSICK, GERALD JOE, entomology educator; b. Ponca City, Okla., May 24, 1940; s. Arlie A. and Leona (Beier) M.; m. Florene Ione Thompson, May 5, 1962; children: Linda Kaye, Mary Louise. BS, Okla. State U., 1962; MS, Iowa State U., 1964; PhD, U. Mo., 1969. Grad. asst. Iowa State U., 1962-64; instr. U. Mo., 1964-69; asst. prof. Ohio State U., Wooster, 1969-71, assoc. prof., 1971-76; dept. head U. Ga., Tifton, 1976-79; prof., dept. head U. Ark., 1979-86, interium dir. agrl. exptl. sta., 1986-87, dean, assoc. v.p. agrl. rsch., 1987-93, univ. prof. entomology, 1993—. Author and co-author numerous publs. Vice-chairperson com. Coop. States Rsch. Svc., 1993, So. Expt. Sta.; chairperson steering com. Midwest Food Safety Consortium, 1991-93. Mem. Entomol. Soc. Am. (pres. S.E. br. 1983-84), Ark. Acad. Sci., Sigma Xi, Gamma Sigma Delta. Lutheran. Avocation: golf. Office: University of Arkansas AG-321 Dept Entomology Fayetteville AR 72701

MUSKIE, EDMUND SIXTUS, lawyer, former secretary of state, former senator; b. Rumford, Maine, Mar. 28, 1914; s. Stephen and Josephine (Czarnecki) M.; m. Jane Frances Gray, May 29, 1948; children—Stephen O., Ellen Muskie Allen, Melinda Muskie Stanton, Martha, Edmund Sixtus. A.B. cum laude, Bates Coll., 1936; LL.B., Cornell U., 1939; hon. degrees, U. N.B., Middlebury Coll., St. Anselm's Coll., William and Mary Coll., U. Md., Alliance Coll., U. N.H., Northeastern U., John Carroll U., Providence Coll., Boston U., Syracuse U., U. Maine, Suffolk U., Bowdoin Coll., Colby Coll., Lafayette Coll., U. Notre Dame, Hanover Coll., George Washington U., U. Buffalo, Nasson Coll., Husson Coll. Bar: Mass. 1939, Maine 1940, U.S. Dist. Ct 1941, N.Y. State 1981, U.S. Supreme Ct. 1981. Practice law Waterville, Maine, 1940, 45-55; gov. of Maine, 1955-59, U.S. senator from Maine, 1959-80; chmn. senate budget com., mem. fgn. relations com., U.S. Senate, chmn. subcom. on intergovtl. relations of senate govt. affairs com., subcom. environ. pollution of environment and pub. works com., subcom. on arms control, asst. majority whip; sec. of state of U.S., 1980-81; ptnr. Chadbourne & Parke, Washington, 1982—; former mem. Adv. Commn. Intergovtl. Relations; nat. exec. dir. Amvets, 1951; dist. dir. OPS, Maine, 1951-52; Maine chmn. citizens com. for Hoover report, 1950; chmn. Roosevelt Campobello Internat. Park Commn. Author: Journeys, 1972; co-author (with McGeorge Bundy) Presidential Promises and Performances, 1980. Mem. Maine Ho. of Reps., 1948-51, Democratic floor leader, 1949-51; mem. Dem. Nat. Com., 1952-55, Dem. candidate for vice pres., U.S., 1968. Served to lt. USNR, 1942-45. Recipient Laetare medal Notre Dame U., 1981, Presdl. Medal of Freedom, 1981, Former Mem. Congress Disting. Service award, 1981. Mem. Maine Bar Assn., Kennebec County Bar Assn., Waterville Bar Assn., Am. Legion, VFW, Amvets, Phi Beta Kappa, Phi Alpha Delta.

MUSKY, JANE MICHELLE, film production designer; b. N.J., May 27, 1954; d. John and Olga (Badaukus) M.; m. Anthony Howard Goldwyn, Apr. 18, 1987. BFA, Boston U., 1976. Asst. designer: (theatre) Barnum, 1980; set designer: (theatre) Marathon 1984, 1984; designer: (theatre) The News, 1985; art dir.: (short film) Split Cherry Tree, 1983 (Academy award nomination best short film 1983), (TV movies) Johnny Bull, 1986, Murrow, 1986; prodn. designer: (films) Blood Simple, 1984, Raising Arizona, 1987, Young Guns, 1988, Patty Hearst, 1988, When Harry Met Sally…, 1989, Ghost, 1990, Glengarry Glen Ross, 1992, Boomerang, 1992, City Hall, 1995, (TV movies) Rockabye, 1986, LBJ: The Early Years, 1987, (TV spls.) Alfred G. Graebner Memorial High School Handbook of Rules and Regulations, 1983 (Emmy award nomination outstanding art direction 1984). Recipient gold medal Nat. Women's Crew Championship, 1976, silver medal, 1978. Democrat. Office: care Gersn Agy 232 N Canon Dr Beverly Hills CA 90221

MUSOLF, LLOYD DARYL, political science educator, institute administrator; b. Yale, S.D., Oct. 14, 1919; s. William Ferdinand and Emma Marie (Pautz) M.; m. Berdyne Peet, June 30, 1944; children—Stephanie, Michael, Laura. B.A., Huron Coll., 1941; M.A., U. S.D., 1946; Ph.D., Johns Hopkins U., 1950. Mem. faculty Vassar Coll., Poughkeepsie, N.Y., 1949-59, assoc. prof. polit. sci., 1955-59; chief of party adv. group Mich. State U., Republic South Vietnam, 1959-61; prof. polit. sci. Mich. State U., East Lansing, 1961-63; prof. polit. sci. U. Calif.-Davis, 1963-87, dir. Inst. Govtl. Affairs, 1963-84, prof. emeritus, 1988—; vis. prof. Johns Hopkins U., Balt., 1953, U. Del., 1954, U. Mich., 1955-56; U.S. Nat. rapporteur for Internat. Congress Adminstrv. Scis., Berlin, 1983; cons. and lectr. in field. Author: Federal Examiners and the Conflict of Law and Administration, 1953, Public

Ownership and Accountability: The Canadian Experience, 1959, Promoting the General Welfare, Government and the Economy, 1965, (with others) American National Government-Policies and Politics, 1971, Mixed Enterprise-A Developmental Perspective, 1972, (with Springer) Malaysia's Parliamentary System-Representative Politics and Policymaking in a Divided Society, 1979, Uncle Sam's Private Profitseeking Corporations-Comsat, Fannie Mae, Amtrak and Conrail, 1983; editor: (with Krislov) The Politics of Regulation, 1964, Communications Satellites in Political Orbit, 1968, (with Kornberg) Legislatures in Developmental Perspective, 1970, (with Joel Smith) Legislatures in Development-Dynamics of Change in New and Old States, 1979; contbr. monographs, chpts. to books, articles to profl. jours. Served to lt. USNR, 1942-45. Johnston scholar Johns Hopkins U., 1946-48; Faculty fellow Vassar Coll., 1954-55; sr. assoc. East-West Ctr., Honolulu, 1968-69; vis. scholar Brookings Instn., Washington, 1980. Mem. Am. Soc. Pub. Adminstrn. (exec. council 1967-70), Nat. Assn. Schs. Pub. Affairs and Adminstrn. (exec. council 1972-75), Western Govtl. Research Assn. (exec. bd. 1966-68), Am. Polit. Sci. Assn., Nat. Assn. State Univs. and Land Grant Colls. (rsch. com. fdiv. urban affairs 1980-81). Home: 844 Lake Blvd Davis CA 95616-2611 Office: U Calif Dept Polit Sci Davis CA 95616

MUSON, HOWARD HENRY, writer, editor; b. Mt. Vernon, N.Y., Mar. 19, 1935; s. Joseph Ernest and Beatrice (Hakmaier) M.; m. Dorothy Regina Tyor, May 21, 1967; children: Eve, Stephanie, Nickolas, Alice. A.B. magna cum laude, Harvard U., Cambridge, Mass., 1956; cert., Johns Hopkins Sch. Advanced Internat. Studies, Bologna, Italy, 1956-57; postgrad., U. Calif., Berkeley, 1957-58. Dir. program research CARE Inc., N.Y.C., 1960-62; bur. chief Hartford Courant, Conn., 1962; newsman, columnist AP, Boston, 1963-66; contbg. editor Time mag., N.Y.C., 1966-70; articles editor N.Y. Times mag., N.Y.C., 1970-77; exec. editor Psychology Today mag., N.Y.C., 1977-82; editor Across The Board, N.Y.C., 1983-89; editor, pub. Family Bus. mag., Phila., 1992—; vis. lectr. in residential colls. Yale U., New Haven, 1982-83; instr. in sci. & environ. reporting program NYU, 1992. Author: Media Violence, 1972, Triumph of the American Spirit: Johnstown, Pennsylvania, 1989; contbr. articles to profl. jours., popular mags. Dir. Project Concern/No. Westchester Walk for Mankind, Mt. Kisco, N.Y., 1985-86. Mem. Nat. Assn. Sci. Writers.

MUSONE, FRED JAMES, manufacturing and logistic executive; b. Sharon, Pa., May 7, 1944; s. Fred A. and Margaret (Mastriani) M.; m. Andrea Helen DiGiammo, Feb. 24, 1982; children: Anthony James, Timothy Wade. BS, Wittenberg U., 1966, postgrad.; postgrad., U. So. Calif. Materials mgmt. developer Rockwell Internat., Pitts., 1966-72; sucessively materials mgr., ops. mgr., plant mgr., gen. mgr., internat. gen. mgr., v.p. and gen. mgr. FM svc. Fed-Mugul Corp., Southfield, Mich., from 1972; now pres. Chassis products ops. Fed-Mogul Corp., Southfield, Mich.; mem. faculty Am. Warehouse Distbn. Assn. Mem. Am. Prodn. Inventory Control Soc., Council Logistics Mgmt. Avocation: conservationist-U.S. and Can. Retriever Field Trials. Home: 2770 E Delhi Rd Ann Arbor MI 48103-9007 Office: Fed-Mogul Corp PO Box 1966 Detroit MI 48235-0906

MUSPRATT, KIRK, conductor. Studied with Georg Mark and Reinhard Schwartz, Vienna (Austria) Conservatory, 1983-84; attended, Tanglewood Inst., 1987. Affiliate artist asst. condr. St. Louis Symphony, 1987-90; music dir. St. Louis Symphony Youth Orch., 1987-90; assoc. condr. Utah Symphony, Salt Lake City, 1990-92; affiliate condr. Pitts. Symphony Orch., 1991-92, resident staff condr., 1992-93, resident condr., 1994—; asst. condr. opera houses Monchengladbach and Krefeld, Germany, 1985-87; guest condr. Utah Opera, 1991, 93, L.A. Philharmonic, 1993, R.I. Philharm., Green Bay Symphony, Montreal Symphony, Que. Symphony, others; condr. Woodstock Mozart Festival, 1994; participant Leighton Artist Colony, Banff Ctr. for Fine Arts. Conducting fellow Aspen Music Festival, 1986, L.A. Philharmonic Inst., 1988; Can. Coun. grantee, Presser Found. grantee; recipient Johann Strauss prize for advanced study in Vienna, 1983, 84, Utah Up'n Comers award. Office: Pitts Symphony Orch Heinz Hall for Performing Arts 600 Penn Ave Pittsburgh PA 15222*

MUSSEHL, ROBERT CLARENCE, lawyer; b. Washington, May 1, 1936; s. Chester Carl and Clara Cecelia (Greenwalt) Mussehl; children: Debra Lee, David Lee; spouse: Misook Chung, Mar. 22, 1987. BA, Am. U., 1964, JD, 1966. Bar: Wash. 1967, U.S. Dist. Ct. (we. dist.) Wash. 1967, U.S. Ct. Appeals (9th cir.) 1968, U.S Supreme Ct. 1971. Sr. ptnr. Thom, Mussehl, Navoni, Hoff, Pierson & Ryder, Seattle, 1967-78, Neubauer & Mussehl, Seattle, 1978-80, Mussehl & Rosenberg, Seattle, 1980—; speaker law convs. and other profl. orgns.; moot ct. judge Nat. Appelate Advocacy Competition, San Francisco, 1987; panel mem. ABA Symposium on Compulsory Jurisdiction of World Ct., San Francisco, 1987; chmn. bd., chief exec. officer The Seattle Smashers profl. volleyball club, 1976-80. Contbr. numerous articles to legal pubs. Mem. Wash. Vol. Lawyers for Arts, 1976-80; statewide chair Lawyers for Nation for Gov., 1976; mem. task force on the single adult and ch. Ch. Coun. Greater Seattle, 1976-78; bd. dirs. Wash. State Pub. Interest Law Ctr., 1976-81; founder, chmn. , exec. com., bd. dirs. Wash. State Lawyers' Campaign Hunger Relief, 1991—. Fellow Am. Bar Found., Am. Acad. Matrimonial Lawyers; mem. ABA (ho. of dels. 1979-91, spl. adv. com. on internat. activities 1989-91, chair marriage and family counseling and conciliation com. family law sect. 1981-83, mem. world order under law standing com. 1983-89, chair, 1986-89, chair ad hoc com. on the assembly 1986-89, mem. assembly resolutions com. 1979-91, mem. blue ribbon com. for world ct. 1987-88, mem. standing com. on dispute resolution, 1992-93; exec. coun. sect. dispute resolution 1993—, others, Achievement award), Wash. State Bar Assn. (exec. com. family law sect. 1973-75, chmn. internat. law com. 1974-76, sec.-treas., exec. com. world peace through law sect. 1980—, chair 1981-82, mem. edit. bd. Family Law Deskbook 1987-89), Wash. State Trial Lawyers Assn., Seattle-King County Bar Assn. (family law sect. 1971-90, other coms. 1970—, chmn. young lawyers sect. 1971-72, sec. 1972-73, trustee), Am. Arbitration Assn. (panel arbitrators), World Assn. Lawyers of World Peace Through Law Ctr. (founding mem.), Heritage Club YMCA Greater Seattle (charter 1977—), UN Assn. U.S.A. (bd. dirs. Seattle chpt. 1989-91). Avocations: biking, tennis, weight training, painting, religious studies. Home: 2250 NW 58th St # 405 Seattle WA 98107 Office: 1111 3rd Ave Ste 2626 Seattle WA 98101-3210

MUSSELMAN, JAMES ARTHUR, army officer; b. Gettysburg, Pa., Sept. 11, 1939; s. Peter Christian and Alice (Spangler) M.; m. Lesley Francis Milks, Sept. 6, 1966; 1 child, Peter Christian. BS in Econs., Fla. So. Coll., 1961; MS in Polit. Sci., Auburn U., 1971. Commd. 2d lt. U.S. Army, 1961, advanced through grades to maj. gen., 1990; various command and staff positions Fed. Republic Germany, Vietnam; grad. student USAF Staff Coll., Montgomery, Ala., 1971, U.S. Army War Coll., Carlisle, Pa., 1980; dep. bn. comdr. 509th Airborne Bn. Combat Team, Vicenza, Italy; comdr. 197th Inf. Brigade, Ft. Benning, Ga.; comdr. 2d region US Army ROTC Cadet Command, Ft. Knox; asst. div. comdr. for ops. adn tng. 4th Inf. Div., Ft. Carson, Colo.; comdg. gen. U.S. Army So. European Task Force, 5th Theater Army Area Command. Decorated Silver Star with oak leaf cluster, Legion of Merit with two oak leaf clusters, DFC, Bronze Star with V device and four oak leaf clusters, Meritorious Svc. medal with four oak leaf clusters, Air medal. Home: CMR 420 Box 5 APO AE 09630 Office: Department of the Army Chief of Public Affairs Office Washington DC 20310

MUSSELMAN, JAMIE P., advertising executive; b. Allentown, Pa., Aug. 4, 1954; d. James P. and Bertha (Lickman) M.; m. Charles L. Garrettson III, June 6, 1981; 1 child, Hadley Helen. BS, Skidmore Coll., 1976; diploma in typography, London Coll. Printing, 1977; MS, Pratt Inst., 1979. Asst. to dir. Skimore Coll., Saratoga Springs, N.Y., 1972-76; show coordinator Soc. Illustrators, N.Y.C., 1975; teaching asst. Cen. Sch. of Art & Design, London, England, 1976-77; graphic designer David Grey Assocs., London, 1976-77, Jack Schecterson Assocs., N.Y.C., 1977-78; pres., creative dir. Musselman Advt. Inc., Allentown, Pa., 1978—; trustee Cedar Crest Coll., Allentown, 1987—; dir. Allentown Econ. Devel. Corp., 1984—, Bethlehem Area C. of C., Bethlehem Musikfest Assn., 1984—. Acct. exec. Colebrook Farms Food Packaging, 1988 (Golden Mummy Mobile Corp. award 1988); creative dir. Musikfest Poster, 1987 (Neographics gold award 1988), Allentown Art Museum Poster, 1987 (Am. Fedn Arts award of Excellence 1988). Bd. dirs. Wildlands Conservancy, Allentown, 1987—; mem. Soc. of Arts/Allentown Art Museum, 1979—, Pa. Soc., Sellersville, 1986—; bd. dirs. United Cerebral Palsy, Bethlehem, 1983-85. Mem. Am. Assn. Advt. Agencies. Avocations: gourmet cooking, travel,

real estate, piano playing. Office: Musselman Advt Inc 601 Hamilton Mall Allentown PA 18101-2103

MUSSELMAN, NORMAN BURKEY, editor; b. Arkansas City, Kans., Mar. 21, 1929; s. Norman Beachy and E. Ruth (Burkey) M.; m. Elizabeth Temple Henry, Oct. 26, 1957; children: Elizabeth Temple Whitson, Norman Henry, Robert Beachy. BA, U. Okla., 1951, MA, 1954. Columnist McGraw Hill Pub. Co., Washington, 1954-67; editor Nat. Assn. Electric Cos., Washington, 1967-80; dir. govt. com. Edison Electric Inst., Washington, 1980—. Pres. Okla. U. Alumni Club, Washington, 1957-58; pres. men of ch. Presbyn. Meeting House, Alexandria, Va., 1962-63, clk. of session, 1980-82; precinct capt. Rep. Party, 1968-69; cubmaster, pack chmn., scout com. Boy Scouts, Alexandria, 1970-73, 78-82. 1st lt. U.S. Army, 1951-53. Mem. Nat. Press Club, Sigma Delta Chi (pres. Okla. U. chpt. 1953-54). Home: 1612 Courtland Rd Alexandria VA 22306

MUSSENDEN, GERALD, psychologist; b. N.Y.C., June 1, 1941; s. Geraldo and Adele (Gimenez) M.; m. Iris Manuela Prado, Aug. 11, 1967; children: Gerald, Ricardo-Antonio, Gina. BA, Tarkio Coll., 1968; MS, Brigham Young U., 1971, PhD, 1974. Diplomate Am. Bd. Profl. Disability Cons., Am. Bd. Forensic Examiners. Dir. child program Albert Einstein Coll. Medicine, N.Y.C., 1974-76; psychologist Mental Health Ctr., Bartow, Fla., 1976-77, Norside Community Mentala Health Ctr., Tampa, Fla., 1977-80; pvt. practice Brandon (Fla.) Counseling Ctr., 1980—; criminal ct. psychologist Fla. Cts., Hillsborough, Fla., 1978—; with children's svcs. State Rehab., Hillsborough, 1977—; rehab. psychologist Vocat. Rehab., Hillsborough; psychologist Div. Blind Svcs., Hillsborough. Fellow Ford Found., 1972-73. Mem. APA, Fla. Psychol. Assn., Bay Area Psychol. Assn., Soc. Personality Assessment. Home: 317 Cactus Rd Seffner FL 33584-6105 Office: Brandon Counseling Ctr 134 N Moon Ave Brandon FL 33510-4420

MUSSER, C. WALTON, physical scientist, consultant; b. Mt. Joy, Pa., Apr. 5, 1909; s. Ezra Nissley and Cora Grace (Weidman) M.; m. Edna Mae Hoak, June 23, 1937; children: Lila Darle (Mrs. Richard Hackman), Yvonne Duane (Mrs. Harold Graham), Stanley Walton (dec.). Student, Chgo. Tech. Coll., 1926-28, Leavitt Sch. Psychology, 1928-29, Wharton Sch. Fin. and Commerce, 1929-30, U. Pa., 1930-32, MIT, 1957. Chief engr. product devel. Indsl. Improvement Corp., Phila., 1936-41; rsch. adviser Dept. Def., 1941-56; pres., dir. rsch. Sci. Rsch., Inc., Glenside, Pa., 1945-52; pvt. practice cons., adviser in rsch. and devel., 1936—. Holder of over 162 U.S. Patents in 32 different classes and more than 60 patents in over 28 countries. Recipient Exceptional Civilian Service award for First Working Recoilless Weapon, Sec. of War, 1945; John C. Jones medal for Disting. Svc., Am. Ordnance Assn., 1951; Machine Design award ASME, 1968; named to Ordnance Hall of Fame, 1976. Mem. Acad. Applied Scis., Am. Def. Preparedness Assn. (hon. life), Nat. Soc. Profl. Engrs., Sigma Xi. Address: 1206 Lela Ln Santa Maria CA 93454-6642 Personal philosophy: Emphasize liking what you do rather than doing what you like. Limiting your activity to only those things you like rapidly decreases your personal universe and eventually assures that much of your activity becomes drudgery.

MUSSER, SANDRA G., lawyer; b. Hollywood, Calif., July 23, 1944; d. Donald Godfrey Gumpertz and Gloria G. (Rosenblatt) King; m. Michael R.V. Whitman, Feb. 19, 1980. BA, UCLA, 1965; JD, Hastings Coll. of Law, 1970. Bar: Calif. 1971, U.S. Dist. Ct. (no. dist.) Calif. 1971, U.S. Ct. Appeals (9th cir.) 1971. Clk. 9th Cir. Ct. of Appeals, 1971-72; lawyer pvt. practice of family law, 1972-86; ptnr. Musser & Ryan, San Francisco, 1986—; judge pro tem San Francisco County Superior Ct., 1988—. Contbr. articles to profl. jours. Fellow Am. Acad. Matrimonial Lawyers; mem. ABA (chair litigation sect. domestic rels. and family law com. 1993-94), Bar Assn. San Francisco, State Bar Calif. (state bar family law sect., 1977—, chair 1982-83, adv. 1983-84). Office: Musser & Ryan 361 Oak St San Francisco CA 94102-5615

MUSSER, STANTON RICHARD, retired air force officer; b. Watsontown, Pa., Apr. 2, 1936; s. Harold Leighton Musser and Marjorie May (Saxton) Musser West; m. Dawn Elizabeth Burg, Sept. 12, 1959; children: Scott Leighton, Shari Dawn, Kristin Leigh. B.S. in Phys. Edn., Gettysburg Coll., 1958; M.A. in Personnel Mgmt., Central Mich. U., 1975; grad., Indsl. Coll. Armed Forces, Fort Lesley J. McNair, 1974; grad. program for sr. execs in nat. and internat. affairs, John F. Kennedy Sch. Govt., Harvard U. Commd. 2d lt. U.S. Air Force, 1958; advanced through grades to maj. gen., 1985; F-100 fighter-bomber aircraft comdr. 417th Tactical Fighter Squadron, Ramstein Air Base, Federal Republic Germany, 1960-64; F-100 pilot, chief wing tng. and scheduling 31st Tactical Fighter Wing, Homestead AFB, Fla., 1964-66; forward air controller Republic of Vietnam; air officer comdg. U.S. Air Force Acad., Colo., 1966; mem. U.S. Air Force Aerial Demonstration Squadron "Thunderbirds", Nellis AFB, 1966-69; asst. ops. officer 469th Tactical Fighter Squadron, Korat Royal Thai AFB, Thailand, 1970; asst. dep. comdr. ops. 388th Tactical Fighter Wing, Korat Royal Thai AFB, Thailand, 1970; chief tactics br., tactical forces div. Directorate Ops., Hdqrs. U.S. Air Force, Washington, 1971-73; asst. dep. comdr. ops. 4th Tactical Fighter Wing, Seymour Johnson AFB, N.C., 1974-75; dep. comdt. cadet wing U.S. Air Force Acad., Colo., 1975-77; vice comdt. cadets U.S. Air Force Acad., 1977; vice comdr. first operational F-15 wing 1st Tactical Fighter Wing, Langley AFB, Va., 1977-79; comdr. 602d Tactical Air Control Wing, Bergstrom AFB, Tex., 1979-80, 33d Tactical Fighter Wing, Eglin AFB, Fla., 1980-82; vice comdr. Ogden Air Logistics Ctr., Hill AFB, Utah, 1982-83; chief Office Mil. Coop., Cairo, Egypt, 1983-85; asst. dep. chief staff logistics and engring. Hdqrs. U.S. Air Force, Washington, 1985-86; dep. dir. Def. Logistics Agy., Washington, 1986-87; comdr. Air Force Inspection and Safety Ctr., Norton AFB, Calif., 1987-89; commandant of cadets Va. Tech U., Blacksburg, 1989—. Decorated Def. D.S.M., Air Force D.S.M., Silver Star, Legion of Merit with three oak leaf clusters, D.F.C. with one oak leaf cluster, Meritorious Service medal, Air medal with ten oak leaf clusters, Air Force Commendation medal, Purple Heart; named Disting. Alumnus, Gettysburg Coll. 1978. Mem. Soc. Logistics Engrs., Daedalians, Air Force Assn., The Ret. Officers Assn., Mil. Order of World Wars, Rotary. Republican. Avocations: golf; racquet ball; tennis. Home: 1777 St Andrews Cir Blacksburg VA 24060-0252 Office: Va Tech Univ Commandant of Cadets Blacksburg VA 24061

MUSSER, THARON, theatrical lighting designer, theatre consultant; b. Roanoke, Va., Jan. 8, 1925; s. George C. and Hazel (Riddle) M. B.A., Berea Coll., 1946; H.H.D., 1979; M.F.A., Yale U., 1950; H.H.D., Emerson Coll., 1980. Lighting designer over 100 Broadway prodns.; lighting designer for repertory theatre including, Jose Limon Dance Co., 1953-56, Group 20 Players of Mass., 1954-56, Phoenix Theatre Co., 1957-60, Am. Theatre Festival, Boston, 1961, Boston Arts Festival, 1962, Empire State Music Festival, 1959, Nat. Repertory Theatre Co., 1961-68, Am. Shakespeare Festival Theatre and Acad., 1963-68, Lincoln Center Repertory Theatre, 1968, Dallas Civic Opera, 1969-77, New Phoenix Repertory Co., 1972, Miami Opera Guild, 1975-78, Wolf Trap Found., Filene Center for Performing Arts, 1977; staff designer, Mark Taper Forum, Los Angeles Center Theatre Group, 1970-86; lighting designer internat. prodns. including, Jose Limon Dance Co. State Dept. Tour, S. Am., 1953; London prodns. Golden Boy, 1968, Mame, 1969, Applause, 1972, A Little Night Music, 1975, They're Playing Our Song, 1979, London Ballet Festival Romeo and Juliet, 1977; London prodn. Ziegfeld, 1988; internat. prodn. A Chorus Line, 1976; lighting designer and cons. internat. prodn., Ford's Theatre Restoration and TV prodn., Washington, 1968, Man and the Universe at, Hemisfair, San Antonio, 1968, Chgo. Auditorium, 1968, Los Angeles Shubert Theatre, 1971, Dallas Music Hall, Berea Coll. Dramatic Arts Center, 1976-80; London prodn. Children of a Lesser God, 1981, 15 Neil Simon shows including, Broadway Bound, Rumors and Lost in Yonkers. Recipient Los Angeles Drama Critics' Circle award for Dream on Monkey Mountain, 1970, for Follies, 1972, for Pacific Overtures, a Chorus Line, 1976-77, for Terra Nova, 1979, Antoinette Perry award for Follies, 1971-72, for A Chorus Line, 1975-76, for Dreamgirls, 1981-82; Yale arts award, 1985; Theatre Hall of Fame award, 1985. Mem. United Scenic Artists, Soc. Brit. Theatrical Lighting Designers, U.S. Inst. Theatre Tech. Address: 21 Cornelia St New York NY 10014-4121

MUSSER, WILLIAM WESLEY, JR., lawyer; b. Enid, Okla., July 17, 1918; s. William Wesley Sr. and Ethel Rice (McElroy) M.; m. Estelle Bee Wiedeman, Jan. 19, 1947; children: James William, Mary Bee Clark. BA, U. Okla., 1939, LLB, 1941. Bar: Okla. 1941. Ptnr. Elam, Crowley & Musser,

Enid, 1946-47; probate judge Garfield County, Okla., 1949-51; ptnr. Otjen, Carter & Musser, Enid, 1952-54; asst. county atty. Garfield County, 1955-56; sole practice Enid, 1957—; chmn. bd. dirs. Tax Roll Corrections, Garfield County, 1950-51; 6th congrl. dist. rep. Okla. Jud. Nominating Com., Enid, 1967-74; judge Okla. Ct. Appeals, Enid, 1982. Pres. Great Salt Plains council Boy Scouts Am., 1955; gen. chmn. St. Mary's Hosp. Bldg. Fund, 1949; bd. dirs. Enid Community Chest, 1950-51, N.W. Okla. Pastoral Care Assn., 1978; v.p. Phillips U., Enid, 1955-74, mem. exec. com., 1955-78, trustee, 1978-82; bd. dirs. Enid Estate Planning Council, 1971-74, sec., 1972, pres., 1973-74. Served to maj. AUS, 1941-45, ETO. Decorated Bronze Star. Fellow Okla. Bar Found.; mem. ABA, Okla. Bar Assn. (v.p. bd. govs. 1957), Garfield County Bar Assn. (pres. 1962), Am. Judicature Soc., U. Okla. Alumni Assn. (bd. 1959-61), Sons and Daus. of Cherokee Strip Pioneers Assn. (exec. bd. dirs. 1970-77), Greater Enid C. of C. (bd. dirs. 1969-71), VFW, Am. Legion, Phi Delta Phi, Alpha Tau Omega. Republican. Mem. Christian Ch. (Disciples of Christ). Clubs: Am. Bus. (pres. 1947), Oakwood Country (Enid). Home: 1301 Indian Dr Enid OK 73703-7012 Office: Broadway Tower 3d Fl 114 E Broadway Enid OK 73701-4534

MUSSEY, JOSEPH ARTHUR, health and medical product executive; b. Cleve., July 17, 1948; s. Arthur Glenn and Mary Jane (Silvaroli) M.; m. Mary Elizabeth Stone, July 11, 1975; 1 child, Joanna Lee. BS in Indsl. Engring. with distinction, Cornell U., 1970; MBA, Harvard U., 1976. Engring. mgmt. officer U.S. Navy Pub. Works Ctr., Pearl Harbor, Hawaii, 1971-75; mktg. exec. B.F. Goodrich, Akron, Ohio, 1976-80; fin. exec. B.F. Goodrich, 1980-84; v.p. fin. Combustion Engring., Stamford, Conn., 1984-85; v.p. ops. Combustion Engring., 1985-86; exec. v.p. Process Automation Bus. Combustion Engring., Columbus, Ohio, 1987-90; pres., CEO Danninger Med. Tech., Inc., Columbus, 1990—; treas., dir. Danninger Med. Tech. Inc. Served as lt. U.S. Navy, 1971-75. Decorated Disting. Naval Grad. (USN), 1971, Disting. Grad. U.S. Navy Civil Engring. Corps., 1971. Mem. Alpha Pi Mu, Tau Beta Pi, Phi Eta Sigma. Republican. Roman Catholic. Club: Skull & Daggar. Home: 8967 Dunskeath Ct Dublin OH 43017-9466 Office: Danniger Med Tech Inc 4140 Fisher Rd Columbus OH 43228-1022

MUSSINA, MICHAEL COLE, professional baseball player; b. Williamsport, Pa., Dec. 8, 1968. BA Econs., Stanford U., 1990. Pitcher Balt. Orioles, 1990—; player Am. League All-Star Team, 1992-94. Named Internat. League Most Valuable Pitcher, 1991. Office: Balt Orioles 333 W Camden St Baltimore MD 21201*

MUSTACCHI, PIERO, physician, educator; b. Cairo, Egypt, May 29, 1920; came to U.S., 1947; naturalized, 1962; s. Gino and Gilda (Rieti) M.; m. Dora Lisa Ancona, Sept. 26, 1948; children: Roberto, Michael. BS in Humanities, U. Florence, Italy, 1938; postgrad. in anatomy, Eleve Interne, U. Lausanne, Switzerland, 1938-39; MB, ChB, Fouad I U., Cairo, Egypt, 1944, grad. in Arabic lang. and lit., 1946; D Medicine and Surgery, U. Pisa, 1986; D Honoris Causa, U. Aix-Marseilles, France, 1988; hon. degree, U. Alexandria, Egypt, 1985. Lic. physician, Egypt, Italy; diplomate Am. Bd. Internal Medicine; qualified med. evaluator, Calif., 1994. House officer English Hosp., Ch. Missionary Soc., Cairo, Egypt, 1945-47; clin. affiliate U. Calif., San Francisco, 1947-48; intern Franklin Hosp., San Francisco, 1948-49; resident in pathology U. Calif., San Francisco, 1949-51; resident in medicine Meml. Ctr. Cancer and Allied Diseases, N.Y.C., 1951-53; rsch. epidemiologist Dept. HEW, Nat. Cancer Inst., Bethesda, Md., 1955-57; cons. allergy clinic U. Calif., San Francisco, 1957-70, clin. prof. medicine and preventive medicine, 1970-90, clin. prof. medicine and epidemiology, 1990—, head occupational epidemiology, 1975-90, head div. internat. health edn. dept. epidemiology and internat. health, 1985-90; med. cons., vis. prof. numerous edn. and profl. instns., including U. Marseilles, 1981, 82, U. Pisa, Italy, 1983, U. Gabon, 1984, U. Siena, Italy, 1985, work clinic U. Calif., 1975-84, Ctr. for Rehab. and Occupational Health, U. Calif., San Francisco, 1984-93; qualified med. evaluator Divsn. Indsl. Accidents, State of Calif., 1990; cons. numerous worldwide govtl. agys. Contbr. chpts. to books, articles to profl. jours. Editorial bd. Medecine d'Afrique Noire, Ospedali d'Italia. Served with USN, USPHS, 1953-55. Decorated Order of Merit (Commander) (Italy), Ordre de la Legion d'Honneur (France), Medal of St. John of Jerusalem, Sovereign Order of Malta, Order of the Republic (Egypt); Scroll, Leonardo da Vinci Soc., San Francisco, 1965; award Internat. Inst. Oakland, 1964; Hon. Vice Consul. Italy, 1971-90. Fellow ACP, Am. Soc. Environ. and Occupational Health; mem. AAAS, Am. Assn. Cancer Rsch., Calif. Soc. Allergy and Immunology, Calif. Med. Assn., San Francisco Med. Soc., West Coast Allergy Soc. (founding), Mex. Congress on Hypertension (corr.), Internat. Assn. Med. Rsch. and Continuing Edn. (U.S. rep.), Villa Taverna Club, Acad. Italiana della Cucina. Democrat. Avocations: mathematics, music, languages. Home: 3344 Laguna St San Francisco CA 94123-2208 Office: U Calif Parnassus Ave San Francisco CA 94143

MUSTARD, JAMES FRASER, research institute executive; b. Toronto, Oct. 16, 1927; s. Allan Alexander and Jean Anne (Oldham) M.; m. Christine Elizabeth Sifton, June 4, 1952; children: Cameron, Ann, Jim, Duncan, John, Christine. MD, U. Toronto, 1953; PhD, Cambridge U., 1956. Asst., then assoc. prof pathology U. Toronto, 1963-66, asst. prof. medicine, 1965-66, hon. prof. pathology, 1990—; prof. pathology McMaster U., Hamilton, Ont., Can., 1966-88, prof. emeritus, 1988—, chmn. pathology, 1966-72, dean faculty health. scis., 1972-80, v.p. faculty health scis., 1980-82; bd. dirs., pres., sr. fellow Can. Inst. Advanced Rsch., Toronto, 1982—; mem. Ont. Premier's Coun. on Econ. Renewal, 1991—; mem. Ont. Coun. Health, 1966-72; founder, chmn. Health Rsch. Com., 1966-73 ; chmn. Spl. Task Force Future Arrangements Health Edn., 1970-71, Task Force Health Planning for Ont., Ministry Health and Govt. Ont., 1973-74; mem. Ont. Coun. Univ. Affairs, 1975-81; chmn. Adv. Coun. Occupational Health and Safety, 1977-83; mem. Royal Commn. Matters Health and Safety Arising Use of Asbestos in Ont., 1980-83; mem. Bovey Commn. Study Future Devel. Univ. in Ont., 1984-85; mem. Premier's Coun. Ont., 1986-91, Premier's Coun. Health Strategy, 1988-91; chmn. ctrs. excellence com. Govt. Ont., 1987-91; mem. Prime Minister's Nat. Adv. Bd. on Sci. and Tech., 1987-91, Ottawa, vice chmn., 1988-91; mem. adv. com. Networks of Ctrs. of Excellence Govt. Can., 1988—; rsch. and analysis adv. com. Stats. Can., Ottawa, 1986—; nat. adv. coun. Can. Adv. Tech. Assn., Ottawa, 1988—; adv. coun. Ctr. Health Econs. and Policy Analysis, McMaster U., 1990-92; chmn. bd. dirs. Steel Co. Can., Hamilton, 1985—, Atomic Energy Can. Ltd., 1990—. Bd. dirs. Heart and Stroke Found. Can., 1971-82, Heart and Stroke Found. Ont., 1982-87; bd. govs. McMaster U., 1978-82; bd. dirs. McMaster U. Med. Centre, 1972-82; trustee Advanced Systems Inst. Found., Vancouver, 1986—, Aga Khan U., Karachi, Pakistan, 1985—; mem. chancellor's commn. Aga Khan U., 1992—. Decorated Officer Order of Canada, 1986, Order of Ont., 1992, Companion Order of Can., 1994; recipient Disting. Svc. award Can. Soc. Clin. Investigation, J. Allyn Taylor Internat. Prize, 1988, Internat. award Gairdner Found., 1967, James F. Mitchell award, 1972, Izaak Walton Killam prize in health sci. Can. Council, 1987, Robert P. Grant award for contbns. to progress Internat. Congress on Thrombosis and Haemostasis, 1987, Disting. Career award for contbns. Internat. Soc. Thrombosis and Haemostasis, 1989, Pvt. Sector Leadership award Can. Advanced Tech. Assn., 1989, R & D Mgmt. award Can. Rsch. Mgmt. and Assn., 1989, Man of Yr. award Can. High Tech. Coun., 1989, Xerox Can.-Forum award Corp. Higher Edn. Forum, 1990, Royal Bank award, 1993, Companion Order of Can., 1994, Order of Ont. 1992. Fellow Royal Coll. Physicians Can.; mem. Am. Soc. Clin. Investigation, Assn. Am. Physicians, Am. Assn. Pathologists, Am. Soc. Hematology (pres. 1970), Can. Atherosclerosis Soc. (councillor exec. com. 1986—), Can. Soc. Clin. Investigation (pres. 1965-66). Home: 422 Sumach St, Toronto, ON Canada M4X 1B5 Office: Can Inst Advanced Rsch, 179 John St Ste 701, Toronto, ON Canada M5T 1X4

MUSTIAN, MIDDLETON TRUETT, hospital administrator; b. Texarkana, Tex., Mar. 27, 1921; s. Thomas William and Hattie (Cornelius) M.; m. Jackie Cain, Dec. 3, 1955; children—Mark Thomas, John Perry, Janet Louise. B.B.A., Baylor U., 1949. Asst. adminstr. Bapt. Hosp., Alexandria, La., 1950-54; asst. adminstr. Miss. Bapt. Hosp., Jackson, 1954-55; adminstr. Meml. Hosp., Panama City, Fla., 1955-60, Alachua Gen. Hosp., Gainesville, Fla., 1960-64, Cen. Unit Meml. Bapt. Hosp., Houston, 1964; asst. dir. Meml. Bapt. Hosp. System, Houston, 1964; pres., chief exec. officer Tallahassee Meml. Regional Med. Center Hosp., 1964-89, pres. emeritus, 1990—; pres., CEO TMH Reg. Med. Ctr. Found., Inc., 1976-89; clin. instr. dept. health adminstrn. U. Gainesville; mem. Hosp. Cost Containment Bd., State of Fla. Contbr. articles to hosp. jours. Bd. dirs. Blue Cross of Fla.; mem. Fla. Statewide Health Coordinating Council. Served to capt. Med. Adminstrv. Corps U.S. Army, 1940-45. Decorated Purple Heart. Fellow Am. Coll. Hosp. Adminstrs. (regent); mem. Am. Hosp. Assn., Fla. Hosp. Assn. (past pres.). Democrat. Baptist. Clubs: Kiwanis, Masons. Home: 6325 Velda Dairy Rd Tallahassee FL 32308-6308 Office: Tallahassee Meml Regional Med Ctr Magnolia Drive Rd Tallahassee FL 32308

MUSTO, DAVID FRANKLIN, physician, historian, consultant; b. Tacoma, Jan. 8, 1936; s. Charles Hiram and Hilda Marie (Hanson) Mustoe; m. Emma Jean Baudendistel, June 2, 1961; children: Jeanne Marie, David Kyle, John Baird, Christopher Edward. BA, U. Wash., 1956, MD, 1963; MA, Yale U. 1961. Lic. physician, Conn., Pa. Clerk Nat. Hosp. for Nervous Disease, London, 1961; intern Pa. Hosp., Phila., 1963-64; resident Yale U. Med. Ctr., New Haven, 1964-67; spl. asst. to dir. NIMH, Bethesda, Md., 1967-69; vis. asst. prof. Johns Hopkins U., 1968-69; asst. prof. Yale U., 1969-73, assoc. prof., 1973-78, sr. rsch. scientist, 1978-81, prof., 1981—, exec. fellow Davenport Coll., 1983-88; mem. adv. editorial com. Yale Edits. Private Papers James Boswell, 1975—; cons. Exec. Office of Pres., 1973-75; mem. White House Strategy Coun., 1978-81; mem. panel on alcohol policy NAS, Washington, 1978-82; cons. White House Conf. on Families, 1979-80; vis. fellow Clare Coll., Cambridge U., 1994; mem. alcohol adv. com. Nat. Assn. Broadcasters, 1994—. Author: The American Disease: Origins of Narcotic Control, 1973, expanded edit., 1987. Historian Pres.'s Commn. on Mental Health, 1977-78; adv. U.S. Del. to UN Commn. Narcotic Drugs, Geneva, 1978-79; mem. nat. coun. Smithsonian Instn., Washington, 1981-90, hon. mem., 1991—; hist. cons. Presdl. Commn. Human Immuno-deficiency Virus Epidemic, 1988; mem. nat. adv. com. on anti-drug program Robert Wood Johnson Found., 1989—; mem. nat. adv. com. on internat. narcotic policy UN Assn. of U.S.A., 1991; mem. adv. com. causes drug abuse Office Tech. Assessment, Congress U.S., 1992-94; commr. Conn. Alcohol and Drug Abuse Commn., 1992-93; bd. dirs. Coll. on Problems of Drug Dependence, 1990-94; trustee Assocs. of Cushing-Whitney Med. Libr., 1994—. With USPHS, 1968-69. Fellow Am. Psychiat. Assn., Coll. Problems of Drug Dependence; mem. New Haven County Med. Assn. (chmn. bicentennial com. 1983), Am. Inst. History of Pharmacy (chmn. Urdang Medal com. 1978, Kremers award), Am. Hist. Assn., Am. Assn. History of Medicine (chmn. edn. com. 1985-85, William Osler medal), English-Speaking Union (pres. New Haven br. 1995—), Soc. of Cin. in the State of Conn., Beaumont Med. Club (pres. 1985-87), Acorn Club, Cosmos Club, Yale Club (N.Y.C.), Athenaeum Club (London). Office: Yale U 333 Cedar St New Haven CT 06520-7900

MUSTO, JOSEPH JOHN, lawyer; b. Pittston, Pa., Nov. 22, 1943; s. James and Rose (Frushon) M.; m. Fortunata Giudice, July 5, 1969; children: Laura, Joseph Robert. BA, King's Coll., Wilkes-Barre, Pa., 1965; JD, Dickinson Sch. Law, Carlisle, Pa., 1968. Bar: Pa. 1968, U.S. Ct. Appeals (3d cir.) 1968, U.S. Dist. Ct. (mid. dist.) Pa. 1971. Asst. dist. atty. City of Phila., 1968-69; assoc. Bedford, Waller, Griffith, Darling & Mitchell, Wilkes-Barre, 1969-73; ptnr. Griffith, Darling, Mitchell, Aponick & Musto, Wilkes-Barre, 1973-75; prin. Griffith, Aponick & Musto, Wilkes-Barre, 1975-90; ptnr. Rosenn, Jenkins & Greeenwald, Wilkes-Barre, 1990-93; judge Ct. Common Pleas of Luzerne County, 1993-94; mem. Hourigan, Kluger, Spohrer & Quinn, Wilkes-Barre, Pa., 1994—; solicitor Yatesville (Pa.) Borough, 1973-80, Duryea (Pa.) Borough, 1975-80, Pittston Area Sch. Dist., 1973-93. Mem. Luzerne County Gov. Study Com., Wilkes-Barre, 1973-74; mem., chmn. No. Luzerne Health Adv. Council, Wilkes-Barre, 1976-80; pres., mem. Health Systems Agy. of Northeast Pa., Avoca, 1980-86; pres. Pa. Health Planning Assn., Harrisburg, 1985-86; mem. civil justice reform act adv. com. Fed. Dist. Pa. Ct., 1991-95. Mem. Fed. Bar Assn. (past pres. Ctrl. Pa. chpt.), Pa. Bar Assn., Wilkes-Barre Law and Libr. Assn. Democrat. Roman Catholic. Home: 7 Prospect Pl Pittston PA 18640-2627 Office: Hourigan Kluger Spohrer & Quinn 700 Mellon Bank Ctr 8 W Market St Wilkes Barre PA 18701-1801

MUSYL, MARC J., lawyer; b. Denver, Jan. 6, 1952; s. Carol L. Curtis, June 3, 1983; children: Amanda Curtis, Rebecca Taylor. BA, Northwestern U., 1972, JD, 1975. Bar: Ill. 1975, U.S. Dist. Ct. (no. dist.) Ill. 1975, U.S. Ct. Appeals (7th cir.) 1975, Colo. 1977, U.S. Dist. Ct. Colo. 1977, U.S. Ct. Appeals (10th cir.) 1977, U.S. Supreme Ct. 1979. Assoc. Arvey Hodes et al, Chgo., 1975-78, Fuller & Evans, Denver, 1978-80; ptnr. Canty Curtis & Musyl, Denver, 1980-84; shareholder Popham Haik et al, Denver, 1984-93; ptnr. Freeborn & Peters, Denver, 1993—. Pres. Cystic Fibrosis Found., Colo., Denver, 1991-94, Children's Legal Clinic, 1994—. Mem. Colo. Bar Assn. (chmn. com. on law and tech. 1992—), Internat. Bus. Assn. Rockies, Japan-Am. Soc., Australian-Am. C. of C. Avocations: sailing, scuba diving, skiing. Office: Freborn & Peters 950 17th St Ste 2600 Denver CO 80202

MUTH, ERIC PETER, ophthalmic optician; b. Munich, Germany, July 25, 1940; s. Erich Walter and Anna Lisa (Pentenrieder) M.; came to U.S., 1948, naturalized, 1955. BS, Charter Oak Coll., 1978; MBA, PhD in Mgmt., Columbia Pacific U., 1983; m. Rachel Hubbard, Apr. 4, 1971; children: Eric Van, Karl George, Ellen Anna. Lic. optician, Conn. Pres. Park Lane Opticians, Inc., Milford, Conn., 1968—; cons. Nat. Acad. Ophthalmology Found. Mus., San Francisco, 1982-88, Nat. Mus. Hist., Smithsonian Inst., 1983-94, Gesell Inst. Human Devel., 1984, 89; mem. adv. com. South Cen. Community Coll., Seattle, 1984; mem. adv. bd. Internat. Scientific Inst., P.R., 1989, adv. bd. Middlesez C.C., 1989 (vice chmn.). Mem. editorial rev. bd. (U.S.A.) Dispensing Optician mag., 1984—; author: Management for Opticians, Butterworths Textbook, 1983; contbr. The Social History of Eyeglasses in Japan, 1991, die Brille, Leipzig, 1989, Thinking on the Edge, Agamennon, 1993; pub. over 200 papers in 6 langs.; contbg. editor Optical Mgmt., 1979-80, OpticScan Canada, 1981-82, Indian Optician, 1982, Prism Mag., Can., 1988; tech. editor Optical Index, 1980-82; reviewer optical books. Presdl. appointment U.S. Selective Svc. Sys., 1991-92; Scoutmaster Boy Scouts Am., 1962; bd. dirs. ARC, Conn. chpt., 1988; advisor Tri Hi-Y YMCA, 1964; chmn. Korea-Vietnam Meml. com., Milford, 1985-86; organizer WWII Monument Com. 1991; trustee Conn. Visual Health Ctr., 1982-84; mem. Soc. 3d U.S. INf. Div., 1987. Served with AUS, 1957-59, Conn. Army N.G., 1960-69. Recipient Eng. National/Wingate prize, 1983, Service Above Self award Rotary, 1986. Fellow Nat. Acad. Opticianry (regional membership chmn., faculty speakers bur., citation 1988), Internat. Acad. Opticianry; mem. Conn. Opticians Assn. (pres. 1974, chmn. membership and ethics coms., Optician of Yr 1975), Conn. Guild Prescription Opticians (pres. 1980, Man of Yr 1981), Opticians Assn. Am. (historian, citation 1993), Assn. Dispensing Opticians Eng., Nat. Commn. on Opticianry Accreditation (commr. 1989—), Brit. Guild Dispensing Opticians, Ednl. Found. in Ophamalic Optics, Calif. Soc. Dispensing Opticians (hon.), Ariz. Soc. Dispensing Opticians (hon.), Am. Legion (citation 1986), Milford C. of C. (chmn. law and safety com. 1975, Community Service award 1986), Internat. Platform Assn., Am. Bd. of Opticianry and Nat. Contact Lens Examiners (cert.), Am. Bd. of Opticianry Master of Ophthalmic Optics, Charter Oak Coll. Alumni Assn. (bd. dirs. 1987, alumni citation 1995). Recipient Senate Citation State of Conn., 1993, German-Am. Friendship award, Germany, 1995, State of Conn. Justice of the Peace, 1995; sr. rsch. fellow Internat. Soc. for Philosophical Inquiry, 1991—. Lodges: Lions, Rotary. Avocations: skydiving, ballooning, motorcycling, Tae Kwan Do (presdl. sports award, 1973). Home: 25 Parkland Pl Milford CT 06460-7723 Office: Park Lane Opticians Inc 50 Broad St Milford CT 06460-3358

MUTH, GEORGE EDWARD, former art and drafting supply company executive; b. Washington, July 1, 1906; s. Edward Everhardt and Edna Elizabeth (Cassidy) M.; m. Lydagene Black, Apr. 19, 1930. A.B., George Washington U., 1931, J.D., 1934; LL.D. (hon.), Gallaudet Coll., 1965. Bar: D.C. 1933. With firm Pennie, Davis, Marvin and Edmonds (patent law), Washington, 1924-36; pres., treas. Geo. F. Muth Co., Inc., Washington, 1936-71; pres. Geo. F. Muth Co., Inc., 1971, 1972—; sec., treas. GFM, Inc., Woodville, Va., 1972-82. Past mem. zoning appeal bd., Rappahannock County, Va.; past mem. Rappahannock County Electoral Bd., Rappahannock County Planning Commn.; past chmn. bd. Gallaudet Coll., Washington, now chmn. emeritus; past trustee Westbrook Sch., Montgomery County, Md., George Washington U.; trustee Rappahannock County Library, Washington, Va.; past mem. fine arts com. U.S. Agr. Grad. School; past pres. Boys Club Washington, Travelers Aid Soc. Washington; past v.p. Nat. Travelers Aid Soc., Nat. Capital Area council Boy Scouts Am.; Washington Soc. for Blind.; bd. dirs., past vice chmn. Culpeper (Va.) Meml.

Hosp.; past bd. dirs., past chmn. Rappahannock-Rapidan Community Services Bd. Mem. Nat. Art Materials Trade Assn. (past pres., dir.), Arts Club (past pres.), Rotary (past pres.), Rappahannock Hunt Club (past pres. Washington, Va.), Masons, Sigma Alpha Epsilon, Gamma Eta Gamma, Omicron Delta Kappa. Presbyterian (elder). Home: 424 Highlands Pl Harrisonburg VA 22801-8348

MUTH, JOHN FRANCIS, newspaper editor, columnist; b. N.Y.C., Sept. 18, 1918; s. Ernest and Mary (Bijot) M.; m. Helen Scanlan, Sept. 26, 1948. Student, Fordham Coll., evenings 1939-40. With King Features Syndicate, 1941—; now asso. editor; editor Nat. Press Photographer mag., 1963-67; syndicated columnist, science writer, 1967—. Served with the USAAF, 1942-45, ETO. Mem. Bellerose Civic Assn., VFW (John F. Prince post). Democrat. Roman Catholic. Club: Caterpillar. Home: 81-33 243d St Bellerose NY 11426 Office: 235 E 45th St New York NY 10017-3305

MUTH, JOHN FRASER, economics educator; b. Chgo., Sept. 27, 1930; s. Merlin Arthur and Margaret Fraser (Ferris) M. B.S.I.E., Washington U., St. Louis, 1952; M.S., Carnegie-Mellon U., 1954, Ph.D., 1962. Research fellow Carnegie-Mellon U., 1956-59, asst. prof. econs., 1959-62, assoc. prof., 1962-64; prof. Mich. State U., 1964-69, Ind. U., 1969-94; ret., 1994. Author: (with others) Planning Production, Inventories, and Work Force, 1960, (with G. K. Groff) Operations Management: Analysis for Decision, 1972; editor: (with G. L. Thompson) Industrial Scheduling, 1963, (with G. K. Groff) Operations Management: Selected Readings, 1969. Fellow Econometric Soc.; mem. Inst. Mgmt. Sci. Home: 21028 4th Ave Sumerland FL 33042

MUTH, RICHARD FERRIS, economics educator; b. Chgo., May 14, 1927; s. Merlin Arthur and Margaret Ferris M.; m. Helene Louise Martin, Dec. 23, 1955; children: Lisa Helene, Laurianne Martin Love. Student, USCG Acad., 1945-47; A.B., Washington U., St. Louis, 1949, M.A., 1950; Ph.D., U. Chgo., 1958. Lectr. polit. economy Johns Hopkins U., Balt., 1955-56; economist Resources for Future, Washington, 1956-58; assoc. prof. urban econs. U. Chgo., 1959-64; economist Inst. Def. Analyses, Arlington, Va., 1964-66, cons., 1966-69; prof. econs. Washington U., St. Louis, 1966-70, Stanford U., (Calif.), 1970-83; Callaway prof. econs. Emory U., Atlanta, 1983—, chmn. dept., 1983-90; vis. assoc. prof. Vanderbilt U., 1958-59; vis. sr. fellow Urban Inst., Washington, 1976-77; vis. prof. Sch. Bus., U. Calif. Berkeley, 1991. Author: (with others) Regions, Resources and Economic Growth, 1960, Cities and Housing, 1969, Public Housing, 1974, Urban Economic Problems, 1975; (with Allen C. Goodman) The Economics of Housing Markets, 1989. Mem. Presdl. Task Force on Urban Renewal, 1969; mem. Presdl. Task Forces on Urban Affairs and on Housing, 1980-81, Presdl. Commn. on Housing, 1981-82. Served with USCG, 1951-52. Mem. Am. Econ. Assn., Am. Real Estate and Urban Econs. Assn., Regional Sci. Assn. (v.p. 1975-76), So. Econ. Assn. Libertarian. Methodist. Office: Emory U Dept Econs Atlanta GA 30322

MUTH, ROBERT JAMES, metal company executive, lawyer; b. Phila., May 13, 1933; s. James H. and Ruth M. (Will) M.; m. Shirley M. Carnes, Jan. 31, 1959; children: Christopher James, Jennifer Augusta. BA, Lafayette Coll., 1954; postgrad., Yale Div. Sch., 1954-55; LLB, Columbia U., 1960. Bar: D.C. 1961, N.Y. 1969. Atty. Covington & Burling, Washington, 1960-68; asst. gen. counsel Asarco, Inc., N.Y.C., 1969-71, asso. gen. counsel, 1971-77, v.p., 1977—; chmn. Lead Industries Assn., N.Y.C., 1986-89, 93—; pres. Silver Inst., Washington, 1987-89; vice chmn. Nat. Legal Ctr. for Pub. Interest, Washington, 1986-90; bd. dirs. So. Peru Copper Corp. Mem. George Sch. Com., Newton, Pa., 1985—; bd. dirs. No. Lights Inst., Missoula, Mont. Lt. inf. U.S. Army, 1955-57, Korea. Mem. ABA, N.Y. State Bar Assn., Met. Club (Washington). Home: 2 Fenwood Pl Morrisville PA 19067-1990

MUTI, RICCARDO, orchestra and opera conductor; b. Naples, Italy, July 28, 1941. Edn., Milan Conservatory; MusD (hon.), U. Pa., Curtis Inst. Music U. Bologna, Mt. Holyoke Coll.; LLD (hon.), Warwick U., Eng.; Doctor Honoris Causa, Westminster Choir Coll., Princeton, N.J. Prin. condr. Orch. Maggio Musicale Florentino, Florence, Italy, 1969-80; guest condr. numerous orchs., Europe and U.S.; music dir. Philharmonia Orch., London, 1973-82; prin. guest condr. Phila. Orch., 1967-78, music dir., 1980-92, laureate condr., 1992—; music dir. La Scala, 1986—, prin. condr., 1973-82; concerts at Salzburg, Edinburgh, Lucerne, Flanders, Vienna and Berlin Festivals; condr. operas at Vienna, Salzburg, La Scala, Milan, Munich, London. Decorated officer of merit Republica Tedesca, Commendatore and Grand Ufficiale Della Republica Italiana, Cavaliere Di Gran Croce; winner Guido Cantelli prize, 1967; recipient Verdienst Kreuz, Fed. Republic of Germany; recipient numerous internat. prizes for recordings. Hon. mem. Royal Acad. Music, Acad. Santa Cecilia, Acad. Luigi Cherubini. Office: Phila Orch Acad of Mus 1420 Locust St Ste 400 Philadelphia PA 19102 also: Orch del Teatro alla Scala, Via dei Filodarmmatici, I-20121 Milan Italy*

MUTO, SUSAN ANNETTE, religion educator, academic administrator; b. Pitts., Dec. 11, 1942; d. Frank and Helen (Scardamalia) M. BA in Journalism and English, Duquesne U., 1964; MA, U. Pitts., 1967, PhD in English Lit., 1970. Asst. dir. Inst. of Formative Spirituality, Duquesne U., Pitts., 1965-80, dir., 1980-88, faculty coordinator grad. programs in foundational formation, 1979-88, prof., 1981—; guest lectr. formative reading various colls. and community orgns., 1970—. Author: (with Adrian van Kaam) The Emergent Self, 1968, (with Adrian van Kaam) The Participant Self, 1969, Approaching the Sacred: An Introduction to Spiritual Reading, 1973, Steps Along the Way, 1975, A Practical Guide to Spiritual Reading, 1976, The Journey Homeward: On the Road of Spiritual Reading, 1977, Tell Me Who I Am, 1977, Celebrating the Single Life, 1982, Blessings That Make Us Be, 1982, Pathways of Spiritual Living, 1984, 89, Mediation in Motion, 1986, (with Adrian van Kaam and Richard Byrne) Songs for Every Season, 1989, (with van Kaam) Commitment: Key to Christian Maturity, 1989, Commitment: Key to Christian Maturity, A Workbook and Guide, 1990, John of the Cross for Today: The Ascent, 1990, Womanspirit, 1991, (with Adrian van Kaam) The Power of Appreciation: A New Approach to Personal and Relational Healing, 1992, John of the Cross for Today: The Dark Night, 1994, Stess and the Search for Happiness: A New Challenge for Christian Spirituality, 1993, Harnessing Stress: A Spiritual Quest, 1993, Healthy and Holy Under Stress: A Royal Road to Wise Living, 1994, Divine Guidance: A Basic Directory to the God-Guided Life for All Believers, 1994, A Practical Guide to Spiritual Reading, 1994, Late Have I Loved Thee: The Recovery of Intimacy, 1995; contbr. articles to religious and secular publs. Mem. Edith Stein Guild, Epiphany Assn. (exec. dir. 1988—), Phi Kappa Phi. Home: 2223 Wenzell Ave Pittsburgh PA 15216-3159 Office: Epiphany Assn Pittsburgh PA 15206-4517

MUTOMBO, DIKEMBE (DIKEMBE MUTOMBO MPOLONDO MUKAMBA JEAN JACQUE WAMUTOMBO), professional basketball player; b. Kinshasa, Zaire, June 25, 1966. Student, Georgetown U. Center Denver Nuggets, 1991—. NBA All-Star, 1992; NBA All-Rookie Team, 1992. Office: Denver Nuggets McNichols Sports Arena 1635 Clay St Denver CO 80204*

MUTSCHLER, HERBERT FREDERICK, retired librarian; b. Eureka, S.D., Nov. 28, 1919; s. Frederick and Helena (Oster) M.; m. Lucille I. Gross, Aug. 18, 1945; 1 dau., Linda M. B.A., Jamestown Coll., 1947; M.A., Western Res. U., 1949, M.S., 1952. Tchr. history high sch. Lemmon, S.D., 1947-48; asst. librarian Royal Oak (Mich.) Libr., 1952-55; head librarian Hamtramck (Mich.) Libr., 1955-56; head public svcs. Wayne County Libr. System, Wayne, Mich., 1956-59; asst. county librarian Wayne County Libr. System, 1960-62; dir. Wayne County Libr. System, Seattle, 1963-89; library bldg. cons. Wayne County Libr. 1956-62, Wash. State Libr., 1966—; cons. Salt Lake County Libr., Pierce County Libr., Wash. Township Libr.; lectr. U. Wash. Sch. Librarianship, 1970-71; bldg. cons. Hoquiam (Wash.) Libr., Olympic (Wash.) Regional Libr., Camas (Wash.) Pub. Libr., N. Cen. (Wash.) Regional Libr., Spokane (Wash.) County Libr., Enumclaw (Wash.) Libr. Puyallup (Wash.) Pub. Libr., Kennewick (Wash.) Pub. Libr., Lopez Island (Wash.) Libr. Contbr. articles profl. jours. Served with AUS, 1941-45; to capt. 1950-52. Decorated Silver Star, Bronze Star with cluster, Purple Heart, Presdl. Unit Citation. Mem. ALA (councilor at large 1965-69, chpt. councilor 1971-75, pres. library adminstrv. div. 1974-75), Pacific N.W. Library Assn., Wash. Library Assn. (exec. bd. 1964-65, 69-71, pres. 1967-

69). Republican. Lutheran. Club: City, Municipal League. Lodge: Kiwanis. Home: 5300 128th Ave SE Bellevue WA 98006-2952

MUTTI, ALBERT FREDERICK, minister; b. Hopkins, Mo., Feb. 13, 1938; s. Albert Frederick and Phyllis Margaret (Turner) M.; m. Etta Mae McClurg, June 7, 1959; children: Timothy Allen, John Frederick, Martin Kent. AB, Cen. Meth. Coll., 1960; MDiv., Garrett Theol. Sem., 1963; DMin., St. Paul Sch. Theology, 1975. Sr. pastor Union Star Charge, Mo., 1963-65, Crossroads Parish, Savannah, Mo., 1965-74; assoc. coun. dir. Mo. West Conf. UMC, Kansas City, 1974-80, coun. dir., 1980-82; sr. pastor First United Meth. Ch., Blue Springs, Mo., 1982-87; dist. supt. Cen. Dist. UMC, Mo., 1987-89; dist. supr. Kansas City N. Dist., 1989-92; bishop Kans. Area United Meth. Ch., Topeka, 1992—. Chair Savannah Cmty. Betterment, 1971; bd. mem. St. Mary's Hosp., Blue Springs, 1986; dir. ARC, Savannah, 1968; bd. Discipleship, Nashville, bd. Global Ministries, N.Y.; pres. Mo. Coun. Chs., Jefferson City, Dean Mo. Area Ministers Sch., Ctrl. Meth. Coll.; trustee St. Paul Sch. Theology; organizer Rural, Religion and labor Coun. Kans. Named Disting. Alumni Ctrl. Meth. Coll.; recipient Grad. award St. Paul Sch. Theology. Home: 6841 SW Dunstan Ct Topeka KS 66610-1406 Office: 4201 SW 15th St Topeka KS 66604

MUTZ, OSCAR ULYSSES, manufacturing and distribution executive; b. Edinburg, Ind., Feb. 12, 1928; s. Harold Winterberg and Laura Belle (Sawin) M.; m. Jean Greiling, Aug. 22, 1948; children: Marcia, H. William. B.S., Ind. U., 1949. Vice pres. Peerless Corp., Indpls., 1954-63; v.p., gen. mgr. Space Conditioning, Inc., Harrisonburg, Va., 1964-66; v.p., treas. Cosco, Inc., Columbus, Ind., 1966-67; exec. v.p., 1967-69, pres., 1969-71; chmn. bd. Court Manor Corp., Columbus, 1971-73; pres. Jenn Air Corp., Indpls., 1973-75; pres., CEO Mutz Corp., 1975-81; pres. Forum Group, Inc. (merger Mutz Corp. and Excepticon, Inc.), Indpls., 1981-91; chmn., chief exec. officer Capital Industries, Inc., Indpls., 1991—; also bd. dirs.; bd. dirs. Ct. Manor Corp., Sargent & Greenleaf; pres. Sovereign Group, Inc., 1991—; also bd. dirs. Nat. trustee Fellowship Christian Athletes, 1985-91, chmn. nat. conf. ctr., 1994—; mem. pres. coun. and dean's adv. coun. Ind. U. Mem. Ind. Mfrs. Assn. (chmn. 1980). Republican. Mem. Christian Ch. Office: Capital Industries Inc 8900 Keystone Crossing Ste 1150 Indianapolis IN 46240

MUUSS, JOHN, public safety and emergency management executive; b. Bklyn., Mar. 8, 1940; s. Leona (Schwanzer; divorced; children: John. Lance, Diana. Student, C.W. Post Coll., Suffolk (N.Y.) C.C., N.Y.C. (N.Y.) Police Acad. Lab. technician Royaltone Photo Finishers, N.Y.C., 1958-59; comml. photographer A. Studley Inc., N.Y.C., 1962-64; police officer N.Y.C. (N.Y.) Police Dept., 1966-70, detective, 1970-78; bonded dep. sheriff Suffolk County, N.Y., 1979—; dir. pub. safety Town of Islip, N.Y., 1978—; dir. emergency mgmt. Town of Islip, 1981—; pvt. practice security cons. East Islip, N.Y., 1986—. Pres., mem. Lakeland Civic Assn., Ronkonkoma, N.Y., 1970-79, Connetquot Bd. Edn., Bohemia, N.Y., 1975-78; campaign chmn. various local and state polit. seats, Islip, 1970—; chmn., mem. MacArthur Airport Adv. Com., Ronkonkoma, 1975-78; vestry mem. St. Marks Episcopal Ch., Islip, 1982-89. With U.S. Army, 1959-62. Mem. Am. Soc. for Indsl. Security, Fire Island Law Enforcement Coun., Internat. Assn. Chiefs of Police, N.Y. State Assn. Chiefs Police, Kiwanis Club of the Islips (charter pres. 1986). Republican. Episcopalian. Avocation: golf. Office: Islip Twp Dept Pub Safety/Emergency 401 Main St Islip NY 11751-3533

MUUSS, ROLF EDUARD, psychologist, educator; b. Tating, Germany, Sept. 26, 1924; came to U.S., 1953, naturalized, 1992; s. Rudolf A. and Else (Osterwald) M.; m. Gertrude Louise Kremser, Dec. 22, 1953; children: Michael John, Gretchen Elise. Diploma, Tchr. Coll., Flensburg, Germany, 1951; student. U. Hamburg, Germany, 1951, Central Mo. State Coll., 1951-52, Columbia Tchrs. Coll., 1952; M.Ed., Western Md. Coll., 1954; Ph.D., U. Ill., 1957. Tchr. pub. sch. Germany, 1945-46, 51, 52-53, substitute prin., 1952-53; tchr. trainee U.S. Office Edn., 1951-52; houseparent Child Study Center, Balt., 1953; grad. asst. U. Ill., 1954-57; research assoc. prof. Iowa Child Welfare Research Sta., State U. Iowa, 1957-59; research cons., 1960, 61; mem. faculty Goucher Coll., 1959—, prof. edn., 1964—, chmn. dept., 1972-75, dir. spl. edn., 1977-92, Elizabeth L. Todd disting. prof., 1980-85, chmn. dept. sociology and anthropology, 1983-85; rsch. assoc. edn. Johns Hopkins, 1962-63; part-time or summer tchr. U. B.C., 1962, Johns Hopkins U., 1962, 65, U. Del., 1965, Towson U., 1967, U. Ill., 1967; teaching assoc. Sheppard and Enoch Pratt Hosp, 1969-80; guest lectr. Tchrs. Coll., Kiel, Fed. Republic Germany, 1977-78. Author: First-Aid for Classroom Discipline Problems, 1962, Theories of Adolescence, 1962, 5th edit., 1988, Grundlagen der Jugendpsychologie, 1982; also numerous articles; editor: Adolescent Behavior and Society: A Book of Readings, 1971, 4th edit., 1990. Served with German Air Force, 1942-45. Recipient award for disting. scholarship Goucher Coll., 1979; grantee Andrew W. Mellon Found., 1976-77. Fellow Am. Psychol. Soc., Am. Psychol. Assn., Md. Psychol. Assn. (treas. 1971-73); mem. Balt. Psychol. Assn. (chmn. membership com. 1966, v.p. 1970-71), Soc. Rsch. Child Devel., Soc. Rsch. on Adolescence, Coun. for Exceptional Children, Kappa Delta Pi (v.p. Alpha chpt. 1956-57), Phi Delta Kappa. Home: 1540 Rickett Rd Lutherville Timonium MD 21093-5822 Office: Goucher Coll Towson MD 21204-2794

MUZEKARI, THOMASINE DABBS, educational consultant; b. Columbia, S.C., Dec. 4, 1941; d. Jesse Thomas and Margaret Salina (Scott) Dabbs; m. William Muzekari, May 7, 1966; children: Laura DuRant, William Theodore. Student, U. S.C., 1961-62, EdD, 1994; BA, Columbia Coll., 1983, MEd, 1987. Cert. tchr., S.C. Tchr. Richland One Sch., Columbia, 1983-89; staff devel. cons. Richland One Sch., 1989—; co-chair Dist. Challenger Space Ctr. Curriculum Com., 1994; pvt. cons. specializing in learning styles, integrated curriculum, active learning, 1993—; adj. prof. U. S.C., 1995—. Writer, producer, narrator televised recert. course for tchrs. Middle School Today, 1991. S.C. Dept. Edn. grantee, 1992—. Mem. S.C. ASCD, S.C. Mid. Sch. Assn., S.C. Assn. Tchrs. Educators, S.C. Network of Women Adminstrs. in Edn. (regional chairperson 1994-95), Nat. Staff Devel. Coun. (S.C. affiliate, gov. com. 1994-95, exec. bd. 1995—), Alpha Delta Kappa (sgt.-at-arms 1988-90). Republican. Methodist. Avocations: gardening, aerobic exercise, reading. Office: Richland One 1616 Richland St Columbia SC 29201-2657

MUZYKA, DONALD RICHARD, specialty metals executive, metallurgist; b. Northampton, Mass., Aug. 23, 1938; s. Stephen S. and Mary (Paul) M.; m. Eileen J. Hannigan, June 10, 1961; children: Steven Richard, James Paul, David Joseph. Supr. high temperature alloy research Carpenter Tech. Corp., Reading, Pa., 1966-73, mgr. alloy research and devel., 1973-76, mgr. high temperature alloys research, 1975-76, gen. mgr. research and devel. labs., 1976-77, gen. mgr. distbn., 1977-79, v.p. tech. div., 1979-82; dir. tech. Cabot Corp., Boston, 1982-85; gen. mgr. refractory metals Cabot Corp., Boyertown, Pa., 1985-87, gen. mgr. elec. and refractory metals, 1987-88; v.p., gen. mgr. Cabot Corp., Boyertown, 1988-89; v.p. rsch. and devel. Cabot Corp., 1989; pres. Spl. Metals Corp., New Hartford, N.Y., 1990—; bd. dirs. Aviall, Inc. Contbr. articles to profl. jours.; patentee in field. Bd. dirs. Wilson Sch. Bd., West Lawn, Pa., 1960-63, Montessori Country Day Sch., Wyomissing, Pa., 1960-63. Recipient Engring. Alumni award U. Mass., 1984. Fellow Am. Soc. Metals (trustee 1982-84, Bradley Stoughton award 1981); mem. The Metall. Soc., Indsl. Research Inst., Am. Ceramic Soc., Am. Soc. Quality Control. Republican. Roman Catholic. Avocation: antique clock collector. Home: 6824 Reservoir Rd Clinton NY 13323-4816 Office: Spl Metals Corp Middle Settlement Rd New Hartford NY 13413

MUZZILLO, RACHEL EVELYN SHEELEY, reporter; b. Richmond, Ind., Nov. 22, 1966; d. Lysle Leavitt and Alecia Eilene (Hindsley) S. BA, Franklin Coll. of Ind., 1989. Intern, writer weekend dept Indpls. Star, 1988; intern, writer Brandon (Man., Can.) Sun, 1989; intern, writer Palladium-Item, Richmond, 1986-89, reporter, 1989—. Winner first prize Bulwer-Lytton Fiction Contest, San Jose State U., 1988, 3rd pl. spot news Best Gannett Corp. award. Mem. Women in Communications, Soc. Profl. Journalists, Phi Alpha Theta. Avocations: reading, writing, tennis, cross stitching, shopping. Home: 516 Riley Rd New Castle IN 47362 Office: Palladium-Item 1175 N A St Richmond IN 47374-3226

MYATT, CLIFFORD E., federal official; b. Boston, Sept. 3, 1929; s. George Myatt and Viola Ryan; m. Graciela de Courceuil, June 28, 1959. BA in Econs., Boston Coll., 1950; Advanced Degree in Acctg., Bentley Coll., 1952. CPA. With Ernst & Ernst, Boston, 1952-59; contr. Internat. Shoe Corp.,

1960-62, Caribe Nitrogen Corp., 1962-68; audit mgr. Ernst & Ernst, San Juan, P.R., 1968-69, ptnr., 1969-89; office mng. ptnr. Ernst & Whinney, San Juan, P.R., 1974-89; adminstr. econ. devel. adminstr. Econ. Devel. Adminstrn., Hato Rey, 1993-94; chief devel. offices for global markets P.R. Dept. Econ. Devel. and Commerce, San Juan, 1995—; bd. dirs. GDB, San Juan, P.R., Ports Authority, San Juan; chmn. bd. dirs. PRIDCO, Hato Rey; vice chmn. bd. dirs., EDB, Hato Rey, 1993-94. Chmn., pres. United Way, P.R., 1972, 73. Mem. Fin. Analyst Club (pres. 1975), Jaycees Internat. (internat. pres. 1967), San Juan Exch. and Rotary (pres. 1969, 82). Office: Econ Devel Adminstrn Roosevelt Ave San Juan PR 00918

MYCIELSKI, JAN, mathematician, educator; b. Wisniowa, Poland, Feb. 7, 1932; s. Jan and Helena (Bal) M.; m. Emilia Przezdziecka, Apr. 25, 1959. MS, U. Wroclaw, Poland, 1955, PhD, 1957. With Inst. Math., Polish Acad. Scis., Wroclaw, 1956-68; prof. math. U. Colo., Boulder, 1969—; vis. prof. Case Western Res. U., Cleve., 1967, U. Colo., 1967, Inst. des Hautes Etudes Scientifiques, Bures-sur-Yvette, 1978-79, dept. math. U. Hawaii, 1987; attache de recherche Centre National de la Recherche Scientifique, Paris, 1972-73; mem. Fin. Analyst Club (pres. 1975); long-term vis. staff mem. Los Alamos Nat. Lab., 1989-90. Author over 140 rsch. papers. Recipient Stefan Banach prize, 1965, Alfred Jurzykowski award, 1977, Waclaw Sierpinski medal, 1990. Mem. Am. Math. Soc., Polish Math. Soc., Assn. for Symbolic Logic. Office: U Colo Dept Math Boulder CO 80309-0395

MYDLAND, GORDON JAMES, judge; b. nr. Hetland, S.D., May 12, 1922; s. Jacob and Anna (Hetl) M.; m. Lorrie Grange, May 29, 1958; 1 child, Gabriel. BS, S.D. State U., 1947; JD, U. S.D., 1956. Bar: S.D. 1956. Pvt. practice law Brookings, S.D., 1956-69, Lake Preston, S.D., 1973; S.D. circuit judge, 1973-87; presiding judge (3d Jud. Circuit), 1975, 79-80; S.D. state's atty. Brookings County, 1959-62; mem. S.D. State Senate, 1963-68; atty. gen. S.D., 1968-72; ret., 1987; part-time instr. constl. and bus. law S.D. State U., 1956-65. Mem. S.D. Code Compilation Commn., 1964-68; mem. S.D. Planning and Adv. Commn. Crime and Juvenile Delinquency, 1970-72; adv. com. S.D. Alcohol Safety Action Project, 1971-72. Served with USNR, 1943-46. Mem. Am. Legion. Lutheran.

MYER, JAMES ALBERT, research science company executive; b. Niagara Falls, Ont., Can., Mar. 15, 1940; came to U.S., 1968; s. Douglas J. and Elizabeth R. (Henderson) M.; m. Elspeth A. Henderson, May 18, 1962; children: James Henderson, Clarissa Annette, Jonathan Joseph. BS, MS, U. Western Ont., 1966; PhD, York U., Toronto, Ont., Can., 1968. Lic. physicist. Sr. scientist GCA Corp., Bedford, Mass., 1968-69; staff scientist AVCO Everett (Mass.) Research Lab., 1969-73; group mgr. Sci. Applications, La Jolla, Calif., 1973-77; pres. Photon Research, La Jolla, 1977—; Contbr. articles to profl. jours.; inventor tunable laser, 1970; patentee, 1972. Bd. dirs. Northwest YMCA, La Jolla, 1965-68; rep. La Jolla Assn., 1976. NRC fellow, Can., 1965-68. Mem. AIAA, Am. Phys. Soc. Republican. Avocations: raquetball, tennis, skiing. Home: 5758 Dolphin Pl La Jolla CA 92037-7519 Office: Photon Research Assocs Inc 10350 N Torrey Pines Rd La Jolla CA 92037-1016

MYERBERG, MARCIA, investment banker; b. Boston, Mar. 25, 1945; d. George and Evelyn (Lewis) Katz; m. Jonathan Gene Myerberg, June 4, 1967 (div. Mar. 1994); 1 child, Gillian Michelle. BS, U. Wis., 1966. Corp. trust adminstr. Chase Manhattan Bank, N.Y.C., 1966-67; asst. cashier Glore Forgan, Wm. R. Staats, Phoenix, 1967-68; bond portfolio analyst Trust Co. of Ga., Atlanta, 1969-72; asst. v.p. 1st Union Nat. Bank, Charlotte, N.C., 1973-78; dir. cash mgmt. Carolina Power & Light Co., Raleigh, N.C., 1978-79; sr. v.p., treas. Fed Home Loan Mortgage Corp., Washington, 1979-85; dir. Salomon Bros. Inc., N.Y.C., 1985-89; sr. mng. dir. Bear, Stearns & Co. Inc., N.Y.C., 1989-93; mng. dir. Bear, Stearns Home Loans, London, 1989-93; chief exec. Myerberg & Co., L.P., N.Y.C., 1994—. Home: Apt P18A 120 E 87th St New York NY 10128 Office: 780 3d Ave New York NY 10017

MYERS, ALBERT G., JR., textile manufacturer; b. Charlotte, N.C., Feb. 15, 1917; s. Albert Gallatin and Elfreida (Nail) M.; m. Kittie Brownlee, Feb. 7, 1942; children—Albert Gallatin III, Barbara Brownlee Melvin. Student, Davidson Coll.; B.S., Erskine Coll., 1940; grad., Exec. Program U. N.C., 1959; LLD (hon.), Belmont Abbey Coll., 1992. With Textiles-Inc. (name changed to Ti-Caro Inc., 1978), Gastonia, N.C., 1939-82; successively mfg. dept., asst v.p., sec.-treas., v.p., treas. Textiles-Inc. (name changed to Ti-Caro Inc., 1978), 1939-61, pres., 1961-70, chmn. bd., 1971-82, also dir.; ret., 1982; with Threads-Inc. (now Threads USA), 1946-82, successively purchasing agt., sec., asst. treas., v.p. and sec., v.p. and treas., 1946-61, pres., 1961-70, chmn. bd., 1971-82, also dir.; ret., 1982; past chmn. bd. Carolina Motor Club. Past pres. Piedmont council Boy Scouts Am., regional chmn.; past mem. adv. bd. Red Shield Boys Club; past pres. Gaston County YMCA; past pres. N.C. Textile Found., Inc., 1967-69; past chmn. bd. First Gaston Found.; past treas. dir. Schiele Mus. Natural History; past trustee Gaston Coll.; trustee Brevard Coll.; past mem. bd. advisers Belmont Abbey Coll.; past chmn. bd. trustees Gaston Meml. Hosp.; trustee Crossnore (N.C.) Sch. Served with USAAF, 1942-46. Mem. Gastonia C. of C. (past pres.), Combed Yarn Spinners Assn. (past pres.), N.C. Textile Mfgrs. Assn. (past dir., 1st v.p. 1970-71), Am. Textile Mfrs. Inst. (dir. 1964-68), Am. Legion, Gaston Country Club, Grandfather Golf and Country Club (Linville, N.C.), Linville Golf Club, Key Largo (Fla.) Anglers Club. Methodist (ofcl. bd.).

MYERS, ALLAN ROSS, construction executive; b. Norristown, Pa., Oct. 26, 1949; s. Allan Carson and Ruth Esther (Markel) M.; m. Jill Bantham, June 25, 1971 (div. Apr. 1988); children: A. Brockway, Aaron Troy, Seth Carson; m. Beth Wilford Turner, June 17, 1989. BSCE, Va. Poly. Inst. and State U., 1972. With Allan D. Myers, Inc., Worcester, Pa., 1972-76, pres., 1976—. Bd. dirs. New Life Youth and Family Svcs., Harleysville, Pa. Recipient Tom Landry award Fellowship Christian Athletes. Mem. Nat. Utility Contractors Assn. (bd. dirs. 1979—), Utility Contractors Assn. Pa. (pres. 1978-80), Antique Automobile Club Am., Sportscare Vintage Racing Assn. Republican. Mem. Schwenkfelder Ch. Avocations: skiing, restoring and collecting antique cars, racing vintage sports cars. Office: Alan A Myers Inc PO Box 98 1805 Berks Rd Worcester PA 19490

MYERS, ALLEN RICHARD, medical school dean, rheumatologist; b. Balt., Jan. 14, 1935; s. Ellis Benjamin and Rosina (Blumberg) M.; m. Ellen Patz, Nov. 26, 1960; children: David Joseph, Robert Todd, Scott Patz. BA, U. Pa., 1956; MD, U. Md., 1960. Diplomate Am. Bd. Internal Medicine, Am. Bd. Rheumatology. Intern Univ. Hosp. Balt., 1960-61; resident in medicine Univ. Hosp., Ann Arbor, Mich., 1961-64; fellow in rheumatology Mass. Gen. Hosp. and Harvard Med. Sch., Boston, 1966-69; dir. clin. ing. rheumatology U. Pa. Sch. Medicine, Phila., 1969-72, chief rheumatology sect., 1972-78; dep. chair medicine Temple U. Sch. Medicine, Phila., 1978-84, acting chmn. medicine, 1984-86, dean, 1991—, prof. medicine, 1978—, assoc. v.p. Health Scis. Ctr., 1994—; vis. prof. Cardiothoracic Inst., U. London, 1988; med. adv. bd. Scleroderma Rsch. Found., Santa Barbara, Calif., 1988. Mem. editorial bd. Arthritis & Rheumatism, 1985-90, Brit. Jour. Rheumatology, 1989-94; editor: Systemic Scleroderma, 1985, Medicine, 1986, 93. Exec. com. Phila. Health Care Congress, 1990—, chmn., 1994; adv. com. Pa. Lupus Found., 1976—. With USPHS, 1964-66. Recipient Margaret Whitaker prize U. Md. Sch. Medicine, 1960, Lindback Found. award Temple, 1981; named Physician of Yr. Temple U. Hosp., 1986. Fellow Phila. Coll. Physicians (councillor 1994—), ACP, Am. Coll. Rheumatolog; mem. Phila. Rheumatism Soc., Am. Fedn. Clin. Rsch., N.Y. Acad. Scis., Brit. Soc. Rheumatology. Avocations: walking, classical music, reading. Office: Temple U Sch Medicine 3400 N Broad St Philadelphia PA 19140

MYERS, ANNE M., church administrator. Sec. Ch. of the Brethren. Office: Church of Brethren 1451 Dundee Ave Elgin IL 60120

MYERS, ARTHUR B., journalist, author; b. Buffalo, Oct. 24, 1917; s. Edward A. and Isabelle (Baker) M.; m. Irma H. Ashley, 1972. BA, Hobart Coll., 1939. Journalist Rochester (N.Y.) Times Union, 1948-52, Washington Post, 1956-57, Berkshire (Mass.) Eagle, 1957-64; contbg. editor Coronet mag., 1965-68; columnist Bergen Record, Hackensack, N.J., 1969-71; exec. editor Berkshire Sampler, Pittsfield, Mass., 1971-77; tchr. writing Mass. U. extension program and Berkshire Community Coll., Pittsfield, 1958-62, Fairleigh Dickinson U., Teaneck, N.J., 1970, Cambridge (Mass.) Coll., 1989. Author: (with J. O'Connell) Safety Last: An Indictment of Auto Industry,

1966, Journalism Careers for the '70's, 1971, Analysis: The Short Story, 1975, Analysis: The Personal Profile Magazine Article, 1976, Kids Do Amazing Things, 1980, The Ghost Hunters, 1980, Sea Creatures Do Amazing Things, 1981; (with Irma Myers) Why You Feel Down and What You Can Do About It, 1982, The Ghostly Register, 1986, Ghosts of the Rich and Famous, 1988, The Ghostly Gazetteer, 1990, Ghost Hunter's Guide, 1993, The Cheyenne, 1992, The Pawnee, 1993, The First Movies, 1993, The First Baseball Game, 1993, The First Football Game, 1993; also short stories, articles. Mem. PEN, Nat. Writers Union, Mensa. Home: 60 Grove St #6202 Wellesley MA 02181

MYERS, BARTON, architect; b. Norfolk, Va., Nov. 6, 1934; s. Barton and Meeta Hamilton (Burrage) M.; m. Victoria George, Mar. 7, 1959; 1 child, Suzanne Lewis. BS, U.S. Naval Acad., 1956; MArch with honors, U. Pa., 1964. Commd. 2d lt. USAF, 1956, resigned, 1961; architect Louis I. Kahn, Phila., 1964-65, Bower, Fradley, Phila., 1967-68; architect, prin. A.J. Diamond & Barton Myers, Toronto, Ont., Can., 1968-75; architect, prin. Barton Myers Assocs., Toronto, 1975—, Los Angeles, 1981—; disting. vis. prof. Ariz. State U., Tempe, 1986; sr. prof. UCLA, 1981—; Thomas Jefferson Prof. U. Va., Charlottesville, 1982; vis. prof., lectr. Harvard U., U. Pa., other univs. U.S. and Can., 1968—. Prin. works include Myers Residence, Toronto (Ont. Assn. Architects Toronto Chpt. Annual Design award, 1971, Can. Housing Design Coun. award, 1971), Wolf Residence, Toronto (Architectural Record: Record Houses of 1977, Twenty-Five Yrs. of Record Houses, 1981), Housing Union Bldg., Edmonton (Can. Housing Design Coun. award, 1974, Design in Steel award, 1975), Citadel Theatre, Edmonton (City of Edmonton Design award, 1978, Stelco Design award, 1978), Seagram Mus., Waterloo, Ont., (Gov. Gen.'s Medal for Architecture, 1986), Howard Hughes Ctr. Master Plan and Wang Tower, L.A., 1986, Phoenix Mcpl. Govt. Ctr. (Winning Competition Entry 1985), Portland Ctr. for the Performing Arts, Portland (Progressive Architecture Design award, 1984), Art Gallery Ont. expansion (Winning Competition Entry, 1987), Film and Drama Facility York U., Toronto, 1987, Cerritos (Calif.) Ctr. Performing Arts, 1987, N.J. Performing Arts Ctr., Newark, 1990, Art Gallery of Ontario, Toronto, 1993, others. Recipient Gov. Gen.'s award for Architecture Woodsworth Coll., 1992, RAIC Gold Medal, 1994, Royal Archtl. Inst. Canada. Fellow AIA, Royal Archtl. Inst. Can.; mem. Soc. Archtl. Historians, Royal Can. Acad. Art, Tau Sigma Delta. Avocations: travel, reading. Office: Barton Myers Assocs Inc 9348 Civic Center Dr Beverly Hills CA 90210-3624

MYERS, CATHERINE R., academic administrator; b. East Orange, N.J., Jan. 5, 1934; d. Joseph Brown and Charlotte (Metzger) Rodgers; m. Franklin G. Myers, Aug. 11, 1966; children: K.C., Anna Marie. BA, Bryn Mawr (Pa.) Coll., 1955; MA, Oxford U., 1961; PhD, Brown U., 1963. Grad. asst. Brown U., Providence, 1957-59; instr., then asst. prof. Bryn Mawr Coll., 1959-67; assoc. prof. to prof. Mahattanville Coll., Purchase, N.Y., 1968—; head Dept. English, 1974-77, dean of studies, 1980-81, dean of faculty, 1981-86, provost, 1986-92; cons. NEH, 1972, 83, 84, Ednl. Testing Service, Princeton, N.J., 1964-82; examiner U. Mid-Am., 1976; project dir. Improvement of Post-Secondary Edn., 1991—; reviewer U.S. Dept. Edn., 1991—. Author (books) Time in the Narrative of the Faerie Queen, 1973, Magic Makers, 1978, (study guides) Paradise Lost, 1966, The Canterbury Tales, 1967, The Faerie Queen, 1968; co-author The Heroic Spirit, 1978. Bd. dirs. A Better Chance in Ridgefield, Conn., 1987. Fulbright scholar, 1955-57; fellow Bryn Mawr Coll., 1963, NEH, 1978. Mem. AAUP, MLA, Am. Assn. Higher Edn., Westchester Consortium Internat. Studies (pres.). Avocation: poetry. Office: Manhattanville Coll Founders 2900 Purchase St Purchase NY 10577

MYERS, CHARLES, medical center director, researcher; b. Wilkes-Barre, Pa., June 24, 1943; s. Charles E. Sr. and Virginia (Rosser) M.; m. Rose Szarlat, July 9, 1968; children: Jessica, Gabriella. BA, Wesleyan U., 1965; MD, U. Pa., 1969. Sr. investigator Nat. Cancer Inst., Bethesda, Md., 1974-81, branch chief, 1981-94; dir. cancer ctr. U.Va., Charlottesville, 1994—. Mem. AAAS, Am. Soc. Clin. Investigation, Am. Assn. Cancer Rsch. Avocations: orchids, bicycling, skiing. Home: 1323 Wimbleton Way Charlottesville VA 22901 Office: U Va Health Sci Ctr Charlottesville VA 22908

MYERS, CHARLES ANDREW, retired economist; b. State College, Pa., June 10, 1913; s. Charles Emory and Christine Alice (Bideispacher) M.; m. Nancy Ellen Nash, June 15, 1937; children—Charles Nash, Anne Howard, Tamson Elizabeth. A.B., Pa. State U., 1934; Ph.D., U. Chgo., 1939. Staff MIT, 1939—, instr., then asst. prof. and assoc. prof., 1939-49, prof. indsl. rels., 1949-67, Sloan Fellows prof. mgmt., 1967-78, prof. emeritus, 1978-81, dir. indsl. rels. sect., 1948-81; with labor div. W.P.B. and service of supply civilian personnel div. War Dept., Washington, 1942-43; pub. panel mem. Region I, Nat. War Labor Bd. Boston, 1944-45; public mem. Presdl. R.R. Commn., 1959-62; chmn. Nat. Manpower Policy Task Force, 1969-71. Author: (with P. Pigors) Personnel Adminstration, 1947, 9th edit., 1981, The Movement of Factory Workers, (with W.R. Maclaurin), 1943, The Dynamics of a Labor Market, (with G.P. Shultz), 1951, Industrial Relations in Sweden Some Comparisons with American Experience, 1951, Labor Problems in the Industrialization of India, 1958, (with F.H. Harbison) Management in the Industrial World, 1959, (with others) Industrialism and Industrial Man, 1960, (with F.H. Harbison) Education, Manpower and Economic Growth, 1964, Computers in Knowledge-Based Fields, 1970, The Role of the Private Sector in Manpower Development, 1971; Editor: The Impact of Computers on Management, 1967; Contbr. articles to profl. jours. Recipient Disting. Alumnus award Pa. State U., 1976. Mem. Indsl. Rels. Rsch. Assn. (pres. 1962), Nat. Acad. Arbitrators (life), Am. Acad. Arts and Scis. (emeritus). Home: 3377 Gulf Shore Blvd N Apt 5B Naples FL 33940-3602

MYERS, CHARLOTTE, secondary educator. Tchr. Lowell (Ind.) Sr. High Sch. Named Outstanding High Sch. Tchr. Inland Steel Ryerson Found., 1992. Office: Lowell Sr High Sch 2051 E Commercial Ave Lowell IN 46356-2115

MYERS, CLARK EVERETT, retired business administration educator; b. Rossville, Kans., Oct. 19, 1915; s. Thad James and Rose I (Page) M.; m. Cora Henley Hepworth, May 7, 1942; children—Clark Everett, Richard G. Hepworth. B.S., U. Kans., 1939, M.B.A., 1946; D.C.S., Harvard, 1956. Tchr. Auburn (Kans.) Sch., 1932-34, prin., 1934-36; instr. U. Kans., 1939-41; asst. prof. U. Tex., 1947-49, assoc. prof., 1949-53, chmn. dept. mgmt., 1950-53; lectr. Harvard Grad. Sch. Bus. Adminstrn., 1953-54; dean Coll. of Commerce, prof. bus. adminstrn. Ohio U., 1954-57; dir. mgmt. devel. inst. Lausanne, Switzerland, 1957-60; lectr. Harvard Grad. Sch. Bus., 1960-61; dean Sch. Bus. Adminstrn., prof. mgmt. U. Miami, Coral Gables, Fla., 1961-68; dean Grad. Sch. Bus. Adminstrn., Emory U., Atlanta, 1968-75; prof. bus. adminstrn. Grad. Sch. Bus. Adminstrn., Emory U., 1975-85, prof. emeritus, 1985—. Editor: (with William R. Spriegel) The Writings of the Gilbreths, 1953. Served as lt. USNR, 1942-45. Fellow Acad. Mgmt.; mem. Am. Assn. Collegiate Schs. Bus. (exec. com. 1965-68, 1969-70, pres. 1970-71), Phi Kappa Phi, Sigma Iota Epsilon, Delta Sigma Pi, Beta Gamma Sigma, Phi Gamma Delta, Beta Alpha Psi. Home: 1082 Vistavia Cir Decatur GA 30033-3411

MYERS, CLAY, retired investment management company executive; b. Portland, Oreg., May 27, 1927; s. Henry Clay and Helen (Mackey) M.; m. Elizabeth Lex Arndt, Oct. 1, 1955; children: Richard Clay (dec.), Carolyn Elizabeth, David Hobson. B.S., U. Oreg., 1949; postgrad., Northwestern Coll. Law, 1950-52; LHD (hon.), Ch. Div. Sch. of the Pacific, 1992. With 1st. Nat. Bank, Portland, 1949-53; with Conn. Gen. Life Ins. Co., Hartford and Portland, 1953-62; state mgr. Conn. Gen. Life Ins. Co., 1960-62; v.p. Ins. Co. Oreg., Portland, 1962-65; asst. sec. state State of Oreg., Salem, 1965-67; sec. state State of Oreg., 1967-77, state treas., 1977-84; v.p. J.P. Morgan Investment Mgmt. Co., N.Y.C., 1984-89, Capital Cons. Inc., Portland, Oreg., 1989-92; chmn. Oreg. House Adv. Com. Legis. Reapportionment, 1961; chmn. Oreg. Gov.'s Commn. on Youth, 1969-74. Author: (with others) Population Reapportionment Initiative Constitutional Amendment, 1952. Bd. dirs., treas. Ch. Divinity Sch. of Pacific, 1977-83; trustee Pacific U., 1989-92; vestryman Trinity Parish, Wall St., 1986-93; pres. Nat. Interfaith Conf., 1986-87; mem. social responsibility in investing com. Nat. Episcopal Ch., 1983-87; trustee Ch. Pension Fund; bd. dirs. Ch. Life Ins. Co. Mem. Nat. Assn. State Treas. (past pres.), Multnomah Athletic Club (Portland), DeMolay Club (Legion of Honor), Lambda Chi Alpha (nat. pres. 1974-78),

Sigma Nu Phi. Republican. Episcopalian. Home: 10456 NW 2d St Portland OR 97231-1072

MYERS, DANIEL N., lawyer, association executive; b. Independence, Kans., Sept. 17, 1942; s. James Kenneth and Evalyn Clair Petty (Feather) M.; m. Eileen Carruthers, Dec. 14, 1968; children: Yvette Christine, John Joseph. AA, Coffeyville Coll., 1961; BA, U. Okla., 1963; JD, Georgetown U., 1975. Bar: Va. 1976, U.S. Ct. Customs and Patent Appeals. Asst. to pres. J.V. Hurson Assoc., Inc., Washington, 1968-74; mgr. fed. legis. affairs AICPA, Washington, 1974-77; dir. legis. svcs., assoc. counsel Nat. LP-Gas Assn., Arlington, Va., 1977-79; gen. counsel, v.p. govt. relations Nat. Propane Gas Assn., Arlington, Va., 1979-88; exec. v.p. Nat. Propane Gas Assn., Oak Brook, Ill., 1989—. Contbr. artilces on good samaritan laws and genealogy to various publs. Bd. dirs. Washington Area State Relations Group, 1980-82, mem. energy task force White House Conf. on Small Bus., 1980; chmn. good samaritan coalition Hazardous Materials Adv. Coun., Washington, 1982—; mem. motor carrier adv. com. Fed. Hwy. Adminstrn., Washington, 1982-88. Sgt. U.S. Army, 1964-68. Mem. Am. Soc. Assn. Execs. (legal sect. coun. 1980—), Greater Washington Soc. Assn. Execs., Spl. Indsl. Radio Svc. Assn. (bd. dirs. 1979-88). Avocations: golf, genealogy, racquetball. Office: Nat Propane Gas Assn 1301 W 22d St Oak Brook IL 60521

MYERS, DANIEL WILLIAM, II, lawyer; b. Camden, N.J., Mar. 21, 1931; s. Charles Rudolph II and Myrtle Henrietta (Kress) M.; m. Eileen Ethel Kohn, Nov. 22, 1959; children: Susan Leigh, Meredith Ann Myers Winner, Kathryn Kress. BS in Commerce, U. Va., 1952, LLB, 1957. Bar: Va. 1957, N.J. 1958, U.S. Dist. Ct. N.J. 1958, U.S. Supreme Ct. 1980. Assoc. Lewis & Hutchinson, Camden, 1958-60; ptnr. Myers, Matteo, Rabii, Norcross & Landgraf, predecessors, Camden, 1960—, Cherry Hill, N.J., 1960-89; ptnr. Montgomery, McCracken, Walker & Rhoads, 1989-94, of counsel, 1994—. 1st lt. U.S. Army, 1952-54. Mem. ABA, N.J. Bar Assn., Va. Bar Assn., Camden County Bar Assn., Am. Arbitration Assn., Exch. Club (pres. Cherry Hill chpt. 1969). Republican. Lutheran. Home: 325 Rhoads Ave Haddonfield NJ 08033-1468 Office: Montgomery McCracken Walker 1010 Kings Hwy S Cherry Hill NJ 08034-2501

MYERS, DAVID N., construction executive; b. June 22, 1900; s. Robert H. and Annie May (Gosberg) M.; m. Inez Pink, Mar. 27, 1929; children: Hal, Dieter. MBA, Dyke Coll., 1922, LHD (hon.), 1981; LHD (hon.), Cleve. State U. Pres. Byerlyte Corp., Cleve., 1931-1965; chmn. bd. Consol. Coatings Corp., 1965-89, Hastings Pavement Co., N.Y.C., 1965—. Life trustee Mt. Sinai Hosp., 1946—; pres. emeritus Menorah Home for Aged; pres. Jewish Community Fedn., 1964-1969; mem. internat. adv. council World Jewish Congress, 1966—; chmn. exec. com. Asphalt Inst., 1953-1955; hon. life trustee ARC; chmn. Ohio State Commn. on Aging, 1983-87; founder Hebrew U. in Jerusalem, Albert Einstein Coll. Medicine, N.Y.C. Recipient United Appeal Disting. Svc. award Eleanor Roosevelt Humanities award, Charles Eisenman award of Jewish Community Fedn., Philos. award ARC, Ollie A. Randall award Nat. Coun. on Aging, 1992; mem. Ohio Sr. Hall of Fame, 1985. Mem. ASTM, Mus. of Art (life), Mus. Natural History, Assn. Asphalt Technologists (life), Am. Ordnance Assn. (life), Oakwood Club, Masons (32 degree). Home: 16900 S Park Blvd Cleveland OH 44120-1643 Office: Investment Plz 1801 E 9th St Cleveland OH 44114-3103 *Retirement at 60 or 65 is folly. Older men are blessed with a perception which allows them, through a recollection of decisions in their past years, to judge things well, whether they be in business or in a profession; or in daily life.*

MYERS, DEE DEE (MARGARET JANE MYERS), former press secretary; b. Quonset Pt., R.I., Sept. 1, 1961; d. Stephen G. and Judith Ann (Burleigh) M. BS, Santa Clara U., 1983. Press asst. Mondal for Pres., L.A., 1984; dep. press sec. Mayor Tom Bradley, L.A., 1985-88; Calif. press sec. Dukakis for Pres., L.A., 1988; press sec. Mayor Tom Bradley, L.A., 1989, Feinstein for Gov., L.A. and San Francisco, 1989-90; campaign dir. Jordan for Mayor, San Francisco, 1991; comm. cons. DeeDee Myers Assocs., Valencia, Calif., 1991; press sec. Clinton for Pres., Little Rock, Ark., 1991-92, White House, Washington, 1993-94. Recipient Robert F. Kennedy award Emerson Coll., Boston, 1993. Roman Catholic. Avocations: running, cycling, music, major league baseball. Office: The White House 1600 Pennsylvania Ave NW Washington DC 20500

MYERS, DENYS PETER, JR., architectural historian; b. Boston, Apr. 23, 1916; s. Denys Peter and Ethel May (Johnston) M.; m. Anne Buchonis, Aug. 24, 1940. S.B., Harvard U., 1940; MA: grad. studies, Fogg Art Mus., 1949-50; M.A., Columbia U., 1948. Asst. reference dept. N.Y. Public Library, 1941-42, charge exbhns., 1942-43; instr. Hunter Coll., N.Y.C., 1947; dir. Art Inst., Zanesville, Ohio, 1947-55, Philbrook Art Center, Tulsa, 1955-58, Des Moines Art Center, 1958-59; asst. dir. Balt. Mus. Art, 1959-64; dir. No. Va. Fine Arts Assn., 1964-66; vis. lectr. Johns Hopkins U., 1962-64; historian Nat. Park Service, U.S. Dept. Interior, 1966-68; prin. archtl. historian Historic Am. Bldgs. Survey, Office of Archaeology and Historic Preservation, Washington, 1968-73; pvt. practice cons. archtl. historian Washington, 1973-78; cons. Faulkner, Fryer and Vanderpool (Architects), Washington, 1975-83; archtl. historian Historic Am. Bldgs. Survey, Nat. Park Service, Dept. Interior, Washington, 1978-85; lectr. Smithsonian Instn., 1974-78, 91, Cath. U. Am., 1966-67. Co-author: A Preservation Index for the Federal Hill Historic District, 1973, Nashville, A Short History and Selected Buildings, 1974, Maine Forms of American Architecture, 1976, Alexandria - A Towne in Transition 1800-1900, 1977, Historic America, 1983; author: Maine Catalog: The Historic Architecture of Maine, 1974, American Gas Lighting: A Guide for Historic Preservation, 1978; introduction to Minard Lafever's Beauties of Modern Architecture, (1835), 1968, Introduction to 1876 Mitchell, Vance & Co. catalog reprint; contbr. articles to MacMillan Ency. Arch., 1982, Dictionary of Art, American National Biography and profl. jours. Ordained perpetual deacon Episcopal Ch., 1954. Served with AUS, 1943-46. Mem. Am. Archtl. Found. (mem. adv. com.), Soc. Archtl. Historians (founding mem., dir. 1962-65, pres. Latrobe chpt. 1975-77), Alexandria Assn. (mem. 1968-69), Victorian Soc. in Am. (dir. 1970-72), Alexandria Library Co. (pres. 1982-83), Alexandria Hist. Soc., Steamship Hist. Soc., Preservation Round Table, Soc. for Preservation New Eng. Antiquities, Hist. Alexandria Found. Club: Cosmos (Washington). Home and Office: 201 N Columbus St Alexandria VA 22314-2411

MYERS, DONALD ALLEN, university dean; b. Nebraska City, Nebr., Dec. 17, 1932; s. Merle D. and Ruth Irene (Potter) M.; m. Dixie Lois Ashton, Aug. 10, 1957; 1 son, Eric; m. Lilian Rose Bautista, Apr. 18, 1966; children: Sherri, Johnny, David; m. Alice L. Twining, July 15. 1990; 1 child, Aaron. B.A., Mcpl. U. Omaha, 1956; M.A., U. Chgo., 1957, Ph.D., 1962. Asst. supt. Sch. Dist. Riverview Gardens, Mo., 1962-65; research assoc. NEA, Washington, 1965-66; curriculum and research specialist Inst. for Devel. of Ednl. Activities, Los Angeles, 1966-70; assoc. prof. SUNY, Albany, 1970-73; head dept. curriculum and instrn. Olka. State U. Stillwater, 1973-79; dean Coll. Edn., U. Nebr., Omaha, 1979-85; dean Sch. Edn. Old Dominion U., Norfolk, Va., 1985—. Author: Teacher Power, 1973, Open Education Reexamined, 1973; contbr. articles, chpts. to profl. jours., books. Washington intern in edn. Ford Found., 1965-66. Democrat. Home: 1272 Belvoir Ln Virginia Beach VA 23464-6746 Office: Old Dominion U Coll Edn 5215 Hampton Blvd Norfolk VA 23508-1506

MYERS, DOUGLAS GEORGE, zoological society administrator; b. L.A., Aug. 30, 1949; s. George Walter and Daydeen (Schroeder) M.; m. Barbara Firestone Myers, Nov. 30, 1980; children: Amy, Andrew. BA, Christopher Newport Coll., 1981. Tour and show host Annheuser-Busch (Bird Sanctuary), Van Nuys, Calif., 1970-74; mgr. zool. ops., 1974-75, asst. mgr. ops., 1975-77; mgr. ops., 1977-78; gen. services mgr. Annheuser-Busch (Old Country), Williamsburg, Va., 1978-80, park ops. dir., 1980-81; gen. mgr. wild animal park Zool. Soc. San Diego, 1981-83, dep. dir. ops., 1983-85, exec. dir., 1985—; cons. in field. Bd. dirs. San Diego Conv. and Visitors Bur.; mem. adv. com. of pres.' assn. Am. Mgmt. Assn. Fellow Am. Assn. Zool. Parks and Aquariums (profl.), Internat. Union Dirs. Zool. Gardens; mem. Internat. Assn. Amusement Parks and Attractions, Calif. Assn. Zoos and Aquariums, Mus. Trustee Assn. Lodge: Rotary. Office: San Diego Zoo PO Box 551 San Diego CA 92111

MYERS, DOUGLAS SCOTT, advertising executive; b. Quincy, Ill., Aug. 31, 1954; s. Frank Earl and Joanna Mae (Boss) M.; m. Lisa Marie Hilton,

Oct. 11, 1986; 1 child, Ariel Terisse. BBA, U. Ariz., 1977. Account exec. Film Creations, Ltd., Tucson, 1979-80; exec. v.p. GEO & Assocs. Advt., Tucson, 1980-82; producer, dir. Taylor Advt., Tucson, 1982-85; producer, dir., writer Duval Advt., Tucson, 1985-86; pres. Hilton & Myers Advt., Tucson, 1986—. Bd. dirs. Ariz. Dance Theatre, Tucson, 1984-86. Mem. Tucson Advt. Club (Tucson Topps award), Phoenix Advt. Dirs. (Prisma award 1986). Office: Hilton & Myers Advt 325 W Franklin St Tucson AZ 85701-8265

MYERS, EDWARD WELLINGTON, hospital administrator; b. Washington, May 29, 1953; married. B, Pa. State U., 1975; M, Temple U., 1977. Various positions, 1977-79; asst. adminstr. Meml. Hosp. Sweetwater County, Rock Springs, Wyo., 1979-82, sr. asst. exec. dir., 1983; CEO, v.p. Meml. Hosp. Sys., Houston, 1985-91; CEO Meml. Hosp. SW, Houston, 1991—. Home: 7702 Penrose Pt Dr Houston TX 77095 Office: Meml Hosp SW 7600 Beechnut St Houston TX 77074-4389

MYERS, EDWIN, think-tank executive. Exec. dir. Southwest Regional Lab., L.A. Office: Southwest Regional Lab 4665 Lampson Ave Los Alamitos CA 90720

MYERS, EUGENE NICHOLAS, otolaryngologist, otolaryngology educator; b. Phila., Nov. 27, 1933; s. David and Rosalind (Nichols) M.; m. Barbara Labov, June 10, 1956; children: Marjorie Rose, Jeffrey N. B.S. in Econs., U. Pa., 1954; M.D., Temple U. Sch. Medicine, 1960. Diplomate: Am. Bd. Otolaryngology. Intern Mt. Sinai Hosp., N.Y.C., 1960-61; resident Mass. Eye and Ear Infirmary, Boston, 1963-65; asst. prof. clin. otolaryngology U. Pa., 1968-72; prof. clin. oncology dept. oral pathology U. Pitts. Sch. Dental Medicine, Pitts., 1975-82, prof. dept. diagnostic services, 1982—; prof., chmn. dept. otolaryngology U. Pitts. Sch. Medicine, 1972—; chief dept. otolaryngology U. Pitts. (Pa.) Med. Ctr., 1972-90, 1990—; cons. VA Med. Ctr., Pitts., 1972—, Children's Hosp., Pitts., 1972—. Editor: Cancer of the Head and Neck, 1981, rev. edit., 1989, Tracheotomy, 1985; mem. editl. bd. Laryngoscope, 1973—, Jour. Head and Neck Surgery, 1978-92, AMA Archives of Otolaryngology, 1983-91, Annals of Otology Rhinology and Laryngology, 1984—, Oncology, 1986—, European Archives of Oto-Rhino-Laryngology, 1990—; editor-in-chief Advances in Otolaryngology, Yr. Book Med. Pubs., 1985—; co-editor Butterworth's Intern Med. Revs., Eng., 1981. Mem. adv. bd. Pa. Lion Hearing Research Found., Pitts., 1983—. Served to capt. M.C., U.S. Army, 1965-67. Recipient Cert of Merit Com. Research, Am. Acad. Otolaryngology-Salicylate Otoxicity, 1965; recipient Award of Merit Am. Acad. Otolaryngology-Head and Neck Surgery Inc., 1978, Robert E. Shoemaker Research award Pa. Acad. Ophthalmology and Otolaryngology, 1979. Fellow ACS (bd. govs. 1981-87, adv. coun. 1988-93), Am. Laryngol. Assn. (sec. 1982-88, pres. 1989-90, coun. mem. 1990-93, James Newcomb award 1993), Am. Acad. Otolaryngology (chmn. com. head and neck surgery 1981-83, bd. dirs. 1985-88, 90, pres. 1994-95); mem. Am. Bd. Otolaryngology (dir. 1981—, pres. elect 1994—), Assn. Acad. Depts. Otolaryngology (coun. 1978-80), Nat. Cancer Inst. (chmn. upper aerodigestive tract working group 1986-89), Am. Soc. Head and Neck Surgery (pres. 1988-89), PanAm. Assn. Otorhinolaryngology Head and Neck Surgery (coun. 1991—, pres. 1988-90), Triological Soc. (coun. mem. 1989-92, v.p. ea. sect. 1994-95), Pitts. Athletic Assn. Republican. Jewish. Office: U Pitts Sch Med Eye & Ear Inst Ste 500 200 Lothrop St Pittsburgh PA 15213-2588

MYERS, EVELYN STEPHENSON, editor, writer; b. N.Y.C.; d. William and Gertrude Maud (Pickett) Stephenson; m. Charles Bogart Myers, June 1, 1946 (dec. Nov. 1990); children—Cynthia Myers Marquardt, Meredith Myers Ballard. Student Simmons Coll., 1940-42; B.A., Barnard Coll., 1943-45; MA in Liberal Studies, Georgetown U., 1976; postgrad. New Sch. Soc. Research, 1945-49, George Washington U., 1977-78. Mng. editor Advance, N.Y.C., 1947-50; editor, Pres.'s Water Resources Policy Commn., Washington, 1950-51; editorial cons. Viet Nam Press, Saigon, 1958-60; chief joint info. service Am. Psychiat. Assn., Nat. Assn. Mental Health, Washington, 1961-63; writer, editor NIMH, Bethesda, Md., 1963-65; mng. editor Am. Jour. Psychiatry, Washington, 1965-87; editor, Eco-Facts, Washington, 1987-91; editorial cons. Mem. A. Psychiat. Assn., Washington, 1993—. Author: (with others) Facing Facts: A Handbook for Reporters in Viet Nam, 1959, Health Insurance and Psychiatric Care: Utilization and Cost, 1972, Health Insurance and Psychiatric Care: Update and Appraisal, 1984, Ethics and Policy in Scientific Publication, 1990. NEH Summer Seminar fellow, 1981. Mem. Council Biology Editors (bd. dirs. 1981-84, editorial policy com. 1984-91), Soc. Scholarly Pub. (program com. 1983-84), LWV, Woman's Nat. Dem. Club, Barnard Club (Washington). Unitarian. Home: 15107 Interlachen Dr Apt 512 Silver Spring MD 20906-5630

MYERS, FRANCES, artist; b. Racine, Wis., Apr. 16, 1938; d. Stephen George and Bernadette Marie (Gales) M.; m. Warrington Colescott, Mar. 15, 1971. MFA, U. Wis., 1965. lectr. St. Martin's Sch. Art, London, 1967; disting. prof. printmaking Mills Coll., Oakland, Calif., 1979; vis. lectr. U. Calif., Berkeley, 1982; currently prof. art U. Wis., Madison. One-woman shows include Horwich Gallery, Chgo., 1977, 81, Haslem Gallery, Washington, 1981, 88, Madison Art Center, 1981, Carnegie Inst., Pitts., 1982, Wis. Acad. Arts, 1985, Perimeter Gallery, Chgo., 1986, 88, 91, 93, Natasha Nicholson Works of Art, 1989, Dittmar Gallery, Northwestern U., Evanston, Ill., 1989, Peltz Gallery, Milw., 1990, 91, 94; group shows include U.S. Pavilion, World's Fair, Osaka, Japan, 1970, Biennale of Prints Musée d'Art Moderne, Paris, 1970, Bklyn. Mus. 20th Biennale Exhbns. of Prints, 1976, 23d Biennale, 1982, 14th and 16th Internat. Biennial Graphic Arts, Ljubljana, Yugoslavia, 1981, 85, Am. Biennial Graphic Arts, Cali, Colombia, 1981, Brit. Internat. Print Biennale, Bradford, Eng., 1984, Bklyn. Mus. 25th Print Biennale, 1986, prints displayed in Am. Consulate, Leningrad, USSR, 1987, USIA, Yugoslavia, 1989-90, Pace Gallery, N.Y.C., 1990, Figurative Graphics, Amerikahaus, Cologne, Fed. Rep. Germany, 1991, Portland (Oreg.) Art Mus., 1992, Milw. Mus. Art, 1990, Nat. Mus. Am. Art, Washington, 1991, Duke U. Mus. Art, Durham, N.C., 1993, Internat. Biennial of Prints, Bhopal, India, 1995; represented in permanent collections Met. Mus. of Art, Victoria and Albert Mus., London, Chgo. Art Inst., Library of Congress, Phila. Mus. Art, Mus. Fine Arts, Boston. Nat. Endowment for the Arts fellow, 1974-75, 85-86, H.I. Romnes fellow U. Wis., 1991. Mem. NAD, Am. Print Alliance Nat. Womens Forum, Phila. Print Club. Home: 8788 County Hwy A Hollandale WI 53544

MYERS, FRANK WAYNE, osteopath, educator; b. Sioux Falls, S.D., 1933. BA, U. S.D., 1955; DO, Coll. Osteo. Medicine and Surgery, 1959. Diplomate Am. Osteo. Bd. of Gen. Practice. Intern Brentwood Hosp., Cleve., 1960, mem. active med. staff, 1960-76, pres. gen. med. staff, 1966, chmn. dept. gen. practice, 1971-73, dir. gen. practice residency program, 1971-73; co-founder, ptnr. Nordonia Hills Clinic, 1960-76; mem. courtesy med. staff O'Bleness Hosp., 1976—; prof. family medicine Coll. Osteo. Medicine Ohio U., 1976—, assoc. dean clin. affairs, 1976-77, dean, 1977—; preceptor Nordonia Hills Clinic, 1967-76; intern interns Brentwood Hosp. and Nordonia Hills Clinic, 1967-76; advisor North Summit County Family and Children Svcs., 1967-76. Bd. dirs., 1972-76; trustee Coll. Osteo. Medicine and Surgery, Des Moines, 1972-77, Physician's Peer Rev. Orgn., Cleve., 1972-76. Mem. editl. consulting bd. Osteo. Physician, 1968—; contbr. articles to profl. jours.; host (radio program) Family Health. Trustee Ohio Osteo. Found., 1973—. Fellow Am. Coll. Gen. Practitioners Osteo. Medicine and Surgery (co-recipient Gen. Practitioner of Yr. award Ohio state soc. 1973); mem. Am. Assn. Colls. Osteo. Medicine (past chairperson bd. govs.), Am. Osteo. Assn. (mem. com. colls., mem. editl. consulting bd. jour. 1973—), Cleve. Acad. Osteo. Medicine of Ohio Osteo. Assn. (mem. exec. com. 1965-76, pres. 1967-68, chair various coms.). Home: 43 Strouds Run Rd Athens OH 45701 Office: Ohio U Coll of Osteopathic Medicine 204 Grosvenor Hall Athens OH 45701

MYERS, FRANKLIN, lawyer, oil service company executive; b. Pensacola, Fla., Nov. 2, 1952; s. T.F. Sr. and D. Bernice (Brewer) M.; m. Melinda Munson, Aug. 9, 1974; children: Amanda C., Adam F., Anne Marie M. BS, Miss. State U., 1974; JD, U. Miss., 1977. Bar: Miss. 1977, Tex. 1978. Ptnr. Fulbright and Jaworski, Houston, 1978-88; sr. v.p., gen. counsel Baker Hughes Inc., Houston, 1988-95; sr. v.p., gen. counsel, corp. sec. Cooper Cameron Corp., Houston, 1995—; adj. prof. U. Tex. Sch. Law, 1990—; bd. dirs. Reunion Resources Co., Convest Energy, Houston, Tex. Bus. Law Found. Bd. dirs. U. St. Thomas, Houston. Fellow Houston Bar Found. (bd.

dirs., treas.); mem. ABA (vice chmn. spl. com. internat. energy law sect. natural resources, energy and environ. law), Tex. Bar Assn., Miss. Bar Assn., Houston Bar Assn. Baptist. Office: Cooper Cameron Corp 515 Post Oak Blvd Ste 1200 Houston TX 77027

MYERS, FREDERICK M., metal products executive; b. 1922; married. Grad., Williams Coll., 1943; LLB, Harvard U., 1948. Assoc. Cravath, Swaine & Moore, N.Y.C., 1948-50, Cain, Hibbard, Myers & Cook, 1951-80; with Lukens, Inc., 1957—, chmn., 1988, vice-chmn., 1988—, also bd. dirs. Office: Lukens Inc 50 S 1st Ave Coatesville PA 19320-5407

MYERS, GEORGE CARLETON, sociology and demographics educator; b. Bklyn., Apr. 8, 1931; s. Francis Murdock and Ruth Emily (Hassinger) M.; m. Pauline Dorothy Kraebel, Apr. 24, 1954; children: George C., Marie E., Peter D., Kathleen A. BA, Yale U., 1953; postgrad., dipl., U. Stockholm, 1956; MA, U. Wash., Seattle, 1960; PhD, U. Wash., 1963. Instr. U. Wash., 1957-59, UCLA, 1960-62; asst. prof. Cornell U., Ithaca, N.Y., 1962-66; assoc. prof. Cornell U., 1966-68; sr. scientist WHO, Geneva, Switzerland, 1968-70; prof. sociology Duke U., Durham, N.C., 1968—; dir. Ctr. for Demographic Studies, 1972—; mem. Nat. Com. on Vital and Health Stats., Washington, 1985-88; mem. com. on aging Nat. Acad. Sci., Washington, 1982-85; mem. Census Adv. Com., 1977-83, WHO Program on Aging, 1988—, NIH Nat. Adv. Com. on Aging, 1991-95; vis. lectr. UN China Nat. Demographic Tng. Ctr., Beijing, 1991; advisor ECE Population Act. Unit, 1992—; vis. prof. U. Geneva Med. Sch., China Nat. 1994, Flinders U. Med. Sch., 1994. Editor: Jour. of Gerontology, 1986-89; contbr. articles to profl. jours. With U.S. Army, 1953-55. NIH grantee, 1969—; sr. vis. fellow Australian Nat. U., 1984; vis. scholar Can. Soc. Human Coun., 1982; sr. internat. fellow Fogarty Ctr., NIH, London, 1978-79. Fellow Gerontol. Soc. Am.; mem. Population Assn. Am. (bd. dirs. 1977-79), So. Demographic Assn. (pres. 1974-76), Triangle Area Population Soc. (pres. 1988-89), Duke Faculty Club (pres. 1972-74). Avocations: sailing, skiing, golf. Home: 12 Scott Pl Durham NC 27705-5719 Office: Duke U Ctr for Demographic Studies 2117 Campus Dr Box 90408 Durham NC 27708-0408

MYERS, GERALD E., humanities educator; b. Central City, Nebr., June 19, 1923; s. Harold W. and Mary (Ferguson) M.; m. Martha Coleman, Aug. 7, 1948; 1 son, Curt. B.A., Haverford Coll., 1947; M.A., Brown U., 1949, Ph.D., 1954. Instr. Smith Coll., 1950-52; asst. prof. Williams Coll., 1952-61; assoc. prof. Kenyon Coll., 1961-65; prof. C.W. Post Coll., L.I. U., 1965-67, Queens Coll. and Grad. Center, City U. N.Y., 1967—; also dep. exec. officer Ph.D. program Queens Coll. and Grad. Center, City U. N.Y. (Grad. Center); dir. intro. philosophy into N.Y.C. High Schs. project.; dir. humanities-and-dance projects Am. Dance Festival, Durham, N.C., 1979; project dir. African-Am. Perspectives in Am. Moslem Dance, Am. Dance Festival/NEH. Author: Self, Religion and Metaphysics, 1961, Self: An Introduction to Philosophical Psychology, 1969, The Spirit of American Philosophy, 1970, William James: His Life and Thoughts, 1986; editor: The Aesthetic and Cultural Signigicance of Modern Dance, 1984, The Black Tradition in American Modern Dance, 1988, African American Genius in Modern Dance, 1992; co-editor: Emotion Philos. Studies, 1983, Echoes from the Holocaust, 1988; contbr. articles to profl. jours. NEH fellow, 1981-82. Mem. Am. Philos. Assn. (past sec.-treas. Western div.), Metaphys. Soc. Am., Soc. Phenomenology and Existential Philosophy, Phi Beta Kapa. Home: 36 Gardner Ave New London CT 06320-4313 Office: 33 W 42nd St New York NY 10036

MYERS, HAROLD MATHEWS, academic administrator; b. Doylestown, Pa., Apr. 13, 1915; s. Carl and Alice W. Myers; m. Margaret F. Smith, July 19, 1944 (dec. Sept. 1963); children: Donald Smith, Dean Chappell, Deborah Kay; m. L. Marjorie Bellau, Nov. 28, 1914. BS in Commerce, Drexel Inst Tech., 1938, DSc in Commerce (hon.), 1983; postgrad., Temple U., 1940-41, U. Omaha, summer 1957. Instr. coop. edn., dir. grad. placement Drexel U. Phila., 1938-46, asst. dean men, dir. student bldgs., adj. instr. labor econs., 1946-52, dean of men, 1952-55, treas., 1955-57, v.p., treas., 1957-80, sr. v.p., 1980-82, sr. v.p. emeritus, 1982-87, interim pres., 1987-88, pres. emeritus, 1988—, life trustee, 1986—; regional dir. Frist Pa. Banking and Trust Co., 1959-76; dir. Sadtler Rsch. Labs., Inc., 1963-69, Almo Indsl. Elecs., Inc., 1966-68; dir., treas. Uni-Coll Corp., 1974-81; dir. dirs. Beulah Cemetary Assn., asst. treas., 1984-89, treas., 1989-90, v.p. and treas., 1990—; bd. dirs., mem. exec. com. Univ. City Sci. Ctr., 1974-90, dir. emeritus, 1991—, chmn. fin. com., 1976-88, vice chmn., 1988-90. Contbr. articles to profl. jours. Bd. dirs. Internat. House of Phila. Inc., 1954-81, exec. com., 1972-81; active Phila. council Boy Scouts Am., 1953—, hon. chmn., 1985—, pres., 1982, 83; mem. citizens fire prevention com. Phila. Fire Dept., 1970-86; bd. dirs. United Fund Greater Phila., 1983-87, Luth. Ch. of Am. Common Investing Fund, 1976-82, Nat. Conf. of Christians and Jews, Inc., Phila. and S. Jersey region NCCJ, 1959-65; dir. Phila. Coun. of Chs., 1954-60; bd. dirs., pres. Ea. Assn. Coll. and Univ. Bus. Officers, 1967-68; pres. Nat. Assn. Coll and Univ. Bus. Officers, 1971-72; treas. Lambda Chi Alpha Found., 1970-84, dir. emeritus, 1984—; pres. Broadmoor Pines Home Owners Assn., 1993-94. Served to comdr. USNR, ret. Recipient Silver Beaver award Boy Scouts Am., 1963, Mary M. Hart award Phila. coun. Boy Scouts Am., 1986, Drexel Alumni Varsity Club award, 1966, Drexel U. Evening Coll. Alumni Assn. award, 1973, Drexel U. Anthony J. Drexel Paul award, 1988, Dept. of Army Cert. of Appreciation for Patriotic Civilian Svc., 1979, Disting. Bus. Officer award Nat. Assn. Coll. and Bus. Officers, 1989, Disting. Svc. in Trusteeship award Assn. Governing Bd. Univs. and Colls., 1989; named Educator of Yr., Phila. coun. Boy Scouts Am., 1989; named to Legion of Honor, Chapel of Four Chaplins; Drexel U. student dormitory named Myers Hall in his honor, 1984; 1 of 100 alumni honored Centennial of Drexel U., 1992. Mem. AARP, Am. Legion, Mil. Order World Wars (perpetual, comdr. Phila. chpt. 1958-59), Ret. Officers Assn. (life), Swedish Colonial Soc. Phila. (sec. 1968), Welsh Soc. Phila. (life), Internat. Frat. Lambda Chi Alpha (pres. 1966-70), Vet. Corps 1st Regiment Infantry, N.G.P. (hon.), Penn Club, Union League Phila. (pres. 1980-81), Sarasota Yacht Club, Masons, Rotary (Paul Harris fellow), Gulf Coast Corvair Club.

MYERS, HARRY J., JR., publisher; b. Denver, Aug. 7, 1931; s. Harry J. and Edith M. (Reed) M.; m. Mary Kay Racine, June 21, 1958; children: Harry J., Hans R. (dec.), Peter C. BA, Colo. U., 1957; postgrad., U. Mo., 1959-60. Advt. dir. Guarantee Mut. Life Ins. Co., Omaha, 1960-61; promotion mgr. Successful Farming mag., Des Moines, 1962-65; promotion dir. Better Homes and Gardens mag., 1965-67, sales mgr. for Mich. and Ohio, Detroit and package goods mgr. N.Y.C., 1967-70; pub. Meredith Pub. Services, Des Moines, 1970-76, Apt. Life, Des Moines, 1976-80, Met. Home, Des Moines, 1980-82, Geo mag., N.Y.C., 1982-83; sr. v.p., group pub. Archtl. Digest, Bon Appetit and Home mags., Knapp Communcations, N.Y.C., 1983-86; sr. v.p., pub. Sci. Am. Mag., N.Y.C., 1986-87, pres., 1987-90; v.p. sales and mktg. The N.Y. Times Co. Mags. Group, N.Y.C., 1990; group v.p., pub. dir. Cowles mag., Harrisburg, Pa., 1990-95; sr. v.p. Cowles mag., Lakewood, Colo., 1995—. Served with USMC, 1953-56. Mem. Kappa Tau Alpha, Phi Gamma Delta. Home: 46 W Ranch Trl Morrison CO 80465-9504 Office: Cowles Mag Ste 300 12265 W Bayand Lakewood CO 80228

MYERS, HERMAN E., JR., life insurance company executive; b. Omaha, Feb. 3, 1926; s. Herman E. Myers.; m. Betty Hopkins, July 27, 1946; children—Sandra Lynn, Cynthia Lee Myers Larson. B.S., Creighton U., 1950. Claim analyst Mut. of Omaha, 1950-51; exec. v.p. Union Casualty Co., Omaha, 1951-61; chmn. Continental Gen. Ins. Co., Omaha, 1961—, also dir.; dir. Cornhusker Motor Club, Continental Print and Photo Co., Firstier Bank-Omaha; mem. exec. coun. Boy Scouts Am. Served to 2d lt. USAF, 1944-46. Mem. Health Ins. Assn. Am., Omaha Businessmans Assn., Am. Council Life Ins., Ins. Fedn. Nebr. Republican. Lutheran. Club: Happy Hollow (Omaha); mem. Omaha Concord Club (hon. life), Jesters Club, Green Fez Club. Lodges: Shriners, Masons. Office: Cont Gen Ins Co 8901 Indian Hills Dr Omaha NE 68114-4071

MYERS, HOWARD MILTON, pharmacologist, educator; b. Bklyn., Dec. 12, 1923; s. Charles and Rose (Nassberg) M.; m. Louise Perry, Mar. 14, 1972; children by previous marriage: Clifford Raymond, Nancy Rose, Stephen Andrew. D.D.S., Western Res. U., 1949; Ph.D., U. Rochester, 1958; M.A. (hon.), U. Pa., 1974; M.A., San Francisco State U., 1964. Prof. oral biology U. Calif., San Francisco, 1965-71; prof. biochemistry U. Pacific Sch. Dentistry, San Francisco, 1971-74; dir. Center for Oral Health

Research, U. Pa., Phila., 1974-78; prof. pharmacology Sch. of Dental Medicine, 1974-86; dir. research/tchr. tng. grant U. Calif., San Francisco, 1965-71; prof. emeritus pharmacology U. Pa.; adj. prof. pharmacology U. Calif.-San Francisco Sch. Medicine, Calif. Coll. Podiatric Medicine; adj. prof. oral biology U. Calif.-San Francisco Sch. Dentistry, 1987-95; pharmacology cons. Nat. Bd. Podiatric Examiners, 1992-95; reviewer U.S.-Israel Binat. Sci. Found., 1982-95. Contbr. articles to profl. jours.; editor: Monographs in Oral Science, 1972-95. Served with U.S. Army, 1942-45. NIH fellow Karolinska Inst., Stockholm, 1964-65; Fogarty Sr. Internat. Research fellow U. Geneva, 1980-81. Mem. AAAS (chmn. sect. dentistry 1974), Am. Assn. Dental Research (pres. 1973-75), Council Biology Editors, Am. Chem. Soc. Home and Office: 3649 Market St Apt 601 San Francisco CA 94131 *Intellectual maturity is the realization that there is more misinformation in the world than there is information.*

MYERS, IONA RAYMER, real estate and property manager; b. Guymon, Okla., Sept. 18, 1931; m. Harold Rudolph Myers, Mar. 28, 1953; children: Richard Galen, Sandra Dawn, Paula Colleen. BS magna cum laude, So. Nazarene U., 1952; MEd, U. Okla., 1959; postgrad., McNeese State U., 1970. Tchr. home econs. Can. County Pub. Schs., Mustang, Okla., 1952-53; tchr. elem. Oklahoma City Pub. Schs., 1955-61, Transylvania County Pub. Schs., Brevard, N.C., 1961-67; elem. tchr., student tchr. supr. Allen Parish Pub. Schs., Oakdale, La., 1967-71; tchr. elem. and jr. high history Lafourche Parish Pub. Schs., Raceland and Lockport, La., 1974-76; tchr. elem. sci. Jefferson Parish Pub. Schs., Metairie, 1976-80; treas. Harold R. Myers Engring. (divsn. Harold R. Myers, Inc.), Metairie, 1993—; mgr. Harion Properties, L.L.C., Metairie, 1980-94, DeRidder Tracts and Comml. Property, Metairie, 1968-94; vol. founding bd. dirs. Jefferson Performing Arts Soc., Metairie, 1977-83; vol. founding mem. community adv. coun. East Jefferson Gen. Hosp., Metairie, 1980-87. Vol. scout leader S.E. La. Girl Scouts U.S. coun., Metairie, 1977-89, fund raising com., 1992-93; vol. tchr. music Harold Keller Elem. Sch., Metairie, 1981-83; life mem. Rep. Nat. Com., Washington, 1980-91, mem. fin. com., 1988; jubilee chmn., fundraiser Jefferson Performing Arts Soc., Metairie, 1987; candidate La. Ho. of Reps. Dist. 88, Baton Rouge, 1991; com. YWCA New Orleans Role Model Luncheon, 1994-95; financier BFW USA Found., 1990-95. New Orleans Mus. of Art fellow, 1984—, So. Nazarene U. fellow, 1985-94; recipient Rice in the Ear award S.E. La. Girl Scouts U.S., 1982, Grand Lady/Great Gentleman award Ladies Aux. East Jefferson Gen. Hosp., 1987, Commendation award Jefferson Performing Arts Soc., 1988, Women as Winners award YWCA New Orleans, 1993. Mem. AAUW (pres. 1988-90, vol. coord. Metairie chpt. 1990-91, del. 4 nat. and 4 regional convs. 1984-94, corr. sec. La. chpt. 1989-91, scholar and grantee 1989, Magnolia editor 1991—, chair nominating com. 1992-93, grant honoree La. 1994), Jefferson Hist. Soc. (life), La. Landmarks Soc. (life), Nat. Assn. Parliamentarians, La. Bus. and Profl. Women (auditor, legis. chmn. 1990-91, rec. sec. 1991-92, membership v.p. 1992-93, pres. Jefferson Parish chpt. 1980-82, 1st v.p. 1993-94, pres.-elect 1994-95, pres. 95—, program v.p. 1993-94, Vision editor 1993—, Jefferson Parish Voice editor 1993—, Outstanding Dist. Dir. award 1985, Nike award 1991, Highest Mem. honor 1992-93, Best Membership Recruiter 1993-94), Metairie Woman's Club (corr. sec. 1994—); New Orleans Mus. Art (fellow 1984-94). Methodist. Avocations: plate collector, gardening, lobbyist. Home: 4701 Chastant St Metairie LA 70006-2059

MYERS, IRA LEE, physician; b. Monrovia, Ala., Feb. 9, 1924; s. Ira W. and Azelea Juanita (Cobbs) M.; m. Dorothy Will Foust, Sept. 4, 1943; children: Martha Crystal, Ira Grady, Stephen Allen, Joanna Lynn. B.S., Howard Coll., Birmingham, Ala., 1945; M.D., U. Ala., 1949; postgrad., Harvard U. Sch. Public Health, 1953. Diplomate: Am. Bd. Preventive Medicine. Commd. officer USPHS, 1949-55; intern USPHS Marine Hosp., Seattle, 1949-50; epidemic intelligence officer Charleston, W.Va., 1950-52, Erie County Health Dept., Buffalo, 1952, Center Communicable Disease, Atlanta, 1952-55; resigned, 1955; adminstrv. health officer Ala. Dept. Health, Montgomery, 1955-63; state health officer Ala. Dept. Health, 1963-86; sec. Ala. Bd. Med. Examiners, 1962-73; chmn. Ala. Bd. Registration Sanitarians, 1964-81, Ala. Air Pollution Control Commn., 1969-82; v.p. Ala. Pollution Control Fin. Authority, 1971-81; assoc. clin. prof. preventive medicine and pub. health U. Ala. Med. Sch.; mem. Ala. vol. med. adv. com. SSS, 1968-86. Pres. Ala. div. Am. Cancer Soc., 1991-93; chmn. bd. dirs. Dalraida Health Ctr., 1992—. Recipient Ala. Sr. Citizens Hall of Fame Golden Eagle award, 1986, St. George medal Nat. Divisional award Am. Cancer Soc., 1989, 1st Ann. Vol. award Montgomery Bapt. Assn., 1993. Mem. AMA, Med. Assn. Ala. (William Henry Saunders award 1968, 1st annual Ira L. Myers Service award, 1986), Montgomery County Med. Soc., Ala. Pub. Health Assn. (D.G. Gill award 1967, established Ira L. Myers Scholarship Endowment), Am. Assn. Pub. Health Physicians, Assn. State and Territorial Health Officers (Arthur N. McCormick award 1976), Ala. Hosp. Assn. (hon.), State. Ala. Nat. Acad. Honor. Democrat. Baptist. Lodge: Montgomery Kiwanis. Initiated state narcotic control program, 1967, state hosp. service for indigent, 1958. Home and Office: 925 Green Forest Dr Montgomery AL 36109-1515

MYERS, IRA THOMAS, physicist; b. Iona, S.D., June 10, 1925; s. Coy Thomas and Elizabeth Ann (Dooley) M.; m. Betty Harrod LaFaver, June 18, 1947; children: Nancy, Sandra, Robert, Alyssa, David, James, Richard, Christopher. BS, Wash. State U., 1948, MS, 1952, PhD, 1958. Cert. health physicist. Chief engr. Radio Sta. KWSC, Pullman, Wash., 1948-49; physicist GE, Richland, Wash., 1949-62, NASA, Cleve., 1962-95; ret., 1995. Author: (with others) Radiation Dosimetry, 1965. Mem. AIAA. Avocations: church work, genealogy. Home: 24931 Westwood Rd Westlake OH 44145

MYERS, JACK EDGAR, biologist, educator; b. Boyds Mills, Pa., July 10, 1913; s. Garry Cleveland and Caroline (Clark) M.; m. Evelyn DeTurck, June 19, 1937; children: Shirley Ann, Jacqueline, Linda Caroline, Kathleen. BS, Juniata Coll., 1934, DSc. 1966; MS, Mont. State Coll., 1935; PhD, U. Minn., 1939. NRC fellow Smithsonian Instn., Washington, 1940-41; asst. prof. zoology U. Tex., 1941-45, assoc. prof., 1945-48, prof., 1948—; prof. botany, 1955—, prof. emeritus, 1980—. Author: (with F.A. Matsen and N.H. Hackerman) Premedical Physical Chemistry, 1947; sci. editor Highlights for Children, 1960—; contbg. author: Algal Culture: from Laboratory to Pilot Plant, 1953, proc. of the World Symposium on Applied Solar Energy, 1956; contbr. articles to profl. jours. Guggenheim fellow, 1959. Mem. Soc. Gen. Physiologists, Am. Soc. Plant Physiologists, Phycol. Soc., AAAS, Nat. Acad. Sci., Tex. Acad. Sci., Am. Soc. Photobiology (pres. 1975), Sigma Xi.

MYERS, JAMES DAVID, municipal government official; b. Salt Lake City, Sept. 16, 1931; m. James William and Pauline (Winsor) M.; m. Carmen Kay Forsland, Mar. 28, 1979 (div.); stepchildren: James Christopher, Jesse Robin; m. Cleo Ester Evitt, Sept. 20, 1986; stepchild: Jennifer Michelle. Student, U. Calif., Berkeley, 1965; BSBA, Calif. State U., Chico, 1968; MPA, Golden Gate U., 1979. Mgr. Unishops, Inc. (Monte Mart), Del Rey Oaks, Calif., 1968-69; acct.-adminstrv. asst. City of Pacific Grove, 1969-79; gen. mgr. Monterey Regional Waste Mgmt. Dist., Marina, Calif., 1979—; dir., sec. Monterey Fed. Credit Union, 1979-91, vice chmn., 1986-87, chmn. supervisory com., 1976-87. Mem. Monterey County Integrated Waste Mgmt. Task Force, Salinas, Calif., 1979—, chmn. tech. com.; dir. Ecology Action of Monterey Peninsula, 1979-82, Milne Home, Residential Treatment Facility for Boys, Carmel Valley, Calif., 1985-87. Staff sgt. USAFR, 1966-72. Mem. Nat. Solid Wast Mgmt. Assn., Calif. Resource Recovery Assn., Solid Waste Assn. N.Am. (dir. No. Calif. chpt. 1988—, internat. landfill gas steering com. 1984-91, internat. conf. 1989, chapt. pres. 1992-93, legis. task force), Calif. Integrated Waste Mgmt. Bd. (local govt. adv. com. 1992—), Commonwealth Club (San Francisco), Mariners' Meml. Club (San Francisco). Democrat. Avocations: bicycling, tennis, record collecting, numismatics. Office: Monterey Regional Waste PO Box 609 Marina CA 93933-0609

MYERS, JAMES NELSON, librarian; b. Buffalo, Aug. 24, 1941; s. James N. and Frances M. (Lennon) M.; m. Victoria A. Montavon; children: James N., Molly P. Houghton, Elizabeth I. Makela. B.A., Canisius Coll., 1963; M.S., U. Ill., 1968; JD, Temple U., 1993. Tchr. Latin Lancaster Central Sch. Dist., N.Y., 1963-65; acquisitions-circulation librarian Canisius Coll., Buffalo, 1965-66; acquisitions librarian Oakland U., Rochester, Minn., 1968-70; assoc. dir. libraries Eastern Wash. State Coll., Cheney, 1970-74; asst. dir. libraries U. Ariz., Tucson, 1974-79; assoc. dir. libraries Stanford U., Calif., 1979-85; libr. Temple U., Phila., 1985—. Co-editor: Disasters: Prevention &

Coping, 1981; bd. of rev. Temple U. Press, 1987-89. Bd. dirs. Friends Free Libr. Phila., 1986-88; mem. libr. com. Balch inst., 1993—, Gov.'s Adv. Coun. on Libr., 1989-93; trustee Balch Inst., 1994—. Mem. ALA, Assn. Coll. and Rsch. Librs., Pa. Libr. Assn. Office: Temple U Librs 13th & Berks St (017-00) Philadelphia PA 19122

MYERS, JEROME KEELEY, sociology educator; b. Lancaster, Pa., Oct. 6, 1921; s. Keeley and Nelie E. (Negley) M.; m. Betsy V. Nolan, June 17, 1944; children—Joseph N., Keeley J., Susan L. B.A., Franklin and Marshall Coll., 1942; M.A., Yale, 1947, Ph.D., 1950. Faculty Yale, 1949—, prof. sociology, 1961-91; prof. emeritus Yale U., 1992—; Cons. Conn. Dept. Health, 1958-59, USPHS, 1960—. Author: (with B.H. Roberts) Family and Class Dynamics in Mental Illness, 1959, (with Lee L. Bean) A Decade Later: A Follow-Up of Social Class and Mental Illness, 1968, (with others) Patient Care Evaluation in Mental Health Programs, 1974, (with M.M. Weissman and C. Ross) Community Surveys of Psychiatric Disorders, 1986. Served with USAAF, 1942-46. Mem. Am., Eastern sociol. assns., AAUP, Phi Beta Kappa. Home: 10 Westerly Rd North Haven CT 06473-4357 Office: Yale U Dept Sociology New Haven CT 06520

MYERS, JERRY K., medal products executive; b. 1940. BS in Real Estate, Mich. State U.; MBA, Northwestern U. With Am. Hosp. Supply, 1970-86, exec. v.p., chief adminstrv. and fin. officer; with TRW Corp., 1986-90; exec. v.p., gen. mgr. automotive sector TRW Corp., Cleve.; pres., CEO Steelcase, Grand Rapids, Mich., 1990—. Office: Steelcase 901 44th St SE Grand Rapids MI 49508-7575

MYERS, JESSE JEROME, lawyer, construction company executive; b. Anthony, Kans., Sept. 30, 1940; s. Claud Lewis and Lucille S. (Robertson) M.; m. Claire H. Conni, Nov., 1966; children: Timothy Todd, Jessica Joy. B.S., McPherson Coll., 1963; J.D., Washburn U., 1970. Bar: Kans. 1970, U.S. Dist. Ct. Kans. 1970. Law clk. U.S. Dist. Ct. Judge Frank Theis, Wichita, KS, 1970-72; individual practice law Wichita, KS, 1972-74; lawyer Cessna Aircraft Co., Wichita, KS, 1974-75; v.p., dir., gen. counsel Martin K. Eby Constrn. Co., Wichita, Kans., 1975-95; pvt. practice Wichita, 1995—. Served with USN, 1963-67. Mem. Am. Bar Assn., Kans. Bar Assn.

MYERS, JIM, church administrator. Chmn. of the bd. Division for Congregational Ministries of the Evangelical Lutheran Church in America, Chicago, Ill. Office: Evang Luthern Ch in Am 8765 Higgins Rd Chicago IL 60631

MYERS, JOHN HERMAN, investment management executive; b. Queens, N.Y., July 2, 1945; s. John Howard and Edna May (Strodthoff) M.; m. JoAnn Barbara Eikamp, Sept. 29, 1973; children: Jennifer Ann, David John, Christina Marie, Kimberly Grace. BS in Math., Wagner Coll., 1967. With GE, 1970—; fin. program trainee GE Internat. GE, N.Y.C. and Frankfurt, Fed. Republic Germany, 1970-74; fin. mgr. Compagnia Generale di Elettricita GE, Milan, 1974-77; fin. mgr. GE, Fairfield, Conn., 1977-81, dep. treas., 1981-84; group fin. mgr. GE, N.Y.C., 1984-86; exec. v.p. GE Investments GE, Stamford, Conn., 1986—; bd. dirs. Butler Capital Corp., N.Y.C., Doubletree Hotel Corp., Phoenix Grimes Aerospace Co., Columbus Hispaland S.A., Madrid, Spain. Bd. trustees Wagner Coll., 1993—. Lt. (j.g.) USN, 1967-70, Vietnam. Mem. Aspetuck Valley Country Club. Republican. Lutheran. Avocations: tennis, basketball, golf.

MYERS, JOHN HOLT, lawyer; b. Washington, Feb. 28, 1923; s. Paul Forrest and Mae Clare (Holt) M.; m. Eleanor Brown, Dec. 18, 1948; children: John Holt Jr., Julie, Lynn, Pamela. AB, Princeton U., 1943; JD, U. Mich., 1949; LLM, Georgetown U., 1955. Bar: U.S. Dist. Ct. D.C. 1950, U.S. Dist. Ct. Md. 1952, Md. 1954, U.S. Claims Ct. 1957, U.S. Tax Ct. 1958, U.S. Supreme Ct. 1960, U.S. Ct. Appeals 1984. Ptnr. Williams, Myers and Quiggle, Washington, 1949-88, Ross, Marsh, Foster, Myers & Quiggle, Washington, 1988—; adj. prof. George Washington U., 1974-80, Law Ctr. U. Miami (Fla.), 1976-80. Author: (with others) Guide to the Administration of Charitable Remainder Trusts, 1978; contbr. over 75 articles to jours. and seminars. Lt. USN, 1943-46. Recipient Disting. Svc. to Higher Edn. award Am. Coll. Pub. Rels. Assn., 1970. Mem. ABA (chair subcom.), Md. Bar Assn., D.C. Bar Assn., Nat. Assn. Coll. & Univ.Attys. (Disting. Svc. award 1988), Cosmos Club, Chevy Chase Club. Democrat. Lutheran. Home: 102 E Melrose St Bethesda MD 20815-3304 Office: Ross Marsh Foster Myers & Quiggle 888 16th St NW Ste 400 Washington DC 20006-4137

MYERS, JOHN JOSEPH, bishop; b. Ottawa, Ill., July 26, 1941; s. M.W. and Margaret Louise (Donahue) M. BA maxima cum laude, Loras Coll., 1963; Licentiate in Sacred Theology, Gregorian U., Rome, 1967; Doctor of Canon Law, Cath. U. Am., 1977; DD (hon.), Apostolic See, Vatican City, 1987. Ordained priest Roman Cath. Ch., 1966, bishop, 1987. Asst. pastor Holy Family Parish, Peoria, Ill., 1967-70; asst. dept. internat. affairs U.S. Cath. Conf., Washington, 1970-71; asst. pastor St. Matthew Parish, Champaign, Ill., 1971-74; vice chancellor Cath. Diocese Peoria, 1977-78, vocation dir., 1977-87, chancellor, 1978-87, vicar gen., 1982-90, co-adjutor bishop, 1987-90; bishop of Peoria, 1990—; bd. govs. Canon Law Soc. Am., Washington, 1985-87; bd. dirs. Pope John XXIII Ctr. for Med.-Moral Rsch. and Edn., Boston; mem. sem. com. Mt. St. Mary's Sem., Md., 1989—. Author: (commentary) Book V of the Code of Canon Law, 1983; contbr. numerous articles to religious pubs. Mem. Canon Law Soc. Am., Nat. Conf. Cath. Bishops. Roman Catholic. Office: Cath Diocese Peoria PO Box 1406 607 NE Madison Ave Peoria IL 61603-3832

MYERS, JOHN LYTLE, historian; b. Findlay, Ohio, June 13, 1929; s. Robert James and Doris Lucille (Lytle) M.; m. Ardene Harriet Muller, June 30, 1957; children: John Lytle II, Jennifer Lucile Myers Hathaway, Jeffrey Lawrence. BS in Edn., Bowling Green U., 1951; MA, U. Mich., 1954, PhD, 1961. Asst. to assoc. prof. Southeast Mo. State Coll., Cape Girardeau, 1957-64; assoc. prof., prof. SUNY, Plattsburgh, 1964—; chmn. faculty senate SUNY, Plattsburgh, 1968-70, 77, 86-88, dean social scis., 1970, acting asst. to pres., 1972. Pres. Clinton-Essex-Franklin Libr. System, Plattsburgh, 1981-84, bd. dirs., 1977-94; bd. dirs. Clinton County Hist. Assn., 1986—, pres., 1988-89; session Presbyn. Ch., Plattsburgh, 1966-69, 82-85, 87-89, 91-95, clk., 1983-85, 92-95. With U.S. Army, 1951-53. Rackham fellow U. Mich., 1956; SUNY fellow, 1965, 67; Penrose fellow Am. Philos. Soc., 1979. Mem. Orgn. Am. Historians, United Univ. Profls. (local pres. 1970), AAUP (local pres. 1963), Soc. Historians of Early Am. Reps. Home: 17 Newell Ave Plattsburgh NY 12901-9752 Office: SUNY Dept History Plattsburgh NY 12901

MYERS, JOHN THOMAS, congressman; b. Covington, Ind., Feb. 8, 1927; m. Carol Carruthers; children: Carol Ann, Lori Jan. B.S., Ind. State U., 1951. Cashier, trust officer Fountain Trust Co.; owner, operator farm; mem. 90th-104th Congresses from 7th Dist. Ind., 1967—; chmn. subcom. on energy & water, appropriations com. Served with AUS, World War II, ETO. Mem. Am. Legion, VFW, Wabash Valley Assn., Res. Officers Assn., U. of C., Sigma Pi. Republican. Episcopalian. Clubs: Mason, Elk, Lion. Office: US-Ho of Reps 2372 Rayburn Washington DC 20515

MYERS, JOHN WESCOTT, aviation executive; b. L.A., June 13, 1911; s. Louis Wescott and Blanche (Brown) M.; m. Lucia Raymond, Mar. 21, 1941; children: Louis W., Lucia E. A.B., Stanford U., 1933; J.D., Harvard U., 1936. Bar: Calif. 1936. Ptnr. law firm O'Melveny & Myers, L.A., 1936-42; from test pilot to sr. v.p., dir. Northrop Corp., 1942-54, 1974-79; chmn. bd. Pacific Airmotive Corp., 1954-79, Airflite, Long Beach, Calif., 1970-89, Flying M Assocs., Long Beach, 1989—; owner Flying M Ranches, Merced, Calif., 1959—. Mem. Calif. Bar Assn., Los Angeles Bar Assn., Soc. Exptl. Test Pilots, Inst. Aerospace Scis. Republican. Clubs: Bohemian, California, Los Angeles Country, Los Angeles Yacht, Sunset, Aviation Country, Conquistadores del Cielo. Home: 718 N Rodeo Dr Beverly Hills CA 90210-3210 Office: 3200 Airflite Way Long Beach CA 90807-5312

MYERS, JOYCE ANNE, fast food chain company executive; b. Aberdeen, Md., Nov. 29, 1948; d. James Day and Helen (Spurling) Bohlken; m. Everett Michael Myers, June 4, 1978. MSW, Va. Commonwealth U., 1975; MBA in Mktg. and Fin., Barry U., 1981. Regional dir., media spokesman Va. Juvenile Justice System, Norfolk, 1973-78; chmn. social work dept. Chris-

topher Newport Campus Coll. William and Mary, Williamsburg, Va., 1978-80; asst. dir. pub. and consumer rels. Miami (Fla.) Herald, 1980-85; mgr. pub. and consumer rels. Burger King Corp., Miami, 1985-87, dir. pub. and consumer rels., 1987-89, v.p. external affairs, 1989-90, sr. v.p. external affairs, 1990—; bd. dirs. Burger King Acad., Miami, 1989-91. Com. mem. United Way, Miami, 1983-85; mem. bd. of 100 Fla. Internat. U., Miami, 1991; bd. dirs. Dade Pub. Edn. Fund, Miami, 1990-91. Recipient commr.'s bus. recognition award Fla. Dept. Edn., 1991, award for social responsibility Women Execs. in Pub. Rels., 1991, Bellringer award Community Rels. Report, 1991, commendation Nat. Sch. Pub. Rels. Assn., 1991. Episcopalian. Avocations: collecting miniatures, dolls and antiques. Office: Burger King Corp 4-South 8700 W Flagler St Miami FL 33174-2428

MYERS, KENNETH ELLIS, hospital administrator; b. Battle Creek, Mich., Jan. 1, 1932; s. Orlow J. and Kathryn (Brown) M.; m. Nancy Lee Lindgren, June 9, 1956; children—Cynthia Lynn, Anne Lisa, Thomas Scot, Susan Elaine. BBA, U. Mich., 1956, MBA, 1957. Research analyst Bur. Bus. Research, U. Mich., 1956-57; in financial mgmt. Burroughs Corp., Detroit, 1957-66; controller William Beaumont Hosp., Royal Oak, Mich., 1966-68; asso. dir. William Beaumont Hosp., 1968-69, hosp. dir., 1969-80, exec. v.p., 1976-80, pres., 1981—; pres. Trinity Loss Prevention Systems, 1980-81; bd. dirs. Chateau Properties, Inc. Elder Bloomfield Hills Christian Ch., 1979-82, Grace Chapel, 1988-92, 95—; bd. visitors Oakland U. Sch. Bus. Adminstrn., 1978-92; mem. adv. bd. Salvation Army, 1985—; bd. dirs. William Tyndale Coll. With U.S Army, 1951-53. Mem. Mich. Hosp. Assn. (past chmn.), Vol. Hosps. Am. Enterprises (bd. dirs. 1984-87), Full Gospel Businessmen's Fellowship, Bloomfield Hills Country Club, Old Club, Phi Delta Theta, Beta Gamma Sigma. Home: 5085 Lakebluff Rd West Bloomfield MI 48323-2430 Office: William Beaumont Hosp Corp 3601 W 13 Mile Rd Royal Oak MI 48073-6769

MYERS, KENNETH M., lawyer; b. Miami, Fla., Mar. 11, 1933; s. Stanley C. and Martha (Scheinberg) M.; div. 1973. AB, U. N.C., 1954; JD, U. Fla., 1957. Bar: Sept. 1957, Colo. 1986, N.Y. 1987. Ptnr. Myers, Kenin Levinson & Richards, Miami, 1957-87, Shea & Gould, N.Y.C., 1987-88, Squire, Sanders & Dempsey, Miami, 1988—; mem. Fla. Ho. Reps., 1965-69, mem. Fla. Senate, 1969-80. Trustee U. Miami, 1985—. Mem. ABA, Dade County Bar Assn., Fla. Bar Assn., Colo. Bar Assn., N.Y State Bar Assn., Am. Law Inst., Nat. Assn. Bond Lawyers. Democrat. Jewish. Office: Squire Sanders & Dempsey 2900 Miami Ctr 201 S Biscayne Blvd Miami FL 33131-4324

MYERS, KENNETH RAYMOND, lawyer; b. N.Y.C., Apr. 14, 1939; s. Cyril Burleigh and Dorothy (Podolyn) M.; m. Susan Kay Plotnick, Sept. 9, 1962; children: Lisa R., Jonathan S., Andrew C. SB, MIT, 1960; JD, Harvard U., 1963. Bar: Ill. 1963, Pa. 1968. Assoc. Ross, Hardies & O'Keefe, Chgo., 1963-68; assoc. Morgan, Lewis & Bockius, Phila., 1968-71, ptnr., 1972—; mem. rules com. Environ. Hearing Bd., Harrisburg, Pa., 1984-89. Editor: Environmental Spill Reporting Handbook, 1992; contbg. author: Environmental Law Practice Guide, 1992; contbr. articles to profl. jours. Mem. exec. com. Water Resources Assn. Del. River Basin, Valley Forge, Pa., 1975—, Am. Jewish Congress, Phila., 1987—, mem. nat. commn., N.Y., 1984—, v.p., 1991—. Mem. ABA (rep. to U.S. Office Personnel Mgmt. 1975—), Pa. Bar Assn., Phila. Bar Assn., Fed. Energy Bar Assn., Eta Kappa Nu. Office: Morgan Lewis & Bockius 2000 One Logan Sq Philadelphia PA 19103

MYERS, LONN WILLIAM, lawyer; b. Rockford, Ill., Nov. 14, 1946; s. William H. and Leona V. (Janvrin) M.; m. Janet L. Forbes, May 14, 1968; children: Andrew, Hillary, Corwin. BA, Mich. State U., 1968; MBA, Ind. U., 1973; JD, Harvard U., 1976. Bar: Ill. 1976, U.S. Ct. of Fed. Claims 1977, U.S. Tax Ct. 1977, U.S. Ct. Appeals (7th cir.) 1977. Ptnr. McDermott, Will & Emery, Chgo., 1976—. Served to maj. USAR, 1968-80. Mem. ABA (chair intangibles com. of capital recovery and leasing com. tax sect. 1994—), Union League Club (Chgo.). Episcopalian. Home: 1711 Highland Ter Glenview IL 60025-2284 Office: McDermott Will & Emery 227 W Monroe St Chicago IL 60606-5016

MYERS, MALCOLM HAYNIE, artist, art educator; b. Lucerne, Mo., June 19, 1917; s. Clyde Emmet and Kathleen M.; m. Roberta Bernice King, May 6. B.F.A., Wichita State U., 1940; M.A., U. Iowa, 1941, M.F.A., 1946. Instr. U. Iowa, 1946-48; prof. art U. Minn., Mpls., 1948—; chmn. dept. art U. Minn., 1957-61. Retrospective print exhbn. include Mr. Possum and Friends, Univ. Art Mus., U. Minn., 1983; traveling exhbn. Worcester (Mass.) Art Mus., 1990-91; paintings also exhibited at Amon Carter Mus., Ft. Worth, and Nelson-Atkins Mus. Art, Kansas City, Mo.; one-man shows include Dolly Fiterman Gallery, Mpls., 1983, 85, 87; represented in permanent collections Bibliotheque Nationale, Paris, Library of Congress, Washington, Los Angeles County Art Mus., Mpls. Inst. Art, St. Louis Art Mus., Seattle Art Mus., Walker Art Center, Mpls., Phoenix Art Mus., Am. Embassy, Bonn, Germany; contbr. art and article to book Am. Prints and Printmakers (Una Johnson). Served with U.S. Mcht. Marines, 1943-45. Recipient Alumni Achievement award Wichita State U., 1973; John Simon Guggenheim fellow Paris, 1950; Guggenheim fellow Mexico City, 1954; trustee Minn. Mus. Art, St. Paul, 1975-78. Mem. Alumni Club U. Minn., Artist Equity (past pres.), Mid-Am. Coll. Art Assn. (past pres.). Presbyterian. Home: 1715 James Ave S Minneapolis MN 55403-2826 Office: U Minn Studio Arts Dept Minneapolis MN 55455

MYERS, MARLEE S., lawyer; b. Washington, Oct. 15, 1950; d. Bertram and Ruth (Shapiro) Lasnik; m. James R. Myers, Apr. 20, 1970; children: Matthew, Erika. Student, Carnegie Mellon U., 1968-70; BA summa cum laude, U. Pitts., 1974, JD summa cum laude, 1977. Assoc. Kirkpatrick & Lockhart, Pitts., 1977-84, ptnr., 1984—; bd. dirs. Pitts. High Tech. Coun.; speaker in field. Contbr. articles to profl. jours. Treas. Pitts. Chamber Music Soc., 1991-92, bd. dirs., 1991—, sec., 1992—; mem. adv. com. United Way of Allegheny County, 1991; mem. Fox Chapel Sch. Dist. Citizens Adv. Com. Mem. ABA, Pa. Bar Assn., World Affairs Coun., Allegheny County Bar Assn., Rivers Club. Avocation: classical music. Office: Kirkpatrick & Lockhart 1500 Oliver Bldg Pittsburgh PA 15222

MYERS, MARY KATHLEEN, publishing executive; b. Cedar Rapids, Iowa, Aug. 19, 1945; d. Joseph Bernard and Marjorie Helen (Huntsman) Weaver; m. David F. Myers, Dec. 30, 1967; children: Mindy, James. BA in English and Psychology, U. Iowa, 1967. Tchr. Lincoln High Sch., Des Moines, 1967-80; editor Perfection Learning Corp., Des Moines, 1980-84, product mgr., 1985-87, v.p., editor-in-chief, 1987-93; pres. Advanced Practical Thinking Tng., Des Moines, 1992—; founding ptnr. orgn. designed to promote Edward de Bono thinking methods, 1992—; co-founder Edward de Bono Creative Fource, 1994. Editor: Retold Classics, 1988-91, (ednl. program) Six Thinking Hats, 1991, Lateral Thinking, 1993; originator numerous other sch. products and programs. Mem. Gov.'s Commn. to Enhance Ednl. Leadership Iowa, Dept. of Edn., 1991-93. Mem. ASTD, Am. Creativity Assn., Am. Soc. Quality Control, Assn. for Quality and Participation. Home: 4315 Urbandale Ave Des Moines IA 50310 Office: APT/T 10520 New York Ave Des Moines IA 50322

MYERS, MICHELE TOLELA, academic administrator; b. Rabat, Morocco, Sept. 25, 1941; came to U.S., 1964; d. Albert and Lilie (Abecassis) Tolela; m. Pierre Vajda, Sept. 12, 1962 (div. Jan. 1965); m. Gail E. Myers, Dec. 20, 1968; children: Erika, David. Diploma, Inst. Polit. Studies, U. Paris, 1962; MA, U. Denver, 1966, PhD, 1967; MA, Trinity U., 1977; LHD, Wittenberg U., 1994. Asst. prof. speech Manchester Coll., North Manchester, Ind., 1967-68; asst. prof. speech and sociology Monticello Coll., Godfrey, Ill., 1968-71; asst. prof. communication Trinity U., San Antonio, 1975-80, assoc. prof., 1980-86, asst. v.p. for acad. affairs, 1982-85, assoc. v.p., 1985-86; assoc. prof. sociology, dean Undergrad. Coll. Bryn Mawr (Pa.) Coll., 1986-89; pres. Denison U., Granville, Ohio, 1989—; comm. anslyst Psychology and Comm., San Antonio, 1974-83; bd. dirs. Am. Coun. on Edn., Nat. Assn. Ind. Coll. and Univs., 1995—; Fed. Res. Bank of Cleve.; mem. pres.'s commn. Nat. Collegiate Athletic Assn., 1993—, Sherman Fairchild Found., 1992—. Author: (with Gail Myers) The Dynamics of Human Communication, 1973, 6th and internat. edits., 1992, transl. into French, 1984, Communicating When We Speak, 1975, 2d edit., 1978, Communication for the Urban Professional, 1977, Managing by Communication: An Organizational Approach, 1982, transl. into Spanish, 1983, internat. edit., 1982. Trustee Phila. Child Guidance Clinic, 1988-89; trustee assoc. The

Bryn Mawr Sch., Balt., 1987-89; v.p., bd. dirs. San Antonio Cmty. Guidance Ctr., 1979-83. Am. Coun. Edn. fellow in acad. adminstrn., 1981-82. Mem. Am. Coun. Edn. (commn. women in higher edn. 1990-92, bd. dirs. 1993—) Great Lake Consortium assn., North Coast Athletic Conf. Home: 204 Broadway W Granville OH 43023-1120 Office: Denison U Office of the President Granville OH 43023

MYERS, MIKE, actor, writer; b. Toronto, Ont., Can., May 25, 1963; s. Eric and Bunny (Hind) M.; m. Robin Ruzan, 1993. Stage appearances: The Second City, Toronto, 1986-88, Chgo., 1988-89; actor, writer: Mullarkey & Myers, Can., 1984-86, (TV show) Saturday Night Live, 1989-94 (Emmy award for outstanding writing in a comedy or variety series 1989), (film) Wayne's World, 1992, So I Married an Axe Murderer, 1993, Wayne's World II, 1993; actor: (TV movie) John and Yoko, 1985. *

MYERS, MINOR, JR., college administrator, political science educator; b. Akron, Ohio, Aug. 13, 1942; s. Minor and Ruth (Libby) M.; m. Ellen Achin, Mar. 21, 1970; children—Minor III, Joffre V.A. B.A., Carleton Coll., Northfield, Minn., 1964; M.A., Princeton U., 1967, Ph.D., 1972. From instr. to assoc. prof. Conn. Coll., New London, 1968-81, prof. govt., 1981-84; provost, dean of faculty, prof. polit. sci. Hobart and William Smith Colls., Geneva, N.Y., 1984-89; pres., prof. polit. sci. Ill. Wesleyan U., Bloomington, 1989—; adv. Numismatic Collection Yale U., 1975-84; chmn. adv. coun. Lyman Allyn Mus., 1976-81, 82-84, pres., 1982-84. Author: Liberty Without Anarchy: A History of the Society of the Cincinnati, 1983, (with others) New London County Furniture, 1974, (with others) The Princeton Graduate School: A History, 1978, (with others) American Interiors: A Documentary History from the Colonial Era to 1915, 1980. Asst. sec. gen. Soc. of the Cin., 1983-86, sec.-gen., 1986-89; trustee Inst. for European Study, 1992—. Mem. Political Sci (N.Y.C.), University (Chgo.). Office: Ill Wesleyan U PO Box 2900 Bloomington IL 61702-2900

MYERS, MOREY MAYER, lawyer; b. Scranton, Pa., Aug. 5, 1927; s. Samuel Z. and Libbye (Kaplan) M.; m. Sondra Gelb, Nov. 25, 1956; children: Jonathan S., David N. AB, Syracuse U., 1949; LLB, Yale U., 1952. Bar: Pa. 1953, U.S. Dist.Ct (mid. dist.) Pa. 1953, U.S. Ct. Appeals (3rd cir.) 1958, U.S. Supreme Ct. 1960, U.S. Dist. Ct. (ea. dist.) Pa. 1981, U.S. Dist. Ct. (we. dist.) Pa. 1988. Asst. solicitor City of Scranton, Pa., 1957-61; asst. atty. gen. Commonwealth of Pa., Harrisburg, 1962-63, chief coun. milk control comn., 1962-63; mng. ptnr. Gelb, Myers, Bishop & Warren, Scranton, 1982-85; sr. ptnr. Hourigan, Kluger, Spohrer, Quinn & Myers, 1985-87; chief coun. Commonwealth of Pa., Harrisburg, 1987-89; ptnr. Schnader, Harrison, Segal & Lewis, Scranton, 1990-95, Myers, Brier & Kelly, Scranton, 1995—; vis. lectr. Hamilton Coll., Clinton, N.Y., 1982-84, Yale U., 1986, 89, 91, Haverford (Pa.) Coll., 1990; chief counsel Gov. of Pa., Harrisburg, 1987-89. Contbr. articles to profl. jours. with USN, 1945-46. Fellow Am. Bar Found.; mem. Nat. Conf. Commrs. Uniform State Laws (comnr.). Office: Myers Brier & Kelly 108 N Washington Ave Scranton PA 18503-1818

MYERS, NORMAN ALLAN, marketing professional; b. Beeville, Tex., Dec. 10, 1935; s. Floyd Charles and Ruby (Lee) Myers; m. Suzanne Carlile, Oct. 11, 1935; children: Lisa Leigh Myers Nowlin, Matthew Scott. BS in Banking and Fin., Okla. State U., 1958. Salesman Jones and Laughlin Steel Corp., Houston, 1958-64; agt. Acacia Mutual Life Ins., Houston, 1964-69; with Browning-Ferris Industries, Houston, 1969—, exec. v.p., 1976-81, chief mktg. officer, 1981—, vice chmn., 1982—; also bd. dirs. bd. dirs. My Friends-A Neuenschwander Found. for Children in Crisis. 2d lt. U.S. Army, 1958-59. Mem. Lakeside Country Club, Hills of Lakeway Club, Barton Creek Lakeside Country Club, Shriners, Holland. Republican. Avocation: golf. Office: Browning-Ferris Ind Inc 757 N Eldridge Pky Houston TX 77079-4435

MYERS, ORIE EUGENE, JR., university official; b. Hagan, Ga., Oct. 14, 1920; s. Orie Eugene and Betty (Shuman) M.; m. Margaret Elizabeth Nesbit, June 7, 1941; children: Orie Eugene III, Curtis Alan, Adrian Marvyn. Student, Ga. Inst. Tech., 1937-38; A.B., Emory U., 1941, M.A., 1957. Personnel asst. Atlanta Personnel Bd., 1940-41; personnel officer Nat. Youth Adminstrn., 1941-43, Office Emergency Mgmt., 1943-44, VA, 1946-48; dir. personnel Emory U., 1948-61, bus. mgr., 1961-73, asst. dir. personnel, dir. health services, 1961-64, v.p. bus., 1973-89, sr. bus. analyst, 1989-91; v.p. bus., dir. Woodruff Med. Center, 1964-73; past chmn. bd. Prime Bancshares, Inc., Prime Bank FSB. Trustee, chmn. med. com. Wesley Homes; bd. dirs., past chmn. DeKalb County unit Am. Cancer Soc. Served to 1st lt. USAAF, 1944-46. Mem. Coll. and Univ. Personnel Assn. (past pres.), Nat. Assn. Coll. and Univ. Bus. Officers (past pres.), So. Assn. Coll. and Univ. Bus. Officers (past pres.), DeKalb C. of C. (past pres.), Sigma Nu. Democrat. Baptist. Home: 236 Mt Vernon Dr Decatur GA 30030-1607

MYERS, PHILLIP FENTON, financial services company executive; b. Cleve., June 24, 1935; s. Max I. and Rebecca (Rosenbloom) M.; m. Hope Gail Strum, Aug. 13, 1961. B in Indsl. Engring., Ohio State U., 1958, MBA, 1960; D in Bus. Adminstrn., Harvard U., 1966. Staff indsl. engr. Procter & Gamble Co., Cin., 1958; sr. cons. Cresap, McCormack & Paget, N.Y.C., 1960-61; staff assoc. Mitre Corp., Bedford, Mass., 1961; cons. Sys. Devel. Corp., Santa Monica, Calif., 1963-64; corp. asst. long range planning Electronic Specialty Co., Los Angeles, 1966-68; chmn. Atek Industries, 1968-72; pres. Myers Fin. Corp., 1973-82; chmn. Amvid Comm. Svcs., Inc., 1975-79, Omni Resources Devel. Corp., 1979-83; chmn., pres. Am. Internat. Mining Co., Inc., 1979-83; pres. Whitehall Internat. Mgmt. Co., Inc., 1982-95; chmn. Global Bond Mktg. Svcs., Inc., 1987-90; pres., CEO Whitehall Container Mfg. Corp., 1988-91; pres. Whitehall Motors Co., 1989—, Allied Metamatter Tech. Corp., 1994—; chmn U.S. Water Resources, Inc., 1994—; pres. Am. Tech. Venture Fund Mgmt., Inc.; pres. Advent Internat. Mgmt. Co., Inc., 1995—, Turbogon, Inc., 1995—; founding dir. Warner Ctr. Bank, 1980-83; lectr. bus. adminstrn. U. So. Calif., L.A., 1967-74; prof. Grad. Sch. Bus. Adminstrn. Pepperdine U., 1974-81. Trustee, treas. Chamber Symphony Soc. Calif., 1971-78; pub. safety commr. City of Hidden Hills, Calif., 1977-83, chmn., 1982-83; co-chmn. budget adv. com. Las Virgenes Sch. Dist., 1983-86; mem. Mayor's Blue Ribbon Fin. Com., 1981-82; mem. dean's select adv. com. Coll. Engring., Ohio State U., 1984—; mem. state exec. com. Calif. Libertarian Party, chmn. region 61, 1989-90, chmn. strategic planning com.; dep. chmn. L.A. County Libertarian Party, 1991-92; chair campaign issues com. Marrou for Pres., 1991-92; chmn. bd. trustees WWII Hist. Soc., 1992—. Capt. USAF, 1958-60. Ford Found. fellow, 1961-64. Mem. Harvard Bus. Sch. Assn., Ohio State Alumni Assn., Harvard Club of So. Calif. (bd. dirs. 1970-74, treas. 1971-73). Office: 682 Laurel Ridge Dr Gahanna OH 43230 Personal philosophy: All out all the time. I stand for the creation of a new system of global governance which stresses individual liberty, freedom and responsibility, and which leads to a world that works for everyone with no one left out. In business, I stand for exceptional vision, creativity, innovation, and success.

MYERS, PHILLIP SAMUEL, mechanical engineering educator; b. Webber, Kans., May 8, 1916; s. Earl Rufus and Sarah Katharine (Breon) M.; m. Jean Frances Alford, May 26, 1943; children: Katharine Myers Muirhead, Elizabeth Myers Baird, Phyllis Myers Rathbone, John, Mark. BS in Math. and Commerce, McPherson Coll., 1940; BSME, Kans. State Coll., 1942; PhDME, U. Wis., 1947. Registered profl. engr., Wis. Instr. mech. engring. Ind. Tech. Coll., Ft. Wayne, summer 1942; instr. U. Wis. Madison, 1942-47, asst. prof., 1947-50, assoc. prof., 1950-55, prof., 1955-86, emeritus prof., 1986—, chmn. dept. mech. engring., 1979-83; cons. Diesel Engine Mfrs. Assn., U.S. Army, various oil and ins. cos.; bd. dirs. Nelson Industries, Echlin Mfg. Corp. Contbr. articles to profl. jours. Chmn. Pine Lake com. W. Wis. Conf. Meth. Ch., 1955-60; Mem. Village Bd., Shorewood Hills, 1962-67. Recipient B.S. Reynolds Teaching award, 1964, McPherson Coll. Alumni citation of merit, 1971; Dugald Clerk award, 1971. Fellow ASME (Diesel Gas Power award 1971, Soichiro Honda award 1993), Soc. Automotive Engrs. (Colwell award 1966, 79, Horning award 1968, nat. pres. 1969, hon. mem.); mem. AAAS, NAE, Am. Soc. for Engring. Edn., Blue Key, Sigma Xi, Phi Kappa Phi, Sigma Tau, Pi Tau Sigma (Gold medal 1949), Tau Beta Pi (Ragnar Onstad Svc. to Soc. award 1978). Mem. Brethren Ch. Achievements include patents in field.

MYERS, PHILLIP WARD, otolaryngologist; b. Evanston, Ill., Nov. 11, 1939; s. R. Maurice and Vivian (Ward) M.; m. Lynetta Sargent, Dec. 22,

1963; children: Andrea, Ward, Alycia, Amanda, Andrew. B.S., Western Ill. U., 1961; M.D., U. Ill., 1965. Diplomate: Am. Bd. Otolaryngology. Intern St. Paul-Ramsey Hosp., 1965-66; resident in otolaryngology U. Louisville, 1966-68; resident Northwestern U., 1968-70, fellow, 1970-71; practice medicine specializing in otolaryngology Springfield, Ill., 1973—; clin. assoc. prof. otolaryngology So. Ill. U., Springfield, 1973—. Served to maj. M.C. AUS, 1971-73. Fellow Am. Soc. for Head and Neck Surgery, Am. Acad. Facial Plastic and Reconstructive Surgery; ACS, Am. Acad. Otolaryngology-Head and Neck Surgery. Research perilymphatic fistulas. Home: 111 Oak Hill Rd Rochester IL 62563-9229 Office: 331 W Carpenter St Springfield IL 62702-4901

MYERS, R. DAVID, library director, dean; b. Hutchinson, Kans., Mar. 27, 1949; s. William Raymond and Elizabeth (Haas) M.; m. Barbara Jean Burridge, Sept. 15, 1973; 1 child, John David. BA, U. No. Colo., 1972, MA, 1974; ABD, U. Mich., 1976; MA, U. Denver, 1979. Manuscript curator Western History Collection, Denver, 1976-79; rsch. assoc. Colo. Legis. Coun., Denver, 1979-81; reference specialist Libr. of Congress, Washington, 1981-84, reference supr., 1984-88; libr. dir. State Hist. Soc. of Wis., Madison, 1988-94; assoc. dean univ. libr. N.Mex. State U. Las Cruces, 1994—; editor Am. history Macmillan Pub., N.Y.C., 1991-94; cons. history of medicine dept. U. Wis., Madison, 1993-94. Author bibliographies for Libr. of Congress, 1987, 88. Mem. ALA, Am. Hist. Assn., Orgn. Am. Historians, Wis. Libr. Assn. Avocations: research, writing, baseball, mysteries. Office: N Mex State U Dept 3475 Box 3006 Las Cruces NM 88003

MYERS, R(ALPH) CHANDLER, lawyer; b. Los Angeles, Jan. 9, 1933; s. Ralph Cather and Winifred (Chandler) M.; m. Rebecca Blythe Borkgren, Jan. 11, 1963; 1 child, Derek Chandler. BA, Stanford U., 1954, JD, 1958; LLD (hon.), Whittier Coll., 1988. Bar: Calif. 1959, U.S. Dist. Ct. (cen. dist.) Calif. 1959, U.S. Supreme Ct. 1971. Law clk., then assoc. Parker, Stanbury, Reese & McGee, Los Angeles, 1958-63; assoc. Nicholas, Kolliner & Van Tassel, Los Angeles, 1963-65; ptnr. Myers & D'Angelo and predecessors, Los Angeles and Pasadena, Calif., 1965—; nat. panelist Am. Arbitration Assn., Los Angeles, 1964—; bd. visitors Stanford U. Law Sch., Calif., 1970-73; mem. judge pro tem panel Los Angeles Mcpl. Ct., 1971-81; mem. Los Angeles County Dist. Atty.'s Adv. Council, Calif., 1976-83. Bd. dirs. Opera Guild So. Calif., Los Angeles, 1971-83, pres., 1980-82,. Guild Opera Co. Los Angeles, 1974-83, pres., 1975-77, Western Justice Ctr. Found., 1993—; pres. Los Angeles Child Guidance Clinic, 1977-79, bd. dirs., 1972-83; nat. vice chmn. Keystone Gifts, Stanford Centennial Campaign, 1987-92; trustee Whittier Coll., Calif., 1973—, chmn. bd. trustees, 1981-87; bd. dirs. Opera Assocs. of the Music Ctr., Los Angeles, 1976-78; trustee Flintridge Prep. Sch., La Canada Flintridge, Calif., 1981-88, chmn. bd. trustees, 1985-88; bd. vis. Whittier Coll. Sch. Law, 1988—. Served to 1st lt. AUS, 1955-57. Recipient Stanford Assocs. award, 1984, Centennial Medallion award, 1991, Gold Spike award Stanford U., 1989, Disting. Svc. award Whittier Law Sch., 1993, Outstanding Achievement award Stanford Assocs., 1995. Mem. Wilshire Bar Assn. (bd. govs. 1972-81, pres. 1979-80), L.A. County Bar Assn. (trustee 1979-81), Stanford Law Soc. So. Calif. (bd. dirs. 1967-72, pres. 1970-71), Stanford Assocs. (bd. govs. 1992—), Jonathan Club, University Club (Pasadena), Stanford Club of L.A. (bd. dirs. 1963-70, pres. 1968-69). Home: La Canada 5623 Burning Tree Dr La Canada Flintridge CA 91011 Office: Myers & D'Angelo Ste 800 301 N Lake Ave Pasadena CA 91101-4108

MYERS, RANDALL KIRK (RANDY MYERS), professional baseball player; b. Vancouver, Washington, Sept. 19, 1962. Student, Clark C.C., Washington. Baseball player N.Y. Mets, 1982-89, Cin. Reds, 1989-91, San Diego Padres, 1991-92, Chicago Cubs, 1992—. Named Calif. League Pitcher of the Yr., 1984, Nat. League Fireman of Yr., Sporting News, 1993. All-Star, 1990, 94; 2d in Nat. League in Saves, 1992. Office: Chicago Cubs Wrigley Field 1060 W Addison St Chicago IL 60613-4397*

MYERS, RAYMOND IRVIN, optometrist, researcher; b. Mishawaka, Ind., Nov. 19, 1943; s. Raymond E. Myers and Adeline S. (Hiler) M.; m. Paulette K. Emerine, July 9, 1966; 1 child, Christopher Raymond. BS, U. Notre Dame, 1966, Ind. U., 1968; OD, Ind. U., 1970. Dir. edn. and manpower div. Am. Optometric Assn., St. Louis, 1970-73; mgr. internat. profl. services Bausch & Lomb, Inc., Rochester, N.Y., 1973-77; research fellow Moorfields Eye Hosp., London, 1977-78; pvt. practice optometry St. Louis, 1979-86; mem. faculty U. Mo., St. Louis, 1986—; mem. faculty, dir. dept. contact lenses La. State U., New Orleans, 1992; faculty dept. ophthalmology Washington U., 1978-86; adj. optometry faculty U. Houston; cons. various contact lens mfrs. Contbr. more than 30 articles to profl. jours. Fellow Am. Acad. Optometry; mem. Am. Optometric Assn., Assn. for Rsch. on Vision and Ophthalmology, St. Louis Optometric Soc. (pres. 1985-86), Internat. Soc. for Contact Lens Rsch. (co-founder, v.p. 1980-93), Am. Optometric Student Assn. (co-founder, pres. 1967). Office: U Mo Sch Optometry 8001 Natural Bridge Rd Saint Louis MO 63121-4499

MYERS, REX CHARLES, academic dean; b. Cleve., July 1, 1945; s. Charles F. and Merial W. (Jones) M.; m. Susan L. Richards, Jan. 10, 1987; children: Gary W., Laura M. BA, Western State Coll., 1967; MA, U. Mont., 1970, PhD, 1972; postgrad., U. Wash., 1983; Mgmt. Devel. Program, Harvard U., 1990. Instr. Palo Verde Coll., Blythe, Calif., 1972-75; reference librarian Mont. Hist. Soc., Helena, 1975-78; prof., div. chmn., dean Western Mont. Coll., Dillon, 1979-86; dean S.D. State U., Brookings, 1986-91; acad. dean Lyndon State Coll., Lyndonville, Vt., 1991—. Author: Montana Symbols, 1976, Montana Trolleys, 1970, Lizzie, 1989; co-author: Marble Colorado, 1970, Montana: Our Land and People, 1978, Montana and the West, 1984; contbr. articles to profl. jours. Bd. dirs. Ctr. for Western Studies, Sioux Falls., S.D., 1990—. Summer stipend NEH, 1973; fellow James J. Hill Library, 1985. Mem. AAUW, Western History Assn. (chmn. membership com. 1980-83), Am. Conf. Acad. Deans, Mont. Oral History Assn. (chmn. 1980-83), N.E. Kingdom C. of C. (bd. dirs.), Phi Kappa Phi. Lutheran. Lodges: Kiwanis (pres. Dillon 1983, lt. gov. 1984), Masons (master 1984). Home: PO Box 45 Lyndon Center VT 05850-0045

MYERS, ROBERT DAVID, judge; b. Springfield, Mass., Nov. 20, 1937; s. William and Pearl (Weiss) M.; m. Judith G. Dickenman, July 1, 1962; children—Mandy Susan, Jay Brandt, Seth William. A.B., U. Mass., 1959; J.D., Boston U., 1962. Bar: Ariz. 1963. Practice in Phoenix, 1963-89; judge, pro tem judge, 1979-89; presiding judge civil dept. Superior Ct. of Arizona in Maricopa County, 1991-92; presiding judge probate and mental health dept. Superior Ct., Ariz., 1992-95; pro tem judge Ariz. Ct. Appeals; judge Ariz. Superior Ct., 1989—; presiding judge Superior Ct. of Ariz. in Maricopa County, 1995—; chmn. com. on exams and admissions Ariz. Supreme Ct., 1974-75, chmn. com. on character and fitness, 1975-76, mem. multi-state bar exam. com., 1976-85. Pres. Valley of Sun chpt. City of Hope, 1965-66, Cmty. Orgn. for Drug Abuse Control, 1972-73, Valley Big Bros., 1975; chmn. Mayors Ad Hoc Com. on Drug Abuse, 1974-75; bd. dirs. Maricopa County Legal Aid Soc., 1978, Phoenix Jewish Cmty. Ctr. Mem. ATLA (nat. chmn. gov.), Ariz. Bar Assn. (gov., com. chmn., sect. pres.), Maricopa County Bar Assn. (dir., pres. 1979-80), Ariz. Trial Lawyers Assn. (pres., dir., co-editor newsletter), Phoenix Trial Lawyers Assn. (pres., dir.), Western Trial Lawyers Assn. (pres. 1977), Am. Judicature Soc. (spl. merit citation outstanding svc. improvement of adminstrn. justice 1986), Am. Bd. Trial Advocates, Sandra Day O'Connor Inn of Ct. (pres. 1991-92). Office: Justice Ctr 201 W Jefferson St Phoenix AZ 85003-2205

MYERS, ROBERT DURANT, biologist, research director, medical educator; b. Phila., Oct. 25, 1931; s. Clarence Norman and Martha Louise (Fox) M.; m. Marjorie Anne Fretz, Dec. 20, 1953; children: Robert, James, Elizabeth, Anne. B.S., Ursinus Coll., 1953; M.S., Purdue U., 1954, Ph.D., 1956; D.h.c., U. Granada, 1984. Asst. prof., assoc. prof. Colgate U., 1956-63; fellow neurol. scis. Johns Hopkins U. Sch. Medicine, 1960-61; research scientist Nat. Inst. for Med. Research, Eng., 1963-65; vis. research neuropharmacology Nat. Inst. for Med. Research, 1969; prof. psychol. and biol. scis. Purdue U., West Lafayette, Ind., 1965-78, co-dir. neurobiology program, 1969-78; prof. psychiatry and pharmacology U. N.C. Sch. Medicine, Chapel Hill, 1978-87; dir. Bowles Biomed. Research Labs., 1980-87; prof. pharmacology and psychiatric medicine East Carolina U. Sch. Medicine, Greenville, N.C., 1987—; vis. prof. Latrobe U. Australia, 1975, 82; mem. psychobiology-neurobiology adv. panels NSF; mem. alcohol adv. panel, also neurosci. neurobiol. tng. and rec. com. NIMH; mem. neurology panel and fellowship rev. panel Nat. Inst. Neurol. and Communicative Disorders and Stroke; cons. Canadian Med. Research Council, Australian Research Grants Council, U.S. VA; mem. peer rev. panel Nat. Council Alcoholism; mem. AIDS related rev. panel NIH; mem. panel Nat. Inst. Environ. Health Scis. Author: Methods in Psychobiology, Vol.I, 1971, Vol.II, 1972, Vol.III, 1977, Neurohumoral Coding of Brain Function, 1974, Handbook Drug and Chemical Stimulation of the Brain, 1974, Neurochemical Analysis of the Conscious Brain, 1986; mem. editorial bd.: Physiol. Behavior, 1967—, Pharmacol. Biochem. Behavior, 1973—, Brain Research Bull. 1976—, Neurosci. and Biobehavioral Rev., 1977—, Prog. Neuropsychopharmacology, 1977—; editor: Alcohol-Biomed. Research Jour., 1984—; contbr. sci. articles to profl. jours. Recipient Alumni award Ursinus Coll., 1967, Sigma Xi research award, 1971, Vol. Service awards Nat. Council Alcoholism, 1974-77; medal Belgrade U. Yugoslavia, 1985, medal Granada U., Spain; NSF grantee, 1960—; NIH grantee, 1980—; Office Naval Research grantee, 1965-81; NIMH grantee, 1969-76. Fellow AAAS, Am. Coll. Neuropsychopharmacology; mem. Collegium Internat. Neuro-Psychopharmacologium, Soc. for Neurosci., Am. Physiol. Soc., Am. Soc. Pharmacology and Exptl. Therapeutics, Rsch. Soc. for Alcoholism, Internat. Soc. Biomed. Rsch., Internat. Behavioral Neurosci. Soc. (pres. 1994-95, pres.-elect 1993-94), N.Y. Acad. Scis., Sigma Xi. Episcopalian. Home: 4006 Sterling Trace Dr Winterville NC 28590-9320

MYERS, ROBERT JAY, retired aerospace company executive; b. Bklyn., Oct. 15, 1934; s. John J. and Clara S. (Martinsen) M.; m. Carolyn Erland, Aug. 10, 1963; children—Susan, Kenneth. BCE, NYU, 1955, postgrad., 1957-65; P.M.D., Harvard U., 1973. With Grumman Corp., Bethpage, N.Y., 1964-94, v.p. resources, 1980-83, sr. v.p. bus. and resource mgmt., 1983-85, sr. v.p. corp. svcs., 1985-86; pres. Grumman Data Systems Corp., Bethpage, 1986-90; pres., chief operating officer, bd. dirs. Grumman Corp., 1991-94; mem. sci. adv. coun. Ala. Space and Rocket Ctr., 1986-91. Mem. adv. panel on econ. devel. N.Y. State Project 2000, 1985-86; mem. L.I. Project 2000; mem. adv. bd. L.I. Youth Guidance, 1986-91; bd. dirs. Huntington Hosp., Poly. U., 1991—. 1st lt. U.S. Army, 1955-57. Fellow Poly. U., 1987, Disting. Alumni award, 1989. Mem. Am. Def. Preparedness Assn. (dir. 1992—), Navy League, Industry Exec. Bd., Nat. Space Club (bd. govs. 1986-89), Huntington Country Club. Lutheran. Home: 7 Heather Ln Huntington NY 11743-1011

MYERS, ROBERT MANSON, English educator, author; b. Charlottesville, Va., May 29, 1921; s. Horwood Prettyman and Matilda Manson (Wynn) M. B.A. summa cum laude, Vanderbilt U., 1941; M.A., Columbia, 1942, Harvard, 1943; Ph.D., Columbia, 1948. Instr. English Yale, 1945-47; asst. prof. Coll. William and Mary, 1947-48, Tulane U., 1948-54; tchr. English Brearley Sch., N.Y.C., 1954-56; chmn. dept. English Osbourn High Sch., Manassas, Va., 1956-59; mem. faculty U. Md., College Park, 1959—; prof. English U. Md., 1968-86, prof. emeritus, 1986—. Author: Handel's Messiah, 1948, From Beowulf to Virginia Woolf, 1952, rev., 1984, Handel, Dryden, and Milton, 1956, Restoration Comedy, 1961, The Children of Pride, 1972, abridged edit., 1984 (Nat. Book award 1973), A Georgian at Princeton, 1976, Quintet: Five Plays, 1991. Fulbright Postdoctoral Research fellow U. London, 1953-54; Fulbright lectr. Restoration, Netherlands, 1958-59. Mem. Modern Lang. Assn. Am., Am. Soc. 18th Century Studies, Jane Austen Soc. N.Am., Phi Beta Kappa. Home: 3900 Connecticut Ave NW Washington DC 20008-2412

MYERS, ROLLAND GRAHAM, investment counselor; b. St. Louis, Aug. 30, 1945; s. Rolland Everett and Lurilien (Graham) M. Diploma, St. Louis Country Day Sch., 1963; AB cum laude in History and Lit., Harvard U., 1966; postgrad. Faculties of Social Scis. and Law, U. Edinburgh, Scotland, 1966-67; postgrad. Fondation Nationale des Sciences Politiques and Faculte de Lettres et des Sciences Humaines, U. Paris, 1967-68. Trainee global credit dept. The Chase Manhattan Bank, N.A., N.Y.C., 1968-69; mem. 32nd spl. devel. program, 1969, strategic planner internat. dept., 1969-70, securities analyst, mktg. rep., fiduciary investment dept., 1970; assoc. Smith, Barney & Co., Inc., N.Y.C., 1971, account exec. N.Y. sales dept., 1971-72, instl. account exec. N.Y. internat. sales dept., 1972-74, 2nd v.p., stockholder, 1975-76; v.p., stockholder Smith Barney, Harris Upham & Co., Inc. (subs. SBHU Holdings, Inc.), N.Y.C., 1976-78; prin. W.H. Graham & Sons, family investment office, 1977-82, investment counsel, 1982—; ltd. ptnr. Croke Patterson Campbell, Ltd., Denver, 1975—; joint founder, gen. ptnr. Mansion Disbursements, Denver, 1979—; pres., chmn. exec. com., bd. dirs. Fifty-Five Residents Corp., N.Y.C., 1980-84; bd. dirs. Fifty-Six Danbury Rd. Assn., Inc., New Milford, Conn. Trustee, mem. corp. Bishop Rhinelander Found. (Episcopal Chaplaincy at Harvard and Radcliffe Colls.), Cambridge, 1973-75; v.p., treas. bd. dirs. The Whitehill Graham Found., St. Louis, 1976—; bd. dirs. fin. com., bylaws com., mem. corp. Eliot Pratt Edn. Ctr., Inc., The Pratt Ctr.: Your Connection with the Natural World, New Milford, 1987-94; bd. dirs., mem. corp. Kent (Conn.) Land Trust, Inc., 1989—, treas., 1989-93; project financier Restoration of 1851 Samuel Curtiss Hosford House, Nat. Register Historic Dist., Falls Village, Conn., 1984-86; commr. Housatonic River Commn., Warren, Conn., 1985-93, vice chmn., 1986-87, chmn., 1988-92; commr., vice chmn. Conservation, Inland Wetlands and Watercourses Commn., Kent, 1988-92; mem. schs. and scholarships com., Office of Admissions and Fin. Aid, Harvard and Radcliffe Colls., 1991—. Mem. Cum Laude Soc., Mary Inst. and St. Louis Country Day Sch. Alumni Assn., Harvard Alumni Assn., Capitol Hill Club (Washington), Harvard Club (N.Y.C.), Hasty Pudding-Inst. of 1770 (Cambridge), Wyoming Heritage Found. Republican. Episcopalian. Office: W H Graham & Sons Investment Counsel 1818 Evans Ave Ste 207 Cheyenne WY 82001-4664

MYERS, RUTH, costume designer. Costume designer: (films) Smashing Time, 1967, Work Is A Four-Letter Word, 1968, A Nice Girl Like Me, 1969, Isadora, 1969, Three into Two Won't Go, 1969, The Twelve Chairs, 1970, The Virgin Soldiers, 1970, Romance of a Horse Thief, 1971, The Ruling Class, 1972, A Touch of Class, 1973, Little Malcolm and His Struggle Against the Eunuchs, 1974, That'll Be the Day, 1974, The Adventures of Sherlock Holmes' Smarter Brother, 1975, Stardust, 1975, Galileo, 1975, The Romantic Englishwoman, 1975, (with Ed Wynigear, Phyllis Garr, Darryl Athons, and Carolina Ewart)The World's Greatest Lover, 1977, Magic, 1978, Silver Bears, 1978, ...And Justice For All, 1979, The Main Event, 1979, The Competition, 1980, In God We Trust, 1980, It's My Turn, 1980, Altered States, 1980, First Monday in October, 1981, Sunday Lovers, 1981, Cannery Row, 1982, Something Wicked This Way Comes, 1983, Crimes of Passion, 1984, Electric Dreams, 1984, (with Norman Burza and Michele Neely) Teachers, 1984, The Woman in Red, 1984, Plenty, 1985, Haunted Honeymoon, 1986, The Accidental Tourist, 1988, Vibes, 1988, Bert Rigby, You're a Fool, 1989, Blaze, 1989, Blood Red, 1989, The Russia House, 1990, The Marrying Man, 1991, Another You, 1991, The Addams Family, 1991 (Acad. award nomination best costume design 1991), Mr. Saturday Night, 1992, The Firm, 1993, (TV movie) Baja Oklahoma, HBO, 1988. Office: Sandra Marsh Mgmt 9150 Wilshire Blvd Ste 220 Beverly Hills CA 90210*

MYERS, SAMUEL LLOYD, education association executive; b. Balt., Apr. 18, 1919; s. David Elkanah and Edith Alexandria (Reid) M.; m. Marion Tama Rieras, Nov. 23, 1943; children—Yvette, Tama, Samuel Lloyd. BS summa cum laude in Social Sci., Morgan State U., Balt., 1940, LLD, 1978; MA in Econs., Boston U., 1942; MA in Econs., Harvard U., 1948, PhD in Econs., 1949; LLD, U. Md., 1983; LHD (hon.), Sojourner-Douglass Coll., 1992, Shaw U., 1994—. Rsch. assoc. Harvard U., Cambridge, Mass., 1949; economist Bur. Labor Stats., Dept. labor, Washington, 1950; prof., dept. chmn. Morgan State Coll., 1950-63, leader in establishment Grad. Sch., 1962; adv. regional integration affairs Bur. Inter-Am. Affairs, Dept. State, Washington, 1963-67; pres. Bowie State Coll., Md., 1967-77, pres. emeritus, 1977—; pres. Nat. Assn. Equal Opportunity in Higher Edn., Washington, 1977—; mem. task Force on Internat. Study Ctrs., 1973; mem. Com. on Future Internat. Studies, 1973; vice chmn. Md. Com. for Humanities and Pub. Policy, 1974-76, Tech. Assistance Consortium for Improved Coll. Services, 1974-77; mem. capital financing adv. bd. Historically Black Coll. and Univs., 1993. Served to capt. U.S. Army, 1942-46, PTO. Decorated comdr. De L'Ordre Nat., (Cote d'Ivoire), 1991; named Alumnus of Yr., Morgan State U., 1976; named to Acad. Disting. Alumni Boston U., 1989; recipient citation for outstanding community service Balt. Urban League, 1964, Samuel Z. Westerfield award Nat. Econ. Assn., 1995; research fellow Harvard U., 1947-49; Rosenwald fellow Harvard U., 1946-47. Mem. Am. Assn. State Colls. and Univs. (bd. dirs. 1976-77), Internat. Tchr. Exchange (chmn. com. on internat. programs 1972-75, mem. pres.'s commn. on fgn.

langs. and internat. studies 1978-80), Alpha Kappa Mu, Alpha Phi Alpha, Sigma Pi Phi. Democrat. Methodist. Office: Nat Assn Equal Opportunity Higher Edn 400 12th St NE Washington DC 20002-6322

MYERS, THEODORE ASH, financial executive; b. Ellwood City, Pa., Aug. 3, 1930; s. Hiram John and Celia (Emery) M.; m. Katharine Louise Hoy, July 2, 1952 (dec.); children: David, Randall, Mark, Katharine, Scott, Christopher; m. Linda Bromley Moore, Nov. 28, 1986. BS in Indsl. Mgmt., Pa. State U., 1952; MBA in Fin., Harvard U., 1966. With indsl. instrument div. Mpls. Honeywell Co., Phila., 1952-56; with Halsey Stuart & Co., N.Y.C., 1957-60, Arnold Malkan & Co., Inc., N.Y.C., 1961-63; mgmt. cons. Belmont, Mass., 1963-66; v.p., treas. Washington Nat. Corp., Evanston, Ill., 1966-74, Whittaker Corp., Los Angeles, 1974-75; asst. v.p. fin. Inland Steel Co., Chgo., 1975-81; v.p. fin. Inland Steel Industries, Inc. (formerly Inland Steel Co.), 1981-89; sr. v.p., chief fin. officer Doskocil Cos., South Hutchinson, Kans., 1990—; bd. dirs. Van Kampen Merritt, Closed End Funds, Doskocil Cos., Inc., Hutchinson, Kans. Mem. Am. Fin. Assn., Machinery and Allied Products Inst., Fin. Execs. Inst. Republican. Clubs: Skokie Country (Glencoe, Ill.), Harvard of N.Y., Harvard Bus. Sch. of Chgo., Econ., Union League (Chgo.), Ventana Canyon Golf and Racquet (Tucson), Prairie Dunes Country (Hutchinson). Home: 550 Washington Ave Glencoe IL 60022-1837 Office: Doskocil Cos 321 N Main St South Hutchinson KS 67505-1127

MYERS, WALTER DEAN, young adult book author; b. Martinsburg, W.Va., Aug. 12, 1937; foster s. Herbert Dean and Florence Brown; children from previous marriage: Karen, Michael Dean; m. Constance Brendel, June 19, 1973; 1 child, Christopher. BA, Empire State U., 1984. Employment supr. N.Y. State Dept. Labor, Bklyn., 1966-69; sr. trade book editor Bobbs-Merrill Co., Inc., N.Y.C., 1970-77. Author: (for children) Where Does the Day Go?, 1969 (Coun. Interracial Books for Children award 1968), The Dragon Takes a Wife, 1972, The Dancers, 1972, Fly, Jiimy, Fly!, 1974, The World of Work: A Guide to Choosing a Career, 1975, Fast Sam, Cool Clyde, and Stuff, 1975 (Woodward Park Sch. Ann. Book award 1976), Social Welfare, 1976, Brainstorm, 1977, Mojo and the Russians, 1977, Victory for Jamie, 1977, It Ain't All for Nothin', 1978 (ALA Best Books for Young Adults citation 1978), The Young Landlords, 1979 (ALA Best Books for Young Adults citation 1979, Coretta Scott King award 1980), The Black Pearl and the Ghost; or, One Mystery After Another, 1980, The Golden Serpent, 1980, Hoops, 1981 (ALA Best Books for Young Adults citation 1982), The Legend of Tarik, 1981 (Notable Children's Trade Book in Social Studies citation 1982), Won't Know Till I Get There, 1982, The Nicholas Factor, 1983, Tales of a Dead King, 1983, Mr. Monkey and the Gotcha Bird, 1984, Motown and Didi: A Love Story, 1984 (Coretta Scott King award 1984), The Outside Shot, 1984, Adventure in Granada, 1985, The Hidden Shrine, 1985, Duel in the Desert, 1986, Ambush in the Amazon, 1986, Sweet Illusions, 1986, Crystal, 1987, Shadow of the Red Moon, 1987, Fallen Angels, 1988, Scorpions, 1988 (Newbery Honor Book 1989), Me, Mop and the Moondance Kid, 1988, The Mouse Rap, 1990, Now Is Your Time!: The African American Struggle for Freedom, 1991 (Coretta Scott King award 1991), Somewhere in the Darkness, 1992 (Newbery Honor book 1993), A Place Called Heartbreak: A Story of Vietnam, 1992, The Righteous Revenge of Artemis Bonner, 1992, Mop, Moondance and the Nagasaki Knights, 1992, Young Martin's Promise, 1992, Malcolm X: By Any Means Necessary, 1993, The Test, 1993, Intensive Care, 1993, Fashion by Tasha, 1993, Dangerous Games, 1993, Brown Angels: An Album of Pictures and Verse, 1993, The Glory Field, 1994, Darnell Rock Reporting, 1994, The Story of the Three Kingdoms, 1995, How Mr. Monkey Saw the Whole World, 1996. Recipient Margaret A. Edwards award ALA's Young Adult Library Services Assn., 1994.

MYERS, WARREN POWERS LAIRD, physician, educator; b. Phila., May 2, 1921; s. John Dashiell and Mary Hall (Laird) M.; m. Katharine Van Vechten, July 1, 1944; children: Warren Powers Laird, Jr., Anne Van Vechten Myers Evans, Duncan McNeir, Sara Myers Gormley. Grad., Episcopal Acad., 1939; B.S., Yale U., 1943; M.D., Columbia U., 1945; M.S. in Medicine, U. Minn., 1952; postgrad. (Eleanor Roosevelt Found. fellow), U. Cambridge, Eng., 1962-63. Diplomate: Am. Bd. Internal Medicine. Rotating intern Phila. Gen. Hosp., 1945-46; intern medicine Maimonides Hosp., N.Y.C., 1948-49; resident fellow in medicine Mayo Clinic, Rochester, Minn., 1949-52; clin. asst. Meml. Hosp., N.Y.C., 1952-54; asst. attending physician Meml. Hosp., 1954-58, assoc. attending physician, 1959, attending physician, 1959-90; instr. Cornell U. Med. Coll., 1955-56, asst. prof., 1956-59, asso. prof., 1959-68, prof. medicine, 1968-86, prof. emeritus, 1986—, assoc. dean, 1977-86; chmn. dept. medicine Meml. Sloan-Kettering Cancer Ctr., N.Y.C., 1967-77; v.p. for ednl. affairs Meml. Hosp., 1977-81, Eugene W. Kettering prof., 1979-86; attending physician N.Y. Hosp., N.Y.C., 1968-86; mem. Sloan-Kettering Inst. Cancer Rsch., N.Y.C., 1969-90; mem. emeritus Meml. Sloan-Kettering Cancer Ctr., N.Y.C., 1990—; cons. Rockefeller U. Hosp., N.Y.C., 1977-86; Mem. clin. cancer tng. com. Nat. Cancer Inst., 1970-73, chmn., 1971-73, chmn. clin. cancer edn. com., 1975-78; adj. prof. medicine Dartmouth Med. Sch., 1987—; cons. staff Mary Hitchcock Meml. Hosp., Hanover, N.H., 1987—. Contbr. articles on cancer, bone metabolism, internal medicine, and med. edn. to med. jours. Bd. dirs. Rye (N.Y.) United Fund, 1969-72, chmn. budget com., 1968-69; bd. dirs. Damon Runyon-Walter Winchell Cancer Fund, 1976-86, pres., 1985-86; trustee Hitchcock Clinic, Hanover, N.H., 1983—, Dartmouth-Hitchcock Med. Ctr., Hanover, 1983—, chmn. exec. com., 1992—; teacher's coll. Columbia U., 1980-86. Served with Med. Corps, USNR, 1946-47. Recipient Alumni award for research Mayo Clinic, 1952, Margaret Hay Edwards Achievement medal Am. Assn. Cancer Edn., 1993. Fellow ACP, N.Y. Acad. Medicine (v.p. 1983-85); mem. Am. Clin. and Climatological Assn., Am. Assn. Cancer Research, Endocrine Soc., Harvey Soc., Am. Fedn. Clin. Research, Practioners' Soc. of N.Y., AMA, Am. Assn. Cancer Edn. (pres. 1984-85), Am. Soc. Clin. Oncology, Founders and Patriots Pa., Alpha Omega Alpha. Presbyterian (elder 1969—). Clubs: Yale, Charaka, Century Assn. (N.Y.C.). Office: Dartmouth Hitchcock Med Ctr Dept Medicine 1 Medical Ctr Dr Lebanon NH 03756 Address: Jericho St RR 2 Box 376 White River Junction VT 05001

MYERS, WAYNE ALAN, psychiatrist, educator; b. N.Y.C., Dec. 13, 1931; s. Harry and Eve Myers; m. Joanne Jackson, Mar. 23, 1969; children: Tracy Victoria, Blake Andrew. BS with high honors, U. Ark., 1952; MD, Columbia U., 1956. Cert. in psychiatry and psychoanalysis. Intern Bellevue Hosp., N.Y.C., 1956-57; resident Payne Whitney Clinic, N.Y. Hosp., N.Y.C., 1957-59, 61-62; instr. psychiatry Cornell U. Med. Ctr., N.Y.C., 1962-72; clin. asst. prof. psychiatry Cornell U. Med. Ctr., 1972-77, clin. assoc. prof. psychiatry, 1977-84, clin. prof. psychiatry, 1984—; tng. and supervising admitting psychoanalyst Columbia U. Ctr. for Psychoanalytic Tng. & Research, N.Y.C., 1983—; sec. Assn. for Psychoanalytic Medicine, N.Y.C., 1987-89. Author: Dynamic Therapy of the Older Patient, 1984, Shrink Dreams, 1992; editor: New Concepts in Psychoanalytic Psychotherapy, 1987, New Techniques in the Psychotherapy of Older Patients, 1991, The Perverse and the Near Perverse in Clinical Practice, 1991, contbr. articles to profl. jours. Capt. U.S. Army, 1959-61. Fellow Am. Psychiat. Assn. (life), Am. Psychoanalytic Assn.; mem. Assn. for Psychoanalytic Medicine (sec.), N.Y. State Med. Soc., N.Y. County Med. Soc., PEN, Author's Guild. Avocations: skiing, squash, creative writing. Office: 60 Sutton Pl S Ste ICN New York NY 10022

MYERS, WENDY SUZANNE, editor; b. North Kansas City, Mo., Sept. 1, 1966; d. F. Dale and Fran L. (Bellinger) Richmond; m. Douglas G. Myers, June 11, 1988. BS in Journalism & Broadcasting, Cen. Mo. State U., 1988; postgrad., Webster U., 1991—. Reporter, photographer Decorah (Iowa) Newspapers, 1988-89; editor Women in Bus. mag., Kansas City, Mo., 1989—. Mem. Soc. Profl. Journalists, Kansas City Soc. Mag. Editors (pres. 1992-93), Kansas City Press Club (treas. 1990-92, membership chmn. 1990-92, pres.-elect 1992-93). Office: Women in Business 9100 Ward Pky Kansas City MO 64114-3306

MYERS, WILLIAM GERRY, III, advocate, lawyer; b. Roanoke, Va., July 13, 1955; s. William Gerry and Ruby Grey (Pollard) M.; m. Susan Louise Benzer, Aug. 27, 1988; children: Katherine Coulter, Molly Benzer. AB, Coll. of William and Mary, 1977; JD, U. Denver, 1981. Bar: Colo. 1981, Wyo. 1982, D.C. 1987, U.S. Supreme Ct. 1990. Assoc. Davis & Cannon, Sheridan, Wyo., 1981-85; legis. counsel U.S. Sen. Alan K. Simpson, Wyo.,

1985-89; asst. to atty. gen. U.S. dept. Justice, Washington, 1989-92; dep. gen. counsel for programs U.S. Dept. Energy, Washington, 1992-93; corp. counsel The Cattlemen Advocating Through Litigation Fund, 1993—; dir. fed. lands Nat. Cattlemen's Assn., 1993—; exec. dir. Pub. Lands Coun., Washington, 1993—; guest lectr. Georgetown U. Sch. Law, Am. U., U. Colo. Sch. Law, Nat. Park Svc. Tng. Ctr., Nat. Acad. Scis., Grazing Lands Forum, Wyo. State Bar. Editl. staff Denver Law Jour., Denver Jour. Internat. Law and Policy; contbr. articles to profl. jours. Office: Public Lands Council Ste 300 1301 Pennsylvania Ave NW Washington DC 20004-1701

MYERS, WILLIAM S., magazine publishing executive; m. Aleksandra Myers; 3 children. BA, Colgate U., 1958. From sales and mktg. rep. to N.Y. divsn. sales mgr. Life Mag., until 1972; advt. sales mgr. Sports Illustrated Mag., 1972-74, N.Y. advt. sales mgr., 1976-82; v.p. mktg. HBO, 1974-75; advt. sales dir. People Mag., 1982-85, assoc. pub., 1985-88; pub. Money Mag., N.Y.C., 1988—. With USN. Office: Money Mag Time & Life Bldg Rockefeller Ctr 33rd fl New York NY 10020

MYERS, WOODROW AUGUSTUS, JR., physician, corporate medical director; b. Indpls., Feb. 14, 1954; s. Woodrow Augustus Sr. and Charlotte T. (Tyler) M.; m. Debra Jackson, June 23, 1973; children: Kimberly Leilani, Zachary Augustus. BS, Stanford (Calif.) U., 1973, MBA, 1982; MD, Harvard U., 1977. Intern in internal medicine Stanford U. Med. Ctr., 1977-78, resident in internal medicine, 1978-80, fellow, critical care medicine, 1980-81; asst. prof. critical care medicine San Francisco Gen. Hosp., 1982-84; physician health advisor com. on labor and human resources U.S. Senate, Washington, 1984; commr. Ind. Dept. of Health, Indpls., 1985-90; health commr. N.Y.C. Dept. of Health, 1990-91; corp. med. dir. Assoc. Group, Indpls., 1991—; asst. prof. medicine Cornell Med. Coll., N.Y.C., 1990-91; bd. trustees Stanford U., 1987-92; assoc. prof. medicine Ind. U. Sch. Medicine, 1992—. Bd. dirs. Stanford Health Systems, 1994—. Robert Wood Johnson clin. scholar, Stanford U., 1980-82. Fellow ACP; mem. AMA, Nat. Med. Assn., Soc. Critical Care Medicine. Office: Assoc Group 120 Monument Cir Indianapolis IN 46204-4906

MYERSON, ALAN, director, film and television writer; b. Cleve., Aug. 8, 1936; s. Seymour A. and Vivien I. (Caplin) M.; m. Irene Ryan, June 2, 1962; 1 son, Lincoln; m. Leigh French, Apr. 15, 1977; children—Sierra Jasmine French, Darcy Anna French-Myerson. Student, Pepperdine Coll., 1956-57, UCLA, 1957. mem. acting faculty U. Calif., Berkeley, 1966, San Francisco State U., 1967. Dir. N.Y. and Off Broadway Prodns., 1958-64, including This Music Crept By Me Upon the Waters, The Committee; dir.: Second City, N.Y.C. and Chgo., 1961, 62; founder, producer, dir. The Committee, San Francisco, L.A. and N.Y., 1963-74; dir.: (films) Steelyard Blues, 1972, Private Lessons, 1981, Police Academy 5, 1988; numerous TV shows, 1975—, including Laverne and Shirley, Rhoda, Bob Newhart Show, Welcome Back, Kotter, Fame, Crime Story, Dynasty, Miami Vice, Hunter, Sisters, Picket Fences, The Larry Sanders Show, Frazier, Friends; TV films The Love Boat, 1976, Hi, Honey, I'm Dead, 1991, Bad Attitudes, 1991; writer It's Showtime. Active in civil rights, anti-war, anti-nuclear power movements, 1957—. Mem. Dirs. Guild Am., Writers Guild Am. West.

MYERSON, ALBERT LEON, physical chemist; b. N.Y.C., Nov. 14, 1919; s. Myer and Dora (Weiner) M.; m. Arline Harriet Rosenfield, May 10, 1953; children: Aimee Lenore, Lorraine Patrice, Paul Andrew. BS, Pa. State U., 1941; postgrad., Columbia U., 1942-45; PhD, U. Wis., 1948. Rsch. asst. Manhattan Project Columbia U., N.Y.C., 1941-45; sr. rsch. chemist Franklin Inst. Labs., Phila., 1948-56; mgr. phys. chemistry Gen. Electric Co., Phila., 1956-60; prin. phys. chemist Aero. Lab. Cornell U., Buffalo, 1960-68; tech. assoc. Exxon Rsch. and Engring. Co., Linden, N.J., 1969-79; head phys. chemistry sect. Mote Marine Lab., Sarasota, Fla., 1979-85; sr. scientist Princeton (N.J.) Sci. Enterprises, Inc., 1985—; cons. in field. Violinist in Venice Symphony; co-editor: Physical Chemistry in Aerodynamics and Space Flight, 1961; contbr. articles in field to profl. jours.; patentee in field. Fellow Am. Phys. Soc.; mem. Am. Chem. Soc., Combustion Inst., Pa. State U. Alumni Assn., Sigma Xi, Phi Lambda Upsilon. Home and Office: 4147 Rosas Ave Sarasota FL 34233-1614 *It has always seemed to me that one's satisfacion with life can be expessed as an integral of the intensity of his or her pursuit of contributions to the world as a function of time, throughout one's life.*

MYERSON, JACOB MYER, former foreign service officer; b. Rock Hill, S.C., June 11, 1926; s. Solomon and Lena (Clein) M.; m. Nicole Neuray, June 10, 1965 (dec. Oct. 1968); 1 child, Sylvie Anne; m. Helen Hayashi, Mar. 9, 1974 (dec. Jan. 1995). Student, Pa. State Coll., 1944; B.A. with distinction, George Washington U., 1949, M.A., 1950; grad., Fgn. Service Inst., 1953. Joined U.S. Fgn. Service, 1950; 3d sec. (Office U.S. High Commr. Germany), Berlin, 1950-52; 2d sec. (U.S. Mission to NATO and European Regional Orgn.), Paris, France, 1953-55; also mem. U.S. permanent del. to coordinating com. InterGovtl. Consultative Group on EastWest Trade; internat. economist, internat. relations officer State Dept., 1956-60; adviser U.S. del. GATT session, Geneva, Switzerland, 1958; ministerial session OEEC, Paris, 1958; 1st sec., chief polit. section U.S. Mission to European Communities, Brussels, Belgium, 1960-65; spl. asst. to under sec. state, 1965-66; officer-in-charge NATO Polit. Affairs, Dept. State, 1966-68; adviser U.S. delegation ministerial sessions North Atlantic Council, 1966-67; dep. polit. adviser, counselor U.S. Mission to NATO, Brussels, Belgium, 1968-70; counselor econ. affairs U.S. Mission to European Communities, Brussels, 1970-74; minister counselor U.S. Mission to European Communities, from 1974; U.S. rep. to UN Econ. and Social Council with rank of ambassador, 1975-77; alt. U.S. del. 30th and 31st sessions UN Gen. Assembly, 1975, 76; alt. U.S. rep. 4th session UN Conf. on Trade and Devel., 1976; ministercounselor for econ. and comml. affairs Am. Embassy, Paris, 1977-80; ret., 1980; dep. sec. gen. OECD, Paris, 1980-88. Served with inf. AUS, 1944-46, ETO. Decorated Bronze Star; Order of the Sacred Treasure Gold and Silver medal (Japan). Recipient Meritorious Service award State Dept., 1960. Mem. Fgn. Service Assn. (Rivkin award 1969), Phi Beta Kappa, Artus, Pi Gamma Mu, Phi Eta Sigma. Address: 2 rue Lucien Gaulard, 75018 Paris France

MYERSON, JOEL ARTHUR, English language educator, researcher; b. Boston, Sept. 9, 1945; s. Edward Yale and Gwenne (Rubenstein) M. AB, Tulane U., 1967; MA, Northwestern U., 1968, PhD, 1971. Asst. prof. English U. S.C., Columbia, 1971-76, assoc. prof., 1976-80, prof., 1980-90, Carolina Rsch. prof. Am. Lit., 1990—, chmn. English dept. 1987-90. Author: Margaret Fuller: An Annotated Secondary Bibliography, 1977, Brook Farm: An Annotated Bibliography and Resources Guide, 1978, Margaret Fuller: A Descriptive Bibliography, 1978, The New England Transcendentalists and the Dial: A History of Magazine and Its Contributors, 1980, Theodore Parker: A Descriptive Bibliography, 1980, Ralph Waldo Emerson: A Descriptive Bibliography, 1982, Emily Dickinson: A Descriptive Bibliography, 1984, Walt Whitman: A Descriptive Bibliography, 1993; co-author: Melville Dissertations: An Annotated Directory, 1972, Emerson: An Annotated Secondary Bibliography, 1985, Ralph Waldo Emerson: An Annotated Bibliography of Criticism, 1980-91, 1994; editor: The American Renaissance in New England, 1978, Margaret Fuller: Esssays on American Life and Letters, 1978, Antebellum Writers in New York and the South, 1979, Critical Essays on Margaret Fuller, 1980, Margaret Fuller, Woman in the Nineteenth Century, 1980, Emerson Centenary Essays, 1982, The Transcendentalists: A Review of Research and Criticism, 1984, The Brook Farm Book: A Collection of First-Hand Accounts of the Community, 1987, The American Transcendentalists, 1988, Critical Essays on Henry David Thoreau's Walden, 1988, Whitman in His Time, 1991, Emerson and Thoreau: The Contemporary Reviews, 1992, The Walt Whitman Archive, 1993, The Cambridge Companion to Henry David Thoreau, 1995, Studies in the American Renaissance, 1977—; co-editor: Critical Essays on American Transcendentalism, 1982, Critical Essays on Ralph Waldo Emerson, 1983, The Selected Letters of Louisa May Alcott, 1987, A Double Life: Newly Discovered Thrillers of Louisa May Alcott, 1988, The Journals of Louisa May Alcott, 1989, Louisa May Alcott: Selected Fiction, 1990, Freaks of Genius: Unknown Thrillers of Louisa May Alcott, 1991, Three Children's Novels by Christopher Pearse Cranch, 1993, Emerson's Antislavery Writings, 1995. Woodrow Wilson Dissertation Yr. fellow, 1970, summer fellow NEH, 1976, rsch. grantee, 1978-81, 88-91, 94-97; Guggenheim Found. fellow, 1981; rsch. grantee Am. Philos. Soc., 1982, 84. Mem. Assn. for Ducumentary Editing (pres. 1989-90, Disting. Svc. award 1986), Philol.

Assn. of Carolinas (pres. 1987-88), Thoreau Soc. (pres. 1992—), MLA (del. assembly 1978-80), Emerson Soc. (pres. 1994-95). Democrat. Home: 6310 Goldbranch Rd Columbia SC 29206-3340 Office: U of SC Dept of English Columbia SC 29208

MYERSON, PAUL GRAVES, psychiatrist, educator; b. Boston, Sept. 15, 1914; s. Abraham and Dorothy (Loman) M.; children: Peter P., Deborah L. Myerson-Kaup, Andrew A., Nancy E. Myerson-Shield. B.S., Harvard, 1935, M.D., 1939. Diplomate Am. Bd. Psychiatry and Neurology. Intern Beth Israel Hosp., Boston, 1939-40; resident neurology Mt. Sinai Hosp., N.Y.C., 1941-42; resident psychiatry N.Y. Psychiat. Inst., 1942-43; tng. analyst Boston Psychoanalytic Soc. and Inst., 1959-85, tng. analyst emeritus 1985—; prof. psychiatry Tufts U. Sch. Medicine, 1962-85, prof. emeritus 1985—, chmn. dept. psychiatry, 1963-79, area dir. Mental Health Ctr., 1968-74; psychiatrist-in-chief New Eng. Med. Ctr. Hosp., 1963-79; vis. prof. psychiatry Harvard Med. Sch., 1979-86; Pres. Boston Psychoanalytic Soc. and Inst., 1972-74. Served to lt. USNR, 1943-46. Fellow Am. Psychiat. Assn. (life); mem. Am. Psychoanalytic Assn., AAAS. Home and Office: 25 Larch Rd Newton MA 02168-1413

MYERSON, ROBERT J., radiologist, educator; b. Boston, May 12, 1947; s. Richard Louis and Rosemarie (Farkas) M.; m. Carla Wheatley, Aug. 8, 1970; 1 child, Jacob Wheatley. BA, Princeton U., 1969; PhD, U. Calif., Berkeley, 1974; MD, U. Miami, 1980. Diplomate Am. Bd. Radiology. Asst. prof. dept. physics Pa. State U., State Coll., 1974-76; fellow Inst. Advanced Studies, Princeton, N.J., 1976-78; resident U. Pa. Hosp., Phila., 1981-84; assoc. prof. radiology Washington U. Sch. Medicine, St. Louis, 1984—, assoc. dir. residency tng. radiation oncology, 1989—. Contbr. articles to profl. jours. Recipient Career Devel. award Am. Cancer Soc., 1985. Mem. Am. Coll. Radiation, Am. Soc. Therapeutic Radiologists, Am. Phys. Soc. Democrat. Jewish. Avocation: bicycling. Office: Washington U Radiation Oncology Ctr Box 8224 4939 Audubon Ave Ste 5500 Saint Louis MO 63110

MYERSON, ROGER BRUCE, game theorist, economist, educator; b. Boston, Mar. 29, 1951; s. Richard L. and Rosemarie (Farkas) M.; m. Regina M. Weber, Aug. 29, 1982; children: Daniel, Rebecca. AB summa cum laude, Harvard U., 1973, SM, 1973, PhD, 1976. Asst. prof. decision scis. Northwestern U., Evanston, Ill., 1976-78, assoc. prof., 1979-82, prof., 1982—, Harold Stuart prof. decision scis., 1986—, prof. econs., 1987—; guest researcher U. Bielefeld, Federal Republic of Germany, 1978-79; vis. prof. econs. U. Chgo., 1985-86. Author: Game Theory: Analysis of Conflict, 1991; mem. editorial bd. Internat. Jour. Game Theory, 1982-92, Games and Econ. Behavior, 1988—; assoc. editor Jour. Econ. Theory, 1983-93; also articles. Guggenheim fellow, 1983-84; Sloan rsch. fellow, 1984-86. Fellow Econometric Soc., Am. Acad. Arts and Scis. Office: Northwestern U Kellogg Grad Sch Mgmt 2001 Sheridan Rd Evanston IL 60208-2009

MYERSON, TOBY SALTER, lawyer; b. Chgo., July 20, 1949; s. Raymond King and Natalie Anita (Salter) M. BA, Yale U., 1971; JD, Harvard U., 1975. Bar: N.Y. 1977, Calif. 1977. Assoc. Coudert Bros., N.Y.C., 1975-77, 81, San Francisco, 1977-81; assoc. Paul, Weiss, Rifkind, Wharton & Garrison, N.Y.C., 1981-83, ptnr., 1983-89; mng. dir. Wasserstein Perella & Co., Inc., N.Y.C., 1989-90; ptnr. Paul, Weiss, Rifkind, Wharton & Garrison, N.Y.C., 1991; lectr. U. Calif. Berkeley, 1979-81, Harvard U., Cambridge, Mass., 1982-83; visiting lectr. Yale U., New Haven, 1983-84; bd. dirs. Myerson, Van Den Berg & Co., Santa Barbara, Calif. Contbg. editor: Doing Business in Japan, 1983, Council on Foreign Rels., 1993—. Sec. Japan Soc. Inc., N.Y.C., 1985-89; bd. dirs. 1058 Corp., N.Y.C., 1985-88. Mem. ABA (subcom. internat. banking, corp. and bus. law sect.), Internat. Bar Assn., N.Y. State Bar Assn., Assn. Bar City N.Y. (com. on fgn. and comparative law, chmn. 1988-89), Calif. Bar Assn. Avocations: art, music, literature, tennis, golf. Home: 1056 Fifth Ave New York NY 10028-0112 Office: Paul Weiss Rifkind Wharton & Garrison 1285 Ave of The Americas New York NY 10019-1532

MYGATT, SUSAN HALL, lawyer; b. Stamford, Conn., Sept. 29, 1947; d. Eben Clarke and Jane Elizabeth (Terhune) Hall; m. Samuel G. Mygatt, June 11, 1977; children: Elizabeth, Jenny, Catherine. BA, Smith Coll., 1969; JD, Boston U., 1977. Bar: Mass. 1977. Adminstrv. asst. HUD, Washington, 1969-73; exec. asst. Urban Devel. Corp., N.Y.C., 1973-74; ptnr. Goodwin, Procter & Hoar, Boston, 1977—. Mem. ABA, Mass. Bar Assn., New Eng. Women in Real Estate. Office: Goodwin Procter & Hoar Exchange Pl Boston MA 02109

MYHRE, BYRON ARNOLD, pathologist, educator; b. Fargo, N.D., Oct. 22, 1928; s. Ben Arnold and Amy Lillian (Gilbertson) M.; m. Eileen Marguerite Scherling, June 16, 1953; children: Patricia Ann, Bruce Allen. B.S., U. Ill., 1950; M.S., Northwestern U., 1952, M.D., 1953; Ph.D., U. Wis., 1962. Intern Evanston (Ill.) Hosp., 1953-54; resident Children's Meml. Hosp., Chgo., 1956-57, U. Wis. Hosp., Madison, 1957-60; assoc. med. dir. Milw. Blood Center, 1962-66; sci. dir. Los Angeles Red Cross Blood Center, 1966-72; dir. Blood Bank Harbor-UCLA Med. Center, Torrance, 1972-85; chief clin. pathology Harbor-UCLA Med. Center, 1985—; prof. pathology UCLA, 1972—. Author: Quality Control on Blood Banking, 1974, (with others) Textbook of Clinical Pathology, 1972, Paternity Testing, 1975; editor seminar procs.; contbr. articles to med. jours., chpts. to books. Served with USAF, 1954-56. Mem. AMA, Am. Soc. Clin. Pathology (dep. commr. commn. on continuing edn.), Am. Assn. Blood Banks (pres. 1978-79), Coll. Am. Pathologists (chmn. blood bank survey com.), Assn. Clin. Scientists (pres. 1993), Calif. Med. Assn., Calif. Blood Bank Systems (past pres.), Wis. Blood Bank Assn. (past pres.), L.A. Acad. Medicine (past pres.), Harbor-UCLA Faculty Soc. (past pres.), Palos Verdes Breakfast Club (treas. 1995). Home: 4004 Via Larga Vis Pls Vrds Est CA 90274-1122 Office: Harbor-UCLA Med Center PO Box 2910 Torrance CA 90509-2910

MYHRE, ROGER L., agricultural products executive; b. 1938. Sr. v.p. Agrex, Inc., Shawnee Mission, Kans. Office: AGREX Inc 9300 W 119th St Ste 500 Shawnee Mission KS 66213-1504

MYHREN, TRYGVE EDWARD, communications company executive; b. Palmerton, Pa., Jan. 3, 1937; s. Arne Johannes and Anita (Blatz) M.; m. Carol Jane Enman, Aug. 8, 1964; children: Erik, Kristen, Tor; m. 2d Victoria Hamilton, Nov. 14, 1981; 1 stepchild, Paige. BA in Philosophy and Polit. Sci., Dartmouth Coll., 1958, MBA, 1959. Sales mgr., unit mgr. Procter and Gamble, Cin., 1963-65; sr. cons. Glendinning Cos., Westport, Conn., 1965-69; pres. Auberge Vintners, 1970-73; exec. v.p. Mktg. Continental, Westport, 1969-73; v.p. gen. mgr. CRM, Inc., Del Mar, Calif., 1973-75; v.p. mktg. Am. TV and Communications Corp., Englewood, Colo., 1975-78, sr. v.p. mktg. and programming, 1978-79, exec. v.p., 1980, pres., 1981, chmn. bd., chief exec. officer, 1981-88; v.p. then exec. v.p. Time Inc., N.Y.C., 1981-88; treas., vice chmn. then chmn. bd. dirs., mem. exec. com. Nat. Cable TV Assn., Washington, 1982-91; mem. adv. com. on HDTV, FCC, 1987-89; bd. dirs. Advanced Mktg. System, Inc., LaJolla, Citizens Bank Corp., Providence; pres. Myhren Media, 1989—, Greenwood Cable Mgmt., 1989-91, Providence Jour. Co., 1990—; pres. CEO King Broadcast Co., 1991—. Vice chmn. Pub. Edn. Coalition; mem. Colo. Forum, 1984-91, chmn. higher edn. com., 1986; bd. dirs., founder Colo. Bus. Com. for the Arts, 1985-91; mem. exec. coun. Found. for Commemoration U.S. Constn., 1987-90; mem. Nat. GED Task Force, 1987-90, Colo. Baseball Commn., 1989-91, Colo. Film Comm., 1989-91; trustee Nat. Nat. Hosp., 1989—, R.I. Hosp., 1991-95, Lifespan Health Sys., 1994—; chmn. Looc 1995 NCAA Hockey Championship. Lt. (j.g.) USNR, 1959-63. Recipient Disting. Leader award Nat. Cable TV Assn., 1988. Mem. Cable TV Adminstrn. and Mktg. Soc. (pres. 1978-79, Grand Tam award 1985, One of a Kind award 1994), Cable Adv. Bur. (founder 1978), Chrons and Colitis Found. Am. (trustee Rocky Mountain chpt.). Episcopalian.

MYLER, RUSSELL CLINTON, social services association administrator; b. St. Louis, June 28, 1944; s. Frank Russell and Lorene (Hayden) Miler; m. Patricia Noland, May 4, 1974; children: Katherine Patricia, Andrew Noland. BA, William Jewell Coll., 1966; MSW, Washington U., St. Louis, 1971. Juvenile officer St. Louis County Juvenile Ct., Clayton, Mo., 1971-73; ctr. coord. Boys Town of Mo., St. Louis, 1973-75; dir. social work Epworth Children's Home, St. Louis, 1975-86; exec. dir. Mo. chpt. Nat. Assn. Social Workers, Columbia, 1986-93; exec. dir. Prader-Willi Syndrome Assn., St. Louis, 1994—. Bd. dirs. Project Start, St. Louis. Mem. NASW, St. Louis

Soc. Assn. Execs. Democrat. Avocation: gardening. Home: 1308 Kirkham Ave Saint Louis MO 63122-3127 Office: Prader-Willi Syndrome Assn 2510 S Brentwood blvd Ste 220 Saint Louis MO 63144

MYLOD, ROBERT JOSEPH, banker; b. Bklyn., Nov. 21, 1939; s. Charles Joseph and Katherine (Normile) M.; m. Monica Manieri, July 11, 1964; children: Rosemary, Robert, Kevin, Paul, Monica, Megan. B.A., St. John's U., 1961. Vice pres. Citibank (N.A.), N.Y.C., 1965-70; V.p. Citicorp., N.Y.C., 1970-73; exec. v.p residential loan div. Advance Mortgage Corp., Detroit, 1973-75; pres. Advance Mortgage Corp., 1975-83; pres., chief operating officer, dir. Fed. Nat. Mortgage, 1983-85; chmn., pres., chief exec. officer, dir. Mich. Nat. Corp., 1985—; chmn., CEO, dir. Mich. Nat. Bank, 1987—, chmn., dir., 1985—. Served to lt. (j.g.) USN, 1961-65. Office: Mich Nat Corp PO Box 9065 Farmington MI 48333-9065

MYLROIE, WILLA WILCOX, transportation engineer, regional planner; b. Seattle, May 30, 1917; d. Elgin Roscoe and Ruth B. (Begg) Wilcox; m. John Ellis Mylroie (dec. 1947); children: Steven Wilcox Mylroie, Jo Mylroie Sohneronne; m. Donald Gile Fassett, Dec. 30, 1966. BS in Civil Engring., U. Wash., 1940, MS in Regional Planning, 1953. Lic. profl. civil engr. Civil engr. U.S. Engring. Dept. C.E., Seattle, 1941-46; affiliate prof. civil engring. U. Wash. Seattle, 1948-51, research asst. prof. civil engring., 1951-56; assoc. prof. civil engring. Purdue U., Lafayette, Ind., 1956-58; research engr. and planner Wash. State Dept. Hwys., Olympia, 1958-69, head research and spl. assignment div., 1969-81; cons. civil engring. and regional planning Olympia, 1981—; cons. King County Design Commn., Seattle, 1981-89; advisor Coll. Engring. U. Wash., 1978-86, affiliate prof. civil engring., 1981-84; advisor Wash. State U. Coll. Engring., Pullman, 1977-85. Active Girls Scouts U.S. coun., Boy Scouts Am., Olympia, Renton, 1950-66; pres. high sch. PTA, Olympia; commr. Thurston County Planning Commn., Olympia; U.S. Coast Guard Auxiliary, 1982-89, U.S. Power Squadron, 1967—; citizen ambo. People to People Trip, Moscow, St. Petersburg, Russia and Muensk, Bolarus. Recipient Profl. Recognition award Women's Transp., Spokane, Spl. Svc. award Transp. Rsch. Bd. Coun., Washington, U. Wash. Coll. Engring. Alumni Achievement award, 1993. Fellow ASCE (ad hoc vis. com. engring. coun. for profl. devel., Edmund Friedman Profl. Recognition award 1978), Inst. Transp. Engrs. (hon. mem., internat. bd. dirs., Tech. Coun. award 1982); mem. Planning Assn. Wash. (bd. dirs.), Sigma Xi. Avocations: sailing, gardening, travel, music, vol. community activities. Home and Office: 7501 Boston Harbor Rd NE Olympia WA 98506-9720

MYNATT, JOHN RUPERT, JR., soft drink bottling executive; b. Knoxville, Tenn., Jan. 29, 1937; s. John Rupert and Eula James (Hansard) M.; m. Gail Janis Hildebrand, Mar. 14, 1958; children: Brenda, Rhonda, John E., Douglas. Student, Lawrence Inst. Tech., 1956, U. Mich., 1957-58. Route mgr. Pepsi Cola Met., Detroit, 1964-66, br. mgr., 1966-69, gen. sales mgr., 1969-75; v.p. sales Seven-Up Ind., Indpls., 1975-79; v.p. gen. mgmt. Pepsi Cola Gen. Bottlers, Aurora, Ill., 1979-81; v.p. gen. mgmt. Chgo. div. Pepsi Cola Gen. Bottlers, 1981—. Mem. exec. bd. Chgo. area council Boy Scouts Am., 1982—, chmn. food, beverage, and hospitality lucheon, Chgo., 1982, 83, 84, chmn. recognition dinner, 1985. Recipient Sales Achiever award Pepsi Cola Co., 1981, Chmns. award I.C. Industries, 1983, Good Scout award Cngo. Area Council, 1985. Mem. Mdse. Exec. Club, Grocers Mfrs. Sales Exec., Ill. Food Retailers, Alpha Tau Omega. Clubs: Society, Medinah Country (Chgo.). Avocations: golf, racquetball. Office: Pepsi-Cola Gen Bottlers Inc 3501 W Algonquin Rd Rolling Meadows IL 60008-3102

MYRA, HAROLD LAWRENCE, publisher; b. Camden, N.J., July 19, 1939; s. John Samuel and Esther (Christensen) M.; m. Jeanette Austin, May 7, 1966; children: Michelle, Todd, Gregory, Ricky, Joshua, Lindsey. B.S., East Stroudsburg State Coll., 1961; Litt.D., John Wesley Coll., 1976; D.Lit., Biola U., 1984; DLitt, Gordon Coll., 1992. Tchr. Pocono Mountain Jointure, Cresco, Pa., 1961; editorial asst. Youth for Christ Internat., Wheaton, Ill., 1961-62; assoc. editor Youth for Christ Internat., 1962-64, mng. editor, 1964-65, dir. of lit., 1965-66; v.p. lit. div., pub. Campus Life, Wheaton, 1966-75; pres., chief exec. officer Christianity Today, Inc., Carol Stream, Ill., 1975—. Author: No Man in Eden, 1969, Michelle, You Scallawag, I Love You, 1972, The New You, 1972, The Carpenter, 1972, Elsbeth, 1975, Is There a Place I Can Scream?, 1976, Santa, Are You For Real?, 1979, Love Notes to Jeanette, 1979, The Choice, 1980, Halloween, 1982, Your Super-Terrific Birthday, 1985, Living By God's Surprises, 1988, Children in the Night, 1991, The Shining Face, 1993, Morning Child, 1994. Presbyterian. Home: 1737 Marion Ct Wheaton IL 60187-3319 Office: Christianity Today 465 Gundersen Dr Carol Stream IL 60188-2498

MYRBERG, ARTHUR AUGUST, JR., marine biological sciences educator; b. Chicago Heights, Ill., June 28, 1933; s. Arthur August and Helen Katherine (Stelle) M.; divorced; children—Arthur August III, Beverly Priscilla. A.B., Ripon Coll., 1954; M.S., U. Ill., 1958; Ph.D. (NIH fellow), UCLA, 1961. Research asst. Ill. Natural History Survey, Champaign-Urbana, 1957; mem. faculty U. Miami, Fla., 1964—; assoc. prof. Sch. Marine and Atmospheric Sci., 1967-72, prof., 1972—; chmn. div. marine biology and fisheries U. Miami, Fla., 1991, academic chmn. div. marine biology and fisheries, 1991-93. Contbr. articles to profl. jours., chpts. to books; assoc. editor Bull. Marine Sci, 1964-73. Mem. Khoury League, 1967-75. Served to 1st lt., inf. U.S. Army, 1954-57. Recipient Disting. Alumni award Ripon Coll., 1991; NIH postdoctoral fellow Max Planck Inst. Behavioral Physiology, Seewiesen, Germany, 1961-64. Fellow Animal Behavior Soc. (Disting. Fellow Lecture award 1993), Am. Inst. Fishery Rsch. Biologists; mem. Am. Soc. Ichthyologists and Herpetologists, Am. Soc. Zoologists, Ecol. Soc. Am., Am. Inst. Biol. Scis., N.Y. Acad. Scis., Internat Assn. Fish Ethologists, Am. Elasmobranch Soc. (gov. 1985-90), Sigma Xi (nat. lectr. 1980-81), Phi Sigma, Omicron Delta Kappa. Achievements include demonstration of the importance of sound production for survival and reproduction in fishes, that sharks are attracted to specific types of underwater sound; reported on the social behavior of sharks. Home: 6001 SW 65th Ave Miami FL 33143-2031

MYRDAL, ROSEMARIE CARYLE, state official, former state legislator; b. Minot, N.D., May 20, 1929; d. Harry Dirk and Olga Jean (Dragge) Lohse; m. B. John Myrdal, June 21, 1952; children: Jan, Mark, Harold, Paul, Amy. BS, N.D. State U., 1951. Registered profl. first grade tchr., N.D. Tchr. N.D., 1951-71; bus. mgr. Edinburg Sch. Dist., 1974-81; mem. N.D. Ho. of Reps., Bismarck, 1984-92, mem. appropriations com., 1991, 92—; lt. gov., State of N.D., Bismarck, 1992—; sch. evaluator Walsh County Sch. Bds. Assn., Grafton, N.D., 1983-84; evaluator, work presenter N.D. Sch. Bds. Assn., Bismarck, 1983-84; mem. sch. bd. Edinburg Sch. Dist., 1981-90; adv. com. Red River Trade Corridor, Inc., 1989—. Co-editor Heritage '76, 1976, Heritage '89, 1989. Precinct committeewoman Gardar Twp. Rep. Com., 1980-86; leader Hummingbirds 4-H Club, Edinburg, 1980-83; bd. dirs. Camp Sioux Diabetic Children, Grand Forks, N.D., 1980-90, N.D. affiliate Am. Diabetes Assn., Families First-Child Welfare Reform Initiative, Region II, 1989-92; dir. N.D. Diabetes Assn., 1989-91; chmn. N.D. Ednl. TelecommunicationsCoun., 1989-90; vice chmn. N.D. Legis. Interim Jobs Devel. Commn., 1989-90. Mem. AAUW (pres. 1982-84 Pembina County area), Pembina County Hist. Soc. (historian 1976-84), Northeastern N.D. Heritage Assn. (pres. 1986-92), Red River Valley Heritage Soc. (bd. dirs. 1985-92). Lutheran. Club: Agassiz Garden (Park River) (pres. 1968-69). Avocations: gardening, architectural history, ethnic foods, historic/cultural preservation. Home: # 302 121 E Arikara Ave Bismarck ND 58501 Office: 600 E Boulevard Ave Bismarck ND 58505

MYREN, RICHARD ALBERT, criminal justice consultant; b. Madison, Wis., Aug. 9, 1924; s. Andrew Olaus and Olyanna (Olson) M.; m. Patricia Ross Hubin, June 12, 1948; children: Nina Ross Schroepfer, Tania Ellis Zobel, Kristina Albee Myren Sheldon, Andrew James. BS, U. Wis., 1948; LLB, Harvard U., 1952; LLD (hon.), U. New Haven, 1976. Bar: N.C. 1954. Research chemist U.S. Dept. Agr., No. Regional Research Lab., Peoria, Ill., 1948-49; asst. to assoc. research prof. pub. law and govt. Inst. Govt., Chapel Hill, N.C., 1952-56; asst. to assoc. prof. Ind. U., 1956-66; dean, prof. Sch. Criminal Justice, State U. N.Y., Albany, 1966-76; dean, prof. Sch. Justice, Am. U., Washington, 1976-86, prof. emeritus, 1986—; cons. Washington, 1987—; vis. prof. Inst. Criminology, Cambridge (Eng.) U., 1973-74, East China Inst. for Politics and Law, Shanghai, People's Republic of China, 1988; cons. law enforcement programs for children and youth Children's Bur., HEW, Washington, 1960-62; cons. Pres.'s. Com. on Juvenile Delinquency and Youth Crime, 1962-64, Pres.'s Commn. on Law Enforcement and Adminstrn. Criminal Justice, 1966, U.S. Law Enforcement Assistance Adminstrn., 1968-82, N.Y. State Temp. Commn. on Constl. Conv., 1967, N.Y. State Dept. Edn., 1967, 69, Calif. Coordinating Council for Higher Edn., 1969-70, Nat. Adv. Commn. on Criminal Justice Standards and Goals, 1971-72, Tenn. Higher Edn. Commn., 1976, Ky. Dept. Justice, 1977-78, NSF, 1978—, U.S. Civil Rights Commn., 1978, others. Author: Coroners in North Carolina: A Discussion of Their Problems, 1953, Indiana Sheriffs' Manual of Law and Practice, rev. edit, 1959, Indiana Conservation Officers' Manual of Law and Practice, 1961; (with Lynn D. Swanson) Police Work With Children, 1962; (with Carroll L. Christenson) The Walsh-Healey Public Contracts Act: A Critical Review of Prevailing Minimum Wage Determinations, 1966, Education in Criminal Justice, 1970, Law and Justice: An Introduction, 1988, Investigation for Determination of Fact: A Primer on Proof, 1989; contbr. to: Bases for Justice Systems: Law and the Social Sciences (Gordon E. Misner), 1980, Five Year Outlook: Problems, Opportunities and Constraints in Science and Technology, 1980; assoc. editor: Jour. Criminal Justice; contbr. articles to profl. jours. Bd. dirs. Sex Info. and Edn. Council U.S., 1972-75. Served with inf. AUS, 1943-46, ETO; with USNR, 1954-68. Fulbright research scholar to Argentina Cordoba, 1964-65. Mem. N.C. Bar Assn., Sociedad Argentina de Sociología. Home: 1051 S Highland St 6D Mount Dora FL 32757-6323

MYRER, ANTON OLMSTEAD, author; b. Worcester, Mass., Nov. 3, 1922; s. Raymond Lewis and Angele (Cormack) M.; m. Patricia McFarland Schartle, May 1, 1970. A.B. magna cum laude, Harvard U., 1944. Author: Evil Under the Sun, 1951, The Big War; movie In Love and War, 1957, The Violent Shore, 1962, The Intruder, 1965, Once an Eagle (Book of Month Club and Readers Digest Book Club selection 1968, basis NBC TV series Bestsellers 1977), 1968, The Tiger Waits, 1973, The Last Convertible (Lit. Guild and Readers Digest Book Club selection; NBC-TV miniseries 1979), 1978; A Green Desire, 1982 (main selection of Lit. Guild). Served with USMCR, 1942-45, PTO. Mem. Authors Guild, PEN, Authors League Am., Signet Soc.

MYRICK, RONALD ERNEST, lawyer, educator; b. Louisville, Ky., July 16, 1943; s. Charles Byron and Lillian (Frances) M.; m. Lynn Kessack, July 31, 1965; children: Amy, Ron Jr., Drew. BEE, U. Louisville, 1966; MEE, Ariz. State U., 1968; JD, Loyola U., Chgo., 1974. Bar: Ill. 1974, Tex. 1980, U.S. Dist. Ct. (no. dist.) Tex., U.S. Ct. Appeals (5th, 7th, 11th and Fed. cirs.), U.S. Patent and Trademark Office 1972, U.S. Trademark Ct., U.S. Supreme Ct., Mass. 1989. Project engr. Sperry Flight Systems, Phoenix, 1966-68; engr. dynamics McDonnel Douglas Astronautics, Nassau Bay, Tex., 1969-70; mem. tech. staff Bell Telephone Labs., Holmdel, N.J., 1970; mem. patent staff Bell Telephone Labs., Naperville, Ill., 1970-74; ptnr. Neuman Williams Anderson & Olson, Chgo., 1974-79; gen. patent counsel, chief legal dept. Mostek Corp. subs. United Techs. Corp., Dallas, 1979-80, gen. counsel, 1980-82, v.p. various depts., 1982-85; v.p. and counsel N.Am. ops. Otis Elevator Co. sub. UTC, Farmington, Conn., 1985-86; mgr. engring. law group Digital Equipment Corp., Maynard, Mass., 1986-88; v.p., asst. gen. counsel Digital Equipment Corp., Maynard, 1988-93, asst. sec., 1989-93; adj. internat. law faculty U. Conn. Law Sch., 1986-88; mem. exec. com. bd. dirs. Intellectual Property Owners Inc.; adj. internat. law faculty Suffolk U. Law Sch., 1993; adv. ELRC of Harvard Law, 1992, AIPLA, 1992, FCA, 1991. Editor: World Litigation Law and Practice, 1989. Bd. dirs. exec. com. Dallas Coun. World Affairs, 1985; co-chmn. coalition contbg. to Nat. Coop. Rsch. Act 1984; mem. adv. group for Implementation of Civil Justice Reform Act U.S. Dist. Ct., Mass., 1991—; rep. 8th meeting Experts World Intellectual Property Orgn., 1990, Diplomatic Conf., 1991, 92; chmn. litigation delary and cost reduction subcom. AIPLA, 1989-91. Recipient Nat. Merit Scholarship. Mem. ABA, ACA, AIPLA, Tex. Bar Assn., Internat. Bar Assn., Southwestern Legal Found. (adv. bd. Internat. and Comparative Law Ctr. 1986-89), Internat. Intellectual Property Assn., Boston Bar Assn., FCA World Affairs Coun. Boston, Boston Patent Law Assn., Computer Law Assn., Mass. Bar Assn., Nat. Assn. Mfrs., U.C. Coun. Internat. Bus., Licensing Execs. Soc., Assn. Corp. Patent Counsel (bd. dirs. 1988-89), Phi Kappa Phi, Omicron Delta Kappa, Sigma Tau. Avocations: sailing, flying, scuba diving, amateur radio, singing. Home: 30 Saddle Ridge Rd Sudbury MA 01776-2772 Office: Fish & Richardson 225 Franklin St Boston MA 02110

MYRICK, SUE, congresswoman, former mayor; b. Tiffin, Ohio, Aug. 1, 1941; d. William Henry and Margaret Ellen (Roby) Wilkins; m. Jim Forest (div.); children: Greg, Dan; m. Wilbur Edward Myrick Jr., Sept. 11, 1977. Student, Heidelberg Coll., 1959-60. Exec. sec. to mayor and city mgr. City of Alliance, Ohio, 1962-63; dir. of office Stark County Ct. of Juvenile and Domestic Rels., Alliance, 1963-65; pres. Myrick Agy., Charlotte, N.C., 1971—; mayor of Charlotte, 1987-91; mem. 104th Congress from 9th N.C. District, Washington, D.C., 1995—; candidate for U.S. Senate from N.C., 1992; active Heart Fund, Multiple Sclerosis, March of Dimes, Arts and Scis. Coun. Fund Dr.; past mem. adv. bd. Uptown Shelter, Uptown Homeless Task Force, bd. dirs. N.C. Inst. Politics; v.p. Sister Cities Internat.; mem. Pres. Bush's Affordable Housing Commn.; founder, coord. Charlotte vol. tornado relief effort; bd. dirs. Learning How; former mem. adv. bd. U.S. Conf. Mayors; mem.-at-large Charlotte City Coun., 1983-85, Strengthening Am. Commn.; lay leader, Sunday sch. tchr. 1st United Meth. Ch.; treas. Mecklenburg Ministries; former trustee U.S. Conf. of Mayors. Recipient Woman of Yr. award Harrisonburg, Va., 1968; named one of Outstanding Young Women of Am., 1968. Mem. Women's Polit. Caucus, Beta Sigma Phi. Republican. Home: 310 W 8th St Charlotte NC 28202-1704 Office: US House Reps 509 Cannon House Office Bldg Washington DC 20515-3309 also: Myrick Enterprises 505 N Poplar St Charlotte NC 28202-1729

MYSAK, LAWRENCE ALEXANDER, oceanographer, climatologist, mathematician, educator; b. Saskatoon, Sask., Can., Jan. 14, 1942; s. Stephen and Nettie (Trojan) M.; m. Diane Mary Eeles, Aug. 15, 1974; children: Paul Alexander, Claire Anastasia. B.Sc., U. Alta., Can., 1961; M.Sc., U. Adelaide, Australia, 1963; M.A., Harvard U., 1964, Ph.D., 1967. Research fellow Harvard U., 1966-67; mem. faculty U. B.C., Vancouver, 1967-86; prof. math. and oceanography U. B.C., 1976-86; Atmospheric Environ. Svc./Natural Scis. Engring. Rsch. Coun.; sr. indsl. rsch. prof. climatology McGill U., Montreal, Que., Can., 1986—; dir. Climate Research Group, 1986-90; Can. Steamship Lines prof. meteorology McGill U., Montreal, Que., 1989—; founding dir. Centre for Climate and Global Change Research, 1990—; vis. research assoc. Oreg. State U., summer 1968; sr. visitor Cambridge (Eng.) U., 1971-72; vis. scientist Inst. Ocean Sci., Sidney, B.C., fall 1976, Nat. Center Atmospheric Research, Boulder, Colo., 1977; vis. prof. U.S. Naval Postgrad. Sch., Monterey, Calif., summer 1981, Swiss Fed. Inst. Tech., Zurich, 1982-83. Co-author: Waves in the Ocean, 1978; also articles in profl. jours.; assoc. editor Jour. Phys. Oceanography, 1977-92, Atmosphere-Ocean, 1988-91, Climatological Bull., 1992-93; contbg. editor Springer-Verlag books on coastal and esturaine studies, 1987—; mem. editorial bd. Geophys. and Astrophys. Fluid Dynamics, 1983—. Mem. Royal Soc. Can., Acad. Sci. Royal Soc. Can. (v.p. 1993-94, pres. 1993—), Can. Meteorol. and Oceanographic Soc. (co-recipient Pres.'s prize 1980), Am. Meteorol. Soc., Am. Geophys. Union, The Oceanography Soc. Office: McGill U, 805 Sherbrooke St W, Montreal, PQ Canada H3A 2K6

MYSLOWKA, MYRON WILLIAM (RON MYSLOWKA), labor union executive; b. Val D'Or, Que., Can., Jan. 14, 1942; s. Anthony and Victoria (Nowosad) M.; m. Janet Florence Hill, July 6, 1963 (div.); children: Lorraine Susan, Myron Shawn, Jason Anthony; m. Donna Clare Fowle, Nov. 2, 1991. Grad., Welland High Sch., Ont. Can., 1961. Electrician Wabasso, 1966-72; with United Textile Workers of Am., 1972—, dir. Ontario and Maritimes, 1974-85, interim Can. dir., 1985-88, Can. dir., 1988-92, pres. Coun. of Can., 1988-92, pres., 1991—. Office: United Textile Workers of Am 2 Echelon Plz Ste 200 Voorhees NJ 08043-2330

NABATOFF, ROBERT ALLAN, vascular surgeon, educator; b. N.Y.C., Nov. 19, 1918; s. Abraham Louis and Emma (Goldin) N.; m. Joan Herman, Sept. 11, 1955; children: Diane, Richard, Ross. BA, U. Mich., 1939; MD, SUNY, N.Y.C., 1943. Intern Mt. Sinai Hosp., N.Y.C., 1943-44, resident in surgery, 1945-46, Dazian Found. pathology fellow, 1944-45; Rosenstock Found. fellow in cardiovascular surgery Presbyn. Hosp., N.Y.C., 1948-49; asst. clin. prof. in vascular surgery Mt. Sinai Hosp., N.Y.C., 1972-74, assoc. clin. prof. in vascular surgery, 1974-79, clin. prof. vascular surgery, 1978—; attending vascular surgeon, 1979—, dir. ambulatory surg. svc., 1982—; cons. vascular surgeon Jewish Hosp. and Home for Aged, N.Y.C., 1978—.

Author 3 book chpts.; contbr. over 60 articles to profl. jours.; inventor 6 surg. devices. Recipient Hon. Medallion, Keio Sch. Medicine, Japan, 1962, Medallion of Honor, Mt. Sinai Alumni Assn., 1965. Fellow AMA, ACS, N.Y. Acad. Medicine; mem. N.Y. State Med. Soc., N.Y. County Med. Soc., N.Y. Soc. for Cardiovascular Surgery, N.Y. Surg. Soc., Pan Am. Med. Assn. (pres. vascular surgery sect.). Avocations: jogging, tennis, walking, theatre, ballet. Office: Medical Office 1020 Park Ave New York NY 10028-0913

NABERS, DRAYTON, JR., insurance company executive; b. Birmingham, Ala., Dec. 2, 1940; s. Drayton Sr. and Jane (Porter) N.; m. Fairfax Smathers, Dec. 31, 1965; children: Drayton III, Mary James, Fairfax Virginia. BA, Princeton U., 1962; LLB, Yale U., 1965. Law clk. to justice Hugo Black U.S. Supreme Ct., Washington, 1965-66; assoc. Cabaniss, Johnston, Gardner, Dumas & O'Neal, Birmingham, Ala., 1966-79; sr. v.p. ops., gen counsel Protective Life Ins. Co., 1979; pres. Empire Gen. Life Ins. Co., 1980-82; pres., COO Protective Life Corp./Protective Life Ins. Co., 1982-92; pres., CEO Protective Life Ins. Co, Birmingham, Ala., 1992-94, chmn., pres., CEO, 1994—; bd. dirs. Protective Life Corp., Protective Life Ins. Co., Am. Found. Life Ins. Co., Energen, Inc., Nat. Bank of Commerce. Mem. steering com. Leadership Birmingham; bd. dirs. Ala. Assn. Ind. Colls.; pres. bd. dirs. Birmingham Alive; trustee So. Rsch. Inst., Berry Coll. Mem. Birmingham Bar Assn., Ala. Bar Assn. Office: Protective Life Corp 2801 Hwy 280 S Birmingham AL 35223 Office: PO Box 2606 Birmingham AL 35202-2606

NABI, STANLEY ANDREW, investment executive; b. Baghdad, Iraq, Sept. 17, 1930; came to U.S., 1947; s. Moshi S. and Victoria T. (Mukamal) N.; m. Bette E. Miller, Mar. 31, 1968; children: Deborah Susan, Lisa Meryl. B.A., Columbia U., 1952; postgrad., NYU, 1954-58. Gen. ptnr. Schweickart & Co., N.Y.C., 1954-72; gen. ptnr., chief investment officer Lazard Freres & Co., N.Y.C., 1973-84; exec. v.p. Bessemer Trust Co., N.A., 1985—; pres., CEO, Bessemer Investors Svcs., 1986-94; lectr. New Sch. Social Research, N.Y.C., 1963-68; investment cons. U.S. Steel and Carnegie Pension Fund, N.Y.C., 1979—; dir. Bargain Town U.S.A., N.Y.C., 1962-69; mem. Pres.'s Coun. New Sch. Social Rsch., N.Y.C., 1989—; adj. prof. fin. Grad. Sch. Bus. Fordham U., N.Y., 1992—. Editor: weekly jour. The Fin. Analysts Jour., 1992; assoc. editor: jour. The Fin. Analysts Jour., 1971-83. Trustee NABI Found. 1964—. Served with U.S. Army, 1952-54. Mem. N.Y. Soc. Security Analysts (pres. 1971-72), Inst. Chartered Fin. Analysts, Fin. Analysts Fedn. (dir. 1972-74). Home: 83 Beach Rd Great Neck NY 11023-1019 Office: 630 Fifth Ave New York NY 10111-0001

NABORS, JAMES THURSTON, actor, singer; b. Sylacauga, Ala., June 12, 1930; s. Fred Nabors. Grad. in bus. adminstrn., U. Ala. Formerly film editor, then jr. cutter for TV; singer at cabaret-theatre, The Horn, Santa Monica, Calif.; first TV appearance on Steve Allen Show; appeared in: own series Gomer Pyle-USMC, 1964-72, Andy Griffith Show, 1963-64, Jim Nabors Hour, 1969-71, Lost Saucer, 1975-76, Sylvan in Paradise, 1986, The Jim Nabors Show, 1987; TV guest appearances on Redd Foxx Show; dramatic appearances in The Rookies; night club headliner in Las Vegas and Lake Tahoe, Nev.; recs. include albums Very Special, The Special Warmth of Jim Nabors, 1986; also 16 single recs.; star: Jim Nabors Polynesian Extravaganza, Honolulu, 1979-81; movie appearances include The Best Little Whorehouse in Tex., 1982, Stroker Ace, 1983, Cannon Ball II, 1984; other TV work includes (movie) Return to Mayberry. Recipient 5 gold albums, 1 platinum album. Office: care William Morris Agy 151 S El Camino Dr Beverly Hills CA 90212-2775

NACE, BARRY JOHN, lawyer; b. York, Pa., Nov. 28, 1944; s. John Harrison and Mildred Louise (Orwig) N.; m. Andrea Marcia Giardini. Apr. 28, 1973; children: Christopher Thomas, Jonathan Barry, Matthew Andrew. BS, Dickinson Coll., 1965, JD, 1969, LLD, 1994. Bar: Md. 1970, D.C. 1971, Pa. 1972, U.S. Ct. Appeals (3d, 4th and D.C. cirs.), U.S. Supreme Ct. Ptnr. Davis & Nace, Washington, 1972-78, Paulson & Nace, Bethesda, Md., 1978-85; sr. ptnr. Paulson, Nace & Norwind, Washington, 1986—. Fellow Roscoe Pound Found. (trustee); mem. Am. Law Inst., D.C. Bar Assn., Montgomery County Bar Assn., Assn. Trial Lawyers Am. (gov. 1976-87, pres. 1993-94), Met. D.C. Trial Attys. (pres. 1977, 87, Atty. of Yr. 1976), Trial Lawyers for Pub. Justice, Civil Justice Found. (trustee), Internat. Acad. Trial Lawyers, Lambert Soc., Am. Inns of Ct. Avocations: golf, tennis, reading, racquetball. Home: 6208 Garnett Dr Bethesda MD 20815-6618 Office: Paulson Nace & Norwind 1814 N St NW Washington DC 20036-2404

NACH, JAMES PETER, foreign service officer; b. Yonkers, N.Y., Aug. 28, 1941; s. Irving Peter and Grace (Sansiper) N.; m. Thuy Duong, Dec. 22, 1978; 1 child, Elizabeth K. BA, St. John's Coll., Annapolis, Md., 1964; Master of Interant. Affairs, Columbia U., 1966; postgrad., Cornell U., 1979-80. Joined fgn. svc. Dept. State, Washington, 1966; with U.S. Consulate, Calcutta, India, 1967-69; with Am. Embassy, Saigon, Vietnam, 1970-74, Manila, 1982-86; various positions U.S. Dept. State, Washington, 1974-82, office dir., 1989-91, with Bur. Pers., 1991-93; polit. counselor Am. Embassy, Kingston, Jamaica, 1986-89; dep. chief mission Am. Embassy, Dhaka, Bangladesh, 1993—; sr. fgn. svc. officer U.S. Dept. State, 1988—. Author 10 Visual Geography texts, 1962-66. Mem. Am. Fgn. Svc. Assn., Sierra Club. Avocations: bicycling, hiking, philately. Home: 7404 Venice St Falls Church VA 22043 Office: Am Embassy Dhaka Dept of State Washington DC 20521-6120

NACHMAN, FREDERICK, public relations executive. Ptnr. Fin. Rels. Bd., Chgo. Office: Fin Rels Bd John Hancock Ctr 875 N Michigan Ave Chicago IL 60611*

NACHMAN, GERALD WEIL, columnist, critic, author; b. Oakland, Calif., Jan. 13, 1938; s. Leonard Calvert and Isabel (Weil) N.; m. Mary Campbell McGeachy, Sept. 3, 1966 (div. 1979). Student, Merritt Coll., 1955-57; BA in Journalism, San Jose State U., 1960. TV and humor columnist San Jose (Calif.) Mercury, 1960-63; feature writer N.Y. Post, N.Y.C., 1963-66; drama critic Oakland (Calif.) Tribune, 1966-71; syndicated humor columnist N.Y. Daily News, 1973-79; critic and columnist San Francisco Chronicle, 1979-93; author, 1995—; juror Pulitzer Prize Com. to choose best play, 1991. Author: The Portable Nachman, 1960, Playing House, 1978, Out on a Whim, 1983, The Fragile Bachelor, 1989; contbr. to (book) Snooze, 1986; contbr. articles to newspapers, mags.; author, co-lyricist (revues) Quirks, 1979, Aftershocks, 1992. Recipient Page One award N.Y. Newspaper Guild, 1965, Deems Taylor award ASCAP, 1989. Home: 281 Juanita Way San Francisco CA 94127-1744

NACHMAN, JAMES L., lawyer; b. Chgo., Mar. 31, 1942. BA, Cornell U., 1963; JD, U. Chgo., 1966. Bar: Ill. 1966. Ptnr. Winston & Strawn, Chgo.; lectr. in field. Mem. ABA (mem. corp., banking and bus. law sects., litigation), Ill. State Bar Assn., Chgo. Bar Assn. (mem. bankruptcy and reorganization com. 1969—, chmn. 1979-80, mem. bankruptcy lawyers referral screening subcom. 1981-85), Law Club Chgo. Office: Winston & Strawn 35 W Wacker Dr Chicago IL 60601-1614

NACHMAN, MERTON ROLAND, JR., lawyer; b. Montgomery, Ala., Dec. 21, 1923; s. Merton Roland and Maxine (Mayer) N.; children: Nancy Nachman Yardley, Linda Nachman Connelly, Betsy Wild, Amy N. DeRoche, Karen Vann; m. Martha Street, June 8, 1968. AB cum laude, Harvard U., 1943, JD, 1948. Bar: Ala. 1949, U.S. Supreme Ct. 1953, U.S. Ct. Appeals (5th and 11th cirs.), U.S. Ct. Claims, U.S. Tax Ct. Asst. atty. gen. State of Ala., 1949-54; ptnr. Knabe & Nachman, Montgomery, 1954-59; adminstrv. asst. to Senator John Sparkman of Ala., 1956; ptnr. Steiner, Crum & Baker, Montgomery, 1959-86; ptnr. Balch & Bingham, 1986-94, coun. 1994—. Chmn. human rights com. Ala. Prison System, 1976-78. With USN, 1943-46. Recipient award of merit Ala. State Bar, 1974; cert. of appreciation Supreme Ct. Ala., 1974. Fellow Am. Coll. Trial Lawyers; mem. ABA (com. on fed. judiciary 1982-88, bd. govs. 1978-81), Ala. State Bar (pres. 1973-74), Am. Judicature Soc. (dir. 1976-80, Herbert Lincoln Harley award 1974), Am. Law Inst., Ala. Law Inst., Unity Club (Montgomery), Am. Acad. Appellate Lawyers. Episcopalian. Office: 2 Dexter Ave PO Box 78 Montgomery AL 36101

NACHMAN, NORMAN HARRY, lawyer; b. Chgo.; s. Harry and Mary (Leibowitz) N.; m. Anne Lev, June 19, 1932; children: Nancy Nachman

Laskow, James Lev, Susan Lev. PhB, U. Chgo., 1930, JD, 1932. Bar: Ill. 1932, U.S. Dist. Ct. (no. dist.) Ill. 1932, U.S. Dist. Ct. (we. dist.) Tex. 1978, U.S. Ct. Apls. (5th cir.) 1978, (8th cir.) 1994, (7th cir.) 1942, U.S. Sup. Ct. 1942. Assoc. Michael Gesas, Chgo., 1932-35; assoc. Schwartz & Cooper, Chgo., 1936-40, ptnr., 1940-46; pvt. practice, Chgo., 1947-67; founder, sr. ptnr. Nachman, Munitz & Sweig, Ltd., Chgo., 1967-87; ptnr. Winston & Strawn, 1987-94; counsel McDermott, Will & Emery, 1994—; mem. adv. com. bankruptcy rules Jud. Conf. U.S., 1960-76, 78-88; mem. Nat. Bankruptcy Conf., 1952—, mem. com. bankruptcy reorganization plans and securities problems, 1977-85; mem. faculty numerous bankruptcy seminars throughout U.S. Contbg. editor: Collier on Bankruptcy, 1981, 84. Chmn. appeals bd. Chgo. Dept. Environ. Control, 1960-80. Served to lt. USN, 1943-46. Mem. ABA (past chmn. comml. bankruptcy com.), Chgo. Bar Assn. (pres. 1963-64), Ill. Bar Assn., Standard Club, Law Club. Jewish. Office: McDermott Will & Emery 227 W Monroe St Chicago IL 60606-5096

NACHMAN, RALPH LOUIS, physician, educator; b. Bayonne, N.J., June 29, 1931; s. Samuel Nachman and Ethel Nelson; m. Nancy Rubin; children: Susan, Steve. BA, Vanderbilt U., 1953, MD, 1956. Lic. physician N.Y.; diplomate Am. Bd. Internal Medicine; subsplty. hematology, med. oncology. Intern in medicine Vanderbilt U. Hosp., 1949-53; asst. resident in medicine Montefiore Hosp., 1960-62; asst. resident in pathology N.Y. Hosp.-Cornell U. Med. Ctr., N.Y.C., 1957-58, rsch. fellow in medicine, 1962-63; dir. labs. for clin. pathology N.Y. Hosp., 1963-69, assoc. attending physician, 1968-72, attending physician, 1972—; from instr. to asst. prof. to assoc. prof. medicine Cornell Med. Ctr., 1963-72, chief divns. hematology, 1968-93, prof. medicine, 1972—; vice chmn. dept. medicine Cornell U. Med. Coll., 1974-78, acting chmn. dept. medicine, 1974-75, dir. Specialized Ctr. Rsch. in Thrombosis, 1976—, acting co-chmn. dept. medicine, 1980-81, bd. overseers, 1987-89; guest investigator Rockefeller U., 1969-70; Wiessberg lectr. Case Western Res. U., 1978; Aggeler lectr. U. Calif., San Francisco, 1981; Patek lectr. Boston U., 1981; Rosenthal lectr. Mt. Sinai, 1982; Beaumont lectr. Wash. U., 1983; Wiener lectr. N.Y. Blood Ctr., 1983; chmn. Gordon Conf. on Hemostasis, 1984; Alpha Omega Alpha lectr. N.Y. Med. Coll., 1985; Sharp lectr. Wayne State U., 1986; Roon lectr. Scripps Rsch. Inst., 1987; Johnson lectr. Internat. Soc. on Thrombosis, 1987; Merck lectr. Cleve. Clinic, 1987; vis. prof. Harvard U., 1991; E. Stanley Emery Jr. Meml. lectr, physician-in-chief pro tempore, 1991; chief resident's vis. prof. Baylor Coll. Medicine, 1991; Samuel S. Riven vis. prof. Vanderbilt U., 1992; Hymie Nossel Meml. lectr. Columbia U., 1992; Pfizer vis. prof. Royal Soc. Medicine, 1992; disting. lectr. Am. Heart Assn., 1994; Seckler lectr. Mt. Sinai Med. Ctr., 1994; Runme Shaw Meml. lectr. Acad. Medicine, Singapore, 1994; chmn. hematology study panel Health Rsch. Coun., N.Y.C., 1973-75; mem. NIH-Program Project Com. Heart and Lung Inst., 1975-79; bd. govs. Am. Bd. Internal Medicine, 1985-88; cons. Manhattan VA Hosp.; vis. physician Rockefeller U. Hosp. Author: Genetics of Coronary Heart Disease, 1992, Systemic Lupus Erythematosus, 1993, (jours.) Blood, 1994, Ann. Internal Medicine, 1993; assoc. editor: Beeson McDermott Textbook of Medicine, XIV edit., 1975, XV edit., 1979, Blood, 1976-82, Am. Jour. Medicine, 1978; adv. editor: Jour. Exptl. Medicine, 1976; editl. bd. Arteriosclerosis, 1983; contbr. articles to med. jours. With USN, 1958-60. Fellow ACP; mem. AAAS, Assn. Am. Physicians, Am. Soc. Clin. Investigation, Am. Fedn. Clin. Rsch., Am. Clin. and Climatol. Assn., N.Y. Acad. Sci., N.Y. Soc. for Study of Blood (pres. 1975), Am. Soc. Hematology (exec. coun. 1978-79), Harvey Soc. (coun. 1980), Am. Physiol. Assn., Internat. Soc. Thrombosis and Hemostasis (coun. 1986-92), Soc. Exptl. Biology and Medicine, Am. Soc. Biol. Chemists, Inst. Medicine of NAS, N.Y. Acad. Medicine, Cornell Med. Alumni (hon.), Nat. Blood Club (pres. 1981-82), Peripatetic Club, Alpha Omega Alpha, Phi Beta Kappa. Home: 657 Floyd St Englewood Cliffs NJ 07632 Office: NY Hosp-Cornell Med Ctr F-433 525 E 68th St New York NY 10021

NACHMAN, RONALD JAMES, research chemist; b. Takoma Park, Md., Feb. 1, 1954; s. Joseph Frank and Rosemary (Anderson) N.; m. Lita Rose Wilson, Dec. 18, 1976 (div. 1987); m. Isidora Austria Panis, May 6, 1989. BS in Chemistry, U. Calif., San Diego, 1976; PhD in Organic Chemistry, Stanford U., 1981. Rsch. asst. Scripps Inst. Oceanography, La Jolla, Calif., 1974-76; chemist Western Regional Rsch. Ctr., USDA, Berkeley, Calif., 1981-89, Vet. Toxicology and Entomology Rsch. Lab., College Station, Tex., 1989—; vis. scientist dept. molecular biology The Salk Inst., La Jolla, 1985, Scripps Rsch. Inst., La Jolla, 1988-89. Contbr. sci. articles to profl. jours. Recipient USDA Cert. of Merit, 1988, 91, Arthur S. Flemming award for sci. achievement, 1994. Fellow Sci. and Humanities Symposia; mem. AAAS, Am. Chem. Soc., N.Y. Acad. Scis., Sigma Xi. Avocations: travel, photography, jogging, racketball. Home: 1015 Pollux PO Box 14D Willis TX 77378-0014 Office: USDA Vet Toxicology Entomology Rsch Lab 2881 F and B Rd College Station TX 77845-9594

NACHMIAS, JACOB, psychologist educator. Prof. psychology dept. U. Pa., Phila. Recipient Edward D. Tillyer award Optical Soc. Am., 1994. Office: U Pa Dept Psychology Philadelphia PA 19104*

NACHT, DANIEL JOSEPH, architect; b. Chgo., Sept. 22, 1915; s. George Carl and Hattie (Zaylor) N.; m. Mary Alice Belcher, Nov. 19, 1960; 1 dau., Pamela Jean. B.S., U. Ill. 1940. Mem. faculty U. Ill., 1940-42; with Skidmore, Owings & Merrill, Chgo., 1946-53; designer Rogers Engring. Co., San Francisco, 1953-55; architect Starks, Jozens & Nacht, Sacramento, 1956-70, Nacht & Lewis, 1970. Prin. works include Consumnes River Coll, Sacramento County Courthouse. Mem. Capitol Bldg. and Planning Commn., 1959-67; mem. Core Area Com. 1962-64; mem. adv. bd. Salvation Army Sacramento area. With USNR, 1942-46. Fellow A.I.A.; mem. Crocker Art Gallery, Alpha Chi Rho. Club: Mason (Shriner). Home: 7604 Pineridge Ln Fair Oaks CA 95628-4855 Office: 7300 Folsom Blvd Sacramento CA 95826-2604

NACHT, SERGIO, biochemist; b. Buenos Aires, Apr. 13, 1934; came to U.S., 1965; s. Oscar and Carmen (Scheiner) N.; m. Beatriz Kahan, Dec. 21, 1958; children: Marcelo H., Gabriel A., Mariana S., Sandra M. BA in Chemistry, U. Buenos Aires, 1958, MS in Biochemistry, 1960, PhD in Biochemistry, 1964. Asst. prof. biochemistry U. Buenos Aires, 1960-64; asst. prof. medicine U. Utah, Salt Lake City, 1965-70; rsch. scientist Alza Corp., Palo Alto, Calif., 1970-73; sr. investigator Richardson-Vicks Inc., Mt. Vernon, N.Y., 1973-76; asst. dir., dir. rsch. Richardson-Vicks Inc., Mt. Vernon, 1976-83; dir. biomed. rsch. Richardson-Vicks Inc., Shelton, Conn., 1983-87; sr. v.p. rsch. and devel. Advanced Polymer Systems, Redwood City, Calif., 1987-93, sr. v.p. sci. and tech., 1993—; lectr. dermatology dept. SUNY Downstate Med. Ctr., Blkyn., 1977-87. Contbr. articles to profl. jours.; patentee in field. Mem. Soc. Investigative Dermatology, Soc. Cosmetic Chemists (award 1981), Dermatology Found., Am. Physiological Soc., Am. Acad. Dermatology. Democrat. Jewish. Home: 409 Wembley Ct Redwood City CA 94061-4308

NACHTIGAL, PATRICIA, equipment manufacturing company executive, general counsel; b. 1946. BA, Montclair State U.; JD, Rutgers U.; LLM, NYU. Tax atty. Ingersoll-Rand Co., Woodcliff Lake, N.J., 1979-83, dir. taxes and legal, 1983-88, sec., mng. atty., 1988-91, v.p., gen. counsel, 1991—. Office: Ingersoll-Rand Co 200 Chestnut Ridge Rd Westwood NJ 07675

NACHTWEY, JAMES ALAN, photojournalist; b. Syracuse, N.Y., Mar. 14, 1948; s. James Vincent and Jean (Stockton) N. BA cum laude, Dartmouth Coll., 1970. Contract photographer Time mag., N.Y.C., 1984—; mem. Magnum Photos, N.Y.C., 1986—; tchr. Internat. Ctr. Photography, N.Y.C., 1993, 94, Sante Fe Workshop, 1994, Jackson Hole (Wyo.) Workshop, 1994. Author; photographer: Deeds of War, 1989 (Leica award 1989), The Inferno, 1995; contbg. photographer (books) War Torn, El Salvador, In Our Time-40 Years of Magnum, The Indelible Image, Odyssey-Photography at the National Geographic, (mags.) Time, Life Nat. Geog. N.Y. Times Mag., Geo, Stern; one-man shows Internat. Ctr. Photography , 1989, Hasseblac Ctr., Gothenburg, Sweden, 1992, Canon Gallery, Amsterdam, The Netherlands, 1992, Carolinum, Prague, Czech Repulic, 1994, Nieuwe Kerk, Amsterdam, 1995. Recipient Robert Capa gold medal Overseas Press Club, 1983, 84, 86, 94, Olivier Rebbot award, 1992, 93; photg. award World Press Photo Found., 1992, 94, Mag. Photographer of Yr. award Nat. Press Photographers Assn. 1983, 86, 88, 90, 92, 94, Canon Photg. essayist award, 1992; Infinity award Internat. Ctr. Photography, 1991, 93, Leica award New Sch. for Social Rsch., 1990, award Budapest Photographic Festival, 1985, Nikon award Maine Workshop, 1985, Nikon World Image award New Sch.-

Parsons Sch. Design, 1991. Avocations: fly fishing, skiing. Office: Magnum Photos 151 W 25th St New York NY 10001

NACKEL, JOHN GEORGE, health care consulting director; b. Medford, Mass., Nov. 4, 1951; s. Michael and Josephine (Maria) N.; m. Gail Helen Becker, Oct. 30, 1976; children: Melissa Anne, Allison Elizabeth. BS, Tufts U., 1973; MS in Pub. Health and Indsl. Engring., U. Mo., 1975, PhD, 1977. Sr. mgr. Ernst & Young, Chgo., 1977-83; nat. dir. health care cons. Cleve., 1983-87, regional dir. health industry svcs., 1987-91; mng. dir. health care Ernst & Young, Cleve., 1991-93; nat. dir. Health Care Cons., L.A., 1994—; editorial bd. Jour. Med. Systems, 1983—. Author: Cost Management for Hospitals, 1987 (Am. Hosp. Assn. book award 1988); contbr. articles to profl. jours. Grantee Dept. Health Edn. Welfare, Washington, 1973-76. Fellow Am. Coll. Health Care Execs., Healthcare Info. and Mgmt. Systems Soc. (articles award); mem. Inst. Indsl. Engrs. (sr.), U. Mo. Health Svcs. Mgmt. Alumni Assn. (pres.), Canterbury Golf Club (Cleve.), La Canada-Flintridge Country Club, Annadale Golf Club, Jonathon Club. Republican. Avocations: golf, tennis, squash, paddle, photography. Home: 666 Linda Vista Ave Pasadena CA 91105-1145

NADAS, ALEXANDER SANDOR, pediatric cardiologist; b. Budapest, Hungary, Nov. 12, 1913; s. Sandor and Margit (Roth) N.; m. Elizabeth McClearen, Nov. 22, 1941; children: Trudi Norman-Murch, Elizabeth Nadas Seamans, John A. M.D., Budapest Med. Sch., 1937, Wayne U., 1945. Diplomate Am. Bd. Pediatrics, Am. Bd. Pediatric Cardiology. Intern Fairview Park Hosp., Cleve., 1939-40, Wilmington Gen. Hosp. 1940-41; resident in pediatrics Mass. Meml. Hosp., Boston, 1941-42; asst. resident Boston Children's Hosp., 1943; chief resident Mich. Children's Hosp., Detroit, 1943-45; practice medicine specializing in pediatrics Greenfield, Mass., 1945-49; asst. physician, asso. chief cardiology Children's Hosp., Boston, 1949-50; assoc. physician Children's Hosp., 1950-51, assoc. cardiologist, 1951-52, cardiologist, 1952-66, sr. asso. in medicine, 1962, chief cardiology div., 1966-69, chief cardiology dept., 1969-83, emeritus chief cardiology, 1983—; research fellow in pediatrics Harvard U. Med. Sch., 1949, instr., 1950-52, clin. assoc., 1952-55, asst. clin. prof. pediatrics, 1955-61, assoc. clin. prof., 1961-64, clin. prof., 1964-69, prof., 1969-83, emeritus prof., 1983—; Fulbright prof. pediatrics U. Groningen, Netherlands, 1956-57; cons. in field. Author: Pediatric Cardiology, 1972, NADAS Pediatric Cardiology, 1991; mem. editorial bd.: Yearbook of Cardiovascular Medicine and Surgery, 1961-85, Circulation, 1968-73, Am. Jour. Cardiology, 1973, Pediatric Cardiology, 1979—; contbr. articles to med. jours. Guggenheim fellow, 1970, recipient Gifted Teacher award., Am. Coll. of Cardiology, 1993. Mem. Mass. Med. Soc., Am. Heart Assn., Am. Acad. Pediatrics, Soc. Pediatric Research, Am. Pediatric Soc. (pres. 1972-73). Home: 865 Central Ave Needham MA 02192-1316 Office: Children's Hosp Dept Cardiology 300 Longwood Ave Boston MA 02115-5737

NADASKAY, RAYMOND, architect; b. Newark, Aug. 26, 1938; s. Charles and Marie (Roncskevitz) N.; m. Nancy Searle, June 29, 1962; 1 child, Cathy. BArch, Washington U., St. Louis, 1962. Registered architect, N.J., Conn., Vt., Mass., Ill., Ohio; registered planner; cert. NCARB. Designer Rotwein and Blake, Architects, Union, N.J., 1962-63, I.M. Pei, N.Y.C., 1963-64; designer, assoc. McDowell Goldstein, Morristown, N.J., 1964-72; pres. Nadaskay Kopelson Architects, P.A., Morristown, 1972—. Mem. Mendham (N.J.) Twp. Hist. Preservation Commn., Mendham Twp. Roadscape Commn. Active mem. Mendham (N.J.) Township Hist. Preservation Soc. Recipient numerous spl. commendations, awards of merit for variety of works. Mem. N.J. Soc. Architects (conv. chmn. 1985-86, past pres. Newark Suburban chpt. 1984, recipient awards for arch. 1982, 83, 85). Club: Porsche (Northern, N.J.). Avocations: woodworking, sailing, auto rally events, swimming. Office: Nadaskay Kopelson Architects 95 Washington St Morristown NJ 07960-6816

NADEAU, BERTIN F., diversified company executive; b. May 26, 1940; s. J.-D. and Irene (Daigle) N.; m. Juliette Angell, July 24, 1971; children: Eric, Shahn, Stephanie. BA, Coll. St-Louis, 1961; grad., Ecole des Hautes Etudes Commerciales de Montreal, 1964; postgrad., Harvard U.; DBA, Ind. U., 1969. Chmn., CEO, GescoLynx Inc., Montreal, 1982-94, chmn., CEO, 1994—; bd. dirs. Sun Life Can., Lafarge Corp., DMR Group, Inc. Office: GescoLynx Inc, 1250 Rene-Levesque Blvd W #4210, Montreal, PQ Canada H3B 5A6

NADEAU, EARL RAYMOND, electronics executive; b. Conrad, Mont., June 8, 1926; s. Raymond Joseph and Marvel Mae (Hunter) N.; m. Frances Ann Gambale, June 30, 1962; children: Nicole Mary, Christopher Earl. Student, Carroll Coll., 1944, U. Wash., 1945, Mont. State U., 1946-48. Supr. method engring., mgr. major subcontracting Boeing Airplane Co., Seattle and Wichita, 1950-55; administr. Atlas program Convair div. Gen. Dynamics, San Diego, 1955-57; chief plans and proposals Boeing Co., Seattle, 1958-59; mgmt. planning and applications cons. Waldwick, N.J., 1960-65; mgr. project engring/applications engring. Lockheed Electronics Co. Inc., Plainfield, N.J., 1966-69, dir. engring., 1970-76, dir. advanced devel., 1976-83; gen. prtnr. Nadeau Assocs., Watchung, N.J., 1984—. Served with USNR, 1943-46, PTO. Electrd to Mont. State U. Athletes Hall of Fame, 1992. Mem. AIAA, Instrument Soc. Am. (sr.), Marine Tech. Soc. Roman Catholic. Home: 132 Sunbright Rd Watchung NJ 07060-6045

NADEL, ELLIOTT, investment firm executive; b. N.Y.C., Nov. 23, 1945; s. Archie and Faye (Braverman) N.; children: Lindsey, Amanda. BBA, Baruch Coll., 1969, MBA, 1971. Portfolio mgr. SwissRe Advisors, N.Y.C., 1973-74; v.p., stockbroker E. F. Hutton, N.Y.C., 1975-84, Shearson Lehman Bros., N.Y.C., 1984-85, Oppenheimer & Co., N.Y.C., 1985, Rooney Pace Inc., N.Y.C., 1986-87, Philips Appel & Walden, N.Y.C., 1987-88; sr. v.p. investments Moore, Schley & Cameron, N.Y.C., 1988-90, Prudential-Securities, N.Y.C., 1990-94; sr. v.p. Gilford Securities, N.Y.C., 1994—. With U.S. Army, 1969-74. Jewish. Avocations: tennis, reading, cars, golf, travel. Office: Gilford Securities 850 3rd Ave New York NY 10022-6222

NADEL, MARK ALAN, hospital executive; b. Columbus, Ohio, Sept. 20, 1945; s. Norman S. and Martha J. (Smith) N.; m. Kimberly J. Grandage, Jan. 16, 1971; children—Leigh, Peter, Sara, Matthew. B.S., Wagner Coll., 1967; M.H.A., Xavier U., Cin., 1975. Administrv. asst. Weiss Meml. Hosp., Chgo., 1971-73; administrv. pres. Aultman Hosp., Canton, Ohio, 1974-75; asst. administr. Timken Mercy Med. Ctr., Canton, Ohio, 1975-76, acting administr., 1976-77, exec. v.p. 1977-83, pres. chief exec. officer, 1983—. Bd. dirs. Catholic Youth Council, Canton, 1979-85; sr. warden St. Mark's Episcopal Ch., Canton, 1982-84; bd. dirs. Walsh Coll., North Canton, 1984—; pres. Xavier U. Grad. program in Health and Hosp. Adminstrn., 1982-84. Fellow Am. Coll. Healthcare Execs.; mem. Forum of Health Services Adminstrs. (pres. 1979-81), Acad. for Cath. Health Care Leadership, Ohio Cath. Health Services (sec./treas.). Clubs: Canton, Brookside Country. Avocations: running; photography; camping; youth soccer coach. Home: 255 21st St NW Canton OH 44709-3909 Office: Health Care Equities Gp 2025 E Beltline Ave SE Grand Rapids MI 49546-7630

NADEL, NORMAN ALLEN, civil engineer; b. N.Y.C., Apr. 10, 1927; s. Louis and Bertha (Julius) N.; m. Cynthia Esther Jereski, July 6, 1952; children: Nancy Sarah Frank, Lawrence Bruce. B.C.E., CCNY, 1949; postgrad., Columbia U., 1949-50. Registered profl. engr., N.Y., Conn. Engr. Arthur A. Johnson Corp., N.Y.C., 1950-53; engr. Slattery Contracting Corp., N.Y.C., 1953-56; mgr., estimator Hartsdale Constrn. Corp., Hartsdale, N.Y., 1956-59; engr. MacLean Grove & Co., Inc., Greenwich, Conn. 1959-63, project mgr., 1963-66, v.p., 1966-70, pres., 1970-94; chmn. Nadel Assocs., Inc., Brewster, N.Y., 1988—; cons. tunnel and underground constrn.; bd. dirs. United Am. Energy Corp., PB-KBB Inc.; mem. com. on tunneling Transp. Resch. Bd., Washington, 1974-75; mem. U.S. Nat. Com. on Tunneling Tech., Washington, 1976-82, chmn., 1980-81; chmn. adv. com. Superconducting Super Collider Underground Tech., 1992-94. Trustee Tunnel Workers Welfare Fund, N.Y.C., 1976-88; mem. exec. coun. Pace U., N.Y.C., 1984—; mem. CCNY Engring. Sch. bd. adv., 1992—. Served with USNR, 1945-46. Named Heavy Constrn. Man of Yr., United Jewish Appeal, 1984; Benjamin Wright award Conn. Soc. Civil Engrs., 1984, Townsend Harris medal City Coll. of N.Y. Alumni Assn., 1987. Fellow ASCE (Constrn. Mgmt. award 1986); mem. Nat. Acad. Engring., Conn. Acad. Sci. and Engring., The Moles (pres. 1982-83, Outstanding Achievement in Constrn. award 1985), Am. Arbitration Assn., Tau Beta Pi, Chi Epsilon.

NADEL, ROGER, radio executive; b. Washington, Oct. 31, 1950; m. Debbie Nadel; children: Adam, Cory. BA in Psychology, U. Pacific, 1971. Newsgatherer AP Audio News Svc., Santa Barbara, Calif., 1974-76; news writer and editor KNX Newsradio, L.A., 1976-82; exec. news producer, 1982-89; dir. news and programming WWJ Newsradio, Detroit, 1989-92; v.p. gen. mgr., 1992—. Bd. trustees New Detroit, Inc.; mem. media subcom.; bd. dirs. Media Partnership for Jobs, chair United Way Ann. Torch Dr. Campaign, 1993; mem. Greater Detroit Pride Enhancement Campaign. Mem. Radio-TV News Dirs. Assn., Soc. Profl. Journalists, Detroit Press Club, Detroit Adcrafter Club, Detroit Econ. Club, Greater Detroit C. of C. (chair Trade and Procurement Fair Com., Crime Prevention/Awareness Com.), Sigma Alpha Epsilon. Office: WWJ/WYST Radio 16550 W 9 Mile Rd Southfield MI 48075-4705

NADEL, STEVEN J., marine instruments adjusting company executive; b. N.Y.C., July 11, 1947; s. William Aaron and Lee Ackerman-Hoffman Nadel. Degree in engring., U. Colo., 1966; degree in math., CCNY, 1968; student, Seaman's Sch., N.Y.C., 1969, U. Southampton, 1971-72. Cert., lic. compass adjuster. Student Marine Instrument Co., N.Y.C., 1960-71, F. Smith & Sons, Ltd., Southampton, Eng., 1971-74; compass adjuster, with nautical instrument svc. Blair's Nautical Supplies Ltd., Cardiff, Wales, 1974-76; compass adjuster, pres. Compass N.W./N.W. Instrument, Seattle, 1976-83; tech. dir., compass adjuster Compass Am./Northstar Navigation Sys., New Orleans, 1982-84; v.p., quality assurance mgr. Marine Instrument Co., Tucson, 1984-90; dir., CEO, quality assurance dir. Navistar/Marine Instrument Corp., N.Y.C., Calif., 1991—. Mem. Royal Inst. Navigation, Soc. Naval Archs. and Marine Engrs., Brit. Nautical Instrument Trade Assn. (compass com.), Am. Nat. Instrument Trade Assn. (founder 1993). Office: NAVISTAR/Marine Ste 102 2505 W Coast Hwy Newport Beach CA 92663

NADELSON, CAROL COOPERMAN, psychiatrist, educator; b. Bklyn., Oct. 13, 1936; m. Theodore Nadelson, July 16, 1965; children—Robert, Jennifer. B.A. magna cum laude, Bklyn. Coll., 1957; M.D. with honors, U. Rochester, N.Y., 1961. Dir. med. student edn. Beth Israel Hosp., Boston, 1974-79, psychiatrist, 1977; assoc. prof. psychiatry Harvard U. Med. Sch., Boston, 1976-79; research scholar Radcliffe Coll., Cambridge, Mass., 1979-80; prof., vice chmn., dir. tng. and edn. dept. psychiatry Tufts-New Eng. Med. Ctr., Boston, 1979-93. Editor: The Woman Patient, Vols. 1, 2 and 3, 1978, 82; Treatment Interventions in Human Sexuality, 1983; Marriage and Divorce: A Contemporary Perspective, 1984, Women Physicians in Leadership Roles, 1986, Training Psychiatrists for the '90s, 1987; editor-in-chief Am. Psychiatric Press, Inc., 1986—; contbr. articles to profl. jours. Trustee Menninger Found., 1988—. Recipient Gold Medal award Mt. Airy Psychiat. Ctr., 1981, award Case Western Res. U., 1983; Picker Found. grantee, 1982-83. Fellow Ctr. for Advanced Study in the Behavioral Scis.; mem. Am. Psychiat. Assn. (pres. 1985-86, Seymour D. Vestermark award 1992), Am. Coll. Psychiatrists, AMA (impaired physicians com. 1984), Group for Advancement of Psychiatry (bd. dirs. 1984). Avocation: travel. Office: 30 Amory St Brookline MA 02146-3909

NADER, RALPH, consumer advocate, lawyer, author; b. Winsted, Conn., Feb. 27, 1934; s. Nadra and Rose (Bouziane) N. AB magna cum laude, Princeton U., 1955; LLB with distinction, Harvard U., 1958. Bar: Conn. 1958, Mass. 1959, U.S. Supreme Ct. 1959. Practiced law in Hartford, Conn., from 1959; lectr. history and govt. U. Hartford, 1961-63; founder Center for Responsive Law, Pub. Interest Research Group, Center for Auto Safety, Pub. Citizen, Clean Water Action Project, Disability Rights Ctr., Pension Rights Ctr., Project for Corporate Responsibility; lectr. to colls. and univs.; lectr. Princeton U., 1967-68; co-founder Princeton Project 55, 1989. Author: Unsafe at Any Speed, 1965, rev., 1972; sponsor: Working on the System: A Manual for Citizen's Access to Federal Agencies, 1972; co-author: Action for a Change, 1972, You and Your Pension, 1973, Taming the Giant Corporation, 1976, Menace of Atomic Energy, 1977, The Lemon Book, 1980, The Big Boys, 1986, Winning The Insurance Game, 1990; editor: Whistle Blowing: The Report on the Conference on Professional Responsibility, 1972, The Consumer and Corporate Accountability, 1973; co-editor: Corporate Power in America, 1973, Verdicts on Lawyers, 1976, Who's Poisoning America, 1981; contbg. editor: Ladies Home Jour., 1973—, also articles. With U.S. Army, 1959. Recipient Nieman Fellows award, 1965-66; named One of 10 Outstanding Young Men of Year U.S. Jr. C. of C., 1967. Mem. ABA, AAAS, Phi Beta Kappa. Address: PO Box 19367 Washington DC 20036 also: 2000 P St NW Washington DC 20036

NADER, ROBERT ALEXANDER, judge, lawyer; b. Warren, Ohio, Mar. 31, 1928; s. Nassef J. and Emily (Nader) N.; m. Nancy M. Veauthier. B.A., Western Res. U., 1950, LL.B., 1953. Bar: Ohio 1953. Ptnr. Paul G. Nader, Warren, 1953-83. Pres. Warren City Police and Fire Pension Bds., 1960-66; trustee Office Econ. Opportunity, 1970-72; mem. Warren City Council, 1960-66, pres. pro tem, 1964-66; mem. Ohio Ho. of Reps., 1971-83, chmn. reference com., 1977-81, chmn. judiciary com., 1981-83; judge Trumbull County Ct. Common Pleas, 1983-91, Ohio 11th Dist. Ct. Appeals, 1991—; trustee Family Service Assn., 1959-65. Served with AUS, 1946-48. Recipient Outstanding Young Man of Yr. award, 1964, award Am. Arbitration Assn., 1965, Community Action award Warren Area Bd. Realtors, 1967, Outstanding Svc. award Kent State U., Trumbull campus, 1978, Outstanding Svc. award Children's Rehab. Ctr., 1980; named to Warren High Sch. Disting. Alumni Hall of Fame, 1993. Mem. Ohio State Bar Assn., Trumbull County Bar Assn. (past pres.), Ct. Appeals Judges Assn., Trumbull County Law Libr. assn. (chmn. legis. com., trustee 1958-72), Trumbull New Theatre (past pres.), KC, Elks, Lambda Chi Alpha (v.p. 1958). Roman Catholic. Home: 798 Wildwood Dr NE Warren OH 44483-4458 Office: 11th Dist Ct # Appeals Warren OH 44481 *My parents provided me with a strong moral background and the inspiration to improve. I will never feel that I have achieved success and thus may continue to improve.*

NADHERNY, FERDINAND, executive recruiting company executive. Sr. mng. dir. Russell Reynolds Assocs. Inc., Chgo. Office: Russell Reynolds Assocs Inc 200 S Wacker Dr Suite 3600 Chicago IL 60606

NADICH, JUDAH, rabbi; b. Balt., May 13, 1912; s. Isaac and Lena (Nathanson) N.; m. Martha Hadassah Ribalow, Jan. 26, 1947; children: Leah N. (Mrs. Aryeh Meir), Shira A. (Mrs. James L. Levin), Nahma M. Nadich (Mrs. David Belcourt). B.A., CCNY, 1932; M.A., Columbia U., 1936; rabbi, M.H.L., Jewish Theol. Sem. Am., 1936, D.H.L., 1953, D.D. (hon), 1966. Rabbi Temple Beth David, Buffalo, 1936-40; co-rabbi Anshe Emet Synagogue, Chgo., 1940-42; lecture tour U.S., South Africa and Rhodesia, 1946-47; rabbi Kehillath Israel Congregation, Brookline, Mass., 1947-57; rabbi Park Ave. Synagogue, N.Y.C., 1957-87, rabbi emeritus, 1987—; conducted first Bat Mitzvah in People's Republic of China, 1990. Author: Eisenhower and the Jews, 1953, Jewish Legends of the Second Commonwealth, 1983, Legends of the Rabbis, 2 vols., 1994; editor, translator: (Menachem Ribalow) The Flowering of Modern Hebrew Literature, 1959; editor: (Louis Ginzberg) Al Halakha v'Aggada, 1960. Pres. Rabbinical Assembly, 1972-74; pres. Jewish Book Coun., 1968-72; bd. dirs., exec. com. Jewish Theol. Sem. Am.; past bd. dirs., mem. exec. com. Nat. Jewish Welfre Bd., Fedn. Jewish Philanthropies N.Y.; mem. hospice com. Beth Israel Med. Ctr.; mem. N.Y.C. Holocaust Meml.; hon. v.p. bd. dirs. Jewish Braille Inst.; bd. dirs. Friends of Jewish Hist. Mus., Warsaw; past pres. Assn. Jewish Chaplains Armed Forces; adv. to Gen. Eisenhower on Jewish affairs, ETO, 1945; com. 50th anniversary World War II U.S. Dept. Defense. Lt. col., chaplain AUS, 1942-46, ETO. Decorated Order Brit. Empire; Croix de Guerre France; Ittur Lohamai Hamdinah Israel; fellow Herbert Lehman Inst. Talmudic Ethics, 1958. Mem. Mil. Chaplains Assn., Phi Beta Kappa. Lodge: Masons. Home: 1040 Park Ave New York NY 10028-1032 Office: Park Ave Synagogue 50 E 87th St New York NY 10128-1002

NADIG, GERALD GEORGE, manufacturing executive; b. Astoria, N.Y., May 9, 1945; s. Charles Edwin and Louise (Hahn) N.; m. Nancy Hanford Stewart, June 20, 1970; children: Sara Hanford, Jennifer, Stewart. AB cum laude, Harvard Coll., 1967, MBA, 1974. Fin. mgr. Rockwell Internat., Hopedale, Mass., 1974-76; materials mgr. Rockwell Internat., Oshkosh, Wis., 1976-78, Marysville, Ohio, 1978-79; ops. mgr. Rockwell Internat., Marysville, 1979-80, plant mgr., 1980-82; regional mgr. Rockwell Internat., Atlanta, 1984-85; mng. dir. Rockwell Maudslay Ltd., Great Alne, Eng., 1982-84; dir. mfg. Toyoda Machinery USA, Arlington Heights, Ill., 1985-87; v.p., gen. mgr. Toyoda Machinery USA, Arlington Heights, 1987-88; v.p.,

gen. mgr. Littell div. Allied Products Corp., Chgo., 1988-89; exec. v.p. pre finish metals Material Scis. Corp., 1989-90; pres. Pre Finish Metals Materials Scis. Corp., 1990-91; pres., chief oper. officer Material Scis. Corp., Chgo., 1991—. Trustee Village of Lake Barrington, 1989-91. With U.S. Army, 1966-70. Mem. Soc. Mfg. Engrs. (sr.), Biltmore Country Club. Avocations: golf, tennis, game theory. Home: 24354 N Grandview Dr Barrington IL 60010-6218 Office: Material Scis Corp 2300 Pratt Blvd Elk Grove Village IL 60007-5919

NADIRI, M. ISHAQ, economics educator, researcher, lecturer, consultant; b. Kabul, Afghanistan, Oct. 16, 1936; s. M. Alam and Gul-Nasa N.; m. Tahira Homayun, Sept. 9, 1978; children: Youssof, Khalid. B.S. with highest distinction, U. Nebr., 1958; M.A., U. Calif.-Berkeley, 1960, Ph.D., 1965; postgrad., Yale U. 1962-63. Asst. prof. Northwestern U., Evanston, Ill., 1964-66, U. Chgo. Bus. Sch., 1966-67; research fellow Nat. Bur. Econ. Research, N.Y.C., 1968-70; research assoc. Nat. Bur. Econ. Research, 1969—; full prof. econs. NYU, 1970—, Jay Gould prof. econs., 1975—, chmn. dept. econs., 1972-78; Disting. vis. prof. U. Cairo, 1993; cons. in field; participant seminars NSF Ctr Strategic Studies, UN Assn. Author: books, including A Disequilibrium Model of Demand for Factors of Production, 1974; research, numerous publs. in field; editor books including The Importance of Technology and the Permanence of Structure in Industrial Growth, 1978, Commodity Markets and Latin American Development: A Modeling Approach, 1980; editorial bd.: Annals of Econs. and Social Measurement. Mem. Com. to Upgrade Central Park, N.Y.C.; mem. Com. to Help Afghan Refugees in the U.S. C. Miller fellow, 1958-59; U. Calif. fellow, 1959-60; Earnhart fellow, 1962-63, 63-64; grantee NSF, Ford Found., IBM Corp., AT&T. Mem. Am. Econs. Assn., Econometrica Soc., Univs.-Nat. Bur. Econ. Research, Internat. Assn. Research in Income and Wealth; mem. AAAS, Am. Statis. Assn., Council Fgn. Relations, Phi Beta Kappa, Pi Sigma Alpha, Beta Gamma Sigma. Office: NYU Dept Econs 269 Mercer St 7th Fl New York NY 10003

NADLER, ALLAN LAWRENCE, institute director; b. Montreal, May 8, 1954; came to U.S., 1976; s. Joseph Y. and Doris (Josevlefsky) N. BA, McGill U., 1976; MA, Harvard U., 1980, PhD, 1988. Ordained rabbi, 1978. Rabbi Charles River Park Synagogue, Boston, 1980-84; asst. prof. McGill U., Montreal, 1982-90; rabbi Congregation Shaar Hashomayim, Montreal, 1984-90; dir. rsch. Yivo Inst. for Jewish Rsch., N.Y.C., 1991—; vis. prof. Cornell U., Ithaca, N.Y., 1993—; adj. prof. NYU. Author: A Religion of Limits, 1995; contbr. articles to profl. jours. Lady Davis fellow Hebrew U., Jerusalem, 1987. Mem. Assn. Jewish Studies, Union for Traditional Judaism (mem. at large at exec. 1990—). Office: Vivo Inst 555 W 57th St New York NY 10019

NADLER, GEORGE L., orthodontist; b. Bklyn., Jan. 13, 1939; s. Rudolph M. and Hannah (Helfman) N.; m. Essie Rubinstein, June 4, 1961; children: Rudolph M., Eric Marc. Student, Bkly. Coll., 1956-59; DDS, NYU Coll. of Dentistry, 1963, postgrad., 1966-70. Diplomate Am. Bd. Orthodontia, 1979. Intern L.I. Coll. Hosp., Bklyn., 1963-64; pvt. practice Bklyn., 1966-70, Tucson, Ariz., 1970—; cons. El Rio Health Ctr., Tucson, 1973—. Contbr. articles to profl. jours. Cons. Ariz. Crippled Children Svc., Tucson, 1973—; exec. bd. Congregation Anshei Israel, 1988—. With USPHS, 1964-66. Fellow NIH, 1961, 62. Mem. ADA, Ariz. Dental Assn., So. Ariz. Dental Assn., Am. Assn. Orthodontists, Pacific Coast Orthodontic Assn., Ariz. Orthodontic Study Club, Tucson Orthodontic Study Club, Tucson Orthodontic Soc. (pres. 1980-81), Ariz. State Orthodontic Soc. (pres. 1988-90), Angle Orthodontic Soc., Golden Key, Skyline Country Club, Omicron Kappa Upsilon. Avocations: tennis, golf, gardening. Home: 6822 N Longfellow Dr Tucson AZ 85718-2422 Office: 5610 E Grant Rd Tucson AZ 85712-2296

NADLER, GEORGIA JANE, nursing administrator; b. Jersey City, Sept. 30, 1949; d. John Patrick and Georgia (Snook) McCarthy; divorced; children: Meredith, Lauren. Diploma, Easton (Pa.) Hosp. Sch. Nursng, 1970; AAS, NYU, 1981; BSN, Hunter Coll., 1983; MBA in Mgmt., Fairleigh Dickinson U., 1986. Staff nurse NYU Med. Ctr., N.Y.C., 1970-71, oper. rm. supr., 1973-82; staff nurse U. Minn. Hosp., Mpls., 1971-73; oper. rm. dir. Manhattan Eye and Ear Hosp., N.Y.C., 1982-85; dir. Surg. Ctr. Med. Ctr. Princeton, N.J., 1985—; v.p. patient svcs. Med. Ctr., Princeton, 1989; presenter, spkr. in field. Co-author, spkr. Healthcare in Law and Ethics, 1992; contbr. articles to profl. publs. Bd. dirs. Ednl. Found., Montgomery Twp., N.J., 1989—. Recipient Nursing Incentive Reimbursement award N.J. State Dept. Health, 1989, 90. Mem. Am. Orgn. Nurse Execs., Nat. League Nursing. Avocations: skiing, jogging. Home: 60 Dogwood Ln Skillman NJ 08558-1301 Office: Med Ctr Princeton 253 Witherspoon St Princeton NJ 08540

NADLER, GERALD, engineering educator, management consultant; b. Cin., Mar. 12, 1924; s. Samuel and Minnie (Krumbein) N.; m. Elaine Muriel Dubin, June 22, 1947; children: Burton Alan, Janice Susan, Robert Daniel. Student, U. Cin., 1942-43; BSME, Purdue U., 1945, MS in Indsl. Engring, 1946, PhD, 1949. Instr. Purdue U., 1948-49; asst. prof. indsl. engring. Washington U., St. Louis, 1949-52, assoc. prof., 1952-55, prof., head dept. indsl. engring., 1955-64; prof. U. Wis., Madison, 1964-83, chmn. dept. indsl. engring., 1964-67, 71-75; prof., chmn. dept. indsl. and systems engring. U. So. Calif., L.A., 1983-93, IBM chair emeritus, 1993—; IBM chair emeritus, prof. emeritus, 1993—; v.p. Artcraft Mfg. Co., St. Louis, 1956-57; dir. Intertherm Inc., St. Louis, 1969-85; pres. Ctr. for Breakthrough Thinking Inc., L.A., 1989—; vis. prof. U. Birmingham, Eng. 1959, Waseda U., Tokyo, 1963, Ind. U., 1964, U. Louvain, Belgium, 1975, Technion-Israel Inst. Tech., Haifa, 1976; speaker in field. Author: The Planning and Design Approach, 1981; (with S. Hibino) Breakthrough Thinking, 1990, 2d edit., 1994, Creative Solution Finding, 1995; (with G. Hoffherr, J. Moran) Breakthrough Thinking in Total Quality Management, 1994; contbr. articles to profl. jours.; reviewer books, papers, proposals. Mem. Ladue Bd. Edn., St. Louis County, 1960-63; acting exec. dir. Higher Edn. Coordinating Coun. Met. St. Louis, 1962-63; chmn. planning com. Wis. Regional Med. Program, 1966-69, mem. steering com., 1969-73. Served with USN, 1943-45. Recipient Gilbreth medal Soc. Advancement Mgmt., 1961, Editorial award Hosp. Mgmt. Mag., 1966, Disting. Engring. Alumnus award Purdue U., 1975; Book of Yr. award Inst. Indsl. Engrs., 1983, Frank and Lillian Gilbreth award, 1992; Phi Kappa Phi Faculty Recognition award U. So. Calif., 1990. Fellow AAAS, Inst. Indsl. Engrs. (pres. 1989-90), Inst. for Advancement Engrs., Am. Soc. Engring. Edn.; mem. NAE, Inst. Mgmt. Scis., Japan Work Design Soc. (hon. adv. 1968—), Sigma Xi, Alpha Pi Mu (nat. officer), Pi Tau Sigma, Omega Rho, Tau Beta Pi. Office: Univ Park GER 240 Dept of I&SE Los Angeles CA 90089-0193

NADLER, HENRY LOUIS, pediatrician, geneticist, medical educator; b. N.Y.C., Apr. 15, 1936; s. Herbert and Mary (Kartiganer) N.; m. Benita Weinhard, June 16, 1957; children: Karen, Gary, Debra, Amy. A.B., Colgate U., 1957; M.D., Northwestern U., 1961; M.S., U. Wis., 1965. Diplomate: Am. Bd. Pediatrics, Am. Bd. Med. Genetics. Intern NYU Med. Ctr., 1961-62, sr. resident pediatrics, 1962-63, chief resident, 1963-64; teaching asst. NYU Sch. Medicine, 1962-63, clin. instr., 1963-64; clin. instr. U. Wis. Sch. Medicine, 1964-65; practice medicine specializing in pediatrics Chgo., 1965—; fellow Children's Meml. Hosp. dept. pediatrics Northwestern U., 1964-65; assoc. in pediatrics Northwestern U. Med. Sch., 1965-66, asst. prof., 1967-68, assoc. prof., 1968-70, prof., 1970-81, chmn. dept. pediatrics, 1970-81; prof. Northwestern U. Med. Sch. (Grad. Sch.), 1971-80; mem. staff Children's Meml. Hosp., 1965-81, head div. genetics, 1969-81, chief of staff, 1970-81; dean, prof. pediatrics, ob-gyn Wayne State U. Med. Sch., Detroit, 1981-88; prof. U. Chgo., 1988-89, U. Ill., 1989—; pres. Michael Reese Hosp. and Med. Ctr., Chgo., 1988-91; market med. dir. Aetna Health Plans, Phoenix, 1993-94, mktg. v.p., CEO, 1994-95; v.p. managed care/physician integration, med. dir. Am. Healthcare Sys., San Diego, 1995—; mem. vis. staff, div. medicine Northwestern Meml. Hosp., 1972-81; staff Children's Hosp. of Mich., 1981-88. Mem. editorial bd. Comprehensive Therapy, 1973-84, Am. Jour. Human Genetics, 1979-83, Pediatrics in Rev., 1980-83, Am. Jour. Diseases of Children, 1983-91; contbr. articles to profl. jours. Recipient E. Mead Johnson award for pediatric rsch., 1973, Meyer O. Cantor award for Disting. Svc. Internat. Coll. Surgeons, 1987; Irene Heinz Given and John La Porte Given rsch. prof. pediatrics, 1970-81. Fellow Am. Acad. Pediatrics; mem. Am. Soc. for Clin. Investigation, Am. Soc. Human Genetics, Am. Pediatric Soc., Soc. for Pediatric Rsch., Midwest Soc. for

Pediatric Rsch., Pan Am. Med. Assn., Alpha Omega Alpha. Home: 25150 N Windy Walk Dr # 23 Scottsdale AZ 85255 Office: Am Healthcare Sys Pointe Corridor Ctr IV 12730 High Bluff Dr Ste 300 San Diego CA 92130-2099

NADLER, JERROLD LEWIS, congressman, lawyer; b. Brooklyn, N.Y., June 13, 1947; s. Emanuel and Miriam (Schreiber) N.; m. Joyce L. Miller, 1976; 1 child, Michael. JD, Fordham U., 1978; AB, Columbia Coll., 1969. Mem. Community Planning Bd. No. 7, Manhattan, 1967-71; Dem. leader 67th Assembly Dist. Part C, 1969-71; exec. dir. Community Free Dem., 1972; law clerk Morgan, Finnegan, Pine, Foley & Lee, 1976; Dem. dist. leader 69th assembly dist. Part A, 1973-77; assemblyman N.Y. State 69th dist., 1977-82, 67th dist., 1983-92; mem. 102d Congress from 17th N.Y. dist., Washington, 1992; mem. 103rd and 104th Congress from 8th N.Y. Dist. 103rd Congress from 8th N.Y. dist., Washington, 1993—; mem. House Subcom. on Comml. and Adminstrv. Law, 1995—; mem. House coms. on judiciary and pub. works and transp., chmn. Assembly Com. on Corps, Authorities and Commns., 1991-92, former chmn. Assembly Consumer Affairs and Protection Com., 1987-89, Assembly Com. on Ethics and Guidance, 1985-86, Assmebly Subcom. on Mass Transit and Rail Freight, 1979-86, mem. Assembly Com. on Judiciary, Gov. Ops., Legis. Tax Study Commn.; past mem. Assembly Com. Ways and Means, Housing, Real Property Tax, Health, Election Law, Ins. Founder, chmn. West Side Peace Com., 1969-71; former mem. exec. coun. N.Y. State New Dem. Coalition; pres. Zionist Orgn. Am. dist. 7A; active Common Cause, Met. Coun. on Housing, West Side Tenants Union, Community Free Dems.; mem. nat. governing coun. Am. Jewish Congress; former bd. dirs. N.Y. State Nat. Abortion Rights Action League, Women's InterArts Ctr. Recipient hon. recognition award N.Y. State Nurses Assn., 1982, Disting. Svc. award Coalition on Domestic Violence, 1989; named Assembly Mem. of Yr. N.Y. chpt. NOW, 1980; Pulitzer scholar Columbia U. Mem. NOW, NAACP, N.Y. Bar Assn., N.Y. Civil Liberties Union (honor roll), Citizens Union, League Conservation Voters, New Dem. Coalition, Ams. for Dem. Action (bd. dirs., nat. v.p.). Office: US Ho of Reps Office of Ho Mems Washington DC 20515

NADLER, MARK B., executive editor; b. N.Y.C., Aug. 2, 1951; s. Leonard and Sylvie (Moret) N.; m. Jan Griffin, Aug. 21, 1978; children: Chloe, Jessica, Charles. BA in English, George Washington U., 1973. Staff writer The Record, Havre de Grace, Md., 1973-74, news editor, 1974-76, mng. editor, 1976-77; staff reporter The Charlotte (N.C.) Observer, 1977-80; city/state editor The Lexinton (Ky.) Herald-Leader, 1980-82, asst. mng. editor, 1982, dep. mng. editor, 1983; second front page The Wall Street Jour., N.Y.C., 1983-84, asst. news editor, 1984-85, editor, spl. reports, 1985-86; mng. editor The Pioneer Press, St. Paul, 1986-90; exec. editor, v.p. The Chicago Sun Times, 1990—. Recipient First Place award N.C. Press Assn., First Place award Md.-D.C. Press. Assn., Grand prize and First prize awards Edn. Writers Assn., 1980. Office: Chicago Sun-Times 401 N Wabash Ave Rm 356 Chicago IL 60611-3532 Office: NW Pubs Inc 345 Cedar St Minneapolis MN 55101*

NADLER, MYRON JAY, lawyer; b. Youngstown, Ohio, July 22, 1923; s. Murray A. and Jean (Davis) N.; m. Alice Blue, Nov. 4, 1951; children: Jed M., Wendy D., John M.S. Student, N.Mex. State Coll., 1943-44; B.S. in Econs, U. Pa., 1947; J.D. with distinction, U. Mich., 1949. Bar: Ohio 1950. Pres., shareholder Nadler, Nadler & Burdman Co., L.P.A., Youngstown, 1950—; asst. editor Mich. Law Rev., 1949; instr. Youngstown U. Law Sch., 1952-59. Author: (with Saul Nadler) Nadler on Bankruptcy, 1965, April's Bankruptcy Forms and Practice, 1964; contbr. articles profl. jours. Chmn. exec. budget com. United Appeal, Youngstown, 1964-66, v.p., 1967-70; co-chmn. Mayor's Commn. Human Rights, 1957; mem. Mahoning County Planning Commn., 1965-71, Nat. Budget and Consultation Com., 1967-70; trustee Community Corp., Youngstown, v.p., 1977-82, chmn. pers. com., 1974-92; bd. dirs. Ctr. for Learning, Villa Maria, Pa., 1969—, pres., 1981-89, chmn. bd., 1989-94, chmn. emeritus, 1994—. With AUS, 1943-45. Decorated Purple Heart with oak leaf cluster. Mem. Fellows of Ohio Bar Assn. Found., Am., Ohio, Mahoning County bar assns., Scribes Assn. Legal Writers, Comml. Law League Am. Clubs: Youngstown, Squaw Creek Country (pres. 1966-68); Hamlet Country. Home: 601 Pine Lake Dr Delray Beach FL 33445 Home: 1313 Virginia Trl Youngstown OH 44505-1641 Office: 20 Federal Plz W Ste 600 Youngstown OH 44503-1423

NADLER, SIGMOND HAROLD, physician, surgeon; b. Bklyn., May 16, 1932; s. Morris and Rose (Levine) N.; m. Beverly Melcher, June 20, 1954; children: Geoffrey, Shail, Tamara, Kimberly. B.A., State U. Iowa, 1955, M.D., 1957. Intern Menorah Med. Center, Kansas City, Mo., 1957-58; surg. resident Menorah Med. Center, 1958-61; surg. resident Roswell Park Meml. Inst., 1961-63, mem. staff, 1962-68, clin. coordinator Eastern region clin. drug evaluation program, 1966-68, project dir. nat. adj. studies, 1966-68, asso. chief cancer research surgery, 1966-68; asso. prof. surgery Jefferson Med. Coll., Phila., 1968-70; also dir. clin. cancer tng.; asst. clin. prof. surgery SUNY-Buffalo, 1970—; staff DeGraff Hosp., North Tonawanda. Mem. Am. Soc. Clin. Oncology, N.Y. State Med. Soc. Erie County. Research in human tumor immunotherapy. Home: 9513 Preston Trail West Ponte Vedra Beach FL 32082 Office: 533 Meadow Dr North Tonawanda NY 14120-2835

NADLEY, HARRIS JEROME, accountant, educator, author; b. Phila., July 6, 1926; s. Michael and Celia (Millman) N.; BS, U. Pa., 1950; MA, PhD, Harvard U., 1952; m. Barbara A. Malone, June 28, 1953; children—Jennifer Beth, Amy Jane, Adam Christopher. Asst. trust officer Provident Trust Co., Phila., 1949; exec. trainee Merrill, Lynch, Pierce, Fenner & Smith, N.Y.C., 1950; ptnr. Michael Nadley Co., CPAs, Phila., 1952—. Teaching fellow Harvard, 1952; instr. fin. Wharton Sch., Phila., 1953-54; adj. prof. bus. adminstrn. St. Joseph's Coll., Phila., Acad. Food Mktg., Pa. Inst. CPAs, N.J. Soc. CPAs, AICPA; cons. Control Data Corp., 1971; participant Current Strategy Forum, Naval War Coll., 1978, Naval War Coll. Found., 1979. Gen. chmn. Marine Corps Birthday Ball, Phila., 1973. Bd. dirs. Montgomery County Assn. for Retarded Children, Cruiser Olympia Assn., ea. Pa. chpt. Arthritis Found.; trustee Lesley Coll., Cambridge, Mass.; pres. adv. council Wharton Sch., U. Pa., 1950; del. White House Conf. on Small Bus., 1986; mem. pres.'s council Chestnut Hill Coll.; mem. Benjamin Franklin Assocs., U. Pa.; chmn. bd. advisors USMC Tun's Tavern Commn., 1991. Served with USMCR, 1944-46; PTO. Mem. Am. Radio Relay League, Fraternal Order Police (hon.), Econometric Soc., Am. Econ. Soc., Mil. Order Fgn. Wars, British Officers' Club, Preservation Soc. Newport County, St. Joseph's Coll. Acad. Food Mktg. (founder), Quarter Century Wireless Assn., Marine Corps Res. Officers Assn., Sixth Marine Div. Assn., Marine Raiders Assn., Navy League, Pa. Soc., Beta Gamma Sigma, Pi Gamma Mu, Beta Sigma Rho. Clubs: Masons, Union League, Harvard, Harvard Faculty, Mercedes-Benz, Urban (Phila.). Author: A Covey of Peacocks, 1969. Contbr. articles to profl. jours.; fin. columnist Phila. mag., Welcomat Newspaper, Phila. Bus. Jour.; cons. Fin. News Network, Phila. Home and Office: 325 S 3d St Philadelphia PA 19106

NADOL, JOSEPH B., JR., otolaryngologist, educator; b. Cambridge, Mass., 1943. MD, Johns Hopkins U., 1970. Surg. intern Beth Israel Hosp., Boston, 1970-71, resident in surgery, 1971-72; resident in otolaryngology Mass. Ear and Eye Infirmary, Boston, 1972-75, asst. on otolaryngology, 1975-80, assoc. surgeon, 1980—, chief otolaryngologist, 1985; asst. prof. otolaryngology Harvard U., Cambridge, Mass., 1976-80, assoc. prof., 1981-85, Walter Augustus Le Compte prof., 1985—, chmn. otolaryngology dept., 1985—. Mem. ACS, AMA, Am. Assn. Ophthalmology and Otolaryngology, Soc. Univ. Otolaryngologists, Soc. Head and Neck Surgeons, Am. Neurolog. Assn. Office: Coll Otology & Laryngology Harvard U Cambridge MA 02138 also: Mass Eye and Ear Infirmary 243 Charles St Boston MA 02114-3004

NADOOLMAN, DEBORAH, costume designer. Costume designer: (films) The Kentucky Fried Movie, 1977, Animal House, 1978, 1941, 1979, The Blues Brothers, 1980, An American Werewolf in London, 1981, Raiders of the Lost Ark, 1981, Trading Places, 1983, Twilight Zone-The Movie ("Back There"), 1983, Spies Like Us, 1985, Into the Night, 1985, Three Amigos, 1986, Coming to America, 1988 (Academy award nomination best costume design 1988), Oscar, 1991, Nothing But Trouble, 1991, Innocent Blood, 1992. Office: care Costume Designer's Guild 13049 Ventura Blvd Ste 309 Sherman Oaks CA 91423*

NAEGELE, CARL JOSEPH, university academic administrator, educator; b. Newark, Jan. 1, 1939; s. Carl Joseph Sr. and Mabel (Flood) N.; n. Elizabeth C. McVey, June 19, 1971; children: Jennifer, Erin. BS, Kean Coll., 1965; MS. Syracuse U., 1969; PhD, Cornell U., 1974. Tchr. physics Summit (N.J.) High Sch., 1965-68; instr. physics Kean Coll., Union, N.J., 1968-70; research assoc. Cornell U., Ithaca, N.Y., 1973-75; prof. Mich. State U., East Lansing, 1975-79; program dir. NSF, Washington, 1979-81, 91-92; dean coll. arts and scis. U. San Francisco, 1981-91; dir. Sci. Inst., 1984—; prof. physics and computer sci. U. San Francisco, 1981—; computer cons. San Rafael, Calif., 1981—. Author: Physics for the Life and Health Sciences, 1974, Laboratory Experiment in General Physics, 1976, Electronic Mail and Communication Networks, 1984, Computer Systems and Applications, 1989; contbr. articles to profl. jours. Served with U.S. Army, 1959-61, Korea. Recipient Outstanding Teaching award Mich. State U., 1978, Leadership award U. San Francisco, 1985; grantee NSF, 1968, 78, 94, Coun. for Basic Edn., 1984-89. Mem. Am. Phys. Soc., Am. Assn. Physics Tchrs., Am. Assn. Univ. Adminstrs., Assn. for Computing Machinery. Avocations: flying, boating, skiing, tennis, running. Office: U San Francisco Coll Arts and Scis Ignatian Heights San Francisco CA 94117-1080

NAEGELE, PHILIPP OTTO, violinist, violist, music educator; b. Stuttgart, Fed. Republic Germany, Jan. 22, 1928; came to U.S., 1940; s. Reinhold and Alice (Nordlinger) N.; m. Susanne Russin (div. 1980); 1 child, Matthias Dominic; m. Barbara Wright, Mar. 1992. BA, Queens Coll., 1949; MFA, Princeton U., 1950, PhD, 1955. Violinist, violist Marlboro (Vt.) Music Festival, 1950—; violinist Cleve. Orch., 1956-64; from asst. prof. to assoc. prof. to prof. violin dept. music Smith Coll., Northampton, Mass., 1964-78; William R. Kenan Jr. prof. music Smith Coll., 1978—; violist Cantilena Piano Quartet, 1980—; mem. Boccherini Ensemble, 1980-84; mem. Resident String Quartet, Kent (Ohio) State U., 1960-64, violin faculty Cleve. Inst. Music, 1961-64, Yale String Quartet, 1977-79; rec. artist Columbia Mus. Heritage Soc., Pro Arte., Nonesuch Records, Bis Records, Marlboro Rec. Soc., Arabesque Records, Da Camera, Spectrum Records, Bayer Records, Sony Classical, Philomusica. Contbr. to New Groves Dictionary of Music, also articles to profl. jours. Served to cpl. U.S. Army, 1955-56. Fellow Am. Council Learned Socs., 1949-50, Proctor, 1952-53, Fulbright, 1953-54. Home: 57 Prospect St Northampton MA 01060-2130 Office: Smith Coll Dept Music Northampton MA 01060

NAESER, MARGARET ANN, linguist, medical researcher; b. Washington, June 22, 1944; d. Charles Rudolph and Elma Mathilda (Meyer) N. BA in German, Smith Coll., 1966; PhD in Linguistics, U. Wis., 1970. Chief speech pathology sect. Martinez (Calif.) VA Med. Ctr., 1972-74, Palo Alta (Calif.) VA Med. Ctr., 1974-77; rsch. linguist Boston VA Med. Ctr., 1977—; dir. CT scan/MRI scan Aphasia Rsch. Lab. Boston U. Aphasia Rsch. Ctr. Sch. Medicine, asst. rsch. prof. neurology, 1978-84, assoc. rsch. prof., 1984—; mem. adv. bd. CT scan/aphasia VA Nat. Task Force, Washington, 1990-91; panel mem. Office Alternative Medicine NIH, 1994. Contbr. articles to Neurology, Archives of Neurology, Brain; author: Outline Guide to Chinese Herbal Patent Medicines in Pill Form, 1990, Laser Acupuncture: An Introductory Textbook, 1994. NDEA fellow, 1967, AAUW fellow, 1970. Mem. Acoustical Soc. Am., Am. Speech, Lang., Hearing Assn., Acad. Aphasia, AAAS, Am. Assn. Acupuncture and Oriental Medicine. Office: Boston VA Med Ctr 150 S Huntington Ave Boston MA 02130

NAESER, NANCY DEARIEN, geologist, researcher; b. Morgantown, W.Va., Apr. 15, 1944; d. William Harold and Katherine Elizabeth (Dearien) Cozad; m. Charles Wilbur Naeser, Feb. 6, 1982. BS, U. Ariz., 1966; PhD, Victoria U., Wellington, New Zealand, 1973. Geol. field asst. U.S. Geol. Survey, Flagstaff, Ariz., 1966; sci. editor, New Zealand Jour. Geology and Geophsyics, New Zealand Dept Sci. and Indsl. Research, Wellington, 1974-76; postdoctoral rsch. assoc., U. Toronto, Ont., Can., 1976-79; postdoctoral rsch. assoc. U.S. Geol. Survey, Denver, 1979-81, geologist, 1981—; adj. prof. Dartmouth Coll., Hanover, N.H., 1985—, U. Wyo., Laramie, 1984—. Editor: Thermal History of Sedimentary Basins - Methods and Case Histories, 1989; contbr. articles on fission-track dating to profl. jours., 1977—. Docent Denver Zoo. Fulbright fellow New Zealand, 1967-68. Fellow Geol. Soc. Am.; mem. Am. Assn. Petroleum Geologists, Soc. Econ. Paleontologists and Mineralogists, Geol. Soc. New Zealand, Mortar Bd., Phi Kappa Phi. Methodist. Office: US Geol Survey Mail Stop 981 12201 Sunrise Valley Dr Reston VA 22092

NAEVE, MILO MERLE, museum curator; b. nr. Arnold, Kans., Oct. 9, 1931; s. Bernhardt and Fern (Yasmer) N.; m. Nancy Jammer, July 18, 1954. BA, U. Colo., 1953; M.A., U. Del., 1955. Curatorial asst. Henry Francis duPont Winterthur Mus., 1957, asst. curator, 1958, sec. of mus., 1959-63, registrar, 1963-65; editor Winterthur Portfolio, 1965-66; asst. dir. dept. collections Colonial Williamsburg, 1967-69, curator, dir. dept. collections, 1970; dir. Colorado Springs (Colo.) Fine Arts Center, 1971-74; curator Am. Arts, Art Inst. Chgo., 1975-91, ret., 1991; curator emeritus Field McCormick. Author: The Classical Presence in American Art, 1978, Identifying American Furniture: A Pictorial Guide to Styles and Terms, Colonial to Contemporary, 1981, 2d edit., 1989, John Lewis Krimmel: An Artist in Federal America, 1987; mem. editorial bd. Am Art Jour.; contbr. articles to profl. jours. Trustee Sewell C. Biggs Mus., Skowhegan Sch. Painting and Sculpture. Wiht AUS, 1955-57. Fellow Royal Soc. Arts; mem. Coll. Art Assn. Am., Nat. Trust Historic Preservation, Am. Assn. Museums, Museums Assn. (Eng.), Ill. Acad. Fine Arts (Lifetime Achievement award 1991). Home: 24 Ingleton Cir Kennett Square PA 19348-2000

NAEYE, RICHARD L., pathologist, educator; b. Rochester, N.Y., Nov. 27, 1929; s. Peter John and Gertrude Ellen (Lookup) N.; m. Patricia Ann Dahl, June 4, 1955; children: Nancy Ellen, Susan Amy, Robert Peter. A.B., Colgate U., 1951; M.D., Columbia U., 1955. Diplomate: Am. Bd. Pathology. Intern N.Y. Hosp., N.Y.C., 1955-56; resident Columbia-Presbyn. Med. Center, 1956-58, Mary Fletcher Hosp., Burlington, Vt., 1958-60; practice medicine, specializing in pathology Burlington, 1960-67, Hershey, Pa., 1967—; asst. attending pathologist Mary Fletcher Hosp., 1960-63; assoc. prof. U. Vt., 1963-67, prof. pathology, 1967; chmn. dept. pathology M.S. Hershey Med. Center, Pa. State U. Coll. Medicine, 1967—; mem. NIH study sect. USPHS, 1968-72. Editorial bd. Human Pathology, 1982—, Pediatric Pathology, 1981—, Pediatric and Perinatal Epidemiology, 1987-94, Modern Pathology, 1993—; contbr. articles to med. jours. Markle scholar in acad. medicine, 1960-65. Mem. Am. Soc. Exptl. Pathology, U.S. Can. Acad. Pathology, Am. Soc. Pathologists, Am. Soc. Clin. Pathologists, Coll. Am. Pathologists, Pediatric Pathology Soc., Pa. Soc. Clin. Pathologists, Investigative Pathology. Home: 50 Laurel Ridge Rd Hershey PA 17033-2513 Office: Pa State U Coll Medicine Dept Pathology 500 University Dr Hershey PA 17033

NAFE, JOHN ELLIOTT, geophysicist; b. Seattle, July 22, 1914; s. Arthur Edward and Muriel (Elliott) N.; m. Sarah Gilpin Underhill, Sept. 6, 1941; children—Mary Malcolm (Mrs. Richard L. Chase), Katharine Elliott (Mrs. Christopher Kenah). B.S., U. Mich., 1938; M.S., Wash. U., 1940; Ph.D., Columbia, 1948. Instr. physics Columbia, 1946-49, adj. asso. prof. geology, 1953-58, prof. geology 1958-80, prof. emeritus, 1980—, chmn. dept., 1962-65; hon. prof. dept. geophysics and astronomy U. B.C., Vancouver, 1980—; asst. prof. physics U. Minn., 1949-51; dir. research Hudson Labs., 1951-53; research scientist Lamont Geol. Obs., 1953-55; chief scientist oceanographic cruises, 1951-62; vis. fellow Cambridge (Eng.) U., 1971-72. Served with USNR, 1941-46. Fellow Geol. Soc. Am., A.A.A.S., Am. Phys. Soc., Am. Geophys. Union; mem. Seismol. Soc. Am., Royal Astron. Soc., Am. Exploration Geophysicists, Am. Assn. Physics Tchrs., Can. Assn. Physicists, Sigma Xi. Research and publs. in physics, geophysics, oceanography. Home: 5775 Toronto Rd, Vancouver, BC Canada V6T 1X4

NAFIE, LAURENCE ALLEN, chemistry educator; b. Detroit, Aug. 9, 1945; s. Marvin Daniel and Edith Allman (Fletcher) N.; m. Dorothy Bondurant Butler, Dec. 28, 1968; children: Bree Lauren, Jordan Wright. B in Chemistry, U. Minn., 1967; MS, U. Oreg., 1969, PhD, 1973. Postdoctoral assoc. U. So. Calif., L.A., 1973-75; asst. prof. chemistry Syracuse (N.Y.) U., 1975-79, assoc. prof., 1979-82, prof., 1982—, chmn. dept., 1984—, assoc. dean Coll. Arts and Scis., 1993-94. Editor BioSpectroscopy; contbr. chpts. to books. With U.S. Army, 1969-71. Alfred P. Sloan Found. fellow, 1978. Mem. Am. Chem. Soc., Am. Phys. Soc., Soc. for Applied Spectroscopy, Coblentz Soc. (pres. 1993—, Coblentz award 1981). Avocations: running;

golf; biking. Home: 208 Crawford Ave Syracuse NY 13224-1712 Office: Syracuse U Dept Chemistry 1-014 CST Syracuse NY 13244-4100

NAFT, BARRY NIEL, waste management administrator, chemical engineer; b. N.Y.C., Mar. 26, 1945; s. Albert A. and Hattie (Cutler) N.; m. Rochelle Susan Weiner, Dec. 26, 1966; children: Jason, David, Rachel. BSChemE, Clarkson U., 1965, MSChemE, 1967; PhD, Purdue U., 1969; AMP, U. Pa., 1988. Registered profl. engr. Calif. Sr. engr. Westinghouse Electric Co., Pitts., 1969-71; br. mgr. Getty Oil Corp., Rockville, Md., 1971-73; dept. mgr. Sci. Applications Inc., McLean, Va., 1973-74; v.p. group exec. NUS Corp., Gaithersburg, Md., 1974-89; pres., chief exec. officer Dow Environ. Inc., Rockville, 1989—. Contbr. numerous articles to profl. jours. Chmn. Potomac (Md.) Citizens Assn., 1979. USAEC fellow, 1967-70. Mem. Am. Nuclear Soc. (chmn. fuel cycle and waste mgmt. divsn. 1978-79), Potomac Squash Club (chmn. 1975). Office: Dow Environ Inc 15204 Omega Dr Rockville MD 20850-4601

NAFTALIS, GARY PHILIP, lawyer, educator; b. Newark, Nov. 23, 1941; s. Gilbert and Bertha Beatrice (Gruber) N.; m. Donna Arditi, June 30, 1974; children: Benjamin, Joshua, Daniel, Sarah. AB, Rutgers U., 1963; AM, Brown U., 1965; LLB, Columbia U., 1967. Bar: N.Y. 1967, U.S. Supreme Ct. 1974, U.S. Ct. Appeals (2d cir.) 1968, U.S. Ct. Appeals (3d cir.) 1973, U.S. Dist. Ct. (so. dist.) N.Y. 1969, U.S. Ct. Appeals (D.C. cir.) 1993. Law clk. to judge U.S. Dist. Ct. So. Dist. N.Y., 1967-68; asst. U.S. atty. So. Dist. N.Y., 1968-74, asst. chief criminal div., 1972-74; spl. asst. U.S. atty. for V.I., 1972-73; spl. counsel U.S. Senate Subcom. on Long Term Care, 1975, N.Y. State Temp. Commn. on Living Costs and the Economy, 1975; ptnr. Orans, Elsen, Polstein & Naftalis, N.Y.C., 1974-81, Kramer, Levin, Naftalis, Nessen, Kamin & Frankel, N.Y.C., 1981—; lectr. in law Law Sch. Columbia U., 1976-88; vis. lectr. Law Sch. Harvard U., 1979; mem. deptl. disciplinary com. Appellate div. 1st Dept., 1980-86. Author: (with Marvin E. Frankel) The Grand Jury: An Institution on Trial, 1977, Considerations in Representing Attorneys in Civil and Criminal Enforcement Proceedings, 1981, Sentencing: Helping Judges Do Their Jobs, 1986; editor: White Collar Crimes, 1980. Trustee Boys Brotherhood Rep., 1978—, Blueberry Treatment Ctr., 1981-91, Joseph Haggerty Children's Fund, 1991—. Fellow Am. Coll. Trial Lawyers; mem. ABA (white collar crime com. criminal justice sect. 1985—), Assn. of Bar of City of N.Y. (com. criminal cts. 1980-83, com. judiciary 1984-87, com. on criminal law 1987-90, com. criminal justice 1985-88), Fed. Bar Coun. (com. cts. 2d cir. 1974-77), N.Y. Bar Assn. (com. state legis. 1974-76, exec. com. comml. and fed. litigation sect.), Internat. Bar Assn. (bus. crimes com. 1988—). Home: 1125 Park Ave Apt 7B New York NY 10128 Office: Kramer Levin Naftalis Nessen Kamin & Frankel 919 Third Ave New York NY 10022

NAFTOLIN, FREDERICK, physician, reproductive biologist educator; b. Bronx, N.Y., Apr. 7, 1936; s. Nathan and Jean (Pesacov) N.; children: Michael Eugene, Joshua Joseph; m. Marcie Myerson, Nov. 1, 1987. A.A., UCLA, 1957; B.A. with honors, U. Calif., Berkeley, 1958; M.D. with honors, U. Calif., San Francisco, 1961; D.Phil., U. Oxford, 1970. Intern King County Hosp., Seattle, 1961-62; resident in ob-gyn UCLA, 1962-66; asst. chief gynecology, endocrine fellow USPHS, Seattle, 1966-68; NIH fellow Oxford (Eng.) U., 1968-70; asst. prof. ob-gyn U. Calif., San Diego Sch. Medicine, 1970-73; asso. prof. ob-gyn Harvard Med. Sch., 1973-75; prof., chmn. ob-gyn dept. McGill Faculty Medicine, Montreal, 1975-78; prof., chmn. dept. ob-gyn Yale Med. Sch., New Haven, Conn., 1978—; prof. dept. biology, 1982—; dir. Yale U. Ctr. for Research in Reproductive Biology, 1986—; vis. prof. U. Geneva, 1982-83, Weizmann Inst., 1991-92. Author 15 books including: Subcellular Mechanisms in Reproductive Neuroendocrinology, 1976, Abnormal Fetal Growth, 1978, Clinical Neuroendocrinology, 1979, Dilatation of the Uterine Cervix, 1980; 2-vol. series Basic Reproductive Medicine, Vol. I, Basis of Normal Reproduction, Vol. II, 1981, Male Reproduction, Vol. III, Metabolism of Steroids by Neuroendocrine Tissues, Follicle Stimulation and Ovulation Induction, 1986; mem. editorial bd. Jour. Soc. Gynecologic Investigation, Menopause, Endocrine Revs.; contbr. over 400 papers, articles to med. jours. Fogarty Internat. fellow, 1982, John Simon Guggenheim fellow, 1983; Berlex Internat. scholar, 1991. Mem. Am. Gynecol. and Obstet. Soc., Soc. Gynecol. Investigation (pres. 1991-92), Endocrine Soc., Internat. Soc. Neuroendocrinology, Internat. Am. Psychoneuroendocrinology, New Haven Ob-Gyn. Soc., Can. Fertility Soc., Soc. for Neurosci. Office: Yale Med Sch Dept Ob-Gyn 333 Cedar St New Haven CT 06510-8063

NAFZIGER, DEAN H., special education research executive. Lab. dir. Far west lab. for edn. rsch. and devel. San Francisco. Office: Far West Lab Educ Rsch & Devlp 730 Harrison St San Francisco CA 94107-1242

NAFZIGER, ESTEL WAYNE, economics educator; b. Bloomington, Ill., Aug. 14, 1938; s. Orrin and Beatrice Mae (Slabaugh) N.; m. Elfrieda Nettie Toews, Aug. 20, 1966; children—Brian Wayne, Kevin Jon. B.A., Goshen Coll., 1960; M.A., U. Mich., 1962; Ph.D., U. Ill., 1967. Rsch. assoc. Econ. Devel. Inst., Enugu, Nigeria, 1964-65; asst. prof. Kans. State U., Manhattan, 1966-73, assoc. prof., 1973-78, prof., 1978—; Fulbright prof. Andhra U., Waltair, India, 1970-71; fellow East West Ctr., Honolulu, 1972-73; vis. scholar Cambridge U., 1976; vis. prof. Internat. U. Japan, Yamato-machi, 1983; external research fellow World Acad. Devel. and Coop., College Park, Md., 1984-85; pres. Kans. State U. Faculty Senate, 1990—. Author: African Capitalism, 1977, Class, Caste and Entrepreneurship, 1978, (with others) Development Theory, 1979, Economics of Political Instability, 1983, Economics of Developing Countries, 1984, 2d edit., 1990, Entrepreneurship Equity and Economic Development, 1986, Inequality in Africa, 1988 (named one of Outstanding Acad. Books, Choice 1989-90), The Debt Crisis in Africa, 1993, Poverty and Wealth, 1994, Learning From the Japanese, 1995. Sec. bd. overseers Hesston Coll., Kans., 1980-85; chmn. Lou Douglas Lecture Series, 1984-91, 92-93; pres. faculty senate Kans. State U., 1990-92. Recipient Honor Lectr. award Mid Am. State U.'s Assn., 1984-85; grantee Social Sci. Found., 1969. Mem. Am. Econ. Assn., AAUP (pres. chpt. 1981-82), African Studies Assn., Soc. Internat. Devel., Assn. Comparative Econ. Studies, Omicron Delta Epsilon (hon.), Phi Kappa Phi (hon.). Democrat. Avocations: reading; running. Home: 1919 Bluestem Ter Manhattan KS 66502-4508 Office: Kans State U Dept Econs Waters Hall Manhattan KS 66506-4001

NAFZIGER, PATTIE LOIS, state legislator; b. Phoenix; married; 4 children. Attended, Colo. Coll., 1947-48, U. Ariz., 1948-50, Ariz. State U., 1967-70, Coll. So. Idaho, 1970-72. Former ptnr. Sunshine Farms; mem. Idaho Ho. of Reps., 1990—. Asst. leader 4-H; active Jr. League of Phoenix. Home: 1787 E 3100 South Wendell ID 83355 Office: Idaho Ho of Reps State Capitol Boise ID 83720

NAGAMIYA, SHOJI, physicist, educator; b. Mikage-shi, Hyogo-Ken, Japan, May 24, 1944; came to U.S., 1973; s. Takeo and Masako Nagamiya; m. Tae Nagamiya, Nov. 9, 1969; children: Masahiko, Kenji. BSc, U. Tokyo, 1967; DSc, Osaka (Japan) U., 1972. Rsch. assoc. U. Tokyo, 1972-75; staff scientist Lawrence Berkeley (Calif.) Lab., 1975-82; assoc. prof. U. Tokyo, 1982-88; prof. Columbia U., N.Y.C., 1986—; chmn. dept. physics 1991-94; adj. prof. Waseda U., 1994—; chmn. Internat. Conf. on Quark Matter, Lennox, Mass., 1987-88. Author: Advances in Nuclear Physics, 1984, Annual Review of Nuclear & Particle Science, 1984; mem. editorial bd. Il Nuovo Cimento, 1989—, Jour. Phys. Soc. Japan, 1984-86; mem. adv. com. Jour. Phys. G, 1992—, Internat. Jour. Modern Phys. E, 1992—. Mem. evaluation com. Swedish Natural Rsch. Coun., 1987; mem. vis. com. Lawrence Berkeley Lab., Oak Ridge (Tenn.) Nat. Lab., Brookhaven Nat. Lab. and others; chmn. Nuclear Physics Com. of Japan, 1985-87. U.S. Dept. of Energy grantee, 1986—, Yamada Sci. Found. grantee, 1989-91; recipient Inoue prize, 1992. Fellow Am. Phys. Soc. Home: PO Box 137 Irvington NY 10533-1923 Office: Columbia U Dept Physics W 120th St New York NY 10027

NAGAN, PETER SEYMOUR, publisher; b. N.Y.C., Dec. 18, 1920; s. Arthur and Anna (Janis) N.; m. Gloria Mesinoff, Dec. 23, 1951; children: Laura Evelyn Brown, Michael Jay. BA, Columbia Coll., 1942; MS in Journalism, Columbia U. 1943, MA in Econs., 1948. Wire editor AP, Newark, N.J., 1943-44; staff writer Sunday Jour. New York Times, 1944-45; staff writer Fortune Mag., N.Y.C., 1946-47; corr. Bus. Week Mag., Washington, 1948-52; mng. editor newsletters Bur. Nat. Affairs, Washington,

1952-60; editor, pub. Bond and Money Market Letter, 1960—; bd. chmn. Newsletter Svcs., Inc., Lanham, Md., 1972—. Author: Medical Almanac, 1961, Fail-Safe Investing, 1981. Recipient Loeb award for Bus. Journalism U. Conn., 1965. Office: Newsletter Svcs Inc 9700 Philadelphia Ct Lanham Seabrook MD 20706

NAGANO, KENT GEORGE, conductor; b. Morro Bay, Calif.. B.A. Sociology & Music (high honors), U of Calif., Santa Cruz; MA in Composition, San Francisco State U.; studied with, Laszlo Varga. Former asst. Opera Co. Boston; former prin. guest condr. Ensemble InterContemporain & the Dutch Radio Orch.; mus. dir. & condr. Berkeley Symphony, 1978—; mus. dir. Opéra de Lyon, 1989—; assoc. prin. & guest condr. LSO, London, England, 1990; mus. dir., prin. condr. designate Hallé Orch., England, 1991-94; mus. dir., prin. condr. Hallé Orch., 1994—. has performed with numerous orchestras around the world; recordings include: Songs of the Auvergne, Peter and the Wolf, Turandot and Arlecchino (Grammy nom.), La Boheme, Dialogues of the Carelites, The Death of Klinghoffer (Grammy nom.), Love for Three Oranges (Grammy nom.), Susannah (Grammy award), La damnation de Faust, The Rite of Spring, Rodrgue et chimene. Recipient Seaver/ NEA Conducting award, 1985; Record of Yr. award Gramophone; named "officer" of France's Order of Arts and Letters, 1993. Office: care Stephen Marcus Pub Rels 110-8 Suburban Ct Rochester NY 14620*

NAGANUMA, KAZUE, automotive executive; b. 1938. Mgmt. Mitsubishi Heavy Industries Ltd., Tokyo, 1960-71, Mitsubishi Motors Corp., Tokyo, 1971-74; exec. v.p. MMC Svcs., Inc., Southfield, Mich., 1974-86; pres. Mitsubishi Motor Sales of Am., Cypress, Calif., 1986—. Office: Mitsubishi Motor Sales Am 6400 Katella Ave Cypress CA 90630-5208

NAGAO, MIKE AKIRA, horticulturist, county administrator; b. Hilo, Hawaii, Oct. 23, 1947. BA, U. Hawaii, 1969, MS, 1971; PhD, U. Mass., 1975. From asst. to assoc. prof. U. Hawaii, Hilo, 1975-81; from asst. to horticulturist U. Hawaii, Honolulu, 1981—; county adminstr., 1991—. Contbr. articles to profl. jours. Mem. Am. Soc. Hort. Sci. Office: Univ of Hawaii Beaumont Rsch Sta 461 W Lanikaula St Hilo HI 96720-4037

NAGARKATTI, JAI PRAKASH, chemical company executive; b. Hyderabad, India, Feb. 18, 1947; came to U.S., 1970; s. Surendranath and Shakuntala (Bai) N.; m. Linda Susan Slaughter, Mar. 14, 1975; 1 child, Shanti. BS, Osmania U., 1966, MS, 1968; MS, East Tex. State U., 1972, EdD, 1976. Group leader Aldrich Chem. Co., Milw., 1977-78, supr. prodn., 1978-79, mgr. prodn., 1979-84, dir. prodn., 1985, v.p., 1985-87, pres., 1987—, also bd. dirs.; lectr. chemistry V.V. Coll., Hyderabad, 1969-70. Contbr. articles to profl. jours. Robert A. Welch fellow East Tex. State U., Commerce, 1974-76. Fellow Indian Chem. Soc.; mem. Am. Chem. Soc. (chmn. membership Milw. chpt. 1981). Avocations: philately, tennis. Office: Aldrich Chem Co Inc 1001 W St Paul Ave Milwaukee WI 53233

NAGATANI, PATRICK ALLEN RYOICHI, artist, art educator; b. Chgo., Aug. 19, 1945; s. John Lee and Diane Yoshiye (Yoshimura) N.; m. Rae Jeanean Bodwell, June 17, 1979; children: Methuen, Hart Gen, Louis-Thomas. BA, Calif. State U., L.A., 1967; MFA, UCLA, 1980. Cert. tchr. K-12, Calif. Instr. Alexander Hamilton High Sch., L.A., 1968-80, West. L.A. C.C., 1980-83; artist in residency Calif. Arts Coun., Juvenile Ct. and Cmty. Schs., L.A., 1986-87; instr. Otis Art Inst. Parson Sch. of Design, L.A., 1987; asst. prof. dept. art/art history Loyola Marymount U., L.A., 1980-87; prof. dept. art & art history U. N.Mex., Albuquerque, 1987—; instr. Fairfax Cmty. Adult Sch., L.A., 1976-79; vis. artist/instr. The Sch. of the Art Inst., Chgo., 1983; conductor numerous seminars and workshops; lectr. in field. One man shows include Pal Gallery, Evergreen State U., Olympia, Wash., 1976, BC Space, Laguna Beach, Calif., 1978, Cityscape Gallery, Pasadena, Calif., 1978, Exploratorium Gallery, Calif. State U., L.A., 1979, Orange Coast Coll., Costa Mesa, Calif., 1980, Susan Spiritus Gallery, Newport Beach, Calif., 1981, 83, 85, Canon Photo Gallery, Amsterdam, The Netherlands, 1982, John Michael Kohler Arts Ctr., Sheboygan, Wis., 1983, 86, Arco Ctr. Visual Arts, L.A., 1983, Clarence Kennedy Gallery, Boston, 1984, Colo. Mountain Coll.. Breckenridge, 1984, Jayne H. Baum Gallery, N.Y.C., 1985, 87, 89, 91, 94, Torch Gallery, Amsterdam, 1985, 87, Fotografie Forum Frankfurt, Fed. Rep. Germany, 1986, Frederick S. Wight Art Gallery, U. Calif., L.A., 1987, San Francisco Cameraworks, 1988, Koplin Gallery, L.A., 1988, 90, 92, 95, Shadai Gallery, Tokyo Inst. Polytech., 1989, Lubbock (Tex.) Fine Arts Ctr., 1990, Haggerty Mus. Art, Marquette U., Milw., 1991, Richard Levy Gallery, Albuquerque, 1992, Stanford (Calif.) Mus. Art, 1993, numerous others; exhibited in group shows at Friends of Photography, Carmel, Calif., 1976, 81, 85, Ctrl. Wash. State Coll., Ellensburg, 1977, Humboldt State U., Arcata, Calif., 1977, Soho/Cameraworks Gallery, L.A., 1978, Libra Gallery, Claremont (Calif.) Grad. Sch., 1978, Cirrus Gallery, L.A., 1979, Skidmore Coll. Art Gallery, Saratoga, N.Y., 1980, Tortue Gallery, Santa Monica, Calif., 1981, Palos Verdes (Calif.) Cmty. Art Ctr., 1982, Fine Arts Gallery, Cypress (Calif.) Coll., 1982, Fay Gold Gallery, Atlanta, 1982, Mus. Photographic Arts, San Diego, 1983, 84, Jayne H. Baum Gallery, N.Y.C., 1983, 87, Arco Ctr. Visual Art, L.A., 1984, Alt. Mus., N.Y.C., 1984, 88, Black Gallery, L.A., 1985, Mus. N.Mex., Santa Fe, 1986, Whitney Mus. Am. Art, Stamford, Conn., 1986, Balt. Mus. Art, 1987, Ctr. Photography, Woodstock, N.Y., 1988, Oakland Mus., Calif., 1989, Alinder Gallery, Gualala, Calif., 1990, 92, Coll. Santa Fe, 1990, Art Ctr., Waco, Tex., 1991, Lintas Worldwide, N.Y.C., 1991, Dirs. Guild of Am., L.A., 1992, Burden Gallery, N.Y.C., 1992, Nat. Arts Club, N.Y.C., 1992, Knoxville (Tenn.) Art Mus., 1993, G. Ray Hawkins Gallery, L.A., 1994, Houston FotoFest, 1994, Riverside (Calif.) Art Mus., 1994, Mass. Coll. Art, Boston, 1994, numerous others; represented in permanent collections Albuquerque Mus., Balt. Art Mus., Continental Ins., N.Y.C., Chrysler Mus. Art, Norfolk, Va., Denver Art Mus., Ga. Power Co., Atlanta, Honolulu Advertiser, L.A. County Mus. Art, Loyola Marymount U., L.A., Mass. Coll. Art, Boston, Met. Mus. Art, N.Y.C., Mus. Fine Arts, Houston, Mus. N.Mex., Santa Fe, Nev. Mus. Art, Reno, Oakland (Calif.) Mus., Prudential Ins. Co. Am., Newark, Roswell (N.Mex.) Mus., St. Louis Art Mus., Shearson/Am. Express, N.Y.C., Tampa (Fla.) Mus. Art, Tokyo Inst. Polytech., numerous others. Travel grantee Ford Found., 1979; Faculty Rsch. grantee Loyola Marymount U., L.A., 1981, 83, U. N.Mex., 1988, 90; Artist-In-Residence grantee Calif. Arts Coun., 1982-83; Visual Artist fellow Nat. Endowment for the Arts, 1984-85, 92-93; Brody Arts Fund fellow, 1986; Polaroid fellow, 1983-90; named Art Waves competition and exhbn. finalist Cmty. Redevel. Agy. L.A., 1987; recipient Calif. Disting. Arist award Nat. Ed. Artn. Assn. Conv., Mus. Contemporary Art, L.A., 1988, Kraszna-Krausz award and Photographic Book Innovation award Kraszna-Krausz Found., 1992. Avocations: gardening, gambling. Office: U NMex Dept Art & Art History Albuquerque NM 87131

NAGATOSHI, KONRAD R., anthropology educator, information systems specialist; b. Chgo., Jan. 18, 1951; s. Paul A. and Dorothea E. (Przybilla) N. BS in Anthropology with honors, Loyola U., 1973; MA in Anthropology, U. Chgo., 1976, PhD in Anthropology, 1984; cert. in data processing-tech., Harper Coll., 1990. Lic. realtor, Ill. Instr. anthropology Loyola U., Chgo., 1979-81; sr. rsch. specialist Ctr. for Craniofacial Anomalies U. Ill., Chgo., 1985-86, clin. asst. prof. biomed. visualization dept., 1987-88, adj. prof. anthropology dept., 1988; comml. real estate sales Samuel Spiro & Assocs., Chgo., 1989; computer micro-asst. Harper Coll., Palatine, Ill., 1990-91, instr. anthropology, 1991—; instr. anthropology Northeastern U., Chgo. 1991; computer programmer and analyst III. Dept. Employment Security, Chgo., 1992—, Kemper Nat. Ins., Long Grove, Ill., 1994—. Abstract reviewer Internat. Jour. Primatology, N.Y.C., 1990, Am. Jour. Physical Anthropology, N.Y.C., 1987; abstract reviewer, organizer U. Ill. Rsch. Forum, 1988; contbr. articles to profl. jours. Organist, song leader Our Lady of Mercy Roman Cath. Ch., Chgo., 1983-88. Found. for Rsch. into the Origins of Man grantee, 1978-84, NSF Found. grantee, 1978-79, Sigma Xi grantee, 1978-79. Fellow Am. Anthropol. Assn.; mem. AAAS, Am. Assn. Phys. Anthropologists. Avocations: piano, art history, fishing, hiking, bicycling. Office: Harper Coll Div Bus/Social Sci 1200 W Algonquin Rd Palatine IL 60067-7398

NAGEL, DARYL DAVID, retail executive; b. Arlington, Minn., Apr. 13, 1939; s. Paul Charles and Frieda L. (Oldenburg) N.; m. Joan Clare Dacey, Dec. 23, 1961; children: Kelly, Andrew, Maureen. BME, U. Minn., 1962; diploma in Advanced Mgmt. Program, Harvard U., 1978. Asst. mdse. mgr. Res. Supply Co., Mpls., 1962-65; mdse. mgr. Reserve Supply Co., Mpls.,

1965-66, v.p., gen. mgr., 1966-69; v.p. area gen. mgr. United Bldg. Ctrs., Winona, Minn., 1969-78, exec. v.p., chief ops. officer, 1978-84, pres., chief exec. officer, 1984-87; pres., CEO Lanoga Corp., Seattle, 1987—; bd. dirs. Lanoga Corp., Seattle, 1987—, Badger Foundry, Winona, 1984-87. Bd. dirs. United Way, Winona, 1978-84. Mem. Home Ctr. Leadership Coun., C. of C. (bd. dirs. 1964-69, 73, 78), Sahalee Country Club. Republican. Lutheran. Avocations: golf, gardening, skiing. Office: Lanoga Corp 17946 NE 65th St Redmond WA 98052-4963

NAGEL, EDWARD MCCAUL, lawyer, former utilities executive; b. Geneva, N.Y., Sept. 6, 1926; s. Edward Samuel and Helen Veronica (McCaul) N.; m. Mary Elizabeth Klein, Sept. 11, 1950; children—Christopher, Linda, Michael, Jeffrey, Ellen. A.B., Harvard, 1949; LL.B., U. Pa., 1952; postgrad., Cornell U. Bus. Sch., 1962. Bar: Pa. 1953. Assoc. Simpson, Thacher & Bartlett, N.Y.C., 1953-54; atty. Pa. Power & Light Co., Allentown, 1952, 54-62; asst. counsel Pa. Power & Light Co., 1962-68, asst. gen. counsel, 1968-71, gen. counsel, 1971-85, sec., 1971-89, v.p., 1973-91; prin. Edward M. Nagel Atty. at Law, 1991—. Chmn. Mayor's Citizens Adv. Com., Allentown, 1968-72; assoc. counsel, bd. dirs. Minsi Trails council Boy Scouts Am. Served with USNR, 1945-46. Mem. Lehigh County Bar Assn. Home: 417 N 28th St Allentown PA 18104-4838

NAGEL, JOACHIM HANS, biomedical engineer, educator; b. Haustadt, Saarland, Feb. 22, 1948; came to U.S., 1986; s. Emil and Margarethe Nagel; m. Monika Behrens. MS, U. Saarbruecken, Fed. Republic Germany, 1973; DSc, U. Erlangen, Fed. Republic Germany, 1979. Rsch. assoc., lectr., instr. U. Saarbruecken, 1973-74; rsch. assoc., lectr., instr. Dept. Biomed. Engring., U. Erlangen-Nuernberg, 1974-75, asst. prof., 1975-79, dir. med. electronics and computer div., 1976-85, acad. councillor, 1980-86; assoc. prof. radiology Med. Sch. U. Miami, Coral Gables, Fla., 1990-91, assoc. prof. psychology Sch. Arts and Scis., 1988-91, assoc. prof. biomed. engring. Coll. Engring., 1986-91, prof. biomed. engring, radiology and psychology, 1991—. Editor: Annals of Biomedical Engineering, Section Instrumentation, 1989-94, IOP Physiological Measurement, 1994—; contbr. numerous articles to profl. jours. NIH grantee since 1986. Mem. IEEE (sr.), IEEE/Engring. in Medicine and Biology Soc. (chmn. Internat. Conf. 1991, chmn. Internat. Progr. Com. Conf. 1989, 90, 92), IEEE/Acoustics, Speech, and Signal Processing Soc., Biomed. Engring. Soc. (sr.), N.Y. Acad. Scis., Internat. Soc. Optical Engring., Romanian Soc. for Clin. Engring. and Med. Computing (hon.), Sigma Xi. Roman Catholic. Achievements include numerous U.S., German and European patents; invention and development of procedure for Sub-Nyquist Sampling of signals for statistic signal processing, NMR imaging of electric currents, passive telemetry for analogue signals, ECG detection; invention of Macro programming; portable drug infusion systems; new techniques for impedance cardiography and perinatal monitors; new techniques for medical image registration and U.S. Doppler analysis. Office: U Miami PO Box 248294 Miami FL 33124-0621

NAGEL, PATRICIA JO, state legislator, consultant, lawyer; b. Billings, Mont., Sept. 24, 1942; d. Robert Mark and Evelyn Margaret (Lipsack) McKeown; m. Robert Wells Nagel, Aug. 18, 1963; children: Stacia, Susanna. BA in Polit. Sci., N.Mex. State U., 1965; JD, U. Wyo., 1984. Bar: Wyo. 1984. Interior designer Nassif's Interiors, Cedar Rapids, Iowa, 1965-67, Cedar Rapids Paint, 1973-74; law clk. to presiding justice 7th jud. dist., Casper, Wyo., 1983-84; sole practice Casper, 1984-88; dir. Wyo. Futures Project, Casper, 1986-88; ptnr. Nagel & Nix, Casper, 1988—; mem. Wyo. Ho. of Reps., 1992—. Sr. editor Land and Water Law Rev., 1982-83. Vice chair Wyo. Community Devel. Authority; mem. planning commn. City of Casper, 1980; pres., bd. dirs. Friends of the Libr., Casper, 1980; pres. Meadowlark Montessori Sch., Casper, 1979; sec. Casper Bicentennial Com., 1976; v.p. Nicolaysen Art Mus., Casper, 1985-86; sec., bd. dirs. Hospice Cancer Treatment Ctr., Casper, 1985-86. Republican. Presbyterian. Avocations: writing, tennis. Home: 1105 S Durbin St Casper WY 82601-4327

NAGEL, PAUL CHESTER, historian, writer, lecturer; b. Independence, Mo., Aug. 14, 1926; s. Paul Conrad and Freda (Sabrowsky) N.; m. Joan Peterson, Mar. 19, 1948; children: Eric John, Jefferson, Steven Paul. B.A., U. Minn., 1948, M.A., 1949, Ph.D., 1952. Historian SAC, USAF, Omaha, 1951-53; asst. prof. Augustana Coll., Sioux Falls, S.D., 1953-54; asst. prof., then assoc. prof. Eastern Ky. U., Richmond, 1954-61; mem. faculty U. Ky., 1961-69, prof. history, 1965-69; dean U. Ky. (Coll. Arts and Scis.), 1965-69; spl. asst. to pres. for acad. affairs U. Mo., 1969-71, v.p. acad. affairs, 1971-74, prof. history, 1969-78; prof., head dept. history U. Ga., 1978-80; dir. Va. Hist. Soc., Richmond, 1981-85; Disting. Lee scholar Lee Meml. Found., 1986-90; vis. prof. Amherst Coll., 1957-58, Vanderbilt U., 1959, U. Minn., 1964; vis. scholar, Duke U., 1991-92, U. Minn., 1992—, Carleton Coll., 1993—. Author: One Nation Indivisible, 1964, 2d edit., 1980, This Sacred Trust, American Nationality, 1798-1898, 1971, 2d edit., 1980, Missouri: A History, 1977 (Best Book award 1977), 2d edit., 1988, Descent from Glory, Four Generations of the John Adams Family, 1983 (Book of the Month Club main selection), The Adams Women: Abigail and Louisa Adams, Their Sisters and Daughters, 1987, The Lees of Virginia: Seven Generations of an American Family, 1990; co-author: Extraordinary Lives, 1986, George Caleb Bingham, 1989, Massachusetts and the New Nation, 1992; contbg. editor American Heritage. Mem. Council Colls. Arts and Scis., 1965-69, Ky. Arts Commn., 1966-69; trustee Colonial Williamsburg Found., 1983—; vice chmn. bd. dirs. Center for Research Libraries, Chgo., 1973-74. Elected a Laureate of Va., 1988. Fellow Soc. Am. Historians, Pilgrim Soc.; So. Hist. Assn. (pres. 1984-85), Mass. Hist. Soc. Home: 1314 Marquette Ave Apt 2206 Minneapolis MN 55403

NAGEL, SIDNEY ROBERT, physics educator; b. N.Y.C., Sept. 28, 1948; s. Ernest and Edith (Haggstrom) N.; married. BA, Columbia U., 1969; MA, Princeton U., 1972, PhD, 1974. Rsch. assoc. Brown U., Providence, R.I., 1974-76; asst. prof. physics U. Chgo., 1976-81, assoc. prof., 1981-84, prof., 1984—. Dir. U. Chgo. Materials Research Lab., 1987-91. Contbr. articles to profl. jours. Alfred Sloan Found. fellow, 1978-82. Fellow AAAS, Am. Phys. Soc. Home: 4919 S Blackstone Ave Chicago IL 60615-3003 Office: U Chgo 5640 S Ellis Ave Chicago IL 60637

NAGEL, STANLEY BLAIR, construction and investment executive; b. Bklyn., Mar. 19, 1926; s. Robert Arthur and Reene Ann Nagel; children: Scott Alan, Robert Arthur. BBA, U. Oreg., 1950. With constrn. dept. Nagel Investment, Portland, Oreg., 1955-58, pres., 1956—; pres. R.A. Constrn., Portland, 1956—; buyer May Co., Portland, 1958-72; gen. mgr. Portland Outdoor Store, 1972-75; owner Nagels Nursery & Greenhouses, Portland, 1975—; pres. E & S Distbrs., Portland, 1982—. Co-inventor pizza machine (patent pending). 2d lt. U.S. Army, 1952-55. Republican. Jewish. Avocations: photography, Malt scotch collector. Home and Office: 5353 SW Martha St Portland OR 97221-1840

NAGEL, STUART SAMUEL, political science educator, lawyer; b. Chgo., Aug. 29, 1934; s. Leo I. and Florence (Pritikin) N.; m. Joyce Golub, Sept. 1, 1957; children: Brenda Ellen, Robert Franklin. Student, U. Chgo., 1954-55; BS, Northwestern U., 1957, JD, 1958, PhD, 1961. Bar: Ill. 1958. Instr. Pa. State U., 1960-61; asst. prof. U. Ariz., 1961-62; prof. polit. sci. U. Ill., 1962—; law and social sci. vis. fellow Yale Law Sch., 1970-71; vis. fellow Nat. Inst. Law Enforcement and Criminal Justice, 1974-75; Sr. scholar East-West Center, Honolulu, 1965; fellow Behavioral Scis. Center, Palo Alto, Calif., 1964-65; dir. O.E.O. Legal Services Agy. of Champaign, 1966-69; vol. atty. Lawyers Constl. Def. Com., Miss., 1967; asst. counsel U.S. Senate Jud. Com., 1966. Author: The Legal Process from a Behavioral Perspective, 1969, Law and Social Change, 1970, New Trends in Law and Politics Research, 1971, Rights of the Accused, 1972, Comparing Elected and Appointed Judicial Systems, 1973, Minimizing Costs and Maximizing Benefits in Providing Legal Services to the Poor, 1973, Improving the Legal Process: Effects of Alternatives, 1975, Operations Research Methods: As Applied to Political Science and The Legal Process, 1976, The Application of Mixed Strategies: Civil Rights and Other Multiple Activity Policies, 1976, Legal Policy Analysis: Finding an Optimum Level or Mix, 1977, Too Much or Too Little Policy: The Example of Pretrial Release, 1977, The Legal Process: Modeling the System, 1977, Decision Theory and the Legal Process, 1979, Policy Analysis: In Social Science Research, 1979, Policy Studies Handbook, 1980, Policy Evaluation: Making Optimum Decisions, 1982, Public Policy: Goals, Means and Methods, 1984, Contemporary Policy Analysis, 1984, Prediction Causation and Legal Analysis, 1986, Law, Policy and Optimizing

Analysis, 1986, Evaluation Analysis with Microcomputers, 1988, Policy Studies: Integration and Evaluation, 1988, Higher Goals for America, 1988, Decision-Aiding Software and Legal Decision-Making, 1988, Introducing Decision-Aiding Software, 1989, Multi-Criteria Dispute Resolution, 1989, Evaluative and Explanatory Reasoning, 1990, Legal Scholarship and Microcomputers, 1990, Decision-Aiding Software: Skills, Obstacles and Applications, 1990, Judicial Decision-Making and Decision-Aiding Software, 1991, Legal Process Controversies and Super-Optimum Solutions, 1991, Public Policy Substance and Super-Optimum Solutions, 1991, Teach Yourself Decision-Aiding Software, 1991, Social Science, Law, and Public Policy, 1991, Policy Analysis Methods and Super-Optimum Solutions, 1992, Professional Developments in Policy Studies, 1992, Developing Nations and Super-Optimum Policy Analysis, 1993, The Policy Process and Super-Optimum Solutions, 1994, others; editor: Policy Studies Jour., The Policy Studies Directory, 1973, Environmental Politics, 1974, Policy Studies in America and Elsewhere, 1975, Policy Studies and the Social Sciences, 1975, Sage Yearbooks in Politics and Public Policy, 1975—, Lexington-Heath Policy Studies Orgn. Series, 1975—, Political Science Utilization Directory, 1975, Policy Studies Review Annual, 1977, Policy Grants Directory, 1977, Modeling the Criminal Justice System, 1977, Policy Research Centers Directory, 1978, Policy Studies Personnel Directory, 1979, Improving Policy Analysis, 1980, Policy Publishers and Associations Directory, 1980, Encyclopedia of Policy Studies, 1982, The Political Science of Criminal Justice, 1982, Productivity and Public Policy, 1983, The Policy Studies Field: It's Basic Literature, 1983, Public Policy Analysis and Management, 1986, Law and Policy Studies, 1987, Social Science and Computers, 1988, Decision-aiding Software and Decision Analysis, 1990, Decision-aiding Software and Public Administration, 1990, Global Policy Studies, 1990, Law, Decision-making and Microcomputers, 1990, Policy Theory and Policy Studies, 1990, Advances in Developmental Policy Studies, 1991—, Applications of Decision-Aiding Software, 19, Applications of Super-Optimum Solutions, 1991, Decision-Aiding Software and Decision Analysis, 1991, Law, Decision-Making, and Microcomputers, 1991, Policy Studies and Developing Nations: A Multi-Volume Treatise, 1991, Public Administration, Public Policy, and The People's Republic of China, 1991, Systematic Analysis in Dispute Resolution, 1991, Computer-Aided Decision Analysis, 1992, Resolving International Disputes Through Win-Win or SOS Solutions, 1992, Computer-Aided Judicial Analysis, 1992, Developing Nations and Super-Optimum Policy Analysis, 1992, Evaluative and Explanatory Reasoning, 1992, Developing Nations and Super-Optimum Policy Analysis, 1993, Legal Scholarship, Super-Optimizing, and Microcomputers, 1993, Encyclopedia of Policy Studies, 1993, African Development and Public Policy, 1994, Asian Development and Public Policy, 1994, East European Development and Public Policy, 1994, Latin American Development and Public Policy, 1994, Policy Studies in Developing Nations, 1994—, Indian Development and Public Policy, 1995, Political Reform, 1995, Policy Studies in Developing Nations, 1994, India Development and Public Policy, 1995, others; mem. editorial bd.: Law and Soc. Assn., 1966—, Law and Policy Studies, 1986—, Pub. Policy Analysis and Mgmt., 1986—. Grantee Social Sci. Research Council, 1959-60; Grantee Am. Council Learned Socs., 1964-65; Grantee NSF, 1970-73; Grantee Rockefeller Found., 1976; Grantee Dept. Transp., 1976; Grantee Ford Found., 1975—; Grantee ERDA, 1977; Grantee Dept. Agr., 1977; Grantee NIE, 1976; Grantee HUD, 1978; Grantee ILEC, 1978; Grantee Dept. Labor, 1978; Grantee NIJ, 1979; Grantee Am. Bar Assn., 1980. Fellow AAAS; mem. ABA, Am. Polit. Sci. Assn., Law and Soc. Assn. (trustee), Policy Studies Orgn. (sec.-treas.). Home: 1720 Park Haven Dr Champaign IL 61820-7153 *There is a need for social scientists to show more interest in applying their knowledge and skills to important policy problems. There is also a need for policy-makers and policy-appliers to become more aware of the relevant knowledge and skills that social scientists have developed. I have tried to stimulate closer relations between social science and public policy by such relevant activities as writing articles, authoring books, editing journals, and founding associations. Those activities will hopefully result in promoting more applications of social science to important public policy problems. I am especially interested in developing solutions to public policy problems whereby liberals, conservatives, and other major viewpoints can all come out ahead of their initial best expectations simultaneously. Such solutions are facilitated by decision-aiding software which enables one to systematically process goals to be achieved, alternatives available for achieving them, and relations be*

NAGEL, THOMAS, philosopher, law educator; b. Belgrade, Yugoslavia, July 4, 1937; came to U.S., 1939, naturalized, 1944; s. Walter and Carolyn (Baer) N.; m. Doris Blum, June 18, 1958 (div. 1973); m. Anne Hollander, June 26, 1979. B.A., Cornell U., 1958; B.Phil., Oxford (Eng.) U., 1960; Ph.D., Harvard, 1963. Asst. prof. philosophy U. Calif., Berkeley, 1963-66; asst. prof. Princeton U., 1966-69, assoc., 1969-72, prof., 1972-80; prof. N.Y. U., 1980—, prof. philosophy and law, 1986—; vis. prof. Rockefeller U., 1973, U. Mex., 1977, U. Witwatersrand, 1982, UCLA, 1986; tanner lectr. Stanford U., 1977, Oxford (Eng.) U., 1979, Howison lectr. U. Calif. Berkeley, 1987, Thalheimer lectr. Johns Hopkins U., 1989, John Locke lectr. Oxford U., 1990, Hempel lectr. Princeton U., 1995, Whitehead lectr. Harvard U., 1995. Author: The Possibility of Altruism, 1970, Mortal Questions, 1979, The View from Nowhere, 1986, What Does It All Mean?, 1987, Equality and Partiality, 1991, Other Minds, 1995; assoc. editor: Philosophy and Public Affairs, 1970-82. Guggenheim fellow, 1966, NSF fellow, 1967-69, NEH fellow, 1978, 84-85, vis. fellow All Souls Coll., Oxford, Eng., 1990. Mem. Am. Philos. Assn., Am. Acad. Arts and Scis., Brit. Acad.

NÄGELE, RAINER, German and comparative literary educator; b. Triesen, Liechtenstein, Aug. 2, 1943; came to U.S., 1967; s. Alwin and Irma (Sele) N.; m. Beryl Schlossman. PhD, U. Santa Barbara, 1971. Asst. prof. U. Iowa, Iowa City, 1971-73; vis. asst. prof. Johns Hopkins U., Balt., 1973-74, assoc. prof., 1976-78, prof. German lang. and comparative lit., 1978—; chmn. German dept., 1987—; assoc. prof. Ohio State U., Columbus, 1974-76. Author: Literatur und Utopie, 1978, Unessbarer Schrift gleich, 1985, Reading after Freud, 1987, Theater Theory Speculation, 1991; editor: Benjamin's Ground, 1988. John S. Guggenheim Found. grantee, 1988. Office: Johns Hopkins U Dept Of German Baltimore MD 21218

NAGERA, HUMBERTO, psychiatrist, psychoanalyst, educator, author; b. Havana, Cuba, May 23, 1927; m. Gloria Maria Hernandez, Sept. 8, 1952; children: Lisette Maria, Humberto Felipe, Daniel. B.Sc., U. Havana, 1945; M.D., Havana Med. Sch., 1952. Intern, resident in psychiatry Havana U. Hosp., 1950-55; sr. staff, chmn. research Anna Freud's Clinic, London, 1958-68; prof. psychiatry U. Mich., Ann Arbor, 1968-87; chief youth services U. Mich., 1973-79, prof. emeritus, 1987; prof. psychiatry U. South Fla., 1987—; dir. adolescent inpatient unit and children's inpatient unit, 1987—. Author: Early Childhood Disturbances, Problems of Developmental Psychoanalytic Psychology, 1966, Vincent Van Gogh, 1966, Basic Psychoanalytic Concepts on the Libido Theory, 1969, Basic Psychoanalytic Concepts on the Theory of Instincts, 1970, Basic Psychoanalytic Concepts of Metapsychology Conflicts, Anxiety, and Other Subjects, 1970, Female Sexuality and the Oedipus Complex, 1975, Obsessional Neurosis: Developmental Psychopathology, 1977, 2nd edit., 1993, The Developmental Approach in Child Psychopathology, 1981; Contbr. articles to profl. jours. Mem. Am. Psychiat. Assn., Internat. Psychoanalytic Assn., Mich. Psychoanalytic Inst. (pres. 1975-77), Am. Assn. Child Psychoanalysis, Cuba Med. Assn. in Exile, South Fla. Tampa Bay Psychoanalytic Soc. (pres. 1992-93). Home: 5202 Dwire Ct Tampa FL 33647-1016 Office: U South Fla Dept Psychiatry 3515 E Fletcher Ave Tampa FL 33613-4788

NAGLE, ARLINGTON, JR., accountant, corporate executive; b. Lancaster, Pa., Feb. 21, 1943; s. Arlington Adam and Kathryn E. (Root) N.; m. Susan E. Wolfe, June 19, 1965; children: Scott A., Christopher A. BA, Moravian Coll., 1965. CPA, Pa. Sr. acct. Price Waterhouse & Co., Phila., 1965-71; sr. v.p. CDI Corp., Phila., 1971—. Mem. AICPA, Pa. Inst. CPAs. Lutheran. Office: CDI Corp 10 Penn Center Plz Philadelphia PA 19103-1628

NAGLE, ARTHUR JOSEPH, investment banker; b. Allentown, Pa., Sept. 11, 1938; s. Paul Arthur and Frances Helene (Kline) N.; m. Paige Carlton, Sept. 12, 1970; children: Katharin Elizabeth, Christopher Paul. BS in Math., Pa. State U., 1961; MBA in Fin., Columbia U., 1967. Systems engr., mktg. rep. IBM, Pitts., 1961-62; trainee to mng. dir. First Boston Corp., N.Y.C., 1967-88; chmn. Vestar Capital Ptnrs., Inc., 1988—; bd. dirs. Chart House Restaurants, Solana Beach, Calif., Super D Drugs, Inc., Memphis, Russell

Stanley Corp., Woodbridge, N.J., La Petite Acad. Inc., Overland Park, Kans., Hampshire Chem. Corp., Lexington, Mass., Prestone Products Corp., Danbury, Conn. Active Community Fund, Bronxville, N.Y.; bd. govs. Lawrence Hosp., Bronxville, Nat. Devel. Coun., Pa. State U., Bronxville Sch. Found. Lt. USN, 1962-66, Vietnam. Office: Vestar Capital Ptnrs Inc 245 Park Ave 40th Fl New York NY 10017

NAGLE, DAVID R., lawyer, former congressman; b. Grinnell, Iowa, Apr. 15, 1943; s. William Nagle; m. Diane Lewis, July 13, 1984; 1 stepchild, Benjamin Norden. Student, U. No. Iowa, 1961-65; LLB, U. Iowa, 1968. Pvt. practice Waterloo and Evansdale, Iowa, 1968-73; ptnr. Ball & Nagle, P.C., Waterloo, 1973-81; sole practice Waterloo, 1981-87, 93—; mem. 100-102nd Congresses from Iowa 3rd Dist., Washington, 1987-93; asst. county atty. Black Hawk County, Waterloo, 1968-70; city atty. Evansdale, 1972-73. Active Black Hawk County Conservation Bd., Cedar Falls, Iowa, 1975-80, pres. 1979; state chmn. Iowa Democrats, Des Moines, 1982-85. Mem. Nat. Dem. Club. Roman Catholic. Avocations: hunting, fishing, golfing.

NAGLE, GEORGE, JR., state mental health administrator; b. Bklyn., July 8, 1932; s. George and Elizabeth (Gaffney) N.; m. Marcia Elynore Moran, July 2, 1964; 1 child, Kristen. BA in Govt. and Bus. magna cum laude, Lehigh U., 1956. Jr. officer trainee CIA, 1956-57; intelligence officer U.S. Intelligence/CIA, 1959-66; dep. dir. adminstrn. Nathan Kline Inst. for Psychiat. Rsch., Orangeburg, N.Y., 1966—; exec. dir. Internat. Com. Against Mental Illness, N.Y.C., 1966—; treas. N.J. Rsch. Found. for Mental Hygiene, 1966—; instr. psychiatry dept. NYU Med. Ctr., N.Y.C., 1979—; mem. adv. bd. refugee assistance program Adelphi U., 1987; adminstr. WHO Mental Health Collaborating Ctr., 1990—; cons. Bus. Counselors, Inc., N.Y.C., 1966-72. Mem. planning and adv. bd. Hampton's Hosp. Fund, Inc., 1968-74; bd. dirs. Assn. for Study Man-Environ. Rels., 1969-75, Rsch. Found. for Mental Hygiene, Inc., Albany, N.Y., 1971—, Friends North Castle Libr.; mem. zoning bd. Town of North Castle. Served to 1st lt. U.S. Army, 1956-58. Mem. Assn. Mental Health Adminstrs. (cert.), Nat. Coun. Univ. Rsch. Adminstrs., Soc. for Rsch. Adminstrs. (cert.), N.Y. State Orgn. Mgmt. Confidential Employees, Big. Bros., Lehigh Club (N.Y.), Westhampton Beach Yachting Club (past commodore), North Cove Yacht Club, Pi Gamma Mu, Phi Alpha Theta. Democrat. Avocations: sailing, gardening, antiques. Home: 92 Byram Ridge Rd Armonk NY 10504-1212 Office: Nathan S Kline Inst Orangeburg NY 10962

NAGLE, HUBERT TROY, JR., electrical engineering educator; b. Booneville, Miss., Aug. 31, 1942; s. Hubert Troy and Mary Elizabeth (Stephens) N.; 1 child, Julia Ann; m. Susan Schiffman, 1989; 1 stepdaughter, Amy Lise. B.S in Elec. Engring. U. Ala., 1964, M.S., 1966; Ph.D., Auburn U., 1968; M.D., U. Miami, 1981. Registered profl. engr., Ala. Faculty Auburn (Ala.) U., 1970-84, prof. elec. engring., 1976-84; prof. elec. and computer engring. N.C. State U., 1984—. Author: (with V.P. Nelson, B.D. Carroll and J.D. Irwin) Digital Logic Circuit Analysis and Design, 1995, (with C. L. Phillips) Digital Control Systems Analysis and Design, 1995; contbr. articles in field to profl. jours. Fellow IEEE (bd. dirs. 1987-88, 1993-95, v.p. tech. activities 1989-90, pres. 1994). Office: NC State U Dept Elec and Computer Engring Raleigh NC 27695

NAGLE, JAMES FRANCIS, lawyer; b. Jersey City, Aug. 5, 1948; s. James Francis and Cecile Marie (Dorgan) N.; m. Ann Marie Thomas, Dec. 28, 1974; children: James, John, Stephen. BS, Georgetown U., 1970; JD, Rutgers U., 1973; LLM, George Washington U., 1981, SJD, 1986. Bar: N.Y. 1973, U.S. Ct. Mil. Appeals 1979, U.S Supreme Ct. 1979, U.S. Ct. Appeals (fed. cir.) 1982, U.S. Ct. Appeals (D.C. cir.) 1983. Enlisted U.S. Army, 1970, advanced through grades to lt. col., 1987; chief of criminal law Presidio of San Francisco, 1974-75; command judge adv. U.S. 8th Army, Korea, 1975-76; chief of administrv. law U.S Army Electronics Command, Ft. Monmouth, N.J., 1976-79; br. chief Army Def. Appellate Div., Falls Church, Va., 1982-85; team chief Army Chief Trial Atty.'s Office, Falls Church 1982-85; contracts atty. U.S. Army Forces Command, Ft. McPherson, Ga., 1985-88; chief adminstrv. law U.S. Third Army, Ft. McPherson, 1986-88; chief logistic and contract law dept. U.S. Army, Washington, 1988-90; ret. U.S. Army, 1990; ptnr. Oles, Morrison & Rinker, Seattle, 1990—. Author: Procurement Regulations, 1987, A History of Government Contracting, 1992, How to Review Federal Contracts, 1990, Federal Construction Contracting, 1992; contbr. articles to profl. jours. Mem. Fed. Bar Assn., N.J. Bar Assn., D.C. Bar Assn. Roman Catholic. Avocations: gardening, karate. Home: 5196 Lynwood Center Rd NE Bainbridge Island WA 98110-4001

NAGLER, ARNOLD LEON, pathologist, scientist, educator; b. N.Y.C., 1935; s. Max and Esther (Finkel) N.; m. Rosalie Groden, Feb. 18, 1961; children: Stephen Marc, Melissa Sue. B.S., CCNY, 1953; M.D., NYU, 1958, Ph.D., 1960. Lic. dir. labs., N.Y. Postgrad. tng. NYU-Bellevue Med. Ctr., 1958-61; research assoc. Mt. Sinai Hosp., N.Y., 1960-61; mem. faculty Albert Einstein Coll. Medicine, Bronx, N.Y., 1961—, assoc. prof. pathology, surgery, 1975—; cons., prof., chmn. pathology dept., dean pre-clin. medicine N.Y. Coll. Osteo Medicine, 1978—; trustee Robert Chambers Microsurgery Research Labs., 1978—; founder, trustee Esther Nagler Dystrophy Research Fund, N.Y. Coll. Osteo. Medicine. Mem. editorial bd.: Circulatory Shock; contbr. articles to profl. jours. Chmn. Jericho council Boy Scouts Am., 1971-73; mem. Pres.'s Task Force, 1981—, Nat. Republican Congressional Com., U.S. Senatorial Club; trustee Liberal Jewish Day Sch., N.Y.C.; corp. mem. Nassau-Suffolk Health Systems Agy., mem. Primary Care Task Force. Served with U.S. Army, 1953-55. NIH grantee, 1961—. Fellow Am. Soc. Clin. Pathologists; mem. N.Y. Acad. Sci., N.Y. Acad. Medicine, AAAS, Am. Trauma Soc. (founder), Sigma Xi. Jewish. Home: 72 Hazelwood Dr Jericho NY 11753-1704 Office: Albert Einstein Coll Medicine 1300 Morris Park Ave Bronx NY 10461-1975 *I was guided by my parents when they were alive and directed by their teachings and precepts after their death to strive to do the best that I possibly may, in any and every endeavor that I undertake. They provided the armoury: Do no harm to anyone—achieve by dedicating yourself to excellence/performance. Do not rally in relegating someone to a lesser state; this is only relative success and is neither satisfying nor worthwhile to the soul, nor is it real.*

NAGLER, LEON GREGORY, management consultant, business executive; b. Buenos Aires, Argentina, Jan. 29, 1932 (parents Am. citizens); s. Morris and Jennie (Golden) N.; BS cum laude, Boston U., 1953, MBA, 1954; J.D., Cleve. State U., 1961; m. F. Elise Charness, Dec. 20, 1953; children: Jeri Lynn, Sandra Michelle. Bar: Ohio 1961. Tchr. psychology Cameron State Agrl. Jr. Coll., Lawton, Okla., 1956-57; supr. employment and tng. Jones & Laughlin Steel Corp., Cleve., 1957-65; exec. dir. indsl. relations Charles Corp., Cleve., 1965-67; dir. personnel ITT Service Industries Corp., Cleve., 1967-72; v.p. personnel Builder Services Corp., Clearwater, Fla., 1972-73; v.p. adminstrn. Damon Corp., Needham Heights, Mass., 1973-77; pres. Nagler & Co., Inc., Wellesley Hills, Mass., 1977—. Mem. Mayfield Heights (Ohio) Planning and Zoning Commn., 1965-67; sec. Mayfield Heights Zoning Bd. Appeals, 1963-65; chmn. Combined Health Fund, Mayfield Heights, 1963; pres. N.E. Ohio region, mem. nat. gov. coun. Am. Jewish Congress, 1972-73; bd. dirs. New Eng. region Anti-Defamation League, 1977-80; bd. dirs. Jewish Vocat. Svc., Boston, 1977—, sec., 1980-83, v.p., 1983-88; bd. dirs. Jewish Community Ctr. Greater Boston, 1988—, Am. Friends Wingate Inst., 1987—, v.p. fin., 1987—; trustee Temple Beth Avodah, Newton, 1978—, v.p., 1979-83, pres., 1983-85; trustee Combined Jewish Philanthropies, Boston, 1985-92; bd. overseers Combined Jewish Philanthropies, 1992—. Served with AUS, 1955-57. Mem. Ohio, Cleve. bar assns., Soc. for Human Resource Mgmt., Internat. Assn. Corp. and Exec. Recruiters, Boston U. Alumni Assn. (pres. N.E. Ohio 1969-73, nat. council 1973—). Democrat. Lodge: Masons. Office: Nagler and Co Inc 65 William St Wellesley MA 02181-3802

NAGLER, MICHAEL NICHOLAS, classics and comparative literature educator; b. N.Y.C., Jan. 20, 1937; s. Harold and Dorothy Judith (Nocks) N.; m. Roberta Ann Robbins (div. May 1983); children: Jessica, Joshua. BA, NYU, 1960; MA, U. Calif., Berkeley, 1962, PhD, 1966. Instr. San Francisco State U., 1963-65; prof. classics, comparative lit. dept. U. Calif., Berkeley, 1966-91, prof. emeritus, 1991—. Author: Spontaneity and Tradition, 1974, America Without Violence, 1982; co-author: The Upanishads, 1987; contbr. articles to profl. publs. Pres. bd. dirs. METTA Ctrs. for Nonviolence Edn. Fellow Am. Coun. Learned Socs., NIH; MacArthur Found. grantee, 1988. Mem. Am. Philolog. Soc. (editor Oral Tradition). Office: U Calif Classics Dept Berkeley CA 94720

NAGLER, STEWART GORDON, insurance company executive; b. Bklyn., Jan. 30, 1943; s. Henry and Mary N.; m. Bonnie Lawrence, Aug. 9, 1964; children: David, Ellen. B.S. summa cum laude, Poly. U., 1963. With Met. Life Ins. Co., N.Y.C., 1963—, exec. v.p., 1978-85, sr. exec. v.p., 1985—; chmn. bd. Century 21 Real Estate Corp., Irvine, Calif. Fellow Soc. Actuaries, Acad. Actuaries. Office: Met Life Ins Co 1 Madison Ave New York NY 10010 also: Century 21 Real Estate Corp 2601 S Main St Santa Ana CA 92707-3432

NAGOURNEY, HERBERT, publishing company executive; b. N.Y.C., Jan. 30, 1926; s. Isidor and Tillie (Burstein) N.; children: Adam, Beth, Eric, Sam. BS, Columbia U., 1946, MS, 1947. Pres. Profl. and Tech. Programs, N.Y.C., 1951-65; v.p. Macmillan Co., N.Y.C., 1965-69; pres. Quadrangle/New York Times Book Co., N.Y.C., 1969-76, New York Times Book Co., N.Y.C., 1971-76, Quartet Books, Inc., N.Y.C. and London, 1976-81, Knowledge Tree Group Inc., 1979-89; v.p., dir. Sci. DataLink, 1981-88, Comtex Sci., 1981-90; pres. Profl. and Tech. Pub. Inc., 1989—, Sci. Datalink, 1990—. Served with AUS, 1944. Home: 320 Joshuatown Rd Lyme CT 06371 Office: 225 Varick St New York NY 10014

NAGRIN, DANIEL, dancer, educator, choreographer, lecturer, writer; b. N.Y.C., May 22, 1917; s. Harry Samuel and Clara (Wexler) N.; m. Helen Tamiris, 1946 (dec. 1966); m. Phyllis A. Steele, Jan. 24, 1992. BS in Edn., CCNY, 1940; DFA, SUNY, Brockport, 1991; LHD, Ariz. State U., 1992; studied dance with Martha Graham, Anna Sokolow, Helen Tamiris, Mme. Anderson-Ivantzova, Nenette Charisse and Edward Caton, 1936-56, studied acting with Miriam Goldina, Sanford Meisner and Stella Adler, 1936-56. Tchr. Silvermine Guild Art, New Canaan, Conn., 1957-66, SUNY, Brockport, 1967-71, U. Md., College Park, 1970, Davis Ctr. Performing Arts, CCNY, 1973-75, Nat. Theatre Inst., Eugene O'Neill Found., Waterford, Conn., 1974, Hartmann Theatre Conservatory, Stamford, Conn., 1975-77; long-term resident tchr., Nat. Endowment for Arts sponsorship U. Hawaii, 1978-80, tchr., 1981; tchr. Bill Evans Dance Workshop, Seattle, 1981; prof. dance dept. Ariz. State U., Tempe, 1982-92; tchr. grad. liberal studies program Wesleyan U., Middletown, Conn., 1984, Dance Workshop for Movement Rsch., N.Y.C., 1984, Improvisation Workshop, Seattle, 1985, Improvisation, Choreography and Acting Technique for Dancers, Seattle, 1985, Dance Workshop, Glenwood Springs, Colo., 1990; prof. emeritus dance Ariz. State U., 1992; tchr. summer sessions Conn. Coll., New London, 1959, 74; Am. Dance Festival at Conn. Coll., 1960, 77, Duke U., Durham, N.C., 1978, 80, 82, 87, 88, 92; summer dance program Conn. Coll., 1979, E. La Tour Dance Workshop, Sedgewick, 1982, 83; dance workshop U. Minn. at Mpls., 1984, Stanford U., 1990; co-dir. Tamiris-Nagrin Summer Dance Workshop, Sedgewick, 1960-61, (with Tamiris) summer dance session C. W. Post Coll., Greenville, N.Y., 1962-63; dir. summer dance workshop Johnson (Vt.) State Coll., 1972, 73, 75, 76. Featured dance soloist on Broadway: Annie Get Your Gun, Lend an Ear, Touch and Go, Plain and Fancy (Billboard Donaldson award 1954-55), 1940-56; appearance in film, Just for You; adapted and performed one-man theatre piece The Fall, from novel by Albert Camus, 1977-79, choreographer (solo works) Spanish Dance, 1948, Man of Action, 1948, Strange Hero, 1948, Indeterminate Figure, 1957, With My Eye and With My Hand, 1968, Jazz: Three Ways, 1958, 66, Path-Silence, 1965, Not Me, But Him, 1965, The Peloponesian War, 1967-68, Untitled, 1974, Ruminations, 1976, Getting Well, 1978, Poems Off the Wall, 1981, Apartment 18C, 1993, others; (for groups) Faces from Walt Whitman, 1950, An American Journey, 1982; asst. choreographer original Broadway prodns.: Up in Central Park, Stovepipe Hat, Show Boat, Annie Get Your Gun, By the Beautiful Sea, others; dir. off-Broadway: Volpone, 1957, The Firebugs, 1960, The Umbrella, 1961, Emperor Jones, (Boston), 1963, others; film choreography: His Majesty O'Keefe; acted in video The Art of Memory, 1985, play, Three Stories High, others; extensive touring U.S, Europe, The Pacific, and Japan, 1957-84; conceived and directed videos: Steps, 1972, The Edge is Also a Circle, 1973, Nagrin Videotape Library of Dances, 1985; author: How to Dance Forever: Surviving Against the Odds, 1988, Dance and the Specific Image: Improvisation, 1993. With spl. svcs. Army Airforce, 1942-43. Grantee Rebekah Harkness Found., 1962, Logan Found., 1965, N.Y. State Coun. on Arts and Humanities, 1967-68, N.Y. State Coun. on Arts and Humanities, 1971-72, 73-74, 75-76, 76-77, 78-79, 80-81, Anne S. Richardson Fund, 1971, 73, 74, 75, 76, 78, Nat. Endowment for Arts, 1975, 79, 81, 83, Ariz. State U., 1983, 84, 85, 86, 88; CAPS fellow N.Y. State Coun. on Arts, 1977-78; fellow Nat. Endowment for Arts, 1977-78, 80, 82, 83, 90, 91; comsd. ballet Rebekah Harkness Ballet Found., 1986. Mem. Actors' Equity, Phi Kappa Phi (hon.). Avocation: reading. Home and Office: 208 E 14th St Tempe AZ 85281-6707

NAGY, ANDREW FRANCIS, engineering educator; b. Budapest, Hungary, May 2, 1932; came to U.S., 1957, naturalized, 1968; s. Bela and Lilly (Dekany) N.; children: Robert Bela, Susan Elizabeth. BE, U. New South Wales, 1957; MSc, U. Nebr., 1959; MS, U. Mich., 1960, PhD, 1963. Design engr. Electric Control and Engring. Co., Ltd., Sydney, Australia, 1956-57; instr. elec. engring. U. Nebr., 1957-59; research engr. U. Mich., Ann Arbor, 1959-63; asst. prof. elec. engring. U. Mich., 1963-67, assoc. prof., 1967-71, prof. space sci., prof. elec. engring., 1971—, assoc. v.p. for rsch., 1987-90; vis. assoc. prof. engring. U. Calif. at San Diego, 1969-70; vis. prof. physics Utah State U., 1976-77. Past editor: Revs. of Geophysics and Space Physics, Geophys. Rsch. Letters. Fulbright scholar, 1957. Fellow Am. Geophys. Union (pres. SPR sect.); mem. IEEE (sr.), Internat. Radio Sci. Union (commns. 3 and 4), Hungarian Acad. Scis., Sigma Xi, Eta Kappa Nu. Home: 338 Rock Creek Dr Ann Arbor MI 48104-1860

NAGY, BARTHOLOMEW STEPHEN, geochemist, educator; b. Budapest, Hungary, May 11, 1927; came to U.S., 1948, naturalized, 1955; s. Stephen and Mary (Mueller) N.; m. Marjorie Lois Bibey, Feb. 1, 1952; 1 child, Erika Anne; m. Lois Anne Brach, Aug. 10, 1967; 1 child, Yvonne Maria. Student, Peter Pazmany U., Budapest, 1945-48; MA, Columbia U., 1950; PhD, Pa. State U., 1953. With Stanolind Oil & Gas Co., Tulsa, 1953-55; supr. geophys. research Cities Service Research & Devel. Co., Tulsa, 1955-57; assoc. prof. Fordham U., 1957-65; vis. assoc. prof. U. Calif., San Diego, 1963-65, assoc. research geochemist, 1965-68; prof. geoscis. U. Ariz., Tucson, 1968—; mem. adv. bd. Lunar Sci. Inst., 1972; rsch. petroleum and organic geochemistry, x-ray crystallography and analytical chemistry, radioactive waste containment, carbonaceous meteorites, and returned lunar samples; mem. steering com. nuclear waste mgmt. program French Atomic Energy Commn. and European Community, 1991—; chmn. U.S. working group internat. geol. correlation program Organics and Mineral Deposits, sponsored by UNESCO, 1993—. Author 3 books; contbr. articles in field; exec. editor Jour. Precambrian Research. Mem. Geochem. Soc. (counselor 1961-64), Am. Chem. Soc., Internat. Soc. for Study of Origin of Life. Home: 245 W Greenock Dr Tucson AZ 85737-7615 Office: U Ariz Lab Organic Geochemistry 522 Gould-Simpson Bldg Tucson AZ 85721 *Lasting achievement can be accomplished only by tackling important problems without regard to praise or criticism.*

NAGY, JOE HOWARD, lawyer; b. Pearsall, Tex., Dec. 17, 1928; s. Joe H. and Pauline (Howard) N.; m. Dorothy Fay Shelton, May 6, 1951; children: Margaret Nagy Dobbs, Joe Howard Jr. BS, Tex. A&M U., 1950; JD, U. Tex., 1958. Bar: Tex. 1958, U.S. Dist. Ct. (no. and we. dists.) Tex. 1958, U.S. Supreme Ct. 1975. Ptnr. Crenshaw, Dupree & Milam, Lubbock, Tex., 1958-65, 1965—. 1st lt. U.S. Army, 1951-53, Korea. Fellow Tex. Bar Found., Tex. Assn. Def. Counsel; mem. State Bar of Tex. (bd. dirs. 1975-78, pres.-elect 1986-87, pres. 1987-89), Lubbock County Bar Assn. (pres.-elect 1971-72, pres. 1972-73, bd. dirs.), Am. Coll. Trial Lawyers. Republican. Methodist. Avocation: hunting. Office: Crenshaw Dupree & Milam 1500 Broadway St Ste 1100 Lubbock TX 79401-3106

NAGY, LOUIS LEONARD, engineering executive, researcher; b. Detroit, Jan. 15, 1942; s. Alex and Helen (Marth) N.; m. Diana M. Skarjune, Aug. 5, 1961; children: Kimberly, Tammy, Kristine, Amanda. BSEE, U. Mich., Dearborn, 1965; MSEE, U. Mich., Ann Arbor, 1969, PhDEE, 1974. Rsch. engr. U. Mich., Ann Arbor, 1962-69; staff rsch. engr. GM Rsch. Labs., Warren, Mich., 1969—. Contbr. articles to profl. jours.; patentee in field. Bd. dirs. Convergency Ednl. Found., Birmingham, Mich., 1991—. Fellow IEEE; mem. Convergence Fellowship (bd. dirs. 1988—), Vehicular Tech.

Soc. (Spl. Recognition award 1979, Avant Garde award 1986, Paper of Yr. 1975), Soc. Automotive Engrs., Tau Beta Pi, Eta Kappa Nu. Avocations: electronics, antennas, radar, automotive radar, microwaves. Office: GM Rsch Labs E-3 Dept Warren MI 48090

NAGY, ROBERT DAVID, tenor; b. Lorain, Ohio, Mar. 3, 1929; s. John Robert and Helen Elizabeth (Polesko) N.; m. Vincenza Rose Ianni, May 1, 1954; children—Robert John, Helena Jean, Gina Kati. Student, Cleve. Inst. Music, 1952-55. tchr., cons. to young opera students. Soloist, Met. Opera, 1957—; appeared in opera houses, throughout U.S., World. Served with U.S. Army, 1950-52, Korea. Weyer Hauser scholar, 1957; Ford Found. scholar, 1959. Winner Met. Opera audition, 1956. Home: 5996 Case Rd North Ridgeville OH 44039-1030

NAGY, STEPHEN FELSOBUKI, investment company executive; b. Celldomolk, Hungary, June 3, 1944; came to U.S., 1956; s. Michael Felsobuki and Carola (Meliorisz) N.; m. Klara Lukats, July 18, 1981. B.S. in Chemistry, Union Coll., Schenectady, 1967; M.S. in Environ. Health, NYU, 1968; M.S. in Indsl. Mgmt., Columbia U., 1970. Prodn. engr. Consol. Edison Co. N.Y., N.Y.C., 1968-71; various mgmt. positions Booz, Allen & Hamilton, Inc., N.Y.C., 1971-76, v.p., 1976-80; v.p., gen. ptnr. Foster Mgmt. Co., N.Y.C., 1980-82, bd. advisors, 1981-85; pres. Foster Med. Corp., Dedham, Mass., 1982-86, also bd. dirs.; exec. v.p. Avon Products, Inc., N.Y.C., 1985-86; chmn. Greenwich Mgmt. Group Inc., 1987—, Top Labs. Inc., 1987—; exec. v.p., gen. ptnr. Foster Mgmt. Co., N.Y.C., 1989—; bd. dirs. Vein Clinics Am. Inc.;. Contbr. articles to profl. jours. Club: N.Y. Athletic. Home: 46 Quail Rd Greenwich CT 06831-3372 Office: Foster Mgmt Co 437 Madison Ave New York NY 10022-7001

NAGY, STEVEN, biochemist; b. Fords, N.J., Apr. 7, 1936; s. Steven and Martha (Moberg) N.; m. Suzanne Nagy; children: Lacey, Nicolette, Steven. BS in Chemistry, La. State U., 1960; MS in Physiology and Biochemistry, Rutgers U., 1962, PhD in Biochemistry, 1965; MEngring. in Indsl. Engring., U. South Fla., 1977. Analytical chemist USPHS, Metuchen, N.J., 1962-65; rsch. assoc. Lever Bros., Edgewater, N.J., 1965-67; rsch. chemist Dept. Agr., Winter Haven, Fla., 1968-79; rsch. scientist Fla. Dept. Citrus, Lake Alfred, 1979—; adj. prof. U. Fla., 1979—; treas. AgScience Inc. Mem. Am. Chem. Soc. (chmn. div. agrl. and food chemistry, disting. svc. award 1988, fellow, 1990), Phytochem. Soc. N. Am. (chmn.), Inst. Food Technologists (chmn. citrus products div.), Am. Soc. for Hort. Sci., Internat. Soc. Citriculture, Fla. Hort. Soc. (v.p.), Sigma Xi. Republican. Author: Citrus Science and Technology, 2 vols., 1977; Tropical and Subtropical Fruits, 1980; Citrus Nutrition and Quality, 1980; Fresh Citrus Fruits, 1986, Adulteration of Fruit Juice Beverages, 1988, Fruits of Tropical and Subtropical Origin, 1990, Fruit Juice Processing Technology, 1993, Methods To Detect Adulteration of Fruit Juice Beverages, 1995; editorial bd. Food Chemistry, Jour. Agrl. and Food Chemistry; contbr. articles to profl. jours. Home: 103 Arietta Shores Dr Auburndale FL 33823-9336 Office: 700 Experiment Station Rd Lake Alfred FL 33850-2243

NAHAI, HAMID, lawyer; b. Tehran, Iran, Oct. 29, 1952; came to U.S., 1977; s. Enayat and Pari (Broumand) N.; m. Gina Barkordarian, Oct. 3, 1982; children: Alexander Shahin, Ashley Leila. LLB, U. London, 1974, LLM, 1975; LLM, U. Calif., 1978. Bar: Eng. 1976, Wales 1976, Calif. 1979, U.S. Dist. Ct. (cen. dist.) Calif. 1980. Barrister Barristers' Chambers, London, 1976-77; assoc. Loeb & Loeb, Los Angeles, 1979-81; assoc. Memel, Jacobs & Ellsworth, Los Angeles, 1981-85, ptnr., 1985-87; ptnr. Finley, Kumble, Wagner, Heine, Underberg, Manley, Myerson & Casey, Los Angeles, 1987, Stroock, Stroock & Lavan, Los Angeles, 1987—; bd. dirs., legal counsel The Magbit Found., 1990; bd. dirs. The Price Found; speaker, lectr. in field. Contbr. articles to profl. jours. Founding mem., bd. dirs. sec., counsel Iranian Am. Rep. Coun., L.A., 1987—; chmn. Am. Friends Bnai Zion Med. Ctr., 1989. Vis. scholar U. Calif., 1978-79. Mem. ABA, Los Angeles County Bar Assn., Nat. Assn. Indsl. and Office Parks, Honourable Soc. Middle Temple (London). Jewish. Office: Stroock & Stroock & Lavan 2029 Century Park E Ste 1800 Los Angeles CA 90067-3086

NAHAS, GABRIEL GEORGES, pharmacologist, educator; b. Alexandria, Egypt, Mar. 4, 1920; came to U.S., 1947, naturalized, 1962; s. Bishara and Gabrielle (Wolff) N.; m. Marilyn Cashman, Feb. 13, 1954; children: Michele, Anthony, Christiane. BA, U. Toulouse, France, 1937, MD, 1944; MS, U. Rochester, 1949; PhD, U. Minn., 1953; DSc (hon.), U. Uppsala, 1988. Rockefeller Found. fellow U. Rochester, 1947-48; Mayo Found. fellow Mayo Clinic, 1949-50; research fellow U. Minn., 1950-53, mem. faculty, 1955-57; staff Walter Reed Army Inst. Research, 1957-59; faculty George Washington U. Med. Sch., 1957-59; mem. faculty Columbia U. Coll. Physicians and Surgeons, N.Y.C., 1959-92, prof. anesthesiology, 1962-92; rsch. prof. anesthesiology NYU Med. Sch., N.Y.C., 1992—; Disting. vis. scientist Addiction Rsch. Ctr., NIDA, 1987; Fulbright scholar, 1966; adj. prof. anesthesiology (rsch.) U. Paris, 1968-71; fellow Coun. Circulation and Basic Sci., Am. Heart Assn., 1961—; com. on trauma NRC, 1964-66; adv. bd. Cousteau Soc.; cons. U.N. Commn. on Narcotics, U.N.D.C.P. Author 700 sci. publs. and 30 books and monographs in English and French. Spl. agt. French Underground, 1941-44; 1st lt. Med., French Army, 1944-45. Decorated Presdl. Medal of Freedom with gold palm U.S.; comdr. Legion of Honor, Croix de Guerre with 3 palms (France); Order Brit. Empire, Order Orange Nassau Netherlands, Silver medal City of Paris; recipient Medal of Honor, Statue of Liberty Centennial, 1986. Fellow AAAS, N.Y. Acad. Sci.; mem. Am. Physiol. Soc., Harvey Soc., Am. Soc. Pharmacology and Exptl. Therapeutics, Am. Soc. Clin. Pharmacology, Soc. Physiol. Langue Française, French Acad. Medicine (laureate), Brit. Pharm. Soc., Sigma Xi. Research on med. instrumentation, pharmacology Tham, acid-base regulation, pharmacology of cannabis and cocaine, drug dependence. Home: 40 E 74th St New York City NY 10021-2732 Office: NYU Med Ctr Dept Anesthesiology 550 First Ave New York NY 10016

NAHAT, DENNIS F., artistic director, choreographer; b. Detroit, Feb. 20, 1946; s. Fred H. and Linda M. (Haddad) N. Hon. degree, Juilliard Sch. Music, 1965. Prin. dancer Joffrey Ballet, N.Y.C., 1965-66; prin. dancer Am. Ballet Theatre, N.Y.C., 1968-79; founder, artistic dir. Cleve. Ballet, 1976—; co-chair Artists Round Table Dance USA, 1991; mem. bd. trustees Cecchetti Council of Am., 1991; adv. bd. Ohio Dance Regional Dance Am. Pin. performer Broadway show Sweet Charity, 1966-67; choreographer Two Gentlemen of Verona (Tony award 1972), 1969-70; (ballet) Celebrations and Ode (resolution award 1985), 1985, Green Table, Three Virgins and a Devil (Isadora Duncan award 1985); co-founder Sch. of Cleve. Ballet, 1972, Cleve. Ballet, 1976; founder, artistic dir. San Jose Cleve. Ballet. Grantee Nat. Endowment Arts, 1978, Andrew Mellow Found., 1985; recipient Outstanding Achievement award Am. Dance Guild, 1995. Avocation: master chef. Office: Cleve Ballet 1375 Euclid Ave Cleveland OH 44115-1803 also: Cleve San Jose Ballet PO Box 1666 San Jose CA 95109-1666

NAHAVANDI, AMIR NEZAMEDDIN, retired engineering firm executive; b. Tehran, Iran, Apr. 6, 1924; came to U.S., 1956, naturalized, 1970; s. Ahmad and Fatima (Razaghi) N. Electromech. Engring. degree, Tehran U., 1947; M.S. in Mech. Engring, Carnegie Inst. Tech., 1957, Ph.D., 1960. Registered profl. engr., Pa. Engr. Tehran U. 1948-50; head design group Nat. Iranian Oil Co., Tehran, 1950-56; adv. engr. Westinghouse Electric Corp., Pitts., 1957-66; prof., chmn. dept. mech. engring. U. Vt., 1967-68; research prof. N.J. Inst. Tech., 1969-77; prof. engring. and applied Sci. Columbia U., N.Y.C., 1977-81; chief scientist Electronic Assocs., Inc., West Long Branch, N.J. 1981-82; pres. Mazen, Inc., Long Branch, N.J., 1982-92. Decorated Sci. medal 1st degree Iran). Fellow ASME; mem. N.Y. Acad. Scis., Phi Kappa Phi, Sigma Xi, Tau Beta Pi. Research and devel. in dynamics of steam generators and boiling systems, dynamic and accident analysis of conventional and nuclear power plants, vibration of reactor structures, thermal pollution of lakes and rivers, solid-fluid interaction. Home: Unit N 470 Ocean Blvd Long Branch NJ 07740-5677

NAHMAN, NORRIS STANLEY, electrical engineer; b. San Francisco, Nov. 9, 1925; s. Hyman Cohen and Rae (Levin) N.; m. Shirley D. Maxwell, July 20, 1968; children: Norris Stanley, Vicki L., Vance W., Scott T. B.S. in Electronics Engring. Calif. Poly. State U., 1951; M.S.E.E., Stanford U., 1952; Ph.D. in Elec. Engring. U. Kans., 1961. Registered profl. engr., Colo. Electronic scientist Nat. Security Agy., Washington, 1952-55; prof. elec.

engring., dir. electronics rsch. lab. U. Kans., Lawrence, 1955-66; sci. cons., chief pulse and time domain sect. Nat. Bur. Standards, Boulder, Colo., 1966-73; chief time domain metrology, sr. scientist Nat. Bur. Standards, 1975-83, group leader field characterization group, 1984-85; v.p. Picosecond Pulse Labs, Inc., Boulder, 1986-90; cons. elec. engr., 1990—; prof., chmn. dept. elec. engring. U. Toledo, 1973-75; prof. elec. engring. U. Colo., Boulder 1966—; Disting. lectr., prin. prof. Ctr. Nat. d' Etude des Telecomm. Summer Sch., Lannion France, 1978; disting. lectr. Harbin Inst. Tech., Peoples Republic China, summer 1982; mem. faculty NATO Advanced Study Inst., Castelvecchio, Italy, 1983, Internat. Radio Sci. Union/NRC; chmn. Internat. Intercomm. Group Waveform Measurements, 1981-90, chmn. Commn. A, 1985-86; affiliate Los Alamos Nat. Lab., 1990—. Contbr. rsch. articles profl. jours.; patentee in field. Asst. scoutmaster Longs Peak coun. Boy Scouts Am., 1970-73, 75-89. With U.S. Mcht. Marine, 1943-46, U.S. Army, 1952-55. Ford Found. faculty fellow MIT, 1962; Nat. Bur. Standards sr. staff fellow, 1978-79; recipient Disting. Alumnus award Calif. Poly. State U., 1972, Order of Arrow Boy Scouts Am., 1976. Fellow IEEE (life), Internat. Sci. Radio Union; mem. Instrumentation and Measurement Soc. of IEEE (admstrv. com. 1982-84, editorial bd. Trans., 1982-86, Andrew H. chi Best Tech. Paper award 1984, Tech. Leadership and Achievement award 1987), Am. Assn. Engring. Edn., U.S. Mcht. Marine Veterans World War II, Am. Legion, Calif. Poly. State U. Alumni Assn. (life), Stanford U. (life), U. Kans. (life), Am. Radio Relay League Club (life), Sigma Pi Sigma, Tau Beta Pi, Eta Kappa Nu, Sigma Tau, Sigma Xi.

NAHMIAS, ANDRÉ JOSEPH, physician, educator, scientist; b. Alexandria, Egypt, Nov. 20, 1930; came to U.S., 1947, naturalized, 1956; s. Gabriel J. and Angela (Arbib) N.; m. Suzanne Beckman; children: Danielle, Gabriel; children from previous marriage: Cynthia, David, Edward. BA, U. Tex., 1950, MA, 1952; MPH, U. Mich., 1953; MD, George Washington U., 1957. Intern USPHS Hosp., S.I., N.Y., 1957-58; resident pediatrics Boston City Hosp., 1960-62; fellow virology Boston U. Sch. Medicine, 1962-64; mem. faculty Emory U., Atlanta, 1964—; asst. prof. Emory U., 1964-67, assoc. prof., 1967-70, prof. pediatrics and chief infectious diseases, epidemiology and immunology div., 1970—, Richard W. Blumberg prof. pediatrics, 1988—, prof. pathology and lab. medicine, 1976—, prof. epidemiology, 1993—; cons. to govt. and non-govtl. agys. and firms, 1969—. Contbr. over 300 articles to various publs.; editor 4 vols. in virology and immunology. Served with USPHS, 1957-60. Recipient Research Career Devel. award NIH, 1966; Mead-Johnson Pediatric Research award, 1975; Josiah Macy Faculty award, 1976; Hardman award Med. Assn. Ga., 1977; Pres.'s award Med. Assn. Atlanta, 1986; Sr. Research Fogerty fellow NIH, 1987. Mem. AAAS, Infectious Disease Soc. Am., Am. Assn. Immunologists, Soc. Pediatric Research, Am. Pediatric Soc., Am. Acad. Pediatrics, Am. Soc. Microbiology, Am. Public Health Assn., Soc. Exptl. Biology and Medicine, Am. Epidemiology Soc. Democrat. Unitarian. Home: 747 Houston Mill Rd NE # 3 Atlanta GA 30329-4248 Office: Emory U 69 Butler St SE Atlanta GA 30303-3033

NAHRWOLD, DAVID LANGE, surgeon, educator; b. St. Louis, Dec. 21, 1935; s. Elmer William and Magdalen Louise (Lange) N.; m. Carolyn Louise Hoffman, June 14, 1958; children: Stephen Henry, Susan Alane, Thomas James, Anne Elizabeth. AB, Ind. U., 1957, MD, 1960. Diplomate Am. Bd. Surgery, Am. Bd. Thoracic Surgery. Intern, then resident in surgery Ind. U. Med. Ctr., Indpls., 1960-65; postdoctoral scholar in gastrointestinal physiology VA Ctr., UCLA, 1965; asst. prof. surgery Med. Sch. Ind. U., 1968-70; assoc. prof. Coll. Medicine Pa. STate U., 1970-73, vice chmn. dept. surgery, 1971-82, assoc. provost, dean health affairs, 1981-82, prof., chief divsn. gen. surgery, 1974-82; Loyal and Edith Davis prof., chmn. dept. surgery Med. Sch. Northwestern U., Chgo., 1982—; surgeon-in-chief Northwestern Meml. Hosp., Chgo., 1982—; mem. Nat. Digestive Disease Adv. Bd., 1985-89; bd. dirs. Am. Bd. Surgery; vice chmn. 1994-95, chmn. 1995-96. Editor-in-chief Jour. Laparoendoscopic Surgery, 1993—; mem. editl. bd. Surgery, 1981-94, Archives of Surgery, 1983-93, Digestive Surgery, 1986—, Am. Jour. Surgery, 1994—, Current Opinion in Gen. Surgery, Jour. Lithotripsy and Stone Disease, 1988-92; contbr. articles to profl. jours. With M.C., U.S. Army, 1964-68. Fellow ACS (bd. govs.); mem. Am. Fedn. Clin. Research, Am. Gastroent. Assn., AMA, Am. Physiol. Soc. (asso.), Am. Surg. Assn. (2d v.p. 1993-94), Assn. Acad. Surgery, Assn. for Surg. Edn., Central Surg. Assn., (sec. 1994—), Chgo. Med. Soc., Chgo. Surg. Soc. (pres. 1993-94), Collegium Internationale Chirurgiae Digestivae (pres. U.S. chpt. 1988-90), Gastroenterology Rsch Group, Ill. State Med. Soc., Ill. Surg. Soc., Internat. Biliary Assn., Soc. Clin. Surgery (sec. 1984-88), Soc. Surgery of Alimentary Tract (sec. 1985-88, pres. 1989-90, trustee), Soc. Univ. Surgeons, Soc. Surg. Chairmen, Soc. for Health and Human Values, Western Surgical Assn., mem. Bd. of Govs. Am. Coll. of Surgs., 1992—; mem. Exec. Com., 1994—, Sigma Xi, Alpha Omega Alpha. Office: Northwestern U Med Sch Dept Surgery 250 E Superior St Ste 201 Chicago IL 60611-2950

NAIBURG, IRVING B., JR., publisher; b. Chgo., Oct. 3, 1942; s. Irving B. and Bobette (Mayer) N. B.A., Harvard U., 1964. Asst. to gen. mgr. Free Press div Macmillan Co., N.Y.C., 1964-66, paperback editor, 1966-68, editor, 1968-72; exec. editor profl. and reference div. Appleton Century Crofts, N.Y.C., 1972-73, editorial dir., 1973-74; founder, pres., editorial dir. Irvington Pubs., Inc., N.Y.C., 1974—. Mem. N.Y. Polit. Action Com., 1978-80. Mem. Tarrytown Group, Soc. Scholarly Pub., Inst. Advancement Health, Network Ind. Pubs. Democrat. Club: Harvard (N.Y.C.). Home: 18 E 64th St New York NY 10021-7265 Office: Irvington Pubs Inc 522 E 82nd St New York NY 10028-7118

NAIDORF, LOUIS MURRAY, architect; b. Los Angeles, Aug. 15, 1928; s. Jack and Meriam (Abbott) N.; m. Dorise D. Roberts, June 4 (div.); children: Victoria Beth Naidorf-Slifer; m. Patricia Ann Shea, June 1, 1968 (div.); m. Patricia Ruth Allen, Dec. 6, 1992. BA, U. Calif., Berkeley, 1949, MA, 1950. Registered architect, Calif. Designer Welton Becket Assocs., L.A., 1950-51, Pereira and Luckman, L.A., 1951-52; project designer Welton Becket Assocs., L.A., 1952-55, sr. project designer, 1955-59, v.p. asst., dir. design, 1959-70, sr. v.p., dir. rsch., 1970-73; sr. v.p., design prin. Ellerbe Becket Assocs., L.A., 1973-95; dean Sch. Architecture and Design Woodbury U., L.A., 1990—; mem. peer rev. panel Nat. Endowment Arts, 1995—; vis. lectr. Calif. Poly. Sch. Architecture, San Luis Obispo, 1975-82; instr. UCLA Sch. Architecture, 1985, UCLA Landscape Archtl. Program, 1980-85, Otis-Parsons, L.A., 1986—. Prin. works include Capitol Records Bldg., Century City, Los Angeles, Hyatt Regency, Dallas, Restoration Calif. State Capitol Bldg. Bd. dirs. Inst. for Garden Studies, L.A., 1986—. Recipient Honor award Nat. Trust for Hist. Preservation, 1985. Fellow AIA (bd. dirs. Los Angeles chpt. 1977-79, Silver Medal 1950, Nat. Honor award 1985). Office: Ellerbe Becket 2501 Colorado Ave Santa Monica CA 90404-3550

NAIFEH, STEVEN WOODWARD, writer; b. Tehran, Iran, June 19, 1952; s. George Amel and Marion (Lamphear) N. AB, Princeton U., 1974; JD, Harvard U., 1977, MA, 1978. Staff lectr. Nat. Gallery Art, Washington 1976; assoc. Milbank, Tweed, Hadley & McCloy, N.Y.C., 1976; v.p. Sabbagh, Naifeh and Assocs., Washington, 1980—. Author: Culture Making: Money, Success and the New York Art World, 1976; (with Gregory White Smith) Moving Up in Style, 1980, Gene Davis, 1981, How to Make Love to a Woman, 1982, What Every Client Needs to Know About Using a Lawyer, 1982, The Bargain Hunter's Guide to Art Collecting, 1982, Why Can't Men Open Up?: Overcoming Men's Fear of Intimacy, 1984, The Mormon Murders: A True Story of Greed, Forgery, Deceit, and Death, 1988, Jackson Pollack: An American Saga, 1989 (Nat. Book award nomination for nonfiction 1990, Pulitzer Prize for biography 1991), Final Justice: The True Story of the Richest Man Ever Tried for Murder, 1993, A Stranger in the Family: A True Story of Murder, Madness, and Unconditional Love, 1995; editor: (with Smith) The Best Lawyers in America, The Best Doctors in America. Address: care Connie Clausen Connie Clausen Assocs 250 E 87th St New York NY 10028 Office: Sabbagh Naifeh & Assocs Inc 4600 Reno Rd NW Washington DC 20008*

NAILOR, RICHARD ANTHONY, SR., research company executive; b. New Haven, July 27, 1935; s. Earl Edward and Theresa Mary (Massaro) N.; m. Sandra Louise Grace, Jan. 16, 1960; children: Richard, Michele, Keith. Student, Fairfield U., 1952-54; AA, USN Elect. Officers, 1964. Enlisted, terrier MSL fire control technician USMC, Egypt, Lebanon and Cuba, 1954-62; radar maintenance officer 9th MEB USMC, Vietnam, 1962-74; logistics analyst Potomac Rsch., Inc., Alexandria, Va., 1974-79, head publs.

br., 1978-80, dir. ILS dept., 1980-82, dir. ILS div., 1982-83, v.p. OPS, 1983-86; sr. v.p. OPS Potomac Rsch. Internat., Alexandria, 1986-94, exec. v.p., COO, 1994—. Troop leader Boy Scouts Council, Woodbridge, Va., 1968-69; pres. Woodbridge Parks Assn., 1978-81; park authority rep. Pr. William County (Va.) Park Authority, 1982-86. Mem. VFW, Ret. Officers Assn., Marine Corps Mustang Assn. (charter), Soc. Logistics Engrs., 1st Marine Aircraft Wing Assn. Republican. Roman Catholic. Avocations: golf, bowling, fishing, genealogy. Home: 300 Beaver Lodge Rd Stafford VA 22554-3427 Office: Potomac Rsch Internat Ste 300 11320 Random Hills Rd Fairfax VA 22030

NAIMARK, ARNOLD, university president, physiologist, internist; b. Winnipeg, Man., Can., Aug. 24, 1933; s. Harvey and Lisa N.; m. Barbara Jean Alder, Feb. 28, 1960; children: David, Mila. MD, U. Man., Winnipeg, 1957, BSc in Medicine, 1957, MSc, 1960; postgrad., U. London, 1962-63, U. Calif., 1960-62; LLD (hon.), Mt. Allison U., 1986. Registrar in medicine Hammersmith Hosp., London, 1962-63; asst. prof. physiology U. Man., 1963-64, asso. prof., 1965-66, prof., 1967-71, acting head dept. physiology, 1966-67, head dept., 1967-71, dean Faculty of Medicine, 1971-81, pres. and vice chancellor, 1981—; bd. govs. St. Boniface Gen. Hosp., Health Scis. Ctr.; cons. to govt. agys. and founds.; chmn. North Portage Devel. Corp., 1984-94; bd. dirs. Can. Imperial Bank Commerce, N.Am. Life Assurance Co., Urban Idea Ctr., North Portage Theatre Corp., Inspiraplex Ltd.; mem. adv. coun. Order of Can., 1988-89; v.p., Can., Inter-Am. Orgn. for Higher Edn., 1993—. Contbr. articles to profl. jours. Mem. nat. hon. bd. dirs. Juvenile Diabetes Fedn. Internat. Can.; trustee Alcoholic Beverage Med. Rsch. Found., 1994—. Lt. Royal Can. Arty., 1950-53. Decorated officer Order of Can.; recipient Queen Elizabeth Silver Jubilee medal; medal in physiology U. Man., 1955; Stefansson Meml. prize, 1957; Prowse prize in clin. rsch., 1959; Isbister scholar, 1950-53, 54-56. Fellow Royal Coll. Physicians, AAAS, Royal Soc. Can. (G. Malcolm Brown award 1987, com. univ. rsch. 1989-91); mem. Can. Med. Assn., Can. Physiol. Soc., Am. Physiol. Soc., Can. Soc. Clin. Investigation, Med. Rsch. Soc. Gt. Brit., Assn. Chairmen Depts. Physiology, Can. Tb and Respiratory Disease Assn., Can. Assn. Univ. Tchrs., Assn. Commonwealth Univs. (council 1985—,) Assn. Univs. and Colls. Am. (pres. 1986-88), Am. Heart Assn., Assn. Commonwealth Univs. (chmn. 1988), Can. Soc. for Acad. Medicine, Nat. Inst. Nutrition (bd. dirs. 1990—). Office: U Man 200 Administrn Bldg, Fort Garry Campus, Winnipeg, MB Canada R3T 2N2

NAIMARK, GEORGE MODELL, marketing and management consultant; b. N.Y.C., Feb. 5, 1925; s. Myron S. and Mary (Modell) N. BS, Bucknell U., 1947, MS, 1948; PhD, U. Del., 1951; m. Helen Anne Wythes, June 24, 1946; children: Ann, Richard, Jane. Rsch. biochemist Brush Devel. Co., Cleve., 1951; dir. quality control Strong, Cobb & Co. Inc., Cleve., 1951-54; dir. sci. svcs. White Labs., Inc., Kenilworth, N.J., 1954-60; v.p. Burdick Assocs., Inc., N.Y.C., 1960-66; pres. Rajah Press, Summit, N.J., 1963—; pres. Naimark and Barba, Inc., Florham Park, N.J., 1966—; mng. ptr. Naimark & Assocs., Florham Park, N.J., 1994—. With USNR, 1944-46. Fellow AAAS, Am. Inst. Chemists; mem. Am. Chem. Soc., N.Y. Acad. Scis., Am. Mktg. Assn. Author: A Patent Manual for Scientists and Engineers, 1961, Communications on Communication, 1971, 3d edit., 1987; patentee in field; contbr. articles in profl. jours. Home: 87 Canoe Brook Pky Summit NJ 07901-1404 Office: Naimark & Barba Inc 248 Columbia Tpke Florham Park NJ 07932-1210

NAIMI, SHAPUR, cardiologist; b. Tehran, Iran, Mar. 28, 1928; s. Mohsen and Mahbuba (Naim) N.; came to U.S., 1959, naturalized, 1968; M.B., Ch.B., Birmingham (Eng.) U., 1953; m. Amy Cabot Simonds, May 11, 1963; children—Timothy Simonds, Susan Lyman, Cameron Lowell. House physician Royal Postgrad Med. Sch. London, 1955; sr. house officer Inst. Diseases of the Chest, London, 1956; fellow in grad. trng. New Eng. Med. Center and Mass. Inst. Tech., 1961-64; cardiologist Tufts New Eng. Med. Center, Boston, 1966—; dir. intensive cardiac care unit, 1973—, assoc. prof. 1970-93, prof. 1993—. Recipient Distinguished Inst. award, 1972, Teaching citation, 1976, Excellence in Teaching award, 1982 (all Tufts Med. Sch.); diplomate Royal Coll. Physicians London, Royal Coll. Physicians Edinburgh, Am. Bd. Internal Medicine (subsplty. bd. cardiovascular disease). Fellow Royal Coll. Physicians (Edinburgh), A.C.P., Am. Coll. Cardiology; mem. Am. Soc. Exptl. Biology and Medicine, Am. Heart Assn., Mass. Med. Soc. Clubs: Country Brookline; Cohasset Yacht. Contbr. to profl. jours. Home: 265 Woodland Rd Chestnut Hill MA 02167-2204 Office: 750 Washington St Boston MA 02111-1526

NAIMOLI, RAYMOND ANTHONY, infosystems specialist, financial consultant; b. Paterson, N.J., Apr. 16, 1942; s. Ralph A. and Margaret Rita (Calabrese) N.; children: Lisa Marie, Dianne, Dolors, Raymond . B.B.A., U. Notre Dame, 1963; M.S., Columbia U., 1976. C.P.A., N.J. Sr. auditor Arthur Young & Co., Newark, 1963-68; asst. controller Universal Mfg. Co., Paterson, 1968-70; corp. controller Scholastic Mags., Inc., N.Y.C., 1970-80; v.p. fin., treas. U.S. News & World Report, Washington, 1980-84; also dir. U.S. News & World Report; exec. v.p. EBM Systems, Inc., Greenbelt, Md., 1986-90; pres. Naimoli & Assocs., Arlington, Va., 1984—; pres. MedLine, Inc., 1991-93, also bd. dirs.; chief fin. officer Ladish Co., Inc., Milw., 1993—; dir. Parkway Communications Corp., Publishers Service Internat., Madana Realty Co., U.S. News Investment Co.; adj. prof. Grad. Sch., Fairleigh Dickinson U., Rutherford, N.J., 1976-80. Mem. Am. Inst. C.P.A.s, Planning Execs. Inst., N.J. Soc. C.P.A.s. Roman Catholic. Office: 5481 S Packard Ave Cudahy WI 53110-2244

NAIMOLI, VINCENT JOSEPH, diversified operating and holding company executive; b. Paterson, N.J., Sept. 16, 1937; s. Ralph A. and Margaret R. (Calabrese) N.; children—Christine, Tory Ann, Alyson, Lindsey. B.S.M.E., U. Notre Dame, 1959; M.S.M.E., N.J. Inst. Tech., 1962; M.B.A., Fairleigh Dickinson U., 1964; grad. Advanced Mgmt. Program, Harvard Bus. Sch., 1974. With Continental Group, 1965-77, v.p., gen. mgr. ops., 1975-77; pres., chief oper. officer Allegheny Beverage Corp., Balt., 1977-78; sr. v.p., group exec. Jim Walter Corp., Tampa, Fla., 1978-81; group v.p. packaging Anchor Hocking Corp., Lancaster, Ohio, 1981-83; chmn. bd., pres., chief exec. officer Anchor Glass Container Corp., Lancaster, 1983-89, Anchor Industries Internat., Tampa, Fla., 1990—; chmn., chief exec. officer Electrolux Corp., Atlanta, 1990-91, Anchor Industries, Tampa, 1991—; chmn., CEO Doehler Jarvis Corp., Toledo, 1991—; mng. gen. ptnr., CEO Tampa Bay Devil Rays, 1992—; chmn., CEO Ladish, Inc., Milw., 1992—; chmn., pres., CEO Harvard Industries, 1993—; bd. dirs. Simplicity Pattern, New River Industries, Russell-Stanley Corp., Fla. Progress. Roman Catholic. Office: Anchor Industries Internat Ste 960 2502 N Rocky Point Dr Tampa FL 33607

NAIPAUL, VIDIADHAR SURAJPRASAD, author; b. Trinidad, Aug. 17, 1932. Student, Queen's Royal Coll., Trinidad, 1943-48; B.A., University Coll., Oxford, Eng., 1953; D.Litt. (hon.), St. Andrews Coll., Scotland, 1979, Columbia U., 1981, Cambridge U., 1983, London U., 1988; DLitt (hon.), Oxford U., 1992. Author: Miguel Street, 1959, A House for Mr. Biswas, 1961, An Area of Darkness, 1964, In a Free State, 1971, Guerrillas, 1975, India: A Wounded Civilization, 1977, A Bend in the River, 1979, Among the Believers, 1981, The Enigma of Arrival, 1987, A Turn in the South, 1989, India: A Million Mutinies Now, 1990, A Way in the World, 1994. Office: Aitken & Stone Ltd, 29 Fernshaw Rd, London SW10 0TG, England

NAIR, RAGHAVAN D., accountant, educator; b. Dehradun, United Provinces, India, Oct. 23, 1951; came to U.S.; 1973; s. Keshavan R. and Parvati Nair; m. Ruth Marie Nair, 1976; 1 child, Andrea. BA, U. Madras, India, 1970, MA, 1972; MBA, U. Mich., 1974, PhD, 1977. CPA, Wis. Prof. U. Wis., Madison, 1978—; sr. assoc. dean acad. affairs Sch. Bus., 1994—; faculty fellow Fin. Acctg. Standards Bd., Norwalk, Conn., 1984-86; faculty resident Arthur Andersen & Co., Chgo., 1991—; dir. PhD Program, 1987-90, chmn. dept. acctg., 1991-94; dir. Arthur Andersen Ctr. Fin. Reporting, 1992-93; prof. acctg. and info. systems Price Waterhouse, 1991—; invited speaker various corps., pub. acctg. firms, mgmt. and exec. edn. groups, 1982—. Contbr. articles to profl. jours. Pres. John Muir PTO, Madison, Wis., 1988-89. Recipient Excellence in Teaching award Lawrence J. Larson Sch. Bus., 1992. Mem. AICPA, Parkwood Hills Community Assn. (treas. 1987-89), Am. Acctg. Assn., Wis. Soc. CPAs (Outstanding Educator award 1989), Blackhawk Country Club. Avocation: golf.

NAIR, VELAYUDHAN, pharmacologist, medical educator; b. India, Dec. 29, 1928; came to U.S., 1956, naturalized, 1963; s. Parameswaran and Ammini N.; m. Jo Ann Burke, Nov. 30, 1957; children: David, Larry, Sharon. Ph.D. in Medicine, U. London, 1956, D.Sc., 1976. Research assoc. U. Ill. Coll. Medicine, 1956-58; asst. prof. U. Chgo. Sch. Medicine, 1958-63; dir. lab. neuropharmacology and biochemistry Michael Reese Hosp. and Med. Center, Chgo., 1963-68; dir. therapeutic research Michael Reese Hosp. and Med. Center, 1968-71; vis. asso. prof. pharmacology Chgo. Med. Sch., 1963-68, vis. prof., 1968-71; prof. pharmacology, 1971—, vice chmn. dept. pharmacology and therapeutics, 1971-76; dean Chgo. Med. Sch. (Sch. Grad. and Postdoctoral Studies), 1976—. Contbr. articles to profl. publs. Recipient Morris Parker award U. Health Scis./Chgo. Med. Sch., 1972. Fellow AAAS, N.Y. Acad. Scis., Am. Coll. Clin. Pharmacology; mem. AAUP, Internat. Brain Rsch. Orgn., Internat. Soc. Biochem. Pharmacology, Am. Soc. Pharmacology & Exptl. Therapeutics, Am. Soc. Clin. Pharmacology & Therapeutics, Radiation Rsch. Soc., Soc. Toxicology, Am. Chem. Soc., Brit. Chem. Soc., Royal Inst. Chemistry (London), Pan Am. Med. Assn. (council on toxicology), Soc. Exptl. Biology & Medicine, Soc. Neurosci., Internat. Soc. Chronobiology, Am. Coll. Toxicology, Internat. Soc. Developmental Neurosci., Sigma Xi, Alpha Omega Alpha. Club: Cosmos (Washington). Office: UHS/Chgo Med Sch 3333 Green Bay Rd North Chicago IL 60064-3095 *Success like happiness is relative and can only be gauged by one's own standards and ideals. There is probably no universal formula for either of them, but I have been guided by the following tenets: Dedication and committment to one's responsibilities and in the conduct of everyday life, honesty and sincerity in personal relations. One must have tolerance for those in less fortunate situations. As one grows older, one recognizes that no one makes it alone. As for me, I have received help from many; some of whom I can never repay except by passing on the gift which I was privileged to share. Above all, a faith that looks beyond the immediate helps to bear the inevitable ups and downs in life.*

NAITO, LISA HEATHER, state legislator; b. Portland, Oreg., May 25, 1955; d. Per Hugo and Christine Annalise (Oertel) Sjogren; m. Steve Lorne Naito; children: Kirsten, Alex. BA, Rice U., 1977; JD, U. Oreg., 1981. Bar: Oreg. Dep. dist. atty. Multnomah County Dist. Atty., Portland, 1981-83; sole practice Portland, 1984-86; atty. Preston, Thorgrimson, Ellis & Holman, Portland, 1988-90; mem. Oreg. Ho. of Reps., Salem, 1991—, vice-chair natural resources subcom. environment and energy, vice chair judiciary subcom. juvenile justice, mem. judiciary subcom. civil law and jud. adminstrn. Oreg. Ho. of Reps.; asst. minority leader Oreg. Ho. of Reps., Salem, 1993; policy coord. Ho. Dem. Caucus. Mem. Child Care Commn. Adviser, 1993—; vice chair House children & families com., 1993; mem. alcohol & drug task force, 1993-94, mem. commerce com., bus. com., 1991, 93, mem. energy & environment com., 1991; bd. dirs. Albertina Kerr, 1992—, Delauney Mental Health Ctr., 1984-86. Mem. Oreg. Womens Polit. Caucus. Democrat. Avocations: gardening, skiing, reading. Home: 3505 SE Ankeny Portland OR 97214 Office: Legislative Assembly State Capitol # 492 Salem OR 97310

NAJAR, LEO MICHAEL, conductor, arranger, educator; b. Grand Rapids, Mich., Jan. 29, 1953; s. Ammiel George and Claire Elizabeth (Grant) N.; m. Tamara Sinkevich, Aug. 24, 1974; m. Jean Anne Van Winkle, May 10, 1986; children: John Andrew, Erik. MusB in Viola Performance, U. Mich., 1976, MusM in Viola Performance, 1977. Asst. condr. Flint (Mich.) Symphony Orch., 1975-80; dir. Flint Community Music Sch., 1976-80; music dir. Saginaw (Mich.) Symphony Orch., 1980—; conductor The Gazebo Orch., 1993—; lectr. music Wayne State U., Detroit, 1983-86; guest asst. prof. music U. Mich., Ann Arbor, 1986-87; artistic adviser Dearborn (Mich.) Symphony Orch., 1987-90, traverse Symphony Orch., 1988-90; spl. artistic adviser Flint Inst. Music, 1991-92; guest prof. Crit. Mich. U., 1995-96. Producer, host radio program Preludio: The String Thing, 1978-80. Mem. adv. panel Mich. Coun. for Arts, 1989-91. Mem. Am. Symphony Orch. League (various coms. 1980—, Helen M. Thompson award 1982), Mich. Orch. Assn. (pres. 1985-88), Condrs. Guild Am. (bd. dirs. 1991-93), Assn. Can. Orchs. Home: 973 S Linwood Beach Rd Linwood MI 48634 Office: Saginaw Symphony Orch 420 Symphony Ln # 415 Saginaw MI 48607-1211

NAJARIAN, HAIGAZOUN, church administrator. Viscar gen. Ea. Diocese of the Armenian Ch. Am. Office: Ea Diocese of the Armenian Ch Am 630 Second Ave New York NY 10016

NAJARIAN, JOHN SARKIS, surgeon, educator; b. Oakland, Calif., Dec. 22, 1927; s. Garabed L. and Siranoush T. (Demirjian) N.; m. Arlys Viola Mignette Anderson, Apr. 27, 1957; children: Jon, David, Paul, Peter. AB with honors, U. Calif., Berkeley, 1948; MD, U. Calif., San Francisco, 1952; LHD (hon.), Univ. Athens, 1980; DSc (hon.), Gustavus Adolphus Coll., 1981; LHD (hon.), Calif. Luth. Coll., 1983. Diplomate Am. Bd. Surgery. Surg. intern U. Calif., San Francisco, 1952-53, surg. resident, 1955-60, asst. prof. surgery, dir. surg. research labs., chief transplant service dept. surgery, 1963-66, prof., vice chmn., 1966-67; spl. research fellow in immunopathology U. Pitts. Med. Sch., 1960-61; NIH sr. fellow and assoc. in tissue transplantation immunology Scripps Clinic and Research Found., La Jolla, Calif., 1961-63; Markle scholar Acad. Medicine, 1964-69; prof., chmn. dept. surgery U. Minn. Hosp., Mpls., 1967-93; med. dir. Transplant Ctr., clin. chief surgery Univ. Hosp., 1967-94; chief hosp. staff U. Minn. Hosp., Mpls., 1970-71, Regents' prof., 1985-95, Jay Phillips Disting. Chair in Surgery, 1986-95; spl. coms. USPHS, NIH Clin. Rsch. Tng. Com., Inst. Gen. Med. Scis., 1965-69; cons. U.S. Bur. Budget, 1966-68. Mem. Nat. Kidney Found., 1968; mem. surg. study sect. A div. rsch. grants NIH, 1970; chmn. renal transplant adv. group VA Hosps., 1971; mem. bd. sci. cons. Sloan-Kettering Inst. Cancer Rsch, 1971-78; mem. screening com. Dernham Postdoctoral Fellowships in Oncology, Calif. div. Am. Cancer Soc. Editor: (with Richard L. Simmons) Transplantation, 1972; co-editor: Manual of Vascular Access, Organ Donation, and Transplantation, 1984; mem. editorial bd. Jour. Surg. Rsch., 1968—, Minn. Medicine, 1968—, Jour. Surg. Oncology, 1968—, Am. Jour. Surgery, 1967—, assoc. editor, 1982—; mem. editorial bd. Year Book of Surgery, 1970-85, Transplantation, 1970—, Transplantation Procs, 1970—, Bd. Clin. Editors, 1981-84, Annals of Surgery, 1972—, World Jour. Surgery, 1976—, Hippocrates, 1986—, Jour. Transplant Coordination, 1990—; assoc. editor: Surgery, 1971; editor-in-chief: Clin. Transplantation, 1986—. Bd. dirs., v.p. Variety Club Heart Hosp., U. Minn.; trustee, v.p. Minn. Med. Found. Served with USAF, 1953-55. Hon. fellow Royal Coll. Surgeons of Eng., 1987; hon. prof. U. Madrid, 1990; named Alumnus of Yr., U. Calif. Med. Sch., San Francisco, 1977; recipient award Calif. Trudeau Soc., 1962, Ann. Brotherhood award NCCJ, 1978, Disting. Achievement award Modern Medicine, 1978, Internat. Gt. Am. award B'nai B'rith Found., 1982, Uncommon Citizen award, 1985, Sir James Carreras award Variety Clubs Internat., 1987, Silver medal IXth Centenary, U. Bologna, 1988, Humanitarian of Yr. award, U. Minn., 1992, Najarian Festschrift award Am. Jour. Surgery, 1993, Jubilee medal Swedish Soc. Medicine, 1994. Fellow ACS; mem. Soc. Univ. Surgeons, Soc. Exptl. Biology and Medicine, AAAS, Am. Soc. Exptl. Pathology, Am. Surg. Assn. (pres. 1988-89), Am. Assn. Immunologists, AMA, Transplantation Soc. (v.p. western hemisphere 1984-86, pres. 1994-96), Am. Soc. Nephrology, Internat. Soc. Nephrology, Am. Assn. Lab. Animal Sci., Assn. Acad. Surgery (pres. 1969), Internat Soc. Surgery, Soc. Surg. Chairmen, Soc. Clin. Surgery, Central Surg. Assn., Minn., Hennepin County med. socs., Mpls., St. Paul, Minn., Howard C. Naffziger, Portland, Halsted surg. socs., Am. Heart Assn., Am. Soc. Transplant Surgeons (pres. 1977-78), Council on Kidney in Cardiovascular Disease, Hagfish Soc., Italian Research Soc., Minn. Acad. Medicine, Minn. Med. Assn., Minn. Med. Found., Surg. Biology Club, Sigma Xi, Alpha Omega Alpha, others. Office: U Minn Surgery Dept Mayo Meml Bldg Box 195 420 Delaware St SE Minneapolis MN 55455-0374

NAJITA, TETSUO, history educator; b. Honokaa, Hawaii, Mar. 30, 1936; s. Niichi and Kikuno (Bamboku) N.; m. Elinor Moon, Aug. 2, 1958; children: Mie Kim, Kiyoshi Young. BA, Grinnell Coll., 1958; MA, Harvard U., 1960, PhD, 1965; LLD, Grinnell Coll., 1989. Asst. prof. Carleton Coll., Northfield, Minn., 1964-66, Wash. Univ. St. Louis, 1966-68; assoc. prof. U. Wis., Madison, 1968-69; Robert S. Ingersoll Disting. Svc. prof. Japanese studies U. Chgo., 1969—, dir. Ctr. for East Asian Studies, 1974-80, assoc. dean, 1983-87, master collegiate div. social scis., 1983-87; John A. Burns disting. visiting chair U. Hawaii, Manoa, 1994; chair dept. history U. Chgo., 1994—. Author: Hara Kei in the Politics of Compromise, 1969 (J.K. Fairbank prize Am. Hist. Assn.), Intellectual Foundations of Modern Japanese Politics, 1974, Visions of Virtue in Tokugawa Japan, 1987.

Recipient Yamagata Banto prize Prefecture of Osaka, 1989; grantee NEH 1973-74, 1980-81; Fulbright fellow 1961-63, 68, Guggenheim fellow 1980-81. Fellow Am. Acad. Arts and Scis.; mem. Am. Hist. Assn., Assn. for Asian Studies (v.p., pres. 1991-93), Phi Beta Kappa. Office: U Chgo Dept History 1126 E 59th St Chicago IL 60637-1580

NAKAGAKI, MASAYUKI, chemist; b. Tokyo, Apr. 19, 1923; s. Sengoro and Shizue N.; m. Hisako Yoshitake, May 3, 1951. BSc, Imperial U., Tokyo, 1945; DSc, U. Tokyo, 1950. Instr. Imperial U., Tokyo, 1945-51; lectr. U. Tokyo, 1951-54; prof. Osaka (Japan) City U., 1954-60; prof. Kyoto (Japan) U., 1960-87, emeritus prof., 1987—; vis. prof. Wayne State U., Detroit, 1955-57, 68-69; dean faculty pharm. sci. Kyoto U., 1978-80; prof. Hoshi U., Tokyo, 1987-92; dir. Tokyo Inst. Colloid Sci., 1992—. Regional editor: Colloid and Polymer Sci., Darmstadt, Germany, 1982—. Recipient rsch. award Takeda Found. 1971. Mem. Membrane Soc. Japan (inspector 1988—, prse. 1978-88), Pharm. Soc. Japan (Rsch. award 1970, merit mem. 1990—). Home: 354 Kotokujicho Teramachi, Kamigoryo, Kyoto 602, Japan Office: Tokyo Inst Colloid Sci, 502 Higashi-Nakano 4-4-3, Tokyo 164, Japan

NAKAGAWA, ALLEN DONALD, radiologic technologist; b. N.Y.C., Mar. 14, 1955; s. Walter Tsunehiko and Alyce Tsuneko (Kinoshita) N. BS in Environ. Studies, St. John's U., Jamaica, N.Y., 1977; MS in Marine Biology, C.W. Post Coll., 1980. Cert. radiologic technologist, in fluoroscopy, Calif.; cert. Am. Registry Radiol. Technologists. Research asst. environ. studies St. John's U., 1976-78; lab. asst. Bur. Water Surveillance, Nassau Co. of Health Dept., Wantaugh, N.Y., 1978; clin. endocrinology asst. U. Calif. VA Hosp., San Francisco, 1981-83; student technologist St. Mary's Hosp., San Francisco, 1985-86; radiologic technologist Mt. Zion Hosp., San Francisco, 1986-88; sr. radiologic technologist U. Calif., San Francisco, 1989—, urosurg. radiologic technologists, 1988-89. Recruiting chmn. hunger project C.W. Post Coll., 1979; participant 33d Annual Radiology Conf., San Francisco, 1990. Mem. AAAS, Calif. Soc. Radiologic Technologists, Marine Mammal Ctr., Calif. Acad. Scis., Planetree Health Resource Ctr., Japanese-Am. Nat. Mus., World Affairs Coun. San Francisco, ACLU, Sigma Xi. Democrat. Methodist. Avocations: assisting handicapped, photography, music, computer illustration, studying advanced technology.

NAKAGAWA, JEAN HARUE, diversified corporation executive; b. Honolulu, Sept. 21, 1943; d. Herbert Haruo and Dorothy Mitsue (Nishimura) Yorita; m. Melvin Katsumi Nakagawa, July 16, 1966; 1 child, Lisa. BBA, U. Hawaii, 1965, MBA, 1968. Rsch. asst. First Hawaiian Bank, Honolulu, 1965-68; dir. planning AMFAC, Inc., Honolulu, 1968-73; v.p. Island Fed. Savings and Loan, Honolulu, 1973-75; dir. rsch. and planning Servco Pacific Inc., Honolulu, 1975—, asst. v.p., 1975-77, v.p., 1977-79, group v.p., 1979-84, sr. v.p., 1984-88, exec. v.p., 1988—; bd. dirs. Servco Pacific Inc., Servco Fin. Corp. Trustee Honolulu Theater for Youth, 1982-89, Hawaii Pub. Employees Health Fund, 1985-89; mem. devel. com. Hawaii Baptist Acad.; bd. dirs. ARC; mem. Pacific Asian Affairs Coun., Hawaii Econ. Edn. Coun., Hawaii Fgn. Rels. Coun. Mem. Hawaii Soc. Corp. Planners (v.p., pres.), Hawaii Econ. Assn. (pres., v.p.) Planning Execs. Inst. (pres.), Orgn. Women Leaders (v.p.). Club: Plaza. Office: Servco Pacific Inc 900 Fort St Mall #600 Honolulu HI 96813

NAKAJIMA, YASUKO, medical educator; b. Osaka, Japan, Jan. 8, 1932; came to U.S., 1962, 69; d. Isao and Taeko Nakagawa; m. Shigehiro Nakajima; children: Hikeko H., Gene A. MD, U. Tokyo, 1955, PhD, 1962. Intern U. Tokyo Sch. Medicine, 1955-56, resident, 1956-57, instr., 1962-67; assoc. prof. Purdue U., West Lafayette, Ind., 1969-76, prof., 1976-88; prof. anatomy and cell biology U. Ill. Coll. Medicine, Chgo., 1988—; vis. rsch. fellow Coll. Physicians and Surgeons, Columbia U., N.Y.C., 1962-64; asst. rsch. anatomist UCLA Sch. Medicine, 1964-65; vis. rsch. fellow Cambridge U., 1967-69. Contbr. articles to sci. jours. Fulbright travel grantee, 1962-65. Mem. AAAS, Soc. Neurosci., Am. Soc. Cell Biology, Am. Assn. Anatomists, Biophys. Soc., Marine Biol. Lab. Corp. Office: U Ill Coll Medicine at Chgo Dept Anatomy-Cell Biology m/c 512 808 S Wood St Chicago IL 60612

NAKAKUKI, MASAFUMI, physician, psychiatry educator; b. Shimotsuma, Ibaragi, Japan, Mar. 1, 1930; came to U.S., 1969, naturalized 1975; s. Keisuke and Toi (Saito) N.; m. Ritsuko Oka, May 25, 1957; children: Mari, Emma; m. Michael McAndrewes, Sept. 1988. MS, U. Ibaragi, 1949; MD, U. Tokyo, 1953. Diplomate Am. Bd. Psychiatry and Neurology. Intern U. Tokyo Hosp., 1953-54, dir. psychiat. inpatient service, 1966-69; resident in psychiatry U. Tokyo, 1954-60, U. Colo.-Denver, 1962-66; asst. prof. psychiatry U. Colo. Med. Ctr., Denver, 1969-73; staff psychiatrist Ft. Logan Mental Health Ctr., Denver, 1973-74, Arapahoe Mental Health Ctr., Englewood, Colo., 1974-76; med. dir. Park East Mental Health Ctr. Denver, 1977-83; pres. Masafumi Nakakuki, M.D., P.C., Denver, 1977—; pres. med. staff Bethesda Hosp., Denver, 1982-83; psychiat. cons. Asian Pacific Devel. Ctr., Denver, 1983—; vis. prof. psychiatry St. Mariana U., Tokyo, 1995—. Author: Textbook of Psychiatry for the General Practitioner, 1968; New Parenting and Culture, 1982. Recipient Letter of Appreciation for Mental Health Svcs. and Leadership from Gov. Romer, 1995. Bd. dirs. Asian Human Service Assn., Denver, 1982. Fulbright scholar, 1961. Fellow Am. Psychiat. Assn.; mem. Colo. Med. Soc. Office: 4770 E Iliff Ave Denver CO 80222-6061 also: 2-1-15-705 Takanawa, Minato-ku Tokyo 108, Japan

NAKAMOTO, KAZUO, chemistry educator; b. Kobe, Hyogo, Japan, Mar. 1, 1922; came to U.S., 1957; s. Tsuneji N. and Ko (Nishikawa); m. Kimiko Hamano, Feb. 21, 1929; children: Takuya, Masaya, Mary. B.S., Osaka U., 1945, D.Sc., 1953; Dr. honoris causa, Tech. U. Wroclaw, Poland, 1978. Postdoctoral fellow Iowa State U., Ames, 1953-55; assoc. prof. Osaka U., Japan, 1955-57; asst. prof. Clark U., Worcester, Mass., 1959-61; assoc. prof. Ill. Inst. Tech., Chgo., 1961-67, prof., 1967-69; Wehr prof. chemistry Marquette U., Milw., 1969-91, prof. emeritus, 1991—; cons. Argonne Nat. Lab., Ill., 1965-73. Author: Infrared and Raman Spectra of Inorganic and Coordination Compounds, 1961, 4th edit., 1986; assoc. editor: Inorganica Chinica Acta, Internat. Jour., 1967-89. Recipient U.S. Sr. Scientist award Alexander von Humboldt Found., Germany, 1974; recipient award Japan Soc. for Promotion of Sci., 1977; named hon. prof. U. La Plata, Argentina, 1983; honoris causa Tech. U. Wroclaw, Poland, 1978. Mem. Am. Chem. Soc. (award Milw. sect. 1979), Japan Chem. Soc., Soc. for Applied Spectroscopy (hon. mem. 1990—, pres. Milw. sect. 1975-76), Sigma Xi (Disting. Sci. Research Achievement award 1988). Office: Marquette U Dept Chemistry PO Box 1881 Milwaukee WI 53201-1881

NAKAMURA, HIROSHI, urology educator; b. Tokyo, Mar. 22, 1933; s. Yataroh and Hideko (Tanaka) N.; m. Miyoko Kodachi, Aug. 13, 1966. MD, Keio U., Tokyo, 1960; PhD, Grad. Sch. Medicine, Keio U., 1966. Med. diplomate. Asst. resident Mt. Sinai Hosp., N.Y.C., 1962-63; rsch. fellow Cornell U. Med. Coll., N.Y.C., 1966-68; asst. Sch. Medicine Keio U., Tokyo, 1968-70; chmn. urology dept. Tokyo Elec. Power Hosp., 1970-73; vis. asst. prof. surgery Cornell U. Med. Coll., N.Y.C., 1973; chmn. urology Kitasato Inst. Hosp., Tokyo, 1973-77; chmn. deptr., prof. urology Nat. Def. Med. Coll., Tokorozawa, Saitama, Japan, 1977—, dir. deptr. acad. affairs, 1994—. Author: New Clin. Urology, 1982, Practice of Renal Transplantation, 1985, Bedside Urology, 1991; editor: Up-to-date Urology, 1983. Recipient Tamura award Keio U. Sch. Medicine, 1967, All-around Med. award, Igaku-Shoin, Ltd., Tokyo, 1967. Buddhist. Avocations: jazz, audiophile, travel, fishing, baseball. Home: 4-403 Boei Idai 3-2 Namiki, Tokorozawa 359 Saitama, Japan Office: Nat Def Med Coll Dept Urol, 3-2 Namiki, Tokorozawa 359 Saitama, Japan

NAKAMURA, JAMES I., economics educator; b. Toppenish, Wash., Mar. 16, 1919; s. Ichihei and Suya (Hirayama) N.; m. Tetsuko Fujii; children—Richard Ken, Leonard Isamu. A.A. Santa Maria Jr. Coll., 1939; B.S., Columbia U., 1952, Ph.D., 1964. Asst. prof. Columbia U., N.Y.C., 1964-68, assoc. prof., 1968-80, prof. econs., 1980-89, prof. emeritus, 1989—; vis. research scholar Kobe U., Japan, 1971-72; co-founder, co-dir., sec.-treas. Japan Econ. Seminar (supported by Columbia U., Harvard U., Georgetown Washington U.), 1965—. Author: Agricultural Production and Economic Development of Japan, 1966, Nihon no Keizai Hatten to Nogyo, 1968; mem. editorial bd. Japan Econ. Studies, 1972—; contbr. numerous articles to profl. jours. Editor newspaper War Relocation Ctr., Gila River, Ariz., 1943-44; legal researcher Shanks Village Com. to Fight Closure, Orangeburg, N.Y.,

1952. Served to lt. U.S. Army, 1945-48, PTO. Ford Found. fellow 1952-55, 62-63; Fulbright-Hays fellow, 1967. Mem. Econ. History Assn., Am. Econ. Assn., Assn. for Asian Studies, Japan Econ. Research Ctr., Phi Beta Kappa. Buddhist. Home: 35 Claremont Ave New York NY 10027-6823 Office: Columbia U 935 IAB New York NY 10027

NAKAMURA, KAZUO, artist; b. Vancouver, Can., Oct. 13, 1926; s. Toichi and Yoshiyo (Uyemoto) N.; m. Lillian Yuriko Kobayakawa, Sept. 15, 1967; children—Elaine Yukae, Bryan Kazuto. Student, Central Tech. Sch., Toronto, 1948-51. Exhibited in one man shows at, Picture Loan Soc., 1952, Hart House, U. Toronto, 1953, Gallery of Contemporary Art, Toronto, 1956, 58, Jerrold Morris Gallery, Toronto, 1962, 65, 67-70, R. McLaughlin Gallery, Oshawa and Can. Tour, 1974-75, Christopher Cutts Gallery, Toronto, 1991; exhibited in group shows at, Fifth Internat. Hallmark Art Award Exhbn., N.Y.C., 1960, Canadian Prints, Drawings and Watercolor, Am. Fedn. Arts Tour, 1960, Seconde Biennale, Musee d'Art Moderne, Paris, France, 1961, Canadian Painting, Polish Tour, 1962, Canadian Painting, Central Africa, 1962, Nineteen Canadian Painters, Louisville, 1962, Commonwealth Painting, London, Eng., 1962, Recent Acquisitions, Mus. Modern Art, N.Y.C., 1963, Canadian Painting, London, 1963, Member's Loan Gallery Acquisitions, Albright-Knox Gallery, Buffalo, 1963, World Show, Washington Sq. Gallery, N.Y.C., 1964, Cardiff Commonwealth Exhbn. of Drawings, Wales, 1965, Centennial Exhbn. of Canadian Prints and Drawings, Australian Tour, 1967, Painters Eleven in Retrospect, Can. tour, 1979-81, Ont. Heritage Found. Firestone Collection, European tour, 1983-84, Nat. Gallery Can., Ottawa, 1989, Nat. Gallery Can., Ottawa, Can. tour, 1993, Mead Mus., Amherst Coll., 1994; others; represented in permanent collections at Nat. Gallery Can., Mus. Modern Art, N.Y.C., Art Gallery of Ont., Toronto, Musée d'Art contemporain, Montreal, R. McLaughlin Gallery, Oshawa, Hirshhorn Mus., Washington, British Mus., London, Art Gallery of Hamilton, Winnipeg Art Gallery, Beaverbrook Art Gallery, Fredericton, N.B., Windsor (Ont.) Art Gallery, Lugano Collection, Hart House, U. Toronto, Victoria Coll., U. Toronto, U. Western Ont., U. Guelph, Concordia U., Univ. Club Montreal, commd. 2 sculptures, Toronto Internat. Airport. (Recipient prize 4th Internat. Exhbn. Drawings and Engravings, Lugano, Switzerland 1956, Purchase award 5th Internat. Hallmark Art Award Exhbn., N.Y.C. 1960).

NAKAMURA, MITSURU JAMES, microbiologist, educator; b. L.A., Dec. 17, 1926; s. Jingo and Michie (Inadomi) N.; m. Judith Ann Frohreich; children: Monica Suzan, Nancy Midori, Mark James. Student, Drake U., 1944-45; AB, UCLA, 1949, postgrad., 1950-52; MS, U. So. Calif., 1950; PhD, Boston U., 1956; ScD (hon.), Albert Szent-Gyorgyi Med. U., 1991. Diplomate Am. Bd. Microbiology. Research asst. U. Calif., San Francisco, 1950-52; asst. prof. Northeastern U., 1952-54, assoc. prof., 1954-56; assoc. prof. U. Mont., Missoula, 1956-62; prof. U. Mont., 1962-86, prof. emeritus, 1986—, chmn. dept., 1963-85; assoc. prof. rsch. Wash. State U., summers 1957, 58; internat. vis. prof. Med. U. Pecs, Hungary, 1987; vis. prof. Yang Ming Med. Coll., Taipei, Taiwan, 1988, Albert Szent Gyorgyi Med. U., Szeged, Hungary, 1989, U. West Indies, Trinidad, 1990, Barbados, 1990, Jozsef Attila U. Scis., Szeged, 1991, Inst. Microbiol. Bulgarian Acad. Scis., 1992; rsch. fellow La. State U. Sch. Medicine, 1959, 60. Contbr. articles profl. jours. With AUS, 1945-47, capt. USPHS, 1959—. U.S. Army rsch. grantee 1959-62, NSF grantee, 1959-67, HEW grantee, 1960-67, Dept. Interior grantee 1964-67; Nat. Acad. Sci. awardee Poland, 1976, Yugoslavia, 1978, Hungary, 1982, 84, 89, Bulgaria, 1985, Czechoslovakia, 1987, ProCultura grantee, Hungary, 1991, 93. Fellow AAAS, APHA, Royal Soc. Tropical Medicine (London), Am. Acad. Microbiology, Bulgarian Acad. Scis., Elks. Home: PO Box 2068 Missoula MT 59806-2068

NAKAMURA, ROBERT MOTOHARU, pathologist; b. Montebello, Calif., June 10, 1927; s. Mosaburo and Haru (Suematsu) N.; m. Shigeyo Jane Hayashi, July 29, 1957; children: Mary, Nancy. AB, Whittier Coll., 1949; MD, Temple U., 1954. Cert. of spl. qualification in pathologic anatomy, clin pathology, immunopathology, Am. Bd. Pathology. Prof. pathology U. Calif., Irvine, 1971-74, adj. prof. pathology, 1974-75; chmn. dept. pathology Scripps Clinic and Rsch. Found., La Jolla, Calif., 1974-92; sr. cons., 1992—; pres. Scripps Clinic Med. Group, La Jolla, 1981-91; adj. prof. pathology U. Calif., San Diego, 1975-93. Author, editor profl. publs.; co-editor Jr. Clin. Lab. Analysis, 1989—. Fellow: Coll. Am. Pathologists, Am. Soc. Clin. Pathologists, Assn. Clin. Scientists, Am. Coll. Nutrition; mem. Internat. Acad. Pathology. Avocation: reading. Home: 8841 Nottingham Pl La Jolla CA 92037-2131

NAKAMURA, YOSHIO, professional sports team executive; b. Japan, 1950; s. of Nagayoshi Nakamura; m. Keiko d. Yuri. Political Law, Keio U., Tokyo, 1973. Prof. sports exec. Fukuoka Lions (later Seibu Lions 1979—), Japan, 1969-87; mgr. operations Lodi Lions, USA, 1971-73; v.p. Seibu Lions, Japan, 1979-87; pres. Kokusai Green Co., Ltd., Japan, 1987—. Lightning Partners Ltd., Tampa Bay, FL, 1991—. Office: care Tampa Bay Lightning 1 Mack Center 501 E Kennedy Blvd Suite 175 Tampa FL 30602*

NAKANISHI, DON TOSHIAKI, Asian American studies educator, writer; b. L.A., Aug. 14, 1949; m. Marsha Hirano; 1 child, Thomas. BA in Polit Sci. cum laude, Yale U., 1971; PhD in Polit. Sci., Harvard U., 1978. Prof. dir. Asian Am. Studies Ctr. UCLA; researcher Social Sci. Rsch. Coun. of N.Y. and the Japan Soc. for the Promotion of Sci. of Tokyo Joint-Project on Am.-Japanese Mut. Images, 1971-73; mem. Asian Am. task force for social studies guideline evaluation, Calif. State Dept. Edn., 1973; guest spkr. Ctr. for the Study of Ednl. Policy, Grad. Sch. Edn., Harvard U., 1974, Metropathways, Ethni-City Sch. Desegregation Program, Boston, 1974; researcher, co-project chair Hispanic Urban Ctr., Project Sch. Desegregation, L.A., 1974. Author: (with others) Mutual Images: Essays in American-Japan Relations, 1975, Eliminating Racism, 1988, Racial and Ethnic Politics in California, 1991; author: In Search of a New Paradigm: Minorities in the Context of International Politics, 1975, The Education of Asian and Pacific Americans: Historical Perspectives and Prescriptions for the Future, 1983, The UCLA Asian Pacific American Voter Registration Study, 1986; contbr. articles to profl. jours. Chair Yale U. Alumni Schs. Com. of So. Calif., 1978—; bd. dirs. Altamed and La Clinica Familiar Del Barrio of East L.A., 1982—; commr. Bd. Transp. Commrs., City of L.A., 1984-90; v.p. Friends of the Little Tokyo Pub. Libr., 1986-88; co-chair nat. scholars adv. com. Japanese Am. Nat. Mus., 1987—; mem., bd. govs. Assn. of Yale Alumni, 1988-91; mem. exec. coun. Mayor's LA's Best Aftersch. Program, City of Los Angeles, 1988-90. Rsch. fellow Japan Soc. for the Promotion of Sci., 1978; recipient Nat. Scholars awrd for Outstanding Rsch. Article on Asian Pacific Am. Edn., Nat. Assn. for Asian and Pacific Am. Edn., 1985, Civil Rights Impace award Asian Am. Legal Ctr. of So. Calif., 1989; grantee Chancellors' Challenge in the Arts and Humanities, 1991, Calif. Policy Seminar, 1992, U. Calif. Pacific Rim Studies, 1992. Mem. Nat. Assn. for Interdisciplinary Ethnic Studies (bd. dirs. 1976-79), Assn. Asian Am. Studies (nat. pres. 1983-85), Nat. Assn. for Asian and Pacific Am. Edn. (exec. bd. dirs., v.p. 1983—). Office: UCLA Asian Am Studies Ctr Los Angeles CA 90024

NAKANISHI, KOJI, chemistry educator, research institute administrator; b. Hong Kong, May 11, 1925; came to U.S., 1969; s. Yuzo and Yoshiko (Sakata) N.; m. Yasuko Abe, Oct. 25, 1947; children: Keiko, Jun. B.Sc., Nagoya U., Japan, 1947; Ph.D., Nagoya U., 1954; DSc (hon.), Williams Coll., 1987, Georgetown U., 1992. Assoc. prof. Nagoya U., 1955-58; prof. Tokyo Kyoiku U., 1958-63, Tohoku U., Sendai, Japan, 1963-69; prof. chemistry Columbia U., N.Y.C., 1969-80; Centennial prof. chemistry Columbia U., 1980—; dir. research Internat. Ctr. Insect Physiology and Ecology, Nairobi, Kenya, 1969-77; dir. Suntory Inst. for Bioorganic Research, Osaka, Japan, 1979-91. Author: Infrared Spectroscopy-Practical, 1962, rev. edit., 1977, Circular Dichroic Spectroscopy-Exciton Coupling in Organic Stereochemistry, 1983, A Wandering Natural Products Chemist, 1991. Recipient Asahi Cultural award Asahi Press, Tokyo, 1968, E.E. Smissmann medal U. Kans., 1979, H.C. Urey award Phi Lambda Upsilon chpt. Columbia U., 1980, Alcon award in ophthalmology, 1986, Pual Karrer gold medal U. Zurich, 1986, Egbert Havinga medal Havinga Found., Leiden, 1989, Imperial Prize of Japan Acad., 1990, Japan Acad. prize, 1990, R.T. Major medal U. Conn., 1991, L.E. Harris award U. Nebr., 1991, Chem. Scis. award Nat. Acad. Sci., 1994. Mem. Chem. Soc. Japan (soc. award 1954, 79), Am. Chem. Soc. (E. Guenther award 1978, Remsen award 1981, A.C. Cope award 1990, Nichols medal 1992, Mosher award 1994, Internat. award in

agrochemistry 1995), Brit. Chem. Soc. (Centenary medal 1979), Swedish Acad. Pharm. Scis. (Scheele award 1992), Am. Acad. Arts and Sci., Am. Soc. Pharmacology (rsch. achievement award 1985), Internat. Chirality Symposium (Chirality gold medal 1995), Pharm. Soc. Japan (hon.), Acad. Nazionalle d'Scienze, Italy (fgn. fellow). Home: 560 Riverside Dr New York NY 10027-3202 Office: Columbia U Dept Chem 116th St & Broadway New York NY 10027

NAKANISHI, TSUTOMU, pharmaceutical science educator; b. Osaka, Japan, Mar. 4, 1939; s. Noboru and Shizuko (Kurata) N.; m. Naoko Nishihara, May 3, 1969; children: Wataru N., Nozomi N., Hiromu N. Diploma in pharm. scis., Osaka U., 1961, PhD, 1968; diploma in organic chemistry, Imperial Coll., London. Lectr. pharm. scis. Osaka U., 1970-78, assoc. prof., 1978-83; prof. faculty pharm. sci. Setsunan U., Osaka, 1983—; rsch. fellow in organic chemistry, Imperial Coll., London, 1973-74. Author; contbr. articles to English and Japanese lang. sci. publs. Mem. Pharm. Soc. Japan, Chem. Soc. Japan, Royal Soc. Chemistry. Office: Pharm Scis Setsunan U, 45-1 Nagaotoge cho, Hirakata 573-01, Japan

NAKANO, TATSUHIKO, chemist, researcher, educator; b. Osaka, Japan, Feb. 4, 1925; s. Denichi and Shie (Kubo) N.; m. Toshiko Kitagawa, Apr. 23, 1965. BA, Kyoto U., 1950, PhD, 1955. Rsch. fellow Kyoto (Japan) U., 1950-55, assoc. prof., 1960-65; rsch. assoc. Wayne State U., Detroit, 1956-59, Stanford (Calif.) U., 1959-60; prof. Inst. Venezolano de Investigaciones Cientificas, Caracas, Venezuela, 1965-94, investigador emerito, 1994; prof. U. Cen. de Venezuela, Caracas, 1981—; disting. prof. Inst. de Tecnología y Estudios Superiores, Monterrey, Mex., 1979; vis. prof. U. N.C., Chapel Hill, 1990, 91, 93; regional editor Revista Latinoamericana de Química, Mex., D.F., 1970—. Contbr. 200 articles to Jour. Chem. Soc., Jour. Chem. Rsch., Tetrahedron, Tetrahedra Letters, etc.; author: Studies in Natural Products Chemistry, 1989, 90. Recipient Spl. Rsch. fellowship IKUEIKAI, 1950, Fulbright Vis. Scientist Travel award, 1956, Rsch. award Rockefeller Found., 1961, NIH, 1962, Fundación José María Vargas, 1969, 80; Decorated Order Andres Bello (3d class, 1979, 2d class, 1989, 1st class, 1995); Emeritus mem., PPI Consejo Nacional de Investigaciones Cientificas y Tecnologicas, 1994; ABI Twentieth Century Achievement award, 1995. Mem. AAAS, Am. Chem. Soc., Royal Soc. Chemistry, N.Y. Acad. Scis., Japan Fulbright Alumni Assn. Office: IVIC Centro de Quimica, Apartado 21827, Caracas 1020-A, Venezuela

NAKASHIMA, MITSUGI, state agency administrator. Chmn. Edn. divsn., Honolulu. Office: Education Dvsn PO Box 2360 Honolulu HI 96804-2360

NAKASONE, ROBERT C., retail toy and game company executive; b. 1947; married. BA, Claremont Coll., 1969; MBA, U. Chgo., 1971. With Brighams Ice Cream Parlor & Sandwich Shops, 1979-82; v.p., gen. mgrs. Jewel Food Stores, 1982-84; Midwest stores v.p. Toys R Us Inc., 1986-89; pres. Toys R Us, USA, 1989—; pres., vice chmn. Toys R Us Worldwide Toy Stores, 1989—; also bd. dirs. 1st lt. U.S. Army, 1979-82. Office: Toys R US Inc 461 From Rd Paramus NJ 07652-3524 Address: 395 W Passaic St Rochelle Park NJ 07662-3016*

NAKATA, HERBERT MINORU, retired microbiology educator, academic administrator; b. Pasadena, Calif., Mar. 10, 1930; s. Russell K. and Fusayo (Osaka) N.; m. Barbara Ann Wescott, Apr. 9, 1960; children: Stephen J., Laura D., Debra L. BS, U. Ill., 1952, MS, 1956, PhD, 1959. Instr. Washington State U., Pullman, asst. prof., assoc. prof., prof. microbiology, chmn. dept. microbiology, 1968-92; ret., 1993. Contbr. articles to profl. jours. Served with U.S. Army, 1952-54. Mem. Am. Soc. for Microbiology (v.p. NW br. 1975-76, 83-84, pres. 1976-77, 84-85, councilor 1980-83), AAAS, Sigma Xi. Avocations: travel, woodworking, fishing, golf. Office: Wash State U Dept Microbiology Pullman WA 99164

NAKATANI, ROY EIJI, biologist, educator; b. Seattle, June 8, 1918; s. Ushinosuke and Fuku N.; m. Harue Okihara, May 28, 1955; children—Ronald L., Dale E., Scott M., Mika L., Mark I. B.S. cum laude in Fisheries, U. Wash., 1947, Ph.D., 1960. Research assoc. U. Wash., 1954-59; biol. scientist Gen. Electric Co., 1959-62; mgr. aquatic biology Hanford Labs., 1962-66; mgr. ecology Battelle-Northwest Labs., 1966-70; assoc. prof. fisheries U. Wash., 1970-73, prof., 1973-88; asst. dir. Fisheries Rsch. Inst., 1970-73, assoc. dir., 1973-88—; prof. emeritus U. Wash., 1988—; cons. in field. Contbr. articles in field to profl. jours. Served as sgt. U.S. Army, 1941-46. Fellow AAAS, Internat. Acad. Fish Sci., Am. Inst. Fishery Rsch. Biologists (nat. sec. 1986-91); mem. Am. Fisheries Soc., Ecol. Soc. Am., Am. Soc. Limnology and Oceanography, Sigma Xi. Home: 6719 152nd Ave NE Redmond WA 98052-4760 Office: Fish Rsch Institute Seattle WA 98195

NAKAYAMA, KEN, psychology educator; b. Englewood, N.J., Mar. 28, 1940. BA in Psychology, Haverford Coll., 1962; PhD in Physiological Psychology, UCLA, 1967. Postdoctoral fellow sch. optometry dept. physiology-anatomy U. Calif., Berkeley, 1967-69; asst. prof. neurophysiology faculty medicine Meml. U. Newfoundland, St. Johns, 1969-71; assoc. scientist Smith-Kettlewell Inst. Visual Scis., San Francisco, 1971-78, sr. scientist, 1978-80; assoc. prof., chmn. dept. visual sci. U. Pacific, San Francisco, 1975-81; assoc. dir. Smith-Kettlewell Eye Rsch. Inst., San Francisco, 1980-90; prof. dept. psychology Harvard U., Cambridge, Mass., 1990—; assoc. Neurosciences Rsch. Program, N.Y.C., 1991—; lectr. Sloan Found. Summer Course in Computational Neuroscience, Cold Spring Harbor Lab., L.I., 1985, 87, 92, McDonnell-Pew Summer Inst. in Cognitive Neuroscience, Dartmouth Coll., Hanover, N.H., 1990, Rockefeller U., 1992. Mem. editorial adv. bd. Perception, 1978—, VNU Press Monograph Series, Amsterdam, 1985; mem. editorial bd. Vision Rsch., 1985-92, Neural Networks, 1987—, Concepts in Neuroscience, 1990—, Jour. Neuroscience, 1990—; contbr. over 60 articles to profl and sci. publs. Trustee Assn. for Rsch in Vision and Ophthalmology, 1989—, v.p., 1993. Fellow Soc. Exptl. Psychologists. Office: Harvard U Cambridge MA 02138

NAKHIMOVSKY, ALICE STONE, foreign language educator; b. Bklyn., Mar. 19, 1950; d. Morton Dramin and Dorothy (Hershkowitz) Stone; m. Alexander David Nakhimovsky, Aug. 27, 1974; children: Isaac, Sharon. AB, Cornell U., 1971, PhD, 1975. Asst. prof. Russian Colgate U., Hamilton, N.Y., 1976-82; assoc. prof. Russian Colgate U., Hamilton, 1982-91, prof. Russian, 1991—, chair dept., 1989—. Author: Laughter in the Void, 1981, Russian-Jewish Literature and Identity, 1992; co-author: Beginning Russian Vol. I, 1981, Vol. II, 1982, 2d edit., 1991; editor: The Semiotics of Russian Cultural History, 1985. Fellow NEH, 1986-87, 95, Meml. Found. for Jewish Culture, 1988-89; Internat. Rsch. and Exch. Bd. grantee, 1988, 94. Mem. Am. Assn. Advancement of Slavic Studies, Am. Assn. Tchrs. Slavic and East European Langs., Nat. Assn. Scholars. Office: Colgate Univ Hamilton NY 13346

NAKHLEH, EMILE A., governmental sciences educator; b. Galilee, Palestine, May 25, 1938; came to U.S., 1960; s. Abdullah J. and Labibeh (Shiban) N.; m. Mary Bird, Dec. 25, 1965 (div. Aug. 1993); children: Charles, Richard; m. Ilonka Lessnau, Dec. 30, 1993. BA in Polit. Sci., St. John's U., 1963; MA in Polit. Sci., Georgetown U., 1966; PhD in Internat. Relation, Am. U., 1968. From asst. prof. to prof. Mt. St. Mary's Coll., Emmitsburg, Md., 1967-94, John L. Morrison prof. internat. studies, 1990—, chmn. dept., 1975-89, dir. internat. studies, 1981-93, chmn. dept. govt. and internat. studies, 1989-93, John L. Morrison prof. in internat. studies, 1990-93; exec. dir. Inst. for Internat. and Contemporary Affairs, 1990-93; scholar-in-residence, sr. analyst U.S. Govt., Washington, 1993—; adj. scholar Am. Enterprise Inst., Washington, 1981-90, Ctr. for Strategic and Internat. Studies, Washington, 1986-90. Author: Gulf Cooperation Council: Policies, Problems and Prospects, 1986, Persian Gulf and American Policy, 1982, A Palestinian Agenda for West Bank and Gaza, 1980, Bahrain: Political Development in a Modernizing Society, 1976. Founding mem. Cumberland Valley Fgn. Policy Study Group, Waynesboro, Pa., 1981-93; Soc. for Gulf Arab Studies, 1989-93; commr. Town of Emmitsburg Coun., 1977; chmn. City Bd. Commrs., Emmitsburg, 1978-79. Fulbright Rsch. fellow, Bahrain, 1972-73; Jerusalem, Israel, 1987, Sr. Rsch. fellow NEH, Washington, 1979-80; resident scholar Woodrow Wilson, Washington, 1979, U.S. Govt., Washington, 1990-91, 93-94. Mem. Md. Assn. for Higher Edn. (Outstanding Educator award 1989), Coun. for Advancement and Support of Edn., Soc. for Gulf Arab Studies (founding mem., pres. 1992-93), Am. Polit. Sci. Assn. Roman Catholic. Avocations: reading, traveling, gardening.

Home: 11415 Bedfordshire Ave Potomac MD 20854-2009 Office: US Govt Washington DC 20505

NALCIOGLU, ORHAN, radiological science educator; b. Istanbul, Feb. 2, 1944; U.S., 1966, naturalized, 1974; s. Mustafa and Meliha N. BS, Robert Coll., Istanbul, 1966; MS, Case Western Res. U., 1968; PhD, U.A. 1970. Postdoctoral fellow dept. physics U. Calif.-Davis, 1970-71; Rsch. assoc. dept. physics U. Rochester, N.Y., 1971-74, U. Wis., Madison, 1974-76; sr. physicist EMI Med. Inc., Northbrook, Ill., 1976-77; prof. depts. radiol. scis., elec. engring., medicine and physics U. Calif.-Irvine, 1977—, head divsn. physics and engring., 1985—; dir. Biomedical Magnetic Resonance Rsch. 1987—, dir. Rsch. Imaging Ctr., 1992—; cons. UN, 1980-86. Editor several books; contbr. articles to profl. jours. Mobil scholar, 1961-66. Fellow IEEE, Am. Assn. Physicists in Medicine; pres. IEEE NPSS, 1993-94; mem. Soc. Magnetic Resonance Imaging, Soc. Magnetic Resonance in Medicine. Republican. Subspecialty: medical physics. Office: U Calif Irvine Coll Medicine Dept Radiol Sci Irvine CA 92717-5000

NALDER, ERIC CHRISTOPHER, investigative reporter; b. Coulee Dam, Wash., Mar. 2, 1946; s. Philip Richard and Mibs Dorothy (Aurdal) N.; m. Jan Christiansen, Dec. 20, 1968; 1 child, Britt Hillary. BA in Communications, U. Wash., 1968. News editor Whidbey News-Times, Oak Harbor, Wash., 1971; reporter Lynnwood (Wash.) Enterprise, 1972, Everett Herald, Lynnwood, 1972-75; gen. assignment reporter Seattle Post-Intelligencer, 1975-78, edn. writer, 1977-78, investigative reporter, 1978-83; chief investigative reporter Seattle Times, 1983—. Author: Tankers Full of Trouble, 1994. Recipient Edn. Writers Assn. award Charles Stewart Mott Found., 1978, Hearst Community Svc. award, 1978, C.B. Blethen awards (12), Outstanding Govt. Reporting award Seattle Mcpl. League, Pub. Svc. in Journalism award Sigma Delta Chi, 1987, Edward J. Meeman award Scripps Howard Found., 1987, Thomas Stokes award, Washington Journalism Ctr., 1990, Pulitzer prize for nat. reporting, 1990, Nat. Headline award, 1991, Pub. Svc. award AP Mags. Editors Assn., 1992, Goldsmith prize for investigative reporting, 1992, Worth Bingham prize for investigative reporting, 1992, Headliner award, 1992, Investigative Reporters and Editors award, 1992. Mem. Investigative Reporters and Editors, Pacific N.W. Newspaper Guild. Avocation: downhill skiing. Office: Seattle Times Fairview Avenue St N Seattle WA 98109*

NALDRETT, ANTHONY JAMES, geology educator; b. London, June 23, 1933; emigrated to Can., 1957; s. Anthony George and Violet Ethel (Latham) N.; m. Sylvia Robb Clark, Apr. 23, 1960 (div.); children: Anne, Jennifer, Penelope; m. Galina Stanislavovna Rylkova, July 6, 1991. B.A., U. Cambridge, 1956, M.A., 1962; M.Sc., Queens U., Can., 1961, Ph.D., 1964. Geologist Falconbridge Nickel Mines, Ltd., Sudbury, 1957-59; fellow Carnegie Inst. Washington, Geophys. Lab., 1964-67; asst. prof. U. Toronto, Ont., 1967-68; assoc. prof. U. Toronto, 1968-72, prof. mineral deposits geology, 1972-84, univ. prof., 1984—; mine geologist Falconbridge Nickel, 1957-59, exploration geologist, summers 1959-63, sr. prin. rsch. officer CSIRO, Australia, 1972-73; vis. prof. U. Pretoria, South Africa, 1979-80; chercheur associé CNRS, Orleans, France, 1986-87; stagière BRGM, Orleans, France, 1993-94. Contbr. articles to profl. jours.; editor: Jour. Petrology, 1984-92. Served with Royal Air Force, 1951-53. Recipient Barlow medal Can. Inst. Mining/Metallurgy, 1974, Duncan Derry medal Geol. Assn. Can., 1980, Logan medal Geol. Assn. Can., 1994, Bownocker gold medal Ohio State U., 1986. Fellow Royal Soc. Can., Mineral. Soc. Am., European Union Geoscientists (hon. fgn.), Soc. Econ. Geologists (v.p. 1982, pres. 1991-92, medal 1982), Geol. Soc. Am., Mineral. Assn. Can. (pres. 1982, 83, Past Pres.'s medal 1991), Société de Mineralogie et Crystallographie (v.p. 1987), Internat. Mineral. Assn. (1st v.p. 1994—). Avocations: sailing, skiing, carpentry. Home: 33 Harbour Sq Ste 1210, Toronto, ON Canada M5J 2G2 Office: Dept Geology, University of Toronto, Toronto, ON Canada M5S 1A1

NALEN, CRAIG ANTHONY, government official; b. Montclair, N.J., Apr. 17, 1930; s. Paul Anthony and Mildred A. (Tucker) N.; m. Katherine Andrews, Dec. 30, 1953; children: Katherine M., David A., Peter H. BA, Princeton U., 1952; MBA, Stanford U., 1957. Mktg. exec. Procter & Gamble, Cin., 1957-62, Foremost-McKesson, San Francisco, 1962-64; divisional gen. mgr., corp. v.p. Gen. Mills Inc., Mpls., 1964-72; pres., also bd. dirs. Am. Photograph Corp., Great Neck, N.Y., 1972-75; pres., chmn. bd. dirs. STP Corp., Ft. Lauderdale, Fla., 1975-80; pres., chief exec. officer Overseas Pvt. Investment Corp. (govt. agy.), Washington, 1981-89, also bd. dirs.; chmn. AES Transpower, Washington, 1989—; bd. dirs. Firan Corp., Ont., Can., Sonex Corp. Bd. dirs., founder Children's World, Denver; bd. dirs. Washington Tennis Found.; chmn. bd. advisors Ctr. for Internat. Studies, Duke U., Durham, N.C. Lt. USNR, 1952-55. Mem. Woodhill Country Club (Wayzata, Minn.), Links Club, Princeton Club (N.Y.C.), Chevy Chase Club (Md.), Gulf Stream Golf Club (Fla.), Ocean Club (Delray Beach, Fla.), Gulf Stream Bath and Tennis Club (Delray Beach), Valley Golf Club (Sun Valley, Idaho). Republican. Home: 6880 N Ocean Blvd Ocean Ridge FL 33435-3317 also: 4419 Chalfont Pl Bethesda MD 20816-1812 also: PO Box 2439 Ketchum ID 83340-2439 Office: AES Transpower 1001 19th St N Arlington VA 22209-1710

NALEWAKO, MARY ANNE, corporate secretary; b. Johnstown, Pa., Aug. 15, 1934; d. Charles and Margaret (Timothy) Rooney; m. Michael S. Nalewako, Apr. 8, 1961; 1 child, Michael. BSBA, Coll. St. Elizabeth, Convent Station, N.J., 1987. Adminstrv. asst. to chmn. Gen. Pub. Utilities, Parsippany, N.J., 1975-88, corp. sec., 1988—. Recipient Twin award Central (N.J.) YWCA, 1989, award Exec. Women of N.J., 1992. Mem. Am. Soc. Corp. Secs., Seraphic Soc., Spring Brook Country Club. Office: Gen Pub Utilities Corp 100 Interpace Pky Parsippany NJ 07054-1113

NALLE, PETER DEVEREUX, publishing company executive; b. N.Y.C., July 26, 1947; s. Peter Borie and Margaret Graham (Josephs) N.; m. Eleanor Jo Graham, June 14, 1969; 1 child, Graham Devereux. B.A., Brown U., 1969. Salesman and mem. sales mgmt. dept. McGraw-Hill Book Co., N.Y.C., 1970-76, editor, mem. editorial mgmt. dept., 1976-81, mktg. dir.-1981-82, gen. mgr., 1982-84, group v.p., 1984-87; pres., chief exec. officer J.B. Lippincott Co., Phila., 1987-90; pres. Simon and Schuster Profl. Info. Group, Englewood Cliffs, N.J., 1990-93; COO Grolier, Inc., Danbury, Conn., 1994—. Bd. dirs. Schuylkill River Devel. Coun. Mem. Assn. Am. Pubs. (exec. council profl. and scholarly div. 1985-87, bd. dirs. 1995-96), Soc. Scholarly Pub., Washington Square Assn. (bd. dirs.), Am. Med. Pubs. Assn. (bd. dirs.), Info. Industry Assn., Friends of Schuylkill River Park (v.p.), Athenaeum of Phila. Club: Brown U. Avocations: sailing; windsurfing; tennis. Home: 2113 Delancey St Philadelphia PA 19103-6511

NALLEY, ELIZABETH ANN, chemistry educator; b. Catron, Mo., July 8, 1942; d. Arthur E. and Thelma L. (King) Frazier; m. Robert L. Mullican, Jan. 2, 1986; 1 child, George L. BS, Northeastern Okla. State U., 1965; MS, Okla. State U., 1969; PhD, Tex. Woman's U., 1975. High sch. tchr. Muskogee (Okla.) Ctrl. High Sch., 1964-65; instr. Cameron U., Lawton, Okla., 1969-72; asst. prof. Cameron U., Lawton, 1972-75, assoc. prof., 1975-78, prof., 1978—. Contbr. articles to profl. jours. Mem. AAAS, Assn. for Advancement of Computers in Edn., Am. Chem. Soc. (councilor 1980—, sec. div. profl. rels. 1987—, Okla. Chemist award 1992), Am. Inst. Chemists (nat. bd. dirs.), Phi Kappa Phi (pres. elect 1981-89, nat. v.p. 1989-92, nat. pres.-elect 1992-95, nat. pres. 1995—, Disting. Faculty award 1978), Sigma Xi, Sigma Pi Sigma, Iota Sigma Pi. Home: RR 3 Box 176-1 Chickasha OK 73018-9544 Office: Cameron U Dept of Chemistry 2800 W Gore Blvd Lawton OK 73505-6320

NAM, CHARLES BENJAMIN, sociologist, demographer, educator; b. Lynbrook, N.Y., Mar. 25, 1926; s. Samuel and Yetta (Huff) N.; m. Marjorie Lee Tallant, Jan. 1, 1956; children: David Wallace, Rebecca Jane. B.A., NYU, 1950; M.A., U. N.C., 1957, Ph.D., 1959. Statistician U.S. Bur. Census, Washington, 1950-53; chief edn. and social stratification br. U.S. Bur. Census, 1957-64; statistician USAF, Montgomery, Ala., 1953-54; rsch. asst. U. N.C., Chapel Hill, 1954-57; prof. sociology Fla. State U., Tallahassee, 1964—; chmn. dept. sociology Fla. State U., 1964-71; dir. Center for Study of Population, 1967-82; disting. rsch. prof. Fla. State U., 1994—; mem. population adv. com. U.S. Bur. Census, 1978-81; cons. population divsn. Orgn. for Econ. Coop. and Devel., 1968-70, UNESCO, 1978-83, Indonesian Ministry of Population and Environment, Jakrarta, 1988-90;

Social Sci. Rsch. Coun., 1981-88. Author: (with John K. Folger) Education of the American Population, 1967, (with Susan Gustavus) Population: The Dynamics of Demographic Change, 1976, Nationality Groups and Social Stratification, 1981, (with Susan Philliber) Population: A Basic Orientation, 1983, (with Mary Powers) The Socioeconomic Approach to Status Measurement, 1983, Our Population: The Face of America, 1988, Understanding Population Change, 1994; editor: Demography, 1972-75; co-editor: (with David Sly, William Serow) International Handbook of Internal Migration, 1990, Handbook of International Migration, 1990; assoc. editor jour. Population Research and Policy Review, 1993-94. Mem. Am. Sociol. Assn. (chmn. sect. on population 1976-78), Population Assn. Am. (pres. 1979), Internat. Union for Sci. Study Population, Am. Statis. Assn. (vice chmn. sect. on population 1976-78), Population Assn. Am. (pres. 1979), Internat. Union for Sci. Study Population, Am. Statis. Assn. (vice chmn. statistics sect. 1974), So. Sociol. Soc. (pres. 1981-82), So. Regional Demographic Group (vice chmn. 1974-75). Home: 820 Live Oak Plantation Rd Tallahassee FL 32312-2413

NAM, SANG BOO, physicist; b. Kyung Nam, Korea, Jan. 30, 1936; came to U.S., 1959, naturalized, 1978; s. Sai Hi and Boon Hi (Kim) N.; m. Wonki Kim, June 1, 1969; children—Sae Woo, Jean Ok. BS, Seoul Nat. U., Korea, 1958; MS, U. Ill., 1961, PhD, 1966. Rsch. assoc. U. Ill., Urbana, 1966; rsch. fellow Rutgers U., New Brunswick, N.J., 1966-68; asst. prof. physics U. Va., Charlottesville, 1968-71; vis. prof. physics Seoul Nat. U., 1970, Belfer Grad. Sch., Yeshiva U., N.Y.C., 1971-74; sr. rsch. fellow in physics Nat. Acad. Sci.-NRC, Washington, 1974-76, 84-86; rsch. prof. physics U. Dayton, Ohio, 1976-80; prof. physics Univ. Rsch. Ctr., Wright State U., Dayton, 1980—. With Korean Army, 1958-59. U. Ill. fellow, 1961. Fellow Am. Phys. Soc., Korean Phys. Soc.; mem. AAAS, N.Y. Acad. Scis., Sigma Xi. Home: 7735 Peters Pike Dayton OH 45414-1713

NAMATH, JOSEPH WILLIAM, entertainer, former professional football player; b. Beaver Falls, Pa., May 31, 1943; s. John Andrew and Rose (Juhasz) N.; m. Deborah Lynn Mays, 1984; 1 child, Jessica Grace. Grad., U. Ala., 1965. Quarterback N.Y. Jets, Am. Football League (merged with NFL 1969), 1965-77, Los Angeles Rams Nat. Football Conf., 1977-78; co-owner Joe Namath Instructional Football Camp, Dudley, Mass. Appeared in films C.C. and Company, 1970, Avalanche Express, 1978, Chattanooga Choo Choo, 1984; TV appearances include The Waverly Wonders, NBC, 1978; frequent guest on Tonight Show; stage appearances include Picnic, 1979, Li'l Abner, 1980, The Caine Mutiny Court-Martial, 1983, Sugar, 1984; leading role in musical Damn Yankees, 1981; author (autobiography): Namath—A Matter of Style; commentator ABC Monday Night Football, 1985-86, TV series The Waverly Wonders, TV Movie Marriage is Alive Well, TV appearances Here's Lucy, The Bradu Bunch. The Love Boat, Kate and Allie. Past chmn. Leukemia Soc. Coin Campaign; hon. chmn. Am. Hungarian Soc.; established scholarship for women athletes U. Ala. Named Am. Football League Rookie of Yr., Sporting News, 1965, to Am. Football League All-Star team, 1968, 72, Most Valuable Player of Super Bowl, 1969, Dodge Man of Yr., N.Y. Jets, to Ala. Sports Hall of Fame, 1981; recipient Hickock Belt for Profl. Athlete of Yr., George Halas Most Courageous Athlete award; named to Pro Football Hall of Fame. Office: care Lantz Office 888 7th Ave New York NY 10106-0001*

NAMBA, TATSUJI, physician, medical researcher; b. Changchun, China, Jan. 29, 1927; came to U.S., 1959, naturalized, 1968; s. Yosuke and Michino (Hinata) N. M.D., Okayama U., Japan, 1950, Ph.D, 1955. Asst., lect. medicine Okayama U. Med. Sch. and Hosp., 1955-62; research assoc. Maimonides Med. Ctr., Bklyn., 1959-66; dir. neuromuscular labs. Maimonides Med. Ctr., 1966-70, dir. neuromuscular disease div., head electromyography clinic, 1966—; instr., asst. prof., assoc. prof. medicine State U. N.Y., Bklyn., 1959-76; prof. State U. N.Y., 1976—; mem. med. adv. bd. Myasthenia Gravis Found., 1968—. Recipient commendation for rsch. and clin. activities on insecticide poisoning Minister Health and Welfare, Japanese Govt., 1958; Fulbright scholar, 1959-62. Fellow ACP, Royal Soc. Medicine; mem. AMA, Am. Acad. Neurology, Am. Soc. Pharmacology and Exptl. Therapeutics, Am. Soc. Clin. Pharmacology and Therapeutics, Am. Assn. Electrodiagnostic Medicine. Office: 4802 10th Ave Brooklyn NY 11219-2916

NAMBOODIRI, KRISHNAN, sociology educator; b. Valavoor, Ind., Nov. 13, 1929; s. Narayanan and Parvathy (Kutty) N.; m. Kadambari Kumari, Sept. 7, 1954; children: Unni (dec.), Sally. B.Sc., U. Kerala, 1950, M.Sc., 1953; M.A., U. Mich., 1962, Ph.D., 1963. Lectr. U. Kerala, India, 1953-55, 58-59; tech. asst. Indian Statis. Inst., Calcutta, 1955-58; reader demography U. Kerala, 1963-66; asst. prof. sociology U. N.C., Chapel Hill, 1966-67; asso. prof. U. N.C., 1967-73, prof., 1973-84, chmn. dept., 1975-80; Robert Lazarus prof. population studies Ohio State U., Columbus, 1984—, chmn. dept. sociology, 1989-93. Author: (with L.F. Carter and H.M. Blalock) Applied Multivariate Analysis and Experimental Designs, 1975; editor: Demography, 1975-78, Survey Sampling and Measurement, 1978, Auth. Matrix Algebra: An Introduction, 1984, (with C.M. Suchindran) Life Table Techniques and Their Applications, 1987, (with R.G. Corwin) Research in Sociology of Education and Socialization: Selected Methodological Issues, 1989, Demographic Analysis: A Stochastic Approach, 1991, The Logic and Method of Macrosociology, 1993, Methods for Macrosociological Research, 1994; contbr. articles to profl. jours. Fellow Am. Statis. Assn.; mem. Population Assn. Am. (dir. 1975-76), Internat. Union Sci. Study Population, Am. Sociol. Assn., Indian Sociol. Assn., Am. Statis. Assn., Sociol. Research Assn. Home: 3107 N Star Rd Columbus OH 43221-2366

NAMBU, YOICHIRO, physics educator; b. Toyko, Jan. 18, 1921; came to U.S., 1952; m. Chieko Hida, Nov. 3, 1945; 1 child, Jun-ichi. Research asst. U. Tokyo, 1945-49; prof. physics Osaka City U., Japan, 1950—; mem. Inst. Advanced Study, 1952-54; research assoc. U. Chgo., 1954-56, mem. faculty, 1956—, prof. physics, 1958, Disting. prof., 1971—; emeritus, 1991—. Contbr. articles to profl. jours. Recipient Wolf Prize in Physics, 1994. Mem. Nat. Acad. Scis., Am. Acad. Arts and Scis., Am. Phys. Soc. Office: Univ of Chicago Dept of Physics 5720 S Ellis Ave Chicago IL 60637-1434

NAMDARI, BAHRAM, surgeon; b. Oct. 26, 1939; s. Rostam and Sarvar Namdari; M.D.; 1966; m. Kathleen Diane Wilmore, Jan. 5, 1976. Resident in gen. surgery St. John's Mercy Med. Ctr., St. Louis, 1969-73; fellow in cardiovascular surgery with Michael DeBakey, Baylor Coll. Medicine, Houston, 1974-75; practice medicine specializing in gen. and vascular surgery and surg. treatment of obesity, Milw., 1976—; mem. staff St. Mary's, St. Luke's, St. Michael, St. Francis hosps. (all Milw.); founder, pres. Famous Mealwaukee Foods Enterprises. Diplomate Am. Bd. Surgery. Fellow ACS, Internat. Coll. Surgeons; mem. Med. Soc. Milw. County, Milw. Acad. Surgery, Wis. Med. Soc., Wis. Surg. Soc., Royal Soc. Medicine Eng. (affiliate), Am. Soc. for Bariatric Surgery, AMA, World Med. Assn., Internat. Acad. Bariatric Medicine (founding mem.), Michael DeBakey Internat. Cardiovascular Soc. Contbr. articles to med. jours.; patentee med. instruments and other devices. Office: Great Lakes Med and Surg Ctr 6000 S 27th St Milwaukee WI 53221-4805

NAMIAS, JEROME, meteorologist; b. Bridgeport, Conn., Mar. 19, 1910; s. Joseph and Saydie (Jacobs) N.; m. Edith Paipert, Sept. 15, 1938; 1 child, Judith Ellen. Student, MIT, 1932-34, M.S., 1941; M.S., U. Mich., 1934-35; Sc.D. (hon.), U. R.I., 1972, Clark U., 1984. Research asst. Blue Hill Meteorol. Obs., Milton, Mass., 1933-35; research assoc. MIT, Boston, 1936-41, Woods Hole (Mass.) Oceanographic Inst.; mgr. extended forecast br. U.S. Weather Bur., Washington, 1941-64; assoc. dir. Nat. Meteorol. Ctr., 1964-66, chief extended forecast div., 1966-71; vis. scientist NYU, N.Y.C, 1966; research meteorologist Scripps Inst. Oceanography, La Jolla, Calif., 1968—; vis. scholar Rockefeller Study and Conf. Center, Bellagio, Italy, 1977; frequent cons. USAAF, USN; developer of system for extending time range of gen. weather forecasts up to a season. Author: An Introduction to the Study of Air Mass and Isentropic Analysis, 1936, Extended Forecasting by Mean Circulation Methods; monograph, 1947, Thirty-Day Forecasting, 1953; Short Period Climatic Variations, Collected Works of Jerome Namias 1934-74, 1975-82, 83, Namias Symposium Volume, 1986; also tech. articles to sci. jours.; Editorial bd.: Geofisica Internacional, Mexico. Recipient citation for weather forecasts North African invasion Sec. of Navy, 1942; Dept. Commerce Meritorious Service award, 1950; Rockefeller Pub. Service award, 1955; Gold medal for disting. achievement Dept. Commerce, 1965; Chancellor's Assocs. award excellence in research U. Calif.-San Diego; Compass award for research Marine Tech. Soc., 1984; Rossby fellow Woods Hole (Mass.) Oceanographic Instn., 1972. Fellow AAAS, Am. Geophys. Union,

Washington Acad. Scis., Am. Meteorol. Soc. (Meisinger award 1983, extraordinary achievement award 1955, Sverdrup Godl medal 1981, Lifetime Achievement award So. Calif. chpt. 1991, councilor 1940-42, 50-53, 60-63, 70-73); mem. NAS, Am. Acad. Arts and Sci., Royal Meteorol. Soc. Great Britain (hon. mem.), Explorers Club. Home: 240 Coast Blvd Apt 2C La Jolla CA 92037-4669 Office: Scripps Inst Oceanography Poss # A-024 La Jolla CA 92093 *I was stimulated by a few exceptionally capable high school teachers to pursue a career in meteorology. This subject became both a vocation and a most challenging hobby and never has ceased to fascinate me. My guiding philosophy has been that one is rewarded if he contributes fundamental ideas which are reasonable and at least partially verifiable. It is not necessary to be highly aggressive to get ahead.*

NANAVATI, GRACE LUTTRELL, dancer, choreographer, instructor; b. Springfield, Ill., Oct. 2, 1951; d. Curtis Loren and Mary Grace (Leaverton) Luttrell; m. P.J. Nanavati, May 11, 1985; 1 child, William P. BA, Butler U., 1973; MA, Sangamon State U., 1978. Owner, dir. Dance Arts Studio, Springfield, 1973—; artistic dir. Springfield (Ill.) Ballet Co., 1975—; compulsary arts programing com. Sch. Dist. 186, Springfield, 1990—; dance panel Ill. Arts Coun., 1990-92. Vol. Meml. Med. Ctr., Springfield 1980-88. Named Women of Yr., YMCA, Springfield, 1982; recipient Mayor award for Arts, City of Springfield, 1985, Best of Springfield award Ill. Times, Springfield, 1990. Home: 1501 Williams Blvd Springfield IL 62704 Office: Dance Arts Studio 2820 So MacArthur Springfield IL 62704

NANCE, ALLAN TAYLOR, lawyer; b. Dallas, Jan. 31, 1933; s. A.Q. and Lois Rebecca (Taylor) N. BA, So. Meth. U., 1954, LLB, 1957; LLM, NYU, 1978. Bar: Tex. 1957, N.Y. 1961. With Simpson Thacher & Bartlett, N.Y.C., 1960-65; asst. counsel J.P. Stevens & Co., Inc., N.Y.C., 1965-70, sec., 1970-78, asst. gen. counsel, 1970-89; counsel J.P. Stevens & Co. Inc. and WestPoint-Pepperell Inc., 1989-93; asst. gen. counsel WestPoint Stevens Inc., N.Y.C., 1993—. With USNR, 1957-59. Woodrow Wilson fellow Columbia U., 1959-60. Mem. Phi Beta Kappa. Home: 201 E 66th St New York NY 10021-6479 Office: WestPoint Stevens Inc 1185 Ave of the Americas New York NY 10036-2601

NANCE, BETTY LOVE, librarian; b. Nashville, Oct. 29, 1923; d. Granville Scott and Clara (Mills) Nance. BA in English magna cum laude, Trinity U., 1957; AM in Library Sci., U. Mich., 1958. Head dept. acquisitions Stephen F. Austin U. Library, Nacogdoches, Tex., 1958-59; librarian 1st Nat. Bank, Fort Worth, 1959-61; head catalog dept. Trinity U., San Antonio, 1961-63; head tech. processes U. Tex. Law Library, Austin, 1963-66; head catalog dept. Tex. A&M U. Library, College Station, 1966-69; chief bibliographic services Washington U. Library, St. Louis, 1970; head dept. acquisitions Va. Commonwealth U. Library, Richmond, 1971-73; head tech. processes Howard Payne U. Library, Brownwood, Tex., 1974-79; library dir. Edinburg (Tex.) Pub. Library, 1980-91; pres. Edinburg Com. for Salvation Army. Mem. ALA, Pub. Library Assn., Tex. Library Assn., Hidalgo County Library Assn. (v.p. 1980-81, pres. 1981-82), Pan Am. Round Table of Edinburg (corr. sec. 1986-88, assoc. dir. 1989-90), Edinburg Bus. and Profl. Womens Club (founding bd. dirs., pres. 1986-87, bd. dirs. 1987-88), Alpha Lambda Delta, Alpha Chi. Methodist. Club: Zonta Club of San Antonio (bd. dirs. West Hidalgo club 1986-88). Home: 5359 Fredericksburg Rd # 806 San Antonio TX 78229

NANCE, CECIL BOONE, JR., lawyer; b. Marion, Ark., Feb. 14, 1925; s. Cecil Boone and Virginia (Essary) N.; m. Harriet Jane McGee, Aug. 7, 1948; children: Janet E., Cecil Boone III. J.D., U. Ark., 1951. Bar: Ark. 1951. Since practiced in West Memphis; mem. firm Nance, Nance & Fleming (named changed to Nance & Nance P.A.), 1951—; Chmn. bd. Fidelity Nat. Bank West Memphis, 1966-71; dir., gen. counsel E. Ark. Savs. & Loan Assn., 1970-83; spl. asso. justice Ark. Supreme Ct. Contbr. articles to profl. jours. Mem. Ark. Ho. of Reps., 1957-68; v.p. Ark. Constl. Conv., 1969. Served with AUS, 1943-46, 52-53. Decorated Bronze Star. Mem. Am. Bar Assn., Ark. Bar Assn. (chmn. jr. bar sect. 1957-58, dir. Ark. Law Rev. and Bar Assn. Jour. 1975), Am. Judicature Soc. Methodist. Club: Rotarian (West Memphis) (pres. 1970-71). Home: 506 Roosevelt Ave West Memphis AR 72301-2961 Office: 203 W Broadway St West Memphis AR 72301-3903

NANCE, JOSEPH MILTON, history educator; b. Kyle, Tex., Sept. 18, 1913; s. Jeremiah Milton and Mary Louise (Hutchison) N.; m. Eleanor Glenn Hanover, Mar. 19, 1944; children: Jeremiah Milton, Joseph Hanover, James Clifton. B.A., U. Tex. 1935, M.A., 1936, Ph.D., 1941; cert. in naval communications, Harvard U., 1944. Tex. supr. Am. imprints, manuscripts and newspaper inventories U.S. Hist. Records Survey, 1938-40; instr. history Tex. A&M U., 1941-42, 46-47, asst. prof., 1947-51, assoc. prof., 1951-57, prof., 1957-58, prof., head dept. history and govt., 1958-68, head dept. history, 1968-73, prof., 1973—; instr. U.S. Naval Tng. Sch., College Station, 1942-43; vis. prof. history SW Tex. State Coll., San Marcos, summers 1956, 58. Author: Checklist of Texas Newspapers, 1813-1939, 1941, 3d edit., 1963, The Early History of Bryan and the Surrounding Area, 1962, After San Jacinto: The Texas-Mexican Frontier, 1836-1841, 1963, Attack and Counter-Attack, The Texas Mexican Frontier, 1842, 1964; co-author: Heroes of Texas, 1964; student guide to accompany A History of the American People (Graebner, Fite, White), 1971; also instr.'s man.; editor: Some Reflections upon Modern America, 1969, A Mier Expedition Diary: A Texan Prisoner's Account (Joseph D. McCutchan), 1978, Dare-Devils All: The Texan Mier Expedition, 1842-1844; mem. editorial bd.: Ariz. and the West, 1980-83; sr. editor: Handbook of Texas, 1983—. Mem. Hood's Brigade-Bryan Centennial Com., 1960-62; panel participant Tex. Legis. Assembly, 1967; mem. Ann. Faculty seminar Standard Oil Co. Calif., summer 1959, Brazos County Hist. Commn., Tex., 1972—. Served to lt. (j.g.) USNR, 1943-46. Recipient 15th Ann. Writers Roundup award Theta Sigma Phi, 1963, Tex. Inst. Letters award, 1964, Walter Prescott Webb award in history U. Tex., 1967, AMOCO Disting. Research award Tex. A&M U., 1979, History award and medal DAR, 1985; 3 ann. scholarships established in his name at Baylor U. Coll. Law, 1979—; ann. lectureship established in his honor Tex. A&M U., 1980—; named Knight of San Jacinto Sons of Republic, 1983. Fellow Tex. State Hist. Assn. (exec. coun.), East Hist. Assn., East Tex. Hist. Assn. (dir. 1980-83); mem. Tex. Inst. Letters, Am. Hist. Assn., So. Hist. Assn., W. Tex. Hist. Assn. (exec. coun., book rev. editor 1975-81, v.p. 1978-81, pres. 1981-82), Orgn. Am. Historians, Western History Assn., Am. Heritage Soc., Am. Studies Assn. Tex. (pres. 1969), Southwestern Social Sci. Assn., Central Tex. Area Writers Conf., Nat. Geog. Soc., Phi Beta Kappa, Phi Kappa Phi, Phi Alpha Theta. Home: 1403 Post Oak Cir College Station TX 77840-2322

NANCE, TONY MAX-PERRY, designer, illustrator; b. Montclair, N.J., Feb. 25, 1955; s. Perry Hedgeman and Ida Delea (King) N.; m. June Anne Percival, Oct. 31, 1986 (div. May 1994); children: Jacqlene, Jihad Conan. Student, U. Denver, 1975; BA, N.Y. Sch. Visual Arts, 1976, postgrad., 1980-81; postgrad., N.J. Inst. Tech., 1977-78, Rutgers U., 1980-82. Design engr. Automation Controls, Montclair, 1975-77; artist, designer Greg Copeland, Inc., Fairfield, N.J., 1976-79; owner, designer Stalhaus, Inc., Montclair, 1976-80; editor contemporary ads Graphics Mag., N.Y.C., 1977-79; illustrator, artist L.C. Graphics, Inc., Clifton, N.J., 1979-80; carrier supr. Montclair Post Office, 1980-93; owner, design engr. Decotech Alternations, Orange, N.J., 1984—, Electronics Tech-Atlas Soundolier, 1993—. Editor Graphis mag.; artist, art dir. (album covers) Bhang, 1984 Ron Smyth I, 1986; artist, illustrator (album cover, tour and advt. promotion) Passport Greatest Hits/Doldinger, 1977 (album cover, internat. poster) Zap and the Wires-The Saga of the Black Silk Jetmen; producer, illustrator (album cover) The Little Things by Dogs Eating Glass with Loren Tindall; one man shows include Discovery Galleries, Montclair, 1978, The Gallery, Fairfield, 1979, Broghton Galleries, Bloomfield, N.J., 1983, Scotland Galleries, Laurinburg, N.C., 1993; various musical and graphic copyrights; mem. Southern Ambition band, 1993—. Art dir. Montclair Coalition for Performing Arts, Montclair, 1982. Mem. Soc. for Creative Anachronism (founding assoc.), Local Musicians Union, Nat. Rifle Assn., Mensa, Scotland County Art Guild, Porsche Club Am., N.C. SCCA. Avocations: music, prop and special effect design, collecting plastic toys, computer software design, collecting guitars. Office: Decotech Alternations Nanceart 1209 N Main St Laurinburg NC 28352

NANCE, WILLIAM BENNETT, economic development specialist; b. Garland, N.C., Nov. 18, 1944; s. Lemon Francis Nance and Hattie McCoy Jones; m. Mildred Elaine McKiever, Dec. 26, 1971; children: William Bennett, David Christopher. BA in Polit. Sci., N.C. Ctrl. U., Durham, 1966; postgrad., Swarthmore Coll., 1966-67; MA in Internat. Affairs, George Washington U., 1979; MA in Pub. Adminstrn., Harvard U., 1989. Asst. program officer, Turkey AID, Ankara, 1971-75; asst. desk officer, Syria AID, Washington, 1975-77, officer-in-charge, Lebanon, 1977-79; chief Office of Program/Planning AID, Kathmandu, Nepal, 1979-83; officer-in-charge, Thailand AID, Washington, 1983-86, officer-in-charge, Philippines, 1986-88, officer-in-charge, Bangladesh, 1989-90; chief Office of Program AID, Rabat, Morocco, 1990-92; rep. to Mongolia AID, Ulaanbaatar, 1992—. Recipient Presdl. award Pres. of U.S., 1993. Avocations: reading, chess, tennis. Home: 4105 Oliver St Chevy Chase MD 20815 Office: Mongolia Psc 461 Box 300 FPO AP 96521-0300

NANDA, VED PRAKASH, law educator, university official; b. Gujranwala, India, Nov. 20, 1934; came to U.S., 1960; s. Jagan Nath and Attar (Kaur) N.; m. Katharine Kunz, Dec. 18, 1982; 1 child, Anjali. MA, Punjab U., 1952; LLB, U. Delhi, 1955, LLM, 1958; LLM, Northwestern U., 1962; postgrad., Yale U., 1962-65. Asst. prof. law U. Denver, 1965-68, assoc. prof., 1968-70, prof. law, dir. Internat. Legal Studies Program, 1970—, Thompson G. Marsh prof. law, 1987—; Evans Univ. prof., 1992—, asst. provost, 1993—; vis. prof. Coll. Law U. Iowa, Iowa City, 1974-75, Fla. State U., 1973, U. San Diego, 1979, U. Colo., 1992; disting. vis. prof. internat. law Chgo. Kent Coll. Law, 1981, Calif. We. Sch. Law, San Diego, 1983-84; disting. vis. scholar Sch. Law, U. Hawaii, Honolulu, 1986-87; cons. Solar Energy Rsch. Inst., 1978-81, Dept. Energy, 1980-81. Author: (with David Pansius) Litigation of International Disputes in U.S. Courts, 1987; editor: Water Needs for the Future, 1977, (with M. Cherif Bassiouni) A Treatise on International Criminal Law, 2 vols., 1973, (with others) Global Human Rights, 1981, The Law of Transnational Business Transactions, 1981, World Climate Change, 1983, Breach and Adaptation of International Contracts, 1992, World Debt and Human Conditions, 1993, Europe Community Law After 1992, 1993, (with George Shepherd) Human Rights and Third World Development, 1985; editor, contbr.: Refugee Law and Policy, 1989; editorial bd. Jour. Am. Comparative Law, Indian Jour. Internat. Law. Co-chmn. Colo. Pub. Broadcasting Fedn., 1977-78; mem. Gov.'s Commn. on Pub. Telecommunications, 1980-82. Mem. World Jurist Assn. (v.p. 1991—, pres. World Assn. Law Profs. 1987-93), UN Assn. (v.p. Colo. div. 1973-76, pres. 1986-88, 93—, nat. coun. UNA-USA 1990—), Am. Assn. Comparative Study Law (bd. dirs. 1980—), Am. Soc. Internat. Law (v.p. 1987-88, exec. coun. 1969-72, 81-84, bd. rev. and devel. 1988—), Assn. Am. Law Schs., U.S. Inst. Human Rights, Internat. Law Assn. (mem. exec. com. 1986—), Colo. Coun. Internat. Orgns. (pres. 1988-90), Assn. U.S. Mems. Internat. Inst. Space Law (bd. dirs., mem. exec. com 1980-88), Order St. Ives (pres.), Rotary, Cactus. Office: U Denver Coll Law 1900 Olive St Denver CO 80220-1857

NANDI, SATYABRATA, zoology educator; b. North Lakhimpur, Assam, India, Dec. 1, 1931; came to U.S., 1954; s. Kunja Bihari Nandi and Jyotirmoyee Sen-Gupta; m. Jean Brandt-Erichsen, July 5, 1957. B.S. with honors, U. Calcutta, India, 1949, M.S., 1951; Ph.D., U. Calif.-Berkeley, 1958. Asst. prof. zoology U. Calif.-Berkeley, 1962-64, assoc. prof., 1964-68, prof., 1968-89, prof. cell and devel. biology, dept. molecular and cell biology, 1989—, Miller prof., 1970-71, vice chmn. zoology, 1965-66, chmn. zoology, 1971-73, dir. cancer research lab., 1974-84; vis. scientist Kyoto U., Japan, 1965. Guggenheim fellow, 1967-68; recipient Spl. Honor for Outstanding Achievement, Ambassador of India, 1979. Mem. Assn. Indians in Am. (award 1980). Office: U Calif Cancer Research Lab 447 Life Scis Addition Berkeley CA 94720

NANFELT, P. N., church administrator. V.p. for Overseas Ministries Christian and Missionary Alliance. Office: PO Box 35000 Colorado Springs CO 80935-3500

NANGLE, JOHN FRANCIS, federal judge; b. St. Louis, June 8, 1922; s. Sylvester Austin and Thelma (Bank) N.; m. Jane Adams, June 7, 1986; 1 child, John Francis Jr. AA, Harris Tchrs. Coll., 1941; BS, U. Mo., 1943; JD, Washington U., St. Louis, 1948. Bar: Mo. 1948. Pvt. practice law Clayton, 1948-73; judge U.S. Dist. Ct., St. Louis, 1973—, chief judge, 1983-90, sr. judge, 1990—. Mem. Mo. Rep. Com., 1958-73; mem. St. Louis County Rep. Cen. Com., 1958-73, chmn., 1960-61; pres. Mo. Assn. Reps., 1961, Reps. Vets. League, 1960; mem. Rep. Nat. Com., 1972-73; bd. dirs. Masonic Home Mo. with AUS, 1943-46. Named Mo. Republican of Year John Marshall Club, 1970, Mo. Republican of Year Mo. Assn. Reps., 1971; recipient Most Disting. Alumnus award Harris-Stowe Coll., Most Disting. Alumnus award Washington U. Sch. Law, 1986. Mem. ABA, Am. Judicature Soc., Legion of Honor DeMolay, Mo. Bar Assn., St. Louis Bar Assn., St. Louis County Bar Assn., 8th Cir. Jud. Coun., Jud. Conf. U.S. (apptd. mem. exec. com.), Jud. Panel on Multidist. Litigation (chmn.).

NANNEY, DAVID LEDBETTER, genetics educator; b. Abingdon, Va., Oct. 10, 1925; s. Thomas Grady and Pearl (Ledbetter) N.; m. Jean Kelly, June 15, 1951; children: Douglas Paul, Ruth Elizabeth Beshears. A.B., Okla. Bapt. U., 1946; Ph.D., Ind. U., 1951; Laurea honoris causa, U. Pisa, Italy, 1994. Asst. prof. zoology U. Mich., Ann Arbor, 1951-56; asso. prof. U. Mich., 1956-58; prof. zoology U. Ill., Urbana-Champaign, 1959-76; prof. genetics and devel. U. Ill., 1976-86, prof. ecology, ethology and evolution, 1987-91, prof. emeritus, 1991—; sr. postdoctoral fellow Calif. Inst. Tech., 1958-59; predoctoral fellow NIH, Ind. U., 1949-51. Author: (with Herbert Stern) The Biology of Cells, 1965, Experimental Ciliatology, 1980. Recipient Disting. Alumnus award Okla. Bapt. U., 1972; named Disting. Lectr. Sch. Life Scis., U. Ill., 1981; Preisträger, Alexander von Humboldt Stiftung, Fed. Republic Germany, 1984. Fellow AAAS, Am. Acad. Arts and Scis.; mem. Genetics Soc. Am., Am. Genetic Assn. (pres. 1982), Soc. Protozoologists. Home: 703 W Indiana Ave Urbana IL 61801-4835 Office: U Ill Dept Ecology Ethology and Evolution 505 S Gregory St Urbana IL 61801

NANNEY, SONDRA TUCKER, dance school executive, small business owner; b. Knoxville, Tenn., Dec. 11, 1937; d. Willard Woodrow and Mary Lou (Pollard) Tucker; m. Red Celestine Nanney, March 11, 1960; children: Stacy Leigh Nanney Courtney, Kristin Kaye. Grad. high sch., Knoxville, 1955. Bookkeeper Miles Siegel, CPA, Knoxville, 1955-56; sales sec. Sta. WBIR-TV, Knoxville, 1956-64, Knoxville News Sentinel, 1965-67; owner Concord Farragut Sch., Knoxville, 1974-79, Knoxville Sch. Dance, 1979-94, Images Dancewear, Knoxville, 1989-94; pres. Knoxville Met. Dance, 1982-94. Mem. Knoxville Symphony League (officer 1982-94, pres. 1989-90), chmn. showcase 1993, nominating com. 1992), Knoxville Met. Dance Theatre (pres. 1994). Republican. Avocations: reading, waterskiing, bridge, the arts. Office: Knoxville Sch Ballet Arts PO Box 23841 Knoxville TN 37933-1841

NANTERMET, PHILIPPE GUY, research scientist; b. Lyon, France, Jan. 18, 1966; came to U.S., 1988; s. Roland and Marie Claire (Finet) N.; m. Pascale Veronique Volle, Jan. 10, 1988; 1 child, Sebastien Andy. Diplome d'Ingenieur Chimiste, Ecole Superieure de Chimie de Lyon, France, 1989; PhD in Organic Chemistry, U. N.C., 1993. Coop. rsch. asst. Rhone Poulenc Agrochemicals, La Dargoire Rsch. Ctr., Lyon, 1987-88; teaching asst. gen. chemistry and advanced synthetic organic lab. U. N.C., Chapel Hill, 1988-89, head teaching asst. gen. chemistry lab., 1989, grad. rsch. asst. chemistry dept., 1989-93; postdoctoral rsch. assoc. chemistry dept. Scripps Rsch. Inst., 1993-94; rsch. scientist II osteoarthritis/rumathoid arthritis rsch. Ciba Geigy corp., Summit, N.J., 1994—. Contbr. articles to profl. jours.; patentee in field. Dobbins fellow U. N.C., 1989, Rhone Poulenc Agrochems. fellow, 1990-92, Rhone Poulenc Rorer fellow, 1993-94. Mem. Am. Chem. Soc.

NANULA, SAVINO P., supermarket and convenience store company executive. Pres., chief operating officer Niagara Frontier Services Inc., Buffalo. Office: Tops Markets Inc 60 Dingens St PO Box 1027 Buffalo NY 14240 also: 60 Dingens St Buffalo NY 14206

NANUS, BURTON BENJAMIN, management educator, researcher; b. N.Y.C., Mar. 21, 1936; s. Max and Mollie (Rothstein) N.; m. Marlene Guttman, June 30, 1969; 1 child, Leora. BSME, Stevens Inst. Tech., 1957; MS in Indsl. Mgmt., MIT, 1959; DBA, U. So. Calif., 1967. Research asst. MIT, Cambridge, 1957-59; mgr. advanced edn. techniques Sperry Rand Univac, N.Y.C., 1959-61; tng. dir. Ops. Research Inc., Santa Monica, Calif., 1962; sr. tech. advisor to mgmt. System Devel. Group, Santa Monica, 1962-

67; pres. Planning Tech., Inc., Los Angeles, 1967-69; prof. mgmt. U. So. Calif., Los Angeles, 1969-94, dir. Ctr. for Futures Research, 1971-87; dir. of rsch. USC Leadership Inst., 1990-94; cons. Am. Inst. CPA's, N.Y.C., 1982-85, Nat. Gov's. Conf., Nashville, 1984, AT&T, Continental Airlines, Honeywell, TRW, Monsanto, others. Co-author: Management Games: A New Technique of Executive Development, 1961, The Social Implications of the Use of Computers Across National Boundaries, 1973, The Emerging Network Marketplace, 1981, Leaders: The Strategies for Taking Charge, 1985; The Leader's Edge: Seven Keys to Leadership in a Turbulent World, 1989, Visionary Leadership, 1992; mem. editorial bd. Jours. Indsl. Engring., 1963-68, Jour. Systems Mgmt., 1967-75, New Mgmt., 1982-87, Futures Rsch. Quarterly, 1985—, Tech. Forecasting and Social Change jour., 1986—. Cons. nat., state and local govt. adv. activities, 1972-82; bd. dirs. Los Angeles Pvt. Industry Council, 1986. Recipient Disting. Contbns. to Planning award So. Calif. Corp. Planners Assn., 1980, Commerce Assocs. award U. So. Calif., 1980, Assn. Systems Mgmt. award, 1972, Am. Inst. Indsl. Engrs. award, 1968. Mem. World Future Soc., Tau Beta Pi. Avocations: tennis, swimming. Office: U So Calif University Park Los Angeles CA 90007

NANZ, ROBERT HAMILTON, petroleum consultant; b. Shelbyville, Ky., Sept. 14, 1923; s. Robert Hamilton and Willie Virginia (O'Brien) N.; m. Norma Lee Peters, Dec. 21, 1944; children—Robert H., Loren P. B.A. in Geology, Miami U., Oxford, Ohio, 1944; Ph.D., U. Chgo., 1952. With Shell Oil Co., 1947-83; exploration mgr. Shell Oil Co., Denver, 1964-66; exploration mgr. Pacific Coast area Shell Oil Co., Los Angeles, 1966-67; dir. exploration research Shell Oil Co., Houston, 1959-64, v.p. exploration and prodn. research center, 1967-70; v.p. exploration Shell Oil Co., N.Y.C., Houston, 1970-75; v.p. Western exploration and prodn. ops. Shell Oil Co., Houston, 1975-81, v.p. tech., 1982-83. Fellow Geol. Soc. Am.; mem. Am. Petroleum Inst. (past chmn. gen. com. exploration affairs, chmn. public lands task force), Am. Assn. Petroleum Geologists (select com. on OCS). Presbyterian. Clubs: Lakeside Country (Houston); Dearborn Country (Ind.). Home: 10102 Briar Dr Houston TX 77042-1209

NAPADENSKY, HYLA SARANE, engineering consultant; b. Chgo., Nov. 12, 1929; d. Morris and Minnie (Litz) Siegel; m. Arnaldo I. Napadensky; children: Lita, Yafa. BS in Math., U. Chgo., MS in Math. Design analysis engineer Internat. Harvester Co., Chgo., 1952-57; dir. rsch. Ill. Inst. Tech. Rsch. Inst., Chgo., 1957-88; v.p. Napadensky Energetics Inc., Evanston, Ill., 1988-94; engring. cons., Lutsen, Minn., 1994—. Contbr. numerous articles to profl. jours. Bd. overseers Armour Coll. Engring. Ill. Inst. Tech., 1988-93. Mem. NAE, Combustion Inst., Sigma Xi. Home and Office: HC 3 Box 458 Lutsen MN 55612-9705

NAPARSTEK, ARTHUR J., social work educator; b. N.Y.C., June 1, 1938; s. Abe and Clara (Meltzer) N.; m. Belleruth Krepon, Sept. 5, 1965; children: Aaron, Keila, Abram. BS, Ill. Wesleyan U., Bloomington, 1960; MSW, NYU, 1962; PhD, Brandeis U., 1972. Sr. health educator USPHS, Chgo., 1962-65; dir. Urban Devel. Inst. Purdue U., Hammond, Ind., 1965-69; dir. rsch. Cath. U., Nat. Ctr. Ethnic Affairs, Washington, 1972-76; dir., prof. Washington Pub. Affairs Ctr. U. So. Calif., Washington, 1976-83; dean, prof. Mandel Sch. Applied Social Sci., Case Western Res. U., Cleve., 1983-88, prof. social work, 1988—; pres. Premier Indsl. Found., Cleve., 1987-89, cons. 1989—. Author: Neighborhood Networks, 1982, Community Support, 1982; author legislation for city govt., 1976-78. Mem. White Ho. Commn. on Neighborhoods, Washington, 1979-80. Lt. PHS, 1962-65. Democrat. Jewish. Office: Case Western Res U Mandel Sch Applied Social Scis Cleveland OH 44106

NAPIER, JOHN, set designer; b. London, England, Mar. 1, 1944; s. James Edward Thomas and Florence (Godbold) N; m. Andreane Neofitou (div.); m. Donna King; children: Julian, Elise, James. Assoc. designer Royal Shakespeare Co., London, England. stage work includes: (with the RSC) Macbeth, The Comedy of Errors, King Lear, Once in a Lifetime, Nicholas Nickleby (Tony award), Hedda Gabler, Peter Pan, Mother Courage, (with the Royal National Theatre) Equus, Trelawny of the Wells, (operas) Lohengrin, Macbeth, Idomeneo, The Devils, (musical theater) Cats (Tony award), Starlight Express (Tony award), Miss Saigon, Les Misérables (Tony award), Sunset Boulevard (Tony award); film work includes: Captain EO, Hook. Office: ML Representaion, 194 Old Brompton Rd, London SW5 0AS, England*

NAPIER, JOHN LIGHT, lawyer; b. Blenheim, S.C., May 16, 1947; s. John Light and Miriam (Keys) N.; m. Pamela Ann Caughman, June 12, 1971; 1 child, Page. A.B., Davidson (N.C.) Coll., 1969; J.D., U. S.C., 1972. Bar: S.C. 1972, U.S. Dist. Ct. 1972, U.S. Ct. Appeals 1975, U.S. Tax Ct. 1975, U.S. Supreme Ct. 1978, D.C. 1983, U.S. Ct. Fed. Claims 1987. U.S. senatorial counsel and asst., 1972-78; atty. Goldberg, Cottingham Easterling & Napier, P.A., Bennettsville, S.C., 1978-80, 83-84; mem. 97th Congress 6th Dist. S.C., mem. agr. com., asst. whip, mem. vets. affairs com., 1981-83; ptnr. Napier & Jennings, Bennettsville, S.C., 1984-86; judge U.S. Ct. Fed. Claims, Washington, 1986-89; ptnr. McNair Law Firm, P.A., Washington and Columbia, S.C., 1989—; mem. Commn. on Grievance and Discipline, S.C. Supreme Ct., 1984-86; chmn. fee dispute panel 4th Jud. Cir. S.C., 1984-86; nat. adv. coun. U.S. Ct. Fed. Claims, 1989—; pvt. judge The Pvt. Adjudication Ctr., Inc., Duke U., 1992; outside spl. counsel U.S. House Reps. House Adminstrn. Com., 1992. Active local United Way, Boy Scouts Am.; pres. Marlborough Hist. Soc., 1978-80. Served as officer USAR, 1969-77. Recipient Disting. Service award Marlboro County Jaycees, 1980. Mem. ABA, S.C. Bar Assn., Marlboro County Bar Assn., D.C. Bar Assn. Republican. Presbyterian. Office: McNair Law Firm Madison Office Bldg 1155 15th St NW Ste 400 Washington DC 20005 also: NCNB Tower Columbia SC 29211

NAPLES, RONALD JAMES, manufacturing company executive; b. Passaic, N.J., Sept. 10, 1945; s. James V. and Lee A. N.; B.S., U.S. Mil. Acad., 1967; M.A., Fletcher Sch. Law and Diplomacy, 1972; M.B.A. with distinction (Walter Heller fellow), Harvard U., 1974; m. Suzanne Lorraine Shoudy, June 17, 1967; children—Regen Jeffrey, Marcus Jamison, Tiffany Marie. Assoc. in corp. fin. Loeb Rhoades Co., 1974; White House fellow, asst. to counselor to Pres., 1974-75; exec. dir. Presdl. Task Force on Energy, Washington, 1975-76; v.p. internat. Hunt Mfg. Co., Phila., 1976, exec. v.p. 1980-81, vice chmn., pres., chief exec. officer, 1981-86, chmn., chief exec. officer, 1987—, also dir.; pres. Hunt Internat. Co., 1977-82. Mem. regional commn. Pres.'s Com. on White House Fellows, 1980—, Fletcher Sch. Law and Diplomacy Adv. Bd., 1982—; chmn./ vice chmn. Greater Phila. 1st Corp., Free Libr. of Phila. Fedn.; bd. dirs. Univ. of the Arts, Pa.-Milw. Ballet, Free Library Phila., Fgn. Policy Research Inst., Childrens Hosp., Phila., Phila. Mus. of Art, Eisenhower Exchange fellowships. Served with U.S. Army, 1967-71. Decorated Bronze Star with oak leaf cluster, Army Commendation medal with oak leaf cluster, Air medal (U.S.); Cross of Gallantry (Vietnam); recipient Mil. Order World Wars award U.S. Mil. Acad., 1967, Phila. Inc. Community Leadership award, 1990; named Outstanding Young Man Am., U.S. Jaycees, 1977, Chief Exec. Officer of decade bus. equipment, 1989-90. Mem. White House Fellows Assn., Young Pres.'s Orgn., Assn. Grad. U.S. Mil. Acad., Harvard Bus. Sch. Alumni Assn. Club: Racquet, Harvard Bus. Sch. (Phila.). Office: Hunt Mfg Co 230 S Broad St Philadelphia PA 19102-3816*

NAPODANO, RUDOLPH JOSEPH, internist, medical educator; b. Rochester, N.Y., Oct. 16, 1933. B.A., U. Buffalo, 1955; M.D., SUNY-HSC, Syracuse, 1959. Diplomate Am. Bd. Internal Medicine, Am. Bd. Cardiovascular Diseases. Intern, asst. resident Highland Hosp., Rochester, 1959-61; fellow in cardiology SUNY-Upstate, Syracuse, 1961-62; chief resident in medicine Highland Hosp., 1962-63; spl. trainee in cardiology U. Rochester, 1968, clin. asst. prof. medicine, 1969-70, asst. prof. medicine, 1970-72, assoc. prof., 1972-79, prof., 1979-93, prof. emeritus, 1993—; with U. Rochester Sch. Medicine and Dentistry, 1970-93; retired 1993; prof. medicine SUNY, Syracuse, N.Y., 1994—. Fellow ACP, Am. Coll. Cardiology; mem. AAAS, Soc. Gen. Internal Medicine, Rochester Acad. Medicine (trustee 1976—, pres. 1980-81), Alpha Omega Alpha.

NAPOLES, VERONICA KLEEMAN, graphic designer, consultant; b. N.Y.C., July 9, 1951; d. Florencio Andres and Elena (Colomar) N.; m. Michael Jeffrey Kleeman, Sept. 5, 1985; 1 child, Samuel Andres. BA, U. Miami, 1972; BArch, U. Calif., Berkeley, 1979. Account supr. Marsh &

McLennan, Miami, Fla., 1974-76; designer Mus. of Anthropology, San Francisco, 1977-79; project dir. Landor & Assocs., San Francisco, 1979-81; prin. Communications Planning, Kentfield, Calif., 1981—; bd. dirs. Mind Fitness, Mill Valley, Calif., Main Arts Coun., Mykytyn Cons. Group; instr. U. Calif.-Berkeley, San Francisco, 1983—, Sonoma State U., Santa Rosa, Calif., 1983-84; tchr. Dynamic Graphics Ednl. Found., San Francisco. Author: Corporate Identity Design, 1987; exhibited at San Francisco Airport, 1992. Bd. dirs. Marin Arts Coun. Recipient Bay Area Hispanic Bus. Achiever award, 1988, Design award PRINT, 1988, Excellence award Am. Corp. Identity, 1989, 90, 91, 92, 93, Excellence award N.Y. Art Dirs. Show, 1989; finalist Sundance Inst., 1991. Mem. Am. Inst. Graphic Arts, Women in Communications. Avocations: painting, writing. Office: Communications Planning 100 Upper Briar Rd San Rafael CA 94904-2824

NAPOLIELLO, MICHAEL JOHN, psychiatrist; b. Feb. 14, 1942; s. Frank J. and Anne M. (Palazzo) N. BS, Fordham U., 1962; MD, NYU, 1966; MBA, Xavier U. Grad. Sch. of Bus., 1980. Diplomate Am. Bd. Psychiatry and Neurology. Attending psychiatrist Bernalillo County Med. Ctr., Albuquerque, 1973-74; dir. behavioral medicine U. N.Mex. Sch. of Medicine, Albuquerque, 1973-74; attending psychiatrist Mary Hitchcock Meml. Hosp., Hanover, N.H., 1974-76; assoc. group dir. Merrell Nat. Labs., Cin., 1976-79; assoc. group dir. clin. pharm. Merrell-Nat. Labs., Cin., 1979-84; dir. clin. investigation Merrell-Dow Research Inst., Cin., 1979-84; sr. dir. Bristol-Myers Internat. Group, N.Y.C., 1984-85; dir. med. & sci. affairs, 1986, v.p. med. & sci. affairs, 1986-90; v.p., cen. nervous system clin. planning Bristol-Myers Squibb, Princeton, N.J., 1990-91; sr. dir. clin. rsch. and prodn. devel. Bristol-Myers Squibb, Tokyo, Japan, 1991-93; exec. dir. internat. clin. devel. Bristol-Myers Squibb, Tokyo, 1993-94, v.p. worldwide med. affairs, 1994—; clin. asst. prof. psychiatry Cornell U. Med. Coll., N.Y.C., 1985—; asst. clin. prof. U. Cin. Coll. Medicine, 1976-80, assoc. prof., 1980-84; lectr. in field. Contbr. over 30 articles to profl. med. jours. Maj. U.S. Army, 1970-73. Recipient Physicians Recognition award AMA, 1969, 72, 76, 79, 82, 85, 88, 91, 94. Mem. Am. Psychiat. Assn., Am. Coll. Neuropsychopharmacology. Roman Catholic. Avocations: foreign languages, creative writing, basketball. Home: 27 Richard Ct Princeton NJ 08540-4000 Office: Bristol-Myers Squibb PO Box 4000 Princeton NJ 08543-4000

NAPOLITANO, GRACE F., state legislator; b. Brownsville, Tex., Dec. 4, 1936; d. Miguel and Maria Alicia Ledezma Flores; m. Frank Napolitano, 1982; 1 child, Yolando M., Fred Musquiz Jr., Edward M., Michael M., Cynthia M. Student, Cerritos Coll., L.A. Trade Tech, Tec Southwest Coll. Mem. Calif. Assembly, 1993—. Councilwoman City of Norwalk, Calif. 1986-92, mayor, 1989-90; active Cmty. Family Guidance. Mem. Cerritos Coll. Found., Lions Club. Democrat. Roman Catholic. Home: 12946 E Belcher St Norwalk CA 90650 Office: Calif Assembly State Capitol Sacramento CA 95814 also: PO Box 942849 Sacramento CA 94249-0001

NAPOLITANO, LEONARD MICHAEL, anatomist, university administrator; b. Oakland, Calif., Jan. 8, 1930; s. Filippo Michael and Angela (De Fiore) N.; m. Jane M. Winer, July 9, 1955; children—Leonard M., Janet Ann, Nancy Angela. B.S., Santa Clara U., 1951; M.S., St. Louis U., 1954, Ph.D., 1956. Instr. anatomy Cornell Med. Coll., N.Y.C., 1956-58; instr. U. Pitts. Sch. Med., 1958-59, asst. prof., 1959-64; asso. prof. U. N.Mex., 1964-68; prof. dept. anatomy U. N.Mex. (Sch. Medicine), 1968—, acting chmn. dept., 1971-72, dean pro tem, 1972-73, dean, 1973—, interim v.p. for health scis., 1976—; dir. U. N.Mex. (Med. Center); dean U. N.Mex. (Sch. Medicine), 1977—; Mem. NIH Rsch. Resource Coun., 1988-91. Contbr. articles on lipid research and ultra structure of cholesterol to profl. jours.; Asso. editor: Anatomical Record, 1968-74. Mem. Am. Assn. Anatomists, Am. Soc. Cell Biology, Electron Microscope Soc. Am., Albuquerque, Bernalillo county Med. Assn. (hon.), Assn. Am. Med. Colls. Council of Deans. Home: 2308 Calle De Panza NW Albuquerque NM 87104-3070 Office: Dean Sch of Medicine U of N Mex Health Sci Center Albuquerque NM 87131

NAPSKY, MARTIN BEN, insurance executive; b. Miami, Fla., June 17, 1938; s. Samuel Ben and Dorothy May N.; m. Carol Ann Rella, Sept. 26, 1978; children: David, Kimberly, Victoria, Bradley, Jason, Keith. BA, Houston (Tex.) U., 1957-61; LLB, Atlanta (Ga.) Law Sch., 1971-74. Ins. agent Continental Casualty Co., Chgo., 1961-70; v.p. Eastern Reg Brokerage, Miami, 1974-88, Western Reg Brokerage, San Diego, 1988—; pres. Fla. Bldg. Contractors, Miami, 1978—. Contbg. editor Wings mag., 1984. Chancellor Nu Beta Epsilon, Atlanta, 1973; mem. George Bush Inner Circle, Washington, 1992, Naders Raiders, Atlanta, 1973-74. Mem. Nat. Assn. Health Underwriters (Health Ins. Quality award 1983), Miami Assn. Health Underwriters, Millionaires Club, Presidents Inner Circle (pres. 1983-84). Republican. Jewish. Avocations: hunting, fishing. Home: 11789 Island Lakes Ln Boca Raton FL 33498-6811

NARAHASHI, TOSHIO, pharmacology educator; b. Fukuoka, Japan, Jan. 30, 1927; came to U.S., 1961; s. Asahachi and Itoko (Yamasaki) Ishii; m. Kyoko Narahashi, Apr. 21, 1956; children: Keiko, Taro. BS, U. Tokyo, 1948, PhD, 1960. Instr. U. Tokyo, 1951-65; research assoc. U. Chgo., 1961, asst. prof., 1962; assoc. prof. Duke U., Durham, N.C., 1962-63, 65-67, assoc. prof., 1967-69, prof., 1969-77, head pharmacology div., 1970-73, vice chmn. dept. physiology and pharmacology, 1973-75; prof., chmn. dept. pharmacology Northwestern U. Med. Sch., Chgo., 1977-94; Alfred Newton Richards prof. Med. Sch. Northwestern U., Chgo., Ill., 1983—; John Evans prof. Northwestern U., Evanston, Ill., 1986—; mem. pharmacology study sect. NIH, 1976-80; mem. rsch. rev. com. Chgo. Heart Assn., 1977-82, vice chmn. rsch. coun., 1986-87, chmn., 1988-90; mem. Nat. Environ. Health Scis. Coun., 1982-86; rev. com. Nat. Inst. Environ. Health Scis., 1991-95. Editor: Cellular Pharmacology of Insecticides and Pheromones, 1979, Cellular and Molecular Neurotoxicology, 1984, Insecticide Action: From Molecule to Organism, 1989; editor Ion Channels, 1988—; contbr. articles to profl. jours. Recipient Javits Neurosci. Investigator award NIH, 1986. Fellow AAAS; mem. Am. Soc. for Pharmacology and Exptl. Therapeutics, Am. Physiol. Soc., Soc for Neurosci., Biophys. Soc. (Cole award 1981), Soc. Toxicology (DuBois award 1988, Merit award 1991), Agrochem. Div. Am. Chem. Soc. (Burdick L. Jackson Internat. award 1989). Home: 175 E Delaware Pl Apt 7911 Chicago IL 60611-1732 Office: Northwestern U Med Sch Dept Mol Pharmaco Biol Chem 303 E Chicago Ave Chicago IL 60611-3008

NARASIMHAN, PADMA MANDYAM, physician; b. Bangalore, India, Mar. 19, 1947; came to U.S., 1976; d. Alasingracher Mandyam and Alamela Mandyam Narasimhan; m. Mandyam N. Venkatesh, Mar. 28, 1981 (div.) 1 child, Ravi. Student, Delhi U., New Delhi, 1964, MBBS, 1969; MD, Maulana Azad Med. Coll., New Delhi, 1970. Diplomate Am. Bd. Internal Medicine. Intern in internal medicine Flushing Hosp., N.Y.C., 1976-77; resident in internal medicine Luth. Med. Ctr., N.Y.C., 1977-79; fellow hematology, oncology Beth-Israel Med. Ctr., N.Y.C., 1979-81; asst. prof. King Drew Med. Ctr., L.A., 1983-87, Harbor UCLA, Torrance, 1987—. Mem. editorial bd. Jour. Internal Medicine, 1986—. Mem. ACP, Am. Soc. Clin. Oncology, So. Calif. Acad. Clin. Oncology. Hindu. Avocations: travel, reading, meeting people, music, walking. Home: 6604 Madeline Cove Dr Palos Verde CA 90275-4608 Office: Harbor UCLA 100 W Carson St Torrance CA 90509

NARASIMHAN, SUBHA, law educator; b. 1948. BS, U. London, 1970, MS, 1972; PhD, Stanford U., 1975; JD, Columbia U., 1980. N.Y. 1981. Law clk. to Hon. Louis H. Polak U.S. Dist. Ct. (ea. dist.), Pa., 1980-81; asst. prof. Columbia U., 1981-86, assoc. prof., 1986-87, prof. U., 1987—. Office: Columbia U Sch Law 435 W 116th St New York NY 10027-7201

NARATH, ALBERT, laboratory administrator; b. Berlin, Mar. 5, 1933; came to U.S., 1947; s. Albert Narath and Johanna Agnes Anne (Bruggeman) Bruckmann; m. Worth Haines Scattergood (div.); children: Tanya, Lise, Yvette; m. Barbara Dean Camp (div. 1983); 1 child, Albert; m. Shanna S. Lindeman. BS in Chemistry, U. Cin., 1955; PhD in Phys. Chemistry, U. Calif., Berkeley, 1959. Mem. tech. staff, mgr. phys. sci. Sandia Nat. Labs., Albuquerque, 1959-68, dir. solid state sci., 1968-71, mng. dir. phys. sci., 1971-73, v.p. rsch., 1973-82, exec. v.p. rsch. and adv. weapons sys., 1982-84, pres., 1989—. Contbr. sci. articles to profl. jours. Fellow AAAS, Am. Phys. Soc. (George E. Pake prize 1991); mem. NAE. Office: Sandia Nat Labs MS 0101 PO Box 5800 Albuquerque NM 87185-0101

NARAYAN, K(RISHNAMURTHI) ANANTH, biochemist; b. Secunderabad, India, Oct. 1, 1930; came to U.S., 1954, naturalized, 1970; s. Ananthnarayan and Rukmani (Sreenivasan) Krishnamurthi; m. Suhasini Naik, Sept. 3, 1961; children—Krishnamurthi, Sheila. B.S. in Chemistry, Christian Coll., India, 1949; M.S. in Chem.Tech., Osmania U., India, 1951; Ph.D. in Food Tech., U. Ill., 1957. Research assoc. Wash. State U., Pullman, 1957-61; asst. prof. U. Ill., Urbana, 1962-71; research biochemist U.S. Army Natick Research and Devel. Ctr., Mass., 1971—. Contbr. chpts. to books. Grantee NIH, 1966-70, Am. Cancer Soc., 1968-70, Am. Heart Assn., 1967-71. Mem. Am. Oil Chemists Soc., Am. Inst. Nutrition, N.Y. Acad. Scis., Biochem. Soc., Soc. Exptl. Biologists. Hindu. Avocations: photography; woodworking; jogging. Home: 84 Indian Head Rd Framingham MA 01701-7920 Office: US Army R and D Ctr SusD/RSD/AFB Natick MA 01760-5020

NARAYAN, RAMESH, astronomy educator; b. Bombay, India, Sept. 25, 1950; came to U.S., 1983; s. G.N. and Rajalakshmi (Sankaran) Ramachandran; m. G.V. Vani, June 6, 1977. BS in Physics, Madras U., 1971; MS in Physics, Bangalore U., 1973, PhD in Physics, 1979. Rsch. scientist Raman Rsch. Inst., Bangalore, India, 1978-83; postdoctoral fellow Calif. Inst. Tech., 1983-84, sr. rsch. fellow, 1984-85; assoc. prof. U. Ariz., Tucson, 1985-90, prof. astronomy, 1990-91; prof. astronomy Harvard U., Cambridge, Mass., 1991—; sr. astronomer Smithsonian Astrophys. Obs., Cambridge, 1991—. Contbr. articles to profl. jours. Named NSF Presdl. Young Investigator, 1989. Mem. AAAS, Am. Astronomical Soc., Internat. Astronomical Union, Astromonical Soc. India. Achievements include research in the general area of theoretical astrophysics, specializing in accretion disks, collapsed stars, gravitational lenses, hydrodynamics, image processing and scintillation. Office: Harvard-Smithsonian Ctr Astrophysics 60 Garden St # 51 Cambridge MA 02138-1596

NARAYANAMURTI, VENKATESH, research administrator; b. Bangalore, Karnataka, India, Sept. 9, 1939; came to U.S., 1961; s. Duraiswami and Janaki (Subramaniam) m. Jayalakshmi Krishnayya, Aug. 23, 1961; children: Arjun, Ranjini, Krishna. BSc, MSc, St. Stephen's Coll., Delhi, India, 1958; PhD, Cornell U., 1965. Instr., rsch. assoc. Cornell U., Ithaca, N.Y., 1965-68; mem. tech. staff AT&T Bell Labs., Murray Hill, N.J., 1968-76, dept.head, 1976-81, dir., 1981-87; v.p. rsch. Sandia Nat. Labs., Albuquerque, 1987-92; dean engring. U. Calif., Santa Barbara, 1992—; chmn. adv. bd. Coll. of Elec. Engring., Cornell U., 1989-90, sci. bd. and regional coun. Santa Fe Inst., 1987-90, microelectric bd., Jet Propulsion Lab., Pasadena, Calif., 1988-90, sci. bd. Stanford Synchroton Lab., Stanford, Calif., 1989-92; mem. IUPAP Comm. on Physics for Devel.; engring. directrorate adv. bd. NSF, 1992—; Fermi award com. Dept. of Energy, 1992—; chair Dept. of Energy Inertial Confinement Fusion Adv. Com., 1992—. Author more than 100 publs.; patentee in field. Fellow IEEE, AAAS, Am. Phys. Soc., Indian Acad. Scis.; mem. NAE, Royal Swedish Acad. Engring. Scis. (fgn.). Avocations: long distance running, squash. Office: U Calif Engring Santa Barbara CA 93106

NARDELLI-OLKOWSKA, KRYSTYNA MARIA, ophthalmologist, educator; b. Myslowice, Poland, June 23, 1939; d. Walerian and Stefania (Jasinska) Nardelli; m. Zbigniew L. Olkowski, Apr. 15, 1963. M.D., Silesian U. Med. Sch., 1964. Diplomate: Am. Bd. Ophthalmology; 1983. Intern, resident ophthalmology Emory U. Med. Sch., Atlanta, 1977-80; fellow in glaucoma Emory U. Med. Sch., 1980-81; asst. prof. dept. ophthalmology Emory U. Med. Sch., Atlanta, 1972—; pvt. practice ophthalmology, 1982—. Postdoctoral fellow Fight for Sight, 1974-75. Mem. Am. Soc. Research in Ophthalmology, Royal Micros. Soc. (Eng.). Home: Villa Sadyba 1018 Mcconnell Dr Decatur GA 30033-3402 Office: 6139 Oakbrook Pky # A Norcross GA 30093-1716

NARDELLO, ROBERT A., medical software company executive; b. Camden, N.J., June 12, 1937; s. Anthony S. and Mary (Colucci) N.; m. Elaine M. Bourgeois, Nov. 19, 1958; children: Debra, Robert M. (dec.), Lorraine, Thomas. Degree in Applied Math., La Salle U., 1970, MBA in Fin., 1978. Mgr. clin. systems Smith Kline & French Labs., Phila., 1970-79, dir. R & D info. systems, 1979-81; dir. corp. EDP Smith Kline Beckman Corp., Phila., 1981-86; v.p. info. svcs. Smith Kline & French, Phila., 1986-88; chief info. officer U.S. Healthcare, Blue Bell, Pa., 1988-90, sr. v.p., 1990-92; pres. Healthcare Data Interchange, Blue Bell, 1992—. Avocations: squash, cycling, recreational computers. Home: 26 Iris Ct Mount Laurel NJ 08054-2520 Office: U S Healthcare 980 Jolly Rd Blue Bell PA 19422-1957

NARDINO, GARY, television and motion picture producer; b. Garfield, N.J., Aug. 26, 1935; s. Louis and Phyllis (Iacovino) N.; m. Florence Peluso, May 1, 1965; children: Caroline, Gary Charles Frank, Teresa. B.S.B.A., Seton Hall U., 1957, LL.D. (hon.), 1983. Agt. William Morris Agy., Ashley Famous Agy., 1959-76; pres. TV prodn. div. Paramount Pictures Corp., Hollywood, Calif., 1977-83; pres. Gary Nardino Prodns., L.A., 1983-89; chmn., chief exec. officer Orion TV Entertainment, L.A., 1989-91, Lorimar TV, Gary Nardino Prodn., Burbank, Calif., 1991—, Warner Bros., 1993—; now exec. prod. Warner Bros. Television. Exec. producer film Star Trek III; producer film Fire with Fire; producer TV series Brothers (Showtime Cable), Hard Knocks (Showtime Cable), Marblehead Manor (1st run synd.), Time Trax (1st run synd. 2nd yr.). Served to 1st lt. inf. U.S. Army, 1957-59. Named Man of Yr., WAIF, Inc., 1983, TV Showman of Yr., Publicist Guild of Am., 1985; recipient Sword of Truth award for Winds of War B'naie B'rith, 1982. Mem. Acad. TV Arts and Scis., Hollywood Radio and TV Soc. (pres. 1981-83), Caucus of Producers, Writers & Dirs., WAIF (nat. chmn.), Alpha Kappa Psi. Roman Catholic. Clubs: N.Y. Athletic; Burning Tree Country (Greenwich, Conn.); Bel Air Country (Los Angeles). Office: Warner Bros TV Producers Bldg 8 #109 300 Television Plz Burbank CA 91505

NARDI RIDDLE, CLARINE, association administrator, judge; b. Clinton, Ind., Apr. 23, 1949; d. Frank Jr. and Alice (Mattioda) Nardi; m. Mark Alan Riddle, Aug. 15, 1971; children: Carl Nardi, Julia Nardi. AB, Ind. U., 1971, JD, 1974; LHD (hon.), St. Joseph Coll., 1991. Bar: Ind. 1974, Conn. 1979, U.S. Dist. Ct. Ind. 1974, Fed. Dist. Ct. Conn. 1980, U.S. Ct. Appeals (2d cir.) 1986, U.S. Ct. Appeals (D.C. cir.) 1994, U.S. Supreme Ct. 1980. Staff atty. Ind. Legis. Svc. Agy., Indpls., 1974-78, legal counsel, 1978-79; dep. corp. counsel City of New Haven, 1980-83; counsel to atty. gen. State of Conn., Hartford, 1983-86, dep. atty. gen., 1986-89, acting atty. gen., 1989, atty. gen., 1989-91; judge Superior Ct. State of Conn., 1991-93; sr. v.p. for govtl. affairs, gen. counsel Nat. Multi-Housing Coun., Nat. Apartment Assn., 1995—; asst. counsel state majority Conn. Gen. Assembly, Hartford, 1979, legal rsch. asst. to prof. Yale U., New Haven, 1979; legal counsel com. on law revision Indpls. State Bar Assn., 1979; mem. Chief Justice's Task Force on Gender Bias, Hartford, 1988-90; mem. ethics and values com. Ind. Sector, Washington, 1988-90. Bd. visitors Ind. U., Bloomington, 1974-92; mem. Gov's Missing Children Com., Hartford, Conn. Child Support Guidelines Com., Gov.'s Task Force on Justice for Abused Children, Hartford, 1988-90. Named Conn. History Maker Women's Bur. & Permanent Commn. on Status of Women, U.S. Dept. Labor, 1989; recipient Citizen award Nat. Task Force on Children's Constl. Rights. Mem. ABA, Conn. Bar Assn. (chair com. on gender bias, Citation of Merit women and law sect. 1989), Nat. assn. Attys. Gen. (chair charitable trusts and solicitation 1988-90), New Haven Neighborhood Music Sch. (bd. dirs.), Am. Arbitration Assn. (arbitration panel 1994). Democrat. Presbyterian.

NARDULLI, PETER F., political science educator; b. Chgo., May 20, 1947; m. Ann Marie Wannemacher. BA, No. Ill. U., 1969; MA, Northwestern U., 1972, JD, 1973, PhD, 1975. Asst. prof. Inst. Pub. Affairs and Dept. Political Sci. U. Ill., Urbana, 1975-80, assoc. prof. Inst. Pub. Affairs and Dept. Political Sci., 1980-85, vis. prof. Coll. of Law, 1985-86, acting dir. Inst. Govt. and Pub. Affairs, 1985-86, prof. Inst. Govt. Pub. Affairs and Dept. Political Sci., 1985—, dir. grad. studies Dept. Political Sci., 1987-91, dept. head and prof. Dept. Political Sci., 1992—. Co-author: (books) The Contours of Justice: Communities and their Courts, 1987, The Tenor of Justice: Felony Courts & The Guilty Plea Process, 1988, The Constitution ans American Political Development: An Institutional Perspective, 1991, The Craft of Justice, 1992. Office: U Ill-Dept Political Sci 361 Lincoln Hall 702 S Wright St Urbana IL 61801

NARENDRA, KUMPATI SUBRAHMANYA, electrical engineering educator, association administrator; b. Madras, India, Apr. 14, 1933; came to U.S., 1954, naturalized, 1974; s. Subrahmanya and Sarada (Alladi) Kumpati; m. Barbara Lamb, Nov. 3, 1961. BEE with honors, U. Madras, 1954; MS, Harvard U., 1955, PhD, 1959; MA (hon.), Yale U., 1968. Lectr., postdoctoral asst. Harvard U., Cambridge, Mass., 1959-61, asst. prof., 1961-65; assoc. prof. Yale U., New Haven, Conn., 1965-68, prof. elec. engring., 1968—, chmn. dept. elec. engring., 1984-87, dir. Neuroengring. and Neurosci. Ctr., 1995—; cons. to comml. firms, 1961—; dir. Ctr. for Systems Sci., 1980—; disting. vis. sci. Jet Propulsion Lab., 1994—; honorary vis. prof. Anna Univ., Madras, India, 1993; mem. adv. bd. Inst. Advanced Engring., Korea; mem. sci. adv. bd. Ctr. for Engring. Sys. Advanced Rsch. Oakridge Nation Lab. Author: Frequency Domain Criteria For Absolute Stability, 1973, Stable Adaptive Systems, 1989, Learning Automata: An Introduction, 1989; editor: Applications of Adaptive Control, 1980, Adaptive and Learning Systems: Theory and Applications, 1987, Advances in Adaptive Control, 1991; editor issue on learning automata Jour. Cybernetics and Info. Sci., vol. I, 1977. Recipient Edn. award Am. Automatic Control Coun., 1990, Leadership award Neural Network Soc., 1994, Hendrik W. Bode Prize/Lectr. award Control Sys. Soc., 1995. Fellow AAAS, Inst. Elec. Engrs. (U.K.), IEEE (Franklin V. Taylor award 1973, George S. Axelby award, 1988, Outstanding Paper of neural network coun. 1991); mem. Sigma Xi. Home: 35 Old Mill Rd Woodbridge CT 06525-1523 Office: Yale U Ctr Systems Sci PO Box 2157 New Haven CT 06520-2157

NARIGAN, HAROLD W., manufacturing company executive; b. Buffalo, Feb. 10, 1925; s. Harold Peter and Lillian (Beale) N.; m. Marjorie Elaine Kalb; 1 child, Beverly Ann. BS in Aeronautical Engring., Purdue U., 1948. Mgr. plastics mfg. engring. conn. products div. AMP, Inc., Harrisburg, Pa., 1964-65, mgr. engring. plastic products div., 1965-69, div. mgr. plastic products div., 1969-74, div. mgr. wiring products div., 1974-78, v.p. gen. products group, 1978-85, v.p. automachine systems group, 1985-89, v.p. corp. quality assurance, 1989-92; pres. Pa. Quality Leadership Found., Inc., Harrisburg, 1992—. Served with USNR, 1943-45. Mem. Soc. Plastic Engrs., Assn. for Quality and Participation, Am. Soc. Quality Control. Avocations: water sports, photography, reading. Home: 1255 Garrison Dr York PA 17404-1267 Office: PO Box 4129 Harrisburg PA 17111-0129

NARIN, STEPHEN B., lawyer; b. Phila., Nov. 23, 1929; s. Bernard E. and Anne (Lipsius) N.; m. Sandra C. Goldberg, Sept. 29, 1963; children: Howard Glen, Brenda Teri. B.S., Temple U., 1951, LL.B. 1953; LL.M. in Taxation, NYU, 1960. Bar: Pa. 1954, U.S. Supreme Ct. 1958; CPA, Pa. Dep. atty. gen. Commonwealth of Pa., Harrisburg, 1955-57; instr. acctg. Temple U., Phila., 1954-55; lectr. in law grad. legal studies div. Temple U. Sch. Law, Phila., 1976-85; lectr. Practicing Law Inst., 1967-69; ptnr. Narin & Chait, Phila., 1970-89, Predecessor Ptnrships., Phila., 1955-70; v.p., gen. counsel Travelco Assocs., Phila., 1989-90; of counsel Krekstein, Wolfson & Krekstein, Phila., 1989-92; v.p., gen. counsel Eagle Nat. Bank, 1990-91; counsel Schachtel, Gerstley, Levine & Koplin, Phila., 1993—; mem. Phila. County Bd. Law Examiners, 1961-65. Mem. nat. governing council Am. Jewish Congress, 1963-84, nat. exec. com., 1978-84, pres. Greater Phila. council, 1965-67; mem. Nat. Commn. on Law and Social Action, 1964-84. Mem. ABA, Am. Judicature Soc., Am. Inst. CPA's, Pa. Inst. CPA's, Pa. Bar Assn., Phila. Bar Assn., Phi Alpha Delta. Office: Schachtel Gerstley et al 4 Penn Center Plz Philadelphia PA 19103-2514

NARITA, HIRO, cinematographer; b. Seoul, Republic of Korea, June 26, 1941; came to Japan, 1945, came to U.S., 1957; s. Masao Morikawa and Masako (Kojima) Morikawa ; m. Barbara Parker, Sept. 9, 1971. BFA in Design, San Francisco Art Inst., 1964. lectr. Mill Valley Film Festival, 1984, Hawaii Internat. Film Festival, 1984. Dir. photography for films: Farewell to Manzanar, 1976 (Emmy nomination 1976), Never Cry Wolf, 1983 (best cinematography award 1983), Solomon Northrup's Odyssey, 1984, Go Tell It on the Mountain, 1985, Amerika, 1987, Honey, I Shrunk the Kids, 1989, The Rocketeer, 1991, Star Trek VI, 1992, Hocus Pocus, 1993, White Fang II, 1994. Served with U.S Army, 1964-66. Mem. Internat. Photographers Guild, Am. Soc. Cinematographers, Acad. Motion Picture Arts and Scis.

NARITA, YUTAKA, advertising executive; b. Japan, Sept. 19, 1929; s. Kiyoomi and Some Narita; m. Michi Narita; children: Chiaki, Akira. BA in Law, U. Tokyo, 1953. Exec. dir. Dentsu Inc., Tokyo, 1981-83, mng. dir. 1983-89, sr. mng. dir., 1989-93, pres., 1993—. Office: Dentsu Inc, 1-11 Tsukiji Chuo-ku, Tokyo 104, Japan

NARKIS, ROBERT JOSEPH, bank executive, lawyer; b. Nashua, N.H., May 23, 1934; s. Joseph John and Stephanie (Kamienecki) N.; m. Mary Ellen Gardner Morris, Oct. 26, 1962 (div. 1974); 1 child Sally Gardner; m. JoAnn Georgetson, Feb. 1975. BA cum laude, U. N.H., 1956; LLB, Yale U., 1961. Sr. ptnr. Gager, Henry and Narkis, Waterbury, Conn., 1961-89; chmn., chief exec. officer Centerbank, Waterbury, Conn., 1989—. Pres., chmn. exec. com. Waterbury Hosp., Conn., 1973-75; bd. dirs. Conn. Bar Assn., Hartford, 1985; trustee Mattatuck Hist. Soc., Waterbury, 1975-78, Waterbury Found., 1984-89, Post Coll., 1984-90, Quinnipiac Coll., Hamden, 1992—. Mem. ABA, Conn. Bar Assn., Supreme Ct. USA Bar, Yale Law Sch. Assn. (exec. com. 1989—), Metropolitan Club, Waterbury Country Club. Avocations: antique collecting, golf, foreign travel, sailing. Home: Charcoal Woods PO Box 385 Middlebury CT 06762-0385 Office: Centerbank 60 N Main St Waterbury CT 06702-1497

NARODICK, SALLY G., corporate executive; b. Clinton, Mass., June 26, 1945; d. Morris and Dorothy Gould; m. Kit G. Narodick, Apr. 11, 1970; children—Lisa, Philip. BA, Boston U., 1962; MA in Teaching, Columbia U., 1969; MBA, N.Y. U., 1973. Security analyst Paine Webber Jackson & Curtis, N.Y.C., 1971-73; security analyst Seattle-First Nat. Bank, 1973-75, mgr. asset-liability, 1975-79, mgr. loan rev. and exams., 1979-80, sr. v.p., controller, 1980-84, sr. v.p., dist. mgr., 1984-87; pres. Narodick, Ross & Assocs., Seattle, 1987-89; chief exec. officer Edmark Corp., Redmond, Wash., 1989—, also bd. dirs.; bd. dirs. Pacific Northwest Bank, Harbor Properties Inc., Wash. Energy Corp. Trustee Lakeside Sch., Penwest Corp., Seattle Found. Mem. Governor's Coun. Edn. Reform & Funding, Seattle C. of C. (treas. 1982-83, bd. dirs., chmn. 1990), Rainier Club (trustee, treas.), Columbia Tower Club. Office: Edmark Corp PO Box 3218 Redmond WA 98073-3218

NARRAMORE, RANDY EARL, protective services official; b. Fullerton, Calif., Oct. 16, 1948; s. Charles Earl and Geraldine (Peterson) N.; m. Marie Edith Seuss, Dec. 5, 1970; 1 child, Ben. AS, Grossmont Coll., El Cajon, Calif., 1973; BS, San Diego State U., 1976; student police adminstrn., FBI Nat. Acad., 1985. Chief detectives El Cajon (Calif.) Police Dept., 1970-88; chief of police Ridgecrest (Calif.) Police Dept., 1988—; instr. Police Sci. Grossmont Coll., El Cajon, Calif., 1975-88, Bakersfield (Calif.) Coll., 1988—. Bd. dirs. Coun. on Substance Abuse, Ridgecrest, Calif., 1988—. Mem. Kern County Police Chiefs' Assn., Calif. Chiefs of Police Assn., Internat. Chiefs Police, Police Officers Rsch. Assn. Calif., Footprinters. Republican. Home: 1219 N Mayflower Cir Ridgecrest CA 93555-5507

NARSAVAGE, GEORGIA ROBERTS, nursing educator, researcher; b. Pittston, Pa., Jan. 1, 1948; d. George H. Roberts and Betty (Smith) Lanphear; m. Peter P. Narsavage, Oct. 26, 1969; children: Peter A., Paul J., Marea L. BSN, U. Md., Washington DC, 1969; MSN, Coll. Misericordia, 1984; PhD in Nursing, U. Pa., Phila., 1990. RN, Pa.; cert. CPR instr. Staff nurse Mercy Hosp., Scranton, Pa., 1970-72; pvt. duty nursing Pa., 1972-79; pvt. duty nurse Community Med. Ctr., Scranton, Pa., 1979; clinical instr. Lackawanna County Vo-Tech Practical Nursing Program, Dunmore, Pa., 1979-82; clinical and theoretical instr. Mercy Hosp. Sch. of Nursing, Scranton, Pa., 1982-84; asst. prof. nursing Dept. of Nursing, U. Scranton, Pa., 1984-93; assoc. prof. U. Scranton Pa., 1993—, chmn. dept., 1991-94; dir. RN program Dept. of Nursing U. Scranton, Pa., 1990-92; cons. in field. Contbr. articles to profl. jours. Gifted program mentor Scranton Sch. Dist.; active in ch. and civic choirs. U. Scranton grantee, 1989, 91; Ea. Nursing Rsch. Soc. Am. Nurses Found. rsch. grantee, 1994. Mem. ANA, Am. Thoracic Soc./Am. Lung Assn., Pa. Nurses Assn. (bd. dirs., chmn. com., conv. del.), Lackawanna Nurses Assn. (bd. dirs., com. chmn., dist. pres.), Nat. League for Nursing, Coun. Nursing Informatics (chair nominating com. 1993-95), Pa. League for Nursing, U. Md. Nurses Alumnae Assn., Am. Pub.

Health Assn., Cmty. Health Nurse Educators Assn. Lutheran. Office: U Scranton O'Hara Hall 118 Scranton PA 18510-4595

NARVER, JOHN COLIN, business administration educator; b. Portland, Oreg., Aug. 5, 1935; s. Ursel Colin and Merle (Wells) N.; children: Gregory, Allison Ann, Colin. B.S., Oreg. State U., 1957; M.B.A. U. Calif.-Berkeley, 1960; Ph.D., 1965. With Boise Cascade Corp., Portland, 1960-61; asst. prof. U. B.C., Can., 1964-66; asst. prof. dept. mktg. and internat. bus. U. Wash., Seattle, 1966-68; assoc. prof. U. Wash., 1968-71, prof., 1971—, chmn. dept., 1974-78; vis. prof. Norwegian Sch. Econs., 1973, Bogazici U., Istanbul, Turkey, 1974; cons. in field. Author: Conglomerate Mergers and Market Competition, 1967; (with R. Savitt) The Marketing Economy: An Analytical Approach, 1971. Served to lt. U.S. Army, 1957-59. Mem. Am. Mktg. Assn., AAUP, Phi Delta Theta. Democrat. Episcopalian. Home: 2015 Federal Ave E Seattle WA 98102-4141 Office: U Wash Sch Bus Adminstrn Seattle WA 98195

NARWOLD, LEWIS LAMMERS, paper products manufacturer; b. Cleve., Sept. 4, 1921; s. Lewis Lammers and Dorothy Marie (Andrus) N.; m. Marilyn Ebner, Oct. 26, 1944; 1 dau., Christine. BBA, Western Res. U., 1942; MBA, Harvard, 1947. Salesman Hoerner Boxes, Inc., 1950-54, gen. sales mgr., 1954-57, v.p., gen. mgr., 1957-62; v.p. So. div. Hoerner Waldorf Corp., St. Paul, 1962-70; sr. v.p., container div. Hoerner Waldorf Corp., 1970-72; pres. SouthWest Packaging Inc., Tulsa, 1972—; dir. UNCA Bankshares, Utica Nat. Bank & Trust, Thermo Chem. Corp., Sooner Box Corp., Hoerner Boxes, Inc., So. Mo. Container Corp.; organizer 1st Bank & Trust Co. of Okla. Chmn. United Fund of Sand Springs, Okla.; pres., trustee Tulsa Charity Horse Show.; Trustee Children's Med. Center of Tulsa, Tulsa Psychiat. Clinic, U. of the Ozarks. Capt. USMC, 1943-45. Decorated Purple Heart; Recieved Presidential Citation. Mem. Sand Springs C. of C. (dir.), Tulsa C. of C. (dir.), N.A.M., Tulsa Mfg. Club. Clubs: Mason. (Tulsa), Summit (Tulsa), Southern Hills Country (Tulsa). Home: 7116 S College Ave Tulsa OK 74136-5601 Office: 6106 W 68th St Tulsa OK 74131-2429

NASAR, SYED ABU, electrical engineering educator; b. Gorakhpur, Uttar Pradesh, India, Dec. 25, 1932; came to U.S., 1956; s. Syed M. and Syeda (Begum) Y.; m. Sara Samad, Sept. 3, 1961; children—Naheed, Sajida. B.Sc., Agra U., 1951; B.Sc. in Elec. Engring., Dacca U., 1955; M.S.E.E., Tex. A&M U., 1957; Ph.D., U. Calif.-Berkeley, 1963. Chartered elec. engr., U.K. Assoc. prof. U. Ky., Lexington, 1968-70, prof. elec. engring., 1970—, Univ. Rsch. prof., 1989—, chmn., 1980-87, dir. grad. studies, 1980-87; visitor Brit. Council, London, 1964. Author or co-author 30 books on elec. engring., 1970-93; editor Elec. Machines and Power Systems Jour., 1976—; contbr. articles to profl. jours. Recipient Aurel Vlaicu award Romanian Nat. Acad., 1978; NSF rsch. grantee, 1966-87, 92—,. Fellow IEEE, Instn. Elec. Engrs. London. Office: U Ky 453 Anderson Hall Lexington KY 40506

NASGAARD, ROALD, museum curator; b. Denmark, Oct. 14, 1941; s. Jens Larsen and Petra (Guldbaek) N.; m. Susan Ursula Watterson, Sept. 8, 1967 (divorced). B.A., U. B.C., 1965, M.A., 1967; Ph.D., Inst. Fine Arts, N.Y. U., 1973. Lectr., asst. prof. U. Guelph, 1971-75; curator contemporary art Art Gallery of Ont., Toronto, 1975-78, chief curator, 1978-89, deputy dir., chief curator, 1989-93, sr. curator rsch., 1993; vis. lectr. U. Guelph, York U., U. Toronto; adj. prof. U. Toronto. Author Ron Martin: World Paintings, 1976, Structures for Behavior, 1977, Garry Neill Kennedy: Recent Work, 1978, Ten Canadian Artists in the 1970's, 1980, Yves Gaucher: A Fifteen Year Perspective, 1978, The Mystic North: Symbolist Landscape Painting in Northern Europe and North America, 1890-1940, 1984, Gerhard Richter: Paintings, 1988, Individualites: 14 Contemporary Artists from France, 1991, Free Worlds: Metaphors and Realities in Contemporary Hungarian Art, 1991, Free Worlds: Metaphors and Realities in Contemporary Hungarian Art, 1991; co-organizer The European Iceberg: Creativity in Germany and Italy Today, 1985. Mem. Toronto Pub. Art Commn., Gershon Iskowitz Found. Can. Council fellow, 1967-68, 70-71. Mem. Coll. Art Assn., Univ. Art Assn. Can., Internat. Art Critics Assn.

NASH, ANNAMARIE, secondary education educator; b. Paterson, N.J., Dec. 26, 1937; d. Karl and Anneliese (Schmidt) Gimmel; m. James John Nash, Aug. 16, 1959; children: James, Brian, Thomas. BA, Montclair State Coll., 1959; MA, William Paterson State Coll., 1980. Cert. tchr., elem. adminstr., secondary adminstr., supr. N.J. Social studies tchr. West New York (N.J.) Bd. Edn., 1959-60, Cedar Grove (N.J.) Bd. Edn., 1968—. Active Nat. Atomic Vets., Salem, Mass., 1982, Disabled Am. Vets. Aux., Cinn., 1988, Little Falls (N.J.) Athletic Club Aux., 1972, Little Falls Jr. Women's Club, 1964-73. Recipient Project Business Program award Jr. Achievement, Inc., 1986; named to Governor's Teacher Recognition Program, 1988. Mem. NEA, N.J. Edn. Assn., Essex County Edn. Assn., Cedar Grove Edn. Assn. (treas., sec. 1968-). Avocations: reading, walking, volleyball, travel. Office: Cedar Grove Bd Edn Cedar Grove High Sch Rugby Rd Cedar Grove NJ 07009

NASH, BOB J. (BOB NASH), under-secretary agriculture rural and small development; b. Texarkana, Ark., 1947. ABA Sociology, U. Ark., 1969; MA Urban Studies, Howard U., 1972. Asst. to dep. mayor Washington, 1970-71; asst. to city mgr. Fairfax, Va., 1971-72; adminstrv. officer Nat. Tng. and Devel. Svc., Washington, 1972-74; dir. community and regional affairs Ark. Dept. Planning, 1974-75; v.p. Winthrop Rockefeller Found., Little Rock, 1975-83; sr. exec. asst. econ. devel. Office Ark. gov., 1983-89; pres. Ark. Devel. Fin. Authority, Little Rock, 1989-92; assoc. dir. personnel White House; dep. dir. personnel Clinton Adminstrn. Transition; under sec. agriculture small community and rural devel. with USDA, Rural Devel. Adminstrn., Farmers Home Adminstrn., Alternative Rsch. & Commercialization Ctr., Rural Electrification Adminstrn., Washington, 1993—. Office: Dept of Agriculture Small Cmty & Rural Devel 14th & Independence Ave SW Washington DC 20250

NASH, BRADLEY DELAMATER, transportation executive; b. Boston, Apr. 7, 1900; s. Edward R. and Allie (DeLamater) N.; m. Ruth B. Cowan, June 30, 1956 (dec. 1994). A.B. cum laude, Harvard, 1923, postgrad., 1924; LHD (hon.), Shepherd Coll., Shepherdstown, W.Va. Banker N.Y.C., 1929-32, 35-40, Washington, 1949-51; sec. to Herbert Hoover, 1927-29; financial adviser RFC, 1932-35, WPB, 1941-42; cons. Pres.'s Adv. Com. Govt. Orgn., 1953; dep. asst. sec. Dept. of Air Force, 1953-56; dep. under sec. transp. Dept. Commerce, 1957-61; cons. U.S. Weather Bur., 1961-63; historian, cons. Nat. Park Svc., Dept. Interior, 1963-64; mayor of Harper's Ferry, W.Va., 1971-77, 81-86; mem. W.Va. R.R. Maintenance Authority, 1977—. Author: Investment Banking in England, 1924, A Hook in Leviathan, 1950, Staffing the Presidency, 1952, (with Milton S. Eisenhower et al) Organizing and Staffing the Presidency, 1980. Bd. advs. Nat. Trust for Historic Preservation; trustee Center for Study Presidency, 1975-84, Storer Coll., Alderson Broaddus Coll. Lt. col. AUS, 1942-45, MTO and Italian campaigns. Decorated Bronze Star, Commendation medal War Dept. Mem. Harvard Club (N.Y.C.), Metropolitan Club (Washington), Nat. Press Club (Washington), Chevy Chase Club (Md.). Address: High Acres Farm Rt 3 Box 122 Harpers Ferry WV 25425

NASH, CHARLES PRESLEY, chemistry educator; b. Sacramento, Calif., Mar. 15, 1932; s. Clarence and Mildred Vida (Johnson) N.; m. Lois Olive Brown, May 29, 1955; children: Nancy Caroline, Sandra Lee, James Roy. BS, U. Calif., Berkeley, 1952; PhD, UCLA, 1958. Instr. chemistry UCLA, 1956-57; from instr. to assoc. prof. U. Calif., Davis, 1957-70, prof., 1970-93; prof. emeritus, 1993—; chmn. acad. senate U. Calif., Davis, 1987-90, chmn. faculty assn., 1993-95; vis. sr. lectr. Imperial Coll., London, 1968-69; disting. vis. prof. USAF Acad., Colorado Springs, 1979-80. Contbr. numerous articles to profl. jours. Trustee Explorit Sci. Ctr. Recipient Disting. Teaching award U. Calif. Davis, 1978. Mem. Am. Chem. Soc., Sigma Xi, Phi Lambda Upsilon. Office: U Calif at Davis Dept Chemistry Davis CA 95616

NASH, CYNTHIA JEANNE, journalist; b. Detroit, Dec. 24, 1947; d. Frederick Copp and Carolyn (Coffin) N.; 1 child, Lydia Anne Mazza; m. Richard Zahler, July 22, 1994. BA, U. Mich., 1969. Reporter, Detroit News, 1970-75, sports columnist, 1975-77, Life Style columnist, 1979-77, Life Style editor, 1979-82; news features editor Seattle Times, 1983, asst. mng. editor Sunday Seattle Times, 1983-86, assoc. mng. editor, 1986—. Mem. Harbor

Sq. Club. Office: Seattle Times PO Box 70 Fairview Ave N & John St Seattle WA 98111-0070

NASH, DONALD GENE, commodities specialist; b. Paris, Ill., July 20, 1945; s. Lelan and Mildred (Washburn) N.; m. Jo Ann Bellew, Aug. 29, 1964; children—Stacey Alan, Ryan Christopher, Shaun Christian. B.S., So. Ill. U., 1967, M.S., 1969; postgrad., DePaul U., 1970-71. Farm mgr., test farms So. Ill. U., Carbondale, 1968-69; economist Commodity Futures Trading Commn., Chgo., 1969-77; v.p.-ops. Mid. Am. Commodity Exchange, Chgo., 1977-86, Div. Enforcement, Commodity Futures Trading Commn., Chgo., 1986—. With Ill. Army N.G., 1968-74. Recipient Outstanding Mktg. award Wall St. Jour., 1966, award of merit Am. Farm Econ. Assn., 1967, cert. of merit Commodity Exch. Authority, merit award Naperville Art League, 1994. Avocations: photography; woodworking; sketching. Home: 923 Bainbridge Dr Naperville IL 60563-2002 Office: Commodity Futures Trading Commn 300 S Riverside Plz Ste 1600N Chicago IL 60606-6615

NASH, EDWARD L., advertising agency executive; b. N.Y.C., Nov. 8, 1936; s. Irving and Mina (Koppel) N.; m. Diana R. Kithcart, June 2, 1968; 1 child, Amelia. B.A., CCNY, 1953. Dir. advt. Crowell, Collier, Macmillan, Inc., N.Y.C., 1961-62; v.p. mktg. LaSalle Extension U., Chgo., 1962-64; pres. Capitol Record Club, Inc., Los Angeles, 1964-69; founder, pres. Nash Pub., Los Angeles, 1969-74; exec. v.p. Rapp & Collins, N.Y.C., 1975-82; pres., chief exec. officer BBDO Direct, N.Y.C., 1982-86; owner, pres. Nash Direct Inc., N.Y.C., 1986-91; chmn. Nash, Wakeman & de Forrest, Inc., 1991-92; exec. v.p. Bozell, Jacobs, Kenyon & Eckhardt, N.Y.C., 1992—; lectr. in field; chmn. Direct Mktg. Day, N.Y.C., 1985. Author: Direct Marketing: Strategy/Planning/Execution, 1982, 2d edit., 1986, 3d edit., 1995; editor: The Direct Marketing Handbook, 1984, 2d edit., 1991, Database Marketing, 1993. Mem. Direct Mktg. Assn. (chmn. mktg. coun. 1980-82). Office: Bozell Jacobs Kenyon & Eckhardt 40 W 23rd St New York NY 10010-5200

NASH, E(DWARD) THOMAS, physicist; b. N.Y.C., July 31, 1943; s. Edward Thomas and Lili Maria (Schvarcz) N.; m. Jessie Madeleine Berry, June 9, 1970. AB, Princeton U., 1965; MA, Columbia U., 1967, PhD, 1970. Rsch. assoc. Nevis Labs., Columbia U., Irvington, N.Y., 1970, MIT, Cambridge, 1970-72; assoc. scientist, then scientist Fermi Nat. Accelerator Lab., Batavia, Ill., 1972—, dep. chmn. dept. physics, 1979-83, head advanced computer program, 1983-89, head computing div., 1989-93; assoc. dir. for tech., info. planning Fermi Nat. Accelerator Lab., 1994—; mem. rsch. briefing panel on computer architectures NAS, 1984, assoc. dir. scientific tech. and lab. info.; chmn. organizing com. Symposium on Recent Devels. in Computing, Processor and Software Rsch. for High-Energy Physics, Guanajuato, Mex., 1984; mem. internat. adv. com. Computing in High Energy Physics Conf., Asilomar, Calif., 1987, Oxford, Eng., 1989, Santa Fe, 1990, Tsukuba City, Japan, 1991, Annecy, France, 1992, Rio de Janeiro, 1995, sci. adv. com. Conf. on Impact Digital Microelectronics and Microprocessors on Particle Physics, Trieste, Italy, 1988; mem. computing/networking rev. panel III. Tech. Challenge Grant Program, State of Ill., 1990; sci. and tech. adv. com. Office Non-Proliferation and Nat. Security U.S. Dept. Energy; rschr. in field. Specialist editor Computer Physics Communications, 1986-93; editorial cons. Ency. Applied Physics, 1988—; contbr. numerous articles, revs. to profl. jours. Carnegie Sci. fellow Ctr. for Internat. Security and Arms Control, Stanford U., 1988-89. Fellow Am. Phys. Soc.; mem. Sigma Xi. Office: Fermi Nat Accelerator Lab PO Box 500 Batavia IL 60510-5000

NASH, FRANK ERWIN, lawyer; b. Pendleton, Oreg., Feb. 27, 1916; s. Frank Lee and Gertrude (Walbridge) N.; m. Elizabeth Ann Kibbe, Apr. 20, 1943; children: Thomas K., Robert L., Carl F., Frances L. B.S., U. Oreg., 1937, J.D., 1939. Bar: Oreg. 1939. Since practiced in Portland; with firm Miller, Nash, Wiener, Hager & Carlsen (and predecessors), 1939-91, ptnr., 1948-91, ret., 1991. Bd. dirs. Tri-County United Good Neighbors, 1961-66, pres., 1963-64; pres. U. Oreg. Found., 1979-81; bd. dirs. Med. Research Found., pres., 1980-81; bd. dirs. Library Assn. Portland, pres., 1978-81; bd. visitors U. Oreg. Law Sch. Served to lt. col., inf. AUS, 1941-46, PTO. Recipient Pioneer award U. Oreg., 1980, Meritorious Svc. award., 1992. Fellow Am. Bar Found.; mem. ABA, Multnomah Bar Assn. (pres. 1964-65), Oreg. State Bar, Order of Coif, Phi Delta Phi, Phi Delta Theta. Republican. Methodist (past chmn. ofcl. bd.). Clubs: Arlington (Portland) (dir. 1963-65), Multnomah Amateur Athletic (Portland) (dir. 1963-65, pres. 1965-66), Waverley (Portland) (pres. 1979-80). Home: 1885 NW Ramsey Dr Portland OR 97229-4240 Office: 111 SW 5th Ave Fl 35 Portland OR 97204-3604

NASH, GARY BARING, historian, educator; b. Phila., July 27, 1933; s. Ralph C. and Edith (Baring) N.; m. Mary Workum, Dec. 20, 1955 (div.); children—Brooke, Robin, Jennifer, David; m. Cynthia Shelton, Oct. 24, 1981. B.A., Princeton U., 1955, Ph.D., 1964. Asst. to dean Grad. Sch., Princeton (N.J.) U., 1959-61, instr., 1964-65, asst. prof. history, 1965-66; asst. prof. history UCLA, 1966-68, assoc. prof., 1968-72, prof., 1972—, dean undergrad. curriculum devel., 1984-91; assoc. dir. Nat. Ctr. for History in the Schs., 1988-94, dir. 1994—; co-chair Nat. Hist. Stds. Project, 1992-95. Author: Quakers and Politics: Pennsylvania, 1681-1726, 1968, rev. edit., 1993, Class and Society in Early America, 1970, The Great Fear: Race in the Mind of America, 1970, Red, White, and Black: The Peoples of Early America, 1974, 2d edit., 1982, 3d edit., 1991, The Urban Crucible, 1979, Struggle and Survival in Colonial America, 1981, Race, Class and Politics: Essays on American Colonial and Revolutionary Society, 1986, (with others) The American People: Creating a Nation and a Society, 1986, 3d edit., 1994, Forging Freedom: The Formation of Philadelphia's Black Community, 1720-1840, 1988, Race and Revolution, 1990, (with Jean R. Soderlund) Freedom by Degrees: Emancipation and Its Aftermath in Pennsylvania, 1991, American Odyssey: The United States in the 20th Century, 1991, rev. edit., 1993; mem. editorial bd. William and Mary Quar., 1974-77, Jour. of Black Studies, 1971-73, Am. Indian Culture and Rsch. Jour., 1978—, Am. Quar., 1980-84, Pa. Mag. History and Biography, 1987—, Social History/Histoire Sociale, 1990—. Served with USN, 1955-58. Guggenheim fellow, 1969-70, Am. Council Learned Socs. fellow, 1973-74. Mem. Am. Hist. Assn., Inst. Early Am. History and Culture, Orgn. Am. Historians (exec. com. 1988-91, pres. 1994-95), Soc. Am. Historians, Am. Antiquarian Soc. Home: 16174 Alcima Ave Pacific Palisades CA 90272-2408

NASH, GERALD DAVID, historian; b. Berlin, July 16, 1928; came to U.S., 1938, naturalized, 1944; s. Alfred and Alice (Kantorowicz) N.; m. Marie L. Norris, Aug. 19, 1967; 1 dau., Stephanie Ann. B.A., NYU, 1950; M.A., Columbia U., 1952; Ph.D., U. Calif., Berkeley, 1957. Instr. history Stanford U., 1957-58, vis. asst. prof., 1959-60; asst. prof. No. Ill. U., DeKalb, 1958-59; postdoctoral fellow Harvard U., 1960-61; mem. faculty U. N.Mex., Albuquerque, 1961—; prof. history U. N.Mex., 1968—, chmn. dept., 1974-80, Presdl. prof., 1985-90, Disting. prof., 1990—; faculty rsch. lectr., 1970; vis. assoc. prof. NYU, 1965-66; George Bancroft prof. Am. History U. Goettingen, Fed. Republic Germany, 1990-91. Author: State Government and Economic Development, 1964, U.S. Oil Policy, 1968, Perspectives on Administration, 1969, The Great Transition, 1971, American West in 20th Century, 1973, Great Depression and World War II, 1979, The American West Transformed; The Impact of World War II, 1985, World War II and the West: Reshaping the Economy, 1990; editor: Issues in American Economic History, 3d edit, 1980, F. D. Roosevelt, 1967, Urban West, 1979, (with Noel Pugach and Richard Tomasson) Social Security in the U.S.-the First Half Century, 1988, (with Richard Etulain) Perspectives on the 20th Century West, 1989, Creating the West: Historical Interpretations, 1991, A.P. Giannini and the Bank of America, 1992, The Crucial Era, 1992; editor The Historian, 1974-84. Fellow Newberry Library, 1959, Huntington Library, 1979; sr. fellow NEH, 1981; Project 87 fellow, 1982-83. Mem. Am. Hist. Assn., Orgn. Am. Historians, Bus. History Soc., Agrl. History Soc., Western History Assn., Phi Beta Kappa. Club: Commonwealth. Office: U NMex Dept History Albuquerque NM 87131 *Anyone reflecting on major trends in the 20th century must conclude that the greatest challenge is to preserve freedom and democratic processes in the effort to achieve greater economic and social equality in America.*

NASH, GRAHAM WILLIAM, singer, composer; b. Blackpool, Lancashire, Eng., 1942. Mem.: Brit. group The Hollies, 1963-68; joined David Crosby and Stephen Stills to form group Brit. group, Crosby, Stills & Nash, 1969, then with Neil Young, to 1971, now soloist and duo (with David Crosby),

then regrouped (with Stephen Stills), 1977; (with Hollies) albums include Bus Stop, 1966, Stop, Stop, Stop, 1967, Hollies' Greatest Hits, 1967, Evolution, 1967, Dear Eloise/King Midas in Reverse, 1967, (with Crosby and Stills) Crosby, Stills & Nash, 1969, CSN, 1977, (with Crosby, Stills and Young) Deja Vu, 1970, 4 Way Street, 1971, (with Crosby) Graham Nash and David Crosby, 1972, Wind on the Water, 1975, Whistling Down the Wire, 1976, Crosby/Nash Live, 1977, After The Storm, 1994; solo albums Songs for Beginners, 1971, Wild Tales, 1974, Earth & Sky, Innocent Eyes, 1986; appeared in film Woodstock, 1970. Recipient Grammy award (with Crosby and Stills) for Best New Artist of Year, 1969. Office: Atlantic Records 75 Rockefeller Plz New York NY 10019*

NASH, HENRY WARREN, marketing educator; b. Tampa, Fla., Sept. 19, 1927; s. Leslie Dikeman and Mildred (Johnson) N.; m. Frances Lora Venters, Aug. 20, 1950; children: Warren Leslie, Richard Dale. B.S. in Bus. Adminstrn, U. Fla., 1950, M.B.A., 1951; postgrad., Ind. U., 1951-53; Ph.D., U. Ala., 1965. Student asst. U. Fla., 1948-50, grad. asst., 1950-51; grad. asst. Ind. U., 1951-53; salesman Field Enterprises, Inc., Chgo., 1953; assoc. prof. bus. and econs. Miss. Coll., 1953-57; assoc. prof. marketing Miss. State U., 1957-66, prof., head dept., 1966—; ptnr. Southland Cons. Assos., 1968—; bd. dirs. Govt. Employees Credit Union, 1969—, v.p., 1969-73, pres., 1973-78. Author: (with others) Principles of Marketing, 1961. Served with USNR, 1945-46. Loveman's Merchandising fellow U. Ala., 1961-62. Mem. Am. Mktg. Assn., Am. Acad. Advt., Acad. Internat. Bus., So. Econ. Assn., So. Mktg. Assn. (sec. 1974-75, pres. 1976-77), Sales and Mktg. Execs. (internat. chmn. educators com. 1967-70), Miss. Retail Mchts. Assn. (bd. dirs.), Pi Sigma Epsilon (Nat. educator, v.p. 1967-69, nat. pres. 1967-71), Kiwanis (treas. Starkville club 1969-70, v.p. 1973-74, pres. 1974-75, lt. gov. 1977-78, gov. 1982-83), Blue Key, Beta Gamma Sigma, Omicron Delta Kappa, Mu Kappa Tau (nat. v.p. 1977-79, 86-88, pres. 1979-81, 88-90), Alpha Kappa Psi, Phi Kappa Phi (v.p. Miss. State U. 1990-91, pres. 1991-92). Baptist (tchr., deacon). Home: 114 Forest Hill Dr Starkville MS 39759-3127 Office: Miss State U Dept Mktg Mississippi State MS 39762

NASH, HOWARD ALLEN, biochemist, researcher; b. N.Y.C., Nov. 5, 1937; s. Harvey and Harriet (Ratner) N.; m. Dominie Maria Shortino, Aug. 31, 1963; children: Janet Elisabeth, Emily Julia. BS, Tufts U., 1957; MD, U. Chgo., 1961, PhD, 1963. Intern U. Chgo. Clinics, 1963-64; rsch. assoc. NIMH, Bethesda, Md., 1964-68, med. officer (res), 1968-84, chief, sec. molecular genetics, 1984—; chmn. Gordon conf. on Nucleic Acids, 1988; vice-chair FASEB Conf. on Genetic Recombination, 1993. Assoc. editor: Cell Jour., 1985-91; editorial bd.: Current Biology Jour., 1993—. Lt. comdr. USPHS, 1964-68. Recipient Superior Svc. award USPHS, 1985, Disting. Svc. award HHS, 1990, Alumni award for Disting. Svc., U. Chgo., 1994. Fellow Am. Acad. Arts and Sci.; mem. NAS. Avocations: choral singing, birdwatching. Office: Lab Molecular Biology NIMH 36 Convent Dr Bethesda MD 20892-4034

NASH, JACK, investment banker; b. Germany, Apr. 10, 1929; s. Joseph and Rachel N.; B.B.A., CCNY, 1953; m. Helen Englander, Oct. 20, 1957; children—Pamela, Joshua. Ptnr. Oppenheimer & Co., N.Y.C., 1952—, pres., 1974-79, chmn., 1979—; ptnr. Odyssey ptnrs., N.Y.C., 1982—; dir. Chgo. Milw. Corp., The Leslie Fay Cos., Inc. Pres. Nathan Miller Ctr. for Nursing Care, Inc., 1969—. Office: 437 Madison Ave New York NY 10022-7001

NASH, JAMES JOHN, superintendent; b. N.Y.C., Nov. 12, 1933; s. James B. and Margaret (Curnyn) N.; m. Annamarie Gimmel, Aug. 16, 1959; children: James, Brian, Thomas. BA, Montclair State U., 1956, MA, 1962. Cert. elem. tchr., adminstr., prin., supr. N.J. Tchr. Little Falls (N.J.) Bd. Edn., 1958-73, prin., 1973-85, supt., 1985—. Pres. Little Falls Recreation Commn., 1975-76. Mem. Am. Assn. Sch. Adminstrs., Nat. Assn. Atomic Vets. (life), Nat. Assn. Radiation Survivors (life), Disabled Am. Vets. (life), N.J. Coun. Edn., N.J. Assn. Sch. Adminstrs. (exec. com. 1989—), N.J. Schoolmaster's Club, Passaic County Assn. Sch. Adminstrs. (pres. 1990-91), Passaic County Assn. Prins. (pres. 1980-81). Avocations: reading, walking, travel, pub. speaking on vets affairs. Office: Little Falls Bd Edn Stevens Ave Sch 1 Little Falls NJ 07424

NASH, JAY ROBERT, III, author, playwright, publisher; b. Indpls., Nov. 26, 1937; s. Jay Robert and Jerrie Lynne (Kosur) N.; m. Janice Patricia Schwartz, Sept. 15, 1962 (div.); children: Lee Travis, Andrea Lynne; m. Judith Anne Anetsberger, Sept. 10, 1983; 1 child, Jay Robert IV. BA in literature, U. Paris, France, 1958. Editor Milw. Lit. Times, 1960-62, Antioch (Ill.) News, 1961-62; mng. editor Am. Trade Mags., Chgo., 1962-66; editorial dir. PRM Corp., Chgo., 1967; editor in chief Chgo. Land Mag., 1967-70; freelance writer Chgo., 1970—; editor in chief, pres. Cine Books, Inc., Chgo., 1984-86; editor in chief, pub., pres. Crime Books, Inc., Wilmette, Ill., 1987—; editor, pub. Lit. Times (jour. of fine arts), Chgo., 1961-70. Author: Lost Natives & Expatriates, 1965, Dillinger: Dead or Alive?, 1970, Hoover and His FBI, 1972, Bloodletters and Badmen: A Narrative Encyclopedia of American Criminals from the Pilgrims to the Present, 1973 (ALA award for best reference book 1973), On All Fronts, 1974, Hustlers and Con Men: An Anecdotal History of the Confidence Man and his Games, 1976, Darkest Hours: A Narrative Encyclopedia of World-Wide Disasters from Ancient Times to the Present, 1976 (ALA award for best reference book 1976), Among the Missing, 1978, Last Rites for the Boys, 1979, Murder America: A Social History of Homicide in the United States from the Revolution to the Present, 1980, Almanac of World Crime, 1981, A Crime Story, 1981, Look for the Woman: A Narrative Encyclopedia of Female Criminals from Elizabethan Times to the Present, 1981, The Innovators, 1981, True Crime Quiz Book, 1981, People to See: A History of Chicago's Makers and Breakers, 1981, The Dark Fountain, 1982, Murder Among the Mighty, 1982, Zanies: A Narrative Encyclopedia of the World's Greatest Eccentrics, 1982, Crime Movie Quiz Book, 1983, The Dillinger Dossier, 1983, Open Files: A Narrative Encyclopedia of the World's Greatest Unsolved Crimes, 1983, The Toughest Movie Quiz Book Ever, 1983, Jay Robert Nash's Crime Chronology: A Worldwide Record, 1900-1983, 1983, The Mafia Diaries, 1984, World Encyclopedia of Twentieth Century Murder, 1989, World Encyclopedia of Organized Crime, 1989, The Encyclopedia of World Crime, 6 vols., 1990 (Edgar Allan Poe award Mystery Writers Am. 1990), Encyclopedia of Western Lawmen and Outlaws, 1992; author, editor, pub.: The Motion Picture Guide (12 vol. ency.), 1986 (ALA award for best reference book 1986). Served with Intelligence Service AUS, 1956-58. Mem. Authors Guild Inc. Office: PO Box 512 Wilmette IL 60091-0512*

NASH, JOHN ARTHUR, bank executive; b. Indpls., Mar. 12, 1938; s. Basil and Harriet Nash; m. Susan Moss; children: John, Bill, Stacia. BS, Ind. U., 1960, MBA, 1961. Account officer Nat. City Bank, Cleve., 1961-66; v.p. Irwin Union Bank, Columbus, Ind., 1966-71, exec. v.p., 1971-75, pres., 1975-79; pres. Irwin Fin. Corp., Columbus, 1979—; also bd. dirs. Irwin Fin. Corp., Columbus, Ind.; bd. dirs. Irwin Union Bank, Irwin Union Investor Svcs., Inc., Inland Mortgage Corp., Affiliated Capital Corp., Irwin Home Equity Corp. Bd. dirs. Columbus Regional Hosp. Found., Columbus Econ. Devel. Bd.; past chmn. Heritage Fund Bartholomew County, Columbus; mem. steering com. Columbus 2000; mem. adv. bd. Ind. U.-Purdue U., Indpls.; trustee Columbus Regional Hosp. 2d lt. U.S. Army, 1961-63. Recipient Sagamore of Wabash award Gov. of Ind., 1991. Mem. Am. Bankers Assn. (mem. bank leadership coun.), Ind. Bankers Assn. (bd. dirs., past chmn., chmn. govt. rels. com.), Ind. U. Alumni Assn. (pres. 1991-92). Office: Irwin Fin Corp 500 Washington St Columbus IN 47201-6230

NASH, JOHN C., research mathematician; b. Bluefield, W.Va., 1928. BS in Math., Carnegie-Mellon U., 1945, MS, 1948; PhD, Princeton U., 1950. Rsch. asst., instr. Princeton (N.J.) U., 1950-51; Moore instr. MIT, 1951-53, asst. prof., 1953-57, assoc. prof., 1957-59; vis. rsch. collaborator math. Princeton U.; cons. RAND Corp., summers 1950, 52; vis. mem. Inst. Advanced Study, Princeton, 1956-57, 61-62, 63-64; rsch. assoc. math. MIT, 1966-67. Co-recipient Nobel Prize in Econ. Scis., 1994; recipient von Neumann Theory prize Ops. Rsch. Soc. Am.; Sloan fellow, NSF fellow; Westinghouse scholar. Fellow Econometric Soc. Office: Princeton U Dept Math Fine Hall Princeton NJ 08544*

NASH, JOHN N., professional basketball team executive; b. Phila., Nov. 28, 1946; s. John N. and Rosemary K. (Noon) N.; m. Anne Kelly (div.); children: Andrea, Carolyn; m. Ann Raley, Oct. 27, 1978; children: Brian, Barbara. Dir. group sales Phila. 76ers, 1969-71, asst. gen. mgr., 1981-86,

gen. mgr., 1986-90; ticket mgr. athletic dept. U. Pa., Phila., 1971-72, Phila. Blazers, 1972-73, Phila. Flyers, 1973-75; exec. sec. Big 5 Basketball, 1975-81; asst. gen. mgr., bus. mgr. Phila. 76ers, 1981-86, gen. mgr., 1986-90; v.p. and gen. mgr. Washington Bullets, 1990—. Office: Washington Bullets USAir Arena Landover MD 20785*

NASH, JONATHON MICHAEL, program manager, mechanical engineer; b. Little Rock, Aug. 10, 1942; s. Bertram B. and Nora B. (Shed) N.; m. Mata W. Smith, Aug. 12, 1972; children: Lillian Kendrick, Caroline Michael. BS in Mech. Engring., U. Miss., 1966, MS in Engring. Sci., 1970, PhD in Engring. Sci., 1973. Registered profl. engr., Ala., Miss., Md. Jr. engr. IBM Fed. Systems div., Huntsville, Ala., 1967-68, Saturn/Apollo manned spacecraft programs sr. assoc. engr., 1973-74, staff engr., 1975-77, solar energy programs project engr., 1977-78, devel. engr., Gaithersburg, Md., 1978-80, adv. engr. synthetic fuels program, 1980-81, tech. planning mgr., 1981-83, sr. engr. FAA programs, Rockville, Md., 1983-88, sr. engr., program mgr. internat. air traffic control programs, 1988-94; program mgr. air traffic control LORAL Fed. Systems, Rockville, Md., 1994—; rsch. assoc. U. Miss., 1970-72, adj. assoc. prof. mech. engring., 1983—; aerospace engr., sci. intern NASA Manned Space Craft Center, summers 1970, 71; instr. U. Ala., Huntsville, 1977-78. Bd. dirs. Arts Council of Frederick City and County, Md., 1981-84, v.p., 1982-83; mem. Lafayette County (Miss.) Rep. Exec. Com., 1972-73. With C.E., U.S. Army, 1968-70, Vietnam; maj. USAR. Decorated Bronze Star; recipient NASA New Tech. award, 1979; NASA Apollo Achievement award 1971; Ala. Young Engr. of Yr. award, Nat. Soc. Profl. Engrs., 1978; Tudor medal for engring. contbns. Soc. Am. Mil. Engrs., 1978; Engring. Achievement award, Huntsville chpt. Soc. Am. Mil. Engrs., 1977; Outstanding Young Engr. of Yr. award Huntsville chpt. Ala. Soc. Profl. Engrs., 1976, others; U.S. fellow, 1970-73. Fellow AIAA (assoc.), ASME (exec. com. solar energy div. 1981-86, sec./treas. 1982-83, vice chmn. 1983-84, chmn. 1984-85, mem. coun. engring. 1992—, mem. operating bd. energy resources group 1984—, Cert. of Appreciation, solar engery div. 1982, 85, chpt. chmn., 1978, vice chmn. 1977-78, treas. 1976-77, mem. nat. bur. standards interaction com., chmn. nat. com. tech. planning 1992—, nat. nominating com. 1988-90, nat. sattelite programs com. 1990-92); mem. NSPE, VFW, ASHRAE (nat. tech. com. on solar energy utilization 1977-80), Am. Inst. Chem. Engrs., Soc. Am. Mil. Engrs. (chpt. pres. 1976-77, bd. dir. 1977-78), Md. Engring. Soc., Ala. Soc. Profl. Engrs. (chpt. dir. 1978), Internat. Solar Energy Soc., Ala. Solar Energy Assn. (chpt. dir. 1978), Am. Def. Preparedness Assn., Sigma Xi (chpt. pres. 1977-78), Omicron Delta Kappa, Alpha Tau Omega (pres. Huntsville alumni 1976-77), Res. Officers Assn. Editor: (with Smok, Thomas and Jenkins) Modeling, Simulation, Testing and Measurements for Solar Energy Systems, 1978; assoc. editor: (jour.) Applied Mechanics Revs., 1985-87, Mfg. Rev., 1987—; contbr. articles to profl. jours.; inventor in field. Home: 300 Rockwell Ter Frederick MD 21701-4912 Office: 9211 Corporate Blvd Rockville MD 20850

NASH, JUNE CAPRICE, anthropology professor; b. Salem, Mass., May 30, 1927; d. Joseph and M. Josephine (Salloway) Bousley; children: Eric, Laura; m. Herbert Menzel, July 1, 1972. BA, CUNY, 1948; MA, U. Chgo., 1953, PhD, 1960. Asst. prof. Chgo. Tchrs. Coll., Chgo.-Ill., 1960-63, Yale U. New Haven, Conn., 1963-68; assoc. prof. NYU, 1968-72; prof. CUNY, 1972—; disting. vis. prof. Am. U., Cairo, 1978, U. Colo., Boulder, 1988—; vis. prof. SUNY, Albany, 1988-89; disting. prof. CUNY, N.Y.C., 1990. Author: In the Eyes of the Ancestor, 1970, We Eat the Mines and the Mines Eat Us: Dependency and Exploitation in Bolivian Mining Communities, 1979, From Tank Town to High Tech: The Clash of Community and Industrial Cycles, 1989; editor: Crafts in the World Market: The Impact of Global Exchange on Middle American Artisans, 1993. Mem. Soc. for the Anthropology of Work (pres. 1988—), Assn. Polit. and Legal Activities (pres. 1983), Am. Anthropology Assn., Am. Ethnographic Soc., Assn. for Feminist Anthropology (pres. 1990-93). Avocations: skiing, hiking. Home: 2166 Broadway 18D New York NY 10024 Office: CUNY 137th Convent New York NY 10031

NASH, LEE J., banker; b. Elgin, Ill., Aug. 17, 1939; s. Richard Lee and Pearl Kepler (June) N.; m. Ruth Ann Ebeling, June 16, 1963; children—Joanne Elizabeth, J.R.; m. Sandra Gail Clegg, Feb. 16, 1980; children—Jason Lee, Jessica Gail. A.B. with honors, Harvard Coll., 1961; M.B.A., Columbia U., 1963. Mgmt. trainee Bankers Trust Co., N.Y.C., 1963-64; v.p. Pitts. Nat. Bank, 1964-70, Crocker Nat. Bank, San Francisco, 1970-75; sr. v.p. Shawmut Corp., Boston, 1975-79; exec. v.p., treas. Mfrs. Hanover Trust Co., N.Y.C., 1979-87; pres., chief exec. officer Mfrs. Hanover Securities Corp., N.Y.C., 1988-90; exec. v.p. Fed. Farm Credit Banks Funding Corp., 1990—. Mem. Am. Bankers Assn. (chmn. fund mgmt. and fin. markets divsn. 1985-87), Pub. Securities Assn. (bd. dirs. 1982-84), Treas. Securities Luncheon Club, Harvard Club (N.Y.C.), Beta Gamma Sigma. Office: Fed Farm Credit Banks Funding Corp 10 Exchange Pl Jersey City NJ 07302-3905

NASH, LEONARD KOLLENDER, chemistry educator; b. N.Y.C., Oct. 27, 1918; s. Adolph and Carol (Kollender) N.; m. Ava Byer, Mar. 3, 1945; children—Vivian C., David B. B.S., Harvard, 1939, M.A., 1941, Ph.D., 1944. Rsch. asst. Harvard U., Cambridge, Mass., 1943-44, instr., 1946-48, asst. prof., 1948-53, assoc. prof., 1953-59, prof. chemistry, 1959-86, chmn. dept., 1971-74; rsch. assoc. Columbia, 1944-45; instr. U. Ill., 1945-46; ret.; staff Manhattan Project, 1944-45. Author: Elements of Chemical Thermodynamics, 1962, The Nature of the Natural Sciences, 1963, Stoichiometry, 1966, Elements of Statistical Thermodynamics, 1968, ChemThermo, 1972. Recipient Mfg. Chemists' award, 1966; James Flack Norris award, 1975. Home: 11 Field Rd Lexington MA 02173-8014

NASH, MARY ALICE, nursing educator; b. Erie, Pa., Nov. 13, 1957; d. Robert Stuart and Jean Marie (Clark) N. BSN, Duquesne U., 1979; postgrad., Edinboro U., 1988—. RN, Pa.; cert. CPR instr. Clin. educator St. Vincent Health Ctr., Erie, 1984, asst. nurse educator, 1988—. Mem. ANA, AACCN, Nat. Nurses Assn., Pa. Nurses Assn., Sigma Theta Tau. Home: 917 W 30th St Erie PA 16508-1645 Office: St Vincent Health Ctr 232 W 25th St Erie PA 16544-0001

NASH, NICHOLAS DAVID, retailing executive; b. Mpls., June 11, 1939; s. Edgar Vanderhoef and Nancy (Van Slyke) N. A.B., Harvard U., 1962; M.Ed., Bowling Green State U., 1970; Ph.D., U. Minn., 1975. Head lower sch. Maumee Valley (Ohio) Country Day Sch., 1965-71; assoc. dir. Univ. Council for Ednl. Adminstrn.; adj. asst. prof. Ohio State U., 1975-78; v.p. programming Minn. Public Radio, St. Paul, 1978-82, Am. Pub. Radio, St. Paul, 1982-85; pres. The Nash Co., 1985—; bd. dirs. Sta. WCAL-FM. Author works in field. Bd. dirs. Schubert Club, Sigurd Olson Environ. Inst., 1992—, Nash Found., 1975—. Mem. University Club St. Paul. Episcopalian. Home: 1340 N Birch Lake Blvd Saint Paul MN 55110-6716 Office: 2179 4th St # 2-h Saint Paul MN 55110-3028

NASH, PAUL LENOIR, lawyer; b. Poughkeepsie, N.Y., Jan. 29, 1931; s. George Matthew and Winifred (LeNoir) N.; m. Nancy Allyn Thouron, Dec. 30, 1961; children—Andrew Gray, Laurie LeNoir, Daphne Thouron. B.A., Yale U., 1953; LL.B., Harvard U., 1958. Bar: N.Y. 1959. Assoc., Dewey, Ballantine, Bushby, Palmer & Wood, N.Y.C., 1958-66, ptnr., 1966—. Pres. bd. trustees Peck Sch., Morristown, N.J., 1978-82. Served to capt. USMC, 1953-55; Japan. Mem. ABA, N.Y. State Bar Assn., Assn. Bar City of N.Y. Republican. Home: 4 Westminster Pl Morristown NJ 07960-5810 Office: Dewey Ballantine 1301 Avenue Of The Americas New York NY 10019-6092

NASH, PETER HUGH JOHN, geographer, educator, planner; b. Frankfurt-on-Main, Germany, Sept. 18, 1921; came to U.S., 1938, naturalized, 1943; s. John Hans Joseph and Alice (Heuman) N.; m. Inez Mae Frost, July 30, 1955 (dec. Apr. 1988); children: Carina Frost Nash Lawrence, Peter Hugh John Jr. A.A. in Earth Scis, Los Angeles City Coll., 1941; B.A. (Gruen Fellow), UCLA, 1942, M.A. in Geography, 1946; Certificat D'Etudes, U. Grenoble, France, 1945; postgrad., U. Wis., 1946-47; M. City Planning (Holtzer fellow), Harvard U., 1949, M.Pub. Adminstrn., 1956, Ph.D. in Archtl. Scis, 1958; postgrad., U. Cin. Law Sch., 1961-63; hon. degree, Aligarh Muslim U., India, 1968. Prin. planning asst. Boston Planning Bd., 1949-50; sr. planner City of Worcester, Mass., 1950-51; asst. chief urban redevel. div. Boston Housing Authority, 1951-52; dir. planning dept. City of Medford, Mass., 1952-56; vis. critic Harvard Grad. Sch. Design, 1955-57, 66-68; assoc. prof. city and regional planning U. N.C., 1957-59;

prof., head dept. geography and regional planning U. Cin., 1959-63; dean Grad. Sch., U. R.I. Kingston, 1963-68, prof. geography and regional planning, dir. grad. curriculum in community planning and area devel., 1963-70; dean faculty of environ. studies U. Waterloo, Ont., Can., 1970-75; prof. architecture, geography and planning U. Waterloo, 1970-93, disting. prof. emeritus, 1993—; instr. Center for Adult Edn., Cambridge, Mass., 1949-57; lectr. Northeastern U., Boston, 1954-56; lectr., acting asst. prof. Boston U., 1956-57; vis. prof. summers U. So. Calif., 1959, 62, Aroostook State Coll., Maine, 1961, Grad. School Ekistics, Athens, Greece, 1967, 70, Inst. Human Scis. Boston Coll., 1969-70; cons. Brookings Inst., 1960-61, ACTION, Inc., 1959-61, Battelle Meml. Inst., Columbus, Ohio and Cleve., 1967-73; corr. Ekistics, 1960-73; Western hemisphere rep. commn. applied geography Internat. Geog. Union, 1964-76. Author 3 books; contbr. over 200 articles, chpts. and revs. in profl. and scholarly jours.; pub. in his honor Peter Nash Festschrift- Abstract Thoughts: Concrete Solutions: Essays, 1987. Participant Delos Symposion, Greece, 1967, 70, 74; mem. alumni council Harvard Sch. Design, pres., 1967-70; mem. exec. coun., sec.-treas. Kennedy Sch. govt., Harvard U., 1982-87; chmn. bd. dirs. K/W Philharm. Choir, 1976-80. Served with AUS, 1942-45. Decorated Purple Heart with oak leaf cluster, Bronze Star; Croix de Guerre (France); recipient Sci. Achievement medal U. Liege, Belgium, 1967; Social Sci. Research Council grantee, 1960; NSF grantee, 1960; Am. Council of Learned Socs. grantee, 1968; Can. Council grantee, 1974, 80, 82; Can. Social Scis. and Humanities Research Council fellow U. Grenoble, France, 1984-85, research grantee, Athens, Greece, 1985, Barcelona, Spain, 1986, research fellowship grantee, 1986-88. Fellow Am. Geog. Soc. (life), Assn. Am. Geographers (life); mem. Inst. Alpine Geography, Grenoble (hon.), Am. Inst. Planners, Internat. City Mgmt. Assn., AAAS, Am. Soc. Pub. Adminstrn., Can. Assn. Geographers, Can. Inst. Planners, Regional Sci. Assn., World Future Soc. (life), New Eng. Conf. on Grad. Edn. (sec.-treas. 1966-68), Assn. Collegiate Schs. Planning (treas. 1968-70), World Soc. Ekistics (v.p. 1994—), Sigma Xi, Sigma Nu, Kappa Delta Pi. Clubs: Mason (Boston and Toronto) (K.T.), Harvard (Boston and Toronto); Rotary Internat. (Kitchener, Ont., Paul Harris fellow). Home: 588 Sugarbush Dr, Waterloo, ON Canada N2K 1Z8 *I have never felt constrained by boundaries, whether geographical, intellectual, disciplinary, or any other type. One has to follow those avenues where one's intellectual curiosity points the way, even if these paths lead to entirely different territories, but the world of reflective thinkers is inhabited primarily by splitters and drillers, but the lumpers and spreaders are increasing rapidly in this era of knowledge explosion, and I am a standard bearer of this salient group as I help to create better futures.*

NASH, ROBERT COUTTS, lawyer; b. Evanston, Ill., May 1, 1944; s. Roscoe Coutts and Dorothy (Cain) N.; m. Roberta M. Spector, Sept. 8, 1968; children: Stephanie A., Scotland E., Whitney S.B. BA cum laude, Dartmouth Coll., 1966; JD, Harvard U., 1969. Bar: Ill. 1969, U.S. Dist. Ct. (no. dist.) Ill. Assoc. Chapman and Cutler, Chgo., 1969-77, ptnr., 1978—; speaker in field. Pres., bd. dirs. Chgo. Vol. Legal Svcs. Found., 1978-88; bd. dirs. Legal Aid Soc., Chgo., 1988—. Mem. Am. Coll. Investment Counsel, Legal Edn. for Fund. (bd. dirs. 1989—). Clubs: Dartmouth Club Chgo., Union League Club Chgo., Dartmouth Club Chgo., Harvard Club Chgo. Office: Chapman and Cutler 111 W Monroe St Chicago IL 60603-4003

NASH, ROBERT FRED, grocery company executive; b. Mpls., Apr. 17, 1933; s. Robert Leich and Marcella Russel (Marfield) N.; m. Mary Elizabeth Armstrong, Sept. 13, 1958; children—Lisa, Robert Fred, David. Student, Williams Coll., 1951-55. With Nash-Finch Co., Mpls., 1960—, tax dept. mgr., 1968-74, treas., 1974—; mem. 1221 adv. bd. Norwest Bank, Mpls., v.p., treas., 1988—. Served with USN, 1955-59.

NASH, RONALD HERMAN, philosophy educator; b. Cleve., May 27, 1936; s. Herman Nash and Viola McAlpin; m. Betty Jane Perry, June 8, 1957; children: Jeffrey A., Jennifer A. BA, Barrington (R.I.) Coll., 1958; MA, Brown U., 1960; PhD, Syracuse U., 1964. Instr. philosophy Barrington Coll., 1958-60, Houghton (N.Y.) Coll., 1960-62; prof. philosophy Western Ky. U., Bowling Green, 1964-91; prof. philosophy religion Ref. Theol. Sem., Orlando, Fla., 1991—; dept. head Western Ky. U., Bowling Green, 1964-84; mem. adv. bd. CEBA, Lynchburg, Va., 1989—. Author: 25 books, including: Poverty and Wealth, 1986, Faith and Reason, 1988, The Closing of the American Heart, 1990, The Gospel and the Greeks, 1992, Beyond Liberation Theology, 1992, World Views in Conflict, 1992, Great Divides, 1992; contbg. editor: The Freeman, 1993—, Christian Rsch. Jour., 1993—; mem. bd. editors Durell Jour. Money and Banking, 1988-91. Advisor U.S. Civil Rights Commn., Washington, 1988-91. Fellow NEH, 1969. Office: Ref Theol Sem PO Box 945120 Maitland FL 32794-5120

NASH, STELLA B., government nutrition administrator; b. Gould, Ark., Nov. 3, 1942; d. Virgil and Lessie B. (Bonner) Riley; m. Solomon Nash, Mar. 31, 1973; children: Chad, Jereme. BS, Ark. AM & N Coll., 1964; MA, NYU, 1970; postgrad., Pa. State U., 1973-74, U. Mo., 1974-75. Nutritionist/spl. asst. to the dir. Ark. Office on Aging, Little Rock, 1975-76; supr. child nutrition Ark. State Dept. Edn., Little Rock, 1976-79; supr. Coop. Extension Svc. USDA, Denver, 1979-85; regional nutrition dir. Mountain Plains region USDA Food and Nutrition Svc., Denver, 1985—; home mgmt. specialist U. Ark. Coop. Extension, Pine Bluff, 1972-73; nutritionist N.J. Coll. Medicine and Dentistry, Newark, 1970-72; dietitian King County Hosp., Bklyn., 1964-66. Co-author: (coloring book) Nutrition Education, 1972; contbr. newpaper articles to Rocky Mountain News, 1992; author (jour.) Ill. Tchr., 1974. State v.p., dist. pres. New Home Makers Am., Ark., 1958-59; mem. Montbello Optimist Club, Denver, 1987-89, Far NE Neighbors Assn., Denver, 1985—; chairperson worship United Ch. of Montbello, Denver, 1989—. Recipient Nutrition Edn. award Western Dairy Coun., 1986; named Outstanding Educator of Am., Outstanding Educators of Am., 1973, Outstanding Young Woman of Am., Outstanding Young Women of Am., 1976. Mem. Am. Dietetic Assn. (registered dietitian), Colo. Dietetic Assn. (scholarship chairperson 1990-91, pub. rels. 1983-84) Soc. Nutrition Edn., Ark. Gerontol. Soc. (charter), Delta Sigma Theta (undergrad. chpt. sponsor 1972-73). Avocations: reading, sewing, visiting museums and art galleries, piano, public speaking. Home: 4743 Chandler Ct Denver CO 80239-4971

NASH, SYLVIA DOTSETH, religious organization executive, consultant; b. Montevedio, Minn., Apr. 25, 1945; d. Owen Donald and Selma A. (Tollefson) Dotseth; divorced; 1 child, Elizabeth Louise; m. Thomas L. Nash, Dec. 20, 1986. Grad., Calif. Luth. Bible Sch., 1965; doctorate (hon.), Pilgrims Theol. Seminary, 1994. Office mgr. First Congl. Ch., Pasadena, Calif., 1968-75; adminstrv. asst. Pasadena Presbyn. Ch., 1975-78; dir. adminstrv. svcs. Fuller Theol. Sem., Pasadena, 1978-81; CEO Christian Mgmt. Assn., Diamond Bar, Calif., 1981-94; pres. Christian Healthcare Network, La Mirada, Calif., 1994—; cons. various orgns., 1985—. Author: Inspirational Management, 1992 (Your Church Mag. award 1992); The Clarion, 1975-78, The Christian Mgmt. Report, 1981-94; mem. editl./adv. bd. Your Church Mag.; mem. editl. bd. Jour. Ministry Mktg. and Mtmg.; contbr. articles to profl. jours. Bd. dirs. Evang. Coun. for Fin. Accountability, Campus Crusade for Christ Internat. Sch. Theology, Nat. Network of Youth Ministries, The Mustard Seed, Int. Nat. Assn. of Ch. Bus. Adminstrn., Found. for His Ministry, Lamb's Players, Gospel Lit. Internat., Rosemead, Calif. Mem. NAFE, Nat. Assn. Ch. Adminstrs. (sec. 1979-81), Am. Soc. Assn. Execs., Christian Mgmt. Assn. Office: Christian Healthcare Network PO Box 1750 La Mirada CA 90637-1750

NASH, WILLIAM ARTHUR, civil engineer, educator; b. Chgo., Sept. 15, 1922; s. William A. and Rose (Keck) N.; m. Verna Lucile Baer, Aug. 8, 1953; children: Rebecca Ann, Phillip Arthur. BS in Civil Engring. Ill. Inst. Tech., 1944, M.S., 1946; Ph.D., U. Mich., 1949. Research engr. David W. Taylor Model Basin, Navy Dept., Washington, 1949-54; mem. faculty U. Fla., Gainesville, 1954-67; head dept. engring. mechanics U. Fla., 1964-67; prof. civil engring. U. Mass., Amherst, 1967—; cons. to govt. and industry; hon. prof. Shanghai Inst. Tech., 1985; pres. Cons. Engring. Amherst, 1992—. Author: Theory and Outline of Strength of Materials, 2d edit., 1973, 3d edit. 1994, Statics and Mechanics of Materials, 1991; also contbr. 105 rsch. articles to profl. jours.; editor Internat. Jour. Nonlinear Mechanics. Recipient Humboldt U.S. Sr. Scientist award to Fed. Republic Germany, 1986; named Outstanding Sr. Faculty Mem. in Engring., U. Mass., 1987. Fellow ASME; mem. Internat. Assn. Shell and Spatial Structures, Am. Soc. Engring. Edn. (Curtis W. McGraw Research award 1961), AIAA, Earth-

quake Engring. Research Inst. Congregationalist. Office: 235 Marston Hall U Mass Amherst MA 01003

NASHE, CAROL, association executive, public relations consultant; b. Boston; d. Max and Sarah Ida (Litcofsky) Naselsky; m. Russell Weinberg (dec. Aug. 1980); children: Richard Dana, Harold Mark (dec.). Student, Mass. Sch. of Art, Boston, 1949. Asst. fashion editor Boston Herald Traveler, 1951; pres., founder Carol Nashe Sch. & Model Agy., Boston, 1951-74; dir. pub. rels. Sheraton Boston Hotel & Tower, 1974-84; cons. Blue Cross and Blue Shield of Mass., Boston, 1984-93; state chmn. U.S. Olympic Com., Mass., 1986-92; bd. dirs. World Trade Ctr., 1987-95; exec. dir., exec. v.p. Nat. Assn. Radio Talk Show Hosts. Bd. dirs. Morgan Meml. Goodwill Industries, Boston, 1986-93, Wang Ctr., Mass. Spl. Olympics, Pub. Action for Arts, Boys and Girls Clubs, Friends of John F. Kennedy Libr.; chmn. bd. Nat. Kidney Found.; advisor Boston organizing com., Mayors Drug Rally; chmn., founder Harold Weinberg Meml. Found., Friends of Mateo's Ballet Theatre of Boston. Named Women of Yr., Nat. Kidney Found., 1983, Woman of Achievement, Big Sisters, 1986, Nat. Humanitarian of Yr., Heaven's Children, 1989; recipient Matrix award Women in Communications, Inc., 1988. Mem. Publicity Club, New Eng. Broadcasters Assn. (bd. dirs. 1985-90), Mass. Women's Polit. Caucus, Internat. Inst. Women's Polit. Leaders, Greater Boston C. of C. (bd. dirs. 1986—), Exec. Club Boston (pres. 1991-92), Boston Club (pub. rels. com. 1987—). Avocations: travel, photography, reading, home decorating, oil painting. Home and Office: 134 Saint Botolph St Boston MA 02115-4819

NASI, JOHN RODERICK, manufacturing executive; b. Ironwood, Mich., May 8, 1940; s. John Frijolf and Katherine Helen (Uremovick) N.; m. Patricia Ann Hosking, May 28, 1960; children: Jeffrey John, John Patrick, James Marshal. B in Mech. Engring., Gen. Motors Inst. Various mgmt. positions GMC Truck and Coach div. Gen. Motors Corp., Pontiac, Mich., 1964-79, gen. supt. prodn., 1979-81, plant mgr., 1981-82; exec. v.p. Transp. Mfg. Corp., Roswell, N. Mex., 1982—; now pres., CEO, bd. dirs. Transp. Mfg. Corp., Roswell, N.Mex.; pres., CEO, bd. dirs. MCI Acceptance Corp., Phoenix; bd. dirs. Dallas Smith Transp. Co., Phoenix, Sunwest Bank of Roswell. Bd. dirs. Boy Scouts of Am., Roswell, 1982—, United Way, Roswell, 1982—, St. Mary's Hosp., Roswell, 1984—. Mem. Soc. Automotive Engrs. Episcopalian. Lodge: Rotary. Avocations: golf, old cars. Home: RR 1 Box 246 Roswell NM 88201-9801 Office: Transp Mfg Corp PO Box 5670 Roswell NM 88202-5670*

NASON, CHARLES TUCKEY, financial services executive; b. Pitts., Apr. 22, 1946; s. Raymond W. and Helen (Tuckey) N.; m. Marlane L. Mulac, Nov. 20, 1967; children—Rebecca Ann, Jill Nicole. B.A., Washington and Jefferson Coll., 1968; M.B.A., U. Pitts. 1969. Cert. fin. planner; chartered fin. cons.; CLU. Dist. sales mgr. Met. Life Ins. Co., Pitts., 1971-77; mng. dir. Acacia Group Cos., Pitts., 1977-88; chmn., pres., chief exec. officer Acacia Mut. Life Ins. Co. , Washington, 1988—; founder, pres. Coordinated Capital Ltd., Pitts., 1982-85. Chmn. exec. com. Washington and Jefferson Coll. Devel. Coun., 1982-85; bd. trustees Washington and Jefferson Coll., 1988—; chmn. Nat. Annual Giving Fund Washington and Jefferson Coll., 1992-94; trustee Washington Federal City Coun., 1988—; bd. dirs. Greater Washington Bd. Trade, 1990—, pres.-elect, 1993, pres., 1994, chmn. 1994; bd. dirs. Blue Cross Blue Shield of Washington, 1991-93, Greater Washington Boys and Girls Clubs, 1991—, Am. Coun. of Life Ins., 1993—. Lt. USAF. 1970-71, Korea. Mem. Gen. Agts. and Mgrs. Assn. (pres. 1984-85), Am. Soc. CLUs (pres. 1981-82), Estate Planning Coun. (bd. dirs.), Nat. Assn. Securities Dealers, Inst. Cert. Fin. Planners (bd. dirs.), Burning Tree Club, Congl. Country Club, Met. Club (Washington), Wexford Plantation Club (Hilton Head, S.C.), Melrose Club. Republican. Roman Catholic. Avocations: reading, golf, guitar. Home: 18 Beman Woods Ct Potomac MD 20854 Office: Acacia Group 51 Louisiana Ave NW Washington DC 20001-2176

NASON, JOHN WILLIAM, retired college president, educational consultant; b. St. Paul, Feb. 9, 1905; s. Albert John and Mary Ethel (Eaton) N.; m. Bertha Deane White, June 15, 1935 (dec. Dec. 1955); children: Charles Kirby, Robert White; m. Elizabeth Mercer Knapp, June 29, 1957; stepchildren: Whitman E. Knapp, Caroline Knapp Hines, Marion E. Knapp. BA, Carleton Coll., 1926, LLD, 1948; postgrad., Yale U., 1926-27; MA, Harvard U., 1928; BA, Oxford (Eng.) U., 1931; LLD, U. Pa., 1941; LittD, Muhlenberg Coll., 1943, Hahnemann Med. Coll. and Hosp., 1943; LHD, Dropsie Coll., 1952, Coll. of Wooster, 1961, St. Olaf Coll., 1970, SUNY, 1992; LLD, Swarthmore Coll., 1953, Hamilton Coll., 1955, Brandeis U., 1958, Johns Hopkins U., 1960. Instr. philosophy Swarthmore Coll., 1931-34, asst. prof., 1934-40, asst. to pres., 1937-38, 39-40, acting chmn. dept. philosophy, 1938-39, pres., 1940-53; asst. to Am. sec. Rhodes Trustees, 1934-40; pres. Fgn. Policy Assn., 1953-62, Carleton Coll., Northfield, Minn., 1962-70; dir. studies Assn. Governing Bds., 1973-75, dir. study presdl. selection and assessment, 1977-79; dir. study on found. trustees Coun. on Founds., 1975-77; ednl. cons., 1979—. Author: American Higher Education in 1980—Some Basic Issues, 1965, Crises in the University, 1970, The Future of Trusteeship: The Role and Responsibilities of College and University Boards, 1975, Trustees & the Future of Foundations, 1977, Presidential Search: A Guide to the Process of Selecting and Appointing College and University Presidents, 1979, Presidential Assessment: Challenge to College and University Leadership, 1980, The Nature of Trusteeship, 1982, Foundation Trusteeship: Service in the Public Interest, 1989; various articles, revs. Chmn. Nat. Japanese-Am. Student Relocation Coun., 1942-45; pres. UN Coun. Phila., 1942-45, World Affairs Coun. Phila., 1949-51, 52-53; mem. Fulbright-Hays Com. Internat. Exchange Persons, 1963-66; mem. educators adv. com. Esso Edn. Found., 1964-68; trustee Edward W. Hazen Found., 1945-67, 68-78; Trustee Phillips Exeter Acad., 1946-50, 52-62, Vassar Coll., 1954-62, Danforth Found., 1961-68, United Negro Coll. Fund, 1966-70, Adirondack Conservancy, 1977-90, N.Y. State Conservancy, 1983-90; bd. govs. Bruce L. Crary Found., 1979-93; bd. dirs. Eisenhower Exchange Fellowship, 1953-65, Fgn. Policy Assn., 1953-62, 71-80 ; mem. adv. coun. Inst. Ednl. Mgmt./Harvard U., 1975-76; mem. vis. com. Harvard Grad. Sch. Edn., 1977-82. Rhodes scholar Oxford U., 1931. Fellow Nat. Coun. Religion in Higher Edn. (pres. 1943-49); mem. Soc. Values in Higher Edn., Phi Beta Kappa (senator united chpts. 1967-73), Delta Sigma Rho. Mem. Soc. of Friends. Home: Crosslands Apt 12 Kennett Square PA 19348

NASON, ROBERT E., accountant; b. Sioux Falls, S.D., July 29, 1936; s. Earl V. and Eileen P. (Henegar) N.; m. Carol Ann Nason, Oct. 6, 1962; children: Steven, Jill. BS, U. S.D., 1958. Staff acct., mgr. Grant Thornton, Mpls., 1958-69, audit ptnr., 1969-71; mng. ptnr. Grant Thornton, Cleve., 1971-76; mng. ptnr. Grant Thornton, Chgo., 1976-88, midwest regional mng. ptnr., 1990-90, exec. ptnr., chief exec. officer, 1990—. Governing mem. Chgo. Symphony Orchestral Assn., 1985—. Mem. AICPA, Ill. CPA Soc., Chgo. Assn. Commerce & Industry, Exmoor Country Club (pres. 1988-90), Mid-Am. Club (bd. dirs. 1988-90), The Plaza Club, Econ. Club Chgo. Avocation: golf. Office: Grant Thorton LLP One Prudential Plz Ste 800 130 E Randolph Dr Chicago IL 60601

NASON, ROCHELLE, conservation organization administrator; b. Oakland, Calif., May 21, 1959; d. Milton and Ann Frances (Reed) N. BA, U. Calif., Berkeley, 1984; JD, U. Calif., San Francisco, 1987. Bar: Calif. 1987. Law clk. to Chief Justice Malcolm Lucas Supreme Ct. of Calif., San Francisco, 1987-88; litigation assoc. Morrison & Foerster, San Francisco, 1988-92; staff lawyer League to Save Lake Tahoe, South Lake Tahoe, Calif., 1992-93, exec. dir., 1993—; adj. instr. Sierra Nev. Coll., Incline Village, 1992—, Lake Tahoe C.C., 1992—. Editor: The Traynor Reader, 1987; sr. rev. editor Hastings Law Jour., 1986-87; editor jour. Keep Tahoe Blue, 1992—; columnist (newspaper) Tahoe Daily Tribune; contbr. articles to profl. jours. V.p., bd. dirs. Jewish Cmty. South Lake Tahoe/Temple Bat Yam, 1992—; mem. leadership coun. Tahoe-Truckee Regional Econ. Coalition, Stateline, Nev., 1992—; bd. dirs. Tahoe Ctr. for Sustainable Future, Glenbrook, Nev., 1995—. Mem. AAUW, Thurston Soc., Order of Coif. Jewish. Avocations: back-packing, skiing. Office: League to Save Lake Tahoe 989 Tahoe Keys Blvd Ste 6 South Lake Tahoe CA 96150

NASSAU, MICHAEL JAY, lawyer; b. N.Y.C., June 3, 1935; s. Benjamin and Belle (Nassau) N.; m. Roberta Bluma Herzlich, June 26, 1971; children: Stephanie Ellen, William Michael. BA summa cum laude, Yale U., 1956, LLB cum laude, 1960. Bar: N.Y. 1960, D.C. 1992, U.S. Dist. Ct. (so. dist.)

N.Y. 1978, U.S. Tax Ct. 1963, U.S. Ct. Appeals (2d cir.) 1963, U.S. Supreme Ct. 1965. Asst. instr. in constl. law Yale U., 1959-60; law clk. to judge U.S. Ct. Appeals 2d. Cir., 1960-61; assoc. tax dept. Paul, Weiss, Rifkind, Wharton & Garrison, N.Y.C., 1961-73; ptnr. Kramer, Levin, Naftalis, Nessen, Kamin & Frankel, and predecessor, N.Y.C., 1974—; mem. adv. bd. Matthew Bender Fed. Pension Law Service, 1975-76; mem. adv. com. NYU Ann. Inst. Employee Plans and Exec. Compensation, 1976-79; mem. steering com. Am. Pension Conf., 1981-83; lectr. in field; panelist various seminars on employee benefits. Mem. ABA (sect. taxation, employee benefits com. 1993—), N.Y. State Bar Assn. (co-chmn. employee benefits sect. taxation 1976-78, mem. exec. com. sect. taxation 1976-79), Assn. of Bar of City of N.Y. (chmn. subcom. pension legis. of com. taxation 1975-76, employee benefits com. 1987-92), WEB (N.Y. chpt. bd. dirs. 1990—, pres. 1993-94), Phi Beta Kappa. Mem. editorial bd. Bank and Corp. Governance Law Reporter, 1989—; contbr. chpts., articles to law publs.; panelist Pension Video Seminar, 1983. Office: Kramer Levin Naftalis Nessen Kamin & Frankel 919 3d Ave New York NY 10022

NASSBERG, EDWARD, chemicals executive. Pres. Plexchem Internat. Inc., Melville, N.Y., 1975—. Office: Plexchem Internat Inc 1121 Old Walt Whitman Rd Melville NY 11747-3083

NASSBERG, RICHARD T., lawyer; b. N.Y.C., Mar. 30, 1942; s. Jules and Rhea (Steinglass) N.; m. Kathryn S. Lynn, May 2, 1981; children: Schuyler M. L., Kathyrn Cupp. BS in Econs., Wharton Sch., U. Pa., 1963; JD, U. Pa., 1968. Bar: N.Y. 1969, U.S. Ct. Appeals (2d cir.) 1970, Pa. 1972, Tex. 1983. With Milbank, Tweed, Hadley & McCloy, N.Y.C., 1968-70; with Schnader, Harrison, Segal & Lewis, Phila., 1971-78, ptnr., 1978-82; ptnr. Mayor, Day & Caldwell, Houston, 1982-90; pvt. practice law, 1990-92; of counsel Mannino & Griffith, Phila., 1992—; planning chmn. courses of study on banking and comml. lending law Am. Law Inst.-ABA, 1979—, mem. adv. com. to subcom. on continuing legal edn., 1982-90 . Served with Army N.G., 1963-65, USAR, 1965-66, USAFR, 1966-69. Mem. NYCYC (standing com. on Nat. Security 1968-71), Am. Law Inst. (advisor comml. law 1985—), ABA, Tex. Bar Assn., Houston Bar Assn. Clubs: Franklin Inn (Phila.). Author: The Lender's Handbook. 1986; editor resource books on banking law; contbr. articles on banking law to profl. publs.; editor U. Pa. Law Rev., 1967-68, assoc. editor, 1966-67. Office: PO Box 5055 Jersey Shore PA 17740

NASSER, JOSEPH YOUSEF, public safety adminstrator, consultant; b. Welch, W.Va., Mar. 19, 1943; s. Joseph H. and Betty Anne (Caldwell) N.; m. Linda Mercer, Aug. 9, 1986; children: Robert, Eric, Melanie, Matthew, Michelle. BS, Pacific Western U., 1989, PhD, 1991. Patrolman, firefighter, emergency med. technician Mich. Dept. Pub. Safety, Oak Park, 1962-75; patrolman Daytona Beach (Fla.) Police Dept., 1975-76; lt., capt., dir. Volusia County (Fla.) Sheriff's Dept., 1976-90; pres., founder, owner Ctr. for Pub. Safety Studies, Ormond Beach, Fla., 1990—; Pres. Associated Pub. Safety Comm. Officer, Inc., 1987-88, Land Mobile Comm. Coun., Washington, 1988-89; chmn. Nat. Pub. Safety Planning Com./F.C.C., 1987-88; life mem. APCO, Inc. Past chmn. Fla. State Standards and Telecommunicator Cert. Com., Fla. State Emergency Mgmt. 9-1-1 Com.; past mem. exec. coun. Volusia County Emergency Med. Found.; past chmn. Volusia County Emergency Med. Svcs. Trust Fund Adv. Bd. Recipient Dayton Beach Cooper-Taylor Pub. Safety Achievement award, 1985, Nat. Achievement award Pub. Safety Comm. Coun., 1987, FCC Recognition award, 1987, APCO Life Mem. award, 1988, Emergency Mgmt. Recognition award State of Fla., 1989, Appreciation award Emergency Med. Found., 1990, Disting. Svc. award Volusia County Sheriff's Dept., 1990. Fellow Radio Club of Am.; mem. Associated Pub. Safety Comms. Ofcls. Internat. (life), Internat. Mcpl. Signal Assn. (sustaining, Journalistic Excellence award 1991). Democrat. Methodist. Avocations: fishing, bowling, jogging, horseback riding. Home: Eagle's Nest Ranch Ormond Beach FL 32174 Office: Ctr for Pub Safety Studies 595 N Nova Rd Ste 207 Ormond Beach FL 32174-4425

NASSIF, THOMAS ANTHONY, business executive, former ambassador; b. Cedar Rapids, Iowa, July 22, 1941; s. George Joseph and Clara Christine (Nofal) N.; m. Zinetta Marie Meherg, Sept. 14, 1968; children—Jaisa Diane, Matthew Christian. BS, Calif. State U.-Los Angeles, 1965; JD, Calif. Western Sch. Law, 1969, LLD (hon.), 1988. Ptnr. Gray, Cary, Ames & Frye, El Centro, Calif., 1980-81; dep. and acting chief of protocol Dept. State, Washington, 1981-83; dep. asst. sec. Bur. Near Eastern and South Asian Affairs, Dept State, Washington 1983-85; U.S. ambassador to Morocco, 1985-88; chmn. bd. Gulf Interstate Internat. Corp., San Diego, 1988-95; chmn. of bd. Gulf Intern. Inc., Houston, 1988-95, Gulf Internat. Consulting Inc., San Diego, 1995—; chmn. Am. Task Force for Lebanon, Washington, 1991—. Active campaign Reagan for Pres., 1980; mem. Calif. State Rep. Cen. Com. Served with U.S. Army and USNG, 1960-67. Recipient Disting. Profl. Achievement award Attiyeh Benevolent Soc., Ellis Island Congl. Medal of Honor, 1993. Office: Gulf Internat Consulting Inc Ste 1025 4660 La Jolla Village Dr San Diego CA 92122-4601

NASSIKAS, JOHN NICHOLAS, lawyer; b. Manchester, N.H., Apr. 29, 1917; s. Nicholas John and Constantina (Gagalis) N.; m. Constantina Andreson, Feb. 21, 1943; children: Kira Hohenadel, Marcy (Mrs. Wade B. C. Weathers, Jr.), Elizabeth (Mrs. Watson Lowery), John Nicholas III. A.B., Dartmouth Coll., 1938; M.B.A., Harvard U., 1940, J.D., 1948; LL.D. (hon.), Notre Dame Coll., Manchester, N.H., 1972. Bar: N.H. and Mass. 1948, D.C. 1968, U.S. Supreme Ct. 1953, Va. 1986. Asst., dep. atty. gen. N.H. 1950-53; sr. partner firm Wiggin, Nourie, Sundeen, Nassikas & Pingree, Manchester, 1953-69; chmn. Fed. Power Commn., 1969-75; partner firm Squire, Sanders & Dempsey, Washington, 1975-86; spl. commr., presiding chmn. N.H. Pub. Utilities Commn., 1984-86; spl. commr., presiding chmn. procs. for reorgn. of Pub. Svc. Co. N.H., N.H. Pub. Utilities Commn., 1989-92; arbitrator Duke Power Co., NCEMC and SALVDA River Elect. Coops., 1992-94. Mem. Adminstrv. Conf. U.S., 1969-75; bd. dirs. U.S. Nat. Com. of World Energy Conf., 1970-74, 77-87; mem. Water Resources Council, 1969-75; mem. exec. com. NARUC, 1970-75; mem. Pres.'s Cabinet Task Force on Oil Import Control, 1969-70; mem. energy subcom. domestic council, 1969-73; mem. Pres.'s Joint Bd. on Fuel Supply and Transport, 1970-73, Pres.'s Energy Resources Council, 1974-75, Nat. Petroleum Council, 1975-79; bd. dirs. Ams. for Energy Independence, 1975-84; trustee Pathfinder Mines Corp., 1976-82; mem. adv. council Gas Research Inst., 1977-87; bd. dirs. corp. Madeira Sch., 1972-80. Served to lt. USNR, 1942-46. Mem. ABA, N.H. Bar Assn., Mass. Bar Assn. (spl. commr. Seabrook Nuclear Fin. Hearings), D.C. Bar Assn., Fed. Bar Assn., Va. Bar Assn., Fed. Energy Bar Assn., Cosmos Club, Met. Club, Farmington Country Club, Ahepa, Kappa Kappa Kappa. Republican. Home and Office: 1131 Litton Ln Mc Lean VA 22101-1823

NAST, DIANNE MARTHA, lawyer; b. Mount Holly, N.J., Jan. 30, 1946; d. Henry Daniel and Anastasia (Lovenduski) N.; m. Joseph Francis Roda, Aug. 23, 1980; children: Michael, Daniel, Joseph, Joshua, Anastasia. BA, Pa. State U., 1965; JD, Rutgers U., 1976. Bar: Pa. 1976, U.S. Dist. Ct. Pa. 1976, N.J. 1976, U.S. Dist. Ct. N.J. 1976, U.S. Ct. Appeals (3d, 6th and 7th cirs.) 1976, U.S. Supreme Ct. 1982, U.S. Dist. Ct. Ariz. 1985. Dir., v.p. Kohn, Nast & Graf, P.C., Phila., 1976-95, Roda & Nast, P.C., Lancaster, Pa., 1995—; mem. lawyers adv. com. U.S. Ct. Appeals (3d cir.), 1982-84, chmn., 1983-84, mem. com. on revision jud. conf. conduct rules, 1982-84; mem. U.S. Ct. Appeals for the 3d Cir. Jud. Conf. Permanent Planning Com., 1983-90; bd. dirs. 3d Cir. Hist. Soc., 1993—; bd. dirs. Phila. Pub. Def., 1980-89; dir. U.S. Fed. Judicial Ctr. Found., 1991—; chmn. lawyers adv. com. U.S. Dist. Ct. (ea. dist.) Pa., 1982-90, pres. Hist. Soc., 1988-91. Mem. Phila. Bar Assn. (bd. govs. 1985-87, chmn. bicentennial com. 1986-87, chmn. bench bar conf. 1988-89), Pa. Bar Assn. (ho. of dels. 1983—), ABA (coun. litigation sect. 1986-89, co-chmn. anti-trust com. litigation sect. 1984-86, div. dir. 1990-91, practical litigation editorial bd. 1989—, ho. of dels. 1992—, mem. task force state of justice system 1993, mem. task force long range planning com. 1994), Am. Law Inst. (chair internat. professionalism com. 1991-94, civil justice task force 1993—), Am. Arbitration Assn. (bd. dirs.), Am. Judicature Soc., N.J. Bar Assn., Pa. Trial Lawyers Assn., Rutgers Law Sch. Alumni Assn., Pa. Acad. Fine Arts. Home: 1059 Sylvan Rd Lancaster PA 17601-1923 Office: Roda & Nast PC 36 E King St Ste 301 Lancaster PA 17602

NASWORTHY, CAROL CANTWELL, education and public policy professional; b. Sapulpa, Okla., Aug. 6, 1939; d. Harlin Forrest and Margaret (Martin) Cantwell; m. Jack Edward Nasworthy. BA in English, Okla. State U., 1962; MA in English, U. Ark.; MEd in Ednl. Adminstrn., Lamar U., 1979; PhD in Ednl. Adminstrn., U. Tex., Austin, 1989. Cert. tchr., Tex. Tchr., dept. chair Tulsa Pub. Schs., 1962-74, Nederland (Tex.) Pub. Schs., 1974-84; legis. aide Tex. Ho. of Reps., Beaumont and Austin, 1982-84; adminstr. Tex. Edn. Agy., Austin, 1985; dir. programs Tex. Gov.'s Office, 1985-87; dir. programs Office Pub./Pvt. Sector Initiatives Tex. Employment Commn., Austin, 1987-93; asst. to comsnr. Tex. Railroad Comsn., Austin, 1993-95; rsch. assoc. S.W. Ednl. Devel. Lab., Austin, 1995—; curriculum cons. Okla. State U., Stillwater and Tulsa, 1967; chair Tex. Com. Practitioners Vocat. Edn., 1990—. Contbr. to profl. publs. Trustee, vice-chair Austin C.C., 1990—. Grantee U.S. Dept. Labor, 1990—, Tex. Dept. Human Svcs., 1990—. Mem. Tex. Coun. Women Sch. Execs. (bd. dirs. 1986-90), Phi Delta Kappa. Democrat. Office: SW Edn Devel. Lab 211 E 7th St Austin TX 78701

NATALICIO, DIANA SIEDHOFF, university president; b. St. Louis, Aug. 25, 1939; d. William and Eleanor J. (Biermann) Siedhoff. BS in Spanish summa cum laude, St. Louis U., 1961; MA in Portuguese lang., U. Tex., 1964, PhD in Linguistics, 1969. Chmn. dept. modern langs. U. Tex., El Paso, 1973-77, assoc. dean liberal arts, 1977-79; acting dean liberal arts, 1979-80; dean Coll. Liberal Arts U. Tex., El Paso, 1980-84, v.p. acad. affairs, 1984-88, pres., 1988—; bd. dirs. El Paso br. Fed. Res. Bd. Dallas, chmn., 1989; mem. Presdl. Adv. Commn. on Ednl. Excellence for Hispanic Ams., 1991; bd. dirs. Tex. Commn. on Humanities, Sandia Corp., Enserch Corp., Nat. Coun. for Minorities in Engring., Fogarty Internat. Ctr. of NIH, U.S.-Mex. Commn. for Ednl. and Cultural Exch., Fund for Improvement of Post-Secondary Edn. Co-author: Sounds of Children, 1977; contbr. articles to profl. jours. Bd. dirs. United Way El Paso, 1990-93, chmn. needs survey com., 1990-91, chmn. edn. divsn., 1989; chmn. Quality Edn. for Minorities Network in Math., Sci. and Engring., 1991-92; chairperson Leadership El Paso, Class 12, 1989-90; mem. adv. coun., 1987-90, participant, 1980-81; active Historically Black Colls. and Univs./Minority Instns. Consortium on Environ. Tech., chairperson, 1991-93, Nat. Sci. Bd., NASA Adv. Coun. Recipient Torch of Liberty award Anti-Defamation League B'nai B'rith, 1991, Conquistador award City of El Paso, 1990, Humanitarian award Nat. Coun. Christians and Jews, El Paso chpt., 1990; mem. El Paso Women's Hall of Fame, 1990. Mem. Am. Assn. Higher Edn. (bd. chair), Philos. Soc. Tex. Avocations: hiking, bicycling, skiing, skating. Home: 711 Cincinnati Ave El Paso TX 79902-2616 Office: U Tex at El Paso Office of the President 500 W University Ave El Paso TX 79968-8900

NATALIE, RONALD BRUCE, lawyer; b. Lynn, Mass., Nov. 29, 1935; s. John Richard and Cecelia Lucy (Fish) N.; m. Betty Ann McEnteggart, Aug. 22, 1958; children: Ronald Bruce Jr., Karen Lorraine, Donna Leslie, John Francis. AB, Tufts Coll., 1957; JD with highest honors, George Washington U., 1962. Bar: D.C. 1962, U.S. Ct. Appeals (D.C. cir.) 1964, U.S. Ct. Appeals (2d cir.) 1970, U.S. Ct. Appeals (5th cir.), 1991, U.S. Ct. Appeals (3d cir.) 1992. Atty. Office of Gen. Counsel, U.S. Commn. on Civil Rights, Washington, 1962-64; assoc. Verner, Liipfert, Bernhard, McPherson and Hand, Washington, 1964-68, ptnr., 1968-81; shareholder Verner Liipfert, Bernarhd, McPherson & Hand, Washington, 1981—; chief counsel Pres.'s Commn. to Investigate the Accident at Three Mil Island, Washington, 1979; vice chmn. Close Up Found., Alexandria, Va., 1971—. Lt. USN, 1957-62. Mem. ABA, D.C. Bar Assn., Ba Assn. of D.C., assn. for Transp., Law, Logistics and Policy, Phi Alpha Delta. Democrat. Home: 3307 39th St NW Washington DC 20016-3711 Office: Verner Liipfert Bernarhd McPherson & Hand 901 15th St NW Washington DC 20005-2327

NATANSON, MAURICE ALEXANDER, philosopher, educator; b. N.Y.C., Nov. 26, 1924; s. Charles and Kate (Scheer) N.; m. Lois Janet Lichenstein, Jan. 21, 1949; children: Charles, Nicholas, Kathy. A.B., Lincoln Meml. U., 1945; M.A., N.Y. U., 1948; Ph.D., U. Nebr., 1950; D.S.Sc. summa cum laude, New Sch. Social Research, 1953; M.A. (hon.), Yale U., 1976. Teaching asst. philosophy U. Neb., Lincoln, 1948-50; instr. U. Neb., 1950-51; lectr. philosophy grad. faculty New Sch. Social Research, N.Y.C., 1952-53; Am. Council Learned Socs. scholar New Sch. Social Research, 1951-53; asst. prof. philosophy U. Houston, 1953-56, asso. prof., 1956-57; assoc. prof. philosophy U. N.C., Chapel Hill, 1957-62; Am. Coun. Learned Socs. fellow, 1961-62; prof. U. N.C., 1962-65; Disting. vis. prof. philosophy, rhetoric Pa. State U., University Park, spring 1963; vis. prof. philosophy U. Calif., Berkeley, 1964-65; prof. philosophy, fellow, Cowell Coll. U. Calif. at Santa Cruz, 1965-76, chmn. bd. philosophy, 1965-67, 68-70, faculty research lectr., 1966; sr. humanities fellow U. Calif., 1967-68; dir. Methuselah, adult edn. program U. Calif., Santa Cruz, summer 1967; prof. philosophy Yale U., 1976—; Guest prof. sociology U. Konstanz, West Germany, spring 1974; Nat. Endowment Humanities sr. fellow, 1971-72, panelist, 1974, dir. summer seminar, 1976, 77, 79; dir. grad. studies in philosophy Yale, 1991-93. Author: A Critique of Jean-Paul Sartre's Ontology, 1951, The Social Dynamics of George H. Mead, 1956, Literature, Philosophy, and the Social Sciences, 1962, The Journeying Self, 1970, Edmund Husserl, 1973, Phenomenology, Role, and Reason, 1974, Anonymity: A Study in the Philosophy of Alfred Schutz, 1986; editor: The Problem of Social Reality (Alfred Schutz), 1962, Philosophy of the Social Sciences, 1963, Essays in Phenomenology, 1966, Psychiatry and Philosophy, 1969, Phenomenology and Social Reality, 1970, Phenomenology and the Social Sciences, 2 vols., 1973, (with Henry W. Johnstone, Jr.) Philosophy, Rhetoric, and Argumentation, 1965; cons. editor Philosophy and Phenomenological Rsch., 1960-84, Ind.-Northwestern U. Press Studies Phenomenology Existential Philosophy, 1963—; Jour. Value Inquiry, 1967-90, Philosophy and Rhetoric, 1968-94, Medicine and Philosophy, 1975-90; book rev. editor: Man and World, 1968-78, Selected Studies Phenomenology Existential Philosophy, 1973-82; mem. editorial adv. bd. Phenomenology and Human Scis., 1981—. Mem. adv. com. Phänomenologische Bibliothek, 1992—. Recipient Nat. Book award Philosophy and Religion, 1974, Yale Coll. award for disting. undergrad. teaching, 1984. Mem. Am. Philos. Assn. (Alfred Schutz lectr. 1969), Soc. Phenomenology and Existential Philosophy (mem. exec. com. 1964-68). Democrat. Jewish. Home: 428 Humphrey St New Haven CT 06511-3711 Office: Yale U Dept Philosophy New Haven CT 06520

NATCHER, STEPHEN DARLINGTON, lawyer, business executive; b. San Francisco, Nov. 19, 1940; s. Stanlus Zoch and Robena Lenore Collie (Goldring) N.; m. Carolyn Anne Bowman, Aug. 23, 1969; children: Tanya Michelle, Stephanie Elizabeth. A.B. in Polit. Sci., Stanford U., 1962; J.D., U. Calif., San Francisco, 1965. Bar: Calif. 1966. Assoc. firm Pillsbury, Madison & Sutro, San Francisco, 1966-68; counsel Douglas Aircraft div. McDonnell Douglas Corp., Long Beach, Calif., 1968-70; v.p., sec. Security Pacific Nat. Bank, 1971-79; asst. gen. counsel Security Pacific Corp., 1979-80; v.p., sec., gen. counsel Lear Siegler, Inc., Santa Monica, Calif., 1980-87; v.p., gen. counsel Computer Scis. Corp., El Segundo, Calif., 1987-88; exec. v.p., gen. counsel, sec. CalFed Inc., 1989-90; sr. v.p. adminstrn., gen. counsel, sec. Wyle Electronics, Irvine, Calif., 1991—. With USCG, 1965-71. Mem. St. Francis Yacht Club (San Francisco). Republican.

NATELSON, NINA BETH, non-profit organization administrator; b. N.Y.C., Nov. 12, 1948; d. Samuel and Ehtel Doris (Nathan) N.; m. Murry Joseph Cohen. BA in French, German, NYU, 1968. Sales asst. Merrill Lynch, Pierce, Fenner & Smith, Inc., Washington, 1971; investment broker Baxter, Blyden, Selheimer, Inc., Washington, 1971-73; mgmt. intern Gen. Svcs. Adminstr., Washington, 1974-76; program analyst Gen. Svcs. Adminstrn., Insp. Gen.'s Office, Office Audits, Washington, 1975-80; program analyst Dept. Labor Insp. Gen.'s Office, Office of Loss Analysis and Prevention, Washington, 1980-82; freelance writer, 1985-92; founder, pres. Concern for Helping Animals in Israel, Alexandria, Va., 1984—. Contbr. articles to profl. jours. Vol. People for the Ethical Treatment of Animals, Washington, 1982-84. Mem. Nat. Fedn. Bus. and Profl. Women (editor local newsletter 1973-74, Disting. Vol. award 1984). Avocation: parapsychology. Home and Office: Concern for Helping Animals Israel PO Box 3341 Alexandria VA 22302

NATELSON, STEPHEN ELLIS, neurosurgeon; b. N.Y.C., Dec. 23, 1937; s. Samuel R. and Ethel D. (Nathan) N.; B.A. magna cum laude, Carleton Coll., 1958; Fulbright scholar in Math., Westfälische-Wilhelms U., Germany, 1958-59; M.D., U. Rochester, 1963; m. Laurie Lou Acred, 1990; children from previous marriage: Lea Jane, Jamie Ann, Jessica Ilana, Benjamin

Henry, Marissa Claire. Intern, USAF Hosp., Wright-Patterson AFB, 1963-64; resident in neurosurgery Ohio State U., 1967-71; chief resident in neurology U. N.Mex., 1971-72; pvt. practice specializing in neurosurgery, Knoxville, Tenn., 1972—; clin. assoc. prof. U. Tenn. Served with USAF, 1962-67. Decorated Air Force Commendation medal; diplomate Am. Bd. Neurol. Surgery. Fellow ACS; mem. Am. Assn. Neurol. Surgeons, Congress Neurol. Surgeons, AMA, Knoxville Acad. Medicine, Tenn. Neurosurg. Soc. (past press.), Am. Physicians Fellowship, Undersea Med. Soc., Phi Beta Kappa, Sigma Xi, Alpha Omega Alpha. Republican. Jewish. Contbr. articles to profl. jours. Office: 103 Newland Profl Bldg Knoxville TN 37916

NATH, JOGINDER, genetics and biology educator, researcher; b. Joginder Nagar, Panjab, India, May 12, 1932; came to U.S. 1957; s. Moti Ram and Vira Wali (Khorana) N.; m. Charlotte Lynn Reese, Apr. 5, 1969; children—Pravene, Brian. B.S. with honors, Panjab U., Amritsar, India, 1953; M.S. with honors, Panjab U., 1955; Ph.D., U. Wis., 1960. Research assoc. Am. Inst. Biol. Research, Madison, Wis., 1960-63; asst. prof. So. Ill. U., Carbondale, Ill., 1964-66; from asst. to assoc. prof. W.Va. U., Morgantown, 1966-72, prof., chmn. dept. genetics and devel. biology, 1972—. Contbr. articles on cytogenetics, mutagenesis, biochem. genetics and cryobiology to profl. jours. Home: bd. Morgantown Day Sch., 1977-79. Grantee NSF, 1967-68, DOE, 1992-95, Nat. Inst. Occupational Safety & Health, 1985-95. Mem. Soc. Cryobiology, Environ. Mutagen Soc., Electron Microscopy Soc., Sigma Xi. Office: WVa U Coll Agr Dept Genetics & Devel Biology Morgantown WV 26506

NATHAN, ANDREW JAMES, political science educator; b. N.Y.C., Apr. 3, 1943; s. Paul S. and Dorothy (Goldeen) N.; 1 child, Chloe; 1 stepchild Alexandra Witke. B.A. summa cum laude, Harvard U., 1963, M.A. in East Asian Regional Studies, 1965, Ph.D. in Polit. Sci., 1971. Lectr. U. Mich., Ann Arbor, 1971; research assoc. Ctr. for Chinese Studies, 1970; asst. prof. polit. sci. Columbia U., N.Y.C., 1971-75, assoc. prof., 1975-82, prof., 1982—; dir. East Asian Inst., 1991—; mem. steering com. China Internat. Bus. Project, 1978—; mem. nat. com. on U.S.-China relations, 1987—. Contbr. book revs. to publs.; manuscript reviewer for U. Calif. Press, Columbia U. Press, Harvard U. Press and jours. in field; author: A History of the China International Famine Relief Commission, 1965, Modern China, 1840-1972; An Introduction to Sources and Research Aids, 1973, Peking Politics, 1918-1923: Factionalism and the Failure of Constitutionalism, 1976, Chinese Democracy, 1985; (with others) Human Rights in Contemporary China, 1986, China's Crisis, 1990; co-editor: Popular Culture in Late Imperial China, 1985. Guggenheim fellow, 1973-74; Luce Found. grantee, 1979-82, 1992-95; Joint Com. onContemporary China, Am. Coun. Learned Soc.-Social Sci. Rsch. Coun. fellow, 1977-78; NEH fellow, 1986-87, 92-93; NSF grantee, 1993-96. Mem. Am. Polit. Sci. Assn., Assn. for Asian Studies. Home: 35 Claremont Ave Apt 6N New York NY 10027 Office: East Asian Inst Columbia U 420 W 118th St New York NY 10027-7213

NATHAN, CARL FRANCIS, medical educator; b. N.Y.C., N.Y., 1946. BA, Harvard U., 1967, MD, 1972. Intern Mass. Gen. Hosp., Boston, 1972-73, resident, 1973-74; clin. assoc. Nat. Cancer Inst., Washington, 1974-76; fellow in med. oncology Yale U., New Haven, 1976-77; attending physician N.Y. Hosp., 1985—; asst. prof. Rockefeller U., N.Y.C., 1977-83, assoc. prof., 1983-85, adj. prof., 1986—; Stanton Griffis prof. medicine Cornell U., N.Y.C., 1986—. Office: Cornell U Med Coll Dept of Medicine 1300 York Ave New York NY 10021-4805

NATHAN, DAVID GORDON, physician, educator; b. Boston, May 25, 1929; s. E. Geoffrey and Ruth (Gordon) N.; m. Jean Louise Friedman, Sept. 1, 1951; children: Deborah, Linda, Geoffrey. BA, Harvard U., 1951, MD, 1955. Diplomate Am. Bd. Internal Medicine, Am. Bd. Pediatrics. Intern dept. medicine Peter Bent Brigham Hosp., Boston, 1955-56, sr. resident, 1958-59; jr. assoc. in medicine Brigham and Women's Hosp., Boston, 1961-67, sr. assoc. in medicine, 1967—; assoc. in medicine, hematology Childrens Hosp., Boston, 1963-68, chief, div. hematology, 1968-73, chief div. hematology and oncology, 1974-84; pediatrician-in-chief Dana Farber Cancer Inst., Boston, 1974-85; Robert A. Stranahan prof. pediatrics Harvard Med. Sch., Boston, 1977—; physician-in-chief Childrens Hosp., Boston, 1985—. Editor: Hematology in Infancy and Childhood, 4th edit., 1993. With USMC, 1948-49. Recipient Nat. Medal Sci. NSF, 1990. Fellow AAAS; mem. Inst. of Medicine of NAS, Am. Acad. Arts & Scis., Am. Pediatric Soc., Soc. Pediatric Rsch., Assn. Am. Physicians, Am. Soc. Clin. Investigators, Am. Soc. Hematology (pres. 1986), Phi Beta Kappa (hon.). Avocations: tennis, hiking. Office: Childrens Hosp 300 Longwood Ave Boston MA 02115-5737

NATHAN, FREDERIC SOLIS, lawyer; b. N.Y.C., June 24, 1922; s. Edgar Joshua and Mabel (Unterberg) N.; m. Frances E., Oct. 28, 1956; children: Jean E., Frederic S., William E. BA, Williams Coll., Williamstown, Mass., 1943; LLD, Yale U., 1948. Bar: N.Y. 1948, U.S. Dist. Ct. (so. and ea. dists) N.Y. 1948, U.S. Ct. Appeals (2d cir.) 1953, U.S. Supreme Ct. 1968. Resident Williams Coll., Williamstown, 1948; assoc. Rathbone Perry Kelley & Drye, N.Y.C., 1948-53; asst. U.S. atty. U.S. Attys.' Office (so. dist.), N.Y.C., 1953-56; assoc. Greenbaum, Wolff & Ernst, N.Y.C., 1956-58, ptnr., 1959-65, 70-82; 1st asst. corp. counsel N.Y.C. Law Dept., N.Y.C., 1966-69; ptnr. Kelley, Drye & Warren, N.Y.C., 1982—. Mem. N.Y. Rep. County Com., N.Y.C., 1948-90; trustee Mt. Sinai Hosp. and Med. Sch., N.Y.C., 1970—; chmn. bd. FOJP Svc. Corp., N.Y.C., 1977-85, chmn. exec. com., 1985—; bd. dirs., v.p. Am. Jewish Soc. for Svc., N.Y.C., 1950—. Served with U.S. Army, 1943-45, ETO. Fellow Am. Coll. Trial Lawyers; mem. ABA, Assn. of Bar of City of N.Y. (exec. com. 1979-81), Fed. Bar Council (pres. 1975-76), N.Y. State Bar Assn. Republican. Jewish. Clubs: Century Assn., Yale of N.Y.C.; Sunningdale Country. Home: 180 East End Ave New York NY 10128-7763 Office: Kelley Drye & Warren 101 Park Ave New York NY 10178-0002

NATHAN, IRWIN, business systems company executive; b. N.Y.C., June 24, 1932; s. Albert Y. and Sarah (Abrams) N.; m. Sandra Alpert, June 18, 1955 (dec. June 1989); children: Alan Bradley, Mitchell Jordan; m. Phyllis Davis, Feb. 16, 1992. BSME, Stevens Inst. Tech., Hoboken, N.J., 1953; MSEE, N.Y.U., 1955, MS in Indsl. Engring., 1960; PhD, Poly. U., Bklyn., 1984. Registered profl. engr., N.Y. Rsch. and devel. engr. Dynamics Corp. of Am., Garden City, N.Y., 1953-56; sr. systems engr. Am. Bosch ARMA, Inc., Garden City, N.Y., 1956-63; prin. engr. Gen. Precision, Inc., Totowa, N.J., 1963-66; from section mgr. to mgr. svc. maintenance strategy Xerox Corp., Stamford, Conn., 1967-94; ret., 1994, cons. in reliability and svc., 1994—; guest lectr. George Washington U., 1969, UCLA, 1971, The Wharton Sch., 1985. Mem. IEEE, Ops. Rsch. Soc. Am. Avocations: boating, fishing, woodworking. Home: 12 Linda Ln Westport CT 06880-3945

NATHAN, JAMES ROBERT, hospital administrator; b. Albuquerque, Nov. 23, 1946; married. B, Miami U., 1968; M, Xavier U., 1974, MHA 1976. Adminstrv. resident Lee Meml. Hosp., Ft. Myers, Fla., 1975-76, v.p., 1976-81, pres., 1982—. Mem. Fla. Hosp. Assn. Home: 3333 Hibiscus Dr Fort Myers FL 33901-6720 Office: Lee Meml Hosp PO Box 2218 Fort Myers FL 33902-2218

NATHAN, LEONARD EDWARD, writer, educator; b. Los Angeles, Nov. 8, 1924; s. Israel and Florence (Rosenberg) N.; m. Carol Gretchen Nash, June 27, 1949; children: Andrew Peter, Julia Irene, Miriam Abigail. Student, Ga. Tech., 1943-44, UCLA, 1946-47; BA summa cum laude, U. Calif.-Berkeley, 1950, MA, 1952, PhD, 1961. Instr. Modesto (Calif.) Jr. Coll. 1954-60; prof. dept. rhetoric U. Calif.-Berkeley, 1960-91, ret., 1991, chmn. dept., 1968-72. Author: Western Reaches, 1958, The Glad and Sorry Seasons, 1963, The Matchmaker's Lament, 1967, The Day The Perfect Speakers Left, 1969, The Tragic Drama of William Butler Yeats, 1963, Flight Plan, 1971, Without Wishing, 1973, The Likeness, 1975, Coup, 1975, Returning Your Call, 1975, The Transport of Love: The Meghaduta by Kalidasa, 1976, Teachings of Grandfather Fox, 1977, Lost Distance, 1978, Dear Blood, 1980, Holding Patterns, 1982, Carrying On: New and Selected Poems, 1985; also record Confessions of a Matchmaker, 1973, De Meester van Het Winterlandschap, Selected Poems in Dutch transl. by Cees Nooteboom, Uitgeverij de Arbiedspers, Amsterdam, 1990; translator: Songs of Something Else, 1982, Grace and Mercy in Her Wild Hair, 1982, (with Czeslaw Milosz) Happy As a Dog's Tail: Poems by Anna Swir, 1985, (with Czeslaw Milosz) With the Skin: Poems of Aleksander Wat, 1989, (with

Arthur Quinn) The Poet's Work: Study of Czeslaw Milosz, 1991. With U.S. Army, 1943-45, ETO. Recipient Phelan award, 1955; Longview prize, 1961; award in lit. Nat. Inst. Arts and Letters, 1971; Poetry medal Commonwealth Club, 1976, 81; U. Calif. Creative Arts fellow, 1961-62, 73-74; U. Calif. Humanities research fellow, 1983-84; Am. Inst. Indian Studies fellow, 1966-67; Guggenheim fellow, 1976-77. Mem. assn. of Lit. Scholars and Critics. Avocation: birdwatching. Home: 40 Beverly Rd Kensington CA 94707-1304

NATHAN, MARSHALL IRA, electrical engineering educator; b. Lakewood, N.J., Jan. 22, 1933; s. Benjamin Charles and Ruth (Blumenthal) N.; m. Nancy Jennens, June 7, 1955 (div. Feb. 1970); children: Eric, Barbara; m. Rosalie Mary Lanzarone, Apr. 10, 1971. BS, MIT, 1954; MA, Harvard U., 1956, PhD, 1958. Mem. rsch. staff, then mgr. IBM, Yorktown Heights, N.Y., 1958-87; prof. dept. elec. engring. U. Minn., Mpls., 1987—; Centennial chair dept. elec. engring., 1990—; vis. prof. Cornell U., Ithaca, N.Y., 1984. Contbr. articles to profl. jours. Recognition award for semiconductor laser Laser and Electro-Optic Soc., 1986. Fellow IEEE (David Sarnoff award 1980), Am. Physical Soc. Office: Univ of Minn Dept Elec Engring 200 Union St SE Minneapolis MN 55455-0154

NATHAN, PAUL S., editor, writer; b. Oakland, Calif., Apr. 2, 1913; s. Alfred Jacobs and Frances (Strause) N.; m. Dorothy Goldeen, July 14, 1935 (dec. Dec. 1966); children: Andrew J., Carl F., Janet D.; m. Ruth Wilk Notkins, May 26, 1972. BA, U. Calif., Berkeley, 1934. Reporter Oakland Post-Enquirer, 1929-36; asst. play editor Paramount Pictures, N.Y.C., 1937-48; hosp. pub. relations Will, Folsom & Smith, N.Y.C., 1948-61; sci. editor Nat. Cystic Fibrosis Research Found., N.Y.C., Atlanta, 1963-73; contbg. editor column Rights and Permissions (now Rights), Pubs. Weekly, N.Y.C., 1946—; U.S. liaison Jerusalem Internat. Book Fair, 1976-77. Author: (play) Ricochet, 1980 (Edgar Allan Poe award of Mystery Writers Am. for best play of 1980), Texas Collects: Fine Arts, Furniture, Windmills, & Whimseys, 1988; co-editor: (anthology) View: Parade of the Avant-Garde, 1991; author: (novel) Protocol for Murder, 1994; contbr. fiction and articles to Story, N.Y. Times mag., Sat. Evening Post, Sat. Rev., others. Mem. P.E.N., Dramatists Guild, Authors Guild, Authors League, Mystery Writers Am., Phi Beta Kappa. Office: care Pubs Weekly 249 W 17th St New York NY 10011-5300

NATHAN, PETER E., psychologist, educator; b. St. Louis, Apr. 18, 1935; s. Emil and Kathryn (Kline) N.; m. Florence I. Baker, Nov. 26, 1959; children: David Edward, Anne Miller, Laura Carol, Mark Andrew. A.B., Harvard U., 1957; Ph.D., Washington U., 1962. Research fellow psychology Harvard U., 1962-64, research asso., 1964-68, asst. prof. psychology, 1968-69; research psychologist Boston City Hosp., 1964-68, dir. alcohol study unit, 1967-70; prof. Rutgers U., New Brunswick, N.J., 1969-89; dir. clin. psychology tng. Rutgers U., 1969-87, dir. Alcohol Behavior Research Lab., 1970-87, chmn. dept. clin. psychology, 1976-87, dir. Ctr. Alcohol Studies, 1983-89, Henry and Anna Starr prof. psychology, 1983-89; sr. program officer, health program MacArthur Found., 1987-89; v.p. acad. affairs, found. disting. prof. psychology U. Iowa, 1990—, dean faculties, 1990-93, provost, 1993—; mem. advisory council VA, 1972-76; chmn. alcoholism com. Nat. Inst. on Alcohol Abuse and Alcoholism, 1973-76, co-chmn. spl. rev. com., 1985, mem. nat. adv. coun., 1990-94; mem. psychol. scis. fellowship rev. com. NIMH, 1977-79; chmn. N.J. State Community Mental Health Bd., 1981-84; mem. working group substance use disorders, DSM-IV. Author: Cues, Decisions, and Diagnoses, 1967, Psychopathology and Society, 1975, 2d edit., 1980, Experimental and Behavioral Approaches to Alcoholism, 1978, Alcoholism: New Directions in Behavioral Treatment and Research, 1978, Clinical Case Studies in the Behavioral Treatment of Alcoholism, 1982, Professionals in Distress, 1987, Neuropsychological Deficits in Alcoholism, 1987, Introduction to Psychology, 1987, 2d edit., 1990, Abnormal Psychology, 1992; mem. numerous editorial bds. including Jour. Cons. Clin. Psychology, 1973—, Jour. Clin. Psychology, 1969—, Profl. Psychology, 1976-89; exec. editor Jour. Studies Alcohol, 1983-90; assoc. editor Am. Psychologist, 1977-85, Contemporary Psychology, 1991—. Fellow Am. Psychol. Assn. (chmn. sect. 3 div. 12 1976-77, rep. to council 1976-79, 82-85, pres. div 12 1984-85). Democrat. Jewish. Home: 248 Black Springs Cir Iowa City IA 52246-3800 Office: Univ Iowa 111 Jessup Hall Iowa City IA 52242-1316

NATHAN, RICHARD ARNOLD, research and development company executive; b. N.Y.C., Sept. 25, 1944; s. Joseph and Mildred (Heller) N.; m. Shelly Ann Michaels, Sept. 5, 1966 (Div. Mar. 1992); children: Wendy Beth, Daniel Scott; m. Onalee Louise Bodi, Apr. 27, 1994. BS in Chemistry, MIT, 1965; PhD in Chemistry, Poly. U., Bklyn., 1969. Researcher Polaroid Corp., Cambridge, Mass., 1969; chemist Battelle Meml. Inst., Columbus, Ohio, 1970-74, project mgr., 1974-79, mgr. environ. chem. sect., 1976-79, dir. programs, 1979-80, mgr. nuclear tech. dept., 1980-85, dir. tech. mgmt., 1985-86, div. gen. mgr., 1986-87, corp. v.p., div. pres., 1987-89, group v.p., gen. mgr., 1989-92; sr. v.p. Mason & Hanger-Silas Mason Co. Inc., Lexington, Ky., 1993—. Editor: Fuels from Sugar Crops, 1976; contbr. articles to profl. publs.; patentee in field. Bd. dirs. Ctrl. Ohio coun. Boy Scouts Am., 1981-90, Ctrl. Sci. and Industry, Columbus, 1988—; chmn. Ohio Sci. Tech. and Industry Hall of Fame, 1989-93. Recipient award Indsl. Rsch. Mag., 1976. Mem. Am. Soc. Macro-Engring. (bd. dirs. 1986—), Am. Nuclear Soc., Am. Mgmt. Assn., Ohio Acad. Sci., Sigma Xi, Phi Lambda Upsilon. Avocations: golf, reading. Office: Mason & Hanger-Silas Mason Co 2355 Harrodsburg Rd Lexington KY 40504-3324

NATHAN, RICHARD P(ERLE), political scientist, educator; b. Schenectady, N.Y., Nov. 24, 1935; s. Sidney Robert and Betty (Green) N.; m. Mary McNamara, June 5, 1957; children: Robert Joseph, Carol Hewit. AB, Brown U., 1957; M in Pub. Adminstrn., Harvard U., 1959, PhD, 1966. Legis. asst. U.S. Senator Kenneth B. Keating, Washington, 1959-62; dir. domestic policy rsch. for Nelson A. Rockefeller, 1963-64; rsch. assoc. The Brookings Inst., Washington, 1966-69, sr. fellow, project dir. monitoring studies gen. revenue sharing, community devel. block grant and pub. svc. employment programs, 1972-79; associated staff The Brookings Inst., Washington, 1980-85; asst. dir. U.S. Office of Mgmt. and Budget, Washington, 1969-71; dep. undersec. U.S Dept. Health, Edn. and Welfare, Washington, 1971-72; prof. pub. and internat. affairs Woodrow Wilson Sch. Pub. and Internat. Affairs Princeton (N.J.) U., 1979-89, also dir. Princeton Urban and Regional Rsch. Ctr., 1979-89; Disting. prof. polit. sci. and pub. policy SUNY, Albany, 1989—, provost Rockefeller Coll. Pub. Affairs and Policy, dir. Rockefeller Inst. Govt., 1989—; assoc. dir. Nat. Adv. Commn. on Civil Disorders, 1967-68; vis. prof. govt., fgn. affairs U. Va., 1972-77; chmn. Nixon Adminstrn. Transition Task Forces on Poverty and Intergovtl. Fiscal Rels., 1968, Domestic Coun. Com. on Welfare Reform Planning, 1969-70; mem. Commn. on Orgn. Govt. D.C., 1970-72, bd. overseers New Sch. for Social Rsch., 1982-88, Working Seminar on Family and Welfare, Marquette U., 1986-87; mem. selection com. Rockefeller Pub. Svc. Awards Program, 1976-78, income maintenance task force Nat. Urban Coalition, 1975-78; treas. Manpower Demonstration Rsch. Corp., 1974-81, chair, 1981—; mem. coun. scholars U.S. Libr. Congress, 1989—; mem. N.Y. State Temp. Commn. Constl. Revision, 1993-94; mem. U.S. Adv. Commn. on Intergovtl. Rels., 1994—. Author: Jobs and Civil Rights, The Role of the Federal Government in Promoting Equal Opportunity in Employment and Training, 1969, The Plot That Failed: Nixon and the Administrative Presidency, 1975, Monitoring Revenue Sharing, 1975, Revenue Sharing, The Second Round, 1977, Monitoring the Public Service Employment Program, 1978, America's Government: A Facct Book of Census Data on the Organization, Finances, and Employment of Federal, State, and Local Governments, 1979, Public Service Employment: A Field Evaluation, 1981, The Administrative Presidency, 1983, Reagan and the States, 1987, Social Sciences in Government Uses and Abuses, 1988, A New Agenda for Cities, 1992, Turning Promises into Performance: The Management Challenge of Implementing Workfare, 1993; contbr. chpts. to books; editor: (with Harvey S. Perloff) Revenue Sharing and the City, 1968, (with John D. DiJulio, Jr.) The View From the States, Making Health Reform Work, Brookings Instn., 1994; mem. editorial bd. Urban Affairs Quar., 1978-85. Eisenhower fellow European Econ. Commn., 1977. Mem. Nat. Acad. Social Ins., Nat. Acad. Pub. Adminstrn. (James E. Webb award 1986), Am. Soc. Pub. Adminstrn. (intergovtl. mgmt. award 1985), Am. Polit. Sci. Assn. (Charles E. Merriam award 1987), Assn. for Pub. Policy Analysis & Mgmt., Phi Beta Kappa, Theta Delta Chi. Republican. Jewish. Club: Princeton (N.Y.), University (Albany). Avocations: reading, squash, tennis, rowing. Home: 9 Pasture Gate Ln Delmar NY 12054-4329 Office: SUNY Rockefeller Coll Provost Office 135 Western Ave Albany NY 12203-1011

NATHANS, DANIEL, biologist; b. Wilmington, Del., Oct. 30, 1928; s. Samuel and Sarah (Levitan) N.; m. Joanne E. Gomberg, Mar. 4, 1956; children: Eli, Jeremy, Benjamin. B.S., U. Del., 1950; M.D., Washington U. 1954. Intern Presbyn. Hosp., N.Y.C., 1954-55; resident in medicine Presbyn. Hosp., 1957-59; clin. assoc. Nat. Cancer Inst., 1955-57; guest investigator Rockefeller U., N.Y.C., 1959-62; prof. microbiology Johns Hopkins Medicine, Johns Hopkins, 1962-72, prof., dir. dept. microbiology, 1972-82, Univ. prof. molecular biology and genetics, 1982—; mem. Pres. Coun. Advisers on Sci. & Tech., 1990-93; sr. investigator Howard Hughes Med. Inst., 1982—. Recipient Nobel prize in physiology or medicine, 1978, Nat. Medal of Sci. 1993. Fellow Am. Acad. Arts and Scis.; mem. NAS. Office: Johns Hopkins U-Sch Med Dept Molecular Biology & Genetics 725 N Wolfe St Baltimore MD 21205-2105

NATHANS, CONSTANCE A., health science organization administrator, sociology educator. Dir. Hopkins Population Ctr., Johns Hopkins U., Balt. Office: Johns Hopkins U Hopkins Population Ctr 615 N Wolfe St Baltimore MD 21205

NATHANSON, HARVEY CHARLES, electrical engineer; b. Pitts., Oct. 22, 1936; s. David Benjamin and Ella (Sachs) N.; m. Esther Janet Mishelevich, Oct. 13, 1963; children: Marc Elliot, Elinor Sharon. B.S.E.E., Carnegie Inst. Tech., 1958, M.S.E.E., 1959, Ph.D., 1962. Sr. engr. Junction Device Physics, Westinghouse, Research/Devel. Center, Pitts., 1962-67; fellow engr. Junction Device Physics, Westinghouse, Research/Devel. Center, 1968-72, mgr. silicon junction physics, 1972-77, mgr. microelectronics dept., 1978-90, chief scientist electronic div., 1990—; instr. Carnegie Inst. Tech., Pitts., 1959-60; chmn. Westinghouse Sat. Sci. Honors Inst. for High Sch. Students, 1970-76; mem. adv. group on electron devices Dept. Def., 1976-86; adviser to Nat. Materials Bd., 1986-87. Contbr. articles to profl. jours.; mem. editorial bd. Solid State Electronics, 1985—. Bd. dirs. Temple Sinai, 1981-83, 95—; pres. Brotherhood, 1993-95. Recipient IR100 award, 1965, hon. mention Outstanding Young Engr. award Eta Kappa Nu, 1967, Best Display Paper award Soc. Info. Display, 1972, Carnegie-Mellon Alumni award, 1982, Westinghouse Top Corp. Patent award, 1990; named to Westinghouse Order of Merit, Westinghouse Electric Corp., 1987. Fellow IEEE (mem. editorial bd. Spectrum mag. 1989-91); mem. IEEE Electron Device Soc. (pres. 1978-80), Fedn. Materials Socs. (bd. dirs. 1987-90), Sigma Xi, Eta Kappa Nu. Democrat. Jewish. Patentee in field. Home: 5635 Marlborough Rd Pittsburgh PA 15217-1404 Office: Westinghouse R & D Labs 1310 Beulah Rd Pittsburgh PA 15235-5098

NATHANSON, KIM, computer support executive; b. 1956. Buyer, in-store mgmt. Sattlers Dept. Store, Buffalo, 1975-84; with Computers Plus, Frederick, Md., chmn., now chmn. bd. Office: Computers Plus Ltd Partnership PO Box 3818 5726 Industry Ln Frederick MD 21705-3818*

NATHANSON, MELVYN BERNARD, university provost, mathematician; b. Phila., Oct. 10, 1944; s. Israel and Sophia (Manstein) N.; m. Marjorie Jane Frankel, Jan. 29, 1978; children: Alexander Philip, Rebecca Anne. BA, U. Pa., 1965; postgrad., Harvard U., 1965-66; MA, U. Rochester, 1968, PhD, 1972. Prof. So. Ill. U., Carbondale, 1971-81; dean Rutgers U., Newark, N.J., 1981-86; provost, v.p. acad. affairs Lehman Coll. CUNY, Bronx, 1986-91; prof. math. Grad. Sch. Lehman Coll. CUNY, 1986—; vis. prof. Moscow State U., USSR, 1972-73, Inst. for Advanced Study, Princeton U., N.J., 1974-75, 76, 90-91, Harvard U., Cambridge, Mass., 1977-78, Rockefeller U., 1982-85, Rutgers U., 1991-93. Author, editor thirteen books; contbr. articles to profl. jours. Fellow N.Y. Acad. Sci.; mem. AAAS, Am. Math. Soc., Math. Assn. Am., Assn. Mems. Inst. for Advanced Study (v.p.). Home: 123 Maplewood Ave Maplewood NJ 07040-1233 Office: CUNY Lehman Coll Dept Math Bronx NY 10468

NATHANSON, MICHAEL, film company executive. Pres. world wide prodn. Columbia Pictures Entertainment Inc., N.Y.C., from 1989, former exec. v.p. prodn.; pres. worldwide prodn. Columbia Pictures Entertainment Inc., Culver City, Calif., to 1993. Office: Columbia Pictures 10202 W Washington Culver City CA 90230

NATHANSON, NEAL, virologist, epidemiologist, educator; b. Boston, Sept. 1, 1927; s. Robert B. and Leah (Rabinowitch) N.; m. Constance Allen, June 8, 1954; children—Katherine L., John A., Daniel R.; m. Phoebe Starfield, Oct. 7, 1984. B.A., Harvard, 1949, M.D., 1953. Chief polio surveillance unit USPHS, 1955-57; research asso., asst. prof. anatomy Johns Hopkins, Balt., 1957-63; asso. prof. epidemiology Johns Hopkins, 1963-68, prof., 1968-79; chmn. dept. microbiology U. Pa., Phila., 1979-93, vice dean rsch., 1993-95. Editor-in-chief: Am. Jour. Epidemiology, 1964-79, Microbial Pathogenesis, 1985-88. Research, publs. pathogenesis, immunology, and epidemiology of viral infections. Home: 1600 Hagys Ford Rd Apt 9W Narberth PA 19072-1049

NATHANSON, RICK, computer company sales and support services executive; b. 1957. CEO Computers Plus Ltd., Frederick, Md., 1984—. Office: Computers Plus Ltd Partnership 5726 Industry Ln Frederick MD 21701*

NATHANSON, WAYNE RICHARD, aerospace company executive; b. Pitts., Dec. 3, 1934; s. Samuel A. and Louise Fredricka (Haisch) N.; m. Shirley Jean Heron, 1954 (div. 1978); children: Lynne, Craig; m. Deborah Ann Geiser, June 1, 1979. BS in Physics, Carnegie Inst. Tech., Pitts., 1956. Engr. McDonnell Aircraft Co., St. Louis, 1956-60, sr. engr., 1960-64, group engr., 1964-65, sr. group engr., 1965-66; sr. group engr. McDonnell Douglas Astronautics Co., St. Louis, 1966-71, sr. program engr., 1971-79, dir., 1979-83, v.p., 1983-88; exec. v.p. McDonnell Douglas Missile Systems Co., St. Louis, 1988—. Bd. dirs. Lindenwood Coll., St. Louis, 1990—. Assoc. fellow AIAA (St. Louis Tech. Mgmt. award 1986); mem Am. Def. Preparedness Assn. (bd. dirs. 1989), Navy League. Avocations: handball, water sports, reading. Office: McDonnell Douglas Aerospace PO Box 516 Saint Louis MO 63166-0516

NATHENSON, STANLEY GAIL, immunology educator; b. Denver, Aug. 1, 1933; s. Abe and Esther (Kurland) N.; m. Susan L., Oct. 16, 1959; children: Matthew, John. BA, Reed Coll., 1955; MD, Washington U. Sch. Medicine, 1959. From asst. to prof. Albert Einstein Coll. Medicine, Bronx, N.Y., 1966—. With USPHS, 1962-64. Mem. AAAS, NAS, Am. Assn. Immunologists. Office: A Einstein Coll of Medicine Dept Microbiology & Immunology Bronx NY 10461

NATION, EARL F., retired urologist, educator; b. Zephyr, Tex., Jan. 16, 1910; s. Joseph Madison and Alma Emily (Johnson) N.; m. Evelyn Stapp Poynter, Aug. 11, 1936; children: William Earl, Robert Joseph. BA, San Diego State U., 1931; MD, Western Res. U., 1935. Lic. urologist, Calif.; diplomate Am. Bd. Urology. Internship, resident in urology Los Angeles County Gen. Hosp., 1935-39; pvt. practice Pasadena, Calif., 1941-90, ret., 1990; instr., assoc. prof. urology U. So. Calif., L.A., 1941-55; sr. attending staff Huntington Meml. Hosp., Pasadena, 1941—, St. Luke Hosp., Pasadena, 1941—, also past pres.; Pasadena Dispensary, 1946; lectr. Coll. Med. Evangelists (now Loma Linda U.), 1941-48. Mem. editorial bd. Jour. of Urology, 1958-66, Calif. Medicine, 1965-69, Forum on Medicine; contbr. articles to profl. jours., contbg. author to numerous books. Sec.-treas. Pasadena Breakfast Forum, 1970-73, pres. 1974-75. Crile rsch. scholar Western Res. U., 1931. Mem. ACS, AMA, Am. Urological Assn. (past pres.), Am. Osler Soc. (past pres.), L.A. County Med. Assn., Calif. Med. Assn., Pasadena Hist. Soc., So. Calif. Hist. Soc., Am. Soc. Clin. Urologists, Pasadena U. Club, Zamorano Club (v.p. L.A. chpt. 1991), Alpha Omega Alpha. Republican. Avocations: book collecting, reading, writing, gardening, fishing. Home: 311 E Sierra Madre Blvd E Sierra Madre CA 91024

NATION, JAMES EDWARD, speech pathologist; b. Springfield, Ill., Aug. 22, 1933; s. John Herbert and Margaret Josephine (Weiss) N. B.S., Ill. State U., 1959; M.S., U. Wis., 1960, Ph.D., 1964. Asst. prof. U. Ga., 1964-66; asst. prof., assoc. prof. Case Western Res. U., Cleve., 1966-86; prof., chmn. dept. communication scis. Case Western Res. U., 1979-85; dir. speech pathology Cleve. Hearing and Speech Center, 1970-74; sr. clin. instr. dept. pediatrics Case Western Res. Sch. Medicine, 1979-86; speech-language pathologist Tucson Unified Sch. Dist. #1, 1985—; chief speech-lang. pathologist craniofacial defects team Rainbow Babies and Childrens Hosp., Univ. Hosps., Case Western Res. U., 1978-85; exec. bd. Nat. Council Grad. Programs in Speech-Lang. Pathology and Audiology; cons. in field. Author: Diagnosis of Speech and Language Disorders, 1977, Child Language Disorders, 1982, 2d rev. edit., 1984; editorial cons.: Cleft Palate Jour.; contbr. chpts. to books; editor: Ohio Speech and Hearing Jour., 1969-73; contbr. articles to profl. jours. Served with U.S. Army, 1953-55. Recipient Wittke award for disting. undergrad. teaching, 1977, Outstanding Service award Ill. State U. Alumni Assn., 1982. Fellow Am. Speech-Lang. and Hearing Assn. (cert. speech-lang. pathologist); mem. Am. Cleft Palate Assn., Ohio Speech and Hearing Assn., Aphasiology Assn. Ohio, Nat. Council Grad. Programs in Speech-Lang. Pathology and Audiology. (Disting. Service award 1982). Home: Apt 19 2600 Skyline Dr Tucson AZ 85718

NATIONS, HOWARD LYNN, lawyer; b. Dalton, Ga., Jan. 9, 1938; s. Howard Lynn and Eva Earline (Armstrong) Lamb; m. Ella Lois Johnson, June 4, 1960 (div. Nov. 1976); 1 child, Cynthia Lynn Nations Garcia; m. Sheree Hope Hamill, May 4, 1991. BA, Florida State U., 1963; JD, Vanderbilt U., 1966. Bar: Tex. 1966. Assoc. Butler, Rice Cook & Knapp, Houston, 1966-71; pres. Nations & Cross, Houston, 1971—; v.p., dir./co-founder Ins. Corp. Am., Houston, 1972—; pres. Caplinger & Nations Galleries, Houston, 1973—, Nations Investment Corp., Houston, 1975—, NCM Trade Corp., Houston, 1975; v.p. Delher Am. Inc., Houston, 1975—; pres. Howard L. Nations, P.C., Houston, 1971—; adj. prof. So. Tex. Coll. Law, Houston, 1967—; speaker in field. Author: Structuring Settlements, 1987; co-author: Texas Workers' Compensation, 1988, (with others) The Anatomy of a Personal Injury Lawsuit, 3rd rev. edit. 1991; editor: Maximizing Damages in Wrongful Death and Personal Injury Litigation, 1985; contbr. articles to profl. jours. Chair, trustee Nat. Coll. Advocacy, Washington, 1985-92. With M.I. Corps, U.S. Army, 1957-60. Fellow Tex. Bar Found., Houston Bar Found. (life); mem. Assn. Trial Lawyers Am. (v.p. 1994-95), Nat. Bd. Trial Advocacy (diplomate civil trial advocacy), So. Trial Lawyers Assn. (pres. 1994-95), Tex. Trial Lawyers Assn. (pres. 1992-93), Tex. Assn. Cert. Trial Lawyers (past pres.). Office: Ste 1400 3000 Post Oak Blvd Houston TX 77056-6598

NATKIN, ALVIN MARTIN, environmental company executive; b. Bklyn., Feb. 4, 1928; s. Max Harvey and Rebecca (Rubenstein) N.; m. Lorraine Rothchild, Aug. 26, 1950; children: Jeff Warren, Stacy Ellen, Marcy Caren. B in Chem. Engring., Poly. Inst. Bklyn., 1952; MBA, Rutgers U., 1954. Engr. Standard Oil Devel. Co., Linden, N.J., 1952-57; mgr. exploratory mktg. Esso Standard Oil Co., N.Y.C., 1957-60, mgr. mktg. rsch., 1960-63; gen. mgr. Esso East Africa, Inc., Nairobi, Kenya, 1963-66; v.p. Esso Philippines, Inc., Manila, 1966-68; mgr. mktg. Esso East, Inc., Houston, 1968-77; environ. mgr. Exxon Corp., N.Y.C., 1977-84; Disting. fellow World Resources Inst., Washington, 1984-86; pres. Continental Environment Co., Summit, N.J., 1986—; internat. chmn. Petroleum Environment Inst., London, 1980-84; dir. World Industry Environment Conf., N.Y.C., 1982-86; cons. Environment & Safety Audit Corp., Midland, Mich., 1986-90. Author: Guidelines for Growth, 1984, Improving Environmental Cooperation, 1985; contbr. articles to profl. jours.; patentee in field, 1958. Served as cpl. U.S. Army, 1946-48. Recipient Disting. Service award U. Tex., 1985; named Hunter of Yr. Profl. Hunters Assn., 1965. Mem. Am. Inst. Chem. Engrs., Am. Assn. Radon Scientists, Am. Chem. Soc., Air Pollution Control Assn., Nat. Assn. Environ. Profls., Explorers Club, Chemists Club (N.Y.C.), Masons, Shriners. Republican. Jewish. Avocations: golf, fishing, hunting. Home: 454200 Prospect Ave West Orange NJ 07052-3215 Office: Continental Environ Co PO Box 384T Summit NJ 07902-0384

NATKIN, ROBERT, painter; b. Chgo., Nov. 7, 1930; s. Phillip and Betty Natkin; m. Judith Dolnick; children: Joshua, Leda. B.A. Art Inst. Chgo., 1952. Exhibited paintings in numerous one-man shows, including Andrè Emmerich Gallery, N.Y.C., Holburne of Menstrie Mus., Bath, Eng., Art Inst. Chgo., Moore Coll. Art, Phila., Ivory/Kimpton Gallery, San Francisco, Gimpel Fils Gallery, London, Gimpel & Weitzenhoffer Gallery, N.Y.C., A.B.C.D. Gallery, Paris, Tortue Gallery, Santa Monica, Calif., Galerie Brusberg, Hannover, Fed. Republic Germany, Hirshhorn Mus. and Sculpture Garden, Washington, Okla. Art Ctr., Oklahoma City, 1982, Lillian Heidenberg Gallery, N.Y.C., 1982, Gloria Luria Gallery, Miami, 1984, Monarides Gallery, Toronto, 1985; group shows include Mus. Art, Pa. State U., 1973, Poindexter Gallery, N.Y.C., 1976; represented in permanent collections, including Art Inst. Chgo., Mus. Modern Art, N.Y.C., Solomon R. Guggenheim Mus., N.Y.C., Whitney Mus. Am. Art, Hirshhorn Mus. and Sculpture Garden, Smithsonian Instn., Washington, Mus. Fine Arts, Houston, Mus. Art, R.I. Sch. Design, San Francisco Mus. Art, Mus. Art, Carnegie Inst., Duke U. Mus. Art, Centre Georges Pompidou (Beaubourg), Paris, Milw. Art Ctr. Office: care Gimpel & Weitzenhoffer Ltd 724 5th Ave Fl 11 New York NY 10019-4106

NATOLI, JOE, newspaper publishing executive. Pres. The Miami Herald, Fla. Office: The Miami Herald 1 Herald Plz Miami FL 33132-1693*

NATORI, JOSIE CRUZ, apparel executive; b. Manila, May 9, 1947; came to U.S., 1964; d. Felipe F. and Angelita A. (Almeda) Cruz; m. Kenneth R. Natori, May 20, 1972; 1 child, Kenneth E.F. BA in Econs., Manhattanville Coll., 1968. V.p. Merrill-Lynch Co., N.Y.C., 1971-77; pres. The Natori Co., N.Y.C., 1977—; bd. dirs. Dreyfus Third Century Fund, The Alltel Corp., Calyx and Corolla. Bd. dirs. Philippine Am. Found., Jr. Achievement, Inc., 1992, Ednl. Found. for Fashion Industries; trustee Manhattanville Coll. Recipient Human Relations award Am. Jewish Com., N.Y.C., 1986, Harriet Alger award Working Woman, N.Y., 1987, Castle award Manhattanville Coll., Purchase, 1988, Galleon award Pres. Philippines, N.Y.C. Asian-Am. award, Friendship award Philippine-Am. Found., Hall of Fame award Mega Mags., Salute to Am. Fashion Designers award Dept. of Commerce. Mem. CFDA, Young Pres.'s Orgn., Fashion Group, Com. of 200. Avocations: pianist, tennis player. Home: 45 E 62nd St New York NY 10021-8025 Office: Natori Co 40 E 34th St Fl 18 New York NY 10016-4401

NATOW, ANNETTE BAUM, nutritionist, author, consultant; b. N.Y.C., Jan. 30, 1933; d. Edward and Gertrude (Jackerson) Baum; m. Harry Natow, Nov. 30, 1955; children: Allen, Laura, Steven. BS, CUNY Bklyn. Coll., 1955; MS, SUNY Coll. Plattsburg, 1960; PhD, Tex. Women's U., 1963. Registered dietitian, N.Y. Asst. prof. SUNY Coll. Plattsburg, 1967-69, CUNY Coll. Lehman, N.Y.C., 1969-70; assoc. prof., chmn. dept. SUNY Downstate Med. Ctr., Bklyn., 1970-76; prof., dir. nutrition programs Adelphi U., Garden City, N.Y., 1976-90, prof. emerita, 1991—; intern Montreal Diet Dispensary, March of Dimes, 1980; pres., writer, cons. NRH Nutrition Cons., Inc., Valley Stream, N.Y., 1980—. Author: No-Nonsense Nutrition, 1978, Geriatric Nutrition, 1980, Nutrition for the Prime of Your Life, 1983, No-Nonsense Nutrition for Kids, 1985, Megadoses: Vitamins as Drugs, 1985, Nutritional Care of the Older Adult, 1986, Pocket Encyclopedia of Nutrition, 1986, The Cholesterol Counter, 1989, 1988, 2d edit., 1989, The Fat Counter, 1989, The Fat Attack Plan, 1990, The Diabetes Carbohydrate and Calorie Counter, 1991, The Pregnancy Counter, 1992, The Iron Counter, 1993, The Sodium Counter, 1993, The Antioxidant Vitamin Counter, 1994, The Fast Food Counter, 1994, The Supermarket Nutrition Counter, 1995; editor Jour. Nutrition for Elderly, 1985—; mem. editorial bd. Environ. Nutrition Newsletter, 1985—; mem. editorial adv. bd. Prevention, 1984-86; contbr. numerous articles to profl. jours. United Hosp. Fund grantee, 1978. Mem. Am. Dietetic Assn., N.Y. State Dietetic Assn., N.Y. State Nutrition Coun. (sec. 1973-74). Avocations: square dancing, music. Home: 100 Rosedale Rd Valley Stream NY 11581-2802 Office: NRH Nutrition Cons Inc 100 Rosedale Rd Valley Stream NY 11581-2802

NATOWITZ, JOSEPH B., chemistry educator, administrator, researcher; b. Saranac Lake, N.Y., Dec. 24, 1936. BS in Chemistry, U. Fla., 1958; Cert. in Meteorology, UCLA, 1959; PhD in Nuclear Chemistry, U. Pitts. 1965. Staff meteorologist, 1st lt. USAF, 1958-61; grad. teaching asst. U. Pitts. 1961-62, grad. rsch. asst., 1962-65; postdoctoral rsch. assoc. SUNY, Stony Brook, 1965-67; rsch. collaborator Brookhaven Nat. Lab., 1965-67; asst. prof. Tex. A&M U., College Station, 1967-72, assoc. prof., 1972-76, prof., 1976—, head dept. chemistry, 1981-85, dir. Cyclotron Inst., 1991—; part-time instr. SUNY-Stony Brook, 1966-67; rsch. collaborator Lawrence Radiation Lab., Berkeley, Calif., 1966, Los Alamos (N.Mex.) Nat. Lab., 1973-74; Alexander Von Humboldt sr. scientist Max Planck Inst. für Kernphysik, Heidelberg, Germany, 1978; vis. prof. Inst. for Nuclear Studies, U. Tokyo, 1979, U. Claude Bernard, Inst. de Physique Nucleaire, 1983, U. de Caen, 1985, Ctr. des Etudes Nucleaires de Saclay, 1986, U. Cath. de Louvain, 1987; with accelerator review com. TASCC, Chalk River, Can.; former mem. adv. com. LBL Superhilac, ORNL Cyclotron, Nat. Superconducting Cyclotron Lab. Contbr. over 130 articles to profl. jours., also to approx. 40 books and procs. Chmn. Cub Scout Pack 802, 1973-75; v.p. College Hills PTO, 1974-75; mem. A&M Consol. Sch. Bd., 1975-78, pres., 1977-78; pres. A&M Consol. Band Boosters, 1980-81. NSF summer fellow, 1962; NASA predoctoral fellow, 1964-65; recipient Disting. Achievment award-rsch. Tex. A&M U., 1988. Fellow Am. Phys. Soc.; mem. Am. Chem. Soc. (vice chmn. div. nuclear chemistry and tech. 1993, chmn. 1994, award in nuclear chemistry 1995), Sigma Xi, Phi Lambda Upsilon. Office: Tex A&M U Cyclotron Inst College Station TX 77843

NATSIOS, NICHOLAS ANDREW, retired foreign service officer; b. Lowell, Mass., July 31, 1920; s. Andrew and Fanny (Papageorgiou) N.; m. Mitzi Peterson, Sept. 2, 1951; children: Christine Daphne, Deborah Diane, Valerie Sophia, Alexandra Roxanne. Student, Lowell Technol. Inst., 1939-40; B.A. cum laude, Ohio State U., 1948; M.A.L.D., Fletcher Sch. Law and Diplomacy, 1983. Civilian spl. adviser polit. problems U.S. Mil. Mission, Salonika, Greece, 1948-50; polit. adviser mil. secretariat U.S. Mil. Mission, Athens, Greece, 1951-56; polit. officer, 1st sec. embassy, spl. asst. to ambassador Am. embassy, Saigon, Viet Nam, 1956-60; attaché Am. embassy, Paris, 1960-62; spl. asst. to ambassador Am. embassy, Seoul, 1962-65; 1st sec. American embassy, Buenos Aires, Argentina, 1965-69; spl. asst. to ambassador Am. embassy, The Hague, The Netherlands, 1969-72; regional affairs officer. Am. embassy, Tehran, Iran, 1972-74; mgmt. cons., 1977—. Served to capt. AUS, 1942-47; comdg. officer Italian Frontier Control Detachment, U.S. Occupation Forces, 1945-47, Milan, Italy. Decorated medal of Merit; decorated Bronze Star U.S.; knight comdr. of Italy; Knight comdr. Order of St. George; medal of Mil. Valor Italy; D.S.C. 1st class Knights of Malta; Order of Eagle Yugoslavia; Distinguished Service medal Greece; Order of Service Merit Korea). Mem. Phi Beta Kappa, Phi Eta Sigma. Address: 77 Lincoln Pky Lowell MA 01851-3405

NATTEL, STANLEY, cardiologist, research scientist; b. Haifa, Israel, Jan. 28, 1951; arrived in Can., 1952; s. William and Julie (Zwirek) N.; m. Celia Anne Reich, Sept. 25, 1973; children: Jonathan, Ilana, Daniel, Sarah. BSc magna cum laude, McGill U., 1972, MD, 1974. Diplomate Am. Bd. Internal Medicine, Am. Bd. Cardiology. Intern in medicine Royal Victoria Hosp., 1974-75, resident in internal medicine, 1975-76; resident in clin. pharmacology Montreal (Que., Can.) Gen. Hosp., 1976-78, cardiologist, clin. pharmacologist, 1981-87, dir. coronary care unit, 1983-87; fellow in cardiology Ind. U., 1978-80; fellow in physiology U. Pa., 1980-81; asst. prof. pharmacology, medicine McGill U., Montreal, 1981-87, assoc. prof., 1987—; cardiologist Montreal Heart Inst., 1987—, dir. rsch. ctr., 1990—; prof. Dept. Medicine, U. Montreal, 1995—; external reviewer Med. Rsch. Coun., 1981—, Ont. Health Ministry, 1983-84, NSF, 1992, others; chmn. libr. com. dept. pharmacology McGill U., 1982-86, mem. grad. com., 1984-89, chmn. grad. tng. com., 1986-89, departmental rep. grad. faculty coun., 1989-91, coord. grad. teaching pharmacology, 1989-91; mem. oper. grants com. Can. Heart Found., 1983-86; chmn. clin. trials com. Montreal Gen. Hosp., 1983-87, chmn. pharmacy and therapeutics com., 1984-87, sec. clin. chemistry rev. com., 1984, course dir. drug therapy, 1984-87, acting dir. divsn. clin. pharmacology, 1984-85, mem. various coms., 1985-87; mem. fellowship awards com. FRSQ, 1988-90, mem. ctr. grants pharmacology/pharmacy com., 1989-90; chmn. pharmacology com. Montreal Heart Inst., 1988-90, mem. search com. pharmacist-in-chief, 1989-90, mem. ethics com., 1991—, chmn. internal rsch. com., 1991—, mem. consultative com. exec. dir., 1991—, chmn. consultative com. rsch. ctr., 1991—; consulting coun. pharmacology Province of Quebec, 1989-90; mem. safety monitoring com. CAMIAT Study, 1990—; assoc. prof. medicine U. Montreal, 1991-95, prof. 1995—, chmn. search com. dir. rsch. Sacré-Coeur Hosp., 1991, mem. rsch. com. CoRMES faculty medicine, 1991—, mem. rsch. com. dept. medicine, 1991—; mem. site visit team program project grant NIH, 1991, cons. program project grant, 1993, spl. reviewer cardiovascular study sect., 1993, 95; mem. oper. grants com. Med. Rsch. Coun. Can., 1988-93; mem. sr. personnel awards com. Can. Heart Found., 1994—; lectr. in field. Assoc. editor Can. Jour. Physiology and Pharmacology, 1990—; mem. editorial bd. Jour. Cardiovascular Electrophysiology, 1991—, Durgs, 1993—, Cardiovascular Drugs and Therapy, 1993—, JACC, 1995—, Circ Res., 1995—; manuscript reviewer Am. Jour. Cardiology, Can. Med. Assn. Jour., European Jour. Pharmacology, New Eng. Jour. Medicine, others; contbr. chpts. to books and articles to profl. jours. Chmn. edn. com. Hebrew Acad. Sch., Montreal, 1991-92. Grantee Quebec Heart Found., 1981—; Nordic Pharms., 1985-87, Knoll Pharms., 1991-93, others; fellow Med. Rsch. Coun. Can., 1979-81; McGill U. scholar, 1967-74, Sir Edward Beatty scholar McGill U., 1967-70, Rsch. scholar Med. Rsch. Coun., 1982-87, Sr. Rsch. scholar Fonds de la Recherche en Santé du Quebec, 1990-93. Fellow Am. Coll. Cardiology, Royal Coll. Physicians Can. (cert. medicine, cardiology); mem. Am. Fedn. Clin. Rsch., Am. Heart Assn. (mem. coun. basic sci.), Am. Soc. Pharmacology and Exptl. Therapeutics, Can. Cardiovascular Soc. (councillor 1992—), Can. Soc. Clin. Pharmacology (Kenneth M. Piafsky Young Investigator award 1985), Pharm. Soc. Can., Biophysical Soc. Avocations: studying Jewish religious works, sports. Home: 5609 Alpine Ave, Côte Saint Luc, PQ Canada H4V 2X6 Office: Montreal Heart Inst, 5000 Belanger St E, Montreal, PQ Canada H1T 1C8

NATTER, ROBERT, JR., federal official, military career officer; b. Trussville, Ala., Apr. 9, 1945; m. Nov. 22, 1975; 3 children. Grad., U.S. Mil. Acad. Commd. ensign USN, 1967, advanced through grades to rear adm., with Coastal Minesweeper Frigate, with 2 amphibious tank landing ships, Spruance Destroyer, comdr. U.S.S. Chandler, U.S.S. Antietam; officer in charge Naval Spl. Warfare USN, Vietnam; co. officer, flag sec. to supt. U.S. Naval Acad. USN, exec. asst. to dir. naval warfare Office Chief Naval Ops., exec. asst. to Comdr.-in-Chief Pacific Fleet; exec asst. to vice chiar Joint Chiefs of Staff, asst. chief naval pers. for distribution; chief legis. affairs Dept. Navy, Washington; mem. staff com. armed svc. U.S. Ho. Reps., Washington. Decorated Silver Star, Def. Superior Svc. Medal, Legion of Merit (5), Bronze Star with Combat V, Purple Heart, Navy Commendation medal with Combat V, Navy Achievement medal with Combat V. Office: Dept Navy Legis Affairs 1300 Navy Pentagon Washington DC 20370-1300

NATZLER, OTTO, ceramic artist; b. Vienna, Austria, Jan. 31, 1908; came to U.S., 1938, naturalized, 1944; s. Sigmund and Frieda (Loewy) N.; m. Gertrud Amon, June 1938; m. Gail Reynolds, Sept. 7, 1973. Author: (with others) Form and Fire—Natzler Ceramics 1939-72, 1973; one man exhbns. include, Fine Art Gallery, San Diego, 1940, 42, San Francisco Mus. Art, 1943, 63, Los Angeles County Mus. Art, 1944, 66, Art Inst. Chgo., 1946, 63, La Jolla Mus. Art, Calif., 1953, Cin. Art Mus., 1954, 60, Joslyn Art Mus., Omaha, 1955, Springfield Mus., Mo., 1955, Jewish Mus., N.Y.C., 1958, Bezalel Nat. Mus., Jerusalem, 1959, Mus. Modern Art, Haifa, Israel, 1959, Kunstgewerbemuseum, Zurich, Switzerland, 1959, Stedelijk Mus., Amsterdam, Holland, 1959, Tulane U., 1961, St. Paul Art Center, 1963, Mus. Contemporary Crafts, N.Y.C., 1963, Birger Sandzen Meml. Gallery, Lindsborg, Kans., 1964, Palm Springs Mus., Calif., 1968, George Walter Vincent Smith Art Mus., Springfield Mass., 1970, Carleton Coll., Northfield, Minn., 1970, retrospective, M.W. deYoung Meml. Mus., San Francisco, 1971, Renwick Gallery, Smithsonian Instn., Washington, 1973, Contemporary Crafts Gallery, Portland, 1975, Craft and Folk Art Mus., Los Angeles, 1977, Scottsdale Center for Arts, Ariz., 1977, No. Ariz. U., Flagstaff, 1978, Los Angeles County Mus. Art, 1980; retrospective show Am. Craft Mus, 1993, Juediaches Museum der Stadt, Wien, 1994; works represented in permanent collections, Renwick Gallery, Smithsonian Inst., Am. Craft Mus., N.Y.C., Cooper-Hewitt Mus., N.Y.C., Fine Arts Gallery, San Diego, Everson Mus. Art, Syracuse, N.Y., Cin. Art Mus., Los Angeles County Mus. Art, Walker Art Center, Mpls., Art Inst. Chgo., Dallas Mus. Fine Arts, Tucson Art Mus., Joselyn Art Mus., Met. Mus. Art, U. Nebr., San Francisco Mus. Art, Kantonales Gewerbemuseum, Bern, Switzerland, Phoenix Art Mus., Nat. Mus. Design, Smithsonian Instn., E.B. Crocker Art Gallery, Sacramento, Balt. Mus. Art, Detroit Inst. Art, Fort Worth Mus. Art, U. Minn., Cranbrook Acad. Art, Bloomfield Hills, Mich., Kunstgewebemuseum, Zurich, Calif. State Fair, Sacramento, Springfield Art Mus., St. Paul Art Center, Phila. Mus. Art, Seattle Art Mus., Slater Meml. Mus., Norwich, Conn., Museo Internazionale delle Ceramiche, Faenza, Italy, Portland Mus. Art,

Oreg., U. Wis., UCLA, Ariz. State Coll., Houston Mus. Fine Art, Krannert Art Mus. at U. Ill., Northwestern U., Oakland Art Mus., Calif., La Crosse State Coll., Ind., Birger Sandzen Meml. Gallery, Mus. Modern Art, N.Y.C., Mills Coll., Oakland, Palm Springs Desert Mus., Newark Mus. Art, George Walter Vincent Smith Mus., Springfield, Mass., U. Oreg., Eugene, Victoria and Albert Mus., London, Minn. Mus. Art, St. Paul, Nat. Mus. Am. History, Smithsonian Instn., Washington, Des Moines Art Center, Santa Barbara Mus. Art, Calif., Maurice Spertus Mus. Judaica, Chgo., Staatliche Museen Preussischer Kulturbesitz, Kunstgewerbemuseum, Berlin, Utah Mus., U. Utah, Salt Lake City, Jewish Mus., N.Y.C., Contemporary Crafts Gallery, Portland, Honolulu Acad. Art, Oesterreichisches Mus fuer Angewandte Kunst, Vienna, Austria, Mus. Bellerive, Zurich Switzerland, Bklyn. Mus., Nelson-Atkins Mus. Art, Kansas City, Mo., Skirball Mus., Los Angeles, Mus. Fine Arts, Boston, Va. Mus. Fine Arts, Richmond, others. Fellow Am. Craft Coun.; Internat. Inst. Arts and Letters. Address: 7837 Woodrow Wilson Dr Los Angeles CA 90046-1213

NAUER, PAULA LOU, physician; b. Norton, Kans., Mar. 18, 1949; d. Paul M. and Louise W. (Duensing) N. BS, Ft. Hays State Coll., 1971; MD, U. Kans., 1974. Diplomate Am. Bd. Family Practice. Resident in family practice Goppert Family Care Ctr., Kansas City, Mo., 1975-78; pvt. practice, Prairie Village, Kans., 1979—. Mem. Am. Academy of Family Practice, Kans. Med. Soc., Johnson County Med. Soc., Am. Med. Soc. Avocations: scuba diving, photography, underwater photography. Office: 7301 Mission Rd Ste 342 Shawnee Mission KS 66208-3096

NAUERT, ROBERT F., insurance company executive. BS, BA, Marquette U., 1945. Pres Pioneer Life Ins., Co. of Ill., Rockford, 1989-93, Continental Life and Accident, Schaumberg, Ill., 1993—. Office: Centinental Life and Accident 304 N Main St Schaumburg IL 60173*

NAUERT, ROGER CHARLES, healthcare executive; b. St. Louis, Jan. 6, 1943; s. Charles Henry and Vilma Amelia (Schneider) N.; B.S., Mich. State U., 1965; J.D., Northwestern U., 1969; M.B.A., U. Chgo., 1979; m. Elaine Louise Harrison, Feb. 18, 1967; children: Paul, Christina. Bar: Ill. 1969. Asst. atty. gen. State of Ill., 1969-71; chief counsel Ill. Legis. Investigating Commn., 1971-73; asst. state comptroller State of Ill., 1973-75; dir. adminstrn. and fin. Health and Hosps. Governing Commn. Cook County, Chgo., 1975-79; nat. dir. health care services Grant Thornton, Chgo., 1979-88; exec. v.p. Detroit Med. Ctr., 1988-91; exec. v.p. Columbia-Presbyn. Med. Ctr., N.Y.C., 1991-93; sr. v.p. Mt. Sinai Med. Ctr., N.Y.C., 1993—; vis. lectr. healthcare mgmt. & fin. Columbia U., Vanderbilt U., U. Chgo., 1978—; preceptor Wharton Sch., U. Pa. Ford Found. grantee, 1968-69. Mem. Am. Hosp. Assn., Am. Public Health Assn., Am. Coll. Healthcare Execs., Nat. Health Lawyers Assn., Health Care Fin. Mgmt. Assn. (faculty mem.), Alpha Phi Sigma, Phi Delta Phi, Delta Upsilon. Clubs: N.Y. Athletic, Mt. Kisco Country. Author: A Sociology of Health, 1977; The Demography of Illness, 1978; Proposal for a National Health Policy, 1979; Health Care Feasibility Studies, 1980; Health Care Planning Guide, 1981; Health Care Strategic Planning, 1982; Overcoming the Obstacles to Planning, 1983; Principles of Hospital Cash Management, 1984; Healthcare Networking Arrangements, 1985; Strategic Planning for Physicians, 1986; HMO's: A Once and Future Strategy, 1987, Mergers, Acquisitions and Divestitures, 1988, Tax Exempt Status Under Seige, 1989, Governance in Multi-Hospital Systems, 1990, Planning Alternative Delivery Systems, 1991, Direct Contracting: The Future is Now, 1992, The Rise and Fall of the U.S. Healthcare System, 1993, A Proposal for National Healthcare Reform, 1994, Academic Medical Centers and the New Age of Managed Care, 1994. Home: 461 Haines Rd Bedford Corners NY 10549 Office: Mt Sinai Med Ctr 1 Gustave L Levy Pl New York NY 10029-6504

NAUGHTON, JAMES, actor; b. Middletown, Conn., Dec. 6, 1945; s. James Joseph and Rosemary (Walsh) N.; m. Pamela Parsons, Oct. 1968; children: Gregory J., Keira P. BA, Brown U., 1967; MFA, Yale U., 1970. Broadway appearances include Edmund in Long Day's Journey Into Night, 1971 (Theatre World award, N.Y. Drama Critics award, Vernon Rice award 1971), Stone in City of Angels (Tony award 1990, Drama Desk award), I Love My Wife, 1977, Whose Life Is It Anyway, 1980. Feature films include Paper Chase, 1972, Second Wind, 1975, A Stranger is Watching, 1981, Cat's Eye, 1982, The Glass Menagerie, 1987, The Good Mother, 1988; TV appearances include: (series) Faraday and Company, 1973-74, Planet of the Apes, 1974, Making the Grade, 1982, Trauma Center, 1983; (movies) F. Scott Fitzgerald and "The Last of the Belles", 1974, The Last 36 Hours of Dr. Durant, 1975, The Bunker, 1981, My Body, My Child, 1982, Parole, 1982, The Last of the Great Survivors, 1984, Between Darkness and the Dawn, 1985, Sin of Innocence, 1986, Necessity, 1988, The Cosby Mysteries, 1994. *

NAUGHTON, JAMES MARTIN, newspaper editor; b. Pitts., Aug. 13, 1938; s. Francis Patrick and Martha Ann (Clear) N.; m. Diana Marie Thomas, Sept. 5, 1964; children—Jenifer Mary, Lara Marie, Michael Thomas, Kerry Marie. B.A. cum laude, U. Notre Dame, 1960. Reporter, photographer Painesville (Ohio) Telegraph, summer, 1955-60; reporter Cleve. Plain Dealer, 1962-69; Washington corr. N.Y. Times, 1969-77; nat. editor Phila. Inquirer, 1977-79, met. editor, 1979-83, assoc. mng. editor, 1980-86, dep. mng. editor, 1986-90, mng. editor, 1990-91, exec. editor, 1991—; Marsh prof. U. Mich., 1977. Served with USMC, 1960-62. Recipient Disting. Service award Sigma Delta Chi, 1973. Roman Catholic. Club: Franklin Inn (Phila.). Home: 8870 Norwood Ave Philadelphia PA 19118-2711 Office: Phila Inquirer 400 N Broad St Philadelphia PA 19130-4099

NAUGHTON, JOHN M., insurance company executive; b. Holyoke, Mass., Dec. 18, 1936; s. James Leo and Catherine (Looney) N.; m. Frances Elaine Willard, Sept. 15, 1962; children: Michael, Matthew. BS, U. Mass., 1959. Pension cons. N.E. Life, Boston, 1959-65; pension cons. Mass. Mut. Life, Los Angeles and Phila., 1965-76; regional sales dir. Mass. Mut. Life, Boston, 1976-78; v.p. Mass. Mut. Life, Springfield, 1978, sr. v.p., 1981, exec. v.p., 1984—; bd. dirs. MML Pension Ins. Co., Oppenheimer Mgmt. Corp., Concert Capital Mgmt., Colebrook Group, APPWP; trustee SIS Bank. Chmn. Greater Springfield United Way, 1987; trustee Am. Internat. Coll., Baystate Med. Ctr.; mem. chancellor's exec. coun. U. Mass.; past chmn. ERISA adv. coun. Dept. Labor. Served to capt. U.S. Army, 1960-61. Mem. Am. Soc. Pension Actuaries, Charter Life Underwriters. Republican. Roman Catholic. Clubs: Colony, Longmeadow Country, StageWest (bd. dirs.). Avocations: reading; skiing; golf; tennis. Office: Mass Mut Life Ins Co 1295 State St Springfield MA 01111-0001

NAUGHTON, JOHN PATRICK, cardiologist, medical school administrator; b. West Nanticoke, Pa., May 20, 1933; s. John Patrick and Anne Frances (McCormick) N.; separated; children: Bruce, Marcia, Lisa, George, Michael, Thomas. AA, Cameron State Coll., Lawton, Okla., 1952; BS, St. Louis U., 1954; MD, Okla. U., 1958. Intern George Washington U. Hosp., Washington, 1958-59; resident U. Okla. Med. Center, 1959-64; asst. prof. medicine U. Okla., 1966-68; assoc. prof. medicine U. Ill., 1968-70; prof. medicine George Washington U., 1970-75, dean acad. affairs, 1973-75; dir. div. rehab. medicine and Regional Rehab. Research and Tng. Center, 1970-75; dean Sch. Medicine, SUNY, Buffalo, 1975—; prof. medicine and physiology Sch. Medicine, SUNY, 1975—, lectr. in rehab. medicine, 1975; acting v.p. for health scis. SUNY, 1983-84, v.p. clin. affairs, 1984—; dir. Nat. Exercise and Heart Disease Project, 1972—; chmn. policy adv. bd. Beta-blocker heart attack trial Nat. Heart, Lung and Blood Inst., 1977-82; pres. Western N.Y. chpt. Am. Heart Assn., 1983-85; v.p. N.Y. State affiliate, 1985, pres. N.Y. state affiliate, 1988-90; chmn. clin. applications and preventions adv. com. Nat. Heart, Lung and Blood Inst., 1984; mem. N.Y. Gov.'s Commn. on Grad. Med. Edn., 1985; mem. N.Y. State Coun. on Grad. Med. Edn., 1988-90; pres. Assoc. Med. Schs. N.Y., 1982-84, mem. adminstrv. com. Council of deans, 1983-89; mem. N.Y. State Dept. of Health Adv. Com. on Physician Recrediting; mem. exec. coun. Nat. Inst. on Disability and Rehab. Rsch., 1991-92. Author: Exercise Testing and Exercise Training in Coronary Heart Disease, 1973, Exercise Testing: Physiological, Biochemical, and Clinical Principles, 1988. Career Devel. awardee Nat. Heart Inst. 1966-71; recipient Brotherhood-Sisterhood award in medicine NCCJ, N.E. Minority Educators award, 1990, Acad. Alumnus of Yr. award Okla. U., 1990, award for svc. to minorities in med. edn., 1991. Fellow ACP, Am. Coll. Cardiology, Am. Coll. Sports Medicine (pres. 1970-71), Am. Coll.

Chest Physicians; mem. N.Y. State Heart Assn. (pres.). Office: SUNY Buffalo Sch Medicine Biomed Scis 3435 Main St Buffalo NY 14214-3001

NAUGHTON, PAUL FRANCIS, financial executive; b. Port Monmouth, N.J., Sept. 1, 1942; s. John Paul and Gertrude (Sheehan) N.; m. Jean Connell, Sept. 18, 1965; children: Thomas, Brian, Jacqueline Ann. BS, LaSalle U., 1964; MBA, St. John's U., 1969. Sr. analyst Dean Witter & Co., N.Y.C., 1968-70; ptnr., sr. analyst F.S. Smithers & Co., N.Y.C., 1970-72; v.p. 1st Boston Corp., N.Y.C., 1972-75; treas. Am. Natural Svc. Co., Detroit, 1975-79; v.p. Dean Witter Reynolds Inc., 1979-81; v.p. fin. Mich. Consol. Gas Co., Detroit, 1981-84, also dir.; sr. v.p. chief fin. officer Primark Corp., McLean, Va.; pres., chief exec. officer Primark Fin. Svcs., Inc., McLean, 1984-86; mng. ptnr. Fin. Resource Enterprises, 1986-87; sr. v.p., chief fin. officer Potomac Capital Investment Corp., 1987-91, pres., COO, dir., 1991—; bd. dirs. Recording for the Blind, 1990. Mem. Fin. Execs. Inst., N.Y. Soc. Security Analysts, Hidden Creek Country Club (Va.), Intenat. Club (Washington), Delta Sigma Pi. Home: 1058 Harriman St Great Falls VA 22066-2533 Office: Potomac Capitol Investment Corp 900 19th St NW Washington DC 20006-2100

NAUHEIM, STEPHEN ALAN, lawyer; b. Washington, Nov. 17, 1942; s. Ferdinand Alan and Beatrice Lillian (Strasburger) N.; children: Terry Beth, David Alan. BS in Acctg., U. N.C., 1964; JD, Georgetown U., 1967; LLM, George Washington U., 1970. Bar: D.C. 1968, U.S. Ct. Claims 1968, U.S. Tax Ct. 1971. Atty. adviser office chief counsel IRS, Washington, 1967-71, asst. br. chief, 1970-71; assoc. Surrey & Morse, Washington, 1971-75, ptnr., 1975-81; prin. Anderson, Hibey, Nauheim & Blair, Washington, 1981-91, Schall, Boudreau & Gore, Washington, 1991-93; pres., gen. counsel CMW Group, Ltd., Washington, 1994—; mem. adv. bd. World Trade Inst., N.Y.C., 1978—, Tax Mgmt. Adv. Bd., Washington, 1980—. Mem. editorial bd. Internat. Tax Jour., N.Y.C., 1982—; contbr. to profl. publs. Mem. ABA (former com. chmn. taxation sect.), Internat. Fiscal Assn., D.C. Bar Assn. (mem. steering com. tax sect. 1987-92, chmn. tax sect. 1990-92), Am. Coll. of Tax Counsel. Avocations: travelling, sailing. Office: CMW Group Ltd 1350 Eye St NW Ste 820 Washington DC 20005

NAULEAU, HEIDI A., holding company executive, metal products executive; b. 1957. Grad., U. Pa., 1978. With Aarque Sec. Corp., Jamestown, N.Y., 1978—, pres.; also bd. dirs. Aarque Mgmt. Corp.; bd. dirs., sec. Cold Metal Products, Youngstown, Ohio. Office: Aarque Sec Corp 111 W 2nd St Jamestown NY 14701*

NAULT, FERNAND, choreographer; b. Montreal, Dec. 27, 1921. Leading character dancer, ballet master Am. Ballet Theatre, N.Y.C., 1944-65; dir. ABT's Sch. of Classical Ballet, N.Y.C., 1960-64; co-artistic dir., resident choreographer Les Grands Ballets Canadiens, 1965-73, resident choreographer, 1973-90, artistic advisor, 1987-90, choreographer emeritus, 1990—; adv. dir. L'École Supérieure de Danse du Québec, 1973-90; guest choreographer Colorado Ballet, 1978-81, artistic dir., 1981-82. Choreographer works. Am. Ballet Theatre, Joffrey Ballet Co., Harkness Co., Colo. Concert Ballet Co., Md. Ballet Co., Atlanta Ballet, Ballet Fedn. Phillipines; works choreographed include Claytonia, 1960, The Lonely Ones, 1960, Iskushenye, 1960, Giosco, 1961, Latin American Symphoniette, 1961, Cyclic, 1962, Roundabout, 1962, The Sleeping Beauty, 1963, Carmina Burana, 1966, Pas d'Eté, 1966, La Lettre, 1966, Hip and Straight, 1970, Tommy, 1970, Coppelia, 1971, Cantique des cantiques, 1974, Liberté Temperée, 1976, La Scouine, 1977. Other choreographed works include Aurki, Ceremonie, Casse-Noisette/The Nutcracker, Chants de douleur chants d'allégresse/Songs of Joy and Sorrow, Gehenne, Incohérence, L'Oiseau de feu, La fille mal gardée, Les sept péchés capitaux/The Seven Deadly Sins, Les sylphides, Miribilia, Mobiles, Paquita (Pas de deux), Pas d'époque, Pas rompu, Quintan, Quintessence, Symphonie de psaumes, Ti-Jean, Try, Ready, Go, Visages. Recipient Silver medal for choreography 7th Internat. Ballet Competition Varna, Bulgaria, 1976; Order of Canada, 1977, Prix Denise-Pelletier, Quebec, 1985, Chevalier de l'ordre national du Quebec, 1990. Office: Les Grands Ballets Canadiens, 4816 rue Rivard, Montreal, PQ Canada H2J 2N6*

NAULT, WILLIAM HENRY, publishing executive; b. Ishpeming, Mich., June 9, 1926; s. Henry J. and Eva (Perrault) N.; m. Helen E. Matthews, Nov. 28, 1946; children: William Henry, Rebecca Nault Marks, Ronald, George, Peter, Julia, Robert, David. AB, No. Mich. U., 1948, LittD (hon.), 1988; MA, U. Mich., 1949; EdD, Columbia U., 1953. Dir. adult edn. Battle Creek, Mich., 1948-49; guidance counselor, 1949-50; prin. W.K. Kellogg High Sch., Battle Creek, 1950-53; research assoc. Columbia U., 1953-54; dir. instrn. pub. schs. Ridgewood, N.J., 1954-55; adj. prof. Patterson State Coll., N.J., 1954-55; dir. research World Book, Inc. (formerly Field Enterprises Edn. Corp.), Chgo., 1955-63; v.p. World Book, Inc. (formerly Field Enterprises Edn. Corp.), 1963-66, v.p., editorial dir., 1966-68, exec. v.p. and editorial dir., 1968-83; pres., pub., chief operating officer World Book, Inc., 1983-84, gen. chmn. editorial adv. bds., 1984—, pub., 1983—; past vice chmn. Govt. Adv. Com. on Internat. Library and Book Programs, U.S. Dept. State; past mem. nat. adv. bd. Ctr. on Ednl. Media and Materials for Handicapped; past mem. exec. bd. Commn. Instns. Higher Edn., North Central Assn. Colls. and Secondary Schs.; mem. dean's adv. council Coll. Bus. and Pub. Adminstrn., U. Mo., Columbia; mem. nat. council Inst. Internat. Edn. Author material on courses of study. Mem. alumni com. Columbia Tchrs. Coll. Capital Campaign; mem. White House Conf. on Youth; pres. Oak Park (Ill.) Bd. Edn., 1960-63; bd. regents Lincoln Acad., Ill.; past trustee Adler Planetarium, De Paul U., Chgo. Geol. Soc.; trustee No. Mich. U. Devel. Fund; bd. dirs. W.V. Phalin Found. Grad. Study; mem. adv. bd. Rosary Coll.; liberal arts and scis. adv. council De Paul U. Served with F.A., AUS, 1944-45. Recipient Columbia U. Tchrs Coll. medal for disting. service in edn.; named Disting. Alumnus, No. Mich. U. Fellow AAAS; mem. ALA, Chgo. Planetarium Soc. (trustee), Chgo. Geog. Soc. (dir.), Am. Acad. Polit. and Social Sci., Am. Edn. Research Assn., Am. Assn. Sch. Adminstrs., Assn. Supervision and Curriculum Devel., Chgo. Pubs. Assn. (past pres.), Ill. Assn. Sch. Adminstrs., Ill. Acad. Sci., Nat. Sci. Tchr. Assn., Nat. Council Tchrs. English, Assn. Am. Geographers, Assn. Childhood Edn. Internat., Nat. Assn. Elementary Sch. Prins., Nat. Assn. Secondary Sch. Prins., Council for Advancement Sch. Writing, Internat. Platform Assn., Nat. Council Social Studies, Nat. Soc. Study Edn. Roman Catholic. Clubs: Mid-Am, Mchts. and Mfrs. Office: World Book Inc 525 W Monroe St Chicago IL 60661-3629

NAULTY, SUSAN LOUISE, archivist; b. Abington, Pa., May 28, 1944; d. Charles J. and Ruth E. (Schick) N. BA, Whittier Coll., 1967; MA, Loyola U., L.A., 1972. Tchr. history and English, Whittier (Calif.) H.S., 1968-70; from libr. asst. to asst. curator Huntington Libr., San Marino, Calif., 1972-91; archivist Richard Nixon Libr. and Birthplace, Yorba Linda, Calif., 1991—. Republican. Roman Catholic. Office: Richard Nixon Libr & Birthplace 18001 Yorba Linda Blvd Yorba Linda CA 92686

NAUMANN, HANS RICHARD ERNST, manufacturing executive; b. N.Y.C., July 24, 1936; s. Frederich and Margarete (Berger) N.; m. Irma Ann Monsees, July 5, 1958; children: Laura Ann, Mark William. BME, Bklyn. Poly. Inst., 1958; MS computer sci., Stevens Inst., Hoboken, N.J., 1962. Registered profl. engr., N.J. Designer mil. R & D products Allen B. DuMont Labs., 1958-60; various positions, mgr. R & D Design Engring. ASCO, Florham Park, N.J., 1960-75, mgr. switch dept., 1975-77, v.p. switch dept., 1977-84, exec. v.p., 1984, pres., chief oper. officer, dir., 1985; pres., chief oper. officer, dir. Emerson Elec. Cos. subs. ASCO, Florham Park, N.J., 1985-87; exec. v.p. Imo Industries Inc., Lawrenceville, N.J., 1987-90; pres., gen. mgr. Landis & Gyr Metering, Inc., Lafayette, Ind. 1st lt. U.S. Army, 1958-59. Mem. Am. Mgmt. Assn., IEEE, Mfrs.' Alliance for Productivity and Innovation, NSPE (registered). Office: Landis & Gyr Metering Inc PO Box 7180 Lafayette IN 47903-7180

NAUMANN, ROBERT BRUNO ALEXANDER, chemist, physicist, educator; b. Dresden, Germany, June 7, 1929; came to U.S., 1932, naturalized 1951; s. Eberhard Bruno and Elsa Henriette (Haege) N.; m. Marina Grot Turkevich, Sept. 16, 1961; children: Kristin Ragnhild, Andrew John Bruno. B.S., U. Calif., Berkeley, 1949; M.A., Princeton U., 1951, Ph.D., 1953. Mem. faculty Princeton U., 1953—, prof. chemistry and physics, 1973-92, prof. emeritus chemistry and physics, 1992—; mem. vis. staff Los Alamos Nat. Lab., 1970-86; rsch. collaborator Brookhaven Nat. Lab., 1984-87; sci. assoc. CERN, Geneva, 1985—; vis. prof. physics dept. Tech. U. Munich,

1988; vis. scholar physics Dartmouth Coll., 1992—. Author articles electromagnetic isotope separation, nuclear structure via radioactive and charged particle nuclear spectroscopy, implantation radioactive isotopes into solids, formation and properties of muonic atoms. Recipient Alexander von Humboldt Stiftung Sr. U.S. Scientist award, 1978, 83; Allied Chem. and Dye Corp. fellow, 1951-52, Procter and Gamble faculty fellow, 1959-60; Deutsche Forschungsgemeinschaft grantee, 1988. Fellow Am. Phys. Soc., AAAS; mem. Am. Chem. Soc. (chmn. Princeton U. sect. 1975, Chmn. Div. Nuclear Chemistry and Technology 1984), Sierra Club, Phi Beta Kappa, Sigma Xi (chmn. Princeton, N.J. sect. 1986-87). Episcopalian. Home: 387 Hawk Pine Hills Norwich VT 05055-9516

NAUMOFF, PHILIP, physician; b. Pitts., Feb. 16, 1914; s. Louis and Celia (Rubenstein) N.; m. Esther Zuckerman, Aug. 21, 1937; children—Carolyn Naumoff Lerner, Susan Naumoff Southern, Lawrence Jay, Elizabeth Anne Naumoff McCarthy, Deborah Jane Naumoff Flynn. B.S., U. Pitts., 1934; M.D., Duke U., 1937. Intern U. Pitts. Hosps., 1937-38; resident Bradford (Pa.) Hosp., 1938-39; gen. practice medicine Charlotte, N.C., 1946—; chmn. dept. family practice Meml. Hosp., 1964-79; Asst. clin. prof. community health scis. Duke Med. Center, Durham, N.C., 1973-79. Served to maj. M.C. AUS, 1942-46. Mem. AMA, Am. Acad. Family Physicians, N.C. Acad. Family Physicians (past pres.), Mecklenburg County Med. Soc. (past pres.), Heart Assn. Mecklenburg County (past pres.), B'nai B'rith (past pres. N.C.). Home: 4214 Woodglen Ln Charlotte NC 28226-7247 Office: 1012 S Kings Dr Charlotte NC 28283-0002

NAUNTON, RALPH FREDERICK, surgeon, educator; b. London, Sept. 26, 1921; came to U.S., 1954, naturalized, 1962; s. Frederick and Violet (Leaker) N.; m. Mary Beatrice Ball, Aug. 25, 1945 (div.); children—Phillip, David; m. Natasha Tjonamon Cofield, Aug. 3, 1978. M.B., B.S., U. Coll., U. London, 1945. Intern U. Coll. Hosp., London, 1945-46; resident in otolaryngology U. Coll. Hosp., 1946-49; mem. Med. Research Council Eng., 1949-54; mem. faculty U. Chgo. Med. Sch., 1954—, prof. surgery, 1964-80, chmn. otolaryngology sect., 1966-79; dir. div. communicative disorders Nat. Inst. Neurol., Communicative Disorders and Stroke, NIH, 1980—. Contbr. articles on physiology and pathology, also treatment hearing and hearing disorders to profl. jours. Fellow ACS, Royal Soc. Medicine; mem. Royal Coll. Surgeons, Am. Otol. Soc., Collegium Oto-Rhino-Laryngol. Soc., Sigma Psi. Home: 3303 Pauline Dr Bethesda MD 20815-3919 Office: NIH Nat Inst Deafness & Comm Disorder 6120 Executive Blvd # 400 C Rockville MD 20852-4909

NAUS, JAMES H., accountant; b. 1944. Ptnr. Cowe Chizek & Co. Office: Cowe Chizek & Co 330 E Jefferson Blvd South Bend IN 46601*

NAUSEDA, ANN JURA See JILLIAN, ANN

NAVA, CYNTHIA D., state legislator. BS, Western Ill. U.; MA, Ea. Ill. U. Dir. spl. edn. Godsden Pub. Sch.; mem. N.Mex. Senate; mem. edn. and rules com. Home: PO Box 493 Mesquite NM 88048 Office: NMex Senate State Capitol New Mexico State Capitol NM 87503

NAVA, ELOY LUIS, financial consultant; b. N.Y.C., May 19, 1942; s. Eloy and Dolores Nava; m. Diane Margret Binder, Dec. 21, 1968; children: Alyson Beth, David Eloy. BMgmt Engring., Rensselaer Poly. Inst., 1964, BMech. Engring., 1965, MSMgmt., 1970. Indsl. engr. Johnson & Johnson Inc., Troy, N.Y., 1965-66; nuclear project engr. and chief nuclear test engr. to ops. analysis project mgr. Electric Boat Div., Gen. Dynamics Corp., Groton, Conn., 1966-78; ptnr., chief fin. officer Collado Ozamiz Co., N.Y.C., 1978-88; pres., chmn. bd. JB Apparel Corp., N.Y.C., 1984-93; v.p., sr. fin. cons. Cruice Investment Advisors, Ltd., 1994—; bd. dirs. Jose Blanco Inc., Santo Domingo, Dominican Republic; mgmt., fin. cons. various orgns. in Dominican Republic. Chmn. water, sewer com. City of Waterford, Conn., 1975-77; mem. Rep. Nat. Com.; swimming ofcl. YMCA, USS. Mem. Midwest Decoy Collectors Assn., NRA, Am. Philatelic Soc., Country Club of Darien (Conn.). Roman Catholic. Avocations: fishing, golf, skiing, stamp and antique decoy collecting. Home: 15 Pasture Ln Darien CT 06820-5618

NAVAB, FARHAD, medical educator; b. Tehran, Iran, Sept. 12, 1938; came to U.S., 1980; s. Hossein and Nahid (Pirnia) N.; m. Nilou Navab, July 22, 1977; children: Sara, June, Linda. BA, Cambridge (Eng.) U., 1960, MD, 1976; MA, MB, B.Chir., Guy's Hosp., London, 1963; MRCP, Westminster Hosp., 1967. Diplomate Am. Bd. Internal Medicine, Am. Bd. Gastroenterology. Asst. prof. U. Tehran, 1972-76, assoc. prof., 1976-79; cons. physician Brook Gen. Hosp., London, 1979-80; assoc. prof. medicine U. Ark. Med. Scis., Little Rock, 1980-87, assoc. prof. physiology, 1985-87, chmn. evaluation com. for gastroenterology, 1986-87; staff physician VA Med. Ctr., Little Rock, 1986-87; chief gastroenterology Baystate Med. Ctr., Springfield, Mass., 1987—; prof. medicine Med. Sch., Tufts U., Boston, 1991—. Fellow ACP, Am. Coll. Gastroenterology, Royal Coll. Physicians; mem. Am. Physiol. Soc., Am. Gastroenterol. Assn., Am. Soc. for Gastrointestinal Endoscopy, Am. Assn. for Study Liver Disease, Mass. Med. Soc., So. Soc. for Clin. Investigation. Avocation: photography. Home: 18 Bittersweet Ln Wilbraham MA 01095-2234 Office: Baystate Med Ctr 759 Chestnut St Springfield MA 01199-0001

NAVAJAS, GONZALO, foreign language educator; b. Barcelona, Spain, May 14, 1946; came to U.S., 1970; s. Jose and Carmen (Navarro) N.; 1 child, Paul. PhD, UCLA, 1975. Prof. SUNY, Stony Brook, 1980-83, Tulane U., New Orleans, 1983-85; prof. dept. Spanish and Portuguese U. Calif., Irvine, 1985—; lectr., mem. editorial bd. various jours. in field. Author 7 books; contbr. articles to profl. publs. Mem. Modern Assn. Am., Internat. Assn. Hispanists. Office: U Calif Dept Spanish Irvine CA 92711

NAVALKAR, RAMCHANDRA GOVINDRAO, microbiologist, immunologist; b. Bombay, May 7, 1924; s. Govindrao Narayan and Shantabai Navalkar; m. Shubhangi Navalkar, Dec. 27, 1966; children: Sushant, Sudevi. BS, Bombay U., 1946, STC, 1952, PhD, 1956. Research asst. Acworth Leprosy Hosp., Bombay, 1952-56, field and research officer, 1959-60; biologist Stanford Research Inst., Menlo Park, Calif., 1956-58; vis. fellow sch. pub. health Harvard U., Cambridge, Mass., 1958; postdoctoral fellow dept. med. microbiology Stanford (Calif.) U., 1956-58; project assoc. dept. med. microbiology U. Wis., Madison, 1960-63, 66-67; research engr. assoc. Inst. Med. Microbiology, U. Gothenburg, Sweden, 1964-65; asst. prof. microbiology Meharry Med. Coll., Nashville, 1967-72, assoc. prof. microbiology, 1972-76, prof. microbiology, 1976-80; prof. microbiology and immunology Morehouse Sch. Medicine, Atlanta, 1980—; mem. site visit com. NIH for tuberculosis rsch. programs, India, 1975; prin. co-ordinator Immunology of Leprosy Project, Al-Azhar U., Cairo, 1977; mem. ad. hoc rev. com. NIH, 1978, 1979, Internat. Leprosy Assn. Workshop on Microbiology, Mexico City, 1978; mem. project site visit com. NIH, Atlanta, 1978, exec com. Sci. Rsch. Inst., Atlanta Univ. Ctr.; cons. MARC program Tenn. State U., Nashville, 1981; disting. guest and cons. to Inst. Dermatology, People's Republic of China, 1982; chmn., mem. NIH spl. study sect. on AIDS-related infections, 1990, on tuberculosis present in lung, 1993. Guest reviewer Internat. Jour. Leprosy, 1984; contbr. numerous articles and rsch. papers to profl. jours. Recipient Golden Apple award Meharry chpt. Student Am. Med. Assn., 1972, Maj. Gen. Sahib Singh Sokhey Outstanding Researcher award, 1976; grantee NIH, 1966-82, 83-87, 89-92, 92-97, PI WHO, 1983-84. Fellow Am. Acad. Microbiology; mem. Am. Soc. Microbiology, The Soc. for Exptl. Biology and Medicine, Internat. Leprosy Assn., Indian Assn. of Leprologists, Acworth Leprosy Hosp. Soc. for Research and Rehab. (life mem.), Assn. Med. Sch. Microbiology Chairmen. Avocations: reading, cooking. Office: Morehouse Sch of Medicine Dept of Microbiology and Immunology Atlanta GA 30310-1495

NAVAR, LUIS GABRIEL, physiology educator, researcher; b. El Paso, Tex., Mar. 24, 1941; s. Luis and Concepcion (Najera) N.; m. Randa Ann Bumgarner, Oct. 15, 1965; children: Tonia, Tess, Gabriel, Daniel. BS, Tex. A&M U., 1962; PhD, U. Miss., 1966, postdoctoral study, 1966-69. Instr. dept. physiology/biophysics U Miss. Jackson, 1966-67, asst. prof. 1967-71, assoc. prof., 1971-74; assoc. prof. U. Ala., Birmingham, 1974-76, prof., 1976-88, assoc. prof. Nephrology Rsch. and Tng. Ctr., 1979-83, prof. 1983-88; prof., chmn. dept. physiology Tulane U. Med. Sch., New Orleans, 1988—; vis. scientist Duke U. Med. Ctr., Durham, N.C., 1972-73. Assoc. editor:

News in Physiol. Scis., 1994—; Am. Jour. Physiology, 1983-89, mem. editorial bd., 1982-83; assoc. editor Hypertension, 1993—; mem. editorial bd. Kidney Internat., 1976-87; Hypertension, 1980-83, assoc. editor, 1993—; editorial bd. Kidney, 1992—, Clinical Science, 1994—; contbr. sci. papers, book chpts., slides and tapes to profl. publs. Chmn. cardiorenal rsch. study com. Am. Heart Assn., 1994-95, mem. nat. rsch. com. 1994-99. Recipient Rsch. Career Devel. award Nat. Heart, Lung and Blood Inst., 1974-79, Merit award, 1988. Mem. AAAS, Am. Physiol. Soc. (coun. 1991-94), Am. Heart Assn. (kidney, high blood pressure couns., nat. rsch. com. 1994—), N.Y. Acad. Sci., Am. Soc. Nephrology, Internat. Soc. Nephrology, Am. Soc. Hypertension (coun. 1992-94), Internat. Soc. Hypertension, Assn. of Chmn. of Depts. of Physiology (councillor 1993-95, pres.-elect 1995—). Democrat. Roman Catholic. Home: 10020 Hyde Pl River Ridge LA 70123-1522 Office: Tulane U Med Sch Dept Physiology 1430 Tulane Ave New Orleans LA 70112-2699

NAVARRE, ROBERT WARD, manufacturing company executive; b. Monroe, Mich., May 21, 1933; s. Joseph Alexander N.; m. Barbara Anne Navarre, June 26, 1953; children—Veo Anne, Robert Ward, Jan Louise. B.S. in Commerce, U. Notre Dame, 1955; grad., exec. program Stanford U., 1979. Sales mgr. Marben Corp., Jackson, Mich., 1958-64; mktg. adminstr. Simpson Industries, Litchfield, Mich., 1964-67; pres., CEO Simpson Industries, 1967-89, chmn., 1989—, also bd. dirs.; bd. dirs. Webster Industries. Chmn. Jackson/Hillsdale Mental Health Service Bd., 1972-78; mem. Hillsdale Schs. Bd. Edn., 1972-76. Mem. NAM (regional vice chmn. 1978-79, chmn. membership com. 1979-80, bd. dirs.), Mich. Mfg. Assn. (bd. dirs., chmn. 1991—). Roman Catholic. Office: Simpson Industries Inc 32100 Telegraph Rd Franklin MI 48025-2452*

NAVARRO, ANTONIO (LUIS), public relations executive; b. Havana, Cuba, Sept. 26, 1922; came to U.S., 1940; s. Antero Navarro and Aurora (Pérez-Zuazo) Todd; m. Avis Hedges, Dec. 28, 1954; children: Antonio, Avis, Alexander. B.S. in Chem. Engring., Ga. Tech., 1944. With Shell Chem. Corp., Calif., 1944-50, Lobo Sugar Trading, Cuba, 1950-54, Textilera Ariguanabo (Hedges Family Textile Bus.), Cuba, 1954-61; mgr. Peruvian ops. W.R. Grace & Co., Lima, Peru, 1961-73; v.p. corp. adminstrn. group, mgr. corp. communications W.R. Grace & Co., N.Y.C., 1973-78, corp. v.p., 1978-82, sr. v.p., 1982-87, group exec., corp. relations group, corp. communications, govt. relations, investor relations, 1986-87; vice chmn. Jack Hilton Inc., 1987-88; dir. Office of Cuba Broadcasting (Radio Marti and TV Marti) USIA, Washington, 1990-93; bd. dirs. Radio Free Europe/Radio Liberty Fund, 1986. Author: (memoir of Cuban revolution) Tocayo, 1981 (Conservative Club Selection award 1981). Bd. dirs. Accion, N.Y.C., 1973-91; mem. Coun. of Ams. (now Ams. Soc.), 1976-86; bd. dirs. Radio Broadcasting to Cuba (Radio Marti), 1985-90; mem. Blue Ribbon panel on minority affairs and indsl. rels. Am. Chem. Soc., 1993—. Recipient Liberty medal N.Y.C., 1986, USIA Superior Honor award, Dir.'s award for superior achievmct, 1993, Cuban-Am. Engr. of Yr. award, Fla., 1994; named to Ga. Tech. Engring. Hall of Fame, 1994. Democrat. Roman Catholic. Avocations: tennis; classical music. Home: 151 Crandon Blvd Miami FL 33149-1527

NAVARRO, BRUCE CHARLES, lawyer; b. West Lafayette, Ind., Oct. 30, 1954; s. Joseph Anthony and Dorothy Gloria (Gnazzo) N.; m. Nancy Elizabeth Pryor; children: Philip Joseph, Joanna Christina, Kelly Finnegan, Ian Chandler Finnegan. BA, Duke U., 1976; JD, Ind. U., 1980. Bar: D.C. 1980. Asst. counsel U.S Senate Labor Subcom., Washington, 1981-84; acting dep. undersec. for legis. affairs Dept. Labor, Washington, 1984-85; atty. advisor EEOC, Washington, 1985-86; dir. Office of Congl. Rels. Office of Pers. Mgmt., Washington, 1986-89; prin. dep. asst. atty. gen. for legis. U.S. Dept. of Justice, Washington, 1989-91; spl. asst. to gen. counsel U.S. Dept. HHS, Washington, 1991; expert cons. U.S. Dept. Def., Washington, 1992; counsel to the vice chmn. U.S. Consumer Product Safety Commn., Bethesda, Md., 1992-95; atty. Bruce C. Navarro Legis. and Regulatory Affairs, Washington, 1995—. Mem. Arlington County Republican Com. (Va.), 1983. Mem. D.C. Bar Assn. Roman Catholic. Avocation: music, golf. Home: 4277 Berwick Pl Woodbridge VA 22192-5119 Office: Ste 550 1201 Connecticut Ave NW Washington DC 20036

NAVARRO, JOSEPH ANTHONY, statistician, consultant; b. New Britain, Conn., July 6, 1927; s. Charles C. and Josephine V. (Bianco) N.; m. Dorothy G. Gnazzo, Feb. 6, 1929; children: Kenneth M., Bruce C., Joseph S. BS, Cen. Conn. State U., 1950; MS, Purdue U., 1952, PhD, 1955. Rsch. staff, cons. GE, 1955-59; rsch. staff, mgmt. IBM, 1962-64; sr. staff mem., asst. dir. Inst. Def. Analyses, Alexandria, Va., 1964-72; pres., chief oper. officer System Planning Corp., Arlington, Va., 1972-86; dep. undersec. test and evaluation Dept. Defense, Washington, 1986-87; now pvt. practice cons., 1987—; pres. Wackenhut Applied Technologies Ctr., Fairfax, Va., 1989-90. Contbr. articles to profl. jours. Mem. Bd. Trade, Washington, 1983-85. Mem. Internat. Test and Evaluation Assn. Republican. Roman Catholic. Club: COSMOS (Washington). Office: JAN Assocs Inc 7825 Fulbright Ct Bethesda MD 20817-3119

NAVAS, WILLIAM ANTONIO, JR., military officer, civil engineer; b. Mayaguez, P.R., Dec. 15, 1942; s. William Antonio Sr. and Ethel Ines (Marin) N.; m. Wilda Margarita Cordova Navas, Aug. 7, 1965; children: William Antonio III, Gretchen Maria. BSCE, U. P.R., 1965; MS in Engring. Mgmt., U. Bridgeport, 1979. Registered profl. engr., P.R. Commd. 2d lt. U.S. Army, 1966, advanced through grades to maj. gen., 1990; served in U.S. Army Corps of Engrs., 1966-70; with Interamerican Def. Coll., Washington, 1981-82; dir. ops. P.R. Army Nat. Guard, San Juan, 1982-84, 84-87; comdr. Engr. Task Force, Panama, 1984; dep. dir. Army Nat. Guard Bur., Washington, 1987—; vice chief Nat. Guard Bur., 1990; project engr. Empresas Navas, Inc., Mayaguez, P.R., 1970-72; ptnr., prin. W.A. Navas Jr. & Assoc., Mayaguez, 1972-80; dir. Navas & Moreda, Inc., Mayaguez, 1973-81; mil. exec. res. forces policy bd. Office of Sec. of Def., 1992-94, dep. asst. sec. of def., 1994—; chmn. Dept. of Army Hispanic Employment Commn., Washington, 1988. Decorated Knight Eq. Order of Holy Sepulchre. Mem. Nat. Guard Assn. of the U.S. (del. 1980-86), Nat. Guard Assn. of P.R., Soc. of Am. Mil. Engrs. Roman Catholic. Avocations: militaria collection, reading, running, travel. Home: Qtrs # 16A Fort Myer VA 22211 Office: Office Sec Def The Pentagon Washington DC 20013

NAVASKY, VICTOR SAUL, magazine editor; b. N.Y.C., July 5, 1932; s. Macy and Esther Blanche (Goldberg) N.; m. Anne Landey Strongin, Mar. 27, 1966; children: Bruno, Miri, Jenny. A.B., Swarthmore Coll., 1954; LL.B., Yale U., 1959. Spl. asst. to Gov. G Mennen Williams, Mich., 1959-60; editor-in-chief, pub. Monocle Mag., 1961-65; editor N.Y. Times mag., 1970-72; editor-in-chief The Nation mag., N.Y.C., 1978—; vis. scholar Russell Sage Found., 1975-76; Ferris prof. journalism Princeton U., 1976-77. Author: Kennedy Justice, 1971 (Nat. Book Award nominee), Naming Names, 1980 (Am. Book award 1981), rev. edit., 1991; editor: (with C. Cerf) The Experts Speak, 1984. Mem. AAAS. Swarthmore Coll., 1991—. Served with U.S. Army, 1954-56. Guggenheim fellow, 1974-75; fellow Inst. of Politics, Harvard U., 1994; Sr. fellow Freedom Forum, 1994. Mem. Author's Guild Coun., PEN (exec. com.), Com. to Protect Journalists (v.p., exec. com.), Phi Beta Kappa. Democrat. Home: 33 W 67th St New York NY 10023-6224 Office: Nation 72 5th Ave New York NY 10011-8004

NAVIA, JUAN MARCELO, biologist, educator; b. Havana, Jan. 16, 1927; came to U.S., 1961; s. Juan and Hortensia (DeLaCampa) N.; m. Josefina Blanca Bonich, Aug. 20, 1950; children: Juan, Carlos, Ana, Beatriz. BS, MIT, 1950, MS, 1951, PhD, 1956. Sr. scientist Inst. Dental Rsch. U. Ala., Birmingham, 1969-88; dir. nutrition and oral health tng. program U. Ala. Birmingham, 1968-88, dir. rsch. tng. Sch. Dentistry, 1971-81, dir. clin. rsch. tng. program - MD, PhD, 1972-75, dir Sparkman Ctr., 1981-94, prof. comparative medicine, 1973-94, prof. biochemistry, 1976-86, prof. nutrition scis., 1977-94; ret., prof. emeritus, 1994—; adv. bd. mem. Fogarty Internat. Ctr., Bethesda, Md., 1985-88, Princeton (N.J.) Dental Resource Ctr., 1987-90; dean U. Ala. Sch. Pub. Health, 1989-92. Author: Animal Models in Dental Research, 1977; editor: The Biologic Basis of Dental Caries, 1980; contbr. Encyclopedia Americana, 1968. Recipient Sr. Internat. Fogarty fellow, 1979, AAAS fellow, 1982, H. Trendley Dean Meml. award Internat. Assn. Dental Rsch., 1990, UAB Pres.'s medal, 1992. Fellow Am. Inst. Nutrition; mem. Internat. Assn. Dental Rsch. (pres. cariology 1983-84), Internat. Soc. Trace Element Rsch. in Humans, Am. Assn. Dental Rsch., Am. Chem. Soc.,

European Orgn. Caries Rsch., Inst. Food Technologists, Nat. Coun. Internat. Health, Sociedad Latinoamericana de Nutricion, N.Y. Acad. Scis., Internat. Serra Club, Sigma Xi, Sigma Delta Pi. Republican. Roman Catholic. Avocations: walking, writing. Office: U Ala at Birmingham Dept Comparative Medicine Volker Hall 403 Birmingham AL 35294

NAVON, IONEL MICHAEL, mathematics educator; b. Bucharest, Romania, Apr. 28, 1940; s. David and Sarah (Schwartzman) N.; m. Lily Marcu, May 11, 1967; children: Daria, Livia. BSc in Math., Hebrew U. Jerusalem, 1967, MSc in Atmospheric Scis., 1971; PhD in Applied Math., U. Witwatersrand, Johannesburg, South Africa, 1979. Sr. rsch. meteorologist Israel Meteorol. Office, Tel Aviv, 1973-74; head applied math. sect. Tamam/Israel Aircraft Industry, Tel Aviv, 1974-76; sr. rsch. officer Counc. Sci. and Indsl. Rsch., Pretoria, South Africa, 1976-78, chief rsch. officer, 1979-80, sr. chief rsch. officer, 1981-83; sr. vis. scientist NASA/Goddard Space Flight Ctr., Greenbelt, Md., 1983-84; cons. NASA/Goddard Space Flight Ctr., Greenbelt, Md., 1984-85; sr. specialist researcher Coun. Sci. and Indsl. Rsch., Pretoria, 1984-85; assoc. scientist Supercomputer Rsch. Inst., Tallahassee, Fla., 1985-87; assoc. prof. math. Fla. State U., Tallahassee, 1987-1990, prof., 1991—, program dir. optimization and optimal control, 1993—, hon. prof. dept. meteorology Supercomputer Rsch. Inst., 1987—, faculty assoc. Supercomputer Computation Rsch. Inst., 1988—, faculty assoc. Geophys. Fluid Dynamics Inst., 1989—; cons. Ctr. Analysis Prediction of Storms, Norman, Okla., 1989; leader Argonne Nat. Lab.; co-organizer Internat. Conf. Element Methods in Geophysics, Tallahassee, 1991; summer lecture series scientist NASA, 1991—; mem. panel nat. experts to rev. and conduct site visiting Okla. Sci. and Tech. Ctr.; keynote speaker Internat. Conf. on Finite Element Methods, South Africa, 1992, Internat. Conf. on Optimization Techniques and Applications, Singapore, 1992, Assimilation of Meteorological and Oceanographic Observations, France, 1993. Editor spl. issues Computer and Math. with Applications; editorial bd. Monthly Weather Rev., 1991-94, Jour. for Numerical Linear Algebra with Applications, 1991, Computational Fluid Dynamics Jour., 1992; contbr. 86 refereed articles. 1st Israel Civil Def., 1960-63. Grantee NSF, 1988, 91, 94—, NASA, 1991, 94, Rsch. grantee Air Force Office Sci., 1989, 91, 94. Mem. Am. Meteorol. Soc., Am. Math. Soc., Am. Geophys. Union, Soc. Indsl. and Applied Math., Israel Assn. Profl. Engrs., Am. Computing Machinery Assn. Avocations: pingpong, photography, books. Home: 3138 Ferns Glen Dr Tallahassee FL 32308-2304 Office: Fla State U Love Building Rm 111 Tallahassee FL 32306

NAVRATIL, GERALD ANTON, plasma physicist; b. Troy, N.Y., Sept. 5, 1951; s. Lloyd George and Frances Mary (Scalise) N.; m. Joan Frances Etzweiler, Sept. 4, 1976; children: Frances, Alexis, Paula. BS, Calif. Inst. Tech., 1973; MS, U. Wis., 1974, PhD, 1976. Project assoc. dept. physics U. Wis.-Madison, 1976-77; asst. prof. engring. sci. Columbia U., N.Y.C., 1977-78, asst. prof. applied physics, 1979-83, assoc. prof., 1983-88, prof., 1988—, chmn. 1988-94, vice dean Sch. Engring. and Applied Sci., 1994—; vis. fellow Princeton U., 1985-86; cons. MIT, 1984-86, Fusion Systems, Inc., 1988, Inst. Def. Analysis, 1992—, com.; mem. Nat. Adv. Coun. TPX Tokomak Project and chair TPX Program Adv. Com., 1993—. Assoc. editor Physics of Plasmas, 1994—. Patentee in field. Cottrell Rsch. grantee, 1978; U.S. Dept. Energy High Beta Tokomak Research contract, 1982—; NSF grantee, 1978-88; Alfred P. Sloan rsch. fellow, 1984. Fellow Am. Phys. Soc. (sec./treas. 1988-94, v.p. 1990, pres. 1991); mem. Univ. Fusion Assn. (sec., treas., pres. 1991), Sigma Xi. Office: Columbia U Dept Applied Physics 500 W 120th St Rm 215 New York NY 10027-6623

NAVRATILOVA, MARTINA, former professional tennis player; b. Prague, Czechoslovakia, Oct. 18, 1956; came to U.S., 1975, naturalized, 1981; d. Miroslav Navratil and Jana Navratilova. Student, schs. in Czechoslovakia. Profl. tennis player, 1975-94. Author: (with George Vecsey) Martina, 1985, (with Liz Nickels) The Total Zone, 1994. Winner Czechoslovak Nat. singles, 1972-74, U.S. Open singles, 1983, 84, 86, 87, U.S. Open doubles, 1977, 78, 80, 83, 84, 87, U.S. Open mixed doubles, 1987, Va. Slims Tournament, 1978, 83, 84, 85, 86, Wimbledon singles, 1978, 79, 82, 83, 84, 85, 86, 87, 90, Wimbledon women's doubles, 1976, 79, 81, 82, 83, 84, 86, Wimbledon mixed doubles, 1985, 94, French Open singles, 1982, 84, Australian Open singles, 1981, 83, 85, Australian Doubles (with Nagelsen), 1980, (with Shriver), 1982, 84, 84, 85, 87, 88, 89, Grand Slam of Women's Tennis, 1984; named Hon. Citizen of Dallas, AP Female Athlete of Yr., 1983. Mem. Women's Tennis Assn. (dir., exec. com., pres.). Address: IMG 1 Erieview Pla Cleveland OH 44114

NAVROTSKY, ALEXANDRA, geophysics educator. BS, U. Chgo., 1963, MS, 1964, PhD, 1967. Rsch. assoc. Technische Hochschule, Clausthal, Germany, 1967-68, Pa. State U., State College, 1968-69; mem. geology and chemistry faculty Ariz. State U., 1969-85, dir. Ctr. Solid State Sci., 1984-85; prof. dept. geol. & geophys. sci. Princeton (N.J.) U., 1985—, Albert G. Blanke Jr. prof. geol. and geophys. scis., 1992—, chair geol. and geophys. scis., 1988-91; Albert G. Blanke Jr. chmn., 1992—. Editor: Physics and Chemistry of Minerals, 1986-91; contbr. articles to profl. jours. Alfred P. Sloan fellow, 1973. Fellow Am. Geophys. Union; mem. NAS, Am. Ceramic Soc., Mineral. Soc. Am. (pres. 1992-93, v.p. 1991-92, award 1981), Princeton Materials Inst., Nat. Acad. Scis., Sigma Xi. Office: Princeton U Dept Geol & Geophys Scis 114 Guyot Ave Princeton NJ 08540-3433*

NAWY, EDWARD GEORGE, civil engineer, educator; b. Baghdad, Iraq, Dec. 21, 1926; came to U.S., 1957, naturalized, 1966; s. George M. and Ava (Marshall) N.; m. Rachel E. Shebbath, Mar. 23, 1949; children: Ava Margaret, Robert M. DIC, Imperial Coll. Sci. and Tech., London, 1951; CE, MIT, 1959; D of Engring., U. Pisa, Italy, 1967. Registered profl. engr. (P.E.), N.J., N.Y., Pa., Calif., Fla. Head structures Israel Water Planning Authority, Tel-Aviv, 1952-57; mem. faculty Rutgers U., New Brunswick, N.J., 1959—; mem. grad. faculty Rutgers U., 1961—, prof. civil engring., 1966-72, Distinguished prof. (prof. II), 1972—, chmn. dept. civil and environ. engring., dir. grad. programs, 1980-86; chmn. Coll. Engring. Del. Assembly, 1969-72; mem. Univ. Senate, 1973-80, also mem. exec. com.; also faculty rep. mem. bd. bovs. and trustee; Guest prof. Nat. U. Tucaman, Argentina, summer 1963, Imperial Coll. Sci. and Tech., summer 1964; vis. prof. Stevens Inst. Tech., Hoboken, N.J., 1968-72; hon. prof. Nanjing Inst. Tech., China, 1987; mem. N.J. Chancellor Higher Edn. for Higher Edn. Master Plan; mem. bridge com., Rutgers U. rep. Transp. Rsch. Bd.; cons. to industry; U.S. mem. commn. on cracking Comité EuroInternat. du Beton; mem. Civil Engring. Tech. Adv. Coun. N.J., 1966-72; concrete sys. cons. FAA, Washington; cons. energy divsn. U.S. Gen. Acctg. Office, Washington; gen. chmn. Internat. Symposium on Slabs and Plates, 1971; mem. hon. presidium RILEM Internat. Conf., Budapest, 1977. Author: Reinforced Concrete, 1985, 3d edit., 1996, Simplified Reinforced Concrete, 1986, Prestressed Concrete, 1989, 2d edit., 1996, High Strength High Performance Concrete, 1995; contbr. over 125 articles to profl. jours. Vice pres. Berkeley Twp. Taxpayers Assn. Ocean City, N.J., 1966-70. Recipient merit citation and award N.J. Concrete Assn., 1966; C. Gulbenkian Found. fellow, 1972. Fellow ASCE (mem. joint com. on slabs), Instn. Civil Engrs. (London), Am. Concrete Inst. (pres. N.J. chpt. 1966, 77-78, chmn. nat. com. on cracking 1966-73, bd. com. chpts. 1969-72, ACI rep. internat. commn. fractures, H.L. Kenneday award 1972, award of recognition N.J. chpt. 1972, chpt. activities award 1978, chmn. nat. com. on deflection 1989—); mem. NSPE, AAUP (chmn. budget and priorities com Rutgers U. chpt. 1972), Am. Soc. Engring. Edn., Prestressed Concrete Inst. (Bridge Competition award 1971, mem. tech. activities com.), N.Y. Acad. Scis., N.J. Bldg., Tall Bldgs. Coun., N.J. Contractors Assn. (cons. educ. com., tall bldgs. coun.), Rotary, Sigma Xi, Tau Beta Pi, Chi Epsilon (hon.). Office: Rutgers State U of NJ Civil Engring Dept New Brunswick NJ 08855 *Success is normally the result of honesty and continuous setting and updating of high goals which have to be perseverely pursued.*

NAY, HOWARD RILEY, surgeon, educator; b. Wheeling, W.Va., Apr. 13, 1930; s. Howard Erwin and Agnes Ellen (Gauld) N.; m. Geraldine Tullock, Oct. 26, 1956; children: Kathryn Nay Clay, Elizabeth Derby Nay Schwengel, Jennifer Hunt. BA, Va. Mil. Inst., 1952; MD, Columbia U., 1956. Diplomate Am. Bd. Surgery; cert. advanced traumal life support, laparoscopic laser cholecystectomy, clin. laparoscopic cholecystectomy, advanced laparoscopic surgery, advanced operative laparoscopy for gen. surgery. Axting asst. attending surgeon St. Luke's Hosp., N.Y.C., 1964-65, asst. attending surgeon, 1965-72, assoc. attending surgeon, 1972-76, attending surgeon, 1976—; sr. attending surgeon St. Luke's/Roosevelt Hosp. Ctr.,

1982—, chief surgery A svc., 1985—, chief surgery A trauma svcs., 1989—; attending srugeon Dr.'s Hosp., N.Yu.C., 1982—, Beth Isreal North Hospice Ctr., 1989—; instr. surgery Columbia U., N.Y.C., 1964-72, asst. clin. prof. surgery, 1972-80, assoc. clin. prof. surgery, 1980—. Contbr. numerous articles to profl. jours. With M.C., USAF, 1959-61, hon. disharge, 1961, USAFR, 1961-70. Fellow ACS: mem. AMA, N.Y. Med. Soc., N.Y. County Med. Soc., N.Y. Surg. Soc., N.Y. Soc. Cardiovascular Surgery, Internat. Soc. Angiology, Internat. Cardiovascular Soc. Office: 925 Park Ave New York NY 10028-0210

NAYAR, BALDEV RAJ, political science educator; b. Gujrat Dist., India, Oct. 26, 1931; emigrated to Can., 1964; s. Jamna Das and Durga Devi (Marwah) N.; m. Nancy Ann Skinner, Aug. 27, 1961; children—Sheila Jane, Kamala Elizabeth, Sunita Maria. B.A., Punjab U., 1953; M.A., 1956, U. Chgo., 1959; Ph.D., U. Chgo., 1963. Asst. prof. Calif. State Coll., Hayward, 1963-64; mem. faculty dept. polit. sci. McGill U., 1964-69, assoc. prof., 1969-71, prof., 1971-94, assoc. chmn., 1990-93; research assoc. Internat. Devel. Research Centre, 1978. Author: Minority Politics in the Punjab, 1966, National Communication and Language Policy, 1969, The Modernization Imperative and Indian Planning, 1972, American Geopolitics and India, 1976, India's Quest for Technological Independence, 1983, India's Mixed Economy, 1989, The Political Economy of India's Public Sector, 1990, Superpower Dominance and Military Aid, 1991, The State and International Aviation in India, 1994. Bd. dirs. Shastri Indo-Canadian Inst., 1970-72, sr. fellow, 1978, 86. Recipient Watumull prize Am. Hist. Assn., 1966; Charles E. Merriam fellow, 1957; Carnegie Study New Nations fellow, 1962; Can. Council sr. fellow, 1967, 74; SSHRC leave fellow, 1982. Mem. Can. Polit. Sci. Assn., Assn. Asian Studies, Assn., Can. Asian Studies Assn. Office: McGill Univ, Dept Polit Sci, Montreal, PQ Canada H3A 2T7

NAYDEN, DENIS J., diversified financial services company executive; b. 1954. BA, U. Conn., MBA. With GE Capital Corp., Stamford, Conn., 1977—, formerly sr. v.p., exec. v.p., 1989—, also bd. dirs. Office: Gen Electric Credit Corp 570 Lexington Ave New York NY 10022-6824

NAYLOR, AUBREY WILLARD, botany educator; b. Union City, Tenn., Feb. 5, 1915; s. Harry Joseph and Clara Mae (Isbell) N.; m. Frances Valentine Lloyd, Dec. 26, 1940; children: Virginia Dawson Naylor Kirby, Edith-Margaret Naylor Eastman DeWitt. BS, U. Chgo., 1937, MS, 1938, PhD, 1940. Mem. staff, bur. plant industry U.S. Dept. Agr., Chgo., 1938-40; instr. botany U. Chgo., 1940-44, Northwestern U., Evanston, Ill., 1944-45; asst. prof. U. Wash., Seattle, 1946-47, Yale U., 1947-52; assoc. prof. Duke U., 1952-59, prof., 1959-72, James B. Duke prof., 1972-85, James B. Duke prof. emeritus, 1985—; program dir. for metabolic biology NSF, Washington, 1961-62, cons., 1960-63; chmn. com. examiners for Grad. (Sch.) Record Examination on Biology, Edn. Testing Svc., Princeton, N.J., 1966-72; cons. Oak Ridge Nat. Lab., 1957-58, Rsch. Triangle Inst., N.C., 1968—, TVA, 1969-75, Schaper and Brümmer Pharm. Co., Salzgitter, Fed. Republic of Germany, 1986-92, Akzo Salt Co., 1991—; mem. summer faculties U. N.C., Chapel Hill, 1960-61, Greensboro, 1964-65; mem. summer faculties Bennett Coll., Greensboro, N.C.; vis. prof. U. Bristol, Eng., 1958-59, U. Tex., Austin, 1977. Contbr. chpts. to books, articles and book revs. to profl. jours. NRC fellow Boyce Thompson Inst. for Plant Rsch., Yonkers, N.Y., 1945-46, Guggenheim fellow, 1958-59; NSF sr. fellow, 1958-59; grantee, 1956-86, Am. Cancer Soc. grantee, 1953-57, Herman Frasch Found. grantee, 1957-72. Fellow AAAS (life mem.); mem. Am. Soc. Plant Physiologists (life, chmn. bd. trustees 1962-74, pres. 1961, exec. com. 1959-60, 62-74, 81-82, Disting. Svc. award So. sect. 1981, Charles Reid Barnes life membership 1981, archivist 1987—), Am. Inst. Biol. Scis., Am. Soc. Cell Biologists, Biochem. Soc., Soc. Exptl. Biologists, Bot. Soc. Am. (life, cert. of merit 1988), Scandinavian Soc. Plant Physiologists, Japanese Soc. Plant Physiologists, Australian Soc. Plant Physiologists, N.C. Acad. Scis., Cosmos Club (Washington), Sigma Xi (life, pres. chpt. 1968-69). Home: 2430 Wrightwood Ave Durham NC 27705-5802

NAYLOR, BRIAN, news correspondent; b. Mt. Kisco, N.Y., Aug. 7, 1955. BA in Broadcasting/Film, U. Maine, 1978. Gen. assignment reporter, anchor, announcer Sta. WLBZ, Bangor, Maine, 1976-78; statehouse reporter Capital News Svc., Augusta, Maine, 1978; gen. assignment reporter, anchor Sta. WLAM, Lewiston, Maine, 1978-79; statehouse reporter, host Sta. WOSU Radio, Columbus, Ohio, 1979-82; prodr., co-host Sta. WOSU-TV, Columbus, 1979-82; newscaster, gen. assignment reporter, White House reporter Nat. Pub. Radio, Washington, 1982-92, Congl. corr., 1992—; adj. prof. Am. U., Washington, 1991. Jefferson fellow, 1990. Office: Nat Pub Radio 635 Massachusetts Ave Washington DC 20001

NAYLOR, BRUCE GORDON, museum director; b. Midale, Sask., Can., Aug. 19, 1950; s. John Raymond Naylor and Mary Lynn (Frisby) Redeberg; m. Marlene Johnstone, Dec. 19, 1981 (dec. July 1992); m. Judith Jeune, June 11, 1994. BS with high honors, U. Sask., 1972; PhD, U. Alta., 1978. Postdoctoral fellow U. Toronto, Ont., 1978-80; lectr. U. Calif., Berkeley, 1979; asst. prof. U. Alta., Edmonton, 1980-82; curator Tyrrell Mus. Drumheller, Alta., 1982-86; asst. dir. Royal Tyrrell Mus., Drumheller, 1986-92, dir., 1992—; adj. prof. U. Alta., 1983—; sen. U. Calgary, Alta., 1989-90. Assoc. editor Jour. Vertebrate Paleontology, 1991-92; contbr. articles to sci. publs. Operating grantee Nat. Sci. & Engring. Rsch. Coun., Ottawa, 1981-82. Fellow Geol. Assn. Can.; mem. Soc. Vertebrate Paleontology, Rotary Club Drumheller. Avocations: horseback riding, gardening. Office: Royal Tyrrell Mus, Box 7500, Drumheller, AB Canada T0J 0Y0

NAYLOR, FRANK WESLEY, JR., financial executive; b. Mulvane, Kans., Feb. 7, 1939; s. Frank Wesley Sr. and Hildred Ethel (Reed) N.; m. Marilyn Everest, May 16, 1987; children: Mary Allison, Frank Wesley III, Erin, Mark. BA, U. Kans., Lawrence, 1961; postgrad., Rockhurst Coll., Kansas City, Mo., 1966-68. Staff mgr. Met. Life Ins. Co., Grand, Kans., 1965-69; dep. mgr. Fed. Crop Ins. Corp., USDA, Washington, 1969-72; exec. asst. to adminstr. VA, Washington, 1972-74; assoc. adminstr. Farmers Home Adminstrn., USDA, Washington, 1974-77; sr. v.p. Farm Credit Banks, Sacramento, 1977-81; under sec. USDA, Washington, 1981-86; chmn. Farm Credit Adminstrn., Washington, 1986-88; pres., chief exec. officer U.S. Agricredit Inc., Washington, 1988—. Mem. Community Services Dist. Bd., Shingle Springs, Calif.; chmn. Eldorado County Fin. Com., Shingle Springs; bd. dirs. Sacramento C. of C., 1977; active Presdl. campaigns, Washington, 1968, 72. Mem. Kansas City (Kans.) Jr. C. of C. Republican. Home: 2 Clapham Ct Sterling VA 20165-5653 Office: US Agricredit Inc 10 Pidgeon Hill Dr Ste 210 Sterling VA 20165-6103

NAYLOR, GEORGE LEROY, lawyer, rail transportation executive; b. Bountiful, Utah, May 11, 1915; s. Joseph Francis and Josephine Chase (Wood) N.; student U. Utah, 1934-36; student George Washington U., 1937; J.D. (Bancroft Whitney scholar), San Francisco, 1953; m. Maxine Elizabeth Lewis, Jan. 18, 1941; children: Georgia Naylor Price, RoseMaree Naylor Hammer, George LeRoy II. Bar: Calif. 1954, Ill. 1968. V.p., sec. legis. rep. Internat. Union of Mine, Mill & Smelter Workers, CIO, Dist. Union 2, Utah-Nevada, 1942-44; examiner So. Pacific Co., San Francisco, 1949-54, chief examiner, 1955, asst. mgr., 1956-61; carrier mem. Nat. R.R. Adjustment Bd., Chgo., 1961-77, chmn., 1970-77; atty. Village of Fox River Valley Gardens, Ill., 1974-77; practice law, legal cons., Ill. and Calif., 1977—, ret. from pvt. practice, 1991; gen. counsel for Can-Veyor, Inc., Mountain View, Calif., 1959-64; adj. instr. dept. mgmt. U. West Fla., 1981. Active Rep. Nat. Com. 1992-93. Served with AUS, World War II. Mem. ABA, Ill. Bar Assn., Calif. Bar Assn., Chgo. Bar Assn., San Francisco Bar Assn. Mormon. Author: Defending Carriers Before the NRAB and Public Law Boards, 1969, Choice Morsels in Tax and Property Law, 1966, Underground at Bingham Canyon, 1944; National Railroad Adjustment Board Practice Manual, 1978. Home and Office: Virginia Lee Rd RR 1 Box 570 Cotter AR 72626

NAYLOR, HARRY BROOKS, microbiologist; b. Hewitt, Minn., Mar. 30, 1914; s. George Brooks and Anna Elmira (Larsen) N.; m. Ellen Florence Haahela, Sept. 8, 1940; children—Lynn Brooks, Roy Allen, Gail Ann. B.S., U. Minn., 1936 Ph.D., Cornell U., 1943. Mem. tech. dept. Sheffield Farms Dairy, Inc., N.Y.C., 1946-47; mem. faculty dept. microbiology Cornell U., Ithaca, N.Y., 1947—; prof. emeritus Cornell U., 1977—. Pasco Labs. Inc., Wheat Ridge, Colo., 1978-86; mem. grant review bd. USPHS, 1967-70; OAS lectr., Brazil, 1972, 73; teaching fellow Fed. U. of Rio de Janeiro, 1978.

Contbr. articles to profl. jours. Served with USNR, 1943-46. Fulbright-Hayes fellow, 1966-67. Mem. Am. Soc. Microbiology, Am. Acad. Microbiology. Home: 5390 Belfern Dr Bellingham WA 98226-9063

NAYLOR, JAMES CHARLES, psychologist, educator; b. Chgo., Feb. 8, 1932; s. Joseph Sewell and Berniece (Berg) N.; m. Georgia Lou Mason, Feb. 14, 1953; children—Mary Denise, Diana Darice, Shari Dalice. B.S., Purdue U., 1957, M.S., 1958, Ph.D., 1960. Asst. prof. Ohio State U., 1960-63, asso. prof., 1963-67, prof. vice chmn. dept. psychology, 1967-68; prof. Purdue U., Lafayette, Ind., 1968-86, head dept. psychol. scis., 1968-79; prof., chmn. dept. psychology Ohio State U., Columbus, 1986—; Fulbright rsch. scholar, Umea, Sweden, 1976; Disting. scholar, vis. scientist Flinders U., South Australia, 1982-83, UNESCO ednl. cons. to Hangzhou U., Peoples Republic of China, 1984; chmn. Coun. Grad. Depts. Psychology, 1993-94. Author: Industrial Psychology, 1968, A Theory of Behavior in Organizations, 1980; founder, editor: Organizational Behavior and Human Decision Processes; mem. editorial bd.: Prof. Psychology; Contbr. articles to profl. jours. Served with USN, 1950-54. Fellow AAAS, Am. Psychol. Soc., Am. Psychol. Assn.; mem. Psychonomic Soc., Psychmetric Soc., Internat. Assn. Applied Psychology, Soc. Organizational Behavior (founder), Phi Beta Kappa, Sigma Xi. Home: 176 Tucker Dr Columbus OH 43085-3064 Office: Ohio State U Dept Psychology Columbus OH 43210

NAYLOR, JOHN THOMAS, telephone company executive; b. Orillia, Ont., Can., Jan. 30, 1913; s. Fred Addison and Ethel (Thompson) N.; m. Ruth Louisa Tissot, Dec. 21, 1934; children: Joan Crosby, Carol Manka. BSEE, Oreg. State U., 1934. Registered profl. engr., Calif., Oreg., Wash. Chief accountant McKesson & Robbins, Inc., Portland, Oreg., 1934-38; engr. Pub. Service Commn. Oreg., 1938-41; v.p. Gen. Telephone Co. Calif., 1941-50; v.p. gen. mgr. Philippine Long Distance Telephone Co. Manila, 1950-56; also dir.; v.p United Utilities, Inc., 1956-59; pres., dir. United Telephone Co.; v.p. Internat. Tel. & Tel. Corp., N.Y.C., 1959-61; pres., dir. Telectronic Systems, Inc., Manila, Philippines, 1962-73; cons., 1973—. Author articles on engring., finance, mgmt., pub. service. Active Boy Scouts Am., YMCA; pres. Am. Sch., Manila; mem. coun. regents Oreg. State U., 1981—. Mem. IEEE, NSPE, Philippine Assn. Mech. and Elec. Engrs., Phi Kappa Phi, Tau Beta Pi, Eta Kappa Nu. Club: Army and Navy. Address: 1451 NE Meier Dr Grants Pass OR 97526

NAYLOR, PAUL DONALD, lawyer; b. St. Bernard, Ohio, May 28, 1925; s. David Frederick and Erna Helen (Miller) N.; m. Geraldine L. Lacy, Jan. 20, 1945; children: Linda S., Paul Scott, Todd L. JD, U. Cin., 1948. Bar: Ohio 1948. Ptnr. Pulse & Naylor, Cin., 1949-65; pvt. practice Cin., 1965—. Mem. Nat. Rep. Com. Lt. (j.g.) USN, 1943-46. Recipient Svc. to Mankind award Sertoma Internat. Mem. Cin. Bar Assn. (real property com. 1966-86), Ohio Bar Assn., Cin. Lawyers Club (pres. 1955), Order of the Coif. Office: 30 E Central Pkwy # 210 Cincinnati OH 45202

NAYLOR, PHYLLIS REYNOLDS, author; b. Anderson, Ind., Jan. 4, 1933; d. Eugene Spencer and Lura Mae (Schield) Reynolds; m. Thomas A. Tedesco, Jr., Sept. 9, 1951 (div. 1960); m. Rex V. Naylor, May 26, 1960; children: Jeffrey, Michael. Diploma, Joliet Jr. Coll., 1953; BA, Am. U., 1963. Author: 86 books including Crazy Love: An Autobiographical Account of Marriage and Madness, 1977, Revelations, 1979, A String of Chances, 1982 (ALA notable book), The Agony of Alice, 1985 (ALA notable book), The Keeper, 1986 (ALA notable book), Unexpected Pleasures, 1986, Send No Blessings, 1990 (YASD best book for young adults), Shiloh, 1991 (ALA notable book, John Newbery medal 1992). Recipient Golden Kite award Soc. Children's Book Writers Am., 1985, Child Study award Bank St. Coll., 1983, Edgar Allan Poe award Mystery Writers Am., 1985, Internat. book award Soc. Sch. Librs., 1988, Christopher award, 1989, Newbery award ALA, 1992, Nat. Endowment of Arts Creative Writing fellow, 1987. Mem. Children's Book Guild of Washington (pres. 1974-75, 83-84), Soc. Children's Book Writers, Authors Guild, PEN, Council for a Livable World, SANE, Physicians for Social Responsibility, Amnesty Internat. Unitarian. Avocations: theater, madrigal singing, swimming. Home and Office: 9910 Holmhurst Rd Bethesda MD 20817-1618

NAYLOR, ROBERT ERNEST, JR., chemical company executive; b. Nashville, Ark., July 14, 1932; s. Robert Ernest and Goldia Geneva (Dalton) N.; m. Mary Jo McDonald, Feb. 23, 1963; 1 son, Robert. B.S., U. S.C. 1951; M.A., Harvard U., 1954, Ph.D., 1956. Various positions in research and mfg. DuPont Co., Wilmington, Del., 1956-76, tech. dir. atomic energy div., 1976-79, dir. research planning corp. plans, 1979-80, dir. central research, 1980-81; v.p. Rohm and Haas Co., Phila., 1981-84, group v.p., 1984—, also bd. dirs.; bd. dirs. Airgas Inc. Republican. Baptist. Home: 479 Cann Rd West Chester PA 19382-1715 Office: 100 Independence Mall W Philadelphia PA 19106

NAYLOR, THOMAS HERBERT, economist, educator, consultant; b. Jackson, Miss., May 30, 1936; s. Thomas Hector and Martha (Watkins) N.; m. Magdalena Raczkowska, Dec. 14, 1985; children: Susanne, Alexander. B.S. in Math., Millsaps Coll., 1958; B.S. in Indsl. Engring., Columbia U., 1959; M.B.A., Ind. U., 1961; Ph.D. in Econs., Tulane U., 1964. Instr. Sch. Bus. Adminstrn. Tulane U., 1961-63; asst. prof. econs. Duke U., 1964-66, assoc. prof., 1966-68, prof. econs., 1968-93, prof. emeritus, 1994—; vis. prof. Middlebury Coll., 1993—; pres. Social Systems, Inc., 1971-80; mng. dir. Naylor Group, 1980; cons., lectr. worldwide. Co-author: Computer Simulation Techniques, 1966, Strategies for Change in the South, 1975, Managerial Economics, 1983; author of 26 books including: Corporate Planning Models, 1978, Strategic Planning Management, 1980, The Corporate Strategy Matrix, 1986, The Gorbachev Strategy, 1988, The Cold War Legacy, 1991, The Search for Meaning, 1994; contbr. numerous articles to profl. publs.; mem. editl. bd. jours. Founder. L.Q.C. Lamar Soc., Washington. Mem. Beta Gamma Sigma, Lambda Chi, Omicron Delta Kappa.

NAYLOR-JACKSON, JERRY, entertainer, public relations consultant, producer; b. Chalk Mountain, Tex., Mar. 6, 1939; s. William Guy and Mary Bernice (Lummus) Jackson; m. Pamela Ann Robinson, Jan. 30, 1966; children: Geoffrey K. Naylor, Kelli A. Naylor, Gregory K. Naylor. Grad., Elkins Electronics Inst., Dallas, 1957; student, U. Md., Fed. Republic of Germany, 1957-58. Life first class radio/TV engring. lic. FCC. Broadcaster various local TV and AM radio stas., San Angelo, Texas, 1955-57; mem. Buddy Holly and the Crickets, 1957-65, lead singer, 1960-65; solo entertainer, performer, recording artist and producer, 1965-83; sr. v.p. corp. devel. Newslink Internat. Satellite Broadcast Comms. Co., Inc., Washington, 1986-88; pres. Internat. Syndications, Inc. subs. Newslink, Inc., Washington, 1986-88; pres., chief exec. officer, owner The Jerry Naylor Co., Inc., Agoura, Calif., 1984—; pres., CEO Media Unlimited/Naylor Prodns., Inc., 1983—; v.p. capital programs, sr. cons. Calif. Luth. Univ., Thousand Oaks, 1990-92; sr. cons., dir. ann. fund Calif. Luth. Univ., 1989-90; polit./media cons. various Rep. candidates and orgns., 1968—; spl. cons. to Violeta Barrios de Chamarro, Pres. of Republic of Nicaragua, 1990-92; disc jockey Sta. KHEY-AM, Sta KINT-AM, El Paso, Tex., 1959; on-air personality Sta. KRLA-AM, Sta. KDAY-AM, L.A., 1960, on-air disc jocky/air personality/celebrity host, KLAC-AM, L.A., Calif., 1974-83; on-camera and voice-over spokesman for Safeway Stores, Inc., Avis Rent-a-Car, Mutual of Omaha, Wrigley Co., 1968-83; U.S. presdl. appointee, chmn. Job Tng. Partnership Act work group/youth at risk subcom. Nat. Commn. for Employment Policy, 1985-92; nat. dir. spl. events Reagan For Pres., 1979-81; apptd. mem. commn. for employment policy Pres. Ronald Reagan, 1985-91. Recording artist maj. labels including CBS Records, Motown Records, Warner Bros. Records, EMI Records, 1965-84; host weekly nat. and internat. radio program Continental Country (Number 1 syndicated country music radio show in Am., Billboard Mag., Country Music Assn., 1974, 77). Active presdl. task force Rep. Nat. Com.: nat. dir. spl. events Reagan for Pres., 1975-76, 79-80; sr. cons. to White House, 1981-88, 89-92. With U.S. Army, 1957-58, Fed. Republic of Germany. Named to Top 40 Male Vocalists of Yr., Billboard Mag., 1970, named #1 Rock Group (Crickets), Billboard Mag./New Music Express Mag., 1958, 62. Mem. NARAS, Am. Film Inst., Country Music Assn., Acad. Country Music (Telly award for TV Documentary 1991, 92), Phi Kappa Phi (alumni). Avocation: writing prose and poetry. Home and Office: Jerry Nalor Co Inc 5308 Ambridge Dr Agoura Hills CA 91301

NAYMARK, SHERMAN, consulting nuclear engineer; b. Duluth, Minn., May 12, 1920; s. David N. and Lena (Naymark); children by previous marriage: Ronald L., Janet Naymark Stone. B.S. in Engring., U.S. Naval Acad., 1941; M.S. in Engring. and Constrn., MIT, 1946. Sr. scientist Argonne Nat. Lab., (Ill.), 1948-52; dir. reactor div. project, engring. mgr. Schenectady office AEC, 1952-56; with Gen. Electric Co., 1956-70; engring. mgr. nuclear turnkey plants San Jose, 1967-69; pres. Quadrex Corp., Campbell, Calif., 1970-86; chmn. Quadrex Corp., 1986; lectr. U. Va., MIT, U.S. Naval Res. Officer tng. Schs.; adviser to U.S. del. 3d Internat. Conf. on Peaceful Uses of Atomic Energy, Geneva, 1964; sr. examiner Profl. Engrs. State of Calif., 1960-70 ; mem. fusion power coordinating com. Dept. Energy. Contbr. numerous articles on nuclear research, devel., engring. to profl. jours. Served to capt. USN, 1941-54. Fellow Am. Nuclear Soc. (gen. chmn ann. meeting, nat. treas. 1978-80), nat. treas. (mem. governing bd. Nuclear Tech. 1979-81); mem. AAAS, Am. Pub. Power Assn. (assoc.), U.S. Naval Inst. (hon. life). Democrat. Jewish. Home: 218 Forrester Rd Los Gatos CA 95032-6509

NAYYAR, MOHINDER LAL, mechanical engineer; b. Jullundur, Punjab, India, Dec. 16, 1943; came to U.S., 1971; s. Dina Nath and Lila (Wati) N.; m. Surendra Prabha Suri, May 23, 1970; children: Mukta Mohi, Manav Mohi, Mahak Mohi. BS in Physics, Chemistry and Math., Agra (Ind.) U., 1963, MA in History, 1969; BE, U. Roorkee, India, 1966. Registered profl. engr., Va.; lic. boiler installer, Mich. Lectr. mech. engring., cons. engr. Tech. Coll., Agra, 1966-71; jr. engr. Charles Besseler Co., Florham Park, N.J., 1971-72; dir. engring. Internat. Inventors, Inc., Alexandria, Va., 1973-74; prin. engr. Bechtel Corp., Gaithersburg, Md., 1974—. Author: (collection of poems) Ghatayen, 1983, Ehsas, 1995; author: (engring. manual) BPC ISI Manual, 1986, 89; editor-in-chief, author: (engring. handbook) Piping Handbook, 1992; editor mags. Recipient Outstanding Participation award Nat. Engrs. Week, 1990-91. Mem. ASME (sect. XI task force 1980-81, power piping code com. 1991—, subcom. C 1993—), Engring. Assn. (sr. pres. 1966-71), UN Club (founding mem.), Internat. Hindi Assn. (founding mem.), Soc. of Naval Architects and Marine Engrs., Metrication Task Force for ANSI BIG 10. Avocations: reading, writing, music, social work. Home: 2917 Gold Mine Rd Brookeville MD 20833-2608 Office: Bechtel Corp 9801 Washingtonian Blvd Gaithersburg MD 20878-5355

NAZARETH, ANNETTE LAPORTE, lawyer; b. Providence, Jan. 27, 1956; d. George Robert and Dolores (LaPorte) N.; m. Roger Walton Ferguson Jr., May 3, 1986. AB in History and Econs., Brown U., 1978; JD, Columbia U., N.Y.C., 1981. Assoc. Davis Polk & Wardwell, N.Y.C., 1981-86; gen. ptnr., gen. counsel Mabon, Nugent & Co., N.Y.C., 1986-91; mng. dir., gen. counsel Mabon Securities Corp., N.Y.C., 1991—. Mem. Securities Industry Assn., Phi Beta Kappa. Home: 160 Overlook Rd New Rochelle NY 10804-3828 Office: Mabon Securities Corp 1 Liberty Plz New York NY 10006-1483

NAZARIAN, JOHN, academic administrator, mathematics educator; b. Pawtucket, R.I., Sept. 6, 1932; s. Zakie and Amenia (Nahas) N. EdB, R.I. Coll., 1954; AM, Brown U., 1956; MA, U. Ill., 1961; PhD, NYU, 1967. Instr. math. R.I. Coll., Providence, 1954-58, asst. prof., 1958-67, assoc. prof., 1967-71, prof., 1971—, assoc. dean Arts and Scis., 1970-72, spl. asst. to pres., 1971-77, v.p adminstrn. and fin., 1977-90, pres., 1990—. Chmn. vice-chmn. Arabic Ednl. Found., Pawtucket, 1966-72; chmn. Sargeant Rehab. Ctr., Providence, 1983-86, Diocesan Pastoral Coun., West Newton, Mass., 1974-78. Recipient Cross of Jerusalem, Patriarch of Melkite Ch., 1976. Avocations: music, golf, reading. Office: RI Coll 600 Mt Pleasant Ave Providence RI 02908-1924

NAZEM, FEREYDOUN F., venture capitalist, financier; b. Tehran, Iran, Dec. 29, 1940; came to U.S., 1960, naturalized, 1976; s. Hassan and Afsar N.; m. Susie Gharib, Jan. 20, 1973; children: Alexander, Taraneh. BSc, Ohio State U., 1964; MSc, U. Cin., 1967; MBA, Columbia U., 1971. Sr. rsch. chemist Matheson Coleman & Bell, Norwood, Ohio, 1967-68; asst. v.p. investment analyst Irving Trust Co., N.Y.C., 1969-74; v.p., venture capital officer Charter N.Y., N.Y.C., 1974-75; mng. dir. Collier Enterprises, N.Y.C., 1976-81; mng. ptnr. Nazem & Co., N.Y.C., 1981—; bd. dir. Applied ImmuneSciences, Menlo Park, Calif., Genesis Health Venture Inc., Kennott Square, Pa., Spatial Tech. Inc., Boulder, Colo., Oxford Health, Darien, Conn., Genetix Corp., Tarrytown, N.Y., Consep Corp., Bend, Oreg. Author: The Chemical Industry and Energy Shortage, 1973; contbr. articles to profl. jours. Mem. N.Y. Soc. Security Analysts, N.Y. Venture Capital Forum. Home: 44 E 73d St New York NY 10021 Office: Nazem & Co 600 Madison Ave 14th Fl New York NY 10022

NAZETTE, RICHARD FOLLETT, lawyer; b. Eldora, Iowa, July 27, 1919; s. Hilmer H. and Genevieve A. (Follett) N.; m. Joan Chekak, June 20, 1942; children—Randall D. Randall A. B.A., U. Iowa, 1942, J.D. with distinction, 1946. Bar: Iowa bar 1946. Practiced in Cedar Rapids, 1946—; partner firm Nazette, Marner, Good, Wendt & Knoll, 1968—; asst. atty. Linn County, Iowa, 1951-56; county atty., 1957-63; dir. United States Bank, Cedar Rapids, 1968-91, State Surety Co., Des Moines, 1966-78. Bd. dirs. Linn County Health Center, 1968-73, chmn., 1968-69; mem. Iowa Bd. Parole, 1981-84. Served with AUS, 1942-44. Fellow Am. Bar Found., Iowa Bar Assn. (bd. govs 1972-76), Iowa State Bar Found.; mem. Linn County Bar Assn. (pres. 1963), Iowa County Attys. Assn. (pres. 1959), Iowa Acad. Trial Lawyers (pres. 1964), Sigma Phi Epsilon, Republican. Presbyterian. Clubs: Masons, Shriners, Jesters, Elks, Optimists (internat. v.p. 1955). Home: 2224 Country Club Pky SE Cedar Rapids IA 52403-1639 Office: 100 1st St SW Cedar Rapids IA 52404

NEAFSEY, JOHN PATRICK, oil company executive; b. Woodside, N.Y., Aug. 4, 1939; s. James F. and Mary C. (Burns) N.; B.S. in Mech. Engring. (Sloan scholar), Cornell U., 1962, M.B.A. in Fin. (univ. bus. sholar), 1963; m. Marilla Bowman, Sept. 2, 1962; children—John Patrick, Terence E., William C. Fin. analyst Esso Research & Engring. Co., 1963-65; planning coordinator Standard Oil Co. (N.J.), 1965-67; with Sun Oil Co., Inc., 1967—, v.p. fin. services, Radnor, Pa., 1975-78, sr. v.p. fin., 1978-86, exec. v.p., 1987—, also bd. dirs.; bd. dirs. Sun Co., Inc., Suncor, Ltd., Toronto, Ont., Can.; bd. dirs. Provident Mutual Life Ins. Co. of Phila., The West Co. Bd. dirs. Crozer-Chester Med. Ctr., Chester, Pa, Crozer-Chester Med. Ctr. Health Systems, Chester, Phila. Drama Guild, Greenwich (Conn.) Capital Markets, Mgmt. Policy Council; mem. adv. council Cornell U. Johnson Grad. Sch. of Mgmt.; bd. trustees Cornell U. Mem. Am. Petroleum Inst., Pi Tau Sigma. Office: Sun Co Inc 100 Matsonford Rd Wayne PA 19087-4527 also: Greenwich Capital Holdings Inc 600 Steamboat Rd Greenwich CT 06830

NEAL, A. CURTIS, retired lawyer; b. Nacogdoches, Tex., Nov. 25, 1922; s. Berry W. and Mattie E. (Shepherd) N.; m. Martha E. Bishop, Apr. 16, 1942; children: Curtis Jr., Patricia Ann, Dick (dec.). BBA, U. Tex. 1948, LLB 1952. Bar: Tex. 1951; CPA, Tex.; soc. lic., Tex.; lic. E.M.T., Tex., 1983. With Office of Tex. Sec. of State 1948-52; pvt. practice, Amarillo, Tex., 1952-90; ret., 1990. Counsel, exec. com., advanced chmn. Boy Scouts Am., 1957-67; mem. Kids, Inc. (bd. dirs. 1954-68, pres. 1960), Western Merchandisers (bd. dirs. 1970-90), Hastings Books, Music, Video (bd. dirs.1971-93); mem. Key Presdl. Legion of Merit (Rep. Presdl. award 1994); formerly active Amarillo Jaycees, Amarillo Symphony, United Fund, Nat. Com. Rep. Presdl. Task Force, Barber Shop Quartett Singing in Am., Inc.; deacon, bd. mem. and vol. Paramount Ter. Christian Ch.; vol. High Plains Bapt. Hosp., Garden Club, Hospice and ch. work. With USN, 1942-45. Decorated with 12 Combat Stars USN, South Pacific. Fellow Tex. Bar Found. (life); mem. ABA, Am. Inst. Accts., State Bar Tex. Assn. (com. assistance to local bar assns. 1979-84, chmn. 1982-83, com. on coordination with accts. 1977-79, spl. services to membership div. 1982, state bar coll. law 1981-90), Tex. Soc. CPAs, Amarillo Bar Assn. (pres. 1981-82), Amarillo Jaycees, Amarillo C. of C., Masons, Amarillo Club, Starlighters Dance Club, Amarillo Knife & Fork Club (dir. 1995—), Tex. Shrine Assn. (all-state dir. gen. 1962, potentate 1970), Cabiri (pres. 1974), Khiva Stage Band (pres. 1978), Downtown Lions Club, Delta Theta Phi, Beta Alpha Psi. Republican. Home: 6205 Jameson Rd Amarillo TX 79106-3518

NEAL, ANN PARKER See PARKER, ANN

NEAL, AVON, artist, author; b. Morgantown, Ind., July 16, 1922; s. Orval Francis and Goldie Agnes (Prather) N.; m. Ann Russell Parker, Oct. 31,

1964. Student, Long Beach Coll., Calif.; M.F.A., Escuela de Bellas Artes, Mex., 1949. Artist-in-residence Altos de Chavon, Dominican Republic, 1983, 84; mem. advisory bd. Mus. Am. Folk Art, 1968-71, Dublin Seminar for New Eng. Folklife, 1976-78; pres. Thistle Hill Press; lectr., radio and TV appearances. Exhibited stone rubbings in one and two man shows, Am. embassy, London, 1965, Hallmark Gallery, N.Y.C., 1968, Amon Carter Mus., Ft. Worth, 1968, 71, Mus. Am. Folk Art, 1970, Mus. Fine Arts, Springfield, Mass., 1972, Altos de Chavon, 1984, Princeton U. Library, N.J., 1986, others; represented in permanent collections at Met. Mus. Art, N.Y.C., Library of Congress, Smithsonian Instn., Washington, Abby Aldrich Rockefeller Mus. Am. Folk Art, Williamsburg, Va., Winterthur Mus., Wilmington, Del.; author: Rubbings From Early American Stone Sculpture, 1963, Ephemeral Folk Figures, 1969, Molas: Folk Art of the Cuna Indians, 1977, Pigs and Eagles, 1978, Scarecrows, 1978, Early American Stone Sculpture Found in the Burying Grounds of New England, 1981, Los Ambulantes, 1982; contbr. articles to profl. jours. Served with USN, World War II. Ford Found. grantee, 1962-64; fiction writing fellow Mass. Artists Found., 1979. Home: Thistle Hill North Brookfield MA 01535

NEAL, DARWINA LEE, government official; b. Mansfield, Pa., Mar. 31, 1942; d. Darwin Leonard and Ina Belle (Cooke) N. BS, Pa. State U., 1965; postgrad., Cath. U., 1968-70. Registered landscape architect. Landscape architect nat. capital region Nat. Pk. Svc., 1965-69, office of White House liaison, 1969-71, office of profl. services, 1971-74, div. design svcs., 1974-89, chief design svcs., 1989—; judge numerous award juries. Contbr. articles to profl. jours.; co-author sects. of profl. bull., mag.; author introduction to book Women, Design and the Cambridge School; columnist: Land monthly, 1975-79. Mem. Women's Coun. on Energy in Environment. Recipient Merit award Landscape Contractors Met. Washington; recipient hon. mention Les Floralies Internationales de Montreal, 1980 Alumni Achievement award Pa. State U. Arts and Architecture Alumni Soc., 1981. Fellow Am. Soc. Landscape Architects (v.p. 1979-81, pres. elect 1982-83, pres 1983-84, trustee 1976-77, nat. treas. 1977-79, legis. coordinator 1975-79, sec. Coun. Fellows 1988-90, (del. to Internat. Fedn. Landscape Architects, del. 1989—, ex-officio rep. to U.S./internat. com. on monuments and sites, liaison to historically black coll. and univ. program Dept. Interior, recipient Pres.' medal 1987); mem. Landscape Archtl. Accreditation Bd. (roster vis. evaluators), Nat. Recreation and Parks Assn., Nat. Soc. Park Resources (bd. dirs. 1978-80), Nat. Trust Hist. Preservation, Pa. State U. Alumni Assn. (Washington met. chpt. trustee 1972-74), Am. Arbitration Assn. (nat. panel arbitrators), Com. 100 for the Fed. City, Preservation Action, Nat. Assn. Olmsted Parks, Beekman Pl. Condominium Assn. (bd. dirs. 1985-91, archtl. control com.), Nat. Parks and Conservation Assn., Alliance for Historic Preservation, World Watch, Worldwide. Office: Nat Pk Svc Nat Capitol Reg Dept Interior Divsn Design Svcs 800 N Capitol St NW Ste 790 Washington DC 20242

NEAL, FRED WARNER, political scientist, educator; b. Northville, Mich., Aug. 5, 1915; s. Frank Stephenson and Bertha (Fendt) N.; m. Grace Irene Repine, Feb. 14, 1952; children: Susan Victoria, Frank Stephenson, Alexander Frederick (dec.); m. Marian Katherine Walker, Jan. 2, 1969; m. Mary Caroline Hall, Jan. 10, 1982. B.A., U. Mich., 1937, Ph.D., 1955; student (Nieman fellow), Harvard U., 1942-43, U. Karlova, Prague, Czechoslovakia, 1949; Fulbright research fellow, U. Paris, 1950. Washington corr. UP and Wall St. Jour., 1938-43; cons. Russian affairs, chief fgn. research State Dept., 1946-48; asst. to pres. Univ. State of N.Y., 1948-49; asst. to chmn. Com. on Present Danger, 1951; asst. prof. polit. sci. U. Colo., 1951-56; asso. prof. UCLA, 1956-57; asso. prof. internat. relations and govt. Claremont (Calif.) Grad. Sch., 1957-60, prof., 1960-83, prof. emeritus, 1983—; Rockefeller prof. internat. relations U. W.I., 1965-66; vis. lectr. U. Mich., 1950, 53-54; asso. Am. U. Field Staff, 1954-55; co-dir. Twentieth Century Fund Study on Yugoslavia, 1958-61; Fulbright fellow, Paris, 1961-62; cons. Center for Study of Democratic Instns.; organizer, dir. Pacem in Terris convocations; chmn. Am. Com. on U.S.-Soviet Relations, 1974-77; exec. v.p. Am. Com. U.S.-Soviet Rels., 1977—. Author: Titoism in Action: The Reforms in Yugoslavia after 1948, 1958, U.S. Foreign Policy and the Soviet Union, 1961, War and Peace and Germany, 1962; co-author: Yugoslvia and the New Communism, 1962; editor: Pacem in Terris III: New Opportunities for American Foreign Policy, 1974, Pacem in Terris IV: American Foreign Policy at Home and Abroad, 1976, Detente or Debacle, 1979; author: A Survey of Detente—Past, Present, Future, 1977. Democratic nominee for Congress 24th Dist. Calif. 1968; Pres. Albert Parvin Found., 1969-70. Served with A.C., USNR, 1943-46, Russia, Siberia. Recipient Decoration of Yugoslav Flag with Golden Wreath, highest honor of Yugoslvia, 1987; Japan Found. fellow, 1978. Mem. Am., Internat., Western polit. sci. assns., Internat. Studies Assn., Am. Assn. Advancement Slavic Studies, AAUP, Soc. Nieman Fellows, Los Angeles Com. Fgn. Relations. Home: 910 N Oxford Ave Claremont CA 91711-3712 *I have become convinced of the essential similarity in human motivations and, also, the essential differences in their expression imposed by different cultures; of the oneness of nature; of the unlikeliness and, usually, the undesirability of extreme solutions; of the difficulties of one generation imparting values to another; of the honor of patriotism and its moral dangers; of the tendency of power to corrupt; and of the incomprehensibility of life as well as the joy of engaging in the struggle to comprehend it.*

NEAL, HOMER ALFRED, physics educator, researcher, university administrator; b. Franklin, Ky., June 13, 1942; s. Homer and Margaret Elizabeth (Holl) N.; m. Donna Jean Daniels, June 16, 1962; children: Sharon Denise, Homer Alfred. BS in Physics with honors, Ind. U., 1961; MS in Physics (John Hay Whitney fellow), U. Mich., 1963, PhD in Physics, 1966. Asst. prof. physics Ind. U., 1967-70, assoc. prof., 1970-72, prof., 1972-81, dean research and grad. devel., 1976-81; prof. physics SUNY, Stony Brook, 1981-87, provost, 1981-86; prof. physics, chmn. U. Mich., Ann Arbor, 1987-93, v.p. rsch., 1993—; mem. Nat. Sci. Bd., 1980-86; chmn. Argonne Zero Gradient Synchrotron Users Group, 1970-72; trustee Argonne Univs. Assn., 1971-74, 77-80; NSF physics adv. panel , 1976-79, chmn. NSF physics adv. panel, 1987-89; high energy physics adv. panel U.S. Dept. Energy, 1977-81; bd. dirs. Ogden Corp. Contbr. articles to profl. jours. Bd. dirs. N.Y. Sea Grant Inst., 1982-86; mem. bd. overseers Superconducting Super Collider, 1989-93; mem. bd. regents Smithsonian Instn., 1989—; trustee Ctr. for Strategic and Internat. Studies, 1990—; trustee Environ. Rsch. Inst. of Mich., 1994—; mem. advisory bd. Oak Ridge (Tenn.) Nat. Lab., 1993—. NSF fellow, 1966-67; Sloan fellow, 1968; Guggenheim fellow, 1980-81. Fellow Am. Phys. Soc., AAAS; mem. Univs. Research Assn. (trustee 1983-87), Sigma Xi. Office: Office VP for Rsch 503 Thompson 4080 Fleming Adminstrn Ann Arbor MI 48109-1340

NEAL, IRENE COLLINS, artist, educator; b. Greensburg, Pa., May 14, 1936; d. Oliver Shupe and Betsey Cowap (Mann) Collins; m. Paul Whitaker Neal, Nov. 24, 1960; children: Paul Collins Gordon, Betsey Whitaker. BA, Wilson Coll., 1958. guest spkr. Coll. Santa Fe, Albuquerque, N.Mex., 1994. Solo exhbns. include Allied Chem. Corp., Morristown, N.J., 1975, Planetarium of Rio de Janeiro, 1977, The Pat Ackerman Gallery, Mphs., 1980, Westmoreland Mus. Art, Greensburg, 1986, Wilson Coll., 1993; group exhbns. include Jersey City Mus., 1975, N.J. State Mus., 1975, Somerset (N.J.) Tri-State Mus., 1975, Nat. Arts Club, N.Y.C., 1975, Garden State Watercolor Soc., 1975, Salao de Marinhas, Rio de Janeiro, 1977, Stamford (Conn.) Mus., 1984, 85, 89, Branchville Soho Gallery, Ridgefield, Conn., 1984, Silvermine Guild, New Canaan, Conn., 1984, Stamford Libr., 1985, Shippee Gallery, N.Y.C., 1986, 110 Greene St., N.Y.C., 1986, Wilton (Conn.) Libr., 1986, Aldrich Mus. Contemporary Art, Ridgefield, 1987, Ariel Gallery, N.Y.C., 1988, 89, Visual Arts Festival, Edmonton, Can., 1989, Mus. Art., Ft. Lauderdale, Fla., 1991-92, Salander-O'Reilly Galleries, Inc., N.Y.; represented in collections Planetarium Rio de Janeiro, Internat. Paper, N.Y.C., Westmoreland Mus. Art, Greensburg, Pepperdine U., Malibu, Calif., Newport Harbor Art Mus., Newport Beach, Calif., Hoover Instn. Stanford (Calif.) U., St. Matthew's Episcopal Ch. Wilton, Conn., Columbia U., N.Y.C., Ctr. Arts, Vero Beach, Fla., Mus. Art., Ft. Lauderdale, Alamo Rent A Car, Ft. Lauderdale, Denver Ctr. Performing Arts, Louis P. Cabot, Boston. Mem. Four Counties Garden Club. Republican. Episcopalian. Avocations: ocean diving, tennis, golf, gardening. Home and Studio: 700 River Rd Greenwich CT 06830

NEAL, JAMES AUSTIN, architect; b. Greenville, S.C., Nov. 23, 1935; s. Charles Albert Neal and Jane (Anderson) Cole; m. Leonette Deming Achor, Apr. 13, 1963; 1 child, Heather Anderson. B. Arch., Clemson U., 1959. Registered arch., S.C. Designer McMillan Architects, Greenville, S.C., 1960-62; project mgr. W.E. Freeman Architects, Greenville, 1963-64; project architect J.E. Sirrine Co., Greenville, 1964-68; pres., prin. Neal, Prince & Browning, Greenville, 1969—; vis. prof. Clemson U. Coll. Architecture, 1974-75; mem. bd. advisors S.C. Nat. Bank. Pres. Leslie Meyer Devel. Ctr., Greenville, 1980-82. Recipient Leadership award Greenville C. of C., 1983. Mem. AIA (Merit Design award 1978, pres. S.C. chpt. 1991, regional dir. S.C., Ga., N.C., mem. nat. bd. 1994—), Greenville Council Architects (past pres.), Interfaith Forum of Religious Art and Architecture (mem. nat. bd.). Baptist. Club: Poinsett (pres. 1985—). Avocations: jogging; flying. Office: Neal Prince & Ptnrs 110 W North St Greenville SC 29601-2727

NEAL, JAMES MADISON, JR., editor; b. Oklahoma City, Aug. 6, 1925; s. James Madison and Tillie Belle (Milliken) N.; m. Caroline Dorothy Becker (dec. Dec. 1974); children: Charles, James W., Jody, Carolyn. BA, U. Colo., 1949; MA, S.D. State U., 1970. Editor various newspapers, Colo., Nebr. and Okla., 1949-59; wire editor Rapid City Journal, Rapid City, S.D., 1959-67; instr. S.D. State U., Brookings, S.D., 1967-71; asst. prof. U. Nebr., Lincoln, 1971-73, assoc. prof., 1973-90; S.D. chmn. AP Mng. Editors Assn., 1962-64. Mem. Soc. Profl. Journalists, Investigative Reporters and Editors, ACLU (bd. dirs. Nebr. chpt. 1979-82), VFW. Unitarian. Avocations: painting, travel. Home: 4700 N Kolb Rd Apt 7207 Tucson AZ 85715-6187

NEAL, JAMES PRESTON, state senator, project engineer; b. Cin., July 1, 1935; s. James Preston and Desha Frank (Thompson) N.; m. Nancy Joan Tyner, June 11, 1961; children: Leslie, Neal Driscoll, Karen Desha, James P. BSME, U. Ill., 1960. Registered profl. engr., Del. Tech. svc. engr. DuPont Co., Parlin, N.J., 1960-62; engr DuPont Co., Waynesboro, Va., 1962-64; instrument engr. DuPont Co., Newburgh, N.Y., 1964-68, Newark, 1966-78; project engr. DuPont Co., 1978-92; dir. Tetra Tech Inc., Christiana, Del., 1992—; mem. Del. Ho. of Reps., 1978-80; mem. Del. Senate, 1980-94. Patentee in field. Councilman City of Newark, 1973-78. With U.S. Army, 1954-56. Recipient Disting. Svc. award Forum to Advance Minorities in Engring., 1989, Disting. Svc. citation Del. Libr. Assn., 1994. Fellow Am. Legis. Exch. Coun. (sr., nat. officer 1991-94, Outstanding Leader 1989, Outstanding Legis. mem. 1994), Conf. World Regions (sr.); mem. IEEE (sr.), Del. Engring. Soc. (Engr. of Yr. 1989), Instrument Soc. Am. Republican. Presbyterian. Avocations: photography, reading. Home: 50 Bridlebrook Ln Newark DE 19711-2061 Office: Tetra Tech Inc 56 W Main St Newark DE 19702

NEAL, JAMES WEATHERLY, investment banker; b. Greensboro, N.C., Nov. 6, 1956; s. James Weatherly and Mildred (Hartzoge) N.; m. Suzanne Jarema, Sept. 15, 1979; children: James Weatherly III, Winston Dwyer. BS, U. N.C., 1978; MBA, U. Chgo., 1983. V.p. Salomon Bros., L.A., 1983-87; mng. dir. Bear, Stearns & Co. Inc., L.A., 1988—. Mem. exec. com. Pres.'s Invitational Golf Tournament, Children's Bur. L.A., 1989. Mem. Sleepy Hollow Country Club (Scarborough, N.Y.), Regency Club (L.A.). Home: 4708 Woodsmith Ct Raleigh NC 27609-5581 Office: 150 Central Park S # 2904 New York NY 10019-1566

NEAL, JERRY EUGENE, controller; b. Columbus, Ohio, Nov. 17, 1941; s. Levert and Anna (Weaver) N.; m. Judith Ann Lehnert; children: Brian, Jeffrey, Timothy. BS, Ohio State U., 1965. Controller Mattel Toys Inc., Hawthorne, Calif., 1979—. Home: 6788 Alta Vista Dr Palos Verdes Peninsula CA 90274-5602 Office: Mattel Toys Inc 333 Continental Blvd El Segundo CA 90245-5032

NEAL, JOHN ERIC, banking executive; b. Mar. 3, 1950. B.A. Harvard U., 1972, M.B.A., 1974. With real estate dept. Continental Bank, Chgo., 1974-83, sr. v.p., mgr. real estate dept., 1983—. Office: Kemper Financial Services 120 S La Salle St 21st Fl Chicago IL 60603

NEAL, JOSEPH C., JR., church administrator. Sec. of fin. Christian Methodist Episcopal Church, L.A. Address: Christian Methodist Episcopal Ch PO Box 75058 Los Angeles CA 90020

NEAL, LEORA LOUISE HASKETT, social services administrator; b. N.Y.C., Feb. 23, 1943; d. Melvin Elias and Miriam Emily (Johnson) Haskett; m. Robert A. Neal, Apr. 23, 1966; children: Marla Patrice, Johnathan Robert. BA in Psychology and Sociology, City Coll. N.Y., 1965; MS in Social Work, Columbia U., 1970, cert. adoption specialist, 1977; IBM cert. community exec. tng. program, N.Y., 1982. Cert. social worker N.Y. state. Caseworker N.Y.C. Dept. Social Service, 1965-67, Windham Child Care, N.Y.C., 1967-73; exec. dir. Assn. Black Social Workers Child Adoption Counseling and Referral Service, N.Y.C., 1975—; cons. adoption, adoption tng. N.Y. State Dept. Social Svc., Columbia U. Sch. Social Work, N.Y.C. Human Resources Adminstrn., U. La., New Orleans; founder Haskett-Neal Publs., Bronx, N.Y., 1993. Co-author: Transracial Adoptive Parenting: A Black/White Community Issue, 1993. Child Welfare League Am. fellow, 1976; recipient cert. No Time to Lose cert. N.Y. State Dept. Social Svcs., 1989. Mem. NAFE, Columbia U. Alumni Assn., CCNY Alumni Assn., Missionary Com. Revival Team (outreach chairperson 1982-88). Democrat. Avocations: writing, history and religious studies, traveling, cultural activities. Office: Assn Black Social Workers 1969 Madison Ave New York NY 10035-1549

NEAL, LOUISE KATHLEEN, life insurance company executive, accountant; b. Seattle, Nov. 25, 1951; d. Paul Bradford and Ruth Catherine (Park) Johnson; m. William Steven Neal, Oct. 25, 1974. B.A. in Bus. Adminstrn. and Acctg., U. Wash., 1974. Sr. acct. Touche Ross & Co., Seattle, 1974-77; internal auditor No. Life Ins. Co., Seattle, 1977-83; auditor Northwestern Nat. Life Ins. Co., Mpls., 1983-84, 2d v.p., auditor, 1984-88; sr. v.p., gen. auditor Transam. Occidental Life Ins. Co., L.A., 1988-89, sr. v.p., 1990-92, sr. v.p., chief adminstrv. officer, 1992-95; pres. USA Admin. Svcs. Inc. sub. Transam. Occidental Life Ins. Co., Overland Park, Kans., 1995—. Fellow Life Mgmt. Inst.; mem. AICPA. Office: USA Admin Svcs Inc PO Box 2948 Overland Park KS 66201-1348

NEAL, MARCUS PINSON, JR., physician, medical educator; b. Columbia, Mo., Apr. 22, 1927; s. M. Pinson and Mathilda (Evers) N.; m. Gail S. Fallon, May 27, 1961; children: Sandra G., M. Pinson III, Ruth-Catherine E. AB, U. Mo., 1949, BS, 1951; MD, U. Tenn., 1953. Intern Med. Coll. Va., Richmond, 1953-54; resident U. Wis. Hosp., Madison, 1954-57; instr. dept. radiology Sch. Medicine U. Wis., Madison, 1957-59; mem. staff U. Wis. Hosps., Madison, 1957-63; asst. prof. radiology, dir. dept. radiology Cen. Wis. Colony, Madison, 1959-63; radiologist Wis. Diagnostic Ctr., Madison, 1962-63; assoc. prof. radiology Med. Coll. Va., U. Commonwealth U., 1963-66, prof. radiology, 1966—; mem. staff Med. Coll. Va. Hosps., Va. Commonwealth U., 1963—; dir. postgrad. edn. dept. radiology Med. Coll. Va., Va. Commonwealth U., 1964-73, chmn. div. diagnostic radiology, 1965-68, asst. dean Sch. Medicine, dir. grad. med. edn., dir. regional med. program, 1968-71, dir. continuing edn. Sch. Medicine., 1969-72, interim dean Sch. Medicine, 1971, asst. v.p. for health scis., 1971-73, provost Health Scis. campus, 1973-78, assoc. dean for continuing med. edn. and quality assurance Sch. Medicine, 1978-79, dir. housestaff edn. Dept. Radiology, 1979-93, dir. section genitourinary radiology, Dept. Radiology., 1981-92; bd. dirs. Common Wealth Bank, Richmond; cons. radiologist Va. Hosp., Madison, 1962-63, USAF Hosp., Truax Field, Madison, 1962-63, McGuire VA Hosp., Richmond, 1963—; bd. forestry Commonwealth of Va., 1990-94, chmn. bd. forestry, 1993-94. Editor: Emergency Interventional Radiology: Practical Aspects, 1988; contbr. articles to profl. jours. Pres. Oxford Civic Assn., Richmond, 1965-67, Three Ridges Condominium Assn., Wintergreen, Va., 1979-84. Served as pharmacist mate USNR, 1945-47. Fellow Oak Ridge Inst. Nuclear Studies, Am. Coll. Radiology (Va. chpt., councilor 1977-83, 85-91, 93—); mem. AMA, Radiol. Soc. N.Am., Am. Roentgen Ray Soc., Med. Soc. Va., Richmond Acad. Medicine, Capitol Club, Commonwealth Club, Bull and Bear Club, Willow Oaks Country Club, Sigma Xi. Avocations: hunting, fishing, gardening, skiing. Home: 4607 Stratford Rd Richmond VA 23225-1066 Office: Med Coll Va PO Box 980295 Richmond VA 23298-0295

NEAL, PHIL HUDSON, JR., manufacturing company executive; b. Birmingham, Ala., Nov. 17, 1926; s. Phil Hudson and Mary (Gross) N.; m. Sarah Swift Britton, Sept. 19, 1959; children: Amy Neal Ager, Phil Hudson, III, Samuel Abney Britton. A.B., Duke U. 1950; M.B.A., Harvard U.,

1952. Investment analyst First Nat. Bank, Birmingham, 1952-55; procedures analyst Gen. Electric Co., Hendersonville, N.C., 1955-58; with Ala. By-Products Corp., Birmingham, 1958-79; asst. treas. Ala. By-Products Corp. 1964-68, treas., 1968-79; dir., v.p. Utility Tool Co., Birmingham, 1979-86; dir., pres. Nutec Metal Finishing Inc., Birmingham, 1986-92, chmn., 1992—; dir. Pounds Ins. Corp., 1986—. Trustee Advent Episcopal Day Sch., 1967—, pres., 1968-89, trustee charitable endowment trust, 1981—; treas. Cathedral Ch. of Advent, 1981-82, mem. chpt., 1983-85, 86-89; bd. dirs. Greater Birmingham Ministries, 1975-77, Advent Episcopal Assn. for Edn., 1968-89, Jefferson County chpt. Ala. Soc. Crippled Children and Adults, Inc., 1977-79; trustee Ala. Found. for Hearing and Speech, 1967-74, v.p., 1968-69, pres., 1969-71. Served with USNR, 1945-46. Mem. Newcomen Soc. N.Am., Phi Beta Kappa, Sigma Nu, Phi Eta Sigma. Episcopalian (vestryman, sr. warden). Clubs: Birmingham Country, The Club. Home: 3336 Hermitage Rd Birmingham AL 35223-2004 also: 81 Old Duck Hole Rd East Orleans MA 02643 Office: 3669 Indsl Pkwy PO Box 170746 Birmingham AL 35217-0746

NEAL, PHILIP, dancer. Grad. magna cum laude, St. Paul's Sch., 1986; trained, Sch. Royal Danish Ballet, Copenhagen, Denmark. With corps. de ballet N.Y.C. Ballet, 1987-91, soloist, 1991-92, prin. dancer, 1992—. Featured in ballets (Balanchine) Divertimento No. 15, Walpurgisnacht, Slaughter on Tenth Avenue, Western Symphony, Swan Lake, Coppelia; (Robbins) Interplay, The Four Seasons, The Goldberg Variations, Glass Pieces, Mother Goose; (Martins) Les Gentilhommes, Ecstatic Orange, Black & White, Fearful Symmetries, The Sleeping Beauty; also appeared in N.Y.C. Ballet's Balanchine Celebration, 1993. Recipient silver medal Internat. Prix de Lausanne ballet competition; summer scholar N.Y.C. Sch. Am. Ballet; named Presdl. scholar of the Arts Nat Found. Advancement of the Arts. Office: New York City Ballet NY State Theater Lincoln Ctr Plaza New York NY 10023*

NEAL, PHILIP MARK, diversified manufacturing executive; b. San Diego, Aug. 28, 1940; s. Philip Mark and Florence Elizabeth (Anderson) N.; children: Brian, Kevin. B.A., Pomona Coll., 1962; M.B.A., Stanford U., 1964. Mgr. financial planning and analysis CBS, Hollywood, 1964-66; cons. McKinsey & Co., Los Angeles, 1966-73; v.p., controller Avery Internat. Corp., Los Angeles, 1974-78; sr. v.p. fin. Avery Internat. Corp., Pasadena, 1979-88, group v.p. materials group, 1988-90; exec. pres. Avery Internat. Corp., 1990, pres., chief operating officer, 1990—; bd. dirs. Ind. Colls. of So. Calif. Trustee Pomona Coll; gov. Town Hall of Calif. Bd. Govs. Mem. Fin. Execs. Inst. Republican. Episcopalian. Office: Avery Dennison Corp PO Box 7090 Pasadena CA 91109

NEAL, RICHARD EDMUND, congressman, former mayor; b. Worcester, Mass., Feb. 14, 1949; s. Edmund J. and Mary H. (Garvey) N.; m. Maureen Conway, Dec. 20, 1975; children—Rory, Brendan, Maura, Sean. B.S., Am. Internat. Coll., Springfield, Mass., 1972; M.P.A., U. Hartford, Conn., 1976; postgrad., U. Mass., Amherst, 1982. Adminstrv. aide to Mayor City of Springfield, Mass., 1973-78, mem. city council, 1978-83, mayor, 1984-88; mem. 101st-103rd Congresses from 2nd. Mass. dist., Washington, DC, 1989—; mem. ways and means com.; lectr. history and politics Springfield Tech. Community Coll., Mass., 1973-83; lectr. bus. and govt. Western New Eng. Coll., Springfield, 1979-82; project dir. Springfield Tech. Community Coll., 1979-82. Trustee ARC, YMCA, Springfield. Named to Outstanding Young Men in Am., U.S. Jr. C. of C., Springfield. Mem. Am. Internat. Coll. Alumni Assn. (pres. 1980, Alumni Achievement award 1985). Springfield Library and Mus. Assn. (trustee). Democrat. Roman Catholic. Clubs: Valley Press. John Boyle O'Reilly (Springfield). Office: US House of Reps 2431 Rayburn Washington DC 20515-2102*

NEAL, RICHARD EDWARD, finance company executive; b. Madison, Ind., June 28, 1925; s. Jacob Edward and Mabel Claire (Litson) N.; m. Florence Marie Ohn, Aug. 27, 1949; 1 child, Richard Lynn. BA, Hanover Coll., 1950; student, Rockhurst Coll., 1944. Account exec. Merrill Lynch, Indpls., 1952-54; v.p., br. mgr. Cruttenden Podesta & Miller, Indpls., 1954-62, Walston & Co., Indpls., 1962-63; pres. Wildman, Neal & Debolt, Indpls., 1963-79; exec. v.p. City Securities Corp., Indpls., 1979—; bd. dirs. Anacomp, Inc., Indpls. Trustee Hanover Coll., 1965—. Sgt. U.S. Army, 1943-45. Mem. Nat. Assn. Securities Dealers (dir. com. 1985-88), Indpls. Security Traders (pres. 1975), Indpls. Bond Club, Indpls. Athletic Club (pres. squash league 1964). Republican. Presbyterian. Avocations: tennis, squash, golf. Home: 8431 Overlook Pky Indianapolis IN 46260-2250

NEAL, STEPHEN C., lawyer; b. San Francisco, Mar. 26, 1949. AB, Harvard U., 1970; JD, Stanford U., 1973. Bar: Ill. 1973. Ptnr. Kirkland & Ellis, Chgo. Office: Kirkland & Ellis 200 E Randolph Dr Chicago IL 60601

NEAL, STEVEN GEORGE, journalist; b. Coos Bay, Oreg., July 3, 1949; s. Ernest L. and Ellen Louise (Williams) N.; m. Susan Christine Simmons, May 8, 1971; children: Erin, Shannon. BS in Journalism, U. Oreg., 1971; MS in Journalism, Columbia U., 1972. Reporter Oreg. Jour., Portland, 1971, Phila. Inquirer, 1972-78; gen. assignment reporter, White House corr., polit. writer Chgo. Tribune, 1979-87; polit. editor Chgo. Sun-Times, 1987-92, polit. columnist, 1987—; bd. govs. White House Corrs. Assn., Washington, 1981-83. Co-author: Tom McCall: Maverick, 1977; author: The Eisenhowers, 1978, Dark Horse: A Biography of Wendell Willkie, 1984, McNary of Oregon, 1985; editor: They Never Go Back to Pocatello: The Essays of Richard Neuberger, 1988; contbr. to Am. Heritage, The Nation, The N.Y. Times Books Rev., Dictionary of Am. Biography. Recipient William H. Jones award Chgo. Tribune, 1984; Robert W. Ruhl lectr. U. Oreg., Eugene, 1984; Col. Robert R. McCormick fellow, McCormick Found., Chgo., 1989; Hoover Libr. Assn. scholar, West Branch, Iowa, 1989. Roman Catholic. Home: 411 N Elm St Hinsdale IL 60521-3709 Office: Chgo Sun-Times Inc 401 N Wabash Ave Rm 110 Chicago IL 60611-3532

NEAL, WILLIAM WEAVER, III, systems integration and software executive; b. Marion, N.C., Apr. 10, 1932; s. William Weaver and Lillian Laura (Long) N.; m. Eleanor Warren Walton, Dec. 23, 1954; children: Laura Ann, Catherine Walton. A.B., Duke U., 1954. Vice pres. mktg. Litton ABS, Montville, N.J., 1971-73; v.p. sales Sweda Internat., Montville, 1973-75; group v.p. Automatic Data Processing, Roseland, N.J., 1975-82 group pres., dir. Automatic Data Processing, 1982-84; gen. ptnr. Venture Capital Partnership, 1985-89; chmn., chief exec. officer Broadway & Seymour, Charlotte, N.C., 1989—. Lay reader Ch. of the Good Shepherd, Midland Park, N.J., 1969-84, jr. warden, 1982, sr. warden, 1983; lay reader, mem. vestry Christ Ch., Short Hills, N.J., 1987-89, lay eucharistic minister, mem. vestry Christ Ch., Charlotte, 1994—. Capt. USAF, 1954-57. Republican. Episcopalian. Home: 228 Fenton Pl Charlotte NC 28207-1914 Office: Broadway & Seymour Inc 128 S Tryon St Charlotte NC 28202-5001

NEAL, WILMER LEWIS, clinical neurophysiologist; b. Indpls., Oct. 20, 1934; s. John Ernest and Hannah Ola (Walker) N.; m. Bonnie Marie Garner, Jan. 25, 1991. MD, Ind. U. Sch. of Medicine, 1961. Ship's surgeon USCG Icebraker Eastwind U.S. Navy's Operation Deepfreeze, McMurdo Sound, Antarctica, 1962-63; med. officer in charge USPHS Clinic, Jacksonville, Fla., 1963-65; Park Ave. physician The Waldorf-Astoria, N.Y.C., 1966-70; physician in charge Tremont Med. Ctr., N.Y.C., 1970-71; resident U. Tenn. Affiliated Hosps., Memphis, 1972-75; pvt. practice clin. neurophysiologist Memphis, 1975-82; neuropsychiatric diagnostician U.S. Vet. Adminstrn., Little Rock, 1982-87; clin. neurophysiologist Lakeshore Inst., Knoxville, Tenn., 1988-89, South Ark. Regional Health Ctr., Magnolia, 1989-92; med. dir. Green River Comp Care/Area East, Owensboro, Ky., 1992—; cons. in field. Author: Serial Anxiety Testing Form WLN-111, 1976, Serial Personality Testing Form WLN-101, 1978. Mem. Am. Psychiat. Assn., Am. Soc. Composers, Authors & Publishers, Sigma Chi Fraternity. Republican. Presbyterian. Avocation: photography. Home: 1609 Griffith Ave Owensboro KY 42301 Office: 1001 Frederica St Owensboro KY 42301

NEALE, E(RNEST) R(ICHARD) WARD, retired university official, consultant; b. Montreal, Que., Can., July 3, 1923; s. Ernest John and Mabel Elizabeth (McNamee) N.; m. Roxie Eveline Anderson, June 3, 1950; children—Richard Ward, Owen Curtis. B.Sc., McGill U., Montreal, 1949; M.S., Yale U., 1950, Ph.D., 1952; LL.D. (hon.), Calgary U., Alta., Can., 1977; DSc (hon.), Meml. U., Nfld., Can. 1989. Asst. prof. geology U. Rochester, N.Y., 1952-54; sect. chief Geol. Survey Can., Ottawa, Ont., 1954-

63; div. chief Geol. Survey Can., 1965-68, Calgary, 1976-81; commonwealth geol. liaison officer London, 1963-65; prof., head geology Meml. U., St. John's, Nfld., Can., 1968-76; v.p. Meml. U., 1982-87; cons., Calgary, Alta., Can., 1987—; chmn. nat. adv. bd. on sci. publs. NRC-Natural Scis. and Engring. Rsch. Coun., Ottawa, 1982-88. Author: Geology and Geophysics in Canadian Universities, 1980. Editor: Some Guides to Mineral Exploration, 1967, Geology in the Atlantic Region, 1968, The Geosciences in Canada, 1968; Editor: Can. Jour. of Earth Science, 1974-79, Science and the Public, 1988. Bd. dirs. Unitarian Ch. Calgary, 1993—, pres., 1995-96. Petty officer Royal Can. Navy, 1943-45. Decorated officer Order of Can., 1990; recipient Queen's Jubilee medal Govt. of Can., 1977, Can. 125 medal, 1992. Fellow Royal Soc. Can. (coun. 1972-75, chmn. com. pub. awareness of sci. 1987-91, Bancroft medal 1975), Geol. Assn. Can. (pres. 1973-74, Ambrose medal 1986, 1st E.R. Ward Neale medal 1995), Can. Geosci. Coun. (pres. 1975-76, R.T. Bell medal Can. Mining Jour. 1977), Geol. Soc. Am.; mem. Assn. Earth Sci. Editors, Nat. Def. (chmn. biol. and chem. def. rev. com. 1990-93), Calgary Elks Golf Club, Chancellor's Club, Crows Nest Club, Calgary Sci. Network (pres. 1989), Sigma Xi (nat. lectr. New Haven 1976, chmn. Avalon chpt. 1986). Avocations: golf, cross-country skiing, hiking, canoeing. Home and Office: 5108 Carney Rd NW, Calgary, AB Canada T2L 1G2

NEALE, GARY LEE, utilities executive; b. Lead, S.D., Mar. 3, 1940; s. Vearl J. and Gladys M. (Trenkle) N.; m. Sandra C. Lovell, June 16, 1962; children: David G., Julie C. BA in Econs., U. Wash., 1962, MBA, 1965. Loan examiner Wells Fargo, 1966-69; sr. fin. analyst Kaiser Industries, 1969-70; chmn., pres., chief exec. officer Planmetrics, Chgo., 1970-89; pres., chief oper. officer No. Ind. Pub. Svc. Co., Hammond, 1989-93, chmn., pres., CEO, 1993—; bd. dirs. Modine Mfg., Racine, Wis., Am. Gas Assn., Arlington, Va., Ind. Gas Assn./Ind. Electric Assn., Indpls., Nipsco Industries Inc., Hammond. Bd. dirs. N.W. Ind. Symphony, 1990; mem. Ind. Energy Policy Forum, 1991. Lt. (j.g.) USN, 1962-64. Mem. Econ. Club Chgo., Chgo. Univ. Club, NYU Club. Office: No Ind Pub Svc Co 5265 Hohman Ave Hammond IN 46320

NEALE, HENRY WHITEHEAD, plastic surgery educator; b. Richmond, Va., July 18, 1940; s. Richard C. and Eva W. Neale; m. Margaret C. Neale, June 20, 1964; children: Leigh, Jennifer, Henry Whitehead Jr., William. BS, Davidson Coll., 1960; MD, Med. Coll. Va., 1964. Diplomate Am. Bd. Surgery, Am. Bd. Plastic Surgery (guest examiner 1986-90, dir. 1990-96, mem. com. on plans and qualifying exam. com. 1993-96, exec. com. 1993—, chmn. certifying examing com. 1993-95, mem. ethics com. 1993, liaison to Am. Bd. Surgery 1993-96, pres.-elect 1995—). Rotating intern Mercy Med. Ctr., Springfield, Ohio, 1964-65; resident in gen. surgery U. Cin. Med. Ctr., 1965-71, dir. div. plastic, reconstructive and hand surgery, 1974—; resident in plastic surgery Duke U. Med. Ctr., Durham, N.C., 1971-74; fellow in hand surgery, Christine Kleinert hand fellow U. Louisville, 1973; asst. prof. surgery U. Cin. Coll. Medicine, 1974-77, assoc. prof., 1977-82, prof., 1982—; active staff, dir. hand surgery and plastic surgery clinics U. Cin. Med. Ctr. Hosp. Group, 1974—; dir. burn reconstructive and plastic surgery, co-dir. hand surgery svc. Shriners Burns Inst., Cin., 1983—; dir. div. plastic, reconstructive and hand surgery and plastic surgery clinic Childrens Hosp. Med. Ctr., Cin., 1983—; assoc. attending staff Good Samaritan Hosp.; courtesy staff Christ Hosp., Jewish Hosp.; numerous presentations in field. Mem. editl. bd. Jour. Plastic and Reconstructive Surgery, 1989—; contbr. numerous articles to med. jours. Capt. M.C., USAF, 1965-70. Rsch. grantee Eli Lilly Co., 1979-91. Fellow ACS; mem. AMA, Am. Assn. Plastic Surgeons, Am. Burn Assn., Am. Cleft Palate Assn., Am. Soc. for Aesthetic Plastic Surgery, Am. Soc. Plastic and Reconstructive Surgeons, Am. Soc. for Surgery of Hand, Acad. Medicine Cin., Assn. Acad. Chairmen in Plastic Surgery, Cin. Surg. Soc., Grad. Surg. Soc. Cin., Greater Cin. Soc. Plastic and Reconstructive Surgeons (pres. 1988-89), Ohio Med. Assn., Ohio Valley Soc. Plaastic and Reconstructive Surgery (pres. 1985-86), Plastic Surgery Rsch. Coun. Home: 2970 Alpine Ter Cincinnati OH 45208 Office: U Cin Coll Medicine Div Pl Reconst Hand Surgery 231 Bethesda Ave Cincinnati OH 45267-0558

NEALE, TIMOTHY ARTHUR, hospital administrator; b. Abington, Pa., Feb. 26, 1948; s. Edwin A. and Helene R. (Rehbaum) N.; m. Cathleen S. Fitzpatrick; children: Adam, Nathan. BA, Amherst (Mass.) Coll., 1970; MA in Teaching, Brown U., 1971; M in Health Svc. Adminstrn., U. Mich., 1980. Asst. dir. admissions Middlebury (Vt.) Coll., 1971-78; assoc. v.p. Meriden-Wallingford (Conn.) Hosp., 1980-83; v.p. Med. Ctr. Hosp. Vt., Burlington, 1983-89, Mt. Auburn Hosp., Cambridge, Mass., 1989—; bd. dirs. Belmont-Watertown (Mass.) VNA. Fellow Am. Coll. Healthcare Execs., Am. Hosp. Assn. Office: Mt Auburn Hosp 330 Mt Auburn St Cambridge MA 02138-5502

NEALON, WILLIAM JOSEPH, JR., federal judge; b. Scranton, Pa., July 31, 1923; s. William Joseph and Ann Cannon (McNally) N.; m. Jean Sullivan, Nov. 15, 1947; children: Ann, Robert, William, John, Jean, Patricia, Kathleen, Terrence, Thomas, Timothy. Student, U. Miami, Fla., 1942-43; B.S. in Econs. Villanova U., 1947; LL.B., Cath. U. Am., 1950; LL.D. (hon.), U. Scranton, 1975. Bar: Pa. 1951. With firm Kennedy, O'Brien & O'Brien (and predecessor), Scranton, 1951-60; mem. Lackawanna County Ct. Common Pleas, 1960-62; U.S. dist. judge Middle Dist. Pa., 1962—, chief judge, 1976-88, sr. status, 1989—; mem. com. on adminstrn. of criminal law Jud. Conf. U.S., 1979—; lectr. bus. law and labor law U. Scranton, 1951-59; mem. jud. council 3d Cir. Ct. Appeals, 1984—; dist. judge rep. from 3d Cir. Jud. Conf. of U.S., 1987—. Mem. Scranton Registration Commn., 1953-55; hearing examiner Pa. Liquor Control Bd., 1955-59; campaign dir. Lackawanna County chpt. Nat. Found., 1961-63; mem. Scranton-Lackawanna Health and Welfare Authority, 1963—; assoc. bd. Marywood Coll., Scranton; pres. bd. dirs. Cath. Youth Center; pres. Father's Club Scranton Prep. Sch., 1966; chmn. bd. dirs. Mercy Hosp., 1991—; chmn. bd. trustees U. Scranton; vice chmn. bd. trustees Lackawanna Jr. Coll., Scranton; bd. dirs. St. Joseph's Children's and Maternity Hosp., 1963-64, Lackawanna County unit Am. Cancer Soc., Lackawanna County Heart Assn., Lackawanna County chpt. Pa. Assn. Retarded Children, Scranton chpt. ARC, Lackawanna United Fund, Mercy Hosp., Scranton, 1975—; trustee St. Michael's Sch. Boys, Hoban Heights; adv. com. Hosp. Service Assn. Northeastern Pa. Served to 1st lt. USMCR, 1942-45. Recipient Americanism award Amos Lodge B'nai B'rith, 1975; Cyrano award U. Scranton Grad. Sch., 1977; Disting. Service award Pa. Trial Lawyers Assn., 1979; named one of 50 Disting. Pennsylvanians Greater Phila. C. of C., 1980, Outstanding Fed. Trial Judge Assn. Trial Lawyers Am., 1983. Mem. Pa. Bar Assn., Lackawanna County Bar Assn. (Chief Justice Michael J. Eagen award 1987), Friendly Sons St. Patrick (pres. Lackawanna County 1963-64), Pi Sigma Alpha. Club: Scranton Country (Clarks Summit, Pa.) (bd. dirs.). Lodge: K.C. Office: US Courthouse PO Box 1146 Scranton PA 18501-1146

NEAMAN, MARK A., health facility administrator. With Riverside Methodist Hosp., Columbus, 1971-74; with Evanston Hosp. Corp., Evanston, Ill., 1974—, now pres., CEO. Office: Evanston Hosp Corp 1301 Central St Evanston IL 60201*

NEAMAN, MARK ROBERT, hospital administrator; b. Buffalo, Oct. 22, 1950; married. B, Ohio State U., 1972, MHA, 1974. Adminstrv. asst. Evanston (Ill.) Hosp., 1974-76, asst. to v.p., 1976-78, asst. v.p., 1978-80, v.p., 1980-84, sr. v.p., 1984-85, pres., exec. v.p., 1985-90, pres., 1990-92, pres., CEO, 1992—. Fellow Am. Coll. Healthcare Execs. (regent northern Cook County, Ill. 1990—, RS Hudgens award 1988). Home: 263 W Onwentsia Rd Lake Forest IL 60045-2826 Office: Evanston Hosp 2650 Ridge Ave Evanston IL 60201-1718

NEAME, RONALD, director, producer; b. Hendon, Middlesex, Eng., Apr. 23, 1911; s. Stuart Elwin and Ivy Lillian (Close) N.; m. Beryl Yolanda Heanly, Oct. 15, 1933; 1 son, Christopher Elwyn; m. Dona Friedberg, Sept. 12, 1993. Student pvt. schs., London and Sussex, Eng. Asst. cameraman Brit. Internat. Pictures, Estree, Eng., 1928-35; chief cameraman Brit. Internat. Pictures. 1935-45. Dir.: photography, prodn. super. various films, including In Which We Serve, 1942, This Happy Breed, 1943, Blithe Spirit, 1944; co-writer, producer: films Brief Encounter, 1945, Great Expectations, 1946; producer: film Oliver Twist, 1947; dir.: films Take My Life, 1948, Golden Salamander, 1949, The Promoter, 1952, Man with a Million, 1953, The Man Who Never Was, 1954, Windom's Way, 1957, The Horse's Mouth, 1958, Tunes of Glory, 1960, I Could Go On Singing, 1962, The Chalk

Garden, 1963, Mr. Moses, 1964, Gambit, 1966, The Prime of Miss Jean Brodie, 1968, Scrooge, 1970, The Poseidon Adventure, 1972, The Odessa File, 1974, Meteor, 1978, Hopscotch, 1979, First Monday in October, 1980-81, Foreign Body, 1985, The Magic Baloon, 1989; co-founder film co. Cineguild Co., Denham, Eng., 1943-44. Mem. Dirs. Guild Am., Am. Film Inst., Acad. Motion Picture Arts and Scis. (gov. 1977-79), Brit. Acad. Film and TV Arts (London and Los Angeles), Savile Club (London). *When I am asked which film I consider to be my best, I reply, "I haven't made it yet. Perhaps next time."*

NEAR, JAMES W., restaurant and franchise executive; b. 1938; married. Student, Hanover Coll., 1961. V.p. BBF Restaurants, 1965-69; exec. v.p., then pres. retail sales Borden, Inc., 1969-74; with Sisters Internat., Inc., 1979-86; pres., chief oper. officer Wendy's Internat., Inc., Ohio, 1986-89, past pres., chief exec. officer, chmn. With USNG. Office: Wendy's Internat Inc 4288 W Dublin Granville Rd Dublin OH 43017-2093

NEARY, PAMELA, state legislator; b. Mar. 16, 1955; m. Court Storey; 4 children. BS in Biology and Polit. Sci., Ft. Lewis St. Coll.; MA in Pub. Affairs, Humphrey Inst. Mem. Minn. Ho. of Reps., 1992—; mem. health and human svcs. com., mem. regulated industries and energy com., mem. transp. and transit com. Active Citizens League. Mem. Minn. Women's Polit. Caucus, Minn. Women's Consortium. Democrat. Home: 1033 Indian Trl S Afton MN 55001-9705 Office: Minn Ho of Reps State Capitol Saint Paul MN 55155

NEARY, PATRICIA ELINOR, ballet director; b. Miami, Fla.; d. James Elliott and Elinor (Mitsitz) N. Corps de ballet Nat. Ballet of Can., Toronto, Ont., 1957-60; prin. dancer N.Y.C. Ballet, 1960-68; ballerina Geneva Ballet (Switzerland), 1968-71; asst. ballet dir., 1973-78; guest artist Stuttgart Ballet, Germany, 1968-71; asst. ballet dir., ballerina West Berlin Ballet, 1970-73; ballet dir. Zurich Ballet (Switzerland), 1978-86, La Scala di Milano ballet co., Italy, 1986-88; tchr., Balanchine ballets, Balanchine Estate, 1987—.

NEARY, ROBERT D., accounting firm executive. Co-chmn. profl. svcs. Ernst & Whinney, Cleve. Office: Ernst & Young 277 Park Ave New York NY 10172 also: Ernst & Young 2000 Nat City Ctr Cleveland OH 44114

NEAS, JOHN THEODORE, petroleum company executive; b. Tulsa, May 1, 1940; s. George and Lillian J. (Kaspar) N.; BS, Okla. State U., 1967, MS, 1968; m. Sally Jane McPherson, June 10, 1966; children: Stephen, Gregory, Matthew. CPA, Okla. With acctg. dept. Rockwell Internat., 1965; with controller's dept. Amoco Prodn. Co., 1966-67; mem. audit and tax staff Deloitte, Haskins & Sells, 1968-75; pres. Nat. Petroleum Sales, Inc., Tulsa, 1975—, John Neas Tank Lines, Inc., 1986—; pres. McPherson Fuels & Asphalts, Inc., 1981-88, sec., 1989—; mem. NPS/Hallmark LLC, 1994—; mem. Bailey Ranch Estates LLC, 1994—; asst. instr. U. Tulsa, 1974; bd. dirs. Waterways Bd. Okla. Dept. Transp. Mem. AICPA, Inst. Mgmt. Accts. (v.p. membership 1976-77), Okla. Soc. CPAs, Am. Petroleum Inst., McClellan-Kerr Arkansas River Navigation System Hist. Soc., Okla. Heritage Assn., Okla. State U. Pres.'s Club, Okla. State U. Coll. Bus. Adminstrn. Assocs. (v.p. memberships 1989-91), Hall of Fame 1991, Acctg. Dept. Hall of Fame, 1993), Oaks Country Club, The Golf Club Okla. Republican. Lutheran. Home: 2943 E 69th St Tulsa OK 74136-4541 Office: Nat Petroleum Sales Inc 5401 S Harvard Ave Ste 200 Tulsa OK 74135-3861

NEASE, STEPHEN WESLEY, college president; b. Everett, Mass., Jan. 15, 1925; s. Floyd William and Madeline Anzelette (Nostrand) N.; m. Dorothy Christine Hardy, June 17, 1946; children: Linda Carol Nease Scott, Floyd William II, Stephen Wesley Jr., David Wayne, Melissa Jo Nease Wallace. A.B., Brown U., 1946; Th.B., Eastern Nazarene Coll., 1947, D.D., 1966; Ed.M., Boston U., 1956; postgrad., Harvard Div. Sch., 1946-48. Ordained to ministry Ch. of the Nazarene, 1951; pastor East Side Ch. of the Nazarene, Newark, Ohio, 1948-50; dean men; instr. religion Ea. Nazarene Coll., Quincy, Mass., 1950-53; dir. devel. Ea. Nazarene Coll., Wollaston, Mass., 1953-66; founding pres. Mt. Vernon (Ohio) Nazarene Coll., 1966-72; pres. Bethany (Okla.) Nazarene Coll., 1973-76, Nazarene Theol. Sem., Kansas City, Mo., 1976-80, Eastern Nazarene Coll., Wollaston, Mass., 1981-89; edn. commr. Ch. of the Nazarene, 1989-94; exec. dir. Capital and Endowment Devel., Mt. Vernon, Ohio, 1994—. Served with USNR, 1943-46. Office: Capital and Endowment Devel 17012 Glen Rd Mount Vernon OH 43050

NEATHAWK, ROGER DELMORE, marketing company executive. BS Pharmacy, Med. Coll. Va., 1961, student, 1968-70; MS Bus., Va. Commonwealth U., 1978, student, 1980. Pharmacist Roanoke (Va.) Meml. Hosps., 1961-63, Melrose Drug Shoppe, Roanoke, Va., 1963-64, River Road Pharmacy, Richmond, Va., 1964-65; various positions from dir. pharmacy and material mgmt. to chief adminstrv. officer St. Mary's Hosp., Richmond, Va., 1965-81; CEO Mary Immaculate Hosp., Newport News, Va., 1981-84; chmn., CEO Market Strategies Inc., Richmond, Va., 1984—; adj. faculty J. Sargeant Reynolds C.C., Richmond, 1973-80; tutor mktg. Mary Baldwin Coll., Staunton, Va., 1985-87. Author: Nursing Recruitment and Retention: Beyond the Cliches, 1988; contbr. articles to profl. jours. Chmn. pub. rels. com. ctrl. Va. Hosp. Coun., chmn. Health Careers com., sec.-treas., v.p., 1967-81; mem. fac. Commonwealth Va. Dept. Volunteerism, 1986, 87; accrediation com. Va. Peninsula C. of C., 1984; Eastern Va. Interhosp. med. edn. com., 1981-84; adv. com. Va. Hosp. Ins. Reciprocal Subscribers (charter mem. 1976-80), chmn. nominating com., risk mgmt. com.; adv. com. Med. Lab. Tech. Program J. Sargeant Reynolds C.C., 1973-80, chmn. ad hoc adv. com. Devel. Master Plan Allied Health, 1973; chmn. bylaws com. Va. Assn. Continuing Edn. in Health Professions, program chmn., needs assessment com., charter mem. 1975-81; Capitol Area Comprehensive Health Planning Coun., 1974; Mktg. Action com. Downtown Richmond Inc., 1992; soc. mem. United Way Svcs. Greater Richmond; bd. dirs. Peninsula Area Health Edn. Ctr., 1983-84, Ctrl. Va. Health Edn. Ctr., 1980-81, Urban League Greater Richmond, 1991-93, chmn. mktg. and mem. com., 1991, 92, pub. rels. com., 1991, nominating com., 1991, ann. banquet com., 1993; Richmond Area Easter Seal Soc. Va., 1992—, V.I.P. team capt., 1990, co-chmn., 1991, chmn. 1992, 93, Old and Historic Broad St. Assn., 1991, 92, 93, chmn. pub. rels. com., 1991, 92, 93, sec. 1993. Recipient Geigy Leadership award Outstanding Hosp. Pharmacist, 1968, Marian award Outstanding Svc. to St. Mary's Hosp., 1974, Commonwealth Va. award Vol. Svc., 1978, Ctrl. Va. Hosp. Leadership award, 1978, Peter N. Pastore award Easter Seal Soc. Va., 1992; named Richmond Area Marketer Yr. Am. Mktg. Assn., 1987, Mid-Atlantic Marketer Yr., 1987. Fellow Am. Coll. Healthcare Adminstrs. (asst. regent commonwealth Va. 1983-85); mem. Am. Soc. Hosp. Mktg. and Pub. Rels. (faculty mem. edn. com. 1988, cert. level. status 1991), VA. Soc. Healthcare Mktg. and Pub. Rels. (charter, chmn. bylaws com. 1971, chmn. mem. com. 1971, program chmn. fall mtg. 1971, presentation to hosp. adminstrn. sch. 1971, treas. 1973, 74, chmn. ann. seminar 1974, budget com. 1981, chmn. 1983, faculty mem. ann. ednl. conf. 1985), Pub. Rels. Soc. Am. (Old Dominion chpt., Va. pub. rels. conf. 1987), Am. Hosp. Assn. (faculty mem. Chgo. 1988). Home: 21 N Granby St Richmond VA 23220 Office: Market Strategies Inc 214 N Jefferson St Ste 600 Richmond VA 23220-4200

NEAVERTH, ELMER JOSEPH, JR., dentist, endodontist, educator; b. Washington, May 26, 1935; s. Elmer Joseph and Dorothy (Crumb) N.; m. Mary Anne Polkowski, July 9, 1960; children: Anthony, Deborah, Michael, James. Student, Georgetown U., 1953-55, DDS, 1959; cert. in Endodontics, Loyola U., Chgo., 1967. Diplomate Am. Bd. Endodontics. Commd. 1st lt. U.S. Army, 1959, advanced through grades to col., 1974; mentor interns and gen. dental residency program Madigan Gen. Hosp., Tacoma, 1967-70; dir. endodontic residency program Madigan Army Med. Ctr., Tacoma, 1970-74; chief endodontic service U.S. Army Dental Activities, Ft. Gordon, Ga., 1974-75; dir. endodnic residency program Dwight D. Eisenhower Army Med. Ctr., Ft. Gordon, 1975-78; chief endodontic services Walter Reed Army Med. Ctr., Washington, 1981-82; clinic chief U.S. Army Dental Hosp., Washington, 1982-83, ret., 1984; prof., chmn. dept. endodontics dental sch. Med. Coll. of Ga., Augusta, 1983-91; pvt. practice in endodontics Augusta and Atlanta, 1991—; cons. in endodontics to surgeon gen. U.S. Army, 1975-76. Contbr. articles to profl. jours. Mem. ADA, Am. Assn. Endodontics, Am. Assn. Dental Schs., So. Endodontic Study Group, Ga. Dental Assn., Ga. Assn. Endodontists, KC. Democrat. Roman Catholic. Avocations: golf, skiing. Office: 13 Corporate Sq Ste 120 Atlanta GA 30329

NEAVES, WILLIAM BARLOW, cell biologist, educator; b. Spur, Tex., Dec. 25, 1943; s. William Fred and Revvie Lee (Hefner) N.; m. Priscilla Wood, Jan. 28, 1965; children: William Barlow, Clarissa D'laine. AB magna cum laude, Harvard U., 1966; postgrad., Med. Sch., 1966-67, PhD, 1969. Lectr. vet. anatomy U. Nairobi, 1970-71, vis. prof., 1978; lectr. anatomy Harvard U., 1972; asst. prof. cell biology U. Tex. Health Sci. Ctr., Dallas, 1972-74; assoc. prof. U. Tex. Health Sci. Ctr., 1974-77, prof., 1977—, Doris and Brian Wildenthal Prof. of Biomed. Sci., 1993—, dean Grad. Sch. Biomed. Scis., 1980-88, interim dean Southwestern Med. Sch., 1986-88, dean Southwestern Med. Sch., 1989—; rsch. assoc. herpetology Los Angeles County Mus., 1970-73; vis. lectr. U. Chgo., 1976-77. Assoc. editor Anat. Record, 1975-87; mem. editl. bd. Biology of Reprodn., 1983-86, Jour. Andrology, 1987-89; contbr. chpts. to books, articles to profl. jours. Bd. dirs. Dallas Zool. Soc., 1989-94, Dallas Mus. Natural History, 1993—, Damon Runyan-Walter Winchell Cancer Fund, 1986-92, v.p., 1990-92. Rockefeller Found. fellow, 1970-71; Milton Fund grantee, 1970-71; Population Council grantee, 1973-75; NIH grantee, 1973-89; Ford. Found. grantee, 1976-78. Fellow AAAS; mem. Am. Assn. Anatomists, Am. Soc. Andrology (Young Andrologist award 1983), Dallas Assembly, N.Y. Acad. Scis., Soc. Study of Reprodn., Liaison Com. on Med. Edn. (joint com. of AMA and Assn. Am. Med. Colls.), Sigma Xi, Alpha Omega Alpha. Methodist. Office: 5323 Harry Hines Blvd Dallas TX 75235-7200

NEAVOLL, GEORGE FRANKLIN, newspaper editor; b. Lebanon, Oreg., Aug. 20, 1938; s. Jesse Hunter and Mazie Maude (Meyer) N.; m. Laney Lila Hunter Hough, June 21, 1969. BS, U. Oreg., 1965. Reporter, photographer Lebanon Express, 1969-70; state editor Idaho State Jour., Pocatello, 1970-72; editorial writer The Jour.-Gazette, Ft. Wayne, Ind., 1972-75, Detroit Free Press, 1975-78; editorial page editor The Wichita (Kans.) Eagle, 1978-91, Portland (Maine) Press Herald, Maine Sunday Telegram, 1991—. Vol. Peace Corps, India, 1967-69; bd. councilors Save-the-Redwoods League, 1980—. Recipient Edward J. Meeman award Scripps-Howard Found., 1973, Honor Roll award, Izaak Walton League Am., 1974; named Hon. Pk. Ranger, Nat. Pk. Svc., 1988. Mem. Inter Am. Press Assn. (bd. dirs. 1985—, Jamaica Daily Gleaner award 1985), Am. Soc. Newspaper Editors, Nat. Conf. Editorial Writers, Soc. Profl. Journalists, Nat. Press Club, Cumberland Club. Home: 45 Eastern Promenade 7D Portland ME 04101 Office: The Portland Newspapers 390 Congress St Portland ME 04101

NEBEKER, FRANK QUILL, federal judge; b. Salt Lake City, Apr. 23, 1930; s. J. Quill and Minnie (Holmgren) N.; m. Louana M. Visintainer, July 11, 1953; children: Caramaria, Melia, William Mark. Student, Weber Coll., 1948-50; B.S. in Polit. Sci. U. Utah, 1953; J.D., Am. U., 1955. Bar: D.C. 1956. Corr. sec. The White House, 1953-56; trial atty. Internal Security div. Justice Dept., Washington, 1956-58; asst. U.S. atty., 1958-69; assoc. judge D.C. Ct. Appeals, 1969-87; dir. Office Govt. Ethics, Washington, 1987-89; chief judge U.S. Ct. of Vets. Appeals, Washington, 1989—; cons. Nat. Commn. on Reform of Fed. Criminal Laws, 1967-68; adj. prof. Am. U. Washington Coll. Law, 1967-85. Mem. Am., D.C. Bar Assns., Am. Law Inst. Office: US Court of Veterans Appeals 625 Indiana Ave NW Ste 900 Washington DC 20004-2901

NEBEKER, STEPHEN BENNION, lawyer; b. Salt Lake City, Feb. 21, 1929; s. Acel Hulme and Lora (Bennion) N.; m. June Wilkins, June 18, 1951; children: Jeanne N. Jardine, Mary N. Larson, Stephen W., Ann W. Wilkinson. JD, U. Utah, 1954. Bar: Utah 1957, U.S. Dist. Ct. Utah 1957, U.S. Ct. Appeals (10th cir.) 1957. Assoc. Ray Quinney & Nebeker, Salt Lake City, 1957-63, ptnr., 1963—, mem. exec. com., 1972—, pres., 1992—. Bd. editors Utah Law Rev., 1953-54. Mem. S.J. and Jessie Quinney Found., Salt Lake City, 1982—; chmn. nat. adv. coun. U. Utah; trustee Ray Quinney & Nebeker Found., Salt Lake City, 1982—. 1st lt. U.S. Army, 1954-57. Recipient Disting. Alumnus award U. Utah, 1992, named Lawyer of Yr. by Law Sch., 1988. Fellow Am. Coll. Trial Lawyers (mem. bd. regents 1984-87), Am. Bd. Trial Advs., Internat. Soc. Counsel, Fedn. Ins. Counsel, Am. Bar Found., Utah Bar Found. (trustee), Utah State Bar (Outstanding Lawyer of Yr. 1986, Trial Lawyer of Yr. 1994), Legal Aid Soc., Am. Inn of Ct. II (pres. 1982-83), Alta Club, Rotary, Salt Lake City Area C. of C. (mem. bd. govs. 1986-89), U. Utah Law Sch. Alumni Assn. (pres. 1985-86). Republican. Mormon. Avocations: skiing, golf, fly fishing, tennis, hunting. Home: 746 16th Ave Salt Lake City UT 84103-3705 Office: Ray Quinney & Nebeker 400 Deseret Bldg Salt Lake City UT 84111

NEBEL, HENRY MARTIN, JR., literature historian, educator; b. N.Y.C., Sept. 29, 1921; s. Henry Martin and Margaret (Naumann) N.; m. Sylvia Sue Fuller, July 13, 1967; children—Althea, Keith, Grant, Blake. B.A., Columbia U., 1943, M.A., 1950, Ph.D., 1960. Researcher analyst Nat. Security Agy., Arlington, Va., 1949-50, U.S. Mcht. Marine Acad., Kings Point, N.Y., 1955-56, Duke U., Durham, N.C., 1956-57; mem. faculty Northwestern U., Evanston, Ill., 1957—, prof. Russian lit., 1960-86, prof. emeritus, 1986—. Author: N.M. Karamzin, A Russian Sentimentalist, 1966, Selected Prose of N.M. Karamzin, 1967, Selected Aesthetic Works of Sumarokov and Karamzin, 1981, others; author articles and translations of Russian topics; editor, contbg. editor various jours. Served with USAF, 1943-45. Mem. Am. Assn. Tchrs. Slavic and East European Langs., Soc. for Eighteenth-Century Lit., AAUP.

NEBEL, KAI ALLEN, lawyer; b. Geneva, N.Y., July 9, 1932; s. Bernard Rudolph and Mabel (Ruttle) N.; m. Maria Agnese Marini, Sept. 15, 1958; children: Natalia, Silvia, Isabella, Erik. BA, Princeton U., 1954; LLB, Harvard U., 1957. Bar: Ill. 1958, U.S. Dist. Ct. (no. dist.) Ill. 1958. Assoc. Clausen, Miller, Caffrey, Witous, Gorman, Chgo., 1958-63; ptnr. Nisen, Elliott, Meier & Bowles, Chgo., 1963-71; ptnr. Boodell, Sears, Giambalvo & Crowley, Chgo., 1971-84, chmn. exec. com., 1982-83; ptnr. Keck, Mahin & Cate, Chgo., 1984—. Contbr. chpt. in profl. jours. Chmn. com. Ill. Gov., 1965, Hyde Park Kenwood Community Org., Chgo., 1968-69; pres. Parents Assn. of Lab. Schs. of U. Chgo., 1970; bd. dirs., mem. adv. bd. Friends of Downtown Chgo., 1982-83; pres. Skokie Sch. Found., Winnetka, Ill., 1984—; mem. design rev. bd. Village of Winnetka, 1988—. Named Man of Yr. Winnetka C. of C., 1986, Vol. of Yr. North Shore Mag. and Neiman Marcus, 1986. Mem. ABA, Ill. Bar Assn., Chgo. Bar Assn., Ill. Tax Increment Assn. (bd. dirs. 1987—), Union League Club. Avocations: photography, gardening, hiking. Home: 362 Hawthorn Ln Winnetka IL 60093-4217 Office: Keck Mahin & Cate 77 West Wacker Dr Ste 4900 Chicago IL 60601-1693

NEBENZAHL, KENNETH, rare book and map dealer, author; b. Far Rockaway, N.Y., Sept. 16, 1927; s. Meyer and Ethel (Levin) N.; m. Jocelyn Hart Spitz, Feb. 7, 1953; children: Kenneth (dec.), Patricia Suzanne Nebenzahl Frish, Margaret Spitz Nebenzahl Quintong, Suzanne Spitz Nebenzahl Nichol. Student, Columbia U., 1947-48; L.H.D. (hon.), Coll. William and Mary, 1983. Solicitor new bus. United Factors Corp., N.Y.C., 1947-50; sales rep. Fromm & Sichel, Inc., N.Y.C., 1950-52; v.p. Cricketeer, Inc., Chgo., 1953-58; pres. Kenneth Nebenzahl, Inc., Chgo., 1957—; bd. dirs. Imago Mundi, Ltd., London, 1976—; cons. Rand McNally and Co., 1966—. Author: Atlas of the American Revolution, 1974, Bibliography of Printed Battle Plans of the American Revolution, 1975, Maps of the Holy Land, 1986, Atlas of Columbus and the Great Discoveries, 1990, also edits. in Spanish, German, Italian, Portugese and French langs.; contbr. articles to profl. jours. and monographs. Trustee Glencoe Public Library, 1963-69, pres., 1966-69; bd. dirs. North Suburban Library System, 1966-69, Beverly Farm Found., Godfrey, Ill., 1961-67, Nature Conservancy of Ill., 1980-88; trustee Adler Planetarium, 1969—, chmn., 1977-81; mem. exec. com. Northwestern U. Library Council, 1973-75; sponsor Kenneth Nebenzahl, Jr. lectures history cartography Newberry Library, Chgo., 1965—; mem. assos. council John Crerar Library, Chgo., 1972—; trustee, 1976-84, mem. vis. com. to library 1974—, chmn., 1987—; trustee U. Chgo., 1982—; co-chair Phillips Soc.- Libr. of Congress, Washington; bd. dirs. Evanston Hosp. Corp., 1978-85, Am. Himalayan Found., 1994—; mem. U.S. nat. adv. coun. World Wildlife Fund, 1993—. Served with USMCR, 1945-46. Recipient IMCoS-Tooley award (London), 1984. Fellow Royal Geog. Soc., Am. Geog. Soc.; mem. Manuscript Soc. (dir. 1965-71), Am. Library Trustees Assn. (nat. chmn. com. intellectual freedom 1967-68), Bibliog. Soc. Am., Newberry Library Assocs. (bd. govs. 1965-78, chmn. 1976-78), Newberry Library (trustee 1979—, chmn. 1994—), Antiquarian Booksellers Assn. Am. (bd. govs. 1965-67, v.p. 1975-77), Am. Antiquarian Soc. (gov. 1981-85), Soc. History Discoveries (dir. 1974-76), Chgo. Map Soc. (dir. 1976-86), Ill. Ctr.

for the Book (pres. 1986-88). Clubs: Caxton (Chgo.) (bd. govs. 1961-68, 74-80, pres. 1964-66), Wayfarers (Chgo.) (pres. 1979-80); Lake Shore Country (Glencoe); Century (N.Y.C.), Grolier (N.Y.C.). Office: PO Box 370 Glencoe IL 60022-0370

NEBERT, DANIEL WALTER, molecular geneticist, research administrator; b. Portland, Oreg., Sept. 26, 1938; s. Walter Francis Nebert and Marie Sophie (Schick) Kirk; m. Myrna Sisk, Mar. 12, 1960 (div. 1975); children: Douglas Daniel, Dietrich Andrew; m. Kathleen Dixon, Aug. 15, 1981; children: Rosemarie Dixon, Rebecca Frances, David Porter, Lucas Daniel. BA, Wesleyan U., 1959; BS and MS in Biochemistry, U. Oreg., MD, 1964. Lic. physician, Calif., Ohio. Pediatric intern UCLA Hosps., Los Angeles, 1964-65; pediatric resident UCLA Hosps., 1965-66; postdoctoral fellow Nat. Cancer Inst., Bethesda, Md., 1966-68; sr. investigator Nat. Inst. Child Health and Human Devel., 1968-71; sect. head Nat. Inst. Child Health and Human Devel., 1971-74, lab. chief, 1974-89; prof. dept. environ. health U. Cin. Med. Ctr., 1989—, prof. dept. pediatrics, 1991—; dir. Ctr. Environ. Genetics, 1992—; mem. faculty bd. cert. in human genetics NIH, 1981-89; coord. med. genetics program U.S-China Coop. Med. Health Protocol, 1982-89; Pfizer lectr. U. Vt., Burlington, 1978, Stanford U., 1979; Wellcome vis. prof. biochemistry and molecular biology U. S.D., Vermillion, 1991. Mem. editorial bd. Archives Biochemistry and Biophysics, 1973-76, Archives Internationales de Pharmacodynamie et de Therapie, 1975-81, Jour. Environ. Scis. and Health, 1976-81, Teratogenesis, Carcinogenesis and Mutagenesis, 1980-86, Anticancer Research, 1981-83, Chemico-Biol. Interactions, 1977-83, Molecular Pharmacology, 1972-84, Devel. Pharmacology and Therapeutics, 1979-87, Biochem. Pharmacology, 1972—, Jour. Exptl. Pathology, 1986—, DNA and Cell Biology, 1986—, Molecular Endocrinology, 1988-91, Endocrinology, 1989—, Pharmacogenetics, 1991—; contbr. over 400 articles to profl. jours. Capt. USPHS, 1966-89. Recipient Meritorious Svc. medal USPHS, 1978, Frank Ayrey fellow award in clin. pharmacology, U.K., 1984, Bernard B. Brodie award, 1986, Ernst A. Sommer Meml. award, 1988; GM nat. scholar, 1956-59, Lawrence Selling scholar, 1961, 63. Fellow AAAS; mem. Am. Soc. Pharmacology and Exptl. Therapeutics, Am. Soc. Biochemistry and Molecular Biology, Am. Soc. Clin. Investigation, Soc. Pediatric Rsch., Am. Soc. Microbiology, Genetics Soc. Am., Endocrine Soc., Soc. Toxicology, Sigma Xi. Republican. Unitarian. Avocations: gardening, golf, piano, skiing, squash, art. Home: 65 Oliver Rd Cincinnati OH 45215-2630 Office: U Cin Med Ctr Dept Environ Health PO Box 670056 Cincinnati OH 45267-0056

NEBIL, CORINNE ELIZABETH, artist; b. Varmland, Sweden, Apr. 30, 1918; came to U.S., 1920, naturalized, 1942; d. Eric and Elisabet (Tillstrom) Erickson; student NAD, 1954, Traphagen Sch. Fashion, 1955-56, Art Students League, N.Y.C., 1949-52, Whitney Sch. Art, 1948, U. Bridgeport, 1955; m. Roland Nebil, 1 dau., Ninette. Co-owner The Little Gallery, Bridgeport, Conn., 1954-60; art dir. Kid Stuff mag., 1964; free-lance fashion illustrator, 1966-81; art instr. Cen. Fla. Jr. Coll., Caytona Beach C.C., 1991-93; one-woman shows: Westport Country Playhouse, 1955, Chappalier Gallery, N.Y.C., 1958, Radio City Music Hall, N.Y.C., 1955, Cen. Fla. Jr. Coll., 1986, 87, others; group shows: Art-U.S.A., Madison Sq. Garden, N.Y.C., 1948, Pastel Soc. Am., N.Y.C., 1982, Smithsonian Instn., Washington, 1965, Lincoln Ctr., Avery Fischer Hall, 1982, Swedish-Am. Artists travelling show, 1967, also others; painter ceiling mural St. Joseph's Ch., Bridgeport, Conn., 1958; represented in numerous pvt. collections; instr. art Famous Artists Schs. Internat., Westport, Conn., 1975-76, Central Fla. Jr. Coll., 1981—, Silvermine Sch. Art, Norwalk, Conn., 1980, Bridgeport Art League and Conn. Classic Arts Workshop, 1981-82; portrait commns. numerous TV and film personalities. Recipient numerous awards, latest best portrait award Conn. Show, 1982. Mem. Nat. League Am. Penwomen, Conn. Classic Arts, Pastel Soc. Am. Designer. Home: 1620 S Oceanshore Blvd Flagler Beach FL 32136-3804

NEBLETT, CAROL, soprano; b. Modesto, Calif., Feb. 1, 1946; m. Philip R. Akre; 3 children. Studies with, William Vennard, Roger Wagner, Esther Andreas, Ernest St. John Metz, Lotte Lehmann, Pierre Bernac, Rosa Ponselle, George London, Jascha Heifetz. Soloist with Roger Wagner Chorale; performed in U.S. and abroad with various symphonies; debut with Carnegie Hall, 1966, N.Y.C. Opera, 1969, Met. Opera, 1979; sung with maj. opera cos. including Met. Opera, N.Y.C., Lyric Opera Chgo., Balt. Opera, Pitts. Opera, Houston Grand Opera, San Francisco Opera, Boston Opera Co., Milw. Florentine Opera, Washington Opera Soc., Covent Garden, Cologne Opera, Vienna (Austria) Staatsoper, Paris Opera, Teatro Regio, Turin, Italy, Teatro San Carlo, Naples, Italy, Teatro Massimo, Palermo, Italy, Gran Teatro del Liceo, Barcelona, Spain, Kirov Opera Theatre, Leningrad, USSR, Dubrovnik (Yugoslavia) Summer Festival, Salzberg Festival, others; rec. artist RCA, DGG, EMI; appearances with symphony orchs., also solo recitals, (film) La Clemenza di Tito; filmed and recorded live performance with Placido Domingo, La Fancivila del West; numerous TV appearances. Office: New Century Artist Mgmt Inc PO Box 802 Tuxedo Park NY 10987•

NECARSULMER, HENRY, investment banker; b. N.Y.C., Mar. 6, 1914; s. Edward and Manuela Fortlouis (Maas) N.; m. Elizabeth Louise Borden, Mar. 21, 1946; children: Susan N. Dallin, John B., Peter B. A.B., Dartmouth Coll., 1934. With Kuhn, Loeb & Co., N.Y.C., 1935-77; gen. partner Kuhn, Loeb & Co., 1956-77, mng. partner, 1969-77, vice chmn., 1977; mng. dir. Lehman Bros. Kuhn Loeb Inc., 1977-81, adv. dir., 1981-84; adv. dir. Shearson Lehman Bros. Inc., 1984-85, mng. dir., 1986-88, adv. dir., 1988-90, cons., 1990-93; cons. Lehman Bros., Inc., 1993—; dir. Polaroid Corp.; past dir. various corps.; Mem. Am. Stock Exchange, 1973-78; mem. governing council Securities Industry Assn., 1972-75; mem. State of N.Y. Judiciary Relations Com., Appellate Div., 1st Jud. Dept., 1973-77; Trustee Jewish Child Care Assn. N.Y. Served to capt. AUS, 1942-46. Office: Lehman Bros Inc 3 World Fin Ctr 17th Fl New York NY 10285

NECCO, ALEXANDER DAVID, lawyer, educator; b. Gary, Ind., Jan. 31, 1936; s. Alesandro Necco and Mary Millonovich; m. Caroline Chappel, Apr. 20, 1958 (dec. Mar. 1978); 1 child, Laurie Ann Necco Stansbury; m. Edna Joanne Painter, July 1, 1989. BA in Philosophy, U. Nev., 1958; JD, Oklahoma City U., 1965. Bar: Okla. 1965, U.S. Dist. Ct. (we. dist.) Okla. 1965, U.S. Ct. Appeals (10th cir.) 1985, U.S. Ct. Claims 1989, U.S. Ct. Vets. Appeals 1994. Assoc. Robert Jordan, Oklahoma City, 1965-66, Stuckey & Witcher, Oklahoma City, 1968-69; atty. Okla. Hwy. Dept., Oklahoma City, 1966, Oklahoma City Urban Renewal, 1966-67; ptnr. Stuckey & Necco, Oklahoma City, 1969-71, Necco & Dyer, Oklahoma City, 1978-82, Dyer, Necco & Byrd, Oklahoma City, 1982-88; pvt. practice, Oklahoma City, 1965—; ptnr. Necco & Byrd, Oklahoma City, 1988—; adj. prof. Oklahoma City U. Sch. Bus., 1965—. Cubmaster Boy Scouts Am., Oklahoma City. With USMC, 1958-61, lt. col. USMCR, 1953-83, ret. Mem. Assn. Trial Lawyers Assn., Okla. Trial Lawyers Assn., Marine Corps Res. Officers Assn. (pres. Oklahoma City 1984-85), Phi Delta Phi, Sigma Nu. Republican. Roman Catholic. Avocations: golf, swimming, tennis. Office: 5700 N Portland Ave Ste 121 Oklahoma City OK 73112-1662

NECHEMIAS, STEPHEN MURRAY, lawyer; b. St. Louis, July 27, 1944; s. Herbert Bernard and Toby Helen (Way) N.; m. Marcia Rosentein, June 19, 1966, (div. Dec. 1981); children: Daniel Jay, Scott Michael; m. Linda Adams, Aug. 20, 1983. BS, Ohio State U., 1966; JD, U. Cin., 1969. Bar: Ohio 1969. Ptnr., Taft, Stettinius & Hollister, Cin., 1969— ; adj. prof. law No. Ky. U., Chase Coll. Law. Tax comment author: Couse's Ohio Form Book, 6th edit., 1984. Mem. Ohio State Bar Assn. (taxation com.), Cin. Bar Assn. (chmn. taxation sect. 1983), Legal Aid Soc. Cin. (pres. trustee). Democrat. Jewish. Home: 777 Cedar Point Dr Cincinnati OH 45230-3755 Office: Taft Stettinius & Hollister 1800 Star Bank Ctr 425 Walnut St Cincinnati OH 45202-3912

NECHIN, HERBERT BENJAMIN, lawyer; b. Chgo., Oct. 25, 1935; s. Abraham and Zelda (Benjamin) N.; m. Susan Zimmerman (div.); 1 child, Jill Rebeca; m. Roberta Fishman, Oct. 24, 1976; 1 child, Stefan. BA with distinction honors in History, Northwestern U., 1956; JD, Harvard U., 1959. Bar: Ill. 1960. From assoc. to ptnr. Brown Fox & Blumberg, Chgo., 1960-75; ptnr. Taussig Wexler & Shaw, Chgo., 1975-79, Fink Coff Stern, Chgo., 1979-81, Holleb & Coff, Chgo., 1981—. Contbr. articles to profl. jours. Pres. Emanuel Congregation, Chgo., 1994—. Staff sgt. USAR, 1960-66. Mem. ABA, Ill. Bar Assn., Chgo. Bar Assn. (chmn. trust law com. 1990-91),

Am. Coll. Trust and Estate Counsel, Univ. Club, Phi Beta Kappa. Office: Holleb & Coff 55 E Monroe St Ste 4100 Chicago IL 60603-5803

NECKERMANN, PETER JOSEF, insurance company executive; b. Wuertzburg, Fed. Republic Germany, Oct. 26, 1935; came to U.S., 1977; s. Josef and Annemarie (Brueckner) N.; m. Jutta Voelk, Feb. 10, 1960; children: Susanne, Christian. Grad., J.W. Goethe U., Frankfurt, Fed. Republic Germany, MA, 1962; PhD, Ohio State U., 1990. Pres. Neckermann Versand KGaA, Frankfurt, 1962-77; dir. econ. analysis and systems Nationwide Ins. Cos., Columbus, Ohio, 1977-79, v.p. econ. and investment services, 1979—. CIV. Mem. Columbus Assn. Bus. Economists, Columbus Coun. on World Affairs (bd. dirs.), Rotary Club of Columbus, Univ. Club of Columbus (bd. dirs.). Avocations: tennis, skiing. Home: 1261 Fountaine Dr Columbus OH 43221-1519 Office: Nationwide Ins Cos 1 Nationwide Plz Columbus OH 43216

NEDD-FRIENDLY, PRISCILLA ANNE, motion picture film editor; b. Indpls., Apr. 6, 1955; d. Jerome Hoard and Betty Anne (Dorn) N. AA, Pierce Jr. Coll., Woodland Hills, Calif., 1975. Assoc. film editor An Officer and a Gentleman, Paramount Pictures, Hollywood, Calif., 1981-82; film editor Eddie and the Cruisers Aurora Prodns., Beverly Hills, Calif., 1982-83; The Flamingo Kid ABC Motion Pictures, Century City, Calif., 1984; No Small Affair Columbia Pictures, Burbank, Calif., 1984; Lucas 20th Century Fox Films, Century City, 1985; Street Smart Canon Pictures, Beverly Hills, 1986; Tucker: The Man and His Dream Lucas Films, Nicasio, Calif., 1987-88; Dead Poet's Society Disney Studio, Burbank, Calif., 1989; Pretty Woman, 1989-90, Guilty by Suspicion, Warner Bros., Burbank, 1990, Doc Hollywood, Warner Bros., Burbank, 1991, That Night, 1991, New Regency Films, 1992. Mem. Motion Picture Editors Guild, Am. Cinema Editors, Acad. Motion Picture Arts and Scis. Office: care Peter Benedek United Talent 9560 Wilshire Blvd Ste 500 Beverly Hills CA 90212 also: care Motion Picture & Videotape Editors Guild 7715 W Sunset Blvd Los Angeles CA 90046-3912

NEDERHOOD, JOEL H., church organization executive, minister; b. Grand Rapids, Mich., Dec. 22, 1930; s. Arthur William and Dena (Homan) N.; m. Mary Lou Nederhood, July 1, 1954; children: Maria, Carol, David. AB, Calvin Coll., 1952; MDiv, Calvin Sem., Grand Rapids, 1957; ThD, Free U. Amsterdam, The Netherlands, 1959. Ordained to ministry Christian Ref. Ch. Broadcast min. Back to God Hour, Christian Ref. Ch., Chgo., 1960-66, dir. Back to God Hour, 1966-81, dir. ministries Back to God Hour, 1981—; host Faith 20 TV, 1980—. Author: God Is Too Much, 1969, The Holy Triangle, 1975, Promises, Promises, Promises, 1980; editor monthly devotional Today. With U.S. Army, 1952-54. Fulbright scholar, 1957. Office: Back to God Hour 6555 W College Dr Palos Heights IL 60463

NEDERLANDER, JAMES LAURENCE, theater owner, producer; b. Detroit, Jan. 23, 1960; s. James Morton and Barbara (Smith) N. Student, Cranbrook Prep, Boston U. Asst. mgr. Pinchnob, Clarkston, Mich.; producer Pineknob, N.Y.C.; v.p. Nederlander, N.Y.C. Assoc. producer plays including The Tragedy of Carmen, 1984 (Tony award 1984), Starlight Express, 1989, assoc. producer musicals On Your Toes, 1987, Legs Diamond, 1988, Barry Manilow on Broadway, 1989; producer show Mort Sahl on Broadway, 1988, Kenny Loggins on Broadway, 1988; coproducer Billy Joel at Yankee Stadium, 1990, Harry Connick Jr. on Broadway, 1990, Yanni on Broadway, 1993, Pink Floyd at Yankee Stadium, 1994, Basia on Broadway, 1994, Shari Lewis and Lambchop on Broadway, 1994, Laurie Anderson on Broadway, 1995, How to Succeed..., 1995. Mem. Com. Am. Candlelite Vigil, 1990, Nat. Hypertension Benefit, N.Y.C., 1988; bd. trustees Entrepid Museum, 1990. Mem. League N.Y. Theatres, Roundabout Theatre Group, City Athletic Club, LaCosta Country Club.

NEDERLANDER, JAMES MORTON, theater executive; b. Detroit, Mar. 31, 1922; s. David T. and Sarah L. (Applebaum) N.; m. Charlene Saunders, Feb. 12, 1969; children: James Laurence, Sharon, Kristina. Student, Detroit Inst. Tech. Chmn., former pres. Nederlander Orgn., Inc. (formerly Nederlander Producing Co. Am., Inc.), N.Y.C., 1966—. Owner and operator of numerous theaters including Palace Theatre, Lunt-Fontanne Theatre, Biltmore Theatre, Nederlander Theatre, Brooks Atkinson Theatre, Biltmore Theatre, Gershwin Theatre, Neil Simon Theatre, Marquis Theatre, Minskoff Theatre, Richard Rodgers Theatre, N.Y.C., Greek Theatre, Pantages Theatre, Henry Fonda Theatre, L.A., Shubert Theatre, Chgo., Fisher Theatre, Masonic Temple, Detroit, Poplar Creek, Hoffman Estates, Ill., Merriweather Post Pavilion, Columbia, Md., Aldwych Theatre, London, Dominion Theatre, London, Adelphi Theatre, London; producer numerous shows for Broadway including She Loves Me, Will Rogers Follies, Me and My Girl, Orpheus Descending, Les Liaisons Dangereuses, Nicholas Nickleby, Annie, La Cage aux Folles, Nine, Applause, Not Now Darling, See Saw, Oliver, Abelard and Heloise, Sherlock Holmes, Treemonisha, Habeus Corpus, Otherwise Engaged, Whose Life is it Anyway?, Betrayal, Woman of the Year, Lena Horne: The Lady and Her Music, The Dresser, Noises Off, Merlin, Night and Day, My Fat Friend, Shirley MacLaine on Broadway, Sweet Charity, Benefactors, Breaking the Code; numerous road show prodns.; revivals: Peter Pan, She Loves Me, Hello Dolly, Porgy and Bess, The Music Man, I Do! I Do!, Oklahoma, On a Clear Day You Can See Forever, Fiddler on the Roof. Office: Nederlander Orgn Inc 810 7th Ave New York NY 10019-5818

NEDERLANDER, ROBERT E., entertainment and television executive, lawyer; b. Detroit, Apr. 10, 1933; s. David T. and Sarah (Applebaum) N.; m. Caren Berman (div.); children: Robert E. Jr., Eric; Gladys Rackmil, Jan. 1, 1988. BA in Econs., U. Mich., 1955, JD, 1958, LLD (hon.), 1990. Ptnr. Nederlander, Dodge & Rollins, Detroit, 1960-90; pres. Nederlander Orgn., Inc., N.Y.C., 1981—; Nederlander TV & Film Prodns., N.Y.C., 1985—; mng. gen. ptnr. N.Y. Yankees, 1990-91. Regent U. Mich., Ann Arbor, 1969-84; trustee Am. Health Found., 1989—; chmn. Gateway Am., 1991—. Recipient Disting. Alumni Svc. award U. Mich., 1985; named Man of Yr. by Gov.'s Com. on Scholastic Achievement, N.Y.C., 1991. Fellow ABA, Mich. Bar Assn. Avocations: tennis, baseball. Office: Nederlander Orgn 810 7th Ave New York NY 10019-5818

NEDOM, H. ARTHUR, petroleum consultant; b. Lincoln, Nebr., Aug. 19, 1925; s. Henry Arthur and Pearle Bertrick (Swan) N.; m. Patricia Margaret Rankin, July 4, 1974; children: Richard A., Robert L., Nicole C. B.S., U. Tulsa, 1949, M.S., 1950; postgrad. in bus. adminstrn., Northwestern U., Evanston, Ill., 1968. Chief engr. Amerada Petroleum Corp., Tulsa, 1961-65; v.p. Amerada Petroleum Corp., 1965-70, Natomas Co., San Francisco, 1971-74; also dir.; pres. Norwegian Oil Co., Houston, 1974-75; pres., mng. dir. Weeks Petroleum Ltd., Westport, Conn., 1975-82; cons., 1982—; chmn. bd. arbitration Prudhoe Bay Unit, 1983-85; chmn. Offshore Tech. Conf., 1971; bd. dirs. Engrs. Joint Council, 1978. Contbr. articles to profl. jours. Served with inf. U.S. Army, 1943-45, ETO. Decorated Bronze Star; named Disting. Alumnus U. Tulsa, 1972. Mem. Soc. Petroleum Engrs. (dir. 1965-68, pres. 1967, Disting. Lectr. 1973, Disting Svc. award 1978, DeGolyer Disting. Svc. medal 1981, Disting. mem. 1983, Disting. lectr. emeritus 1989, v.p. SPE Found. 1988-89), AIME (dir. 1966-69, 76-79, pres. 1977, hon. mem. 1982, Disting. Svc. award 1993), Am. Assn. Engring. Soc. (dir. 1980-82, chmn. 1981, Spl. award 1979, Engring. Svc. award 1980). Episcopalian. Home: 21 Deerwood Ln Westport CT 06880-2648

NEE, SISTER MARY COLEMAN, college president emeritus; b. Taylor, Pa., Nov. 14, 1917; d. Coleman James and Nora Ann (Hopkins) N. AB, Marywood Coll., 1939, MA, 1943; MS, Notre Dame U., 1959. Joined Order of Sisters, Servants of Immaculate Heart of Mary, 1941; assoc. prof. math. Marywood Coll., Scranton, Pa., 1959-68; pres. Marywood Coll., 1970-88, pres. emerita, 1988—; apostolic coord. Sisters, Servants Immaculate Heart of Mary, Scranton, Pa., 1968-70. Home and Office: Cathedral Convent 333 Wyoming Ave Scranton PA 18503-1223

NEE, OWEN D., JR., lawyer; b. Bronxville, N.Y., Nov. 22, 1943; s. Owen D. and Elisabeth (Osborn) N.; m. Amber W., Dec. 11, 1971. BA, Princeton U., 1965; JD, Columbia U., 1973. Bar: N.Y. 1973. Assoc. Coudert Bros., Hong Kong, 1973-81, ptnr., 1981-91; ptnr. Coudert Bros., N.Y.C., 1992-93, Hong Kong, 1994—. Author: CHINA, 1986; Commercial, Business and Trade Laws of PRC, 3 vols., 1991. Capt. U.S. Army, 1969-71, Vietnam.

Decorated Bronze star U.S. Army, Vietnam, 1971. Mem. Apawamis Club. Office: Coudert Bros, Nine Queen's Rd, Central, Hong Kong Hong Kong

NEECK, BERNARD J., insurance company executive; b. 1927. Sr. acct. Price Waterhouse & Co., N.Y.C., 1951-56; corp. mgr. gen. acctg. Kennecott Cooper Corp., N.Y.C., 1956-66; contr. Conrock Machinery, Clifton, N.J., 1967; v.p., contr. The Okonite Co., Ramsey, N.J., 1967-73; v.p. fin. HIP-NY, N.Y.C., 1973-82; med. dir. Staten Island Med. Group; now exec. v.p, CFO Health Ins. Plan of Greater N.Y., N.Y.C. Office: Health Insur Plan of Grter NY 7 W 34th St New York NY 10001-8100

NEEDHAM, CHARLES WILLIAM, neurosurgeon; b. Bklyn., Oct. 14, 1936; s. William and Jeanne (Studioso) N.; m. Constance Taft, June 15, 1958; children: Susan, Andrew, Jennifer, Sarah, Benjamin. B.S. cum laude Wagner Coll., 1957; M.D., Albany Med. Coll., 1961; M.Sc., McGill U., 1969. Cert. Am. Bd. Neurol. Surgery; lic. physician Conn. Asst. prof. neurol. surgery UCLA Sch. Medicine, 1969-71; clin. assoc. prof. neurol. surgery U. Ariz., Tucson, 1971-84; staff neurosurgeon Norwalk (Conn.) Hosp., Greenwich (Conn.) Hosp., 1984—; clin. instr. neurosurgery Yale U. Sch. Medicine 1989—; postdoctoral fellow Nat. Inst. Neurol. Diseases & Blindness, 1967-69. Author: Neurosurgical Syndromes of the Brain, 1973, Cerebral Logic, 1978, Principles of Cerebral Dominance, 1982, Neurosurgical Signs, 1986; contbr. articles to profl. jours. Served to capt. USAF MC, 1963-65. Recipient numerous awards for excellence in medicine including AMA Continuing Edn. awards, 1978—, Yale U. Sch. Medicine award, 1986. Fellow ACS; mem. AAAS, Am. Assn. Neurol. Surgeons, Congress Neurol. Surgeons, Brain and Behavioral Scis. Assn., N.Y. Acad. Scis., New Eng. Neurosurg. Soc., Conn. State Neurosurg. Soc. (pres. 1992—), Fairfield (Conn.) County Med. Soc. Avocations: philosophy, physics, anthropology, writing. Home: 1 Sipperleys Hill Rd Westport CT 06880-1245 Office: 5 Elmcrest Ter Norwalk CT 06850-3938

NEEDHAM, GEORGE AUSTIN, investment banker; b. Beverly, Mass., Jan. 27, 1943; s. Everett Austin and Edith Strode (Walton) N.; m. Ellen Ann Levin, July 9, 1978; children—Michael Austin, Sarah Elisabeth, Paul Everett. B.S. in Bus. Adminstrn., Bucknell U., 1965; M.B.A., Stanford U., 1971. Portfolio mgr. Bankers Trust Co., N.Y.C., 1967-69; mng. dir. First Boston Corp., N.Y.C., 1971-84; chmn., CEO Needham & Co. Inc., N.Y.C., 1985—. Trustee Stanford Bus. Sch. Trust, Palo Alto, Calif., 1983-89. Served to 1st lt. U.S. Army, 1965-67. Mem. Fin. Analysts Fedn., Bond Club N.Y. Republican. Clubs: University (N.Y.C.); Sleepy Hollow County (Scarborough, N.Y.); Coral Beach Club (Bermuda). Home: 79 E 79th St New York NY 10021-0202 Office: Needham & Co Inc 400 Park Ave New York NY 10022-4406

NEEDHAM, GEORGE MICHAEL, library association executive; b. Buffalo, July 3, 1955; s. Paul James and Dolores Ann (Duffy) N.; m. Joyce Elaine Leahy, Nov. 28, 1992; 1 stepchild, Katherine Wallace. BA in English, SUNY, Buffalo, 1976, MLS, 1977. Various profl. positions Charleston (S.C.) County Libr., 1977-84; dir. Fairfield County Dist. Libr., Lancaster, Ohio, 1984-89; mem. svcs. dir. Ohio Libr. Assn., Columbus, 1990-92; exec. dir. Pub. Libr. Assn., Chgo., 1993—; cons. Wright Meml. Libr., Oakwood, Ohio, 1992; mem. adv. bd. Southeastern Correctional Inst., Lancaster, Ohio, 1984-89; cons. Reference Point Found., Columbia, Md., 1994—. Author (book revs.) Booklist, 1994—, (video revs.) Libr. Jours., 1979—. Bd. dirs. Fairfield County chpt. ARC, Lancaster, 1985-88, Info. and Crisis Svc., Lancaster, 1984-88, Mt. Prospect Theatre Soc., Mt. Prospect, Ill., 1993—. Mem. ALA, ACLU, Am. Soc. Assn. Execs., Pub. Libr. Assn. Democrat. Avocations: acting, traditional folk music, writing, 2-time Jeopardy champion. Office: Pub Libr Assn 50 E Huron St Chicago IL 60611

NEEDHAM, HAL, director, writer; b. Memphis, Mar. 6, 1931; s. Howard and Edith May (Robinson) N.; m. Dani Janssen, June 28, 1981 (separated); children: Debra Jean, Daniel Albert, David Allyn. Student pub. schs. Founder Stunts Unltd., Los Angeles, 1956; stuntman Stunts Unltd., 1956-68, dir. and stunt coordinator second unit, 1968-76, dir., writer, 1976—; chmn bd. Camera Platforms Internat., Inc., 1986—. Dir., writer films Smokey and The Bandit, 1977, Hooper, 1978, The Villain, 1979, Smokey and The Bandit, II, 1980, The Cannonball Run, 1981, Mega Force, 1982, Stroker Ace, 1983, Cannonball Run Part 2, 1984, Rad, 1986, Body Slam, 1987; dir., writer, exec. prodr. Bandit, 1993; dir. pilot TV series Stunts Unltd.; movie of the week Death Car on the Freeway, B.L. Stryker, 1989. Served with Paratroopers U.S. Army, 1951-54. Mem. Screen Actors Guild, Dirs. Guild Am., Writers Guild Am., AFTRA. Owner Budweiser Rocket Car (fastest car in the world) displayed at Smithsonian Inst. Office: c/o Laura Lizer & Assocs 12711 Ventura Blvd Ste 440 Studio City CA 91604-2431 *I feel that if I can become successful with less than ten years of education, anyone in this country is capable of the same goals with positive thinking and total dedication.**

NEEDHAM, JAMES JOSEPH, consultant; b. Woodhaven, N.Y., Aug. 18, 1926; s. James Joseph and Amelia (Pasta) N.; m. Dolores A. Habick, July 1, 1950 (dec. Feb. 1993); children: James Joseph, Robert, Ravenna, Michael, Catherine. Student, Cornell U., 1946; BBA, St. John's U., 1951, LLD (hon.), 1972. CPA, N.Y. Acct. Price Waterhouse & Co., N.Y.C., 1947-54; ptnr. R. T. Hyer & Co., Port Washington, N.Y., 1954-57; ptnr., mem. exec. com. A. M. Pullen & Co., N.Y.C., 1957-69; commr. SEC, Washington, 1969-72; chmn., chief exec. officer N.Y. Stock Exch., 1972-76; v.p. Internat. Fedn. Stock Exchs., 1973-75; pres. Internat. Fedn. Stock Exchanges, 1976-90; councilman Town of Southampton, N.Y., 1986—; Disting. prof. grad. div. Coll. Bus. Adminstrn., St. John's U., Jamaica, N.Y.; U.S. amb. to Japan Expo '85, 1982-85; bd. dirs. Axe-Houghton Mut. Funds, Standard Register Co. Treas. Central Sch. Dist. 4, 1951-52, mem. budget and finance com., 1951, 63, chmn. high sch. planning com., 1947; active local Boy Scouts Am., 1962-65; mem. bishop's com. of laity Catholic Charities, Rockville Center, N.Y., 1960-68; mem. lay adv. bd. Cath. Youth Orgn., 1964-67; bd. advs. Coll. Bus. Adminstrn., St. John's U.; mem. hon. com. Am. Cancer Soc.; N.Y. State co-chmn. fin. Reagan for Pres. Campaign, 1980; Past dir., auditor Plainview (N.Y.) Republican Club; Bd. govs. Fed. Hall Meml. Assos.; trustee N.Y. Foundling Hosp. Served with USNR, 1944-46. Recipient Disting. Citizen award N.Y. U. Law Sch., Disting. Service award in investment edn. Nat. Assn. Investment Clubs; named Bus. Person of Year Bus. Adminstrn. Soc. St. John's U., 1975; fellow Aspen Inst. for Humanistic Studies. Mem. N.Y. Soc. CPA's (past dir., treas., past pres. Nassau-Suffolk chpt., recognition award), Am. Inst. CPA's (past mem. council), L.I. Assn., N.Y. Chamber Commerce and Industry, Internat. C. of C. (U.S. council), Downtown-Lower Manhattan Assn. (dir., mem. exec. com.), N.Y. Credit and Fin. Mgmt. Assn. (Laurel award), Cath. Accountants Guild (past pres.), Accountants Club Am., NYU Fin. Club (adv. council), Bond Club N.Y., Beta Alpha Psi. Clubs: Serra (Nassau) (past pres.); Cornell of Nassau County, Wheatley Hills Golf (past treas.), Siwanoy Country; Economic, University, Board Room, Downtown A.C. (N.Y.C.); Burning Tree, Capitol Hill (Washington); Blind Brook (Port Chester, N.Y.). Home: PO Box 1229 Bridgehampton NY 11932-1229

NEEDHAM, JOSEPH, biochemist, historian of science, orientalist; b. 1900; s. Joseph and Alicia N.; m. Dorothy Mary Moyle, 1924 (dec. 1979), m. Lu Gwei-Djen, 1989 (dec. 1991). M.A., Ph.D., Sc. D., Cambridge U.; F.R.S., F.B.A., hon. F.R.C.P.; D.Sc. (hon.), U. Brussels, U. Norwich, Chinese U. Hong Kong; U. Newcastle upon Tyne, U. Hull, U. Chgo., U. N.C., Wilmington, U. Cambridge, U. Peradeniya, Sri. Lanka; D.Univ. (hon.), U. Surrey; Ph.D. (hon.), U. Uppsala; Companion of Honor awarded by the Queen, 1992. Fellow Gonville and Caius Coll., Cambridge, 1924—, librarian, 1959-60, pres., 1959-66 master, 1966-76, sr. fellow, from 1976, emeritus sr. fellow; univ. demonstrator in biochemistry Cambridge U., 1928-33, Sir William Dunn reader in biochemistry, 1933-66, now emeritus; vis. prof. biochemistry Stanford U., 1929; Hitchcock prof. U. Calif., 1950; vis. prof. U. Lyon, 1951, U. Kyoto, 1971, Collège de France, Paris, 1973, U. B.C., Vancouver, 1975; hon. prof. Inst. History of Sci., Peking, 1982, Grad. Sch., Nat. Acad. Natural Scis., Peking, 1984; head Brit. Sci. Mission, China, and sci. counsellor Brit. Embassy, Chungking, adv. to Chinese Nat. Resources Commn., Chinese Army Med. Adminstrn., and Chinese Air Force Research Bur., 1942-46; dir. dept. natural sci. UNESCO, 1946-48; chmn. Ceylon Govt. Univ. Policy Commn., 1958. Recipient Sir William Jones medal Asiatic Soc. Bengal, 1963; George Sarton medal Soc. History of Sci., 1968; Leonardo da Vinci medal

Soc. History of Tech., 1968; Dexter award for History of Chemistry, 1979; Nat. award 1st class Chinese Sci. and Tech. Commn., 1988, Fukuoka gold medal, 1990, UNESCO Einstein Gold medal, 1994. Mem. Internat. Union History of Sci. (pres. 1972-74), Nat. Acad. Sci. U.S. (fgn.), Am. Acad. Arts and Scis. (fgn.), Nat. Acad. Scis. China (fgn., 1994), Royal Danish Acad. (fgn.), Internat. Acads. History of Sci. and Medicine, Sigma Xi (hon.). Author: Man a Machine, 1927; The Skeptical Biologist, 1929; Chemical Embryology (3 vols.), 1931; The Great Amphibium, 1932; A History of Embryology, 1934; Order and Life, 1935; Adventures before Birth, 1936; Biochemistry and Morphogenesis, 1942; Time, the Refreshing River, 1943; History is on Our Side, 1945; Chinese Science, 1946; Science Outpost, 1948; Science and Civilisation in China (7 vols. in 30 parts), 1954—; The Development of Iron and Steel Technology in China, 1958; Heavenly Clockwork, 1960; Within the Four Seas, 1970; The Grand Titration, 1970; Clerks and Craftsmen in China and the West, 1970; Moulds of Understanding, 1976; Celestial Lancets, a history and rationale of Acupuncture and Moxa, 1980; Trans-Pacific Echoes and Resonances—Listening Once Again, 1985; The Hall of Heavenly Records; Korean Clocks and Astronomical Instruments, 1380 to 1780, 1986; editor: Science, Religion and Reality, 1925; Christianity and the Social Revolution, 1935; Background to Modern Science, 1938; Hopkins and Biochemistry, 1949; The Chemistry of Life, 1970, (with Mansel Davies) Selections from the Writings of Joseph Needham, 1990; contbr. articles to profl. jours. Home: 2 A Sylvester Rd, Cambridge England CB3 9AF Office: East Asian History of Sci Libr, 8 Sylvester Rd, Cambridge England

NEEDHAM, KATHLEEN ANN, gerontology educator, consultant; b. Saginaw, Mich., Aug. 30, 1944; d. George Whitcomb and Ann (Drensky) N.; m. Kenneth Edward Cassady, June 19, 1982. BA, Olivet (Mich.) Coll., 1967; MA, Mich. State U., 1970, postgrad., 1972-76, 90—; cert., U. Mich., 1977. Cert. tchr., Mich. High sch. tchr. Pontiac (Mich.) schs., 1968-72; grad. asst. Mich. State U., East Lansing, 1972-76; asst. prof., chmn. dept. gerontology Madonna U., Livonia, Mich., 1981-90; mem. faculty Madonna Coll., Livonia, Mich. 1991—; grant project dir. Adminstrn. on Aging, Washington, 1977-83, Mich. Dept. Labor, Lansing, 1985-86; grant project supr. NIMH, Washington, 1981-83; cons. in field. Producer tapes in field. Del. Mich. White House Conf. on Aging, Dearborn, 1981; mem. com. Mich. Offie Svcs. to Aging, Lansing, 1983-92; bd. dirs. United Community Svcs., 1985-94, mem. health svcs. com., 1991—; chmn. Mich. Minimum Stds. for Aging, 1987; vol. Focus Hope, Detroit, Mich. Lupus Found.; mem. Mich. Task Force on Older Worker, Lansing, 1987, Mich. Exec. Commn. on Older Learner Summit, 1990-93; chair Mich. Gov.'s Conf. on Aging, 1991; cons. to bd. Mich. Assoc. Svc. Orgns., 1991-93; Mich. regional facilitator and del. White House Conf., 1994; mem. annual conf. planning com. Mich. Soc. Gerontology, 1994, 95. Recipient Svc. award Internat. Healthcare Assn., 1988, 89. Mem. Gerontol. Soc. Am., Detroit Women's Econ. Club, Mich. Soc. Gerontology (bd. dirs. 1987), Assn. Gerontology in Higher Edn. (membership com. 1982, pub. policy com. 1988, pub. rels. and fund raising 1992, 93), Am. Soc. Aging. Presbyterian. Home: 22760 Clear Lake Dr Farmington MI 48335-3834 Office: Madonna Univ 36600 Schoolcraft Rd Livonia MI 48150-1176

NEEDHAM, LUCIEN ARTHUR, musician, educator; b. Hull, Yorkshire, Eng., Apr. 5, 1929; s. Arthur and A. Nita (Sims) N.; m. Louise Chapman, Aug. 16, 1974 (dec. Oct. 3, 1988). Student, Guildhall Sch. Music, London, 1952-56. Condr. Winnipeg (Man., Can.) Philharm. Choir, 1956-60, Winnipeg Male Voice Choir, 1957-60; vis. instr. voice and theoretical subjects Brandon (Man.) U. Sch. Music, 1959-62, asst. prof. voice, organ and theoretical subjects, 1962-64, asso. prof., 1964-67; founding condr., mus. dir. Western Man. Philharm. Choir, 1965-67; assoc. prof. U. Lethbridge, Alta., 1967-69, prof. voice and theoretical subjects, 1970-87; chmn. dept. music U. Lethbridge, 1967-71, condr. Univ. Choir, 1968-74; condr. Lethbridge Symphony Orch., 1970-76; lectr., speaker, condr. master classes, 1956-87; examiner Western Bd. Music, 1957-87; adjudicator regional, interstate, provincial and local music festivals, scholarship competitions, 1957-87; mem. Alta. Registered Music Tchrs. Assn., 1967-87, pres., 1980-81. Tchr. singing, pianist, accompanist, condr. public concerts and on radio and TV, 1952-87; composer: Christmas Gradual, 1963, The Fields Abroad, 1967; contbr. articles, monographs to music jours. Served with RAF, 1948-50. Fellow Guildhall Sch. Music, 1965; grantee Nuffield Found., 1965; grantee Can. Council, 1966, 71; grantee U. Lethbridge, 1974, 85.

NEEDHAM, RICHARD LEE, magazine editor; b. Cleve., Jan. 16, 1939; s. Lester Hayes and Helen (Bender) N.; m. Irene Juechter, Aug. 7, 1965; children—Margaret, Richard, Trevor. B.A., Denison U., 1961; M.A., U. Mo., 1967. Copy editor Sat. Rev., N.Y.C., 1967-68; editor-in-chief Preview Internat., N.Y.C., 1968-69; financial and N.Y. editor Instns. mag.; also editor Service World Internat., N.Y.C., 1969-70; copy dir. American Home mag., N.Y.C., 1970-71; exec. editor Ski Mag., N.Y.C., 1971-74, editor, 1974-92, editor-in-chief, 1992-94, editor-at-large, 1994—; editor Ency. of Skiing, 1978, Ski Fever, 1995. Broadcaster: Ski Spot, CBS Radio, N.Y.C., 1978-83, On the Slopes, Audio Features Syndicate, 1984-87; author: Ski—50 Years in North America. Served to lt. USNR, 1961-65. Recipient Lowell Thomas award, 1985. Mem. N.Am. Ski Journalists Assn., Internat. Assn. Ski Journalists. Home: 115 Old Post Rd Croton On Hudson NY 10520 Office: SKI mag Times-Mirror Mags 2 Park Ave New York NY 10016-5603

NEEDLEMAN, ALAN, mechanical engineering educator; b. Phila., Sept. 2, 1944; s. Herman and Hannah (Goodman) N.; m. Wanda Sapolsky, Apr. 12, 1970; children—Deborah, Daniel. B.S., U. Pa., 1966; M.S., Harvard U., 1967, Ph.D., 1970. Instr. applied math. MIT, Cambridge, 1970-72, asst. prof., 1972-75; asst. prof. engring. Brown U., Providence, 1975-78, assoc. prof., 1978-81, prof., 1981—; mem. faculty, dean engring., 1988-91; vis. asst. prof. Tech. U. Denmark, Lyngby, 1973; vis. fellow Clare Hall, U. Cambridge, Eng., 1978; vis. prof. MIT, Cambridge, 1991. Contbr. articles to profl. jours. Guggenheim fellow, 1977. Fellow ASME; mem. Am. Acad. Mechanics, ASME, Danish Ctr. for Applied Math. and Mechanics (fgn.), Groupe Francais de Mecanique des Matériaux (fgn.). Home: 24 Elton St Providence RI 02906-4106 Office: Brown U Div Engring Providence RI 02912

NEEDLEMAN, HARRY, lawyer; b. N.Y.C., Oct. 13, 1949; s. Jack and Sarah (Finar) N.; m. Roseann Marie Eppolito, Jan. 15, 1971. BA, Bklyn. Coll., 1970; JD, St. John's U., Queens, N.Y., 1975. Bar: N.Y. 1976, U.S. Dist. Ct. (so. dist.) N.Y. 1979, U.S. Supreme Ct. 1980. Staff atty. Merrill Lynch, N.Y.C., 1975-80; gen. counsel Cantor Fitzgerald, L.P., N.Y.C., 1980-93. Address: 13 Crestview Dr Pleasantville NY 10570

NEEDLEMAN, HERBERT LEROY, psychiatrist, pediatrician; b. Phila., Dec. 13, 1927; s. J. Joseph and Sonia Rita (Shupak) N.; m. Shirley Weinstein, Sept. 12, 1948 (div. 1957); 1 child, Samuel; m. Roberta Pizor, June 2, 1963; children Joshua, Sara. BS, Muhlenberg Coll., Allentown, Pa., 1948; MD, U. Pa., 1952. Intern Phila. Gen. Hosp., 1952-54; resident in pediatrics Children's Hosp. of Phila., 1957-58, chief resident in pediatrics, 1958-59; resident in psychiatry Temple U. Med. Ctr., Phila., 1962-65, asst. prof. psychiatry, 1967-71; spl. fellow in psychiatry NIMH, Bethesda, Md., 1965-67; assoc. prof. psychiatry Harvard Med. Sch., Boston, 1971-81; prof. psychiatry and pediatrics U. Pitts. Sch. Medicine, 1981—; cons. and lead criteria document EPA, Washington, 1977; editor Ctrs. for Disease Control, Atlanta, 1978; mem. adv. com. on childhood lead poisoning prevention, 1990; chmn. devel. toxicology subpanel NAS, 1986. Editor: Low Level Lead Exposure: The Clinical Implications of Current Research, 1980; contbr. articles to profl. jours. Chmn. Com. of Responsibility, Boston, 1966-75, Alliance to End Childhood Lead Poisoning, Washington, 1991—; bd. dirs. Mass. Advocacy Ctr., Boston, 1972-80. Capt. U.S. Army, 1955-57. Recipient Sarah L. Poiley Meml. award N.Y. Acad. Sci., 1985, The Charles A. Dana award, 1989; NAS IOM, 1990. Fellow Am. Acad. Pediatrics; mem. Soc. of Toxicology, Am. Pediatric Soc., Am. Acad. of Child and Adolescent Psychiatry, Am. Acad. of Pediatrics Com. on Environ. Hazards, Phi Beta Kappa, Sigma Xi. Democrat. Jewish. Avocations: trout fishing, carpentry. Home: 5734 Aylesboro Ave Pittsburgh PA 15217-1412 Office: Univ Pitts Sch Medicine 305 Iroquois Ave Pittsburgh PA 15237-4724

NEEDLEMAN, JACOB, philosophy educator, writer; b. Phila., Oct. 6, 1934; s. Benjamin and Ida (Seltzer) N.; m. Carla Satzman, Aug. 30, 1959 (div. 1989); children: Raphael, Eve; m. Gail Adelman, Dec. 1990. BA, Harvard U., 1956; grad., U. Freiburg, 1957-58; PhD, Yale U., 1961. Clin.

psychology trainee West Haven (Conn.) Veterans Hosp. Adminstrn., 1960-61; rsch. assoc. Rockefeller Inst., N.Y., 1961-62; from asst. prof. to assoc. prof. philosophy San Francisco State U., 1962-66, prof philosophy, 1967—, chair dept. philosophy, 1968-69; vis. scholar Union Theol. Seminary, 1967-68; dir. Ctr. Study New Religions, 1977-83; lectr. psychiatry, cons. med. ethics U. Calif., 1981-84. Author: Being-in-the-World, 1963, The New Religions, 1970, Religion for a New Generation, 1973, A Sense of the Cosmos, 1975, On The Way to Self-Knowledge: Sacred Tradition and Psychotherapy, 1976, Lost Christianity, 1980, Consciousness and Tradition, 1982, The Heart of Philosophy, 1982, Sorcerers, 1986, Sin and Scientism, 1986, Lost Christianity: A Journey of Rediscovery to the Centre of Christian Experience, 1990, Money and the Meaning of Life, 1991, Modern Esoteric Spirituality, 1992, The Way of the Physician, 1993, The Indestructible Question, 1994; (trans.) The Primary World of Senses, 1963, Essays on Ego Psychology, 1964; editor Care of Patients with Fatal Illness, 1969, The Sword of Gnosis, 1973, Sacred Tradition and Present Need, 1974, Understanding the New Religions, 1978, Speaking of My Life: The Art of Living in the Cultural Revolution, 1979, Real Philosophy: An Anthology of the Universal Search for Meaning, 1991; contbr. Death and Bereavement, 1969, To Live Within, 1971, My Life with a Brahmin Family, 1972, The New Man, 1972, The Universal Meaning of the Kabbalah, 1973, The Phenomenon of Death, 1974, Search, 1979. Grantee Religion in Higher Edn., 1967-68, Marsden Found., Ella Lyman Cabot Trust, 1969, Marsda Found, Far West Inst., 1975; Fulbright scholar Germany, 1957-58; Fels Found. fellow Munich, 1959; fellow Rockefeller Found. Humanities, 1977-78. Office: San Francisco State U Dept Philosophy 1600 Holloway Ave San Francisco CA 94132

NEEDLER, GEORGE TREGLOHAN, oceanographer, researcher; b. Summerside, P.E.I., Can., Feb. 2, 1935; s. Alfred Walker Holinshead and Alfreda Alice (Berkeley) N.; m. Catherine Lebedoff de Badrihaye, June 11, 1984; 1 child, Frederick Hoelbl; children from previous marriage: Mary Catherine, Kirstie Ann, Ian Berkeley, Peter Alfred. BS in Math. and Physics with honours, MS in Theoretical Physics, U.B.C., 1958; PhD in Theoretical Physics, McGill U., 1963. Research scientist dept. fisheries and ocean Bedford Inst. Oceanography, Dartmouth, N.S., Can., 1962-75, head ocean circulation div., 1975-79, dir., 1979-85, rsch. scientist, 1992—; scientific dir. World Ocean Circulation Experiment Inst. Oceanographic Scis., Deacon Lab., Wormley, Godalming, Surrey, Eng., 1985-89, chief scientist, 1989-92; rsch. assoc. Dalhousie U., Halifax, N.S., 1965-85; mem. UN body Joint Group of Experts on Scientific Aspects of Marine Pollution, 1980-85, chmn. working group on oceanographic model of wastes disposed in the deep sea, 1980-83; mem. Can. Nat. Com. Internat. Union Geodesy and Geophysics, 1979-83, chmn., 1983-85; mem. Can. Nat. Com. for Sci. Com. Oceanographic Rsch., 1978-79; bd. dirs., rsch./policy com. Can. Global Change Program. Rossby Meml. fellow Woods Hole Oceanographic Instn., 1970. Fellow Royal Soc. Can.; mem. Can. Meteorological and Oceanographic Soc. (scientific com. 1977-80). Avocations: golf, squash. Office: Bedford Inst Oceanography, PO Box 1006, Dartmouth, NS Canada B2Y 4A2

NEEL, HARRY BRYAN, III, surgeon, scientist, educator; b. Rochester, Minn., Oct. 28, 1939; s. Harry Bryan and May Birgitta (Bjornsson) N.; m. Ingrid Helene Vaga, Aug. 29, 1964; children: Carlton Bryan, Harry Bryan IV, Roger Clifton. BS, Cornell U., 1962; MD, SUNY-Bklyn., 1966; PhD, U. Minn., 1976. Diplomate Am. Bd. Otolaryngology. Intern Kings County Hosp., Bklyn., 1966-67; resident in gen. surgery U. Minn. Hosps., Mpls., 1967-68; resident in otolaryngology Mayo Grad. Sch. Medicine Mayo Clinic, Rochester, Minn., 1970-74, cons. in otohinolaryngology, 1974—, cons. in cell biology, 1981—, assoc. prof. otolaryngology and microbiology Med. Sch., 1979-84, prof., 1984—, also chmn. dept. otolaryngology. Author: Cryosurgery for Cancer, 1976; contbr. chpts. to books, articles to profl. jours. Vice-pres. bd. dirs. Minn. Orch. in Rochester, Inc., 1982, pres., chmn. 1983-84; mem. devel. com. Minn. Orchestral Assn., 1983, Mayo Found. bd. devel., 1983-86; bd. dirs. Mayo Health Plan, 1986-92, chmn. 1990-92; mem. bd. Mayo Mgmt. Svcs., Inc., 1992—; mem. bd. regents U. Minn., 1991—, chair faculty staff, student affairs com.; bd. dirs. Greater Rochester Area Univ. Ctr., 1993—. With USPHS, 1968-70. Recipient travel award Soc. Acad. Chmn. Otolaryngology, 1974, Ira J. Tresley rsch. award Am. Acad. Facial and Reconstructive Surgery, 1982, Notable award Nat. Assn. Collegiate Women Athletic Adminstrs., 1992, The Best Doctors in Am. award Woodward/White, 1992-93, 94-95. Mem. AMA, ACS (bd. govs. 1985-90, devel. bd. 1988—, treas. 1990—, sec.-treas. Minn. chpt. 1983-85, pres. 1988-89), Am. Acad. Otolaryngology-Head and Neck Surgery (prize for basic research in otolaryngology 1972, bd. dirs. 1988-91, established Neel Disting. Rsch. Lectureship Endowment Fund 1994), Minn. Med. Assn., Zumbro Valley Med. Soc., Am. Broncho-Esophagological Assn. (pres. elect 1988, pres. 1989-90), Am. Rhinological and Otol. Soc. (Mosher award 1980), Am. Laryngological Assn. (Casselberry award 1985, sec. 1988-93, v.p. 1994, pres. 1994—), Assn. for Research in Otolaryngology, Assn. Acad. Depts. in Otolaryngology (sec.-treas. 1984-86, pres. elect 1986, pres. 1988-90), Alumni Assn. Cornell U. (Outstanding Alumni award 1985, Collegium ORL Amicitiae Sacrum 1990—), Am. Bd. Otolaryngology (bd. dirs. 1986—, most admired man of decade 1992). Republican. Presbyterian. Club: Rochester Golf and Country. Home: 828 8th St SW Rochester MN 55902-6310 Office: Mayo Clinic 200 1st St SW Rochester MN 55905-0001

NEEL, JAMES VAN GUNDIA, geneticist, educator; b. Hamilton, Ohio, Mar. 22, 1915; s. Hiram Alexander and Elizabeth (Van Gundia) N.; m. Priscilla Baxter, May 6, 1943; children—Frances, James Van Gundia, Alexander Baxter. A.B., Coll. Wooster, 1935, D.Sc. (hon.) 1959; Ph.D., U. Rochester, 1939, M.D., 1944, D.Sc. (hon.) 1974; D.Sc. (hon.), Med. Coll. Ohio, 1981. Instr. zoology Dartmouth, 1939-41; fellow zoology NRC, 1941-42; intern, asst. resident medicine Strong Meml. Hosp., 1944-46; assoc. geneticist lab. vertebrate biology, asst. prof. internal medicine U. Mich. Med. Sch., 1948-51, geneticist Inst. Human Biology, asso. prof. med. genetics, 1951-56, prof. human genetics, chmn. dept., 1956-85, prof. internal medicine 1957-85, Lee R. Dice U. prof. human genetics, 1966-85, prof. emeritus, 1985—; Galton lectr. U. London,, 1955; Cutter lectr. Harvard U., 1956; Russel lectr. U. Mich.; 1966; Wilhemene E. Key lectr. Am. Genetic Assn., 1982; Jacobson lectr. U. Newcastle upon Tyne, 1988; Baker lectr. Pa. State U., 1989; Andros lectr. U. Chgo., 1991; Lederberg lectr. Rockefeller U., 1995; cons. USPHS, AEC, NRC, WHO, EPA, VA; pres. 6th Internat. Congress Human Genetics; chmn. 7th Internat. Symposium Smithsonian Instn., Washington, 1981. Author med. articles; mem. editorial bd.: Blood, 1950-62, Perspectives in Biology and Medicine, 1956—, Human Genetics Abstracts, 1962—, Mutation Research, 1964-75. Served to 1st lt. M.C. AUS, 1943-44, 46-47; acting dir. field studies Atomic Bomb Casualty Commn., 1947-48. Recipient Albert Lasker award, 1960, Allan award Am. Soc. Human Genetics, 1965, Nat. Medal of Sci., 1974, medal Smithsonian Instn., 1981, Conte award Conte Inst. for Environ. Health, 1991, James D. Brice award ACP, 1995; named Mich. Scientist of Yr., 1984. Fellow Am. Coll. Med. Genetics (hon.), Royal Soc. Medicine; mem. Am. Philos. Assn., Am. Acad. Arts and Scis., Inst. of Medicine, Nat. Acad. Scis. (mem. coun. 1970-72), Genetics Soc. Am., Am. Soc. Human Genetics (v.p. 1952-53, pres. 1953-54), Internat. Genetic Epidemiology Soc. (pres. 1992-93), Am. Fedn. Clin. Rsch., Am. Soc. Naturalists, Assn. Am. Physicians, ACP (Laureate award 1987), Brazilian Soc. Human Genetics, Phi Beta Kappa, Sigma Xi, Alpha Omega Alpha. Avocation: orchid cultivation.

NEEL, JOHN DODD, memorial park executive; b. McKeesport, Pa., Aug. 7, 1923; s. Harry Campbell and Anna (Dodd) N.; m. Jean Wyatt, Feb. 11, 1948; children: Harry C., John Dodd II, W. Wyatt, Jeffrey J. BA, Pa. State U., 1946. From salesman to pres. Jefferson Meml. Park, Pitts., 1946-88, chmn. bd. dirs., 1988—. Mem. Zoning Hearing Bd., Pleasant Hills, Pa., 1970—. Mem. adv. bd. Pa. State U., McKeesport; campus mem. Pa. State Real Estate Commn. 1st lt. USAAF, 1943-45. Decorated Air medal with 4 clusters, D.F.C. Recipient George Washington cert. Freedom Found., 1974. Mem. Cemetery Assn. Pa. (pres. 1963-65), Am. Cemetery Assn. (pres. 1973-74), West Jefferson Hills C. of C. (pres. 1984), VFW, Am. Legion, 57th Bomb Wing Assn., South Hills Country Club, Indian Lake Golf Club, Aero Club, Kiwanis (pres. 1959). Masons, Shriners. Presbyterian. Avocations: golf, travel, reading, hunting. Office: Jefferson Meml Pk PO Box 10898 Pittsburgh PA 15236-0898

NEEL, JUDY MURPHY, association executive; b. Rhome, Tex.; d. James W. and Linna B. (Vess) Neel; m. Ellis F. Murphy, Jr., Dec. 30, 1975; children from previous marriage: Mary B. Schmidt, Janet E. Wescott, Susan E. Salinas. BS, Northwestern U., 1976; MBA, Roosevelt U., 1983. V.p.

Murphy, Tashjian & Assocs., Chgo., 1960-73; exec. dir. Automotive Affiliated Rep. Assn., Chgo., 1973-78; mgr. Automotive Svc. Ind. Assn., Chgo., 1978-80; exec. dir. Am. Soc. Safety Engrs., Des Plaines, Ill., 1980—. Mem. Chgo. Soc. Assn. Execs. (bd. dirs. 1979—, pres. 1985—, Shapiro award 1991), Am. Soc. Assn. Execs. (sec.-treas. 1994, found. dir. 1986-90, bd. dirs. 1990—, Key award 1986). Republican. Office: Am Soc Safety Engrs 1800 E Oakton St Des Plaines IL 60018-2187

NEEL, RICHARD EUGENE, economics educator; b. Bluefield, Va., Jan. 7, 1932; s. Charles Richard and Zell LaVerne (Bowling) N.; m. Binnie Jo LeFever, June 10, 1961; children: Jeffrey Richard, Cynthia Jo. BS, U. Tenn., 1954, MS, 1955; PhD, Ohio State U., 1960. Instr. econs. Ohio State U., 1958-60; asst. prof. econs. Coll. William and Mary, 1960-61; asst. prof. U. South Fla., 1961-63, assoc. prof., 1963-66, chmn. econs. and fin. programs, 1964-66, acting chmn. grad. program Coll. Bus Adminstrn., 1965-66; dir. instl. planning Fla. Tech. U., 1966-68, chmn. dept. econs., prof. econs., 1968-69; assoc. dean Sch. Bus. Adminstrn. Ga. State U., 1969-77, dean grad. studies Sch. Bus. Adminstrn., 1973-77, prof. econs. Sch. Bus. Adminstrn., 1969-78; dean Coll. Bus. Adminstrn. U. N.C., Charlotte, 1978-93, econ. prof., 1993—. Contbg. author: The Case Study of Off-Campus Postsecondary Education on Military Bases, 1980; contbr. numerous articles, monographs to profl. publs.; editor: Readings in Price Theory, 1973. Sec., bd. dirs. Charlotte Fgn. Trade Zone; mem. fin. com. United Way Ctrl. Carolinas, Inc.; mem. Mayor's Pvt. Industry Coun., Urban League/Nations Bank Loan Rev. Bd. Mem. Charlotte Sales and Mktg. Execs., Rotary, Phi Kappa Phi, Beta Gamma Sigma. Presbyterian. Office: U NC at Charlotte Charlotte NC 28223

NEEL, SAMUEL ELLISON, lawyer; b. Kansas City, Mo., Feb. 22, 1914; s. Ellison Adger and Serena (Smith) N.; m. Mary Wilson, Oct. 11, 1941; children: James Adger, Amy Bowen, Wilson (dec. 1947), Wendy Busselle, Mary Ellison, Sophia Talbot. B.A., Westminster Coll., Mo., 1935; LL.B. Yale U., 1938. Bar: Mo. 1938, D.C. 1946, Va. 1953. Spl. asst. to atty. gen. anti-trust div. U.S. Dept. Justice, Washington, 1938-40, rep. State-War Dept. Mission on Japanese Combines, 1946; legal staff adv. commn. Coun. Nat. Def., OPM, WPB, 1940-42; pvt. practice Washington and McLean, Va., 1946-93; bd. dirs. emeritus Rouse Co. Mem. Fed. City Coun., Washington, 1954-58; pres. McLean Citizens Assn., 1953-54, Pub. Utilities Commn., Fairfax County, Va., 1956-57, The Squam Lakes Assn., N.H., 1987-89; chmn. Fairfax County Water Authority, 1957-63, Fairfax County Housing Authority, 1970-72; adv. com. Mortgage Fin. FHA, 1956-66; pres. Neel Found., trustee Westminster Coll. Lt. commdr. USNR, 1942-46; staff commdr. USAF, Pacific Fleet. Mem. Mortgage Bankers Assn. Am. (exec. v.p. 1965-66, gen. counsel 1946-74), Soc. Cin., Beta Theta Pi, Omicron Delta Kappa. Democrat. Episcopalian (past trustee). Clubs: Lawyers (Washington), Metropolitan (Washington); N.Y. Yacht. Home: 1157 Chain Bridge Rd Mc Lean VA 22101-2215 Office: PO Box 385 Mc Lean VA 22101-0385

NEEL, SPURGEON HART, JR., physician, retired army officer; b. Memphis, Sept. 24, 1919; s. Spurgeon Hart and Pyrle (Womble) N.; m. Alice Glidewell Torti, Nov. 18, 1939; children: Spurgeon Hart III, Alice Leah Neel Zartarian. Student pre-med., Memphis State U., 1939; M.D., U. Tenn., 1942; M.P.H., Harvard U., 1958; M.S.B.A., George Washington U., 1965. Diplomate: Am. Bd. Preventive Medicine. Intern Meth. Hosp., Memphis, 1943; resident x-ray Santa Ana (Calif.) AFB, 1944; resident aviation medicine USAF Sch. Aerospace Medicine, 1960; commd. 2d lt. U.S. Army, 1942, advanced through grades to maj. gen., 1970; various assignments U.S., 1943-44, 47-48, ETO, 1944-47; chief surgeon service Ft. McPherson, Ga., 1949; med. service, 1949; div. surgeon (82d Airborne Div.), Ft. Bragg, N.C., 1949-51; comdr. (30th Med. Group), Korea, 1953-54; dep. div. physiology and pharmacology (WRAIR, WRAMC), 1956; chief aviation br. (OTSG), 1957; chief aviation medicine Ft. Rucker, Ala., 1960; comdg. officer U.S. Army Hosp., post surgeon, 1961-64; stationed in Vietnam, 1965-66, 68-69; dep. surgeon gen. U.S. Army, Washington, 1969-73; comdr. (U.S. Army Health Services Command), 1973-77; clin. assoc. prof. family practice U. Tex. Health Sci. Ctr., San Antoniko, now prof. emeritus occupl. and aerospace medicine U. Tex. Sch. Pub. Health; med. cons. U.S. Automobile Assn., other industries, San Antonio. Contbr. articles med. jours. Decorated D.S.M. with oak leaf cluster, Legion of Merit with 4 clusters, Bronze Star with oak leaf cluster, Air medal with 3 oak leaf clusters, Joint Service Commendation medal, USAF Commendation medal, Purple Heart, others.; Recipient Seaman award Assn. Mil. Surgeons U.S., 1950, Gary Wratten award, 1967; McClelland award Army Aviation Assn. Am., 1962; named to U.S. Army Aviation Hall Fame, 1976; recipient Lyster award Aerospace Med. Assn., 1977. Fellow A.C.P., Am. Coll. Preventive Medicine (past v.p.), Royal Soc. Health, Aerospace Med. Assn. (past pres.), Internat. Acad. Aviation and Space Medicine, Am. Acad. Med. Adminstrs., Am. Coll. Health Care Execs.; mem. AMA (past-sec. mil. medicine), Assn. Mil. Surgeons U.S., Assn. U.S. Army, Army Aviation Assn. Am.; asso. mem. Phi Chi. Home: 1321 Spanish Oaks San Antonio TX 78213-1606

NEELANKAVIL, JAMES PAUL, marketing educator, consultant, researcher; b. Anjoor, India, May 29, 1940; came to U.S., 1973, naturalized, 1985; s. Paul V. and Mary (Velara) N.; m. Salvacion Querol Pena, July 15, 1973; children: Mary Angel, Jacques Prince. BS, St. Thomas Coll., India, 1961; MBA, Asian Inst. Mgmt., Philippines, 1972; PhD, NYU, 1976. Asst. prof. N.Y. Inst., 1976-78; assoc. prof. Montclair State Coll., N.J., 1978-80; asst. prof. NYU, 1980-84; chmn. mktg. and internat. bus. dept. Hofstra U., Hempstead, N.Y., 1984-86, assoc. dean sch. bus., 1986-89, acting dean, 1989-91, prof. mktg. and internat. bus., 1991—; supr. Firestone, Bombay, India, 1961-70; cons. Internat. Advt. Assn., N.Y.C., 1979-88, GTE Inc., Stamford, Conn., 1980-85, Healthchem Inc., N.Y.C., 1980-83. Author: Self-Regulation, 1980, Agency Compensation, 1982, Advertising Regulation, 1985, Advertising Regulations in Selected Countries, 1987; co-author Advertising Self-Regulation: A Global Perspective, 1980; also articles. Min. Resurrection Ascension Ch., N.Y.C., 1990—. Mem. Internat. Advt. Assn., Am. Mktg. Assn., Acad. Internat. Bus., Advt. Research Found. Avocations: reading, tennis, travel.

NEELD, ELIZABETH HARPER, author, researcher, consultant; b. Brooks, Ga., Dec. 25, 1940; d. Tommie Frank and Rachel (Leach) Harper; m. Gregory Cowan, Feb. 24, 1975 (dec. 1979); m. Jerele Don Neeld, 1983. BS, U. Chattanooga, 1962, MEd, 1966; PhD, U. Tenn., Knoxville, 1973. Dir. English programs MLA, N.Y.C., 1976-78; prof. English Tex. A&M U., College Station, 1976-83; exec. prof. Coll. Bus. Adminstrn., U. Houston, 1990—. Author: Seven Choices: Taking the Steps to New Life After Losing Someone You Love, 1990, Sister Bernadette: Cowboy Nun from Texas; author, editor 14 additional books; author: (audiocassette series) Yes! You Can Write; subject, anchor PBS documentary The Challenge of Grief, 1991. Big sister Big Sister Orgn., Houston, 1991. Democrat. Methodist. Avocations: cooking, ballet, opera, music, weaving. Home: 716 Euclid St Houston TX 77009-7229

NEELEY, DELMAR GEORGE, human resources executive; b. Charleston, Ill., June 4, 1937; s. Glenn Truman and Gladys Bernice (Dittman) N.; m. Yvonne Tamara Penrod, Mar. 2, 1957 (div. Feb. 1969); children: Timothy Del, Kimberly Yvonne, Terry; m. Terry Anne Barbour, Aug. 28, 1971; children: Robert James, Stephen Edward. BA in Philosophy, Olivet Nazarene U., 1965, MA in Lit., 1969; postgrad., U. Sarasota, 1993-95. Mgr. mgmt. devel. Rauland Divsn. Zenith Corp., Chgo., 1967-70; sr. personnel cons. Mid. West Svc. Co., Chgo., 1971-73; dir. human resources Nichols-Homeshield Inc., West Chicago, Ill., 1974-76, Gould Inc./Ind. Battery Divsn., Langhorne, Pa., 1976-81; pres., owner Barbour-Neeley Inc., Sarasota, Fla., 1982-92. Counselor Chgo. Boys Club, 1968-70, Spl. Olympics, Chgo., 1967-70, Sarasota, 1982-85. With USAF, 1954-59. Recipient Meritorious Svc. award Chgo. Boys Club, 1970, Svc. award Chgo. Jaycees, 1967-71. Mem. Ctr. for Study of Presidency, The Century Club (life), Libr. of Congress Assocs. (charter mem.), Acad. Polit. Sci., Nat. Trust for Historic Preservation. Independent. Methodist. Avocations: teaching, business consultant, physical rehabilitation counseling. Home: 5161 Cedar Hammock Dr Sarasota FL 34232-2243

NEELEY, KATHLEEN LOUISE, librarian; b. Pitts., Feb. 22, 1946; d. George Edward Jr. and Mildred Jane (Snellbacher) Kratt; m. James Dalton Neeley, July 20, 1968; children: Laura Elizabeth, Alan Dalton. BS in Chemistry, Chatham Coll., Pitts., 1968; MS in LS, Syracuse U., 1972.

Analytical chemist U.S. Plant, Soil and Nutrition Lab., Cornell U., Ithaca, N.Y., 1968-69, libr. asst. Olin Libr., 1969-70; libr. Syracuse (N.Y.) U. Sch. Nursing Libr., 1971; libr. Logan Lewis Libr., Carrier Corp., Syracuse, 1971-72; med. libr. Health Sci. Libr., U. Minn., Duluth, 1973-74; tech. libr. Nuclear Energy Sys. Libr., Westinghouse Electric Corp., Pitts., 1974-77; asst. sci. libr. U. Kans. Librs., Lawrence, 1977-85, acting head sci. librs., 1985-86, head sci. librs., 1986—; mem. access to health info. task force Kans. Libr. Network Bd. Contbr. articles to profl. jours. Mem. ALA (programming planning com. sci. and tech. sect.), Am. Chem. Soc., Assn. Coll. and Rsch. Librs., Beta Phi Mu. Avocations: reading, gardening, travel. Office: U Kans 424 Anschutz Sci Libr University Of Kansas KS 66045

NEELY, CAMERON MICHAEL, professional hockey player; b. Comox, B.C., Can., June 6, 1965. Hockey player Vancouver Canucks, 1983-86, Boston Bruins, 1986—; player NHL All-Star Game, 1988-91. Recipient Bill Masterton Meml. trophy, 1993-94; named to Sporting News All-Star Team, 1987-88, 93-94. Office: Boston Bruins 150 Causeway St Boston MA 02114-1310*

NEELY, CHARLES LEA, JR., retired physician; b. Memphis, Aug. 3, 1927; s. Charles Lea and Ruby Perry (Mayes) N.; m. Mary Louise Buckingham, Mar. 30, 1957; children: Louise Mayes, Charles Buckingham. A.B., Princeton U., 1950; M.D., Washington U., St. Louis, 1954. Diplomate: Am. Bd. Internal Medicine. Intern Cornell Service, Bellevue Hosp., N.Y.C., 1954-55; resident Barnes Hosp., St. Louis, 1955-57; fellow in hematology Barnes Hosp., 1957-58; dir. U. Tenn. Cancer Clinic, 1979-87; mem. staffs Bapt. Meml. Hosp., Regional Med. Ctr. at Memphis, U. Tenn. Med. Center; prof. medicine and pathology U. Tenn., 1971-87. Served with USNR, 1945-47. Fellow A.C.P.; mem. AMA, Am. Soc. Clin. Oncology, Am. Soc. Hematology, Am. Fedn. Clin. Research, Sigma Xi, Alpha Omega Alpha. Home: 4743 Mint Dr Memphis TN 38117-4010

NEELY, EDGAR ADAMS, JR., lawyer; b. Atlanta, May 8, 1910; s. Edgar A. and Emily Levering (Eckfeldt) N.; m. Ruth Nevenzel, Dec. 17, 1966; children by previous marriage to Claire Graham: Edgar Adams III, Michael G., Alan S., Claire G., Constance L. B.A., U. N.C., 1931; LL.B., Emory U., 1934. Bar: Ga. 1934, U.S. Supreme Ct. 1963. Practiced Atlanta, 1934—; chief personnel and labor relations naval contract Arundel Corp., Consol. Engring. Co., Hardaway Contracting Co., 1942-43; asso., then partner Neely, Marshall and Greene, 1934-51; partner Marshall, Greene and Neely, Atlanta, 1951-59, Greene, Neely, Buckley and DeRieux, Atlanta, 1960-66, Neely, Freeman & Hawkins, 1966-76, Neely and Player (and predecessors), Atlanta, 1976—; mem. legal staff Bell Aircraft, Inc., Marietta, Ga., 1943-45, asst. to mgr., 1945-46; mem. faculty Products Liability Seminars, U. Balt., 1976-77. Author: Gain and Maintain Vibrant Drive from 25 to 95. Good cheer reporter Sta. WSB, 1934-39; chmn. Speakers Bur. Community Chest Fund, ARC, Atlanta, 1930's and 40's; vestryman St. Luke's Episcopal Ch., Atlanta. Named Disting. Alumnus, Emory Univ. Sch. of Law, 1994; recipient six-diamond 60 yr. pin for Norfolk So. Corp. and subs., 1995. Fellow Am. Coll. Trial Lawyers; mem. State Bar Ga., Trial Attys. Am., Nat. Assn. of R.R. Trial Counsel (pres. 1965-66), Ga. Bar Assn. (tradition of excellence award 1984), Internat. Assn. of Defense Counsel, ABA, Atlanta Bar Assn., Lawyers Club Atlanta (Fifty Yr. award 1984), Terminus Tennis Club, Commerce Club, Piedmont Driving Club, Amelia Island Plantation Club, Old War Horse Club (pres. 1986). Clubs: Terminus Tennis, Commerce, Piedmont Driving, Amelia Island Plantation, Old War Horse (pres.). Home: 1650 Nottingham Way NE Atlanta GA 30309-2628 also: 4150 S Fletcher Ave Fernandina Beach FL 32034 Office: Neely & Player 191 Peachtree St Ste 900 Atlanta GA 30303-1757

NEELY, J. RANDALL, public relations executive; b. Houston, Jan. 16, 1943. BS in Journalism, U. Tenn., 1966. PI spec. NASA, 1966-68; A/E Holder-Kennedy, 1968-69, v.p., 1969-70; exec. v.p. Wenz-Neely Co., 1970-85, pres., 1985—. Mem. PRSA, PRSA/Bluegrass (pres., v.p., sec., treas.). Office: The Wenz-Neely Co 505 W Ormsby Ave Louisville KY 40203

NEELY, MARK EDWARD, JR., writer; b. Amarillo, Tex., Nov. 10, 1944; s. Mark Edward and Lottie (Wright) N.; m. Sylvia Eakes, June 15, 1966. BA, Yale U., 1966, PhD, 1973; LHD (hon.), Lincoln Coll., 1981. Former dir. Louis A. Warren Lincoln Library and Museum, Ft. Wayne, Ind.; vis. instr. Iowa State U., Ames, 1971-72; editor Lincoln Lore, 1973—; mem. adv. bd. Ind. Historical Bureau, 1980—; mem. editorial adv. com. Ind. Mag. of History, 1981—; mem. editorial bd. Ulysses S. Grant Assn., 1981—. Author: The Abraham Lincoln Encyclopedia, 1981, The Lincoln Family Album: Photographs From The Personal Collection of a Historic American Family, 1990, The Fate of Liberty: Abraham Lincoln and Civil Liberties, 1991 (Pulitzer Prize for history 1992), The Last Best Hope on Earth: Abraham Lincoln and the Promise of America, 1993; (with Harold Holzer and Gabor S. Boritt) The Lincoln Image: Abraham Lincoln and the Popular Print, 1984, The Confederate Image: Prints of the Last Cause, 1987; (with R. Gerald McMurty) The Insanity File: The Case of Mary Todd Lincoln, 1986; (with Holzer) Mine Eyes Have Seen the Glory: The Civil War in American Art, 1993. Mem. Abraham Lincoln Assn., Soc. Ind. Archivists (pres. 1980-81), Ind. Assn. of Historians (pres. 1987-88). *

NEELY, PAUL, newspaper editor; b. San Francisco, July 30, 1946; s. Ralph and Virginia (Gaylord) N.; m. Linda Borsch, Oct. 6, 1977; children: David King, Michael Paul. BA, Williams Coll., 1968; MS in Journalism, Columbia U., 1970, MBA, 1970. Reporter, editorial writer Press Enterprise, Riverside, Calif., 1970-73; copy editor, asst. mng. editor Courier Jour., Louisville, 1973-79; news features editor St. Petersburg Times (Fla.), 1980-83; mng. editor Chattanooga Times, 1983-91, editor, dep. pub., 1991-92, pub. 1992—; mem. Commn. on Future Tenn. Judicial Sys. Mem. Am. Assn. Sunday and Feature Editors (pres. 1981-82), Am. Soc. Newspaper Editors. Home: 1000 Skillet Gap Chattanooga TN 37419 Office: The Chattanooga Times Po Box 951 100 E 10th St Chattanooga TN 37402-4230

NEELY, RICHARD, lawyer; b. Aug. 2, 1941; s. John Champ and Elinore (Forlani) N.; m. Carolyn Elaine Elmore, 1979; children: John Champ, Charles Whittaker. AB, Dartmouth Coll., 1964; LLB, Yale U., 1967. Bar: W.Va. 1967. Practiced in Fairmont, W.Va., 1969-73; chmn. Marion County Bd. Pub. Health, 1971-72; mem. W.Va. Ho. of Dels., 1971-73; justice, chief justice W.Va. Supreme Ct. of Appeals, Charleston, 1973-95; ptnr. Neely & Hunter, Charleston, 1995—; chmn. bd. Kane & Keyser Co., Belington, W.Va., 1970-88. Author: How Courts Govern America, 1980, Why Courts Don't Work, 1983, The Divorce Decision, 1984, Judicial Jeopardy: When Business Collides with the Courts, 1986, The Product Liability Mess: How Business Can Be Rescued from State Court Politics, 1988, Take Back Your Neighborhood: A Case for Modern-Day Vigilantism, 1990, Tragedies of our Own Making: How Private Choices have Created Public Bankruptcy, 1994; contbr. articles to nat. mags. Capt. U.S. Army, 1967-69. Decorated Bronze Star, Vietnam Honor medal 1st Class. Mem. W.Va. Bar Assn., Am. Econ. Assn., Internat. Brotherhood Elec. Workers, VFW, Am. Legion, Moose, Phi Delta Phi, Phi Sigma Kappa. Episcopalian. Office: Neely & Hunter 159 Summers St Charleston WV 25301

NEELY, SALLY SCHULTZ, lawyer; b. L.A. BA Stanford U., 1970, JD, 1971. Bar: Ariz. 1972, Calif. 1977. Law clk. to judge U.S. Ct. Appeals (9th cir.), Phoenix, 1971-72; assoc. Lewis and Roca, Phoenix, 1972-75; asst. prof. Harvard U. Law Sch., Cambridge, Mass., 1975-77; assoc. Shutan & Trost, P.C., Los Angeles, 1977-79, ptnr., 1979-80, Sidley & Austin, L.A., 1980—; faculty ABA Chapt. 11 Bus. Reorgns., 1989—, Bankruptcy Law Inst. and Bankruptcy Litigation Inst., 1987-92, Nat. Conf. Bankruptcy Judges, 1988, 90, 95, Fed. Jud. Ctr., 1989, 90, 94-95, Workshop Bankruptcy and Bus. Reorganization NYU, 1992—; rep. 9th cir. jud. conf., 1989-91; mem. Nat. Bankruptcy Conf., 1993—. Chair Stanford Law Sch. Reunion Giving, 1986; bd. visitors Stanford Law Sch., 1990-92. Fellow Am. Coll. Bankruptcy; mem. ABA, Calif. State Bar Assn. (debtor-creditor rels. and bankruptcy subcom. bus. law sect. 1985-87). Office: Sidley & Austin 555 W 5th St Ste 4000 Los Angeles CA 90013

NEELY, THOMAS EMERSON, lawyer; b. Pitts., Oct. 19, 1943; s. William Homer and Frances Elizabeth (Curtis) N.; m. Janice Elaine Fay, July 6, 1968; children: Daniel, Morgan, Benjamin. BA, Williams Coll., 1965; JD, Harvard U., 1968. Bar: Mass. 1968. Assoc. Hale and Dorr, Boston, 1971-

80, ptnr., 1980—. With U.S. Army, 1969-71, Vietnam. Office: Hale and Dorr 60 State St Boston MA 02109-1803

NEENAN, THOMAS FRANCIS, association executive, consultant; b. Kansas City, Mo., Apr. 3, 1923; s. Emmet Joseph and Mary Helen (Liebst) N.; m. Eileen Margaret Vala, Aug. 4, 1951; children: Nancy, Tom Jr., Pamela, Kathleen, Maureen. BA, Iowa U., 1948; MA, Iowa State U., 1978. Trademark researcher Lampa Christopherson, Chgo., 1948-50; sales mgr. Cedar Rapids (Iowa) Block Co., 1950-53; owner Tywal Co., Center Point, Iowa, 1953-60; mem. sales staff Capp Homes, Center Point, Iowa, 1960-78; property mgr. Center Point, Iowa, 1978-86; exec. dir. Iowa Trails Coun., Center Point, Iowa, 1984—. Editor: (mag.) Trails Advocate, 1986—. Mayor City of Center Point, 1959-61, 65-69; chmn. City Planning an dzoning Com., Center Point, 1970—; active County Dem. Ctrl. Com., Linn County, Iowa, Linn County Conservation Bd., 1972-83; vice chair state legis. com. AARP, Des Moines, 1988-93; active leader Boy Scouts Am. Recipient Silver Beaver award Boy Scouts Am., 1961, St. George award Cath. Archdiocese of Dubuque, 1973. Mem. Am. Hiking Soc. (bd. dirs., Kern award 1986), Rails to Trails Conservancy, Am. Trails (treas., bd. dirs., award of excellence 1992). Democrat. Roman Catholic. Avocation: trail acquisition, development, and promotion. Home: 1201 Central Ave Center Point IA 52213 Office: Trails Coun Inc PO Box 131 Center Point IA 52213-0131

NEER, CHARLES SUMNER, II, orthopaedic surgeon, educator; b. Vinita, Okla., Nov. 10, 1917; s. Charles Sumner and Pearl Victoria (Brooke) N.; m. Eileen Meyer, June 12, 1990; children: Charlotte Marguerite, Sydney Victoria, Charles Henry. BA, Dartmouth Coll., 1939; MD, U. Pa., 1942. Intern U. Pa. Hosp., Phila., 1942-43; asso. in surgery N.Y. Orthopedic-Columbia-Presbyn. Med. Center, N.Y.C., 1943-44; instr. in surgery Coll. Physicians and Surgeons, Columbia U., N.Y.C., 1946-47; instr. orthopaedic surgery Coll. Physicians and Surgeons, Columbia U., 1947-57, asst. prof. clin. orthopaedic surgery, 1957-64, asso. prof., 1964-68, prof. clin. orthopaedic surgery, 1968-90, prof. clin. orthopaedic surgery emeritus, spl. lectr. orthopaedic surgery, 1990—; attending orthopaedic surgeon Columbia-Presbyn. Med. Ctr., N.Y.C.; chief adult reconstructive svc. N.Y. Orthopaedic Hosp.; chief shoulder and elbow clinic Presbyn. Hosp.; cons. Orthopaedic Surgeon emeritus, N.Y. Orthopaedic Columbia Presbyterian Med. Ctr., 1991—, chmn. 4th internat. Congress Shoulder Surgeons. Founder, chmn. bd. trustees Jour. Shoulder and Elbow Surgery, 1990—; contbr. articles to books, tech. films, sound slides. Served with U.S. Army, 1944-46. Fellow ACS (mem. nat. com. on trauma), Am. Acad. Orthopaedic Surgeons (com. on upper extremity, shoulder com.); mem. AMA, Am. Bd. Orthopaedic Surgeons (Disting. Svc. award 1975, bd. dirs. 1970-75), Am. Shoulder and Elbow Surgeons (inaugural pres.), Am. Assn. Surgery of Trauma, Am. Orthopaedic Assn. Am. Coll. Surgeons (mem. com. trauma), Mid-Am. Orthopaedic Assn. (hon.), N.Y. Acad. Medicine, Allen O. Whipple Surg. Soc., N.Y. State Med. Soc., N.Y. County Med. Soc., Pan Am. Med. Assn., Am. Trauma Soc., Sociedad Latino Americana de Ortopedia y Traumatologia, Internat. Soc. Orthopaedic Surgery and Traumatology, Va. Orthopaedic Soc. (hon.), Carolina Orthopaedic Alumni Assn. (hon.), Conn. Orthopaedic Club (hon.), Houston Orthopaedic Assn. (hon.), Soc. Française de Chirurgie Orthopédique et Traumatologique (honneur), Soc. Italiana Ortopedia Etravmatologia (Onorario); patron, Shoulder and Elbow Soc. of Australia, Internat. Bd. of Shoulder Surgery (chmn. 1992—), Alpha Omega Alpha, Phi Chi. Home and Office: 231 S Miller St Vinita OK 74301-3625 *Forever grateful I could be a doctor and especially to work in the exciting area of shoulder surgery.*

NEERHOUT, JOHN, JR., petroleum company executive; b. 1931. BSME, U. Calif., 1953. With Bechtel Petroleum, Inc. (now Bechtel, Inc.), San Francisco, 1966—; pres. Bechtel Petroleum, Inc. (now Bechtel, Inc.), 1983-86, also dir. Bechtel Group, Inc. Office: Bechtel Group Inc 50 Beale St San Francisco CA 94105-1813

NEESE, ELBERT HAVEN, retired paper machinery manufacturing executive; b. Chgo., Nov. 8, 1923; s. Elbert Haven and Laura Janvrin (Aldrich) N.; m. Margaret Eda Knorpp, Apr. 22, 1947; children: Laura Ann, Mary Jane, John, Robert, Margaret, Walter. B.S. in Mech. Engring., Purdue U., 1944. With Beloit Corp.(Wis.), 1946-86, dir., 1952-86, pres., 1974-78, chmn. bd., pres., 1978-84, chmn. bd., chief exec. officer, 1984-86; dir. Regal-Beloit Corp., First Nat. Bank & Trust Co. Beloit; pres. Syracuse (N.Y.) Pulp and Paper Found., 1981-83. Trustee Beloit Coll.; pres. Beloit Found.; mem. Beloit City Council, 1956-59. Served with AUS, 1944; Served with USNR, 1944-47. Mem. TAPPI. Republican.

NEESON, LIAM, actor; b. Ballymena, No. Ireland, June 7, 1952; s. Barney and Kitty N.; m. Natasha Richardson, July 3, 1994; 1 son: Micheál Richard Antonio. Theatrical appearances include (Broadway) Anna Christie, 1993; films include Excalibur, 1981, Krull, 1983, The Bounty, 1984, The Innocent, 1984, Lamb, 1986, Duet for One, 1986, The Mission, 1986, A Prayer for the Dying, 1987, Suspect, 1987, Satisfaction, 1988, The Dead Pool, 1988, High Spirits, 1988, The Good Mother, 1988, Next of Kin, 1989, Darkman, 1990, Crossing the Line, 1990, Shining Through, 1992, Under Suspicion, 1992, Husbands and Wives, 1992, Leap of Faith, 1992, Ethan Fromme, 1993, Ruby Cairo, 1991, Schindler's List, 1993 (Best Actor Acad. award nominee 1994), Nell, 1994, Rob Roy, 1995, Before and After, 1995, Michael Collins, 1995. Office: c/o Susan Culley & Assocs 150 S Rodeo Dr Ste 220 Beverly Hills CA 90212

NEF, EVELYN STEFANSSON, psychotherapist, author, editor, specialist polar regions; b. N.Y.C., July 24, 1913; d. Jeno and Bella (Klein) Schwartz; m. Bil Baird, 1932 (div. 1938); m. Vilhjalmur Stefansson, 1941 (dec. 1962); m. John Ulric Nef, Apr. 21, 1964 (dec. Dec. 1988). Student, Traphagen Art Sch., N.Y.C., summer 1927, Art Student League, 1931, Inst. Study Psychotherapy, N.Y.C., 1974-77, Advanced Psychoanalytic Seminar, 1977-83. Librarian Stefansson Polar Library, N.Y.C., 1941-52; librarian Stefansson collection Baker Library, Dartmouth Coll., 1952-63, also lectr. polar studies program, 1960-61; administrv. officer Am. Sociol. Assn., Washington, 1963-64; freelance writer book reviews, newspaper articles N.Y. Times Book Review, also Washington Post, 1942-72; research assoc. dept. dermatology Washington Hosp. Ctr., 1976—; coordinator psoriasis social adjustment study, 1977-80; guest worker Inst. Brain Evolution and Behavior, NIHM; guest on radio and TV programs; mem. vis. com. U. Chgo. Libr., 1973-84, vice chmn., 1977-84; mem. vis. com. on social scis. U. Chgo., 1978-83; bd. dirs. MacDowell Colony, 1992—, fellow, summer 1993. Author: Within the Circle, 1945, Here is the Far North, 1957, Here is Alaska, 4th rev. edit. (with Linda C. Yahn), 1983, also contbg. author other books; editor-in-chief: Beyond the Pillars of Heracles (Rhys Carpenter), 1966, South from the Spanish Main (Earl Hanson), 1967, Silk, Spices and Empire (Owen and Eleanor Lattimore), 1968, West and By North (Louis B. Wright and Elaine Fowler), 1971, The Moving Frontier (Louis B. Wright and Elaine Fowler), 1972; foreward writer for Eleanor Lattimonew's Turkestan Reunion, 1995; editor, contbr.: Polar Notes, 1960-63, Eleanor Holgate Lattimore, 1895-1970, 1970, Jour. of Polar Studies, 1984; contbr. to: A Chronological Bibliography of the Published Works of Vilhjalmur Stefansson, 1978, Vilhjalmur Stefansson and The Development of Arctic Terrestial Science, 1984. Pres. Evelyn S. Nef Found., 1992—; trustee Corcoran Gallery Art, Washington, 1974-89; bd. dirs. Reginald S. Lourie Ctr. for Infants and Young Children, 1989-93, Washington Opera, 1993—, Nat. Symphony, MacDowell Colony, 1991—, Paget Found.; mem. adv. coun. dept. geriatrics Mt. Sinai Hosp., N.Y.C. 1988—. Recipient Vol. Activist award, 1978, recognition award Young Audiences, 1992. Mem. Washington Acad. Scis., Smithsonian Assocs. (mem. women's com. 1971-74), Soc. Women Geographers (nat. v.p., chmn. Washington chpt. 1969-71, nat. pres. 1972-75). Research on psychosomatic skin diseases, progressive aging. Home: 2726 N St NW Washington DC 20007-3323

NEFF, CRAIG, periodical editor. Student, Colgate U. Mng. editor Sports Illustrated for Kids, N.Y.C. Office: Sports Illustrated for Kids Rockefeller Ct Time & Life Building New York NY 10020-1393

NEFF, DONALD LLOYD, news correspondent, writer; b. York, Pa., Oct. 15, 1930; s. Harry William and Gertrude Marie N.; m. Abigail Trafford; 1 son, Gregory Harry. Student, Trinity Coll., San Antonio, 1949, York Coll., 1950-52, N.Y. U., 1953. Reporter York Dispatch, 1954-56, L.A. Mirror-News, 1956-57, UPI, L.A., 1957-61; with L.A. Times, 1961-64; bur. chief

L.A. Times, Tokyo, 1964; with Time mag., 1965-81; corr. Time mag., Vietnam, 1965-66; writer Time mag. N.Y.C., 1966-68; bur. chief Time mag., Houston, 1968-70, L.A., 1970-73, Jerusalem, 1975-78; bur. chief Time mag., N.Y.C., 1978-79, sr. editor, 1973-75; news svcs. editor Washington Star, 1979-80; Washington corr. Middle East Internat., 1989—. Author: Warriors at Suez: Eisenhower Takes America into the Middle East, 1981, Warriors for Jerusalem, The Six Days That Changed the Middle East, 1984; Warriors Against Israel, 1988, Fallen Pillars; U.S. Policy Toward Palestine and Israel since 1945, 1995. Served with AUS, 1948-50. Recipient Theta Sigma Phi Matrix award, 1962, Calif.-Nev. AP Writing Contest best met. spot news story award, 1962, Overseas Press Club award for best fgn. article in a mag., 1979; finalist Am. Book Award History category, 1982. Mem. Fgn. Press Assn. (Israel pres. 1977, v.p. 1978).

NEFF, EDWARD AUGUST, manufacturing company executive; b. Chgo., Feb. 7, 1947; s. Russell Jack and Betty Rae (Heins) N.; m. Janet Irene Picerno; children: Kathleen Rae, David Russell. BA, Ohio Wesleyan U., 1969. Mgmt. trainee Phoenix Trimming Co., Chgo., 1970-73, dir. research and devel., 1973-77; dir. research and devel. Phoenix Trimming Co., Tarboro, N.C., 1977-86, v.p. mfg., 1986-87; v.p. mfg. Murdock Webbing Co., Central Falls, R.I., 1987—. Deacon, treas. Howard Meml. Presbyn. Ch., Tarboro, N.C., 1984-88; treas. Christ Ch., East Greenwich, R.I., 1994—. Mem. Narrow Fabrics Inst. (pres. 1985-88), Web Sling Assn. (v.p. 1974-76). Republican. Avocations: golf, bridge. Home: 1065 South Rd East Greenwich RI 02818-1333 Office: Murdock Webbing Co 27 Foundry St Pawtucket RI 02863-2317

NEFF, FRANCINE IRVING (MRS. EDWARD JOHN NEFF), former federal government official; b. Albuquerque, Dec. 6, 1925; d. Edward Hackett and Georga (Henderson) Irving; m. Edward John Neff, June 7, 1948; children: Sindle, Edward Vann. A.A., Cottey Coll., 1946; B.A., U. N.Mex., 1948. Div. and precinct chmn. Republican Party, Albuquerque, 1966-71; mem. central com. Bernalillo County (N.Mex.) Republican Party, 1967-74, mem. exec. bd., 1968-70; mem. N.Mex. State central com. Republican Party, 1968-74, 77-82, mem. exec. bd., 1970-74, 81-83; Rep. nat. committeewoman State of N.Mex., 1970-74; also mem. exec. com.; Treas. of U.S. U.S. Dept. Treasury, Washington, 1974-77; nat. dir. U.S. Savs. Bonds, 1974-77; mktg. v.p. Rio Grande Valley Bank, Albuquerque, 1977-81; dir. Hershey Foods Corp., Pa., E-Systems Inc., Dallas, La.-Pacific Corp., Portland, Oreg., D.R. Horton, Inc., Arlington, Tex. N.Mex. state adviser Teenage Reps., 1967-68; del. Rep. Nat. Conv., Miami, 1968, 72; campaign coordinator Congressman Lujan of N.Mex., 1970; pres. Albuquerque Federated Rep. Women's Club, 1977; Leader Camp Fire Girls, Albuquerque, 1957-64; pres. Inez (N.Mex.) PTA, 1961; den mother Cub Scouts Am., Albuquerque, 1964-65; former mem. exec. bd. United Way of Albuquerque; former mem. adv. council Mgmt. Devel. Center, Robert O. Anderson Grad. Sch. Bus. and Adminstrv. Scis., U. N.Mex.; former mem. Def. Adv. Com. on Women in the Services, 1980-83; trustee Cottey Coll., Nevada, Mo., 1982-89. Recipient Exceptional Service award Dept. Treasury, 1976, Horatio Alger award, 1976. Mem. P.E.O. (pres. Albuquerque chpt. 1958-59, 63-64), Albuquerque City Panhellenic Assn. (pres. 1959-60), Greater Albuquerque C. of C. (bd. dirs. 1978-81), Alpha Delta Pi, Sigma Alpha Iota, Phi Kappa Phi, Pi Lambda Theta, Phi Theta Kappa. Episcopalian.

NEFF, GREGORY PALL, manufacturing engineering educator, consultant; b. Detroit, Nov. 23, 1942; s. Jacob John and Bonnie Alice (Pall) N.; m. Bonita Jean Dostal, Apr. 27, 1974; 1 child, Kristiana Dostal Neff. BS in Physics, U. Mich., 1964, MA in Math., 1966, MS in Physics, 1967; MSME, Mich. State U., 1982. Registered profl. engr., Ind.; cert. mfg. engr.; cert. mfg. technologist; cert. sr. indsl. technologist. Rsch. asst. cyclotron lab U. Mich., Ann Arbor, 1968-72, teaching fellow physics dept., 1973; instr. sci. dept. Lansing (Mich.) C.C., 1976-82; guest lectr. Purdue U. Calumet, Hammond, Ind., 1982-83, asst. prof., 1984-91, assoc. prof. mfg. engring. technologies and supervision, 1991—; cons. Inland Steel Co., Indsl. Engring., East Chicago, Ind., 1984-86, Polyurethane div. Pinder Industries, East Chicago, 1990-92, Elevated div. Pitts. Tank & Tower, Henderson, Ky., 1990-91. Contbr. articles to profl. jours. County commr. Ingham County Bd. of Commr., Mason, Mich., 1977-80, Tri-County Regional Planning Commn., Lansing, 1978-80, chair, non-motorized adv. coun. Mich. Dept. Transp., Lansing, 1982-83. Mem. ASME, AAUP, Soc. Mfg. Engrs. (chpt. 112 bd. dirs. 1986—, Appreciation award 1990, 92, Outstanding Faculty Advisor award 1991,), Ind. Soc. Profl. Engrs., Am. Soc. for Engring. Edn. (Merl K. Miller award 1994), Nat. Assn. Indsl. Tech., Order of the Engr. Democrat. Roman Catholic. Office: Purdue U Calumet 2200 169th St Hammond IN 46323-2094

NEFF, HOWARD, bank executive; b. 1933. Pres. Thunderbird Bank, Phoenix; with Bluebonnet Savings Bank FSB, Dallas, 1989—, now vice chmn. Office: Bluebonnet Savs Bank FSB 3100 Monticello Ave Dallas TX 75205*

NEFF, JACK KENNETH, apparel manufacturing company executive; b. N.Y.C., Feb. 23, 1938; s. William K. and Rose T. N.; m. Barbara Joan Neff, Nov. 4, 1961; 1 son, Craig William. A.A.S., Queens Coll., 1968; postgrad., Stanford Advanced Mgmt. Coll., 1973. Gen. mdse. mgr. youthwear Levi Strauss & Co., 1973-78, v.p. mktg., 1978-80; pres. Salant & Salant Co., N.Y.C., 1980-81; exec. v.p. Salant Corp., N.Y.C., 1981-84; pres., chief exec. officer Thomson Co., N.Y.C., 1984-87; exec. v.p., chief operating officer Stanley Blacker Co., N.Y.C., 1987-90; with Inside Mgmt. Assocs., N.Y.C., 1991-93; v.p. and gen. mgr. Reebok Worldwide Apparel Div., 1993-94; sr. v.p., 1994—. Served in USN, 1956-59.

NEFF, JAMES DENNIS, manufacturing company executive, consultant; b. Ft. Wayne, Ind., Aug. 24, 1937; s. James Marion and Margaret Ann (Lynch) N.; m. Jeanette Ann Day, Apr. 8, 1966; children: Bryan James, Julie Ann, Sarah Lynn. Student, Purdue U., 1955-57; BSME, U. Ill., 1959; MBA, Ind. U., 1963. Sr. mktg. analyst Allison div. Gen. Motors Corp., Indpls., 1963-67; mgr. Merwins Internat. Harvestor Truck Dealership, St. Croix, V.I., 1967-68; sr. v.p. Hexcel Corp., Dublin, Calif., 1968—; coll. instr. V.I., 1967-68. Served with U.S. Army, 1960. Mem. Aerospace Industries Assn., Am. Def. Preparedness Assn. (bd. dirs. 1975), Soc. Advancement of Material and Process Engring. (presenter). Office: Hexcel Corp 11555 Dublin Blvd Dublin CA 94568-2854

NEFF, JOHN, recording engineer, producer; b. Birmingham, Mich., Mar. 13, 1951; s. Robert Leslie Joseph and Mary Therese (McElvarr) N.; m. Nancy Louise Boocks, Aug. 29, 1987; children: Jennifer Lyn Neff, Bryan C. Groves, Kenneth John Neff. Student, Oakland Community Coll., Auburn Hills, Mich., 1970-72. Freelance recording artist, session musician Detroit, 1965-73; freelance record producer Toronto, Phoenix, L.A., 1974-79; radio announcer, engr. Stas. KVIB, KHEI, KMVI, KLHI, KAOI, 1981-88; record producer Maui Recorders, Kula, Hawaii, 1986-92; cons. studio design Roadrunner Audio Svcs., Glendale, Ariz., 1993—; rec. engr. for Walter Becker (Steely Dan), Buffy Ste Marie, Willie Nelson, Sagan Lewis; touring musician Detroit, Toronto, Phoenix, L.A., 1965-79. Recipient Grammy award nomination for Kamakiriad, 1994. Mem. ASCAP, Audio Engring Soc. (cert.), Am. Fedn. Musicians. Avocations: photography, hiking, travel. Home and Office: Roadrunner Audio Svcs 23846 N 38th Dr Glendale AZ 85310

NEFF, JOHN BROWN, financial portfolio manager; b. Wauseon, Ohio, Sept. 19, 1931; s. John Franklin Neff and Barbara (Brown) Hutton; m. Lillian Elizabeth Tulak, Oct. 4, 1935; children: Lisa, Stephen. BBA summa cum laude, U. Toledo, 1955; MBA, Case Western Reserve U., 1958; MA (hon.), U. Pa., 1984. Chartered fin. analyst. Asst. v.p security analysis Nat. City Bank of Cleve., 1955-63; mng. ptnr., sr. v.p., portfolio mgr. Wellington Mgmt. Co., Valley Forge, Pa., 1963—; bd. dirs. Gen. Accident Ins. Trustee U. Pa., Phila. Served with USN, 1951-53. Mem. Chartered Fin. Analysts Fedn., Fin. Analysts of Phila. Avocations: tennis, golf, travel, history. Home: 1271 Argyle Rd Berwyn PA 19312-2001 Office: Wellington Mgmt Co PO Box 823 Valley Forge PA 19482

NEFF, JOHN SAMUEL, astronomy educator; b. Milw., Nov. 24, 1934; s. Samuel O. and Esther Ann (Johnson) N.; m. Darlyne Katherine DeTuncq, Aug. 20, 1960; children—Paul, James. B.S., U. Wis., 1957, M.S., 1958, Ph.D., 1961. Atmospheric physicist Sacramento Peak Solar Obs., 1961;

research assoc. U. Chgo. 1961-64; asst. prof. astronomy U. Iowa, Iowa City, 1964-68; assoc. prof. U. Iowa, 1968-79, prof. astronomy, 1979—. Steward Obs. fellow, U. Ariz., 1959-60. Fellow Royal Astron. Soc.; mem. Am. Astron. Soc., Astron. Soc. Pacific, Internat. Astron. Union.

NEFF, JOYA LEE, community health nurse, administrator; b. Ohio, Jan. 17, 1936; d. John and Orpha Jane (McGee) Disbennett; m. Robert R. Neff, Aug. 8, 1971. BSN, Ohio State U., 1957; MPH, U. Mich., 1967. Pub. health nurse Columbus (Ohio) City Health Dept.; DON Erie County Health Dept., Sandusky, Ohio; chief div. nursing Ohio Dept. Health, Columbus. Named Woman of Yr. Buckeye chpt. Am. Bus. Women's Assn., 1981. Mem. ANA, APHA, Ohio Nurses Assn., Ohio Pub. Health Assn., Assn. State and Terr. Dirs. Nursing (past pres.), Sigma Theta Tau. Office: Ohio Dept Health PO Box 118 246 High Columbus OH 43266

NEFF, KENNETH D., realtor, mayor; b. Montpelier, Ind., Oct. 19, 1929; s. Clyde A. and Cora I. N.; m. Nancy Stiffler, Dec. 26, 1951; children: David, Susan, Julie, Bradley. BS in Bus., Ball State U. Mayor City of Montpelier, 1953—; owner Neff Realty, Montpelier, 1956—. Mem. air pollution bd. Ind. Dept. Environ. Mgmt., Indpls., 1991—; mem. Purdue Hwy. Extension and Rsch. Project, Ind. Counties and Cities Bd., West Lafayette, 1991—; chmn. adminstrv. coun. Montpelier United Meth. Ch. Lt. col. USAF, 1958-81. Mem. Ind. Dem. Editorial Assn., Ind. Assn. Cities and Towns (exec. bd., legis. com.), North Ctrl. Mayor's Roundtable (pres. 1991-92), Kiwanis (past state lt. gov.). Democrat. Home: 129 S Huntington St Montpelier IN 47359 Office: 109 W Huntington St Montpelier IN 47359

NEFF, P. SHERRILL, health care executive; b. Balt., Dec. 18, 1951; s. Paul Heston and Mary (Poulnot) N.; m. Sarah B. Barrett, June 20, 1976 (div. 1985); 1 child, Jacob Colin; m. Alicia Phyll Felton, May 26, 1988; 1 child, Michael Felton. BA, Wesleyan U., 1974; JD magna cum laude, U. Mich., 1980. Bar: Pa. 1980. Atty. Morgan Lewis & Bockius, Phila., 1980-84; investment banker Alex Brown & Sons, Inc., Balt., 1984-93, mng. dir., 1992-93; sr. v.p. corp. devel. U.S. Healthcare, Blue Bell, Pa., 1993-94; pres., CFO Neose Pharms. Inc., Horsham, Pa., 1994—, also bd. dirs.; bd. dirs State Bancshares, Inc., Phila. Trustee Zero Moving Dance Co., Phila., 1984-93. Democrat. Jewish. Home: 619 Revere Rd Merion Station PA 19066-1007 Office: Neose Pharms Inc PO Box 1109 102 Witmer Rd Horsham PA 19044

NEFF, PETER JOHN, chemicals, mining and metal processing executive; b. New Brunswick, N.J., Oct. 31, 1938; s. Peter and Carrie (Colasurdo) N.; m. Joan Ruth Knapp, June 18, 1960; children: Lisa, Kristopher, Greg. BS in Chemistry, Rutgers U., 1969; MBA, Rider Coll., Lawrenceville, N.J., 1978. Rsch. chemist Exxon Chems., Linden, N.J.; product mgr. Standard Brands Chem. Industries, Edison, N.J., 1970-73; sales mgr. St. Joe Minerals Corp., N.Y.C., 1973-77; dir. planning St. Joe Zinc Co., Pitts., 1977-80; v.p. St. Joe Internat. Corp., N.Y.C., 1980-83, pres., 1983-85; pres., chief exec. officer St. Joe Minerals Corp., St. Louis, 1985-89; pres., chief oper. officer Rhone-Poulenc Inc., Princeton, N.J., from 1987, now pres., chief exec. officer, also bd. dirs.; pres. Interchem., Inc., New Castle, Del. With USN, 1956-59. Mem. Chem. Mfg. Assn. (bd. dirs.), French. Am. C. of C. Avocations: furniture design and construction. Home: 47 Dogwood Ln Skillman NJ 08558-1302 Office: Rhone-Poulenc Inc 125 Black Horse Ln Monmouth Junction NJ 08852

NEFF, RAY, insurance company executive. MS in Actuarial Sci., U. Mich. With Mich. and Fla. ins. depts.; dir. divsn. workers compensation Fla. Dept. Labor and Security; ops. mgr. Fla. Constrn. Commerce Industry, Sarasota, Fla., now administrator. Office: Fla Constr Commerce Ind 2601 Cattlemen Rd Sarasota FL 34232*

NEFF, RAY QUINN, electric power educator, consultant; b. Houston, Apr. 29, 1928; s. Noah Grant and Alma Ray (Smith) N.; m. Elizabeth McDougald, Sept. 4, 1982. Degree in Steam Engring., Houston Vocat. Tech., 1957; BSME, Kennedy Western U., 1986. Various positions Houston Lighting & Power Co., 1945-60, plant supr., 1960-70, plant supt. asst., 1970-80, tech. supr., 1980-85, tng. supr., 1985-87; owner, operator Neff Enterprises, Bedias, Tex., 1987—; tng. supr. Tex. A&M U., 1991—; cons. Houston Industries, 1987-89. Author: Power Plant Operation, 1975, Power Operator Training, 1985, Power Foreman Training, 1986. Judge Internat. Sci. and Engring. Fair, Houston, 1982, Sci. Engring. Fair Houston, 1987. Mem. ASME, Assn. Chief Operating Engrs., Masons. Republican. Methodist. Avocations: farming, ranching, classic cars. Home: Hwy 90 Rte 2t Box 193-A Bedias TX 77831 Office: Tex A&M U Power Plant College Station TX 77843

NEFF, RICHARD B., consumer products company executive; b. 1948. BS, Fairleigh Dickinson U., 1970. CPA. With Arthur Andersen & Co., 1970-73; various exec. positions including exec. v.p., CFO and dir. Transco Group, Inc., 1973-86; mng. ptnr. Greenwood Meadows Devel. Co., 1988—; exec. v.p., CFO, dir. Di Giorgio Corp., 1990—; pres. Las Plumas Lumber, 1991—; officer White Rose Foods, Inc., 1992—. Office: Di Giorgio Corp PO Box 6715 Somerset NJ 08875-6715

NEFF, ROBERT WILBUR, church official, educator; b. Lancaster, Pa., June 16, 1936; s. Wilbur Hildebr and Hazel Margaret (Martin) N.; m. Dorothy Rosewarne, Aug. 16, 1959; children: Charles Scott, Heather Lynn. BS, Pa. State U., 1958; BD, Yale Div. Sch., 1961, MA, 1963, PhD, 1969; DD, Juniata Coll., 1978, Manchester Coll., 1979; DHL, Bridgewater Coll., 1979. Asst. prof. Bridgewater Coll., 1964-65; mem. faculty dept. Bibl. studies Bethany Theol. Sem., 1965-77, prof., 1973-77; gen. sec. Ch. of the Brethren, Elgin, Ill., 1978-86; pres. Juniata Coll., 1986—; mem. faculty North Park Sem., No. Baptist Sem., Theol. Coll. No. Nigeria. bd. dirs. Mellon Bank (Ctrl.) Nat. Assn., exec. com., 1989—, chair exec. com., 1993. Mem. governing bd. Nat. Coun. Chs. of Christ, 1976-86, mem. exec. com. 1979-86; mem. Mid-East panel, 1980, 2d v.p., 1985-86; mem. ctrl. com. World Coun. Chs., 1983-92; rep. Assembly of World Coun. Chs., 1983, mem. exec. com. on interch. rels., 1980-84, mem. del. to China, 1981, chmn. presdl. panel, 1982-84; bd. dirs. Bethany Theol. Sem., 1978-86; campaign chmn. United Way, Huntington County, 1989; chair higher edn. com. Ch. of Brethren, 1993—. Danforth fellow, 1958-69. Mem. Soc. Bibl. Lit., Soc. Old Testament Study, Chgo. Soc. Bibl. Rsch., Soc. Values in Higher Edn., Coun. of Ind. Colls. (nat. bd. dirs. 1991-94, treas. 1995—), Pa. Coun. Ind. Colls. and Univs. (mem. exec. com. 1988-90, 92—, chairperson ann. conf. nominating com. 1993-94). Democrat. Home: 2201 Washington St Huntingdon PA 16652-9762 Office: Juniata Coll 1700 Moore St Huntingdon PA 16652-2196

NEFF, THOMAS JOSEPH, executive search firm executive; b. Easton, Pa., Oct. 2, 1937; s. John Wallace and Elizabeth Ann (Dougherty) N.; m. Susan Culver Paul, Nov. 26, 1971 (dec.); children: David Andrew, Mark Gregory, Scott Dougherty; m. Sarah Brown Hallingby, Jan. 20, 1989; stepchildren: Brooke, Bailey. BS in Indsl. Engring., Lafayette Coll., 1959; MBA, Lehigh U., 1961. Assoc. McKinsey & Co., Inc., N.Y.C. and Australia, 1963-66; dir. mktg. planning Trans-World Airlines, N.Y.C., 1966-69; pres. Hosp. Data Scis., Inc., N.Y.C., 1969-74; prin. Booz, Allen & Hamilton, Inc., N.Y.C., 1974-76; regional ptnr. Spencer Stuart, Inc., N.Y.C., N.Am., 1976-79; bd. dirs. Spencer Stuart & Assocs., N.Y.C., 1976-79, pres., 1979—, also bd. dirs.; bd. dirs. Lord Abbett & Co. Mut. Funds, Affiliated Fund, Brunswick Sch. Trustee Lafayette Coll. Served with U.S. Army, 1961-63. Mem. Links Club, Sky Club, Racquet and Tennis Club, Blind Brook Club, Quogue (N.Y.) Beach Club, Quogue Field Club, Round Hill Club, Mill Reef Club, Coral Beach Club. Republican. Roman Catholic. Home: 25 Midwood Rd Greenwich CT 06830-3807 Office: Spencer Stuart & Assocs Park Ave Plz 277 Park Ave New York NY 10172

NEFF, WALTER PERRY, financial consultant; b. Madison, Wis., Apr. 2, 1927; s. Ezra Eugene and Ruth (Perry) N.; m. Diane Michele Dubois, Mar. 12, 1963; children: Christopher (dec.), Taylor E., Stewart P. (by previous marriage), Michael W.P., Laura D. B.A., Williams Coll., 1950; LL.B., U. Wis., 1954; grad. advanced mgmt. program, Harvard U., 1969. Bar: Wis. 1954. Practiced in Madison, 1954-57; with Chem. Bank N.Y. Trust Co. (now Chem. Bank), N.Y.C., 1957-71; v.p. personal trust dept. Chem. Bank N.Y. Trust Co. (now Chem. Bank), 1965-68, sr. v.p., head fiduciary adminstrn. dept., 1968-71; exec. v.p. Chem. Bank, N.Y.C., 1971-73; sr. operating officer, adminstrv. head trust and investment Chem. Bank, 1973-

82; fin. cons., 1983—; bd. dirs. Petroleum & Resources Corp., Balt., Adams Express Corp., Balt., N.Am. Life Assurance Co., Toronto; mem. adv. bd. Mchts. Bank, Burlington, Vt.; chmn. Hanover Funds, Hanover Investment Funds; police justice Village of Centre Island, Oyster Bay, N.Y., 1965-74. Served with USNR, 1945-46. Mem. N.Y. State Bankers Assn. (exec. com. trust div.), Seawanhaka Corinthian Yacht Club (former commodore) (Oyster Bay), Royal Bermuda Yacht Club, Ekwanok Country Club (Manchester, Vt.), Phi Alpha Delta, Psi Upsilon. Home: Holden Hill Rd Weston VT 05161 Office: 370 Park Ave New York NY 10017

NEFT, DAVID SAMUEL, marketing professional; b. N.Y.C., Jan. 9, 1937; s. Louis and Sue (Horowitz) N.; m. Naomi Silver, May 31, 1964; children: Michael Louis, Deborah Isabel. BA, Columbia U., 1957, MBA, 1959, PhD, 1962. Dir. info. pub. Info. Concepts, Inc., N.Y.C., 1965-68, treas., chief exec. officer, 1968-70; gen. mgr. Sports Illustrated Enterprises, N.Y.C., 1970-73; pres. Sports Products Inc., Ridgefield, Conn., 1973-76; chief statistician Louis Harris and Assocs., N.Y.C., 1963-65, sr. v.p., 1977-78, exec. v.p., chief exec. officer, 1978-85; dir. research Gannett Co., Inc., N.Y.C., 1985-90, v.p rsch., 1990—; cons. Fed. Energy Adminstrn., Washington, 1973-75. Author: Statistical Analysis for Areal Distributions, 1966; editor: The Baseball Encyclopedia, 1969; author (with others) The World Book of Odds, 1978, The Sports Encyclopedia: Baseball, 1974, 76-77, 81-82, 85, 87-89, 90—, The Sports Encyclopedia: Pro Football, 1974, 76, 78, 83, 87, 88-89, 90—, Pro Football: The Early Years, 1978, 83, 87, The World Series, 1976, 79, 86, The Sports Encyclopedia: Pro Basketball, 1975, 89, 90-91, All-Sports World Record Book, 1974, 75, 76, The Scrapbook History of Pro Football, 1976, 77, 79, The Scrapbook History of Baseball, 1975, The Notre Dame Football Scrapbook, 1977, The Ohio State Football Scrapbook, 1977, The University of Michigan Football Scrapbook, 1978, The Football Encyclopedia, 1991, 94; contbr. articles to profl. and acad. jours. Served with U.S. Army, 1961-63. Mem. Am. Assn. Pub. Opinion Rsch., Profl. Football Rsch. Assn. (v.p. 1985-87), Soc. for Am. Baseball Rsch. Jewish. Home: 525 E 86th St New York NY 10028-7512

NEGELE, JOHN WILLIAM, physics educator, consultant; b. Cleve., Apr. 18, 1944; s. Charles Frederick and Virgil Lea (Wettich) N.; m. Rose Anne Meeks, June 18, 1967; Janette Andrea, Julia Elizabeth. B.S., Purdue U., 1965; Ph.D., Cornell U., 1969. Research fellow Niels Bohr Inst., Copenhagen, 1969-70; vis. asst. prof. MIT, Cambridge, 1970-71, faculty mem., 1971—, prof. physics, 1979—, William A. Coolidge prof., 1991—, assoc. dir. Ctr. for Theoretical Physics, 1988-89, dir. Ctr. for Theoretical Physics, 1989—; cons. Los Alamos Sci. Lab., Brookhaven Nat. Lab., Lawrence Livermore Nat. Lab., Oak Ridge Nat. Lab.; mem. physics div. rev. com. Argonne Nat. Lab., (Ill.), 1977-83; mem. nuclear sci. div. rev. com. Lawrence Berkeley Lab., (Calif.), 1982—; mem. adv. bd., steering com. Inst. for Theoretical Physics, U. Calif.-Santa Barbara, 1982-86; mem. adv. bd. inst. for Nuclear Theory U. Washington, 1990—, chair 1992-94; program adv. com. Tandem Van de Graaff Accelerator, Brookhaven Nat. Lab., 1977-78, Bates Linear Accelerator, 1977-80, Los Alamos Meson Prodn. Facility, 1986-89, Brookhaven Alternating Gradient Synchraton, 1987-90. Author: Quantum Many Particle Systems, 1987; contbr. articles to profl. jours.; editor: Advances in Nuclear Physics, 1977—. Grantee NSF, 1965-69; grantee Danforth Found., 1965-69, Woodrow Wilson Found., 1965, Alfred P. Sloan Found., 1979, Japan Soc. for Promotion Sci., 1981, John Simon Guggenheim Found., 1982. Fellow Am. Phys. Soc. (exec. com. 1982-84, program com. 1980-82, editorial bd. Phys. Rev. 1984-92, exec. com. topical group on computational physics 1992-93, chair divsn. of computational physics 1992-93, exec. com. 1992-94, Bonner prize com. 1984-85), AAAS (nominating com. 1987-91, mem. physics sect. com. 1991—), Fedn. Am. Scientists. Home: 70 Buckman Dr Lexington MA 02173-6000 Office: MIT Dept Physics 6-308 77 Massachusetts Ave Cambridge MA 02139-3594

NEGREPONTIS, MICHAEL (TIMOTHY), bishop; b. Athens, Greece, June 7, 1930; s. Anastasios and Maria Negrepontis. Sacred Theology, U. Thessalonika, Greece; M.Div., Holy Cross Greek Orthodox Theol. Sch., Boston; B.A. with honors, Hellenic Coll. Ordained deacon Greek Orthodox Ch., 1950, ordained priest, 1952. Pastor St. Nicholas Ch., Bethlehem, Pa., 1955-61, Parish of Sts. Constantine and Helen, Middletown, Ohio, 1961-62; pastor Holy Trinity Ch., London, Ont., Can., 1962-67, Harrisburg, Pa.; pastor Dionysios Ch., Kansas City, Kans., St. Barbara; dean Holy Trinity Archdiocesan Cathedral, N.Y.C., until 1969; spl. asst. to chancellor and personnel dir. archdiocesan staff Archdiocesan Hdqrs., N.Y.C., from 1969; pastor St. Anargyroi Ch., Marlboro, Mass., until 1973, Ch. Holy Ascension, Fairview, N.J.; elevated to Titular Bishop of Pamphilos, 1973, consecrated bishop, 1974; bishop Greek Orthodox Diocese in S.Am., 1974-79; aux. bishop to the Archbishop 7th Archdiocesan Dist. Detroit, 1979; bishop Greek Orthodox Diocese of Detroit, 1979—; apptd. pastor Greek Orthodox Communities of Republic of Panama. Decorated Grand Master of Order of Vasco Nuñez de Balboa, Republic of Panama; Grand Taxiarch, Order Orthodox Crusaders of Holy Sepulcher. Address: 19405 Renfrew Rd Detroit MI 48221

NEGRON, JAIME, college administrator; b. San Juan, P.R., Dec. 23, 1939; came to U.S., 1952; s. Rito and Tomasa (Otero) N.; m. Barbara Charlotte Stovall, Nov. 5, 1959; children: Jeannette Michelle, Victoria Frances. BA in Econs., Howard U., 1987. Lic. realtor. Chief receiving & shipping Am. Univ., Washington, 1960-62; book dept. mgr. Am. U., Washington, 1968-71; bookstore mgr. Follett Corp., Chgo., 1962-68, Cath. U., Washington, 1971-74; dir. Howard U. stores Howard Univ., Washington, 1974-87; dir. aux. enterprises Howard U., Washington, 1987-91; real estate agt. Shannon & Luchs, Vienna, Va., 1988-92; asst. dir. aux. enterprises DeKalb Coll., Atlanta, 1992—; cons. U. Del., Newark, 1988, Wesley Sem., Washington, 1984, R.R. Moton Meml. Inst., N.Y.C., 1974-79. Active Vienna Jaycees, 1970-80. With USN, 1958-60. Mem. Middle Atlantic Coll. Stores (pres. 1984), Nat. Assn. Coll. Stores, Nat. Bd. Realtors, Va. Bd. Realtors. Episcopalian. Avocation: dancing. Office: DeKalb Coll 555 N Indian Creek Dr Bldg S Clarkston GA 30021-2361

NEGRONI, PETER JOSEPH, school system administrator; b. Guantanamo, Cuba, Apr. 17, 1942; s. Silvestre Antonio Negroni and Maria Casas de Prieto; divorced; children: Daniel, Paul, Deborah, Amy. BA, Iona Coll., 1963; MS, CUNY, 1967; Cert. Advanced Grad. Studies, CCNY, 1971; EdD, Fairleigh Dickinson U., 1978. Tchr. N.Y. Pub. Schs., N.Y.C., 1963-68; asst. prin. Bilingual Community Sch. 211, Bronx, N.Y., 1969-71; prin. Community Sch. 234, Bronx, 1971-78; supt. Community Sch. Dist. 12, Bronx, 1978-88; exec. dir. Coun. for Ednl. Excellence Catawba County, N.C., 1988-89; supt. Springfield (Mass.) Pub. Schs., 1989—; tchr. Hunter Coll., CUNY, CCNY, Columbia U., N.Y.C., 1966—; examination asst. bd. examiners N.Y.C. Bd. Edn., 1973-88; mem. adv. bd. Harvard Doctoral Urban Supts. Program, Cambridge, Mass., 1991-94; cons. N.Y. State Edn. Dept., Conn. State Edn. Dept. Boston Pub. Schs. Bd. trustees Community Svc. N.Y.C.; bd. dirs. Uniyted Way, Springfield. Recipient Headliner of Yr. award Valley Press Club. 1991, Outstanding Educator award P.R. Cultural Ctr., 1993; named Supt. of Yr., Sch. Psychologists Assn., 1991, One of Top 100 Educators, Exec. Educator, 1993. Mem. ASCD, AM. Assn. Sch. Adminstrs., Nat. Assn. Sch. Bds., Nat. Assn. Bilingual Edn., Mass. Assn. Sch. Supts., Assn. for Sch. Supts. Home: 98 Elliot St Springfield MA 01105-1728 Office: Springfield Pub Schs 195 State St Springfield MA 01103-1410

NEGROPONTE, JOHN DIMITRI, diplomat; b. London, July 21, 1939; s. Dimitri John and Catherine (Coumantaros) N.; m. Diana Mary Villiers, Dec. 14, 1976. B.A., Yale U., 1960. Commd. fgn. service officer Dept. of State, 1960; vice consul Dept. of State, Hong Kong, 1961-63; 2d sec. Dept. of State, Saigon, 1964-68; mem. U.S. Del. to Paris Peace Talks on Viet Nam, 1968-69, Nat. Security Council Staff, 1970-73; polit. counselor Quito, Ecuador, 1973-75; consul gen. Thessaloniki, Greece, 1975-77; dep. asst. sec. of state for oceans and fisheries affairs Washington, 1977-79; dep. asst. sec. for East Asian and Pacific affairs Dept. State, Washington, 1980-81; U.S. amb. to Honduras, 1981-85, asst. sec. for oceans and internat. environ. and sci. affairs, 1985-87; dep. asst. Pres. for Nat. Security Affairs, 1987-89; U.S. amb. to Mexico, 1989-93, U.S. amb. to The Philippines, 1993—. Mem. Am. Fgn. Service Assn., Council on Fgn. Relations. Greek Orthodox.

NEHAMAS, ALEXANDER, philosophy educator; b. Athens, Greece, Mar. 22, 1946; came to U.S., 1964; s. Albert and Christine (Yannuli) N.; m. Susan Glimcher, June 22, 1983; 1 child, Nicholas Albert Glimcher. BA,

Swarthmore Coll., 1967; PhD, Princeton U., 1971, D in Philosophy (hon.) Athens, 1993. Asst., then assoc. prof. philosophy U. Pitts., 1971-81, prof., 1981-86; prof. philosophy U. Pa., 1986-90; vis. prof. Princeton U., N.J., 1978-79, 87, Edmund Carpenter prof. humanities, prof. philosophy and comparative lit., 1990—; chair humanities coun., 1990—; program in Hellenic studies, 1994—; Mills vis. prof. U. Calif., Berkeley, 1983, Sather vis. prof., 1993; vis. prof. U. Calif., Santa Cruz, 1988; bd. dir. Princeton Univ. Press; bd. trustees Nat. Humanities Ctr. Author: Nietzsche: Life as Literature, 1985; translator: Plato's Symposium, 1989, Plato's Phaedrus, 1995; co-editor: Aristotle's Rhetoric: Philosophical Essays, 1994; contbr. articles to profl. jours.; mem. editorial bd. Am. Philos. Quar., 1981-86, History of Philosophy Quar., 1983-88, Ancient Philosophy, 1984—, Jour. Modern Greek Studies, 1986—, Arion, 1989—, Philosophy and Lit., 1989—, Philosophy and Phenomenological Rsch., 1990—. Recipient Lindback Found. Teaching award, U. Pa., 1989; Guggenheim fellow 1983; NEH grantee, 1978. Mem. MLA, Am. Philos. Assn. (chmn. program 1982-83, exec. com. 1990-92), Modern Greek Studies Assn., Am. Soc. Aesthetics, North Am. Nietzsche Soc. (exec. com. 1988-91), Phi Beta Kappa (vis. scholar 1991). Office: Princeton U Dept Philosophy Princeton NJ 08544

NEHER, TIMOTHY PYPER, cable company executive; b. Jersey City, Sept. 9, 1947; s. Harry Paul and Alice (Pyper) N.; m. Mary Ann King, June 13, 1970; children: Amy, Victoria. BA in Math., Cornell U., 1969; MBA in Fin., Boston U., 1971. Loan officer Bank New Eng., Boston, 1971-74; regional mgr. Continental Cablevision, Boston, 1974-77, v.p., gen. mgr., 1977-80, v.p., treas., 1980-82, exec. v.p., 1982-85, pres., chief operating officer, 1985-90, vice chmn., 1991—; also bd. dirs.; bd. dirs. Turner Broadcasting Inc., Atlanta, Viewers' Choice Network Inc., N.Y.C. Mem. Weston Golf Club (Mass.), Boston Racquet Club, Old Marsh Golf Club, Lost Tree Golf Club (North Palm Beach, Fla.), Oyster Harbors Club (Osterville, Mass.). Republican. Office: Continental Cablevision Inc 5 Niblick Rd Enfield CT 06082-4443

NEHLS, ROBERT LOUIS, JR., school system administrator; b. Berkeley, Calif., Dec. 27, 1944; s. Robert Louis and Inda May (Kean) N.; m. Diana Jean Smith, June 17, 1967; 1 child, Patrick Robert. AA, Coll. Marin, 1965; BS, San Jose State U., 1967, MA, 1976; EdD, U. San Francisco, 1991. Cert. tchr., sch. adminstr., Calif. Tchr. Diablo Valley Coll., Pleasant Hill, Calif., 1979-86; acct. Kelly and Tama, CPAs, Walnut Creek, Calif., 1978-79; tchr. Pleasanton (Calif.) Unified Sch. Dist., 1970-78, 79-81, dir. fiscal svcs., 1981-83; dep. supt. San Leandro (Calif.) Unified Sch. Dist., 1983-87, 90—; asst. supt. Acalanes Union High Sch. Dist., Lafayette, Calif., 1987-89; supt. Orinda (Calif.) Union Sch. Dist., 1989-90; exec. adv. com. Calif. Found. Improvement of Employee/Employer Relationships, Sacramento, 1992—. Contbr. articles to profl. jours. Mem. Assn. Calif. Sch. Adminstrs. (comptr. 1992-95, pres.-elect, pres. 1995-96), Calif. Assn. Sch. Bus. Ofcls. (bd. dirs. no. sect. 1984-89), No. Calif. Sch. Bus. Execs. (past pres.), Acad. Sci., Phi Kappa Phi. Avocations: fishing, skiing. Home: 1004 Leland Dr Lafayette CA 94549-4130 Office: San Leandro Unified Sch Dist 14735 Juniper St San Leandro CA 94579-1222

NEHMER, STANLEY, economics consultant; b. N.Y.C., Dec. 8, 1920; s. Alexander and Laura (Kessler) N.; m. Phyllis Fleischman, Nov. 30, 1946; children: Sheryl Rae, Jonathan Craig. BSS, CCNY, 1941; MA, Columbia U., 1942; postgrad. George Washington U., 1943-44, Am. U., 1946-47. Faculty CCNY, 1941-42; with OSS, 1942-45; economist Dept. State, 1945-57; dep. dir. Office Internat. Resources, Washington, 1961-64, dir., 1964-65; dep. asst. sec. for resources Dept. Commerce, 1965-73; sr. economist IBRD, 1957-61; prin. and dir. econ. cons. services Wolf & Co., Washington, 1973-78; pres. Econ. Cons. Services Inc., Washington, 1978-88, chmn., 1988—; adj. prof. Am. bus. history Am. U., 1948-63; U.S. rep. commodities com. UN Conf. on Trade and Devel., Geneva, 1965; chmn. Interagy. Textile Adminstrv. Com., 1965-72; chmn. U.S. rep. OECD Textiles Com., 1971-73; mem. U.S. Oil Import Appeals Bd., 1973-83; chmn. Com. for Implementation of Textile Agreements, 1972-73; alt. mem. Oil Policy Com., 1970-73; mem. U.S. Govt. Industry Sector Adv. Com. for Trade Negotiations, 1976-88, Treasury Dept. Adv. Com. on Customl. Ops. of Customs Svc., 1988-92. Contbr. to: Ency. Americana, Ency. Brit., U.S. Competiveness in the World Economy, 1985. Served with AUS, 1943-45. Recipient Commendable Service award Dept. State, 1956, Superior Honor award, 1964; certificate appreciation Sec. Commerce, 1967; Gold medal Dept. Commerce, 1971; N.Y. Bd. Trade Ann. Textile award, 1972; No. Textile Assn. Distinguished Service award, 1973. Fellow Am. Council Learned Socs., mem. Nat. Economists Club, Am. Econ. Assn. Home: 15100 Interlachen Dr Silver Spring MD 20906-5611 also: 2600 S Ocean Blvd Boca Raton FL 33432 Office: 1225 19th St NW Washington DC 20036-2410

NEHRBASS, SETH MARTIN, lawyer; b. Lafayette, La., Nov. 10, 1960; s. Neil Martin and Janet (Himbert) N.; m. Isabel Hortelano, July 10, 1982 (div. Feb. 1993); children: Gabriel, Fabian. Student, U. Catholique de l'Ouest, Angers, France, 1980, U. Paul Valéry, Montpellier, France, 1981; BS in Physics summa cum laude, U. Southwe. La., 1982; JD cum laude, Loyola U., 1990. Bar: U.S. Patent & Trademark Office 1984, La. 1990, U.S. Dist. Ct. (ea., mid., and we. dists.) La. 1990, U.S. Ct. Appeals (5th and fed. cirs.) 1990; cert. notary public, La. Patent examiner U.S. Patent & Trademark Office, 1982-84; patent agt. with law firm New Orleans, 1986-87; assoc. Pravel, Hewitt, Kimball & Krieger, New Orleans, 1987—; judge practice round moot ct. teams Loyola Law Sch., 1992—; preparer questions patent bar exam PTO Q & A Bd., 1992-93; presenter numerous seminars. Contbr. articles to profl. jours. Den leader 2d grade Cub Scouts, Boy Scouts Am., Lusher Sch. Audubon Dist., 1991-92, asst. den leader 3d grade Cub Scouts, 1992-93, 4th grade, 1993-94, den leader 3d grade, 1994-95; soccer coach Carrollton Booster Club, New Orleans, 1993; coach Lakeview Soccer Club, New Orleans, 1995—. Recipient Hornbook award West Pub. Co., 1986-87, 87-88, Corpus Juris Secundum award, 1986-87, Am. Jurisprudence awards (2), 1986; scholar La. State U. Alumni Fedn., 1978, Coun. Devel. French La./French Govt., 1980-81, Loyola Law Sch., 1986. Mem. ABA (sect. law, sci., tech. 1988-91, law student divsn. liaison patent trademark and copyright law 1988-90, intellectual property law sect. 1988—, student law com. 1989—, chmn. spl. com. drug crisis 1990-93, co-chmn. ann. meeting arrangements com. 1993-94, internat. treaties and laws com. 1994—), Am. Intellecual Property Assn. (mem. ADR com. 1994—, internat. and fgn. law com. 1994—, patent law com. 1994—), State Bar Assn. (internat. law sect. 1992-94), New Orleans Bar Assn. (interim chmn. ad hoc com. drug crisis 1991-92, chmn. charter mem. intellectual property law com. 1991—), Loyola Law Sch. Moot Ct. Alumni Assn., Sigma Pi Sigma, Pi Delta Phi, Alpha Sigma Nu. Democrat. Roman Catholic. Avocations: gardening, dancing, traveling, hunting, fishing. Office: Pravel Hewitt Kimball & Krieger 1515 Poydras St Ste 2300 New Orleans LA 70112-3723

NEHRT, LEE CHARLES, management educator; b. Baldwin, Ill., Sept. 12, 1926; s. Martin William and Amanda Fredarika (Tillock) N.; m. Ardith Ann Saltzman, Mar. 26, 1952; children: Chadwick Charles, Philip Lee, Dana Ann. BS, USCG Acad., 1949; certificat d'Etudes Politiques, U. Paris, 1955; MBA, Columbia U., 1956, PhD, 1962. Fgn. ops. supr. Atomics Internat., Canoga Park, Calif., 1956-60; prof. internat. bus. Ind. U., 1962-65, 67-69, 71-74; Ford Found. adv. to minister planning, economy and industry Tunisia, 1965-67; chief adv. group U. Dacca, E. Pakistan, 1969-71; R.P. Clinton prof. internat. mgmt. Wichita (Kans.) State U., 1974-78; pres. World Trade Inst., N.Y.C., 1978-81; Owens-Ill. prof. internat. mgmt. Ohio State U., Columbus, 1981-86; cons. UN, World Bank, advisor Ministry Planning Govt. Indonesia, 1987-89; dir., curator The Blacksmith Mus., 1991-92. Author monographs, books, papers, reports in field. Served to lt. (j.g.) USCG, 1949-53. Mem. Acad. Internat. Bus. (pres. 1972-74, dean fellows 1978-81), Soc. Internat. Devel. (gov. 1968-71).

NEIDELL, MARTIN H., lawyer; b. Bklyn., Apr. 5, 1946; s. Sidney B. and Sophie (Goldstein) N.; m. Suzan C. Rucker, June 23, 1968; children: Michael, Sari. BA magna cum laude, Lehigh U., 1968; JD cum laude, NYU, 1971. Bar: N.Y. 1972, U.S. Dist. Ct. (ea. and so. dists.) N.Y. 1973, U.S. Ct. Appeals (2d cir.) 1973. Law clk. to presiding justice Sub. Dist. Ct. (ea. dist.) N.Y., Bklyn., 1971-73; assoc. Stroock & Stroock & Lavan, N.Y.C., 1973-79, ptnr., 1980—; legal advisor Am. Arbitration Assn., N.Y.C., 1983—. Editor NYU Law Rev., 1971. Trustee North Shore Synagogue, Syosset, N.Y., 1984-90. Mem. ABA. Office: Stroock & Stroock & Lavan 7 Hanover Sq New York NY 10004-2616

NEIDERT, KALO EDWARD, accountant, educator; b. Safe, Mo., Sept. 1, 1918; s. Edward Robert and Margaret Emma (Kinsey) N.; m. Stella Mae Vest, June 22, 1952; children—Edward, Karl, David, Wayne, Margaret. B.S. in Bus. Adminstrn. with honors, Washington U., St. Louis, 1949, M.S. in Bus. Adminstrn, 1950; postgrad., U. Minn., 1950-54. CPA, Nev. Mem. faculty U. Minn., 1950-54; mem. faculty U. Miss., 1954-57, U. Tex., Austin, 1957-61, Gustavus Adolphus Coll., St. Peter, Minn., 1961-62, U. Nev., Reno, 1962—; prof. acctg. and info. systems U. Nev., 1962-90, prof. emeritus, 1990—; auditor Washoe County Employee Fed. Credit Union, 1969-82, dir., treas., 1982-86. Author: Statement on Auditing Procedure in Decision Tree Form, 1974. Asst. scoutmaster local Boy Scouts Am.; Bd. dirs. Tahoe Timber Trails, 1980-82, treas., 1981-82, v.p. fin., 1982-84; Bd. dirs. St. Johns Child Care Center, 1982-84; cen. com. mem. Washoe County Rep. Party, Reno, 1986-88, 90—. Mem. AICPA, Assn. System Mgmt. (treas. Reno chpt. 1984—), Am. Acctg. Assn., Am. Econ. Assn., Am. Fin. Assn., Fin. Mgmt. Assn., Nev. Soc. CPAs, Western Fin. Assn., Oddfellows, Beta Alpha Psi, Beta Gamma Sigma. Presbyterian. Office: U Nev Coll Bus Adminstrn Reno NV 89557 *I am the descendent of a second generation American. In addition I was raised on a farm in rural America. Early in life, I learned that achievements come only with hard work and taking advantage of each opportunity that comes along, not waiting to see if there was a better opportunity around the corner. All through life this has been my philosophy; take advantage of each opportunity and work hard to make it succeed.*

NEIDHARDT, FREDERICK CARL, microbiologist; b. Phila., May 12, 1931; s. Adam Fred and Carrie (Fry) N.; m. Elizabeth Robinson, June 9, 1956 (div. Sept. 1977); children: Richard Frederick, Jane Elizabeth; m. Germaine Chipault, Dec. 3, 1977; 1 son, Marc Frederick. BA, Kenyon Coll., 1952, DSc (hon.), 1976; PhD, Harvard U., 1956; DSc (hon.), Purdue U., 1988, Umea U., 1994. Research fellow Pasteur Inst., Paris, 1956-57; H.C. Ernst research fellow Harvard Med. Sch., 1957-58, instr., then assoc., 1958-61; mem. faculty Purdue U., 1961-70, assoc. prof, then prof., assoc. head dept. biol. scis., 1965-70; mem. faculty U. Mich., Ann Arbor, 1970—, chmn. dept. microbiology and immunology, 1970-82, F.G. Novy disting. univ prof., assoc. dean faculty affairs, 1990-93, assoc. v.p. for rsch., 1993—; Found. for Microbiology lectr. Am. Soc. Microbiology, 1966-67; cons. Dept. Agr., 1964-65; mem. grant study panel NIH, 1965-69; mem. commn. scholars Ill. Bd. Higher Edn., 1978; mem. test com. for microbiology Nat. Bd. Med. Examiners, 1975-79, chmn., 1979-83; mem. sci. adv. com. Neogen Corp., 1982-92; Wellcome vis. prof. in microbiology U. Ky., 1986. Author books and papers in field; mem. editorial bd. profl. jours. Recipient award bacteriology and immunology Eli Lilly and Co., 1966; Alexander von Humboldt Found. award for U.S. sr. scientist, 1979; NSF sr. fellow U. Copenhagen, 1968-69. Mem. Am. Soc. Microbiology (pres. 1981-82), Am. Soc. Biochemistry and Molecular Biology, Am. Inst. Biol. Scis., Genetics Soc. Am., Soc. Gen. Physiology, Phi Beta Kappa, Sigma Xi. Office: U Mich Med Sch Dept Microbiology and Immunology Ann Arbor MI 48109-0620

NEIDHART, JAMES ALLEN, physician, educator; b. Steubenville, Ohio, Aug. 30, 1940; s. James Leonard and Mary Jane (Daniels) N.; m. Patricia Irene Harpkamp, Aug. 16, 1964 (div. Apr. 1985); children—James, Jeffrey, Jennifer; m. Mary Gagen, Feb. 1986; children: Andrew, Rae Ann. B.S., Union Coll., Alliance, Ohio, 1962; M.D. Ohio State U., 1966. Diplomate Am. Bd. Internal Medicine, Am. Bd. Hematology and Oncology. Intern Bronson Hosp., Kalamazoo, Mich., 1966-67; resident Ohio State U., Columbus, Ohio, 1969-71; postdoctoral fellow Coll. Medicine, Ohio State U., Columbus, 1972-74, asst. prof. medicine, 1974-78, assoc. prof., 1978-84, dir. interdisciplinary oncology unit Comprehensive Cancer Ctr., 1975-80, dep. dir. Comprehensive Cancer Ctr., 1980-84; prof. medicine U. Tex.-Houston-M.D. Anderson Hosp. and Tumor Inst., 1984-86, Hubert L. and Olive Stringer prof. oncology, 1984-86, dep. head div. medicine, 1984-86, chmn. dept. med. oncology, 1984-86; dir. Cancer Rsch. and Treatment Ctr., U. N.Mex., Albuquerque, 1986—, chief hematology and oncology, 1986-91. Contbr. chpts. to Recent Advances in Clinical Therapeutics, Clinical Immunotherapy. Former mem. bd. dirs. Am. Cancer Soc., Columbus; former v.p. Ohio Cancer Research Assocs. Served to lt. USN, 1967-69, Vietnam. Mem. Am. Soc. Hematology, Am. Soc. Clin. Oncology, Am. Assn. Cancer Research, ACP, S.W. Oncology Group, Wilderness Soc., Sierra Club. Home: 83 Kootz Rd Corrales NM 87048-9000 Office: U N Mex Cancer Rsch & Treatment Ctr 900 Camino de Salud NE Albuquerque NM 87131

NEIDICH, GEORGE ARTHUR, lawyer; b. N.Y.C., Feb. 22, 1950; s. Hyman and Rosalyn (Eisenberg) N.; m. Alene Wendrow, Jan. 10, 1982. BA, SUNY, Binghamton, 1971; JD magna cum laude, SUNY, 1974; MLT, Georgetown U., 1981. Bar: N.Y. 1975, D.C. 1979, U.S. Ct. Appeals (2d cir.) 1975, U.S. Dist. Ct. (we. dist.) N.Y. 1975, U.S. Tax Ct. 1976, Conn. 1990. Assoc. Runfola & Birzon, Buffalo, 1973-75, Duke, Holzman, Yaeger, & Radlin, Buffalo, 1975-77; gen. counsel subcom. on capital, investments and bus. opportunity. com. on small bus. U.S. Ho. of Reps., Washington, 1977-79, subcom. on gen. oversight, 1979-80; sr. legal advisor Task Force Product Liability and Accident Compensation, Office of Gen. Counsel, Dept. Commerce, Washington, 1980-81; assoc. Steptoe & Johnson, Washington, 1981-86, of counsel, 1986-89; gen. counsel, sr. v.p. Preferred Health Care, Ltd., Wilton, Conn. (now Value Behavioral Health, Inc.), 1989-93, COO, 1993-95, cons., 1995—; adj. prof. Georgetown U. Law Ctr., 1985-87. Author: Report on Product Liability, 1980. Contbr. articles to profl. jours. Mem. N.Y. State Bar Assn. Home: 9301 Morison Ln Great Falls VA 22066 Office: PO Box 536 Great Falls VA 22066

NEIGHMOND, PATRICIA, reporter; b. Boston, Sept. 25, 1949; d. Howard Francis and Joyce (Ghiglia) N. BA, U. Md., 1971. Researcher Community Nutrition Inst., Washington, 1974-77; news reporter Sta. WPFW- FM, Washington, 1977-78; bur. chief Pacific Found., Washington, 1978-80; reporter Nat. Pub. Radio, Washington, 1981-84, editor/producer, 1984-87, reporter, 1987—; lectr. Am. Soc. of Journalists and Authors; U.S. Indo Subcommn., Bangalore, India, U.S. Inf. Agy, Recife, Sao Paulo, Brazil, 1989. Recipient George Polk award L.I. U., 1989, Best Consumer Journalism award Nat. Press Club, Washington, 1988, Radio Documentary award Pol. Inst., Washington, 1984, 87, Best Radio Documentary award Corp. for Pub. Broadcasting, 1982. Democrat. Avocation: creative writing. Office: Nat Pub Radio 635 Massachusetts Ave NW Washington DC 20001-3752

NEIKIRK, WILLIAM ROBERT, journalist; b. Irvine, Ky., Jan. 6, 1938; s. Lewis Byron and Nancy Elizabeth (Green) N.; m. Ruth Ann Clary, Sept. 10, 1960; children: Paul Gregory, John Stuart, Christa Lynn. B.A. in Journalism, U. Ky., 1960. Reporter Lexington (Ky.) Herald, 1959-60; state capital corr. AP, Frankfort, Ky., 1961-66, Baton Rouge, 1966-69; econ. corr. AP (Washington Bur.), 1970-74; nat. econ. writer Chgo. Tribune, Washington, 1974-83, White House corr., 1977, 94—, econ. columnist, 1980—; news editor Washington bur., 1983, fin. editor, 1988-91, sr. writer, 1991—. Author: The Work Revolution, 1983, Volcker: The Money Man, 1987. Recipient Beck award Chgo. Tribune, 1975, Bus. Writing award U. Mo., 1978, 80, Bus. Writing award Amos Tuck Grad. Sch. Bus., Dartmouth Coll., 1980, John Hancock Bus. Writing award Wharton Sch. Fin., U. Pa., 1979, finalist, 1990, 91, John Hancock Bus. Writing award U. Houston, 1980, Loeb Bus. Writing award UCLA Grad. Sch. Mgmt., 1979, Chgo. Headliner Club award, 1979, 84, Raymond Clapper Meml. award, 1981, Barnet Nover award, 1994, Merriman Smith award, 1995. Mem. Gridiron Club. Mem. United Ch. of Christ. Home: 5121 38th St N Arlington VA 22207-1827

NEIL, FRED APPLESTEIN, public relations executive; b. Balt., Nov. 26, 1933; s. Frank and Mollie (Schapiro) Applestein; m. Sheila Tilles, Aug. 30, 1959 (div. May 1980); children: Jay Alan, Brian Mark Applestein, Gail Renee Applestein; m. Dawn Francis Fisher, July 6, 1986. BA, U. Md., 1959. News and sports editor Sta. WITH, Balt., 1959-60; dir. news and sports Sta. WCBM, Metromedia, Balt., 1960-69; press officer Mayor William Donald Schaefer, Balt., 1970-71; gen. mgr. Balt. Banners World Team Tennis League, 1971-72; pres. Fred Neil Assocs., Pub. Rels., Balt., 1972—; staff specialist pub. info. Md. Rehab. Ctr., Balt., 1980-91; owner Cruising for Mems., Ellicott City, 1987—, Dir. Office of Comm. and Community Rels., Divsn. Rehab. Svcs., Balt., 1980—; co-owner Carrolltowne Card & Gift Shop. Author: It's A Very Simple Game! Charley Eckman, Whistle Blower and More, 1995; editor, contbr. Lafayette Sq. Newsletter, 1974-82, Fed. Hill Newsletter, 1974-82, Greater Penn Ave. Newsletter, 1974-82, MPCA News Letter, 1982—, Md. Rehab. Assn. News Letter, 1985—, Front and Center newsletter, 1980-92, Rehab Digest, 1992—; contbr. articles to mags., newspapers and newsletters. Bd. dirs. Liberty Showcase Theater, 1985-87, Howard County Summer Theatre, 1992—, pres. 1995. With U.S. Army, 1956-58. Recipient award for spot reporting Chesapeake AP, 1967, award for in-depth sports reporting, 1967, 69, Media Appreciation award U.S. Intercollegiate Lacrosse Assn., 1970, Humanitarian award Md. Rehab. Assn., 1982, Appreciation award 1986, Profl. Svc. award Md. Rehab. Counseling Assn., 1985, Ams. with Disabilities Act award The Task Force on the Rights and Empowerment of Ams. with Disabilities, 1991, Outstanding Contbns. award, 1994. Mem. Md. Rehab. Assn. (pres. 1985, 87), Md. Press Club (pres. 1988-89, bd. dirs. 1990-91), Balt. Sports Reporters Assn. (pres. 1964), Balt. Press Reporters Assn. (pres. 1965), Mid-Atlantic Rehab. Adminstrs. Assn. (pres. 1990). Home: 4029 Pebble Branch Rd Ellicott City MD 21042

NEILL, DENIS MICHAEL, government relations consulting executive; b. Grand Rapids, Mich., Apr. 27, 1943; s. Thomas Patrick and Agnes Josephine (Weber) N.; m. Mary Kathleen Golden, June 11, 1966; children: Mark, Erin. AB cum laude, St. Louis U., 1964, JD cum laude, 1967. Bar: Mo. 1967, D.C. 1969., 1981—; Gen. atty. Office of Asst. Regional Counsel IRS, Newark, 1967-68; assoc. Arent, Fox, Kintner, Plotkin & Kahn, Washington, 1969-71, Morgan, Lewis & Bockius, Washington, 1971-72; atty. advisor office gen. counsel AID, Washington, 1972-73, asst. gen. counsel legis. and policy coordination, 1973-75, asst. adminstr. legis. affairs, 1975-77; sr. v.p., gen. counsel Aeromaritime Internat. Corp., Washington, 1977-80; counsel Surrey & Morse, Washington, 1980-81; sr. ptnr. Neill & Shaw, Washington, 1981-92; sr. law ptnr. Dalley, Neill, Assevero, Carroll & Nealer, Washington, 1992-93; pres. Neill & Co., Inc., Washington, 1981—. Bd. dirs. Barker Found., 1988-89, Fed. City Nat. Bank, Washington, 1987. Lt. USCG, 1968-71. Recipient Superior Unit Citation AID, 1976, Disting. Honor award, 1977. Mem. ABA, FBA, D.C. Bar Assn., Mo. Bar Assn., Nat. Security Indsl. Assn. (bd. dirs. 1982-90), Capitol Hill Club, Columbia Country Club (Chevy Chase, Md.), Jefferson Islands Club. Democrat. Home: 5945 Searl Ter Bethesda MD 20816-2022 Office: Neill & Co Ste 800 5945 Searl Ter Bethesda MD 20816-2022

NEILL, RICHARD ROBERT, retired publishing company executive; b. N.Y.C., June 20, 1925; s. Robert Irving and Mildred Mary (Hall) N.; m. Patricia Mae Robinson, Dec. 27, 1952; 1 son, Robert Kenneth. A.B. summa cum laude, Princeton U., 1948; M.A., N.Y. U., 1953. With Prentice-Hall, Inc., N.Y.C. and Englewood Cliffs, N.J., 1948-85; advt. mgr. Prentice-Hall, Inc., N.Y.C. and Englewood Cliffs, 1953-58, v.p. advt., 1958-62; pres. Exec. Reports Corp. div., 1962-85, ret., 1985; Regional chmn. Princeton Alumni Giving, Yonkers, N.Y., 1966-83, Tarrytown-Irvington, N.Y., 1977-80. Pres. Tarrytown (N.Y.) Jr. High Sch. PTA, 1971-72; bd. dirs. Martling Owners, Tarrytown, 1980-84, 89-93. Lt. (j.g.) USNR, 1943-46, PTO. Mem. USN Meml. Found., Princeton Terrace Club (bd. govs. 1986-92), Great Harbour Cay Club (Bahamas), Phi Beta Kappa. Republican. Mem. Reform Ch. Home: 222 Martling Ave Tarrytown NY 10591-4756

NEILL, ROLFE, newspaper executive; b. Mount Airy, N.C., Dec. 4, 1932; s. Kenneth A. and Carmen (Goforth) N.; m. Rosemary Clifford Boney, July 20, 1952 (div.); children: Clifford Randolph, Sabrina Ashley, Dana Catlin, Jessica Rosemary Ingrid, Quentin Roark Robinson; m. Ann Marshall Snider, Sept. 24, 1988. A.B. in History, U.N.C. 1954. Reporter Franklin (N.C.) Press, 1956-57; reporter Charlotte (N.C.) Observer, 1957-58, bus. editor, 1958-61; editor, pub. Coral Gables (Fla.) Times and The Guide, 1961-63, Miami Beach (Fla.) Daily Sun, 1963-65; asst. to pub. N.Y. Daily News, 1965-67, suburban editor, 1967-68, asst. mng. editor, 1968-70; editor Phila. Daily News, 1970-75; v.p., dir. Phila. Newspapers Inc., 1970-75; chmn., pub. Charlotte (N.C.) Observer, 1975—. Served with AUS, 1954-56. Office: Knight Pub Co 600 S Tryon St PO Box 32188 Charlotte NC 28232

NEILL, SAM, actor; b. Northern Ireland, Sept. 14, 1947; m. Noriko Watanabe; 3 children. Student, U. Canterbury, Eng. Appearances include (film) Land Fall, 1976, Sleeping Dogs, 1977, The Journalist, 1979, Just Out of Reach, 1979, My Brilliant Career, 1980, Attack Force Z, 1981, The Final Conflict, 1981, Possession, 1981, Enigma, 1983, The Country Girls, 1983, Robbery Under Arms, 1984, Plenty, 1985, For Love Alone, 1986, The Good Wife, 1987, A Cry in the Dark, 1988, Dead Calm, 1989, La Révolution Française, 1989, The Hunt for Red October, 1990, Death in Brunswick, 1990, Until the End of the World, 1991, Memoirs of An Invisible Man, 1992, The Piano, 1993, Jurassic Park, 1993, In the Mouth of Madness, 1993, Country Life, 1994, Rudyard Kipling's Jungle Book, 1994, Restoration, 1994, Sirens, 1994, In the Mouth of Madness, 1995, Country Life, 1995, (TV miniseries) Kane and Abel, 1985, Reilly Ace of Spies, 1986, Amerika, 1987, (TV movies) From a Far Country: Pope John Paul II, 1981, Ivanhoe, 1982, The Blood of Others, 1984, Arthur Hailey's Strong Medicine, 1986, Leap of Faith, 1988, Fever, 1991, One Against the Wind, 1991, The Sinking of the Rainbow Warrior, 1991, Family Pictures, 1993. Recipient O.B.E. award, 1991. Office: Internat Creative Mgmt 8942 Wilshire Blvd Beverly Hills CA 90211*

NEILL, VE, make-up artist; b. Riverside, Calif., May 13, 1951; d. Charles and Eileen Anne (Bernasco) Flores. Grad., Louisville H.S., Woodland Hills, Calif. Credits include (TV movies) Cry for Help, 1978, The London Affair, 1978, Sultan and the Rock Star, 1979, Muppets Go to the Movies, 1981, First Lady of the World, 1982, Money on the Side, 1982, Jane Doe, 1986; (TV Spls.) Sold Out-Lily Tomlin, 1981, Lily for President, 1982, Comedy Store 15th Yr. Reunion, 1988; (TV pilots) One Night Band, 1981, T.J. Hooker, 1981, Madeline (Madeline Kahn), 1982, Girls Life, 1982, A-Team, 1982, Rock & Roll Mom, 1987, Kowalski Loves, 1987; (TV show) Pee Wee's Playhouse (Emmy award 1988, Emmy award nominee 1989); (feature films) Star Trek: The Motion Picture (Saturn award 1981), The Incredible Shrinking Woman, 9 to 5, Monty Python at the Hollywood Bowl, Sword and the Sorcerer, The Last Star Fighter, All of Me, The Lost Boys, 1986 (Saturn award 1987), Beetlejuice, 1987 (Acad. award 1987, Saturn award 1988, Brit. Acad. award nominee 1988), Cocoon II, 1988, Big Top Pee Wee, 1988, Dick Tracy, 1989, Flatliners, 1989, Edward Scissorhands, 1990 (Acad. award nominee 1989, Brit. Acad. award nominee 1990), Curly Sue, 1990, Hook, 1991, Batman Returns, 1991 (Saturn award 1992, Acad. award nominee 1992, Brit. Acad. award nominee 1992), Hoffa, 1992 (Acad. award nominee 1992), Rising Sun, 1992, Mrs. Doubtfire, 1993 (Acad. award 1993), Ed Wood, 1993 (Acad. award 1994), Cobb, 1994, Junior, 1994, Batman Forever, 1995. Mem. Acad. Motion Picture Arts and Scis. (mem. exec. bd.), Brit. Acad. Film and TV. Avocations: collecting antiques, beading with antique Am. trade beads, hiking, traveling the U.S. Office: IATSE Local 706 11519 Chandler Blvd North Hollywood CA 91607

NEILL, WILLIAM ALEXANDER, magazine editor; b. Atlanta, Feb. 17, 1957; s. William A. and Sara Ann Neill. BA in English, Wesleyan U., 1979. Editor Car Audio and Electronics, Woodland Hills, Calif., 1989—. Office: Avcom Pub 21700 Oxnard St Ste 1600 Woodland Hills CA 91367-7305

NEILL, WILLIAM HAROLD, JR., biological science educator; b. Wynne, Ark., Oct. 21, 1943; s. William H., Sr. and Shirley A. (Ellis) N.; m. Charlotte A. Jackson, Dec. 20, 1964; 1 child, Amanda K. BS in Zoology, U. Ark., 1965, MS in Zoology, 1967; PhD, U. Wis., 1971. Rsch. fishery biologist Southwest Fisheries Ctr. Nat. Marine Fisheries Svc., Honolulu, 1971-74; assoc. prof. Tex. A&M U./Tex. Agrl. Expt. Sta., College Station, 1975-83; prof. Tex. A&M U./TAES, College Station, 1983—; interim head Dept. Wildlife and Fisheries Sci., College Station, 1992-93; mem. organizing com. Advanced Rsch. Inst. on Mechanisms Fish Migration, NATO, 1980-82; mem. tech. com. So. Regional Aquaculture Ctr., USDA, 1987-89. Editor Tex. Jour. Sci., 1983-85; mem. editl. adv. bd. Critical Revs. in Aquatic Sci., 1986-91; contbr. 60 articles to sci. jours. Grantee numerous orgns., 1989—. Fellow Tex. Acad. Sci.; mem. AAAS, Am. Fisheries Soc. (life; award of Excellence com. 1987, 89, chair Publ. Awards com. 1993), Am. Inst. Fishery Rsch. Biologists, Internat. Soc. Ecol. Modelling, World Aquaculture Soc., Phi Beta Kappa, Sigma Xi, Phi Sigma. Office: Texas A&M U Dept Wildlife & Fisheries Sci College Station TX 77843-2258

NEILLY, ANDREW HUTCHINSON, JR., publisher; b. Balt., 1923; m. Janet Dayton, 1949; children: Susan, Thomas, Sarah. Grad., U. Rochester, 1947. Coll. sales rep. John Wiley & Sons, Inc., N.Y.C., 1947-51, asst. sales mgr., 1951-57, asst. v.p. domestic sales and promotion, 1957-61, v.p. mktg.

div., 1961-67, exec. v.p., chief operating officer, 1967-71, pres., chief operating officer, 1971-79, pres., chief exec. officer, 1979-89, vice chmn., 1989—; also bd. dirs. Trustee U. Rochester, Columbia U. Press. Mem. Internat. Pubs. Assn. (pres. 1988-92), Internat. Group STM Pubs. (exec. com.). Club: Century Assn. Office: John Wiley & Sons Inc 605 3rd Ave New York NY 10158-0180 Also: Columbia Univ Press 562 W 113th St New York NY 10025

NEILSON, ELIZABETH ANASTASIA, health sciences educator, association executive, author, editor; b. Medford, Mass., Oct. 13, 1913; d. William H. and Anastasia (Mahony) N. Diploma, Tufts U., 1933; B.S. in Edn, Boston U., 1934, M.Ed., 1945, Ed.D., 1957. Tchr. pub. schs. Medford, 1934-43; instr. health and phys. edn. Boston Coll., 1954-55; mem. faculty State Coll., Lowell, Mass., 1944-72; prof. edn., chmn. dept. health and phys. edn. State Coll., 1966-72; dir. continuing edn. Am. Sch. Health Assn., Kent, Ohio, 1972—; adj. prof. Kent State U., 1971-77; adj. prof. health edn. Boston-Bouvé Coll. Human Devel. Professions, Northeastern U., 1974—; lectr. extension div. Harvard U., 1975—; vis. prof. Boston U., 1960-62, Ind. U., summers 1966-72, Utah State U., summer 1968; del. Internat. Conf. Health and Edn., Madrid, 1965, Pa., 1962, Dusseldorf, Germany, 1959; health edn. cons. to govt. agys., industry, ednl. instns.; del. White House Conf. Children and Youth, 1970; mem. membership com. Am. Nat. Council for Health, 1967-73; chmn. resources council Mass. Sch. Health Council, 1964-69; mem. Nat. Adv. Council on Smoking and Health Edn., 1964-74, Gov.'s Council for Health and Fitness, 1964-69, Gov.'s Council for Nutrition Edn., 1971-74; mem. program evaluation team N.H. State Bd. Edn. Author: Health Living Program, 1977, also school health textbooks; contbg. author: coll. text Personal and Community Health; editor in chief coll. text Journal-Health Values: Achieving High Level Wellness, 1976—; contbr. articles to profl. jours. V.p. bd. dirs. March Against Dental Disease Found.; bd. dirs. Middlesex TB and Health Assn., Mass. Cancer Soc., Lowell MEntal Health Assn., Lowell Heart Assn., Lowell Diabetes Assn., New Hampshire Lung Assn.; mem. Jackson Sch. Bd.; trustee Jackson Libr.; pres., bd. dirs. Flintlock Village Assn.Inc., Wells, Maine, 1988—; founder Elizabeth A. Neilson-George H. Neilson Advanced Grad. Endowed Scholarship Fund for the Promotion of Health Edn., dept. physiology and health scis., Ball State U., 1992. Recipient William A. Howe award Am. Sch. Health Assn., 1969, Disting. Svc. award 1965, Disting. Svc. award ea. dist. AAHPER, 1967, Profl. Svc. award Mass. chpt. 1965, Svc. award Nat. ARC, 1960, Disting. Alumni award Northeastern U., Boston, 1983, Profl. Svc. award Am. Alliance for Health Edn., 1987; inducted into Mass. Hall of Fame, Medford High, 1990; hon. fellow Ball State U., Muncie, Ind., 1993. Fellow Am. Sch. Health Assn. (life, pres. 1964-66, chmn. study coms. 1969-72, mem. governing assn. 1960-65, Howe award), Royal Soc. Health; mem. Am. Assn. Higher Edn., Am. Soc. Assn. Execs., Nat. Bus. and Profl. Women's Club, Assn. Supervision and Curriculum Devel., UN Assn. U.S.A., Internat. Union for Health, Smithsonian Assos., Nat. Parks and Conservation Assn., New Eng. Health Assn., Am. Coll. Health Assn. (research council 1954-57), Am. (editorial bd. 1958-60, chmn. coll. health com. Eastern dist. 1948-51, chmn. resolutions com. sch. health div. 1951-53), Mass. assns. health, phys. edn. and recreation, Am. Pub. Health Assn., Soc. Health Educators, Phi Lambda Theta. Home and Office: PO Box 890 Wells ME 04090-0890 Since childhood my life has been guided by the concept that it is best to prevent illness by healthful living. On this premise I have devoted my life toward achieving a high level of wellness for myself and my family. As a professor of health education and an exemplar of the concepts associated with the daily application of scientific health information, I have worked toward helping others achieve the level of health their inherited potential would permit.

NEILSON, ERIC GRANT, physician, educator, health facility administrator; b. Bklyn., Sept. 14, 1949; s. Jack Drew and Lynette Elsie (Lundquist) N.; m. Linda Rae Apolzon, May 27, 1972; children: Tinsley, Sigrid. BS magna cum laude, Denison U., 1971; MD magna cum laude, U. Ala., 1975; MD (hon.), U. Pa., 1987. Asst. prof. U. Pa., Phila., 1980-87, assoc. prof. 1987-91, prof., 1991—, C. Mahlon Kline prof., 1993—, chief renal-electrolyte sect. dept. medicine, 1988—; attending physician Hosp. of U. Pa., 1980—; cons. in field. Med. editorial bds. on sci. jours.; contbr. numerous articles to profl. jours. Chmn. med. adv. bd. Lupus Found. of Phila., 1985-95; chmn. pathology A study sect. NIH, Bethesda, Md., 1990-92; chmn. grant rev. com. Nat. Kidney Found. of Delaware Valley. Recipient Clin. Scientist award Am. Heart Assn., 1980, Young Investigator award Am. Soc. Nephrology/Am. Heart Assn., 1985, Established Investigator award Am. Heart Assn., President's medal Am. Soc. Nephrology, 1994. Fellow ACP; mem. Am. Soc. Clin. Investigation, Assn. Am. Physicians, Am. Soc. Nephrology, Am. Assn. Immunologists, Am. Fedn. Clin. Rsch., Assn. Subsplty. Profs. (pres. 1994—). Mem. Soc. of Friends. Office: U Pa Renal Electrolyte Sect 700 Clin Rsch Bldg 422 Curie Blvd Philadelphia PA 19104-6140

NEILSON, ROBERT MCKENZIE, JR., materials scientist; b. Buffalo, July 1, 1949; s. Robert McKenzie and Jean E. (Feist) N.; m. Georgette P. Mullen, May 22, 1971 (div. May 1984); 1 child, Robert McKenzie III; m. Laurel Kim Moncur, Dec. 22, 1984; 1 child, Amber. B Engring. Sci., SUNY, Stony Brook, 1971, MS in Materials Sci., 1973, MS in Indsl. Mgmt., 1979. Sci. assoc. Brookhaven Nat. Lab., Upton, N.Y., 1974-82; sr. scientist EG&G Idaho, Inc., Idaho Falls, 1982-88, rsch. and devel. mgr., 1988—; cons., Idaho Falls, 1983—; lectr. ASME, N.Y.C., 1978-82; U.S. rep. IAEA, Vienna, Austria, 1980. Editor Jour. Nuclear and Chem. Waste, 1980-83; contbr. articles to profl. jours.; patentee tritum waste disposal field. Bd. dirs. Bonneville County unit Am. Cancer Soc., 1984—; mem. Idaho Innovation Ctr., 1988—. Recipient R & D 100 award R & D mag., 1988. Mem. Am. Ceramic Soc., Am. Soc. for Metals (bd. dirs. local chpt. 1980-82), Am. Nuclear Soc. (standards com. 1981—), ASTM (C-28 com. 1986—), U.S. Power Squadron (sec. Patchogue, N.Y. 1980-82), Idaho Falls Ski Club, Tau Beta Pi. Republican. Episcopalian.

NEILSON, WINTHROP CUNNINGHAM, III, communications executive, financial communications consultant; b. N.Y.C., Jan. 7, 1934; s. Winthrop Cunningham, Jr. and Frances Fullerton (Jones) N.; m. Ilse Rossenbeck, Jan. 4, 1957; children: Luise R., Victoria F.; m. Demaris King Hetrick, July 5, 1985; 1 child, Whitney C.; stepchildren: Norman P. Hetrick Jr., D. Page Hetrick. B.A., Harvard U., 1956; grad. in security analysis, N.Y. Inst. Finance, 1963. Asst. producer, asst. dir. Rangley Lakes Theater, 1955; gen. assignment reporter Albany (N.Y.) Times-Union, 1959-60; pub. info. writer, speaker Consol. Edison, 1960-61; asst. dir. pub. relations Union Service Corp., 1962; with Georgeson & Co., N.Y.C., 1962-81, prin., 1969-81; sr. v.p. D.F. King & Co. Inc., N.Y.C., 1982-86; founder, mng. dir. Krone Communications, Harrisburg, Pa., 1986-89; pres. Krone Group Inc., Harrisburg, 1987-89; mng. dir. Neilson/Hetrick Group, Montclair, N.J., 1990—, Harrisburg, Pa., 1993—; chmn. Neilson/Hetrick Group, Montclair, N.J., 1993—; mng. dir. Corp. Investor Communications, Carlstadt, N.J., 1991-93; guest lectr. NYU, 1991; bd. dirs. Guardman Products. Author: series Aunt Jane, 1971, 73, The Reluctant Marriage, 1978, Investorism, 1981, Annual Reports, The Agony and the Ecstasy, 1985, Individual Investors, a Counterbalance to Institutional Investors, 1986; writer, assoc. editor: Trends, 1965-81; contbr. articles to profl. jours. Mem. Mountain Lakes (N.J.) Econ. Devel. Council, 1974-79, chmn., 1977-79; pres. Robert A. Taft Republican Club, Queens, N.Y., 1964-65, chmn., 1966-67; treas. 23d Assembly Dist. Rep. Party, 1966-67; county committeeman, 1964-67; del. N.Y. State Nominating Conv., 1966; campaign mgr. for 2 assemblymen and state senator. Served with AUS, 1956-59. Recipient Investor Edn. Disting. Service award Nat. Assn. Investors Clubs, 1986. Mem. Nat. Investor Rels. Inst. (dir. 1980-84, v.p. manpower 1980-81, v.p. long-range planning 1981-84), Pub. Rels. Soc. Am. (charter, exec. com. investor rels. 1982-90, vice chmn. 1986, chmn. 1987, Pres. award 1987, inducted into Hall of Fame for Investor Rels.) Corp. Rels. Soc. Ctrl. Pa. (v.p. 1986-89, pres. 1994—), Ctrl. Pa. Entrepreneurial Assn. (bd. dirs. 1988-89, adv. bd. tech. coun. Ctrl. Pa. 1994—), Colonial Country Club, DU Club, Hasty Pudding Club, Ausable Club. Mem. Soc. of Friends. Home: 5778 Nesbit Dr Harrisburg PA 17112-2200 Office: 5778 Nesbit Dr Ste 12 Harrisburg PA 17112-2200

NEIMAN, JOHN HAMMOND, lawyer; b. Des Moines, Jan. 8, 1917; s. Donald Edwin and Bessie A. (White) N.; m. Madeline Clare Flint, July 2, 1941; children—Richard F., Donald F., Nancy J. Student, Grinnell Coll., 1935-37; B.A., Drake U., 1939, J.D. 1941. Bar: Iowa 1941. Ptnr. Neiman, Neiman, Stone & Spellman, Des Moines, 1946-92, Neiman, Stone, McCormick & Wendl, Attys., Des Moines, 1992—; exec. v.p., sec. Nat.

Assn. Credit Mgmt., Des Moines, 1956-83; mem. ethics com. Iowa Senate, 1969-73, probate rules com. Iowa Supreme Ct., 1977-81; mem., chmn. Client Security and Atty. Disciplinary Commn., Iowa, 1974-85. Pres. bd. councilors Drake U. Law Sch., 1968; pres. Northwest Community Hosp., Des Moines, 1974-77. Recipient Centennial award Drake U., 1981. Fellow Am. Bar Found., Comml. Law Found., Iowa State Bar Found.; mem. ABA (bd. govs. 1984-85, ho. dels. 1978-87, profl. discipline com 1979-84, forum com. 1985-89, responsibility for clients protection, 1989-90), Iowa Bar Assn. (bd. govs. 1963-67, pres. 1967-68, award of merit 1975), Polk County Bar Assn. (pres. 1960-61), Comml. Law League Am., Iowa State Bar Found. (sec. 1975-78, pres. 1988-92), Wakonda Club (pres. 1973), Met. Club (pres. 1981-82, 84-86). Republican. Methodist. Home: 3514 Wakonda Ct Des Moines IA 50321-2648 Office: Neiman Stone McCormick & Wendl 2910 Westown Pky Ste 104 West Des Moines IA 50266-1303

NEIMAN, LEROY, artist; b. St. Paul, June 8, 1927; s. Charles and Lydia (Serline) Runquist; m. Janet Byrne, June 22, 1957. Student, St. Art Inst., Chgo., 1946-50, U. Ill., 1951, DePaul U., 1951; LittD (hon.), Franklin Pierce Coll., 1976; hon. doctorate, St. John's U., 1980; hon. Doctorate, Iona Coll., 1985. Instr. Sch. Art Inst. Chgo., 1950-60, Saugatuck (Mich.) Summer Sch. Painting, 1957-58, 63, Sch. Arts and Crafts, Winston-Salem, N.C., 1963; instr. painting Atlanta Youth Council, 1968-69; printmaker-graphics, 1971—; artist Olympics, ABC-TV, Munich, 1972; ofcl. artist Olympics, ABC-TV, Montreal, 1976, U.S. Olympics, 1980, 84; computer artist CBS-TV (Superbowl), New Orleans, 1978; ofcl. artist Goodwill Games CNN-TV, Moscow, USSR, 1986. Exhibited one-man shows, Oehlshlaeger Gallery, Chgo., 1959, 61, O'Hana Gallery, London, Gallerie O. Bosc, Paris, 1962, Hammer Gallery, N.Y.C., 1963, 65, 67, 70, 72, 76, 78, 79, 81-83, 85-87, 89, 92, Huntington-Hartford Gallery Modern Art, N.Y.C., 1967, Heath Gallery, Atlanta, 1969, Abbey Theatre, Dublin, Ireland, 1970, Museo de Bellas Artes, Caracas, Indpls. Inst. Arts, 1972, Hermitage Mus., Leningrad, Tobu Gallery, Tokyo, 1974, Springfield (Mass.) Mus. Fine Arts, 1974, 84, Knoedler Gallery, London, 1976, Casa gratica, Helsinki, 1977, Renée Victor, Stockholm, 1977, Okla. Art Ctr., Oklahoma City, 1981, Harrod's, London, 1982; retrospective show, Minn. Mus. Art, St. Paul, 1975, Meredith Long Galleries, Houston, 1978, Hanae Mori Gallery, Tokyo, 1988, New State Tretyakov Mus., 1988, Butler Inst., Youngstown, Ohio, 1990, Galerie Marcel Bernheim, Paris, 1993, Ky. Derby Mus., Louisville, 1995, two man show, Neiman-Warhol, Los Angeles Inst. Contemporary Art, 1981; exhibited in group shows, Art Inst. Chgo., 1954-60, Carnegie Internat., 1956, Corcoran Gallery Am., Washington, Walker Art Center, Mpls., 1957, Ringling Mus., Sarasota, Fla., 1959, Salon d'Art Mus., Paris, 1961, Nat. Gallery Portraiture, Smithsonian Instn., Washington, Minn. Mus. Art, 1969, Rotunda Della Basana, Milan, Italy, 1971, Royal Coll. Art, London, 1971, Minn. Mus. Art Nat. Tour, 1976-77, Whitney Mus., 1985 ; Master Prints of 19th and 20th Centuries, Hammer Galls., N.Y., 1987, Salon d'Automne, Paris, 1992, 93; represented in permanent collections, Mpls. Inst. Arts, Ill. State Mus., Springfield, Joslyn Mus., Omaha, Wodham Coll., Oxford, Eng., Nat. Art Mus. Sport, N.Y.C., Museo De Ballas Artes Caracas, Hermitage Mus., Indpls. Inst. Arts, U. Ill., Balt. Mus. Fine Art, The Armand Hammer Collection, Los Angeles; executed murals at, Merc. Nat. Bank, Hammond, Ind., Continental Hotel, Chgo., Swedish Lloyd Ship S.S. Patricia, Stockholm, ceramic tile mural, Sportsmans Park, Chgo.; author: LeRoy Neiman—Art and Life Style, 1974, Horses, 1979, LeRoy Neiman. Posters, 1980, LeRoy Neiman. Catalogue Raisonné, 1980, Carnaval, 1981, LeRoy Neiman: Winners, 1983, Japanese translation, 1985, LeRoy Neiman, Monte Carlo Chase, 1988, The Prints of LeRoy Neiman, 1980-90, Big Time Golf, 1992, LeRoy Neiman, An American in Paris, 1994; illustrator: 12 paintings deluxe edit. Moby Dick, 1975. Served with AUS, 1942-46. Recipient 1st prize Twin City Show, 1953, 2d prize Minn. State Show, 1954, Clark Meml. prize Chgo. Show, 1957, Hamilton-Graham prize Ball State Coll., 1958, Municipal prize Chgo. Show, 1958, Purchase prize Miss. Valley Show, 1959, Gold medal Salon d'Art Modern Paris, 1961; award of merit as nation's outstanding sports artist AAU, 1976; Olympic Artist of Century award, 1979, Gold Medal award St. John's U., 1985. Address: 1 W 67th St New York NY 10023-6200

NEIMARK, PHILIP JOHN, financial consultant, editor; b. Chgo., Sept. 13, 1939; s. Mortimer William and Hortense (Peters) N.; m. Vassa Lynn; children: Tanya Lee, Joshua Daniel, Dashiel Charles, Darq-Amber. Student U. Chgo., 1956-58, Northwestern U., 1958-59; D in Bus. Mgmt. (hon.), Ricker Coll., Houlton, Maine, 1976. Ordained minister Babalawo of IFA Ch. of Nigeria, 1989. Mem. Chgo. Mercantile Exchange, 1968-74; owner Josephson Neimark Trading Co., Chgo., 1972-73; ptnr. Rosenthal & Co., Chgo., 1973-77; owner, prin. Philip J. Neimark Investments, Miami, Fla., 1977-79, Chgo., 1979—; pres. Neimark Fin. Pub. Co., 1985—; pres., Croesus Assocs., 1988-90; editor, pub. Philip J. Neimark Viewpoint, N.Y.C., 1976-85, editor Pro Trade, 1984—, Low Priced Stock Edit., 1984-91; fin. editor Money Maker mag., 1979-85; mem. Internat. Monetary Market, 1971-74, N.Y. Mercantile Exchange, 1973-74, Chgo. Bd. of Options Exchange, 1973-75; editor, Low Priced Stock Edition 1984-91, Pro Trade, 1985—; instr. Omega Inst., 1994, Esalen Inst., 1994. Author: How to Be Lucky, 1975, Way of the Orisa, 1992, The Sacred Ifa Oracle, 1995; syndicated columnist Ask the Shaman, 1994—; contdg. editor Consumers Digest mag., 1977-85. Bd. dirs. Luth. Gen. Med. Found. (emeritus), Principal Vassa Inc.; chmn. IFA Found N.Am., 1989—. Mem. Fla. Exec. Planning Assn., South Fla. Fin. Planners Assn., Investment Co. Inst., Nat. Paso Fino Assn. (founder).

NEIMARK, SHERIDAN, lawyer; b. Youngstown, Ohio, Apr. 7, 1935; s. David and Anne (Kamisar) N.; m. Dana Ellen Perlzweig, Jan. 5, 1963; children: David, Rebecca, Matthew. B.S. in Chem. Engring., Carnegie-Mellon U., 1957; J.D., George Washington U., 1961. Bar: Va. 1962, D.C. 1962, U.S. Ct. of Customs and Patent Appeals 1963, U.S.C. Ct. Appeals (Fed. cir.) 1982, U.S. Supreme Ct. 1973. Patent examiner U.S. Patent Office, Washington, 1957-62; practiced in Washington, 1962—; patent atty. firms K. Flocks and A. Browdy, Washington, 1962-68; mem. firm Browdy and Neimark, Washington, 1969—; sr. ptnr., 1989—. Contbr. articles, papers to profl. jours. Charter mem. Gov.'s Planning and Adv. Coun. on Devel. Disabilities, State of Md., 1971-86, vice chmn., 1975-77; mem. Legal and Human Rights Task Force, Montgomery County (Md.) Com. for Employment of Handicapped, 1972-73; bd. dirs., co-founder Cmty. Svcs. for Autistic Adults and Children; past bd. dirs. Tifereth Israel Congregation. Recipient Gov.'s citation State of Md., 1986. Mem. Am. Bar Assn. (mem. adv. bd. developmental disabilities model legis. project 1977-81, mem. adv. bd. mental and phys. disabilities law reporter 1979—), D.C. Bar, Va. State Bar, Am. Intellectual Property Law Assn. (mem. com. patent law 1965-69, chem. practice 1970—), Md. Patent Law Assn., Internat. Assn. Jewish Lawyers and Jurists, Patent Office Soc., Autism Soc. Am. (nat. dir. 1973-77, dir. Montgomery County chpt. 1970-72, nat. Plaque awards 1972, 77), Md. State Soc. for Autistic Children (founder, dir. 1971), Am. Jewish Com., Am. Jewish Congress, B'nai Brith. Home: 12908 Ruxton Rd Silver Spring MD 20904-5278 Office: 419 7th St NW Suite 300 Washington DC 20004

NEIMS, ALLEN HOWARD, university dean, medical scientist; b. Chgo., Oct. 24, 1938; s. Irving Morris and Ruth (Geller) N.; m. Myrna Gay Robins, June 18, 1961; children: Daniel Mark, Susan Roberta, Nancy Elizabeth. B.A., B.S., U. Chgo., 1957; M.D., Johns Hopkins U., 1961, Ph.D., 1966. Intern, resident in pediatrics Johns Hopkins Hosp., 1961-62, 66-68; research assoc. Lab. Neurochemistry, NIH, 1968-70; asst. prof. physiol. chemistry and pediatrics Johns Hopkins Med. Sch., 1970-72; assoc. prof. McGill U., 1972-77, prof. pharmacology and pediatrics, 1977-78; dir. Roche developmental pharmacology unit, 1972-78; prof., chmn. dept. pharmacology and therapeutics, prof. pediatrics U. Fla., Gainesville, 1978-89, dean Coll. Medicine, 1989—; Fulton Bequest prof. U. Melbourne, Australia, 1974; mem. human embryology and devel. study sect. NIH, 1979-83; sci. cons. Can. Found. for Study of Sudden Infant Death, 1974-77, Nat. Soft Drink Assn., 1976-78, Internat. Life Scis. Inst., 1978-89; bd. sci. counsellors Nat. Inst. Child Health and Human Devel., 1984-89. Contbr. to books, articles to med. jours. Served to comdr. USPHS, 1968-70. NIH, Can. Med. Research Council grantee. Mem. Can. Assn. Medical Research (pres. 1976-78), Am. Soc. Pharmacology and Exptl. Therapeutics (past mem. exec. coms. clin. pharmacology and drug metabolism), Pediatric Research Soc., Am. Soc. Clin. Pharmacology and Therapeutics, Assn. Am. Med. Colls. Coun. of Deans, Am. Pediatric Soc., Am. Acad. Pediatrics. Office: U Fla Coll Medicine PO Box 100215 Gainesville FL 32610-0215

NEINAS, CHARLES MERRILL, athletic association executive; b. Marshfield, Wis., Jan. 18, 1932; s. Arthur Oscar and Blanche Amelia (Reeder) N.; children: Andrew, Toby. B.S., U. Wis., 1957. Asst. exec. dir. Nat. Collegiate Athletic Assn., Kansas City, Mo., 1961-71; commr. Big Eight Conf., Kansas City, 1971-81; exec. dir. Coll. Football Assn., 1981—; Dr. Patricia L. Pacey prof. econs. U. Colo., Boulder, 1981—, econs. cons. 1981—. Served with USNR, 1952-54. Home: 4977 Idylwild Trl Boulder CO 80301-3651 Office: College Football Assoc 6688 Gunpark Dr Boulder CO 80301-3372

NEINER, A(NDREW) JOSEPH, corporate executive; b. Ft. Scott, Kans., Feb. 15, 1950; s. Andrew W. and Celeste H. (Beck) N.; m. Linda M. Koenig, Aug. 21, 1969; children: Carrie L., Christine M., Joseph M., Elizabeth A. BSBA, U. Mo., St. Louis, 1972; MBA, St. Louis U., 1976; postgrad. in advanced mgmt. program, Harvard U., 1990. Fin. analyst Chrysler Corp., Fenton, Mo., 1972-75; fin. mgr. Gen. Cable Corp., St. Louis, 1975-79; contr. Consol. Aluminum Corp., St. Louis, 1979—, group contr., 1980-84, corp. contr., 1983-85, dir. corp. planning, 1985-86, v.p., chief fin. officer, 1986-91, dir., 1987—; exec. v.p. strategic planning Alusuisse-Lonza of America, 1987-94; exec. v.p. fin. and planning Clarke Am., Inc., San Antonio, 1994—; also bd. dirs.; conducted fin. workshops Alusuisse Lonza (Holding) Ltd., Interlaken Switzerland, 1985, St. Gallen, Switzerland, 1992, Morschach and Wegis, Switzerland, 1993; instr. St. Louis Jr. Coll., 1978-80, U. Mo., St. Louis, 1987; bd. Dirs. Electro Savs. Credit Union, 1988-90, 93-94. Recipient Disting. Leadership award Am. Biog. Inst., 1987-88, Disting. Am., 1987, 90, 91; counseling recognition certs. SBA, 1975, 76. Mem. Am. Mgmt. Assn., Fin. Execs. Inst., Assn. for Corp. Growth (v.p. officer, dir. 1993-94), Strategic Mgmt. Soc., The Planning Forum. Roman Catholic. Home: 23 Inwood Autumn San Antonio TX 78248-1679

NEIS, ARNOLD HAYWARD, pharmaceutical company executive; b. N.Y.C., Feb. 13, 1938; s. Harry H. and Mary Ruth (Bishop) N.; m. Lucy de Puig, Dec. 8, 1989; children by previous marriage: Nancy R., Robert C. B.S. cum laude, Columbia U., 1959; MBA, N.Y.U., 1967. With Scott Chem. Co., 1959-64; v.p. mktg., then v.p. Odell, Inc., N.Y.C., 1964-71, pres. Knomark div., 1969-71; pres., chief exec. officer E.T. Browne Drug Co., Inc., Englewood Cliffs, N.J., 1971—; dir. Esquire A.B. Stockholm, Knomark Can. Ltd., E.T. Browne Internat. Fellow Royal Soc. Chemists, Royal Geog. Soc., Am. Inst. Chemists, N.Y. Acad. Scis.; mem. AAAS, Am. Chem. Soc., Am. Pharm. Assn., New Eng. Soc. (bd. dirs.), Explorers Club (v.p., bd. dirs.), Chemists Club, Lotos Club, Soldiers, Sailors and Airmans Club (bd. dirs.), St. Georges Soc. Episcopalian. Home: 898 Park Ave New York NY 10021-0234 Office: PO Box 1613 140 Sylvan Ave Englewood NJ 07632-2502

NEIS, ARTHUR VERAL, healthcare and development company executive; b. Lawrence, Kans., May 30, 1940; s. Veral Herbert and Louise (Schlegel) N.; m. Fleeta Weigel, Apr. 12, 1969; children: Frederich Arthur, Benjamin Jason, Sarah Louise. BS in Bus., U. Kans., 1962, MS in Acctg., 1963. CPA, Kans., Iowa. Mgmt. cons. Arthur Andersen & Co., Kansas City, Mo. and Mpls., 1963-74; chief corp. acctg. Carlson Co., Mpls., 1974-76; controller The Fullerton Cos., Mpls., 1976-78; asst. treas. Fru-Con Corp., St. Louis, 1978-80, asst. controller, 1981, controller, 1982-86; corp. contr. LCS Holdings, Inc. (Weitz Corp. and Subsidaries), Des Moines, 1986-87; treas., chief fin. officer The Weitz Corp., Des Moines, 1987—; treas., CFO Weitz Co., Des Moines, 1987-93, Life Care Services Corp., Des Moines, 1987—; bd. dirs. LCS Holdings, Inc. (Weitz Corp.); mem. adv. group NAIC, 1990-93. Bd. dirs. Inst. Humane Studies George Mason U., Fairfax, Va., 1973—, exec. com., 1975-83, chmn., 1978-83; bd. dirs. Lake Country Sch., Mpls., 1973-78; treas. Villa de Maria Montessori Sch., St. Louis, 1982-86, bd. dirs.; trustee Crossroads Sch., St. Louis, 1984-86, exec. com. bd., 1984-86; vice chair, bd. dirs. Alliance for Arts and Understanding, 1993—; trustee Fin. Execs. Rsch. Found., 1994—; trustee Plymouth Congrl. United Ch. of Christ, 1993—. Mem. AICPA, Kans. Soc. CPAs, Iowa Soc. CPAs, Fin. Execs. Inst. (bd. dirs. Iowa chpt. 1986, 88-94, sec. 1988-90, v.p. 1990-91, pres. 1991-92). Avocations: bibliophile, Kans. history, orientalia. Home: 1575 NW 106th St Clive IA 50325-6604 Office: Life Care Svcs Corp 800 2nd Ave Des Moines IA 50309-1328

NEIS, JAMES M., lawyer; b. Chgo., Mar. 3, 1946. BA, DePaul U., 1969, JD, 1973. Bar: Ill. 1973, U.S. Tax Ct. 1974. Mng. ptnr. Winston & Strawn, Chgo.; adj. prof. law DePaul U., 1979-86. Mem. ABA, Ill. State Bar Assn., Chgo. Bar Assn. Office: Winston & Strawn 35 W Wacker Dr Chicago IL 60601-1614

NEISER, BRENT ALLEN, public affairs consultant; b. Cin., Sept. 16, 1954; s. Rodger John and Hazel Jean Neiser; m. Marion Alice Hutton, Apr. 1, 1978; children: Christy Jean, Steven Jose, April Reneé. BA in Pub. Affairs, George Washington U., 1976; MA in Urban Studies, Occidental Coll., 1978; MBA, U. Louisville, 1979; postgrad. in internat. affairs, U. Denver, 1987—. Cert. fin. planner, 1985; cert. assn. exec., 1994. Project mgr., analyst Legis. Research Com., Frankfort, Ky., 1978-84; pres. Moneyminder, Denver and Frankfort, 1983-91; dir. edn., govt. affairs and ethics Inst. Cert. Fin. Planners, Denver, 1985-91, exec. dir., 1991-94; pub. affairs, telecomms., govt. rels. bus. strategies cons. pvt. practice, Englewood, Colo., 1994—; mng. dir. Fin. Products Stds. Bd., Denver, 1985-91; co-creator Personal Econ. Summit '93, Washington; dir. Nat. Endowment for Fin. Edn. Author: EPCOT/World Showcase External Directions, Walt Disney Imagineering, 1977; co-inventor: Trivia Express (game) Denver, 1986. Vol., v.p. Big Bros./Big Sisters, Frankfort, 1982; del. Colo. Model Constnl. Conv. 1987; mem. citizens budget rev. com. Greenwood Village; parent trainer Rocky Mountain Adoption Exch., Denver, 1988, mem. long range planning com., 1992-93, bd. dirs., 1993—; polit. action dir. Frankfort NAACP, 1983, legis. chmn. state conf., 1984; troop com. mem., asst. scoutmaster Boy Scouts Am., Englewood, 1993—; bd. dirs. Young Ams. Bank Edn. Found., 1993—; Leadership Denver, 1993. Lt. (j.g.) USNR, 1985—. Recipient Outstanding Service award Frankfort NAACP, 1981; named Man of Yr., Frankfort NAACP, 1983; Pub. Affairs fellow Coro Found., 1976-77. Mem. Investors Edn. Assn. Colo. (bd. dirs.), Nat. Assns. in Colo., Denver C. of C. (pub. affairs coun.), Adoptive Families of Am., Inst. Cert. Fin. Planners, Assn. for Fin. Counseling and Planning Edn., Am. Soc. Assn. Execs., Inst. Mgmt. Cons., Internat. Assn. Fin. Planners (bd. dirs. Rocky Mountain chpt. 1990-92), N.Am. Securities Adminstrs. Assn. (investment adviser and fin. planner adv. com.), Nat. Soc. Compliance Profls. (bd. dirs. 1987-89), Am. Film Inst. (writers workshop). Office: 5860 Big Canyon Dr Englewood CO 80111-3516

NEISER, RICHARD WILLIAM, utility executive; b. Covington, Ky., June 16, 1938; s. Richard William Neiser Sr. and Elizabeth Mildred (Marz) Raible; m. Joy Lee, Aug. 27, 1960; children: David, Linda, Mary Beth. BA, Centre Coll., 1960; JD, Stetson Coll. Law, 1963. Trust rep., trust officer Barnett Bank & Trust Co., St. Petersburg, Fla., 1963-64; sole practice, St. Petersburg, 1965; staff atty. Fla. Power Corp., St. Petersburg, 1966-68, asst. counsel, 1968-74, asst. gen. counsel, 1974-76, asst. v.p., asst. gen. counsel, 1976-78, v.p., asst. gen. counsel, 1978-83, sr. v.p., gen. counsel, 1983-87, sr. v.p. corporate services, 1987—. Mem. Leadership St Petersburg Alumni Assn. Mem. ABA, Fla. Bar Assn., St. Petersburg Bar Assn., Am. Judicature Soc., Fla. C. of C., St. Petersburg C. of C., Edison Electric Inst. Legal Com. Republican. Club: Suncoast Tiger Bay (St. Petersburg). Avocations: water sports, tennis, woodworking. Office: Fla Power Corp 3201 34th St S Saint Petersburg FL 33711-3897

NEISSER, ULRIC, psychology educator; b. Kiel, Germany, Dec. 8, 1928; came to U.S., 1933; s. Hans Philip and Charlotte (Schroeter) N. BA, Harvard U., 1950, PhD, 1956; MA, Swarthmore Coll., 1952; Laurea Honoris Causa, U. Rome, 1988, U. Aarhus, Denmark, 1993, U. Cluj, Romania, 1994. Instr. Swarthmore (Pa.) Coll., 1953-54, Harvard U., Cambridge, Mass., 1956-57; from asst. to assoc. prof. Brandeis U., Waltham, Mass. 1957-66; prof. psychology Cornell U., Ithaca, N.Y., 1967-80, Susan Linn Sage prof. psychology, 1980-83; Robert W. Woodruff prof. psychology Emory U., Atlanta, 1983—. Author: Cognitive Psychology, 1967, Cognition and Reality, 1976; editor: Memory Observed, 1982, The School Achievement of Minority Children, 1987, Concepts and Conceptual Development, 1987, Remembering Reconsidered, 1988, The Perceived Self, 1993. Ctr. for Advanced Study in Behavior Scis. fellow, 1973-74, Guggenheim fellow, 1987-88. Fellow APA; mem. NAS, Am. Acad. Arts and Scis., Cognitive Sci. Soc., Internat. Soc. Ecol. Psychology, Psychonomic Soc. Office: Emory U Dept of Psychology Atlanta GA 30322

NEITER, GERALD IRVING, lawyer; b. L.A., Nov. 11, 1933; s. Harry and Ida Florence (Alperin) N.; m. Margaret P. Rowe, Mar. 5, 1961; children: David, Karen, Michael. BSL, U. So. Calif., 1957, JD, 1957. Bar: Calif. 1958. Judge pro tem Mcpl. Cts., L.A. and Beverly Hills, 1970—; judge pro tem and mediator Calif. Superior Ct., L.A. County, 1974—; family law mediator, 1976—; prin. Geralt I. Neiter, P.C., L.A., 1981—; lectr. State Bar of Calif., 1968, 76, 79, 81; former referee State Bar Ct.; arbitrator Am. Arbitration Assn. Mem. Am., Los Angeles County (arbitrator), Beverly Hills, Century City bar assns., State Bar Calif. Office: 1925 Century Park E Ste 200 Los Angeles CA 90067-2703

NEJELSKI, PAUL ARTHUR, judge; b. Chgo., Feb. 24, 1938; s. Leo Lawrence and Rena Grace (Martin) N.; m. Marilyn Ray Mills, Oct. 2, 1965; children: Nicole Rena, Stephen Downing. BA magna cum laude, Yale U., 1959, LLB, 1962; MPA, Am. U., 1969; cert. of theol. studies, Georgetown U., 1989. Bar: N.J. 1963. Law clk. appellate div. N.J. Superior Ct., 1962-63; asst. U.S. atty. U.S. Dist. Ct. N.J., 1964-65; atty., later chief immigration unit Dept. Justice, Washington, 1965-69; chief cts. desk Nat. Inst. Justice, Washington, 1969-70; asst. dir. Criminal Justice Ctr., Harvard U., 1970-71; dir. planning phase Inst. Jud. Adminstrn.-ABA Juvenile Justice Standards Project, N.Y.C., 1971-73; dir. Inst. Jud. Adminstrn., NYU, 1973-76; dep. ct. adminstrn. Conn. Jud. Dept., Hartford, 1976-77; dep. asst. atty. gen. Office for Improvements in Adminstrn. Justice, Dept. Justice, Washington, 1977-79; dir. Action Commn. to Reduce Ct. Costs and Delay, ABA, Washington, 1979-81; cir. exec. 3rd Cir., Phila., 1981-84; ct. adminstr. U.S. Tax Ct., 1984-89; immigration judge Dept. Justice, Arlington, Va., 1989—; mem. faculty law NYU, 1972-74, U. Conn., 1976-77, U. Md., 1981-82; cons. Author: (with C.O. Philip) Where Do Judges Come From?, 1976; editor: Social Research in Conflict With Law and Ethics, 1976; contbr. articles to profl. jours. With U.S. Army, 1963-64. Office: 901 N Stuart St Ste 708 Arlington VA 22203-1853

NELKIN, DOROTHY, sociology and science policy educator, researcher; b. Boston, July 30, 1933; d. Henry and Helen (Fine) Wolfers; m. Mark Nelkin, Aug. 31, 1952; children: Lisa, Laurie. B.A., Cornell U., 1954. Research assoc. Cornell U., Ithaca, N.Y., 1963-69, sr. research assoc., 1970-72, assoc. prof., 1972-76, prof. sci. tech. sociology program, 1976-90, prof. sociology, 1977-90; Univ. prof., prof. sociology, affiliate prof. law NYU, 1990—, Clare Boothe Luce vis. prof., 1988-90; cons. OECD, Paris, 1975-76, Inst. Environ., Berlin, 1978-79; maitre de conference U. Paris, 1975-76; maitre de recherche Ecole Polytechnique, Paris, 1980-81. Author: The Atom Besieged, 1981, The Creation Controversy, 1982, Science as Intellectual Property, 1983, Workers at Risk, 1984, Selling Science: How the Press Covers Science and Technology, 1987, Dangerous Diagnostics: The Social Power of Biological Information, 1989, 2d edit. 1994, A Disease of Society: Cultural Impact of AIDS, 1991, The Animal Rights Crusade, 1991, Controversy: Politics of Tecnical Decision, 3d edit., 1992, The DNA Mystique: The Gene as Cultural Icon, 1995. Adviser Office Tech. Assessment, 1977-79, 82-83; expert witness ACLU, Ark., 1982; mem. Nat. Adv. Coun. to NIH Human Gerome Project, 1991—. Vis. scholar Resources for the Futures, 1980-81; vis. scholar Russell Sage Found., N.Y.C., 1983; Guggenheim fellow, 1983-84. Fellow AAAS (bd. dirs.), Hastings Inst. Soc. Ethics and Life Scis.; mem. NAS Inst. of Medicine, Soc. for Social Studies Sci. (pres. 1978-79). Home: 3 Washington Square Vlg New York NY 10012-1835 Office: NYU Dept Sociology 269 Mercer St New York NY 10003-6633

NELLERMOE, LESLIE C., lawyer; b. Oakland, Calif., Jan. 26, 1954; d. Carrol Wandell and Nora Ann (Conway) N.; m. Darrell Ray McKissic, Aug. 9, 1986; 1 child, Devin Anne. BS cum laude, Wash. State U., 1975; JD cum laude, Willamette U., 1978. Bar: Wash. 1978, U.S. Dist. Ct. (ea. dist.) Wash. 1979, U.S. Dist. Ct. (we. dist.) Wash. 1983. Staff atty. Wash. Ct. Appeals, Spokane, 1978-79; asst. atty. gen. Wash. Atty. Gen. Office, Spokane, 1979-83, Olympia, 1983-85; assoc. Syrdal, Danelo, Klein, Myre & Woods, Seattle, 1985-88; ptnr. Heller Ehrman White & McAuliffe, Seattle, 1989—. Bd. dirs. Campfire Boys & Girls, Seattle, 1991—. Mem. ABA, Wash. State Bar Assn., King County Bar Assn. Office: Heller Ehrman White & McAuliffe 6100 Columbia Ctr Seattle WA 98104

NELLES, MAURICE, mechanical engineer, author; b. Madison, S.D., Oct. 19, 1906; s. Hubert Tilman and Anne (Benson) N.; m. Cecelia Nelson, Aug. 28, 1929; 1 son, Maurice Tilman; foster daus., Sally Sue Hopkins, Merrill Sherwin. A.B., U.S.D., 1927, A.M., 1928; Ph.D., Harvard, 1932; D.Sc., U. S.D., 1955. Prof. physics Columbus Coll., 1928-29; instr. chemistry U. S.D., 1929-30; research chemist Nat. Aniline Chem. Co., 1932-34, Union Oil Co., 1934-36; camp dir. Civilian Conservation Corps, Ft. Lewis, 1936-37; research engr. Riverside Cement Co., 1937-39; engr. Permanente Corp., 1939-40; staff asst. Lockheed Aircraft, 1940-46; prof. aero. engring., mgr. Allan Hancock Found., U. So. Calif., 1947-50; prof., dir. engring. expt. sta. Pa. State U., 1950-51; dir. research Borg-Warner, also v.p. petro-mechanics div., 1951-54; dir. research and diversification, mgr. graphic arts div. Technicolor Corp., 1954-57; v.p. engring. Crane Co., Chgo., 1957-59; v.p. Am. Electronics, Inc., 1959-62, Quail Products, Inc.; pres. Corwith Co. div. Crane Co., Locked-Lattice Steel Co.; dir. Merd Corp., Lamb-Weston, Inc., Scientia Corp., Hydro-Aire Co., Crane, Ltd., Can., Western Optics, Inc., Radix Corp.; Rust prof. bus. adminstrn. U. Va.; exec. dir. Tayloe Murphy Inst.; prof. Grad. Sch. Bus. Adminstrn., 1966-70, Christian Heritage Coll.; cons. Nat. Acad. Sci.; Dep. dir. WPB; mem. war mobil. com. NACA; dir. Sch. Ministry World Evangelism, Inc., 1977-81; chief engr. Office Prodn. Research and Devel. Author: Satan's 20th Century Strategy, 1971, Precious Christian Thought Patterns, 1973, The Deal, 1976, also articles mgmt. research and engring., new research technique. Trustee Midwest Research Inst., Marine Studies Inst.; commr. to synod United Presbyn. Ch. Charles Coffin fellow; George H. Emerson scholar; Harvard U. fellow. Fellow Am. Inst. Chemists; mem. Am. Soc. M.E., Soc. Automotive Engrs., Inst. Aero. Scis., I.E.E.E., Am. Chem. Soc., Am. Soc. Naval Engrs., Am. Soc. Metals, AIAA, Am. Soc. Motion Picture and TV Engrs., Internat. Soc. Visual Literacy, Optical Soc. Am., Am. Mgmt. Assn., A.A.A.S., Sigma Xi, Tau Beta Pi, Alpha Tau Omega, Tau Kappa Alpha, Sigma Phi Delta, Gamma Alpha, Alpha Chi Sigma. Presbyn. (elder, mem. San Diego Presbytery). Clubs: Mason, Los Angeles Athletic; Montecito (Santa Barbara); Chemists (N.Y.C.); Farmington Country (Charlottesville, Va.). Sci. expdns. aboard U. So. Calif. Marine Lab. Ship. Sci. expdns. aboard U. So. Calif. Marine Lab. Ship. Home: 5522 Rutgers Rd La Jolla CA 92037-7821 *I have walked with God since I was eight years of age. While in college I made the decision not to work with any one organization in any one field for more than three years. As a result I have an unusually diverse set of thought patterns and material in my memory that makes it possible to quickly accomplish much by analogical actions and to use for creative planning.*

NELLI, D. JAMES, business school executive, accountant; b. Seneca Falls, N.Y., Feb. 19, 1917; s. Thomas and Vita N.; m. Victoria Margaret Serino, Aug. 31, 1941 (dec. May 1980); children: Thomas, Diane, Joseph, John; m. 2d, Carmel L. Dowd, Sept. 19, 1981; BS, Syracuse U., 1948. CPA, N.Y. Staff acct. Seidman & Seidman, N.Y.C., 1948-49, Stover, Butler & Murphy, Syracuse, N.Y., 1949-55; instr. Syracuse U., 1953; instr. acctg. Central City Bus. Inst., Syracuse, 1955-58, pres., 1958—, also pvt. practice acctg., Syracuse. Served with USNR, 1943-46. CPA, N.Y. Mem. Am. Inst. CPAs, N.Y. State Soc. CPAs, Am. Acctg. Assn., AAUP. Roman Catholic. Clubs: Lakeshore Yacht and Country (Clay, N.Y.), Italian Am. Athletic (Syracuse). Home: 7929 Boxford Rd Clay NY 13041-8606 Office: Cen City Bus Inst 224 Harrison St Syracuse NY 13202-3028

NELLIGAN, KATE (PATRICIA COLLEEN NELLIGAN), actress; b. London, Ont., Can., Mar. 16, 1951; d. Patrick Joseph and Alice (Dier) N. Attended, York U., Toronto, Ctrl. Sch. Speech and Drama, London. Appeared in plays in Bristol, London, and New York: Barefoot in the Park, 1972, Misalliance, A Streetcar Named Desire, The Playboy of the Western World, London Assurance, Lulu, Private Lives, Knuckle, 1974, Heartbreak House, 1975, Plenty, 1975, As You Like It, A Moon for the Misbegotten, 1984, Virginia, 1985, Serious Money, 1988, Spoils of War, 1988, BAd Habits; films include: The Count of Monte Cristo, 1979, The Romantic Englishwoman, 1979, Dracula, 1979, Mr. Patman, 1980, Eye of the Needle, 1980, Agent, 1980, Without a Trace, 1983, Eleni, 1985, Frankie and Johnnie, 1991, The Prince of Tides, 1991, Shadows and Fog, 1992, Fatal Instinct, 1993, Wolf, 1994, How to Make an American Quilt, 1995; TV appearances include: The Onedin Line, The Lady of the Camellias, Licking Hitler,

Measure for Measure, Therese Raquin, 1980, Forgive Our Foolish Ways, 1980, Love and Hate: A Marriage Made in Hell, 1990, Terror Strickes the Class Reunion, 1992, The Diamond Fleece, 1992, Liar Liar, 1993. Recipient Best Actress award Evening Standard, 1978. Avocations: reading, cooking. Office: Internat Creative Mgmt 8942 Wilshire Blvd Beverly Hills CA 90211*

NELLIGAN, WILLIAM DAVID, professional association executive; b. Halstead, Kans., Aug. 10, 1926; s. William D. and Katherine (Roberts) N.; m. Dorothy Meyer, Aug. 17, 1952; children: Richard, Arthur, Mark. Student, U. Wichita, 1944-46; BS, U. Kans., 1949. Display advt. salesman Kansas City Star and Times, Mo., 1949-51; mgr. SW Kans. Extension Ctr. U. Kans., Garden City, 1951-55; exec. dir. dept. postgrad. med. edn. Sch. Medicine U. Kans., Kansas City, Kans., 1955-64; asst. to pres. Med. Coll. Ga., Augusta, 1964-65; exec. v.p. Am. Coll. Cardiology, Bethesda, Md., 1965-92; v.p. Marion Merrell DOW, Inc., Kansas City, Mo., 1992-94; exec. dir. Am. Soc. Nuc. Cardiology, Bethesda, 1994—. mem. Nat. Commn. Diabetes, 1975-76, adv. council Nat. Diabetes and Digestive and Kidney Diseases, 1987-88; bd. dirs. Arthur E. Hertzler Research Found., Halstead, Kans., 1961—. Recipient Man with a Heart award N.Y. Cardiol. Soc., 1970, Presdl. citation Am. Coll. Cardiology, 1975, Disting. Service award Am. Coll. Cardiology, 1986, CLC Hall of Leaders award, 1986. Fellow Am. Coll. Cardiology; mem. AMA (citation of layman for disting. svc. 1993), Profl. Conv. Mgmt. Assn. (pres. 1974-75, Disting. Svc. award 1990), Am. Med. Writers Assn. (dir., exec. com., treas. 1970-78, Harold Swanberg Disting. Svc. award), Am. Soc. Assn. Execs. (cert., dir. 1975-78, sec.-treas. 1987-88, Key award 1984), Am. Assn. Med. Soc. Execs. (pres. 1986-87), Brit. Cardiac Soc. (hon.), Alliance for Continuing Med. Edn. (Pres.'s award 1994), Masons. Office: 9111 Old Georgetown Rd Bethesda MD 20814

NELMS, CHARLIE, academic administrator. Chancellor Ind. U. East, Richmond; now chancellor U. Mich., Flint. Office: U Mich Office of Chancellor 221 University Pavilion Flint MI 48502

NELSEN, BETTY JO, government administrator; b. Boston, Oct. 11, 1935; B.S., Mass. State Coll., 1957; married; 3 children. Mem. Wis. Ho. of Reps., 1979-90; adminstr. Food and Nutrition Svc. USDA. Mem. Citizens' Govtl. Research Bur.; former pres. Jr. League Milw.; bd. dirs. Milw. Mgmt. Support Orgn.; mem. North Shore Republican Club; trustee Shorewood Civic Improvement Found.; bd. dirs. United Way of Greater Milw.; mem. Goals for Milw. 2000. Office: USDA Food & Nutrition Svc 3101 Park Center Dr Alexandria VA 22302

NELSEN, HART MICHAEL, sociologist, educator; b. Pipestone, Minn., Aug. 3, 1938; s. Noah I. and Nova (Ziegler) N.; m. Anne Kusener, June 13, 1964; 1 dau., Jennifer. B.A., U. No. Iowa, 1959, M.A., 1963; M.Div., Princeton Theol. Sem., 1963; Ph.D. (NSF faculty fellow), Vanderbilt U., 1972. Asst. prof. sociology Western Ky. U., Bowling Green, 1965-70; assoc. prof. Western Ky. U., 1970-73; assoc. prof. Catholic U. Am., 1973-74, prof., 1974-81, chmn. dept. sociology, 1974-77, mem. Boys Town Ctr. for Study Youth Devel., 1974-81; prof. sociology La. State U., Baton Rouge, 1981-84, chmn. dept. sociology, head dept. rural sociology, 1981-84, coordinator rural sociology research, 1981-84; dean Coll. Liberal Arts Pa. State U., 1984-90, prof. sociology, 1984—. Author: (with Anne K. Nelsen) Black Church in the Sixties, 1975; co-author: The Religion of Children, 1977, Religion and American Youth, 1976; editor: (with others) The Black Church in America, 1971; adv. editor: Sociol. Quar, 1976-82; assoc. editor: Sociol. Analysis, 1977-80, Rev. Religious Research, 1977-80, 84—, editor, 1980-84; mem. editorial bd.: Social Forces, 1983-86. Co-rec. sec. Capitol Hill Restoration Soc., 1979-80, v.p., 1980-81; mem. exec. bd. Lafitte Hills Assn., 1983-84. Presbyterian Chs. grantee, 1966-69; NIMH co-grantee, 1969-72; Russell Sage Found. co-grantee, 1972-73; La. Gov.'s Commn. on Alcoholism and Drug Abuse grantee, 1982. Mem. Assn. Sociology Religion (exec. council 1974-76, 78-82, v.p. 1978-79, pres. 1980-81), Religious Research Assn. (dir. 1977-80, pres.-elect 1985-86, pres. 1987-88), Soc. Sci. Study Religion (council 1981-83, exec. sec. 1984-87), Am. Sociol. Assn., So. Sociol. Soc. (chmn. membership com. 1983-85), AAAS (rep. 1984—). Presbyterian. Office: Pa State U Oswald 306 Dept Sociology University Park PA 16802

NELSEN, MARTIN CLAUDE, management services professional; b. Kankakee, Ill., Nov. 12, 1942; s. Claude Brink and Mildred Pauline (Paraday) N.; m. Darlene Marie Buckardt, Mar. 31, 1962; children: Dawn Therese (dec.), Deena Marie Nelsen Hyatt, Martin Arthur. AS, Waubonsee C.C., Sugar Grove, Ill., 1973; B in Mgmt., Elmhurst Coll., 1983; cert. gen. mgr., Planty Sr. Seminar. Cert. laundry/linen mgr. Nat. Assn. Instnl. Linen Mgmt., advanced devel. program for mgrs. Prodn. control mgr. Lyon Metal Products, Aurora, Ill., 1969-72; plant mgr. Lyon Metal Products, Aurora, 1972-80, dir. mfg., 1980-85; gen. mgr. Marriott Mgmt. Svcs., Opa Locka, Fla., 1985—. Contbr. articles to profl. jours. and in-house news periodicals. Active Mens Rep. Club Boca Raton, Fla., 1986-94. Named Laundry Mgr. of Yr., Nat. Assn. Instnl. Linen Mgmt. South Fla. Chpt., 1987, 92, 95. Mem. Am. Soc. ASHES, South Fla. Healthcare Exec. Forum, South Fla. Chpt. Nat. Assn. Instnl. Linen Mgmt. (pres. 3 terms, sec.-treas. 5 terms), Elks, Moose. Lutheran. Avocations: golf, boating, corvette restoration, travel. Office: Marriott/Combined Svcs 2358 NW 151st St Opa Locka FL 33054-2712

NELSEN, TIMOTHY ALAN, lawyer; b. Chgo., Nov. 14, 1947; s. Theodore Allen and Betty Jane (Freeman) Nelsen. BA, Carleton Coll., 1969; JD, U. Mich., 1972. Bar: N.Y. 1973, U.S. Dist. Ct. (so. and ea. dists.) N.Y. 1973, U.S. Ct. Appeals (2d cir.) 1973, U.S. Tax Ct. 1981, U.S. Ct. Appeals (5th cir.) 1985, Ill. 1986, U.S. Dist. Ct. (no. dist.) Ill. 1986, U.S. Ct. Appeals (7th cir.) 1986, U.S. Supreme Ct. 1987, U.S. Dist. Ct. (ea. dist) Mich. 1992, U.S. Ct. Appeals (6th cir.) 1992, U.S. Dist. Ct. Ariz. 1993; cert. ICC, 1982. Ptnr. Skadden, Arps, Slate, Meagher & Flom, N.Y.C., 1972-85, Chgo., 1985—. Home: 2800 N Lake Shore Dr Apt 3601 Chicago IL 60657-6253 Office: Skadden Arps Slate et al 333 W Wacker Dr Chicago IL 60606-1218

NELSEN, WILLIAM CAMERON, foundation president, former college president; b. Omaha, Oct. 18, 1941; s. William Peter and Ellen Lucella (Cameron) N.; m. Margaret Leone Rossow, May 30, 1981; children by previous marriage: William Norris, Shawna Lynn; 1 adopted dau., Sarah Ruth. B.A., Midland Lutheran Coll., Fremont, Nebr., 1963; M.A. (Danforth Grad. fellow 1963, Woodrow Wilson fellow 1963), Columbia U., 1966; Ph.D., U. Pa., 1971; Fulbright scholar, U. Erlangen, W. Ger., 1964; D (hon.), Midland Luth. Coll., 1995. Program exec. Danforth Found., St. Louis, 1970-73; asst. dean, then v.p. dean coll. St. Olaf Coll. Northfield, Minn., 1973-80; pres. Augustana Coll., Sioux Falls, S.D., 1980-86, Citizens' Scholarship Found. of Am., St. Peter, Minn., 1986—; bd. dirs. 1st Nat. Bank, St. Peter, Minn., Coun. of Ind. Colls.; adv. bd. Consortium for Advancement of Pvt. Higher Edn., 1988—. Author: Effective Approaches to Faculty Development, 1980, Renewal of the Teacher Scholar, 1981, also articles. Bd. dirs. S.D. Symphony, 1980-85, Sioux Falls YMCA, 1980-86, Luth. Ednl. Conf. N.Am., 1982-86, Sioux Falls United Way, 1983-86. Mem. Am. Assn. Higher Edn., Assn. Am. Colls. (bd. dirs. 1984-86, dir. project faculty devel. 1979). Republican. Lutheran. Home: 804 Spruce Pl Saint Peter MN 56082-1598 Office: Citizens' Scholarship Found Am PO Box 297 Saint Peter MN 56082-0297

NELSON, ALAN CURTIS, government official, lawyer; b. Oakland, Calif., Oct. 18, 1933; s. Albert C. and Martha (Peters) N.; m. JoAnn Wallen, Jan. 31, 1960; children: Kristine Ann, Kathryn Donna, Karin Martha. BS, U. Calif., Berkeley, 1955, JD, 1958. Bar: Calif. 1959, U.S. Dist. Cts. Calif. 1959, U.S. Supreme Ct. 1984. Atty. Rogers, Clark & Jordan, San Francisco, 1959-64; dep. dist. atty. Alameda County (Calif.), 1964-69; asst. dir. State of Calif. Human Resource Dept., Sacramento, 1969-72; dir. State of Calif. Dept. Rehab., Sacramento, 1972-75; gen. atty. Pacific Telephone & Telegraph, San Francisco, 1975-81; dep. commr. Immigration and Naturalization Service, Washington, 1981-82, commr. 1982-89; cons. fed. Am. immigration reform U.S. Dept. Justice, Washington, 1989-90, 91-94; gen. counsel employment devel. dept. State of Calif., 1990-91; atty. and cons. on immigration Sacramento, 1994—; adj. prof. McGeorge Sch. Law, U. Pacific. Chmn. Calif. Gov. Com. for Employment of Handicapped, 1981-82. Recipient Alumnus of Yr. award Tau Kappa Epsilon, 1987; Border Patrol Sta., Imperial Beach, Calif. dedicated to Commr. Nelson, 1988. Mem. State Bar Calif., Assn. Calif. Tort Reform (dir.), Bar Assn. San Francisco, Legal Aid Soc. San

Francisco (dir.), Assn. Fed. Investigators (pres. 1987). Republican. Club: Commonwealth. Office: Law Offices of Alan Nelson 835 Shoreside Dr Sacramento CA 95831-1422 *Four Key Personal and Management Concepts: Pride, Integrity, Innovation and Persistence. Pride: pride in ones country, family and traditions are a foundation for all meaningful personal actions. Integrity: most individuals have an innate sense of integrity; this pins integrity which is learned in one's life experience must also form the foundation for all actions. Innovation: constantly pursue new challenges and approaches, innovation, which makes our system so effective, is essential in all business and government. Persistence: in any bureacratic setting a lack of persistence can often equate to failure because most obstacles must be overcome with some difficulty.*

NELSON, ALAN RAY, internist, medical assocation executive; b. Logan, Utah, June 11, 1933; s. Ray J. and Leah B. (Olson) N.; m. Gwen L. Sparrow, Jan. 2, 1959; children: John R., Shannon, Alan L. Student, Utah State U., 1951-54; MD, Northwestern U., 1958. Diplomate Am. Bd. Internal Medicine, Am. Bd. Endocrinology and Metabolism. Intern Highland Alameda County Hosp., Oakland, Calif., 1958-59; resident in internal medicine U. Utah, Salt Lake City, 1959-62, assoc. clin. prof., 1964-89; clin. prof. U. Utah, 1989-92; practice medicine specializing in internal medicine and endocrinology Salt Lake City, 1964-91; assoc. Meml. Med. Ctr., Salt Lake City, 1964-91; exec. v.p. Am. Soc. Internal Medicine, Washington, 1992—; mem. Nat. Profl. Standard Rev. Coun., 1973-77; pres. Utah Profl. Rev. Orgn., 1971-75; mem. AMA Coun. on Legis., 1977-80, trustee 1980—, chmn. 1986-88, pres.-elect 1988-89, pres. 1989-90; commr. Joint Commn. on Accreditation of Hosps., 1982-86, sec.-treas., 1985-86. Served with M.C. USAF, 1962-64. Recipient Spl. Recognition award Am. Soc. Internal Medicine, 1973, Disting. Internist award, 1989. Fellow ACP; mem. Utah Med. Assn. (pres. from 1976, award 1973, 79), Inst. Medicine of NAS, (governing coun. 1984-87), World Med. Assn. (pres.-elect 1990-91, pres. 1992-92). Home: 11905 Parkside Dr Fairfax VA 22033 Office: ASIM 2011 Pennsylvania Ave NW Washington DC 20006

NELSON, ALFRED JOHN, retired pharmaceutical company executive; b. Dalmuir, Scotland, Jan. 24, 1922; came to U.S., 1972; s. John and Mary Catherine (Duncan) N.; m. Frances C. Hillier, Dec. 5, 1952; children: J. Stuart, Andrew D. MBChB, U. Glasgow, Scotland, 1945, MD with commendation, 1957; DPH, Royal Inst. Pub. Health and Hygiene, London, 1948. Resident Ayr County Hosp., 1945, Belvidere Fever Hosp., Glasgow, Scotland, 1948; cons. N.Y. State Dept. Health, Albany, 1950-51; dir. venereal disease control B.C. Dept. Health and Welfare, Vancouver, Can., 1952-55, cons. epidemiology, 1954-55; asst. dean medicine, assoc. prof. pub. health U. B.C., Can., 1955-57; dir. health services B.C. Hydro and Power Authority, Vancouver, Can., 1957-70; v.p. Hoechst-Roussel Pharm., Inc., Somerville, N.J., 1972-81, sr. v.p., med. dir., 1981-87, ret., 1987; hon. mem. staff Vancouver Gen. Hosp. Served with RCAF, 1953-56. Recipient John J. Sippy Meml. award APHA, 1959, Spl. award, 1960; named Officer Brother, Order of St. John of Jerusalem, 1967. Fellow ACP, Royal Coll. Physicians and Surgeons Can., Am. Coll. Preventive Medicine, N.Y. Acad. Medicine; mem. Can. Med. Assn. (sec. com. 1954-57). Presbyterian. Home: 29436 Port Royal Way Laguna Niguel CA 92677-7947

NELSON, ARTHUR HUNT, real estate management development company executive; b. Kansas City, Mo., May 21, 1923; s. Carl Ferdinand and Hearty (Brown) N.; m. Eleanor Thomas, Dec. 27, 1954; children: Carl F., Frances, Pamela. AB, U. Kans., 1943; JD, Harvard U., 1949. Bar: Mass. 1949. Staff radiation lab. MIT, 1943-44; sr. engr., cons. Raytheon Mfg. Co., Boston, 1948-52; pvt. practice Boston, 1949; v.p., treas., dir. Gen. Electronic Labs., Inc., Cambridge, Mass., 1951-64, chmn. bd., 1959-63; treas., dir. Sci. Electronics, Inc., Cambridge, 1955-64; treas., dir. Assocs. for Internat. Rsch., Inc., Cambridge, 1954—, pres., 1968—; treas., dir. Victor Realty Devel., Inc., Cambridge, 1959-76, pres., 1972-76, gen. ptnr., 1976—; gen. ptnr. Prospect Hill Exec. Office Park, Waltham, Mass., 1977—; chmn. Nelson Cos., 1990—, Cambridge Devel. Lab., 1994—; bd. dirs. Internat. Data Group, Inc., Sterling Bank; chmn. Cambridge Devel. Lab., Inc., 1994—. Pres., trustee Tech. Edn. Rsch. Ctrs., Inc., 1965—; trustee Winsor Sch., Boston, 1978-88, treas., 1978-82; bd. dirs. Charles River Mus. Industry, Waltham, 1986—, pres. 1994. Lt. USRN, 1944-46. Mem. ABA, Mass. Bar Assn., Boston Bar Assn., Boston Computer Soc. (bd. dirs. 1985—, chmn. 1994), Greater Boston C. of C., Harvard Club Boston, Beta Theta Pi, Phi Beta Kappa, Sigma Xi. Home: 75 Robin Rd Weston MA 02193-2436 Office: 100 5th Ave Waltham MA 02154-8704

NELSON, BEN, JR., air force officer; b. Ft. Lewis, Wash., Jan. 31, 1942; s. Ben and Marie (Warn) N.; m. Suzanne Wiseman, Dec. 22, 1963; 1 child: William Bryant. BBA, U. Tex., 1964; MPA, Golden Gate U., 1976. Commd. 2d lt. USAF, 1964, advanced through grades to brig. gen., 1988; instr. pilot 3525th Fighter Tng. Squadron, Williams AFB, Ariz., 1965-70; flight comdr. 390th Tactical Fighter Squadron, DaNang, Vietnam, 1970-71, Sheppard AFB, Tex., 1971-74; chief pers. tng. br. Office Dep. Chief of Staff for Pers., Hdqrs. Tactical Air Command, Langley AFB, Va., 1974-77; ops. officer, comdr. 428th Tactical Fighter Squadron, Nellis AFB, Nev., 1977-81; student Naval War Coll., Newport, R.I., 1981-82; chief fighter plans br. Office Dep. Chief of Staff Ops., Hdqrs. USAF, Washington, 1982-84; vice comdr. 32d Tactical Fighter Squadron, Soesterberg Air Base, The Netherlands, 1984-85; vice comdr., then comdr. 50th Tactical Fighter Wing, Hahn Air Base, Fed. Republic Germany, 1985-88; asst. dep. chief of staff for plans Hdqrs. Tactical Air Command, Langley AFB, 1988-89; comdr. 56th Fighter Wing, MacDill AFB, Fla., 1989-92; dep. comdr. 5th Allied Tactical Air Forces (NATO), Vincenza, Italy, 1992-94; CEO regional office ARC, Tampa Bay, Fla., 1994—. Recipient Phoenix award Dept. Def., 1987, O'Malley award Dept. Air Force. Mem. Air Force Assn., Tampa C. of C. (bd. dirs. 1989-92), Order of Daedalians. Episcopalian. Avocation: golf.

NELSON, BERNARD EDWARD, lawyer; b. Miles City, Mont., May 9, 1950; s. Theodore M. and Lucille K. Nelson; m. Jane Walker, Sept. 8, 1978; children: Iain, Colin, Stuart. BA, Yale U., 1972; JD, Harvard U., 1975. Bar: N.Y. 1976. Assoc. White & Case, N.Y.C., 1975-84; ptnr. White & Case, N.Y.C. and London, 1984—, London, 1988—. Mem. Union Internationale Des Avocats (U.S. rep. permanent tax commn.). Democrat. Avocations: antique map collecting, antiquarian books. Office: White & Case, 7 Moorgate, London EC2R 6HH, England

NELSON, BERNARD WILLIAM, foundation executive, educator, physician; b. San Diego, Sept. 15, 1935; s. Arnold B. and Helene Christina (Falck) N.; m. Frances Davison, Aug. 9, 1958; children—Harry, Kate, Anne, Daniel. A.B., Stanford U., 1957, M.D., 1961. Asst. prof., asst. dean medicine Stanford U., Palo Alto, Calif., 1965-67, assoc. dean medicine, 1968-71, cons. assoc. prof., 1980-86; assoc. dean U. Wis., Madison, 1974-77, acting vice chancellor, 1978-79; exec. v.p. Kaiser Family Found., Menlo Park, Calif., 1979-81, 1981-86; chancellor U. Colo. Health Sci. Ctr., Denver, 1986—; mem., v.p., pres. Nat. Med. Fellowships, 1969-77. Trustee Morehouse Med. Sch., 1981-83. Fellow Inst. Medicine; mem. Calif. Acad. Sci., Alpha Omega Alpha (bd. dirs. 1978—). Avocations: fishing; photography; gardening; carpentry. Office: U Colo Health Sci Ctr Office of Chancellor 4200 E 9th Ave Denver CO 80220-3706

NELSON, BRUCE SHERMAN, advertising agency executive; b. Lansing, Mich., Nov. 3, 1951; s. Max and Blanche (Sherman) N.; m. Minette Raskin. AB, UCLA, 1973. Sr. copywriter Ogilvy & Mather, Los Angeles, 1977-78, Young & Rubicam, N.Y.C., 1978-79; assoc. creative dir. McCann Erickson, Inc., N.Y.C., 1979-80, v.p. 1980-81, sr. v.p., 1981-83, exec. v.p., creative dir., 1983-86, exec. v.p., worldwide dir. strategic creative devel., 1987-93; exec. v.p., creative dir. worldwide accounts, 1994—; founder, chief exec. officer Ira Madris, Bruce Nelson & Colleagues, 1986?; lectr. Columbia Bus. Sch. Exec. Programs, N.Y.C., 1993—. Mgmt. fellow Sch. orgn. and Mgmt. Yale U., 1993—. Office: McCann-Erickson Worldwide 750 3rd Ave New York NY 10017-2703

NELSON, CARL ROGER, retired lawyer; b. Gowrie, Ia., Dec. 26, 1915; s. Carl Helge and Inez Olivia (West) N.; m. Elizabeth Boswell Campbell, Apr. 27, 1946; children: Thomas C., Nancy L. AB, Grinnell Coll., 1937; MA, Columbia, 1938, LLB, 1941. Bar: N.Y. 1941, D.C. 1947, U.S. Supreme Ct. 1947. Law clk. to Chief Justice Stone, 1941-42; Washington asso. firm Root,

Ballantine, Harlan, Bushby & Palmer, 1946-51; mem. firm Purcell & Nelson, Washington, 1951-80; firm Reavis & McGrath, 1980-83, Nelson Thurston Jones & Blouch, 1984-88; Mem. Adminstrv. Conf. U.S., 1967-73. Served to capt. AUS, 1942-46. Fellow Am. Bar Found.; mem. ABA (mem. ho. dels. 1964-66, mem. coun. 1960-66, chmn. sect. adminstrv. law 1963-64), D.C. Bar Assn. (chmn. corp. law, com. 1954-55, 58-60), Mediation Panel U.S. Ct. Appeals (D.C. cir.), Chevy Chase (Md.) Club, Lawyers Club (Washington), Met. Club (Washington), Phi Beta Kappa. Mem. United Ch. of Christ.

NELSON, CHARLES ARTHUR, publisher, consultant; b. Berwyn, Ill., Dec. 21, 1922; s. Arthur A.R. and Florence Dorothy (Lagergren) N.; m. Anne Ballou Higgins, July 1946; children: Christopher, Janet, Colin, Edward. BA, St. John's Coll., Annapolis, Md., 1947. Dir. liberal arts program, humanities lectr. U. Chgo., 1947-52; exec. dir. Am. Found. For Polit. Edn., Chgo., 1947-56; sr. cons. Cresap, McCormick & Paget, N.Y.C., 1956-58; pres. Nelson Assocs., N.Y.C., 1958-68; prin. Peat Marwick Mitchell & co., N.Y.C., 1968-83; pres. Exec. Search, Croton-on-Hudson, 1983—; pub. Croton-Cortlandt Gazette, Croton-on-Hudson, 1986—. Author: Developing Responsible Public Leaders, 1963; co-author: The University, The Citizen, & World Affairs, 1956, Financial Management for the Arts, 1975, Ratio Analysis in Higher Education, 1980, Ethics, Leadership and the Bottom Line, 1991; contbr. articles to jours. Chmn. bd. Exec. Council on Fgn. Diplomats, N.Y.C.; chmn. bd. St. John's Coll., Annapolis, Md., Santa Fe, 1978-83, trustee, 1952-91, Linfield Coll., McMinville, Oreg., 1983-88. Mem. N.Y. Press Assn. Democrat. Home and Office: PO Box 247 Croton On Hudson NY 10520-0247

NELSON, CHARLES J., university administrator, international consultant, diplomat, consultant; b. Mich., Mar. 5, 1920; m. Maureen Tinsley. A.B., Lincoln U., 1942; M.P.A., NYU, 1948. Research assoc. state govt., 1949-52; program asst. MSA Manila, 1952-53; pub. adminstrn. analyst FOA, 1953-54, pub. adminstrn. specialist, 1954-55; dep. spl. asst. for community devel. ICA, 1955-57; chief community devel. adviser Tehran, 1958; community devel. adviser Dept. State, 1960, chief Africa-Latin Am. br., 1960-61, detailed African br., 1961; assoc. dir. Office Program Devel. and Coordination PC, Washington, 1961-63; dir. Office Devel. Resources, AID, 1963-64, dir. North African affairs, 1964-66; dep. mission dir. Addis Ababa, 1966-68; mission dir. Dar es Salaam, 1968-71; ambassador to Botswana, Lesotho and Swaziland, 1971-74; mission dir. counsellor internat. devel. AID, Nairobi, Kenya, 1974-78; adminstr. program in internat. studies Sch. Human Ecology, Howard U., 1978-81. Mem. Overseas Devel. Coun.; chair Mayor's Internat. Adv. Council; bd. dirs. Nations Capital council Girl Scouts U.S.A., 1981-87, also mem. retention extension outreach com.; bd. dirs. D.C. Council Internat. Programs, 1981-87; v.p. nat. bd. dirs. Sister Cities Internat.; mem. U.S. D.C.-Beijing Friendship Council; mem. Thai-Am. Assn. Coun. Am. Ambassadors, U.S.-Dakar Capital Cities Friendship Council; co-chmn. Soc. for Internat. Devel., Africa Roundtable. Served to capt. AUS, 1942-47. Mem. Georgetown Citizens Assn., Voice of Informed Community Expression, Smithsonian Instn., Overseas Devel. Coun., The Atlantic Coun., Am. Polit. Sci. Assn., UN Assn., Diplomatic and Counselor Officers Ret., Friends of Ethiopia, Nat. Press Club, Internat. Club (Washington). Address: 1401 35th St NW Washington DC 20007

NELSON, CHARLES ROWE, economist, educator; b. Milw., Aug. 21, 1942; s. Elmer Rowe and Julia (Hydar) N.; B.A., Yale U., 1963; M.A., U. Wis., 1967, Ph.D., 1969; m. Kathleen Norman Yoerg, Sept. 6, 1969; children—John Charles, Roger Rowe. Mem. faculty Grad. Sch. Bus., U. Chgo., 1969-75; prof. U. Wash., Seattle, 1975—, chmn. dept. econs., 1979-84; dir. Stein Roe and Farnham mut. funds. Recipient Irving Fisher Grad. Monograph award Omicron Delta Epsilon, 1971. Mem. Am. Econ. Assn., Am. Fin. Assn., Am. Statis. Assn., Econometric Soc., Nat. Assn. Bus. Economists. Author: The Term Structure of Interest Rates, 1972; Applied Time Series Analysis for Managerial Forecasting, 1973. Home: 4921 NE 39th St Seattle WA 98105-5208 Office: U Wash DK 30 302 Savery Hall Dept Econs Seattle WA 98195

NELSON, CLIFFORD ARNOLD, retired bank executive; b. Lodi, Wis., Feb. 15, 1923; s. Henry Abel and Corine (Femreite) N.; m. Elizabeth Jean McCargo, Apr. 30, 1949; children: Paul, David, James, Janet, Robert. Ba, U. Wis., 1947. CPA, Wis. V.p., treas. West Bend (Wis.) Co., 1963-67, sr. v.p. fin., 1968-71; v.p. Dart Industries, West Bend, 1972-74; v.p. M&I 1st Nat. Bank, West Bend, 1975-79, pres., 1980-88, also bd. dirs.; bd. dirs. West Bend Mutual Ins. Co., Gehl Co., West Bend; chmn. bd. trustees Marsden Found, Oscar and Augusta Schlegal Found. Pres. West Bend Bd. Edn., 1969, Kettle Moraine YMCA, 1984; campaign chmn. Washington County United Way, West Bend, 1986. Mem. West Bend C. of C. (pres. 1985). Republican. Methodist. Club: West Bend Country. Lodge: Rotary (pres. West Bend 1979).

NELSON, CRAIG ALAN, management consultant; b. San Rafael, Calif., July 11, 1961; s. Kenneth Alfred and Anne Catherine (Laurie) N. BS in Fin., San Diego State U., 1984. Loan assoc. Union Bank, San Diego, 1984-85, commi. loan officer, 1985-86, corp. banking officer, 1986-87, asst. v.p., 1987-89, v.p. corp. banking, 1989-93; v.p. Alexander & Alexander, San Diego, 1993—. Corp. recruiter United Way, San Diego, 1988; community group chair San Diego chpt. Am. Cancer Soc., 1989; mem. com. Juvenile Diabetes Assn.; bd. dirs. San Diego State Found., 1989—. Mem. San Diego State U. Young Alumni Assn. (pres. 1988-89, bd. dirs. emeritus 1989). Home: 1233 San Dieguito Dr Encinitas CA 92024-5116 Office: Alexander and Alexander 9255 Towne Centre Dr Ste 225 San Diego CA 92121-3035

NELSON, CRAIG T., actor; b. Spokane, Wash., Apr. 4, 1946. Appeared in (feature films) And Justice for All, 1979, The Formula, 1980, Where the Buffalo Roam, 1980, Private Benjamin, 1980, Stir Crazy, 1981, Poltergeist, 1982, Man, Woman, and Child, 1983, The Osterman Weekend, 1983, All the Right Moves, 1983, The Killing Fields, 1984, Silkwood, 1984, Poltergeist II: The Other Side, 1986, Red Riding Hood, 1987, Action Jackson, 1988, Me and Him, 1988, Troup Beverly Hills, 1989, Rachel River, 1989, Turner & Hooch, 1989; (stage prodns.) Friends, 1983-84, (TV movies) How the West Was Won, 1978, Diary of a Teenage Hitchhiker, 1979, Rage, 1980, Inmates: A Love Story, 1981, Murder in Texas, 1981, Paper Dolls, 1983, Alex: The Life of a Child, 1986, The Ted Kennedy, Jr. Story, 1986, Murderers Among Us: The Simon Wiesenthal Story, 1989, Extreme Close-Up, 1990, Drug Wars: The Camarena Story, 1990, The Josephine Baker Story, 1991, The Fire Next Time, 1993; (TV series) Heroes: Made in the U.S.A. (host), 1986, Coach, 1993— (Emmy award, Leading actor in a comedy series, 1992); producer (film documentaries) American Still; screenwriter (TV shows) The Lohman and Barkley Show, The Tim Conway Show, The Alan King Special. Office: care Universal TV Coach 100 Universal City Plz Universal City CA 91608*

NELSON, CRAIG WAYNE, academy administrator; b. Mpls., Mar. 8, 1932; s. Clarence August and Blanche Adeline (Nordell) N.; m. Betty Ann McLouth, Oct. 27, 1956; children: Cynthia Ann, Jon Craig. AA, North Pk. Coll., 1951; student, Trinity Coll., Hartford, Conn., 1951-52; BA, Northwestern U., 1955, MA in History, 1959; BD, North Pk. Theol. Sem., 1956; postgrad., Ea. Mich. U., 1970-71. Ordained clergyperson Covenant Ch. Am. Intern pastor Queen St. Congl. Ch., Bristol, Conn., 1952-53; pastor Evang. Covenant Ch., Villa Park, Ill., 1956-61, 1st Covenant Ch., Red Wing, Minn., 1961-66, Dearborn (Mich.) Evang. Covenant Ch., 1966-71, Bloomington (Minn.) Covenant Ch., 1971-77; pres. Minnehaha Acad., Mpls., 1977-94; ednl. cons., 1995—; tchr. North Pk. Coll., 1958-59, Minnehaha Acad., 1979-90; chaplain Mpls. Police Dept., 1972-77, Bloomington Police Dept., 1973-77; area co-dir. Evangelism N.W. Conf., mem. exec. bd.; sec. N.W. Covenant Ministerium; active Covenant Bd. Ministry, Covenant Stewardship Commn. Active Bloomington Bd. Health, 1975-77; trustee Minn. Ind. Sch. Fund, 1979-91, v.p. 1980-81, 92-93, treas., 1991-92, pres., 1993-94. Named Disting. Alumni, North Pk. Coll., 1985. Mem. Coun. for Advancement and Support of Edn., North Ctrl. Assn. Bloomington Ministerial Assn. (chmn. 1974-75), Mpls. Ministerial Assn. (chmn. 1976-77), MISF (chairperson 1993-95). Avocations: fishing, hunting, boating, reading.

NELSON, DARRELL W., university administrator; b. Aledo, Ill., Nov. 28, 1939; s. Wayne Edward and Olive Elvina (Peterson) N.; m. Nancyann Hyer, Aug. 27, 1961; children: Christina Lynne, Craig Douglas. BS in Agriculture, U. Ill., 1961, MS in Agronomy, 1963; PhD in Agronomy, Iowa State U., 1967. Cert. profl. soil scientist. Div. chief U.S.

Army Chem. Corps., Denver, 1967-68; asst. prof. Purdue U., West Lafayette, Ind., 1968-73, assoc. prof., 1973-77, prof. agronomy, 1977-84; dept. head U. Nebr., Lincoln, 1984-88, dean for agr. rsch. and dir. Nebr. Agrl. Experiment Sta., 1988—; cons. U.S. EPA, Washington, 1977-79, Ind. Bd. of Health, Indpls., 1977-83, Eli Lilly Co., Indpls., 1976. Editor: Chemical Mobility and Reactivity in Soils, 1983. Served to capt. U.S. Army, 1967-68. Fellow AAAS, Am. Soc. Agronomy (bd. dirs., CIBA-Geigy award 1975, Agronomic Achievement award 1983, Environ. Quality Rsch. award 1985), Soil Sci. Soc. Am. (bd. dirs., pres. elect 1992, pres. 1993, past. pres. 1994); mem. Internat. Soil Sci. Soc., Lions Lodge (treas. 1980-83, Lafayette, Ind. chpt.). Presbyterian. Avocations: fishing, skiing, jogging. Office: Univ of Nebr Agrl Rsch Div Lincoln NE 68583-0704

NELSON, DAVID ALDRICH, federal judge; b. Watertown, N.Y., Aug. 14, 1932; s. Carlton Low and Irene Demetria (Aldrich) N.; m. Mary Dickson, Aug. 25, 1956; 3 children. A.B., Hamilton Coll., 1954; postgrad., Cambridge U., Eng., 1954-55; LL.B., Harvard U., 1958. Bar: Ohio 1958, N.Y. 1982. Atty.-advisor Office of the Gen. Counsel, Dept. of the Air Force, 1959-62; assoc. Squire, Sanders & Dempsey, Cleve., 1958-67, ptnr., 1967-69, 72-85; cir. judge U.S. Ct. Appeals (6th cir.), Cin., 1985—; gen. counsel U.S. Post Office Dept., Washington, 1969-71; sr. asst. postmaster gen., gen. counsel U.S. Postal Svc., Washington, 1971; mem. nat. coun. Coll. Law, Ohio State U., 1988—. Trustee Hamilton Coll., 1984-88. Served to maj. USAFR, 1959-69. Fulbright scholar, 1954-55; recipient Benjamin Franklin award U.S. Post Office Dept., 1969. Fellow Am. Coll. Trial Lawyers; mem. Fed. Bar Assn., Ohio Bar Assn., Cleve. Bar Assn., Cin. Bar Assn., Emerson Lit. Soc., Ct. of Nisi Prius (sgt. emeritus), Phi Beta Kappa. Office: US Ct Appeals 6th Cir Potter Stewart US Ct House 5th and Walnut St Cincinnati OH 45202-3988

NELSON, DAVID BRIAN, physicist; b. Lincoln, Nebr., Oct. 23, 1940; s. Carl Leroy and Charlotte Mary (Butler) N.; m. Kathryn Muriel Puester, May 12, 1964; children: Mark, Laura. AB, Harvard U., 1962; MA, NYU, 1965, PhD, 1967. Mem. research staff in engring. physics Oak Ridge (Tenn.) Nat. Lab., 1966-71, mem. research staff in plasma physics, 1971-79; chief fusion theory and computer services Office Fusion Energy, Dept. Energy, Washington, 1979-84, dir. applied plasma physics, 1984-87; dir. sci. computing Office Energy Research, 1987, exec. dir., 1987—; mem. adv. com. on civil def. Nat. Research Council, Washington, 1968-71; vis. mem. Courant Inst., NYU, 1975-76. Contbr. articles to profl. jours. Council pres. bd. trustees Christ Luth. Ch., Bethesda, Md., 1986-87. Recipient Appreciation award Def. Electric Power Adminstrn., Washington, 1973. Mem. Am. Phys. Soc. Avocations: tennis, skiing, music, drama. Office: US Dept Energy Office Energy Research Washington DC 20585

NELSON, DAVID EDWARD, lawyer; b. Passaic, N.J., Oct. 26, 1930; s. David Charles and Ann Ellen (Pardoe) N.; m. Stuart McKenna, May 28, 1953; children: Douglas, Kathryn, Ann; m. Elizabeth A. Carlston, Dec. 28, 1974; children: Lynnen, Kathleen. A.B., UCLA; LL.B., U. Calif.-Berkeley; Diploma in Comparative Legal Studies, U. Cambridge, Eng., 1960. Bar: Calif. Assoc. Morrison & Foerster, San Francisco, 1960-65, ptnr., 1965—. Bd. dirs. Berkeley Bd. Edn., 1967-69; chmn. bd. Head-Royce Sch., Oakland, Calif., 1974-79. Served to lt. (j.g.) U.S. Navy, 1952-56. Mem. San Francisco Bar Assn. (pres. Barrister Club), ABA (chmn. bus. law sect. 1988-89), Calif. Bar Assn. (com. bar examiners 1973-77, chmn. 1976-77), Southwestern Legal Found., Bankers Club. Office: Morrison & Foerster 345 California St San Francisco CA 94104-2606

NELSON, DAVID LEONARD, process management systems company executive; b. Omaha, May 8, 1930; s. Leonard A. and Cecelia (Steinert) N.; m. Jacqueline J. Zerbe, Dec. 26, 1952; 1 child, Nancy Jo. BS, Iowa State U., 1952. Mktg. adminstr. Ingersoll Rand, Chgo., 1954-56; with Accuray Corp., Columbus, Ohio, 1956-87, exec. v.p., gen. mgr., 1967, pres., 1967-87, chief exec. officer, 1970-87; pres. process automation bus. unit Combustion Engring., Inc., Columbus, 1987-90; pres. bus. area process automation Asea Brown Boveri, Stamford, Conn., 1990-91, v.p. customer satisfaction Ams. region, 1991-93, v.p. customer support Ams. region, 1994—; bd. dirs. Herman Miller Inc. Patentee in field. Bd. dirs. Cardinal Govt. Obligations Fund, Columbus, Cardinal Govt. Securities Trust, Columbus, Cardinal Tax Exempt Money Trust, Columbus, Cardinal Govt. Guaranteed Fund, Columbus, Cardinal Aggressive Growth Fund, Columbus, Cardinal Balanced Fund, Columbus. Served to capt. USMCR, 1952-54. Mem. IEEE, Instrument Soc. Am., Newcomen Soc. N.Am., Tau Beta Pi, Phi Kappa Phi, Phi Eta Sigma, Delta Upsilon. Home: 18 Janes Ln Stamford CT 06903-4825 Office: Asea Brown Boveri Inc 501 Merritt #7 PO Box 5308 Norwalk CT 06856

NELSON, DAVID ROBERT, physics educator; b. Stuttgart, Federal Republic of Germany, May 9, 1951; came to U.S., 1953; s. Robert Charles and Faye Scott (Abernethy) N.; m. Patricia Schneider, Dec. 30, 1975; children: Meredith, Leigh. Christopher David, Peter Charles. AB, Cornell U., 1972, MS, 1974, PhD, 1975; MA (hon.), Harvard U., 1980. Jr. fellow Harvard Soc. Fellows, Cambridge, Mass., 1975-78; assoc. prof. physics Harvard U., 1978-80; prof. Harvard U., Cambridge, 1980-91, Mallinckrodt prof. physics, 1992—; cons. IBM, Yorktown Heights, N.Y., 1976-82, Mitre Corp., Bedford, Mass., 1985—, AT&T Bell Labs., Murray Hill, N.J., 1988—, Exxon Rsch. and Engring., 1994—. Co-author: Phase Transitions and Critical Phenomena, Vol. 7, 1983; co-author, editor: Statistical Mechanics of Membranes and Interfaces, 1989. A.P. Sloan Found. fellow, 1979-83, MacArthur Found. Prize fellow, 1984-89, Guggenheim fellow, 1993—; recipient award for initiatives in rsch. NAS, 1986. Fellow Am. Phys. Soc., Harvard Soc. Fellows (sr.); mem. APS, AAAS, NAS, Am. Acad. Arts and Scis. Office: Harvard U Dept Physics Cambridge MA 02138

NELSON, DAVID S., federal judge; b. Boston, Mass., Dec. 2, 1933; s. Maston A. and Enid M.N. BS, Boston Coll., 1957, JD, 1960. Ptnr. Crane, Inker & Oteri, 1960-73; U.S. commr., 1968-69; asst. atty. gen. State of Mass., 1971-73; justice Superior Ct. Mass., Boston, 1973-79; judge U.S. Dist. Ct. Mass., Boston, 1979-91, sr. judge, 1991—. Fellow Am. Bar Found.; mem. Am. Law Inst. Office: US Dist Ct 90 Devonshire St Rm 1805 Boston MA 02109-4570

NELSON, DEWEY ALLEN, neurologist, educator; b. Eldrado, Ark., Dec. 2, 1927; s. Herman Eugene and Pearl Estelle (Shirley) N.; m. E. Jem Nolt, Oct. 7, 1951; children: Allen, Stephen, Jean, John, Daniel. BS, Cornell U., 1948, MD, 1951. Diplomate Am. Bd. Psychiatry and Neurology, Am. Bd. Neurophysiology. Resident Bellevue Hosp., N.Y.C., 1951-52, 54-57; chief neurology Med. Ctr. Del., Wilmington, 1957-83, sr. neurology, 1983-88, hon. sr. neurology, 1988—; chief neurology St. Francis Hosp., Wilmington, 1957-83; founder, neurologist Neurology Assocs., Wilmington, 1957-85; assoc. clin. prof. neurology Thomas Jefferson U. Med. Ctr., Phila., 1971-75 prof. neurology, 1975—; med. expert, advisor to ct. Social Security Adminstrn., 1982—. Contbr. 70 articles to profl. jours., poetry to periodicals. 1st lt. U.S. Army, 1952-54, Korea. Decorated Bronze Star; recipient Bronze Hope Chest award Nat. Multiple Sclerosis Soc., 1960, Plaque award Multiple Sclerosis Clinic, 1979; Teagle Found. scholar, 1946-51. Republican. Presbyterian (ruling elder). Avocations: metal work cast iron, antique cars, choir. Home: 206 N Spring Valley Rd Wilmington DE 19807

NELSON, DON HARRIS, gas and oil industry executive; b. Phila., Mar. 18, 1932; s. Morris Daniel and Catherine (Kaplan) N.; m. Ruth Kaiser Nelson, Aug. 31, 1959 (div. 1981); children: Michael Stewart, Pamela Blair, Randolph Miles, Timothy Blake; m. Karen Fulton, Feb. 12, 1982. BA, Yale U., 1953; MBA, U. Pa., 1957. Project engr. GE, Phila., 1957-60; mgr. exploration Kaiser Francis Oil Co., Tulsa, 1960-77; CEO Sanguine, Ltd, Greenwich, Conn., 1977—; mem. Yale Devel. Bd., 1988—; chmn. Mus. African Art, N.Y.C., 1991-94. Pres. Family and Childrens Svc. Agy., Tulsa, 1975. Capt. USMC, Korea. Mem. Stanwich Club, Yale Club (N.Y.C.), Tulsa Tennis Club. Avocations: post-impressionistic and African art, tennis, skiing, scuba diving. Home: 1121 Lake Ave Greenwich CT 06831 Office: Sanguine Ltd 3 Pickwick Plz Greenwich CT 06830

NELSON, DON JEROME, electrical engineering and computer science educator; b. Nebr., Aug. 17, 1930; s. Irvin Andrew and Agnes Emelia (Nissen) N. BSc, U. Nebr., 1953, MSc, 1958; PhD, Stanford U., 1962. Registered profl. engr., Nebr. Mem. tech. staff AT&T Bell Labs.,

Manhattan, N.Y., 1953, 55; instr. U. Nebr., Lincoln, 1955-58, from asst. to assoc. prof., 1960-63, dir. computer ctr., 1963-72, prof. electrical engring., 1967—; prof. computer sci., 1969—, co-dir. Ctr. Comm. & Info. Sci., 1988-91, dir. rsch. computing group, 1993—; cons. Union Life Ins., Lincoln, 1973, Nebr. Pub. Power Dist., Columbus, 1972-83, Taiwan Power Co., Taipei, 1974. 1st lt. USAF, 1953-55. Mem. IEEE (sr., Outstanding Faculty award 1989), Assn. Computing Machinery. Republican. Home: 1620 East Manor Dr Lincoln NE 68506 Office: U Nebr 209N Wsec Lincoln NE 68588

NELSON, DONALD ARVID (NELLIE NELSON), professional basketball coach; b. Muskegon, Mich., May 15, 1940. Student, U. Iowa. Player NBA teams, Chgo. Zephyrs, 1962-63, Los Angeles Lakers, 1963-65, Boston Celtics, 1965-76; from asst. to head coach Milw. Bucks NBA, 1976-87, also dir. player personnel; exec. v.p., part owner Golden State Warriors, NBA, Oakland, Calif., 1987-95; mem. Nat. Basketball championship teams, 1966, 68, 69, 74, 76; head coach Golden State Warriors, 1988-95, New York Knicks, 1995—; coach Dream Team II, 1994. Named Coach of Yr. NBA, 1983, 85, 92. Office: care New York Knicks Two Pennsylvania Plaza New York NY 10121*

NELSON, DONALD J., engineering executive. Exec. v.p. corp. devel. and comms. Michael Baker Corp., Coraopolis, Pa., 1965—. Office: Michael Baker Corp 420 Rouser Rd 3 Coraopolis PA 15108

NELSON, DOROTHY PATRICIA, health policy analyst, educator; b. Herrin, Ill., July 4, 1921; d. Hugh and Catherine (Disney) Mercer; m. John Robert Nelson, Aug. 18, 1945; children: Eric Mercer, William John. BS, So. Ill. U., 1942; MPH, Yale U., 1946; MBA, Boston U., 1977, PhD, 1984. Dir. edn. Children's Hosp., Boston, 1971-74; asst. prof., administr. sch. medicine Boston U., 1974-76; dir. planning Carney Hosp., Boston, 1976-83; mgr. planning Tex. Med. Ctr., Houston, 1985-86; spl. asst. to pres. U. Tex. Health Scis. Ctr., Houston, 1986-88; assoc. prof. health care Tex. Women's U., Houston, 1985-87; pres., exec. dir. Health Access Tex. Inc., Houston, 1988—; adj. prof. health mgmt. U. St. Thomas, Houston, 1988—; nat. bd. dirs. Health Planning Forum, Washington, Founder, pres. Neighbors of Hermann Park, Houston, 1991-93; bd. dirs. The Planning Forum, 1988-94. Recipient Health Security award Sen. Edward Kennedy, 1968. Fellow Am. Coll. Healthcare Execs.; mem. APHA, Yale Club Houston (bd. dirs. 1991—), Rotary Club Houston. Democrat. Methodist. Office: Health Access Tex 1111 Hermann Dr Ste 19A Houston TX 77004-6930

NELSON, DOROTHY WRIGHT (MRS. JAMES F. NELSON), federal judge; b. San Pedro, Calif., Sept. 30, 1928; d. Harry Earl and Lorna Amy Wright; m. James Frank Nelson, Dec. 27, 1950; children: Franklin Wright, Lorna Jean. B.A., UCLA, 1950, J.D., 1953; LL.M., U. So. Calif., 1956; LLD honoris causa, Western State U., 1980, U. So. Calif., 1983, Georgetown U., 1988, Whittier U., 1989, U. Santa Clara, 1990. Bar: Calif. 1954. Research assoc. fellow U. So. Calif., 1953-56; instr., 1957, asst. prof., 1958-61, assoc. prof., 1961-67, prof., 1967, assoc. dean., 1965-67, dean., 1967-80; judge U.S. Ct. Appeals (9th cir.), 1980—; cons. Project STAR, Law Enforcement Assistance Adminstrn.; mem. select com. on internal procedures of Calif. Supreme Ct., 1987—; co-chair Sino-Am. Seminar on Mediation and Arbitration, Beijing, 1992; dir. Dialogue on Transition to a Global Soc., Weinacht, Switzerland, 1992. Author: Judicial Adminstration and The Administration of Justice, 1973; Contbr. articles to profl. jours. Co-chmn. Confronting Myths in Edn. for Pres. Nixon's White House Conf. on Children, Pres. Carter's Commn. for Pension Policy, 1974-80, Pres. Reagon's Madison Trust; bd. visitors U.S. Air Force Acad., 1978; bd. dirs. Council on Legal Edn. for Profl. Responsibility, 1971-80, Constnl. Right Found., Am. Nat. Inst. for Social Advancement; adv. bd. Nat. Center for State Cts., 1971-73; chmn. bd. Western Justice Ctr., 1986—; mem. adv. com. Nat. Jud. Edn. Program to promote equality for woman and men in cts. Named Law Alumnus of Yr. UCLA, 1967; recipient Profl. Achievement award, 1969; named Times Woman of Yr., 1968; recipient U. Judaism Humanitarian award, 1973; AWARE Internat. award, 1970; Ernestine Stalhut Outstanding Woman Lawyer award, 1972; Pub. Sc. award Coro Found., 1978, Pax Orbis ex Jure medallion World Peace thru Law Ctr., 1975, Hollzer Human Rights award Jesish Fedn. Coun. L.A., 1988, Medal of Honor UCLA, 1993; Lustman fellow Yale U. 1977. Fellow Am. Bar Found., Davenport Coll., Yale U.; mem. Bar Calif. (bd. dirs. continuing edn. bar commn. 1967-74), Am. Judicature Soc. (dir., Justice award 1985), Assn. Am. Law Schs. (chmn. com. on edn. in jud. adminstrn.), Am. Bar Assn. (sect. on jud. adminstrn., chmn. com. on edn. in jud. adminstrn. 1973-89), Phi Beta Kappa, Order of Coif (nat. v.p. 1974-76), Jud. Conf. U.S. (com. to consider standards for admission to practice in fed. cts. 1976-79). Office: US Ct Appeals Cir PO Box 91510 125 S Grand Ave Pasadena CA 91105-1652

NELSON, DOTSON MCGINNIS, JR., clergyman; b. Clinton, Miss., Mar. 11, 1915; s. Dotson McGinnis and Mary (White) N.; m. Grace Elizabeth Philpot, Oct. 8, 1941; children—Carol Lois, Dotson McGinnis III, Mary Grace, William Philpot. B.A. summa cum laude, Miss. Coll., 1935; Th.M., So. Bapt. Theol. Sem., 1938, Ph.D., 1945; D.D., Furman U., 1958, Miss. Coll., 1973, Samford U., 1981. Ordained to ministry Bapt. Ch., 1935; pastor Vinton Bapt. Ch., Roanoke, Va., 1941-42, Second Bapt. Ch., Richmond, 1942-44, Calvary Bapt. Ch., Kansas City, Mo., 1946-52, 1st Bapt. Ch., Greenville, S.C., 1952-61, Mountain Brook Bapt. Ch., Birmingham, Ala., 1961-81; now pastor emeritus. Mountain Brook Bapt. Ch.; Mem. fgn. mission bd. So. Bapt. Conv., 1942-43, 47-52, 54-60, 1st v.p., 1976-77; exec. com., 1977-88; chmn. exec. bd. Ala. Bapt. Conv., 1966-68, mem. exec. bd., 1966-72, 78—, pres. conv., 1973-74, 74-75, mem. ednl. adv. com., 1975-81, chmn. ednl. adv. com., 1975-79; chmn. (Edn. Commn.), 1979-81; mem. Commn. Religious Liberty and Human Rights, Bapt. World Alliance, 1970-75; Bus. activities dir. Home Savs. & Loan, Kansas City, Mo., 1949-52. Chmn. bd. dirs. Found. for Pastoral Counseling and Consultation; dir. Spastic Aid Ala., 1961; trustee So. Bapt. Theol. Sem., William Jewell Coll., 1948-52, Samford U., 1961-66; trustee Furman U., 1957-61, chmn. trustees, 1959-61; bd. visitors Mo. Bapt. Hosp., 1949-52; bd. dirs. YMCA, Birmingham, So. Bapt. Found., 1968-70, Bapt. Hosp. Found. Birmingham, So. Bapt. Hosps., 1968-70. Served to lt. Chaplains Corps USNR, World War II. Recipient Service to Humanity award Miss. Coll., 1976. Mem. So. Bapt. Sem. Alumni Assn. (pres. Ala. 1980-81), Greater Birmingham Ministers Assn. (pres. 1971). Lodge: Kiwanis. Home: Ste 211 3850 Galleria Woods Dr Birmingham AL 35244 Office: Mountain Brook Bapt Ch 3631 Montevallo Rd South Birmingham AL 35213-4422

NELSON, DOUGLAS A., pathologist, educator; b. Windom, Minn., 1927. MD, U. Minn., 1954. Diplomate Am. Bd. Pathology (trustee 1979-90, pres. 1988), Am. Bd. Hematology. Intern Phila. Gen. Hosp., 1954-55; resident in pathology Mallory Inst. Pathology, Boston, 1955-58; chief resident Boston City Hosp., 1957-58; med. fellow Affiliated Hosps. U. Minn. Hosps., 1958-60; instr., lab. medicine U. Minn., 1960-63, asst. prof., 1963-64; assoc. prof., dep. dir. clin. pathology SUNY, Syracuse, 1964-69, prof., dep. dir. clin. pathology, 1969-93, prof. emeritus, 1993—; mem. Res. Rev. Com. for Pathology, 1985-90. With USNR, 1945-46. Mem. AMA, Am. Soc. Clin. Pathologists, Am. Soc. Hematology, Acad. Clin. Lab. Physicians and Scientists, Phi Beta Kappa, Sigma Xi, Alpha Omega Alpha. Office: SUNY Health Sci Ctr 750 E Adams St Syracuse NY 13210-2306

NELSON, DOUGLAS LEE, insurance company executive; b. Washington, Mar. 7, 1944; s. John Jacob and Sharett L. (Legreid) N. BA, U. So. Calif., 1967. Planning USAID/MACV, Republic of Vietnam, 1968-69; life mgmt. staff Prudential Ins. Co., L.A., 1971-75; planning cons. Prudential Ins. Co., Roseland, N.J., 1975-77; small group health staff Prudential Ins. Co., L.A., 1978-82; svc. support staff Prudential Ins. Co., Mpls., 1983-87, mutual funds staff, 1988-90; quality svc. exec. Prudential Ins. Co., Newark, 1990-93; quality officer Prudential Direct, Newark, 1993-95; gen. mgr. pub. rels. Prudential Policyowners, 1995—. Bd. dirs. treas. Self Reliance Str., Mpls. 1986-88, Pax World Found., Washington, 1991—; mem. aviation adv. coun. NJDOT, 1994—. Mem. Am. Soc. Quality Control, Internat. Svc. Quality Assn. (edn. com. 1991—), Quality Productivity Mgmt. Assn., Assn. Quality and Participation, Life Ins. Mktg. Rsch. Assn. (quality bus. com. 1991—; examiner, N.J. Quality Achievement award 1993-94, Exptl. Aircraft Assn. (chpt. pres. 1991—), Conf. Bd., Sierra Club (exec. com. Northstar chpt. 1989-90). Avocations: skiing, sailing, flying, airplane building and restoration. Office: Prudential Ins Co Am PO Box 17100 New Brunswick NJ 08906-7100

NELSON, DOUGLAS W., social service administrator; b. 1946. With State of Wis., Madison, 1967-85, Ctr. for Study Policy, Washington, 1985-90, The Annie E. Casey Found., Greenwith, Conn., 1990—; now exec. dir., pres. The Annie E. Casey Found., Greenwith. Office: The Annie E Casey Found 1 Lafayette Pl Greenwich CT 06830*

NELSON, E. BENJAMIN, governor; b. McCook, Nebr., May 17, 1941; s. Benjamin Earl and Birdella Ruby (Henderson) N.; B.A., U. Nebr., 1963, M.A., 1966, J.D., 1970; LLD (hon.) Creighton U., 1992, Peru State Coll., 1993; m. Diane C. Gleason, Feb. 22, 1980; children by previous marriage—Sarah Jane, Patrick James; stepchildren—Kevin Michael Gleason, Christine Marie Gleason. Bar: Nebr. 1970. Instr. dept. philosophy U. Nebr., 1963-65; supr. Dept. Ins., State of Nebr., Lincoln, 1965-72, dir. ins., 1975-76; asst. gen. counsel, gen. counsel, sec., v.p. The Central Nat. Ins. Group of Omaha, 1972-75, exec. v.p., 1976-77, pres., 1978-81, CEO, 1980-81, of counsel, Kennedy, Holland, DeLacy & Svoboda, Omaha, 1985-90; gov. State of Nebr., Lincoln, 1991—. Co-chmn. Carter/Mondale re-election campaign, Nebr., 1980; chair Nat. Edn. Goals Panel, 1992-94, Gov.'s Ethanol Coalition, 1991-94, chair 1991, 94; pres. Coun. of State Gov's., 1994. Named Amb. Plenipotentiary, 1993. Mem. Consumer Credit Ins. Assn., Nat. Assn. Ind. Insurers, Nat. Assn. Ins. Commissioners (exec. v.p. 1982-85), Nebr. Bar Assn., Am. Bar Assn., Midwestern Gov's. Assn. (chair 1994), Western Gov.'s Assn. (vice chair 1994), Happy Hollow Club, Omaha Club, Hillcrest Country Club. Democrat. Methodist. Home: 1425 H St Lincoln NE 68508-3759 Office: State Capitol 2nd Floor Lincoln NE 68509*

NELSON, EDITH ELLEN, dietitian; b. Vicksburg, Mich., Sept. 26, 1940; d. Edward Kenneth and Anna (McManus) Rolffs; m. Douglas Keith Nelson; children: Daniel Lee, Jennifer Lynn. BS, Mich. State U., 1962; MEd in Applied Nutrition, U. Cin., 1979. Lic. dietitian, Fla. Clin. dietitian Macon (Ga.) Gen. Hosp., Blodgett Meml. Hosp., Grand Rapids, Mich.; grad. teaching asst. U. Cin., 1978-79; dir. nutrition svcs. Dialysis Clinic, Inc., Cin., 1979-88; cons. dietitian Panama City Devel. Ctr., Ft. Walton Beach Devel. Ctr., Fla., 1988-94, N.W. Fla. Community Hosp., Chipley, Fla., 1993-94, Beverly Enterprises, Panama City Beach, 1994—; renal dietitian Dialysis Svcs. Fla., Ft. Walton Beach, 1989-92. Mich. Edn. Assn. scholar, 1958; Nat. Kidney Found. grantee, 1986. Mem. Am. Dietetic Assn., Fla. Dietetic Assn., Panhandle Dist. Dietetic Assn., Nat. Kidney Found. (coun. on renal nutrition, Fla. coun. on renal nutrition), Omicron Nu. Home: 150 Grand Lagoon Shores Dr Panama City Beach FL 32408

NELSON, EDWARD GAGE, merchant banking investment company executive; b. Nashville, May 17, 1931; s. Charles and Polly (Prentiss) N.; m. Carole Olivia Frances Minton, Sept. 17, 1960; children—Carole Gervais, Emily Minton, Ellen Prentiss. B.A. in Polit. Sci., U. of South, Sewanee, 1952. Exec. v.p. Clark, Landstreet & Kirkpatrick, Inc., Nashville, 1955-64; exec. v.p. Commerce Union Bank, Nashville, 1968-72, pres., 1972-82, cons., 1985—, chmn., chief exec. officer, 1982-84; chmn., pres. Nelson Capital Corp., Nashville, 1985—; hon. consul gen. Japan; dir. Werthan Packaging, SouthCap Corp., Franklin Industries, Osborn Comm., A Plus Comm., Trans Arabian Investment Bank, ClinTrials, Inc., Berlitz Internat., Inc., Ctrl. Parking Sys., Advocat Inc.; mem. 1st adv. coun. Japan/Tenn. Soc. Trustee Vanderbilt U. Nashville, 1979—, chmn. med. ctr. bd., 1984—; vice chmn. Pub. Edn. Nashville Citizens; mem. De Tocqueville Soc. of United Way. Spl. agt. U.S Army, 1955, Japan. Mem. Belle Meade Country Club, Cumberland Club, River Club (N.Y.C.). Republican. Episcopalian. Home: 1305 Chickering Rd Nashville TN 37215-4521 Office: Nelson Capital Corp 3401 W End Ave Ste 300 Nashville TN 37203-1085

NELSON, EDWARD HUMPHREY, architect; b. Winchester, Mass., Sept. 2, 1918; s. Richard MacDonald and Evelyn Miller (Humphrey) N.; m. Lois Whitaker Renouf, Sept. 24, 1948 (dec.); children: Susan, David, Sarah; m. Miriam P. Ketcham, Jan. 2, 1988. Grad., Lenox Sch., 1936; B.Arch., Yale, 1950. Pvt. archtl. practice Tucson, 1953-61; sr. v.p. CNWC Architects, Tucson, 1961-88, pres., 1989-94; bd. dirs. CNWC & Steppe Archs.; mem. adv. com. U. Ariz. Coll. Arch., 1984-93. Works include: design for Tucson Community Ctr. Pres. Tucson Cmty. Coun., 1969-71, Tucson Art Ctr., 1960, Tucson Housing Found., 1969-92; bd. dirs. Tucson Trade Bur., 1976-91, pres., 1984; bd. dirs. Tucson Symphony, 1977-84, Tucson United Way, 1980; trustee Green Fields Sch., 1960-74, Tucson Art Mus.; vestry St. Philips Episc. Ch., 1967-69, sr. warden, 1987-90, parish warden, 1993-94; convenor Episcopal Interparish Coun., 1990-92; mem. Episcopal Diocese of Ariz., W.W. Regional Parish. Served to capt. AUS, 1940-41, WWII, ETO. Decorated Bronze Star with oak leaf cluster, Purple Heart; recipient Disting. Citizen award U. Ariz., 1981. Fellow Am. Inst. Architects (pres. So. Ariz. chpt. 1962, chmn. Ariz. fellows 1986-90); mem. Ariz. Soc. Architects (pres. 1963). Democrat. Episcopalian. Clubs: Yale (Tucson) (pres. 1962, 83, dir. 1979—); U. Ariz. Pres.'. Home: 2020 E 4th St Tucson AZ 85719-5114

NELSON, EDWARD SHEFFIELD, lawyer, former utility company executive; b. Keevil, Ark., Feb. 23, 1941; s. Robert Ford and Thelma Jo (Mayberry) N.; m. Mary Lynn McCastlain, Oct. 12, 1962; children: Cynthia, Lynn (dec.), Laura. BS, U. Cen. Ark., 1963; LLB, Ark. Law Sch., 1968; JD, U. Ark., 1969. Mgmt. trainee Ark. La. Gas Co., Little Rock, 1963-64; sales engr. Ark. La. Gas Co., 1964-67, sales coordinator, 1967-69, gen. sales mgr., 1969-71, v.p., gen. sales mgr., 1971-73, pres., dir., 1973-79, pres., chmn., chief exec. officer, 1979-85; ptnr., chmn. bd., chief exec. officer House, Wallace, Nelson & Jewel, Little Rock, 1985-86; pvt. practice law Little Rock, 1986—; of counsel Jack, Lyon & Jones, P.A., 1991—; bd. dirs. Fed. Res. Mem. N.G., 1957-63; bd. dirs. U. Ark., Little Rock, vice chmn. bd. visitors, 1981; bd. dirs. Philander Smith Coll., 1981; chmn. Ark. Indsl. Devel. Commn., 1987, 88; past chmn. Little Rock br. Fed. Res. Bd. St. Louis; chmn. Econ. Expansion Study Commn., 1987—; bd. dirs. Ark. Ednl. TV Found., Ark. Game and Fish Commn. Found.; founder, 1st pres. Jr. Achievement Ark., 1987-88; Rep. nominee for Gov. of Ark., 1990, 94; co-state chmn. Ark. Reps., 1991-92, nat. committeeman Ark. GOP, 1993—. Named Ark.'s Outstanding Young Man Ark. J. C. of C., 1973; One of Am.'s Ten Outstanding Young Men U.S. Jr. C. of C., 1974; Citizen of Yr. Ark. chpt. March of Dimes, 1983; Humanitarian of Yr. NCCJ, 1983; Best Chief Exec. Officer in Natural Gas Industry Wall Street Transcript, 1983; recipient 1st Disting. Alumnus award U. Cen. Ark., 1987. Mem. Am., Ark., Pulaski County bar assns., Ark. C. of C. (dir.), Little Rock C. of C. (dir., pres. 1981), Sales and Mktg. Execs. Assn. (pres. 1975, Top Mgmt. award 1977), U. Ark. Law Sch. Alumni Assn. (pres. 1980). Methodist. Office: 6th and Broadway 3400 Tcby Bldg Little Rock AR 72201

NELSON, EDWIN CLARENCE, academic administrator, emeritus; b. Dallas, S.D., Apr. 19, 1922; s. Clifford and Vera (Usher) N.; m. Avis Hedrix, Nov. 15, 1941; children—Judy, Roger. A.B., Kearney (Nebr.) State Coll., 1950; M.E., West Tex. State U., 1953; Ed.D., U. Nebr., 1959; postgrad., U. Minn., 1959; LHD (hon.), U. Nebr., Kearney, 1993. Tchr. math. and sci. pub. schs. Nebr., 1947-50; supt. schs. Huntley, Nebr., 1950-52, Wilcox, Nebr., 1953-56, Red Cloud, Nebr., 1956-59; tchr. aircraft mechanics Amarillo (Tex.) AFB, 1952-53; asso. prof. edn. Kearney State Tchrs. Coll., 1959-61; dean coll., dir. grad. studies Chadron (Nebr.) State Coll., 1961-67, pres., 1967-73, 75-86, pres. emeritus, Disting. Service prof., 1986—; community devel. specialist, 1988—; Leadership Seminars, 1988—; exec. officer bd. trustees Nebr. State Colls., 1973-75; Mem. Council State Coll. Presidents, Nebr. Ednl. TV Commn., Nebr. Council Econ. Edn.; rep. Am. Assn. State Colls. and Univs.; pres. Nebr. Ednl. TV Council for Higher Edn., 1967, 85; exec. com. Nebr. Council Tchr. Edn. Served with AUS, 1942-45. Recipient Disting. Svc. award Kearney State Coll., 1968, Disting. Svc. award Chadron State Coll., 1989; named Boss of Yr., Chadron Jaycees, 1971, Chadron Citizen of the Yr., 1985, AK-SAR-BEN Ike Friedman Community Leader, 1994. Mem. Nebr. Edn. Assn. (pres. 1967), Chadron C. of C. (Magic Key award 1988), Phi Delta Kappa. Republican. Methodist. Clubs: Elk, Kiwanian. I have appreciated my opportunities to serve education at all levels.

NELSON, EDWIN L., federal judge; b. 1940. Student, U. Ala, 1962-63, Samford U., 1965-66; LLB, Samford U., 1969. Mem. firm French & Nelson, Ft. Payne, Ala., 1969-73; pvt. practice law French & Nelson, 1974; magistrate U.S. Dist. Ct. (no. dist.) Ala., Birmingham, 1974-90, judge, 1990—. With USN, 1958-62. Mem. Ala. Bar Assn., Birmingham Bar Assn., 11th Cir. Assn. U.S. Magistrates, Nat. Coun. Magistrates, Phi Alpha Delta. Office: US Dist Ct Hugo L Black Courthouse 1729 5th Ave N Fl 7 Birmingham AL 35203-2000

NELSON, ELMER KINGSHOLM, JR., educator, writer, mediator, consultant; b. Laramie, Wyo., Sept. 14, 1922; s. Elmer Kingsholm and Alice (Downey) N.; m. Jane Beckwith Oliver, Aug. 4, 1945; 1 son, Elmer Kingsholm III (Kirk). BA, U. Wyo., 1943, JD, 1948, MA, 1949; Dr. Pub. Adminstrn., U. So. Calif. 1959. Instr. psychology U. Wyo., 1947-49; psychologist, staff psychologist dept. probation Contra Costa County, Calif., 1949-51; sr. psychologist Cal. State Dept. Corrections, San Quentin and Chino Prisons, 1951-52; asst. prof. criminology U. B.C., Can., 1952-54; assoc. prof. U. B.C., 1954-56, head criminology div., 1953-56; warden Haney Correctional Instn., B.C., 1956-58; assoc. dir. Youth Studies Ctr. U. So. Calif., 1958-59, dir. Youth Studies Ctr., 1959-64, assoc. prof. pub. adminstrn., 1958-61, prof., 1961—, dean Sch. Pub. Adminstrn., 1971-76, prof., co-dir. Sacramento Pub. Affairs Ctr.; head Bay Area Research Center, Berkeley, 1979—; dep. adminstr. Youth and Adult Corrections Agy., State of Calif., Sacramento, 1964-65; interim exec. dir. Office Criminal Justice Planning, spring 1975; dir. Nat. Study Probation and Parole, 1976-77; chmn. task force on corrections, asso. dir. Pres.'s Commn. on Law Enforcement and Adminstrn. of Justice, Washington, 1966-67; dir. nat. study of correctional adminstrn. U. So. Calif. for Joint Commn. on Correctional Manpower and Tng., 1967-69. Co-author: Corrections in America, 1975; contbr. articles, monographs, research reports to profl. jours. Advisor on mgmt. Boys Republic, Chino, Calif., 1967—; bd. dirs., v.p. Am. Justice Inst., Sacramento; bd. dirs. Human Interaction Rsch. Inst., L.A. Recipient Disting. Alumnus award U. Wyo., 1975, Exemplary Alumni award U. Wyo. Coll. Arts and Scis., 1994; Ford Found. Travel Study grantee, 1970-71; E. Kim Nelson endowed doctoral fellowship established at U. So. Calif. 1987. Mem. Nat. Acad. Pub. Adminstrn., Wyo. Bar Assn., Alpha Tau Omega. Home: 2825 Ptarmigan Dr # 1 Walnut Creek CA 94595

NELSON, ERLAND RANDALL, educator, neurologist; b. Blair, Nebr., June 4, 1928; s. Erland P. and Naida (Randall) N.; divorced; children—Pamela, Katherine. B.S. cum laude, Carthage Coll., 1947, Sc.D. (hon.), 1973; M.D., Columbia U., 1951; Ph.D., U. Minn., 1961. Diplomate: Am. Bd. Neurology and Psychiatry. Intern U. Chgo. Clinics, 1951-52; resident neurology U. Minn. Hosps., 1952-55; from instr. to asso. prof. neurology U. Minn. Med. Sch., 1957-64; prof. neurology, head dept. U. Md. Med. Sch., 1964-80; vis. prof. cardiology Tokyo Med. and Dental Sch., 1972-73; mem. Residency Rev. Com. for Psychiatry and Neurology, 1974-78; chmn. dept. neurology Mt. Sinai Hosp., Chgo., 1981—; prof. neurology Rush Med. Sch., 1981—. Author: Outline of Neuropathology, 1959; co-author: Cerebrovascular Diseases, 1980; editorial bd.: Stroke, 1969-74, Jour. Neuropathology and Exptl. Neurology, 1973-78. Bd. dirs. Epilepsy Found. Am., 1974-76; mem. nat. exec. com. Stroke Council of Am. Heart Assn., 1974-76, 83—. Served to capt. USAF, 1955-57. NIH fellow neuropathology Munich, Germany, 1960-61. Fellow Acad. Neurology; mem. Am. Neurol. Assn., Am. Assn. Neuropathologists, Electron Microscope Soc. Am., Assn. U. Profs. Neurology (pres. 1972-73), Balt. Neurol. Soc. Office: Mt Sinai Hosp Dept Neurology Rm 551 S California Ave & 15th St Chicago IL 60612-3323

NELSON, FREDA NELL HEIN, librarian; b. Trenton, Mo., Dec. 16, 1929; d. Fred Albert and Mable Carman (Doan) Hein; m. Robert John Nelson, Nov. 1, 1957 (div. Apr. 1984); children: Thor, Hope. Nursing diploma, Trinity Luth. Hosp., Kansas City, Mo., 1950; B. Philosophy, Northwestern U., 1961; MS in Info. and Libr. Sci., U. Ill., 1986. RN. Operating rm. nurse Trinity Luth. Hosp., Kansas City, Mo., 1950-52, Johns Hopkins Hosp., Balt., 1952, Wesley Meml. Hosp., Chgo., 1952-58, Tacoma Gen. Hosp., 1958-59, Chgo. Wesley Hosp., 1959-61; libr. asst. Maple Woods Campus Met. Community Colls., Kansas City, 1987-89, libr., libr. mgr. Blue Springs Campus, 1989—; co-founder Coll. for Kids, Knox Coll., Galesburg, Ill., 1982. Nurses scholar Edgar Bergen Found., 1947; recipient Award of Merit, Chgo. Bd. Health, 1952. Avocations: swimming, walking, cross-word puzzles. Home: 7000 N Elm St Pleasant Valley MO 64068 Office: Blue Springs Campus Libr 1501 W Jefferson St Blue Springs MO 64015-7242

NELSON, FREDERICK CARL, mechanical engineering educator; b. Braintree, Mass., Aug. 8, 1932; s. Carl Edwin and Marjorie May (Miller) N.; m. Delia Ann Dwaresky; children: Jeffrey, Karen, Richard, Christine. BSME, Tufts U., 1954; MS, Harvard U., 1955, PhD, 1961. Registered profl. engr., Mass. Instr. Tufts U., Medford, Mass., 1955-57, asst. prof. mech. engring., 1957-64; assoc. prof. mech. engring. Tufts U., Medford, 1964-71, prof. mech. engring., 1971—, dean engring., 1980-94; bd. dirs. Mass. Tech. Park Corp., Westboro. Translator: (book) Mechanical Vibrations for Engineers, 1983. Fellow ASME (Centennial Medal award 1980), Acoustical Soc. Am.; mem. AAAS, Nat. Inst. Applied Scis. of Lyons (medal 1988), Korea Advanced Inst. Sci. and Tech. (medal 1988), Tufts U. Alumni Assn. (medal 1991). Office: Tufts U Coll Engring Medford MA 02155-5555

NELSON, GARETH JON, zoologist, curator, educator; b. Chgo., Dec. 23, 1937; s. Harry Walfred and Nina Elizabeth (Torke) N.; m. Brenda Gill, Oct. 20, 1971 (div. 1982); children: Annelise, Jennifer. Student, U. Chgo., 1953-55; BS, Roosevelt U., 1962; PhD, U. Hawaii, 1966. Curator Am. Mus. Natural History, N.Y.C., 1967—; adj. prof. biology CUNY, 1974—; vis. fellow U. Melbourne, 1989-90. Co-author: Systematics and Biogeography, 1981, Vicariance Biogeography, 1981. With U.S. Army, 1955-58. Postdoctoral fellow NSF, 1966, Winston Churchill traveling fellow English-Speaking Union, 1981. Fellow Willi Henning Soc. (councillor 1985—); mem. Soc. Systematic Zoology (pres. 1985-86), Am. Soc. Ichthyologists and Herpetologists (Stoye award 1965), Linnean Soc. London (fgn.). Office: Am Mus Natural History Central Park St West New York NY 10026

NELSON, GARRETT R., retail food company executive. Sr. v.p., CFO, The Vons Cos. Inc., Arcadia, Calif., until 1987, exec. v.p. retail support group, 1987-91, exec. v.p., chief exec. officer. Office: Vons Cos Inc 618 Michillinda Ave Arcadia CA 91007-6300

NELSON, GARY, county councilman, engineer; b. Spokane, Wash., Apr. 11, 1936; s. Nels Alfred and Laura Marie (Winberg) Nelson; m. JoAnne Laura Knudson, Nov. 27, 1959; children: Grant, Geoffrey, Gregory. BSEE, Wash. State U., 1958; MSEE, U. Wis., 1963. Engr. RCA, Camden, N.J., 1958-59; officer USAF, Madison, Wis., 1959-62; mgr. U.S. West, Seattle, 1963-90; pvt. practice Edmonds, Wash., 1990-94; bd. dirs. Stevens Hosp. Found., Edmonds, Olympic Ballet, Snohomish County Health Dist., 1994—, United Way of Snohomish County, Everett, 1986-92; Wash. State Legislator, 1972-94. planning commn. City of Edmonds, 1964-67, city coun., 1968-74. Capt. USAF, 1959-62. Mem. Sons of Norway, Rotary. Republican. Lutheran. Home: 9710 Wharf St Edmonds WA 98020-2363 Office: Snohomish County Coun 3000 Rockefeller M/S 609 Everett WA 98201

NELSON, GAYLORD ANTON, former senator, association executive; b. Clear-Lake, Wis., June 4, 1916; s. Anton and Mary (Bradt) N.; m. Carrie Lee Dotson, Nov. 14, 1947; children—Gaylord, Cynthia, Jeffrey. Grad., San Jose State Coll., Calif., 1939, U. Wis. Law Sch., 1942. Bar: Admitted Wis. bar 1942. Practiced in Madison, 1946-58; mem. Wis. Senate, 1949-58, Democratic leader, 1948-52; gov. Wis., 1958-62, U.S. senator from Wis., 1963-81; mem. finance com., chmn. subcom. on Social Security; chmn. employment, poverty and migratory labor subcom. of human resources com.; chmn. select com. on small bus., chmn. monopoly subcom. Author: Environmental Education Act, 1970, Nat. Environmental Education Act, 1972; co-author: The National Teacher Corps, 1965. Counselor Wilderness Soc., Washington, 1981—; founder Earth Day. 1st lt. AUS, World War II. Recipient Conservationist of the Year Award, Nat. Wildlife Fedn., 1989, Only One Earth Award, Environmental Leadership Award, UN Environment Prog., 1992, Presdl. Freedom medal, 1995. Mem. State Bar Assn. Wis. Home: 3611 Calvend Ln Kensington MD 20895-3154 Office: Wilderness Soc 900 17th St NW Washington DC 20006-2500

NELSON, GLEN DAVID, medical products executive, physician; b. Mpls., Mar. 28, 1937; s. Ralph and Edna S. Nelson; m. Marilyn Carlson, June 30, 1961; children: Diana, Curtis, Wendy. AB, Harvard U., 1959; MD, U. Minn., 1963. Diplomate Am. Bd. Surgery, also sub-bd. bariatric and peripheral vascular surgery. Intern Hennepin County Gen. Hosp., Mpls., 1963-64, resident in gen. surgery, 1964-69; staff surgeon Park Nicollet Med. Ctr.

(formerly St. Louis Park Med. Ctr.), Mpls., 1969-86, pres., chmn. bd. trustees, 1975-86; chmn., CEO Am. Med Ctrs., Mpls., 1984-86; exec. v.p. Medtronic, Inc., Mpls., 1986-88, vice chmn., 1988—, also bd. dirs.; clin. prof. dept. surgery U. Minn.; bd. dirs. Northwestern Nat. Life Inst. Co., Mpls., Carlson Holdings, Inc., Mpls., St. Paul Cos., Medtronic, Inc., Mpls. Fellow ACS (del.); mem. AMA, Am. Acad. Med. Dirs., Am. Coll. Physician Execs., Hennepin County Med. Assn., Greater Mpls. C. of C. (chmn. 1987), Jackson Hole Group. Office: Medtronic Inc 7000 Central Ave NE Minneapolis MN 55432

NELSON, GORDON LEIGH, chemist, educator; b. Palo Alto, Calif., May 27, 1943; s. Nels Folke and Alice Virginia (Fredrickson) N. BS in Chemistry, U. Nev., 1965; MS, Yale U., 1967, PhD, 1970; DSc (hon.), William Carey Coll., 1988. Staff research chemist corp. research and devel. Gen. Electric Co., Schenectady, N.Y., 1970-74; mgr. combustibility tech. plastics div. Gen. Electric Co., Pittsfield, Mass., 1974-79, mgr. environ. protection plastics div., 1979-82; v.p. materials sci. and tech. Springborn Labs. Inc., Enfield, Conn., 1982-83; prof., chmn. dept. polymer sci. U. So. Miss., Hattiesburg, 1983-89; dean Coll. Sci. and Liberal Arts, prof. chemistry Fla. Inst. Tech., Melbourne, 1989—, mem. coun. sci., soc. pres., sec., 1989-90, chair-elect, 1991, chair, 1992; cons. in field. Author: Carbon-13 Nuclear Magnetic Resonance for Organic Chemists, 1972, 2d edit., 1980; co-author: Polymer Materials-Chemistry for the Future, 1989, Carbon Monoxide and Human Lethality, 1993; editor: Fire and Polymers--Hazard Identification and Prevention, 1990, Fire and Polymers II--Materials and Tests for Hazards Prevention, 1995; editor books on coatings sci. tech.; contbr. articles to profl. jours. Mem. Am. Inst. Chemists (Mems. and Fellow lectr. award 1989), Soc. Plastics Engrs., Am. Chem. Soc. (pres. 1988, bd. dirs. 1977-85, 87-89, 92-94, Henry Hill award 1986), Info. Tech. Industry Coun. (chmn. Plastics Task Group), ASTM (E5 cert. of appreciation 1985), Ctr. Sci., Tech. and the Media (bd. dirs. 1991—), So. Soc. for Coatings Tech., IEC (U.S. tech. adv. group on info. processing equipment), Structural Plastics divsn. Soc. of the Plastics Industry (Man of Yr. 1979), Coun. Colls. Arts and Scis., Yale Chemists Assn. (pres. 1981—), Nev. Hist. Soc., Sigma Xi. Republican. Presbyterian. Avocations: travel, western U.S. history. Office: Fla Inst Tech Coll Sci & Liberal Arts 150 W University Blvd Melbourne FL 32901-6967

NELSON, GRANT STEEL, lawyer, educator; b. Mitchell, S.D., Apr. 18, 1939; s. Howard Steel and Clara Marie (Winandy) N.; m. Judith Ann Haugen, Sept. 22, 1962; children: Mary Elizabeth, Rebekah Anne, John Adam. B.A. magna cum laude, U. Minn., 1960; J.D. cum laude, 1963. Bar: Minn. 1963, Mo. 1971. Assoc. firm Faegre & Benson, Mpls., 1963-67; mem. law faculty U. Mo., Columbia, 1967-91; assoc. prof. U. Mo., 1970-72, prof., 1972-91, Enoch H. Crowder prof. law, 1974-91; prof. UCLA, 1991—; bd. legal advs. Great Plains Legal Found., 1978-85; vis. asst. prof. law U. Mich., Ann Arbor, 1969-70, Brigham Young U., Provo, Utah, summer 1976; vis. prof. law U. Minn., Mpls., 1981-82, UCLA, 1989-90; disting. vis. prof. Pepperdine U., 1987-88; commr. Nat. Conf. Commrs. Uniform State Laws, 1983-91; mem. West Pub. Law Sch. Adv. Bd. Author: (with Van Hecke and Leavell) Cases and Materials on Equitable Remedies and Restitution, 1973, (with Whitman) Cases and Materials on Real Estate Finance and Development, 1976, Cases and Materials on Real Estate Transfer, Finance and Development, 1981, (with Osborne and Whitman) Real Estate Finance Law, 1979, (with Leavell and Love) Cases and Materials on Equitable Remedies and Restitution, 1980, (with Whitman) Land Transactions and Finance, 1983, rev. edit., 1988, (with Whitman) Real Estate Finance Law, 1985, rev. edit., 1994, (with Leavell and Love) Cases and Materials on Equitable Remedies, Restitution and Damages, 1986, rev. edit., 1994, (with Whitman) Cases and Materials on Real Estate Transfer, Finance and Development, 1987, (with Browder, Cunningham, Steobuck and Whitman) Basic Property Law, 1989, (with Whitman) Cases and Materials on Real Estate Transfer, Finance and Development, 1992; co-reporter ALI Restatement of Land Security; contbr. articles to profl. jours. Served to 1st lt. AUS, 1964-65. Recipient award for meritorious service and achievement U. Mo. Law Sch. Found., 1974; recipient Disting. Faculty Service award U. Mo.-Columbia Alumni Assn., 1978, Disting. Faculty award, 1986, Disting. Non-Alumnus award, 1991. Fellow Am. Bar Found.; mem. ABA, Mo. Bar Assn. (vice chmn. property law com. 1974-75, chmn. 1975-77), Assn. Am. Law Schs. (sect. chmn. 1976-77), Am. Law Inst., Am. Coll. Real Estate Lawyers, Order of Coif, Phi Beta Kappa, Phi Delta Phi. Home: 24609 Plover Way Malibu CA 90265 Office: UCLA Sch Law 405 Relgard Ave Los Angeles CA 90024

NELSON, H. H. RED, insurance company executive; b. Herman, Nebr., June 2, 1912; m. Ruth Hansen; children: John, Steve. B.A., U. Nebr., 1934, J.D., 1937. Bar: Nebr. 1938; C.L.U., 1948. Asst. mgr. life accident group depts. Travelers Inc. Co., Omaha, 1939-44; chmn. bd. Redlands Ins. Co., 1945—, Ins. Agts. Inc., Council Bluffs, Iowa, 1945—, Am. Agrisurance Co., 1945—, Homestead Ins. Co., 1987—, U.S. Agrl., Texas, 1988—; chmn. Redland Group Cos. Pres. United Fund, Western Iowa council Boy Scouts Am.; bd. dirs. Nat. Scout Council; pres. Christian Home Orphanage, Council Bluffs Indsl. Found. Mem. Ind. Ins. Agts. Am. (pres. 1964-65, Woodworth Meml. award 1966), Iowa Assn. Ins. Agts. (nat. dir., pres. 1957-60, Heritage award 1986), C. of C. (bd. dirs.). Lodges: Elks (past exalted ruler), Masons, Shriners. Office: Redland Group Inc 535 W Broadway Council Bluffs IA 51503-0812

NELSON, HAROLD BERNHARD, museum director; b. Providence, R.I., May 14, 1947; s. Harold B. and Eleanor (Lavina) N. BA, Bowdoin Coll., 1969; MA, U. Del., 1972. Rsch. fellow NMAA Smithsonian Inst., Washington, 1976-77; curator Am. art Mus. Art & Archeol., U. Mo., Columbia, 1977-79; registrar Solomon R. Guggenheim Mus., N.Y.C., 1979-83; exhibition program dir. Am. Fedn. Arts, N.Y.C., 1983-89; dir. Long Beach (Calif.) Mus. of Art, 1989—; juror Annual Art Exhibition Mus. Art, Sci. & Industry, Bridgeport, Conn., 1988, Annual Art Exhibition, Clark County Dist. Libr., Las Vegas, Nev., 1984; speaker Am. Assn. Mus. Annual Conf., Detroit, 1985, annual meeting Western Mus. Conf., Portland, Oreg., 1987, Grantmakers in Art Symposium, N.Y.C., 1986, annual meeting Western Mus. Conf., Salt Lake City, 1985; mem. adv. com. APA, Assn. Sci. and Tech. Ctrs.; panelist Aid to Spl. Exhibitions, NEA, Washington, 1986; participant Am. Legal Assn., ABA Conf., San Francisco, 1986; observer, respondent Mus. Symposium, NEA, Dallas, 1985. Author: Sounding the Depths: 150 Years of American Seascape, 1989. Office: Long Beach Mus Art 2300 E Ocean Blvd Long Beach CA 90803-2442

NELSON, HARRY, journalist, medical writer; b. Interlachen, Fla., Apr. 18, 1923; s. Knut Alfred and Edith Farr (Wilkes) N.; m. Diane Gabriella Meerschaert, Aug. 29, 1948 (div. 1977); children--Tanya Ann, Lawrence Stephen, Ronald Gerard, James Anthony, John Christopher; m. Gita Doris Wheelis, Jan. 29, 1984. B.A., U. So. Calif., 1949. Reporter, photographer Bakersfield Press, Calif., 1949; reporter, photographer Bakersfield Community Chest, Calif., 1949; promotion writer Los Angeles Times, 1949-57, reporter, 1957-58, med. writer, 1958-88, sr. writer, 1977-80; freelance med. writer, 1988—; med. writer Milbank Meml. Fund, 1993—. Charter mem. bd. dirs. Los Angeles County Comprehensive Health Planning Assn., Los Angeles, 1968-69. Served with USAAF, 1941-45. Recipient spl. commendation AMA, 1974, John Hancock award John Hancock Ins. Co., 1978, Journalism award Am. Acad. Pediatrics, 1979, Disting. Svc. by non-physician award Calif. Med. Assn., 1988, Lifetime Achievement in med. writing award AMA, 1988, Peter Lisagor award for exemplary journalism Chgo. Headliners Club, 1988. Mem. Nat. Assn. Sci. Writers (pres. 1966). Avocations: sailing; hiking; ceramics. Address: Med Writers Internat PO Box N 14016 Yellowstone Dr Frazier Park CA 93222

NELSON, H(ARRY) DONALD, communications executive; b. Chgo., Nov. 23, 1933; s. Harry Emmanual and Elsie Ina (Liljedahl) N.; m. Carol Jacqueline Stewart, Mar. 31, 1956; children: Donald S., David S., Sharon Nelson Arnold. BS in Bus., Northwestern U., 1955, MBA with distinction, 1959. Salesperson Procter & Gamble, Chgo., 1955-58; product mgr. Gen. Electric Corp., Syracuse, N.Y., 1959-72; mktg. mgr. Tex. Instruments, Dallas, 1972-74; v.p. mktg. Rockwell Internat., Anaheim, Calif., 1974-75, HMW-Pulsar, Lancaster, Pa., 1975-77; mgr. market and product devel. Gen. Electric Corp., Louisville, 1977-80; v.p. mktg. Genesco, Nashville, 1981-83; v.p. cellular bus. Telephone and Data Systems, Chgo., 1983-85; pres., chief exec. officer U.S. Cellular, Chgo., 1986—; mem. mgmt. alumni adv. bd. dirs. Kellogg Grad. Sch. With U.S. Army. Mem. Cellular Telecomm. Industry Assn. (bd. dirs. 1984—, com. chmn. 1985-89, exec. com. 1991—, treas.), Am. Stock Exch.

(listed co. adv. coun.). Republican. Baptist. Office: US Cellular 8410 W Bryn Mawr Ave Ste 700 Chicago IL 60631-3486

NELSON, HARVEY FRANS, JR., retired foreign service officer; b. Long Beach, Calif., Jan. 26, 1924; s. Harvey Frans and Marian (Norris) N.; m. Celia Anne Kendrick, June 27, 1947 (dec. June 1985); children--Erik Frans, Kai David, Peter Norris, Annika Di Vittorio; m. Esta Harrie de Fossard, May 31, 1987; children: Granville, Beatrice. B.A., Occidental Coll., 1948; postgrad., Stockholm U., 1948-49; M.A., Fletcher Sch. Internat. Law and Diplomacy, Medford, Mass., 1950. Commd. fgn. service officer Dept. State, 1951; dep. chief of mission Am. embassy, Pretoria, Republic of South Africa, 1976-79; diplomat in residence Ariz. State U., Tempe, 1979-80; dep. commandant U.S. Army War Coll., Carlisle, Pa., 1980-84; ambassador Am. embassy, Mbabane, Swaziland, 1985-88; sr. advisor U.S. Del. to UN, 1988, 90. Served to lt. (j.g.) USN, 1942-46.

NELSON, HELAINE QUEEN, lawyer; b. Hamtramck, Mich., Mar. 15, 1945; d. Willard Myron and Helen Victoria (Nebraska) Bowers; m. William Michael Nelson, Apr. 19, 1970; 1 child, Lindsey Paige. BS, Western Mich. U., 1969, MS, 1971; JD, U. Detroit, 1977. Bar: Ohio 1977, U.S. Dist. Ct. (no. and so. dists.) Ohio 1978, Ill. 1985. Corp. counsel Beverage Mgmt., Inc., Columbus, Ohio, 1977-79, assoc. gen. counsel, 1979-80, gen. counsel, 1980-84; sr. atty. Abbott Labs., Abbott Park, Ill., 1984-87; div. counsel Abbott Labs., Columbus, 1987—. Mem. Ohio Bar Assn., Am. Corp. Counsel Assn. Unitarian. Avocations: freelance writing, jogging, reading. Office: Ross Products Divsn 625 Cleveland Ave Columbus OH 43215-1754

NELSON, HELEN MARTHA, retired library director; b. Anaconda, Mont., Dec. 20, 1929; d. Ole Bertin and Caroline Helen (Massey) N. BA with honors, U. Mont., 1951; MLS, U. Wash., 1960. Asst. documents and serials libr. U. Mont., Missoula, 1951-52; tchr. English and history, libr. Laurel H.S., 1952-54; tchr. English, libr. Beaverhead County H.S., 1954-56; tchr. English, journalism Anaconda Sr. H.S., 1956-59; libr., adminstr. U.S. Army, 1960-68; libr. dir. Oceanside (Calif.) Libr., 1968-94; chmn. Serra Coop. Libr., 1973-74, 84-85, 90-91; mem. coun. Serra Coop. Sys., 1969-94. Chmn. Christian Sponsors, Oceanside, 1975; congl. pres. King of Kings Luth. Ch., Oceanside, 1974, 77, 84, mem. coun. 1971-77, 82-84, 92-94; bd. dirs. Oceanside/Carlsbad ARC, 1970-71; del. Calif. Gov.'s Conf. Librs. and Info. Sci. Mem. ALA, AAUW, LWV, Mont. Libr. Assn., Calif. Libr. Assn. (coun. 1978-80, v.p. Palomar chpt. 1978), Rep. Club, Libr. Execs. of So. Calif., Oceanside C. of C., Calif. Inst. Libr. Offs. (bd. dirs. 1978-80). Avocations: photography, travel, crewel embroidery.

NELSON, HERBERT LEROY, psychiatrist; b. Eddyville, Iowa, June 15, 1922; s. Albert and Bessie Mae (Durham) N.; m. Carol Lorayne Hofert, Dec. 23, 1943; children--Richard Kent, Vicki Lurae, Thadeus Leroy, Cylda Vermae. B.A., U. Iowa, 1943, M.D. 1946. Diplomate Am. Bd. Psychiatry and Neurology. Intern Univ Hosps. of U. Iowa, Iowa City, 1946-47; resident Brooke Army Med. Ctr, Fort Sam Houston, Tex., 1947-49, U.S. VA Hosp., Knoxville, Iowa, 1949-51; resident Oreg. State Hosp., Salem, 1951-52, clin. dir., 1952-63; asst. prof. psychiatry U. Iowa, Iowa City, 1963-66; assoc. prof. U. Iowa, 1966-73, prof., 1973-84, prof. emeritus, 1984—; dir. Iowa Mental Health Authority, Iowa City, 1968-82; med. dir. Mideast Iowa Community Mental Health Ctr., Iowa City, 1969-84; adj. prof. Tulane U., New Orleans, 1974-77. Co-author 4 monographs; also articles, 1965-83. Served as capt. M.C., U.S. Army, 1947-49. Fellow Am. Psychiat. Assn.; mem. Iowa Psychiat. Soc. (pres. 1970-71, chmn. subcom. on psychiat. care 1973-77), AMA, Johnson County Med. Soc., Am. Assn. Psychiat. Adminstrs., Am. Coll. Mental Health Adminstrs. Republican. Methodist. Avocations: gardening; fishing; woodworking; painting; travel. Home and Office: 1400 Laura Dr Iowa City IA 52245-1539

NELSON, HOWARD JOSEPH, educator, geographer; b. Gowrie, Iowa, Jan. 12, 1919; s. Joseph A. and Hannah (Swanson) N.; m. Betty Marie Garlick, June 18, 1944; children: Linda Ann, James Allan. B.A. with high honors, Iowa State Tchrs. Coll., 1942; M.A., U. Chgo., 1947, Ph.D., 1949. Mem. faculty UCLA, 1949—, prof. geography, 1963-86, prof. emeritus, 1986—, chmn. dept., 1966-71. Author: (with W.A.V. Clark) Los Angeles, The Metropolitan Experience, 1976, The Los Angeles Metropolis, 1983. Served with AUS, 1943-46. Mem. Assn. Am. Geographers (regional councillor 1968-71), Sigma Xi. Home: 6136 Kentland Ave Woodland Hills CA 91367-1719 Office: Univ Calif Los Angeles CA 90024

NELSON, IVORY VANCE, university president; b. Curtis, La., June 11, 1934; s. Elijah H. and Mattie (White) N.; m. Patricia Robbins, Dec. 27, 1985; children: Cherlyn, Karyn, Eric Beatty, Kim Beatty. BS, Grambling (La.) State U., 1959; PhD, U. Kans., 1963. Assoc. prof. chemistry So. U., Baton Rouge, 1963-67, head div. sci., 1966-68; prof. chemistry Prairie View (Tex.) A&M U., 1968-83, asst. acad. dean, 1968-72, v.p. rsch., 1972-82, acting pres., 1982-83; exec. asst. Tex. A&M U. System, College Station, 1983-86; chancellor Alamo C.C. Dist., San Antonio, 1986-92; pres. Cen. Wash. U., Ellensburg, 1992—; DuPont teaching fellow U. Kans., 1959; rsch. chemist Am. Oil Co., 1962; sr. rsch. chemist Union Carbide Co., 1969; vis. prof. U. Autonomous Guadalajara, Mex., 1966, Loyola U., 1967; Fulbright lectr., 1966; cons. evaluation coms. Oak Ridge (Tenn.) Assoc. Univs., NSF, Nat. Coun. for Accreditation Tchr. Edn., So. Assn. Colls. and Schs. Author: regional policy coms. on minorities Western Interstate Com. on Higher Edn., 1986-88; mem. exec. com. Nat. Assn. State Univs. and Land Grant Colls., 1980-82. Contbr. articles to profl. jours. Bd. dirs. Target 90, Goals San Antonio, 1987-89, Commn. on Student Learning, Wash., 1992—, United Way San Antonio, 1987-89, Alamo Area coun. Boy Scouts Am., 1987-89, San Antonio Symphony Soc., 1987-91, Key Bank of Wash.; mem. com. fir jud. reform State of Tex., 1991; mem. edn. adv. bd. Tex. Rsch. Park, 1987-89; bd. givs. Am. Inst. for character Edn., Inc., 1988-91; mem. adv. com. Tex. Ho. of Reps., 1978; chmn. United Way Campaign Tex. A&M U. System, 1984, others. Staff sgt. USAF, 1951-55, Korea. T.H. Harris scholar Grambling State U., 1959; fellow Nat. Urban League, 1969. Mem. AAAS, Am. Chem. Soc., Tex. Acad. Sci., NAACP, Phi Beta Kappa, Sigma Xi, Phi Lambda Upsilon, Beta Kappa Chi, Alpha Mu Gamma, Kappa Delta Pi, Sigma Pi Sigma, Omega Psi Phi, Sigma Pi Phi, Phi Kappa Phi. Avocations: fishing, photography, sports. Home: 211 E 10th Ave Ellensburg WA 98926-2911 Office: Office of Pres Cen Wash U Ellensburg WA 98926

NELSON, J. GORDON, geography educator. Prof. dept. geography U. Waterloo, Ont., Can. Recipient Massey medal Royal Can. Geog. Soc., 1993. Office: U Waterloo, Dept Geography, Waterloo, ON Canada N2L 3G1*

NELSON, J. ROBERT, lawyer; b. Santa Monica, Calif., Apr. 3, 1944. Attended, U. Utah; BS, UCLA, 1968, JD, 1971. Bar: Calif. 1972, Utah, 1985, U.S. Dist. Ct. (so. and no. dists.) Calif. 1975, U.S. Ct. Military Appeals 1973. Ptnr. Sidley & Austin, L.A. Editor notes and comments UCLA Law Review, 1970-71. Lt. JAGC, USN, 1972-75. Mem. ABA, State Bar Calif., Utah State Bar, L.A. County Bar, Order of Coif. Office: Sidley & Austin 555 W 5th St 40th Fl Los Angeles CA 90013-1010

NELSON, JACK LEE, education educator; b. Cheyenne, Wyo., Nov. 2, 1932; s. Myron Alfred and Mary Elizabeth (Baker) N.; m. Gwen Margret Names, Mar. 13, 1953; children: Barbara Louise Nelson Vollmer, Steven Lee. B.A., U. Denver, 1954; M.A., Calif. State U.-Los Angeles, 1958; Ed.D., U. So. Calif., 1961. Tchr. pub. schs., Riverside, Calif., 1956-58; instr. Calif. State U., Los Angeles, 1958-59, asst. prof., 1959-63; instr. Citrus Community Coll., Glendora, Calif., 1959-63; assoc. prof. SUNY, Buffalo, 1963-68, chmn. dept., 1966-68; prof. edn. Rutgers U., New Brunswick, N.J., 1968—, Disting. prof., 1975; dean, prof. Sch. Edn. San Jose (Calif.) State U., 1986-87; chmn. dept. sci. and humanities edn. Rutgers U., 1972-75; vis. prof. Cambridge U., Eng., 1974, 75, 79, 80, 83, 84, 85; vis. scholar U. Calif., Berkeley, 1975-76, Stanford U., 1982-83, Western Australia Inst. Tech., 1985, U. Colo., 1989, U. Wash., 1993, U. Sydney, Australia, 1994-95; cond. editor Random House Inc., McGraw-Hill Inc.; mem. adv. coun. New World Dictionary. Author: (with J. Michaelis) Secondary Social Studies, 1980, (with V. Green) International Human Rights, 1980, (with Frank Besag) Foundations of Education, 1984, (with S. Palonsky and K. Carlson) Critical Issues in Education, 1990, 2nd edit., 1993; contbr. numerous articles to profl. jours.; editor: Social Sci. Record, Theory and Research in Social Education, 1982-85. Mem. exec. bd. ACLU, Middlesex County, N.J., 1968-83; mem. Erie County Dem. Com., 1967-68, N.J. Gov.'s Task Force on

Rehab. Edn. for Prisoners, 1970-74; mem. Highland Park Bd. Edn., N.J., 1972-75, pres., 1974-75; mem. Highland Park Hist. Commn., 1980-86; mem. nat. panel Project Censored, 1976—; mem. N.J. Rural Adv. Commn., 1992—. Robert Taft Found. grantee Inst. in Govt., 1970, 86; Inst. for World Order grantee Rutgers U., 1973—; Rutgers U. grantee; SUNY-Buffalo grantee, 1967-68; ACLU of N.J. grantee, 1972-73; U.S. Office Edn. grantee, 1967-68; N.J. Dept. Higher Edn. grantee, 1985-86. Mem. Am. Acad. Polit. and Social Sci., AAUP (editorial bd. 1977-80, rep. nat. council 1982-85, com. on acad. freedom and tenure 1983-86, com. on legis. affairs 1992-95), Am. Ednl. Research Assn., Internat. Studies Assn., Nat. Council for Social Studies, Social Sci. Edn. Consortium (bd. dirs. 1983-85), Phi Delta Kappa. Home: 299 Woodbridge Ave Metuchen NJ 08840-2039 Office: Rutgers U Grad Sch Edn Rutgers U Grad Sch Edn New Brunswick NJ 08903

NELSON, JAMES ALBERT, librarian, state official; b. Grand Junction, Colo., June 13, 1941; s. Gerhardt Melvin and Lettie Louise (Sanders) N.; m. Judith Ann Brown, Sept. 5, 1965 (div. July 1972); children: Colm Corbett, Rebekah Sanders; m. Carol Stern, Aug. 8, 1982 (div. Apt. 1992); 1 child, Michael Leland. B.A. in English, U. Colo., 1965; M.S. in L.S., U. Ky., 1969. Head librarian Hardin County Pub. Library, Elizabethtown, Ky., 1969-70; dir. interlibrary coop. Ky. Dept. Libraries and Archives, Frankfort, 1970-72; state libr., commr. Ky. Dept. Librs. and Archives, Frankfort, 1980—; speech writer Gov. Ky., Frankfort, 1972-73; dir. continuing edn. Coll. Libr. Sci., U. Ky., Lexington, 1973-77; asst. prof. libr. sci. U. Wis., Madison, 1977-80; vol. U.S. Peace Corps, Bulan, Sorsogon, Philippines, 1965-66; mem. Ky. Sci. and Tech. Coun., 1990—, Ky. Task Force on Open Meetings and Open Records, 1990—. Editor column Jour. Edn. for Librarianship, 1976-79, Gateways to Comprehensive State Information Policy, 1990; contbr. articles to jours. Pres. Increase Lapham Community Edn., Madison, 1979; mem. Ky. Gov.'s Commn. on Literacy; mem. exec. bd. Ky. Oral History Commn.; mem. KISC Comm. Adv. Coun., 1991—. Recipient Outstanding Alumnus award U. Ky. Coll. Library and Info. Sci., 1985. Mem. ALA (chmn. continuing edn. com. 1976-78, pres. 1984-85, chair 1988-89), Assn. coop. and Specialized Libr. Agys., Ky. Info. Systems Commn. (chair info. policy spl. com. 19916), Continuing Libr. Edn. Network and Exch. (pres. 1979-80), Soc. Am. Archivist (task force archives and soc.), Chief Officers State Libr. Agys. (treas. 1989-91, chair legis. com. 1991-92), Beta Phi Mu (chpt. pres. 1969). Democrat. Home: 222 Raintree Rd Frankfort KY 40601 Office: Ky Dept Libr and Archives PO Box 537 Frankfort KY 40602-0537

NELSON, JAMES ALONZO, radiologist, educator; b. Cherokee, Iowa, Oct. 20, 1938; s. Joe George and Ruth Geraldine (Jones) N.; m. Katherine Metcalf, July 16, 1966; children: John Metcalf, Julie Heaps. AB, Harvard U., 1961, MD, 1965. Asst. prof. radiology U. Calif. San Francisco, 1972-74; assoc. prof. U. Utah, Salt Lake City, 1974-79, prof., 1979-86; prof. U. Wash., Seattle, 1986—; dir. radiol. rsch. U. Calif.-San Francisco/Ft. Miley VAH, 1973-74, U. Utah, 1984-85, U. Wash., 1986—. Contbr. articles to Aj. Jour. Roentgenology, Radiology, Investigative Radiology, others; contbr. chpts. to books. Capt. USAF, 1967-69. John Harvard scholar, 1957-61, James Picker Found. scholar, 1973-77; recipient Mallinkrodt prize Soc. Body Computerized Tomagraphy, 1990, Roscoe Miller award Soc. Gastrointestinal Radiology, 1991. Fellow Am. Coll. Radiology (diplomate); mem. Radiol. Soc. N.Am., Assn. Univ. Radiology. Achievements include patents (with others) for Non-Surgical Peritoneal Lavage, Recursive Band-Pass Filter for Digital Angiography, for Unsharp Masking for Chest Films, Improved Chest Tube, Oral Hepatobiliary MRI Contrast Agent. Office: U Wash Dept Radiology SB-05 Diagnostic Imaging Sci Ctr Seattle WA 98195

NELSON, JAMES AUGUSTUS, II, real estate executive, architect, banker; b. Damrascotta, Maine, July 26, 1947; s. Robert Maynard and Margret Rebbeca (Harmision) N.; m. Linda Ray, Aug. 15, 1975 (div. 1985); m. Tina Nides, Oct. 22, 1986 (div. 1991); 1 child, Jennifer Alexandria. BArch, Columbia U., 1973, MBA, 1974. Resident v.p. Citibank, N.Y.C., 1974-77; group v.p. Bank of San Francisco, 1977-82; assoc. John Portman and Assocs., Atlanta, 1983-85; pres. J.A. Nelson and Assocs., L.A., 1986-88; dir. real estate planning and devel. MCA Devel. Co., L.A., 1988-94; founder Mother Co., Hollywood, Calif., 1995. Author: Banker's Guide to Construction, 1978, Doing Business in Saudi Arabia, 1979. Chmn. Laurel Canyon Coalition, L.A.; bd. dirs. Laurel Canyon Area Assn., Hollywood Heritage, Hillside Fedn., L.A., Lookout Mountain Assocs., L.A. Avocations: gardening, architecture. Home: 8306 Grandview Dr West Hollywood CA 90046-1918 Office: Mother Co 8306 Grandview Dr Los Angeles CA 90046-1918

NELSON, JAMES CARMER, JR., advertising executive, writer; b. Denver, Nov. 10, 1921; s. James Carmer and Helen (McClelland) N.; m. Mary-Armour Ransom, Sept. 9, 1950; children--James Carmer III, Marie-Louise Nelson Masters, Jeffrey Armour, Rebecca McClelland Nelson Sylla. A.B., Yale, 1943. Mktg. editor Bus. Week mag., N.Y.C., 1946-48; illustration editor Bus. Week mag., 1948-52; freelance author Sonoma, Calif., 1952-57; copy chief Hoefer, Dieterich & Brown, Inc., San Francisco, 1957-59; v.p., creative dir. Hoefer, Dieterich & Brown, Inc., 1959-66, exec. v.p., 1966-76, pres., 1976-79, vice chmn., 1979-80; ptnr. John H. Hoefer & Assocs., 1972—; vice chmn. Chiat/Day/Hoefer, 1980; prit. advt. cons., 1980—; bd. dirs. McKinney, Inc., Phila.; instr. Golden Gate Coll., San Francisco, 1958-59; alternate mem. Nat. Advt. Rev. Bd., 1971-75. Author: The Trouble With Gumballs, 1957, Great Cheap Wines: A Poorperson's Guide, 1977, Great Wines Under $5, 1983; contbr. articles and fiction to popular mags. Mem. Harold Brunn Soc. for Med. Research, Mt. Zion Hosp., San Francisco; bd. assos. Linus Pauling Inst. Sci. and Medicine, Palo Alto, Calif.; mem. Colony Found., New Haven; trustee Coro Found., 1965-75, Marin Art Complex; bd. mgrs. Marin County YMCA. Served with USNR, 1942-46. Mem. ASCAP. Club: Villa Taverna (San Francisco). Home: 649 Idylberry Rd San Rafael CA 94903-1231

NELSON, JAMES F., judge, religious organization administrator. BS, U. Calif., LLB, Loyola U., Los Angeles. Bar: Calif. 1954. Judge, Los Angeles Mcpl. Ct. Chmn. Baha'i Faith Nat. Spiritual Assembly Bahais of the U.S., Wilmette, Ill. Address: Nat Spiritual Assembly Bahai Faith 536 Sheridan Rd Wilmette IL 60091-2849

NELSON, JAMES SMITH, pathologist, educator; b. St. Louis, Mar. 19, 1933; s. Victor Paul and Dorothy Gertrude (Smith) N.; children: Paul F., Andrew S. BS, St. Louis U., 1950-53, MD, 1957. Pathology intern, resident St. Louis U. Hosps., 1957-59, 60-61; neuropathology fellow Columbia U. Coll. Phys. & Surgery, N.Y.C., 1959-60; neurochemistry fellow Washington U. Med. Sch., St. Louis, 1961-63, instr. in pathology, 1963-64, asst. prof. prof. pathology & pediatrics, 1973-87; asst. prof., assoc. prof. pathology St. Louis U. Med. Sch., 1964-73; head divsn. neuropathology Henry Ford Hosp., Detroit, 1987-89; clin. prof. neuropathology U. Mich. Med. Sch., Ann Arbor, 1988-89; prof. pathology La. State U. Med. Ctr., New Orleans, 1989—; intern. dept. neuropathology Armed Forces Inst. Pathology, Washington, 1990-94; ad hoc cons. NIH, Washington, 1973-92; mem. Nat. Cancer Inst. CNS Oncology Working Group, Washington, 1986-89; mem. neuropathology test com. Am. Bd. Pathology, Tampa, Fla., 1984-90; mem. WHO Brain Tumor Working Group, Zurich, Switzerland, 1990—; adv. mem. neuropathology com. Coll. Am. Pathologists, Chgo., 1992—. Author: Medical School Admission: A Systematic Guide, 1974; author, editor: Principles and Practice of Neuropathology, 1993; contbr. over 150 articles to profl. jours. Col M.C., U.S. Army, 1990-94. Decorated Legion of Merit; recipient U.S. Sr. Scientist award Alexander von Humboldt Found., Free U. Berlin, 1979-80, Cert. of Achievement, U.S. Surgeon Gen., 1985, Res. Components Achievement medal U.S. Army, 1986; NIH spl. rsch. fellow in neurochemistry, 1961-63; NIH grantee, 1986-87. Mem. AMA, Coll. Am. Pathologists (com. mem.), Am. Soc. Clin. Pathologists, Am. Assn. Neuropathologists (com. mem.), U.S. & Can. Acad. Pathology, Am. Soc. for Investigative Pathology, Am. Inst. Nutrition. Roman Catholic. Avocations: sailing, fishing, photography, skydiving. Home: 3443 Esplanade Ave Apt 415 New Orleans LA 70119 Office: Dept of Pathology La State Univ Med Ctr 1901 Perdido St New Orleans LA 70112

NELSON, JOHN HOWARD (JACK HOWARD NELSON), journalist; b. Talladega, Ala., Oct. 11, 1929; s. Howard Alonzo and Barbara Lena (O'Donnell) N.; m. Virginia Dare Dickinson, Aug. 4, 1951 (div. Nov. 1974);

children: Karen Dare, John Michael, Steven Howard; m. Barbara Joan Matusow, Dec. 7, 1974. Student econs., Ga. State Coll., 1953-57; Nieman fellow, Harvard U., 1961-62. Reporter, Biloxi (Miss.) Daily Herald, 1947-51; Reporter Atlanta Constitution, 1952-65; So. bur. chief Los Angeles Times, Atlanta, 1965-70; with Washington bur. Los Angeles Times, 1970—, Washington bur. chief, 1975—; mem. steering com. Reporters Com. for Freedom of Press. Author: (with Gene Roberts, Jr.) The Censors and the Schools, 1963, (with Jack Bass) The Orangeburg Massacre, 1970, (with R.J. Ostrow) The FBI and the Berrigans, 1972, Captive Voices, Shocken Books, 1974, Terror in the Night, 1993. Mem. vis. com. U. Md. Sch. Journalism, U. Miami Sch. Communications. With AUS, 1951-52. Recipient Pulitzer prize for local reporting under deadline pressure, 1960; Drew Pearson award for gen. excellence in investigative reporting, 1974. Mem. Fgn. Policy Coun., The Gridiron Club. Home: 4 Wynkoop Ct Bethesda MD 20817-5936 Office: 1875 I St NW Ste 1100 Washington DC 20006-5409

NELSON, JOHN HOWARD, food company research executive; b. Chgo., May 29, 1930; s. Harold Eugene and Zoe (Peters) N.; m. Jacqueline Raff, Apr. 30, 1952; children: Keith E., Kevin E., Kristen E. BS in Horticulture and Food Tech., Purdue U., 1952, MS in Food Tech. and Microbiology, 1953; PhD in Biochemistry and Microbiology, U. Minn., 1961. From rsch. biochemist to head R&D dept. Gen. Mills., Mpls., 1955-67; dir. R&D to v.p. R&D Peavey Co., Mpls., 1968-76; ptnr. Johnson Powell & Co., Mpls., 1976-78; v.p. R&D, then v.p. mktg. and product devel. Am. Maize Products Co., Hammond, Ind., 1978-82; v.p. corp. devel., then chief oper. officer Roman Meal Co., Tacoma, Wash., 1982-86; corp. dir. R&D, then v.p. R&D McCormick & Co. Inc., Hunt Valley, Md., 1986-88, v.p. sci. and tech., 1988-94; ret., 1994; prof. food sci. dept. Purdue U., West Lafayette, Ind., 1994—; sci. program advisor Charles F. Kettering Rsch. Lab., Dayton, Ohio, 1976-77. Trustee St. Joseph Hosp., Towson, Md., 1989—; mem. chancellor's adv. com. U. Md., 1989—; chmn. Ind./Acad. bd. Towson State U., 1990-92. Visking fellow Visking Corp., 1958. Fellow League for Internat. Food Edn. (pres. 1981-82, chmn. Project SUSTAIN 1988-89); mem. Am. Assn. Cereal Chemists (pres. 1974-75, William F. Geddes award 1979), Am. Chem. Soc., Inst. Food Technologists, Elks, Sigma Xi, Gamma Sigma Delta, Alpha Zeta. Republican. Avocations: travel, golf, gardening. Office: Purdue Univ 1160 Smith Hall West Lafayette IN 47907

NELSON, JOHN KEITH, electrical engineering educator; b. Oldham, Lancashire, Eng., July 3, 1943; s. John Collins and Joyce Palfrey (Simmons) N.; m. Christine Anne Baker, Feb. 10, 1968; children: David John, Peter Mark. BS in Engring., U. London, 1965, PhD, 1969. Rsch. fellow U. London, 1966-69, lectr., 1969-78, reader, 1978-79; rsch. mgr. Gen. Electric, Schenectady, 1979-82; prof. elec. power engring. Rensselaer Poly. Inst., Troy, N.Y., 1982—, head dept.; examiner U. Sri Lanka, 1970-85; cons. in field. Contbr. articles to profl. jours. Patentee in field. Recipient Snell Premium, IEEE, London, 1972, J.R. Beard award, 1976, Rsch. award, Brit. Council, 1974, 76; Travel award, Royal Soc., London, 1976, Power Engring. Educator award Edison Electric Inst., 1994. Fellow Inst. Elec. Engrs. (U.K.), IEEE (tech. v.p. Dielectrics and Elect. Insulation Soc. 1991-92, administrv. v.p., 1993-94, pres. 1995—, Meml. lectr. 1993); mem., Council of Engring. Inst. Episcopalian. Avocations: squash, sailing, scuba diving, flying. Office: Rensselaer Poly Inst Dept Elec Power Engring Troy NY 12180-3590

NELSON, JOHN MARTIN, corporate executive; b. N.Y.C., Aug. 9, 1931; s. Martin H. and Margaret (Larkin) N.; m. Linda Crocker Moore, Aug. 30, 1992; children: Murrey E., Christopher L. A.B., Wesleyan U., 1953; M.B.A., Harvard U., 1959. With Norton Co., Worcester, Mass., 1959-90; pres., chief exec. officer Norton Christensen Inc. subs. Norton Co., Salt Lake City, 1978-86; pres., chief operating officer Norton Co., Worcester, 1986-88, chmn., chief exec. officer, 1988-90; chmn., chief exec. officer Wyman-Gordon Co., Worcester, 1991—; dir. Brown and Sharpe Mfg. Co., Kingstown, R.I., Cambridge Biotech. Corp., Worcester, Mass., Stocker &Yale, Inc., Beverly, Mass., Commerce Holdings, Inc., Webster, Mass. The TJX Cos., Inc., Framingham, Mass. Trustee Wesleyan U., 1978-81, Worcester Poly. Inst., 1986—, Worcester Found. for Exptl. Biology, 1993—; bd. dirs. Worcester Mcpl. Rsch. Bur., 1989—, Alliance for Edn., 1991—, U. Mass. Med. Ctr. Found., Inc., 1991—, United Way Ctrl. Mass., chmn., 1993; chmn. Greater Worcester Cmty. Found., 1990-94; mem. Worcester Airport Commn., 1994—. Lt. (j.g.) USN, 1953-56. Home: 7 Massachuetts Ave Worcester MA 01609-1157 Office: Wyman-Gordon Co 244 Worcester St Box 8001 North Grafton MA 01536-8001

NELSON, JOHN ROBERT, theology educator, clergyman; b. Winona Lake, Ind., Aug. 21, 1920; s. William John and Agnes Dorothy (Soderborg) N.; m. Dorothy Patricia Mercer, Aug. 18, 1945; children: Eric Mercer, William John. AB, DePauw U., 1941, LHD, 1960; BD, Yale U., 1944; DTheol., U. Zürich, Switzerland, 1951; LLD, Wilberforce U., 1954; DD, Ohio Wesleyan U., 1964; LHD, Loyola U., 1969; DH, Hellenic Coll., 1985. Ordained to ministry Meth. Ch., 1944; dir. Wesley Found., Chapel Hill, N.C., 1946-48; assoc. dir. Wesley Found., Urbana, Ill., 1951-53; study sect. United Student Christian Council, N.Y.C., 1951-53; sec. commn. on faith and order World Council Chs., Geneva, Switzerland, 1953-57, chmn. working com., 1967-75; dean; prof. theology Vanderbilt Div. Sch., 1957-60; vis. prof. ecumenics Princeton Theol. Sem., 1960-61; vis. prof. United Theol. Coll., Bangalore, India, and Leonard Theol. Coll., Jabalpur, India, 1961-62; Fairchild prof. Christian theology Grad. Sch. Theology, Oberlin Coll., Ohio, 1962-65; prof. systematic theology Boston U. Sch. Theology, 1965-84, dean, 1972-74; Peyton lectr. So. Meth. U., 1961; Merrick lectr. Ohio Wesleyan U., 1964; Lowell lectr., 1966; Burke lectr. U. Calif.-San Diego, 1985; Willson lectr. Centenary Coll., 1985; Nobel lectr. Gustavus Adolphus U., 1985; vis. prof. Pontifical Gregorian U., Rome, 1968-69; Mendenhall lectr. DePauw, 1974; Russell lectr. Tufts U., 1976, Wattson lectr., Cath. U., 1989; cons. Pres.'s Commn. for Study Ethical Problems in Biomed. Research, 1980-82; dir. Inst. Religion, Tex. Med. Ctr., Houston, 1985-92, sr. rsch. fellow 1992—; adj. prof. medicine Baylor Coll. Medicine, 1985—, adj. prof. religious studies Rice U., 1987-91; program dir. Genetics, Religion and Ethics, Baylor Coll. Medicine, 1990—. Author: The Realm of Redemption, 1951, One Lord, One Church, 1958, Overcoming Christian Divisions, rev. edit, 1962, Criterion for the Church, 1963, Fifty Years of Faith and Order, (with J. Skoglund), 1963, Crisis in Unity and Witness, 1968, Church Union in Focus, 1968, Science and Our Troubled Conscience, 1980, Human Life: a Biblical Perspective for Bioethics, 1984, On the New Frontiers of Genetics and Religion, 1994; editor: The Christian Student and the World Struggle, 1952, Christian Unity in North America, 1958, No Man Is Alien, 1971, Life as Liberty, Life as Trust, 1992; editor-at-large, The Christian Century, 1958-91; assoc. editor Jour. Ecumenical Studies; mem. editorial bd. Human Gene Therapy. Del. all 7 assemblies World Coun. Chs., 5th World Conf. on Faith and Order, 1993, United Meth. Gen. Conf., 1968, 72; mem. commn. on faith and order Nat. Coun. Chs.; mem. U.S. Commn. for UNESCO, 1974-80; bd. dirs. Value of Life Com. Fellow Am. Acad. Arts and Scis.; mem. Am. Theol. Soc. (past pres.), N.Am. Acad. Ecumenists (past pres.), Soc. Europeénne de Culture (v.p.), Houston Philosophy Soc., Phi Beta Kappa, Beta Theta Pi. Clubs: St. Botolph, Doctors, Country (Brookline, Mass.), Lodge: Rotary. Home: 1111 Hermann Dr 19-A Houston TX 77004 Office: Inst of Religion Tex Med Ctr 1129 Wilkins St Houston TX 77030-2805 The sequence of my persuasions and commitments has been from Christian unity to human unity to basic concern for the value of human life itself; and these are cumulative convictions from which I cannot deviate.

NELSON, JOHN THILGEN, hospital administrator, physician; b. Aurora, Ill., Feb. 11, 1921; s. George William and Margaret Mary (Thilgen) N. Student, Wheaton (Ill.) Coll., 1941-44; M.D., Chgo. Med. Sch., 1949. Intern Macon (Ga.) Hosp., 1948-49; resident anesthesiology U. Ill. Sch. Medicine, 1949-51, clin. instr., 1949-57; attending physician VA Hosp., Hines, Ill., 1951-57; pvt. practice medicine, specializing in anesthesiology Chgo., 1951-52, Elgin, Ill., 1954-69; chief of dept. St. Joseph Hosp., Elgin, 1954-69; sec. med. staff St. Joseph Hosp., 1966, v.p. med. staff, 1967, pres., 1968; supt. Chgo.-Read Mental Health Center, 1969-74; med. dir. Elgin Mental Health Center, 1974-87; coordinator med. services Ill. Dept. Health and Devel. Disabilities, 1976-87; ret. Served with AUS, 1952-54. Fellow Am. Coll. Anesthesiology; mem. Am., Ill., Chgo., Kane County med. socs., Am., Ill., Chgo. socs. anesthesiology. Home: RR 1 Box 313 Rohrssen Rd Elgin IL 60120

NELSON, JOHN WILTON, symphonic conductor; b. San Jose, Costa Rica, Dec. 6, 1941; came to U.S., 1953; s. Wilton Mons and Thelma (Agnew) N.; m. Anita Christine Johnsen, Sept. 4, 1964; children: Kirsten, Kari. B. Music, Wheaton Coll., 1963; M.M. (Teaching fellow), Juilliard Sch., 1965, postgrad. diploma (teaching fellow), 1967. Conducting faculty Juillard Sch., N.Y.C., 1968-72; dir. Aspen Choral Inst., 1968-73. Music dir., ProArte Chorale, Ridgewood, N.J., 1965-75; condr., N.Y. Mozart Festival, 1967, Juilliard Opera Theatre, N.Y.C., 1968; music dir., Greenwich Philharmonica Orch., N.Y.C., 1966-74; condr., N.Y.C. Opera, 1973-75, Santa Fe Opera, 1973, Geneva Grand Theatre, 1974, Met. Opera, N.Y.C., 1974—, Lyon Opera, 1991, Geneva Opera, 1992; condr., music dir., Indpls. Symphony Orch., 1976-87; music adviser, Nashville (Tenn.) Symphony, 1975; conducted, Chgo. Symphony, N.Y Philharm., Boston Symphony, Phila. Orch., Indpls. Symphony Orch., Cin. Orch., L.A. Philharmonic, London Royal Philharmonic, Suiss Romande and others; music dir. St. Louis Opera, 1981-91, prin. guest condr., 1991—. Recipient Irving Berlin Conducting award, 1967, Diapason d'Or award recording Beatrice & Benedict, 1993, Best Operatic Rec. Grammy award for Handel's Semele with English Chamber Orch./Kathleen Battle, 1993. Office: care IMG Artists Media House, 3 Burlington Ln, London Chiswick W4 2TH, England

NELSON, JOHN WOOLARD, neurology educator, physician; b. Hagerstown, Ind., Mar. 9, 1928; s. John Hans and Marvel May (Woolard) N.; m. Nancy Louise Elam, July 21, 1966; 1 son, John Hancock. A.B., Earlham Coll., 1950; M.D., Ind. U., 1953. Diplomate: Am. Bd Psychiatry and Neurology (clin. neurophysiology). Instr. neurology U. Tenn. Coll. Medicine, 1959-61; asst. prof. neurology W. Va. U. Sch. Medicine, 1961-63; assoc. prof. neurology U. Tenn., 1963-66; assoc. prof. to prof. Med. Coll. Wis., Milw., 1966-72; clin. prof. neurology U. Minn., Duluth, 1972-73; prof., head dept. neurology U. Okla. Coll. of Medicine, Oklahoma City, 1973-88, prof. emeritus neurology, 1989—. Served with M.C. U.S. Army, 1955-56. Mem. Okla. County Med. Soc., Okla. Med. Soc., AMA, Am. Acad. Neurology, Am. Electroencephalographic Soc., Am. Med. Electroencephalographic Soc. Home: 2608 Greenfield Dr Edmond OK 73003-6528

NELSON, JOSEPH CONRAD, lawyer, business executive, educator; b. Rochester, N.Y., Sept. 20, 1926; s. Joseph F. and Louise (Mairhuber) N.; m. Anita Elizabeth Rougal, May 19, 1945 (dec. Feb. 1982); children: Lynn Louise Nelson Crow, Lisa Ann Nelson Harris; m. Maurine Helen Trautz, Oct. 4, 1990. AB magna cum laude, U. Rochester, 1947; JD, Harvard U., 1949. Bar: Mich. 1949, Ill. 1958, Mo. 1966, Tex. 1967, D.C. 1991, Md. 1994, U.S. Supreme Ct. 1965. Atty., N.Y.C. R.R., Detroit, 1949-52; atty. Mich. Wis. Pipe Line Co., 1952-56; asst. sec. Am. La. Pipe Line Co., Detroit, 1956-58; atty. Sears, Roebuck and Co., Chgo., 1958-63, coordinator mdse. mgmt. com. on staff vp merchandising, 1963-65; sec., gen. counsel Kellwood Co., Chgo. and St. Louis, 1965-67; sec., gen. atty. Tex. Industries, Inc. and subs., Dallas, 1967-72, v.p., 1969-72, v.p., sec., gen. counsel Centex Corp., Dallas, 1972-81, assoc. prof. law Tex. Tech U., 1981-82; v.p., gen. counsel, sec. Tex. Industries Inc., Dallas, 1982-85; vis. scholar/researcher Harvard U. Law Sch., Cambridge, Mass., 1985-86; v.p., gen. counsel, sec. Overhead Door Corp., Dallas, 1987-90, legal cons., 1990-91; cons. Office Econ. Devel., Montgomery County, Md. Government, Rockville, 1992-93; legal cons. Office County Atty., Montgomery County, Rockville, 1993-94; lectr. Detroit Coll. Law, 1950-58, Grad. Program in Internat. Mgmt., U. Tex.-Dallas, 1984. Mem. scholarship com. Telluride Assn. Greater Detroit, 1956-58; Dallas regional scholarship chmn. U. Rochester, 1969-75; legis. chmn. Birmingham (Mich.) PTA, 1957-58; chmn. Winnetka (Ill.) Cancer Crusade, 1964; sec. Kellwood Found., 1965-67; bd. dirs. Chgo. North Shore unit Am. Cancer Soc., 1965, Dallas County unit, 1968-70; sec., bd. dirs. Pub. Communication Found. for North Tex., 1969-81; trustee Dallas Symphony Orch., 1968-73. Mem. Md. Bar Assn., Dallas Bar Assn. (chmn. corp. counsel sect. 1976-77), D.C. Bar Assn., Harvard Law Sch. Assn. (bd. dirs. Dallas-Ft. Worth chpt. 1984-85), Order of Coif, Phi Beta Kappa. Home: 14920 Bradwill Ct Rockville MD 20850-3934

NELSON, JUDD, actor; b. Portland, Maine, Nov. 28, 1959. Student, Bryn Mawr Coll., Stella Adler Conservatory. mem. Shoestring Theatre Co. Performances include: (stage prodns.) Mozart and Salieri, Domino Courts; (feature films) Making the Grade, 1984, Fandango, 1985, The Breakfast Club, 1985, St. Elmo's Fire, 1986, Blue City, 1986, (voice only) Transformers: The Movie, 1986, From the Hip, 1987, Relentless, 1989, Far Out Man, 1990, New Jack City, 1991, The Dark Backward, 1991, Every Breath, 1993, Blindfold, 1993; (TV episode) Moonlighting; (TV movies) Billionaire Boys Club, 1987, Hiroshima: Out of the Ashes, 1990. Office: The Gersh Agency 232 N Canon Dr Beverly Hills CA 90210*

NELSON, JULIE D., lawyer; b. N.Y.C., Sept. 8, 1954; d. John D. and Eileen M. (Canning) Krohn; m. James L. Nelson, Dec. 29, 1973; children: Morgan, Max. BS, U. Iowa, 1975, JD, 1978. Bar: D.C., Colo., Tex. Law clk. to presiding justice Iowa Supreme Ct., Des Moines, 1978-79; assoc. Sidley & Austin, Washington, 1979-84; atty. AT&T Info. Systems, Denver, 1984-87, AT&T Communications, Austin, Tex., 1987-91, AT&T Fed. Sys., 1991-92; sr. v.p., counsel AT&T Universal Card Svcs. Corp., 1993—; instr. U. Iowa Sch. Law, summer 1983, U. Phoenix, 1986-87. Mem. Order of Coif, Phi Beta Kappa. Democrat. Office: AT&T Universal Card 8787 Baypine Rd 3-2-A720 Jacksonville FL 32256

NELSON, KARIN BECKER, child neurologist; b. Chgo., Aug. 14, 1933; d. George and Sylvia (Demansly) Becker; m. Phillip G. Nelson, Mar. 10, 1955; children: Sarah Nelson Hammack, Rebecca Nelson Miller, Jenny Nelson Walker, Peter. MD, U. Chgo., 1957; Student, U. Minn., 1950-53. Cert. child neurology Am. Bd. Psychiatry and Neurology. Intern rotating Phila. Gen. Hosp., 1957-58; asst. resident neurology U Md. Sch. Medicine, Balt., 1958-59; resident neurology George Washington U. Sch. Medicine, Washington, 1959-62; cons. in med. neurology St. Elizabeth's Hosp., Washington, 1960-62; registrar to outpatients Nat. Hosp., Queen Sq., London, 1963; med. officer perinatal rsch. br. Nat. Inst. of Neurol. Disorders and Blindness, NIH, 1964-67; asst. prof. neurology George Washington U., Washington, 1970-72; assoc. neurologist Children's Hosp. of D.C., Washington, 1967-71; instr. neurology George Washington U., Washington, 1967-70; attending neurologist Children's Hosp., Washington, 1971-73, 78—; assoc. clin. prof. neurology George Washington U., Washington, 1972—; cons. Nat. Inst. Child Health and Human Devel., 1975-80, orphan products devel. initial rev. group FDA, 1983-86, Boston Collaborative Drug Surveillance Group, 1985-86, vaccine Am. Acad. Pediatrics, 1985, 87, Dept. Health, State of Calif. Birth Monitoring Group, 1986—, Ctr. for Disease Control Birth Defects Monitoring Com., 1987; med. officer Nat. Inst. Neurol. Disorders and Blindness, NIH, Bethesda, 1972—; med. staff Children Hosp., Washington, 1962—; mem. adv. bd. Internat. Sch. Neuroscis., Venice, Italy, Little Found./World Fedn. Neurology, 1992—; mem. bd. Nat. Inst. Aging; mem. epidemiology steering com. NIH, 1993—. Editor: Workshop on the Neurobiological Basis of Autism, 1979, (with J.H. Ellenberg) Febrile Seizures, 1981; editorial bd. Pediatric Neurology, 1984-90, Brain and Development, 1984—, Neurology, 1985-88, Paediatric and Perinatal Epidemiology, 1987—, Developmental Medicine and Child Neurology, 1988; field editor Epilepsy Advances; contbr. papers to profl. jours. Recipient Spl. Recognition award USPHS, 1977, Spl. Achievement award 1981, United Cerebral Palsy Weinstein-Goldenson Rsch. award 1990, Dirs. award NIH, 1992. Fellow Am. Acad. Neurology (sec. bd. 1989-91, councillor); mem. Soc. Perinatal Obstetricians (hon.), Child Neurology Soc. (program chmn. 1973, liaison nat. Inst. of Neurol. and Communicative Disorders and Blindness 1977-80, ethics com. 1985-87, by-laws com. 1990—, ad hoc com. for consensus statement of DPT immunications and the cen. nervous system 1990, long range planning com. 1991—), Hower award 1991), Am. Acad. for Cerebral Palsy and Devel. Medicine (program chmn. 1985), Am. Epilepsy Soc. (Disting. Basic Neuroscientist Epilepsy Rsch. award 1992), Am. Neurol. Assn. (membership com. 1994—), Internat. Child Neurology Assn. (sci. selection com. 1993-94), Can. Assn. Child Neurology (hon.), Soc. Perinatal Obstetricians (hon.), Baltic Child Neurology Soc., Dana Alliance Brain Initiatives, Alpha Omega Alpha. Democrat. Jewish. Office: NIH 7550 Wisconsin Ave Rm 700 Bethesda MD 20892-9130

NELSON, KARL EMIL, hospital administrator, healthcare consultant; b. N.Y.C., Apr. 2, 1938; s. Carl Emil and Elsie Catherine (Lock) N.; m. Margaret Worthy, June 21, 1963 (div. Dec. 1992); children: Jeanne Marie Nelson Leo, Keith Eric. BA, U. Rochester, 1959; postgrad., Fairleigh Dick-

inson U., 1960; MS in Hosp. Adminstrn., Columbia U., 1963. With various hosps. The Salvation Army, Cleve., Buffalo, Cin., 1963-70; exec. dir., chief oper. officer Booth Meml. Hosp., Flushing, N.Y., 1970-82; exec. dir. Coler Meml. Hosp., N.Y.C., 1982-84, Beekman Downtown Hosp., N.Y.C., 1984-86; mgr. bus. devel. Turner Constrn. Co., N.Y.C., 1987-92; cons. Helme Assocs., Hampton Bays, N.Y., 1992-95; site adminstr. Bklyn. Hosp., 1995—; bd. dirs. Health Sys. Agy. of Nassau-Suffolk, Plainview, N.Y., 1989—, Health Sys. Agy. N.Y.C., 1974-82. Bd. dirs. N.Y. Inst. Tech.; bd. dirs. Heart Assn. Nassau County, chmn. devel. com., 1989-92. Fellow Am. Coll. Healthcare Execs. Presbyterian. Home: Helme Assos 24 Clay St Huntington Station NY 11746 Office: Bklyn Hosp Ctr 100 Parkside Ave Brooklyn NY 11226

NELSON, KEITH ADAM, chemistry educator; b. N.Y.C., Dec. 8, 1953; s. Sidney and Doris Nelson; m. Martha Leticia Cortes, Oct. 5, 1981; children: Hannah, Dylan. BS in Chemistry, Stanford U., 1976, PhD in Phys. Chemistry, 1981. Postdoctoral scholar UCLA, 1981-82; asst. prof. chemistry MIT, Cambridge, 1982-87, assoc. prof., 1987-92, prof., 1992—. Contbr. over 100 articles to profl. jours. Recipient Presdl. Young Investigator award NSF, 1985-90, Coblentz prize Coblentz Soc., 1988; fellow Alfred P. Sloan Found., 1987-89. Fellow Am. Phys. Soc.; mem. Am. Chem. Soc., Optical Soc. Am., Materials Rsch. Soc., Inter-Am. Photochem. Soc. Avocations: chess, soccer, topless coed roller derby. Office: MIT Dept Chemistry 77 Massachusetts Ave Cambridge MA 02139-3594

NELSON, KEITHE EUGENE, lawyer, state court administrator; b. Grand Forks, N.D., Mar. 23, 1935; s. Herman William and Hannah Marie (Anderson) N.; m. Shirley Jeanne Jordahl, June 10, 1955; children: Kirsti Lynn Nelson Hoerauf, Scott David, Kenen Edward, Karen Lee Nelson Strandquist. PhB, U. N.D., 1958, JD, 1959. Bar: N.D. 1959, U.S. Ct. Mil. Appeals 1967, U.S. Supreme Ct. 1967. With Armour & Co., Grand Forks, 1958-59; commd. 2d lt. USAF, 1958, advanced through grades to maj. gen., 1985; judge advocate USAF, N.D. and, Fed. Republic Germany and Eng., 1959-73; chief career mgmt. USAF, Washington, 1973-77; comdt. USAF JAG Sch., Montgomery, Ala., 1977-81; staff judge adv. Tactical Air Command USAF, Hampton, Va., 1981-82, SAC, Omaha, 1984-85; dir. USAF Judiciary, Washington, 1982-84; dep. JAG, USAF, Washington, 1985-88, JAG., 1988-91; ret., 1991; dir. jud. planning Supreme Ct. N.D.; state ct. administr., 1992—. Chmn. editorial bd. USAF Law Rev., 1977-81. Decorated D.S.M., Legion of Merit with two oak leaf clusters. Mem. ABA. Lutheran. Avocations: skeet shooting, hunting, tennis. Home: 800 Munich Dr Bismarck ND 58504

NELSON, KENNETH EDWARD, consulting engineer; b. Chgo., Dec. 13, 1948; s. Kenneth C and Mary A. (Leisten) N.; m. Wendy E. Mollner, Apr. 21, 1974; children: Emily M., Sam M. BS in Urban Systems Engring., U. Ill., Chgo., 1970; MSCE, Northwestern U., 1972; MBA, Loyola U., Chgo., 1981. Registered profl. engr., Ill., Wis., Mich., Ind., Pa., Ohio. Sr. transp. engr. Lester B. Knight, Chgo., 1978-80; exec. v.p HDR Engring., Chgo., 1980-89; v.p. Rust Environ. and Infrastructure Inc., Chgo., 1989—. Contbr. articles to tech. publs. Mem. planning and devel. com., Morton Grove, Ill., 1973-74; mem. architecture and environ. bd. Winnetka, Ill., 1978-79; chmn. Glencoe Plan Commn., 1986—. Walter P. Murphy fellow Northwestern U., 1971-72. Mem. ASCE, NSPE, Transp. Rsch. Bd., Inst. Transp. Engrs., Western Soc. Engrs. (past trustee), Ill. Soc. Profl. Engrs., Cons. Engrs. Coun. Ill. (bd. dirs.), Beta Gamma Sigma. Office: Rust Environ & Infrastructure Inc 111 N Canal St Ste 305 Chicago IL 60606-7203

NELSON, KENT C., delivery service executive; b. 1937. BS, Ball State U., 1959. With United Parcel Svc. Am., Inc., 1959-80, exec. v.p. fin., 1980-86, exec. v.p., 1986-88, vice chmn., 1988-89, chmn. bd., CEO, 1989—; chmn. bd., CEO United Parcel Svc. Inc., N.Y., Ohio. Office: United Parcel Svc AM Inc 400 Perimeter Ctr Terraces Atlanta GA 30346*

NELSON, KIRK N., insurance company executive. Pres., coo Federated Mutual Ins. Co., Owatonna, Minn. Office: Federated Mutual Insurance Co 121 E Park Sq Owatonna MN 55060-3046

NELSON, LARRY A., statistics educator, consultant; b. Omaha, Oct. 28, 1932; s. Rudolph Lawrence and Elizabeth Coleman (Lewis) N. BS in Agronomy, Iowa State U., 1954; MS in Soil Sci., Tex. A&M U., 1958; PhD in Soil Sci.-Stats., N.C. State U., 1961. Soil scientist Iowa Agrl. Exptl. Sta., Ames, 1954-55; soils instr. Tex. A&I Coll., Kingsville, 1955; rsch. soil scientist Tex. A&M Rsch. Found., College Station, 1956; soils instr. Tex. A&M U., College Station, 1956-58; rsch. asst. N.C. State U., Raleigh, 1959-61, asst. prof. exptl. stats., 1964-66, assoc. prof. exptl. stats., 1966-71, prof. stats., 1971-89, prof. emeritus stats., 1989—; asst. specialist in land classification Land Study Bur., U. Hawaii, Honolulu, 1961-63; lectr., tchr., cons. in field; spl. advisor head dept. stats. Kasetsart U., Bangkok, Thailand, 1973; evaluator quantitative skills IADS, Bangladesh, 1984; mem. rev. team Ctr. for Agrl. Econs. and Ctr. for Data Processing, Winrock Internat., Indonesia, 1985; statis. cons. PROCAFE, El Salvador, 1990—; ptnr. Statis. Rsch. Assocs., Honolulu, 1962-63. Assoc. editor Geoderma, 1976-84, Agronomy Jour., 1981-87; contbr. numerous articles to profl. publs. NATO fellow Data Analysis Lab., Lynbgy, Denmark, 1978. Fellow AAAS, Am. Stat. Assn. (mem. biometrics sect. com. 1989-90), Am. Soc. Agronomy, Soil Sci. Soc. Am.; mem. Statis. Assn. Thailand (life), Internat.Biometric Soc. (bus. mgr. and treas. 1969-79, awards com. 1987-94, 1990-93), Sigma Xi, Gamma Sigma Delta (internat. pres. 1984-86, Award of merit 1973-74, rep. to AAAS 1978-86), Phi Kappa Phi. Baptist. Avocations: music, genealogy, diving, bicycling, travel. Home: 1422 Banbury Rd Raleigh NC 27607 Office: NC State U Dept Stats Box 8203 Raleigh NC 27695-8203

NELSON, LARS-ERIK, newspaperman; b. N.Y.C., Oct. 15, 1941; s. Arthur and Freda (Rappaport) N.; m. Mary Elizabeth Cantwell, Dec. 28, 1963; children—Peter, Amanda. A.B., Columbia U., 1964. Editorial asst. N.Y. Herald Tribune, N.Y.C., 1959-63; Russian translator Current Digest, N.Y.C., 1963-64; rewriteman The Record, Hackensack, N.J., 1965-66; corr. Reuters, London, Moscow, Prague and Washington, 1966-77; Newsweek, Washington, 1977-79; corr. N.Y. Daily News, Washington, 1979—, bur. chief, 1981-93; columnist Newsday, 1993—. Editor: International Bus News, 1977-81. Mem. State Dept. Corrs. Assn. (pres. 1978-79), Overseas Writers, White Ho. Corrs. Assn. (Merriman Smith award 1980), Gridiron Club (Washington). Office: Newsday 1001 Pennsylvania Ave NW Washington DC 20004-2505

NELSON, LAWRENCE EVAN, business consultant; b. Chgo., Dec. 3, 1932; s. Evan Thomas and Elizabeth Marie (Stettka) N.; m. Jean H. Clayton, July 11, 1953; children: Lori Jean, Lawrence Evan. BS with honors, So. Ill. U., 1959; MBA, U. Chgo., 1969. CPA, Ill. Sr. acct Price Waterhouse & Co., CPA's, Chgo., 1959-65; sec.-treas. Bradner Cen. Co., Chgo., 1965-73; pres. Protectoseal Co., Bensenville, Ill., 1973-84, Plan Ahead Inc., Palos Park, Ill, 1984—. Author: (book) Personal Financial Planning, 1985. Treas. City of Palos Heights, Ill., 1964-68, alderman, 1970-71; trustee Palos Heights FPD, 1977—. Served with USNR, 1952-56. Mem. Am. Inst. CPA's, Ill. Soc. CPA's. Office: Plan Ahead Inc PO Box 164 Palos Park IL 60464-0164

NELSON, LINDA SHEARER, child development and family relations educator; b. New Kensington, Pa., Dec. 8, 1944; d. Walter M. and Jean M. (Black) Shearer; m. Alan Edward Nelson, Dec. 29, 1973; children: Amelia (Amy), Emily. BS in Home Econs. Edn., Pa. State U., 1966; MS in Child Devel. and Family Rels., Cornell U., 1968; PhD in Higher Edn. and Child Devel., U. Pitts., 1982. Head tchr.-lab. nursery sch. Dept. of Psychology, Vassar Coll., Poughkeepsie, 1966-69; instr. child devel. dept. home econs. edn. Indiana U. Pa., 1969-72, asst. prof., 1972-77, assoc. prof., 1977-84, prof., 1984—, dept. chair, 1991-93, with human devel. environ. studies dept. coll. health and human svcs., 1993—; cons., trainer Head Start Programs, Pa., 1971-72, Child Care Programs and Agys., Pa., 1970—; child devel. assoc. rep. Coun. for Early Childhood Profl. Recognition, Washington, 1989-91; field rep. Keystone U. Rsch. Corp., Erie, 1990-91; keynote/guest spkr. Child Devel./Child Care and Home Econs. confs., Pa. and nat., 1985—; refocusing com. Ind. U. Pa., 1993-94, strategic planning com., 1995-96. Mem. adv. bd. Early Childhood Edn., Annual Edits., 1985, Interface: Home Econs. and Tech. Newsletter, 1993—; contbr. articles to profl. jours. Bd. dirs. Indiana County Child Care Program, 1970-92; guest spkr. Delta Kappa Gamma, Indiana, 1990, Bus. and Profl. Women, Indiana, 1991.

Grantee in field, 1985—. Mem. AAUW, Nat. Assn. for the Edn. Young Children, Pitts. Assn. for the Edn. Young Children (conf. co-chair 1983-85), Assn. Pa. State Coll. and Univ. Faculties, Kappa Omicron Nu, Phi Upsilon Omicron. Democrat. Presbyterian. Avocations: photography, reading, Chautauqua Instn. programs. Office: Indiana U of Pa Human Devel and Environ Studies Dept 207 Ackerman Hall Indiana PA 15705

NELSON, LINDSEY, sportscaster; b. Pulaski, Tenn., May 25, 1919; s. John Lee and Osie (Baker) N.; m. Mildred Murphy Lambert, May 9, 1946 (dec. Jan. 1973); children: Sharon, Nancy Lynne. BA, U. Tenn., 1941. With WKGN and WROL, Knoxville, Tenn., 1947-50, Liberty Broadcasting System, Dallas, 1951-52, NBC, N.Y.C., 1952-62; baseball announcer N.Y. Mets, 1962-78, San Francisco Giants, 1979—; freelance football announcer CBS, NBC, ABC, Notre Dame Network, MBS, 1962—; Conducted baseball clinics for U.S. Army in Europe, 1960. Author: (with Al Hirshberg) Backstage at the Mets, 1966; Hello Everybody, I'm Lindsey Nelson, 1985. Mem. Pres.'s Council on Youth Fitness, 1956. Served to capt., inf. AUS, 1941-45, ETO. Decorated Bronze Star medal; recipient Golden Mike award Nat. Touchdown Club, 1978. Mem. Nat. Sportscasters and Sportswriters Assn. (pres., named Nat. Sportscaster of Yr. 1959-63, named to Hall of Fame 1979), Overseas Press Club Am. Office: care Internat Creative Mgmt 40 W 57th St New York NY 10019-4001*

NELSON, LLOYD STEADMAN, statistics consultant; b. Norwich, Conn., Mar. 29, 1922; s. Ronald Richbourg and Marion Shapley (Rogers) N.; m. Almeda Christine Ponder, Feb. 21, 1947; children: Peter Reid, Fay Hulett-Nelson, Barbara Nelson Ramey; m. Frances Betty Pallant, Mar. 13, 1982. BS, U. N.C., 1943; PhD, U. Conn., 1950. Registered profl. engr., Calif. Instr. physics U. Conn., Storrs, 1943-44; instr. chemistry Ill. Inst. Tech., Chgo., 1949-51; research chemist Gen. Electric Co., Waterford, N.Y., 1951-53; research assoc. Gen. Electric Research Lab., Schenectady, N.Y., 1953-56; cons. statistician Gen. Electric Lamp Div., Cleve., 1956-68; lectr. in math. Case Inst. Tech., Cleve., 1963-64; mgr. applied math. lab. Gen. Electric Major Appliance Group, Louisville, 1968-80; dir. statis. methods Nashua (N.H.) Corp., 1980-92; pvt. practice statis. cons., 1992—. Editor: Indsl. Quality Control, 1966-68; founding editor: Jour. Quality Tech., 1969-71; contbr. over 100 articles to sci. jours. Served with USN, 1944-46. Fellow AAAS, Am. Soc. Quality Control (Shewhart medal, 1978, Deming medal 1985), Am. Statis. Assn. (outstanding statistician of yr. award 1983). Home: 17 Jefferson Dr Londonderry NH 03053-3647

NELSON, LYLE MORGAN, communications educator; b. Yamhill, Oreg., Feb. 28, 1918; s. Guy Calvin and Bessie Alzine (Morgan) N.; m. Corrine Marlis Wignes, Oct. 2, 1941; children: Gayle Kathryn, Judith Lee. AB, U. Oreg., 1941; LHD (hon.), Linfield (Oreg.) Coll., 1981; Dr. honoris causa, U. Autónoma de Guadalajara, Mex., 1981. Acting dir. Univ. News Service, U. Oreg., 1941-43, asst. to pres., asso. prof. journalism, 1947-53; with U.S. Army Ordnance Dept., 1943-45; asst. regional info. officer Bur. Reclamation, Boise, Idaho, 1945-47; asst. to pres., sec. bd. dirs. Ednl. TV and Radio Center, Ann Arbor, Mich., 1953-55; asst. to pres., prof. communications San Francisco State Coll., 1955-57; v.p., prof. journalism U. Mich., 1957-60, v.p., 1960-62; dir. univ. relations Stanford, 1962-72, prof. communications, chmn. dept., 1968-78; dir. John S. Knight profl. journalism fellow program, 1972-86, Thomas M. Storke distinguished prof. emeritus, 1986—; hon. prof. journalism Autonomous U. Guadalajara; cons. edn. Ford Found., 1962-63, 65; acad. cons. Xiamen U. Author: (with W. Schramm) Financing of Public Television, Bold Experiment: The Impact of Television on American Samoa; Editor: (with Dan Lerner) Communication Research: A Half Century Appraisal. Exec. dir. White House Conf. Edn., 1965; spl. cons. U.S. Commr. Edn., 1963, 67-70; cons. USIA, 1966-69; cons. higher edn. master plans, Ohio, N.Y., Kans.; mem. Greenbrier Conf. Higher Edn., 1958, U.S. ednl. del. to USSR, 1959; UNESCO ednl. TV Study Team; mem. UNDP/UNEDCO team to Evaluate TV Tng. in India, 1973; 1st vice chmn., bd. govs. Nature Conservancy, 1972-74; chmn. bd. fgn. scholarships State Dept., 1973-75; chmn. bd. trustees Alliance for Devel. of Latin Am. Higher Edn., 1974-79; trustee Hewlett Found., 1975-94. Recipient award for disting. svc. to higher edn. Am. Coll. Pub. Rels. Assn., 1953, 66, award for exceptional svc. to Stanford U., 1984, Disting. Svc. award U. Oreg., 1994; sr. Fulbright scholar, Australia, New Zealand, 1978. Mem. Am. Coll. Pub. Rels. Assn. (bd. dirs. 1956-65, pres. 1959-60), Bohemian Club (San Francisco), Lamplighters Club, Phi Kappa Phi, Sigma Delta Chi, Sigma Chi. Clubs: Bohemian (San Francisco); Lamplighters. Home: 732 San Rafael Pl Stanford CA 94305-1007

NELSON, MARK BRUCE, interior designer; b. Los Angeles, Dec. 8, 1921; s. Mark Bruce and Rubie (Henrionnet) N. B.A. in Art, U. Calif., Los Angeles, 1943, postgrad., 1949-50; postgrad., Art Center Sch., Los Angeles, 1946-49. Tchr. Pasadena (Calif.) City Coll., 1950-54; propr. Mark Nelson Interiors, Los Angeles, 1954—; designer DuPont Corp. exhibit N.Y. World's Fair, 1964; co-chmn. Los Angeles show com. Am. Inst. Interior Designers, 1960-67, Living with Famous Paintings, 1964-65; Mem. Los Angeles adv. council Am. Arbitration Assn., 1971-72; chmn. Los Angeles N.C.I.D.Q., 1973-80, Design House West, 1978. Mem. Los Angeles Beautiful Com., 1966. Served as officer USNR, 1942-46, 52-53, ETO, Korea. Fellow Am. Soc. Interior Designers (life mem., exam. chmn. 1972—, chmn. nat. by-laws com. 1973, pres. Los Angeles 1969-71, Calif. regional v.p. 1970-73, pres. Los Angeles found. 1980. Presdl. citation 1973); mem. Phi Kappa Sigma. Home and Office: 554 Lillian Way Los Angeles CA 90004-1106 *During my thirty years as a interior designer, I have enjoyed many successes, while watching the profession grow and mature. Designing the homes of rich and famous Americans has not altered my concept that it is the middle class American consumer who needs and can afford the services of professional designers.*

NELSON, MARSHALL J., lawyer; b. Portland, Oreg., Mar. 25, 1943; s. Leo B. and Eunice Elizabeth (Johnson) N.; m. Ann Laird Jarrett, May 20, 1967; children: Laird Jarrett, Sarah Elizabeth. BA, Northwestern U., 1965, JD, 1972. Bar: Wash. 1972, U.S. Supreme Ct. 1982. Assoc. Davis Wright Todd Riese & Jones, Seattle, 1972-78; ptnr. Davis Wright Tremaine, Seattle, 1978—; instr. U. Wash., 1976. Contbr. articles to profl. jours. Adv. bd. Cable TV, Seattle; dir. Wash. Vol. Lawyers for the Arts, Seattle. 1st Lt. U.S. Army, 1966-69, Germany. Recipient Nathan Burkan meml. Copyright Competition Nat. award ASCAP, 1971. Office: Davis Wright Tremaine 1501 4th Ave Seattle WA 98101-1662

NELSON, MARTHA JANE, magazine editor; b. Pierre, S.D., Aug. 13, 1952; d. Bernard Anton and Pauline Isabel (Noren) N. BA, Barnard Coll., 1976. Mng. editor Signs: Jour. of Women in Culture, N.Y.C., 1976-80; editor Ms. Mag., N.Y.C., 1980-85; editor-in-chief Women's Sports and Fitness Mag., Palo Alto, Calif., 1985-87; exec. editor Savvy, N.Y.C., 1988-89, editor-in-chief, 1989-91; asst. mng. editor People, 1993; editor In Style Mag., N.Y.C., 1993-95. Editor: Women in the American City, 1980; cons. editor Who Weekly, Sydney; contbr. articles to profl. jours. Bd. dirs. Painting Space 122, N.Y.C., 1982-85, Urban Athletic Assn. Mem. Am. Soc. Mag. Editors, Women in Film.

NELSON, MARVIN BERNARD, financial executive; b. N.Y.C., Jan. 2, 1931; s. Nathan and Bessie Nelson; m. Reasha Mary Kagan, Mar. 21, 1959; children: Alyson, Bradley. BS in Acctg., U. N.Y.C., 1954, MBA, 1958. Cert. fin. planner. Contr. New Am. Libr., Inc., N.Y.C., 1960-65; treas. Ziff Davis Pub. Co., Inc., Teaneck, N.J., 1965-68; dir acquisitions and planning New Eng. Industries, Inc., N.Y.C., 1968-69; v.p. Babbage Systems, Inc., N.Y.C., 1969-75; v.p. adminstrn. Action Computer, Inc., N.Y.C., 1978-82; pres. Global, Inc., N.Y.C., 1976-83; exec. v.p., CFO Alliance for Health, Inc., N.Y.C., 1983—; bd. dirs. Vis. Home Health Svc., Hackensack, N.J. Sgt. U.S. Army, 1951-53, Europe. Mem. Inst. Cert. Fin. Planners, Nat. Assn. Accts., Am. Mgmt. Assn. Avocations: golf, hiking, travel. Office: 6143 Jericho Tpke Commack NY 11725-2809

NELSON, MARVIN RAY, retired life insurance company executive; b. Thornton, Iowa, Aug. 29, 1926; s. Clarence Anton and Rose Bessie (Nicolet) N.; m. Juanita Mae Brown, May 26, 1951; children: Nancy, Kenneth. BS, Drake U., 1951. Actuary Security Mut. Life Ins. Co., Lincoln, Nebr., 1951-58; assoc. actuary Life Ins. Co. N.Am., Phila., 1958-59; group actuary Bankers Life of Nebr., Lincoln, 1959-66; actuary Mut. Service Life Ins. Co., St. Paul, 1966-68; sr. v.p. Horace Mann Educators Corp., Springfield, Ill., 1968-77; sr. v.p. Security Life of Denver, 1977-83, exec. v.p., 1988-91; pres.,

chief oper. officer, dir., mem. investment com. Midwestern United Life Ins. Co., Ft. Wayne, Ind., 1983-89; ret., 1991. Bd. dirs., treas. Ft. Wayne Urban League, 1983-87; bd. dirs. Taxpayers Research Assn., Ft. Wayne, 1984-88. Served with U.S. Army, 1946-47. Fellow Soc. Actuaries; mem. Am. Acad. Actuaries, Pi Kappa Phi. Home: 7636 E Windford St Parker CO 80134-5927

NELSON, MARY S., former state legislator; b. Boston, May 3, 1943; children: John, Michael, Jamie. Tchr. Perkins Sch. Blind, 1967-77; lectr. River Coll., 1977-78; selectman Nashua, N.H., 1983-85; mem. N.H. Ho. of Reps., 1983-85, N.H. State Senate, 1986-92; del. Dem. State Conv., 1982, 84; cons. on employment and tng. of handicapped, 1977—. Talk show host Sta. WMVU. Mem. N.H. Order of Women Legislators (pres. 1986—), Phi Delta Kappa. Democrat. Roman Catholic. Home: 18 Stanley Ln Nashua NH 03062-3237

NELSON, MERLE CHANDLER, real estate executive; b. Nicholson, Ga., June 30, 1908; d. Berry G. and Addie Lavina (Harris) Chandler; m. Ealton Louis Nelson, Dec. 2, 1938; children: Joan Harris Nelson Mulholland, Jean Nelson Amann. Student, Am. U., 1938-41, George Washington U., 1937-38. Exec. sec. Civil Aeros. Bd., Washington, 1938-41; real estate broker No. Va. Bd. Realtors, Fairfax, 1957-87; pres. Nelson Realty, Inc., Arlington, Va., 1957-87, also chmn. bd. dirs. Mem. Arlington County Dem. com., Arlington, 1955-56. Mem. Lake Barcroft Civic Assn. Democrat. Home: 3816 Lakeview Ter Falls Church VA 22041-1313

NELSON, MERLIN EDWARD, international business consultant, company director; b. Fargo, N.D., Jan. 30, 1922; s. Theodore G. and Eva C. (Hultgren) N.; m. Nancy Ellen Craig, June 1952 (div. June 1962); children: Craig Edward, Brian Anthony; m. Janet April Pope, Aug. 30, 1963; children: Claudia Jane, Rolf Merlin. BS in Polit. Sci., U. Oreg., 1943; postgrad. Fordham U., 1943-44; JD, Yale U., 1948. Bar: Oreg. 1948, N.Y. 1954, U.S Dist. Ct. D.C. 1954. Atty. Office Gen. Counsel, ECA, Washington and Paris, 1949-52; assoc. Davis, Polk, Wardwell, Sunderland & Kiendl, 1952-59; exec. asst. to v.p. AMF, Inc., N.Y.C., 1960-62; chmn., mng. dir. AMF Internat., Ltd., London, 1962-63; v.p., group exec. AMF, Inc., 1963-70, exec. v.p., vice chmn., dir., 1970-84, now cons., 1984—; ret., 1984; bd. dirs. Indsl. Bank Japan Trust Co., Derby Internat. Corp., S.A., Exeter Internat. Corp., S.A., Mitsui Found.; chmn. IBJ Found.; chmn. adv. coun. Trust for Pub. Land; chmn. Econ. Literacy Project, Ltd. Mem. Coun. Fgn. Rels., Overseas Devel. Coun., Avon Internat. Adv. Coun. Decorated Purple Heart. Mem. Phi Beta Kappa. Home and Office: 215 E 72nd St New York NY 10021-4576

NELSON, MICHAEL UNDERHILL, aerospace company executive, association executive; b. Balt., May 5, 1932; s. Cyril Arthur and Elise (Macy) N.; m. Barbara Gail Hutchins, June 25, 1960; children: Kevin Underhill, Bronwyn Hastings, Gayle Hutchins, Corey Williams. AB, Rutgers U., 1957, EdM, 1968. Salesman J & N Distbg. Co., New Brunswick, N.J., 1957-59; extension assoc. Univ. Coll., Rutgers U., New Brunswick, 1959-61; asst. dir. summer session Rutgers U., 1961-68; asst. dean sch. continuing edn., dir. summer sch. Washington U., St. Louis, 1969-81, dir. div. of profl. and community programs sch. continuing edn., 1975-78; exec. sec. N.Am. Assn. Summer Sessions, 1979—; account exec. Trio Printing Co., 1982-84; sr. procedures analyst McDonnell Douglas Corp, St. Louis, 1984—. Bd. dirs. Adult Edn. Council of Greater St. Louis, 1975-78. Served with USMC, 1951-54. Mem. North Ctrl. Conf. Summer Schs. (pres. 1974-75), Am. Assn. Univ. Adminstrs., Assn. Univ. Summer Sessions, Am. Summer Sessions Senate, N.Am. Assn. Summer Sessions (pres. 1978), Alpha Sigma Lambda, Phi Delta Kappa. Episcopalian. Home: 11728 Summerhaven Dr Saint Louis MO 63146-5444 Office: McDonnell Douglas Corp Mailcode 306 4168 Dept 804 Saint Louis MO 63166-0516

NELSON, NANCY ELEANOR, pediatrician, educator; b. El Paso, Apr. 4, 1933; d. Harry Hamilton and Helen Maude (Murphy) N. B.A. magna cum laude, U. Colo., 1955, M.D., 1959. Intern, Case Western Res. U. Hosp., 1959-60, resident, 1960-63; pvt. practice medicine specializing in pediatrics, Denver, 1963-70; clin. prof. U. Colo. Sch. Medicine, Denver, 1988—; asst. dean Sch. Medicine, 1982-88, assoc. dean, 1988—. Mem. Am. Acad. Pediatrics, AMA (sect. med. schs. governing coun. 1994—), Denver Med. Soc. (pres. 1983-84), Colo. Med. Soc. (bd. dirs. 1985-88, judicial coun. 1992—). Home: 1265 Elizabeth St Denver CO 80206-3241 Office: 4200 E 9th Ave Denver CO 80262

NELSON, NELS ROBERT, drama critic; b. Phila., Feb. 8, 1923; s. Nels Adolph and Agnes (Moorhead) N.; m. Lee Ciorletti, Oct. 5, 1963. B.S. in Journalism, Temple U., 1950. Reporter, Daily Local News, West Chester, Pa., 1950-52; reporter, copy editor Intelligencer Jour., Lancaster, Pa., 1952-55; with Phila. Daily News, 1955—; music columnist, 1959—, drama critic, 1982-94; critic-at-large, 1994—. Served with AUS, 1943-46. Recipient awards Phila. Press Assn., awards Pa. Newspaper Pubs. Assn. Mem. Sigma Delta Chi. Office: 400 N Broad St Philadelphia PA 19130-4099

NELSON, NORMAN CROOKS, surgeon, academic administrator, educator; b. Hibbing, Minn., July 24, 1929; s. Sander Noble and Lillian Olive (Olsen) N.; m. Annie Lee Pitre, June 25, 1955; children—Norman, Charles, Jennifer. B.S., Tulane U., 1951, M.D., 1954. Diplomate: Am. Bd. Surgery. Intern Charity Hosp. La., New Orleans, 1954-55; resident Charity Hosp. La., 1958-62; USPHS fellow Nat. Inst. Arthritis and Metabolic Diseases, Harvard and Mass. Gen. Hosp., 1962-63; pvt. practice Houston, 1955-56; instr. surgery, Sch. Medicine La. State U., New Orleans, 1963-65; asst. prof., Sch. Medicine La. State U., 1965-68, assoc. prof., Sch. Medicine, 1968-71, prof., assoc. dean Sch. Medicine, 1969-71, dean Sch. Medicine, 1971-73; vice chancellor health affairs, dean Sch. Medicine, prof. surgery U. Miss. Med. Ctr., Jackson, 1973-94, vice chancellor health affairs emeritus, prof. surgery emeritus, 1993-94. Bd. dirs. Miss. div. Am. Cancer Soc.; trustee Miss. Sch. for Deaf and Blind; bd. govs. Addie McBryde Rehab., Ctr. for Blind, Jackson. Capt. AUS, 1956-58. John and Mary Markle scholar in acad. medicine, 1965-70; recipient Outstanding Alumnus award Tulane U. Sch. Medicine, 1989. Fellow ACS, Southeastern Surg. Congress; mem. AAAS, AMA, Assn. Acad. Surgery, Assn. Am. Med. Colls., Central Med. Soc. Miss., Endocrine Soc., James D. Rives Surg. Soc. (founders group), Miss. Acad. Scis., Miss. Med. Assn., Miss. Hosp. Assn. (hon.), New Orleans Surg. Soc., N.Y. Acad. Scis., Soc. Exptl. Biology and Medicine, Soc. Head and Neck Surgeons, Soc. Univ. Surgeons, Am. Surg. Assn., So. Surg. Assn., Soc. Internationale de Chirurgie, Surg. Assn. La. (pres. 1973), Allen O. Whipple Surg. Soc., Univ. Club (Jackson), Sigma Xi, Alpha Omega Alpha, Phi Kappa Phi, Omicron Delta Kappa, Omicron Kappa Upsilon (hon.), Alpha Eta Soc. Home: 109 Cardinal Cir Brandon MS 39042-6418

NELSON, NORMAN DANIEL, career officer; b. Dec. 30, 1968. BSBA, U. Fla., 1991. Intern internat. trade and commerce dept. ctrl. Europe office Fla. Dept. Commerce, Frankfurt, Germany, 1992; intern corp. fin. divsn. mergers and acquisitions Commerzbank AG, Frankfurt, 1992; intern corp. fin. divsn. internat. leasing and new stock issues Deutsche Bank AG, Frankfurt, 1992; commd. 2d lt. USAR, 1991; advanced through grades to 1st lt. U.S. Army, 1993; platoon leader 44th engr. bn., 2d inf. divsn. U.S. Army, Republic of South Korea, 1993-94; tng. officer 6th transp. bn. U.S. Army, Ft. Eustis, Va., 1994—. Vol. Amer-Asian orphanage, Seoul, Republic of Korea, 1993-94; asst. scout master Boy Scouts Am., 1994—. Decorated Army Commendation medal; scholar Army ROTC, 1987-91, Acad. scholar State of Fla., 1987-91, Fed. Chancellor scholar Alexander-von-Humboldt Found., 1991-92. Mem. Phi Kappa Phi. Home: 1010 Ridgefield Dr Valrico FL 33594

NELSON, OLIVER EVANS, JR., geneticist, educator; b. Seattle, Aug. 16, 1920; s. Oliver Evans and Mary Isabella (Grant) N.; m. Gerda Kjer Hansen, Mar. 28, 1943. A.B., Colgate U., 1941; M.S., Yale, 1943, Ph.D., 1947. Asst. prof. genetics Purdue U., 1947-49, assoc. prof., 1949-54, prof., 1954-69; prof. genetics U. Wis., Madison, 1969—, chmn. Lab. of Genetics, 1986-89; vis. investigator Biochem. Inst., U. Stockholm and Nat. Forest Research Inst., Stockholm, 1954-55; NSF, sr. postdoctoral fellow Calif. Inst. Tech., Pasadena, 1961-62. Contbr. articles on controlling elements, genes affecting starch synthesis and genes affecting storage protein synthesis to profl. publs. Recipient John Scott medal City of Phila., 1967; Hoblitzelle award Tex. Research Found., 1968; Browning award Am. Soc. Agronomy, 1974; Donald F. Jones medal

Conn. Agrl. Exptl. Sta., 1976. Mem. NAS, AAAS, Am. Acad. Arts and Scis., Genetics Soc. Am., Am. Genetics Assn., Am. Soc. Plant Physiologists (Stephen Hales award, 1988), Sigma Xi. Home: Apt 325 325 S Yellowstone Dr Madison WI 53705-4355 Office: U Wis Lab Genetics Madison WI 53706

NELSON, PAUL EDWARD, science educator; b. Franklin Township, Wis., May 26, 1927; s. John Richard and Zella Mae (Merritt) N.; m. Barbara Jean Enyeart, June 18, 1950; children: Kathryn, John, Nancy. AA in Plant Sci., Fullerton Jr. Coll., 1949; BS in Plant Pathology, U. Calif., Berkeley, 1951, PhD in Plant Pathology, 1955. Asst. prof. plant pathology Cornell U., Ithaca, 1955-61, assoc. prof., 1961-65; assoc. prof. Pa. State U., University Park, 1965-67, prof., 1967—; interim dept. head, 1981-82; adj. prof. Cornell U., 1975—; hon. assoc. dept. plant pathology and agrl. entomology U. Sydney, Australia, 1981; mem. various coms. Pa. State U.; cons. med. mycology sect. M.D. Anderson Cancer Ctr., Houston; mem. rev. panel USDA, Southeast Area, Agrl. Rsch. rev. culture collection rsch. No. Regional Rsch. Ctr., Peoria, Ill., Coop. States Rsch. Svc. rev. grad. program and rsch. and tng. programs dept. entomology and plant pathology U. Tenn., Knoxville, comprehensive program rev.,. Contbr. articles to profl. jours. Recipient Alex & Jessie C. Black award Coll. Agrl. Scis., Pa. State U., 1992. Fellow Am. Phytopathological Soc. (northeastern divsn., mem. various coms., asst. editor Phytopathology 1970, sr. editor 1970-72, Award of Merit 1986); mem. Mycological Soc. Am., U.S. Fedn. Culture Collections, Am. Soc. Microbiology. Home: 535 Outer Dr State College PA 16801-7936 Office: Pa State U Fusarium Rsch Ctr 211 Buckhout Lab University Park PA 16802

NELSON, PAUL WILLIAM, real estate broker; b. Mpls., Mar. 7, 1952; s. William H. and Jean (Darrington) N.; m. Jill Brownson, Oct. 18, 1986 (dec. Nov. 1990); 1 child, Emily J. BS, U. Colo., 1974. Lic. real estate broker, Colo. Advt. dir. Denver Beechcraft, 1976-77; real estate broker Coldwell Banker, Grand Junction, Colo., 1977—; bd. dirs. Colo. Assn. Realtors, Denver, 1981-83. Mem. Grand Junction City Coun., 1985-93, also mayor pro tem; mem. Downtown Devel. Authority, Grand Junction, 1985-91; bd. dirs. Mesa County Planning Commn., Grand Junction, 1980-85, Colo. Nat. Monument Assn., 1989-91, Grand Junction Visitors and Conv. Bur., 1993—, Club 20 (20 counties west of continental divide) Lobbying Group; mem. Mesa County Uranium Mill Tailings Removal Citizens Com.; mem., co-chmn. Mesa County Riverfront Commn.; mem. dist. resource adv. coun. Bur. Land Mgmt., 1990-93, Grand Junction Visitors and Convention Bureau bd. dirs., 1992—. Recipient Citizen Svc. award Mesa County, 1985. Mem. Grand Junction Bd. Realtors (bd. dirs. 1981-83), Rotary. Republican. Avocations: pvt. pilot, skiing. Office: Coldwell Banker PO Box 3117 Grand Junction CO 81502-3117

NELSON, PHILIP EDWIN, food scientist, educator; b. Shelbyville, Ind., Nov. 12, 1934; s. Brainard R. and Alta E. (Pitts) N.; m. Sue Bayless, Dec. 27, 1955; children: Jennifer, Andrew, Bradley. BS, Purdue U., 1956, PhD, 1976. Plant mgr. Blue River Packing Co., Morristown, Ind., 1956-60; instr. Purdue U., West Lafayette, Ind., 1961-76, head dept. food sci., 1984—; cons. PEN Cons., West Lafayette, 1974; chair Food Processors Inst., Washington, 1990-92. Editor: Fruit Vegetable Juice Technology, 1980, Principles of Aseptic Processing and Packaging, 1987. Fellow Inst. Food Techs. (Indsl. Achievement award 1976, Nicholas Appert award 1995); mem. AAAS, Sigma Xi, Phi Tau Sigma (pres. 1976-77). Achievements include 11 U.S. and foreign patents. Office: Purdue U Dept Food Sci 1160 Smith Hall West Lafayette IN 47907-1160

NELSON, PHILIP FRANCIS, musicology educator, consultant, choral conductor; b. Waseca, Minn., Feb. 17, 1928; s. Elmer Philip and Frances (Bretzke) N.; m. Georgia Ann Yelland, June 5, 1950; children: Curtis Ann, Philip Francis Jr. A.B., Grinnell Coll., 1950; A.M., U. N.C., 1956; Ph.D., U.N.C. 1958; Diplome (Fulbright scholar). U. Paris, 1957; student, Conservatoire Nat. de Paris, 1956-57; M.A. (hon.), Yale U., 1971; L.H.D. (hon.), Grinnell Coll., 1981. Asst. prof. Ariz. State U., 1958-62, assoc. prof., 1962-63; prof., chmn. dept. music SUNY, Binghamton, 1963-70; prof., dean Sch. Music, Yale U., 1970-81; prof., provost, dean U. Calif., Santa Cruz, 1981-83; chmn. trustee com. Curtis Inst., 1982-83; sr. v.p. ABE N.Y.C., 1984-87; v.p. Aspen Inst. for Humanistic Studies, 1987-89; interim chancellor Sch. Arts, U. N.C., 1989-90; assoc. fellow Nat. Humanities Ctr., 1990-91; interim vice chancellor U. N.C., Chapel Hill, 1991; cons. edn., arts, 1992-93; chmn. grad. sch. adv. coun. U. N.C., Chapel Hill, 1993—; music critic Phoenix Gazette, 1959-62; music cons. Taliesin West, 1959-63; chmn. Nat. Screening Com. for Fulbright Awards in Musicology, 1965-68; cons. Nat. Endowment for Arts, 1984—. Contbg. editor: College and Adult Reading List, 1962, Nicolas Bernier, Principles of Composition, 1964, Recherches sur la musique Française classique, 1979, 80; contbr. to Groves Dictionary of Music, 6th edit.; editor publs. in the arts for The Aspen Inst. for the Humanities, 1987-89. Bd. dirs. various symphonies, chamber music socs., arts groups; trustee Curtis Inst. Music, Phila., 1980-83; mem. exec. com. Conn. State Golf Assn., 1975-81; founder Seven Springs Soc., 1975; bd. dirs. Conn. Hospice, 1983-87, Nat. Soc. to Prevent Blindness, 1987—; bd. dirs., v.p. 1987-93; mem. Chapel Hill Arts Ctr., 1992—; mem. Triangle J. Coun. Govt., 1992—. Served from ensign to lt. comdr. USCGR, 1952-72. Found. grantee. Mem. Am., Internat. musicol. socs., Coll. Music Soc. (nat. council. editor jour. 1966-69), Société Française de Musicologie, Soc. Ethnomusicology, U.S. Srs. Golf Assn. Clubs: Mory's (New Haven); Yale (N.Y.C.); Elizabethan Grads., New Haven Country, Yale Golf, Finley Golf, Chapel Hill Country. Home: 621 Greenwood Rd Chapel Hill NC 27514-5921

NELSON, PRINCE ROGERS See PRINCE

NELSON, RALPH ALFRED, physician; b. Mpls., June 19, 1927; s. Alfred W. and Lydia (Johnson) N.; m. Rosemary Pokela, Aug. 7, 1954; children—Edward Ancher, Audrey Anne, Elizabeth Marie, Andrew William, Evan Robert. B.A., U. Minn., 1949, M.D., 1953, Ph.D., 1961. Diplomate Am. Bd. Internal Medicine. Intern Cook County (Ill.) Hosp., 1953-54; resident U. Minn. Hosps., Mpls., 1954-55, U. Minn., Mpls., 1955-56; fellow in physiology Mayo Grad. Sch., Rochester, Minn., 1957-60, resident in internal medicine, 1976-78; practice medicine specializing in internal medicine and clin. nutrition Sioux Falls, S.D., 1978-79, Urbana, Ill., 1979—; bd. dirs. Scott Research Lab., Fairview Park Hosp., Cleve., 1962-67; assoc. in physiology Western Res. U., Cleve., 1962-67; asst. prof. physiology Mayo Grad. Sch., 1967-73, Mayo Med. Sch., 1973, assoc. prof. nutrition, 1974; cons. in nutrition Mayo Clinic, 1967-76; assoc. prof. medicine U.S.D. Sch. Medicine, Sioux Falls, 1978-79; prof. nutrition U. Ill. Coll. Medicine, Urbana-Champaign, 1979—, chmn. dept. medicine prof. nutritional sci., physiology, biophysics dept. food sci. Sch. Agr., 1979—, also prof. medicine, exec. head dept. internal medicine , 1989—; dir. research Carle Found. Hosp., Urbana, 1979—; head nutritional support service Danville (Ill.) VA Hosp., 1980—. Co-author: The Mayo Clinic Renal Diet Cookbook, 1974; contbr. articles on nutrition, physiology, and hibernation to sci. jours.; editor: Geriatrics, 1980—, The Physician and Sportsmedicine, 1980-88, Am. Jour. Clin. Nutrition, 1980-83. Cons. in nutrition Nat. Cancer Inst., 1976; cons. in nutrition HEW, 1976, 79, 89, Nat. Heart and Lung Inst., 1976. Served with USAF, 1945-47. Fulbright scholar, Morocco, 1988. Mem. Am. Physiol. Soc., Am. Inst. Nutrition, Am. Soc. Clin. Nutrition, Central Soc. Clin. Research, Am. Gastroent. Assn. Lutheran. Home: 2 Illini Cir Urbana IL 61801-5813 Office: Carle Foundation Hospital 611 W Park St Urbana IL 61801-2529

NELSON, RALPH LOWELL, economics educator; b. St. Paul, June 9, 1926; s. Ralph Edward and Beulah (Pierce) N.; m. Ann Eileen Carson, Apr. 18, 1954; children—David Lowell, Rachel Jean. B.S., U. Minn., 1949; M.A., Columbia U., 1953, Ph.D., 1955. Instr. econs. Adelphi Coll., 1950-54; asst. prof. fin. Northwestern U., 1956-59; econ. census monographist Social Sci. Research Council, 1958-59; research staff Nat. Bur. Econ. Research, 1959-72; dir. Found. Investment Study, Found. Library Ctr., 1962-64; assoc. prof. econs. Queens College, CUNY, 1964-67, prof. econs., 1968—, acting assoc. dean grad. div., 1969-70; acad. visitor London Sch. Econs. and Polit. Sci., 1970-71; mem. securities industry task force 20th Century Fund, 1972-74; spl. cons. Commn. on Pvt. Philanthropy and Pub. Needs, 1974-76; cons. Dept. Treasury, 1977; mem. rsch. staff Philanthropic Found. rsch. project, 1980-87; cons. Am. Assn. Fund-Raising Counsel, 1984—; bd. dirs. trust for philanthropy, 1985-90. Author: Merger Movements in American Industry, 1959, Concentration in the Manufacturing Industries of the United States, 1963, The Investment Policies of Foundations, 1967, Economic Factors in Corporation Giving, 1970, Total Personal Giving in the United States, 1986, An Economic History of Large Foundations, 1987; contbr. articles to profl. jours. Bd. govs. Caroline Veatch Assistance and Extension Program, 1974-76. Served with USNR, 1944-46. Mem. AAUP, Am. Econ. Assn.; Royal Econ. Soc. Phi Beta Kappa, Beta Gamma Sigma. Unitarian. Home: 346 Mill Spring Rd Manhasset NY 11030 Office: Queens Coll Econs Dept Flushing NY 11367

NELSON, RALPH STANLEY, lawyer; b. Mpls., Mar. 15, 1943; s. Stanley L. and Louise M. Nelson; m. Judy E. Nelson, July 8, 1867; children: Sara C., Amy E., David A. BS in Bus. Adminstrn., U. Minn., 1966; JD with honors, Drake U., 1972. Bar: Minn. 1973, Wash. 1982, Tex. 1985, Ind. 1993. Assoc. Wiese and Cox, Ltd., Mpls., 1973-76; atty. Burlington No. R.R. St. Paul, Minn., 1976-81; sr. corp. counsel Burlington No. Inc., Seattle, 1981-85; v.p. law and adminstrn. Burlington Motor Carriers Inc., Ft. Worth, Tex., 1985-88; exec. v.p. and gen. counsel Burlington Motor Carriers Inc., Ft. Worth, 1988-92; exec. v.p., gen. counsel Burlington Motor Carriers, Inc., Daleville (Indpls.), Ind., 1992—. Mem. law rev. Drake U. Capt. USMC, 1966-70. Mem. Order of the Coif.

NELSON, RAYMOND JOHN, mathematics and philosophy educator; b. Chgo., Oct. 8, 1917; s. Emil and Florence (Anderson) N.; m. Hendrieka Rinkema, Aug. 11, 1942; children: Susan Nelson McGuire, Steven, Peter. AB, Grinnell Coll., 1941; PhD, U. Chgo., 1949. Prof. philosophy U. Akron, 1946-52; mathematician IBM, 1952-55; staff engr. Link Aviation Corp., 1955-56; prof. math., dir. Computing Ctr. Case Western Res. U., 1956-65, prof. math. and philosophy, 1965-72, Truman P. Handy prof. philosophy, 1972-81; prof. emeritus, 1981—; Rockefeller Scholar, Belagio, 1982; cons. to industry, 1956—; spl. rsch. on computer logic, philosophy of sci.; bd. dirs. CHI Corp.; adj. prof. of computer sci. U. N.C., 1986—. Author: Introduction to Automata, 1967, The Logic of Mind, 1982, 2d edit., 1989, Naming and Reference, 1992; contbr. articles to profl. jours.; patentee electronic switching device, large data processing device. Mem. Ohio Environ. Health Com. Capt. AUS, 1942-46. Mem. AAUP, Am. Philos. Assn., Am. Math. Soc., Assn. Symbolic Logic, Assn. Computing Machinery, Philos. Sci. Assn., Sigma Xi. Home: 2400 Demington Dr Cleveland OH 44106-3652

NELSON, RAYMOND JOHN, English literature educator, university dean, author; b. Waterbury, Conn., Sept. 5, 1938; s. Raymond John and Eileen (McGrath) N.; m. Claudine Eva Ligot, Aug. 20, 1972; children: Sylvie, Christopher. BA, U. Conn., 1965; MA, Stanford U., 1967, PhD, 1969. Prof. English U. Va., Charlottesville, 1969—, dean faculty arts and scis., 1989—. Author: Van Wyck Brooks: A Writer's Life, 1981, Kenneth Patchen and American Mysticism, 1984 (Melville Cane award Poetry Soc. Am. 1984); also articles. With USCG, 1958-62. Woodrow Wilson fellow, 1965-66, fellow NEH, 1971-72. Mem. Colonnade Club (U. Va.), Phi Beta Kappa. Avocation: photography. Home: RR 3 Box 14 Earlysville VA 22936-9756 Office: U Va Dean of Faculty Office 419 Cabell Hall Charlottesville VA 22903

NELSON, RICHARD ARTHUR, lawyer; b. Fosston, Minn., Apr. 8, 1947; s. Arthur Joseph and Thelma Lillian Nelson; m. Kathryn Louise Sims, Sept. 25, 1976; children: Jennifer Kathryn, Kristen Elizabeth. BS in Math., U. Minn., 1969, JD, 1974. Bar: Minn. 1974, U.S. Ct. Appeals (D.C. cir.) 1975, U.S. Dist. Ct. Minn. 1975. Law clk. U.S. Ct. Appeals (D.C. cir.), Washington, 1974-75; ptnr. Faegre and Benson, Mpls., 1975—; seminar lectr. in employee benefits and labor laws, 1983—. Note and articles editor Minn. Law Rev., 1973-74. Active Dem.-Farmer-Labor State Cen. Com., Minn., 1976—, del. dist. and local coms. and convs., 1970—, state exec. com., 1990—; student rep. bd. regents U. Minn., Mpls., 1973-74; v.p. Minn. Student Assn., 1968-69. Served with U.S. Army, 1970-72. Mem. ABA, Minn. Bar Assn., Order of Coif, Tau Beta Pi. Lutheran. Office: Faegre and Benson 2200 Norwest Ctr 90 S 7th St Minneapolis MN 55402

NELSON, RICHARD BURTON, patent consultant; b. Powell, Wyo., Dec. 10, 1911; s. Severt A. and Sedona Lenora (Fesenbeck) N.; m. Maxine Caroline George, Feb. 25, 1950 (div. June 1963); 1 child, Anna Afton Ghandour; m. Pauline Wright, Dec. 29, 1969. Student, San Diego State Coll., 1930-32; BS in Physics with honors, Calif. Inst. Tech., 1935; PhD, MIT, 1938. Registered patent agt. Physicist R.C.A. Mfg. Co., Harrison, N.J., 1938-41, NRC, Ottawa, Ont., Can., 1941-42; rsch. assoc. GE Rsch. Lab., Schenectady, 1942-50; div. mgr. Varian Assocs., Palo Alto, Calif., 1960-63, chief engr., 1963-74, patent agt., 1974-77, cons., 1977-91; bd. dirs. 1st Nat. Bank, Powell (Wyo.), 1st Co., Powell. Author of numerous tech. papers; patentee in field. Fellow IEEE; mem. N.W. Wyo. Coll. Found. Home and Office: Villa 28 23350 Sereno Ct Cupertino CA 95014

NELSON, RICHARD COPELAND, hotel executive; b. Millington, Md., May 12, 1930; s. Roland H. and Marion (Beauchamp) N.; m. Helen Kowaleski, Feb. 22, 1964 (dec.). BA., Duke, 1952; B.S., Cornell U., 1957. Food and beverage mgr. Hilton Inn, New Orleans, 1960-63; mgr. Hilton Inn, Seattle, 1963-64; exec. asst. mgr. Hilton Inn, San Francisco, New Orleans, 1964-66; resident mgr. Statler Hilton, Dallas, 1966-68, Palmer House, Chgo., 1968-69; asst. to sr. v.p. Hilton Hotels Corp., 1969; gen. mgr. Capitol Hilton, Washington, 1969-72, Hyatt Regency Hotel, Houston, 1972-80; regional v.p., mng. dir. Hyatt Regency Washington, 1980-86, Grand Hyatt Washington, 1986—. Bd. dirs. exec. com. U.S. Navy Meml. Found. Served as lt. (j.g.) USNR, 1952-54. Mem. Hotel Assn. Washington (pres.), Washington Conv. & Visitors Assn. (pres.), Greater Washington Bd. Trade (bd. dirs., Leader of Yr. award 1994), Cornell Soc. Hotelmen (regional v.p.), Am. Hotel & Motel Assn. (sec.-treas. 1989, v.p. 1990, pres. 1991), Skal Club, Chaine des Rotisseurs, Alfalfa Club, Washington Golf and Country Club, Burning Tree Club. Republican. Roman Catholic. Address: 1000 H St NW Washington DC 20001-4310

NELSON, RICHARD DAVID, lawyer; b. Chgo., Jan. 29, 1940; s. Irving E. and Dorothy (Apolsky) N.; m. Davida Distenfield, Dec. 17, 1960; children: Cheryl, Laurel. BS in Acctg., U. Ill., 1961, LLB, 1964. Bar: Ill. 1964. Ptnr. Defrees & Fiske Law Offices, Chgo., 1964-81; ptnr., counsel, CFO, chief adminstrv. officer Heidrick & Struggles, Inc., Chgo., 1981—; bd. dirs., exec. com. Heidrick & Struggles, Inc., Chgo., 1981—. Pres. Jewish Cmty. Ctrs. of Chgo., 1987-89; chmn. Sign Graphics Task Force, Highland Park, Ill., 1986-88, Bus. and Econ. Devel. Commn., Highland Park; mem. Econ. Devel. Commn. Highland Park, 1993—. Mem. ABA, Ill. State Bar Assn., Chgo. Bar Assn., Standard Club, Northmoor Country Club. Office: Heidrick & Struggles Inc 125 S Wacker Dr Ste 2800 Chicago IL 60606-4590

NELSON, RICHARD HENRY, manufacturing company executive; b. Norfolk, Va., May 24, 1939; s. Irvin Joseph and Ethel Blair (Levy) N.; m. Carole Ellen Rosen, Mar. 12, 1966; children: Christopher, Karin. BA, Princeton U., 1961; postgrad., Georgetown U., 1962-63. Spl. asst. to dir. Peace Corps, Washington, 1961-62; mil. aide to U.S. v.p. Office of the V.P., Washington, 1962-63; asst. to U.S. Pres. Office of the Pres., Washington, 1963-66; spl. asst. to sec. HUD, Washington, 1966-68; v.p. Am. Internat. Bank, N.Y.C., 1968-70, Studebaker-Worthington, N.Y.C., 1970-73; pres. Sartex Corp., N.Y.C., 1973-80; pres., CEO Cogenic Energy Systems, Inc., N.Y.C., 1981-91; CEO U.S. Envirosystems, Inc., West Palm Beach, Fla., 1992—; bd. dirs. Nelco Corp., Laurel, Md.; chmn. bd. Powerwave Inc., N.Y.C., 1984-92; chmn. bd., chief exec. officer Utility System Fla., Inc. Bd. dirs. Nat. Hypertension Assn., N.Y.C., 1982-90; exec. com. Southampton Assn., N.Y., 1983—; advisor to mayor Historic Preservation Com. Southampton, 1986—; prin. Ctr. Excellence in Govt., Washington, 1987—. 1st lt. U.S. Army, 1962-64. Recipient Presdl. Medal Office of Pres. of U.S., 1965. Mem. Internat. Cogeneration Assn., Am. Gas Assn., Am. Cogeneration Coalition, Ind. Power Producers, Princeton Club, Doubles Club, Southampton Hunt and Polo Club (chmn. bd.), Palm Beach Polo and Country Club, U.S. Polo Assn., Meadow Club. Democrat. Avocations: horseback riding, polo. Home: 12012 Longwood Green Dr West Palm Beach FL 33414-7070 Office: US Envirosystems Inc 777 S Flagler Dr Ste 8002 West Palm Beach FL 33401

NELSON, RICHARD JOHN, playwright; b. Chgo. Oct. 17, 1950; s. Richard Finis and Viola (Gabriel) N.; m. Cynthia Blair Bacon, May 21, 1972; children: Zoe Elizabeth, Jocelyn Anne. BA, Hamilton Coll. 1972. Literary mgr. Bklyn. Acad. Music Theater Co., 1979-81; assoc. dir.

Goodman Theatre, Chgo., 1980-83; dramaturg Tyrone Guthrie Theater, Mpls., 1981-82. Author: (plays) The Killing of Yablonski, 1975, Conjuring an Event, 1976, Scooping, 1977, Jungle Coup, 1978, The Vienna Notes, 1978 (Obie award for disting. playwriting 1979), Bal, 1980, Rip Van Winkle or 'The Works', 1981, The Return of Pinocchio, 1983, Between East and West, 1985 (HBO Playwrights USA award 1986), Principia Scriptoriae, 1985 (ABC-TV Playwriting award 1985, Timeout London Theatre award 1987), An American Comedy, 1986, Roots in the Water, 1989, Some Americans Abroad, 1989, Sensibility and Sense, 1989, Two Shakespearean Actors, 1990, Columbus and the Discovery of Japan, 1992, (with Alexander Gelman) Misha's Party, 1993, Life Sentences, 1993, New England, 1994; (radio plays) Languages Spoken Here, 1987 (Giles Cooper award 1988), Eating Words, 1989 (Giles Cooper award 1990), Advice to Eastern Europe, 1990; (book of musical) Chess, 1988; (teleplays) Terror in the Sky, 1971, Houston, We've Got a Problem, 1974, The End of a Sentence, 1991; (screenplay) Ethan Frome, 1993; contbr., editor: Strictly Dishonorable and Other Lost American Plays, 1986; translator: Don Juan (Moliere) 1979, The Wedding (Brecht) 1980, The Suicide (Erdman) 1980, Il Campiello (Goldoni) 1980, Jungle of Cities (Brecht) 1981, The Marriage of Figaro (Beaumarchais) 1982, Three Sisters (Chekhov) 1984, Accidental Death of an Anarchist (Dario Fo) 1984, Jitterbugging, 1989. Thomas J. Watson Travelling fellow, 1972, Creative Writing fellow NEA, 1979, Guggenheim fellow, 1983, Playwriting fellow NEA, 1986-87; Office of Advanced Drama Rsch. grantee, 1976, Rockefeller grantee, 1979, 88; recipient Obie award for innovative programming, 1980, Lila Wallace Writers award Readers Digest Fund, 1991-93. Office: care William Morris Agy 1350 Ave of the Americas New York NY 10019*

NELSON, RICHARD R., law educator. Prof. internat. and pub. affairs, law, bus. Columbia U., N.Y.C. Office: Columbia U Sch Internat & Pub Affairs 435 W 116th St New York NY 10027

NELSON, ROBERT BRUCE, lawyer; b. Chgo., Feb. 21, 1935; s. Albert G. and Julia (Stevens) N.; m. Jeanne Bambas Denton, June 21, 1986. BA in Econs., U. Mich., 1957, JD, 1960. Bar: Ohio 1961, Fla. 1976. Assoc. Jones, Day, Reavis & Pogue, Cleve., 1960-68, ptnr., 1968-95. Spl. counsel to atty. gen. Ohio for Litigation regarding Battelle Meml. Inst., Columbus, 1973-75; v.p. Children's Aid Soc., Cleve., 1977-79, pres., 1979-81, trustee, 1970-95, hon. trustee 1995—; chmn. Inner City Renewal Soc., Cleve., 1971-73, trustee, 1965-89; trustee Cleve. Playhouse, 1987-94. Mem. Fla. Bar Assn., Ohio Bar Assn., Cleve. Bar Assn., Am. Coll. Trust and Estate Counsel, Order of Coif, Phi Beta Kappa, Phi Kappa Phi, Phi Eta Sigma. Congregationalist. Avocation: swimming. Home: 4614 L Honoapillani Rd Lahaina HI 96761

NELSON, ROBERT CHARLES, newspaper executive; b. Phila., Dec. 10, 1924; s. Charles Emil and Florence E. (Kelly) N.; m. Jeanne H. Wallace, Mar. 10, 1945; children—John R., Barbara J., Nancy A. Student, The Citadel, 1942-43; M.E., Stevens Inst. Tech., 1949. Asst. mech. supt. N.Y. News, N.Y.C., 1949-52; with Detroit News, 1952—, prodn. mgr., 1952-69, ops. mgr., 1969-75, v.p., 1973-79, gen. mgr., 1975-81, pres., 1981-87, pres., pub., 1982-87, spl. asst. to chmn., 1987—; exec. v.p. newspaper div. Evening News Assn., Detroit, 1978-87; dir. Evening News Assn., 1985-90, ret., pub. emeritus, 1990—; Bd. dirs., sec. Greater Detroit Safety Council, 1973—; bd. dirs. Engring. Sci. Fair, Detroit, 1975—; bd. dirs., mem. exec. com. Better Bus. Bur., Detroit, 1976—. Trustee New Detroit, 1980—. Served with USNR, 1943-46, PTO. Mem. Engring. Soc. Detroit, Greater Detroit C. of C. (bd. dirs. 1980—, vice chmn. 1985—), Acad. Sr. Profls. at Eckerd Coll., Detroit Club, Orchard Lake Country Club, Adcraft Club of Detroit, Econ. Club, St. Petersburg Yacht Club.

NELSON, ROBERT E., public relations executive, political consultant; b. Jefferson, Wis., Oct. 25, 1951; s. Clifford H. and Mary Ann (Lundquist) N.; m. Heidi Nelson. Fiscal svcs. officer Orange (Calif.) County Med. Ctr., 1968-73; exec. asst. Orange County Bd. Suprs., Santa Ana, 1973-75; sr. assoc. Butcher-Forde Cons., Newport Beach, Calif., 1976-77; chmn., CEO Nelson Comm. Group, Irvine, Calif., 1979—. dep. asst. dir. pub. outreach presdl. transition, Little Rock, 1993; presdl. appointee U.S. Competitiveness Policy Coun., Washington, 1994—. Recipient Rocky Mountain regional Emmy award TV. advt., 1986. Mem. Internat. Assn. Polit. Cons. (bd. dirs. 1992—), Young Pres. Orgn. (bd. dir.s 1994—), Pacific Club. Avocations: fly fishing, scuba, horses, skiing. Office: Nelson Comm Group 18401 Von Karman Ave #120 Irvine CA 92715-1542

NELSON, ROBERT EARL, JR., financial services company executive; b. Mobile, Ala., May 15, 1938; s. Robert Earl Sr. and Frances Lucille (Till) N.; m. Sandra Anne Berry, Aug. 3, 1964; children: Robin Lynne, Robert Earl III, Patricia Anne. BS in Indsl. Mgmt., Ga. Inst. Tech., 1960; MBA, U. Ala., 1963. CPA, Ga., N.Y. Prodn. mgr. Borg Warner Corp., Chgo., 1963-65; mgr., mgmt. cons. Peat, Marwick, & Mitchell, Atlanta, 1965-71; corp. controller VF Corp., Reading, Pa., 1971-73; ptnr., mgmt. services Arthur Young & Co., N.Y.C., 1973-81; sr. v.p., CFO Cable Am. Inc., Atlanta, 1981-84; exec. v.p., chief ops. officer Kroh Bros. Devel. Co., Kansas City, Mo., 1984-87; chief exec. officer Nelson & Co., Atlanta, 1987—. Contbr. articles to profl. jours. Served to 1st lt. USMC, 1960-62. Mem. AICPA, Am. Inst. Indsl. Engrs., Fin. Execs. Inst., Bus. and Tech. Alliance, Venture Forum, Union League Club (N.Y.C.), Carriage Club (Kansas City). Republican. Episcopalian. Avocations: golf, tennis, biking, scuba diving. Home: 5100 Jett Forest Trl NW Atlanta GA 30327 Office: Nelson & Co 1100 Circle 75 Pky NW Ste 800 Atlanta GA 30339-3097

NELSON, ROBERT GARY, textile executive; b. Queens, N.Y., Oct. 12, 1948; s. HOrace T. and Irene A. (Robertson) N.; m. Marla A. Svoboda, May 20, 1989; children: Ian A., Jessica L., Robert G. Jr. BBA, Dowling Coll., 1971. Various mktg. positions Springs Industries, N.Y.C., 1972-85; dir. bus. planning, 1985-88; pres. Walton Fabrics divsn. Avondale Mills Inc., Monroe, Ga., 1988—. Program chair Leadership Ga., Athens, 1994; elder Lawrenceville (Ga.) Presbyn. Ch., 1992—. Mem. Ga. Textile Manufacturers Assn. (bd. dirs. 1992—), Am. Textile Mfg. Assn. (advisor, com. mem. 1986-87). Avocations: skiing, golf, boating.

NELSON, ROBERT LOUIS, lawyer; b. Dover, N.H., Aug. 10, 1931; s. Albert Louis and Alice (Rogers) N.; m. Rita Jean Hutchins, June 11, 1955; children: Karen, Robin Andrea. B.A., Bates Coll., Lewiston, Maine, 1956; LL.B., Georgetown U., 1959. Bar: D.C. 1960. With U.S. Commn. Civil Rights, 1958-63, AID, 1963-66; program sec. U.S. Mission to Brazil, 1965-66; exec. dir. Lawyers Com. Civil Rights Under Law, 1966-70; dep. campaign mgr. Muskie for Pres., 1970-72; v.p. Perpetual Corp., Houston, 1972-74; sr. v.p., gen. counsel Washington Star, 1974-76; pres. broadcast div. Washington Star Communications, Inc., 1976-77; asst. sec. of state U.S. Dept. Def., 1977-79; spl. advisor to chief N.G. Bur., Dept. Def., 1980-85; pres., dir. Mid-Mal. Communications Corp., 1981-85; ptnr. Verner, Liipfert, Bernhard, McPherson and Hand, 1979-87; gen. counsel Paralyzed Vets. Am., 1988—. Vice chmn. D.C. Redevel. Land Agy., 1976-77; bd. dirs. Community Found. Greater Washington, 1977-78; bd. dirs. Friends of Nat. Zoo, 1975—, pres., 1982-84; bd. dirs. Downtown Progress, 1976-77, Fed. City Council, 1976-77, 83-87, Pennsylvania Ave. Devel. Corp., 1976-77. Served with AUS, 1953-54. Mem. ABA, D.C. Bar Assn., Army Navy Club (Washington). Democrat. Episcopalian. Home: 3819 Ingomar St NW Washington DC 20015-1929 Home (summer): Robins Nest Orrs Island ME 04066 Office: 801 18th St NW Washington DC 20006-3517

NELSON, ROGER HUGH, management educator, business executive; b. Spring City, Utah, Mar. 7, 1931; s. Hugh Devere and Maudella Sarah (Larsen) N.; m. DeEtte Munk, Aug. 26, 1955; children—Steven R., Deanne, Mark L. B.S., U. Utah, 53, M.S., 1953; Ed.D., Columbia U., 1958. Mem. faculty U. Utah Coll. Bus., 1953—, prof. mgmt. 1970—, dir. programs in emerging bus., 1989—, chmn. mgmt. dept., 1976-82, asst. dean, 1969-74; dir. MBA integrative field studies, 1993—; pres. David Eccles Sch. of Bus. Faculty, 1995—; mem. faculty Utah Mgmt. Inst., 1968-75; v.p. Computer Logic Corp., 1970-73; pres. Am. Leisure & Sports Investment Corp., 1973-75, Oil Resources, Inc., 1980-88, Puma Energy Corp., 1981-88, The Ultimate Choice Catalog Co., 1986—; fin. and mgmt. cons., 1965—; founder Utah Small Bus. Devel. Center, U. Utah, 1979. Author: Personal Money Management, 1973, The Utah Entrepreneur's Guide, 1995, also articles, reports, manuals. Active local Am. Heart Assn.; Am. Cancer Soc. campaigns; mem. exec. bd. Utah Opera Co., 1981-85, gen. bd., 1985-89. Danforth Teaching fellow, 1957. Mem. Acad. Mgmt., Adminstrv. Mgmt. Soc., NEA,

AAUP, Phi Kappa Phi, Beta Gamma Sigma, Phi Delta Kappa, Delta Phi Epsilon. Inventor comml. color separation camera and related dye-transfer processes. Home: 2662 Skyline Dr Salt Lake City UT 84108-2855 Office: U Utah David Eccles Sch Bus Salt Lake City UT 84112

NELSON, RON, composer, conductor, educator; b. Joliet, Ill., Dec. 14, 1929; s. Walter E. and Lois (Fulton) N.; m. Helen Mitchell, 1954 (dec. 1967); children: Marc W., Kristen R. Mus.B., Eastman Sch. Music, 1952, Mus.M., 1953, Mus.D., 1956; postgrad., L'Ecole, Normale, Paris, 1954-55; M.A., Brown U., 1959. Prof. Brown U. Providence, chmn. dept. music, 1963-73, Acuff chair of excellence in creative arts, 1991; prof. emeritus Brown U., 1993—. film composer, HEW, Eastman Kodak, ARC, Columbia Pictures, comms. from, Cin. Symphony, Lima Symphony, Rochester Philharmonic, R.I. Philharm., Am. Bapt. Soc., U. Minn., Dartmouth Coll., Brown U., New Music Ensemble, LaSalle Coll., Western Mich. U., Classic Chorale, U.S. Air Force Band; composer (for orch.) Savannah River Holiday, 1954, Sarabande: For Katherine in April, 1954, (opera) The Birthday of the Infanta, 1956; (cantata) The Christmas Story, 1958: (for orch.) Tocatta for Orchestra, 1963; (oratorio) What is Man?, 1964; (orch./wind ensemble) Rocky Point Holiday, 1968-69; This is the Orchestra; (orch. and tape trilogy) Trilogy: JFK-MLK-RFK, 1969; (choral) Prayer of Emperor of China, 1973; (choral) Thy Truth is Great, 1973; (choral) Psalm 95, 1974; (orch.) Five Pieces for Orchestra after Paintings by Andrew Wyeth, 1975; (choral) Prayer of St. Francis of Assisi, 1976; (orch.) Meditation and Dance for Orch., 1976; (choral) Six Pieces for Chamber Ensemble, 1977, Four Choral Pieces After the Seasons, 1978, Three Autumnal Sketches, 1979, Here We Come As in The Beginning, 1979, Mass in Honor of St. LaSalle, 1981, Three Nocturnal Pieces, 1982, Three Seasonal Reflections, 1982; composer: Fanfare for a Celebration, 1982; (choral) On Christmas Night, 1982; Medieval Suite, 1983; (choral) Dreams, 1982; (band) Fanfare for a Celebration, 1983; (cello-piano) And the Moon Rose Golden, 1983; (band) Medieval Suite, 1983; composer: Aspen Jubilee, 1984; (organ-brass) Pebble Beach Sojourn, 1984; (chorus-band) Te Deum Laudamus, 1985; (choral) Lost and Found, 1985, Light Years, 1985, Three Settings of the Moon, 1985, (strings-trumpet) Elegy, 1986, (brass) Brevard Fanfare, 1986, (chorus/band) Prime: The Hour of Sunrise, 1987, (choral) White, 1987, (choral) Another Spring, 1987, (choral) Miniatures from a Bestiary Parts I and II, 1988, (saxophone-band) Danza Capriccio, 1988, (choral) Three Pieces after Tennyson (1988), (choral) Three Mountain Ballads, 1989, (brass-winds-percussion) Fanfare for the Hour of Sunrise, 1989, (band) Morning Alleluias for the Winter Solstice, 1989, (band) Resonances, 1990; (chorus) And This Shall Be for Music, 1990, Invoking the Powers, 1991, Songs of Praise and Reconciliation, 1991, The Meadow, 1991, (band) Lauds: Praise High Day, 1992, To the Airborne, 1991, Passacaglia (Homage on B-A-C-H), 1992, Chaconne (In Memoriam), 1994, Sonoran Desert Holiday, 1994, (orch.) Epiphanies, 1993. Recipient ASCAP awards, 1962-94, Found. award for World tour, 1965-66, Nat. Band Assn. award, 1992, John Philip Sousa medal of merit, 1994; Fulbright fellow, 1954; Ford Found. commn., 1962, NEA grantee, 1973, 76, 79; awarded Acuff Chair of Excellence on the Creative Arts, 1991; winner Am. Bandmasters Assn. Ostwald Contest, 1993, Am. Band Assn. contest, 1992, Sudler Internat. Wind Band Competition, 1993. Office: Brown U Dept Music Providence RI 02912

NELSON, RONALD HARVEY, animal science educator, researcher; b. Union Grove, Wis. Aug. 10, 1918; s. Harvey August and Myra Frances (Sheen) N.; m. Elizabeth Jane Lappley, Apr. 13, 1940; children: David Peter, Marjorie Jean, Linda Louise, Ronda Elizabeth. BS, U. Wis., 1939; MS, Okla. A&M U., 1941; PhD, Iowa State U., 1943. Mem. faculty Mich. State U., 1946-85, prof., head, animal sci. dept., 1950-84, prof. emeritus, 1985—; chief of party Mich. State U. tech. assistance project Balcarce, Pcia, Buenos Aires, 1966-68. Recipient Grad. Distinction award Okla State U., 1987, Nat. Saddle and Sirloin Portrait award, 1990. Fellow Am. Soc. Animal Sci. (Internat. Animal Agr. award 1978, Animal Industry award 1984); mem. Am. Angus Assn. (chmn. research advisory com. 1956-60), Mich. Angus Assn. (pres. 1977-78), Animal Sci. Assn., Sigma Xi, Phi Kappa Phi, Alpha Zeta. Home: 1545 N Harrison Rd East Lansing MI 48823-1801

NELSON, RUSSELL MARION, surgeon, educator; b. Salt Lake City, Sept. 9, 1924; s. Marion C. and Edna (Anderson) N.; m. Dantzel White, Aug. 31, 1945; children: Marsha Nelson McKellar, Wendy Nelson Maxfield, Gloria Nelson Irion, Brenda Nelson Miles, Sylvia Nelson Webster, Emily Nelson Wittwer (dec.), Laurie Nelson Marsh, Rosalie Nelson Ringwood, Marjorie Nelson Helsten, Russell Marion Jr. BA, U. Utah, 1945, MD, 1947; PhD in Surgery, U. Minn., 1954; ScD (hon.), Brigham Young U., 1970; DMS (hon.), Utah State U., 1989; LHD (hon.), Snow Coll., 1994. Diplomate: Am. Bd. Surgery, Am. Bd. Thoracic Surgery (dir. 1972-78). Intern U. Minn. Hosps., Mpls., 1947; asst. resident surgery U. Minn. Hosps., 1948-51; first asst. resident surgery Mass. Gen. Hosp., Boston, 1953-54; sr. resident surgery U. Minn. Hosps., Mpls., 1954-55; practice medicine (specializing in cardiovascular and thoracic surgery), Salt Lake City, 1959-84; staff surgeon Latter-day Saints Hosp., Salt Lake City, 1959-84; dir. surg. research lab. Latter-day Saints Hosp., 1959-72, chief cardiovascular-thoracic surg. div., 1967-72, also bd. govs., 1970-90, vice chmn., 1979-89; staff surgeon Primary Children's Hosp., Salt Lake City, 1960; attending in surgery VA Hosp., Salt Lake City, 1953-84, Univ. Hosp., Salt Lake City, 1955-84; asst. prof. surgery Med. Sch. U. Utah, Salt Lake City, 1955-59, asst. clin. prof. surgery, 1959-66, assoc. clin. prof. surgery, clin. prof., 1966-69, research prof. surgery, 1970-84, clin. prof. emeritus, 1984—; staff services Utah Biomed. Test Lab., 1970-84; dir. tng. program cardiovascular and thoracic surgery at Univ. Utah affiliated hosps., 1967-84; mem. policyholders adv. com. New Eng. Mut. Life Ins. Co., Boston, 1976-80. Contbr. articles to profl. jours. Mem. White House Conf. on Youth and Children, 1960; bd. dirs. Internat. Cardiol. Found.; bd. govs. LDS Hosp., 1970-90, Deseret Gymnasium, 1971-75, Promised Valley Playhouse, 1970-79. 1st lt. to capt. M.C., AUS, 1951-53. Markle scholar in med. scis., 1957-59; Fellowship of Medici Publici U. Utah Coll., 1967; Gold Medal of Merit, Argentina, 1974; named Hon. Prof. Shandong Med. U., Jinan, People's Republic of China, 1985; Old People's U., Jinan, 1986; Xi-an (People's Republic of China) Med. Coll., 1986, Legacy of Life award, 1993. Fellow A.C.S. (chmn. adv. council on thoracic surgery 1973-75), Am. Coll. Cardiology, Am. Coll. Chest Physicians; mem. Am. Assn. Thoracic Surgery, Am. Soc. Artificial Internal Organs, AMA, Dirs. Thoracic Residencies (pres. 1971-72), Utah Med. Assn. (pres. 1970-71), Salt Lake County Med. Soc., Am. Heart Assn. (exec. com. cardiovascular surgery 1972, dir. 1976-78, chmn. council cardiovascular surgery 1976-78), Utah Heart Assn. (pres. 1964-65), Soc. Thoracic Surgeons, Soc. Vascular Surgery (sec. 1968-72, pres. 1974), Utah Thoracic Soc., Salt Lake Surg. Soc., Samson Thoracic Surg. Soc., Western Soc. for Clin. Research, Soc. U. Surgeons, Am., Western, Pan-Pacific surg. assns., Inter. Am. Soc. Cardiology (bd. mgrs.), Phi Beta Kappa, Sigma Xi, Alpha Omega Alpha, Phi Kappa Phi, Sigma Chi. Mem. Ch. of Jesus Christ of Latter-day Saints (pres. Bonneville Stake 1964-71, gen. pres. Sunday sch. 1971-79, regional rep. 1979-84, Quorum of the Twelve Apostles 1984—). Home: 1347 Normandie Cir Salt Lake City UT 84105-1919 Office: 47 E South Temple Salt Lake City UT 84150

NELSON, SANDRA KAY, foundation administrator; b. Hicksville, Ohio, July 12, 1961; d. Deloy LaVerl and Bettie E. Lucille (Wonderly) Osmun; m. Gregory Lynn Thompson, May 22, 1982 (div. Aug. 1988); 1 child, Andrew Braden; m. Dean Marshall Nelson, July 17, 1993; 1 child, Tanner Marshall. Student, Internat. Bus. Coll., Ft. Wayne, Ind., 1979-80, N.W. Tech. Coll., 1990—. Supr. Ohio Art Co., Bryan, 1984-87; nat. devel. dir. Nat. Reye's Syndrome Found., Bryan, 1987-93, acting exec. dir., 1993-94, exec. dir., 1994—. Editor (newsletter) In The News, 1989—. Den leader Cub Scout Pack 3186, Fremont, Ind., 1993—. Mem. Nat. Voluntary Health Agys. (chairperson 1994-95, trustee 1993—, nat. com. rep. 1993—), Clear Lake Yacht Club (social chair 1993-94). Lutheran. Avocations: sailing races, bike treks. Office: Reyes Syndrome Found 426 N Lewis PO Box 829 Bryan OH 43506

NELSON, SARAH MILLEDGE, archaeology educator; b. Miami, Fla., Nov. 29, 1931; d. Stanley and Sarah Woodman (Franklin) M.; m. Harold Stanley Nelson, July 25, 1953; children: Erik Harold, Mark Milledge, Stanley Franklin. BA, Wellesley Coll., 1953; MA, U. Mich., 1969, PhD, 1973. Instr. archaeology U. Md. extension, Seoul, Republic Korea, 1970-71; asst. prof. U. Denver, 1974-79, assoc. prof., 1979-85, prof. archaeology, 1985—, chair dept. anthropology, dir. women's studies program, 1985-87; vis. asst. prof. U. Colo., Boulder, 1974. Co-editor: Powers of Observation, 1990,

Equity Issues for Women in Archaeology, 1994; author: Archaeology of Korea, 1993; editor: The Archaeology of Northeast China, 1995. Active Earthwatch, 1989. Southwestern Inst. Rsch. on Women grantee, 1981, Acad. Korean Studies grantee, Seoul, 1983, Internat. Cultural Soc. Korea grantee, 1986, Scholarly Communication award People's Republic of China, NAS, 1988; recipient Outstanding Scholar award U. Denver, 1989. Fellow Am. Anthrop. Assn.; mem. Soc. Am. Archaeology, Assn. Asian Studies, Royal Asiatic Soc., Sigma Xi (sec.-treas. 1978-79), Phi Beta Kappa. Democrat. Avocations: skiing, gardening. Home: 5878 S Dry Creek Ct Littleton CO 80121-1709 Office: U Denver Dept Anthropology Denver CO 80208

NELSON, SHELLEY MARIE, lawyer; b. Fairmont, Minn., Nov. 1, 1956; d. Maynard Melvin and Anita Pauline (Myhrvold) N. BS in Polit. Sci., French summa cum laude, Mankato State U., 1978; JD magna cum laude, U. Minn., 1981. Bar: Minn. 1981, U.S. Dist. Ct. Minn. 1982. Assoc. Dorsey and Whitney, Mpls., 1981-83; atty. Minn. Mining and Mfg., St. Paul, 1983-86, counsel, 1986-89, sr. counsel, 1989—; counsel The Hague Acad. Internat. Law, 1988. Contbr. articles to profl. jour. Mem. Minn. Internat. Human Rights Com., 1988—; team capt. United Arts Fund Drive, 1988; bd. dirs., legal advisor Minn. Women's Polit. Caucus, 1989-90. Mem. Minn. State Bar Assn., Ramsey County Bar Assn., Am. Immigration Lawyers Assn., Order of Coif, Phi Kappa Phi.

NELSON, STEVEN CRAIG, lawyer; b. Oakland, Calif., May 11, 1944; s. Eskil Manfred and Florence Lucille (Boatman) N.; m. Kathryn Cassel Stoltz, Nov. 30, 1974; children: Carleton Philip, Whitney Cassel. BA in Econs. with exceptional distinction, Yale U., 1966, LLB, 1969. Bar: DC 1969, Minn. Supreme Ct. 1973, U.S. Supreme Ct. 1973. From atty. adviser to asst. legal adviser U.S. Dept. State, Washington, 1969-74; from assoc. to ptnr. Oppenheimer, Wolff, Foster, Shepard & Donnelly, St. Paul and Mpls., 1975-85; ptnr. Dorsey & Whitney, Mpls., 1985—; mem. bd. appeals NATO, Brussels. 1977—; adj. prof. law U. Minn. 1980—; speaker in field. Contbr. articles to profl. jours. Mem. ABA (chmn. internat. law and practice 1988-89), Minn. Bar Assn., Am. Fgn. Law Assn., Am. Soc. Internat. Law, Internat. Bar Assn., Union Internat. des Avocats. Presbyterian. Club: Minikahda (Mpls.). Avocations: golf, tennis, skiing, sailing. Office: Dorsey & Whitney 220 S 6th St Minneapolis MN 55402

NELSON, STEVEN DOUGLAS, lawyer; b. Houston, Oct. 13, 1950; s. Stewart L. and Jean (Boyd) N.; m. Elizabeth (Betsy) Lane Brown, Mar. 25, 1972; children: Elizabeth K., D. Andrew, Allison L., Amanda J. BA in Econs., So. Meth. U., 1972, JD, 1976. Bar: Tex. 1976, U.S. Dist. Ct. (no. dist.) Tex. 1980, U.S. Ct. Claims 1980, U.S. Ct. Appeals (5th cir.) 1979, U.S. Ct. Appeals (fed. cir.) 1982, U.S. Supreme Ct. 1980. Shareholder, chmn. constrn. law practice group Winstead, Sechrest & Minick, P.C., Dallas, 1976—; participant Surety Claims Inst., Mo., 1982, 84-86, 89, 91; leader constrn./fidelity/surety sect. Winstead, Sechrest & Minick, 1983-85, 89—, mem. mgmt. com., 1985-86, compensation com., 1991-93, co-chmn. bus. devel. com., 1986-87, practice and procedures com., 1990-91, chmn. facilities, systems and tech. com., 1988-90; mem. AIA/AGC liaison com. Dallas chpt. Associated Gen. Contractors, 1984-88, legis. com. Dallas bldg. br., 1988-90, bd. dirs., 1991—; speaker in field. Author: Bonds and Liens in Texas, 1991; co-author: Texas Lien Law Digest, 1984; contbg. editor: Design and Construction Market Strategist, 1993, Mexican Business Review, 1993, Dallas Construction Industry Practices, 1986-89; author: (audiovisual presentations) Insurable Risks, 1985. Mem. adv. com. magnet ctr. pub. svcs., govt. and law Dallas Ind. Sch. Dist., 1989—, adv. coun. Ctr. Non-Profit Mgmt., 1992-93, Pub. Safety Com., City University Park, Tex., 1992-93; bd. dirs. Greater Dallas Crime Comsn., 1990—, chmn. legis. com., 1990, v.p. crime stoppers, 1990-91, pres., 1992, gen. counsel, 1993; bd. dirs. and v.p. The City Club, Dallas, 1992—; asst. scoutmaster Boy Scout Troop # 72, Dallas, 1992—. Staff sgt. USAR, 1971-77. Mem. ABA (fidelity and surety subcommittee tort and ins. practice sect., pub. contract law sect., forum com. construction law), Am. Surety Assn. (vice-chmn. claims com. 1981-82, chmn. 1982-83, dir. 1983-84, 86-90, v.p. 1988-90), Am. Arbitration Assn. (nat. panel arbitrators), U.S. Arbitration and Mediation, Inc. (nat. constrn. panel), State Bar Tex. (co-founder constrn. law sect., various offices, editor Constrn. Law Newsletter 1992-93), Def. Rsch. Inst., Dallas Bar Assn. Republican. Presbyterian. Avocations: backpacking, genealogy, computers. Home: 4011 Amherst Dallas TX 75225 Office: Ford and Nelson PC 1100 Highland Park Pl 4514 Cole Ave Dallas TX 75205

NELSON, STUART OWEN, agricultural engineer, researcher, educator; b. Pilger, Nebr., Jan. 23, 1927; s. Irvin Andrew and Agnes Emilie (Nissen) N.; m. Carolyn Joye Fricke, Dec. 27, 1953 (dec. Nov. 1975); children: Richard Lynn, Jana Sue; m. Martha Ellen White Fuller, Apr. 8, 1979. BS in Agrl. Engring., U. Nebr., 1950, MSc in Agrl. Engring., 1952, MA in Physics, 1954; PhD in Engring., Iowa State U., 1972, hon. DSc U. Nebr., 1989. Grad. asst. U. Nebr., Lincoln, 1952-54, research assoc., 1954-60, assoc. prof., 1960-72, prof., 1972-76; project leader Farm Electrification Research, Agrl. Research Service, U.S. Dept. Agr., Lincoln, 1954-59, research investigations leader, 1959-72, research leader, 1972-76, research agrl. engr. Russell Research Ctr., Athens, Ga., 1976—; adj. prof. U. Ga., 1976—; sci. adv. council Am. Seed Research Found.; mem. CAST Task Force on Irradiation for Food Preservation and Pest Control; adv. com. grain moisture measurement Nat. Council Weights and Measures; mem. sci. bd. 4th Internat. Conf. on Phys. Properties Agrl. Materials, Prague, 1985. Served with USN, 1946-48. Recipient HM Crops and Soils award Am. Soc. Agronomy, 1966; recipient Founders Gold medal as named Fed. Engr. of Yr., NSPE, 1985; Superior Service award U.S. Dept. Agr., 1986; Profl. Achievement Citation Engring. award Iowa State U., 1987. Fellow Am. Soc. Agrl. Engrs. (Tech. Paper award 1965, 94, Engr. of Yr. award Ga. sect. 1988, chmn. Ga. sect. 1988-89). Fellow Internat. Microwave Power Inst. (Decade award 1981); mem. AAAS, IEEE (sr.), The Electromagnetics Acad., Internat. Soc. Agromaterials Sci. and Engring., Ga. Soc. Profl. Engrs. (Engr. of Yr. in Govt. award 1991), Nat. Accad. Engring., Nat. Soc. Profl. Engrs., Orgn. Profl. Employees of Dept. of Agr. (pres. Athens area chpt. 1984-86, nat. coun. rep. 1988-95, Profl. of Yr. award 1987), Sigma Xi, Sigma Nu, Gamma Sigma Delta, Tau Beta Pi. Methodist. Club: Athens Optimist (pres. 1980-81, lt. gov. Ga. dist. 1983-84, Optimist of Yr. award 1982, disting. and outstanding lt. gov. Ga. dist. 1985), Assoc. editor Jour. Microwave Power, 1975-76; contbr. more than 300 articles to sci. and tech. jours. Home: 270 Idylwood Dr Athens GA 30605-4610 Office: Rsch Agr Engr USDA ARS PO Box 5677 Athens GA 30604

NELSON, SUZANNE MOSEY, association executive, non-profit management consultant; b. Sioux Falls, S.D., Feb. 23, 1949; d. Albert Ali and Fatima (Hasson) Mosey; m. Jeffrey T. Nelson, Aug. 6, 1971 (div. 1985); children: Leia, Kristoffar. BA, Augustana Coll., Sioux Falls, S.D., 1971, postgrad., 1976-78. Cert. tchr., S.D. Tchr. Sioux Falls Pub. Schs., 1971-76; instr. Augustana Coll., 1976-78, asst. dir. student acitivies, 1982-84; personnel adminstr. First Nat. Bank Sioux Falls, 1984-87; exec. dir. S.D. Symphony Orch., Sioux Falls, 1987-91, YWCA, Sioux Falls, 1991—; cons. non-profit mgmt., NEA pilot project, S.D., South for Dakotans Arts, 1991—. Vol. Meals on Wheels/Sr. Citizens Ctr., Sioux Falls; active PTA, Sioux Falls, 1981—; mem. adv. bd. Sioux Empire Youth Symphony; trustee S.D. Symphony Orch. League; pres., bd. dirs. Sioux Falls Community Playhouse, 1978-83. Mem. Nat. Soc. Fund Raising Execs., Nat. Assn. YWCA Execs., YWCA U.S.A., Sioux Falls Personnel Assn., Sioux Falls C. of C. (diplomat). Lutheran. Avocations: antiques, gardening, water sports, choir. Office: YWCA Sioux Falls 300 W 11th St Sioux Falls SD 57102

NELSON, SYDNEY B., lawyer, state senator; b. Mar. 12, 1935; BBA, U. Okla.; JD, La. State U.; m. Gail Anderson. Law clk. U.S. Dist. Ct., 1963-64; pvt. practice law, Shreveport, La., 1964—; Mem. La. Senate, 1980-92. Mem. adminstrv. bd. 1st Meth. Ch., Shreveport; adv. bd. Norwella coun. Boy Scouts Am. Served as officer USN, 1957-60. Assoc. editor La. Law Rev. Mem. ABA, La. Bar Assn., Shreveport Bar Assn. (pres. 1989), Order of Coif. Republican. Office: 705 Milam St Ste A Shreveport LA 71101-3507

NELSON, THOMAS CARL, association executive; b. St. Louis, Dec. 28, 1943; s. Carl William and Thora E. (Herr) N.; m. L. Brooke Morrison, Aug. 14, 1965; children: Ashley, Jay. BA, Drake U., 1965; MPA, Kans. U., 1967. Asst. village mgr. Winnetka, Ill., 1966-68, Titusville, Fla., 1968-69; exec. asst. Am. Acad. Family Physicians, Kansas City, Mo., 1969-70; adminstrv.

asst. AMA, Chgo., 1970-71; asst. exec. dir. Am. Acad. Orthopedic Surgeons, Chgo., 1971-78, exec. dir., 1984—; pres. Thomas Nelson Assocs., Chgo., 1978-84; bd. dirs. Orthopaedic Resource Coordinating Co., Chgo. Mem. Assn. Med. Soc. Execs. (adv. com.), Profl. Convention Mgmt. Assn. (editorial bd. 1985—, legis. com. 1986—), Am. Orthopedic Soc. Sports Medicine (hon.). Office: Am Acad Orthopaedic Surgeons 6300 N River Rd Des Plaines IL 60018

NELSON, THOMAS G., federal judge; b. 1936. Student, Univ. Idaho, 1955-59, LLB, 1960. Ptnr. Parry, Robertson, Daly and Larson, Twin Falls, Idaho, 1965-79, Nelson, Rosholt, Robertson, Tolman and Tucker, Twin Falls, from 1979; judge U.S. Cir. Ct. (9th cir.), San Francisco, Calif., 1990—. With Idaho Air N.G., 1962-65, USAR, 1965-68. Mem. ABA (ho. of dels. 1974, 86-88), Am. Bar Found., Am. Coll. Trial Lawyers, Idaho State Bar (pres., bd. commrs.), Idaho Assn. Def. Counsel, Am. Bd. Trial Advocates (pres. Idaho chpt.), Phi Alpha Delta, Idaho Law Found., Internat. Assn. Def. Counsel. Office: US Ct Appeals 9th Circuit PO Box 1339 Boise ID 83701-1339

NELSON, THOMAS R., lawyer; b. St. Paul, Apr. 29, 1936. BA, U. Okla., 1958, LLB, 1960. Bar: Ill. 1964, N.Y. 1968. Ptnr. Baker & McKenzie, Chgo. Office: Baker & McKenzie 1 Prudential Plz 130 E Randolph St Chicago IL 60601

NELSON, THOMAS WILLIAM, management consultant, former government official; b. Rupert, Idaho, June 9, 1921; s. John Glenn and Jessie Olive (Wise) N.; m. Frances Grace Rotanzi, Oct. 17, 1948; children: Janet, Neal, Eric, Karen. A.B., San Diego State U., 1948; grad., Fed. Exec. Inst., 1968. Personnel technician U.S. Air Force, 1948-61; chief civilian salary and wage adminstrn. Hdqrs. U.S. Air Force, 1961-66; chief mgmt. div. Office of Sec. of Air Force, 1966-69; dep. adminstrv. asst. to Sec. Air Force, 1969-71, adminstrv. asst., 1971-80; pres., mgmt. cons. Thomas W. Nelson & Assoc. Inc., 1981—; mgmt. cons. ManTech Internat. Corp., 1981-85. Pres. Buffalo Hill Citizens Assn., Falls Church, Va., 1968, Sleepy Hollow Recreation Assn., 1962—. Served with U.S. Army, 1943-45, ETO. Decorated Purple Heart, Bronze Star; recipient Meritorious Service award Dept. Air Force, 1961, Exceptional Civilian Service award, 1971, 73, 75, 77, 79, 80; Disting. Civilian Service medal Dept. Def., 1980. Mem. Sigma Phi Epsilon. Home and Office: 6344 Nicholson St Falls Church VA 22044-1912

NELSON, VIRGINIA SIMSON, pediatrician, educator; b. L.A.; d. Jerome and Virginia (Kuppler) Simson; children: Eric, Paul. AB, Stanford U., 1963, MD, 1970; MPH, U. Mich., 1974. Diplomate Am. Bd. Pediatrics, Am. Bd. Phys. Medicine and Rehab. Pediatrician Inst. Study Mental Retardation and Related Disabilities, U. Mich., Ann Arbor, 1973-80; mem. faculty phys. medicine and rehab. dept. U. Mich. Med. Ctr., Ann Arbor, 1980-83, resident PM&R, 1983-85, chief pediatric PM&R, 1985—. Contbr. articles to profl. jours. Office: Univ Mich Med Ctr F7822 Mott Hospital Ann Arbor MI 48109-0230

NELSON, WALDEMAR STANLEY, civil engineer, consultant; b. New Orleans, July 8, 1916; s. Bernard Stanley and Mary Lockett (Hutson) N.; widowed; children: Mary Sue Nelson Roniger, Martha Nelson Frost, Charles W., Virginia Nelson Dodge, Kenneth H. BS in Mech. and Elec. Engring., Tulane U., 1936. Registered civil, elec. and mech. engr., 44 states. Jr. engr. A. M. Lockett & Co., 1936-37; civil engr. Jeff. Lake Sulphur Co., Brazoria, Tex., 1937-38; chief survey party N.O. Pub. Belt. R.R., New Orleans, 1938; resident engr. James M. Todd, Buras, La., 1938-39; pvt. practice New Orleans, 1939-40; asst. chief engr. W. Horace Williams Co., Camp Claiborne, La., 1940-41; sr. engr. U.S. Engr. Dept., Camp Claiborne, 1941-44; prin. Waldemar S. Nelson and Co., Inc., New Orleans, 1945—, chmn. bd. dirs.; past chmn. La. State Bd. Registration Profl. Engrs. and Land Surveyors; founding mem., pres. bd. advisors sch. engring. Tulane U. Chmn. Tulane Alumni Fund, Mems' Coun., 1984; mem. bd. visitors Tulane U.; active The Chamber/New Orleans, Boy Scouts Am.; past chmn. Com. of 50; past pres. bd. commrs. NewOrleans City Pk. Improvement Assn.; mem. exec. bd. Christmas New Orleans, 1988; past sr. warden of vestry St. Andrew's Episcopal Ch.; past chmn. bd. dirs. St. Andrew's Episcopal Sch.; past pres. bd. trustees St. Martin's Protestant Episcopal Sch.; trustee Tulane Engring. Found.; bd. dirs. River Region, MetroVision. Recipient Outstanding Engring. Alumnus award Tulane U., 1976, Honor award Constrn. Industry Assn. New Orleans, Inc., 1982, Role Model of Yr. award Young Leadership Coun., 1987, Vol. of Yr. award Tulane U. Alumni Affairs, 1992. Fellow ASCE (life), ASME (life, past chmn. New Orleans sect.); mem. IEEE, NSPE (past v.p., past chmn. bd. ethical rev.), Am. Pub. Works Assn. (life), Am. Acad. Environ. Engrs. (diplomate), Nat. Coun. Engring. Examiners (past treas., Disting. Svc. award), Soc. Am. Mil. Engrs., La. Engring. Soc. (hon., past pres., Charles M. Kerr Pub. Rels. award, Leo M. Odom Profl. Svcs. award, A.B. Paterson medal, Andrew M. Lockett medal), La. Engring. Found. (trustee 1990, treas. 1991-91, sec. 1994—), Soc. Tulane Engrs. (past pres.), French-Am. C. of C. (pres. La. chpt. 1992-93, chmn. 1994), Tulane Alumni Assn. (past pres.), Engrs.' Club New Orleans (past pres.), Tau Beta Pi, Pi Tau Sigma, Eta Kappa Nu, others. Avocations: fishing, boating, gardening, shop work, photography. Office: Waldemar S Nelson & Co Inc 1200 Saint Charles Ave New Orleans LA 70130

NELSON, WALLACE BOYD, economics and business administration educator; b. Oilton, Okla., Mar. 17, 1923; s. Frank and Notie (Ferguson) N.; m. Merietta Josephine Lair, Sept. 1, 1942; 1 child, Larry Frank. BS, So. Ill. U., 1947; MA, U. Ia., 1948; PhD, U. Iowa, 1950. From asst. to prof. econs. Kans. State U., 1950-61; prof., chmn. dept. bus. adminstrn. Arlington (Tex.) State Coll., 1961-65; prof. econs. and bus. adminstrn., dean U. Tex. Sch. Bus. Adminstrn., Arlington, 1965-73; prof. econs. and bus. adminstrn. U. Tex., Arlington, 1973-93, prof. emeritus, 1993—; pres. Nelson Assocs., 1974—; cochmn. regional devel. com. N. Tex. Commn., 1972-77, bd. dirs. commn., 1973-77; personal injury litigation cons. Contbr. articles to profl. jours. With USAAF, 1943-46, USAF, 1951-53. Honor guest Brazil at Celebration Brazil's 150th Anniversary, 1972; Ford Motor Co. fellow, 1955, rsch. fellow Claremont Men's Coll., 1957. Mem. Am. Arbitration Assn., Fed. Mediation Conciliation Service, Nat. Acad. Arbitrators, Arlington, Dallas, Ft. Worth C. of C., Am. Econ. Assn., Indsl. Relations Research Assn., Southwestern Social Sci. Assn., Order of Artus (pres. 1948). Presbyn. (trustee). Club: Rotarian. Home: 917 Sherwood Dr Arlington TX 76013-1571

NELSON, WALLACE WARREN, retired superintendent experimental station, agronomy educator; b. Tracy, Minn., Feb. 17, 1928; s. Elmer R. and Mabel K. (Anderson) N.; m. Arlene S. Michelson, June 18, 1949; children: Thomas W., Kathryn J. BS, U. Minn., 1950, PhD, 1956. Asst. supt., agronomist N.E. Exptl. Sta. U. Minn., Duluth, 1953-59; supt., agronomist S.W. Exptl. Sta. U. Minn., Lamberton, 1959-72, supt., prof., 1972-95; ret.; bd. dirs. North Star Ins., Cottonwood, Minn. Bd. dirs. Minn. Pollution Control Agys., 1980-83. Recipient Outstanding Alumni award U. Minn., 1989. Fellow Am. Soc. Agronomists (chmn. A-7 1988). Lutheran.

NELSON, WALTER GERALD, retired insurance company executive; b. Peoria, Ill., Jan. 2, 1930; s. Walter Dennis and Hazel Marie (Tucker) N.; m. Mary Ann Olberding, Jan. 28, 1952 (dec. Nov. 1989); children—Ann (Mrs. Michael Larkin), Michael, Susan (Mrs. Jay Boor), Patrick, Timothy, Molly (Mrs. David Edwards); m. Mary Jo Sunderland, Apr. 6, 1991. Student, St. Benedict's Coll., Atchison, Kans., 1947-49, Bradley U., Peoria, Ill., 1949; JD, Creighton U., Omaha, 1952. Bar: Nebr. 1952, Ill. 1955; CLU. Practice in Peoria, 1955-56; with State Farm Life Ins. Co., Bloomington, Ill., 1956—; counsel State Farm Life Ins. Co., 1968—, v.p. 1970—; past dir. Ill. Life Ins. Coun.; past chmn. legal sect. Am. Coun. Life Ins.; speaker in field. Contbr. articles to profl. jours. Community bd. dirs. St. Joseph Med. Ctr., Bloomington, Ill., 1994. Mem. ABA, Ill. Bar Assn., Nebr. Bar Assn., Assn. Life Ins. Counsel (bd. govs., past pres.), Nat. Orgn. Life and Health Ins. Guaranty Assns. Bloomington Country Club, KC. Republican. Roman Catholic.

NELSON, WENDEL LANE, medicinal chemist, educator; b. Mason City, Nebr., Apr. 7, 1939; s. Clayton W. and Joyce E. (Wilson) N.; m. Karen A. Hansen, June 14, 1968; children—Christopher E., Timothy D. B.S., Idaho State U., 1962; Ph.D., U. Kans., 1965. Asst. prof. med. chemistry U. Wash., Seattle, 1965-70; asso. prof., 1970-76, prof., 1976—. NSF fellow, 1963-65; recipient career devel. award NIH, 1971-76. Mem. Am. Chem. Soc., N.Y.

Acad. Sci., Am. Assn. Colls. Pharmacy. Office: Dept Med Chem U Wash Seattle WA 98195

NELSON, WILLIAM BRUCE, newspaper company executive; b. Mpls., July 13, 1950; s. William Harry and Marian (Anderson) N.; m. Sherry Graham, Dec. 28, 1974; children: Timothy, Jeffrey, Michael. BS in Indsl. Engring., Northwestern U., MBA in Mgmt. Loan rep. 1st Nat. Bank Chgo., 1975-77; fin. analyst Tribune Co., 1977-78, mgr. fin. planning, 1978-79; dir. fin. planning Chgo. Tribune Co., 1979-82, v.p., chief fin. officer, 1982—. Mem. Inst. Newspaper Fin. Execs. Avocations: stamp collecting, baseball.

NELSON, WILLIAM EDWARD, lawyer, educator; b. 1940. A.B., Hamilton Coll., 1962; LL.B., NYU, 1965; Ph.D., Harvard U., 1971. Bar: N.Y. 1966. Law clk. to assoc. justice, Byron R. White, U.S. Supreme Ct., Washington, 1971-72; asst. prof. U. Pa., Phila., 1971-74, assoc. prof., 1974-75; assoc. prof. Yale U., New Haven Conn., 1975-80; prof. NYU, N.Y.C., 1980—. Mem. Order of Coif. Author: Americanization of the Common Law: The Impact of Legal Change on Massachusetts Society, 1760-1830, 1975; The Roots of American Bureaucracy, 1830-1900, 1982, The Fourteenth Amendment: From Political Principle to Judicial Doctrine, 1988. Office: NYU Law Sch 40 Washington Sq S New York NY 10012-1099

NELSON, WILLIAM GEORGE, IV, software company executive; b. Phila., May 26, 1934; s. William George III and Eleanor (Boyle) N. BA in Chemistry, Swarthmore Coll., 1956; MBA in Finance, U. Pa., 1958; PhD in Econs., Rice U., 1965. Various positions Du Pont Co., 1957-62, Monsanto Co., St. Louis, 1965-76; vis. assist. prof. Washington U., St. Louis, 1965-75; sr. v.p. Chase Econs./Interactive Data, Waltham, Mass., 1976-83; pres. Pansophic Systems, Lisle, Ill., 1983-90; pres., CEO OnLine Software, Ft. Lee, N.J., 1990-91, bd. dirs.; pres., CEO Pilot Software, Boston, 1992-94; CEO Harris Data Corp., 1990—; bd. dirs. GEAC, Toronto, Manugistics, Rockville, Md., Harris Data, Waukesha, Wis., HPR, Inc., Boston, Project Software and Devel. Inc., Cambridge, Mass. Bd. dirs. Swarthmore Coll., Hampton U. NFS fellow in econs., 1963-65. Office: Harris Data 611 N Barker Rd Brookfield WI 53045-5977

NELSON, WILLIAM O., pharmaceutical company executive; b. Upland, Calif., Mar. 30, 1941; s. William Orestas and Glenice Irene (Pearson) N.; m. Sue Farmer, Jan. 27, 1962 (div. Jan. 1971); 1 child, Terri Lynn; m. Deborah Marie Goodwin, Oct. 5, 1985. AA, Pima Coll., Tucson, 1976; BS, U. Phoenix, 1980. Sales rep. Sandoz Pharms., Riverside, Calif., 1966-71, Tucson, 1971-79; regional sales mgr. Sandoz Pharms., Phoenix, 1979-87, western area mgr., med. scis. liaison, 1987-94; assoc. dir. oncology bus. ops. Sandoz Pharms., East Hanover, N.J., 1994—. With USN, 1959-63. Republican. Avocations: golf, trap shooting, audiophile. Home: 8768 Banyan St Rancho Cucamonga CA 91701-3355

NELSON, WILLIAM RANKIN, surgeon; b. Charlottesville, Va., Dec. 12, 1921; s. Hugh Thomas and Edith (Rankin) N.; m. Nancy Laidley, Mar. 17, 1956 (div. 1979); children: Robin Page Nelson Russel, Susan Kimberly Nelson Wright, Anne Rankin Nelson Cron; m. Pamela Morgan Phelps, July 5, 1984. BA, U. Va., 1943, MD, 1945. Diplomate Am. Bd. Surgery. Intern Vanderbilt U. Hosp., Nashville, 1945-46; resident in surgery U. Va. Hosp., Charlottesville, 1949-51; fellow surg. oncology Meml. Sloan Kettering Cancer Ctr., N.Y.C., 1951-55; instr. U. Colo. Sch. Medicine, Denver, 1955-57; asst. clin. prof. U. Colo. Sch. Medicine, 1962-87, clin. prof. surgery, 1987—; asst. prof. Med. Coll. Va., Richmond, 1957-62; mem. exec. com. U. Colo. Cancer Ctr.; mem. nat. bd., nat. exec. com. Am. Cancer Soc. Contbr. articles to profl. jours. and chpts. to textbooks. Capt. USAAF, 1946-48. Recipient Nat. Div. award Am. Cancer Soc., 1979. Fellow Am. Coll. Surgeons (bd. govs. 1984-89); mem. AMA, Internat. Soc. Surgery, Brit. Assn. Surg. Oncology, Royal Soc. Medicine (U.K.), Soc. Surg. Oncology (pres. 1975-76), Soc. Head and Neck Surgeons (pres. 1986-87), Am. Cancer Soc. (pres. Colo. div. 1975-77, exec. com. nat. bd. dirs., del. dir. from Colo. div. 1975—), Am. Soc. Clin. Oncology, Western Surg. Assn. Colo. Med. Soc., Denver Med. Soc., Denver Acad. Surgery, Rocky Mt. Oncology Soc., Univ. Club, Rotary. Republican. Presbyterian. Avocations: skiing, backpacking, travel, bicycling, fly fishing.

NELSON, WILLIAM SHANNON, II, lawyer; b. Columbia, S.C., Oct. 9, 1938; s. Patrick Henry and Elizabeth (Nicholson) N.; m. LeGrand M. Nelson, July 23, 1966; children: Patrick Henry, William Shannon III, Francis Pickens, Caroline LeGran Nelson. BA, U. S.C., 1960, LLB, 1963. Bar: S.C. 1963. Ptnr. Nelson, Mullins, Riley & Scarborough, Columbia, S.C., 1964—; Episcopalian. Office: Nelson Mullins Riley & Scarborough 1330 Lady St Columbia SC 29201-3300

NELSON, WILLIE, musician, songwriter; b. Abbott, Tex., Apr. 30, 1933; children: Jacob, Lukas, Paula Carlene, Amy, Lana, Susie, Billy. Student, Baylor U. Worked as salesman; announcer, host country music shows local Tex. stas.; bass player, Ray Price's band; then formed own band, personal appearances at Grand Ole Opry, Nashville and throughout U.S., 1964—; rec. artist, Atlantic, Columbia and RCA records; albums include One for the Road, Here's Willie Nelson, 1963, Country Willie, 1973, Red Headed Stranger, 1975, The Troublemaker, 1976, Willie Nelson and His Friends, 1976, Willie Before His Time, Wanted/The Outlaw, The Willie Way, The Best of Willie Nelson, Stardust, 1978, Family Bible, 1980, Tougher Than Leather, 1983, City of New Orleans, 1984, Me and Paul, 1985, (with Johnny Cash, Kris Kristofferson and Waylon Jennings) Highwayman, 1985, The Promise Land, 1986, Partners, 1986, Island in the Sea, 1987, Seashores of Old Mexico, 1987, What a Wonderful World, 1988, A Horse Called Music, 1989, Highwayman II, 1990, Born for Trouble, 1990, Clean Shirt Waylon and Willie, 1991, Across the Borderline, 1993, Across the Borderline, 1993, Moonlight Becomes You, 1993; film appearances include: Electric Horseman, 1979, Honeysuckle Rose, 1980, Thief, 1981, Barbarosa, 1982; star, co-writer mus. score TV film Stagecoach, 1986; theme song performed, film Welcome Home, 1989; TV films include Where the Hell's That Gold, 1988, Once upon a Texas Train, 1989, A Pair of Aces, 1990, Born for Trouble, 1990, Another Pair of Aces: Three of a Kind, 1991; author: (autobiography) I Didn't Come Here and I Ain't Leading, 1988. Served in USAF. Recipient Grammy award for song Blue Eyes Crying in the Rain 1975, for Georgia on My Mind 1978, for Mammas Don't Let Your Babies Grow Up to Be Cowboys (with Waylon Jennings) 1978, Billboard mag. citation for Top Album Artist 1976, Country Music Assn. award for single Good Hearted Woman, for vocal duo with Waylon Jennings and for album Wanted: The Outlaws, Grammy award for Best Album, 1984, Special Humanitarian award Nat. Farmers Orgn., 1986, (with Julio Iglesias) Best Vocal Duo award Country Music Assn., Grammy Lifetime Achievement award, 1989; named to Nashville Songwriters Assn. Hall of Fame, 1973, CMA Entertainer of Yr., 1979, Country Music Hall of Fame, 1993. Office: care Mark Rothbaum & Assocs Inc PO Box 2689 Danbury CT 06813-2689

NELSON-HUMPHRIES, TESSA (TESSA UNTHANK), English language educator, writer, lecturer; b. Yorkshire, Eng.; came to U.S., 1955; m. Kenneth Nelson Brown, June 1, 1957 (dec. 1962); m. Cecil H. Unthank, Sept. 26, 1963 (dec. 1979). BA, U. London, 1953; MA, U. N.C., 1965; PhD in English, U. Liverpool (Eng.), 1973. Head English dept. Richard Thomas Girls Sch., Elmore Green Sch., Walsall, Eng., 1953-58, 59-60; dir. English studies Windsor Coll., Buenos Aires, Argentina, 1958-59; prof. English, Cumberland Coll., Williamsburg, Ky., 1964-90; prof. English, N.Mex. State U., 1990-91. Best Actress award Carlsbad (N.Mex.) Little Theatre, 1962, Cumberland Coll., 1979; Fulbright fellow, 1955-56, Danforth fellow, 1971, James Still fellow, 1983; Mellon travel/study grantee, China, 1981, 87; recipient awards for fiction Eng., 1986, 87, 88. Fellow AAUW; mem. Soc. Women Writers and Journalists (Short Story prize 1975, 87, Poetry prize 1988, 89, Julia Cairns Silver trophy for Poetry, 1978, article prize, London, 1986, poetry prizes, 1994, U.K. 1994-95), Soc. Women Writers and Journalists Eng., Soc. Children's Book Writers, Vegetarian Soc. (life), Mensa. Episcopalian. Contbr. articles to Cats Mag., Let's Live, The Lookout, Child Life, Children's Digest, Vegetarian Times, Alive!, The Dalesman, Mich. Quar. Rev., Bull. of Soc. Children's Book Writers, Bull. Soc. Women Writers and Journalists, others; columnist, British Vegetarian mag., 1976-85; contbr. poetry to various mags. including Joycean Lit. Arts Guild, Z-Miscellaneous, Blue Unicorn, Appalachian Heritage, Aireings-U.K., ENVOI (HardBack Anthology)-U.K.

NELSON-MAYSON, LINDA RUTH, art museum curator; b. Vincennes, Ind., Jan. 9, 1954; d. Robert Arthur and Darleen Marie (Andrews) N.; m. William A. Mayson, June 12, 1982; 1 child, Eric Nelson. BFA, Miami U., Oxford, Ohio, 1976; MFA, Ohio State U., 1981. Co-dir. Artreach Gallery, Columbus, Ohio, 1980-82; art instr., gallery asst. Ohio U., Chillicothe, 1982-83; asst. curator Ross County Mus., Chillicothe, 1982-83; art dir. Aaron Copland Music & Arts Program, White Plains, N.Y., 1982-85; artist-in-residence Nebr. Arts Council, Omaha, 1983-85; curator Art Mus. South Tex., Corpus Christi, 1985-89; curator collections Columbia (S.C.) Mus. Art, 1989-92, dep. dir. curatorial svcs., 1992-94; ind. curator, cons. no name exhbns. Minn. Mus. Am. Art, New Hope, Minn., 1994—; juror art exhibits Corpus Christi Arts Found., 1986-88, Hardin Simmons U., 1987, Anderson Coll., 1989, Hilton Head Art League, 1994; mem. pub. art selection panel S.C. Arts Coun., 1990; mem. steering com. South Tex. Regional Arts Conf., 1986-88; adj. lectr. art history U.S.C., 1989-94; chmn. curators com. S.E. Mus. Conf., 1991-93, chmn. local program com., 1992, mem program com. 1992-93; mem. Midwest Mus. Conf., 1994-95. Grantee NEA, S.C. Arts Coun., Tex. Coun. on Arts, Kress Found., Inst. Mus. Svcs. Mem. Am. Assn. Mus. (co-chmn. exhibits competition 1991-93, chmn. curator's com. 1993-95, chmn. of chairmen 1994-95, nominating com. 1994-95). Democrat. Avocations: dogs, gardening.

NEMAN, DANIEL LOUIS, movie critic; b. Cin., May 18, 1960; s. Albert Henry and Beth Maxine (Smilansky) N. BA in English Lang. and Lit., U. Chgo., 1982. Movie critic, entertainment writer Bryan-College Sta., Tex., 1983-86; movie critic, features writer Richmond (Va.) News Leader, 1986-92, Richmond Times-Dispatch, 1992—. Recipient 3rd Pl. awards Art and Leisure Va. Press Women, 1989, 90, 91, 92, First Pl. awards Revs. Va. Press Women, 1988, 89, 90, 91, 93, 2nd Pl. award Critical Writing Va. Press Assn., 1991, 2nd Pl. award Humor Va. Press Women, 1992, 1st Pl. award Critical Writing Va. Press Women, 1992, 2nd Pl. award Revs. Nat. Fedn. Press Women, 1993, 1st Pl. award Entertainment Harte-Hanks Newspapers, 1985, others. Mem. Soc. Profl. Journalists, Va: Press Assn. Office: Richmond Times-Dispatch 333 E Grace St Richmond VA 23293-1000

NEMAN, THOMAS EDWARD, advertising and marketing executive, researcher; b. Milw., Aug. 7, 1940; s. Edward Louis and Helen (Lawler) N.; m. Jo Ann Spahn, Oct. 14, 1967. A.B., Marquette U., 1962; M.A., Ind. U.-Bloomington, 1963, Ph.D., 1967. Sr. economist, Smith Kline and French, Phila., 1967-69; corp. mgr. statis. applications Gen. Foods Corp., White Plains, N.Y., 1969-72; v.p., assoc. research dir. J. Walter Thompson, N.Y.C., 1972-76; v.p., research dir. Leber, Katz Ptnrs., N.Y.C., 1976-79; sr. v.p., dir. planning and research BBDO, Worldwide Inc., N.Y.C., and Detroit, 1979—; mem. council Advt. Research Found., N.Y.C., 1972—. Mem. Advt. Research Found., Am. Acad. Advt., Econ. Club Detroit, Am. Mktg. Assn. Am. Statis. Assn. (sec. N.Y. chpt. 1977-78). Republican. Home: 21590 E Valley Woods Dr Franklin MI 48025-2633 Office: BBDO Detroit 26261 Evergreen Rd Southfield MI 48076-4447

NEMANICK, RICHARD CHARLES, business executive; b. St. Louis, Dec. 8, 1942; s. Charles John and Kathryn (Shank) N.; m. Colleen Elizabeth Hennessy, Aug. 26, 1967; children: Richard C. Jr., Jeffery R., Eric J. BS, U. Mo., 1964; JD, St. Louis U., 1967; LLM, Washington U., St. Louis, 1978. Bar: Mo. V.p. N.Am. Security Corp., St. Louis, 1967-70; v.p. The Lorvic Corp., St. Louis, 1969-86, pres., 1986—. Alderman City of Town and Country, Mo., 1986-94; commr. Police & Fire Commn., Town and Country, 1986-94; bd. dirs. Cen. County Dispatching, Ballwin, Mo., 1986-94, bd. chmn., 1991. Mem. Mo. Athletic Club, Elks. Avocations: golf, swimming, fishing, reading, walking. Home: 900 Cabernet Town and Country MO 63017 Office: The Lorvic Corp 8810 Frost Ave Saint Louis MO 63134

NEMEC, JOSEPH C., III, production designer. Prodn. designer: (TV movies) Blind Justice, 1986, Amerika, 1987, (films) Extreme Prejudice, 1987, Fatal Beauty, 1987, Alien Nation, 1988, The Abyss, 1989, Another 48 Hours, 1990, Fear, 1990, Patriot Games, 1993, The Getaway, 1993. Office: care Marty Barkin CNA & Associates 1801 Ave of the Stars Ste 1250 Los Angeles CA 90067*

NEMECEK, ALBERT DUNCAN, JR., retail company executive, investment banker, management consultant; b. Helena, Mont., Mar. 10, 1936; s. Albert Duncan and Geneva (Reindle) N.; m. Marilyn Ann Shaughnessy, Sept. 7, 1963 (div.); children: Maureen Ann, Steven Mathew; m. Judith Eileen Swift, Sept. 18, 1981 (div.); 1 child, Jennifer Eileen. B.S., U. Md., 1960, postgrad. in econs., 1961. Agt. IRS, Washington, 1961-65; tax dir. Macke Co., Washington, 1965-69; tax dir., then sec. Garfinckle, Brooks Bros., Miller & Rhoads, Inc., Washington, 1969-76; treas. Garfinckle, Brooks Bros., Miller & Rhoads, Inc., 1976—, v.p., 1979—; mng. ptnr. Nemecek & Falleroni, 1987, Nemecek & Jacknis, investment bankers, mgmt. cons., Falls Church, Va., 1989; founder Nemecek & Co., Inc., Falls Church, 1990; founder Entreprenurial Growth Fund, Falls Church, 1990. Home: 18724 Walker's Choice Rd #5 Gaithersburg MD 20879 *A man's success is measured by the respect he has gained from his peers, his understanding and compassion, respect for the feelings of others, appreciation of the world's beauty, and his attempts to leave the world better than he found it.*

NEMECEK, GEORGINA MARIE, molecular pharmacologist; b. Mineola, N.Y., Aug. 27, 1946; d. George and Frances Valerie (Masaryk) N. AB, Mt. Holyoke Coll., 1968; PhD, U. Pa., 1972. Rsch. assoc. dept. biochemistry U. Mass. Med. Sch., Worcester, 1972-73, postdoctoral fellow of Am. Heart Assn., dept. biochemistry, 1974, asst. prof., 1974-80, assoc. prof., 1981-83; sr. scientist platelet dept. Sandoz Pharm. Corp., East Hanover, N.J., 1983-85, mem. sr. sci. staff, platelet dept., 1986, fellow, sect. head molecular biology, 1987-91, fellow diabetes, 1991-93; fellow regulatory toxicology Sandoz Pharm. Corp., East Hanover, 1993—; vis. scientist dept. molecular biology, Princeton (N.J.) U., 1987, Sea Pharm. Inc., 1984, NATO, U. Libre, Brussels, 1979, biotechnology dept. Sandoz AG, Basel, Switzerland, 1988. Contbr. articles to profl. jours. Named Nat. Heart, Lung, and Blood Inst. Young Investigator, NIH, 1977-81. Mem. Am. Assn. Cancer Research, Exptl. Therapeutics, N.Y. Acad. Sci. (chmn. 1992-94), Tissue Culture Asn., Sigma Xi. Avocations: boating, gardening, riding, needlework. Office: Sandoz Pharm Corp 59 State Route 10 East Hanover NJ 07936-1080

NEMEROFF, CHARLES BARNET, neurobiology and psychiatry educator; b. Bronx, N.Y., Sept. 7, 1949; s. Philip Peace and Sarah (Greenberg) N.; m. Melissa Ann Pilkington, May 24, 1980; children: Matthew P., Amanda P., Sarah-Frances P. B.S., CCNY, 1970; M.S., Northeastern U., 1973; Ph.D., U.N.C., 1976, M.D., 1981. Diplomate Am. Bd. Psychiatry and Neurology; lic. physician, N.C., Ga. Research asst. ichthyology Am. Mus. Natural History, 1968-71, neurochemistry lab. McLean Hosp., Belmont, Mass., 1971-72; research assoc. surgery Beth Israel Hosp, Boston, 1972-73; teaching asst. biology Northeastern U., 1972-73; postdoctoral fellow Biol. Scis. Research Ctr., U. N.C., Chapel Hill, 1976-77, research fellow, 1977-83, clin. instr. psychiatry, 1983; resident in psychiatry N.C. Meml. Hosp., Chapel Hill, 1981-83; asst. prof. psychiatry and pharmacology Duke U., Durham, N.C., 1983-85, assoc. prof. psychiatry, 1985-89, assoc. prof. pharmacology, 1986-89, prof. depts. psychiatry and pharmacology, 1989-91; chief div. biological psychiatry, 1988-91, prof., chmn. dept. psychiatry and behavioral scis. Emory U. Sch. Medicine, 1991-94, Reunette W. Harris prof. psychiatry and behavioral scis., 1994—; vis. prof. physiology Cath. U., Santiago, Chile, 1978. Predoctoral fellow Schizophrenia Research Found., Soc. Scottish Rite, Lexington, Mass., 1975-76; postdoctoral fellow Nat. Inst. Neurol., Communicative Disorders and Stroke, 1977; recipient Michiko Kuno award U. N.C., 1978, 79, Merck award for acad. excellence, 1981; grantee Nat. Inst. Aging, 1982-83, NIMH, 1983—; Merck award for young investigators Am. Geriatrics Soc., 1985, 2d prize Anna Monica Found. for Research in Endogenous Depression, 1987, Merit award NIMH, 1987; Nanaline Duke fellow Duke U. Med. Ctr., 1985-87; Rsch. prize World Fedn. Societies of Biol. Psychiatry, 1991; recipient Edward J. Sachar award Columbia U., 1993, Edward A. Strecker prize Instl. Pa. Hosp., 1993. Fellow Am. Coll. Neuropsychopharmacology (Mead Johnson travel award 1982, coun. 1993—), Am. Coll. Psychiatrists (chmn. contbns. com. 1991-93, edn. com. 1993—,bd. regents 1994—); mem. Soc. Neurosci., AAAS, N.Y. Acad. Scis., Internat. Soc. Psychoneuroendocrinology (pres. 1993—, Curt P. Richter award 1985), Internat. Soc. Neurochemistry, Am. Soc. Neurochemistry (Jordi-Folch-Pi award 1987), Endocrine Soc., Internat. Soc. Neuroendocrinology, Soc. Biol. Psychiatry (A.E. Bennett award 1979), Am.

Fedn. Clin. Research, AMA, Am. Pain Soc., Am. Psychiat. Assn. (Kempf award 1989, Samuel Hibbs award 1991, coun. rsch. 1993—, chmn. 1994-95), Argentine Assn. Psychoneuroendocrinology (sci. council), Sigma Xi. Democrat. Jewish. Editor: (with A.J. Prange, Jr.) Neurotensin, a Brain and Gastrointestinal Peptide, 1982, (with A.J. Dunn) Peptides, Hormones and Behavior, 1984, (with P.T. Loosen) Handbook of Clinical Psychoneuroendocrinology, Neuropeptides in Psychiatric and Neurological Disorders, 1987, Neuropeptides in Psychiatric Disorders, 1991, Neuroendocrinology, 1992, (with P. Kitabgi) The Neurobiology of Neurotensin, 1992, (with A.F. Schatzberg) Textbook of Psychopharmacology, 1995; editor-in-chief: Depression, 1993—; co-editor-in-chief: Critical Revs. in Neurobiology, 1992—; contbr. numerous articles and abstracts to profl. jours., chpts. in books. Office: Emory U Sch Medicine Dept Psychiatry 1639 Pierce Dr Atlanta GA 30322

NEMEROFF, MICHAEL ALAN, lawyer; b. Feb. 16, 1946; s. Bernard Gregor and Frances (Gotleib) N.; m. Sharon Lynn Leininger, Sept. 22, 1974; children: Theodore, Patrick, James. BA, U. Chgo., 1968; JD, Columbia U., 1971. Asst. counsel Subcom. on Juvenile Delinquency of Senate Jud. Com., Washington, 1971-73; assoc. Sidley & Austin, Washington, 1973-78, ptnr., 1978—. Treas. Friends of Jim Sasser, 1978—, Andy Ireland Campaign Com., 1984-92. Office: Sidley & Austin 1722 I St NW Washington DC 20006-3705

NEMEROVSKI, STEVEN H., lawyer; b. Oak Park, Ill., Nov. 9, 1951. BA, U. Pa., 1972; JD, U. Ill., 1976. Bar: Ill. 1977, U.S. Dist. Ct. (no. dist.) Ill. 1977; CPA, Ill. Parliamentarian Ill. Ho. Reps., Chgo.; instr. Roosevelt U., 1979—. Mem. Chgo. Bar Assn. Office: Lavin & Waldon 111 E Wacker Dr Ste 2800 Chicago IL 60601

NEMETH, CHARLAN JEANNE, psychology educator; b. St. Louis, Dec. 29, 1941; d. Joseph Frank and Loretto Julia (Linkul) N.; children: Brendan Gibbs Nemeth-Brown, Lauren Loretto Nemeth-Brown. B.A., Washington U., 1963; M.A., U. Wis., 1965; postgrad. Oxford (Eng.) U., 1965-66; Ph.D., Cornell U., 1968. Fellow in law and psychology Battelle Seattle Rsch. Ctr., 1974-75; asst. prof. dept. psychology U. Chgo., 1968-73, U. Va., Charlottesville, 1973-75, U. B.C. Can., 1975-77, U. Calif., Berkeley, 1977—; vis. prof. U. Bristol, Eng., 1969-70, Ecole des Hautes Etudes, Paris, 1969-70, U. Mannheim, Fed. Republic of Germany, summer, 1977, Ecole des Hautes Etudes en Sciences Sociale, 1984, 89; cons. in psychology and law. Author: Social Psychology: Classic and Contemporary Integrations, 1974, Differential Contributions of Majority and Minority Influence, 1986; contbr. chpts. to books, articles to profl. jours. Grantee NIMH, 1970-81, NSF, 1986-89; Hon. Woodrow Wilson fellow, 1963. Fellow Am. Psychol. Assn., Am. Psychol. Soc.; mem. Soc. for Exptl. Social Psychology, European Assn. Soc. Psychology (affiliate), Phi Beta Kappa. Democrat. Roman Catholic. Office: U Calif Dept Psychology Berkeley CA 94720 *Maintain respect both for yourself and your profession by never compromising excellence or ethical conduct.*

NEMETH, PATRICIA A., school nurse; b. New Brunswick, N.J., Jan. 1, 1941; d. Charles and Genevieve Theresa (Yacuk) N. Diploma, St. Francis Sch. Nursing, Trenton, N.J., 1961; BA in Sch. Nursing, Health Edn., Trenton State Coll., 1968, MA in Health Edn., 1972; postgrad., Rutgers U., 1992. Lic. sch. nurse, health tchr., N.J. Relief health employee supr. Middlesex Gen. Hosp., New Brunswick, N.J., 1970-72, staff nurse surg. unit; sch. nurse, health educator Franklin Twp. Bd. Edn., Somerset, N.J., 1963—; liaison between Franklin nurses and Bd. Health, 1969-72; panelist Role of Sch. Nurse with Exceptional Children and Child Study Team, Exceptional Children Assn., 1976; panelist An Innovative Approach to Obesity, N.J. Pub. Health Assn., 1979; coord. Franklin Twp. Health Fair, 1974; mem. Franklin Twp. Adv. Bd. Health, 1973-79, 85—, chair, 1974-76; participant Live for Live Sch. Nurse fellowship Rutgers U., 1992. Trustee Somerset County Mental Health Assn., 1973-77, 1st vice-chair, 1976-77; chair Somerset County Mental Health Plan, 1989, Somerset County Mental Health Bd., 1987—; mem. com. Franklin Twp. Alliance Against Drug Abuse and Youth Svc. Commn., 1991-92; bd. trustees N.J. Pub. Health Assn., 1990. Recipient Pres.'s award N.J. Pub. Health Assn., 1991. Mem. NEA, Somerset County Sch. Nurses (co-chair programs), Franklin Twp. Edn. Assn. (corr. sec. 1966-68, chair newsletter 1966-67), Somerset County Edn. Assn., N.J. Edn. Assn., N.J. Sch. Nurses Assn. Home: 107 Dayton Ave Somerset NJ 08873-1967

NEMETZ, NATHANIEL THEODORE, lawyer, former chief justice of British Columbia; b. Winnipeg, Man., Can., Sept. 8, 1913; s. Samuel and Rebecca (Birch) N.; m. Bel Newman, Aug. 10, 1935 (dec.); 1 son, Peter Newman. B.A. with 1st class honors, U. B.C., 1934; LL.D. (hon.), Notre Dame, Nelson, B.C., 1972, U. B.C., 1975, Simon Fraser U., 1975, U. Victoria, 1976; PhD honoris causa, Tel Aviv U., 1991. Bar: Created King's Counsel 1950. Spl. counsel Public Utilities Commn., 1958-61; spl. counsel to cities of Vancouver, Burnaby, New Westminster, Can., 1959-63; justice Supreme Ct. B.C., 1963-68, Ct. Appeal, 1968-73; chief justice B.C. Supreme Ct., 1973-78, B.C., 1979-88; assoc. counsel Russell & DuMoulin, Vancouver, 1990—; mem. Royal Commn. to investigate election irregularities, 1965; arbitrator fishing, lumber and hydro industries West Coast shipping dispute, 1966-73; del. Govt. Can. to Internat. Labor Orgn., Geneva, 1973; chmn. Legal Conf., Stanford U., 1986; co-chmn. 1st Can.-Australasian Legal Conf., Canberra, Australia, 1988; mem. appeal bd. Can.-U.S. Free Trade Agreement; chmn. Japan-Can. Coal Dispute Arbitration, 1988; hon. consul gen. Singapore, 1989. Contbr. articles in field to profl. publs. Mem. senate, chmn. bd. govs. U. B.C., 1957-68, chancellor, 1972-75; chmn. Can. edn. del. to China, 1974; chmn. Univ. Dist. Sch. Bd., 1957-59; hon. chmn. Crusade Against Cancer, 1988; hon. trustee B.C. Govt. Ho. Found., 1988; mem. Freeman City of Vancouver, 1988; hon. chm. Vancouver Sun Children's Fund, 1990, 91. Named hon. fellow Hebrew U., Jerusalem, 1976; recipient award Can. Council Christians and Jews, 1958; Great Trekker award U.B.C., 1969; Beth Emeth Brotherhood award, 1969; Canada medal, 1967; award of distinction U. B.C. Alumni, 1975; Queen Elizabeth medal, 1977, 125th Can. medal, Alumni award U. B.C., 1988; medal of Flag of Yugoslavia with ribbon, 1989; Companion Order of Can., 1990; Order of Brit. Columbia; Nathan T. Nemetz chair in Legal History created in his honor U. B.C., 1988. Mem. Can. Jud. Coun. (exec. 1973-88, vice chmn. 1988), Can. Bar Assn. (George Goyer Meml. award B.C. br. 1994), Faculty Assn. U. B.C. (hon.), Alumni Assn. U. B.C. (pres. 1957). Jewish. Clubs: Faculty (U. B.C.), Vancouver. Office: Russell & DuMoulin, 2100-1075 W Georgia St, Vancouver, BC Canada V6E 3G2

NEMHAUSER, GEORGE L., industrial, systems engineer, operations research educator; b. N.Y.C., July 27, 1937; s. Martin and Rose (Schwartz) N.; m. Ellen Krupsaw, Sept. 14, 1959; children: Wendy, Dennis. B.Chem.Engring., CCNY, 1958; M.S., Northwestern U., 1959, Ph.D. 1961. Prof. ops. research Johns Hopkins U., Balt., 1961-69; prof. Cornell U., Ithaca, N.Y., 1969-84, Leon C. Welch prof. engring., 1984-85, dir. Sch. Ops. Research and Indsl. Engring., 1977-83; Chandler prof. indsl. and systems engring. Ga. Inst. Tech., 1985—, inst. prof., 1992—; vis. prof. U. Leeds, U.K., 1963-64; vis. prof., dir. research Center for Ops. Research and Econometrics, U. Louvain, Belgium, 1975-77; cons. NSF (others). Author: Introduction to Dynamic Programming, 1966, Integer Programming, 1972, Integer and Combinatorial Optimization, 1988; editor-in-chief: Ops. Research, 1975-78, Ops. Research Letters, 1981—; contbr. articles to profl. jours. NSF faculty fellow, 1969-70. Mem. NAE, Ops. Research Soc. Am. (pres. 1981-82, Lanchester prize 1977, 89, Kimball medal 1988), Inst. Mgmt. Sci., Soc. Indsl. and Applied Math., Am. Inst. Indsl. Engrs., Math. Programming Soc. (chmn. 1989-1992). Home: 1208 Villa Dr NE Atlanta GA 30306-2567

NEMIR, DONALD PHILIP, lawyer; b. Oakland, Calif., Oct. 31, 1931; s. Philip F. and Mary (Shavor) N. AB, U. Calif., Berkeley, 1957, JD, 1960. Bar: Calif. 1961. Pvt. practice, San Francisco, 1961—; pres. Law Offices Donald Nemir. Mem. ABA, Calif. State Bar Assn., Phi Delta Phi. Home: PO Box 1089 Mill Valley CA 94942 Office: One Sansome St Ste 2000 San Francisco CA 94104

NEMIROW, ARNOLD MYLES, manufacturing executive; b. Hartford, Conn., Mar. 25, 1943; s. Benjamin and Elsie (Nozik) N.; m. Barbro Sandberg, Dec. 22, 1967 (dec. Aug. 1983); children: Matthew, Adam; m.

Sharon Green, April 23, 1988. AB cum laude, Harvard U., 1966; JD, U. Mich., 1969. Bar: N.Y. Atty. Carter, Ledyard & Milburn, N.Y.C., 1969-73; asst. gen. counsel Coleco Industries Inc., Hartford, 1973-74; atty., asst. gen. counsel Gt. No. Nekoosa Corp., Stamford, Conn., 1974-80, dir. indsl. rels., 1981-83, v.p., 1984-90; pres. Gt. Southern Paper Co., Cedar Springs, Ga., 1984-87, Nekoosa Papers Inc., Port Edwards, Wis., 1988-90; pres., CEO Wausau Papers, Wausau, Wis., 1990-94; CEO, pres. Bowater Inc., 1995—. Office: 55 E Camperdown Way Greenville SC 29602

NEMSER, EARL HAROLD, lawyer; b. N.Y.C., Jan. 17, 1947; s. Harold Summers and Eleanor Patricia (Beckerman) N.; m. Randy Lynn Lehrer, June 17, 1974 (div.); children: Eliza Sarah, Maggie Lehrer. B.A., NYU, 1967; J.D. magna cum laude, Boston U., 1970. Bar: N.Y. 1970, U.S. Supreme Ct. 1975, U.S. Claims Ct. 1979, U.S. Tax Ct. 1985. Law clk. Hon. Collins J. Seitz, Chief Judge U.S. Ct. appeals 3rd Cir., 1970-71; ptnr. Cadwalader, Wickersham & Taft, N.Y.C., 1971—; dir. Timber Hill, Inc., Valhalla, N.Y., 1989—. Mem. ABA, Assn. Bar City of N.Y., Fed. Bar Council, Boston U. Law Sch. Alumni Assn. (pres. 1984). Clubs: Downtown Assn.; Contbr. note to legal rev. Office: Cadwalader Wickersham & Taft 100 Maiden Ln New York NY 10038-4818

NEMSER, ROBERT SOLOMON, visual communications consultant, art director, designer, educator; b. Bklyn., May 30, 1938; s. Leo Lewis Nemser and Mae (Silver) Wolf; m. Fredda Carol Siegel, Oct. 15, 1960; children: Lori, Adam, Alec, Ian. AAS, N.Y. Coll. Arts and Scis., 1960; MFA, Syracuse U., 1990. Designer Inst. Life Ins., N.Y.C., 1960, Dell Pub. Co., N.Y.C., 1962-65; art. dir. Universal Pub. Co., N.Y.C., 1965-67; v.p. Corp. Ann. Reports, N.Y.C., 1967-73; pres., owner Robert S. Nemser Assocs., N.J. and N.Y., 1974—; mem. adj. faculty Rutgers U. Mason Gross Sch. Arts, 1987-91; asst. prof. art Trenton (N.J.) State Coll., 1993-94; spkr. on Psychedelic Art in the '60s and the San Francisco Music Scene, The Art of Seeing: Creating with Your Camera, The Psychology and Design of Coffee-Table Books, Photoluminescence: Painting with the Camera. Designer, photo editor (books) Martin Luther King Jr., 1976 (Gold medal 1977), The Eternal Sea (Gold medal 1977), Your Future in Space, 1986, King Remembered, 1986, He Had a Dream: Martin Luther King Jr. and the Civil Rights Movement, 1995 (Silver medal 1995); designer Ctrl. N.J. Jewish Home for Aged logo, 1975, East Brunswick (N.J.) Libr. logo, 1976; work exhibited at Art Dirs. Club N.J., 1970—, Rutgers U., 1990. Bd. dirs. East Brunswick Jewish Ctr., 1975-77, publicity chmn., 1976; TV photo show host East Brunswick Channel 8 Cable TV, 1986. Served to sgt. U.S. Army, 1960-62. Recipient numerous design awards from various profl. orgns. Mem. Art Dirs. Club N.J. (life, pres. 1976-77, chmn. edn. coun. 1987-92, numerous awards), Advt. Club N.Y. (Andy award 1973). Avocations: collecting military medals and paraphernalia, elephants and police badges, racquetball, paddleball, noted authority on Rock and Roll and Doo Wopp music of 1950's and 1960's. Office: PO Box 992 East Brunswick NJ 08816-0992

NENNEMAN, RICHARD ARTHUR, retired publishing executive; b. Chgo., Oct. 13, 1929; s. William T. and Fannie (Peterson) N.; m. Katherine Ann LaBrunerie, June 29, 1954; children: Ann Walker, Mary Lisa, Katherine Conley. A.B. magna cum laude, Harvard U., 1951, M.A. in Internat. Affairs, 1953. With No. Trust Co., Chgo., 1957-58; v.p., treas., dir. First Fed. Savs. & Loan Assn. St. Joseph, Mo., 1958-60; with Valley Nat. Bank. Phoenix, 1960-65; asst. v.p., 1963-65; bus. and financial editor Christian Sci. Monitor, Boston, 1965-74; v.p. dir. investment research Girard Bank, Phila., 1974-77; sr. v.p., chmn. trust investment policy com. Girard Bank, 1977-82; mng. editor Christian Sci. Monitor, Boston, 1983-86; editor, exec. prodr., TV broadcasting Christian Sci. Pub. Soc., Boston, 1987; editor-in-chief Christian Science Monitor, 1988-93; ret., 1993; mem. investment com. Gen. Accident Ins. Group., until 1982; dir. DLB Fund Group, 1994—. Contbr. to Understanding Our Century, 1984; editor: (with Earl Foell) How Peace Came to the World, 1986, The New Birth of Christianity, 1992. Trustee Barnes Found., until 1982; selectman Town of Weston, Mass., 1973-74; chmn. Boston Com. on Fgn. Rels. Served with AUS, 1954-57. Mem. Coun. on Fgn. Rels., Am. Coun. Ger., Harvard Grad. Coun. Home: PO Box 634 East Orleans MA 02643

NEPPL, WALTER JOSEPH, retired retail store executive; b. Halbur, Iowa, June 15, 1922; s. Frank and Anna (Halbur) N.; m. Marian Maher, Oct. 15, 1945; children: Eugenie Neppl Kauffman, Marilee Neppl Cumming, Deborah Neppl Johnson, John, Thomas (dec.), Christina Neppl Totino, Nancy Neppl Tripucka. Grad. h.s., Carrol, Iowa. With J.C. Penney Co., Inc., 1940—; mgr. store J.C. Penney Co., Inc., Albuquerque, 1954-55; dist. mgr. J.C. Penney Co., Inc., Pitts., 1955-61; store coordination mgr. J.C. Penney Co., Inc., N.Y.C., 1961-64; asst. to dir. dist. mgmt. dept. J.C. Penney Co., Inc., 1964-65, gen. mdse. mgr. hard lines, 1965-67, v.p., 1967-68, gen. sales and mdse. mgr., 1968-71, dir. merchandising, 1971-72, exec. v.p., 1972-76, pres., chief operating officer, 1976-81, vice-chmn. bd., 1981-82, ret., 1982, dir., 1968-85. Trustee Geraldine R. Dodge Found., FFB Funds Trust; Hosp. Served to capt. USAAF, 1943-45. Decorated D.F.C. Roman Catholic. Home: The Enclave 5345 Annabel Ln Plano TX 75093-3428

NEPTUNE, JOHN ADDISON, chemistry educator, consultant; b. Barnesville, Ohio, Nov. 27, 1919; s. George Addison and Lola Mae (Skinner) N.; m. Ruth Elizabeth Dorsey, Aug. 24, 1947; 1 child, Benjamin. BS summa cum laude, Muskingum Coll., 1942; MS, U. Wis., 1949, PhD, 1952. Instr. chemistry Muskingum Coll., New Concord, Ohio, 1943-44, 45-48; foreman Tenn. Eastman Corp., Manhattan Project, 1944-45; asst. prof. chemistry Bowling Green State U., Ohio, 1949-50; instr. pharm. chemistry U. Wis.-Madison, 1952-55; asst. prof. chemistry San Jose State U., Calif., 1955-58, assoc. prof., 1958-61, prof. 1961-90, chmn. dept., 1973-86. Mem. Am. Chem. Soc., AAUP. Methodist. Home: 50 Cherokee Ln San Jose CA 95127-2513 Office: San Jose State U Dept Chemistry San Jose CA 95192

NEPTUNE, RICHARD ALLAN (DICK NEPTUNE), superintendent of schools; b. Lawton, Okla., Oct. 1, 1934; s. Everett and Mary Louise (Green) N.; m. Carol Faye Brewer; stepchildren: Derek Knowles, Larrie Knowles, Ronnie Joe Knowles. BS, Okla. Bapt. U., 1956; MEd, U. Okla., 1962. Cert. standard supt. Photography tchr. Lawton (Okla.) Pub. Schs., 1957-60, dir. activities, 1960-62, asst. prin. behavior, 1962-66, asst. prin. instrn., 1966-69, prin., 1969-77, asst. supt., 1977-79, assoc. supt., 1979-80, dep. supt., 1980-85, supt., 1985—. Bd. dirs. Hotel Lawtonian, Lawton Indsl. Svc., Lawton Pub. Libr., Lawton Jaycees, McMahon Cmty. Auditorium Theatre League, Mus. of the Great Plains, United Way, C. of C., Nat. PTA; pres. USO, v.p. With USAR, 1957-63. Recipient Nat. Pub. Rels. Assn. award, 1987, Exec. Educators 100, 1989, Kennedy Ctr. Sch. Adminstrs. award, 1990, State of Okla. medal, 1990. Mem. Am. Assn. of Sch. Personnel Administrs., Am. Assn. of Sch. Administrs., Am. Mgmt. Assn., Am. Soc. Tng. and Devel., Lawton Assn. of Secondary Sch. Prins. (pres.), Nat. Assn. Secondary Sch. Prins., Nat. Edn. Assn., Nat. Sch. Bds. Assn., Okla. Assn. Secondary Sch. Prins. (bd. dirs., chmn. leadership com.), Okla. Assn. for Supervision and Curriculum Devel., Okla. Curriculum Improvement Commn. (pres. 1988), Okla. Edn. Assn. Secondary Sch. Prins., Kappa Delta Pi, Phi Delta Kappa. Home: 453 NW Chimney Creek Dr Lawton OK 73505-5919 Office: Lawton Pub Sch PO Box 1009 753 NW Ft Sill Blvd Lawton OK 73502

NEQUIST, JOHN LEONARD, retired food company executive; b. Sparta, Mich., July 31, 1929; s. John Ormond and Leola Irene (Fessenden) N.; m. Patricia Ann Kelley, Jan. 7, 1950; children: Eric Martin, Kelley Jo; m. Donna Jean Williams, 1990. B.B.A., U. Mich., 1956. With Kellogg Co., Battle Creek, Mich., 1957-88; chief accountant, then asst. controller Kellogg Co., 1967-75, controller, 1975-79, v.p., controller U.S. Foods Products div., 1979-84, dir. spl. assignments McCanly Sq. div., hotel and retail area, 1984-88. Chmn. planning and budget com. Battle Creek United Fund, 1969-70, Battle Creek Family/Childrens Service, 1973, Battle Creek United Arts Council, 1975; dir. spl. assignments Gov.'s Exec. Corps, 1984-85; bd. dirs. ARC, Battle Creek; chmn. bd. Downtown Bus. Assn., Battle Creek, 1987-88; mem. South Haven (Mich.) City Council. Served with USAF, 1948-52. Mem. Beta Alpha Psi. Home: 36 Lake Shore Dr South Haven MI 49090-1131 Home (winter): 196 Furse Lakes Cir Naples FL 33942

NEREM, ROBERT MICHAEL, engineering educator, consultant; b. Chgo., July 20, 1937; s. Robert and Borghild Guneva (Bakken) N.; m. Jill Ann Thomson, Dec. 21, 1958 (div. 1977); children: Robert Steven, Nancy Ann Nerem Chambers; m. Marilyn Reed, Oct. 7, 1978; stepchildren: Christina

Lynn Maser, Carol Marie Maser. BS, U. Okla., 1959; MS, Ohio State U., 1961, PhD, 1964; D (honoris causa), U. Paris, 1990. Asst. prof. Ohio State U., Columbus, 1964-68, assoc. prof. 1968-72, prof., 1972-79, assoc. dean Grad. Sch., 1975-79; prof. mech. engring., chmn. dept. U. Houston, 1979-86; Parker H. Petit prof. Ga. Inst. Tech., Atlanta, 1987—, Inst. prof., 1991—; mem. Ga. Gov.'s Adv. Coun. on Sci. and Tech. Devel., Atlanta, 1992—; ALZA disting. lectr. Biomed. Engring. Soc., 1991, ASME Thurston lectr. 1994. Contbr. over 80 articles to profl. jours. Fellow Am. Inst. Med. and Biol. Engring. (founding pres. 1992-94), ASME, AAAS; mem. NAE, Biomed. Engring. Soc., Inst. Medicine, Internat. Union for Phys. and Engring. Scis. in Medicine (pres. 1991-94), Internat. Fedn. for Med. and Biol. Engring. (pres. 1988-91), U.S. Nat. Com. on Biomechanics (1988-91 chmn.), Polish Acad. Scis. Home: 2950 Waverly Ct Atlanta GA 30339-4200 Office: Ga Inst Tech Sch Mech Engring Ferst and Cherry Sts Atlanta GA 30332-0405

NERENBERG, AARON, lawyer; b. Phila., Sept. 22, 1940; s. Jacob and Rose (Solominsky) N.; m. Adrianne Daufman, May 30, 1965; children: Jeffrey, Kimberly. BSME, Pa. State U., 1963; MSME, Villanova U., 1967; JD, Temple U., 1971. Bar: Pa. 1971, U.S. Dist. Ct. (ea. dist.) Pa. 1973, U.S. Ct. Appeals (3d cir.),1973, U.S. Supreme Ct., 1974, U.S. Patent Office, 1972. Devel. engr. Naval Air Engring. Ctr., Phila., 1963-71; sole practice Phila., 1971-72; patent advisor Naval Air Devel. Ctr., Warminster, Pa., 1972-74; patent atty, SPS Techs. Inc., Jenkintown, Pa., 1974-78, patent counsel, 1978-82, assoc. gen. counsel, Newtown, Pa., 1982-86, gen. counsel, 1986—, sec., 1986—, v.p., 1988. Mem. ABA, Phila. Patent Law Assn. (chmn. placement com. 1977-85), Pa. State Alumni Assn. (v.p. 1982-86, Disting. Alumni award 1982). Republican. Jewish. Avocations: golf, swimming. Office: SPS Techs Inc Jenkintown Plz 101 Greenwood Ave Ste 470 Jenkintown PA 19046

NERI, MANUEL, sculptor; b. Sanger, Calif., Apr. 12, 1930; s. Manuel and Guadalupe (Penilla) N.; children: Raoul Garth, LaTicia Elizabeth, Noel Elmer, Maximilian Anthony, Ruby Rose Victoria, Julia Marjorie, Gustavo Manuel. Student, San Francisco City Coll., 1949-50, U. Calif., Berkeley, 1951-52, Calif. Sch. Arts and Crafts, 1952-57, Calif. Sch. Fine Arts, 1957-59. Mem. faculty art Calif. Sch. Fine Arts, San Francisco, 1959-64; prof. art U. Calif., Davis, 1964-90. One-man shows of sculpture, from 1957, recent exhbns. include, Oakland Mus. Art, Oakland, Calif., 1976, Western Assn. Art Mus. Travelling Exhbn., 1980-83, Seattle Art Mus., 1981, Mexican Mus., San Francisco, 1981, John Berggruen Gallery, San Francisco, 1981, 84, 88, Charles Cowles Gallery, N.Y.C., 1981, 82, 86, 89, 93, Middendorf Gallery, Washington, 1983, 84, Gimpel-Hanover & Andre Emmerich Galerien, Zurich, Switzerland, 1984, James Corcoran Gallery, Santa Monica, Calif., 1988, San Francisco Mus. Modern Art, 1989, Dia Ctr. for the Arts, Bridgehampton, N.Y., 1993, Campbell-Thiebaud Gallery, San Francisco, 1993; numerous group shows, from 1955, recent exhbns. include San Francisco Mus. Modern Art, 1980, 83, 84, 85, 86, Am. Acad. Arts and Letters, N.Y.C., 1981, 82, 84, Oakland Mus. (Calif.), 1982, 84, 85, Seattle Art Mus., 1983, 84, 1983, Inst. Contemporary Art, Richmond, Va., 1983, Hirshhorn Mus., 1984, Contemporary Arts Ctr., Cin., 1985, Mus. Fine Arts, Houston, 1987, Bronx Mus. Arts, 1988; represented in permanent collections: Oakland Mus., Seattle Art Mus., San Francisco Mus. Modern Art, Honolulu Acad. Arts, Des Moines Arts Ctr., also numerous pvt. collections including Verlaine Found., New Orleans, Bank Am. Corp., San Francisco, Lannan Found., Los Angeles; represented by Campbell-Thiebaud Gallery, San Francisco, Charles Cowles Gallery, N.Y., James Corcoran Gallery, Santa Monica, Yares Gallery, Scottsdale, Ariz., Greg Kucera Gallery, Seattle, Ive Mannes Gallery, Atlanta. Recipient 1st Award in Sculpture Oakland Art Mus., 1953, Nat. Art Found. award, 1965, award San Francisco Art Inst., 1963, award in art Am. Acad. and Inst. Arts and Letters, 1982, award of merit in sculpture San Francisco Arts Commn., 1985; Guggenheim fellow, 1979; Nat. Endowment for the Arts grantee, 1980. Roman Catholic. Office: care Anne Kohs and Assocs Inc 251 Post St Ste 540 San Francisco CA 94108-5004

NERLINGER, JOHN WILLIAM, association executive; b. Detroit, June 22, 1920; s. John W. and Bessie Prudence (Beith) N.; m. Pearl Pauline Procup, Nov. 4, 1943; children: John Charles, Ruth Marie Nerlinger Blazevich. Student, Detroit Bus. Inst., 1938-39; BA, Detroit Inst. Tech., 1950; LLD (hon.), Northwood U., Midland, Mich., 1990. Bus. mgr. Retail Gasoline Dealers Assn. Mich., Detroit, 1939-51; exec. sec. Retail Gasoline Dealers Assn. Mich., 1951-63, Nat. Congress Petroleum Retailers, Detroit, 1951-63; asst. exec. v.p. Automotive Service Industry Assn., Chgo., 1963-73; exec. v.p Automotive Service Industry Assn., 1973-80, pres., 1981-91; ret., 1991; Vice chmn. Automotive Hall of Fame; Served with AUS, 1942-45, PTO. Recipient Petroleum Man of Yr. award Gasoline News, 1961, Automotive Replacement Edn. award Northwood U., Midland, Mich., 1975, Disting. Svc. citation Automotive Hall of Fame, 1978, Industry Leadership award Automotive Svc. Industry Assn., 1978. Mem. Am. Soc. Assn. Execs. (mem. edn. com.), Chgo. Soc. Assn. Execs., Automotive Old Timers, Automotive Info. Council (dir.), Automotive Boosters Clubs Internat., Chgo. Assn. Commerce and Industry (mem. govt. relations com.), Nat. Assn. Wholesalers-Distbrs. (exec. com., dir. distbn. research and edn. found,) Automotive Acad. Lutheran. Clubs: Mid-America, Inverness Golf. Lodge: Masons (32 deg.), Shriners. Home: 601 E Fairview St Arlington Heights IL 60005-2770

NERLOVE, MARC LEON, economics educator; b. Chgo., Oct. 12, 1933; s. Samuel Henry and Evelyn (Andelman) N.; children: Susan, Miriam. BA, U. Chgo., 1952; MA, Johns Hopkins U., 1955, PhD, 1956. Analytical statistician USDA, Washington, 1956-57; assoc. prof. U. Minn., Mpls., 1959-60; prof. Stanford (Calif.) U., Stanford U., 1960-65, Yale U., 1965-69; prof. econs. U. Chgo., 1969-74; F.W. Taussig rsch. prof. Harvard Coll., Cambridge, Mass., 1967-68; vis. Cook prof. Northwestern U., Evanston, Ill., 1973-74, Cook prof. 1974-82; prof. econs. U. Pa., Phila., 1982-86, Univ. prof., 1986-93; prof. agriculture and resource econs. U. Md., College Park, 1993—. Author: Dynamics of Supply, 1958, Distributed Lags and Demand Analysis, 1958, Estimation and Identification of Cobb-Douglas Production Functions, 1965, Analysis of Economic Time Series: A Synthesis, 1979, Household and Economy: Welfare Economics of Endogenous Fertility, 1987; contbr. numerous articles to profl. jours. 1st lt. AUS, 1957-59. Recipient award Am. Farm Econ. Assn., 1956, 58, 61, 79, PS Mahalanobis medal Indian Econ. Soc., 1975. Fellow Am. Statis. Assn., Econometric Soc. (v.p. 1980, pres. 1981), Am. Acad. Arts and Scis., Am. Agrl. Econ. Assn.; mem. NAS, Am. Econ. Assn. (mem. exec. com. 1977-79, John Bates Clark medal 1969), Royal Econ. Soc., Phi Beta Kappa, others. Achievements include research on economics of agriculture with particular reference to developing countries, population and economic growth; analysis of categorical data, particularly business and household surveys. Office: U Md Dept Agri & Rsch Econs College Park MD 20742-5535

NERO, ANTHONY VINCENT, JR., physicist, environmental scientist; b. Salisbury, Md., Apr. 11, 1942; s. Anthony V. Nero and Anna Elizabeth Coladonato. BS summa cum laude, Fordham U., 1964; PhD in Physics, Stanford U., 1971. Rsch. fellow physics dept. Fordham U., summers 1962-63; grad. rsch. asst. Nuclear Physics Lab., Stanford (Calif.) U., 1966-70; postdoctoral rsch. fellow Kellogg Radiation Lab., Calif. Inst. Tech., Pasadena, 1970-72; asst. prof. physics Princeton (N.J.) U., 1972-75; physicist energy and environ. div. Lawrence Berkeley (Calif.) Lab., 1975—, leader indoor radon group, 1980-86, sr. scientist, 1986—, dep. leader indoor environ. program, 1986-94; visitor nuclear power div. Electric Power Rsch. Inst., summers 1974-75; phys. sci. officer Non-Proliferation Bur., ADCA, 1978; lectr. dept. mech. engring. U. Calif., Berkeley, 1979, lectr. energy and resources program, 1980, lectr. Sch. Pub. Health, 1989, mem. environ. health scis. ctr., 1992-94, acad. coord. energy and resources program, 1993-94; mem. adv. com. 3d Internat. Conf. on Indoor Air Quality and Climate, Stockholm, 1984, symposium organizer, rapporteur for radon 4th Conf. Berlin, 1987; mem. various adv. and rev. panels EPA, 1984—; mem. program com. 4th Internat. Symposium on Natural Radiation Environ, Lisbon, 1987, 5th internat. syposium, Salzburg, Austria, 1991. Author: A Guidebook to Nuclear Reactors, 1979; co-author: Instrumentation for Environmental Monitoring, Vol. 1, 1983, Radon and Its Decay Products in Indoor Air, 1988; contbr. articles to profl. and popular publs., chpts. to books. Gen. Motors Corp. nat. scholar, 1960-64; NSF undergrad. summer rsch. fellow, 1962, 63, NSF grad. fellow, 1964-68. Fellow Am. Physics Soc. (panel on pub. affairs 1981-83, Leo Szilard award for Physics in the Pub. Interest 1989, exec. com. forum on physics and soc. 1988-90, vice-chair forum on physics and soc. 1992-93, chair-elect 1993-94, chair 1994-95); mem. AAAS, Health

---

Physics Soc., Fedn. Am. Scientist, Soc. Risk Analysis, Phi Beta Kappa, Sigma Xi. Office: Lawrence Berkeley Lab 1 Cyclotron Rd Rm 3058 Berkeley CA 94720

NERO, PETER, pianist, conductor, composer, arranger; b. N.Y.C., May 22, 1934; s. Julius and Mary (Menasche) N.; m. Marcia Dunner, June 19, 1956; children—Beverly, Jedd; m. Peggy Altman, Aug. 31, 1977. Student, Juilliard Sch., N.Y.C. Nat. tour with Paul Whiteman on TV and in concert, 1953-57, appearances concert halls, theatres, colls., TV and supper clubs throughout U.S., Eng., France, Holland, Italy, Scandinavia, 1962—; appeared at Grand Gala du Disque, Amsterdam, The Netherlands, 1964, five TV specials on BBC-TV; arranged, appeared and recorded with Boston Pops Orch.; pops music dir. Tulsa Philharm., 1987—; music dir., Philly Pops Orch., 1979—, Fla. Philharm., 1981—; rec. artist for Arista Records, Pro Arte, Columbia; albums include Peter Nero Now, The Sounds of Love, Anything But Lonely and Peter Nero and Friends, 1993; appeared in film Sunday in New York; composer, condr. more than 150 symphony orchs., 1971—; recordings include (with the Rochester Philharmonic) Classic Connections. Honored by Internat. Soc. Performing Arts Adminstrs., 1986; recipient 8 Grammy nominations, 2 Grammy awards; named #1 Instrumentalist Cashbox Mag. Office: Tulsa Philharm 2901 S Harvard Tulsa OK 74114 also: care Gurtman & Murtha Assoc 450 7th Ave # 603 New York NY 10123 also: Pro Arte 90 Intersound Internat Inc P O Box 1724 Roswell GA 30077*

NERREN, GEORGE N., school system administrator. Supt. Dyersburg (Tenn.) City Schs. State finalist Nat. Supt. Yr., 1993. Office: Dyersburg City Schs PO Box 1507 1025 Phillips St Dyersburg TN 38024-4114

NESBIT, ROBERT CARRINGTON, historian; b. Ellensburg, Wash., July 16, 1917; s. Sidney Shaw and Verna Mildred (Carrington) N.; m. Marie Richert, Nov. 24, 1942. B.A., Central Wash. Coll., 1939; M.A., U. Wash., 1947, Ph.D., 1957. Tchr. Cashmere (Wash.) Pub. Schs., 1939-41; state archivist Wash., 1951-57; adminstrv. asst. Wash. Dept. Gen. Adminstrn., 1958-59, supr. state purchasing, 1959-62; assoc. prof. U. Wis., Madison, 1962-68; prof., assoc. chmn. dept. history U. Wis., 1967-80. Author: He Built Seattle: A Biography of Judge Thomas Burke, 1961, Wisconsin, A History, 1973 (award of merit Am. Assn. State and Local History 1975), rev. edit. (with William F. Thompson Jr.), 1990; The History of Wisconsin, Vol. III, Industrialization and Urbanization, 1873-1893, 1985. Served with USAAF, 1941-46. Named Hon. fellow State Hist. Soc. Wis., 1986. Wis. History Found. grantee, 1971-72; NEH grantee, 1980-82. Home: 2406 Fir St SE Olympia WA 98501-3048

NESBIT, ROBERT GROVER, management consultant; b. Scranton, Pa., Feb. 8, 1932; s. George Archibald and Mildred Maude (Bohl) N.; m. Nancy Elizabeth Wilson, June 17, 1961; children: Robert, Jonathan. B.S., U. Scranton, 1957; M.S., NYU, 1958. Asst. to dean NYU, N.Y.C., 1960-64; mdse. mgr. Associated Merchandising Corp., N.Y.C., 1964-67; dir. corp. mktg. Genesco, Inc., Nashville, 1968-77; v.p., div. gen. mgr. Levi Straus & Co., San Francisco, 1977-79; sr. partner Korn/Ferry Internat., N.Y.C., 1979—. Trustee Rollins Coll. Served with U.S. Army, 1953-55. Mem. Nat. Retail Mchts. Assn., Am. Apparel Mfrs. Assn., Sigma Nu. Presbyterian. Club: N.Y. Athletic. Home: 71 Bank St New Canaan CT 06840-6812 Office: 237 Park Ave New York NY 10017-3142

NESBIT, WILLIAM TERRY, small business owner, consultant; b. Pitts., Jan. 30, 1945; s. William Frank and Glenna (Cleeton) N.; divorced. Owner, CEO Narrow Gauge Car Shop, Evergreen Outdoor Ctr., Shiremanstown, Pa., 1972—; mem. faculty Millersville (Pa.) U., 1976-81, Temple U., Phila., 1979, Nat. Aquatic and Small Craft Sch., Bemis Point, N.Y., 1980, Harrisburg (Pa.) Area C. C., 1981-82, 91, Dickinson Coll., Carlisle, Pa., 1982-83; judge 32d Capital Area Sci., Engring. Fair, Dickinson Coll., Carlisle, Pa., 1989. Co-developer American Red Cross Basic and Whitewater Canoeing Programs for Instruction, 1977-79; developer The Z Drag for Boat Rescues, 1980; contbr. The Brown Book, 2nd edit. 1982. Vol. ARC, 1961—. Recipient award for Humanity ARC, 1967, award for 30 Yrs. Vol. Svc., 1991; named Class I Radiological Protection Officer, U.S. Dept. of Defense, 1993. Mem. Math. Assn. Am., Nat. Assn. Canoe Liveries and Outfitters (founding), Nat. Model Railroad Assn. (life). Episcopalian. Office: Evergreen Outdoor Ctr PO Box 3081 Shiremanstown PA 17011-3081

NESBITT, ARTHUR WALLACE, mail order and manufacturing executive; b. Enon Valley, Pa., July 29, 1927; s. William and Frances Mildred (Gilmore) N.; m. Donna Saviers Fox, Aug. 19, 1967; children: Warren P., David G.; stepchildren: Marsha, Marilyn, William, Leann, Sandra Fox. B.S., Pa. State U., 1950. Asst county agt. Pa. State U., Clarion, 1950-51; exec. sec. Pa. Holstein Assn., State College, 1952-59; v.p. sales Nasco, Fort Atkinson, Wis., 1959-71; exec. v.p. Nasco Internat., Inc., 1972-74, pres., CEO, 1974—; bd. dirs., v.p World Dairy Expo, 1967-90; bd. dirs., treas. Nat. Dairy Shrine, 1969-93; chmn. bd., dir. Gehl Co., Bank Ft. Atkinson, Geneve Corp. Bd. govs. Agrl. Hall of Fame; bd. dirs. Wis. 4-H Found., Competitive Wis., Blue Cross-Blue Shield United Wis., 1990—, United Wis. Svc., 1991—; trustee Pa. State U., 1987-88. With U.S. Army, 1945-46. Recipient Nat. 4-H Alumni award, 1979, Fellow award Pa. State U., Disting. Alumnus award Pa. State U., 1987; named Hon. County Agt., 1988, Person of Yr. World Dairy Expo. Industry, 1989, Guest of Honor Nat. Dairy Shrine, 1993. Mem. Dairy and Food Industries Supply Assn. (bd. dirs., past pres. 1974—), Wis. Mfg. and Commerce Assn. (bd. dirs 1980—, chmn. 1990-91), Nat. Speakers Assn., Am. Dairy Sci. Assn., Holstein-Friesian Assn. Am., Pa. State U. Soc. for Disting. Alumni (pres. 1993—), Delta Theta Sigma (past pres.), Gamma Sigma Delta. Mem. United Ch. of Christ. Home: 711 Blackhawk Dr Fort Atkinson WI 53538-1047 Office: Nasco Internat Inc 901 Janesville Ave Fort Atkinson WI 53538

NESBITT, CHARLES RUDOLPH, lawyer, energy consultant; b. Miami, Okla., Aug. 30, 1921; s. Charles Rudolph and Irma Louise (Wilhelmi) N.; m. Margot Dorothy Lord, June 6, 1948; children: Nancy Margot Nesbitt Nagle, Douglas Charles, Carolyn Jane Nesbitt Gresham. B.A., U. Okla., 1942; LL.B., Yale, 1947. Bar: Okla. 1947, U.S. Supreme Ct. 1957. Pvt. practice Oklahoma City, 1948-62, 67-69, 75-91; atty. gen. Okla., 1963-67; mem. Okla. Corp. Commn., 1968-75, chmn., 1969-75; sec. of energy State of Okla., Oklahoma City, 1991-95; pvt. practice Oklahoma City, 1995—; Okla. rep., v.p. Interstate Oil and Gas Compact. Bd. dirs., trustee endowment fund St. Gregory's Coll.; trustee Oklahoma City U.; pres. Hist. Preservation, Inc.; pres. bd. trustees Okla. Mus. Art; v.p., bd. dirs Western History Collections Assocs., U. Okla. Librs.; mem. panel arbitrators Am. Arbitration Assn., NASD, NYSE; mem. Ecclesiastical Ct., Diocese Okla. With AUS, 1942-46. Mem. Am., Okla. bar assns., Oklahoma City C. of C., Phi Beta Kappa, Phi Delta Phi. Episcopalian. Home: 1703 N Hudson Ave Oklahoma City OK 73103-3428 Office: 125 NW 6th St Oklahoma City OK 73102

NESBITT, LENORE CARRERO, federal judge; b. Joseph Nesbitt; 2 children: Sarah, Thomas. A.A., Stephens Coll., 1952; BS, Northwestern U., 1954; student U. Fla. Law Sch., 1954-55; LLB, U. Miami, 1957. Rsch. asst. Dist. Ct. Appeal, 1957-59, Dade County Cir. Ct., 1963-65; pvt. practice Nesbitt & Nesbitt, 1960-63; spl. asst. attorney gen., 1961-63; with Law Offices of John Robert Terry, 1969-73; counsel, Fla. State Bd. Med. Examiners, 1970-71; with Petersen, McGowan & Feder, 1973-75; judge Fla. Cir. Ct., 1975-82, U.S. Dist. Ct. (so. dist.) Fla., Miami, 1983—. Bd. trustees U. Miami; bd. dirs. Miami Children's Hosp. Mem. FBA, Fla. Bar Assn., U.S. Jud. Conf. Com. on Criminal Law and Probation Adminstrn. Office: US Dist Ct 301 N Miami Ave Miami FL 33128-7701

NESBITT, LLOYD IVAN, podiatrist; b. Toronto, Ont., Can., Sept. 24, 1951; s. Allan Jay and Rose (Shuster) N.; m. Marlene Cindy Wegler, May 13, 1984; children: Hilary Liza, Andrea Eve, Jeffrey Ryan. D in Podiatric Medicine, Calif. Coll. Podiatric Medicine, San Francisco, 1975. Diplomate Internat. Soc. Podiatric Laser Surgery. Residency program Vancouver (B.C.) Gen. Hosp., Can., 1975-76; pvt. practice podiatric medicine Toronto; cons. podiatry Alan Eagleson Sports Medicine Clinic, Toronto, 1979—; lectr. numerous colls., fitness ctrs. and sports medicine confs., Ont., 1979—. Contbr. numerous articles to sports medicine books and jours; editor Canadian Podiatrist Jour., 1979-88. Fellow Can. Podiatric Sports Medicine Acad. (pres. 1979-89, editor newsletter 1977-89), Am. Acad. Podiatric Sports Medicine; mem. Internat. Soc. Podiatric Laser Surgery (diplomate), Am.

Podiatric Med. Assn., Sierra Club. Avocations: skiing, in-line skating, sailing, cycling, gardening. Home: 122 Argonne Crescent, Willowdale, ON Canada M2K 2K1 Office: Madison Ctr Office Tower, 4950 Yonge St Ste 2414, Toronto, ON Canada M2N 6K1

NESBITT, MARK, management consultant; b. Ottawa, Ont., Can., Dec. 31, 1952; s. William Alonzo and Barbara (Ellis) N.; 1 child, Karen Elizabeth. BSc, Carleton U., Ottawa, 1973, BA, 1974; MBA, Harvard U., 1978. Cert. Mgmt. Cons. Cons. Peat Marwick & Ptnrs., Ottawa, 1978; assoc./ mgr. Veritas Cons. Inc., Toronto, Ont., Can., 1978-86, pres., 1986-93; pres., CEO Vertex Cons. Inc., Toronto, 1993—; IS com. mem. YMCA Metro Toronto, 1992-93. Mem. Am. Mktg. Assn., Inst. Cert. Mgmt. Cons. Ont. (firms com.), Assn. for Creative Change, Internat. Mgmt. Devel. (v.p.). Anglican. Avocations: bicycling, photography, programming. Office: Vertex Cons Inc, 14 Dundonald St, Toronto, ON Canada M4Y 1K2

NESBITT, ROBERT EDWARD LEE, JR., physician, educator; b. Albany, Ga., Aug. 21, 1924; s. Robert E.L. and Anne Louise (Hill) N.; m. Ellen Therese Morrissey. B.A., Vanderbilt U., 1944, M.D., 1947. Diplomate: Am. Bd. Ob-Gyn (asso. examiner). Asst. prof. Johns Hopkins U., 1954-56, chief obstetric pathology lab., acting chief obstetrics, 1955-56; prof., chmn. dept. ob-gyn Albany (N.Y.) Med. Coll., Union U., 1956-61; prof., chmn. dept. ob-gyn SUNY Health Sci. Ctr., Syracuse, 1961-81, dir. gen. gynecology service, 1982-84, prof. and chmn. emeritus dept. ob-gyn; obstetrician-gynecologist-in-chief Albany Hosp., 1956-61; obstetrician, gynecologist-in-chief Syracuse Meml. Hosp., 1961-65; obstetrician-gynecologist-in-chief Crouse-Irving Hosp., 1963-70, attending staff, 1970-84; prof. surgery U. South Fla., Tampa, 1988-92, prof. ob.-gyn., 1988-92; chief ob-gyn State U. Hosp., 1964-81, chmn. med. staff and med. bd., 1964-66; attending staff St. Joseph's Hosp.; cons. chief gynecology sect. surg. service Syracuse VA Hosp., 1984-88; chief gynecology sect., asst. chief surgery, dir. urogynecology VA Med. Ctr., Bay Pines, Fla., 1988-92, acting chief of staff, 1990, interim chief surgery, 1992-92, chmn. O.R. com. surg. svc., 1988-92, chmn. patient care evaluation com., 1989-90, chmn. clin. exec. bd., 1990, chmn. drug usage evaluation com., 1990-91, chmn. profl. standards bd., 1990; cons. Syracuse Psychiat. Inst.; mem. cancer tng. grants and edn. com. Nat. Cancer Insts.; mem. adv. com. Bur. Maternal and Child Health, N.Y. State Dept. Health, 1957-61; nat. adviser to Children, publ. of Children's Bur., HEW, 1959-63; cons. Children's Bur., 1959-62; mem. prenatal care guide subcom. Am. Pub. Health Assn., 1962-64; cons. to regional adviser in maternal and child health Pan Am. San. Bur., WHO, 1963-65; numerous guest professorships including univs. in Mex., Chile, Uruguay, Colombia, St. Vincent (W.I.), Venezuela, People's Republic of China; numerous guest professorships including univs. in others. Author: Perinatal Loss in Modern Obstetrics, 1957; sect. on ob-gyn in Rypin's Med. Licensure Exams; also chpts. in numerous anthologies; co-author: Infant, Perinatal, Maternal and Childhood Mortality in U.S, 1968; editor: sect. on obstetrics and gynecology Stedman's Medical Dictionary, 1958-64; sect. on fetus Funk and Wagnalls Universal Standard Ency, 1959; 1st guest editor: sect. on fetus Clinics in Perinatology, 1974; 1st editor: sect. on fetus Clinical Diagnosis Quiz for Obstetrics and Gynecology, 1976, Clini-Pearls in Obstetrics and Gynecology, 1977; contbr. to: sect. on fetus Attorneys' Textbook of Medicine. Capt. M.C., U.S. Army, 1952-54. Named One of Ten Outstanding Young Men in Am., U.S. Jr. C. of C., 1957; Robert E.L. Nesbitt Jr. scholarship, Sr. Resident in Ob-Gyn, and Robert E.L. Nesbitt Jr. student scholarship established in his honor, SUNY Health Sci. Ctr. at Syracuse, 1987. Fellow Am. Assn. Maternal and Child Health, Am. Coll. Obstetricians and Gynecologists (chmn. com. mental retardation and perinatal health 1966), A.C.S. (com. forum fundamental surg. problems 1962-67), Venezuelan Obstetrics-Gynecol. Soc. (hon.), N.Y. Acad. Scis.; mem. AMA, Soc. for Gynecol. Investigations (council), Pan Am. Med. Assn. (med. ambassador goodwill life mem. sect. on cancer), Med. Soc. N.Y. State (regional obstetrics chmn., subcom. Maternal and Child Welfare), Onondaga County Med. Soc., Am. Soc. Cytology, Pub. Health Council N.Y. State, Alpha Omega Alpha; hon. mem. Southwest, Fla. obstet. and gynecol. socs., others. Research and 230 publs. on cytologic, cytochem. and histochem. study of early cervical cancer, perinatal and placental pathology, cytologic and hormonal studies in normal and high-risk obstet. patiens, exptl. prodn. of abruptio placentae, reproductive endocrinology, animal experimentation, induced endocrine insults upon pregnant and nonpregnant ewes and hormonal influence on placentation, invitro placenta perfusion, fetal growth and devel., female urology, new surgical technique for restoration of female pelvic floor integrity while preserving the uterus (published 1989); creation science. Home: 11639 Grove St North Seminole FL 34642-7137

NESBITT, ROSEMARY SINNETT, theatre educator; b. Syracuse, N.Y., Oct. 12, 1924; d. Matthew A. and Mary Louise (Kane) Sinnett; m. George R. Nesbitt, June 18, 1955 (dec. Nov. 1971); children: Mary, Anne, George R., Elizabeth. BS magna cum laude, Syracuse U., 1947, MS, 1952. Instr. in speech Wells Coll., Aurora, N.Y., 1949-52, Syracuse U., 1952-57; asst. prof. SUNY, Oswego, 1965-68, assoc. prof., 1968-72, prof. theatre, 1972-77, Disting. teaching prof., 1977—, dir. children's theatre, 1969—; cons., lectr. pub. schs., N.Y. and New Eng., 1965—; lectr. in field. Author: The Great Rope, 1968, Colonel Meacham's Giant Cheese, 1971; (play) The Great Rope, 1975 (George Washington medal Freedom Found. 1975); plays for children. Founding mem. Oswego Heritage Found., 1963; historian City of Oswego, 1973-80, 88—; founder, bd. dirs. H. Lee White Marine Mus., Oswego, 1983—; chmn. bd. dirs. Port of Oswego Authority, 1986-88, bd. dirs., 1978-88. Recipient George R. Arents Disting. Alumnus award Syracuse U., 1975, Jefferson award Jefferson Award Com., 1984, Svc. to Arts award Cultural Resources Coun. Onondaga County, 1985, Franklin award for Disting. Svc. in Transp. Syracuse U. Sch. mgmt., 1989, Amelia Earhart Woman of the Yr. award Zonta Club of Oswego; named Woman of Yr. in Cultural Devel., Syracuse Post Standard, 1971, Citizen of Yr., City of Oswego, 1974. Mem. AAUW, Alpha Psi Omega. Democrat. Roman Catholic. Avocations: history, reading, travel. Home: 119 W 4th St Oswego NY 13126-2002 Office: SUNY Theatre Dept Oswego NY 13126

NESBURG, ALAN D., lawyer; b. Muskegon, Mich., Oct. 8, 1947. BA, Kalamazoo Coll., 1969; JD, Northwestern U., 1972. Bar: Ill. 1972, Fla. 1977. Ptnr. McDermott, Will & Emory, Chgo. Mem. ABA, Ill. State Bar Assn., Fla. Bar, Chgo. Bar Assn. Office: McDermott Will & Emery 111 W Monroe St Chicago IL 60603-4003

NESHEIM, MALDEN C., university administrator. Provost Cornell U., Ithaca, N.Y. Office: Cornell U Office Provost Ithaca NY 14853

NESHEIM, ROBERT OLAF, food products executive; b. Monroe Center, Ill., Sept. 13, 1921; s. Olaf M. and Sena M. (Willms) N.; m. Emogene P. Sullivan, July 13, 1946 (divorced); children: Barbara Mowry, Susan Yost (dec.), Sandra Rankin; m. doris Howes Calloway, July 4, 1981. BS, U. Ill., 1943, MS, 1950, PhD, 1951; postgrad. in advanced mgmt. program, Harvard U., 1971. Farm mgr. Halderman Farm Mgmt. Svc., Wabash, Ind., 1946-48; instr. U. Ill., 1951; mgr. feed rsch. The Quaker Oats Co., Barrington, Ill., 1952-64; prof., head of dept. animal sci. U. Ill., 1964-67; dir. nutrition rsch. The Quaker Oats Co. Barrington, Ill., 1967-69, v.p R & D, 1969-78; v.p. sci. & tech. The Quaker Oats Co., Chgo., 1978-83; sr. v.p. sci. & tech. Avadyne, Inc., Monterey, Calif., 1983-85; pres. Advanced Healthcare, Monterey, 1985-91; ret., 1991. Capt. U.S. Army, 1943-46, South Pacific. Fellow Am. Inst. Nutrition (treas. 1983-86), AAAS; mem. Inst. Food Technologists, Fed. Socs. Exptl. Biologists (treas. 1973-79), APHA, Corral de Tierra Club (Salinas, Calif.). Avocations: gardening, golf.

NESI, VINCENT, apparel executive. With A. Smile Inc., N.Y.C., 1974-77; pres. Bugle Boy, Simi Valley, Calif., 1977—. Office: Bugle Boy 2900 N Madera Rd Simi Valley CA 93065-6236

NESIN, JEFFREY D., academic administrator; b. N.Y.C.; m. Diane Garvey, 1968; children: Kate Dillon, Sarah Grace. BA in Eng. Lit., Hobart Coll., 1966; MA in Eng. Lit, SUNY, Buffalo, 1971, MA in Am. Studies, 1973. Faculty dept. humanities & scis. Sch. Visual Arts, N.Y.C., 1974-91; pres. Memphis Coll. Art, 1991—; adj. lectr. CCNY, Hunter Coll.; advisor dept. fine arts Sch. Visual Arts, 1975-82, dir. spl. programs, 1978-91, asst. to pres., 1982-91; cons. Smithsonian Instn., IBM, 1st Tenn. Bank; panelist, speaker in field. Contbg. editor: High Fidelity, Creem; contbr. reviews, interviews, essays to mags.; adv. editor Jour. Popular Music and Society.

Mem. Am. Studies Assn., Met. Am. Studies Assn. (past pres.), Assn. Ind. Colls. Art & Design (bd. dirs. 1991—), Memphis Rotary, Nat. Assn. Schs. Art & Design (commn. accreditation 1993—). Avocations: mystery novels, barbecue, baseball. Office: Memphis Coll Art Office of President 1930 Poplar Ave Memphis TN 38104 Home: 1545 Vinton Ave Memphis TN 38104-4923

NESMITH, MICHAEL, film producer, video specialist; b. Houston, Dec. 30, 1942; s. Warren and Bette Nesmith; m. Phyliss Nesmith; children: Christian, Jonathan, Jessica; m. 2d, Kathryn Nesmith. Chmn., chief exec. officer Pacific Arts Corp. (div. Nesmith Enterprises), L.A., 1987—. Author, producer, performer various records, 1968-77; mem. (rock group) The Monkees; co-author, exec. producer: (films) Timerider; actor: (films) Head, 1968, Burglar, 1987, (TV series) The Monkees; exec. producer: (films) Repo Man, 1984, Square Dance, 1986, Tapeheads, 1988; exec. producer, actor: (video) Dr. Duck's Super Secret All-Purpose Sauce; producer: (series) Television Parts, 1985; co-author, producer: (pilot) for TV Pop Clips, original concept for MTV.; creator PBS Home Video. Trustee Gihon Found., 1970—, McMurray Found., 1970—. Recipient 1st Video Grammy for Elephant Paris. Christian Scientist. Office: Pacific Arts Corp 11858 La Grange Ave Ste 210 Los Angeles CA 90025

NESMITH, RICHARD DUEY, clergyman, theology educator; b. Belleville, Kans., Jan. 9, 1929; s. Eugene Gordon and Edith Mae (Duey) N.; m. Patricia N. Nichols, Aug. 24, 1985; children: Leslie Ann, Lisa Lorraine, Laurel Sue, Lana Louise, Christopher Toscano. B.A., Nebr. Wesleyan U., 1950; M.Div., Garrett Evang. Sem., 1953; Ph.D., Boston U., 1957. Ordained to ministry United Methodist Ch., 1953; dean students MacMurray Coll. Jacksonville, Ill., 1957-61; prof. sociology of religion St. Paul's Sch. Theology, Kansas City, 1961-67; dir. planning Nat. div. Methodist Bd. of Global Ministries, N.Y.C., 1967-73; pastor Trinity Ch., Lincoln, Nebr., 1973-77; dean Sch. Theology Boston U., 1977-88, prof., 1988—; bd. dirs. State Line Farms, Inc.; pres. Nesmith Inc. Producer religious TV program, Perspectives. Office: Boston U Sch Theology 745 Commonwealth Ave Rm 438 Boston MA 02215-1401

NESS, ALBERT KENNETH, artist; b. St. Ignace, Mich., June 21, 1903; s. Albert Klingberg and Violet Matilda (Sutherland); m. Lenore Consuelo Chrisman, Aug. 4, 1926; children: Peter, James Kenneth, Jane Lenore. Student U. Detroit, 1923-24, Detroit Sch. of Applied Art, 1924-26, Wicker Sch. of Fine Art, 1926-28; Diploma, Sch. of Art Inst., 1932. Show-card writer, window display man S.S. Kresge Co., Detroit, 1923-24; artist poster and advt. Cunningham Drugs, Detroit, 1924-26; artist layout lettering and design W.L. Flemming Studios, Detroit, 1926-28, McAleer Displays, Chgo., 1929-32; artist, design asst. Layman-Whitney Assocs., 1933 World's Fair, Chgo.; layout artist, poster designer Elevated Advt. Co., Chgo., 1934-37; instr., art dir. Sch. of Applied Art, Chgo., 1938-40; Carnegie resident artist U. N.C., Chapel Hill, 1941-43, dir. War Art Ctr., 1942-43, resident artist, assoc. prof. art, 1943-49, acting head dept. art, acting dir. Person Hall Art Gallery, 1944-45, resident artist, prof. art, 1949-73, acting head dept. of art, acting dir. Person Hall Art Gallery, 1955, 57-58, resident artist, prof. emeritus, 1973—. One man shows include: Chester Johnson Galleries, Chgo., 1932, Evanston Art Ctr., Ill., 1940, Person Hall Art Gallery, 1941, N.C. Art Soc. Gallery, Raleigh, 1942, Duke U. Art Gallery, Durham, N.C., 1955, Louisburg Coll. Gallery, N.C., 1964, Ackland Art Mus., U.N.C. Chapel Hill, 1973; Internat. Water Color Exhbn. Chgo. Art Inst., 1934-39; Golden Gate Internat. Exposition, San Francisco, 1939, exhibited in group shows: Whitney Mus., N.Y.C., 1933, U. Chattanooga, Tenn., 1946, Centennial Exhbn. U. Fla., Gainesville, 1953, Jacksonville Art Mus., Fla., 1960; exhibited nationally Am. Artists' Anns., Chgo. Art Inst., 1935-37, Butler Art Inst., Youngstown, Ohio, 1951, Pa. Acad. Am. Annuals, Phila., 1953-54, Optique Gallery, Lambertville, N.J., 1991—, Ross-Constantine Gallery, N.Y.C., 1991—, Marita Gilliam Gallery, Raleigh, N.C., 1993—; others; works in pub. collections include: N.C. Mus., Raleigh, Ackland Art Mus., Reynolds Found., Winston Salem, Duke U. Art Mus., Durham. Contbr. to local and state newspapers. Editor, designer, photographer: A brochure on art study, 1964. Recipient Jenkins Meml. prize 38th Ann. Chgo. Artists' Exhbn., 1934, Purchase award N.C. Artists' Ann., Raleigh, 1953; 2-Star award Movie Maker Competition, London, 1970, N.C. award in Fine Arts, 1973, Purchase award Reynolds Competition, Winston Salem, 1977. Home: PO Box 14 Chapel Hill NC 27514-0014

NESS, ANDREW DAVID, lawyer; b. San Francisco, Oct. 29, 1952; s. Orville Arne and Muriel Ruth (Trendt) N.; m. Rita M. Kobylenski, May 25, 1980; children: Katherine, Austin, Emily. BS, Stanford U., 1974; JD, Harvard U., 1977. Bar: Calif. 1977, D.C. 1979, U.S. Dist. Ct. (no. dist.) Calif. 1977, U.S. Dist. Ct. D.C. 1983, U.S. Dist. Ct. (ea. dist.) Va. 1988, U.S. Ct. Appeals (4th cir.) 1989. Law clk. U.S. Dist. Ct., San Francisco, 1977-78; assoc. Lewis, Mitchell & Moore, Vienna, Va., 1979-82, ptnr., 1982-87; ptnr. Morgan, Lewis & Bockius, Washington, 1987—; instr. U. Md., College Park, 1987-90; mem. faculty seminars Stanford (Calif.) U., 1984-87. Contbr. chpt. to book, 1990, also articles to profl. jours. Mem. ABA (forum on constrn. industry, chair ins. and indemnification com., pub. contract law sect.). Avocations: hiking, bicycling. Office: Morgan Lewis & Bockius 1800 M St NW Washington DC 20036-5802

NESS, FREDERIC WILLIAM, former academic administrator, educator, consultant; b. York, Pa., Feb. 2, 1914; s. Harry and Rosalyn Barbara (Eichelberger) N.; m. Dore Roberts, June 30, 1943 (dec. May 1959); children: Lynne, Diane, Merryl, Melanie Barbara; m. Eleanor H. Hedge, Sept. 1, 1962 (dec. May 1994); 1 child, Brook H. A.B., Dickinson Coll., 1933, LL.D., 1973; student, Cin. Conservatory Music, 1930, 31, 33-35; A.M., U. Cin., 1935; Ph.D., Yale U., 1940; Litt.D., Ursinus Coll., 1971, Coll. Idaho, 1972, Monmouth Coll., 1976; L.H.D., Beaver Coll., 1972, Millikin U., 1972, Coll. St. Scholastica, 1972, Ottawa U., 1976, York Coll., 1978, Moravian Coll., 1984; Ped. D., Hofstra U., 1975; H.H.D., Rider Coll., 1975, Bridgewater Coll., 1977; LL.D., Elizabethtown Coll., 1976, New Eng. Coll., 1982. Instr. English, dean men Cin. Conservatory Music, 1938-39; instr. English U. Cin., 1939, Yale U., 1939-42; fellow Berkeley Coll., Yale U., 1940-42; asst. to vice chancellor, dean, NYU, 1945-52; dean, prof. English Dickinson Coll., 1952-60, acad. v.p., 1955-60, chmn. dept. English 1956-58, William W. Edel prof. humanities, 1959-60; v.p., provost, dean Grad. Sch. L.I. U., 1960-62; v.p. Hofstra U., 1962-64; pres. Fresno (Calif.) State Coll., 1964-69, pres. emeritus, 1975—; pres. Assn. Am. Colls., Washington, 1969-78, pres. emeritus, 1978—; founding dir. Presdl. Search Consultation Svc., 1979-86, sr. cons., 1986-94; vis. prof. Poly. Inst., San German, P.R., 1955; mem. Pa. Gov.'s Com. Edn., 1958-60; pres. Western Colls. Assn. 1967-68. Author: The Use of Rhyme in Shakespeare's Plays, 1941; co-author: Graduate Study in the Liberal Arts College, 1961; editor, author: The Role of the College in the Recruitment of Teachers, 1958, A Guide to Graduate Study, 1957, 61, A Regional Faculty Orientation Program, 1961, An Uncertain Glory, 1970. Chmn. bd. dirs. Community Chest, Carlisle, Pa., 1960; bd. dirs. Bklyn. Acad., 1960-62, Fresno Philarmonic Orch., 1965-69, Am. Coun. Edn., 1966-69, Change, 1970-72, Common Fund, 1970-76, Catalyst, 1974-78, Ind. Colls. Fund Am., 1976-86, Moravian Coll., 1976-84, Am. U., 1980-88, Annapolis Life Care, 1994—, Md. Hall for Creative Arts, 1990—; bd. dirs., pres. Teaching Film Custodians, 1970-73; mem. acad. adv. bd. U.S. Naval Acad., 1978-86. Lt. commdr. USNR, 1942-46. Mem. Elizabethan Club, Cosmos Club, Annapolis Yacht Club, Phi Beta Kappa, Beta Gamma Sigma, Omicron Delta Kappa, Phi Mu Alpha, Beta Theta Pi. Presbyterian. Office: 3105 River Crescent Dr Annapolis MD 21401-6211

NESS, NORMAN FREDERICK, astrophysicist, educator, administrator; b. Springfield, Mass., Apr. 15, 1933; s. Herman Hugo and Eva (Custard) N.; children: Elizabeth Ann, Stephen Andrew. BS, Mass. Inst. Tech., 1955, Ph.D., 1959. Space physicist, asst. prof. geophysics UCLA, 1959-61; Nat. Acad. Sci.-NRC post doctoral research assoc. NASA, 1960-61; research physicist in space scis. Goddard Space Flight Center, Greenbelt, Md., 1961-86; head extraterrestrial physics br. Goddard Space Flight Center, 1968-69; chief Lab. for Extraterrestrial Physics, 1969-86; pres., prof. Bartol Research Inst., U. Del., 1987—; lectr. math. U. Md., 1962-64, assoc. research prof., 1965-67. Contbr. articles profl. jours. Recipient Exceptional Sci. Achievement award NASA, 1966, 81, 86, Arthur S. Flemming award, 1968, Space Sci. award AIAA, 1971, Disting. Svc. medal NASA, 1986, Nat. Space Club award, 1993, Emil Wiechert medal German Geophys. Soc., 1993. Fellow

Am. Geophys. Union (John Adam Fleming award 1968), Royal Astron. Soc.; mem. NAS, Accademia Nazionale dei Lincei, Royal Ocean Racing Club. Achievements include research, experimental studies of interplanetary and planetary magnetic fields by satellites and space probes. Home: 9 Wilkinson Dr Landenberg PA 19350-9359 Office: U Del Bartol Research Inst Newark DE 19716-4793

NESS, OWEN MCGREGOR, retired aluminum company executive; b. Howick, Que., Can., Apr. 3, 1930; s. John Earle and Jane Ella (McGregor) N.; m. Carolyn Mary Graham, Sept. 12, 1953; children: David Graham (dec.), Peter Earle, William Bruce (dec.), Richard Andrew. BSc in Agr., McGill U., Montreal, Que., 1952; postgrad., Ctr. Indsl. Studies, Geneva, 1961. Various positions including works pers. mgr. Alcan Smelters & Chems., Arvida, Que., 1954-71; various positions in compensation Alcan Can., Montreal, 1971-76, dir. pers., 1985-89; pers. dir. Alcan Aluminium (UK) Ltd., 1979-84; mgr. R & D, Alcan Internat. Ltd., Montreal, 1984-85; regional pers. mgr. Alcan Aluminium Ltd., Montreal, 1976-79, v.p. pers., 1989-93; mem. internat. human resource mgmt. coun. Conf. Bd., 1990-93. Mem. agrl. and environ. scis. adv. bd. Macdonald Coll., McGill U., 1988-93. Mem. Montreal Amateur Athletic Assn., Ormstown Golf Club (Que.). Avocations: farming, golf, badminton, aerobics. Home: 1595 Rte 202, Athelstan, PQ Canada J0S 1A0

NESSE, MARK A., library director; b. Redwing, Minn., Mar. 10, 1943; s. Marvin Edgar and Ruth (Huus) N.; m. Sheila Joan Powers, Apr. 5, 1967; children: Rachel, Eric, John. BA in Edn., Pacific Luth. U., Tacoma, 1965; MS in LS, U. N.C., 1971. Cert. Mln. Secondary tchr. U.S. Peace Corps, Yrgalem and Hosanna, Ethiopia, 1965-67; tng. instr. at U. Utah U.S. Peace Corps, Salt Lake City, summer 1967; tchr. jr. h.s. Tacoma Pub. Schs., 1967-69; extension head Durham County Libr., Durham, N.C., 1971-73; dir. Beverly (Mass.) Pub. Libr., 1973-77, Everett (Wash.) Pub. Libr., 1977—. Contbr. chpt. to book. Bd. dirs. Marie Weeks Varley Campfire Found., Everett, 1988-88, Snohomish chpt. ARC, Everett, 1991-94; mem. Everett Sch. Bd., 1993—. Mem. ALA, Rotary Club of Everett (pres. 1988-89). Avocations: restoring Jeepster automobiles, antiques. Office: Everett Pub Libr 2702 Hoyt Ave Everett WA 98201

NESSELROADE, JOHN RICHARD, psychology educator; b. Silverton, W.Va., Mar. 13, 1936; s. John S. and Emma E. (Suck) N.; m. Carolyn S. Boyles, July 12, 1959; children: Cynthia Anne, Jennifer Sue. BS, Marietta Coll., 1961; MA, Univ. Ill., 1965, PhD, 1967. Asst. prof. W. Va. U., Morgantown, 1967-70, assoc. prof., 1970-72; assoc. prof. human devel. Pa. State U., University Park, 1972-75, prof., 1975-83, rsch. prof., 1983-90, disting. rsch. prof., 1990-91, dir. Ctr. for Devel. and Health Rsch. Methodology, 1989-91; Hamilton prof. psychology U. Va., Charlottesville, 1991—. Editor: Handbook of Multivariate Exptl. Psychology, 1988. Sgt. USMC, 1954-57, Japan. Recipient Cattell award Soc. of Multivariate Exptl. Psychology, 1972. Fellow AAAS, APA (Disting. Contbns. award Divsn. 20 1994), Am. Psychol. Soc. (charter), Gerontol. Soc. Am. Avocations: music, tennis, golf. Home: 116 Chestnut Ridge Rd Charlottesville VA 22901-8544

NESSEN, RONALD HAROLD, public affairs executive; b. Washington, May 25, 1934; s. Frederick E. and Ida Edith (Kaufman) N.; m. Johanna Neuman, Feb. 14, 1988; children: Caren Jayne, Edward Song. B.A., Am. U., 1959; LL.D. (hon.), Heidelberg Coll., 1975, Ursinus Coll., 1977. News announcer Sta. WEPM, Martinsburg, W.Va., 1952-54, Sta. WARL, Arlington, Va., 1954-55; writer Montgomery County (Md.) Sentinel, Rockville, 1955-56; editor UPI, Washington, 1956-62; news corr. NBC News, Washington, 1962-74; press sec. to Pres. Gerald R. Ford, 1974-77; freelance writer, lectr., 1977-80; exec. v.p. Marston & Rothenberg Public Affairs, Inc., Washington, 1980-84; sr. asso. Robert Marston & Assos., N.Y.C., 1980-84; moderator Pro-Con TV series Pa. Pub. Broadcasting System, 1983-84; v.p. MBS, Arlington, Va., 1984-92; v.p. pub. affairs, comm. Cellular Telecommunications Industry Assn., 1992—. Author: It Sure Looks Different From the Inside, 1978, The First Lady, 1979, The Hour, 1984; contbr. articles to popular publs. Recipient George Foster Peabody Broadcasting award, 1964, George Polk Meml. award Overseas Press Club, 1967, Edward R. Murrow Brotherhood award, 1988, 1989, Grand award Internat. Radio Festival, 1988, Nat. Headliner award, 1989. Mem. Nat. Press Club. Home: 6409 Walhonding Rd Bethesda MD 20816-2264

NESSEN, WARD HENRY, typographer, lawyer; b. Empire, Mich., Nov. 29, 1909; s. Henry L. and Louise (Stecher) N.; m. Jane Randall, Apr. 4, 1959. AB, U. Mich., 1931; JD, John Marshall Law Sch., Chgo., 1937; course in acctg. Northwestern U. Grad. Sch., 1946. Bar: Ill. 1937. With trust dept. No. Trust Co., Chgo., 1934-41; sales planning Am. Home Products, 1946-51; sales exec. Permacel Tape Corp., 1951-55; pres. The Highton Co., Newark, 1955-75; sr. v.p. Arrow Typographers, Newark, 1975-84; chmn. Coll. Communications Seminar, 1973. Mem. Civic Clubs Council Greater Newark Area, 1957-59, Bd. Comml. Arbitration N.Y.C., 1982-86; pres. Dale Carnegie course, 1964; chmn. selection com. Advt. Hall of Fame of N.J., 1983. Lt. col. AUS, 1941-46, ETO, assigned ETOUSA. Decorated Bronze Star with oak leaf cluster, Army Commendation medal; recipient Svc. to Industry award Printing Industries, N.J., 1973, recipient award of Excellence for Exhbn. Insides Am. Inst. Graphic Arts, 1974, Elmer G. Voigt award, 1975; named to Advt. Hall of Fame N.J., 1990. Mem. Internat. Platform Assn., Typographers Internat. Assn. (pres. 1970-71), N.J. Typographers Assn. (pres. 1957-59), Print/N.J. (pres. 1967-69), Assn. Graphic Arts N.Y. (bd. govs. 1967-69), Advt. Club N.J. (chmn. com. Constnl. bylaws 1980-81), John Monteith Soc., Pres.'s Club of U. Mich., Order of John Marshall, Sigma Phi. Republican. Episcopalian. Clubs: Type Dirs.; Advt. N.J. (bd. govs 1972-84). Home: 11 Euclid Ave Summit NJ 07901-2114

NESSON, CHARLES R., lawyer, educator; b. 1939. A.B., Harvard U., 1960, LL.B., 1963. Bar: D.C. 1964, Mass. 1971. Law clk. to assoc. justice Harlan, U.S. Supreme Ct., Washington, 1964-65; spl. asst. Civil Rights Div., Dept. Justice, 1965-66; asst. prof. Harvard U., Cambridge, Mass., 1966-69, prof., 1969—. Author: (with E. Green) Federal Rules of Evidence, 1984. Mem. Media and Soc. Office: Law Sch Harvard U Cambridge MA 02138

NESSON, H. RICHARD, medical administrator, physician; b. Boston, May 6, 1932; s. Edward Donald and Ruthe (Zakon) N.; m. Lois Feinberg, Aug. 25, 1957; children—Edward D., Sara F. A.B., Harvard Coll., 1954; M.D., Boston U., 1959. Med. dir. Harvard Community Health Plan, Boston, 1967-73; dir. Office of Extramural Health Programs Harvard Sch. Pub. Health, Boston, 1973-76; dir. div. Gen. Medicine and Primary Care, dept. medicine Brigham & Woman's Hosp., Boston, 1976-82, v.p. ambulatory and community health services, 1976-82, pres., 1982—; CEO Partners HealthCare System, Inc., 1994—; sr. program cons. Robert Wood Johnson Found., Princeton, N.H., 1979-82; bd. dirs. Mercy Hosp. Sys. Contbr. articles to profl. jours. Chmn. Brookline Adv. Council of Pub. Health, Mass. 1971-76; mem. adv. com. of Radcliffe Seminars Program, Cambridge, Mass., 1975-82; bd. dirs. United Way, Boston, 1985-90; mem. policy adv. com. Mass. Supreme Judicial Ct., 1991. Recipient Disting. Alumni award Boston U. Sch. Medicine, 1983. Mem. AAAS, APHA, Assn. Am. Med. Colls., Mass. Pub. Health Assn., Med. Adminstrs. Conf. (sec. 1982), Soc. Med. Adminstrs., Am. Fedn. Clinic Rsch., Mass. Med. Soc., Am. Hosp. Assn. (mem. coun. of mgmt. 1984-87, chmn. 1994-95), Mass. Hosp. Assn. (chmn. 1994-95), Group Health Assn. Am., Harvard Club of Boston, Alpha Omega Alpha. Avocation: tennis. Office: Ptnrs HealthCare Sys Inc Ste 1150 800 Boylston St Boston MA 02199-8001

NESTER, EUGENE WILLIAM, microbiology educator; b. Johnson City, N.Y., Sept. 15, 1930; married, 1959; 2 children. BS, Cornell U., 1952; PhD, Western Reserve U., 1959. Am. Cancer Soc. genetics Stanford U., 1959-62, instr. microbiology, 1962-63; from asst. to assoc. prof. microbiology and genetics, 1963-72; prof. microbiology U. Wash., Seattle, 1972—. Recipient Chiron Corp. Biotechnology Rsch. award, Australia prize, 1990. Fellow NAS, AAAS, Am. Acad. Microbiology; mem. Am. Soc. Microbiology. Achievements include bacterial-plant relationships. Office: U Wash Microbiology Dept SC-42 Seattle WA 98195

NESTER, WILLIAM RAYMOND, JR., retired university chancellor and educator; b. Cin., May 19, 1928; s. William Raymond and Evelyn (Blettner) N.; m. Mary Jane Grossman, Aug. 21, 1950; children: William Raymond, Mark Patrick, Brian Philip, Stephen Christopher. BS, U. Cin., 1950, EdM,

1953, EdD, 1965. Tchr. high sch. English and history Cin., 1950-52; dir. student union U. Cin., 1952-53, asst. dean of men, 1953-60, dean of men, 1960-67, assoc. prof. edn., 1965-70, dean of students, 1967-69, vice provost student and univ. affairs, 1969-76, prof. edn., 1970-78, assoc. sr. v.p., assoc. provost, 1976-78; vis. student svcs. Ohio State U., Columbus, 1978-83, prof. edn., 1978-83; pres. Kearney State Coll., Nebr., 1983-91, prof. edn., 1983-93; chancellor U. Nebr., Kearney, 1991-93, prof. emeritus, chancellor emeritus, 1993—; pres. emeritus Mus. Nebr. Art, 1991—; cons. on edn., 1993—. Pres. Metro-Six Athletic Conf., 1975-76, Cen. States Intercollegiate Conf., 1986-89. Mem. AAUP, Am. Assn. State Colls. and Univs. (bd. dirs. 1991—), Am. Intercollegiate Athletics (pres.), Nat. Assn. Student Pers. Adminstrs. (past regional v.p., mem. exec. com.), Am. Assn. Higher Edn., Ohio Assn. Student Pers. Adminstrs. (past pres.), Nat. Intrafrat. Conf. (pres. 1991-92), Frat. Scholarship Officers Assn. (past pres.), Mortar Bd., Pi Kappa Alpha (nat. pres. 1978-80, past pres. ednl. found.), Omicron Delta Kappa, Phi Delta Kappa, Phi Alpha Theta, Phi Eta Sigma, Sigma Sigma. Episcopalian. Home: 7674 Coldstream Dr Cincinnati OH 45255-3932

NESTOR, SUSAN E., health services executive; b. Nov. 28, 1956. BA, U. Notre Dame, 1978; MHA, St. Louis U., 1980. Hosp. adminstrv. resident People's Community Hosp. Authority, Wayne, Mich., 1979-80; dir. svcs. for the aged, hosp. planning St. Joseph Mercy Hosp., Pontiac, Mich., 1980-83; mgr. corp. planning Health Resources, Inc., St. Paul, Minn., 1983-84; dir. hosp. planning Health One Corp., Mpls., 1984, v.p. strategic planning, 1984-87, v.p. strategic devel., 1987—; instr. Roosevelt High Sch., Mpls., 1990, U. Minn. Grad. Program, St. Paul, 1984—, Mercy Coll., Detroit, 1981-83. Author: Afterimages as a Function of Adult Age and Exposure Duration, 1977, Experimental Aging Research, 1977. Sponsor, immigrant family Cath. Charities, Mpls., 1987; chmn. Gov.'s Commn. Promoting Minn. Healthcare, 1988-89; v.p. Planning Forum, 1988-89; bd. dirs. St. Louis U., 1989—, class sec., 1980—; bd. dirs. Minn. Internat. Health Vols. Regional finalist White House fellowship, 1988. Mem. Notre Dame Alumni Club of Minn. (bd. dirs. 1987-88). Office: Health One Corp 2810 57th Ave N Minneapolis MN 55430-2467

NESTVOLD, ELWOOD OLAF, oil service company executive; b. Minot, N.D., Mar. 19, 1932; came to Netherlands 1979; s. Ole Enevold and Ragnhilda (Quanbeck) N.; m. Simone Chriqui, Dec. 6, 1955 (dec. Jan. 1990); children: Rebecca Lynn, Paul Stephen; m. Jeannette Garvin, Mar. 23, 1991; stepchildren: Michele Marie, Jennifer Ann, Michael Dennis. BA, Augsburg Coll., Mpls., 1952; postgrad., U. Wash., 1952-53; MS, U. Minn., 1959, PhD, 1962. Physics instr. U. Minn., Mpls., 1956-61; physicist and section leader Shell EP Rsch. Lab., Houston, 1962-68, mgr. geophysics rsch., 1968-71; mgr. geophysics Shell Western Div., Denver, Houston, 1971-74, Pecten Internat., Houston, 1974-77; chief geophysicist Woodside Petroleum, Perth, Australia, 1977-78; mgr. EP processing ctr. Shell EP Rsch. Lab., Rijswijk, Netherlands, 1979-81; chief geophysicist Shell Internat. Petroleum, The Hague, 1981-86, dir. geophysics and topography, 1986-92; chief geophysicist GECO-Prakla div. Schlumberger Ltd., Paris, 1992-94; v.p. mktg. GECO-Prakla div. Schlumberger Ltd., Paris, 1993-94; sr. geophysics cons. Schlumberger Oilfield Svcs., Houston, 1994—; cons. Lighting and Transients Rsch. Inst., Mpls., 1957-61; lectr. Australian Petroleum Exploration Assn, 1991, Internat. Assn. Geophysical Contractors, 1992, European Assn. Exploration Geophysicists, 1994 and others. Presenter keynote addresses; contbr. articles to profl. and trade jours. 1st lt. USAF, 1952-56. Recipient award of appreciation Internat. Assn. Geophys. Contractors, 1992. Mem. IEEE, Am. Assn. Petroleum Geologists (Disting. lectr. 1993-94), Am. Assn. Physics Tchrs., European Assn. Petroleum Geoscientists, European Assn. Exploration Geophysicists, Soc. Exploration Geophysicists, N.Y. Acad. Scis., Soc. Petroleum Engrs. (Disting. lectr. 1994—), Sigma Xi. Avocations: hiking, museums. Home: 6423 Genstar Ln Dallas TX 75252-5403 Office: 1325 S Dairy Ashford Houston TX 77077

NETER, JOHN, statistician; b. Germany, Feb. 8, 1923; m. Dorothy Rachman, June 24, 1951; children: Ronald J., David L. B.S., U. Buffalo, 1943; M.B.A., U. Pa., 1947; Ph.D., Columbia U., 1952. Asst. prof. Syracuse (N.Y.) U., 1949-55, chmn. dept. bus. stats., 1952-55; prof. U. Minn., Mpls., 1955-75; chmn. dept. quantitative analysis U. Minn., 1961-65; C. Herman and Mary Virginia Terry prof. mgmt. sci., stats. U. Ga., Athens, 1975-89, prof. emeritus, 1990—; supervisory math. statistician U.S. Bur. Census, 1959-60; chmn. panel on quality control of fed. assistance programs Nat. Acad. Scis., 1986-87; cons. in field. Co-author: Statistical Sampling for Auditors and Accountants, 1956, Fundamental Statistics for Business and Economics, 4th edit., 1973, Applied Linear Statistical Models, 1974, 4th edit., 1996, Applied Statistics, 1978, 4th edit., 1993, Applied Linear Regression Models, 1983, 3d edit., 1996; editor: Am. Statistician, 1976-80; assoc. editor: Decision Scis., 1973-74; contbr. articles to profl. jours. Chmn. citizens adv. com., City of St. Louis Park, Minn., 1972, mem. planning commn., 1974-75. Served with AUS, 1943-45. Ford Found. faculty research fellow, 1957-58. Fellow Am. Statis. Assn. (council 1963-64, 67-70, dir. 1975-80, pres. 1985), AAAS (chmn., sec. on statistics 1991), Decision Scis. Inst. (pres. 1978-79); mem. AAUP (chpt. pres. 1969-70), Inst. Mgmt. Sci., Inst. Math. Stats., Internat. Statis. Inst. Home: 310 St George Dr Athens GA 30606-3910 Office: Terry Coll Bus Univ Ga Athens GA 30602-6255

NETHERCUT, PHILIP EDWIN, honorary consul; b. Indpls., Apr. 3, 1921; s. William Richard and Ruth Salome (Habbe) N.; m. Leah Teresa Diehl, Apr. 9, 1949; children: Bruce Philip, Gail Ellen, Anne Louise. B.S., Beloit Coll., 1942; M.S., Lawrence Coll., 1944, Ph.D., 1949. With Watervliet Paper Co., Mich., 1949-50; research mgr. Scott Paper Co., 1951-56; with TAPPI, N.Y.C., now Atlanta, 1957-86; sec.-treas. TAPPI, 1959-60, exec. sec., 1960-75, treas., 1964-75, exec. dir., 1975-82, vice. chmn. bd., 1983-86; hon. consul for Finland in Ga., 1976—; trustee Inst. Paper Chemistry, 1979-83, TAPPI Found., 1990—. Bd. dirs. Met. Atlanta Boys' and Girls' Club, 1979—. Served to lt. (j.g.) USNR, 1944-46. Recipient Distinguished Service citation Beloit Coll., 1967; Clarke award Ga. Soc. Assn. Execs., 1979; decorated Knight Finnish Order of White Rose, 1987. Fellow TAPPI; mem. Am. Soc. Assn. Execs. (CAE award 1968, Key award 1981), Inst. Paper Chemistry Alumni Assn. (chmn. 1960), Council Engring. and Sci. Soc. Execs. (pres. 1968), Finnish-Am. C. of C. S.E., Atlanta Consular Corps, Phi Beta Kappa, Beta Theta Pi. Club: Mountain View. Home: 9240 Huntcliff Trace NE Atlanta GA 30350-1603

NETHERCUTT, GEORGE RECTOR, JR., congressman, lawyer; b. Spokane, Wash., Oct. 4, 1944; s. George Rector and Nancy N.; m. Mary Beth Socha Nethercutt, Apr. 2, 1977; children: Meredith, Elliott. BA in English, Wash. State U., 1967; JD, Gonzaga U., 1971. Bar: 1972. Law clk. to Hon. Ralph Plummer U.S. Dist. Ct., Ala., Anchorage, 1971; staff counsel to U.S. Senator Ted Stevens Washington, 1972, chief of staff to U.S. Senator Ted Stevens, 1972-76; pvt. practice Spokane, Wash., 1977-94; mem. 104th Congress from 5th Wash. dist., Washington, 1994—. Chmn. Spokane County Rep. Party, 1990-94, co-founder Vanessa Behan Crisis Nursery, pres. Spokane Juvenile Diabetes Found., 1993-94. Mem. Masons (lodge #34), Lions Club (Spokane Ctrl.), Sigma Nu. Republican. Presbyterian. Avocations: running, handball, squash. Office: US House Reps 1527 Longworth House Office Bldg Washington DC 20515-4705

NETHERS, ELENA SOTO, lawyer; b. St. Louis, Mar. 20, 1963; d. Alberto Arturo and Maria (Vila) Soto; m. Mark Raymond Nethers; children: Patricia Elena, Alexander Mark. BA in Internat. Rels., Newcomb Coll., 1985; JD, Wash. U., St. Louis, 1989. Bar: Nebr. 1989. Counsel Mut. of Omaha Ins. Co., 1989-92, sr. counsel, 1992-95; asst. v.p., counsel, 1995—. Bd. dirs. YWCA, Omaha, 1993. Mem. Nebr. Bar Assn. (exec. com. corp. counsel 1993), Omaha Bar Assn. Office: Mutual of Omaha Ins Co Mutual of Omaha Plz Omaha NE 68175

NETHERY, JOHN JAY, government official; b. Mpls., June 4, 1941; s. Ronald Jay and Mary Vesta (McVeety) N.; m. Sonya Elisabeth Magin, July 27, 1968; children: William Jay, Mary Elisabeth (dec.), Sarah Ann. BA, U. Denver, 1963, MPA, 1968. Mgmt. intern USAF Logistics Command, San Antonio, 1969-71; budget analyst USAF Logistics Command, Dayton, Ohio, 1971-72; chief, fiscal analysis USAF Hdqrs., Washington, 1973-80, chief investment div., 1980-81, chief budget mgmt., 1981-85; dep. asst. sec. Dept. of USAF, Washington, 1986-88, asst. to undersecretary, 1988-89, dep. asst. sec., 1989—; mem. Air Force bd. for the correction of mil. records, Washington, 1980—. Recipient Gov.'s Scholastic award Gov. of Colo., 1968,

Presdl. Rank award, 1988. Mem. Sr. Execs. Assn., Air Force Assn. Presbyterian. Avocations: history, military minatures. Home: 12349 Coleraine Ct Reston VA 22091-1627 Office: Dept USAF SAF/FM The Pentagon Washington DC 20330-1130

NETRAVALI, ARUN N., communications executive; b. Bombay, May 26, 1946; m. Chitra Netravali; 2 children. BS in Tech. with honors, Indian Inst. Tech., Bombay, 1967; MS, Rice U., 1969, PhD, 1970; PhD (hon.), Ecole Polytechnique Federale, Lausanne, Switzerland, 1994. With NASA, Orlando, Fla., 1970-72; mem. tech. staff AT&T Bell Labs., Holmdel, N.J., 1972-78; head visual comm. rsch. dept. AT&T Bell Labs., Murray Hill, N.J., 1978-83, dir. computing systems rsch., 1983-92, exec. dir. rsch., comm. scis. divsn., 1992-94; v.p. AT&T Bell Labs., 1994—; adj. prof. media lab. MIT, Cambridge, Mass., 1984—; lectr. City Coll. N.Y., Columbia U., MIT, Rutgers U.; advisor Ctr. for Telecomm. Rsch. of Columbia U., 1987—; EPFL Swiss Fed. Inst. Tech., Lausanne, 1986—, Beckman Inst. of U. Ill. Co-author: Digital Pictures: Representation and Compression, 1987, Visual Communication Systems, 1989; contbr. 100 tech. papers to sci. jours.; patentee for 64 inventions. Recipient Journal award Soc. of Motion Pictures and TV Engrs., 1982, Ann. Asian Am. Corp. Employees award Orgn. Chinese Ams., 1991, Engr. of Yr. award Asian Am. Engrs. of India, 1992. Fellow IEEE (editor Communications 1984—, mem. editorial bd. Proceedsings of IEEE 1980-84, Fink prize 1980, L.G. Abraham prize 1985, 91, Alexander Graham Bell medal 1991, mem. digitals TV com.), AAAS; mem. NAE, Tau Beta Pi, Sigma Xi. Avocation: tennis. Home: 10 Byron Ct Westfield NJ 07090-2250 Office: AT&T Bell Labs Rsch Comm Sci Divsn 101 Crawfords Corner Rd Holmdel NJ 07733-1900

NETSCH, DAWN CLARK, state official, law educator; b. Cin., Sept. 16, 1926; BA with distinction, Northwestern U., 1948, JD magna cum laude, 1952; m. Walter A. Netsch. Bar: Ill, D.C. Law clk. U.S. Dist. Ct. Chgo.; adminstrv. and legal aide Ill. Gov. Otto Kerner, 1961-65; prof. law Northwestern U., 1965—; pvt. practice, Washington and Chgo.; mem. Ill. Senate; elected Ill. comptroller, 1990. Del. Ill. Constl. Conv. Author: (with Daniel Mandelker and Peter Salsich) State and Local Government in a Federal System; contbr. articles to legal jours. Mem. ABA, LWV, ACLU (bd. dirs. Ill. div. leadership coun.), Chgo. Bar Assn., Econ. Club. Office: Office of Comptr 201 State House Springfield IL 62706 also: Office of Comptr 100 W Randolph St # 500 Chicago IL 60601-3218

NETTELS, ELSA, English language educator; b. Madison, Wis., May 25, 1931; d. Curtis Putnam and Elsie (Patterson) N. BA, Cornell U., 1953; MA, U. Wis., 1955, PhD, 1960. From instr. to asst. prof. English Mt. Holyoke Coll., South Hadley, Mass., 1959-67; asst. prof. to prof. English Coll. William and Mary, Williamsburg, Va., 1967—. Author: James and Conrad, 1977 (South Atlantic Modern Lang. Assn. award 1975), Language, Race and Social Class in Howells' America, 1988; contbr. articles to profl. jours. NEH fellow, 1984-85. Mem. Modern Lang. Assn., South Atlantic Modern Lang. Assn. (edit. bd. 1977-83), Henry James Soc. (edit. bd. 1983—), Am. Studies Assn. Home: 211 Indian Springs Rd Williamsburg VA 23185-3940 Office: Coll William and Mary Dept English Williamsburg VA 23185

NETTELS, GEORGE EDWARD, JR., mining executive; b. Pittsburg, Kans., Oct. 20, 1927; s. George Edward and Mathilde A. (Wulke) N.; m. Mary Joanne Myers, July 19, 1952; children: Christopher Bryan, Margaret Anne, Katherine Anne, Rebecca Jane. B.S. in Civil Engring, U. Kans., Lawrence, 1950. With Black & Veatch Engrs., Kansas City, Mo., 1950-51, Spencer Chem. Co., Kansas City, Mo., 1951-55, Freeto Constrn. Co., Pittsburg, 1955-57; pres. Midwest Minerals, Inc., Pittsburg, 1957—; chmn. bd. McNally Pittsburg Mfg. Corp., 1970-76, pres., chief exec. officer, 1976-87; ret. McNally Pitts. Inc., 1987; bd. dirs. Bank IV, Pitts., Kansas City Power & Light Co.; past chmn. bd. Nat. Limestone Inst.; bd. dirs. Pitts. Indsl. Devel. Com. Bd. advisers Kans. U. Endowment Assn.; mem. Kans. U. Chancellor's Club, Kans., Inc.; past pres. Bd. Edn. 250, Pittsburg; past chmn. bd. trustees Mt. Carmel Hosp.; past mem. Kans. Common. Civil Rights; chmn. Kans. Republican Com., 1966-68; Kans. del. Rep. Nat. Conv., 1968, Kans. Bus. and Industry Com. for Re-election of the President, 1972. Served with AUS, 1946-47. Recipient Disting. Service citation U. Kans., 1980, Disting. Engring. citation U. Kans., 1985; named Kansan of Yr., 1986. Mem. ASCE, NAM (past. dir.), Kans. C. of C. and Industry (dir., chmn. 1983-84), Kans. Right to Work (dir.), Pittsburg C. of C. (past dir.), Kans. U. Alumni Assn. (pres. 1977), Kans. Leadership Com., Tau Beta Pi, Omicron Delta Kappa, Beta Theta Pi. Presbyterian. Clubs: Crestwood Country (Pittsburg); Wolf Creek Golf (Olathe). Office: Midwest Minerals Inc 509 W Quincy St Pittsburg KS 66762-5531

NETTER, IRENE M., secondary education educator; b. N.Y.C., Oct. 29, 1926; m. Emile Netter Sr., 1951; children: Michael Eliot, Emile Jr.; m. Lance Allan Dohe, 1994. BS summa cum laude, NYU, 1948, MA, 1949; postgrad., Rutgers U., San Diego State U., Sarah Lawrence Coll. Cert. elem. tchr. (life), profl. growth adv., Calif. Bd. dirs., writer Copley Press, San Diego; pres. bd. Christian edn., supt. Sunday sch. and Vacation Bible sch. Holy Cross Luth. Ch., San Diego; mentor speech, drama tchr., coach, sponsor San Diego (Calif.) Unified Sch. Dist. Prodr., dir., writer, actress Messiah's Messengers, King's Players, San Diego. Named Tchr. of Yr., San Diego, 1986, Vol. of Yr., San Diego, 1992; recipient EXCEL award for excellence in teaching. Mem. ASCD, Nat. Coun. Tchrs. English, Newspaper in Edn., Optimist Internat. (chmn. optimist oratorical and essay contest), Kappa Delta Pi. Home: 4606 La Cuenta Dr San Diego CA 92124-3011

NETTER, KURT FRED, building products company executive; b. Mannheim, Fed. Republic Germany, Dec. 3, 1919; came to U.S., 1941, naturalized, 1944; s. Arthur and Kate (Gruenfeld) N.; m. Alice Dreyfus, May 26, 1942; children: Nadine, Ronald, Alfred. Student, Swiss Inst. Tech., 1938-39, U. Toronto, 1939-41; BS, Columbia U., 1942. Ptnr. Interstate Engring. and Machinery Co., N.Y.C., 1942-44; officer, dir. Supradur Cos., Inc., 1946—, pres., CEO, 1953-93; chmn., 1986—; also bd. dirs. Supradur Cos., Inc., 1946—; bd. dirs., chmn. subs. Supradur Mfg. Corp., Wind Gap, Pa., Precision Fabricators, Inc., Garden City Park, N.Y., Triton Co., Inc., Rye, Supradur Investments Inc., Montreal, Que., Can. Bd. dirs Selfhelp Community Svcs., Inc., treas., 1970-85, pres., 1985-90, chmn., 1990—. With AUS, 1944-46. Home: 203 Griffen Ave Scarsdale NY 10583-7905 Office: Supradur Cos Inc 411 Theodore Fremd Ave Rye NY 10580-0908

NETTL, BRUNO, anthropology and musicology educator; b. Prague, Czechoslovakia, Mar. 14, 1930; s. Paul and Gertrud (Hutter) N.; m. Wanda Maria White, Sept. 15, 1952; children: Rebecca, Gloria. A.B., Ind. U., 1950, Ph.D., 1953; M.A. in L.S., U. Mich., 1960; LHD (hon.), U. Chgo., 1993. Mem. faculty Wayne State U., Detroit, 1953-64; asst. prof. Wayne State U., 1954-64, music librarian, 1958-64; mem. faculty U. Ill., Urbana, 1964—; prof. music and anthropology U. Ill., 1967—, chmn. div. musicology 1967-72, 75-77, 82-85; vis. lectr., Fulbright grantee U. Kiel, Fed. Republic of Germany, 1956-58; cons. Ency. Britannica, 1969—, also on ethomusicology to various univs.; vis. prof. Williams Coll., 1971, Wash. U., 1978, U. Louisville, 1983, U. Wash., 1985, 88, 89, 93, Fla. State U., 1988, Harvard U., 1989, U. Alta, 1991, Colo. Coll., 1992, Northwestern U., 1993, U. Minn., 1994. Author: Theory and Method in Ethnomusicology, 1964, Music in Primitive Culture, 1956, Folk and Traditional Music of the Western Continents, 1965, 2d edit., 1973, Eight Urban Musical Cultures, 1978, The Study of Ethnomusicology, 1983, The Western Impact on World Music, 1985, The Radif of Persian Music, 1987, rev. edit., 1992, Blackfoot Musical Thought, 1989, Comparative Musicology and Anthropology of Music, 1991, Heartland Excursions, 1995; co-author Excursions in World Music, 1992; editor Ethnomusicology, 1961-65, Yearbook of the International Folk Music Council, 1975-77; contbr. articles to profl. jours. Recipient Koizumi prize in ethnomusicology, Tokyo, 1994. Mem. Soc. Ethnomusicology (pres. 1969-71), Am., Internat. musicol. socs., Internat. Coun. for Traditional Music. Home: 1423 Cambridge Dr Champaign IL 61821-4958 Office: Sch Music U Ill Urbana IL 61801

NETTLE, ROBERT DALE, state legislator, former insurance and real estate broker; b. Barberton, Ohio, Jan. 19, 1924; s. Lewis H. and Katie (Biskopski) N.; m. Dorothy M. Hansel, Feb. 25, 1944; children: Karen Nettle Butler, Deborah Nettle Crawford, Renee Nettle Ramunni, Claudia Nettle Ward, Jennifer Nettle Samples. Student, U. Akron, 1945-46. Safety dir.

Barberton, Ohio, 1966; 6th ward councilman Barberton, 1967-73; pres. Barberton City Coun., 1973-77; state rep. 41st dist., Barberton, 1977-86; senator 28th dist., Barberton, 1986-92, Akron, 1992-94; elected asst. minority whip, 1990, 93, elected minority whip, 1990, 93, 95. Bd. dirs. Portage Path Mental Health Orgn. Cpl. A.C., U.S. Army, 1943-45. Mem. VFW, Kiwanis (pres. Barberton club 1971-72), Shriners. Avocations: camping, golf, fishing, photography. Office: State Senate Bldg State Capital Columbus OH 43215

NETTLES, JOHN BARNWELL, obstetrics and gynecology educator; b. Dover, N.C., May 19, 1922; s. Stephen A. and Estelle (Hendrix) N.; m. Eunice Anita Saugstad, Apr. 28, 1956; children: Eric, Robert, John Barnwell; m. 2d, Sandra Williams, Sept. 14, 1991; stepchildren: Steven Williams, Clayton Williams. B.S., U. S.C., 1941; M.D., Med. Coll. S.C., 1944. Diplomate: Am. Bd. Obstetrics and Gynecology. Intern Garfield Meml. Hosp., Washington, 1944-45; research fellow in pathology Med. Coll. Ga., Augusta, 1946-47; resident in ob-gyn. U. Ill. Rsch. and Ednl. Hosps., Chgo., 1947-51; instr. to asst. prof. ob-gyn. U. Ill. Coll. Medicine, Chgo., 1951-57; asst. prof., assoc. prof., prof. ob-gyn. U. Ark. Med. Ctr., Little Rock, 1957-69; dir. grad. edn. Hillcrest Med. Ctr., Tulsa, 1969-75; prof. ob-gyn Coll. Medicine, U. Okla., Oklahoma City, 1969—; chmn. dept. ob-gyn. U. Okla.-Tulsa Med. Coll., 1975-80, prof. 1980—, mem. coun. on residency edn. in ob-gyn., 1974-79; dir. Tulsa Obstet. and Gynecol. Edn. Found., 1969-80; Coordinator med. edn. Nat. Def., Ark., 1961-69; mem. S.W. regional med. adv. com. Planned Parenthood Fedn. Am., 1974-78; mem. adv. com. Health Policy Agenda Am. People, 1982—, rev. com. Accreditation Council for Continuing Med. Edn., 1987-92. Contbr. articles on uterine malignancy, kidney biopsy in pregnancy, perinatal morbidity and mortality, human sexuality sch. age pregnancy to profl. jours. Served as lt. (j.g.) M.C. USNR, 1945-46; as lt. 1953-54. Fellow Am. Coll. Obstetricians and Gynecologists (dist. sec.-treas. 1964-70, dist. chmn. exec. bd. 1970-73, v.p. 1977-78), A.C.S. (bd. govs. 1969-71, program com. 1970-71, Surg. forum 1977-84, adv. com. gyn/ob 1985—), Royal Soc. Health, Royal Soc. Medicine; mem. Ark. Obstet. and Gynecol. Soc. (exec. sec. 1959-69), Central Assn. Obstetrics and Gynecology (exec. com. 1966-69, pres. 1978-79), Internat. Soc. Advancement Humanistic Studies in Gynecology, Assn. Mil. Surgeons U.S., AMA (sect. council on obstetrics and gynecology 1975—, chmn. 1982—, del. from Am. Coll. Obstetricians and Gynecologists 1987—, Young at Heart award Young Physicians sect. 1994), Nurses Assn. Am. Coll. Obstetricians and Gynecologists (exec. bd. 1970-73, assoc. 1980—), So. Med. Assn. (chmn. obstetrics 1973-74), Okla. Med. Soc., Tulsa County Med. Soc., Chgo. Med. Soc., Am. Assn. for Maternal and Infant Health, Assn. Am. Med. Colls., Am. Public Health Assn., Am. Assn. Sex Edn. Counselors and Therapists (S.W. regional bd. 1976-79), Soc. for Gynecol. Investigation, AAAS, Am. Soc. for Study Fertility and Sterility, Internat. Soc. Gen. Semantics, Aerospace Med. Assn., So. Gynecol. and Obstet. Soc. (pres. 1981-82), Am. Cancer Soc. (pres. Okla. div. 1979-83, St. George's medal 1991), Com. on In-Tng. Exam. in Obstetrics and Gynecology, Am. Coll. Nurse Midwives (governing bd. examiners 1979-83), Sigma Xi (pres. Tulsa chpt. 1992-93), Phi Rho Sigma. Lutheran. Office: U Okla Tulsa Med Coll 2808 S Sheridan Rd Tulsa OK 74129 To live life fully, with faith and trust in God and his people, working with others to make our world a little better, and willing to fill the gaps wherever they are.

NETTLESHIP, PATRICIA SHARYN, investment group executive; b. Calif.; A.A., Stephens Coll.; A.B., U. Mo.; A.M.P., Harvard U.; children—Stephen, Lisa, Gunnar. Co-founder, sec.-treas. North Pacific Constrn. Co., Yakima, Wash., 1969-72, chmn., pres., chief exec. officer, 1973—; chmn. bd. North Pacific Investment Group; chief exec. officer NPCC CM; dir. Western Bank Commerce, SAPLASA, Sacramento de la plata; chmn. Competitive Enterprise Found. Mem. tax policy subcom. Econ. Council, Republican Nat. Com.; bd. regents Loyola Marymount U.; nat. bd. dirs. Jr. Achievement; chmn. Competitive Enterprise Found.; nat. vice chmn. Bus. for Reagan-Bush; mem. Pres.' Adv. Com. on Women's Bus. Ownership. Mem. Young Pres. Orgn. (rep. to various fgn. countries, chmn. Washington Nat. Conf. 1979, chmn. econ. edn. workshop), Constrn. Mgmt. Assn. Am. (bd. dirs., chmn. 1984 ann. conf.) Episcopalian. Clubs: Seattle Yacht, Harvard Bus. Sch., Wash. Athletic. Office: The Nettleship Group 2665 Main St Ste 220 Santa Monica CA 90405-4000

NETTLETON, DAVID, religious administrator. Chmn. Gen. Assn. Regular Bapt. Chs., Schaumburg, Ill., 1988—. Office: Gen Assn Regular Bapt Chs 1300 N Meacham Rd Schaumburg IL 60173-4806

NETUSIL, NOELWAH ROSE, economics educator; b. Port Jefferson, N.Y., Nov. 10, 1964; d. Louis and Noelwah (Hottenstein) N. BS, Allegheny Coll., 1986; MS, U. Ill., 1988, PhD, 1992. Asst. prof. econs. Reed Coll., Portland, Oreg., 1990—. Sloan Found. grantee, 1992. Mem. Am. Econ. Assn., We. Econ. Assn., Assn. Environ. and Resource Economists. Avocation: hiking. Office: Reed Coll Dept Econs 3203 SE Woodstock Blvd Portland OR 97202-8199

NETZEL, PAUL ARTHUR, fund raising management executive, consultant; b. Tacoma, Sept. 11, 1941; s. Marden Arthur and Audrey Rose (Jones) N.; BS in Group Work Edn., George Williams Coll., 1963; m. Diane Viscount, Mar. 21, 1963; children: Paul M., Shari Ann. Program dir. S. Pasadena-San Marino (Calif.) YMCA, 1963-66; exec. dir. camp and youth programs Wenatchee (Wash.) YMCA, 1966-67; exec. dir. Culver-Palms Family YMCA, Culver City, Calif., 1967-73; v.p. met. fin. devel. YMCA Met. Los Angeles, 1973-78, exec. v.p. devel., 1979-85; pres. bd. dirs. YMCA Employees Credit Union, 1977-80; chmn. N.Am. Fellowship of YMCA Devel. Officers, 1980-83; adj. faculty U. So. Calif. Coll. Continuing Edn. 1983-86, Loyola Marymount U., L.A., 1986-90, Calif. State U. L.A., 1991—; pvt. practice cons., fund raiser. Chmn. Culver-Palms YMCA, Culver City, 1991-93, chmn. 1989-91, bd. mgrs. 1985—; pres. bd. Culver City Guidance Clinic, 1971-74; mem. Culver City Bd. Edn., 1975-79, pres. 1977-78; mem. Culver City Edn. Found., 1982-91; bd. dirs. Los Angeles Psychiat. Svc., 1971-74, Goodwill Industries of So. Calif., 1993—; mem. Culver City Council, 1980-88, vice-mayor, 1980-82, 84-85, mayor, 1982-83, 86-87; mem. Culver City Redevel. Agcy., 1980-88, chmn., 1983-84, 87-88, vice chmn. 1985-86; bd. dirs. Los Angeles County Sanitation Dists., 1982-83, 85-87, Western Region United Way, 1986-93, vice chmn, 1991-92; chmn. bd. dirs. Calif. Youth Model Legislature, 1987-92; mem. World Affairs Coun., 1989—. Recipient Man of Yr. award Culver City C. of C., 1972. Mem. Nat. Soc. Fund Raising Execs. (nat. bd. dirs. 1989-91, vice chmn. 1994, v.p. bd. dirs. Greater L.A. chpt. 1986-88, pres. bd. dirs. 1989-90, Profl. of Yr. 1983), Calif. Club, Rotary (L.A. # 5, pres. 1992-93), Mountain Gate Country. Address: Netzel Assocs Inc 9696 Culver Blvd Ste 204 Culver City CA 90232-2753

NETZER, DICK, economics educator; b. N.Y.C., May 14, 1928; s. Solomon and Sue (Dick) N.; m. Carol Risika, Dec. 30, 1945; children: Jenny, Katherine. B.A., U. Wis., 1946; M.A., M.P.A., Harvard U., 1948, Ph.D., 1952. Successively economist, sr. economist, asst. v.p. Fed. Res. Bank Chgo., 1948-60; econ. cons. Regional Plan Assn., N.Y.C., 1960-80; assoc. prof. N.Y. U., 1961-64, prof. econs., 1964—, dean Grad. Sch. Pub. Adminstrn., 1969-82, dir. Urban Research Center, 1981-86; cons. in field, 1960—. Author: Economics of the Property Tax, 1966, The Economics of Public Finance, 1974, The Subsidized Muse, 1978, Urban Politics New York Style, 1990; editor: N.Y. Affairs, 1973-88. Mem. Mayor N.Y.C. Fiscal Adv. com., 1969-73; treas. Colony-South Bklyn. Houses, 1968-73; mem. Mcpl. Securities Rulemaking Bd., 1978-81, vice chmn., 1980-81; bd. dirs. Mcpl. Assistance Corp., N.Y.C., 1975—, Citizens Union Found., 1981—; bd. dirs., treas. Adolph and Esther Gottlieb Found., 1975—, v.p. 1979-88, pres. 1989—. Mem. Am. Econs. Assn., Regional Sci. Assn., Nat. Tax Assn., Am. Inst. Cert. Planners, Assn. Cultural Econs. Internat. (pres. 1993-94). Home: 25 Clinton St Brooklyn NY 11201-6144 Office: 4 Washington Sq N New York NY 10003-6671

NETZER, LANORE A(GNES), retired educational administration educator; b. Laona, Wis., Apr. 27, 1916; d. Henry N. and Adam M. (Niquette) Netzer; m. Glen G. Eye, 1979. Diploma, Oconto County Normal Sch., 1935; BS, State Tchrs. Coll., Oshkosh, Wis., 1943; MS, U. Wis., 1948, PhD, 1951. Tchr. Goldhorn Rural Sch., Pound, Wis., 1935-36; tchr. Goldfield Sch., Pound, 1936-37, tchr., acting prin., 1937-39; prin. Spruce (Wis.) Grade Sch., 1939-41; tchr. pub. schs. Neenah, Wis., 1943-46; demonstration and critic tchr. Campus Sch. State Tchrs. Coll., Oshkosh, 1946-48; supr. student

tchrs.' coll. instrn. State Tchrs. Coll., Milw., 1950-55; teaching asst. U. Wis. Madison, 1948-50; assoc. prof. edn. U. Wis., Milw., 1955-63; prof. ednl. adminstrn. U. Wis., Madison, 1963-77, emeritus prof., 1977—; rsch. assoc. U.S. Office Edn., 1963-66; supr. student tchrs. coll. instrn. State Tchrs. Coll., Milw., 1950-55; mem. curriculum adminstrn. com. Wis. Coop. Curriculum Planning Program, 1945-52; mem. Wis. Joint Com. on Edn., 1957-59, E.B. Fred Fellowship U. Wis., 1966—; ednl. cons. Educators Progress Svc., 1970—. Author: The Use of Industry Aids in Schools, 1952, (with Glen G. Eye) Supervision of Instruction: A Phase of Administration, 1965, 2d. edit., 1971, (with others) Interdisciplinary Foundations of Supervision, 1969, (with G. Eye) School Administrators and Instruction, 1969, (with others) Education Administration and Change, 1970, (with others) Supervision of Instruction, 1971, Strategies for Instructional Management, 1977; contbr. articles to profl. jours. Rsch. grantee Hill & Knowlton, Inc., N.Y.C., 1969; grantee Wis. Mfrs. Assn., 1954; recipient award of Distinction Nat. Coun. of Adminstrv. Women in Edn., 1975. Mem. AAUP, Wis. Edn. Assn. (life), So. Wis. Edn. Assn., Nat. Assn. Supervision and Curriculum Devel., Wis. Assn. Supervision and Curriculum Devel., Southwestern Assn. Supervision and Curriculum Devel., Wis. Elem. Sch. Prins. Assn., Am. Assn. Sch. Adminstrs., Wis. Assn. Sch. Dist. Adminstrs., Am. Edn. Rsch. Assn., Wis. Edn. Rsch. Assn., Univ. Coun. Ednl. Adminstrn., U. Wis. Alumni Assn. (life), U. Wis. Meml. Union (life), Phi Beta Sigma, Kappa Delta Pi, Pi Lambda Theta, Phi Delta Kappa. Home: 110 S Henry St Apt 1506 Madison WI 53703-3168 Office: U Wis Dept Ednl Adminstrn 1025 W Johnson St Madison WI 53706-1706 My life achieves meaning as I help people to appreciate, reinforce, and serve each other. Kindness may be a goal, a process of living, or a product of effort, but to me it is the main road to self-realization.

NETZLOFF, MICHAEL LAWRENCE, pediatric educator, endocrinologist; b. Madison, Wis., Sept. 11, 1942; s. Harold Harvey Netzloff and Garnet Lucille (Wilson) MacFarlane; m. Cheryl Lynne Crandall, July 20, 1963; children: Michelle Lynne, Rochelle Anne, Cherie Lucille. BS with high honors, Eckert Coll., 1964; MS, U. Fla., 1968, MD, 1969. Diplomate Am. Bd. Pediatrics, Diplomate Am. Bd. Pediatric Endocrinology. Rsch. fellow, rsch. trainee dept. of anat. scis. U. Fla. Coll. Medicine, Gainesville, 1965-69, intern and resident in pediatrics, 1969-71, clin. and rsch. fellow div. genetics, endocrinology and metabolism, dept. pediatrics, 1971-73, instr. in pediatrics, 1973-74, asst. prof. of pediatrics, 1974-79; assoc. prof. of pediatrics and human devel. Mich. State U. Coll. of Human Medicine, East Lansing, 1979-85, dir. of pediatric endocrinology, pediatrics and human devel., 1981-89, dir. div. of human genetics, genetic toxicology, endocrinology and oncology, pediatrics and human devel., 1982-89, prof. dept. pediatrics and human devel., 1985—, chmn. dept., 1987-91; vis. prof. dept. pediatrics U. Mich., 1992-93; cons. Juvenile Diabetes Found., Lansing, 1981—; mem. diabetes adv. coun. Mich. State Dept. Pub. Health and Chronic Disease Control, Lansing, 1980-90. Recipient Carithers award for Child Health and Human Dev., U. Fla. Coll. Medicine, 1969, Edward Bogen fellowship U. Fla. Coll. Med., 1972, Basil O'Connor rsch. grant Nat. Found. March of Dimes, 1973, pediatric residency teaching award, Grad. Med. Edn., Inc., Mich. State U. Affiliated Residency program, 1982, 86. Fellow Am. Acad. Pediatrics; mem. Assn. Clin. Scis. Inst. (sci. com 1979—), Am. Diabetes Assn. (coun. on diabetes in youth 1979—), Am. Pediatric Soc., Lawson-Wilkins Pediatric Endocrine Soc., Mich State Med. Soc., Ingham County Med. Soc., Soc. for Pediatric Rsch., Sigma Xi. Democrat. Lutheran. Home: 4432 Greenwood Dr Okemos MI 48864-3044 Office: Mich State U Dept Pediatrics B240 Life Scis East Lansing MI 48824-1317

NEU, CARL HERBERT, JR., management consultant; b. Miami Beach, Fla., Sept. 4, 1937; s. Carl Herbert and Catherine Mary (Miller) N.; BS, MIT, 1959; MBA, Harvard U., 1961; m. Carmen Mercedes Smith, Feb. 8, 1964; children—Carl Bartley, David Conrad. Cert. profl. mgmt. cons. Indsl. liaison officer MIT, Cambridge, 1967-69; coord. forward planning Gates Rubber Co., Denver, 1969-71; pres., co-founder Dyna-Com Resources, Lakewood, Colo., 1971-77; pres., founder Neu & Co., Lakewood, 1977—; mng. dir. Pro-Med Mgmt. Systems, Lakewood, 1981—; lectr. Grad. Sch. Pub. Affairs, U. Colo. Denver, 1982-84. Mem. exec. coun. Episcopal Diocese Colo., 1974; mem. Lakewood City Coun., 1975-80, pres., 1976; chmn. Lakewood City Charter Commn., 1982, Lakewood Civic Found., Inc., 1986—; pres. Lakewood on Parade, 1978, bd. dirs., 1978-80; pres. Classic Chorale, Denver, 1979, bd. dirs., 1978-83; pres. Lakewood Pub. Bldg. Authority, 1983—; bd. dirs. Metro State Coll. of Denver Found., 1990—, treas., 1994—; bd. dirs. Kaiser Permanente Health Adv. Com., 1990—. With U.S. Army, 1961-67. Decorated Bronze Star medal, Army Commendation medal; recipient Arthur Page award AT&T, 1979; Kettering Found. grantee, 1979-80. Mem. World Future Soc., Internat. City Mgrs. Assn., Lakewood-So. Jefferson County C. of C. (bd. dirs. 1983-89, chmn. 1988, chmn. 1987-88), Jefferson County C. of C. (chmn. 1988). Republican. Episcopalian. Contbr. articles to profl. jours. Home: 8169 W Baker Ave Denver CO 80227-3129

NEU, CHARLES ERIC, historian, educator; b. Carroll, Iowa, Apr. 10, 1936; s. Arthur Nicholas and Martha Margaret (Frandsen) N.; m. Deborah Dunning, Sept. 2, 1961 (div. 1978); children: Hilary Adams, Douglas Bancroft.; m. Susan Jennifer Kane, May 14, 1983 (div. 1991). B.A., Northwestern U., 1958; Ph.D., Harvard U., 1964. Instr. history Rice U., 1963-64, asst. prof., 1964-67, asso. prof., 1968-70; asso. prof. history Brown U., Providence, 1970-76; prof. Brown U., 1976—; fellow Charles Warren Center for Studies in Am. History, 1971-72; dir. summer seminar NEH, 1979, 86-87, 89, 92. Author: An Uncertain Friendship: Theodore Roosevelt and Japan, 1906-1909, 1967, The Troubled Encounter: The United States and Japan, 1975; co-editor: The Wilson Era: Essays in Honor of Arthur S. Link, 1991. Woodrow Wilson fellow, 1958-59; NEH younger scholar, 1968-69; Am. Council Learned Socs. fellow, 1975-76; Howard Found. fellow, 1976-77; Guggenheim fellow, 1981-82; guest scholar Woodrow Wilson Ctr., summer 1988. Mem. Am. Hist. Assn., Orgn. Am. Historians, Soc. Historians of Am. Fgn. Policy, Phi Beta Kappa. Democrat. Club: Agawam Hunt (Providence). Home: 346 Rochambeau Ave Providence RI 02906-3516 Office: Brown U Dept History Providence RI 02912

NEU, HAROLD CONRAD, physician, educator; b. Omaha, Aug. 19, 1934; s. Harold N. and Othilla M. (Miller) N.; m. Carmen Irene Ortiz, Nov. 24, 1962; children—Maria, Natalie, Harold. A.B., Creighton U., 1956; M.D., Johns Hopkins U., 1960. Intern, resident Presbyn. Hosp., N.Y.C., 1960-62; rsch. assoc. NIH, Bethesda, Md., 1962-64; asst. prof. medicine and pharmacology Columbia U., N.Y.C., 1965-70; asso. prof. Columbia U., 1970-74, prof., 1974—; chief infectious diseases Columbia-Presbyn. Med. Center, 1971—. Author: 21 books in field; contbr. 943 articles to med. jours.; editor Antibiotics Newsletter; assoc. editor J. Clin. Pharm., Infection, Diagnostic Microbiology and Infectious Diseases, Infectious Diseases in Chem. Practice; mem. editorial bd. 18 jours. Served with USPHS, 1962-64. N.Y. Health Research Council grantee, 1965-71. Fellow ACP (master); mem. Am. Soc. Clin. Investigation, Infectious Diseases Soc. Am., Am. Soc. Microbiology, Am. Soc. Biologic Chemists, Am. Soc. Clin. Pharmacology (Outstanding Rsch. award 1990), Am. Coll. Clin. Pharmacology (regent, Hoechst Roussel Outstanding Rsch. Antimicrobial Chemotherapy award 1983), N.Y. Acad. Scis. (Rhone-Poulenc-Rorer award for Quinolone rsch. 1990). Roman Catholic. Home: 51 Burnside Dr Hastings On Hudson NY 10706-3002 Office: Presbyn Hosp Columbia-Presbyn Med Ctr New York NY 10032 Out of chaos I have sought to bring an orderly approach to an understanding of how microorganisms continue to overcome developments to hold them in check. Diligent work, being in the right place at the right time, has made it possible for me to contribute to society and achieve success.

NEUBAUER, CHARLES FREDERICK, investigative reporter; b. Berkeley, Ill., Feb. 13, 1950; s. Fred Charles and Dolores Jeanne (Pries) N.; m. Sandra Carol Bergo, Oct. 4, 1975; 1 child, Michael Frederick. B.S.J., Northwestern U., 1972, M.S.J., 1973. Investigator Better Govt. Assn., Chgo., 1971-73; investigative reporter Chgo. Today, 1973, Chgo. Tribune, 1974-83, Chgo. Sun Times, 1983—. Recipient Pulitzer prize local reporting, 1976; Edward Scott Beck award for domestic reporting Chgo. Tribune, 1980. Office: 401 N Wabash Ave Chicago IL 60611-3532

NEUBAUER, JOSEPH, food services company executive; b. Oct. 19, 1941; s. Max and Herta (Kahn) N.; children: Lawrence, Melissa. B.S. in Chem. Engring, Tufts U., 1963; M.B.A. in Fin, U. Chgo., 1965. Asst. treas. Chase

Manhattan Bank, 1965-68, asst. v.p., 1968-70, v.p., 1970-71; asst. treas. Pepsico Inc., Purchase, N.Y., 1971-72; treas. Pepsico Inc., 1972-73, v.p., 1973-76; v.p. fin. and control Wilson Sporting Goods Co., River Grove, Ill., 1976-77, sr. v.p., gen. mgr. team sports div., 1977-79; exec. v.p. fin. and devel., chief fin. officer, dir. ARA Svcs., Inc., Phila., 1979-81; pres., chief operating officer, dir. ARA Services, Inc., Phila., 1981-83, pres., chief exec. officer, 1983-84; chmn., CEO ARA Svcs., Inc., Phila., 1984—; bd. dirs. 1st Fidelity Bancorp, Bell Atlantic, Federated Dept. Stores; trustee Penn Mut. Life Ins. Co. Chmn., CEO Phila. Orch. Assn., Mann Music Ctr., Inroads/Phila., Inc.; trustee Hahnemann U., Tufts U., Mus. Am. Jewish History, Greater Phila. First Corp., Com. for Econ. Devel., U. Chgo.; bd. govs. Joseph H. Lauder Inst. Mgmt. and Internat. Studies, U. Pa. Mem. Phila. C of C., Union League Club, Locust Club, Phila. Club, Bus. Coun., Bus. Roundtable. Office: ARAMARK Corp ARAMARK Tower 1101 Market St Philadelphia PA 19107-2934

NEUBAUER, PETER BELA, psychoanalyst; b. Krems, Austria, July 5, 1913; came to U.S., 1941, naturalized, 1946; s. Samuel and Rose (Blau) N.; m. Susan Rachlin, Nov. 25, 1953 (dec.); children—Joshua Rachlin, Alexander Lewis. M.D., U. Berne, 1938. Intern Lawrence Meml. Hosp., New London, Conn., 1941, Beth-El Hosp., Bklyn., 1942; resident in psychiatry Bellevue Hosp., N.Y.C., 1943-45; dir. Child Devel. Ctr., Jewish Bd. Family and Children's Services, N.Y.C., 1951-83; clin. prof. psychiatry Psychoanalytic Inst., N.Y. U., 1979—; lectr. child psychoanalysis Psychoanalytic Inst. for Tng. and Research Columbia U., 1973. Author: Children in Collectives: Child Rearing Aims and Practices in Kibbutzim, 1965, Early Child Day Care, 1974, Process of Child Development, 1976, (with Alexander Neubauer) Nature's Thumbprint, 1990; contbg. author: Fathers and Their Families, 1989; mem. editorial bd. Psychoanalytic Study of the Child, 1978. Recipient Hulse award N.Y. Council Child Psychiatry, 1975, Heinz Hartmann award N.Y. Psychoanalytic Soc., 1981, Mary S. Sigourney award, 1994. Mem. Am. Psychoanalytic Assn., Am. Acad. Child Psychiatry, Assn. Child Psychoanalysis, Internat. Assn. Child and Adolescent Psychiatry, Assn. for Child Psychoanalysis (pres. 1974-76). Office: 33 E 70th St New York NY 10021-4946

NEUBAUER, RICHARD A., library science educator, consultant; b. Meadville, Pa., Oct. 9, 1933; s. Carl Gustave and Velma Winston (Watson) N.; m. Janice Ernest; children: David, Lynda, Karl, Jennifer; m. Carol Barton. BS, Clarion U., 1955; MLS, SUNY, Geneseo, 1966; attended, Kent St. U., 1966-68, Simmons Coll., 1970-72. Cert. profl. libr., sch. libr., tchr. Tchr. geography Franklin (Pa.) Sch. Dept., 1957-58, N. Bedford City Schs., Woodbury, Mass., 1958-60; tchr. history Hornell (N.Y.) Jr. High Sch., 1960-62, sch. libr., 1962-65; prof. libr. sci. Edinboro (Pa.) U., 1965-68, assoc. libr. Hamilton Librr., 1965-68; dir. sch. librs. Duxbury (Mass.) Sch. Dept., 1968-69; dir., cons. Pub. Libr., Lincoln, Mass., 1969-70; prof. libr. sci. Bridgewater (Mass.) State Coll., 1969-78, chair dept. libr. sci., 1978-80, prof. libr. sci., 1980-91, coord. libr. media program, 1991—; adj. prof. libr. sci. U. R.I., Kingston, 1975-88; cons. Tabor Acad., Marion, Mass., 1970-71, Abington (Mass.) Pub. Libr. Trustees, 1973-76, Duxbury Free Libr., 1968-72. Author: Planning the Elementary School Library, 1968; author, editor Exploring the U.S.-Northeast, 1994. Chmn. Mass. Dept. Edn. Cert., Quincy, 1989-90; resource cons. Project Contemporary Competitiveness, Bridgewater, Mass., 1973-83. 1st lt. USMC, 1955-57. Inst. grantee HEA of 1965 Edinboro U., 1968. Mem. NEA, Am. Libr. Assn., Intellectual Freedom Found., Mass. Assn. of Edn. Media, Mass. Sch. Libr. Media Assn., Mass. Tchrs. Assn. Democrat. Avocations: gardening, woodworking, reading. Office: Bridgewater St College Maxwell Libr Bldg 211 Bridgewater MA 02325

NEUBERGER, EGON, economics educator; b. Zagreb, Croatia, Yugoslavia, Feb. 27, 1925; came to U.S., 1940; s. Paul and Ann (Freund) N.; m. Florence Perlmutter, Dec. 22, 1949; children: Leah Ruth, Marc Joseph. BA, Cornell U., 1947; MA, Harvard U., 1949, PhD, 1958. Econ. analyst State Dept., Washington, 1949-54; asst. prof. econ. Amherst (Mass.) Coll., 1957-60; economist RAND Corp., Santa Monica, Calif., 1960-67; prof. econ. SUNY, Stony Brook, 1967-81, leading prof. econs., 1982—, dean social and behavioral scis., 1982-88; vice provost for undergraduate studies SUNY, 1989-90; econ. officer Am. Embassy, Moscow, 1952-53; vis. prof. U. Mich., Ann Arbor, 1965-66, U. Konstanz, Germany, 1995. Served with U.S. Army, 1943-46, ETO. Mem. Am. Comparative Econ. Studies (mem. exec. com. 1974-76, pres. 1990-91), Am. Econ. Assn., Assn. Study of Grants Economy (adv. bd.), Omicron Delta Epsilon (pres. 1979-81, exec. bd., Disting. Ser. award 1981). Democrat. Jewish. Home: 5 Somerset Ct East Setauket NY 11733 Office: SUNY Dept Econs Stony Brook NY 11794

NEUBERGER, ROY R., investment counselor; b. Bridgeport, Conn., July 21, 1903; s. Louis and Bertha (Rothschild) N.; m. Marie Salant, June 29, 1932; children—Ann Marie Neuberger Aceves, Roy S., James A. Ed., NYU, U. Sorbonne; D.F.A. (hon.), SUNY Coll.-Purchase, N.Y., 1982; L.H.D. (hon.), Parsons Sch. Design, New Sch. for Social Research, N.Y.C., 1985; D.H.L. (hon.), Bar-Ilan U., Israel, 1987. Buyer B. Altman & Co., 1922-25; art student Paris, 1925-29; broker Halle & Stieglitz, N.Y.C., 1929-40; sr. partner Neuberger & Berman, N.Y.C., 1940—; pres. Guardian Mut. Fund, Inc., 1950-79, chmn. bd., 1979-91, chmn. emeritus, 1991—; chmn. bd. Genesis Fund, Inc., 1988-91; chmn. emeritus, 1991—; chmn. bd., dir. Neuberger & Berman Asset Mgmt., Inc. (formerly Neuberger & Berman Pension Mgmt. Inc.), 1976-87, chmn. emeritus, 1991—; chmn. bd., dir. Neuberger & Berman Mgmt. Inc. (formerly Cedar St. Cons.), 1970—. Art collector, collection exhibited museums throughout, U.S. and abroad, 1936—. Bd. dirs. City Center Music and Drama, N.Y.C., 1957-74, trustee, 1974—, fin. chmn., 1971-74; chmn. adv. council on arts N.Y.C. Housing Authority, 1960-70; trustee Whitney Mus. Am. Art, 1961-69, trustee emeritus, 1969-94, hon. trustee, 1994—; mem. collector's com. Nat. Gallery Art, Washington, 1975—; trustee, mem. exec. com. New Sch. Social Research, 1967-75; hon. trustee Met. Mus. Art, N.Y.C., 1968—; council of friends Inst. Fine Arts, NYU, 1961—; mem. president's council Mus. City N.Y.; trustee Purchase Coll. Found., 1971-85, chmn., 1974-85; bd. dirs. Bard Coll. Center, 1979-91; donor Roy R. Neuberger Mus. State U. N.Y. at Purchase, 1969—. Recipient award Artists Equity Assn., 1972; Gari Melchers medal Artists Fellowship, Inc., N.Y.C., 1984, Arts award Council for Arts in Westchester, 1985, Art in Am. award, 1959, North Shore Com. Arts Ctr. award, 1971; Benjamin Franklin fellow Royal Soc. Arts, 1969—; fellow R.I. Sch. Design, 1981. Fellow in perpetuity NAD; mem. Am. Fedn. Arts (pres. 1955-67, hon. pres. 1968—), N.Y. Soc. Security Analysts, Soc. Ethical Culture N.Y.C. (treas. 1956-64, pres. 1965-68). Clubs: Century Assn., Williams Club, City Athletic (N.Y.C.), Harmonie. Home: 625 Park Ave New York NY 10021-8401 Office: Neuberger & Berman 605 3rd Ave New York NY 10158-0001

NEUBERT, GEORGE W., museum director, sculptor; b. Mpls. Oct. 24, 1942; s. George W. and Juanita Neubert; m. Eva Saenz, 1965; 1 child, Evangeline. BS, Hardin-Simmons U., 1965; postgrad., San Francisco Art Inst., 1967; MFA, Mills Coll., 1969. Curator art Oakland Mus., 1970-80; assoc. dir. San Francisco Mus. Modern Art, 1980-83; dir. Sheldon Meml. Art Gallery, Lincoln, Nebr., 1983—; mem. adv. bd. Archives of Am. Art, Smithsonian, 1972—; mem. Project Sculpture/Public Site, San Francisco 1980-83; mem. panel Art in Pub. Places, NEA, 1976-79, 1978; project dir. 4th Triennial New Delhi/USIA, 1977-78. Co-author: Robert Graham Statues, 1981; Nathan Oliveira Survey, 1984; editor catalogues various exhbns., 1970-84. One-man shows include Gallery Paule Anglim, San Francisco, 1971; Gallery 72, Omaha, 1984, U. Houston, 1987; group shows include Mus. Conceptual Art, San Francisco, 1981, Impressions Gallery, Boston, 1982, Sculpture, Traditions in Steel, N.Y.C., 1983. Mem. Nebr. Art Invitation Com., Mayor's Design Com. Trefethen fellow Mills Coll. 1969, Ctr. for Great Plains Studies fellow, 1983—; NEA grantee, 1980. Mem. Art Mus. Assn. Am. (bd. dirs.), Assn. Art Mus. Dirs. Office: U Nebr Art Galleries-Sheldon Meml Art Gallery 12th & R Sts Lincoln NE 68588-0300

NEUBORNE, BURT, law educator; b. 1941. AB, Cornell U., 1961; LLB, Harvard U., 1964. Bar: N.Y. 1965. Assoc. Casey, Lane & Mittendorf, N.Y.C., 1964-67; staff counsel N.Y. Civil Liberties Union, N.Y.C., 1967-72; asst. legal dir. ACLU, N.Y.C., 1972-74; assoc. prof. NYU, 1974-76, prof. 1976-94, John Norton Pomeroy prof. of law, 1994—; legal dir. ACLU, 1983-86, spl. counsel, 1978—; spl. counsel Now Legal Def. and Edn. Fund, 1991—. Co-author: Political and Civil Rights in The United States, Vol. I, 1976, Vol. II, 1979. Active N.Y.C. Human Rights Commn., 1988-92. Office: NYU Sch Law 40 Washington Sq S New York NY 10012-1099

NEUDECK, GEROLD WALTER, electrical engineering educator; b. Beach, N.D., Sept. 25, 1936; s. Adolph John and Helen Annette (Kramer) N.; m. Mariellen Kristine MacDonald, Sept. 1, 1962; children: Philip Gerold, Alexander John. BSEE, U. N.D., 1959, MSEE, 1960; PhD in Elec. Engring., Purdue U., 1969. Asst. prof. U. N.D., Grand Forks, 1960-64; grad. instr. Purdue U., West Lafayette, Ind., 1964-68; asst. prof. Purdue U., 1968-71, assoc. prof., 1971-77, prof. elec. engring., 1977—; asst. dean engring. Purdue U., West Lafayette, 1988-90, assoc. dir. NSF/ERC Engring., 1988-94, dir. Optoelectronics Rsch. Ctr., 1993—; cons. in field. Author: Electric Circuit Analysis and Design, 1976, 2d edit., 1987, Junction Diode/Bipolar Transisters, 1983, 2d edit., 1989; author, editor: Modular Series on Solid State Devices, 1983; contbr. over 200 articles to profl. jours.; inventor, patentee in field. Bd. dirs. W. Lafayette Devel. Commn., 1990—, Greater Lafayette Pub. Transp., 1975-80; pres. Lafayette Tennis, 1976-78. Recipient Dow Outstanding Faculty award Am. Soc. Engring. Edn., 1972, Western Elec. Fund award, 1974-75, D.D. Ewing award Purdue U., 1973, A.A. Potter award, 1973, Honeywell Teaching award, 1995. Fellow IEEE (Harry S. Nyquist award 1992); mem. Am. Vacuum Soc., Sigma Xi, Eta Kappa Nu, Sigma Tau, Sigma Pi Sigma. Avocations: tennis, backpacking, fishing, woodworking, baking. Office: Purdue U Elec Engring Bldg West Lafayette IN 47907

NEUEFEIND, WILHELM, economics educator, university administrator; b. Viersen, Rheinland, Germany, Mar. 6, 1939; came to U.S., 1977; m. Ingrid Leuchtenberg, Mar. 30, 1966; children: Nicole, Bettina. MBA, U. Cologne, Germany, 1962, MA in Math., 1969; PhD in Econs., U. Bonn, 1972. Lectr. econs. U. Bonn, 1973-77; prof. Washington U., St. Louis, 1977—; chmn. dept. econs. Wash. U., St. Louis, 1983—; contbr. articles to profl. jours. Mem. Econometric Soc., Am. Econ. Assn., Assn. for Advancement Econ. Theory. Office: Washington U Dept Econs 1 Brookings Dr # 1208 Saint Louis MO 63130-4899

NEUFELD, EDWARD PETER, retired economist; b. Sask., Can., Nov. 16, 1927; s. Henry Gerhard and Anna Neufeld; m. Myrtle Christina Schoonover, July 6, 1948 (dec. 1972); children—Dwight, Anna-Marie, Derek; m. Arlette Deloge, Dec. 28, 1974; 1 child, Valery Deloge. B.A. with honors, U. Sask., Saskatoon, Can., 1951; Ph.D., London Sch. Econs. and Polit. Sci., 1954. With Bank of Eng., London, 1954-55; prof. U. Toronto, Ont., Can., 1955-70; vis. scholar Stanford U., Calif., 1970-71; asst. dep. minister Govt. of Can., Ottawa, Ont., Can., 1973-80; exec. v.p. econ. and corp. affairs Royal Bank of Can., Toronto, Ont., Can., 1980—; bd. dirs. C.D. Howe Inst., Toronto, 1985, Atlantic Council Can., Toronto, 1983, Le Cercle Canadian, 1990, internat. adv. bd. Canadian Coun. for the Americas, 1990. Author: Bank of Canada Operations and Policy, 1958; editor, contbr.: Money and Banking in Canada, 1964, A Global Corporation, 1969, The Financial System of Canada, 1972; author studies in field. Fellow London Sch. Econs. and Polit. Sci. (hon.). Avocations: curling; skiing; tennis; bicycling. Office: Royal Bank of Can, 200 Bay St, Toronto, ON Canada M5J 2J5

NEUFELD, ELIZABETH FONDAL, biochemist, educator; b. Paris, Sept. 27, 1928; U.S. citizen; m. 1951. Ph.D., U. Calif., Berkeley, 1956; D.H.C. (hon.), U. Rene Descartes, Paris, 1978; D.Sc. (hon.), Russell Sage Coll., Troy, N.Y., 1981, Hahnemann U. Sch. Medicine, 1984. Asst. research biochemist U. Calif., Berkeley, 1957-63; with Nat. Inst. Arthritis, Metabolism and Digestive Diseases, Bethesda, Md., 1963-84, research biochemist, 1963-73, chief sect. human biochem. genetics, 1973-79, chief genetics and biochem. br., 1979-84; prof., chmn. dept. biol. chemistry UCLA Sch. Medicine, 1984—. Passano Found. sr. laureate, 1982; named Calif. Scientist of Yr., 1990; recipient Dickson prize U. Pitts., 1974, Hillebrand award, 1975, Gairdner Found. award, 1981, Albert Lasker Clin. Med. Rsch. award, 1982, William Allan award, 1982, Elliott Cresson medal, 1984, Wolf Found. prize, 1988, Christopher Columbus Discovery award for biomed. rsch., 1992, Nat. Medal. of Sch., 1994. Fellow AAAS; mem. NAS, Inst. Medicine of NAS, Am. Acad. Arts and Scis., Am. Soc. Human Genetics, Am. Chem. Soc., Am. Soc. Biochemistry and Molecular Biology (pres. 1992-93), Am. Soc. Cell Biology, Am. Soc. Clin. Investigation. Office: UCLA Sch Medicine Dept Biol Chemistry Los Angeles CA 90024

NEUFELD, MACE, film company executive; b. N.Y.C., July 13, 1928; s. Philip M. and Margaret Ruth (Braun) N.; Feb. 28, 1954; children: Bradley David, Glenn Jeremy, Nancy Ann. B.A., Yale U., 1948; postgrad., NYU, 1958-60. Photographer various N.Y. pubs., 1943-45; prodn. asst. Raymond E. Nelson, 1949-50; founder, owner Ray Bloch Assos., Inc., N.Y.C., 1951-59; ptnr. BNB Prodns., N.Y.C., 1959-70, Neufeld-Davis Prodns., Inc., Beverly Hills, Calif., 1981—; Trustee Am. Film Inst., 1978—; chmn. life achievement award nominating com. and scholarship fund. Producer in assn. with Harvey Bernhard The Omen, 1976, Damien - Omen II, 1977, Omen III - The Final Conflict, 1980; producer: The Frisco Kid, 1979, Angel on My Shoulder, 1980, The American Dream, 1980; ABC-TV mini-series East of Eden, 1981; CBS-TV series Cagney and Lacey, 1984; MGM film The Aviator, 1984, ABC-TV A Death in California, 1985; producer films Transylvania 6-5000, 1985, No Way Out, 1987, The Hunt for Red October, 1989, Flight of the Intruder, 1990, Necessary Roughness, 1991, Patriot Games, 1992, Clear and Present Danger, 1994, Gettysburg, 1994, Beverly Hills Cop 3, 1994. Photograph entitled Sammy's Home voted Picture of Yr. N.Y. World Telegram-Sun, 1955; recipient Grand prize Eastman Kodak's First Nat. Salon of Photography, 1945; named N.A.T.O./Showest Producer of the Yr., 1993. Mem. Acad. TV Arts and Scis., Acad. Motion Picture Arts and Scis., ASCAP, Am. Film Inst. Democrat. Clubs: Friars, Yale of N.Y. Home: 624 N Arden Dr Beverly Hills CA 90210-3510 Office: Paramount Pictures 5555 Melrose Ave Los Angeles CA 90038-3197

NEUFELD, MICHAEL JOHN, curator, historian; b. Edmonton, Alta., Can., July 5, 1951; s. Henry John and Isabel Grace (Mitchell) N.; m. Sheila Faith Weiss, May 29, 1983 (div. Dec. 1992); m. Karen Lee Levenback, June 14, 1994. BA with 1st class honors, U. Calgary, Alta., 1974; MA, U. B.C., Vancouver, Can., 1976, Johns Hopkins U., 1980; PhD in History, Johns Hopkins U., 1984. Hist. rschr. Dept. Supply and Svcs., Ottawa, Ont., Can., summer 1973, 74; teaching asst. Johns Hopkins U., Balt., 1979-80; instr. Clarkson U., Potsdam, N.Y., 1983-84, from part-time instr. to part-time asst. prof., 1983-85; vis. asst. prof. SUNY, Oswego, 1985-86, Colgate U., Hamilton, N.Y., 1986-88; Verville fellow Nat. Air and Space Mus., Washington, 1988-89, Smithsonian postdoctoral fellow, 1989-90, curator dept. aeronautics, 1990—; curator Air Power in WWII series, 1991-94. Author: The Skilled Metalworkers of Nuremberg, 1989, The Rocket and the Reich, 1995; contbr. articles and book revs. to profl. jours. Recipient History Manuscript award AIAA, 1995, NSF Scholar's award History of Sci. and Tech. Program, 1989-90; Johns Hopkins U. grad. fellow and jr. instructorship, 1978-80, Social Scis. and Humanities Rsch. Coun. Can. doctoral fellow, 1980-82; travel grantee Internat. Congress of History of Sci., Hamburg and Munich, 1989, U. B.C. grad. fellow and summer scholar, 1974-76. Mem. Am. Hist. Assn., Conf. Group on Cen. European History, Soc. for History of Tech., History of Sci. Soc. Avocation: amateur astronomy. Office: Nat Air & Space Mus Dept Aeronautics Smithsonian Instn Washington DC 20560

NEUFELD, VICTOR, television executive; m. Lois Neufeld; 1 child, Stephanie. BS, Rutgers U., 1967; M in Broadcasting, Bklyn. Coll., 1969. Assignment editor, prodr. The Ten O'Clock News Sta. WNEW-TV, N.Y.C., 1969-73; with ABC News, N.Y.C., 1973—, prodr. The Weekend Report, sr. prodr. ABC Evening News; sr. prodr. 20/20, N.Y.C., 1979-87, exec. prodr., 1987—. Recipient 38 Emmy awards, 12 Nat. Headliner awards, 7 awards Am. Women in Radio and T.V., 2 Clarion awards, Alfred I. duPont-Columbia award. Office: c/o 20/20 ABC News 157 Columbus Ave New York NY 10023

NEUGARTEN, BERNICE LEVIN, social scientist; b. Norfolk, Nebr., Feb. 11, 1916; d. David L. and Sadie (Segall) Levin; m. Fritz Neugarten, July 1, 1940; children: Dail Ann, Jerrold. B.A., U. Chgo., 1936, Ph.D., 1943; D.Sc. (hon.), U. So. Calif., 1980; PhD (hon.), Calif. U., Nijmegen, 1988. Rsch. assoc. Com. on Human Devel., U. Chgo., 1948-50; asst. prof. U. Chgo., 1951-60, assoc. prof., 1960-64, prof., 1964-80, chmn., 1969-73, prof. social svc. adminstrn., 1978-80; mem. com. on policy studies, 1979-80, Rothschild disting. scholar, prof. emeritus, 1988—; prof. human devel. and social policy Northwestern U., 1980-88; mem. council U. Chgo. Senate, 1968-71, 72-75, 78-80, chmn. council on univ. women, 1969-70; nat. adv. council Nat. Inst. on Aging, 1975-76, 78-81, Fed. Council on Aging, 1978-81; dep. chmn. White House Conf. on Aging, 1980-81. Author: (with R.J. Havighurst)

American Indian and White Children: A Social-Psychological Investigation, 1955, reprint, 1969, (with R.J. Havighurst) Society and Education, 1957, rev., 1962, 67, 75, (with Assocs.) Personality in Middle and Late Life, 1964, reprint, 1980, (with J.M.A. Munnichs et al) Adjustment to Retirement, 1969, (with R.P. Coleman) Social Status in the City, 1971, Middle Age and Aging, 1968; co-editor: (with H. Eglit) Age Discrimination, 1981, Age or Need? Public Policies for Older People, 1982; assoc. editor Jour. Gerontology, 1958-61, Human Devel., 1962-68; adv. or cons. editor other profl. jours., 1959—; author monographs, research papers and reports. mem. various adv. bodies. Recipient Am. Psychol. Found. Disting. Tchg. award, 1975, Disting. Psychologist award Ill. Psychol. Assn., 1979, Sandoz Internat. Prize for Gerontol. Rsch., 1987, Ollie Randall award Nat. Coun. on Aging, 1993, Gold Medal award for lifetime contbn. as a psychologist in the public interest Am. Psychol. Found., 1994. Fellow AAAS, Am. Psychol. Assn. (coun. rep. 1967-69, 73-76, Disting. Sci. Contbn. award 1980, honoree Women's Heritage Exhibit 1992, Gold Medal award 1994), Am. Sociol. Assn., Gerontol. Soc. Am. (pres. 1968-69, Kleemeier award 1971, Brookdale award 1982, Disting. Mentor award 1988), Am. Acad. Arts and Scis., Internat. Assn. Gerontology (governing coun. 1975-78, chmn. N.Am. exec. com. 1983-85, disting. creative contbn. to gerontology award); mem. Inst. Medicine of NAS. Home: 5801 S Dorchester Ave Chicago IL 60637-1731

NEUGEBAUER, GERRY, astrophysicist, educator; b. Göttingen, Germany, Sept. 3, 1932; came to U.S., 1939; s. Otto E. and Grete (Brück) N.; m. Marcia MacDonald, Aug. 26, 1956; children: Carol, Lee. B.S., Cornell U., 1954; Ph.D., Calif. Inst. Tech., 1960. Mem. faculty Calif. Inst. Tech., Pasadena, 1962—, prof. physics, 1970—, Howard Hughes Prof. Physics, 1985—, chmn. divsn. physics, math and astronomy, 1988-93; mem. staff Hale Obs., 1970-80; acting dir. Palomar Obs., 1980-81, dir., 1981—. Served with AUS, 1961-63. Recipient Except. Sci. Achievement medal NASA, 1972, 1984, Richtmyer Lectr. award, 1985, Space Sci. award Am. Inst. Aeronaut and Astronaut, 1985, Rumford Premium Am. Acad. Arts & Sci., 1986. Fellow Am. Acad. Arts and Scis.; mem. NAS, Am. Philos. Soc., Am. Astron. Soc., Royal Astron. Soc., Internat. AStron. Union. Office: Calif Inst Tech Down Lab of Physics 320-47 Pasadena CA 91125*

NEUGEBAUER, MARCIA, physicist, administrator; b. N.Y.C., Sept. 27, 1932; d. Howard Graeme MacDonald and Frances (Townsend) Marshall; m. Gerry Neugebauer, Aug. 25, 1956; children: Carol, Lee. B.S., Cornell U., 1954; M.S., U. Ill., 1956. Grad. asst. U. Ill., Urbana, 1954-56; vis. fellow Clare Hall Coll., Cambridge, Eng., 1975; sr. research scientist Jet Propulsion Lab. Calif. Inst. Tech., Pasadena, 1956—; vis. prof. planetary sci. Calif. Inst. Tech., Pasadena, 1986-87; mem. com. NASA, Washington, 1960—, NAS, Washington, 1981—; Regents lectr. UCLA, 1990-91. Contbr. numerous articles on physics to profl. jours. Named Calif. Woman Scientist of Yr. Calif. Mus. Sci. and Industry, 1967; recipient Exceptional Sci. Achievement medal NASA, 1970, Outstanding Leadership medal NASA, 1993. Fellow Am. Geophys. Union (sec., pres. solar planetary relationships sect. 1979-84, editor-in-chief Rev. Geophysics 1988-92, pres.-elect 1992-94, pres. 1994-96). Democrat. Home: 1720 Braeburn Rd Altadena CA 91001-2708 Office: Calif Inst Tech Jet Propulsion Lab/MS 169-506 4800 Oak Grove Dr Pasadena CA 91109-8001

NEUGROSCHEL, ARNOST, electrical engineering educator; b. Prešov, Czechoslovakia, June 18, 1942; came to U.S., 1973; s. Ludovit and Irene (Gottfried) Neugröschl; m. Susan M. Pertz, June 20, 1982. Diploma in engring., Slovak Tech. U., Bratislava, Czechoslovakia, 1965; PhD, Technion-Israel Inst. Tech., Haifa, 1973. Engr. Tesla, Inc., Piešťany, Czechoslovakia, 1966-67; instr. Technion-Israel Inst. Tech., 1969-73; postdoctoral rsch. assot. dept. elec. engring. U. Ill., Urbana, 1973-75; asst. prof. U. Fla., Gainesville, 1975-79, assoc. prof., 1979-83, prof., 1983—; on leave Interuniv. Microelectronic Ctr., Louvain, Belgium, 1986; mem. summer faculty IBM T.J. Watson Rsch. Ctr., Yorktown Heights, N.Y., 1982. Contbr. over 75 articles to profl. jours.; patentee in field. Fellow IEEE. Avocations: tennis, travel. Office: U Fla Dept Elec Engring Gainesville FL 32611

NEUHARTH, ALLEN HAROLD, newspaper publisher; b. Eureka, S.D., Mar. 22, 1924; s. Daniel J. and Christina (Neuharth) N.; m. Loretta Fay Helgeland, June 16, 1946 (div. 1972); children: Daniel J. II, Jan; m. Lori Wilson, Dec. 31, 1973 (div. 1982). BA cum laude, U. S.D., 1950. Reporter Rapid City (S.D.) Jour., 1948; sports writer Mitchell (S.D.) Daily Republic, 1949; staff writer AP, Sioux Falls, S.D., 1950-52; editor, pub. SoDak Sports, Sioux Falls, 1952-54; with Miami (Fla.) Herald, 1954-60, asst. mng. editor, 1958-60; asst. exec. editor Detroit Free Press, 1960-63; gen. mgr. Times-Union and Democrat and Chronicle, Rochester, N.Y., 1963-66; exec. v.p. Gannett Co., Inc., Washington, 1966-70, pres., chief operating officer, 1970-73, pres., chief exec. officer, 1973-79, chmn., chief exec. officer, 1979-86; founder, chmn. USA Today, 1982; chmn. Gannett Co., Inc., Washington, 1986-89, Gannett Found., Arlington, Va., 1989-91, Freedom Forum, 1991—. Author: Confessions of an S.O.B., 1989. Trustee, chmn. Gannett Found. Served with inf. AUS, 1943-46, ETO, PTO. Decorated Bronze Star; recipient Horatio Alger award, 1975; named Outstanding Chief Exec. of Yr. in Pub. and Printing Industry for 3 consecutive yrs. Mem. Am. Newspaper Pubs. Assn. (bd. dirs. 1968-82, chmn., pres. 1979-80), Jockey Club (Miami), Ocean Reef Club (Key Largo, Fla.), Sky Club, Sigma Delta Chi (past nat. region I dir.). Office: Freedom Forum 1101 Wilson Blvd Arlington VA 22209-2248*

NEUHAUS, JULIUS VICTOR, III, architect; b. Houston, Sept. 9, 1926; s. Julius Victor, Jr. and Vera Inez (Richardson) N.; m. Judith Ann Brown, Oct. 22, 1976; children: Nancy Neuhaus Holden, Patricia Neuhaus Napoleon, Alicia Brownell. B.Arch., U. Tex., 1951. Co-founder 3D/Internat. (and predecessor Neuhaus & Taylor, Architects and Planning Cons.), Houston, 1955; pres., chmn. bd. dirs., chief exec. officer 3D/Internat. (and predecessor Neuhaus & Taylor, Architects and Planning Cons.), 1971—; moderator panel central cities Gov. Tex. Conf. Urban and Community Affairs, 1969; mem. Citizens Adv. Com. Housing, Houston, 1966; mem. regional adv. panel GSA, 1971; mem. chancellor's council and archtl. adv. com. U. Tex.; adv. bd. Sch. Architecture, U. Houston, 1984—. Served with USNR, 1944-46. Fellow AIA; mem. Tex. Soc. Architects, Houston C. of C. Republican. Methodist. Clubs: River Oaks Country, University (Houston). Office: 3D Internat Inc 1900 West Loop S Ste 600 Houston TX 77027-3206

NEUHAUS, MAX, artist, composer; b. Beaumont, Tex., Aug. 9, 1939; s. Max Werner N. and Harriet Rachel Ocker. B.Mus., Manhattan Sch. Music, 1961, M.Mus., 1962. Fellow DAAD Kunstler Program, W. Berlin, 1977; founder, 1974; since dir. HEAR Inc. (aural environ. as a resource), N.Y.C.; created sound events for nat. radio networks and telephone systems Radio Net, 1977; series permanent sound installations for specific urban sites Times Sq., 1977, also for: museums, Abby Aldrich Rockefeller Sculpture Garden, Mus. Modern Art, N.Y.C., 1978, Mus. Contemporary Art, Chgo., 1979, Domaine de Kerguehennel, Bignan, France, 1986, Documenta IX, Kassel, Germany, 1992, CACP Musée D'Art Contemporain, Bordeaux, France, 1993. Percussion soloist, Karlheinz Stockhausen, others, 1963-64, solo recitalist, Carnegie Hall, N.Y.C., 1964-65, artist-in-residence U. Chgo., 1964-65, solo tour of Europe, 1965-66; one-person exhbns. Musee d'Art Moderne de la Ville de Paris, 1983, Kunsthalle Basel, 1983, Kunsthalle Bern, Switzerland, 1988, Dallas Mus. Art, 1990. Nat. Endowment Arts music fellow, 1973; NEA visual arts fellow, 1977, 81, 90. Introduced concept of sound installation, 1967. Address: 350 5th Ave Ste 3304 New York NY 10118-0100 *The first work of mine which can be called a sound installation was done in 1967. It was a radical departure from the current and still prevalent form of sound art, i.e., the arrangement where a group of people gather together at a specific time and place to watch and listen to a small and more specialized group make sound. I had spent the previous ten years functioning wholly within this context and felt confined by its 18th and 19th century habits. I began exploring new materials—electronics offered limitless possibilities—new contexts—ones which entered peoples' patterns of daily activity—and ways of working with a broad spectrum of society.*

NEUHAUS, OTTO WILHELM, biochemistry educator; b. Zweibrucken, Germany, Nov. 18, 1922; came to U.S., 1927, naturalized, 1931; s. Clemens Jakob and Johanna Amalie (Schnorr) N.; m. Dorothy Ellen Rehn, Aug. 30, 1947; children: Thomas William, Carol Alida, Joanne Marie. B.S., U. Wis., 1944; M.S., U. Mich., 1947, Ph.D., 1953. Research chemist Huron Milling Co., 1951-54; mem. faculty Wayne State U., Detroit, 1954-66; assoc. prof. Wayne State U., 1965-66; prof., chmn. dept. biochemistry U. S.D., Vermillion, 1966-76, acting chmn. dept. physiology and pharmacology, 1975-76, 82-83, prof., chmn. div. biochemistry, physiology and pharmacology, 1976-82, prof., 1982-88, chmn. dept. biochemistry, 1982-86; prof. emeritus U. S.D., 1988—. Author: (with John Halver) Fish in Research, 1969, (with James Orten) Human Biochemistry, 1982; also research articles. NATO Research fellow, 1961-62. Fellow AAAS; mem. Am. Chem. Soc., Am. Soc. Biol. Chemists, Sigma Xi, Phi Sigma, Alpha Chi Sigma, Phi Lambda Upsilon. Lutheran. Home: 1090 Valley View Vermillion SD 57069

NEUHAUS, PHILIP ROSS, investment banker; b. Houston, Dec. 25, 1919; s. Hugo Victor and Kate Padgitt (Rice) N.; m. Elizabeth Lacey Thompson, Oct. 31, 1942 (div. 1967); children: Philip Ross (dec.), Lacey Neuhaus Dorn, Elizabeth Neuhaus Armstrong, Joan Thompson Neuhaus; m. Barbara R. Haden, Aug. 14, 1968; 5 stepchildren. Grad., St. Mark's Sch. Southborough, Mass., 1938; BA, Yale, 1942. With Nat. City Bank of Cleve., 1946-47, McDonald & Co., Cleve., 1947; with Neuhaus & Co., 1947; chmn. Underwood, Neuhaus & Co., Inc., Houston, 1948-89; hon. chmn. Lovett Underwood Neuhaus & Webb, Houston, 1989-92; sr. v.p. Kemper Securities Inc., Houston, 1992—. Trustee Tex. Childrens Hosp.; assoc. Rice U.; advisory bd. Salvation Army, Houston, 1969-91. Served to capt., cav. AUS, 1942-45. Mem. Securities Industry Assn. Am. (bd. govs., chmn. Tex. dist. 1973, exec. com. 1975), Houston Soc. Financial Analysts (pres. 1959), Stock and Bond Club Houston (past pres.), Nat. Fedn. Financial Analysts (v.p. 1963, dir.). Clubs: Bayou, Houston Country, Houston, Eagle Lake Rod and Gun. Home: 407 Thamer Ln Houston TX 77024-6939 Office: Kemper Securities Inc. 909 Fannin St Houston TX 77010-1060

NEUHAUS, SYDNEY ANN, public relations executive. Grad., Cornell U. With med. comms. group Daniel J. Edelman Pub. Rels.; asst. dir., project mgr. Sutton Pub. Rels., 1990; v.p. Medicus Intercon Pub. Rels., 1991-92; sr. v.p., dir. pub. rels. Harrison Star Wiener & Beitler Pub. Rels., 1992—. Office: Harrison Star Wiener & Beitler Pub Rels 16 W 22nd St New York NY 10010

NEUHAUS, WILLIAM OSCAR, III, architect; b. Houston, Mar. 16, 1944; s. W. Oscar and Betty Palmer (Bosworth) N.; m. Kay Ficklen; children: Kimberly Sautelle, Sara Palmer. BArch, Ga. Inst. Tech., 1967. Registered architect, Tex., N.Mex. Intern architect Caudill Rowlett Scott, Houston, 1967-69; assoc. Charles Tapley Assocs., Houston, 1969-72; prin. W.O. Neuhaus Architecture/Planning, Houston, 1972-83; owner, mgr. W.O. Neuhaus Assocs., Houston, 1984—. Co-author trading Toilets: The Subterranean Zoning of Houston, 1982; author Foreward, 1992. Pres. Rice Design Alliance, Houston, 1982-83, bd. dirs. 1978-84; pres. Armand Bayou Nature Ctr. Found., 1986-90, Stages Repertory Theatre, Houston, 1988-89; mem. Mayor's Land Use Strategy com., Houston, 1990. Fellow Am. Leadership Forum, AIA (pres. 1990-91, chair design com. 1988-89); mem. Tex. Soc. Architects (mem. design com. 1989-90). Office: WO Neuhaus Assocs 4100 Montrose Blvd Ste D Houston TX 77006-4912

NEUHAUSEN, BENJAMIN SIMON, auditor, accountant; b. Urbana, Ill., Apr. 23, 1950; s. Stanley Edward and Dolores Renee (Epstein) N.; m. Madeline Cohen, Sept. 6, 1987; 3 children. BA, Mich. State U., 1971; MBA, NYU, 1973. CPA, Ill. Staff auditor Arthur Andersen & Co., N.Y.C., 1973-75, sr. auditor, 1975-78, audit mgr., 1978-79, 81-85; audit ptnr. Arthur Andersen & Co., Chgo., 1985—; practice fellow Fin. Acctg. Standards Bd., Stamford, Conn., 1979-81. Contbr. articles to profl. jours. Bd. dirs. The Renaissance Soc., Chgo., 1987-90. Recipient Charles W. Haskins medal N.Y. Soc. CPAs, 1974. Mem. AICPA, Ill. SOc. CPAs, Chgo. Athletic Assn. Jewish. Office: Arthur Andersen & Co 69 W Washington St Chicago IL 60602-3004

NEUHAUSER, DUNCAN VON BRIESEN, health services educator; b. Phila., June 20, 1939; s. Edward Blaine Duncan and Gernda (von Briesen) N.; m. Elinor Toaz, Mar. 6, 1965; children: Steven, Ann. B.A., Harvard U., 1961; M.H.A., U. Mich., 1963; M.B.A., U. Chgo., 1966, Ph.D., 1971. Research assoc. U. Chgo., 1965-70; asst. prof. Sch. Pub. Health, Harvard U., Boston, 1970-74; assoc. prof. Sch. Pub. Health, Harvard U., 1974-79; cons. in medicine Mass. Gen. Hosp., Boston, 1975-80; assoc. dir. Health Systems Mgmt. Ctr. Case Western Res. U., Cleve., 1979-85, prof. epidemiology, biostatistics and organizational behavior, 1979—, prof. medicine, 1981—, prof. family medicine, 1990—, co-dir. Health Systems Mgmt. Ctr., 1985—; cons. in medicine Cleve. Met. Gen. Hosp., 1981—; adj. mem. med. staff Cleve. Clinic Found., 1984—. Author numerous books, sci. papers; editor: jours. Health Matrix, 1982-90, Med. Care, 1983—. Vice chmn. bd. dirs. Vis. Nurse Assn. Greater Cleve., 1983-84, chmn., 1984-85; bd. dirs. New Eng. Grenfell Assn., Boston, 1972—, Braintree (Mass.) Hosp., 1975-86; trustee Internat. Grenfell Assn. St. Anthony, Nfld., Can., 1975-83, Blue Hill (Maine) Hosp., 1983-89; trustee Hough Norwood Health Ctr., 1983-94, chmn., 1993-94. Keck Found. scholar, 1982—; Kellogg fellow, 1963-65; Neuhauser lectr. Soc. Pediatric Radiology, 1982; Freedlander lectr. Ohio Permanente Med. Group, 1986; recipient E.F. Meyers Trustee award Cleve. Hosp. Assn., 1987. Mem. Inst. Medicine of NAS, Soc. for Clin. Decision Making, Cleve. Skating Club, St. Botolph Club (Boston), Kollegewidgwok Yacht Club (Blue Hill, Maine, commodore 1991-93), Beta Gamma Sigma. Home: 2655 N Park Blvd Cleveland Heights OH 44106-3622 Office: Case Western Res U Med Sch 10900 Euclid Ave Cleveland OH 44106-4945

NEUMAIER, GERHARD JOHN, environment consulting company executive; b. Covington, Ky., July 27, 1937; s. John Edward and Elli Anna (Raudies) N.; m. Ellen Elaine Klepper, Oct. 24, 1959; children: Kevin Scott, Kirsten Lynn. BME, Gen. Motors Inst., 1960; MA in Biophysics, U. Buffalo, 1963. Research ecologist, project mgr. Cornell Aero. Lab., Buffalo, 1963-70; pres., chief exec., chmn. bd. Ecology and Environment Inc., Buffalo, 1970—. Recipient Theodore Roosevelt Citizen of Yr. award City of Buffalo, 1990. Mem. APHA, Air Pollution Control Assn., Internat. Assn. Gt. Lakes Research, Inst. Environ. Scis., Ecol. Soc. Am., Am. Inst. Biol. Scis., Urban Land Inst., Arctic Inst. N.Am., Nat. Parks and Conservation Assn., Defenders of Wildlife, Nat. Wildlife Fedn., Wilderness Soc., Am. Hort. Soc., Smithsonian Assocs., Nat. Audubon Soc. Home: 284 Mill Rd East Aurora NY 14052-2805 Office: Ecology & Environment Inc 368 Pleasant View Dr Lancaster NY 14086-1397

NEUMAN, CHARLES P., electrical and computer engineering educator, consultant; b. Pitts., July 26, 1940; s. Daniel and Frances G. Neuman; m. Susan G. Neuman, Sept. 4, 1967. B.S. in Elec. Engring. with honors, Carnegie Inst. Tech., 1962; S.M., Harvard U., 1963, Ph.D in Applied Math., 1968. Teaching fellow Harvard U., Cambridge, Mass., 1962-64, research asst., 1964-67; mem. tech. staff Bell Telephone Labs., Whippany, N.J., 1967-69; asst. prof. elec. engring. Carnegie-Mellon U., Pitts., 1969-71, assoc. prof., 1971-78, prof. elec. engring., 1978-83; prof. elec. and computer engring., 1983—. Mem. editorial bd. Internat. Jour. Modelling and Simulation, Control and Computers; contbr. numerous articles to profl. jours. Mem. IEEE (sr., assoc. editor Trans. on Systems, Man and Cybernetics), Inst. Mgmt. Scis., AAAS, Instrument Soc. Am. (sr.), Soc. Harvard Engrs. and Scientists, Soc. Indsl. and Applied Math., Sigma Xi, Phi Kappa Phi, Tau Beta Pi, Eta Kappa Nu. Office: Carnegie-Mellon U Dept Elec & Computer Engring Pittsburgh PA 15213

NEUMAN, CURTIS WILLIAM, computer systems company executive; b. Pitts., July 22, 1942; s. Joel McKee and Margaret Lucille (Baer) N.; m. Susan Marie Naderer, Feb. 5, 1980 (div. July 1985); children: Brett Jerris Nadan, Tal Devery Nadan. BS, Case Western Res. U., 1971. Cert. in prodn. and inventory control. Systems analyst, mgr. White Motor Corp., Eastlake, Ohio, 1972-80; mgr. prodn. and systems True Temper Corp., Cleve., 1980-83; cons. Avon Co., Rye, N.Y., 1983-85; sr. cons. Coopers & Lybrand, N.Y.C., 1985-90; pres. Nadan Neuman Assocs., Norwalk, Conn., 1990—. Team leader Clinton Campaign, Washington, 1992. Capt. U.S. Army, 1967-70, Viet Nam. Mem. Am. Prodn. and Inventory Control Soc., Conn. PC Users Group. Democrat. Avocations: personal computers, golf, arts, movies, literature. Home: 50 Aiken St Apt 412 Norwalk CT 06851-2034 Office: Nadan Neuman Assocs 50 Aiken St Apt 412 Norwalk CT 06851-2034

NEUMAN, NANCY ADAMS MOSSHAMMER, civic leader; b. Greenwich, Conn., July 24, 1936; d. Alden Smith and Margaret (Mevis) Mosshammer; BA, Pomona Coll., 1957, LLD, 1983; MA, U. Calif. at

Berkeley, 1961; LHD, Westminster Coll., 1987; m. Mark Donald Neuman, Dec. 23, 1958; children: Deborah Neuman Metzler, Jennifer Neuman Joye, Jeffrey Abbott. William A. Johnson Disting. lectr. Am. govt. Pomona Coll., 1990; disting. vis. prof. Washington and Jefferson Coll., 1991, 94, Bucknell U., 1992. Pres., Lewisburg (Pa.) area League Women Voters, 1967-70; bd. dirs. LWV Pa., 1970-77, pres., 1975-77; bd. dirs. LWV U.S., 1977-90, 2d v.p., 1978-80, 1st v.p., 1982-84, pres., 1986-90; bd. dirs., pres. Pathmakers, Inc., 1993—; mem. Pa. Gov.'s Commn. on Mortgage and Interest Rates, 1973, Pa. Commonwealth Child Devel. Com., 1974-75, Nat. Commn. on Pub. Svc., 1987-90; bd. dirs. Housing Assistance Council, Inc., Washington, 1974—, pres., 1978-80; bd. dirs. Nat. Council on Agrl. Life and Labor, 1974-79, Nat. Rural Housing Coalition, 1975—, Pa. Housing Fin. Agy., 1975-80, Jud. Inquiry and Rev. Bd. Pa., 1989-93; Disciplinary Bd. Supreme Ct. Pa., 1980-85; mem. Pa. Gov.'s Task Force on Voter Registration, 1975-76, Nat. Task Force for Implementation Equal Rights Amendment, 1975-77; mem. adv. com. Pa. Gov.'s Interdepartmental Council on Seasonal Farmworkers, 1975-77; mem. Appellate Ct. Nominating Commn. Pa., 1976-79; mem. Fed. Jud. Nominating Commn. Pa., 1977-85, chmn., 1978-81, 82-83; mem. Pa. Gov.'s Study Commn. on Pub. Employee Relations, 1976-78; del. Internat. Women's Yr. Conf., 1977; bd. dirs. ERAmerica, Inc., 1st v.p., 1977-79, Nat. Low Income Housing Coalition, 1979-82; Rural Am., 1979-81, Fed. Home Loan Bank Pitts., 1979-82; mem. Nat. Adv. Com. for Women, 1978-79; mem. nat. adv. com. Pa. Neighborhood Preservation Support System, 1976-77; bd. dirs. Pa. Women's Campaign Fund, 1984-86, 92—, pres., 1992—, Rural Coalition, Washington, 1984-90, Com. on the Constitutional System, 1988-90, Am. Judicature Soc., 1989-93; exec. com. Leadership Conf. Civil Rights, 1986-90; bd. dirs. Pennsylvanians for Modern Cts., 1986— trustee Citizen's Rsch. Found., 1989—; mem. mid. dist. Pa. adv. com. judicial and U.S. atty nominations, 1993-94. Virginia Travis lectureship Bucknell U., 1982. Recipient Disting. Alumna award MacDuffie Sch. for Girls, 1979, Liberty Bell award Pa. Bar Assn., 1983, Barrows Alumni award Pomona Coll., 1987, Thomas P. O'Neill Jr. award for exemplary pub. svc., 1989; named Disting. Daughter of Pa., 1987 Woodrow Wilson vis. fellow, 1993—. Mem. ABA (com. election law and voter participation, 1986-90, accreditation com. 1990—), Am. Arbitration Assn. (bd. dirs. 1986-90). Home: 132 Verna Rd Lewisburg PA 17837-8747

NEUMAN, ROBERT HENRY, lawyer; b. N.Y.C., Oct. 14, 1936; s. Sydney A. and Ethel (Pekelner) N.; m. Emily Mann, Dec. 30, 1960 (div. 1975); children: David Marshall, Anthony Howard, Amanda Sarah; m. Joyce Thompson, May 5, 1975; 1 child, Nicole Joyce. AB magna cum laude, Harvard U., 1958, JD, 1961. Bar: N.Y. 1962, D.C. 1962. Ford Found. fellow West Africa, 1961-62; Assoc. Meyers & Batzell, Washington, D.C., 1962-64; asst. legal adviser U.S. Dept. of State, Washington, D.C., 1964-70; ptnr. Arent, Fox, Kintner, Plotkin & Kahn, Washington, D.C., 1970-92, Baker & Hostetler, Washington, 1993—. U.S. rep. to U.N. Conf. on Marine Pollution, 1969. Recipient Superior Honor award Dept. State, 1965. Mem. ABA, Fed. Bar Assn., Am. Soc. Internat. Law, Phi Beta Kappa. Avocation: sailing. Home: 3408 34th Pl NW Washington DC 20016-3136 Office: Baker & Hostetler 1050 Connecticut Ave NW Washington DC 20036-5303

NEUMAN, ROBERT STERLING, art educator, artist; b. Kellogg, Idaho, Sept. 9, 1926; s. Oscar C. and Katherine (Samuelson) N.; m. Helen Patricia Feddersen, Apr. 6, 1947 (div. 1971); children—Ingrid Alexandra, Elizabeth Catherine; m. Sunne Savage, June 3, 1979; 1 dau., Christina Mary. Student, U. Idaho, 1944-46; B.A.A., M.F.A., Calif. Coll. Arts and Crafts, 1947-51; student, San Francisco Sch. Fine Arts, 1950-51, Mills Coll., 1951. Assoc. prof. art Brown U., 1962-63; lectr. drawing Carpenter Center for Visual Arts, Harvard, 1963-72; prof. art, chmn. dept. Keene (N.H.) State Coll., 1972-90. Exhbns. include, Mus. Modern Art, Whitney Mus. Am. Art, Carnegie Internat., San Francisco Mus. Art, Boston Mus. Fine Arts, Worcester (Mass.) Art Mus., also, Japan and Europe. Served with AUS and USAAF, 1945-46. Recipient Howard Found. award for painting, 1967; Fulbright grantee, 1953-54; Guggenheim fellow, 1956-57; Bender grantee San Francisco Art Assn., 1952. Home: 135 Cambridge St Winchester MA 01890-2411

NEUMAN, SHLOMO P., hydrology educator; b. Zilina, Czechoslovakia, Oct. 26, 1938; came to U.S., 1963, naturalized, 1970; s. Alexander Neuman and Klara (Pikler) Lesny; m. Yael B. Boritzer, Jan. 30, 1965; children: Gil, Michal, Ariel. BSc in Geology, Hebrew U., Jerusalem, 1963; MS in Engring. Sci., U. Calif., Berkeley, 1966, PhD in Engring. Sci., 1968. Cert. profl. hydrogeologist. Acting asst. prof., asst. rsch. engr. dept. civil engring. U. Calif., Berkeley, 1968-70; vis. assoc. prof. dept. civil engring., 1974-75; sr. scientist, assoc. rsch. prof. Inst. Soil and Water Agrl. Rsch. Orgn., Bet-Dagan, Israel, 1970-74; prof. hydrology dept. hydrology and water resources U. Ariz., Tucson, 1975-88, Regents' prof. dept. hydrology and water resources, 1988—; vis. scientist dept. isotope Weizmann Inst. Sci., Rehovot, Israel, 1976; maitre de rsch. Ctr. d'Informatique Geologique, Ecole Mines Paris, Fountainebleau, France, 1978, dir. rsch., 1981; vis. prof. dept. fluid mechanics and heat transfer Tel-Aviv U., 1981; disting. lectr. in field. Mem. editorial adv. bd. Jour. Hydrology, 1977-84, Water Sci. and Tech. Libr. (The Netherlands), 1983-86, Stochastic Hydrology and Hydraulics, 1992—; assoc. editor Water Resources Rsch. Jour., 1987-93; contbr. articles to profl. jours. Hebrew U. scholar, 1962-63, Edwin Letts Oliver scholar, 1965-66; Jane Lewis fellow, 1966-68; recipient Cert. of Appreciation award USDA, 1975, C.V. Theis award Am. Inst. Hydrology, 1990. Fellow Geol. Soc. Am. (O.E. Meinzer award 1976, Birdsal Disting. Lectr. 1987), Am. Geophys. Union (Robert E. Horton award 1969, assoc. editor Water Resources Rsch. 1987—); mem. Soc. Petroleum Engrs. of AIME, U.S. Nat. Acad. Engring., Assn. Groundwater Scientists and Engrs. of Nat. Well Water Assn. (Sci. award 1989), Ariz. Hydrol. Soc., Internat. Assn. Hydrogeologists, Sigma Xi. Jewish. Office: U Ariz Dept Hydrology & Water Resources Tucson AZ 85721

NEUMAN, TED R., principal. Prin. Duluth (Ga.) High Sch. Recipient Blue Ribbon award U.S. Dept. Edn., 1990-91. Office: Duluth High Sch 3737 Brock Rd Duluth GA 30136-2799

NEUMAN, TOM S., emergency medical physician, educator; b. N.Y.C., July 23, 1946; s. Otto and Susan Ann (Baltaxe) N.; m. Doris Rubin, Aug. 24, 1969; children: Allison Rachel, Russell Solomon. AB, Cornell U., 1967; MD, NYU, 1971. Diplomate Nat. Bd. Med. Examiners, Am. Bd. Internal Medicine, Am. Bd. Preventative Medicine, Am. Bd. Emergency Medicine. Intern Bellevue Hosp., N.Y.C., 1971-72, resident, 1972-73; commd. med. officer USN, 1973; advanced through grades to capt. USNR, 1990; instr. Naval Undersea Med. Inst., New London, Conn., 1973-74; staff med. officer Submarine Devel. Group One, San Diego, 1974-76, 78-80; emergency room physician Chula Vista (Calif.) Community Hosp., 1975-80; attending physician VA Med. Ctr., La Jolla, Calif., 1976-78; fellow in pulmonary medicine and physiology U. Calif. Sch. Medicine at San Diego, 1976-78, clin. instr., 1978-80, asst. clin. prof., 1980-84, flight physician Life Flight Aeromed. Program, 1980-86, asst. dir. dept. emergency medicine, 1980-94; assoc. dir. dept. emergency medicine, 1994—; attending physician pulmonary divsn. U. Calif. Sch. Medicine at San Diego, 1980—, assoc. clin. prof. medicine and surgery, 1984-87, base hosp. physician, 1984—, dir. Hyperbaric Med. Ctr., 1984—; med. officer UDT/SEAL Res. Unit 119, San Diego, 1980-84, Mobile Diving and Salvage Unit One, USNR, San Diego, 1984-86, PRIMUS Unit 1942-A, U. Calif. at San Diego, 1988-90; sr. med. officer Seal Teams 1/3/5, USNR, Coronado, Calif., 1986-87; asst. officer in charge Med. Unit 1942-A, U. Calif. at San Diego, 1990—; mem. med. adv. bd. western regional underwater lab. program U. So. Calif. Marine Sci. Ctr., Catalina, 1985-89; assoc. adj. prof. medicine and surgery U. Calif. Sch. Medicine at San Diego, 1987-90, adj. prof. medicine and surgery, 1990—; mem. San Diego Coroner's com. for investigation of diving fatalities, 1974; med. diving cons. Vocat. Diver Tng. Facility Calif. Inst. Med, Chino, Calif., 1967; mem. task force City Mgr. on Carbon Monoxide Poisoning, San Diego, 1991; active Am. Nat. Stds. Inst. com. for minimal course content for recreational scuba instr. cert., 1992-94; chmn. emergency med. physician quality improvement com., 1992—; speaker in field. Author book chpts.; contbr. articles to profl. jours. Fellow Am. Coll. Physicians, Am. Coll. Preventative Medicine; mem. Am. Thoracic Soc., Am. Lung Assn., Indersea and Hyperbaric Med. Soc. (mem. program com. 1981-82, mem. nominations com. 1982-83, chmn 1988-89, mem. edn. com. 1982-87, chmn awards com. 1983-84, v.p. exec. com. 1983-84, mem. 1988-92, cp-chmn. credentials com. 1984-85, mem. editorial bd. Undersea and Hyperbaric Medicine, mem. North Pacific chpt.), Profl. Assn. Diving Instructors (emeritus). Avocations: scuba diving, fishing,

photography. Office: Dept Emergency Medicine UCSD Med Ctr 200 W Arbor Dr Bldg 8676 San Diego CA 92103-1911

NEUMANN, ALFRED KURT, public health physician, educator; b. Milw., July 25, 1930; s. Alfred P. and Hannah A. (Lange) N.; B.A., U. Wis., 1952, M.A., 1955; M.D., NYU, 1958; M.P.H., Harvard U., 1960; m. Charlotte Grantz, Sept. 10, 1959; children—Frederick, Peter, Daniel. Diplomate Am. Bd. Preventive Medicine. Intern, Kings County Gen. Hosp., Bklyn., 1958-59; resident in preventive medicine Mass. Dept. Pub. Health-Harvard U., 1960-62; gen. practice medicine, Marathon, Wis., 1959; pub. health physician Mass. Dept. Pub. Health, 1960-61, asst. med. dir., 1961-65; instr. Tufts U. Sch. Medicine, Boston, 1963-65; dir. Health Dept. Brookline (Mass.), 1964-65; lectr. Johns Hopkins U., Balt., 1965-68; asst. prof. UCLA, 1968-71, assoc. prof., 1972-76; prof. Sch. Pub. Health, 1977—, dir. preventive medicine residency program, 1986—; assoc. dean of students, sch. pub. health, 1986-88; vis. prof. People's Republic China, 1983, 85, 86; officer rural health project Narangwal, India, 1965-68; prin. investigator, co-dir. Danfa Comprehensive Rural Health Project, Ghana, 1970-79; cons. World Bank, WHO, UNFPA, Am. Pub. Health Assn.; chmn. Internat. Health Adv. Com., Project Concern Internat.; sec., bd. dirs. New Era Found. for Internat. Devel., Inc., N.Y.C.; sr. adv. Health for Humanity, 1994—; Fellow Soc. Applied Anthropology, Am. Pub. Health Assn.; mem. Wis. Acad. Sci., Arts and Letters, African Studies Assn., Internat. Health Soc. (pres. 1985-86), Delta Omega. Baha'i. Contbr. articles to profl. jours. Home: 520 20th St Santa Monica CA 90402-3028 Office: UCLA Sch Pub Health Rm 36-081 CHS Los Angeles CA 90024-1300

NEUMANN, ANDREW CONRAD, geological oceanography educator; b. Oak Bluffs, Mass., Dec. 21, 1933; s. Andrew Conrad Neumann and Faye Watson (Gilmore) Gilmour; m. Jane Spaeth, July 7, 1962; children: Jennifer, Christopher, Jonathan. BS in Geology, Bklyn. Coll., 1955; MS in Oceanography, Tex. A&M U., 1958; PhD in Geology, Lehigh U., 1963. Asst. prof. marine geology Lehigh U., Bethlehem, Pa., 1963-65; asst. prof. marine sci. U. Miami, Fla., 1965-69, assoc. prof. marine sci., 1969-72; prof. marine sci. U. N.C., Chapel Hill, 1972-85, Bowman and Gray prof. geol. oceanography, 1985—; program dir. NSF, Washington, 1969-70; Kenan prof. U. Edinburgh, Scotland, 1978; summer vis. investigator U.S. Geol. Survey, Woods Hole, Mass., 1981—, Woods Hole Oceanographic Inst., 1981—; vis. prof. U. Naples, Italy, 1984, Eötvös U., Budapest, Hungary, 1991. Contbr. articles to profl. jours. Trustee Bermuda Biol. Sta. for Research Inc., 1972-76. Recipient Disting. Alumni award Bklyn. Coll., 1987. Fellow Geol. Soc. Am.; mem. Soc. Econ. Paleontologists and Mineralogists, N.C. Acad. Sci. Avocations: fishing, gardening, sailing. Office: U NC Dept Marine Scis 1205 Venable Hall 045a Chapel Hill NC 27599-3300*

NEUMANN, CHARLES HENRY, mathematics educator; b. Washington, Jan. 30, 1943; s. Bernhardt Walter and Emma (Habitz) N.; m. Cheryl Elaine Girard, June 18, 1965; children: Matthew Roy, Kristen Elizabeth. AS, Alpena (Mich.) C.C., 1962; BS in Math., Mich. State U., 1964, M.A.T. in Math., 1965. Sci. tchr. Alpena Pub. Schs., 1965-66; instr. math. Alpena C.C., 1966-84, math. sci. dept. chair, 1969-84; instr. math. Oakland C.C., Bloomfield Hills, Mich., 1984—; bd. dirs. Blue Cross Blue Shield-Mich., Detroit, 1986-94. Scoutmaster troop 92 Boy Scouts Am., Alpena, 1981-84; bd. dirs. Mich. Vision Svc. Assn., Lansing, 1984-89, Ohio Vision Svc. Assn., Columbus, 1988-89; mem. exec. com. Oakland County (Mich.) Dem. Mem. NEA (del. 1974-80, adv. com. on membership 1993—), Math. Assn. Am., Am. Math. Assn of Two-Yr. Colls., Mich. Edn. Assn. (bd. dirs. 1974-80), Mich. Edn. Spl. Svcs. (trustee 1975-93, pres. 1976-93), Mich. Math. Assn. of Two-Yr. Colls., Mich. Assn. Higher Edn. (v.p. two-yr. colls. 1977—), Oakland C.C. Faculty Assn. (v.p. 1994-95, pres. 1995—), Phi Kappa Phi. Lutheran. Avocations: collecting antique books, racquetball, cross country skiing. Home: 5871 Warbler Dr Clarkston MI 48346 Office: Oakland C C 2900 Featherstone Auburn Hills MI 48326

NEUMANN, FORREST KARL, hospital administrator; b. St. Louis, Oct. 7, 1930; s. Metz Earl and Ruth (McGhee) N.; m. Erika Stefanie Turkl, Feb. 11, 1955; children: Tracey Neumann Liberson, Karen Neumann Kruger, Scott, Lisa. B.S., Roosevelt U., 1953; M.S. in Hosp. Adminstrn., Northwestern U., 1955. Adminstrv. resident Louis A. Weiss Hosp., Chgo., 1954-55; mem. staff Sparrow Hosp., Lansing, Mich., 1958—; chief exec. officer, dir. Edward W. Sparrow Hosp., Lansing, Mich., 1962—; pres., chief exec. officer, dir. Mason Gen. Hosp., Mich., 1973-83; chmn. bd. Caymich Ins. Co. Ltd., Cayman Islands, 1979—, Caymich Ins. Co. (Barbados) Ltd., 1986—, Mich. Hosp. Assn. Mut. Ins. Co., 1979—; pres., chief exec. officer Sparrow, Inc., 1984—; bd. dirs. First Am. Bank-Central, First Am. Bank Corp., Auto Owners Ins. Co., Physician's Health Plan, PHP-Lansing. Chmn. hosp. div. United Community Chest, 1965-68, chmn. budget steering com., 1970-71, bd. dirs., mem. exec. com., 1969-75; mem. adv. com. Capitol Area Comprehensive Health Planning Assn., 1969, bd. dirs., 1971-75, treas., 1974-75; mem., vice chmn. Mich. Arbitration Adv. Com., 1975-80; bd. dirs. Grad. Med. Edn., Inc., 1971-80, pres., 1972-73, treas. 1973. Fellow Am. Coll. Hosp. Adminstrs.; mem. Southwestern Mich. Hosp. Council (trustee 1968-73, pres. 1970-71), Am. Hosp. Assn. (del. 1979-87), Mich. Hosp. Assn. (1st v.p. 1972-73, bd. dirs., exec. com., treas. 1974-75, chmn. 1976-77, Meritorious Key award 1979). Lodge: Rotary (Lansing). Office: Michigan Hospital Assoc Ins Co 6215 West St Joseph Highway Lansing MI 48917

NEUMANN, FREDERICK LOOMIS, accounting educator, academic administrator, consultant; b. New Britain, Conn., Nov. 16, 1930; s. Carl Samuel and Rachel Louise (Clark) N.; m. Elizabeth Ann Robinson, Sept. 10, 1960; children: Bradford E., Carla C., Marshall G. A.B magna cum laude, Dartmouth Coll., 1952; M.B.A. with highest distinction, Amos Tuck Sch. Bus. Adminstrn., 1953; M.B.A., U. Chgo., 1965, Ph.D., 1967. CPA, Ill., Conn.; cert. internal auditor. Sr. acct. Arthur Andersen & Co., N.Y.C., 1956-62; mem. faculty U. Ill., Urbana-Champaign, 1965—, asst. prof. accountancy, 1965-70, assoc. prof., 1970-75, prof., 1975—; Price Waterhouse prof. auditing, 1979—, head dept. accountancy, 1981-86, assoc. dean acad. affairs, 1992—; cons. in field; pres. Fedn. Schs. of Accountancy, 1987—; sec. Adminstrs. of Accountancy Programs, 1986. Author: Case Studies in Computer Control and Auditing, 1975, Questions and Problems in Auditing, 11th edit., 1995; editor: Issues in Acctg. Edn., 1991—; contbr. numerous articles to profl. jours., chpts. to books. Cons. Champaign County Headstart and Child Devel. Corp., 1970-87; treas. Wesley Meth. Ch., 1987—; chmn. com. Champaign County Regional Blood Ctr., 1982—; bd. govs. Univ. YMCA, 1990—, chmn., 1992—; mem. Univ. Senate. Lt. (j.g.) USNR, 1953-56, comdr. Res. Ford Found. fellow, 1962-65, Ernst & Whinney fellow, 1972-73. Mem. Inst. Decision Scis., Am. Acctg. Assn. (chmn. auditing sect. 1976-77, chmn. teaching and curriculum sect. 1991-92, named Outstanding Audit Educator 1991, named for Disting. Svc. in Auditing Abroad, 1994, dir. pubs.-elect 1994—, mem. exec. com. 1995), Ill. CPA Soc. (bd. dirs. 1983-85), Am. Inst. CPAs, Inst. Internal Auditors (Leon Radde Outstanding Educator award 1986), EDP Auditors Assn., Acctg. Historians, Inst. Mgmt. Accts., Fin. Execs. Inst., Phi Beta Kappa (treas. local chpt. 1981—), Beta Gamma Sigma, Beta Alpha Psi. Home: 2211 S Cottage Grove Ave Urbana IL 61801-6815 Office: U Ill 1206 S 6th St Champaign IL 61820-6915

NEUMANN, HARRY, philosophy educator; b. Dormoschel, Germany, Oct. 10, 1930; came to U.S., 1937, naturalized, 1948; s. Siegfried and Frieda (Lion) N.; m. Christina Sephnt, Sept. 25, 1959. B.A., St. John's Coll., 1952; M.A., U. Chgo., 1954; Ph.D., Johns Hopkins U., 1962; postgrad., U. Heidelberg, Germany, 1956-58. Mem. faculty Mich. State U., 1962-63, Lake Forest Coll., 1963-65; prof. philosophy and govt. Claremont Grad. Sch. Scripps Coll., Claremont (Calif.) Grad. Sch., 1966—; research assoc. Rockefeller Inst., N.Y.C., 1963. Author: Liberalism, 1991; contbr. articles profl. jours. With AUS 1954-56. Classical Philosophy fellow Ctr. Hellenic Studies, Dumbarton Oaks, Washington, 1965-66; rsch. fellow Salvatori Ctr. for Study of Individual Freedom in the Modern World, 1970; rsch. fellow Earhart Found., 1973-74, 78, 82, 86, 90, 94. Mem. Univ. Ctrs. Rational Alternatives, Univ. Profs. for Acad. Order, John Brown Cook Assn. for Freedom (advisor). Home: Scripps Coll Claremont CA 91711

NEUMANN, HERSCHEL, physics educator; b. San Bernardino, Calif., Feb. 3, 1930; s. Arthur and Dorothy (Greenhood) N.; m. Julia Black, June 15, 1951; 1 child, Keith. B.A. U. Calif., Berkeley, 1951; MS, U. Oreg., 1959; PhD, U. Nebr., 1965. Theoretical physicist Gen. Electric Co., Richland, Wash., 1951-57; instr. physics U. Nebr., Lincoln, 1964-65; asst. prof. physics

U. Denver, 1965-71, assoc. prof. physics, 1971-85, prof., chmn. physics, 1985—. Contbr. over 20 articles to profl. jours. Dir. numerous pub. outreach programs in physics. Mem. Am. Phys. Soc., Am. Assn. Physics Tchrs. Home: 2425 S St Paul St Denver CO 80210-5516 Office: U Denver Dept Physics and Astronomy Denver CO 80208-0202

NEUMANN, L. N., grain company executive; b. 1941. With Ctrl. Soya Co., Inc., Fort Wayne, Ind., 1964-73, Cook Grain Co. of Minnesota, Mpls., 1973-76, Porr Corp., Mpls., 1976-79; chmn. bd., CEO Benson-Quinn Co., Mpls., 1979—. Office: Benson-Quinn Co 1075 Grain Exchange Bldg Minneapolis MN 55415

NEUMANN, MARK W., congressman; b. Waukesha, Wis., Feb. 2, 1954; m. Sue; 3 children. BS, U. Wis., 1975. Real estate developer Neumann Devels., 1980—; mem. 104th Congress from 1st Wis. dist., 1994—. Office: US House Reps 1719 Longworth House Office Bldg Washington DC 20515-4901*

NEUMANN, ROBERT GERHARD, ambassador, consultant; b. Vienna, Austria, Jan. 2, 1916; s. Hugo and Stephanie (Taussky) N.; m. Marlen Eldredge, July 27, 1941; children: Ronald E., Gregory W. Diplome superieur, U. Rennes, France, 1936; diploma Consular Acad. Vienna, Geneva Sch. Internat. Studies, 1937; student, U. Vienna, 1938; M.A., Amherst Coll., 1940; Ph.D. (Shevlin fellow 1940-41), U. Minn., 1946. Instr. State Tchrs. Coll., Oshkosh, Wis., 1941-42; lectr. U. Wis., 1946-47; asst. prof. UCLA, 1947-52, asso. prof., 1952-58, prof., 1958-70; dir. Inst. Internat. and Fgn. Studies, 1959-65, chmn. Atlantic and West European Program, 1965-66; U.S. ambassador to Afghanistan Kabul, 1966-73; to Morocco Rabat, 1973-76; dir. transition team Dept. State, 1980-81; to Saudi Arabia Jidda, 1981; sr. staff assoc. Center for Strategic and Internat. Studies, 1976-80, vice chmn., 1980-81, cons., 1980-81, sr. advisor, 1982—; cons. to bus. and govt., 1983—. Author: The Government of the German Federal Republic, 1966, European and Comparative Government, 4th edit, 1968, Toward a More Effective Executive-Legislative Relationship in the Conduct of America's Foreign Policy, 1977; contbr.: The Austrian Solution, 1982; Contbr. articles to jours.; Editorial writer: Los Angeles Times, 1952-59. Chmn. internat. relations sect. Town Hall, 1956-62; mem. Calif. Rep. Cen. Com., 1954-60; bd. dirs. Coun. Am. Ambs., 1982—; vice chmn., trustee Moroccan-Am. Found., 1982-90; vice chmn. Am.-Saudi Bus. Roundtable, 1982-83, chmn., 1984-91; mem. exec. com. Islam and the West, 1984-88; mem. nat. adv. coun. Am. Inst. Islamic Affairs, 1985—; v.p. Am. Friends of Afghanistan, 1985—; hon. dir. Afghanistan Relief Com., 1985—; mem. regional task force Am.-Russian Rels., 1984—; mem. adv. bd. Nat. Coun. U.S.-Arab Rels., 1989—; founding mem. Reps. Abroad. Served from pvt. to 1st lt. AUS, 1942-46. Haynes Found. fellow, 1950-51; Social Sci. Research Council fellow, 1950-51; Fulbright fellow France, 1954-55; Nat. Woodrow Wilson Found. fellow, 1984-93; recipient hon. medal U. Brussels, 1955; decorated Legion of Honor (France), 1957; officers cross Order of Merit (Fed. Republic of Germany), 1963; Comdr.'s Cross, 1974; Order of the Star (Afghanistan), 1973; grand officier Order and Star of Ouissam Alaoui (Morocco), 1976; Knight Comdr.'s Cross and Star (Austria), 1991. Mem. Atlantic Council U.S. (sponsor), Inst. Strategic Studies London, Am., Internat. polit. sci. assns., Internat. Law Assn. Roman Catholic. Home: 4986 Sentinel Dr apt 301 Bethesda MD 20816-3580 The following thoughts and principles, forged on the ladder to success, took their roots earlier when I was a prisoner in Nazi concentration camps and then a penniless immigrant to America: 1. When in doubt, choose the road of courage. The dynamics of action will carry others with you and confound your opponents. 2. While action must be carefully considered, it is generally better to act than not to act. It is easier to correct the course of action than to move from inaction to action. 3. Dream big and without restraint. There will always be time afterwards to reduce the scope of your action in the light of confining realities. But if you start dreaming small, you shackle your imagination before that moment. 4. Have some reasonable and constant ideas as to what you will not put up with and examine your conscience from time to time to check the possible corrosion success might have wrought. It might keep you honest, or, at least—humble.

NEUMANN, ROY COVERT, architect; b. Columbus, Nebr., Mar. 1, 1921; s. LeRoy Franklin and Clara Louise (Covert) N.; m. Hedy Charlotte Schultz, Aug. 28, 1948; children: Tali, Scott. Student, Midland Coll., 1939-40, U. Calif.-Berkeley Armed Forces Inst., overseas, 1942-43; AB, U. Nebr., 1948, BArch, 1949; MA, Harvard U., 1952; postgrad., U. Wis., Iowa State U. Registered profl. architect, Iowa, Nebr., Kans., Minn., S.D., N.Y., N.J., Mass., Ohio, Pa., Tenn., Ky., Va., W.Va., Ga., Mich., Mo., Ill., Wis., Tex., Colo. Ptnr., architect R. Neumann Assocs., Lincoln, Nebr., 1952-55; officer mgr. Sargent, Webster, Crenshaw & Folley, Schenectady, N.Y., 1955-59; dir. architecture, ptnr. A.M. Kinney Assocs., Cin., 1959-65; officer mgr. Hunter, Campbell & Rea, Johnstown, Pa., 1965-66; dir. architecture, ptnr. Stanley Cons., Muscatine, Iowa, 1966-76; pres., chmn. bd. Neumann Monson P.C., Iowa City, 1976—; ptnr. Clinton St. Ptnrs., Iowa City, 1983—, Iris City Devel. Co. Mt. Pleasant, Iowa, 1986. Prin. works include Harbour Facilities, Antigua, W.I., S.C. Johnson Office Bldg., Racine, Wis., Iowa City Transit Facility Bldg., addition to Davenport Ctrl. High Sch., V.A. Administrv. Office Bldg., Iowa City, Johnson County Office Bldg., Iowa City Mercer Park Aquatic Ctr., Iowa City, Coll. Bus. U. Iowa, Iowa City, renovation Lawrence County Courthouse, Deadwood, S.D. Mem. bd. edn. Muscatine Community Sch. Dist., 1974-76. Served with USN, 1942-46, PTO. Recipient Honor award Portland Cement Assn., 1949. Mem. AIA (Honor award 1975), Constrn. Specifications Inst. (pres. 1974-76, Honor award 1983, 84, 85, 86), Soc. Archtl. Historians, Archtl. Assn. London, U. Nebr. Alumni Assn., Harvard U. Alumni Assn., Iowa City U. of C., Phi Kappa Psi, Univ. Athletic Club (Iowa City), Masons, Ea. Star, Elks. Republican. Presbyterian. Avocations: golf, fishing, medieval history, big band music. Home: 2014 Burnside Dr Muscatine IA 52761-3510 Office: Neumann Monson Architects 111 E College St Iowa City IA 52240-4002

NEUMANN, W. MICHAEL, chemicals executive. Grad., U. Conn., 1970. With Oxy (formally Cities Scv.), Houston, 1970-91; pres., COO Trident NGL, Inc., The Woodlands, Tex., 1991—. Office: Trident NGL Inc 10200 Grogans Mill Rd The Woodlands TX 77380

NEUMANN, WILLIAM ALLEN, judge; b. Minot, N.D., Feb. 11, 1944; s. Albert W. and Opal Olive (Whitlock) N.; m. Jaqueline Denise Buechler, Aug. 9, 1980; children: Andrew, Emily. BSBA, U. N.D., 1965; JD, Stanford U., 1968. Bar: N.D. 1969, U.S. Dist. Ct. N.D. 1969. Pvt. practice law Williston, N.D., 1969-70, Bottineau, N.D., 1970-79; former judge N.D. Dist. Ct., Rugby, 1979-92; justice N.D. Supreme Ct., Bismarck, 1993—; chmn. elect N.D. Jud. Conf., 1985-87, chmn. 1987-89. Mem. ABA, State Bar Assn. N.D., Am. Judicature Soc. Lutheran. Avocation: pvt. pilot. Office: ND Supreme Ct Judicial Wing 1st Fl 600 E Boulevard Ave Bismarck ND 58505-0660

NEUMARK, GERTRUDE FANNY, materials science educator; b. Nuremberg, Germany, Apr. 29, 1927; came to U.S., 1939; d. Siegmund and Bertha (Forchheimer) N.; m. Henry Rothschild, Mar. 18, 1950. BA, Barnard Coll., 1948; MA, Radcliffe Coll., 1949; PhD, Columbia U., 1951. Advanced rsch. physicist Sylvania Rsch. Labs., Bayside, N.Y., 1952-60; sr. mem. tech. staff Philips Labs., Briarcliff Manor, N.Y., 1960-85; cons. Am. Inst. Physics, N.Y.C., 1968-69; NSF vis. prof., 1982; panelist NRC; panelist, reviewer NSF. Contbr. Encyclopedia of Advanced Materials, numerous articles to sci. jours., chpt. to books; patentee in field. Rice fellow, 1948, Dana fellow, 1948, AAUW Anderson fellow, 1951. Fellow Am. Phys. Soc. (Goeppert-Meyer award com. 1987-89); mem. Materials Rsch. Soc., Electrochem. Soc. (sr.), Soc. Women Engrs. (sr.), Am. Chem. Soc. Office: Columbia U 1137 SW Mudd Bldg New York NY 10027

NEUMARK, MICHAEL HARRY, lawyer; b. Cin., Oct. 28, 1945; s. Jacob H. and Bertha (Zubor) N.; m. Sue Daly, June 5, 1971; children: Julie Rebecca, John Adam. BS in Bus., Ind. U., 1967; JD, U. Cin., 1970. Bar: Ohio 1970, D.C. 1972. Atty. chief counsel's office IRS, Washington, 1970-74; acting br. chief IRS, 1974-75; sr. atty. regional counsel's office IRS, Cin., 1975-77; assoc. Paxton & Seasongood Legal Profl. Assn., Cin., 1977-80; ptnr. Thompson, Hine & Flory, 1980—, mem. mgmt. com., 1993—; chmn. So. Ohio Tax Inst., 1987; mem. IRS and Bar Liaison Com.; speaker at profl. confs. Contbr. articles to profl. jours. Bd. dirs. 1987 World Figure Skating Chamionship, Cin., 1986-89; precinct exec. Hamilton County Rep. Orgn.,

1980-86; vol. referee Hamilton County Juvenile Ct., 1980-86; adv. bd. Cin. Entrepreneurship Inst.; trustee St. Rita Sch. for Deaf, 1991—. Recipient Commendation Resolution Sycamore Twp., 1987. Mem. ABA (tax sect. S corp. subcom. chmn. 1981-88), Ohio State Bar ssn., Cin. Bar Assn. (recognition award 1985, treas., bd. trustees 1988-91, trustee 1992—, chair tax sect., 1990-91, pres.-elect 1995), Kenwood Country Club, Indian Hill Club. Republican. Avocations: golf, travel. Office: Thompson Hine & Flory 312 Walnut St Cincinnati OH 45202-4024

NEUMEIER, JOHN, choreographer, ballet company director; b. Milw., Feb. 24, 1942; s. Albert and Lucille N. BA, Marquette U., 1961, DFA (hon.), 1987; student, Stone-Camryn Ballet Sch., Chgo., 1957-62, Royal Ballet Sch., London, 1962-63; student of Vera Volkova, Copenhagen, 1962-63. Dancer Sybil Shearer Co., Chgo., 1960-62, Stuttgart (Fed. Republic Germany) Ballet, 1963-69; artistic dir. Frankfurt (Fed. Republic Germany) Opera Ballet, 1969-73, Hamburg (Fed. Republic Germany) State Opera Ballet, 1973—; prof. City of Hamburg, 1987; found. ballet sch. Hamburg State Opera, 1978; found. ballet ctr. John Neumeier, ballet sch., Hamburg State Opera co. tng. under one roof., 1989. Guest choreographer for various cos. including Am. Ballet Theatre, Royal Ballet London, Royal Danish Ballet, Nat. Ballet Can., Royal Winnipeg Ballet, Stuttgart Ballet, Munich Opera, Vienna Opera, Ballet du XX siecle, Brussels, Opera de Paris, Opera of Stockholm; guest opera dir.: Otello, Munich Opera, Hamburg State Opera, ballet dir.: films Rondo, 1971 (Prix Italia 1972), Third Symphony of Gustav Mahler (Golden Camera award 1978), Legend of Joseph, Wendung (String Quintet in C major by Schubert), 1979, Scenes of Childhood, The Lady of the Camellias, 1986, Othello, 1987. Decorated knight's cross Danebrog Order (Denmark); recipient Dance mag. award, 1983, Fed. German Cross of Merit, 1987, German Dance prize, 1988; title of Prof. conferred by City of Hamburg, 1987, Deutscher Tanzpreis, Fed. Republic of Germany, 1988; recipient Prix Diaghilev award, France, 1988, Order Des Arts et des Lettres award French Minister Culture, 1991, Carina Ari award, Stockholm, 1994. Mem. Acad. der Kuenste Hamburg, Acad. der Kuenste Berlin. Roman Catholic. Office: Ballettzentrum Hamburg, Caspar-Voght-Strasse 54, D-20535 Hamburg Germany

NEUMEYER, JOHN LEOPOLD, research company administrator, chemistry educator; b. Munich, Germany, July 19, 1930; came to U.S., 1945, naturalized, 1950; s. Albert and Martha (Stern) N.; m. Evelyn Friedman, June 24, 1956; children: Ann Martha, David Alexander, Elizabeth Jean. BS, Columbia U., 1952; PhD, U. Wis., 1961. Rsch. chemist Ethicon Inc., New Brunswick, N.J., 1952-57, FMC Corp., Princeton, N.J., 1961-63; sr. staff chemist Arthur D. Little Inc., Cambridge, Mass., 1963-69; prof. medicinal chemistry, chemistry Northeastern U., Boston, 1969-91, dir. grad. sch., 1978-85, disting. emeritus prof., 1992—; chmn. bd., co-founder Rsch. Biochem. Internat., Natick, Mass., 1981—; cons. in field. Patentee in field. Contbr. articles to profl. jours., also chpts. to books in field. Mem. Bd. Health, Wayland, Mass., 1968-75, Pesticide Bd., Mass., 1972-75. Served to capt. U.S. Army, 1953-55. Recipient Lunsford Richardson award, 1961, Marie Curie award in Nuclear Medicine, 1992; Sr. Hayes Fulbright fellow, 1975-76. Fellow AAAS (mem. at large 1983-87, chmn. pharm. sci. sect. 1992-93), Am. Assn. Pharm. Scis., Acad. Pharm Scis. (rsch. achievement award in medicinal chemistry 1982, Northeastern U. faculty lectr. award 1978, U. disting. prof. 1982-92); mem. Am. Soc. Neurosci., Am. Soc. Exptl. Pharm. & Exptl. Therapeutics, Am. Chem. Soc. (councilor 1985—, trustee 1989-93, bd. editors Jour. Medicinal Chemistry 1974-88, chmn. div. medicinal chem. 1982). Office: Rsch Biochems Internat 1 Strathmore Rd Natick MA 01760

NEUNZIG, CAROLYN MILLER, middle school educator; b. L.I., May 5, 1930; kd. Stanley and Grace (Walsh) Miller; m. Herbert Neunzig, May 28, 1955; children: Kurt Miller, Keith Weidler. BA, Beaver Coll., Glen Side, Pa., 1953; MSSc, Syracuse U., 1989; postgrad., Adelphi U.; Cert., N.C. State U., Raleigh. Reading tchr. grades K-6 St. Timothy's Sch., Raleigh, N.C., 1971-83, 5th grade tchr., 1983-88, 5th grade lead tchr., 1986-88; tchr. English and geography 7th grade St. Timothy's Mid. Sch., Raleigh, 1991—; tchr Am. govt. 12th grade St. Timothy's Mid. Sch./Hale High Sch., Raleigh, 1991-93; instr. continuing edn. program history Meredith Coll., Raleigh, 1990-91, spl. high sch. registration commr., 1991-93, instr. continuing edn. program in history, 1995-96. Mem. Am. Acad. Polit. and Social Sci., Acad. Polit. Sci., Nat. Coun. for Social Studies, Nat. Coun. Tchrs. English.

NEUSCHEL, ROBERT PERCY, educator, former management consultant; b. Hamburg, N.Y., Mar. 13, 1919; s. Percy J. and Anna (Becker) N.; m. Dorothy Virginia Maxwell, Oct. 20, 1944; children:—Kerr Anne Ziprick, Carla Becker Neuschel Wyckoff, Robert Friedrich (Fritz). B.A., Denison U., 1941; M.B.A., Harvard U., 1947. Indsl. engr. Sylvania Elec. Products Co., Inc., 1947-49; with McKinsey & Co., Inc., 1950-79, sr. partner, dir., 1967-79; prof. corp. governance, assoc. dean J. L. Kellogg Grad. Sch. Mgmt.; former dir. Northwestern U., assoc. dean J.L. Kellogg Sch. Mgmt.; mem. exec. coun. Internat. Air Cargo Forum, 1988—; mem. com. study air passenger svc. and safety NRC, 1989—; bd. dirs. Butler Mfg. Co., Combined Ins. Co. Am., Templeton, Kenly & Co., TNT Freightways Co.; lectr. in field; mem. McKinsey Found. Mgmt. Research, Inc.; transp. task force Reagan transition team. Contbr. to profl. jours. Pres. Bd. Edn., Lake Forest, Ill., 1965-70; rep. Nat. council Boy Scouts Am., 1970—, mem. N.E. exec. coun., 1969—; chmn. bd. Lake Forest Symphony, 1973; bd. dirs. Loyola U., Chgo., Chgo. Boys' Club, Nat. Ctr. Voluntary Action, Inst. Mgmt. Consultants; trustee N. Suburban Mass Transit, 1972-73, Loyola Med. Ctr.; mem. adv. coun. Kellogg Grad. Sch. Mgmt., Northwestern U., White House conferee Drug Free Am.; mem. Nat. Petroleum Coun. Transp. and Supply Com. Served to capt. USAAF, World War II. Named Transporation Man of Yr. Chitransp. Assoc., 1994. Fellow Acad. Advancement Corp. Governance; mem. Transp. Assn. Am., Nat. Def. Transp. Assn. (mem. subcom. transp. tech. agenda 1990—). Presbyterian (ruling elder). Clubs: Harvard Bus. Sch. (pres. 1964-65), Economic, Executive, Chicago, Mid America, Mid-Day (Chgo.); Onwentsia (Lake Forest). Home: 101 Sunset Pl Lake Forest IL 60045-1834 Office: 1936 Sheridan Rd Evanston IL 60208-0002 My observations and experiences with corporate executives convince me that leadership is based less on sheer intelligence and more on fundamental qualities of character. By traits of character I would suggest such things as trust, staying power, guts, fairness, maturity, and the capacity to be 'big'. And the primary task of the individual leader is, above all else, to manage himself—his time, talents, emotions, sense of values, and priorities, as a living example to those who follow his leadership.

NEUSNER, JACOB, humanities and religious studies educator; b. Hartford, Conn., July 28, 1932; m. Suzanne Richter, Mar. 15, 1964; children: Samuel Aaron, Eli Ephraim, Noam Mordecai Menahem, Margalit Leah Berakhah. AB in History magna cum laude, Harvard U., 1953; postgrad. (Henry fellow), Lincoln Coll., Oxford, Eng., 1953-54; postgrad. (Fulbright scholar), Hebrew U., 1957-58; M.H.L., Jewish Theol. Sem. Am., 1960, DHL (hon.), 1987; Ph.D. in Religion (Univ. scholar), Columbia U., 1960; A.M. ad eudem, Brown U., 1969; L.H.D., U. Chgo., 1978; D.Phil. (hon.), U. Cologne, 1979. Instr. religion Columbia U., 1960-61; asst. prof. Hebrew U. Wis.-Milw., 1961-62; research assto. Brandeis U., 1962-64; asst. prof. religion Dartmouth Coll., 1964-66; assoc. prof. Dartmouth Coll., Providence, 1966-68; prof. religious studies Brown U., Providence, 1968-75, prof. religious studies, Ungerleider Disting. scholar Judaic studies, 1975-82, Univ. prof., Ungerleider Disting. scholar, 1982-90; Disting. Rsch. prof. religious studies U. S. Fla., Tampa, 1990—; vis. prof. Jewish Theol. Sem. Am., summer 1977, Iliff Sch. Theology, Denver, summer 1978; Hill vis. prof. U. Minn., 1978; pres. Max Richter Found., 1969—; mem. bd. advisors I. Edward Kiev Library Found., 1977—, Ancient Biblical Manuscript Center Library, Sch. Theology, Claremont, 1978—; mem. Nat. Council for the Humanities, governing bd. Nat. Endowment Humanities, 1978-84; lectr. various orgns. Author: A Life of Yohanan ben Zakkai, 1962 (Abraham Berliner prize in Jewish history), A History of the Jews in Babylonia, 1965-70, Development of a Legend: Studies on the Traditions Concerning Yohanan ben Zakkai, 1970, Aphrahat and Judaism: The Christian-Jewish Argument in Fourth Century Iran, 1971, The Rabbinic Traditions about the Pharisees before 70, 1971, Eliezer ben Hyrcanus: The Tradition and the Man, 1973, The Ideal of Purity in Ancient Judaism, 1973, A History of the Mishnaic Law of Purities, 1974-80, Judaism: The Evidence of the Mishnah, 1981, others; author numerous textbooks including American Judaism, Adventure in Modernity, 1972, From Politics to Piety: The Emergence of Pharisaic Judaism, 1973, 78, Invitation to the Talmud: A Teaching Book, 1974, Between Time and Eternity: The Essentials of Judaism, 1976, Form-Analysis and Exegesis: A Fresh

Approach to the Interpretation of Mishnah, 1980; editor numerous books including Studies in Judaism in Late Antiquity, 1973—, Studies in Judaism in Modern Times, 1975—, Library of Judaic Learning, 1975—, Brown Judaic Studies, 1976—, Chicago Studies in the History of Judaism, 1980—, Basic Jewish Ideas, 1981—; founder, editor-in-chief Brown Studies on Jews and their Societies, 1985—; mem. bd. cons.: Religious Traditions, 1977—; mem. editorial bd.: The Second Century, 1980—, Studies in Religion/Sciences Religieuses, 1981-83, Assn. for Jewish Studies Rev, 1981-83, Jour. Am. Acad. Religion, 1985—, Hebrew Ann. Rev., 1985—, Religious and Theol. Studies, 1985—; contbg. editor: Moment, 1977—, The Reconstructionist, 1983—. Kent fellow Nat. Council for Religion in Higher Edn., 1957-60; Lown fellow, 1962-64; Guggenheim Found. fellow, 1973-74, 79-80; Am. Council Learned Socs. fellow, 1966-67, 70-71; research grantee Am. Philos. Soc., 1965, 67; recipient Univ. Medal for Excellence Columbia U., 1974, Von Humboldt prize Von Humboldt Found., 1981, Disting. Humanitarian award Ohio State U., 1983. Fellow Royal Asiatic Soc., Am. Acad. Jewish Research (exec. com. 1976—); mem. Am. Acad. Religion (v.p., program chmn. 1967-68, pres. 1968-69, chmn. sect. on history of judaism 1979-81, 1981—), Am. Oriental Soc., Assn. Jewish Studies, N.Am. Soc. Study of Religion (founding com. 1986—, exec. com.), Am. Hist. Assn., Soc. Bibl. Lit., Phi Beta Kappa. Home: 735 14th Ave NE Saint Petersburg FL 33701-1413 Office: U South Fla Dept Religious Studies Tampa FL 33620 What makes us different from animals is our mind, our capacity to reason, to ask why. That is how we are "like God" in the Biblical sense: knowing the difference between good and evil, but also between what is true and what is untrue. That is, further, how we know God. My life is spent in the places where people learn to use their minds as best they can, and I teach, as best I can, how my student can do so. What a privilege!.

NEUSTADT, BARBARA MAE, artist, illustrator, etcher; b. Davenport, Iowa, June 21, 1922; d. David and Cora (Wollensky) N.; children: Diane Elizabeth Walbridge Wheeler, Laurie Barbara Meyer Hall. B.A., Smith Coll., 1944; postgrad., U. Chgo., 1945-46; Art Student's League scholar, Ohio U. Sch. Fine Arts, 1952. Art dir., designer Shepherd Cards, Inc., N.Y.C., 1956-63; dir., instr. Studio Graphics Workshop, Woodstock, N.Y., 1970—; lectr. on printmaking; participant artist in schs. program N.Y. State Schs., 1972-74; Bd. dirs., editor bull. LWV of Woodstock, 1969-70. Illustrator: The First Christmas, 1960, A Dream of Love (by Joseph Langland), 1986 (exhibited in Sarasota, Fla., 1986, Ga. So. Coll., Statesboro, 1987); commd. etching edits to Collectors Am. Art, N.Y.C., 1956, 58, 61, Internat. Graphic Arts Soc., N.Y.C., 1960, N.Y. Hilton Art Collection, N.Y.C., 1961; one-man shows include Ruth White Gallery, N.Y.C., 1958, Phila. Art Alliance, 1959, Portland (Maine) Mus. Art, 1965, L.I. U., Bklyn., 1973, Smith Coll., Northampton, Mass., 1974, Manatee Art League, Bradenton, Fla., 1980, 91, Sarasota, Fla., 1985, 86, Unity Gallery, Sarasota, 1994; group shows include Mus. Modern Art, N.Y.C., 1958-59, Yale U. Art Gallery, New Haven, 1960, Soc. Am. Graphic Artists nat. and internat. exhbns., 1954, 55, 57, 59, 60, 61, 73, 75, 76, 78, L'Antipoete Galerie Librairie, Paris, 1961, Quito, Ecuador, S.Am., 1987, Fla. Printmakers, 1987, 88, So. Printmakers, U. of S. Ala., 1988, Springfest '89, Bradenton, Fla., 1989, Invitational Manatee Art League, Bradenton, 1992, 93, 94, Soc. Exptl. Artists, Longboat Key, juried 1992, juried Shreveport, La., 1993, Nat. Mus. Women Arts, Washington, 1993-94, Longboat Key Art Ctr., 1994; represented in permanent collections including Met. Mus. Art, N.Y.C., Library of Congress, Nat. Gallery Art, Washington, Phila. Mus. Art, USIA, Bonn, Germany, N.Y. Public Library N.Y.C., Rare Book Rm., William A. Neilson Libr., Smith Coll., Henderson Libr., Ga. So. Coll. Found., Statesboro, Ga., McFarlin Libr., Spl. Collections, U. of Tulsa, 1990, Ward Meml. Collection, Gilkey Ctr. for Graphic Arts, Portland (Oreg.) Art Mus., 1992, Nat. Mus. Women Arts. Recipient prize Boston Printmakers, 1957, Joseph Pennell Meml. medal Phila. Watercolor Club, 1972; Yasuo Kuniyoshi Meml. award, 1978; Am. the Beautiful Fund of N.Y. of Natural Area Council grantee, 1973. Mem. Soc. Am. Graphic Artists (prize 1954, 78), Phila. Water Color Club (prize 1972), Soc. Exptl. Artists Fla., Fla. Printmakers, The So. Graphics Coun., Art Uptown Inc. Gallery (Sarasota, Fla.), Gallery Two (Rockville, Md.). Studio: Graphic Workshop Pleiades Press 3014 Ave C Holmes Beach FL 34217

NEUSTADT, DAVID HAROLD, physician; b. Evansville, Ind., Dec. 2, 1925; s. Mose and Leah (Epstein) N.; m. Carolyn Jacobson, June 15, 1952; children: Susan Miriam, Jeffrey Bruce, Robert Alan. Student, DePauw U., 1943-44, 46-47; M.D., U. Louisville, 1950. Intern Morrisania City Hosp., N.Y.C., 1950-51; resident in internal medicine Lenox Hill Hosp., N.Y.C., 1951-52; NIH trainee in rheumatic diseases Lenox Hill Hosp., 1952-53, resident in gastroenterology, 1953-54; practice medicine specializing in rheumatic diseases Louisville, 1954—; chief arthritis clinic Louisville Gen. Hosp., 1960-76; asst. prof. medicine St. Medicine, U. Louisville, 1963-67, asso. prof. clin. medicine, 1967-75, clin. prof. medicine, 1974—, head sect. rheumatic diseases, 1960-76; chief dept. medicine Jewish Hosp., Louisville, 1965-67; pres. med. staff Jewish Hosp., 1967-69; cons. in rheumatology VA, 1970—; advisor Network for Continuing Med. Edn., 1983—. Author: The Chemistry and Therapy of Collagen Diseases, 1963, (with other) Aspiration and Injection Therapy in Arthritis and Musculoskeletal Disorders, 1972; editor: (with other) Arthritis Abstracts, References Indexes, 1970-75; contbr. articles to profl. jours. Former pres., chmn. bd. med. sci. com. Ky. chpt. Arthritis Found. Served with AUS, 1944-46. Master Am. Coll. Rheumatology (mem. editorial bd. 1989—); fellow Am. Med. Writers Assn., ACP; mem. AMA, N.Y. Acad. Sci., Am. Rheumatism Assn. (exec. com., pres. ctrl. region 1982-84), N.Y. Rheumatism Soc., Ky. Rheumatism Assn. (pres. 1956-57), Internat. Soc. Internal Medicine, So. Med. Assn. (edn. com., sect. rheumatology), Am. Physicians Fellowship (nat. trustee 1984—), Spondylitis Assn. (adv. bd. 1986—, contbg. editor 1989—, mem. editorial bd. Arthritis Care and Rsch. Newsletter 1989—), Masons, Shriner. Jewish. Home: 216 Smithfield Rd Louisville KY 40207-1267 Office: Med Towers Louisville KY 40202 I believe the qualities necessary to achieve success include a combination of ability, commitment to hard work, enthusiasm or enjoyment of your work, plus a liberal chunk of optimism, faith, luck, and a supporting family and co-workers.

NEUSTADT, RICHARD ELLIOTT, political scientist, educator; b. Phila., June 26, 1919; s. Richard Mitchells and Elizabeth (Neufeld) N.; m. Bertha Frances Cummings, Dec. 21, 1945 (dec. 1984); children: Richard Mitchells, Elizabeth Ann; m. Shirley Williams, Dec. 19, 1987. AB, U. Calif., Berkeley, 1939; MA, Harvard U., 1941, PhD, 1951. Economist OPA, 1942; mem. staff Bur. Budget, 1946-50, White House, 1950-53; prof. pub. administrn. Cornell U., 1953-54; prof. govt. Columbia U., 1954-64; prof. govt. Harvard U., 1965-78, Lucius N. Littauer prof. pub. adminstrn., 1978-87, Douglas Dillon prof., 1987-89, assoc. dean John Fitzgerald Kennedy Sch. Govt., 1965-75, dir. Inst. Politics, 1966-71, prof. emeritus, 1989—; spl. cons. subcom. on nat. policy machinery U.S. Senate, 1959-61; mem. adv. bd. Commn. Money and Credit, 1960-61; spl. cons. to Pres. elect Kennedy, 1960-61, to subcom. on nat. security staffing and ops. U.S. Senate, 1962-68; cons. to Pres. Kennedy, 1961-63, Pres. Johnson, 1964-66, Dept. State, 1962-69, Bur. Budget, 1961-70, AEC, 1962-68, Rand Corp., 1964-79, Pres.'s Reorgn. Project, Office Mgmt. and Budget, 1977-79; vis. lectr. Nuffield Coll., Oxford, Eng., 1961-62, assoc. mem., 1965-67, 90-92; vis. prof., Princeton U., 1957, U. Calif., Berkeley, 1986, Cornell U., 1992, U. Essex, UK, 1994—. Author: Presidential Power, 1960, rev. 1990, Alliance Politics, 1970; (with Harvey V. Fineberg) The Swine Flu Affair, 1978, reissued as The Epidemic That Never Was, 1983; (with Ernest R. May) Thinking in Time, 1986; contbr. articles to mags., revs. Mem. staff Dem. Platform Com., 1952, 56, chmn., 1972; trustee Radcliffe Coll., 1976-80; mem. exec. bd. Coll. Letters & Scis., U. Calif., Berkeley, 1994—. With USNR, 1942-46. Fellow Ctr. Advanced Study in the Behavioral Scis., 1978-79. Fellow Am. Acad. Arts Scis; mem. Am. Polit. Sci. Assn., Nat. Acad. Pub. Adminstrn., Council Fgn. Rels., Inst. Strategic Studies, Am. Philos. Soc., Cosmos Club. Home: PO Box 1123 Wellfleet MA 02667-1123 Office: Kennedy Sch Govt Harvard U Cambridge MA 02138

NEUTHALER, PAUL DAVID, publisher; b. N.Y.C., Nov. 2, 1942; s.Jacob and Frances (Poses) N.; m. Paula Diane Wool, Nov. 20, 1965 (div.) 1976; m. Abbi Mae Greenfield, Dec. 19, 1982; children: Mindy, Howard, Jamie, Jacob. BA, Columbia U., 1964, MA, 1965, PhD, 1972. Pres. pub. Gen. Health Pub. Corp., N.Y.C., 1977-79; pres., chief exec. officer Warren Gorham & Lamont Inc., N.Y.C., 1980-84; pres., chief exec. officer and tech. pub. Bertelsmann Pub. Co., N.Y.C., 1984-86; exec. v.p. JPT Pub. Group, N.Y.C., 1986-90; chmn., chief exec. officer Bantam Doubleday Pub. Group, N.Y.C., 1990-91; pres., chief exec. officer prof. and tech. pub.

Bertelsmann Pub. Group Internat., N.Y.C., 1991—. Honoree United Jewish Appeal, N.Y.C., 1991. Mem. Assn. Am. Publishers (bd. dirs. 1990-91), University Club (N.Y.C.). Home: 33 E 70th St New York NY 10021-4946 Office: Bertelsmann Pub Group Internat 1540 Broadway New York NY 10036-4039

NEUTRA, DION, architect; b. Los Angeles, Oct. 8, 1926; s. Richard Joseph and Dione (Niedermann) N.; children: Gregory, Wendy, Haig, Nicholas. Student, Swiss Inst. Tech., 1947-48; B.Arch. cum laude, U. So. Calif., 1950. With Richard J. Neutra (architect), Los Angeles, 1942-55; assoc. Neutra & Alexander, Los Angeles, 1955-60; asso. Robert E. Alexander, Los Angeles, 1960-62; prin. Dion Neutra and Assos., Los Angeles, 1962-65; prin. Richard & Dion Neutra, Architects and Assos., Los Angeles, 1965—; pres. Richard J. Neutra, Inc., 1970—; exec. cons. Inst. for Survival Through Design, L.A.; lectr. Calif. State U., L.A., Sacramento City Coll., Mira Costa State U., Cabrillo State U., Soka U. Tokyo, San Diego City Coll., Germany, Switzerland, Eng., Austria; vis. prof. Calif. State U.-Pomona 1970, 85-86; vis. lectr. USC. Prin. works include various residential, ednl., religious and instnl. facilities including Am. Embassy Karachi, Pakistan, Gettysburg Meml., Simpson Coll. Libr., Adelphi Coll. Libr., Libr. and Resource Ctr. for City of Huntington Beach, Calif., Treetops Townhouses, 1980; exhbns. "View from Inside", 1984, 86, 92, "Visions & Exiles", Vienna, 1995. Mem. Silver Lake-Echo Park Dist. Plan Adv. Com., Master Plan City of Los Angeles, 1970-71; mem. Citizens to Save Silver Lake, 1973-76; Dir. Child Care and Devel. Services, 1970-71. Served with USNR, 1944-46. Neutra Place a street named in firm's honor in Silverlake, the site of 10 Neutra designs, 1992; Neutra Centennial named in his honor, 1992. Mem. AIA, Nat. Council Archtl. Registration Bds., Alpha Rho Chi. Studio: Richard & Dion Neutra 2440 Neutra Pl Los Angeles CA 90039-3141

NEUTS, MARCEL FERNAND, statistician, educator; b. Ostend, Belgium, Feb. 21, 1935; came to U.S., 1958; s. Achille Jan and Marceline (Neuts) N.; m. Olga Alida Topff, June 27, 1959; children: Chris, Myriam, Catherine, Debbie. Lic. in math., U. Louvain, Belgium, 1956; MS in Stats., Stanford U., 1959, PhD in Stats., 1961. Instr. Lovanium U., Leopoldville, Zaire, 1956-57; researcher U. Louvain, 1960-62; asst. prof. Purdue U., 1962-64, assoc. prof., 1964-68, prof., 1968-76; vis. prof. Cornell U., 1968-69; Unidel prof. U. Del., 1976-85; prof. systems and indsl. engring. U. Ariz., Tucson, 1985—; lectr. math. scis. Johns Hopkins U., Balt., 1979. Author: Probability, 1973, Matrix-Geometric Solutions in Stochastic Models - An Algorithmic Approach, 1981, Structured Stochastic Matrices of M/G/1 Type and Their Applications, 1989, Algorithmic Probability: A Collection of Problems, 1995; editor: Algorithmic Methods in Probability, 1977; contbr. articles to profl. jours.; coord. editor Jour. Applied Probability and Advances Applied Probability, 1982—; editor in chief, founding editor: Stochastic Models, 1983—. Fellow Commn. Relief Belgium, 1958-60. Recipient Sr. U.S. Scientist award Alexander von Humboldt Found., Fed. Republic of Germany, 1983; Rsch. fellow Ctr. Advanced Study U. Del., 1980-81. Fellow Inst. Math. Stats.; mem. Math. Assn. Am. (Lester R. Ford award 1969), Ops. Rsch. Soc. Am. (Rsch. Excellence prize computer sci. tech. sect. 1989), Ops. Rsch. Soc. Israel, Am. Statis. Assn., Internat. Statis. Inst., Bernoulli Soc., Belgian Soc. Stats. (hon.), Alumnus Assn. Fondation Universitaire Belgium, Alumnus Assn. Founds. Nat. Recherche Scientifique Belgium, Sigma Xi, Omega Rho (hon.). Home: 925 N Smoketree Cir Tucson AZ 85745-9666 Office: U Ariz Dept Systems & Indsl Engring Tucson AZ 85721

NEUWIRTH, ALAN JAMES, lawyer; b. N.Y.C., July 4, 1943; s. Bernard and Audrey (Hattenbach) N.; m. Patricia E. Neuwirth, Sept. 4, 1966; children: John A., Daniel P. BA, Lehigh U., 1965; JD, NYU, 1969. Bar: NY 1970, U.S. Dist. Ct. (so. and ea. dists.) N.Y. 1972, U.S. Ct. Appeals (2d cir.) 1972, U.S. Ct. Internat. Trade 1983, U.S. Ct. Appeals (Fed. cir.) 1984, U.S. Supreme Ct. 1988. Assoc. Miller & Summit, N.Y.C., 1970-72, Ratheim, Hoffman, Kassel & Silverman, N.Y.C., 1973-75; ptnr. Kassel, Neuwirth & Geiger, N.Y.C., 1976-86, Webster & Sheffield, N.Y.C., 1987-90; sr. ptnr. Morgan, Lewis & Bockius, N.Y.C., 1990—; bd. dirs. various cos. With U.S. Army, 1969-74, USAR. Mem. ABA, Assn. of Bar of City of N.Y., N.Y. County Lawyers Assn., Internat. Trade Commn., Trial Lawyers Assn. Office: Morgan Lewis & Bockius 101 Park Ave New York NY 10178-0060

NEUWIRTH, BEBE, dancer, actress; b. Newark, Dec. 31; d. Lee Paul and Sydney Anne Neuwirth; m. Paul Dorman. Student, Juilliard Sch., 1976-77. Appeared on Broadway and internationally as Sheila in A Chorus Line, 1978-81; other stage appearances include West Side Story, 1981, Little Me, 1982, Upstairs at O'Neal's, 1982-83, The Road to Hollywood, Just So, 1985, Sweet Charity, 1985-87 (Tony award for Best Supporting Actress in a Musical 1985-86), Waiting in the Wings: The Night the Understudies Take the Stage, 1986, Showing Off, 1989, Chicago, 1992, Kiss of the Spider Woman (London), 1993, Damn Yankees, 1994, Pal Joey, 1995; prin. dancer Dancin', 1982; choregrapher, leading dance role Kicks, 1984; TV series Cheers, 1984-93 (Emmy award for Best Supporting Actress in a Comedy Series 1990, 1991); TV guest appearances Frasier, 1994, Aladdin, 1994; TV movies Without Her Consent, 1990, Unspeakable Acts, 1990, Wild Palms, 1993; films Say Anything, 1989, Green Card, 1990, Penny Ante, 1990, Bugsy, 1991, Painted Heart, 1992, Malice, 1993. Vol. performances for March of Dimes Telethon, 1986, Cystic Fibrosis Benefit Children's Ball, 1986, Ensemble Studio Theater Benefit, 1986, Circle Repertory Co. Benefit, 1986, all in N.Y.C. Democrat. Office: Internat Creative Mgmt 8942 Wilshire Blvd Beverly Hills CA 90211 Office: Internat Creative Mgmt 40 W 57th Str New York NY 10019*

NEUWIRTH, ROBERT SAMUEL, obstetrician, gynecologist; b. N.Y.C., July 11, 1933; s. Abraham Alexander and Phyllis Neuwirth; children from previous marriage: Susan, Jessica, Laura, Michael, Alexander. BS, Yale U., 1954, MD, 1958. Intern Presbyn. Hosp., N.Y.C., 1958-59, resident, 1959-64; asst. prof. ob-gyn. Columbia U., 1964-68, assoc. prof., 1968-71, prof., 1972—, Babcock prof., 1977—; dir. ob-gyn Bronx Lebanon Hosp., N.Y.C., 1967-72, Woman's Hosp., N.Y.C., St. Luke's Hosp. Ctr., 1974—; prof. Albert Einstein Coll. Medicine, 1971-72; cons. WHO, NIH, AID, FDA. Author: Hysteroscopy, 1975; contbr. articles to profl. jours. Mem. Am. Coll. Obstetricians and Gynecologists, Soc. Gynecologic Investigation, N.Y. Obstet. Soc., Am. Assn. Profs. Ob-Gyn., Assn. Vol. Sterilization (chmn. biomed. com. 1971—). Office: 1090 Amsterdam Ave 6th Fl New York NY 10025

NEVA, FRANKLIN ALLEN, physician, educator; b. Cloquet, Minn., June 8, 1922; s. Lauri Albin and Anna (Lahti) N.; m. Alice Hanson, July 5, 1947; children: Karen, Kristin, Erik. SB, U. Minn., 1944, MD, 1946; AM (hon.), Harvard U., 1964. Diplomate Am. Bd. Internal Medicine. Intern Harvard Med. Services, Boston City Hosp., 1946-47, resident, 1949-50; research fellow Harvard Med. Sch., 1950-53; asst. prof. U. Pitts. Med. Sch., 1953-55; mem. faculty Harvard Sch. Pub. Health, 1955-69, John LaPorte Given prof. tropical pub. health, 1964-69; chief Lab. Parasitic Diseases, Inst. Allergy and Infectious Diseases, NIH, 1969-95; mem. commn. parasitic diseases, assoc. mem. commn. virus infections Armed Forces Epidemiol. Bd., 1963-68; mem. Latin Am. sci. bd. Nat. Acad. Scis.-NRC, 1963-68; bd. sci. counselors Inst. Allergy and Infectious Diseases, NIH, 1966-69. Served to lt. (j.G.) USNR, 1947-49. Mem. Soc. Exptl. Biology and Medicine, Infectious Diseases Soc. Am. (Joseph Smadel lectr. 1985), Am. Soc. Tropical Medicine and Hygiene (Bailey K. Ashford award 1965, Craig lectr. 1986), Assn. Am. Physicians (Presdl. Meritorious Exec. Rank award 1985). Achievements include special research infectious diseases especially tropical, parasitic and virus infections. Home: 10851 Glen Rd Potomac MD 20854-1401 Office: NIH Inst Allergy & Infectious Diseases Bethesda MD 20892

NEVAS, ALAN HARRIS, federal judge; b. Norwalk, Conn., Mar. 27, 1928; s. Nathan and Eva (Harris) N.; m. Janet S. Snyder, Sept. 13, 1959; children: Andrew, Debra, Nathaniel. B.A., Syracuse U., 1949; LL.B., NYU, 1951. Bar: Conn. 1951, U.S. Dist. Ct. Conn. 1955, U.S. Supreme Ct. 1959, U.S. Ct. Appeals for 2d circuit 1967, U.S. Tax. Ct. 1981. Ptnr. firm Nevas Nevas & Rubin, Westport, Conn., 1954-81; U.S. atty. for Dist. of Conn., 1981-85; judge U.S. Dist. Ct., Hartford, 1985—. Mem. Conn. Ho. Reps., 1971-77, dep. house majority leader, 1973-75, dep. house minority leader, 1975-77; justice of the peace, Westport, Conn., 1976-81. Served with AUS, 1952-54. Named One of 10 Most Outstanding Mems. Conn. Gen. Assembly Conn.

Mag., 1975-77. Mem. Conn. Bar. Assn. (gov. 1978-81). Republican. Jewish. Office: US Dist Ct 915 Lafayette Blvd Bridgeport CT 06604-4768

NEVELOFF, JAY A., lawyer; b. Bklyn., Oct. 11, 1950; s. Cydelle (Weber) Elrich; m. Arlene Sillman, Aug. 26, 1972; children: David, Kevin. BA, Bklyn. Coll., 1971; JD, NYU, 1974. Bar: N.Y. 1975, D.C. 1992, U.S. Dist. Ct. (so. and ea. dists.) N.Y. 1975, U.S. Ct. Appeals (2d cir.) 1975, U.S. Supreme Ct. 1982. Assoc. Marshall, Bratter, Greene, Allison & Tucker, N.Y.C., 1974-82; assoc. Rosenman, Colin, Freund, Lewis & Cohen, N.Y.C., 1982-83, ptnr., 1983-88; ptnr. Kramer, Levin, Naftalis, Nessen, Kamin & Frankel, N.Y.C., 1988—. Editor N.Y. Real Property Service. Mem. ABA (vice chmn. com. partnerships, joint ventures and other investment vehicles 1988—), Am. Law Inst., Am. Coll. Real Estate Attys., N.Y. State Bar Assn. (financing com.), Practising Law Inst. (lectr. 1988—, mem. adv. bd. 1991—), N.Y. County Lawyers Assn. (lectr. 1984—), Assn. of Bar of City of N.Y. (real property law com., chmn. condominium resale contract com., lectr., 1984-88), Cmty. Assns. Inst. (lectr. 1986), Law Jours. Seminars (lectr. 1987—), Strategic Resources Inst. (lectr. 1994—), Inst. Internat. Rsch. (lectr. 1994—). Home: 134 Alder Dr Briarcliff Manor NY 10510-2218 Office: Kramer Levin Naftalis Nessen Kamin & Frankel 919 Third Ave New York NY 10022

NEVEU, JEAN, printing company executive. Chmn., CEO, Quebecor Printing Inc., Montreal, Que., Can. Office: Quebecor Printing Inc, 612 Saint-Jacques St, Montreal, PQ Canada H3C 4M8

NEVIASER, ROBERT JON, orthopedic surgeon, educator; b. Washington, Nov. 21, 1936; s. Julius Salem and Jane Frances (Gibbons) N.; m. Anne Maclean Shedden, Dec. 3, 1966; children: Jeanne Nicole, Robert Jon Jr., Ian Maclean, Andrew Shedden. Grad., Phillips Acad., Andover, Mass., 1954; AB, Princeton U., 1958; MD, Jefferson Med. Coll., 1962. Diplomate Am. Bd. Orthopaedic Surgery with cert. of added qualification in surgery of hand. Intern N.Y. Hosp., Cornell Med. Center, N.Y.C., 1962-63; asst. resident N.Y. Hosp., Cornell Med. Center, 1963-64; asst. resident in orthopaedic surgery N.Y. Orthopaedic Hosp., Columbia-Presbyn. Med. Center, N.Y.C., 1964-66; resident N.Y. Orthopaedic Hosp., Columbia-Presbyn. Med. Center, 1966-67; fellow in surgery of the hand Orthopaedic Hosp., Los Angeles, 1969-70; asst. prof. div. orthopaedic and hand surgery, chmn. dept. U. Conn., Hartford, 1970-71; assoc. prof. orthopaedic surgery George Washington U., Washington, 1971-76; prof. George Washington U., 1976—, dir. orthopedic edn., assoc. chmn. dept. orthopedic surgery, 1984-87, chmn. dept. orthopedic surgery, 1987—. Contbr. articles in field to profl. jours. Served to lt. comdr. USNR, 1967-69. Fellow Am. Soc. Surgery of the Hand, Am. Acad. Orthopaedic Surgeons, Ea. Orthopaedic Assn., Am. Shoulder and Elbow Surgeons, Am. Orthopaedic Assn.; mem. Alpha Kappa Kappa. Republican. Clubs: Princeton (N.Y. and Washington), Darnestown Swim and Racquet, Cosmos. Office: 2150 Pennsylvania Ave NW Washington DC 20037-2396

NEVILL, WILLIAM ALBERT, chemistry educator; b. Indpls., Jan. 1, 1929; s. Irwin Lowell and Mary Marie (Barker) N.; m. Nancy Neiman Roll, May 19, 1979; children: Paul David, John Michael, Steven Joseph, Anne Marie, Deborah Ruth. BS magna cum laude, Butler U., 1951; PhD, Calif. Inst. Tech., 1954. Research chemist Proctor-Gamble, Cin., 1954; prof. chemistry, chmn. dept. Grinnell Coll., 1956-67; prof. chemistry Ind. U.-Purdue U., Indpls., 1967-83, chmn. dept., 1967-72; dean Sch. Sci. Ind. U.-Purdue U., 1972-79; dir. grad. studies, 1979-83; pres. B&N Cons. Co., 1972-93; vice chancellor acad. affairs La. State U., Shreveport, 1983-85; prof. La. State U., 1983-94; pres. Catoctin Assocs., 1993—; arbitrator, mediator Ind. Employment Rels. Bd., 1975-83. Author: General Chemistry, 1967, Experiments in General Chemistry, 1968. Bd. dirs. Indpls. Sci. and Engring. Found., 1972-75, 79-82, Westminster Found., Lafayette, Ind., 1972-74, Am. Chem. Soc., 1986-92. With U.S. Army, 1954-56; col. USAR, 1956-84. Grantee NSF, 1959-74; Grantee NIH, 1963-70; Grantee Office Naval Research, 1953. Mem. Ind. Acad. Sci., Am. Chem. Soc. (chmn. sect. 1972, counselor 1973-92). Presbyterian. Home: 2229 Greenpark Dr Richardson TX 75082-4219

NEVILLE, AARON, musician; m. Joel; 1 d., Ernestine; 3 s., Aaron, Jr., Ivan, Jason. Singer (singles): Over You, 1959, Tell It Like It Is, 1966, 91; (albums): Orchid in the Storm, 1990, The Classic: My Greatest Gift, 1990, Warm Your Heart, 1991, The Grand Tour, 1993, Aaron Neville's Soulful Christmas, 1993; singles (with Linda Ronstadt) Don't Know Much, 1989 (Grammy award), All My Life, 1990, albums (with Neville Brothers) The Neville Brothers, 1978, Fiyo On the Bayou, 1980, Neville-ization, 1984, Uptown, 1987, Treacherous: A History of the Neville Brothers, 1987, Yellow Moon, 1989, Brother's Keeper, 1990, Treacherous Too, 1991, Family Groove, 1992, Live on Planet Earth, 1994. Recipient Down Beat Blues, Soul, R&B Group award, 1990; 2 Grammy nominations, 1994. Office: care A&M Records Inc 1416 N La Brea Ave Los Angeles CA 90028-7563*

NEVILLE, ART, musician. Albums include: Mardi Gras Rock 'N' Roll, 1987, (with Neville Brothers) The Neville Brothers, 1979, Treacherous: A History of the Neville Brothers, 1987, Brother's Keeper, 1990, Fiyo On the Bayou, 1980, Neville-ization, 1984, Uptown, 1987, Yellow Moon, 1989, Treacherous Too, 1991, Family Groove, 1992, Live on Planet Earth, 1994; (with The Meters) Sophisticated Sissy, 1968, Sissy Strut, Look-Ka Py Py, Chicken Strut, Cabbage Alley, also backup for many groups until 1980's. Recipient Down Beat Blues, Soul, R&B Group award, 1990. Office: care A & M Records Inc 1416 N La Brea Ave Los Angeles CA 90028-7563*

NEVILLE, CHARLES, musician. Albums include: (with Neville Brothers) The Neville Brothers, 1979, Fiyo on the Bayou, 1980, Neville-ization, 1984, Uptown, 1987, Treacherous: A History of the Neville Brothers, 1987, Yellow Moon, 1989, Brother's Keeper, 1990, Treacherous Too, 1991, Family Groove, 1992, Live on Planet Earth, 1994. Office: care A & M Records Inc 1416 N La Brea Ave Los Angeles CA 90028-7563*

NEVILLE, CYRIL, musician. Albums include: (with Neville Brothers) The Neville Brothers, 1979, Fiyo on the Bayou, 1980, Neville-ization, 1984, Uptown, 1987, Treacherous: A History of the Neville Brothers, 1987, Yellow Moon, 1989, Brother's Keeper, 1990, Treacherous Too, 1991, Family Groove, 1992, Live on Planet Earth, 1994. Recipient Down Beat Blues, Soul, R&B Group award, 1990. Office: care A & M Records Inc 1416 N La Brea Ave Los Angeles CA 90028-7563*

NEVILLE, GWEN KENNEDY, anthropology educator; b. Taylor, Tex., Mar. 23, 1938; d. Matthew Ranken and Gwendolyn (Harrison) Kennedy; m. William Gordon Neville (div.); children: Katherine, Mary Grace, William Kennedy; m. Jack Gregory Hunnicutt, Jr., 1975. BA, Mary Baldwin Coll., Staunton, Va., 1959; MA, U. Fla., 1968, PhD, 1971. Asst. prof. Emory U., Atlanta, 1971-78; assoc. prof., 1978-79; assoc. prof. Southwestern U. Georgetown, Tex., 1979-84, prof. anthropology, 1984—; Elizabeth Root Paden chairholder, 1979—; cons. Wenner-Gren Conf., Mt. Kisco, N.Y., 1983; grant holder NEH, Washington, 1972, 89; researcher, writer Lilly Endowment, Indpls., 1988—; bd. dirs. Soc. for Anthropology of Europe, 1988—. Author: Kinship and Pilgrimage, 1987, The Mother Town, 1994; co-author: Generation to Generation, 1973, Learning Through Liturgy, 1978; contbr. articles to profl. jours. Fellow Am. Anthropol. Assn.; mem. Am. Ethnological Soc., Am. Folklore Soc., Soc. for Anthropology of Europe (bd. dirs. 1989-92), Assn. for Scottish Ethnography, Coun. on Anthropology and Edn. (bd. dirs. 1971-74), So. Anthropol. Soc. (editor 1974-77). Methodist. Office: University at Maple Southwestern U Georgetown TX 78626

NEVILLE, JAMES MORTON, food company executive, lawyer; b. Mpls., May 28, 1939; s. Philip and Maurene (Morton) N.; m. Judie Martha Proctor, Sept. 9, 1961; children: Stephen Warren, Martha Maurene. BA, U. Minn., JD magna cum laude, 1964. Bar: Minn. 1964, Mo. 1984. Assoc. firm Neville, Johnson & Thompson, Mpls., 1964-69, ptnr., 1969-70; assoc. counsel Gen. Mills, Inc., Mpls. 1970-77, sr. assoc. counsel, 1977-83, corp. sec., 1976-83; v.p., sec., asst. gen. counsel Ralston Purina Co., St. Louis, 1983-84, v.p., gen. counsel, sec., 1984—; lectr. bus. law U. Minn., 1967-71. Named Man of Yr. Edina Jaycees, 1967. Mem. ABA, Minn., Mo. Bar Assns., U.S. Supreme Ct. Bar Assn., Hennepin County Bar Assn., St. Louis Bar Assn., U.

Minn. Law Sch. Alumni Assn., Am. Soc. Corp. Secs., Old Warson Country Club, Ladue Racquet Club, Noonday Club, Order of Coif, Phi Delta Phi, Psi Upsilon. Episcopalian. Home: 9810 Log Cabin Ct Saint Louis MO 63124-1133 Office: Ralston Purina Co Checkerboard Sq Saint Louis MO 63164-0002

NEVILLE, MARGARET COBB, physiologist, educator; b. Greenville, S.C., Nov. 4, 1934; d. Henry Van Zandt and Florence Ruth (Crozier) Cobb; m. Hans E. Neville, Dec. 27, 1957; children: Michel Paul, Brian Douglas. BA, Pomona Coll., 1956; PhD, U. Pa., 1962. Asst. prof. physiology U. Colo. Med. Sch., Denver, 1968-75, assoc. prof., 1975-82, prof., 1982—; dir. med. scientist tng. program, 1985-94. Editor: Lactation: Physiology, Nutrition, Breast Feeding, 1983 (Am. Pubs. award 1984), Human Lactation I, 1985, The Mammary Gland, 1987, Jour. Mammary Gland Biology and Neoplasia, 1995—; contbr. numerous articles to profl. jours. Recipient Rsch. Career Devel. award NIH, 1975, NIH merit award, 1993. Mem. AAAS, Am. Physiol. Soc., Am. Soc. Cell Biology, Internat. Soc. Rsch. in Human Milk and Lactation, Phi Beta Kappa. Office: U Colo Dept Physiology PO Box 240C Denver CO 80262

NEVILLE, PHOEBE, choreographer, dancer, educator; b. Swarthmore, Pa., Sept. 28, 1941; d. Kenneth R. and Marion (Eberbach) Balsley. Student, Wilson Coll., 1959-61. Cert. practitioner body-mind centering; registered movement therapist. Instr. Bennington (Vt.) Coll., 1981-84, 87-88; vis. lectr. UCLA, 1984-86. Dancer, choreographer Judson Meml. Ch., N.Y.C., 1966-70, Dance Uptown Series, N.Y.C., 1969, Cubiculo Theatre, N.Y.C., 1972-75, Delacorte Dance Festival, N.Y.C., 1976, Dance Umbrella Series, N.Y.C., 1977, Riverside Dance Festival, N.Y.C., 1976, 78, N.Y. Seasons, 1979—; dancer, artistic dir. Phoebe Neville Dance Co., N.Y.C., 1975—, Jacob's Pillow Splash! Festival, 1988, Dance Theater Workshop Winter Events, 1988. Recipient Creative Artist Public Svc. award, 1975; Nat. Endowment for Arts fellow, 1975, 79, 80, 85-87, 92-94, Choreographic fellow N.Y. Found. for Arts, 1989. Mem. Laban Inst. Movement Studies, Dance Theater Workshop, Body-Mind Centering Assn. (cert. practitioner and tchr.), Internat. Movement Therapy Assn. (registered), Internat. Assn. Healthcare Practitioners. Buddhist. Club: Recluse.

NEVILLE, ROBERT CUMMINGS, philosophy and religion educator; b. St. Louis, May 1, 1939; s. Richard Perry and Rose Naomi (Cummings) N.; m. Elizabeth Egan, June 8, 1963; children: Gwendolyn (dec.), Naomi, Leonora. BA, Yale U., 1960, MA, 1962, PhD, 1963. Ordained as elder United Meth. Ch., 1966. Instr. philosophy Yale U., New Haven, Conn., 1963-65; from asst. to assoc. prof. philosophy Fordham U., Bronx, 1965-71; assoc. prof. philosophy SUNY-Purchase, 1971-74, prof. 1974-77; prof. philosophy and religion, chair religion dept. SUNY-Stony Brook, N.Y., 1978-82, dean humanities and arts, 1982-85, chmn. dept. religion, 1986-87; prof. religion, philosophy and theology, chmn. religion dept. Boston U., 1987-88, dean Sch. of Theology, 1988—. Author: God the Creator, 1968, 2d edition, 1992, The Cosmology of Freedom, 1974, reprinted, 1995, Soldier, Sage, Saint, 1978, reprinted, 1995, Creativity and God, 1980, Reconstruction of Thinking, 1981, The Tao and the Daimon, 1982, The Puritan Smile, 1987, Recovery of the Measure, 1989, Behind the Masks of God, 1991, A Theology Primer, 1991, The Highroad around Modernism, 1992, Eternity and Time's Flow, 1993, Normative Cultures, 1995, The Truth of Broken Symbols, 1995; editor: (with Gaylin and Meister) Operating on the Mind, 1975; New Essays in Metaphysics, 1987; contbr. articles to profl. jours. Mem. Mo. E. Ann. Conf., United Meth. Ch., 1963—. Mem. Am. Acad. Religion (bd. dirs. 1982-93, chmn. rsch. com. 1984-89, v.p., pres. elect, pres. 1990-92), Am. Theol. Soc. (exec. com. 1980-83), Am. Philos. Assn. (exec. com. 1983-85), Metaphys. Soc. Am. (pres. 1988), Internat. Soc. Chinese Philos. (pres. 1992-93). Democrat. Avocations: t'ai chi ch'uan, singing. Office: Boston U Sch Theology Boston MA 02215

NEVILLE, ROY GERALD, scientist, chemical management and environmental consultant; b. Bournemouth, Dorsetshire, Eng., Oct. 15, 1926; came to U.S., 1951, naturalized, 1957; s. Percy Herbert and Georgina Lallie (Jenkins) N.; m. Jeanne Frances Russ, July 26, 1952; children: Laura Jean, Janet Marilyn. BSc with honors, U. London, 1951; MSc, U. Oreg., 1952, PhD, 1954; FRIC, Royal Inst. Chemistry, London, 1963, DSc (hon.), 1973. Research chemist Monsanto Chem. co., Seattle, 1955-57; sr. chem. engr. Boeing Co., Seattle, 1957-58; sr. research scientist Lockheed Missiles & Space Co., Palo Alto, Calif., 1958-61; sr. staff scientist Aerospace Corp., El Segundo, Calif., 1961-63; prin. scientist Rockwell Internat. Corp., Los Angeles, 1963-67; head dept. materials Scis. Lab., Boeing Sci. Research Labs. Boeing Co., Seattle, 1967-69; sr. environ. engring. specialist Bechtel Corp., San Francisco, 1969-73; pres. Engring. & Tech. Cons., Inc., Redwood City, Calif., 1973—. Contbr. numerous sci. articles on organic synthesis, polymers, pollution control processes to profl. jours. and books; many U.S. and fgn. patents in field. Fulbright scholar to U.S., 1951; USPHS fellowship, 1951-52, Research Corp. fellow, 1952-54; chartered chemist, London. Fellow Royal Soc. Chemistry (London), Am. Inst. Chemists, AAAS; mem. Am. Chem. Soc., Am. Inst. Chem. Engrs., History Sci. Soc., Soc. Study Early Chemistry, Royal Instn. Great Britain, Research Soc. Am., Soc. Mining Engrs. of AIME, Calif. Mining Assn., Sigma Xi. Office: 1068 Eden Bower Ln Redwood City CA 94061-1806

NEVIN, CROCKER, investment banker; b. Tulsa, Mar. 14, 1923; s. Ethelbert Paul and Jennie Crocker (Fassett) N.; m. Mary Elizabeth Sherwin, Apr. 24, 1952 (div. 1984); children: Anne, Paul, Elizabeth, Crocker; m. Marilyn Elizabeth English, Nov. 3, 1984; 1 child, Jennie Fassett. Grad. with high honors, St. Paul's Sch., 1942; A.B. with high honors, Princeton U., 1946. With Vick Chem. Co., 1949-50, John Roberts Powers Cosmetic Co., 1950-52; with Marine Midland Grace Trust Co. of N.Y., 1952—, exec. v.p., 1964-66, pres., 1966-70, chmn. bd., chief exec. officer, 1968-73; also dir.; vice chmn. bd. Evans Products Co., N.Y.C., 1974-76, Drexel Burnam Lambert Co., investment bankers, N.Y.C., 1976-88; chmn. bd., chief exec. officer CF & I Steel Corp., Pueblo, Colo., 1985-93; dir. Medco Containment Services Inc., Magnatck, Inc., BOC Group PLC; bd. govs. U.S. Postal Svc. Chmn. exec. com. ACCION Internat. Lt. (j.g.) AUS USN, 1942-46. Mem. River side Yacht Club, N.Y. Yacht Club (N.Y.C.), Blind Brook Club. Home: 20 Hope Farm Rd Greenwich CT 06830

NEVIN, JOHN JOSEPH, tire and rubber manufacturing executive; b. Jersey City, Feb. 13, 1927; s. Edward Vincent and Anna (Burns) N.; m. Anna Filice, June 16, 1951; children: Stanley James, John Joseph, Richard Charles, Paul Edward, Gerald Patrick, Mary Anne. B.S., U. Calif., 1950; M.B.A., Harvard U., 1952. Various positions fin., product planning and mktg. Ford Motor Co., Dearborn, 1952—; v.p. mktg. Ford Motor Co., 1969-71; pres. Zenith Radio Corp., Chgo., 1971-76; chmn. Zenith Radio Corp., 1976-79; pres. Firestone Tire & Rubber Co., Akron, Ohio, 1979-82, chief exec. officer, 1980—, chmn., 1981—. Gen. chmn. Summit County United Way, 1980. Served with USNR, 1945-46. Office: Budget Rent-A-Car Corp 200 N Michigan Ave Chicago IL 60601-5909

NEVIN, JOHN ROBERT, business educator, consultant; b. Joliet, Ill., Jan. 27, 1943; s. Robert Charles and Rita Alice (Roder) N.; m. Jeanne M. Conroy, June 10, 1967; children: Erin, Michael. BS, So. Ill. U., 1965; MS, U. Ill., 1968, PhD, 1972. Asst. prof. bus. U. Wis., Madison, 1970-77, assoc. prof. bus., 1977-83, prof. bus., 1983—, Wis. disting. prof. bus., 1988-89, Grainger Wis. disting. prof. bus., 1989—, dir. Grainger Ctr. for Distrbn. Mgmt., 1992—; mem. editorial bd. Jour. of Mktg. Channels, The Haworth Press, Inc., 1991—; mem. investment adv. com. Venture Investors of Wis., Inc., Madison 1986—. Author: International Marketing: An Annotated Bibliography, 1983; contbr. articles to profl. jours. Bd. dirs. Madison Civic Ctr., 1983—. Mem. Am. Mktg. Assn. (bd. dirs. PhD consortium 1979, editorial bd. Jour. of Mktg. Chgo. chpt. 1983—), Am. Coun. on Consumer Interests, Assn. for Consumer Rsch. Avocations: golf, skiing, running. Home: 7514 Red Fox Trail Madison WI 53717 Office: U Wis 975 University Ave Madison WI 53706-1397

NEVIN, JOSEPH FRANCIS, computer systems engineer; b. Washington, Mar. 20, 1947; s. John Joseph and Mary Frances (O'Donnell) N.; m. Kathleen Cecelia Ridgell, Mar. 16, 1991; children: Christopher, Andrew, Amy, Megan. BA, Georgetown U., 1969; MS, Am. U., 1977. Chief of systems devel. USPHS, Rockville, Md., 1980—, BPHS, Rockville, Md.; historian Smithsonian Assocs., Washington, 1982—. Pres. Balt. RR Hist. Soc.,

1982-83, 94—, v.p. 1984-94, Ohio RR Hist. Soc. Recipient Adminstrs. award Health Resources and Svcs., 1983; pub. health spl. recognition award, 1984. Avocations: railroad and transportation history. Office: Balt and Ohio RR Hist Soc PO Box 13578 Baltimore MD 21203

NEVIN, ROBERT CHARLES, information systems executive; b. Dayton, Ohio, Nov. 4, 1940; s. Robert Steely and Virginia (Boehme) N.; m. Linda Sharon Fox, Apr. 16, 1966; children: Heather, Andrew. B.A., Williams Coll., 1962; M.B.A., U. Pa., 1970. Fin. planning mgr. Huffy Corp., Dayton, Ohio, 1971-72, asst. treas., 1972-73, treas., 1973-75, v.p. fin., 1975-79, exec. v.p., 1982-85; pres., gen. mgr. Frabill Sporting Good, Milw., 1979-82; exec. v.p. Reynolds & Reynolds, Dayton, Ohio, 1985-88, pres. bus. forms div., 1988—; bd. dirs. Reynolds & Reynolds, Olympic Title Ins. Co. Bd. dirs., pres. Camp Fire Girls, Dayton 1975; bd. dirs. ARC, 1977; participant, then trustee Leadership Dayton, 1978; chmn. bd. trustees Miami Valley Hosp., Dayton; vice chmn. Med Am. Corp.; trustee, treas. Victory Theater Assn., Dayton Mus. Natural History, Theater Assn., 1992; trustee, treas. Dayton Mus., trustee Alliance for Edn. 1st lt. USN, 1962-70. Mem. Beta Gamma Sigma, Racquet (Dayton), Dayton Country, Country Club of the North. Republican. Episcopalian. Office: Reynolds & Reynolds 115 S Ludlow St Dayton OH 45402-1812

NEVINS, ALBERT J., publisher, editor, author; b. Yonkers, N.Y., Sept. 11, 1915; s. Albert J. and Bessie (Corcoran) N. Ed., Venard Coll., Clarks Summit, Pa., 1936, Maryknoll (N.Y.) Sem., 1942; LHD (hon.), St. Benedict's Coll., Atchinson, Kans., 1963, Universidad Catolica de Puerto Rico, 1978. Ordained priest Roman Catholic Ch., 1942. Dir. social communications Cath. Fgn. Mission Soc. Am., 1960-69; v.p., pub., editor-in-chief Our Sunday Visitor, Inc., 1969-80; editor The Pope Speaks, 1980—, Diaconate Mag., 1985-91, Nova, 1989—; editor Maryknoll mag., 1955-69, World Campus mag., 1958-67; dir. World Horizon Films, 1945-68; cons. internat. visitors office U.S. Cath. Conf.; treas. Inter-Am. Tech. Ctr., 1972-88. Author: The Catholic Year, 1949, Adventures of Wu Han of Korea, 1951, Adventures of Kenji of Japan, 1952, Adventures of Pancho of Peru, 1953, Adventures of Ramon of Bolivia, 1954, St. Francis of the Seven Seas, 1955, The Adventures of Duc of Indochina, 1955, The Meaning of Maryknoll, 1956, Adventures of Men of Maryknoll, 1957, The Maryknoll Golden Book, 1956, The Making of a Priest, 1958, Away to Africa, 1959, The Maryknoll Book of Peoples, 1959, The Young Conquistador, 1960, Aways to the Lands of the Andes, 1962, Maryknoll Catholic Dictionary, 1964, Church in the Modern World, 1964, Away to Mexico, 1966, Away to Central America, 1967, Maryknoll Book of Treasures, 1968, Away to Venezuela, 1969, The Prayer of the Faithful, 1970, Our American Catholic Heritage, 1972, General Intercessions, 1977, A Saint for Your Name, 1980, Life After Death, 1983, The Sunday Readings, 1984, Builders of Catholic America, 1985, The Life of Jesus Christ, 1987, American Martyrs, 1987, Strangers at Your Door, 1988, Ask Me a Question, 1989, Answering a Fundamentalist, 1990, Scriptures of Faith, 1991, Catholicism, 1994, Indulgences, 1995; prodr., author, photographer numerous films, from 1946, including The Story of Juan Mateo (Film Festival award), 1957, A Problem of People (Film Festival award), 1961, The Gods of Todos Santos (Film Festival award 1966, 67). Comdr. Westchester group Civil Air Patrol; pres. Cath. Journalism Scholarship Fund; bd. dirs. Cath. League for Religious and Civil Rights, 1975—. Recipient Nat. Brotherhood award NCCJ, 1958, Maria Moors Cabot prize Columbia, 1961, St. Augustine award Villanova U., 1962, Benemerenti gold medal Holy See, 1980. Mem. Inter-Am. Press Assn. (treas. tech. ctr., bd. dirs. 1965-94), Cath. Press Assn. (pres. 1959-61, bd. dirs. award 1961), Cath. Inst. Press (co-founder, mem. exec. bd. 1945-60), U.S. Cath. Hist. Soc., Latin Am. Studies Assn., Cath. Assn. Internat. Peace, Fellowship of Cath. Scholars, Overseas Press Club. Address: 4606 W Loughman Tampa FL 33616

NEVINS, JOHN J., bishop; b. New Rochelle, N.Y., Jan. 19, 1932. Student, Iona Coll. (N.Y.), Cath. U. Washington. Ordained priest, Roman Catholic Ch., 1959. Ordained titular bishop of Rusticana and aux. bishop Diocese of Miami, Fla., 1979-84; first bishop Diocese of Venice, Fla., 1984—. Office: PO Box 2006 1000 Pinebrook Rd Venice FL 34292-1426

NEVINS, LOUIS H., lawyer; b. Cleve., Aug. 4, 1938; s. Charles E. and Ruth Francis (Altschul) N.; divorced; children: David, Jennifer, Elizabeth. BS in Econs., U. Pa., 1960, LLB, 1963. Bar: Ohio 1963, D.C. 1969. Atty. FHA, Washington, 1963-67; asst. dir. legis. rels. Nat. Assn. Realtors, Washington, 1967-70; sr. v.p., dir. Washington office Nat. Assn. Mut. Savs. Banks, 1971-83; ptnr. Thacher Proffitt & Wood, Washington, 1983-93; pres. Western League of Savs. Instns., L.A., Washington, 1993—; lectr. on banking and mortgage fin. matters. Columnist U.S. Banker mag., 1984-88. Bd. dirs. Big Bros., Washington, 1964-71. Recipient Disting. Svc. award Amherst (Mass.) Coll., 1991. Mem. ABA, City Club (Washington). Office: Western League Savs Instns 1301 Pennsylvania Ave # 500 Washington DC 20004

NEVINS, ROBERT CHARLES, insurance broker; b. N.Y.C., Dec. 19, 1933; m. C. Ann Nevins; children: Beth, Mary, Tom. BS, Miami U., Oxford, Ohio, 1955, AA in Risk Mgmt., 1974. Asst. mgr. INA, San Francisco, 1955-64; pres., mng. ptnr. Dinner Nevins, San Francisco, 1964-83; chmn., pres. Fred S. James of Calif., 1983-84, exec. v.p., chief operating officer, 1984-86; exec. v.p. mktg. The Home Ins. Co., N.Y.C., 1986-88; vice chmn. Alexander & Alexander of Calif., Inc., San Francisco, 1989—. Mem. Nat. Soc. CPCU (past pres.), Soc. Ins. Brokers (past chmn. 1975), Ins. Ednl. Assn. (chmn. 1984-85), Ins. Forum, Risk Mgmt. Forum, Ins. Inst. Am. (bd. dirs.), Western Assn. Ins. Brokers, CNA Agts. Group (chmn. 1973), NASCA, San Francisco C. of C. (bd. dirs.), Am Inst. Property and Liability. Home: 3355 Mcgraw Ln Lafayette CA 94549-2313 Office: Alexander & Alexander Calif Inc 2 Embarcadero Ctr Ste 1400 San Francisco CA 94111-3800

NEVINS, SHEILA, television programmer and producer; b. N.Y.C.; d. Benjamin and Stella N.; B.A., Barnard Coll., 1960; M.F.A. (Three Arts fellow), Yale U., 1963; m. Sidney Koch; 1 son, David Andrew. TV producer Great Am. Dream Machine, NET, 1970-72, The Reasoner Report, ABC, 1973, Feeling Good, Children's TV Workshop, 1975-76, Who's Who, CBS, 1977-78; v.p. documentary and family programming HBO, N.Y.C., 1978-82, dir. documentary programming Home Box Office, N.Y.C., 1986—. Bd. dirs. Women's Action Alliance. Recipient Peabody award, 1986, 92, Acad. Award Documentary, 1993, Emmy award, 1994; named Woman of Achievement YWCA, 1991. Mem. Writers Guild Am., Women in Film.

NEVISON, CHRISTOPHER HARRY, computer science educator; b. Phila., Nov. 24, 1945; s. John A. and Dorothy A. (Metcalfe) N.; m. Joyce Elizabeth Gordon, June 3,1 972; children: Christopher Sean, Colin Michael. BA in Math., Dartmouth Coll.; BA in Philosophy, Politics, Economics, Oxford U. Eng., 1969; MS in Math., Stanford U., 1970, PhD in Math., 1974. Lectr. math. U. Calif., Davis, 1973-74; from asst. prof. math. to assoc. prof. math. Colgate U., Hamilton, N.Y., 1974-83, assoc. prof. computer sci., 1983-84, prof. computer sci., 1984—; mem. AP exam com. computer sci. Coll. Bd. Edn. Testing Svc., Princeton, N.J., 1991, AP cons. computer sci., 1985—. Author: Turing Machines and What Can Be Computed, 1992; co-author: Statistical Tables and Formulae, 1989. EMT South Madison County Ambulance Corps., Hamilton, 1986—. Mem. Assn. Computing Machinery, Ops. Rescue Soc. Am., Math. Assn. Am. Avocation: coaching youth soccer. Office: Colgate U 13 Oak Dr Hamilton NY 13346-1338

NEVLING, J. KELLEY, JR., lawyer; b. Clearfield, Pa., Nov. 15, 1942; s. James K. and Frances (Wilson) N.; m. Judy Goulding, Apr. 15, 1972. BA cum laude, Harvard U., 1964; JD magna cum laude, Columbia U., 1969. Bar: N.Y. 1970, U.S. Dist. Ct. (so. dist.) N.Y. 1972, U.S. Dist. Ct. (ea. dist.) N.Y. 1978, U.S. Dist. Ct. (no dist.) Calif. 1985, U.S. Ct. Appeals (2d cir.) 1972. Law clk. to Hon. Charles M. Metzner U.S. Dist. Ct. (so. dist.) N.Y., N.Y.C., 1969-70; assoc. Rosenman, Colin, Freund, Lewis & Cohen, N.Y.C., 1970-78; ptnr. Rosenman & Colin, N.Y.C., 1978-93; with Citibank Legal Affairs Office, N.Y.C. Mem. bd. editors Columbia Law Rev., 1967-69. Served to 1st lt. U.S. Army, 1964-66. Mem. N.Y. State Bar Assn. Office: Rosenman & Colin 575 Madison Ave New York NY 10022-2511

NEVUE, SARAH PAULSON, museum administrator. Former exec. dir. Am. Advt. Mus., Portland, Oreg.; now devel. dir. Oregon Symphony Orch., Portland. Office: Oreg Symphony Orch 711 SW Alder Ste 200 Portland OR 97205

NEW, ELOISE OPHELIA, special education educator; b. Jeffersonville, Ind., Jan. 14, 1942; d. Ivan Foster and Nellie Katherine (Harman) Baugh; m. Paul Eugene New, Nov. 23, 1961; children: Paula, Paul Jr. BS in Elem. Edn., Eastern Ky. U., 1963; MA in Edn., Coll. Mt. St. Joseph, 1987. Cert. elem. K-8, and developmentally handicapped tchr. K-12, Ohio. Tchr. Newport (Ky.) City Schs., 1963-69, Ross County and Chillicothe (Ohio) City Schs., 1977-78; developmentally handicapped tchr. Mt. Logan Middle Sch. Chillicothe, 1979—. Tchr. Sunday sch. Tabernacle Bapt. Ch., Chillicothe, 1987-93, chmn. elem. edn. com., 1989-93, Sunday sch. supt., 1994—, mem. Christian bd. edn.; spokesperson for edn. selection Chillicothe Edn. Found., 1989. Recipient Excellence in Edn. award Pilasco-Ross Adminstrn. Conf. for Spl. Educators, 1984, Ohio Jennings Scholar award, 1991-93. Mem. NEA, Ohio Edn. Assn., Chillicothe Edn. Assn. (rep. 1986-88). Baptist. Home: 828 Orange St Chillicothe OH 45601-1340 Office: Mt Logan Mid Sch 841 E Main St Chillicothe OH 45601-3509

NEW, MARIA IANDOLO, physician, educator; b. N.Y.C.; d. Loris J. and Esther B. (Giglio) Iandolo; m. Bertrand L. New, 1949 (dec. 1990); children: Erica, Daniel, Antonia. B.A., Cornell U., 1950; M.D., U. Pa., 1954. Diplomate: Am. Bd. Pediatrics. Med. intern Bellevue Hosp., N.Y.C., 1954-55; resident pediatrics N.Y. Hosp., 1955-57; fellow NIH, 1957-58, 61-64; practice medicine specializing in pediatrics N.Y.C., 1955—; mem. staff N.Y Hosp., N.Y.C.; dir. Pediatric Metabolism Clinic, N.Y. Hosp., 1964—, attending pediatrician, 1971-80, pediatrician-in-chief, 1980—; asst. prof. dept. pediatrics Cornell U. Med. Coll., N.Y.C., 1963-68, assoc. prof., 1968-71, prof., 1971—, Harold and Percy Uris prof. pediatric endocrinology, 1978—, prof., chmn. dept. pediatrics, 1980—; asso. dir. Pediatric Clin. Research Ctr., 1980-88; adj. prof. Rockefeller U.; career scientist N.Y.C. Health Research Council, 1966-75; adj. attending pediatrician dept. pediatrics Meml. Sloan-Kettering Cancer Ctr., 1979—; cons. United Hosp., Port Chester, N.Y., 1977—, North Shore Univ. Hosp., 1982—, dept. pediatrics Cath. Med. Ctr. Bklyn. and Queens, N.Y., 1987; vis. physician Rockefeller U. Hosp., N.Y.C. 1973—; mem. endocrine study sect. NIH, 1977-81, Gen. Clin. Research Ctrs. Adv. Com.; chmn. Div. Research Resources Gen. Clin. Research Ctrs. Com. NIH, 1987-88; bd. dirs. Robert Wood Johnson Clin. Scholars Program; mem. N.Y. State Gov.'s Task Force on Life and Law, 1985—; mem. NIH Reviewers Res.; mem. FDA endocrinology and metabolism drug adv. cm., 1994—; panelist ACGME bd. appeals, 1994—. Mem. editorial bd. Jour. Clin. Endocrinology and Metabolism, 1973-80, editor-in-chief, 1994-99; assoc. editor Metabolism, 1981—; contbr. articles to med. jours. Trustee Irma T. Hirschl Trust. Recipient Mary Jane Kugel award Juvenile Diabetes Found., 1977, Katharine D. McCormick Disting. Lectureship, 1981, Robert H. Williams Disting. Leadership award, 1988, Albion O. Bernstein award Med. Soc. State N.Y., 1988, medal N.Y. Acad. Medicine, 1991, Disting. Grad. award U. Pa. Sch. Medicine, 1991, Optimate Recognition award Assn. Student-Profl. Italian-Ams., 1991, Outstanding Woman Scientist award N.Y. chpt. Am. Women in Sci., 1986, Maurice R. Greenberg Disting. Svc. award, 1994, Humanitarian award Juvenile Diabetes Found., 1994; grantee. Fellow Italian Soc. Endocrinology (hon.); mem. AAAS, Am. Soc. Human Genetics, Am. Acad. Pediatrics, Soc. for Pediatric Research, Harvey Soc., Endocrine Soc. (mem. coun. 1981-84, pres. 1991-92), Lawson Wilkins Pediatric Endocrine Soc. (pres. 1985-86), Am. Soc. Nephrology, Am. Soc. Pediatric Nephrology, Am. Pediatric Soc., Am. Fedn. Clin. Research, Am. Diabetes Assn., European Soc. Pediatric Endocrinology, Am. Coll. Clin. Pharmacology, Am. Clin. & Climatol. Assn., N.Y. Acad. Scis., Pan Am. Med. Assn., Assn. Am. Physicians, Am. Fertility Soc., U.S Pharmacopeial Conv. (elected), Am. Acad. of Arts and Scis. (elected 1992), Alpha Omega Alpha. Office: New York Hosp-Cornell Med Ctr Dept Pediatrics 525 E 68th St New York NY 10021-4885

NEW, WILLIAM NEIL, physician, retired naval officer; b. Atoka, Okla., Oct. 24, 1908; s. Robert Calvin and Nommar Bell (Willmore) N.; m. Ruth Anderson Pride, Mar. 30, 1940. B.A., Central State Tchrs. Coll., Edmond, Okla., 1931; B.S. in Medicine, U. Okla., 1932, M.D. 1934; postgrad., Northwestern U. Med. Sch., 1947-48. Diplomate: Am. Bd. Dermatology and Syphilology. Intern So. Pacific R.R. Hosp., San Francisco, 1934-35; commd. lt. (j.g.), U.S. Navy, 1935, advanced through grades to rear adm., 1963; resident dermatology and syphilology Naval Hosp., Phila., 1946-47; med. officer on gunboat and USMC Hosp., Shanghai, 1937-39; regtl. surgeon 7th Marines in Guadalcanal; later div. surgeon 5th Marine Div. (Japanese occupation), 1945; established Naval Med. Field Research Lab., Camp Lejeune, 1943; chief dermatology services naval hosps. Great Lakes, Ill., 1948-51, Phila., 1951-53, San Diego, 1956-59; force surgeon Fleet Marine Force, Pacific, 1954-56; comdg. officer U.S. Naval Hosp., Yokusaka, Japan, 1959-62; dir. staff Office Dep. Asst. Sec. Def. for Health and Med., 1962-66; pvt. practice dermatology Dallas Med. and Surg. clinic, 1968-91; ret., 1991; clin. assoc. prof. dermatology Southwestern Med. Sch., U. Tex., Dallas, 1966-92. Mem. ACP (life), Am. Acad. Dermatology (life), Pacific Dermatol. Assn. (life), Assn. Mil. Dermatologists (past pres.), N.Am. Clin. Dermatol. Soc. (co-founder, life), Space Dermatol. Found. (co-founder), Cutaneous Therapy Soc. (co-founder, life). Home: 3310 Fairmount St # 17C Dallas TX 75201 *Love and live today as we plan a rewarding tomorrow.*

NEWBAUER, JOHN ARTHUR, editor; b. Newport, R.I., Apr. 24, 1928; s. John Arthur and Theo Caroline (Trewhella) N.; m. Marilyn Mahler, Oct. 14, 1956; children: April, Dana, Miranda. B.A., U. Calif.-Berkeley, 1951. Sr. editor and writer sci. and engring., rocket devel. dept. U.S. Naval Ordnance Test Sta., China Lake, Calif., 1951-56; editor in chief Astronautics and Aeronautics jour., N.Y.C., 1963-83; adminstr. sci. publs. AIAA, 1983-91, cons. editor, 1991—; editor in chief Aerospace Am., 1983-87, acquisitions editor, 1987-89. Fellow AIAA (assoc.), Brit. Interplanetary Soc. Home: 356 Bay Ridge Ave Brooklyn NY 11220-5315 Office: AIAA-TIS 555 W 57th St New York NY 10020

NEWBERG, DOROTHY BECK (MRS. WILLIAM C. NEWBERG), portrait artist; b. Detroit, May 30, 1919; d. Charles William and Mary (Labedz) Beck; student Detroit Conservatory Music, 1938; m. William C. Newberg, Nov. 3, 1939; children: Judith Bookwalter Bracken, Robert Charles, James William, William Charles. Trustee Detroit Adventure, 1967-71, originator A Drop in Bucket Program for artistically talented inner-city children. Cmty. outreach coord. Reno Police Dept.; bd. dirs. Bloomfield Art Assn., 1960-62, trustee 1965-67; bd. dirs. Your Heritage House, 1972-75, Franklin Wright Settlement, 1972-75, Meadowbrook Art Gallery, Oakland U., 1973-75; bd. dirs. Sierra Nevada Mus. Art, 1978-80; bd. dirs. Nat. Conf. Christians and Jews, Gang Alternatives Partnership. Recipient Heart of Gold award, 1969, Mich. vol. leadership award, 1969, Outstanding Vol. award City of Reno, 1989-90. Mem. Nevada Mus. Art, No. Nev. Black Cultural Awareness Soc. (bd. dirs.), Hispanic 500 C. of C. No. Nev., Sierra Art Found, Serra Club of Reno. Roman Catholic. Home: 2000 Dant Blvd Reno NV 89509-5193

NEWBERG, JOSEPH H., lawyer; b. Middletown, Conn., May 20, 1947; s. Mendel and Annette (Gold) N.; m. Alice V. Melnikoff, Sept. 23, 1973; children: Mark, Emily. BA, U. Mich., 1969; JD, Harvard U., 1972; LLM, Boston U., 1976. Bar: Mass. 1972, U.S. Tax Ct. 1975. Assoc. Sullivan & Worcester, Boston, 1972-80, ptnr., 1980—; lectr. grad. tax program Boston U., 1982-84; adj. asst. prof. Bentley Grad. Tax Program, Waltham, Mass., 1985, 86. Mem. ABA, Boston Bar Assn. Office: Sullivan & Worcester One Post Office Sq Boston MA 02109

NEWBERN, WILLIAM DAVID, state supreme court justice; b. Oklahoma City, May 28, 1937; s. Charles Banks and Mary Frances (Harding) N.; m. Barbara Lee Rigsby, Aug. 19, 1961 (div. 1968); 1 child, Laura Harding; m. Carolyn Lewis, July 30, 1970; 1 child, Alistair Elizabeth. B.A., U. Ark., 1959, J.D., 1961; LL.M., George Washington U., 1963; M.A., Tufts U., 1967. Bar: Ark. 1961, U.S. Dist. Ct. (we. dist.) Ark. 1961, U.S. Supreme Ct. 1968, U.S. Ct. Appeals (8th cir.) 1983. Commd. 1st lt. advanced to maj. U.S. Army JAGC, 1961-70; Prof. law U. Ark., Fayetteville, 1970-84; adminstr. Ozark Folk Ctr., Mountain View, Ark., 1973; judge Ark. Ct. Appeals, Little Rock 1979-80; assoc. justice Ark. Supreme Ct., Little Rock 1985—; mem. faculty sr. appellate judges seminar NYU, 1987-91. Editor Ark. Law Rev., 1961; author: Arkansas Civil Practice and Procedure, 1985, 2d edit., 1993. Mem. Fayetteville Bd. Adjustment, 1973-79; bd. dirs. Decision Point, Inc., Springdale, Ark., 1980-85; pres. Little Rock Wind Symphony, Inc., 1993—. Mem. Am. Judicature Soc. (bd. dirs. 1985-89), Washington County Bar Assn., Inst. Jud. Adminstrn., Ark. IOLTA Found. (bd. dirs. 1985-87). Democrat. Avocation: string band-guitar, mandolin, banjo and brass quintet-tuba. Office: Ark Supreme Ct 625 Marshall St Little Rock AR 72201-1020

NEWBERRY, CONRAD FLOYDE, aerospace engineering educator; b. Neodesha, Kans., Nov. 10, 1931; s. Ragan McGregor and Audra Aenia (Newmaster) N.; m. Sarah Louise Thonn, Jan. 26, 1958; children: Conrad Floyde Jr., Thomas Edwin, Susan Louise. AA, Independence Jr. Coll., 1951; BEME in Aero. Sequence, U. So. Calif., 1957; MSME, Calif. State U., Los Angeles, 1971, MA in Edn., 1974; D.Environ. Sci. and Engring., UCLA, 1985. Registered profl. engr., Calif., Kans., N.C., Tex. Mathematician L.A. divsn. N.Am. Aviation Inc., 1951-53, jr. engr., 1953-54, engr., 1954-57, sr. engr., 1957-64; asst. prof. aerospace engring. Calif. State Poly. U., Pomona, 1964-70, assoc. prof. aerospace engring., 1970-75, prof. aerospace engring., 1975-90, prof. emeritus, 1990—; staff engr. EPA, 1980-82; engring. specialist space transp. systems div. Rockwell Internat. Corp., 1984-90; prof. aeronautics, astronautics Naval Postgrad. Sch., Monterey, Calif., 1990—, acad. assoc. space systems engring., 1992-94. Recipient John Leland Atwood award as outstanding aerospace engring. educator AIAA/Am. Soc. Engring. Edn., 1986. Fellow AIAA (dep. dir. edn. region VI 1976-79, dep. dir. career enhancement 1982-91, chmn. L.A. sect. 1989-90, chmn. Point Lobos sect. 1990-91, dir. tech.-aircraft systems 1990-93), Inst. Advancement Engring. Brit. Interplanetary Soc.; mem.IEEE, AAAS, ASME, NSPE, Royal Aeronautical Soc., Calif. Soc. Profl. Engrs., Am. Acad. Environ. Engrs. (cert. air pollution control engr.), Am. Soc. Engring. Edn. (chmn. PIC II 1995—, chmn. aerospace div. 1979-80, div. exec. com. 1976-80, 89-94, chmn. ocean and marine engring. div. 1993-95, program chmn. 1991-93, chmn. 1993-95, exec. com. 1982-85, 90—), Am. Soc. Pub. Adminstrn., Am. Meteorol. Soc., U.S. Naval Inst., Am. Helicopter Soc., Soc. Naval Architects and Marine Engrs., Air and Waste Mgmt. Assn., Inst. Environ. Scis., Exptl. Aircraft Assn., Water Environment Fedn., Soc. Automotive Engrs., Soc. Allied Weight Engrs., Assn. Unmanned Vehicle Systems, Calif. Water Pollution Control Assn., Nat. Assn. Environ. Profls., Am. Soc. Naval Engrs., Planetary Soc., Tau Beta Pi, Sigma Gamma Tau, Kappa Delta Pi. Democrat. Mem. Christian Ch. (Disciples of Christ). Achievements include research on aircraft, space, missile and engine design and related impacts on exergy, quality, conservation engineering, cost and environmental controls. Home: 9463 Willow Oak Rd Salinas CA 93907-1037 Office: Naval Postgrad Sch Dept Aeronautics and Astronautics AA/NE 699 Dyer Rd Monterey CA 93943-5106

NEWBERRY, ROBERT CURTIS, SR., newspaper columnist; b. Port Arthur, Tex., Feb. 20, 1945; s. Ira and Nona (Houston) N.; m. Carolyn Annette Ponder, Dec. 21, 1968; children: Renita, Renona, Robert Jr.; m. Jackolyn Cone, Oct. 8, 1994. BA, U. Houston, 1967. Sports editor The Houston Informer, 1964-65, Sports World, Houston, 1965; asst. news editor, columnist The Houston Post, 1967-87, columnist, 1987—; adj. prof. journalism Tex. So. U., 1988-92; bd. dirs. I Have a Dream, Houston, Citizens for Better Health, Houston Child Guidance Ctr., 1988-92, tutor and mentor, 1991—. Bd. dirs. Citizens Better Health, 1990—. Recipient Life Svc. award Tex. So. U., Houston, 1972, Print Media award Mental Health Assn., 1987, Print Media award Tex. Mental Health Assn., 1988, Julia C. Hester Achievement award Trailblazer, 1988, Awards of Excellence Dallas Press Club, 1989, Houston Press Club, 1990, 1st Pl. award UPI Regional Awards, 1990, Disting. Alumnus award U. Houston, 1990. Fellow Am. Leadership Forum (sr., bd. dirs. 1990—); mem. Nat. Assn. Black Journalists, Soc. Profl. Journalists (bd. dirs. 1968), Houston Assn. Black Journalists, U. Houston Alumni Orgn. (bd. dirs. 1991—). Democrat. Avocations: writing, fishing, boating. Office: The Houston Post 4747 South Fwy Houston TX 77004-6063

NEWBERRY, WILLIAM MARCUS, physician, educator, university administrator; b. Columbus, Ga., Nov. 13, 1938; s. William Marcus and Georgia Evelyn (Jones) N.; m. Nancy Elaine Harris, May 22, 1965; children: William Marcus, III, Thomas William, Judith Alison. B.A., Northwestern U., 1960; M.D., Emory U., 1964. Intern in medicine Ohio State U. Hosp., Columbus, 1964-65; with epidemic intelligence service Center Communicable Disease, USPHS, Atlanta, 1965-67; resident in medicine Barnes Hosp., St. Louis, 1967-69; research fellow U. Tex. Med. Sch., Dallas, 1969-71; asst. prof. medicine U. Tex. Med. Sch., 1970-71; mem. faculty internal medicine Med. U. S.C., Charleston, 1971—, prof. medicine, 1975—, dean Coll. Medicine, 1974-85, interim pres., 1982, acting v.p. acad. affairs, 1983, v.p. acad. affairs, provost, 1985-95; interim pres. Winthrop Coll., Rock Hill, S.C., 1986; mem. deans' com. Charleston VA Hosp. Contbr. med. jours. Trustee Trident United Way, 1984-86. Served as surgeon USPHS, 1965-67. Mem. AMA, S.C. Med. Assn., Charleston County Med. Soc., Am. Fedn. Clin. Rsch., So. Soc. Clin. Investigation, Assn. Am. Med. Colls., Charleston C. of C., Alpha Omege Alpha. Avocations: golf, rowing. Home: 1172 Farm Quarter Rd Mount Pleasant SC 29464-9543 Office: Med Univ SC 171 Ashley Ave Charleston SC 29425-0001

NEWBLATT, STEWART ALBERT, federal judge; b. Detroit, Dec. 23, 1927; s. Robert Abraham and Fanny Ida (Gregory) N.; m. Flora Irene Sandweiss, Mar. 5, 1965; children: David Jacob, Robert Abraham, Joshua Isaac. B.A. with distinction, U. Mich., 1950, J.D. with distinction, 1952. Bar: Mich. bar 1953. Ptnr. firm White & Newblatt, Flint, Mich., 1953-62; judge 7th Jud. Cir. Mich., 1962-70; ptnr. firm Newblatt & Grossman (and predecessor), Flint, 1970-79; judge U.S. Dist. Ct. (ea. dist.) Mich., Flint, 1979—; adj. instr. U. Mich.-Flint, 1977-78, 86. Mem. Internat. Bridge Authority Mich., 1960-62. Served with AUS, 1946-47. Mem. Fed. Bar Assn., State Bar Mich., Dist. Judges Assns. 6th Circuit. Jewish. Office: US Dist Ct 140 Federal Bldg 600 Church St Flint MI 48502-1214

NEWBOLD, ARTHUR, lawyer; b. Harrisburg, Pa., 1942. AB cum laude, Harvard U., 1964; LLB magna cum laude, U. Pa., 1967. BAr: Pa. 1967. Ptnr. Dechert Price & Rhodes, Phila. Comment editor U. Pa. Law review, 1966-67. Fellow Am. Coll. Trial Lawyers; mem. Order of Coif. Office: Dechert Price & Rhoads 4000 Bell Atlantic 1717 Arch St Philadelphia PA 19103

NEWBOLD, BENJAMIN MILLARD, JR., library manager, education consultant; b. La Grange, Ga., June 20, 1941; s. Benjamin Millard and Zeppa (Dasher) N.; married, 1968 (div. 1977); 2 children. BA in Sociology, Roger Williams Coll., 1970; MEd in Spl. Edn., Mid. Tenn. State U., 1975; MLS, U. So. Fla., 1985. Cert. tchr., Tenn., Fla., Ga., S.C., La. Tchr. psychotic, emotionally disturbed, mentally retarded Montanari Clin. Sch., Hialeah, Fla., 1970-72, 76-77; tchr. educatable mentally retarded Colleton County Bd. Edn., Walterboro, S.C., 1972-73, John Coleman Sch., Smyrna, Tenn., 1973-76, Hahnville High Sch., Boutte, La., 1978-79, Gulf Comprehensive High Sch., New Port Richie, Fla., 1979-80; tchr. severely mentally retarded, psychology supr. Sunniland Tng. Ctr., Ft. Myers, Fla., 1983-84; grad. asst. U. So. Fla., Tampa, 1984-85; adult reference libr. Houston Pub. Libr., 1986-89, libr. br. mgr., 1989-94, collection devel. mgr. Scenic Woods Regional Cluster, 1994—; geneal. researcher Clayton Libr./Ctr. for Geneal. Rsch., 1994—; pilot project tchr. Garrison Environ. Model, Rutherford County Bd. Edn., Murfreesboro, 1973-76; county coord. Spl. Edn. Grad. Credit, Murfreesboro, 1973-76; supr., adminstr., cons. pub. schs., pub. and pvt. facilities, librs.; active community pub. rels. P.T.A., sch. dists., librs. Active CONNECTEXAS, Austin, Fonwood P.T.A., Houston, Fontaine-Scenic Woods Civic Club, Houston, positive interaction program Houston Police Dept.; past mem. exec. bd. Houston Pub. Libr. Staff Assn. Recipient Spirit award Wall Street-The Club, 1991. Republican. Avocations: education, art, writing, politics, acting. Home: 401 S Bender Ave Apt 1109 Humble TX 77338-7706 Office: Clayton Libr Ctr Gen Rsch 5300 Caroline Houston TX 77004-6896

NEWBOLD, JOHN LOWE, banker; b. Washington, Dec. 26, 1935; s. John Lowe and Katharine Emily (Wilkins) N.; m. Judith Allen Bourne, June 20, 1959; children: Jennifer Hathaway, Timothy Bourne, Michael Fleming. BS, Yale U., 1957; MBA, NYU, 1963; sr. execs. program cert. MIT, 1970. Asst. v.p., credit instr. Citibank, N.A., N.Y.C., 1968-69, v.p. retail trade unit, 1969-70, v.p. info. svcs. dept., 1970-72, v.p., corp. bank head, Tokyo, 1972-73, v.p., country head, Singapore, 1974-76, sr. v.p., shipping dept. head, N.Y.C., 1976-85, div. exec. Global Shipping Div., 1985-89, Global Transp.

Div., 1989—; pres., dir. Mchts. Fund, Inc., Silver Spring, Md., 1981—; bd. dirs. First Olsen Tankers Ltd., Bermuda. Trustee Summit Area Community Coun., N.J., 1983-86, United Way, Summit, 1984-92; pres. PTA Presidents' Coun., Summit, 1981-83. Served as lt. (j.g.) USNR, 1957-60. Mem. Yale of Cen. N.J. Club (trustee 1980—), Met. Club (Washington), Beacon Hill Club (Summit). Episcopalian. Home: 47 Hillcrest Ave Summit NJ 07901-2011 Office: Citibank NA 399 Park Ave New York NY 10043-0001

NEWBORG, GERALD GORDON, historical agency administrator; b. Ada, Minn., Dec. 13, 1942; s. George Harold and Olea (Halstad) N.; m. Jean Annette Gruhl, Aug. 14, 1964; children: Erica, Annette. BA, Concordia Coll., Moorhead, Minn., 1964; MA, U. N.D., 1969; MBA, Ohio State U. 1978. Cert. archivist. Tutor, preceptor Parsons Coll., Fairfield, Iowa, 1964-67; state archivist Ohio Hist. Soc., Columbus, 1968-76; v.p. Archival Systems Inc., Columbus, 1978-81; state archivist State Hist. Soc. of N.D., Bismarck, 1981—; instr. Franklin U., Columbus, 1974; adj. prof. Bismarck State Coll. 1985-86. Co-author: North Dakota: A Pictorial History, 1988. Recipient Resolution of Commendation Ohio Ho. of Reps., Columbus, 1976. Mem. Soc. Am. Archivists, Nat. Assn. Govt. Archives & Records Adminstrs. (bd. dirs. 1984-86, sec. 1994—), Midwest Archives Conf., N.D. Libr. Assn. (exec. bd. 1985-86). Home: 1327 N 18th St Bismarck ND 58501-2827 Office: State Hist Soc 612 E Boulevard Ave Bismarck ND 58505-0664

NEWBORN, IRA, composer. Scores include (films) The Blues Brothers, 1980, All Night Long, 1981, Sixteen Candles, 1984, Into the Night, 1985, Weird Science, 1985, Ferris Bueller's Day Off, 1986, Wise Guys, 1986, Dragnet, 1987, Amazon Women on the Moon, 1987, Planes, Trains and Automobiles, 1987, Caddyshack II, 1988, The Naked Gun, 1988, Uncle Buck, 1989, Short Time, 1990, My Blue Heaven, 1990, The Naked Gun 2 1/2: The Smell of Fear, 1991, Brain Donors, 1992, Innocent Blood, 1992, The Opposite Sex and How to Live with Them, 1993, Naked Gun 33 1/3: The Final Insult, 1994, Ace Ventura, Pet Detective, 1994, (TV movies) Cast the First Stone, 1989. Office: The Robert Light Agency 6204 Wilshire Blvd Ste 900 Los Angeles CA 90048*

NEWBORN, JUD, cultural anthropologist, writer; b. N.Y.C., Nov. 8, 1952; s. Solomon and Rita (Cohen) N. BA magna cum laude in Anthropology and English, NYU, 1974; postgrad., Clare Hall, Cambridge U., 1974-75; MA in Anthropology, U. Chgo., 1977, PhD with distinction, 1994. Free-lance writer N.Y.C., Munich, Chgo., 1974—; publicist Oxford U. Press, N.Y.C. 1975-76; mus. historian, curatorial cons. Mus. Jewish Heritage (N.Y. Holocaust Meml. Commn.), N.Y.C., 1986—; cons. Sci. Inst. for Pub. Info., N.Y.C., 1987—; cons., speaker, lectr. in field. Author: Shattering the German Night: The Story of the White Rose Anti-Nazi Resistance, 1986, "Work Makes Free": The Hidden Cultural Meaning of the Holocaust, 1995, German Translator. Fulbright fellow, 1980-82; Newcombe fellow, 1984-85. Mem. ASCAP, Am. Anthrop. Assn., The Am. Hist. Assn., The Authors' Guild, Phi Beta Kappa. Office: Elaine Markson Lit Agy 44 Greenwich Ave New York NY 10011

NEWBORN, KAREN B., lawyer; b. Cleve., Oct. 30, 1944. BA, Goucher Coll., 1966; JD summa cum laude, Cleve. State U., 1976. Bar: Ohio 1976, U.S. Dist. Ct. (no. dist.) Ohio 1976, U.S. Ct. Appeals (6th cir.) 1978, U.S. Dist. Ct. (ea. dist.) Mich. 1984, U.S. Supreme Ct. 1988. Ptnr. Baker & Hostetler, Cleve.; asst. law dir. City Cleve., 1976-79; adj. instr. teaching trial advocacy, 1987. Mem. ABA, Ohio State Bar Assn., Cleve. Bar Assn. (bd. trustees 1989-92, chair commn. women in the law 1987-90), Inn of Ct. Office: Baker & Hostetler 3200 Nat City Ctr 1900 E 9th St Cleveland OH 44114-3303

NEWBRAND, CHARLES MICHAEL, advertising firm executive; b. Staten Island, N.Y., May 2, 1944; s. Charles Henry and Edith (Kotte) N.; m. Clare Ann Holmes, Aug. 26, 1967; 1 child, Alexis Christina. B.A., U. Notre Dame, 1965; J.D., U. Pa., Phila., 1968. Bar: N.J. 1968. Media planner Ogilvy & Mather, N.Y.C., 1968-71, account exec., 1971-74, account supr., 1974-77, v.p. mgmt. supr., 1977-82, sr. v.p. mgmt. supr., 1982-85, sr. v.p., group dir., 1985-89; mem. N.Y. oper. bd. Ogilvy & Mather, 1987-89; sr. v.p., group acct. dir., mem. exec. com. Foote, Cone & Belding, Inc., Chgo., 1990; sr. v.p. The Martin Agy., Richmond, Va., 1991—. Recipient Stephen E. Kelly award Mag. Pubs. Assn., 1981, Golden Effie Am. Mktg. Assn., N.Y. chpt., 1982, 87. Office: The Martin Agy 500 N Allen Ave Richmond VA 23220-2904

NEWBRANDER, WILLIAM CARL, health economist, management consultant; b. Irumagawa, Japan, Sept. 14, 1951; s. Virgil Ray and Ella Jeannette (Rae) N.; m. Nancy Sharon Wilson, June 15, 1974; children: Sharon, Billy, Andrew, Jonathan, Daniel. BA, Wheaton Coll., 1973; M of Hosp. Adminstrn., 1975; M of Applied Econs., U. Mich., 1981, PhD, 1983. Teaching/rsch. asst. U. Mich., Ann Arbor, 1979-83; mgmt. specialist V-HSR&D, Ann Arbor, 1980-83; hosp. adminstr. Whittaker Corp., Tabuk, Saudi Arabia, 1983-85; health economist WHO, Geneva, Switzerland, 1985-92; sr. assoc. Mgmt. Scis. for Health, Boston, 1992—. Author: Decentralization in a Developing Country, (booklet) Hospital Economics and Financing in Developing Countries, 1992, (jours.) Health Policy and Planning, 1988, 89, 90, 91, 94, Health Planning and Mgmt., 1988, 90, 91, World Health Forum, 1994. Eagle Scout advisor Boy Scouts Am., Geneva and Hopkinton, Mass., 1990—; mgr. Little League baseball team, Geneva and Hopkinton, 1990—. Capt. U.S. Army, 1975-79. VA Rsch. fellow, 1981-83. Fellow Am. Coll. Healthcare Execs. Office: Health Fin Program Mgt Sciences Health 165 Allandale Rd Boston MA 02130

NEWBROUGH, EDGAR TRUETT, retired management consultant; b. Madison, Ill., June 22, 1917; s. Edgar M. and Iris M. (Webb) N.; m. Muriel E. Amos, Nov. 26, 1936; children—Sherrill (Mrs. T.D. McIntyre), Sandra (Mrs. D. S. Cole), Arthur T. B.A., San Diego State U., 1938. Registered profl. engr., Pa., Mo., Ill., Mich. cert. mgmt. cons. With Solar Aircraft Co., San Diego, 1937-43; supt. Des Moines plant, 1943-45; mem. staff Albert Ramond & Assos., Chgo., 1943-72, v.p., 1956-61, pres., 1962-72; spl. cons. Theodore Barry & Assocs., L.A., 1977-82, ind. mgmt. cons., 1982-89, cons. fellow; ret. Author: Effective Maintenance Management; also articles. Mem. Inst. Indsl. Engrs., Assn. Cons. Mgmt. Engrs. (dir. 1964-66), Am. Inst. Plant Engrs., Inst. Mgmt. Cons.'s (charter), Bald Mountain Country Club, Masons, Shriners. Presbyterian. (elder). Home: Fairfield Mountains 106 Gateway Dr Lake Lure NC 28746

NEWBURG, ANDRE W. G., lawyer; b. Berlin, Jan. 9, 1928; s. Hugo and Olga (Cherniak) N.; m. Ellen French Vanderbilt, Dec. 27, 1953; children: Michael W., Anne C., Daniel F., Thomas H. AB, Harvard U., 1949, LLB, 1952. Bar: N.Y. 1952. Mem. Cleary, Gottlieb, Steen & Hamilton, N.Y.C., 1952-91, Paris, 1956-59, 1964-76, Brussels, 1960-64, N.Y.C., 1964-74, 76-91, Hong Kong, 1980; ptnr. Cleary, Gottlieb, Steen & Hamilton, 1963-91; gen. counsel European Bank for Reconstrn. and Devel., London, 1991—. Mem. Coun. on Fgn. Rels., 1973—; trustee Am. Sch. Classical Studies at Athens, 1965—; bd. dirs. Belgian-Am. Ednl. Found., 1979-94. Decorated Order of Leopold II (Belgium). Mem. ABA, Am. Assn. Internat. Commn. Jurists (bd. dirs. 1971—, chmn. 1989-91), Internat. Bar Assn., Interant. Law Assn. (monetary law com.), Assn. Bar City N.Y. chmn. spl. com. on Soviet affairs 1989-91), Century Assn., Travellers Club, Polo Club (Paris), Royal Automobile Club. Office: European Bank for Reconstrn and Devel 1 Exchange Sq, London EC2A 2EH, England

NEWBURGER, BETH WEINSTEIN, medical telecommunications company executive; b. Schenectady, July 8, 1937; d. H. Edward and Shirley (Diamond) Weinstein; m. Alan C. Newburger, Jan. 23, 1963 (dec. Oct. 1980); children: Mark, Lori, Eric, Jill; m. Richard Schwartz, May 26, 1989. BA, Cornell U., 1959. Dir. advt. New Republic, Washington, 1974-77; mktg. mgr. Washington Post, 1977-84; pres. Owlcat/Digital Rsch., Inc., Monterey, Calif., 1984-86; pres., chief exec. officer Corabi Internat. Telemetrics, Inc., Alexandria, Va., 1986—; chmn. bd. dirs. Health Street, Inc., Bethesda, Md., 1985—; bd. dirs. Tysons Nat. Bank, Vienna, Va. Bd. dirs. Arena Stage, Washington, 1993—; mem. Nat. Learning Ctr./Capital Children's Mus., Washington, 1984—. Named Woman of Yr., Svc. Guild, Washington, 1972, 73. Mem. Women in Advt. and Mktg. (bd. dirs. 1986-89). Home: 1401 N Oak St Arlington VA 22209-3648 Office: Corabi Internat Telemetrics 890 S Pickett St Alexandria VA 22304-4614

NEWBURGER, FRANK L., JR., retired investment broker; b. Phila., Nov. 26, 1908; s. Frank L. and Helen (Langfeld) N.; m. Dorothy Hess, Nov. 7, 1946 (dec.); children: Patricia S. (dec.), Frank L., III; m. Jane Berger, Aug. 19, 1973. AB, Cornell U., 1929. Ptnr. Newburger, Loeb & Co., Phila., 1930-46, Newburger & Co., 1946-70, Advest Co.; mng. partner Newburger & Co. div. Advest, 1970-77; sr. v.p. Newburger & Co. div. Advest, Phila., 1977-84; Bd. govs. N.Y. Stock Exchange, 1959-62; bd. govs. Phila.-Balt. Stock Exchange, 1946-56, pres., 1954-57. Vice chmn. United Fund, 1957-63; dir. Fedn. Jewish Agys., 1950—, pres., 1966, 67; emeritus bd. dirs., past treas., trustee (hon.) Acad. Natural Scis.; emeritus trustee Albert Einstein Med. Center, treas., 1957-60; mem. council Cornell U., 1965-71, 74-77, emeritus, 1978-88, life mem., 1989; mem. Health and Welfare Council, 1965-70. Mem. Bond Club Phila. (pres. 1966). Home: 8302 York Rd Apt B-63 Elkins Park PA 19027 Office: 7 Penn Ctr Pla 11th Fl 1635 Market St Philadelphia PA 19103-2217

NEWBURGER, HOWARD MARTIN, psychoanalyst; b. N.Y.C., May 16, 1924; s. Bernhard and Bertha (Travers) N.; m. Doris Schekter, July 3, 1949; children: Amy, Barry, Cary. B.A., N.Y. U., 1948, M.A., 1950, Ph.D., 1952; tng. in Jungian, Neo-Freudian and Horneyian psychoanalysis. Cert. in group psychotherapy and psychodrama. Rotating intern N.J. Dept. Instns. and Agys., 1948-49; chief psychologist N.J. State Instn., Annandale, 1949-52; dir. psychoanalysis Div. Social Def. UN, 1952; pvt. practice in psychoanalysis and group psychotherapy, 1952—; instr. HEW, 1958; rsch. assoc. Beth Israel Hosp., 1958-69; staff mem. St. Agnes Hosp., White Plains, 1991—; lectr., adj. assoc. prof. NYU, 1951-60, chmn. dept. exceptional child and youth, 1954-62; chmn. faculty and supr. treatment Inst. Applied Human Dynamics, 1960—; lectr., cons. in field; prelect prof. psychology John Jay Coll. Criminal Justice, 1969-72; chmn. bd. dirs. Inst. Applied Human Dynamics, N.Y.C. and Westchester, N.Y., 1960-81, exec. v-p., 1983-85. Co-author: Winners and Losers. Assoc. editor: Excerpta Medica, 1951-62. Contbr. articles and papers to tech. jours. Trustee Acad. Jewish Religion, 1991—. Served with AUS, World War II, ETO; with AUS, MTO. Recipient Outstanding Service to Humanity award Inst. Applied Human Dynamics for Handicapped, 1970. Mem. Am. Psychol. Assn., Am. Soc. Group Psychotherapy and Psychodrama (sec.-treas. 1954-55). Office: Timber Trail Rye NY 10580-1935 *Our country affords tremendous opportunity. Through the development of our inner resources, and their assertion, we can all have happy and effective lives.*

NEWBY, JILL JEANINE, airline pilot; b. Mpls., Oct. 8, 1960; d. Clinton Warner and Betty Jane (Mandelcorn) Erickson; m. Thomas William Newby, Jr., Oct. 18, 1986. BS in Aviation Adminstrn., U. N.D., 1983. Flight coord. Fed. Express Corp., Memphis, 1982-83; flight instr. U. N.D., Grand Forks, 1982-83; ramp handler Fed. Express Corp., L.A., 1984-85; flight instr. Gunnell Aviation, Santa Monica, Calif., 1984-85; with pub. rels. U. N.D., Grand Forks, 1983-84; reservation sales agt. Northwest Airlines, L.A., 1984-85; pilot Desert Sun Airlines, Long Beach, Calif., 1985, United Airlines, L.A., 1985—. Vol. speaker Career Days L.A. Pub. Schs., 1988. Mem. Airline Pilots Assn., Internat. Soc. Women Airline Pilots, Aircraft Owners and Pilots Assn., U. N.D. Flying Team, Alpha Eta Rho. Democrat. Lutheran. Avocations: snow and water skiing, gardening, travel, cooking.

NEWBY, TIMOTHY JAMES, education educator, researcher; b. Nampa, Idaho, Oct. 9, 1955; s. Neal Arthur and Margy Lou (Hooker) N.; m. Deedra Diane Hays May 3, 1978; children: Timbre, Landon, Alexis, Brayden. BS, Brigham Young U., 1979, PhD, 1984. Assoc. prof. Purdue U., West Lafayette, Ind. Mem. Am. Edn. Rsch. Assn. Home: 216 Berwick Dr Lafayette IN 47905 Office: Purdue U Curriculum and Instruction 1442 LAEB West Lafayette IN 47907

NEWCOMB, DANFORTH, lawyer; b. Tarrytown, N.Y., Jan. 24, 1943; s. Russell Ladd and Louise Munroe (Blazer) N.; m. Elizabeth W. Newcomb, Nov. 25, 1966; children—Alexander, Thomas. B.A., U. Vt., 1965; LL.B. Columbia U., 1968. Bar: N.Y. 1968, D.C. 1990, U.S. Dist. Ct. (so. and ea. dists.) N.Y. 1971, U.S. Ct. Claims 1971, U.S. Tax Ct. 1971, U.S. Ct. Appeals (2d and 3d cir.) 1971, U.S. Supreme Ct. 1981, U.S. Dist. Ct. (ea. dist.) Mich. 1983, U.S. Ct. Appeals (11th cir.) 1983, U.S. Ct. Appeals (6th cir.) 1986. Assoc., Shearman & Sterling, N.Y.C., 1968-69, 71-78, ptnr., 1979—; mem. panel of mediators U.S. Dist. Ct. (so. dist.) N.Y. Served to capt. U.S. Army, 1969-70. Decorated Bronze Star. Mem. ABA, Fed. Bar Council, Am. Arbitration Assn. (panel of arbitrators). Office: Shearman & Sterling 153 E 53rd St New York NY 10022-4611

NEWCOMB, ELDON HENRY, retired botany educator; b. Columbia, Mo., Jan. 19, 1919; s. Ernest Henry and Ruby Josephine (Anderson) N.; m. Joyce Bright Rieling, June 21, 1949; children—Norman Robert, Barbara Pauline, Cynthia Irma. Student, U. Kansas City, 1936-38; A.B., U. Mo., 1940, A.M., 1942; Ph.D., U. Wis., 1949; DS honoris causa, U. Mo., Columbia, 1993. Asst. prof. botany U. Wis.-Madison, 1949-54, assoc. prof., 1954-58, prof., 1958-90, prof. emeritus, 1990—; dir. Inst. Plant Devel., 1979-88; chmn. dept. botany U. Wis.-Madison, 1982-88, Folke Skoog prof. botany, 1987—; cons. Shell Devel. Co., 1954-59. Sr. author: Plants in Perspective, 1963; mng. editor Protoplasma, 1969-73; mem. editorial bd. Ann. Rev. Plant Physiology, 1965-69, Protoplasma, 1973—, Planta, 1981-90; contbr. articles to profl. jours. Served with AUS, 1942-45. NRC predoctoral fellow U. Wis., 1946-49; Guggenheim Found. fellow U. Calif. at Berkeley, 1951-52; Sci. Faculty fellow Harvard, 1963-64; Fulbright Sr. Research scholar Australian Nat. U., Canberra, 1976. Mem. NAS, Am. Soc. Cell Biologists, Am. Acad. Arts and Scis., Bot. Soc. Am., Am. Soc. Plant Physiologists, Soc. Devel. Biology, Phi Beta Kappa (pres. Wis. Alpha chpt. 1978-79), Sigma Xi. Mem. expdn. to Great Barrier Reef, 1973. Home: 52 Oak Creek Trl Madison WI 53717-1510

NEWCOMB, JONATHAN, publishing executive; b. Chappaqua, N.Y., June 12, 1946; s. Russell L. and Louise B. N.; m. Deborah Small, Dec. 11, 1970; children: Thaddeus, Zachary. AB in Econs., Dartmouth Coll., 1968; MBA, Columbia U., 1970. Mgr. Dun & Bradstreet, N.Y.C., 1972-74; mgr. Standard & Poor's Corp, N.Y.C., 1974-75, dir. 1976-79, v.p., 1979-80, sr. v.p., 1980-82, group v.p., 1982-84, exec. v.p., 1984-85; pres. McGraw-Hill Fin. & Econ. Info. Co., N.Y.C., 1985-88, Simon & Schuster Profl. Info. Group, N.Y.C., 1989-91; pres., CEO, Simon & Schuster, N.Y.C., 1991-94, pres., chief executive officer, 1994—; bd. dirs. CorpTech, Boston, Teltech, Mpls. Bd. overseers Amos Tuck Sch. Bus. Dartmouth Coll. Tuck Sch.; bd. dirs. Bklyn. Acad. of Music. 1st lt. U.S. Army, 1969-71, Vietnam. Club: Heights Casino (Bklyn.). Home: 61 Pierrepont St Brooklyn NY 11201-2453 Office: Simon & Schuster Inc 1230 Ave of Americas New York NY 10020-1513

NEWCOMB, LAWRENCE HOWARD, agricultural educator; b. Chase City, Va., July 20, 1947; s. George W. and Doris A. (Ashworth) N.; m. Beverly Hope Spain, July 12, 1968; children: Rodney, Angela. BS, Va. Poly. Inst., 1969, MS, 1971; PhD, Ohio State U., 1973. Vocat. agriculture tchr. Pulaski County (Va.) Sch. Bd., 1969-71; asst. prof. agrl. edn. Ohio State U., Columbus, 1973-81, prof., 1981—, chmn. dept., 1986-89, assoc. dean Coll. Agr., 1989—; cons. Coll. Agriculture U. Wis., Madison, U. Fla., Gainesville, Dept. Animal Sci., Okla. State U., Stillwater. Co-author: The FFA and You, 1979, Methods of Teaching Agriculture, 1986. Lay leader Northwest United Meth. Ch., Columbus, 1984-87, chairperson adminstrv. bd., 1988-90. Mem. Am. Assn. Tchr. Educators in Agriculture (chmn. nat. agrl. edn. rsch. meeting 1982-83, outstanding paper award 1985, editing-mng. bd., Author of Yr. award 1984), Am. Vocat. Assn., Nat. Future Farmers Am. Alumni Coun., Gamma Sigma Delta (pres. 1984-85). Home: 4146 Checkerberry Ct Hilliard OH 43026-3017 Office: Ohio State Univ 2120 Fyffe Rd Columbus OH 43210-1067

NEWCOMB, MARTHA FREEMAN, lawyer; b. R.I., Aug. 4, 1955; d. Peter Hendrix and Juliette Adams (Freeman) N. AB, Smith Coll., Northampton, Mass., 1976; JD, Northeastern U., Boston, 1984. Bar: Mass. 1984, R.I. 1985, U.S. Supreme Ct. 1993. Editor, reporter Phoenix-Times Newspapers, Bristol, R.I., 1976-79; reporter The New Review, Clackamas County, Oreg., 1979-80; staff writer RIOICC, Providence, 1981; staff atty. R.I. Supreme Ct., Providence, 1984-86, chief staff atty., 1986—. Editor: (pamphlet) Beyond the Pipe Dream, 1979. Mem. ABA (chair Nat. Coun. Appellate Staff Attys. 1992-93), R.I. Bar Assn. Avocations: long-distance bicycling, sailing, traveling. Office: RI Supreme Ct 250 Benefit St Providence RI 02903

NEWCOMB, ROBERT WAYNE, electrical engineering educator; b. Glendale, Calif., June 27, 1933; s. Robert Dobson and Dorothy Opal (Bissinger) N.; m. Sarah Eleanor Fritz, May 22, 1954; children: Gail E., Robert W. BSEE, Purdue U., 1955; MS, Stanford U., 1957, PhD, U. Calif., Berkeley, 1960. Registered profl. engr., Calif. Rsch. intern Stanford Rsch. Inst., Menlo Park, Calif., 1955-57; teaching assoc. U. Calif., Berkeley, 1957-60; asst. and assoc. prof. Stanford U., 1960-70; prof. elec. engring. U. Md., College Park, 1970—; bd. dirs. PARCOR Rsch. program, Universidad Politecnica de Madrid, Spain. Author: Linear Multiport Synthesis, 1966, Active Integrated Circuit Synthesis, 1968, Concepts of Linear Systems and Control, 1968, Network Theory, 1967. Fulbright fellow, 1963; Fulbright-Hays fellow, 1976. Fellow IEEE; mem. Soc. Indsl. and Applied Math., Math. Assn. Am., Acad. Am. Poets. Avocations: film, literature, poetry. Home: 13120 Two Farm Dr Silver Spring MD 20904-3418 Office: Univ Md Microsystems Lab Elec Engring Dept College Park MD 20742

NEWCOMBE, GEORGE MICHAEL, lawyer; b. Newark, Nov. 11, 1947; s. George Anthony and Mary Hellen Newcombe; m. Joan Sharon Hanlon, May 30, 1969; children: Sean Michael, Scott Ryan, Jennifer Leigh. B-SChemE, N.J. Inst. Tech., 1969; JD, Columbia U., 1975. Bar: N.J. 1975, U.S. Dist. Ct. N.J. 1975, U.S. Ct. Appeals (3d cir.) 1975, N.Y. 1976, U.S. Dist. Ct. (so. dist.) N.Y. 1976, U.S. Dist. Ct. (we. dist.) Tex. 1985, U.S. Ct. Appeals (5th cir.) 1986, U.S. Supreme Ct., 1987. Ptnr. Simpson, Thacher & Bartlett, N.Y.C., 1975—; dir. Columbia Law Sch. Assn., Inc.; legal sec. Am. Ditchlay Found., 1994. Mem. coun. com. law offices vol. divsn. Legal Aid Soc., N.Y.C., 1980-86. Lt. USPHS, 1970-72. James Kent scholar Columbia Law Sch., 1974, Harlan Fiske Stone scholar Columbia Law Sch., 1975. Mem. Am. Law Inst., ABA, AICE, Assn. of Bar of City of N.Y., Tau Beta Epsilon, Omicron Delta Kappa. Office: Simpson Thacher & Bartlett 425 Lexington Ave New York NY 10017-3903

NEWCOMBE, HOWARD BORDEN, biologist, consultant; b. Kentville, N.S., Can., Sept. 19, 1914; s. Edward Borden and Mabel Elsie (Outerbridge) N.; m. Beryl Honor Callaway, Feb. 14, 1942; children—Kenneth Donald, Charles Philip, Richard William. B.Sc., Acadia U., Wolfville, N.S., 1935; Assoc., Imperial Coll. Tropical Agr., Trinidad, 1938; Ph.D., McGill U., Montreal, P.Q., Can., 1939; D.Sc. (hon.), McGill U., 1966, Acadia U., 1970. Sci. officer Brit. Ministry of Supply, London, 1940-41; research assoc. Carnegie Instn. Washington, 1946-47; research sci. Atomic Energy of Can. Ltd., Chalk River, Ont., 1947-79; head biology br. Atomic Energy of Can. Ltd., 1949-70, head population research br., 1970-79; vis. prof. genetics Ind. U., Bloomington, 1963; mem. Internat. Commn. on Radiol. Protection, 1965-77, chmn. com. on biol. effects, 1965-72. Contbr. articles to profl. jours. Served to lt. Brit. Royal Naval Vol. Res., 1941-46. Fellow Royal Soc. Can.; mem. Genetics Soc. Am. (sec. 1956-58), Am. Soc. Human Genetics (pres. 1965), Genetics Soc. Can. (pres. 1964-65). Home: 67 Hillcrest Ave, PO Box 135, Deep River, ON Canada K0J 1P0

NEWCOMER, CLARENCE CHARLES, federal judge; b. Mount Joy, Pa., Jan. 18, 1923; s. Clarence S. and Marion Clara (Charles) N.; m. Jane Moyer Martin, Oct. 2, 1948; children: Judy (Mrs. Kenneth N. Birkett Jr.), Nancy Jane Newcomer (Mrs. Edward H. Vick), Peggy Jo Pollack. A.B., Franklin and Marshall Coll., 1944; LL.B., Dickinson Sch. Law, 1948. Bar: Pa. 1950. Practiced law Lancaster, 1950-57; partner firm Rohrer, Honaman, Newcomer & Musser, Lancaster, 1957-60; with Office of Dist. Atty., Lancaster, 1960-64; 1st asst. dist. atty. Office of Dist. Atty., 1964-68, dist. atty., 1968-72; partner Newcomer, Roda & Morgan, 1968-72; fed. dist. judge Eastern Dist. Pa., Phila., 1972—; Spl. dep. atty. gen. Pa. Dept. Justice, 1953-54. Served to lt. (j.g.) USNR, 1943-46, PTO. Office: US Dist Ct 13614 US Courthouse 601 Market St Philadelphia PA 19106

NEWELL, BARBARA WARNE, economist, educator; b. Pitts., Aug. 19, 1929; d. Colston E. and Frances (Corbett) Warne; m. George V. Thompson, June 15, 1954 (dec. 1954); m. George S. Newell, June 9, 1956 (dec. 1964); 1 dau., Elizabeth Penfield. BA, Vassar Coll., 1951; MA, U. Wis., 1953, PhD, 1958, D. Pub. Svc.; LHD, Trinity Coll., 1973, Lesley Coll., 1978; LLD, Central Mich. U., 1973, Williams Coll., 1974, Rollins Coll., 1981, Butler U., 1983, Monmouth Coll., 1986; DLitt, Northeastern U., 1974, Mt. Vernon Coll., 1975, Lesley Coll., 1978, Denison U., 1978, Eckerd Coll., 1982, Gettysburg Coll., 1982, Dennison U., 1978, D.Adminstrn., Purdue U., 1976; DSc, Fla. Inst. Tech., 1981; LHD, Eckerd Coll., 1982; LLD, Butler U., 1983; D Pub. Service, Alaska Pacific U., 1986; DsPS, U. Md., 1987. Govt. intern NLRB, 1948, Hudson Shore Labor Sch., 1949; research, teaching asst. U. Wis., 1951-54, asst. to chancellor, 1965-67; research, teaching asst., assoc. U. Ill., 1954-59; asst. prof., then assoc. prof. economics Purdue U., 1959-65; asst. to pres., assoc. prof. econs. U. Mich., Ann Arbor, 1967-71, acting v.p. student affairs, 1968-70; prof. econs., assoc. provost grad. study and research U. Pitts., 1971; pres. Wellesley (Mass.) Coll., 1972-79; U.S. rep. with rank ambassador to UNESCO, Paris, 1979-81; chancellor State U. System Fla., Tallahassee, 1981-85; Regents prof. Fla. State U., 1985—; vis. scholar Harvard U., 1985-86, vis. lectr., 1986-87; cons. Fla. Dept. Labor, 1991—; State Job Tng. Coordinating Com., 1991; mem. Fla. Supreme Ct. Racial and Ethnic Bias Study Commn., 1990-92. Author: Chicago and the Labor Movement, 1961, (with Lawrence Senesh) The Pulse of the Nation, 1961, Our Labour Force, 1962; editorial bd.: (with Lawrence Senesh) Labor History, 1975—; mem. editorial bd. Jour. for Higher Edn. Mgmt., 1984—; contbr. articles and revs. to profl. jours. and mags. Mem. Disting. Review Panel Gov's. Challenge to State Colls. of N.J., 1985-87; mem. Task Force on Edn. at Earlham Coll., 1985-86; mem. Gov's. Council on High Technology, Fla., 1983-85; mem. Council of 100, Fla., 1981-85; steering com. of pres. to assist the Boston Sch. Dept., 1975-79; U.S. del. World Conf. on Women Leaders, Israel, 1979, Conf. on Women's Edn., Orgn. of Am. States, Buenos Aires, 1973; sec. County of Dane (Wis.) Community Action Council, 1964-66; bd. overseers Boston Symphony Orch., 1974-79, bd. dirs. WGBH-TV, Boston, 1974-79, County of Dane (Wis.) Community Welfare Council, 1964-66; Consortium on Financing Higher Edn., 1974-76, vice chmn., 1975-76; mem. ad hoc com. Future of State Univs. Nat. Assn. State Univs. and Land Grant Colls., N.Y., 1984-85, Internat. U. Consortium for Telecommunications in Learning, 1985-86; chmn. Nat. Commn. on Med. Care for Women of Am. Coll. Ob-Gyn, 1976-77; advisor to bd. of trustees Wesleyan U., Middletown, Conn., 1970-74, So. Regional Edn. Bd., 1981-85; trustee U. Pitts., 1973-76, Brookings Inst., 1973-79, Carnegie Endowment for Internat. Peace, 1973—, Carnegie Found. for the Advancement of Tchg., 1976-79, Am. Coll. of Paris, 1980, UN Internat. Research and Tng. Inst. for the Advancement of Women, 1986—, Com. for Econ. Devel., 1979—; mem. Pres.'s Commn. on Future of U. Mass., 1988-89; bd. dirs. Mass. Mutual Life Ins. Co., 1981-86, DeVry Corp., 1985-87, Americans for thr Universality of UNESCO, 1984—; mem. Fla. State Job Tng. Com., 1991—, mem. Fla. Edn. and Employment Coun. for Women and Girls, 1992—. Wells fellow, 1981. Mem. Soc. for Values in Higher Edn., Nat. Assn. Ind. Colls. and Univs. (bd. dirs. 1977-80), Assn. Am. Colls. (mem. task force on presdl. selection and career devel. 1974). Club: Cosmopolitan (N.Y.C.). Office: Florida State U Dept of Econ Tallahassee FL 32306-2045

NEWELL, BYRON BRUCE, JR., clergyman, former naval officer; b. Long Beach, Calif., July 31, 1932; s. Byron Bruce and Eleanor Whitaker (Davis) N.; m. Ingrid Charlotte Asche, June 11, 1955 (dec. July 1989); children: Thomas, Susan, Robert, Michael; m. Theresa Ann Troncale, Sept. 1, 1990. Student, Wesleyan U., 1950-51; BS, U.S. Naval Acad., 1955; MSEE, U.S. Naval Postgrad. Sch. Monterey, 1962; postgrad. nuclear power tng., 1964-65; MDiv, U. Theol. Sem., 1987. Ordained priest, Episcopal Ch., 1988. Commd. ensign U.S. Navy, 1955, advanced through grades to rear adm., 1980; weapons officer U.S.S. Lowry, Hull (destroyers), 1955-58; comdg. officer salvage ship, 1962-64, exec., comdg. officer nuclear cruisers, 1968-77, manpower/tng. surface ship personnel, 1977-79; with Nat. Mil. Command Center, Washington, 1979-80, chief navy info., 1980-82, chief navy legis. affairs, 1982-84; assoc. dean Trinity Episcopal Sch. for Ministry, Ambridge, Pa., 1990—; chmn., trustee Breakthrough, Inc. Decorated Legion of Merit, D.S.M. Mem. Naval Inst., Naval Hist. Soc., Met. Club. Home: 256 Thorn St Sewickley PA 15143-1204

NEWELL, CHARLDEAN, public administration educator; b. Ft. Worth, Oct. 14, 1939; d. Charles Thurlow and Mildren Dean (Looney) N. BA, U. North Tex., 1960, MA, 1962; PhD, U. Tex., 1968; cert., Harvard U., 1988. Instr. U. North Tex., Denton, 1965-68, asst. prof., 1968-72; assoc. prof., dir. Fedn. North Tex. Area Univs., Denton, Dallas, 1972-74; assoc. prof., assoc.

v.p. acad. affairs U. North Tex., Denton, 1974-76, assoc. prof., chair dept. polit. sci., 1976-80, prof. polit. sci., 1980-92, assoc. v.p., spl. asst. to chancellor, 1982-92, regents prof. pub. adminstrn., 1992—; cons. Miss. Bd. Trustees State Instns. Higher Learning, Jackson, 1983-84, Ednl. Testing Svc., Princeton, N.J., 1980, 82, 85, Spear, Down & Judin, Dallas, 1994-95, North Tex. Inst. Edn. in Visual Arts, Denton, 1993-94; bd. dirs. Mcpl. Clks. Ednl. Found., San Dimas, Calif.; bd. regents Internat. City/County Mgmt. Assn., Washington. Author: (with others) Texas Politics, 1993, The Effective Local Government Manager, 1993, City Executives: Leadership Roles, Work Characteristics and Time Management, 1989, Essentials of Texas Politics, 1995; contbr. articles to profl. jours. Chair charter rev. com. City of Denton, 1978-79; mem. adv. com. Ann's Haven Hospice, Denton, 1981-85; mem. exec. coun. Epsic. Diocese Dallas, 1985-88; mem. Civil Svc. Commn., City of Denton, 1989—, chmn., 1992—. Recipient Elmer Staats Career Pub. Svc. award Nat. Assn. Sch. Pub. Affairs Adminstrn., 1993. Mem. Am. Soc. Pub. Adminstrn. (sect. chmn 1982-83, mem. editorial bd. 1985-88), Internat. Pers. Mgmt. Assn. (regional program com. 1982-83), Am. Polit. Sci. Assn., Southwestern Polit. Sci. Assn. (sec., treas. 1975-79), Denton C. of C., Denton Tennis Assn., Pi Sigma Alpha (exec. coun. 1988-92). Democrat. Avocations: walking, reading. Home: 709 Mimosa Dr Denton TX 76201-0858 Office: U North Tex PO Box 5367 Denton TX 76203-0367

NEWELL, ERIC JAMES, financial planner, tax consultant, former insurance executive; b. Toronto, Ont., Can., Sept. 24, 1930; came to U.S., 1959, naturalized, 1970; s. James and Anne (Brown) N.; m. Essie Miskelly, Sept. 30, 1950; 1 son, Eric Wayne. Student, U. Toronto, 1951-53. Pub. acct. W.J. Wilcox & Co., Toronto, 1949-53; chief acct. Toronto Mut. Life Ins. Co., 1953-57; asst. sec. Holland Life Ins. Co., Toronto, 1957-59; with Penn Mut. Life Ins. Co., Phila., 1959-86; assoc. controller Penn Mut. Life Ins. Co., 1965-70, 2d v.p., controller, 1970-84, v.p., controller, 1984-86, ret. 1986; fin., tax cons., 1986—; dir. Hotel Brunswick, Lancaster, Pa., 1982-85. Mem. Traffic and Transp. Bd., Cherry Hill, N.J., 1971-73, Zoning Bd., 1975-78; vice chmn. Cherry Hill Econ. Devel. Bd., 1973-75; pres. Greater Kingston Civic Assn., Cherry Hill, 1970-76; Democratic committeeman, Camden County, 1976-79; vice chmn. Dem. Party, Cherry Hill, 1976. Fellow Life Mgmt. Inst., Royal Commonwealth Soc.; mem. Fin. Execs. Inst., Am. Inst. Corp. Contrs., N.Y. Ins. Accts. Club (chmn. 1984), Nat. Soc. Tax Profls., Royal Black Knights of Ireland, Loyal Orange Assn., Scotch-Irish Soc. of U.S., Am. Legion. Presbyterian (deacon 1969—). Home and Office: 137 E Partridge Ln Cherry Hill NJ 08003-4407

NEWELL, FRANK WILLIAM, ophthalmologist, educator; b. St. Paul, Jan. 14, 1916; s. Frank John and Hilda (Turnquist) N.; m. Marian Glennon, Sept. 12, 1942; children: Frank William, Mary Susan newell O'Connell, Elizabeth Glennon, Newell Murphy. M.D., Loyola U., Chgo., 1939; M.Sc., U. Minn., 1942. Diplomate Am. Bd. Ophthalmology (chmn. bd. 1967-69). James and Anna Raymond prof. dept. ophthalmology U. Chgo., 1953—; prof. extraordinario Autonomous U. Barcelona, Spain, 1972—; hon. prof. Tech. U. Japan, 1986—; sci. counselor Nat. Inst. Neurol. Diseases and Blindness, 1959-62, chmn., 1961-62; mem. nat. adv. eye coun. NIH, 1972-75; mem. Internat. Council Ophthalmology, 1977-85; bd. dirs. Heed Ophthalmic Found., 1965-93, chmn. 1975-90; dir. Ophthalmic Pub. Co., 1962, sec.-treas. 1971—. Author: Ophthalmology: Principles and Concepts, 1965, 7th edit., 1992, The American Ophthalmological Society, 1964-89, 1989; also articles; editor in chief Am. Jour. Ophthalmology, 1965-91, pub. 1972—; editor: Trans Claucoma Conf., Vols. 1-15, 1955-61, Amblyopia and Strabismus, 1975, Hereditary Diseases of the Eye, 1980, Stedman's Medical Dictionary, 25th edit., 1990. Trustee Loyola U., Chgo., 1977-81. Served from 1st lt. to maj. M.C. AUS, 1942-46. Recipient Alumni Citation award Loyola U., 1962, Stritch medal, 1966, Outstanding Achievement award U. Minn., 1975, 92, Gold Key U. Chgo., 1981, Lang medal Royal Soc. Medicine, London, 1974, medal honor Soc. Eye Surgeons, 1975, Vail medal Internat. Eye Found., 1986, medalla André Bello U. Chile, 1977, medalla de Oro Instituto Barraquer, Barcelona, Spain, 1982; Disting. Svc. award Physicians Edn. Network, 1983; decorated knight Order of St. John. Mem. Nat. Soc. Prevention Blindness (dir., v.p. 1970-81, pres. 1981-83, chmn. bd. 1983-85, Dunnington medal 1976), AMA (chmn. sect. ophthalmology 1964-65, Howe prize 1968), Am. Acad. Ophthalmology and Otolaryngology (pres. 1975), Inst. Barraguer (pres. 1970-88, hon. pres. 1988—), Assn. Univ. Profs. Ophthalmology (trustee 1966-69, pres. 1968-69), Assn. Research Ophthal. (chmn. bd. trustees 1967-68), Pan-Am. Assn. Ophthalmology (dir. 1969—, pres. 1981-83), Am. Ophthal. Soc. (pres. 1986-87, Howe medal 1979), Chgo. Ophthal. Soc. (pres. 1957-58), Oxford (Eng.) Ophthal. Congress (hon. mem., dep. master 1980), Hellenic Ophthal. Soc. (hon.), Royal Soc. Medicine (hon.), Academia Ophthalmologica Internationalis (pres. 1980-84), Columbia Ophthal. Soc. (hon.), Sigma Xi, Alpha Omega Alpha. Roman Catholic. Clubs: Literary (Chgo.), Quadrangle (Chgo.). Home: 4500 N Mozart St Chicago IL 60625-3817 Office: 77 W Wacker Dr Chicago IL 60601-1632

NEWELL, NORMAN DENNIS, paleontologist, geologist, museum curator, educator; b. Chgo., Jan. 27, 1909; s. Virgil Bingham and Nellie (Clark) N.; m. Valerie Zirkle, Feb. 25, 1928 (dec. 1972); m. Gillian Wendy Wormall, Apr. 28, 1973. B.S., U. Kans., 1929, M.A., 1931; Ph.D. in Geology, Yale U., 1933. Faculty mem. U. Kans., Lawrence, 1934-37; assoc. prof. geology U. Wis.-Madison, 1937-45; prof. geology Columbia U., N.Y.C., 1945-77, prof. emeritus, 1977—; curator Am. Mus. Nat. History, N.Y.C., 1945-77, curator emeritus, 1977—; geologist Kans. Geol. Survey, Lawrence, 1929-37; cons. on petroleum geology Peruvian Govt., 1942-45. Author: Permian Reef Complex of the Guadalupe Mountains Region, Texas and New Mexico, 1953, Creation and Evolution: Myth or Reality?, 1982, also numerous sci. articles and papers. Recipient Disting. Svc. Alumni award Kans. U., 1961, Hayden award Phila. Acad. Sci., 1965, Verrill medal Yale U., 1966, Gold medal for achievment in sci. Am. Mus. Natural History, 1978, Raymond C. Moore medal Soc. Econ. Paleontologists and Mineralogists, 1980, Scientific Freedom and Responsibility award AAAS, 1987. Mem. Nat. Acad. Scis. (Mary Clark Thompson medal 1960), Am. Philos. Soc., Am. Acad. Arts and Scis., Geol. Soc. Am. (Penrose medal 1990), Soc. Study Evolution (pres. 1949), Soc. Systematic Zoology (pres. 1972-73), Paleontol. Soc. (pres. 1960-61, medal 1979), Can. Soc. Petroleum Geologists (hon.). Avocations: geologic field expeditions. Home: 135 Knapp Ter Leonia NJ 07605-1216 Office: Am Mus Natural History Central Park St W New York NY 10026

NEWELL, PAUL HAYNES, JR., engineering educator, former college president; b. Nashville, July 1, 1933; s. Paul Haynes Newell; m. Martha A. Newell; children—Paul Haynes III, Mike, Nan. B.M.E., U. Tenn., 1958, M.M.E., 1961; Mech.E., Mass. Inst. Tech., 1964, Ph.D., 1966. Registered profl. engr., Ala., Tenn., N.J. Student asst. mech. engring. U. Tenn., 1957, instr. mech. engring., 1958-62; NSF Sci. faculty fellow Mass. Inst. Tech., 1962-65; assoc. prof. mech. engring. U. Ala. Coll. Engring., 1966-69; prof. mech. engring. Tex. A. and M. U., 1969-72, assoc. dean engring., 1972; prof. biomed. engring., dept. phys. medicine Baylor Coll. Medicine, 1969-74, prof. biomed. engring., dept. physiology, 1970-74, prof. biomed. engring., dept. community medicine, 1972-74, prof. biomed. engring., dept. rehab., 1972—, mem. grad. faculty, 1970-74; prof., head indsl. engring. dept. Tex. A. & M. U., 1972-74, prof., head combined programs of behavioral engring., bioengring., cybernetic engring., hygiene and safety engring., indsl. engring., 1972-74; pres., prof. Newark Coll. Engring., N.J. Inst. Tech., 1974-78; prof. Adminstrn. Prosthetics Ctr., N.Y., 1973-75, VA Hosp., Houston, 1972-75, Baylor Coll. Medicine, Houston, from 1971; pres. Newell Engring., Greenbrier, Tenn., 1979—; dir. N.J. Bell Telephone Co., Mid Atlantic Nat. Bank, Thomas-Betts Corp. Contbr. articles to profl. jours., chpts. to books. Mem. NSF liaison com., Newark Transp. Council, N.J. Safety Council; sec. exec. com. council Boy Scouts Am., Birmingham, Ala., 1966-68; bd. dirs. N.J. State Opera, United Hosps. Newark. Served with USMCR, Korean Conflict. Recipient NSF Sci. Faculty fellowship. Mem. Am. Soc. Tool and Mfg. Engrs., N.Y., Ala. acads. scis., AAAS, Am. Congress Rehab. Medicine, Am. Heart Assn., Am. Inst. Indsl. Engrs., Am. Soc. Artificial Internal Organs, Am. Soc. Engring. Edn., ASME, Biomed. Engring. Soc., Inst. Engring. Deans, Internat. Soc. Prosthetics and Orthotics, Nat. Soc. Profl. Engrs., Soc. Advanced Med. Systems, Soc. Engring. Sci., Pres. Newark Engring. Green-brier, Tenn., 1979—; dir. N.J. Bell Telephone Co., Mid Atlantic Nat. Bank, Soc., N.J. Soc. Engrs., Sigma Xi, Tau Beta Pi, Phi Kappa Phi, Pi Tau Sigma. Club: Rotary. Address: 1855 Lake Rd Greenbrier TN 37073-4619 Office: Newell Engring Greenbrier TN 37073-4619

NEWELL, REGINALD EDWARD, physics educator; b. Peterborough, Eng., Apr. 9, 1931; came to U.S., 1954, naturalized, 1969; s. Harold Aubrey and Edith (Swiffin) N.; m. Maireen W. Lees, Sept. 6, 1954; children:

Madeleine, Elizabeth, Oliver, Nicholas. B.S. in Physics, U. Birmingham, Eng., 1954; M.S., Mass. Inst. Tech., 1956, Sc.D., 1960. With Brit. Meteorol. Office, 1947-50; successively research staff asst., asst. prof., assoc. prof., prof. MIT, Cambridge, 1954—; mem IUGG Internat. Commn. Meteorology Upper Atmosphere, 1967-75; mem. Internat. Commn. Atmospheric Chemistry and Global Pollution, 1971-83; pres. Internat. Commn. on Climate, 1977-83. Joint author: The General Circulation of the Tropical Atmosphere, Vol. 1, 1972, and Vol. 2, 1976, Global Ocean Surface Temperature Atlas, 1990; contbr. articles to profl. jours. Served with RAF, 1950-51. Fellow Royal Meteorol. Soc., Am. Meteorol. Soc.; mem. Am. Geophys. Union. Home: 45 Jason St Arlington MA 02174-6446 Office: MIT 54-1824 77 Massachusetts Ave Cambridge MA 02139

NEWELL, ROBERT LINCOLN, retired banker; b. Hartford, Conn., Dec. 2, 1922; s. Robert B. and Helen C. (Lincoln) N.; m. Sally C. Erdman, July 28, 1944; children: Sally Newell Huss, Helen Newell Douglas, Robert Lincoln, Katharine Newell Chiodo, William Henry II. Student, Wesleyan U., Middletown, Conn. With Conn. Nat. Bank, Hartford, 1946-88, exec. v.p., 1967-72, 1st exec. v.p., 1972-75, pres., 1975-78, chmn., 1978-87, ret., 1987; bd. dirs. Kaman Corp.; former chmn. Hartford Nat. Corp. Corporator Hartford Hosp., Mt. Sinai Hosp.; bd. dirs. Mustic Seaport Mus. Lt. USNR, 1943-46. Home: 42 Mountain View Dr West Hartford CT 06117-3029

NEWELL, WILLIAM TALMAN, JR., hospital administrator; b. Newport News, Va., Apr. 4, 1932; s. William Talman and Helen Louise (Woolfolk) N.; m. Mary Hill Chilton, Feb. 11, 1956; children—William Talman III, John Chilton, Anne Caroline. B.S. in Hotel Adminstrn., Cornell U., 1954; M.B.A. in Health Care Adminstrn., George Washington U., 1967. Asst. mgr. Dayton (Ohio) Biltmore Hotel, 1956-57; restaurant mgr. Marriott Corp., Washington, 1957-60; food service mgr. The Fairfax Hosp., Falls Church, Va., 1960-63, asst. dir. gen. services div., 1963-64, dir. gen. services div., 1964-66, asst. to the adminstr., 1966-67; asst. dir. Yale-New Haven (Conn.) Hosp., 1967-70, assoc. dir., 1970-75; chief exec. officer U. Miss. Hosp., 1975-83; exec. dir. Univ. Hosp., SUNY, Stony Brook, 1983-94, ret., 1994; lectr. Sch. Epidemiology and Pub. Health, Yale U. Sch. Medicine, 1969-75; dir. Miss. Blue Cross & Blue Shield, 1979-83; mem. Appalachian Council Teaching Hosps., 1979; mem. Miss. Gov.'s Health Care Task Force on Children and Youth, 1982-83. Chmn. bd. Vocat. Rehab. Ctr. for Blind, Jackson, Miss.; adminstrv. bd. Nassau-Suffolk Hosp. Council Bd.; v.p. ops. Suffolk County council Boy Scouts Am.; bd. dirs. U. Hosp. Consortium; pres. bd. dirs. Miss. Blood Services, 1977-83; bd. dirs. Hosp. Assn. N.Y. Served to 1st lt. U.S. Army, 1954-56. Mem. Am. Coll. Health Care Adminstrs. Episcopalian.

NEWEY, PAUL DAVIS, lawyer; b. Mpls., July 4, 1914; s. Paul S. and Mary (Yonan) N.; m. Viola W. Raymond, Dec. 16, 1943 (dec. June 1982); children: Paul S. Newey II, Davis Raymond, Dean Alan, Arthur Tyler. A.A. Cen. YMCA, 1935; LLB, JD, John Marshall Law Sch., 1940; AB, Detroit Inst. Tech., 1947; diploma, U.S. Treasury Dept. Law Enforcement Sch., 1943; spl. courses, U.S. Gov. and Mil. Intelligence Schs., 1951-53. Bar: Ill. 1946. Squad leader Bur. Census, Dept. Commerce, 1940; officer Uniformed Force U.S. Secret Svc., 1940-42; agt. Bur. Narcotics, Treasury Dept., 1942-47; pvt. practice law, real estate and ins. broker Chgo., 1948-51; spl. rep. CIA, 1951-57; asst. state's atty.-investigator County of Cook, Ill., 1957-58; asst. state's atty.-chief investigator, chief state's atty.'s police County of Cook, 1958-60; pvt. practice law Chgo., 1961-65, spl. investigator, 1961—; ptnr. Adamowski, Newey & Adamowski, Chgo., 1965-82; spl. atty. Ill. Sec. of State, 1975-80; ptnr. firm Adamowski & Newey, Chgo., 1982-89; ret., 1989; sec., dir. Master Fishing Gear, Inc., 1956-57. Pvt. AUS, 1941; 1st lt. Counter Intelligence Corps. USAR, 1949-54. Recipient Medal of Merit and elected to Hall of Fame Nat. Police Officers Assn. Am., 1960, Disting. Citizen award Assyrian-Am. Welfare Council, 1970, Hammurabi award Assyrian Heritage Orgn., 1985; recipient Outstanding Svc. citation John Marshall Law Sch., 1975, Disting. Alumnus merit citation, 1970; honored by proclamation by Ill. gov., resolution by City of Chgo. aldermen and granted by mayor of Chgo. setting June 8, 1985 as Paul D. Newey Day. Mem. ABA, Fed. Bar Assn., Ill. Bar Assn., Chgo. Bar Assn., Internat. Assn. Investigators and Spl. Police (chmn. bd. dirs.), N. Am. Inst. Police Sci. (bd. dirs.), N.Am. Detective Agy. (bd. dirs.), Spl. Agts. Assn. (3d v.p. and legal counsel 1977—), U.S. Treasury Agts. Assn. (pres. 1970-71), John Marshall Law Sch. Alumni Assn. (treas. 1973-75, bd. dirs. 1964-84), Internat. Assn. Chiefs of Police (life), Spl. Agts. Assn. Chgo. (life), Amvets, Am. Legion, Assn. Former Fed. Narcotic Agents, Fed. Criminal Investigators Assn., Edward T. Lee Found. John Marshall Law Sch. (life), Amvets, Am. Legion, Smithsonian Assocs., Congl. Club (pres. 1963-64, bd. dirs., trustee 1962-65), Masons (32 degree, life), Medina Temple, Shriners (life), Lawyers Shrine Club (life). Mem. United Ch. of Christ. Home: 1034 W Altgeld St Chicago IL 60614-2209 *Life is an interlude in eternity, and material gain, by itself, makes it a nullity. The Master's admonition, "whatsoever ye have done for the least of these thy brethren, ye have done it unto me!" demands pro bono conduct; or perish without paying your debt for existence. I know that "man does not live by bread alone!" and try to shape my sojourn here accordingly.*

NEWFIELD, JACK, columnist. Columnist N.Y. Post, N.Y.C. Office: NY Post Corp 210 South St New York NY 10002

NEWFIELD, MAYER ULLMAN, lawyer; b. Birmingham, Ala., Apr. 5, 1905; s. Morris and Leah (Ullman) N.; m. Bertha Lehman, June 8, 1938 (dec. 1973); children: Jane, Melanie (Mrs. Harvey Seigle); m. Loretta Schneiderman Ostrow, Nov. 29, 1978. A.B., Samford U., 1927; postgrad., Harvard Law Sch., 1928-29; LL.B., U. Ala., 1931. Bar: Ala. 1931, U.S. Supreme Ct 1931. Asso. firm London, Yancey & Brower, Birmingham, 1931-34; supervising atty. HOLC, 1934-35; sr. trial atty., chief proxy unit, chief litigation and enforcement sect., asst. regional adminstr. SEC, Atlanta, Washington, Phila. and N.Y.C., 1935-47; co-author Rule 10b-5, 1942; asst. atty. City of Birmingham, 1948-56; gen. practice Birmingham, 1956—; mem. firm Newfield & Minisman, Birmingham, 1972-73; counsel Sirote & Permutt, 1972—; gen. ptnr., v.p. N. Ala. Mineral Devel. Co. Pres. Civic Opera Assn., 1964-66; Ala. co-chmn. NCCJ, 1964-74, Ala. chmn., 1974-75, mem. nat. bd. govs., 1974-80; nat. commr. Anti-Defamation League, 1956-82, exec. com., 1957-71, now hon. life mem.; pres. Jewish Community Council, 1975-77; bd. dirs. Am. Lung Assn., 1958-90; pres. Jewish Community Center, 1970-71; bd. dirs. Birmingham Music Club, 1986—, Urban League, 1967-74, Leo N. Levi Hosp., Hot Springs, Ark., 1968-74, Jewish Children's Home, New Orleans, 1968-74; mem. nat. adv. com. Am Israel Public Affairs Com., 1977-81; pres. Temple Emanu-El, 1976-77. Mem. ABA, Ala., Birmingham bar assns., B'nai B'rith (pres. Ala. 1949). Democrat. Home: 2900 Thornhill Rd Birmingham AL 35213-3521 Office: 2222 Arlington Ave S Birmingham AL 35205-4070

NEWHALL, CHARLES WATSON, III, venture capitalist; b. Washington, Nov. 18, 1944; s. Charles Watson Jr. and Gladys (Brantley) N.; m. Mary W. Newhall, Oct. 14, 1967 (dec. 1982); children: Charles Ashton, Adair Brantley; m. Amy Louise Liebno, June 4, 1983. BA in English with honors, U. Pa., 1967; MBA, Harvard U., 1971. Investment analyst T. Rowe Price Assocs., Balt., 1971-73, asst. v.p., 1973-74; v.p. New Horizons Fund, Balt., 1974-77; co-founder New Enterprise Assocs., Balt., 1978—; bd. dirs. Am. Day Treatment Ctrs., Inc., Annapolis, Md., Communication Systems Tech., Columbia, Md., Cellco, Inc., Germantown, Md., Healthsouth Rehab. Corp., Birmingham, Ala., Genetic Therapy, Inc., Gaithersburg, Md., MedPartners, Inc., Birmingham, Ala., Zymark Corp., Hopkinton, Mass., Scandipharm, Inc., Birmingham, Ala., Surg. Health Corp., Atlanta, Ga. Integrated Health Svcs., OPTA Food Ingredients, Cambridge, Mass., Americaid, Virginia Beach, Va. Trustee Balt. Mus. Art, Balt. Mus. Art. Lt. U.S. Army, 1967-69, Vietnam. Decorated Silver Star, Vietnam Svc. medal, oak leaf cluster, Bronze Star, Purple Heart, Air medal. Mem. Balt.-Washington Venture Capital Group (chmn.), Somerset Club, Rolling Rock Club, Greenspring Valley Hunt Club, Coral Beach Club. Office: New Enterprise Assocs 1119 Saint Paul St Baltimore MD 21202-2699

NEWHALL, DAVID, III, former federal government official; b. Phila., Dec. 6, 1937; s. David Jr. and Jane Martyn (Dunn) N. AB in Politics, Princeton U., 1961. Mgr. Bell Tel. Co. of Pa., Norristown, 1961-63; adminstrv. asst. to U.S. Rep. R.S. Schweiker Washington, 1963-69, chief of staff to U.S. Senator R.S. Schweiker, 1969-81; chief of staff HHS, Washington, 1981-83; pres.

Marmion Plantation Co., King George, VA., 1983-91; prin. dep. asst. sec. def.(health affairs) U.S. Dept. Def., Washington, 1985-90, acting asst. sec. def. (health affairs), 1989-90; gen. ptnr. Marmion Partnership Restorations, 1990—. Republican. Episcopalian. Club: Princeton Tower. Avocation: beef cow-calf operation. Home and Office: 7382M Marmion Ln King George VA 22485

NEWHALL, DAVID SOWLE, history educator; b. Burlington, Vt., July 26, 1929; s. Chester Albert and Nella Perry (Tillotson) N.; m. Edna Irene Newton, Mar. 25, 1952; children: Rebecca, John Newton, Jesslyn, Melissa, David Chester. BA. U. Vt., 1951; postgrad., Boston U., 1951; AM, Harvard U., 1956, PhD, 1963. Instr., asst. prof. U. Vt., Burlington, 1959-66; asst. prof., assoc. prof. history Centre Coll., Danville, Ky., 1966, prof., 1970, disting. prof. humanities, 1987, Pottinger disting. prof. history, 1994; mem. adv. com. Danville High Sch., 1980-81; cons. dept. history Berea (Ky.) Coll., 1983; rep. Ky. Coun. on Internat. Edn., Lexington, 1984-85. Author: Clemenceau: A Life at War, 1991; contbr. to Historical Dictionary of the Third French Republic, 1988, Kentucky Ency., 1992, Historical World Leaders, 1994. Elder Presbyn. Ch., U.S.A., Danville, 1969—; officer Danville High Sch. Band Parents Assn., 1982-86; bd. dirs. Project Opportunity, Lee and Breathitt Counties, Ky., 1968-74; mem. Citizens Com. on Coal-Hauling Traffic, Boyle County, Ky., 1982—. With U.S. Army, 1951-53, Korea. Recipient Acorn award Ky. Advocates for Higher Edn., 1994; Nat. Meth. scholar Boston U., 1953-55. Mem. Soc. for French Hist. Studies, World History Assn., Phi Beta Kappa (officer Centre Coll. 1971—), Omicron Delta Kappa, Phi Alpha Theta. Avocations: church choir, railroading. Home: 634 N 3d St Danville KY 40422 Office: Centre Coll Danville KY 40422

NEWHALL, JOHN HARRISON, management consultant; b. Phila., Sept. 29, 1933; s. Blackwell and Mary Large (Harrison) N.; m. Jane Carol Ward, July 15, 1961; children: Carol Newhall Neilson, Thomas Blackwell, Daniel Ward. BA, Williams Coll., 1955; MBA, Harvard U., 1960. Dir. corp. planning, gen. mgr. Europe H.J. Heinz Co., Pitts., 1970-77; v.p. mktg. Sun Co., Phila., 1977-81; chmn., chief exec. officer Aitkin-Kynett Co. (subs. Foote Cone & Belding), Phila., 1981-84; mng. dir., exec. v.p. Campbell-Ewald Co., N.Y.C., 1984-86; prin. mgmt. cons. SRI Internat., Menlo Park, Calif., 1987-90; mng. dir. Strategic Directions, Narberth, Pa., 1990—; pres. Advanced Promotion Techs., Deerfield Beach, Fla., 1992-93, Harvard Bus. Sch. Club of Phila., 1994—. mem. devel. council Williams Coll., Williamstown, Mass., 1977-87, Reg. v. chmn. Capital Campaign, 1991-93; mem. Com. of 70, Phila., 1981-84; bd. dirs. Bryn Mawr (Pa.) Hosp., 1982-88, The Haverford (Pa.) Sch., 1980-86, Headmaster sel. comm., 1992, Strategic Planning Comm., 1994, World Affairs Council, Phila., 1982-86, Found. for Vascular Hypertension Research, Phila., 1982—, chmn., 1987, Jr. Achievement, Phila., 1977-81, vice chmn., 1981, SE chpt. ARC, Phila., 1981-84, Pa. Economy League, 1981-84; vestryman, lay reader Episc. Ch., 1964-70. Served to lt. USN, 1955-58. Recipient Cert. of Merit Chapel of Four Chaplains, 1983, 85. Mem. Assn. Nat. Advertisers (exec. com. 1977-81). Republican. Episcopalian. Clubs: Union League (Phila.); Merion Cricket (Haverford); Gulph Mills (Pa.) Golf; Harbor (Seal Harbor, Maine). Avocations: skiing, tennis, sailing. Home and Office: Strategic Directions 414 Righters Mill Rd Narberth PA 19072-1423

NEWHART, BOB, entertainer; b. Oak Park, Ill., Sept. 29, 1929; m. Virginia Quinn, Jan. 12, 1963; 4 children. BS, Loyola U., Chgo., 1952. Acct. U.S. Gypsum Co.; copywriter Fred Niles Film Co.; appeared on Jack Paar Show, 1960; TV performer numerous guest appearances, 1961—; star TV series Newhart, 1982-90. Rec. artist (album) Button Down Mind on TV; royal command performance, London, 1964, appeared in films Hot Millions, 1968, Catch 22, 1970, Cold Turkey, 1971, First Family, 1980, Little Miss Marker, 1982; TV films include Thursday's Game, 1978, Marathon, 1980. Grand marshall Tournament Roses Parade, 1991. Served with U.S. Army, 1952-54. Recipient Emmy award, 1961, Peabody award, 1961, Sword of Loyola award, 1976, Legend to Legend award, 1993; named to Acad. Hall of Fame, 1993. Office: c/o David Capell 1875 Century Park E # 2250 Los Angeles CA 90067

NEWHOUSE, ALAN RUSSELL, federal government executive; b. N.Y.C., Feb. 27, 1938; s. Russell Conwell and Clara Lucille (Scovell) N.; m. Margo Stiles Hicks, Feb. 3, 1960; children: Daryl, Jeffrey, William. BEE, Cornell U., 1960. Engr. Bur. of Ships, Washington, 1964-66; nuclear power engr., chief West Milton field office AEC, Schenectady, N.Y., 1966-69; sr. exec. AEC, ERDA, U.S. Dept. Energy, Washington, 1969-92; dep. asst. sec. Space and Def. Power Systems Office Nuclear Energy, Washington, 1992-93; dir. Office Space and Def. Power Systems, 1993—. Composer numerous musical works. Bd. trustees River Road Unitarian Ch., Bethesda, Md., 1973-75; mem. McLean Symphony Orchestra, Washington Men's Camerata, Musica Antiqua, Interamerican Chamber Singers, Continuum Chamber Singers, U. Md. Chorus. Lt. USN, 1960-64. Mem. IEEE, AIAA, Am. Nuclear Soc., Am. Soc. Naval Engrs., Soc. Naval Architects and Marine Engrs., Am. Astronautical Soc. Republican. Unitarian. Home: 11108 Deborah Dr Potomac MD 20854-2721 Office: Space Def Power Systems Nuclear Energy NE # 50 Washington DC 20585

NEWHOUSE, BRIAN E., lawyer; b. Galion, Ohio, Feb. 22, 1953. BA with honors, Denison U., 1975; JD cum laude, U. Mich., 1978. Bar: Conn. 1978, Ill. 1984, Calif. 1985. Ptnr. Mayer, Brown & Platt, L.A.; lectr. Banking Law Inst., 1985. Mem. ABA (mem. corp., banking and bus. law sects.), State Bar Calif. Office: Mayer Brown & Platt 350 S Grand Ave Los Angeles CA 90071-1503

NEWHOUSE, DONALD E., newspaper publishing executive; b. 1930; s. Samuel N. Student, Syracuse U. With Advance Publs., Staten Island, N.Y., 1951—, now pres.; co-founder Newhouse Newspapers, N.Y.C., 1963, now v.p.; pres. Newark (N.J.) Star-Ledger; v.p. Times Picayune Pub. Corp., New Orleans; treas. Herald Am., Syracuse, 1960—, The Post Standard, Syracuse, 1960—, The Syracuse Herald Journal, 1960—, The Herald Co. Inc., 1960—; co-founder Metro-Suburbia, Inc., N.Y.C., 1963; prin. The Trenton (N.J.) Times, Times of Trenton Pub. Corp. Office: Star-Ledger 1 Star Ledger Plz Newark NJ 07102-1200*

NEWHOUSE, IRVING RALPH, state legislator; b. Mabton, Wash., Oct. 16, 1920; s. John and Tina (Bos) N.; m. Ruth Martha Gardner, July 14, 1945; children: Joyce, James, Linda, Laura, Daniel, Dorothy. BS, Wash. State U., 1943. County agt. Egrl. Extension Svc., Ellensburg, Wash., 1946; farmer Mabton, 1947—; mem. Wash. Ho. of Reps., Olympia, 1964-80; mem. Wash. State Senate, Olympia, 1980—, Rep. floor leader. Lt. (j.g.) USNR, 1943-45, PTO. Republican. Mem. Christian Reformed Ch. Home: 1160 Murray Rd Mabton WA 98935-9714 Office: Wash State Sen 403 Legislative Bldg Olympia WA 98504

NEWHOUSE, JOSEPH PAUL, economics educator; b. Waterloo, Iowa, Feb. 24, 1942; s. Joseph Alexander and Ruth Linnea (Johnson) N.; m. Margaret Louise Locke, June 22, 1968; children: Eric Joseph, David Locke. BA, Harvard U., 1963, PhD, 1969; postgrad (Fulbright scholar), Goethe U., Frankfort, Germany, 1963-64. Staff economist Rand Corp., Santa Monica, Calif., 1968-72, dep. program mgr., health and biosci. rsch., 1971-88, sr. staff economist, 1972-81, head econs. dept., 1981-85, sr. corp. fellow, 1985—; John D. MacArthur prof. health policy and mgmt., dir. div. Health Policy Rsch. and Edn., Harvard U., 1988—; lectr. UCLA, 1970-83, adj. prof., 1983-88; mem. faculty Rand Grad. Sch., 1972-88; dir. Rand-UCLA Ctr. for Study Health Care Fin. Policy, 1984-88, co-dir., 1988-92. prin. investigator health ins. study grant HHS, 1971-86; chmn. health svcs. rsch. study sect. HHS-Agy. for Health Care Policy and Rsch., 1989-93; mem. Nat. Commn. Cost Med. Care, 1976-77; mem. health svcs. devel. grants study sect. HEW, 1978-82, Inst. Medicine of NAS, 1978—, mem. coun., 1992—; mem. Physician Payment Rev. Commn., 1993—. Author: The Economics of Medical Care, 1978, The Cost of Poor Health Habits, 1991, A Measure of Malpractice, 1993, Free for All?, 1993; editor Jour. Health Econs., 1981—; assoc. editor Econ. Perspectives, 1992—; contbr. articles to profl. jours. Recipient David Kershaw award and prize Assn. Pub. Policy and Mgmt., 1983, Baxter Am. Found. prize, 1988, Adminstr.'s citation Health Care Fin. Adminstrn., 1988. Fellow Am. Acad. Arts and Scis.; mem. Assn. for Health Svcs. Rsch. (Article of Yr. award 1989, bd. dirs. 1991—, pres. 1993-94), Am. Econ. Assn., Royal Econ. Soc., Econometric Soc., Phi Beta Kappa. Office:

Harvard U Health Policy Rsch and Edn 25 Shattuck St Fl 1 Boston MA 02115-6027

NEWHOUSE, MARK WILLIAM, publishing executive; b. N.Y.C., Oct. 14, 1948; s. Norman Nathan and Alice (Gross) N.; m. Lorry A. Whitehead, June 1, 1974; children: Jesse Louis, Charlotte Ann. BA, Yale U., 1969. V.p., gen. mgr. The Star-Ledger, Newark, N.J., 1980—. Bd. dirs. N.Y.C. Opera, 1992—, pres., 1993—; bd. dirs. Audit Bur. of Circulations, 1995—. Office: Newark Morning Star Ledger Co One Star Ledger Plz Newark NJ 07102-1200

NEWHOUSE, NANCY RILEY, newspaper editor; b. Bellingham, Wash.; d. Fenwick Charles and Elizabeth (Grace) Riley; m. John Newhouse, Sept. 27, 1961 (div. 1970); m. Michael Iovenko, Mar. 6, 1983. BA, Vassar Coll., 1958. Sr. editor N.Y. Mag., N.Y.C., 1970-75, House & Garden Mag., N.Y.C., 1976; successively home editor, style editor and travel editor N.Y. Times, N.Y.C., 1976—. Editor: Hers: Through Women's Eyes, 1985; editor Hers column N.Y. Times, 1976-92; mem. adv. bd. Vassar Quar., Poughkeepsie, N.Y., 1995—. Recipient Penney-Mo. Newspaper award U. Mo. Sch. Journalism, 1982-83. Mem. The Century Assn. (admissions com.), Women's Forum N.Y. Office: NY Times Co 229 W 43rd St New York NY 10036-3913*

NEWHOUSE, ROBERT J., JR., insurance executive. Ret. vice chmn. bd. Marsh & McLennan Cos., Inc.; chmn. bd. Mid Ocean Reins. Co. Ltd., Bermuda; dir., chmn. exec. com. ACE Ltd., Bermuda; dir. Trident Corp., Bermuda. Office: 55 Madison Ave Ste 450 Morristown NJ 07960

NEWHOUSE, SAMUEL I., JR., publishing executive; b. 1928; m. Victoria Newhouse. Chmn. Condé Nast Publs. Inc., N.Y.C.; also chmn. bd. dirs., CEO Advance Publs., Inc., S.I., N.Y. Recipient Henry Johnson Fisher award Mag. Pubs. Assn., 1985. Office: Condé Nast Publs Inc 350 Madison Ave New York NY 10017-3704 also: Advance Pubs Inc 950 Fingerboard Rd Staten Island NY 10305-1453

NEWICK, CRAIG DAVID, architect; b. Orange, N.J., Feb. 14, 1960; s. Russel Forester and Helen (Welch) N.; m. Linda Hammer Lindroth, June 6, 1987; 1 child, Zachary Eran. BA in Architecture, Lehigh U., 1982; MArch, Yale U., 1987. Registered architect, Conn. Ptnr. Lindroth & Newick, New Haven, 1991—; architect, cons. Riverfront Recapture Inc. Design, Hartford, Conn., 1991. Out Of Bounds (fisrt prize artists books 1994). Grantee New Eng. Found. for Arts, 1992, NEA Interarts grantee Rockefeller Found., 1989-90, Found. for Contemporary Performance Art, 1989, 90; New Eng. for Arts Regional fellow, 1993; recipient 1st place award Am. Visionary Set Design Competition, 1989, 3d place award Astronauts Meml. Design Competition, 1988, 2d prize African Burial Ground Competition Mcpl. Arts Soc. N.Y., 1994. Mem. Architecture League N.Y. (young architects forum 1991). Office: Lindroth & Newick 219 Livingston St New Haven CT 06511-2209

NEWKIRK, INGRID, animal rights activist; b. Surrey, Eng., 1949; m. Steve Newkirk, 1967 (div. 1980). Poundmaster D.C., 1978; dir. cruelty investigations Washington Humane Soc., D.C., 1978-80; co-founder (with Alex Pacheco) People for the Ethical Treatment of Animals, D.C., 1980—, also nat. dir. Author: Save the Animals! 101 Easy Things You Can Do, 1990. Office: PETA Box 42516 Washington DC 20015

NEWKIRK, JOHN BURT, metallurgical engineer, administrator; b. Mpls., Mar. 24, 1920; s. Burt Leroy and Mary Louise (Leavenworth) N.; m. Carolyn Mae Jordan, Aug. 4, 1951; children: Jeffrey Burt (dec.), John Jordan, Victoria Louise Leinheimer, Christina Brooks. B. Metall. Engring. Rensselaer Poly. Inst., Troy, N.Y., 1941; M.S., Carnegie Inst. Tech., 1947, Sc.D., 1950. Metall. investigator Bethlehem Steel Co., Pa., 1941-42; Fulbright postdoctoral fellow Cambridge (Eng.) U., 1950-51; research metallurgist research lab. Gen. Electric Co., Schenectady, 1951-59; prof. Cornell U. 1959-65; Phillipson prof. U. Denver, 1965-74, prof. phys. chemistry, 1975-84, Phillipson prof. emeritus, 1984—; pres. Colo. Biomed., Inc. 1969—, ret. Editor Rews. on High Temperature Materials, 1973-78; 16 ann. volumes Advances in X-Ray Analysis; contbr. over 75 articles profl. jours. With USNR, 1942-46. Fellow Am. Soc. Metals (life); mem. Sigma Xi, Tau Beta Pi, Phi Kappa Phi, Alpha Sigma Mu (internat. pres. 1950), Alpha Tau Omega. Republican. Presbyterian. Office: Colo Biomed Inc 6851 Hwy 73 Evergreen CO 80439-6543

NEWLAND, CHESTER ALBERT, public administration educator; b. Kansas City, Kans., June 18, 1930; s. Guy Wesley and Mary Virginia (Yoakum) N. BA, U. N. Tex., Denton, 1954; MA, U. Kans., 1955, PhD, 1958. Social Sci. Rsch. Coun. fellow U. Wis. and U.S. Supreme Ct., 1958-59; instr. polit. sci. Idaho State U., Pocatello, 1959-60; mem. faculty U. North Tex., Denton, 1960-66, prof. govt., 1963-66, dir. dept. govt., 1963-66; prof. polit. sci. U. Houston, 1967-68; dir. Lyndon Baines Johnson Libr., Austin, Tex., 1968-70; prof. pub. adminstrn. U. So. Calif., 1966-67, 68-71, 76-82, 84-92, Duggan disting. prof. pub. adminstrn., 1992—; prof. George Mason U., Fairfax, Va., 1982-84; mem. faculty Fed. Exec. Inst., 1971-76, dir. 1973-76, 80-81; mgr. task force on fed. labor-mgmt. rels. U.S. Pers. Mgmt. Project, Pres.'s Reorgn., Washington, 1977-78. Editor in chief Pub. Adminstrn. Rev., 1984-90; contbr. articles to profl. jours. Chmn. Mcpl. Rsch. Coun., Denton, 1963-64; city councilman Denton, 1964-66; mem. Pub. Sector Commn. on Productivity and Work Quality, 1974-78; trustee Sacramento (Calif.) Mus. History, Sci. and Tech., 1993-95. Recipient Staats award Nat. Assn. Schs. of Pub. Affairs and Adminstrn. Mem. Nat. Acad. Pub. Adminstrn., Southwestern Social Sci. Assn. (chmn. govt. sect. 1964-65), Am. Soc. Pub. Adminstrn. (pres. Dallas-Ft. Worth chpt. 1964-65, nat. coun. 1976, 78-81, editorial bd. jour. 1972-76, chmn. publ. com. 1975-79, program chmn. 1977, nat. pres. 1981-82, Dimock award 1984), Am. Polit. Sci. Assn., Internat. Pers. Mgmt. Assn. (program chmn. 1978, Stockberger award 1979), Am. Acad. Polit. and Social Sci., Internat. City Mgmt. Assn. (hon.), Nat. Assn. Schs Pub. Affairs and Adminstrn. (Staats Pub. Svc. award 1989). Office: Univ Southern California 1201 J St Sacramento CA 95814-2919

NEWLAND, LARRY J., orchestra conductor; b. Winfield, Kans., Jan. 24, 1935; s. Roy E. and Frances M. (Hammond) N.; m. Paula Kahn, Feb. 18, 1977; children: Lee Ann, Sara. MusB, Oberlin Conservatory, 1955; MusM, Manhattan Sch. Music, 1957. artistic adminstr. Sr. Concert Orch., N.Y.C., 1987-89. Asst. condr., musician N.Y. Philharm., N.Y.C., 1960-85; music dir., condr. Harrisburg (Pa.) Symphony, 1978-94, Philharm. Chamber Orch. (formerly Diabolus Musicus Chamber Orch.), N.Y.C., 1974—; music dir. Sr. Concert Orch. N.Y., 1987-89; regular guest condr. Seoul (Republic of Korea) Philharm.; prof., dir. ensembles Adelphi U., Garden City, N.Y., 1990—, acting chair music dept., 1993-94, chair music dept., 1994—. Served with U.S. Army, 1957-60. REcipient Harold Bauer Meml. award, 1957, Koussevitzky Conducting prize, 1963, Pa. Gov.'s citation, 1982, Pa. Ho. of Reps. citation, 1988, Disting. Pub. Svc. award City of Harrisburg, 1982, Golden Baton award Harrisburg Symphony, 1994, Pa. State Senate commendation, 1994; Leonard Bernstein conducting fellow, 1964. Mem. Am. Symphony Orch. League, Am. Fedn. Musicians, Condrs. Guild (pres. 1993-95). Avocations: tennis, sailing, mountain climbing, hiking, reading.

NEWLAND, MATTHEW JOHN, state legislator; b. Middletown, Conn., Dec. 6, 1967; s. Marshall Lee Jr. and Arline Ann (Stafford) N.; Heather Catherine Clough, Oct. 2, 1993. A Bus. Mgmt., N.H. Tech. Inst., 1990; BBA, U. N.H., 1993. Mem. N.H. Ho. of Reps., Concord, 1992—. Trustee U. Sys. of N.H., Lee, 1991-92; mem. Civic Ctr. Commn., Concord, 1994; mem. N.H. State Dem. Com., Concord, 1993-94; bd. mem. Cmty. Svc. Coun., 1994—. Mem. Sachem Soc., World Wildlife Fund. Democrat. Roman Catholic. Avocations: reading, skiing, movies. Home: 81 Fisherville Rd Apt 29 Concord NH 03303-4155 Office: State House Rm 306 Concord NH 03301

NEWLAND, RON, airport executive. Mgr. of airport svcs. Rickenbacker Internat Airport, Columbus, OH. Office: Rickenbaker Intl Airport 2365 Fred Haise Ave Columbus OH 43217

NEWLIN, CHARLES FREMONT, lawyer; b. Palestine, Ill., Nov. 18, 1953; s. Charles Norris and Regina Helen (Correll) N.; m. Jean Bolt, Jan. 6, 1975; children: Christian N., Charles W., Ethan A. BA in Polit. Sci. summa cum laude, Ill. Wesleyan U., 1975; JD cum laude, Harvard U., 1978. Bar: Ill. 1978, U.S. Dist. Ct. (no. dist.) Ill. 1978, U.S. Tax Ct. 1980. Law clk. Sugarman, Rogers, Barshak & Cohen, Boston, 1976-78; assoc. Mayer, Brown & Platt, Chgo., 1978-84, ptnr., 1985—; adj. prof. law DePaul U., Chgo., 1986-90; lectr. in field. Contbg. author: Am. Law of Property, 1975, Trust Adminstrn. Ill., 1983, 87, 92, Bogert on Trusts, 1986-91, The Lawyer's Guide to Retirement, 1991, 94; contbr. articles to profl. jours. Scouting coord. DuPage area coun. Boy Scouts Am., Woodridge, Ill., 1984-86; bishop's counselor Mormon Ch., Woodridge, 1984-86; mem. planned giving com. Ill. div. Am. Cancer Soc., 1988—, Boys and Girls Clubs of Chgo., 1993—; vol. legal cons. The Tower Chorale, Western Springs, Ill., 1989-91. Fellow Am. Coll. Trust and Estate Counsel; mem. Chgo. Bar Assn., Chgo. Estate Planning Coun. Democrat. Methodist. Office: Mayer Brown & Platt 190 S La Salle St Chicago IL 60603-3410

NEWLIN, LYMAN WILBUR, bookseller, consultant; b. Buda, Ill., May 26, 1910; s. Fred Matheny and Maude Lillian (Potter) N.; m. Evy Ottonia Magnusson, 1966; children: Fred M. II, Erik B.M. Student, Coll. Emporia, Kans., 1928-30, U. Chgo., 1930-32. Buyer, bus. mgr. Follett Book Co., Chgo., 1934-44; mgr. Minn. Book Store and Macalester Coll. Book Store, Mpls. and St. Paul, 1944-48; co-owner Broadwater Lodge, Hackensack, Minn., 1948-65; founder, owner Broadwater Books, Lewiston, N.Y., 1948—; buyer, dept. mgr. Kroch's & Brentano's Book Store, Chgo., 1951-65; regional mgr. Richard Abel and Co., Portland, Oreg. and Zion, Ill., 1966-69, asst. to pres., 1969-75; founder, prin. counselor Lyman W. Newlin Book Trade Counsellors, Lewiston, N.Y., 1975—; mdse. mgr. Coutts Library Services, Inc., Lewiston, 1976-90; pub. rels. advisor The Charleston (Coll. Libr.) Conf., 1985—; pub. liaison Book News, Inc., Portland, 1989—; program coord. Acad. of Scholarly Pub. seminar Coll. of Charleston, 1995; cons. Rutgers U. Press, New Brunswick, N.J., 1975-81; judge Hawkins awards Assn. Am. PUbs., 1976-81; panelist and lectr. to acad. librs. and schs., booksellers. Pub. Rev. Index Quar. Guide to Profl. Revs., 1941-43; pub. rels. advisor, contbr. Quar. Publ. Against the Grain, 1985—; contbr. articles to profl. jours. Founder, 1st pres. Boy River Chain of Lakes Improvement Assn., Cass County, Minn., 1961-65, Concerned Parents Orgn., Freehold, 1976-79; trustee, v.p., sec., chmn. new libr. bldg. com. Lewiston Pub. Libr., 1985—; committeeman Niagara County Dem. Party, 1987—, sec., 1988-90; mem. coun. Luth. Ch. Messiah, Lewiston, 1982-93, deacon, 1992—; mem. Town of Lewiston Sr. Citizens Adv. Bd., 1992—. Mem. Assn. Book Travelers (50 Yr. award 1984), Am. Booksellers Assn. Assc Scholarly Pub. (program com. 1985), ALA, Can. Libr. Assn., Book Industry Study Group, Pi Kappa Delta. Democrat. Avocations: amateur ornithology, jazz. folk music, New Orleans jazz, book collecting. Office: PO Box 278 Lewiston NY 14092-0278

NEWLIN, PETER CAVERLY, architect; b. Bryn Mawr, Pa., Feb. 26, 1947; s. J. Shipley and Virginia (Strong) N.; m. M. Gale Tucker, Oct. 17, 1992; 1 child, Julia Kimble Ramsey. BA magna cum laude, Conn. Coll., 1972; MArch, U. Va., 1977; postgrad., St. John's Coll., 1975, 78. Registered architect; cert. Nat. Coun. Achtl. Registration Bds. Prin. Peter Newlin, Builder, Chestertown, Md., 1973-78; mgr. James Wood Burch, FAIA & Assocs., Chestertown, Md., 1978-83; pres. Chesapeake Associated Architects, Inc., Chestertown, 1983—; instr. archtl. history and design theory Chesapeake Coll., 1979, 80, Washington Coll., 1981, 82; lectr. Washington Coll.-sponsored energy workshop SENSE; instr. architecture State of Md.'s Gifted and Talented Summer Program, 1984-85, 86, 87; chosen as one of 6 Am. architects to visit The Netherlands to study architecture. Mem. Hist. Dist. Commn. of Chestertown, 1986-87, Kent County Housing Code Com., 1991, Gov.'s Task Force for State-wide Bldg. Code, 1992; profl. advisor Chester Valley Habitat, 1990; co-chmn. Chesapeake Bay Chpt. Govt. & Pub. Affairs, 1990-92; chmn. Kent County Bldg. Code Com., 1991-92; pres. Queen St. Cmty. Assn., 1983-84. German translator U.S. Army, 1966-70. Recipient Gov. Citation for pub. svc., Gov. of Md., 1993, Most Innovative Energy Conserving Design award Delmarva Power, 1991. Mem. AIA, Md. Soc. AIA (pres. 1993, regis. chmn. 1995, Pres.'s award for pub. svc. 1991), Chesapeake Bay Chpt. AIA (pres. 1989, Award for Design Excellence 1986, 89, Citation for Design Merit 1991, 92). Office: Chesapeake Architects 104 Church St Chestertown MD 21620-1506

NEWMAN, ANDREW EDISON, retail executive; b. St. Louis, Aug. 14, 1944; s. Eric Pfeiffer and Evelyn Frances (Edison) N.; m. Peggy Gregory, Feb. 14, 1984; children: Daniel Mark, Anthony Edison. BA, Harvard U., 1966, MBA, 1968. With Office of Sec. Def., Washington, 1968-70; With Edison Bros. Stores, Inc., St. Louis, 1970—, v.p. ops. and adminstrn., 1975-80, dir., 1978—; exec. v.p., 1980-86; chmn. Edison Bros. Stores, Inc., 1987—; bd. dirs. Washington U., St. Louis, Boatmen's Bancshares, St Louis, Sigma-Aldrich Corp., St. Louis, Lee Enterprises, Davenport, Iowa. Bd. dirs., commr. St. Louis Sci. Ctr. Office: Edison Bros Stores Inc 501 N Broadway Saint Louis MO 63102-2196

NEWMAN, ARNOLD, photographer; b. N.Y.C., Mar. 3, 1918; s. Isidore and Freda (Perell) N.; m. Augusta Rubenstein, Mar. 6, 1949; children—Eric Allan, David Saul. Student, U. Miami, Coral Gables, Fla., 1937-38, DFA (hon.), 1981; HHD (hon.), Art Ctr. Coll. Design, Pasadena, Calif., 1985; hon. univ. doctorate, U. Bradford, Eng., 1989; DFA (hon.), New Sch. Social Rsch./Parson Sch. Design, 1990. Began photography, 1938, exptl. portraiture, 1941, opened N.Y.C. studio, 1946; adj. prof. photography Cooper Union, N.Y.C., 1968-75; resident dir.s visitor/lectr. Inst. for Advanced Study, Princeton, N.J., 1991; lectr. U.S. and abroad. Exhibited and represented in collections, Mus. Modern Art, N.Y.C., Met. Mus. Art, N.Y.C., Art Inst. Chgo., Smithsonian Instn., Washington, Phila. Mus. Art, Internat. Mus. Photography at George Eastman House, Rochester, N.Y., Photography Gallery, London, Israel Mus., Jerusalem, Victoria and Albert Mus., London, Moderna Museet, Stockholm, Australian Nat. Gallery, Camberra, Nat. Portrait Gallery, London, Nihon U. Coll. Art, Tokyo, Odakyu Gallery, Tokyo, Japan, others; traveling retrospective exhbn., Arnold Newman-Five Decades, Mus. of Photographic Arts, San, Diego, 1986, Art Inst. of Chgo., 1986, Mpls. Inst. Art, 1987, Norton Gallery & Sch. Art, MIT Mus., Cambridge, 1988, Modern Art Mus., Ft. Worth, 1988-89, Cin. Art Mus., 1989, De Nieuwe Kerk, Amsterdam, The Netherlands, 1989, The Joan Miró Fedn., Barcelona, Spain, 1990, Frankfurter Kunstverein, Germany, Musee de l'Elysee, Lausanne, Switzerland, 1992, Mus. Modern Art, Oxford, England, 1992, Arnold Newman's Ams., Nat. Portrait Gallery, Washington, 1992; author: Bravo Stravinsky, 1967, One Mind's Eye: The Portraits and Other Photographs of Arnold Newman, 1974, Faces USA, 1978, The Great British, 1979, Artists: Portraits from Four Decades, 1980, I Grandi Fotografhi Arnold Newman, 1983, Arnold Newman-Five Decades, 1986, Arnold Newman in Florida, 1987, Arnold Newman's Americans, Portrait Gallery, Washington, 1992, The Detroit Inst. Arts, 1993, LBJ Libr. & Mus., Austin, Tex., 1993, Columbus (Ga.) Mus. Art, 1993-94, Greenville (S.C.) County Mus. Art, 1994, Worcester (Mass.) Art Mus., 1994, Arnold Newman's Gift, George Eastman House, Rochester, N.Y., 1994; contbr. to Travel and Leisure, Life, Look, Holiday, Fortune, Esquire, Town & Country, Vanity Fair, 1946—; subject of Nebr. Ednl. TV program The Image Makers: The Environment of Arnold Newman, 1977; invited exhbn. and lecture tour throughout country Czechoslovakian govt., 1989, Mus. Contemporary History, Budapest, Hungary, 1990. Recipient Photokina award, Cologne, Germany 1951, Newhouse citation Syracuse (N.Y.) U. 1961, Gold medal 4th Biennale Internazionale della Fotagrafic, Venice, Italy 1963, Andy award Advt. Club N.Y., 1983, Mo. Honor medal for journalism U. Mo., 1985, Medal of Merit, 1986, Medal of Merit Lotos Club, 1986, Lifetime Achievement in Photography award Photographic Adminstrs., 1989, others; named Hon. Fellow of Israel Mus. of Jerusalem, 1986, Commemorative medal in hon. 150th anniversary photography Ministry of Culture Czechoslovakia, 1989, Disting. Alumnus award U. Miami, 1993; named N.Y. Alumnus of Yr. U. Miami, 1993; The Arnold Newman Scholarship Fund named in honor Parsons Sch. Design, N.Y.C., 1993. Mem. Am. Soc. Mag. Photographers (Life Achievement in Photography award 1975), Inst. for Advanced Study (bd. dirs. visitor Princeton chpt. 1991). Home: 33 W 67th St New York NY 10023-6224 Office: 39 W 67th St New York NY 10023-6244

NEWMAN, BARBARA POLLOCK, journalist, television writer, producer.; b. N.Y.C., June 15, 1939; d. Irving G. and Jeanne (Ginsberg) Pollock; div.; 1 child, Penelope. BA, Mount Holyoke Coll., 1960; MA, Columbia U., 1962. Legis. asst. Rep. James Scheuer, Washington, 1964-65, Mayor John Lindsay, N.Y.C., 1965-67; mem. President's Nat. Adv. Commn. on Civil Disorders, Washington, 1967-79; reporter, interviewer Nat. Pub. Radio, N.Y.C., 1971-

78; investigative reporter, producer "20/20" ABC News, Washington, 1978-81; exec. producer Jack Anderson Confidential, Washington, 1982-83; pres. Praetorian Prodns., Inc., Washington, 1984—; moderator Nat. Town Meetings, Pub. TV, 1975-78; Hostess McNeill Lehrer Report, Aug. 1977; mem. adv. bd. Washington Journalism Review, 1977-80. Author: The Covenant: Love and Death in Beirut, 1989; contbr. news and editl. articles to newspapers and popular jours.; sr. prodr. Now It Can Be Told, 1991; prodr. documentaries for investigative reports Arts and Entertainment Network; prodr. Channel 4 and Ctrl. TV, London. Recipient Peabody award thorugh Nat. Pub. Radio, 1972, Ohio State award, 1973, 74, 76, Silver Gavel award, ABA, 1974, Cadmus award, Am. Lebanese League, 1981; Emmy nominee, 1981 for investigative reporting. Home: 5336 29th St NW Washington DC 20015-1332

NEWMAN, BARRY INGALLS, retired banker, lawyer; b. N.Y.C., Mar. 19, 1932; s. M.A. and T.C. (Weitman) N.; BA, Alfred U., 1952; JD, NYU, 1955; m. Jean Short, Mar. 6, 1965; children: Suzanne, Cathy, David. Bar: N.Y. 1957, Ohio 1957, U.S. Supreme Ct. 1967, Calif. 1990; practiced in N.Y.C., 1957; assoc., then ptnr. firm Shapiro Persky Marken & Newman, Cleve., 1957-63; asst. v.p. Meinhard & Co. (now Meinhard Comml. Corp.), N.Y.C., 1963-65; v.p. Amsterdam Overseas Corp., N.Y.C., 1966-68; pres. No. Fin. Corp., L.A., 1968-72; sr. v.p. Aetna Bus. Credit, Inc., Hartford, Conn., 1972-78; exec. v.p. Security Pacific Fin. Group, San Diego, 1978-81, chmn., pres, chief exec. officer, 1981-82; sr. exec. v.p. Gt. Am. First Savs. Bank, 1982-88; ret. 1988; chmn. bd. dirs. San Diego County Capital Asset Leasing Corp. With U.S. Army, 1955-57. Recipient Disting. Svc. award Cleve. Jr. C. of C., 1961. Mem. ABA, N.Y. State Bar Assn., Ohio Bar Assn., Calif. Bar Assn., San Diego Bar Assn., Masons. Republican. Home: 3308 Avenida Sierra Escondido CA 92029-7937

NEWMAN, BRUCE MURRAY, antiques dealer; b. N.Y.C., Jan. 27, 1930; s. Meyer and Evelyn (Kantor) N.; m. Judith S. Brandus, June 26, 1965; 1 child, Emily Rachel. BA, Pratt Inst., 1953. Pres. Newel Art Galleries Inc., N.Y.C., 1975—; lectr. mus. and univs. Author: Fantasy Furniture, 1989; featured on numerous TV & radio programs, mags. and other publs.; guest CBS Morning Show, 1988; prime time host PBS Chanel 13, N.Y.C. Bd. dirs. N.Y.C. Ctr., 1988-90; assoc. mem. Mt. Sinai Med. Ctr., 1981—; trustee Pratt Inst., Bklyn., 1983—. Recipient Designer award Art Dirs. Club, 1984, Man of Yr. award Pratt Inst., 1993; featured on Lifestyles of the Rich and Famous, 1991, other TV programs, Cover Connoisseur Mag., 1989, (story) Architectural Digest, 1989, N.Y. Times, 1983, 84, (2) 89, 92, 95, Internat. Herald Tribune, 1992, others. Mem. Am. Soc. Interior Designers (bd. dirs. 1989—), Victorian Soc. Am. Avocations: golfing, reading, jogging, traveling. Office: Newel Art Galleries Inc 425 E 53rd St New York NY 10022-5122

NEWMAN, CAROL L., lawyer; b. Yonkers, N.Y., Aug. 7, 1949; d. Richard J. and Pauline Frances (Stoll) N. AB/MA summa cum laude, Brown U., 1971; postgrad. Harvard U. Law Sch., 1972-73; JD cum laude, George Washington U., 1977. Bar: D.C., 1977, Calif., 1979. With antitrust div. U.S. Dept. Justice, Washington and L.A., 1977-80; assoc. Alschuler, Grossman & Pines, L.A., 1980-82, Costello & Walcher, L.A., 1982-85, Rosen, Wachtell & Gilbert, 1985-88, ptnr., 1988-90; ptnr. Keck, Mahin & Cate, 1990-94; pvt. practice, L.A., 1994—; adj. prof. Sch. Bus., Golden Gate U., spring 1982. Candidate for State Atty. Gen., 1986; L.A. city commr. L.A. Bd. Transp. Commrs., 1993—. Mem. ABA, State Bar Calif., L.A. County Bar Assn., L.A. Lawyers for Human Rights (co. pres. 1991-92), Log Cabin (bd. dirs. 1992—), Calif. Women Lawyers (bd. dirs., bd. govs. 1991-94), Order of Coif, Phi Beta Kappa.

NEWMAN, CHARLES A., lawyer; b. L.A., Mar. 18, 1949; s. Arthur and Gladys (Barnett) N.; m. Joan Kathleen Meskiel, Aug. 8, 1971; children: Anne R., Elyse S. BA magna cum laude, U. Calif., 1970; JD, Washington U., 1973. Bar: Mo. 1973, D.C. 1981, U.S. Dist. Ct. (ea. dist.) Mo. 1973, U.S. Ct. Appeals (8th and 11th cirs.) 1973, U.S. Tax Ct. 1981, U.S. Claims Ct. 1981, U.S. Supreme Ct. 1976. From assoc. to ptnr. Thompson & Mitchell, St. Louis, 1973—; lectr. law Washington U., St. Louis, 1976-78. Trustee Mo. Bar Found., 1990—, mem. Mo. Bar Bd. Govs, 1980-84; bd. dirs. United Israel Appeal, N.Y.C., 1990-93, Coun. Jewish Fedns., N.Y.C., 1992—, United Jewish Appeal Young Leadership Cabinet, N.Y.C., 1985-88, Ctr. for Study of Dispute Resolution, 1985-88, Legal Svcs. Ea. Mo., 1985-94, St. Louis Community Found., 1992—, St. Louis chpt. Young Audiences 1993—, Planned Parenthood St. Louis, 1986-89, Jewish Fedn., St. Louis, 1986—, asst. treas., 1989-90, v.p.h. fin. planning, 1990-93, asst. sec., 1994—; v.p. Repertory Theatre, St. Louis, 1986-89, sr. v.p., 1990-91, St. Louis Opportunity Clearinghouse, 1974-78. Recipient Lon O. Hocker Meml. Trial award Mo. Bar Found., 1984. Mem. Bar Assn. Met. St. Louis (Merit award 1976). Democrat. Avocations: golf, tennis, reading, music. Office: Thompson & Mitchell 1 Mercantile Ctr Ste 3000 Saint Louis MO 63101

NEWMAN, DAVID, composer; b. L.A., Mar. 11, 1954; s. Alfred N. music dir. Sundance Inst. Film scores include Critters, 1985, Vendetta, 1986, The Kindred, 1987, The Brave Little Toaster, 1987, Malone, 1987, My Demon Lover, 1987, Dragnet, 1987, Throw Momma from the Train, 1987, Pass the Ammo, 1988, Heathers, 1989, Bill & Ted's Excellent Adventure, 1989, Disorganized Crime, 1989, Little Monsters, 1989, The War of the Roses, 1989, Gross Anatomy, 1989, Madhouse, 1990, Fire Birds, 1990, The Freshman, 1990, Mr. Destiny, 1990, Duck Tales: The Movie, 1990, Meet the Applegates, 1991, The Marrying Man, 1991, Don't Tell Mom the Babysitter's Dead, 1991, Bill & Ted's Bogus Journey, 1991, Rover Dangerfield, 1991, Talent for the Game, 1991, Paradise, 1991, Other People's Money, 1991, Honeymoon in Vegas, 1992, The Runestone, 1992, The Mighty Ducks, 1992, That Night, 1992, Hoffa, 1992, The Sandlot, 1993, Coneheads, 1993, Undercover Blues, 1993, The Air Up There, 1994, My Father, the Hero, 1994, The Flintstones, 1994, The Cowboy Way, 1994, I Love Trouble, 1994, Boys On the Side, 1995. Office: Marks and Vangelos Mgt 19301 Ventura Blvd Ste 206 Tarzana CA 91356*

NEWMAN, DAVID WHEELER, lawyer; b. Salt Lake City, Apr. 5, 1952; s. Donnell and Vera Mae (Siratt) N.; m. Mahnaz Navai, Mar. 14, 1981; 1 child, Anthony Dara. BA cum laude, Claremont Men's Coll., 1973; JD, UCLA, 1977; LLM in Taxation, NYU, 1979. Bar: Calif. 1978, U.S. Dist. Ct. Calif. 1978, U.S. Tax Ct. 1979. Tax ptnr. Mitchell, Silberberg & Knupp, L.A., 1982—; bd. dirs. Indsl. Bank, Nat. Com. on Planned Giving; mem. exec. com. tax sect. L.A. County Bar, 1991—. Mem. Calif. Club. Avocations: tennis, skiing. Office: Mitchell Silberberg & Knupp 11377 W Olympic Blvd Los Angeles CA 90064-1625

NEWMAN, DELLA M., ambassador; married Wells B. McCurdy. Pres., owner Village Real Estate, Inc., Seattle; treas. Pacific Factors Ltd.; propr. Braemar Assocs.; amb. to New Zealand and Western Samoa, Wellington, 1989—. Bd. dirs. Wash. Inst. for Policy Studies, Wash. Coun. for Econ. Edn., Assn. Wash. Bus.; del. Rep. Nat. Conv., 1980, 88; spl. events dir. Wash. Reagan-Bush Campaign, 1980; co-chmn. Reagan-Bush Fin. Com., 1984; chmn. Wash. George Bush for Pres. Campaign, 1987-88. Office: Am Embassy, 29 Fitzherbert Ter, Thorndon Wellington New Zealand also: US Embassy Wellington PSC 467 Box 1 FPO AP 96531-1001

NEWMAN, DENIS, merchant banker; b. Short Hills, N.J., June 9, 1930; s. Rockwell and Helen (O'Brien) N.; m. Mary McMorrow, Aug. 4, 1966; children—Stephen, Brian, Kerry. B.A., Yale U., 1952; M.B.A., Harvard U., 1954. Mng. dir. First Boston Corp., N.Y.C., 1954-87; pres. The Dunmore Group, Inc., Morristown, N.J., 1987-89; mng. dir. MidMark Mgmt., Inc., Chatham, N.J., 1989—; fin. officer IBRD, Washington, 1960-62; sr. advisor Investment Corp. of Pakistan, Karachi, 1967-68, Devel. and Indsl. Bank of Iran, Teheran, 1975; bd. dirs. First Branch Corp., Danbury, Conn., Charles River Data, Framingham, Mass., GMIS Inc., Malvern, Pa. Author: (with others) The International Banking Handbook, 1983. Mem. Republican County Com., N.J., 1975-80, Millburn-Short Hills Cable Adv. Com., (N.J.), 1981—. Served with U.S. Army, 1954-56. Mem. Securities Industry Assn. (chmn. internat. com. 1980-82), Fin. Analysts Fedn., N.Y. Soc. Security Analysts, Bond Club, Links Club, Shorts Hills Club, Morristown Club.

NEWMAN, DENNIS COLLINS, SR., accountant; b. Memphis, Apr. 9, 1932; s. Dennis Garland and Dorothy Elenora (White) N.; m. Debra Marlene Stone, Dec. 10, 1983; children: Denise, Terry, Phyllis, Dennis Jr., John, Paul. BBA, U. Tenn., 1956, MBA, 1958; M Acctg., Stanford U.,

1961; PhD in Bus., Harvard U., 1965. Cert. tax profl. V.p. ops. Holiday Inns of Am., Memphis, 1965-72; dir. Popeyes Fried Chicken, New Orleans, 1972-76; v.p. so. div. McDonald's, New Orleans, 1976-84; v.p. tng. Burger King, New Orleans, 1984-88; gen. ptnr. Newman & Hastings P.A., Biloxi, Miss., 1988—. Author: Tax of Small Business, 1978, How to Work Smarter, 1983, Tax Professionals, 1989. Dep. chmn. State Rep. Party, Jackson, Miss., 1991. 1st lt. U.S. Army, 1951-53, Korea. Mem. Nat. Soc. Pub. Accts. (del. at large 1992), Nat. Soc. Mgmt. Cons. (pres. 1992), Nat. Soc. Tax Profls. (bd. mem. 1992), Am. Mgmt. Assn., Nat. Assn. Ind. Paralegals (membership com. 1991), Nat. Paralegal Assn. (rules com. 1991-92), Am. Fedn. Police (bd. mem. 1991-92), Miss. Assn. Pub. Accts. (bd. dirs. 1992), Nat. Fedn. Ind. Bus. (guardian mem.). Republican. Baptist. Avocations: golf, fishing, hunting, boating.

NEWMAN, DIANA S., community foundation executive; b. Toledo, June 15, 1943; d. Fred Andrew and Thelma Elizabeth (Hewitt) Smith; m. Dennis Ryan Newman, Feb. 15, 1964; children: Barbara Lynn Newman LaBine, John Ryan, Elizabeth Anne. Student, Oberlin Coll., 1961-64. Asst. treas. Marble Cliff Quarries Co., 1964-68; community vol., 1968-83; dir. Ohio Hist. Found., Columbus, 1983-90; v.p. advancement The Columbus (Ohio) Found., 1990—. Chair governing com. First Community Ch., 1983-88; bd. dirs. LWV, 1968-72; Ohio Mus. Assn., 1985-90, Nat. Soc. Fundraising Execs. Cen. Ohio chpt., Columbus, 1983-88, Crittenton Family Svcs., Columbus, 1992—; founder Franklin County Com. on Criminal Justice, Columbus, 1972; past pres. Jr. League Columbus. Mem. Ctrl. Ohio Planned Giving Coun. (bd. dirs. 1990—), Columbus Female Benevolent Soc. (bd. dirs. 1984—). Home: 1944 Chatfield Rd Columbus OH 43221-3702 Office: The Columbus Foundation 1234 E Broad St Columbus OH 43205-1463

NEWMAN, DON MELVIN, federal agency administrator; b. Chgo., July 31, 1923; s. Lee and Florence G. (White) N.; m. Mary Louise Strait, Jan. 23, 1945 (dec. Feb. 1988); children: Barbara Newman Martin, Kathryn Newman Grieser. BS in Pharmacy, Purdue U., 1947; MS in Bus. Adminstrn., Ind. U., 1972; JD, Georgetown U., 1979; MBA, Ind. U., 1989; PharmD (hon.), Ll U., 1987, Purdue U., 1987. Pharmacist Kellog Pharmacy, New Carlisle, Ind., 1947-48, Bushbaum Pharmacy, South Bend, Ind., 1948-52, Rex Pharmacy, South Bend, 1952-53, Byron Childress Pharmacy, Mishawaka, Ind., 1953-55; owner, operator Newman's Pharmacy, 1955-73, Medical Arts Pharmacy, 1963-65; dir. Washington Office State of Ind., 1973-85; under sec. HHS, Washington, 1985-89, acting sec., 1989; U.S. min. Internat. Civil Aviation Orgrn., 1990—. Pres. Penn-Madison-Harrison Sch. Bd., Mishawaka, 1964-68; bd. dirs. Mishawaka Airport, 1965-66, South Bend Airport, 1962-66, Ind. Red Cross, South Bend, 1968-72; chmn. Pharmacists for Reagan-Bush '84 campaign, Washington, hon. chmn. for Bush-Quale '88 campaign. Recipient Pharm.'s award Am. Soc. Pharmacy Law, 1989. Mem. ABA, D.C. Bar Assn., Am. Pharm. Assn. (Hubert Humphrey award 1986), Ind. Pharm. Assn. (Bowl of Hygeia award 1970), Nat. Assn. Retail Druggists (Dargaual award 1987), Masons. Republican. Presbyterian. Avocation: flying, sports. Home and Office: 200 Independence Ave SW # 614 Washington DC 20201-0004

NEWMAN, EDWARD M., engineering executive; b. Bay Shore, N.Y., Jan. 22, 1945; s. Edward and Eleanor Newman; m. Catherine Newman, June 29, 1968; children: Edward, John. BSEE, Rensselaer Poly. Inst., 1967; MSEE, Poly. Inst. Bklyn., 1973; MS in Acctg., L.I. U., 1978. Engr. Sanders Assocs., Nashua, N.H., 1967-69; various engring. positions Hazeltine Corp., Greenlawn, N.Y., 1969-82, head Wheeler labs., 1982-87, dir. advanced tech., 1987-89, dir. advanced devel., 1989-93, v.p. advanced devel., 1993—. Mem. IEEE. Avocation: sailing. Home: 19 Robinhood Ct Nesconset NY 11767 Office: Hazeltine Corp 450 E Pulaski Rd Greenlawn NY 11740

NEWMAN, EDWIN DAVID, textile company executive; b. Bklyn., Sept. 18, 1933; s. Emanuel and Rose Kate (Kopp) N.; 1 child, Valerie. AAS, Fashion Inst. Tech., N.Y.C., 1953. Fabric stylist Lowensteins & Sons, N.Y.C., 1953-66; v.p., dir. design Wm. Anderson Fabrics, N.Y.C., 1966-70; v.p., creative dir. Dan River Inc., N.Y.C., 1970-85; pres. Design Libr., N.Y.C., 1985-86; v.p., editor in chief Am. Fabrics and Fashion Mag., N.Y.C., 1986-87; profl. Fashion Inst. Tech., N.Y.C., 1987-90, dir. alumni affairs, design dir., 1990-93; v.p., creative dir. Whisper Soft Mills, Inc., N.Y.C., 1993—. Recipient Disting. Alumni award SUNY, 1984, Tommy award Am. Print Coun., 1985. Mem. AAUP, ASID (affiliate), Internat. Furnishing and Design Assn. (mem. spl. events, edn. and membership coms.), Fashion Inner Cirlce (mem. spl. events com.), Fashion Inst. Tech. Alumni Assn. (past pres., bd. dirs., Ritter award 1980), N.Y. Arbitration Bd. Democrat. Avocations: animal welfare, old home restoration. Home: 123 E 37th St New York NY 10016-3030 Office: Whisper Soft Mills Inc 111 W 40th St New York NY 10018-2506

NEWMAN, EDWIN HAROLD, news commentator; b. N.Y.C., Jan. 25, 1919; s. Myron and Rose (Parker) N.; m. Rigel Grell, Aug. 14, 1944; 1 child, Nancy (Mrs. Henry Drucker). BA, U. Wis., 1940; postgrad. (fellow), La. State U., 1940. With Washington bur. Internat. News Svc., 1941, U.P., 1941-42, 45-46, N.Y. Daily PM, 1946-47; ind. Washington news bur., 1947; asst to Eric Sevareid at Washington bur. CBS, 1947-49; freelance writer, broadcaster London, 1949-52; with European Recovery Program, 1951-52, NBC, 1952—; chief news bur. NBC, London, 1956-57, Rome, 1957-58, Paris, 1958-61; news commentator NBC, N.Y.C., 1961-83; columnist King Features Syndicate, 1984-89; moderator 1st Ford-Carter Debate, 1976, 2d Reagan-Mondale debate, 1984; moderator ann. conf. former secs. of state, 1983—, former secs. of def., 1987—. Narrator: TV spls. including Japan: East is West, 1961, Orient Express, 1964, Who Shall Live?, 1965, Pensions-The Broken Promise, 1972, Violence in America, 1977, I Want It All Now, 1978, Spying for Uncle Sam, 1978, Oil and American Power, 1979, The Billionaire Hunts, 1981, Congress: We the People, 1983-84, On Television, 1985-86, Freud, 1987, The Borgias, 1988; host Saturday Night Live, 1984; drama critic WNB C-TV, 1965-71 (Emmy awards 1966, 68, 70, 72, 73, 74, 82, Peabody award 1966); author: Strictly Speaking: Will America Be The Death of English?, 1974, A Civil Tongue, 1976, Sunday Punch, 1979, I Must Say, 1988; contbr. articles and revs. to various periodicals, U.S., Can. and Eng.; chmn. usage panel Am. Heritage Dictionary, 1975-80. Served from ensign to lt. USNR, 1942-45. Decorated chevalier Legion of Honor France; recipient awards Overseas Press Club, 1961, awards U. Wis. Sch. Journalism, 1967, awards U. Mo. Sch. Journalism, 1975. Mem. AFTRA, Authors Guild, Screen Actors Guild. Address: care Richard Fulton Inc 66 Richfield St Plainview NY 11803-1441

NEWMAN, EDWIN STANLEY, lawyer, publishing company executive; b. N.Y.C., Apr. 26, 1922; s. Gordon H. and Rosalind (Zieph) N.; m. Evaline Ada Lipp, Sept. 2, 1945; children: Scott D., Linda S. Newman Perl. BA summa cum laude, CCNY, 1940; LLB, Columbia U., 1943. Admitted to N.Y. State bar, 1943, U.S. Ct. Internat. Trade. Asst. to pres. Am. Jewish Com., 1946-60; ins. co. exec., 1960-69; v.p., gen. counsel Oceana Publs., Inc., Dobbs Ferry, N.Y., 1969-94, exec. v.p., 1994—, also dir.; past lectr. New Sch. Social Research. Author: Freedom Reader, 1963, Hate Reader, 1964, Law of Philanthropy, 1955, Fundraising Made Easy, 1954, Law of Civil Liberty and Civil Rights, 7th edit., 1987; editor: U.S. Internat. Trade Reports, 1981—. Chmn. bd. Elmont Jewish Ctr., 1953-57. Served with U.S. Army, 1943-46, 51-52. Named James Kent scholar, 1941, 42, 43. Internat. Bar Assn., Columbia Law Sch. Alumni Assn., Internat. Assn. Jurists (Italian-Am. sect.), Am. Corp. Counsel Assn., Dobbs Ferry Rotary, Phi Beta Kappa. Home and Office: 75 Main St Dobbs Ferry NY 10522-1601

NEWMAN, ELIAS, artist; b. Staszow, Poland, Feb. 12, 1903; came to U.S., 1913, naturalized, 1928; s. Simon and Rebecca (Becker) N.; m. Lillian Judith Tesser, Feb. 26, 1945 (dec. June 1990). Student, N.A.D., 1919-20, Edn. Alliance Art Sch., 1920-25, Academie du Chaumiere, Paris, 1929. Art instr. Ednl. Alliance Art Sch., 1946-48; instr. painting YMHA 92nd St. Art Sch., 1949-51, Elias Newman Sch. of Art, Rockport, Mass., 1951-64; art dir. Palestine Pavilion, N.Y. World's Fair, 1939-40; cons. Internat. Exposition, Cleve., 1941; chmn. Conf. Am. Artists, 1971-75; exec officer Artists Welfare Fund, Inc., 1975-88, pres. emeritus, 1988—; lectr. art of Israel, trends in Am. art. Editor: Improvisations, 1950, 51, 52, Artists' Equity, N.Y.; author: Art in Palestine, 1939; one-man shows, 1927—, including Salon Henri Brendle, Zurich, Switzerland, 1929, High Mus. Art, Atlanta, 1928, Yorke Gallery, Washington, 1929, Balt. Mus. Art, 1928, 30, 34, 41, The Art Ctr., N.Y.C. 1931, Montross Gallery, N.Y.C., 1932, Sears Roebuck & Co. Art Gallery,

Washington, 1932, Md. Art Inst., Balt., 1932, 35, 36, Maxwell Galleries, San Francisco, 1945, Modernage Art Gallery, N.Y., 1945, Phila. Art Alliance, 1946, Jewish Mus., N.Y.C., 1949, Babcock Galleries, N.Y.C., 1947, 49, 51, 53, 60, Tel Aviv Mus., (Israel) 1934, 38, 49, 62, Werbe Galleries, Detroit, 1956, Doll & Richards Galleries, Boston, 1947, 50, 60, Rubin Mus. Found., Tel viv, Israel, 1986; participated juried exhbns. including Ohel Group of Modern Artists, Tel Aviv, 1927, The Group of Palestinian Artists, Tel Aviv, 1930, N.A.D., Am. Acad. Arts and Letters, Am. Watercolor Soc., Nat. Soc. Painters in Casein and Acrylics, Audubon Artists, Rockport Art Assn., Am. Soc. Contemporary Artists, Butler Mus. Art, Youngstown, Ohio, The Currier Gallery of Art, Manchester, N.H., Cape Ann Soc. Modern Artists; works in permanent collections Nat. Mus. Am. Art of Smithsonian Instn., Washington, Jewish Mus., N.Y.C., San Francisco Mus. of Art, Balt. Art Mus., John Herron Mus. Art, Indpls., Denver Mus. Art, Tel Aviv Mus. (Israel), Bklyn. Mus. Art, Haifa Mus. Modern Art, Israel, Histadruth House, Tel Aviv, Butler Mus. Am. Art, Youngstown, Ohio, Boston Mus. Fine Arts, Nebr. U. Gallery, Inst. Man and Sci., Rensselaerville, N.Y., Brandeis U., Hillel House, Boston U., Jasper Rand Art Mus., Westfield, Mass., Joslyn Mus., Omaha, Addison Gallery Am. Art, Andover, Mass., George Washington Carver Mus., Tuskegee, Ala., Arnot Art Mus., Elmira, N.Y., Everson Mus. Art, Syracuse, N.Y., Ga. Art Mus., Athens, Slater Meml. Mus., Norwich, Conn., Norfolk (Va.) Mus. Arts and Scis., Phoenix Mus. Art, Met. Ins. Co., Newark, DeCordova Mus., Lexington, Mass., Tel Aviv Municipality, Israel, Mishkan Le'omanut Mus. Art, Ein Harod, Israel, others. Served with C.A.C. AUS, 1942-43. Recipient Minnie R. Stern Meml. medal and prize Audubon Artists 18th Ann. Exhibit, N.Y., 1960; Pauline Mintz Meml. award 28th Ann. Exhibit, 1970; Stanley Grumbacher Meml. medal and prize 35th Ann. Exhibit, 1977, Elaine and James Hewitt award, 1988; awards Nat. Soc. Painters in Casein and Acrylics; Joseph Meyer Co. prize, 1966; Gramercy prize, 1968; M.J. Kaplan Meml. prize, 1970; Today's Art mag. medal merit, 1971; Shiva award for casein painting, 1980, 91, The Elizabeth Erlanger Meml. award, 1992; Beatrice S. Katz prize Am. Soc. Contemporary Artists, 1971; Morrilla Co. award, 1981; Grumbacher art award, 1983; Philip Reisman Meml. award, 1994; Municipality Tel-Aviv-Jaffo, Isreal medal, 1987; Pres.' Spl. Citation of Merit 47th Ann. Exhibit, 1989, Audubon Artists. Mem. Palestine Artists and Sculptors Assn. (organizer 1935), Am. Artists for Israel (chmn. 1949), Cape Ann Soc. Modern Artists (pres. 1958-59), Am. Soc. Contemporary Artists (bd. dir. 1970, 87), Artists Equity Assn. (nat. sec. 1954, exec. dir. 1959-60, pres. N.Y. chpt. 1960-62, v.p. 1963-64, 67, 68), N.Y. Artists Equity Assn. (pres. 1970-75, pres. emeritus 1975—), Audubon Artists (bd. dir. 1971-74, treas. 1976-77, bd. dir. 1977-78, v.p. 1978-82), Nat. Soc. Painters in Casein and Acrylics (bd. dir. 1963, chmn. ways and means com. 1966, pres. 1967-71, hon. pres. 1971—), Am. Jewish League for Israel. Club: Overseas Press. Home: 215 Park Row New York NY 10038-1115 *I have tried in the course of my life in art to be guided by the following concepts: Art is a continuum that expresses the time in which we live. I am involved with the phenomenon of nature, the changing scene and the life around me. I believe that each painting should be the result of an experience deeply felt. I try to absorb influences, refine them and recreate them in my own image. I believe great works of art always had affinity with humanity, nature, and the soul of mankind.*

NEWMAN, ERIC PFEIFFER, retail chain store executive; b. St. Louis, May 25, 1911; s. Samuel Elijah and Rose (Pfeiffer) N.; m. Evelyn Edison, Nov. 29, 1939; children: Linda Newman Schapiro, Andrew Edison. BS, Mass. Inst. Tech., 1932; J.D., Washington U., St. Louis, 1935; D.H.L. (hon.), U. Mo., 1980. Bar: Mo. 1935. Practice in St. Louis, 1935-43; with Edison Bros. Stores, Inc., St. Louis, 1944, sec., 1951-87, v.p., 1964-68, exec. v.p., 1968-87, retired, now bd. dirs. Author: Coinage for Colonial Virginia, 1957, The Secret of the Good Samaritan Shilling, 1959, The Fantastic 1804 Dollar, 1962, The Early Paper Money of America, 1967, rev. edit., 1976, 90; editor: Studies on Money in Early America, 1976. Pres. Community Sch., 1952-53, Mark Twain Summer Inst., 1963-67; treas. Jefferson Nat. Expansion Meml. Assn., 1970-77; chmn. U.S. Assay Commn., 1967; chmn. coins and medals panel Am. Revolution Bicentennial Commn., 1972-74; trustee Harry Edison Found., 1959—, pres., 1988—; pres. Eric P. Newman Numis. Edn. Soc. (operator Mercantile Money Mus., St. Louis), 1959—. Recipient Farran Zerbe award, 1969, Archer M. Huntington medal, 1978, Royal Numismatic Soc. medal, 1991. Mem. Am. Numis. Soc. (council (dir.) 1963—), Am. Numism. Assn. (16 Heath Lit. awards), Am. Antiquarian Soc. Club: Explorers. Home: 6450 Cecil Ave Saint Louis MO 63105-2225 Office: 501 N Broadway Saint Louis MO 63102-2196

NEWMAN, FRANK CECIL, legal educator, retired state supreme court justice; b. Eureka, Calif., July 17, 1917; s. Frank J. and Anna (Dunn) N.; m. Frances Burks, Jan. 14, 1940; children: Robert, Julie, Ralph, Carol. A.B., Dartmouth Coll., 1938; LL.B., U. Calif., 1941; LL.M., Columbia U., 1947, J.S.D., 1953; LL.D., U. Santa Clara, 1978. Bar: Calif. 1942. Prof. law U. Calif., Berkeley, 1946—, dean Sch. Law, 1961-66, Jackson H. Ralston prof. internat. law, 1974-77, 82-88, prof. emeritus, 1988—; justice Calif. Supreme Ct., 1977-82; atty. OPA, N.Y.C. and Washington, 1942-43, Office Gen. Counsel Dept. Navy, 1943-46; vis. prof. law schs. Harvard U., 1953-54, U. Wash., summer 1952, Salzburg Sem. in Am. Studies, Austria, summer 1954, 64, Inst. Human rights, Strasburg, France, summer 1970, 71, 75, 77, People's U., Beijing, spring 1985, Global Security Studies program Meiji Gakuin U., Yokohama, spring 1992, U. San Francisco, 1992—, Trinity Coll., Dublin, summer 1993, Golden Gate U., 1994—; cons. OPS, 1951; counsel Gov. Calif. Commn. on Unemployment Compensation, 1952; cons. GAO, 1959, Calif. Agr. and Services Agy., 1975-76; dir. Fed. Home Loan Bank, San Francisco, 1962-70. Author: (with Stanley S. Surrey) Newman and Surrey on Legislation, 1955, (with Richard B. Lillich) International Human Rights: Problems of Law and Policy, 1979, (with David S. Weissbrodt) International Human Rights: Law, Policy, and Process, 1990, supplement, 1994. Mem. exec. com., chmn. drafting com. Calif. Constn. Revision Commn., 1964-72. Served from ensign to lt. USNR, 1943-46. Mem. Internat. Inst. Human Rights. Office: U Calif Sch Law Berkeley CA 94720

NEWMAN, FRANK NEIL, federal official; b. Quincy, Mass., Apr. 20, 1942; s. Robert David and Ethel F. N.; 1 child: Daniel. B.A. in Econs. magna cum laude, Harvard U., 1963. Exec. v.p., CFO Wells Fargo & Co. and Wells Fargo Bank, San Francisco, 1980-86; CEO, vice chmn. bd. dirs. Bank Am. Corp, Bank of Am., San Francisco, 1986-93; under sec. domestic fin. Dept. Treasury, Washington, 1993-94, dep. sec., 1994—. Office: Dep Sec Dept Treasury 15th & Pennsylvania Ave NW Washington DC 20220

NEWMAN, FREDRIC SAMUEL, lawyer, business executive; b. York, Pa., June 22, 1945; s. Nat. Howard and Josephine (Farkas) N.; m. Mary E. Kiley, May 19, 1973; children: Lydia Ann, Anne Marie, Pauline. AB cum laude, Harvard U., 1967; JD, Columbia U., 1970; cert. the exec. program, U. Va., 1984. Bar: N.Y. 1971, U.S. Dist. Ct. (so. and ea. dists.) N.Y. 1972, U.S. Ct. Appeals (2d cir.) 1974, U.S. Ct. Claims 1993. Assoc. White & Case, N.Y.C., 1970-80; asst. gen. counsel Philip Morris Cos., N.Y.C., 1981-87; gen. counsel, v.p., sec. Philip Morris, Inc., N.Y.C., 1987-90; chief exec. officer TeamTennis, Inc., 1991; prin. Law Office of Fredric S. Newman, N.Y.C., 1992—; pres., CEO, Pathe Comm. Corp., N.Y.C., 1993—; bd. dirs. Exel Ins. Co., Bermuda. Trustee Calhoun Sch., N.Y.C., 1985-88; bd. dirs. N.Y. Fire Safety Found., N.Y.C., 1985-88. Fellow Am. Bar Found. Office: 10 E 40th St New York NY 10016

NEWMAN, GERALDINE ANNE, advertising executive; b. Boston, Apr. 1; d. Joseph M. and Clara (Bistry) N. BS, UCLA; postgrad., Alliance Francaise, Paris, Los Angeles Sch. Fine Arts, NYU. Writer Tinker Dodge and Delano, N.Y.C., 1970-72, Ketchum Advt., N.Y.C., 1972-75, Advt. to Women, N.Y.C., 1975-78; v.p., creative supr. Young and Rubicam, N.Y.C., 1978-83; v.p., assoc. creative dir. Backer Spielvogel Bates Worldwide Internat. Div., N.Y.C., 1983-90; pres. Geraldine Newman Commn., Inc., N.Y.C., 1990—. County committeewoman Dem. Party, N.Y.C., 1972; advt. adviser Youth at Risk, Breakthrough Found., Food Bank, Food for All, Gifts that Give Back. Featured in Adweek mag., 1986; winner Andy award 1975, 78, 82, 84, Clio award 1982, numerous others. Mem. Ad-net (bd. dirs. 1984-89, creative dir. 1986-89, Pres.'s award 1988). Avocations: painting, travel. Home and Office: 315 E 72nd St New York NY 10021-4674

NEWMAN, GLEN CARROLL, superintendent of schools; b. Guthrie, Okla., July 20, 1935; s. Nathaniel Clark and Evelyn Irene (Miller) N.; m.

Nancy Jo Kennedy, Feb. 24, 1961; 1 child, Geoffrey William. BA, Cen. State U., Edmond, Okla., 1955; MA in Teaching, U. Redlands, 1966; MA, Calif. State U., Fullerton, 1969; EdD, U. So. Calif., 1978. Tchr. Hemet (Calif.) Unified Sch. Dist., 1956-58, 61-74, dir. spl. svcs., 1974-78; dist. supt. schs. Menifee Union Sch. Dist., Sun City, Calif., 1978—; instr. U. Calif. Extension, Riverside, 1969-70, Calif. State U. Extension, San Diego, 1970-71; NDEA cons. in English, Calif. Dept. Edn., 1969-71; cons. on lang. arts Riverside County Interns, 1970. Bd. dirs. Hemet Hosp. Found., 1987—; vice chmn. Sun City-Menifee Valley Community Plan Adv. Com., 1988-89. Recipient award of appreciation and leadership Riverside County Governance Coun., 1985. Mem. Am. Assn. Sch. Adminstrs., Assn. Supervision and Curriculum Devel., Assn. Calif. Sch. Adminstrs. (chmn. supt.'s com. region 12, 1988—), Riverside County Reading Assn. (pres. 1975-78), Rotary (pres. Sun City 1984-85), Phi Delta Kappa. Avocations: Home: 26570 Vassar St Hemet CA 92544-7509 Office: Menifee Union Sch Dist 28125 Bradley Rd Ste 210 Sun City CA 92381

NEWMAN, HARRY RUDOLPH, urologist, educator; b. Russia, Sept. 10, 1909; naturalized, 1919, came to U.S., 1935, naturalized, 1944; s. Abraham and Mary (Rudolph) N.; m. Lillian Lear, Aug. 18, 1942; children: Nancy Ellen, Robert Lear, Suzanne Mary. M.D., U. Toronto, 1935; M.S., U. Pa., 1940. Diplomate: Am. Bd. Urology. Resident urology U. Minn. Hosps., 1936-37, All Saints Hosp., London, Eng., 1937-38; sr. resident urology N.Y. Postgrad. Med. Sch. and Hosp., 1939-40, Boston Long Island Hosp., 1941-42; resident surgery N.Y. Postgrad. Hosp., 1942; resident gen. surgery Prince of Wales Hosp., Plymouth, Eng.; attending urologist Yale New-Haven Hosp.; attending univ. service Yale U., asst. clin. prof. urology, 1949—; dir. urology Albert Einstein Coll. Medicine, also clin. prof. surgery, chief urology, 1957—, clin. prof. urology, 1957-62, prof. urology, 1963-65, 66-80, emeritus chmn. and prof. urology, 1980—, chmn. dept., 1966-80; prof. history; chief urology Bronx Mcpl. Hosp., 1966—; chief urology community div. Grace New Haven Hosp., 1965-66; cons. urologist Stamford (Conn.) Hosp., St. Joseph Hosp., Stamford, 1965—; former asst. clin. prof. urology NYU; dir. urology City N.Y. Bronx Mcpl. Med. Center, 1954-65; chief urology Regional Hosp., Hunter Field, Savannah, Ga. Served from capt. to maj. USAAF, 1942-46. Fellow ACS, N.Y. Acad. Medicine, Royal So. of Health (Great Britian); mem. Soc. Univ. Urologists, Masons (32 deg.), Shriners, Yale Club (N.Y.), Sigma Xi. Clubs: Masons (New Haven) (32 deg.), Shriners (New Haven), Yale (New Haven); Woodbridge (Conn.) Country. Home: 95 Broadfield Rd Hamden CT 06517-1543 Office: 2 Church St S New Haven CT 06519-1717

NEWMAN, HERBERT S., architect, educator; b. N.Y.C., Mar. 6, 1934; s. Bernard and Gertrude (Weitz) N.; m. Edna Lee Greenberg, June 7, 1956; children: Matthew, Peter. BA, Brown U., 1955; MArch, Yale U., 1959. Designer I. M. Pei & Ptnrs., N.Y.C., 1959-64; vis. critic Sch. of Architecture Yale U., New Haven, 1965-73, asst. profl. archtl. design, 1973-75, assoc. prof., 1975-87, critic archtl. design, 1987—. Mem. exec. coun. Jewish Fedn. New Haven, mem. exec. and community rels. coms., 1990—; pres. Jewish Family Svc., New Haven, 1974-77; mem. steering com. Bus. Vols. for the Arts, 1987—; mem. adv. bd. Habitat for Humanity of New Haven, Inc., 1989—. Recipient Thomas Jefferson award for pub. architecture, 1995, others. Fellow AIA; mem. Conn. Soc. Architects (state com. on design New Haven chpt. 1979). Home: 12 Round Hill Ln Woodbridge CT 06525-1269 Office: Herbert S Newman & Ptnrs 300 York St New Haven CT 06511-3627

NEWMAN, HOWARD NEAL, law educator, lawyer; b. N.Y.C., June 11, 1935; s. Herman and Sarah (Steinsaltz) N.; m. Carol Redstone, Dec. 25, 1960; children: Leslie, Amy. A.B., Dartmouth Coll., 1956, M.B.A., 1957; M.S., Columbia U., 1959; J.D., Temple U., 1970. Trainee to asst. v.p. Roosevelt Hosp., N.Y.C., 1957-65; assoc. adminstr. Pa. Hosp., Phila., 1965-70; commr. Med. Services Adminstrn., Washington, 1970-74; pres. Dartmouth-Hitchcock Med. Center, Hanover, N.H., 1974-80; adminstr. Health Care Financing Adminstr., Dept. Health and Human Services, Washington, 1980-81; ptnr. Memel, Jacobs, Pierno & Gersh, Washington, 1982-86, Powell, Goldstein, Frazer & Murphy, Washington, 1986-88; deam, prof. health policy and mgmt. NYU, 1988-94, prof. health policy and mgmt., 1994—. Served with USAR, 1959. White House fellow, 1967-68. Mem. Nat. Inst. for Dispute Resolution, D.C. Bar Assn. Jewish. Office: 4 Washington Sq N New York NY 10003-6671

NEWMAN, JAMES AUSTIN, financial journalist; b. Covington, Okla., Apr. 24, 1932; s. James Austin and Olive Elizabeth (Adair) N. BA, Westminster Coll., 1952. Bus. editor AP, Washington, 1974-76; bus. reporter NBC, N.Y.C., 1976-79; pres. Newman Econs., L.A., 1979-81; bus. reporter Sta. KTLA-TV, L.A., 1981-82, CBS, L.A., 1982-83; bus. corr. Satellite News Channel Bus. Week Mag. ABC, N.Y.C., 1983-84; fin. editor Sta. KFWB, L.A., 1984—; Sta. KTLA, L.A. With U.S. Army, 1952-54. Recipient Janus award Mortgage Bankers, Washington, 1974, Bus. Reporting award L.A. Press Club, 1982. Mem. Overseas Press Club, Soc. Profl. Journalists, Jonathan Club. Avocations: horses, early Am. books and European furniture. Home: PO Box 1246 Beverly Hills CA 90213-1246 Office: Westinghouse Broadcasting 6232 Yucca St Los Angeles CA 90028-5217

NEWMAN, JAMES MICHAEL, communications company executive; b. Terre Haute, Ind., Aug. 10, 1949; s. Roy Johnson; m. Georgina Crabb, June 6, 1970; 1 child, Jonathan. BA in Math., DePaul U., 1974; MBA, U. Chgo., 1987. Dir. planning support GTE, Northlake, Ill., 1982-83, dir. corp. systems, 1983-86, dir. info. svcs., 1986-87; v.p. strategic planning U.S. Sprint, Kansas City, Mo., 1987-88, v.p. corp. systems, 1988-91; dir. GTE Mobile Communications, 1991-93; GM Contel Cellular, 1993-94; v.p. info. tech. Dial Call Inc., Atlanta, 1994—. Mem. IEEE, Assn. Computing Machinery. Republican. Lutheran. Avocations: golfing, tennis, sailing, skiing. Office: Dial Call Inc 6575 The Corners Pky Ste 100 Norcross GA 30092

NEWMAN, JAMES WILSON, business executive; b. Clemson, S.C., Nov. 3, 1909; s. Charles Carter and Grace (Strode) N.; m. Clara Collier, July 1934; children: Clare Adelaide, Mildred Bledsoe, James Wilson, Charles Carter II. B.S., Clemson U., 1931, also LL.D. (hon.); student, Am. Inst. Banking, 1931-32; J.D., N.Y. U., 1937. Bar: N.Y. bar 1937. Reporter R.G. Dun & Co., 1931-46; v.p. Dun & Bradstreet, Inc., 1946-52, pres., chief exec. officer, 1952-60, chmn., chief exec. officer, 1960-68, chmn. finance com., 1968-80, dir., to 1980; adv. bd. Chem. Bank, Gen. Foods Corp., 1963-81, Internat. Paper Co., until 1982; trustee Atlantic Mut. Ins. Co., Mut. Life Ins. Co. Am., until 1982; chmn. spl. rev. com. Lockheed Corp., 1976-78. Chmn. Pres.'s Task Force on Small Bus., 1969; mem. Commn. on Bankruptcy Laws U.S., 1970-73; chmn. Nat. Bur. Econ. Rsch., 1974-78; trustee Com. Econ. Devel., Va. Mus. Fine Arts, 1978-94; mem. coun. Miller Ctr. Pub. Affairs, U. Va., 1983-94; mem. Price Commn., 1971-72; chmn. Sweet Briar Coll., 1963-69. Mem. ABA, Univ. Club (N.Y.C.), Ocean Club (Fla.), Farmington Country Club (Va.), Commonwealth Club (Richmond, Va.), Army and Navy Club (Washington), Phi Delta Theta. Home: 4 Apple Tree Ln Charlottesville VA 22901 Office: 503 Falconer Dr Madison Park Suite 4A Charlottesville VA 22903

NEWMAN, JANE, advertising agency executive; b. Woking, Surrey, Eng., Oct. 22, 1947; came to U.S., 1978; d. Ronald William and Victoria (Brady) N.; 1 child. BA, Sussex U., Eng., 1969; MA, Lancaster U., Eng., 1970. Account planner Boase Massimi & Pollitt, London, 1970-78; account mgr. Needham Harper & Steers, Chgo., 1978-79, Ammirati & Puris, N.Y.C., 1979-81; vice chmn. Chiat/Day Advt., N.Y.C., 1981-93; ptnr. Merkley Newman Harty Advt. Agy., N.Y.C., 1993—. Avocation: traveling. Office: Merkley Newman Harty 200 Varick St New York NY 10014-4810

NEWMAN, JOAN MESKIEL, lawyer; b. Youngstown, Ohio, Dec. 12, 1947; d. John F. and Rosemary (Scarmuzzi) Meskiel; m. Charles Andrew Newman, Aug. 8, 1971; children: Anne R., Elyse S. BA in Polit. Sci., Case-Western Reserve U., 1969; JD, Washington U. St. Louis, 1972, LLM in Taxation, 1973. Bar: Mo. 1972. Assoc. Lewis & Rice, St. Louis, 1973-80, ptnr., 1981-90; ptnr. Thompson & Mitchell, St. Louis, 1990—; adj. prof. law Washington U. Sch. Law, St. Louis, 1975-92; past pres., mem. Midwest Pension Conf., St. Louis chpt.; lectr. in field. Chmn. bd. dirs. Girl Scout Coun. Greater St. Louis, 1988-92, officer, 1978-92; mem. bd. dirs. and exec. com. Girl Scouts of U.S.A., 1993—; chmn. bd. dirs. Met. Employment and Rehabilitation Svcs., 1994—; bd. dirs. Jewish Fedn. St. Louis, 1991—,

Jewish Ctr. Aged, 1990-92; chmn. bd. dirs. Women of Achievement, 1993—; mem. community wide youth svcs. panel United Way Greater St. Louis, 1992—; fin., futures task force Kiwanis Camp Wyman, 1992-93; mem. nat. coun. Washington U. Sch. Law, 1988-91; chmn. staff blue ribbon fin. com. Sch. Dist. Clayton, 1986-87; vol. Women's Self Help Ctr. Named Woman of Achievement St. Louis, 1991. Mem. Mo. Bar Assn. (staff pension and benefits com. 1991—), Bar Met. St. Louis (past chmn. taxation sect.), St. Louis Forum, Order of Coif (hon.). Office: Thompson & Mitchell 1 Mercantile Ctr Ste 3300 Saint Louis MO 63101-1622

NEWMAN, JOHN KEVIN, classics educator; b. Bradford, Yorkshire, Eng., Aug. 17, 1928; came to U.S., 1969, naturalized, 1984; s. Willie and Agnes (Shee) N.; m. Frances M. Stickney, Sept. 8, 1970: children: Alexandra, John, Victoria. B.A. in Lit.-Humaniores, Exeter Coll., Oxford U., 1950, B.A. in Russian, 1952, M.A., 1953; Ph.D., Bristol U., 1967. Classics master St. Francis Xavier Coll., Liverpool, Eng., 1952-54, Downside Sch., Somerset, Eng., 1955-69; mem. faculty U. Ill., Urbana, 1969—, prof. classics, 1980—, chmn. dept., 1981-85. Author: Augustus and the New Poetry, 1967, Latin Compositions, 1976, Pindar's Art, 1984, The Classical Epic Tradition, 1986, Roman Catullus, 1990, Lelio Guidiccioni, Latin Poems, 1992; editor: Ill. Classical Studies, 1982-87; contbr. The New Princeton Encyclopedia of Poetry and Poetics, 1993. mem. sr. common room Corpus Christi Coll., Oxford U., 1985-86. Recipient silver medals Vatican, Rome, 1960, 62, 65. Roman Catholic. Home: 703 W Delaware Ave Urbana IL 61801-4806 Office: Dept Classics U Ill 4072 Fgn Lang Bldg 707 S Mathews Ave Urbana IL 61801-3625

NEWMAN, JOHN M., JR., lawyer; b. Youngstown, Ohio, Aug. 15, 1944. BA, Georgetown U., 1966; JD, Harvard U., 1969. BAr: Ill. 1970, Calif. 1970, Ohio 1976. Law clerk ctrl. dist. U.S. Dist. Ct., Calif., 1969-70, asst. U.S. Atty. ctrl. dist., 1970-75; ptnr. Jones, Day, Reavis & Pogue, Cleve. Fellow Am. Coll. Trial Lawyers; mem. Phi Beta Kappa. Office: Jones Day Reavis & Pogue North Point 901 Lakeside Ave E Cleveland OH 44114-1190

NEWMAN, JOHN NICHOLAS, naval architect educator; b. New Haven, Mar. 10, 1935; s. Richard and Daisy (Neumann) N.; m. Kathleen Smedley Kirk, June 16, 1956; children—James Bartram, Nancy Kirk, Carol Ann. B.S. Mass. Inst. Tech, 1956, M.S., 1957, Sc.D., 1960; postgrad., Cambridge (Eng.) U., 1958-59; D Technicae honoris causa, U. Trondheim, Norway, 1992. Research naval architect David Taylor Model Basin, Navy Dept., Washington, 1959-67; assoc. prof. naval architecture MIT, Cambridge, 1967-70, prof., 1970—; vis. prof. U. New South Wales, Australia, 1973, U. Adelaide, Australia, 1974, Tech. U. Norway, 1981-82; cons. Navy Dept., Dept. Justice, pvt. firms. Author: Marine Hydrodynamics, 1977; Contbr.: articles to profl. jours., including Sci. Am. Recipient prize Am. Bur. Shipping, 1956; Walter Atkinson prize Royal Instn. Naval Architects, 1973, also Bronze medal, 1976; Guggenheim fellow, 1973-74; research grantee Office Naval Research; NSF. Mem. AAAS, NAE, Soc. Naval Architects and Marine Engrs. (Davidson medal 1988), Norwegian Acad. Sci. Home: 60 Campbell Rd Wayland MA 01778-1024 Office: MIT Cambridge MA 02139

NEWMAN, JOHN SCOTT, chemical engineer, educator; b. Richmond, Va., Nov. 17, 1938; s. Clarence William and Marjorie Lenore (Saucerman) N.; m. Nguyen Thanh Lan, June 30, 1973; children—Natalie Diane, Michael Alexander. B.S., Northwestern U., 1960; M.S., U. Calif., Berkeley, 1962, Ph.D. 1963. Asst. prof. chem. engring. U. Calif., Berkeley, 1963-67, assoc. prof., 1967-70; prof. U. Calif., 1970—; prin. investigator energy & environ. divsn. Lawrence Berkeley Lab., 1963—; vis. prof. U. Wis., Madison, 1973; summer participant Oak Ridge Nat. Lab., 1965, 66. Author: Electrochemical Systems, 1973, rev. edit. 1991; assoc. editor Jour. Electrochem. Soc., 1990—; contbr. articles to profl. jours. Mem. Electrochem. Soc. (Young Author's prize 1966, 69, David C. Grahame award 1985, Henry B. Linford award 1990, Olin Palladium medal 1991), Am. Inst. Chem. Engrs. Home: 114 York Ave Kensington CA 94708-1045 Office: U Calif Dept Chem Engring Berkeley CA 94720-1462

NEWMAN, JON O., federal judge; b. N.Y.C., N.Y., May 2, 1932; s. Harold W. Jr. and Estelle L. (Ormond) N.; m. Martha G. Silberman, June 19, 1953; children: Leigh, Scott, David. Postgrad., Hotchkiss Sch., 1949; AB magna cum laude, Princeton U., 1953; LLB, Yale U., 1956; LLD (hon.), U. Hartford, 1975, U. Bridgeport, 1980. Bar: Conn. 1956, D.C. 1956. Law clk. to Hon. George T. Washington U.S. Ct. Appeals, 1956-57; sr. law clk. to chief justice U.S. Supreme Ct., 1957-58; ptnr. Ritter, Satter & Newman, Hartford, Conn., 1958-60; counsel to majority Conn. Gen. Assembly, 1959; spl. counsel to gov. Conn., 1959-61; asst. to sec. HEW, 1961-62; adminstrv. asst. to U.S. senator, 1963-64; U.S. atty. Dist. of Conn., 1964-69; pvt. practice law, 1969-71; U.S. dist. judge Dist. of Conn., 1972-79; U.S. cir. judge 2d Cir. Ct. of Appeals, 1979-93, chief judge, 1993—. Co-author: Politics: The American Way. With USAR, 1954-62. Recipient Learned Hand medal Fed. Bar Coun., 1987. Fellow Am. Bar Found.; mem. ABA, Am. Law Inst., Conn. Bar Assn., Am. Judicature Soc. Democrat. Office: US Ct Appeals 450 Main St Hartford CT 06103-3001

NEWMAN, JOSEPH HERZL, advertising executive; b. N.Y.C., Dec. 1, 1928; s. Max A. and Tillie C. (Weitzman) N.; m. Ruth Z. Marcus, Dec. 19, 1954 (div. Feb. 1987); children: Deborah Lynn, David Alan, Mark Jonathan; m. Nancy K. Deutschman, Aug. 19, 1990; stepchildren: Pamela Sue Deutschman, Douglas Hayes Deutschman, Cindi Elaine Deutschman. AB, Bethany Coll., W.Va., 1949; MS, Columbia U., 1956. With 20th Century Fox Film Corp., N.Y.C., 1949-53; media supr. Fred Wittner Advt. Agy. (now Hammond Farrell Inc.), N.Y.C., 1953-56; media dir. O.S. Tyson & Co. (now Poppe Tyson, Inc.), N.Y.C., 1956-64; v.p., media dir. Marsteller Inc. (now Lord, Dentsu and Ptnrs.), N.Y.C., 1965-85; v.p., assoc. media dir. HBM/Creamer, N.Y.C., 1985-87, Della Femina, McNamee, Inc., N.Y.C., 1987-89; pres. Newman and Assocs., Cleve., 1989—; mem. faculty Advt. Age Media Workshop, 1972; past chmn. media mgrs. adv. com. Bus. Publs. Audit of Circulation Inc., N.Y.C.; conducted profl. media planning seminars, 1989—. Contbr. articles to profl. jours. Past chmn. bus.-to-bus. media com. Am. Assn. Advt. Agys.; mem. tax incentive rev. coun. City of Mayfield Heights, Ohio, 1994—. With U.S. Army, 1950-52. Mem. Bus. Mktg. Assn. (mem. media comparability coun., media data form com. and rsch. resource com., Agy. Exec. of Yr., N.Y. chpt. 1960, 66, 71, 73). Home and Office: 6338 Woodhawk Dr Cleveland OH 44124-4153

NEWMAN, JOYCE KLIGERMAN, sculptor; b. Atlantic City, July 7, 1927; d. Louis and Anne (Levine) Kligerman; m. Melvin Micklin Newman, Sept. 11, 1949; children—Rebecca, Morris Henry. B.A., Cornell U., 1948; Ph.D. in Biochemistry, U. Chgo., 1955; student, Art Students League, N.Y.C., 1962. Research asso. biochemistry U. Colo. Med. Center, Denver, 1963-70; mem. faculty dept. chemistry Met. State Coll., 1976-77. Profl. sculptor, Denver, 1968-84, Pasadena, Calif., 1984—, sculpture installed, Douglas County (Colo.) Pub. Library, 1971; commd. public sculpture, City of Littleton (Colo.), 1979, U. No Colo., Greeley, 1981, City of Chandler, Ariz., 1986; Contbr. numerous articles on biochemistry, also artists' rights to profl. jours. Mem. Artists Equity Assn. (pres. Colo. chpt. 1970-72, nat. pres. 1973-75), U. Chgo. Alumni Assn. (pres. Denver club 1967-84, bd. dirs. L.A. club 1985—, v.p. 1987-91, pres. 1992-94). Address: 1750 E Mountain St Pasadena CA 91104-3937

NEWMAN, JUSTINA ANNE, nursery school administrator, consultant; b. New Brunswick, N.J., Dec. 21, 1943; d. John S. and Louise B. (Marcks) Hilman; m. Raymond William Newman, Sept. 15, 1962; children: Raymond, Steven, Michelle. BA in Elem. Edn., nursery sch. endorse., Georgian Ct. Coll., 1982, cert. spl. edn., 1986. Dir., owner, child dcare cons. Beachwood (N.J.) Nursery Sch. Inc., 1986—. Exec. bd. Pine Beach Sch. PTA, Little League, Pine Beach/Beachwood, Cub Scouts; co-leader Brownies, Toms River (N.J.) High Sch. band Wagon. Recipient Accredation award Nat. Acad. Early Childhood Programs, 1992—. Mem. Nat. Assn. for the Edn. of Young Children (Ocean chpt., editor, founder N.J. chpt. newsletter 1988—, N.J. Assn. for the Edn. of Young Children (pres. Ocean chpt. 1984-88, corr. sec. 1990-92, fin. com. 1990—, grant program com.), Assn. for Childhood Edn. Internat. (early childhood divsn. 1990—). Roman Catholic. Avocations: music, writing, traveling. Home: 525 Admirals Cir Pine Beach NJ 08741-1413 Office: Beachwood Nursery Sch 1014 Pinewood Rd Beachwood NJ 08722

NEWMAN, LAWRENCE, lawyer; b. N.Y.C., May 31, 1931; s. Herman and Sarah (Steinsaltz) N.; m. Helaine J. Glickstein, June 6, 1954; children: Debra, Daniel, Karen. A.B., Dartmouth Coll. 1952; LL.B., Yale U., 1955; S.J.D., N.Y. Law Sch., 1963. Bar: N.Y. 1956. Law clk. to Hon. Lawrence E. Walsh U.S. Dist. Ct., N.Y.C., 1955-57; ptnr. Kaye, Scholer, Fierman, Hays & Handler, N.Y.C., 1962-94; cons. Friedman & Kaplan, N.Y.C., 1994—; adj. prof. U. Pa. Law Sch., Phila., 1969—, Yale U. Law Sch., 1983-85; lectr. Columbia U. Law Sch., N.Y.C., 1994—. Author: (with Albert Kalter) Postmortem Estate Planning, 1976, 2nd edit., 1994. Mem. exec. com. Am. Friends of Hebrew U. Fellow Am. Bar Found., Am. Coll. Trust and Estate Coun.; mem. ABA (chmn. sect. legal edn. 1979-80, chmn. com. estate & gift taxation 1976-78), Estate Planning Council N.Y.C. (pres. 1979-80), N.Y. State Bar Assn. Office: 875 3d Ave New York NY 10022

NEWMAN, LAWRENCE WALKER, lawyer; b. Boston, July 1, 1935; s. Leon Bettoney and Hazel W. (Walker) N.; m. Cecilia Isette Santos, Nov. 29, 1975; children: Reynaldo W., Timothy D., Virginia I.S., Isabel B., Thomas H. A.B., Harvard U., 1957, LL.B., 1960. Bar: D.C. 1961, N.Y. 1965. Atty. U.S. Dept. Justice, 1960-61, Spl. Study of Securities Markets and Office Spl. Counsel on Investment Co. Act Matters, U.S. SEC, 1961-64; asst. U.S. atty. So. Dist. N.Y., 1964-69; assoc. Baker & McKenzie, N.Y.C., 1969-71, ptnr., 1971—; mem. internat. adv. coun. World Arbitration Inst., 1984-87; mem. adv. com. Asia Pacific Ctr. for Resolution of Internat. Trade Disputes, 1987—; mem. adv. bd.Inst. for Transnational Arbitration, 1988—; chmn. U.S. Iranian Claimants Com., 1982—. Co-author: The Practice of International Litigation, 1992, 93; columnist N.Y. Law Jour., 1982—; mem. adv. bd. World Arbitration and Mediation Report; contbr. articles to profl. jours. and books on litigation and internat. arbitration. Mem. ABA (internat. litigation com., internat. arbitration com.), Internat. Bar Assn. (com. dispute resolution, com. constrn. litigation), Inter-Am. Bar Assn., Fed. Bar Coun., Am. Fgn. Law Assn., Maritime Law Assn. U.S., Assn. Bar City N.Y. (com. on arbitration & alternative dispute resolution 1991-94), Am. Arbitration Assn. (corp. counsel com. 1987—, panel comml. arbitrators), U.S. Coun. Internat. Bus., Ct. Arbitration of Polish Chamber Fgn. Trade (panel of arbitrators), Brit. Col. Internat. Comml. Abitration Ctr. Home: 1001 Park Ave New York NY 10028-0935 Office: Baker & McKenzie 805 3d Ave New York NY 10022

NEWMAN, LAWRENCE WILLIAM, financial executive; b. Chgo., Jan. 14, 1939; s. Eskil William and Adele Diane (Lawnicki) N.; m. Christine Harriet Jaronski, Sept. 22, 1962; children: Paul, Scott, Ron. BBS, U. Ill., 1965; MBA, Northwestern U., 1970. CPA, Ill. Controller ECM Corp., Schaumburg, Ill., 1966-70; controller Nachman Corp., Des Plaines, Ill., 1970-76, v.p., treas., controller, 1976-79; v.p. fin. P & S Mgmt. Inc., Schiller Park, Ill., 1979-83; controller Underwriters Labs., Northbrook, Ill., 1983-85, asst. treas., 1985-89; v.p., treas. Underwriters Labs., 1990—. Mem. Fin. Execs. Inst., Am. Inst. CPA's. Club: Exec. of Chgo. Office: Underwriters Labs 333 Pfingsten Rd Northbrook IL 60062-2002

NEWMAN, MALCOLM, civil engineering consultant; b. N.Y.C., June 29, 1931; s. George and Evelyn (Weber) N.; m. Estelle Ruth Glotzer, June 11, 1955; children: Roberta Gail, Leonard Scott, Alisha Gwen. BSCE, CCNY, 1952; MS in Civil Engring., Columbia U., 1957; D in Engring. Sci., NYU, 1962. Registered profl. engr., N.Y. Chief structural mechanics Republic-Fairchild Hiller Corp., Farmingdale, N.Y., 1962-65, staff cons., 1970-71; dir. structural mechanics and design Analytical Mechanics Assn., Jericho, N.Y., 1969-70; prof. mech. engring. Tel Aviv U., 1972-75; pres., tech. dir. Inner-City Testing and Consulting, Mineola, N.Y., 1979—; pres. Athletic Safety Products Inc., Mineola, 1985—. Contbr. over 80 articles to profl. jours.; patentee in field. Bd. dirs. Cinema Arts Ctr., Huntington, N.Y., 1989—. Mem. NSPE, Am. Soc. Safety Engrs., Nat. Assn. Profl. Accident Reconstruction Specialists, Soc. Automotive Engrs., System Safety Soc. (pres. 1983-85). Office: Inter-City Testing & Cons 167 Willis Ave Mineola NY 11501-2621

NEWMAN, MARGARET ANN, nursing educator; b. Memphis, Oct. 10, 1933; d. Ivo Mathias and Mamie Love (Donald) N.; BSHE, Baylor U., 1954; BSN, U. Tenn., Memphis, 1962; MS, U. Calif., San Francisco, 1964; PhD, NYU, 1971. Dir. nursing, asst. prof. nursing Clin. Research Center, U. Tenn., 1964-67; asst. prof. N.Y.U., 1971-75, assoc. prof., 1975-77; prof. in charge grad. program and research dept. nursing Pa. State U., 1977-80, prof. nursing, 1977-84; prof. nursing U. Minn., 1984—; disting. resident Westminster Coll., Salt Lake City Utah, 1991. Travelling fellow New Zealand Nursing Ednl. & Rsch. Fund, 1985; Am. Jour. Nursing scholar, 1979-80; recipient Outstanding Alumnus award U. Tenn. Coll. Nursing, 1975, Disting. Alumnus award NYU Div. Nursing, 1984; Disting. Scholar in Nursing award NYU Div. Nursing, 1992, Sigma Theta Tau Founders Rsch. award, 1993, Nursing Scholar award St. Xavier U., 1994. Fellow Am. Acad. Nursing. Author: Theory Development in Nursing, 1979; Health as Expanding Consciousness, 1986, 2nd edit., 1994; A Developing Discipline, 1995; editor: (with others) Source Book of Nursing Research, 1973, 2d edit., 1977. Research on patterns of person-environment interaction as indices of health as expanding consciousness; also models of profl. practice. Office: 6-101 Health Scis Unit F 308 Harvard St SE Minneapolis MN 55455-0353

NEWMAN, MONROE, retired economist, educator; b. Bklyn., Jan. 31, 1929; s. David A. and Ida Mary (Leight) N.; m. Ruth Zielinski, Feb. 6, 1951. BA, Antioch Coll., 1950; MA, U. Ill., 1953, PhD, 1954. Mem. rsch. staff AFL, 1947-48; examiner NLRB, 1949-50; rsch. analyst U. Ill., 1950-54; research analyst Assn. Casualty and Surety Cos., 1954-55; mem. faculty Pa. State U., University Park, 1955-86; prof. econs. Pa. State U., 1961-86, prof. emeritus, 1986—, head dept., 1958-62, 78-85, chmn. grad. program regional planning, 1971-72; dir. Ctr. for Study of Environ. Policy, 1972-73; vis. rsch. prof. econs. U. Pitts., 1964-65; economist Appalachian Regional Commn., Washington, 1964-65, rsch. dir., 1965-66, spl. cons., 1966-86, sr. econ. advisor, 1986-93. Co-author: Insurance and Risk, 1964, Acid Mine Drainage in Appalachia, 1969, Experiment in Appalachia, 1973; author: Political Economy of Appalachia, 1972, also articles. Mem. So. Regional Sci. Assn. (pres.), Am. Econ. Assn., Regional Sci. Assn. Home: 4101 Cathedral Ave NW Washington DC 20016-3585

NEWMAN, MORRIS, mathematician; b. N.Y.C., Feb. 25, 1924; s. Isaac and Sarah (Cohen) N.; m. Mary Aileen Lenk, Sept. 18, 1948; children: Sally Ann, Carl Lenk. A.B., N.Y.U., 1945; M.A., Columbia U., 1946; Ph.D., U. Pa., 1952. Mathematician applied math div. Nat. Bur. Standards, Washington, 1951-63, chief numerical analysis sect., 1963-70, sr. rsch. mathematician, 1970-76; prof. math. U. Calif., Santa Barbara, 1976—; dir. Inst. Interdisciplinary Applications of Algebra and Combinatorics, 1976-94, emeritus, 1994—; lectr. U. B.C., 1960, U. Calif.-Santa Barbara, 1965, Am. U., Cath. U., U. Md. Author: Matrix Representations of Groups, 1968, Integral Matrices, 1972; editor: Jour. Research Nat. Bur. Standards, 1966-76, Math. of Computation, 1975-86; assoc. editor: Jour. Linear and Multilinear Algebra, 1973—, Letters in Linear Algebra, 1979—; contbr. articles to profl. jours. Recipient Gold medal U.S. Dept. Commerce, 1966. Mem. Am. Math. Soc. (council 1980-86), London Math. Soc., Math. Assn. Am., Washington Acad. Scis., AAAS, sigma Xi. Home: 1050 Las Alturas Rd Santa Barbara CA 93103-1608 Office: U Calif Dept Math Santa Barbara CA 93106

NEWMAN, MURIEL KALLIS STEINBERG, art collector; b. Chgo., Feb. 25, 1914; d. Maurice and Ida (Nudelman) Kallis; m. Albert H. Newman, May 14, 1955; 1 son by previous marriage, Glenn D. Steinberg. Student, Art Inst. Chgo., 1932-36, Ill. Inst. Tech., 1947-50, U. Chgo., 1958-65. hon. life trustee, benefactor Met. Mus. Art, N.Y.C., mem. vis. com. dept. 20th Century Art, mem. acquisitions com., 1981—, mem. decorative arts com., 1989; also Costume Inst. Dir. 20th Century Painting and Sculpture Com., Art Inst. Chgo., 1955-80, governing mem. inst., 1975—, major benefactor, 1979—; pioneer collector Am. abstract expressionist art, 1949—, major show of collection, Met. Mus. Art, N.Y.C., 1981, also show of personal collection of costumes and jewelry, 1981. Bd. govs. Landmarks Preservation Council, Chgo., 1966-78; mem. woman's bd. U. Chgo., 1960-81, Art Inst. Chgo., 1953—; trustee Mus. Contemporary Art, 1970—, benefactor, 1970—; trustee Chgo. Sch. of architecture Found., 1971—, Archives Am. Art, 1976—; mem. bd. Bright Hebrew U. Urban Affairs Lecture Series, 1966—. Recipient Scroll Recognition of Public Service U.S. Dept. State, 1958. Mem. Antiquarian Soc. of Art Inst. Chgo., Chgo. Hist. Soc. (mem. guild 1958—). Clubs: Arts

(Chgo.), Casino (Chgo.). *Searching for truth is a given for a life of value. For me visual art ontologically reveals the truth of the search. Striving for excellence is the spearhead with which to proceed.*

NEWMAN, MURRAY ARTHUR, aquarium administrator; b. Chgo., Mar. 6, 1924; emigrated to Can., 1953, naturalized, 1975; s. Paul Jones and Virginia (Murray) N.; m. Katherine Greene Rose, Aug. 8, 1952; 1 child, Susan. B.Sc., U. Chgo., 1949; postgrad., U. Hawaii, 1950; M.A., U. Calif., Berkeley, 1951; Ph.D., U.B.C. (Can.), Vancouver, 1960. Curator fisheries UCLA, 1951-53, Ichthyology Museum, U.B.C., 1953-56; curator Vancouver Public Aquarium, 1956-66, dir., 1966-93; pres. Mana Aquarium Cons.; fgn. adv. Nat. Mus./Aquarium Project, Taiwan, Republic of China; past chmn. adv. com. Western Can. Univs. Marine Biol. Soc. Author: Life in a Fishbowl: Confessions of an Aquarium Director, 1994. Served with USN, 1943-46. Decorated Order of Can.; recipient Man of Yr. award City of Vancouver, 1964; Centennial award Govt. Can., 1967, cert. of merit, 1988; Harold J. Merilees award Vancouver Visitors Bur., 1976, 75 Achievers award, 1987, Silver Bravery medal Royal Soc. Canada, 1992, Canada 125 medal, 1992. Mem. Am. Assn. Zool. Parks and Aquariums, Internat. Union Dirs. Zool. Gardens, Can. Assn. Zool. Pks. and Aquariums (pres. 1978-79), Vancouver Club (bd. dirs.), Round Table Club. Office: Vancouver Pub Aquarium, PO Box 3232, Vancouver, BC Canada V6B 3X8

NEWMAN, NANCY MARILYN, ophthalmologist, educator, consultant, inventor, entrepreneur; b. San Francisco, Mar. 16, 1941. BA in Psychology magna cum laude, Stanford U., 1962, MD, 1967. Diplomate Am. Bd. Ophthalmology. NIH trainee neurophysiology Inst. Visual Scis., San Francisco, 1964-65; clin. clk. Nat. Hosp. for Nervous and Mental Disease, London, 1966-67; intern Mount Auburn Hosp., Cambridge, Mass., 1967-68; NIH trainee neuro-ophthalmology, from jr. asst. resident to sr. asst. resident to assoc. resident dept. ophthalmology sch. medicine Washington U., St. Louis, 1968-71; NIH spl. fellow in neuro-ophthalmology depts. ophthalmology and neurol. surgery sch. medicine U. Calif., San Francisco, 1971-72, clin. asst. prof. ophthalmology sch. medicine, 1972; asst. chief, chief divsn. neuro-ophthalmology Pacific Med. Ctr., San Francisco, 1972-73, assoc. prof., chief, 1973-88; physician, cons. dept. neurology sch. medicine U. Calif., VA Med. Ctr., Martinez, Calif., 1978—; prof. dept. spl. edn. Calif. State U., San Francisco, 1974-79; vis. prof. Centre Nat. D'Ophtalmologie des Quinze-Vingts, Paris, 1980; clin. assoc. prof. optometry U. Calif., Berkeley, 1990—; bd. dirs., adv. bd. Frank B. Walsh Soc., 1974-91, Rose Resnick Ctr. for the Blind and Handicapped, 1988-92, Fifer St. Fitness, Larkspur, 1990-92; Internat. Soc. for Orbital Disorders, 1983—, North Calif. Soc. Prevention of Blindness, 1978-88, North African Ctr. for Sight, Tunis, Tunisia, 1988—; pres., CEO Minerva Medica; cons. in field. Author: Eye Movement Disorders; Neuro-ophthalmology: A Practical Text, 1992; mem. editorial bd. Jour. of Clin. Neuro-ophthalmology, Am. Jour. Opthalmology, 1980-92, Soc. Francaise d'Ophtalmogie, Ophthalmology Practice, 1993—; contbr. numerous articles to profl. jours. Recipient NSPI award Self Instrnl. Materials Ophthalmology, Merit award Internat. Eye Found., fellow 1971; Smith-Kettlewell Inst. Vis. Scis. fellow, 1971-72. Mem. AMA (leader Calif. del. continuing med. edn. 1982, 83), San Francisco Med. Soc., Calif. Med. Assn. (sub com. med. policy coms. 1984—, chair com. on accreditation continuing med. edn. 1981-88, chair quality care rev. commn. 1984), Assn. for Rsch. in Vision and Ophthalmology, Pan Am. Assn. of Ophthalmology, Soc. of Heed Fellows, Pacific Coast Oto-Ophthalmology Soc., Lane Medical Soc. (v.p. 1975-76), Internat. Soc. of Neuro-Ophthalmology (founder), Cordes Soc., Am. Soc. Ophthalmic Ultrasound (charter), Orbital Soc. (founder), West Bay Health Systems Agy., Oxford Opthalmology Soc., Pacific Physician Assocs., Soc. Francaise D'Ophtalmologie (mem. editorial bd. jour.). Home: 819 Spring Dr Mill Valley CA 94941-3924

NEWMAN, NORMAN, lawyer; b. Bklyn., Nov. 7, 1952; s. Irving and Rachel (Manheim) N.; m. Gitta Stern, Feb. 4, 1981; children: Evan Michael, Jennifer Danielle, Stephanie Gabrielle, Adam Jay. BA, Yeshiva U., N.Y., 1974; JD, Columbia U. Sch. of Law, N.Y., 1977. Bar: N.Y. 1978, U.S. Supreme Ct. N.Y. 1978, U.S. Tax Ct. 1978. Student clk. Roberts & Holland, N.Y., 1976-77; summer clk. Hale and Dorr, Boston, 1976; assoc. Mudge, Rose, Guthrie, Alexander & Ferdon, N.Y., 1977-79, Zimet, Haines et al, N.Y., 1979-82, Baer, Marks & Upham, N.Y., 1982-86; ptnr., chmn. Baer, Marks & Upham Employee Benefits Dept., N.Y., 1986-92; ptnr. Winston & Strawn, N.Y.C., 1992—, chmn. employee benefits dept., 1994—; mem. mgmt. com., bus. devel. com. Baer Marks & Upham, N.Y., 1990-92; mem. commrs. ad-hoc adv. com. exempt plans IRS, Washington, 1988-91. Contbr. editor: Compensation and Benefit Management Journal, United States Employee Benefit Plans and Executive Compensation, New Business Law mag., 1989. Bd. dirs. Hartmann YMHA, N.Y., 1989-91, Peninsula Counseling Ctr., 1991—, Minyan for the Stars, 1991-92; dir. v.p. exec. com. Yeshiva Toras Chaim, N.Y., 1989-91, pres. 1991—. Mem. N.Y.S. Bar Assn., Am. Bar Assn., Bar Assn. of N.Y.C. Avocations: tennis, biking. Home: 180 Lakeside Dr S Lawrence NY 11559-1721 Office: Winston & Strawn 175 Water St New York NY 10038

NEWMAN, PAUL, actor, professional race-car driver, food company executive; b. Cleve., Jan. 26, 1925; s. Arthur S. and Theresa (Fetzer) N.; m. Jacqueline Witte, Dec. 1949; children: Scott (dec.), Susan, Stephanie; m. Joanne Woodward, Jan. 1958; children: Elinor, Melissa, Clea. BA, Kenyon Coll., 1949; postgrad., Yale Sch. Drama, 1951; studied with Lee Strasborg; LHD, Yale U., 1988. Pres. Newman's Own Found., Inc., Westport, Conn. Appeared on Broadway in: Picnic, 1953-54, Desperate Hours, 1955, The Long Hot Summer, 1958 (Cannes Internat. Film Festival, Best Actor, 1958), Sweet Bird of Youth, 1959, Baby Want a Kiss, 1964; motion pictures include Somebody Up There Likes Me, 1956, Cat on a Hot Tin Roof, 1958, From the Terrace, 1960, Exodus, 1960, The Hustler, 1961, Sweet Bird of Youth, 1962, Hud, 1963, The Outrage, 1964, The Prize, 1964, Lady L, 1965, Harper, 1966, Hombre, 1967, Cool Hand Luke, 1967, Winning, 1969, Butch Cassidy and the Sundance Kid, 1969, WUSA, Sometimes a Great Notion, 1971, Pocket Money, 1972, The Life and Times of Judge Roy Bean, 1972, The MacIntosh Man, 1973, The Sting, 1973, The Towering Inferno, 1974, Drowning Pool, 1975, Buffalo Bill and the Indians, 1976, Slap Shot, 1977, Quintet, 1979, Fort Apache, The Bronx, 1980, When Time Ran Out, 1980, Absence of Malice, 1981, The Verdict, 1982, The Color of Money, 1986, (Acad. award for best actor, 1987), Blaze, 1989, Mr. and Mrs. Bridge, 1989, The Hudsucker Proxy, 1994, Nobody's Fool, 1994; dir. motion pictures including: The Effect of Gamma Rays on Man-in-the-Moon Marigolds, 1973, Rachel, Rachel, 1968, Glass Menagerie, 1987; dir., screenwriter, actor in film Harry and Son, 1984; producer, actor Nat. Acad. Motion Picture Arts and Scis. 1959-61, 63, 81, 82; recipient Man of Year award Hasty Pudding Theatrical, Harvard U., 1968; elected World film favorite Golden Globe awards 1967; named Best Motion Picture Producer of Yr., Producers Guild Am. 1968; recipient hon. Acad. award for career achievement, 1986. Served with AC USNR, 1943-46. Recipient D.W. Griffith Best Actor award Nat Bd. Rev. Motion Pictures, 1986; Jean Hersholt Humanitarian Award (Academy Award), 1994. *

NEWMAN, PAULINE, federal judge; b. N.Y.C., N.Y., June 20, 1927; d. Maxwell Henry and Rosella N. B.A., Vassar Coll., 1947; M.A., Columbia U., 1948; Ph.D., Yale U., 1952; LL.B., NYU, 1958. Bar: N.Y. 1958, U.S. Supreme Ct. 1972, U.S. Ct. Customs and Patent Appeals 1978, Pa. 1979, U.S. Ct. Appeals (3d cir.) 1981, U.S. Ct. Appeals (fed. cir.) 1982. Research chemist Am. Cyanamid Co., Bound Brook, N.J., 1951-54; mem. patent staff FMC Corp., N.Y.C., 1954-75; mem. patent staff FMC Corp., Phila., 1975-84, dir. patent and licensing, 1969-84; judge U.S. Ct. Appeals (fed. cir.), Washington, 1984—; bd. dir. Research Corp., 1982-84; program specialist Dept. Natural Scis. UNESCO, Paris, 1961-62; mem. State Dept. Adv. Com. on Internat. Indsl. Property, 1974-84; lectr. in field. Contbr. articles to profl. jours. Bd. dirs. Med. Coll. Pa., 1975-84, Midgard Found., 1973-84; trustee Phila. Coll. Pharmacy and Sci., 1983-84. Mem. ABA (council sect. patent trademark and copyright 1983-84), Am. Patent Law Assn. (bd. dirs. 1981-84), U.S. Trademark Assn. (bd. dirs. 1975-79, v.p. 1978-79), Am. Chem. Soc. (bd. dirs. 1972-81), Am. Inst. Chemists (bd. dirs. 1960-66, 70-76), Pacific Indsl. Property (pres. 1979-80). Clubs: Vassar, Yale. Office: US Ct Appeals 717 Madison Pl NW Washington DC 20439-0002

NEWMAN, PETER CHARLES, journalist; b. Vienna, Austria, May 10, 1929; emigrated to Can., 1940, naturalized, 1945; s. Oscar C. and Wanda

(Newman) N. Ed., Upper Can. Coll., 1948; M.A., U. Toronto, 1951; LL.D. (hon.), Brock U., 1974; D.Litt. (hon.), York U., 1975; LL.D. (hon.) Wilfrid Laurier U., 1983, Royal Mil. Coll., 1986, Queens U., 1986. Asst. editor The Financial Post, 1951-55; Ottawa editor Maclean's Mag., 1955-64; Ottawa editor Toronto Daily Star, 1964-69, editor-in-chief, 1969-71; editor Maclean's, Toronto, 1971-82, sr. contbg. editor, 1982; Dep. chmn. for Can. Internat. Press Inst., 1970-74; vis. assoc. prof. polit. sci. McMaster U., Hamilton, Ont., 1970—; adj. prof. Sask. Indian Federated Coll., 1985; prof. creative writing U. Victoria, 1986; vis. prof. York U., 1979; dir. Maclean Hunter Ltd., 1972-82, Key Radio Ltd., 1982. Author: Flame of Power, 1959, Renegade in Power, 1963, The Distemper of Our Times, 1968, Home Country, 1973, The Canadian Establishment, 1975, Bronfman Dynasty, 1978, The Acquisitors, 1981, The Establishment Man, 1982, True North: Not Strong and Free, 1983, The Debrett's Guide to the Canadian Establishment, 1983, Company of Adventurers, 1985, Caesars of the Wilderness, 1987, Sometimes a Great Nation, 1988, Empire of the Bay, 1989, Merchant Princes, 1992, Canada: 1892-Portrait of a Promised Land, 1994, The Canadian Revolution: From Deference to Defiance, 1995. Gov. Shaw Festival, 1984; bd. dirs. Can. Coun. Native Bus., 1985, Can. Coun. Econ. Edn. 1985; dir. St. Paul's Hosp. Capt. Royal Can. Navy Res. Decorated companion Order of Can., knight commdr. St. Lazarus; recipient Nat. Newspaper award for feature writing, 1966, Wilderness award CBC, 1967, Michener award for journalism, 1971, Pres.'s medal U. We. Ont., 1974, Quill award-Journalist of Yr., 1977, Best TV Program of Yr. award Assn. Can. TV and Radio Artists, 1981, Nat. Bus. Writing award for disting. svc., 1986; elected to News Hall of Fame, 1989. Home: 2324 W 1st Ave Ste 1205, Vancouver, BC Canada V6K 1G3 Office: Maclean Hunter Bldg, 777 Bay St, Toronto, ON Canada

NEWMAN, PETER KENNETH, economist, educator; b. Mitcham, Eng., Oct. 5, 1928; s. Charles Francis and Harriet Anne (Newbold) N.; m. Jennifer Mary Hugh-Jones Steed, Sept. 30, 1974; children by previous marriage: Jean Ellen, John Lincoln, Katherine Rachel, Alan Peter. B.Sc. in Econs, Univ. Coll. U. London, Eng., 1949, M.Sc. in Econs, 1951, D.Sc. in Econs, 1962. Lectr. U. West Indies, Jamaica, 1957-59, sr. lectr., 1959-61; prof. econs. U. Mich., Ann Arbor, 1961-63; prof. econs. Johns Hopkins U., Balt., 1964-65, 66-90, prof. emeritus, 1990—; sr. assoc. Robert R. Nathan Assocs., Washington, 1965-66. Author: British Guiana, 1964, Malaria Eradication and Population Growth, 1965, Theory of Exchange, 1965; co-editor: The New Palgrave: A Dictionary of Economics, 4 vols., 1987; chief editor: The New Palgrave: Dictionary of Money and Finance, 3 vols., 1992.

NEWMAN, PHILLIP BARBOUR, III, distilling company executive; b. Louisville, May 31, 1932; s. Phillip Barbour and Francis (Powell) N.; m. Eleanor Griffith Tarrant, May 15, 1965; children: Phillip IV, John Tarrant. B in Engring., Yale U., 1956, BS, 1957. Engr. Westinghouse Electric Co., Balt., 1960-64; v.p. Glenmore Distilleries Co., Louisville, 1964-68, 1st v.p., 1968-90, exec. v.p., 1990-92, also bd. dirs.; pres., dir. Mr. Boston Distillers Corp., 1977—, Viking Distilling Co., Albany, Ga., 1977—; v.p. United Distillors Mfg. Inc., Louisville, 1992—. Served lt. (j.g.) USNR, 1956-60. Mem. Ky. Distillers Assn. (bd. dirs., treas. 1980—), Soc. Colonial Wars. Club: Louisville Country, Pendennis (Louisville). Avocation: sailing.

NEWMAN, RACHEL, magazine editor; b. Malden, Mass., May 1, 1938; d. Maurice and Edythe Brenda (Tichell) N.; m. Herbert Bleiweiss, Apr. 6, 1973 (div. Apr. 1989). B.A., Pa. State U., 1960; cert., N.Y. Sch. Interior Design, 1963. Accessories editor Women's Wear Daily, N.Y.C., 1964-65; designer, publicist Grandoe Glove Corp., N.Y.C., 1965-67; assoc. editor McCall's Sportswear and Dress Merchandiser mag., N.Y.C., 1967; mng. editor McCall's You-Do-It Home Decorating, 1968-70, Ladies Home Jour. Needle and Craft mag., N.Y.C., 1970-72; editor-in-chief Am. Home Crafts mag., N.Y.C., 1972-77; fashion dir. Good Housekeeping mag., N.Y.C., 1977-78; home bldg. and decorating dir. Good Housekeeping mag., 1978-82; editor-in-chief Country Living mag., 1978—; founding editor Country Cooking mag., 1985—, Dream Homes mag., 1989—, Country Kitchens mag., 1990—, Country Living Gardener Mag., 1993—. Pa. State U. Alumni fellow, 1986; recipient Cir. of Excellence award IFDA, 1992, YMCA Hall of Fame, 1992; named Disting. Alumni Pa. State U., 1988. Mem. N.Y. Fashion Group, Nat. Home Fashions League, Am. Soc. Interior Designers, Am. Soc. Mag. Editors. Office: Country Living 224 W 57th St New York NY 10019-3203

NEWMAN, RALPH GEOFFREY, literary scholar historian; b. Chgo., Nov. 3, 1911; s. Henry and Dora (Glickman) N.; m. Estelle Hoffman, 1934 (div.); children: Maxine (Mrs. Richard B. Brandenburg), Carol (Mrs. John Fox); m. Patricia Lyons Simon, 1972. Litt.D., James Milliken U. (Lincoln Coll.), 1950, Knox Coll., Rockford Coll.; LL.D., Iowa Wesleyan Coll.; Litt. D., Meisei U., Tokyo. Founder Abraham Lincoln Book Shop, Inc., Chgo., 1933-84; pres. Americana House, Inc., 1946-89, Lincoln's New Salem Enterprises, Inc., 1952-92, Ralph Geoffrey Newman, Inc., 1967—, Civil War Enterprises, Ltd., 1985-90; cons. Broadcast Music, Inc., 1941-89, Chgo. Sports Hall of Fame, 1989—. Author: (with Otto Eisenschiml) The American Iliad, 1947, Abraham Lincoln: An Autobiographical Narrative, 1970; Editor: The Diary of a Public Man, 1945, The Railsplitter, 1950, (with Otto Eisenschiml, E.B. Long) The Civil War, 1956; radio series The Abraham Lincoln Story, 1958-59; Lincoln for the Ages, 1960, (with Otto Eisenchiml) Evewitness, 1960, (with E.B. Long) The Civil War Digest, 1960, Pictorial Autobiography of Abraham Lincoln, 1962, Time-Table for the Lincoln Funeral, 1965, Abraham Lincoln: His Story in His Own Words, 1975, Abraham Lincoln's Last Full Measure of Devotion, 1981, The Lincoln Academy: A History, 1984, rev. edit., 1994, We Shall Pay Any Price, 1988, The General's Greatest Victory, 1989, (with G. N. Wiche) Great and Goods Books, 1989, Preserving Lincoln for the Ages, 1989, Lincoln: Day by Day, 1992; contbr. The Continuing Civil War, 1992, A Vermont 14, 1992; mem. editorial bd.: Civil War History, 1955-75. Chmn. Ill. com. N.Y. World's Fair, 1963-65; chmn. Ill. Sesquicentennial Commn., 1965-69; mem. Ill. Spl. Events Commn., 1969-73, Book and Libr. Commn., USIA, 1983—; past pres. Adult Edn. Council Greater Chgo.; bd. regents Lincoln Acad. Ill.; city archivist, City of Chgo., 1979-80; pres. bd. dirs. Chgo. Public Library, 1964-79; trustee Lincoln Coll.; past chmn. bd. dirs. Ford's Theatre Soc., Washington; pres. Urban Libraries Council, 1970-78; bd. dirs. Chgo. Fund on Ageing and Disability, 1987-89. Served with USNR, 1944-45. Recipient diploma of honor Lincoln Meml. U., 1952; Am. of Year award Independence Hall Assn., 1958; Nevins-Freeman award, 1975; laureate Lincoln Acad. Ill., 1983, Barondess award Lincoln Group of N.Y., 1987. Mem. Civil War Round Table Chgo. (founder 1940, Harry S. Truman award Kansas City chpt. 1966), Royal Arts Soc. (London), Abraham Lincoln Assn. (dir.), Stephen A. Douglas Assn. (chmn., bd. dirs.), Ulysses S. Grant Assn. (pres. 1962-90), pres. emeritus 1990—), Am., Ind., Ill., Iowa, Kans., Chgo. hist. socs., Am. Legion, ALA, Am. Booksellers Assn., Bibliog. Socs. Am., U.S. Info. Agy. (book and library com.), Soc. Am. Historians, Newberry Library Assocs. Chgo., Phi Alpha Theta. Clubs: Arts, Casino, Caxton, Internat. (Chgo.), Sangamo (Springfield, Ill.), Union League. Address: 175 E Delaware Pl Chicago IL 60611-1734 Office: Fine Arts Bldg 410 S Michigan Ave Chicago IL 60605-1302 *I believe opportunity exists wherever you are if you are willing to work hard enough to achieve it. No goal is impossible. If you are willing to forego dependence on anyone else and realize that your own, and only your own, efforts will bring success, you can be successful.*

NEWMAN, RANDY, singer, songwriter, musician; b. Los Angeles, Calif., Nov. 28, 1943; s. Irving and Adele N.; m. Roswitha Newman; children: Amos, Eric, John. Degree, U. Calif. Arranger, singer, songwriter, musician various record firms; singer-composer: (albums) including Randy Newman, 1968, Twelve Songs, 1969, Live, 1971, Sail Away, 1972, Good Old Boys, 1974, Little Criminals, 1977, Born Again, 1979, Trouble In Paradise, 1983, Land of Dreams, 1988; appeared in film: Ragtime, 1981; also TV and concert engagements; music composer for films: Performance, 1970, Pursuit of Happiness, 1971, Cold Turkey, 1971, Ragtime, 1981, The Natural, 1984, Three Amigos (also co-wrote screenplay), 1986, Parenthood, 1989, Avalon, 1990, Awakenings, 1990. Recipient Grammy award for best instrumental composition, 1984. Office: care Renaissance Mgmt Corp 21241 Ventura Blvd Suite 251 Woodland Hills CA 91364*

NEWMAN, RICHARD, engineering executive. With Cahn Engr Inc., L.A., 1960-77; pres. of subsidiary Daniel Mann Johnson & Mendenhall, L.A., 1977-88; pres. Aecom Tech Corp., L.A., 1989—, now chmn. bd. dirs.,

pres., CEO. Office: Aecom Tech Corp 3250 Wilshire Blvd # 5 Los Angeles CA 90010-1438*

NEWMAN, RICHARD ALAN, publisher, editor and consultant; b. Watertown, N.Y., Mar. 30, 1930; s. Gordon Leon and Belle (Burton) N.; m. Ann Cowan Meredith, 1955 (div. 1960); m. Peggy J. Hyot, Oct. 23, 1964 (div. 1978); stepchildren: David W. Bauer, Paul W. Bauer, Nancy E. Beck. B.A., Maryville Coll., 1952; M.Div., Union Theol. Sem., 1955; postgrad., Syracuse U., 1959-61, Harvard U., 1966. Ordained to ministry Presbyn. Ch., 1955, demitted, 1977; minister Westminster Presbyn. Ch., Syracuse, N.Y., 1955-59; instr. religion Vassar Coll., Poughkeepsie, N.Y., 1962-63; prof., chmn. dept. social scis. Boston U., 1964-73; sr. editor G.K. Hall Co., Boston, 1973-79; exec. editor Garland Pub. Co., N.Y.C., 1978-81; mgr. publs. N.Y. Pub. Libr., 1981-92; cons. Columbia U., N.Y.C., 1992-93; pubs. officer and mng. editor The Harvard Guide to African-Am. History, W.E.B. DuBois Inst., Harvard U., 1993—. Author: Black Index, 1981, Bless All Thy Creatures, Lord, 1982, Lemuel Haynes, 1984, Afro-American Education, 1984, Black Access: A Bibliography, 1984, Black Power and Black Religion, 1987, Words Like Freedom, 1989, Black Preacher to White America, 1990; editor: Treasures from the New York Public Library, 1985; contbr. articles to profl. jours. Dem. candidate for N.Y. State Assembly from Onondaga County, 1960. Mem. Friends of Union Sem. Libr., Boston Athenaeum, Studio Mus. in Harlem, Friends of Amistad Rsch. Ctr., Schomburg Commn. for Preservation of Black Culture. Home: 160 Commonwealth Ave Apt 614 Boston MA 02116

NEWMAN, RICHARD OAKLEY, utilities executive, consultant; b. Enid, Okla., Aug. 30, 1920; s. O. B. and Grace E. N.; m. Betty Lou Bennett, Mar. 13, 1940; children: Linda Lou Newman Weathers, Richard Oakley, Mark B. B.S. in Mech. Engring. Okla. State U., 1942. With Pub. Svc. Co. of Okla., Tulsa, 1946; exec. v.p. Pub. Svc. Co. of Okla., 1968-70, exec. v.p., dir., 1970-72, pres., chief exec. officer, dir., 1972-82, chmn. bd., 1982-85, dir., 1970-86; pres., bd. dirs. Prodek, Inc., 1986-89; pres. R.O. Newman & Assocs., Inc., 1989—; past chmn. bd., chief exec. officer, dir. Transok Pipe Line Co.; past chmn., bd. dirs Ash Creek Mining Co.; past chmn. S.W. Underground Distbn. Exch., S.W. Power Pool; bd. dirs. Williams Cos., Panda Energy Co.; trustee N.Am. Electric Reliability Coun. Past chmn. ofcl. bd., deacon, elder, trustee, Sunday Sch. supt. East Side Christian Ch.; dir. Tulsa Christian Found.; past pres. Tulsa Area Christian Missionary Soc.; mem. Gov.'s Energy Advisory Council, from 1973; past chmn. and dir. Industries for Tulsa, Inc.; past pres. and dir. Goodwill Industries of Tulsa; bd. dirs Indian Nations council Boy Scouts Am.; past mem. bd. dirs. Goodwill Industries Am., Inc., Okla. State U. Found.; trustee St. Francis Hosp., Phillips U.; mem. advisory bd. Downtown Tulsa Unlimited, Inc.; bd. dirs. U. Tulsa. Served with AUS, 1942-46. Mem. IEEE, Am. Nuclear Soc., ASME, Nat., Okla. socs. profl. engrs., Okla. Petroleum Council, Mid-Continent Oil and Gas Assn., Tulsa C. of C. (past pres. and dir.), Nat. Alliance Businessmen (past met. chmn.), Edison Electric Inst. (former dir.). Mo. Valley Electric Assn. (past pres. and mem. exec. com.). Clubs: So. Hills Country, Tulsa Press. Lodge: Masons (32 deg.). Office: 7130 S Lewis Ave # 245 Tulsa OK 74136-5484

NEWMAN, ROBERT GABRIEL, physician; b. The Netherlands, Oct. 26, 1937; came to U.S., 1939; s. Randolph H. and Eva E. (Feilchenfeld) N.; m. Seiko Kusuba, Oct. 26, 1968; children—Henry Seiji, Hana Marie. B.A. NYU, 1958; M.D. with honors, U. Rochester, 1963; M.P.H., U. Calif.-Berkeley, 1969. Intern and resident in surgery Univ. Hosps., Cleve., 1963-65; dist. health officer N.Y.C. Health Dept., 1968; dir. Nat. Nutrition Survey of N.Y.C., 1969-70; asst. commr. N.Y.C. Health Dept., 1970-74; health cons., 1974-76; assoc. gen. dir. Beth Israel Med. Ctr., N.Y.C., 1976-78; chief exec. officer, pres. Beth Israel Med. Ctr., 1978—, pres., 1985—; prof. dept. community medicine Mt. Sinai Sch. Medicine, N.Y.C., 1982-94; prof. depts. epidemiology and social medicine/psychiatry Albert Einstein Coll. of Medicine, 1994—; cons. addiction problems Govt. of Hong Kong, 1975-85. Author book in field of methadone treatment; contbr. articles to profl. jours. Served with USAF, 1965-67. WHO fellow, 1972. Fellow N.Y. Acad. Medicine, Am. Coll. Preventive Medicine; mem. Public Health Assn. N.Y.C. Hosp. Assn. N.Y. State (past chmn. 1992), Greater N.Y. Hosp. Assn. (past chmn. bd.), Am. Public Health Assn. Office: Beth Israel Med Ctr 1st Ave # 16th St New York NY 10003

NEWMAN, SAMUEL, trust company executive; b. N.Y.C., Mar. 12, 1938; s. Aaron and Rachel (Hershkowitz) N.; m. Carolyn Gropper, Oct. 27, 1963; children: Marci Ann, Jodi Robin, Michael David. BBA, CUNY, 1971; grad. Advanced Mgmt. Program, Harvard U., 1982. Methods analyst Bankers Trust Co., N.Y.C., 1960-67; project leader Clark O'Neill SVC Corp., Fairview, N.J., 1967-68; sr. v.p. Irving Trust Co., N.Y.C., 1968-85; sr. v.p., gen. mgr. trade svcs. and GEOSERVE legal and regulatory support Mfrs. Hanover Trust (merger with Chem. Bank 1992), N.Y.C., 1985-92; sr. v.p., gen. mgr. funds transfer and trade svcs. Chem. Bank, N.Y.C., 1992-93; sr. v.p. and bus. head payment products First Fidelity Bank NA, Newark, 1993-95; head dept. product support Natwest Svcs. Inc., Scranton, Pa., 1995—; past chmn. bd. dirs. S.W.I.F.T. Terminal Svcs.; past chmn. N.Y. Clearing House funds transfer com.; speaker industry confs. Contbr. articles to profl. jours. Advisor Nat. Coun. of Commrs. on Uniform State Laws; former mem. U.S. coun. Internat. Banking Exec. Com., U.S. del. to Uncitral Working Group on Internat. Payments; former chief U.S. del. to tech. com. 168 Internat. Standards Orgn. Mem. Soc. Worldwide Fin. Telecom. (bd. dirs. 1978-92, dep. chmn 1989-92). Avocations: numismatist; collecting Hummel figurines and plates. Office: Natwest Svcs Inc PO Box 5600 Scranton PA 18505-5600

NEWMAN, SARAH WINANS, neuroanatomist, educator; b. Hannibal, Mo., Apr. 23, 1941; d. Edwin Christian and Marian (Aldrich) Schilling; m. Richard Mark Newman, June 11, 1981 (dec. 1987). BA in Zoology, Cornell U., 1963, PhD in Anatomy, 1969. Instr. anatomy Downstate Med. Ctr.-SUNY, Bklyn., 1968-70; asst. prof. anatomy U. Mich., Ann Arbor, 1970-75, assoc. prof. anatomy, 1975-83, prof. anatomy, 1983—; acting chmn. anatomy, 1983-86, assoc. v.p. for rsch., 1991-94; Javits neurosci. investigator NIH, 1988-95. Co-author: Essentials of Clinical Neuroanatomy and Neurophysiology, 8th edit., 1992; contbr. articles to profl. jours. Mem. AAAS, Soc. for Neurosci. (chpt. pres. 1984-86), Mich. Soc. Fellows, Sigma Club, Sigma Xi. Office: U Mich Med Sci II Dept Anatomy and Cell Bio Ann Arbor MI 48109-0616

NEWMAN, SASHA MARY, art historian, curator; b. New Haven, Sept. 4, 1955; s. Harry Rudolph and Lillian Estelle (Lear) N.; m. Mark Benjamin DuBois, Aug. 23, 1986. Student, Conn. Coll., 1973-74; BA, Tufts U., 1978; MA, NYU, 1981, MPhil, 1983. Curatorial asst., assoc. curator The Phillips Collection, Nat. Gallery Art, Washington, 1978-85, Kress fellow CASVA, 1986-87; Seymour A Knox Jr. curator European and contemporary art Yale U. Art Gallery, New Haven, 1987—; cons., contbr. Met. Mus. Art, N.Y.C., 1987-89; Meyer Shapiro prof. The Studio Sch., N.Y.C., 1989—. Author: Arthur Dove and Duncan Phillips, 1981; editor, author: Pierre Bonnard: The Late Workks, 1984, Felix Vallotton, 1991; contbg. author: Pierre Bonnard: the Graphic Work, 1989; also articles. Robert Goldwater fellow Inst. Fine Arts, 1981, Theodore Rousseeau fellow Met. Mus., 1982-84, Samuel Kress fellow Nat. Gallery Art, 1984-86. Democrat. Avocation: competitive equestrian sports (dressage). Office: Yale U Art Gallery 201 York St New Haven CT 06511-4803

NEWMAN, SCOTT DAVID, lawyer; b. N.Y.C., Nov. 5, 1947; s. Edwin Stanley and Eveline Ada (Lipp) N.; m. Judy Lynn Monchik, June 24, 1972; 1 child, Eric. B.A. magna cum laude, Yale U., 1969; J.D., Harvard U., 1973, M.B.A., 1973; LL.M. in Taxation, NYU, 1977. Bar: N.Y. 1974, U.S. Dist. Ct. (so. and ea. dists.) N.Y. 1975, U.S. Ct. Appeals (2d cir.) 1975, U.S. Ct. Claims 1976, U.S. Tax Ct. 1979. Assoc. Dewey, Ballantine, Bushby, Palmer & Wood, N.Y.C., 1973-76, Stroock & Stroock & Lavan, N.Y.C., 1976-78; assoc., ptnr. Zimet, Haines, Moss & Friedman, N.Y.C., 1978-81; tax counsel Phibro-Salomon Inc., N.Y.C., 1981-84; ptnr. Baer, Marks & Upham, N.Y.C., 1984-87; ptnr. Wiener, Zuckerbrot, Weiss & Newman, N.Y.C., 1987-90; ptnr. Whitman & Ransom, N.Y.C., 1990—. Co-author tape cassettes: New Tax Reform Act of 1976, Tax Reform' '78, 1978. Tax Reform Act of 1984, 1986, Tax Reform Act of 1986, 1986; contbr. article to profl. jour. Mem. Phi Beta Kappa. Home: 21 Kipp St Chappaqua NY 10514-2518 Office: Whitman & Ransom 200 Park Ave New York NY 10166-0001

NEWMAN, SHELDON OSCAR, computer company executive; b. N.Y.C., June 25, 1923; s. Morris and Anna (Schlanger) N.; m. Miriam Jasphy, July 30, 1950; children: Barry Marc, Amy Stacy, Andrew Eric. BS in Elec. Engring., CUNY, 1944. Project engr. NASA, Sunnyvale, Calif., 1946-47; gen. mgr. info. and communications div. Sperry Corp., Gt. Neck, N.Y., 1947-67; chmn. bd., chief exec. officer Algorex Corp., Hauppauge, N.Y., 1968-93. Chmn. bd. trustees Hosp. for Joint Diseases, Orthopaedic Inst., N.Y.C.; trustee NYU Med. Ctr.; bd. dirs. HJD Rsch. and Devel. Found., Sjogrens Syndrome Found., Woodbridge Assn., Boca Raton, Fla.; pres. Pine Lake Park Coop. Assn., Peekskill, N.Y. Patentee in field. Lt. (j.g.), USN, 1944-46. Recipient Disting. Trustee award United Hosp. Fund, 1995. Mem. IEEE (sr.), Archaeol. Inst. Am. (pres.), L.I. Soc., Masons, Tau Beta Pi, Eta Kappa Nu.

NEWMAN, SLATER EDMUND, psychologist, educator; b. Boston, Sept. 8, 1924; s. Max and Gertrude (Raphael) N.; m. Corrine Lois Silfen, June 18, 1950 (div. 1968); children—Kurt Douglas, Donald Mark, Eric Bruce; m. Patricia Ellen Christopher Thomas, July 2, 1969; 1 stepchild, Arthur C. Thomas III. B.S., U. Pa., 1947; M.A., Boston U., 1948; Ph.D., Northwestern U., 1951. Research psychologist U.S. Air Force, 1951-57; mem. faculty N.C. State U., Raleigh, 1957—; now prof. psychology N.C. State U.; vis. fgn. mem. Exptl. Psychology Soc. U.K., 1973-74, 82-83, 90. Contbr. chpts. to books, articles to profl. publs. Bd. dirs. ACLU, 1992—, mem. biennial conf. com., 1994—, mem. task force internat. human rights, 1994—; pres. N.C. Civil Liberties Union, 1980-82, exec. com., 1986-87, bd. dirs., 1969-73, 76-82, 84-90, 91—; pres. Wake County chpt. ACLU, 1969-72, 84-86, bd. dirs., 1969-73, 76-82, 84-90, 91—; chair com. on Internat. Human Rights, 1988—; mem. steering com. ACLU-Affiliate Leadership NEtwork, 1991—; mem. Mayor's Com. UN Week, Raleigh, 1986—; active Amnesty Internat.; coord. Com. to Reverse Arms Race, 1982—; mem. steerong com. North Carolinians Against Apartheid, 1985-87; mem. Wake County com. bicentennial U.S. Constitution, 1987-89; co-chair N.C. Com. for Celebration of Human Rights, 1989—. Served to 2d lt. USAF, 1943-46, 52-53. USPHS spl. rsch. fellow U. Calif.-Berkeley, 1965-66; U. London hon. rsch. fellow, 1973-74, 82-83, 90. Fellow AAAS, Am. Psychol. Assn., Am. Psychol. Soc.; mem. NAAPC, Psychonomic Soc., UN Assn. (bd. dirs. Wake County chpt. 1991—) People for Am. Way, Southeastern Psychol. Assn., Soc. Soc. Philosophy and Psychology, Cognitive Sci. Soc., Soc. Rsch. in Child Devel., Southeastern Workers in Memory (founder), N.C. Cognition Group (founder), Ea. Psychol. Assn., AAUP (pres. N.C. State U. chpt. 1968-69), Carolinas Conf. for Undergrad. Rsch. in Psychology (co-founder 1976), Sigma Xi, Psi Chi (v.p. southeastern region 1990-94, mem. nat. coun.). Home: 315 Shepherd St Raleigh NC 27607-4031 Office: Dept Psychology NC State U Raleigh NC 27695-7801

NEWMAN, STANLEY RAY, oil refining company executive; b. Milo, Idaho, Mar. 5, 1923; s. Franklin Hughes and Ethel Amelda (Crowley) N.; student Tex. A&M U, 1944-45; B.S., U. Utah, 1947, Ph.D., 1952. m. Rosa Klein, May 27, 1961 (div. Mar. 1980); children: Trudy Lynn, Susan Louise, Karen Elizabeth, Paul Daniel, Phillip John; m. Madelyn Wycherly, Jan. 10, 1991; children: Heidi, Heather, Amy. With Texaco Res. Ctr., Beacon, N.Y., 1951-82, technologist, 1973-77, sr. technologist research mfg.-fuels, 1977-82, profl. cons. on fuels and chems., 1983—. Chmn., Planning Bd., Village of Fishkill, N.Y., 1973- 77; village trustee, 1990-92; mem. Dutchess County Solid Waste Mgmt. Bd., 1974-76. With inf. Signal Corps U.S Army, 1944-46. Mem. AAAS, N.Y. Acad. Sci., Dutchess County Geneal. Soc. (pres. 1981-87, exec. v.p. 1987-88), N.Y. Fruit Testing Assn., Sigma Xi (pres. Texaco Res. Ctr. br. 1980-81). Republican. Mormon. Patentee in field. Home: 285 Plantation Cir Idaho Falls ID 83404-7990

NEWMAN, STEPHEN ALEXANDER, chemical engineer, thermodynamicist; b. Auburn, N.Y., Apr. 12, 1938; s. Solomon and Anna (Reich) N.; m. Mary Ellen Lassow, July 26, 1964; children: Sharon Rose, Lori Suzanne. BSChemE, Rensselaer Poly. Inst., 1960; MSChemE, MIT, 1962; PhD, Rutgers U., 1976. Registered profl. engr., N.J. Rsch. engr. M.W. Kellogg Co., Piscataway, N.J., 1962-67; tech. mgr. Foster Wheeler Energy Corp., Clinton, N.J., 1967—; frequent speaker nat. and internat. sci. meetings; organizer, conf./symposium chmn. Nat. Thermodynamics Conf., 1978, World Congress Chem. Engring., Montreal, 1981, Co-Data Congress, Jerusalem, 1984; panel NAS, 1980-82; cons. Nat. Bur. Standards, Washington, 1979; chmn. various project coms. U.S. Dept. Energy, 1977-84. Editor: Thermodynamics of Aqueous Systems with Industrial Applications, 1980, Chemical Engineering Thermodynamics 1983, Shale Oil Upgrading and Refining, 1983, Acid and Sour Gas Treating Processes, 1985; book and article reviewer Chem. Engring. mag., Gulf Publs., 1980—; contbr. numerous articles to profl. jours. Pres. Mens' Club Temple Israel, Union, N.J., 1980-81. AEC fellow, 1961-62; grantee NSF, 1978, 84. Fellow AIChE (chmn. nat. rsch. com. 1984-85, co-founder Design Inst. Phys. Property Data 1977, vice chmn. 1979-85, award 1989); mem. Am. Petroleum Inst. (chair contractors com. on tech. data 1978—), Gas Processors Assn. (project monitor 1976-85, tech. com.). Am. Assn. Engring. Socs. Jewish. Home: 941 Douglas Ter Union NJ 07083-6523 Office: Foster Wheeler Energy Corp Perryville Corp Park Clinton NJ 08809

NEWMAN, STEPHEN MICHAEL, lawyer; b. Buffalo, Jan. 12, 1945; s. Howard A. and Mildred (Ballow) N.; m. Gayle Mallon, May 24, 1969; children: Holly, Deborah. AB, Princeton U., 1966; JD, U. Mich., 1969. Bar: N.Y. 1969, Fla. 1976. Assoc. Hodgson, Russ, Andrews, Woods & Goodyear, Buffalo, 1969-73, ptnr., 1973—; lectr. various seminars, confs., profl. groups throughout the U.S. Bd. dirs. Leukemia Soc., United Jewish Fedn. Buffalo Inc., Jewish Ctr. Greater Buffalo Inc., Temple Beth Zion; bd. dirs., chpt. chmn., exec. com. Am. Jewish Com., Buffalo chpt.; active Vol. Action Ctr. United Way of Buffalo and Erie County. Fellow Am. Coll. Trusts and Estates Coun., mem. ABA (personal svc. corps. com. tax sect.), N.Y. State Bar Assn. (exec. com. trusts and estates law sect.), Princeton Club of Western N.Y. (sch. com.). Office: Hodgson Russ Andrews Woods & Goodyear 1 Montana Ave Ste 1800 Buffalo NY 14211-1638

NEWMAN, STEVEN HARVEY, insurance company executive; b. Bklyn., Apr. 26, 1943; s. Charlotte (Segal) Newman Bart; m. Lenore Blaustein, June 14, 1964; children: Richard, Michael, Stephanie. B.S., Bklyn. Coll., 1963. Actuarial asst. Royal Globe Ins. Co., N.Y.C., 1963-65; asst. sec. Ins. Rating Bd., N.Y.C., 1965-69; v.p., sr. casualty actuary Am. Internat. Group, N.Y.C., 1969-82; exec. v.p. Home Ins. Co., N.Y.C., 1982-85, also dir. pres., 1985-86; chmn., CEO Underwriters Reinsurance Co., Woodland Hills, Calif., 1987—. Fellow Casualty Actuarial Soc. (pres. 1981-82); mem. Am. Acad. Actuaries, Internat. Actuarial Assn.

NEWMAN, TERRY E., lawyer; b. Chgo., Jan. 15, 1947. BA, Loyola U., Ill., 1969; JD, DePaul U., 1977. Bar: Ill. 1977, U.S. Dist. Ct. (no. dist.) Ill. 1977, D.C. 1991. Asst. states atty. Cook County, 1977-78; ptnr. Katten Muchin & Zavis, Chgo. Sec. bd. trustees City Coll. Chgo., 1989. Mem. ABA, Ill. State Bar, D.C. Bar, Chgo. Bar Assn. (real estate tax sect.). Address: Katten Muchin & Zavis 525 W Monroe St Ste 1600 Chicago IL 60661-3693

NEWMAN, THEODORE ROOSEVELT, JR., judge; b. Birmingham, Ala., July 5, 1934; s. Theodore R. and Ruth L. (Oliver) N. A.B., Brown U., 1955, LL.D., 1980; J.D., Harvard U., 1958. Bar: D.C. 1958, Ala. 1959. Atty. civil rights div. Dept. Justice, Washington, 1961-62; practiced law in Washington, 1962-70; assoc. judge D.C. Superior Ct., 1970-76; judge D.C.Ct. Appeals, 1976-91, chief judge, 1976-84; sr. judge, 1991—; bd. dirs. Nat. Center for State Cts., v.p., 1980-81, pres., 1981-82. Trustee Brown U. With USAF, 1958-61. Fellow Am. Bar Found.; mem. Nat. Bar Assn. (past pres. jud. coun., C. Francis Stradford award 1984, William H. Hastie award 1988).

NEWMAN, THOMAS, composer. Scores include (films) Grandview, U.S.A., 1984, Reckless, 1984, Revenge of the Nerds, 1984, Girls Just Want to Have Fun, 1985, Desperately Seeking Susan, 1985, The Man with One Red Shoe, 1985, Real Genius, 1985, Gung Ho, 1986, Jumpin' Jack flash, 1986, Quicksilver, 1986, Light of Day, 1987, The Lost Boys, 1987, Less Than Zero, 1987, The Great Outdoors, 1988, The Prince of Pennsylvania, 1988, Cookie, 1989, Men Don't Leave, 1990, Naked Tango, 1990, Welcome Home, Roxy Carmichael, 1990, Career Opportunities, 1991, Deceived, 1991, The Rapture, 1991, Fried Green Tomatoes, 1991, The Linguini Incident, 1992, The Player, 1992, Whispers in the Dark, 1992, Scent of a Woman, 1992,

Flesh and Bone, 1993, Josh and S.A.M., 1993, The Favor, 1994, Threesome, 1994, The Shawshank Redemption, 1994 (Academy award nomination best original score 1994), Little Women, 1994 (Academy award nomination best original score 1994), (TV movies) The Seduction of Gina, 1984, Heat Wave, 1991, Those Secrets, 1992, Citizen Cohn, 1992. Office: Gorfaine Schwartz Agency 3301 Barham Blvd Ste 201 Los Angeles CA 90068*

NEWMAN, W. JOE, financial planner, municipal official; b. Phenix City, Ala., Mar. 29, 1948; s. William Harvey and Lena Belle (Mancil) N.; m. M. Jackie Olah, Dec. 15, 1984; children: Sara, Susan. B in Bus. Adminstrn., Mktg. and History, Troy State U., 1970. Prin. W. Joe Newman and Assocs., Chesapeake, Va. Councilman City Chesapeake, Va., 1994—. Republican. Baptist. Office: W Joe Newman & Assocs 528 Forest Rd Chesapeake VA 23322

NEWMAN, WADE DAVIS, trade association executive; b. Chgo., June 23, 1936; s. Clifford and Mary Gwendolyn (Parsons) N.; m. Rita Esmoer, Apr. 30, 1960; children—Erik Parsons, Sherrill Susan. Student, Northwestern U., 1954-57. Sales mgr. Schramm Fiberglass Products, Inc., Chgo., 1958-65; sales promotion mgr. Monogram Models, Inc., Morton Grove, Ill., 1965-68; dir. info. Nat. Sch. Supply & Equipment Assn., Chgo., 1968-72; product mgr. Skillcraft Corp., Chgo., 1972-73; dir. communications and convs. Nat. Bldg. Material Distrbrs. Assn., Chgo., 1973-79; exec. dir. Nat. Assn. Floor Covering Distbrs., Chgo., 1979-91, Steel Plate Fabricators Assn., Des Plaines, Ill., 1992—. Bd. dirs. Edison Park (Ill.) Community Council, 1973—, pres., 1975. Mem. Am. Soc. Assn. Execs. (on. mgmt. cert.), Chgo. Soc. Assn. Execs., Assn. Econ. Coun. Republican. Methodist. Home: 7300 W Ibsen St Chicago IL 60631-1151 Office: Assn 3158 Des Plaines Ave Des Plaines IL 60018-4211

NEWMAN, WILLIAM, real estate executive; b. N.Y.C., July 6, 1926; s. Morris B. and Ida (Singer) N.; m. Anita Eagle, Dec. 12, 1948; children: Steven (dec.), Sharon (dec.), Debra Newman Bernstein. BBA, CCNY, 1947. CPA, N.Y. Ptnr. Morris B. Newman & Co., N.Y.C., 1947-61; pres. New Plan Realty Corp., N.Y.C., 1961-72; chief exec. officer New Plan Realty Trust, N.Y.C., 1972—, also chmn. bd. trustees. Trustee Baruch Coll. Fund. Lt. USNR, 1944-46. Recipient Gold award Wall St. Transcript, 1986, Bronze award, 1989, Silver award, 1990, 91, Outstanding Achievement award Baruch Coll. Alumni Assn., 1991; Baruch Coll. Libr. designated William and Anita Newman Libr. Mem. Nat. Assn. Real Estate Investment Trusts (chmn. 1990-92), Chief Execs. Orgn., Met. Pres.'s Orgn., Aspinal-Curzon Club (London), Brae Burn Country Club, Boca Rio Golf Club, Sky Club. Office: New Plan Realty Trust 1120 Ave Of The Americas New York NY 10036-6700

NEWMAN, WILLIAM BERNARD, JR., railroad executive; b. Providence, Nov. 16, 1950; s. William Bernard and Virginia (Crosby) N.; m. Karen O'Connor, Jan. 11, 1951. B.A., Ohio Wesleyan U., 1972; J.D., George Mason U., Arlington, Va., 1977; attended advanced mgmt. program, Harvard U., 1987. Bar: N.Y. 1977, D.C. 1978. Atty. com. energy Ho. of Reps., Washington, 1978-81; v.p., Washington counsel Consol. Rail Corp. Dept. Govt. Affairs, Washington, 1981—. Mem. ABA, Va. Bar Assn., D.C. Bar Assn. Home: 1009 Priory Pl Mc Lean VA 22101-2134 Office: Consol Rail Corp 990 Lenfant Plz SW Washington DC 20024-2116 also: Consol Rail Corp 6 Penn Center Plz Philadelphia PA 19103-2919

NEWMAN, WILLIAM C., bishop; b. Balt., Aug. 16, 1928. Student, St. Mary Sem., Cath. U., Loyola Coll. Ordained priest Roman Cath. Ch., 1954. Aux. bishop Archdiocese of Balt., 1984—. Address: 5300 N Charles St Baltimore MD 21210-2023 Office: Chancery Office 320 Cathedral St Baltimore MD 21201-4492*

NEWMAN, WILLIAM E., naval officer; b. Chgo., Dec. 27, 1939; s. William Benedict and Florence Vivian (Skorup) N.; m. Judith Ann Morgan; children: Elizabeth, Matthew, David, Joseph. BS, U.S. Naval Acad., 1961; grad., Brit. Empire Test Pilot's Sch., Farnborough, Eng., 1966. Cert. pilot, test pilot, material profl. Commd. ensign USN, 1961, advanced through grades to rear adm., 1990; test pilot Naval Air Test Ctr. NAS, Patuxent River, Md., 1966-69; commanding officer Attack Squadron 195 USS Kitty Hawk NAS, Lemoore, Calif., 1975-77; commanding officer, flight leader The Blue Angels flying team NAS, Pensacola, Fla., 1978-79; comdr. Carrier Air Wing 9 USS Constellation, 1980-81; head air weapons requirements Chief of Naval Ops. Staff Washington, 1981-84; commanding officer USS White Plains Guam, 1984-86; maj. program mgr. Naval Air Systems Command Washington, 1987-89, dir. tactical aircraft programs, 1989-90; comdr. Pacific Missile Test Ctr. USN, Point Mugu, Calif., 1990—. Contbr. articles to profl. jours. Decorated Legion of Merit, D.F.C. Mem. Soc. Exptl. Test Pilots, Assn. Naval Aviation, U.S. Naval Inst., D.C. Masters Swimming Club (pres. 1987-89). Republican. Roman Catholic. Competitive masters swimmer, 1987, 90. Home: 7808 Valleyfield Dr Springfield VA 22153-4118 Office: Pacific Missile Test Ctr Office Of Comdr Point Mugu CA 93042

NEWMAN, WILLIAM LOUIS, geologist; b. Rockford, Ill., July 14, 1920; s. Lyle Winfred and Carrie (Waterman) N.; m. Lucille Mary Hagen, Feb. 21, 1946; children: William Dwight, Christopher. BS, Beloit Coll., 1942; postgrad., Mont. Sch. Mines, 1946, U. Mont., 1948-50. Geologist Anaconda Mining Co., Butte, Mont., 1946-48; geologist U.S. Geol. Survey, 1950-80; uranium exploration U.S. Geol. Survey, Colo. Plateau, 1950-57; staff asst. to asso. dir. U.S. Geol. Survey, 1957-59; chief Metallogenic Map Project, 1959-62; staff asst. Office of Chief Geologist, 1962-63, staff geologist, 1963-67, chief nontech. reports, 1967-78; dep. chief Office Sci. Publs., 1978-80; cons., 1981—. Served with AUS, 1942-46. Recipient Superior Performance awards, 1963, 70; Superior Service award, 1972. Fellow AAAS, Geol. Soc. Am., Soc. Econ. Geologists; mem. Am. Assn. Petroleum Geologists (rep. Capital dist. 1966-68), Geochem. Soc., Fed. Editors Assn., Assn. Earth Sci. Editors, Am. Geol. Inst. (sec.-treas., bd. dirs. 1971-72), Geol. Soc. Washington (program chmn. 1963, sec. 1968-69), Geol. Soc. Grand Junction (Colo.) (sec. 1954), SAR, KC, Sigma Chi. Home and Office: 5624 E Wethersfield Rd Scottsdale AZ 85254-4317

NEWMAN, WILLIAM STEIN, music educator, author, pianist, composer; b. Cleve., Apr. 6, 1912; m. Claire Louise Murray, Dec. 20, 1947; 1 son, Craig William (dec. 1983). B.S., Cleve. Inst. Music, 1933, hon. doctorate, 1986; B.S. in Mus. Edn. (Cleve. Pub. Sch. Music scholar), Western Res. U., 1933, M.A. in Musicology (grad. fellow), 1935, Ph.D., 1939; postgrad. in Europe, Columbia U., 1940. Pvt. tchr. piano and theory, 1926—; fed. relief adminstr. Cleve., 1933-34; asst. choral dir. Western Res. U., 1934-36, instr. undergrad., grad. music courses, summer 1942; music tchr. Wilson Jr. High Sch., Cleve., 1935-37, Collinwood High Sch., 1937-42, Cleve. Music Sch. Settlement, 1937-38; vocal coach, accompanist Juilliard Sch. Music, Chautauqua, summer 1937; lectr. recitalist Juilliard Sch. Music, summer 1948; instr. music history Bennington Coll., summer 1940; instr. grad. courses Columbia Tchrs. Coll., summer 1941, asst. prof., summers 1946-48; asst. to librarian Cleve. Pub. Library System, 1941-42; asst. prof. U. N.C., 1945-46, mem. grad. faculty, 1946—, Carnegie research grantee, 1947, 48, asso. prof. music, chmn. piano instrn., 1949-69, prof., 1955-62, Alumni Disting. prof., 1962—, dir. grad. studies in music, 1966—, prof. emeritus, 1977—; prof. music summers U. Colo., 1956, U. Mont., 1963, U. Oreg., 1965, 69, Harpur Coll., 1966, Northwestern U., 1974, U. Mo., 1978, U. Alta., 1982; piano recitals, lectrs. throughout U.S. Author: The Pianists' Problems, rev. edit, 1956 (London 1952), 1974, 84, Understanding Music, rev. edit, 1961, 67, The Sonata in the Baroque Era, rev. edit, 1966, 72, 83, Sonata in the Classic Era, 1963, 72, 83, The Sonata Since Beethoven, (vols. 1, 2, and 3 of a History of the Sonata Idea, 1969, rev. edit., 1972, 83), Performance Practices in Beethoven's Piano Sonatas, 1971; Beethoven on Beethoven-Playing His Piano Music His Way, 1988; editor: Thirteen Keyboard Sonatas of the 18th and 19th Centuries, 1947, Two-Part Inventions of J.S. Bach, 1957, A Chopin Anthology, 1957, Diabelli Variations, 16 Contemporaries of Beethoven on a Waltz Tune, 1958, Six Keyboard Sonatas from the Classic Era, 1965; Contbg. editor: Piano Quar; antho. Numerous articles to profl. jours., reference works. Served with USAAF, 1943-45. Recipient Ann. Composition award Fortnightly Mus. Club, Cleve., 1935, Disting. Alumnus award Cleve. Inst. Music, 1986; scholarship Concord (Mass.) Sch. Music, 1935; Kenan rsch. leave U. N.C. 1956; Ford Found.-U. N.C. Rsch. grantee, 1958; Ford Found. Teaching grantee WUNC-TV, 1959; Guggenheim fellow musicology, 1960-61; Am. Council Learned Socs. grantee-in-aid, 1960, 61, 66-67, 80-81; sr. fellow NEH

1973; summer seminars, 1975, 79; dir. year-long seminar, 1977-78; fellow Nat. Humanities Ctr., 1983-84. Mem. Music Tchrs. Nat. Assn. (chmn. theory forum 1940, membership chmn. N.C. 1949, chmn. sr. piano com. 1950-53, exec. bd. 1952-56), Am. Musicological Soc. (hon. life, exec. coun. 1955-57, nat. v.p. 1968-69, pres. 1969-70, program chmn. 1958, 66, editor jour. summer 1959), Internat. Musicological Soc. (U.S. rep. on directorium 1971-82), N.C. Music Educators, Music Libr. Assn., Coll. Music Soc. Home: 808 Old Mill Rd Chapel Hill NC 27514-3928

NEWMAN-GORDON, PAULINE, French language and literature educator; b. N.Y.C., Aug. 5, 1925; d. Bernard and Eva Newman; m. Sydney A. Gordon, Sept. 13, 1959 (dec.). BA, Hunter Coll., 1947; MA, Columbia U., 1948; PhD, Sorbonne U., Paris, 1951. Instr. French Wellesley (Mass.) Coll., 1952-53; mem. faculty Stanford (Calif.) U., 1953—, prof. French lit., 1969-93, prof. emerita, 1994—. Author: Marcel Proust, 1953, Eugene Le Roy, 1957, Corbiere, Laforgue and Apollinaire, 1964, Helen of Troy Myth, 1968, (poetry) Mooring to France, (prose poem) Sydney: editor: Dictionary of Ideas in Marcel Proust, 1968, also articles in field; contbr. articles to profl. jours. Scholar Internat. Fund, 1948-51, MLA, 1956-57, AAUW, 1962-63, Am. Philos. Soc., 1970-71, NEH, 1989; elected to Hall of Fame, Alumni Assn. Hunter Coll. of CUNY, 1990. Mem. MLA, Am. Assn. Tchrs. French, Soc. Friends Marcel Proust. Office: Stanford U Dept French and Italian Stanford CA 94305

NEWMARCH, MICHAEL GEORGE, insurance company executive; b. May 19, 1938; m. Audrey Newmarch; children: Tim, Kate, Jo. Student, London U., 1957-63. Econ. intelligence unit Prudential Assurance Co. Ltd., London, 1955-81; CEO Prudential Portfolio Mgrs., London, 1981-90; chmn. PPM Ltd., London, 1990—; group chief exec. Prudential Corp. London, 1990—; chmn. Jackson Nat. Life Ins. Co. 1991—; dir. Assn. Brit. Insurers, London, The Node, London; mem. Brit. Invisibles China Com., City Rsch. Project, Pers. Stds. Lead Body, The Geneva Assn. Avocations: keen salmon and trout fishing, bridge, concert and theatre. Office: Prudential Corp PLC, 142 Holborn Bars, London EC1N 2NH, England

NEWMARK, EMANUEL, ophthalmologist; b. Newark, May 25, 1936; s. Charles Meyer and Bella (Yoskowitz) N.; m. Tina Steinberg, Aug. 25, 1957; children: Karen Beth, Heidi Ellen, Stuart Jeffry. BS in Pharmacy, Rutger's U., 1959; postgrad., Univ. Amsterdam, The Netherlands, 1960-63, Armed Forces Instn. Pathology, Washington, 1971; MD, Duke U., 1966; Lancaster course in ophthalmology, Harvard U., 1967. Diplomate Am. Bd. Ophthalmology. Intern George Washington U. Hosp., Washington, 1966; trainee NIH rsch. Univ. Fla., Gainesville, 1967-70; resident ophthalmology U. Fla. Hosp., 1967-70; instr. dept. ophthalmology Univ. Fla., 1970; cons. ophthalmology Gainesville VA Hosp., 1970; clin. instr. ophthalmology U. Tex. Med. Sch., San Antonio, 1971-72; cons. ophthalmology Kerrville (Tex.) VA Hosp., 1971-72; asst. chief ophthalmology svc. Brooke Army Gen. Hosp., Fort Sam, Tex., 1971-72; assoc. clin. prof. Bascom Palmer Eye Inst., Miami, Fla., 1973—; clin. assst. prof. ophthalmology Bexar County Hosp. and Clinics, San Antonio, 1971-72; teaching faculty Joint Com. Allied Health Pers. Ophthalmology, St. Paul, 1981—; chief ophthalmology svc. JFK Med. Ctr., Atlantis, Fla., 1982; cons. Bascom Palmer Eye Inst., 1983—; dir., sec., treas. Palm Beach Eye Assocs., Atlantis, 1973—; mem. pharm. adv. com. Fla. Dept. Profl. Regulation, 1991; mem. med. adv. bd. Fla. east coast chpt. Nat. Sjorgren's Syndrome Assn., 1990—; bd. dirs. Fla. Eye Injury and Disease Registry. Contbr. chpts. to 4 textbooks, over 12 articles to med. jours. Alumni assoc Rutgers Coll. Pharmacy, 1960—; chmn. reunion 1986 Duke U. Med. Alumni Assn., N.C., 1967—; centurian Davison Club-Duke U. Med. Sch., N.C., 1982—; campaign chmn., nat. vice chmn. Israel Bonds, Palm Beach County, Fla., 1988—; participant cvharitable orgns.; pres. Palm Beach Liturgical Culture Found., 1987-94, trustee, 1987—; v.p., 1994—. Decorated Lion of Judea State of Israel, 1984, recipient Gates of Jerusalem medal, 1991. Fellow ACS, Am. Acad. Ophthalmology (alt. del. coun., Fla. state chmn. ednl. trust), Am. Castrovoieio Cornea Soc.; mem. AMA, Internat. Platform Assn., Assn. for Rsch. in Vision and Ophthalmology, Am. Orgn. for Rehab. Through Tng. Fedn. (nat. exec. com.-campaign cabinet 1987, pres. 1990—, Palm Beach Men's Achievement award 1988, Presdl. award 1989), Fla. Med. Assn. (Ho. Dels. 1993-95), Palm Beach County Ophthal. Soc. (pres. 1984-85), Fla. Soc. Ophthalmology (ethics chmn. 1985-90, pres. 1990-91), Founder's Soc. Duke Univ. Jewish. Avocations: travel, radio broadcasting, teaching. Home: 335 Glenbrook Dr Atlantis FL 33462-1009 Office: Palm Beach Eye Assocs 140 JFK Dr Atlantis FL 33462-1159

NEWMARK, HOWARD, surgeon, entrepreneur; b. Perth Amboy, N.J., Mar. 12, 1944; s. Carl and Ruth (Kestenbaum) N.; m. Mary Ella Adkins, Feb. 19, 1989. BA, Duke U., 1966; MD, Meharry Med. Coll., 1970; MBA, Ohio U., 1988. Diplomate Am. Bd. Abdominal Surgery. Intern Cook County Hosp., Chgo., 1971; resident in surgery Med. Coll. of Ohio, Toledo, 1975; resident in thoracic surgery U. Louisville, 1979; chief exec. officer, pres. Summa Med. Systems, Ashland, Ky., Ironton, Ohio, Huntington, W.Va., 1987—; pvt. practice surgeon Portsmouth, Ohio, 1979, Ashland, 1981-83, Ironton, 1983—, Huntington, 1990; surgeon Lawrence County Med. Ctr., Ironton, Cabell-Huntington Hosp., Huntington. Maj. USAF, 1975-77. Named Eagle Scout Boy Scouts Am. Fellow Am. Soc. Phlebology, Am. Soc. Abdominal Surgeons, Am. Coll. Angiology, Internat. Coll. Angiology, Internat. Coll. Surgeons; mem. AMA, ASPCA, PETA, Am. Thoracic Soc., N.Am. Soc. Pacing and Electrophysiology, Soc. Vascular Tech., Internat. Endovascular Soc., Am. Coll. Chest Physicians, Am. Coll. Physician Execs. (alt. del.), Ohio State Med. Assn. (pres.-elect), Lawrence County Med. Assn., Am. Mgmt. Assn., Pres.'s Assn., Greenpeace, Costeau Soc. Republican. Jewish. Avocations: golf, stamp collecting, art collecting, writing. Office: 207 7th St Ironton OH 45638 also: 1631 Offnere St Portsmouth OH 45662

NEWMARK, LEONARD DANIEL, linguistics educator; b. Attica, Ind., Apr. 8, 1929; s. Max Jacob and Sophie (Glusker) N.; m. Ruth Broessler, Sept. 16, 1951; children: Katya, Mark. AB, U. Chgo., 1947; MA, Ind. U., 1951, PhD, 1955. Instr. English U. Ill., Urbana, 1951; vis. asst. prof. linguistics U. Mich., Ann Arbor, 1961; assoc. prof. English Ohio State U., 1954-62; assoc. prof. linguistics Ind. U., Bloomington, 1962-63; prof. linguistics U. Calif., San Diego, 1963-91, prof. emeritus, 1992—, chmn. dept., 1963-71, 79-85, head program in Am. lang. and culture, 1979-84, rsch. linguist Ctr. for Rsch. in Lang., 1992—. Author: Linguistic History of English, 1963, Spoken Albanian, 1981, Standard Albanian, 1982; inventor memory aid device. Mem. Linguistics Soc. Am., Dictionary Soc. N.Am., Phi Beta Kappa. Home: 2643 St Tropez Pl La Jolla CA 92037-3541 Office: U Calif San Diego La Jolla CA 92093

NEWMARK, MILTON MAXWELL, lawyer; b. Oakland, Calif., Feb. 24, 1916; s. Milton and Mary (Maxwell) N.; m. Marion Irene Johnson, July 31, 1941 (dec.); children—Mari Newmark Anderson, Lucy Newmark Sammons, Grace Newmark Lucini; m. Aylene Pruett Rosselli, June 21, 1991. A.B., U. Calif.-Berkeley, 1936, J.D., 1947. Bar: Calif. 1940, U.S. Supreme Ct. 1944. Ptnr. Milton Newmark, San Francisco, 1941-56; sole practice, 1956-62; sole practice, Lafayette, Calif., 1962-80, Walnut Creek, Calif., 1980—; lectr. bankruptcy State Bar of Calif. Continuing Edn. Program. Served with U.S. Army, 1942-46; to lt. col. USAR. Mem. Alameda County Rep. Cen. Com., 1940-41; pres. Alameda Rep. Assembly, 1950. Mem. Am. Legion, ABA, San Francisco Bar Assn., Contra Costa Bar Assn., Alameda County Bar Assn., Scabbard and Blade. Lodges: Masons, Shriners, Rotary. Home: 609 Terra California # 6 Walnut Creek CA 94595

NEWMEYER, FREDERICK JARET, linguist, educator; b. Phila., Jan. 30, 1944; s. Alvin S. and Fritzie B. (Nisenson) N.; m. Carolyn V. Platt, Apr. 28, 1968 (div. 1974); m. Marilyn M. Goebel, Dec. 25, 1993. BA, U. Rochester, 1965, MA, 1967; PhD, U. Ill., 1969. Asst. prof. linguistics U. Wash., Seattle, 1969-75, assoc. prof., 1975-81, prof., 1981—; chair, 1990—; vis. prof. U. London, 1979, Cornell U., 1981, U. Md., 1982, UCLA, 1982-83, La Trobe U., Australia, 1987. Author: English Aspectual Verbs, 1975, Linguistic Theory in America, 1980, Grammatical Theory, 1983, Politics of Linguistics, 1986; editor: Linguistics: The Cambridge Survey, 1988, Natural Language and Linguistic Theory, 1987—; assoc. editor: Language, 1980-85. NEH fellow, 1973-74. Mem. Linguistic Soc. Am. (sec.-treas. 1989-94). Avocations: gardening. Home: 4621 NE 107th St Seattle WA 98125-6947 Office: Univ of Wash Dept Linguistics Seattle WA 98195

NEWNAM, PHYLLIS SUE See SAND, PHYLLIS SUE NEWNAM

NEWPORT, JOHN PAUL, philosophy of religion educator, former academic administrator; b. Buffalo, Mo., June 16, 1917; s. Marvin Jackson and Mildred (Morrow) N.; m. Eddie Belle Leavell, Nov. 14, 1941; children: Martha Ellen, Frank M., John P. Jr. BA, William Jewell Coll., Liberty, Mo., 1938; ThM, So. Bapt. Theol. Sem., Louisville, 1941, ThD, 1946; PhD, U. Edinburgh, Scotland, 1953; MA, Tex. Christian U., 1968; LittD, William Jewell Coll., 1967. Assoc. prof. Baylor U., 1949-51, New Orleans Bapt. Theol. Sem., 1951-52; prof. Southwestern Bapt. Theol. Sem, Ft. Worth, 1952-76, Rice U., 1976-79; v.p. acad. affairs, provost Southwestern Bapt. Theol. Sem., 1979-90, v.p. emeritus, spl. asst. to pres., 1990—, disting. prof. philosophy of religion, 1990—; vis. prof. Princeton Theol. Sem., 1982. Author: Theology and Contemporary Art Forms, 1971, Demons, Demons, Demons, 1972, Why Christians Fight over the Bible, 1974, Christ and the New Consciousness, 1978, Christianity and Contemporary Art Forms, 1979, Nineteenth Century Devotional Thought, 1981, Paul Tillich, 1984, What Is Christian Doctrine? 1984, The Lion and the Lamb, 1986, Life's Ultimate Questions, 1989; contbr. numerous articles to jours. and mags. Seatlantic fellowship Rockefeller Found., Harvard U. 1958-59. Mem. Am. Acad. Religion (pres. S.W. div. 1967-68), Soc. Bibl. Lit. and Exegesis, Southwestern Philos. Assn., N.Am. Paul Tillich Soc. (dir. 1984-86), Southside of C. (Ft. Worth), Downtown Rotary Cub (Ft. Worth), Ft. Worth Club. Democrat. Avocations: golf, swimming, tennis. Office: Southwestern Bapt Theol Sem PO Box 22000 Fort Worth TX 76122

NEWQUIST, DON, federal agency administrator; b. Stamford, Tex., Aug. 23, 1943. BBA, McMurry U., 1966; postgrad., Tex. Tech U. Farmer Jones County, 1973—; asst. gen. mgr. C. of C., Corpus Christi, Tex., 1969-72; gen. mgr. C. of C., Denver, 1972-74; asst. v.p. Valero Energy Corp., San Antonio, 1974-80, v.p., then sr. v.p., dir. subs. cos., 1980—; commr. U.S. Internat. Trade Commn., Washington, 1988—, chmn., 1991-94. With USN, 1967-69, Vietnam. Mem. South Tex. C. of C. (past pres.). Office: US Intl Trade Commn Ste 704 500 E St SW Washington DC 20436

NEWS, KATHRYN ANNE, editor, educator, writer; b. McPherson County, Kans., Mar. 16, 1934; d. Henry J. and Mary J. (Kauffman) Goering; m. Albert D. Klassen Jr. (div. June 1976); children: Teresa C., Jean A., Eric P., Rachel S.; m. Francis W. News, Mar. 4, 1982. Student, Bethel Coll., 1952-54, Washburn U., 1964-67; BA, Roosevelt U., 1968; MA, Ind. U., 1971. Assoc. editor Holiday mag. Curtis Pub. Co., Indpls., 1973-74, mng. editor, 1974-77; travel page cons. Sat. Evening Post, 1976-77, Country Gentleman, 1976-77; editor Going Places mag. Chilton Publs., Radnor, Pa., 1977-79; mng. editor Réalités mag., 1979-81, Spring mag. Rodale Press, 1981-82; assoc. prof. communications Temple U., Phila., 1982—. Author: Great Escapes: An Executive's Guide to Fine Resorts, 1980. Recipient cert. of merit Atlantic Monthly, 1958; 1st Place Fellowship award Ind. U. Writers Conf., 1970, Golden Basset award, 1973, Chilton Editorial award, 1978. Office: Temple U Dept Journalism Philadelphia PA 19122

NEWSOM, CAROLYN CARDALL, management consultant; b. South Weymouth, Mass., Feb. 27, 1941; d. Alfred James and Bertha Virginia (Roy) Cardall; m. John Harlan Newsom, Feb. 4, 1967; children: John Cardall, James Harlan. AB, Brown U., 1962; MBA, Wharton Sch., 1978; PhD, U. Pa., 1985. Systems engr. IBM, Seattle, 1964-70, Newsom S.E. Services, Seattle, 1970-76; instr. U. Pa. Wharton Sch., Phila., 1978-81; v.p., prin. sr. cons. PA Cons. Group, Princeton, N.J., 1981-88; pres. Newsom Assocs., Yardley, Pa., 1988; ptnr. Bus. Strategy Implementation, Princeton, N.J., 1989-90; pres. Strategy Implementation Solutions, Yardley, Pa., 1990—; examiner N.J. Quality Award, 1993-94. Trustee St. Mary Hosp., Langhorne, Pa., 1986-94; bd. dirs. Chandler Hall. Mem. AAUW, Acad. Mgmt., Am. Mgmt. Assn., Am. Soc. for Quality Control, Am. Bus. Women's Assn., Associated Alumni Brown U. (pres.-elect 1993-95, pres. 1995-97), Quality N.J. Home: Cardalls Corner PO Box F Yardley PA 19067-0403 Office: Strategy Implementation Solutions 1588 Woodside Rd Yardley PA 19067-2611

NEWSOM, DAVID DUNLOP, foreign service officer, educator; b. Richmond, Calif., Jan. 6, 1918; s. Fred Stoddard and Ivy Elizabeth (Dunlop) N.; m. Jean Frances Craig, Nov. 17, 1942; children: John, Daniel, Nancy, David, Catherine. AB, U. Calif., 1938; MS, Columbia U., 1940; LLD, U. Pacific, 1979. Pulitzer traveling scholar, 1940-41; pub. Walnut Creek (Calif.) Courier-Jour., 1946-47; 3d sec., info. officer Am. embassy, Karachi, Pakistan, 1948-50; 2d sec., vice consul Oslo, 1950-51; pub. affairs officer Baghdad, Iraq, 1952-55; officer-in-charge Arabian peninsula affairs Dept. State, Washington, 1955-59; with Nat. War Coll., 1959-60; 1st sec. Am. embassy, London, 1960-62; dep. dir. Office No. African Affairs, Dept. State, Washington, 1962-63; dir. Office No. African Affairs, Dept. State, 1963-65; U.S. ambassador Libya, 1965-69; asst. sec. state for African affairs, 1969-74; U.S. ambassador Indonesia, 1974-77, Philippines, 1977-78; undersec. state of polit. affairs Washington, 1978-81; dir. Inst. Study of Diplomacy, Sch. Fgn. Svc., Georgetown U., 1981-90, Marshall Coyne rsch. prof. diplomacy, 1989-91; Cumming Meml. prof. internat. rels. U. Va., 1991-95; interim dean Sch. Fgn. Svc. Georgetown U., Washington, 1995—; spl. adviser U.S. del. UN Gen. Assembly, 1972, 78, 79, 80. Served to lt. USNR, 1942-46. Recipient Commendable Service award USIS, 1955; Dept. State Meritorious Service award, 1958; Nat. Civil Service League award, 1972; Rockefeller Pub. Service award, 1973. Mem. U.S. Fgn. Svc. Assn., Coun. Fgn. Rels., Cosmos Club. Presbyterian. Home: 4990 Sentinel Dr Apt 102 Bethesda MD 20816

NEWSOM, DOUGLAS ANN JOHNSON, author, journalism educator; b. Dallas, Jan. 16, 1934; d. J. Douglas and R. Grace (Dickson) Johnson; m. L. Mack Newsom, Jr., Oct. 27, 1956 (dec.); children: Michael Douglas, Kevin Jackson, Nancy Elizabeth, William Macklemore; m. Bob J. Carrell, 1993. BJ cum laude, U. Tex., 1954, BFA summa cum laude, 1955, M in Journalism 1956, PhD, 1978. Gen. publicity State Fair Tex., 1955; advt. and promotion Newsom's Women's Wear, 1956-57; publicist Auto Market Show, 1961; lab. instr. radio-tv news-writing course U. Tex., 1961-62; local publicist Tex. Boys Choir, 1964-69, nat. publicist, 1967-69; pub. rels. dir. Gt. S.W. Boat Show Dallas, 1966-72, Family Fun Show, 1970-71, Horace Ainsworth Co., Dallas, 1966-76; pres. Profl. Devel. Cons., Inc. 1976-89; faculty Tex. Christian U., Ft. Worth, 1969—, prof. dept. journalism, thmn. dept., 1979-86, adviser yearbook and mag. 1969-79; dir. ONEOK Inc., diversified energy co., 1980—; Fulbright lectr. in India, 1988. Author: (with Alan Scott) This is PR, 1976, 3d edit., 1984, (with Alan Scott and Judy Van Slyke Turk) 4th edit., 1989, 5th edit., 1992, (with Bob Carrell) Writing for Public Relations Practice, 4th edit., 1994, (with Jim Wollert) Media Writing, 1984, 2d edit., 1988; mem. editorial bd. Pub. Rels. Rev., 1978—. Sec.-treas. Pub. Rels. Found., 1979-80; also trustee; pub. rels. chmn. local Am. Heart Assn., 1973-76, state pub. rels. com. 1974-82, chmn., 1980-82; trustee Inst. for Pub. Rels. Rsch. and Edn., 1985-89; mem. Gas Rsch. Adv. Coun., 1981—; Fellow Pub. Rels. Soc. Am. (chmn. Coll. Fellows 1992, nat. edn. com. 1975, chmn. 1978, nat. faculty adviser, chmn. edn. sect.); mem. Assn. Edn. in Journalism and Mass Communication (pres. pub. rels. div. 1974-75, nat. pres. 1984-85), Women in Communications (nat. conv. treas. 1967, nat. pub. rels. chmn. 1969-71), Tex. Pub. Rels. Assn. (v.p. 1976-84, v.p. 1980-82, pres. 1982-83), Mortar Bd. Alumnae (adviser Tex. Christian U. 1974-75), Phi Kappa Phi, Kappa Tau Alpha, Phi Beta Delta. Episcopalian. Home: 4237 Shannon Dr Fort Worth TX 76116-8043 Office: Tex Christian U Dept Journalism PO Box 32930 Fort Worth TX 76129

NEWSOM, GERALD HIGLEY, astronomy educator; b. Albuquerque, Feb. 11, 1939; s. Carroll Vincent and Frances Jeanne (Higley) N.; m. Ann Catherine Bricker, June 17, 1972; children: Christine Ann, Elizabeth Ann. BA, U. Mich., 1961; MA, Harvard U., 1963, PhD, 1968. Research asst. McMath-Hulbert Obs., Pontiac, Mich., summers 1959, 61; research asst. astronomy dept. U. Mich., Ann Arbor, 1959-61; research asst. Shock Tube Lab. Harvard U. Cambridge, Mass., 1962, 64-68; research asst. dept. physics Imperial Coll., London, 1968-69; asst. prof. astronomy Ohio State U., Columbus, 1969-73, assoc. prof., 1973-82, prof., 1982—, acting chmn. dept. astronomy, 1991-93, vice chmn. dept. astronomy 1993—, acting asst. dean, 1985-86; sr. post-doctoral research asst. Physikalisches Institut, Bonn, Fed. Republic of Germany, 1978. Author: Astronomy, 1976, Exploring the Universe, 1979; contbr. articles to profl. and scholarly jours. Fellow Woodrow Wilson Found., 1961-62, NSF, 1961-63; grantee Noble Found., 1961-64. Mem. Internat. Astron. Union, Am. Astron. Soc. Home: 46 W

Weisheimer Rd Columbus OH 43214-2545 Office: Ohio State U Dept Astronomy 174 W 18th Ave Columbus OH 43210-1106

NEWSOM, JAMES T., lawyer; b. Carrollton, Mo., Oct. 6, 1944; s. Thomas Edward and Hazel Love (Mitchell) N.; m. Sherry Elaine Retzloff, Aug. 9, 1986; stepchildren: Benjamin A. Bawden, Holly K. Bawden. AB, U. Mo. 1966, JD, 1968. Bar: Mo. 1968, U.S. Supreme Ct. 1971. Assoc. Shook, Hardy & Bacon, London and Kansas City, Mo., 1972, ptnr., 1976—. Mem. Mo. Law Rev., 1966-68. Lt. comdr. JAGC, USNR, 1968-72. Mem. ABA, Internat. Bar Assn., Kansas City Met. Bar Assn., Lawyers Assn. Kansas City, U. Mo. Law Sch. Law Soc., Kansas City Club, U. Mo. Jefferson Club, Order of Coif. Avocations: skiing, sailing, car racing. Office: Shook Hardy & Bacon One Kansas City Pl 1200 Main St Ste 3100 Kansas City MO 64105

NEWSOM, MELVIN MAX, retired research company executive; b. El Paso, Tex., Dec. 27, 1931; s. Melvin William and Dorthy Maxine (Kinnison) N.; m. Rose Marie Neill, June 5, 1953; children—Terri Laine, Cherri Leigh, Michael Dirk, Thomas Cody. B.S. in Elec. Engring, Tex. A. and M. U., 1955, M.S. in Elec. Engring. (Tex. Power & Light fellow), 1956. Mem. tech. staff Sandia Lab., Albuquerque, 1956—; sect. supr. Sandia Lab., 1961-64, div. supr., 1964-77, dept. mgr., 1977-92, dir. Ctr. for Applied Def. Tech., 1992-94; cons. Dept. Energy; mem. U.S. group on petroleum tech. Joint U.S./USSR Energy Program; participant several programs Nat. Acad. Engring. Contbr. numerous articles to profl. jours. Pres. coaches council Young Am. Football League, 1975—, mem. bd., 1977—; Dist. chmn. Republican Party, 1960-61, asst., 1963-64. Served with USN, 1951-53. Decorated Am. Spirit Honor medal; Dept. Energy grantee. Mem. Am. Inst. Mining Engrs., Am. Rose Soc., Tau Beta Pi, Etta Kappa Nu. Presbyterian. Club: Coronado (chmn. bd. 1965-66, 69-70, 73-74, 76-79, dir.). Research in improved drilling tech. for petroleum, geothermal and sci. drilling, and on high temperature well logging. Home: 1517 Eastridge Ct NE Albuquerque NM 87112-4507 Office: Dept 9120 PO Box 5800 Albuquerque NM 87185

NEWSOME, GEORGE LANE, JR., education educator; b. Bessemer, Ala., Oct. 5, 1923; s. George Lane and Mary Viola (Mobbs) N.; m. Martha Cornelia Merchant, June 8, 1947; children: George Lane III, Mary Virginia, Elizabeth Ann. BS, U. Ala., 1949, MA, 1950; PhD, Yale, 1956. Asst. prof. edn. U. Bridgeport, 1955-57, assoc. prof., 1957-58; assoc. prof. philosophy edn. U. Ga., 1958-63, prof., head dept., 1963-85, prof. emeritus philosophy edn., 1990—, mem. dept. curriculum and supervision, 1985-90; guest prof. Philosophy Inst., No. Ill. U., U. Pacific, 1970; guest lectr. U. Bridgeport, 1954-55. Author: Philosophical Perspectives, 1961; editor: Philosophy of Education Proces., 1968, (with William T. Blackstone) Education and Ethics, 1969; mem. editorial bd. Ga. Rev., 1973-75, Ednl. Theory, 1976-78; co-editor Jour. R & D in Edn., 1982-85, editor, 1985-89, bd. cons., 1991—. With AUS, 1943-46. Mem. Philosophy of Edn. Soc. (sec.-treas. 1964-66, pres. 1981-82), Southea. Philosophy of Edn. Soc. (sec.-treas. 1961, pres. 1962), U. Ga. Ret. Tchrs. Assn. (v.p. 1994-95), Phi Kappa Phi, Kappa Delta Pi. Home: 145 Tuxedo Rd Athens GA 30606-3133

NEWSOME, JON P., insurance company executive. With Central Life, Des Moines, 1970-75, The Statesman Group, Des Moines, 1975-80; pres. American Life & Casualty Inc., Fargo, N.D., 1980-88, USG Annuity & Life Ins. Co., Des Moines, 1988—. Office: USG Annuity & Life Insur Co 700 Locust St # 201 Des Moines IA 50309-3700

NEWSOME, MARY DE SÉVIGNÉ, psychoanalyst; b. South Bend, Ind., Dec. 23, 1929; d. Herman Lafayette and Irene Aurora (de Sévigné) N. BA, U. Chgo., 1950; MD, U. Ill., 1959. Mem. faculty Inst. Psychoanalysis, Chgo., 1989—; lectr. U. Chgo., 1993—; assoc. prof. psychiatry Rush Med. Coll., Chgo., 1993—. Contbr. articles to sci. jours. incl. The Annual of Psychoanalysis, Psychoanalytic Inquiry and Progress in Self Psychology. Office: Inst Psychoanalysis 180 N Mich Ave Chicago IL 60601

NEWSOME, RANDALL JACKSON, judge; b. Dayton, Ohio, July 13, 1950; s. Harold I. and Sultana S. (Stony) N.; B.A. summa cum laude, Boston U., 1972; J.D., U. Cin., 1975. Bar: Ohio 1975, U.S. Dist. Ct. (so. dist.) Ohio 1977, U.S. Ct. Appeals (6th cir.) 1979, U.S. Supreme Ct. 1981. Law clk. to chief judge U.S. Dist. Ct., So. Dist. Ohio, 1975-77; assoc. Dinsmore & Shohl, Cin., 1978-82; judge U.S. Bankruptcy Ct., So. Dist. Ohio, Cin., 1982-88, No. Dist. Calif., Oakland, 1988—. Faculty mem. Fed. Jud. Ctr., ALI-ABA, 1987—; mem. Nat. Conf. of Bankruptcy Judges, 1983—, mem. bd. govs., 1987-88. Fellow Am. Coll. Bankruptcy; mem. Am. Bankruptcy Inst., Phi Beta Kappa. Democrat. Mem. United Ch. of Christ. Office: US Bankruptcy Ct PO Box 2070 Oakland CA 94604-2070

NEWSOME, WILLIAM ROY, JR., state official; b. Asheville, N.C., July 8, 1934; s. William R. and Mary (Morgan) N.; m. Mary Grace Daniel, Dec. 22, 1958; children: William Daniel, Bo Nathan. Cert., Tollare Folkhögskola, Stockholm, 1959; BS, U. Tenn., 1960; M in Regional Planning, U. N.C., 1962. Planner Tenn. State Planning Commn., Knoxville, 1959-62; city planner Athens (Tenn.) City Govt., 1962-64; campus planner U. Tenn., Knoxville, 1964-66; regional planner Atlanta Regional Planning Commn., 1966-68; planner Pa. State Planning Bd., Harrisburg, 1968-70; spl. advisor Pa. Dept. Community Affairs, Harrisburg, 1970-77; spl. asst. Fed. Emergency Mgmt. Agy., Washington, 1977-81; ptnr. The GNP Firm, Harrisburg, 1982-87; dir. Gov.'s Policy Office, Harrisburg, 1987-88; spl. asst. Pa. Housing Fin. Agy., Harrisburg, 1988—; bd. dirs. Pa. Community Devel. and Fin. Corp., Harrisburg. Bd. dirs. Cen. Pa. Literary Coun., Harrisburg, 1992—; mem. Gov.'s Bldg. Energy Conservation Com., Harrisburg, 1989—. Served with USMC, 1954-57. Mem. Am. Inst. Cert. Planners (charter). Democrat. Home: 112 Maple Rd Harrisburg PA 17109-2730 Office: Pa Housing Fin Agy 2101 N Front St Harrisburg PA 17110-1081

NEWTON, BLAKE TYLER, III, lawyer; b. Richmond, Va., June 21, 1942; s. Blake Tyler Jr. and Anne Rodgers (Walker) N.; m. Belle Carter Blanchard, May 12, 1979; 1 child, Samuel Tyler Blanchard. AB, Coll. William & Mary, 1964; LLB, U. Va., 1967. Assoc. Hall, McNicol, Hamilton & Clark, N.Y.C. 1969-75, ptnr., 1975-92; ptnr. Keck, Mahin & Cate (previously Hall McNicol), N.Y.C., 1992—; bd. dirs. Roothbert Fund, N.Y.C. With U.S. Army, 1967-69, Korea. Mem. ABA, N.Y. Bar Assn., Assn. Bar City N.Y. Office: Keck Mahin & Cate 220 E 42nd St New York NY 10017-5806

NEWTON, CHARLES CHARTIER, architect; b. Albuquerque, Feb. 18, 1933; s. Charles Edward and Aileen (Chartier) N.; m. Patricia Clarke, Sept. 6, 1958; children: Heather Ann, Amy Marie, April Chartier. BArch, Tex. A&M U., 1956; MArch, Cranbrook Acad. of Art, 1957. Lic. architect, Tex. Designer Caudill, Rowlett & Scott, Architects, Bryan, Tex., 1958, Eero Saarinen & Assocs., Birmingham, Mich., 1959-60; head design dept. Harrell & Hamilton, Architects, Dallas, 1960-63; project architect Matthews and Assocs., Bryan, 1963-66; assoc. prof. design, dir. Basic Architecture Program Tex. A&M U., College Station, 1963-68; assoc. prof. Sch. Architecture Rice U., Houston, 1968-70; designer Rapp, Tacket, Fash, Houston, 1968; assoc. Van Ness and Mower, Houston, 1969-70; ptnr. Emerson, Fehr, Newton, Austin, Tex., 1970-74; pres. Chartier Newton & Assocs., Austin, 1975-89; prin., v.p. Jessen, Inc., Austin, 1989-91; prin. Chartier Newton & Assocs., Austin, 1991—. Major projects include Clear Lake Grad. Ctr., 1972 (Houston AIA merit award), additions to Robert Mueller Airport, 1976 (Austin AIA design award), Chartier Newton family residence, 1976 (Austin AIA hon. award), Pecan Sq. Splty. Shopping Ctr. (Austin AIA design citation), restoration Henry Hirshfield House and Cottage, 1980 (Austin AIA design award with others), South Austin Multi-Purpose Ctr., 1980 (Austin AIA design award with others), Cedar St. Ct., 1981 (Austin Heritage Soc. award, Austin AIA design award, Tex. Soc. Architects award 1983, Carl W. Burnett award Austin Devel. Found. 1983), office Moore Trust Group, 1982 (Austin AIA design award), Seay House, 1982 (Austin AIA award), renovation Sutton Hall U. Tex. Austin, 1983 (Tex. Soc. Architects design award with others), Riverbend Bapt. Ch., 1985 (merit award ch. architecture dept. Sun. Sch. Bd. So. Bapt. Conv.), Goldsmith Hall U. Tex. (Tex. Soc. Architects honor award with others 1989), Corps of Cadets Ctr. Tex. A & M U. Pres. Environ. Conservancy Austin and Cen. Tex., 1978-79; vice chmn. Sierra Club Austin, 1973-75; mem. Rollingswood (Tex.) Planning and Zoning Commn., 1980-83; mem. guild bd. Austin History Ctr., 1981-82; sr. warden St. Michael's Episc. Ch., 1990. 1st Lt. USAR, 1957-58. Fellow AIA (pres. Austin chpt. 1981, Loop 361 Bridge Task Force 1978); mem. Tex. Soc. Architects (chmn. educators liaison com. 1989-90). Episcopalian. Rotary

(bd. dirs. Austin Westlake club, 1982-83). Avocations: backpacking, sketching, fishing. Office: Chartier Newton & Assocs 3001 S Lamar Blvd Ste 301 Austin TX 78704

NEWTON, CHRISTOPHER, artistic director. BA with honors, Univ. Leeds; MA, U. Ill.; LLD (hon.), Brock U., U. Guelph. Founder, artistic dir. Theatre Calgary, 1968-71; artistic dir. Vancouver Playhouse, 1971-79, Shaw Festival, 1979—. Dir. Sherlock Holmes; Busman's Honeymoon, The Silver King, Candida, Pointe Valaine, Lulu, Pygmalion, Misalliance, Man and Superman, Don Juan in Hell, Saint Joan, You Never Can Tell, Caesar and Cleopatra, Heartbreak House, Major Barbara, The Millionairess, (opera) Barber of Seville, Madama Butterfly, Die Fledermaus, Patria I, Porgy and Bess, I Due Foscari, Candida, The Silver King; actor (stage) The Marrying of Ann Leete, Charley's Aunt, Peter Pan, Private Lives, Camille, A Flea in Her Ear, Present Laughter; writer (stage plays) Slow Train to St. Ives, You Stay Here, The Rest Come With Me, Trip, The Sound of Distant Thunder, Where Are You When We Need You Simon Fraser. Recipient Queen's Silver Jubilee medal, 1977, Dora award, 1986; Royal Conservatory of Music, fellow (hon.), 1993. Office: Shaw Festival Theatre Found, PO Box 774, Niagara-on-the-Lake, ON Canada L0S 1J0

NEWTON, DON ALLEN, association executive; b. Laurel, Miss., Oct. 19, 1934; s. Wilfred L. and Mary (McMullan) N.; m. Coleta Farrell, Oct. 11, 1958; children: Don Jr., Coleta Midge. AA, Meridian Jr. Coll., 1954; BA in Journalism, U. Ala., 1956; postgrad. bus. mgmt., U. N.C.; postgrad., U. Okla. Asst. mgr. Meridian C. of C., Miss., 1956; mgr. Winston County C. of C., Louisville, Miss., 1960-61; asst. dir. Delta Council Indsl. and Community Devel. Bd., Stoneville, Miss., 1961-62; dir. Delta Coun. Indsl. and Cmty. Devel. Bd., Stoneville, Miss., 1963-70; exec. v.p. Met. Devel. Bd., Birmingham, Ala., 1970-74, Birmingham Area C. of C., 1974-88; pres. Birmingham Area C. of C. Found., Inc., 1988—; pub. Birmingham Mag., Birmingham Bus. Mag. Contbr. articles to profl. jours., newspapers. Appointee Ala. Export Coun.; bd. dirs. Met. Devel. Bd., Birmingham, Ala. Sports Found. Lt. USNR, 1957-60. Named Ala. Mktg. Man of Yr., 1972. Mem. Ala. C. of C. Execs., Econ. Devel. Assn. Ala., Am. C. of C. Execs., U. Ala. Commerce Execs. Soc., Sigma Chi. Home: 2541 Canterbury Rd Birmingham AL 35223-1909 Office: Birmingham Area C of C PO Box 10127 2027 First Ave N Birmingham AL 35202-0127

NEWTON, EARLE WILLIAMS, editor, museum director, library and museum consultant; b. Cortland, N.Y., Apr. 10, 1917; s. Earle Williams Sr. and Anna (Moore) N.; m. Josephine A. Lyon, June 20, 1938; children: Earle W. III, Antoinette Lyon. AB magna cum laude, Amherst Coll., 1938; MA, Columbia U., 1939, postgrad., 1939-40, PhD, 1974; diploma in Mus. Adminstrn., Bristol U., Eng., 1956. Dir. hist. research Webster Pub. Co., St. Louis, 1939-41; dir. Vt. Hist. Soc., Montpelier, 1942-50, Old Sturbridge Village, 1950-54, Inst. on Hist. and Archival Mgmt. Radcliffe-Harvard U., 1954-55; founder, editor Vt. Life Mag., 1946-50; founder, editor Am. Heritage, 1949-54, cons. editor, 1954-55; sr. rsch. scholar U. London, 1955-56; lectr. U. Uppsala, Sweden, 1956. Author: Before Pearl Harbor, 1942, The Vermont Story, 1949; editor: Growth of Vermont, 1946-50, Old Cities of the New World, 1967, In Search of Gulf Coast History, 1970, Historic Architecture of Pensacola, 1970, Spain and Her Rivals, 1971; mem. editorial bd. Art in America, 1953-56. Dir. Pa. Bur. Museums and Historic Properties, 1956-59, Mus. Art, Sci. and Industry, Bridgeport, Conn., 1959-62; exec. dir. St. Augustine Hist. and Restoration Commn., 1960-68; exec. dir. Historic St. Augustine Pres. Bd., 1989-91; dir.-gen. Nat. Quadricentennial Commn., 1962-66; pres. St. Augustine Restoration, Inc., 1965-68, 1989-94; acting dir. libraries Flagier Coll., St. Augustine, Fla., 1967-68; exec. dir. Pensacola Hist. Restoration and Preservation Commn., 1968-72; cons. U. of West Fla., 1968-72; acting chancellor Mark Hopkins Coll., 1972; mem. acad. bd. Walden U., 1973; chmn. New England Conf. Museums, 1953, Northeast Conf. Museums, v.p., 1957-59; mng. editor History News, 1944-49; exec. sec. Am. Assn. State and Local History, 1947-52, sec. Soc. Am. Historians, 1947-50; exec. dir. Richmondtown Restoration, 1976-78; adj. prof. humanities, asst. to pres. Norwich U., 1979-86, mem. bd. fellows, 1986—; dir. Mus. of the Americas, 1986—. Lt. (j.g.) USNR, 1944-46. Decorated comdr. Order of Isabella la Catolica; Order of Merit (Spain); recipient Spl. award of Merit Am. Assn. State and Local History, 1949, editorial awards Am. Inst. Graphic Arts, 1950, 51, 52. Fellow Internat. Inst. Arts and Letters (life); mem. Am. Assn. Museums, Am. Assn. for State and Local History, Am. Hist. Assn., Nat. Trust for Hist. Preservation, Vt. Hist. Soc., Inter-Am. Inst. Fine Arts (pres. 1966-68), British Mus. Assn., Internat. Coun. on Museums, PEN, Newcomen Soc., Rotary, Phi Beta Kappa, Cum Laude Soc., Sigma Delta Chi. Lodge: Rotary. Avocations: English and Am. maps, paintings. Home: 27 Solana Rd Ponte Vedra Beach FL 32082 Office: Mus of Ams Rte 14 Brookfield VT 05036

NEWTON, GEORGE ADDISON, investment banker, lawyer; b. Denver, Apr. 2, 1911; s. George Addison and Gertrude (Manderson) N.; m. Mary Virginia Powell, Sept. 18, 1937; children: George Addison IV, Nancy Ella Newton Bollman, Virginia Powell Newton Jacobi. A.B., U. Colo., 1933; LL.B., Harvard U., 1936. Bar: Ill. 1937, Mo. 1946. Asso. firm Scott, MacLeish & Falk, Chgo., 1936-42; partner G.H. Walker & Co., St. Louis, 1946-62; mng. partner G.H. Walker & Co., 1962-72; chmn. bd. Stifel Nicolaus & Co., Inc., St. Louis, 1972-82, chmn. emeritus, 1982—; chief exec. officer Stifel Nicolaus & Co., Inc., 1974-78. Bd. govs. Greater St. Louis Cmty. Chest; mem. Coun. on Civic Needs; bd. dirs. Goodwill Industries, 1963—, chmn. bd., 1980-82; bd. dirs. U. Colo. Improvement Corp., U. Colo. Found., St. Louis Conservatory Music; dir. devel. fund U. Colo., 1954-55, chmn., 1955; trustee Fontbonne Coll., 1972-80, chmn., 1974-77; trustee Govtl. Rsch. Inst.; trustee Whitfield Sch., 1978—, chmn., 1986-88, 89-90. Served to maj., USAAF, 1942-45. Decorated Order of the Rising Sun, Gold Rays and Rosette, Emperor of Japan, 1991; recipient C. Fobb award U. Colo., 1955, alumni Recognition award, 1958, named to C Club Hall of Fame, 1968, Silver Ann. All Am. award Sports Illustrated, 1957, Norlin award U. Colo., 1968; U. Colo. medal, 1984. Mem. Investment Bankers Assn. Am. (pres. 1961), Nat. Assn. Securities Dealers (gov. 1954-56, vice chmn. 1956), Assn. Stock Exchange Firms (gov. 1969-72), Sales Execs. Assn. (dir. 1955-60), U. Colo. Assn. Alumni (dir. 1965-67), Japan-Am. Soc. St. Louis (dir. 1980—, pres. 1982-85), The Robert Burns Club of St. Louis (pres. 1993), Phi Beta Kappa, Phi Gamma Delta. Episcopalian (treas. diocese of Mo., 1958-69; sr. warden; trustee diocesan investment trust). Clubs: Racquet (St. Louis), Noonday (St. Louis), St. Louis (St. Louis), Bellerive Country (St. Louis); Denver Country; Boulder (Colo.) Country. Home: 6428 Cecil Ave Saint Louis MO 63105-2225 Office: Stifel Nicolaus & Co Inc 500 N Broadway Saint Louis MO 63102-2110 *A reward of one's own accomplishment is realizing how help of others made it possible.*

NEWTON, GEORGE DURFEE, JR., lawyer; b. Rochester, N.Y., Apr. 19, 1931; s. George Durfee and Nora (Dexter) N.; m. Marja Lee Hodson, July 16, 1955; children: Patricia, George Durfee III, Melinda, Deborah. B.A., Harvard U., 1953; LL.B., Yale U., 1958. Bar: Ill. 1958, N.C. 1989. Assoc. Kirkland & Ellis, Chgo., 1958-64; ptnr. Kirkland & Ellis, 1964-85; v.p., dep. gen. counsel RJR Nabisco, Inc., Winston-Salem, N.C., 1985-91, ret., 1991. Author: Firearms and Violence in American Life, 1969. Dir. task force on firearms Nat. Comm. Causes and Prevention of Violence, Washington, 1968-69. Served with CIC, U.S. Army, 1953-55, Korea. Republican. Clubs: Indian Hill, Old Town, Piedmont, Landings. Home: 2818 Lazy Ln Winston Salem NC 27106-5825

NEWTON, JAMES QUIGG, JR., lawyer; b. Denver, 1911; s. James Quigg and Nelle (Singleton) N.; m. Virginia Shafroth, June 6, 1942; children: Nancy, Nelle Grainger, Abby Hornung, Virginia Rice. AB, Yale U., 1933, LLB, 1936, MA (hon.), 1951; DPS (hon.), U. Denver, 1952; LLD, Adams State Coll., 1960, Colo. Coll., 1962, U. Colo., 1975. Bar: Colo. 1938. Legal sec. to W.O. Douglas SEC, 1936-37; practiced in Denver, 1938-42, 46-47; lectr. U. Denver, 1938-41; with Ford Found., N.Y.C., 1955-56; v.p. Ford Found., 1956; pres. U. Colo., 1956-63, Commonwealth Fund, N.Y.C., 1963-75; vice chmn. Commonwealth Fund, 1975-76, dir., 1951-55, 57-78; sr. cons. Henry J. Kaiser Family Found., Menlo Park, Calif., 1978-80; of counsel firm Davis, Graham & Stubbs, 1981—; dir. N.Y. Life Fund, 1972-95, Kaiser Found. Hosps./Health Plan, 1972-80; trustee Dry Dock Savs. Bank; mem. Yale Corp., 1951-55, Western Interstate Com. Higher Edn., 1957-63; mem. nat. adv. mental health coun. NIH, 1964-68; mem. Inst. Medicine, Nat. Acad. Scis., 1972—; VA Spl. Med. Adv. Group, 1968-74; fellow Ctr. for

Advanced Study in Behavioral Scis., 1977-78. Mayor, City and County of Denver, 1947-55; Sec. bd. trustees U. Denver, 1938-42, pres., 1946-47; pub. trustee Nutrition Found.; chmn. bd. YMCA Greater N.Y., 1976-77. Served with USNR, 1942-46. Fellow Acad. Arts and Scis.; mem. Am. Municipal Assn. (pres. 1950), Am. Council Edn. (dir. 1959-62), Am. Arbitration Assn. (dir., exec. com.), Fgn. Bondholders Protective Council (dir. 1975—), Phi Delta Phi, Alpha Delta Phi. Home: 2552 E Alameda Ave Denver CO 80209-3320 Office: Davis Graham & Stubbs 370 17th St Denver CO 80202-5656

NEWTON, JOHN MILTON, acadmeic administrator, psychology educator; b. Schenectady, Feb. 25, 1929; s. Harry Hazleton and Bertha A. (Lehmann) N.; m. Elizabeth Ann Slattery, Sept. 11, 1954; children: Patricia, Peter, Christopher. B.S., Union Coll., Schenectady, 1951; M.A., Ohio State U., 1952, Ph.D., 1955. Lic. psychologist, Nebr. Research psychologist Electric Boat div. Gen. Dynamics Corp., Groton, Conn., 1957-60; mem. faculty U. Nebr., Omaha, 1960—; prof. psychology U. Nebr., 1966—, chmn. dept., 1967-74; dean U. Nebr. (Coll. Arts and Scis.), 1974-94; acting vice chancellor academic affairs U. Nebr., Omaha, 1994—; cons. in field, 1960-72. Author research papers in field. Served to 1st lt. Med. Service Corps, AUS, 1955-57. Mem. Am. Psychol. Assn., Psychonomic Soc., Midwestern Psychol. Assn., Omaha-West Rotary. Home: 5611 Jones St Omaha NE 68106-1232 Office: U Nebr Office Academic Affairs Omaha NE 68182

NEWTON, JOHN T., towel and baby products manufacturing company executive; b. 1916; grad. U. Ga. With Dundee Mills Inc., Griffin, Ga., 1938—, chmn., chief exec. officer, Dundee Mills, Inc., 1986, supt. mill #1, v.p., 1957, pres., 1979, also dir.; v.p., dir. Hartwell Mills; chmn. bd. 1st Nat. Bank Griffin. Office: Dundee Mills Inc 301 Railroad Ave Griffin GA 30223*

NEWTON, JOHN THOMAS, utility company executive; b. Shelbyville, Ky., 1936. BS, Western Ky. U., 1952. With Ky. Pub. Svc. Commn., 1952-53; asst. treas. Commonwealth Water Co., 1953-55; office mgr. Campbell County Water Dist., 1955-58; with Ky. Utilities Co., 1958—, asst. sec., asst. treas., 1964-68, sec., treas., 1968-73, v.p., sec., 1973-78, sr. v.p., 1978-87, chmn., pres., 1987—; chmn., pres. KU Energy Corp., 1988—. Office: Ky Utilities Co 1 Quality St Lexington KY 40507-1428

NEWTON, LISA HAENLEIN, philosophy educator; b. Orange, N.J., Sept. 17, 1939; d. Wallen Joseph and Carol Bigelow (Cypiot) Haenlein; m. Victor Joseph Newton, June 3, 1972; children: Tracey, Kit, Cynthia Perkins, Daniel Perkins, Laura Perkins. Student, Swarthmore Coll., 1957-59; BS in Philosophy with honors, Columbia U., 1962, PhD, 1967. Asst. prof. philosophy Hofstra U., Hempstead, N.Y., 1967-69; asst. prof. philosophy Fairfield U., Conn., 1969-73, assoc. prof., 1973-78, prof., 1978—; dir. program in applied ethics, 1983—; dir. program in environ. studies, 1986—; lectr. in medicine Yale U., 1984—; lectr., cons. in field. Author: Ethics in America: co-author: Watersheds, 1994, Wake-up Calls, 1995; co-editor: Taking Sides: Controversial Issues Business Ethics, 4th edit., 1996; contbr. articles to profl. jours. Mem. exec. bd. Conn. Humanities Council, 1979-83. Mem. Am. Soc. Value Inquiry (past pres.), Am. Philos. Assn., Am. Soc. Polit. and Legal Philosophy, Acad. Mgmt., Am. Soc. Law and Medicine, Soc. Bus. Ethics (past pres.), Phi Beta Kappa. Home: 4042 Congress St Fairfield CT 06430-2041 Office: Fairfield U Dept Philosophy Fairfield CT 06430-7524

NEWTON, RHONWEN LEONARD, writer, microcomputer consultant; b. Lexington, N.C., Nov. 13, 1940; d. Jacob Calvin and Mary Louse (Moffitt) Leonard; children: Blair Armistead, Newton Jones, Allison Page, William Brockenbrough III. AB, Duke U., 1962; MS in Edn., Old Dominion U., 1968. French tchr. Hampton (Va.) Pub. Schs., 1962-65, Va. Beach (Va.) Pub. Schs., 1965-66; instr. foreign lang. various colls. and univs., 1967-75; foreign lang. cons. Portsmouth (Va.) Pub. Schs., 1973-75; dir. The Computer Inst., Inc., Columbia, S.C., 1983; pres., founder The Computer Experience, Inc., Columbia, 1983-88, RN Enterprises, Columbia, 1991—. Author: WordPerfect, 1988, All About Computers, 1989, Microsoft Excel for the Mac, 1989, Introduction to the Mac, 1989, Introduction to DOS, 1989, Introduction to Lotus 1-2-3, 1989, Advanced Lotus 1-2-3, 1989, Introduction to WordPerfect, 1989, Advanced WordPerfect, 1989, Introduction to DisplayWrite 4, 1989, WordPerfect for the Mac, 1989, Introduction to Microsoft Works for the Mac, 1990, Accountant, Inc for the Mac, 1992, Introduction to Filemaker Pro, 1992, Quicken for the MAC, 1993, Quicken for Windows, 1993, WordPerfect for Windows, 1993, Advanced WordPerfect for Windows, 1993, Lotus 1-2-3 for Windows, 1993, Introduction to Quick Books, 1994, Quick Book for Windows, 1994. Mem. Columbia Planning Commn., 1980-87; bd. dirs. United Way Midlands, Columbia, 1983-86; bd. dirs. Assn. Jr. Leagues, N.Y.C., 1980-82; trustee Heathwood Hall Episcopal Sch., Columbia, 1979-85. Republican. Episcopalian. Avocations: golf, walking. Home and Office: 1635 Kathwood Dr Columbia SC 29206-4509

NEWTON, RICHARD AARON, lawyer; b. Lyons, Ga., Jan. 11, 1935; s. Boyd Brymbrick and Emolyn (Mobley) N.; m. Josephine Reid Bogle, Aug. 10, 1957; children: Richard Aaron Jr., Malcolm Reid, Boyd Bogle. AB, Emory U., 1957; LLB, U. Ga., 1961. Bar: Ga. 1961, U.S. Dist. Ct. Ga. (no. dist.) 1964. Assoc. Kilpatrick & Cody, Atlanta, 1961-65; ptnr. Troutman Sanders, Atlanta, 1965—; bd. dirs. SouthTrust Bank Atlanta, chmn., 1984-92. Chmn. bd. trustees Andrew Coll., Cuthbert, Ga., 1987-92. Mem. ABA, Ga. Bar Assn., Atlanta Bar Assn. Republican. Presbyterian. Home: 3661 Hadden Hall Rd NW Atlanta GA 30327-2627 Office: Troutman Sanders 600 Peachtree St NE Atlanta GA 30308-2214

NEWTON, ROBERT EUGENE, mechanical engineering educator; b. St. Louis, Oct. 16, 1917; s. H. Melville and Lily C. (Peterson) N.; m. Dorothy M. Fairbank, Jan. 31, 1942; children: Peggy D. (Mrs. Alan L. Rector), Gary Fairbank. B.S. in Mech. Engring. Washington U., St. Louis, 1938, M.S. 1939; Ph.D., U. Mich. 1951. From asst. applied math. to assoc. prof. Washington U., 1938-51; head structural methods unit Curtiss-Wright Corp., 1941-45; sr. engr. McDonnell Aircraft Corp., 1945; prof. mech. engring. Naval Postgrad. Sch., Monterey, Calif., 1951-86; prof. emeritus Naval Postgrad. Sch., Monterey, 1986—, chmn. dept., 1953-67; vis. prof. U. Wales, Swansea, 1968-69, Universite de Nantes, 1981-82; cons. to industry, 1938—. Author articles, chpt. in book. Trustee Carmel (Calif.) Unified Sch. Dist., 1961-68, pres., 1962-67; Gov. Cmty. Theatre Monterey Peninsula, 1971-73; dir. Cypress Fire Protection Dist., 1993—. Recipient Distinguished Service award St. Louis County Jr. C. of C. Fellow ASME (Jr. award 1940); mem. Am. Soc. Engring. Edn., Soc. for Exptl. Mechanics, Sigma Xi, Tau Beta Pi, Omicron Delta Kappa. Home: 3810 Whitman Cir Carmel CA 93923-8326 Office: Naval Postgrad Sch Monterey CA 93943

NEWTON, V. MILLER, medical psychotherapist, neuropsychologist, writer; b. Tampa, Fla., Sept. 6, 1938; s. Virgil M. Jr. and Louisa (Verri) N.; m. Ruth Ann Klink, Nov. 9, 1957; children: Johanna, Miller, Mark. BA, U. Fla., 1960; MDiv, Princeton Theol. Sem., 1963; postgrad., U. Geneva, Switzerland, 1962; PhD in Med. Anthropology, The Union Inst., 1981, PhD in Clin. Neuropsychology, 1993. Min. dir. Flectcher Pl. Urban Social Ministry, Indpls., 1963-65; coord. staff tng. and community rels. Breckinridge Job Corps Ctr., Ky., 1965-66; asst. prof., program dir. social scis. Webster Coll., St. Louis, 1966-69; assoc. prof., program dir. edn. U. South Fla., Tampa, 1969-73; clk. of the cir. ct. Pasco County, Fla., 1973-76; exec. dir. Fla. Alcohol Coalition, Inc., 1979-80; program and nat. clin. dir. Straight, Inc., St. Petersburg, Fla., 1980-83; dir. KIDS of North Jersey, Inc., 1983—; mem. Sec. Task Force Confidentiality and Client Info. System, Fla. Dept. of Health and Rehab. Svcs., 1979-80; chmn.'s pres's adv. Coun. Webster-1968-69; guest lectr. at the Grad. Inst. of Community Devel. So. Ill. U., 1968-69; cons. Tampa Model Cities Program, 1969-70; chmn. planning com. Nchtr. Corps. Nat. Conf.; faculty mem. Internat. U. for Pres., Munich; co-chmn. Mayor's com. on Pre-sch. Edn., Indpls., 1964-65; speaker in field. Author: Gone Way Done: Teenage Drug-Use is a Disease, 1981, Kids, Drugs, and Sex, 1986, Adolescence: Guiding Youth Through the Perilous Ordeal, 1995; co-author: Not My Kid: A Parent's Guide to Kids and Drugs, 1984; appeared on TV programs NBC Mag., 1982, 1986 NBC, 1986, Drugs: A Plague upon America with Peter Jennings ABC, 1988; contbr. articles to profl. jours. Member drug abuse adv. coun. State of N.J., 1985-91; chmn., bd. dirs. Adjustment Madeira Beach, Fla., 1981—, Alcohol Community Treatment Svcs., Inc., Tampa, 1979; pres. Pasco County Coun.

on Aging, 1977-79; chmn. bd. San Antonio Boys Village, 1975-76; chmn. Pasco County Data Ctr. Bd., 1973-75, Cen. Pasco Urban Planning Commn., 1972-73; adult del. White House Conf. on Youth, 1971; chmn. Nat. Tchr. Corps Field Coun., 1970-71; pres. Christian Inner City Issues, Indpls., 1964-65; mem. Gov. Ashew's Adv. Com., Pasco County, 1974-76. Aldersgate fellow, 1962; recipient Honor award Nat. LWV, 1963, Cert. Appreciation Pinellas County Bd. of County Commrs., 1982; named Outstanding Young Man of Yr., Indpls. Jaycees, 1965, Outstanding Govt. Leader, Dade City Jaycees, Fla. 1973-74. Mem. ACA, APHA, APA, Am. Bd. Med. Psychotherapists, Am. Anthrop. Assn., Nat. Acad. Neuropsychology (assoc.), Soc. Med. Anthropology, Ea. Psychol. Assn., Psychol. Anthropology, Soc. Behavioral Medicine, Soc. Adolescent Medicine (provisional mem.), Phi Delta Theta, Rotary Internat., Order of DeMolay (state master counselor 1957). Democrat. Methodist. Home: 7003 Boulevard E Apt 4-14K Guttenberg NJ 07093-4801 Office: KIDS of North Jersey PO Box 2455 Secaucus NJ 07096-2455

NEWTON, VERNE WESTER, library director; b. Long Beach, Calif., Mar. 21, 1944; s. Robert Thomas and Bette (Wester) N. BA, Am. U., Washington, 1967; PhD candidate, Syracuse U., 1967-69. V.p. MPG Capital Corp., N.Y.C., 1975-77; exec. sec. AID, Washington, 1977-80; writer, internat. cons., 1980-91; dir. Franklin D. Roosevelt Presdl. Libr., Hyde Park, N.Y., 1991—; sr. cons. Nat. Dem. Inst., Washington, 1992; cons. The Creative Factory, Palm Beach, Fla., 1989-91, Ctr. for Nat. Policy, Washington, 1989-91. Author: Cambridge Spies, 1991; writer, producer documentary film Harry Hopkins: At FDR's Side; contbr. articles to profl. jours. Democrat. Congregationalist. Avocations: tennis, squash, rollerblading. Office: Franklin D Roosevelt Libr 511 Albany Post Rd Hyde Park NY 12538

NEWTON, VIRGINIA, archivist, historian, librarian; b. Walters, Okla., Oct. 5, 1938; d. John Walter and Reba Catherine (Mawdsley) N.; m. Gary J. Mounce, Dec. 27, 1963 (div. 1982). Student, Inst. Tecnológico y de Estudios Superiores de Monterrey, Nuevo Leon, Mex., 1957; AA in Bus. Adminstrn., Stephens Coll., 1958; BA in History, Okla. State U., 1960; M of Librarianship, U. Wash., 1963; cert. in libr. sci., U. Tex., 1968, MA in History Archives and Libr. Sci., 1975, PhD in History, Archives and Libr. Sci., 1983. Libr. Inst. Pub. Affairs U. Tex., Austin, 1965-65, libr. Art Libr., 1965-67; coord. Sr. Community Svcs. Program Econ. Opportunities Devel. Corp., San Antonio, 1968-69; archivist, spl. collections libr. Trinity U., San Antonio, 1969-73; spl. collections and reference libr. Pan Am. U., Edinburg, Tex., 1974-77; archivist, records analyst Alaska State Archives and Records Svc., 1983-84, dep. state archivist, 1984-87; state archivist Alaska State Archives & Records Mgmt. Svcs., 1988-93; dir. Columbus Meml. Libr. OAS, Washington, 1993—; archives cons. Ford Found. for Brazilian Archivists Assn. 1976, Soc. for Ibero-Latin Thought, 1980, Project for a Notarial Archives Computerized Guide, 1980; reviewer grant proposal NEH, 1978—; chair Alaska State Hist. Records Adv. Bd., 1988-93, coords. steering com., 1991-93. Author: An Archivists' Guide to the Catholic Church in Mexico, 1979; contbr. articles to profl. publs. founder jail libr. Bexar County Jail, San Antonio; hon. dep. sheriff Bexar County, 1972-75; mem. Dem. party; chair Dems. Abroad in Mex., 1979-81; mem. Dems. Abroad Del. The Dem. Nat. Conv., N.Y., 1980; vice- chair Bill Egan Forum Greater Juneau Dem. Precinct, 1986-88. Recipient Commendation award Gov. of Alaska William Sheffield, 1985, Masonic Scholarship for internat. rels. George Washington U., 1960-61; univ. fellow U. Tex.-Austin, 1982-83, post masters fellow U.S. Dept. Edn.-U. Tex., Austin, 1967-68; scholar Orgn. Am. States, 1980, 81, Fulbright-Hays scholar, 1979, 80, scholar Nat. Def. Fgn. Lang.-U. Tex., Austin, 1978-79, scholar Calif. State Libr., 1962-63. Mem. AAUW (bd. dirs. 1983-86, scholar 1983), Nat. Assn. Govt. Archives and Records Adminstrs. (bd. dirs. 1989-93, chair membership com. 1989-93), Alaska Hist. Soc. (bd. treas. 1988-94), Alaska Libr. Assn., Acad. Cert. Archivists (cert. 1989), Rotary, Phi Kappa Phi. Democrat. Unitarian. Avocations: skiing, dancing, researching, reading, hiking. Home: 2801 Park Center Dr A909 Alexandria VA 22302 Office: Columbus Meml Libr OAS 19th & Constitution Ave NW Washington DC 20006-4499

NEWTON, WAYNE, entertainer, actor, recording artist; b. Norfolk, Va., Apr. 3, 1942; s. Patrick and Evelyn (Smith) N.; m. Elaine Okamura, 1968 (div.); 1 child, Erin; m. Kathleen McCrone, April 9, 1994. L.H.D. (hon.), U. Nev.-Las Vegas, 1981. Owner Tamiment Internat. Resort. Appearances include Sands, Caesar's Palace, Desert Inn, Flamingo and Frontier hotels, Las Vegas, Harrah's Club, Reno and Lake Tahoe, I Love N.Y. Concert, Americana Hotel, N.Y.C., Talk of the Town, London, London Paladium, Grand Ole Oprey House, Nashville, 4th of July, Washington, Astrodome, Houston, Hollywood (Calif.) Bowl, Melodyland, Anaheim, Calif., Circle Star, San Francisco, Sea World, Orlando, Fla., Sherman House, Chgo., Wis. State, Iowa State fairs, Valley Forge Music, Westbury Music fairs, Deauville and Eden Roc hotels, Miami Beach, Carlton Club, Bloomington, Minn., hotels Atlantic City, N.J., before U.S. troops, Beirut; TV appearances on shows of Red, White & Wow, A Christmas Card, miniseries North and South: Book II, 1986; film appearance in 80 Steps to Jonah, 1969, The Adventures of Ford Fairlane, 1990; numerous recs. including Moods and Moments, Greatest Hits; author (with Dick Maurice): Once Before I Go, 1989. A supporter St. John's Indian Mission, Levene, Ariz. Recipient citation as distinguished recording artist and humanitarian, 1971; Freedom Lantern award Commonwealth of Mass., 1979; Entertainer of Yr. award Variety Clubs So. Nev., 1973; Gov.'s award Commonwealth of Mass., 1976; cert. of appreciation Gov. of Nev., 1978; Outstanding Indian Entertainer of Yr. Navajo Nation, 1980; Founders award St. Judes Childrens Hosp.; Humanitarian award AMC Cancer Research Ctr.; Recipient award for Daddy Don't Walk So Fast ASCAP; platinum record for Danke Schoen, also gold album and gold records; also others.; named One of 10 Outstanding Young Men of Am. Nat. Jaycees, 1976, Most Disting. Citizen of Yr. NCCJ. *

NEWTON, WILLIAM ALLEN, JR., pediatric pathologist; b. Traverse City, Mich., May 19, 1923; s. William Allen and Florence Emma (Brown) N.; m. Helen Patricia Goodrich, Apr. 21, 1945; children: Katherine Germain, Elizabeth Gale, William Allen, Nancy Anne. B.Sc. cum laude, Alma (Mich.) Coll., 1943; M.D., U. Mich., 1946. Diplomate: Am. Bd. Pathology, Am. Bd. Pediatrics. Intern Wayne County Gen. Hosp., Detroit, 1947; resident in pediatric pathology/pathology/hematology Children's Hosp. Mich., Detroit, 1948-50; res. in pediatrics Children's Hosp. Phila., 1950; dir. labs. Children's Hosp. Columbus, Ohio, 1952-88, rsch. pathologist, 1989—; mem. faculty Coll. Medicine, Ohio State U., 1952—, prof., 1965—, chief pediatric pathology, 1952-89, chief div. pediatric hematology, 1952-88, prof. emeritus, 1989—; chmn. pathology com. Children's Cancer Study Group, 1965-91; chmn. Pathology Com. Intergroup Rhabdomyosarcoma Study Group; chmn. pathology com. Late Effects Study Group. Contbr. articles to med. jours. Trustee, mem. exec. com. Am. Cancer Soc., Ohio div., 1972-86; mem. adv. com. on childhood cancer Am. Cancer Soc.; chmn. exec. com. Consortium for Cancer Control of Ohio, 1982-86; mem. sci. adv. com. Armed Forces Inst. Pathology. Served to capt. M.C. U.S. Army, 1950-52, brig. gen. Res. ret. Mem. Ohio State Med. Assn. (com. on cancer), Midwest Soc. Pediatric Research (mem. council 1960-63, pres. 1964-65), Soc. Pediatric Research, Am. Pediatric Soc., Pediatric Pathology Club (pres. 1968-69), Am. Soc. Clin. Oncology, Internat. Soc. Pediatric Oncology, Sigma Xi, Phi Sigma Pi. Republican. Baptist. Home: 2500 Harrison Rd Johnstown OH 43031-9540 Office: 700 Childrens Dr Columbus OH 43205-2666

NEWTON-JOHN, OLIVIA, singer, actress; b. Cambridge, Eng., Sept. 26, 1948; d. Brin and Irene (Born) N-J.; m. Matt Lattanzi; 1 child, Chloe. Student pub. schs. Co-owner Koala Blue, 1982—. Singer, actress in Australia, Eng. and U.S., 1965—; actress: (films) Grease, 1978, Xanadu, 1980, Two of a Kind, 1983; albums include: Let me Be There, 1973, If You Love Me Let Me Know, 1974, Long Live Love, 1974, First Impressions, 1974, Have You Ever Been Mellow, 1975, Clearly Love, 1975, Come on Over, 1976, Don't Stop Believing, 1976, Making a Good Thing Better, 1977, Greatest Hits, 1977, Totally Hot, 1978, Grease, 1978, Xanadu, 1980 Physical, 1981, Greatest Hits, 1982, (with John Travolta) Two of a Kind 1984, Soul Kiss, 1985, The Rumour, 1988, Warm And Tender, 1989, Back To Basics-The Essential Collection, 1992; TV prodn. In Australia, 1988. Decorated Order Brit. Empire; recipient Acad. Country Music, 1973, Country Music Assn. U.K., 1974-75, Country Music Assn. award, 1974, Grammy award 1973-74, AGVA award, 1974, Billboard Mag. award, 1974-75, People's Choice award 1974, 76, 79, Record World award, 1974-76, 78,

Nat. Assn. Retail Merchandisers/Cashbox, 1974-75, Am. Music award 1974-76, Nat. Juke Box award, 1980. Address: care Bill Sammeth Orgn PO Box 960 Beverly Hills CA 90213-0960*

NEXSEN, JULIAN JACOBS, lawyer; b. Kingstree, S.C., Apr. 14, 1924; s. William Ivey and Elizabeth (Jacobs) N.; m. Mary Elizabeth McIntosh, Jan. 28, 1948; children: Louise Ivey (Mrs. Heyward Harles Bouknight, Jr.), Julian Jacobs Jr. Student, The Citadel, 1941-43; BS magna cum laude, U. S.C., 1948, JD magna cum laude, 1950. Bar: S.C. 1950, U.S. Supreme Ct. 1960. Partner firm Nexsen Pruet Jacobs & Pollard, Columbia, S.C., 1950—. Trustee Richland County Pub. Libr., chmn., 1976-77; trustee Providence Hosp., chmn. 1984-86; trustee Providence Found., Sisters of Charity of st. Augustine Health System; past bd. dirs. Columbia Music Festival Assn. ARC Richland-Lexington counties, Cen. Carolina Community Found.; mem. U.S. C. Law Sch. partnership bd.; elder Presbyterian Ch. trustee Congaree Presbytery, 1967-87, Synod S.C., 1969-74, mem. Trinity Presbytery Coun., 1991—. Served to lt. inf. AUS, 1943-46, ETO; capt., 1950-51, Korea. Decorated Silver Star, Bronze Star with oak leaf cluster. Mem. ABA, S.C. Bar (treas., bd. govs. 1974-79, ho. of dels. 1980-92), Richland County Bar Assn. (pres. 1974-75, Disting. Svc. award 1987), Am. Bar Found., S.C. Bar Found. (pres. 1971-72), S.C. Law Inst. (coun., exec. com. 1986—), Am. Law Inst., Am. Coll. Trust and Estate Counsel (regent 1973-82), Am. Judicature Soc., Forest Lake Country Club, Palmetto Club, Summit Club, Kiwanis (bd. dirs. 1972-74, 77-79), Phi Beta Kappa. Home: 2840 Sheffield Rd Columbia SC 29204-2332 Office: Nexsen Pruet Jacobs & Pollard Drawer 2426 1441 Main St Columbia SC 29201-2848

NEY, EDWARD N., ambassador, advertising and public relations company executive; b. St. Paul, May 26, 1925; s. John Joseph and Marion (Noonan) N.; m. Suzanne Hayes, 1950 (div. 1974); children: Nicholas, Hilary, Michelle; m. Judith I. Lasky, May 24, 1974. B.A. (Lord Jeffrey Amherst scholar 1942), Amherst Coll., 1947. With Young & Rubicam, Inc., N.Y.C., 1951-86; chmn., pres. CEO Young & Rubicam, Inc., 1970-86; chmn. Paine Webber/ Young & Rubicam Ventures, N.Y.C., 1987-89; vice-chmn. Paine Webber, Inc., N.Y.C., 1987-89; amb. to Can., Am. Embassy, Ottawa, Ont.. 1989-92; chmn. bd. advisors Burson-Marsteller, N.Y.C., 1992—; bd. dirs. Ctr. for Comm., 1986—, Am. Barrick Corp., Toronto, Ont., Horsham Corp., Toronto, Mattel Corp., L.A., Power Fin. Corp., Montreal, Que., Can., World Times Pub., Boston. Trustee Amherst Coll., 1979—, Mus. of Broadcasting, 1982—; bd. govs. Fgn. Policy Assn., 1980—; mem. adv. bd. Ctr. for Strategic and Internat. Studies, 1986—, Coun. on Fgn. Rels., 1975—, Lt.(j.g.) USNR, 1943-46. Office: Burson-Marsteller 230 Park Ave South New York NY 10003-1566

NEY, JAMES WALTER EDWARD COLBY, English language educator; b. Nakaru, Kenya, July 28, 1932; came to U.S., 1951; s. Reginald Osborne and Elizabeth Grace Colby (Aikins) N.; m. Joan Marie Allen, June 12, 1954; children: Cheryl Lynn, James Allen Colby, Peter Cameron. AB, Wheaton Coll., 1955, AM, 1957; EdD, U. Mich., 1963. Cons. Dade County (Fla.) schs., 1961-62; mem. Faculty U. Ryukyus, Okinawa, 1962-64; asst. prof. Mich. State U., Hunt Valley, 1964-69; prof. English Ariz. State U., Tempe, 1969—; vis. prof. U. Montreal, 1962, George Peabody Coll., Nashville, 1965, U. Hawaii, 1967, Western N.Mex. U., 1971; pres. Ariz. Bilingual Council, 1973-74; appointed to council on practice The Am. Assn. Nurse Anesthetists, 1976-83. Author: Readings on American Society, 1969, Exploring in English, 1972, Discovery in English, 1972, American English for Japanese Students, 1973, Linguistics, Language Teaching and Composition in the Grade, 1975, Semantic Structures for the Syntax of the Modal Auxiliaries and Complements in English, 1982, Transformational Grammar: Essays for the Left Hand, 1988, American College Life in English Communication, 1991, GMAT Study Guide and Time Saver, 1993, English Proficiency through American Culture, 1994, others. Instr. workshop Community Assn. Inst. Tech. Writing, 1988; cons. TESL and bilingual edn. with Sta. KFYI, 1986-88. Recipient Best Pedagogical Article award Am. Assn. Tchrs. of Spanish and Portuguese and Hispania mag., 1976. Mem. Am. Linguistic Assn., Nat. Council Tchrs. English, Can. Linguistic Assn., Nat. Assn. Fgn. Student Affairs. Home: 13375 N 96th Pl Scottsdale AZ 85260-6302 Office: Ariz State U Dept English College and University Sts Tempe AZ 85287-0302

NEY, ROBERT TERRENCE, lawyer; b. Pensacola, Fla., July 18, 1944; s. Robert Jackson and Maybelle (Carriere) N.; m. Ursula Christa Deutsch, Sept. 17, 1983; children: Ashley Chamberlain, Shaler Brooke Lindsay. BA, Harvard U., 1966; JD, U. Tex., 1969. Bar: Va. 1970, U.S. Ct. Appeals (4th cir.) 1971, U.S. Supreme Ct. 1975. Atty. Bauknight, Prichard, McCandlish & Williams, Fairfax, Va., 1969-71; ptnr. Boothe, Prichard & Dudley, Fairfax, McLean, Va., 1971-87, McGuire Woods Battle & Boothe, McLean, Va., 1987—. Editor, chpt. author: Appellate Practice, 1986, 2d edit., 1992. Mem. Va. Bar Assn. (pres. 1995). Home: Rte 734 Box 206 Philomont VA 22131 Office: McGuire Woods Battle & Boothe 8280 Greensboro Dr Ste 900 Mc Lean VA 22102-3892

NEY, ROBERT W., congressman; b. Wheeling, W. Va., July 5, 1954; m. Candy; children: Bobby, Kayla Marie. BS in Edn., Ohio State U., 1976. Am. Embassy tchr., supr. affiliate school of Shiraz (Iran), 1978; health and edn. program mgr. Ohio Office of Appalachia, 1979; safety dir. City of Bellaire, Ohio, until 1980; mem. Ohio Ho. of Reps., 1980-84, Ohio Senate, 1984-94, 104th Congress from 18th Ohio dist., 1995—; mem. banking and fin. svc. com., mem. vets. affairs com., mem. house oversight com., dep. whip, mem. subcom. on fin. instns. and consumer credit, mem. subcom. on domestic and internat. monetary policy, mem. subcom. on housing/cmty. opportunity. Mem. Kiwanis, Elks, Lions, Sportsmen clubs, NRA. Office: 1605 Longworth HOB Washington DC 20515 also: 3201 Belmont St Rm 504 Bellaire OH 43908*

NEYER, JEROME CHARLES, consulting civil engineer; b. Cin., July 15, 1938; s. Urban Charles and Marie Helen (Hemsteger) N.; m. Judy Ann Drolet, June 17, 1961; children: Janet, Karen. B.C.E., U. Detroit, 1961; M.C.E., U. Wash., 1963. Registered profl. engr. 16 states. Facilities engr. Boeing Co., Seattle, 1961-62; found. engr. Metro Engrs., Seattle, 1962-65; project engr. Hugo N. Helpert Assocs., Detroit, 1965-70; pres. NTH Cons. Ltd., Farmington Hills, Mich., 1970—; adj. prof. U. Detroit, 1973-79. Contbr. articles to profl. jours. Chmn. bldg. appeals bd. City of Farmington Hills, 1983; mem. mineral well adv. bd., Lansing, Mich., 1975, mem. constrn. safety standards bd., 1982. Mem. ASTM, ASCE (br. pres. 1973-74), Engring. Soc. of Detroit, Cons. Engrs. of Mich. (pres. 1981), Mich. Soc. Profl. Engrs. (bd. dirs. 1980), Assn. Engring. Firms Practicing in the Geoscis, (pres. 1991). Roman Catholic. Avocations: golfing; tennis. Home: 37972 Tralee Trl Northville MI 48167-9030 Office: Neyer Tisco & Hindo Ltd 38955 Hills Tech Dr Farmington MI 48331-3434

NEYLON, MARTIN JOSEPH, bishop; b. Buffalo, Feb. 13, 1920; s. Martin Francis and Delia (Breen) N. PhL, Woodstock Coll., 1944, ThL, 1951; MA, Fordham U., 1948. Ordained priest Roman Cath. Ch., 1950. Bishop Roman Cath. Ch., 1970; mem. Soc. of Jesus; tchr. Regis High Sch., N.Y.C., 1952-54; master Jesuit novices Poughkeepsie, N.Y., 1955-67; chaplain Kwajalein Missile Range, Marshall Islands, 1967-68; superior Residence for Jesuit Students, Guam, 1968-70; coadjutor bishop Caroline and Marshall Islands, 1970-80; Vicar apostolic, 1971—; residential bishop New Diocese of Carolines-Marshalls, 1980—. Address: PO Box 250 Chuuk FM 96942

NGAI, SHIH HSUN, physician; b. Wuchang, China, Sept. 15, 1920; came to U.S., 1946, naturalized, 1953; s. Chih F. and Shen (Shih) N.; m. Hsueh-hwa Wang, Nov. 6, 1948; children: Mae, Janet, John. M.B., Nat. Central U. Sch. Medicine, China, 1944. Mem. staff Presbyn. Hosp., N.Y.C. 1949-88; attending anesthesiologist Presbyn. Hosp., 1965-88; faculty Columbia Coll. Phys. and Surg., 1949—, prof. anesthesiology, 1965-88, prof. pharmacology, 1974-88, prof. emeritus, 1988—, chmn. dept. anesthesiology, 1970-73; mem. com. on anesthesia NRC-Nat. Acad. Scis., 1961-70; cons. NIH, 1963-67, 78-82. Author: Manual of Anesthesiology, 1959, 62, Metabolic Effects of Anesthesia, 1962, Highlights of Clinical Anesthesiology, 1971; contbr. to: Physiol. Pharmacology, 1963, Handbook of Physiology, 1964, Modern Trends in Anesthesia, 1966, Advances in Anesthesiology-Muscle Relaxants, 1967, Handbook of Experimental Pharmacology XXX, Modern Inhalation Anesthetics, 1972, Muscle Relaxants, 1975, Enzymes in Anesthesiology, 1978; editor: Anesthesiology, 1967-77. Mem. Am. Physiol. Soc., Am. Soc. Pharmacology and Exptl. Therapeutics, Assn. Univ. Anesthetists, Am. Soc.

Anesthesiologists, Academia Sinica. Home: 281 Edgewood Ave Teaneck NJ 07666-3023

NGUYEN, AN DUC, industrial development, consultant; b. Hai-Hung, Vietnam, Feb. 27, 1930; came to U.S., 1983; s. Giat Duc and Bien Thi (Pham) N.; m. Thuoc Thi Bui, Dec. 21, 1948; children: Tuan, Khoi, Thang, Phuong Nguyen Khanh Nguyen, Long Nguyen Kein Nguyen. BA, U. Hanoi, Vietnam, 1952. Custom officer Directorate of Vietnam Customs, Haiphong, Saigon, Vietnam, 1952-63; dist. mgr. Royal Dutch Shell, Saigon, Vietnam, 1964-75; pres. Windeco World Industrial Devel., Inc., Houston, Hanoi, 1990—. Pres. Lion Internal., Saigon, 1970-71; coord. United Medical Found., 1992. Decorated Economic medal Minister of Econ., Saigon, 1974. Avocations: sports, music, gardening. Office: Windeco Inc 1010 Lamar St Ste 1150 Houston TX 77002-6314

NGUYEN, KING XUAN, language educator; b. Hue, Vietnam, Dec. 20, 1930; came to U.S., 1975; s. Duong Xuan Nguyen and Thi Thi Ton-Nu. BA, U. Saigon, 1960, LLB, 1963; MEd, Boise State U., 1980. Tchr. Boise Sch. Dist., 1975—; lectr. S.E. Asian Studies Summer Inst./U. Wash., 1992-93, SEASSI, U. Wis., 1994—; spl. lectr. Boise State U., 1975-77. Col. Vietnamese Air Force to 1975. Recipient Red Apple Award for Outstanding Svc. to Edn., Boise, 1990. Mem. NEA, Idaho Edn. Assn., Boise Edn. Assn., Consortium Tchrs. Southeast Asian Langs., Assn. of TESOL. Home: 9674 W Pattie Ct Boise ID 83704-2824 Office: Boise Lang Acad 300 Fort St Boise ID 83702-5493

NGUYEN, TAI ANH, minister. Supt. Vietnamese Ministry Dist. of the Christian and Missionary Alliance. Office: 1681 W Broadway Anaheim CA 92802-1113

NGUYEN, TRUYEN THANH, computer and communications company executive; b. Thua-Thien, Vietnam, Apr. 20, 1930; came to U.S., 1962; s. Con Thanh Nguyen and Que Thi Tran; m. Thoa Thi, June 18, 1956; children: Son, Quang, Tu, Ha, Minh, My. BS in Math., Saigon (Vietnam) U., 1960; MA in Econs., Georgetown U., 1966. Asst. mil. attaché Embassy of Vietnam, Washington, 1962-64; computer programmer Drug Fair Co., Alexandria, Va., 1964-66; systems analyst Capital Car Distbr., Inc., Landover, Md., 1966-69; mgr. systems and programming The Hecht Co., Washington, 1969-77; dir. systems devel. J.L. Hudson Co., Detroit, 1977-81; v.p. info. svcs. Carter, Hawley, Hale Stores, Inc., Anaheim, Calif., 1981-87; v.p. mgmt. info. systems Brooks Fashion Stores, Inc., N.Y.C., 1987-91; pres., chief exec. officer Computer, Communications Svcs., Rockville, Md., 1988—; cons. Authorization Systems Inc., Rockville, 1975-88. Chmn. ADRIFT, Mich., 1979; mem. adv. comm. Vietnamese-Am. Buddhist Assn., Calif., 1985. Avocations: swimming, reading, gardening. Home: 260 NE 19th St Gresham OR 97030-2712 Office: Computer Communications Svc 12300 Twinbrook Pky Ste 220 Rockville MD 20852-1606

NGUYEN-TRONG, HOANG, physician, consultant; b. Hue, Republic of Vietnam, Sept. 4, 1936; s. Nguyen-Trong Hiep and Nguyen-Phuoc Ton-nu-Thi Sung. B in Math., Lycée d'Etat Michel Montaigne, Bordeaux, 1956; state diploma of medicine, Sch. Medicine, Paris, 1966, also cert. aeronautical medicine and health and sanitation, 1965, diploma Health and Smoking, 1993. Resident surgeon Compiegne State Hosp., 1963-64, Meaux State Hosp., 1964-66, Lagny State Hosp., 1966; specialist in health and sanitation Paris Sch. Medicine, 1965—; specialist in family planning French Action of Family Planning, Paris, 1968—; practice medicine, Nanterre, France, 1969—; cons. physican various pharm. labs., Paris, 1987; investigator physician WHO regional office for Europe, 1991. Contbr. articles to profl. jours. Active mem. task force on tobacco dependency Biomed. Saints Péres Rsch. Unit, Paris, 1993, AIDS treatment assn. Le Val de Seine, 1993. Recipient World Decoration of Excellence, 1990, Commemorative Medal of Honor, 1990, Internat. Order of Merit, 1990. Mem. French Soc. Aviation and Space Physiology and Medicine (titulary, specialist in aviation medicine), Assn. Nanterre Physicians, Assn. Vietnamese Practitioners in France, Assn. Le Val de Seine, Chambre Syndicale des Medecins des Hauts de Seine, Ordre des Medecins des Hauts de Seine, Les Ex du XIV Shooting Club. Avocations: painting, poetry, classical and modern jazz music, riflery, martial arts. Home: 3 Rue Gazan, 75014 Paris France Office: Cabinet Med Privé, 38 Rue des Fontenelles, 92000 Nanterre France

NIBLEY, ANDREW MATHEWS, editorial executive; b. Maxwell AFB, Ala., May 25, 1951; s. Owen Smoot and Frances Elizabeth (Browder) N.; m. Mary Elizabeth Michael, Nov. 24, 1984; children: Kevin Mathews, Carlyle Gower, Leath Michael. Attended, Montgomery Coll. Rockville, Md., 1970-72, Univ. Md., 1973. Legis. corr. UPI, Hartford, Conn., 1975-78; bur. chief UPI, Concord, N.H., 1979; Treasury corr. UPI, Washington, 1980; Treasury corr. Reuters N.Am., Washington, 1980-82, editor-in-charge, 1982, news editor, 1982-85; news editor Reuters N.Am., N.Y.C., 1985-87; news editor Europe Reuters Holdings, London, 1987-89; editor, America Reuters America Inc., N.Y.C., 1989-94; sr. v.p., news and TV Reuters America Inc., 1993-94; editor, exec. v.p., bd. dirs. Reuters New Media Inc., N.Y.C., 1994—; bd. dirs. Reality Online Techs., Inc., 1994-95, InGenius Inc., 1994—. Mem. Gov.'s Coun. on Alcoholism and Drug Abuse, mem. media subcom., 1991-92; trustee N.J. Ctr. for Family Studies; bd. advisors Grad. Sch. Journalism U. Calif., Berkeley. Recipient Meritorious Service award Nat. Press Club. Mem. Am. Soc. Newspaper Editors (editl. bd. 1992-93), Overseas Press Club (program vice chmn. 1990-93, bd. govs. 1993—), Fgn. Press Assn., Internat. Platform Assn., N.Y. New Media Assn., Montclair Golf Club (Verona, N.J.), Essex Running Club, The Athletic and Swim Club (N.Y.C.). Avocations: golf, tennis, jogging, racquetball, triathlons. Office: Reuters New Media Inc 1700 Broadway New York NY 10019

NIBLEY, ROBERT RICKS, retired lawyer; b. Salt Lake City, Sept. 24, 1913; s. Joel and Teresa (Taylor) N.; m. Lee Allan, Jan. 31, 1945 (dec.); children—Jane, Annette. A.B., U. Utah, 1934; J.D., Loyola U., Los Angeles, 1942. Bar: Calif. bar 1943. Accountant Nat. Parks Airways, Salt Lake City, 1934-37, Western Air Lines, Los Angeles, 1937-40; asst. mgr. market research dept. Lockheed Aircraft Corp., Burbank, Calif., 1940-43; asso. firm Hill, Farrer and Burrill, Los Angeles, 1946-53; partner Hill, Farrer and Burrill, 1953-70, of counsel, 1971-78. Served from ensign to lt. comdr. USNR, 1943-46. Mem. ABA, L.A. Bar Assn., Calif. Club, Phi Delta Phi, Phi Kappa Phi, Phi Delta Theta. Home: 4860 Ambrose Ave Los Angeles CA 90027-1866

NIBLOCK, WILLIAM ROBERT, manufacturing executive; b. Phila., Aug. 15, 1928; s. William and Grace Neary (Rennie) N.; m. Barbara Ann Parsons, Sept. 26, 1956; children: Elizabeth Ann, Christopher Parsons. BSchemE, Drexel U., 1951; MBA, U. Chgo., 1956. Dir. corp. devel. and planning Pitts. Coke and Chem. Co., 1956-68, U.S. Chems., Inc., Pitts., 1966-70; v.p. corp. devel. Courtaulds Coatings, Inc., Louisville, 1970-95; v.p. investments Courtaulds Coatings Inc. (Porter Paint Co.), Louisville, 1995—; bd. dirs. Internat. Paint of Am. Inc., v.p., 1988; chmn., bd. dirs. The Hanseatic Group Inc., Louisville, 1990. Bd. dirs. Ky. Bell. Found., Lexington, 1984—; bd. dirs. Jr. Achievement of Kentuckiana; pres., co-dir. Porter Paint Found. Inc; pres., dir. Porter Paint Found., Inc. Lt. USN, 1952-55. Mem. Wynn-Stay Club, Jefferson Club. Republican. Episcopalian. Avocations: sailing, skiing, coins, computers. Home: 2210 Wynnewood Cir Louisville KY 40222-6342 Office: Courtaulds Coatings Inc 400 S 13th St Louisville KY 40203-1700

NICANDROS, CONSTANTINE STAVROS, oil company executive; b. Port Said, Egypt, Aug. 2, 1933; came to U.S., 1955, naturalized, 1963; s. Stavros Constantine and Helen (Lianakis) N.; m. Tassie Boozalis, May 24, 1959; children: Steve Constantine, Vicky Ellen. Diploma, HEC Ecole des Hautes Etudes Commerciales, 1954; lic. en droit, Law Sch. U. Paris, 1954, doctorate in econ. sci., 1955; MBA, Harvard Coll., 1957. With planning dept. Conoco Inc., Houston, 1957-61; with planning dept. Conoco Inc., N.Y.C., 1961-64, with land acquisition internat. exploration-prodn. dept., 1964-66, dir. planning ea. hemisphere, 1966-71, gen. mgr., then v.p. supply and transp. ea. hemisphere, 1971-74, exec. v.p. ea. hemisphere refining, mktg., supply, transp., 1974-75; exec. v.p. worldwide supply and transp. Conoco Inc., Stamford, Conn., 1975-78; group exec. v.p. petroleum products Conoco Inc., Houston, 1978-83, pres. international ops., 1983-87, pres., CEO, 1987—, also bd. dirs.; vice chmn., bd. dirs. E.I. du Pont de Nemours & Co.; bd. dirs. strategic direction com. E.I. du Pont de Nemours & Co.; bd. dirs. Tex. Commerce Bank, Cooper Industries, Inc., Consolidation Coal Co.; active mem. adv. bd. Tex. Ctr. for Superconductivity, U. Houston, 1989-91. Bd. dirs. Houston Symphony, Greater Houston Partnership, 1989-95, Tex. Gulf Coast affiliate United Way, 1986-91, campaign chmn., 1988; bd. trustees Mus. Fine Arts, Houston, 1987-94, Houston Ballet Found., Baylor Coll. Medicine; chmn. bd. trustees Houston Grand Opera; chmn. Tex. chpt. Am. Com. on French Revolution Bicentennial, 1989. Mem. Am. Petroleum Inst. (bd. dirs.), Tex. Rsch. League (bd. dirs.), The Houston Forum (mem. bd. govs.), Nat. Petroleum Coun. Greek Orthodox. Office: Conoco Inc PO Box 2197 Houston TX 77252-2197

NICASTRO, FRANCIS EFISIO, defense electronics and retailing executive; b. N.Y.C., Apr. 21, 1942; s. Louis and Janet Amalia (Onnis) N.; m. Rosalind Piperno, Nov. 22, 1972; 1 child, Jason. BS in Econs., U. Pa., 1964. Audit analyst ops., coordinator audit and procedures S.H. Kress and Co., N.Y.C., 1967-68; mgr. audit and acctg. Singer Co., N.Y.C., 1968-76, dir. acctg. and budgets, 1976-77, dir. cons. acctg., 1977-79; dir. domestic treasury ops. Singer Co., Stamford, Conn., 1979-80, asst. treas., 1980-86, treas., 1986-89; corp. v.p., treas. Grand Union Co., Wayne, N.J., 1989—. Served to 1st lt. U.S. Army, 1964-66. Republican. Home: 141 Doubling Rd Greenwich CT 06830-4040 Office: The Grand Union Co 201 Willowbrook Blvd Wayne NJ 07470-7025

NICASTRO, NEIL DAVID, business executive, lawyer; b. N.Y.C., Oct. 25, 1956; s. Louis Joseph and Rosalie Laura (Vanson) N.; m. Kimberly Ann Hyland, May 23, 1981; children: Nicholas L., Mark T., Kelly Ann. BA, Kenyon Coll., Gambier, Ohio, 1978; JD, John Marshall Law Sch., 1981. Dir. stockholder rels. WMS Industries, Inc., N.Y.C., v.p., treas., 1986-88, exec. v.p., 1988-90, COO; pres. WMS Industries, Inc., Chgo., 1991—. Office: WMS Industries Inc 3401 N California Ave Chicago IL 60618

NICCOLINI, DREW GEORGE, gastroenterologist; b. Rockville Center, N.Y., July 27, 1945; s. George D. and Elaine A. (Augsbury) N.; m. Martha Dodge, Jan. 3, 1971; children: Alyssa, Rachael, Lesley, Matthew, Adam. BA, Johns Hopkins U., 1967; MD, Tufts U., 1971. Diplomate Am. Bd. Internal Medicine, Am. Bd. Gastroenterology. Intern St. Elizabeth Hosp., Boston, 1971-72, resident, 1972-74, gastrointestinal fellow, 1974-75; gastrointestinal fellow Faulkner Hosp., Boston, 1975-76; clinician Pentucket Med. Assocs., Haverhill, Mass., 1976—; staff physician Hale Hosp., Haverhill, 1976—, Lawrence (Mass.) Gen. Hosp., 1976—; cons. Holy Family Hosp., Methuen, Mass., 1976—; chief medicine Hale Hosp., haverhill, Mass., 1987-88. Capt. U.S. Army, 1971-77. Fellow Am. Coll. Gastroenterology; mem. ACP, AMA, New Eng. Endoscopy Soc., Am. Soc. Gastroent. Endoscopy, Alpha Omega Alpha. Avocations: skiing, tennis. Office: Pentucket Med Assocs PO Box 502 Haverhill MA 01831-0602

NICE, CARTER, conductor, music director; b. Jacksonville, Fla., Apr. 5, 1940; s. Clarence Carter and Elizabeth Jane (Hintermister) N.; m. Jennifer Charlotte Smith, Apr. 4, 1983; children: Danielle, Christian, Olivia. MusB, Eastman Sch. Music, 1962; MusM, Manhattan Sch. Music, 1964. Asst. condr., concert master New Orleans Philharm., 1967-79; condr., music dir. Sacramento Symphony, 1979-92; music dir., conductor Bear Valley Music Fest., 1985—. Office: 200 P St Apt B36 Sacramento CA 95814-6231

NICE, CHARLES MONROE, JR., physician, educator; b. Parsons, Kans., Dec. 21, 1919; s. Charles Monroe and Margaret (McClenahan) N.; m. Mary Ellen Cranmer, Dec. 21, 1940; children: Norma Jane Nice Murphy, Pamela, Deborah, Julianne, Charles Monroe III, Thomas, Mary Ellen, Rebecca. AB, U. Kans., MD, 1943; MSc in Medicine, U. Colo., 1948; PhD, U. Minn., 1956. Intern Grasslands Hosp., 1943-44; resident in radiology U. Minn. Hosp., 1948-50; mem. faculty U. Minn. Hosp., Mpls., 1951-58; prof. radiology Tulane U. Sch. Medicine, New Orleans, 1958—; chmn. dept. Tulane U. Sch. Medicine, 1960-85; mem. staff Charity Hosp., New Orleans, 1958—; mem. tng. com.investigative radiology NIH, 1967-69, mem. subcom. Sickle Cell, heart, lung, blood com., 1982-83; mem. com. on radiology NRC, 1965-67; chmn. tng. adv. com. Bur. Radiol. Health, 1970-72; guest lectr. Congress of Radiology, Japan, Colombian Radiol. Soc.; U.S. counselor Inter Am. Coll. Radiology, 1985-90. Author: Roentgen Diagnois of Abdominal Tumors in Childhood, 1957, Clinical Roentgenology of Collagen Disease, 1966, Differential Diagnosis of Cardiovascular Disease by X-ray, 1966, Cardiovascular Roentgenology; a validated program, 1967, Cerebral Computed Tomography; contbr. articles to profl. jours. Served with AUS, 1944-46, PTO. Fellow Am. Coll. Chest Physicians (bd. gov's 1975-81), Am. Coll. Radiologists. Home: 508 Millaudon St New Orleans LA 70118-3805 Office: 1430 Tulane Ave New Orleans LA 70112-2699

NICEWANDER, DAN LEON, lawyer, rancher; b. Bartlesville, Okla., June 22, 1941; s. Daniel Andrew and Margaret Dorthy (Kloss) N.; m. Andrea Ruth Elkenbaum, Mar. 3, 1967; children: Mary, Patricia. BA with highed honors, U. Tex., 1963; LLB, Columbia U., 1966. Bar: U.S. Dist. Ct. (no. dist.) Tex. 1969. Ptnr. Gardere & Wynne, Dallas, 1966—; speaker various profl. orgns. including State Bar Insts., U. Tex. Mortgage Lending Inst., Dallas Bar Assn. Clinics, Tex. Tech Continuing Edn. Confs., Bank Adminstrn. Insts., other; past instr. comml. law Am. Inst. Banking. Contbr. articles to profl. jours. Mem. lay adv. bd. Perkins Sch. Theology, Dallas, 1987-90. Fellow Tex. Bar Found.; mem. ABA, Tex. Bar Assn. (legal forms com. 1981-84, fin. instns. com. 1987-89), Dallas Bar Assn., Coll. of State Bar Tex., Tex. Assn. Bank Counsel. Republican. Methodist. Avocations: gardening, fishing. Home: 1813 Greenway Dr Plano TX 75075-6462 Office: Gardere & Wynne 1601 Elm St Dallas TX 75201-4701

NICHOL, FRED JOSEPH, federal judge; b. Sioux City, Iowa, Mar. 19, 1912; s. Ralph Edwin and Florence (Young) N.; m. Evelyn Parrish, June 2, 1939; children: Allen H., Janet M. AB., Yankton Coll., 1933; J.D., U. S.D., 1936; LL.D. (hon.), Dakota Wesleyan U., 1975. Bar: S.D. bar 1936. Mem. firm Hitchcock, Nichol & Lasegard, Mitchell, 1938-58; mem. S.D. Ho. of Reps. from, Davison County, 1951-52, 57-58; state's atty. Davison County, 1947-51; circuit judge 4th Jud. Circuit S.D., 1959-65; U.S. dist. judge for S.D., 1965-66; chief judge, 1966-80, sr. judge, 1980—; Mem. exec. com. Legis. Research Council, 1951; S.D. del. Nat. Trial Judges Conv., 1962, 63, 64. Mem. sch. bd. and library bd., Mitchell, 1958-64; del. White House Conf. on Aging, 1961; Sec. S.D. delegation Democratic Nat. Conv., 1956; Mem. corp. bd., also trustee Yankton Coll., from 1954. Served to lt. USNR, World War II. Mem. ABA, Am. Judicature Soc., Phi Delta Phi. Congregationalist (past chmn.). Clubs: Elks, Masonic (32 Shriner, K.T.), Rotarian. Office: US Dist Ct 400 S Phillips Ave Rm 202 Sioux Falls SD 57102-0959

NICHOL, HENRY FERRIS, former government official, environment consultant; b. Charleston, S.C., Jan. 21, 1911; s. A. Ferris and Ella (Humphrey) N.; m. Elizabeth B. Holmes, Apr. 15, 1944; children: Susan (Mrs. William C. Thompson), Elizabeth (Mrs. Robert McC. McConnell III), David, Peter. AB, Davidson Coll., 1933; postgrad., Georgetown U. Law Sch., 1936-37. Clk. HOLC, 1934-37; adminstrv. asst. FSA, 1937-46; fgn. affairs specialist Dept. State, 1946-63; fgn. service officer, 1955-63; conf. attache Geneva, Switzerland, 1952-58; consul Liverpool, Eng., 1958-63; acting prin. officer, 1958-59; sec. U.S. delegations to numerous confs.; adviser U.S. delegations, exec. com. Internat. Refugee Fund, Geneva, 1956-57; asst. dir., asst. to adminstr. Rural Community Devel. Service, U.S. Dept. Agr., 1963-66; staff rep. to Pres.'s Recreation Adv. Council, 1963-66, vice chmn. staff, 1964-66; mem. staff Pres.'s Council on Recreation and Natural Beauty, 1966-69; asst. to asso. adminstr. Soil Conservation Service, 1966-70; environ. cons., 1970—; Liaison officer U.S. Dept. Agr. to White House Conf. Natural Beauty, 1965; sr. warden Am. Ch., Geneva, Switzerland; Eastern rep. Nat. Outdoor Leadership Sch.; chmn. Montgomery County Citizens Adv. Com. on Bikeways and Trails; chmn. Potomac Com. Bikeways and Trails; trustee Potomac Conservation Found., Wilderness Edn. Assn.; v.p. Potomac Appalachian Trail Club; founder Potomac Clean and Green. Served to comdr. USNR, 1942-45. Recipient Pres. Theodore Roosevelt Conservation award Pres. of U.S., 1990, Community Svc. award Potomac Almanac, 1990; named Outstanding Citizen of Yr. Potomac C. of C., 1976. Mem. Explorers Club, Diplomatic and Consular Officers Ret., Am. Fgn. Svc. Assn., Phi Beta Kappa. Episcopalian. Home: 9616 Accord Dr Potomac MD 20854-4304

NICHOL, NORMAN J., manufacturing executive; b. East Cleveland, Ohio, Feb. 12, 1944; s. Norman George and Irene Josephine (Peters) N.; m. Janice E. Nichol, Oct. 19, 1968; children: Gerard, Katherine. B.B.A., Kent State U. Mktg. trainee A.B. Dick Co., Chgo., 1968, sales rep., supr.-spl. markets

mgr., 1971-75, br. mgr. Indpls. and Chgo., 1975-80, dir.-gen. mgr. internat., 1980-82, pres., 1982—; pres. Rycoline Products Co., 1985—, Sun Graphic Inc., Robersol Inc. Served with U.S. Army, 1964-70. Home: 1021 Dover Ct Libertyville IL 60048-3509 Office: Rycoline Products Inc 5540 N Northwest Hwy Chicago IL 60630-1116

NICHOL, VICTOR E., JR., banking executive. CEO Secor Bank. Office: Secor Bank 201 Office Park Dr Birmingham AL 35223-2495

NICHOLAS (RICHARD G. SMISKO), bishop; b. Perth Amboy, N.J., Feb. 23, 1936; s. Andrew and Anna (Totin) S. Grad., Christ the Saviour Sem., Johnstown, Pa., 1959; student, Patriarchal Theol. Acad., Istanbul, Turkey; BA, U. Youngstown, 1961; BTh, U. Pitts. Ordained priest Am. Carpatho-Russian Orthodox Greek Cath. Diocese, 1959. Pastor Sts. Peter and Paul Ch., Windber, 1959-62; prefect of discipline, tchr. Christ the Saviour Sem., Johnstown, 1963-65; pastor Sts. Peter and Paul Ch., Homer City, 1965-71, St. Michael's Ch., Clymer, 1971-72, St. Nicholas Ch., N.Y.C., 1972-78; elevated to archimandrite Am. Carpatho-Russian Orthodox Greek Cath. Diocese, 1976; abbot Monastery of Annunciation, Tuxedo Park, N.Y., 1978-82; elected titular bishop of Amissos, aux. bishop Ukrainian Orthodox Diocese of Ecumenical Patriarchate, 1983; consecrated bishop Am. Carpatho-Russian Orthodox Greek Cath. Diocese, 1985, bishop, 1985—; asst. Christ the Saviour Cathedral, 1963-65; chmn. XIV Diocesan Coun., New Brunswick, N.J., 1985, XV Diocesan Coun., Pitts., 1991. Office: 312 Garfield St Johnstown PA 15906-2122

NICHOLAS, ARTHUR SOTERIOS, manufacturing company executive; b. Grand Rapids, Mich., Mar. 6, 1930; s. Samuel D. and Penelope A. (Kalapodes) N.; m. Bessie Zazanis, Aug. 25, 1957; children: Niki Stephanie, Arthur S., Thomas. B.S. in Chem. Engring, U. Mich., 1953; B.A. in Indsl. Mgmt, Wayne State U., 1957. Registered profl. engr., Mich. Project engr. B.F. Goodrich Co., 1953-54; plant mgr. Cadillac Plastics and Chem. Co., 1954-69; pres., chief exec. officer Leon Chem. and Plastics, Inc., Grand Rapids, 1960-69; with U.S. Industries, Inc., 1969-73, pres., chief operating officer, 1973; now pres. The Antech Group; bd. dirs. ERO Industries Inc., Crellin Internat. Inc., Transco Corp. Judge Jr. Achievement, Chgo. Served with USNR, 1948-49. Recipient Distinguished Alumni award Grand Rapids Jr. Coll., 1970. Mem. Young Pres. Orgn., Soc. Plastic Engrs., Mich. Acad. Sci., Arts and Letters, Chgo. Coun. on Fgn. Rels., Pres.' Assn. Mem. Greek Orthodox Ch. Clubs: Chgo. Athletic Assn. (Chgo.), Executives (Chgo.). Patentee in field. Home: 655 Oak Rd Barrington IL 60010-3135 Office: Ste 1224 135 S La Salle St Chicago IL 60603

NICHOLAS, FAYARD ANTONIO, dancer, actor, entertainer; b. Mobile, Ala., Oct. 20, 1914; s. Ulysses Domonick and Viola (Harden) N.; m. Geraldine Pate (div. 1955); children: Anthony Fayard, Paul Didier; m. Barbara January, Sept. 17, 1967. Pvt. ed. in, high sch. and coll. related courses. Owner, dancer Cotton Club, Phila., from 1932; guest lectr. San Francisco State U., UCLA, U. So. Calif., U. Hawaii. Appeared in films Kid Millions, 1934, The Big Broadcast, 1936, Down Argentine Way, 1940, Tin Pan Alley, 1940, The Great American Broadcast, 1941, Sun Valley Serenade, 1941, Orchestra Wives, 1942, Stormy Weather, 1943, The Pirate, 1948, others; Broadway shows include Ziegfeld Follies, 1936, Babes in Arms, 1937, St. Louis Woman, 1946; actor The Liberation of L.B. Jones, 1970; choreographer Broadway musical Black and Blue (Tony award), 1989; starred in ballet Nutcracker, San Diego Ballet Co., 1990; commd. Japan Satellite Broadcasting Co., 1991; performer maj. TV shows; entertainer (with Bob Hope) troops in Vietnam. Supporter numerous charity events including Danny Thomas-St. Jude Hosp., Jerry Lewis Telethon, Negro Coll. Fund, Drug Abuse, Spl. Concern with the Plights of Homeless. With U.S. Army, 1943-44. Recipient Emmy award, 1965, Bumps Blackwell Life Achievement award, 1980, Ellie award Nat. Film Soc., 1984, City of L.A. award, 1984, resolution, 1991, City of Hope award, 1986, Golden Angel award, 1986, Josephine Baker award, 1986, Ebony Life Achievement award, 1987, Jeanne Golden Halo award, 1988, Tony award, 1989, Lafayette Players West award, 1991, Paul Robeson award Black Am. Cinema Soc., 1992, Dance Mag. award, 1995, numerous others; named to Black Filmmakers Hall of Fame, 1989; with brother Harold honored at White House and Kennedy Ctr., 1991; honored TV Documentary, 1992; honored Lincoln Ctr., N.Y.C., 1993. Mem. Acad. Arts and Sci. (life), Dance Gallery, Friars Club (life), San Fernando Valley Art Coun. Home: 23388 Mulholland Dr Woodland Hills CA 91364-2792

NICHOLAS, LYNN HOLMAN, writer; b. New London, Conn., Nov. 11, 1939; d. William Grizzard Holman and Carol (Ackiss) Wakelin; m. Robert Carter Nicholas III, Dec. 20, 1965; children: William C., R. Carter, Philip H. Student, Radcliffe Coll., 1957-59; diploma, U. Madrid, 1960; BA, Oxford (Eng.) U., 1964. Author: The Rape of Europa, 1994 (Cir. award Nat. Book Critics 1995).

NICHOLAS, RALPH WALLACE, anthropologist, educator; b. Dallas, Nov. 28, 1934; s. Ralph Wendell and Ruth Elizabeth (Oury) N.; m. Marta Ruth Weinstock, June 13, 1963. B.A., Wayne U., 1957; M.A., U. Chgo., 1958, Ph.D., 1962. Asst. prof. to prof. Mich. State U., East Lansing, 1964-71; prof. anthropology U. Chgo., 1971—, chmn. dept., 1981-82, dep. provost, 1982-87, dean of coll., 1987-92, dir. Ctr. Internat. Studies, 1984—; William Rainey Harper prof. of Anthropology and Social Scis., 1992—; pres. Internat. House of Chgo., 1993—; cons. Ford Found., Dhaka, Bangladesh, 1973. Author: (with others) Kinship Bengali Culture, 1977; editor: Jour. Asian Studies, 1975-78. Trustee Am. Inst. Indian Studies, 1974-76, treas., 1993—; trustee Bangladesh Found. Ford Found. fgn. area tng. fellow, India, 1960-61; Sch. Oriental and African Studies research fellow, London, 1962-63; sr. Fulbright fellow, West Bengal, India, 1968-69. Fellow AAAS, Am. Anthrop. Assn., Royal Anthrop. Inst. (Eng.); mem. Assn. Asian Studies, India League of Am. Found. (trustee). Home and Office: Internat House of Chicago 1414 E 59th St Chicago IL 60637

NICHOLAS, ROBERT B., lawyer; b. N.Y.C., June 7, 1944. AB, St. Lawrence U., 1966; JD, Boston U., 1969. Bar: Mass. 1969, Pa. 1971, D.C. 1982. Spl. asst. to Atty. Gen. U.S. Atty. Gen. Office, Pa., 1971-73; dep. atty. gen., 1974-77; counsel toxic substances and environ. health U.S. Pres. Coun. on Environ. Quality, 1977-79; sr. staff mem., 1979-81; chief counsel, staff dir. Subcom. on Investigations and Oversight, Com. on Sci. and Tech., Ho. of Reps., Washington, 1982-85; ptnr. McDermott, Will & Emory, Washington; mem. U.S. Expert Group on Chem. Data Confidentiality OECD, 1978-81; chmn. Superfund-Nat. Contingency Plan Revision Com., 1980-81. Mem. editorial bd. Biotechnology Law Reporter, 1984—. Mem. ABA (mem. natural resources, energy and environ. law sects., vice chair spl. com. on biotechnology 1990—), Fed. Bar Assn. Office: McDermott Will & Emery 1850 K St NW Ste 500 Washington DC 20006-2296

NICHOLAS, ROBERT B., insurance executive; b. 1929; married. BA, Denison U., 1950; MS, Columbia U., 1954. With Mobile Oil Corp., 1956-60; mgr. corp. planning Atlantic Richfield Co., 1960-71; v.p. corp. planning Aetna Casualty & Surety Co., Hartford, Conn., 1971-76, v.p. fin. and planning, 1976-86, sr. v.p. corp. planning and devel., 1986—; 1st lt. U.S. Army, 1951-53. Office: Aetna Casualty & Surety Co 151 Farmington Ave Hartford CT 06156-0001

NICHOLAS, THOMAS ANDREW, artist; b. Middletown, Conn., Sept. 26, 1934; s. Michael and Lena (Sequnzia) N.; m. Gloria R. Spencer, Oct. 11, 1958; 1 son, Thomas Michael. Student of Ernst Lohrmann, 1949-53; scholarship student, Sch. Visual Arts, N.Y.C., 1953-55. Instr. Famous Artists Schs., Inc., Westport, Conn., 1958-60; instr. painting, Rockport, Mass., 1963-66. Commd. by Franklin Mint Gallery Am. Art to produce lithographs of Am. coastline, 1977; one-man shows include Grand Cen. Galleries, N.Y.C., 1962, 64, 66, 68, 70, 78, I.F.A. Galleries, Washington, 1964-92, A. Huney Gallery, San Diego, 1980, 82;, Carolyn Hill Gallery, Soho, N.Y.C., 1988-89, 3 person show, 1992; represented in permanent collections Butler Inst. Am. Art, Youngstown, Ohio, Ga. Mus., Athens, New Britain (Conn.) Art Mus., U. Utah, Adelphi U., Greenshields Mus., Montreal, Can., Farnsworth Mus., Rockland, Maine, Springfield (Mo.) Art Mus., Ranger Collection at NAD (2 works); author articles; recipient numerous awards 1957—, including, Emile Lowe award watercolor Am. Watercolor Soc. 1961, watercolor prize 1964, Gold medal honor 1969, Clare Stout award 1971, Mary S. Litt award 1972, medal honor for watercolor Knickerbocker

Artists 1962, Purchase award watercolor Butler Inst. Am. Art 1962, Henry Ward Ranger Fund purchase watercolor NAD 1962, 71, Obrig prize watercolor 1964, 66, 79, 87, gold medal honor watercolor Allied Artists Am. 1962, Grumbacher prize 1978, Today Mag. Art medal 1970, 74, gold medal honor watercolor Am. Artists Profl. League 1964; best landscape award 1974, gold medal 1978, Edwin S. Webster award honor watercolor Boston Soc. Watercolor 1964, gold medal honor watercolor Hudson Valley Art Assn. 1964, DuMond Meml. award 1971, Isabel Stinschneider Meml. award 1972, Herman Wick Meml. award Salmagundi Club, N.Y.C. 1966, 2d prize 1966, June Justin J. Impasto award 1972, Arthur T. Hill prize 1973, Arthur T. Hill Meml. prize 1975, Louis Z. Seley prize 1978, Gwynne Lennon prize 1979, Gold medal honor oil Rockport Art Assn. 1966, 69, 76, 86, cash award Wichita Centennial Watercolor 1970, Providence Art Club prize 1972, gold medal Franklin Mint Competition 1974, Gold medal Honor Acad. Assn. 1976, others. Elizabeth Greenshields grantee, 1961, 62; recipient Gold medal of Honor New Eng. Watercolor Soc., Boston, 1985, Acad. Artists Assn., 1985; named Knickerbocker Honoree Artist of Yr., 1989; recipient Grumbacher award watercolor, Acad. Artists Assn., 1990, Grumbacher Gold medal Gouache New Eng. Watercolor Soc., 1992. Mem. NAD (cert. merit watercolor 1992), Am. Watercolor Soc. (ea. v.p. 1994—, Dolphin fellow), Boston Watercolor Soc., Conn. Watercolor Socs., Allied Artists Am., Knickerbocker Artists (dir.'s prize 1971, Golf medal 1989), Boston Guild Artists (Grumbacher Gold medallion award Watercolor 1988, No. Shore Arts Assn. award oil 1991), Rockport Art Assn. (Silver medal 1988, 94, Darrand award oil 1992, Cirino award 1st prize Gouache 1992, Clark Popular award Gouache 1992), Hudson Valley Artists (Gold medal 1974, 85, 94). Home: 7 Wildon Heights Rockport MA 01966 Office: 71 Main St Rockport MA 01966-1512 *I have been fortunate to have been encouraged by my family at an early age and have a number of people to thank for their support, especially my wife. I feel artists must never compromise their ideals and principles, no matter how high their standards. Originality and professional ethics with one's work make goals achieved meaningful. On the one hand, an artist should inwardly feel that there is little he can't accomplish, and yet he must learn to work within his realized limitations.*

NICHOLAS, THOMAS PETER, library administrator, community television consultant, producer; b. Laramie, Wyo., Dec. 6, 1948; s. Thomas Lloyd Nicholas and Frances (Collins) Chambers; m. Tanya Michelle Villont; 1 child, Ja'el Michelle. AA in Fine Arts, Cabrillo Coll., 1970; BA in English, U. Colo., 1972; MS in Librarianship and Info. Sci., U. Denver, 1982. Real estate salesperson Sun Country, Lakewood, Colo., 1972-74; v.p. Nicholas Properties, Denver, 1971-77; libr. City of Aurora, Colo., 1975-80, system support mgr., 1981-83, dir. libr. and TV svcs., 1984—; pres. bd. Irving Libr. Network Inc., Denver, 1985—; advisor CL System Inc., Boston, 1985—; acting pers. dir. City of Aurora. Exec. producer TV programs: Election Night 85 (Franny award 1986), Miss Plumjoy's Place, 1988 (Starwards 1988), Aurora's Can't Afford Not To, 1988 (Starwards 1988). Mem. exec. bd., chmn. Arapahoe Pub. Access to Librs., 1984-85; site coordinator Am. Cancer Soc., Aurora, 1988; adv. Youth at Risk, Aurora, 1989; bd. dirs. Cen. Colo. Libr. System, Lakewood, 1985-87; mem. exec. bd. Colo. Libr. Legis. Com., Denver, 1988—; pres. Greater Metro Cable Consortium, 1992—; acting dep. city mgr. City of Aurora, 1993—. Mem. ALA, Colo. Libr. Assn. (advisor 1982-83, Programming award 1982, 1st Colo. Childrens Program award 1983, 88), Nat. Assn. Telecommunications Officers and Advisors (regional pres. 1983-84, T.V. Program award 1986), Rotary (program chmn. 1987-88), Eastgate Lions Club (pres. 1989-90). Democrat. Greek Orthodox. Avocations: fine art, poetry, automobile restoration, martial arts (Black Belt). Office: Aurora Pub Libr 14949 E Alameda Dr Aurora CO 80012-1500

NICHOLAS, WILLIAM RICHARD, lawyer; b. Pontiac, Mich., June 19, 1934; s. Reginald and Edna Irene (Bartlett) N.; m. Diana Lee Johnson, Aug. 20, 1960; children: Susan Lee, William Richard Jr. BS in Bus., U. Idaho, 1956; JD, U. Mich., 1962. Bar: 1963. Ptnr. Latham & Watkins, Los Angeles, 1962—. Contbr. numerous articles on taxation. Served to lt. (j.g.) USN, 1956-59. Mem. Calif. Bar Assn., Los Angeles County Bar Assn., Am. Coll. Tax Counsel. Home: 1808 Old Ranch Rd Los Angeles CA 90049-2207 Office: Latham & Watkins 633 W 5th St Ste 4000 Los Angeles CA 90071-2059

NICHOLAW, GEORGE, communications executive; b. Salinas, Calif., Nov. 17, 1927; s. Costas and Anna G. (Melissa) N.; m. Betty Baron. B in Fgn. Trade, Am. Grad. Sch. Internat. Mgmt.; BS, U. Calif., Berkeley. Program dir. Sta. KDON, Salinas, 1953-55; asst. dir. promotion, publicity Sta. KNXT-TV, Los Angeles, 1955-63; dir. info. services and community relations Sta. WBBM-TV, Chgo., 1963-66; dir. community services Sta. WCBS-TV, N.Y.C., 1966-67; v.p. CBS radio div., gen. mgr. Sta. KNX, Los Angeles, 1967—. Commr. Los Angeles Energy Commn.; active Communications Task Force Greater Los Angeles Urban Coalition., Calif. Air Pollution Emergency Traffic Control Com. Served with U.S. Army. Recipient Abe Lincoln award, Peabody award, Ohio State award, Alfred I DuPont award, Columbia U. Mem. Nat. Assn. Broadcasters, Calif. Broadcasters Assn. (dir. Los Angeles chpt.), Hollywood Radio and TV Soc. (dir. Los Angeles chpt.), Arbitron Radio Adv. Council (past chmn.), Calif. Inst. Cancer Research (bd. dirs.), Permanent Charities Com. Entertainment Industries (bd. dirs.). Office: Sta KNX-AM 6121 W Sunset Blvd Los Angeles CA 90028-6455

NICHOLLS, DAVID G., editor; b. Indpls., Oct. 6, 1965; s. Thomas G. and Natalie A. (Keinonen) N. AB, Bowdoin Coll., 1988; MA, U. Chgo., 1989, PhD, 1995. Nonfiction editor Chgo. Rev., 1989-91, editor, 1991—. Co-editor: The Penguin New Writing in India, 1994. Javits fellow U.S. Dept. Edn., 1989-93, Mellon fellow U. Chgo., 1993-94; Witter Bynner Found. grantee, 1991. Office: Chicago Review 5801 S Kenwood Ave Chicago IL 60637-1766

NICHOLLS, RICHARD H., lawyer; b. Toronto, Ont., Can., Oct. 27, 1938; s. Richard S. and Roberta T.; m. Judy Carter, Apr. 15, 1963; children: Christopher T., Jamie C.; m. Anne Delaney, June 10, 1978. BA can. Law and, Amherst Coll., 1960; LLB, Stamford U., 1963; LLM, NYU, 1964. Bar: Calif. 1964, N.Y. 1965, D.C. Assoc. Mudge Rose Guthrie, Alexander & Ferdon and predecessor, N.Y.C., 1964-70, ptnr., 1971-94, of counsel, 1995—. Mem. ABA, N.Y. State Bar Assn., Nat. Bond Lawyers, Stamford Yacht Club. Home: 159 Ocean Dr W Stamford CT 06902-8004 Office: Mudge Rose Guthrie Alexander & Ferdon 180 Maiden Ln New York NY 10038-4925

NICHOLS, ALBERT L., economics consultant; b. Poughkeepsie, N.Y., Feb. 13, 1951; s. Albert and Margaret (Schaefer) N.; m. Eve Kaufman, June 16, 1973; children: Matthew, Elizabeth. AB, Stanford U., 1973; M of Pub. Policy, Harvard U., 1975, PhD, 1981. Assoc. prof. Harvard U., Cambridge, Mass., 1977-83, 85-88, dir. adminstrv. planning, 1988-89; dir. econ. analysis EPA, Washington, 1983-85; v.p. Nat. Econ. Rsch. Assocs., Cambridge, 1989—; cons. various corps., 1976-89. Author: Targeting Economic Incentives for Environmental Protection, 1984; contbr. numerous articles to profl. jours. Nat. Merit scholar, 1969. Mem. Am. Econ. Assn., Soc. for Risk Analysis, Assn. Environ. and Resource Economists, Phi Beta Kappa. Avocation: woodworking. Home: 14 Baskin Rd Lexington MA 02173-6929 Office: Nat Econ Rsch Assocs 1 Main St Cambridge MA 02142-1517

NICHOLS, C. WALTER, III, retired trust company executive; b. N.Y.C., Aug. 25, 1937; s. Charles Walter and Marjorie (Jones) N.; B.A., U. Va., 1959; m. Anne Sharp, Aug. 8, 1959; children:—Blair, Sandra, Walter, Hope. Vice pres. Citibank, N.Y.C., 1962-78, Morgan Guaranty Trust Co. N.Y., N.Y.C., 1979-93; 1st v.p. Republic Nat. Bank N.Y., N.Y.C., 1994—; mng. dir. Fissell, Laidlaw & Co. Inc., 1995—. Bd. dirs. Nichols Found., Inc., 1969—, pres. 1988-90; bd. dirs. Greenwich House, 1969-94, pres., 1984-90; bd. dirs. Choate Rosemary Hall, 1972-77, 82-89, Lower Hudson (N.Y.) chpt. Nature Conservancy, 1978-87, hon. trustee, 1988—, John Jay Homestead, 1980—, Nat. Audubon Soc., 1983-87; mem. adv. bd. N.Y. Zool. Soc. (Bronx Zoo), 1987-94; mem. adv. bd. Caramoor Music Festival, 1994—. Served to 1st lt. U.S. Army, 1960-62. Decorated Army Commendation medal. Mem. Naturist Soc. Clubs: Bedford (N.Y.) Golf and Tennis, Pilgrims of U.S. Office: 42 Main St Bedford Hills NY 10507

NICHOLS, CARL WHEELER, retired advertising agency executive; b. Ottawa, Kans., Oct. 9, 1923; s. Carl Wheeler and Cora Merle (Hanks) N.; children: Christine, Carl Wheeler, Nancy, Matthew; m. Anna Norris, Apr. 18, 1992. Student, Baker U., 1940-41, U. Mo., 1941-43; B.A., U. Mich.,

1944. Research analyst Cunningham & Walsh, Inc. (advt. agy.), N.Y.C., 1946-49; copywriter Cunningham & Walsh, Inc. (advt. agy.), 1949-56, co-creative dir., v.p., 1956-59, dir. account mgmt., 1959-61, pres., 1961-69, chmn., chief exec. officer, 1969-85, chmn. emeritus, 1986. Capt. USMCR, 1943-46, 50-52, Korea. Named to Advt. Hall of Fame, 1986. Mem. N.Y. Advt. Coun. (bd. dirs. 1974-85), Am. Advt. Fedn. (dir. 1972-75, chmn. 1975-76), Advt. Ednl. Found. (bd. dirs., sec., treas. 1983-91), Woodway Country Club, John's Island Club, Bent Pine Club, Sigma Xi. Presbyterian (elder). Home: 241 Island Creek Dr Vero Beach FL 32963-3304

NICHOLS, CAROL D., real estate professional, association executive. BA, U. Pitts., 1964; cert. in advanced mgmt., U. Chgo. From mgmt. trainee to buyer May Dept. Stores Co., Pitts., 1964-70; various mgmt. positions, then mng. dir. mortgage and real estate div. Tchrs. Ins. and Annuity Assn. Am., N.Y.C., 1970—; instr. real estate div. continuing edn. Marymount Manhattan Coll., N.Y.C., 1975-76, Woman's Sch. Adult Edn. Ctr., N.Y.C., 1976-77; v.p. instn. owners div. Real Estate Bd. N.Y., past chmn. fin. com., mem. seminar and gen. meetings coms. Trustee, mem. investment com. Nat. Jewish Ctr. for Immunology and Respiratory Medicine; bd. dirs. N.Y. region NCCJ. Recipient Nat. Humanitarian award Nat. Jewish Ctr. for Immunology and Respiratory Medicine, Nat. Brotherhood award NCCJ. Mem. Assn. Real Estate Women (past pres.), Urban Land Inst. (trustee, chmn. urban devel. and mixed use coun., coun. coord. and inner city). Home: 165 Winfield St East Norwalk CT 06855-1622 Office: Teachers Ins & Annuity Assn 730 3rd Ave New York NY 10017-3206

NICHOLS, CHARLES LEE, professional services executive; b. Seminole, Okla., Nov. 1, 1941; s. Calvin Eugene Nichols and Irene Frances (Newport) Christopher; m. Ofelia Luna, Nov. 27, 1967 (div. Oct. 1986); 1 child, William C. BA in English, Tex. A&M U., 1963; LLB, U. Tex., 1966. Bar: Tex. 1966, Calif. 1971. Sr. v.p. Sci. Applications Internat. Corp., San Diego, 1970—. Bd. dirs. Profl. Services Council, Washington, 1985. Capt USAF, 1966-70. Mem. Calif. Bar Assn., Tex. Bar Assn. Club: San Diego Yacht. Avocations: yacht racing, skiing. Home: 6455 La Jolla Blvd La Jolla CA 92037-6627 Office: Sci Applications Internat Corp 10260 Campus Point Dr San Diego CA 92121-1522

NICHOLS, COLIN GRAHAM, bioscience educator; b. Leicester, Eng., Aug. 27, 1960; came to U.S., 1985; s. Graham P. and Margaret Ann Nichols; m. Diana L. Coleman, Oct. 17, 1992. BSc, Leeds (Eng.) U., 1982, PhD, 1985. Postdoctoral fellow U. Md., Balt., 1985-90; vis. rsch. assoc. Baylor Coll. Medicine, Houston, 1990-91; asst. prof. cell biology Washington U., St. Louis, 1991—; established investigator Am. Heart Assn., 1993—. Contbr. numerous articles to sci. jours. Mem. Biophys. Soc., Soc. Gen. Physiologists. Avocations: avid cricket player. Office: Washington U Sch Medicine Dept Cell Biology 660 S Euclid Ave Saint Louis MO 63110

NICHOLS, DAVID, production designer. Prodn. designer: (films) Box Car Bertha, 1972, The Wild Party, 1975, (with Robb Wilson King) Swamp Thing, 1982, Testament, 1983, Heartbreaker, 1983, Reckless, 1984, The Best of Times, 1986, Hoosiers, 1986, The Serpent and the Rainbow, 1988, Great Balls of Fire!, 1989, A Midnight Clear, 1992, Groundhog Day, 1993, Airheads, 1994, (TV movie) Finnegan Begin Again, 1985; visual cons.: (films) Mean Streets, 1973. Office: care Spyros Skouras Sanford Skouras Gross & Assocs 1015 Gayley Ave 3rd Fl Los Angeles CA 90024*

NICHOLS, DAVID ARTHUR, mediator, retired state justice; b. Lincolnville, Maine, Aug. 6, 1917; s. George E. and Flora E. (Pillsbury) N. A.B. magna cum laude, Bates Coll., 1942; J.D., U. Mich., 1949. Bar: Maine bar 1949, Mass. bar 1949, U.S. Supreme Ct 1954. Pvt. practice Camden, Maine, 1949-75; justice Maine Superior Ct., 1975-77, Maine Supreme Jud. Ct., 1977-88; mediator, 1988—; mem. Maine Exec. Council, 1955-57; moderator Lincolnville Town Meeting, 1950-74. Mem. editorial bd. Picton Press, 1989—; contbr. to legal and geneal. pubs. Chmn. Maine Republican Com., 1960-64; mem. Rep. Nat. Com., 1960-68; chmn. Maine council Young Reps., 1950-54; New Eng. council Young Reps., 1952-54; trustee, past pres. Penobscot Bay Med. Center. Served with USAAF, 1942-45. Fellow Am. Bar Found., Am. Coll. Trial Lawyers; mem. Am. Law Inst., Camden-Rockport C of C. (past pres.), Maine Hist. Soc., Camden Hist. Soc. (past pres.), Camden Bus. Men's Assn. (past pres.), ABA (bd. govs. 1960-63, ho. dels. 1957-78), Maine Bar Assn., Am. Judicature Soc. (dir. 1960-64), New Eng. Historic Geneal. Soc. (trustee), Bates Coll. Alumni Assn. (past pres.), Maine Trial Lawyers Assn. (past pres.), Phi Beta Kappa, Delta Sigma Rho. Clubs: Odd Fellows, Rotary (past pres.). Home: PO Box 76 Lincolnville ME 04849-0076

NICHOLS, DAVID HARRY, gynecologic surgeon, obstetrics and gynecology educator, author; b. Utica, N.Y., July 30, 1925; s. Harry Harrison and Katherine Valentine (Belknap) N.; m. Lorraine Elizabeth Landel, June 23, 1948; children: David L., Laurie L., Nancie L., Daniel A., Julie L. MD, U. Buffalo, 1947; MA (hon.), Brown U., 1982. Diplomate Am. Bd. Ob-Gyn. Intern E.J. Meyer Meml. Hosp., Buffalo, 1947-48; resident in ob-gyn Millard Fillmore Hosp., Buffalo, 1948-51; assoc. cancer rsch. gynecologist Roswell Pk. Meml. Inst., Buffalo, 1953-60; asst. clin. prof. ob-gyn. SUNY, Buffalo, 1958-68, clin. prof., 1968-75, prof., 1975-80; prof. Brown U., Providence, 1980-92, chmn. dept. ob-gyn., 1980-91, dir. Ctr. for Women's Surgery, 1990-91; chief of pelvic surgery Mass. Gen. Hosp., Boston, 1991—; pres. Erie County unit Am. Cancer Soc., 1962-68, Buffalo Ob/Gyn. Soc., 1975-76; vis. prof. ob-gyn., reproductive biology Harvard U. Sch. Med., 1991—. Author: Atlas of Gynecological Pathology, 1951, Vaginal Surgery, 1976, 4th edit., 1995; author/editor: (med. monograph) Clinical Problems, Injuries, and Complications of GYN Surgery, 1983, 3rd edit., 1995, Ambulatory Gynecology, 1985, 2d edit 1995, Reoperative Gynecologic Surgery, 1991, Gynecologic and Obstetric Surgery, 1993. Maj. M.C., USAF, 1949-53. Fellow ACS, Am. Coll. Ob-Gyn., Internat. Coll. Surgeons, Boston Obstet. Soc.; mem. Soc. Pelvic Surgeons, Soc. Gynecol. Surgeons (nat. pres. 1984-85), N.E. Obstet. Soc., Agawam Hunt Club, Boston Obstet. Soc., Am. Gyn. Club (pres. 1993-94), Harvard Club. Republican. Roman Catholic. Avocations: travel, music, literature. Office: Mass Gen Hosp Vincent 1 Boston MA 02114 Address: 101 Prospect St Providence RI 02906-1440

NICHOLS, DAVID L., retail executive; b. Toledo, Sept. 1, 1941; s. Lee Roy and Marianne (smith) N.; children: Fredericka, JoLynn, Jennifer, Laurie, Martha, Meredith; m. Lenore Grotke Nichols, Sept. 15, 1990. BA in Bus., U. Toledo, 1990. With The McAlpin Co., Cin., 1963-76; store mgr. McAlpin's Northgate, Cin., 1976-78; gen. mdse. mgr. Mercantile Stores Co., Inc., N.Y.C., 1978-82, v.p., CFO, treas., 1989-91, exec. v.p., CFO, treas., 1991-92, chmn., CEO, 1992—; pres. Lion Store, Toledo, 1982-89. Active Cin. Bus. Com., 1992. Recipient Green Thumb award Am. Apparel Mfr. Assn., 1993. Avocations: golf, gourmet cooking. Office: Mercantile Stores Co Inc 1100 N Market St Wilmington DE 19801*

NICHOLS, DONALD ARTHUR, economist, educator; b. Madison, Conn., Dec. 20, 1940; s. Edward Charles and Ruth (Nilson) N.; m. Linda Powley, Aug. 19, 1962 (dec. Oct. 1982); children: Charles Spencer, Elizabeth Clarke; m. Barbara Jakubowski Noel, May 22, 1983. B.A., Yale U., 1962, M.A., 1963, Ph.D., 1968. Mem. faculty dept. econs. U. Wis., Madison, 1966—, prof., 1977—, chmn. dept. econs., 1983-86, 88-90, mem. exec. com. faculty senate, 1987-90, chmn., 1989-90; lectr. Yale U., 1970-71; sr. economist Senate Budget Com., Washington, 1975-76; dep. asst. sec. for econ. policy and rsch. Dept. Labor, Washington, 1977-79; dir. Ctr. for Rsch. on Wis. Economy; econ. advisor to Gov. State of Wis., 1983-86; exec. sec. Gov.'s Coun. Econ. Advisors, 1983-86; mem. Gov.'s Export Strategy Commn., Wis., 1994-95; bd. dirs. Thompson, Plumb Funds, 1987—, Plumb Fund, Inc., PROFS, 1987-90, treas., 1987-88, pres., 1988-89; cons. in field. Author: (with Clark Reynolds) Principles of Economics, 1970, Dollars and Sense, 1994; contbr. articles to profl. jours. Trustee U. Wis. Bookstore, 1990—; bd. advisors Am. Players Theatre, Spring Green, Wis., 1993—. NSF fellow, 1963-66, 70-72; Nat. Commn. Employment Policy rsch. grantee, 1980-82; recipient William H. Kiekhofer Meml. Teaching prize U. Wis., 1973. Mem. Am. Econ. Assn., Econometric Soc., Royal Econ. Soc. Office: U Wis 1180 Observatory Dr Madison WI 53706-1393

NICHOLS, DONALD RICHARDSON, medical educator; b. Mpls., Feb. 22, 1911; s. Arthur R. and Agusta (Fisher) N.; m. Margery Spicer, Mar. 5, 1942 (dec.); children: Virginia (Mrs. Gregory Blanchfield), John; m. Mary

Jean Scholberg, Mar. 2, 1957 (dec.); children: Arthur, Edwin, Mary Jean (Mrs. Vincent Grimaldi), Barbara (Mrs. Todd McCallister). AB, Amherst Coll., 1933; MD, U. Minn., 1938, MS in Medicine, 1942. Diplomate: Am. Bd. Internal Medicine. Intern Milw. County Hosp., 1939; fellow medicine Mayo Found., 1939-42; mem. faculty Mayo Grad. Sch. Medicine, U. Minn., 1948-72, prof. clin. medicine, 1965-72; prof. medicine Mayo Med. Sch., 1972-81; cons. medicine Mayo Clinic, 1942-81, chmn. divsn. infectious diseases, 1963-73, sr. cons. medicine, 1973-81; dir. health svc. Rochester (Minn.) C.C., (Minn.), 1981-86. Treas. Rochester Human Rights Commn., 1983-89. Surgeon U.S. Mcht. Marines, 1941. Fellow Infectious Diseases Soc. Am., ACP; mem. AMA, Minn. State Med. Assn., Central Soc. Clin. Research, Mayo Alumni Assn., Sigma Xi, Nu Sigma Nu, Theta Delta Chi. Methodist. Home: 207 5th Ave SW Rochester MN 55902-3100

NICHOLS, ELIZABETH GRACE, nursing educator, administrator; b. Tehran, Iran, Feb. 1, 1943; came to U.S., 1964; d. Terence and Eleanor Denny (Payne) Quilliam; m. Gerald Ray Nichols, Nov. 20, 1965; children: Tina Lynn, Jeffrey David. BSN, San Francisco State U., 1969; MS, U. Calif.-San Francisco, 1970, Dr. Nursing Sci., 1974, MA Idaho State U., 1989. Staff nurse Peninsula Hosp., Burlingame, Calif., 1966-72; asst. prof. U. Calif.-San Francisco Sch. Nursing, 1974-82; comm. dept. nursing Idaho State U., Pocatello, 1982-85 ; assoc. dean Coll. Health Scis. Sch. Nursing U. Wyo., Laramie, 1985—; cons. U. Rochester, N.Y., 1979, Carroll Coll., Mont., 1980, div. Nursing Dept. HHS, Washington, 1980, 84, 85, 86, 87, Stanford Hosp. Nursing Service, Calif., 1981-82, Ea. N.Mex. U., 1988. Contbr. articles on nursing to profl. jours. Mem. adv. bd. dirs. Ombudsman Service of Contra Costa Calif., 1979-82, U. Calif. Home Care Service, San Francisco, 1975-82, Free Clinic of Pocatello, 1984. ACE fellow U. Maine system 1990-91. Fellow ACE, Gerontol. Soc. Am., Am. Acad. Nursing; mem. Gerontol. Soc. Am. (chmn. clin. medicine section 1987, sec. 1990—), Am. Nurses Assn., Wyo. Nurses Assn., Idaho Nurses Assn. (dist. 51 adv. bd. dirs. 1982-84), Western Inst. Nursing (chair, 1995-96). Club: Oakland Ski (1st v.p. 1981-82). (Calif.). Office: U Wyo Laramie WY 82071

NICHOLS, EUGENE DOUGLAS, mathematics educator; b. Rovno, Poland, Feb. 6, 1923; came to U.S., 1946, naturalized, 1951; s. Alex and Anna (Radchuk) Nichiporuk; m. Alice Bissell, Mar. 31, 1951. BS, U. Chgo., 1949, postgrad., 1949-51; MEd, U. Ill., 1953, MA, 1954, PhD, 1956. Instr. math. Roberts Wesleyan Coll., North Chili, N.Y., 1950-51, U. Ill., 1951-56; assoc. prof. math. edn. Fla. State U., 1956-61, prof., head dept., 1961-73; dir. Project for Mathematical Devel. of Children, 1973-77; dir. math program NSF, 1958-61; dir. Math. Inst. Elem. Tchrs., 1961-70; pres. Nichols Schwartz Pub., 1992—; prof. math. edn. Fla. State U., 1974-90; Chmn. U. Ill. Com. on Sch. Math., 1954-55; cons. editor math McGraw-Hill Book Co., summer 1956. Co-author: Modern Elementary Algebra, 1961, Introduction to Sets, 1962, Arithmetic of Directed Numbers, 1962, Introduction to Equations and Inequalities, 1963, Introduction to Coordinate Geometry, 1963, Introduction to Exponents, 1964, Understanding Arithmetic, 1965, Elementary Mathematics Patterns and Structure, 1966, Mathematics Patterns and Structure, 1966, Algebra, 1966, Modern Geometry, 1968, Modern Trignomometry, 1968, Modern Intermediate Algebra, 1969, Analytic Geometry, 1973, Holt Algebra 1, 1974, 78, 82, 86, 92, Holt Algebra 2, 1974, 78, 82, 86, 92, Holt Geometry, 1974, 78, 82, 86, Holt School Mathematics, 1974, 78, 81, Holt Mathematics, 1981, 85, Pre-Algebra Mathematics, 1980, 86, Holt Pre-Algebra, 1992, Elementary School Mathematics and How to Teach It, 1982, Geometry, 1991, Mathematics Dictionary and Handbook, 1993, 95; author: Pre-Algebra Mathematics, 1970, College Mathematics for General Education, rev. edit., 1975, Introductory Algebra for College Students, 1971, Mathematics for the Elementary School Teacher, 1971, College Mathematics, 1975. Named Fla. State U. Disting. Prof., 1968-69; recipient Disting. Alumni award U. Ill. Coll. Edn., 1970. Mem. Am. Math. Soc., Math. Assn. Am., Sch. Sci. and Math Assn., Nat. Coun. Tchrs. Math., Coun. Basic Edn., Pi Mu Epsilon, Phi Delta Kappa. Home: 3386 W Lakeshore Dr Tallahassee FL 32312-1305

NICHOLS, GUY WARREN, institute executive, former utilities executive; b. Colchester, Vt., Oct. 27, 1925; s. Guy W. and Gladys (Tomlinson) N.; m. Shirley Hibbard, June 21, 1947; children: Pamela, Gail, Sally. BSCE, U. Vt., 1947; postgrad., Worcester Poly. Inst. Sch. Indsl. Mgmt., 1953-56; MS in Bus. Adminstrn., MIT, 1961. With New Eng. Electric System, Westborough, Mass., 1947-84, exec. v.p., 1968-70, pres., 1970-84, chief exec. officer, 1972-84, chmn. bd., 1978-84; bd. dirs. State Mut. Life Assurance Co. Am., Allmerica Property & Casualty Cos. Inc., Noble Affiliates. Chmn., trustees Woods Hole Oceanographic Instn., 1985—. Served with AUS, 1944-46. Sloan fellow, MIT, 1961. Fellow Am. Acad. Arts and Scis. Office: 25 Research Dr Westborough MA 01582

NICHOLS, HAROLD NEIL, corporate executive, former pipeline company executive; b. Digby, N.S., Can., June 15, 1937; s. Harold A. and Lillian (Nielsen) N.; m. Doris E. Outhouse, Mar. 2, 1957; children—Michael, Dale, Sherri, Susan, Lori. Grad. high sch. Cert. Mgmt. Acct. Various fin. positions TransCan. PipeLines Ltd., Toronto, Ont., from 1956, chief fin. officer, from 1983, exec. v.p., 1988-89; mgmt. cons. Unionville, Ont., 1989-92; chmn. Battery Techs., Inc.; bd. dirs. Union Bank Switzerland (Can.), Corrosion Interventions Ltd., Metocean Data Sys. Ltd. Mem. Fin. Execs. Inst. Home: 7 Blackwell Ct, Unionville, ON Canada L3R 0C2

NICHOLS, HENRY ELIOT, lawyer, savings and loan executive; b. N.Y.C., Jan. 3, 1924; s. William and Elizabeth (Lisse) N.; m. Frances Griffin Morrison, Aug. 12, 1950 (dec. July 1978); children: Clyde Whitney, Diane Spencer; m. Mary Ann Wall, May 31, 1987. BA, Yale U., 1946; JD, U. Va., 1948. Bar: D.C. 1950, U.S. Dist. Ct. 1950, U.S. Ct. Appeals 1952, U.S. Supreme Ct. 1969. Assoc. Frederick W. Berens, Washington, 1950-52; sole practice, Washington, 1952—; real estate columnist Washington Star, 1966-81; pres., gen. counsel Hamilton Fed. Savs. & Loan Assn., 1971-74; vice chmn. bd. Columbia 1st Bank (formerly Columbia 1st Fed. Savs. & Loan Assn.), Washington, 1974-90, bd. dir.; pres. Century Fin. Corp., 1971-90; regional v.p. Preview, Inc., 1972-78; bd. dir., exec. com. Columbia Real Estate Title Ins. Co., Washington, 1968-78; bd. dir. Greater Met. Bd. Trade, 1974-78, Dist. Realty Title Ins. Co., 1978-88. Nat. adv. bd. Harker Prep. Sch., 1975-80; exec. com. Father Walter E. Schmitz Meml. Fund, Cath. U., 1982-83; bd. dirs. Vincent T. Lombardi Cancer Rsch. Ctr., 1979-84; del. Pres. Johnson's Conf. Law and Poverty, 1967; vice chmn. Mayor's Ad Hoc Com. Housing Code Problems, Washington, 1968-71; mem. Downtown Progress, 1970; bd. dirs. Washington Mental Health Assn., 1973, Washington Med Ctr., 1975. Capt USAAF, 1942-46. Mem. Am. Land Devel. Assn., Nat. Assn. Realtors, Nat. Assn. Real Estate Editors, Washington Bd. Realtors (pres. 1970, Realtor of Yr. 1970, Martin Isen award 1981), Greater Met. Washington Bd. Trade (bd. dirs. 1974-80), U.S. League Savs. Assns. (attys. com. 1971-80), Washington Savs. and Loan League, ABA, D.C. Bar Assn. Internat. Real Estate Fedn., Omega Tau Rho. Episcopalian. Clubs: Yale, Cosmos, Rolls Royce, Antique Auto, St. Elmo. Patentee med. inventions; contbr. articles profl. jours. Address: 1 Kittery Ct Bethesda MD 20817 Office: 1112 16th St NW Washington DC 20036-3906

NICHOLS, HENRY LOUIS, lawyer; b. Collin County, Tex., Nov. 7, 1916; s. Jesse Cleveland and Leva (Stiff) N.; m. Elaine Guentherman, May 17, 1949; children: David Michael, Martha Marie. LL.B., So. Meth. U., 1940. Bar: Tex. 1939. Asst. city atty. Dallas, 1946-50, sole practice, 1951—; bd. dirs. Southwestern Legal Found; mem. adv. bd. Ctr. for Legal Mcpl. Studies. Served to lt. col. AUS, 1941-46; col. USAR ret. Rsch. fellow Southwestern Legal Found., 1964. Fellow Am. Bar Found.; mem. ABA, Dallas Bar Assn. (pres. 1963-64), State Bar Tex., Tex. Bar Found. (charter). Club: Lakewood Country. Home: 3131 Maple Ave Apt 4F Dallas TX 75201-1204 Office: 1800 Lincoln St Dallas TX 75226-2248 *As a night-school graduate (Law School), I believe the opportunities in America are unlimited for anyone willing to work. Nowhere in the world are such opportunities available. We who live in the U.S.A. are blessed and the most fortunate of all people. We should strive to maintain that which our fathers preserved for us.*

NICHOLS, HORACE ELMO, state justice; b. Elkmont, Ala., July 16, 1912; s. William Henry and Lou Ella (Bates) N.; m. Edith Bowers, Oct. 20, 1945; children: Nancy (Mrs. Lewis Glenn), Carol (Mrs. Scott Henwood), Horace Elmo Jr. Mus.B., Columbia U., 1933, postgrad. in constnl. law,

1937-38; LL.B., Cumberland Law Sch., 1936. Bar: Ga. 1935. Practice in Canton, Ga., 1938-40, Rome, Ga., 1940-48; judge Superior Ct., Rome, 1948-54; mem. Ct. Appeals Ga., 1954-66; justice Supreme Ct. Ga., Atlanta, 1966-80; chief justice Supreme Ct. Ga., 1975-80. Vocal soloist, World's Fair, Chgo., 1933. Mem. Sigma Alpha Epsilon, Blue Key. Democrat. Presbyterian. Clubs: Coosa Country (Rome); Piedmont Driving (Atlanta), Capitol City (Atlanta), Atlanta City (Atlanta). Lodge: Elks (Rome). Home: 13 Virginia Cir Rome GA 30161-4473 Office: 28 Jud Bldg Atlanta GA 30334

NICHOLS, IRBY COGHILL, JR., historian, educator, entrepreneur; b. Baton Rouge, Apr. 10, 1926; s. Irby Coghill and Pauline (Wright) N.; m. Margaret Sunshine Irby, Apr. 18, 1953; children—Nina Keith, Irby Coghill III. B.A., La. State U., 1947; M.A., U.N.C., 1949; Ph.D., U. Mich., 1955. Instr. Catawba Coll., 1949; tchg. fellow U. Mich., 1949-52; instr. N.Mex. Mil. Inst., 1952-55; asst. prof. Northwestern U., Denton, 1955-57, assoc. prof., 1957-67, prof., 1967-92, prof. emeritus, 1992—; adj. prof. North Ctrl. Tex. Coll., Gainesville, Tex., 1993-94; vis. assoc. prof. La. State U., summer 1962, U. London, fall 1991; participant several programs Consortium on Revolutionary Europe, 1750-1850; v.p., bd. dirs. Whispering Hills Estates, Cooke County, Tex. Author: The European Pentarchy and the Congress of Verona, 1822, 1971; (with Paul Smith and Dwane Kingery) U. North Tex.: A Self-Study, 1962; history assoc. editor Social Sci. Quar. (formerly Southwestern Social Sci. Quar.), 1961-64; contbr. articles to profl. publs. Served with USMC, 1944-46. Recipient Louis Knott Koontz award Pacific Hist. Assn., 1968, First Ann. Jo Houston Shelton award U. North Tex., 1976; faculty research grantee U. North Tex., 1956—. Mem. Am. Acad. Arts and Scis., So Hist. Assn., Soc. French Hist. Studies, Southwestern Soc. Sci. Assn. (chmn. sessions 1971—, chmn. history sect. 1969-70), Smithsonian Instrn., World Future Soc., Phi Kappa Phi, Phi Alpha Theta, Kappa Mu Epsilon. Democrat. Episcopalian. Home: PO Box 392 Gainesville TX 76241-0392 Office: Univ North Tex Box 13735 N Tex Sta Denton TX 76203

NICHOLS, IRIS JEAN, illustrator; b. Yakima, Wash., Aug. 2, 1938; d. Charles Frederick and Velma Irene (Hacker) Beisner; (div. June 1963); children: Reid William, Amy Jo; m. David Gary Nichols, Sept. 21, 1966. BFA in Art, U. Wash., 1978. Freelance illustrator, graphic designer Seattle, 1966—; med. illustrator, head dept. illustration Swedish Hosp. Med. Ctr., Seattle, 1981-86; owner, med. and scientific illustrator Art for Medicine, Seattle, 1986—; part-time med. illustrator U. Wash., Seattle, 1966-67; part-time med. illustrator, graphic coord. dept. art The Mason Clinic, 1968-78; instr. advanced illustration Cornish Coll. Arts, Seattle, 1988—. Illustrator various books including Bryophytes of Pacific Northwest, 1966, Microbiology, 1973, 78, 82, 94, Introduction to Human Physiology, 1980, Understanding Human Anatomy and Physiology, 1983, Human Anatomy, 1984 Regional Anesthesia, 1990, and children's books on various subjects; exhibited in group shows at Seattle Pacific Soc. Ctr., summer 1979, & Seattle, U. Wash. Med. Surgeons (1st prize 1974), N.W. Urology Conf. (1st prize 1974, 76, 2d prize 1975). Pres. ArtsWest (formerly West Seattle Arts Coun.), 1983; active Seattle Art Mus. Named to West Seattle High Sch. Alumni Hall of Fame, 1986, Matrix Table, 1986-95. Mem. Assn. Med. Illustrators (Murial McLatchie Fine Arts award 1981), Nat. Mus. Women in the Arts (Wash. state com., bd. dirs. 1987-95, pres. 1993-94), Women Painters of Wash. (pres. 1987-89), U. Wash. Alumni Assn., Lambda Rho. Avocations: artwork, printmaking, entering juried art exhibitions.

NICHOLS, J. HUGH, economic development consultant; b. Sprott, Ala., Nov. 27, 1930; s. Joseph Gordon and Mary Roberta (Stone) N.; m. Annie Sue Ratliff, Dec. 30, 1948; children: Duane A., Sharon K., Gerald Hugh, Jonathan G.; 1 foster child, John Dorsey. AB, U. Ala., 1957; MA, The Am. U., 1967. Sr. scientist Dunlap & Assocs., Washington, 1963-67; dir. plans and programming Informatics, Inc., Bethesda, Md., 1967-73; dir. pub. affairs Ocean Data Systems, Inc., Rockville, Md., 1973-77; asst. budget sec. State of Md., Annapolis, 1977-78; county exec. Howard County Md., Ellicott City, 1978-86; dir. econ. devel. Entergy Corp., New Orleans, 1986-93; prin. ICA, Maplesville, Ala., 1993—; cons. NSF, Washington, 1972-78. Contbr. articles to profl. jours. Charter mem., bd. dirs. Howard County, 1966-68, mem. county coun., 1969-70; mem. state legislature Md. Ho. of Dels., Annapolis, 1970-77; mem. Howard County Exec., 1978-86. Served with U.S. Army, 1948-54, ETO. Mem. AAAS (life), VFW (life), Acad. Polit. Sci. (life), Am. Acad. Scis. (Space Application Bd. 1983-86), Nat. Rifle Assn. (life), Am. Legion (life), Mensa, Phi Beta Kappa, Phi Alpha Theta, Pi Sigma Alpha. Republican. Methodist. Lodges: Alcazar Temple, Patmos. Avocations: writing, flying, boating, traveling. Home: 318 Chilton Rd 214 Maplesville AL 36750 Office: ICA PO Box 223 Maplesville AL 36750-0223

NICHOLS, J. LARRY, energy company executive, lawyer; b. Oklahoma City, July 6, 1942; s. John Whiteman and Mary (Davis) N.; m. Polly Puckett, Oct. 16, 1971; children: Tyler, Sally. BA in Geology, Princeton U., 1964; JD, U. Mich., 1967. Bar: Okla. 1967. Law clk. to chief justice U.S. Supreme Ct., Washington, 1967-68; spl. asst. to asst. atty. gen. U.S. Dept. Justice, Washington, 1968-70; pres. Devon Energy Corp., Oklahoma City, 1970—. Commr. Urban Renewal Authority Bd., Oklahoma City, 1989; pres. domestic petroleum coun. Okla. Nature Conservancy. Mem. Okla. Bar Assn. (bd. dirs., v.p.), Ind. Petroleum Assn. Am. (bd. dirs.), NAM (bd. dirs.), Oklahoma City C. of C., Econ. Club (pres. 1988-89). Office: Devon Energy Corp 20 N Broadway Ave Oklahoma City OK 73102-8202

NICHOLS, JAMES RICHARD, civil engineer, consultant; b. Amarillo, Tex., June 29, 1923; s. Marvin Curtis and Ethel (Nichols) N.; m. Billie Louise Smith, Dec. 24, 1944; children: Judith Ann, James Richard Jr., John M. B.S. in Civil Engring., Tex. A&M U., 1949, M.S. in Civil Engring., 1950. Registered profl. engr., Tex., Okla., N.Mex. Ptnr. Freese & Nichols, Inc., Cons. Engrs., Fort Worth, 1950-76; pres. Freese & Nichols, Inc., Cons. Engrs., 1977-88, chmn., 1988—; bd. dirs. Cornerstone Investment Group. Chmn. Ft. Worth Conv. and Visitors Bur.; bd. dirs. United Way Tarrant County, Pub. Comm. Found. North Tex., Tex. A&M Rsch. Found., Tex. Wesleyan U. With U.S. Army, 1943-46. Fellow Am. Cons. Engrs. Council; mem. Cons. Engrs. Council, ASCE, Nat. Soc. Profl. Engrs., Fort Worth C of C. (bd. dirs., mem. adv. council), Newcomen Soc. Methodist. Clubs: Masons, Rotary, Fort Worth, Exchange. Home: 4821 Overton Woods Dr Fort Worth TX 76109-2429 Office: Freese & Nichols Inc 4055 Internat Plz Ste 200 Fort Worth TX 76109-4895

NICHOLS, JAMES ROBBS, university dean; b. Jackson, Tenn., May 30, 1926; s. William Ed and Buelha (Robbs) N.; m. Johnnie Jones; 1 dau., Tina Jean Nichols Benson. BS, U. Tenn., 1949; MS, U. Minn., 1955, PhD, 1957. Former mem. faculty Pa. State U., U. Tenn.; mem. faculty Va. Poly. Inst. and State U., Blacksburg, 1964-71, 73—; head dairy sci. dept. Va. Poly. Inst. and State U., 1964-69; assoc. dean Va. Poly. Inst. and State U. (Coll. Agr.), 1969-71, 73-75; dean Coll. Agr. & Life Scis., dir. Va. Agr. Exptl. Sta., 1975—; exec. v.p., gen. mgr. Select Sires, Inc., Columbus, Ohio, 1971-73. Served with USAAF, World War II. Named Man of Yr. in Agr. in Va. Progressive Farmer mag., 1975; hon. state farmer Tenn. Mem. AAAS, Am. Dairy Sci. Assn., Sigma Xi, Phi Kappa Phi, Alpha Zeta. Methodist. Clubs: Rotary. Office: Va Poly Inst and State U Coll Agr and Life Scis 104G Hutcheson Hall Blacksburg VA 24061-2903

NICHOLS, JOHN D., church administrator. Dir. of ministry to the military Ch. of God. Office: Church of God PO Box 2430 Cleveland TN 37320-2430

NICHOLS, JOHN DOANE, diversified manufacturing corporation executive; b. Shanghai, China, 1930; m. Alexandra M. Curran, Dec. 4, 1971; children: Kendra E., John D. III. BA, Harvard U., 1953, MBA, 1955. Various operating positions Ford Motor Corp., 1958-68; dir. fin. controls ITT Corp., 1968-69; exec. v.p., chief operating officer Aerojet-Gen. Corp., 1969-79; exec. v.p., COO Ill. Tool Works Inc., Chgo., 1980-81; chief exec. officer, dir. Ill. Tool Works Inc., 1982—, chmn., 1986—; bd. dirs. Household Internat., Philip Morris Cos., Inc., Rockwell Internat., Stone Container Corp.; overseer Harvard U. Trustee U. Chgo. 1987-93, Chgo. Symphony Orch., 1986-94, Lyric Opera Chgo., Mus. Sci. and Industry, Jr. Achievement Chgo., Chgo. Commerce Civic Com., Bus. Roundtable, Art Inst. Chgo.; overseer Argonne (Ill.) Nat. Lab., 1988-93. Mem. Harvard Club (N.Y., Chgo.), Indian Hill Club (Winnetka, Ill.), Chgo. Club, Comml. Club, Econ.

Club Chgo. Home: 900 Mount Pleasant Rd Winnetka IL 60093-3613 Office: Ill Tool Works Inc 3600 W Lake Ave Glenview IL 60025-1215

NICHOLS, KENNETH DAVID, consulting engineer; b. Cleve., Nov. 13, 1907; s. Wilbur Loren and Minnie May (Colbrunn) N.; m. Jacqueline Darrieulat, Dec. 15, 1932; (children: Jacqueline Anne Thompson, K. David. BS, U.S. Mil. Acad., 1929; CE, Cornell U., 1932, MCE, 1933; postgrad., Technische Hochschule, Charlottenburg, Fed. Republic Germany, 1934-35; PhD in Hydraulics, U. Iowa, 1937. Commd. 2d lt. C.E. U.S. Army, 1929, advanced through grades to maj. gen., 1948, various mil. positions, 1929-41, dep. and dist. engr., Manhattan Engr. Dist., 1942-46; prof. mechanics U.S. Mil. Acad., West Point, N.Y., 1947-48; chief armed forces spl. weapons project (atomic) Pentagon, Va., 1948-50; dep. dir. guided missiles Office of Sec. of Def., Pentagon, Va., 1951-53; chief R&D Office of Chief of Staff, U.S. Army, Pentagon, Va., 1952-53; ret. U.S. Army, 1953; gen. mgr. U.S. AEC, Washington, 1953-55; cons. engr. Md., 1955-92; with World War II prodn. plants plutonium and uranium U-235, 1942-46; Cold War chief Armed Forces Spl. Weapons Project, 1948-50; cons. Yankee Atomic Power Plant, Conn. Atomic Power Plant, 1955-71. Author: The Road to Trinity, 1987. Trustee Thomas Alva Edison Found., Detroit, 1963-76; bd. dirs., v.p. Army Distaff Found., Washington, 1960-66; mem. at large engring. and indsl. rsch. div., NRC, Washington, 1954-58. Decorated DSM, DSM with oak leaf cluster; named to Comdr. Brit. Empire Order, Brit. Amb., 1946; recipient Presdl. Medal of Merit, Pres. of Nicaragua, 1931, Disting. Svc. medal Commn. AEC, 1955, Chiefs of Engrs. award for Outstanding Pub. Svc. Fellow Am. Nuclear Soc.; mem. ASME (hon.), Nat. Acad. Engring., ASCE (Collinwood Prize 1938). Republican. Home: Knollwood 6200 Oregon Ave NW Apt 345 Washington DC 20015-1543

NICHOLS, KYRA, ballerina; b. Berkeley, Calif., July 2, 1958. Studied with Alan Howard, Pacific Ballet, Sch. Am. Ballet, N.Y.C. With N.Y.C. Ballet, 1974—, prin. dancer, 1979—. Created roles in Tricolore, 1978, A Sketch Book, 1978, Jerome Robbins' Four Seasons, 1979, John Taras' Concerto for Piano and Wind Instruments, Stravinsky Centennial Celebration, 1982, Jacques d'Amboise's Celebration, 1983; performed in N.Y.C. Ballet's Balanchine Celebration, 1993. Ford Found. scholar; recipient Dance Mag. award, 1988. Office: Peter S Diggins Assocs 133 W 71st St New York NY 10023-3834 also: NYC Ballet Inc NY State Theater Lincoln Ctr Pla New York NY 10023

NICHOLS, MARY D., federal agency administrator, lawyer. BA, Cornell U.; JD, Yale U. Sr. staff atty., dir. L.A. office Nat. Resources Def. Coun.; asst. adminstr. for air and radiation EPA, Washington, 1993—; chair Calif. Air Resources Bd.; bd. commns. L.A. Dept. Water and Power; instr. U. So. Calif., UCLA; founding trustee Calif. Environ. Trust; bd. dirs. L.A. 2000 Partnership; cons. in field. Office: Enviromental Protection Agency Air & Radiation 401 M St SW Washington DC 20001

NICHOLS, MIKE, stage and film director; b. Berlin, Nov. 6, 1931; s. Nicholaievitch and Brigitte (Landauer) Peschowsky; m. Patricia Scott, 1957 (div.); m. Margot Callas, 1974 (div.); m. Annabel (div.); m. Diane Sawyer, Apr. 29, 1988. Student, U. Chgo., 1950-53; student acting, Lee Strasberg. Ptnr. with Elaine May in comedy act; first appeared at Playwrights Theatre Club, Compass Theatre, Chgo.; N.Y. debut An Evening with Mike Nichols and Elaine May, 1960; acted in A Matter of Position, Phila., 1962; dir.: (plays) Barefoot in the Park, 1963 (Tony award), The Knack, 1964, Luv, 1964 (Tony award), The Odd Couple, 1965 (Tony award for best dir.), The Apple Tree, 1966, The Little Foxes, 1967, Plaza Suite, 1968 (Tony award), The Prisoner of 2d Avenue, 1971 (Tony award), Uncle Vanya (co-adapted), 1973, Streamers, 1976, Comedians, 1976, The Gin Game, 1977, Billy Bishop Goes to War, Lunch Hour, 1980, Fools, 1981, The Real Thing, 1984 (Tony award 1984,), Hurlyburly, 1984, Social Security, 1984, Elliot Loves, 1990, Death and the Maiden, 1992; (films) Who's Afraid of Virginia Woolf?, 1966, (Academy award nomination best director 1966), The Graduate, 1967 (Academy award best director 1967), Catch-22, 1970, Carnal Knowledge, 1971, The Day of the Dolphin, 1973, The Fortune, 1975, Gilda Live, 1980, Silkwood, 1983 (Academy award nomination best director 1983), Heartburn, 1986, Biloxi Blues, 1987, Working Girl, 1988 (Academy award nomination best director 1988), Postcards From the Edge, 1990, Regarding Henry, 1991, Wolf, 1994; producer: (musical) Annie, 1977; performed at N.Y. musical Pres. Johnson's Inaugural Gala, 1965; TV appearances include Today Show. Office: care Mike Ovitz CAA 9830 Wilshire Blvd Beverly Hills CA 90212

NICHOLS, RALPH ARTHUR, lawyer; b. Clinton, N.Y., Jan. 27, 1919; s. Arthur Britcher and Carrie Lena (Pitcher) N.; m. Pamela Crow Berninghausen, May 3, 1947 (dec. Feb. 1980); children: Jeremy Nichols Pierce, Ralph A. Jr., Melinda Nichols Mayer; m. Victoria Requa Lalli, Sept. 5, 1981. AB, Hamilton Coll., 1940; LLB, Yale U., 1947. Bar: Conn. 1949, N.Y. 1947, U.S. Dist. Ct. (so. dist.) N.Y. 1949, U.S. Dist. Ct. Conn. 1950, U.S. Supreme Ct. 1959. Assoc. Burke & Burke, N.Y.C., 1947-49, Maguire, Walker & Middleton, Stamford, Ct., 1949-54; assoc., then ptnr. Cummings & Lockwood, Stamford, 1954—. Founder, former bd. dirs. Stamford Land Conservation Trust; former bd. dirs. Conservationists Stamford, Inc., Stamford YMCA; former bd. dirs., sec. Stamford Area Commerce and Industry; trustee Stamford YMCA. Lt. USNR, 1942-46, ETO, PTO. Fellow Am. Coll. Trust and Estate Counsel; mem. ABA, Woodway Country Club (Darien, Conn.), Yale Club (N.Y.C.), Phi Delta Phi. Republican. Episcopalian. Home: 656 Den Rd Stamford CT 06903-3824 Office: Cummings & Lockwood PO Box 120 10 Stamford Forum Stamford CT 06901-3215

NICHOLS, RICHARD DALE, former congressman, banker; b. Ft. Scott, Kans., Apr. 29, 1926; s. Ralph Dale and Olive Marston (Kittell) N.; m. Constance Weinbrenner, Mar. 25, 1951; children: Philip William, Ronald Dale, Anita Jane Nichols Bomberger. BS in Agr. and BS in Journalism, Kans. State U., 1951. Info. counsel Kans. State Bd. Agr., Topeka, 1951-54; assoc. far, dir. Sta. WIBW, WIBW-TV, Topeka, 1954-57; agr. rep. to v.p. Hutchinson (Kans.) Nat. Bank and Trust, 1957-69; pres., chief exec. officer Home State Bank, McPherson, Kans., 1969-79, chmn., pres. chief exec. officer, 1979-91; mem. 102d Congress from 5th Kans. dist., 1991-92; chmn. Home State Bank & Trust, McPherson, Kans., 1993—. Pres. Arts Coun., McPherson, 1979; dist. chmn. Rep. Party, Kans., 1986-89. Ensign USN, 1944-47, ATO; bd. trustees Ctrl. Coll. mem. VFW, Kans. Bankers Assn. (pres. 1985-86), Am. Bankers Assn. (advisor 1986-88), Kans. Assn. Banking Ag. Reps. (pres. 1965), Am. Legion, McPherson C. of C. (pres. 1977), Optimist (pres. Hutchinson club 1965), Rotary (pres. McPherson club 1978), Kans. Cavalry (cmdg. gen. 1986-89). Methodist. Home: 404 N Lakeside Dr Mc Pherson KS 67460-3600 Office: Home State Bank and Trust PO Box 1266 Mc Pherson KS 67460-1266

NICHOLS, ROBERT EDMUND), editor, writer, journalist; b. Daytona Beach, Fla., Feb. 14, 1925; s. Joe D. and Edna A. (Casper) N.; m. Diana R. Grosso; children by previous marriage: Craig S., Kim S., Robin K. Student, San Diego State Coll., 1942-43, St. John's Coll., 1944-45, George Washington U., 1948-49. Reporter San Diego Union, 1942-44; corr. Washington bur. N.Y. Herald Tribune, 1945-48, CBS, 1948-51, Time, Inc., 1951-61; contbg. editor Time, asst. edn. dir. Life mag., N.Y.C., 1951-52; corr. representing Time, Life, Fortune, Sports Illus. mags., San Diego area, 1952-61; Sunday editor San Diego Union, 1952-61; fin. editor Los Angeles Times, 1961-68, mem. editorial bd., 1965-68; spl. asst. to bd. govs. Fed. Res. System, 1968-70; v.p., dir. various editorial svcs. Bank of Am., 1970-85; prin. Robert E. Nichols Communications, San Francisco, 1985—. Writer, dir. film and radio documentaries. Mem. U.S. Antarctic Expedition, 1946-47. Recipient Loeb Newspaper Spl. Achievement award, 1963, Loeb award disting. fin. reporting, 1964. Fellow Royal Geog. Soc., Explorers Club; mem. Am. Polar Soc., Calif. Scholarship fedn. (hon., life), Soc. Am. Bus. Editors and Writers (hon., life, pres. 1967-68), South Polar Press Club. Home and Office: 38 Ord Ct San Francisco CA 94114-1417

NICHOLS, ROBERT LEE, food company executive; b. Clarksburg, W.Va., Nov. 4, 1924; s. Clarence Garfield and Reatha Maude (Berry) N.; m. Vianne Hope Demaray, Oct. 21, 1973; children: Donna Beth, Michael Alan, Jeffrey Mark. Student, Bus. Coll., 1944, U. Detroit, 1959. Sales rep. Kellogg Sales Co., Battle Creek, Mich., 1944-50; dist. mgr. Kellogg Sales Co., 1950-61, asst. div. mgr., 1961-64, sales promotion dir., 1964-69, exec. v.p., gen. sales mgr., 1969-71, pres., 1976-78; pres. Fearn Internat., 1971-76, dir., 1971-82;

group exec. v.p. Kellogg Co., Battle Creek, 1979-82, dir., 1977-89, vice chmn., 1983-89; pres., dir. Mrs. Smith's Frozen Foods Co., 1979-82, McCamly Square Corp., 1983-89; dir., pres. Battle Creek Unltd., 1985-87; bd. dirs. Cereal Inst., 1976-79, Am. Frozen Food Inst., 1982, Cereal City Devel. Corp., 1986; bd. govs. Acad. Food Mktg., St. Joseph U., 1976-79. Exec. v.p., bd. dirs. Jr. Achievement, Battle Creek, 1970-71; trustee Mich. Colls. Found., 1985-89, Thomas Jefferson Found., Lakeview Schs., 1986-89, Mich. Biotechnology Inst., 1985-89, Citizens Research Council of Mich, 1985-90; mem., bd. dirs United Way of Greater Battle Creek Area, 1984-89, campaign chmn. 1985; pres. Battle Creek Unltd., 1985-87; vice chmn. Battle Creek Airport Adv. Com., 1984-89; mem. Nat. Corp. Council Interlochen Ctr. for the Arts, 1986-89; mem. adminstrv. bd. 1st United Meth. Ch., Stuart, Fla., 1990—. Mem. Svc. Core Ret. Execs. (vice chair 1991-93), Snug Harbor Yacht Club (vice commodore 1990-92, commodore 1992-93), First Nat. Bank & Trust of the Treasure Coast (adv. bd. 1993—), Martin County Coun. for the Arts (dir. 1992—), Masons. Office: Kellogg Co 1 Kellogg Sq PO Box 3599 Battle Creek MI 49016-3599

NICHOLS, ROBERT LEIGHTON, civil engineer; b. Amarillo, Tex., June 24, 1926; s. Marvin Curtis and Ethel N.; m. Frances Hardison, June 8, 1948; children—Eileen, William C., Michael L. B.S.C.E., Tex. A&M U., 1947, M.S.C.E., 1948. Grad. asst., instr. Tex. A&M U., 1947-48; assoc. Freese & Nichols (and predecessors), Ft. Worth, 1948-50; partner Freese & Nichols (and predecessors), 1950-77, v.p., 1977-88, pres., 1988-91, vice chmn., 1991-92, pres. emeritus, 1992—; mem. Bldg. Standards Commn., 1956-62. Chmn. Horn Frog dist. Boy Scouts Am., pres. Longhorn coun., 1990-93. Mem. ASCE, NSPE (pres. 1977-78), Tex. Soc. Profl. Engrs. (pres. 1965-66, Engr. of Yr. Ft. Worth chpt. 1966), Am. Water Works Assn., Tex. Water Conservation Assn., Water Environ. Fedn., Water Environ. Assn. Tex. (pres. 1962-63), Am. Pub. Woks Assn., Tex. Water Utilities Assn., Tex. Pub. Works Assn., Masons, Tau Beta Pi, Chi Epsilon. Methodist. Office: 4055 Internat Plz Fort Worth TX 76109-4895

NICHOLS, RONALD LEE, surgeon, educator; b. Chgo., June 25, 1941; s. Peter Raymond and Jane Eleanor (Johnson) N.; m. Elsa Elaine Johnson, Dec. 4, 1964; children: Kimberly Jane, Matthew Bennett. M.D., U. Ill., 1966, M.S., 1970. Diplomate: Am. Bd. Surgery (assoc. cert. examiner, New Orleans, 1991), Nat. Bd. Med. Examiners. Intern U. Ill. Hosp., Chgo., 1966-67, resident in surgery, 1967-72, instr. surgery, 1970-72, asst. prof. surgery, 1972-74; assoc. prof. surgery U. Health Scis. Chgo. Med. Sch., 1975-77, dir. surg. edn., 1975-77; William Henderson prof. surgery Tulane U. Sch. Medicine, New Orleans, 1977—, staff surgeon, 1977—, prof. microbiology and immunology, 1979—; vice chmn. dept. surgery Tulane U. Sch. Medicine, New Orleans, $D, 1982-91; cons. surgeon VA Hosp., Alexandria, La., 1978-93, Huey P. Long Hosp., Pineville, La., 1978—, Lallie Kemp Charity Hosp., Independence, La., 1977-85, Touro Infirmary, New Orleans, Monmouth Med. Ctr., Long Branch, N.J., 1979-88; mem. VA Coop. Study Rev. Bd., 1978-81, VA Merit Rev. Bd. in Surgery, 1979-82; mem. sci. program com. 3d Internat. Conf. Nosocomial Infections, Ctr. Disease Control; bd. dirs. Nat. Found. Infectious Diseases, 1989—; hon. fellow faculty Kasr El Aini Cairo U. Sch. Medicine, 1989; mem. adv. com. on infection control Ctrs. for Disease Control, 1991—; disting. guest, vis. prof. Royal Coll. Surgeons Thailand 14th Ann. Clin. Congress, 1989, 17th Ann. Clin. Congress, 1992; mem. infectious deseases adv. bd. Roche Labs., 1988-95, Abbott Labs., 1990-92, Kimberly Clark Corp., 1990—, Smith Klein Beecham Labs., 1990-95, Fujisawa Pharm., chmn. 1990—, Miles Pharm., 1994—. Author: (with Gorbach, Bartlett and Nichols) Manual of Surgical Infection, 1984; (with Nichols, Hyslop Jr. and Bartlett) Decision Making in Surgical Sepsis, 1991; guest editor: Surgical Sepsis 1993 and Beyond, 1993; mem. editorial bd. Current Surgery, 1977—, Hosp. Physician, 1980—, Infection Control, 1980-86, Guidelines to Antibiotic Therapy, 1976-81, Am. Jour. Infection Control, 1981—, Internat. Medicine, 1983—, Confronting Infection, 1983-86, Current Concepts in Clin. Surgery, 1984—, Fact Line, 1984—, Host/Pathogen News, 1984—, Infectious Diseases in Clin. Practice, 1991—, surg. sect. editor, 1992—, Surgical Infections: Index and Reviews, So. Med. Jour., 1992—, ANAEROBE; mem. adv. bd. Physicians News Network, 1991-95; patentee (with S.G. Schoenberger and W.R. Rank) Helical-Tipped Lesion Localization Needle Device; patentee in field. Elected faculty sponsor graduating class Tulane Med. Sch., 1979-80, 83, 85, 87, 88, 91-92. Served to major USAR, 1972-75. Recipient House Staff teaching award U. Ill. Coll. Medicine, 1973, Rsch. award Bd. Trustees U. Health Scis.-Chgo. Med. Sch., 1977, Owl Club Teaching award, 1980-86, 90; named Clin. Prof. of Yr. U. Health Scis., Chgo. Med. Sch., 1977, Clin. Prof. of Yr., Tulane U. Sch. Medicine, 1979; Douglas Stubbs Lectr. award Surg. Sect. Nat. Med. Assn., 1987, Prix d'Elegance award Men of Fashion, New Orleans, 1993. Fellow Infectious Disease Soc. Am. (mem. FDA subcom. to develop guidelines in surg. prophylaxis 1989-93, co-recipient Joseph Susman Meml. award 1990), Am. Acad. Microbiology, Internat. Soc. Univ. Colon and Rectal Surgeons, ACS (chmn. operating room environment com. 1981-83, sr. mem. 1984-87, 94—, internat. relations com. 1987-93); mem. AMA, Nat. Found. for Infectious Diseases (bd. dirs. 1988—, v.p. 1994—), Joint Commn. on Accreditation of Health Care Orgn. (Infection Control adv. group, 1988—, sci. program com. 3d internat. conf. nosocomial infections CDC/Nat. Found. Infectious Diseases 1990, FDA Subcom. to Develop Guidelines in Surg. Prophylaxis, AIDS commr. State of La. 1992-94), 5th Nat. Forum on AIDS (sci. program com.), Assn. Practitioners in Infection Control (physician adv. coun. 1991—), Internat. Soc. Anaerobic Bacteria, So. Med. Assn. (vice chmn. sect. surgery 1980-81, chmn. 1982-83), Assn. Acad. Surgery, N.Y. Acad. Sci., Warren H. Cole Soc. (pres.-ele Assn. VA Surgeons, Soc. Surgery Alimentary Tract, Inst. Medicine Chgo., Midwest Surg. Assn., Cen. Surg. Assn., Ill. Surg. Soc., European Soc. Surg. Rsch., Collegium Internationale Chirugiae Digestivae, Chgo. Surg. Soc. (hon.), New Orleans Surg. Soc. (bd. dirs. 1983-87), Soc. Univ. Surgeons, Surg. Soc. La., Southeastern Surg. Soc., Phoenix Surg. Soc. (hon.), Hellenic Surg. Soc. (hon.), Cen. N.Y. Surg. Soc. (hon.), Tulane Surg. Soc., Alton Ochsner Surg. Soc., Am. Soc. Microbiology, Soc. Internat. de Chirugie, Surg. Infection Soc. (sci. study com. 1982-83, fellowship com. 1985-87, ad hoc sci. liaison com. 1986-89, program com. 1986-87, chmn. ad hoc com. rels. with industry 1990-93, mem. sci. liaison com. 1995—), Soc. for Intestinal Microbial Ecology and Disease, Soc. Critical Care Medicine, Am. Surg. Assn., Kansas City Surg. Soc., Bay Surg. Soc. (hon.), Cuban Surg. Soc. (hon.), Panhellenic Surg. Soc. (hon.), Sigma Xi, Alpha Omega Alpha. Episcopalian. Home: 1521 7th St New Orleans LA 70115-3322 Office: 1430 Tulane Ave New Orleans LA 70112-2699

NICHOLS, RUSSELL JAMES, manufacturing company executive; b. Brockton, Mass., Nov. 12, 1943; s. Clarence Willard and Hattie Matilda (Harlow) N.; m. Patricia Anna Rogers, Aug. 1, 1964; children: James E., Sharon L., Deborah L. Student, Rutgers U., 1966-68, Marion (Ohio) Tech. Coll., 1973-75, Findlay (Ohio) Coll., 1979-80. Registered profl. engr., Ohio. Rsch. technician Princeton Rsch. Ctr. Columbian Carbon divsn. Cities Svc. Co., Cranberry, N.J., 1965-68; tech. svc. engr. HPM Corp., Mount Gilead, Ohio, 1969-71, rsch. engr., 1971-73, product engr., 1974, area sales mgr., 1975, product mgr., 1976-77; process engring. mgr. Hancor Inc., Findlay, 1977-80; dir. devel. and tech. dir. Welding Engrs., Inc., Blue Bell, Pa., 1981-88; v.p. engring. Farrel Corp., Ansonia, Conn., 1989-90, v.p. quality, 1991—. Contbr. articles to profl. jours.; patentee in field. With USN, 1961-64. Mem. NSPE, Soc. Plastics Engrs. (sr. mem.), Am. Mgmt. Assn., Am. Soc. Quality Control, Am. Chem. Soc. (Akron Rubber Group divsn.). Avocations: computers, reading. Home: 292 Elmwood Cir Cheshire CT 06410 Office: Farrel Corp 25 Main St Ansonia CT 06401

NICHOLS, STEPHEN GEORGE, Romance languages educator; b. Cambridge, Mass., Oct. 24, 1936; s. Stephen George and Marjorie (Whitney) N.; m. Mary Winn Jordan, June 22, 1957 (div. 1972); children: Stephen Frost (dec.), Sarah Winn; m. Edith Karetzky, 1972; stepchildren: Laura Natalie Karetzky, Sarah Alexandra Karetzky. A.B. cum laude, Dartmouth Coll., 1958; A.B., Rotary Found. fellow, Université d'Aix-Marseilles, France, 1958-59; Ph.D., Yale U., 1963; Docteur ès lettres honoris causa, Université de Genève, 1992. Asst. prof. French UCLA, 1963-65; assoc. prof. comparative lit. U. Wis.-Madison, 1965-68, chmn. dept., 1967-68; prof. Romance langs. and comparative lit. Dartmouth Coll., 1968-84, chmn. dept. comparative lit., 1969-72, 74, 79-82, chmn. Romance langs., 1974-77, Edward Tuck prof. French, 1984-85, chmn. dept. French and Italian, 1982-85, liaison officer Sch. Criticism and Theory, 1983-85; faculty Dartmouth Inst., 1980-85, faculty dir., 1984-85; prof. Romance langs. U. Pa., 1985-86, Edmund J. Kahn Disting. prof. humanities, 1986-92; James M. Beall prof. French and humanities Johns Hopkins U., Balt., 1992—; grad. group chmn. French and

Italian U. Pa., 1986-88, chmn. dept. romance langs., 1987-88, assoc. dean for humanities, 1988-91; acting chair French, 1993-94; dir. grad. studies dept. French The Johns Hopkins U., Balt., 1992-94; R. Champlain and Debbie Sheridan interim dir. Eisenhower Libr., Johns Hopkins U., 1994-95, chair dept of French, 1995—; vis. prof. U. Tel Aviv, 1977, NYU, 1979-81, Exeter (Eng.) U., 1980, Ariz. State U., 1982, U. Calif., Irvine, 1985, Sch. of Criticism and Theory, 1989, 95, Humanities Rsch. Inst., U. Calif., 1990, NEH fellow, 1978-79, rev. panelist 1979-81, 84, 91, Guggenheim fellow, 1987-88; Phi Beta Kappa vis. scholar, 1983-84; Lauder fellow Aspen Inst. for Humanistic Study, 1988; mem. adv. bd. Institut d'Etudes françaises d'Avignon, Bryn Mawr Coll., 1965—; dir. seminar NEH, 1975, 79, Mellon Summer Seminar in Humanities, Johns Hopkins U., 1993, 94, dir. Louis Marin Ctr. for French Cult. Studies, Johns Hopkins U., 1993—; exec. com. Eastern Comparative Lit. Conf.; mem. adv. coun. dept. comparative lit. Princeton U., 1982-88, chmn., 1984-88; co-dir. Cultural Study, U. Pa., 1986-92; advisor Waverly Consort, 1987—; adv. bd. Soc. Humanities Cornell U., 1993—; dir. assoc. studies Ecole Pratique des Hautes Etudes, Paris, 1994-95; dir. Sch. of Criticism and Theory, 1995—. Author: Formulaic Diction and Thematic Composition in the Chanson de Roland, 1961, The Songs of Bernart de Ventadorn, 1962, Comparatists at Work, 1968, The Meaning of Mannerism, 1972, Romanesque Signs: Early Medieval Narrative and Iconography (James Russell Lowell prize MLA 1984), 1983, paperback edit., 1985, Mimesis: from Mirror to Method, Augustine to Descartes, 1982, Images of Power: Medieval History/Discourse/Literature, 1986, The Legitimacy of the Middle Ages, 1988, The New Philology, 1990, The New Medievalism, 1991, Boundaries and Transgressions in Medieval Literature, 1990, Annotation as Cultural Artifact, 1993; also articles in profl. jours.; mem. editl. bd. French Rev., 1968-69, Comparative Lit. Studies, 1987—, Medievalia et Humanistica, 1974—, Medievalia, 1974—, Oliphant, 1974—, PMLA, 1980-85, 88-89; co-editor Parallax: Revisions of Culture and Society, 1987—, Figurae: New Studies in Medieval Literature and Culture, 1991-94; adv. editor Utrecht Publications in General and Comparative Literature, 1987—; mem. adv. bd. Romanic Rev., 1986—. Fellow Inst. Research in Humanities, 1966-67; sr. fellow Sch. of Criticism and Theory, 1988—. Fellow Medieval Acad. Am.; mem. Acad. Lit. Studies (nominating com. 1974-78, sec.-treas. 1978-87), Dante Soc., Internat. Comparative Lit. Assn., New Eng. Medieval Assn. (adv. com. 1985-85), MLA (chmn. com. on careers 1985-86, James Russell Lowell prize com. 1986-88, com. on profl. ethics 1987-88, del. assembly 1994—), Medieval Acad. Am., Société Rencevals (sec.-treas. Am. sect. 1964-69). Home: 5 Saint Martins Rd Baltimore MD 21218-1815

NICHOLS, STEVEN PARKS, mechanical engineer, university official; b. Cody, Wyo., July 1, 1950; s. Rufus Parks Nichols and Gwen Sena (Frank) Keyes; m. Mary Ruth Barrow, Aug. 5, 1990; 1 child, Nicholas Barrow Nichols. PhD, U. Tex., Austin, 1975, JD, 1983. Assoc. dir. Tex. Space Grant Consortium, Austin, 1989-91; dep. dir. ctr. for energy studies U. Tex., Austin, 1988-91, dir. Ctr. for Energy Studies, 1991—, acting dir. ctr. for electromechanics, 1994—. Patentee (with others) railgun igniter, inert burner, other patents pending. Mem. NSPE, ASME, ABA, Am. Soc. Engring. Edn., Nat. Inst. Engring. Ethics (bd. govs. 1987-93). Home: 105 Laurel Ln Austin TX 78705-2813 Office: U Tex Ctr for Energy Studies 10100 Burnet Rd Austin TX 78758-4445

NICHOLS, WADE HAMPTON, III, lawyer; b. Bronxville, N.Y., Dec. 7, 1942; s. Wade Hampton Jr. and Edith Lou (Docekal) N.; m. Brenda Gail Downing, June 27, 1981; children: Scot, Laura, Eric Black, Gregory Black. BA, Yale U., 1964; LLB, Columbia U., 1967. Bar: N.Y. 1967. Assoc. Paul, Weiss, Rifkind, Wharton & Garrison, N.Y.C., 1971-78; sr. counsel Revlon Inc., N.Y.C., 1978-81; sec. Revlon Inc., N.Y.C., 1981-92, v.p., 1984-92, sr. v.p., gen. counsel, 1992—; v.p. MacAndrews & Forbes Holdings, Inc., 1986—. Served to lt. JAGC, USNR, 1967-71. Mem. ABA, Am. Soc. Corp. Secs. Democrat.

NICHOLS, WILLIAM CURTIS, psychologist, family therapist, consultant; b. Fayette, Ala., Apr. 16, 1929; s. William Curtis and Eva (Hargett) N.; m. Alice Louise Mancill, May 29, 1954 (dec. 1990); children: Alice Camille, William Mancill, David Paul; m. Mary Anne Pace, Feb. 29, 1992. AB, U. Ala., 1953; EdD, Columbia U., 1960. Diplomate Am. Bd. Profl. Psychology. Asst. prof. sociology U. Ala., Birmingham, 1960-63; postdoctoral fellow Merrill-Palmer Inst., 1963-64, mem. psychotherapy faculty, 1965-69; prof. sociology Samford U., Birmingham, Ala., 1963-65; pvt. practice clin. psychology and marital and family therapy Grosse Pointe, Mich., 1969-73, 76-87; pvt. practice psychology, marital and family therapy Birmingham, Mich., 1976-87; prof. home and family life, dir. marriage and family counseling Fla. State U., 1973-76; exec. dir. Gov.'s Constituency Children, Fla., 1987-89; pvt. practice marital and family therapy S.E. Family Inst., 1989-90; pres. William Nichols Assocs., Organizational Cons., 1990-91; cons., marital and family therapist Atlanta, 1992—; adj. prof. clin. psychology U. Detroit, 1976-83; adj. prof. family therapy Fla. State U., 1990-91; adj. prof., grad. faculty child and family devel. dept. U. Ga., 1992—, founder, chair adv. com. Family Therapy Archives, 1993—. Author: Marital Therapy: An Integrative Approach, 1988, Treating Adult Survivors of Childhood Sexual Abuse, 1992, The AAMFT: Fifty Years of Marital and Family Therapy, 1992; co-author: Systematic Family Therapy, 1986; editor The Family Coord., 1970-75, Jour. of Marriage and Family Counseling, 1974-76, Contemporary Family Therapy: An International Jour., 1986—, Family Therapy News, 1986-91; mem. editorial bd. Internat. Jour. of Family Therapy, 1977-85, Jour. of Divorce and Remarriage, 1976-83, 1985—, Internat. Jour. of Family, Sage Family Studies Abstracts, 1977—, Family Systems Medicine, 1982—, Jour. Marital and Family Therapy, 1984—, Jour. Family Psychotherapy, 1990—, Jour. Family Psychology, 1986-90. Mem. mental health and health coms. Mayor's Commn. on Children and Youth, 1966-69; bd. dirs. Family and Children's Svc., Oakland, Mich., 1977-87, chmn., 1984-86, dir. emeritus, 1987—. With C.E., U.S. Army, 1948-49. Recipient Svc. award Ala. Assn. for Mental Health, 1962, Spl. award for Outstanding Contbns. Fla. Assn. Marriage and Family Therapy, 1977, 82, 90; NSF fellow U. Colo., 1963. Fellow APA, Am. Psychol. Soc., Am. Assn. Marriage and Family Therapy (dir. 1969-72, 1979-83, chmn. accreditation com. 1976-77, co-chmn. Atlanta Multiregional Conf. 1975, 77, founding editor Jour. Marital and Family Therapy 1974-76, Spl. awards 1976, 78, Disting. Leadership awards 1982, 83, pres.-elect 1979-80, pres. 1981-82, Disting. Leadership award 1991, Orgnl. Contributions award 1992), Acad. of Clin. Psychology; mem. Am. Assn. Marriage and Family Therapy Edn. and Rsch. Found. (trustee 1992-94), Am. Assn. Marital and Family Therapy Regulation Bds. (mem. MFT Examination Adv. bd. 1989-92), Mich. Inter-Profl. Assn. on Marriage, Divorce and Family (Organizational Contbn. award 1992, trustee 1977-80, com. chmn. 1968-71, 76—), Mich. Assn. Marriage Counselors (pres. 1969-71, chmn. profl. liaison com. 1972-73), Nat. Coun. on Family Rels. (pres. 1976-77, dir., mem. exec. com. 1969-78), Mich. Bd. Marriage Counselors (chair 1980-87), Ga. Assn. for Marriage and Family Therapy (pres.-elect 1994—). Home: 1041 Ferncreek Dr Watkinsville GA 30677-4212 Office: The Family Workshop 752 Houston Mill Rd NE Atlanta GA 30329

NICHOLS, WILLIAM DEMING, lawyer; b. New Haven, Nov. 12, 1924; s. Malcolm Parrot and Mabel (Turck) N.; m. Nancy Bird; children: Nathaniel, Malcolm, William, Deborah. BA, Amherst Coll., 1951; LLB, Harvard U., 1954. Sr. ptnr. Sullivan & Worcester, Boston, 1962-94, of counsel, 1995—. Sgt. USMC, 1942-45, PTO. Republican. Protestant. Home: 245 Main Ave South Hampton NH 03827 Office: Sullivan & Worcester 1 Post Office Sq Boston MA 02109-2103

NICHOLS, WILLIAM FORD, JR., foundation executive, business executive; b. Palo Alto, Calif., July 4, 1934; s. William Ford and Elizabeth (Woodyatt) N.; m. Rosemary Peterson, 1988; children: Deborah, John, Andrew. A.B. Stanford U., 1956, M.B.A., 1958. C.P.A., Calif. With Price Waterhouse, San Francisco, 1958-69, Price Waterhouse Co., Sydney, Australia, 1960; asst. controller Saga Corp., Menlo Park, Calif., 1969-72; controller Saga Corp., 1972—, asst. treas., 1981-83; assoc. prof. San Jose State U., 1983-88; treas. William and Flora Hewlett Found., Menlo Park, 1985—; Mem. bd. trustees The Investment Fund for Founds., 1991—. Mem. Am. Inst. C.P.A.'s, Calif. Soc. C.P.A.'s, Nat. Assn. Acct. (nat. v.p. 1974-75, dir.), Fin. Execs. Inst. (pres. Santa Clara Valley chpt. 1979-80). Home: 330 August Cir Menlo Park CA 94025-5829

NICHOLSON, BRUCE, graphics expert, executive. With Ray Mercer & Co., Apogee, Future Gen.; from optical camera asst. to optical supr. Indsl. Light & Magic, San Rafael, Calif., 1976-83, visual effects supr., 1984—. Optical camera asst. (films) Close Encounters of the Third Kind, 1976, Star Wars, 1977; optical supr. (films) The Empire Strikes Back, 1980 (Oscar award), Raiders of the Lost Ark, 1981 (Oscar award), Dragonslayer, 1981, Poltergeist, 1982, Return of the Jedi, 1983, Indiana Jones and the Temple of Doom, 1984; visual effects supr. (films) Starman, 1985, Explorers, 1986, Batteries Not Included, 1987, Field of Dreams, 1989, Always, 1989, Ghost, 1990, Memories of An Invisible Man, 1991, Meteor Man, 1993, In The Mouth of Madness, 1994, (commls.) HDTV, 1988, Panasonic, 1988, Subaru, 1989, Honda, 1990, Choice Hotels, 1994. Office: Indsl Light and Magic PO Box 2459 San Rafael CA 94912-2459

NICHOLSON, BRUCE J., insurance company executive. With Ministers Life Ins. Co., Mpls., 1975-1984, Towers Perrin Co, Mpls., 1984-1990; now with Lutheran Brotherhood Inc., 1990—. Office: Lutheran Brotherhood Inc 625 4th S Minneapolis MN 55415

NICHOLSON, DOUGLAS ROBERT, accountant; b. Avon, N.Y., Dec. 4, 1921; s. Robert William and Ruth (Neff) N.; m. Gertrude Jane Scott, Apr. 24, 1944; children—Laurie, Scott, Susan, Steven. A.B., U. Rochester, 1942, M.S., 1948. Baseball player St. Louis Cardinal Farm Teams, 1942, 46; Staff acct. Oliver & Clapp, 1948-49; sr. acct. Charles L. Clapp & Co., 1949-51; tchr. income taxes U. Rochester, 1950-61; office mgr. Williams, Clapp & Co., 1951-53, ptnr., 1953-56; prin. Haskins & Sells, CPA's, Rochester, N.Y., 1956-59, ptnr., 1959-67, ptnr.-in-charge Rochester office, 1967-82. Pres. Estate Planning Council Rochester; team capt. YMCA capital fund drive, 1961, Rochester Inst. Tech. new campus fund drive, 1964; chmn. spl. gifts com. U. Rochester, 1965, group leader 38 million capital fund campaign, 1966; mem. accounting adv. bd. Syracuse U., 1968; adv. com. M.S. program Rochester Inst. Tech. Bd. dirs.; treas. Highland Hosp., Rochester; bd. dirs. Hosp. Computer Center Rochester, Rochester Regional Research Library Council; mem. deferred giving adv. council Rochester Inst. Tech.; mem. N.Y. State Bd. Pub. Accountancy, 1977. Served to lt. USN, 1942-45. Recipient Gannett Newspapers award, 1956. Mem. Am. Inst. C.P.A.'s, N.Y. State Soc. C.P.A.'s (past pres. Rochester), Nat. Assn. Accountants, Am. Accounting Assn., Am. Mgmt. Assn., Rochester C. of C., Beta Alpha Psi. Democrat. Unitarian (trustee). Clubs: Oak Hill Country, University, Genesee Valley. Home and Office: 663 Lake Rd Webster NY 14580-1552

NICHOLSON, G. RANDY, petroleum company executive. Pres., dir. E-Z Serve Inc., Abilene, Tex. Office: E-Z Serve Inc PO Box 612007 Dallas TX 75261-2007

NICHOLSON, GEORGE, judge; b. Dallas, Feb. 15, 1941; s. George William and Delighon (Ross) N.; m. Brenda Hommel, Nov. 14, 1959; children: Peggy, Christopher. AA, Oakland City Coll., 1962; BA in Polit. Sci., Calif. State U., Hayward, 1964; JD, U. Calif., San Francisco, 1967. Bar: Calif. U.S. Ct. Appeals (9th cir.), U.S. Dist. Ct. (ea. and no. dists.) Calif., U.S. Supreme Ct. Sr. trial dep. dist. atty. Alameda County, Oakland, Calif., 1966-76; exec. dir. Calif. Dist. Atty.'s Assn., Sacramento, 1976-79; sr. asst. atty. gen. Calif. Dept. Justice, Sacramento, 1979-83; legal and ednl. advisor Gov. Calif., Sacramento, 1983-84; dir. and chief counsel Nat. Sch. Safety Ctr., Sacramento, 1984-86; sole practice Sacramento, 1986-87; Judge Sacramento Mcpl. Ct., 1987-89; judge Sacramento County Superior Ct., 1989-90; assoc. justice Ct. of Appeal Third Appellate Dist., Sacramento, 1990—; adv. bds. Fed. Office Juvenile Justice and Delinquency Prevention-Nat. juvenile justice code project, Nat. restitution project; pres.'s adv. com. Victims of Crime, 1980-81; adj. prof. edn. Grad. Sch. Edn. Psychology, Pepperdine U., Malibu, Calif.; exec. com. Commn. on the Future of the Calif. Cts., 1991-1994 (chmn. tech. com., appellate cts. com.). Prin. author Proposition 8, California Victims' Bill Rights, 1982, California Constitutional Right to Safe Schools; (with others) Forgotten Victims: An Advocate's Anthology, 1977, Crime Victims' Handbook, 1981, School Crime and Violence: Victims' Rights, 1986, 2nd edit., 1992; editor School Safety Legal Anthology, 1985; contbr. articles to profl. jours. Vol. legal counsel Parents of Murdered Children, Los Angeles, 1982; Laws at Work, Los Angeles, 1980-82; Calif. Rep. exec. com., 1983-86; Rep. nominee Calif. Atty. Gen., 1982. Mem. ABA (judicial admin. divsn.), Am. Judges Assn., Am. Judicature Soc., Calif. Judges Assn. Presbyterian. Avocations: legal edn. subjects, skiing, baseball. Office: Court of Appeal 914 Capitol Mall Sacramento CA 95814-4811

NICHOLSON, GEORGE ALBERT, JR., financial analyst; b. Baldwin City, Kan., May 7, 1908; s. George Albert and Nellie May (Ruthrauff) N.; m. Elizabeth Farnham, Sept. 1, 1933; children: George Albert III, Edwin F., John R., Elizabeth C. (Mrs. David D. Hamm). A.B., U. Mich., 1928; M.B.A., Harvard U., 1930; LL.D., Carthage Coll., 1972. Chartered fin. analyst. With Hudson Motor Co., 1930-31, Union Guardian Trust Co., 1931-33; fin. analyst Whitlock, Smith & Co., Detroit, 1933-37, Am. Industries, Detroit, 1941; civilian renegotiator USAF, 1942-45; fin. analyst Watling, Lerchen & Co., Detroit, 1945-58; rsch. dir. Smith, Hague & Co. Inc., Detroit, 1958-90; columnist Better Investing Mag.; cons. 1st of Mich. Merger, Detroit; chmn. Investment Edn. Inst., Internat. Investment Edn. Inst., World Fedn. Investment Clubs. Nicholson awards for best ann. reports for individual investors established by Nat. Assn. Investors, 1978. Mem. Fin. Analyst Soc. Detroit (pres. 1957), Nat. Assn. Investment Clubs (chmn. adv. bd.), Delta Kappa Epsilon. Republican. Episcopalian. Clubs: Country (Detroit), Indian Village (Detroit). Home: 1017 Cadieux Rd Grosse Pointe MI 48230-1511

NICHOLSON, JACK, actor, director, producer; b. Neptune, N.J., Apr. 28, 1937; s. John and Ethel May N.; m. Sandra Knight, 1961 (div. 1966); children: Jennifer, Lorraine Broussard. Acting debut Hollywood stage prodn. Tea and Sympathy; films include Cry-Baby Killer, 1958, Studs Lonigen, 1960, Little Shop of Horrors, 1960, Ensign Pulver, 1964, The Trip, 1967, Easy Rider, (Acad. award nomination for best supporting actor), 1969, Five Easy Pieces, 1970, Carnal Knowledge, 1971, A Safe Place, 1971, The Last Detail, 1974 (Cannes Film Festival prize), Chinatown, 1974 (Acad. award nomination, N.Y. Film Critics Circle award), Tommy, The Passenger, 1975, The Fortune, 1975, One Flew Over the Cuckoo's Nest (Golden Globe award, Acad. award for best actor), N.Y. Film Critics Circle award), 1975, The Missouri Breaks, 1976, TheLast Tycoon, 1976, The Shining, 1980, The Postman Always Rings Twice, 1981, Reds,1981 (Acad. award nomination for best supporting actor), The Border, 1982, Termsof Endearment (Acad. award for best supporting actor), 1983, Prizzi's Honor,1985 (Acad. award nomination for best actor), Heartburn, 1986, The Witches of Eastwick, 1987, Broadcast News, 1987, Ironweed, 1987 (Acad. award nomination for bestactor), Batman, 1989, Man Trouble, 1991, A Few Good Men, 1992, Hoffa, 1992, Wolf, 1994, The Crossing Guard, 1995; producer films Head, 1968, Ride the Whirlwind, The Shooting; dir. films Drive, He Said, 1971; dir., actor films Goin' South, 1978, The Two Jakes, 1990. Co-recipient with Bobby McFerrin) Grammy award for best recording for children,1987. Office: Bresler Kelly Kipperman 15760 Ventura Blvd Ste 1730 Encino CA 91436*

NICHOLSON, JOSEPH BRUCE, real estate developer; b. San Jose, Calif., Jan. 21, 1940; s. Wilmot Joseph and Ruth (Russell) N.; m. Susan Knight, Nov. 1963 (div. 1972); children: Kelsey Erin, Craig Wilmot; m. Linda Mirassou, Aug. 1992. BArch, U. Oreg., 1963. Exec. v.p. Nicholson-Brown Inc., Santa Clara, Calif., 1967-80; prin. Nicholson Assocs., Aptos, Calif., 1977—; v.p., gen. mgr. Nicholson-Wilson Co., Santa Clara, 1980-83; prin. The Nicholson Co., Campbell, Calif., 1984—; v.p. Pacific Property Ventures Inc., Campbell, 1988—; pres. Nicholson Constrn. Inc. Campbell, 1989—; v.p. Nicholson Property Mgmt. Inc., Campbell, 1989—; bd. dirs. Transmetrics Inc., San Jose. Bd. dirs. Triton Mus., Santa Clara, 1979, Hope Rehab. Svc., San Jose, 1979, United Way Cen. Area, San Jose, 1991; pres. adv. bd. de Saisset Mus., Santa Clara U., 1991; trustee Art Mus. Santa Cruz County, 1993. Lt. USN, 1963-67. Mem. Rotary, Commonwealth Club (San Francisco), World Trade Club (San Francisco). Republican. Avocations: travel, reading, art collecting, cooking, tennis. Home: 218 Shoreview Dr Aptos CA 95003-4621 Office: The Nicholson Co 75 Cristich Ln Campbell CA 95008-5403

NICHOLSON, LELAND ROSS, retired utilities company executive, energy consultant; b. Carrington, N.D., Feb. 21, 1924; s. Malcom and Lena May

(Kerlin) N.; m. Virginia E. Blair, Mar. 16, 1946; children: Heather Le Nicholson Studebaker, Leland B., Holly Kay. Student, Northwestern U., 1940-41; BSEE, U. N.D., 1949; postgrad. in utility mgmt., U. Minn., 1952. Planning and mktg. engr. Minkota Power Coop., Grand Forks, N.D., 1949-54; dir. new bus. Kans. Power & Light Co., Topeka, 1954-64, v.p. mktg., 1964-76, sr. v.p., 1976-80, exec. v.p., 1980-83, also bd. dirs.; pres. Kans. Power & Light Gas Service, Topeka, 1985-88, ret., 1988; pres., chief operating officer The Gas Service Co., Kansas City, Mo., 1983-85; pres. Indsl. Devel. Corp.; chmn. Kans. Council on Electricity and Environment; exec. com. Kansas City Labor Mgmt. Council, 1986-89; mem. Mktg. Execs. Conf.; bd. dirs. Gas Service Energy Corp., Kansas City, Merchants Nat. Bank, Topeka. Idea innovator heat pump water heater, photo cell controlled yard light, electric grill. Bd. dirs., area relations com. Kansas City (Mo.) Area Econ. Devel. Council, 1983-89; bd. dirs. Kansas City Pvt. Industry Council, 1986-89, Kansas City Downtown Council; trustee U. Mo., Kansas City, 1984-91; mktg. chmn. Kansas City Full Employment Council; past chmn., mem. Topeka-Shawnee County Planning Commn.; adult adv. com. Sea Scouts. Served to master sgt. USMC, 1942-46. Mem. Am. Gas Assn., Midwest Gas Assn. (bd. dirs. 1985-89), Mo. Valley Electric Assn. (chmn. 1979-81), Edison Electric Inst. (mktg. chmn. 1978-80), Assoc. Industries of Mo., Kans. Assn. Commerce and Industry, Greater Kansas City (Mo.) C. of C. (bd. dirs. 1979-82), Shawnee Yacht Club (Topeka) (commodore 1972-74), Lake Gaston Assn. (pres. 1993—), Kansas City Club, Rotary. Republican. Congregationalist. Avocations: sailing, canoeing, fishing, reading, electronics.

NICHOLSON, LUTHER BEAL, financial consultant; b. Sulphur Springs, Tex., Dec. 15, 1921; s. Stephen Edward and Elma (McCracken) N.; B.B.A. So. Meth. U., 1942, postgrad., 1946-47, Tex. U., 1947-48; diploma Southwestern Grad. Sch. Banking, 1967; m. Ruth Wimbish, May 29, 1952; children—Penelope Elizabeth, Stephen David. Controller, Varo, Inc., Garland, Tex., 1946-55, dir., 1947-72, v.p. fin., 1955-66, sr. v.p., 1966-67, exec. v.p., 1967-70, pres., 1970-71, chmn. bd., 1971-72, cons. to bd. dirs., 1972-75; gen. mgr. Challenger Lock Co., Los Angeles, 1956-58; dir. Varo Inc. Electrokinetics div., Varo Optical, Inc., Biometrics Instrument Corp., Varo Atlas GmbH, Micropac Industries, Inc., Gt. No. Corp., Garland Bank & Trust Co. Bd. dirs., exec. v.p. Harriett Stanton-Edna Murray Found. Served with AUS, 1942-46. Mem. Fin. Execs. Inst. (past pres.), Am. Inst. C.P.A.'s, AIM, Am. Mgmt. Assn., NAM. Home: 1917 Melody Ln Garland TX 75042-8442 Office: 610 Main St Garland TX 75040-6323

NICHOLSON, MORRIS EMMONS, JR., metallurgist, educator; b. Indpls., Feb. 15, 1916; s. Morris Emmons and Jessie (Cox) N.; m. Norma Story, Aug. 21, 1943; children: Morris Emmons III, Robert A., Richard A. BS, MIT, 1939; ScD, Mass. Inst. Tech., 1947. Registered profl. engr., Minn. Sect. head engring. research dept. Standard Oil Co., Ind., 1947-50; asst. prof. Inst. Study Metals, U. Chgo., 1950-55; prof. metallurgy U. Minn., 1956-85, prof. emeritus 1985—, head dept., 1956-62, dir. continuing edn. in engring. and sci., 1973-85; mem. Materials Adv. Bd., 1960-62. Active Boys Scouts Am., 1952—, dist. commr., 1961-64, 70-71; trustee Inst. Dist. 623 Sch. Bd., 1959-65, treas., 1965-77; bd. dirs. 916 AVTI, 1976-83, 916 Found., 1984—, sec., 1984-90; bd. dirs. Minn. Sch. Bd. Assn., 1973-79; amb. N.W. Youth and Family Svcs., 1988-93; mem. Falcon Heights Parks and Recreation Commn., 1992—. Recipient Silver Beaver, Boy Scouts Am., 1966; named Outstanding Sch. Bd. Mem., Minn. Sch. Bd. Assn., 1981. Mem. Am. Soc. Engring. Edn. (chmn. U. Minn. chpt. 1957-58, CPD divsn. 1962—, archivist 1985-94, Disting. Svc. award 1980), Am. Soc. Metals (chmn. Minn. chpt. 1958, mem. hist. sites com. 1989-92, chmn. 1991-92), Minerals, Metals and Materials Soc. (profl. registration com. 1982-93, chmn. 1986-93, Disting. Svc. award 1994), Nat. Assn. Corrosion Engrs., Assn. for Media-Based Continuing Edn. for Engrs. (bd. dirs. 1976-85), Sigma Xi, Theta Delta Chi, Tau Beta Pi, Alpha Chi Sigma. Mem. United Ch. Christ. Home: 1776 Pascal Ave N Saint Paul MN 55113-6259

NICHOLSON, R. STEPHEN, organization administrator; b. Radford, Va., Mar. 4, 1926; s. Roy S. and Ethel Dovie (Macy) N.; m. Carol Peterson, 1987; 1 child, Suzanne Carpenter. A.B., Marion Coll., 1950; M.A., Syracuse U., 1956; Ph.D., Mich. State U., 1971. Prof. Lansing (Mich.) Community Coll., 1963-66, Acad. dean, 1966-69; pres. Daley Coll., Chgo., 1969-71, Clark County Community Coll., 1971-76, Mt. Hood Community Coll. Dist., 1976-85; chancellor Oakland Community Coll., 1985-90; vice chancellor Higher Colls. of Tech., United Arab Emirates, 1990-92; CEO Internat. Christian Leadership, 1992-93; pres. emeritus Mt. Hood Coll., 1993—; CEO Mercy Corps Internat., 1994-95. Internat. corp. advisor M.J. Murdock Trust, 1993—. Mem. Am. Assn. Community and Jr. Colls. (pres. Pres.'s Acad. 1982, bd. dirs. 1985-87), N.W. Assn. Community and Jr. Colls. (pres. 1976), Am. Sch. Adminstrs. Assn., Am. Sociology Assn., Am. Acad. Polit. and Social Scis., Gresham C. of C. (dir. 1977-79), Japan-Am. Soc., World Affairs Council, Am. Futurist Soc., Phi Delta Kappa. Club: Rotary (pres. 1983, Paul Harris fellow 1986). Home: 3901 SW 22nd Dr Gresham OR 97080-8381

NICHOLSON, RALPH LESTER, botanist, educator; b. Lynn, Mass., Aug. 25, 1942; s. Nathan Aaron and Muriel Spinney (Buxton) N. BA, U. Vt., 1964; MS, U. Maine, 1967; PhD, Purdue U., 1972. Prof. dept. botany and plant pathology Purdue U., West Lafayette, Ind., 1972—; Contbr. chpts. to books, more than 100 articles to profl. jours. Active Big Bros./Big Sisters, Lafayette, Ind., 1974—. Fellow Am. Phytopathol. Soc. Office: Purdue U Botany and Plant Pathology Lafayette IN 47907

NICHOLSON, RICHARD JOSEPH, trust banking executive; b. N.Y.C., Feb. 19, 1932; s. Robert William and Mary Elizabeth (McShane) N.; m. Barbara Helen Malisky, Oct. 15, 1955; 1 child, Richard Jr. BS in Social Sci., Georgetown U., 1952; MBA, NYU, 1957. Asst. cashier Citibank Trust Div., N.Y.C., 1952-66; sr. v.p. 1st Fidelity Bank, Newark, 1966-90, ret., 1990; mem. exec. com. N.J. Bankers Assn. Trust Div., Princeton, 1983-85. Bd. dirs. Family Service Bur. of Newark, 1976—; mem. council Newark Mus., 1979-90. Served as cpl. U.S. Army, 1952-54. Mem. N.J. Bond Club. Republican. Roman Catholic. Avocations: tennis, travel, history.

NICHOLSON, RICHARD SELINDH, educational association administrator; b. Des Moines, Apr. 5, 1938; s. George Eugene and Margaret (Selindh) N.; m. Mary Lou Weisbrod, Aug. 1, 1958 (div. 1971) 1 child, Jeffrey Richard; m. Lois Ann Karls, Aug. 15, 1976; 1 child, Gregory Michael. BS, Iowa State U., 1960; PhD, U. Wis., 1964; LHD (hon.), CUNY, 1994; DHL (hon.), CUNY-Mt. Sinai Med. Ctr., 1994. Rsch. assoc. U. Wis., Madison, 1963-64; asst. prof. Mich. State U., East Lansing, 1964-67, assoc. prof., 1967-70; program dir. NSF, Washington, 1970-77, div. dir., 1977-82, chief of staff, 1983-85, asst. dir., 1985-89; exec. dir. Nat. Sci. Bd. Commn., Washington, 1982-83; exec. officer, pub. Science AAAS, Washington, 1989—; cons. on sci. affairs Pres. of U.S., Washington, 1978-79; exec. sec. Pres.' Com. on Nat. Medal Sci., Washington, 1976-84; mem. Pres.' Nat. Commn. on Superconductivity, 1989; vice chair Commn. on Phys. Scis., Math and Resources NRC, 1989—, Edn. Coordinating Coun., 1991—, com. on environ. rsch., 1991-92, co-chair coun. on competitiveness, 1991—; mem. statutory vis. com. Nat. Inst. of Standards and Tech., 1990-93; vis. com. chemistry dept. Harvard U., 1989—; bd. dirs. Qaulity Edn. for Minorities Network, 1989—; trustee Gordon Rsch. Conf., 1989—; science policy adv. com. space, science and tech. U.S. Ho. Reps., 1992—; chmn. edn. adv. com. Genentech, 1993—. Mem. editorial bd. Analytical Chemistry, 1980-82, Chem. and Engring. News, 1985-88; contbr. articles to profl. jours. and chpts. to books. Served as seaman USN, 1956-63. Recipient Presdl. Disitng. Ranking, Pres. Reagan, 1982, Alumni Citation Merit award Iowa State U., 1983. Fellow AAAS; mem. Am. Chem. Soc. (chmn. Mich. State U. sect. 1968-70), Chem. Soc. Washington (nominations com. 1977), Cosmos Club, Nat. Press Club. Avocations: sports, tennis, reading. Home: 1020 Union Church Rd Mc Lean VA 22102-1115 Office: AAAS 1333 H St NW Washington DC 20005-4707

NICHOLSON, ROBERT ARTHUR, college president; b. Pepin, Wis., Oct. 13, 1923; s. Arthur W. and Ethel (Weeden) N.; m. Dorothy Nelis, June 17, 1944; children: Paul, Gary. BS, Anderson U., ind., 1944; MA, NYU, 1946, Ph.D., 1953. With Anderson U., 1945-90, successively instr. asst. prof., assoc. prof. music, chmn. dept., asst. to dean, 1945-58, dean, 1958-83, v.p., 1964-83, pres., 1983-90, pres. emeritus, 1990—. Author: Handbook to the Hymnal of the Church of God, 1953; Editor: Hymnal of the Church of God, 1953, 71. Mem. pub. bd. Church of God, 1955-80, chmn. commn. higher

edn., 1963-70, 83-86, vice chmn., 1970-83, cons., 1990—; cons. Warner Pacific Coll., Oreg., 1990—, N. Ind. United Meth. Found., Inc., 1992—; bd. dirs. Anderson Symphony Orch., 1974-87, 93—, United Way Madison County, 1985-89, 91—, Minnetrista Cultural Found., 1988—; bd. dirs., v.p. Anderson Internat., 1990-93; bd. dirs. Community Hosp. Madison County, 1986—, vice chmn., 1988—, interim pres., chief exec. officer, 1991; pres. Madison County Community Found., Inc., 1991—. Mem. Associated Colls. of Ind., Ind. Colls. and Univs. of Ind. (chmn. 1988-89), Anderson Area C. of C. (bd. dirs. 1985-90, vice chmn. and chmn. elect 1988, chmn. 1989). Home: 721 Maplewood Ave Anderson IN 46012-3028

NICHOLSON, WALTER, economist, educator; b. Phila., Sept. 23, 1942; s. Walter E. and Emily (Hay) N.; B.A., Williams Coll., 1964; Ph.D., M.I.T., 1970; M.A. (hon.), Amherst Coll., 1978; m. Susan Atkinson, Aug. 12, 1967; children—Kate, David, Tory, Paul. Dir. research Mathematica Policy Research, 1971-72, sr. fellow, 1974—; vis. assoc. prof. Grad. Sch. Public Policy, U. Calif, Berkeley, 1977; vis. scholar Doshisha U., Kyoto, Japan, 1982-83; mem. faculty Amherst Coll., 1968, prof. econs., 1978—. Chmn. Grad. Records Exam. in Econ., 1986-89. Woodrow Wilson fellow, 1964-65. Mem. Am. Econ. Assn. Author: Microeconomic Theory, 1995. Home: 131 Middle St Amherst MA 01002-3011 Office: Amherst Coll Dept of Econ Amherst MA 01002

NICHOLSON, WILL FAUST, JR., bank holding company executive; b. Colorado Springs, Colo., Feb. 8, 1929; s. Will Faust and Gladys Olivia (Burns) N.; m. Shirley Ann Baker, Nov. 26, 1955; children: Ann Louise Nicholson Naughton, Will Faust III. S.B., M.I.T., 1950; M.B.A., U. Denver, 1956. V.p. Van Schaack & Co., Denver, 1954-66; pntr. N. G. Petry Constrn. Co., Denver, 1966-70; sr. v.p. Colo. Nat. Bankshares, Inc., Denver, 1970-75; pres. Colo. Nat. Bankshares, Inc., 1975-95, chmn. bd., chief exec. officer, 1985-95; chmn. Rocky Mountain Bankcard Sys., Denver, 1995—; bd. dirs. Pub. Svc. Co., Colo., First Bank Sys.; bd. dirs., chmn. VISA USA, Inc., VISA Internat. Bd. dirs. Boys and Girls Clubs of Metro Denver; active Downtown Denver, Inc., Colo. Assn. of Commerce and Industry, chmn. 1990-91, Denver Urban Renewal Authority, 1958-59, Denver Bd. Water Commrs., 1959-65, pres. 1964, 65; Nat. Western Stock Show; bd. Health One. With USAF, 1950-53. Mem. Assn. Bank Holding Cos. (bd. dirs. 1979-87, 89-91, exec. com. 1980-85, vice chmn. 1981-82, chmn. 1983-84), U.S. C. of C. (bd. dirs. 1990—), U.S. Golf Assn. (exec. com. 1974-82, v.p. 1978, 79, pres. 1980, 81), Denver Country Club, Denver Club, Univ. Club Colo., Univ. Club N.Y., Castle Pine Golf Club, Royal and Ancient Golf Club (St. Andrews, Scotland), Augusta (Ga.) Nat. Golf Club. Republican. Episcopalian. Home: 37 Polo Club Circle Denver CO 80209 Office: Colo Nat Bankshares PO Box 5168 Denver CO 80217-5168

NICHOLSON, WILLIAM MAC, naval architect, marine engineer, consultant; b. Napa, Calif., June 15, 1918; s. William John and Hazel (McIlmoil) N.; m. Lynda Bishop, Feb. 10, 1947 (div. Aug. 1959); children: Lynda Joanne, Samuel Bishop; m. Leslie Marie Earle-Thomas, Apr. 1, 1964; children: Richard Thomas, Glenn Thomas, Ronald Thomas. BS, U.S. Naval Acad., 1941; MS, MIT, 1948. Commd. ensign USN, 1941, advanced through grades to capt., 1960; ret., 1971; design supt. Boston Shipyard, 1951-52; project officer minesweeping, hydrofoils Bur. of Ships, Washington, 1955-59; comptr. Puget Sound Naval Shipyard, Bremerton, Wash., 1959-62; prof. naval constrn. MIT, Cambridge, 1962-65; dir. ship design dir. Bur. of Ships, Washington, 1965-66; program mgr. deep submergence Chief of Naval Material, Washington, 1966-71; assoc. dir. Nat. Ocean Survey, NOAA, Washington, 1971-81; retired, 1981. chmn. U.S.-Japan panel on marine facilities under U.S.-Japan Natural Resource Agreement., 1972-81; vice-chmn. marine bd. Acad. Engring., NAS, Washington, 1984-85; pres., 1983, chmn., bd. dirs., 1984, Sea-Space Symposium. Decorated Legion of Merit. Mem. Soc. Naval Architects and Marine Engrs. (sect. chmn. N.E. 1964-65), Soc. Naval Engrs. (coun. 1966-68), Marine Tech. Soc. (sect. chmn. 1974-75), N.Y. Yacht Club, Sigma Xi, Tau Beta Pi. Republican. Home: 4000 Towerside Ter # 2307 Miami FL 33138

NICHOLSON, WILLIAM THOMAS, advertising executive; b. N.Y.C., Oct. 12, 1944; s. John Joseph and Margaret m. (Abdale) N.; m. Amy Bivona (div. July 1983); 1 child, Dina Marie; m. Nancy Musser, Oct. 17, 1987. BS, St. John's U., Jamaica, N.Y., 1973, MBA, 1976. Dir. corp. acctg. Pan Am World Airways, N.Y.C., 1969-81; controller Seiko Time Corp., N.Y.C., 1981-83; sr. v.p., chief fin. officer Cunningham & Walsh, N.Y.C., 1983-86; exec. v.p., chief ops. officer Kornhauser & Calene Inc., N.Y.C., 1986—; also bd. dirs. Cornhauser & Calene, N.Y.C.; bd. dirs. Sun Coast Airlines, Ft. Lauderdale, Fla. Mem. Fin. Execs. Inst. (chmn. com. 1987). Republican. Episcopalian. Clubs: Lotos, Doubles. Avocations: reading, travel. Office: Lintas New York 1 Dag Hammarskjold Plz New York NY 10017-2201

NICHOLSON-GUTHRIE, CATHERINE S. See GUTHRIE, CATHERINE S. NICHOLSON

NICITA, RICK, agent. Agent Creative Artists Agy. Office: Creative Artists Agy 9830 Wilshire Blvd Beverly Hills CA 90212-1825*

NICKEL, ALBERT GEORGE, advertising agency executive; b. Pitts., July 12, 1943; s. Frank George and Dorothy (Wiefling) N.; children: Melissa, Mark. AB, Washington and Jefferson Coll., 1965; MBA, Ind. U., 1967. Mktg. rsch. analyst Pfizer, Inc., N.Y.C., 1967, profl. svc. rep., 1967-68, mktg. rsch. mgr., 1968-69, product mgr., 1969-70; product mgr. USV Internat., Tuckahoe, N.Y., 1970-71; account exec. J. Walter Thompson (Deltakos), N.Y.C., 1971-72; account supr., 1972-73; account supr. Sudler & Hennessey, N.Y.C., 1973-77; sr. v.p. mgmt. group supr. Young and Rubicam, N.Y.C., 1977-79; pres., chief oper. officer Dorritie Lyons & Nickel, Inc., N.Y.C., 1979-94; pres., COO Lyons, Lavey, Nickel, Swift, Inc., 1994—. Trustee Wilton YMCA, Five Town Found., Dominican Coll.; bd. dirs., exec. com. Wilton LaCrosse Assn.; bd. dirs. Healthcare Businesswoman's Assn. Wilton High Sch. Long Range Planning Team, Am. Coun. on Sci. and Health. Capt. USAF, 1969. Mem. Pharm. Rsch. and Mfrs. Assn. (bd. dirs.), Healthcare Mktg. and Comm. Coun. Club. Med. Advt. Hall of Fame, Midwest Healthcare Mktg. Assn., Wilton Riding Club (pres.), Shore and Country Club, Silver Spring Country Club. Home: 65 Keelers Ridge Wilton CT 06897-4234

NICKEL, DONALD LLOYD, engineering executive; b. Hortonville, Wis., June 19, 1933; s. Lloyd Harrison and Norma Irene (Anderson) N.; m. Harriet Elizabeth Stitzer, Mar. 28, 1959 (div. 1981); children: Kenneth, Carol; m. Florence Margaret Knoch, Sept. 18, 1981; children: Sandra, David, Linda, Karen, Janice. B.S. in Math. and Physics, U. Wis., 1957; postgrad., U. Pitts., 1958-66. Computer engr. Westinghouse Elec. Corp., East Pittsburgh, Pa., 1957-63, cons., 1963-72, engring. mgr., 1972-76, adv. engr., 1976-84, power systems engr. mgr. process control projects, 1984-88, mgr. devel. projects, 1988-89; mgr. transient analysis and special projects ABB Transmission Tech. Inst., Pitts., 1989-92; cons. ABB Power T & D Co., Inc., Raleigh, N.C., 1992—. Author: (with others) Underground Distribution, 1966. Treas. First Baptist Ch., Monroeville, Pa., 1971-80. Served with U.S. Army, 1954-56, Japan. Mem. IEEE. Republican. Baptist. Lodge: Masons. Home: 1200 Silas Ridge Ct Raleigh NC 27609-3502 Office: ABB Power T & D Co Inc 1021 Main Campus Dr Raleigh NC 27606-5202

NICKEL, JANET MARLENE MILTON, geriatrics nurse; b. Manitowoc, Wis., June 9, 1940; d. Ashley and Pearl (Kerr) Milton; m. Curtis A. Nickel, July 29, 1961; children: Cassie, Debra, Susan. Diploma, Milw. Inst., 1961; ADN, N.D. State U., 1988. Nurse Milw. VA, Wood, Wis., 1961-62; supervising nurse Park Lawn Convalescent Hosp., Manitowoc, 1964-65; newsletter editor Fargo (N.D.) Model Cities Program, 1970-73; supervising night nurse Rosewood on Broadway, Luth. Hosps. and Homes, Fargo, 1973-92; assoc. dir. nursing Elim Nursing Home, Fargo, 1992-94, night supr., 1994—. Mem. Phi Eta Sigma. Home: 225 19th Ave N Fargo ND 58102-2352 Office: 3534 S University Dr Fargo ND 58104-6228

NICKEL, MELVIN EDWIN, metallurgical engineer; b. St. Louis, Aug. 24, 1915; s. Jacob William and Mary Anna (Madsen) N.; m. Mary Louise Breuer, Sept. 12, 1942; children: Elizabeth Ann Nickel Medve, Mary Patricia Nickel Hepburn, Sheila Breuer Nickel Stojak, William Louis. BS in Metall. Engring., U. Mo., Rolla, 1938, Profl. Degree of Metall. Engring., 1967. Mgmt. trainee Bethlehem (Pa.) Steel Corp., 1938-39; asst. to supt. blast furnaces Wis. Steel div. Internat. Harvester Co., Chgo., 1939-43, gen. foreman furnaces, blast furnaces, 1943-48, asst. supt. blast furnaces, 1948-49, supt. open hearths, 1949-61, supt. basic oxygen furnaces, mgr. steel prodn., 1961-68, mgr. primary ops., 1968-77; mgr. facilities planning and appropriations, works mgr. Envirodyne Industries, Inc., Wis. Steel Corp., 1977-80; pres. Melvin E. Nickel & Assocs., Inc., Chgo., 1980—. Contbr. articles to profl. jours.; developer early practices for prodn. of spl. bar quality and alloy steel in top blown basic oxygen furnace, 1962-64. Bd. trustees Iron and Steel Soc. Found., Warrensdale, Pa., 1980-91. Recipient Disting. Merit award U. Mo., Rolla, 1960; inducted Mo. Sch. Mines/U. Mo.-Rolla Athletic Hall of Fame U. Mo., Rolla, 1993. Mem. AIME (hon., nat. v.p., dir. 1974-76), Iron and Steel Soc. of AIME (nat. pres. 1974-75), Metall. Soc. of AIME (nat. chmn. iron and steel divsn. 1972-74), Assn. of Iron and Steel Engrs., Western States Blast Furnaces and Coke Assn., U. Mo., Rolla Alumni Assn. (pres. 1956-59, bd. dirs.), Triangle Fraternity, Jackson Hole Wildlife Soc., Ridge Country Club of Chgo., Beverly Hills Univ. Club. Republican. Roman Catholic. Avocations: hunting, fishing, carpentry, mineral collecting, boating. Home and Office: 10601 S Hamilton Ave Chicago IL 60643-3127

NICKELS, ROBERT EDWARD, plastic manufacturing company executive; b. Detroit, Jan. 23, 1943; s. William Edward and Winifred June (Hocking) N.; m. Carol Lee Johnson, Jan. 26, 1963; children: Tracy Lee, Robbie Lynn. BS in Mech. Engring., Mich. State U., 1966, MBA, 1967; postgrad., Stanford U., 1978. With Procter & Gamble, Chgo., 1967-69; prodn. mgr. Roper Lawn Products, Newark, Ohio, 1969-71; v.p., gen. mgr. Roper Lawn Products, Savannah, Ga., 1971-77; v.p. mfg. Roper Outdoor Products, Bradley, Ill., 1977-79, exec. v.p., 1979-81, pres., 1981-83; v.p. mfg. Sewell Plastics, Inc., Atlanta, 1983-84, exec. v.p., 1984-85, pres., chief exec. officer, 1985—; sr. v.p. Constar Internat. subs. Sewell Plastics, Inc., Chattanooga, 1986—; adv. bd. Allendale Ins., Johnson, R.I., 1986—; pres. MONTPLAS subs. Sewell Plastics, Inc.; bd dirs. Wellstar, Didam, the Netherlands. Mem. Nat. Assn. for Plastic Container Recovery (chmn. 1987-89), Flying Rebel Club. Republican. Presbyterian. Avocation: flying. Home: 646 Gunby Rd Marietta GA 30067-5132 Office: Constar Plastics Inc 5375 Drake Dr SW Atlanta GA 30336-2498

NICKENS, JACKS CLARENCE, lawyer; b. McCamey, Tex., Feb. 7, 1949; s. Jacks C. Nickens and Elsie Louise (Jordan) Donohue; m. Linda M. Colangelo, June 13, 1970 (div. 1984); 1 child, Marie Louise; m. Melinda Jo Hubbert, Oct. 13, 1990. AB magna cum laude, Harvard U., 1971, JD cum laude, 1975. Bar: Tex. 1975, U.S. Dist. Ct. (so. dist.) Tex. 1975. Assoc. Vinson & Elkins, Houston, 1975-79; ptnr. Scott Douglass & Keeton (now Miller, Bristow & Brown), Houston, 1979-90; prin. Jacks C. Nickens & Assocs., Houston, 1990-91; ptnr. Mayer, Brown & Platt, Houston, 1991—. Home: 3418 S Parkwood Dr Houston TX 77021-1238 Office: Mayer Brown & Platt 700 Louisiana St Ste 3600 Houston TX 77002-2730

NICKERSON, EUGENE H., federal judge; b. Orange, N.J., Aug. 2, 1918; m. Marie-Louise Steiner; children—Marie-Louise, Lawrie H., Stephanie W., Susan A. A.B., Harvard U., 1941; LL.B. (Kent scholar), Columbia U., 1943; LL.D. (hon.), Hofstra U., 1970, Bklyn. Law Sch., 1991. Bar: N.Y. 1944, U.S. Supreme Ct. 1948. Law clk. to Judge Augustus N. Hand, 2d circuit U.S. Ct. Appeals, 1943-44; to Chief Justice Harlan F. Stone U.S. Supreme Ct., 1944-46; county exec. Nassau County, N.Y., 1962-70; practice law N.Y.C., 1946-61, 71-77; judge U.S. Dist. Ct., Bklyn., 1977—; Counsel N.Y. Gov.'s Com. Pub. Employee Procedures, 1956-58; mem. N.Y. State Law Revision Commn., 1958-59, 77; mem. Met. Regional Council, 1962-70, chmn., 1969-70; mem. adv. council pub. welfare HEW, 1963-65; mem. pub. ofcls. adv. council OEO, 1968. Mem. ABA, Nassau County Bar Assn., Assn. Bar City N.Y. (com. fed. legislation 1971-74, com. on communications 1971-77, com. on judiciary 1974-77), Am. Law Inst., Phi Delta Phi. Office: US Dist Ct US Courthouse 225 Cadman Plz E Brooklyn NY 11201

NICKERSON, GARY LEE, secondary education educator; b. Cleve., Nov. 7, 1942; s. Alto Lee and Louise Evelyn (Watson) N.; m. Barbara Marie Butler, Aug. 17, 1968; 1 child, L'Oreal. BS, Ohio U., 1966; MA, Atlanta U., 1971. Cert. secondary tchr., Ohio. With Cleve. Pub. Schs., 1966—; sci. dept. chmn. John F. Kennedy High Sch., Cleve., 1985—; physics instr. Case Western Res. U., Cleve., summer, 1988; sci instr. Standard Oil Elem. Teaching Retraining Program summmer 1986; mem. adv. panel Ednl. Devel. Ctr., Inc., Newton, Mass., 1989—; sci. instr. Cleve. Ednl. Found. Elem. Teaching Retraining Program, 1990, Baldwin Wallace U. Upward Bound Program, 1992; engring. project instr. MEIOP Summer Program Case Western Res. U., 1991; tchr. trainer Kent State U. Trivet program, 1991—. Coauthor curriculum guides. Recipient Cert. of Excellence in Teaching Rotary, 1990. Mem. NAACP, Urban League, Cleve. Regional Coun. Sci. Tchrs. (bd. dirs. 1986-87), Metrocabse Assn., Nat. Sci. Tcrhrs. Assn., Sci. Edn. Coun. Ohio, Kappa Alpha Psi. Democrat. Baptist. Avocations: ice skating, tennis, swimming, singing, weight lifting. Home: 5871 White Pine Dr Cleveland OH 44146-3075 Office: John F Kennedy High Sch 17100 Harvard Ave Cleveland OH 44128-2299

NICKERSON, GUY ROBERT, lumber company executive; b. Salt Lake City, May 20, 1956; s. Charles Augustus and Florence May (Fogel) N.; m. Maggie Rose McDonnell, May 30, 1992; children: Melissa Marie, Rebecca Rose. B Acctg., U. Utah, 1977, M Profl. Accountancy, 1978. CPA, Utah. Sr. mgr. Deloitte Haskins & Sells, Salt Lake City and N.Y.C., 1978-87; v.p fin. Anderson Lumber Co., Ogden, Utah, 1987—. Office: Anderson Lumber Co 4700 Harrison Blvd Ogden UT 84409

NICKERSON, JAMES FINDLEY, education consultant; b. Gretna, Nebr., Dec. 16, 1910; s. Elmer Samuel and Lulu Perkins (Patterson) N.; m. Juanita M. Bolin, Mar. 3, 1934; children: Ann Rogers Nickerson Lueck, Maria De Miranda. BS, Nebr. Wesleyan U., 1932; MA, Columbia Tchrs. Coll., 1940; PhD, U. Minn., 1948; ScD (hon.), Yankton (S.D.) Coll., 1971. Tchr. pub. schs. Giltner, Nebr., 1932-35; sch. music supr. Gordon, Nebr., 1936-38, Bayshore, L.I., 1939-41, Grand Island, Nebr., 1941-42; instr. Coll. Edn., music supr. high sch. U. Minn., 1942-46, vis. prof. Coll. Edn., summer 1948; asst. prof. music edn. U. Kans., 1946-48, assoc. prof., 1948-53; rsch. assoc. dept. psychology U. So. Calif., assigned human factors div. U.S. Navy Electronics Lab., San Diego, 1953-54; dean edn., dir. summer quar., prof. psychology Mont. State U., 1954-64, head dept. psychology, 1954-56, rsch. assoc. Electronics Rsch. Lab, 1958-64; v.p. acad. affairs N.D. State U., Fargo, 1964-66; pres. Mankato (Minn.) State U., 1966-73, then pres. emeritus, disting. svc. prof., 1973-76; dir. Svc. Mems. Opportunity Colls., Am. Assn. State Colls. and Univs., Washington, 1973-81; dir. Northwestern Nat. Bank, Mankato, 1967-69; cons. publ. edn. Office Gov. Wash., 1964; exec. sec., study dir. interim com. edn. Wash. Legislature, 1959-60; chmn. regional conf. womanpower Nat. Manpower Coun. and Mont. State Coll., 1957; mem. steering com. Pacific N.W. Con. Higher Edn., 1962; mem. nat. adv. com. sci. edn. NSF, 1968-71, chmn., 1970-71; mem. vis. com. Harvard Grad. Sch. Edn., 1970-76, Schola Cantorum, N.Y.C., 1938-39, Choral Arts Soc., Washington, 1969-71. Stringbass Mont. State Coll. Symphonette, 1959-63, Mankato Symphony Orch., 1967-73, 83—, bd. dirs., 1987-90. Recipient citation interim study Wash. Legislature and Gov., 1960, Outstanding Achievement award Bd. Regents U. Minn., 1968, Alumni award Nebr. Wesleyan U., 1968; Sec. Def. medal for outstanding pub. svc., 1981, citation Am. Coun. Edn., 1981; James F. Nickerson Medal of Merit for outstanding svc. to mil. edn. created by Am. Assn. Sr. Colls. and Univs., 1981; Danforth Found. adminstrn. grantee, 1969. Mem. Nat. Assn. State Univs. and Land Grant Colls. (senate, chmn. div. tchr. edn. 1962-65, sec. coun. acad. officers 1965), Am. Assn. State Colls. and State Univs. (bd. dirs. 1966-71), Am. Assn. Colls. Tchr. Edn. (bd. dirs. 1966-71), Am. Assn. Higher Edn. (chmn. resolutions com. 1974), Assn. Minn. Colls. (pres. 1972), Edn. Commn. States (commr. 1967-73, mem. task force on coordination, governance and structure postsecondary edn. 1973), Sigma Xi, Phi Mu Alpha Sinfonia. Home and Office: PO Box 204 Elysian MN 56028-0204

NICKERSON, JERRY EDGAR ALAN, manufacturing executive; b. North Sydney, N.S., Can., Apr. 28, 1936; s. Jeremiah Beldon and Jean Frances (Innes) N.; m. Jean Frances Ritcey, Sept. 20, 1958; children: Mark Alan, Jerry Ross. B.Commerce, Dalhousie U., 1958. Chmn. bd. H.B. Nickerson & Son, Ltd., North Sydney; bd. dirs. Gt. West Life & Annuity, Gt. West Life Assurance Co., Bank of Montreal, Seaside Cable TV Ltd. Mem. Zeta Psi. Office: HB Nickerson & Sons Ltd PO Box 130, North Sydney, NS Canada B2A 3M2

NICKERSON, JOHN MITCHELL, political science educator; b. Lewiston, Maine, July 1, 1937; s. Elmer Winfield and Marion Gertrude (Howard) N. B.A., U. Maine, 1959; M.A., Wash. State U., 1966; Ph.D., U. Idaho, 1971. Commd. 2d lt. U.S. Army, 1959, advanced through grades to capt., resigned, 1967; rsch. assoc. Bur. Pub. Administrn. U. Maine, Orono, 1967-68, mem. grad. faculty, 1970-88; assoc. prof. polit. sci. U. Maine, Augusta, 1970-81, prof., 1981—; developer Baccalaureate program in pub. adminstrn.; dir. New Eng. Govtl. Research Inst., Inc., Waterville, Maine, 1971; lectr. Colby Coll., Waterville, Maine, 1979, Maine State Dedimus Justice; cons. in field. Author: The Control of Civil Disturbances, 1968, Municipal Police in Maine - A Study of Selected Personnel Practices with Emphasis on Recruit Selection and Training, 1969, (with others) A Study of Policy-Making: The Dynamics and Adaptability of the U.S. Federal System, 1971; editor, author foreward: Is the Municipality Liable for Insufficiently Trained Police? (James P. Murphy), 1968; contbr. articles to profl. jours. Mem. Maine State Police Planning Adv. Group, Maine State Bd. Assessment Rev., Maine Hwy. Safety Com.; vice chmn. adv. bd. Salvation Army, Augusta; trustee, treas. Lithgow Library; incorporator Kennebec Valley Med. Ctr., Augusta. Dept. Justice grantee, 1967. Mem. AAUP, Am. Polit. Sci. Assn., New Eng. Polit. Sci. Assn., Northeastern Polit. Sci. Assn., Acad. Polit. Sci. (life), Am. Acad. Polit. and Social Sci. (life), Am. Soc. for Pub. Adminstrn., ACLU (life), Kennebec Hist. Soc. (life), Kennebec Valley Humane Soc. (life), Maine Civil Liberties Union (life, legis. com.), Pi Sigma Alpha, Pi Alpha Alpha. Home: 190 Capitol St Augusta ME 04330-6236 Office: U Maine University Heights Augusta ME 04330

NICKERSON, RICHARD GORHAM, research company executive; b. Harwich, Mass., Nov. 20, 1927; s. Ephriam Gorham and Elizabeth (Wardle) N.; m. Eileen Florence Tressler, June 7, 1957; children: Holly Anne, Wendy Elyse, Susan Denise. BS cum laude, U. Mass., 1950; PhD, Northwestern U., 1955; postgrad., Poly. Inst. Bklyn., 1955-57; MBA cum laude, Boston U., 1983. Rsch. chemist DuPont, Cellophane Tech. Sect., Richmond, Va., 1954-55, W.R. Grace, Dewey & Almy Div., Cambridge, Mass., 1957-60; v.p. rsch. and devel. Electronautics Corp., Maynard, Mass., 1960-61; pres. Electronautics Corp., Maynard, 1961-63; project leader Polyco Borden Chem. div. Borden, Inc., Leominister, Mass., 1963-65, group leader, 1965-67, devel. mgr., 1967-81, lab. mgr., 1981-87; pres., mng. dir. Boston Profls. Internat., Inc., Hopkinton, Mass., 1987—. Patentee in field; design and devel. of water based polymers to meet specific performance requirement. With Chem. Corps, U.S. Army, 1955-57. Mem. Am. Chem. Soc., Soc. Plastics Engrs., Sigma Xi, Phi Lambda Upsilon, Alpha Chi Sigma. Avocations: sailing, photography, antique autos, classical music, dancing. Home: 16 Valleywood Rd Hopkinton MA 01748-1635

NICKERSON, RUTH, sculptor; b. Appleton, Wis., Nov. 23, 1905; d. Robert Wellington and Kate Mary (Ellis) N.; m. Edmund Greacen, Jr., Dec. 30, 1935; children: Elizabeth Ruth, Barbara Eleanor. Ed., Simcoe Collegiate Inst., 1921-23, Nat. Acad. Schs., 1928-32; student stone carving, Ahron Ben-Shmuel. Works represented in permanent collections, Newark Mus., Cedar Rapids (Iowa) Mus. Art, New Brunswick, N.J., Eden Post Office, N.C., children's br. Bklyn. Pub. Libr., New Rochelle City Hall, Grasslands Hosp., Valhalla, N.Y., Montclair (N.J.) Mus. Art, Interchurch Ctr., N.Y.C. Mem. White Plains Civic Arts Commn., 1948-60, Mitchell Wolfson Mus., Miami, Fla., Queensborough Pub. Libr., Jamaica, N.Y., permanent and pvt. collections. Recipient Nat. ARts Club medal, 1933, Saltus Gold medal N.A.D., 1933, Montclair Mus. medal, 1936, Am. Artists Profl. League medal, 1947, Allied Artists Religious award, 1981, Therese Wright Richard award Nat. Sculpture Soc., 1982, Bertelson prize N.A.D., 1993; Guggenheim fellow, 1946-47. Fellow Nat. Sculpture Soc. (council 1981-83); mem. N.A.D. (diplomate, council mem. 1978-81), Audubon Artists. Address: 30 Lake St Apt 8K White Plains NY 10603-4002 *The principles I have tried to express in all my sculpture are simplicity, dignity and strength. My belief that the ultimate purpose of creation is to integrate wildly disparate elements into a unified and harmonious whole is the basis for all my creative work. My goal has been to use a God-given talent to give others a glimpse of that same concept through my use of human character and forms. My standard of conduct has been to act with integrity and forthrightness.*

NICKERSON, T. B., think-tank organization executive. Pres. Nova Scotia Rsch., Sartmouth, Canada. Office: Nova Scotia Research Fndn Corp, 101 Research Dr Box 790, Dartmouth, NS Canada B2Y 3Z7

NICKERSON, WILLIAM MILNOR, federal judge; b. Balt., Dec. 6, 1933; s. Palmer Rice and Eleanor (Renshaw) N.; m. Virginia Airen Bourne, Apr. 25, 1954; children: Carol Lee, Deborah, Susan, Wendy, Laura. BA, U. Va., 1955; LLB, U. Md., Balt., 1962. Bar: Md. 1962. Mem. Md. Senate, 1979-80; mem. U.S. Senate from Okla., 1981—, chmn. Senate Rep. policy com.; assoc. judge Cir. Ct. Baltimore County, Towson, Md., 1985-90; judge U.S. Dist. Ct. Md., Balt., 1990—. Served to lt. USCGR, 1955-59. Mem. ABA (judicial adminstrn. div.), Am. Judicature Soc., Fed. Judges Assn., Md. State Bar Assn.,. Office: US Dist Ct 101 W Lombard St Baltimore MD 21201

NICKFORD, JUAN, sculptor, educator; b. Havana, Cuba, Aug. 8, 1925; s. Basil and Maria (Hoshko) N.; m. Jene Rashkind, Aug. 16, 1952; children—Dena, Marc. M.F.A., Bellas Artes, Havana, 1945; postgrad., U. Havana, 1944-46. Head welding dept. Sculpture Center of N.Y., 1955-62; vis. artist Vasar Coll., 1962-63, Smith Coll., 1966-67, U. Hartford, 1965-66, Bklyn. Mus. Art Sch., 1968-70, Finch Coll., San Marino, 1975; prof. art CCNY, 1975-91, prof. emeritus, 1991—. One man shows, Leonard Gallery, Woodstock, N.Y., 1981, Emanuel Coll. Gallery, Boston, 1977, Sculpture Center, 1974, Art Glass Gallery, Toronto, Can., 1985, numerous others; retrospective Hopper House, Nyack, N.Y., 1986; group shows include, Thorpe Intermedia Gallery, Sparkill, N.Y., 1974, Hopper House, Nyack, N.Y., 1978, Sculpture Center, N.Y.C., 1978, Sculpture Gallery, Palo Alto, Calif., 1981, numerous museums; represented in permanent collection, Newberger Coll., N.Y., numerous pvt. collections. Cintas Found. grantee, 1970-71, CUNY Faculty Research Found. grantee, 1982-83; recipient Bronze medal N.Y. State Expn., 1964. Mem. Sculptors Guild. Home: 161 Old Tappan Rd Tappan NY 10983-2311

NICKLAS, ROBERT BRUCE, cell biologist; b. Lakewood, Ohio, May 29, 1932; s. Ford Adelbert and Marthabelle (Beckett) N.; m. Sheila Jean Counce, Sept. 17, 1960. B.A., Bowling Green State U., 1954; M.A. (Eugene Higgins fellow), Columbia U., 1956, Ph.D., 1958. Instr. in zoology Yale U., 1958-61, asst. prof. zoology, 1961-64, assoc. prof., 1964-65; assoc. prof. Duke U., 1965-71, prof., 1971—; chairperson dept., 1983-86; mem. NSF Postdoctoral Fellowship Panel, 1969-71, Am. Cancer Soc. Sci. Adv. Com. for Virology and Cell Biology, 1975-78; mem. adv. bd. 12th Internat. Chromosome Conf., 1994. Contbr. numerous articles to profl. publs.; mem. editorial bd. Chromosoma, 1966-83, Jour. Exptl. Zoology, 1970-72, Jour. Cell Biology, 1980-81, Jour. Cell Sci., 1984-91, European Jour. Cell Biology, 1985-89. Recipient award for disting. teaching Duke Alumni, 1975; Yale fellow in scis., 1963-64; John Simon Guggenheim fellow, 1972-73; grantee Inst. Gen. Med. Scis. USPHS, 1960—. Fellow AAAS; mem. Am. Soc. Cell Biology (exec. com. 1976-78, council 1975-78), Am. Soc. Naturalists, Genetics Soc. Am., Sigma Xi. Home: 3101 Camelot Ct Durham NC 27705-5405 Office: Duke U Dept Zoology Durham NC 27708-1000

NICKLAUS, CHARLES EDWARD, sales training executive; b. Columbus, Ohio, Nov. 2, 1915; m. Hazel Stine, Aug. 31, 1940; children: Carol Marie, James Frank. BSBA, Franklin U., Columbus, 1980. Dir. rsch. lab. H. Braun Co., Columbus, 1939-41; gen. mgr. Edmont Co. Br. Mt. Sterling, Ohio, 1943-48; internat. sales tng. dir. Warren-Teed Pharm. Co., Columbus, 1948-75; prof. mktg. Columbus State C.C., 1986-90; adj. faculty Franklin U., Columbus, 1975-90, Svc. Corps of Ret. Execs. and Active Corps Execs., U.S SBA # 285, Charleston, S.C.; seminar moderator, 1986—. Mem. Kappa Psi (pres. 1936-38), Columbus C. of C., Masons (Mt. Sterling, Ohio).

NICKLAUS, JACK WILLIAM, professional golfer; b. Columbus, Ohio, Jan. 21, 1940; s. Louis Charles, Jr. and Helen (Schoener) N.; m. Barbara Bash, July 23, 1960; children: Jack William II, Steven Charles, Nancy Jean, Gary Thomas, Michael Scott. Student, Ohio State U., 1957-62; D of Athletic Arts (hon.), 1972; LLD (hon.), U. St. Andrews, 1984. Chmn., chief exec. officer Golden Bear Internat., Inc. Author: My 55 Ways to Lower Your Golf Score, 1964, Take a Tip From Me, 1968, The Greatest Game of All, 1969, Jack Nicklaus' Lesson Tee, 1972, Golf My Way, 1974, Jack Nicklaus' Playing Lessons, 1976, On and Off the Fairway, 1978, Play Better Golf, Vols. 1-3, 1980, 81, 83, The Full Swing, 1982, My Most Memorable Shots in the Majors, 1988. Chmn. Ohio div. Am. Cancer Soc., 1967; chmn. sports div. Nat. Easter Seal Soc., 1967. Named PGA Player of Year, 1967, 72, 73, 75, 76, Dunlop Profl. Athlete of Yr., 1972, Golfer of Year Profl. Golfers Assn., 1973, Byron Nelson award, 1964, 65, 72, 73, Bob Jones award, 1975; named Sportsman of Year, Sports Illus. mag., 1978; named to World Golf Hall of Fame; named Athlete of the Decade for 1970-79, 1979, Golfer of the '70s, 1979, Golfer of the Century, 1988. Mem. President's Club Ohio State U., Phi Gamma Delta. Over 105 golf courses on 5 continents, 12 ranked in U.S. Top 100; hosted 185 profl. tournaments 1973—; won 71 tournaments including 20 maj. championships; maj. tournaments won include Tournament of Champions, 1963, 64, 71, 73, 77, U.S. Amateur, 1959, 61, U.S. Open, 1962, 67, 72, 80, U.S. Masters, 1963, 65, 66, 72, 75, 86, Brit. Open, 1966, 70, 78, PGA Championship, 1963, 71, 73, 75, 80, Internat. Pro-Amateur, 1973, Atlanta Golf Classic, 1973, Walt Disney World Golf Classic, 1971-73, 75, Hawaiian Open, 1974, Tournament Players Championship, 1974, 76, 78, Hawaiian Open, 1974, Doral-Eastern Open, 1975, Heritage Classic, 1975, Australian Open, 1964, 68, 71, 75, 76, 78, World Series of Golf, 1962, 63, 67, 70, 76, Gleason Inverrary Classic, 1976, 77, 78, Phila. Classic, 1965, 78, Colonial Nat. Invitational, 1982, PGA Seniors Championship, 1991, U.S. Senior Open, 1991, 93, Mercedes Sr. Championship, 1994, others. Office: Golden Bear Internat Inc 11780 US Hwy #1 North Palm Beach FL 33408*

NICKLE, DENNIS EDWIN, electronics engineer, church deacon; b. Sioux City, Iowa, Jan. 30, 1936; s. Harold Bateman and Helen Cecilia (Killackey) N. BS in Math., Fla. State U., 1961. Reliability mathematician Pratt & Whitney Aircraft Co., W. Palm Beach, Fla., 1961-63; br. supr. Melpar Inc., Falls Church, Va., 1963-66; prin. mem. tech. staff Xerox Data Systems, Rockville, Md., 1966-70; sr. tech. officer WHO, Washington, 1970-76; software tech. mgr. Melpar div. E-Systems, Inc., Falls Church, 1976—; lectr. in field. Ordained deacon Roman Catholic Ch., 1979. Chief judge for computers Fairfax County Regional Sci. Fair, 1964-88; mem. Am. Security Council; scoutmaster, commr. Boy Scouts Am., 1957-92; youth custodian Fairfax County Juvenile Ct., 1973-87; chaplain No. Va. Regional Juvenile Detention Home, 1978-88; moderator Nocturnal Adoration Soc.; parochial St. Michael's Ch., Annandale, Va., 1979-89, Christ the Redeemer, Sterling, Va., 1990-93. Served with U.S. Army, 1958-60. Recipient Eagle award, Silver award, Silver Beaver award, other awards Boy Scouts Am.; Ad Altare Dei, St. George Emblem, Diocese of Richmond. Mem. Assn. Computing Machinery, Computer Soc., Am. Soc. For Quality Control, CODSIA (mem. chmn working groups), ORLANDO II (Govt./industry working group), Old Crows Assn., Rolm Mil-Spec Computer Users Group (internat. pres.), San Antonio I (select industry coordination group), Nat. Security Indsl. Assn. (convention com. 1985—, software quality assurance subcom., regional membership chmn 1981-89, nat. exec. vice-chmn. 1989-94, chmn. 1994—), Am. Security Coun., IEEE (sr. mem. standards working group in computers 1983—), Defense Software Devel. Standards Avd. Bd. (chmn. 1991—), Soc. Software Quality, Hewlett Packard Users Group, Smithsonian Assn., Internat. Platform Assn., NRA (endowment), Nat. Eagle Scout Assn. (life), Alpha Phi Omega (life), Sigma Phi Epsilon. Club: KC (4 deg.). Author: Stress in Adolescents, 1986; co-author: Handbook for Handling Non-Productive Stress in Adolescence, Standard For Software Life Cycle Processes, IMPEESA Junior Leader Training Guide, Standard for Software Quality Assurance, 1984-91, Standard for Developing Software Life Cycle Processes, Configuration Management Procedures, Software Quality Assurance Procedures, Software Development Procedures; contbr. to profl. jours. Office: 7700 Arlington Blvd Falls Church VA 22042-2902

NICKLES, DONALD (DON NICKLES), senator; b. Ponca City, Okla., Dec. 6, 1948; s. Robert C. and Coeweene (Bryan) N.; m. Linda L. Morrison, Sept. 5, 1968; children—Donald Lee II, Jennifer Lynn, Kim Elizabeth, Robyn Leigh. BA in Bus. Adminstrn., Okla. State U., 1971. Owner, operator Don Nickles Profl. Cleaning Svc., Stillwater, Okla., 1968-71; v.p., gen. mgr. Nickles Machine Corp., Ponca City, 1972—; mem. Okla. Senate, 1979-80; mem. U.S. Senate from Okla., 1981—, chmn. Senate Rep. policy com.; chem. Senate Rep. policy com., mem. com. on energy and natural resources, com. on rules and adminstrn., com. on budget fin. and select com. on Indian affairs, mem. arms control observer group, coal caucus, rail caucus, rural health caucus, world climate conv. observer group, Rep. task force on nat. security and regulatory reform; passed legislation to provide for econ. and employment impact statement for all new laws and regulations. Chmn. platform com. Rep. Nat. Conv., 1992; bd. dirs. Ponca City United Way; bd. advisors Close Up Found.; mem. Kay Coun. for Retarded Children, Ponca City, St. Mary's Roman Cath. Parish Coun.; mem. adv. bd. Salvation Army, Ponca City. With USNG, 1970-76. Named one of Outstanding Young Men of Am., U.S. Jaycees, 1983. Mem. Fellowship Christian Athletes, Ponca City C. of C. Republican. Club: Rotary. Office: US Senate 133 Hart Senate Office Bldg Washington DC 20510

NICKLIN, EMILY, lawyer; b. Cooperstown, N.Y., June 24, 1953; d. George Leslie Jr. and Katherine Mildred (Aronson) N.; m. Jay Schleusener, Dec. 28, 1974; children: Max, Lucas, Anna. BA, U. Chgo., 1975, JD, 1977. Bar: Ill. 1977, U.S. Dist. Ct. (no. dist.) Ill. 1977, U.S. Ct. Appeals (7th cir.) 1979. Law clk. to judge U.S. Dist. Ct. (no. dist.) Ill., Chgo., 1977-79; assoc. Kirkland & Ellis, Chgo., 1979-83, ptnr., 1983—; tchr. Ill. Continuing Legal Edn. Bar Program, Chgo., 1983—; fellow Salzburg Seminar, Austria, 1983; dep. corp. counsel City of Chgo., 1989-91. Mem. Nat. Inst. Trial Advocacy (tchr., team leader 1982—), Order of Coif, Phi Beta Kappa. Office: Kirkland & Ellis 200 E Randolph Dr Chicago IL 60601-6401

NICKLIN, GEORGE LESLIE, JR., psychoanalyst, educator, physician; b. Franklin, Pa., July 25, 1925; s. George Leslie and Emma (Reed) N.; m. Katherine Mildred Aronson, Sept. 30, 1950. B.A., Haverford Coll., 1949; M.D., Columbia U., 1951; postgrad. psychoanalysis, William A. White Inst., N.Y.C., 1962. Resident, then chief resident Bellevue Psychiat. Hosp., N.Y.C., 1953-56; pvt. practice specializing in psychoanalytic psychiatry, 1956—; staff Bellevue Hosp., 1956—; asst. clin. prof. psychiatry NYU Med. Sch., 1962-70, assoc. clin. prof. psychiatry, 1970—; dir. L.I. Inst. Psychoanalysis, 1978-88, dir. emeritus, 1988—; attending psychiatrist Nassau County Med. Center Clin. Campus; assoc. clin. prof. psychiatry SUNY-Stony Brook Health Sci. Ctr., 1976—; mem. Com. to Award Martin Luther King Peace Prize. Founder Friends World Coll., 1958, trustee, 1968-83. Served with AUS, 1943-46, ETO. Decorated Purple Heart with oak leaf cluster, Bronze Star with oak leaf cluster and three battle stars. Fellow Am. Acad. Psychoanalysis, Am. Psychiat. Assn.; mem. AAAS, NAACP, Soc. Med. Psychoanalysts (pres. 1986-87), White Psychoanalytic Soc., Assn. for World Edn. (charter trustee, treas. 1970-78), 9th Inf. Divsn. Assn. Mem. Soc. of Friends. Clubs: Gardiner's Bay Country (Shelter Island, N.Y.); Penn (London). Home and Office: 6 Butler Pl Garden City NY 11530-4603 *Education is essential to the future evolution of human society. But education alone is not enough. Integrity, creative thinking and informed action opens the path to the future.*

NICKON, ALEX, chemist, educator; b. Poland, Oct. 6, 1927; came to U.S., 1955, naturalized, 1961; s. Steve and Maria (Nickon) N.. m. Beulah Monica Godby, Aug. 22, 1950; children—Dale Beverly, Linda Cheryl, Leanne Marie. B.Sc., U. Alta., 1949; M.A., Harvard U., 1951, Ph.D. 1953. Vis. lectr. Bryn Mawr Coll., 1953; postdoctoral fellow Birkbeck Coll., U. London, Eng., 1953-54, NRC, Ottawa, Can., 1954-55; NSF sr. fellow, Imperial Coll., London, 1963-64, U. Munich, Germany, 1971-72; mem. faculty Johns Hopkins, 1955—, prof. chemistry, 1964-94, Vernon K. Krieble prof. chemistry, 1975-94, prof. emeritus, 1994—; vis. asso. Am. Chem. Soc. on Profl. Tng., 1975—; Mem. medicinal chem. panel NIH, 1966-70; postdoctoral panel NRC, 1968-69. Sr. editor: Jour. Organic Chemistry, 1965-71; Am. exec. editor: Tetrahedron Reports, 1978—. Recipient Md. Chemist award, 1990; Sloan Found. fellow, 1957-61. Fellow N.Y. Acad. Scis.; mem. Am. Chem. Soc. (nat. awards com. 1974-76), Brit. Chem. Soc. Home: 1009 Painters Ln Cockeysville Hunt Valley MD 21030-1729 Office: Dept Chemistry Johns Hopkins U Baltimore MD 21218-2685

NICKS, STEVIE (STEPHANIE NICKS), singer, songwriter; b. Calif., May 26, 1948. albums include: (with Lindsey Buckingham Buckingham Nicks, 1973, (with Fleetwood Mac) Fleetwood Mac, 1975, Rumours, 1977 (co-winner, Billboard award for Album of the Year, Group of Year 1977), Tusk,

1979, Fleetwood Mac Live, 1980, Mirage, 1982, Tango in the Night, 1987, Greatest Hits, 1989, Behind The Mask, 1990, 25 Years-The Chain, 1992; (solo) Bella Donna, 1981, The Wild Heart, 1983, Rock a Little, 1985, The Other Side of the Mirror, 1989, Time Space, 1991, Street Angel, 1994; composer songs Rhiannon, 1975, Landslide, 1975, Leather and Lace, 1975, Dreams, 1977, Sara, 1979, Edge of Seventeen, 1981, If Anyone Falls (with Sandy Stewart), 1982, Stand Back (with Prince Rogers Nelson), 1983, I Can't Wait (with others), 1985, Seven Wonders (with Sandy Stewart), 1987. Office: Modern Records care WEA 111 N Hollywood Way Burbank CA 91505*

NICOL, ROBERT DUNCAN, architect; b. La Jolla, Calif., Sept. 16, 1936; s. Duncan and Catherine (Muffly) N.; m. Susann Kay Larson; 1 child, Jennifer E. AA, Principia Coll., 1967; BArch, U. Calif., Berkeley, 1961. Registered arch., Ariz., Calif., Mont., Wash. Designer Kawneer Mfg. Co., Richmond, Calif., 1961-62, Claude Oakland, San Francisco, 1962-64; project arch. David T. Johnson, Oakland, Calif., 1964-68; pvt. practice Oakland, Calif., 1968—. Mem. bd. appeals City of Alameda, 1971-73, vice chair planning commn., 1973-77, founder, chair, vice chair design rev. bd., 1974-80, founder, chair, vice chair hist. adv. bd., 1976—, co-founder, chair, vice chair mayor's com. for handicapped, 1980-86;. Recipient Design award Am. Registered Archs., 1969, Harper Plz. Design award Calif. Bldg. Officials Assn., 1985. Fellow AIA; mem. Soc. Am. Registered Archs., Nat. Coun. Archtl. Registration Bds. (sr.), Alexander Graham Bell Assn. for Deaf (lectr.), Oral Hearing Impaired Sec., San Leandro Hist. Railway Soc. (founder, charter mem., chair, vice-chair), Alameda Jr. C. of C. (project dir. 1969), Alameda Victorian Preservation Soc. Republican. Office: 455 17th St Oakland CA 94612-2101

NICOLA, JAMES B., stage director, composer, playwright; b. Worcester, Mass., Oct. 28, 1958; s. George Anthony and Settimia (Palumbo) Balko. BA cum laude, Yale U., 1980; studies with Maury Yeston, Lehman Engel. Script cons. Manhattan Theatre Club, 1980-82; assoc. dir. Am. Stage Festival, 1985; guest dir. Cen. Washington U., Ellensburg, Wash., 1987, Spokane (Wash.) Interplayers Ensemble, 1987-88, Shakespeare-by-the-Sea, Virginia Beach, Va., 1988; artistic dir. Youngstown Playhouse, 1988-89; asst. prof. William Patterson Coll., N.J., 1989; vis. asst. prof., guest dir. U. Mont., Missoula, 1987, 91; dir. Ark. Repertory Theatre, 1992, Worcester Foothills Theatre, Mass., 1990-92, Heritage Repertory, Charlottesville, Va., 1990, Telluride (Colo.) Repertory Theatre, 1992, 93, 94, 95; dir. Indsl. Arts Theater, Denver, 1993, 94; guest dir. Ohio Northern U., 1993; assoc. dir. Mint Theatre Co., N.Y.C., 1993—. Dir. (plays) Macbeth, Long Day's Journey Into Night, Lady Windermere's Fan, The Importance of Being Earnest, The House of Bernarda Alba, 1994; All My Sons, The Menaechmi, Amadeus (Pierrot award for Best Dir./Best Prodn. 1987), Romeo and Juliet, The Attic, Children of a Lesser God, Steel Magnolias, Hannah Davis, Noises Off, Rapid Transit, The Elephant Man, Diary of Anne Frank, Measure for Measure, Uncle Vanya, Much Ado About Nothing, Fat Lucy; (mus.) Anything Goes, Kiss Me Kate, A Little Night Music, I Do! I Do!, Working, Swing It!, You're a Good Man Charlie Brown, My Fair Lady, Round for Four; composer: Round for Four, 1987, The Tempest, Goodbye Columbus Ave.; playwright: Donuts, 1987. Madolin Cervantes grantee, SDC Workshop Found., 1984, 87, Meet the Composers grantee, 1987; semi-finalist Christina Crawford award, U. S.D., 1987. Mem. Soc. Stage Dirs. and Choreographers, Dramatists Guild. Home and Office: Apt 45-0 484 W 43d St New York NY 10036

NICOLA, JAMES C., theater director; b. Hartford, Conn., July 5, 1950; s. Renato Nicola and Joyce Arlene Skates Bruckner. BA, Tufts U., 1972. Adminstrv. asst. Theatre Comms. Group, N.Y.C., 1973-75; casting asst. N.Y. Shakespeare Festival, N.Y.C., 1975-78, casting coord., 1978-80; NEA dir. fellow Arena Stage, Washington, 1980-81, producing assoc., 1981-88; artistic dir. N.Y. Theatre Workshop, N.Y.C., 1988—; freelance dir. WPA Theatre, N.Y.C., 1974-77, Studio Theatre, Washington, 1986, New Playwrights Theatre, Washington, 1981-85, Round House Theatre, Washington, 1987. Recipient Cmty. Svc. award League of Washington Theaters, 1988, Obie award Village Voice, 1991. Democrat. Office: My Theatre Workshop 79 E 4th St New York NY 10003

NICOLAI, EUGENE RALPH, public relations consultant, editor, writer; b. Renton, Wash., June 26, 1911; s. Eugene George and Josephine (Heidinger) N.; student U. Wash., 1929, Whitman Coll., 1929-30; B.A., U. Wash., 1934; postgrad. Am. U., 1942; M.A., George Washington U., 1965; m. Helen Margaret Manogue, June 5, 1935; 1 son, Paul Eugene. Editor, U. Wash. Daily, Seattle, 1934; asst. city editor, writer, nat. def. editor Seattle Times, 1934-41; writer Sta. KJR, Seattle, 1937-39; writer, editor, safety info. officer Bur. Mines, Washington, 1941-45; news dir. Grand Coulee Dam and Columbia Basin Project, Washington, 1945-50; regional info. dir. Bur. Mines, Denver and Pitts., 1950-55, asst. chief mineral reports, Washington, 1955-61, news dir. office of oil and gas, 1956-57; sr. info. officer, later sr. public info. officer Office Sec. Interior, Washington, 1961-71, staff White House Nat. Conf. on Natural Beauty, spl. detail to White House, 1971, ret.; now public relations cons., tech. editor, writer. Formerly safety policy adviser Interior Dept.; com. mem. Internat. Cooperation Year, State Dept., 1971. With George Washington U. Alumni Found.; founder, mng. dir. Josephine Nature Preserve; pres. Media Assocs. Bd. dirs. Wash. State Council on Alcoholism; adviser Pierce Transit Authority, Pierce County Growth Mgmt., Pierce County Ethics Commn. Named Disting. Alumnus, recipient Penrose award, both Whitman Coll., 1979. Mem. Nature Conservancy, Wash. Environ. Council, Nat. Audubon Soc. (Am. Belgian Tervuren dist. rep.), Crook County (Oreg.) Hist. Soc., Washington State Hist. Soc., Emerald Shores Assn, Sigma Delta Chi, Pi Kappa Alpha. Presbyn. Clubs: George Washington U., Purdy (pres.). Lodge: Masons. Author: The Middle East Emergency Committee; editor: Fed. Conservation Yearbooks. Home: 9809 N Seminole Dr Spokane WA 99208-8608

NICOLAIDES, MARY, lawyer; b. N.Y.C., June 7, 1927; d. George and Dorothy Nicolaides. BCE, CUNY, 1947; MBA with distinction, DePaul U., 1975, JD, 1981. Bar: Ill. 1982, U.S. Dist. Ct. (no. dist.) Ill. 1982, U.S. Patent Office 1983. Sr. design engr. cement subs. U.S. Steel Corp., N.Y.C., then Pitts., 1948-71; sole practice Chgo., 1982—. Mem. ABA. Republican. Greek Orthodox. Address: 233 E Erie St Suite 1804 Chicago IL 60611

NICOLAOU, KYRIACOS COSTA, chemistry educator; b. Karavas, Kyrenia, Cyprus, June 5, 1946; came to U.S., 1972; s. Costa and Helen (Yettimi) N.; m. Georgette Karayianni, July 15, 1973; children; Colette, Alexis, Christopher, Paul. BSc, Bedford Coll., London, 1969; PhD, U. Coll., London, 1972. Rsch. associate Columbia U., N.Y.C., 1972-73, Harvard U., Cambridge, Mass., 1973-76; from asst. prof. to Rhodes-Thompson prof. chemistry U. Pa., Phila., 1976-89; Darlene Shiley prof. chemistry, chmn. dept. Rsch. Inst. Scripps Clinic, La Jolla, Calif., 1989—; prof. chemistry U. Calif., La Jolla 1989—; vis. prof. U. Paris, 1986; mem. exec. com. Biann. Cyprus Conf. on Drug Design; mem. med. study sect. B, NIH, 1988-90. Author: (with N. A. Petasis) Selenium in Natural Products Synthesis, 1984; co-editor; Synthesis, Germany, 1984-90; editorial bd. Prostaglandins, Leukotrienes and Medicine, 1978-88, Synthesis, 1990—, Accounts of Chem. Rsch., 1992—, Carbohydrate Letters, 1993—; mem. bd. consulting editors Tetrahedron Publs., 1992—; mem. adv. bd. Contemporary Organic Synthesis, 1993—; mem. regional adv. bd. J. C. S. Chem. Comm., 1989—, J. C. S. Perkin I, 1991—.; contbr. numerous articles to profl. jours.; patentee in field. Recipient Japan Soc. for Promotion Sci. award, 1987-88, U.S. Sr. Scientist award Alexander von Humboldt Found., 1987-88, Alan R. Day award Phila. Organic Chemisyts Club, 1993; fellow A. P. Sloan Found., 1979-83, J. S. Guggenheim Found., 1984; Camille and Henry Dreyfus scholar, 1980-84, Arthur C. Cope scholar, 1987. Fellow N.Y. Acad. Scis.; mem. AAAS, Am. Chem. Soc. (Creative Work in Synthetic Organic Chemistry award 1993), Chem. Soc. London, German Chem. Soc., Japanese Chem. Soc. Office: Univ California at San Diego Dept Chemistry 0332 9500 Gillman Dr La Jolla CA 92093-5003*

NICOLAY, JANICE, state legislator; b. Watertown, S.D.; m. Jerry Nicolay. MEd, S.D. State U. Mem. S.D. Ho. of Reps., 1983—; chair appropriations com., pub. sch. administr.; bd. dirs. 1st Bank S.D. Mem. United Way. Recipient Leadership award YWCA. Mem. Nat. Edn. Assn., S.D. Edn. Assn. Republican. Home: 1401 Suburban Dr Sioux Falls SD 57103-3762 Office: SD House of Reps Office of House Mems Pierre SD 57501

NICOLETTE, ARCHIE JOHN, local government official, retired secondary education educator; b. Nashwauk, Minn., Sept. 4, 1918; s. Frank P. Nicolette and Rachel DeMark; m. Barbara Mae Boelsen, June 7, 1947; children: Archie Jr., Cathrine, Frank, David, Lorinda, Anna Marie. Student, St. Norbert Coll., 1936-39; B in Sci. Edn., U. Superior, 1942; student, U. Ark., 1959, 60, 61; M in Sci. Edn., U. No. Mich., 1965. Sci. tchr. Comins Sch. Dist., Fairview, Mich., 1942-44, Rib Lake (Wis.) Sch. Dist., 1944-45; sci. tchr., coach Fairchild Sch. Dist., 1945-46, Arbor Vitae-Woodruff (Wis.) Sch. Dist., 1946-57; sci. dept. chmn. Lakeland Union High Sch., Minocqua, Wis., 1957-81; ret. from teaching, 1981; dist. 9 supr. Oneida County, Woodruff, 1982-90. Mem. Lakeland Union Sch. Dist. Bd., Minocqua, 1983-90; assessor Woodruff Twp., 1958-70; presenter 16th Ann. Sci. Tchrs. Assn. Conv., Washington, 1968; participant Elderhostel Program, Weed, Calif., 1986, Brandon, Ont., 1987; scoutmaster Boy Scouts of Am., 1957-68; mem. Oneida County Commn. on Aging, 1986—, No. Area Agy. on Aging, 1988—, treas. 1991—. Recipient Ron Gibbs award Wis. Soc. Sci. Tchrs., 1980, 3 NSF awards, 1956, 68, 71. Mem. Nat. Sci. Tchr. Assn., Wis. Edn. Assn., Lakeland Edn. Assn., 4H Club (v.p. Oneida County 1968), Lions Club (chpt. pres. 1960), KC (grand knight 1989-91). Roman Catholic. Avocations: photography, video, skiing. Home: 8741 Nicks Dr Woodruff WI 54568-9626

NICOLETTI, PAUL LEE, veterinarian, educator; b. Goodman, Mo., Oct. 26, 1932; s. Felix and Clarice Nicoletti; m. Earlene Blackburn, June 6, 1954; children: Diana, Julie, Nancy. BS in Agr., U. Mo., 1956, DVM, 1956; MS, U. Wis., 1962. Diplomate Am. Coll. Vet. Preventative Medicine. Veterinarian, U.S. Dept. Agr., Mo., Wis., N.Y., 1956-68, UN Food and Agr. Orgn., Tehran, Iran, 1968-72, U.S. Dept. Agr., Jackson, Miss., 1972-75, Gainesville, Fla., 1973-78; prof. veterinarian medicine U. Fla., Gainesville, 1978—. Contbr. numerous articles to profl. jours. Recipient awards from Fla. Cattleman's Assn., 1978, Dairy Farmers, Inc., 1978, Borden award, 1979, Gold Star award Fla. Veterinary Medicine Assoc., 1981, 1986, Universidad Austral de Chile, 1981, Puerto Rico Dairy Assn., 1978, Faculty Alumni award U. Mo., 1987; named Basic Scis. Tchr. of Yr., Nat. Student Am. Veterinary Med. Assn., 1994; Veterinarian of the Yr. award, Fla. Veterinary Med. Assn., 1994, (pres. 1995—). Mem. Am. Veterinary Medicine Assn. (int. prize 1991), Am. Assoc. Bovine Practice. Home: 2552 SW 14th Dr Gainesville FL 32608-2042 Office: Univ of Fla Coll Vet Medicine PO Box 110880 Gainesville FL 32611-0880

NICOLITZ, ERNST, ophthalmologist, educator; b. Surabaja, Java, Indonesia, Jan. 7, 1947; came to U.S., 1956; naturalized, 1961; s. Alexander Renauld and Augustine Adeline (Godschalk) N.; m. Elizabeth Ann Perkins, July 30, 1971; children:3 Ryan, Marlana, Jennifer. B.S. in Chemistry, N.Mex. State U., 1969; grad. UCLA, 1969-70; M.D., U. N.Mex., 1974. Diplomate Am. Bd. Ophthalmology, Nat. Bd. Med. Examiners. Resident in eye surgery U. Ala., Birmingham, 1974-77; oculoplastic fellow Wills Eye Hosp., Phila., 1977-78; practice medicine specializing in ophthalmology, Jacksonville, Fla., 1978—; chief ophthalmology Baptist Med. Ctr., Jacksonville, 1984-86, 88-90, co-founder Bapt. Eye Inst.; asst. clin. prof. U. Fla., Gainesville, 1979—. Contbr. articles to profl. jours. Med. advisor Prevent Blindness, Jacksonville, 1978—. Recipient Physician Recognition award AMA, 1984. Fellow ACS, Am. Soc. Ophthalmic Plastic Surgery, Am. Acad. Ophthalmology (Honor award 1993), Am. Acad. Facial Plastic and Reconstructive Surgery. Republican. Presbyterian. Avocations: fishing, travel, photography, tennis, hunting. Office: Bapt Eye Inst 1235 San Marco Blvd Jacksonville FL 32207-8554

NICOLL, CHARLES SAMUEL, physiologist, educator; b. Toronto, Ont., Can., Apr. 11, 1937; came to U.S., 1951, naturalized, 1958; s. Robert Knox and Annie (Young) N.; m. Sharon M. Russell, Apr. 14, 1974; children: Katherin Ann, Eric Robert, Scott Frank. B.S., Mich. State U., 1958, M.S., 1960, Ph.D. (NIH fellow), 1962. Am. Cancer Soc. postdoctoral fellow U. Calif., Berkeley, 1962-64, asst. prof. physiology, 1966-70, assoc. prof., 1970-74, prof., 1974—; staff fellow Nat. Cancer Inst. NIH, 1964-66. Recipient award for meritorious rsch. Sigma Xi, 1960, City of Nice, France, 1977, Grace Pickford medal for outstanding rsch. Internat. Soc. for Comparative Endocrinology, 1989, Richard Simpson Meml. award Incurably Ill for Animal Rsch., 1992. Fellow AAAS; mem. Calif. Biomed. Rsch. Assn. (cert. of appreciation for outstanding svc. 1991), Am. Soc. Zoologists, Am. Physiol. Soc., Endocrine Soc. Research on hormones, growth, development and cancer; achievements include co-founding coalition for animals and animal research, a proactive organization that supports the use of animals in research.

NICOSIA, JOSEPH A., transportation company executive; b. Phila., Mar. 16, 1943; s. Frank R. and Rose (Cola) N.; m. Janet A. Aldrich, Dec. 6, 1972. BS, Pa. State U., 1965. Traffic supr. Air Products & Chems. Inc., Allentown, Pa., 1965-67; mgr. leased equipment Roadway Express, Akron, 1969-70; prin. William Kordisemon & Assocs., Chgo., 1970-72; dir. nat. accts. Rollins Leasing Corp., Wlimington, Del., 1972-80; v.p. sales, mktg. McDonnell Douglas Truck Svcs., Phila., 1980-83, Leaseway Transp., Cleve., 1983-87, Customized Transp. Inc., Jacksonville, Fla., 1987—. Lt. USN, 1967-69. Mem. Coun. Logistics Mgmt., Warehouse Edn. Rsch. Coun., Delta Nu Alpha, Marsh Landing Country Club, Rolling Green Golf Club. Home: 7130 Fountains Way Ponte Vedra Beach FL 32082-1909 Office: GATX Logistics Inc 1301 Gulf Life Dr Jacksonville FL 32207

NICOTRA, JOSEPH CHARLES, artist; b. Corona, N.Y., Aug. 9, 1931; s. Charles C. and Constanta (Maglienti) N.; m. Mary C. Losquadro, Sept. 9, 1951; children: Therese, Nanette, Marie. Student, Art Students League, N.Y.C., 1955-59, Art Students League, Woodstock, N.Y., 1959-60, Am. Art Sch., N.Y.C., 1960-61; diploma of merit, U. Art, Italy, 1982. Registered artist, N.Y.C., GSA, Met. Transp. Authority N.Y. Freelance artist, N.Y.C., 1962—. One-man shows include Armstrong Mural Gallery, Flushing, N.Y., 1968, La Galerie Mouffe, Paris, 1976, Long Beach Artists Assn. Gallery, N.Y.C., 1978, 79, Long Beach Libr. Art Gallery, 1979, Cam Art Ctr., Bayshore, N.Y., 1982, Pricilla Redford Roe Gallery, Suffork, N.Y., 1982, Queens Mus., 1982, 84, Pla. Del Malfestazione, Italy, 1983, 6th Internat. Biennale, Garbo, Bulgaria, 1983, Flushing Coun. on Culture & Arts, 1986, Atlanta Gallery Geneve, 1987 (Primo Milano Gold medal 1988), St. Paul's Ch., Beth Page, N.Y., 1992, "Time Capsule-Schedule Mail Call" from the people of the Borough of Queens 1992 A.D., for 2292 A.D.; group shows include 57th St. Gallery, N.Y., 1957, Woodstock, N.Y., 1961, Long Beach (N.Y.) Mus., 1976, Flushing Coun. on Culture & Arts, 1986; represented in permanent collections Nat. Archives, Washington, Queens Mus. Art; prin. works include mural for Queens Mus. Title Wall for Nat. Travel Show; contbrs. Smithsonian Inst., Kennedy Gallery. Vol. Artist, tchr., docent, lectr. Queens Mus. Art, Flushing, N.Y., 1972—. With U.S. Army, 1952-54; mem. Queens Coun. Arts, Flushing Coun. Culture and Arts. Recipient Outstanding Svc. award Queens Mus. Art, 1972-91, 1st prize for Oil, Long Beach Mus., 1976; Bernsay scholar, 1958, scholar VA, 1959, 1st prize Long Beach Artists Assn., 1980, Accademia delle Art Gold medal, Italy, 1980, Gold medal for Safety, Peace & Artist Merit, Internat. Parliament, U.S.A., 1983, Accademia D'Europa award, 1983, Statue of Victory, Com. for World Culture, 1984, European Banner of Arts award 1985, Gold Plaque award Italian Accademia, 1987. Mem. Art Students League (life), Orgn. Ind. Artists, Internat. Confedn. Over of Artists (hon.), Queens Mus. Art (hon.), DAV (life). Home and Studio: 59-32 156th St Flushing NY 11355

NIDA, JANE BOLSTER (MRS. DOW HUGHES NIDA), retired librarian; b. Chgo., July 19, 1918; d. Chalmer A. and Elsie R. (Sonderman) Bolster; m. Dow Hughes Nida, Sept. 1, 1946; 1 child, Janice Beth (Mrs. Robert M Michaels). B.A., Aurora (Ill.) U., 1942; B.S. in Library Sci, U. Ill., 1943. Circulation librarian Aurora Pub. Library, 1940-42, 43-44, reference librarian, 1946; program dir. A.R.C. Eng., France, 1944-46; acquisitions librarian Ohio U., Athens, 1947; dir. Falls Church (Va.) Pub. Library, 1951-54; asst. dir. Arlington County Dept. Libraries, Arlington, Va., 1954-57; dir. Arlington County Dept. Libraries, 1957-80; on loan to AID, 1979-80; Mem. Va. Adv. Legis. Council, Com. to Revise State Library Laws, 1968-69, Women's Joint Congl. Com., 1968-80. Vol. Am. Cancer Soc., 1971-84, bd. dirs. Arlington chpt., 1974-84; mem. exec. com. Regional Adv. Group, Va. Regional Med. Program, 1971-76; v.p., founder, dir. Cultural Laureate Found. Recipient Meritorious Service award A.R.C., World War II, Outstanding Alumnus award Aurora U., 1979. Mem. AAUW, ALA, D.C. Libr. Assn., Va. Libr. Assn. (pres. 1969-70), Arlington Hist. Soc. (charter, bd. dirs. 1989-93), Army-Navy Country Club. Baptist. Home: 4907 29th St N

Arlington VA 22207-2755 also: 1617 Bayhouse Ct Apt 218 Sarasota FL 34231-6771

NIDETCH, JEAN, health service executive; b. Bklyn., Oct. 12, 1923; d. David and May (Rodin) Slutsky; children—David, Richard. Founder, pres. Weight Watchers Internat., Inc., Manhasset, L.I., until 1973, now cons.; cons. N.Y. State Assembly Mental Hygiene Com., 1968; adviser Joint Legis. Com. on Child Care Needs, Legislature N.Y.; pres. Weight Watchers Found. Author: Jean Nidetch: Weight Watchers Cookbook, 1966, The Story of Weight Watchers, 1970, Weight Watchers Party & Holiday Cookbook, 1984. Named Marketing Woman of Yr., Hon. Adm. Gt. Navy Nebr.; Woman of Year, Forest Hills Youth Assn.; recipient Woman of Achievement award, Speakers award Sales Promotion Execs. Assn. Mem. Washington Sq. Bus. and Profl. Womens Club, AFTRA. Home: 203 E 72nd St Apt 11B New York NY 10021-4568

NIEBRUEGGE, MICHAEL E., lawyer; b. Alton, Ill., Mar. 21, 1952. BA, Harvard U., 1974; JD, Cornell U., 1977. Bar: Ill. 1977, U.S. Dist. Ct. (no. dist.) Ill. 1977, Tex. 1982, U.S. Dist. Ct. (so dist.) Tex. 1988. Ptnr. Mayer, Brown & Platt, Houston; lectr. Northwestern U., Chgo., 1979-80. Mem. State Bar Tex., Tex. Assn. Bank Counsel. Office: Mayer Brown & Platt 3600 NCNB Ctr 700 Louisiana St Houston TX 77002-2730

NIED, THOMAS H., publishing company executive; b. Queens, N.Y., May 4, 1942; s. Herman Joseph and Margaret (Jos) N.; m. Carol J. Thomas, June 6, 1964; children: Stacey, Allison. BA, Rutgers U., 1964, LLB, 1967; LLM in Taxation, NYU, 1972. CPA, N.J., Ga. Tax mgr. Ernst & Young, N.Y.C., Atlanta, Newark and Trenton, N.J., 1968-77, N.Y. Times Co., N.Y.C., 1977—. Mem. ABA, AICPA, Tax Execs. Inst. (bd. dirs. 1986-91, pres. N.Y. chpt. 1991-92, exec. com. 1992-93). Avocations: travel, reading, philately, tennis. Home: 31 Vreeland Ct Princeton NJ 08540-6760 Office: NY Times Co 229 W 43rd St New York NY 10036-3913

NIEDEL, JAMES E., pharmaceuticals executive; b. Milw., Mar. 30, 1944; m. Selaine Benaim, Mar. 11, 1969; children: Ian Edward, Felisa Ann, Shira Beth. BS, U. Wis., 1965; MD, U. Miami, 1973, PhD, 1974. Diplomate Am. Bd. Internal Medicine. Scientist Burroughs-Wellcome, Research Triangle Park, N.C., 1977-80; prof. medicine Duke U., Durham, N.C., 1980-89; v.p. rsch. Glaxo Rsch. Inst., Research Triangle Park, 1989-92, sr. v.p. R & D, 1992-95, also bd. dirs., dir. group rsch. & devel., 1995—; bd. dirs. Amylin Corp. Bd. overseers Duke Cancer Ctr., Durham, 1990—. Searle scholar, 1981-84; recipient Career Devel. award NIH, 1981-84. Mem. Am. Soc. Clin. Investigation, Am. Soc. Biochemistry and Molecular Biology, Am. Soc. Immunology. Office: Glaxo Rsch Inst PO Box 13408 5 Moore Pl Research Triangle Park NC 27709

NIEDERAUER, GEORGE H., bishop; b. Los Angeles, CA, June 14, 1936; s. George and Elaine N. B.A. Philosophy, St. John's Seminary, Camarillo, CA, 1959; B.A. Sacred Theology, Catholic U., Washington, DC, 1962; M.A. English Lit., Loyola U., Los Angeles, CA, 1962; Ph.D. English Lit., USC, 1966. ordained priest April 30, 1962; named prelate of honor (monsignor) 1984; named bishop of Diocese of Salt Lake City, Nov. 3, 1994. Asst. pastor Our Lady of the Assumption Parish, Claremont, CA, 1962-63; priest in residence Holy Name of Jesus Parish, Los Angeles, CA, 1963-65; instr. English Lit. St. John's Seminary Coll., Camarillo, CA, 1965-79; instr. of English Lit. Mt. St. Mary's Coll., Los Angeles, CA, 1967-74; English Dept. chmn. St. John's Seminary Coll., Camarillo, CA, 1968-77; spiritual dir. St. John's Seminary Coll., 1972-79; part-time instr. of Spiritual Theology St. John's Seminary Theologate, 1976-79, full-time instr. of Spiritual Theology, 1979-87; part-time instr. of English Lit. St. John's Seminary Coll., 1979-92; rector St. John's Seminary, 1987-92, spiritual dir., 1979—; co-dir. Cardinal Manning House of Prayer for Priests, Los Angeles, CA, 1992—; mem. Nat. Fedn. of Spiritual Dirs. (pres. 1975-77); mem. Alpha Sigma Nu (Jesuit Honor Soc. - LMU Chapter); pres. Western Assn. of Spiritual Dirs., 1973-75; mem. bd. of the Comm. of Priests' Retreat, Archdiocese of Los Angeles; mem. select comm. for the revision of the U.S. Catholic Conf. "Program for Priestly Formation" 3rd edition; mem. Vatican Visitation Team for Theologates; speaker World Vision Internat, Fuller Theological Seminary, Calif. Lutheran Coll.; mem. Camarillo Ministerial Assn. Avocations include: classical music, stamp collecting, reading, film appreciation. Office: Chancery Office 27 C St Salt Lake City UT 84103*

NIEDERHUBER, JOHN EDWARD, surgical oncologist and molecular immunologist, university educator and administrator; b. Steubenville, Ohio, June 21, 1938; s. William Henry and Helen (Smittle) N.; m. Tracey J. Williamson; children: Elizabeth Ann, Matthew John. B.S., Bethany Coll., 1960; M.D., Ohio State U., 1964. Diplomate Am. Bd. Surgery. Internship, surgery Ohio State U. Hosp., Columbus, 1964-65; resident, surgery U. Mich. Med. Ctr., Ann Arbor, 1967-69, NIH acad. trainee in surgery, 1969-71, resident, surgery, 1971-72, chief resident surgery, 1972-73, asst. prof. surgery and asst. prof. microbiology, 1973-77, dir. transplantation program, 1975-76, assoc. prof. surgery and assoc. prof. microbiology, 1977-80, chief divsn. surg. oncology and transplantation, sect. gen. surgery, 1979-82, sr. assoc. dean med. sch., 1983-86, assoc. dean research, 1982-86, chief divsn. surg. oncology sect. gen. surgery, 1982-86, prof. surgery, prof. microbiology and immunology, 1980-87; cons. Wayne County Gen. Hosp. Mich., 1973-84; cons. surgery Ann Arbor VA Hosp., 1973-87; prof. surgery, oncology, molecular biology and genetics The Johns Hopkins U. Sch. Med., Baltimore, 1987-91; Emile Holman prof. surgery, chair, dept. surgery, head sect. surgical scis. Stanford (Calif.) U. Sch. Medicine, 1991—, prof. microbiology and immunology, 1991—; chief of surgery Stanford (Calif.) U. Hosp., 1991—; dir. Comp. Cancer Ctr. Stanford (Calif.) Med. Ctr., 1991—; vis. prof. Howard Hughes Med. Inst. Dept. Molecular Biology and Genetics The Johns Hopkins U. Sch. Medicine, Baltimore, 1986-87. Authored books on cancer; mem. editorial bd. Jour. Immunology, 1981-85, Jour. Surg. Res., 1989—, Current Opinion in Oncology, 1989—, Annals of Surgery, 1991—, Surg. Oncology, 1991—, Cancer, 1992—, Jour. Clin. Oncology, 1993, Annals of Surg. Oncology, 1993—, Jour. Am. Coll. Surgeons, 1994—; contbr. articles to profl. jours. Active NCI divsn. Cancer Treatment Bd. Scientific Councilors, 1986-91, chmn., 1987-91, Gen. Motors Cancer Rsch. Found. Awards Assembly, 1988-92. Served to capt. U.S. Army, 1965-67. Recipient USPHS Rsch. Career Devel. award Nat. Inst. Allergy and Infectious Disease, 1974-79, Disting. Faculty Svc. award U. Mich., 1978, Alumni Achievement award Ohio State U. Coll. Medicine, 1989, Alumni Achievement award in Medicine Bethany Coll., 1995; vis. rsch. fellow divsn. immunobiology Karolinska Inst., Stockholm, 1970-71, Am. Cancer Soc. Jr. Faculty Clin. fellow, 1977-79. Fellow ACS; mem. Am. Soc. Transplant Surgeons, Transplantation Soc., Am. Surg. Assn., Am. Assn. Immunologists, Coller Surg. Soc., Soc. Univ. Surgeons, Assn. Acad. Surgeons, Soc. Surg. Oncology, Ctrl. Surg. Soc., Am. Assn. Cancer Rsch., Am. Soc. Clin. Oncology, Soc. Clin. Surgery, Biology Club II, Robert M. Zollinger-Ohio State U. Surg. Soc., Pacific Coast Surg. Assn. Avocations: tennis, golf, gardening. Office: Stanford Univ Sch Medicine Dept of Surgery MSOB X300 Stanford CA 94304-5408

NIEDERJOHN, RUSSELL JAMES, electrical and computer engineering educator; b. Schenectady, June 13, 1944; s. Russell Kelly and Jeanette Ody (Burnison) N.; m. Susan A Swenson, June 7, 1969; children: Matthew Scott, Jeremy Michael. B.S. in Elec. Engring., U. Mass., Amherst, 1967, M.S. in Elec. Engring., 1968, Ph.D. in Elec. Engring., 1971. Registered profl. engr., Wis. Research asst. elec. engring. dept. U. Mass., Amherst, 1968-71; asst. prof. elec. engring. dept. Marquette U., Milw., 1971-75, assoc. prof., 1975-80, prof. elec. engring. and computer sci., dir. computer sci. and engring., 1980-87, prof., chmn. elec. and computer engring. dept., 1987-94; prof. elec. and computer engring. dept., 1994—; dir. speech and signal processing lab. Marquette U., Milw., 1973—, co-dir. signal processing rsch. ctr., 1991—; cons. William C. Brown Co. Pubs., Dubuque, Iowa, 1981-85, Eaton Corp., Milw., 1978-85, Seaman Nuclear Corp., Milw., 1979-81, 92-93, MacMillan Pubs., Encino, Calif., 1983-86. Contbr. articles to profl. jours. Mem. Milw. Ednl. TV Auction Com., 1978-81. Recipient Dow Outstanding Young Faculty award, 1977, award Western Electric Fund, 1981, Marquette U. Faculty award for teaching excellence, 1984. Fellow IEEE (mem. exec. com. Milw. sect. 1974-75, 76-79, 82-89, treas. 1982-83, sec. 1983-84, vice chmn. 1984-85, chmn. 1985-86, edn. chmn. 1977-80, chmn. nominating com. 1986-87, awards chmn. 1987-89; Meml. award 1979); mem. IEEE Signal Processing Soc., IEEE Computer Soc. (bd. dirs. Milw. chpt. 1981-85), IEEE Ind.

Elec. Soc. (adminstrv. com. 1986—, edn. com. 1986-89, soc. chpt. coord. 1989-91, assoc. editor Trans. 1988—, vice chmn. for confs. 1992, vice chmn. for pubs., 1993, vice chmn. adminstrn., 1994—), IEEE Systems, Man and Cybernetics Soc. (bd. dirs. Milw. chpt. 1975-79), Am. Soc. Engring. Edn. (exec. com. North Midwest sect. 1974-89), Acoustical Soc. Am., Milw. Symposium on Automatic Control (program chmn. 1975), Sigma Xi (pres.-elect Marquette U. chpt. 1986-87, pres. 1987-88, scientific achievement award, 1993), Eta Kappa Nu (C. Holmes MacDonald Outstanding Elec. Engring. Prof. in U.S. 1978, Marquette U. chpt. adv. 1986—, bd. dirs. 1993—), Tau Beta Pi. Home: 2545 S Brookside Pky New Berlin WI 53151-2907 Office: 1515 W Wisconsin Ave Milwaukee WI 53233-2286

NIEDERMAN, JAMES CORSON, physician, educator; b. Hamilton, Ohio, Nov. 27, 1924; s. Clifford Frederick and Henrietta (Corson) N.; m. Miriam Camp, Dec. 12, 1951; children—Timothy Porter, Derrick Corson, Eliza Orton, Caroline Noble. Student, Kenyon Coll., 1943-44, D.Sc. (hon.), 1981; M.D., Johns Hopkins U., 1949. Intern Johns Hopkins Hosp., Balt., 1949-50; asst. resident in medicine Yale-New Haven Med. Center, 1950-51, assoc. resident, 1953-55; med. ctr. practice specializing in internal medicine, infectious disease and clin. epidemiology New Haven, 1955—; instr. Yale U., 1955-58, asst. prof., 1958-66, assoc. prof., 1966-76, clin. prof. medicine and epidemiology, 1976—; mem. Nat. Coun. for Johns Hopkins Medicine. Trustee Kenyon Coll.; bd. counselors Smith Coll., 1970-77; mem. Alumni Coun. Johns Hopkins U.; mem. Conn. Soc. of Arts and Scis. Served to 1st lt. M.C. U.S. Army, 1951-53. Fellow Silliman Coll., Yale U. Fellow Am. Coll. Epidemiology; mem. Infectious Diseases Soc. Am., Am. Epidemiol. Soc., Johns Hopkins Med. and Surg. Assn., Democrat. Episcopalian. Clubs: Yale (N.Y.C.); New Haven Lawn. Research in clin. epidemiology. Home: 429 Sperry Rd Bethany CT 06524-3544 Office: 60 College St New Haven CT 06510-3210

NIEDERREITER, HARALD GUENTHER, mathematician, researcher; b. Vienna, June 7, 1944; s. Simon and Erna (Emig) N.; m. Gerlinde Hollweger, Aug. 30, 1969. PhD, U. Vienna, 1969. Asst. prof. So. Ill. U., Carbondale, 1969-72, assoc. prof., 1972-73; mem. Inst. Advanced Study, Princeton, N.J., 1973-75; vis. prof. UCLA, 1975-76; prof. U. Ill., Urbana, 1976-78, U. W.I., Kingston, Jamaica, 1978-81; researcher Austrian Acad. Scis., Vienna, 1981-89, dir. Inst. Info. Processing, 1989—. Author: Uniform Distribution of Sequences, 1974, Russian transl., 1985, Finite Fields, 1983, Russian transl. 1988, Introduction to Finite Fields and Their Applications, 1986, rev. edit., 1994, Random Number Generation and Quasi-Monte Carlo Methods, 1992; contbr. over 200 rsch. articles to math. jours.; assoc. editor Mathematics of Computation, 1988—, ACM Trans. Modeling and Computer Simulation, 1990—; mem. editorial bd. Caribbean J. Math., 1982—, Applicable Algebra, 1990—, Stochastic Optimization and Design, 1991—, J. Ramanujan Math. Soc., 1991—, Acta Arithmetica, 1992—, Monatshefte Math., 1993—, Finite Fields and Their Applications, 1993—, Jour. Info. and Optimization Scis., 1995—. Named hon. prof. U. Vienna, 1986. Mem. Am. Math. Soc., Austrian Math. Soc., Austrian Acad. Scis. (elected corr. 1993), Internat. Assn. Cryptologic Rsch., Austrian Computer Soc., Gesellschaft für Informatik, Soc. Indsl. Applied Math. Home: Sieveringer Str 41, A1190 Vienna Austria Office: Austrian Acad Scis, Sonnenfelsgasse 19, A1010 Vienna Austria

NIEDZIELSKI, HENRI ZYGMUNT, French and English language educator; b. Troyes, France, Mar. 30, 1931; came to U.S., 1956, naturalized, 1963; s. Zygmunt and Anna (Pelik) N.; children: Henri Zygmunt, Daniel Domenic, Robert Nicholas, Anna-Pia Irene. B.A., U. Conn., 1959, M.A., 1963, Ph.D., 1964. Instr. U. Mass., 1962-64, asst. prof., 1965-66; free-lance interpreter, 1960—; asst. prof. U. Laval, Quebec, Can., 1964-65; assoc. prof. U. Hawaii, 1966-72, prof., 1972-90, chmn. div. French, 1968-70, prof. emeritus; linguistic specialist NDEA, Edn. Profl. Devel. Act, 1963-69; Fulbright lectr. linguistics and TESL Krakow, Poland, 1972-74, Bujumbura, Burundi, 1980-81, Poznan, Poland, 1990-92; guest prof. Avignon, France, 1983-84, Bonn, Fed. Republic Germany, 1986-87; Disting. fellow Auckland U., New Zealand, 1989. Author: Le Roman de Helcanus, 1966, Basic French: A Programmed Course, 1968, Handbook of French Structure; A Systematic Review, 1968, Intermediate French: An Individualized Course, 1972, The Silent Language of France, 1975, French Sound Visuals, 1976; Films in Polish Body Language, 1989; editor: Language and Literature in Hawaii, 1968-72, Jean Misrahi Memorial Volume: Studies in Medieval Languages and Literature, 1977, Studies on the Seven Sages of Rome, 1978; assoc. editor: The Phonetician, 1994—. Pres. Family Counseling Center Hawaii, 1968-70; chmn. bd. Family Edn. Centers Hawaii, 1969-72. Served with French Armored Cav., 1951-53. Mem. Hawaii Assn. Lang. Tchrs. (pres. 1968-69), Modern Lang. Assn., Chopin Soc. Hawaii (dir. 1990—), Am. Translators Assn., Internat. Sociol. Assn., Alliance Française Hawaii (pres. 1978-80), Hawaii Assn. Translators (founding pres. 1982—), Am. Assn. Tchrs. French (pres. Hawaii 1981-83), Am. Council Teaching Fgn. Langs. (dir. 1970-72), Hawaii Second Lang. Articulation Com. (chmn. 1986-89), Rotary, Elks, Phi Beta Kappa, Pi Delta Phi, Phi Kappa Phi, Sigma Delta Pi. Lodge: Rotary, Elks. There is more than one way to help people but there is only one way to live: Help people.

NIEFELD, JAYE SUTTER, advertising executive; b. Mpls., May 27, 1924; s. Julius and Sophia (Rosenfeld) N.; m. Piri Elizabeth Von Zabrana-Szilagy, July 5, 1947; 1 child, Peter Wendell. Cert., London U., 1945; B.A., U. Minn., 1948; B.S., Georgetown U., 1949; Ph.D., U. Vienna, 1951. Project dir. Bur. Social Sci. Research, Washington, 1952-54; research dir. McCann-Erickson, Inc., N.Y.C., 1954-57; v.p. dir. mktg. Keyes, Madden & Jones, Chgo., 1957-60; pres., dir. Niefeld, Paley & Kuhn, Inc., Chgo., 1961-71; exec. v.p. Bozell, Inc., Chgo., 1971-89; pres. The Georgetown Group, Inc., 1991—; cons. U.S. Dept. State Commerce, HEW, also others; lectr. Columbia U., Northwestern U., U. Chgo., 1989-94; chmn. Ctr. Advanced Comm. Rsch.; pres. Glencoe Angus Farms, J&J Enterprises, The Georgetown Group Inc., 1991—; bd. dirs. Mktg. Decisions, Inc. Author: The Making of an Advertising Campaign, 1989; (with others) Marketing's Role in Scientific Management, 1957, Advertising and Marketing to Young People, 1965, The Ultimate Overseas Business Guide for Growing Companies, 1990; contbr. articles to profl. jours. Mem. adv. bd. Glencoe Family Svc.; bd. dirs. Big Bros. Met. Chgo.; exec. v.p. City of Hope. Capt. AUS, 1942-46. Decorated Bronze Star. Mem. Am. Assn. Pub. Opinion Rsch., Am. Film Inst., Am. Mktg. Assn., Am. Sociol. Assn., Smithsonian Instn. Home: 1011 Bluff St Glencoe IL 60022-1120

NIEFORTH, KARL ALLEN, university dean, educator; b. Melrose, Mass., July 7, 1936; s. Reginald Lemuel and Mabel (Zeimetz) N.; children from previous marriage: Scott, Keith, Karla, Kraig; m. Joan Carolyn Whitney, Feb. 14, 1989. BS, Mass. Coll. Pharmacy, 1957; MS in Med. Chemistry, Purdue U., 1959, PhD, 1961. Lic. pharmacist, Conn., Mass. Asst. prof. med. chemistry St. Pharmacy, U. Conn., Storrs, 1961-68, assoc. prof., 1968-75, prof., 1975—; asst. dean, 1967-76, assoc. dean, 1976-81, dean, 1981-93; lectr. psychiatry Yale U., 1970-76; mem. evaluation panels NSF, 1974-76, NIH, 1972-75; bd. dirs. Ctr. Drug and Alcohol Studies, Farmington, Conn., 1976-78; mem. pharmacy educators com. Nat. Assn. Chain Drugstores, 1988-93. Mem. adv. com. Conn. Dept. Mental Health, 1972-75; bd. dirs. Ea. Conn. Drug Action Program, 1970-72; mem. pharm. tripartite com. Conn. Dept. Consumer Protection, 1979-82, 89-95. Mem. Am. Found. Pharm. Edn. (Charles Lynn Fellow 1960-61), Am. Chem. Soc., Am. Pharm. Assn., Am. Assn. Colls. Pharmacy, Conn. Pharm. Assn., Conn. Soc. Hosp. Pharmacists, Acad. Pharm. Scis., Sigma Xi, Kappa Psi, Phi Lambda Sigma, Phi Lambda Upsilon, Rho Chi, Phi Kappa Phi. Republican. Home: 83 Brookside Ln Mansfield Center CT 06250-1109 Office: U Conn Sch Pharmacy Storrs CT 06269

NIEHANS, DANIEL JURG, lawyer; b. Basel, Switzerland, July 9, 1949; came to U.S., 1966, naturalized, 1972; s. Jurg Max and Gertrud Helen (Heusler) N.; m. Patricia Delano Lazowska, July 14, 1979; 1 child, Christina Claire. BA, Johns Hopkins U., 1971; JD, U. Chgo., 1974. Bar: Calif. 1974, U.S. Dist. Ct. (no. dist.) Calif. 1974, U.S. Tax Ct. 1981. Assoc. Pillsbury, Madison & Sutro, San Francisco, 1974-81, ptnr., 1982—. Mem. ABA, Western Pension and Benefits Conf. Republican. Office: Pillsbury Madison & Sutro 235 Montgomery St San Francisco CA 94104

NIEHAUS, LENNIE, composer, jazz saxophonist; b. St. Louis, Mo., June 1, 1929. Scores include (films) Tightrope, 1984, City Heat, 1984, Sesame Street: Follow That Bird, 1985, Pale Rider, 1985, Never Too Young to Die, 1986, Ratboy, 1986, Heartbreak Ridge, 1986, Emanon, 1987, Bird, 1988, Hot Men, 1989, White Hunter, Black Heart, 1990, The Rookie, 1990, Unforgiven, 1992, A Perfect World, 1993, The Bridges of Madison County, 1995, (TV movies) The Child Saver, 1988, Lush Life, 1994. Office: The Robert Light Agency 6404 Wilshire Blvd Ste 900 Los Angeles CA 90048*

NIEHAUS, MERLE H., agricultural educator, international agriculture consultant; b. Enid, Okla., Mar. 25, 1933; s. Roy H. and Hazel (Farris) N.; m. Allene Rollier, Aug. 20, 1954; children: Lisa, Mark. BS, Okla. State U., 1955, MS, 1957; PhD, Purdue U., 1964. From asst. prof. to prof. agr. Ohio Agrl. Research and Devel. Ctr., Wooster, 1964-75, assoc. chmn. dept. agr., 1975-78; head dept. agronomy N.Mex. State U., Las Cruces, 1978-83, dir. agrl. exptl. sta., 1983-84; dean Coll. Agrl. Scis. Colo. State U., Ft. Collins, 1984-91, prof., 1991-92, dir. internat. R & D, 1993—; cons. FAO, UN, Rome, 1982. Contbr. articles to profl. jours. Mem. Wooster Sch. Bd., 1976-77. Fellow AAAS, Crop Sci. Soc. Am., Am. Soc. Agronomy. Office: Colo State U Internat R & D Fort Collins CO 80523

NIEHAUS, ROBERT JAMES, investment banking executive; b. Ann Arbor, Mich., Jan. 6, 1930; s. Julius Herman and Mary Johanna (Koch) N.; m. Jacqueline C. Mallier, Aug. 5, 1982. BBA, U. Mich., 1951; MBA, U. Detroit, 1958. Asst. sr. buyer Ford Motor Co., Dearborn, Mich., 1954-58; gen. purchasing agt. Hercules Motors Co., Canton, Ohio, 1959-60; v.p. procurement Schwitzer Corp., Indpls., 1960-66; sr. v.p. Wallace Murray Corp., N.Y.C., 1966-82; v.p. spl. projects Fischbach Corp., N.Y.C., 1983-84, sr. v.p., 1985-87; pres., chief exec. officer, vice chmn. Fischbach & Moore, Inc., Dallas, 1987-90; pres. Fischbach Corp., 1989-90, 1st Phila. Corp., Radnor, Pa., 1991-92; dir. Computone Corp., Atlanta, Ga., 1993-95; pres. Mile Marker Inc., Pompano Beach, Fla., 1994—, also bd. dirs.; bd. dirs. Software Group, Woodbridge, Ont., Can. Served to lt. USN, 1951-54. Mem. Am. Mgmt. Assn. (gen. mgmt. council 1982—). Clubs: Union League (N.Y.C.); Greenwich (Conn.) Country. Avocations: boating, music, tennis, golf, swimming. Home: 201 Brighton Cir Devon PA 19333-1041

NIEHM, BERNARD FRANK, mental health center administrator; b. Sandusky, Ohio, Feb. 7, 1923; s. Bernard Frank and Hedwick (Panzer) N.; m. Eunice M. Patterson, Oct. 4, 1924; children—Julie, Patti, Bernie. B.A., Ohio State U., 1951, M.A., 1955, Ph.D., 1968. Tchr. pub. schs. Sandusky, 1951-57; chief adml., vocat. and occupational therapy svcs. Vineland (N.J.) Tng. Sch., 1957-61; exec. dir. Franklin County Coun. Retarded Children, Columbus, Ohio, 1962-64; dir. Ohio Sheltered Workshop Planning Project Mental Retardation, 1964-66; coordinator mental retardation planning Ohio Bur. Planning and Grants, Div. Mental Health and Mental Retardation, 1966-68; project dir. Ohio Gov.'s Citizen Com. on Mental Retardation Planning, 1966-68; adminstr. Franklin County Program for Mentally Retarded, 1968-70; supt. Gallipolis (Ohio) State Inst., 1970-76; tchr. spl. edn. Ohio U., 1975—; dir. consultation and edn. Gallia-Jackson-Meigs Community Mental Health Ctr. (now Woodland Ctrs. Inc.), Gallipolis, 1977-79, dir., 1979—; pres. Gallco (sheltered employment and workshop, for mentally retarded and developmentally disabled), 1989-90. Contbr. articles to profl. jours. Mem. Foster Grandparents Adv. Coun. Gallia County, 1974-76, Gallipolis State Inst. Parent Vol. Assn., 1970—; chmn. MGM dist. Tri-State Boy Scout coun.; chmn. Meigs, Gallia, Mason Counties Boy Scout Dist., 1972-94; mem. Franklin County Bd. Mental Retardation, 1967-68; pres. Gallipolis Girls Athletic Assn. Booster Club, 1976—, Gallia County Arthritis Unit, 1986—, Galleo Industries Bd. to serve handicapped adults, 1987-94; bd. dirs. United Cerebral Palsy Columbus, 1968-70. With U.S. Army, 1943-46. Mem. Am. Assn. Mental Deficiency (past chmn. Ohio chpt., chmn. Great Lakes region), Am. Mental Health Adminstrs. (nat. Ohio chpts.), Nat. Rehab. Assn., Ohio Rehab. Assn., Ohio Assn. Retarded Children (2d v.p. 1974-76, dir.), Vocat. Rehab. Assn., Ohio Coun. Community Mental Health Ctrs., Gallia County Arthritis Assn. (pres. 1991—), Gallipolis Area C of C., Rotary, Lutheran. Home: 1525 Mill Creek Rd Gallipolis OH 45631-8616 Office: Woodland Ctr Inc 3086 State Rte 160 Gallipolis OH 45631-8418

NIEHOFF, KARL RICHARD BESUDEN, financial executive; b. Cin., May 11, 1943; s. Karl George and Jean (Besuden) N.; children: K. Richard B Jr., Kelly B. B.A., U. Cin., 1967. Corp. trust officer 5th-3d Union Trust, Cin., 1968-74; v.p., gen. mgr. Sabina (Ohio) Water Co., 1974-76; v.p. sec. Weil, Roth and Irving, Inc., 1974-76; co-mgr., mgmt. fin. dept. Thomson McKinnon Securities, Cin. and N.Y.C., 1976-79; trustee Cin. Stock Exch., 1974-80, 87-90, chmn. bd. trustees, 1978-79, pres., chief oper. officer, 1979-90; exch. rep. Consol. Quote, Consol. Tape Oper. Coms., 1979-90, alt., 1991-92; pres. Fin. Instruments Svcs. Corp., Cin., Chgo., London, 1985-90; v.p. Trading Svcs. NASDAQ Inc., 1991-92, D.E. Shaw & Co., N.Y.C., 1992-94; pres., mng. ptnr. Niehoff and Assocs., N.Y.C., 1994—; mgr. OTC Project, Warsaw, Poland, 1995—; voting mem. Inter-Market Trading Com., 1980-90, Stock Exch. Chief Execs. Com., 1988-90; mem. Cin. Stock Exch., 1974-89, P.B.W. Stock Exch., 1975-76; mgr. OTC Project for Mass Privitazion for the Country of Poland, 1995—. Trustee, sec. Contemporary Arts Ctr., Cin., 1975-83; mem. Young Mens Mercantile Libr. Assn., 1974-90, adv. com., 1974-77; mem. devel. com. Tangeman Gallery of Art, 1981-82. Mem. Securities Traders Assn. N.Y., Univ. Club (Cin.), Miami Club (Miamitown), Keeneland Assn. (Lexington, KY.), N.Y. Stock Exch. Luncheon Club, N.Y. Athletic Club, Cin. Stock and Bond Club (trustee and 1st v.p. 1974-90), Queen City Mcpl. Bond Club (trustee 1974-80), India House, Phi Alpha Theta. Office: Niehoff and Assocs 2001 M St NW Washington DC 20036

NIELDS, MORGAN WESSON, medical supply company executive; b. Springfield, Mass., Jan. 25, 1946; s. Robert Littleton and Florence (Wesson) N.; m. Belinda Gammon, Aug. 14, 1968; children: William, Michael, Stefan, Morgan, Lindsey, Hunter. Cert. d'Etudes Francaises, Université de Lausanne, Switzerland, 1966; BA, Williams Coll., 1968; MBA, Dartmouth Coll., 1970. Mgr. mgmt. svcs. Graco Inc., Paris, 1970-73; chmn., chief exec. officer Fischer Imaging Corp., Denver, 1973—, also bd. dirs.; pres., chief operating officer Diasonics Inc., Milpitas, Calif., 1983-84; bd. dirs. Scinticor, Inc., Milw., Columbia Hosp. Corp., Ft. Worth. Trustee Humana, Mountain View Hosp., Thornton, Colo., 1988-89. Mem. Nat. Elec. Mfrs. Assn. (bd. govs. 1986-87, 91—, bd. dirs. diagnostic imaging and therapy systems div. 1976-89), U.S. Ski Assn. (masters div., pres. Rocky Mountain region 1987-88). Avocations: ski racing, tennis, golf. Office: Fischer Imaging Corp 12300 Grant St Denver CO 80241-3120

NIELSEN, ALDON DALE, retired government agency official, economist; b. Mason City, Nebr., Jan. 13, 1922; s. Seren and Sena (Nielsen) N.; m. Vivian Leola Lee, Mar. 24, 1944; children: Carol Ann, Aldon Lynn, Dennis Lee, Brian Paige. Student, Biarittz Am. U., France, 1945; B.Sc., U. Nebr., 1948, postgrad., 1951. With Bur. Reclamation, Dept. Interior, 1948-86; successively economist Bur. Reclamation, Dept. Interior, Grand Island, Nebr., 1948-60; regional agrl. economist Bur. Reclamation, Dept. Interior, Denver, 1960-63; contract and repayment specialist Bur. Reclamation, Dept. Interior, 1963-65; chief economics and program analysis br. Bur. Reclamation, Dept. Interior, Washington, 1965-77; asst. chief div. water and land Bur. Reclamation, Dept. Interior, 1977-78; dir. operation and maintenance policy staff Bur. Reclamation, Dept. Interior, Washington, 1978-83, dir. Office of Water Research, 1983-85; asst. chief div. fgn. activities Dept. Interior, 1985-86; mem. Internat. Commn. on Irrigation and Drainage. Pres. Nebr. Baptist Men, 1957-59; bd. mgrs. Nebr. Bapt. Conv., 1957-59; mem. Nebr. Bapt. Lay Devel. Com., 1957-58; bd. dirs. Colo. Bapt. Conv., 1960-63; sec. Colo. Bapt. Men., 1961-63; exec. v.p. Am. Bapt. Men, 1962-65, pres. 1965-67; mem. exec. bd. D.C. Bapt. Conv., 1974-92, 76-78, 80-82, 88-95, v.p. 1989-90, pres. 1990-91; active U.S. Com. on Irrigation and Drainage. Served with AUS, 1944-46, ETO. Decorated Bronze Star; recipient Superior Service award Dept. Interior, 1958, 59, 61, 66, Meritorius Service award, 1973, Spl. Achievement award, 1978, Disting. Service award, 1985. Mem. Internat. Water Resources Assn. Home: 519 S Harrison St Arlington VA 22204-1217

NIELSEN, ALVIN HERBORG, university dean, physicist; b. Menominee, Mich., May 30, 1910; s. Knud and Maren (Nielsen) N.; m. Jane Ann Evans, Dec. 29, 1942; 1 dau., Margaret Arthur Wayne. B.A., U. Mich., 1931, M.S., 1932, Ph.D., 1934. Research fellow Ohio State U., 1934-35; faculty U. Tenn., 1935—, prof. physics, 1946-80, prof. emeritus, 1980—, head dept., 1956-69, dean Coll. Liberal Arts, 1963-77; dean emeritus U. Tenn. (Coll. Liberal Arts) 1977—, Mace Bearer and Phi Kappa Phi disting. faculty lectr.,

1962-63; Research asso. for OSRD Ohio State U. Research Found., 1944-46; cons. Oak Ridge Gaseous Diffusion Plant Labs. and Oak Ridge Nat. Lab., 1947-80. Author articles molecular spectroscopy.; Asso. editor: Jour. Chem. Physics, 1955-57. Mem. Knoxville Symphony Soc. Bd., 1963—, v.p., 1965-68, 75-76, 77-78, pres., 1968-69, 76-77; bd. dirs. Greater Knox Council for the Arts, 1974—, v.p., 1977-74. NRC fellow elect, 1942; Fulbright research scholar Astrophys. Inst., U. Liege, Belgium, 1951-52; Alvin H. Nielsen Physics Bldg., U. Tenn. dedicated Oct. 1980; recipient Mayor's award for support of arts, 1978. Fellow Am. Phys. Soc. (Pegram award S.E. sect. 1980), Optical Soc. Am., AAAS; mem. AAUP, Tenn. Acad. Sci. (exec. com. 1959-61), Coblentz Soc., Am. Inst. Physics, Am. Conf. Acad. Deans (dir. 1968-75, chmn. 1972), Phi Beta Kappa, Sigma Xi, Phi Kappa Phi, Sigma Pi Sigma, Pi Delta Phi, Omicron Delta Kappa. Episcopalian. Clubs: Faculty, Irving. Home: 3605 Timberlake Rd Knoxville TN 37920-2856 *Died Nov. 3, 1994.*

NIELSEN, BARBARA STOCK, state educational administrator. State supt. S.C. Dept. Edn., Columbia. Office: SC Dept Edn 1429 Senate St 1006 Rutledge Bldg Columbia SC 29201

NIELSEN, EDWARD L., medical association administrator; b. Alexandria, Va., June 8, 1951; s. Edward and Alice (Poulton) N.; m. Elizabeth Gay Holston, Sept. 8, 1984; children: Elizabeth, Alexandra. Grad., Elizabethtown Coll., 1970; M in Human Svcs., Lincoln U., 1980. Outreach counselor Individual and Family Devel. Ctr., Mechanicsburg, Pa., 1975-77; tng. coord. Cumberland-Perry Assn. of Retarded Citizens, Carlisle, Pa., 1977-79; svc. coord. Tressler-Luth. Svcs. Assns., Camp Hill, Pa., 1979-87; mng. ptnr. Metzner-Nielsen Assocs., Harrisburg, Pa., 1985-87; exec. asst. Pa. Acad. Family Physicians, Harrisburg, Pa., 1987-88, exec. v.p., 1988—. Mem. Am. Tng. Soc. (bd. dirs. Pa. chpt. 1989—), Am. Soc. Assn. Execs., Am. Assn. Med. Soc. Execs., Profl. Conv. Mgmt. Assn., Aircraft Owners and Pilots Assn. Avocations: aircraft and sailplane pilot, tennis, skiing. Office: Pa Acad Family Physicians 5600 Derry St Harrisburg PA 17111-3592

NIELSEN, EMIEL THEODORE, JR., retired manufacturing company executive; b. Cupertino, Calif., Dec. 3, 1914; s. Emiel Theodore and Bessie (Kimball) N.; m. Marjorie Bothwell, July 14, 1940; children: Philip B., John K. A.B., Stanford U., 1936, M.B.A., 1938. With Gen. Mills, Inc., 1938-42; with FMC Corp., Chgo., 1942—; vice chmn. FMC Corp., to 1979; dir. Bank of the West, Talley Industries, Inc. Mem. Am. Def. Preparedness Assn. Republican. Clubs: Sainte Claire, San Jose Country.

NIELSEN, FORREST HAROLD, research nutritionist; b. Junction City, Wis., Oct. 26, 1941; s. George Adolph and Sylvia Viola (Blood) N.; m. Emily Joanne Currie, June 13, 1964; children: Forrest Erik, Kistin Emily. BS, U. Wis., 1963, MS, 1966, PhD, 1967. NIH grad. fellow, dept. biochemistry U. Wis., Madison, 1963-67; rsch. chemist, Human Nutrition Rsch. Inst. USDA, Beltsville, Md., 1969-70; rsch. chemist Human Nutrition Rsch. Ctr., USDA, Grand Forks, N.D., 1970-86, ctr. dir. and rsch. nutritionist, 1986—; rsch. assoc. dept. biochemistry, U. N.D., Grand Forks, 1971—, speaker in field. Assoc. editor Magnesium and Trace Elements Jour., 1990-93; mem. editl. bd. Jour. Trace Elements in Exptl. Medicine, 1988—, Biol. Trace Element Rsch. Jour., 1979—, Jour. Nutrition, 1984-88; contbr. articles to profl. jours. Capt. U.S. Army, 1967-69. Recipient Klaus Schwarz Commemorative medal and award Internat. Assn. of Bioinorganic Scientists; named Scientist of Yr. U.S. Dept. Agrl., 1993. Mem. Internat. Soc. Trace Element Rsch. in Humans (gov. bd. 1989—, pres. 1992-95), Internat. Assn. Bioinorganic Scis., Soc. for Exptl. Biology and Medicine, Am. Inst. Nutrition, N.D. Acad. Sci. (pres. 1988-89), Sigma Xi (pres. U. N.D. chpt. 1976-77). Lutheran. Achievements include patent for use of Boron Supplements to Increase in Vivo Production of Hydroxylated Steroids; discovery of the nutritional essentiality of the trace elements boron and nickel. Office: USDA ARS GFHNRC PO Box 9034 Grand Forks ND 58202-9034

NIELSEN, GEORGE LEE, architect; b. Ames, Iowa, Dec. 12, 1937; s. Verner Henry and Verba Lucile (Smith) N.; m. Karen Wall, Feb. 28, 1959; children: David Stuart, Kristina, Melissa. B.Arch., Iowa State U., 1961, M.Arch., M.I.T., 1962. Registered architect, Mass., Ohio. Designer Perry, Shaw, Hepburn & Dean, Boston, 1961-64, F.A. Stahl & Assos., Cambridge, Mass., 1964-65; project architect Peirce & Pierce, Boston, 1965-70; project mgr. A.M. Kinney Assos., Cin., 1970—, partner, 1978—; sec. A.M. Kinney Assocs., Inc., Cin., 1993—, also dir.; v.p. A.M Kinney Inc., Cin., 1992-94, pres., 1994—, also dir. Architect assoc. with major projects for Avco Rsch. Lab., Children's Hosp. Med. Ctr., Square D. Corp., Nalco Chem. Co., Olin Corp., Mead Johnson/Bristol Myers Squib, Cin. Gas and Electric Co., Sandoz Pharm. Corp., Hoechst Celanese, Witco Corp., Sotheby's, Shell Chem. Co. Served with U.S. Army, 1962-64. Mem. AIA (design awards 1970-71, 74, 78, 81, 91, 94). Episcopalian. Home: 3419 Ault View Ave Cincinnati OH 45208-2518 Office: A M Kinney Inc 2900 Vernon Pl Cincinnati OH 45219-2436

NIELSEN, GLADE BENJAMIN, mayor, former state senator; b. Hyrum, Utah, Mar. 8, 1926; s. George Benjamin and Katie Ione (Jensen) N.; m. Alpha Fern Strempke, Oct. 15, 1955; children: Karen Lynn, Sharon Kay, Roger Glade, Laura Mae, Lance Eric. BS, Utah State U., 1949. Supt. various constrn. cos., Wyo., Nev., and Calif., 1949-55; pres. Glade Nielsen Builder, Roy, Utah, 1955-86; mem. Utah State Senate, Salt Lake City, 1987-92; may Roy City, 1994—. Pres. Weber Basin Homebuilders Assn., 1967-68, Home Builders Assn. Utah, 1972-73; v.p. Nat. Assn. Home Builders, Washington, 1974-75, mem. exec. com. 1976-79; exec. com. Weber Econ. Devel. Corp.; pres. Roy C. of C., 1980; bd. dirs. Utah Housing Fin. Agy., Salt Lake, 1975-83. With USN, 1944-46, PTO. Recipient Builder of Yr. award Home Builders Assn. Utah, 1988, Svc. award Utah State Com. Consumer Svcs., 1989, Recognition award Utah State Dept. Commerce, 1989, Hon. Commendation award Ogden Air Logistics Command, 1989, Roy City Outstanding Citizen award, 1993. Mem. VFW, Am. Legion, Thunderbird Motor Club Utah (pres.), Elks, Ogden/Weber C. of C. (dir.). Republican. Avocations: travel, antique cars.

NIELSEN, GREG ROSS, lawyer; b. Provo, Utah, Sept. 24, 1947; s. Ross T. and Carma (Peterson) N.; m. Jo Rita Beer, Sept. 3, 1971; children: Jennifer, Jerilyn, Eric Michael, Brittany Anne. BA in Polit. Sci. magna cum laude, Brigham Young U., 1971; JD cum laude, Harvard U., 1975. Bar: Ariz. 1975, U.S. Dist. Ct. Ariz. 1975, U.S. Ct. Appeals (9th cir.) 1977, Utah 1990. Assoc. Snell & Wilmer, Phoenix, 1975-80, ptnr., 1981-91; mng. ptnr. Snell & Wilmer, Salt Lake City, 1991—; adminstrv. coord. real estate practice group Snell & Wilmer, Phoenix, 1988-90. Mem. elect com. Theodore Roosevelt coun. Boy Scouts Am., 1988-90, Valley Partnership, Phoenix, 1989-90. Hinckley scholar Brigham Young U., 1970; fellow Ford Found., 1970. Mem. ABA, State Bar Ariz., Utah Bar Assn. Republican. Mem. LDS Ch. Office: Snell & Wilmer 111 E Broadway Ste 900 Salt Lake City UT 84111-5235

NIELSEN, HARALD CHRISTIAN, retired chemist; b. Chgo., Apr. 18, 1930; s. Svend Aage and Seena (Hansen) N.; m. Eloise Wilma Soule, Dec. 19, 1953; children—Brenda Mae, Paul Erick, Gloria Lynn. B.A., St. Olaf Coll., 1952; Ph.D., Mich. State U. 1957. Cereal grain proteins chemist Nat. Ctr. for Agrl. Utilization Rsch. (formerly No. Regional Research Ctr.), Agrl. Research Service, USDA, Peoria, Ill., 1957-87. Contbr. articles to profl. jours. Pres. local 3247 Am. Fedn. Govt. Employees, AFL-CIO, 1977-86; mem. Peoria Area Combined Fed. Campaign Coordinating Com., 1980-87. Fellow AAAS; mem. ACLU, Am. Assn. Cereal Chemists, Nat. Assn. Ret. Fed. Employees (officer chpt. 268 1989-92, pres. chpt. 268 1991), Sigma Xi. Democrat. Lutheran. Home: 2318 N Gale Ave Peoria IL 61604-3229

NIELSEN, JOYCE, former state legislator; b. Askov, Minn., Nov. 20, 1933; d. Clarey Burnhardt and Dorothy Elaine (Saastad) Jensen; m. Eric Hans Nielsen, June 11, 1955; 1 child, Cindy. Grad., Cloquet (Minn.) H.S. Fin. cons. Nielsen Fin. Cons., Inc., Cedar Rapids, Iowa, 1984-88; mem. Iowa Ho. of Reps., Des Moines, 1989-93; facilitator Parenting Edn. Programs 1993—. Bd. dirs., treas. Peoples Ch., Cedar Rapids, 1983; bd. dirs., sec. UN Assn., Cedar Rapids, 1988; bd. dirs., mem. exec. com. United Way, Cedar Rapids. Named Woman of Yr., Coalition of Women's Groups; recipient Outstanding Svc. award YWCA, Community Action Agy. Mem. LWV (bd. dirs.). Democrat. Mem. Unitarian Ch. Home: 2702 Q Ave NW Cedar Rapids IA 52405

NIELSEN, LELAND C., federal judge; b. Vesper, Kans., June 14, 1919; s. Carl Christian and Christena (Larson) N.; m. Virginia Garland, Nov. 27, 1958; 1 child, Christena. A.B., Washburn U., 1946; J.D., U. So. Calif., 1946. Bar: Calif. 1947. Practice law Los Angeles, from 1947; dep. city atty. City of Los Angeles, 1947-51; judge Superior Ct. Calif. San Diego County, 1968-71, U.S. Dist. Ct. (so. dist.) Calif., San Diego, 1971—. Served to maj. A.C., U.S. Army 1941-46. Decorated Purple Heart, Disting. Svc. Cross, Air medal with oak leaf clusters. Mem. Am. Coll. Trial Lawyers. Republican. Presbyterian. Office: US Dist Ct 940 Front St San Diego CA 92189-0010

NIELSEN, LESLIE, actor; b. Regina, Sask., Can., Feb. 11, 1926; s. Ingvard and Maybelle N. Student, Neighborhood Playhouse, N.Y.C. Former announcer, disk jockey, Can. radio; feature films include The Vagabond King, 1956, Forbidden Planet, 1956, Ransom!, 1956, The Opposite Sex, 1956, Hot Summer Night, 1957, Tammy and the Bachelor, 1957, Night Train to Paris, 1964, Harlow, 1965, Dark Intruder, 1965, Beau Geste, 1965, Gunfight in Abilene, 1967, The Reluctant Astronaut, 1967, Rosie, 1967, Counterpoint, 1967, Dayton's Devils, 1969, How to Commit Marriage, 1969, Change of Mind, 1969, The Resurrection of Zachary Wheeler, 1971, The Poseidon Adventure, 1972, Viva, Knievel, 1977, City of Fire, 1979, Airplane!, 1980, Wrong is Right, 1982, Creepshow, 1983, Spaceship, 1983, Soul Man, 1986, The Patriot, 1986, Nuts, 1987, Nightstick, 1987, Home Is Where the Hart Is, 1987, The Naked Gun, 1988, Dangerous Curves, The Repossessed, The Naked Gun 2 1/2: The Smell of Fear, 1991, All I Want for Christmas, 1991, Surf Ninjas, 1993, The Naked Gun 33 1/3: The Final Insult, 1994; TV films include Crime Syndicated, 1952, Man Behind The Badge, 1954, See How They Run, 1964, Shadow Over Elveron, 1968, Hawaii Five-O, 1968, Companions in Nightmare, 1968, Trial Run, 1969, Deadlock, 1969, Night Slaves, 1970, The Aquarians, 1970, Hauser's Memory, 1970, Monty Nash, 1971, They Call It Murder, 1971, Incident in San Francisco, 1972, Snatched, 1973, The Letters, 1973, Can Ellen Be Saved?, 1974, Brinks! The Great Robbery, 1976, Little Mo, 1978, miniseries Back Stairs At the White House, 1979, Institute For Revenge, 1979, Ohms, 1980, The Night The Bridge Fell Down, 1980, Murder Among Friends, 1982, Cave-In, 1983, Blade in Hong Kong, 1985, The Loner, Fatal Confession: A Father Dowling Mystery, Chance of a Lifetime, 1991; numerous other TV appearances including dramatic series Studio One, Armstrong Circle Theater, Goodyear Playhouse; TV series include The New Breed, 1961, The Bold Ones, 1963-67, Peyton Place, 1965, Bracken's World, 1969-70, Shaping Up, 1984, Police Squad, 1982, The Golden Girls, 1992; toured country in one man show Darrow, 1979; co-author: The Naked Truth, 1993. Office: Bresler Kelly Kipperman 15760 Ventura Blvd Encino CA 91436*

NIELSEN, NANCY, publishing executive; b. Jeffersonville, Ind., 1950. BA, Univ. Calif., Berkeley, 1975. Asst. city editor, weekend mag. editor Dallas Times Herald, 1975-77; cons. McKinsey & Co. Inc.; dir. office of comm. Capital Cities/ABC Inc., N.Y.C., 1984-86; deputy dir. corp. rels. The N.Y. Times Co., N.Y.C., 1986-88, dir. corp. rels./Pa., 1987-93, v.p. corp. comm., 1992—; bd. dir. Inst. of Journalism Edn. Recipient Alumni Assn. award for outstanding performance in journalism Univ. Calif. Berkeley. Office: The New York Times Co 229 W 43rd St New York NY 10036

NIELSEN, NIELS CHRISTIAN, JR., theology educator; b. Long Beach, Calif., June 2, 1921; s. Niels Hansen and Frances (Nofziger) N.; m. Erika Kreuth, May 10, 1958; children—Camilla Regina, Niels Albrecht. BA, George Pepperdine Coll., L.A., 1942; BD, Yale U., 1946, PhD, 1951. Ordained to ministry Meth. Ch., 1946. Pastor Woodbury (Conn.) Meth. Ch., 1944-46; instr. religion Yale U., New Haven, 1948-51; faculty Rice U., Houston, 1951—; J. Newton Rayzor prof. religious studies. Rice U., prof. emeritus, 1991—; Amax presdl. prof. humanities Colo. Sch. Mines, Golden, 1982-83; scholar in residence St. Paul's United Meth. Ch., Houston. Author: Philosophy and Religion in Contemporary Japan, 1957, Geistige Landerkunde USA, 1960, A Layman Looks at World Religions, 1962, God in Education, 1966, Solzhenitsyn's Religion (Nelson), 1975, The Religion of Jimmy Carter, 1977, The Crisis of Human Rights, 1978, Religions of the World, 1982, Revolutions in Eastern Europe: The Religious Roots, 1991, Fundamentalism, Mythos and World Religions, 1993; editor: Religion After Communism in Russia, 1994; contbr. articles to profl. jours. Mem. Am. Acad. Religion, Am. Philos. Soc., Am. Soc. Study Religion (sec. 1977-89), Soc. European Culture, Am. Soc. for Values in Higher Edn. Democrat. Home: 2424 Swift Blvd Houston TX 77030-1806

NIELSEN, STEVEN B., medical products executive; b. 1947. BA, Calif. State U., Long Beach, 1973. With Acme United Corp., 1973-76, Bergen Brunswig Med. Surgical Inc., 1976-78, 80-84, Hosp. Pharmacies Inc., 1978-80; exec. v.p. Gen. Med. Corp., Richmond, Va., 1984-88, pres., 1988-89, dir., 1989-93, chm. bd., CEO, 1993—. Office: General Medical Corp 8741 Landmark Rd Richmond VA 23228-2801

NIELSEN, WILLIAM FREMMING, federal judge; b. 1934. BA, U. Wash., 1956, LLB, 1963. Law clk. to Hon. Charles L. Powell U.S. Dist. Ct. (ea. dist.) Wash., 1963-64; mem. firm Paine, Hamblen, Coffin, Brooke & Miller, 1964-91; judge U.S. Dist. Ct. (ea. dist.) Wash., Spokane, 1991—. lt. col. USAFR. Fellow Am. Coll. Trial Lawyers; mem. ABA, Wash. State Bar Assn., Spokane County Bar Assn. (pres. 1981-82), Fed. Bar Assn. (pres. 1988), Spokane County Legal Svcs. Corp. (past pres.), Lawyer Pilot Bar Assn., Assn. Trial Lawyers Am., Wash. State Trial Lawyers Assn., Assn. Def. Trial Attys., Am. Inns of Ct., Charles L. Powell Inn (pres. 1987), The Spokane Club, Rotary, Alpha Delta Phi, Phi Delta Phi. Office: US Dist Ct PO Box 2208 W920 W Riverside Ave Spokane WA 99201-1007

NIELSON, HOWARD CURTIS, former congressman, retired educator; b. Richfield, Utah, Sept. 12, 1924; s. Herman Taylor and Zula May (Curtis) N.; m. Julia Adams, June 18, 1948; children: Noreen (Mrs. Stephen Astin), Elaine (Mrs. Stanley Taylor), John, Mary Lee (Mrs. Paul Jackson), James, Jean (Mrs. Clay Cundick), Howard Curtis Jr. BS in Math., U. Utah, 1947; MS in Math., U. Oreg., 1949; MBA, Stanford U., 1956, PhD in Bus. Adminstrn. and Stats., 1958. Statistician C & H Sugar Refining Corp., 1949-51; rsch. economist and statistician Stanford Rsch. Inst., 1951-57; mem. faculty Brigham Young U., Provo, Utah, 1957-82; prof. statistics Brigham Young U., 1961-82, chmn. dept., 1960-63; sr. econ. engr. Hercules, Inc., 1960-66; dir. Ctr. for Bus. and Econ. Rsch., 1971-72; sr. statistician, acting field mgr. C.E.I.R, Inc., 1963-64, mgr., cons., Hawaii 65-75; prin. scientist GCA Corp., 1965-67; dir. econ. rsch. Eyring Rsch. Inst., 1974-75; assoc. commr. higher edn. State of Utah, 1976-79; mem. 98th-101st Congresses from 3d dist. Utah; missionary LDS Ch., Australia, 1991-92, Hungary, 1993-94; econ. adviser Kingdom of Jordan, Ford Found., 1970-71; prof. Am. U. Beirut, 1970; adj. prof. U. Utah, 1972-76. Author: The Efficiency of Certain Truncated Order Statistics in Estimating the Mean of Various Distributions, 1949, Population Trends in the United States Through 1975, 1955, The Hows and Whys of Statistics, 1963, Experimental Designs Used in Industry, 1965, Membership Growth of the Church of Jesus Christ of Latter-Day Saints, 1957, 67, 71, 75, 78, Evaluation of the Seven Year Plan for Economic Development in Jordan, 1971, Economic Analysis of Fiji, Tonga, Western and Am. Samoa, 1972; co-author: The Newsprint Situation in the Western Region of North America, 1952, America's Demand for Wood, 1954, also reports. Mem. Utah Gov.'s Econ. Rsch. Adv. Coun., 1967-72; dir. bur. ch. studies Ch. of Jesus Christ of Latter-day Saints, 1958-63; rsch. dir. Utah Republican Party, 1967-68; mem. Utah Ho. of Reps, 1967-75, majority leader, 1969-71, speaker, 1973-75, mem. legis. budget-audit com., 1967-73, chmn., 1971-73, chmn. legis. coun., 1973-75; mem. Utah 3d Dist., U.S. Ho. of Reps, 1983-91; chmn. Utah County Rep. Com., 1979-81. Mem. Am. Statis. Assn. (pres. Utah br. 1964-65, mem. nat. coun. 1967-70), Sci. Rsch. Soc. Am., Order of Artus, Phi Beta Kappa, Sigma Xi, Pi Mu Epsilon, Sigma Pi Sigma.

NIELSON, NORMA LEE, business educator; b. Augusta, Ga., Dec. 26, 1953; d. Norman Lyle and Betty Lou (Buckner) Parrott; m. Mark G. Nielson, Nov. 20, 1985 (div. 1988); 1 child, Eric Gordon. BS, Northwest Mo. State U., 1974; MA, U. Pa., 1976, PhD, 1979. CLU. Asst. prof. Iowa State U., Ames, 1977-79, U. So. Calif., L.A., 1979-84; cons. profl. Mercer-Meidinger, L.A., 1984-85; assoc. prof. Oreg. State U., Corvallis, 1985-90; prof. Oreg. State U., 1990—; bd. examiners Internat. Bd. Stds. and Practice for CFP, 1991-94. Developer software; contbg. author: Handbook for Corporate Directors, 1995; contbr. articles to profl. publs. Vol. Linn-Benton Food Share, Corvallis; bd. dirs. Corvallis Cmty. Dare Care, Inc., 1988-91;

---

candidate for Oreg. Ho. of Reps., 1994. Andrus Found. rsch. grantee, 1989-91. Mem. Am. Risk and Ins. Assn. (bd. dirs. 1990—, officer 1993—), Western Risk and Ins. Assn. (officer 1981-84), Risk and Ins. Mgmt. Soc. Avocations: piano, stained glass, flying. Office: Oreg State U Coll Bus Bexell Hall 200 Corvallis OR 97331-2603

NIELSON, THEO GILBERT, law enforcement official, university official; b. Roosevelt, Utah, June 29, 1938; s. John Gilbert and Mazie (Alexander) N.; m. Martha Perez, May 22, 196l; children: Lucille Marie, Sherry Lou, Mark Andrew, Rex Alexander, Theo Gilbert Jr., Cristal Ina, Gregory Angus, Mazie Leah, Rosanna Alma. Grad., FBI Nat. Acad., 1970; BA, Ariz. State U., 1975, MS, 1977. Officer Univ. Police, Ariz. State U., Tempe, 1963-67, sgt., 1967-70, lt., 1970-79; chief police Douglas (Ariz.) Police Dept., 1979-82; div. adminstr. Ariz. Criminal Intelligence Systems Agy., Tucson, 1982-84; dir. campus safety and security No. Ariz. U., Flagstaff, 1984-92; chief police Ariz. Dept. Adminstrn., 1993—. Mem. Am. Soc. for Indsl. Security (chmn. No. Ariz. chpt. 1987), Internat. Assn. Chiefs Police, Internat. Assn. Campus Law Enforcement Adminstrs., Ariz. Assn. Campus Law Enforcement (pres. 1989-90). Republican. Mormon. Avocations: genealogy, hiking, grandchildren. Home: 3335 E Hampton Ave Mesa AZ 85204-6410 Office: Ariz State Capitol Police 1700 W Washington Ave Ste B15 Phoenix AZ 85007

NIEMAN, JOHN FRANCIS, advertising executive; b. St. Louis, Jan. 8, 1949; s. John Francis and Virginia N.; m. Janice Seidel, Apr. 25, 1981; children: Lindsay Briana, John III, Scott Parker, James August. BA in English, U. Mo., 1971. From assoc. creative dir. to v.p. Gardner Advt. Co., St. Louis, 1971-79; from group creative dir. to sr. v.p. Young and Rubicam, N.Y.C., 1979-86, DDB Needham, Chgo., 1986; exec. creative dir., exec. v.p. McCann-Erickson, N.Y.C., 1986-89; vice chair, chief creative officer USA D'Arcy Masius Benton & Bowles, N.Y.C., 1989-91, vice chair, chief creative officer, N.Am., 1991—; dir.-at-large The Advt. Coun., N.Y.C. Chmn. Best of N.Y. Addy Awards, 1992; finalist judge Addy Awards, 1993; blue ribbon judge Andy Awards, 1990-93; mem. creative commn. Partnership for Drug Free Am., N.Y.C., 1991—. Recipient numerous Clios, Andy, Addy and Cannes awards. Office: D'Arcy Massius Benton & Bowles 1675 Broadway New York NY 10019-5809

NIEMANN, BERNARD JOHN, JR., land and geographical system educator, researcher, consultant; b. Highland Park, Ill., July 23, 1937; s. Bernard J.. and Emma (Gaeble) N.; m. Sondra Sue, Dec. 29, 1962; 1 child, Ben. BA, U. Ill., 1960; MLA, Harvard U., 1964. Site planner Leo A. Daly Co., Omaha, 1960-63, Sasaki-Walker & Assocs., Watertown, Mass., 1963-64; asst. prof. dept. landscape architecture U. Wis., Madison, 1963-68, assoc. prof., 1969-71, chmn. dept., 1971-75, prof. dept. landscape architecture Inst. Environ.. Studies, adj. prof. urban and regional planning, 1976—, dir. land info. and computer graphics facility Sch. Natural Resources, 1988—; cons. resource and land investigations program U.S. Dept. Interior, Reston, Va., 1976-80; mem. com. on integrated land data mapping NRC, Washington, 1981-82, mem. com. mapping sci. NRC, Washington, 1990-94; prin. Landscapes Ltd., Madison, 1964-73; cons. Wis. Dept. Justice, Office Pub. Intervenor, Madison, 1978-84; mem. Lower Wis. Riverway Planning Task Force, Wis. Dept. Natural Resources, Madison, 1983-87; vice chair Wis. Gov.'s Land Records Com., 1985-87; adviser nat. geodetic survey U.S. Dept. Commerce. Author: (with others) Modernization of the Public Land Survey System, 1982; editor: Land Records Can and Should Be Improved, 1980; editor Wis. Land Info. Newsletter, 1983—; co-editor Jour. Urban and Regional Systems Assn., 1988—. Bd. dirs. Wis. Land Info. Bd., 1989—, chmn., 1989-90. vice chmn., 1990—; pres. Wis. Land Info. Assn., 1989-90. Recipient Educator of Yr. award Coun. Educators in Landscape Architecture, 1986, Wis. Idea award in natural resource policy, 1991, award of distinction and svc. Wis. Land Info. Assn., 1990, Pres. award, 1995. Mem. Am. Soc. Landscape Architects (award of achievement 1959, award of merit 1970, 74, 88, award of honor 1982, 84, 89, Horwood Merit award), Urban and Regional Info. Assn. (bd. dirs. 1986-88), Gamma Sigma Delta. Home: 2501 Marshall Pky Madison WI 53713-1030 Office: U Wis Land Info & Computer Graphics 25 Agrl Hall 1450 Linden Dr Madison WI 53706-1562

NIEMANN, LEWIS KEITH, lamp manufacturing company executive; b. Alliance, Nebr., Dec. 10, 1930; s. William Grover and Vivian Zelma (Holloway) N. BS in Mktg. with honors (Standard Oil grantee), San Diego State Coll., 1956. Mdse. mgr. Fed Mart Corp., San Diego, 1954-61; store mgr. GEX, Atlanta, 1961-63; mdse. mgr. J. C. Penney Co., Pitts., 1963-67; mgr. sales planning and product devel. RCA Sales Corp., 1967-70; spl. asst. to pres. Magnavox Consumer Electronics Co., 1970-73, v.p. internat. and comml. sales, 1973-74; v.p. mktg., div. mfg. Beatrice Foods Co., Chgo., 1974-75; v.p. mktg., div. luggage Samsonite Corp., Denver, 1975-78; pres. Stiffel Co., Chgo., 1978-80, Westwood Lighting Group, Inc., Paterson, N.J., 1980-87, El Paso, Tex., 1987-90, Sunset-Richards Lighting, City of Commerce, Calif., 1990-91. Bd. dirs. Jr. Achievement, Denver, 1976-78, Pvt. Industry Council, Passiaic County. Served with USMC, 1948-52, Korea. Recipient CLIO award for Best TV Comml. in class, 1978. Republican. Episcopalian.

NIEMANN, RICHARD HENRY, grocery executive; b. Quincy, Ill., Feb. 18, 1931; s. Ferdinand Elmer and Antoinette E. (Heckenkamp) N.; m. Constance M. Volm, Oct. 6, 1951; children—Linda M., Connie A., Richard Henry, Daniel M., Ted M., Christopher J., Margaret M., Amy E. B.S. in Mktg., Quincy Coll., 1953. Warehouse mgr. Niemann Bros., Quincy, 1953-69; pres., chief exec. officer Niemann Foods Inc., Quincy, 1969—; v.p. A'Village Land Corp., Quincy, 1969-82; mng. ptnr. FoodCo Land Trust, Quincy, 1973—; pres. Johannes Meats Inc., Quincy, 1979-83; ptnr. Niemann Farms, Quincy, 1953—; trustee Quincy Foods Profit Sharing Trust, 1971—; dir. State Street Bank & Trust, Quincy. Chmn. Ill. Food Distbrs. Polit. Action Com., Lombard, 1983—; dir., exec. com. Great River Econ. Devel. Found.; trustee Culver Stockton Coll.; mem. pres.'s bd. advisors Quincy Coll.; bd. dirs. Western Ill. U. Found., Quincy Area Project, Quincy Catholic Charities; past pres. bd. trustees St. Mary Hosp.; past pres. bd. edn. Quincy Pub. Sch.; past pres. Deanery Council Catholic Men. Mem. Ill. Food Retailers Assn. (dir., exec. com 1972—), Ill. Retail Mchts. Assn. (dir. 1981—), Quincy Area C. of C. (dir.). Democrat. Roman Catholic. Club: Quincy Country. Lodges: K.C. (former master), Quincy Rotary (past pres.). Home: 2 Old Orchard Rd Quincy IL 62301-6524 Office: Niemann Foods Inc 1501 N 12th St Quincy IL 62301-1996

NIEMETH, CHARLES FREDERICK, lawyer; b. Lorain, Ohio, Nov. 25, 1939; s. Charles Ambrose and Christine Cameron (Mollison) N.; m. Anne Marie Meckes, Oct. 12, 1968. B.A., Harvard U., 1962; J.D., U. Mich., 1965. Bar: Calif. 1966, N.Y. 1984. Assoc. O'Melveny & Myers, Los Angeles, 1965-72, ptnr., 1973—. Mem. nat. com. Mich. Law Sch. Fund; trustee Challengers Boys and Girls Club, 1968-83; mem. bus. adv. coun. UCLA, 1979-83; mem. exec. com. Internat. Student Ctr., 1979-83; bd. dirs. Olympic Tower Condominium, 1986-92; bd. visitors Mich. Law Sch., mem. Tri-Bar Opinion Com. Mem. Riviera Tennis Club, Regency Club, N.Y. Athletic Club, Field Club (Greenwich, Conn.), Bel-Air Bay Club. Democrat. Roman Catholic. Home: 10660 Bellagio Rd Los Angeles CA 90077-3713 also: 70 Oneida Dr Greenwich CT 06830-7131 Office: O'Melveny & Myers 1999 Avenue of the Stars Los Angeles CA 90067-6035 also: O'Melveny & Myers 153 E 53rd St 54th Fl New York NY 10022-4611

NIEMEYER, GERHART, political science educator; b. Essen, Germany, Feb. 15, 1907; came to U.S., 1937, naturalized, 1943; s. Victor and Kaethe (Ley) N.; m. Lucie Lenzner, Sept. 18, 1931; children: A. Hermann, Lucian L., Paul V., Lisa M., Christian B. Student, Cambridge U., 1925-26, Munich U., 1926-27; J.U.D., Kiel U., 1932. Ordained priest Episcopal Ch. 1980, canon, 1987. Lectr., asst. prof. Princeton U., 1937-44; prof., head div. Oglethorpe U., 1944-50; fgn. affairs officer Dept. State, 1950-53; research analyst Council Fgn. Relations, 1953-55; prof. U. Notre Dame, 1955-76 emeritus, 1976—; mem. Bd. Fgn. Scholarships, 1981-84, chmn., 1982-84; vis. prof. Yale U., 1942, 46, 54-55, Columbia U., 1952, Vanderbilt U., 1962-66; faculty Nat. War Coll., 1958-59, 61; Fulbright prof. U. Munich, 1962-63; Distinguished vis. prof. Hillsdale Coll., 1976-82. Author: Law Without Force, 1941, An Inquiry into Soviet Mentality, 1956, Facts on Communism, vol. 1: The Communist Ideology, 1959, Handbook on Communism, 1962, Between Nothingness and Paradise, 1971, Deceitful Peace, 1971, Aftersight and Foresight, 1988, Within and Above Ourselves, 1995; assoc. editor

---

Modern Age, 1965—. Mem. task force on fgn. policy Republican Nat. Com., 1965-68. Mem. Am. Polit. Sci. Assn. Roman Catholic. Home: 806 E Angela Blvd South Bend IN 46617-1309

NIEMEYER, GLENN ALAN, academic administrator, history educator; b. Muskegon, Mich., Jan. 14, 1934; s. John T. and Johanna F. (Walhout) N.; m. Betty Sikkenga, July 8, 1955; children—Kristin, Alexis, Sander. B.A. in History, Calvin Coll., 1955; M.A. in History, Mich. State U., 1959, Ph.D. in History, 1962. Tchr. soc. sci. Grand Haven Christian Sch., Mich., 1955-58; teaching asst., asst. instr. Mich. State U., East Lansing, 1958-63; asst. prof. history Grand Valley State U., Allendale, Mich., 1963-66, assoc. prof., 1966-70, prof., 1970—; dean Coll. Arts and Scis., 1970-73, v.p. of colls., 1973-76, v.p. acad. affairs. North Ctrl. Assn., Chgo., 1974—, vice chair, 1993-94, chair, 1995; mem. Acad. Officers, Pres.'s Coun. State Univs. of Mich. Author: The Automotive Career of Ransom E. Olds, 1963; contbr. articles and book revs. to profl. publs. Trustee Calvin Coll., Grand Rapids, Mich., 1974-80; trustee Unity Christian High Sch., Hudsonville, Mich., 1978-80, pres. bd., 1979-80. Mem. Am. Coun. on Edn., Am. Assn. Higher Edn. Mem. Christian Ref. Ch. Office: Grand Valley State U Allendale MI 49401

NIEMEYER, PAUL VICTOR, federal judge; b. Princeton, N.J., Apr. 5, 1941; s. Gerhart and Lucie (Lenzner) N.; m. Susan Kinley, Aug. 24, 1963; children Jonathan K., Peter E., Christopher J. AB, Kenyon Coll., 1962; student, U. Munich, Federal Republic of Germany, 1962-63; JD, U. Notre Dame, 1966. Bars: Md. 1966, U.S. Dist. Ct. Md. 1967, U.S. Ct. Appeals (4th cir.) 1968, U.S. Supreme Ct. 1970, U.S. Dist Ct. (so. dist.) Tex. 1977, U.S. Ct. Appeals (5th cir.) 1978, U.S. Ct. Appeals (3d cir.) 1980. Assoc. Piper & Marbury, Balt., 1966-74, ptnr., 1974-88; U.S. dist. judge U.S. Dist. Ct. Md., Balt., 1988-90; fed. judge U.S. Ct. Appeals (4th cir.), Balt., 1990—; lectr. advanced bus. law Johns Hopkins U., Balt., 1971-75; lectr. Md. Jud. Conf., Md. Ct. Clks. Assn.; mem. standing com. on rules of practice and procedure cts. appeals, 1973-88, atty. grievance com.-hearing panel, 1978-81; select com.-profl. conduct, 1983-85, adv. com. on Fed. Rules of Civil Procedure, 1993—. Co-author: Maryland Rules Commentary, 1984, supplement, 1988, 2d edit., 1992; contbr. articles to profl. jours. Recipient Spl. Merit citation Am. Judicature Soc., 1987. Fellow Am. Coll. Trial Lawyers, Am. Bar Found., Md. Bar Found., Md. Bar Assn. (Disting. Svc. award litigation sect. 1981), Am. Law Inst.; mem. Wednesday Law Club, Lawyers' Round Table. Republican. Episcopalian. Office: US Cir Ct Md 101 W Lombard St Rm 910 Baltimore MD 21201

NIEMI, JANICE, lawyer, former state legislator; b. Flint, Mich., Sept. 18, 1928; d. Richard Jesse and Norma (Bell) Bailey; m. Preston Niemi, Feb. 4, 1953 (divorced 1987); children—Ries, Patricia. BA, U. Wash., 1950, LL.B, 1967; postgrad. U. Mich., 1950-52; cert. Hague Acad. Internat. Law, Netherlands, 1954. Bar: Wash. 1968. Assoc. firm Powell, Livengood, Dunlap & Silverdale, Kirkland, Wash., 1968; staff atty. Legal Service Ctr., Seattle, 1968-70; judge Seattle Dist. Ct., 1971-72, King County Superior Ct., Seattle, 1973-78; acting gen. counsel, dep. gen. counsel SBA, Washington, 1979-81; mem. Wash. State Ho. of Reps., Olympia, 1983-87, chmn. com. on state govt., 1984; mem. Wash. State Senate, 1987-95; sole practice, Seattle, 1981—; mem. White House Fellows Regional Selection Panel, Seattle, 1974-77, chmn., 1976, 77; incorporator Sound Savs. & Loan, Seattle, 1975. Bd. dirs. Allied Arts, Seattle, 1971—, Ctr. Contemporary Art, Seattle, 1981-83, Women's Network, Seattle, 1981-84, Pub. Defender Assn., Seattle, 1982-84; bd. visitors dept. psychology U. Wash., Seattle, 1983-87, bd. visitors dept sociology, 1988—. Named Woman of Yr. in Law, Past Pres.'s Assn., Seattle, 1971; Woman of Yr., Matrix Table, Seattle, 1973, Capitol Hill Bus. and Profl. Women, 1975. Mem. Wash. State Bar Assn., Wash. Women Lawyers. Democrat. Home: PO Box 20516 Seattle WA 98102-1516

NIEMI, RICHARD GENE, political science educator; b. Green Bay, Wis., Jan. 10, 1941; s. Eugene H. and Dorothy M. (Stevens) N.; m. Shirley A. Gill, Aug. 4, 1962; children: Nancy, Patricia, Jennifer, Julie. BA, Lawrence Coll., 1962; PhD, U. Mich., 1967. Asst. prof. polit. sci. U. Rochester, N.Y., 1967-71, assoc. prof., 1971-75, prof., 1975—, disting. grad. tchg. prof., 1983-86, chmn. dept. polit. sci., 1979-83, assoc. dean, 1986-89, sr. assoc. dean, 1989-91; vis. prof. U. Lund, Sweden, 1974, 81, U. Iowa, 1985; vis. rschr. Kobe U., Japan, 1991. Author: (with M. Kent Jennings) The Political Character of Adolescence, 1974, Generations and Politics, 1981, How Family Members Perceive Each Other, 1974, (with Bernard Grofman/Lisa Handley) Minority Representation and the Quest for Voting Equality, 1992; editor: (with Herbert Weisberg) Controversies in Voting Behavior, 1976, 3d edit., 1994, Classics in Voting Behavior, 1993, (with Harold Stanley) Vital Statistics in American Politics, 1988, 4th edit., 1994; co-author: Trends in Public Opinion. Rsch. grantee NIMH, 1969-70, NSF, 1974-77, 80-86, 94—, Ford Found., 1972-73; fellow Guggenheim Found., 1983-84, Ctr. for Advanced Study in Behavioral Sci., 1989. Mem. Am. Polit. Sci. Assn., Phi Beta Kappa. Lutheran. Home: 45 Boniface Dr Rochester NY 14620-3333 Office: U Rochester Dept Polit Sci Rochester NY 14627

NIEMIEC, DAVID WALLACE, investment company executive; b. Midland, Mich., Dec. 17, 1949; s. George G. and Eleanor (Yack) N.; m. Melanie Taveau Mason, Oct. 4, 1975; children—Elizabeth Street, Margaret Johnson. A.B., Harvard U., 1972, M.B.A., 1974. Assoc. Dillon, Read & Co., Inc., N.Y.C., 1974-78, v.p., 1979-81, sr. v.p., chief adminstrv. officer, 1982-83, mng. dir., chief adminstrv. officer, 1984—, vice chmn., 1991—; dir. Nat. Securities Clearing Corp., N.Y.C., 1989-92. Trustee Nightingale-Bamford Sch., N.Y.C., 1993—. Republican. Unitarian. Clubs: Union, Down Town (N.Y.C.). Office: Dillon Read & Co Inc 535 Madison Ave New York NY 10022-4212

NIEMIEC, EDWARD WALTER, professional association executive; b. Detroit, Nov. 1, 1936; s. Walter A. and Mary N.; m. Nancy M. Bennett, Aug. 25, 1962; children: Lisa, Julie, Brenda. B.S., U. Detroit, 1959, M.B.A., 1961. With Paine Webber Jackson & Curtis, N.Y.C., 1959-80, exec. v.p., dir. adminstrv. div., to 1980; v.p., bd. dirs. Moseley, Hallgarten, Estabrook, Weeden, Inc., 1980-82; also bd. dirs. Moseley, Hallgarten, Estabrook & Weeden Holding Corp.; pres., chief exec. officer, dir., mem. exec. com. Securities Settlement Corp. (subs. The Travelers 1982), N.Y.C., 1980-87; pres., dir. Inc Trading Co. subs. Instinet Corp., 1989-89; chief oper. officer Instinet Corp. subs. Reuters Holdings Plc., 1988-89; group v.p. AICPA, N.Y.C., 1989—. Served with U.S. Army. Roman Catholic. Office: AICPA Harborside Fin Ctr 201 Plaza Three Jersey City NJ 07311

NIEMIEC, PETER JUDE, lawyer; b. Yonkers, N.Y., Mar. 9, 1951; m. Ann Majchrzak. BA, Columbia U., 1973; JD, NYU, 1976. Bar: Calif. 1976, U.S. Dist. Ct. (cen. dist.) Calif. 1976, D.C. 1982, Ind. 1983. Sr. atty. U.S. EPA, Washington, 1980-83; dep. atty. gen. State of Ind., Indpls., 1983-86; sr. counsel Pacific Enterprises, L.A., 1986-89; ptnr. Greenberg, Glusker, Fields, Claman & Machtinger, L.A., 1990—; adj. prof. Ind. U. Sch. of Law, Indpls., 1984. Assoc. editor Ann. Survey of Am. Lawyers, 1975. Mem. ABA (natural resources, energy and environ. law sect.), L.A. County Bar Assn. (exec. com. 1990-91), Nat. Rsch. Coun. (com. review and evaluation Army chem. stockpile disposal program, 1992-95). Office: Greenberg Glusker Fields Claman & Machtinger 1900 Avenue Of The Stars Los Angeles CA 90067-4301

NIEMOLLER, ARTHUR B., electrical engineer; b. Wakefield, Kans., Oct. 4, 1912; s. Benjamin Henry and Minnie Christine (Carlson) N.; m. Ann Sochor, May 29, 1937 (dec. June 1982); children: Joanna Matteson, Arthur D. BSEE, Kans. State U., 1933. Registered profl. engr., N.Y., N.J., Pa., Ill., Ohio. Engr. Westinghouse, Newark, N.J., 1937-48, Hillside, N.J., 1948-59, Chgo., 1959-61, Pitts., 1961-65, Cin., 1965-77; pvt. practice engr. Montgomery, Ohio, 1977—. Patentee in field. Elder Presbyterian Church. Served with USN, 1933-37. Mem. AAAS, IEEE, NSPE, N.Y. Acad. Scis. Republican. Home and Office: 7888 Mitchell Farm Ln Cincinnati OH 45242-6410

NIENBURG, GEORGE FRANK, photographer; b. N.Y.C., Feb. 14, 1938; s. Carl George and Louise Elizabeth (Baum) N. Grad., Germain Sch. Photography, 1989. Veterinarian asst. Stamen Animal Hosp., New Rochelle, N.Y., 1966-70; trainer guard dogs Paradise Guard Dog Service, N.Y.C., 1970-71; animal care technician Am. Soc. for Prevention Cruelty to Animals, N.Y.C. 1971-82; security guard Cen. Nat. Investigation agy., New Rochelle,

1983-88; mem. rsch. bd. advisors Am. Biographical Inst., 1989—. Mem. Nat. Rep. Com., Washington, 1986—; mem. nat. leadership coalition Campaign Am., Washington, 1987—; mem. Nat. Rep. Sen. Com., 1989—; sustaining sponsor Ronald Reagan Found., 1987—; chartered founder Presdl. Trust Fund, 1992; charter mem., supporter Battle Normandy Mus., 1988—; sponsor Nat. Rep. Congl. Com., 1983; life mem. Rep. Presdl. Task Force, 1988; charter founder Ronald Reagan Ctr., 1988—; mem. Pres.'s Congl. Task Force, 1990, Rep. Campaign Com., 1991; supporter USN Meml. Owner Navy Plank, 1991. Recipient Congl. Order of Liberty award, 1993, Rep. Presdl. Legion of Merit; named in inscription in U.S. Pres. Bush's Spl. Honor Roll, Honor Roll Commemorating the Reagan-Bush Adminstrn., 1991; included in the "Life Mem. Wall of Honor" at Ronald Reagan Rep. Ctr.; inducted to Rep. Nat. Senatorial com.'s full and complete presdl. commn., 1992, The Ronald Reagan Presdl. Libr. Register, 1991; named to Ronald Reagan Freed Flame, 1994, Election Registry, Washington, 1994. Mem. Washington Legal Found. (patron), U.S. Sen. Club, Internat. Freelance Photographer Orgn. (life), Westchester Photographic Soc., Nat. Fedn. Rep. Women, English First, Nat. Wildlife Fedn. (assoc.), Am. Mus. Natural History, Nat. Trust for Hist. Preservation, Am. Space Frontier Com. (sustaining mem.), Nat. Flag Found. (std. bearer 1987—), Internat. Platform Assn., Masons (master 1986—, royal arch and knight templer 1992), Golden Heart Club, Mil. Order Purple Heart Svc. Found., HeartHighlander Club, Oxford Club. Avocations: music, photography. Home: 22 Edgewood Park PO Box 511 New Rochelle NY 10802-0511

NIENHUIS, ARTHUR WESLEY, physician, researcher; b. Hudsonville, Mich., Aug. 9, 1941; s. Willard M. and Grace (Prince) N.; m. Sheryl Ann Kalmink Nienhuis, Sept. 20, 1968; children: Carol Elizabeth, Craig Wesley, Kevin Robert, Heather Grace. Student, Cornell Coll., 1959-61; MD, U. Caif., L.A., 1963-68. Am. Bd. Internal Medicine, Am. Bd. Hematology. Intern Mass. Gen. Hosp., Boston, 1968-69, asst. resident, 1969-70; clin. assoc. NHLBI, NIH, Bethesda, Md., 1970-72; clin. fellow hematology Children's Hosp., Boston, 1972-73; chief. clin. svc. Molecular Hematology NIH, Bethesda, Md., 1973-77; dept. clin. dir. NHLBI, NIH, Bethesda, Md., 1976—, chief clin. Hematology Branch, 1976-93; dir. St. Jude Children's Rsch. Hosp., Memphis, 1993—; editor BLOOD-J Am. Soc. Hematology, Bethesda, Md., 1988-92; chmn. Hematology Bd. Am. Bd. Internat Med., Phila., 1988-92; mem. bd. dirs. Am. Bd. Internat Med., Phila., 1988-92. Editor: Molecular Basis of Blood Diseases, 1986, 93. Mem. Am. Soc. Hematology (pres. 1994), Am. Soc. Clin. Investigation, Assn. Am. Physicians. Office: St Jude Children's Rsch Hosp 332 N Lauderdale St Memphis TN 38105-2729

NIERENBERG, ROGER, symphony conductor; b. N.Y.C., June 14, 1947; s. Gerard I. and Julliet L. N.; BA, Princeton U., 1969; postgrad. diploma Mannes Coll. Music, 1971; Mus.M., Juilliard Sch. Music, 1979. Mus. dir. Pro Arte Chorale, Paramus, N.J., 1976-85, Juilliard Pre-Coll. Orchestra, N.Y.C., 1979-84, Stamford (Conn.) Symphony Orchestra, 1980—, Jacksonville Symphony (Fla.), 1984—; also condr. Office: Stanford Symphony Orch 1 Stamford Plz 263 Tresser Blvd Stamford CT 06901-3236*

NIES, BOYD ARTHUR, hematologist, oncologist; b. Orange, Calif., Jan. 12, 1935; s. Arthur J. and Mary Dora (Sheffer) N.; m. Helen May Salter, July 28, 1957; children: Nancy, Linda, Boyd Jr. AB, Stanford U., 1956, MD, 1959. Diplomate Am. Bd. Internal Medicine, Am. Bd. Internal Medicine: Hematology, Med. Oncology. Intern UCLA, 1959-60, asst. resident, 1960-61; assoc. resident Wadsworth VA Hosp., L.A., 1961-62; clin. assoc. Nat. Cancer Inst., Bethesda, Md., 1962-64; fellow in hematology Stanford U., Palo Alto, Calif., 1964-65; pvt. practice internal medicine and hematology Redlands, Calif., 1965-68; pvt. practice hematology and med. oncology San Bernardino, Calif., 1968—. Contbr. articles to profl. jours. Bd. dirs. First United Meth. Ch., Redlands, 1985-88, St. Bernardine Hosp., San Bernardino, 1975-77, Riverside-San Bernardino Counties Blood Bank, 1984—, pres. 1988-90, bd. dirs. Inland Med. Providers, 1990-93. Fellow ACP; mem. AMA, Am. Soc. Internal Medicine, Am. Soc. Hematology, Am. Soc. Clin. Oncology, Internat. Soc. Hematology, Redlands Country Club, Redlands Swim and Tennis Club. Republican. Methodist. Avocations: tennis, photography, stamp collecting. Home: 645 E Mariposa Dr Redlands CA 92373-7353 Office: Inland Hematology Oncology 401-C Highland Ave Ste 552 San Bernardino CA 92404-3801

NIES, HELEN WILSON, federal judge; b. Birmingham, Ala., Aug. 7, 1925; d. George Earl and Lida Blanche (Erckert) Wilson; m. John Dirk Nies; children: Dirk, Nancy, Eric. BA, U. Mich., 1946, JD, 1948. Bar: D.C. 1961, U.S. Supreme Ct. 1962. Atty. Dept. Justice, Washington, 1948-51, Office Price Stblzn., Washington, 1951-52; assoc. Pattishall, McAuliffe and Hofstetter, Washington, 1960-66, resident ptnr., 1966-77; ptnr. Howrey & Simon, Washington, 1978-80; judge U.S. Ct. Customs and Patent Appeals, 1980-82; cir. judge U.S. Ct. Appeals Fed. Cir., 1982—; chief judge U.S. Ct. Appeals (fed. cir.), 1990-94; mem. jud. conf. U.S. Com. on Bicentennial of Constitution, 1986-90; mem. pub. adv. com. trademark affairs Dept. Commerce, 1976-80; mem. adv. bd. BNA's Patent Trademark and Copyright Jour., 1976-78; bd. visitors U. Mich. Law Sch., 1975-78; bd. visitors U. Mich. Law Sch., 1975-78; adv. for restatement of law and unfair competition Am. Law Inst., 1986—; speaker World Intellectual Property Orgn., Forum of Judges, Calcutta, 1987, European Judges Conf., Hague, 1991, Kyoto (Japan) Comparative Law Ctr., 1992, others. Recipient Athena Outstanding Alumna award U. Mich., 1987, Jefferson medal N.J. Patent Law Assn., 1991, Judicial Honoree award Bar Assn. D.C., 1992, D. of Laws, Honoris Causa, John Marshall Law Sch., Chgo., 1993. Mem. ABA (chmn. com. 203, 1972-74, com. 504, 1975-76), Bar Assn. D.C. (chmn. patent trademark copyright sect. 1975-76, dir. 1976-78), U.S. Trademark Assn. (chmn. lawyers adv. com. 1974-76, bd. dirs. 1976-78), Am. Patent Law Assn., Fed. Bar Assn., Nat. Assn. Women Lawyers (Woman Lawyer of Yr. 1980), Women's Bar D.C., Order of Coif, Phi Beta Kappa, Phi Kappa Phi. Office: US Ct Appeals Fed Cir 717 Madison Pl NW Washington DC 20439*

NIESE, WILLIAM A., lawyer, newspaper publishing executive. BS, Cornell U., 1958; LLB, SUNY, Buffalo, 1961. Bar: N.Y. 1961, Ariz. 1963, Calif. 1966. Corp. counsel, asst. sec. Times Mirror Co., L.A., 1969-73, asst. gen. counsel, asst. sec., 1973-82; assoc. gen. counsel, asst. sec. L.A. Times, 1982-90, v.p., gen. counsel, 1985-90, sr. v.p. law and human resources, 1990—. Capt., JAGC, U.S. Army, 1961-66. Office: Times Mirror Co Times Mirror Sq Los Angeles CA 90053

NIESEN, JAMES LOUIS, theater director; b. St. Louis, Feb. 15, 1946; s. James Louis and Emily Elise (Brennecke) N. BFA, Ill. Wesleyan U., 1968; MFA, Ohio U., 1974. Actor Stage South, Columbia, S.C., 1974-75, Long Wharf Theatre, New Haven, 1977-78, Geva Theater, Rochester, N.Y., 1978-79; freelance dir., 1980-83; stage mgr. Roundabout Theater, N.Y., 1982-83; artistic dir. Irondale Ensemble Project, N.Y., 1983—; panelist N.Y. Found. on the Arts, N.Y., 1988-89. Author: (book) Game Guide, 1988; contbr. articles to profl. jours.; dir. (play) St. Joan of the Stockyards, 1993, Donton's Death, 1994. Mem. Actor's Equity Assn. Avocations: country music, tennis. Home: 419 Pacific St Brooklyn NY 11217 Office: Irondale Ensemble Project 351 W 18th St New York NY 10011

NIETO DEL RIO, JUAN CARLOS, marketing executive; b. Mexico City, Mar. 1, 1962. BA, Tufts U., 1984. Latin Am. sales TELEVISA, Miami, Fla., 1984-86; rsch. assoc. UNIVISION, N.Y.C., 1986-87; asst. to v.p. UNIVISA, L.A., 1987-88; pres. Spanish Comm., A Divsn. of Western Media, L.A., 1989-93; pres. mktg. HES, L.A., 1993—. Vol. Hermandad Mexicana, L.A. Avocations: travel, languages, multimedia computers. Office: HES 3726 Laurel Canyon Blvd Studio City CA 91604-3718

NIEVERGELT, JURG, computer science educator; b. Luzern, Switzerland, June 6, 1938; came to U.S., 1962; s. Albert and Hedwig Nievergelt; m. Teresa Quiambao; children: Mark, Derek. Diploma in math., Swiss Fed. Inst. Tech. (ETH), Zurich, Switzerland, 1962; PhD in Math., U. Ill., 1965. Research fellow Dept. Computer Sci. and Math., U. Ill., 1962-65; asst. prof. computer sci. and math. U. Ill. Urbana, 1965-68, assoc. prof. computer sci., 1968-72, prof., 1972-77; prof. Swiss Fed. Inst. Tech. (ETH), Zurich, 1975-85, 89—; Kenan prof., chmn. dept. computer sci. U. N.C., Chapel Hill, 1985-89; rsch. scientist various rsch. labs. and univs., including U. Grenoble, U. Stuttgart, Keio U.; mem. Computing Rsch. Bd., 1987-89. Author: (with E.M. Reingold and N. Deo) Combinatorial Algorithms: Theory and Prac-

tice, 1977, (with A. Ventura and H. Hinterberger) Interactive Computer Programs for Education—Philosophy, Techniques and Examples, 1986, (with K. Hinrichs) Algorithms and Data Structures, with Applications to Graphics and Geometry, 1993; mem. editorial bd. Sci. Computer Programming, Jour. Symbolic Computation, Decision Support Systems, Informatik Spektrum; contbr. articles to profl. jours. Grantee NSF, 1972-76, 86-89, Office Naval Rsch., 1986-89. Fellow IEEE, AAAS; mem. Assn. Computing Machinery. Research interests include algorithms and data structures, parallel computation, interactive systems. Office: ETH Informatik, CH-8092 Zurich Switzerland

NIEWIAROSKI, TRUDI OSMERS (GERTRUDE NIEWIAROSKI), social studies educator; b. Jersey City, Apr. 30, 1935; d. Albert John and Margaret (Niemeyer) Osmers; m. Donald H. Niewiaroski, June 8, 1957; children: Donald H., Donna, Margaret Anne, Nancy Noel. AB in History and German, Upsala Coll., East Orange, N.J., 1957; MEd, Montgomery County Pub. Schs., Rockville, Md., 1992. Cert. tchr., Md. Tchr. geography Colego Americano, Quito, Ecuador, 1964-66; tchr. speed reading Escuela Lincoln, Buenos Aires, Argentina, 1966-67; substitute thcr. Montgomery County Pub. Schs., Rockville, 1978-83, tchr. social studies, 1984—; bd. dirs. Coto Paxi Acad., Quito, 1964-66; del. Eisenhower People to People Del. Vietnam, 1993. Author curricula; contbr. chpts. to books, articles to profl. jours.; lectr. at workshops. Pres. Citizens Assn., Potomac, Md., 1977-81; leader Girl Scouts U.S., 1975-76. Fulbright fellow India, 1985, China, 1990, Japan Keizai Koho Ctr. fellow, 1992; recipient Md. Tchr. of Yr. award State of Md. Edn. Dept., 1993, Finalist Nat. Tchr. of Yr., 1993, Disting. Alumni award Upsala Coll., 1993, Milkin Nat. Educator award, 1994. Mem. Nat. Coun. Social Studies, Md. Coun. for Social Studies, Asia Soc., Smithsonian Instn., Montgomery County Hist. Soc., Spl. Interest Group-China, Kappa Delta Pi. Avocations: cake and cookie decorating, travel. Office: R Montgomery High Sch Rockville MD 20852

NIEWIAROWSKI, STEFAN, physiology educator, biomedical research scientist; b. Warsaw, Poland, Dec. 4, 1926; came to U.S., 1972, naturalized, 1978; s. Marian and Janina (Sledzinska) N.; m. Marta Ciswicka (div. 1974); children: Agata, Tomasz. MD, Warsaw U., 1952, PhD, 1960, Dozent, 1961. Lic. physician, Pa.; cert. Ednl. Coun. Fgn. Med. Grads. Intern, med. resident Inst. Hematology, Warsaw, 1951-54; rsch. fellow, rsch. assoc. dept. physiol. chemistry Warsaw U. Med. Sch., 1948-54; rsch. assoc., sr. rsch. assoc. Lab. Clin. Biochemistry, Inst. Hematology, Warsaw, 1951-61; physician in charge Outpatient Dept. for Hemophiliacs, Warsaw, 1957-61; head dept., prof. physiol. chemistry Med. Sch., Bialystok, Poland, 1961-68; assoc. prof. pahtology dept. pathology McMaster U., Hamilton, Ont., Can., 1970-72; rsch. prof. medicine, head coagulation sect. Specialized Ctr. Thrombosis Rsch., Temple U. Sch. Medicine, Phila., 1972-78; prof. physiology Temple U. Sch. Medicine, Phila., 1975—, prof. physiology Thrombosis Rsch. Ctr., 1978—; cons. dept. infectious diseases Warsaw U. Med. Sch., 1954-60; vis. scientist Centre Nat. de Transfusion Sanguine, Paris, 1959; cons. dept. pediatrics Warsaw U. Med. Sch., 1961-65; vis. scientist Vascular Lab., Lemeul Shattuck Hosp., Boston, 1965, 68-70; vis. prof. medicine Tufts U. Sch. Medicine, Boston, 1968-70; dir. Blood Components Devel. Lab., Hamilton Red Cross and McMaster U., 1971-72; mem. sr. coun. Internat. Com. on Haemostatis and Thrombosis, 1973—; mem. NIH rsch. rev. coms., 1975—. Editor Thrombosis Rsch., 1972-80; mem. editorial com. Procs. of Soc. of Exptl. Biology and Medicine, 1980-82, mem. editorial bd., 1980—; reviewer Jour. Clin. Investigation, Jour. Lab. and Clin. Medicine, Blood, Biochimica et Biophysica Acta, Archives of Biochemistry and Biophysics, Jour. Biol. Chemistry, Am. Jour. Physiology; author, co-author 250 articles in the field of blood coagulation, platelet physiology and cell adhesion; contbr. articles to profl. jours. Ont. Heart Found. fellow, 1970-71; recipient Jurzykowski Found. award, 1990, rsch. awards NIH, 1972—. Mem. Internat. Soc. Hematology, Internat. Soc. Thrombosis and Hemostasis, Am. Physiology Soc., Am. Soc. Hematology, Coun. of Thrombosis of Am. Heart Assn., Soc. Exptl. Biology and Medicine, Polish Inst. Arts and Scis. in Am., Am. Soc. Exptl. Pathology, Polish Am. Med. Soc. (hon.). Achievements include patent for trigramin a platelet aggregation inhibiting polypeptide. Home: 445 S Woodbine Ave Narberth PA 19072-2027 Office: Temple U Sch Medicine 3400 N Broad St Philadelphia PA 19140-5104

NIEWYK, ANTHONY, lawyer; b. Utrecht, The Netherlands, Feb. 28, 1941; arrived in U.S., 1956; s. John and Anthonia B. (Thomassen) N.; m. Ruth Ann Hunderman, Aug. 20, 1965; children: Robert, Deborah. BS, Calvin Coll., 1961; BSEE, U. Mich., 1963, MSEE, 1964; JD, George Washington U., 1972. Engr. Whirlpool Corp., Benton Harbor, Mich., 1965-69; patent agt. Whirlpool Corp., Benton Harbor, 1969-72, patent atty., 1972-78, dir. labor rels., 1978-84; atty. Jeffers, Irish, Hoffman, Wayne, Ind., 1984-86; ptnr. Jeffers, Hoffman, Niewyk, Ft. Wayne, Ind., 1987-91, Baker & Daniels, Ft. Wayne, Ind., 1991—. Avocations: reading, golf, fishing, flying, gardening. Home: 12215 Glen Lake Dr Fort Wayne IN 46804-4572 Office: Baker & Daniels 2400 Ft Wayne Nat Bank Bldg Fort Wayne IN 46802

NIGAM, BISHAN PERKASH, physics educator; b. Delhi, India, July 14, 1928; came to U.S., 1952; s. Rajeshwar Nath and Durga (Vati) N.; m. Indira Bahadur, Nov. 14, 1956; children—Sanjay, Shobhna, Ajay. B.S., U. Delhi, 1946, M.S., 1948; Ph.D., U. Rochester, N.Y., 1955. Research fellow U. Delhi, 1948-50; lectr. in physics, 1950-52, 55-56; postdoctoral fellow Case Inst. Tech., Cleve., 1954-55; postdoctoral research fellow NRC, Ottawa, Can., 1956-59; research assoc. U. Rochester, 1959-60, asst. prof. physics, part-time 1960-61; prin. scientist Gen. Dynamics/Electronics, Rochester, N.Y., 1960-61; assoc. prof. physics SUNY, Buffalo, 1961-64; prof. physics Ariz. State U., Tempe, 1964—, U. Wis., Milw., 1966-67. Author: (with R.R. Roy) Nuclear Physics, 1967; also articles. Govt. of India scholar U. Rochester, 1952-54. Fellow Am. Phys. Soc. Office: Ariz State U Dept Physics Box 871504 Tempe AZ 85287-1504

NIGG, BENNO MAURUS, biomechanics educator; b. Walenstadt, St. Gallen, Switzerland, Apr. 10, 1938; s. Josef B. Nigg and Edwina Nigg-Widrig; m. Margaretha J. Bolleter, Aug. 28, 1965; children: Andreas, Reto, Claudio, Sandro. Diploma in physics, ETH, Zurich, Switzerland, 1965, Dr. sci. nat., 1975. Instr. Lyceum Alpinum Zuoz, Switzerland, 1965-71; rsch. Biomechs. Lab. Eidgenössische Technische Hochschule (ETH), Zurich, 1971-76, dir., 1976-81; prof. U. Calgary, 1981—, dir. Human Performance Lab, 1981—; cons. Adidas, Germany, 1976—, Nike, 1981-85; mem. steering com. World Congress on Biomechs., 1988—. Recipient Michael Jaeger award Gesellschaft für Orthopaedie und Traumatologie in Sport, Munich, 1986, Wartenweiler Meml. award Internat. Soc. for Biomechs., UCLA, 189, NOVEL award, Vienna, 1991. Mem. Am. Soc. Biomechanics, Can. Soc. Biomechanics, Internat. Soc. Biomechanics (pres. 1983-85). Office: U Calgary, Human Performance Lab, Calgary, AB Canada T2N 1N4*

NIGH, GEORGE, university administrator, former governor; b. McAlester, Okla., June 9, 1927; s. Wilber and Irene (Crockett) N.; m. Donna Mashburn, 1963; children: Mike, Georgeann. Student, Ea. A&M Coll., 1946-48; BA, E. Cen. State U., 1950. Ptnr. Nigh Grocery, McAlester, 1956-60; mem. Okla. Legislature, 1950-58; lt. gov. Okla., 1958-63, 67-79, gov., 1963, 79-87; pres. U. Cen. Okla., Edmond, OK, 1992—; bd. dirs. J.C. Penney Co., Boatmen's First Nat. Bank. Mem. Okla. Young Democrats (pres.), Okla. Jr. C. of C. (sec.), Am. Legion, V.F.W., Am. Vets. Presbyterian. Club: Mason (32 deg., Shriner). Office: U Ctrl Okla Office of President 100 N University Dr Edmond OK 73034

NIGHTINGALE, ELENA OTTOLENGHI, geneticist, physician, administrator; b. Livorno, Italy, Nov. 1, 1932; came to U.S., 1939; d. Mario Lazzaro and Elisa Vittoria (Levi) Ottolenghi; m. Stuart L. Nightingale, July 1, 1965; children—Elizabeth, Marisa. A.B. summa cum laude, Barnard Coll., 1954; Ph.D., Rockefeller U., 1961; M.D., NYU, 1964. Asst. prof. Cornell U. Med. Coll., N.Y.C., 1965-70, Johns Hopkins U., Balt., 1970-73; fellow in clin. genetics and pediatrics Georgetown U. Hosp., Washington, 1973-74; sr. staff officer NAS, Washington, 1975-79, sr. program officer Inst. Medicine, 1979-82, sr. scholar in residence, 1982-83; spl. advisor to pres. Carnegie Corp. N.Y., N.Y.C., 1983-94, sr. program officer, 1989-94; scholar-in-residence Nat. Acad. Scis., Washington, 1995—; vis. assoc. prof. Harvard U. Med. Sch., Boston, 1980-84, vis. lectr. 1984—; adj. prof. pediatrics Georgetown U. Med. Ctr., 1983—, George Washington U. Med. Ctr., 1994—; mem. recombinant DNA adv. com. NIH, Bethesda, Md., 1979-83. Editor: The Breaking of Bodies and Minds: Torture, Psychiatric Abuse and the Health Professions,

1985, Prenatal Screening, Policies and Values: The Example of Neural Tube Defects, 1987; co-author: Before Birth: Prenatal Screening for Genetic Disease, 1990, Promoting the Health of Adolescents: New Directions for the 21st Century, 1993; contbr. numerous sci. articles to profl. publs. Bd. dirs. Ctr. for Youth Svcs., Washington, 1980-84, Sci. Svc. Inc., Washington, 1985—, Amnesty Internat., U.S.A., 1989-91. Sloan Found. fellow, 1974-75. Fellow AAAS (chmn. com. on sci. freedom and responsibility 1985-88), N.Y. Acad. Scis., Royal Soc. Medicine; mem. Harvey Soc., Am. Soc. Microbiology, Am. Soc. Human Genetics (social issues com. 1982-85), Genetics Soc. Am., Inst. Medicine of NAS (chmn. com. on health and human rights 1987-90), Phi Beta Kappa, Sigma Xi. Office: Nat Acad Scis 2101 Constitution Ave NW Washington DC 20418

NIGHTINGALE, GEOFFREY J., communications company executive, consultant; b. New Haven, Conn., Sept. 5, 1938; s. Louis M. and Evelyn G. (Carr) N.; m. Gisela I. Staats, Apr. 7, 1961; children: Alyssa M., Christopher G. BA, CCNY, 1963. Editor Trench Pubs., N.Y.C., 1961-64; pub. relations AE W. Alec Jordan Assocs., N.Y.C., 1964-68; pub. relations AE Burson-Marsteller, N.Y.C., 1968-71, group mgr., v.p. pub. relations, 1971-73, creative dir. pub. relations, v.p., 1973-78, exec. v.p., worldwide creative dir., 1983-93; pres. Syner Genics div. Burson-Marsteller, N.Y.C., The Hague (The Netherlands), 1986-93; pres. Syner Genics divsn. Young & Rubicam Inc., 1993—; dir. strategy and devel. Nightingale & Ptnrs., Cold Spring Harbor, N.Y., 1991—; creative cons. N.Y.C., 1978-83; cons. Port of Galveston, Tex., 1984-86. Author: The Highway Gourmet, 1992; contbr. articles to profl. jours. Cons. Conservative Party, 1977-78, USA for Africa, 1985-86. Served with U.S. Army, 1958-60. Mem. Internat. Assn. Bus. Communicators, Corp. Communication Cons., World Future Soc. Democrat. Universalist-Unitarian. Avocations: dog breeding, sailing, writing non-fiction. Office: Nightingale & Ptnrs 3 Harbor Rd Cold Spring Harbor NY 11724

NIGHTINGALE, RETHA LEE, federal agency administrator; b. Wichita, Kans., Dec. 15, 1954; d. L.D. and Barbara Louise (McClain) Figgins; m. William Boyd III, Dec. 30, 1982; children: Theodore Jacob, Katharine Ann. BA, U. Kans., 1977. Hydrologic technician U.S. Geol. Survey, Lawrence, Kans., 1975-78; personnel clk. U.S. Geol. Survey, Denver, 1978-79, position class specialist, 1979-80; personnel mgmt. specialist Office of Personnel Mgmt., Denver, 1980-81; personnel officer USDA Forest Service, Glenwood Springs, Colo., 1981-83; adminstrv. officer USDA Forest Service, Nemo, S.D., 1983-87, Bighorn Nat. Forest, Sheridan, Wyo., 1987-88; acting dist. ranger Ketchikan (Alaska) Ranger Dist., 1990; adminstrv. officer Tongass Nat. Forest, Ketchikan, Alaska, 1989—; chmn. exec. com. Regional Adminstrv. Team, 1987-88. Rep. Pres. Carter's Adv. Com. on the Status of Women, Denver, 1980, Civil Rights Commn., Custer, S.D., 1986-87; bd. dirs. Ketchikan Youth Svcs., 1989-91. Named one of Outstanding Young Women in Am., Jaycees, 1983, 87. Mem. Am. Soc. Pers. Adminstrn. (treas. 1975-76), Bus. and Profl. Women (dir. young career woman program 1984-85, Young Career Women award for Western Colo. 1983), Fed. Employed Women (sec. 1980-81), Rotary, Epsilon Sigma Alpha (dir. pub. rels. 1982-83), Alpha Delta Pi. Democrat. Presbyterian. Avocations: bicycling, swimming, hiking, reading.

NIGHTINGALE, STUART LESTER, physician, public health officer; b. N.Y.C., Jan. 26, 1938; s. Lester M. Nightingale and Beatrice L. N. (Liebowitz) Helpern; m. Elena Ottolenghi, July 1, 1965; children: Elizabeth S., Marisa O. BA, Yale U., 1959; MD, NYU, 1964. Diplomate Am. Bd. Internal Medicine. Intern in medicine and surgery Montefiore Hosp. and Med. Ctr., Bronx, N.Y., 1964-65, resident in internal medicine, fellow in adolescent medicine, 1965-66, 67-69, asst. attending physician, 1969-70; resident in anatomical pathology NYU Sch. Medicine, 1966-67; med. dir. drug abuse adminstrn. Dept. Health and Mental Hygiene State of Md., Balt., 1971-72; chief treatment and rehab., office of programs, spl. action office for drug abuse prevention Exec. Office of Pres., Washington, 1972-74, chief office treatment and rehab., spl. action office for drug abuse prevention, 1974-75; dir. divsn. resource devel. Nat. Inst. on Drug Abuse, Rockville, Md., 1974-76; asst. to dir. Bur. Drugs, Food and Drug Adminstrn., Rockville, 1976-79; dep. assoc. commr. for health affairs FDA, Rockville, 1979-82, acting assoc. commr. for health affairs, 1979-82, assoc. commr. for health affairs, 1982—; med. dir. The Fort Greene/Bklyn.-Cumberland Narcotic Detoxification Program, Bklyn., 1969-70; vis. physician Balt. City Hosps., 1970-72; clin. instr. dept. medicine Coll. Medicine SUNY, Bklyn., 1970; asst. physician out-patient dept., instr. dept. medicine Johns Hopkins U. Sch. Medicine, Balt., 1970-72, med. dir. drug abuse ctr., 1970-71, instr. dept. med. care and hosps. Sch. Hygiene and Pub. Health, 1971-74, rsch. program mgr. health svcs. rsch. and devel. ctr., 1970-71; chmn. rsch. involving human subjects com. FDA, 1979-84; liaison mem. Commn. on Fed. Drug Approval Process, U.S. Congress, 1980-81; mem.-at-large U.S. Pharmacopeial Conv., Inc., 1985—; bd. trustees The Milton Helpern Libr. of Legal Medicine, N.Y.C., 1982—; bd. dirs. Nat. Coun. on Patient Info. and Edn., Washington; mem. forum on drug devel. and regulation Inst. Medicine, NAS, Washington, 1986—. Contbg. author Jour. AMA, 1985—, Am. Family Physician, 1986—. Capt. med. corps USAR, 1966-72; with USPHS. Recipient Disting. Svc. Spl. Action Office for Drug Abuse Prevention award Exec. Office of Pres., 1975, Pub. Health Superior Svc. award, 1983, Disting. Contbn. award Nat. Coun. Patient Info. and Edn., 1987, Achievement award Am. Assn. Physicians for Human Rights, 1990, Presdl. Meritorious Exec. Rank award, 1990, Pub. Health Svc. Spl. Recognition award, 1993. Fellow ACP (mem. clin. pharmacology subcom., health and pub. policy com. 1984-87, 87-88); mem. AMA, Sr. Execs. Assn., Cosmos Club, Yale Club of Washington. Office: FDA 5600 Fishers Ln Rockville MD 20857

NIGHTINGALE, WILLIAM JOSLYN, management consulting company executive; b. Mpls., Sept. 16, 1929; s. William Issac and Gladys (Joslyn) N. B.A., Bowdoin Coll., 1951; M.B.A., Harvard U., 1953; children: Paul, Sara, William Joslyn, Margaret. Mktg. mgr. Gen. Mills Inc., Mpls., 1957-66; sr. assoc. Booz, Allen & Hamilton Inc., N.Y.C., 1966-68; v.p./fin. Hanes Corp., Winston-Salem, N.C., 1969; pres. Bali Co. Inc., N.Y.C., 1970-75; chmn. Nightingale & Assocs. Inc., Stamford, Conn., 1975—; bd. dirs. Ring's End Lumber Inc., Spreckles Industries, Inc., GlassTec Inc.; trustee Naraganseft Tax Free Bond Fund, Churchill Money Mkt. Fund, Churchill Tax Free Bd. Fund. Active numerous charitable orgns.; vestryman St. Luke's Episcopal Ch., 1975-78, sr. warden, 1989-91; mem. Darien Representative Town Meeting, 1971-74. Lt. (j.g.) USNR, 1953-57. Republican. Clubs: Wee Burn Country; Harvard (N.Y.C.); Noroton (Conn.) Yacht. Home: 195 Rowayton Ave Norwalk CT 06853 Office: Soundview Plz 1266 E Main St Stamford CT 06902-3546

NIGUIDULA, FAUSTINO NAZARIO, surgeon; b. Pasay City, Philippines, June 27, 1926; s. Aquilino Uriarte and Encarnacion (Nazario) N.; MD, U. of Philippines, 1953; m. Barbara Ann Brooks, Dec. 17, 1977; children: Andrew, Nicole; children by previous marriage—David, Diane, Susan, John, Stephen, Daniel, Nancy, Kathy. Came to U.S., 1953, naturalized, 1970. Intern, Arnot-Ogden Meml. Hosp., Elmira, N.Y., 1953-54; resident surgery Strong Meml. Hosp., Rochester, N.Y., 1954-59; resident in thoracic surgery Buffalo Gen. Hosp., 1959-61; fellow pediatric cardiothoracic surgery Children's Hosp., Buffalo, 1961-62, Hosp. Sick Children, Toronto, Ont., Can., 1963-64; instr. surgery U. Rochester (N.Y.), 1958-59; clin. instr. surgery U. Buffalo, 1965-66; asst. prof. surgery Temple U. Phila., 1967-70, asso. prof. surgery, pediatrics, 1970-75; clin. assoc. prof. surgery U., 1979-83; prof. surgery, prof. pediatrics N.Y. Med. Coll., 1983—; dir. pediatric cardio-thoracic surgery Deborah Heart and Lung Center, Browns Mills, N.J., 1975-83; chief pediatric cardiothoracic surgery St. Christopher's Hosp. for Children, Phila., 1967-75, Westchester Med. Ctr., Valhalla, N.Y., 1983—. Recipient 7th commemorative medal Cardiology Soc. Poland, 1982. Mem. ACS, Soc. Thoracic Surgeons, Am. Heart Assn., Assn. Thoracic and Cardiovascular Surgeons Asia, Westchester County Med. Soc., N.Y. State Med. Soc., Westchester Acad. Medicine, AAAS, Soc. Philippine Surgeons in Am., N.Y. Acad. Scis. Presbyterian. Home: 2 Pine Hill Ct Briarcliff Manor NY 10510-1742 Office: Westchester County Med Ctr Valhalla NY 10595

NIHART, FRANKLIN BROOKE, museum consultant, writer and editor; b. Los Angeles, Mar. 16, 1919; s. Claude Eugene and Vera Howard (Brooke) N.; m. Mary Helen Brosius, Feb. 11, 1945; children: Mary Catherine, Virginia Brooke Nihart-Martinez. BA, Occidental Coll., 1940. Commd. 2d lt. USMC, 1940, advanced through grades to col., 1957; dep. dir. Marine Corps. History and Mus. USMC, Washington, 1973-92; fellow, past gov., pres. Co. Mil. Historians, 1967-71; founder Marine Corps Hist. Found., 1979. Assoc. editor: Jour. Am. Mil. Past; contbg. editor: Almanac of Seapower. Bd. advisors Am. Mil. U. Decorated Navy Cross, Bronze Star with one gold star; named to Order del Mar Oceano; recipient Disting. Svc. award Co. Mil. Historians, 1982, Disting. Svc. award Marine Corps. Hist. Found., 1992. Mem. Am. Assn. Mus., Internat. Coun. Mus., Nat. Firearms Mus. (bd. dirs.), Nat. Hist. Intelligence Mus. (bd. dirs.), Va. Mus. Mil. Vehicles (bd. dirs.), Internat. Assn. Mus. Arms and Mil. History (hon. life), Orgn. Mil. Mus. Can. (hon. life), Washington Naval Corrs. Circle, Army and Navy Club, Mil. Order of Carabao (Disting. Svc. award 1987), Dacor House, Ends of the Earth Club, Masons. Republican. Presbyterian. Avocations: history, politics, travel, shooting, writing.

NIHILL, JULIAN DUMONTIEL, lawyer; b. Nairobi, Kenya, Apr. 17, 1950; s. Alan Barclay and Jeannine (Morgan-Davies) N.; m. Catherine Lynn Brittingham, Aug. 28,1977; children: Natalie Penn, Edward Barclay. Student, Ampleforth Coll., Eng., 1967; LLB with honors, Exeter U., Eng., 1972; barrister at law, Inner Temple, Eng., 1973; JD, Boston U., 1977. Bar: Ill. 1977, Tex. 1982, U.S. Tax Ct. 1982. Assoc. McDermott, Will & Emery, Chgo., 1977-79, Baker & McKenzie, Chgo., 1979-83; ptnr. Gardere & Wynne, Dallas, 1984—; chmn. Tex. State Bar Internat. Sect., Internat. Sect. Gardere & Wynne. Contbr. articles to profl. jours. Mem. U.S.-Mex. C. of C., Cavalry and Guards Club. Avocations: Playing piano, sailing, flyfishing. Office: Gardere & Wynne 3000 Thanksgiving Tower 1601 Elm St Dallas TX 75201-4701

NIJENHUIS, ALBERT, mathematician, educator; b. Eindhoven, Netherlands, Nov. 21, 1926; came to U.S., 1952, naturalized, 1959; s. Hendrik and Lijdia (Koornneef) N.; m. Marianne Dannhauser, Aug. 14, 1955; children: Erika, Karin, Sabien, Alaine. Candidaat, U. Amsterdam, Netherlands, 1947, Doctorandus, 1950, Doctor cum laude, 1952. Assoc. Math. Ctr., Amsterdam, Netherlands, 1951-52; asst. Inst. Advanced Study, Princeton, N.J., 1955; mem. Inst. Advanced Study, 1953-55, 61-62; instr., rsch. assoc. U. Chgo., 1955-56; faculty U. Wash., Seattle, 1956-63, prof., 1961-63, affiliate prof., 1988—; prof. math. U. Pa., Phila., 1963-87, prof. emeritus, 1987—; Fulbright lectr. U. Amsterdam, 1963-64; vis. prof. U. Geneva, Switzerland, 1967-68, Dartmouth Coll., 1977-78; researcher and author publs. on subjects including differential geometry, deformation theory in algebra, combinatorics, especially tensors, holonomy groups, graded lie algebras, algorithms. Co-author: Combinatorial Algorithms, 1975, 78; editor: Jour. Algorithms. Postdoctoral fellow Princeton, 1952-53; Fulbright grantee, 1952-53, 63-64; Guggenheim fellow, 1961-62. Mem. Am. Math. Soc., Math. Assn. Am., Netherlands Math. Soc., Assn. for Computing Machinery, AAUP, Royal Netherlands Acad. Scis. (corr.). Office: U Wash Dept Math Box 354350 Seattle WA 98195-4350

NIKIFORUK, PETER N., university dean; b. St. Paul, Alta., Can., Feb. 11, 1930; s. DeMetro and Mary (Dowhaniuk) N.; m. Eugenie F. Dyson, Dec. 21, 1957; children: Elizabeth, Adrienne. B.Sc., Queen's U., Ont., Can., 1952; Ph.D., Manchester U., Eng., 1955, D.Sc., 1970. Engr. A.V. Roe Ltd., Toronto, Ont., 1951-52; def. sci. service officer Def. Research Bd., Quebec, Que., Can., 1956-57; systems engr. Canadair Ltd., Montreal, Que., 1957-59; asst. prof. U. Sask., Saskatoon, 1960-61; assoc. prof. U. Sask., 1961-65, prof., 1965—, chmn. div. control engring., 1964-69, head mech. engring., 1966-73, dean engring., 1973—; cons. in field.; mem. council NRC, 1973-78. Contbr. articles to profl. jours. Bd. dirs. Sask. Research Council, Can. Inst. Indsl. Tech. Fellow IEEE (Kelvin Premium, Centennial medal), RSC, Royal Soc. Arts, Inst. Physics, Can. Acad. Engring., Engring. Inst. Can. (C. Julian Smith medal), Can. Soc. Mech. Engr. (past v.p.); mem. Assn. Profl. Engrs. Sask. (chmn. bd. examiners, Disting. Svc. award). Home: 31 Bell Crescent, Saskatoon, SK Canada S7J 2W2

NIKKEL, RONALD WILBERT, social services administrator; b. Lethbridge, Alta., Can., June 8, 1946; came to U.S., 1978; s. Henry Peter and Katharine (Penner) N.; m. Celeste Carisa Friesen, June 11, 1970. BA, U. Winnipeg (Can.), 1970; MPS, Loyola U., Chgo., 1983. Nat. dir. YFC/Youth Guidance, Toronto, Ont., Can., 1973-78, Chgo., 1978-82; field dir. Prison Fellowship Internat., Washington, 1982-84, v.p., 1984-88, pres., 1988—. Editor: Guidelines for Volunteer Programs in Justice, 1988. Chmn. Non Govtl. Orgns. Alliance in Crime Prevention and Criminal Justice, N.Y.C., 1988—; bd. dirs. Love and Action, Annapolis, Md., 1989—, Jericho Rd. Found., Chgo., 1992—, Advocates Internat., 1993—. Mem. Acad. Criminal Justice Scis. Episcopalian. Avocations: photography, hiking, gardening. Office: Prison Fellowship Internat PO Box 17434 Washington DC 20041-0434

NIKLAS, KARL J., plant biology educator. Prof. dept. plant biology Cornell U., Ithaca, N.Y. Recipient Cichan award Botanical Soc. Am., 1993. Office: Cornell U Dept Plant Biology 237 Plant Sci Bldg Ithaca NY 14853-0001*

NIKOLAI, JAMES A., insurance executive. V.p. Farmers Group Inc., L.A., Farmers Ins. Cos. Office: Farmers Ins Group Cos 4680 Wilshire Blvd Los Angeles CA 90010-3807

NIKOLAI, LOREN ALFRED, accounting educator, author; b. Northfield, Minn., Dec. 14, 1943; s. Roman Peter and Loyola (Gertrude) N.; m. Anita Carol Baker, Jan. 15, 1966; children: Trishia, Jay. BA, St. Cloud State U., 1966, MBA, 1967; PhD, U. Minn., 1973. CPA, Mo. Asst. prof. U. N.C., Chapel Hill, 1973-76; assoc. prof. U. Mo., Columbia, 1976-80, prof., 1980-82, Ernst & Young Disting. prof. Sch. Accountancy, 1982—; Author: Principles of Accounting, 3d edit., 1990, Financial Accounting: Concepts and Uses, 3d edit., 1995, Intermediate Accounting, 6th edit., 1994. Recipient Faculty award of merit Fedn. Schs. of Accountancy, 1989, Disting. Alumni award St. Cloud U., 1990, Coll. of Bus. Faculty Mem. of Year award, 1991, Mo. Outstanding Educator award, 1993; Kemper fellow, U. Mo., 1992. Mem. AICPA, Am. Acctg. Assn., Mo. Soc. CPAs, Fedn. Schs. of Acctg. (pres. 1994). Office: U Mo Sch Accountancy 226 Middlebush Columbia MO 65211

NILES, GEDDES LEROY, private investigator; b. Haines, Alaska, Oct. 31, 1926; s. Geddes William and Gladys Bell (McCormack) N.; m. Aline Terii Tehei, June 17, 1960; children: Diana Mareva Niles-Hansen, Stephen Lloyd Teva. BA, U. Calif., Berkeley, 1949. Investigator and hearing officer U.S. Civil Service Commn., San Francisco, 1955-62, Honolulu, 1962-78; pres. Niles Realty Ltd., Honolulu, 1979—; dir. The Niles Agy., Honolulu, 1983—. Mem. Neighborhood Bd., Kailua, Hawaii, 1979-80. Club: Iaorana Tahiti (Honolulu) (treas. 1985-89). Avocation: mystery writer. Office: 350 Ward Ave Ste 106 Honolulu HI 96814-4004

NILES, JOHN GILBERT, lawyer; b. Dallas, Oct. 5, 1943; s. Paul Dickerman and Nedra Mary (Arendts) N.; m. Marian Higginbotham, Nov. 21, 1970; children: Paul Breckenridge, Matthew Higginbotham. BA in History, Stanford U., 1965; LLB, U. Tex., 1968. Bar: Tex. 1968, Calif. 1969, U.S. Dist. Ct. (cen. dist.) Calif. 1973, U.S. Ct. Appeals (9th cir.) 1973, U.S. Dist. Ct. (so. dist.) Calif. 1977, U.S. Supreme Ct. 1979, U.S. Dist. Ct. (no. dist.) Calif. 1983. Assoc. O'Melveny & Myers, Los Angeles, 1973-77, ptnr., 1978—; judge pro tem mcpl. ct. L.A.; spkr., panel mem. Practicing Law Inst., Calif. CEB. Served to lt. comdr. USNR, 1968-72, Vietnam. Served to lt. comdr. USNR, 1968-72, Viet Nam. Mem. ABA, Los Angeles County Bar Assn., Am. Judicature Soc. Clubs: Bel-Air Bay (Pacific Palisades, Calif.) Calif. (Los Angeles). Avocation: sailing. Home: 1257 Villa Woods Dr Pacific Palisades CA 90272-3953 Office: O'Melveny & Myers 400 S Hope St Los Angeles CA 90071

NILES, NICHOLAS HEMELRIGHT, publisher; b. Carbondale, Pa., Oct. 17, 1938; s. John Southworth and Helen (Hemelright) N.; m. Margaretta Linen Goodbody, Aug. 19, 1961; children—Jennifer Collett, Arthur David. B.S., Columbia U., 1965; M.B.A. Fordham U., 1976. With Time Inc., 1965-75; assoc. pub. New Times mag., N.Y.C., 1975-79, The Runner mag., 1978-79; pub. Changing Times mag., N.Y.C., 1979-88; v.p., pub. Food & Wine mag., N.Y.C., 1988-90; exec. v.p. Sprinhouse (Pa.) Corp., 1990-92; pres., CEO The Sporting News, N.Y.C., 1992—; pres., CEO, pub. Golf Mag. Properties, N.Y.C., 1995—; sr. v.p. Times Mirror Mags., N.Y.C., 1995; bd. dirs. Kiplinger Washington Editors, 1981-88; chmn. bd. Internat. Art of

Jazz, Inc., 1985-89; mem. adv. bd. Cornell U. Alumni Mag., 1981-89; mem. mag. policy com. Times Mirror Mag. Chmn. PTA Hinley Sch., Darien, Conn., 1974-76; bd. dirs., mem. exec. com. Urban League Southwestern Fairfield County, Conn., 1976-82; bd. dirs. Guthrie Clinic Found., Sayre, Pa., 1977, Call for Action, 1984-88, League for Hard of Hearing, Guthrie Research Inst., 1982—; pub. relations com. League for the Hard of Hearing, bd. dirs. 1986—. Served to lt. U.S. Army, 1961-63. Mem. Met. Advt. Golf Assn., Mag. Pub. Assn., Wee Burn Country Club, Union League, Blooming Grove Hunting and Fishing Club, Bohemian Club (San Francisco), Anglers Club, TPC Sawgrass Golf Club. Office: The Sporting News 2 Park Ave New York NY 10016-5603

NILES, THOMAS MICHAEL TOLLIVER, ambassador; b. Lexington, Ky., Sept. 22, 1939; s. John Jacob and Rena (Lipetz) N.; m. Carroll C. Ehringhaus, July 22, 1967; children: John Thomas, Mary Chapman. BA, Harvard U., 1960; MA, U. Ky., 1962. Commd. fgn. service officer Dept. State, Washington, 1961; U.S. ambassador to Can., 1985-1989; then permanent rep. EEC, Brussels; amb. to Greece Athens, 1993—. Recipient Superior Honor award Dept. State, 1982, 85. Mem. Phi Beta Kappa. Office: Psc 108 Box 56 APO AE 09842-5009

NILES, WALTER H., aviation manufacturing company executive, retired; b. N.Y.C., Mar. 9, 1915; s. Issac and Rebecca Niles; m. Rose Reiss, Nov. 10, 1940; children: Richard, Barbara, Russell. BS in Engring., CUNY, 1936, M in Civil Engring., 1938; D Prof. Studies, Pace U., 1970. Lic. prof. engr., Ohio. Assoc. engr. Sperry Gyroscope, Garden City, N.Y., 1938-39; asst. engr. U.S. Engrs., N.Y.C., 1939-40; ptnr. Bruce Kamp Assocs., N.Y.C. and Phila., 1946-48; v.p. engring. Cameraflex Corp., N.Y.C., 1948-51; v.p. Sterling Precision Instruments, N.Y.C., 1953-54; exec. v.p. East Coast Aeronautics, Pelham, N.Y., 1954-56; sr. v.p. Lawrence Aviation Industries, Port Jefferson Sta., N.Y., 1957—; mem. pres.'s coun., tchr. ctr., SUNY, 1986—; pres. Rye Brook (N.Y.) Archtl. Rev. Bd., 1984-93. Lt. col. USAF, 1941-46, World War II, 1951-53, Korea. Decorated Legion of Merit. Mem. Jewish War Vets, Masons, Pres. Club., Retired Officers Assn., Reserve Officers Assn., Jewish War Veterans. Home: 101 Country Ridge Dr Rye Brook NY 10573-1043 Office: Lawrence Aviation Inc Sheep Pasture Rd Port Jefferson Station NY 11776

NILLES, JOHN MATHIAS (JACK NILLES), entrepreneur; b. Evanston, Ill., Aug. 25, 1932; s. Elmer Edward and Hazel Evelyn (Wickum) N.; m. Laila Padorr, July 8, 1957. BA magna cum laude, Lawrence Coll., 1954; MS in Engring., U. Calif., Los Angeles, 1964. Sr. engr. Raytheon Mfg. Co., Santa Barbara, Calif., 1956-58; section head. Ramo-Woodridge Corp., L.A., 1958-59; project engr. Space Technology Lab., L.A., 1960; dir. The Aerospace Corp., L.A., 1961-67; sr. systems engr. TRW Systems, L.A., 1967-69; assoc. group dir. The Aerospace Corp., L.A., 1965-72; dir. interdisciplinary programs U. So. Calif., L.A., 1972-81, dir. info. technology program, 1981-89; pres. JALA Internat. Inc., L.A., 1980—; coord. EC Teleforum, Brussels, 1992—; dir. Telecommuting Adv. Coun., L.A., 1991—, pres., 1993-94; pres. Telecommuting Rsch. Inst., Inc., L.A., 1990—. Author: The Telecommunications Transportation Tradeoff, 1976, Japanese edit., 1977, Exploring the World of the Personal Computer, 1982, French edit., 1985, Micros and Modems, 1983, French edit., 1986, Making Telecommuting Happen, 1994. Capt. USAF, 1954-56. Recipient Rod Rose award Soc. Rsch. Adminstrs., 1976, Environ. Pride award L.A. Mag., 1993, Environ. Achievement award Renew Am., 1994. Mem. IEEE, IEEE Computer Soc., AAAS, Assn. Computing Machinery, Inst. Mgmt. Scis., World Future Soc., Calif. Yacht Club. Avocations: sailing, photography. Office: JALA Internat Inc 971 Stonehill Ln Los Angeles CA 90049-1412

NILLES, JOHN MICHAEL, lawyer; b. Langdon, N.D., Aug. 20, 1930; s. John Joseph and Isabele Mary (O'Neil) N.; m. Barbara Ann Cook, June 22, 1957; children: Trese M., Daniel J., Marcia L., Thomas M., Margaret J. BA cum laude, St. Johns U., 1955; JD cum laude with distinction, U. N.D., 1958. Bar: N.D. 1958, U.S. Dist. Ct. N.D. 1958, U.S. Ct. Appeals (8th cir.) 1958, Minn. 1991. Shareholder, dir., pres. Nilles, Hansen and Davies, Ltd., Fargo, N.D., 1958-90, of counsel, 1990—; exec. v.p., gen. counsel Met. Fin. Corp., Mpls., 1990-95, First Bank F.S.B., Mpls., 1995—; pres., bd. dirs. Legal Aid Soc. N.D., Fargo, 1970-76, Red River Estate Planning Coun., 1980-87; vice-chmn. disciplinary bd. Supreme Ct. N.D., 1984-90. Bd. editors N.D. Law Rev., 1957-58. Exec. bd. Red River Valley coun. Boy Scouts Am., 1959-70; bd. regents Mary Coll., Bismarck, N.D., 1967-77; pres., bd. dirs. Cath. Charities, Fargo, 1959-65, Southeast Mental Health Ctr., Fargo, 1972-80. Staff sgt. USAF, 1951-54. Fellow Am. Coll. Trust and Estate Counsel (state dir. 1979-90); mem. ABA, State Bar Assn. N.D., Minn. Bar Assn., Order of Coif. Republican. Roman Catholic. Avocations: tennis, downhill skiing, cross-country skiing, hunting. Home: 10412 Fawns Way Eden Prairie MN 55347-5117 Office: First Bank Sys 601 2d Ave S Minneapolis MN 55402

NILSON, GEORGE ALBERT, lawyer; b. N.Y.C., Jan. 15, 1942; s. Howard Seth and Beatrice Ethyl (McCurdy) N.; m. Elizabeth Hughes Logan, July 18, 1942; children: Scott Logan, Douglas George. BA, Yale U., 1963, LLB, 1967, M of Urban Studies, 1967. Bar: Md. 1967, U.S. Dist. Ct. Md., U.S. Ct. Appeals (4th cir.), U.S. Supreme Ct. Assoc. Piper & Marbury, Balt., 1967-73, ptnr., 1982—; asst. atty. gen. Md. State Law Dept., Balt., 1973-76, dep. atty. gen., 1976-82; chmn. Gen. Assembly Compensation Commn., Annapolis, Md., 1984-93, Commn. to Rev. Md. Elections Laws, Annapolis 1986-87. Pres. Guilford Assn., Balt., 1990-92. Mem. Rule Day Club, The Wranglers, Sergeants Inn. Democrat. Avocations: fishing, golf. Office: Piper & Marbury 36 S Charles St Baltimore MD 21201-3020

NILSSON, A. KENNETH, investor; b. L.A., Mar. 16, 1933; s. Arthur V. and Esther (Dean) N.; m. Lesley Swanson, Sept., 1965; children: Kerstin, Keith. BA, U. So. Calif., 1955; MA, U. Calif., 1960; grad., U.S. Defense Language Inst., 1956. Founder Koken, Ltd., Tokyo, 1960-63; mng. dir. Pfizer Internat., Tokyo, 1963-66; pres. Pfizer Inc., Manila, The Philippines, 1966-68, Max Factor & Co. Japan Ltd., Tokyo, 1968-72, Cooper Labs Internat., Inc. Geneva and Brussels, 1972-80, Cooper Labs, Inc., N.Y.C. and Palo Alto, Calif., 1980-85, Cooper Lasersonics, Inc., Palo Alto, 1985; now chmn. Eureka Group, Inc. Monterey, Calif., 1985—; chmn. Monterey Inst. Internat. Studies, 1983—. Contbr. articles to profl. jours. Mem. Coun. on Foreign Rels., World Affairs Coun. Served 1st lt. U.S. Army, 1955-58. Fellow Am. Soc. Laser Medicine, Internat. Inst. Stragetic Studies. Avocation: philology.

NILSSON, BIRGIT, soprano; b. Karup, Sweden, May 17, 1918; d. Nils P. and Justina (Paulsson) Svensson; m. Bertil Niklasson, Sept. 10, 1948. Student, Royal Musical Acad., Stockholm; MusD (hon.), Amherst U. Mass., Andover U. Manhattan Sch. Music, 1982, Mich. State U., 1982. Tchr. master classes Manhattan Sch. Music, N.Y.C., 1983—. Appeared opera and concert houses in Europe, N.Am., S.Am., Japan and Australia; most famous roles include: Isolde, Brünnhilde, Turandot, Elektra; now ret. Decorated 1st comdr. Order of Vasa (Sweden); comdr. Order of St. Olav 1st class (Norway); comdr. Arts et Lettres (France); recipient Swedish Golden medal Illis Quorum Cl.18; Austrian and Bavarian Kammersaengerin; named Swedish Royal Court Singer. Hon. mem. Royal Acad. Music London, Royal Acad. Music Stockholm, Vienna State Opera. *

NILSSON, NILS JOHN, computer science educator, researcher; b. Saginaw, Mich., Feb. 6, 1933; s. Walter A. and Pauline (Glerum) N.; m. Karen Braucht, July 19, 1958; children: Kristen, Lars. MS, Stanford U., 1956, PhD, 1958. Sr. scientist SRI, Menlo Park, Calif., 1961-84; chmn. computer sci. dept. Stanford U., Palo Alto, Calif., 1985—; founder Tioga Pub. Co., 1979—; bd. dirs. Morgan Kaufmann Pub. Served to lt. USAF, 1958-61. Avocations: hiking, skiing. Home: 150 Coquito Way Menlo Park CA 94028-7404 Office: Stanford U Dept of Computer Sci Stanford CA 94305

NIMETZ, MATTHEW, lawyer; b. Bklyn., June 17, 1939; s. Joseph L. and Elsie (Botwinik) N.; m. Gloria S. Lorch, June 24, 1975; children: Alexandra Elise, Lloyd. B.A., Williams Coll., 1960, LL.D. (hon.), 1979; B.A. (Rhodes scholar), Balliol Coll., Oxford (Eng.) U., 1962; M.A., Oxford (Eng.) U., 1966; LL.B., Harvard U., 1965. Bar: N.Y. 1966, D.C. 1968. Law clk. to Justice John M. Harlan, U.S. Supreme Ct., 1965-67; staff asst. to Pres. Johnson, 1967-69; asso. firm Simpson Thacher & Bartlett, N.Y.C., 1969-71; partner Simpson Thacher & Bartlett, 1972-77; counselor Dept. of State, Washington, 1977-80; acting coordinator refugee affairs Dept. of State, 1979-

80, under sec. of state for security assistance, sci. and tech., 1980; partner firm Paul, Weiss, Rifkind, Wharton & Garrison, N.Y.C., 1981—; commr. Port Authority N.Y. and N.J., 1975-77; dir. World Resources Inst., chmn., 1982-94; dir. Coun. for U.S. and Italy, Inc.; mem. N.Y. State Adv. Coun. on State Productivity, 1990-92; presdl. envoy Greek-Macedonian Negotiations, 1994—. Trustee Williams Coll., 1981—; chmn. UN Devel. Corp., 1986-94; bd. dirs. Charles H. Revson Found., 1990—. Mem. Assn. of Bar of City of N.Y., Coun. on Fgn. Rels. Club: Harvard (N.Y.C.). Office: Paul Weiss Rifkind Wharton & Garrison 1285 Ave of the Americas New York NY 10019-6028

NIMITZ, CHESTER WILLIAM, JR., manufacturing company executive; b. Bklyn., Feb. 17, 1915; s. Chester William and Catherine V. (Freeman) N.; m. Joan Leona Labern, June 18, 1938; children: Frances Mary, Elizabeth Joan, Sarah Catherine. BS, U.S. Naval Acad., 1936. Commd. ensign USN, 1936, advanced through grades to rear adm., 1957, principally assigned to submarines and destroyers, ret., 1957; with Tex. Instruments Co., 1957-61; with Perkin-Elmer Corp., Norwalk, Conn., 1961—, pres., chief exec. officer, 1965-73, chmn. bd., 1973—, chief exec. officer, 1973-78, chmn. exec. com., 1980-85. Decorated Navy Cross, Silver Star (3). Home: PO Box 1485 Boca Grande FL 33921

NIMKIN, BERNARD WILLIAM, retired lawyer; b. N.Y.C., Apr. 15, 1923; s. Myron Benjamin and Anabel (Davidow) N.; m. Jean Horowitz, Feb. 9, 1947; children—David Andrew, Margaret Lee, Katherine. B.S. cum laude, Harvard U., 1943, LL.B. cum laude, 1949. Bar: N.Y. State bar 1949. Asso. firm Carter, Ledyard & Milburn, N.Y.C., 1949-58; asso. and partner firm Kaye, Scholer, Fierman, Hays & Handler, N.Y.C., 1958-91; lectr. Practising Law Inst., Banking Law Inst.; Mem. Am. Law Inst.; vis. com. U. Miami Law Sch.; mem. adv. bd. Rev. of Securities Regulation. Contbr. articles to profl. jours. Mem. Conservation Commn., Town of Mamaroneck, N.Y., 1970-74; bd. dirs., sec. United Way of Tri-State, 1985-91. Served to 1st lt. U.S. Army, 1943-46. Mem. ABA (mem. fed. regulation of securities com. 1975—, corp. laws com. 1984-92, legal opinions com. 1989—), N.Y. State Bar Assn. (chmn. sect. banking corp. and bus. law 1979-81, ho. of dels. 1981-84, chmn. corp. law com. 1976-79), Assn. Bar City of N.Y. (chmn. uniform state laws com. 1962-65), Tribar Opinion Com. Democrat. Jewish. Home: 116 E 63rd St New York NY 10021-7343 Office: Kaye Scholer Fierman Hays & Handler 425 Park Ave New York NY 10022-3506

NIMMER, RAYMOND T., lawyer, law educator; b. Chgo., May 2, 1944; s. Raymond O. and Helen (Barscz) N. BA in Math., Valparaiso U., 1966, JD with distinction, 1968. Bar: Ill. 1968, Tex. 1984, U.S. Ct. Appeals (5th cir.) 1984, U.S. Supreme Ct. 1985. Rsch. atty. Am. Bar Found., 1968-75; assoc. dean U. Houston Law Sch., 1975-87, Childs prof. Law, 1979—; counsel Sheinfeld, Maley & Kay, Houston, 1985-91, Weil, Gotshal & Manges, Houston, 1991—; vis. prof. law U. Tex., Austin, 1985, U. Mich., Ann Arbor, 1987; mem. adv. com. U.S. State Dept., Washington, 1990—; vice chmn. computer law divsn., sect. sci. and tech. ABA, Chgo., 1991—; reporter UCC Art. 2 rev. com. Nat. Conf. Commrs. on Uniform State Laws, Chgo., 1992—. Author: Commercial Asset-Based Financing, 1989, The Law of Computer Technology, 2d edit., 1993; co-author: Secured Financing in Personal Property, 1992, Bankruptcy and Creditors Rights, 1992. Recipient 5th Nat. award Nathan Burkan Copyright Competition, ASCAP, 1970. Fellow Am. Coll. Comml. Fin. Lawyers; mem. Am. Intellectual Property Law Assn., Am. Law Inst., Licensing Law Execs. Soc., Law and Soc. Assn., Tex. Bar Found. Office: Weil Gotshal & Manges 700 Louisiana Ste 1600 Houston TX 77002

NIMMONS, PHILLIP RISTA, composer, conductor, clarinetist, educator; b. Kamloops, B.C., Can., June 3, 1923; s. George Rista and Hilda Louise (McCrum) N.; m. Noreen Liese Spencer, July 5, 1950; children: Holly Jayne, Carey Jocelyn, Phillip Rista. BA, U. B.C., 1944; scholar, Juilliard Sch. Music, 1945-47, Royal Conservatory Music, U. Toronto, 1948-50. Performances include CBC radio and TV spls., 1948-79, CBC drama, mus. comedy, variety shows and own jazz program, 1953—; appearances include Royal Alexander Theatre, Crest Theatre, Toronto Symphony Orch., Expo 67, 1976 Olympics; composer numerous jazz works including: The Atlantic Suite, 1974, Transformations, 1975, Invocation, 1976, Contemporary Piano Suite/Jazz Band, 1980; commd. works: Duologue, 1985, PS42JS, 1985, L'Images Entre Nous, 1987, all by Ont. Arts Coun., Plateaux, 1986, by Can. Broadcasting Corp., The Torch, 1988, (Winter Olympics, Calgary); commd. works Trumpet Concerto, 1988, Skyscape, 1988, Bach in My Own Back Yard, 1988, Twosome: Concerto for Piano and Vibraphone, 1988, Of Moods and Contrasts: A Sound Poem, 1994, Riverscape, 1994; rec. artist; co-founder Advanced Sch. Contemporary Music, 1960, dir., 1961-66; on tour of Can. bases with CBC, 1965-72; tour of Atlantic Provinces, 1974, 77; dir. jazz program, prof. U. Toronto, 1970-80, adj. prof., 1980—, dir. emeritus Jazz Faculty, 1991; prof., dir. jazz program U. N.B., summers 1967—, Banff Sch. Fine Arts, 1972, U. Western Ont., 1968—; leader Nimmon 'n Nine Plus Six jazz ensemble, 1953—; pres. Nimmons 'N Music, Ltd., 1975—; lectr. schs., colls. and community groups; dir. Can. Stage Band Festival, 1981—; adjudicator numerous festivals. Mem. adv. bd. Number Coll., Banff Sch. Fine Arts; trustee, then chmn. York Edn. Clinic, 1968-74; mem. parents adv. bd. Thornhills Secondary Sch., 1967-72; bd. dirs. Toronto Arts Award; artistic dir. Courtenay Youth Music Camp, B.C., 1985—, Jazz Camp, Manitouwabing, Ont., Can., 1986—. Recipient cert. for music contbn. to Expo '67 Govt. Can., 1967, Cert. of Honour BMI, Can., 1968, Cert. Recognition City of Fredericton, N.B., 1976, Juno award Can. Soc. Rec. Arts and Scis., 1976, Toronto Arts award for excellence, 1986, Best Jazz Clarinetist award Can. Jazz Report, 1994; named officer of Order of Can., 1994, Order of Ont., 1994. Mem. Can. Fedn. Musicians, Performance Rights Orgn. Can. (award 1980), Can. League Composers (charter), Can. Music Centre, Guild Can. Film Composers (dir. 1981—), Celebrity Club (Toronto), Performing Arts Lodge (adv. bd.). Home and Office: 114 Babcombe Dr, Thornhill, ON Canada L3T 1N1

NIMMONS, RALPH WILSON, JR., federal judge; b. Dallas, Sept. 14, 1938; s. Ralph Wilson and Dorothy (Tucker) N.; m. Doris Penelope Pickels, Jan. 30, 1960; children—Bradley, Paige, Bonnie. BA, U. Fla., 1960, JD, 1963. Bar: Fla. 1963, U.S. Dist. Ct. (mid. dist.) Fla. 1963, U.S. Ct. Appeals (5th cir.) 1969, U.S. Supreme Ct. 1970. Assoc. Ulmer, Murchison, Ashby & Ball, Jacksonville, Fla., 1963-65, ptnr., 1973-77; asst. pub. defender Pub. Defender's Office, Jacksonville, 1969-71; chief asst. gen. counsel City of Jacksonville, Jacksonville, 1969-71; chief asst. gen. counsel City of Jacksonville 1971-73; judge 4th Jud. Cir. Ct., Jacksonville, 1977-83, First Dist. Ct. of Appeal Fla., Tallahassee, 1983-91; judge U.S. Dist. Ct. Mid. Dist. Fla., 1991—; mem. faculty Fla. Jud. Coll., Tallahassee, 1985, 86; mem. Fla. Bar Grievance Com., 1973-76, vice chmn., 1975-76; mem. Fla. Conf. Cir. Judges, 1977-83, mem. exec. com., 1980-83; mem. Met. Criminal Justice Adv. Council, 1977-79; mem. Fla. Gov.'s Task Force on Prison Overcrowding, 1983; mem. Trial Ct. Study Commn., 1987-88. Chmn. lay bd. Riverside Baptist Ch., Jacksonville, 1982; chmn. deacons First Bapt. Ch., Tallahassee, 1988—; trustee Jacksonville Wolfson Children's Hosp., 1973-83. Recipient Carroll award for Outstanding Mem. Fla. Judiciary Jacksonville Jr. C. of C., 1980, Disting. Svc. award Fla. Council on Crime and Delinquency, 1981; named Outstanding Judge in Duval County, Jacksonville Bar Assn. Young Lawyers Sect., 1981. Mem. Phi Alpha Delta (pres. chpt. 1962-63), Am. Inns of Ct. (master of bench), Delta Tau Delta (pres. chpt. 1959-60). Office: 611 N Florida Ave Tampa FL 33602

NIMNI, MARCEL EPHRAIM, biochemistry educator; b. Buenos Aires, Feb. 1, 1931; came to U.S., 1955; s. Sam and Sarah Dora (Freedman) N.; children: Elizabeth, Brian Sam. BS in Pharmacy, U. Buenos Aires, 1954, PhD, 1960; MS, U. So. Calif., 1957. Cert. nutrition specialist. Rsch. fellow U. So. Calif., L.A., 1960-61, asst. prof. biochemistry, 1963-66, assoc. prof., 1966-72, prof., 1972—; dir. biology Don Baxter Labs., Glendale, Calif., 1962; cons. Hancock Labs., Anaheim, Calif., 1970-78, pathobiochemistry study sect. NIH, 1980-85, orthopaedics and biomechanics study sect., 1987-90; dir. biochemistry rsch. Orthopaedic Hosp., L.A., 1990-91; cons. Tillots-Pharma Labs, Basle, Switzerland, 1986—; dir. surg. rsch. Children's Hosp. of L.A., 1991—; adv. bd. Maimonides Univ., Buenos Aires. College: Biochemistry, Biotechnology and Molecular Biology, Vols. 1-V, 1987-91; editor Matrix, 1980—, Connective Tissue Rsch., 1973—, Jour. Orthopaedic Rsch., 1989—; patentee collagen technology, transdermal drug delivery. Research grantee NIH Arthritis Inst., 1966—, NIH Aging Inst., 1982—; recipient

Merit award NIH, 1987. Fellow AAAS, Soc. Biomaterials (Founders award 1986); mem. Am. Inst. Nutrition, Am. Assn. Biochem. and Molecular Biology. Office: Childrens Hosp LA Mailstop # 35 4650 W Sunset Blvd Los Angeles CA 90027-6016

NIMOY, LEONARD, actor, director; b. Boston, Mar. 26, 1931; s. Max and Dora (Spinner) N.; m. Sandi Zober, Feb. 21, 1954 (div.); children: Julie, Adam; m. Susan Bay, 1988. Student (drama scholar), Boston Coll., Pasadena (Calif) Playhouse, Jeff Corey, 1960-63; M.A., Antioch U., Austin, Tex. Operator drama studio San Fernando Valley; tchr. Synanon; owner Adajul Music Pub. Co. Appeared in television including Eleventh Hour, Kraft Theatre, Profiles in Courage, Bonanza, The Twilight Zone, Wagon Train, The Virginian, The Outer Limits, Rawhide, Dr. Kildare, Night Gallery, Columbo, T.J. Hooker, Star Trek: The Next Generation; (series) Star Trek, 1966-69, Mission: Impossible, 1969-71, In Search Of..., 1976-80 (host); (movies) Assault on the Wayne, 1971, Baffled!, 1973, The Alpha Caper, 1973, The Missing Are Deadly, 1975, Seizure: The Story of Kathy Morris, 1979, The Sun Also Rises, 1984, A Woman Called Golda, 1982, Never Forget, 1991 (also co-producer); appeared in movies including: Queen for a Day, 1951, Rhubarb, 1951, Kid Monk Baroni, 1952, The Brain Eaters, 1958, The Balcony, 1963, Catlow, 1971, Invasion of the Body Snatchers, 1978, Star Trek: The Motion Picture, 1979, Star Trek II: The Wrath of Khan, 1982, Transformers: The Movie, 1986 (voice only), Star Trek V: The Final Frontier, 1989, The Pagemaster, 1994 (voice only); (dir., actor) Star Trek III: The Search for Spock, 1984; (dir., co-story, actor) Star Trek IV: The Voyage Home, 1986; (exec. producer, co-story, actor) Star Trek VI: The Undiscovered Country, 1991; (dir.) Three Men and a Baby, 1987, The Good Mother, 1988, Funny About Love, 1990, Holy Matrimony, 1994; appeared on stage in Dr. Faustus, Stalag 17, Streetcar Named Desire, Cat on a Hot Tin Roof, Deathwatch, Monserrat, Irma La Douce, Visit to a Small Planet, Fiddler on a Roof, The Man in the Glass Booth, 6 Rms Riv Vu, Equus, Vincent (dir., writer), Love Letters, others; composed, rec. albums including The New World of Leonard Nimoy; composer other songs; author poetry and photography Will I Think of You; biography I Am Not Spock, 1975, We Are All Children, 1977, Come Be With Me, 1979. Mem. ACLU; mem. sch. com. adv. bd. Parents for Peace Western Los Angeles.; del. Dem. Central Com., 1971, 72. Served with AUS, 1954-56. Office: care The Gersh Agy Inc 222 N Canon Dr Beverly Hills CA 90210-5320*

NIMS, ARTHUR LEE, III, federal judge; b. Oklahoma City, Jan. 3, 1923; s. Arthur Lee and Edwina (Peckham) N.; m. Nancy Chloe Keyes, July 28, 1950; children: Chloe, Lucy. B.A., Williams Coll., 1945; LL.B., U. Ga., 1949; LL.M. in Taxation, NYU, 1954. Bar: Ga. 1949, N.J. 1955. Practice law Macon, Ga., 1949-51; spl. atty. Office Chief Counsel, IRS, N.Y.C. and Washington, 1951-55; assoc. McCarter & English, Newark, 1955-61; ptnr. McCarter & English, 1961-79; judge U.S. Tax Ct., Washington, 1979-88, chief judge, 1988-92. Mem. standing com. Episcopal Diocese of Newark, 1971-75; pres. Colonial Symphony Soc., Madison, N.J., 1975-78. Served to lt. (j.g.) USNR, 1943-46. Recipient Kellogg award Williams Coll., 1990, Career Achievement award The Tax Soc. NYU, 1990. Fellow Am. Coll. Tax Counsel; mem. ABA (sec. sect. taxation 1977-79), N.J. Bar Assn. (chmm. sect. taxation 1969-71, Am. Law Inst., J. Edgar Murdock Am. Inn of Ct. (pres. 1988-92). Office: US Tax Ct 400 2nd St NW Washington DC 20217-0002

NIMS, JOHN FREDERICK, writer, educator; b. Muskegon, Mich., Nov. 20, 1913; s. Frank McReynolds and Anne (McDonald) N.; m. Bonnie Larkin, Sept. 11, 1947; children—John (dec.), Frank, George (dec.), Sarah Hoyt, Emily Anne. A.B., U. Notre Dame, 1937, M.A., 1939; Ph.D., U. Chgo., 1945. Mem. faculty U. Notre Dame, 1939-45, 46-52, 54-58, U. Toronto, 1945-46, Bocconi U., Milan, Italy, 1952-53, U. Florence, Italy, 1953-54, U. Madrid, 1958-60, Harvard U., 1964, 68-69, summer 1974, U. Ill.-Urbana, 1961-65, U. Ill., at Chgo., 1965-85, Bread Loaf Writers Conf., 1958-71, Bread Loaf Sch. English, 1965-69, U. Fla., fall 1972, 73-77; Margaret Scott Bundy prof. lit. Williams Coll., fall 1975; prof. lit. Coll. of Charleston, spring 1987; mem. editorial bd. Poetry mag., 1945-48, vis. editor, 1960-61, editor, 1978-84; Phi Beta Kappa poet Harvard U., 1978; Cockefair chair U. Mo., Kansas City, spring 1986; Kilby cons. in poetry Wheaton (Ill.) Coll., fall 1988. Author: The Iron Pastoral, 1947, A Fountain in Kentucky, 1950, The Poems of St. John of the Cross, 1959, rev., 1979, Knowledge of the Evening, 1960, Of Flesh and Bone, 1967, Sappho to Valéry: Poems in Translation, 1971, rev. edit., 1990, Western Wind, 1974, rev. edit., 1992, The Kiss: A Jambalaya, 1982, Selected Poems, 1982, A Local Habitation; Essays on Poetry, 1985, The Six Cornered Snowflake, 1990, Zany in Denim, 1990; contbr.: Five Young American Poets, 1944, The Complete Greek Tragedies, 1959; also anthologies, mags.; editor: Ovid's Metamorphoses, 1965, (James Shirley) Love's Cruelty, 1980, Harper Anthology of Poetry, 1981; assoc. editor: The Poem Itself, 1960; editorial adviser, Princeton U. Press, 1975-82. Recipient Harriet Monroe Meml. award Poetry mag., 1942, Guarantors prize, 1943, Levinson prize, 1944, Disting. fellowship Acad. Am. Poets, 1982; Fulbright grantee, 1952, 53; Smith Mundt grantee, 1958, 59; Nat. Found. Arts and Humanities grantee, 1967-68; award for creative writing Am. Acad. Arts and Letters, 1968, Aiken Taylor award, 1991, Melville Cane award 1992, Hardison Poetry prize, 1993; Creative Arts citation in Poetry Brandeis U., 1974; fellow Inst. Humanities U. Ill., 1983-84; Guggenheim fellow, 1986-87. Democrat. Roman Catholic. Address: 3920 Lake Shore Dr Chicago IL 60613

NIMS, MICHAEL A., lawyer; b. Manhattan, Kans., Oct. 18, 1946. AB, Murray State U., 1968; JD, U. Mich., 1971. Bar: Ohio 1971. Ptnr. Jones, Day, Reavis & Pogue, Cleve. Office: Jones Day Reavis & Pogue North Point 901 Lakeside Ave E Cleveland OH 44114-1190

NING, TAK HUNG, physicist, microelectronic technologist; b. Canton, China, Nov. 14, 1943; came to U.S., 1964; s. Hong and Kwai-Chan (Lee) N.; m. Yin Ngao Fan; children: Adrienne, Brenda. BA in Physics, Reed Coll., 1967; MS in Physics, U. Ill., 1968, PhD in Physics, 1971. IBM Rsch. Div., Yorktown Heights, N.Y., 1973-78, Mgr. bipolar devices and cirs., 1978-82, mgr. Advanced Silicon Technology Lab., 1982-83, mgr. silicon devices and technology, 1983-90; mgr. VLSI design and tech. IBM Rsch. Div., 1990-91; IBM fellow, 1991—. Patentee in field. Fellow IEEE (assoc. editor Trans. on Electron Devices 1988-90, J.J. Ebers award 1989, Jack A. Morton award 1991); mem. Nat. Acad. Engring. Home: 3085 Weston Ln Yorktown Heights NY 10598-1962 Office: IBM T J Watson Research Ct Yorktown Heights NY 10598

NING, XUE-HAN (HSUEH-HAN NING), physiologist, researcher; b. Peng-Lai, Shandong, People's Republic of China, Apr. 15, 1936; came to U.S., 1984; s. Yi-Xing and Liu Ning; m. Jian-Xin Fan, May 28, 1967; 1 child, Di Fan. MD, Shanghai 1st Med. Coll., People's Republic of China, 1960. Rsch. investigator Shanghai Inst. Physiology, 1960-72, leader cardiovasc. rsch. group, 1973-83, head, assoc. prof. cardiovasc. rsch. unit, 1984-87, prof. and chair hypoxia dept., 1988-90, vice chairperson academic com., 1988-90; NIH internat. rsch. fellow U. Mich., Ann Arbor, 1984-87, vis. prof. dept. physiology, agl. prof. dept. surgery, 1991-95; prof. and dir. Hypoxia Physiology Lab. Academia Sinica, Shanghai, 1989—; acting leader High Alt. Physiology Group, Chinese mountaineering and sci. expdn. team to Mt. Everest, 1975, Dept. Metall. Industry of China and Ry. Engring. Corps, 1979; vis. prof. dept. physiology Mich. State U., East Lansing, 1988-90; vis. prof. dept. pediatrics U. Wash., Seattle, 1994—. Author: High Altitude Physiology and Medicine, 1981, Environment and Ecology of Qinghai-Xizong (Tibet) Plateau, 1982; mem. editorial bd. Chinese Jour. Applied Physiology, 1984—, Acta Physiologica, 1988—; contbr. articles to profl. jours. Recipient Merit award Shanghai Sci. Congress, 1977, All-China Sci. Congress, Beijing, 1978, Super Class award Academia Sinica, Beijing, 1986, 1st Class award Nat. Natural Scis., Beijing, 1987. Mem. Am. Physiol. Soc., Internat. Soc. Heart Rsch., Royal Soc. Medicine, Shanghai Assn. Physiol., Chinese Assn. Physiol. (bd. dirs., 1988—, com. applied physiology 1984—, com. blood, cardiovascular, respiratory and renal physiology 1988—), Chinese Soc. Medicine, Chinese Soc. Biomed. Engring. Achievements include research in predictive evaluation of mountaineering performance, paradox phenomenon of cardiac pump function injury after climbing or giving oxygen, blood flow-metabolism-function relationship of heart during hypoxia and ischemia, effect of medicinal herbs on cardiac performance, cardiovascular adaptation and tolerance to hypoxia and ischemia; first electrocardiograph recording at summit of Mt. Everest. Home: 7033 43rd Ave

NE Seattle WA 98115 Office: U Washington Dept Pediatrics RD-20 1959 NE Pacific St Seattle WA 98195

NINOS, NICHOLAS PETER, retired military officer, medical consultant; b. Chgo., May 11, 1936; s. Peter Spiros and Ann (Lesczynsky) N. BA in Art, Bradley U., 1958, BS in Chemistry, 1959; MD, U. Ill., Chgo., 1963. Diplomate Am. Bd. Internal Med., Am. Bd. Cardiology, Am. Bd. Critical Care Medicne. Intern Cook County Hosp., Chgo., 1963-64, resident in internal medicine, 1964-67, fellow in cardiology, 1967-68; commd. capt. U.S. Army, 1968, advanced through grades to col., 1979; chief dept. medicine U.S. Army Community Hosp. U.S. Army, Bremerhaven, Fed. Republic Germany, 1968-69, Wurzberg, Fed. Republic Germany, 1969-72; chief critical care Letterman Army Med. Ctr., San Francisco, 1976-91; dep. comdr. San Francisco med. command Letterman Army Med. Ctr./Naval Hosp. of Oakland, San Francisco and Oakland Calif., 1988-90; ret., 1991; assoc. prof. medicine and surgery Uniformed Svcs., U. Health Scis., Bethesda, Md., 1981—; critical care medicine cons. to U.S. Army Surgeon Gen., 1981-91; lectr. in field. Author (jour.): Ethics, 1988; co-editor: Nutrition, 1988, Problems in Critical Care, Nutrition Support; mem. editorial bd. Jour. Critical Care Medicine, 1988-91; illustrator: Medical Decision Making, 1988. 2d v.p. Twin Springs Condominium Homeowners Assn., Palm Springs, Calif., 1993-94, sec., 1994—; ch. bd. councilman St. George Orthodox Ch. of the Desert, Palm Desert, Calif., 1993—; active Palm Springs Comm., 1993—. Decorated Legion of Merit, Meritorious Svc. medal with oak leaf cluster. Fellow Am. Coll. Critical care Medicine; mem. AMA, Soc. Critical Care Medicine (pres. uniformed svcs. sect. 1987-90, Shubin/Weil award 1988), Am. Coll. Critical Care Medicine (bd. regents 1989-94, chmn. 1989-91), Soc. Med. Cons. to Armed Forces (assoc.), Inst. Critical Care Medicine (exec. v.p. 1991-92), Toastmasters Internat. (sec.-treas. Palm Springs chpt. 1993-94, pres. 1994, area gov. 1994—). Avocations: art, skiing, jogging, traveling, music.

NINTEMANN, TERRI, legislative staff member; b. Rochester, Minn., Mar. 16, 1963; d. John F. and Janice A. (Blair) Nintemann; m. Vincent J. Kiernan, Aug. 27, 1994. BS, U. Minn., 1985. Legis. asst. Farm Credit Svcs., St. Paul, Minn., 1986; intern, receptionist U.S. Senator Rudy Boschwitz, Washington, 1985, legis. corr., 1986-87, legis. asst., 1987-91; legis. dir. U.S. Rep. Dave Camp, Washington, 1991-92; profl. staff mem. Senate Agrl. Com., U.S. Senate, Washington, 1992—. Mem. U. Minn. Alumni, FFA Alumni (life mem.), Rep. Women of Capital Hill. Republican. Roman Catholic. Avocations: movies, yoga, volunteer work. Office: Senate Agrl Com 328 A Russell Senate Office Bldg Washington DC 20510

NIRENBERG, LOUIS, mathematician, educator; b. Hamilton, Ont., Can., Feb. 28, 1925; came to U.S., 1945, naturalized, 1954; s. Zuzie and Bina (Katz) N.; m. Susan Blank, Jan. 25, 1948; children: Marc, Lisa. BSc, McGill U., Montreal, 1945, DSc (hon.), 1986; MS, NYU, 1947, PhD, 1949; DSc (hon.), U. Pisa, Italy, 1990, U. Paris Dauphine, 1990. Mem. faculty N.Y. U., 1949—, prof. math., 1957—, dir. Courant Inst., 1970-72; visitor Inst. Advanced Study, 1958; hon. prof. Nankai U., Zhejiang U. Author research articles. Recipient Crafoord prize Royal Swedish Acad., 1982; NRC fellow, 1951-52; Sloan Found. fellow, 1958-60; Guggenheim Found. fellow, 1966-67, 75-76; Fulbright fellow, 1965. Mem. NAS, Am. Acad. Arts and Scis., Am. Math. Soc. (v.p. 1976-78, M. Böcher prize 1959, L. P. Steele prize 1994), Am. Philos. Soc., French Acad. Scis. (fgn. mem.), Accademia dei Lincei (fgn. mem.), Istituto Lombardo, Accad. de Scienze e Lettere (fgn. mem.), Ukrainian Acad. Sci. (fgn. mem.). Home: 221 W 82nd St New York NY 10024-5406 Office: Courant Inst 251 Mercer St New York NY 10012-1185

NIRENBERG, MARSHALL WARREN, biochemist; b. N.Y.C., N.Y., Apr. 10, 1927; s. Harry Edward and Minerva (Bykowsky) N.; m. Perola Zaltzman, July 14, 1961. BS in Zoology, U. Fla., 1948, M.S., 1952; Ph.D. in Biochemistry, U. Mich., 1957. Postdoctoral fellow Am. Cancer Soc. at NIH, 1957-59; postdoctoral fellow USPHS at NIH, 1959-60; mem. staff NIH, 1960—; research biochemist, chief lab. biochem. genetics Nat. Heart, Lung and Blood Inst., 1962—; researcher mechanism protein synthesis, genetic code, nucleic acids, regulatory mechanisms in synthesis macromolecules, and neurobiology. Recipient Molecular Biology award Nat. Acad. Scis., 1962, award in biol. scis. Washington Acad. Scis., 1962, medal HEW, 1964, Modern Medicine award, 1963, Harrison Howe award Am. Chem. Soc., 1964, Nat. Medal Sci. Pres. Johnson, 1965, Hildebrand award Am. Chem. Soc., 1966, Research Corp. award, 1966, A.C.P. award, 1967, Gairdner Found. award merit Can., 1967, Prix Charles Leopold Meyer French Acad. Scis., 1967, Franklin medal Franklin Inst., 1968, Albert Lasker Med. Research award, 1968, Priestly award, 1968; co-recipient Louisa Gross Horowitz prize Columbia, 1968, Nobel prize in medicine and physiology, 1968. Fellow AAAS, N.Y. Acad. Scis.; mem. Am. Soc. Biol. Chemists, Am. Chem. Soc. (Paul Lewis award enzyme chemistry 1964), Am. Acad. Arts and Scis., Biophys. Soc., Nat. Acad. Scis., Washington Acad. Scis., Soc. for Study Devel. and Growth, Soc. Devel. Biology, Harvey Soc. (hon.), Leopoldina Deutsche Akademie der Naturforscher, Pontifical Acad. Scis. Office: NIH Lab Biochemical Genetics Bldg 36 Rm 1C06 Bethesda MD 20892*

NISBET, JOANNE, ballet mistress; b. Karachi, Pakistan, July 15, 1931; d. James Maltman Wilson and Victoria (Dickie) Nisbet; m. David Robert Scott, Apr. 15, 1957. Studied with, Lubov Egorova, Paris, 1946-48, Anna Ivanova, London. Mem. corps de ballet Ballet Rambert, London, 1945-46; dancer Palladium Theatre, London, 1949; mem. corps de ballet Sadler's Wells Theatre, London, 1950-55, Festival Ballet, London, 1955-59; mem. corps de ballet Nat. Ballet Can., 1959-61, asst. ballet mistress, 1961-62, ballet mistress, 1962-83, prin. ballet mistress, 1983—. Staged (with David Scott) prodns. The Sleeping Beauty for Vienna State Opera, 1979, Etudes (by Harold Lander) for Am. Ballet Theatre, 1987. Office: Nat Ballet Can, 157 King St E, Toronto, ON Canada M5C 1G9*

NISBET, JOHN STIRLING, electrical engineering educator; b. Darval, Scotland, Dec. 10, 1927; s. Robert George Jackson and Kathleen Agnes (Young) N.; m. J. Valerie Payne, Jan. 10, 1953; children: Robert John, Alexander Stevens. B.S., London U., 1950; M.S., Pa. State U., 1957, Ph.D., 1960. Trainee, engr. Nash & Thompson Ltd., Surbiton, Eng., 1944-51; engr. Decca Radar Ltd., Surbiton, 1951-53, Can. Westinghouse, Hamilton, Ont., 1953-55; research assoc. electric engring. dept. Pa. State U., University Park, 1955-60, prof., 1960—; Disting. Alumni prof. electric engring. Pa. State U., 1985-90, Disting. Alumni prof. elec. engring. emeritus, 1990—, dir. Ionosphere Rsch. Lab., 1971-84, dir. Communications and Space Scis. Lab., 1984-86. Author numerous sci. papers; mem. editorial bd.: Jour. Atmospheric and Terrestrial Physics. NSF sr. postdoctoral fellow Brussels, 1965; Fulbright Hays lectr. Council Internat. Exchange Scholars, USSR, 1979; NRC-Nat. Acad. Sci. fellow Goddard Space Flight Ctr., 1980. Sr. mem. IEEE, Am. Geophys. Union, Sigma Xi, Phi Kappa Phi. Unitarian. Home: 618 Glenn Rd State College PA 16803-3474 Office: Communications & Space Scis Lab 316 Electrical Eng Univ Park PA 16802

NISBET, ROBERT A., historian, sociologist; b. Los Angeles, Sept. 30, 1913; s. Henry S. and Cynthia (Jenifer) N.; m. Emily P. Heron (div.); children: Martha Rehrman, Constance Field; m. Caroline Burks Kirkpatrick; 1 child, Ann Nash. AB, U. Calif., Berkeley, 1936, MA, 1937, PhD, 1939, Berkeley citation, 1970; LHD (hon.), Hofstra U., 1974. Instr. social instns. U. Calif. at Berkeley, 1939-43; asst. dean U. Calif. at Berkeley (Coll. Letters and Sci.), 1942-43, 46, asst. prof. social instns., 1943-48, asso. prof. sociology, 1948-52; prof. sociology U. Calif., Riverside, 1953-72; vice chancellor U. Calif., 1960-63; dean U. Calif. (Coll. Letters and Sci.), 1953-63; vis. prof. Columbia U., 1949, Albert Schweitzer prof. humanities, 1974-78, emeritus, 1978—; resident scholar Am. Enterprise Inst., Washington, 1978-80, adj. scholar, 1980-86; prof. history and sociology U. Ariz., 1972-74; vis. prof. U. Bologna, Italy, 1956-57; Rieker lectr. U. Ariz., 1956; lectr. all univs., Calif., 1961, Guggenheim fellow, 1963-64; Cooper lectr. Swarthmore Coll., 1966; John Dewey lectr. John Dewey Soc., 1970; William A. Neilson research prof. Smith Coll., 1971-72; Blazer lectr. U. Ky., 1971; Phi Beta Kappa Nat. vis. scholar, 1971-72; vis. fellow Princeton U., 1963-64; Johns Hopkins Centennial scholar, 1975-76; W.G. Sumner lectr. Yale U., 1976; Leon lectr. U. Pa., 1982; Benjamin Rush lectr. Am. Psychiat. Assn., 1983; Jefferson lectr. in Humanities NEH, 1988. Author: The Quest for Community, 1953, Human Relations in Administration, 1956, Emile Durkheim, 1965, The Sociological Tradition, 1966, Tradition and Revolt, 1968, Social Change and History, 1969, The Social Bond, 1970, The Degradation of the Academic Dogma,

1971, The Social Philosophers, 1973, rev. edit., 1983, The Sociology of Emile Durkheim, 1974, Twilight of Authority, 1975, Sociology as an Art Form, 1976, History of the Idea of Progress, 1980, Prejudices: A Philosophical Dictionary, 1982, Conservatism: Dream and Reality, 1986, The Making of Modern Society, 1986, The Present Age, 1988, Roosevelt and Stalin, 1989, Teachers and Scholars, 1992; editor: Social Change; co-editor: Contemporary Social Problems, 1961, 66, 71, 1976, History of Sociological Analysis, 1978; bd. editors Am. Jour. Sociology, 1970-74; mem. publ. com. The Public Interest, 1976-84; mem. editorial bd. The American Scholar, 1975-80; contbr. articles to profl. jours. Mem. Nat. Council Humanities, 1975-78; mem. N.Y. Gov.'s Health Adv. Council, 1975-76, Parkman Prize Com., 1978-80; bd. dirs. Am. Council Learned Socs., 1974-79, Council Acad. Advisers, Am. Enterprise Inst., Washington, 1972-86, Rockford Inst., 1978-84. Served with AUS, 1943-45, PTO. Decorated cavaliere ufficiale Order of Merit Italy; recipient Ingersoll award in humanities, 1985; Rockefeller Found. grantee, 1975-78. Fellow Am. Acad. Arts and Scis. (councillor 1977-80), Am. Philos. Soc. (councillor 1977-80, Penrose Meml. lectr. 1982), Soc. Am. Historians; mem. Société Européene de Culture, Columbia Soc. Fellows, Institut Internationale de Sociologie, Phi Beta Kappa. Address: 2828 Wisconsin Ave NW Apt 102 Washington DC 20007-4713

NISBETT, RICHARD EUGENE, psychology educator; b. Littlefield, Tex., June 1, 1941; s. R. Wayne and Helen (King) N.; m. Susan Ellen Isaacs, June 29, 1969; children: Matthew, Sarah. A.B. summa cum laude, Tufts U., 1962; Ph.D., Columbia U., 1966. Asst. prof. psychology Yale U., New Haven, 1966-71; assoc. prof. psychology U. Mich., Ann Arbor, 1971-77, prof., 1977—; Theodore M. Newcomb prof. psychology, 1989-92, Theodore M. Newcomb disting. univ. prof. of social scis., 1992—. Author: (with others) Attribution: Perceiving the Causes of Behavior, 1972, Induction: Processes of Inference, Learning, and Discovery, 1986, Rules for Reasoning, 1992, (with L. Ross) Human Inference: Strategies and Shortcomings of Social Judgment, 1980, The Person and the Situation, 1991; editor: (with others) Social Psychology: Explorations in Understanding, 1974—. Recipient Donald T. Campbell award for disting. rsch. in social psychology APA, 1982, Disting. Sci. Contbn. award APA, 1991, Disting. Sr. Scientist award Soc. Exptl. Social Psychology; fellow Ctr. for Advanced Studies in Behavioral Scis. Office: U Mich 5261 ISR Rsch Ctr Group Dynamics Ann Arbor MI 48109

NISENHOLTZ, MARTIN ABRAM, telecommunications executive, educator; b. Phila., Apr. 1, 1955; s. Louis William and Rhoda Greta (Koenig) N.; m. Anne Ermine Stockler, July 26, 1987; children: Johanna, Marjorie. BA, U. Pa., 1977, MA, 1979. Research scientist NYU, N.Y.C., 1979-83; mgr. Ogilvy & Mather, N.Y.C., 1983-84, v.p., 1984-89, sr. v.p., 1989-94; dir. content strategy Ameritech Corp., Chgo., 1994—; mem. oper. com. Ogilvy & Mather Direct, 1992-94; adj. assoc. prof. NYU, 1983—; dir. Worldview Corp., 1994—. Grantee Nat. Endowment Arts, 1981. Mem. Interactive Svcs. Assn. (dir. 1985-94, chmn. 1991, Disting. Svc. award 1994). Office: Ameritech Corp 30 S Wacker Dr Chicago IL 60606

NISHIDA, ATSUTOSHI, computer company executive. Pres. Toshiba Am. Info. Systems Inc., Irvine, Calif., 1975—. Office: Toshiba Amer Info Systems Inc 9740 Irvine Blvd Irvine CA 92718-1608

NISHIMURA, JOSEPH YO, retired retail executive, accountant; b. Berkeley, Calif., Nov. 4, 1933; s. Masamoto and Kimiko (Ishihara) N.; m. Joyce Toshiye Mori, Sept. 1, 1956; children: Brenda Joyce, Stephen Lloyd. AB cum laude, Princeton U., 1956; MBA, Stanford U., 1961. CPA, Calif., N.Y.; cert. Employee Benefit Specialist. Audit supr. Touche Ross & Co., San Francisco, 1961-66; contr. Scott Co. of Calif., Oakland, 1966-67, Purity Stores, Inc., Burlingame, Calif., 1967-69; pres. Cubit Systems Corp., Burlingame, 1969-72; sr. v.p. Golden West Fin. Corp., Oakland, 1972-73; exec. v.p. Victory Markets, Inc., Norwich, N.Y., 1973-90, dir., 1976-90; dir. Carl's Drug Co., Rome, N.Y., 1988-90; gen. ptnr. Mori Enterprises, 1994—. V.p., bd. dirs. Chenango Meml. Hosp., Norwich, 1981-87; bd. dirs. United Fund, Norwich, 1984-90, N.Y. State Food Mchts. Assn., 1988-90, Binghamton (N.Y.) Symphony Orch, 1988—, treas., 1990-93; gen. ptnr. Mori Enterprises, 1994—. Served to lt. (j.g.) USN, 1956-59; Japan. Mem. AICPA, N.Y. State Soc. CPA's, Calif. Soc. CPAs. Democrat. Presbyterian. Club: Princeton (N.Y.C.).

NISHIMURA, PETE HIDEO, oral surgeon; b. Hilo, Hawaii, Aug. 7, 1922; s. Hideichi and Satsuki N.; m. Tomoe Nishimura, June, 1949; children—Dennis Dean, Grant Neil, Dawn Naomi. Student, U. Hawaii, 1940-44; D.D.S., U. Mo.; 1947; M.S.D., Northwestern U., 1949. Practice dentistry specializing in oral surgery Honolulu, 1952—; pres. Oral Surgery Group, 1978—; mem. coun. Nat. Bd. Dental Examination; dir. Hawaii Dental Svc., 1962-85, pres., 1970-72, 76-78; pres. State Bd. Dental Examiners, Delta Sigma Delta, Fedn. Dentaire Internat. Served with U.S. Army, 1952-54. Fellow Am. Coll. Dentists, Internat. Coll. Dentists; mem. Hawaii Dental Assn. (past pres.), Delta Dental Plans Assn. (dir.), Honolulu County Dental Soc., ADA, Hawaii Soc. Oral Surgeons, Am. Assn. Oral and Maxillofacial Surgeons, Western Soc. Oral and Maxillofacial Surgeons, Am. Assn. Dental Examiners, Pierre Fauchard Acad. Democrat. Home: 494 Halemaumau St Honolulu HI 96821-2135 Office: 848 S Beretania St Honolulu HI 96813-2551

NISHITANI, MARTHA, dancer; b. Seattle, Feb. 27, 1920; d. Denjiro and Jin (Aoto) N. B.A. in Comparative Arts, U. Wash., 1958; studied with, Eleanor King, Mary Ann Wells, Perry Mansfield, Cornish Sch., Conn. Coll. Sch. Dance, Long Beach State U. Founder, dir. Martha Nishitani Modern Dance Sch. and Co., Seattle, 1950—; dance dir. Helen Bush Sch. and Central YWCA, 1951-54; choreographer U. Wash. Opera Theater, 1955-65, Intiman Theater, 1972—; dance instr. Elementary and Secondary Edn. Act Program, 1966; dance specialist spl. edn. program Shoreline Pub. Schs., 1970-72; condr. workshops and concerts King County Youth Correctional Instns., 1972-73; Dance adv. counsel Wash. Cultural Enrichment Program; dance adv. bd. Seattle Parks and Recreation. Dancer Eleanor King Co., Seattle, 1946-50, dance films, 1946-51, Channel 9, Ednl. TV, 1967-68; lectr. demonstrator numerous colls., festivals, convs., childrens theater.; author articles on dance; one of the subjects: A Celebration of 100 Years of Dance in Washington, 1989. Trustee Allied Arts Seattle, 1967. Recipient Theta Sigma Phi Matrix Table award, 1968, Asian Am. Living Treasure award Northwest Asian Am. Theater, 1984; listed Dance Archives, N.Y.C. Libr., 1991, N.Y.C. Lincoln Ctr. Dance Archives, 1991, U. Wash. Libr. Archives, 1993, exhibit of Japanese Am. Women of Achievement, Burke Mus., 1994, 40th Anniversary of Martha Nishitani Modern Dance Sch. Mem. Am. Dance Guild (exec. com. 1961-63), Com. Research in Dance, Seattle Art Mus., Internat. Dance Alliance (adv. council 1984), Smithsonian Assos., Progressive Animal Welfare Soc. Address: 4205 University Way NE PO Box 45264 Seattle WA 98145-0264 Until a few years ago a compelling force within me would let nothing interfere with performing, teaching, and directing dance. My belief: "I must be selfish about that which means most to me." This dedication was in constant battle with loneliness, frugality and neglect of loved ones. My first solo dance was Credo in Conflict. I have earned a degree of success, satisfaction, joy and recognition. My thoughts are now that I have learned to pursue a balance in life as I battle. The scars of selfishness persist but the broader view brings validity to my beliefs.

NISKANEN, WILLIAM ARTHUR, JR., economist; b. Bend, Oreg., Mar. 13, 1933; s. William Arthur and Nina Elizabeth (McCord) N.; children—Lia, Pamela, Jaime. BA, Harvard U., 1954; MA, U. Chgo., 1955, PhD, 1962. Staff economist RAND Corp., Santa Monica, Calif., 1957-62; staff dir. Dept. Def., Washington, 1962-64; div. dir. Inst. Def. Analyses, Washington, 1964-70; asst. dir. Office of Mgmt. and Budget, Washington, 1970-72; prof. U. Calif., Berkeley, 1972-75; chief economist Ford Motor Co., Dearborn, Mich., 1975-80; prof. UCLA, 1980-81; mem. Coun. Econ. Advisers, Washington, 1981-85; chmn. CATO Inst., Washington, 1985—. Author: Bureaucracy and Representative Government, 1971, Reaganomics, 1988; editor Regulation mag., 1990—. Founder Nat. Tax Limitation Com. Mem. Am. Econ. Assn., Pub. Choice Soc., Atlantic Econ. Assn. (former pres.). Republican. Office: Cato Inst 1000 Massachusetts Ave NW Washington DC 20001-5400

NISONOFF, ALFRED, biochemist, educator; b. N.Y.C., Jan. 26, 1923; s. Hyman and Lillian (Klein) N.; m. Sarah Weinraub, July 17, 1946; children: Donald Michael, Linda Ann. B.S. (State scholar), Rutgers U., 1942; M.A., Johns Hopkins U., 1948, Ph.D. (AEC fellow), 1951. Postdoctoral fellow

Johns Hopkins Med. Sch., 1951-52; research chemist U.S. Rubber Co., Naugatuck, Conn., 1952-54; sr. cancer research scientist Roswell Park Meml. Inst., Buffalo, 1954-57; assoc. cancer research scientist Roswell Park Meml. Inst., 1957-60; assoc. prof. microbiology U. Ill., Urbana, 1960-62; prof. U. Ill., 1962-66; prof. microbiology U. Ill. Coll. Medicine, Chgo., 1966-69; head dept. biol. chemistry U. Ill. Coll. Medicine, 1969-75; prof. biology Rosenstiel Research Center, Brandeis U., Waltham, Mass., 1975-93, prof. emeritus, 1993—; Mem. grant rev. bd. allergy and immunology study sect. NIH, 1965-67, 71-74, chmn., 1984-87; grant rev. bd. Nat. Multiple Sclerosis Soc., 1972-75, 77-80. Author: The Antibody Molecule, 1975, Introduction to Molecular Immunology, 1982; Editorial bd.: Jour. Immunology, 1962-67, 69-74, sect. editor, 1971-74, sr. editor, 1975-79; editorial bd.: Immunochemistry, 1964-70, Bacteriological Revs, 1968-70, Jour. Exptl. Medicine, 1974-78, Critical Reviews in Immunology, 1980—, European Jour. Epidemiology, 1986—; contbr. articles to profl. jours. Served to lt. (j.g.) USNR, 1943-46. Recipient Research Career award NIH, 1962-69; Pasteur Inst. medal, 1970. Fellow Am. Acad. Arts and Scis.; mem. NAS, Am. Assn. Immunologists (coun. 1985-92, pres. 1990-91), Belgian Royal Acad. Medicine (fgn. corr.), Phi Beta Kappa, Phi Lambda Upsilon. Home: 116 Florence St Apt I Chestnut Hill MA 02167-1938 Office: Brandeis Univ Rosenstiel Rsch Ctr Dept Biology Waltham MA 02254

NISONSON, IAN, urologist; b. Montreal, Que., Can., Jan. 10, 1937; came to U.S., 1947; s. Nathan and Rebecca (Etzkovich) N.; m. Myrna J. Goodman, Apr. 9, 1960; children: Evan J., Andrea B., Lauren R., Ronald S. BA, Columbia U., 1958, MD, 1962. Diplomate Am. Bd. Urology. Intern Strong Meml. Hosp.U. Rochester, 1962-64; resident Squire Urological Clinic Presbyn. Hosp. Columbia U., N.Y.C., 1966-70; NIH Fellow infectious diseases, 1967-68; pvt. practice, Miami, Fla., 1970—; chief surgery Bapt. Hosp., Miami, 1986-87. Editor-in-chief Miami Medicine, 1987-90. Capt. M.C., USAF, 1964-66. Fellow ACS (pres. Greater Miami chpt. 1979-80, bd. govs. Fla. 1990-93), Greater Miami Urol. Soc. (pres. 1986). Home: 7400 N Kendall Dr Miami FL 33156-7706 Office: South Fla Urology Assocs 7800 SW 87th Ave Miami FL 33173-3570

NISSEL, MARTIN, radiologist, consultant; b. N.Y.C., July 29, 1921; s. Samuel David and Etta Rebecca (Ostrie) N.; m. Beatrice Goldberg, Dec. 26, 1943; children: Philippa Lyn, Jeremy Michael. BA, NYU, 1941; MD, N.Y. Med. Coll., 1944. Diplomate Am. Bd. Radiology. Intern Met. Hosp., N.Y.C., 1944-45, Lincoln Hosp., N.Y.C., 1947-48; resident in radiology Bronx Hosp., 1948-50, attending radiologist, 1952-54; resident in radiotheraphy Montefiore Hosp., Bronx, 1950-51, attending radiotherapist, 1954-65; attending radiologist Buffalo (N.Y.) VA Hosp., 1951-52; attending radiotherapist Univ. Hosp. Boston City Hosp., 1965-69; asst. prof. radiology Boston U. Sch. of Medicine, 1965-69; chief radiotherapist,dir. radiation ctr. Brookside Hosp., San Pablo, Calif., 1969-77; group leader, radiopharm. drugs FDA, Rockville, Md., 1977-86; pvt. cons. radiopharm. drug devel., 1986—. Contbr. articles to profl. jours. Lectr. Am. Cancer Soc., Contra Costa County, Calif., 1973-76. Capt. MC AUS, 1945-47, Korea. Recipient Contra Costa County Speakers Bur. award Am. Cancer Soc., 1973, 76, Responsible Person for Radiol. Health Program for Radiopharm. Drugs award FDA, 1980-86. Mem. Am. Coll. Radiology, Radiol. Soc. N.Am. Avocations: photography, model train building, travel. Office: PO Box 5537 Eugene OR 97405-0537

NISSEN, CARL ANDREW, JR., minister, retired procurement analyst; b. Manhattan, Kans., June 26, 1930; s. Carl Andrew and Bernice Lydia (Varney) N. Student, Denison U., 1948-49; BA, Ohio State U., 1960; postgrad., Grad. Sch. Theology, Oberlin, Ohio, 1959, Berkeley Bapt. Divinity Sch., 1960-61. Ordained to ministry Ohio Bapt. Conv. Supply pastor Ohio Bapt. Conv., various, 1958-61, 82-85; pastor Sinking Creek Bapt. Ch., Springfield, Ohio, 1985-90; chaplain gen. SAR, Louisville, 1989-90; ret., 1990; procurement analyst Def. Electronics Supply Ctr., Dayton, Ohio, 1963-90, ret., 1990. Sgt. U.S. Army, 1950-53, Korea; lt. col. Ohio Mil. Res., 1984-91. Recipient George Washington Honor medal Freedom's Found., 1972, Minute Man medal SAR, 1991. Home: 1001 Fordham Dr Ruskin FL 33573-5236 *Faith in the presence of Almighty God in our lives makes the challenges we face opportunities for change.*

NISSEN, WILLIAM JOHN, lawyer; b. Chgo., July 28, 1947; s. William Gordon Jr. and Ruth Carolyn (Banas) N.; m. Patricia Jane Press, Jan. 16, 1971; children: Meredith Warner, Edward William. BA, Northwestern U., 1969; JD magna cum laude, Harvard U., 1976. Bar: Ill. 1976, U.S. Dist. Ct. (no. dist.) Ill. 1976, U.S. Ct. Appeals (7th cir.) 1981. Assoc. Sidley & Austin, Chgo., 1976-83, ptnr., 1983—; gen. counsel Heinold Commodities, Inc., Chgo., 1982-84. Editor Harvard U. Internat. Law Jour., 1974-76. Served to lt. USN, 1969-73. Mem. ABA (co-chmn. futures regulation subcom. on internat. futures matters 1985—), Chgo. Bar Assn. (chmn. futures regulation com. 1985-86), Am. Legion (comdr. union league post 758 1994-95), Union League Club Chgo. Home: 348 Foss Ct Lake Bluff IL 60044-2753 Office: Sidley & Austin 1 First National Plz Chicago IL 60603

NISSINEN, MIKKO PEKKA, dancer; b. Helsinki, Finland, Mar. 4, 1962; came to U.S., 1987; s. Pekka and Pirkko (Pukkinen) N. Grad., Finnish Nat. Ballet Sch., 1977; postgrad., Leningrad Acad. Ballet Sch., 1979-80. Mem. corps de ballet Finnish Nat. Ballet, Helsinki, 1977-79, soloist, 1980-82; grand sujete Dutch Nat. Ballet, Amsterdam, The Netherlands, 1982-84; soloist Basel (Switzerland) Ballet, 1984-87; soloist San Francisco Ballet, 1987-88, prin. dancer, 1988—; guest artist La Bayadere, Nat. Ballet Can., 1989, Oberlin Dance Collective, 1993; advisor to sch. dir. Nat. Ballet Sch., Toronto, Ont., Can., 1992; bd. dirs. Le Don Des Etoiles, 1989—; guest tchr. Royal Acad. of Dancing, 1993, Kennedy Ctr. Ballet. Program, 1994, Nat. Ballet Sch., Toronto, 1994; lectr. on dance history and state of dance today Standord U., St. Mary's Coll., Christensen Soc. Repertoire includes (with San Francisco Ballet) The Sleeping Beauty, Swan Lake, Bizet Pas de Deux, Handel-a-Celebration, Haffner Symphony, Con Brio, Ballet d'Isoline, Giuliani: Variations on a Theme, Tchaikovsky Pas de Deux, Symphony in C, Theme and Variations, Ballo della Regina, The Nutcracker, Airs de Ballet, Variations de Ballet, Rodin, Rodeo, Maelstrom, Dark Elegies, Harvest Moon, Napoli, Job, The Wanderer Fantasy, In the middle, somewhat elevated, Calcium Light Night, Le Corsaire Pas de Deux, Dreams of Harmony, Pulcinella, The Dream; (with other cos.) Don Quixote, Giselle, A Midsummer Night's Dream, Les Biches, Sleeping Beauty, Pyrrich Dances, Masse, Le Tombeau de Couperin, Symphony in C, The Four Temperaments, The Prodigal Son, Rodin, Pierrot Lunaire, La Fille mal gardée, Swan Lake, Henze, Five Tangos, In and Out, Bits and Pieces, Jeu de Cartes; appeared in the Canadian Internat. Ballet Gala, 1989, 90, 91, 92, 93, 94, Reykjavik Arts Festival, 1990, Internat. Ballet Gala, Kuodio, Finland, 1992, Internat. Ballet Gala, Vail, Colo., 1993, Night of Stars Ballet Gala, Helsinki, 1993; profiled in nat. and internat. radio and TV programs, including CNN Worldwide Report, 1992; featured on cover of Dance Mag., 1992. Recipient 1st prize 1st Nat. Dance Competition Kuopio, Finland, 1978. •

NISWENDER, GORDON DEAN, physiologist, educator; b. Gillette, Wyo., Apr. 21, 1940; s. Rex Lel and Inez Irene (Dillinger) N.; m. Joy Dean Thayer, June 14, 1964; children: Kevin Dean, Kory Dean. B.S., U. Wyo., 1962; M.S., U. Nebr., 1964; Ph.D., U. Ill., 1967. NIH postdoctoral fellow U. Mich., 1967-68, asst. prof. physiology, 1968-72; mem. faculty Colo. State U., Ft. Collins, 1972—; prof. physiology Colo. State U., 1975—; assoc. dean research Coll. Veterinary Medicine and Biomed. Scis., 1982—; dir. animal reproduction and biotech. lab., 1986—, disting. prof., 1987—; mem. rev. panels NIH; cons. FDA. Recipient Merit award NIH, grantee, 1968—. Mem.Am. Animal Scientists (Outstanding Young Scientist award western sect. 1974, Animal Physiology and Endocrinology award 1983), Soc. Study Reprodn. (treas. 1972-75, pres. 1981-82, rsch. award 1988). Office: Colo State U Animal Reprod & BiotechnologyLab College of Veterinary Medicine Fort Collins CO 80523

NITECKI, JOSEPH ZBIGNIEW, librarian; b. Dabrowa Górnicza, Poland, Jan. 31, 1922; came to U.S., 1951, naturalized, 1956; s. Henryk W. and Antonina S. N.; m. Sophie V. Zboinski, June 17, 1945; children: Zbigniew H., Danuta A. B.A. in Philosophy, Wayne State U., 1955; M.A., Roosevelt U., 1959; M.A. in L.S., U. Chgo., 1963. Various profl. and adminstrv. positions in libraries U. Chgo. 1961-63, Chgo. City Coll., 1963-66, U. Wis., Milw., 1967-70, Temple U., Phila., 1970-78; prof., exec. dir. libraries U. Wis., Oshkosh, 1978-80; dir. libraries SUNY, Albany, 1980-88, prof. Sch. Info Sci.

and Policy, 1988-90, prof. emeritus, 1990—; cons. library issues. Author, editor compiler and reviewer in field; ref. and manuscript reader. Served with Polish Armed Forces under Brit. command, 1939-48. Mem. ALA, Beta Phi Mu. Home: 22 Shetland Dr Delmar NY 12054-3630

NITECKI, ZBIGNIEW HENRY, mathematician, educator; b. Plymouth, UK, May 2, 1946; came to U.S., 1950; s. Joseph Zbigniew and Zofia (Zboinska) N.; m. Alicia Korzeniowska, Mar. 25, 1972; 1 child, Elizabeth Lauren. SB, U. Chgo., 1965; MA, PhD, U. Calif., Berkeley, 1969. Gibbs instr. Yale U., New Haven, 1969-71; asst. prof. CUNY, 1971-72; asst. prof. Tufts U., Medford, Mass., 1972-75, assoc. prof., 1975-80, prof. math., 1980—; program dir. for geometric analysis NSF, Washington, 1982-83. Author: Differentiable Dynamics, 1971; co-author: Differential Equations—A First Course, 1984, Differential Equations with Linear Algebra, 1986; contbr. articles to profl. jours. Mem. Am. Math. Soc., Soc. for Indsl. and Applied Maths. Office: Dept of Mathematics Bromfield-Pearson Bldg Tufts University Medford MA 02155

NITIKMAN, FRANKLIN W., lawyer; b. Davenport, Iowa, Oct. 26, 1940; s. David A. and Janette (Gordon) N.; m. Adrienne C. Drell, Nov. 28, 1972. BA, Northwestern U., 1963; LLB, Yale U., 1966. Bar: Ill. 1966, U.S. Dist. Ct. (no. dist.) Ill. 1967, U.S. Tax Ct. 1972, Fla. 1977, D.C. 1981. Assoc. McDermott, Will & Emery, Chgo., 1966-72, ptnr., 1973—. Co-author: Drafting Wills and Trust Agreements, 1990. Bd. dirs. Owen Coon Found., Glenview, Ill., 1985—, Spertus Inst. Jewish Studies, Chgo., 1991—, Jewish United Fund, Jewish Fedn. Metro. Chgo., 1994—. Fellow Am. Coll. Trust and Estate Coun., Am. Bar Found.; mem. Standard Club, Arts Club (Chgo.). Home: 365 Lakeside Pl Highland Park IL 60035-5371 Office: McDermott Will & Emery 227 W Monroe St Chicago IL 60606-5096

NITSCHE, JOHANNES CARL CHRISTIAN, mathematics educator; b. Olbernhau, Fed. Republic Germany, Jan. 22, 1925; came to U.S., 1956; s. Ludwig Johannes and Irma (Raecke) N.; m. Carmen Dolores Mercado Delgado, July 1, 1959; children: Carmen Irma, Johannes Marcos and Ludwig Carlos (twins). Diplom für Mathematik, U. Göttingen, 1950; PhD, U. Leipzig, 1951; Privatdozent, Tech. U. Berlin, 1955. Asst. U. Göttingen, 1948-50; rsch. mathematician Max Planck Institut für Strömungsforschung Göttingen, 1950-52; asst. Privatdozent Tech. U., Berlin, 1952-56; vis. assoc. prof. U. Cin., 1956-57; assoc. prof. U. Minn., Mpls., 1957-60; prof. math. U. Minn., 1960—, head Sch. Math., 1971-78; vis. prof. U. P.R., 1960-61, U. Hamburg, 1965, Tech. Hochschule Vienna, 1968, U. Bonn, 1971, 75, 77, 80, 81, U. Heidelberg, 1979, 82, 83, U. Munich, 1983, U. Florence, 1983; keynote speaker Festive Colloquium, U. Ulm, 1986; co-organizer workshop statis. thermodynamics and differential geometry U. Minn., 1991; keynote speaker Meml. Colloquium Tech. U. Berlin, 1991, speaker Internat. Workshop on Geometry and Interfaces, Aussois, France, 1990. Author: Vorlesungen uber Minimalflachen, Springer-Verlag, 1975, Lectures on Minimal Surfaces, 1989; editor: Analysis, 1980—; assoc. editor: Contemporary Math., 1980-88, Zeitschrift für Analysis und ihre Anwendungen, 1993—; contbr. articles to profl. jours. Mem. Am. del. joint Soviet-Am. Symposium on Partial Differential Equations, Novosibirsk, 1963, U.S.-Japan Seminar on Differential Geometry, Tokyo, 1977; speaker 750th Berlin Anniversary Colloquium, Free U. Berlin, 1987. Recipient Lester R. Ford award for outstanding expository writing, 1975, George Taylor Disting. Svc. award U. Minn. Found., 1980, Humboldt prize for sr. U.S. scientists Alexander von Humboldt Found., 1981; Fulbright rsch. fellow Stanford, 1955-56. Fellow AAAS; mem. Am. Math. Soc., Circolo Matematico di Palermo, Deutsche Mathematiker-Vereinigung, Edinburgh Math. Soc., Gesellschaft für Angewandte Mathematik und Mechanik, Math. Assn. Am., N.Y. Acad. Scis., Österreichische Mathematische Gesellschaft, Soc. Natural Philosophy. Home: 2765 Dean Pky Minneapolis MN 55416-4382

NITTA, DIANE E., nursing administrator; b. Calif., Oct. 15, 1944; d. Amos C. and Mary E. (Lopes) Kirk; m. Hitoshi A. Nitta, Aug. 21, 1971; children: David, Lisa. Diploma in nursing, Highland Alameda County Hosp., 1966; BA, U. of Redlands, 1974; MA, U. of the Redlands, 1978. Cert. nurse adminstr.-advanced. Staff nurse recovery rm. Lawton (Okla.) Pub. Hosp.; staff nurse labor and delivery newborn nursery 30th Field Hosp., Augsberg, Fed. Republic Germany; staff nurse to charge nurse acute med. and intensive care Orange County Med. Ctr., Orange, Calif., head nurse hemodialysis unit; head nurse cardiac intensive care unit U. Calif. Irvine Med. Ctr., Orange, head nurse emergency svcs., nursing supr. emergency dept., assoc. dir. nursing, ops. officer; assoc. adminstr. patient care svcs., dir. nursing Valley Med. Ctr., Fresno, Calif.; assoc. clin. prof. Calif. State U., Fresno; asst. clin. prof. U. Calif., San Francisco. Author: (with others) Human Resource Management Handbook: Contemporary Strategies for Nursing Managers, 1987; contbr. articles to profl. jours. Mem. Orgn. Nurse Execs. Calif., Nursing Adminstrs. Coun. San Juaquin Valley (past pres.), San Joaquin Valley Health Consortium, Sigma Theta Tau.

NITTA, KENJIRO, Computer company executive. With NEC Corp., Tokyo, Japan, 1961-1991; chmn., ceo Nec Technologies Inc., Boxboro, Mass., 1991—. Office: Nec Technologies Inc 1414 Massachusetts Ave Boxboro MA 01719-2205

NITTOLY, PAUL GERARD, lawyer; b. Bklyn., July 13, 1948; s. Edward Joseph and Philomena (Lorenzo) N.; m. Maryann Racioppi, May 31, 1970; children: Melissa Beth, Matthew Edward. AB, Rutgers U., 1970; JD, N.Y. Law Sch., 1973. Bar: N.J. 1973, U.S. Dist. Ct. N.J. 1973, U.S. Supreme Ct. 1979; cert. trial atty. (civil and criminal) N.J. Supreme Ct. Asst. prosecutor, sr. trial atty. Essex County Prosecutor's Office, Newark, 1974-79; ptnr. Shanley & Fisher, P.C., Morristown, N.J., 1984—; moot trial ct. judge Seton Hall Law Sch., Newark, 1982—; lectr. symposium on perinatal malpractice Am. Coll. Ob-Gyn and Rutgers U. Med. Sch., Morristown, N.J., 1984; mem. practitioner's adv. group to U.S. Sentencing Commn., 1992—. Author: Readings in White Collar Crime, 1991; contbr. chapts to books; mem. editorial bd. Corporate Criminal Liability Reporter. Served to capt. U.S. Army, 1972. Mem. ABA, N.J. Bar Assn., Essex County Bar Assn., Morris County Bar Assn., Nat. Assn. Criminal Defense Lawyers, Assn. Criminal Defense Attys. N.J., Trial Attys. N.J., Park Avenue Club (Morristown), Morristown Club, Delta Upsilon. Roman Catholic. Home: 275 Meetinghouse Ln Mountainside NJ 07092-1305 Office: Shanley & Fisher 131 Madison Ave Morristown NJ 07962

NITZE, PAUL HENRY, international studies educator; b. Amherst, Mass., Jan. 16, 1907; s. William A. and Anina (Hilken) N.; m. Phyllis Pratt, Dec. 2, 1932 (dec.); children: Heidi, Peter, William II, Phyllis; m. Elisabeth Scott Porter, Jan. 23, 1993. AB cum laude, Harvard U., 1928; LLD (hon.), New Sch. Social Research, Pratt Inst., Johns Hopkins U., Holy Cross Coll., Harvard U., Amherst Coll., Williams Coll., Brown U. With Dillon, Read & Co. (investment bankers), N.Y.C., 1929-37; v.p. Dillon, Read & Co. (investment bankers), 1939-41; pres. P.H. Nitze & Co., Inc., 1938-39; U.S. govt. fin. dir., coord. Inter-Am. Affairs; chief metals and minerals br. Bd. Econ. Warfare; dir. fgn. procurement and devel. br. Fgn. Econ. Adminstrn.; dir., then vice chmn. U.S. Strategic Bombing Survey, 1944-46; dep. dir. Office Internat. Trade Policy, Dept. State, 1946; dep. to asst. sec. state for econ. affairs, 1948-49; dir. policy planning staff Dept. State, 1950-53; pres. Fgn. Service Ednl. Found., Washington, 1953-61; asst. sec. def. for Internat. Security Affairs, 1961-63; sec. of Navy, 1963-67, dep. sec. of def., 1967-69; mem. U.S. del. Strategic Arms Limitation Talks, 1969-74; head U.S. negotiating team Arms Control Talks, Geneva, 1981-84; spl. advisor to pres. and sec. state on arms control matters, 1984-89; founder, diplomat-in-residence, disting. rsch. prof. in strategic studies and Am. fgn. policy Paul H. Nitze Sch. Advanced Internat. Studies, Johns Hopkins U., Washington; mem. internat. adv. council Inst. Internat. Studies.; chmn. Washington Inst. Fgn. Affairs. Author: From Hiroshima to Glasnot: A Memoir, 1989 (Adolph Bentinck Lit. prize 1990), Tension Between Opposites: Reflections on the Practice and Theory of Politics, 1993. Recipient Medal for Merit, Medal of Freedom, George C. Marshall, Knight Comdrs. Cross (badge and star) Order of Merit (Fed. Republic Germany); grand officier de l'Ordre de la Couronne Royaume de Belgique, 1989, Grosse Goldene Ehrenzeiche des Landes Steiermark (Austria), 1991, other awards from The Netherlands, Italy, Sec. Gen. Atlantic award (NATO Man of Yr.), 1988, Sec. State Disting. Svc. award, 1988, Sylvanus Thayer award, 1991, Doolittle award, 1993. Home: 2416 Tracy Pl NW Washington DC 20008-1627 Office: Paul Nitze

Sch Advanced Internat Studies Johns Hopkins U 1619 Massachusetts Ave NW Washington DC 20036-2213

NITZE, WILLIAM ALBERT, lawyer, government official; b. N.Y.C., Sept. 27, 1942; s. Paul Henry and Phyllis (Pratt) N.; m. Ann Kendall Richards, June 5, 1971; children: Paul Kendall, Charles Richards. BA, Harvard U., 1964, JD, 1969; BA, Oxford U., 1966. Bar: N.Y. 1970, U.S. Supreme Ct. 1987. Assoc. Sullivan and Cromwell, N.Y.C., 1970-72; v.p. London Arts, Inc., N.Y.C., 1972-73; counsel Mobil South, Inc., N.Y.C., 1974-76; gen. counsel Mobil Oil Japan, Tokyo, 1976-80; asst. gen. counsel exploration and producing div. Mobil Oil Corp., N.Y.C., 1980-87; dep asst. sec. for environment, health and natural resources U.S. Dept. State, Washington, 1987-90; pres. Alliance to Save Energy, Washington, 1990-94; asst. adminstr. for internat. activities U.S. EPA, Washington, 1994—; mem. adv. com. Sch. Advanced Internat. Studies, Washington, 1982—; professorial lectr. 1993-94; vis. scholar Environ. Law Inst., Washington, 1990; dir. Charles A. Lindbergh Fund, Mpls., 1990-94, Nat. Symphony Orch. Assn., Washington. Trustee Aspen Inst., Queenstown, Md., 1988—. Mem. Assn. of Bar of City of N.Y., Coun. on Fgn. Rels., Met. Club, Links Club. Republican. Episcopalian. Avocations: running, piano, collecting art. Home: 1336 30th St NW Washington DC 20007-3349 Office: US EPA 401 M St SW Washington DC 20460

NITZSCHE, JACK, composer; b. Mich.. 1937. music arranger Phil Spector, 1962-66, Specialty Records, Original Sound Records; session musician Rolling Stones, 1965-66, Buffalo Springfield, 1967; keyboardist, prodr. Crazy Horse, 1970-71; keyboardist Stray Gators, 1973; prodr. Lee Hazlewood, Rolling Stones, James Gang. Neil Young, Ringo Starr, Buffy Sainte-Marie, Rick Nelson, Graham Parker, Mink DeVille. Composer, music dir.: (films) Village of the Giants, 1965; composer, music dir., orchestrator: (films) When You Comin' Back, Red Ryder?, 1979; composer: (films) Performance, 1970, Greaser's Palace, 1972, The Exorcist, 1973, One Flew Over the Cuckoo's Nest, 1975 (Academy award nomination best original score 1975), (with Richard Hazard) Heroes, 1977, (with Ry Cooder) Blue Collar, 1978, Hardcore, 1979, Heart Beat, 1979, Melvin and Howard, 1980, Cruising, 1980, Cutter's Way, 1981, An Officer and a Gentleman, 1982 (Academy award nomination best original score 1982), Cannery Row, 1982, Personal Best, 1982, Without a Trace, 1983, Breathless, 1983, The Razor's Edge, 1984, Starman, 1984, Windy City, 1984, The Jewel of the Nile, 1985, (with Michael Hoenig) 9 1/2 Weeks, 1986, Stand By Me, 1986, Streets of Gold, 1986, (with Buffy Sainte-Marie) Stripper, 1986, The Whoopee Boys, 1986, The Seventh Sign, 1988, Next of Kin, 1989, Revenge, 1990, The Hot Spot, 1990, The Last of the Finest, 1990, Mermaids, 1990, The Indian Runner, 1991, (TV movies) Middle Ages, 1992, (TV series) Starman, 1986-86, (songs) (with Sonny Bono) Needles and Pins, 1963, The Lonely Surfer, 1963, Gone Dead Train, 1970, (with Cooder and Paul Schrader) Hard Working Man, 1978, No One Knows Better Than You, 1979, I Love Her Too, 1979, We're Old Enough to Know, 1981, (with Wil Jennings and Sainte-Marie) Up Where We Belong, 1982 (Academy award best original song 1983), Hit and Run Lovers, 1984; album: The Lonely Surfer, 1963, St. Giles Cripplegate, 1972. Office: Creative Artists Agency 9830 Wilshire Blvd Beverly Hills CA 90210*

NITZSCHKE, DALE FREDERICK, university president; b. Remsen, Iowa, Sept. 16, 1937; m. Linda Hutchinson, June 24, 1971; children: Mary Beth, Stephen, Lori, Eric, David. BA in Edn. cum laude, Lora Coll., 1959; MEd in Guidance and Counseling, Ohio U., 1960, PhD in Guidance and Counseling, 1964. Instr. edn. Loras Coll., Dubuque, Iowa, 1964-65, chmn. dept. edn., 1964-65; asst. prof., dir. edn. placement bur. Ohio U., Athens, 1967-72; assoc. dean profl. and gen. studies, dean edn. State U. Coll. Arts and Sci., Plattsburgh, N.Y., 1972-76; prof. edn., dean Coll. Edn. U. No. Iowa, 1976-80; prof. edn., v.p. acad. affairs U. Nev., Las Vegas, 1980-84; pres. Marshall U., Huntington, W.Va., 1984-90, U. N.H., Durham, 1990—; workshop dir. Evaluation Elem. Schs.; dir. Martha Holden Jennings Founds. Lectureship Series; cons. Athens non-graded high sch.; cons. on personnel mgmt. U. Nev. Reno Med. Sch. Contbr. articles to profl. jours. Bd. dirs., blood chmn. Athens County Red Cross; v.p. Kootoga council Boy Scouts Am.; mem. N.Y. State Policy Bd. in Spl. Edn., 1975-76; nat. adv. com. Personalized Adult Counseling Experience (PACE); coordinator Coll. Drug Edn. Program, Ohio U.; dir. Student Tutors for Ednl. Progress (STEP); coordinator Preparation Program for Inner City and Appalachian Tchrs.; sec. State of Ohio Edn. Deans; bd. dirs. Elvis Presley Mus. and Entertainment Inst., Las Vegas; bd. acad. advisors Am. Inst. for Fgn. Study; chmn. bd. regents State Adv. Com. for Iowa Sch. for Deaf, Iowa Braille and Sight Saving Sch.; mem. State-wide Inter-Instl. Gerontology Com.; bd. dirs. W.Va. Council on Econ. Devel., W.Va. Roundtable, Cabell-Wayne United Way, River Cities Cultural Devel. Council, Community Players, W.Va. Edn. Fund, Inc., Boys Club Huntington, Ronald McDonald House, Huntington, W.Va. Com. on Employment Opportunities and Econ. Devel.; mem. com. on self regulation initiatives Am. Council on Edn.; mem. selection com. Harry S. Truman Scholarship Program; incorporator Trust for N.H. Lands, 1992—; bd. dirs. New Eng. Coun. Recipient Community Leader of Am. award, 1969; Disting. Service award Rotary, 1969; Alexander Meiklejohn award for acad. freedom AAUP, 1984. Mem. Assn. Higher Edn., Am. Personnel Guidance Assn., Nat. Vocat. Guidance Assn., Am. Counselor Edn. Assn., Student Personnel Assn. for Tchr. Edn., Nat. Assn. State Univs. and Land Grant Colls. (chmn. commn. on outreach and tech. transfer 1991—), Huntington C. of C. (bd. dirs.), Athens Jaycees (past pres., chmn. bd., Young Man of Yr. award 1969), Nature Conservancy (trustee N.H. chpt. 1992—). Home: 2 Garrison Ave Durham NH 03824-2315 Office: U NH Office of Pres Main St Durham NH 03824-2521

NIVEN, LAURENCE VAN COTT, author; b. Los Angeles, Apr. 30, 1938; s. Waldemar Van Cott and Lucy Estelle (Doheny) N.; m. Marilyn Joyce Wisowaty, Sept. 6, 1969. Student, Calif. Inst. Tech., 1956-58; BA in mathematics, Washburn U., Topeka, 1962, LLD, 1984. Free-lance writer. Contbr. numerous stories to mags., also TV scripts; author: (novels) World of Ptavvs, 1966, A Gift From Earth, 1968, Ringworld, 1970 (Nebula award Sci. Fiction Writers Am. 1970, Hugo award World Sci. Fiction Conv. 1971, Ditmar award 1972), (with David Gerrold) The Flying Sorcerers, 1971, Protector, 1973, A World Out of Time, 1976, The Magic Goes Away, 1978, The Ringworld Engineers, 1980, The Patchwork Girl, 1980, The Integral Trees, 1984, The Smoke Ring, 1987, Green Lantern: Ganthet's Tale, 1992, Crashlander, 1994; (with Jerry Pournelle) The Mote in God's Eye, 1974, Inferno, 1976, Lucifer's Hammer, 1977, Oath of Fealty, 1981, Footfall, 1985, Fallen Angels, 1991, The Gripping Hand, 1993; (with Steven Barnes) Dream Park, 1981, The Descent of Anansi, 1982, Dream Park II: The Barsoom Project, 1989, Achilles' Choice, 1991, The California Voodoo Game, 1992; (with Barnes and Pournelle) The Legacy of Heorot, 1987, Beowulf's Children, 1995; (with others) "Man-Kzin Wars" series, 1988—; story collections include Neutron Star, 1968, The Shape of Space, 1969, All the Myriad Ways, 1971, The Flight of the Horse, 1973, Inconstant Moon, 1973, A Hole in Space, 1974, Tales of Known Space, 1975, The Long ARM of Gil Hamilton, 1976, Convergent Series, 1979, Niven's Laws, 1984, The Time ofthe Warlock, 1984, Limits: Collected Stories, 1985, N-Space, 1990, Playgrounds of the Mind, 1991; editor: The Magic May Return, 1981, More Magic, 1984. Recipient Hugo award for short stories World Sci. Fiction Conv., 1967, 72, 75, 76, E.E. Smith Meml. award, 1978, Inkpot award San Diego Comic Conv., 1979. Mem. Sci. Fiction Writers Am., Los Angeles Sci. Fantasy Soc. Republican. Address: 136 El Camino Dr Beverly Hills CA 90212 *If you don't know what you're talking about, you should be listening. If you're talking anyway, don't treat your listener like an idiot. If he is an idiot, find someone else to talk to.*•

NIVISON, DAVID SHEPHERD, Chinese and philosophy educator; b. Farmingdale, Maine, Jan. 17, 1923; s. William and Ruth (Robinson) N.; m. Cornelia Green, Sept. 11, 1944; children—Louise, Helen Thom, David Gregory, James Nicholas. A.B. summa cum laude, Harvard U., 1946, M.A., 1948, Ph.D., 1953. Instr. Chinese Stanford U., 1948-52, Ford Found. faculty fellow, 1952-53, instr. Chinese and philosophy, 1953-54; Fulbright research scholar Kyoto, Japan, 1954-55; lectr. philosophy Stanford U., 1955-58, asst. prof. Chinese and philosophy, 1958-59, assoc. prof., 1959-66, prof., 1966-88, Walter Y. Evans-Wentz prof. Oriental Philosophies, Religions and Ethics, 1983-88, chmn. dept. philosophy, 1969-72, 75-76, acting chmn. dept. Asian langs., 1968-69; emeritus, 1988—. Author: The Life and Thought of Chang Hsüeh-ch'eng, 1738-1801, 1966; editor, co-compiler: Stanford Chinese Concordance Series, 1979; co-editor: Confucianism in Action, 1959; contbr. articles profl. jours. Served with AUS, 1943-46. Recipient Prix Stanislas-Julien Inst. de France, 1967; Am. Council Learned Socs. fellow, 1973; John Simon Guggenheim fellow, 1973-74. Mem. Assn. Asian Studies, Am. Philos. Assn. (v.p. Pacific div. 1978-79, pres. 1979-80), Am. Oriental Soc. (Western br. v.p. 1964-65, sec. 1965-70, pres. 1971-72), AAUP (pres. No. Calif. Conf. 1964-66), Internat. Acad. Chinese Culture (Beijing, Peoples Republic of China), Phi Beta Kappa. Home: 1169 Russell Ave Los Altos CA 94024-5066 Office: Stanford U Philosophy Dept Stanford CA 94305

NIWA, NORIO, computer company executive. Pres., ceo Epson Am. Inc., Torrance, Calif., 1992—. Office: Epson AMerica Inc 20770 Madrona Ave Torrance CA 90503-3777

NIX, EDMUND ALFRED, lawyer; b. Eau Claire, Wis., May 24, 1929; s. Sebastian and Kathryn (Keirnan) N.; m. Mary Kathryn Nagle Daley, Apr. 27, 1968; children: Kim, Mary Kay, Norbert, Edmund Alfred, Michael. B.S., Wis. State U., 1951; LL.B., U. Wis., 1954, postgrad. in speech, 1956-57. Bar: Wis. 1954. Practice in Eau Claire, 1954-65; dist. atty. Eau Claire County, 1958-64; U.S. atty. Western Dist. Wis., Eau Claire, 1965-69; U.S. magistrate Western Dist. Wis., 1969-70; dist. atty. La Crosse County, Wis., 1977-91; mcpl. judge City of La Crosse, 1992—. Co-chmn. United Fund, Eau Claire, 1958; Pres. Young Democrats Wis., 1951-53; mem. adminstrv. bd. Wis. Dem. party, 1953-54; chmn. 10th Congl. dist., 1965; sec. Kennedy for Pres. Club Wis., 1959-60. Served with AUS, 1954-56. Mem. Fed. Bar Assn., Wis. Bar Assn. (state chmn. crime prevention and control com.), La Crosse County Bar Assn. (pres.), Nat. Dist. Attys. Assn., KC. Roman Catholic. Office: 123 4th St N La Crosse WI 54601-3235

NIX, JAMES RAYFORD, nuclear physicist, consultant; b. Natchitoches, La., Feb. 18, 1938; s. Joe Ebbin and Edna (Gain) N.; m. Sally Ann Wood, Aug. 19, 1961; children—Patricia Lynne, David Allen. B.S. in Physics, Carnegie Inst. Tech., 1960; Ph.D. in Physics, U. Calif.-Berkeley, 1964. Summer physicist Lawrence Livermore Nat. Lab., Livermore, Calif., 1961; research asst. Lawrence Berkeley Lab., Berkeley, Calif., 1961-64, postdoctoral physicist, 1966-68; NATO postdoctoral fellow Niels Bohr Inst., Copenhagen, Denmark, 1964-65; staff mem. Los Alamos Nat. Lab., 1968-77, 89-94, group leader, 1977-89, fellow, 1994—; vis. prof. Centro Brasileiro de Pesquisas Físicas, Rio de Janeiro, Brazil, 1974; cons. Calif. Inst. Tech., Pasadena, 1976, 79; chmn. Gordon Research Conf. Nuclear Chemistry, New London, N.H., 1976; chmn. physics div. adv. com. Oak Ridge Nat. Lab., 1976, chmn. nuclear sci. div. vis. com. Lawrence Berkeley Lab., 1979-80. Contbr. articles to numerous publs. Alfred P. Sloan Found. scholar, Pitts., 1956-60; Phi Kappa Phi fellow, Berkeley, Calif., 1960-61; Alexander von Humboldt Sr. U.S. Scientist award Univ. Munich and Max-Planck Inst. for Nuclear Physics, 1980-81. Fellow Am. Phys. Soc. (exec. com. 1973-75); mem. AAAS, Sigma Xi, Phi Kappa Phi. Democrat. Home: 12 Los Pueblos Los Alamos NM 87544-2659 Office: Los Alamos Nat Lab Nuclear Theory T-2 MS B243 Los Alamos NM 87545

NIX, JOHN B., aeronautical engineer. Chief fighter divsn. Air Force Materiel Command, Wright-Patterson AFB, Ohio. Recipient Aircraft Design award AIAA, 1994. Office: Attn ASC/PA Air Force Materiel Command Wright Patterson AFB OH 45433-6309*

NIX, ROBERT LYNN, minister; b. Belleville, Ark., Nov. 24, 1940; s. Huey Watson and Edna Mae (Johnson) N.; m. Patricia Sue Palmer, Aug. 27, 1961; children: Kevin Lynn, Robert Keith, Jonathan Kyle, Kelly Eugene. Diploma, Jackson (Miss.) Coll. Ministries, 1965. Ordained to ministry United Pentecostal Ch. Internat., 1963. Prof. Pentecostal Bible Inst., Tupelo, Miss., 1965-66; missionary to Peru, United Pentecostal Ch. Internat., 1966-69; missionary supt. United Pentecostal Ch., Peru, 1966-85; pres. United Pentecostal Sem., Peru, 1969-85; missionary supt. United Pentecostal Ch., Costa Rica, Cen. Am.; pres. United Pentecostal Sem. United Pentecostal Ch., Costa Rica, Cen. Am., 1983-85; pastor United Pentecostal Spanish Ch., Hilsboro, Oreg., 1985-86, Christian Apostolic Ch., San Antonio, 1987—. Bd. dirs. Tex. Bible Coll., Houston, 1993—. Home and Office: 12016 White Birch St San Antonio TX 78245-3350 *The Apostle Paul said, "For me to live is Christ." (Phil. 1:21). In this age of hedonism and materialism many believe that life consists of worldly goods and human achievements. How mistaken they are! People never really live until they die to self and allow Jesus Christ to become the Supreme Lord of their lives.*

NIX, ROBERT N(ELSON) C(ORNELIUS), JR., state supreme court chief justice; b. Phila., July 13, 1928; s. Robert Nelson Cornelius and Ethel (Lanier) N.; m. Renate Bryant; children from previous marriage: Dorthy Lewis (dec.), Robert Nelson Cornelius III, Michael, Anthony, S. Jude. A.B., Villanova U., LLD (hon.); J.D., U. Pa.; postgrad. bus. adminstrn. and econs., Temple U.; LLD (hon.), St. Charles Sem., Dickinson U. Sch. Law, Scranton U., Delaware Law Sch., Lafayette Coll. Bar: Pa. 1956, U.S. Dist. Ct. (ea. dist.) Pa., U.S. Ct. Appeals (3d cir.). Dep. atty. gen. Commonwealth of Pa., 1956-58; then Nix, Rhodes & Nix, Phila., 1958-68; judge Common Pleas Ct., Phila., 1968-71; justice Supreme Ct. Pa., Phila., 1972-84, chief justice, 1984—; adj. chmn. bd. dirs. Nat. Ctr. for State Cts., 1990-91. Bd. dirs. Nat. Ctr. for State Cts., 1985—; Scranton U. Duquesne U., Lincoln U.; life mem. bd. consultors Villanova U., trustee, 1986—; bd. overseers U. Pa. Sch. Law, 1987—; bd. mgrs. Archdiocese of Phila. Served with AUS, 1953-55. Recipient First Pa. award, Benjamin Franklin award Poor Richard Club Pa., James Madison award Nat. Soc. Profl. Journalists; named Knight Comdr. Order of St. Gregory the Great. Fellow Am. Bar Found.; mem. ABA, Pa. Bar Assn., Phila. Bar Assn., Nat. Bar Assn. (past chmn. jud. coun.), Barristers Club, Am. Law Inst., Conf. of Chief Justices (bd. dirs., pres. 1990-91), The Legal Club, Omega Psi Phi. Lodge: KC. Office: Pa Supreme Ct Ea Dist Office City Hall Rm 468 Philadelphia PA 19107 Office: 1 South Penn Sq Widener Bldg Rm 500 Philadelphia PA 19107 *America is slowly becoming aware of the vast potential she possesses because of the varied backgrounds and cultures of her citizens. When this fact is fully appreciated and full advantage is taken of this resource, she will reach an unprecedented level of civilization.*

NIX, WILLIAM DALE, materials scientist, educator; b. King City, Calif., Oct. 28, 1936; s. Earl Thomas and Ethel Lula (Jackson) W.; m. Jean Aldene Telford, June 15, 1958; children—Cynthia Lea, Jeffrey Alan, Rebecca Jean. B.S., San Jose State Coll., 1959; M.S., Stanford U., 1960, Ph.D., 1963. Asst. prof. materials sci. Stanford U., 1962-66, assoc. prof., 1967-72, prof., 1972—, dir. Ctr. Materials Research, 1968-70, assoc. chmn. dept., 1975-86, acting chmn. dept., 1986-87, Lee Otterson prof. Sch. of Engring., 1989—, chmn. dept., 1991—; asst. to dir. technology Stellite div. Union Carbide Corp., Kokomo, Ind., 1966; cons. to govt. and indsl. orgns. Author: (with C.R. Barrett and A.S. Tetelman) The Principles of Engineering Materials, 1973; contbr. articles to profl. jours. Recipient Teaching Excellence award Western Electric Fund, 1964, Disting. Alumni award San Jose State U., 1980, Gold medal Acta Metallurgica, 1993. Fellow Am. Soc. Metals (Bradley Stoughton award 1970, Edward DeMille Campbell lectr. 1989), Metall. Soc.; mem. AIME (Mathewson Gold medal 1979, R.F. Mehl medal 1988, Inst. Metals lectr 1988), NAE, Am. Soc. Engring. Edn., Sigma Xi. Republican. Presbyterian. Home: 1526 Apple Creek Ln Santa Rosa CA 95401-7619 Office: Stanford U Dept Materials Sci Stanford CA 94305

NIX, AGNES ECKHARDT, television writer, producer; m. Robert Nixon; 4 children. Student, Sch. Speech, Northwestern U. Writer for radio and TV; freelance writer for: TV programs Hallmark Hall of Fame, Robert Montgomery Presents, Studio One; creator, packager, head writer: daytime TV series All My Children; creator nightime mini-series The Manions of America; creator, packager daytime TV series One Life to Live; creator, packager: daytime TV series Loving; co-creator: daytime TV series As The World Turns; formerly head writer, The Guiding Light, daytime TV series Another World. Recipient Trustees award Nat. Acad. TV Arts and Scis., 1981, Super Achiever award Jr. Diabetes Found.; Wilmer Eye Inst. award, Communicator award Am. Women in Radio & TV, 1984, Gold Plate award Am. Acad. Achievement, 1983; inducted into TV Hall of Fame, 1993. Mem. Internat. Radio and TV Soc. Nat. Acad. TV Arts and Scis., The Friars Club, Bd. of Havard Found. Address: 774 Conestoga Rd Rosemont PA 19010-1257

NIXON, DAVID, dancer; b. Windsor, Ont., Can.. Student, The Nat. Ballet Sch. With Nat. Ballet of Can., 1978-84, 1st soloist, 1982-84, prin. dancer,

1984-90; prin. dancer: Berlin Opera Ballet, 1985-88, 90, Bayerisches Staatsoper Ballet Munich, 1990-91; prin. dancer and 1st Ballet master, Deutsche Opera Ballet Berlin, 1994-95; various guest appearences including Alexander Godunov and Stars summer, 1982, Milw. Ballet, 1984, Sydney Ballet Australia, 1984, World Ballet Festival Tokyo, 1985, 88, Hamburg Ballet, 1988-89, Staatsoper Berlin, 1989-91, Komische Opera Berlin, 1991-93, Birmingham Royal Ballet, 1990-93, prodr.; David Nixon's Dance Theater, Hebbel Theater, Berlin, 1990-91; artistic dir. BalletMet, 1994—; choreographer Butterfly, 1983, La Follia, 1984, Dangerous Liasions, 1990, African Fantasy, 1990, Celebrate Mozart, 1991, Sudden Impulse, 1994.

NIXON, DAVID LEE, lawyer; b. Concord, Mass., Mar. 19, 1932; s. Louis Gerard and Patricia (Williams) N.; children: Leslie C., Melanie D., Wendy W. N. Branch, Amy W., David L. Jr., Louis G. II. BA cum laude, Wesleyan U., Middletown, Conn., 1953; LLB, U. Mich., 1958. Bar: N.H. 1958, U.S. Dist. Ct. N.H. 1959, U.S. Ct. Appeals (1st cir.) 1961, U.S. Supreme Ct. 1968. Assoc. McLane, Graf, Greene & Brown, Manchester, N.H., 1958-61; ptnr. King & Nixon, Manchester, N.H., 1961-69, Nixon, Christy & Tessier, Manchester, N.H., 1969-76; dir. Brown & Nixon P.A., Manchester, N.H., 1976-88; pres. Nixon, Hall & Hess P.A., Manchester, N.H., 1988-93, of counsel, 1993-94; pres., dir. Nixon, Raiche, Brown, Manning & Branch P.A., 1994—; mem. N.H. Ct. Accreditation Commn., 1985—, N.H. Jud. Coun., 1980-83, 93—. Rep. N.H. Legis., Concord, 1969-74, senate pres., 1973-74; moderator Town of New Boston, N.H., 1964-92. With U.S. Army, 1953-55. Named Trial Lawyer of the Decade N.H. Trial Lawyers Assn., 1988. Mem. ABA (ho. of dels. 1970-72), Manchester Bar Assn. (pres. 1973-74), N.H. Bar Assn. (pres. 1980-81, Disting. Svc. award 1982, award for professionalism 1993), New Eng. Bar Assn. (pres. 1970-72), Internat. Soc. Barristers (bd. govs. 1988—), Inner Circle Advs., Manchester Bar Assn. (Lawyer of Yr. award 1995). Home: Dockside II Unit 6 51 River Front Dr Manchester NH 03102-3243 Office: Nixon Raiche Brown Manning & Branch PA 77 Central St Manchester NH 03101-2423

NIXON, EUGENE RAY, chemist, educator; b. Mt. Pleasant, Mich., Apr. 14, 1919; s. William S. and Grace (Brookens) N.; m. Phyllis R. Jones, June 10, 1945; children—Cynthia L., Emily E. Sc.B. summa cum laude, Alma Coll., 1941; Ph.D., Brown U., 1947. Research chemist Manhattan Project, 1942-46; instr. chemistry Brown U., 1947-49; mem. faculty U. Pa., Phila., 1949—; prof. chemistry U. Pa., 1965—, vice dean grad. sch., 1958-62, acting chmn. dept. chemistry, 1965-66, dir. materials research lab., 1969-72; vis. prof. U. London, 1963-64; vis. lectr. Bryn Mawr Coll., 1957-58. Mem. Am. Chem. Soc., Am. Phys. Soc., Soc. Applied Spectroscopy (Jour. award 1965, Spectroscopist of Yr. award Del. Valley sect. 1988), Coblentz Soc. (bd. mgrs.), Sigma Xi. Research, publs. on phys. chemistry, molecular structure and molecular spectroscopy, properties of crystals, intermolecular interactions, laser chemistry and laser spectroscopy. Home: 35 Julio Dr Apt 106 Shrewsbury MA 01545 Office: Univ Pa Dept Chemistry Philadelphia PA 19104

NIXON, HARVEY, lawyer; b. Chgo., Nov. 22, 1931. BA, Grinnell Coll., 1953; LLB, Harvard U., 1960. Bar: Ill. 1960. Office: Mayer Brown & Platt 190 S La Salle St Chicago IL 60603

NIXON, JAMES ALEXANDER, cosmetic company executive; b. Detroit, Aug. 30, 1932; s. David S. and Kathleen (Garlick) N.; m. Elizabeth Fitzwater, Apr. 27, 1935; children: James Jeffery, Richard Scott. BA, Amherst Coll., 1954; MA, Harvard U., 1955. Mgr. advt. Campbell Soup Co., Camden, N.J., 1957-67; dir. mktg. Miles Labs., Elkhart, N.J., 1967-78; v.p. mktg. Keydata Corp., Boston, 1970-73, Bristol Myers Corp., N.Y.C., 1973-76; exec. v.p. Cosmair, Inc., N.Y.C., 1976—. Served with U.S. Army, 1955-57. Republican. Episcopalean. Clubs: Greenwich Country (Conn.); Pine Valley Golf (N.J.). Avocations: golf, squash, tennis. Home: 11 Hillside Rd Greenwich CT 06830-4834

NIXON, JEREMIAH W. (JAY NIXON), state attorney general; b. DeSoto, Mo., Feb. 13, 1956; s. Jeremiah and Betty (Lea) N.; m. Georganne Nixon; children: Jeremiah, Will. BS in Polit. Sci., U. Mo., 1978, JD, 1981. Ptnr. Nixon, Nixon, Breeze & Roberts, Jefferson County, Mo., 1981-86; mem. Mo. State Senate from Dist 22, 1986-93; atty. gen. State of Mo., 1993—; chmn. select com. ins. reform.; created video internat. devel. and edn. opportunity program. Honoree, Conservation Fedn. Mo., 1992; named Outstanding Young Missourian Mo. Jaycees, 1994, Outstanding Young Lawyer, Barrister's Mag., 1993. Mem. Nat. Assn. Attys. Gen. (antitrust com., chair FTC working group, criminal law com., consumer protection com.), Midwest Assn. Attys. Gen. (chmn.), Mo. Assn. Trial Attys. Democrat. Methodist. Office: Atty Gen Office PO Box 899 Jefferson City MO 65102

NIXON, JOAN LOWERY, writer; b. L.A., Feb. 3, 1927; d. Joseph Michael and Margaret Mary (Meyer) Lowery; m. Hershell Howard Nixon, Aug. 6, 1949; children: Kathleen Nixon Brush, Maureen Nixon Quinlan, Joseph Michael, Eileen Nixon McGowan. BA in Journalism, U. So. Calif., L.A., 1947; Elem. Edn. Credentials, Calif. State Coll., L.A., 1949. Tchr. L.A. Elem. Schs., 1947-50; free-lance writer Houston, 1944—; creative writing tchr. Midland (Tex.) Jr. Coll., 1971-73, U. Houston Continuing Edn., 1974-77; columnist The Houston Post, 1969-76. Author: The Mystery of Hurricane Castle, 1964, The Mystery of the Grinning Idol, 1965, The Mystery of the Hidden Cockatoo, 1966, The Mystery of the Haunted Woods, 1967, The Mystery of the Secret Stowaway, 1968, Delbert, The Plainclothes Detective, 1971, The Alligator under the Bed, 1974 (Tex. Inst. Letters award, 1975), The Secret Box Mystery, 1974 (Jr. Lit. Guild), The Mysterious Red Tape Gang, 1974 (Edgar scroll Mystery Writers of Am. 1975), The Mysterious Prowler, 1976, Who Is My Neighbor?, 1976, Five Loaves and Two Fishes, 1976, The Son Who Came Home Again, 1977, Writing Mysteries for Young People, 1977, The Boy Who Could Find Anything, 1978 (reprinted Scott Foresman text), Danger in Dinosaur Valley, 1978, (Jr. Lit. Guild), Muffie Mouse and the Busy Birthday, 1978, (Jr. Lit. Guild), When God Speaks, 1978, When God Listens, 1978, The Kidnapping of Christina Lattimore, 1979 (Edgar Allan Poe award Mystery Writers Am., 1980), The Grandmothers's Book, 1979, The New Year's Day Mystery, 1978, The Halloween Mystery, 1979, The Butterfly Tree, 1979, Bigfoot Makes a Movie, 1979, The Valentine's Day Mystery, 1979, The Happy Birthday Mystery, 1979, The Seance, 1980 (Edgar Allan Poe award best juvenile mystery 1981), Gloria Chipmunk, Star! 1980, If You Say So, Claude, 1980 (Book of Month Club), Before You Were Born, 1980, Casey and the Great Idea, 1980, The Thanksgiving Day Mystery, 1980, The April Fools Day Mystery, 1980, Kleep, The Space Detective Series: Kidnapped on Astarr, The Mysterious Queen of Magic, The Mystery Dolls of Planet Ur, 1981, The Christmas Eve Mystery, 1981, The Easter Mystery, 1981, The Spotlight Gang and the Backstage Ghost, 1981, The Specter, 1982, The Gift, 1983, Days of Fear, 1983, Magnolia's Mixed-Up Magic, 1983 (Crabbery childrens choice award Prince George County, Md.), A Deadly Game of Magic, 1983 (Ind. Young Adult Hoosier award 1989), The Ghosts of Now, 1984 (Edgar Allan Poe award nomination), The House on Hackman's Hill (Mich. Children's Choice award 1987), The Stalker, 1985 (Calif. Young Readers medal 1989), Maggie, Too, 1987, Beats Me, Claude, 1986 (Lit. Guild), The Other Side of Dark, 1987 (Edgar award Mystery Writers Am., other awards, Calif. Young Readers medal 1990), And Maggie Makes Three, 1986, Haunted Island, 1987, Maggie Forevermore, 1987, Fat Chance, Claude, 1987, The Dark and Deadly Pool, 1987, Orphan Train Quartet: (vol. 1) A Family Apart, 1987 (Best Juvenile Western Book award Western Writers Am.), (vol. 2) Caught in the Act, 1988, (vol.3) In The Face Of Danger, 1988 (Best Juvenile Western Book award We. Writers of Am. 1989), (vol. 4) A Place to Belong, 1989, If You Were a Writer, 1988 (Jr. Lit. Guild), Secret, Silent Screams, 1988, The Island of Dangerous Dreams, 1989, You Bet Your Britches, Claude, 1989, Whispers From the Dead, 1989, Hollywood Daughters: A Family Triology: (vol. 1) Star Baby, 1989, (vol. 2) Overnight Sensation, 1990, (vol. 3) Encore, 1990, A Candidate for Murder, 1991, The Nic-Nacs and the Nic-Nac News Series (The Mystery Box, Watch Out for Dinosaurs, The Honeycutt Street Celebrities, and The Haunted House on Honeycutt Street), 1991, High Trail to Danger, 1991, The Deadly Promise, 1992, The Weekend Was Murder!, 1992, Ellis Island: Land of Hope, 1992, That's the Spirit, Claude, 1992, The Name of the Game Was Murder, 1993 (Edgar award Mystery Writers Am., 1994), Land of Promise, 1993, Land of Dreams, 1994, When I Am Eight, 1994, Will You Give Me A Dream?, 1994, A Dangerous Promise, 1994, Shadowmaker, 1994; co-author textbooks: This I Can Be, 1975, People and Me, 1975; co-author: (with Hershell Nixon) Oil and Gas, from Fossils to

Fuels, 1977, Volcanoes: Nature's Fireworks, 1978 (Outstanding Sci. Books for Children cert. Nat. Sci. Tchrs. Assn. and Children's Book Coun.), Glaciers: Nature's Frozen Rivers, 1980 (Outstanding Sci. Books for Children cert. Nat. Sci. Tchrs. Assn. and Children's Book Coun.), Earthquakes: Nature in Motion, 1981 (Outstanding Sci. Books for Children cert. Nat. Sci. Tchrs. Assn. and Children's Book Coun.), Land Under the Seas, 1985; author under pseudonym Jaye Ellen: The Trouble With Charlie, 1982; numerous of these books pub. in fgn. langs., paperbacks, reprints. Recipient Children's Choice awards in over 7 states, 1984-89, Best Children's Book award Tex. Inst. Letters, Austin, 1975, Outstanding Contbn. to Children's Lit. award Bishop Byrne Chpt. Cath. Librs. Am., 1980, Cen. Mo. State U., 1982. Mem. Mystery Writers of Am., Inc. (regional v.p. southwest chpt. 1984-86, gen. awards chmn. N.Y. 1988-89, nat. bd. dirs. 1994-95), Soc. Children's Book Writers (bd. dirs. 1974-78), Am. Crime Writers League, Western Writers Am., The Authors Guild, Sisters in Crime, Kappa Delta. Republican. Roman Catholic. Avocations: reading, travel. Home: 10215 Cedar Creek Dr Houston TX 77042-2049 Office: care Writers House Inc 21 W 26th St New York NY 10010-1003

NIXON, JOHN HARMON, economist; b. Mpls., Apr. 7, 1915; s. Justin Wroe and Ida Elisabeth (Wickenden) N. AB, Swarthmore Coll. 1935; AM, Harvard U., 1949, PhD, 1953. Analyst U.S. R.R. Retirement Bd., Washington, 1938-41; economist U.S. Office of Price Adminstrn., Washington, 1941-46; teaching fellow, sr. tutor Harvard Coll., Cambridge, Mass., 1947-50; asst. prof. econs. CCNY, 1953-56; dir. econ. devel. N.Y. State Dept. Commerce, Albany, 1956-59; dir. area devel. Com. for Econ. Devel., N.Y.C., 1959-65; dir. tech. assistance U.S. Econ. Devel. Adminstrn., Washington, 1966-67; urban economist U.S. AID, Saigon, Vietnam, 1967; economist Ralph M. Parsons Co., Washington, 1968-70; chief economist/systems Ralph M. Parsons Co., Pasadena, Calif., 1971-82; mem. adv. bd. U.S. Area Devel. Adminstrn., Washington, 1963-65. Co-author, editor: Community Economic Development Efforts, 1964, Living Without Water (Cairo), 1980. Vice chmn. Mayor's Com. on Econ. Devel., L.A., 1974-75; pres. Pasadena Devel. Corp., 1982-84. Mem. Nat. Economists Club, Nat. Assn. Bus. Economists, Harvard Club N.Y.C., Town Hall of Calif., Phi Beta Kappa. Democrat. Presbyterian. Office: PO Box 76267 Los Angeles CA 90076

NIXON, JOHN TRICE, federal judge; b. New Orleans, La., Jan. 9, 1933; s. H. C. and Anne (Trice) N.; m. Betty Chiles, Aug. 5, 1960 (div. Nov. 1985); children: Mignon Elizabeth, Anne Trice. A.B. cum laude, Harvard Coll. 1955; LL.B., Vanderbilt U., 1960. Bar: Ala. bar 1960, Tenn. bar 1972. Individual practice law Anniston, Ala., 1960-62; city atty. Anniston, 1962-64; trial atty. Civil Rights Div., Dept. Justice, Washington, 1964-69; staff atty., comptroller of Treasury State of Tenn., 1971-76; pvt. practice law Nashville, 1976-77; cir. judge, 1977-78, gen. sessions judge, 1978-80; judge U.S. Dist. Ct. (mid. dist.) Tenn., Nashville, 1980—. Served with U.S. Army, 1958. Democrat. Methodist. Clubs: D.U. (Cambridge); Harvard-Radcliffe (Nashville). Home: 1026 18th Ave S Nashville TN 37212-2105 Office: US Dist Ct 825 US Courthouse Nashville TN 37203

NIXON, JUDITH MAY, librarian; b. Gary, Ind., June 14, 1945; d. Louis Robert Sr. and Mable Sophia (Reiner) Vician; m. Cleon Robert Nixon III, Aug. 20, 1967; 1 child, Elizabeth Marie. BS in Edn., Valparaiso U., 1967; MA in LS, U. Iowa, 1974. Tchr. U.S. Peace Corps, Kingdom of Tonga, 1968-69; popular books libr. Lincoln Libr., Springfield, Ill., 1971-73; reference libr. Cedar Rapids (Iowa) Pub. Libr., 1974-76; reference coord. U. Wis., Platteville, 1976-82; bus. libr. U. Ariz., Tucson, 1982-84; consumer and family sci. libr. Purdue U., West Lafayette, La., 1984-93; Krannert mgmt. and econs. libr. Purdue U., West Lafayette, 1993—. Editor: Industry and Company Information, 1991, Organization Charts, 1992, Hotel and Restaurant Industries, 1993; editor quar. serial Lodging and Restaurant Index, 1985—. Leader Girl Scouts, Lafayette, Ind., 1985—. Recipient John H. Moriarty award Purdue U. Librs., 1989. Mem. ALA (chair bus. reference and svcs. sect. 1995—), GALE Rsch. award for excellence in bus. librarianship 1994). Home: 2375 N 23d St Lafayette IN 47904 Office: Purdue U Mgmt and Econs Libr Krannert Grad Sch Mgmt West Lafayette IN 47907

NIXON, MARNI, singer; b. Altadena, Calif., Feb. 22, 1930; d. Charles and Margaret (Wittke) McEathron; m. Ernest Gold, May 22, 1950 (div. 1969); children: Andrew Maurice, Martha Alice, Melani Christine; m. Lajos Frederick Fenster, July 23, 1971 (div. July 1975); m. Albert David Block, Apr. 11, 1983. Student opera workshop, Los Angeles City Coll., UCLA, U. So. Calif., Tanglewood, Mass. Dir. vocal faculty Calif. Inst. Arts, Valencia, 1970-72; pvt. tchr., vocal coacn, condr. master classes, 1970—, pvt. voice tchr., coach, condr. master classes, 1970—; head apprentice div. Santa Barbara Music Acad. of West, 1980; formerly dir. opera workshop Cornish Inst. Arts, Seattle.; tchr. in field; judge Met. Opera Internat. Am. Music Awards, Nat. Inst. Music Theatre, 1984, 85-86, 87; panelist New Music, Nat. Assn. Tchrs. Singing, pres. (N.Y. chpt.), 1994—; dialect dir., opera recs. Child actress Pasadena (Calif.) Playhouse, 1940-45, soloist Roger Wagner chorale, 1947-53, appeared with New Eng. Opera Co., Los Angeles Opera Co., also Ford Found. TV Opera, 1948-63, San Francisco Spring Opera, 1966, Seattle Opera, 1971, 72, 73; classical recitals and appearances with symphony orchs. throughout U.S., Can., also Eng., Israel, Ireland; appeared on Broadway as Eliza Doolittle in My Fair Lady, 1964; in motion picture as Sister Sophia in Sound of Music, 1964; also in numerous TV shows and night clubs; star children's ednl. TV show Boomerang, ABC-TV, from 1975; off-Broadway show Taking My Turn, from 1983, Opal, from 1992; appeared in (stage plays) Romeo & Juliet, N.Y.C.; taped for Great Performances PBS-TV Role of Edna, 1994; voice dubbed in for musical motion pictures My Fair Lady, The King and I, An Affair to Remember, West Side Story, and others; rec. artist for Columbia, Mus. Heritage Records, Capital, RCA Victor, Ednl.Records, Reference Recs., Varese-Sarabande, Nonesuch; played violin at age 4; studied in youth orch., 10 yrs; studied voice at age 10. Recipient 4 Emmy awards for best actress, 2 Action for Childrens TV awards, 1977; nominee Drama Desk award; recipient Chgo. Film Festival award, 1977, Gold Record for Songs from Mary Poppins, 2 time Grammy award nominee Nat. Acad. Rec. Arts and Scis. (1st rec. Cabaret Songs and Early Songs by Arnold Schoenberg, RCA, 1977 and 1st rec. Emily Dickinson Songs by Aaron Copland, Reference Recs., 1988. Mem. Nat. Assn. Tchrs. Singing (pres. N.Y. chpt. 1994—).

NIXON, PHILIP ANDREWS, diversified company executive; b. Bklyn., Nov. 23, 1938; s. Philip A. and Hilda (Weidman) N.; m. Brooke Nichols, June 9, 1963; children: Lucia, Rachel, Eliot, Oliver, Preya, Malini, Biplab, Jasmine, Hilda. B.A., Yale U., 1960. Vol. Peace Corps, Sierra Leone, Africa, 1965-67; aide to gov. State of Maine, Augusta, 1967-70; asst. to chmn. Dead River Co., Bangor, Maine, 1970-71, v.p., 1971-73, exec. v.p. 1973, pres., chief exec. officer, 1974—; pres., chief exec. officer Dead River Group of Cos., Bangor, Maine, 1974-85; chmn. bd. Dead River Group of Cos., 1985—; dir. Fleet/Norstar Bank Maine, Forster Mfg. Co., Wilton, Maine. Sec. Maine Pulp & Paper Found., 1976-86; bd. dirs. New Eng. Council, 1978-86, Maine Community Found.; trustee Kenduskeag Found., Bangor, 1979—, Portland Sch. Art, 1983—; chmn. Maine Community Found., 1989-94. Served with USN, 1961-65. Mem. M. C. of C. of U.S. Conf. Bd. Democrat. Clubs: Union (Boston). Home: 71 Federal St Brunswick ME 04011-2114 Office: Dead River Co 1 Dana St Portland ME 04101-4014

NIXON, RALPH ANGUS, psychiatrist, educator, research neuroscientist; b. Somerville, Mass., Jan. 29, 1947; s. Ralph Angus and Eleanor Nixon; m. Katharine Sangree Faulkner, Aug. 20, 1974; children: Abigail, Rebecca. AB, Brandeis U., 1968; PhD in Cell and Devel. Biology, Harvard U., 1974; MD, U. Vt., 1976. Intern Mass. Gen. Hosp., 1976, Salem Hosp., 1977; resident in psychiatry Mass. Gen. Hosp., 1977-79, McLean Hosp., 1979-80; clin. assoc. in psychiatry Mass. Gen. Hosp., Boston, 1980—; assoc. in neurosci. Children's Hosp Med. Ctr., Boston, 1982-88; staff physician Rehab. Ctr. for Aged, Boston, 1984-90; asst. prof. psychiatry Harvard Med. Sch., Boston, 1982-86, assoc. prof., 1986—; assoc. neuropathologist McLean Hosp., Belmont, Mass., 1982-90, assoc. psychiatrist, 1988-93, neuropathologist, 1991; psychiatrist, 1993—; mem. sci. rev. com. Am. Fedn. for Aging Rsch., 1990—; mem. neurosci., behavior and sociology of aging rev. com., subcom. A, Nat. Inst. on Aging, NIH, 1991—; dir. labs. for molecular neuroscience McLean Hosp., 1992. Mem. editorial bd. Jour. neurochemistry, 1986—, Neurochem. Rsch., 1988—, harvard Rev. Psychiatry, 1992, Neurobiology of Aging 1994—; contbr. articles to sci. Jour. Cell Biology; Jour. Biology Chem., Annals N.Y. Acad. Sci., Proc. NAS, chpts. to books;

Proteases and protease Inhibitors Banner C Nixon R.A. eds Annals Acad. Sci. vol. 67, 1992. Hon. bd. dirs. Ch. League for Civic Concerns, Boston, 1987-89. Recipient Merit award NIH, 1990, Leadership and Excellence in Alzheimer Disease award, Nat. Inst. Aging, 1992; Ethel DuPont Warren Fellow, 1979-80, rsch. fellw Med. Found., 1980-82, Alfred P. Sloan Found., 1981-83, Scottish Rite Schizophrenia Rsch. Program, 1983-85. Mem. AAAS, Soc. for Neurosci., Fedn. Am. Scientists, Am. Soc. for Neurochemistry, Internat. Soc. for Neurochemistry, Am. Psychiat. Assn. Am. Soc. for Cell Biology, Am. Assn. for Geriatric Psychiatry, Gerontol. Soc. Am., Am. Assn. Neuropathologists. Achievements include patents (with others) on cupric chloride spot test and neural calcium-activated neutral proteinase inhibitors; four patents pending. Office: McLean Hosp-Harvard Med Sch 115 Mill St Belmont MA 02178-1048

NIXON, RALPH EDWARD, financial executive; b. Brockton, Md., Apr. 29, 1944; s. Ralph Edward and Ilta EMily (Oman) N.; m. Cheryl Ann Ortendahl, Sept. 9, 1967; children: Kristin Ann, Amy Lynne. BS in Econs., Northwestern U., 1971. Mgmt. trainee to v.p Plymouth-Home Nat. Bank, Brockton, 1967-74; v.p., pres., chief exec. officer Mutual Adv. Corp., Boston, 1974-83; pres., chief exec. officer Liberty Securities Corp., Boston, 1983—. Treas. United Way, Brockton, 1970-72. Served to sgt. USAF, 1963-67. Mem. Strategic Planning Inst. (bd. dirs. 1980-82), NE Bair Mktg. Assn. (bd. dirs. 1972-74). Republican. Lutheran. Avocations: sailing, skiing, traveling, being with his family. Office: Liberty Securities Corp 600 Atlantic Ave Boston MA 02210-2211

NIXON, ROBERT OBEY, SR., business educator; b. Pitts., Feb. 14, 1922; s. Frank Obey and Margurite (Van Buren) N.; m. Marilyn Cavanagh, Oct. 25, 1944 (dec. 1990); children: Nan Nixon Friend, Robert Obey, Jr., Dwight Cavanagh. BS in bus. adminstrn., U. Pitts., 1948; MS, Ohio State U., 1964; MBA, U. Phoenix, 1984. Commd. 2d lt. USAF, 1943, advanced through grades to col., 1970, master navigator WWII, Korea, Vietnam; sales adminstrn. U.S. Rubber Corp., Pitts., 1940-41; asst. engr. Am. Bridge Corp., Pitts., 1941-42; underwriter, sales Penn Mutual Life Ins. Corp., Pitts., 1945-50; capt., nav. instr. USAF Reserves, 1945-50; ret. USAF Col., divsn. chief Joint Chiefs of Staff, 1973; educator, cons. U. Ariz., 1973-79; bus. dept. chmn., coord., founder weekend coll. Pima Community Coll., Tucson, 1979-90, prof. mgmt., coord. Weekend Coll. program, 1991—; founder, pres. Multiple Adv. Group ednl. cons., Tucson, 1978—. Contbr. articles to profl. jours. Mem. Soc. Logistics Engrs. (sr., charter mem.), Phi Delta Theta. Presbyterian. Avocations: tennis, hiking, swimming. Home: 1824 S Regina Cleri Dr Tucson AZ 85710-8664

NIXON, SCOTT WEST, oceanography science educator; b. Phila., Aug. 24, 1943; s. Robert Scott West and Elizabeth (Wright) West Nixon; m. Pendleton Hall, (div.); children: Carter Hall, Elizabeth Pendleton; m. Virginia Lee. BA, U. Del., 1965; Ph.D, U.N.C., 1970. Prof. oceanography U.R.I. Kingston, 1970—; dir. sea grant coll. program, 1983—; owner Coastal Ecology, Wakefield, R.I., 1980—. Author: (with others) A Coastal Marine Ecosystem, 1978, The New England High Salt Marshes, 1982; editor-in-chief Estuaries, 1988—; also articles. Grantee NSF, NOAA, EPA, Office Water Resources Research, State of R.I. Mem. Am. Soc. Limnology and Oceanography (governing bd. 1984-87), Estuarine Research Fedn., Nat. Assn. State Univs. Land-Grant Colls. Office: Univ of RI Dept Of Oceanography Kingston RI 02881

NIZZE, JUDITH ANNE, physician assistant; b. L.A., Nov. 1, 1942; d. Robert George and Charlotte Ann (Wise) Swan; m. Norbert Adolph Otto Paul Nizze, Dec. 31, 1966. BA, UCLA, 1966, postgrad., 1966-76; grad. physician asst. tng. program, Charles R. Drew Sch. Postgrad., L.A., 1979; BS, Calif. State U., Dominguez, 1980. Cert. physician asst., Calif. rsch. assoc. I-II Wadsworth Vet. Hosp., L.A., 1965-71; staff rsch. assoc. III-IV John Wayne Clinic Jonsson Comprehensive Cancer Ctr., UCLA, 1971-78; clin. asst. Robert S. Ozeran, Gardena, Calif., 1978; physician asst. family practice Fred Chasan, Torrance, Calif., 1980-82; sr. physician asst. Donald L. Morton prof., chief surg. oncology Jonsson Comprehensive Cancer Ctr., UCLA, 1983-91; adminstrv. dir. clin. rsch. John Wayne Cancer Inst., Santa Monica, Calif., 1991—. Contbr. articles to profl. jours. Fellow Am. Acad. Physician Assts., Am. Assn. Surgeons Assts., Calif. Acad. Physician Assts.; mem. Assn. Physician Assts. in Oncology, Am. Sailing Assn. Republican. Presbyterian. Avocations: sailing, tennis, skiing, photography, computers. Home: 13243 Fiji Way Unit J Marina Dl Rey CA 90292-7079 Office: John Wayne Cancer Inst St John's Hosp & Health Ctr 1328 22nd St Santa Monica CA 90404-2091

NOAKES, BETTY L., elementary school educator; b. Oklahoma City, Okla., Aug. 28, 1938; d. Webster L. and Willie Ruth (Johnson) Hawkins; m. Richard E. Noakes, Apr. 22, 1962 (dec.); 1 child, Michele Monique. Student, Oklahoma City U., MEd, 1971; BS, Cen. State U., 1962. Cert. therapeutic recration specialist, Okla. Elem. tchr. Merced (Calif.) Pub. Schs., 1966-67, Oklahoma City Schs., 1971-73, Mid-Del Schs., Midwest City, Okla., 1973—. 2nd v.p. PTA, Pleasant Hill, 1991, cert. recognition 1992-93; active Nat. PTA, 1991-92. Recipient Cert. Appreciation YMCA, 1992-92, Disting. Svc. award Mid-Del PTA, 1992. Mem. NEA, ASCD, AAUW, NAACP, Nat. Therapeutic Recreation Assn., Okla. Edn. Assn., Okla. Reading Assn., Okla. Therapeutic Recreation Assn. (charter), Smithsonian Inst., Oklahoma City U. Alumni Assn., United Meth. Women Assn., Cen. State U. Alumni Assn., Okla. Ea. Star (Lilly of the Valley chpt. 7), Phi Delta Kappa (sgt.-at-arms), Zeta Phi Beta. Avocations: aerobics, singing, piano, clarinet, folk dancing. Home: 5956 N Coltrane Rd Oklahoma City OK 73121-3409 Office: 4346 NE 36th St Oklahoma City OK 73121-5400

NOALL, ROGER, bank executive; b. Brigham City, Utah, Apr. 1, 1935; s. Albert Edward Noall and Mabel Clayton; m. Judith Ann Stelter, Mar. 16, 1962 (div.); children: Brennan, Tyler; m. Colleen Henrietta Mannion. BS, U. Utah, 1955; LLB, Harvard U., 1958; LLM, NYU, 1959. Legal asst. Donavan, Leisure, Newton & Irvine, N.Y.C., 1959-61; assoc. Olwine, Connelly, Chase, O'Donnell & Weyher, N.Y.C., 1961-65, ptnr., 1965-67; with Bunge Corp., N.Y.C., 1967-85, exec. v.p, 1975-83; exec. v.p., chief fin. officer Centran Corp., Cleve., 1985-; sr. v.p., chief adminstrv. officer Key Corp., Cleve., 1994—. Served in USNG, 1959. Office: Society Corp 127 Public Sq Cleveland OH 44114-1306

NOBACK, CHARLES ROBERT, anatomist, educator; b. N.Y.C., Feb. 15, 1916; s. Charles Victor and Beatrice (Cerny) N.; m. Eleanor Louise Loomis, Nov. 23, 1938 (dec. Mar. 24, 1981); children: Charles Victor, Margaret Beatrice, Ralph Theodore, Elizabeth Louise. BS, Cornell U., 1936; MS, NYU, 1938; postgrad., Columbia U., 1936-38; PhD, U. Minn., 1942. Asst. prof. anatomy U. Ga., 1941-44; faculty L.I. Coll. Medicine, 1944-49, assoc. prof., 1948-49; mem. faculty Columbia Coll. Phys. and Surg., 1949—, assoc. prof. anatomy, 1953-68, prof., 1968-86, prof. emeritus 1986—, spl. lectr. 1986-92, acting chmn. dept., 1974-75. Author: The Human Nervous System, 1967, 75, 81, Spinal Cord, 1971, The Nervous System Introduction and Review, 1972, 77, 86, 91, 95; co-author: (with N. Strominger and R. Demarest) Human Anatomy and Physiology, 1990, 2d edit., 1992, 3d edit. 1995, (with D. Van Wysberghe and R. Carola) Human Anatomy, 1992, (with R. Carola and H. Harley), editor: The Primate Brain, 1970, Sensory Systems of Primates, 1978; sr. editor: Advances in Primatology; series editor: Contbns. to Primatology; contbr. articles to profl. jours., sects. to Ency. Brit., McGraw Hill Ency. Sci. and Tech., Collier's Ency. Fellow N.Y. Acad. Scis. (past rec. sec.), AAAS; mem. Am. Assn. Anatomists, Histochem. Soc., Internat. Primatological Soc., Am. Soc. Naturalists, Cajal Club Am. (past pres.), Assn. Phys. Anthropologists, Harvey Soc., Am. Acad. Neurology, Soc. Neurosci., Sigma Xi. Home: 116 7th St Cresskill NJ 07626-2005 Office: Columbia U Anatomy And Cell Dept New York NY 10032

NOBACK, RICHARDSON KILBOURNE, medical educator; b. Richmond, Va., Nov. 7, 1923; s. Gustav Joseph and Hazel (Kilborn) N.; m. Nan Jean Gates, Apr. 5, 1947; children: Carl R., Robert K., Catherine E. BA, Columbia U., 1943; MD, Cornell U., 1947; BA, Columbia U., 1993. Diplomate Am. Bd. Internal Medicine. Intern N.Y. Hosp., 1947-48; asst. resident Cornell Med. div. Bellevue Hosp., N.Y.C., 1958-50, chief resident, 1950-52; instr. medicine Cornell U., N.Y.C., 1950-53; asst. prof. medicine SUNY Upstate Med. Ctr., Syracuse, 1955-56; assoc. prof. medicine U. Ky. Med. Ctr., Lexington, 1956-64; exec. dir. Kansas City (Mo.) Gen. Hosp. and

Med. Ctr., 1964-69; assoc. dean, prof. medicine U. Mo. Sch. Medicine, Columbia, 1964-69; founding dean U. Mo. Sch. Medicine, Kansas City, 1969-78, prof. medicine, 1969-90, prof. and dean emeritus, 1990—; cons. U. Tenn., U. Mich., U. Del., Northeastern Ohio Group, U. Mo., Eastern Va. Med. Sch., Tex. Tech. U. Contbr. numerous articles to profl. jours. Bd. dirs. Kansas City Gen. Hosp., Truman Med. Ctr., Wayne Miner Health Ctr., Jackson County Med. Soc., The Shepherd's Ctr., Am. Fedn. Aging Rsch., Mo. Gerontol. Inst., The Shepherd's Ctrs. of Am.; dir. Mo. Geriatric Edn. Ctr., 1985-88. Capt. USAF Med. Svcs. 1953-55. Recipient medal of honor Avila Coll., Kansas City, 1968, merit award Met. Med. Soc., 1991, recognition award Mo. Soc. Internal Medicine, 1993. Mem. AMA, Mo. Med. Assn. (former mem. ho. of dels., v.p. 1992), Am. Geriatric Soc., Alpha Omega Alpha, Phi Kappa Phi. Avocations: photography, writing, travel. Home: 2912 Abercorn Dr Las Vegas NV 89134 Office: U Mo-Kansas City Sch Medicine 2411 Holmes St Kansas City MO 64108-2796

NOBE, KEN, chemical engineering educator; b. Berkeley, Calif., Aug. 26, 1925; s. Sidney and Kiyo (Uyeyama) N.; m. Mary Tagami, Aug. 31, 1957; children: Steven Andrew, Keven Gibbs, Brian Kelvin. B.S., U. Calif., Berkeley, 1951; Ph.D, UCLA, 1956. Jr. chem. engr. Air Reduction Co., Murray Hill, N.J., 1951-52; asst. prof. chem. engring. UCLA, 1957-62, assoc. prof., 1962-68, prof., 1968—, chmn. dept. chem., nuclear and thermal engring., 1978-83, founding chmn. chem. engring., 1983-84. Div. editor: Jour. Electrochem. Soc. 1967-91, Electrochimica Acta, 1977-85. Served with U.S. Army, 1944-46. Mem. Electrochem. Soc. (Henry B. Linford award 1992), Am. Chem. Soc., Nat. Assn. Corrosion Engrs., Internat. Soc. Electrochemistry, Sigma Xi. Office: UCLA Dept Of Chemical Engin Los Angeles CA 90095

NOBEL, JOEL J., biomedical researcher; b. Phila., Dec. 8, 1934; s. Bernard D. and Golda R. (Nobel) Judovich; m. Bonnie Sue Goldberg, June 19, 1960 (div.); children—Erika, Joshua; m. Loretta Schwartz, Oct. 28, 1979; 1 child, Adam. AB, Haverford Coll., 1956; MA, U. Pa., 1958; MD, Thomas Jefferson Med. Coll., Phila., 1963. Intern Presbyn. Hosp., Phila., 1963-64; resident in surgery Pa. Hosp., 1964-65; resident in neurosurgery U. Pa. Hosp., 1965-66; practice medicine specializing in biomed. engring. rsch. and healthcare tech. assessment, Phila., 1968—; dir. research Emergency Care Research Inst., Plymouth Meeting, Pa., 1968-71; dir., pres. Emergency Care Research Inst., 1971—; pres. Emergency Care Research Inst., 1971—; cons. in field; bd. dirs. Consumers Union, 1976-79, 80—, chmn. tech. policy com., exec. bd. Publisher Health Devices, 1971—, Health Devices Alerts, 1977—. Contbr. articles to profl. jours. Served with USNR, 1966-68. Smith, Kline & French fgn. fellow, 1962; grantee HEW, 1968-72; grantee Am. Heart Assn., 1965-66. Mem. AMA, APHA, Assn. Advancement Med. Instrumentation, Critical Care Med. Soc., Pa. Med. Assn., Navy League, U.S. Naval Inst., Sunday Breakfast Club. Home: 1434 Monk Rd Gladwyne PA 19035-1315 Office: ECRI 5200 Butler Pike Plymouth Meeting PA 19462-1298

NOBILE, JOHN FRANK, food flavor company executive; b. N.Y.C., Dec. 20, 1940; s. Frank and Josephine (Russo) N.; m. Geraldine Claire Fanelli, May 9, 1987; children: Jennifer Lori, Liana Marie, Raquel Lynne. BS in Chemistry, NYU, 1961; MBA, Fordham U., 1971. New products mgr. Fisher Sci. Co., Fairlawn, N.Y., 1961-68; bus. devel. mgr. Union Carbide Corp., N.Y.C., 1968-78; dir. mktg. ITT Corp., Stamford, Conn., 1978-87; v.p., gen. mgr. Flavor Key 2000, Inc., Fairfield, N.J., 1987-90; v.p., chief operating officer Frutarom, U.S.A., Fairfield, 1990—. Author: Single Cell Proteins, 1982; patentee in field. Staff sgt. USAF, 1961-63. Recipient Energy Mgmt. award Am. Paper Inst./Nat. Fibrous Pulp Assn. Roman Catholic. Avocations: sailing, golf, music. Home: 2 Van Fleet Rd Neshanic Station NJ 08853-4300 Office: Frutarom USA Inc 9500 Railroad Ave North Bergen NJ 07046

NOBLE, DOUGLAS ROSS, museum administrator; b. Sturgis, Ky., Jan. 19, 1945; s. Roscoe and Robbie Rae (Martin) N.; m. Catherine Ann Richardson, Nov. 3, 1973; children: Kate Faxon, Jennifer Martin. BS, Okla. State U., 1967; MSA, Ga. Coll., 1978; D of Pub. Adminstrn., U. Ga., 1987. Asst. to dir. Savannah Sci. Mus., Ga., 1971-73; exec. dir. Mus. of Arts and Scis., Macon, Ga., 1973-80; dir. of museums Memphis Mus. System, 1980—; mem. mus. assessment program Inst. of Mus. Services, Washington, 1982—, grant reviewer, 1983—; cons. Mus. Mgmt. Program, Sarasota, Fla., 1985. Contbr. articles to profl. jours. Grad. Leadership Memphis, 1984; bd. dirs. Leadership in May Internat. Festival. 1st lt. U.S. Army, 1968-70; Vietnam. Decorated Bronze Star. Mem. Natural Sci. for Youth Found. (trustee 1980-87), Naumburg award 1978), Am. Assn. Museums (S.E. rep. 1984-87, chmn. mus. assessment program adv. com. 1987-89, treas., v.p. fin. 1990-92), chmn. nature ctr. accreditation com. 1985), Southeastern Museums Conf. (pres. 1982-84), Memphis Museums Roundtable (co-founder). Episcopalian. Home: 330 Belhaven Memphis TN 38117 Office: Memphis Pink Palace Mus & Planetarium 3050 Central Ave Memphis TN 38111-3399

NOBLE, ERNEST PASCAL, physician, biochemist, educator; b. Baghdad, Iraq, Apr. 2, 1929; came to U.S., 1946; s. Noble Babik and Barkev Grace (Kasparian) Babikian; m. Inga Birgitta Kilstromer, May 19, 1956; children—Lorna, Katharine, Erik. B.S. in Chemistry, U. Calif.-Berkeley, 1951; Ph.D in Biochemistry, Oreg. State U., 1955; M.D., Case Western Res. U., 1962. Diplomate Nat. Bd. Med. Examiners. Sr. instr. biochemistry Western Res. U., Cleve., 1957-62; intern Stanford Med. Ctr., Calif., 1962-63, resident in psychiatry, 1963-66, research assoc., asst. prof., 1965-69; assoc. prof. psychiatry, psychobiology and pharmacology U. Calif.-Irvine, 1969-71, prof., chief neurochemistry, 1971-76, 79-81; dir. Nat. Inst. Alcohol Abuse and Alcoholism HEW, 1976-78, assoc. adminstr. sci., alcohol, drug abuse and mental health, 1978-79; Pike prof. alcohol studies, dir. Alcohol Research Ctr. UCLA Sch. of Medicine, 1981—. Mem. various med./sci. jour. editorial bds.; contbr. numerous articles to profl. jours., chpts. to books. v.p Nat. Coun. on Alcoholism 1981-84; pres. Internat. Commn. for the Prevention of Alcoholism and Drug Dependency, 1988. Fulbright scholar, 1955-56; Guggenheim fellow, 1974-75; Sr. Fulbright scholar, 1984-85; recipient Career Devel. award NIMH, HEW, 1966-69. Fellow Am. Coll. Neuropsychopharmacology; mem. Internat. Soc. Neurochemistry, Am. Soc. Pharmacology and Exptl. Therapeutics, Research Soc. on Alcoholism. Office: UCLA 760 Westwood Plz Los Angeles CA 90024-8300

NOBLE, JAMES KENDRICK, JR., media industry consultant; b. N.Y.C., Oct. 6, 1928; s. James Kendrick and Orrel Tennant (Baldwin) N.; m. Norma Jean Rowell, June 16, 1951; children: Anne Rowell, James Kendrick III. Student, Princeton U., 1945-46; BS, U.S. Naval Acad., 1950; postgrad., USN Gen. Line Sch., 1955-56; MBA, NYU, 1961; postgrad., Sch. Edn., 1962-68. CFA. Commd. ensign USN, 1950; transferred to USNR, 1957; advanced through grades to capt. USNR, 1973; asst. gunnery officer in U.S.S. Thomas E. Fraser, 1950-51; student naval aviator USNR, 1951-52 pilot asst. ops. officer, 1952-55; instr. U.S. Naval Acad. 1956-57, Officer Candidate Sch., Newport, R.I., 1958; asst. to pres. Noble & Noble, Pub., Inc., N.Y.C., 1957-60; dir. spl. projects Noble & Noble, Pub., Inc., 1960-62, v.p., 1962-65, exec. v.p., 1965-66, dir., 1957-65; dir., v.p. Transl. Pub. Co. N.Y.C., 1958-65; cons. Transl. Pub. Co., 1965-66; v.p. dir. Elbon Realty Corp., Bronxville, N.Y., 1965-66; cons. Elbon Realty Corp., 1965-66; comdg. officer NAIRU R2, 1968-70; staff NARS W2, 1970-71, NRID 3-1, 1971-74; comdg. officer NRCSG 302, 1974-76; sr. analyst F. Eberstadt & Co., 1966-69; sr. analyst Auerbach, Pollak & Richardson, 1969-75, v.p., 1972-75, mgr. spl. rsch. projects 1973-75, dir., 1975; v.p. rsch. Paine, Webber, Jackson & Curtis, Inc., 1975-77, assoc. dir. rsch., 1976-77; v.p. Paine Webber, N.Y.C., 1977-79; 1st v.p. Paine Webber, 1979-91; pres. Noble Cons. Inc., 1991—; bd. dirs. Curriculum Ctr, Denver, 1972-78; instl. investor All Am. Rsch. Team, 1972-90. Author: Ploob, 1949, rev., 1956; editor pub.: The Years Between, 1966; also articles in various pubs. Mem. Bronxville Bd. Edn., 1968-74, pres., 1970-72; Rep. co-leader 21st Dist., Eastchester, N.Y. 1961-65; dir. Merit; cons., dir. Space and Sci. Train, 1962-63; trustee St. John's Hosp., Yonkers, N.Y. 1972-92. com. chmn., 1980-92. Freedom Forum Ctr. for Media Studies fellow, 1993-94. Fellow emeritus AAAS; mem. Info. Industry Assn. (disting. profl. mem.), Nat. Inst. Social Scis., N.Y. Soc. Security Analysts (mem. com. 1971-91, dir. 1975-84, v.p 1977-81, exec. v.p., 1981-82, pres. 1982-83), Am. Textbook Pub. Inst. (com. chmn. 1964-66), AIAA (mem. com. 1957-61), Media and Entertainment Analysts Assn. (pres. 1969-71), Fin. Analysts Fedn. (dir. 1984-87), Naval Res. Assn. (v.p. N.Y. Navy chpt. 1968-76), Wings Club, Siwanoy Country Club. Mem.

Reformed Ch. Home: 45 Edgewood Ln Bronxville NY 10708-1946 Office: Noble Cons 45 Edgewood Ln Bronxville NY 10708-1946

NOBLE, JAMES WILKES, actor; b. Dallas, Mar. 5, 1922; s. Ralph Byrne and Lois Frances (Wilkes) N.; m. Carolyn Owen Coates, May 19, 1956; 1 child: Jessica Katherine. Student, North Tex. Coll., Arlington, 1939-41, So. Methodist U., Dallas, 1941-43, 1946-47. lectr. acting and mime Am. Acad. Dramatic Art, 1956-59. Mem. Lydia Tarnower Modern Dance Co., 1937-39; title role in 1st TV drama, The Egoist on Dumont TV, 1943; 1st N.Y. Stage appearance Helena's Room, 1947; 1st Broadway appearance: The Big Knife, 1949; others include: The Velvet Glove, 1949; Medea, 1951; Come of Age, 1952; A Far Country, 1961; Strange Interlude, 1963; 1776, 1971; The Runner Stumbles, 1976; mem. Am. Mime Theatre, 1952-59; appeared in numerous TV dramas and soap operas; appeared in more than 200 plays in theatres throughout the world most recent: Stratford Characters in Stratford-Upon-Avon, England, T.S. Eliot in The Poet's Theatre, Cambridge, Mass.; TV appearances include the role of the Governor on Benson, ABC-TV, 1979-86, series First Impressions, CBS-TV, 1987—, series Archies, NBC-TV, 1990—, Law and Order, 1991; movies include: Dragonfly, 1965; The Sporting Club, 1967; 1776, 1972; Promises in the Dark, 1978; Ten, 1979; Being There, 1979; Airplane II, 1983; You Talkin' To Me?, 1986; Tiger's Tale, 1987, Chances Are, 1988, Absent Minded Professor, 1989, Law and Order, 1991, All My Children, 1992; numerous other appearances. Author jour. article on Am. mime. Served as lt. USNR, 1943-46, P.T.O. Named Hon. Gov., N.J., N.Y., 1982; appreciation award Am. Heart Assn., 1983. Mem. Actors Studio (life), Actors Equity, SAG, AFTRA. Democrat. Roman Catholic. Avocation: Photography. Office: Paradigm Agy 10100 Santa Monica Blvd Los Angeles CA 90067

NOBLE, JOSEPH VEACH, fine arts administrator; b. Phila., Apr. 3, 1920; s. Joseph Haderman and Helen Elizabeth (Veach) N.; m. Olive Ashley Mooney, June 21, 1941 (dec. Sept. 1978); children: Josette, Ashley, Laurence; m. Lois Cook Cartwright, Oct. 27, 1979. Student, U. Pa., 1942. Cameraman, dir. DeFrenes and Co. Studios, Phila., 1939-41; studio mgr. WPTZ, Philco TV Sta., Phila., 1941-42, DeFrenes and Co. Studios, 1946-49; gen. mgr. Murphy-Lillis Prodns., N.Y.C., 1949-50; exec. v.p Film Counselors, Inc., N.Y.C., 1950-56, dir., 1950-82; operating adminstr. Met. Mus. Art, 1956-67, vice dir. adminstrn., 1967-70; dir. Mus. City N.Y., 1970-85; exec. dir. Soc. Medalists, 1985—; photog. salon exhibitor, from 1936; lectr. CCNY, 1949-51. Author: The Techniques of Painted Attic Pottery, 1965, The Historical Murals of Maplewood, 1961, Forgery of the Etruscan Terracotta Warriors, 1961; Contbr.: Ency. Brit, 1970. Chmn. N.Y. State Bd. Hist. Preservation, 1972-76; co-chmn. Save Venice, Inc., 1972; trustee Brookgreen Gardens, pres., 1976-90, chmn., 1990—; trustee Corning Mus. of Glass, 1970—. Served with AUS, 1942-46. Recipient Venice Film Festival medal for photography in sci., 1948, Sigma Xi award 1963, Maple Leaf award Maplewood, N.J., 1966, 87, Gold medal for The Big Apple N.Y. Film Festival, 1979, Disting. Svc. award Maplewood C. of C., 1987. Fellow Soc. Antiquaries London; mem. N.Y. State Assn. Museums (pres. 1970-72), NAD (medal 1976), Nat. Sculpture Soc. (medal 1978, 91), Artists' Fellowship (medal 1978), Archeol. Inst. Am. (treas. 1963-70), Museums Council N.Y.C. (chmn. 1965-67), Am. Assn. Museums (pres. 1975-78, Disting. Svc. Awd., 1991), Cultural Instns. Group N.Y.C. (chmn. 1984-85), Soc. Promotion Hellenic Studies; Am. Watercolor Soc. (medal 1982). Clubs: Maplewood Country; Explorers (N.Y.C.), Century Assn. (N.Y.C.). Office: Brookgreen Gardens Murrells Inlet SC 29576

NOBLE, MERRILL EMMETT, retired psychology educator, psychologist; b. Las Vegas, N.Mex., July 25, 1923; s. Merrill Emmett and Martha (Van Petten) N.; m. Joy Lind, July 18, 1953; children: Margaret Lind, Eric Severin. B.A., N.Mex. Highlands U., 1947; M.A., Ohio State U., 1949, Ph.D., 1951. Research asso. Ohio State U., 1951-54, summers 1956, 58; mem. faculty Kans. State U., 1954-67, prof. psychology, 1961-67, chmn. dept., 1962-67; prof. psychology Pa. State U., 1967-88, chmn. dept., 1967-77, ret., 1989; Vis. scientist Inst. for Perception TNO, Soesterberg, Netherlands, 1973-74, 77-78, 80, also NATO vis. lectr. several univs. Mem. editorial bd. Psychol. Bull., 1963-64, Jour. Exptl. Psychology, 1967-78, Acta Psychologica, 1978-82, Human Performance, 1987-92. Bd. dirs. Environ. Research Found., Topeka, 1965-68. Fellow Am. Psychol. Assn. (com. on adv. services for edn. and tng. 1967-70, accreditation com. 1979-82), AAAS; mem. Psychonomic Soc., Midwestern Psychol. Assn. (mem. council 1967-70), Sigma Xi. Home: 2562 Calle Delfino Santa Fe NM 87505-6488

NOBLE, RICHARD LLOYD, lawyer; b. Oklahoma City, Oct. 11, 1939; s. Samuel Lloyd and Eloise Joyce (Millard) N. AB with distinction, Stanford, 1961, LLB, 1964. Bar: Calif. 1964. Assoc. firm Cooper, White & Cooper, San Francisco, 1965-67; assoc., ptnr. firm Voegelin, Barton, Harris & Callister, Los Angeles, 1967-70; ptnr. Noble & Campbell, Los Angeles, San Francisco, 1970—; dir. Langdale Corp., L.A., Gt. Pacific Fin. Co., Sacramento; lectr. Tax Inst. U. So. Calif., 1970; mem. bd. law and bus. program Stanford Law Sch. Contbr. articles to legal jours. Bd. govs. St. Thomas Aquinas Coll. Recipient Hilmer Dehlman Jr. award Stanford Law Sch., 1962; Benjamin Harrison fellow Stanford U., 1967. Mem. ABA, State Bar Calif., L.A. Bar Assn., San Francisco Bar Assn., Commercial Club (San Francisco), Commonwealth Club (San Francisco), Petroleum Club (L.A.), Capitol Hill Club (Washington), Pi Sigma Alpha. Republican. Home: 2222 Avenue of the Stars Los Angeles CA 90067-5655 Office: Noble & Campbell 333 N Grand Los Angeles CA 90014

NOBLE, RONALD K., government official, lawyer; b. Ft. Dix, N.J., Sept. 24, 1956. BA cum laude, U. N.H., 1979; JD, Stanford U., 1982. Sr. law clk to A. Leon Higginbotham Jr. U.S. Ct. Appeals for 3d Cir., 1982-84; asst. U.S. atty. for ea. dist. Pa., 1984-88; with U.S. Dept. Justice, 1988-89, dep. asst. atty. gen., chief staff, spl. counsel criminal, 1988-89; assoc. prof. law NYU Sch. Law, N.Y.C., 1989-93; asst. sec. for enforcement U.S. Dept. Treasury, Washington, 1993-94, under sec. for enforcement, 1994—; pres. Fin. Action Task Force, 1994—; mem. exec. com. INTERPOL, 1994—; mem. Root-Tilden Scholar Selection Bd., 1990—. Articles editor Stanford Law Rev. Office: Dept of Treasury Ste 4330 1500 Pennsylvania Ave Washington DC 20220

NOBLE, RONALD NELSON, hospital administrator; b. Listowel, Ont., Can., July 16, 1956; s. Stanly and Beatrice Lillian (Smith) N. BSc in Kinesiology with honours, U. Waterloo, Ont., 1980; MBA in Health Svcs. Adminstrn., McMaster U., Hamilton, Ont. Mktg. rep. Becton-Dickinson Co. Can. Ltd., Mississauga, Ont., 1980-81; adminstrv. asst. Henderson Gen. Hosp. div. Hamilton Civic Hosps., 1984-85, asst. adminstr., 1985-86; asst. exec. dir. Vernon (B.C., Can.) Jubilee Hosp., 1986-89; v.p. ops. and profl. svcs. Kitchener (Ont.) Waterloo Hosp., 1989—; advisor deptl. mgmt. program Can. Hosp. Assn., 1987-89. Contbr. articles to profl. jours. Mem. exec. com. Hamilton-Wentworth dist. coun. Boy Scouts Can., 1984-86; bd. dirs. North Okanagan Boy Scouts Assn., 1987-89; treas., Vernon and Dist. Hospice Soc., 1987-89; vice chmn. Kitchener Waterloo Big Bros. Assn., 1992-94; sector chmn. for pub. instns. United Way Campaign for Kitchener Waterloo, 1992-94. Recipient lit. award Health Exec. Forum, 1991, Agnew Peckham award for lit. excellence, 1991. Fellow Am. Coll. Healthcare Execs. (regent adv. coun. for B.C. and Yukon 1987-88, for Ont. 1990-91, 92-94), Can. Coll. Health Svc. Execs. (cert., bd. dirs. Hamilton chpt. 1990-91, pres. 1990-91, 92-94, award for lit. excellence 1991); mem. McMaster U. MBA Alumni Assn., Vernon Kinsmen Club (2d v.p. 1987-89, pres. 1987-89), Waterloo Grand River Kinsmen Club (bd. dirs. 1990-91). Avocations: travel, team sports, camping, cross-country and downhill skiing, jogging. Home: 365 Bennington Gate Apt 2, Waterloo, ON Canada N2T 2L1 Office: Kitchener Waterloo Hosp, 835 King St W, Kitchener, ON Canada N2G 1G3

NOBLE, STUART HARRIS, newspaper executive; b. Vancouver, B.C., Can., Jan. 11, 1941; s. Stewart Ian and Mina Rebecca (Harris) N.; m. Ann Rosalind Thorne, June 20, 1964 (dec. Dec. 1983); children: Kirsten Ann, Kenneth Stuart, William Frank, Catherine Marguerite; m. Susan Carmen Melnechuk, May 12, 1984; 1 child, Justin Arthur. BS in Forestry, U. B.C., Vancouver. From trainee to mgr. employee relations MacMillan Bloedel Ltd., Vancouver, 1965-77; dir. human resources Fording Coal Ltd., Calgary, Alta., Can., 1977-85; v.p. human resources Pacific Pres Ltd., Vancouver, 1985, v.p. human resources and ops., 1988—. Recipient Outstanding Service award Big Bros. of B.C., 1973. Mem. Indsl. Relations Mgmt. Assn., Can.

and Am. Newspaper Assns., Vancouver Bd. Trade. Lodge: Rotary (sec.; treas. local chpt. 1974-76). Avocations: home renovations, racquetball, skiing, reading. Home: 6700 Whiteoak Dr, Richmond, BC Canada V7E 4Z9 Office: Pacific Press Ltd, 2250 Granville St, Vancouver, BC Canada V6H 3G2

NOBLE, (TERRY) THOM, film editor. Editor: (films) Fahrenheit 451, 1966, The Man Who Had Power over Women, 1970, Senza Ragione, 1972, And Now for Something Completely Different, 1972, The Strange Vengeance of Rosalie, 1972, The Apprenticeship of Duddy Kravitz, 1974, (with Peter Thornton) Rosebud, 1975, Inside Out, 1976, Joseph Andrews, 1977, Black Joy, 1977, Who Is Killing the Great Chefs of Europe?, 1978, All Things Bright and Beautiful, 1979, Boardwalk, 1979, Improper Channels, 1981, Tattoo, 1981, Red Dawn, 1984, Witness, 1985 (Academy award best film editing 1985), Poltergeist II: The Other Side, 1986, The Mosquito Coast, 1986, Switching Channels, 1988, Winter People, 1989, Mountains of the Moon, 1990, Thelma and Louise, 1991 (Academy award nomination best film editing 1991), Body of Evidence, 1993, The Hudsucker Proxy, 1994; editor, visual cons.: (films) First Blood, 1982; editorial cons.: (films) North Dallas Forty, 1979, Uncommon Valor, 1983; editor, prodn. designer: (films) Final Analysis, 1992. Office: The Gersh Agency 232 N Canon Dr Beverly Hills CA 90210*

NOBLES, LAURENCE HEWIT, retired geology educator; b. Spokane, Sept. 28, 1927; s. Harry and Florence (Giffin) N.; m. Barbara Joanne Smith, Aug. 28, 1948; children: Heather C., Laurence F. BS, Calif. Inst. Tech., 1949, MS, 1949; PhD, Harvard, 1952. Instr. geology Northwestern U., 1952-55, asst. prof., 1955-61, assoc. prof., 1961-67, prof., 1967-90, prof. emeritus, 1990—; also asst. dean Northwestern U. (Coll. Arts and Scis.), 1966-67, asso. dean, 1968-70, acting dean, 1970-72, dean adminstrn., 1972-81, v.p. adminstrn. and fin. planning, 1981-86. Trustee Adler Planetarium, 1980-86; faculty rep. Big Ten Conf., 1976-81; trustee Chgo. Acad. Scis., 1967-87, pres., 1973-78, hon. trustee, 1987—. Mem. Am. Geophys. Union, Geol. Soc. Am., Univ. Club Chgo., Sigma Xi.

NOBLES, LEWIS, college president; b. Meridian, Miss., Sept. 11, 1925; s. Julius Sidney and Ruby Rae (Roper) N.; m. Joy Ford, Aug. 29, 1948; children—Sandra Jeanne (Mrs. Ben Nash), Glenda Suzanne (dec.). Student, Ursinus Coll., 1944-45; B.S. in Pharmacy, U. Miss., 1948, M.S., 1949; Ph.D., U. Kans., 1952; NSF postdoctoral fellow, U. Mich., 1958-59. Mem. faculty U. Miss., 1952-68, prof. pharm. chemistry, 1955-68; dean U. Miss. (Grad. Sch.), 1960-68, coordinator univ. research, 1964-68; pres. Miss. Coll., Clinton, 1968—. Co-author: Physical and Technical Pharmacy; contbr. to books; editorial adv. bd.: Jour. Pharm. Scis, 1965-71. Mem. regional adv. group Miss. Regional Med. Program 1969-76; chmn. 1971-76; mem. nat. adv. council on regional med. programs HEW, 1976-79; bd. grants Am. Found. Pharm. Ed., 1972-80; trustee New Orleans Baptist Theol. Sem., 1976-82. Served to lt. (j.g.) USNR, 1944-46. Am. Found. Pharm. Edn. fellow, 1949; Gustavus A. Pfeiffer Meml. Research fellow, 1955; recipient award for stimulation of research Am. Pharm. Assn. Found., 1966; named one of Top 18 Most Effective Coll. Pres. in U.S. Exxon Ednl. Found., 1986. Fellow AAAS; mem. Am. Chem. Soc., Chem. Soc. Gt. Britain, N.Y. Acad. Sci., Acad. Pharm. Scis. (chmn. medicinal chemistry sect. 1967-68), Am. Pharm. Assn. Internat. Platform Assn., Jackson C. of C., Am. Assn. Pres. Ind. Colls. and Univs. (trustee 1987—), Nat. Assn. Ind. Colls. and Univs. (bd. dirs. 1990-92), Soc. assn. of Colls. and Schs. (mem. commn. on colls.), Rotary, Sigma Xi, Rho Chi, Kappa Psi, Phi Eta Sigma, Pi Kappa Pi. Baptist. Office: Miss Coll PO Box 4186 Clinton MS 39058

NOBLITT, HARDING COOLIDGE, political scientist, educator; b. Marion, N.C., Oct. 31, 1920; s. Walter Tate and Nellie Mae (Horton) N.; m. Louise Hope Lester, July 3, 1943; 1 son, Walter Thomas. B.A., Berea Coll., 1942; M.A., U. Chgo., 1947, Ph.D. 1955. Mem. faculty Concordia Coll., Moorhead, Minn., 1950-90, prof. polit. sci., 1956-90, Wije Disting. prof., 1979-82; chmn. dept. Concordia Coll., 1964-72, prof. emeritus, 1990. Mem. editorial bd.: Discourse: A Review of the Liberal Arts, 1957-67, acting editor, 1959-60. Democratic candidate Congress, 1962; del. Dem. Nat. Conv., 1964; chmn. Profs. for Johnson-Humphrey, Minn., 1964; chmn. platform com. Dem. State Conv., 1968; mem. Gov's Citizens Council on Aging, 1963-68; mem. City Charter Commn., Moorhead, 1985—; mem. Minn. Higher Edn. Coordinating Bd., 1971-81, sec., 1974-75, pres., 1979-80. Served with AUS, 1943-46, ETO. Recipient 1st ann. Great Tchr. award Concordia Coll., 1960; recipient Flaat Disting. Service award Concordia Coll., 1982. Mem. Am. Polit. Sci. Assn., Am. Legion, Phi Kappa Phi, Pi Gamma Mu, Tau Kappa Alpha, Pi Kappa Delta. Presbyterian (elder). Home: 2014 4th St S Moorhead MN 56560-4131 Office: Concordia Coll Dept Polit Sci Moorhead MN 56560

NOCAS, ANDREW JAMES, lawyer; b. Los Angeles, Feb. 2, 1941; s. John Richard and Muriel Phyliss (Harvey) N.; m. Beverly De La Mare, June 27, 1964; 1 son, Scott Andrew. B.S., Stanford U., 1962, J.D., 1964. Bar: Calif. 1965. Assoc. Thelen, Marrin, Johnson & Bridges, Los Angeles, 1964-71, ptnr., 1972-91; pvt. practice L.A., 1992—; del. Calif. Bar Conv., 1972—. Served to capt. JAGC, USAR. Mem. Los Angeles County Bar Assn. (chmn. sect. law office mgmt. 1980-82, chair errors & ommissions com. 1987-88, chair litigation sect. 1988-89), ABA (chmn. arbitration com. 1981). Club: San Marino City. Office: 201 N Figueroa St Ste 1300 Los Angeles CA 90012-2636

NOCE, ROBERT HENRY, neuropsychiatrist, educator; b. Phila., Feb. 19, 1914; s. Rev. Sisto Julius and Madeleine (Saulino) N.; m. Carole Lee Landis, 1987. A.B., Kenyon Coll., 1935; M.D., U. Louisville, 1939; postgrad., U. Pa. Sch. Medicine, 1947, Langley-Porter Neuropsychiat. Inst., 1949, 52. Rotating intern Hamot Hosp., Erie, Pa., 1939-40; resident psychiatrist Warren (Pa.) State Hosp., 1940-41, staff psysician, 1946-48; staff physician Met. State Hosp., Norwalk, Calif., 1948-50; dir. clin. services Pacific State Hosp., Spadra, Calif., 1950-52; dir. clin. services Modesto (Calif.) State Hosp., 1952-58, asst. supt. psychiat. services, 1958-64; pvt. practice medicine specializing in neuropsychiatry, 1965-73; Mem. faculty postgrad. symposiums in psychiatry for physicians U. Calif., 1958, 66. Author: (film) Reserpine Treatment of Psychotic Patients; contbr. articles to profl. jours. Served from lt. (j.g.) to lt. comdr. M.C. USNR, 1941-46. Recipient Albert and Mary Lasker award for integration reserpine treatment mentally ill and mentally retarded, 1957; Wisdom award of honor, 1970. Life fellow Am. Psychiat. Assn. (sec. 1954, 55); fellow Royal Soc. Health; mem. Phi Beta Kappa, Delta Psi. Episcopalian. Home: 407 E Colgate Dr Tempe AZ 85283-1809 *I was fortunate in being raised in a Christian home. My late father was an Episcopal priest, and my eldest brother follows the same profession. All of my achievements are due to God's guidance. I feel that one must lead a balanced life, between worship, work, and leisure. Ideals, rather than material goals, should prevail at all times. Love of God and one's fellowman are of cardinal importance. Daily exercise, with observation of the marvels of nature, such as walking on the beach, promote physical and mental health. Listen intently to other people, but follow your own star.*

NOCE, WALTER WILLIAM, JR., hospital administrator; b. Neptune, N.J., Sept. 27, 1945; s. Walter William and Louise Marie (Jenkins) N.; m. Cinda Ann Miller, Apr. 15, 1967; children: Krista Suzanne, David Michael. B.A., LaSalle Coll., Phila., 1967; M.P.H., UCLA, 1969. Regional coordinator USPHS, Rockville, Md., 1969-71; v.p. Hollywood Presbyn. Hosp., Los Angeles, 1971-75; sr. v.p. Hollywood Presbyn. Med. ctr., 1975-77; v.p. adminstrn. Huntington Meml. Hosp, Pasadena, Calif., 1977-83; pres., chief exec. officer St. Joseph Hosp., Orange, Calif., 1983-90; pres. so. Calif. region St. Joseph Health System, 1987-90, exec. v.p., 1990-94; pres., CEO Children's Hosp., L.A., 1995—; preceptor UCLA Health Services Mgmt. Program, 1977—; chmn. bd. Health Plan of Am., 1985-91; chmn. Hosp. Coun. So. Calif., 1989. Exec. v.p. Mental Health Assn. in Los Angeles County, 1979-82; regional v.p. Calif. Mental Health Assn., 1982-83. W. Glenn Ebersole finalist Assn. Western Hosp., 1969; recipient USPHS letter commendation, 1971. Mem. Am. Coll. Hosp. Adminstrs., Am. Hosp. Assn. (ho. of dels. 1994—), Calif. Assn. Hosps. (chmn. 1990-91), Calif. Assn. Hosps. and Health Sys. (chmn. 1992), UCLA Hosp. Adminstrn. Alumni Assn. (pres. 1979-80), Pasadena C. of C. (v.p. 1980-82). Home: 20388 Via Marwah Yorba Linda CA 92686-4522 Office: Children's Hosp Los Angeles 4650 Sunset Blvd Los Angeles CA 90027 *Ambition is necessary for success, but success achieved at the expense of others is failure.*

NOCHIMSON, DAVID, lawyer; b. Paterson, N.J., June 19, 1943; s. Samuel S. and Mildred (Singer) N.; m. Roberta Maizel, June 5, 1966 (div. 1972); m. Gail Burgess, May 26, 1978. BA, Yale U., 1965; LLB, Columbia U., 1968; LLM, Australian Nat. U., Canberra, 1969. Bar: N.Y. 1970, Calif. 1977. Assoc. Paul, Weiss, Rifkind, Wharton and Garrison, N.Y.C., 1970-72; sr. v.p. Comprog Equities Corp., N.Y.C., 1972-76; assoc. Mitchell, Silberberg and Knupp, L.A., 1977-80, ptnr., 1980-83; ptnr. Ziffren, Brittenham and Branca, L.A., 1983—; mem. planning com. UCLA Entertainment Symposium, Los Angeles, 1979—, co-chmn. 1981-82. Contbr. articles to Encyclopedia of Investments, 1982, profl. jours. Fulbright scholar, 1968-69. Mem. ABA (forum com. on entertainment and sports industries 1982—, editor The Entertainment and Sports Lawyer 1982-89, chmn. 1989-92), Internat. Bar Assn. (Vice chmn. entertainment com. 1986-90), Am. Bar Found., Beverly Hills Bar Assn. Democrat. Jewish. Avocations: tennis, racquetball, playing piano, hiking. Office: Ziffren Brittenham & Branca 2121 Avenue of the Stars 32 D Los Angeles CA 90067-5010

NOCHLIN, LINDA, art history educator; b. N.Y.C., Jan. 30, 1931; d. Jules and Elka (Heller) Weinberg; m. Richard Pommer, June 3, 1968; children: Jessica Nochlin, Daisy Pommer. B.A., Vassar Coll., 1951; M.A., Columbia U., 1952; Ph.D., NYU, 1963; D (hon.), Colgate U., 1987. Instr. Vassar Coll., Poughkeepsie, N.Y., 1952-63, asst. prof., 1963-66, assoc. prof., 1966-69, prof., 1969-71, Mary Conover Mellon prof. art history, 1971-79; vis. prof. Columbia U. N.Y.C., 1967-68, 75-76, Stanford (Calif.) U., 1971, Hunter Coll., N.Y.C., 1970, City U. N.Y. Grad. Ctr., N.Y.C., 1975-76, Disting. prof. art history, 1980—; fellow Inst. of Humanities, 1980. Author: Realism, 1967, (with A.S. Harris) Women Artists: 1550-1950, 1976; contbr. (with A.S. Harris) articles to profl. jours.; bd. editors: (with A.S. Harris) Art Bull. Recipient Kingsley Porter prize, 1968; Harbison award for gifted teaching Danforth Found., 1972; Mademoiselle mag. Woman of Yr. award, 1977; CAA Critics prize, 1977; Fulbright fellow, 1959-59; Fels fellow, 1962-63; Am. Council Learned Socs. fellow, 1972-73; NEH fellow, 1977-78, Guggenheim fellow, 1984-85, Inst. for Advanced Studies fellow, 1985. Mem. AAUP, NOW, Coll. Art Assn. Am., Phi Beta Kappa. Office: Yale U Dept History of Art Yale Station New Haven CT 06520

NOCK, WILLIAM H., bank executive; b. Salisbury, Md., June 14, 1945; s. William H. Jr. and Ruth Esther (Green) N.; m. Linda Hughes, June 22, 1968; children: Susan Hunter, Meredith Allen. BS, U.S. Coast Guard Acad., 1967; MBA, U. Pa., 1973; postgrad., Rutgers U., 1981. Credit analyst 1st Union Nat. Bank, Charlotte, N.C., 1974; sr. loan officer 1st Union Nat. Bank, Statesville, N.C., 1974-76, Rocky Mount, N.C., 1976-77; br. adminstr. Nat. Bank S.C., Columbia, 1977-78, city exec., 1978-81; banking div. adminstr. Nat. Bank S.C., Sumter, 1981-85, pres., 1985—, also bd. dirs.; bd. dirs. NBSC Corp., SumBank Life Ins. Co, Sumter. Served to lt. USCG, 1967-72, Vietnam. Office: The Nat Bank of SC 207 N Main St Sumter SC 29150-4958

NOCKS, JAMES JAY, psychiatrist; b. Bklyn., Apr. 17, 1943; s. Henry and Pearl (Klein) N.; m. Ellen Jane Leblang, June 21, 1964; children: Randy, Jason. BA in English Lit., U. Pa., 1964, MD, 1968. Diplomate Nat. Bd. Med. Examiners, Am. Bd. Psychiatry and Neurology (psychiatry and addiction psychiatry), Am. Bd. Med. Mgmt. Rotating intern Chgo. Wesley Meml. Hosp., Northwestern U., 1968-69; resident psychiatry U. Pa., Phila., 1969-73; chief alcoholism program VA Med. Ctr., West Haven, Conn., 1975-87; asst. chief psychiatry svc. VA Med. Ctr., 1978-87; chief staff VA Med. Ctr., Coatesville, Pa., 1987—; sr. resident psychiatry U. Pa., 1971-72, chief resident psychiatry, 1972-73; asst. instr. psychiatry, 1971-73; clin. asst. prof. psychiatry Health Sci. Ctr. U. Tex., San Antonio, 1973-75; asst. clin. prof. psychiatry Yale U. Sch. Medicine, New Haven, 1975-80, assoc. clin. prof. psychiatry, 1980-87; clin. prof. psychiatry and human behavior Jefferson Med. Coll., Phila., 1987-91; prof. psychiatry Temple U. Sch. Medicine, Phila., 1991—. Contbr. chpts. in Psychiatry: Pre-Test, Self-Assessment and Review, 2d edit., 1982, 3d edit., 1984, Alcoholic Liver Disease, 1985; contbr. articles to profl. jours. Mem. exec. com. Med. Alumni Soc., U. Pa., 1989—. Major Med. Corps, USAF, 1973-75. Fellow Am. Psychiat. Assn. (cert. adminstrv. psychiatry); mem. Pa. Psychiat. Soc., Phila. Psychiat. Soc., Am. Soc. of Addiction Medicine (cert.), Assn. for Med. Edn. & Rsch. in Substance Abuse, Am. Assn. for Social Psychiatry, Am. Acad. Psychiatrists in Alcoholism & Addictions. Jewish. Avocations: bicycling, tennis, music. Office: VA Med Ctr Blackhorse Hill Rd Coatesville PA 19320-3313

NODA, HIROSHI, automotive company executive; b. Osaka, Japan, Feb. 13, 1938; came to the U.S., 1974; s. Feb. 13, 1938, Takeshi and Hisae (Fujii) N.; m. Takako Nishii, Apr. 24, 1966; children: Satoshi, Yasushi. BBA, Kobe U., Japan, 1961. Gen. mgr. sales Kawasaki Motors Japan, Akashi, 1969-73; mgr. planning Kawasaki Heavy Industries, Akashi, 1974, sr. mgr. planning, 1978-82; mgr. nat. dealer procurement Kawasaki Motor Corp. U.S.A., Santa Ana, Calif., 1974-76, mgr. market devel., 1976-78, v.p. mktg., 1982-86, pres., 1991—. Avocation: swimming. Home: 15 Skycrest Irvine CA 92715 Office: Kawasaki Motors Corp USA 9950 Jeronimo Rd Irvine CA 92718

NODDINGS, NEL, education educator, writer; b. Irvington, N.J., Jan. 19, 1929; d. Edward A. Rieth and Nellie A. (Connors) Walter; m. James A. Noddings, Aug. 20, 1949; children: Chris, Howard, Laurie, James, Nancy, William, Sharon, Edward, Vicky, Timothy. BA in Math., Montclair State Coll., 1949; MA in Math. Rutgers U., 1964; PhD in Edn., Stanford U., 1973; PhD (hon.), Columbia Coll., 1995. Cert. tchr., Calif., N.J. Tchr. Woodbury (N.J.) Publ Schs., 1949-52; tchr. math. dept. Matawan (N.J.) High Sch., 1958-62, chair, asst. prin., 1964-69; curriculum supr. Montgomery Twp. Pub. Schs., Skillman, N.J., 1970-72; dir. precollegiate edn. U. Chgo., 1975-76; asst. prof. Pa. State U., State College, 1973; from asst. prof. to assoc. prof. Stanford (Calif.) U., 1977-86, prof., 1986—, assoc. dean, 1990-92, acting dean, 1992-94, Lee L. Jacks prof. child edn., 1992—; bd. dirs. Ctr. for Human Caring Sch. Nursing, Denver, 1986-92; cons. NIE, NSF and various other sch. dists. Author: Caring: A Feminine Approach to Ethics and Moral Education, 1984, Women and Evil, 1989, (with W. Paul Shore) Awakening the Inner Eye: Intuition in Education, 1984, (with Carol Witherell) Stories Lives Tell, 1991, The Challenge to Care in Schools, 1992, Educating for Intelligent Belief or Unbelief, 1993, Philosophy of Education, Voices of Care (with Suzanne Gorden and Patricia Benner); mem. adv. bd. Am. Jour. Edn., Ednl. Theory, Sci. and Edn.; contbr. articles to profl. jours. Mem. disting. women's adv. bd. Coll. St. Catherine. NSF fellow Rutgers U., 1962-64; recipient Anne Roe award for Contbns. to Profl. Devel. of Women, Harvard Grad. Sch. Edn., 1993, Disting. Svc. medal Tchrs. Coll. Columbia, 1994. Fellow Philosophy of Edn. Soc. (pres.-elect 1990-91, pres. 1991-92); mem. Am. Ednl. Rsch. Assn., Am. Philos. Assn., John Dewey Soc. (pres. 1994—), Phi Beta Kappa (vis. scholar), Kappa Delta Pi, Laureate. Avocation: gardening. Office: Stanford U Sch of Edn Stanford CA 94305

NODELMAN, JARED ROBERT, investment advisor; b. N.Y.C., May 24, 1937; s. George and Ray (Mayerson) N.; children: Seth, Ilisa. BA, Ohio State U., 1958. Registered investment advisor. Pres. Commonwealth Assocs. Inc., San Juan, P.R., 1964-74, Inversiones Metropolitanas, Inc., Santa Rosa, Calif., 1974—, Orinoco Capital Advisers Ltd., N.Y.C. Mem. cabinet Marin Gen. Hosp., Pres.' Coun. Meml. Sloan Kettering Cancer Ctr. Recipient Leadership award Meml. Sloan-Kettering Cancer Ctr., N.Y.C., 1989. Mem. World Trade Club, St. Francis Yacht Club, San Francisco Yacht Club, San Francisco Rotary, Villa Taverna, Olympic Club. Avocation: sailing. Office: Orinco Capital Advisers Ltd Ste 903 1250 Jones St San Francisco CA 94109

NOE, ELNORA (ELLIE NOE), retired chemical company executive; b. Evansville, Ind., Aug. 23, 1928; d. Thomas Noe and Evelyn (West) Dieter. Student Ind. U.-Purdue U., Indpls. Sec., Pitman Moore Co., Indpls., 1946; with Dow Chem. Co., Indpls., 1960-90, pub. rels. asst. then mgr. employee commn., 1970-87, mgr. commty. rels., 1987-90, DowBrands Inc., 1986-90; vice chmn. corp. affairs discussion group, 1988-89, chmn. 1989-90; mem. steering com. Learn About Bus. Recipient 2d pl. award as Businesswoman of Yr., Indpls. Bus. and Profl. Women's Assn., 1980, Indpls. Profl. Woman of Yr. award Zonta, Altrusa, Soroptomist & Pilot Svc. Clubs, 1985, DowBrands Great Things Cmty. Svc. award, 1991. Mem. Am. Bus. Women Assn. (Woman of Yr. award 1965, past pres.), Ind. Assn. Bus. Communicators (hon., communicator of yr. 1977), Women in Comm. (Louise Eleanor Kleinhenz award 1984), Zonta (dist. pub. rels. chmn. 1978-80, area dir. 1980-

82, pres. Indpls. 1977-79, bd. dirs. 1993-95), Dow Indpls. Retiree Club (pres. 1995—).

NOE, GUY, social services administrator; b. Brussels, Jan. 28, 1934; came to U.S., 1955, naturalized, 1961; s. Marinus Cornelis and Johana Dorothea (Beijne) N.; 1 dau., Jeanette Sue. B.S., Regional Agrl. Sch., Loiret, France, 1954. Social worker State of Wyo., Casper, 1962-66; dir. Natrona County (Wyo.) Dept. Public Assistance, Casper, 1966-79; dir. Wyo. Div. Mental Health, Cheyenne, 1979-82, asst. adminstr. Divsn. of Youth Svcs., 1992—; former mgr. Platte County Office Pub. Assistance and Social Services, Wheatland, Wyo.; dir. low income energy assistance programs, 1994—; lectr. in field. V.p. Wyo. chpt. Big Bros., 1976-77; chmn. adv. coun. social svcs. State of Wyo., 1969-79; bd. dirs. Casper United Way, 1970—, Casper Salvation Army, 1970—, Casper chpt. ARC, 1977—; mem. Gov.'s Drug Abuse Adv. Bd., 1992—; pres. State Employees Assn. Named Outstanding Adminstr. State of Wyo., 1976; recipient Youth Svcs. award Wyo. Human Resources Confederation, 1988. Mem. Am. Public Welfare Assn. (Wyo. membership chmn.), Am. Soc. Public Adminstrn. Democrat. Club: Toastmasters. Home: 2731 Deming Blvd Cheyenne WY 82001-5709 Office: Dept Pub Assistance & Social Services Hathaway Bldg Cheyenne WY 82002

NOE, JAMES ALVA, judge; b. Billings, Mont., May 25, 1932; s. James Alva Sr. and Laura Madlen (Parmenter) N.; m. Patricia Arlene Caudill, Aug. 4, 1956; children: Kendra Sue, Jeffrey James, Bradley John, Kirkwood Merle. BA in Polit. Sci., U. Wash., 1954, LLB, 1957; LittD hon., Christian Theol. Sem., 1986. Bar: Wash. 1958, U.S. Dist. Ct. (we. dist.) Wash. 1958, U.S. Ct. Appeals (9th cir.) 1959. Dep. prosecuting atty. King County, Seattle, 1958-61; trial lawyer Williams, Kastner & Gibbs, Seattle, 1961-67; judge Seattle Mcpl. Ct., 1967-71, King County Superior Ct., 1971—. Moderator Christian Ch. (Disciples of Christ) in the U.S. and Can., 1977-79. Fellow Am. Bar Found.; mem. ABA (ho. of dels. 1976-78, 82-87, 91—, bd. govs. 1991-94, chmn. jud. adminstrn. divsn. 1988-89, chmn. nat. conf. state trial judges 1981-82), Wash. State Superior Ct. Judges Assn. (pres. 1984-85), Nat. Jud. Coll. (bd. dirs. 1988-91, 95—). Home: 8250 SE 61st St Mercer Island WA 98040-4902 Office: King County Courthouse 3rd And James W # 711 Seattle WA 98104

NOE, JERRE DONALD, computer science educator; b. McCloud, Calif., Feb. 1, 1923; s. Charles J. and Mae H. (Linebarger) N.; m. Mary A. Ward, Oct. 20, 1943 (dec.); children: M. Sherill (Mrs. Michael F. Roberts), Jeffrey W., Russell H.; m. Margarete Wöhlert, Sept. 10, 1983. B.S., U. Calif., 1943; Ph.D., Stanford U., 1948. Rsch. assoc. Radio Research Lab. Harvard and Am. Brit. Lab., Malvern, Eng., 1943-45; devel. engr. Hewlett-Packard Co., Palo Alto, Calif., 1946-48; rsch. engr. Stanford Research Inst., Menlo Park, Calif., 1948-53; asst. dir. engring. rsch., 1954-60, exec. dir. info. sci. and engring., 1961-68; prof. computer sci. U. Wash., Seattle, 1968-89, prof. emeritus, 1990—; chmn. dept. U. Wash., 1968-76; lectr. Stanford U., 1955-68; vis. prof. Virje Universiteit, Amsterdam, 1976-77; guest rsch. scientist Gesellschaft fur Mathematik und Datenverarbeitung (GMD), Bonn, Fed. Republic Germany, 1986-87; mem. Army Sci. Bd., 1984-90; trustee Internat. Computer Sci. Inst., 1991-93; panelist NRC, 1991-92. Mem. Assn. Computing Machinery, IEEE (nat. chmn. profl. group electronic computers 1956-57), Sigma Xi, Eta Kappa Nu, Tau Beta Pi. Tech. dir., devel. 1st computer for banking industry Bank Am. ERMA system, 1950-56. Home: 7524 34th Ave NW Seattle WA 98117-4723 Office: U Wash Dept Computer Sci & Engring Sieg Hall Seattle WA 98195-2350

NOEHREN, ROBERT, organist, organ builder; b. Buffalo, Dec. 16, 1910; s. Alfred H. and Juliet (Egelhoff) N.; m. Eloise Southern, Aug. 27, 1938; children: Judith, Arthur. Student Inst. Mus. Art, N.Y.C., 1929-30, Curtis Inst. Music, Phila., 1930-31; BMus, U. Mich., 1948; DMus (hon.), Davidson Coll., 1957. Instr., Davidson Coll., 1946-49; prof., univ. organist U. Mich., 1949-77, prof. emeritus, 1977—; vis. prof. Eastman Sch. Music, 1967, U. Kans., 1975; organ builder; important instruments include organ in St. John's Roman Cath. Cathedral, Milw., 1st Unitarian Ch., San Francisco, 1st Presbyn. Ch., Buffalo, St. Andrew's Episc. Ch., Newport News, Va., Calvary Episc. Ch., Rochester, Minn.; designer, cons., 1954—; concert tours of Europe, 1948—; soloist Phila. Orch., Philharmonia Hungarica, New Sinfonia; rec. artist Lyrichord, Urania, Orion, Delos records; spl. research old organs Europe, 17th and 18th century organs in France. Recipient Grande Prix du Disque. Contbr. articles profl. jours. Composer pieces for organ, piano, voice, chorus. Patentee combination action for organs. Home: 17605 Drayton Hall Way San Diego CA 92128-2057

NOEL, BARBARA HUGHES MCMURTRY, music educator; b. Mt. Vernon, Wash., Feb. 27, 1929; d. Lowell Robinson and Mary Evelyn (Hayton) Hughes; children: Sarah Kathleen, Martha Elizabeth. BM, U. Ky., 1951, MM, 1952; PhD, U. Ill., 1972; student, Oberlin Conservatory, 1947-49. Instr. music Union Coll., Barbourville, Ky., 1952-54; instr. music and fine arts Annie Wright Sem., Tacoma, Wash., 1957-63; organist, choirmaster Episc. churches, Calif., Wash., 1954-66; chmn. music dept. U. Richmond (Va.), 1971-76, Mankato (Minn.) State U., 1978-81; dean coll. humanities and fine arts Tex. Woman's U., Denton, 1978-81; prof. music U. Mass., Dartmouth, North Dartmouth, 1981-89; prof. music U. Mass., Dartmouth, 1990—; cons. for various music orgns. and univs., 1976—, textbook pubs., 1980—; reviewer Nat. Endowment for the Humanities. Book reviewer Providence Sunday Jour., 1984—; contbr. articles to music jours; contbr. New Grove Dictionary of Music, 1974. Bd. dirs. Community Symphony Orchs., Mankato, 1976-78, New Bedford, Mass., 1981-87. Grad. fellow Danforth Found., U. Ill., 1966-71. Mem. Coll. Music Soc. (treas. 1983-87, v.p. 1979-83, coun. mem.), Nat. Assn. Schs. Music (undergrad. commr. 1978-81). Episcopalian. Avocations: reading, traveling, hiking. Home: 73 Tucker Ln North Dartmouth MA 02747-3529 Office: U Mass Dartmouth North Dartmouth MA 02747

NOEL, CRAIG, performing arts company executive, producer. LHD (hon.), U. San Diego. Actor Old Globe Theatre, San Diego, 1937—, dir., 1939—, exec. prodr.; instituted Globe Ednl. Tours, 1974, Old Globe's multicultural theater component Teatro Meta, 1983; established Play Discovery Program, 1974—; Shakespeare Festival, 1949—; founder Calif. Theatre Coun.; former v.p. Calif. Confedn. Arts.; introduced various playwrights, such as Beckett, Ionesco, to San Diego at La Jolla Mus. Contemporary Art, then Falstaff Tavern renamed Cassius Carter Centre Stage, 1969; presenter original drama, 1939—. Dir. more than 200 works; prodr. 290 works; recent prodns. include Morning's at Seven, Shirley Valentine, The Norman Conquests, 1979, Taking Steps, 1984, Intimate Exchanges, 1987, The Night of the Iguana, 1987, The Boiler Room, 1987, The White Rose, 1991, Mr. A's Amazing Maze Plays, 1994. Receipient Gov.'s award for Arts, San Diego's Living Treasure award, Conservator Am. Arts award Am. Conservatory Theatre, Headliner award San Diego Press Club, San Diego Gentlemen of Distinction award, combined tribute Pub. Arts Adv. Coun. and San Diego County Bd. Suprs.; named Outstanding Citizen contbn. fine arts dept. U. Ariz. Alumni Assn., one of 25 persons who shaped city's history San Diego Union; year proclaimed in his honor Mayor Maureen O'Connor, San Diego, 1987. Office: Old Globe Theatre PO Box 2171 San Diego CA 92112-2171*

NOEL, DON OBERT, JR., newspaper columnist; b. Elizabeth, N.J., Nov. 27, 1931; s. Don O. and Catherine (Pyle) N.; m. Elizabeth Bradford Foulds, Aug. 29, 1953; 1 child, Emily Rebecca. BA in Am. Studies, Cornell U., 1954. Reporter Hartford (Conn.) Times, 1958-68, asst. mng. editor, 1968-69, editorial page editor, 1969-74, editor in chief, 1974-75; sr. corr. WFSB-TV, host Face The State Post-Newsweek Stas., 1975-84; polit. columnist op-ed page Hartford Courant, 1984—. Bd. sec. Blue Hills Civic Assn., Hartford, 1988—. Served alt. mil. duty Am. Friends Svc. Com., Tokyo, 1954-56. Recipient Sevellon Brown Meml. award New England AP, 1964, Nat. Journalism award AMA, 1972, Nat. Journalism award Am. Soc. Planning Officials, 1972, 74; fellow Alicia Patterson Found., 1966-67; finalist Pulitzer Prize for non-deadline reporting, 1964. Mem. Soc. of Friends. Avocations: gardening, birdwatching, language study. Home: 141 Ridgefield St Hartford CT 06112-1837 Office: Hartford Courant Co Op-Ed Page 285 Broad St Hartford CT 06115-2510

NOEL, EDWIN LAWRENCE, lawyer; b. St. Louis, July 11, 1946; s. Thomas Currie and Christine (Jones) N.; m. Nancy Carter Simpson, Feb. 7, 1970; children: Caroline, Edwin C. BA, Brown U., 1968; JD cum laude, St. Louis U., 1974. Bar: Mo. 1974, U.S. Dist. Ct. (ea. dist.) Mo. 1974, U.S. Ct.

Appeals (8th cir.) 1974, U.S. Ct. Appeals (6th cir.) 1978, U.S. Ct. Appeals (7th cir.) 1994, U.S. Supreme Ct. 1986. Ptnr. Armstrong, Teasdale, Schlafly & Davis, St. Louis, 1974—; mng. ptnr., 1993—; bd. dirs. Elcom Industries, St. Louis, Home Fed. Savs. Bank of Mo., 1988-93. Bd. dirs. Edgewood Children's Ctr., St. Louis, 1982-92, St. Louis Assn. for Retarded Citizens, 1984-87, Churchill Sch., 1988-94, Whitfield Sch., 1991—; chmn. Mo. Clean Water Com., Jefferson City, 1982-86; chmn. environ. com. St. Louis Regional Commerce and Growth Assn., 1982-88. Mem. Mo. Bar Assn., Bar Assn. Met. St. Louis. Republican. Episcopalian. Home: 301 S Mcknight Rd Saint Louis MO 63124-1884 Office: Armstrong Teasdale Schlafly & Davis 1 Metropolitan Sq Saint Louis MO 63102-2740

NOEL, FRANKLIN LINWOOD, federal magistrate judge; b. N.Y.C., Dec. 7, 1951; s. Charles Alexander and Mayme (Loth) N.; m. Ellen Barbara Perl, Sept. 15, 1979; children: Kate Alexandra, Charles David. BA, SUNY, Binghamton, 1974; JD, Georgetown U., 1977. Bar: D.C. 1977, U. S. Dist. Ct. D.C. 1978, U.S. Ct. Appeals (D.C. cir.) 1977, Pa. 1979, Minn. 1983, U.S. Ct. Appeals (8th cir.) 1983, U.S. Dist. Ct. Minn. 1984. Assoc. Arnold & Porter, Washington, 1977-79; asst. dist. atty. Phila. Dist. Attys. Office, 1979-83; asst. U.S. atty. U.S. Attys. Office, Mpls., 1983-89; U.S. magistrate judge U.S. Dist. Ct., St. Paul, 1989—; legal writing instr. U. Minn., Mpls., 1989-92. Mem. League of Am. Wheelman, Phi Beta Kappa. Episcopalian. Avocation: bicycling. Office: US Dist Ct 638 US Courthouse 316 N Robert St Saint Paul MN 55101

NOËL, LAURENT, bishop, educator; b. St. Just de Bretenieres, Que., Can., Mar. 19, 1920; s. Remi and Albertine (Nadeau) N. B.A., Coll. de Levis, 1940; L.Th., Laval U., 1944, L.Ph., 1948; D.Th., Inst. Angelicum, Rome, 1951. Ordained priest Roman Catholic Ch., 1944; prof. theology Laval U., 1946-48, 52-63, prof. ethics Med. Sch., 1952-63; vice rector Grand Sem., Sch. Theology, 1961-63; aux. bishop Que., 1963-74; apostolic administr. Diocese of Hauterive, 1974-75; bishop Diocese of Trois-Rivieres, Que., 1975—; Provincial chaplain Assn. des Infirmieres Catholiques, 1958—; chaplain Syndicat Profl. des Infirmieres Catholiques, 1958-63. Author: Precis. de morale medicale, 1962. Address: Bishop's House, CP 879, Trois Rivières, PQ Canada G9A 5J9

NOEL, MICHAEL LEE, utility executive; b. Rapid City, S.D., Apr. 5, 1941; s. Milton George and Merel Lyreen (Roth) N.; children—Christy Carole, Craig Arnold. B.S. in Finance cum laude, Calif. State U., Long Beach, 1964; M.B.A. summa cum laude, U. So. Calif., 1973. With So. Calif. Edison Co., Rosemead, 1964—, mgr. corp. planning, 1974-75, asst. treas., 1975-76, treas., 1976—, v.p., 1980—; guest lectr. U. So. Calif., Fullerton, Calif. State U., Long Beach; bd dirs. Current Income Shares, Inc., Hancock Savs. and Loan Assn., Software Toolworks Inc. Chmn., bd. dirs. Los Angeles Jr. C. of C. Mem. L.A. Soc. Fin. Analysts, Pacific Coast Elec. Assn., L.A. Treas., Seacliff Tennis Club. Club: Seacliff Balboa Yacht. Home: 353 Ultimo Ave Long Beach CA 90814-3200 Office: So Calif Edison Co 2244 Walnut Grove Ave Rosemead CA 91770-3714

NOEL, RANDALL DEANE, lawyer; b. Memphis, Oct. 19, 1953; s. D.A. and Patricia G. Noel; m. Lissa Johns, May 28, 1977; children: Lauren Elizabeth, Randall Walker. BBA with honors, U. Miss., 1975, JD, 1978. Bar: Miss. 1978, U.S. Dist. Ct. (no. and so. dists.) Miss. 1978, Tenn. 1979, U.S. Dist. Ct. (we., mid. and ea. dists.) Tenn. 1979, U.S. Ct. Appeals (5th and 6th cirs.) 1984, U.S. Supreme Ct. 1986. Assoc. Armstrong, Allen, Braden, Goodman, McBride & Prewitt, Memphis, 1978-85; ptnr. Armstrong, Allen, Prewitt, Gentry, Johnston & Holmes, Memphis, 1985—, mgr. litigation practice group, 1990—. Mem. fin. com. Memphis in May Internat. Festival, 1980-81; sec., gen. counsel Carnival Memphis, 1981—; bd. dirs. Christ United Meth. Ch., Memphis, 1984-87, 89-91, trustee, 1991-93; mem. Leadership Memphis, 1994-95. Fellow Tenn. Bar Found.; mem. ABA (Young Lawyers Divsn., fellow, dir. 1988-90, editor The Affiliate newsletter 1987-88, dir. Affiliate Outreach project 1988—, vice chmn. Award of Achievement com. 1986, ALI-ABA bd. 1992—, ALI-ABA continuing edn. com. 1993—), Am. Counsel Assn. (bd. dirs. 1992—), Tenn. Bar Assn. (pres. young lawyers conf. 1990—, pres. litigation sect. 1988, treas. 1986, mem. bd. govs. 1989—, Pres.'s Disting. Svc. award 1988, 89), Memphis and Shelby County Bar Assn. (mem. jud. recommendations, law week and memberships coms.), Miss. Bar Assn., Def. Rsch. Inst., Tenn. Def. Lawyers Assn., Am. Judicature Soc. (bd. dirs. 1992—. Home: 2938 Tishomingo Ln Memphis TN 38111-2627 Office: Armstrong Allen Prewitt Gentry Johnston & Holmes 80 Monroe Ste 700 Memphis TN 38103

NOËL HUME, IVOR, retired antiquary, consultant; b. London, Eng., 1927; s. Cecil and Gladys Mary (Bagshaw Mann) Noël H. Student, Framlingham Coll., Suffolk, 1936-39, St. Lawrence Coll., Kent, 1942-44; L.H.D. (hon.), U. Pa., 1976, Coll. William and Mary, 1983. Archaeologist Guildhall Mus. Corp., London, 1949-57; chief archaeologist Colonial Williamsburg, Va., 1957-64; dir. dept. archaeology Colonial Williamsburg, 1964-72, resident archaeologist, 1972-87, ret., 1987; guest curator Steuben Glass Co., 1990, dir. Roanoke Project, 1991-93; rsch. assoc. Smithsonian Instn., 1959—; archaeol. cons. to Govt. of Jamaica, 1967-69; vice chmn. gov's adv. com. Va. Rsch. Ctr. for Hist. Archaeology, 1970-76; mem., 1971-76; mem. Va. Historic Landmarks Bd., 1985-87; mem. rev. Panel NEH, 1973-77; mem. Coun. Inst. Early Am. History and Culture, 1974-77; chair Jamestown Rediscovery Adv. Bd., 1994-95. Author: Archaeology in Britain, 1953, (with Audrey Noël Hume) Tortoises, Terrapins and Turtles, 1954, Treasure in the Thames, 1956, Great Moments in Archaeology, 1957, Here Lies Virginia, 1963, 1994, 1775; Another Part of the Field, 1966, Historical Archaeology, 1969, Artifacts of Early America, 1970, All the Best Rubbish, 1974, Early English Delftware, 1977, Martin's Hundred, 1982, The Virginia Adventure, 1994, Shipwreck; History from the Bermuda Reefs, 1995; contbr. articles to profl. jours.; Writer-dir.: (film) Doorway to the Past, 1968; writer, narrator: (TV movie) The Williamsburg File, 1976, Search for a Century, 1981; author pseudonymous novels, 1971, 72. Bd. dirs. Jamestown-Yorktown Found., 1987-91, Flowerdew Hundred Found., 1988—. With Indian Army, 1944-45. Recipient spl. award for hist. archaeology U.S.C., 1975, Achievement award Nat. Soc. Daus. Founders and Patriots Am., 1989, Nat. Soc. Daus. of the Am. Colonists, 1990; named Officer of the Brit. Empire (OBE), 1992. Fellow Soc. Antiquaries London, Am. Antiquarian Soc., Zool. Soc. London; mem. Soc. Hist. Archaeology (Harrington medal 1991), Soc. for Post-Medieval Archaeology (v.p. 1967-76), Kent Archaeol. Soc. (Gt. Britain), Va. Archeol. Soc. (hon., profl. Archaeologist of Yr. award 1980), English Ceramic Circle, Glass Circle. Home: 2 W Circle Williamsburg VA 23185

NOELKE, PAUL, lawyer; b. La Crosse, Wis., Feb. 10, 1915; s. Carl Bernard and Mary Amelia (O'Meara) N.; m. Mary Jo Kamps, May 4, 1943; children: Paul William, Mary Nesius, Ann Witt, Kate Helms. A.B. magna cum laude, Marquette U., 1936, J.D. cum laude, 1938; LL.M., U. Chgo., 1947; D.H.L. (hon.), Mt. Senario Coll., 1976. Bar: Wis. 1938, D.C. 1975, U.S. Dist. Ct. (ea. dist.) Wis. 1938, U.S. Supreme Ct. 1960. Assoc. firm Miller, Mack & Fairchild, 1938-40; asst. prof. law Marquette U., 1940-42; spl. asgt. FBI, 1942-45; assoc. Quarles & Brady and predecessor firms, Milw., 1943-52, ptnr., 1952-85, of counsel, 1985—. Trustee Viterbo Coll., LaCrosse, Sacred Heart Sch. of Theology, Hales Corners, Wis.; mem. adv. bd. Cardinal Stritch Coll., Milw.; past chmn. Pres.'s Coun. Marquette U.; past pres. Serra Internat., Chgo.; past chmn. Bd. Tax Rev., Village of Shorewood, Wis. Recipient Alumnus of Yr. award Marquette U., 1980; recipient Conf. award NCCJ, 1967. Mem. ABA, Wis. State Bar Assn., Milw. Bar Assn., Am. Judicature Soc., Order Holy Sepulchre, Alpha Sigma Nu. Roman Catholic. Home: 2462 N Prospect Ave Milwaukee WI 53211 Office: 411 E Wisconsin Ave Milwaukee WI 53202-4409

NOER, RICHARD J., physics educator, researcher; b. Madison, Wis., July 3, 1937; s. Rudolf J. and Anita M. (Showerman) N.; m. Raymonde Tasset, Aug. 17, 1967; children—Geoffrey, Catherine. B.A., Amherst Coll., 1958; Ph.D., U. Calif., Berkeley, 1963. Physicist Atomic Energy Research, Harwell, Eng., 1963-64; asst. prof. physics Amherst Coll., Mass., 1964-66; asst. prof. physics Carleton Coll., Northfield, Minn., 1966-68, assoc. prof. physics, 1968-72, prof. physics, 1972—; dept. chair, 1974-77, 89-92; vis. physicist U. Paris, Orsay, France, 1972-73; physicist Ames Lab., Iowa, summers 1977-80, 82-84; rsch. physicist U. Geneva, 1980-81, 84-85; vis. scientist Cornell U. summers 1986, 88-91; vis. physicist Centre d'Etudes Nucléaires, Saclay, France, 1992-93. Co-author: Revolutions in Physics, 1972; contbr. articles to profl. jours. Mem. Am. Phys. Soc., Am. Assn.

Physics Tchrs., AAAS, Phi Beta Kappa, Sigma Xi. Home: 101 Winona St Northfield MN 55057-2232 Office: Carleton Coll Dept Physics Northfield MN 55057

NOETHER, EMILIANA PASCA, historian, educator; b. Naples, Italy; came to U.S., 1919; d. Guglielmo and Bianca (Dramis) Pasca; m. Gottfried E. Noether, Aug. 1, 1942; 1 dau., Monica Gail. AB, Hunter Coll., N.Y.C., 1943; MA, Columbia U., 1944, PhD, 1948. Instr., then asst. prof. history Douglass Coll., Rutgers U., 1947-52; research asso. Center Internat. Studies, Mass. Inst. Tech., 1952-54; from lectr. to prof. history Regis Coll., Weston., Mass., 1959-66; prof. history Simmons Coll., Boston, 1966-68, U. Conn., Storrs, 1968-87. Editor: Italian sect. Am. Hist. Rev, 1958-75, Recently Published Articles, 1976-90, Garland Modern History Dissertation Series (Italy), 1989—; author: Seeds of Italian Nationalism, 2d edit, 1969, also articles.; co-editor, contbr.: Modern Italy: A Topical History Since 1861, 1974; contbg. editor: The American Constitution as a Symbol and Reality for Italy, 1989. AAUW fellow, 1946-47, 62-63; Bunting Inst. fellow, 1961-62; sr. Fulbright scholar Florence, Italy, 1965-66; Rome, 1982; research grantee Am. Philos. Soc., summer 1970; U. Conn. Research Found. grantee, 1969-71, 73-77, 81-86. Mem. Am. Hist. Assn. (council 1975-78, chmn. com. women historians 1976), Soc. Italian Studies (chmn. prize award and citation com. 1968-69, adv. council 1979-82, adv. council v.p. 1981-83, pres. 1983-85), Berkshire Conf. Women Historians (sec. 1962-64, pres. 1967-71), Coordinating Com. on Women in Hist. Profession, AAUW, Phi Beta Kappa, Pi Gamma Mu., Phi Kappa Phi. Home: 988 Blvd of Arts Apt 1117 Sarasota FL 34236

NOFER, GEORGE HANCOCK, lawyer; b. Phila., June 14, 1926. B.A., Haverford Coll., 1949; J.D., Yale U., 1952. Bar: Pa. 1953. Pvt. practice Phila., 1953—; ret. ptnr. Schnader, Harrison, Segal & Lewis, Phila., 1961-91, sr. counsel, 1992—; lectr. probate law, 1955—. Pres. bd. sch. dirs. Upper Moreland Twp., Pa., 1965-73; trustee Beaver Coll., Glenside, Pa., 1969-76; elder, trustee, deacon Abington Presbyn. Ch., Pa.; vice chmn. bd. dirs. Phila. Presbyn. Homes, Inc.; bd. dirs. A.C. Bell Assn. for the Deaf, Washington. Fellow Am. Coll. Trust and Estate Counsel (regent 1975—, pres. 1983-84, chmn. Pa. 1973-78), Am. Law Inst., Am. Bar Found.; mem. ABA (standing com. on specialization 1980-86, chmn. 1983-86), Pa. Bar Assn., Phila. Bar Assn., Internat. Acad. Estate and Trust Law, Phi Beta Kappa, Phi Delta Phi. Home: 241 Pine St Philadelphia PA 19106-4313 Office: Schnader Harrison Segal & Lewis 1600 Market St Ste 3600 Philadelphia PA 19103-7236

NOFFSINGER, ANNE-RUSSELL L., former nursing administrator, educator; b. Frankfort, Ky., Feb. 4, 1932; d. Charles Russell and Hettie Lee (Ward) Lillis; m. J. Philip Noffsinger, July 1, 1966; children: Ward, Gretchen, Hans. Diploma, Good Samaritan Hosp., Lexington, Ky., 1952; BA in English, U. Ky., 1966, MA in Counseling, 1968, EdD in Psychology, 1979; MSN, U. Tenn., 1986. Instr. fundamentals of nursing Good Samaritan Hosp., Lexington, 1955-56; assoc. dir. nursing St. Joseph Hosp., Lexington, 1958-61; instr. pediatric nursing Good Samaritan Hosp. Sch. Nursing, Lexington, 1961-68; prof., chmn. nursing Lexington Community Coll., 1968-94; asst. to pres. for resource devel. and external rels., 1994—. Co-author: Counseling. Recipient U. Ky. Alumni Great Teaching award; Helene Fuld grantee. Mem. ANA (del.), KNA (former pres.), Nat. League for Nursing, KLN (former pres.), ODK, KCADN, Sigma Theta Tau, Omicron Delta Kappa, Phi Delta Kappa.

NOFSINGER, WILLIAM MORRIS, engineering executive; b. Orange, N.J., Sept. 11, 1932; s. Charles William and Grace Elizabeth (Morris) N.; m. Bonnie Jean Haisler, Nov. 6, 1965; children: Barry Jean, Betsy Jayne. BS in Chem. Engring., U. Kans., 1955. Registered profl. engr. With The C.W. Nofsinger Co., Kansas City, Mo., various positions to v.p., 1959-78, pres., 1978—. Lt. USAF, 1955-58, capt. Res. Fellow Am. Inst. Chem. Engrs.; mem. NSPE, Am. Chem. Soc., Mo. Soc. Profl. Engrs., Kans. Engring. Soc. Republican. Lodge: Rotary (v.p. 1983-84, pres. elect 1984-85, pres. 1985-86). Home: 6645 Brookside Rd Kansas City MO 64113-1837 Office: The CW Nofsinger Co 4700 E 63rd St Kansas City MO 64130-4630

NOFZIGER, SALLY ALENE, diversified utility company executive; b. San Francisco; m. Charles E. Nofziger; 1 child, Paul. BS in Bus. Administrn. and Econs., Portland State U., 1980, MBA, 1986. Asst. sec. PacifiCorp, Portland, Oreg., 1980-83, corp. sec., 1983-89, v.p., corp. sec., 1989—. Mem. Am. Soc. Corp. Secs. (regional group pres. 1988-87, nat. bd. dirs. 1988-91). Office: PacifiCorp 700 NE Multnomah St Portland OR 97232-2131

NOGALES, LUIS GUERRERO, communications company executive; b. Madera, Calif., Oct. 17, 1943; s. Alejandro Cano and Florence (Guerrero) N.; children: Alicia Fipp, Maria Cristina. BA in Polit. Sci., San Diego State U., 1966; JD, Stanford U., 1969. Asst. to pres. Stanford U., Calif., 1969-72; White House fellow, asst. to sec. U.S. Dept. Interior, Washington, 1972-73; exec. v.p., dir. Golden West Broadcasters, L.A., 1973-80; pres. Nogales, Bermudex, Chase and Tamayo, L.A., 1981-82; chmn., chief exec. officer UPI, Washington, 1983-86; pres. ECO Internat. News Svc., 1987, Univision, 1987-88; gen . ptnr. Nogales Castro Ptnrs., 1989-90; pres. Nogales Ptnrs., L.A., 1990—; bd. dir. The Bank of Calif., San Francisco, Stanford U. Ctr. for Pub. Svc., The Ford Found. Bd. dirs. State of Calif. Bd. Higher Edn., Sacramento, 1973-79, Los Angeles Redevel. Agy., 1973-76, United Way Am., Alexandria, Va., 1984-88; trustee Claremont U. Ctr. and Grad. Sch., 1987, Stanford U.; chmn. MALDEF, 1980-82. Office: 2049 Century Park E Bldg 39 Los Angeles CA 90067-1905

NOGAWA, KIYOSHI, computer company executive. Sr. v.p., chief adminstrn. officer Fujitsu Am. Inc., San Jose, Calif. Office: Fujitsu America Inc 3055 Orchard Dr San Jose CA 95134

NOGELO, ANTHONY MILES, health care company executive; b. Framingham, Mass., Apr. 2, 1943; s. Anthony Joseph and Lillian Carol (Nowick) N.; m. Gerry C. Stugis, Mar. 20, 1965; children: Laura Elizabeth, Michael Joseph. B.A. in Econs., Tufts U., 1964; M.B.A., Harvard Bus. Sch., 1968. Mgr. fin. planning and analysis Gen. Foods Corp., White Plains, N.Y., 1968-73; ptnr. Paul E. Dean, Greenwich, Conn., 1973-74; asst. treas. Ludlow Corp., Needham Heights, Mass., 1974-80; v.p., treas. Nat. Med. Care Inc., Boston, 1980-85; v.p., chief fin. officer, treas. Nat. Med. Care Inc., 1985—. Served to lt. j.g. USNR, 1964-66. Mem. Fin. Execs. Inst., Treas. Club Boston. Home: 19 Washington Dr Sudbury MA 01776-2935 Office: Nat Med Care Inc 1601 Trapelo Rd Waltham MA 02154-7350

NOGUCHI, THOMAS TSUNETOMI, author, forensic pathologist; b. Fukuoka, Japan, Jan. 4, 1927; came to U.S., 1952; s. Wataru and Tomika Narahashi N. D of Medicine, Nippon Med. Sch., Tokyo, 1951; LLD (hon.), U. Braz Cubas Fedn. Faculties Mogi Das Cruzes, Sao Paolo, Brazil, 1980; DSc (hon.), Worcester State Coll., 1985. Dep. med. examiner Los Angeles County Dept. Chief Med. Examiner, L.A., 1961-67, coroner, 1967-82; prof. forensic pathology U. So. Calif., L.A., 1982—. Author: Coroner, 1983 (N.Y. Times Bestseller 1984), Coroner At Large, 1985; (fiction) Unnatural Causes, 1988, Physical Evidence, 1990. Fellow Am. Acad. Forensic Sci. (chmn. sect. 1966); mem. Nat. Assn. Med. Examiners (pres. 1983), Calif. State Coroners Assn. (pres. 1974), World Assn. Med. Law (v.p.). Republican. Avocations: fine arts, gourmet Oriental cooking, painting stills and abstracts. Home: 1110 Avoca Ave Pasadena CA 91105-3405 Office: U So Calif Med Ctr 1200 N State St Rm 2520 Los Angeles CA 90033

NOHA, EDWARD J., insurance company executive; b. N.Y.C., Aug. 25, 1927; married. BBA, Pace Coll. With Dept. Justice, 1944-52, Met. Life Ins. Co., 1952-55; exec. v.p. Allstate Ins. Co., Chgo., 1955-74; chmn. bd., pres., CEO Continental Assurance Co., Chgo., 1955-74, CNA Ins. Cos., Chgo., 1975-92; chmn. bd. CNA Fin. Corp., 1992—; chmn. bd. Nat. Fire Ins. Co. of Hartford, Inc., Transcontinental Ins. Co.; dir. Loews Corp.; mem. Property-Casualty Ins. Coun.; trustee Am. Inst. Property & Liability Underwriters, Ins. Inst. Am.; chmn. Chgo. Econ. Devel. Commn., 1992—. Office: CNA Fin Corp CNA Plz 33 South Wacker Chicago IL 60685

NOHRNBERG, JAMES CARSON, English language educator; b. Berkeley, Calif., Mar. 19, 1941; s. Carson and Geneva Gertrude (Gibbs) N.; m. Stephanie Payson Lamport, June 14, 1964; children: Gabrielle L., Peter Carson L. Student, Kenyon Coll., 1958-60; BA, Harvard Coll., 1962, post-

grad., 1965-68; PhD, U. Toronto, Ont., Can., 1970. Teaching fellow dept. English U. Coll., U. Toronto, 1963-64; jr. fellow Soc. of Fellows Harvard U., 1965-68; acting instr. dept. English Yale U., New Haven, 1968-69, lectr. dept. English, 1969-70, asst. prof. dept. English, 1970-75, assoc. prof., 1975; prof. English U. Va., Charlottesville, 1975—; adj. instr. English Harvard U., Cambridge, 1967; lectr. various univs., 1974-94; Gauss seminar in criticism lectr. Princeton U., 1987. Author: The Analogy of the Faerie Queene, 1976, 81, Like Unto Moses: The Constituting of an Interruption, 1995; mem. editl. bd. Spenser Ency., 1977-90; editor vols.; contbr. articles to profl. jours. Woodrow Wilson fellow, 1962, jr. fellow Harvard U., 1965-68, Morse fellow Yale U., 1974-75, U. Va. Ctr. for Advanced Studies fellow, 1975-78, Guggenheim fellow, 1981-82, Ind. U. Inst. for Advanced Studies fellow, 1991. Mem. MLA, Spenser Soc. Presbyterian. Avocations: writing poetry, collecting books and records. Home: 1874 Wayside Pl Charlottesville VA 22903-1631 Office: U Va Dept English Bryan Hall Charlottesville VA 22903

NOIA, ALAN JAMES, utility company executive; b. Selbitz, Germany, Feb. 18, 1947; came to U.S., 1949; s. Fiore and Anneliese (Gossler) N.; m. Cynthia Dee Rathman. BSEE, U. Va., Charlottesville, 1969. Engr. Potomac Edison Co., Hagerstown, Md., 1969-72; data base administr., supr. tech. svcs. Allegheny Power Svc. Corp., Greensburg, Pa., 1973-75; staff asst. Allegheny Power Svc. Corp., N.Y.C., 1975-79; asst. v.p., treas. Allegheny Power System, N.Y.C., 1979-80, treas., 1980-82, v.p., treas., 1983-84, v.p. bulk power supply, CFO, 1987-90; pres. Potomac Edison Co., Hagerstown, Md., 1990-94; pres., COO Allegheny Power System, Inc., N.Y.C., 1994—, also bd. dirs.; bd. dirs. Allegheny Power Svc. Corp., Monongahela Power Co., Potomac Edison Co., West Penn Power Co., Allegheny Generating Co.; mem. Balt.-Washington Internat. Airport Commn. Trustee East Ctrl. Nuclear Group, N.Y.C., 1979—; chmn. elec. engring. indsl. adv. bd. U. Va. Mem. Md. C of C. (bd. dirs.), Phi Eta Sigma, Eta Kappa Nu, Tau Beta Pi. Roman Catholic. Home: Childacrest Dr Boonsboro MD 21713 Office: Allegheny Power System Inc 12 E 49th St New York NY 10017

NOJUNAS, THOMAS MICHAEL, hospital executive; b. Harrisburg, Pa., Feb. 3, 1950; s. William James and Ann Marie (Moleski) N.; m. Patricia Ann Murphy, Sept. 19, 1970; children: Tara, Michael. BS in Bus. Adminstrn., Drexel U. 1971; M Health and Hosp. Adminstrn., U. Fla., 1973. Ops. analysis asst. mgmt. info. systems dept. Lankenau Hosp., Phila., 1969-70; grad. asst. office planning and budgeting J. Hillis Miller Health Ctr., Gainesville, Fla., 1972; adminstrv. resident, asst. The Milton S. Hershey Med. Ctr. Pa. State U., Hershey, 1972-73; pres Bryn Mawr Rehab. Hosp., Malvern, Pa., 1973—; adv. grad. program health service adminstrn. Pa., Am. Hosp. Assn., Chgo., Nat. Assn. Rehab. Facilities, McLean, Va. Fellow Am. Coll. Health Care Execs., Hosp. Fin. Mgmt. Assn. Roman Catholic. Office: Nojunas & Assos 1327 Karen Lane Radnor PA 19087

NOKES, JOHN RICHARD, retired newspaper editor, author; b. Portland, Oreg., Feb. 23, 1915; s. James Abraham and Bernice Alfaretta (Bailey) N.; m. Evelyn Junkin, Sept. 13, 1936; children: Richard Gregory, William G., Gail (Mrs. William M. Hulden), Douglas J., Kathy E. B.S., Linfield Coll., 1936, LHD (hon.), 1988. With The Oregonian, Portland, 1936-82, city editor, 1950-65, asst. mng. editor, 1965-71, mng. editor, 1971-75, editor, 1975-82; disting. vis. prof. journalism Linfield Coll., 1982-85; cons. editor The Hong Kong Standard, 1994. Author: American Form of Government, 1939, Columbia's River: The Voyages of Robert Gray 1787-1793, 1991; editor Oreg. Edn. Jour., 1944. Bd. dirs. Portland U.S.O., 1968-72, U.S. Coast Guard Acad. Found., 1972-74, Portland Opera Assn., 1976-78; trustee Linfield Coll., 1977-93; v.p. Oreg. Sch. Assn., 1983-85, chmn. Oreg. UN Day, 1983. Lt. (j.g.) USNR, 1944-46; comdr. Res. (ret.). Mem. Navy League U.S. (pres. Portland coun. 1969-71), Linfield Coll. Alumni Assn. (pres. 1940), World Affairs Coun. Oreg. (pres. 1973-74), AP Mng. Editors Assn. (dir. 1973-80), Am. Soc. Newspaper Editors, N.W. China Coun., Sigma Delta Chi (pres. Willamette Valley chpt. 1975-76). Republican. Methodist. Club: Multnomah Athletic (Portland). Home: 14650 SW 103rd Ave Tigard OR 97224-4740

NOKES, MARY TRIPLETT, educator, counselor, artist; b. Weatherford, Okla., Sept. 6, 1920; d. Ernest Carlton and Eva Hannah (Claridge) Triplett; m. George Willis Malcom Nokes, July 11, 1937; 1 child, William Careton. BA, Cen. State U., 1943; Masters Degree, U. Okla., 1949, Doctors Degree, 1969. Tchr., sec. Okla. Edn. Assn., Oklahoma City, 1955-83; 1st v.pv. Interant. Porcelain Artist, 1966-68, pres., 1968-70, sec. bd., 1989-92; pres. Olka. State U., 1975-91. Sponsor Student Coun., 1955-83; pres. Okla. State China Painting Tchr., 1986-87. Named Vol. Woman of Yr. Salvation Army, Okla., 1992-93, Personality of South, 1994-95, Cmty. Leader for Noteworthy Ams., 1994-95, Cmty. Leader Okla. City, 1994-95; recipient proclamation Mayor Okla. City, 1994-95. Mem. Internat. Porcelain Art Tchrs. (past v.p., past pres., regional chmn., sec. to internat. bd. dirs.), Intercontinental Biographical Assn., C. of C. (sec.), Les Lefeyetts Home Club (pres. 1941-43), Garden Club (pres.), Sooners Art Club (pres. 1991-93, 93-94, 94-95), Kermac Art Club, Alpha Phi Sigma, Kappa Delta Phi, Kappa Kappa Iota. Baptist. Home: 4125 NW 57th St Oklahoma City OK 73112-1505

NOLAN, ALAN TUCKER, retired lawyer; b. Evansville, Ind., Jan. 19, 1923; s. Val and Jeannette (Covert) N.; m. Elizabeth Clare Titsworth, Aug. 26, 1947 (dec. Nov. 1967); children: Patrick A., Thomas C., Mary F., Elizabeth T., John V.; m. Jane Ransel DeVoe, Feb. 7, 1970; adopted children: John C. DeVoe, Ellen R. DeVoe, Thomas R. DeVoe. AB in Govt., Ind. U., 1944, DHL (hon.), 1993; LLB, Harvard U., 1947. Bar: Ind. 1947. Law clk U.S. Ct. Appeals (7th Cir.), Chgo., 1947-48; assoc. Ice, Miller, Donadio & Ryan, Indpls., 1948-58, ptnr., 1958-93, ret., 1993—; chmn. Disciplinary Commn. Supreme Ct. Ind., Indpls., 1966-73; vice-chmn. bd. dirs. Union City Body Co., Inc., 1982-92. Author: The Iron Brigade, 1961, As Sounding Brass, 1964, Lee Considered, 1991; contbg. editor The Civil War, 1985-89; contbr. numerous articles to profl. jours. Life mem. NAACP Indpls., v.p., 1950-54; bd. dirs., founder Ind. Civil Liberties Union, Indpls., 1953-60; bd. dirs. Indpls. Art League 1981-87; chmn., bd. trustees Ind. Hist. Soc., Indpls. 1986—; trustee Eiteljorg Mus., Indpls., 1987-93. Fellow Co. Mil. Historians, Am. Bar Found.; mem. ABA, Ind. Bar Assn., Indpls. Bar Assn. (bd. mgrs. 1958-60, chmn. Grievance Com. 1960-64), Indpls. Civil War Round Table. Democrat. Roman Catholic. Avocations: travel, gardening, reading. Home: 4118 N Pennsylvania St Indianapolis IN 46205-2611 Office: PO Box 82001 1 American Sq Indianapolis IN 46282-0001

NOLAN, BARRY HANCE, publishing company executive; b. Easton, Pa., Sept. 15, 1942; s. Arthur James Nolan and Marion (Hance) Slater; m. Janet Lynch, Mar. 20, 1971 (dec. Mar. 1981); 1 child, Tracy; m. Catherine McDermott, Feb. 19, 1983; children: Craig, Kelsey. AB in Econs., Princeton U., 1964; MBA, Columbia U., 1966. Account exec. Papert, Koenig, Lois Advt., N.Y.C., 1966-68; group mgr. new bus.'s Butterick div. Am. Can, N.Y.C., 1969-72; dir. mktg. planning Current Inc. subs. Deluxe Check Printers, Colorado Springs, Colo., 1973-77; v.p. mktg., 1977-79, pres., chief exec. officer, 1980-89; pres., chief exec. officer ECM, Inc., Colorado Springs, Colo., 1991—; asst. to pres. Pacific Water Works Supply Co., Seattle, 1979-80. Pres. bd. dirs. Pikes Peak br. Cystic Fibrosis Found., Colorado Springs, 1984-89, nat. trustee-at-large, Washington, 1985-92. Mem. Parcel Shippers Assn. (bd. dirs. 1987-89). Republican. Presbyterian. Clubs: Cheyenne Mountain Country (Colorado Springs); Sahalee Country (Redmond, Wash.), Broadmoor Golf, Garden of the Gods. Avocations: golf, landscape architecture, photography. Home: 35 Elm Ave Colorado Springs CO 80906-3169 Office: ECM Inc PO Box 50065 Colorado Springs CO 80949-0065

NOLAN, CAROLE RITA, broadcasting executive; b. Chgo., Jan. 28, 1932; d. Martin Francis and Caroline Rita (Alton) N.; B.A., De Paul U., 1954, M.A., 1961. Tchr. Chgo. public schs., 1954-61, sci. cons., 1961-66, dir. instructional TV, 1966-71; dir. bur. telecommunications and broadcasting, mgr. Sta. WBEZ-FM, Chgo., 1971-90; pres, gen. mgr, 1990—; mem. faculty Northeastern U., 1964-65, De Paul U., 1975—; cons. Comptons Ency., 1964-65, Chgo. Area Sch. TV, 1964-72, Ill. TV Adv. Council, 1969. Bd. dirs. Chicagoland Radio Info. Services. Mem. Chgo. Network (v.p.), Nat. Pub. Radio, DePaul Univ. Women's Alumni Assn. (bd. dirs.), Delta Kappa Gamma. Office: Sta WBEZ-FM 105 W Adams St Chicago IL 60603-6201

NOLAN, CARY J., medical products manufacturer; b. 1942. BA, Notre Dame, BS in Elec. Engring. With Xerox Corp.; pres. Xerox Med. Systems; pres., CEO Cooper Surgical subs The Cooper Co., Picker Internat. Inc., 1989—. Office: Picker Internat Inc 595 Miner Rd Cleveland OH 44143

NOLAN, HAROLD JOSEPH, JR., marketing educator; b. Red Bank, N.J., Mar. 21, 1947; s. Harold J. Sr. and Marie I. (Suess) N.; m. Janet M. Kazawic; children: Tara H., Erin M., Dayle M., Harold J. III. BA, J.F. Kennedy Coll., Wahoo, Nebr., 1969; MA, Montclair State Coll., 1974; PhD, U. Utah, 1976; MBA, Monmouth Coll., West Long Branch, N.J., 1985. Cert. planner, N.J. Program dir Middletown (N.J.) Dept. Parks and Recreation, 1969-70; dir. recreation, parks and tourism City of Long Branch, 1970-74; sr. planner Bur. of Land Mgmt., Salt Lake City, 1974-75; asst. prof. U. Nebr., Omaha, 1975-77; assoc. prof., dir., acting assoc. dean Franklin Pierce Coll., Rindge, N.H., 1977-79; assoc.prof., chmn. Kean State Coll., Union, N.J., 1979-85; prof., dir. Georgian Ct. Coll., Lakewood, N.J., 1985—; dir. Inst. Tourism & Recreation Mgmt., 1986—; prin. Nolan Cons. Group, Navesink, N.J., 1979-86. Author: Management of Tourism Attractions, 1994; contbr. over 25 articles to profl. jours. Chmn. Landmarks Com. Middletown Twp., N.J., 1982-89, Monmouth County Tourism Coun. Freehold, N.J., 1981-90; chmn. bd. Shore Region Tourism Coun. Manasquan, N.J., 1980-92; mem. gov.'s coun. tourism State of N.J., Trenton, 1983-90. Named Outstanding Young Man Am., 1977, All-Am. Cross Country, Nat. Assn. Intercollegiate Athletics, 1968, Hall of Fame, coll., high sch., club and state, 1969-92, and various profl. awards, 1975—, Monmouth Ocean Devel. Coun. Silver Gull award in Tourism Devel.,1994-95. Fellow Nat. Recreation and Park Assn.; mem. Am. Mktg. Assn., Soc. Travel and Tourism Educators, Travel and Tourism Rsch. Assn., Shore Athletic Club N.J. Roman Catholic. Avocations: running, sailing, camping, back-packing, environmental activities. Home: PO Box 83 Navesink NJ 07752-0083 Office: Georgian Ct Coll Sch Bus Lakewood Ave Lakewood NJ 08701

NOLAN, JEAN, federal agency official; b. Collingdale, Pa., Oct. 25, 1959; d. John Thomas and Elizabeth (Gillan) N.; m. Robert Schwaninger, Mar. 3, 1984 (div. Sept. 1989). BA, Temple U., 1981. Reporter Inside Radio, Cherry Hill, N.J., 1978-82; staff reporter Phila. Bus. Jour., 1982-84, Washington Bus. Jour., Tysons Corner, Va., 1984-85, Housing & Devel. Reporter, Washington, 1985-89; dir. publs. Enterprise Found., Columbia, Md., 1989-91, dir. comms., 1991-93; asst. sec. pub. affairs U.S. Dept. HUD, Washington, 1993—. Mem. Comms. Affinity Group Coun. Found. Democrat. Office: US Dept HUD 451 7th St SW Rm 10032 Washington DC 20410

NOLAN, JOHN BLANCHARD, lawyer; b. Providence, Aug. 30, 1943; s. John O'Leary and Elizabeth Rita (Blanchard) N.; m. Marguerite Ruth Hartley, Mar. 1, 1969 (dec. Aug. 1988); children: Suzanne, Caroline, Danielle; m. Lillian B. Prestley, 1989. AB, Brown U., 1965; JD, Georgetown U., 1968. Bar: Conn. 1968, U.S. Dist. Ct. Conn. 1969, U.S. Ct. Appeals (2d cir.) 1969, U.S. Dist. Ct. (so. dist.) N.Y. 1973, N.Y. 1974, U.S. Ct. Appeals (1st cir.) 1991, U.S. Dist. Ct. Ariz. 1994, U.S. Supreme Ct. 1995. Assoc. Day, Berry & Howard, Hartford, 1968, 1976-79, ptnr., 1976—; bd. dirs. Spiritus Wines, Inc., Hartford; chmn. Local Rules of Practice Adv. Com. to U.S. Bankruptcy Ct., 1981—. Corporator St. Francis Hosp. Med. Ctr. Hartford, 1982—; trustee St. Mary Home Found., 1983—, U. Hartford Art Sch., 1988-94; bd. dirs. Greater Hartford Arts Coun., Inc., 1993—. Mem. ABA, Am. Bankruptcy Inst., Conn. Bar Assn., Hartford County Bar Assn, Insolvency Internat., Hartford Club. Democrat. Roman Catholic. Avocations: golf, skiing, travel, wines. Home: 150 Scarborough St Hartford CT 06105-1107 Office: Day Berry & Howard Cityplace Hartford CT 06103

NOLAN, JOHN EDWARD, retired electrical corporation executive; b. Bklyn., Apr. 15, 1925; s. John C. and Elizabeth (Reighton) N.; m. Dorothea Scheuermann, Aug. 23, 1952; children: Kathleen, Elizabeth, John Edward, James, Michael, Patricia, Maureen. BEE, Cooper Union, 1950; MSEE, U. Pitts., 1955. With Westinghouse Electric Corp., 1950-90, mem. staff Bettis Atomic Power Lab., 1951-69, with Advanced Reactors div., 1969-79, dir. Hanford Engring. Devel. Lab., 1980-87, pres. Westinghouse Hanford Co., 1988-90; ret., 1990. With U.S. Army, 1943-46, ETO. Mem. IEEE, ASME, Am. Nuclear Soc. Home: 411 Snyder Rd Richland WA 99352-1945

NOLAN, JOHN EDWARD, JR., lawyer; b. Mpls., July 11, 1927; s. John E. and Teresa (Franey) N.; m. Joan Dobbins, June 3, 1950; children: Carol N. Klatt, John Edward III (dec.), Kelly N. Spencer, Richard Clark, Patricia N. McNeill. BS, U.S. Naval Acad., 1950; JD, Georgetown U., 1955. Bar: D.C. 1955, U.S. Supreme Ct. 1959, Md. 1961. Law clk. to Justice Clark U.S. Supreme Ct., 1955-56; adminstrv. asst. to Atty. Gen. Robert F. Kennedy, 1963-64; assoc. Steptoe & Johnson, Washington, 1956-62; ptnr. Steptoe & Johnson, 1962-63, 65—; assoc. counsel Cuban families com. Cuban Prisoners Exch., Havana, 1962-63; spl. counsel refugee subcom. Senate Jud. Com., Vietnam, 1967-68; mem. CPR Panel of Disting. Neutrals, Washington, U.S. Ct. Appeals mediator D.C. cir.; mem. exec. com. Lawyers Com. for Civil Rights Under the Law; bd. dirs. Hooper Holmes, Inc., Iomega Corp.; vis. fellow Wolfson Coll., Cambridge (Eng.) U., 1987, 92. Trustee Robert F. Kennedy Meml., 1969—; bd. dirs. Fund Dem. Majority; moderator Aspen Inst., 1980—. Capt. USMC, 1950-54, Korea. Decorated Silver Star, Bronze Star with Combat V, Purple Heart. Mem. ABA, D.C. Bar Assn. (gov.), Am. Law Inst. Democrat. Roman Catholic. Clubs: Met. (Washington); Congl. Home: 7830 Persimmon Tree Ln Bethesda MD 20817-4520 Office: 1330 Connecticut Ave NW Washington DC 20036-1704

NOLAN, JOHN THOMAS, JR., retired oil industry administrator; b. Boston, Apr. 15, 1930; s. John T. Sr. and Margaret M. (Craig) N.; m. Mary Sharkey, May 7, 1955; children: Anne, Margaret, John T. III, Stephen, Michael. AB, Cath. U. Am., 1951; PhD, MIT, 1955. Chemist Texaco, Inc., Beacon, N.Y., 1955-59; group leader Texaco, Inc., Beacon, 1959-69, supr., 1969-79, asst. mgr., 1979-82, assoc. dir., 1982-87, dir. strategic rsch., 1987-92; mem. adv. bd. Dutchess County Sci. Fair, Poughkeepsie, N.Y., 1990—. Contbr. over 5 articles to profl. jours. Mem. blue ribbon panel Beacon Sch. Dist., 1987-92; chmn. bd. Dutchess C.C. Found., Poughkeepsie, 1989-92, chmn. planning com., 1992—. Mem. Am. Chem. Soc., Greater So. Dutchess C. of C. (bd. dirs. 1989-92), Sigma Xi, Phi Beta Kappa. Achievements include patents in field. Home: 18 Relyea Ter Wappingers Falls NY 12590-5824

NOLAN, JOSEPH THOMAS, journalism educator, communications consultant; b. Waterbury, Conn., Apr. 11, 1920; s. Thomas Francis and Mary Margaret (Gaffney) N.; m. Virginia Theodate Tappin, May 6, 1943; children—Carol Nolan Rigolot, David J. A.B., Holy Cross Coll., 1942; M.A. in English, Boston U., 1945; Ph.D. in Econs, NYU, 1973. Washington corr. UPI, 1943-49; writer, copy editor N.Y. Times, N.Y.C., 1949-55; mgr. editorial and press services RCA Corp., N.Y.C., 1955-62; sr. v.p. corporate communications Chase Manhattan Bank, N.Y.C., 1962-74; prof. journalism and pub. affairs U.S.C., Columbia, 1974-76; v.p. pub. affairs Monsanto Co., St. Louis, 1976-85; Gannett vis. prof. communications U. Fla., 1985-86; prof. communications U. North Fla., Jacksonville, 1986-92; adj. prof. bus. comm. Flagler Coll., St. Augustine, Fla., 1992—. Contbr. articles to various mags. Mem. Pub. Relations Soc. Am. Roman Catholic. Home: 30 Park Terrace Dr Saint Augustine FL 32084

NOLAN, KATHLEEN D., public relations executive; b. Phila., Aug. 9, 1949; d. John T. and Margaret (Kane) N.; m. Barry Eigen, Sept. 8, 1979; 1 child, Christopher. BA, Coll. Notre Dame of Md., 1971. Account exec. Brovillard Communications Div. J. Walter Thompson, N.Y.C., 1980-84; account supr. Creamer Dickson Basford, N.Y.C., 1984-86; account supr. Fleishman Hillard, Washington, 1986-87, v.p., 1987—.

NOLAN, PATRICK JOSEPH, screenwriter, playwright, educator; b. Bronx, N.Y., Jan. 2, 1933; s. Patrick John and Catherine Katrina (O'Malley) N.; children: Patrick, Christian, Mark. BA, Villanova U., 1955; MA, U. Detroit, 1961; PhD, Bryn Mawr Coll., 1973. Teaching fellow and mem. faculty dept. English U. Detroit, 1959-62; instr. English Villanova (Pa.) U., 1962-80, prof., 1980—. TV playwright: The Hourglass Moment, 1968-69; playwright: Chameleons, 1980, Midnight Rainbows, 1991; TV screenwriter: The Hourglass Moment, 1968, The Jericho Mile, 1979 (Emmy award). Served to lt. (j.g.) USNR, 1955-59, PTO. Recipient teaching excellence award Philadelphia mag., 1980, Alumni Medallion award Villanova U., 1986.

Mem. Writers Guild Am. (West chpt.), Dramatists Guild. Roman Catholic. Avocations: swimming, biking. Office: Villanova U Villanova PA 19085

NOLAN, PAUL T., telephone company executive. With Gen. Telephone of Pa., from 1949; then with Cen. Telephone of Ind., v.p. mktg., customer svc., from 1971, v.p. regulatory affairs; pres. GTE NW, Inc., 1985-89, GTE North, Inc., Westfield, Ind., 1989—. Office: GTE N Inc 19845 Us Highway 31 N Westfield IN 46074-9685

NOLAN, PAUL THOMAS, retired English and humanities educator; b. Rochester, N.Y., Apr. 4, 1919; s. John J. and Anna (Sweeney) N.; m. Peggy Hime, June 1, 1947; children: John Michael, Peter Andrew, Elizabeth Anne Nolan Fellows. Student, Aquinas Inst. Rochester, 1933-37; B.A., Central Ark. U., 1947; M.A., Tulane U., 1949, Ph.D., 1953. Instr. English, dir. News Bur. Central Ark. U., 1947; asst. prof. English, dir. pub. relations Centenary Coll. of La., 1949-54; Ford Found. vis. prof. Ark. State U., 1954-55; prof. English, Dupré prof. humanities U. Southwestern La., Lafayette, 1955-88, emeritus, 1988—. Author: Round-The-World Plays, 1961, One-Act Plays of Lee Arthur, 1962, Chaucer for Children, 1963, Writing the One-Act Play, 1964, Death For The Lonely, 1964 (Nat. Workshop Players award), Three Plays by John W. Crawford, 1965, Marc Connelly, 1969, Drama Workshop Plays, 1969, Describing People, 1970, The Loneliest Game, 1971, Hedda Gabler, South, 1972, Last Week I Was Ninety-Five, 1973, Squeak to Me of Love, 1973, (with James Burke) Between Hisses 1973, The Highwayman, 1975, The Eavesdrop Theatre, 1976, John Wallace Crawford, 1981, Folk Tale Plays, 1982, Directing the Amateur Stage, 1985. Served with USAAF, 1942-45. Mem. Modern Lang. Assn., Playwrights' Theatre La., Am. Studies Assn. Democrat. Home: 219 Renee Ave Lafayette LA 70503-3331 Office: PO Box 4 Lafayette LA 70504

NOLAN, PETER FRANCIS, lawyer, entertainment company executive; b. N.Y.C., Mar. 31, 1943; s. Frank Michael and Mary Elizabeth (Flanigan) N.; married, 1967; 1 child, Kevin Sean. AB, Georgetown U., 1965, JD, 1968. Bar: D.C. 1968, Calif. 1972. Assoc. Pattishall, McAuliffe & Hofstetter, Washington, 1968-69; atty. examiner U.S. Copyright Office, Washington, 1969-71; staff atty. Walt Disney Co., Burbank, Calif., 1971-79, sr. counsel, 1979-82, v.p., counsel, 1982—. Contbr. articles to profl. jours. Mem. ABA (council patent trademark and copyright sect. 1985—). Roman Catholic. Office: The Walt Disney Co 500 S Buena Vista St Burbank CA 91521-0001

NOLAN, PETER JOHN, physics educator; b. N.Y.C., Mar. 25, 1934; s. Peter John and Nora (Gleeson) N.; divorced 1978; children: Thomas, James, John, Kevin. BS in Physics, Manhattan Coll., 1956; cert. in meteorology, UCLA, 1958; MS in Physics, Adelphi U., 1966, PhD in Physics, 1974. Engr. various corps., N.J., N.Y., 1956-63; systems analysis engr. Gruman Aircraft Engring. Corp., Bethpage, N.Y., 1963-66; asst. prof. Physics SUNY, Farmingdale, 1966-68, assoc. prof. Physics, 1968-71, prof. Physics, 1971—; chmn. Physics dept. SUNY, Farmingdale, 1970-77. Author: Experiments in Physics, 1982, Fundamentals of College Physics, 1993; contbr. articles to profl. jours. Mem. Am. Assn. Physics Tchrs. Home: 47 Fairdale Dr Brentwood NY 11717-1337 Office: Suny Farmingdale NY 11735

NOLAN, ROBERT, management consulting company executive; b. Hartford, Conn., Oct. 13, 1933; s. Robert Emmett and Marian (Sobanski) N.; m. Eileen Luke, July 7, 1955; children: Daniel, Kathleen, Michael, Pamela, Mary. BA, U. Conn. 1958. Sr. analyst Aetna Life & Casualty Co., Hartford, 1958-62; v.p. Serge A. Birn Co. Inc., Louisville, 1962-73; chmn., chief exec. officer Robert E. Nolan Co. Inc., Simsbury, Conn., 1973—; sr. examiner Malcolm Baldridge Nat. Quality Award, Gaithersburg, Md., 1988-89. Co-author: Work Measurement in Accounting, 1963, Office Work Measurement, 1970, Improving Productivity through Advanced Office Controls, 1980, White Collar Productivity, 1982. With USAF, 1950-54, Korea. Mem. Am. Soc. for Quality Control, Inst. Indsl. Engrs., Assn. for Systems Mgmt., Adminstrn. Mgmt. Soc. Office: Robert E Nolan Co Inc 90 Hopmeadow St Simsbury CT 06070-2413

NOLAN, ROBERT D., advertising company executive. Vice chmn., dir. creative svcs. - Leo Burnett USA Leo Burnett Co., Inc., Chgo. Office: Leo Burnett Co Inc Prudential Plz 17 Bougainvillea Ave Key West FL 33040-6226

NOLAN, STANTON PEELLE, surgeon, educator; b. Washington, May 29, 1933; s. James Parker and Ellen Dubose (Peelle) N.; m. Marion Faro, June 16, 1955; children—Stanton Peelle Jr., Tiphanie Ravenel. B.A., Princeton U., 1955; M.D., U. Va., 1959, M.S., 1962. Cert. Am. Bd. Surgery, Am. Bd. Thoracic Surgery. Intern U. Va. Med. Ctr., Charlottesville, 1959-60, asst. resident gen. surgery, 1960-61, research fellow surgery, 1961-62, sr. asst. resident gen. surgery, 1962-64, chief resident gen surgery, 1964-65, chief resident thoracic cardiovascular surgery, 1965-66; sr. rsch. assoc. Clinic of Surgery Nat. Heart Inst., NIH, Bethesda, Md., 1966-68; asst. prof. surgery U. Va. Med. Ctr., Charlottesville, 1968-70, assoc. prof. surgery, 1970-74, surgeon in charge div. thoracic cardiovascular surgery, 1970-93, prof. surgery, 1974—, Claude A. Jessup prof. surgery, 1981—, med. dir. Thoracic Cardiovascular post-operative unit, 1989-93; established investigator Am. Heart Assn., 1969-74; cons. thoracic cardiovascular surgery VA Hosp., Salem, Va., 1968—, Am. Bd. Surgery to qualifying examination com., 1988-91; surg. cons. Bur. Crippled Children, Charlottesville, 1968—; vis. cons. cardiothoracic surgery Aga Khan U., Karachi, Pakistan, 1995; mem. surgera A study sect. NIH, 1972-76, surgery and bioengring. study sect., 1984-87, chmn., 1985-87. Mem. editl. bd. Jour. Surg. Rsch., 1973-79, Annals of Thoracic Surgery, 1977-89; mem. sci. adv. bd. Jour. for Heart Valve Disease, 1993-94; mem. editl. adv. bd. ECRI Operating Rm. Risk Mgmt., 1992—; co-editor: Comprehensive Thoracic Surgery Curriculum, TSDA, 1995; contbr. numerous articles to profl. jours., chpts. to books. Recipient John Horsley Meml. prize U. Va. Med. Sch., 1962; Merit award Research Forum of Am. Coll. Chest Physicians, 1968; research fellow Va. Heart Assn., 1961-62, Am. Cancer Soc., 1963-64; grantee NIH, 1968-84, Am. Heart Assn., 1970-73, Medtronic Corp., 1975-81. Fellow ACS, Am. Coll. Cardiology, Am. Surg. Assn.; mem. Am. Assn. Thoracic Surgery (rep. to exec. Am. Med. Colls., Am. Bd. Cardiovascular Perfusion, Am. Soc. Extracorporeal Tech., others), Am. Heart Assn. (coun. on cardiovascular surgery 1969—, anesthesiology, radiology and surgery study com. 1991-94), Andrew G. Morrow Soc., Assn. Acad. Surgery, Assn. Advancement ofMed. Instrumentation (co-chmn. cardiac vavle protheses stds. com. 1974—, mem. internat. stds. com. 1989—; bd. dirs. 1990—, stds. bd. 1991-94, edn. com. 1992-93), Internat. Stds. Orgn. (chmn. subcom. on cardiovascular surg. implants 1982—), Assn. Clin. Cardiac Surgeons, Halsted Soc. (exec. com. 1985-89), Coordinating Com. on Perfusion Affairs (chmn. 1990—), Internat. Assn. Cardiac Biological Implants (sci. com. 1994), Internat. Cardiovascular Soc., Muller Surg. Soc. (pre.s 1979), Societé Internat. de Chururgie, Soc. Vascular Surgery, Soc. Thoracic Surgeons (ad hoc com. on industry rels. 1992—, stds. and ethics com. 1991—), Soc. Univ. Surgeons, Southeastern Surg. Congress, So. Surg. Assn. (2d v.p. 1982), Va. Surg. Soc. (v.p. 1980-83, pres. 1984), Va. Vascular Soc. (exec. coun. 1985-86), Soc. Critical Care Medicine, Raven Soc., Assn. Am. Med. Colls. (rep. coun. acad. socs. 1992—), Alpha Omega Alpha, Omicron Delta Kappa. Clubs: Chevy Chase (Md.); Farmington Country (Va.); Princeton (N.Y.C.). Office: U Va Dept Surgery Box 181-6 Charlottesville VA 22908

NOLAN, TERRANCE JOSEPH, JR., lawyer; b. Bklyn., Mar. 29, 1950; s. Terrance Joseph Sr. and Antonia (Pontecorvo) N.; m. Irene M. Rush, Aug. 2, 1980; children: Maryjane Frances, David Anthony. BA, St. Francis Coll., Bklyn., 1971; JD, St. Johns U., Jamaica, N.Y., 1974; LLM, NYU, 1982. Bar: N.Y. 1975, U.S. Dist. Ct. (ea. and so. dists.) N.Y. 1975, U.S. Ct. Appeals (2d cir.) 1975, U.S. Supreme Ct. 1980. Atty. N.Y.C. Transit Authority, Bklyn., 1974-77; specialist labor rels. Pepsi-Cola Co. Purchase, N.Y., 1977-80; asst. gen. counsel, assoc. dir. labor rels. NYU, N.Y.C., 1980-89, assoc. gen. counsel, dep. dir. labor rels., 1989—. Mem. Am. Corp. Coun. Assn., N.Y. State Bar Assn., Indsl. Rels. Rsch. Assn. Nat. Assn. Coll. and Univ. Attys. N.Y.-N.J. Arbitration Group. Home: 41 Russell St Lynbrook NY 11563-1135 Office: NYU 70 Washington Sq S New York NY 10012-1091

NOLAN, VAL, JR., biologist, lawyer; b. Evansville, Ind., Apr. 28, 1920; s. Val and Jeannette (Covert) N.; m. Susanne Howe, Dec. 23, 1946 (div. Aug. 29, 1980); children: Val, Ann Clare, William Alan; m. Ellen D. Ketterson,

Oct. 17, 1980. A.B., Ind. U., 1941, J.D., 1949. Bar: Ind. 1949. Dep. U.S. marshal, 1941; agt. White House Detail, U.S. Secret Service, 1942; asst. prof. law Ind. U., 1949-52, assoc. prof., 1952-56, prof., 1956-85, prof. emeritus, 1985—, research scholar in zoology, 1957-68, prof. zoology, 1968-77, prof. biology, 1977-85; prof. emeritus, 1985—, acting dean Sch. Law, 1976, 80. Author: (with F.E. Horack, Jr.) Land Use Controls, 1955, Ecology and Behavior of the Prairie Warbler, 1978; editor Ind. Law Jour., 1945-46; co-editor Current Ornithology, 1994—. Served with USNR, 1942-46. Guggenheim fellow, 1957; recipient Ind. U. Disting. Alumni Svc. award, 1987; named to Acad. Law Alumni Fellows, Ind. U., 1988. Fellow AAAS, Am. Ornithologists Union (v.p. 1989-90, Brewster Meml. award 1986); mem. Brit. Ornithologists Union, Cooper Ornithol. Soc., Wilson Ornithol. Soc., Assn. Field Ornithologists, Ecol. Soc. Am., Am. Soc. Naturalists, Animal Behavior Soc., Deutsche Ornithologen-Gesellschaft, Nederlandse Ornithologische Unie, Soc. for Study of Reprodn., Phi Beta Kappa, Sigma Xi. Democrat. Home: 4675 E Heritage Woods Rd Bloomington IN 47401-9312

NOLAN, VICTORIA HOLMES, theater director; b. Portland, Maine, June 15, 1952; d. Herbert Wallace and Diane Katharine (Kremm) N.; m. Clarkson Newell Crolius, Aug. 30, 1980; children: Covey Emmeline, Wilhelmina Adams. BA magna cum laude, U. Maine, 1976. Publicity asst. Loeb Drama Ctr. Harvard U., Cambridge, Mass., 1975; pub. rels. asst. to dir. Sch. for Arts Boston U., 1975-76; mgmt. asst. TAG Found., N.Y.C., 1976-77; mng. dir. Ram Island Dance Co., Portland, 1977-78; dir. devel. Ctr. Stage, Balt., 1979-81, assoc. mng. dir., 1981-87; mng. dir. Ind. Repertory Theatre, Indpls., 1988-93, Yale Repertory Theatre, New Haven, 1993—; cons. Fedn. for Extension and Devel. Am. Profl. Theatre, N.Y.C., 1979-87; prog. evaluator NEA, Washington, 1988—, panelist, 1991; mem. Indpls. Cultural Consortium, v.p., 1991—; bd. dirs. Greater Indpls. Progress Com., Indpls. Urban League, Arts Coun. Indpls.; nat. bd. Theatre Comms. Group, N.Y.C. Mem. exec. com. League Resident Profl. Theatres. Nat. Performing Arts Mgmt. fellow Exxon, Doner Fedn. and NEA, 1978. Home: 120 Rimmon Rd Woodbridge CT 06525-1915 Office: Yale Repertory Theater PO Box 1903A Yale Station 222 York St New Haven CT 06520-8244*

NOLAN, WILLIAM JOSEPH, III, banker; b. N.Y.C., Apr. 6, 1947; s. William J. Jr. and Alice Nettleton (Edwards) N.; m. Wendy Collison French, Mar. 21, 1981; children: William J. IV, Anina Chrysler. Student, Hackley Sch., Tarrytown, N.Y., 1958-65; E.S.U. scholar, Eastbourne Coll., U.K., 1966; BA, Colgate U., 1970; MBA, Stanford U., 1973. V.p. Bankers Trust Co., N.Y.C., 1973-83; mng. dir. Becker-Paribas, N.Y.C., 1983-84, PaineWebber, N.Y.C., 1984—. Bd. dirs. Eastbourne Coll. N.Am. Ednl. Found., Mahwah, N.J., 1984-93. Mem. Pub. Securities Assn. (money market exec. com. 1985-89, chmn. 1987, bd. dirs. 1988-91, treas. 1990), Adirondack League, Piping Rock Club, Union Club of N.Y.C. Home: 1088 Park Ave New York NY 10128-1132 Office: PaineWebber Inc 1285 6th Ave New York NY 10019-6028

NOLAND, CHRISTINA A., judge. BA, La. State Univ., JD. Law clk. to Hon. John V. Parker U.S. Dist. Ct. (La. mid. dist.), 5th circuit; magistrate judge U.S. Dist. Ct. (La. mid. dist.), 5th circuit, Baton Rouge, 1987—. Mem. Am. Bar Assn., La. State Bar, La. Trial Lawyers Assn., Baton Rouge Bar Assn. Office: Russell B Long Fed Bldg & Courthouse 777 Florida St Rm 265 Baton Rouge LA 70801-1713

NOLAND, GARY LLOYD, vocation educational administrator; b. Lindsborg, Kans., July 29, 1942; s. Willard L. and Florence L. (Waggoner) N.; m. Deborah L. Homan, Mar. 20, 1981; children: Krista L., Timothy L. BSBA, Cen. Mo. State U., 1971, MEd, 1974. Cert. vocat. dir., Mo. V.p. sales First Nat. Land Co., Scottsdale, Ariz., 1961-66; student grad. asst. Cen. Mo. State U. Warrensburg, 1968-72; instr. State Fair CC., Sedalia, Mo., 1972-74, dir. job placement, 1974-79; dir. Statewide Job Placement Svc., Sedalia, 1979-84, State Fair Area Vocat. Sch., Sedalia, 1984—; dir. State Fair C.C. Found., Sedalia, 1986—; mgr. State Fair Coll. Farm, Sedalia, 1987-92. Author: Help Yourself to Successful Employment, 1980; author instructional modules. Mem., chmn. ctrl. Mo. chpt. March of Dimes, Sedalia, 1979; v.p. Pettis County Farm Bur., Sedalia, 1987-91, pres., 1991—; dir. Am. Cancer Soc., Sedalia, 1989-92. Named Outstanding Young Man Am., 1979, Outstanding Placement Specialist, Mo. Guidance and Placement, 1980, Outstanding Vocat. Program Area VII, U.S. Dept. Edn., 1982. Mem. VFW (life), Am. Simmental Assn., Am. Legion, Mo. Coun. Local Adminstrs., Mo. Assn. Secondary Prins., Mo. Cattleman's Assn., Pettis County Cattleman's Assn., Lions (pres. Sedalia 1979-80), Masons, Sedalia Area C. of C. (amb. 1975-92). Baptist. Avocations: farming, golfing, fishing. Home: RR 3 Box 90-D Sedalia MO 65301-9504 Office: State Fair Area Vocat Sch 3201 W 16th St Sedalia MO 65301-2199

NOLAND, JON DAVID, utility corporation executive, lawyer; b. Peru, Ind., Dec. 4, 1938; s. Edward Donald and Gladys (Hosman) N.; m. Dorothea Karoline Silbernagel, Aug. 10, 1966; children: Mark Richard, Christopher Edward. B.A., Ind. U., 1960; LL.B., Harvard U., 1964. Bar: Ind. 1964, U.S. Supreme Ct. 1972. Assoc. firm Barnes, Hickam, Pantzer & Boyd, Indpls., 1966-71, ptnr., 1972-81; sr. v.p., gen. counsel Pub. Svc. Co. of Ind., Inc., Plainfield, 1981-82, sr. v.p. law, Ind. svcs., 1983-86; exec. v.p., 1986—. Bd. dirs. Tri County Mental Health Ctr. Inc., 1989—; Capt. AUS, 1964-66. Mem. ABA, Ind. State Bar Assn., Phi Beta Kappa. Republican. Lutheran. Home: 701 Mayfair Ln Carmel IN 46032-8653 Office: Pub Svc Co Ind Inc 1000 E Main St Plainfield IN 46168-1765*

NOLAND, LLOYD U., III, wholesale utility supplies company executive; b. Balt., 1943; married. BA, U. Va., 1966; MBA, U. Pa., 1968. Sales trainee Noland Co., Newport News, Va., 1968-69, salesman, 1969-71, mgr. Durham (N.C.) br., 1971-73, mgr. Nashville br., 1973-77, mgr. merchandising, plumbing and heating South div., 1977-80, mgr. merchandising, plumbing and heating, 1980-81, v.p. merchandising, plumbing and heating, 1981, now chmn., pres., chief exec. officer, also bd. dirs.; bd. dirs. Cen. Fidelity Bank, N.A., So. Wholesalers Assn. Mem. Am. Supply Assn. (bd. dirs.), So. Wholesalers Assn. (pres.). Office: Noland Co 2700 Warwick Blvd Newport News VA 23607-4030

NOLAND, MARCUS, economist, educator; b. Greensboro, N.C., Mar. 29, 1959. BA, Swarthmore Coll., 1981; PhD, Johns Hopkins U. 1985. Sr. fellow Inst. for Internat. Econs., Washington, 1985—; asst. prof. U. So. Calif., L.A., 1990-91; sr. economist Coun. Econ. Advisers, Washington, 1993-94; vis. prof. Saitama U., Urawa, Japan, 1988-89; vis. scholar Korea Devel. Inst., Seoul, 1991; vis. assoc. prof. Johns Hopkins U., Balt., 1991—; cons. N.Y. Stock Exch., 1990, Adv. Com. on Trade Policy, Washington, 1989-92, World Bank, Washington, 1990—. Author: Pacific Basin Developing Countries, 1991; co-author: Japan in the World Economy, 1988, Reconcilable Differences?, 1993; co-editor: Pacific Economic Dynamism, 1993. Japan Soc. for Promotion of Sci. fellow, 1988; Internat. Affairs fellow Coun. on Fgn. Rels., 1993. Mem. Coun. on Fgn. Rels. Office: Inst for Internat Econs 11 DuPont Cir NW Washington DC 20036

NOLAND, ROBERT LEROY, retired manufacturing company executive; b. Lawrence, Kans., Sept. 7, 1918; s. Harry L. and Angela (Scola) N.; m. Delpha Mae Mierndorf, June 16, 1962; children: Gary, Fabra Jeanine, Derice Elizabeth. B.S. in Mech. Engring. Calif. Inst. Tech., 1941. Design and devel. rocket propelled devices Calif. Inst. Tech., 1941-45; supr. propulsions Naval Ordnance Test Sta., China Lake, Calif., 1945-46; asst. chief engr. Aerojet Gen. Corp., 1946-52; cons. engr. plastic components, rockets and missiles, 1952-54; exec. v.p. Reinhold Engring. and Plastics Co., 1954-57, pres., 1957-59; exec. v.p. Haveg Industries, Wilmington, Del., 1959-66; exec. v.p. Ametek, Inc., Paoli, Pa., 1966-68, pres., bd. dirs. 1968-88; pres., chief exec. officer, dir. Ketema Inc., Bensalem, Pa., 1988-92; ret., chmn.; chmn. bd. Myricom, 1994—. Home: 5555 Eastlake Blvd Carson City NV 89704-9266

NOLAND, ROYCE PAUL, association executive, physical therapist; b. Walla Walla, Wash., Dec. 6, 1928; s. Homer Vernon and Mildred Bessie (Royce) N.; m. April Lynn Hawkes, Feb. 10, 1979; children—Royce Paul, Richard Mitchell. B.A., Whitman Coll., Walla Walla, Wash., 1951; Cert. in phys. therapy, Stanford U., 1952. Pvt. practice in phys. therapy Santa Cruz, Calif., 1961-68; exec. dir. Calif. Chpt. Am. Phys. Therapy Assn., Santa Cruz, Calif., 1965-69; exec. dir. Am. Phys. Therapy Assn., Washington, D.C., 1969-87; pres., chief exec. officer Inst. Profl. Health Service Adminstrs.,

Alexandria, 1988-91; exec. dir., CEO Fedn. of State Bds. of Phys. Therapy, Arlington, Va., 1992—. Co-inventor phys. therapy device; contbr. articles to profl. publs. Mem. Am. Soc. Assn. Execs. (cert.), Presdl. Commn. Employment of Handicapped, Am. Pub. Health Assn. Republican. Club: Belle Haven Country (Alexandria). Avocation: golf. Home: 2302 Popkins Ln Alexandria VA 22306-2443 Office: Fedn of State Bds of Phys Therapy 2231 Crystal Dr Ste 500 Arlington VA 22202-3711

NOLD, CARL RICHARD, state historic parks and museums administrator; b. Mineola, N.Y., Nov. 26, 1955; s. Carl Frederick and Joan Catherine (Heine) N.; m. Mary Beth Krivoruchka (div.). BA in History magna cum laude, St. John's U., Jamaica, N.Y., 1977; MA in History Mus. Studies, SUNY, Oneonta, 1982. Pres. Gregory Mus. Hicksville, N.Y., 1977; registrar N.Y. State Hist. Assn., Cooperstown, 1978-80; dir.: curator Gadsby's Tavern Mus., Alexandria, Va., 1980-84; dir. State Mus. Pa., Harrisburg, 1984-91; exec. dir. Mackinac State Hist. Parks, Lansing, Mackinac Island, Mich., 1992—; grant reviewer Inst. Mus. Svcs., Washington, 1982-90, 95—, mus. assessment prog. reviewer, 1985—, panelist, 1992-94; panelist mus. grant prog. Nat. Endowment for Humanities, 1990-93. Co-author: Gadsby's Tavern Mus. Interpretive Master Plan, 1984; contbr. articles to profl. jours. Mem. adv. bd. for Grad. History George Mason U., Fairfax, Va., 1982-84, adv. com. Susquehanna Mus. Art, Harrisburg, 189-91; bd. dirs. Harrisburg-Hershey-Carlisle Tourism and Visitor Bur., 1987-91, bd. sec., 1990-91; mem. mayor's adv. bd. city of Mackinac Island, 1993—. Mem. Midwest Mus. Assn., Mich. Mus. Assn., Am. Assn. Mus. (vis. com. mus. accrditation 1989—), Am. Assn. for State and Local History (elections chmn. 1990), Cooperstown Grad. Assn. (bd. dirs. 1985-87).

NOLEN, JERRY AFTEN, JR., physicist; b. Washington, Nov. 17, 1940; s. Jerry Aften and Roxie Ann (Stout) N.; m. Geraldine Janet Meads, Oct. 4, 1980; children by previous marriage: Greer Roxanne, Joyce Lynne, Paige Hamilton; stepchildren: Jeffrey Brian, Tara Leigh, Christopher Allen. B.S., Lehigh U., 1961; Ph.D., Princeton U., 1965. Instr. Princeton (N.J.) U., 1965-66; postdoctoral appointee Argonne (Ill.) Nat. Labs., 1966-68; asst. prof. U. Md., College Park, 1968-70; assoc. prof. Mich. State U., East Lansing, 1970-76; prof. physics Mich. State U., 1976-92, assoc. dir. Nat. Superconducting Cyclotron Lab, 1984-92; Max Planck fellow Heidelberg, Ger., 1977; dir. Atlas Argonne Nat. Lab., Argonne, Ill., 1992—. Contbr. articles to profl. jours.; editor: (with W. Benenson) Atomic Masses and Fundamental Constants, 1980. Woodrow Wilson grad. fellow, 1961-62. Fellow Am. Phys. Soc. (mem. exec. com. div. nuclear physics 1989-91); mem. Sigma Xi, Phi Beta Kappa, Tau Beta Pi. Home: 14611 S Hawthorne Ct N Lockport IL 60441-8559 Office: Argonne Nat Lab Physics Div Bldg 203 Argonne IL 60439

NOLEN, ROY LEMUEL, lawyer; b. Montgomery, Ala., Nov. 29, 1937; s. Roy Lemuel Jr. and Elizabeth (Larkin) N.; m. Evelyn McNeill Thomas, Aug. 28, 1965; 1 child, Rives Rutledge. BArch, Rice U., 1961; LLB, Harvard U., 1967. Bar: Tex. 1968, U.S. C. Appeals (5th cir.) 1969. Law clk. to sr. judge U.S. Ct. Appeals (5th cir.), 1967-68; assoc. Baker & Botts, Houston, 1968-75, ptnr., 1976—; co-head Corp. Dept., 1985-90, mem. exec. com., 1988-91. Bd. dirs. Houston Ballet Found., 1980-92; mem. exec. com. Contemporary Arts Mus., 1987—; mem. exec. com., gen. counsel Houston Symphony Soc., 1994—; sr. warden Christ Ch. Cathedral, 1991-92; bd. dirs. Rice Design Alliance, 1995—. Mem. ABA, State Bar of Tex., Houston Bar Assn., Coronado Club, Allegro, Paul Jones Club. Episcopalian. Office: Baker & Botts 3000 One Shell Plz 910 Louisiana St Houston TX 77002

NOLEN, WILFRED E., church administrator. Exec. sec. Brethren Benefit Trust. Office: Church of the Brethren Gen Offices 1505 Dundee Ave Elgin IL 60120-1619

NOLEN, WILLIAM GILES, lawyer, accountant; b. Fayetteville, Ark., Aug. 4, 1931; s. William Jefferson and Marie (Giles) N.; m. Carole Turner, Aug. 25, 1957; children: Kathy, Thomas. B.S.B.A., U. Ark., 1960; J.D., U. Houston, 1980. Bar: Tex. 1980; C.P.A., Tex. Auditor Arthur Anderson & Co., Houston, 1960-66; sec., treas. Brown & Root (U.K.) Ltd., London, 1966-69; v.p. Highlands Ins. Co., Houston, 1969-73, sr. v.p., 1973-80, dir., 1973-88; v.p. Halliburton Co., Dallas, 1980-82; sr. v.p. Brown & Root, Inc., Houston, 1982-86; exec. v.p. Highlands Ins. Co., Houston, 1986-88; of counsel Whitmore, Sheppard & Pollicoff, Houston, 1988-92, Policoff, Smith & Myres LLP, Houston, 1992—. Maj. USAF, 1951-56. Mem. ABA, Am. Assn. of Atty. CPAs (treas., bd. dirs.), Tex. Soc. CPAs (Tex. CPA of Yr. 1961), Mensa, Sugar Creek Country Club. Republican. Presbyterian.

NOLF, DAVID MANSTAN, financial executive; b. Hartford, Conn., Nov. 25, 1942; s. Richard A. and Erreld I. (Manstan) N.; m. Linda J. Anderson, June 20, 1964; 1 child, Cristina E. BSChemE, Lafayette Coll., 1964; MBA, U. Conn., 1968. Prodn. engr. Am. Cyanamid, Wallingford, Conn., 1664-66; adminstrn. supr. Electric Boat Div. Gen. Dynamics, Groton, Conn., 1966-71; chief fin. and adminstrv. officer, corp. sec. Analysis and Tech. Inc., North Stonington, Conn., 1971—; bd. dirs. Analysis and Tech., Inc., North Stonington, Conn., Applied Sci. Assocs., Butler, Pa., Gen. Systems Solutions, Groton, Continental Dynamics, Inc., Reston, Va., Integrated Performance Decisions, Inc., North Stonington. Sec. Sch. Bldg. Com., Stonington, 1989-92; chmn. Ch. Fin. Com., Westerly, R.I., 1989-93; trustee Westerly Hosp., 1993—. Mem. Nat. Contract Mgmt. Assn., Am. Mgmt. Assn., Def. Preparedness Assn., Tau Bet Pi, Beta Gamma Sigma. Avocations: fishing, golf. Home: 11 Meadow Rd Pawcatuck CT 06379-2013 Office: Analysis & Tech Inc Technology Park PO Box 220 North Stonington CT 06359-9801

NOLL, ANNA CECILIA, curator; b. Alexandria, Va., July 22, 1950; d. Louis Richard and Barbara Lucille (Curtice) N. BS in Psychology, Va. Poly. Inst. and State Univ., 1974; MA in Art History, George Washington U., 1983. Asst. curator Queens Mus., Flushing, N.Y., 1984-86; curator Fort Wayne (Ind.) Mus. Art, 1986-89, Heckscher Mus., Huntington, N.Y., 1989—; guest essayist June Kelly Gallery, N.Y.C., 1994, Bernice Steinbaum Gallery, N.Y.C., 1989; mem. benefit com. Ctr. for Book Arts Auction, N.Y.C., 1991. Vol. Gay Men's Health Crisis AIDS Dance-a-thon, N.Y.C., 1990, Cold Spring Harbor (N.Y.) Lab. Centennial Celebration, 1990. Hilla von Rebay fellow Solomon R. Guggenheim Mus., 1981, Univ. fellow George Washington U., 1981-83. Mem. Am. Assn. Mus. (mem. curators com., co-chair exhibit competition 1994-95), Coll. Art Assn. (presenter ann. meeting 1994), Alliance Française. Avocations: garden history, cooking, travel. Office: Heckscher Mus 2 Prime Ave Huntington NY 11743-2741

NOLL, CHARLES HENRY, former professional football coach; b. Cleve., Jan. 5, 1932; m. Marianne Noll; 1 son, Chris. BE, U. Dayton, 1953. Football player Cleve. Browns, 1953-59; asst. coach San Diego Chargers, 1960-65, Balt. Colts, 1966-68; head coach Pitts. Steelers, 1969-91; winner Super Bowl games, 1975-76, 79-80. Named Am. Football Coach of Yr., UPI, 1972; inductee Pro Football Hall of Fame, 1993. Office: 300 Stadium Cir Pittsburgh PA 15212-5729 Office: The Football Hall of Fame 2121 George Halas Dr NW Canton OH 44708-2630

NOLL, JOHN F., sales and marketing executive, investment banker; b. Ft. Wayne, Ind., Feb. 2, 1945; s. Martin F. and Viola N.; m. Ann E. Files, Sept. 23, 1972; children: Eric, Scott. BA in Philosophy, Athanaeum of Ohio Coll., 1966; MA in English, Purdue U., 1968; MBA in Mktg., U. of Colo., 1970. From sales rep. to dist. mgr. Procter & Gamble, Cin., 1968-83; v.p. sales Software Distrbn. Svcs., Buffalo, 1983-85; adminstrv. v.p. trusts M&T Bank, Buffalo, 1985-88; dir. sales and mktg. Select Interior Door, Ltd., N Java, N.Y., 1988-93; dir. corp. fin. Capital Formation Group, 1994—; co-founder, bd. dirs. NORAM Group, Ltd., Buffalo, 1988—; owner Sales Resources, Orchard Park, N.Y., 1989-90. Bd. dirs. Orchard Park Little League, 1973-85, Boys and Girls Club of Orchard Park, 1986-93; bd. dirs., pres. Eagle Ridge Recreation Assn., Orchard Park, 1986-88. Mem. Am. Mktg. Assn., Sales and Mktg. Execs. (bd. dirs. 1989-91), Resource Group (founder, bd. dirs. 1981—), Orchard Park Country Club. Republican. Presbyterian. Avocations: golf, skiing, tennis. Home and Office: 46 Knob Hill Rd Orchard Park NY 14127-3931

NOLL, JONATHAN BOYD, lawyer; b. Summit, N.J., Mar. 21, 1944; s. Clyde Miller and Florence Elizabeth (Boyd) N.; m. Martha Jane Lentz, Nov. 27, 1974. BS, Bucknell U., 1966; JD, Harvard U., 1969. Bar: N.J. 1969,

Wash. 1971, Alaska 1982. Dep. pros. atty. King County Prosecuting Atty.'s Office, Seattle, 1972-76; assoc. Foster, Pepper & Shefelman, Seattle, 1976-80, ptnr., 1980—. Instr. ARC, Seattle, 1975—. 1st lt. U.S. Army, 1969-71, Vietnam. Mem. Wash. State Bar Assn. (exec. com. litigation sect. 1983-91, chmn. 1990-91), Mountaineers Club. Avocations: mountain climbing, skiing, soccer. Home: 2525 E Calhoun St Seattle WA 98112-2615 Office: Foster Pepper & Shefelman 1111 3rd Ave 34th Fl Seattle WA 98101

NOLL, ROGER GORDON, economist, educator; b. Monterey Park, Calif., Mar. 13, 1940; s. Cecil Ray and Hjordis Alberta (Westover) N.; m. Robyn Schreiber, Aug. 25, 1962; 1 child, Kimberlee Elizabeth. B.S., Calif. Inst. Tech., 1962; A.M., Harvard U., 1965, Ph.D. in Econs, 1967. Mem. social sci. faculty Calif. Inst. Tech., 1965-84, prof., 1973-82, Inst. prof., 1982-84, chmn. div. humanities and social scis., 1978-82; prof. econs Stanford U., 1984—, dir. pub. policy program, 1986—, Morris M. Doyle centennial prof. of pub. policy, 1990—; Jean Monnet prof. European U. Inst., 1991; sr. staff economist Council of Econ. Advs. Washington, 1967-69; sr. fellow Brookings Instn., Washington, 1970-72; mem. tech. adv. bd. Com. for Econ. Devel., 1978-82; mem. adv. council NSF, 1978-89, SERI, 1982-90; mem. Pres.' Commn. for Nat. Agenda for the Eighties, 1980; mem. adv. council NASA, 1978-81; chmn. Los Angeles Sch. Monitoring Com., 1978-79; mem. Commn. on Behavioral and Social Scis. and Edn., NAS, 1984-90; mem. Energy Rsch. Adv. Bd. Dept. Energy, 1986-89; mem. Soc. of Energy Adv. Bd., 1990—. Author: Reforming Regulation, 1971, The Economics and Politics of Deregulation, 1991; co-author: Economic Aspects of Television Regulation, 1973, The Political Economy of Deregulation, 1983, The Technology Pork Barrel, 1991; editor: Government and the Sports Business, 1974; Regulatory Policy and the Social Sciences, 1985; supervisory editor Info. Econs. and Policy Jour., 1984-92. NSF grantee, 1973-82; Recipient 1st ann. book award Nat. Assn. Ednl. Broadcasters, 1974; Guggenheim fellow, 1983-84. Mem. Am. Econ. Assn. Democrat. Home: 4153 Hubbart Dr Palo Alto CA 94306-3834 Office: Stanford U Dept Econs Stanford CA 94305

NOLLER, HARRY FRANCIS, JR., biochemist, educator; b. Oakland, Calif., June 10, 1939; s. Harry Francis and Charlotte Frances (Silva) N.; m. Betty Lucille Parnow, Nov. 25, 1964 (div. 1969); 1 child, Maria Irene; m. Sharon Ann Sussman; 1 child, Eric Francis; stepchildren: Django Sussman, Seb Sussman. AB, U. Calif., Berkeley, 1960; PhD, U. Oreg., 1965. Postdoctoral fellow MRC Lab. of Molecular Biology, Cambridge, Eng., 1965-66, Inst. Molecular Biology, Geneva, Switzerland, 1966-68; asst. prof. biology U. Calif., Santa Cruz, 1968-73, assoc. prof., 1973-79, prof. biology, 1979—, Robert Louis Sinsheimer prof. molecular biology, 1987—; Harvey lectr. Rockefeller U., 1989; Sherman Fairchild Disting. scholar, Calif. Inst. Tech., 1990; Harvey lectr., 1989. Mem. NAS. Office: Sinsheimer Labs U Calif Santa Cruz High St Santa Cruz CA 95064-1099

NOLLY, ROBERT J., hospital administrator, pharmaceutical science educator; b. Amsterdam, N.Y., Jan. 8, 1947; m. Diera R. Lehtonen, June 21, 1969; children: Shelby Alexandra, Kirby Alycia, Kendall Alexis. BS in Pharmacy with honor, Albany Coll. Pharmacy, 1970; MSc in Hosp. Pharmacy, Ohio State U., 1979. Pharmacy extern Matt Pharmacy, Canajoharie, N.Y., 1967-70; pharmacy intern Park Row Drugs, Canajoharie, 1970-71, asst. mgr., 1971-72; staff pharmacist Mary Imogene Bassett Hosp., Cooperstown, N.Y., 1972-74, 75-77; med. svc. rep. Dista Products Co., Eli Lilly and Co., Indpls., 1974-75; resident hosp. pharmacy Grant Hosp., Columbus, Ohio, 1977-79; asst. dir. pharmacy svcs. City of Memphis Hosp., 1979-81; asst. dir. pharmacy svcs. U. Tenn. Bowld Hosp., Memphis, 1980-82, dir. pharmacy svcs. and materials mgmt., 1982-85, asst. adminstr. pharmacy svcs. and materials mgmt., 1985-91, adminstr., 1991—; asst. prof. dept. pharmacy practice Coll. Pharmacy U. Tenn., Memphis, 1979-83, asst. prof. dept. health sci. adminstrn. dept. pharmaceutics, 1983-92, assoc. prof. divsn. pharmacy adminstrn. dept. pharmaceutical scis., 1992—; attended confs., mgmt. tng. programs in field; lectr. Columbus Tech. Inst., 1978-79, City of Memphis Hosp., 1980-81; trustee Diversified Svcs., Inc. Tenn. Hosp. Assn., 1990-93, mem. pharmacy adv. com., 1990; bd. dirs. Ava Marie Nursing Home, chmn. nom. com., 1988, 89, mem. long range planning com., 1989, 90, mem. constitution and by-laws com., 1990, mem. govtl. rels. com., 1991-93. Contbr. articles to profl. jours.; presenter in field; editor newsletter U. Tenn. Bowld Hosp. Pharmacy Newsletter 1987-91; mem. editorial bd. Drug and Therapeutics Newsletter drug info. ctr. coll. pharmacy U. Tenn., 1989, 90. Usher Ch. of Holy Spirit, 1988-93; mem. Am. Cancer Soc., recipient Order of Sword, 1992. Mem. Am. Soc. Hosp. Pharmacists, Tenn. Soc. Hosp. Pharmacists (mem. com. 1980, constitution and by-laws com. 1985, 88, 89, 90, chmn. nom. com. 1989, orgn. and goals com. 1991, strategic planning com. 1992), Tenn. Pharmacists Assn. (pharmacy tech. task force 1988, 89, 90, ho. dels. 1988, 89, 90, 91, 92, chmn. tech. curriculum com. 1991, tech. edn. accreditation com. 1991, 92), Memphis Area Soc. Hosp. Pharmacists (pres.-elect 1984, pres. 1985, past pres. 1986, chmn. nom. com. 1991), Tenn. Hosp. Assn. (jt. liaison Tenn. Med. Assn. com. 1991), Mid-South Healthcare Materials Mgmt. Assn. (co-chmn. founding orgnl. com. 1991), Kappa Psi, Rho Chi. Home: 2927 Mikeyair Dr Germantown TN 38138-7148 Office: UT Bowld Hosp 951 Court Ave Memphis TN 38103-2813

NOLTE, HENRY R., JR., lawyer, former automobile company executive; b. N.Y.C., Mar. 3, 1924; s. Henry R. and Emily A. (Eisele) N.; m. Frances Messner, May 19, 1951; children: Gwynne Conn, Henry Reed III, Jennifer Stevens, Suzanne. BA, Duke U., 1947; LLB, U. Pa., 1949. Bar: N.Y. 1950, Mich. 1967. Assoc. Cravath, Swaine & Moore, N.Y.C., 1951-61; assoc. counsel Ford Motor Co., Dearborn, Mich., 1961, asst. gen. counsel, 1964-71, assoc. gen. counsel, 1971-74, v.p., gen. counsel, 1974-89; v.p., gen. counsel Philco-Ford Corp., Phila., 1961-64; v.p., gen. counsel, sec. Ford of Europe Inc., Warley, Essex, Eng., 1967-69; gen. counsel fin. and ins. subs. Ford Motor Co., 1974-89; sr. ptnr. Miller, Canfield, Paddock & Stone, Detroit, 1989-93, of counsel, 1993—; bd. dirs. First Fed. Mich. Corp. Trustee Cranbrook Ednl. Community; mem. Internat. and Comparative Law Ctr. of Southwestern Legal Found.; bd. dirs. Detroit Symphony Orch.; trustee Beaumont Hosp. Lt. USNR, 1943-46, PTO. Mem. ABA (past chmn. corp. law depts.), Mich. Bar Assn., Assn. Bar City N.Y., Assn. Gen. Counsel, Orchard Lake Country Club, Bloomfield Hills Country Club, Everglades Club (Fla.), Gulfstream Golf Club (Fla.), Ocean Club (Fla.). Episcopalian. Office: Miller Canfield Paddock & Stone 1400 N Woodward Ave Ste 100 Bloomfield Hills MI 48303-2014

NOLTE, JUDITH ANN, magazine editor; b. Hampton, Iowa, Sept. 17, 1938; d. Clifford P. and Sigrid M. (Johnson) N.; m. Randers H. Heimer, May 7, 1971. BS, U. Minn., 1960; MA in English, NYU, 1965. Tchr. English Middletown (N.Y.) High Sch., 1960-62, High Sch. of Commerce, N.Y.C., 1962-64; merchandising editor Conde Nast Publs., N.Y.C., 1964-69; editor-in-chief Am. Baby Mag., Cahners Pub. Co., N.Y.C., 1969—, Weight Watchers mag., 1980-83; editorial dir. Cahners Childcare Group, N.Y.C., 1990—; hostess Am. Baby Cable TV Show. Chmn. media adv. bd. N.Y. chpt. March of Dimes. Mem. Am. Soc. Mag. Editors (pres. 1986-88), Mortar Bd., Delta Gamma (pres. 1960). Office: Am Baby/Healthly Kids Cahners Publishing Company 249 W 17th St New York NY 10011

NOLTE, NICK, actor; b. Omaha, 1942; m. Rebecca Linger, Feb. 19, 1984; 1 child, Brawley King. Student, Pasadena City Coll., Phoenix City Coll.; studies with, John Paul, Allen Dutton. Actor: (play) The Last Pad, 1973, (TV movies) Winter Kill, 1974, The California Kid, 1974, Death Sentence, 1974, Adams of Eagle Lake, 1975, The Treasure Chest Murder, 1975, The Runaways, 1975, (mini-series) Rich Man, Poor Man, 1976; (films) The Deep, 1977, Return to Macon County, 1975, Who'll Stop the Rain, 1978, North Dallas Forty, 1979, Heartbeat, 1980, Cannery Row, 1982, 48 Hours, 1982, Under Fire, 1983, The Ultimate Solution of Grace Quigley, 1984, Teachers, 1984, Down and Out in Beverly Hills, 1986, Weeds, 1987, Extreme Prejudice, 1987, Farewell to the King, 1988, Three Fugitives, 1988, New York Stories, 1989, Everybody Wins, 1989, Q & A, 1990, Another 48 Hours, 1990, Prince of Tides, 1991, Cape Fear, 1991, Lorenzo's Oil, 1992, Blue Chips, 1994, I'll Do Anything, 1994, Jefferson in Paris, 1995. Address: 6173 Bonsall Dr Malibu CA 90265*

NOLTE, RICHARD HENRY, political science researcher, consultant; b. Duluth, Minn., Dec. 27, 1920; s. Julius Mosher and Mildred (Miller) N.; m. Jeanne McQuarrie, Mar. 27, 1945; children: Charles McQuarrie, Roger Reed, Douglas Mitchell, Jameson Jay. A.B., Yale, 1943, M.A., 1947; B.A. (Rhodes scholar), Oxford (Eng.) U., 1950, MA, 1954, Inst. Current World

Affairs fellow, 1948-54; D.Sc. (hon.), U. Wis., Milw., 1979. Assoc. on Middle East Am. Univs. Field Staff, 1953-58; asst. dir. humanities Rockefeller Found., Inc., N.Y.C., 1958-59; exec. dir. Inst. Current World Affairs, N.Y.C., 1959-78, Alicia Patterson Found., N.Y.C., 1965-78; exec. v.p. Hamilton, Johnston & Co., Inc., N.Y.C., 1978-81; cons. Middle East Dillon, Read & Co., Inc., N.Y.C., 1981-82; assoc. for Middle East HME Internat. Adv. Assocs., Inc., N.Y.C., 1982-90; gen. ptnr. Washburn Island Res. Ltd. Partnership, East Falmouth, Mass., 1981-89; pres. Near East Found., N.Y.C., 1984-87, now bd. dirs.; ambassador to Egypt Cairo, 1967. Editor: The Modern Middle East, 1963. Vice chmn. Stamford Forum for World Affairs; bd. dirs. Pro Bono, Inc., 1994—. Pilot USNR, 1943-45. Mem. Am. Geog. Soc. (pres. 1973-80, now chmn. bd.), Nat. Aphasia Assn. (bd. dirs. 1990—, bd. dirs. Fund for Peace 1993—), Coun. on Fgn. Rels., Phi Beta Kappa. Clubs: Yale, Mid-Atlantic. Home and Office: 516 Harvest Commons Westport CT 06880

NOLTE, WALTER EDUARD, retired retirement home executive, foundation counsel, former banker; b. Joplin, Mo., Oct. 28, 1911; s. Ernest Henry and Clara (Meyer) N.; m. Sara Elizabeth Mumford, Oct. 6, 1939 (dec. May 1990); children: Walter Eduard, Craig R. (dec.). AB, U. Nebr., 1934, JD, 1936. Bar: Nebr. 1936, Tex. 1952, U.S. Supreme Ct 1952. With firm Beghtol, Foe & Rankin, Lincoln, Nebr., 1936-48; asst. atty. gen. Neb., 1948-50; dep. atty. gen., 1950-52; pres. Nolte Nat. Bank, Seguin, Tex., 1952-59; v.p. 1st Nat. Bank & Trust Co., Lincoln, 1959-60; exec. v.p. 1st Nat. Bank & Trust Co., 1960-76; pres. Gateway Manor, Inc., 1976-89; dir. Am. Combined Life Ins. Co., Chgo. Co-editor: Nebraska Restatement of Trusts, 1941. Pres. Lincoln Better Bus. Bur., 1964-65; Past pres. Lincoln Gen. Hosp. and Lincoln Hosp. Assn.; gen. chmn. Lincoln United Fund, 1973-74; bd. dirs. Lincoln Symphony Assn.; pres. Tb Assn., 1970. Served to lt. comdr. USNR, 1943-45. Mem. Nebr. Bar Assn., State Bar Tex., Lincoln C. of C. (pres. 1967-68), Nebr. Assn. Commerce and Industry (pres. 1975-76), Lincoln U. Club, Ak-Sar-Ben Club, Lincoln Country Club, Beta Theta Pi, Phi Delta Phi. Republican. Episcopalian. Home and Office: 225 N 56th St Lincoln NE 68504-3515

NOLTE, WILLIAM HENRY, English language educator; b. Tulia, Tex., May 2, 1928; s. Eugene Arch Nolte and Myrtle (Burns) Goldman; m. Alice Froehling, June 12, 1954; 1 child, Katherine Ann. Student, Tex. Tech U., 1947-49; BA, U. Mo., 1951; MA, U. Tex., 1952; PhD, U. Ill., 1959. Teaching asst. U. Ill., Urbana, 1954-59; asst. prof. English U. Oreg., Eugene, 1959-65; assoc. prof. U. Mo., St. Louis, 1965-67; prof. U. S.C., Columbia, 1967-89, disting. prof. emeritus English, 1989—. Author: H.L. Mencken, Literary Critic, 1966, H.L. Mencken's Smart Set Criticism, 1968, Rock and Hawk: Robinson Jeffers and the Romantic Agony, 1978. Served to cpl. USAAF, 1946-47. Holder endowed chair U. S.C. Ednl. Found., Columbia, 1978. Democrat. Home: 4502 Storkland Ave Columbia SC 29206-1245 Office: Univ of SC Dept of English Lang & Lit Columbia SC 29208

NOLTIMIER, HALLAN COSTELLO, geology educator, researcher, consultant; b. Los Angeles, Mar. 19, 1937; s. Frederick Henry and Corinne Marie (Scheel) N.; m. Judith Walford Summers, July 14, 1961; children: Mark Andrew, Romy Ann. B.S. in Sci., Calif. Inst. Tech., 1958; Ph.D. in Geophysics, U. Newcastle upon Tune, (Eng.), 1965. Lectr. physics and geophysics U. Newcastle upon Tyne, 1966-68; asst. prof. U. Okla., Norman, 1968-71; assoc. prof. U. Houston, 1971-72; assoc. prof. geology Ohio State U., Columbus, 1972-78, prof., 1978—; faculty rep. Research Found., 1982-86; cons. energy cos, Ohio and Tex., 1980—; geosci. commentator Swedish Nat. Radio, 1981. Contbr. chpts., numerous articles to profl. publs. Mobile Oil Co. scholar, 1957; Dept. Sci. and Indsl. Research studentship, 1958-61; Fulbright Found. fellow Goettingen, W. Ger., 1958; Petroleum Research Fund grantee Wales, 1976-81; Dept. State grantee Spain, 1978-82. Fellow Royal Astron. Soc.; mem. Am. Geophys. Union, Geol. Soc. Am., AAAS, N.Y. Acad. Sci., Ohio Acad. Sci., Sigma Xi (sec. chpt. 1969-71). Office: Ohio State U Dept Geology and Mineralogy 125 S Oval Mall Columbus OH 43210-1308 *The most influential event in my life was the offer by Professor S.K.Runcorn, upon my graduation from California Institute of Technology to do graduatework in geophysics at the University of Newcastle-upon-Tyne in England. That offer shaped my professional academic career, led to my marriage in England and our family, and encouraged me to understand the world in which I live. That 'travel broadens one' may be the most valid cliche of our time.*

NOMURA, MASAYASU, biological chemistry educator; b. Hyogo-Ken, Japan, Apr. 27, 1927; s. Hiromichi and Yaeko N.; m. Junko Hamashima, Feb. 10, 1957; children—Keiko, Toshiyasu. Ph.D., U. Tokyo, 1957. Asst. prof. Inst. Protein Research, Osaka (Japan) U., 1960-63; assoc. prof. genetics U. Wis., Madison, 1963-66, prof., 1966-70, Elvehejem prof. in Life Sci. genetics and biochemistry, 1970-84, co-dir. Inst. for Enzyme Research, 1970-84; prof. biol. chemistry, Grace Bell chair U. Calif., Irvine, 1984—. Recipient U.S. Steel award in molecular biology Nat. Acad. Scis., 1971; recipient Acad. award Japanese Acad. Arts and Sci., 1972. Mem. Am. Acad. Arts and Scis., Nat. Acad. Scis., Royal Danish Acad. Scis. and Letters, Royal Netherlands Acad. Arts and Scis. Home: 74 Whitman Ct Irvine CA 92715-4066 Office: U Calif Dept Biol Chemistry Med Sci I # D240 Irvine CA 92717

NONES SUCRE, CARLOS ENRIQUE, political organization executive; b. Caracas, Venezuela, Oct. 12, 1936; arrived in U.S., 1980; s. Abraham Alberto Nones Fonseca and Delfina Mercedes (Sucre) De Nones; m. Antonieta Paulina Landaeta de Nones, Dec. 26, 1986. BSCE, MIT, 1957, MS in Interdisciplinary Studies, 1974; ingeniero quimico, Univ. Central de Venezuela, 1960; postgrad. diploma in applied chem. kinetics, Sorbornne, U. Paris, 1961; MPhil in Polit. Sci., CUNY, N.Y.C., 1992, PhD in Polit. Sci., Internat. Politics, 1994. Chem. engr. Nat. Petrochemical Enterprise, Caracas, Venezuela, 1957-60; asst. prof. chemistry Venezuelan Naval Acad., Maiquetia, Venezuela, 1958-60; programme specialist, internat. exchange svc. UNESCO, Paris, 1961-63; asst. to dir. regional ctr. in western hemisphere UNESCO, Havana, Cuba, 1963-65, dep. dir. regional ctr. in western hemisphere, chief of Cuban mission, 1965-67; dep. chief Latin Am. and Caribbean divsn., Office of Rels. with Member States UNESCO, Paris, 1968-71, programme specialist, engring. edn. sect., divsn. tech. rsch. and higher edn., 1971-75, sr. programme specialist, divsn. technological rsch. and higher edn., 1975-81; dep. dir. Ctr. for Sci. and Tech. for Devel., UN, N.Y.C., 1981-91, dep. exec. dir. 1991-92; head sci. and tech. br., dept. econs. and social devel. UN, N.Y.C., 1992-93, dep. dept. devel. support and mgmt. scis., 1993-94; amb. to Netherlands Govt. Venezuela, The Hague, 1994—; mem. adv. bd. Ctr. Hemisphere Cooperation in Rsch. and Edn. in Engring. and Applied Scis., Mayaguez, P.R., 1992—. Contbg. author: Temas Internacionales 1994, 1994; contbr. articles to profl. jours. Recipient Andres Bello medal Min. Edn., Venezuela, 1986, Francisco de Miranda medal Pres. of Venezuela, 1991; Ctr. for Advanced Engring. Studies fellow MIT, 1973-74. Mem. Colegio de Ingenieros de Venezuela, UN Staff Assn., Assn. Promotion of Humor in Internat. Affairs, World Assn. Indsl. and Tech. Rsch. Orgns. (mem. exec. com. 1991—), Internat. Assn. Tech. Assessment and Forecasting (promoter founder). Roman Catholic. Avocations: art collecting, swimming. Home: Villa Coromoto, 91 Buurtweg, 2244 AB Wassenaar The Netherlands Office: Embassy of Venezuela, 2 Nassaulaan, 2514 JS The Hague The Netherlands

NONET, PHILIPPE, law educator; b. Liège, Belgium, Feb. 25, 1939; s. Leon and Helene (Reginster) N.; m. Pamela Jean Utz, Mar. 21, 1978; children—Michael, Genevieve, Beatrice. Docteur en Droit, U. Liège, 1961; Ph.D., U. Calif., Berkeley, 1966. Prof. law U. Calif.-Berkeley, 1966—. Author: Administrative Justice, 1969; (with others) Law and Society in Transition, 1978. Mem. Am. Soc. for Polit. and Legal Philosophy, Amintaphil, Law and Soc. Assn. Home: 885 Creed Rd Oakland CA 94610-1853 Office: U Calif-Berkeley Sch Law Berkeley CA 94720

NONG, artist, sculptor; b. Seoul, Korea, Oct. 10, 1930; came to U.S., 1952, naturalized, 1958; Commr. Asian Art Commn. Asian Art Mus. San Francisco, The Avery Brundage Collection, City and County of San Francisco, 1981-84. One-man exhbns. paintings and/or sculpture include Ft. Lauderdale (Fla.) Mus. Arts, Santa Barbara (Calif.) Mus. Art, Crocker Art Mus., Sacramento, Calif., 1965, Ga. Mus. Art, Athens, 1967, El Paso (Tex.) Mus. Art, 1967, Galerie Vallombreuse, Biarritz, France, 1970, Nat. Mus. History, Taiwan, 1971, Nihonbashi Gallery, Tokyo, Japan, 1971, Shinsege

Gallery, Seoul, Korea, 1975, Nat. Mus. Modern Art, Seoul, 1975, San Francisco Zool. Garden, 1975, Tongin Art Gallery, Seoul, 1978, Consulate Gen. Republic of Korea, Los Angeles, 1982, Choon Chu Gallery, Seoul, 1982, Mee Gallery, Seoul, 1984, 86, Leema Art Mus., Seoul 1985, Tong-A Dept. Store, Taegu, Korea, 1986, Tongso Gallery, Masan, Korea, 1986, Han Kwang Art Mus., Pusan, Korea, 1986, Union de Arte, Barcelona, Spain, 1987, Acad. de Belles Arts, Sabadell, Spain; 1987; numerous group exhibits Mus. and Art Ctr., Douglaston, N.Y., 1961, Nat. Collection Fine Arts, Smithsonian Instn., Washington, 1961, Mus. Fine Arts, Springfield, Mass., 1961, Conn. Acad. Fine Arts, Hartford, Conn., 1962, Charles and Emma Frye Art Mus., Seattle, 1962, The Denver Art Mus., 1965, Jersey City Mus., 1967, U. Santa Clara (Calif.) Mus., 1967, U. Calif., Berkeley, 1968, Maison de la Culture du Havre, Le Havre, France, 1970, Oakland (Calif.) Art Mus., 1971, Gallerie des Champs Elysees, Paris, 1971, Nat. Sculpture Soc., Lever House, N.Y.C., 1971, Taipei Provincial Mus., Republic of China, 1971, San Francisco Mus. Modern Art, 1972, Galerie Hexagramme, Paris, 1975, Galeria de Arte Misrachi, Mexico City, 1979, The Mun Ye Art Ctr., Seoul, 1986, Salon de Artistes Francais, Paris, France, 1971, Salon d'Automne, Paris, 1969-71, Salon Grands et Jeunes d'Aujourd'hui, Paris, 1971-77; represented in numerous permanent collections including, Santa Barbara Mus. Art, Anchorage (Alaska) Hist. and Fine Art Mus., Museo de Arte, Lima, Peru, Govt. Peru, Nat. Mus. History, Govt. of Republic of China, Oakland (Calif.) Art Mus., Ga. Mus. Art, Athens, Korean Embassy, Lima, Peru, Nat. Mus. of Modern Art, Nat. Mus. Korea, Govt. of Republic of Korea, Seoul, Nat. Gallery of Modern Art, New Delhi, India, Asian Art Mus. San Francisco, Govt. of People's Republic China, Beijing and Shanghai, Palacio de la Zarzuela, Madrid, Palacio de la Moncloa, Madrid, The Korean Embassy, Madrid, Mus. of Arte de Sabadell, Spain, Mus. Nat. des Beaux-Arts, Monte Carlo, Monaco, others; author: Nong Questions, 1982. Chmn. San Francisco-Seoul Sister City Com., City and County San Francisco, 1981-84. Served with U.S. Army, 1956-59; Served with USAF, 1959-60. Recipient numerous awards including citations from Republic of Korea, Cert. Disting. Achievement State of Calif., 1982, Proclamation City and County of San Francisco, 1982. Home: 7013 Union Mill Rd Clifton VA 22024 *Beauty and ugliness, good and bad, right and wrong. Which test should I choose to measure these? Then, how long can I rely on the test I choose?.*

NONNA, JOHN MICHAEL, lawyer; b. N.Y.C., July 8, 1948; s. Angelo and Josephine (Visconti) N.; m. Jean Wanda Cleary, June 9, 1973; children: Elizabeth, Caroline, Marianne, Timothy. AB, Princeton U., 1970; JD, NYU, 1975. Bar: N.Y. 1976, U.S. Dist. Ct. (so. dist.) N.Y. 1978, U.S. Ct. Appeals (2d cir.) 1978, U.S. Ct. Appeals (9th cir.) 1980, U.S. Dist. Ct. Conn. 1988. Law asst. to Hon. D.L. Gabrielli N.Y. Ct. Appeals, Albany, 1975-77; assoc. Reid & Priest, 1977-84; ptnr. Werner & Kennedy, 1984—. Contbr. articles to profl. jours. Trustee Village of Pleasantville, N.Y., 1990—, dep. mayor, 1993-95, acting justice, 1983-89. With USNR, 1970-75. U.S. Olympic Team, Munich, 1972, Moscow, 1980. Recipient Bar Found.; mem. ABA (torts and ins. practice sect. com. chair 1986-87, 92-93), N.Y. State Bar Assn. (exec. com. comml. and fed. litigation sect. 1984—, INCL sect. 1993—), Assn. of Bar of City of N.Y., N.Y. Fencers Club (pres. 1990-93). Avocations: fencing, running, piano. Office: Werner and Kennedy 1633 Broadway Fl 46 New York NY 10019-6708

NOON, PATRICK, museum curator; b. Phila., Oct. 13, 1951; s. Francis Joseph and Marion (Henneberry) N.; m. Diane Meade Tsurutani, May 18, 1991. BA in Art History, Brown U., 1973; MA in Art History, U. Mich., 1974. Asst. curator Yale Ctr. for Brit. Art, New Haven, 1977-80, curator, 1980—; mem. adv. bd. Walpole Soc., London, 1989—. Author: English Portrait Drawings, 1979, English Miniatures, 1981, Richard Parkes Bonington, 1991; mem. editorial bd. Print Quar., 1986—, Master Drawings, 1989—; contbr. articles to profl. jours. Nat. Endowment of Art fellow, 1974, 86. Mem. Print Coun. Am. Democrat. Office: Yale Ctr for Brit Art Yale Sta PO Box 2120 New Haven CT 06520

NOONAN, FRANK R., business executive; b. Boston, July 21, 1942; s. Russell F. and Barbara (Yutronich) N.; m. Patricia Bernadette Saulnier, Aug. 22, 1964; children: Kathleen, Kelly, Kristin. BA, U. N.H., 1964. Fin. mgmt. trainee Gen. Electric Co., Lynn, Mass., 1966-69; corp. auditor Gen. Electric Co., Schenectady, N.Y., 1969-74, audit adminstr., 1974-76; fin. mgr. mechanical drive turbine dept. Gen. Electric Co., Fitchburg, Mass., 1976-78; fin. mgr. air conditioning div. Gen. Electric Co., Louisville, 1978-81; sr. v.p., chief fin. officer Union Mutual Ins. Co., Portland, Maine, 1981-86, UNUM Corp., Portland, 1986-89; sr. v.p., group fin. The Dun & Bradstreet Corp., N.Y.C., 1989-90; chmn., CEO Reuben H. Donnelly Corp., Purchase, N.Y., 1991—. Bd. dirs. Maine Coll. of Art; v.p. Found. Blood Rsch. Scarborough, Maine, 1982-89. Mem. Fin. Execs. Inst. Republican. Avocations: tennis, skiing, music, golf, model trains. Home: 8 Lincoln Ln Purchase NY 10577 Office: Reuben H Donnelly Corp 287 Bowman Ave Purchase NY 10577-2517

NOONAN, JACQUELINE ANNE, pediatrics educator; b. Burlington, Vt., Oct. 28, 1928. BA, Albertus Magnus Coll., 1950; MD, U. Vt., 1954, DSc (hon.), 1980. Diplomate Am. Bd. Pediatrics, Am. Bd. Pediatric Cardiology. Intern N.C. Meml. Hosp., Chapel Hill, 1954-55; resident in pediatrics Children's Hosp., Cin., 1955-57; rsch. fellow Children's Med. Ctr., Boston, 1957-59; asst. prof. pediatrics State U. Iowa Sch. Medicine, 1959-61; asst. prof. pediatrics cardiology U. Ky. Coll. Medicine, Lexington, 1961-64, assoc. prof., 1964-69, prof., 1969—, chmn. dept. pediatrics, 1974-92; mem. embryology and human devel. study sect. NIH, 1973-78; mem. U.S.-USSR Symposium on Congenital Heart Disease, 1975; mem. sub. bd. pediatric cardiology Am. Bd. Pediatrics, 1977-82; examiner, mem. test. com. Nat. Bd. Med. Examiners, 1984-90, exec. com., 1991-95; participant various confs. in field; vis. prof. Vanderbilt U., Nashville, 1987; spkr. in field. Contbr. articles, revs. to med. publs.; mem. editl. bd. Am. Jour. Diseases Children, 1970-80, Am. Jour. Med. Edn., 1975-78, Pediatric Cardiology, 1978-90, Am. Heart Jour., 1994—, Clin. Pediatrics, 1990—. Mem. AMA, Am. Acad. Pediatrics (cardiology sect. chmn. 1972-74), Am. Coll. Cardiology (gov. Ky. chpt. 1989-92), Am. Fedn. Clin. Rsch., Assn. Med. Sch. Pediatric (dept. chmn. exec. com. 1978-81), Fayette County Med. Soc., Irish-Am. Pediatric Soc., Am. Pediatric Soc., Ky. State Med. Assn., NIH Alumni Assn., Soc. Pediatric Rsch., So. Soc. Pediatric Rsch. (pres. 1972). Office: U Ky Med Ctr Pediatrics Ky Clinic Lexington KY 40536-0284

NOONAN, JOHN MICHAEL, aluminum company executive; b. Syracuse, N.Y., Apr. 21, 1933; s. Michael Joseph and Rose (Early) N.; m. Barbara A. Boland, July 23, 1955; children: Michael, John, Karen, Eileen, Bryan, Paul. B.A., LeMoyne Coll., 1955; M.P.A., Syracuse U., 1956. Project dir. Reynolds Metals Devel. Co., Washington, 1959-69; v.p. Reynolds Metals Devel. Co., Providence, 1969-72, exec. v.p., 1972-77; pres. Reynolds Metals Devel. Co., Richmond, Va., 1977—; dir. corp. real estate Reynolds Metals Co., Richmond, 1978-81; v.p. Reynolds Metals Co., 1981—; bd. dirs. Citizens Bank, Providence. Chmn. bd. Providence Found., 1975-79; trustee Salve Regina Coll., Newport (R.I.), 1977—. Mem. greater Providence C. of C. (dir. 1976-79), Riverfront Devel. Corp., 1990—. Roman Catholic. Home: 8706 Tarrytown Dr Richmond VA 23229-7134 Office: Reynolds Metals Co 6601 W Broad St Richmond VA 23269-0001

NOONAN, JOHN T., JR., federal judge, legal educator; b. Boston, Oct. 24, 1926; s. John T. and Marie (Shea) N.; m. Mary Lee Bennett, Dec. 27, 1967; children: John Kenneth, Rebecca Lee, Susanna Bain. B.A., Harvard U., 1946, LL.B., 1954; student, Cambridge U., 1946-47; M.A., Cath. U. Am., 1949, Ph.D., 1951, LHD, 1980; LL.D., U. Santa Clara, 1974, U. Notre Dame, 1976, Loyola U. South, 1978; LHD, Holy Cross Coll., 1980; LL.D., St. Louis U., 1981, U. San Francisco, 1985; student, Holy Cross Coll. 1980, Cath. U. Am. 1980, Gonzaga U., 1986, U. San Francisco, 1986. Bar: Mass. 1954, U.S. Supreme Ct. 1971. Mem. spl. staff Nat. Security Council, 1954-55; pvt. practice Herrick & Smith, Boston, 1955-60; prof. law U. Notre Dame, 1961-66; prof. law U. Calif., Berkeley, 1967-86, chmn. religious studies, 1970-73, chmn. medieval studies, 1978-79; judge U.S. Ct. Appeals (9th cir.), San Francisco, 1985—; Oliver Wendell Holmes, Jr. lectr. Harvard U. Law Sch., 1972, Pope John XXIII lectr. Cath. U. Law Sch., 1973, Cardinal Bellarmine lectr. St. Louis U. Div. Sch., 1973, Baum lectr. U. Ill., 1988, Strassberger lectr. U. Tex., 1989; chmn. bd. Games Rsch. Inc., 1961-76; overseer Harvard U., 1991—. Author: The Scholastic Analyst of Usury, 1957; Contraception: A History of Its Treatment by the Catholic Theo-

logians and Canonists, 1965; Power to Dissolve, 1972; Persons and Masks of the Law, 1976; The Antelope, 1977; A Private Choice, 1979; Bribes, 1984; editor: Natural Law Forum, 1961-70, Am. Jour. Jurisprudence, 1970, The Morality of Abortion, 1970. Chmn. Brookline Redevel. Authority, Mass., 1958-62; cons. Papal Commn. on Family, 1965-66, Ford Found., Indonesian Legal Program, 1968; NIH, 1973, NIH, 1974; expert Presdl. Commn. on Population and Am. Future, 1971; cons. U.S. Cath. Conf., 1979-86; sec., treas. Inst. for Research in Medieval Canon Law, 1970-88; pres. Thomas More-Jacques Maritain Inst., 1977—; trustee Population Council, 1969-76, Phi Kappa Found., 1970-76, Grad. Theol. Union, 1970-73, U. San Francisco, 1971-75; mem. com. theol. edn. Yale U., 1972-77; exec. com. Cath. Commn. Intellectual and Cultural Affairs, 1972-75; bd. dirs. Ctr. for Human Values in the Health Scis., 1969-71, S.W. Intergroup Relations Council, 1970-72, Inst. for Study Ethical Issues, 1971-73. Recipient St. Thomas More award U. San Francisco, 1974, Christian Culture medal, 1975, Laetare medal U. Notre Dame, 1984, Campion medal Cath. Book Club, 1987; Guggenheim fellow, 1965-66, 79-80, Laetare medal U. Notre Dame, 1984, Campion medal, 1987, Alemany medal Western Dominican Province, 1988; Ctr. for advanced Studies in Behavioral Scis. fellow, 1973-74; Wilson Ctr. fellow, 1979-80. Fellow Am. Acad. Arts and Scis., Am. Soc. Legal Historians (hon.); mem. Am. Soc. Polit. and Legal Philosophy (v.p. 1964), Canon Law Soc. Am. (gov. 1970-72), Am. Law Inst., Phi Beta Kappa (senator United chpts. 1970-72, pres. Alpha of Calif. chpt. 1972-73). Office: US Ct Appeals 9th Cir PO Box 193939 San Francisco CA 94119-3939*

NOONAN, JOSEPH PATRICK, engineering educator; b. Somerville, Mass., Aug. 19, 1944. BS in Elec. Engring., Tufts U., 1967, MS in Elec. Engring., 1969, PhD in Statis. Comm., 1973. Sr. engr. missile systems divsn. Raytheon Co., Bedford, Mass., 1969-73; mgr. signal processing group RDP, Inc., Bedford, Mass., 1973-78; pres., founder, chmn. bd. Bedford Rsch. Assocs., Bedford, 1978-85; assoc. prof. elec. engring. Tufts U., Medford, Mass., 1985—; lectr. Tufts U., Medford, 1985; tech. cons. Bedford Rsch. Assocs., Bedford, 1985—; reviewer Jour. Signal Processing, MacMillan Pub. Co. Contbr. articles to profl. jours. Mem. IEEE (reviewer), Eta Kappa Nu (faculty adv.), Tau Beta Pi. Office: Tufts U Dept Electrical Engrin Medford MA 02155

NOONAN, NORINE ELIZABETH, academic administrator, researcher; b. Phila., Oct. 5, 1948; d. Alaric Edwin and Norine (Radford) Freeman. BA, summa cum laude, U. Vt., 1970; MA, Princeton U., 1972, PhD, 1976. Asst. prof. Coll. Vet. Medicine, U. Fla., Gainesville, 1976-81, assoc. prof., 1981; research assoc. prof. Georgetown U., Washington, 1981-82; Am. Chem. Soc. sci. fellow U.S. Senate Commerce Com., Washington, 1982-83; program and budget analyst Office Mgmt. and Budget, Washington, 1983-87, acting br. chief sci. and space programs, 1987-88, br. chief, 1988-92; v.p. rsch. Fla. Inst. Tech., Melbourne, 1992—, dean grad. sch., 1993—; bd. advisors U.S. Found. for the Internat. Space U., 1989-90; disting. lectr. MITRE Corp. Inst., 1991; vis. faculty Exec. Seminar Ctrs., Office Personnel Mgmt.; cons. Am. Chem. Soc. com. chem. and pub. affairs; mem. NASA space sci. adv. com.; mem. com. Antarctic policy & sci. and future of space sci. NRC; councilor Oak Ridge Assn. Univs.; trustee Southeast Univs. Rsch. Assn.; also chair finance com. Contbr. articles to sci. jours. Vol. Balt. City Fair, 1982-91. Bd. dirs. Brevard Symphony Orchestra, 1993—, Wolf Trap Farm Pk. Assocs., Wolf Trap Farm Pk. for the Performing Arts, 1988-92, exec. com. 1990-92, exec. vice chmn., 1991-92, treas., 1992; mem. adv. coun. Brookings Instn. Ctr. for Pub. Policy Edn., 1989-93; treas. White House Athletic Ctr., 1990-92, Potomac Basset Hound Club, Space Coast Tiger Bay Club. Recipient Spl. Performance award Office Mgmt. and Budget, 1987, 88; grantee Fla. Div. Am. Cancer Soc., 1977, NIH, 1979, NSF, 1979. Fellow AAAS (mem. at large sect. gen. interest in sci. and tech. 1994—, mem. sci., engring. and pub. policy com.); mem. Am. Soc. Cell Biology, Sigma Xi, Phi Beta Kappa (pres. Fla. chpt. 1980-81). Mem. United Ch. of Christ. Avocations: running, purebred dogs, reading, cooking, aerobics. Home: 2480 Grassmere Dr Melbourne FL 32904-9715 Office: Fla Inst Tech 150 W University Blvd Melbourne FL 32901-6967

NOONAN, PATRICK FRANCIS, conservation executive; b. St. Petersburg, Fla., Dec. 2, 1942; s. Francis Patrick and Henrietta (Donovan) N.; m. Nancy Elizabeth Peck, Aug. 15, 1964; children: Karen Elizabeth, Dawn Wiley. A.B., Gettysburg Coll., 1961-65; M.City and Regional Planning, Catholic U. Am., 1967; M.B.A., Am. U., 1971. Dir. ops. The Nature Conservancy, Arlington, Va., 1969-73; pres. The Nature Conservancy, 1973-80; chmn. The Conservation Fund, 1985—. Trustee Nat. Geographi Soc. 1990—, Gettysburg Coll., 1978-91, Duke U. Sch. Environment, 1979—, Ind. Sector, 1984-91, dir. Ashland, 1991—, Internat. Paper, 1993—, Saul Ctrs., 1993—, Rushmore Funds, 1987—; mem. Pres.' Commn. on Am. Outdoors, 1985-87, Pres.' Commn. on Environ. Quality, 1991-93; trustee Catholic Youth Orgn., 1975—, Am. Conservation Assn., 1986—, Am. Farmland Trust, 1987—). MacArthur Found. fellow, 1985-90. Home: 11901 Glen Mill Rd Potomac MD 20854-1920

NOONAN, STEPHEN JOSEPH, accounting firm executive; b. Millbury, Mass., June 13, 1945; s. Joseph Andrew and Evelyn Mary (Devoe) N.; m. Helen Stephanie Wolochowicz, May 20, 1967; children: John Patrick, Karen Marie. Diploma, N.E. Sch. Acctg., Worcester, 1965. Enrolled agt. Acct. George Cagan, CPA, Worcester, 1965-66; mgr. Greenberg, Rosenblat & Assocs., Worcester, 1966-85; proprietor Stephen J. Noonan Assocs., Millbury, Mass., 1985—; cons. Sisters of the Assumption, Worcester, 1991—. Mem. sch. com. Assumption Sch., Millbury, Mass., 1979—; youth soccer coach Sutton (Mass.) Soccer Club, 1979-87; organizer Good Shepherd Endowment Fund, Worcester, 1984. Mem. Mass. Soc. CPAs, Estate and Bus. Planning Coun. of Worcester County. Democrat. Roman Catholic. Avocations: wood carving, photography, writing, soccer, music. Home: 18 Juniper Dr Millbury MA 01527 Office: Stephen J Noonan and Assocs PO Box 431 Millbury MA 01527

NOONAN, SUSAN ABERT, public relations counselor; b. Lancaster, Pa., May 10, 1960; d. James Goodear and Carole (Althouse) Abert; m. David Lindsay Noonan, July 28, 1986; children: Caroline du Pont, Elizabeth Augusta. BA, Mt. Holyoke Coll., 1982. Account exec. Merill Lynch, N.Y.C., 1982-83; sr. v.p. Cameron Assocs., N.Y.C., 1983-88; pres., founder Noonan/Russo Comm., N.Y.C. 1989—. Mem. Nat. Investor Rels. Inst. Office: Noonan/Russo Comm Inc 220 5th Ave New York NY 10001

NOONAN, THOMAS SCHAUB, history educator, Russian studies educator; b. N.Y.C., Jan. 20, 1938; s. Thomas M. and Martha M. (Schaub) N.; m. Norma L. Corigliano, May 19, 1937; 1 child, Thomas R. A.B., Dartmouth Coll., 1959; M.A., Ind. U., 1962, Ph.D., 1965. Cert. Russian Inst., Ind. U. Asst. prof. Otterbein Coll., Westerville, Ohio, 1965-66; asst. prof. dept. history U. Minn.-Mpls., 1966-74, assoc. prof., 1974-79, prof., 1979—; chmn. dept. Russian and East European studies, 1981-91; assoc. chmn. dept. history U. Minn.-Mpls., 1992-93, 94—; acting chmn. dept. history, 1994-95. Co-editor Archivum Eurasiae Medii Aevi, 1980—, Russian and East European Studies, 1986—; mem. adv. bd. Russian History, 1980-88, Soviet Studies in History, 1986-89; contbr. articles to profl. jours. Recipient Royal medal Swedish Numismatic Soc., 1984; Kraay vis. fellow Oxford U., 1983; Social Sci. Rsch. Coun. fellow, 1980-81; Reference Tools grantee NEH, 1990-91. Fellow Am. Numismatic Soc., Royal Numismatic Soc.; mem. Am. Hist. Assn., Am. Assn. Advancement Slavic Studies, Assn. Advancement Baltic Studies. Home: 10224 Rich Rd Minneapolis MN 55437-2503 Office: Univ Minn Dept History 614 Social Sciences Bldg Minneapolis MN 55455

NOONAN, WILLIAM FRANCIS, public relations company executive; b. Irvington, N.J., Sept. 29, 1932; s. Thomas Leo and Rose Anna (O'Reilly) N.; m. Alyce K. Normoyle; children: Jessica L., Shannon C.; children by previous marriage: William J., Thomas M., Robert P., Carol J. B.A. in Journalism, U. Notre Dame, 1954. Asst. promotion mgr. plastics div. Union Carbide Corp., N.Y.C., 1956-62; with Burson-Marsteller, N.Y.C., 1962-94; account exec., account supr., group mgr. Burson-Marsteller, 1962-72, exec. v.p., gen. mgr. N.Y.C. office, 1972-83, pres./Americas, 1983-84, vice chmn., pres. internat., 1985-90; vice chmn. Burston-Marsteller, 1992-94; also bd. dirs. Burson-Marsteller; chmn., CEO Dentsu Burson-Marsteller, N.Y.C., 1990-94; prin. Princeton Pub. Rels. Group, Somerset, N.J., 1994—. Served with U.S. Army, 1954-56. Roman Catholic. Office: Princeton Pub Rels Group Somerset NJ 08873

NOONAN, WILLIAM MOSS, information systems executive, consultant; b. Plainfield, N.J., Nov. 8, 1942; s. Raymond Edgar and Edna Maida (Sanger) N.; m. Jo Ann Gardiner, July 3, 1966 (div. July 1984); m. Cynthia Gail Lynch, Aug. 22, 1985; children by previous marriages: Larissa, Leigh, Matthew, Duncan, Darby. BSBA, U. Richmond, 1964; MBA, Stanford U., 1966. Asst. acct. exec. Benton & Bowles, N.Y.C., 1966-67; cons. Arthur Andersen & Co., San Francisco, 1969-71, mgr., 1971-79; ptnr. Arthur Andersen & Co., Rio de Janeiro, 1979-82, Houston, 1982-84; sr. cons. Arthur D. Little, San Francisco, 1984-86; sr. mgr. Price Waterhouse, San Francisco, 1986-88, ptnr., 1988—; spkr. info. tech. mgmt., change mgmt., bus. process reengineering. vol. U.S. Peace Corps, Colombia, 1967-69; asst. treas. Am. Sch. of Rio de Janeiro, 1980-82; dir. fundraising peninsula chpt. Amigos de las Americas, 1987; vice-chmn. fundraising bus. sch. Stanford U., 1983—; bd. dirs. Rio de Janeiro chpt. Am. C. of C., 1981-82. Mem. Assn. for Systems Mgmt. (sec. San Francisco chpt. 1989-90, program chmn. 1990-92, v.p. 1990-91, pres. 1991-92), Coun. Logistics Mgmt. Avocations: sailing, golf, travel, symphony, San Francisco history. Office: Price Waterhouse 555 California St San Francisco CA 94104-1502

NOONE, ROBERT BARRETT, plastic surgeon; b. Scranton, Pa., Oct. 30, 1939; s. Robert Patrick and Margaret Ann (Barrett) N.; m. Barbara Ellen Atkins, May 29, 1965; children: Robert B. Jr., Megan J., Genevieve C., Rebecca B., Theresa Ann. BS, U. Scranton, 1961; MD, U. Pa., 1965. Diplomate Am. Bd. Surgery, Am. Bd. Plastic Surgery. Rotating intern Hosp. of U. Pa., Phila., 1965-66, resident in surgery, 1966-71, resident in plastic surgery, 1971-73; asst. prof. surgery Sch. Medicine, U. Pa., Phila., 1974-83, clin. assoc. prof. surgery, 1983-89; clin. prof. surgery Sch. Medicine, U. Pa., 1989—; head sect. on plastic surgery Pa. Hosp., Phila., 1974-80; chief svc. plastic surgery Bryn Mawr Hosp., Bryn Mawr, Pa., 1977—, Lankenau Hosp., Phila., 1980-91; clin. mem. dept. surgery Bryn Mawr (Pa.) Hosp., 1991—; bd. dirs. Am. Bd. Plastic Surgery, Phila., 1987-94, vice chmn. 1993-94; bd. dirs. Plastic Surgery Ednl. Found., Chgo., 1981-91, pres. 1989-90. Contbr. articles to profl. jours. Bd. dirs., trustee Rosemont (Pa.) Sch. of the Holy Child, 1983-87. Capt. USAF, 1967-69. Recipient Frank J. O'Hara Disting. Alumnus award U. Scranton, 1986. Fellow Am. Coll. Surgeons (bd. govs. 1994—); mem. AMA (del. plastic srugery 1986-88), Am. Soc. Plastic & Reconstructive Surgery (bd. dirs. 1989-90, 92-95, chmn. bd. trustees 1994), Northeastern Soc. Plastic Surgeons (pres. 1985-86), Robert H. Ivy Soc. (pres. 1982-83), Am. Assn. Plastic Surgeons (trustee 1990-93), Merion Cricket Club, Phila. Country Club, Eagles Mere Country Club (Pa.). Republican. Roman Catholic. Avocations: golf, tennis, photography, swimming, fly fishing, reading. Home: 234 Cheswold Hill Rd Haverford PA 19041-1814 Office: Plastic & Reconstructive Surg Assocs 888 Glenbrook Ave Bryn Mawr PA 19010-2506

NOONE, STEPHEN J., association executive; b. Indpls., Sept. 5, 1942; s. Dennis J. and Helen M. (McGinty) N.; m. Kathleen A. Thornburgh, June 18, 1966; children: Patrick (dec.), Lisa, Brendan. BA, Marian Coll., 1964; MS, Butler U., 1970. Cert. assn. exec., Am. Soc. Assn. Execs.; cert. secondary edn. tchr., adminstr., Ind. Tchr. Bishop Chatard High Sch., Indpls., 1964-70, prin., 1970-77; dir. schs. Office of Cath. Edn., Archdiocese of Indpls., 1977-84; exec. dir. Ind. Assn. of Osteo. Physicians, 1984-92, Am. Acad. Osteopathy, 1992—. Contbr. articles to profl. jours. and pubs. Adv. bd. Our Lady of Grace Monastery, Beech Grove, Ind., 1989—; bd. dirs. Westview Osteopathic Hosp. Found., Indpls., 1988-92; mem. religious svcs. com. Pan Am. Games, Indpls., 1986-87; at-large del. and interviewer for Congress, Ind. Congress on Edn., 1983-84; rep. Nat. Forum on Excellence in Edn., 1983; mem. Christ the King Cath. Ch., 1968—, eucharistic minister, lector, choir mem., others; steering com. Sesquicentennial Celebration of the Archdiocese of Indpls., 1982-84, others. Mem. Am. Soc. Assn. Execs., Ind. Soc. Assn. Execs. (bd. dirs. 1989-93, Exec. Dir. of Yr. 1993), Am. Osteopathic Assn., Assn. Osteopathic State Exec. Dirs. Roman Catholic. Home: 5935 Hillside Ave W Dr Indianapolis IN 46220

NOONKESTER, JAMES RALPH, retired college president; b. Flatridge, Va., June 10, 1924; s. Reggie L. and Arcie (Parks) N.; m. Naomi Hopkins, June 10, 1947; children: Myron Craig, Lila. BA, U. Richmond, 1944, LLD, 1968; ThM, So. Bapt. Theol. Sem., 1947, PhD, 1949; LHD (hon.), Blue Mountain Coll., 1982; postgrad., Harvard U., 1980. Minister edn. 1st Bapt. Ch., Charlottesville, Va., 1950-52; prof., head div. religion and philosophy William Carey Coll., Hattiesburg, Miss., 1952-53; acad. dean William Carey Coll., 1953-56, pres., 1956-89, pres. emeritus, 1989—; pres. Miss. Found. Ind. Colls.; mem. Edn. commn. So. Bapt. Conv., chmn., 1983; bd. dirs. Miss. Sch. Bds. Assn. Workers Compensation Trust, 1993—, chmn., 1994. Chmn. bd. dirs. Am. Cancer Soc., Miss. div., 1966; campaign chmn. United Givers Fund, 1975-76, pres. 1976-77; coun. chmn. Boy Scouts Am., dir. Planned Giving Pine Burr Area Boy Scouts Am., 1990—; trustee Hattiesburg Pub. Schs., 1990—, pres. bd. trustees, 1992—. Recipient award Outstanding Grad. English U. Richmond, 1944; named Hattiesburg's Outstanding Young Man of 1956; recipient Silver Beaver award Boy Scouts Am., 1981, HUB award, 1983; named Sales and Mktg. Execs. Man of Yr., 1983. Mem. NEA, Miss. Edn. Assn., Hattiesburg Concert Assn. (bd. dir.), So. Assn. Bapt. Colls. and Schs. (pres.), Miss. Assn. Colls. (pres.), Hattiesburg C. of C. (pres. 1966), Phi Beta Kappa, Phi Delta Kappa, Chi Beta Phi, Omicron Delta Kappa. Club: Kiwanian. Home: 100 Lesley Ln Hattiesburg MS 39402-2922

NOOR, AHMED KHAIRY, engineering educator, researcher; b. Cairo, Egypt, Aug. 11, 1938; s. Mohamed Sayed and Fatma Mohamed (El-Zeini) N.; m. Zakia Mahmoud Taha, Aug. 18, 1966; 1 child. Mohamed. BS with honors, Cairo (Egypt) U., 1958; M.S., U. Ill., Urbana, 1961, PhD, 1963. Asst. prof. aeros. and astronautics Stanford U., 1963-64; sr. lectr. structural mechanics, Cairo (Egypt) U., 1964-67; vis. sr. lectr. structural mechanics U. Baghdad, Iraq, 1967-68; sr. lectr. structural mechanics U. New South Wales, Australia, 1968-71; NRC sen. resident postdoct. res. assoc. NASA Langley Rsch. Center, Hampton, Va., 1971-72; prof. engring. and applied sci. George Washington U., Hampton Va., 1972-90; Ferman W. Perry prof. aerospace structures and applied mechanics U. Va.; dir. computational structures tech. ctr. NASA Langley Rsch. Ctr., Hampton, Va.; mem. coms. computational mechanics and large space systems Nat. Acad. Engring. Fellow AIAA, ASME, ASCE, Am. Acad. Mechanics, Internat. Assn. for Computational Mechanics (founder mem.), U.S. Assn. for Computational Mechanics, Sigma Xi. Editor-in-chief Computing Systems in Engineering; editor books on structures and solids and computational mechanics; mem. editorial bd. of several tech. jours.; contbr. articles to profl. jours. Home: 31 Towler Dr Hampton VA 23666-2659 Office: Univ Va NASA Langley Rsch Ctr Ms # 369 Hampton VA 23681

NOORDA, RAYMOND J., computer software company executive; b. Ogden, Utah., 1949. BSEE, Utah, 1949. CEO Novell Inc., 1982—. Office: MTI Technology Corp 4905 E La Palma Ave Anaheim CA 92807

NOORDERGRAAF, ABRAHAM, biophysics educator; b. Utrecht, Netherlands, Aug. 7, 1929; s. Leendert and Johanna (Kool) N.; m. Geertruida Alida Van Nee, Sept. 6, 1956; children: Annemiek (Mrs. James A. Young), Gerrit Jan, Jeske Inette, Alexander Abraham. B.Sc., U. Utrecht, 1953, M.S., 1955, Ph.D., 1956, M.A. (hon.), U. Pa., 1971. Teaching asst. U. Utrecht, 1949-50, asst. dept. physics, 1951-53, research asst. dept. med. physics, 1953-55, research fellow dept. med. physics, 1955-58, sr. research fellow dept. med. physics, 1959-65; tchr. math. and physics Vereniging Nijverheidsonderwijs, Utrecht, 1951; research asst. U. Amsterdam, Netherlands, 1952; vis. fellow dept. therapeutic research U. Pa., Phila., 1957-58; assoc. prof. biomed. engring. Moore Sch. Elec. Engring., 1964-70, acting head electromed. div., 1968-69, prof. biomed. engring., 1970—; prof. physiology Sch. Vet. Medicine, 1976—, prof. Dutch culture Sch. Arts and Scis., 1983—; prof. medicine Med. Sch. U. Pa., 1990—; assoc. dir. biomed. engring. tng. program Moore Sch. Elec. Engring., 1971-76, asso. dir. sch., 1972-74, chmn. grad. group in biomed. electronic engring., 1973-75, chmn. dept. bioengring., 1973-76, chmn. grad. group bioengring., 1975-76, dir. systems and integrative biology tng. program, 1979-84; vis. prof. biomed. engring. U. Miami, 1970-79, Erasmus U. Med. Sch., Rotterdam, Netherlands, 1970-71, Tech. U., Delft, 1970-71, Polish Acad. Scis., Warsaw, 1975; hon. vis. prof. of physiology U. Ljubljana, 1994—; mem. cardiovascular study sect., 1985-89; cons. sci. affaris divsn. NATO, 1973—; participant numerous internat. confs. in field. Author: (with I. Starr) Ballistocardiography in Cardiovascular Research, 1967, Circulatory System Dynamics, 1978; contbg. author: Biological Engineering, 1969; Editor: (with G.N. Jager and N. Westerhof) Circulatory Analog Computers,

1963, (with G.H. Pollack) Ballistocardiography and Cardiac Performance, 1967, (with E. Kresch) The Venous System: Characteristics and Function, 1969, (with J. Baan and J. Raines) Cardiovascular System Dynamics, 1978, (with Reichenbach-Consten) Two Hundred Years of Netherlands-American Interaction; sci. editor Biophysics and Bioengring. Series, 1976-94; contbr. numerous articles to profl. jours.; Referee: Biophys. Jour., 1968—; Physics in Medicine and Biology, 1969—, Bull. Math. Biophysics, 1972-84, Circulation Research, 1973—; mem. editorial adv. bd.: Jour. Biomechanics, 1969-84; assoc. editor: Bull. Math. Biology, 1973-84. Vice pres. Haverford Friends Sch. PTA, 1968-70. Recipient S. Reid Warren Jr. award U. Pa. Sch. Engring. and Applied Sci., 1986, Christian and Mary Lindback award U. Pa., 1988. Fellow IEEE (mem. adminstrv. com. engring. in medicine and biology group 1967-70, mem. edn. com. group biomed. engring. 1968-70, sec. Phila. chpt. 1974-75, mem. regional council profl. group engring. in medicine and biology 1974-77), N.Y. Acad. Scis., AAAS, Explorers Club, Coll. Physicians Phila., Am. Coll. Cardiology, Royal Soc. Medicine London; mem. Nederlandse Natuurkundige Vereniging, Ballistocardiograph Research Soc. U.S.A. (sec.-treas. 1965-67, pres. 1968-70), Biophys. Soc. (charter), European Soc. for Noninvasive Cardiovascular Research (co-founder 1960, sec.-treas. 1960-61, mem. com. on nomenclature 1960-61, officer 1961-62, Herman C. Burger award 1978, Disting. Rsch. Award, 1993), Cardiovascular System Dynamics Soc. (co-founder 1976, pres. 1976-80, hon. life 1986), Franklin Inst., John Morgan Soc., Biomed. Engring. Soc. (founding mem., chmn. membership com. 1978-79, dir. 1972-75), Am. Heart Assn., Instrument Soc. Am. (sr. mem.), Soc. Math. Biology (charter mem.), Am. Physiol. Soc., Microcirculatory Soc., Am. Assn. Med. Systems and Informatics, Pa. Acad. Sci., Sigma Xi, Phi Zeta. Presbyterian. Home: 620 Haydock Ln Haverford PA 19041-1208 Office: U Pa 101 Hayden Hall Philadelphia PA 19104-6392

NORA, AUDREY HART, physician; b. Picayune, Miss., Dec. 5, 1936; d. Allen Joshua and Vera Lee (Ballard) H.; m. James Jackson Nora, Apr. 9, 1966; children: James Jackson Jr., Elizabeth Hart. BS, U. Miss., 1958, MD, 1961; MPH, U. Calif., 1974. Diplomate Am. Bd. Pediatrics, Am. Bd. Hematology and Oncology. Resident in pediatrics U. Wis. Hosp., Madison, 1961-64; fellow in hematology/oncology Baylor U., Tex. Childrens Hosp., Houston, 1964-66, asst. prof. pediatrics, 1966-70; assoc. clin. prof. pediatrics U. Colo. Sch. Medicine, Denver, 1970—; dir. genetics Denver Childrens Hosp., 1970-78; cons. maternal and child health USPHS, Denver, 1978-83, asst. surgeon gen. regional health adminstr., 1983-92; dir. maternal & child health bur., health resources and svc. adminstrn. USPHS, commd. med. officer, 1978, advanced through grades to asst. surgeon gen., 1983; adv. com. NIH, Bethesda, 1975-77; adv. bd. Metronet Health, Inc., Denver, 1986—, Colo. Assn. Commerce and Industry, Denver, 1985—. Author: (with J.J. Nora) Genetics and Counseling in Cardiovascular Disease, 1978, (with others) Blakiston's Medical Dictionary, 1980, Birth Defects Encyclopedia, 1990, (with J.J. Nora and K. Berg) Cardiovascular Diseases: Genetics, Epidemiology and Prevention, 1991; contbr. articles to profl. jours. Recipient Virginia Apgar award Nat. Found., 1976. Fellow Am. Acad. Pediatrics; mem. Am. Pub. Health Assn. (governing coun. 1990-92, coun. mem. maternal and child health 1990—), Commd. Officers Assn., Am. Soc. Human Genetics, Teratology Soc., Western Soc. Pediatric Rsch. Presbyterian. Avocations: quilting, cooking, hiking. Office: USPHS Room 18-05 Parklawn Bldg 5600 Fishers Ln Rockville MD 20857

NORA, JAMES JACKSON, physician, author, educator; b. Chgo., June 26, 1928; s. Joseph James and May Henrietta (Jackson) N.; m. Barbara June Fluhrer, Sept. 7, 1949 (div. 1963); children: Wendy Alison, Penelope Welbon, Marianne Leslie; m. Audrey Faye Hart, Apr. 9, 1966; children: James Jackson Jr., Elizabeth Hart Nora. AB, Harvard U., 1950; MD, Yale U., 1954; MPH, U. Calif., Berkeley, 1978. Intern Detroit Receiving Hosp., 1954-55; resident in pediatrics U. Wis. Hosps., Madison, 1959-61, fellow in cardiology, 1962-64; fellow in genetics McGill U. Children's Hosp., Montreal, Can., 1964-65; assoc. prof. pediatrics Baylor Coll. Medicine, Houston, 1965-71; prof. genetics, preventive medicine and pediatrics U. Colo. Med. Sch., Denver, 1971—; dir. genetics Rose Med. Ctr., Denver, 1980—; dir. pediatric cardiology and cardiovascular tng. U. Colo. Sch. Medicine, 1971-78; mem. task force Nat. Heart and Lung Program, Bethesda, Md., 1973; cons. WHO, Geneva, 1983—; mem. U.S.-U.S.S.R. Exchange Program on Heart Disease, Moscow and Leningrad, 1975. Author: The Whole Heart Book, 1980, 2d edit., 1989; (with F.C. Fraser) Medical Genetics, 4th edit., 1994, Genetics of Man, 2d edit., 1986, Cardiovascular Diseases: Genetics, Epidemiology and Prevention, 1991; (novels) The Upstart Spring, 1989, The Psi Delegation, 1989, Sabbatical, 1995. Com. mem. March of Dimes, Am. Heart Assn., Boy Scouts Am. Served to lt. USAAC, 1945-47. Grantee Nat. Heart, Lung and Blood Inst., Nat. Inst. Child Health and Human Devel., Am. Heart Assn., NIH; recipient Virginia Apgar Meml. award. Fellow Am. Coll. Cardiology, Am. Acad. Pediatrics, Am. Coll. Med. Genetics; mem. Am. Pediatric Soc., Soc. Pediatric Rsch., Am. Heart Assn., Teratology Soc., Transplantation Soc., Am. Soc. Human Genetics, Authors Guild, Authors League, Acad. Am. Poets, Mystery Writers Am., Rocky Mountain Harvard Club. Democrat. Presbyterian. Avocations: writing fiction, poetry. Home: 3110 Fairweather Ct Olney MD 20832-3021 Office: Parklawn Bldg 5600 Fishers Ln Rm 18-05 Rockville MD 20857-0001

NORBACK, CRAIG THOMAS, writer; b. Pitts., Nov. 14, 1943; s. Howard George and Maybelle Veronica Montaigne (Cosse) N.; m. Judith Carol Shaul, Oct. 12, 1976. BS, Washington U., St. Louis, 1967; postgrad., Drew U., 1986—. Author, co-author, compiler, producer over 130 books, including: The Misspeller's Dictionary, 1972, Everything You Can Get from the Government for Free or Almost for Free, 1975, The Dream Machine: The Golden Age of American Automobiles 1946-65, 1976, Great Songs of Madison Avenue, 1976, Great North American Indians, 1977, The Health Care Directory, 1977, The Older American's Handbook, 1977, The Educational Marketplace, 1978, Famous American Admirals, 1978, Newsweek Travel Guide to the U.S., 1978, The Dow Jones-Irwin Guide to Franchising, 1979, The Horseman's Catalog, 1979, The Must Words, 1979, The Practical Inventor's Handbook, 1979, ABC Complete Book of Sports Facts, 1980, ABC Monday Night Football, 1980-81, 1980, The Bible Almanac, 1980, Check Yourself Out, 1980, The Signet Book of World Winners, 1980, The TV Guide Almanac, 1980, The World's Great News Photos (1840-1980), 1980, The Allergy Encyclopedia, 1981, American Expressions, 1981, The Computer Invasion, 1981, The Consumer's Energy Handbook, 1981, 500 Questions New Parents Ask, 1982, Business Week Almanac, 1982, The International Yellow Pages, 1982, The Puzzle King's Bafflers, 1982, The Associated Press Sunday Crossword Puzzle Book, 1983, Chilton's Job Textbook Series: Advertising Management, 1983, Office Management, 1983, It's a Fact, 1983, National Education Association Parent and Child Success Library: Helping Your Child Read, 1983, How Letters Make Words, 1983, How to Prepare Your Child for School, 1983, Learning the Alphabet, 1983, Learning to Add, 1983, The Ultimate Toy Catalog, 1983, U.S. Publicity Directory, various years, Advertising and Promotion Management, 1983, America Wants to Know, 1983, Certified Professional Secretary modules I through VI, 1984, East Coast Publicity Directory, 1984, Human Resources Yearbook, 1987, 88, 89, 90, Princeton Area Job Finder, 1987, 88, Career Encyclopedia, 1987, Travel Publicity Directory, 1987, 88, 89, 90, Arthur Young Guide to Venture Capital, 1987, Hazardous Chemicals on File, 1988, Joint Ventures, 1992. Home: 131 S Mill Rd Princeton Junction NJ 08550

NORBERG, ARTHUR LAWRENCE, JR., historian, physicist educator; b. Providence, Apr. 13, 1938; s. Arthur Lawrence Sr. and Margaret Helen (Riley) N.; m. Kerry J. Freedman. BS in Physics, Providence Coll., 1959; MS in Physics, U. Vt., 1962; PhD in History of Sci., U. Wis., 1974. Asst. prof. physics St. Michael's Coll., Winooski, Vt., 1961-63, 64-68; assoc. scientist Westinghouse Electric Co., Pitts., 1963-64; instr. in physics U. Wis., Whitewater, 1968-71; rsch. historian U. Calif., Berkeley, 1973-79; program mgr. NSF, Washington, 1979-81; dir. Charles Babbage Inst. for History of Info. Processing U. Minn., Mpls., 1981-93, assoc. prof. history of sci. and tech., 1981—, assoc. prof. computer sci., 1981-95, prof. computer sci., 1995—; del. Am. Coun. Learned Socs., N.Y.C., 1981-87; mem. adv. coun. NASA, Washington, 1988-93; endowed ERA Land Grant chair U. Minn., 1989-93; mem. adv. com. Am. Inst. Physics Ctr. for History of Physics, 1995—. Editor: Annals of the History of Computing, 1982-93; adv. editor Tech. and Culture, 1985-92 Changing Computer Technology: The Pentagon's Role, 1962-87, (book) Chanign Computer Technology: The Role of the Pentagon, 1962-87; contbr. articles to profl. jours. Founding pres. City Works-A Tech. Ctr., Mpls., 1987-90; bd. dirs. Charles Babbage Found., 1984-94. Fellow AAAS; mem. History of Sci. Soc. (treas. 1975-80), Brit.

Soc. for History of Sci., Soc. for History of Tech., Sigma Xi. Office: U Minn Dept Computer Sci 4-192 EE/CS Bldg Minneapolis MN 55455-0290

NORBERG, CHARLES ROBERT, lawyer; b. Cleve., July 25, 1912; s. Rudolf Carl and Ida Edith (Roberts) N. B.S. in Adminstrv. Engring, Cornell U., 1934; M.A. in Internat. Econs, U. Pa., 1937; LL.B., Harvard U., 1939. Bar: Pa. bar 1940, U.S. Supreme Ct. bar 1946, D.C. bar 1947. Lab. research asst. Willard Storage Battery Co., Cleve., 1934-35; assto. firm Hepburn and Norris, Phila., 1939-42; with Office of Assn. Secretary for Public Affairs, Dept. State, 1948-51; asst. dir. psychol. strategy bd. Exec. Office of the Pres., 1952-54; mem. staff U.S. Delegation to UN Gen. Assembly, Paris, 1951; adviser U.S. Delegation to UNESCO Gen. Conf., Montevideo, 1954; assoc. firm Morgan, Lewis and Bockius, Washington, 1955-56; individual practice law Washington, 1956—; treas., gen. counsel Inter-Am. Comml. Arbitration Commn., 1968-83, dir. gen., 1983—; chief Spl. AID Mission to Ecuador, 1961; spl. Aid Mission to Uruguay, 1961; mem. U.S. delegation to Specialized Inter-Am. Conf. on pvt. internat. law, Panama, 1975. Chmn. Internat. Visitors Info. Service, Washington, 1965-69; chmn. Mayor's Com. on Internat. Visitors, 1971-78; chmn., pres. Bicentennial Commn. of D.C., Inc., 1975-81. Served with USAF, 1942-46. Mem. Phila. Bar Assn., Pa. Bar Assn., Inter-Am. Bar Assn., Washington Fgn. Law Soc. (pres. 1959-63), Am. Soc. Internat. Law, Am. Law Inst., Am. Bar Assn. (chmn. internat. legal exchange program 1974-79), Bar Assn. of D.C. (chmn. internat. law com. 1977-79), Inter-Am. Bar Found. (founder, dir. 1957, pres. 1969-84, chmn. bd. 1984—), Diplomatic and Consular Officers Retired (Washington), Washington Inst. Fgn. Affairs, Academia Colombiana de Jurisprudencia, Inter-Am. Acad. Internat. and Comparative Law, Colegio de Abogados de Quito. Clubs: Met. (Washington); Dacor (Washington); Racquet (Phila.); Harvard (N.Y.C.). Home: 3104 N St NW Washington DC 20007-3413 Office: 1819 H St NW Washington DC 20006-3603

NORBERG, JARON B., public service company executive; b. 1937; married. JD, U. Utah, 1967; postgrad., Brigham Young U. Ptnr. Snell & Wilmer, 1967-73; gen. counsel Ariz. Pub. Svc. Co., Phoenix, 1972-82, sr. v.p., corp. counsel, from 1982, now exec. v.p., chief fin. officer, also bd. dirs. Office: Ariz Pub Svc Co PO Box 53999 Phoenix AZ 85072-3999

NORBERG, RICHARD EDWIN, physicist, educator; b. Newark, Dec. 28, 1922; s. Arthur Edwin and Melita (Roefer) N.; m. Patricia Ann Leach, Dec. 27, 1947 (dec. July 1977); children—Karen Elizabeth, Craig Alan, Peter Douglas; m. Jeanne C. O'Brien, Apr. 1, 1978. B.A., DePauw U., 1943; M.A., U. Ill., 1947, Ph.D., 1951. Research assoc., control sytems lab. U. Ill., 1951-53, asst. prof., 1953; vis. lectr. physics Washington U., St. Louis, 1954—; mem. faculty Washington U., 1955—, prof. physics, 1958—, chmn. dept., 1962-91; dir. Technilab Inc. Mem. editorial bd. Magnetic Research Rev. Served with USAAF, 1943-46. Fellow Am. Phys. Soc., Internat. Soc. Magnetic Research. Home: 7134 Princeton Ave Saint Louis MO 63130-2308 Office: Washington U Dept Physics PO Box 1105 Saint Louis MO 63188-1105

NORBERG-CALIENDO, LYNDA JOY, school system administrator; b. Bklyn., Oct. 16, 1941; d. Harold I. and Shirley Claire (Karp) Levy; m. Jon Norberg (div. 1988); children: Paige, Toby, Hilary; m. Richard Caliendo, July 28, 1990. BFA, Ohio U.; MS in Reading, Hofstra U., postgrad. Cert. supt., Conn.; cert. adminstr., N.Y.; cert. tchr., Mass., Ohio. Instr. Montessori Sch., Dallas, 1968-69; tchr. reading and LD Fiedel County Day Sch., Glen Cove, N.Y., 1969-72; reading cons., asst. prin. Stagecoach Elem. Sch., Centereach, N.Y., 1972-83; dir. curriculum and instruction Elmont (N.Y.) Union Free Sch. Dist., 1983-86; edn. cons. Scott, Foresman & Co., Oakland, N.J., 1986-87; asst. supt. instruction Valley Stream (N.Y.) Union Free Sch. Dist. 30, 1987-90; dep. supt. Hamden (Conn.) Pub. Schs., 1990—. Mem. adv. bd. Global Edn., Early Childhood Edn., N.Y. State Coun. Social Studies; ednl. coord. Internat. Games for the Disabled; commr. World Games of Spl. Olympics-Spkrs. Bur. Mem. ASCD, AASA, Anti Defamation League-A World of Difference, Phi Delta Kappa. Home: 631 Whitney Ave New Haven CT 06511-2218 Office: Shepherd Glen Elem Sch Skiff St Ext Hamden CT 06514-2825

NORBY, RONALD BRANDON, nurse executive; b. Jacksonville, Fla., Nov. 15, 1943; s. John K. and Corliss J. (Hisey) N. BS, Baylor U., 1965; MS in Nursing, U. Wash., 1970, postgrad., 1970-71; postgrad., U. Hawaii, 1973-74. Charge nurse, open heart surg. team Baylor U. Med. Ctr., Dallas, 1965; dir. nursing Mother Frances Hosp., Tyler, Tex., 1966; charge nurse, nursing dir. USN Nurse Corps., 1966-69; asst. dir. nursing U Hosp., Seattle, 1972-73; asst. prof. U. Hawaii Sch. Nursing, Honolulu, 1972-74; dir. div. nursing Medicus Systems Corp., Chgo., 1974-77; v.p. nursing St. Francis Hosp., Evanston, Ill., 1977-79; dir. div. nursing Am. Hosp. Assn., Chgo., 1979-80; sr. v.p. Med. Scientific Internat., Corp., Washington, 1980-82; chief nursing svc. Edward Hines, Jr. VA Hosp., Chgo., 1983-86; asst. dean clin. nursing affairs Marcella Neifhoff Sch. Nursing, Loyola U., Chgo. 1983-86; assoc. chief of staff/nursing VA Med. Ctr., San Diego, 1986; adj. faculty San Diego State U., 1986; instr. Calif. State U. at Domenguez Hills; chair nat. devel. effort for expert panel-based nurse staffing methology for Dept. of Vets. Affairs; chair nursing conf., Las Vegas, 1992; dir. field support/clin. integration ctrl. office Dept. Vets. Affairs, Washington, 1994; cons. in field. Author: (with M. Mayers) Quality Assurance for Patient Care: Nursing Perspectives, 1977; Taking the Pain Out of Care Planning, 1976, A Realistic Approach to the Teaching and Implementation of Care Planning, 1976; (with others) Implementing Research in Nursing Practice, 1985, Identification of the Nursing Minimum Data Set, 1988, Positioning for Success, 1990. Chmn. hosp. disaster com. U. Hosp., 1970, mem. Nat. Commn. Nursing Implementation Project, 1985-86; treas. Being Alive, San Diego; mem. HIV Care Coalition, County of San Diego. Mem. Am. Hosp. Assn. (sr. staff coun. on nursing 1979-80, coord. Nat. Comm. Nursing 1980), Am. Orgn. Nurse Execs., (com. on nominations 1985), ANA, Nat. League Nursing, Calif. Soc. Nursing Svc. Conference Group, Calif. Nurses Assn., Hawaii Nurses Assn. (v.p. 1973), Ill. Nurses Assn., Chief Med. Dir. Clin. and Programs Adv. Coun. (chair VA western region ambulatory care and edn. nursing subcom.), Sigma Theta Tau (internat. treas. 1987-91, chmn. fin. com. 1987-91, chmn. membership enhancement task force 1988-91, pres. Gamma Gamma chpt. 1989-91). Home: PO Box 50932 Washington DC 20091-0932 Office: Dept Vets Affairs Nursing Svc (118E) 810 Vermont Ave NW Washington DC 20420

NORBY, WILLIAM CHARLES, financial consultant; b. Chgo., Aug. 10, 1915; s. Oscar Maurice and Louise (Godejohann) N.; m. Camilla Edbrooke, June 12, 1943; children: Martha Norby Fraundorf, Richard James. AB, U. Chgo., 1935. With Harris Trust & Savs. Bank, Chgo., 1935-70, v.p., 1953-64, sr. v.p., 1964-70; exec. dir. Fin. Analysts Fedn., N.Y.-1970-72; sr. v.p., bd. dirs. Duff & Phelps, Inc., Chgo., 1973-81; mem. Fin. Acctg. Standards Adv. Coun., 1975-79. mem. Fin. Acctg. Stds. Adv. Coun., 1975-79. Mem. AICPA (com. on auditors responsibilities 1975-78), Fin. Analysts Fedn. (bd. 1962-68, pres. 1963-64, Disting. Svc. award 1973, Nicholas Molodovsky award 1979), Investment Analysts Soc. Chgo. (pres. 1955-56), U. Chgo. Alumni Assn. (citation 1961), Phi Beta Kappa. Congregationalist (trustee 1950-56, chmn. 1955-56). Home: 337 Blackstone Ave La Grange IL 60525-2107

NORCEL, JACQUELINE JOYCE CASALE, educational administrator; b. Bklyn., Nov. 19, 1940; d. Frederick and Josephine Jeanette (Bestafka) Casale; m. Edward John Norcel, Feb. 24, 1962. BS, Fordham U., 1961; MS, Bklyn. Coll., 1966; 6th yr. cert. So. Conn. State U., 1980; postgrad. Bridgeport U. Elem. tchr., pub. schs., N.Y.C., 1961-80; prin. Coventry Schs., Conn., 1980-84, Trumbull Schs., Conn., 1984—; guest lectr. So. Conn. State U., 1980—; cons. Monson Schs., Mass., 1984; mem. Conn. State Prin. Acad. Adv. Bd., 1986-88; mem. adj. faculty Sacred Heart U., Fairfield, Conn., 1986—, So. Conn. State U., summer 1991. Editor: Best of the Decade, 1980; mem. editorial adv. bd. Principal Matters; contbr. articles to profl. jours. Chmn. bldg. com. Trumbull Bd. Edn., 1978-80; chmn. Sch. Benefit Com., Trumbull, 1985-86; catechist Bridgeport Diocese, Roman Cath. Ch., Conn., 1975-85, youth minister, 1979-84, coord., evaluator leadership tng. workshops for teens and adults, 1979-84; mem. St. Stephen's Parish Coun., 1993—. Recipient Town of Trumbull Service award, 1982, Nat. Disting. Prin. award, 1988, Joseph Formica Disting. Svc. award EMSPAC, 1994. Mem. N.E. Regional Elem. Prins. Assn. (rep. 1984-86, sec. 1986-87), Elem. Mid. Sch. Prins. Assn. (pres. 1985-86, Citizen of Year award, 1991, Pres.'s award 1981-

85, state elected rep. 1989-90, fed. rels. coord. 1990-94), Adminstrn. and Supervision Assn. (sec. 1980-81, pres. 1981-82, exec. bd. 1982-93), Hartford Area Prins. and Suprs. Assn. (local pres. 1981-82), Nat. Assn. Elem. Sch. Prins. (zone I dir. 1987-90, del. to gen. assemblies 1984-90, bd. dirs. 1987-90), Assn. Supervision and Curriculum Devel., Conn. Assn. Supervision and Curriculum Devel., Trumbull Adminstrs. Assn. (pres.-elect 1989-91, pres. 1991-93), Eastern Conn. Council of Internat. Reading Assn., New Eng. Coalition Ednl. Leaders, Associated Tchrs. of Math. in Conn., Phi Delta Kappa (Disting. Fellow award 1992, v.p. rsch. and projects 1993-95), Pi Lambda Theta (Beta Sigma chpt.), Delta Kappa Gamma. Republican. Home: 5240 Madison Ave Trumbull CT 06611-1016 Office: Tashua Sch 401 Stonehouse Rd Trumbull CT 06611-1651

NORCIA, STEPHEN WILLIAM, advertising executive; b. N.Y.C., Jan. 21, 1941; s. William Matthew and Amelia (Marrone) N.; m. Martha Elizabeth Whelan, Apr. 22, 1978; children: Matthew F., Daniel P., Anne E. BA, U. Conn., 1962. Media planner and buyer SSC&B, N.Y.C., 1965-66; account exec. McCann-Erickson Co., Chgo., 1966-68; v.p., dep. mgr. McCann-Erickson Co., Milw., 1971-72; v.p., mgr. supervisor McCann-Erickson Co., N.Y.C., 1972-74; sr. v.p., gen. mgr. McCann-Erickson Co., Atlanta, 1974-78; exec. v.p., gen. mgr. McCann-Erickson Co., N.Y.C., 1978-81; exec. v.p., mem. exec. policy com., mem. mgmt. com. Lintas, N.Y.C., 1981—; exec. v.p., 1989-91, world wide client dir., dir. bus. devel., 1991—; also bd. dirs.; mng. ptnr. Earle Palmer Brown, N.Y.C., 1994—; account exec. Needham, Harper & Steers, Chgo., 1968-70; dir. mktg. product devel. workshop Interpub., N.Y.C., 1970-71; bd. dirs. Communication Counselors Network. Bd. dirs. U. Ga. Master of Br. Mgmt. Program, 1985, 86, 87. 1st lt. U.S. Army, 1962-65. Recipient Robert E. Healy award Interpub. Group Cos., 1975, Effie award Am. Mktg. Assn., 1985, Grand Effie award Am. Mktg. Assn., 1984. Mem. Am. Assn. Advt. Agys., Advt. Club N.Y., Am. Yacht Club. Republican. Roman Catholic. Avocations: tennis, boating, skiing. Home: 1 Topsail Ln Rye NY 10580-3116 Office: Earle Palmer Brown 345 Hudson St New York NY 10014

NORCROSS, DAVID FRANK ARMSTRONG, lawyer; b. Camden, N.J., Mar. 30, 1937; s. David Kincaid and Elizabeth S. (Norcross) Armstrong; m. Laurie Lee Michel, Nov. 11, 1988; children: Spencer Kincaid Cook, Victoria Lynn Armstrong. BA, U. Del., 1958; LLB, U. Pa., 1961. Bar: N.J. 1961, U.S. Ct. Appeals (3d cir.) 1971, U.S. Supreme Ct. 1987, D.C. 1993. Ptnr. Archer & Greiner, Haddonfield, N.J., 1965-71; exec. asst. to gov. State of N.J., Trenton, 1971-73; exec. dir. N.J. Election Law Enforcement Commn., Trenton, 1973-76; of counsel Brandt, Haughey, Penberthy & Lewis, Haddonfield, 1976; ptnr. Myers, Matteo, Rabil & Norcross, Cherry Hill, N.J. 1977-89, Montgomery, McCracken, Walker & Rhoads, Washington, Cherry Hill, 1989-94, Blank, Rome, Comisky & McCauley, Cherry Hill, 1994—; cons. Fed. Election Com., Washington, 1976, White House Conf. Drug Free Am., 1987-88; dir. Rep. Inst. Internat. Affairs, Washington, 1984—, gen. counsel, 1984-93; bd. dirs. Ctr. for Democracy, Washington, 1985-95; gen. counsel Rep. Nat. Com., 1993—. Rep. candidate U.S. Senate, N.J., 1976; chmn. N.J. Rep. Party, 1977-81; counsel to chmn. Rep. Nat. Com., Washington, 1983-89, mem., 1992—; vice chmn. Commn. on Presdl. Debates, 1988-93. Mem. N.J. Bar Assn., Burlington County Bar Assn., D.C. Bar Assn., Camden County Bar Assn., St. Andrews Soc. Washington, Capitol Hill Club, Moorestown Field Club, Univ. Club. Episcopalian. Office: Blank Rome Comisky McCauley 1156 15th St NW Ste 550 Washington DC 20005-1704

NORCROSS, DAVID WARREN, physicist, researcher; b. Cin., July 18, 1941; s. Gerald Warren and Alice Elizabeth (Downey) N.; m. Mary Josephine Boudrias, Aug. 26, 1967; children: Joshua David, Sarah Elizabeth. A.B., Harvard Coll., 1963; M.Sc., U. Ill., 1965; Ph.D., Univ. Coll., London, 1970. Research assoc. U. Colo., Boulder, 1970-74; physicist Nat. Bur. Standards, Boulder, 1974—; chief quantum physics divsn. Nat. Inst. Stds. and Tech., 1989-93, dir. Boulder Labs., 1994—; fellow Joint Inst. Lab. Astrophysics, Boulder, 1976—. Contbr. articles to profl. jours. Recipient Bronze medal Nat. Bur. Standards, 1982, Silver medal U.S. Dept. Commerce, 1994. Fellow Am. Phys. Soc. Office: Nat Inst Standards & Tech 325 Broadway Boulder CO 80303

NORCROSS, MARVIN AUGUSTUS, veterinarian, government agency official; b. Tansboro, N.J., Feb. 8, 1931; s. Marvin A. and Katherine V. (McGuigan) N.; m. Diane L. Tuttle, Nov. 22, 1956 (div. 1991); children: James, Janet. Student, Rutgers U., 1954-55; V.M.D., U. Pa., 1959, Ph.D., 1966. Pathologist Merck Sharp & Dohme Research Labs., Rahway, N.J., 1966-69; dir. clin. research Merck Sharp & Dohme Research Labs., 1969-72, sr. dir. domestic vet. research, 1972-75; dir. div. vet. med. research Ctr. Vet. Medicine, FDA, Rockville, Md., 1975-78; assoc. dir. for research Ctr. Vet. Medicine, FDA, 1978-82, assoc. dir. for human food safety, 1982-84, assoc. dir. for new animal drug evaluation, 1984-87; asst. dep. adminstr., then dep. adminstr. Sci. and Tech., Food Safety and Inspection Svc. USDA, Washington, 1987-93, exec. asst. to the adminstr., 1993-94; U.S. coord. for Codex Alimentarius Codex Alimentarius USDA, Washington, 1994—; adj. prof. faculty Va.-Md. Regional Coll. Vet. Medicine, Blacksburg, Va., 1980-85. Contbr. articles to profl. jours. Trustee Scotch Plains (N.J.) Community Fund, 1969-72. Served to lt. AUS, 1952-54; col. Res., 1954-83 (ret.). Recipient FDA Merit award, 1978, Meritorious Presdl. Rank award, 1989. Mem. Am. Vet. Med. Assn., AAAS, Am. Assn. Avian Pathologists, Soc. Toxicologic Pathologists, Assn. Mil. Surgeons U.S., Civil Affairs Assn., Inst. Food Technologists, Nat. Assn. Fed. Veterinarians, N.J. Acad. Sci., N.Y. Acad. Scis., Res. Officers Assn., Sigma Xi. Home: 14304 Brickhowe Ct Germantown MD 20874-3431 Office: USDA Food Safety & Inspection Svc 1255 22d St NW Rm 311 Washington DC 20250-3700

NORD, ELFRIDA, community health nurse; b. N.D., Oct. 8, 1933; d. Helmer Emil and Elfrida (Gjesbakk) N. Diploma, Sacred Heart Hosp., 1954; BS in Nursing, U. Wash., 1969; MPH, U. Hawaii, 1983. Staff nurse Sacred Heart Hosp., Havre, Mont., 1954-55; staff nurse oper. rm. Vancouver (Wash.) Meml. Hosp., 1955-58, 59-64; staff nurse Ulleval Hosp., Oslo and Hammerfest Hosp., Norway, 1958-59; nurse advisor USPHS/USAID, Cantho, Nha Trang, Vietnam, 1964-67; staff nurse Vancouver (Wash.) Meml. Hosp., 1970; head nurse Alaska Native Health Svcs. Hosp., Bethel, 1970-73; itinerant pub. health nurse Sect. of Nursing Div. Pub. Health, Bethel, 1973-76; nurse cons. Sect. of Communicable Disease Control Div. Pub. Health, Anchorage, 1976-82, 84; chief sect. of nursing Div. of Pub. Health, Juneau, Alaska, 1984—. Mem. Alaska Nurses Assn. (dist. 3), Alaska Pub. Health Assn., Am. Pub. Health Assn., Am. Soc. Circumpolar Health (charter), Assn. of State and Territorial Dirs. of Nursing (sec.), Sigma Theta Tau. Home: 1135 Slim Williams Way Juneau AK 99801-8759

NORD, ERIC THOMAS, manufacturing executive; b. Amherst, Ohio, Nov. 8, 1917; s. Walter G. and Virginia C. (Greive) N.; m. Jane H. Baker; children: Virginia, Emily, Carlotte, Richard. BS in Mech. Engring., Case Inst. Tech., 1939. Pres., chief exec. officer Nordson Corp., Amherst, Ohio, 1954-73; chmn. Nordson Corp., Amherst, 1973—. Pres. Oberlin (Ohio) Bd. Edn., 1965; chmn. Oberlin City Council, 1959; bd. trustees Oberlin Coll., 1977—.

NORD, HENRY J., transportation executive; b. Berlin, May 1, 1917; came to U.S., 1937, naturalized, 1943; s. Walter and Herta (Riess) N.; children: Stephen, Philip. Student, U. Oxford, Eng., 1934, Northwestern U., 1938-40, Ill. Inst. Tech., 1942; JD, De Paul U., 1949. CPA, Ill. Apprentice in export Hamburg, Germany, 1935- 37; with GATX Corp., Chgo., 1938-85; comptroller GATX Corp., 1961—, v.p., exec. v.p., 1971-78, sr. v.p., 1978-80, v.p. 1980-82, cons. 1982-88, fin. cons., 1982—, dir. 1964-78; dir. Planned Lighting, Inc. to 1988. Trustee DePaul U. Served to 1st lt. AUS, 1944-46. Mem. Internat. Law Assn. Club: Tavern (Chgo.). Home: 1000 N Lake Shore Plz Chicago IL 60611-1354 Office: 55 W Monroe St Ste 500 Chicago IL 60603-5003

NORD, PAUL ELLIOTT, accountant; b. Carona, N.Y., Mar. 22, 1936; s. Abe and Rose (Guss) N.; m. Marcia B. Gross, June 13, 1965; children—Howard, Aimee, Samuel. Student U. Utah, 1952-56; student, LaSalle Extension Inst., 1966. C.P.A., Calif. Staff acct. Robinson, Nowell & Co. (merged with Muncy McPherson & Co., Muncy McPherson McCune Dieckman 1967), 1966-73, ptnr., 1973-81, mng. ptnr., 1981-87, ptnr. BDO Seidman, 1988—. Bd. dirs. Congregation Beth Sholom, San Francisco,

1969—, pres., 1979-81; mem. budget and allocations com. Jewish Fedn., East Bay, 1981-84. With U.S. Army, 1957-58, 61-62. Ford Found. scholar. Mem. Am. Inst. C.P.A.s (acctg. standards exec. com. 1979-81), Calif. Soc. C.P.A.s (chmn. sub-com. acctg. principles 1981-83), C.P.A. Assocs. Bd. dirs. 1986-87) San Francisco Estate Planning Coun., Mensa, San Francisco Comml. Club, San Francisco City Club. Jewish. Home: 931 Walnut Ave Walnut Creek CA 94598-3738 Office: 1 Sansome St 11th Fl San Francisco CA 94014

NORD, PETER ROBERT, advertising executive; b. N.Y.C. Aug. 22, 1929; s. Samuel and Esther (Eichner) N.; m. Rita Carol Alperin; children: Lisa Susan, Gail Anne. BA in Liberal Arts, Queens Coll., 1951. Copy chief Hicks & Greist Advt., N.Y.C., 1955-62; creative dir. Solow Wexton Advt., N.Y.C., 1962-70; assoc. creative dir. Benton & Bowles Advt., N.Y.C., 1972-80; creative dir. Geers Gross Advt., N.Y.C., 1980-86; group creative dir. D'Arcy Masius Benton & Bowles, N.Y.C., 1986—. Contbr. articles to popular periodicals. Lt. (j.g.) USNR, 1951-55. Recipient Gold Key award Copy Club, Clio award Am. TV & Radio Festival. Jewish. Home: 301 E 66th St New York NY 10021-6205 Office: D'Arcy Masius Benton & Bowles 1675 Broadway New York NY 10019-5865

NORD, ROBERT EAMOR, lawyer; b. Ogden, Utah, Apr. 11, 1945; s. Eamor Carroll and Ella Carol (Winkler) N.; m. Sherryl Anne Smith, May 15, 1969; children: Kimberly, P. Ryan, Debra, Heather, Andrew, Elizabeth. BS, Brigham Young U., 1969; JD, U. Chgo., 1972. Bar: Ill. 1972, U.S. Dist. Ct. (no. dist.) Ill. 1972, U.S. Ct. Appeals (D.C. cir.) 1974, U.S. Dist. Ct. (mid. dist.) Fla. 1976, U.S. Ct. Appeals (7th cir.) 1977, U.S. Dist. Ct. (no. dist.) Ind. 1978, U.S. Dist. Ct. (no. dist.) Fla. 1979, U.S. Supreme Ct. 1981, U.S. Dist. Ct. (ea. dist.) Mich. 1984, U.S. Ct. Appeals (11th cir.) 1985. Assoc. Chadwell & Kayser, Chgo., 1972-75; from assoc. to ptnr. Hinshaw & Culbertson, Chgo., 1975—. Republican. Mormon. Club: University (Chgo.). Home: 481 Woodlawn Ave Glencoe IL 60022-2175 Office: Hinshaw & Culbertson 222 N La Salle St Ste 300 Chicago IL 60601-1081

NORD, THOMAS ALLISON, hospital administrator; b. Boise, Idaho, Dec. 29, 1934; s. Everett Oliver and Alice Susan (Sherry) N.; m. Kay Hahn, Apr. 19, 1958; children: Mark Allison, Matthew Brendan, Julia Christian Nord Jenkins, Christopher Thomas. BSBA, Denver U., 1957, MBA, 1971; post-grad., Cornell U., 1974. Office mgr. Mountain States Sprinkler Supply, Denver, 1957-61; owner, mgr. Desert Rain, Roswell, N.Mex., 1961-68; sheriff Chaves County, Roswell, 1966-71; adminstr. St. Vincent Gen. Hosp., Leadville, Colo., 1972-78, Grand River Hosp. Dist., Rifle, Colo., 1980-83; planner, coord. outreach St. Mary's Hosp. and Med. Ctr., Grand Junction, Colo., 1978-80, assoc. adminstr., 1980; pres., CEO Ivinson Meml. Hosp., Laramie, Wyo., 1983—; Mem. Garfield County Human Svc. Commn., 1980-83, chmn., 1982-83; mem. governing bd. Westrn Colo. Health Sys. Agy., 1980; chmn. steering com. Southeastern Colo. Health Sys. Agy., 1975, chmn. governing bd., 1976-79; mem. liaison com. for U. Wyo. Sch. Nursing, 1984-85; mem. clin. faculty programs in health svcs. adminstrn. U. Minn. Sch. Pub. Health, 1984; bd. dirs. Blue Cross/Blue Shield Wyo., 1988—, mem. exec. com., 1993—; mem. Wyo. Healthcare Reform Commn., 1994; chmn. bd. VHA Mountain States. Active Boy Scouts Am., United Way. Fellow Am. Coll. Healthcare Execs. (Wyo. regent 1994); mem. Am. Hosp. Assn. (Colo. Hosp. Assn. bd. 1980-83, mem. task force for input price adjustments 1988, del. regional policy bd. 1994), Wyo. Hosp. Assn. (bd. dirs. 1984—, chmn. 1986), Healthcare Forum (membership com. 1985, bd. dirs. 1986-89), Laramie C. of C., Rotary, Lions, Elks. Republican. Avocations: skiing, hunting, hiking, fishing, woodworking. Home: PO Box 155 Centennial WY 82055 Office: Ivinson Memorial Hospital 255 N 30th St Laramie WY 82070-5195

NORD, WALTER ROBERT, business administration educator, researcher, consultant; b. Mt. Kisco, N.Y., July 2, 1939; s. Arthur William and Elizabeth (Reimstedt) N.; m. Anne Feagan, June 10, 1967. BA in Econs., Williams Coll., 1961; MS in Organizational Behavior, Cornell U., 1963; PhD in Social Psychology, Washington U., St. Louis 1967. Asst. prof. organiza social psychology Washington U., 1967-70, assoc. prof., 1970-73, prof., 1973-89; prof. mgmt. U. South Fla., 1989—; vis. prof. faculty commerce U. B.C. (Can.), Vancouver, 1975-76, Northwestern U., 1981. Author: (with S. Tucker) Implementing Routine and Radical Innovations, 1987; editor: Concepts and Controversy in Organizational Behavior, 1972, rev. edit, 1976; (with P. Frost and V. Mitchell) Organizational Reality, 1978, rev. edit., 1982, 86, 92; (with H. Meltzer) Making Organizations Humane and Productive, 1982; (with P. Frost and V. Mitchell) Managerial Reality, 1989, HRM Reality, 1992; (with A. Brief) Meanings of Occupational Work, 1990. Fellow Am. Psychol. Assn.; mem. Acad. Mgmt., Union for Radical Polit. Econs. Home: 6004 Pratt St Tampa FL 33647-1043 Office: U South Fla Sch Bus Tampa FL 33620-5500

NORDBERG, JOHN ALBERT, federal judge; b. Evanston, Ill., June 18, 1926; s. Carl Albert and Judith Ranghild (Carlson) N.; m. Jane Spaulding, June 18, 1947; children: Carol, Mary, Janet, John. Student, Carleton Coll., 1943-44, 46-47; J.D., U. Mich., 1950. Bar: Ill. 1950, U.S. Dist. Ct. (no. dist.) Ill. 1957, U.S. Ct. Appeals (7th cir.) 1961. Assoc. Pope & Ballard, Chgo., 1950-57; ptnr. Pope, Ballard, Shepard & Fowle, Chgo., 1957-76; judge Cir. Ct. of Cook County, Ill., 1976-82, U.S. Dist. Ct. (no. dist.) Ill., Chgo., 1982—; lectr. Nat. Inst. Trial Advocacy, 1979—. Editor-in-chief, bd. editors Chgo. Bar Record, 1966-74. Magistrate of Cir. Ct. and justice of peace Ill., 1957-65. Served with USN, 1944-46; PTO. Mem. ABA, Chgo. Bar Assn., Am. Judicature Soc., Law Club Chgo., Union League, Legal Club Chgo., Order of Coif. Office: US Dist Ct 219 S Dearborn St Chicago IL 60604

NORDBY, EUGENE JORGEN, orthopedic surgeon; b. Abbotsford, Wis., Apr. 30, 1918; s. Herman Preus and Lucille Violet (Korsrud) N.; m. Olive Marie Jensen, June 21, 1941; 1 child, Jon Jorgen. B.A., Luther Coll., Decorah, Iowa, 1939; M.D., U. Wis., 1943. Intern Madison Gen. Hosp., Wis., 1943-44, asst. in orthopedic surgery, 1944-48; practice medicine specializing in orthopedic surgery Madison, Wis., 1948—; pres. Bone and Joint Surgery Assocs., S.C. 1969-91; chief staff Madison Gen. Hosp., 1957-63; assoc. clin. prof. U. Wis. Med. Sch., 1961—; chmn. Wis. Physicians Svc., 1979—; dir. Wis. Regional Med. Program, Chgo. Madison and No. RR; bd. govs. Wis. Health Care Liability Ins. Plan; chmn. trustees S.M.S. Realty Corp.; mem. bd. attys. Profl. Responsibility of Wis. Supreme Ct., 1992—. Assoc. editor Clin. Orthopaedics and Related Research, 1964—. Pres. Vesterheim Norwegian Am. Mus., Decorah, Iowa, 1968—. Served to capt. M.C., AUS, 1944-46. Decorated Knight 1st class Royal Norwegian Order St. Olav; recipient Disting. Svc. award Internat. Rotary, 1987, Den Hoyeste Aere award Vesterheim, 1993. Mem. Am. Acad. Orthopaedic Surgeons (dir. 1972-73), Clin. Orthopaedic Soc., Assn. Bone and Joint Surgeons (pres. 1973), Internat. Soc. Study Lumbar Spine, State Med. Soc. Wis. (chmn. 1968-76, treas. 1976—, Coun. award 1976), N.Am. Spine Soc., Internat. Intradiscal Therapy Soc. (sec. 1987—), Wis. Orthopaedic Soc., Dane County Med. Soc. (pres. 1957), Nat. Exchange Club, Madison Torske Klubben (founder, pres. 1978—), Norwegian-Am. Orthopaedic Soc., Phi Chi. Lutheran. Home: 6234 S Highlands Ave Madison WI 53705-1115 Office: 2704 Marshall Ct Madison WI 53705-2297

NORDBY, GENE MILO, engineering educator; b. Anoka, Minn., May 7, 1926; s. Bert J. and Nina Grace N.; m. Arlene Delores Anderson, Aug. 27, 1949 (dec. Nov. 1974); children: Susan Pamela, Brett Gene, Lisa Lea; m. Dusilla Anne Rycroft, July 8, 1975 (div. July 1988); m. Catherine Lynn Short, Dec. 23, 1992. BSCE, Oreg. State U., 1948; MSCE, U. Minn., 1949, Ph.D. in Civil Engring., 1955. Registered profl. engr., Colo. Ariz., Okla. Grad. asst. U. Minn., 1948-50; instructional instr., then asst. prof. civil engring. U. Colo., Boulder, 1950-56; assoc. prof., rsch. engr. Joint Hwy. Rsch. Project Purdue U., East Lafayette, Ind., 1956; engr. program dir. engring. scis. NSF, Washington, 1956-58; lectr. civil engring. George Washington U., Washington, 1956-58; dir., then chmn. adv. com. Ariz. Transp. and Traffic Inst. at univ., 1959-62; prof. engring. U. Okla., Norman, 1962-77, dean Coll. Engring, 1962-70, v.p. for adminstrn. and fin. Coll. Engring, 1969-77; v.p. for bus. and fin., prof. civil engring. Ga. Inst. Tech., Atlanta, 1977-80; chancellor U. Colo., Denver, 1980-85; chancellor emeritus, 1985—; prof. civil engring. U. Colo., Denver and Boulder, 1985-86; prof. civil engring. head dept. civil engring. U. Ariz., 1958-62; prof. agrl. engring. U. Ariz., Tucson, 1986-94, prof. emeritus, 1994—, head dept. agrl. engring., 1986-91; mem. Reinforced Concrete

Research Council Engring. Found., 1954-60; trustee Frontiers of Science Found., Okla., 1963-70; pres. Tetracon Assos., Inc., 1968-86; cons. structural engring., research financing and programming, ednl. facilities planning and constrn., reinforced concrete, also higher edn. adminstrn., engring. program accreditation, NSF, 1984-87, panel engring. ctrs. of excellence, 1983-87; bd. dirs. Higher Edn. and the Handicapped, Am. Council on Edn., 1980-83; pres. Accreditation Bd. for Engring. and Tech., 1985-86, fellow, mem. Related Accreditation Commn., 1986—, chair, 1993-94; gen. chmn. Nat. Congress on Engring. Edn., Washington, 1986; commr. at large N. Cen. Assn. Schs. and Colls., 1988-92. Co-author: Introduction to Structural Mechanics, 1960; Cons. editor, MacMillan Co., 1962-70. Mem. bd. vis. Air Force Inst. Tech., 1985-87. With AUS, 1943-46. Recipient Citation for Svc., State of Okla. Ho. Reps., 1977, Linton E. Grinter Disting. Svc. award Accreditation Bd. for Engring. and Tech., 1982. Fellow ASCE (com. on engring edn., 1964-68, com. on research needs, 1965-70, com. on ednl. research, 1976-79, Edmund Friedman Profl. Devel. award 1982); mem. Am. Soc. Engring. Edn. (projects bd. 1969-70, chmn. Curtis W. McGraw award com. 1968, Dean's Inst. com. 1966-69, accreditation process com. 1979-81), Nat. Soc. Profl. Engrs., Am. Arbitration Assn., Am. Soc. Agrl. Engrs. (com. in egring. and tech. accreditation 1987-93), Engrs. Council for Profl. Devel. (chmn. engring. edn. and accreditation com. 1970, dir. 1976-79, 83-87), Ariz. Soc. Profl. Engrs., Okla. Soc. Profl. Engrs. (dir. 1966-69), Nat. Assn. State Univs. and Land Grant Colls. (commn. edn. engring. profession 1966, 70-73), Engring. Colls. Adminstrv. Council (mem. exec. bd. 1966), Ga. Soc. Profl. Engrs. (bd. dirs. Atlanta chpt. 1978-79), Nat. Assn. Coll. and Univ. Bus. Officers (chmn. personnel com. 1977-79), Sigma Tau, Omicron Delta Kappa, Tau Beta Pi, Chi Epsilon, Alpha Episilon. Club: Mason. Office: U Ariz 403 Shantz Bldg 38 Tucson AZ 85721

NORDELL, HANS RODERICK, journalist, retired editor; b. Alexandria, Minn., June 26, 1925; s. Wilbur Eric and Amelia (Jasperson) N.; m. Joan Projansky, Apr. 30, 1955; children: Eric Peter, John Roderick, Elizabeth Sabin. AB magna cum laude, Harvard U., 1948; B Litt, U. Dublin, 1951. With Christian Sci. Monitor, Boston, 1948-93, arts editor, 1968-73, asst. chief editorial writer, 1973-83, home forum editor, 1983-85, feature editor, 1985-87, exec. editor World Monitor: The Christian Science Monitor Monthly (new mag.), 1988-93. Bd. dirs. Community Music Ctr., Boston, 1970-94, corp. chair, 1994—; bd. dirs. Young Audiences, 1970-88; mem. Com. for Harvard Theatre Collection, 1977-91; trustee Berklee Coll. Music, 1970—. With USMCR, 1943-46. Fellowship Rotary Found., 1950-51. Mem. St. Botolph Club, Phi Beta Kappa. Christian Scientist. Home: 25 Meadow Way Cambridge MA 02138-4635

NORDENBERG, MARK ALAN, legal educator, university administrator; b. Duluth, Minn., July 12, 1948; s. John Clemens and Shirley Mae (Tappen) N.; m. Nikki Patricia Pirillo, Dec. 26, 1970; children: Erin, Carl, Michael. BA, Thiel Coll., 1970; JD, U. Wis., 1973. Bar: Wis. 1973, Minn. 1974, U.S. Supreme Ct. 1976, Pa. 1985. Atty. Gray, Plant, Mooty & Anderson, Mpls., 1973-75; prof. law Capital U. Law Ctr., Columbus, Ohio, 1975-77; prof. law U. Pitts., 1977—, acting dean Sch. Law, 1985-87, dean Sch. Law, 1987-93, interim univ. sr. vice chancellor and provost, 1993-94, Univ. Disting. Svc. prof., 1994—; mem. U.S. Supreme Ct. Adv. Com. on Civil Rules, Washington, 1988-93, Pa. Supreme Ct. Civil Procedure Rules Com., Phila., 1986-92; mem. large and complex case panel Am. Arbitration Assn.; reporter civil justice adv. group U.S. Dist. Ct., Pitts., 1991—. Author: Modern Pennsylvania Civil Practice, 1985. Trustee Thiel Coll., Greenville, Pa., 1987—; bd. dirs. Lawyers Concerned for Lawyers of Pa., Harrisburg. Fellow Am. Bar Found.; mem. ABA, Pa. Bar Assn., Allegheny County Bar Assn., Acad. Trial Lawyers Allegheny County, Law Club Pitts., Univ. Club. Office: U Pitts 524 Law Sch Pittsburgh PA 15260-0001

NORDGREN, RONALD PAUL, engineering educator, researcher; b. Munising, Mich., Apr. 3, 1936; s. Paul A. and Martha M. (Busse) N.; m. Joan E. McAfee, Sept 12, 1959; children: Sonia, Paul. BS in Engring., U. Mich., 1957, MS in Engring., 1958; PhD, U. Calif., Berkeley, 1962. Rsch. asst. U. Calif., Berkeley, 1959-62; mathematician Shell Devel. Co., Houston, 1963-68, staff rsch. engr., 1968-74, sr. staff rsch. engr., 1974-80, rsch. assoc., 1980-90; Brown prof. civil and mech. engring. Rice U., Houston, 1989—; mem. U.S. nat. com. on theoretical and applied mechanics NRC, 1984-86, U.S. nat. com. for rock mechanics, 1991-95. Contbr. tech. papers to profl. jours.; assoc. editor Jour. Applied Mechanics, 1972-76, 81-85; patentee in field. Fellow ASME; mem. NAE, ASCE, Soc. Industrial and Applied Math., Soc. Engring. Sci., Sigma Xi. Office: Rice U 6100 S Main St Houston TX 77005-1892

NORDHAUS, ROBERT RIGGS, lawyer; b. Albuquerque, Mar. 27, 1937; s. Robert J. and Virginia (Riggs) N.; m. Jean Friedberg, June 27, 1964; children: Ronald E., Hannah E. BA, Stanford U., 1960; LLB, Yale U., 1963. Bar: N.Mex. 1963, D.C. 1981, U.S. Supreme Ct. 1982. Asst counsel U.S. House Reps., Washington, 1963-74, counsel interstate and fgn. commerce com., 1975-76; asst. adminstr. FEA, Washington, 1977; gen. counsel Fed. Energy Regulatory Commn., Washington, 1977-80; ptnr. Van Ness, Feldman & Curtis, Washington, 1981-93; gen. counsel Dept. of Energy, Washington, 1993—; adj. prof. Georgetown U. Law Ctr., Washington, 1980-85. Served to 2d. lt. U.S. Army, 1960-68. Mem. Fed. Energy Bar Assn. (bd. dirs. 1989—). Office: Gen Coun 1000 Independence Ave SW Washington DC 20585-0001

NORDIN, VIDAR JOHN, forestry educator, consultant; b. Ratansbyn, Sweden, June 28, 1924; s. John Herman and Beda Catherina (Wahlen) N.; m. Julianne Leona Zerr, Oct. 11, 1947; children: Christopher Eric, Katrin Anne. B.A., U. B.C., 1946, B.Sc.F., 1947; Ph.D., U. Toronto, 1951. Registered profl. forester, Ont. In charge Forest Pathology Lab., Fredericton, N.B., Can., 1949-51; officer in charge Calgary, Alta., Can., 1952-57; asso. dir. forest biology div. Fed. Agr. Dept., 1958-65; research mgr. Fed. Environment Dept., Ottawa, Ont., Can., 1965-71; prof., dean faculty forestry U. Toronto, Ont., 1971-84, prof. emeritus, 1986—; chmn. bd. Algonquin Forestry Authority Corp., 1974-82; pres. U.J. Nordin Assocs. Ltd., 1974—; dir. Can. Forestry Accreditation Project, 1987-89; sr. cons. Assn. Univs. and Colls. of Can., 1989—; hon. lectr. U. N.B., 1949-51. Mem. editl. bd. European Jour. Forest Pathology, 1970-84; co-editor: Forestry Chronicle, 1995—; contbr. articles to profl. jours. Co-chmn. U. Toronto United Way Campaign, 1973-74; mem. Provincial Parks Adv. Council, 1974-77. Fellow Canadian Inst. Forestry (past pres.); mem. Internat. Union Forestry Research Orgns. (past subject group chmn.), Internat. Soc. Tropical Foresters (treas., dir., v.p.), Ont. Forestry Assn. (dir.), Ont. Profl. Foresters Assn., Soc. Am. Foresters, Assn. Univ. Forestry Schs. Can. (past pres.), Chinese Soc. Forestry (hon.), Can. Owners and Pilots Assn., Rockcliffe Flying Club. Home: 403-A Echo Dr, Ottawa, ON Canada K1S 1N5

NORDLAND, GERALD, art museum administrator, historian, consultant; b. Los Angeles. A.B., U. So. Calif., J.D. Dean of faculty Chouinard Art Sch., L.A., 1960-64; dir. Washington Gallery of Modern Art, 1964-66, San Francisco Mus. Art, 1966-72, Frederick S. Wight Art Galleries, UCLA, 1973-77, Milw. Art Mus., 1977-85; ind. curator, author, editor Chgo., 1985—. Author: Paul Jenkins, 1972, Gaston Lachaise/The Man and His Work, 1974, Richard Diebenkorn, 1987. Gaston Lachaise Found. grantee, 1973-74; John Simon Guggenheim Found. fellow, 1985-86. Home and Office: 645 W Sheridan Rd Chicago IL 60613-3316

NORDLEY, GERALD DAVID, writer, investor; b. Mpls., May 22, 1947; s. V. Gerald and Evelyn May (Whitesel) N.; (div. 1973); 1 child, Sharon; m. Gayle Ann Wiesner, May 9, 1976; children: Jeffrey Goldberg, Andrew Nordley. BA in Physics, Macalester Coll., 1969; MS in System Mgmt., U. So. Calif., L.A. 1980. Enlisted USAF, 1970, commd. 2nd lt., 1970, advanced through grades to maj., 1982; inter-range ops. officer Network Ops. Div., Sunnyvale AFB, Calif., 1974-76; chief orbital ops. br. Def. Satellite Communications Directorate, L.A. AFB, 1976-81; chief spacecraft engr. br. DSCS III Program Office, L.A. AFB, 1981-82; battle dir. Mangilsan Liason Annex, Mang Il San, South Korea, 1983; chief advanced propulsion br. A.F. Rocket Propulsion Lab., Edwards AFB, Calif., 1984-86; rsch. staff mgr. ARIES office Astronautics Lab., Edwards AFB, 1986-89; ret. USAF, 1989; writer, pvt. investor Sunnyvale, 1990—. Mem. dir. Macalester Coll. Rep. Club, St. Paul, 1967-68; pres. Park Knowles Estates Property Owners Assn., Boron, Calif., 1988; co-chair Silicon Valley Writers Workshop, Cupertino, Calif., 1992, 93. Decorated Air Force Commendation medal with 4 oak leaf clusters, Meritorious Svc. medal with 1 oak leaf cluster; recipient Anlab award

Analog Mag., 1992, 93. Fellow Brit. Interplanetary Soc.; mem. AIAA (elec. propulsion com. 1984-86), Air Force Assn., Sci. Fiction Writers Am., Whensday People Writers Group, Ft. Mason's Officers Club, Am. Legion. Unitarian. Avocation: amateur astronomy.

NORDLIE, ROBERT CONRAD, biochemistry educator; b. Willmar, Minn., June 11, 1930; s. Peder Conrad and Myrtle (Spindler) N.; m. Sally Ann Christianson, Aug. 23, 1959; children: Margaret, Melissa, John. B.S. St. Cloud State Coll., Minn., 1952; M.S., U. N.D., 1957, Ph.D., 1960. Teaching and research asst. biochemistry U. N.D. Med. Sch., Grand Forks, 1955-60, Hill research prof. biochemistry, 1962-74, Chester Fritz disting. prof. biochemistry, 1974—, Cornatzer prof., chmn. dept. biochemistry and molecular biology, 1983—; hon. prof. San Marcos U., Lima, Peru, 1981, 82—; NIH fellow Inst. Enzyme Rsch., U. Wis., 1960-61; mem. biochemistry study sect. NIH; merit rev. com. VA, 1994—; cons. exzymology Oak Ridge, 1961—; vis. prof. Tokyo Biomed. Inst., 1984; mem. predoctoral fellowship rev. group Howard Hughes Inst., 1990-93. Mem. editorial bd.: Jour. Biol. Chemistry, Biochimca et Biophysica Acta. Research publs. on enzymology relating to metabolism of various carbohydrates in mammalian livers, regulation blood sugar levels. Served with AUS, 1953-55. Recipient Disting. Alumnus award St. Cloud State U., 1983; recipient Sigma Xi Rsch. award, 1969, Golden Apple award U. N.D., 1968, Edgar Dale award U. N.D., 1983, Burlington No. Faculty Scholar award, 1987, Thomas J. Clifford Faculty Achievement award for excellence in rsch. U. N.D. Found., 1993. Mem. Am. Soc. Biol. Chemistry and Molecular Biology, Am. Chem. Soc., AAAS, Internt. Union Biochemists, Am. Soc. Microbiology, Soc. Exptl. Biology and Medicine, Am. Inst. Nutrition, Brit. Biochem. Soc., Sigma Xi, Alpha Omega Alpha. Home: 162 Columbia Ct Grand Forks ND 58203-2947

NORDLING, BERNARD ERICK, lawyer; b. Nekoma, Kans., June 14, 1921; s. Carl Ruben Ebben and Edith Elveda (Freeburg) N.; m. Barbara Ann Burkholder, Mar. 26, 1949. Student, George Washington U., 1941-43; AB, McPherson Coll., 1947; JD, U. Kans., 1949. Bar: Kans. 1949, U.S. Dist. Ct. Kans. 1949, U.S. Ct. Appeals (10th cir.) 1970. Pvt. practice Hugoton, Kans., 1949—; ptnr. Kramer & Nordling, 1950-65; ptnr. Kramer, Nordling, Nordling & Tate, 1966-94, of counsel, 1994—; city atty. City of Hugoton, 1951-87; county atty. Stevens County, Kans., 1957-63; Kans. mem. legal com. Interstate Oil Compact Commn., 1969—; mem. supply tech. adv. com. nat. gas survey FPC, 1975-77. Editor U. Kans. Law Rev., 1949. Mem. Hugoton Sch. Bds., 1954-68, pres. grade sch. bd., 1957-63; trustee McPherson Coll., 1971-81, mem. exec. com., 1975-81; mem. Kans. Energy Adv. Coun., 1975-78, mem. exec. com., 1976-78. With AUS, 1944-46. Recipient Citation of Merit, McPherson Coll., 1987, Disting. Alumnus award Kans. U. Law Sch., 1993, Lifetime Achievement award Hugoton Kans. Area C. of C., 1994. Fellow Am. Bar Found. (Kans.); mem. ABA, Kans. Bar Assn., S.W. Kans. Bar Assn., Am. Judicature Soc., City Attys. Assn. Kans. (exec. com. 1975-83, pres. 1982-83), Nat. Assn. Royalty Owners (bd. govs. 1980—), S.W. Kans. Royalty Owners Assn. (exec. sec. 1968-94, asst. exec. sec. 1994—), U. Kans. Law Soc. (bd. govs. 1984-87), Kans. U. Endowment Assn. (trustee 1989—), Kans. U. Alumni Assn. (bd. dirs. 1992—), Order of Coif, Phi Alpha Delta. Home: 218 N Jackson St Hugoton KS 67951-2040 Office: 209 E 6th St Hugoton KS 67951

NORDLOH, DAVID JOSEPH, English language educator; b. Cin., May 3, 1942; s. Joseph Westerman and Josephine (Fusz) N.; m. Barbara Jane Beddow, June 29, 1968; children: Geoffrey David, Jennifer Ellen. AB in English, Coll. of Holy Cross, 1964; PhD in English, Ind. U., 1969. Asst. prof. English Ind. U., Bloomington, 1969-75, assoc. prof. English, 1975-81, prof. English, 1981—; vis. assoc. prof. U. Va., Charlottesville, 1978; dir. Am. Studies Program, Ind. U., 1987-94. Gen. editor: A Selected Edition of W.D. Howells, 1974—; editor: Twayne's United States Author's Series, 1978-90; co-editor: American Literary Scholarship, 1986—; mem. editl. bd. Walter Scott Edition, 1984—; mem. adv. bd. The Writings of James Fenimore Cooper, 1995—. Pres. Bloomington Symphony Orch., 1986-88, 93-94. Fulbright scholar, 1982-83. Mem. MLA (chmn. div. methods of lit. rsch. 1987), Soc. for Textual Scholarship (adv. bd. 1980—), Midwest MLA (chmn. bibliography sect. 1990-91), South Atlantic MLA, Am. Lit. Assn. Home: 3123 E Diana Ct Bloomington IN 47401-4407 Office: Ind U English Dept Ballantine Hall #442 Bloomington IN 47405

NORDLUND, DONALD CRAIG, corporate lawyer; b. Chgo., May 23, 1949; s. Donald E. and Jane (Houston) N.; m. Sally Baum, Sept. 7, 1975; children: Courtney Elizabeth, Michael Andrew, Laurie Katherine. AB, Stanford U., 1971; JD, Vanderbilt U., 1974. Assoc. Ware & Freidenrich, Palo Alto, Calif., 1974-77; atty. Hewlett-Packard Co., Palo Alto, 1977-80, sr. atty., asst. sec., 1980-81, asst. sec., corp. counsel, 1981-85, sec., corp. counsel, 1985-86, sec., asst. gen. counsel, 1986-87, assoc. gen. counsel, sec., 1987—; bd. dirs. Hewlett-Packard Hellas, Palo Alto, Hewlett-Packard European Distbn., Ops., Inc., The Netherlands, Hewlett-Packard Labs. Japan, Inc., Hewlett-Packard Del. Holding Inc., Eon System, Palo Alto, Hewlett-Packard Employees Fed. Credit Union, other Hewlett-Packard subs.; sec. Hewlett-Packard Co. Found., Palo Alto, 1979—, Hewlett-Packard Fin. Co., Palo Alto, 1983—; Apollo Computer, Inc., 1989—; panelist disclosure documents seminar Practicing Law Inst., 1982-94, also contbg. author to course handbook; cons. pub. guide series, CEB, 1991. Mem. exec. com., bd. dirs. Santa Clara County chpt. Jr. Achievement, 1989—. Mem. Am. Soc. Corp. Sec. Inc. (pres. San Francisco region 1986-88, bd. dirs. 1987-90, chmn. sec.'s issues seminar 1986, mem. exec. com. 1988-89), Am. Corp. Counsel Assn. (bd. dirs. San Francisco chpt. 1984—, treas. Bay area chpt. 1986-87, sec. 1987-88, v.p. 1988-89, pres. 1989-90), Foothills Tennis and Swimming Club (Palo Alto). Avocations: tennis, skiing, sailing, golf. Office: Hewlett-Packard Co 3000 Hanover St Palo Alto CA 94304-1112

NORDLUND, DONALD ELMER, manufacturing company executive; b. Stromsburg, Nebr., Mar. 1, 1922; s. E.C. and Edith O. (Peterson) N.; m. Mary Jane Houston, June 5, 1948; children: Donald Craig, William Chalmers, Sarah, James. A.B., Midland Coll., 1943; J.D., U. Mich., 1948. Bar: Ill. 1949. With Stevenson, Conaghan, Hackbert, Rooks and Pitts, Chgo., 1948-55, A.E. Staley Mfg. Co., Decatur, Ill., 1956-85; v.p., dir., mem. exec. com. A.E. Staley Mfg. Co., 1958-65, pres., chief operating officer, 1965-80, dir., mem. exec. com., 1965-85, also chmn., 1975-85; chief exec. officer Staley Continental, Inc., Rolling Meadows, Ill., 1985-88, chmn. and chief exec. officer, 1985-88; bd. dirs. Amsted Industries, Inc., Sentry Ins., Sundstrand Corp. Past chmn. bd. trustees Millikin U., now hon. trustee; trustee Vanderbilt U., Mus. Sci. and Industry, Chgo. Rush-Presbyn. St. Lukes Med. Ctr., Chgo.; bd. dirs. Lyric Opera Chgo.; mem. grad. dirs. coun. Decatur Meml. Hosp. Mem. ABA, Chgo. Bar Assn., Corn Refiners. Assn. (bd. dirs., past chmn., now hon. dir.). The Lincoln Acad. of Ill. Legal Club, Commercial Club, Chgo. Club, Tavern Club, Barrington Hills Club, Phi Alpha Delta.

NORDLUND, JAMES JOHN, dermatologist; b. St. Paul, Aug. 11, 1939; m. Mary Flanagan, Sept. 28, 1963; children: Christa, Michael, Marguerite. BA, St. John's U., 1961; BS, U. Minn., 1963, MD, 1965. Diplomate Am. Bd. Internal Medicine, Am. Bd. Dermatology. Clin. investigator VA, West Haven, Conn., 1977-80; assoc. prof. dermatology Yale U., New Haven, 1978-82, prof. dermatology, 1982-83; prof., chmn. U. Cin., 1983—; mem. nat. adv. com. St. John's U., Collegeville, Minn. Editor: Dermatology Resource Manual, 1988, Pigmentary Disorders, 1988, Cutaneous Aging, 1988. Lt. comdr. USPHS, 1967-69. Mem. Soc. Investigative Dermatology, Am. Dermatol. Assn., Pan Am. Soc. for Pigment Cell Rsch. (pres. 1986-91), Am. Acad. Dermatology (bd. dirs. 1987-91), N.Y. Acad. Sci., Assn. Profs. Dermatology, Internat. Fedn. Pigment Cell Socs. (sec.-treas. 1989-92), Sigma Xi. Avocations: scuba, hiking, woodworking, gardening. Office: U Cin Coll Medicine 231 Bethesda Ave # 592 Cincinnati OH 45267

NORDLUND, JAMES ROBERT, state agency administrator; b. St. Paul, Minn., Dec. 23, 1952; s. Leonard Gustav and Catherine Ann (Lindow) N. BS, St. John U., 1975; MPA, U. Colo., 1982. Journeyman carpenter Carpenter's Locals Denver and Anchorage, 1981-85; housing rehab. specialist Anchorage Neighborhood Housing Svcs., 1983-86; legis. asst. Alaska State Legislature, Anchorage, Juneau, 1986-92, state legislator, 1993-95; dir. divsn. pub. assistance State of Alaska, Juneau, 1995—; pres., CEO Macuir Co. Inc., Anchorage, 1990—; comml. fisherman, Alaska, 1987—; Founding pres. Anchorage Waterways Coun., 1985. Democrat. Roman

Catholic. Avocations: outdoor sports, team sports, photography, running. Office: PO Box 110640 Juneau AK 99811-0640

NORDLUND, WILLIAM CHALMERS, lawyer; b. Chgo., Aug. 29, 1954; s. Donald E. and Jane H. (Houston) N.; m. Elizabeth Apell, Oct. 1, 1983; children: William Chalmers Jr., Scott Donald. BA, Vanderbilt U., 1976; JD, Duke U., 1979; MM, Northwestern U., 1990. Bar: Ill. 1979, Md. 1991, Mich. 1992. Assoc. Winston & Strawn, Chgo., 1979-87, ptnr., 1987-90; atty. Constellation Holdings, Inc., 1990-91; v.p., sec., gen. counsel The Oxford Energy Co., Dearborn, Mich., 1991-92, sr. v.p., sec., gen. counsel, 1992-93; gen. counsel Panda Energy Co., Dallas, 1993-94, v.p. and gen. counsel, 1994—. Bd. dirs. Orch. of Ill., Chgo., 1983-85; bd. dirs., sec. Literacy Vols. of Am.-Ill., Chgo., 1985-88, treas., 1988-90. Mem. Gleneagles C.C. Avocations: golf, tennis, skiing. Office: Panda Energy Corp 4100 Spring Valley Rd Ste 1001 Dallas TX 75244-3646

NORDMAN, CHRISTER ERIC, chemistry educator; b. Helsinki, Finland, Jan. 23, 1925; came to U.S., 1948, naturalized, 1960; s. Eric Johan and Gertrud (Nordgren) N.; m. Barbara Lorraine Neal, Nov. 28, 1952 (div. 1993); children: Christina, Aleta, Eric, Carl; m. Outi Marttila, Dec. 28, 1994. Dipl. Ing., Finnish Inst. Tech., Helsinki, 1949; Ph.D., U. Minn., 1953. Research assoc. Inst. Cancer Research, Phila., 1953-55; mem. faculty U. Mich., Ann Arbor, 1955—; prof. chemistry U. Mich., 1964—. Mem. U.S. Nat. Com. Crystallography, 1970-72. Served with Finnish Army, 1943-44. NIH spl. fellow, 1971-72. Fellow AAAS; mem. Am. Chem. Soc., Am. Phys. Soc., Am. Cyrstallographic Assn. Home: 2200 Fuller Rd Apt 207B Ann Arbor MI 48105-2309 Office: Univ Mich Dept Chemistry Ann Arbor MI 48109

NORDMAN, RICHARD DENNIS, chemical company executive; b. Iowa, Sept. 30, 1946; s. Victor and Dorothy Nordman; m. Patricia Lynn Boehnke, Aug. 27, 1966; children: Sarah, Matthew, Angela. BSBA, Iowa State U., 1968. CPA, Ill. Mgr. Arthur Andersen & Co., Chgo., 1968-74; treas. Lawter Internat., Inc., Northbrook, Ill., 1974-80, v.p. fin., 1983-85, exec. v.p., 1983-86, pres., chief operating officer, 1986—, also bd. dirs., 1982—; bd. dirs. Kemper Corp., Long Grove, Ill. Trustee Cornerstone Found. Luth. Social Svcs. of Ill. Mem. AICPA, Ill. Soc. CPAs, Chgo. Sunday Evening Club (trustee), Econ. Club, Exec. Club. Avocations: golf, tennis, flying. Office: Lawter Internat Inc 990 Skokie Blvd Northbrook IL 60062-4096

NORDMANN, GARY ARNOLD, corporate executive; b. Berwyn, Ill., Jan. 29, 1942; s. Arnold Friedrich and Mildred Ellen (Forslund) N.; m. Nancy Olivia House, June 9, 1966 (div. Sept. 1982); 1 child, Leila Olivia; m. Caroline C. Brune, Feb. 20, 1988. BS in Indsl. Mgmt., Purdue U., 1964; MBA, Harvard U., 1970. Asst. to v.p. fin. S.C. Johnson & Sons, Inc., Racine, Wis., 1970-72; controller Wilson Sporting Goods Co., River Grove, Ill., 1972-77; v.p. corp. devel. Mattel, Inc., Hawthorne, Calif., 1977-81; v.p. fin. Marriott Corp., Inc., Gurnee, Ill., 1981-83; exec. v.p. Whitbread N.Am., Inc., Lake Success, N.Y., 1983—; instr. U. Wis., Parkside, 1970-73. Lt. USN, 1965-68. Mem. Nat. Assn. Accts., Cold Spring Harbor Beach Club, Huntington Country Club. Office: Whitbread N Am Inc PO Box 33005 Detroit MI 48232-5005

NORDQUIST, MYRON HARRY, lawyer; b. Kalispell, Mont., Oct. 22, 1940; s. Harry and Guida (Sorenson) N.; m. Barbara Kay Altpeter, Dec. 28, 1967; children: Nels, Silvy, Ingrid. BS, Oreg. State U., 1966; JD, Calif. Western U., San Diego, 1969; SJD, U. Va., 1977. Bar: Calif. 1970, D.C. 1975, Mass. 1983. Atty. Office of Legal Adviser, U.S. Dept. State, Washington, 1970-77; ptnr. Nossaman, Krueger & Marsh, Washington, 1978-82, Duncan, Allen & Mitchell, Washington, 1982-83, Herrick & Smith, Washington, 1984-85, Kelley, Drye & Warren, Washington, 1985-89; pres. Core Corp., Washington, 1989-90; dep. gen. counsel Dept. Air Force, Washington, 1990-93, acting gen. counsel, 1993—. Editor: (books) New Directions in Law of the Sea, 1970-78, Commentary: 1982 Convention on Law of the Sea, 1985—; editor-in-chief Annual Proc. Mem. Ctr. for Oceans Law and Policy, U. Va., Charlottesville, 1978—. Capt. USMC, 1966-69, Vietnam. Office: Dept Air Force 4E856 General Counsel The Pentagon Washington DC 20330

NORDQVIST, ERIK ASKBO, shipping company executive; b. Copenhagen, Aug. 8, 1943; s. Joergen and Lissie (Moeller) A.; m. Kirsten Vibeke Kenholt, Sept. 17, 1970; children: Ken-Martin, Alexander. Student, Danish Comml. Coll. Commerce, London, 1963-64, U. S.C., London, 1964-65. Vice pres. Import Center W.S., L.A., 1964-65; mng. Denning Freight Forwarders Ltd., Toronto, Ont., Can., 1965-66; sales dir. overseas Samson Transp. Co., Copenhagen, 1967-68; mng. dir., pres. Seair AS, Copenhagen, 1969-71, Nordbird Group, Vedbaek, Denmark, 1971—, Nordbird AS, 1971—; also Nordbird Oil, Nordbird Fin., Copenhagen, Nordbird Internat. Financing Ltd., Toronto, Ont.; v.p. N. Sea Products Inc., High Point, N.C., 1980—; bd. dirs. Frano Aps, Copenhagen, 1979-80, Fino Travel, Odense, Denmark, 1979—, Annex Furniture Galleries, 1980—, European Broadcast Communication, Vedbaek, 1989—, On Holding Ltd., Gibraltar, 1989—, Olsen & Nordqvist Holding, Holbaek, Denmark, 1984—, pres., 1986—, NQ-Byg Aps, Holbaek, 1986—, Auto Dan-Am., Holbaek, 1986—, Autotel Internat. Roskilde, 1987—, On Holding APS, Vedbaek Dansk-Fransk Osters Aps, 3 Danish Open, U.S., Great Britain, Japan, 1988—, Tins and Cans, Denmark, 1988—; chmn. European Broadcast Comm., Charlottenlund, Denmark, London, European Aid Found., Vedbaek, Denmark, Lac, Albanien; cons. Frederikshavns. Skibsvaerf AS, Copenhagen Community. Chmn. European Broadcast Comm., Copenhagen and London, 1992—, European Aid Found., Copenhagen and N.Y.C.; del. Internat. Red Cross, Copenhagen, 1994—. Recipient Devel. honor for shipping City of Le Havre, France, 1971. Mem. Det Udenrigspolitiske Selskab, Funen Soc. (founder, past pres.). Conservative. Lutheran. Office: 35 Flintemarken, 2950 Vedbaek Denmark

NORDSTRAND, RAYMOND WILLIAM, broadcasting company executive; b. Evanston, Ill., Sept. 13, 1932; s. Nels Eric and Frida Elise (Kuehl) N.; m. Susan Diane Ports, June 15, 1963 (div.); 1 child, Susan Erika. BA, Northwestern U., 1953, MS, 1966; PhD (hon.), Columbia Coll., 1985, Shimer Coll., 1987. Instr. econs. Northwestern U., Evanston, 1953-55; announcer Sta. WFMT, Chgo., 1953-57, asst. mgr., 1957-63, comml. mgr., 1963-68, sta. mgr., 1968-70, gen. mgr., 1970-85, pres., 1970—, pres. WFMT Fine Arts Network, dir. WFMT Fine Arts Cir.; pub. Chgo. mag., 1970-85, dir. devel., 1990—; with Cinema/Chgo., 1978-88, chmn., trustee. Co-producer nationally syndicated radio program Midnight Spl.; syndicator radio series, Sta. WFMT Fine Arts Network, Beethoven Satellite Network; contbr. articles to profl. publs. Trustee, Old Town Sch. of Folk Music; bd. govs. Chgo. Symphony Orch.; bd. dirs. Lyric Opera Chgo., Arts & Bus. Coun. Chgo. Recipient Maj. Armstrong award, 1971, 86, Broadcast Receptor award San Francisco State U., 1982, George Foster Peabody award U. Ga., 1985; named Outstanding Citizen by resolution of Mayor and City Coun. Chgo., 1973, 78. Mem. Concert Mus. Broadcasters Assn. (exec. com., chmn 1975-76), City and Regional Mag. Assn. (v.p., exec. com.), Phi Beta Kappa. Office: Sta WFMT 303 E Wacker Dr Chicago IL 60601-5212

NORDSTROM, BRUCE A., department store executive; b. 1933; married. BA, U. Wash., 1956. With Nordstrom, Inc., Seattle, 1956—, v.p., 1964-70, pres., 1975-77, chmn., 1975-77, co-chmn., 1977—; dir. Office: Nordstrom Inc 1501 5th Ave Seattle WA 98101*

NORDSTROM, JAMES F., department store executive; b. 1940; married. BBA, U. Wash., 1962. Various positions Nordstrom, Inc., Seattle, 1960—, exec. v.p., 1975-78, pres., 1975-78, from 1978, co-chmn., also bd. dirs. Office: Nordstrom Inc 1501 5th Ave Seattle WA 98101-1603*

NORDSTROM, JOHN N., department store executive; b. 1937; married. BA, U. Wash., 1958. With Nordstrom, Inc., Seattle, 1958—, v.p., 1965-70, exec. v.p., 1970-75, pres., 1975-77, co-chmn., 1977—; bd. dirs. Fed. Res. Bank San Francisco. Office: Nordstrom Inc 1501 5th Ave Seattle WA 98101-1603*

NORELL, MARK ALLEN, paleontology educator; b. St. Paul, July 26, 1957; s. Albert Donald Norell and Helen Louise Soltau; m. Vivian Pan, Nov. 1, 1991. BS, Long Beach State U., 1980; MS, San Diego State U., 1983; PhD, Yale U., 1988. Asst. curator Am. Mus., N.Y.C., 1989-94, assoc.

curator, 1994—; adj. asst. prof. biology dept. Yale U., New Haven, 1991—. Author: All You Need to Know About Dinosaurs, 1991; (with others) Discovering Dinosaurs, 1995; forward to: Bones: The Unity of Form & Function, 1994; contbr. articles to profl. jours. Fellow Willi Hennig Soc., Explorers Club; mem. Soc. Vertebrate Paleontology (Romer prize 1987). Office: Am Mus Natural History 79th At Ctrl Park West New York NY 10024

NOREM, RICHARD FREDERICK, SR., musician, music educator; b. Joliet, Ill., June 28, 1931; s. Oscar Lewis and Mabel Vera (Meyer) N.; m. Sally Lou Jarvis, July 24, 1954; 1 son, Richard Frederick II. Mus.B., U. Rochester, 1953, Mus.M., 1958; postgrad., Guildhall Sch. London, 1974. Instr. Joliet Musical Coll., Ill., 1951-53; tchr. Rochester Pub. Schs., N.Y., 1956-57; mem. faculty La. State U., Baton Rouge, 1957—; prof., asst. dean music La. State U., 1969-84; dir., sec.-treas. Bank Commerce, 1983—; bd. dirs., sec.-treas. NBC Fin. Corp., 1988—. Mem. Baton Rouge Symphony Orch., 1957—, Timm Woodwind quintet, 1957—. Served with band USMC, 1953-56. Mem. Baton Rouge Symphony Orch., 1957—, Timm Woodwind quintet, 1957—. With USMC Band, 1953-56. Trumpeter. Episcopalian. Clubs: Rolls-Royce Owners (sec.-treas. So. Delta region), Starlighters, LSU Faculty. Home: 4821 Sweetbriar St Baton Rouge LA 70808-8660 Office: La State U Sch Music Baton Rouge LA 70803 *I have been blessed by the divine creator with an artistic talent in music to which I have dedicated my life. Early during my performing career I knew I must share with others the knowledge I had obtained in music; consequently my goals have been to train and educate the hundreds of music students I have taught during my teaching career. I have also tried to continue to bring beauty to our world in my own way as an active performing musician.*

NORFLEET, ROBERT F., JR., banking executive; b. Richmond, Va., 1940. BA, Washington & Lee U., 1962; grad., Rutgers U., 1972. Corp. exec. v.p., sr. credit officer Crestar Bank Corp., Richmond, Va., 1994. Office: Crestar Bank Corp 919 E Main St Richmond VA 23219-4625

NORFOLK, WILLIAM RAY, lawyer; b. Huron, S.D., Mar. 15, 1941; s. James W. and Helen F. (Thompson) N.; m. Marilyn E. Meadors; children: Stephanie G., Allison T., Meredith H. BA, Miami U., Oxford, Ohio, 1963; student, U. London, 1963-64; LLB, Duke U., 1967. Bar: N.Y. 1968, U.S. Dist. Ct. (so. and ea. dists.) N.Y. 1969, U.S. Ct. Appeals (2d cir.) 1969, U.S. Ct. Appeals (9th cir.) 1977, U.S. Ct. Appeals (5th cir.) 1979, U.S. Ct. Appeals (3d and 11th cirs.) 1981, U.S. Dist. Ct. (ea. dist.) Mich. 1986, U.S. Ct. Appeals (6th and 8th cirs.) 1986, U.S. Ct. Appeals (Fed. cir.) 1990, U.S. Ct. Internat. Trade 1990, U.S. Dist. Ct. (we. dist.) Mich. 1992. Assoc. Sullivan & Cromwell, N.Y.C., 1967-74, ptnr., 1974—. Trustee N.Y. Meth. Hosp. Mem. ABA, N.Y. State Bar Assn., Am. Soc. Internat. Law. Office: Sullivan & Cromwell 125 Broad St New York NY 10004-2400

NORGLE, CHARLES RONALD, SR., federal judge; b. Mar. 3, 1937. BBA, Northwestern U., Evanston, Ill., 1964; JD, John Marshall Law Sch., Chgo., 1969. Asst. state's atty. DuPage County, Ill., 1969-71, dep. pub. defender, 1971-73, assoc. judge, 1973-77, 78-81, cir. judge, 1977-78, 81-84; judge U.S. Dist. Ct. (no. dist.) Ill., Chgo., 1984—; mem. exec. com. No. Dist., Ill.; mem. 7th Cir. Judicial Coun.; mem. Fed. Defender Svcs. Com. Mem. ABA, Fed. Bar Assn., Ill. Bar Assn., DuPage Bar Assn., Nat. Attys. Assn., DuPage Assn. Women Attys., Chgo. Legal Club. Office: US Dist Ct 219 S Dearborn St Rm 1703 Chicago IL 60606-7206

NORGREN, C. NEIL, retired manufacturing company executive; b. Silt, Colo., Aug. 23, 1923; s. Carl August and Juliet (Lien) N.; m. Carolyn Sutherland, Apr. 12, 1980; children by previous marriage: Jeraldine Leigh, Carol Ann, John Carl, David Laurence. Student, U. Colo., 1941-43. With C.A. Norgren Co. (mfrs. pneumatic products), Englewood, Colo., 1938-84; asst. gen. mgr. C.A. Norgren Co. (mfrs. pneumatic products), 1947-53, v.p., 1953-55, exec. v.p., 1955-62, pres., 1962-84, also dir.; chmn., chief exec. officer Butler Fixture Co., Denver, 1984-91; dir. United Bank of Denver (mem. exec. com. 1957-90). Bd. dirs. Bus. and Industry Polit. Action Com., 1967-89, Carl A. Norgren Found., 1955-90, Unitog Co., 1971-84; pres. Met. Denver chpt. Jr. Acheivement, 1954-56, nat. exec. com. 1956-62; bd. dirs. Denver Mus. Natural History, 1st v.p., 1983-88, pres., 1988-91; pres. C. Neil and Carolyn S. Norgren Found., 1990—; bd. dirs. U. Colo. Found., 1961-68, 81—, vice chmn., 1985-87, chmn., 1987-90, chmn. exec. com., 1990-92; Colo. divsn. exec. com. Am. Cancer Soc., 1961-67. Staff sgt. USAAF, 1942-46. Mem. NAM (bd. dirs. 1964-87, regional v.p. 1966-71, div. v.p. 1972-78, exec. com. 1966-78), Nat. Fluid Power Assn., Nat. Coun. Profit Sharing Industries (past chmn. exec. com.), Nat. Western Stock Show Assn. (former bd. dirs.), Inst. Dirs. London, Met. Denver Execs. Club (co-founder, past pres.), Athletic Club, Pinehurst Country Club, Air Force Acad. Golff Club (Colorado Springs), Met. Club, Greencroft Club, Flatirons Club, Beta Theta Pi. Home: 350 Barracks Hl Charlottesville VA 22901-8845

NORGREN, WILLIAM ANDREW, religious denomination administrator; b. Frostburg, Md., May 5, 1927; s. William Andrew and Martha Elizabeth Leona (Richardson) N. BA, Coll. William and Mary, 1948; STB, now STM, Gen. Theol. Sem., N.Y.C., 1953; LittB, Oxford (Eng.) U., 1959; DD (hon.), Gen. Theol. Sem., N.Y.C., 1984, Berkeley Divinity Sch., 1995. Ordained to ministry Episcopal Ch., 1953. Chaplain Christ Ch. Cathedral, Oxford, 1955-59; exec. dir. Commn. on Faith and Order Nat. Coun. Chs. of Christ in U.S.A., N.Y.C., 1959-71; mem. gen. bd. Nat. Coun. Chs. in Christ in U.S.A., N.Y.C., 1979-94; pastoral asst. Trinity Ch., N.Y.C., 1972-74; assoc. ecumenical officer Episcopal Ch., N.Y.C., 1975-79, ecumenical officer, 1979-94, theol. cons., 1995—; observer 2d Vatican Coun., Roman Cath. Ch., Vatican City, 1963-65; mem. assemblies World Co. Chs., various cities, 1961, 68, 83, 91. Editor: Living Room Dialogues, 1965, Implications of the Gospel, 1988, Toward Full Communion and Concordat of Agreement, 1991; compiler: What Can We Share, 1985. Fellow Gen. Theol. Sem., 1953-55. Democrat. Avocations: art, music, theatre, walking. Office: Episcopal Church Ctr 815 2nd Ave New York NY 10017

NORIAN, ROGER W., plastic manufacturing company executive; b. Chgo., Apr. 16, 1943; s. Richard and Eunice (Sandusky) N.; m. Ann Steel, Apr. 29, 1989; children from previous marriage: Jennifer, Michelle, Kristina. BS in Bus. Adminstrn, Northwestern U., 1965, M.B.A., 1966. Assoc. corp. fin. dept. A.G. Becker & Co., N.Y.C., 1966-68; asst. to chmn., CFO Duplan Corp., N.Y.C., 1968-75; CFO Kerr Glass Corp., L.A., from 1975, now pres., chmn. bd., CEO. Office: Kerr Group 1840 Century Park E Los Angeles CA 90067-2101

NORICK, RONALD J., mayor of Oklahoma City; b. Oklahoma City, Aug. 5, 1941; m. Carolyn Norick; children: Allyson, Lance. BS in Mgmt., Oklahoma City U., LHD (hon.), 1990. Pres. Norick Bros., Inc., 1981-92; mayor City of Oklahoma City, Oklahoma City, 1987—; gen. ptng. Norick Investment Inc.; former chmn. bd. Norick Software, Inc. Trustee Community Ch. of Redeemer; mem. Ctrl. Okla. Transp. and Parking Authority, Oklahoma City Water Utilities Trust, Myriad Gardens Authority; bd. dirs. Okla. State Fair' mem. McGee Creek Authority; bd. dirs. Oklahoma City Philharm.; mem. exec. com. Oklahoma City U., Allied Arts Found. Mem. Nat. League Cities, U.S. Conf. Mayors, Okla. Mcpl. League, Oklahoma City C. of C. (bd. dirs.), South Oklahoma City C. of C. (bd. dirs.), Econ. Club Okla., Men's Dinner Club, Rotary. Avocations: golf, tennis, fishing, boating. Office: Office of Mayor City Hall 200 N Walker Ave Oklahoma City OK 73102-2247*

NORIEGA, RUDY JORGE, hospital administrator; b. Havana, Cuba, Apr. 23, 1937; s. Rodolfo and Iris (Santini) N.; came to U.S., 1961; naturalized, 1966; BS, Masonic U., 1960; m. Rosa E. Del Castillo, Jan. 2, 1960; children: Rudy A., George. Acct., Continental Can Co., Havana, Cuba, 1961, Am. Fgn. Ins. Assn., N.Y.C., 1961-62, North Miami Gen. Hosp., Miami, Fla., 1962-64; asst. controller Jackson Meml. Hosp., Miami, 1964-65; asst. adminstr. Plantation (Fla.) Gen. Hosp., 1965-72, adminstr., trustee, 1972-80; v.p., trustee Internat. Hosp., Miami, 1980-83; exec. v.p., chief operating officer Gen. Health L.P., Miami, 1983—; sr. v.p. Ornda So. Fla., 1993—; pres., chmn. Golden Glades Gen. Hosp., 1991—; mem. sch. bldg. com. U. Miami Law Sch., 1989—; bd. dirs. Kendall Hosp., 1989—; coord. health needs for Pope John Paul II's U.S. Visit, 1987. Mem. jud. nominating commn. 3rd dist. ct. appeals. Mem. Am. Coll. Hosp. Adminstrs., jud. nominating commn. Fla. Supreme Ct., 1992—, So. Fla. Hosp. Assn. (pres.

1979-80), Broward County Hosp. Assn. (pres. 1978-79), Fla. League Hosps. (pres. 1974-75), Fedn. Am. Hosps. (dir. 1973-74), Hosp. Fin. Mgmt. Assn. (dir. 1971-72), Plantation C. of C. (pres. 1978-79), Kiwanis (v.p. 1978-79). Office: Ornda So Fla Miami FL 33152

NORINS, ARTHUR LEONARD, physician, educator; b. Chgo., Dec. 2, 1928; s. Russell Joseph and Elsie (Lindemann) N.; m. Mona Lisa Wetzer, Sept. 12, 1954; children: Catherine, Nan, Jane, Arthur. B.S. in Chem. Engring, Northwestern U., 1951, M.S. in Physiology, 1953, M.D., 1955. Diplomate: Am. Bd. Dermatology; subcert. in dermatopathology. Intern U. Mich., Ann Arbor, 1955-56; resident in dermatology Northwestern U., Chgo., 1956-59; asst. prof. Stanford U., 1961-64; prof., chmn. dept. dermatology, prof. pathology Ind. U. Sch. Medicine, Indpls., 1964-93, prof. emeritus, 1993—; mem. staff Riley Children's Hosp.; Wishard Hosp., Univ. Hosp.; cons. VA Hosp. Contbr. articles to profl. jours. Capt. M.C. U.S. Army, 1959-61. Recipient Pres.' award Ind. U., 1979. Fellow ACP; mem. Am. Acad. Dermatology (bd. dirs.), Am. Dermatol. Assn., Soc. Pediatric Dermatology (founder, past pres.), Am. Soc. Dermatopathology, Am. Soc. Photobiology (founder), Soc. Investigative Dermatology. Home: 1234 Kirkham Ln Indianapolis IN 46260-1637 Office: 550 W University Blvd Ste 3240 Indianapolis IN 46202-5267

NORKUS, MICHAEL, management consultant; b. Stuttgart, W. Ger., July 4, 1946; came to U.S. 1973; s. Hans and Gisela (Fritz) N.; m. Andrea G. Gluck, June 13, 1975; 1 child, Tyler David. MBA, Harvard U., 1975; PhD, U. Hamburg, W.Ger., 1973; Law Diplome, U. Paris, 1971. V.p., dir. Boston Cons. Group, 1975-86; pres., founder Alliance Cons. Group, Cambridge, Mass., 1986—. Author: Market Dominance and Anti-Trust Law, 1976. Lt. W. German Navy, 1966-68. Office: Alliance Cons Group One Kendall Sq Bldg 700 Cambridge MA 02139

NORLAND, DONALD RICHARD, retired foreign service officer; b. Laurens, Iowa, June 14, 1924; s. Norman and Aletta (Brunsvold) N.; m. Patricia Bamman, Dec. 13, 1952; children: Richard Boyce, David, Patricia D. Student, Iowa State Tchrs. Coll., 1941-43, N.W. Mo. State Tchrs. Coll., 1943-44; BA, U. Minn., 1948, MS, 1950; postgrad., U. Mich., 1951-52, Grenoble (France) U., 1948-49. Instr. history and polit. sci. U. No. Iowa, 1949-51; teaching fellow U. Mich., 1951-52; with Fgn. Svc., U.S. Dept. State, 1952-81; posts include Rabat, Morocco, 1952-56, Washington, 1956-58, Abidjan, Ivory Coast, 1958-60; mem. NATO del., Paris, 1961-63, NATO delegation, The Hague, The Netherlands, 1964-69; dep. chief mission Conakry, Guinea, 1970-72; U.S. Dept. State fellow Stanford (Calif.) U., 1969-70; dep. dir. Office Mil. Assistance and Sales, Bur. Politico-Mil. Affairs, Dept. State, Washington, 1972-73, chief polit. officers counseling br. Office Pers., 1973-75; dep. dir. Office Mgmt. Ops., 1975-76; amb. to Botswana, Lesotho and Swaziland Gaborone, Botswana, 1976-79; amb. to Chad, 1979-81; ret. Fgn. Svc., U.S. Dept. State, 1981; lectr. African affairs; internat. cons., specialist econ. devel.; chmn. African studies Fgn. Svc. Inst. of U.S. Dept. State, Washington, 1987-89; program dir. Ctr. for Internat. Pvt. Enterprise affiliate U.S. C. of C., Washington, 1990-91. Bd. dirs. Calvert New Africa Fund, 1995. Lt. (j.g.) USNR, 1943-46. Mem. Am. Fgn. Svc. Assn. (v.p. for retirees 1993—, sr. policy advisor 1991—, mem. governing bd., mem. editorial bd. Fgn. Svc. Jour. 1992—). Home: 4000 Cathedral Ave NW Apt 138B Washington DC 20016-5249

NORLANDER, JOHN ALLEN, hotel executive; b. Chgo., Nov. 19, 1930; s. Everett C. and Anna (Hall) N.; m. Diana A. Dahl, June 29, 1957; children: Lisa D., Erik D., Krist D., Britt H. Student, Carleton Coll., 1948-50; BS in Hotel Adminstrn., Cornell U., 1953; PhD (hon.), Johnson and Wales U., 1991. Sales mgr. Hilton Hotels, Chgo., 1956-59; nat. sales mgr. Hilton Hotels, Washington, 1959-60; exec. asst. mgr. Hilton Hotels, Chgo., 1960-64; gen. mgr. Hilton Hotels, St. Paul, 1966-68, Washington, 1968-70, Beverly Hills, Calif., 1970-75; exec. v.p. Radisson Hotel Corp., Mpls., 1975-83, pres., 1984—; v.p. Carlson Cos., 1984—; bd. dirs. Radamer Point Venture, Moscow, Diamond Cruise, Helsinki, Finland. Bd. dirs. Ednl. Inst., Lansing, Mich., Mpls. Conv. Bur. With USN, 1953-56, Korea. Recipient cert. of merit Calif. Hotel Assn., 1975. Mem. Am. Hotel Mgrs. Assn. (cert.), Chaine des Rotisseurs (chevallier). Avocations: oil painting, tennis.

NORLING, JAMES A., electronics company executive. BSEE, U. Ill., 1964, MSEE, 1965. Engring. trainee Motorola Inc., Schaumburg, Ill., 1965-70, ops. mgr. spl. products, 1970-71, ops. mgr. bipolar digital integrated cir. businesses, timepiece electric ops. mgr., bipolar ops. planning mgr., power metal transistors ops. mgr., 1971-73, power products dir. ops., 1973-79, gen. mgr. power products div., 1979-83, sr. v.p., gen. mgr. internat. group semicondr., 1981-85, sr. v.p., asst. gen. mgr. semicondr. products sector, 1985-86, exec. v.p., gen. mgr. semicondr. products sector, 1986—. Office: Motorola Inc Semiconductor Products Sector 56th St & Thomas Ave Phoenix AZ 85008

NORMAN, ALBERT GEORGE, JR., lawyer; b. Birmingham, Ala., May 29, 1929; s. Albert G. and Ila Mae (Carroll) N.; m. Catherine Marshall DeShazo, Sept. 3, 1955; children: Catherine Marshall, Albert George III. B.A., Auburn U., 1953; LL.B., Emory U., 1958; M.A., U.N.C., 1960. Bar: Ga. 1957. Assoc. Moise, Post & Gardner, Atlanta, 1958-60, ptnr., 1960-62; ptnr. Hansell & Post, Atlanta, 1962-86, Long, Aldridge & Norman, Atlanta, 1986—; dir. Atlanta Gas Light Co. Served with USAAF, 1946-49. Mem. ABA, Ga. Bar Assn., Atlanta Bar Assn., Lawyers Club Atlanta (pres. 1973-74), Am. Law Inst., Am. Judicature Soc. (dir. 1975-78), Old War Horse Lawyers Club, (pres. 1991-92), Cherokee Town and Country Club. Episcopalian.

NORMAN, ANTHONY WESTCOTT, biochemistry educator; b. Ames, Iowa, Jan. 19, 1938; s. A. Geoffrey and Marian Ester (Foote) N.; children—Thea C., Jacqueline E., Derek P.G. M.S., U. Wis., 1960, Ph.D., 1963. From asst. prof. to prof. dept. biochemistry U. Calif., Riverside, 1963—, chmn. dept.; 1975-80, prof. biomedical scis., 1986—, divisional dean biomed. scis., 1986-91; asst. dean UCLA Sch. Medicine, 1986-91. Recipient Ernst Oppenheimer award Endocrine Soc., 1977; Prix Andre Lichwitz award French Govt., 1981; Fulbright fellow, 1970. Mem. AAAS, Am. Inst. Nutrition (Mead Johnson award 1977, Osborne-Mendel award 1989), Am. Chem. Soc., Am. Soc. Biol. Chemists. Home: 7225 Lenox Ave Riverside CA 92504-4922 Office: U of Calif-Riverside Dept of Biochemistry Riverside CA 92521

NORMAN, ARNOLD McCALLUM, JR., engineer; b. Little Rock, May 1, 1940; s. Arnold McCallum and Ann Carolyn (Gibson) N.; m. Sylvia Burton, July 1, 1962 (div. 1967); m. Marisha Irene Malin, June 7, 1969; children: Frank Lee, Paul James. BS in Physics, Ga. Inst. Tech., 1962. Test engr. Rocketdyne div. Rockwell Internat., Canoga Park, Calif., 1962-64, engr. in charge of various programs, 1964-75, engr. in charge, project engr. large chem. lasers, 1975-85, project engr. space sta. propulsion system, 1985-87, project engr. nat. launch system health mgmt. systems, 1987-92, project engr. kinetic energy weapons, 1993-94; project engr. advanced propulsion systems Rockwell Internat., Canoga Park, Calif., 1994-95, sr. engring. specialist, 1995—; mem. ops. com. health mgmt. ctr. U. Cin., 1988-94; mem. program com. Am Internat. Conf. on Engring. Applications of Artificial Intelligence, 1988-90; presenter in field. Mem. editorial bd. Jour. Applied Intelligence, 1990—; author numerous papers in field. Fellow AIAA (assoc., section chair sr. adv. com. 1991-93, SFV sect., chmn. 1989-90, system effectiveness & safety tech. com. 1995—), Inst. Advancement Engring; mem. Tau Beta Pi. Home: 20238 Mobile St Canoga Park CA 91306-4241 Office: Rockwell Internat Rocketdyne divsn 6633 Canoga Ave Canoga Park CA 91303-2790

NORMAN, CHARLES HENRY, broadcasting executive; b. St. Louis, June 13, 1920; s. Charles Henry and Grace Vincent (Francis) N. BS, U. So. Calif., L.A., 1942. Announcer WIL, KSTL Radio Stas., St. Louis, 1948-55; owner Norman Broadcasting Co. St. Louis, 1961—. Lt. USN, 1943-45. Mem. St. Louis Ambassadors, Phi Kappa Phi. Congregation. Office: Portland Towers 275 Union Blvd Ste 1315 Saint Louis MO 63108-1231

NORMAN, COLIN ARTHUR, astrophysics educator; b. Melbourne, Australia, May 3, 1948; came to U.S., 1984; s. Howard Arthur Norman and Jean Olice (Macgregor) Downing; m. Wen Shen, June 2, 1988; children: Alexandra Jean, Arthur Shen, Victoria Amelia. BE with honours, U. Melbourne,

1969; DPhil, Oxford U., 1973. Rsch. fellow Magdalen Coll., Oxford (Eng.) U., 1973-77, U. Calif., Berkeley, 1975-77; asst. prof. U. Leiden (Netherlands), 1977-84; prof. physics and astronomy Johns Hopkins U., Balt., 1984—, head acad. affairs div. Space Telescope Sci. Inst., 1987-91, head Hubble Fellow program Space Telescope Sci. Inst., 1991—; sr. rsch. fellow Inst. Astronomy, Cambridge, Eng., 1981-84, European So. Obs., Munich, 1983-84; vis. prof. U. Paris, 1983; bd. dirs. Norman Bros. Pty. Ltd., Melbourne; trustee Norman Family Trusts, Melbourne. Editor: Stellar Populations, 1987, Quasar Absorption Lines, 1988, Massive Stars and Star Formations, 1991; contbr. articles to astrophysics jours. Rhodes scholar, 1970-73. Fellow Royal Astron. Soc.; mem. Am. Phys. Soc., Am. Astron. Soc., Amnesty Internat., Greenpeace, Johns Hopkins Club, Hamilton St. Club. Office: Johns Hopkins U Dept Physics and Astronomy Baltimore MD 21218

NORMAN, DAVID A., business equipment company executive; b. St. Paul, Nov. 15, 1935; s. Robert Albin and Nellie (Williams) N.; m. M. Ruth Landrum, July 19, 1959; children: David, Susan. BS in Mech. Engring., U. Minn., 1963; MS in Indsl. Engring., Stanford U., 1966. Engr. Lockheed Missiles and Space Co., Sunnyvale, Calif., 1963-67; project leader Stanford Research Inst., Calif., 1967-69; v.p., dir. Creative Strategies, Inc., Palo Alto, Calif., 1969-71; pres., chief exec. officer Dataquest, Inc., San Jose, Calif. 1971-82; pres., chief exec. officer Businessland, Inc., San Jose 1982—. Served with USN, 1955-60.

NORMAN, DONALD ARTHUR, cognitive scientist; b. N.Y.C., Dec. 25, 1935; s. Noah N. and Miriam F. N.; m. Martha Karpati (div.); children—Cynthia, Michael; m. Julie Jacobsen; 1 child, Eric. B.S.E.E., MIT, 1957; M.S.E.E., U. Pa., 1959, Ph.D. in Psychology, 1962; degree in Psychology (hon.), U. Padua, Italy, 1995. Lectr. Harvard U., 1962-66; Prof. dept. psychology U. Calif.-San Diego, La Jolla, 1966-92, prof. emeritus, 1992—, prof., chair dept. cognitive sci., 1988-92, chair dept.psychology, 1974-78, dir. cognitive sci. program, 1977-88, dir. Inst. for Cognitive Sci., 1981-89; Apple fellow Apple Computer Inc., Cupertino, Calif., 1993—; mem. sci. adv. bd. Naval Pers. Rsch. Ctr., San Diego, 1982-86; cons. to industry on human interaction and user-centered design. Author: Learning and Memory, 1982, Human Information Processing, 2d edit., 1977, User Centered System Design, 1986, The Psychology of Everyday Things, 1988, The Design of Everyday Things, 1989, Turn Signals Are the Facial Expressions of Automobiles, 1992, Things That Make Us Smart, 1993; editor: Perspectives on Cognitive Science, 1981, Exploration in Cognition, 1975, Cognitive Sci. Jour., 1981-85; series editor Cognitive Sci. Series Lawrence Earlbaum Assoc., 1979—. Recipient Excellence in Rsch. award U. Calif., 1984. Fellow Am. Psychol. Soc., Am. Acad. Arts and Scis.; mem. Am. Assn. Arts and Scis., Am. Assn. for Artificial Intelligence, Assn. for Computational Machinery, Cognitive Sci. Soc. (chmn. founding mem.). Office: Apple Computer Inc MS 301-4UE 1 Infinite Loop Cupertino CA 95014

NORMAN, DUDLEY KENT, hospital administrator, nurse; b. Cleve., July 27, 1949; s. George R. and Coral L. (Henrickson) N.; m. Martha Alice; children: David, Nicholas. BS in Edn., MEd, Kent State U., 1976; BS in Nursing, Case Western Res. U., 1976; MS, MSN, Tex. Women's U., 1981; EdD, U. Houston, 1990. RN; cert. nursing home administr. Tchr. Beachwood City Schs., Cleve., 1972-74; clin. nurse Univ. Hosp., Cleve., 1976-78; asst. administr. Parkland Hosp., Dallas, 1979-83, St. Lukes Hosp./Tex. Heart Inst., Tex. Children's Hosp., Houston, 1983-84; asst. dean U. Tex. Med. Sch., Houston, 1984-85; administr. U. Tex. Mental Scis. Inst., Houston, 1985-87; asst. administr. U. Tex.-Harris County Psychiat. Ctr., Houston, 1987-90; administr. U. Tex. Med. Br., Galveston, 1990—; cons. St. Lukes Hosp., N.Y.C., 1980; dir. nurse tng. Bd. Nurse Examiners Approved Program, Dallas, 1979-81. Recipient Chemistry Scholar prize Lubrizol Found., Cleve., 1971, Cushing Robb prize Case Western Res. U., Cleve., 1976; named One of Outstanding Young Men of Am., U.S. Jaycees, 1978. Fellow Am. Coll. Health Care Execs.; mem. ANA, Assn. for Study of Higher Edn., Healthcare Fin. Mgmt. Assn., Sigma Theta Tau. Methodist. Office: U Tex Med Br Galveston TX 77550

NORMAN, E. GLADYS, business computer educator, consultant; b. Oklahoma City, June 13, 1933; d. Joseph Eldon and Mildred Lou (Truitt) Biggs; m. Joseph R.R. Radeck, Mar. 1, 1953 (div. Aug. 1962); children: Jody Matti, Ray Norman, Warren Norman (dec. May 1993), Dana Norman; m. Leslie P. Norman, Aug. 26, 1963 (dec. Feb. 1994); 1 child, Elayne Pearce. Student, Fresno (Calif.) State Coll., 1951-52, UCLA, 1956-59, Linfield Coll., 1986-95. Math. aid U.S. Naval Weapons Ctr., China Lake, Calif., 1952-56, computing systems specialist, 1957-68; systems programmer Oreg. Motor Vehicles Dept., Salem, 1968-69; instr. in data processing, dir. Computer Programming Ctr., Salem, 1969-72; instr. in data processing Merritt-Davis Bus. Coll., Salem, 1972-73; sr. programmer, analyst Teledyne Wah Chang, Albany, Oreg., 1973-79; sr. systems analyst Oreg. Dept. Vets. Affairs, Albany, 1979-80; instr. in bus. computers Linn-Benton Community Coll., Albany, 1980-95; ret., 1995; computer cons. for LBCC Ret. Sr. Vol. Program, 1995—; presenter computer software seminars State of Oreg., 1991-93, Oreg. Credit Assoc. Conf., 1991, Oreg. Regional Users Group Conf., 1992; computer cons. in field. Mem. Data Processing Mgmt. Assn. (bd. dirs. 1977-84, 89-95, sec. 1995, assoc. v.p. 1988, Diamond Individual Performance award 1985). Democrat. Avocations: family, sewing, crocheting. Office: Linn-Benton CC Bus Mgmt Dept 6500 Pacific Blvd SW Albany OR 97321-3755

NORMAN, GEOFFREY ROBERT, financial executive; b. Orpington, Kent, Eng., Jan. 31, 1944; came to U.S., 1968, naturalized, 1974; s. Leonard Robert and Minnie Rose (Carter) N.; m. Christina Norman, June 8, 1968; children—Catarina, Camilla. B.A., St. Catharine's Coll., Cambridge, Eng., 1966, M.A., 1968. Corp. auditor Gen. Electric Co., Schenectady, 1971-74, comptroller GE Española, Bilbao, Spain, 1974-78, cons. corp. fin., Fairfield, Conn., 1978-81, mgr. fin., Bridgeport, Conn., 1981-83; v.p., treas. Gen. Electric Fin. Services, Inc. and Gen. Electric Capital Corp., N.Y.C., 1983-85, Stamford, Conn., 1985-88; exec. v.p. GE Investments, 1988—. State scholar U.K. Govt., 1962, Open Exhbn. scholar St. Catharine's Coll., 1962. Office: GE Investments 3003 Summer St Stamford CT 06905-4317

NORMAN, GREG, professional golfer; b. Mt. Isa, Australia, Feb. 10, 1955. Profl. golfer, 1976—. Winner Martini Internat., 1977, 79, 81, French Open, 1980, Australian Open, 1980, 85, 87, Dunlop Masters, 1981, 82, Hong Kong Open, 1981, Australian Masters 1981, 83, 84, 87, 89, 90 State Express Classic, 1982, Benson and Hedges, 1982, Canadian Open, 1984, 92, Kemper Open, 1984, Las Vegas Invitational, 1986, Kemper Open, 1986, British Open, 1986, 93, European Open, 1986, Suntory World Match, 1986, Queensland Open, 1986, New South Wales Open, 1985, 86, 88, Australian Tournament Players Championship, 1988, 89, Heritage Classic, 1988, Italian Open, 1988, Doral Ryder Open, 1990, 93, Memorial Tournament, 1990, Tournament Players Championship, 1994, Johnnie Walker Asian Classic, 1994. Leading Money Winner PGA Tour 1986, 90. Address: Great White Shark Enterprises Inc PO Box 1189 Hobe Sound FL 33475-1189*

NORMAN, HOWARD A., writer; b. Toledo, Mar. 4, 1949; s. Lawrence and Estelle N.; m. Jane Shore; 1 child, Emma. Instr. U. Md. Translator: The Wishing Bone Cycle: Narrative Poems from the Swampy Cree Indians, 1976, The Woe Shirt: Caribbean Folk Tales, 1980, Where the Chill Came From: Cree Windigo Tales and Journeys, 1982; author: The Owl Scatterer, 1986, The Northern Lights, 1987 (Nat. Book award nomination 1987), Who Paddled-Backward-with-Trout, 1987, Kiss in the Hotel Joseph Conrad and Other Stories, 1989, How Glooskap Outwits the Ice Giants: And Other Tales of the Maritime Indians, 1989, The Bird Artist, 1994 (Nat. Book award nomination 1994); editor: Coyote Stories for Children, 1991, Northern Tales, 1994. Whiting Found. grantee, 1987. Office: Univ of Maryland Dept of English College Park MD 20742-0001*

NORMAN, JACK LEE, church administrator, consultant; b. Lancaster, Ohio, Aug. 5, 1938; s. Clarence Herbert and Jeanette Belle (Bennett) N.; m. Boneda Mae Coppock, June 30, 1957; children: Anthony Lee, Becky Lynn Norman Huss. Student, Circleville Bible Coll., Olivet U. Ordained min. Ch. of Christ, 1961. Pastor Chs. of Christ in Christian Union, Chillicothe, Ohio, 1959-62, 65-90, Winchester, Ohio, 1962-65; dist. supt. Chs. of Christ in Christian Union, Circleville, Ohio, 1990—; trustee Chs. of Christ in Christian Union, mem. dist. bd., mem. ch. ext. bd., mem. bd. exam. and ordination, mem. Evang. Christian Youth Bd. Trustee Circleville Bible Coll. Sgt.

USNG, 1956-59. Avocations: fishing, boating, classic cars. Office: Ch of Christ in Christian Union PO Box 30 Circleville OH 43113-0030

NORMAN, JESSYE, soprano; b. Augusta, Ga., Sept. 15, 1945; d. Silas Sr. and Janie (King) N. B.M. cum laude, Howard U., 1967; postgrad., Peabody Conservatory, 1967; M.Mus., U. Mich., 1968; MusD (hon.), U. South, 1984, Boston Conservatory, 1984, U. Mich., 1987, U. Edinburgh, 1989, Cambridge U., 1989. Debut, Deutsche Oper, Berlin, 1969, Italy, 1970; appeared: in operas Die Walküre, Idomeneo, L'Africaine, Marriage of Figaro, Aida, Don Giovanni, Tannhauser, Gotterdammerung, Ariadne auf Naxos, Les Troyens, Dido and Aeneas, Oedipus Rex, Hérodiade, Les Contes d'Hoffmann; debut in operas, La Scala, Milan, Italy, 1972, Salzburg Festival, 1977, U.S. debut, Hollywood Bowl, 1972, appeared with, Tanglewood Festival, Mass., also Edinburgh (Scotland) Festival, debut, Covent Garden, 1972; appeared in 1st Great Performers recital, Lincoln Center, N.Y.C., 1973—; other guest performances include, L.A. Philharm. Orch., Boston Symphony Orch., Am. Symphony Orch., Chgo. Symphony Orch., San Francisco Symphony Orch., Cleve. Orch., Detroit Symphony, N.Y. Philharm. Orch., London Symphony Orch., London Philharm. Orch., BBC Orch., Israel Philharm. Orch., Orchestre de Paris, Nat. Symphony Orch., English Chamber Orch., Royal Philharm., London Phila. Orch., Milw. Symphony Orch., Stockholm Philharm. Orch., Vienna Philharm. Orch., Berlin Philharm. Orch.; tours, Europe, S. Am., Australia, numerous recs., Columbia, EMI, Philips Records; PBS TV spcls. include Kathleen Battle and Jessye Norman Sing Spirituals, 1991, Concert at Avery Fisher Hall, 1994. Recipient 1st prize Bavarian Radio Corp. Internat. Music Competition, 1968, Grand Prix du Disque, Acad. du Disque Francais, 1973, 76, 77, 82, 84, Deutsche Schallplatten, Preis, 1975, 81, Alumni award U. Mich., 1982, Outstanding Musician of Yr. award Musical Am., 1982, Grand Prix du Disque Academie Charles Cros, 1983, Commandeur de l'Ordre des Arts et des Lettres, France, 1984, Grammy awards, 1980, 82, 85, numerous other awards; named hon. life mem. Girl Scouts U.S., 1987. Mem. Royal Acad. Music (hon.), Alpha Kappa Alpha, Gamma Sigma Sigma, Sigma Alpha Iota, Pi Kappa Lambda. Club: Friday Morning Music (Washington). Office: care Shaw Concerts Inc 1900 Broadway New York NY 10023-7004*

NORMAN, JOE G., JR., chemistry educator, college dean; b. Brevard, N.C., Aug. 8, 1947; s. Josephus Gaston and Nelle Livingston (Bookout) N. BA in Chemistry, Rice U., 1969; PhD in Chemistry, MIT, 1972. Asst. prof. U. Wash., Seattle, 1972-77, assoc. prof., 1977-82, prof., 1982—, assoc. dean grad. sch., 1980-87, dean arts and scis., 1987—; bd. dirs. Wash. Tech. Ctr., Biomembrane Inst., CARE Northwest; cons. Monsanto Co., Gen. Motors, Bell Labs., Boeing, 1976-82; proposal reviewer NSF, Am. Chem. Soc., Research Corp., 1974—; invited lectr. various universities and socs., 1976-80. Editorial bd. Jour. Computational Chemistry, 1980-89. Mem. Seattle-King County Leadership Tomorrow, 1985-86, Seattle-King County Mcpl. League, 1985—, Wash. Environ. Coun., Seattle, 1971—; bd. dirs. Seattle Repertory Theatre, Pacific Northwest Ballet. Alfred P. Sloan Found. fellow, 1978-80; NSF research grantee, 1976-83, Am. Chem. Soc. research grantee, 1972-83. Mem. Am. Crystallography Assn., Henry Gallery Assn. (bd. dirs. 1987). Avocations: photography, internat. natural history, performing arts. *

NORMAN, JOHN BARSTOW, JR., designer, educator; b. Paloa, Kans., Feb. 5, 1940; s. John B. and Ruby Maxine (Johnson) N.; m. Roberta Jeanne Martin, June 6, 1967; children: John Barstow III, Elizabeth Jeanne. BFA, U. Kans., 1962, MFA, 1966. Designer and illustrator Advt. Design, Kansas City, Mo., 1962-64; asst. instr. U. Kans., Lawrence, 1964-66; art dir. Hallmark Cards, Inc., Kansas City, Mo., 1966-69; instr. dept. art U. Denver, 1969-73, asst. prof., 1973-78, assoc. prof., 1978—, Disting. prof., 1980; sr. designer Mo. Coun. Arts and Humanities, 1966-67; cons. designer Rocky Mountain Bank Note Corp., Denver, 1971—; Signage Identity System, U. Dever; bd. dirs. communications U. Denver; tech. cons. Denver Art Mus., 1974—, designed exhbns., 1974-75; adv., cons. Jefferson County (Colo.) Sch., System, 1976—; chmn. Design and Sculpture Exhbn., Colo. Celebration of the Arts, 1975-76. One man shows include: Gallery Cortina, Aspen, Colo., 1983; commd. works include: Jedda, Saudi Arabia, Synegistics Corp., Denver; represented in permanent collections Pasadena Ctr. for the Arts, N.Y. Art Dirs. Club, Calif. State U./Fiber Collection, Pasadena (Calif.) Ctr. for the Arts, 1984, N.Y. Art Dirs. Club, 1985 Midland Art Coun./Fiber Collection, 1985, Geologic Soc. Am.; represented in traveling exhbns. L.A. Art Dirs. Show and N.Y. Art Dirs. Show, U.S., Europe, Japan, 1985; fearured in Denver Post, 1984, Post Electric City Mag., 1984, Rocky Mt. News, 1984, Douglas County Press, 1984, Mile High Cable Vision, 1985, Sta. KWGN-TV, 1985, Les Krantz's Am. Artists, 1988, Illustrated Survey of Leading Contemporaries, 1988, U.S. Surface Design Jour., 1988; co-work represented in film collection Mus. Modern Art, N.Y.C.; selected fashion show designs displayed to Sister City dels., Denver, 1987. Co-recipient Silver Medal award N.Y. Internat. Film and Video Competition, 1976, Design awards Coun. Advancement and Support of Edn., 1969, 71, 73, 76, Honor Mention award L.A. Art Dirs. Club, 1984, Honor Mention award N.Y. Art Dirs. Club, 1984, Native Am. Wearable Art Competition, 1985, 5th pl. Nat. Wind Sail Am. Banners Competition, Midland, Mich., 1985, also awards for surface designs in Colo. Ctr. for the Arts Wearable Art Competition, 1984-85, Foothills Art Gallery Nat. Wearable Art Competition, 1984-85, Fashion Group of Denver Competition, 1984-85. Mem. Art Dirs. Club Denver (Gold medals 1974-82, Best of Show Gold medal 1983, Honor Mention award, 1984, 3 Gold medals 1989), Univ. Art Dirs. Assn. Home: PO Box 302 751 Willow Lake Dr Franktown CO 80116 Office: U Denver Sch Art 2121 E Asbury Ave Denver CO 80208-0001

NORMAN, LALANDER STADIG, insurance company executive; b. Binford, N.D., Apr. 10, 1912; s. John and Corinne (Stadig) N.; m. Garnet Johnston, Nov. 8, 1941; children: Eric John, Martha Mary Norman Neely, Carol Jean Norman Wellborn, Shirley Ann Norman Cook. A.B., U. Mich., 1935, M.B.A., 1937. Actuarial asst. Central Life Ins. Co. of Ill., Chgo., 1937-40; mgr. Eastern dept. Central Life Ins. Co. of Ill., 1940-41; actuary Mich. Life Ins. Co., Detroit, 1941-43; asst. actuary Guarantee Mut. Life Co., Omaha, 1946-49; asso. actuary Am. United Life Ins. Co., Indpls., 1949; actuary Am. United Life Ins. Co., 1950-77, dir., 1959-77, v.p., exec. Sr. v.p., 1969-77; ret., 1977; bd. mgrs. AUL Fund B, 1969-84, chmn., 1973-84; actuary Ind. Dept. Ins., 1977-79. Bd. dirs. Cypress Village Assn., 1981, 83-85. Served with USNR, 1943-46. Recipient Navy Commendation award, 1946, Theta Xi Distinguished Service award, 1958. Fellow Soc. Actuaries; mem. Am. Acad. Actuaries, Indpls. Actuarial Club (past pres.), Woodland Country Club (Carmel), Sugarmill Woods Golf and Racquet Club, So. Woods Golf Club, Phi Beta Kappa, Theta Xi (regional dir. 1953-59), Phi Kappa Phi, Beta Gamma Sigma. Republican. Home: Sugarmill Woods 21 Graytwig Ct W Homosassa FL 34446 Office: 1 American Sq Indianapolis IN 46204-1926

NORMAN, MARSHA, playwright; b. Louisville, Sept. 21, 1947; d. Billie Lee and Bertha Mae (Conley) Williams; m. Michael Norman (div. 1974); m. Dann C. Byck Jr., 1978 (div.); m. Timothy Dykman; 2 children: Angus, Katherine. B.A., Agnes Scott Coll., 1969; M.A.T., U. Louisville, 1971. Author: (plays) Getting Out, 1977 (John Gassner New Playwrights medalion, Outer Critics Circle award 1979, George Oppenheimer-Newsday award 1979), Third and Oak, 1978, Circus Valentine, 1979, The Holdup, 1980, 'Night, Mother, 1982 (Susan Smith Blackburn prize 1982, Tony award nomination for best play 1983, Pulitzer Prize for Drama 1983, Elizabeth Hull-Kate Warriner award Dramatists Guild 1983), Traveler in the Dark, 1984, Sarah and Abraham, 1987, D. Boone, 1992; (book of musical, lyrics) The Secret Garden, 1991 (Tony award for best book of musical 1991, Tony award nominee for best original score 1991, Drama Desk award for best book of musical 1991); (screenplay) 'Night, Mother, 1986; (teleplays) It's the Willingness, 1978, In Trouble at Fifteen, 1980, The Laundromat, 1985, Third and Oak: The Pool Hall, 1989, Face of a Stranger, 1991; (novel) The Fortune Teller, 1987; (collection) Four Plays by Marsha Norman, 1988. NEA grantee, 1978-79, Rockefeller playwright-in-residence grantee, 1979-80, Am. Acad. and Inst. for Arts and Letters grantee; recipient Lit. Lion award N.Y. Pub. Libr., 1986. Office: Jack Tantleff 375 Greenwich St Ste 700 New York NY 10013-2338*

NORMAN, PEGGY ROCKER, retired secondary school educator; b. Richland, Ga., Aug. 14, 1938; d. Evelyn (Rigdon) Bland Womack; m. L Roy Norman; children: Cecilia McAllister, Rodney. BSE, Ga. So. U., 1959;

MEd, U. Ga., 1976, EdS, 1985. Tchr., dept. head Dekalb County Schs., Decatur, Ga., 1962-65; tchr. Marietta (Ga.) City Schs., 1966; tchr., dept. head Cobb County Schs., Marietta, 1966-80; tchr. Lafayette (La.) Parish Schs., 1980-84; tchr., dept. head Cobb County Schs., Marietta, 1984-94; ret., 1994; supervising student tchrs. U. Ga., Marietta, 1985—. Outreach leader Holt Rd. Bapt. Ch., Marietta, 1990-92; active textbook adoption com., 1989, curriculum revision com. Parenting grantee Fed., 1987-90; named Tchr. of Yr., 1993. Mem. Am. Vocat. Assn., Ga. Vocat. Assn., Ga. Home Econs. Assn., Parent-Tchr.-Student Assn., 4-H Club (life), Phi Delta Kappa (treas. 1987, 88, 89), Alpha Delta Kappa. Republican. Avocations: sewing, gourmet cooking, spectator sports, shopping, playing cards. Home: 1269 Channel Park SW Marietta GA 30064

NORMAN, PETER MINERT, fundraising consulting company executive; b. Rochester, N.Y., Mar. 23, 1932; s. Jesse George and Doris (Colony) N.; m. Janet G. Wasson, Sept. 6, 1952; children: Susan Jane, Paula Lea, Christa MacLeod, Peter Minert II. BA, Trinity Coll., Hartford, Conn., 1954; MDiv, Yale U., 1957. Ordained priest Episcopal Ch., 1957; lic. nursing home administr. Curate St. Stephen's Episc. Ch., Rochester, 1957-60; rector Zion Episc. Ch., Avon, N.Y., 1960-68; cons. Health and housing programs, Rochester and Washington, 1968-73; dir. Ward, Dreshman, Reinhardt, Worthington, Ohio, 1973-77; v.p. Seabury Western Sem., Evanston, Ill., 1977-80; exec. dir. Cathedral Found., Jacksonville, Fla., 1980-82; chmn. CEO Ward, Dreshman & Reinhardt, Worthington, 1982-92, WDR Community Svcs., Worthington, 1990-92; exec. v.p. Goettler Assocs., Columbus, Ohio, 1992-93; corp. v.p. of devel. svcs. St. Francis Acad., Salina, Kans., 1993-94; dir. fund devel. Episcopal Retirement House, Cin., 1994—; pres. Clan MacLeod Soc. U.S.A., 1988-89; chmn. Dunvegan Fund, N.Y./Edinburgh, 1988; chmn. World Fundraising Counsel, Amsterdam, 1990-92. Author: How to Assure Successful Every Member Canvass, 1979, Hospital Prayer Book, 1958. Mem. Worthington Hills Country Club, Am. Assn. Fundraising Counsel (treas. 1989-90, vice-chmn. 1990-91), Phi Beta Kappa, Pi Gamma Mu. Republican. Home: 1308 Clubview Blvd S Columbus OH 43235-1643 Office: Episcopal Retirement Homes 3870 Virginia Ave Cincinnati OH 45227-3427

NORMAN, PHILIP SIDNEY, physician; b. Pittsburg, Kans., Aug. 4, 1924; s. P. Sidney and Mildred A. (Lawyer) N.; m. Marion Birmingham, Apr. 15, 1955; children: Margaret Reynolds, Meredith Andrew, Helen Elizabeth. A.B., Kans. State Coll., 1947; M.D. cum laude, Washington U., St. Louis, 1951. Intern Barnes Hosp., St. Louis, 1951-52; resident Vanderbilt U. Hosp., Nashville, 1952-54; fellow Rockefeller Inst., 1954-56; instr. medicine Johns Hopkins U. Sch. Medicine, Balt., 1956-59; asst. prof. Johns Hopkins U. Sch. Medicine, 1959-64, assoc. prof., 1964-75, prof., 1975—; chief allergy and immunology div., 1971-91. Editor Jour. of Allergy and Clin. Immunology, 1993—; contbr. chpt. to books, articles to profl. jours. Served with USAAF, 1943-46; Served with USPHS, 1954-56. Fellow Am. Acad. Allergy (pres. 1975); mem. Am. Fedn. Clin. Research, Am. Assn. Immunologists, Am. Soc. Clin. Investigation, Am. Assn. Physicians, N.Y. Acad. Scis., Soc. Exptl. Biology and Medicine, Am. Thoracic Soc., Am. Clin. and Climatol. Assn., Johns Hopkins Med. Soc., Alpha Omega Alpha. Episcopalian. Home: 13500 Manor Rd Baldwin MD 21013-9775 Office: Johns Hopkins U Asthma and Allergy Ctr 5501 Hopkins Bayview Cir Baltimore MD 21224-6821

NORMAN, RALPH DAVID, consulting psychologist, former university administrator; b. N.Y.C., June 2, 1915; s. Selig J. and Rose (Bernstein) N.; m. Rose Libovsky, Aug. 23, 1942; children—Robert, Patricia. B.S., CCNY, 1934; M.A., Columbia U., 1936; Ph.D., Ohio State U., 1946. Diplomate: Am. Bd. Profl. Psychology. Psychologist Juvenile Ct., N.Y.C., 1936-37, N.Y. State Prison, Dannemora, N.Y., 1937-38, Miss. State Hosp., Whitfield, 1938-39, U.S. Reformatory, Chillicothe, Ohio, 1939-40; personnel technician U.S. Army Air Force, Chanute Field, Ill., 1941-42; asst. prof. psychology Princeton U., 1947-48, U. Mich., 1948-49; faculty U. N.Mex., Albuquerque, 1949—; prof. U. N.Mex., 1957-80, prof. emeritus, 1980—; asso. dean Arts and Scis. Coll., 1970-80; pvt. practice, 1980—; mem. N.Mex. State Bd. Psychol. Examiners, chmn., 1963-66; cons. in field. Contbr. articles to profl. publs. Served with USNR, 1942-46. Fellow Am. Psychol. Assn.; mem. AAUP, Rocky Mountain Psychol. Assn. (pres. 1952-53), Sigma Xi, Phi Delta Kappa. Home: 5012 Sunningdale Ave NE Albuquerque NM 87110-5850

NORMAN, RALPH LOUIS, physicist, consultant; b. Kingston, Tenn., Mar. 25, 1933; s. Walter Hugh and Helen Irene (Smith) N.; m. Agnes Irene Pickel, Sept. 5, 1964; children: Mark Alan, Max Alvin. B.S., U. Tenn., 1959; LL.B., Blackstone Sch. Law, 1967, J.D., 1971; certificate, Indsl. Coll. Armed Forces, 1969; M.A. in Pub. Adminstrn, U. Okla., 1971; D.Sci. (hon.), Apollo Research Inst., 1976. Engr. Chrysler Corp. Missile Div., Huntsville, Ala., 1959-60; physicist Army Rocket & Guided Missile Agy., Redstone Arsenal, Ala., 1960-61; asst. project mgr. Army Missile Command, Redstone Arsenal, 1961-62; project mgr. Army Missile Command, 1962-89, ret., 1989; cons. to several def. contractors, 1989—; faculty Athens (Ala.) Coll., 1970-71, Calhoun Jr. Coll., Decatur, Ala., 1971-74, 85-90, U. Montevallo, Ala., 1973-74, U. Ala. at Huntsville, 1976-77, Columbia (Mo.) Coll., 1977-79; cons. firm Bishop and Sexton, 1973—, Athens (Ala.) State Coll.; reviewer NSF, 1974-76; FAA examiner. Contbr. articles profl. jours. Served with USN, 1951-55. Recipient Dept. Def. commendations, 1961, 65, Dept. Army commendation, 1972. Mem. N.Y. Acad. Scis., Assn. U.S. Army. Home: 13889 Dupree Worthy Rd Harvest AL 35749-9620 *I strive to make the knowledge gained through my research benefit all mankind.*

NORMAN, RICHARD ARTHUR, educator; b. Columbus, Ohio, July 11, 1915; s. Norman Oscar and Marie (Falter) Kuhnheim. BA, George Washington U., 1951; MA, Columbia U., 1952, PhD, 1957. Instr. Columbia U., N.Y.C., 1952-57; asst. prof. English Barnard Coll., 1957-64, assoc. prof., 1964-72, prof., 1972-81, spl. lectr., 1981-85, prof. emeritus, 1985—; instr. grad. div. Hunter Coll., 1960-62; Speech cons. CBS News, 1971-85; reader Talking Books Am. Found. for Blind, 1973-80. Radio announcer, producer, actor, 1934-50; commentator for chamber music concert; broadcast, from Library of Congress, Washington, 1948-50; Author: (with George W. Hibbitt) A Guide to Speech Training, 1964; radio series The Wonder of Words, 1962. Vice pres. Axe-Houghton Found., now emeritus. Served to capt. USAAF, 1942-45. Home: 9 Branchville Rd Ridgefield CT 06877

NORMAN, RONALD, church officer; b. Watertown, Wis., Mar. 1, 1945; m. Sandra Lang; children: Corey, Chanda, Cherie. Student, Carroll Coll.; BA, Sioux Falls Coll., 1968; MA, N.Am. Bapt. Sem., 1972, postgrad. Ordained pastor Bapt. Ch., 1972. Student pastor United Ch. of Christ, Valley Springs, S.D., 1971-72, 1st Presbyn. Ch., Bridgewater, S.D., 1970-71, St. Paul's Presbyn. Ch., Emergy, S.D., 1970-71; dir. church edn. and youth Bismarck (N.D.) Bapt. Ch., 1972-74, sr. pastor, 1974-79; sr. pastor Village Green Bapt. Ch., Glen Ellyn, Ill., 1982-86; dir. growth dept. Nat. Am. Bapt. Ch. Ext., 1982-86; sr. pastor 1st Bapt. Ch., Elk Grove, Calif., 1986—; moderator Nat. Am. Bapt. Coun. Office: North Am Baptist Con 1 S 210 Summit Ave Villa Park IL 60181

NORMAN, STEPHEN PECKHAM, financial services company executive; b. Norwich, Conn., May 20, 1942; s. Richard Leonard and Mary Ellen (Carr) N.; m. Jacqueline Mary Batten, June 29, 1968; children—Adrian Gates, Hilary Batten, Philip Douglas, Matthew Jeremy Mitchell. B.A., Yale U., 1964; J.D., U. Pa., 1967. Bar: Conn. 1967, N.Y. 1972. Atty. Am. Express Co., N.Y.C., 1970-78, v.p. corp. office, 1978-82, sec., 1982—; chmn. NYSE Commn. on Shareholder Comm. Served to sgt. U.S. Army, 1968-70; Vietnam. Mem. Conn. Bar Assn., N.Y. Bar Assn., Am. Soc. Corp. Secs. (chmn.), U.S. Working Com. Group 30. Republican. Episcopalian. Club: Am. Yacht (Rye). Home: 6 Highland Park Pl Rye NY 10580-1736 Office: Am Express Co World Fin Ctr 200 Vesey St New York NY 10285-0001

NORMAN, WILLIAM STANLEY, travel and tourism executive; b. Roper, N.C., Apr. 27, 1938; s. James Colbitt and Josephine Cleo (Woods) N.; m. Elizabeth Patricia Patterson, May 31, 1969; children: Lisa Renée, William Stanley II. BS, West Va. Wesleyan U., 1960; MA, Am. U., 1967; exec. program, Stanford U., 1976. Math. tchr. Washington High Sch., Norfolk, 1961; commd. USN, 1962; advanced through grades to comdr., 1971; naval flight officer Airborne Early Warning Squadron Eleven, 1962-65; asst. combat info. ctr. officer U.S.S. Constellation, 1965; staff officer air weapons systems analysis Office Chief Naval Ops., Pentagon, Washington, 1965-66; history and fgn. affairs instr. U.S. Naval Acad., 1967-69; social aide The White House, 1967-69; carrier div. staff officer SE Asia, 1969-70, spl. asst. to Chief Naval Ops. for Minority Affairs, 1970-72, asst. to Chief Naval Ops. for Spl. Projects, 1972-73; dir. corp. action Cummins Engine Co. Inc., Columbus, Ind., 1973-74, exec. dir. corp. responsibility, 1974-76; exec. mktg. mgr., 1976-77; exec. dir. distbn. mktg. Cummins Engine Co. Inc., Columbus, Ind., 1977-78; v.p. eastern divsn., 1978-79; v.p. sales and mktg. Amtrak, Washington, 1979-81, group v.p., 1981-84, exec. v.p., 1984-94; pres., CEO Travel Industry Assn. of Am., Washington, 1994—; chmn. adv. coun. on travel and tourism industry U.S. Senate Com. on Commerce, Sci. and Transp.; bd. dirs. CPC Internat., Englewood Cliffs, N.J., Logistics Mgmt. Inst., McLean, Va. Bd. dirs. USN Meml. Found., Washington, 1980—; bd. visitors Am. U. Kogod Sch. of Bus. Capt. USNR. Mem. Travel Industry Assn. Am. (bd. dirs. 1980—, chmn. bd. 1987-89, chmn. bd. dirs. of found. 1990-92), UN Assn. U.S. (bd. dirs. 1983—, bd. govs. 1985—), Coun. on Fgn. Rels., Inst. Cert. Travel. Agts., Bretton Woods Com., Travel and Tourism Govt. Affairs Coun. (bd. dirs. 1988—). Democrat. Episcopalian. Avocations: golf, tennis, jogging, walking, cycling. Home: 1308 Timberly Ln Mc Lean VA 22102-2504 Office: Travel Industry Assn of Am 1100 New York Ave Ste 450 Washington DC 20005-3934

NORMAND, ROBERT, lawyer; b. Montreal, Que., Can., Sept. 24, 1936; s. Lucien and Eva (Rochon) N.; m. Madeleine Scott, Sept. 16, 1961; children: Eric, Yves, Genevieve. BA, U. Montreal, 1956; LLL, U. Sherbrooke, Que., 1960; diploma, Inst. d'etudes politiques, Paris, 1962. Bar: Que. 1960. Legal adviser Nat. Assembly, Quebec City, 1962-67, law clk., 1967-71; asst. dep. min. justice Que. Govt., Quebec City, 1970-71, dep. min. justice, 1971-77, dep. min. intergovtl. affairs, 1977-82, dep. min. fin., 1982-87; pres., pub. Le Soleil (Hollinger), Quebec City, 1987-93; v.p. corp. affairs UniMedia Inc., 1993-94, dep. min. internat. affairs, 1994—; bd. dirs. Credit Lyonnais Can., Montreal, 1989-94; sec. Study Com. on Expropriation 1967-69; guest prof. legislation law faculty Laval U., Ottawa U., 1971; pres. Que. Policy Inst., 1974; chmn. Com. Supervising Olympic Security, 1974-76; chmn. Uniform Law Conf. Can; dir. Caisse de Dèpot et Placement du Quèbec, 1982-87; v.p. Can. delegation Diplomatic Conf. on travel contracts, Brussels, 1970; pres. Can. delegation at convs. Internat. Inst. French Lang. Law, 1974, 76. V.p. Hosp. du Saint-Sacrement, Quebec City, 1988-94; vice chmn. Inst. Rsch. on Pub. Policy, Montreal, 1988-94; pres. Que. Symphony Orch., Quebec City, 1989-92; consul gen. Sweden, Quebec City, 1989-94; co-pres. United Way Campaign Greater Quebec Region, 1989, hon. chmn. Telethon for Cerebral Palsy, 1990; mem. Citizens Forum, Spicer Commn., 1990-91. Capt. Can. Army, 1954-60. Named Queen's Counsel, 1971; recipient Pub. Adminstrn. award of excellence Nat. Sch. Pub. Adminstrn. Alumni, Quebec City, 1986. Mem. Investment Dealers Assn. Can. (dir. 1989-94), Que. Garrison Club (dir. 1991-94), Profl. Liability Ins. of Que. Bar (dir. 1991-94), Que. Bar (supervisory com. 1988-93), Can. Bar Assn., la Commanderie de Bordeaux, l'Ordre Internat. des Anysetiers. Roman Catholic. Avocations: fishing, hunting. Home: 2750 de L'Anse, Sainte-Foy, PQ Canada G1W 2G5 Office: 525 boul René-Lévesque est, Quebec, PQ Canada G1R 5R9

NORMANDEAU, ANDRE GABRIEL, criminologist, educator; b. Montreal, Que., Can.; May 4, 1942; s. Gabriel E. and Laurette D. (Sauve) N.; m. Pierrette La Pointe, Aug. 14, 1965; children: Alain, Louis, Jean. M.A. in Criminology, U. Pa., 1965, Ph.D. in Sociology, 1968. Asst. prof. criminology U. Montreal, 1968-71, assoc. prof., 1971-76, prof., 1976—, chmn. dept. criminology, 1970-80, dir. Internat. Ctr. Comparative Criminology, 1983-89, dir. Rsch. Inst. on Police, 1990—. Author: Public Attitudes and Crime, 1970, The Measurement of Crime, 1975, Patterns of Robbery, 1980, Crimes of Violence, 1985, A Vision of the Police, 1990, Crime Prevention, 1993, Justice and Minorities, 1995. Woodrow Wilson fellow, 1964-68. Mem. Internat. Soc. Criminology, Am. Soc. Criminology, Am. Sociol. Assn., Can. Criminal Justice Assn. Roman Catholic. Home: 3150 Ave Kent, Montreal, PQ Canada H3S 1N1 Office: Dept Criminology U Montreal, Montreal, PQ Canada H3C 3J7 Happiness is achieved by working for it, not by waiting for it to come to you.

NORMANDY, GEORGE MITCHELL, JR., electrical engineer; b. Decatur, Ga., Oct. 23, 1935; s. George Mitchell and Martha Randolph (Jones) M.; m. Marcia Del Farris, May 23, 1955 (div. Sept. 1969); children: Penny, Patricia, George III, Pamela, Paulette; m. Jean Edna Stolberg, Jan. 15, 1971; children: Jo Ann, John, Penny. AA in Phys. Sci, AA in Math., San Diego Evening Coll., 1977; BSEE, San Diego State U., 1981; AA in Psychology, AS in Mfg. Tech., San Diego City Coll., 1984; MS in Engring. Mgmt., West Coast U., 1992. Registered profl. engr., Calif. Enlisted USN, 1954-69, resigned, 1969; with customer svc. Motor Machine Co., San Diego, 1969-80; engr. Gen. Atomic Co., San Diego, 1980-82; sr. engr. GA Techs. Inc. (name now Gen. Atomics), San Diego, 1982—. Mem. IEEE, Am. Nuclear Soc., Indsl. Computer Soc. (founding mem.), Mensa. Republican. Lutheran. Avocation: home computer. Home: 3842 Basilone St #3 San Diego CA 92110-5402 Office: Gen Atomics PO Box 85608 San Diego CA 92186-5608

NORQUIST, JOHN OLOF, mayor; b. Princeton, N.J., Oct. 22, 1949; s. Ernest O. and Jeannette (Nelson) N.; m. Susan R. Mudd, Dec. 1986; 1 child, Benjamin Edward. Student, Augustana Coll., Rock Island, Ill., 1967-69; BS, U. Wis., 1971, MPA, 1988. Assemblyman Wis. State Assembly, Madison, 1974-82, co-chmn. state joint com. fin., 1980-81; mem. Wis. State Senate, 82-88, asst. majority leader, 1984-85, 87; mayor City of Milw., 1988—. Sgt. USAR, 1971-77. Mem. Nat. League of Cities, Wis. Alliance of Cities, U.S. Conf. of Mayors (mem. adv. com. 1989—). Democrat. Presbyterian. Avocation: map collecting. Office: Office of Mayor City Hall Rm 201 200 E Wells St Milwaukee WI 53202-3515*

NORRED, WILLIAM PRESTON, JR., pharmacologist, educator; b. Tallassee, Ala., July 11, 1945; s. William Preston and Halley May (Ingham) N.; m. Carol Joyce Nelson, Sept. 13, 1969; children: Amy, Leigh, Richard. BA, Emory U., 1966; BS in Pharm., U. Ga., 1969, PhD, 1971. Rsch. pharmacologist Agrl. Rsch. Ctr. USDA, Athens, Ga., 1971-81, supervisory pharmacologist, 1984—; adj. asst. prof. U. Ga., Athens, 1976-84, assoc. prof., 1984—. Author: (with others) Diagnosis of Mycotoxicoses, 1986; contbr. more than 75 articles to profl. jours. Mem. Am. Soc. for Pharmacology and Exptl. Therapeutics, Ga. Acad. Sci., Soc. Toxicology, Sigma Xi, Phi Sigma, Rho Chi, Phi Kappa Phi. Avocations: golf, woodworking, fishing. Office: USDA/ARS Russell Rsch Ctr 950 College Station Rd Athens GA 30605-2720

NORRGARD, KRISTIN ANN, magazine publisher; b. London, June 19, 1957; came to U.S., 1959; d. John Thomas and Barbara Ann (Erikson) N. BA, William Smith Coll., 1979. Account mgr. The Media Book, N.Y.C., 1979-80; dir. advt. Ad Forum mag., N.Y.C., 1980-83; nat. account mgr. Ladies' Home Jour., N.Y.C., 1983-85; dir. advt. Savvy Woman mag., N.Y.C., 1985-86, pub. 1986-90, v.p., 1988-90; assoc. pub. Inc. Mag., N.Y.C., 1990—. Active Jr. League of Greenwich (Conn.), 1979-80, Jr. League of N.Y.C. 1980-87, Fountain House, N.Y.C., The Manhattan Soc., N.Y.C. Mem. Advt. Women N.Y.C., Ad Club N.Y. Republican. Congregationalist. Avocations: skiing, swimming, windsurfing, traveling, cycling. Office: Working Woman 230 Park Ave New York NY 10169

NORRIE, K. PETER, manufacturing executive; b. Madison, Wis., Mar. 7, 1939; s. Kenneth Peter and Clara Frances (Storey) N.; m. Susan Kelliher, Sept. 6, 1960 (dec. 1975); children: Peter Clark, David Doherty, Charles Kelliher; m. Betty Buzard, Oct. 14, 1978 (div. Apr. 1989). BCE, Gonzaga U., 1961; MBA, Harvard U., 1964. Estimator H. Halvorsen Contractors, Spokane, Wash., 1961-62; gen. mgr. Boise (Idaho) Cascade Corp., 1964-70, mgr. gen. sales, 1970-72, v.p., 1972-76, sr. v.p., 1976—, also bd. dirs. Trustee UCLA Found. With USMCR, 1956-62. Recipient Disting. Alumni Merit award Gonzaga U., 1987. Republican. Roman Catholic. Avocation: golf. Office: Boise Cascade Corp 1 Jefferson Sq Boise ID 83728-0001

NORRIS, ALAN EUGENE, federal judge; b. Columbus, Ohio, Aug. 15, 1935; s. J. Russell and Dorothy A. (Shrader) N.; m. Nancy Jean Myers, Apr. 15, 1962 (dec. Jan. 1986); children: Tom Edward Jackson, Tracy Elaine; m. Carol Lynn Spohn, Nov. 10, 1990. BA, Otterbein Coll., 1957, HLD (hon.), 1991; cert., U. Paris, 1956; LLB, NYU, 1960; LLM, U. Va., 1986. Bar: Ohio 1960, U.S. Dist. Ct. (so. dist) Ohio 1962, U.S. Dist. Ct. (no. dist) Ohio 1964. Law clk. to judge Ohio Supreme Ct., Columbus, 1960-61; assoc. Vorys,

Sater, Seymour & Pease, Columbus, 1961-62; ptnr. Metz, Bailey, Norris & Spicer, Westerville, Ohio, 1962-80; judge Ohio Ct. Appeals (10th dist.), Columbus, 1981-86, U.S. Ct. Appeals (6th cir.), Columbus, 1986—. Contbr. articles to profl. jours. Mem. Ohio Ho. of Reps., Columbus, 1967-80. Named Outstanding Young Man, Westerville Jaycees, 1971; recipient Legislator of Yr. award Ohio Acad. Trial Lawyers, Columbus, 1972. Mem. ABA, Am. Judicature Soc., Inst. Jud. Adminstrn., Ohio Bar Assn., Columbus Bar Assn. Republican. Methodist. Lodge: Masons (master 1966-67). Office: US Ct Appeals 328 US Courthouse 85 Marconi Blvd Columbus OH 43215-2823

NORRIS, ALBERT STANLEY, psychiatrist, educator; b. Sudbury, Ont., Can., July 14, 1926; s. William and Mary (Zell) N.; m. Dorothy James, Sept. 2, 1950; children: Barbara Ellen, Robert Edward, Kimberly Ann. M.D., U. Western Ont., 1951. Intern Ottawa (Ont.) Civic Hosp., 1951-52; resident in psychiatry U. Iowa, Psychopathic Hosp., Iowa City, 1953-55, Boston City Hosp., 1955-56; practice medicine Kingston, Ont., Can., 1956-57; instr. Queen's U., Kingston, 1956-57; asst. prof. psychiatry U. Iowa, 1957-62, asso. prof., 1962-64, 1965-66, prof., 1966-72; asso. prof. U. Oreg., 1964-65; prof. So. Ill. U. Sch. Medicine, Springfield, 1972-84, chmn. dept. psychiatry, 1972-82; prof. emeritus, 1984—; practice medicine specializing in psychiatry Cedar Rapids, Iowa, 1984—; vis. prof. U. Auckland, N.Z., U. Otago, New Zealand, U. Liverpool. Contbr. chpts. to books, articles to med. jours. Fellow Am. Psychiat. Soc. (life); mem. AMA, Am. Psychopath. Assn., Soc. Biol. Psychiatry, Can. Psychiat. Soc., Am. Soc. Psychosomatic Ob-Gyn, Royal Soc. Medicine. Republican. Presbyterian. Home: 5 Penfro Dr Iowa City IA 52246-4927 Office: Ste 133 1730 1st Ave NE Cedar Rapids IA 52402 A life is only fulfilled by a quest, a vision of the future and a commitment to a greater value than one's self.

NORRIS, ALFRED LLOYD, theological seminary president, clergyman; b. Bogalusa, La., Feb. 6, 1938; s. Leslie Henry Peter and Adele Theresa (Washington) N.; m. Mackie Lyvonne Harper, Sept. 9, 1961; children: Alfred Lloyd II, Angela Renee. BA, Dillard U., 1960; MDiv, Gammon Theol. Sem., Atlanta, 1964, DD (hon.), 1976; DD (hon.), Centenary Coll., 1989; LLD, Dillard U., 1989. Ordained ministry United Meth. Ch., 1963. Pastor Haven United Meth. Ch., New Orleans, 1963-66, Peck United Meth. Ch., New Orleans, 1966-68, First Street United Meth. Ch., New Orleans, 1972-74, Mt. Zion United Meth. Ch., New Orleans, 1980-85; dist. supt. New Orleans dist. United Meth. Ch., New Orleans, 1974-80; dir. recruitment Gammon Theol. Sem., 1968-72, pres., 1985—; now bishop of New Mexico United Methodist Church, Albuquerque, N.Mex.; mem. Am. Preaching Mission, 1967; mem. bd. publs. United Meth. Pub. House, Nashville, 1980—; bd. dirs. Gulfside Assembly, Waveland, Miss., 1975—; mem. La. Conf. Bd. Higher Edn. and Campus Ministry; chmn. bd. ordained ministry La. Ann. Conf., 1980-88; guest preacher Liberia, West Africa, 1988. Trustee Centenary Coll., Shreveport, La., 1979—; mem. exec. com. NAACP, New Orleans, 1980-85; bd. dirs. New Orleans Urban League, 1981-84, Wesley Homes, Inc., Atlanta, 1986—; mem. exec. com. Met. Area Com., New Orleans, 1983-85; chmn. bd. dirs. Lafon Home for Elderly, New Orleans, 1983-85. Crusade scholar, 1961-63. Mem. Assn. United Meth. Theol. Schs. (sec. 1986-88), Adminstrv. Deans' Coun. (v.p. 1986—), Masons, Sigma Pi Phi, Theta Phi. Democrat. Avocations: reading, spectator sports.

NORRIS, ANDREA SPAULDING, art museum director; b. Apr. 2, 1945; d. Edwin Baker and Mary Gretchen (Brendle) Spaulding. BA, Wellesley Coll., 1967; MA, NYU, 1969, PhD, 1971. Intern dept. western European arts Met. Mus. Art, N.Y.C., 1970, 72; rsch. and editorial asst. Inst. Fine Arts NYU, 1971, lectr. Washington Sq. Coll., 1976-77; lectr. Queens Coll. CUNY, 1973-74; asst. to dir. Art Gallery Yale U., New Haven, 1977-80, lectr. art history, 1979-80; chief curator Archer M. Huntington Art Gallery, Austin, Tex., 1980-88; lectr. art history Dept. Art U. Tex., Austin, 1984-88; dir. Spencer Mus. Art U. Kans., Lawrence, 1988—. Co-author: (catalogue) Medals and Plaquettes from the Molinari Collection at Bowdoin College, 1976; author: (exhbn. catalogues) Jackson Pollock: New-Found Works, 1978; exhbn. The Sforza Court: Milan in the Renaissance 1450-1535, 1988-89. Mem. Renaissance Soc. Am., Coll. Art Assn., Assn. Art Mus. Dirs., Phi Beta Kappa. Office: Spencer Mus Art U Kans Lawrence KS 66045

NORRIS, CHUCK (CARLOS RAY), actor; b. Ryan, Okla., Mar. 10, 1940; m. Dianne Norris (div.); children: Mike, Eric. Appeared in films The Wrecking Crew, 1969, Return of the Dragon, 1972, Breaker, Breaker, 1976, Good Guys Wear Black, 1977, Force of One, 1978, The Octagon, 1979, An Eye for an Eye, 1980, Silent Rage, 1981, Forced Vengeance, 1981, Lone Wolf McQuade, 1982, Missing in Action, 1984, Missing in Action II-The Beginning, 1985, Code of Silence, 1985, (co-screenwriter) Invasion, U.S.A., 1985, Delta Force, 1986, Firewalker, 1986, (co-screenwriter) Braddock: Missing in Action III, 1987, Hero and the Terror, 1988, Delta Force 2: Operation Stranglehold, 1990, The Hitman, 1991, (co-exec. prodr.) Sidekicks, 1993, Top Dog, 1994; TV series Walker: Texas Ranger, 1993—; author: (with Joe Hyams) The Secret of Inner Strength: My Story, 1988; host: The Ultimate Stuntman: A Tribute to Dar Robinson. Profl. world middleweight karate champion, 1968-74. Office: PO Box 872 Navasota TX 77868

NORRIS, CURTIS BIRD, journalist, publisher; b. Quincy, Mass., July 14, 1927; s. Lowell Ames and Helen (Curtis) N.; m. Eileen Patricia Schindler, Mar. 23, 1959; children: Katharine Eileen, Helen Carolyn, Suzanne Elizabeth. AB, Middlebury Coll., 1951; postgrad., Bridgewater (Mass.) State Coll., 1986-95. Free-lance writer, 1945—; writer Sikorsky Aircraft Co., Stratford, Conn., 1957-59, N.Am. Aviation, Downey, Calif., 1959-61; editor Hughes Aircraft Co., Fullerton, Calif., 1961-62, Whitman (Mass.) News, 1962-65; sci. writer U. Vt., 1965-66; editor Wareham (Mass.) Courier, 1966-69; med. sci. editor Brown U., Providence, 1969-77; dir. pub. affairs Stonehill Coll., North Easton, Mass., 1977-83; staff columnist Quincy (Mass.) Patriot Ledger, 1982—; news dir. Bridgewater State Coll., 1985-87; indsl. rels. dir. Morgan Meml. Goodwill Industries, Boston, 1987-88; instr. Stonehill Coll., North Easton, 1991—; lectr., feature writer Boston Sunday Herald-Traveler, 1963-76, Yankee mag., 1963—; staff investigative reporter Globe Communications, Montreal, Can., 1973—; bd. dirs. pub. rels. programs Composite Tech. Alloys Co., Attleboro, Mass., 1975—; coord. Ea. Writers Conf., Salem, Mass., 1982; cons. pub. rels., 1983—; instr. Stonehill Coll., 1991. Author: Seldom Heard Tales of New England, 1964, American Holocaust, 1975, Phantom P. 40, 1981, Little Known Mysteries of New England, 1992, Ghosts I Have Known, 1993, The Boston Bogeyman, 1995, The Man Who Talked to Trees, 1995; assoc. editor: Stonehill Alumni News, 1977-81; editor: Stonehill Rev., 1977-83; originator (TV programs) Health Call, Science Call, Providence; prodr.: (cable TV program) Seldom Heard Tales of New Eng. 1986-88; represented in anthologies including Yankees Under Steam, 1970, Mysterious New England, 1971, Danger, Disaster and Horrid Deeds, 1974, Best Detective Cases, 1975-77, True Police Yearbook, 1975, 77, Startling Detective Yearbook, 1975-77, The World Wars Remembered, 1979, Best of Old Farmers Almanac, 1991; author manuscripts in Norris Collection, Brown U.; contbr. numerous stories to mags., TV Unsolved Mysteries, 1989. Chmn. publicity Wareham chpt., Am. Cancer Soc., 1966, cmty. chmn., 1967-69; assoc. mem. Federated Ea. Indian League; bd. dirs. Opera New Eng. of Greater Brookton. With USAAF, 1945-57; maj. Mass. N.G. Recipient Grand award Coun. Advancement and Support of Edn., 1976-77. Mem. New Eng. Press Assn., Am. Defenders of Bataan and Corregidor, Am. Med. Writers Assn., Assn. Am. Med. Colls., Mystery Writers Am., State Def. Force Assn. of U.S., Ret. Officers Assn., Kappa Delta Rho. Unitarian. Home: 166 E Main St Norton MA 02766-2310

NORRIS, DARELL FOREST, insurance company executive; b. Pontiac, Mich., Oct. 19, 1928; s. Forest Ellis and Mabel Marie (Smith) N.; m. Thordis Marie Johansen, Aug. 21, 1955; children: Dara Lee, Jennifer, Lisa, Nancy. BS, U. Kans., 1950. CLU, chartered fin. cons. Reporter, sports staff Kansas City Star, Mo., 1950-51; pilot TWA, 1955-56; div. agy. mgr. Merced region Farmers Group, Inc., Calif., 1959, sales rep., Colorado Springs region, 1962, regional agy. mgr., Aurora, Ill., 1964, regional sales mgr., Santa Ana, Calif., 1966, mgmt. tng. program staff, div. agy. mgr., Austin, Tex., 1971, v.p. sales, L.A., 1973, v.p. field ops. midwestern zone, 1976, v.p. field ops., western zone, 1979—; pres. Farmers New World Mgmt. Co., 1977-81, v.p. staff ops., 1981-85, sr. v.p. life co. ops. and staff support svcs., 1985-90, farmers cons., 1990-93; gen. ins. cons., 1993—. Chmn. bd. deacons First Baptist Ch., Granada Hills, Calif., 1977-89; sustaining mem. Rep. Nat. Com. Capt. USAF, 1951-55. Mem. Am. Soc. CLUs, Chartered Fin. Cons.

NORRIS, DAVID STUART, bank executive; b. Balt., May 17, 1938; s. Norman W. and June (Aler) N.; m. Ann King, July 8, 1967; children: Virginia A., Robert S. BS in Acctg., Va. Commonwealth U., 1963. Acct. A.M. Pullen, Richmond, Va., 1962-65; tax mgr. Ernst and Whinney, Richmond, 1966-72; v.p. Sovran, Richmond, 1973; exec. v.p., controller Signet Banking Corp., Richmond, 1974—. Served with USAF, 1961-62. Fellow Am. Inst. CPA's, Va. Soc. CPA's, Fin. Execs. Inst. (nat. dir., area v.p., exec. com.); mem. Assn. Bank Holding Cos. Clubs: Bull and Bear, Willow Oaks Country (Richmond). Avocation: fishing. Office: Signet Banking Corp 7 N 8th St Richmond VA 23219-3301

NORRIS, DENNIS E., religious organization executive. Dir. Am. Baptist Chs. Cleve. Region. Office: Amer Baptist Churches USA 1737 Euclid Ave Ste 603 Cleveland OH 44115

NORRIS, DOLORES JUNE, elementary school educator; b. Belmore, N.Y., Feb. 10, 1938; d. Abe and Doris Cyril (Stahl) Wanser; m. William Dean Norris, June 11, 1960; children: William Dean II, Ronald Wayne, Darla Cyrille. BS in Elem. Edn., So. Nazarene U., 1959; MS in Computer Edn., Nova U., 1988, EdS in Computer Applications, 1990. Cert. elem. edn. and computer sci. tchr., Fla. Tchr. 4th and 5th grades Ruskin (Fla.) Elem. Sch., 1959-61; tchr. 5th grade Emerson Elem. Sch., Kansas City, Kans., 1961-63; tchr. 1st grade Hickman Mills, Mo., 1964-65; tchr. 3d and 4th grades Lake Mary Elem. Sch., Sanford, Fla., 1968-72; tchr. 1st grade St. Charles Cath. Sch., Port Charlotte, Fla., 1976-77; primary tchr. Meadow Park Elem. Sch., Port Charlotte, 1977-89; computer specialist Vineland Elem. Sch., Rotanda West, Fla., 1989-90, Myakka River Elem. Sch., Port Charlotte, 1990—; reading coun. Charlotte County Schs., Port Charlotte, 1987—, rep., 1989-90, in-svc. com. 1990-93; program planner Meadow Park Elem. Sch., 1988-89; program planner Myakka River Elem. Sch. 1991-93. Mem. Rotary, Punta Gorda, Fla., 1982-86; co-dir. teens Touring Puppet Group, Punta Gorda, 1982-86; puppet co-dir. NOW Teens, Punta Gorda, 1976-80. Mem. Fla. Assn. Computers in Edn. Avocations: piano, swimming, travel. Home: 1171 Richter St Port Charlotte FL 33952

NORRIS, EDWIN L., lawyer; b. Columbus, Ohio, Oct. 6, 1946. BA, Duke U., 1968; JD, Yale U., 1972; LLM, NYU, 1978. Bar: N.Y. 1973, U.S. Tax Ct. 1979, Calif. 1987. Ptnr. Sidley & Austin, L.A. Mem. ABA (mem. fgn. activities on U.S. taxpayers com. sect. taxation 1984—), State Bar Calif. (mem. tax sect.), L.A. County Bar Assn. Office: Sidley & Austin 555 W 5th St 40th Fl Los Angeles CA 90013-1010

NORRIS, FLOYD HAMILTON, lawyer; b. Tahlequah, Okla., Oct. 24, 1908; s. Thomas Franklin and Sudie (Gates) N.; m. Martha B. Norris, July 1944 (dec.); 1 child, Floyd Hamilton II; m. Tania McKnight, June 28, 1991. BS, Northeastern State U., 1932; LLD, Okla. U., 1935. Bar: N.Mex. 1935, Okla. 1935, Calif. 1946. Pvt. practice law L.A., 1935—. Mem. Okla. Legis., Cherokee County, 1936-38. Col. U.S. Army, 1940-46. Decorated Bronze Star medal. Mem. Masons (Shriner). Democrat. Presbyterian. Avocations: gardening, woodworking. Office: Norris Bldg Inc 714 S Hill St Ste 405 Los Angeles CA 90014

NORRIS, FLOYD HAMILTON, financial journalist; b. L.A., Sept. 6, 1947; s. Floyd H. and Martha Leota (Buntin) N.; m. Mary Christine Bockelmann, Oct. 5, 1984; 1 child, John Buntin. Student, U. Calif., Irvine, 1965-68; MBA, Columbia U., 1982. Reporter Coll. Press Svc., Washington, 1969-70, Manchester (N.H.) Am., 1970-72, Concord (N.H.) Monitor, 1972-74, UPI, Vt. and Ala., 1974-77; press sec. Sen. John Durkin, Washington, 1977-78; fin. writer AP, N.Y.C., 1978-81; columnist Barron's, N.Y.C., 1982-88; fin. columnist N.Y. Times, N.Y.C., 1988—. Office: N Y Times 229 W 43rd St New York NY 10036-3913

NORRIS, FRANKLIN GRAY, surgeon; b. Washington, June 30, 1923; s. Franklin Gray and Ellie Narcissus (Story) N.; m. Sara Kathryn Green, Aug. 12, 1945; children: Gloria Norris Sales, F. Gray III. BS, Duke U., 1947; MD, Harvard U., 1951. Resident, Peter Bent Brigham Hosp., Boston, 1951-54, Bowman Gray Sch. Medicine, 1954-57; practice medicine specializing in thoracic and cardiovascular surgery, 1957—; pres. Norris Assocs., Orlando, 1985—; mem. staff Brevard Meml. Hosp., Melbourne, Fla., Waterman Meml. Hosp., Eustis, Fla., West Orange Meml. Hosp., Winter Garden, Fla., Orlando Regional Med. Ctr., Fla. Hosp., Lucerne Hosp., Arnold Palmer Children Hosp., Princeton, Fla. Hosp. N.E. and South (all Orlando). Bd. dirs. Orange County Cancer Soc., 1958-64, Central Fla. Respiratory Disease Assn., 1958-65. Served to capt. USAAF, 1943-45. Decorated Air medal with 3 oak leaf clusters. Diplomate Am. Bd. Surgery, Am. Bd. Thoracic and Cardiovascular Surgery, Am. Bd. Gen. Vascular Surgery. Mem. Fla. Heart Assn. (dir. 1958—), Orange County Med. Soc. (exec. com. 1964-75, pres. 1971-75), Cen. Fla. Hosp. Assn. (bd. dirs. 1980-85), ACS, Soc. Thoracic Surgeons, So. Thoracic Surg. Assn., Am. Coll. Chest Physicians, Fla. Soc. Thoracic Surgeons (pres. 1981-82), Am. Coll. Cardiology, So. Assn. Vascular Surgeons, Fla. Vascular Soc., Phi Kappa Psi. Presbyterian (elder). Clubs: Citrus, Orlando Country. Home: 1801 Bimini Dr Orlando FL 32806-1515 Office: Norris Assocs 55 W Columbia St Orlando FL 32806-1101

NORRIS, GENIE M., political organization executive; b. N.Y.C., July 15, 1951; d. Eugene and Peggy (Carter) Martell; m. Larry Specht, Apr. 22, 1982; children: Amanda Michele, Joshua Albert, Rachel Elizabeth. Adminstr. Senator Patrick Moynihan, N.Y.C., 1976; exec. asst. U.S. Senate, Washington, 1982-86; dep. field dir. Carter/Mondale Presdl. Campaign, Washington, 1979; dep. dir. Dem. Nat. Com., Washington, 1980-81; dir., v.p. assoc. Francis Assocs., Ltd., Washington, Germany, 1981-82; exec. asst. Senator Patrick Moynihan, Washington, 1982-86; guest lectr. USIA, Washington, 1987-90; mgr. Amb. Residence, Bonn, Germany, 1987-90; sr. assoc. FMR Group, Washington, 1990; dep. exec. dir. Dem. Congl. Campaign Com., Washington, 1990-91, exec. dir., 1991-94; dep. Asst. Sec. for ops. Dept. of State, Washington, 1995—; com. rep. Dem. Nat. Com. South Africa, 1980, Dem. Congl. Campaign Com., Republic of China, 1992; Peace Corp. transistion team leader Pres. Transition Team, Washington, 1992-93; South Africa elections obs. UN, 1994. With U.S. Army, 1975-78. Democrat. Roman Catholic. Avocations: art history, 1st edition books, horseback riding, music, antiques. Home: 1630 Davidson Rd Mc Lean VA 22101 Office: Dept of State Washington DC 20520

NORRIS, GEOFFREY, geology educator, consultant; b. Romford, Essex, Eng., Aug. 6, 1937; came to Can., 1964; s. Alfred Frederick Henry and Winifred Lucy (Camps) N.; m. Anne Frances Facer, Sept. 20, 1958; children—Grant, Theresa, Brett, Sonia. B.A., Cambridge U., Eng., 1959, M.A., 1962, Ph.D., 1964. Sci. officer N.Z. Geol. Survey, Lower Hutt, 1961-64; postdoctoral fellow McMaster U. Hamilton, Ont., Can., 1965; rsch. scientist Pan Am. Petroleum, Tulsa, Okla., 1965-67; prof. U. Toronto, Ont., Can., 1967—, chmn. dept. geology, 1980-90; rsch. assoc. Royal Ont. Mus., Toronto, 1967—; A.V. Humboldt fellow Cologne U., W.Ger., 1976; Ptnr. Austin and Cumming Exploration, Calgary, Alta., Can., 1980-87; vis. scientist Fla. Marine Research Lab., St. Petersburg, 1986, Fla. Mus. Natural History, U. Fla., Gainesville, 1994. Contbr. articles to profl. jours. Pres. White Light Hospice Found., Toronto, 1987—; dir. Metro Toronto Residents Action Com. for Rail Safety, 1980—. Recipient numerous operating, equipment and travel grants, Nat. Scis. and Engring. Research Council of Can., 1975—. Fellow Am. Assn. Stratigraphic Palynologists (pres. 1972), Royal Soc. Can. (sec. divsn. earth, ocean and atmospheric scis. 1990-92, dir. 1993—), Geol. Assn. Can. (councilor 1987-90), Geol. Soc. Am.; mem. Can. Assn. Palynologists (pres. 1982), Internat. Commn. Palynology (sec.-treas. 1975-80), Internat. Union Geol. Scis. (Can. nat. com. 1990—). Home: 12 Astley Ave, Toronto, ON Canada M4W 3B4 Office: U Toronto, Dept Geology, Toronto, ON Canada M5S 3B1

NORRIS, H. THOMAS, pathologist, academic administrator; b. Johnson City, Tenn., Nov. 24, 1934; s. Herbert Thomas and Ruth M. (Church) N.; m. Patricia Henry, June 19, 1956; children: Ruth Eileen, Margaret Ann, Edward Robert. BS with honors, Wash. State U., 1956; MD, U. So. Calif., 1959. Diplomate Am. Bd. Anatomic and Clin. Pathology. Resident pathology Mallory Inst. Pathology, Boston, 1960-62, 64-65; instr. Tufts U.

NORRIS, JAMES ARNOLD, government executive; b. Fargo, N.D., May 26, 1937; s. Cedric Leon and Gladys Louise (Arnold) N.; m. Catherine Anne Wright, Mar. 2, 1963; children: Suzanne, Erica, James. SB, MIT, 1959, SM, 1965; PhD, U. Calif., 1963. Economist Agy. Internat. Devel., Tunis, Tunisia, 1966-71, Jakarta, Indonesia, 1971-76, Cairo, 1976-80; dir. Bangladesh-India office Agy. Internat. Devel., Washington, 1980-82; mission dir. Agy. Internat. Devel., Dhaka, Bangladesh, 1982-84, Islamabad, Pakistan, 1988-92, Moscow, 1992—; counselor to agy. Agy. Internat. Devel., Washington, 1984-85, dep. asst. adminstr. Asia, 1985-88. Recipient Presdl. Meritorious Svc. award President U.S., 1984, 87, Presdl. Disting. Svc. award President U.S., 1989. Home: Psc 77 Aid APO AE 09721

NORRIS, JAMES HAROLD, lawyer; b. New Kensington, Pa., Sept. 18, 1953; s. J. Harold and Eleanore Rose (Arch) N.; m. Ann Marie Annase, Nov. 25, 1988; children: Ryan, Scott, Nicholas. BA, Washington Jefferson Coll., 1975; JD, Duquesne U., 1978. Bar: Pa. 1978, U.S. Dist. Ct. (we. dist.) Pa. 1978, U.S. Ct. Appeals (3d cir.) 1994. Assoc. Ruffin Hazlett Snyder Brown & Stabile, Pitts., 1979-83; ptnr. Eckert Seamans Cherin & Mellott, Pitts., 1983—. Mem. Allegheny County Bar Assn., Pa. Bar Assn. (com. adminstrv. law sect. 1992-94, asst. del., sports, entertainment and art law com., spl. achievement award 1993). Home: 2545 Country Side Ln Wexford PA 15090-7941 Office: Eckert Seamans & Mellott 600 Grant St Pittsburgh PA 15219-2702

NORRIS, JAMES RUFUS, JR., chemist, educator, consultant; b. Anderson, S.C., Dec. 29, 1941; s. James Rufus and Julia Lee (Walker) N.; m. Carol Anne Poetzsch, Dec. 28, 1963; children: Sharon Adele, David James. BS, U. N.C., 1963; PhD, Washington U., St. Louis, 1968. Postdoctoral appointee Argonne (Ill.) Nat. Lab., 1968-71, asst. chemist, 1971-74, chemist, 1974-79, photosynthesis group leader, 1979—, sr. chemist, 1981—; prof. chemistry U. Chgo., 1984—; chmn. internat. organizing com. 7th Internat. Conf. on Photochemical Conversion and Storage of Solar Energy, Northwestern U., Evanston, Ill., 1988. Co-editor: Photochemical Energy Conversion, 1989; mem. editorial bd. Applied Magnetic Resonance Jour., 1989—. Recipient Disting. Peformance award U. Chgo., 1977, 2 R&D 100 awards R&D mag., 1988, E.O. Lawrence Meml. award Dept. of Energy, 1990, Rumford Premium AAAS, 1992, Humboldt Rsch. award for Sr. Scientists, 1992. Mem. Am. Chem. Soc., Biophysical Soc. Achievements include discovery that the primary donor of photosynthesis is a dimeric special pair of chlorophyll molecules. Office: U Chgo Dept Chemistry 5735 S Ellis Ave Chicago IL 60637-1403*

NORRIS, JOHN, school system administrator. PhD. Supt. schs., dir. child-youth ministry Archdiocese of Milw. Office: Schs and Child Youth Ministry PO Box 07912 Milwaukee WI 53207-0912

NORRIS, JOHN ANTHONY, health sciences executive, lawyer, educator; b. Buffalo, Dec. 27, 1946; s. Joseph D. and Maria L. (Suite) N.; m. Kathleen E. Mullen, July 13, 1969; children: Patricia Marie, John Anthony II, Joseph Mullen, Mary Kathleen, Elizabeth Mary. BA, U. Rochester, 1968; JD, MBA with honors, Cornell U., 1973; cert., Harvard U. Sch. Govt., 1986. Bar: Mass. 1973. Assoc. Peabody, Brown, Boston, 1973-75; assoc. Powers Hall, Boston, 1975-76, ptnr., mem. exec. com., 1976-80, v.p., dir., 1979-80, chmn. adminstrv. com., 1976-79, chmn. hiring com., 1979-80; chmn. bd., pres., chief exec. officer, founder Norris & Norris, Boston, 1980-85; dep. commr. and chief operating officer FDA, Washington, 1985-88, chmn. action planning and cap coms., 1985-88, chmn. reye syndrome com., 1985-87, chmn. trade legis. com., 1987-88; corporate exec. v.p. Hill & Knowlton, Inc., N.Y.C., 1988—; worldwide dir. Health Scis. Cons. Group., 1988—, chmn. health scis. policy coun., 1989—; mem. faculty Tufts Dental Sch., 1974-79, Boston Coll. Law Sch., 1976-80, Boston U. Law Sch., 1979-83, Harvard U. Public Health Sch., 1988—; mem. bd. editors FDA Drug Bulletin and FDA Consumer Report, 1985-88. Founder, faculty editor-in-chief Am. Jour. Law and Medicine, 1973-81, emeritus 1981—; editor-in-chief Cornell Internat. Law Jour., 1971-73; reviewer New Eng. Jour. Medicine Law-Medicine Notes, 1980-81; assoc. editor Medicolegal News, 1973-75. Mem. U.S. Del. to Japan (chmn.), Austria, Saudi Arabia, 1987, mem., Finland, Denmark, Italy, 1986; chmn. Mass. Statutory Adv. Com. on Regulation of Clin. Labs., 1977-83; chmn. Boston Alumni and Scholarship Com., U. Rochester, 1979-85; mem. trustees council U. Rochester, 1979-85; mem. exec. com. Cornell Law Sch. Assn., 1982-85; mem. Mass. Gov.'s Blue Ribbon Task Force on DON, 1979-80, bd. trustees Jordan Hosp., 1978-80, mem. exec. com., 1979-80, chmn., chief exec. officer search com., 1980; chmn. Joseph D. Norris Health, Law and Pub. Policy Fund, 1979—; chmn. bd. Boston Holiday Project, 1981-83; mem. U.S. Pres. Chernobyl Task Force, 1986, vice-chmn. health affects sub-com.; mem. U.S. Intra-Govtl. AIDS Task Force, 1987; mem. IOM Drug Devel. Forum, 1986—, co-chmn. end points sub-com., 1987-88, Fed. Pain Commn., 1984-85. With U.S. Army, 1972-73, with res. Fed. Comprehensive Health Planning fellow, 1970-73; recipient Kansas City Hon. Key award, 1988, Nat. Health Fraud Conf. award, 1988, TOYL award, 1982, FDA Award of Merit, 1987, 88, PHS award, 1987, HHS Sec. award, 1988. Mem. ABA (vice chmn. medicine and law com. 1977-80), Mass. Bar Assn., Am. Soc. Hosp. Attys., Nat. Health Lawyers, Am. Soc. Law and Medicine (1st v.p. 1975-80, chmn. bd. 1981-84, life mem. award 1981), Soc. Computer Applications to Med. Care (mem. bd. 1984-85), Phi Kappa Phi. Home: 531 W Washington St Hanson MA 02341-1067

NORRIS, JOHN HART, lawyer; b. New Bedford, Mass., Aug. 4, 1942; s. Edwin Arter and Harriet Joan (Winter) N.; m. Anne Kiley Monaghan, June 10, 1967; children: Kiley Anne, Amy O'Shea. BA, Ind. U., 1964; JD, U. Mich., 1967. Bar: Mich. 1968, U.S. Ct. Mil. Appeals 1969, U.S. Supreme Ct. 1974, U.S. Ct. Claims 1975, U.S. Tax Ct. 1979. Assoc., then ptnr. Monaghan, Campbell, LoPrete, McDonald and Norris, 1970-83; of counsel Dickinson, Wright, Moon, Van Dusen & Freeman, 1983-84, ptnr.1985—; natural gas law counsel to claims mediator Columbia Gas Transmission Corp.; chpt. 11 bankruptcy proceedings in Wilmington, Del. Bankruptcy Ct., 1992—; bd. dirs. Prime Securities Corp., Ray M. Whyte Co., Ward-Williston Drilling Co. Mem. Rep. State Fin. Com.; founder, co-chmn. Rep. majority club; bd. trustees Boys and Girls Clubs of Southeastern Mich., 1979—, Mich. Wildlife Habitat Found., Mercy Coll., Detroit, Detroit Hist. Soc., 1984—; bd. trustees, bd. dirs. African Wildlife Found.; trustee and 1st vice chmn. Salk Inst. With M.I., U.S. Army, 1968-70. Recipient numerous civic and non-profit assn. awards. Fellow Mich. State Bar Found.; mem. ABA (litigation and natural resources sects.), Mich. Oil and Gas Assn. (legal and legis. com.), State Bar Mich. (chmn. environ. law sect. 1982-83, probate and trust law sect., energy conservation task force, oil and gas com.), Oakland County Bar Assn., Detroit Bar Assn. (pub. adv. com.), Am. Arbitration Assn., Fin. and Estate Planning Council of Detroit, Def. Orientation Conf. Assn., Detroit Zool. Soc., Blue Key Nat. Hon. Fraternity, Phi Delta Phi. Roman Catholic. Clubs: Bloomfield Hills Country; Thomas M. Cooley, Detroit Athletic, Economic (Detroit); Hundred, Prismatic, Turtle Lake, Yondotega. Contbr. articles to profl jours. Home: 1325 Buckingham Ave Birmingham MI 48009-5881 Office: Dickinson Wright 525 N Woodward Ave Bloomfield Hills MI 48304-2971

NORRIS, JOHN WINDSOR, JR., manufacturing company executive; b. Marshalltown, Iowa, Feb. 10, 1936; s. John Windsor Norris and Mary Merrill Margerin; m. Terry Reibsamen, Dec. 26, 1956; children: John Windsor III, Julie, Jeffrey. B.S. in Bus. Administrn., M.I.T., 1960. With Lennox Industries Inc., Dallas, 1960—, sr. v.p., 1975-77; pres. Lennox Industries Inc., 1977-80, past pres., chief exec. officer, 1980—, dir.; past pres., chief exec. officer Lennox Internat., Dallas, now chmn. bd., CEO; dir. Central Life Assurance Co., Des Moines. Chmn. parents div., mem. ann. gifts council Tex. Christian U. Mem. ARI (dir. at large, vice chmn. cert. programs and policy com., vice chmn. communications com.), GAMA (chmn. furnace div. 1978-79, chmn. bd. 1980). Club: Bent Tree Country (Dallas). Office: Lennox Industries Inc 2100 Lake Park Blvd Richardson TX 75080*

NORRIS, KENNETH L., accountant; b. Hartville, Ohio, Jan. 9, 1939; s. William J. and Thelma A. (Bennett) N.; m. M. Sue Weathers, June 17, 1957 (div. Mar. 1963); 1 child, W. Gregory; m. Ursel I. Simon, July 4, 1969. BSBA, U. Fla., 1961; MBA, Brenau Coll., 1989. CPA, Ga. Audit mgr. Arthur Andersen and Co., Atlanta, 1961-69; treas. Buck Creek Industries, Inc., Atlanta, 1969-81; v.p. fin. So. Aggregates Co., Atlanta and Augusta, Ga., 1982-84, Beaulieu of Am., Inc., Dalton, Ga., 1985—. Mem. Am. Inst. CPA's, Ga. Soc. CPA's, Nat. Assn. of Accts. Avocation: golf. Home: 1235 Covie Dr Dalton GA 30720-2524

NORRIS, LOUISE, religious organization executive. Nat. supr. Women's Dept. of the Ch. of God in Christ Internat. Office: Women's Dept of the Ch of God in Christ Internat 360 Colorado Ave Bridgeport CT 06605

NORRIS, MARTIN JOSEPH, lawyer; b. N.Y.C., Mar. 23, 1907; s. Louis and Esther (Wohlgemuth) Knaris; m. Helen Stella Hecht, June 5, 1930; 1 child, Barbara. LL.B., Bklyn. Law Sch., 1930. Bar: N.Y. 1932. Pvt. practice law N.Y.C., 1932-35; atty. U.S. Shipping Bd. Bur., Dept. Commerce, Washington, 1935-36, U.S. Maritime Commn., Washington and N.Y.C., 1936-42, War Shipping Administrn., N.Y.C., 1945-50; admiralty trial atty. admiralty and shipping sect. Dept. Justice, N.Y.C., 1950-56; adminstrv. law judge U.S. Coast Guard, N.Y.C., 1956-70; lectr. Sch. for World Trade, N.Y.C., Practicing Law Inst., N.Y.C., Lawyers Sq. Club, N.Y.C., U.S. Merchant Marine Acad., N.Y. State Maritime Coll.; cons. maritime law, shipping. Author: Your Boat and the Law, 1965, The Law of Seamen, 3 vols., 4th edit., 1985, The Law of Maritime Personal Injuries, 2 vols., 4th edit., 1990, The Law of Salvage, 1990; contbr. articles in field to legal jours. Served to capt. U.S. Army, 1942-45. Mem. Am. Soc. Writers on Legal Subjects. Jewish.

NORRIS, MELVIN, lawyer; b. Cambridge, Mass., Aug. 17, 1931. A.B., Northeastern U., Boston, 1954; J.D., Boston Coll., 1959. Bar: Mass. 1959, U.S. Supreme Ct. 1965. Atty. FTC, Boston, 1960-62; individual practice law Boston, 1962-76; ptnr. Norris, Kozody, Krasnoo & Fong, Boston, 1976-90, Norris, Kozody & Fong, Boston, 1991—. Bd. editors Mass. Lawyers Weekly, 1984-93. Vice chmn. Newton (Mass.) Crime Commn., 1966-67; mem. Newton Bldg. Code Revision Com., 1972-73; chmn. bd. dirs., pres. Waterville Estates Assn., Campton, N.H., 1992-94. With USCG, 1954-56. Mem. Fed. Bar Assn. (pres. Boston chpt. 1977-78, v.p. 1st circuit 1978—; exec. com. 1982-83), Mass. Bar Assn. Address: 18 Tremont St Boston MA 02108-2301

NORRIS, MICHAEL R., engineering administrator. Comdr. U.S. army beloir rsch. Devel. and Engring. Ctr., Fort Belvoir, Va. Office: US Army Belvoir Rsch Devel & Engring Ctr ATTN STRBE-Z Fort Belvoir VA 22060*

NORRIS, PATRICIA, costume designer. Costume designer: (films) The Good Guys and the Bad Guys, 1969, Support Your Local Gunfighter, 1971, The Candidate, 1972, Prime Cut, 1972, A Reflection of Fear, 1973, Zandy's Bride, 1974, Smile, 1975, The Sunshine Boys, 1975, The Missouri Breaks, 1976, Silent Movie, 1976, High Anxiety, 1977, California Suite, 1978, Capricorn One, 1978, Days of Heaven, 1978 (Acad. award nomination best costume design 1978), Movie Movie, 1978, Heart Beat, 1979, The Fish That Saved Pittsburgh, 1979, On the Nickel, 1980, The Elephant Man, 1980 (Acad. award nomination best costume design 1980), Fatso, 1980, The Baltimore Bullet, 1980, Four Friends, 1981, History of the World Part I, 1981, Frances, 1982, Victor/Victoria, 1982 (Acad. award nomination best costume design 1982), Scarface, 1983, The Star Chamber, 1983, Johnny Dangerously, 1984, Micki and Maude, 1984, Racing With the Moon, 1984, 2010, 1984 (Acad. award nomination best costume design 1984), The Best of Times, 1986, A Fine Mess, 1986, Spacecamp, 1986, The Whoopee Boys, 1986, Black Widow, 1987, Little Nikita, 1988, Sunset, 1988 (Acad. award nomination best costume design 1988), (TV movies) Harpy, 1971, Sybil, 1974, Cat on a Hot Tin Roof, 1984; prodn. designer: (films) Blue Velvet, 1986; costume designer, prodn. designer: (films) Tap, 1989, Wild at Heart, 1990, Leaving Normal, 1992, Twin Peaks: Fire Walk With Me, 1992, Amos and Andrew, 1993, (TV series) Twin Peaks, 1990 (Emmy awardoutstanding costume design for a series 1990). Office: Smith/Gosnell/Nicholson & Assoc PO Box 1166 1294 Calle de Sevilla Pacific Palisades CA 90272*

NORRIS, RICHARD ANTHONY, accountant; b. Birmingham, Eng., July 6, 1943; s. Albert Edward and Audrey (Rowley) N.; m. Geri M., Jan. 20, 1947; 1 child, Karen Louise. BA, U. Leeds, York, Eng., 1966. Chartered acct., Can. Auditor Price Waterhouse & Co., Bristol, Eng., 1966-70; mgr. Price Waterhouse & Co., Montreal, Que., Can., 1970-78; from mgr. corp. acctg. to controller Can. Pacific Enterprises, Montreal and Calgary, Alta., Can., 1978-85; v.p. fin. U.S. Ops. Laidlaw Waste Systems Inc., North Richland Hills, Tex., 1986—. Home: 2401 Hillside Ct Southlake TX 76092-8793

NORRIS, RICHARD PATRICK, museum director, history educator; b. Galveston, Tex., May 21, 1944; s. William Gerard and Iris Elsa (Allington) N.; m. Therese Louise Aalid, July 24, 1976; children: William Gerard, John Patrick. BA, Ohio State U., 1966; MA, SUNY, Binghamton, 1968; PhD, U. Minn., 1976. Instr. U. Minn., Mpls., 1970-76; lectr. U. Md., Europe/Asia, 1976-78; dir. Chippewa Valley Mus., Eau Claire, Wis., 1978-80, Kalamazoo (Mich.) Pub. Mus., 1985—; curator of history Mus. Sci. & Hist., Fort Worth, 1980-85; lectr. Tex. Christian U., Fort Worth, 1981-85; cons. Am. Assn. Mus., Washington, 1979—, NEH, 1989; grant reviewer Inst. Mus. Svcs., Washington, 1984—; Mich. Coun. Humanities, Lansing, 1985—; adj. prof. Western Mich. U., Kalamazoo, 1986—. Author: History by Design, 1984; book reviewer Mus. News, History News; contbr. articles to profl. jours. Dir. at large Arts Coun. Greater Kalamazoo, 1987-93; chmn. internat. com. Fort Worth 500 Com., 1984. 1st lt. U.S. Army, 1968-70. Mem. Am. Assn. Mus., Am. Assn. State and Local Hist., Internat. Coun. Mus., Midwest Mus. Conf., Tex. Assn. Mus., Rotary (dir. Kalamazoo club 1991-93). Democrat. Roman Catholic. Office: Kalamazoo Pub Mus PO Box 4070 315 S Rose St Kalamazoo MI 49003-4070

NORRIS, ROBERT F., food products company executive; b. 1922; married. BS, U. Kans. 1946. With Fleming Cos., Oklahoma City, 1946-71; former exec. v.p., pres. M. Loeb Ltd., Ottawa, Can., 1971-73; chmn., pres., chief exec. officer S.M. Flickinger Co., 1973-81; v.p. sales Associated Grocers, Phoenix, 1981-83; vice chmn. Godfrey Co., Waukesha, Wis., 1983-86, chief exec. officer, 1983—, chmn., 1986—; dir. Godfrey Co., Waukesha. Served to lt. USN, 1942-46. Office: Godfrey Co 1200 W Sunset Dr Waukesha WI 53186-6597

NORRIS, ROBERT MATHESON, geologist; b. Los Angeles, Apr. 24, 1921; s. Robert DeWitt and Jessie (Matheson) N.; m. Virginia Grace Oakley, Jan. 5, 1952; children—Donald Oakley, James Matheson, Elizabeth Anne. A.B., UCLA, 1943, M.A., 1949; Ph.D. Scripps Inst. Oceanography, U. Calif., San Diego, 1951. Teaching asst. UCLA, 1946-49; asso. marine geology Scripps Inst. Oceanography, 1951-52; mem. faculty U. Calif., Santa Barbara, 1952—; prof. geology U. Calif., 1968-86, prof. emeritus, 1986—; also dir. Channel Islands Field Sta., 1970-75. Contbr. articles profl. jours. Served with USNR, 1944-46. Fulbright scholar, 1961-62. Mem. Geol. Soc. Am., Geol. Soc. N.Z., Nat. Assn. Geology Tchrs. (pres. 1988-89), Am. Assn. Petroleum Geologists, Soc. Econ. Paleontologists and Mineralogists, Sigma Xi, Phi Kappa Sigma, Phi Delta Kappa. Congregationalist. Address: 4424 Nueces Dr Santa Barbara CA 93110-2006

NORRIS, ROBERT WHEELER, lawyer, military officer; b. Birmingham, Ala., May 22, 1932; s. Hubert Lee and Georgia Irene (Parker) N.; m. Martha Katherine Cummins, Feb. 19, 1955; children—Lisha Katherine Norris Utt, Nathan Robert. B.A. in Bus. Adminstrn., U. Ala., 1954, LL.B., 1955; LL.M., George Washington U., 1979; postgrad., Air Command & Staff Coll., 1968, Nat. War Coll., 1975. Commd. 2d lt. USAF, advanced through grades to maj. gen.; dep. judge advocate gen. USAF, Washington, 1983-85, judge advocate gen., 1985-88; gen. counsel Ala. Bar Assn., Montgomery, 1988—. Decorated D.S.M., Legion of Merit, Meritorious Svc. medal. Mem. ABA. Methodist. Office: Ala Bar Assn Office of Gen Counsel 415 Dexter Ave Montgomery AL 36104-3742

NORRIS, STEPHEN LESLIE, merchant banking, tax and finance executive; b. Mobile, Ala., Apr. 3, 1950; s. Thomas G. and Jean (Branyon) N.; m. Frances McMurtray, Oct. 8, 1981; 1 child, Christopher Edward. BS, Ala. U., 1972, JD, 1975; LLM in Taxation, NYU, 1976. Bar: Ala. 1975, D.C. 1976. Fellow Yale Law Sch., New Haven, Conn., 1977; tax atty. Cohen and Uretz, Washington, 1978-81; v.p. corp. officer Marriott Corp., Washington, 1981-86; mng. dir. The Carlyle Group, 1986-94; founder The Appian Group, 1995; asst. prof. Georgetown U. Law Sch., Washington, 1983; prof. law Am. U., Washington, 1983-86. Named one of Outstanding Young Men Am., 1983. Mem. ABA (real estate com.), D.C. Bar. Club: Athletic (N.Y.C.), Univ. (Washington).

NORRIS, T. H., retired oil industry executive; b. 1929. Iowa State U., 1951, Pa. State U., 1969. With Cities Svc. Pipeline Co., Bartlesville, Okla., 1951-52; chief inspector Colonial Pipeline Co., Atlanta, 1962-63, with engring. dept., 1963-64, divsn. engr., 1964-65, asst. mgr. engring dept., 1965-69, asst. mgr. western region, 1969-73, mgr. products movement dept., 1974-75, v.p. adminstrn., 1975-78, v.p. ops., 1978-94. Office: Colonial Pipeline Co 945 E Paces Ferry Rd NE Atlanta GA 30326-1125

NORRIS, THOMAS CLAYTON, paper company executive; b. York, Pa., May 9, 1938; m. Joan G. Wachob, Mar. 24, 1962; children: Robert, Richard, Mary Catherine. B.A., Gettysburg Coll., 1960. Chmn., pres., chief exec. officer P.H. Glatfelter Co., Spring Grove, Pa., 1980—. Home: 330 Rhonda Dr York PA 17404-6117 Office: P H Glatfelter Co 228 S Main St Spring Grove PA 17362-1000*

NORRIS, WILLIAM ALBERT, federal judge; b. Turtle Creek, Pa., Aug. 30, 1927; s. George and Florence (Clive) N.; m. Merry Wright, Nov. 23, 1974; children: Barbara, Donald, Kim, Alison; m. Jane Jelenko. Student, U. Wis., 1945; B.A., Princeton U., 1951; J.D., Stanford U., 1954. Bar: Calif. and D.C. 1955. Assoc. firm Northcutt Ely, Washington, 1954-55; law clk. to Justice William O. Douglas U.S. Supreme Ct., Washington, 1955-56; sr. mem. firm Tuttle & Taylor, Inc., L.A., 1956-80; judge U.S. Ct. Appeals (9th cir.), L.A., 1980—; spl. counsel Pres.' Kennedy's Com. on Airlines Controversy, 1961; mem., v.p. Calif. State Bd. Edn., 1961-67. Trustee Calif. State Colls., 1967-72; pres. L.A. Bd. Police Commrs., 1973-74; Democratic nominee for atty. gen. State of Calif., 1974; founding pres. bd. trustees Mus. Contemporary Art, L.A., 1979—; trustee Craft and Folk Art Mus., 1979—. With USN, 1945-47. Home: 1473 Oriole Dr West Hollywood CA 90069-1155 Office: US Ct Appeals 9th Cir 312 N Spring St Los Angeles CA 90012-4701*

NORROD, JAMES DOUGLAS, computer subsystems company executive; b. Detroit, Feb. 18, 1948; s. Charles Douglas and Bonnie Gene (Phillips) N.; m. Vickie Carolyn Newsom, Aug. 23, 1969; children: Heather Victoria, April Elizabeth. BS cum laude, Oakland U., Rochester, Mich., 1970; MBA, U. Detroit, 1975. Sales rep. IBM Corp., Detroit, 1970-77, mktg. mgr., 1977-80; v.p. Auto-trol Tech. Corp., Denver, 1980-86; pres., chief exec. officer CGX Corp., Acton, Mass., 1986-87, Adage, Inc., Billerica, Mass., 1987—. Republican. Home: 161 Ember Ln Carlisle MA 01741-1309 Office: Emerald Systems Corp PO Box 500550 San Diego CA 92150-0550 also: Octocom Systems Inc 1 Executive Dr Chelmsford MA 01824-2558

NORSTRAND, IRIS FLETCHER, psychiatrist, neurologist, educator; b. Bklyn., Nov. 21, 1915; d. Matthew Emerson and Violet Marie (Anderson) Fletcher; m. Severin Anton Norstrand, May 20, 1941; children: Virginia Helene Norstrand Villano, Thomas Fletcher, Lucille Joyce. BA, Bklyn. Coll., 1937, MA, 1965, PhD, 1972; MD, L.I. Coll. Medicine, 1941. Diplomate in neurology and geriatric psychiatry Am. Bd. Psychiatry and NEurology. Med. intern Montefiore Hosp., Bronx, N.Y., 1941-42; asst. resident in neurology N.Y. Neurol. Inst.-Columbia-Presbyn. Med. Ctr., N.Y.C., 1944-45; pvt. practice Bklyn., 1947-52; resident in psychiatry Bklyn. VA Med. Ctr., 1952-54, resident in neurology, 1954-55, staff neurologist, 1955—, asst. chief neurol. svc., 1981-91; neurol. cons. Indsl. Home for Blind, Bklyn., 1948-51; clin. prof. neurology SUNY Health Sci. Ctr., Bklyn., 1981—; attending neurologist Kings County Hosp., Bklyn., State U. Hosp., Bklyn. Contbr. articles to med. jours. Recipient spl. plaque Mil. Order Purple Heart, 1986, Spl. Achievement award PhD Alumni Assn. of CUNY, 1993, others. Fellow Am. Psychiat. Assn., Am. Acad. Neurology, Internat. Soc. Neurochemistry, Am. Assn. U. Profs. Neurology, Am. Med. EEG Soc. (pres. 1987-88), Nat. Assn. VA Physicians (pres. 1989-91, James O'Connor award 1987), N.Y. Acad. Scis., Sigma Xi. Republican. Presbyterian. Avocations: writing, piano, travel, reading. Home: 7624 10th Ave Brooklyn NY 11228 Office: Bklyn VA Med Ctr 800 Poly Pl Brooklyn NY 11209-7104

NORSWORTHY, LAMAR, petroleum company executive; b. 1946. With Holly Corp., Dallas, 1967—, pres., 1971-75, treas., from 1975, now chmn., pres.; chmn., pres. Navajo Refining Co., Artesia, N.Mex., 1982—. Office: Holly Corp 100 Crescent Ct Ste 1600 Dallas TX 75201-1832 also: Navajo Refining Co 501 E Main St Artesia NM 88210

NORTH, DANIEL WARNER, consulting analyst; b. N.Y.C., Mar. 12, 1941; s. James Dennis and Margaret P. North; m. Diane M. Tarantino, Nov. 26, 1978 (div. May 27, 1993); 1 child, Evan Armstrong; m. Cheryl Jeanne Bonham, May 27, 1993. BS, Yale U., 1962; MS, Stanford U., 1964, PhD, 1970. Analyst SRI Internat., Menlo Park, Calif., 1967-74, asst. dir. decision analysis dept., 1974-77; sr., v.p. Decision Focus Inc., Mountain View, Calif., 1977—; consulting prof. Dept. of Eng.-Econ. Sys., Stanford U., 1975-77; mem. sci. adv. bd. EPA, Washington, 1978—; gov.'s sci. adv. panel Calif. Propostion 65, 1987-89, Nuc. Waste Tech. Review Bd., 1989-94. Mem. Soc. Risk Analysis, (pres. 1991-92), Inst. Ops. Rsch. Mgmt. Sci., Sigma Xi. Office: Decision Focus Inc 650 Castro St Ste 300 Mountain View CA 94041-2055

NORTH, DORIS GRIFFIN, physician, educator; b. Washington, Nov. 30, 1916; d. Edward Lawrence and Ruth Gladys (Spray) Griffin; m. Victor North, Nov. 2, 1940 (dec. 1984); children: James, Daniel, Frederick. BA, U. Kans., 1938, MT, 1939; MD, Kans. State U., 1947. Med. tech. Ralph G. Ball, M.D., Manhattan, Kans., 1939-40, St. Francis Hosp., Pitts., 1940-41, John Minor, M.D., Washington, 1941-43; intern Wesly Hosp., Wichita, Kans., 1947-48; resident in pediat. and internal medicine Sedgwick Hosp., Wichita, 1948-49; pvt. practice family physician Wichita, Kans., 1951—; clin. asst. prof. medicine Kans. State U. Sch. Medicine, Wichita, 1974—. Mem. AMA, Am. Acad. Family Practice, Kans. Med. Soc., Med. Soc. Sedgwick County, Phi Beta Kappa, Alpha Omega Alpha. Home: 1000 S Woodlawn Apt 408 Wichita KS 67218 Office: 1148 S Hillside Wichita KS 67211

NORTH, DOUGLASS CECIL, economist, educator; b. Cambridge, Mass., Nov. 5, 1920; s. Henry Emerson and Edith (Saitta) N.; m. Elisabeth Willard Case, Sept. 28, 1972; children by previous marriage: Douglass Alan, Christopher, Malcolm Peter. B.A., U. Calif., Berkeley, 1942, Ph.D., 1952; D Rer. Pol. (hon.), U. of Cologne, Federal Republic of Germany, 1988, U. Zurich, Switzerland, 1993, Stockholm Sch. of Econs., Sweden, 1994. Asst. prof. econs. U. Wash., 1950-56, assoc. prof., 1957-60, prof., 1960-83, prof. emeritus, 1983—, chmn. dept., 1967-79; dir. Inst. Econ. Research, 1960-66, Nat. Bur. Econ. Research, 1967-87; Luce prof. law and liberty, prof. econs. Washington U., St. Louis, 1983—; Pitt prof. Am. history and instns. Cambridge U., 1981-82; fellow Ctr. for Advanced Study on Behavioral Scis., 1987-88. Author: The Economic Growth of the U.S. 1790-1860, 1961, Growth and Welfare in the American Past, 1966, (with L Davis) Institutional Change and American Economic Growth, 1971, (with R. Miller) The Economics of Public Issues, 1971, 74, 76, 78, 80, (with R. Thomas) The Rise of the Western World, 1973, Structure and Change in Economic History, 1981, Institutions, Institutional Change and Economic Performance, 1990. Guggenheim fellow, 1972-73; grantee Social Sci. Rsch. Coun., 1962, Rockefeller Found., 1960-63, Ford Found., 1961, 66, NSF, 1967-73, Bradley Found., 1986—. Recipient Nobel Prize in Economic Science, Nobel Foundation, 1993. Fellow Am. Acad. Arts and Scis.; mem. Am. Econ. Assn., Econ. History Assn. Home: 14 Lenox Pl Saint Louis MO 63108-1902 Office: Washington U PO Box 1208 Saint Louis MO 63188-1208

NORTH, HELEN FLORENCE, classicist, educator; b. Utica, N.Y.; d. James H. and Catherine (Debbold) N. A.B., Cornell U., 1942, M.A., 1943, Ph.D., 1945; LL.D. (hon.), Rosary Coll., 1982; D.Litt. (hon.), Trinity Coll., Dublin, 1984; L.H.D. (hon.), La Salle U., 1985, Yale U., 1986. Instr. classical lang. Rosary Coll., River Forest, Ill., 1946-48; mem. faculty Swarthmore Coll., 1948-91, prof. classics, 1961-91, chmn. dept., 1959-91, emerita, 1991—, Centennial prof. classics, 1966-73, 78-91, Kenan prof., 1973-78; vis. asst. prof. Cornell U., 1952—; vis. asso. prof. Barnard Coll., 1954-55; vis. prof. LaSalle Coll., Phila., 1965. Am. Sch. Classical Studies, Athens, 1975, 87; Blegen disting. vis. research prof. Vassar Coll., 1979. Author: Sophrosyne: Self-Knowledge and Self-Restraint in Greek Literature, 1966, From Myth to Icon: Reflections of Greek Ethical Doctrine in Literature and Art, 1979; translator: John Milton's Second Defense of the English People, 1966; editor: Interpretations of Plato: A Swarthmore Symposium, 1977; co-editor: Of Eloquence, 1970; editor: Jour. History of Ideas; mem. editorial bd.: Catalogus Translationum et Commentariorum, 1979—. Bd. dirs. Am. Coun. Learned Socs., 1977-85; chmn. bd. trustees LaSalle U., 1991-93; trustee King's Coll., Am. Acad. in Rome; chmn. com. on Classical Sch. Recipient Harbison prize Danforth Found., 1969; named Distinguished Daughter of Pa., 1989, del. of Am. Philological Assn. to Am. Coun. Learned Studies, 1991-95 ; grantee Am. Council Learned Socs., 1943-45, 73, fellow, 1971-72, 87-88; Mary Isabel Sibley fellow Phi Beta Kappa Found., 1945-46, Ford Fund Advancement Edn. fellow, also Fulbright fellow Rome, 1953-54; grantee Danforth Found., 1962, Lindbach Found., 1966; fellow AAUW, 1963-64; NEH sr. fellow, 1967-68; NEH Coll. Tchrs. fellow, 1983-84; Martin classical lectr. Oberlin Coll., 1972; Guggenheim fellow, 1958-59,75-76. Mem. Am. Philol. Assn. (dir. 1968—, pres. 1976—, Charles J. Goodwin award of merit 1969), Classical Assn. Atlantic States, Catholic Commn. Intellectual and Cultural Affairs (chmn. 1968-69), Am. Acad. Arts and Scis., Am. Philos. Soc., Soc. Religion Higher Edn., Phi Beta Kappa (mem. bd. vis. scholars 1975-76, senate 1991—), Phi Kappa Phi. Home: 604 Ogden Ave Swarthmore PA 19081-1131

NORTH, JOHN ADNA, JR., accountant, real estate appraiser; b. Atlanta, Oct. 20, 1944; s. John Adna and Julia Osborn (Napier) N.; m. Alexa Ruth Bryans, Mar. 20, 1976; 1 child, William Bryans. BA in Econs., U. Ga., 1966; M of Profl. Accountancy, Ga. State U., 1977, M of Taxation, 1980; JD, Woodrow Wilson Coll. Law, Atlanta, 1980. CPA, Ga.; cert. real estate appraiser. Trust administr. Trust Co. Bank, Atlanta, 1968-71; fin. produce sales exec. Dean Witter Reynolds Inc., Atlanta, 1971-73; with acctg. firm and in pvt. practice Atlanta, 1973-80; multi-state tax, staff, gen. tax counsel Texaco Inc., White Plains, N.Y., 1980-87; multi-state tax Price Waterhouse, Atlanta, 1987-88; dir. various corps. MacMillan Bloedel (USA) Inc., Wilmington, Del., 1988-91; pres. Cobb Svc. Assocs. Inc., Marietta, Ga., 1991—; chmn. supervisory com. Texaco Fed. Credit Union, Atlanta, 1980-88; bd. dirs., treas. Atlanta Credit Union League, 1986-87; v.p. The Planning Forum, Atlanta, 1984-85. Alumni trustee The Lovett Sch., Atlanta, 1985-89. Capt. U.S. Army, 1966-68. Mem. Ga. Soc. CPAs, Nat. Soc. Scabbard and Blade, SCV, Mil. Order of Stars and Bars, Beta Alpha Psi. Anglican. Avocations: personal computers, building custom fly fishing rods, genealogy. Home: 3242 Old Mill Ter Marietta GA 30067-5119

NORTH, MARJORIE MARY, columnist; b. Mt. Clemens, Mich., Oct. 21, 1945; d. Robert Haller and Hilla Beryl (Willard) Wright; m. Thomas Lee North (div.); children: Laura, Christina, Angela. Student, Wayne State U., 1963-65. Features editor Elizabeth City (N.C.) Daily Advance, 1966-69; news/mng. editor Brandon (Fla.) News, 1977-78; city editor Leesburg (Fla.) Daily Comml., 1978-79; metro editor Sarasota (Fla.) Herald Tribune, 1979-80, Fla. West editor, 1980-85, daily columnist, 1985—. Author: Sarasota: A City For All Seasons, 1994, (play) With the Best Intentions, 1994. Paul Harris fellow, 1994; recipient Layout, Creativity and Overall Publ. awards Fla. Press Assn., 1977, numerous cmty. awards and citations; winner Fla. shorts competition Fla. Studio Theatre New Play Festival, 1994. Avocations: sailing, tennis, interviewing, theater. Office: Sarasota Herald-Tribune PO Box 1719 Sarasota FL 34230-1719

NORTH, PHIL RECORD, retired banker; b. Fort Worth, July 6, 1918; s. James M. and Lottie R. N.; m. Janis Harris, July 28, 1944; children: Phillip Kevin, Kerry Lawrence, Mairin Kathleen, Deirdre Aine. A.B., U. Notre Dame, 1939. With Fort Worth Star Telegram, 1937-62, exec. editor, 1956-62, asst. gen. mgr., 1959-62; v.p. Carter Publs., Inc., 1949-62; with Tandy Corp., Fort Worth, 1966-82; chief exec. officer Tandy Corp., 1978-81, pres., 1978-81, chmn. bd., 1978-82; chmn. bd. 1st City Nat. Bank, Ft. Worth, 1982-86; chmn. bd. dirs. JMJ Fin. Corp., Ft. Worth, CXE, inc., Plano, Tex., Haeco II, Inc., Hillsboro, Ohio; bd. dirs. Del Norte Tech., Euless, Tex. Served to maj. AUS, 1940-46. Decorated Bronze Star. Mem. Ft. Worth Club, River Crest Club, Shady Oaks Club, Rockport Country Club, Rockport Yacht Club, Corpus Christi Yacht Club. Roman Catholic.

NORTH, PHILLIP J., lawyer; b. Charlottesville, Va., June 29, 1949. AB, W.Va. U., 1975, JD, 1978; LLM, London Sch. Econs., 1983. Bar: W.Va. 1978, Calif. 1978, Va. 1988. Alfred P. Sloan fellow London Bus. Sch., 1984; ptnr. Baker & Hostetler, Denver. Office: Baker & Hostetler 303 E 17th Ave Ste 1100 Denver CO 80203-1264

NORTH, ROBERT CARVER, political science educator; b. Walton, N.Y., Nov. 17, 1914; s. Arthur W. and Irene (Davenport) N.; m. Dorothy Anderson, Mar. 12, 1977; children by previous marriage: Woesha Kristina, Mary Davenport, Elizabeth Katrynka, Robert Cloud, Renya Catarina. A.B., Union Coll., 1936; M.A., Stanford U., 1948, Ph.D., 1957. Tchr. English, History Milford (Conn.) Sch., 1939-42; research asst. Hoover Instn., Stanford, Calif., 1948-50, research assoc., 1950-57; assoc. prof. polit. sci. Stanford (Calif.) U., 1957-62, prof., 1962-85, prof. emeritus, 1985—. Author: Revolt in San Marcos, 1941 (Commonwealth Gold medal), Moscow and Chinese Communists, 1952, The World That Could Be, 1976, (with Nazli Choucri) Nations in Conflict, 1975, War, Peace, Survival, 1990, (with Nazli Choucri and Susumu Yamakage) The Challenge of Japan: Before World War II and After, 1992. Served to capt. USAAF, 1942-46. Mem. Am. Polit. Sci. Assn. (Conflicts Processes Sect. Lifetime Achievement award 1993), Internat. Studies Assn. (pres. 1970-71), Internat. Peace-Sci. Assn., Explorers Club. Democrat. Unitarian. Office: Stanford U Dept Polit Sci Stanford CA 94305

NORTH, ROBERT JOHN, biologist; b. Bathurst, Australia, Aug. 22, 1935; s. Herbert John North and Loraine (Grace) Lamrock. BS, Sydney U., Australia, 1958; PhD, Nat. U., Canberra, Australia, 1967; DSc (hon.), SUNY, 1992. Vis. investigator Trudeau Inst., Saranac Lake, N.Y., 1967-70; assoc. mem. Trudeau Inst., 1970-74, mem., 1974-76, dir., 1976—. Mem. editorial bd. Jour. Exptl. Medicine, Infection and Immunity, Cancer Immunology and Immunotherapy; contbr. articles on immunity to infections and cancer to profl. jours. Recipient Friedrich Sasse sci. prize, 1984, rsch. award Soc. of Leukocyte Biology, 1990; grantee NIH, Am. Cancer Soc. Mem. Am. Assn. Immunologists, Reticuloendothelial Soc. (pres. 1983), Transplantation Soc., AAAS, Am. Soc. Microbiologists. Avocation: classical music. Office: Trudeau Inst Inc PO Box 59 Saranac Lake NY 12983

NORTH, WARREN JAMES, government official; b. Winchester, Ill., Apr. 28, 1922; s. Clyde James and Lucille Adele (Bishop) N.; m. Mary Strother; children—James Warren, Mary Kay, Susan Lee, Diane. B.S. in Engring. Purdue U., 1947; M.S., Case Inst. Tech., 1953, Princeton, 1956. Engr. and test pilot NACA, Cleve., 1947-55; asst. chief aerodynamics br. NACA, 1955-59; chief manned satellites NASA, Washington, 1959-62; chief flight crew support div. NASA (Manned Spacecraft Center), Houston, 1962-71; asst. dir. space shuttle NASA (Flight Ops. Directorate), 1972-85; pres. Spalding Edn. Found., Glendale, Ariz., 1986—. Contbr. articles to profl. jours. Served with USAAF, 1943-45. Recipient DeFlorez tng. award, 1966; NASA award for exceptional service, 1968, 69. Mem. Am. Inst. Aero. and Astronautics

---

(asso. fellow 1955), Tau Beta Pi, Pi Tau Sigma. Club: Mason. Home: 6933 W Kimberly Way Glendale AZ 85308-5757 Office: Spalding Edn Found 5930 W Greenway Ste 4 Glendale AZ 85306

NORTH, WHEELER JAMES, marine ecologist, educator; b. San Francisco, Jan. 2, 1922; s. Wheeler Orrin and Florence Julia (Ross) N.; m. Barbara Alice Best, Apr. 25, 1946; children: Hannah Catherine, Wheeler Orrin. BS in Engring, Calif. Inst. Tech., 1944, BS in Biology, 1949; MS in Oceanography, U. Calif. at San Diego, 1953; Ph.D., 1953. NSF postdoctoral fellow Cambridge (Eng.) U.; Electronics engr. U.S. Navy Electronics Lab., Point Loma, Calif., 1947-48; asst. research biologist Scripps Inst. Oceanography, U. Calif. at San Diego, 1953, Rockefeller postdoctoral fellow, 1955-56; asst. research biologist Inst. Marine Resources Scripps Inst. Oceanography, 1956-63; assoc. prof. Calif. Inst. Tech., Pasadena, 1963-70; prof. Calif. Inst. Tech., 1970-92, prof. emeritus, 1992—; Cons. marine biology U.S. Govt., State of Calif., San Francisco, Los Angeles, San Diego, numerous industries, 1957—; Phi Beta Kappa vis. scholar, 1973-74; mem. Calif. Adv. Commn., 1972-73, Nav. and Ocean Devel. Commn., 1973-76; dir. Marine Biol. Cons. Contbr. articles to profl. jours. Recipient NOGI award Underwater Soc. Am., 1975. Mem. Am. Littoral Soc. (James Duggan award), AAAS, Am. Soc. Limnology and Oceanography, Am. Soc. Zoology, Soc. Gen. Physiology, Calif. Acad. Sci., Fish Protective Assn. (dir.), N.Y. Acad. Sci., Am. Geophys. Union, Smithsonian Instn., Am. San Diego museums, Marine Tech. Soc., Western Soc. Naturalists, Calif. Soc. Profl. Engrs., Am. Zoomalac Soc., Internat. Oceanographic Found., Sigma Xi. Home: 205 Carnation Ave Apt 5 Corona Del Mar CA 92625-2807 Office: Calif Inst Tech Div Engring and Applied Sci Pasadena CA 91125

NORTH, WILLIAM HAVEN, foreign service officer; b. Summit, N.J., Aug. 17, 1926; s. Eric M. and Gladys (Haven) N.; m. Jeanne Foote, Sept. 2, 1950; children: Jeannette Haven, William Ashby, Charles Eric. B.A. with high distinction and honors in History, Wesleyan U., Middletown, Conn., 1949; M.A. In History, Columbia, 1951. Program officer ICA, Ethiopia, 1953-57; then dep. chief program div. ICA (African-European Regional Office), Washington; asst. dir. for program Lagos, Nigeria, AID, until 1965; dir. central and W. African affairs AID, Washington, 1966-70; dir. U.S. AID mission to Ghana, 1970-76; dep. asst. administr. Africa Bur. AID, 1976-82, spl. asst. Office of the Administr., 1982-83, assoc. asst. administr. Ctr. Devel. Info. and Evaluation, 1983-89, ret.; pvt. cons. Internat. Devel. for World Bank, 1989—, UN Devel. Program USAID, 1989—; coord. Evaluation of Global Environ. Facility, 1993; fellow Ctr. for Internat. Affairs, Harvard U. 1965-66; chmn. experts group on evaluation Devel. Assistance Commn., OECD, 1985-88; vice-chmn. editl. bd. Fgn. Svc. Jour., 1983-86; mem. adv. panel on evaluation Inter-Am. Devel. Bank, 1993-94; prin. evaluator Internat. Fin. Corp., 1994-95, U.S. AID Africa Program. Served with AUS, 1944-46. Recipient Meritorious Svc. award for exemplary achievement in pub. adminstrn., W.A. Jump Honor cert., Superior Honor award for Nigerian Relief Adminstrn., Equal Employment Opportunity award, Disting. Honor award AID, Presdl. Meritorious Svc. medal, Administrs. Career Svc. award. Mem. Soc. for Internat. Devel., African Studies Assn. Methodist. Club: Appalachian Mountain. Home and Office: Internat Development 6748 Brigadoon Dr Bethesda MD 20817-5436

NORTHCUTT, CLARENCE DEWEY, lawyer; b. Guin, Ala., July 7, 1916; s. Walter G. and Nancy E. (Homer) N.; m. Ruth Eleanor Storms, May 25, 1941; children: Gayle Marie (Mrs. John J. Young), John E. A.B., U. Okla., 1939, LL.B., 1938. Bar: Okla. 1938. Pvt. practice Ponca City, 1938—; Mem. bd. visitors U. Okla. Served with AUS, 1941-46. Decorated Bronze Star, Air medal with oak leaf cluster., Order St. John of Jerusalem; named Outstanding Citizen of Ponca City, 1982. Fellow Am. Coll. Trial Lawyers, Am. Coll. Trust and Estate Attys., Am. Bar Found.; mem. Acad. Univ. Fellows, Internat. Soc. Barristers, Am. Bd. Advocacy, Internat. Acad. Trial Lawyers, Okla. Bar Assn. (pres. 1975, bd. govs.), Ponca City of C. (past pres.). Democrat. Baptist. Clubs: Mason, Kiwanian. Home: 132 Whitworth Ave Ponca City OK 74601-3438 Office: PO Box 1669 Ponca City OK 74602-1669

NORTHEN, CHARLES SWIFT, III, banker; b. Birmingham, Ala., Jan. 25, 1937; s. Charles Swift and Jennie Hood (Hunt) S.; m. Margaret Carson Robinson, Dec. 27, 1959 (div. 1972); children—Margaret Allen, Charles Swift IV, Bryce Robinson; m. Betty Jean Taylor, Oct. 3, 1981. B.A. cum laude, Vanderbilt U., 1959, M.A., 1961. Chartered fin. analyst. Mem. staff trust dept. Birmingham Trust Nat. Bank, 1960-64; with First Ala. Bank Birmingham, 1964-80, sr. v.p., trust officer, 1975-80; sr. v.p., trust officer Central Bank of South, Birmingham, 1981-85; exec. v.p. 1st Ala. Bancshares, 1985—; Corp. Investment Officer, 1993—. lectr. So. Trust Sch., Birmingham So. Coll.; pres. First Ala. Investments Inc.; dir. Hubbard Press, Findlay, Ohio. Bd. dirs. United Presbyn. Found, N.Y.C., 1977—; mem. Birmingham Com. Fgn. Relations, 1970—. Mem. Ala. Security Dealers Assn. (pres.), Ala. Soc. Fin. Analysts (pres.), Inst. Chartered Fin. Analysts, Newcomen Soc., SAR. Presbyterian. Clubs: Mountain Brook, The Club. Lodge: Kiwanis. Home: 3024 N Woodridge Rd Birmingham AL 35223-2748 Office: PO Box 10247 Birmingham AL 35202-0247

NORTHINGTON, DAVID K., research center director, botanist, educator. BA in Biology, U. Tex., 1962, PhD in Systematic Botany, 1971. Prof. Texas Tech U., 1971-84; exec. dir. Nat. Wildflower Rsch. Ctr., Austin, Tex., 1984—; vis. assoc. prof. Southwest Tex. State U., 1985—; adj prof. dept. botany U. Tex., 1984—; curator E.L. Reed Herbarium Tex. Tech. U.; dir. Tex. Tech. Ctr., Junction. Co-author 3 sci. books; contbr. numerous articles to profl. jours., mags., newspapers, newsletters. Mem. Am. Assn. Bot. Gardens and Arboreta, Am. Soc. Plant Taxonomists, Nature Conservancy (bd. dirs. Tex. chpt.). Office: Nat Wildlife Rsch Ctr 4801 La Crosse Blvd Austin TX 78739

NORTHRIP, ROBERT EARL, lawyer; b. Sleeper, Mo., May 8, 1939; s. Novel and Jessie (Burch) N.; m. Linda Kay Francis, June 15, 1968; children: Robert E. Jr., William F., Darryl F., David F. BA, Southwest Mo. State, 1960; MA, U. N.C., 1965; JD, U. Mo., 1968. Bar: Mo. 1968, U.S. Dist. Ct. (we. dist.) Mo. 1968, U.S. Ct. Appeals (10th cir.) 1976, U.S. Ct. Appeals (8th cir.) 1980, U.S. Ct. Appeals (9th cir.) 1983, U.S. Ct. Appeals (3d cir.) 1987, U.S. Supreme Ct. 1978. Ptnr. Shook, Hardy & Bacon, Kansas City, Mo., 1968—. Active Nelson Art Gallery, Soc. of Fellows, Kans. City, Mo. 1st lt. US Army, 1963-65. Mem. ABA, Mo. Bar Assn., Lawyers Assn. Kansas City, Mo. Orgn. Def. Lawyers, Kansas City Met. Bar Assn., U. Mo. Alumni Assn. (past pres. Kansas City chpt.), Nat. Soc. Arts and Letters. Republican. Avocations: baseball, football. Office: Shook Hardy & Bacon 1200 Main St Kansas City MO 64105

NORTHROP, CARL WOODEN, lawyer; b. Princeton, N.J., Sept. 30, 1950; s. M. Starr and Margaret Leigh (Wooden) N.; m. Michaelanne Provencher, July 21, 1972; children: Lisa Erin, Kristen Elizabeth. BBA, U. Mich., 1972; JD, Georgetown U., 1976. Assoc. Norm Jorgensen Law Office, Washington, 1976-78; ptnr. Jorgensen, Johnson & Northrop, Washington, 1978-81; ptnr. Kadison, Pfaelzer, Woodard, Quinn & Rossi, Washington, 1981-85, mng. ptnr., 1985-87; ptnr. Bryan Cave, Washington, 1987—. Editor Georgetown U. Law Jour., 1975-76. Mem. Fed. Communications Bar Assn. Office: Bryan Cave 700 13th St NW Washington DC 20005-3960

NORTHROP, DOUGLAS ANTHONY, English educator, college official and dean; b. Ontario, N.Y., Apr. 12, 1935; s. Adren Henry and Anna Susanna (Hamelink) N.; m. Lynn Bradley Post, Sept. 22, 1956; children: Christopher, Jennifer, Timothy, Gregory. BA, Wesleyan U., 1956; MA, U. Chgo., 1957, PhD, 1966. Instr. English (Wis.) Coll., 1960-63, asst. prof., 1963-68, assoc. prof., 1968-74, prof. English, 1974—, v.p., dean of faculty, 1977-94. Contbr. articles and revs. to profl. jours. Mem., treas., v.p., pres. Ripon Sch. Bd. Edn. 1973-83; mem. exec. com., vice chmn., then chmn. Wis. Humanities Com., Madison, 1985-92. Recipient Severy award for Teaching, Ripon Coll., 1966, Uhrig award for Teaching Ripon Coll. 1971. Mem. Renaissance Soc. Am. Home: 528 Woodside Ave Ripon WI 54971-1639 Office: Ripon College PO Box 248 Ripon WI 54971-0248

NORTHROP, EDWARD SKOTTOWE, federal judge; b. Chevy Chase, Md., June 12, 1911; s. Claudian Bellinger and Eleanor Smythe (Grimke) N.; m. Barbara Middleton Burdette, Apr. 22, 1939; children: Edward M., St. Julien (Mrs. Kevin Butler), Peter. LL.B., George Washington U., 1937.

Bar: Md. 1937. Village mgr. Chevy Chase, Md., 1934-41; pvt. practice Rockville, Md., Washington, D.C., 1937-61; mem. Md. Senate, 1954-61, chmn. fin. com., joint com. taxation fiscal affairs, majority leader, 1959-61; judge U.S. Dist. Ct. Md., Balt., 1961—; chief judge U.S. Dist. Ct. of Md., Balt., 1970-81; mem. Met. Chief Judges Conf., 1970-81; mem. Jud. Conf. Com. on Adminstrn. of Probation System, 1973-79, Adv. Corrections Council U.S., 1976—, Jud. Panel on Multidist. Litigation, 1979—; judge U.S. Fgn. Intelligence Surveillance Ct. of Rev., 1985—. Trustee Woodberry Forest Sch.; founder Washington Met. Area Coun. Govts. & Mass Transp. Agy. Served to comdr. USNR, 1941-45. Decorated Army commendation medal, Navy commendation medal; recipient Profl. Achievement award George Washington U., 1975, Disting. Citizen award State of Md., 1981, Spl. Merit citation Am. Judicature Soc., 1982. Mem. ABA, Md. Bar Assn. (Disting. Svc. award 1982), D.C. Bar Assn., Montgomery County Bar Assn., Barristers, Washington Ctr. Met. Studies. Democrat. Episcopalian. Club: Chevy Chase (Md.). Lodge: Rotary. Office: US Dist Ct 101 W Lombard St Baltimore MD 21201

NORTHROP, MONROE, lawyer; b. Houston, Jan. 1, 1931; s. Joseph Walter and Mary (Harris) N.; m. Jane Ann Palmer, Dec. 4, 1970; 1 child, Ronald Northrop Viator. BBA, U. Tex., 1953, LLB, 1954. Bar: Tex. bar 1954. Asst. dist. atty. Harris County, Houston, 1957-59; asst. to U.S. atty. So. Dist. Tex., Houston, 1959-61; ptnr. Austin, Dabney, Northrop & Garwood, 1963-75, Austin & Arnett, 1975-84; sr. asst. City Atty., Houston, 1985—. With C.I.C. AUS, 1955-57. Fellow Tex. Bar Found. (life); mem. Tex. Bar Assn., Tex. Ctr. for Legal Ethics and Professionalism (founding), Sigma Chi. Republican. Episcopalian. Home: 4722 Waring St Houston TX 77027-6220 Office: Legal Dept PO Box 1562 Houston TX 77251-1562

NORTHROP, STUART JOHNSTON, manufacturing company executive; b. New Haven, Oct. 22, 1925; s. Filmer Stuart Cuchow and Christine (Johnston) N.; divorced; children: Christine Daniell, Richard Rockwell Stafford. B.A. in Physics, Yale U., 1948. Indsl. engr. U.S. Rubber Co., Naugatuck, Conn., 1948-51; head indsl. engring. dept. Am. Cyanamid Co., Wallingford, Conn., 1951-54; mfg. mgr. Linear, Inc., Phila., 1954-57; mgr. quality control and mfg. Westinghouse Electric Co., Pitts., 1957-58; mfg. supt. SKF Industries, Phila., 1958-61; v.p. mfg. Am. Meter Co., Phila., 1961-69; founder, v.p., gen. mgr. water resources div. Singer Co., Phila.; pres., dir. Buffalo Meter Co., Four Layne Cos.; dir. Gen. Filter Co., 1969-72; chmn., CEO Huffy Corp., Dayton, Ohio, 1972-85, chmn. exec. com., 1985-94; bd. dirs. Lukens, Inc., Coatesville, Pa., Union Corp., N.Y.C., Power Spectra, Sunnyvale, Calif., Wolverine Worldwide, Rockford, Mich., DSLT Inc., St. Clair, Mich., Elbit Sys. Am., Ft. Worth. County fin. chmn. George Bush Presdl. campaign, 1980; presdl. appointee Pres.'s Commn. on Ams. Outdoors, 1985-86; chmn. nat. hwy. safety adv. com. Dept. Transp., 1986—; founder, dir. emeritus Recreation Roundtable, Washington. Served with USAAF, 1944-46. Named Chief Exec. Officer of Yr. for leisure industry Wall Street Transcript, 1980. Mem. Del. Valley Investors (past pres.), Interlocutors, Elihu, Am. Bus. Conf. (founding), Fin. Commn. of Funds Am. Future, Boulders Club (Scottsdale), KOA Soc., Delta Kappa Epsilon. Home: 7474 E Boulders Pkwy # 4 Scottsdale AZ 85262-9999 Office: Huffy Corp 7701 Byers Rd Miamisburg OH 45342-3657

NORTHROP, THOMAS WEBSTER, health care facility administrator; b. Bridgeport, Conn., Dec. 27, 1948; s. Alvin Jennings and Margaret Gwendolyn (Webster) N.; m. Margaret Carol Joseph, Jan. 1, 1972; children: Justin Bradley, Heather, Kristen. BA, Lafayette Coll., 1970; MHA, Duke U., 1974. Adminstrv. asst. Meml. Hosp. Alamance County, Burlington, N.C., 1973-74; exec. asst. to pres. Vista Hill Found., San Diego, 1974-76; acting dir. Imperial County Mental Health Services, El Centro, Calif., 1976-77; asst. administr. Mesa Vista Hosp., San Diego, 1977-78; administr. Vista Hill Hosp., Chula Vista, N.C., 1978-83, Anson County Hosp., Wadesboro, N.C., 1983-87; v.p. Md. and Del. Sunhealth, Inc., Charlotte, N.C., 1987—. Healthcare columnist local newspaper, 1984-87. Mem. Am. Coll. Healthcare Execs., Assn. Mental Health Adminstrs., Hosp. Fin. Mgmt. Assn., Anson County Heart Assn. (pres. 1985, 86), Anson County C. of C. (bd. dirs. 1985, 86). Lodge: Rotary. (pres. 1986-87). Office: Sunhealth Inc Ste 100 10480 Little Patuxent Pky Columbia MD 21044-3506

NORTHRUP, HERBERT ROOF, economist, business executive; b. Irvington, N.J., Mar. 6, 1918; m. Eleanor Pearson, June 3, 1944; children: James Pearson, Nancy Warren, Jonathan Peter, David Oliver, Philip Wilson. A.B., Duke U., 1939; A.M., Harvard U., 1941, Ph.D., 1942. Instr. econs. Cornell U., 1942-43; sr. hearing officer Nat. War Labor Bd., 1943-45; asst. prof. econs. Columbia U., 1945-49; labor economist Nat. Indsl. Conf. Bd., 1949-52; indsl. relations cons. Ebasco Services, 1952-55; v.p. indsl. relations Penn-Texas Corp., N.Y.C., 1955-58; employee relations mgr. Gen. Electric Co., 1958-61; prof. industry Wharton Sch., U. Pa., Phila., 1961-88; prof. emeritus Wharton Sch. U. Pa., Phila., 1988—; chmn. dept. industry Wharton Sch., U. Pa., 1964-69; dir. indsl. research unit, 1964-88, chmn. Labor Relations Council, 1968-85; cons. and expert witness on manpower, pers. and labor rels. problems for many cos.; arbitrator in labor rels. disputes. Author: Organized Labor and the Negro, 1944, Unionization of Professional Engineers and Chemists, 1946, Economics of Labor Relations, 1950, 9th edit., 1981, Government and Labor, 1963, Readings in Labor Economics, 1963, Boulwarism: Labor Policies of General Electric Company, 1964, Negro and Employment Opportunity, 1965, Hours of Labor, 1965, Compulsory Arbitration and Government Intervention in Labor Disputes, 1966, Restrictive Labor Practices in Supermarket Industry, 1967, Negro in the Automobile Industry, 1968, Negro in the Aerospace Industry, 1968, Negro in the Rubber Tire Industry, 1969, Negro in Paper Industry, 1969, Negro in the Tobacco Industry, 1970, Negro Employment in Basic Industry, 1970, Negro Employment in Southern Industry, 1970, Negro Employment in Land and Air Transport, 1971, Impact of Government Manpower Programs, 1975, Open Shop Construction, 1975, The Impact of OSHA, 1978, Objective Selection of Supervisors, 1978, Black and Other Minority Participation in the All-Volunteer Navy and Marine Corps, 1979, Manpower in the Retail Pharmacy Industry, 1979, The Impact of the ATT-EEO Consent Decree, 1979, Multinational Collective Bargaining Attempts, 1979, Multinational Union Organizations in the Manufacturing Industries, 1980, Employee Relations and Regulations in the 80s, 1982, Internat. Transport Workers' Federation and Flag of Convenience Shipping, 1983, Open Shop Construction Revisited, 1984, Personnel Policies for Engineers and Scientists, 1985, Doublebreasted Operations and Pre-Hire Agreements in Construction: The Facts and the Law, 1987, The Federal Government as Employer: The Federal Labor Relations Authority and the PATCO Challenge, 1988, The Changing Role of Women in Research and Development, 1988, Government Protection of Employees in Mergers and Acquisitions, 1989, The Railway Labor Act, 1990, Union Corporate Campaigns and Inside Games as a Strike Form, 1994, also over 275 articles in field. Mem. Am. Econ. Assn., Indsl. Relations Research Assn., Am. Arbitration Assn., Phi Beta Kappa. Clubs: Harvard (N.Y.C.); Harvard-Radcliffe (Phila.); University (Washington); Faculty (U. Pa.). Home and Office: 205 Avon Rd Haverford PA 19041-1612

NORTHRUP, WILLIAM STEPHEN, JR., television producer; b. South Kingstown, R.I., Aug. 18, 1946; s. William Stephen and Elizabeth (Northrup) N.; m. Lynn Louise Henneberry, July 27, 1968. Grad., Northeast Broadcasting Sch., Boston, 1965; cert., Inst. for Orgn. Mgmt., Washington, 1975. News dir. Sta. WPRO, Providence, 1972-74; v.p. communications Providence C. of C., 1974-76; reporter Sta. WJAR-TV, NBC, Providence, 1977-81; asst. news dir. Sta. WLNE-TV, CBS, Providence, 1981-83, news dir., 1983-84; exec. producer news Sta. KHJ-TV, L.A., 1984—. Mem. Acad. TV Arts and Scis. (Emmy award 1986), Radio-TV News Assn. So. Calif. (judges search com. 1988—, Golden Mikew award 1986), Am. Film Inst. Episcopalian. Office: Sta KHJ-TV News 5515 Melrose Ave Los Angeles CA 90038-3199

NORTHUP, ANNE MEAGHER, state legislator; b. Louisville, Jan. 22, 1948; d. James L. and Floy Gates (Terstege) Meagher; m. Robert Wood Northup, Apr. 12, 1969; children: David, Katherine, Joshua, Kevin, Erin, Mark. BA in Econs., St. Mary's Coll. Notre Dame, South Bend, Ind., 1970. Mem. Ky. Ho. of Reps., Frankfort, 1987—; mem. fin. adv. bd. EPA, 1989-93. Recipient Cath. Schs. Disting. Alumni award, U. Notre Dame award of the yr. Ky. Alumni Assn., Clearing the Air award Am. Lung Assn. of Ky., 1991. Mem. Nat. Order Women Legislators, Nat. Conf. State Legislators (Task Republican Legis. Conf., So. Legis. Conf. (alternat from Ky. to fiscal affairs and governmental com.). Roman Catholic. Home: 3340 Lexington

Rd Louisville KY 40206-3050 Office: Ky Ho of Reps State Capitol Frankfort KY 40601

NORTHUP, JOHN DAVID, management consultant, inventor; b. Toledo, Sept. 8, 1910; s. Charles S. and Alice Delia (Bachelder) N.; m. Ruth Bender, Jan. 15, 1937; children: John David, Mary Elizabeth, Nancy Ross (Mrs. H.T. Lehrkind). B.S., MIT, 1932. With Owens-Ill. Glass Co., 1933-74; mgr. Owens-Ill. Glass Co., Clarion, Pa., 1943-46, Charleston, W.Va., 1946-47; gen. purchasing agt. glass container div. Owens-Ill. Glass Co., 1947-49, gen. mgr. corrugated package ops., 1949-53, dir. engring., 1953-55, v.p. administrv. div., 1956-61, v.p. gen. mgr. Closure div., 1961-72, v.p. charge glass container mfg., 1972-74; ind. inventor, mgmt. cons., 1974—; chmn. closure com. Glass Container Mfrs. Inst., 1966-69; tech. adviser on poison prevention packaging FDA, 1971-72. Mem. TAPPI, Am. Ceramic Soc., Inverness Club, Beta Theta Pi. Republican. Home: 2460 Underhill Rd Toledo OH 43615-2332

NORTON, ANDRE ALICE, author; b. Cleve., Sept. 17, 1912; d. Adalbert and Bertha Stemm N. Librarian Cleve. Public Library, until 1951. Author: 125 books including The Sword is Drawn (Dutch Gov. award 1946) 1944, Sword in Sheath (Ohioana Juevenile award Honor Book 1950) 1949, Starhunter (Hugo award nomination World Sci. Fiction Convention 1962) 1961, Witch World (Hugo award nomination World Sci Fiction Convention 1964) 1963, Night of Masks (Boy's Club of Am. Certificate of Merit 1965) 1964; series include Swords Trilogy, Star Ka'at Sci. Fiction Series, Witch World Fantasy Series. Recipient Invisible Little Man award Westercon XVI, 1963, Phoenix award 1976, Gandalf Master Fantasy award World Sci. Fiction Convention, 1977, Andre Norton award Women Writers of Sci. Fiction, 1978, Balrog Fantasy award 1979, Ohioana award, 1980, Fritz Leiber award, 1983, E.E. Smith award, 1983, Nebula Grand Master award Sci. Fiction Writers of Am., 1984, Jules Verne award, 1984, Second Stage Lensman award, 1987; named to Ohio Hall of Fame, 1981. Mem. PEN Women, Sci. Fiction Writers Am., Theta Sigma Phi (Headliner award 1963).

NORTON, AUGUSTUS RICHARD, political science educator; b. Bklyn., Sept. 2, 1946; m. Deanna Lampros, Dec. 27, 1969; 1 child, A. Timothy. BA in Polit. Sci. magna cum laude, U. Miami, Fla., 1974, MA in Polit. Sci., 1974; PhD in Polit. Sci., U. Chgo., 1984. Commd. 2d lt. U.S. Army, 1967, advanced through grades to col., 1990, ret., 1993; prof. polit. sci., dept. social scis. U.S. Mil. Acad., West Point, N.Y., 1981-93; prof. internat. rels. Boston U., 1993—; dir. Civil Soc. in Mid. East program NYU, 1992-94. Author: Amal and the Shi'a: Struggle for the Soul of Lebanon, 1987; co-author: International Terrorism: An Annotated Bibliography and Research Guide, 1980, UN Peacekeepers: Soldiers With A Difference, 1990, Political Tides in the Arab World, 1992; contbr., sr. editor: Studies in Nuclear Terrorism, 1979, The International Relations of the PLO, 1989, Touring Nam: The Vietnam War Reader, 1989; editor: Civil Society in the Middle East, vol. I, 1994, vol. II, 1995; mem. editorial bd. Ethics and Internat. Affairs, 1990—, Current History, 1992—, Global Goverance, 1994. Sr. rsch. fellow Internat. Peace Acad., 1990-92, Woodrow Wilson Nat. fellow, 1990-93; Fulbright rsch. prof., Norway, 1989; grantee NEH summer 1986, MacArthur Found. 1989-90, Ford Found., 1991—, Rockefeller Found., 1993-94. Fellow Inter-Univ. Seminar on Armed Forces and Soc. (assoc. chmn., regional rep. N.E. region 1982—); mem. Am. Polit. Sci. Assn., Coun. Fgn. Rels., Internat. Inst. Strategic Studies, Mid. East Studies Assn., Am. Rsch. Ctr. Egypt, Columbia Univ. Seminar on Middle East, Mid. East Inst. Columbia U., Conf. Group on Mid. East (co-founder), Phi Kappa Phi, Pi Sigma Alpha. Office: Dept Internat Rels Boston U 152 Bay State Rd Boston MA 02215

NORTON, DAVID C., federal judge; b. Washington, July 25, 1946; s. Charles Edward and Louise Helen (Le Feber) N.; m. Dee Holman, June 16, 1973; children: Phoebe Elizabeth, Christine Baron. BA in History, U. of the South, 1968; JD, U. S.C., 1975. Assoc. Holmes & Thomson, Charleston, S.C., 1975-77, 80-82, ptnr., 1982-90; dep. solicitor 9th Jud. Ct., Charleston, 1977-80; U.S. Dist. judge Charleston, 1990—. With USN, 1969-72. Mem. ABA, Fed. Judges Assn., Charleston County Bar Assn. (sec.-tres. 1983-90). S.C. Def. Trial Attys. Assn. (exec. com. 1988-90), S.C. Bar Assn. (mem. Ho. Dels. 1986-90). Episcopalian. Avocations: boating, racquet ball. Office: Hollings Judicial Ctr PO Box 835 Broad & Meeting Sts 3rd Fl Charleston SC 29402-0835

NORTON, DELMAR LYNN, candy company executive, video executive; b. Vernal, Utah, Sept. 6, 1944; s. La Mar and Velma (Hullinger) N.; m. Connie Jean Bryan, Mar. 10, 1967; children: Bryan Lynn, Christopher Max, Wendy, Nicholas Delmar. Student, U. Utah, 1962-63, Famous Artists Sch., 1966-69. Nat. sales mgr. Maxfield Candy Co., Salt Lake City, 1965-72; sec.-treas. Ice Cream & Candy Shops, Salt Lake City, 1972-73; pres., gen. mgr. Ostlers' Candy Co., Salt Lake City, 1973—; chmn. bd. Nat. Mktg. Co., Salt Lake City, 1974—; pres., gen. mgr. Rent-A-Flick, Inc., Salt Lake City.; v.p. Redi-Therm Insulation, Inc., Salt Lake City, 1991-94; nat. sales mgr. Uphill Down U.S.A., 1994—. Mem. Ch. Jesus Christ of Latter-Day Saints (missionary). Home: 4240 S 1650 E Salt Lake City UT 84124-2556

NORTON, DONN H., insurance company executive; b. 1942. BBA, Nichols Coll., 1066. CPA. Acct. Arthur Young & Co., 1966-70; with Bellemend Devel. Corp., 1970—; from sr. v.p. to exec. v.p. Chubb Corp., Warren, NJ. with USN, 1959-62. Office: Chubb Corp PO Box 1615 15 Mountain View Rd Warren NJ 07061-1615 Office: Bellmead Development Corp 4 Becker Farm Rd Roseland NJ 07068-3790

NORTON, DUNBAR SUTTON, economic developer; b. Hoquiam, Wash., Jan. 30, 1926; s. Percy Dunbar and Anna Fedelia (Sutton) N.; m. Kathleen Margaret Mullarky, Dec. 21, 1948 (dec. Apr. 1994); children: Priscilla K., Rebecca C., Jennifer A., Douglas S. Student, U. Oreg., 1946-48; diploma, U.S. Army Command & Gen. Staff, 1964. Commd. 2d lt. U.S. Army, 1948, advanced through grades to lt. col., ret., 1974; dir. econ. devel. dept. Yuma (Ariz.) County C. of C., 1974-83; exec. v.p. Lakin Enterprises, Yuma, 1983-87; owner Norton Cons., Yuma, 1987—; corp. mem. Yuma Econ. Devel. Corp., 1984—, vice chmn., 1993—. Mem. Yuma County Indsl. Devel. Authority, 1984-90, 92—, pres., 1992—; chmn. fundraising com. Yuma Cross Park Coun., 1984-88, sec., 1988-90, v.p., 1990-92, bd. dirs., 1982-95; chmn. devel. com. Yuma County Airport Authority, 1985-92, v.p., 1992—; vice chmn. Yuma Main St. Bd., 1988-90, Yuma County Geog. Info. System Task Force, 1991—, Yuma Kids Voting, 1990-91; bd. dirs. Ariz. Partnership Air Transp., 1990—, v.p., 1993—; bd. dirs. Yuma County Civic Trusteeship, 1993-95. Decorated Legion of Merit with oak leaf cluster, Bronze Star. Mem. Ariz. Assn. for Indsl. Devel. (bd. dirs. 1975-82, pres. 1982-83, Developer of the Yr. 1977), Yuma Execs. Assn. (sec., treas., exec. dir. 1987—). Republican. Episcopalian. Avocations: golf, swimming, singing. Home: 12267 Del Norte Yuma AZ 85367-8923 Office: 11411 S Fortuna Rd Ste 205 Yuma AZ 85367

NORTON, ELEANOR HOLMES, congresswoman, lawyer, educator; b. Washington, June 13, 1937; d. Coleman and Vela (Lynch) Holmes; m. Edward W. Norton (div.); children: Katherine Felicia, John Holmes. BA, Antioch Coll., 1960; MA in Am. Studies, Yale U., 1963, LLB, 1964; LLD (hon.), Cedar Crest Coll., Allentown, Pa., 1969, Bard Coll., Annandale-on-Hudson, N.Y., 1971, Princeton U., 1973, Marymount Coll., 1974, CCNY, 1975, NYU, 1978, Howard U., 1978, Brown U., 1978, Wilberforce U., 1978, Wayne State U., 1980, Syracuse U., 1981, Yeshiva U., 1981, Lawrence U., 1981, Emanuel Coll., 1981, Spelman Coll., 1982, U. Mass., 1983, Smith Coll., 1983, Med. Coll. Pa., 1983, Tufts U., 1984, Bowdoin Coll., 1985. Bar: Pa., 1965, U.S. Supreme Ct., 1968. Law clk. presiding justice Fed. Dist. Ct., 1964-65; asst. legal dir. ACLU, 1965-70; exec. asst. to mayor City of N.Y., 1971-74, chmn. commn. humanities, 1970-77; chmn. commn. humanities EEOC, Washington, 1977-81; sr. fellow Urban Inst., Washington, 1981-82; prof. law Georgetown U., Washington, 1982—; chmn. nat. adv. coun. ACLU; mem. 100th-104th Congresses from D.C. dist., 1990—; lead Dem. mem. D.C. subcom., water resources and environ. subcom., pub. bldgs. and econ. devel. subcom.; vice chair Congl. Caucus on Women's Issues; mem. exec. com. Dem. Study Group; active Congl. Black Caucus, Congl. Arts Caucus, Environ. and Energy Study Conf., Fed. Govt. Svc. Caucus, Congl. Tourism Caucus. Author: (with others) Sex Discrimination and the Law: Causes and Remedies, 1975; contbr. articles to profl. jours. Trustee Community Found. Greater Washington, Rockefeller Found., Yale Corp.; bd. dirs. A. Philip Randolph Inst., Bethune Mus. and Archives Nat. Historic

Site; catalyst Ctr. Nat. Policy, Manpower Demonstration Research Corp., Martin Luther King, Jr. Ctr. Social Change, Nat. Black Leadership Roundtable, Nat. Polit. Congress Black Women, Nat. Urban Coalition, Pitney Bowes Corp., So. Christian Leadership Conf.; adv. bd. Nat. Women's Polit. Caucus, Women's Law and Policy Fellowship, Workplace Health Fund; chmn. Commn. Future of Women in Workplace, Nat. Adv. Council ACLU; mem. Am. Council Edn., Council Minority Edn., Council Fgn. Relations, U.S. Citizens Com. Monitor Helsinki Accords, exec. panel Ford Found. Project Future of Welfare State, Nat. Acad. Scis. Com. Effects Tech. Change Employment and Working Environment. Recipient Young Woman of Year award Jr. C. of C., 1965, Yale Wilbur Cross medal Yale U. Grad. Sch.; Named one of 25 Most Influential Women in Am. award Newspaper Enterprise Assn., 1977; Louise Waterman Wise award Am. Jewish Congress, 1971; Harper fellow Yale Law Sch., 1976; vis. Phi Beta Kappa scholar, 1985. Mem. NAS (numerous coms.). Office: 1424 Longworth HOB Washington DC 20515 also: Georgetown U Law Ctr 600 New Jersey Ave NW Washington DC 20001

NORTON, ELIZABETH WYCHGEL, lawyer; b. Cleve., Mar. 25, 1933; d. James Nicolas and Ruth Elizabeth (Cannell) Wychgel; m. Henry Wacks Norton Jr., July 16, 1954 (div. 1971); children: James, Henry, Peter, Fred; m. James Cory Ferguson, Dec. 14, 1985 (div. Apr. 1988). BA in Math., Wellesley Coll., 1954; JD cum laude, U. Minn., 1974. Bar: Minn. 1974. Summer intern Minn. Atty. Gen.'s Office, St. Paul, 1972; with U.S. Dept. Treasury, St. Paul, 1973; assoc. Gray, Plant, Mooty, Mooty & Bennett, P.A., Mpls., 1974-79, prin., 1980-94, of counsel, 1995—; mem. Minn. Lawyers Bd. Profl. Responsibility, 1984-89; mem. U. Minn. Law Sch. Bd. Visitors, 1987-92. trustee YWCA, Mpls., 1979-84, 89-91, co-chmn. deferred giving com., 1980-81, chmn. by-laws com., bd. dirs., 1976-77, lectr.; treas. Minn. Women's Campaign Fund, 1985, guarantor, 1982-83, budget and fin. com. bd. dirs., 1984-87; trustee Ripley Meml. Found., 1980-84; treas. Jones-Harrison Home, 1967, bd. dirs., 1962-69, 2d v.p., chmn. fin., 1968-69; mem. Sen. David Durenberger's Women's Network, 1983-88. Durant award. Fellow Am. Bar Found.; mem. ABA (mediation task force family law sect. 1983-84), Minn. Bar Assn. (human rights com. family law sect., task force uniform marital property act 1984-85), Minn. Bar Found. (bd. 1991-94), Hennepin County Bar Assn. (pres. 1987-88, chmn. task force on pub. edn. 1984, chmn., mem. exec. com. family law sect. 1979-94), Minn. Inst. Legal Edn., Minn. Women's Lawyers (exec. com.), U. Minn. Law Sch. Alumni Assn. (dir. 1975-81, exec. com. 1981-83), Wellesley Club, Phi Beta Kappa. Home: 4980 Dockside Dr # 204 Fort Myers FL 33919-4657 Office: Gray Plant Mooty Mooty & Bennett 33 S 6th St Ste 3400 Minneapolis MN 55402-3796

NORTON, EUNICE, pianist; b. Mpls., June 30, 1908; d. Willis I. and Charlotte (O'Brien) N.; m. Bernard Lewis, May 4, 1934; 1 child, Norton Lewis. Student, U. Minn., 1922-24, Tobias Matthay Pianoforte Sch., London, 1924-31, Artur Schabel Master Piano Classes, Ger., 1931-33, Arthur Schabel Master Piano Classes, Italy, 1933; MusD (hon.), Wooster Coll., 1977. vis. prof. piano Carnegie Mellon U.; lectr. U. Pitts., Cath. U. Am.; lectr., condr. master piano classes univs.; condr. pvt. master classes, Pitts., N.Y.C., Vt.; dir. Peacham (Vt.) Piano Festivals; founder, musical dir. Pitts. New Friends of Music, Pitts. Concert Artists. Concert pianist U.S. Europe, 1927—; soloist with numerous symphony orchs. including N.Y. Philharm., Boston Symphony Orch., Phila. Symphony Orch., Pitts. Symphony Orch., Mpls. Symphony Orch., London Symphony Orch., Berlin Symphony Orch., also orchs. in Leipzig, Germany, Vienna, Austria, Birmingham, Eng., Manchester, Eng.; chamber musician with Budapest, Juilliard and Griller string quartets, Am. Chamber Orch.; recorded Well Tempered Clavier (J.S. Bach); performed Beethoven's entire piano sonatas, Carlow Coll., Pitts., 1983, U. Pitts., 1988, recorded ltd. edit., 1988; recorded 4 one-hour illustrated lectrs. on video "Teaching of Artur Schnabel", U. Pitts., 1987. Recipient Bach prize, 1927; recipient Chappell Gold medal Chappell Piano Co., London, 1928. Mem. Am. Matthay Piano Assn. (founder mem.), Sigma Alpha Iota (hon.). Club: Tuesday Musical (hon.) (Pitts.). Home: 5863 Marlborough Rd Pittsburgh PA 15217-1415 *I am convinced that music is not an ornament but an essential part of life. It is a serious activity. I live with the principle of uncompromising adherence to musical values without regard for popular approval and economic gain.*

NORTON, FLOYD LIGON, IV, lawyer; b. Shreveport, La., Oct. 23, 1950; s. Floyd Ligon III and Grace Louise (Julian) N.; m. Kathleen Fair Patterson, Nov. 24, 1979; children: Caroline, Elizabeth. BA with honors, U. Va., 1972, JD, 1975. Bar: Va. 1975, D.C. 1975. Assoc. Reid & Priest, Washington, 1975-83, ptnr., 1983—. Mem. ABA, Fed. Energy Bar Assn. Episcopalian. Home: 4107 Bradley Ln Bethesda MD 20815-5236 Office: Reid & Priest 701 Pennsylvania Ave NW Washington DC 20004-2608

NORTON, GALE A., state attorney general; b. Wichita, Mar. 11, 1954; d. Dale Bentsen and Anna Jacqueline (Lansdowne) N.; m. John Goethe Hughes, Mar. 26, 1990. BA, U. Denver, 1975, JD, 1978. Bar: Colo. 1978, U.S. Supreme Ct. 1981. Jud. clk. Colo. Ct. of Appeals, Denver, 1978-79; sr. atty. Mountain States Legal Found., Denver, 1979-83; nat. fellow Hoover Instn. Stanford (Calif.) U., 1983-84; asst. to dep. sec. U.S. Dept. of Agr., Washington, 1984-85; assoc. solicitor U.S. Dept. of Interior, Washington, 1985-87; pvt. practice law Denver, 1987-90; atty. gen. State of Colo., Denver, 1991—; Murdock fellow Polit. Economy Rsch. Ctr., Bozeman, Mont., 1984; sr. fellow Ind. Inst., Golden, Colo., 1989-90; policy analyst Pres. Coun. on Environ. Quality, Washington, 1985-88; lectr. U. Denver Law Sch., 1989; transp. law program dir. U. Denver, 1978-79. Contbr. chpts. to books, articles to profl. jours. Participant Rep. Leadership Program, Colo., 1988, Colo. Leadership Forum, 1989; past chair Nat. Assn. Attys. Gen. Environ. Com.; co-chair Nat. Policy Forum Environment Coun. Named Young Career Woman Bus. and Profl. Wome, 1981, Young Lawyer of Yr., 1991. Mem. Federalist Soc., Colo. Women's Forum, Order of St. Ives. Republican. Methodist. Avocation: skiing. Office: Colo Dept of Law 1525 Sherman St 5th Fl Denver CO 80203

NORTON, GEORGE DAWSON, retired banker; b. Dry Ridge, Ky., Sept. 6, 1930; s. George Ruddle and Bessie (Caldwell) N.; m. Ellen Sue Hirsh, Mar. 1, 1949; children: June Karen Norton Hannah, Teresa Darlene Norton Bajkowsky, Hilary Janine. BS, Ea. Ky. U., 1952; LLB, Temple U., 1959; postgrad., Stonier Grad. Sch. Banking, Rutgers U., 1968. Exec. v.p., cashier CoreStates Bank, N.A., 1975-93; exec. v.p. CoreStates Fin. Corp., Phila., 1983-93; vice chmn. CoreStates Bank Del., Phila., 1985-93; pres., CEO Clymer Realty Corp., Phila., 1986-93; nat. chmn. Bank Adminstrn. Inst., Chgo.; mem. exec. com., dir. Cen. Phila. Devel. Corp., 1989; mem. exec. com. Ctrl. Phila. Devel. Corp., Ho. of Kids, Inc., Camden, N.J. Author: Payable Through Drafts, 1966 (Stonier award 1966). Capt. U.S. Army, 1951-54. Mem. Phila. Clearing House Assn. (pres. 1984-85), Pa. Bankers Assn. (mem. gov. coun., bd. dirs. 1983-86), Union League, Riverton (N.J.) Country Club. Republican. Baptist. Avocations: pilot, golf, bowling.

NORTON, GERALD PATRICK, lawyer; b. West Roxbury, Mass., Jan. 25, 1940; s. Thomas W. and Genevieve (Sweeny) N.; m. Judith C. Ralphs, Apr. 24, 1965 (dec. Oct. 1969); children: Jeremy, Elizabeth; m. Amanda B. Pedersen, Sept. 25, 1971; 1 child, Adam. AB magna cum laude, Princeton U., 1961; LLB magna cum laude, Columbia U., 1964. Bar: N.Y. 1964, D.C. 1966. Law clk. to judge U.S. Ct. Appeals (2d cir.), N.Y.C., 1964-65; assoc. Covington & Burling, Washington, 1965-73; asst. to solicitor gen. Dept. Justice, Washington, 1973-75; dep. gen. counsel FTC, Washington, 1975-79; ptnr. Pepper Hamilton & Scheetz, Washington, 1979-92, Harkins Cunningham, Washington, 1992—; mediator U.S. Dist. Ct. for D.C.; lectr. various seminars. Mng. and research editor Columbia U. Law Rev., 1963-64; contbr. articles to profl. jours. Bd. dirs. Washington Lawyer Com. for Civil Rights, 1984—; 1st v.p. dirs. Washington Met. Planning and Housing Assn., 1969-70; vol. atty. ACLU Washington. Recipient Arthur E. Flemming award Jaycees of Nat. Capital Area, 1979; named Grad. of Yr., Province I Phi Delta Phi, 1964. Mem. ABA, D.C. Bar Assn. (spl. com. on profl. responsibility for govt. employees, legal ethics com.), D.C. Cir. Jud. Conf., Nat. Assn. Atty.'s Gen., Supreme Ct. Moot Ct. Democrat. Office: Harkins Cunningham 1300 19th St NW Washington DC 20036-1609

NORTON, GLYN PETER, French literature educator; b. Exeter, Devonshire, Eng., May 22, 1941; s. Trevor Thomas and Betty (Marshall) N.; m. Victoria Josefina Perez, Oct. 28, 1966; children—Alexandra, Leslie. A.B., U. Mich., 1963, A.M., 1965, Ph.D., 1968. Asst. prof. Dartmouth Coll., Ha-

nover, N.H., 1968-71; prof. French lit. Pa. State U., University Park, 1971-88; prof. French lit., chmn. dept. romance langs, dir. Ctr. for Fgn. Langs., Lits. and Cultures Williams Coll., Williamstown, Mass., 1988-93, Adsit prof. Internat. Studies, 1993—. Author: Montaigne and the Introspective Mind, 1975; The Ideology and Language of Translation in Renaissance France, 1984; editor: The Cambridge History of Literary Criticism, vol. III; contbr. articles to ednl. jours. NEH fellow, 1973-74, Guggenheim fellow, 1986-87; Am. Council of Learned Socs. grantee, 1980-81, 85; recipient medal City of Melun, France, 1985. Mem. MLA, Renaissance Soc. Am., Soc. Franç aise des Seiziemistes. Avocations: music; gardening; traveling. Office: Williams Coll Dept Romance Langs Weston Hall Williamstown MA 01267

NORTON, HOWARD CHERRINGTON, leasing company executive; b. Payson, Utah, Apr. 29, 1955; s. Merlin J. Norton and Jane (Cherrington) Hinckley; m. Christine Lynne Stones, July 23, 1982; children: Alexandra, Dax, Mikelle. Grad., Westside High Sch., 1973. Gen. mgr. Transport Leasing, Ltd., Salt Lake City, 1973-75; regional v.p. F-B Truck Line Co., Salt Lake City, 1975-76; pres., chief exec. officer Lester Smith Trucking Inc., Denver, 1976-78; v.p., then pres. Great Western Leasing, Salt Lake City, 1978-82, chief exec. officer, 1988—; gen. mgr., sec. Oliver Internat., Inc., Salt Lake City, 1983-85; v.p. ops. PST Vans, Inc., Salt Lake City, 1985-88; v.p., bd. dirs. Norton Enterprises, Salt Lake City, 1987-89; mem. lessors conf. com. Ariz. Motor Transport Assn., Phoenix, 1989-90; mem. Nat. Truck Leasing System, Oakbrook, Ill., 1990—. Mem. Young Pres.' Orgn. Mormon. Office: Great Western Leasing Co 1305 W 2100 S Salt Lake City UT 84119-1403

NORTON, HUGH STANTON, economist, educator; b. Delta, Colo., Sept. 18, 1921; s. Cecil A. and Olive S. (Stanton) N.; m. Miriam Jarmon, Dec. 19, 1949 (dec. 1983); children: Pamela, John; m. Mary Jo Roberts. A.B., George Washington U., 1947, Ph.D., 1956. Johnson prof. econs. U. S.C., Columbia, 1968—; disting. prof. emeritus U. S.C., 1988—; cons. anti-trust and transp. econs. to indsl. firms. Author: The Role of the Economist in Government Policy Making, 1969, The World of the Economist, 1973, 2d edit., 1977, The Employment Act and the Council of Economic Advisers 1946-76, 1977, The Quest for Economic Stability: Roosevelt to Reagan, rev. edit., 1990. Served with Signal Corps AUS, 1942-45. Club: Cosmos (Washington). Home: 3335 Overcreek Rd Columbia SC 29206-5145

NORTON, JAMES ADOLPHUS, higher education administrator and consultant, retired academic administrator, political science educator; b. Haynesville, La., May 28, 1922; s. George Thurman and Sue Annie (Tinsley) N.; m. Fay-Tyler Murray, Mar. 4, 1945; 1 child, Diana Maurine Norton Dicks. Student, La. Poly. Inst., 1939-42; B.A., La. State U., 1945, M.A., 1946; M.A., Harvard U., 1949, Ph.D., 1950; LL.D. (hon.), Cleve. Marshall Law Sch.; L.H.D. (hon.), Kent State U., 1973; D.Litt. (hon.), Urbana Coll., 1977; D.Public Service (hon.), Bowling Green State U., 1973; Litt.D. (hon.), Baldwin Wallace Coll., 1978. Instr. U. Tex., 1946-47; vis. asst. prof. La. State U., 1949; asst. prof. Fla. State U., 1949-52, assoc. prof., 1952-56, prof., 1956; lectr. Sch. Pub. Health, Harvard U., 1954-55; vis. prof. Western Res. U., 1959-60; prof. area devel. Case Inst. Tech., 1960-62; exec. dir. Cleve. Met. Services Commn., 1956-59; pres. Greater Cleve. Associated Found., 1962-73; exec. dir. Cleve. Found., 1968-73; chancellor Ohio Bd. Regents, 1973-78; vis. chancellor Case Western Res. U., 1978-79; urban scholar in residence Cleve. State U., 1979-80; prof. U.Va., Charlottesville, 1981-88; dir. Ctr. for Pub. Service U. Va., 1981-88; interim pres. Hiram (Ohio) Coll., 1988-89; interim chancellor U. Md. System, Adelphi, 1989-90, ret., 1990; cons. in field Charlottesville, Va., 1990—; interim chancellor Lamar U. System, Beaumont, Tex., 1992-94; Fla. corr. Pub. Mgmt. and Municipal Yearbook, 1952-56; lectr. Murray Seasongood Good Govt. Fund, 1957-65; radio announcer, 1945-46, TV moderator, 1961-62, cons. state programs in higher edn., 1979—; dir. Third Century Project on Higher Edn. in N.C.; chmn. Coalition to Improve Mgmt. in State and Local Govt. Author: The Metro Experience, 1963, Continuing the Conversation, 1987; contbr. articles to profl. jours. Spl. projects officer Fla. Civil Def. Council, 1956; chmn. housing com., trustee Cleve. Urban League, 1959-62; mem. Mayor's Com. on Met. Charter, 1957-61; chmn. research com. Greater Cleve. Growth Bd., 1962-68; chmn. econ. research com. Ohio Dept. Devel., 1965-69; adv. com. Urban poverty, met. govt. Council for Econ. Opportunity, 1968-69; mem. Ohio Citizens Council for State Legislature, 1970-71; co-chmn. Va. Commn. of Higher Edn. Task Force on Evaluation of Grad. Edn. Programs, 1982-83; trustee Cleve. Baptist Assn., 1959-63, Hiram Coll., 1979—, St. Mary's Sem., 1970-73; bd. dirs. Lincoln Inst. Land Policy, 1986-94. Served with USAAF, 1942-43. Recipient Fruin-Colnon award Nat. Municipal League, 1959, Distinguished Service award United Appeal, 1964, Exec. Order Ohio Commodores, 1966; Distinguished Service award Kent State U., 1969; Disting. Service award Feds. Community Planning, 1973; named Ernest J. Bohn Adminstr. of Yr., 1979. Mem. Am. Polit. Sci. Assn., Nat. Mcpl. League (trustee 1975-78), State Higher Edn. Exec. Officers Orgn. (chmn. fed. rels. com. 1977-78), Internat. City Mgrs. Assn., Am. Soc. Pub. Adminstrn. (past pres., chmn. Found. 1985-89), Nat. Acad. Pub. Adminstrn., James A. Garfield Soc. Hiram Coll., Pi Sigma Alpha, Phi Alpha Sigma, Kappa Sigma. Democrat. Baptist. Home: 2617 C Barracks Rd Charlottesville VA 22901

NORTON, JAMES J., union official; b. Boston, June 9, 1930; s. Patrick P. and Anne (Flaherty) N.; m. Patricia A. Tuley, Sept. 19, 1953; children: James, Ann Marie, Robert, Thomas, Donald, David, Brian. Treas. Boston Photo Engravers Union, 1957-60, pres., 1960-62; internat. rep. Graphic Arts Union, Boston, 1962-78; sec. treas. Graphic Arts Union, Washington, 1979-83; rec. and fin. sec. Graphic Communications Internat. Union, 1983-85, pres., 1983—; exec. coun. AFL-CIO, Union Labor Life Ins. Co.; bd. govs. ARC. Coach Peewee-Bantum level Dorchester Youth Hockey Program, Boston, 1958-79; coach Midget level Fairfax (Va.) Hockey Program, 1980-81; exec. bd. mem. ARC. Mem. AFL-CIO (exec. coun.), Montclair C. of C. Roman Catholic. Lodge: K.C. Office: Graphic Comms Internat Union 1900 L St NW Washington DC 20036-5002

NORTON, JODY (JOHN DOUGLAS NORTON), English language educator; b. Princeton, N.J., Nov. 13, 1943; s. Paul Foote and Alison Edmunds (Stuart) N.; m. Alexandra Holt Morey, Aug. 20, 1977; children: Joselle, Jackson, Tayo. BA, U. Mass., Amherst, 1966; MA, U. Calif., Berkeley, 1981, PhD, 1988. Vis. asst. prof. Rice U., Houston, 1988-89, Albion (Mich.) Coll., 1989-94; lectr. Ea. Mich. U., Ypsilanti, 1994—. Contbr. articles to profl. jours. Fellow U. Calif., 1979-80, 80-81, 84-85, 87-88, Yale U., 1966-67; faculty rsch. grantee Albion Coll., 1992, 93, 94. Mem. MLA, Midwest MLA, Soc. for Critical Exch., Phi Beta Kappa, Phi Kappa Phi. Avocations: tennis, mountain climbing, camping, playing electric bass, blues and country western music. Home: 415 Ventura Ct Ann Arbor MI 48103 Office: Eastern Mich U Dept English Lang and Lit Ypsilanti MI 48197

NORTON, JUDY, actress; b. Santa Monica, Calif., Jan. 29; d. Harry Vincent and Constance (Glazebrook) Norton; m. Randy Apostle, Apr. 8, 1991. Participated in 2 world skydiving records. Appeared in film Hotel, 1966; actress repertory co. The Stable Players, 1969-71, Cinderella, 1981, Annie Get Your Gun, 1983, I Ought to Be in Pictures, 1983, Perfect Pitch, 1984, Spring at Marino, 1984, Times of Your Life, 1985, Social Security (Stage West, Calgary, Can.), 1987, Sound of Music, 1989, Alive & Kicking, 1989, Move Over, Mrs. Markham (Stage West, Can.), 1991, Weekend Comedy (Stage West, Can.), 1991, Volstead Blues (Souris Valley Theatre, Can.), 1993, Ranchers & Rustlers (Can.), 1994; TV movies include The Homecoming, 1971, Valentine, 1978, Valentine's Day-A Love Story, 1982, A Day of Thanks, 1982, Volstead Blues (Souris Valley Theatre, Can.), 1993, dir. 1994; appeared in TV series The Waltons, 1972-81, also Circus of the Stars, 1983, 84; TV movie A Walton Thanksgiving, 1993, A Walton Wedding, 1995; TV guest appearances in The Love Boat, 1981, Trial by Jury, 1989; co-writer Knaughty Knights, 1992, Ranchers And Rustlers, 1992; co-dir., co-writer Laura & Johnny Were Lovers, 1992, Hot Summer Nights, 1992, Gillian's Island, 1992, Murder on the Prairie Express, 1993, Mugs and Molls, 1993, I Dream of Jimmy, 1993, Rock N Roll Candidate, 1993, Star Trax, 1993, There's No Life Like It, 1993, He Shoots, She Scores, 1994, Of Course, Elvis Will Be Here, 1994, Monster High Reunion, 1994, Don't Touch That Dial, 1994, Ranchers and Rustlers II, 1994, Captain Vancouver & The Land Pirates, 1995, Philip Harlow, 1995, Phantom of the Theatre, 1995. Mem. AFTRA, SAG, Actors Equity, Can. Actors Equity.

NORTON, MARY BETH, history educator, author; b. Ann Arbor, Mich., Mar. 25, 1943; d. Clark Frederic and Mary Elizabeth (Lunny) N. BA, U. Mich., 1964; MA, Harvard U., 1965, PhD, 1969; DHL (hon.), Siena Coll., 1983, Marymount Manhattan Coll., 1984, De Pauw U., 1989; DLitt (hon.), Ill. Wesleyan U., 1992. Asst. prof. history U. Conn., Storrs, 1969-71; from asst. prof. to prof. Cornell U., Ithaca, N.Y., 1971-87, Mary Donlon Alger prof. Am. history, 1987—. Author: The British-Americans: The Loyalist Exiles in England, 1774-1789, 1972, Liberty's Daughters: The Revolutionary Experience of American Women, 1750-1800, 1980 (Berkshire prize for Best Book Woman Historian 1980); co-author: A People and A Nation, 1982, 4th rev. edit., 1994; editor: Major Problems in American Women's History, 1989, AHA Guide to Historical Literature, 3d rev. edit., 1995; co-editor: Women of America: A History, 1979, To Toil the Livelong Day: America's Women at Work, 1790-1980, 1987; contbr. articles to profl. jours. Trustee Cornell U., 1973-75, 83-88; mem. Nat. Coun. Humanities, Washington, 1979-84. Woodrow Wilson Found. fellow, 1964-65, NEH fellow, 1974-75, Shelby Cullom Davis Ctr. fellow Princeton U., 1977-78, Rockefeller Found. fellow, 1986-87, Soc. for Humanities fellow Cornell U., 1989-90, John Simon Guggenheim Meml. Found. fellow, 1993-94. Fellow Soc. Am. Historians (exec. bd. 1974-87, Allan Nevins prize 1970); mem. Am. Hist. Assn. (v.p. for rsch. 1985-87) Orgn. Am. Historians (exec. bd. 1983-86), Berkshire Conf. Women Historians (pres. 1983-85). Democrat. Methodist. Office: Cornell U Dept History Ithaca NY 14853

NORTON, NATHANIEL GOODWIN, marketing executive; b. Chgo., Jan. 7, 1948; s. Wilbur H. and Eva (Geneen) N.; m. Ariel Taylor, Nov. 15, 1980 (div. July 1987). BA, U. N.C., 1969. Mktg. mgr. Canteen Corp., Chgo., 1971-74; sr. v.p. Mathieu, Gerfen & Bresner, N.Y.C., 1974-83; pres., ptnr. Rand Pub. Rels., N.Y.C., 1983-89; ind. marketing cons. North Hampton, N.H., 1989—.

NORTON, NORMAN JAMES, exploration geologist; b. Du Quoin, Ill., Apr. 26, 1933; s. James Harlan Norton and Helen Jane (Riley) Norton Rosen; m. Bettie Jean Greer, July 7, 1955; children—Matthew James, Jane Alison. B.S., So. Ill. U., 1958; M.S., U. Minn., 1960, Ph.D., 1963. Successively, asst., assoc., then full prof. biology Hope Coll., Holland, Mich., 1964-74; prof., chmn. dept. biology Ball State U., Munice, Ind., 1974-78, acting v.p. acad. affairs, 1978-79; acting dean Coll. Arts and Scis. Ball State U., 1979-81; provost, v.p. acad. affairs Ind. U. Pa., 1981-83; cons. geologist Gulf Oil Corp., Houston, 1970-83; sr. staff geologist Gulf Oil Exploration and Prodn. Co., Houston, 1983-85; biostratigrapher, stratigraphic services, exploration Chevron Overseas Petroleum Inc., San Ramon, Calif., 1985-91; supr. biostratigraphy sect. Chevron U.S.A., Inc., Houston, 1991—; acting divsn. geologist Chevron U.S.A. Inc., Houston, 1993-95, divsn. geologist, 1995—. Contbr. articles to profl. jours. Served with USAF, 1952-56. Recipient Outstanding Tchr. Educator award Sr. Class of Hope Coll., 1969; acad. citation for disting. achievement Mich. Acad. Scis., Arts and Letters, 1969. Mem. Am. Assn. Stratigraphic Palynologists (Disting. Svc. award 1978, chmn. bd. trustees found., archives com. 1970—, constn. revision com.), Paleobot. Soc. Am. Home: 4419 St Michaels Ct Sugar Land TX 77479-2989 Office: CUSA PO Box 1635 Houston TX 77251-1635

NORTON, PAUL ALLEN, insurance executive; b. Ardmore, S.D., Sept. 10, 1913; s. Albert James and Leota (Clute) N.; m. Ruth Stephens Richards, July 4, 1941; children: Richard Allen, Carolyn Ruth (Mrs. Robert Padgette). BA magna cum laude, Chadron State Coll., 1935, LLH (hon.), 1987; M.B.A. with distinction, Harvard U., 1937; LL.D., Bethany Coll., 1973. Mgr. N.Y. Life Ins. Co., Worcester, Mass., 1938-41, Boston., 1941-43; mgr. N.Y. Life Ins. Co., Phila., 1944-47; asst. supt. agys. N.Y. Life Ins. Co., 1947; mgr. N.Y. Life Ins. Co., Houston, 1948-49; supt. agys. N.Y. Life Ins. Co., N.Y., 1947; mgr. N.Y. Life Ins. Co., Houston, 1948-49; supt. agys. N.Y. Life Ins. Co., N.Y.C., 1950; v.p. charge group sales N.Y. Life Ins. Co., 1951, agy. v.p., 1952, field v.p., 1952, regional v.p., 1953, v.p., 1954-59, v.p. in charge sales mgmt., 1959-62, v.p. in charge mktg., 1962-64, sr. v.p. in charge mktg., 1964-69, exec. v.p., 1969-73. Contbr. articles to profl. publs. Hon. chmn. Greater N.Y. council Boy Scouts Am. Mem. Life Ins. Agy. Mgmt. Assn. (past pres.), Nat. Assn. Life Underwriters (v.p. Worcester chpt. 1940-41), Exec. Assn. (pres. Worcester chpt. 1939-41), Am. Soc. C.L.U.s (dir.). Clubs: Harvard, Economic (N.Y.C.); Am. Yacht (Rye, N.Y.). Home: 20 Church St Greenwich CT 06830-5631 Office: Church Pension Fund 800 2nd Ave New York NY 10017-4709

NORTON, PETER BOWES, publishing company executive; b. London, May 4, 1929; came to U.S., 1969; s. James Peter and Margaret (Bowes) N.; m. Heather Pearch, Jan. 16, 1954; children: Jan Heather, Fiona Mary. Student, S.E. Essex Tech. Coll., 1942-45, Royal Naval Colls., 1949-54. Commd. officer Royal Navy, 1945, advanced through grades to lt., 1954, ret., 1960; pers. officer United Dominions Trust, London, 1960-63; jr. exec. to mng. dir. Ency. Britannica, London, 1963-68, mng. dir., 1968-69; v.p. internat. div. Ency. Britannica, Chgo., 1969-70; pres. Ency. Britannica Can., 1970-73, Ency. Britannica U.S.A., Chgo., 1974-85; pres. Ency. Britannica Inc., 1986-93, pres., CEO, 1993—; also bd. dirs. Ency. Britannica Inc., Chgo.; bd. dirs. Ency. Universalis (Paris); chmn., bd. dirs. Ency. Britannica Ednl. Corp., Chgo., 1988—. Bd. dirs. William Benton Found. Fellow Chartered Inst. Secs. (Eng.), Chartered Inst. Administrs. U.K., Chartered Inst. Dirs. U.K.; mem. Japan Am. Soc. Chgo., Inc., Chgo. Club. Mem. Ch. of Eng. Clubs: Royal Automobile (London); Chgo., Carlton. Avocations: tennis, reading. Home: 180 E Pearson St Apt 3401 Chicago IL 60611-2125 Office: Ency Britannica Inc 310 S Michigan Ave Chicago IL 60604

NORTON, PETER J., publishing executive. Chmn. of the bd. Merriam-Webster Inc., Springfield, Mass. Office: Merriam Webster Inc 47 Federal St Springfield MA 01105-3805

NORTON, ROSANNA, costume designer. Costume designer: (films) Carrie, 1976, (with Pam Scrape) Outlaw Blues, 1977, I Wanna Hold Your Hand, 1978, Head Over Heels, 1979, Airplane!, 1980, The Stunt Man, 1980, (with Elois Jenssen) Tron, 1982 (Academy award nomination best costume design 1982), Hard to Hold, 1984, Explorers, 1985, Nothing in Common, 1986, Ruthless People, 1986, Innerspace, 1987, Loverboy, 1989, The 'Burbs, 1989, Robocop 2, 1990, Gremlins 2: The New Batch, 1990, Frankie and Johnny, 1992, The Flintstones, 1994, Angels in the Outfield, 1994, (TV movies) Rascals and Robbers: The Secret Adventures of Tom Sawyer and Huckleberry Finn, 1982. Office: Smith Gosnell Nicholson & Assoc PO Box 1166 1515 Palisades Dr Pacific Palisades CA 90272*

NORTON, STEPHEN ALLEN, geological sciences educator; b. Newton, Mass., May 21, 1940; m. Anne Peer, Apr. 25, 1970; children: David S., Lisa A., Stephen A. B.A., Princeton U., 1962; M.A., Harvard U., 1963, Ph.D., 1967. Prof. geol. scis. U. Maine, Orono, 1978—; chmn. dept. U. Maine-Orono, 1978-82, 93—, dean arts and scis., 1984-86. Fellow Geol. Soc. Am.; mem. Am. Soc. Limnology and Oceanography, Sigma Xi. Office: U Maine Dept Geol Scis Boardman Hall Orono ME 04469-5711

NORTON, THOMAS EDMOND, state senator, engineer; b. Bremerton, Wash., July 31, 1940; s. Edmond Stanley and Violet Marian (Gustafson) N.; children by previous marriage: Konnie, Kent, Kim; m. Pamalyn Kay McEver, Dec. 23, 1976; children: Paige, Whitney. BS in Civil Engring., Colo. State U., 1964, MS in Sanitary Engring., 1969. Profl. engr. V.p. engring. svcs. Nelson, Haley, Patterson, Quirk, Greeley, Colo., 1963-76; v.p. Norton, Underwood and Lamb/KLH Engring., Greeley, 1976—; rep. Colo Legis., Denver, 1986-88, senator, 1988—; pres. Colo. State Senate, Denver, 1993—; bd. dirs. First Nat. Bank, Greeley, Colo. Natural Gas Assistance Found., Denver. Recipient Annual Right Cole awrd Colo. Community Corrections Coalition, 1990, Spl. Recognition award Am. Inst. Architects, 1989; named Bus. Legislator of Yr. Colo. Pub. Affairs Coun., 1989. Republican. Methodist. Office: Colo State Senate State Capital Denver CO 80203

NORUM, DAVID P., retail company executive; b. 1931; married. BS, Ill. Wesleyan U., 1958; JD, John Marshall Law Sch., 1964. Staff asst. Sears, Roebuck & Co., Chgo., 1959-68, nat. coordinator sales use taxes, 1968-71, asst. mgr. state & local taxes, 1971-73, territorial tax mgr. Midwest region, 1973-80, asst. to v.p. taxes, 1980, corp. v.p. taxes, 1988—. Served as capt. U.S. Army, 1973-74. Office: Sears Roebuck & Co Sears Towers Chicago IL 60684

NORVELL, PATSY, artist; b. Greenville, S.C., July 13, 1942; d. Wendell Norvell and Margaret Marie (Schaefer) Nichols; m. Robert Rahway Zakanitch, May 2, 1982; 1 child, Amelia Zakanitch Norvell. BA, Bennington Coll., 1964; studied with David Smith, Bolton Landing, N.Y., 1964; MA, CUNY-Hunter Coll., 1970. Asst. instr. Colo. Springs (Colo.) Fine Arts Ctr., 1967; instr. dept. art Rutgers U., Newark, 1969-70, Montclair (N.J.) State Coll., 1970-74; assoc. in sculpture Columbia U., N.Y.C., 1977; instr. pvt. studio seminar, N.Y.C, 1973-74; adj. lectr. in sculpture SUNY, Queens, 1978-79; adj. asst. prof. dept. art Hunter Coll., N.Y.C., 1979-81, vis. asst. prof., 1982-83; vis. artist N.Y. Exptl. Glass Workshop, 1980, 84; cons. sculpture panel N.Y. State Creative Artist Pub. Svc., 1980, 81; panelist sculpture fellowship N.J. State Coun. Arts, 1983, gen. svc. adminstrn. NEH, 1984, Hunter's Point Selection Com., 1987; presenter numerous seminars. One woman shows include A.I.R. Gallery, N.Y.C., 1973, 75, 78, 80, 82, 87, 91, LaGrangeville, N.Y., 1977, Vassar College & Barrett Ho., Poughkeepsie, N.Y., 1979, Avery Fisher Hall, Lincoln Ctr., N.Y.C., 1980, Matthew Hamilton Gallery, Phila., 1984; exhibited in group shows at 117 Prince St, N.Y.C., 1972, Kent (Ohio) State Galleries, 1972, Alonzo Gallery, N.Y.C., 1972, Newark Mus., 1973, Nancy Hoffmann Gallery, N.Y.C., 73, Erotic Art Gallery, N.Y.C., 1973, Indpls. Mus. Art, Cin., 1974, Taft Mus., Cin., 1974, Central Hall Gallery, Port Washington, N.Y., 1975, 77, Skidmore Coll., Saratoga Springs, N.Y., 1975, Fine Arts Bldg., N.Y.C., 1976, Webb and Parsons, Bedford Village, N.Y., 1976, Hurlbutt Gallery, Greenwich, Conn., 1977, County Mus. Fine Arts, Roslyn, N.Y., 1977, Whitney Downtown Mus., N.Y.C., 1978, 79, Robert Freidus Gallery, N.Y.C., 1978, Ginza Kaigaken, Tokyo, 1978, Battery Park Landfill, N.Y.C., 1978, Thorpe Intermedia Gallery, Sparkill, N.Y., 1979, Perkins Ctr. Arts, Moorestown, N.J., 1979, McKintosch/Drysdale Gallerym Washington, 1980, Danforth (Mass.) Mus., 1981, Berkshire (Mass.) Mus., 1981-82, Women's Hall of Fame, Seneca Falls, N.Y., 1981, U. Houston, 1981, Sidney Janis Gallery, N.Y.C., 1982, Norton Gallery Art, West Palm Beach, Fla., 1983, High Mus. Art, Atlanta, 1983, Nat. Gallery Art, Washington, 1984, Palladium, N.Y.C., 1985, Tanabaum Gallery, N.Y.C., Contemporary Arts Ctr., Cin., 1986, Lowe Art Mus., Coral Gables, Fla., 1987, Max Protetch Gallery, N.Y.C., 1987, Toledo Mus. Art, 1988, Fort Wayne (Ind.) Mus. Art, 1988, The Home Saving Tower, L.A., 1989, Md. Coll. Art and Design, 1989, Bernice Steinbaum Gallery, 1989-93, Noyes Mus., Oceanville, N.J., 1990, Art Mus., Southampton, N.Y., 1991, Midtown-Payson Gallery, 1992, Willow Gallery, N.Y.C., 1993, Steinbaum-Krauss Gallery, N.Y.C., 1993; others; commd. works include glass, mirror, railing, and stone sculptures for Nicholas Recital Hall, Douglass Coll., New Brunswick, N.J., 1981-82, Bridgeport (Conn.) Fed. Bldg. and Courthouse, 1983-85, Battery Park City Authority, N.Y.C., 1983-86, 4600 East-West Hwy, Bethesda, Md., 1984-88, Bellevue Hosp., 1986, Home Savings Am. Tower, L.A., 1987-88, 14th St. Union Sq. Local Devel. Corp., 1988-94, Beverly and Cortelyou Subway Stas., M.T.A., N.Y.; represented in permanent collections including Jim Henson Apt., N.Y.C., Brown's Residence, Bethesda, Md., Steinbaum Residence, L.I., N.Y., Bille Norma Roth Collection, Winterhaven, Fla. Recipient Spl. Recognition award Art Commn. N.Y.C., 1993; Nat. Endowment for Arts artist fellow, 1976-77. Home: 78 Greene St New York NY 10012

NORVILLE, CRAIG HUBERT, lawyer; b. N.Y.C., June 10, 1944; s. Hubert G. and Harriett (Johnson) N.; 1 child, Margaret Amelia. AB, Harvard U., 1966; LLB, U. Va., 1969. Bar: N.Y. 1971, Pa. 1979, Tenn. 1985. Instr. law U. Mich., 1969-70; assoc. Cravath, Swaine & Moore, N.Y.C., 1970-76; sr. atty. Bethlehem (Pa.) Steel Corp., 1976-80; v.p., assoc. gen. counsel Holiday Corp. (name changed to The Promus Cos. Inc.), Memphis, 1980-84, v.p., gen. counsel, 1984-86, sr. v.p., gen. counsel, 1986-93, spl. counsel, 1993—. Articles editor U. Va. Law Rev. Mem. Raven Soc., Hasty Pudding Inst. of 1770, Order of Coif, Harvard Varsity Club (Cambridge, Mass.), Univ. Club (Memphis). Avocations: tennis, golf, skiing, fishing. Office: Brinkley Plz 80 Monroe 7th Flr Memphis TN 38104

NORVILLE, DEBORAH, news correspondent; b. Aug. 8, 1958; m. Karl Wellner; 2 children: Karl Nikolai, Kyle Maximilian. BJ, U. Ga., 1979. Reporter Sta. WAGA-TV, Atlanta, 1978-79; anchor, reporter, 1979-81; anchor, reporter Sta. WMAQ-TV, Chgo., 1982-86; anchor NBC News, N.Y.C., 1987-89; news anchor Today Show, NBC, N.Y.C., 1989, co-anchor, 1990-92; corr. Street Stories, CBS, N.Y.C., 1992-94; co-anchor America Tonight, CBS, N.Y.C., 1994; anchor Inside Edition, King World Prodns., 1994—; contbg. editor McCall's, N.Y.C. Bd. dirs. Greater N.Y. coun. Girl Scouts US. Recipient Outstanding Young Alumni award Sch. Journalism, U. Ga., Emmy award, 1985-86, 89; named Person of Yr., Chgo. Broadcast Advt. Club, 1989, Anchor of Yr. 2000, Washington Journalism Rev., 1989. Mem. Soc. Profl. Journalists. Office: Inside Edition 402 E 76th St New York NY 10021

NORWOOD, BERNARD, economist; b. Boston, Nov. 21, 1922; s. Hyman and Rose (Fink) N.; m. Janet Lippe, June 25, 1943; children: Stephen Harlan, Peter Carlton. B.A., Boston U., 1947; M.A., Fletcher Sch. Law and Diplomacy, 1948, Ph.D., 1957. Internat. economist State Dept., 1949-58; joined U.S. Fgn. Service, 1955; 1st sec. U.S. mission to European Communities, Brussels, Belgium, 1958-62; asst. chief commi. policy and treaties div. Dept. State, 1962; chmn. trade staff com. Office Spl. Rep. for Trade Negotiations, Exec. Office Pres., 1963-67; assigned The Nat. War Coll., 1967-68; adviser div. internat finance bd. govs. Fed. Res. System, 1968-75; prin. assoc., sr. cons. Nathan Assocs., Inc., 1975-94; Mem. U.S. delegation to negotiations and confs. GATT, Geneva, Switzerland, 1953-67. Served with AUS, 1943-46. Home: 6409 Marjory Ln Bethesda MD 20817-5805

NORWOOD, CAROLE GENE, middle school educator; b. Odessa, Tex., Feb. 27, 1943; d. Perry Eugene and Jeffie Lynn (Stephens) Knowles; m. James Ralph Norwood, Aug. 4, 1973. BA, U. Tex., 1966; MA, N. North Tex., 1975; cert. ESL, Our Lady of the Lake U., San Antonio, 1988. Cert. Sec. Edn. English, Spanish, ESL. Student intern Dept. of the Interior, Washington, 1962; receptionist Senate Chambers, Austin, Tex., 1965; English instr. Universidade Mackenzie, Sao Paulo, Brazil, 1966-67, Uniao Cultural Brasil-Estados Unidos, Sao Paulo, 1966-67; tchr. Terrell (Tex.) Jr. Sr. High Sch., 1967-68, Agnew Jr. High Sch., Mesquite, Tex., 1968-70; teaching asst. U. North Tex. Denton, Tex., 1970-71; sec. to pres. The Village Bank, Dallas, 1971-72; tchr. Plano (Tex.) High Sch., 1972-74; ESL adult edn. tchr. Dallas, 1972-73; tchr. Brentwood Middle Sch., San Antonio, 1975-90; instructional specialist Gus Garcia Jr. High Sch., San Antonio, 1990—; interdisciplinary team leader, 1992-93; yearbook and newspaper sponsor, Agnew Jr. High Sch., 1969-70. Contbr. articles to profl. jours. Mem. World Wildlife Fund, Audubon Soc., Nat. Wildlife Fedn., Nature Conservancy, San Antonio Museum Assn., San Antonio Zoological Soc., Los Padrinos (Mission Rd. Devel. Ctr.); U.I.L. coach 1976-87, 92-93. Named Outstanding Young Woman of Am., 1972. Mem. AAUW, NEA, ASCD, Nat. Coun. Tchrs. English, San Antonio Area Coun. Tchrs. English, Tex. State Tchrs. Assn., Edgewood Classroom Tchrs. Assn. (faculty rep. 1991-94), Longhorn Singers Alumni Assn., Tex. Execs. Alumni Assn. Delta Kappa Gamma (chpt. pres. 1990-92, San Antonio coordinating coun. chair 1995—, state program com. mem. 1995—). Presbyterian. Office: Edgewood Ind Sch Dist Gus Garcia Jr School 3306 Ruiz San Antonio TX 78228

NORWOOD, CHARLES W., JR., congressman; b. Valdosta, Ga., July 27, 1942; m. Gloria Norwood; 2 children. BS, Ga. So. U., 1964; DDS, Georgetown U., 1967. Pvt. practice Augusta, Ga., 1969—; owner Norwood Tree Nursery, 1984—; mem. 104th Congress from 10th Ga. dist., 1995—. Capt. U.S. Army, 1967-69, Vietnam. Decorated Combat Medic badge, Bronze Star for Valorous Svc., Bronze Star for Meritorious Achievement. Mem. Ga. Dental Assn. Republican. Methodist. Office: US Ho of Reps Washington DC 20515

NORWOOD, DEBORAH ANNE, law librarian; b. Honolulu, Nov. 12, 1950; d. Alfred Freeman and Helen G. (Papsch) N.; 1 child, Nicholas. BA, U. Wash., 1972; JD, Willamette U., 1974; M in Law Librarianship, U. Wash., 1979. Bar: Wash. U.S. Dist. Ct. (we. dist) 1975, U.S. Ct. Appeals (9th cir.) 1980. Ptnr. Evans and Norwood, Seattle, 1975-79; law librarian U.S. Courts Library, Seattle, 1980-89; state law librarian Wash. State Law Libr., Olympia, 1989—, reporter of decisions, 1994—; adv. bd. mem. U. Wash. Library Automation Cert. Program, Seattle, 1988-89. Mem. Am. Assn. Law Librs., Am. Libr. Assn. Office: Wash State Law Libr PO Box 40751 Temple of Justice Olympia WA 98504-0751

NORWOOD, GEOFFREY ALEXANDER, hospital administrator; b. Erwin, N.C., Feb. 26, 1950; s. George McIntosh and Zabelle (Corwin) N.; m. Christine Cramer, July 12, 1975; children: Bryan Teague, Kathryn Blakely. BA in English, U. N.C., 1972; M in Hosp. Adminstrn., George Washington U., 1978. Fin. planner Meridian Engring., Phila., 1972-75; adminstrv. resident St. Luke's Med. Ctr., Phoenix, 1977-78; with planning dept. Scottsdale (Ariz.) Meml. Hosp., 1978-80, mgr. Family Health Unit, 1980-82; asst. adminstr. United Gen. Hosp., Sedro Woolley, Wash., 1982-84, chief exec. officer, 1984—. Pres. Babe Ruth Baseball League, Skagit County, Wash.; bd. dirs. United Way, Skagit County. Mem. Am. Coll. Health Care Execs., Wash. State Hosp. Assn. (mem. planning com. 1985), Hosp. Shared Services Assn. Presbyterian. Lodge: Rotary (bd. dirs. local chpt.). Avocations: baseball, fishing, traveling. Office: Phoebe Putney Mem Hosp PO Box 1828 417 3rd Ave Albany GA 31703

NORWOOD, GEORGE JOSEPH, pharmacy educator; b. Clover, Va., Oct. 7, 1938; s. George Washington and Sara (Bailey) N.; m. Elaine Preece, Aug. 20, 1960; children: Joseph Derrick, Kevin Todd. Student, Randolph Macon Coll., 1957-58; B.S., Med. Coll. Va., N.D., 1970. Registered pharmacist. Va., N.D. Asst. prof. pharmacy adminstrn. U. Iowa, Iowa City, 1969-72, assoc. prof., 1972-74, assoc. prof. pharm. socioecons., 1974-77, prof., 1977-78, head dept. pharm. socioecons., 1974-78, dir. health services Research Ctr., 1978-81; dean Coll. Pharmacy N.D. State U., Fargo, 1981-86; dean Southeastern U. Coll. Pharm., North Miami Beach, Fla., 1986-90; prof., chmn. pharm. adminstrn. Sch. Pharmacy, U. N.C., Chapel Hill, 1990—; cons. in field. Author: Capitation for Pharmacy Services, 1982; contbr. articles to profl. jours. Mem. health manpower com. Iowa Office for Programming and Planning, Des Moines, 1975-76, mem. health personnel info. services bd., 1975-76. HEW grantee, 1976; Nat. Ctr. for Health Services Research grantee, 1978, 79, 80. Fellow Acad. Pharm. Scis. (chmn. econ. and adminstrv. scis. 1976-77); mem. Am. Pharm. Assn. (del. 1976-81), Am. Assn. Colls. Pharmacy (del. 1974-76), Sigma XI, Rho Chi, Kappa Psi. Home: 321 Azalea Dr Chapel Hill NC 27514 Office: U NC Sch Pharmacy Beard Hall A 7360 Chapel Hill NC 27599

NORWOOD, JANET LIPPE, economist; b. Newark, Dec. 11, 1923; d. M. Turner and Thelma (Levinson) Lippe; m. Bernard Norwood, June 25, 1943; children—Stephen Harlan, Peter Carlton. BA, Douglass Coll., 1945; MA, Tufts U., 1946; PhD, Fletcher Sch. Law and Diplomacy, 1949; LLD (hon.), Fla. Internat. U., 1979; LL.D. (hon.), Carnegie Mellon U., 1984. Instr. Wellesley Coll., 1949-49; economist William L. Clayton Ctr., Tufts U., 1953-58; with Bur. Labor Stats., U.S. Dept. Labor, Washington, 1963-91; dep. commr., then acting commr. Bur. Labor Stats. Dept. Labor, Washington, 1975-79, commr. labor stats., 1979-92; sr. fellow The Urban Inst., Washington, 1992—; dir. Republic Nat. Bank, CIESIN, chair adv. coun. unemployment compensation, 1993—; mem. com. on nat. stats. Nat. Acad. Sci. Author papers, reports in field. Recipient Disting. Achievement award Dept. Labor, 1972, Spl. Commendation award, 1977, Philip Arnow award, 1979, Elmer Staats award, 1982, Pub. Svc. award, 1984; named to Hall Disting. Alumni, Rutgers U., 1987; recipient Presdl. Disting. Exec. rank, 1988. Fellow AAAS, Am. Statis. Assn. (pres. 1989), Royal Statis. Soc., Nat. Assn. Bus. Economists; mem. Am. Econ. Assn., Indsl. Rels. Rsch. Assn., Women's Caucus in Stats., Com. Status Women Econs. Profession, Internat. Statis. Inst., Internat. Assn. Ofcls. Stats., Nat. Acad. Pub. Adminstrn. (vice chair bd. trustees), Nat. Inst. Statis. Sci. (bd. trustees); mem. Cosmos Club (v.p.), Douglas Coll. Soc. Disting. Achievement. Home: 6409 Marjory Ln Bethesda MD 20817-5805 Office: The Urban Inst 1000 Wilson Blvd # 2710 Arlington VA 22209-3901

NORWOOD, PHILIP WELTNER, lawyer; b. Tallahassee, July 25, 1947; s. William Usher and May Pope (Weltner) N.; m. Marianne Battistone, Jan. 18, 1992; children from previous marriage: Elizabeth Pritchard, Hopewell Hull, Catherine Dalton. BA with honors, Washington & Lee U., 1969; MA, Duke U., 1970; JD cum laude, U. Ga., 1975. Bar: Ga. 1975, Ala. 1975, D.C. 1981, Tex. 1984. Mgr. So. Bell Telephone, Jacksonville, Fla., 1970-72; assoc., ptnr. Haskell, Slaughter & Young, Birmingham, 1975-80; ptnr. Trammell Crow Co., Washington, 1980-82; ptnr. adminstrn. and fin. Trammell Crow Co., Dallas, 1982-85, ptnr. TC ventures, 1985-89, nat. ptnr. TC ventures, 1988—; pres. Trammell Crow Real Estate Investors, Dallas, 1985-91, Trammell Crow Internat. Ptnrs., Dallas, 1986-91; mng. ptnr., CEO Trammell Crow Realty Advisors, 1992-93, chmn., 1993; pres., CEO Faison Assocs., Charlotte, N.C., 1994—; real estate rep. Tex. Econ. Forum, Austin; mem. Urban Land Inst. Mem. assoc. bd. Edwin L. Cox Sch. Bus. So. Meth. U., Dallas. Republican. Episcopalian. Home: 2633 Richardson Dr Charlotte NC 28211-3355 Office: Faison Assocs 121 W Trade St 1900 Interstate Tower Charlotte NC 28202

NORZ, CHARLES HENRY, oil company executive; b. Bklyn., Aug. 23, 1937; s. Charles and Edna Monica (Schweikert) N.; m. Judith K. Keenan, Feb. 4, 1961; children—Susan M., Mary Beth, Jennifer L. B.S., U.S. Mcht. Marine Acad. U.S. Coast Guard Lic., 3d Mate Oceans Unltd. Ops. asst. States Marine Lines, N.Y.C., 1960-63; chartering mgr. Triton Shipping, Inc., N.Y.C., 1963-74; sr. v.p. Am. Hess Corp., N.Y.C., 1974—. Bd. dirs. Knollwood Beach Assn., Old Saybrook (Conn.), 1978-84. Home: 5 Easterly Ct Huntington NY 11743-1605 Office: Amerada Hess Corp 1185 Ave Of The Americas New York NY 10036-2601

NOSANOW, BARBARA SHISSLER, museum director; b. Roanoke, Va.; d. Willis M. and Kathryne (Bradford) Johnson; m. Lewis H. Nosanow, Oct. 15, 1973; m. John Lewis Shissler, July 1957 (dec. 1971); children: John Lewis III, Ada Holland. BA, Smith Coll., 1957; MA, Case Western Res. U., 1959. Mng. editor Jour. Aesthetics and Art Criticism, 1959-62; dir. publs. Mpls. Inst. Arts, 1964-72; dir. Univ. Gallery, U. Minn., Mpls., 1972-76; spl. project dir. The Art of Russia, 1800-1850, Washington, 1976-79; dir. edn. and exhibits Nat. Archives, Washington, 1976-79; curator edn. Smithsonian Instn., Nat. Mus. Am. Art, 1979-82, asst. dir., 1982-87; dir. Portland (Maine) Mus. Art, 1988—. Office: Portland Mus Art 7 Congress Sq Portland ME 04101-1119

NOSEK, LAURA J., health facility administrator; b. Cleve.; d. LeRoy VanPelt and Florence Isabel (Acker) John; m. Frank Joseph Nosek, Sept. 9, 1961; children: Karin Beth, Kevin Bruce. Diploma in nursing, Good Samaritan Sch. Nursing, 1958; BSN, Western Res. U., 1961; MSN, Case Western Res. U., 1981, PhD, 1986. RN, Vt. Adminstrv. nurse clin. U. Hosps. Cleve., dir. nursing mgmt. svcs.; asst. clin. prof. nursing Case Western Res. U., Cleve.; assoc. v.p. nursing and patient svcs. Med. Ctr. Hosp. Vt., Burlington; adj. assoc. prof. nursing U. Vt. Contbr. articles to profl. jours. Mem. ANA, Am. Orgn. Nurse Execs., Nat. League Nursing, Am. Nurses Found., Vt. Nurses Assn. (pres.), Vt. Orgn. Nurse Execs. (pres.), Sigma Theta Tau (Info. Resources Tech. award). Office: Med Ctr Hosp Vt Colchester Ave Burlington VT 05401

NOSHPITZ, JOSEPH DOVE, child and adolescent psychiatrist; b. N.Y.C., Aug. 31, 1922; s. Israel Abraham and Sarah (Stolar) N.; m. Charlotte S., Sept. 20, 1956; 1 child, Claude A.S. BA, U. Louisville, 1943, MD, 1945. Diplomate: Am. Bd. Psychiatry and Neurology (psychiatry and child psychiatry). Intern, Morrisania City Hosp., Bronx, N.Y., 1945-46; resident in psychiatry Winter VA Hosp., Topeka, 1948-51; resident in child psychiatry Menninger Found., 1952-54; chief children's service Topeka State Hosp., 1951-56; chief children's unit, child research for NIMH, 1956-60; mem. faculty dept. psychiatry George Washington U. Sch. Medicine, 1971-77, prof., 1977-88, clin. prof., 1988—; sr. attending staff psychiatrist Children's Hosp. Nat. Med. Center, Washington, 1976-89; dir. psychiatry Crittenton Barrett Program, Washington, 1977-82; cons. in child psychiatry Area B Community Mental Health Center, 1973-82; bd. dirs. Joint Commn. on the Mental Health of Children, 1966-69; mem. Task Force on Financing, Pres.'s Commn. on Mental Health, 1978-79. Editor-in-chief: Basic Handbook of Child Psychiatry, 5 vols., 1979. Psychiatrist-in-chief Am. Health Group Inc., 1989-93. Capt. M.C., AUS, 1943-45, 46-47. Fellow Am. Orthopsychiat. Assn. (life), Am. Acad. Child Psychiatry (life, past pres.), Am. Assn. Children's Residential Ctrs. (life, past pres.), Am. Psychiat. Assn. (life), Group for Advancement of Psychiatry (corr.), Internat. Soc. for Adolescent Medicine. Am. Psychoanalytic Assn. Home and Office: 3141 34th St NW Washington DC 20008-3308

NOSTRAND, HOWARD LEE, language and literature educator; b. N.Y.C., Nov. 16, 1910; s. Elijah H. and Ida Josephine (Maeder) N.; m. Frances Anne Levering, June 23, 1933 (div. Aug. 1967); children: David L., Richard L., Robert M.; m. Frances Helen Brewer, Aug. 9, 1967. BA, Amherst Coll., 1932; MA, Harvard U., 1933; D, l'Université de Paris, 1934. Tchr. U. Buffalo, 1934-36, U.S. Naval Acad., 1936-38, Brown U., 1938-39; prof. romance langs. U. Wash., Seattle, 1939-81, chmn. dept., 1939-64, prof. emeritus, 1981—; vis. prof. Coll. de France, 1975, Simon Fraser U., 1982.; Fulbright lectr., France, 1970-71; cons. Am. Coun. on Teaching Fgn. Langs., 1982, chair Nat. Commn. on Ethnography, 1974-80; Am. Assn. of Tchr. of French (pres.1960-62); Nat. Commn. Profl. Stds., 1986—; mem. Nat. Commn. on Proficency, 1986-93, mem., chair Nat. Commn. on Telematics, 1990-92; co-chair Nat. Commn. on Cultural Competence, 1992—; mem. Nat. Commn. Student Stds., 1993—; cons. Ednl. Testing Svc., 1988—. Author: Le Théâtre antique, 1934, Mission of the University, 1944, The Cultural Attaché, 1947, Research on Language Teaching ... International Bibliography, 1962, 65, The University and Human Understanding, 1963, Film-Recital of French Poems and Cultural Commentary, 1964, Bakcground Data for the Teaching of French, 1967; (with others) La France en mutation, 1979, Savoir vivre en français, 1988, Databases: Our Third Technical Revolution, 1991; contbr over 100 articles to profl. jours. Mem. Seattle Nantes Sister City Assn., 1980-90, pres., 1987-89; bd. mem. U.S. Com. for a Cmty. Democracies, 1983-92, hon. chair, Seattle, 1986-92. Guggenheim fellow, 1953-54; named Order of Sun Peru, 1947, French Govt. Palmes Académiques, 1950, Chevalier, Legion d'Honneur, 1962, Officer, 1994; recipient Pro Lingua award Wash. Assn. Fgn. Lang. Tchrs., 1977, award for leadership N.E. Conf. on Teaching Fgn. Langs., 1978, Nelson Brooks award Am. Coun. Teaching Fgn. Langs., 1980, Outstanding Pub. Svc. award U. Wash. Alumni, 1980, award for vision and leadership Vols. of Bonjour Seattle Festival, 1979-80. Mem. Assn. pour la recherche interculturelle (hon.). Democrat. Unitarian. Home: U Washington 18550 29th Ave NE Seattle WA 98155-4137

NOTARBARTOLO, ALBERT, artist; b. N.Y.C., Jan. 12, 1934; s. Leopold and Elvira (Caputo) N.; m. Valerie Cervelli, June 1, 1962. Student (scholar), Nat. Acad. Fine Arts, 1950; apprentice to mural painter, Ignacio LaRussa, 1951-53. Tchr., 1967—. Represented in permanent collections, Smithsonian Instn., Washington, Mus. Modern Art, N.Y.C.; one-man shows include Hemisphere Gallery of Time-Life Inc., 1973, U. P.R., 1966, David Gavin Gallery, Millerton, N.Y., 1993; exhibited group shows, Tate Gallery, London, 1965, Corcoran Gallery Art, Washington, 1968, Del. Art Mus., Wilmington, 1970, Mus. Modern Art, N.Y.C., 1971, 74, 76, Nat. Gallery Art, Washington, 1976, Smithsonian Instn., Washington, 1976, Santa Barbara (Calif.) Mus. Art, 1976, Taft Mus., Cin., Bell Gallery, Greenwich, Conn., 1977, Huntsville (Ala.) Mus. Art, 1978, Hokin Gallery, Palm Beach, Fla., 1982. Served with AUS, 1957-59. Recipient Nat. Community Art Competition award HUD, 1973; U.S. Bicentennial Flag Competition award, A Flag for the Moon, 1976. Mem. Nat. Soc. Lit. and the Arts. Home: 99 Battery Pl Ste 27H New York NY 10280 *When I turned thirteen my Aunt Rosa Pucci gave me a gift—a small packet of reproductions of Raphael's paintings. On the overleaf she inscribed, "Art does affect the lives of men; it moves to ecstasy, thus giving colour and movement to what be otherwise a rather grey and trivial affair." The intonation of this phrase today makes me believe that an act of art echoes on, invoking a continuing music, a vitality for the future while all else turns into the dust of history.*

NOTARI, PAUL CELESTIN, communications executive; b. Chgo., Sept. 8, 1926; s. Peter and Mae Rose (Luvisi) N.; m. Marlene Fineman, Feb. 21, 1969; children: Cathy Notari Davidson, Kenneth, Sharon Notari Westover, Mindy Lubell, Debbie McGrath. B.S. in Physics, DePaul U., 1952; M.S. in Comml. Sci., Rollins Coll., 1968. Mgr. publs. and tng. Motorola Inc., Chgo., 1952-65; supr., publs. engr. Martin Co., Orlando, Fla., 1966-67; dir. communications Bus. Equipment Mfrs. Assn., N.Y.C., 1967-70; dir. publs. pub. jour. Am. Water Works Assn., Denver, 1971-79; mgr. tech. info. Solar Energy Research Inst., Denver, 1979-91; pres. SciTech Communications, Inc., Denver, 1992—; lectr. bus. communications Northwestern U. Served with USNR, 1944-46. Mem. Assn. Computer Programmers and Analysts (founding pres. 1970-73), Soc. Tech. Writers and Pubs. (chmn. chpt. 1965-66), Am. Solar Energy Soc. (nat. commn 1990-91). Office: SciTech Comm Inc 1000 S Monaco Pkwy Ste 77 Denver CO 80224 *In this complex world we live in, a nation lives or dies by its technological achievements, made possible by a steady flow of information between scientists, engineers, technicians and producers. I believe I have made a significant contribution on this behalf.*

NOTARO, MICHAEL R., data processing and computer service executive; b. Chgo., Nov. 1, 1914; s. Anthony and Felicia (Franzese) N.; m. Irene Hapsude, May 5, 1936 (dec.); children: Michael R., Phyllis Ann; m. Ruth Bostrom, Mar. 10, 1984. Student, Northwestern U. Sch. Commerce, 1930-36, Chgo. Law Sch., 1930-32; LL.D., DePaul U. dir. St. Paul Fed. Savs. Bank. Bd. dirs. Cath. Charities of Archdiocese of Chgo., Boys Clubs Chgo., Loyola U.; trustee De Paul U. Decorated knight Malta, knight St. Gregory, Knight comdr. Order Merit Italy). Roman Catholic (lay trustee). Clubs: Union League, Mid-Am., Tavern, Chgo. Athletic Assn. (Chgo.); Butterfield Country (Hinsdale, Ill.). Home & Office: 500 Linden Ave Oak Park IL 60302-1659

NOTE, KESSAI H., federal official; b. Ailinglaplap, Marshall Islands, Aug. 7, 1950; s. Hesa and May (Samson) N.; m. Mary Neimoj Yamamura, Dec. 15, 1975; children: Carlo, Mariana, Annette, Eugenia, Michael. BS in Agriculture, U. Papua, New Guinea, 1974. Min. natural resources Marshall Islands Govt., Majuro, 1979-83, min. internal affairs, 1983-84, min. transport, 1984-86; speaker Parliament Marshall Islands Nitijela, Majuro, 1986—; pres. Airline Marshall Islands, Majuro, 1980-86; chmn. Marshall Islands Planning Commn., Majuro, 1980-84. Chmn. Marshalls Community Action Agy., Majuro, 1979-82; mem. 1978 Constl. Conv., Majuro, 1977-78; president 1990 Constl. Conv., Majuro, 1990-91. Mem. Marshall Islands Tennis Club, Marshall Islands Billfish Club. Avocations: fishing, reading, sailing, volleyball, basketball. Office: Nitijela Parliament Bldg Majuro MH 96960

NOTEBAERT, RICHARD C., telecommunications industry executive; b. 1948; married. With Wisconsin Bell, 1969-83; v.p. marketing and operations Ameritech, Chicago, 1983-86; pres. Ameritech Mobile Comm., 1986-89, Indiana Bell Telephone Co., 1989-92, Ameritech Services, Chicago, 1992-94; chmn., pres., CEO Ameritech Corp., Chicago, 1993—. Office: Ameritech Corp 30 S Wacker Dr Chicago IL 60606-7402*

NOTESTINE, WILBUR EDMUND, energy company executive, lawyer; b. Big Spring, Tex., Jan. 30, 1931; s. Edmund and Virginia (Barnett) N.; m. Frances Elaine Folley, May 28, 1954; children: Alice Jennings Waters, Martha Claire. BS, U. Tex., 1951, LLB, 1954. V.p. gen. counsel Maxus Energy Corp., Dallas. 1st lt. AUS, 1955-58. Mem. ABA, Tex. Bar Assn., Dallas Bar Assn., Tex. Mid Oil and Gas Assn., Dallas Petroleum Club. Office: Maxus Energy Corp 717 N Harwood St Dallas TX 75201-6505

NOTHMANN, GERHARD ADOLF, retired engineering executive, research engineer; b. Berlin, Germany, Dec. 9, 1921; came to U.S., 1939, naturalized, 1944; s. Rudolf and Margarete (Caro) N.; m. Charlotte Braude, June 23, 1943; children—Joyce Anne, Ruth Ellen, Barbara Fay. B.S. in Mech. Engring, Purdue U., 1942, M.S. in Mech. Engring. 1942; Ph.D., Cornell U., 1948. Tchr. machine design and kinematics Cornell U., 1942-44, 46-48, instr., 1942-44, 46-48, asst. prof., 1948; engr. for design spl. bindery R. R. Donnelley & Sons, 1946-47; research engr. Armour Research Found., Ill. Inst. Tech., Chgo., 1948-59; successively asst. supr., asst. chmn., chmn., mgr. dept. mech. engring. research Armour Research Found., Ill. Inst. Tech., 1952-59; dir. creative and devel. engring. Miehle div. Miehle-Goss-Dexter, Inc., 1959-62, dir. research and devel., 1962-64, dir. engring., 1964-67, dir. tech. research, 1967-68; dir. engring. Robertson Photo-Mechanix, Inc., 1968-69, v.p. engring., 1969-71; chief engr. duplicators Addressograph Multigraph Corp., 1971-77; dir. engring. Visual Graphics Corp. Tamarac, Fla., 1977-79; prin. engr. Xerox Corp., Pasadena, Calif., 1979-89, ret., 1989; chmn. mechanics colloquim Ill. Inst. Tech., 1953-54; mem. adv. com. Graphic Arts Tech. Found. Author: Nonimpact Printing, 1989. Pres. bd. dirs. Wilmette United Fund, 1963; mem. Wilmette Sch. Bd., 1968-74; pres. Pasadena Jewish Temple and Ctr., 1989-91. With USNR, 1944-46. Named one of six outstanding young men in Chgo. area. Chgo. Jr. Assn. Commerce and Industry, 1954. Mem. ASME, Am. Soc. Engring. Edn., Tech. Assn. for

---

Graphic Arts, Jewish Geneal. Soc. of L.A., Sigma Xi, Tau Beta Pi, Pi Tau Sigma. Home: 3760 Edgeview Dr Pasadena CA 91107-1309

NOTKIN, LEONARD SHELDON, architect; b. N.Y.C., Apr. 1, 1931; s. Murry and Evelyn (Mofshatz) N.; m. Ann Mathilda Stefanko, Nov. 24, 1956; children: Jennifer, Mead. B.Arch., U. Pa., 1954. Registered architect, N.Y., Mass., Ohio, Pa., Nat. Council Archtl. Registration Bds. Architect, Percival Goodman (Architect), N.Y.C., 1956-58; Architect Bloch and Hesse (Architects), N.Y.C., 1958-59, Resnick and Green (Architects), N.Y.C., 1959-60; architect, prin., v.p. The Architects Collaborative, Inc., Cambridge, Mass., 1960—; chief design critic Boston Archtl. Center, 1964-69; mem. Lexington (Mass.) Design Adv. Com., 1970-73, chmn., 1972; profl. studio critic Harvard Grad. Sch. Design, 1974-76. Major recent works include Intermediate Sch. 137, Bronx, N.Y., 1976, Visual Arts Instructional Facility, SUNY Coll. at Purchase, 1976, Lahey Clinic Med. Center, Burlington, Mass., 1976—, W. Penn Hosp, Pitts., 1977, St. Francis/St. George Hosp, Cin., 1978, Blue Cross/Blue Shield of Conn. Hdqrs, North Haven, Temple U. Hosp, Phila., composite hosp. Loring AFB, Limestone, Maine, Med. Facilities, Fort Drum, N.Y., Health Care Internat. Ltd., Glasgow, Scotland, Intensive Care Hosp. and Hotel, Univ. Ky. Cancer Rsch. Ctr., Children's Hosp. Med. Ctr. Rsch. Lab., Cin., Lahey Clinic Med. Ctr., Burlington, Mass., 1990, new main entrance, lobby and admissions facilities Hosp. of U. Pa., Phila. (spl. design citation Boston Soc. Architects 1993). Served with U.S. Army, 1954-56. Recipient Design award for IBM Hdqrs., Gaithersburg, Md. Progressive Architecture mag., 1964; 1st pl. award for Worcester (Mass.) Community Center AIA, 1966; Design award for Worcester Found. Exptl. Biology bldg. Mass. chpt. AIA, 1968; Design award NIH Research Lab., Bethesda, Md. GSA, 1972; Best Bldg. of Yr. award for Norwalk (Conn.) High Sch. Assn. for Better Community Design, 1972; Honor award Conn. Soc. Architects AIA, 1974. Mem. AIA, Boston Soc. Architects (dir. 1976-79), Mass. State Assn. Architects. Office: 46 Brattle St Cambridge MA 02138-3705

NOTKIN, RICHARD T., ceramic sculptor, educator; b. Chgo., Oct. 26, 1948; s. Nathan T. and Thelma N. (Tutilman) N.; children: Jessica, Ethan. BFA, Kansas City (Mo.) Art Inst., 1970; MFA, U. Calif., Davis, 1973. Freelance ceramic sculptor Myrtle Point, Oreg., 1974-94, Helena, Mont., 1994—; vis. asst. prof. U. Utah, Salt Lake City, 1975; vis. instr. Md. Inst. Coll. of Art, Balt., 1977; vis. artist, lectr. Ohio State U., Columbus, 1982; adj. asst. prof. Mont. State U., Bozeman, 1981; vis. artist Kansas City Art Inst., 1984, Bezalel Acad. of Art & Design, Jerusalem, 1990; artist-in-industry Kohler (Wis.) Co., 1976, 78; artist-in-residence Archie Bray Found., Helena, Mont., 1981. Sculptor nmerous pub. and pvt. collections. Western States Arts Found. fellow, 1976, NEA fellow, 1979, 81, 88, Oreg. Arts Commn. fellow, 1985, John Simon Guggenheim Meml. Found. fellow, 1990, Louis Comfort Tiffany Found. fellow, 1991. Mem. Nat. Coun. on Edn. for the Ceramic Arts, Am. Crafts Coun., Archie Bay Found. (bd. dirs.).

NOTKINS, ABNER LOUIS, physician, researcher; b. New Haven, May 8, 1932; s. Louis Adolph and Sair Rosalyn (Mathog) N.; m. Susan Woodward, Aug. 9, 1969. BA Yale U., 1953; MD, NYU, 1958. Intern Johns Hopkins U., Balt., 1959, asst. resident, 1960; research assoc. Nat. Cancer Inst., NIH, Bethesda, Md., 1960-61; prin. investigator Nat. Inst. Dental Research, NIH, Bethesda, Md., 1961-67, sect. chief, microbiology lab., 1967-73, chief, oral medicine lab., 1973—; dir., intramural research program, 1985—; cons. Nat. Commn. on Diabetes, 1975, Virology Task Force, 1976, Nat. Diabetes Research Interchange, 1981—, Wistar Inst. Persistent Virus Program, 1983—, NASA, 1983; lectr. various univs. and orgns. Mem. editorial bd. Infection and Immunity, 1970-73, Jour. of Virology, 1984—, Microbial Pathogenesis, 1985—; contbr. numerous articles to profl. jours.; editor 3 books. Served to med. dir. PHS, 1960-85. Recipient Meritorious Service medal Dept. HHS, 1973, David Rumbough Sci. award Juvenile Diabetes Found., 1980, Distinguished Service award Dept. HHS, 1981, Paul E. Lacey research award Nat. Diabetes Research Interchange, 1982, Paul Ehrlich prize, Paul Ehrlich Found., Fed. Republic of Germany, 1986. Mem. Assn. U. Pathologists (Pluto Soc.), Assn. Am. Physicians, Alpha Omega Alpha. Home: 1179 Crest Ln Mc Lean VA 22101-1805 Office: HHS Nat Inst of Dental Research 9000 Rockville Pike Bldg 30 Bethesda MD 20892-0001

NOTO, LUCIO A., gas and oil industry executive; b. 1939. With Mobil Corp., 1962—; pres. Mobil Saudi Arabia, 1981-85, chmn., 1985-86; v.p. planning and econs. Mobil Corp./Mobil Oil Corp., 1986-88, CFO, 1989-93, pres., 1993—, chmn. bd., CEO, COO, 1994—. Office: Mobil Corp 3225 Gallows Rd Fairfax VA 22037

NOTOPOULOS, ALEXANDER ANASTASIOS, JR., lawyer; b. Altoona, Pa., Jan. 29, 1953; s. Alexander Anastasios Sr. and Christine (Economou) N.; m. Alexis J. Anderson, Aug. 4, 1984. BA, Amherst Coll., 1974; JD, Harvard U., 1977. Bar: Mass. 1978, U.S. Dist. Ct. Mass. 1979. Law clk. to judge U.S. Ct. Appeals (3d cir.), Phila., 1977-78; assoc. Sullivan & Worcester, Boston, 1978-85, ptnr., 1985—. Home: 96 Shornecliffe Rd Newton MA 02158-2421 Office: Sullivan & Worcester One Post Office Sq Boston MA 02109

NOTTINGHAM, EDWARD WILLIS, JR., federal judge; b. Denver, Jan. 9, 1948; s. Edward Willis and Willie Newton (Gullett) N.; m. Cheryl Ann Card, June 6, 1970 (div. Feb. 1981); children: Amelia Charlene, Edward Willis III; m. Janis Ellen Chapman, Aug. 18, 1984; 1 child, Spencer Chapman. AB, Cornell U., 1969; JD, U. Colo., 1972. Bar: Colo. 1972, U.S. Dist. Ct. Colo. 1972, U.S. Ct. Appeals (10th cir.) 1973. Law clk. to presiding judge U.S. Dist. Ct. Colo., Denver, 1972-73; assoc. Sherman & Howard, Denver, 1973-76, 78-80, ptnr., 1980-87; ptnr. Beckner & Nottingham, Grand Junction, Colo., 1987-89; asst. U.S. atty. U.S. Dept. Justice, Denver, 1976-78; U.S. dist. judge Dist. of Colo., Denver, 1989—. Bd. dirs. Beaver Creek Met. Dist., Avon, Colo., 1980-88, Justice Info. Ctr., Denver, 1985-87, 21st Jud. Dist. Victim Compensation Fund, Grand Junction, Colo., 1987-89. Mem. ABA, Colo. Bar Assn. (chmn. criminal law sect. 1983-85, chmn. ethics com. 1988-89), Order of Coif, Denver Athletic Club, Delta Sigma Rho, Tau Kappa Alpha. Episcopalian. Office: US Dist Ct 1929 Stout St Denver CO 80294-2900

NOTTINGHAM, JAMES (LEROY NOTTINGHAM), retired protective services official, professional society administrator; b. Ft. Myers, Fla., Sept. 6, 1937; s. George M. and Josephine E. (Holcomb) N.; m. Bonita Jean Hager, Sept. 2, 1957; children: James Jr., Mark, Dale, Valarie. Student, Fla. State Fire Coll., 1964—, St. Pete Jr. Coll., 1966—. Cert. firefighter, Fla., cert. EMT, cert. real estate agt., ins. salesman, notary; instr., Fla.; security lic.; bus. agt. permit, Fla. Firefighter, engr., capt. Ft. Myers Fire Dept., 1963-94; negotiator Ft. Myers Firefighters L. 1826, 1971—; instr. Fla. Standard Firefighters, Fla. State, 1973—, mem. and chmn., 1981-94; chmn. MDA, 12th Dist. IAFF, N.C., S.C., Ga., Fla., V.I., 1986—. Mem. Civil Svc. Bd. Ft. Myers City, 1968-71; pres. N. Ft. Myers Little League, 1971-76, N. Ft. Myers Pop Warner, 1973, Peace River Conf., 1974; head coach N. Ft. Myers Babe Ruth 16-18, 85-85, state champions, 1978, 81; fire commr. N. Ft. Myers Fire and Rescue, 1993. Named Firefighter of Yr., City of Ft. Myers, 1992, Fla. State Cabinet and Fla. Profl. Firefighters, 1993; recipient Good Neighbor award TV Sta. 20, NBC, Ft. Myers, 1993. Mem. Nat. Fire Protection Assn., Ft. Myers and S.W. Fla. Profl. Firefighters (pres. 1970—), Fla. Profl. Firefighters (lobbyist 1970—, dist. v.p. 1978—), Masons (32 deg.), Shriners. Democrat. Baptist. Avocations: golf, scuba diving, fishing, RV camping. Home: 53 Victoria Dr North Fort Myers FL 33917 Office: SW Fla Profl Firefighters 1601 Lee St Fort Myers FL 33901

NOTTINGHAM, ROBINSON KENDALL, life insurance company executive; b. Balt., Apr. 4, 1938; s. Robinson Jr. and Juliet (Moore) N.; m. Elizabeth LeViness, Aug. 26, 1960; children: Robinson Kendall Jr., Charles Denmead. BA in Polit. Sci., Johns Hopkins U., 1959; postgrad., Johns Hopkins U., Washington, 1965. With Am. Internat. Group, Inc., Hong Kong and Bangkok, 1968-71; chief exec. officer for Japan and Korea Am. Internat. Group, Inc., Tokyo, 1986-89; mng. dir. Hanover Ins. Co., Universal Ins. Co., Bangkok, 1971-73, Am. Internat. Ins. Co., Lagos, Nigeria, 1973-75; regional pres. African div. Am. Internat. Underwriters, N.Y.C., 1975-78, Middle Ea. div., 1978-83, European div., 1983-86; chmn., bd. dirs., CEO Am. Life Ins. Co., Wilmington, Del., 1989—; bd. dirs. AIG Overseas Fin. (Japan) Inc., Tokyo, Am. Home Assurance Co., N.Y.C., AIU Ins Co., N.Y.C. Pres. USO Coun., Tokyo, 1987-89; mem. world bd. govs. USO, Washington,

---

1987—; mem. adv. coun. Johns Hopkins U. Sch. Advanced Internat. Studies, Washington, 1984—, Reischauer Ctr. Japan Studies, Washington, 1986—. Served to lt. comdr. USNR, 1960-68. Mem. Princeton Club (N.Y.C.), Short Hills Club (N.J.), Bay Head Yacht Club (N.J.), Baltusrol Club (Springfield, N.J.), Chevy Chase (Md.) Club, Delta Phi. Republican. Episcopalian. Avocation: sailing. Home: 393 Charlton Ave South Orange NJ 07079-2405 Office: Am Life Ins Co 1 Alico Plz Wilmington DE 19899

NOTTINGHAM, WILLIAM JESSE, church mission executive, minister; b. Sharon, Pa., Nov. 22, 1927; s. Jess William and Alice May (Green) N.; m. Patricia Clutts, Feb. 1, 1949; children: Theodore Jess, Deborah Joan Selke, Nancy Alice, Gregory Philip. BA, Bethany Coll., W.Va., 1949, DD (hon.), 1987; BD, Union Theol. Sem., N.Y.C., 1953; PhD, Columbia U., 1962; DD (hon.), Christian Theol. Sem., Indpls., 1984. Ordained to ministry Christian Ch. (Disciples of Christ), Oct. 21, 1945. Pastor Ch. of Christ, Canoe Camp and Covington, Pa., 1949-50; field worker Ch. of the Master, N.Y.C., 1950-53; assoc. min. Nat. City Christian Ch., Washington, 1954-58; fraternal worker Coun. on Christian Unity, France, 1958-65; with youth dept. World Coun. of Chs., Geneva, 1965-68; exec. sec. for Latin Am. and Caribbean Divsn. Overseas Ministries, Christian Ch. (Disciples of Christ and United Ch. Christ), Indpls., 1968-76, exec. sec. East Asia and Pacific, 1976-83, pres., 1984-94; affiliate prof. missions Christian Theol. Sem., 1995—. Author: Christian Faith and Secular Action, 1968, The Preaching and Practice of Liberation, 1986; translator: God's Underground, 1970, Prayer at the Heart of Life, 1975, Materialist Approaches to the Bible, 1985, Madeleine Barot, 1991. Fulbright scholar, Strasbourg, France, 1953-54. Mem. Nat. Coun. Chs. of Christ in USA (gen. bd.), Assn. Disciples for Theol. Discussion. Democrat.

NOTZ, JOHN KRANZ, JR., lawyer; b. Chgo., Jan. 5, 1932; s. John Kranz and Elinor (Trostel) N.; m. Janis Wellin, Apr. 23, 1966; children: Jane Elinor, John Wellin. BA, Williams Coll., 1953; JD, Northwestern U., 1956. Bar: Ill. 1956, Fla. 1957, Wis. 1989, U.S. Supreme Ct. 1960. Assoc. 1st Nat. Bank Chgo., 1954, 1956; assoc. Gardner, Carton & Douglas, Chgo., 1960-66, ptnr., 1966-89, of counsel, 1990—; arbitrator, mediator CPR Inst. for Dispute Resolution, Am. Arbitration Assn., Nat. Assn. Securities Dealers, Nat. Futures Assn., N.H. Stock Exchange, Am. Stock Exchange. Contbr. numerous articles to profl. jours. Mem. Ill. Sec. State Corp. Acts Adv. Com. 1982—, chmn. 1987-89; bd. dirs., treas. Chgo. Lit. Club; bd. dirs. Ill. Inst. Continuing Legal Edn., 1980-91, chmn. 1990-91; bd. dirs. Inspired Ptnrs.; bd. trustees Graceland Cemetery. 1st lt. USAF1957-60. Recipient Svc. award Northwestern U., 1978. Fellow Am. Bar Found.; mem. Am. Law Inst., Ill. State Bar Assn., Chgo. Bar Assn., Fla. Bar Assn., Wis. State Bar, Law Club City Chgo. (pres. 1989-90), Racquet Club Chgo., John Evans Club (Northwestern U., bd. dirs.), Lake Geneva Country Club. Office: Gardner Carton & Douglas 3400 Quaker Tower 321 N Clark St Chicago IL 60610-4795

NOUMOFF, SAMUEL JOSEPH, political scientist, researcher; b. Bklyn., Nov. 14, 1935. Ba, Clark U., 1956; MA, NYU, 1965, PhD with distinction, 1975. Lectr. Hunter Coll., N.Y.C., 1965, U. N.B., Can., 1966-67; asst. prof., then assoc. prof. polit. sci. McGill U., Montreal, 1967—, assoc. dir. Ctr. for East Asian Studies, 1970-81, dir. Ctr. for Developing Area Studies, 1988—; guest lectr. Sophia U., Japan, Coll. Sacred Heart, Japan, Hosei U., Japan, Inst. Am. Studies, Japan, Meiji U., Japan, Assn. Negro Studies, Japan, Jawaharlal Nehru U., India, Delhi U., India, Nodal Rsch. Ctr., India, Chulalongkorn U., Thailand, U. Dhaka, Bangladesh, Nat. U. Malaya, Malaysia, U. Hong Kong, Inst. Contemporary Internat. Rels., China, Inst. L.Am. Studies, China, State Econ. Commn., China, Nankai U., China, Shandong U., China, Wuhan U., China, Peking U., China, Xiamen U., China, Guangdong Overseas Chinese U., China, Jiangsu Econ. Commn., China, Inner Mongolia Econ. Commn., China, Xinjiang Econ. Commn. Higher Party Sch., China, Beijing Mcpl. Party Sch., China, Tianjin Mcpl. Party Sch., China, Shangong Provincial Party Sch., Fiundan U., China, Nanjing U., China, Qufu Normal U., China, U. Havana, Cuba; cons. U. East Asia, Macau on Univ. Governance, Task Force of Sec. State for External Rels.: Can. Aid Policy to China; commentary on radio and TV for CBC, CTV Networks. Editor The Korean Rev.; mem. editl. bd. Labor, Capital and Soc., Socialist Alternatives; contbr. articles to profl. jours. Mem. Can. Polit. Sci. Assn., Can. Asian Studies Assn., Can. Assn. Studies in Devel., Quebec Com. for Asian Studies, Can. China Soc., Com. for New Direction in U.S. Korea Policy, Zimbabwe Ednl. Cultural Inst., Third World Scis. Office: McGill Univ, 3715 Peel St, Montreal, PQ Canada H3A 1X1

NOVA, CRAIG, writer; b. Los Angeles, July 5, 1945; s. Karl and Elizabeth (Sinclair) N.; m. Christina Barnes, July 2, 1977; children: Abigail, Tate. B.A., U. Calif.-Berkeley, 1967; M.F.A., Columbia U., 1969. Author: Turkey Hash, 1972, The Geek, 1975, Incandescence, 1978, The Good Son, 1982, The Congressman's Daughter, 1986, Tornado Alley, 1989, Trombone, 1992, The Book of Dreams, 1994. Recipient Harper-Saxton prize Harper and Row, Pubs., 1972; recipient award in lit. Am. Acad. and Inst. Arts and Letters; Guggenheim Found. fellow, 1977; fellow Nat. Endowment for Arts, 1973, Nat. Endowment for Arts, 1975, Creative Artists Pub. Service, 1976; NEA fellow, 1985; story included in Best Am. Short Stories, 1987.

NOVACEK, JAY MCKINLEY, professional football player; b. Martin, S.D., Oct. 24, 1962. BS in Indsl. Edn., U. Wyoming, 1986. With St. Louis Cardinals, 1985-87, Phoenix Cardinals (formerly St. Louis Cardinals), 1988-89; tight end Dallas Cowboys, 1990—; player Pro Bowl, 1991-93, Super Bowl XXVII, 1992, XXVIII, 1993. Office: Dallas Cowboys 1 Cowboys Pky Irving TX 75063*

NOVACEK, MICHAEL JOHN, curator, museum administrator; b. Evanston, Ill., June 3, 1948; s. Albin John and June Shirley (White) N.; m. Vera Ellen Novacek, June 19, 1971; 1 child, Julie. BA in Zoology, UCLA, 1971; MA in Biology, San Diego State U., 1973; PhD in Paleontology with honors, U. Calif., Berkeley, 1978. Lectr. dept. zoology San Diego State U., 1976-77, asst. prof., 1977-79, assoc. prof., 1979-82; asst. curator dept. vertebrate paleontology Am. Mus. Natural History, N.Y.C., 1983-85, chmn., 1983-89, assoc. curator, 1985-89, curator, 1989—, v.p., dean sci., 1989—; v.p., provost sci., 1994—; adj. prof. San Diego State U., 1982—; panel mem. systematic biology program NSF, 1986-90, mem. bioadv. com., 1992—; adj. prof. dept. biology CUNY, 1987—; chmn. biospherics com. Yale U., New Haven, 1993—; expedition leader, Wyo., Mex., Chile, Mongolia; lectr. in field. Editor: Extinction and Phylogeny, 1992, Mammal Phylogeny, 1993; contbr. over 100 articles to profl. jours. Grantee Nat. Geog. Soc., 1985-86, 88-90, Eppley Found., 1986-88, NSF, 1989-95, Sloan Found., 1990, Internat. Rsch. and Exch. Bd.; Nat. Needs postdoctoral fellow NSF, 1979-80. Fellow Explorer's Club; mem. AAAS (bd. dirs. 1995—), Soc. Study Evolution, Soc. Systematic Biologists (pres. 1992-93), Systematics Agenda 2000 (co-chair 1992—). Avocations: music, climbing, cycling, skiing, art. Office: Am Mus Natural History Central Park West at 79th New York NY 10024

NOVACK, ALVIN JOHN, physician; b. Red Lodge, Mont., Mar. 11, 1925; s. John and Anna Geraldine (Maddio) N.; m. Betty F. Novack, Jan. 10, 1952; children—Vance, Deborah, Michelle, Mitchel, Craig, Brad, Mary Ellen, Garth. M.D., U. Wash., 1952. Intern Harper Hosp., Detroit, 1952; resident in surgery Harper Hosp., 1953; resident in otolaryngology Johns Hopkins U., 1954-57; resident in surgery Columbia-Presbyn. Med. Center, N.Y.C., 1957-60; fellow head and neck surgery Columbia-Presbyn. Med. Center, 1957-60; dir. head and neck surgery Swedish Hosp., Seattle, Wash., 91; dir. otolaryngology Children's Orthopedic Hosp., Seattle, 1965-78; ret., 1991. Contbr. articles to med. jours. Served to lt. AUS, 1940-43. Nat. Cancer Inst. fellow, 1957-60. Fellow A.C.S.; mem. AMA, Am. Acad. Otolaryngology and Head and Neck Surgery, Soc. Head and Neck Surgeons, North Pacific Surg. Assn., Pacific Coast Surg. Assn., Seattle Surg. Soc.

NOVACKY, ANTON JAN, plant pathologist, educator; b. Bratislava, Czechoslovakia, June 3, 1933; came to U.S., 1968; s. Jan Martin and Katarina (Fischer) N.; m. Dorothy Edit Hyross, June 28, 1958; children: Andrea Novacky Congdon, Thomas Martin. Student, Charles U., Prague, Czechoslovakia; BS, Comenius U., Bratislava, 1955, MS, 1956; PhD, Czechoslovak Acad. Sci. Prague, 1965. Postgrad. fellow U. Moscow, Russia. 1964; postdoctoral fellow U. Ky., Lexington, 1966-69; postdoctoral rsch. assoc. U. Mo., Columbia, 1969-70, asst. prof., 1970-74, assoc. prof., 1974-82, prof., 1982—; rsch. phytopathologist Inst. Exptl. Phytopathology and Entomology, Bratislava, Czechoslovakia, 1962-68. Author: (with R.N. Goodman) The Hypersensitive Reaction in Plants to Pathogens, 1994; speaker various seminars and meeting presentations; contbr. articles to profl. jours. Grantee NSF, 1986-89, 1978-82, USDA, 1978-83, 93-95, MSMC, 1986-89; fellow Japanese Soc. for Promotion of Sci. Rsch., 1984; recipient German Academic Exch. award, 1976, Alexander von Humboldt Sr. U.S. Scientist, 1983. Mem. AAAS, Am. Phytopathol. Soc. (fellow 1986, chair 1984-85), Am. Soc. Plant Physiologists, Sigma Xi. Roman Catholic. Home: 311 Crown Pt Columbia MO 65203-2202 Office: U Mo Agriculture Bldg 3-18 Columbia MO 65211

NOVAK, ALFRED, retired biology educator; b. Chgo., Jan. 28, 1915; s. Phillip and Celia (Kaplan) N.; m. Helen Ascher, Feb. 19, 1944 (dec. Oct. 20, 1985); children—Paul, Gregory, David. A.A., U. Chgo., 1934, B.S., 1936; M.S., 1941; M.Ed., Chgo. Tchrs. Coll., 1940; Ph.D., Mich. State U., 1950. Mem. faculty Mich. State U., 1945-61, asso. prof. biology, 1951-55, prof., 1955-61; sci. coordinator, prof. emeritus biology Stephens Coll., Columbia, Mo., 1961-80; prof. biology div. U. Mo., Columbia, 1980-81; cons., writer Biol. Sci. Curriculum Study, Boulder, Colo., 1960-61; cons. sci. curriculum, facilities planning for colls. and univs., 1955—; heart damage research U. Bologna (Italy) Med. Sch., 1972; bd. dirs. Allied Health Programs. Adv. biology editor, writer: Ency. Americana, 1959-69. Served with USAAF, 1941-44. Recipient Favilli medal Istituto di Patologia Generale, Bologna, 1972; Guggenheim fellow Cambridge (Eng.) U., 1957-58; NIH fellow Cal. Inst. Tech., 1950. Mem. Am. Assn. Gen. Liberal Edn. (past pres.), Nat. Assn. Biology Tchrs., AAAS. Discovered cold pack treatment for mumps orchitis, 1945. Home: 4954 W 60th Ter Mission KS 66205-3079 *I have lived through two major wars, the 1929 depression, the turbulent 60's, distressing inflation of the 70's and rejuvenation in the early 80's. I am dismayed with bureaucratic waste, the decay in character, honesty & morality. I am also appalled by the ineptitude of the U.S. judicial system. There are too many laws and too many corrupt lawyers. Our freedoms are being eroded, yet democracy is still the greatest hope of the world.*

NOVAK, BARBARA, art history educator; b. N.Y.C.; d. Joseph and Sadie (Kaufman) N.; m. Brian O'Doherty, July 5, 1960. B.A., Barnard Coll., 1951; M.A., Radcliffe Coll., 1953, Ph.D., 1957. TV instr. Mus. Fine Arts, Boston, 1957-58; mem. faculty Barnard Coll., Columbia U., N.Y.C., 1958—; prof. art history Barnard Coll., Columbia U., 1970—, Helen G. Altschul prof., 1984—; adv. council Archives of Am. Art, NAD. Editorial bd.; Am. Art Jour.; co-editor Next to Nature, 1980; author: American Painting of the 19th Century, 1969, Nature and Culture, 1980, The Thyssen-Bornemisza Collection 19th Century American Painting, 1986, Alice's Neck, 1987, (play) The Ape and the Whale: Darwin and Melville in Their Own Words, 1987 (performed at Symphony Space, 1987), Dreams and Shadows: Thomas H. Hotchkiss in 19th Cen. Italy, 1993. Commr. Nat. Portrait Gallery; trustee N.Y. Hist. Soc. Fulbright fellow Belgium, 1953-54; Guggenheim fellow, 1974; Nat. Book Critics nominee, 1980; Los Angeles Times Book Award nominee, 1980; Am. Book Award paperback nominee, 1981. Fellow Soc. Am. Historians, Phila. Atheneum; mem. Soc. Am. Historians, Am. Antiquarian Soc., Coll. Art Assn. (dir. 1974-77), N.Y. Hist. Soc. (trustee), PEN. Office: Barnard Coll Art History Dept 606 W 120th St New York NY 10027-5706

NOVAK, DAVID, Judaic studies educator, rabbi; b. Chgo., Aug. 19, 1941; s. Syd and Sylvia (Wien) N.; m. Melva Ziman, July 3, 1963; children: Marianne, Jacob George. AB in Classics and Ancient History, U. Chgo., 1961; M in Hebrew Lit., Jewish Theol. Sem. Am., 1964; PhD, Georgetown U., 1971. Ordained rabbi, 1966. Rabbi Shaare Tikvah Congregation, 1966-69; dir. Jewish chaplaincy St. Elizabeth's Hosp., 1966-69; rabbi Emanuel Synagogue, Oklahoma City, 1969-72, Beth Tfiloh Congregation, Balt., 1972-77, Congregation Beth El, Norfolk, Va., 1977-81, Congregation Darchay Noam, Far Rockaway, N.Y., 1981-89; Edgar M. Bronfman prof. modern Judaic studies U. Va., Charlottesville, 1989—; lectr. philosophy Oklahoma City U., 1969-72, New Sch. for Social Rsch., 1982-84; lectr. Jewish studies Balt. Hebrew Coll., 1972-77; adj. asst. prof. philosophy Old Dominion U., 1977-81; vis. assoc. prof. Talmud Jewish Theol. Sem. Am., 1986-88; adj. assoc. prof. Baruch Coll., CUNY, 1984-88, adj. prof., 1989; founder, v.p., coord. panel Halakhic inquiry Union Traditional Judaism/Inst. Traditional Judaism. Compiling. editor Sh'ma, First Things. Sec.-treas. Inst. on Religion and Pub. Life. Essay winner Hyman G. Enelow prize Jewish Theol. Sem. Am., 1975; recipient Rabbi Jacob B. Augus award Jewish Theol. Sem. Am., 1984. Fellow Acad. for Jewish Philosophy; mem. Am. Theol. Soc., Assn. for Jewish Studies, Am. Acad. Religion, Jewish Law Assn., Leo Baeck Inst. Home: 5311 Cutshaw Ave Richmond VA 23226-1105 Office: U Va Dept Religious Studies Cocke Hall Charlottesville VA 22903-3281

NOVAK, EDWARD FRANK, lawyer; b. Berwyn, Ill., Sept. 25, 1947; s. Edward F. and Myrtle L. (Weese) N.; 1 child, Jay P. BA, Knox Coll., 1969; JD, DePaul U., 1976. Bar: Ill. 1976, Ariz. 1979, D.C. 1985. Assoc. Coffield, Ungaretti & Harris, Chgo., 1976-79, Jordan Green, P.C, Phoenix, 1979-81; assoc. Lewis and Roca, Phoenix, 1981-83, ptnr., 1983—. Sgt. U.S. Army, 1969-72, Vietnam. Mem. State Bar Ariz. (vice chmn. criminal justice sect. 1985, chmn. 1986-88). Office: Lewis and Roca 40 N Central Ave Phoenix AZ 85004

NOVAK, EUGENE FRANCIS, advertising executive; b. Johnstown, Pa., May 4, 1925; s. John F. and Amelia (Havel) N.; m. Joan Tross, Apr. 12, 1947; children: Gregory, Mark. B.A., U. Pitts., 1948. With radio sta. WKBW, Buffalo, 1950-52; mgr. continuity dept. sta. WBEN-TV, Buffalo, 1952-54; TV writer, dir. Comstock Advt., Buffalo, 1954-58; radio-TV dir Rumrill-Hoyt (advt.), N.Y.C., 1959-69; pres., creative dir. Rumrill-Hoyt (advt.), 1969-82; chmn., creative dir. Rumrill-Hoyt, 1983—. Author articles. Bd. dirs. Fair Campaign Practices Com., Washington, Nat. Advt. Rev. Bd., Advt. Council. Served with AUS, 1943-46, ETO. Mem. Pi Delta Epsilon. Office: 635 Madison Ave New York NY 10022-1009

NOVAK, JOSEPH DONALD, science educator, knowledge studies specialist; b. Mpls., Dec. 2, 1930; s. Joseph Daniel and Anna (Podany) N.; m. Joan Owen, July 18, 1953; children: Joseph Mark, Barbara Joan, William John. BS, U. Minn., 1952, MA, 1954, PhD, 1958. Teaching asst. U. Minn., Mpls., 1952-56, instr., 1956-57; asst. prof. Kans. State Tchrs. Coll., 1957-59; asst. prof. Purdue U., West Lafayette, Ind., 1959-62, assoc. prof., 1962-67; prof. Cornell U., Ithaca, N.Y., 1967—; knowledge constrn. and orgn. cons. to Procter & Gamble and other cos.; cons. to over 300 schs. and colls., 1975—; vis. fellow Harvard U., 1965-66; disting. vis. prof. U. N.C., Wilmington, 1980, U. Western Fla., 1987-88; vis. prof. U. South Fla., 1995. Author: Learning How to Learn, 1984, Educational Psychology: A Cognitive View, 1978, A Theory of Education, 1977, 15 others; contbr. over 100 articles to profl. jours. Fellow Tozer Found., Lydia Anderson, 1955-56; research assoc. Harvard U., 1965-66; Fulbright-Hayes Sr. Scholar, Australia, 1980. Fellow AAAS (sec. sect. Q); mem. APA, Am. Inst. Biol. Scis., Nat. Sci. Tchrs. Assn., Nat. Assn. Rsch. in Sci. Teaching (Outstanding Contbns. Sci. Teaching Through Rsch. award 1990), Nat. Assn. Biology Tchrs., Assn. for Edn. of Tchrs. of Sci., Am. Ednl. Rsch. Assn., Sigma Xi. Avocations: hiking; swimming; dancing; music. Home: 1403 Slaterville Rd Ithaca NY 14850-6207 Office: Cornell U Dept Edn Kennedy Hall Ithaca NY 14853

NOVAK, KIM (MARILYN NOVAK), actress; b. Chgo., Feb. 13, 1933; d. Joseph A. and Blanche (Kral) N.; m. Richard Johnson, April 1965 (div.); m. Robert Malloy, Jan. 1977. Student, Wright Jr. College, Chgo.; A.A., Los Angeles City College, 1958. appeared in: (films) The French Line, 1953, Pushover, 1954, Phfft, 1954, Five Against the House, 1955, Son of Sinbad, 1955, Picnic, 1955, The Man with the Golden Arm, 1956, The Eddie Duchin Story, 1956, Jeanne Eagles, 1957, Pal Joey, 1958, Vertigo, 1958, Bell, Book and Candle, 1958, Middle of the Night, 1959, Strangers When We Meet, 1960, Pépé, 1960, Boys' Night Out, 1962, The Notorious Landlady, 1962, Of Human Bondage, 1964, Kiss Me Stupid, 1964, The Amorous Adventures of Moll Flanders, 1965, The Legend of Lylah Clare, 1968, The Great Bank Robbery, 1969, Tales That Witness Madness, 1973, The White Buffalo, 1977, Just a Gigolo, 1979, The Mirror Crack'd, 1980, Liebestraum, 1991; (TV movies) Third Girl from the Left, 1974, Satan's Triangle, 1975, Malibu, 1983. Named one of 10 most popular movie stars by Box-Office mag. 1956, All-Am. Favorite 1961, Brussels World Fair poll as favorite all-time actress in world 1958. Office: 24700 Outlook Dr Carmel CA 93923*

NOVAK, MICHAEL (JOHN), religion educator, author, editor; b. Johnstown, Pa., Sept. 9, 1933; s. Michael John and Irene (Sakmar) N.; m. Karen Ruth Laub, June 29, 1963; children: Richard, Tanya, Jana. AB summa cum laude, Stonehill Coll., North Easton, Mass., 1956; BT cum laude, Gregorian U., Rome, 1958; MA, Harvard U., 1966; LLD, Keuka (N.Y.) Coll., 1970, Stonehill Coll., Mass., 1977, Thomas More Coll., 1992; LHD, Davis and Elkins (W.Va.) Coll., 1971, LeMoyne (N.Y.) Coll., 1976, Sacred Heart U., 1977, Muhlenberg Coll., 1979, D'Youville Coll., 1981, Boston U., 1981, New Eng. Coll., 1983, Rivier Coll., 1984, Marquette U., 1987; D en Ciencias Sociales, U. Francisco Marroquin, Guatemala, 1993. Teaching fellow Harvard U., 1961-63; asst. prof. Stanford U., 1965-68; assoc. prof. philosophy and religious studies State U. N.Y., Old Westbury, 1968-71; assoc. dir. humanities Rockefeller Found., N.Y.C., 1973-75; provost Disciplines Coll., SUNY, Old Westbury, 1969-71; vis. prof. Jan. session Carleton Coll., Northfield, Minn., 1970, Immaculate Heart Coll., Hollywood, Calif., 1971; vis. prof. U. Calif., Santa Barbara, 1972, Riverside, 1975; Ledden-Watson disting. prof. religion Syracuse U., 1977-79; journalist nat. elections Newsday, 1972; writer in residence The Washington Star, 1976, syndicated columnist, 1976-80, 84-89; columnist Forbes Mag., 1989—; resident scholar in religion and public policy Am. Enterprise Inst., Washington, 1978—; George Frederick Jewett chair pub. policy research, 1983—, dir. social and polit. studies, 1987—; chmn. working seminar on family and Am. welfare policy Inst., 1986; faculty U. Notre Dame, Ind., 1986-87, vis. W. Harold and Martha Welch Prof. Am. Studies, 1988, 88; judge Nat. Book awards, 1971, DuPont Broadcast Journalism awards, 1971-80; speechwriter nat. polit. campaigns, 1970, 72; mem. Bd. Internat. Broadcasting, 1983—; mem. Presdl. Task Force Project Econ. Justice, 1985-87, Council Scholars Library of Congress, 1986—; mem. monitoring panel UNESCO, 1984; vice chmn. Lay Commn. Cath. Social Teaching and U.S. Economy, 1984-86; U.S. Ambassador to Experts Meeting on Human Contacts of the Conf. On Security and Cooperation in Europe, Bern, Switzerland, 1986; U.S. rep. to human rights commn. UN, 1981-83; hon. prof. U Cuyo, Argentina, 1992. Author: novel The Tiber was Silver, 1961, A New Generation, 1964, The Experience of Marriage, 1964, The Open Church, 1964, Belief and Unbelief, 1965, A Time to Build, 1967, A Theology for Radical Politics, 1969, American Philosophy and the Future, 1968, Story in Politics, 1970, (with Brown and Herschel) Vietnam: Crisis of Conscience, 1967; Politics: Realism & Imagination, 1971, Ascent of the Mountain, Flight of the Dove, 1971, A Book of Elements, 1972, All the Catholic People, 1971, novel Naked I Leave, 1970, The Experience of Nothingness, 1970, The Rise of the Unmeltable Ethnics, 1972, Choosing Our King, 1974, The Joy of Sports, 1976, The Guns of Lattimer, 1978, The American Vision, 1978, Rethinking Human Rights I and II, 1981, 82, The Spirit of Democratic Capitalism, 1982, Confession of a Catholic, 1983, Moral Clarity in the Nuclear Age, 1983, Freedom with Justice, 1984, Human Rights and the New Realism, 1986, Will It Liberate? Questions About Liberation Theology, 1986, Character and Crime, 1986, The New Consensus on Family and Welfare, 1987, Taking Glasnost Seriously: Toward an Open Soviet Union, 1988, Free Persons and the Common Good, 1989, This Hemisphere of Liberty, 1990, The Spirit of Democratic Capitalism, 1991 (Anthony Fisher award 1992), Choosing Presidents, 1992, The Catholic Ethic and the Spirit of Capitalism, 1993; numerous other articles and books transl. into all maj. langs.; assoc. editor Commonweal mag., 1966-69; contbg. editor Christian Century, 1967-80, Christianity and Crisis, 1968-76, Jour. Ecumenical Studies, 1967—, This World, 1982-89, First Things, 1990—; religion editor Nat. Review, 1979-86; founder, pub. Crisis, 1982—, editor-in-chief, 1993—; fellow Hastings Inst., 1970-76; named Most Influential Prof. Sr. Class Stanford U., 1967, 68; Man of Yr. Johnstown, Pa., 1978; recipient Faith and Freedom award Religious Heritage Am., 1978, HIAS Liberty award, 1981, Friend of Freedom award, 1981; Newman Alumni award CCNY, 1984; George Washington Honor medal, 1984; award of Excellence, Religion in Media, 8th annual Angel Awards, 1985, Ellis Island Honor medal, 1986; recipient Anthony Fisher award, 1992; Templeton Progress in Religion prize, 1994; diploma as vis. prof. U. Francisco Marroquin, 1985; named acad. corr. mem. from U.S., Argentina Nat. Acad. Scis., Morals & Politics, 1985, others. Mem. Soc. Religion in Higher Edn. (crnl. com. 1970-73), Am. Acad. Religion (prog. dir. 1968-72), Coun. Fgn. Rels., Cath. Theol. Soc., Soc. Christian Ethics, Inst. Religion and Democracy (dir. 1981—), Nat. Ctr. Urban and Ethnic Affairs (dir. 1982-86). Office: Am Enterprise Inst 1150 17th St NW Washington DC 20036-4603 *Many persons have found a certain emptiness at the heart of human life —an experience of nothingness. Hidden in it, implicit in it, are prior commitments to honesty, courage, freedom, community. To increase the frequency of such acts in our lives is to grow, and to feel them diminish is to wither.*

NOVAK, PAUL, hotel industry executive; b. Lansing, Mich., May 19, 1946; s. Alfred and Helen Betty (Ascher) N.; m. Karen Juelg, Aug. 21, 1976; children: Sarah Ashley, Amanda Christine. BA, Mich. State U., 1973. Supervising cons. Pannell Kerr Forster and Co., Atlanta, 1970-76; v.p. devel. Accommodation Services, Inc., Atlanta, 1976-77; regional devel. analyst Holiday Inns, Inc., Memphis, 1977-78; dir. real estate La Quinta Motor Inns, Inc., San Antonio, 1978-81; sr. v.p. lodging devel. Marriott Corp., Washington, 1981—. Named one of Outstanding Young Men Am., 1981. Mem. Mich. State Alumni Club (v.p. Atlanta chpt. 1972-74), Travel and Tourism Rsch. Assn. (pres. Tex. chpt. 1979, internat. chpt. 1983, chmn. 1984), Mich. State Hotel, Restaurant and Instnl. Alumni Assn. (bd. dirs. 1989—), Nat. Assn. Indsl. and Office Parks (bd. dirs. 1989—). Jewish. Office: Marriott Corp Marriott Dr Washington DC 20058

NOVAK, PETER JOHN, lawyer; b. Chgo., Apr. 16, 1939; s. Peter and Ann (Jakocko) N.; m. Sarah Ellen Tayntor, Sept. 18, 1965; children: Nancy Ann, Natalie Hastings. AB, U. Ill., 1960, LLB, 1962. Bar: Ill. 1963, Ariz. 1972. Regional atty. Great Atlantic & Pacific Tea Co., Chgo., 1963-68; from staff atty. to gen. solicitor Greyhound Corp., Phoenix, 1968-93, v.p. brokerage, 1973-75; gen. counsel Sevices Co.-The Dial Corp., Phoenix, 1993—. Bd. dirs. Ariz. Zool. Assn.-Phoenix Zoo, The Phoenix Symphony. With U.S. Army, 1962-63. Mem. ABA, Ariz. Bar Assn., Maricopa County Bar Assn., Ill. Bar Assn., Chgo. Bar Assn., Internat. Assn. Ins. Counsel, Fedn. Ins. and Corp. Counsel, Am. Corp. Counsel Assn. Republican. Home: 4309 E Palo Verde Dr Phoenix AZ 85018-1127 Office: The Dial Corp 1850 N Central Ave Phoenix AZ 85077-0001

NOVAK, RAYMOND FRANCIS, research institute director, pharmacology educator; b. St. Louis, July 26, 1946; s. Joseph Raymond and Margaret A. (Cerutti) N.; m. Frances C. Holy, Apr. 12, 1969; children: Jennifer, Jessica, Janelle, Joanna. BS in Chemistry, U. Mo., St. Louis, 1968; PhD in Phys. Chemistry, Case Western Res. U., 1973. Assoc. in pharmacology Northwestern U. Med. Sch., Chgo., 1976-77, asst. prof. pharmacology, 1977-81, assoc. prof., 1981-86, prof., 1986-88; prof. pharmacology Wayne State U. Sch. Medicine, Detroit, 1988—; dir. Inst. Chem. Toxicology Wayne State U., Detroit, 1988—, dir. NIEHS Ctr. in Molecular and Cellular Toxicology with Human Application, 1994—; mem. toxicology study sect. NIH, Bethesda, Md., 1984-88; adj. sci. Inhalation Toxicology Rsch. Inst., Lovelace Biomed. and Environ. Rsch. Inst., 1991-95. Assoc. editor Toxicol. Applied Pharmacology, 1992—; editor Drug Metabolism and Disposition, 1994—; mem. editorial bd. Jour. Toxicology and Environ. Health, 1987-92, In Vivo, 1986—, Toxic Substances Jour., 1993—; mem. bd. pub. trustees Am. Soc. Pharmacology and Experimental Therapeutics, 1994—; contbr. articles to profl. jours. Recipient Disting. Alumni award U. Mo., St. Louis, 1988; grantee Nat. Inst. Environ. Health Sci., 1979—, Gen. Medicine sect. NIH, 1979—. Mem. Am. Soc. for Biochem. and Molecular Biology, Soc. Toxicology, Am. Assn. for Cancer Rsch., Am. Soc. for Pharmacology and Exptl. Therapeutics, Am. Chem. Soc. Hematology, Am. Chem. Soc., Biophys. Soc., Internat. Soc. for Study of Xenobiotics. Office: Wayne State U Inst Chem Toxicology 2727 2nd Ave Rm 4000 Detroit MI 48201-2654

NOVAK, ROBERT DAVID SANDERS, newspaper columnist, television commentator; b. Joliet, Ill., Feb. 26, 1931; s. Maurice Pall and Jane Ann (Sanders) N.; m. Geraldine Williams, Nov. 10, 1962; children: Zelda, Alexander. AB, U. Ill., 1952; LLD (hon.), Kenyon Coll., 1987. Reporter Joliet (Ill.) Herald-News, 1947-51, Champaign-Urbana (Ill.) Courier, 1951-52, AP, Omaha, Lincoln, Nebr., Indpls. and Washington, 1954-58, Wall St. Jour., Washington, 1958-63; syndicated columnist N.Y. Herald-Tribune, Washington, 1963-66; commentator Corinthian Broadcasting, Washington, 1963-65, Metromedia, Washington, 1966-76, RKO-Features, Washington, 1976-78; syndicated columnist Chgo. Sun-Times, Washington, 1966—; commentator Cable News Network, Washington, 1980—, Nat. Empowerment

TV, 1993—; pub. Evans-Novak Polit. Report, Washington, 1967—, Evans-Novak Tax Report, Washington, 1985-92, Evans-Novak Japan Report, Washington, 1989-92; roving editor Readers Digest, 1979—. Author: The Agony of the GOP, 1965, (with Rowland Evans) Lyndon B. Johnson: The Exercise of Power, 1967, Nixon In The White House, 1971, The Reagan Revolution, 1981. Trustee Bullis Sch., Potomac, Md., 1987—, Phillips Found., 1991—. 1st lt. U.S. Army, 1952-54. Recipient ACE award Cable Broadcasting Industry, 1990. Mem. Soc. Profl. Journalists, Washington Gridiron Club, Nat. Press Club, Army and Navy Club. Home: 801 Pennsylvania Ave NW Washington DC 20004-2615 Office: Ste 802 1750 Pennsylvania Ave NW Washington DC 20006-4502

NOVAK, ROBERT LOUIS, civil engineer, pavement management consultant; b. Chgo., Feb. 9, 1928; s. Louis and Frances (Kucera) N.; m. Virginia Staas, Jan. 22, 1955 (div. 1962); children: Susan Grace, Nina Louise; m. Joyce Eloise Keen, May 7, 1966; stepchildren: Robert John Moore, William Keen Moore, Marilyn Joyce Moore, James Clifford Moore. BCE, Ga. Inst. Tech., 1948. Soils engr. Soil Testing Svc., Chgo., 1952-54; chief materials engr. Skidmore Ownings and Merrill USAF Acad., Colorado Springs, 1954, dir. field invest, 1954-58; asst. dir. engring. O'Hare field constrn. Naess & Murphy, Chgo., 1958-60; pres. Novak, Dempsey & Assocs., Palatine, Ill. 1960-85; ptnr. Infrastructure Mgmt. Svcs., Arlington Heights, Ill., 1985-89, cons., 1989—. Contbr. articles to profl. jours. With U.S. Army, 1950-52. Mem. ASTM, Am. Pub. Works Assn. (meritorious svc. award 1990), Transp. Rsch. Bd. Achievements include development of one of the first pavement management programs. Home: 813 N Auburn Woods Dr Palatine IL 60067-2435

NOVAK, TERRY LEE, public adminstration educator; b. Chamberlain, S.D., Sept. 1, 1940; s. Warren F. and Elaine M. N.; m. Barbara Hosea, Aug. 29, 1981; children: Stephen, David. B.Sc., S.D. State U., 1962; postgrad. (Rotary fellow), U. Paris, 1962-63; M.P.A., Colo. U., 1965, Ph.D., 1970. Asst. city mgr. City of Anchorage, 1966-68; city mgr. City of Hopkins, Minn., 1968-74, City of Columbia, Mo., 1974-78, City of Spokane, Wash., 1978-91; v.p. bus. and fin. Ea. Wash. U., Cheney, 1991-92, prof. public adminstrn., 1992—, dir. grad. program pub. adminstrn., 1994—; acting dir. Joint Ctr. for Higher Edn., 1995-96; asst. adj. prof. U. Mo., Columbia, 1975, 77; adj. instr. Gonzaga U., Spokane, 1986-88; mem. nat. adv. coun. on environ. policy and tech. EPA. Author: Special Assessment Financing in American Cities, 1970; contbr. articles to profl. jours. Mem. Internat. City Mgrs. Assn. (Acad. Profl. Devel.), Am. Soc. Public Adminstrn. Episcopalian. Office: Ea Wash U Spokane Ctr 705 W 1st Ave Spokane WA 99204-0409

NOVAK, VICTOR ANTHONY, semi-retired manufacturing company executive; b. Antigo, Wis., Mar. 23, 1930; s. Joseph F. and Mary C. (Jerovic) N.; m. Marcella A. Tessmer, Nov. 3, 1951; children: Deborah, Mark, Jeffrey, Lori. Cert. in Mgmt., Marquette U., 1980. Mgr. repairshop Novak's Machineshop, Antigo, 1947-52; model maker AC Spark Plug co., Oakcreek, Wis., 1952-66; supr. experimental div. Oster Corp., Glendale, Wis., 1966-72; gen. foreman toolroom Square D Co., Milw., 1972-82, mgr. tool engring., 1982-89; sr. mfg. engr. Square D Co., Milw., Wis., 1993—; tchr. Milw. Area Tech. Coll., 1973—. Avocations: golf, bowling, fishing, skiing. Home: 6705 N Braeburn Ln Milwaukee WI 53209-3327 Office: Square D Co 4080 N 1st St Milwaukee WI 53212

NOVAK, WILLIAM ARNOLD, author, lecturer; b. Toronto, Ont., Can., Aug. 1, 1948; s. George Joseph and Esther (Brill) N.; m. Linda Mali Manaly, June 19, 1977; children: Ben, Jesse, Lev. BA, York U., Toronto, 1969; MA, Brandeis U., 1973. Editor Reponse mag., 1969-74; exec. editor Moment mag., 1976-78; editor New Traditions mag., 1984-86. Author: High Culture: Marijuana in the Lives of Americans, 1980, The Great American Man Shortage, 1983; co-author: (with Moshe Waldoks) The Big Book of Jewish Humor, 1981, (with Lee Iacocca) Iacocca: An Autobiography, 1984, (with Sydney Biddle Barrows) Mayflower Madam, 1986, (with Herb Schmertz) Goodbye to the Low Profile, 1986, (with Tip O'Neill) Man of the House, 1987, (with Nancy Reagan) My Turn, 1989, (with Moshe Waldoks) The Big Book of New American Humor, 1990, (with Oliver North) Under Fire, 1991, (with Magic Johnson) My Life, 1992. Jewish. Office: care Axelrod Agy 66 Church St Lenox MA 01240-2554

NOVAKOV, GEORGE JOHN, JR., gifted and talented education educator; b. New Orleans, Apr. 1, 1945; s. George John Novakov Sr. and Gloria (Edwards) Frost; m. Ann Marie Mariano, Dec. 27, 1969; children: Jay, Jaime. BA, U. New Orleans, 1967, MEd, 1970, postgrad., 1985; postgrad., Tulane U., Loyola U., 1985. Tchr. New Orleans Pub. Schs., 1967—; adminstrv. asst. Edna Karr Magnet Sch., 1994—; grant writer asst. New Orleans Pub. Libr., 1987-89. Author: (play) The Christmas Caper, 1980. Ind. Study Humanities fellow, 1991. Mem. La. Assn. of Computer Using Educators (assoc. editor newsletter, 1992), Greater New Orleans Coun. of Tchrs. of English. Democrat. Roman Catholic. Avocations: opera, science fiction, computers. Home: 7340 Edward St New Orleans LA 70126-2012 Office: Edna Karr Magnet Sch 3332 Huntlee Dr New Orleans LA 70131-7099

NOVALES, RONALD RICHARDS, zoologist, educator; b. San Francisco, Apr. 24, 1928; s. William Henry and Dorothy (Richards) N.; m. Barbara Jean Martin, Dec. 19, 1953; children: Nancy Ann, Mary Elizabeth. B.A., U. Calif., Berkeley, 1950, M.A., 1953, Ph.D., 1958; postgrad., U. Calif., Los Angeles, 1951-52. Asst. prof. biol. scis. Northwestern U., Evanston, Ill., 1958-64; assoc. prof. Northwestern U., 1964-70, prof., 1970-80, prof. neurobiology and physiology, 1981-93, emeritus prof. neurobiology and physiology, 1993—; cons. A.J. Nystrom Co., 1969. Mem. editorial bd.: The American Zoologist, 1969-73; Contbr.: articles to profl. jours. Ency. Brit. Book of Year. Served with U.S. Army, 1953-55. NSF research grantee, 1959-73, 75-78. Fellow AAAS. Unitarian. Home: 2008 Mcdaniel Ave Evanston IL 60201-2125

NOVAS, JOSEPH, JR., advertising agency executive; b. Bueu, Pontevedra, Spain, Sept. 21, 1921; came to U.S., 1928; s. Joseph and Josephine (Regueira) N.; m. Carmen Ramos, Feb. 9, 1989; children by previous marriage: Stephen, Robert, Paul, Patricia. A.B., Brown U., 1946; postgrad., Columbia U., 1948-49. Asst. advt. mgr. Colegate-Palmolive, Jersey City, 1946-49; internat. advt. mgr. The Gillette Co., Boston, 1949-53; founder, pres. Laradiotel, C.A., Havana, Caracas, Mexico, San Juan, N.Y.C., 1953-58; founder Telefilms, C.A., Venezuela, 1955; founder, pres. Novas-Criswell Advt., Caracas, Mexico City, Madrid, Bogota, Sao Paulo, San Juan, Buenos Aires, 1958-74; chmn. and mem. exec. com. Leo Burnett Co., Inc., Spain, Portugal, 1974-77; sr. v.p. Leo Burnett Co., Inc., Chgo., 1977-83, also bd. dirs.; chmn. Leo Burnett Europe/ME Ltd., London, 1983-86; cons. CMQ-TV, Havana, Cuba, 1953-54, Channel 2, Caracas, Venezuela, 1951-58, Heinz Co., Europe, 1985-87, Leo Burnett, 1986—; lectr. Caracas Central U., Caracas Andres Bello U., Mich. State U., Ohio U., Eastern Ill. U., McGill U., Montreal, Can. Served to lt. (j.g.) USN, 1942-46. Named Advt. Man of Yr., Venezuela. Mem. Internat. Advt. Assn. (world pres. 1974-76), Sales and Mktg. Execs. (pres. Venezuela chpt. 1962-64), Las Brisas Club (Marbella, Spain), Broken Sound Club (Boca Raton). *Frankness, forthrightness—always with the cards on the table. You lose some but you win most, and you always look in the mirror with pride and self respect.*

NOVATNEY, JOHN F., JR., lawyer; b. Cleve., May 26, 1930. AB, Brown U., 1952; LLB, U. Va., 1955. Bar: Ohio 1959. Ptnr. Baker & Hostetler, Cleve. Office: Baker & Hostetler 3200 Nat City Ctr 1900 E 9th St Cleveland OH 44114-3303

NOVELLO, ANTONIA COELLO, United Nations official, former U.S. surgeon general; b. Fajardo, P.R., Aug. 23, 1944; d. Antonio and Ana D. (Flores) Coello; m. Joseph R. Novello, May 30, 1970. BS, U. P.R. Rio Piedras, 1965; MD, U. P.R., San Juan, 1970; MPH, Johns Hopkins Sch. Hygiene, 1982; DSc (hon.), Med. Coll. Ohio, 1990, U. Ctrl. Caribe, Cayey, P.R., 1990, Lehigh U., 1992, Hood Coll., 1992. Diplomate Am. Bd. Pediatrics. Intern in pediatrics U. Mich. Med. Ctr., Ann Arbor, 1970-71, resident in pediatrics, 1971-73, pediatric nephrology fellow, 1973-74; pediatric nephrology fellow Georgetown U. Hosp., Washington, 1974-75; project officer Nat. Inst. Arthritis, Metabolism and Digestive Diseases NIH, Bethesda, Md., 1978-79, staff physician, 1979-80; exec. sec. gen. medicine B study sect., div. of rsch. grants NIH, Bethesda, 1981-86; dep. dir. Nat. Inst. Child Health & Human Devel., NIH, Bethesda, 1986-90; surgeon gen. HHS, Washington, 1990-93; spl. rep. for health and nutrition UNICEF, N.Y.C., 1993—; clin. prof. pediatrics Georgetown U. Hosp., Washington, 1986, 89, Uniformed Svcs. U. of Health Scis., 1989; mem. Georgetown Med. Ctr. Interdepartmental Rsch. Group, 1984—; legis. fellow U.S. Senate Com. on Labor and Human Resources, Washington, 1982-83; mem. Com. on Rsch. in Pediatric Nephrology, Washington, 1981—; participant grants assoc. program seminars Nat. Inst. Arthritis, Diabetes and Digestive and Kidney Diseases, NIH, Bethesda, 1980-81; pediatric cons. Adolescent Medicine Svc., Psychiat. Inst., Washington, 1979-83; nephrology cons. Met. Washington Renal Dialysis Ctr. affiliate Georgetown U. Hosp., Washington, 1975-78; phys. diagnosis class instr. U. Mich. Med. Ctr., Ann Arbor, 1973-74; chair Sec.'s Work Group on Pediatric HIV Infection and Disease, DHHS, 1988; cons. World Health Organ., Geneva, 1989; mem. Johns Hopkins Soc. Scholars, 1991. Contbr. numerous articles to profl. jours. and chpts. to books in field; mem. editorial bd. Internat. Jour Artificial Organs, Jour. Mexican Nephrology. Served to capt. USPHS, 1978—. Recipient Intern of Yr. award U. Mich. Dept. Pediatrics, 1971, Woman of Yr. award Disting. Grads. Pub. Sch. Systems, San Juan, 1980, PHS Commendation medal HHS, 1983, PHS Citation award HHS, 1984, Cert. of Recognition, Div. Research Grants NIH, 1985, PHS Outstanding medal HHS, 1988, PHS Unit Commendation, 1988, PHS Surgeon Gen.'s Exemplary Svc. medal, 1989, PHS Outstanding Unit citation, 1989, DHHS Asst. Sec. for Health cert. of commendation, 1989, Surgeon Gen. Medallion award, 1990, Alumni award U. Mich. Med. Ctr., 1991, Elizabeth Blackwell award, 1991, Woodrow Wilson award for disting. govt. svc., 1991, Congrl. Hispanic Caucus medal, 1991, Order of Mil. Med. Merit, 1992, Washington Times Freedom award, 1992, Charles C. Shepard Sci. award, 1992, Golden Plate award, 1992, Elizabeth Ann Seton award, 1992, Ellis Island Congrl. Medal of Honor, 1993, Legion of Merit medal, 1993, Athena award Alumnae Coun., 1993, Nat. Citation award Mortar Bd., 1993, Disting. Pub. Svc. award, 1993; named Health Leader of Yr., COA, 1992. Fellow Am. Acad. Pediatrics (Excellence Pub. Svc. award 1993); mem. AMA (Nathan Davis award 1993, Meritorious Svc. award 1993), Internat. Soc. Nephrology, Am. Soc. Nephrology, Latin Am. Soc. Nephrology, Soc. for Pediatric Rsch., Am. Pediatric Soc., Assn. Mil. Surgeons U.S., Am. Soc. Pediatric Nephrology, Pan Am. Med. and Dental Soc. (pres.-elect sec. 1984), D.C. Med. Soc. (assoc.), Johns Hopkins U. Soc. Scholars, Alpha Omega Alpha. Avocation: collecting antique furniture. Home: 1315 31st St NW Washington DC 20007-3334 Office: UNICEF Rm 634 3 United Nations Plaza New York NY 10017

NOVELLO, DON, writer, comedian, actor; b. Ashtabula, Ohio, Jan. 1, 1943; s. A.J. and Eleanor (Finnerty) N. BA, U. Dayton, 1964. Writer, performer TV show Smothers Brothers Show, 1975; author novel The Lazlo Letters, 1977; writer, performer TV show Saturday Night Live, 1978-80; performer feature film Gilda Live, 1979; writer, performer rec. Live At St. Douglas Convent, 1980; producer TV series SCTV, 1982; author novel The Blade, 1985; performer TV spl. Father Guido Sarducci Goes To College, 1985; writer, performer rec. Breakfast in Heaven, 1986; performer feature film Head Office, 1986; performer TV spl. The Vatican Inquirer, 1987; performer feature film Tucker, 1988, N.Y. Stories, 1989, Godfather III, 1990, La Pastorela, 1991. Author: (children's mus.) Full Moon Over Tutti, 1992, (novel) Citizen Lazlo, 1992; contbr. articles to Rolling Stone, Playboy, Washington Post, Mother Jones, Spy Mag. Founder The People's Cath. Ch. Mem. AFTRA, Writers Guild Am., Screen Actors Guild. Club: Cavalier's. Office: care Vesuvio Olive Oil Co PO Box 245 Fairfax CA 94930

NOVELLY, PAUL A., petrochemical and refining company executive; b. 1941; married. With Shell Oil Co., St. Louis, 1962-68; with Apex Oil Co., Inc., St. Louis, 1968—, Clark Oil & Refining Co., St. Louis; now vice-chmn., dir. Clark Oil & Refining Co. Office: Apex Oil Corp 8182 Maryland Ave Saint Louis MO 63105-3786

NOVER, NAOMI, journalist, editor, author; b. Buffalo; d. B.B. and Rebecca (Shane) Goll; m. Barnet Nover. Student, U. Buffalo; BS, N.Y. State Tchrs. Coll.; MA, George Washington U., 1951. News, features, editorial asst. Buffalo Times; tchr. pub., pvt. schs. Buffalo Park Sch. (demonstration sch. of U. Buffalo), Snyder, N.Y.; music critic Denver Post at Goethe Music Festival, Aspen, Colo.; news corr., columnist Washington Bur. Denver Post; editor, bur. chief Nover News Bur., Washington, 1972—; corr. mission to Europe Portland Oregonian, Italian Peace Treaty Conf., Luxembourg Palace, Paris, Ladybird Johnson trips to nat. parks, 1963; attended various econ. summits; White House corr. Pres. Ford European tour, Switzerland, Spain, Finland, England, France, Germany, Poland, 1975, Pres. Ford trips to China, South Korea, Indonesia, Japan, Philippines, Hawaii, 1978, Pres. Carter trips to India, Saudi Arabia, Israel, Egypt, S.Am., Africa, Eng., Europe, Japan, etc., 1978, Pres. Reagan trips to Peoples Republic of China, Europe, Cen. Am., Caribbean, Iceland, Bali, Indonesia, Finland, 1988, Pres. Bush's trips to Italy, The Vatican, Poland, Hungary, France, NATO, London, Costa Rica, Fed. Republic Germany, Belgium, The Netherlands, 1989, to Finland for Bush-Gorbachev Summit, 1990, Can., Martinique, Bermuda, Paris, London, Athens, Crete, Greece, Ankara, Turkey, Istanbul, Turkey, 1991, Moscow, Kiev, Russia, 1991, Honolulu, Sydney, Australia, Canberra, Australia, Melbourne, Australia, Singapore, Seoul, Korea, Osaka, Japan, Tokyo, 1992, Pres. Clinton trip to UN, N.Y., 1993. Writer, dir. plays produced in Buffalo; participated radio and television plays; producer: nationally syndicated radio program Views and Interviews; author: nationally syndicated feature stories and column Washington Dateline, 1952—; contbr. articles to mags. Formerly active ARC, U.S Treasury War Bonds; chmn. Kalorama area Community Chest, 1947-49; originator embassy participation groups, jr. hostess, chmn., originator embassy tour Goodwill Industries; past chmn., producer program with 1,000 Girl Scouts at Pan Am. Union; past mem. council Girl Scouts U.S.A.; chmn. program com. Columbian Women of George Washington U., 1953-56; nat. chmn. War Nurses Meml.; mem. women's bd. George Washington U. Hosp. Recipient award pin U.S. Treasury Dept.; Silver Eagle award Girl Scouts U.S.A.; chosen to christen ship SS Syosset for vol. and charity activities; named honor citizen Colonial Williamsburg (Va.). Mem. White House Corrs. Assn., State Dept. Corrs. Assn., Congl. Press Galleries Corrs. Assn., U.S. Capitol, AAUW, U.S. Capitol Hist. Soc., U.S. Supreme Ct. Hist. Soc., Founding Friend of Blair House, The Circle of Nat. Gallery of Art, Nat. League Am. Pen Women, Smithsonian Assocs., U.S. Archives, Hist. Preservation, Libr. of Congress Assocs., Women in Radio and TV Assn., Women in Arts Mus., Am. Hist. Assn., Welcome to Washington, Ikebana, Phi Beta Kappa Assocs., Sigma Delta Chi, Pi Lambda Theta (past corr. ofcl. publ., nat. scholastic honors). Office: Nat Press Bldg Washington DC 20045

NOVETZKE, SALLY JOHNSON, former ambassador; b. Stillwater, Minn., Jan. 12, 1932; married; 4 children. Student, Carleton Coll., 1950-52; HHD (hon.), Mt. Mercy Coll., 1991. Amb. to Malta, Am. Embassy, Valletta, 1989-93. Past mem., legis. rep. Nat. Coun. on Vocat. Edn.; past mem. adv. coun. for career edn., past mem. planning coun. Kirkwood C.C.; bd. dirs., lifetime trustee Cedar Rapids (Iowa) Community Theater; bd. dirs. James Baker III Pub. Policy Inst. Rice U.; trustee Shattuck/St. Mary's Sch., Faribault, Minn.; vice chmn., lifetime trustee, exec. com. Hoover Presdl. Libr.; past precinct chmn. Iowa Rep. Com., 1976-88, mem. cen. com., 1982-85; state chmn., 1985-87; chmn. Linn County Rep. Com., 1980-83; adv. bd. Iowa Fedn. Rep. Women, 1987-89; vice chmn. campaign adv. bd. Nat. Fedn. Rep. Women, 1987-89; co-chmn. V.P. Bush Inauguration, 1980; Iowa co-chmn. George Bush for Pres., 1988; bd. dirs. Greater Cedar Rapids Found., also chmn. grants com., Coun. of Am. Ambs.; bd. dirs. Ambs. Forum; trustee Shahuck/St. Mary Sch., Fairmont, Minn. Decorated dame Order of Knights of Malta; recipient Disting. Alumnus award Stillwater High Sch., 1991; Disting. Alumni award for outstanding achievement Carleton Coll., 1994. Office: 4747 Mount Vernon Rd SE Cedar Rapids IA 52403-3941

NOVICH, BRUCE ERIC, materials engineer; b. Phila., Mar. 15, 1957; s. Samuel David and Vivian Rose Novich; m. Susan S. Novich, Sept. 5, 1982; children: Scott, Spencer, Cory. BA, Colgate U., 1979; BSChemE, MIT, 1980, MS in Geology, 1982, MS in Civil Engring, 1982, PhD, 1984. V.p. rsch., devel., engring. Ceramics Process System, Milford, Mass., 1984—. Contbr. over 30 articles to profl. jours. Achievements include 15 patents in particulate processing. Home: 55 Pleasant St Lexington MA 02173-6114 Office: Cermics Process Systems 8 Avenue E Hopkinton MA 01748-2211

NOVICK, ALVIN, biology educator; b. Flushing, N.Y., June 27, 1925; s. Isidore and Lena (Janowitz) K. A.B., Harvard U., 1947, M.D., 1951; M.A. (hon.), Yale U., 1983. Diplomate Am. Bd. Med. Examiners. Instr. to prof. biology Yale U., New Haven, 1957—. Author: The World of Bats, 1969; Animal Structure and Funcion, 1969; (with others) The Biology of Bats., 1977. Faculty affiliate Peabody Mus. Natural History, New Haven, 1958—; co-founder AIDS Project, New Haven, 1983; chmn. Conn. Stonewalls Found., Hartford, Conn., 1984—; chmn. Mayor's Task Force on AIDS, New Haven, 1986—; bd. dirs. Nat. AIDS Network, 1987—; mem. Task Force on AIDS, Archdiocese of Hartford, 1987—, Conn. Task Force Rev. Research and Recommanend State Policy on AIDS, 1987-88. Served with inf. U.S. Army, 1943-45, ETO. Mem. Am. Assn. Physicians for Human Rights (pres. 1985—). Avocations: breeder of shih tzu; gardening; dwarf conifers. Home: 1998 Hartford Tpke North Haven CT 06473-1004 Office: Yale Univ Dept of Biology PO Box 6666 New Haven CT 06511-8161

NOVICK, ANDREW CARL, urologist; b. Montreal, Que., Can., Apr. 5, 1948; came to U.S., 1974; s. David and Rose (Ortenberg) N.; m. Thelma Silver, June 29, 1969 (div. Dec. 1983); 1 child, Lorne J.; m. Linda Friedman, May 24, 1992; children: Rachel H., Eric D. BSc, McGill U., Montreal, 1968, MD, CM, 1972. Diplomate Am. Bd. Urology. Resident in surgery Royal Victoria Hosp., Montreal, 1972-74; resident in urology Cleve. Clinic Found., 1974-77, staff dept. urology, 1977—, head sect. renal transplant, 1977—, chmn. dept. urology, 1985—, chmn. Organ Transplant Ctr., 1985—. Editor: Vascular Problems in Urology, 1982, Stewart's Operative Urology, 1989; contbr. over 400 articles to profl. jours. Fellow ACS, Med. Coun. Can.; mem. Am. Urol. Assn., Am. Assn. Genito-Urinary Surgeons, Clin. Soc. Genito-Urinary Surgeons. Home: 22325 Canterbury Ln Cleveland OH 44122-3901 Office: Cleve Clinic Found 9500 Euclid Ave Cleveland OH 44195-0001

NOVICK, DAVID, civil engineer, educator; b. N.Y.C., May 14, 1926; s. Harry and Charlotte (Menzin) N.; m. Minna Sommer, Aug. 28, 1953; children: Martha, Linda, Emily. BSCE, Columbia U., 1948, MS, 1954. Registered profl. engr., Ill., N.Y.; registered structural engr., Ill. Founds. and soils engr. Tippetts-Abbett-McCarthy-Stratton, N.Y.C., 1948-54; found., structural engr., exec. v.p. Goodkind & O'Dea, Inc., Hamden, Conn., 1954-56, Chgo., 1956-60; pres. Westenhoff & Novick, Inc., Chgo., 1960-77; exec. v.p. Lester B. Knight & Assos., Chgo., 1977-81; sr. v.p. Parsons, Brinckerhoff, Quade & Douglas, Inc., Chgo., 1981-92, cons., 1992-93; assoc. dir. Urban Systems Lab., U. Ill., Chgo., 1977; adj. prof. systems engring. U. Ill., 1977-80; prin. Dana Engring. Corp., 1993—; mem. Dispute Resolution Bd., Washington, 1995—; lectr. civil engring. Ill. Inst. Tech., 1970-76; mem., sec. Ill. sTructural Engr. Exam. Com., 1970-75; Crom lectr. U. Fla., 1982; bd. overseers Armour Coll., Ill. Inst. Tech., 1989-94. Author: Life Cycle Considerations in Infrastructure Management, FHWA Life Cycle Cost Symposium, 1993. Trustee North Suburban Mass Transit Dist., 1970-74; bd. dirs. Open Lands Project, 1986—, exec. com., 1989-92; active METRA Commuter Rail System, Citizen's Adv. Bd., 1992—. With AUS, 1944-46. Fellow ASCE (nat. dir. 1977-80, pres. Ill. sect., co-chmn. task com. nat. civil engring. edn. conf. 1979, Washington Award Comm. 1972-78, 91—, chmn. publs. com. 1979-80, task com. on civil engring. edn. 1981-85, chmn. task com. on Civil Engring. Rsch. Found. 1986-88, chmn. com. engring. mgmt. at orgn. level 1987-88, mem. strategic planning com., 1988-90, Ill. sect. Chgo. Civil. Engr. of Yr. 1987, Profl. Activities Com. 1991—), Civil. Engr. Rsch. Found. (chmn. implementation task force 1991-92, ASCE practitioner-in-residence program 1992, 93), Am. Cons. Engrs. Coun. (chmn. com. fellows 1992-94, mem. ACEC constrn. liaison com. 1995—); mem. NSPE (life), ASTM, Am. Ry. Engring. Assn., Ill. Soc. Prfl. Engrs. (v.p. 1963-64), Cons. Engrs. Coun. Ill. (bd. dirs. 1989—, v.p. 1991-92, pres.-elect 1993, pres. 1994, nat. dir. 1995—), Western Soc. Engrs. (trustee 1972-78), Internat. Soc. Bridge and Structural Engrs., Internat. Soc. Soil Mechanics and Found. Engrs., Soc. Am. Mil. Engrs. (Pub. Svc. award Chgo. Post 1981), Am. Arbitration Assn. (panel arbitrators and mediatirs), Univ. Club (Chgo.), Chi Epsilon (hon.). Home: 1335 N Astor St Chicago IL 60610-2152 Office: Dana Engring Corp 1335 N Astor St Chicago IL 60610-2152

NOVICK, JULIUS LERNER, theater critic, educator; b. N.Y.C., Jan. 31, 1939; s. Solomon Joseph and Ethel (Lerner) N.; m. Phyllis Belle Spaeth, May 27, 1983; 1 child, Ilana. B.A., Harvard U., 1960; D.F.A., Yale U., 1966. Theatre critic WNDT-TV, Channel 13, N.Y.C., 1968-70; asst. prof. English NYU, N.Y.C., 1969-72; assoc. prof. lit. SUNY-Purchase, 1972-80, prof., 1980—; theatre critic The Village Voice, N.Y.C., 1958-89, The N.Y. Observer, N.Y.C., 1987-91, Newsday, N.Y.C., 1992-94, The Threepenny Rev., Berkeley, Calif., 1994—; vis. lectr. drama div. Juilliard Sch., N.Y.C., 1968-71; dramaturg The Acting Co., N.Y.C., 1971-73; vis. critic Dartmouth Summer Repertory Co., Hanover, N.H., 1976, 79, 80, 82, 83, 84; master critic Nat. Critics Inst., Waterford, Conn., 1971—. Author: Beyond Broadway, 1968. Fulbright scholar, 1960-61; Woodrow Wilson fellow, 1961-62; Guggenheim fellow, 1977; recipient George Jean Nathan award for dramatic criticism, 1981-82. Mem. Drama Desk, Am.Soc. for Theatre Rsch., Am. Theatre Critics Assn. (adv. coun.). Jewish.

NOVICK, MARVIN, investment company executive, former automotive supplier executive, accountant; b. N.Y.C., July 16, 1931; s. Joseph and Anna Novick; m. Margaret A. Blau, Apr. 9, 1960; children: Jeffrey, Stuart, Barry. BBA, CCNY, 1952; MBA, NYU, 1955, postgrad., 1955-58. CPA, N.Y., Mich., La., N.C. Sr. v.p. Mich. Blue Cross/Blue Shield, Detroit, 1961-70; v.p., dir. fin. Meadowbrook Ins. Southfield, Mich., 1970-72; ptnr. Touche Ross and Co., Detroit, 1972-84; vice chmn. Dura Corp., Southfield, 1984-87, Wesnovtek Corp., Birmingham, Mich., 1987—. Chmn. Oak Park-Huntington Woods-Pleasant Ridge (Mich.) Dem. Org., 1970-72, 18th Dem. Congl. Dist., 1972-74; trustee Mich. Assn. for Emotional Children, 1965—, also past pres.; trustee Providence Hosp., Southfield, 1975-83, also past chmn., trustee bldg. bd., 1982-89; trustee Oak Park (Mich.) Bd. Edn., 1964-71, also past pres.; trustee Temple Beth El, Birmingham, Mich., 1968—, also past pres.; trustee, vice chmn. Union of Am. Hebrew Congregation, 1981—; chmn. fin. com., fin. sec. World for Prog. Judaism-Internat., 1985—; chmn. personnel com. Jewish Welfare Found., 1987-91, assoc. chmn. cultural and edn. fedn. com., 1984—, chmn. sub-com. Israel and Overseas Com., 1988—; mem. com. Jewish Aggy. in Israel, 1987—; vice chmn. fin. com., trustee Sinai Hosp., 1988-92; trustee, fin. com. Mich. Cancer Found., 1992—; bd. dirs. B'nai Brith Centennial Lodge, 1970-79, past v.p.; trustee, mem. exec. com. Rose Hill Ctr., Inc., 1992—; mem. com. Hillel Ctr., U. Mich.; mem. various coms. Jewish Welfare Fedn. Recipient Honor and Service cert. Oak Park Bd. Edn., 1972, Past Pres. award Mich. Assn. Emotionally Disturbed Children, 1986; named one of Outstanding Young Men of Am., Outstanding Am. Found., 1968. Mem. Am Inst. CPA's, Mich. Assn. CPA's, N.Y. State Assn. CPA's. Home: 12820 Burton St Oak Park MI 48237-1679

NOVICK, NELSON LEE, dermatologist, internist, writer; b. Bklyn., June 27, 1949; s. Benjamin and Vivian (Meltzer) N.; m. Meryl Sohnis, June 20, 1971; children: Yonatan, Yoel, Ariel, Daniel, Avraham. BA in Biology magna cum laude, Bklyn. Coll., 1971; MD, Mt. Sinai Sch. Medicine, 1975. Diplomate Am. Bd. Internal Medicine, Am. Bd. Dermatology, Am. Bd. Med. Examiners. Resident in internal medicine Mt. Sinai Med. Ctr., N.Y.C., 1975-78, assoc. attending, 1980—, postgrad. preceptee, 1980-83, outpatient dept. clinic chief, dermatology svc., 1983; resident Skin and Cancer Unit NYU Med. Ctr., N.Y.C., 1978-80; assoc. clin. prof. Mt. Sinai Sch. Medicine, N.Y.C., 1980—; cons. Westwood-Squibb Skin Care Info. Ctr., Vaseline Intensive Care Rsch., Bausch & Lomb, Schering-Plough, Sandoz Internat., Proctor & Gamble, Lever-2000. Author: Saving Face, Skin Care for Teens, Super Skin, Baby Skin, You Can Do Something About Your Allergies, Diseases of the Mucous Membranes, You Can Look Younger At Any Age, (novel) In the Path of the Wolf; co-author: The External Ear; reviewer Annals Internal Medicine, Jour. Am. Acad. Dermatology, Jour. Dermatol. Surgery and Oncology, Internat. Jour. Dermatology; editorial advisor Exec. Health's Good Health Report, Snyder Comm., Your Baby Wallboard Program; former med. editor Current Podiatric Medicine, Jour. Am. Analgesia Soc.; contbr. articles to profl. pubs. Regent's Coll. scholar, 1971, Max and Leah Strauss Fund scholar, 1971, Grand St. Found. scholar, 1971. Fellow ACP (direct election), Am. Acad. Dermatology, Am. Soc. Dermatol. Surgery, Skin Cancer Found. (hon.), Am. Acad. Cosmetic Surgery; mem. AMA, AAAS, Soc. Investigative Dermatology, Skin Phototrauma Found., Internat. Soc. for Androgenic Disorders, Skin Cancer Found. (charter), N.Y. Acad. Scis., N.Y. County Med. Soc., Am. Soc. Dermatologic Surgery, Am. Analgesia Soc. (past bd. dirs.), Nature Conservancy, Audubon Soc., Nat.

Geog. Found., N.Y. Zool. Soc., Am. Mus. Natural History, Smithsonian Instn., Nat. Wildlife Fedn., The Wilderness Soc., Author's Guild, Author's League Am., Phi Beta Kappa. Jewish. Office: 328 E 75th St New York NY 10021-3305

NOVICK, PETER, historian, educator; b. Jersey City, July 26, 1934; s. Michael and Esther (Liebman) N.; m. Carroll Ott, July 10, 1957 (div. 1962); m. Joan Kroll, May 24, 1964; 1 child, Michael. BS, Columbia U., 1957, PhD, 1965. Asst. prof. U. Calif., Santa Barbara, 1965-66; asst. prof. history U. Chgo., 1966-69, assoc. prof., 1969-87, prof., 1987—; lectr. Rutgers U., New Brunswick, N.J., 1961-62, Columbia U., N.Y.C., 1961-65. Author: The Resistance vs. Vichy: The Purge of Collaborators in Liberated France, 1969 (Clark M. Ansley award Columbia U. Press 1969), That Noble Dream: The "Objectivity Question" and the American Historical Profession, 1988 (Albert J. Beveridge prize Am. Hist. Assn. 1989). With U.S. Army, 1953-55. French Govt. fellow, 1960-61, William Bayard Cutting travelling fellow, 1962-63, NEH fellow, 1990-91, Ctr. for Advanced Study in Behavioral Scis: fellow, 1991-92. Mem. Am. Hist. Assn. Home: 5000 S Cornell Ave Chicago IL 60615-3041 Office: U Chgo Dept History 1126 E 59th St Chicago IL 60637-1580

NOVICK, ROBERT, physicist, educator; b. N.Y.C., May 3, 1923; s. Abraham and Carolyn (Weisberg) N.; m. Bernice Lehrman, July 3, 1947; children: Beth, Amy, Peter. M.E., Stevens Inst. Tech., 1944, M.S., 1949; Ph.D., Columbia, 1955. Microwave engr. Wheeler Lab., Inc., Great Neck, L.I., N.Y., 1946-47; instr. physics Columbia U., 1952-54, research assoc. 1954-57, assoc. prof. physics, dir. radiation lab., 1960-62, prof., co-dir. Astrophysics Lab., 1968-77, 86-92, dir. Astrophysics Lab., 1977-86, prof., 1977-93, prof. of physics emeritus, 1993—, chmn. dept. physics, 1983-88; asst. prof. physics U. Ill., Urbana, 1957-59, assoc. prof., 1959-60; Cons to labs., research insts.; chmn. subpanel on atomic and molecular physics Nat. Acad. Sci., 1964-65; mem. NASA Commn. on Sci. Uses of Space Sta., 1984-86. Recipient Exceptional Sci. Achievement medal NASA, 1980, Honor award Stevens Inst. Tech., 1989; A.P. Sloan fellow, 1958-70. Fellow Am. Phys. Soc., IEEE, AAAS; mem. Am. Astron. Soc. (sec.-treas. high energy astrophysics sect. 1975-78), Internat. Astron. Union. Research, publs. on atomic physics, atomic collisions, quantum electronics, atomic frequency standards, nuclear spins and moments, X-ray astronomy. Home: 366 W 245th St Bronx NY 10471-3902 Office: Dep Physics Columbia Univ 538 W 120th St New York NY 10027-6601

NOVICK, SHELDON M., author, lawyer; b. N.Y.C., June 19, 1941; s. Irving and Ruth (Rosenblatt) N.; m. Carolyn M. Clinton; children: Melia Bensussen, Michael Clinton. BA, Antioch Coll., 1963; JD, Washington U., 1977. Adminstr. Center for Biology of Natural Systems, Washington U., St. Louis, 1966-69; assoc. editor Environment mag., St. Louis, 1964-69; editor Environment mag., 1969-77, pub., 1972-74; assoc. firm Milgrim Thomajan Jacobs & Lee, N.Y.C., 1977-78; regional counsel U.S. EPA, Phila., 1978-86; staff atty. Environ. Law Inst., 1986-87; scholar in residence Vt. Law Sch., 1987—. Author: The Careless Atom, 1969, The Electric War, 1976, Law of Environmental Protection, 1987, Honorable Justice: The Life of Oliver Wendell Holmes, 1989; editor (with Dorothy Cottrell) Our World in Peril, 1971, The Collected Works of Justice Holmes, 1995. Town agt., grand juror Strafford Twp., 1988—; mem. Vt. Water Resources Bd., 1988-92. Home: PO Box 259 South Strafford VT 05070

NOVINGER, CATHY BLACKBURN, utility company executive; b. Portsmouth, Ohio, Apr. 7, 1949; s. Donald E. and Leona (Collingsworth) Blackburn; m. Robert L. Novinger, June 8, 1968; 1 child, Travis Andrew. Diploma, Portsmouth Bus. coll., 1968; cert. sec., U. S.C., 1977; student, Limestone Coll., 1980-81, Edison Electric Inst., 1984. Adminstrv. asst. to pres. S.C. Electric and Gas Co., Columbia, 1979-81, exec. asst. to pres., 1981-82, v.p. corp. services, 1982-83, v.p. group exec. adminstrn., 1983, sr. v.p. adminstrn. and mktg., 1984-88; sr. v.p. adminstn. and govt. affairs SCANA Corp., 1988—; sem. instr. U.S.C., Columbia, 1982—. Bd. dirs. Nat. Soc. Prevent Blindness, Columbia, pres., 1986; adv. bd. Salvation Army, Columbia, 1986—; personel relations com. Edison Electric Inst.; bd. dirs. Jr. Achievement, Columbia, 1981—; bd. dirs. exec. com. Community Relations Council, Columbia, 1984—. Recipient Tribute to Women in Industry award YWCA, 1982; Ind. Bus. Women award, 1984; named Career Woman of Yr., Nat. Fedn. Bus. and Profl. Women, 1983; named to Tribute to Women in Industry Acad., YWCA, 1987. Mem. SE Electric Exchange (employee relations com.). Republican. Baptist. Avocations: tennis, cooking, reading. Office: SCANA Corp 1426 Main St Box 764 Columbia SC 29201*

NOVINS, DOUGLAS K., psychiatrist, educator. Prof. psychiatry divsn. child and adolescent psychiatry U. Colo., Denver. Recipient Presdl. Scholar award Am. Acad. Child and Adolescent Psychiatry, 1993. Office: U CO Divsn Child & Adolescent Psychiatry/Health Sciences Ctr PO Box C-259 / 4200 E 9th Ave Denver CO 80262*

NOVITCH, MARK, physician, educator, retired pharmaceutical executive; b. New London, Conn., Apr. 23, 1932; s. Charles Weinger and Mary (Margolick) N.; m. Katherine Louise Henderson, Oct. 9, 1971; 1 dau., Julia Drummond. A.B., Yale U., 1954; M.D., N.Y. Med. Coll., 1958. Intern, asst. resident in medicine Boston City Hosp., 1958-60; rsch. fellow Harvard Med. Sch., 1960-62, asst. in medicine, 1962-64, instr. medicine, 1964-67; mem. med. staff Peter Bent Brigham Hosp., Boston, 1962-67; asst. physician Univ. Health Svcs., Harvard U., 1961-67; asst. to dep. asst. sec. for health and sci. affairs HEW, Washington, 1967-71; dep. assoc. commr. for med. affairs FDA, Washington, 1971-78; assoc. commr. for health affairs FDA, 1978-81; dep. commr. food and drugs HHS, 1981-85; corp. v.p. The Upjohn Co., Kalamazoo, 1985-86, sr. v.p. sci. adminstrn., 1986-88, exec. v.p., 1989-90, vice-chmn. bd. dirs., 1991-93; prof. health scis. George Washington U., Washington, 1994—; bd. dirs. Biomed. Svcs. Bd. ARC, Nat. Orgn. for Rare Disorders, Neurogen Corp., Osiris Therapeutics, Inc., Alteon, Inc., Challenger Ctr. for Space Sci.; trustee and past pres. U.S. Pharmacopeial Conv. Inc. Trustee Coun. for Excellence in Govt., Kalamazoo Coll.; mem. com. Bretton Woods. USPHS fellow, 1960-62; Brookings Instn. fed. exec. fellow, 1970-71. Mem. AMA, Mass. Med. Soc., Am. Pub. Health Assn., Am. Soc. Clin. Pharmacology and Therapeutics, Nat. Acad. Social Ins. Home: 3558 Albemarle St NW Washington DC 20008-4214

NOVITZ, CHARLES RICHARD, television executive; b. Chgo., Oct. 25, 1934; m. Eve Krzyzanowski, Feb. 11, 1988; 1 child, Alexandra Maris. BS in Journalism, U. Ill., Champaign-Urbana, 1956; MS, Columbia U., 1960; MPA, NYU, 1971. Reporter, writer, editor City News Bur., Chgo., 1956-57, UPI, Chgo., 1957-59; editor, writer, field producer NBC News, N.Y.C. and Chgo., 1959-60; with ABC News (TV network syndication), 1973-79; mng. dir. Ind. TV News Assn., N.Y.C., 1979-81; producer, exec. NBC News, N.Y.C., 1982-85, 87; assoc. Rowan & Blewitt, Inc./Exec. TV Workshop, N.Y.C., 1985—; pres. NovaNews Comm. Cons. N.Y.C., 1994—; on-air talent Money Call News, 1988; freelance TV producer, cable and pub. TV series, 1985—; adj. instr. LIU, 1967-69, NYU, 1969-70; asst. adj. prof. Lehman Coll., 1970-71; adj. prof., producer interactive televised course CUNY, 1972-75. Mem. Broadcast Pioneers, Radio TV News Dirs. Assn., Alumni Assn. Columbia Grad. Sch. Journalism (pres. 1979, Deadline Club (N.Y.C.; pres. 1969), Soc. Profl. Journalists-Sigma Delta Chi (pres. 1981-82). Address: 160 West End Ave Apt 29D New York NY 10023-5604 Office: 3 Park Ave 39th Flr New York NY 10016

NOVOGROD, NANCY ELLEN, editor; b. N.Y.C., Jan. 30, 1949; d. Max and Hilda (Kirschbaum) Gerstein; m. John Campner Novogrod, Nov. 7, 1976; children: James Campner, Caroline Anne. AB, Mt. Holyoke Coll., 1971. Sec. fiction dept. The New Yorker, N.Y.C., 1971-73; reader, 1973-76; asst. editor Clarkson N. Potter, Inc., N.Y.C., 1977-78, assoc. editor, 1978-80, editor, 1980-83, sr. editor, 1984-86, exec. editor, 1987; sr. editor HG (formerly House and Garden mag.), N.Y.C., 1987-88, editor-in-chief, 1988-93; editor-in-chief Travel & Leisure, N.Y.C., 1993—. Bd. dirs. N.Y. Bot. Garden, 1991, Mount Holyoke Coll., 1992—. Office: Travel & Leisure 1120 Ave of the Americas New York NY 10036

NOVOTNEY, DONALD FRANCIS, school system administrator; b. Streator, Ill., July 10, 1947; s. Andrew Steven and Irene Marie (Lux) N.; m. Jane Frances Loeffelholz, June 3, 1972; children: Nicole, Tara, Thomas,

Michael, Theresa. BA in English and Social Studies, Loras Coll., 1969; MST, U. Wis., Platteville, 1973; MS, U. Dayton, 1984. Tchr. Holy Ghost Sch., Dickeyville, Wis., 1969-70, prin., 1970-75; prin. St. John Sch., Green Bay, Wis., 1975-76, St. Peter Sch. Beaver Dam, Wis., 1976-83; coord. Jordan Cath. Sch., Rock Island, Fla., 1983-85; supt. schs. Diocese of Fargo, N.D., 1985-87; dir. schs. Diocese of LaCrosse, Wis., 1987—. Ch. lecter, eucharistic minister St. Pius Ch., LaCrosse, Wis., 1986—. Mem. Nat. Cath. Edn. Assn. (mem. resource for mktg. 1992—, del. to nat. congress for cath. schs. 1992), Wis. Assn. Nonpub. Schs. Republican. Home: 3314 33rd St S La Crosse WI 54601-7706 Office: PO Box 4004 La Crosse WI 54602-4004

NOVOTNY, DONALD WAYNE, electrical engineering educator; b. Chgo., Dec. 15, 1934; s. Adolph and Margaret N.; m. Louise J. Eenigenburg, June 26, 1954; children: Donna Jo, Cynthia Novotny. B.E.E., Ill. Inst. Tech., 1956, M.S., 1957; Ph.D., U. Wis., 1961. Registered profl. engr., Wis. Instr. Ill. Inst. Tech., 1957-58; mem. faculty U. Wis., Madison, 1958—, prof. elec. engring., 1969—, chmn. dept. elec. and computer engring., 1976-80, Grainger prof. power electronics, 1990—; vis. prof. Mont. State U., 1966, Eindhoven (The Netherlands) Tech. U., 1974, Tech. U. Louvain, Belgium, 1986; Fulbright lectr. Tech. U. Ghent, Belgium, 1981; dir. Wis. Elec. Machines and Power Electronics Consortium, 1981—; assoc. dir. Univ.-Industry Rsch. Program, 1982-93; chmn. elec. engring. program Nat. Technol. U., 1989—; cons. to industry. Author: Introductory Electromechanics, 1965; also research papers; assoc. editor Electric Machines and Power Systems, 1976—. Fellow Gen. Electric Co., 1956; Ford Found., 1960; recipient Kiekhofer Teaching award U. Wis., 1964, Benjamin Smith Reynolds Teaching award, 1984; Outstanding Paper award Engring. Inst. Can., 1966; grantee numerous industries and govt. agencies. Fellow IEEE (prize papers awards 1983, 84, 86, 87, 90, 91, 93); mem. Am. Soc. Engring. Edn., Sigma Xi, Tau Beta Pi, Eta Kappa Nu. Congregationalist. Lodge: Rotary. Home: 1421 E Skyline Dr Madison WI 53705-1132 Office: U Wis Dept Elec and Computer Engring 1415 Johnson Dr Madison WI 53706-1691

NOVOTNY, MILOS VLASTISLAV, chemistry educator; b. Brno, Czechoslovakia, Apr. 19, 1942; came to U.S., 1969; BS, U. Brno, Czechoslovakia, 1962, PhD, 1965. Rsch. assoc. Inst. Analytical Chemistry Czechoslovak Acad. Scis., Brno, 1965-68; rsch. assoc. Royal Karolinska Inst., Stockholm, 1968-69; rsch. assoc. dept. chemistry U. Houston, 1969-71; from instr. to Rudy prof. of chemistry Ind. U., Bloomington, 1971—. Office: Ind U Dept of Chemistry Bloomington IN 47405

NOVOTNY, SUSAN M., judge; b. Norfolk, Nebr., June 13, 1951; d. Richard J. and Blanche M. (Mensik) N.; m. Scott R. Laidig, Jan. 22, 1978. BA cum laude, Cath. Univ. of Am., D.C., 1973; JD, Cath. Univ. of Am. Law Sch., D.C., 1979. Bar: Fla. 1980, Escambia Santa Rosa 1980. Adminstrv. asst., paralegal specialist Dept. of Justice, D.C., 1973-79; trial atty. Criminal Div. Fraud Sect. U.S. Dept. of Justice, D.C., 1979-80; assoc. Kerrigan, Estess & Rankin, Pensacola, Fla., 1980-82; asst. state atty. Pensacola, Fla., 1982-84, asst. U.S. atty., 1984-86; magistrate judge U.S. Dist. Ct. (no. dist.) Fla., Pensacola, 1986—; adj. prof. Pensacola Jr. Coll., 1980-85, Law Enforcement Tng. Acad., 1981-85; instr. Nat. Inst. of Trial Advocacy, 1984-88, Emory Law Sch. Trial Techniques Program, Atlanta, 1985, Atty. Gen.'s Advocacy Inst., Dept. of Justice, 1985-89. Recipient Spl. Achievement award U.S. Dept. of Justice, 1985, Cert. of Appreciation U.S. Dept. of Treasury Bureau of Alcohol, Tobacco & Firearms, 1985. Mem. Am. Bar Assn., Fla. Bar Assn., Escambia Santa Rosa Bar Assn. Office: US Courthouse 100 N Palafox St Rm 204 Pensacola FL 32501-4839

NOVY, MILES JOSEPH, obstetrician/gynecologist, educator; b. Berlin, Germany, Nov. 23, 1937; s. Joseph Miloslav and Helena (Lukowski) N.; m. Katherine Stephens, Dec. 20, 1978 (div.); children: Milena, Julia. BA, Yale U., 1959; MD, Harvard U., 1963. Diplomate Am. Bd. Obstetrics and Gynecology. Fellow dept ob/gyn Harvard U., Boston, 1969-70; asst. prof. dept. ob/gyn Oreg. Health Scis. U., Portland, 1970-72; assoc. prof. Oreg. Health Scis. U., 1972-78, asst. chmn. ob/gyn., 1986-88, co-dir. reprodn./endocrine infertility svc., 1984-88, dir. div. reproductive endocrine fertility div., 1988—; prof. ob/gyn., 1978—; assoc. scientist reproductive biology behavior Oreg. Reg. Primate Rsch. Ctr., Beaverton, 1970-72; scientist Oreg. Reg. Primate Rsch. Ctr., 1972—; cons. Kaiser Permanente, Portland, 1980—; lectr. in field. Contbr. articles to profl. jours., chpts. to books; inventor in field. Lt. comdr., USPHS, 1965-68. NIH Merit awardee, 1989; recipient Outstanding Movie award, Am. Fertility Soc., 1989. Fellow Am. Coll. Obstetricians and Gynecologists (Hoechst award 1969); mem. Am. Fertility Soc. (postgrad. prog. com. 1990—), Yale U. Alumni Assn. (del. 1988-90), Am. Physiol. Soc., Soc. for Gynecologic Investigation, AMA, Am. Gynecology and Obstetrical Soc., Soc. of Reproductive Surgeons, Pacific Coast Ob/Gyn Soc. (Meml. Found. award 1974). Avocations: tennis, scuba diving, skiing. Home: 3107 SW Nottingham Dr Portland OR 97201-1611 Office: Oregon Regional Primate Ctr 505 NW 185th Ave Beaverton OR 97006-3448

NOWACKI, JAMES NELSON, lawyer; b. Columbus, Ohio, Sept. 12, 1947; s. Louis James and Betty Jane (Nelson) N.; m. Catherine Ann Holden, Aug. 1, 1970; children: Carrie, Anastasia, Emma. AB, Princeton U., 1969; JD, Yale U., 1973. Bar: Ill. 1973, N.Y. 1982, U.S. dist. Ct. (no. dist.) Ill. 1973, U.S. Ct. Appeals (7th cir.) 1978, U.S. Ct. Appeals (6th cir.) 1987, U.S. Supremem Ct. 1992. Assoc. Isham, Lincoln & Beale, Chgo., 1976-80; ptnr. Kirkland & Ellis, Chgo., 1980—. Mem. Winnetka Sch. Bd. Dist. 36, Ill., 1983-91, bd. pres., 1989-91, Winnetka caucus, 1995-96. Harlan Fiske Stone prize Yale U., 1972. Mem. ABA (forum com. on constrn. industry, litigation sect.), Mid-Am. Club, Skokie Country Club. Home: 708 Prospect Ave Winnetka IL 60093-2320 Office: Kirkland & Ellis 200 E Randolph Dr Chicago IL 60601

NOWAK, JACQUELYN LOUISE, administrative officer, realtor, consultant; b. Harrisburg, Pa., Sept. 2, 1937; d. John Henry and Irene Louise (Clark) Snyder; children: Andrew Alfred, IV, Deirdre Anne. Student, Pa. State U., 1973-74; BA, Lycoming Coll., 1975. Editorial writer Patriot News Co., Harrisburg, Pa., 1957-58; dir. West Shore Sr. Citizens Ctr., New Cumberland, Pa., 1969-72; exec. dir. Cumberland County Office Aging, Carlisle, Pa., 1972-80; bur. dir. Bur. Advocacy, Pa. Dept. Aging, Harrisburg, 1980-88; exec. asst. to Pa. Senator John D. Hopper, Senate Com. on Aging and Youth, 1989; owner D&J Prodns., Art and Handcrafted Teddy Bears 1986, Ted E. Bear's Emporium, Harrisburg, 1988-92; assoc. Century 21 Piscioneri Realty, Inc., Camp Hill, Pa.; spl. projects coord. Pa. div. Am. Trauma Soc., 1991-93; adminstr. Country Meadows of West Shore II. Mechanicsburg, Pa., 1993-94; adminstrv. officer Am. Trama Soc., 1994—; recorder Pa. Gov's. Coun. Aging Cen. Region, 1972-74; chmn. pub. rels., 1973-74; mem. state planning com. Pa. State Conf. Aging, 1974, panelist, 1975-78; mem. state bd. Pa. Coun. Homemakers-Home Health Aide Svcs., 1972-80, v.p., 1975, chmn. ann. meeting, 1973-75; sr. citizens subcom. chmn. Pa. Atty. Gens. Commn. to Prevent Shoplifting, 1983; mem. adv. com. Tri-County Ret. Sr. Vol. Program, 1972-74; bd. dirs. Coun. Human Svcs. Cumberland, Dauphin, and Perry Counties, 1973-74; mem. svc. com. Family and Children's Svc. Harrisburg, 1970-74, mem. policy com., 1973-74, bd. dirs. Cumberland County unit Am. Cancer Soc., 1964-76, state del., 1964-66, chmn. county pub. rels. 1965-66, cancer crusade chmn., 1964. Recipient Herman Melitzer award, Pa. Conf. Aging, 1978; named Woman of the Yr. Sta. WIOO Radio, Carlisle, Pa., 1979. Mem. Nat. Assn. Area Ags. on Aging (bd. dir. 1975-80, pres. 1976-77; sec. 1978-79), Pa. Watercolor Soc., Harrisburg Art Assn., Mechanicsburg Art Ctr. (pres. 1987-90, bd. dirs. 1984—), Gerontol Soc. Am., Am. Trauma Soc. (Pa. div. state bd. 1985-88), Older Women's League (founder chpt.), Lycoming Coll. Alumni Assn. (exec. bd. 1987-90), Bus. and Profl. Women's Club (div. chmn. 1972-76), Torch Club (pres. 1987-88, 2d v.p. 1985-86), Zonta Internat. (sec. 1986-89). Home: 15 Paddock Ln Camp Hill PA 17011-1268

NOWAK, JAN ZDZISLAW, writer, consultant; b. Warsaw, Poland, May 15, 1913; came to U.S.A., 1977; s. Waclaw Adam and Elisabeth (Piotrowski) Jezioranski; m. Jadwiga Zaleski, Sept. 7, 1944. M.S., U. Poznan, Poland, 1936; Doctorate honoris causa, U. Poznan. Sr. researcher U. Poznan, 1937-39; emissary Polish resistance movement, 1941-45; editor BBC, London, 1947-51; dir. Polish Service Radio Free Europe, Munich, Fed. Republic of Germany, 1951-76; nat. dir. Polish Am. Congress, Washington, 1979-92; cons. Nat. Security Coun., 1979-92. Author: Courier from Warsaw, 1982, War on Airways, 1985, Poland From Afar, 1988; contbr. articles to mags.

Served to maj. Polish Army, 1939-45. Decorated Virtuti Militari; decorated Cross of Valour, King's medal for Courage, Order of White Eagle, Poland, gt. ribbon Polonia Restituta, Comdrs. Cross of Merit with star (Poland). Roman Catholic. Home: 3815 Forest Grove Dr Annandale VA 22003-1959

NOWAK, JOHN E., law educator; b. Chgo., Jan. 2, 1947; s. George Edward and Evelyn (Bucci) N.; m. Judith Johnson, June 1, 1968; children: John Edwin, Jeffrey Edward. AB, Marquette U., 1968; JD, U. Ill., 1971. Law clk. Supreme Ct. of Ill., Chgo., 1971-72; asst. prof. U. Ill., Urbana, 1972-75, assoc. prof., 1975-87, law prof., 1978—, grad. coll. faculty, 1982—, Baum Prof. Law, 1993—; chmn. Constl. Law Sch. Sect.; faculty rep. Big Ten Intercollegiate Conf. Schaumburg, Ill., 1981—; vis. prof. law U. Mich., Ann Arbor, 1985; Lee Disting. vis. prof. Coll. William and Mary, 1993. Coauthor: Constitutional Law, 4th edit. 1991, Treatise on Constitutional Law, 1986, 2nd edit., 1992, Story's Commentaries on the Constitution, 1987. Scholar-in-Residence, U. of Ariz., Tucson, 1985, 87. Mem. Assn. of Am. Law Schs. (chm. constl. law sect., accreditation com. 1980-88), Nat. Collegiate Athletic Assn. (mem. infractions com. 1987—), Am. Law Inst., Am. Bar Assn., Ill. Bar Assn., Order of the Coif (Triennial Book award com.). Roman Catholic. Home: 1701 Mayfair Rd Champaign IL 61821-5522 Office: U Ill Coll Law 504 E Pennsylvania Ave Champaign IL 61820-6909

NOWAK, JOHN MICHAEL, air force officer; b. Grand Rapids, Mich., Dec. 17, 1941; s. John F. and Dorothy F. (Smigiel) N.; m. Maureen K. Henry, Apr. 20, 1963; children: Kimberly, Susan, John, Michael, Lynn. BA in Sociology and Polit. Sci., Aquinas Coll., Mich., 1963; M in Mgmt., U. So.Calif., 1973. Commd. 2d lt. U.S. Air Force, 1963, advanced through grades to lt. gen., 1993; dir. maintenance Ogden Air Logistics Ctr., Hill AFB, Utah, 1984-86; dep. chief staff for maintenance Air Force Logistics Command, Wright-Patterson AFB, Ohio, 1986-89; dep. chief staff for logistics and engring. Hdqrs. Mil. Airlift Command, Scott AFB, Ill., 1989-92; dep. chief staff for logistics Hdqrs. Air Mobility Command, Scott AFB, 1992; dir. of supply Hdqrs. U.S. Air Force, Washington, 1992-93, dep. chief for logistics, 1993—. Decorated DSM, Legion of Merit, Bronze Star medal, Meritorious Svc. medal with 3 oak leaf clusters, Air Force Commendation medal. Avocations: golf, reading. Office: HQ USAF/LG 1030 Air Force Pentagon Washington DC 20336

NOWAK, NANCY STEIN, judge; b. Des Moines, Sept. 17, 1952; d. Russell D. and Christine (Evanoka) Stein; m. Raymond A. Nowak, May 26, 1973. BA, Drake Univ., Iowa, 1974, MA, 1976; JD, George Washington Univ., D.C., 1980. Bar: D.C. 1980, Iowa 1982, Tex. 1986. Briefing atty. Judge Jamie Boyd, 1983-84, Judge Edward Prado, 1984-87; asst. U.S. atty., 1987-88, asst. U.S. trustee, 1988-89; magistrate judge U.S. Dist. Ct. (Tex. we. dist.), 5th circuit, San Antonio, 1989—. Office: US Courthouse 655 E Durango Blvd San Antonio TX 78206

NOWEL, DAVID JOHN, marketing professional; b. New Britain, Conn., Mar. 29, 1935; s. John Joseph and Sophie C. (Nowel) Bonkowski; m. July 20, 1961 (div. 1979); children: Lynn Marie, Bruce Edward. BA in Chemistry and Psychology, Hobart Coll., 1959; MA in Bus., Bklyn. Coll. of Pharmacy, 1964. Neurophysiology tech. technician Inst. of Living Rsch. Lab., Hartford, 1955-57; sales rep. Sandoz Pharms., Bklyn., 1961-65, Becton Dickenson, Huntington Beach, Calif., 1965-71; sales mgr. Scott Labs., N. Hollywood, Calif., 1971-79; area mgr. Beckman Instruments, Fullerton, Calif., 1979-86; sales rep. Indsl. Tng. Corp.; sales mgr. Pacific Toxicology Lab., L.A., 1987-89, The Mark Group, Santa Ana, Calif., 1989-91; dir. of mktg. Remedial Mgmt. Corp., Newport Beach, Calif., 1991-92; bus. devel. mgr. Tech. Waste Inc., Placentia, Calif., 1993-94; sales engr. Nat. Tech. Sys., Calabasas, Calif., 1994—. Author: Space Station "ARK," 1987, 2nd edit., 1994. Chairperson energy Orange County C. of C., 1989, mem. air subcom. 1991; co-chairperson environment Irvine C. of C., 1989. With USN, 1959-61. Mem. Assn. of Hazardous Materials Profls. Republican. Unitarian. Home: 19585 Seagull Ln Huntington Beach CA 92648 Office: Nat Tech Sys Environ Svcs 1536 E Valencia Dr Fullerton CA 92631

NOWELL, ELIZABETH CAMERON CLEMONS, author; b. Berkeley, Calif.; d. Alfred George and Edith (Catton) Cameron; AB San Jose State Coll., 1928; MA, Stanford U., 1937; m. Wood Clemons, Dec. 22, 1946 (div. Dec. 1958); m. Arthur G. Robinson, May 27, 1961 (dec. Jan. 1967); m. Nelson T. Nowell, Feb. 15, 1969 (dec. Sept. 1973). With edn. dept. San Jose State Coll., 1928-39, in service tng. U. Calif. Extension Div., 1939-42; elem. editor The John C. Winston Co., 1942-43, Silver Burdett Co., 1943-44, D.C. Heath, 1944-46; instr. English dept. U. Minn., 1947; writing, editing publs. services Gen. Mills, 1947-50; freelance writer, 1950—; mem. faculty Monterey Peninsula Coll., Monterey, Calif., 1978-83; reading cons. Monterey City Sch., 1959-62, assoc. editor Calif. edit. Am. Home Mag., 1965-70; mem. seminar faculty Embroiderers Guild, 1980; judge needle-work Good Samaritan Hosp., L.A.s, 1977, 79, 83, 87, Montalvo Center for Arts, Saratoga, Calif., 1980, 82, Status Needle Art Show, Burlingame, Calif., 1982, Altrusa Needlework Exhbn., Santa Maria, Calif., 1982, Scripps Meml. Hosp., La Jolla, Calif., 1980, 86, others. Bd. dirs. Community Hosp. Aux.; bd. dirs. Harrison Meml. Library, 1971-76, Monterey Symphony Assn., 1974-75; vestryman St. Dunstan's Episcopal Ch., 1974-77. Mem. Nat. League Am. Pen Women, Authors Guild, LWV, Nat. Embroidery Tchrs. Assn. (nat. dir. 1978-81), Embroiderers Guild Am. (hon. mem. 1991—, nat. dir. 1978-81, nat. fin. com. 1984-87; nat. fin. guidelines chmn. 1986-87; nat. judges cert. com. 1984-89, chmn. 1987; pres. chpt. 1977-78; judge needlework exhbns. 1977-90, historian 1988-89), Kappa Alpha Theta, Pi Lambda Theta, Delta Phi Upsilon, Kappa Delta Pi, Delta Kappa Gamma. Republican. Episcopalian. Clubs: Casa Abrego (historian 1979-83), Monterey Peninsula Country, Soroptimist. Author: The Pixie Dictionary, 1953; the Catholic Child's First Dictionary, 1954; The Winston Dictionary for Canadian School Children, 1955; Away I Go, 1956; All About Baby, 1956; I Live on A Farm, 1956; A Wish for Billy, 1956; Wings, Wheels, and Motors, 1957; The Big Book of Real Fire Engines, 1958; The Big Book of Real Trains, 1958; The Big Book of Real Trucks, 1958; Rodeo Days, 1960; Shells Are Where You Find Them, 1960; Rocks and The World Around You, 1960; Big and Little, 1961; Tide Pools and Beaches, 1964; Waves, Tides, and Currents, 1967; Here and There Stories; Now and Then Stories; Near and Far Stories; A Source Book for the Teaching of Literature for Children (all 1967); The Seven Seas, 1971; The Friendly Frog, 1971; What I Like, 1971; Guidelines for Treasurers, 1987, Wind by the Sea, 1989, Skylines, 1989; also feature articles in nat. mags. Address: 200 Glenwood Cir E7 Monterey CA 93940

NOWELL, GLENNA GREELY, librarian, consultant; b. Gardiner, Maine, Apr. 15, 1937; d. Bion Mellon and Faith Louise (Hutchings) Greely; m. Dana Richard Nowell, Sept. 1, 1956 (div. 1971); children: Dana A., Mark R., Dean E. BA in English, U. Maine, 1986. Dir. Gardiner Pub. Libr., 1974—; bd. dirs. Gardiner Bd. Trade; mem. Maine Libr. Commn., 1980-88, Gov.'s Commn. Employment of Handicapped, 1978-81; mem. adv. bd. Gardiner Savs. Bank, 1986—; trustee J. Walter Robinson Welfare Trust, 1986—. Creator, editor Who Reads What publ., 1988—. Mem. Gardiner Econ. Devel. Com., 1989—; interim city mgr. City of Gardiner, 1991. Recipient Hugh Hefner 1st Amendment award Playboy Found., 1987, Outstanding Libr. award Maine Libr. Assn., 1993, Cmty. Svc. award Kennebec Valley C. of C., 1991. Mem. Rotary (pres. Gardiner chpt. 1993-94). Office: Gardiner Pub Libr 152 Water St Gardiner ME 04345-2195

NOWELL, PETER CAREY, pathologist, educator; b. Phila., Feb. 8, 1928; s. Foster and Margaret (Matlack) N.; m. Helen Worst, Sept. 9, 1950; children: Sharon, Timothy, Karen, Kristin, Michael. B.A., Wesleyan U., Middletown, Conn., 1948; M.D., U. Pa., 1952. Intern Phila. Gen. Hosp., 1952-53; resident pathology Presbyn. Hosp., Phila., 1953-54; med.-teaching, research specializing in cancer Phila., 1956—; from instr. to prof. pathology Sch. Medicine U. Pa., 1956—, chmn. dept. pathology, 1967-73; dir. (Cancer Center), 1973-75. Served to lt., M.C. USNR, 1954-56. Recipient Research Career award USPHS, 1964-67, Parke-Davis award, 1965, Lindback Disting. Teaching award, 1967, Passano award, 1984, Rous-Whipple award Am. Assn. Pathology, 1986, de Villers award Leukemia Soc. Am., 1987, Mott prize GM Cancer Rsch. Found., 1989, 3M award, FASEB, 1993. Mem. AMA, APHA, Am. Assn. Advancement Med. Instrumentation, Critical Care Med. Soc., Pa. Med. Assn., Navy League, U.S. Naval Inst., Sunday Breakfast Club. Home: 345 Mt Alverno Rd Media PA 19063-5313 Office: U

Pa Sch Medicine Dept Pathology and Lab Medicine Philadelphia PA 19104-6082

NOWICK, ARTHUR STANLEY, metallurgy, materials science educator; b. N.Y.C., Aug. 29, 1923; s. Hyman and Clara (Sperling) N.; m. Joan Franzblau, Oct. 30, 1949; children: Jonathan, Steven, Alan, James. A.B., Bklyn. Coll., 1943; A.M., Columbia U., 1948, Ph.D., 1950. Physicist NACA, Cleve., 1944-46; instr. U. Chgo., 1949-51; asst. prof., then assoc. prof. metallurgy Yale U., 1951-57; mgr. metallurgy research IBM Corp Research Center, Yorktown Heights, N.Y., 1957-66; prof. metallurgy Columbia U., 1966-90, Henry Marion Howe prof. metallurgy and materials sci., 1990—; A. Frank Golick lectr. U. Mo., 1970; vis. prof. Technion, Haifa, Israel, 1973; co-chmn. Internat. Conf. Internal Friction, 1961, 69 (medal 1989); cons. in field. Co-author: Anelastic Relaxation in Crystalline Solids, 1972; co-editor: Diffusion in Solids, 1975, Diffusion in Crystalline Solids, 1984; contbr. articles to profl. jours. Fellow Am. Phys. Soc., AIME; mem. Am. Ceramic Soc., Materials Research Soc. (Turnbull lectr. 1994), Sigma Xi (pres. Kappa chpt. 1983-85). Office: 1144 Mudd Bldg Columbia U New York NY 10027

NOWICKI, GEORGE LUCIAN, retired chemical company executive; b. Rutherford, N.J., Dec. 4, 1926; s. Justin Nowicki; m. Mary Elisabeth Baker, Aug. 30, 1947; children: Barbara, Peter, Paul, James. BSChemE, CCNY, 1949; MSChemE, NYU, 1956. Registered profl. engr., N.Y., Pa. Chemist Ideal Toy Co., N.Y.C., 1949; chem. engr. Bklyn. Union Gas Co., 1949-50, Sonotone Corp., Elmsford, N.Y., 1950-52; dept. head Burroughs Wellcome Co., Tuckahoe, N.Y., 1952-70; v.p. mfg. Quaker Chem. Corp., Conshohocken, Pa., 1970-79, v.p. domestic ops., 1984-89; ret. Quaker Chem. Corp., Conshohocken, 1989; pres. Selby Batersby Co., Phila., 1979-81; mng. dir. Quaker Chem. Holland BV, Uithoorn, The Netherlands, 1981-84; chmn. bd. Overdale Corp., Alsip, Ill., 1987-89, Quaker Chem. Can. Ltd., Toronto, 1985-89. Pres. Citl. Sch. Dist. 7, Hartsdale, N.Y., 1960-69, Westchester County Sch. Bds. Assn., White Plains, N.Y., 1965; bd. dirs. Suburban Gen. Hosp., Norristown, Pa., 1986; mem. governing bd. Vt. Common Cause, 1993—; bd. dirs. Martha Canfield Libr., Arlington, Vt., 1994—; counselor Svc. Corps Ret. Execs., 1993-95. Mem. Am. Inst. Chem. Engrs., Mfrs. Assn. Del. Valley (bd. dirs. 1987-89). Avocations: swimming, skiing, video photography, stamps. Home: RR 1 Box 1809 Arlington VT 05250-9716

NOWLAN, GEORGE JOSEPH See DAVIS, DANNY

NOWLIN, JAMES ROBERTSON, federal judge; b. San Antonio, Nov. 21, 1937; s. William Forney and Jeannette (Robertson) N. BA, Trinity U., 1959, M.A., 1962; J.D., U. Tex., Austin, 1963. Bar: Tex. 1963, Colo. 1993, U.S. Dist. Ct. D.C. 1966, U.S. Ct. Claims 1969, U.S. Supreme Ct. 1969, U.S. Dist. Ct. (we. dist.) Tex. 1971. Assoc. Kelso, Locke, & King, San Antonio, 1963-65; assoc. Kelso, Locke & Lepick, San Antonio, 1966-69; legal counsel U.S. Senate, Washington, 1965-66; propr. Law Offices James R. Nowlin, San Antonio, 1969-81; mem. Tex. Ho. of Reps., Austin, 1967-71, 73-81; judge U.S. Dist. Ct. (we. dist.) Tex., Austin, 1981—; instr. Am. govt. and history San Antonio Coll., 1964-65, 71-73. Served to capt. U.S. Army, 1959-60, USAR, 1960-68. Life fellow State Bar Found; mem. ABA, Travis County Bar Assn., San Antonio Bar Assn. Republican. Presbyterian. Avocations: pilot; skiing; hiking; jogging. Office: US Courthouse 200 W 8th St Austin TX 78701-2333

NOYCE, PHILLIP, film director; b. Griffith, New South Wales, Austalia, Apr. 27, 1950; films include: (dir., writer): Backroads, 1977 (also prodr.), Newsfront, 1979, Heatwave, 1983; (dir.): Shadows of the Peacock, 1987 (in U.S. as Echoes of Paradise, 1989), Dead Calm, 1989, Blind Fury, 1990, Patriot Games, 1992, Sliver, 1993, Clear and Present Danger, 1994; television work includes (as dir.): The Dismissal, 1983, The Cowra Breakout, 1985, The Hitchhiker (The Curse), 1986, Nightmare Cafe (pilot), 1992. Office: ICM 8942 Wilshire Blvd Beverly Hills CA 90211-1908*

NOYES, ANNE LOUISE, lawyer; b. Milw., Feb. 6, 1958; d. Ralph Paul and Nancy (Dammann) Rosenheimer; m. Christopher Benson Noyes, June 23, 1984. Student, Occidental Coll., 1976-78; BS in Internat. Politics cum laude, Georgetown U., 1978-80; JD cum laude, U. Wis., 1981-84. Assoc. Quarles & Brady, Milw., 1984—. Assoc. editor Wis. Law Review; author (newsletter) Wis. Marital Property Act, 1986. Vol. atty. Milw. Zool. Soc., 1985-86; chmn. Law Explorers, Milw., 1984-86; fund raiser Milw. Performing Arts Ctr., Milw., 1985-86. Named Rookie Adv. of Yr. Boy Scouts Am., 1985. Mem. Assn. Women Lawyers, ABA, Wis. Bar Assn. (young lawyers div.), Milw. Met. Assn. Profl. Women (publicity co-chmn.). Avocation: tennis. Home: 2119 E Kenilworth Pl Milwaukee WI 53202-1326 Office: Quarles & Brady 780 N Water St Milwaukee WI 53202-3512

NOYES, H(ENRY) PIERRE, physicist; b. Paris, Dec. 10, 1923; s. William Albert and Katharine Haworth (Macy) N.; m. Mary Wilson, Dec. 20, 1947; children—David Brian, Alan Guinn, Katharine Hope. B.A., Harvard U., 1943; Ph.D., U. Calif., Berkeley, 1950. Physicist MIT, 1943-44, U. Calif. Berkeley, 1949-50; Fulbright fellow U. Birmingham, Eng., 1950-51; asst. prof. U. Rochester, N.Y., 1951-55; group leader Lawrence Livermore Lab., 1955-62; Leverhulme lectr. U. Liverpool, Eng., 1957-58; adminstrv. head theory sect. Stanford Linear Accelerator Center, 1962-69; assoc. prof. Stanford U., 1962-67, prof., 1967—; vis. scholar Center Advanced Study Behavioral Scis., Stanford, 1968-69; cons. in field. Author papers in field. Chmn. Com. for Direct Attack on Legality of Vietnam War, 1969-72; mem. steering com. Faculty Political Action Group, Stanford U., 1970-72; mem. policy com. U.S. People's Com. on Iran, 1977-79. Served with USNR, 1944-46. Fellow NSF, 1962; Fellow Nat. Humanities Faculty, 1970; recipient Alexander von Humboldt U.S. Sr. Scientist award, 1979. Mem. Alternative Natural Philosophy Assn. (pres. 1979-87, 1st alternative natural philosopher award 1989), Am. Phys. Soc., AAAS, Sigma Xi. What success I may have had has come because I have tried to bring together my physics and politics and family to serve the people. I aim to achieve a unified materialist philosophy that might help others to greater success than my own. I sum up this philosophy as "fixed past - uncertain future".

NOYES, JUDITH GIBSON, library director; b. N.Y.C., Apr. 19, 1941; d. Charles II and Alice (Klauss) Gibson; m. Paul V. Noyes, June 1, 1991; children from previous marriage: Andrea Elizabeth Green, Michael Charles Green. BA, Carleton Coll., 1962; MLS, U. Western Ont., London, Can., 1972. Librarian edn. U. New Brunswick, 1972-86; libr. Can. Inst. Sci. and Tech. Info., Ottawa, Ont., Can., 1975-86; univ. librarian Colgate U., Hamilton, N.Y., 1986—; mem. OCLC Adv. Com. on Coll. and Univ. Librs., 1991—; pres. bd. trustees Ctrl. N.Y. Libr. Resources Coun., 1992—. Mem. ALA, Am. Coll. and Rsch. Librs. (nominating com. 1988-89, 92-93, legis. com. coll. libr. sect. liaison 1989-91, chair task force on intellectual freedom 1992-94), Internat. Standards Orgn. (tech. com. 46, 1981-89). Office: Colgate U Everett Needham Case Libr 13 Oak Dr Hamilton NY 13346-1379

NOYES, RICHARD HALL, bookseller; b. Evanston, Ill., Feb. 12, 1930; s. George Frederick and Dorothy (Hall) N.; m. Judith Claire Mitchell, Oct. 10, 1953; children—Catherine, Stephanie, Matthew. B.A., Wesleyan U., 1952. Tng. program, elementary-high sch. salesman Rand McNally & Co., Colo., Utah, Idaho, Wyo., 1955-59; founder, owner, mgr. The Chinook Bookshop, Colorado Springs, Colo., 1959—. Contbr. to A Manual on Bookselling, 1974, The Business of Book Publishing, 1984; contbr. articles to newspapers and trade jours. Chmn. Colo. Media Coalition, 1974—; bd. dirs. Colorado Springs Fine Arts Ctr. 1977-81, Citizens Goals for Colorado Springs, 1976-88; trustee Fountain Valley Sch., 1979-81; vice chmn. Colorado Springs Charter Rev. Commn., 1991-92. Served with AUS, 1952-54. Recipient Intellectual Freedom award Mountain Plains Librs. Assn., 1977, Disting. Svc. award U. Colo., 1980, Recognition award Pikes Peak Arts Coun., 1989, Charles S. Haslam award, 1990. Entrepreneur of Yr. award U. Colo., 1992. Mem. Am. Booksellers Assn. (pres., dir.). Home: 1601 Constellation Dr Colorado Springs CO 80906-1609 Office: The Chinook Bookshop Inc 210 N Tejon St Colorado Springs CO 80903-1314

NOYES, RICHARD MACY, physical chemist, educator; b. Champaign, Ill., Apr. 6, 1919; s. William Albert and Katharine Haworth (Macy) N.; m. Winninette Arnold, July 12, 1946 (dec. Mar. 1972); m. Patricia Jean Harris, Jan. 26, 1973. A.B. summa cum laude, Harvard U., 1939; Ph.D., Calif. Inst. Tech., 1942. Research assoc. rocket propellants Calif. Inst. Tech., 1942-46;

mem. faculty Columbia U., 1946-58, assoc. prof., 1954-58; Guggenheim fellow, vis. prof. U. Leeds, Eng., 1955-56; prof. chemistry U. Oreg., 1958—, head dept., 1963-68, 75-78, ret., 1984—. Editorial adv. com.: Chem. Revs. 1967-69; editorial adv. com.: Jour. Phys. Chemistry, 1973-80; assoc. editor: Internat. Jour. Chem. Kinetics, 1972-82, Jour. Phys. Chemistry, 1980-82; Contbr. to profl. jours. Fulbright fellow; Victoria U. Wellington, New Zealand, 1964; NSF sr. postdoctoral fellow Max Planck Inst. für Physikalische Chemie, Göttingen, Fed. Republic Germany, 1965; sr. Am. scientist awardee Alexander von Humboldt Found., 1978-79. Fellow Am. Phys. Soc.; mem. NAS, Am. Acad. Arts and Scis., Am. Chem. Soc. (chmn. div. phys. chemistry 1961-62, exec. com. div. 1960-75, mem. coun. 1960-75, chmn. Oreg. sect. 1967-68, com. on nominations and elections 1962-68, com. on pubs. 1969-72), Chem. Soc. (London), Wilderness Soc., ACLU, Hungarian Acad. Scis. (hon.), Sierra Club (past chmn. Atlantic and Pacific N.W. chpts., N.W. regional v.p. 1973-74), Phi Beta Kappa, Sigma Xi. Achievements include research mechanisms chemical reactions, developing general theories, intrepretation physical properties chemicals. Home: 2014 Elk Ave Eugene OR 97403-1734 Office: U of Oregon Dept Chemistry Eugene OR 97403 *When I was young, I wanted to be an "explorer" I am fortunate to have a job in which I can make discoveries as exciting as those of the explorers who first sailed uncharted seas. Then I can try to convey the excitement to another generation. As an avocation, I try to influence government policies toward our least developed lands. It is a gratifying mix of satisfying curiousity and serving society.*

NOYES, ROBERT EDWIN, publisher, writer; b. N.Y.C., June 22, 1925; s. Clarence A. and Edith (LaDomus) N.; m. Janet Brown, Mar. 24, 1952 (div. June 1963); children—Keith, Steven, Mark, Geoffrey; m. Mariel Jones, July 24, 1964; children—Rebecca, Robert. B.S. in Chem. Engring, Northwestern U., 1945. Chem. engr. Am. Cyanamid Co., Pearl River, N.Y., 1947; sales exec. Titanium Pigment Corp., N.Y.C., 1948-55; market research mgr. U.S. Indsl. Chem. Co., N.Y.C., 1956-58; sales mgr. atomic energy Curtiss Wright Export, N.Y.C., 1958-60; founder, pres., chmn. bd. Noyes Data Corp., Park Ridge, N.J., 1960—; pub. Noyes Press, Noyes Publs., Park Ridge, 1961—. Author numerous books in fields of internat. fin., devel., tech. Served to lt. (j.g.) USNR, 1945-47. Mem. Am. Chem. Soc., Am. Inst. Chem. Engrs., Indian Harbor Yacht Club (Conn.), N.Y. Yacht Club. Episcopalian. Office: Noyes Bldg Park Ridge NJ 07656

NOYES, RONALD TACIE, agricultural engineering educator; b. Leedey, Okla., Jan. 4, 1937; s. Johnnie Lyle and Anna Madeline (Allen) N.; m. Zona Gail McMillen, Apr. 16, 1960; children: Cynthia Gail, Ronald Scott, David Eric. BS in Agrl. Engring., Okla. State U., 1961, MS in Agrl. Engring., 1964; postgrad., Purdue U., 1966-68, U. Okla., 1988-93. Profl. engr., Ind., Okla. Asst. prof. Purdue U., West Lafayette, Ind., 1964-68; chief engr. Beard Industries, Inc., Frankfort, Ind., 1968-81, v.p. engring., 1981-85; assoc. prof. Okla. State U., Stillwater, 1985-88, prof., 1988—; cons. Ronald T. Noyes, Profl. Agrl. Engr., Stillwater, 1988—. Co-author: Designing Pesticide and Fertilizer Containment Facilities, 1991; contbr. chpts. to books. 1st lt. U.S. Army, 1961-63. Recipient Disting. Svc. award U.S. Dept. Agr., 1992, Outstanding Ext. Faculty award Okla. State U., 1991. Fellow Am. Soc. Agrl. Engrs.; mem. Aircraft Owners & Pilots Assn., Nat. Agrl. Aviation Assn. (assoc.). Achievements include 6 patents in field; developed new aeration management procedure for controlling insects in stored grain that reduces chemical use. Home: 1116 Westwood Dr Stillwater OK 74074-1116 Office: Oklahoma St Univ Agrl Engring Dept 224 Ag Hall Stillwater OK 74074-0469

NOZATO, RYOICHI, metallurgy educator, researcher; b. Amagasaki, Hyogo, Japan, May 27, 1926; s. Mitsujiro and Kokame (Ashida) N.;m. Kazuko Ando, Nov. 15, 1955 (dec. 1981); children: Kimiko, Kohei; m. Harumi Miura, May 23, 1985. BEng, Osaka (Japan) U., 1950, DEng, 1962. Instr. metallurgy U. Osaka Prefecture, Sakai, Japan, 1963-64, assoc. prof., 1964-83; prof. metallurgy Himeji (Japan) Inst. Tech., 1983-92, chmn. dept. material engring., 1984-85, 89-90, prof. emeritus, 1992—. Contbr. articles on phase diagram of alloys and precipitation in alloys to profl. jours. Recipient Hofmann Meml. prize Lead Devel. Assn., 1977. Mem. Japan Inst. Metals, Japan Soc. Applied Physics, Atomic Energy Soc. Japan, Hyogo Indsl. Assn. (hon.). Buddhist. Avocations: painting, golf. Home: 15-13 Yamate-cho, Tondabayashi 584, Japan

NOZICK, ROBERT, philosophy educator, author; b. Bklyn., Nov. 16, 1938; s. Max and Sophie (Cohen) N.; m. Barbara Fierer, Aug. 15, 1959 (div. 1981); children: Emily, David; m. Gjertrud Schnackenberg, Oct. 5, 1987. A.B., Columbia U., 1959; A.M., Princeton U., 1961, Ph.D., 1963; A.M. (hon.), Harvard U., 1969; DHL (hon.), Knox Coll., 1983. Asst. dir. Social Sci. Research Council Summer Inst., 1962; instr. philosophy Princeton U., 1962-63, asst. prof., 1964-65; Fulbright scholar Oxford (Eng.) U., 1963-64; asst. prof. philosophy Harvard U., Cambridge, Mass., 1965-67; prof. Harvard U., 1969—, chmn. dept., 1981-84, Arthur Kingsley Porter prof., 1985—, sr. fellow Soc. Fellows; assoc. prof. Rockefeller U., 1967-69. Author: Anarchy, State, and Utopia, 1974 (Nat. Book award 1975), Philosophical Explanations, 1981 (Ralph Waldo Emerson award 1982), The Examined Life, 1989, The Nature of Rationality, 1993; mem. bd. editors Philosophy and Pub. Affairs; contbr. articles to profl. jours. Fellow Center Advanced Study Behavorial Scis., 1971-72, Rockefeller Found. Humanities fellow, 1979-80, NEH fellow, 1987-88. Mem. Am. Philos. Assn., Am. Acad. Arts and Scis., Council of Scholars, Library of Congress, Phi Beta Kappa. Office: Harvard U Emerson Hall Cambridge MA 02138

NUBER, PHILIP WILLIAM, air force officer; b. Bozeman, Mont., Sept. 27, 1939; s. Carl Philip and Harriet Catherine (Shane) N.; m. Maureen Jill Pepper, Mar. 24 1962; children: Greg, Jennifer. BS, Mont. State U., 1962. Commd. 2d lt. USAF, 1962, advanced through grades to major gen., 1992; ops. officer 35th Tactical Fighter Squadron, Davis-Monthan AFB, Ariz., 1975-78; chief officer assignments Hdqrs. Tactical Air Command/DP, Langley AFB, Va., 1978-80; comdr. 425th Tactical Fighter Tng. Squadron, Williams AFB, Ariz., 1980-82; dep. comdr., then comdr. 833d Combat Support Group, Holloman AFB, N.Mex., 1982-84; vice comdr., then wing comdr. 343d Tactical Fighter Wing, Eielson AFB, Alaska, 1984-88; dep. dir. for ops. Air Forces/X00, Washington, 1988-89; dep. comdr. Joint Task Force, USS LaSalle, Mid. East, 1989; dir. internat. programs Hdqrs. USAF/PRI, Washington, 1989-91; asst. dep. undersec. for internat. affairs SAF/IA, Washington, 1991-92; chief Joint U.S. Military Mission for Aid to Turkey, 1992. Home: 4780 Lanmar Ln Andrews AFB MD 20335 Office: HQ DMA 8613 Lee Hwy Fairfax VA 22031-2137

NUCCI, LEO, baritone; b. nr. Bologna, Italy, 1942. Studied with, Guiseppe Marchesi, Ottaviano Bizzarri. Mem. chorus la Scala, Milan, Italy, 1969-75. Debut as Figaro in The Barber of Seville at Spoleto, 1967, Covent Garden, London, 1987, San Francisco; 1987; appeared in La Boheme, La Fenice, Venice, Italy, 1975, as Rodrigo in Don Carlo, La Scala, Milan, as Belcore in L'Elisir d'amore, as Francesco Foscari in I due Foscari, as Miller in Luisa Miller, Covent Garden, 1978, as Renato in Un Ballo in Maschera, Met. Opera, N.Y., 1980, Paris Opera, 1981, La Scala, 1987, Barber of Seville Met. Opera, 1984, Falstaff, London, Adriana Levouvreur, San Francisco Opera, 1985, La Traviata, Met. Opera, 1985, Don Carlo, 1986, Madame Butterfly, 1986, Aida, 1986, Rigoletto, Hamburg, Barcelona, Spain, 1987, Il Trovatore, Lyric Opera Chgo., 1987, Met. Opera, 1987; The Force of Destiny, Lyric Opera Chgo., 1988, Macbeth, Marseille, 1988, Il Trovatore and Barber of Seville, Met. Opera, 1988, Rigoletto, Met. Opera, 1989, Un Ballo in Maschera, Salzburg Festival, 1989, Rigoletto, Houston Grand Opera, 1990, Elisir d'amore, Vienna State Opera, 1990, Rigoletto and Simone Boccanegra, Vienna, Rigoletto Lyric Opera Chgo., 1990, Rigoletto in Bologna, Italy and Munich, 1990, Luisa Miller, Ballo in Maschera Met. Opera, 1991; Otello Chgo. Symphony; Rigoletto Rome Opera, Verona Festival, Covent Garden, 1991, Simon Boccanegra in Santiago, Chile, Trovatore in Torino, Rigoletto in Venice, 1992; opera recs. include La Rondine, Le Villi, Andrea Chenier, The Barber of Seville, Don Pasquale, Tosca, Turco in Italia, Ernani, Aida, Falstaff, Don Carlo, Macbeth, 1987, Un Ballo in Maschera, Simone Boccanegra, Otello, Rigoletto, bel canto arias Il Viaggio a Reims, Idomeneo, Elisir d'Amore, Simon Boccanegra Popular Italian Songs, Gianni Schicchi, Italian Songs, Bel Canto Arias from Puritani, Pirata, Beatrice di Tenda, Guglielmo Tell, Poliuto, Duca d'Alba, Don Sebastiano, Favorita; films include: Macbeth, 1987. Office: care Allied Artists Agency, 42 Montpellier Square, London SW7 152, England*

NUCCIARONE, A. PATRICK, lawyer; b. Denville, N.J., Aug. 29, 1947; s. H. Joseph and Alice Marie (McGuirk) N. BA, U. So. Calif., 1969; JD, George Washington U., 1973. Bar: N.J. 1973, N.Y. 1981, Vt. 1984, U.S. Dist. Ct. N.J. 1973, U.S. Dist. Ct. (no. dist.) Ohio 1986, U.S. Ct. Appeals (3d cir.) 1976, U.S. Supreme Ct. 1995. Com. staff asst. U.S. House of Reps., Washington, 1971-72; staff asst. Exec. Office of Pres. of U.S., Washington, 1972-73; asst. U.S. Atty. Office of U.S. Atty., Newark, 1974-83, chief environ. sect., 1978-83; spl. asst. Atty. Gen. Office of Atty. Gen., Montpelier, Vt., 1984; ptnr. Hannoch Weisman, Roseland, N.J., 1984-91, Dechert, Price & Rhoads, Princeton, N.J., 1991—; co-chmn. N.J. Hazardous Task Force, Trenton, 1978-83; supr. Rutgers U. Environ. Law Clinic, Newark, 1978-83; mem. Environ. Expn. Adv. Bd., Trenton, 1985-90; chmn. ann. seminar on impacts of environ. law bus. trans. Practicing Law Inst., 1986-92. Contbr. articles to profl. jours. Recipient Outstanding Service award U.S. Dept. Justice, Washington, 1980, Spl. Achievement awards U.S. Dept. Justice, 1978, 79, Presdl. Citation for Excellent Performance Exec. Office of Pres., Washington, 1973. Mem. ABA (vice chmn. sect. on natural resources, energy and environ. law 1987-93), N.J. State Bar Assn. (bd. dirs. environ. law sect. 1985-89), Monmouth County Bar Assn. Avocations: sailing, skiing, hiking. Office: Dechert Price & Rhoads PO Box 5218 Princeton NJ 08543-5218

NUCCITELLI, SAUL ARNOLD, civil engineer, consultant; b. Yonkers, N.Y., Apr. 25, 1928; s. Agostino and Antoinette (D'Amicis) N.; m. Concetta Orlandi, Dec. 23, 1969; 1 child, Saul A. BS, NYU, 1949, MCE, 1954; DCE, MIT, 1960. Registered profl. engr., N.Y., Mo., Colo., Conn., Mass.; lic. land surveyor, Mo., Colo., Conn., Mass. Asst. civil engr. Westchester County Engrs., N.Y.C., 1949-51, 53-54; project engr. H.B. Bolas Enterprises, Denver, 1954-55; asst. prof., rsch. engr., U. Denver, 1955-58; mem. staff MIT, 1958-60; asst. prof. engring. Cooper Union Coll., N.Y.C., 1960-62; pvt. practice cons. engring., Springfield, Mo., 1962—; organizer, bd. dirs. Met. Nat. Bank, Springfield; former adviser, bd. dirs. Farm & Home Savs. and Loan Assn. Contbr. articles to profl. jours. Past chmn. Adv. Council on Mo. Pub. Drinking Water; chmn. Watershed Com. of the Ozarks; bd. dirs. YMCA; Greene County Mus. of Ozarks; past chmn. Bd. City Utilities, Springfield; past pres. Downtown Springfield Assn. 1st lt. U.S. Army, 1951-53. Recipient Cert. of Appreciation, Mo. Mcpl. League, 1981; named Mo. Cons. Engr. of Yr., 1973. Fellow ASCE, Nat. Soc. Profl. Engrs., Mo. Soc. Profl. Engrs. (past pres. Ozark chpt.), Boston Soc. Civil Engrs., Am. Concrete Inst., Am. Inst. Steel Constrn., Am. Welding Soc., ASTM, Am. Soc. Mil. Engrs., Springfield C. of C. (past v.p.), Rotary (past pres.). Home: 2919 S Brentmoor Ave Springfield MO 65804-3925 Office: 122 Park Central Sq Springfield MO 65806-1311

NUCKOLLS, JOHN HOPKINS, physicist, researcher; b. Chgo., Nov. 17, 1930; s. Asa Hopkins and Helen (Gates) N.; m. Ruth Munsterman, Apr. 21, 1952 (div. 1983); children—Helen Marie, Robert David; m. Amelia Aphrodite Liaskas, July 29, 1983. B.S., Wheaton Coll., 1953; M.A., Columbia U., 1955; D.Sc. (hon), Fla. Inst. Tech., 1977. Physicist U. Calif. Lawrence Livermore Nat. Lab., 1955—, assoc. leader thermonuclear design div., 1965-80, assoc. leader laser fusion program, 1975-83, div. leader, 1980-83, assoc. dir. physics, 1983-88, dir., 1988-94, assoc. dir. at large, 1994—. Recipient E.O. Lawrence award AEC, 1969, Fusion Leadership award Fusion Power Assocs., 1983, Edward Teller medal Internat. Workshop Laser Interaction and Related Plasma Phenomena, 1991. Fellow AAAS, Am. Phys. Soc. (J.C. Maxwell prize 1981); mem. NAE. Office: Lawrence Livermore Nat Lab PO Box 808 Livermore Ca 94551-0808

NUCKOLLS, LEONARD ARNOLD, retired hospital administrator; b. Park City, Utah, Feb. 22, 1917; s. Harry Leonard and Mabel Hill (Ganson) N.; m. Rachel A. Beckner, Apr. 18, 1942; children: Rachel Nuckolls Conine, Peter Leonard. AB, Pueblo Jr. Coll., 1938; BA, U. Colo., 1940. Commd. U.S. Army, 1942, advanced through grades to lt. col., 1962; adj. gen. 2d Army Div., Ft. Hood, Tex., 1960-62; ret., 1962; acct. Colo. State Hosp., Pueblo, 1963-64; caseworker N.Mex. Dept. Pub. Welfare, Clovis, 1964-66; unit coord. N.Mex. Dept. Hosps. and Instns., Las Vegas State Hosp., 1966-69; hosp. adminstr. Las Vegas Med. Ctr., 1969-76; adminstr. Vista Sandia Hosp., Albuquerque, 1980-83. Vol. Internat. Exec. Svc. Corp. Mem. Ret. Officers Assn., Mensa, Rotary. Home: 810 Faldas De La Sierra Santa Fe NM 87501-1252

NUCKOLLS, ROBERT THEODORE, cemetery executive; b. Welch, W.Va., Jan. 30, 1933; s. John Samuel and Maude (Barteé) N.; children: Robert Lance, Mark Theodore; m. Lillian Mosley, Jan. 5, 1980; children: Ashley-Marie Barteé, Andrew Boyd. Cert. cemetery exec., Am. Cemetery Assn. Vice pres. Ft. Lincoln Cemetery, Washington, 1953-63; founder, pres. Eastern Meml. Inc., Wilmington, Del., 1963-69; pres. Cross Mausoleums Funeral Homes Corp., Nashville, 1969-72; exec. v.p. Loudon Park and Druid Ridge Cemeteries, Balt., 1972-92; pres. Loudon Park, Druid Ridge, Cedar Hill, and Crest Lawn Cemeteries, Md., 1992—; chmn. Md.-D.C. Cemetery Assn. Legis. Com., 1976—; lectr. faculty exec. mgmt. Washington U., St. Louis; pres. Stewart Enterprises Mid-Atlantic No. region, 1992—. Contbr. numerous articles on cemetery mgmt. and mktg. to trade jours. Recipient medallion Am. Inst. Commemorative Art, 1978. Mem. Am. Cemetery Assn. (dir. 1981, exec. com. 1981, 92-93, cert. cemetery exec. 1989, chmn. ethics and inquiry com. 1991-95), Cemetery Assn. (mem. faculty Memphis State U. summer mktg. seminar, pres. 1977-78, 89), Execs. Assn. Balt. (dir. 1975—), Am. Assn. (pres. 1978), Md. Freestate Cemetery Assn. (pres. 1994—). Home: 6306 N Charles St Baltimore MD 21212-1042 Office: PO Box 2926 Baltimore MD 21229-0926

NUCKOLS, FRANK JOSEPH, psychiatrist; b. Akron, Ohio, Apr. 7, 1926; s. William Alexander Jr. and Jean (Harrison) N.; m. Jane Fleetwood McIntosh, June 16, 1948; children: Claud Alexander, John Andrew. BA, U. Louisville, 1946; MD, U. Ala., 1951. Diplomate Am. Bd. Psychiatry and Neurology. Intern Holy Name Jesus Hosp., Gadsden, Ala., 1951; ward physician Ala. State Hosp., Tuscaloosa, 1951-52; resident U. Louisville, USPHS Hosp., Lexington, Ky., 1953-56; mem. faculty psychiatry U. Ala. Med. Ctr., Birmingham, 1958-68, dir. tng. psychiat. residents, 1964-68, head div. community psychiatry, 1964-68, head continuing psychiat. edn. for physicians, 1964-68; chief psychiat. staff in-patient svc. U. Hosp., Birmingham, 1966-68; dir. tng. Hill Crest Hosp., Birmingham, 1975-79; pvt. practice Birmingham, 1968-93; cons. Ala. Div. Disability Determinations, Birmingham, 1993—; staff Med. Ctr. East Hosp., Birmingham, Bapt. Med. Ctr. Montclair, Birmingham; cons. staff St. Vincent's Hosp., Birmingham, Lloyd Noland Hosp., Birmingham, South Highland Hosp., Birmingham; vis. faculty, mem. interuniv. forum in cmty. psychiatry Harvard U., Boston, 1963-66; vis. faculty Baylor U. Med. Sch., Houston, 1967-71. Ensign USNR, 1941-43; sr. surgeon USPHS, 1956—. Fellow Am. Psychiat. Assn. So. Psychiat. Assn.; mem. Med. Assn. Ala., So. Med. Assn., Jefferson County Mental Health Assn. (v.p. 1960), Jefferson County Med. Soc., Mental Health Assn. State Ala. (charter past-profl. adv. com. 1961), Nat. Assn. Disability Examiners, Phi Beta Pi, Tau Kappa Epsilon. Home and Office: 3741 River Oaks Cir Birmingham AL 35223-2117

NUDELMAN, PHILLIP M., insurance company executive. V.p. Geriatric Health Corp., Seattle, 1968-1973; pres., ceo Group Health Coop of Puget Sound, Seattle, 1973—. Office: Group Health Coop of Puget Sound 521 Wall St Seattle WA 98121-1524

NUERNBERG, WILLIAM RICHARD, lawyer; b. Pitts., July 7, 1946; s. William W. and Frances (Hubler) N. BA cum laude, Denison U., 1968; JD cum laude, U. Mich., 1971. Bar: Pa. 1971, U.S. Dist. Ct. (we. dist.) Pa. 1971. Ptnr. Eckert Seamans Cherin & Mellott, Pitts., 1981—. Pitt fellow U. Pitts. Sch. Bus., 1987-88. Mem. ABA, Pa. Bar Assn., Allegheny County Bar Assn., Rivers Club. Office: Eckert Seamans Cherin & Mellott 701 Brickell Ave 18th Fl Miami FL 33131

NUESSE, CELESTINE JOSEPH, retired university official; b. Sevastopol, Wis., Nov. 25, 1913; s. George and Salome Helen (Martens) N.; m. Margaret O'Donoghue, 1969. B.E., Central State Tchrs. Coll., Stevens Point, Wis., 1934; M.A., Northwestern U., 1937; Ph.D., Cath. U. Am., 1944, L.H.D., 1982; LL.D., Merrimack Coll., 1960. Tchr. social studies Pub. High Sch., Antigo, Wis., 1934-40; instr. sociology Coll. St. Catherine, St. Paul, 1943, Marquette U., 1943-45; instr. Cath. U. Am., Washington, 1945-48, asst. prof., 1948-52, assoc. prof., 1952-64, prof., 1964-81, prof. emeritus, 1981—,

dean Sch. Social Sci., 1952-61, exec. v.p., 1967-81, provost, 1968-79, provost emeritus, 1981—; Spl. rep. in Germany, Nat. Cath. Welfare Conf., 1950-51; mem. U.S. Nat. Commn. for UNESCO, 1950-56, 63-69, exec. com., 1954-56; mem. gov. bd. UNESCO Youth Inst., Munich, Germany, 1955-56; mem. U.S. Bd. Fgn. Scholarships, 1954-58, chmn., 1956-58; mem. D.C. Commr.'s Council Human Relations, 1958-64, D.C. Commn. on Postsecondary Edn., 1975-80. Author: The Social Thought of American Catholics, 1634-1829, 1945, The Catholic University of America: A Centennial History, 1990; co-author, co-editor: The Sociology of the Parish, 1951; staff editor New Cath. Ency., 1963-66, chmn. editl. bd. supplements, 1973-79; contbr. articles to profl. jours. Mem. Am. Cath. Hist. Assn., Am. Cath. Sociol. Soc. (pres. 1954), Am. Sociol. Assn., Cath. Assn. Internat. Peace (pres. 1954-56), Cath. Commn. Intellectual and Cultural Affairs, Inst. Internat. Sociologie, Internat. Conf. on Sociology of Religion (past v.p.), Nat. Cath. Ednl. Assn., Cath. Interracial Council Washington (pres. 1962-66), Phi Beta Kappa (hon.), Alpha Kappa Delta, Pi Gamma Mu, Sigma Tau Delta, Phi Sigma Epsilon. Club: Cosmos (Washington). Lodge: KC. Home: 8108 River Crescent Dr Annapolis MD 21401-7276

NUGENT, CHARLES ARTER, physician; b. Denver, Nov. 18, 1924; s. Charles Arter and Florence (Cohn) N.; m. Margaret Flint, Aug. 30, 1950; children—Stephen, Sara, Daniel. Student, U. Chgo., 1941-43, Ill. Inst. Tech., 1943, U. Minn., 1944, U. S.D., 1944-46; M.D., Yale U., 1951. Intern, asst. resident New Haven Hosp., 1951-53; resident Salt Lake County Gen. Hosp., Salt Lake City, 1954-56; mem. faculty U. Utah Coll. Medicine, 1956-67, assoc. prof. medicine, 1965-67; prof. dept. internal medicine U. Hawaii Med. Sch., 1967-70; prof. sect. endocrinology dept. internal medicine U. Ariz. Coll. Medicine, Tucson, 1970—. Contbr. articles to profl. jours. Served with U.S. Army, 1943-46, 53. James Hudson Brown Meml. fellow, 1949-50. Mem. AAUP, Endocrine Soc., Western Assn. Physicians, Physicians Forum, Am. Soc. Clinical Investigators. Home: 3242 E 5th St Tucson AZ 85716-4902 Office: 1501 N Campbell Ave Tucson AZ 85724-0001

NUGENT, DANIEL EUGENE, business executive; b. Chgo., Dec. 18, 1927; s. Daniel Edward and Pearl A. (Trieger) N.; m. Bonnie Lynn Weidman, July 1, 1950; children: Cynthia Lynn, Mark Alan, Dale Alan. BSME, Northwestern U., 1951. With U.S. Gypsum Co., Chgo., 1951-71, dir. corp. devel., to 1971; pres. Am. Louver Co., Chgo., 1971-72; v.p. ops. ITT Corp., Cleve., 1972-74; exec. v.p. ITT Corp., St. Paul, 1974-75; v.p. ops. Pentair, Inc., St. Paul, 1974-75, pres., COO, 1975-81, pres., CEO, 1981-86, chmn., CEO, 1986-92, chmn. exec. com., 1992—; chrm., dir. Pentair, Inc.; bd. dirs Apogee Enterprises, Inc. Vice-chmn. local planning commn., 1968-72; cochmn. Wellspring, 1989—; trustee Harper Coll., Palatine, 1970-73; mem. adv. commn. McCormick Engring. and Kellogg Schs. at Northwestern U., MBA Sch. of St. Thomas U., St. Paul; mem. exec. com. Indian Head coun. Boy Scouts Am. With AUS, 1946-47. Mem. North Oaks Golf Club, Mpls. Club. Republican. Presbyterian. Office: Pentair Inc 1700 West Highway 36 Saint Paul MN 55113

NUGENT, G. EUGENE, manufacturing company executive; b. 1927; married. BSME, Northwestern U., 1951. With U.S. Gypsum Co., 1951-71; pres. Am. Louver Co., 1971-72; v.p. ITT Svc. Industry, 1972-74; exec. v.p. ITT Indusl. Credit, 1974-75; v.p. ops. Pentair Inc., St. Paul, 1975-76, pres., 1976-86, COO, from 1976, CEO, 1981-92, chmn., 1986-92. With U.S. Army, 1946-47.

NUGENT, JOHNNY, tractor company executive, state senator; b. Cleve., July 18, 1939; s. Carl Howard and Velma (Holland) N.; m. Nancy Carol Whiteford, Dec. 16, 1960; 1 child, Suzette. Grad. high sch., Aurora, Ind. Owner, mgr. Nugent Tractor Sales, Lawrenceburg, Ind., 1960—; mem. Ind. Senate, Indpls., 1978—; bd. dirs. 1st Nat. Bank Aurora. Commr. Dearborn County, Lawrenceburg, 1966-74. With USAR, 1957-64. Republican. Baptist. Office: State Senate State Capital Indianapolis IN 46204

NUGENT, NELLE, theater, film and television producer; b. Jersey City, May 24, 1939; d. John Patrick and Evelyn Adelaide (Stern) N.; m. Donald G. Baker, June 6, 1960 (div. 1962); m. Benjamin Janney, June 22, 1969 (div. Apr., 1980); m. Jolyon Fox Stern, Apr. 7, 1982; 1 child, Alexandra Fox Stern. BS, Skidmore Coll., 1960, DHL (hon.), 1981. Chmn. bd. McCann & Nugent, Prodns. Inc. (mgmt. and prodn. co.), N.Y.C., 1976-86; pres. Foxboro Prodns., Inc., N.Y.C., 1985—; pres., CEO Foxboro Entertainment, 1990—; pres. The Foxboro Co., Inc. Stage mgr. various off-Broadway shows, 1960-64; prodn. asst.: Broadways plays Any Wednesday, 1963-64, Dylan, 1964, Ben Franklin in Paris, 1964-65; stage mgr. Broadway shows, 1964-68; prodn. supr., then gen. mgr., 1969-76, assoc. mng. dir. Nederlander Corp., operating theaters and producing plays in N.Y.C. and on tour, 1970-76; prodr.: Dracula, 1977 (Tony award), The Elephant Man, 1978 (Tony award, Drama Critics award), Morning's at Seven, 1980 (Tony award), Home, 1980 (Tony nomination), Amadeus, 1981 (Tony award); also produced: Rose and Piaf, 1980, The Life and Adventures of Nicholas Nickleby, 1981 (Tony award, Drama Critics award), The Dresser (Tony award nominee), 1981, Mass Appeal, 1981; The Lady & The Clarinet, 1982; The Glass Menagerie (revival), 1983; Painting Churches (Obie award), 1983; Total Abandon, 1983; All's Well That End's Well, 1983 (Tony nominee); Pilobolus Dance Company, 1983; Pacific Overtures (revival), 1984; Much Ado about Nothing/Cyrano de Bergerac (repertory) (Tony award nominees), 1984; Leader of the Pack (Tony award nominee), 1985, The Life and Adventures of Nicholas Nickleby (revival) (Tony award nominee), 1986; prodr.: TV spls.: Morning's At Seven, Piaf; Pilobolus; producer A Fighting Choice, Walt Disney Prodns., 1986, Phoenix Entertainment Group, 1986-88, A Conspiracy of Love, New World TV, 1987, The Final Verdict, TNT, 1990 (Cable Ace award nominee Best Picture); exec. prodr. (TV pilot) Morning Maggie, 1987, Dick Clark Prodns., 1988-90, (feature film) Student Body, 1993, (Showtime) In the Presence of Mine Enemies, 1995. Mem. Am. Women's Econ. Devel. Corp. (bd. dirs.). Office: Foxboro Co Inc 133 E 58th St Ste 301 New York NY 10022-1236

NUGENT, ROBERT J., JR., fast food company executive; b. 1942. BBA, U. Cin., 1964. loan officer Citizens Savs., 1964-67; asst. v.p. Gem City Savs., 1967-69; v.p. Ponderosa System Inc., 1969-78, Ky. Fried Chicken, 1978-79; v.p. Foodmaker Inc., San Diego, from 1979, exec. v.p. ops., mktg., 1985—. Office: Foodmaker Inc PO Box 783 San Diego CA 92112-4126

NUGENT, THEODORE ANTHONY, musician; b. Detroit, Dec. 13, 1948; s. Warren Henry and Marion Dorothy (Johnson) N.; divorced; children: Sasha Emma, Theodore Tobias. Ed.: Oakland Community Coll., Detroit. Also prcfd. off-road racer, 1981—. Guitarist, 1958—, mem. group, Amboy Dukes, 1965, solo artist, 1965—; recs. include: (with Amboy Dukes) Ted Nugent and the Amboy Dukes, 1968, Journey to the Center of the Mind, 1968, Marriage on the Rocks, 1970, Survival of the Fittest, 1974, Call of the Wild, 1974, Tooth, Fang, and Claw, 1975; (solo album) Ted Nugent, 1975, Free for All, 1976, Cat Scratch Fever, 1977, Double Live Gonzo, 1977, Weekend Warriors, 1978, State of Shock, 1979, Scream Dream, 1980, Great Gonzos/The Best of, 1981, Intensities in Ten Cities, 1981, Penetrator, 1984, Little Miss Dangerous, 1986, If You Can't Lick 'Em...Lick 'Em, 1988; (with Damn Yankees) Damn Yankees, 1990, Don't Tread, 1992. Mem. ASCAP, Nat. Rifle Assn. (life), Ducks Unlimited (life sponsor), Nat. Trappers Assn., Mich. Bowhunters, Safari Club Internat. Address: PO Box 15108 Ann Arbor MI 48106-5108 also: Sony Music Entertainment Inc. 550 Madison Ave New York NY 10022-3211*

NUGENT, THOMAS D., food products executive; b. 1943; married. BS, Northern Ill. U., 1966; student, U. of Illinois, 1982. With Arthur Andersen & Co., Chgo., 1970-77, Polk Brothers Inc., Chgo., 1977-79, Coopers & Lybrand, Chgo., 1979-82; sr. v.p.finance Otasco Inc., Tulsa, 1982-86; c.f.o., exec. v.p. Wholesale Club Inc. served AUS 1968-70. Office: Wholesale Club 7260 Shadeland Sta Indianapolis IN 46256-3929

NUGENT, WALTER TERRY KING, historian; b. Watertown, N.Y., Jan. 11, 1935; s. Clarence A. and Florence (King) N.; children from previous marriage: Katherine, Rachel, David, Douglas, Terry, Mary; m. Suellen Hoy, 1986. A.B., St. Benedict's Coll., 1954, D.Litt., 1968; M.A., Georgetown U., 1956; Ph.D., U. Chgo., 1961. Instr. history Washburn U., 1957-58; asst. prof. Kans. State U., 1961-63; asst. prof. history Ind. U., 1963-64, assoc. prof., 1964-68, prof., 1968-84, assoc. dean Coll. Arts and Scis., 1967-71, dir.

overseas study, 1967-76, chmn. history dept., 1974-77; Andrew V. Tackes prof. history U. Notre Dame, 1984—; Paley lectr., Fulbright vis. prof. Hebrew U. Jerusalem, 1978-79; vis. prof. U. Hamburg, 1980, U. Warsaw, 1982; Mary Ball Washington Fulbright prof. U. Coll., Dublin, 1991-92. Author: The Tolerant Populists, 1963, Creative History, 1967, The Money Question During Reconstruction, 1967, Money and American Society 1865-1880, 1968, Modern America, 1973, From Centennial to Worl War: American Society 1876-1917, 1977, Stuctures of American Social History, 1981, Crossings: The Great Transatlantic Migrations, 1870-1914, 1992. Newberry Libr. fellow, 1962; Guggenheim fellow, 1964-65; seminar dir., Nat. Endowment for Humanities, 1979, 84, 86; Huntington Libr. fellow, 1979, 85; Beinecke fellow Yale U., 1990. Mem. Western Hist. Assn., Soc. Am. Historians, Coun. on Fgn. Rels. Democrat. Office: U Notre Dame Notre Dame IN 46556

NUGTEREN, CORNELIUS, air force officer; b. Colton, S.D., Feb. 7, 1928; s. Adrian Joe and Marie Johanna N.; m. Liane Albrecht, Sept. 22, 1956; children: Cecile, Aneli. B.A., Central Coll., Pella, Iowa, 1951. Commd. 2d lt. USAF, 1953, advanced through grades to maj. gen., 1980; advisor Vietnam Air Force, 1970-71, served in Germany, 1971-77; vice comdr. (Air Logistics Center), Utah, 1977-79; comdr. (Aerospace Rescue and Recovery Service), Scott AFB, Ill., 1979-81; chief (Joint U.S. Mil. Aid Group), Greece, 1981-82; comdr. Air Logistics Ctr., Robins AFB, Ga, 1983-88, ret.; cons. for def. industries Warner Robins, Ga., 1988—; v.p. Chem. Tech. Internat., Warner Robins; 1988—. Decorated D.S.M., Legion of Merit, Bronze Star, Superior Service medal; recipient USAF EEO award, 1979. Mem. Air Force Assn., Order Daedalians, Internat. Order Hansen, Order of the Sword. Office: 114 Holly Dr Warner Robins GA 31088-6615 *Service to one's country is not just a job...it's a calling. Integrity to and within the institution to which you belong is an absolute necessity. Loyalty to peers and subordinates is equally important as loyalty to your superiors. Attitude toward life, humankind and profession is key determinant to success. Goals should be set high enough so as to be unattainable. Standard of conduct must always include duty, honor, country.*

NULAND, SHERWIN, surgeon, author; b. N.Y.C., Dec. 8, 1930; s. Meyer and Violet (Lutsky) N.; m. Sarah Peterson, May 29, 1977; children: Victoria Jane, Andrew Meyer, William Peterson, Amelia Rose. BA, NYU, 1951; MD, Yale U., 1955. Surgeon Yale-New Haven Hosp. (Conn.), 1962-91; clin. prof. surgery Yale Sch. Medicine, New Haven, 1962—. Author: The Origins of Anesthesia, 1983, Doctors: The Biography of Medicine, 1988, Medicine: The Art of Healing, 1991, The Face of Mercy, 1993, How We Die: Reflections on Life's Final Chapter, 1994 (Nat. Book award for non-fiction 1994). Pres. med. com. Jewish Home Aged, New Haven, 1985-87; v.p. Conn. Hospice, New Haven, 1978-80. Fellow ACS; mem. New Eng. Surg. Soc., Assocs. of Yale Med. Sch. Libr. (chmn. 1982-94), Yale-China Assn. (chmn. med. 1988-93). Democrat. Jewish. Avocation: tennis. Home: 29 Hartford Tpke Hamden CT 06517-1813 Office: PO Box 6356 Hamden CT 06517-0356

NULL, JACK ELTON, schools superintendent; b. New Haven, Ind., May 22, 1938; s. Clifford Lewis and Violet Alice (Shuler) N.; m. Carolyn Wastjer, June 9, 1962 (div.); 1 child, Richard Lance. BS in Bus. Mgmt., Ind. U., 1960; MA in Elem. Edn., Ball State U., 1963; EdD in Ednl. Adminstrn., Ariz. State U., 1974. Cert. elem. edn. tchr., prin., bus. mgr., supt., Ariz. Adminstrv. asst. to dir. of purchasing Cummins Engine Co., Columbus, Ind., 1960-61; tchr. Randolph Cen. Schs., Winchester, Ind., 1963; tchr., coach East Allen County Schs., New Haven, 1963-66; from prin. to adminstrv. asst. to prin. Wilson Sch. Dist. 6, Phoenix, 1966-73; acting supt., exec. asst. Washington Sch. Dist. 7, Phoenix, 1973-79; supt. Fowler Sch. Dist. 45, Phoenix, 1979—; supt.'s chmn. Westside IMPACT, Phoenix, Tolleson, Avondale, Goodyear and Litchfield, Ariz., 1988-92; All Ariz. Supt., 1992-93. Football ofcl. PAC-10, Big Sky, Ariz. C.C. Athletic Conf., Ariz. Interscholastic Assn., 1966—; basketball ofcl., 1963-85; sports statist. Ariz. State U., Tempe, 1968—; clock operator NFL, Phoenix, 1987—; vice chmn. West Phoenix Cactus League Baseball Coalition, 1991-93, Ariz. edn. reform com., 1993—. Staff sgt. USAFR, 1961-66. Named Football Ofcl. Yr. ACCAC, 1990. Mem. Am. Assn. Sch. Adminstrs., Ariz. Sch. Administrs., Inc. (charter, active various coms., chmn. legis. com. 1992—, bd. dirs. supts. divsn. 1993—), Maricopa County Supt. Assn. (treas. 1970-71, pres. 1971-72), Greater Phoenix Supts. Assn. Democrat. Congregationalist. Avocations: investments, sports.

NULL, PAUL BRYAN, minister; b. Oakland, Calif., May 7, 1944; s. Carleton Elliot and Dorothy Irene (Bryan) N.; m. Renee Yvonne Howell, Aug. 23, 1969; children: Bryan Joseph, Kara Renee. BS, Western Bapt. Coll., 1973; MDiv, Western Conservative Bapt. Sem., 1979; DMin, Trinity Theol. Sem., 1994. Ordained to ministry Bapt. Ch., 1982. Asst. pastor Bethel Bapt. Ch., Aumsville, Oreg., 1972-74; sr. pastor, 1974-87; sr. pastor The Calvary Congregation, Stockton, Calif., 1987-94; pastor Sierra Comty. Ch., South Lake Tahoe, Calif., 1994—; trustee Conservative Bapt. Assn. of Oreg., 1982-85, mem. Ch. extension com., 1975-85. Radio show commentator Food for Thought, 1987. Panel mem. Presdl. Anti-Drug Campaign, 1984. Served with U.S. Army, 1965-67. Named Outstanding Young Man Am., 1979. Mem. Conservative Bapt. Assn. of Am., No. Calif. Conservative Bapt. Assn. (pres. 1992-93), Delta Epsilon Chi. Avocations: weight training, aerobics, writing, hiking, cross-country skiing. Home: 1399 Iroquois Circle South Lake Tahoe CA 96150 Office: Sierra Comty Ch 1165 Sierra Blvd South Lake Tahoe CA 96150

NULTON, WILLIAM CLEMENTS, lawyer; b. Pittsburg, Kans., Feb. 22, 1931; s. Perley Edgar and Mary Celia (Anderson) N.; m. Vicki Smith, Aug. 20, 1956; children: Carnie, Erica. BA, Kans. U., 1953, LLB with honors, 1958; postgrad., NYU, 1953-54. Bar: Kans. 1958, Mo. 1959. Sr. atty. Great Lakes Pipe Line Co., Kansas City, Mo., 1958-66, asst. sec., 1961-68; Blackwell, Sanders, Matheny, Weary & Lombardi, Kansas City, 1966-68, ptnr., 1968-81; assoc. Shughart Thomson & Kilroy, Kansas City, 1981-83, ptnr., 1983-94. Contbr. articles to profl. jours. Bd. dirs. Corinth Hills Home Assn., Shawnee Mission, 1974-76; bd. dirs. Elder Village United Presbyn. Ch., Prairie Village, Kans., 1976—, trustee, 1992-94; bd. dirs. Kansas City Civil Rights Consortium, 1993—, Marillac Acad., 1994—; mem. Kans. adv. com. U.S. Civil Rights Commn., 1994—; mem. Shawnee Mission Unified Bd. Edn., 1969-73, v.p., 1973; pres. Corinth Elem. Bd. Edn. Johnson County, Kans., 1969; chmn. Full Employment Task Group on Employment Disabled, Kansas City, 1987. Summerfield scholar Kans. U., 1949-53, Root-Tilden scholar NYU, 1953-54. Mem. ABA (mgmt. chmn. labor and employment law sect., com. on arbitration and collective bargaining 1989-92), Am. Acad. Hosp. Attys. (co-chmn. task group on bylaws for small rural hosps. 1992—), Mo. Bar Assn. (chmn. labor law com. 1982), Nat. Health Lawyers Assn. (co-chmn. task group on alternative dispute resolution in health care field 1990—), Phi Beta Kappa. Republican. Home: 7908 El Monte St Shawnee Mission KS 66208-5047

NUNES, GEOFFREY, lawyer, corporate executive; b. N.Y.C., July 7, 1930; s. Kenneth Neville and Helen (Landsberg) N.; m. Clare Harwood, Sept. 13, 1958; children: Geoffrey, John Kenneth, Margaret Hamilton. AB, Princeton U., 1952; LLB, Harvard U., 1957. Bar: N.Y. 1957, N.J. 1968, Mass. 1978. Assoc. atty. Breed Abbott & Morgan, N.Y.C., 1957-61, Shea & Gould, N.Y.C., 1961066; v.p., gen. counsel Lenox, Inc., Princeton, N.J., 1966-76; sr. v.p., gen. counsel Millipore Corp., Bedford, Mass., 1976—; bd. dirs. Reebok Internat, Stoughton, Mass., Scottish Widows Internat. Mut. Found., Reading, Pa. Trustee, bd. dirs. DeCordova Mus., Lincoln, Mass., Boston Biomed. Rsch. Inst., 1992. With USN, 1952-54. Office: Millipore Corp 80 Ashby Rd Bedford MA 01730-2271

NUNEZ-PORTUONDO, RICARDO, investment company executive; b. N.Y.C., June 9, 1933; s. Emilio and Maria (Garcia) N-P.; m. Dolores Maldonado, Sept. 7, 1963; children—Ricardo Jose, Emilio Manuel, Eduardo Javier. LL.D., U. Havana, Cuba; postdoctoral in law, U. Fla., 1975. Bar: Cuba, Fla. Editor Latin Am. div. USIA, Miami, Fla., 1961-71; editor Latin Am. div. USIA, Washington, 1961-71; nat. dir. Cuban Refugee Program, Washington, 1975-77; pres. Cultural Pub., Inc., Miami, 1994—, Central Investment Trust, Coral Gables, Fla., 1977—; chmn. bd. Interstate Bank of Commerce, Miami, 1986-88; v.p. Century 21, Coral Gables, 1989—. Author: A Critique on the Linowitz Report, 1975, Cuba: La Otra Imagen, 1994, Un Procer Cubano, 1994, Cuban Refugee Program, The Early Years, 1995. dir. Nat. Hispanic Scholarship Fund, San Francisco, 1978—; dir. COSSMHO,

Washington, 1980—; trustee emeritus Fla. Internat. U., 1984—; pres. Mercy Hosp. Found., Miami, 1985—; bd. dirs. ARC, Greater Miami. Recipient numerous awards for civic contbns. including day named in honor Ricardo Nunez Day, Miami, 1975. Mem. Cuban Lawyers Assn., Cuban Acad. History, Metro. Club, Lyford Cay Club, Ocean Reef Club, Key Biscayne Yacht Club, Big Five Club, 200 Club. Republican. Roman Catholic. Home: 675 Solano Prado Miami FL 33156-2373 Office: PO Box 141720 Coral Gables FL 33114-1720

NUNIS, DOYCE BLACKMAN, JR., historian, educator; b. Cedartown, Ga., May 30, 1924; s. Doyce Blackman and Winnie Ethel (Morris) N. B.A., U. Calif. Los Angeles, 1947; M.S., U. So. Calif., 1950, M.Ed., 1952, Ph.D., 1958. Lectr. U. So. Calif., 1951-56; instr. El Camino Coll., 1956-59; asst. prof. edn. and history UCLA, 1959-65; assoc. prof. history U. So. Calif., 1965-68, prof., 1968-89, emeritus, 1989—; asst. research historian U. Calif. Los Angeles, 1959-63; asso. U. Calif., 1963-65, lectr., 1960-61, asst. prof. edn. and history, 1961-64, asso. prof., 1964-65. Author: Andrew Sublette, Rocky Mountain Prince, 1960, Josiah Belden, 1841 California Overland Pioneer, 1962, The Golden Frontier: The Recollections of Herman Francis Rinehart, 1851-69, 1962, The California Diary of Faxon Dean Atherton, 1836-39, 1964, Letters of a Young Miner, 1964, The Journal of James H. Bull, 1965, The Trials of Isaac Graham, 1967, The Medical Journey of Pierre Garnier in California, 1851, 1967, Past is Prologue, 1968, Hudson's Bay Company's First Fur Brigade to the Sacramento Valley, 1968, Sketches of a Journey on Two Oceans by H.J.A. Alric, 1850-1867, 1971, San Francisco 1856 Vigilance Committee: Three Views, 1971, The Drawings of Ignatio Tirsh, Los Angeles and Its Environs in the 20th Century, A Bibliography, 1973, A History of American Political Thought, 2 vols, 1975, The Mexican War in Baja California, 1977, Henry Hoyt's A Frontier Doctor, 1979, Los Angeles from the Days of the Old Pueblo, 1981, The 1769 Transit of Venus, 1982, The Missionary Letters of Jacob Baegert, 1982, Men, Medicine and Water, 1982, Southern California Historical Anthology, 1984, George Coe's Frontier Fighter, 1984, Life of Tom Horn, 1987, A Guide to the History of California, 1989, Great Doctors of Medicine, 1990, The Bidwell-Bartleson Party, 1991, The Life of Tom Horn Revisited, 1992, Southern California's Spanish Heritage, 1992, Southern California Local History, A Gathering of W.W. Robinson's Writings, 1993, From Mexican Days to the Gold Rush, 1993, Tales of Mexican California, 1994, Women in the Life of Southern California, 1995; editor So. Calif. Quar., 1962—; contbr. articles to profl. jours. Trustee Mission Santa Barbara Archives-Libr., 1970—, pres., 1972—. Decorated Denemerenti, Papal medal, 1984; recipient Distinction award Calif. Com. for Promotion of History, 1985 award Calif. Conf. Hist. Socs., 1986, Franciscan Hist. award, 1990, Disting. Emeritus award U. So. Calif., 1993, Knight Comdr. of St. Gregory, 1993; Henry E. Huntington Libr. grantee-in-aide, 1960, grantee Am. Philos. Soc., 1969; Guggenheim fellow, 1963-64. Fellow Calif. Hist. Soc. (trustee 1987-93, v.p. 1989-93, Henry R. Wagner award 1981), Hist. Soc. So. Calif.; mem. Am. Antiquarian Soc., Am. Hist. Assn., Orgn. Am. Historians, Western Hist. Assn., Zamorano Club, L.A. Corral Westerners, Phi Alpha Theta, Pi Sigma Alpha. Home: 4426 Cromwell Ave Los Angeles CA 90027-1250

NUNIS, RICHARD ARLEN, amusement parks executive; b. Cedartown, Ga., May 30, 1932; s. Doyce Blackman and Winnie E. (Morris) N.; m. Mary Nunis; 1 child from previous marriage, Richard Dean. B.S. in Edn, U. So. Calif., 1954. With The Walt Disney Co., 1955—; dir. ops. Disneyland, Calif., 1961-68; chmn. park ops. com. Disneyland, 1968-74; corp. v.p. Disneyland Ops. (Disneyland, Walt Disney World, Tokyo Disneyland), 1968-91, Walt Disney World, Orlando, Fla., 1971—; exec. v.p., then pres. Walt Disney Attractions and Disneyland Internat., 1972-91; chmn. Walt Disney Attractions, 1991—; mem. exec. com. Walt Disney Co.; adv. bd. Travel and Tourism, U.S. Dept. of Commerce; chmn. Recreation Roundtable; bd. dirs. SunBanks, N.A., Orlando, Fla., Progress Capital Holdings Inc., Electric Fuels Corp. Exec. adv. bd. dirs. Give the Kids the World; co-chmn. Orange County Com. on Children, Orlando; bd. dirs. Fla. Progress Bd., Corp. Coun. Econ. Devel. Commn. Mid-Fla. Inc., U. Cen. Fla. Found., Inc.; deputy chair Heart of Fla. United Way; bd. dirs. Fla. Econ. Growth and Internat. Devel. Commn., Workforce 2000, Fla. Coun. 100; treas. United Arts of Cen. Fla.; chmn. Major Gifts for United Arts of Cen. Fla., 1990; adv. bd. in initiation and operation of drug rehab. ctr. Fla. Ho. of Reps.; mem. econ. devel. adv. coun. Fla. Dept. of Commerce. Named first acad. All-Am., U. So. Calif., 1952. Mem. Fla. C. of C. (bd. dirs.), Fla. Coun. of 100, Citrus Club (bd. govs.) Isleworth Golf and Country Club. Republican. Avocations: sports, fishing, golf. Office: Walt Disney World Resorts #257D PO Box 10,000 Teaqm Disney-2N Lake Buena Vista FL 32830 also: 1313 Harbor Blvd Anaheim CA 92803 *Do the best job you can with the job you are given to do. Those who look over the hill never climb over the mountain.*

NUNN, G. RAYMOND, history educator; b. Pirbright, Surrey, Eng., May 18, 1918; came to U.S., 1951; s. Alfred Gerald Cole and Sybil Amy (Bolton) N.; m. E. Margaret Brown; children: Pamela Elizabeth, Michael David, Lesley Margaret. BA honours, U. London, 1951, Dip. Librarianship, 1952; MA, U. Mich., 1954, PhD Far Eastern studies, 1957. Head Asia Library Univ. Mich. Library, Ann Arbor, 1951-61; instr. history Univ. Mich., Ann Arbor, 1959-61; prof. history U. Hawaii, Honolulu, 1961-64, prof. history and Asian studies, 1964-92, dir. rsch. collections East-West Ctr., 1961-64; prof. history, chair Asian studies program U. Hawaii, 1990-92, prof. emeritus, 1993—. Author: Asia and Oceania, A Guide to Archival and Manuscript Sources in the U.S., Publishing in Mainland China, Southeast Asian Periodicals an International Union List, Japanese Periodicals and Newspapers in Western Languages an International Union List, Asia Reference Works. Maj. inf., Indian Army, 1940-47. Ford Found. fellow, 1956. Mem. Internat. Assn. Orientalist Librarians (pres. 1976-80). Episcopalian. Home: 2631 Ferdinand Ave Honolulu HI 96822-1740 Office: U Hawaii SHAPS 1890 E West Rd Honolulu HI 96822-2318

NUNN, GRADY HARRISON, political science educator emeritus; b. Arlington, Tex., Apr. 12, 1917; s. William Roy and Floy Brooke (Dugan) N.; m. Ann Torrey Welsh, June 15, 1951 (dec. 1980); 1 child, Therese von Hohoff.; m. Virginia Cotton Chivington, Dec. 18, 1982. B.A., U. Okla., 1939, M.A., 1941; Ph.D. (Penfield fellow), N.Y.U., 1961. Instr. N.Y.U., 1946-49; from instr. to asso. prof. U. Ala., Tuscaloosa, 1949-65; prof., chmn. dept. polit. sci. U. Ala., Birmingham, 1969-83, prof. emeritus, 1983—; vis. asst. prof. Ind. U., 1960-61; asst. prof., asso. prof. U. Pitts. at Ahmadu Bellu U., Nigeria, 1964-68; assoc. prof. U. Pitts., 1968, Auburn U., 1968-69; Bd. dirs. Unitarian Universalist Service Com., 1978-84, v.p., 1981-82. Assoc. editor: Background on World Politics, 1957-62; Contbr. to: Readings in Government in American Society, 1949, Federalism in the Commonwealth, 1963, The Politics and Administration of Nigerian Government, 1965; editorial bd.: Jour. of Politics, 1971-74. Served to capt., F.A. AUS, 1942-46. Ford Found. Fgn. Area fellow, 1956-57. Mem. Am. Polit. Sci. Assn., So. Polit. Sci. Assn. (exec. council 1974-77), Royal African Soc., AAUP (pres. Ala. conf.), Phi Beta Kappa, Pi Sigma Alpha, Phi Eta Sigma, Alpha Tau Omega, Omicron Delta Kappa. Unitarian. Home: 1152 52nd St S Birmingham AL 35222-3925

NUNN, ROBERT WARNE, lawyer; b. Salem, Oreg., Sept. 20, 1950; s. Warne Harry and Delores (Netz) N.; m. Kandis Brewer; 1 child, Hayley Elisabeth. Student, U. Vienna, Austria, 1971; BS, Willamette U., 1972; MS in Acctg., Northeastern U., Boston, 1973; JD, U. Oreg., 1976. Bar: Oreg 1976, U.S. Dist. Ct. Oreg. 1977, U.S. Ct. Appeals (9th cir.) 1977, U.S. Supreme Ct. 1982, Wash. 1986. Ptnr. Schwabe, Williamson & Wyatt, Portland, Oreg., 1976-92; ptnr., chmn. corp. dept. Preston, Gates & Ellis, Portland, 1992—. Mem. exec. com. Am. Leadership; bd. mgrs. Multnomah metro br. YMCA, Portland, 1983-86, chmn., 1984-85; pres. Oreg. div. Am. Cancer Soc., Portland, 1986-87, bd. dirs. 1987-88, trustee Marylhurst Coll., Oreg., 1985-91, Willamette U. 1991—, World Affairs Coun. Oreg., 1991—; bd. dirs. United Way of Columbia-Willamette, Portland, 1984-87. Am. Leadership fellow, 1987; named Order of Red Sword Am. Cancer Soc., 1985. Mem. ABA, Oreg. Bar Assn. (CPA joint com., past chmn. legal assts. and legal investigators com., cert. subcom., fee arbitration panel), Internat. Bar Assn., Nat. Assn. Bond Lawyers (vice-chmn. mcpl. utility obligations com.), Pacific N.W. Internat. Trade Assn., Portland C. of C. (chmn. internat. trade com.), Univ. Club, Multnomah Athletic Club (Portland). Republican. Lutheran. Avocations: computers, skiing, sailing. Home: 10910 SW 29th Ct Portland OR 97219-7585

NUNN, SAMUEL (SAM NUNN), senator; b. Perry, Ga., Sept. 8, 1938; s. Samuel Augustus and Elizabeth (Cannon) N.; m. Colleen O'Brien, Sept. 25, 1965; children: Michelle, Brian. Student, Ga. Tech. Coll., 1956-59; A.B., LL.B., Emory U., 1962. Bar: Ga. 1962. Legal counsel armed services com. U.S. Ho. Reps., 1963; mem. firm Nunn, Geiger & Rampey, Perry, Ga., 1964-73; mem. Ga. Ho. Reps., 1968-72; U.S. senator from Ga., 1972—; ranking minority mem. Armed Services Com.; mem. Govtl. Affairs Com., Small Bus. Com., Senate Dem. Steering and Coordination Com.; chmn. Permanent Subcom. on Investigations of Govt. Affairs; farmer, Perry, 1964—. Office: US Senate 303 Dirksen Senate Bldg Washington DC 20510*

NUNN, THOMAS CALVIN, school supervisor, retired army officer; b. Weleetka, Okla., Mar. 28, 1928; s. Ernest Howard and Beatrice (Thomas) N.; m. Agnes Ruth Zaletel, Sept. 2, 1950; children: Thomas C. Jr., Pamela, Becky, Marilyn, Linda. BA, Okla. State U., 1952; MA, U.S. Army Command & Gen. Staff Coll., 1967. Cert. sch. supr. Platoon leader 1st armored div. U.S. Army, Ft. Hood, Tex., 1950-52; provost marshal U.S. Army, Fairbanks, Alaska, 1953-55; co. comdr. 1st cav. div. U.S. Army, Korea, 1960-61; ops. officer U.S. Army, Berlin, 1963-65; battalion comdr. 25th infantry div. U.S. Army, Vietnam, 1967-68; chief plans and ops. fifth hdqrs. U.S. Army, Ft. Sheridan, Ill., 1968-72; dep. comdr. criminal investigation command U.S. Army, Heidleberg, Germany, 1972-74; supr. Lafourche Parish Sch. Bd., Thibodaux, La., 1974-95; dir. army inst. LaFourche Parish Sch. Bd., Thibodaux, 1974-95. Co-chmn. Civic Com., Thibodaux, 1979. Lt. Col. U.S. Army, 1950-74. Decorated Legion of Merit (3 awards), D.F.C., Purple Heart (3 awards), others; named Outstanding La. Educator, State Dept. Edn., Baton Rouge, 1981; recipient Svc. award Citizen of Yr. City Svc. League, Thibodaux, 1990. Mem. DAV (life), VFW (life), Purple Heart Assn. (life), Am. Legion (v.p. 1975-79), Gulf South Suprs. Assn., La. Sch. Suprs. Assn., Lions Club (prs. 1978-79, Lion of Yr. 1979-80). Avocations: fishing, golfing, gardening. Home: 305 Edgewood Dr Thibodaux LA 70301-3809

NUNN, TREVOR ROBERT, director; b. Ipswich, Eng., Jan. 14, 1940; s. Robert Alexander and Dorothy May (Piper) N.; m. Janet Suzman, 1969 (div. 1985); 1 child; m. Sharon Lee Hill, 1986 (div. 1991); 2 children: m. Imogen Stubbs, 1994; 1 child. Student, Ipswich Coll., Downing Coll., Cambridge, Eng.; LLD, U. Warwick, 1982; MA (hon.), U. Newcastle-upon-Tyne, 1982. Trainee dir. Belgrade Theatre, Coventry; assoc. dir. Royal Shakespeare Co., Warwickshire, Eng., 1964-68, artistic dir., 1968-78, joint artistic dir., 1978-86, chief exec., 1968-86, dir. emeritus, 1986—. Dir. plays including Tango, 1965, The Revenger's Tragedy, 1965, 69, The Taming of the Shrew, The Relapse, The Winter's Tale, 1969, Hamlet, 1970, Henry VIII, 1970, Roman Season: Antony and Cleopatra, Coriolanus, Julius Caesar, Titus Andronicus, 1970, Macbeth, 1974, 76, Hedda Gabler (own version) 1975, Romeo and Juliet, 1976, Comedy of Errors, 1976, The Alchemist, 1977, As You Like It, 1977, Every Good Boy Deserves Favour, 1977, Three Sisters, 1978, The Merry Wives of Windsor, 1979, Once in a Lifetime, 1979 (Evening Standard Best Dir. award), Juno and the Paycock, 1980, The Life and Adventures of Nicholas Nickleby (with John Caird), 1980 (Tony Best Dir. award 1981, Evening Standard Best Dir. award), touring revival, 1985, Cats, 1981 (Best Dir. Tony award 1982), All's Well That Ends Well, 1981, Henry IV (parts I and II), 1981, 82, Peter Pan (with John Caird), 1982, Starlight Express, 1984, Les Miserables (with John Caird), 1985 (Tony award for best dir. 1987), Fair Maid of the West, 1986, Chess, 1986, Aspects of Love, 1989, Othello, 1989, The Baker's Wife, 1989, Timon of Athens, 1991 (Evening Standard Best Dir. award, Best Dir. Critics' Cir. award), The Blue Angel, 1991, Measure for Measure, 1991, Heartbreak House, 1992, Arcadia, 1993, Sunset Boulevard, 1993 (Tony nominee - Direction of a Musical, 1995); (opera) Idomeneo, 1982, Porgy and Bess, 1986, revived 1987,92, Cosi Fan Tutte, 1991, Peter Grimes, 1992, Katya Kabanova, 1994; TV shows Include: Anthony and Cleopatra, 1975, Comedy of Errors, 1976, Every Good Boy Deserves Favour, 1978, Three Sisters, 1978, Macbeth, 1978, Great Hamlets, 1983, Othello, 1990, Porgy and Bess, 1993; writer, dir. Shakespeare Workshops Word of Mouth, 1979, films Hedda, Lady Jane, 1985; author: British Theatre Design, 1989. Recipient London Theatre Critics Best Dir. award, 1969; Soc. Film and TV Arts award, 1975, Ivor Novello award for best Brit. Musical, 1976; numerous others. Office: Homevale Ltd, Gloucester Mansions 3d Fl, Cambridge Circus London WC2H 8HD, England

NUNNELLY, WALTER SANDELS, III, corporate executive; b. Union City, Tenn., Sept. 13, 1943; s. Walter Sandels and Betty Jane (Cox) N.; m. Sarah Anne Chaffin, June 23, 1984. BA, Vanderbilt U., 1966. Customer svc. rep. Robert Orr/SYSCO, Nashville, 1969-71; nat. accounts exec., 1971-77, nat. accounts dir., 1978-81, v.p. mktg., 1982-85, v.p. sales, 1985-87, exec. v.p., 1987—. Pres. Cockrill Bend Bus. Coun., Nashville, 1990. With USAF, 1967-69. Mem. Tenn. Hotel and Motel Assn. (bd. dirs. 1982-90), Nashville City Club, Masons. Methodist. Avocations: reading, snow skiing, hunting, farming. Home: 159 N Berwick Ln Franklin TN 37064-7132 Office: Robert Orr/SYSCO 1 Hermitage Plz Nashville TN 37230

NUNZ, GREGORY JOSEPH, aerospace engineer and educator; b. Batavia, N.Y., May 28, 1934; s. Sylvester Joseph and Elizabeth Marie (Loesell) N.; m. Georgia Monyea Costas, Mar. 30, 1958; children: Karen, John, Rebecca, Deirdre, Jaimie, Marta. BSChemE, Cooper Union, 1955; postgrad., U. So. Calif., Calif. State U.; MS in applied Math., Columbia Pacific U., 1991, PhD in Mgmt. Sci., 1993. Adv. design staff, propulsion mgr. U.K. project Rocketdyne div. Rockwell, Canoga Park, Calif., 1955-65; mem. tech. staff Aerospace Corp., El Segundo, Calif., 1965-70; mem. tech. staff propulsion div. Jet Propulsion Lab., Pasadena, Calif., 1970-72; chief. monoprop. engring. Bell Aerospace Corp., Buffalo, N.Y., 1972-74; group supr. comb. devices Jet Propulsion Lab., Pasadena, 1974-76; asst. div. leader, program mgr. internat. HDR geothermal energy program, project mgr. space-related projects Los Alamos (N.Mex.) Nat. Lab., 1977—; assoc. prof. electronics L.A. Pierce Coll., Woodland Hills, Calif., 1961-72; instr. No. N.Mex. Community Coll., Los Alamos, 1978-80, div. head scis., 1980-92; adj. prof. math. U. N.Mex., Los Alamos, 1980—. Author: Electronics Lab Manual I, 1964, Electronics in Our World, 1972; co-author: Electronics Mathematics, vol. I, II, 1967; contbg. author Prentice-Hall Textbook of Cosmetology, 1975, Alternative Energy Sources VII, 1987; contbr. articles to profl. jours.; inventor smallest catalytic liquid N2H4 rocket thrustor, co-inventor first monoprop/biprop bimodal rocket engine, tech. advisor internat. multi-prize winning documentary film One With the Earth. Mem. Aerial Phenomena Research Orgn., L.A., 1975. Fellow AIAA (assoc.); mem. Tech. Mktg. Soc. Am., Math. Assn. Am., ARISTA, Shrine Club, Masons, Ballut Abyad Temple. Avocations: travel, archaeology, fgn. langs., golf. Office: Los Alamos Nat Lab PO Box 1663 MS D460 Los Alamos NM 87545

NUNZIATO, CARL ANTHONY, lawyer, banker; b. Youngstown, Ohio, Dec. 19, 1938; s. Thomas J. and Antoinette (Candela) N.; m. Clara J. Scarpine, Aug. 26, 1961; 1 child, Elizabeth. BA, Youngstown State U., 1961; JD, Case Western Res. U., 1971. Bar: Ohio 1971. Commd. U.S. Army, 1961, advanced through grades to maj., resigned, 1971; trust atty. Dollar Savs. and Trust Co., Youngstown, 1971—, corp. sec., 1971—, sec. holding co., 1971—. Trustee Youngstown chpt. Easter Seal Soc., Youngstown State U.; commr. Ohio Rehab. Assn. Named Disabled Citizen of Yr. Easter Seal Soc., 1985; recipient award Govt. of Ohio, 1980. Mem. Ohio Bar Assn., Mahoning County Bar Assn., Youngstown Estate Planning Coun. (officer 1978-80), DAV (Vet.of Yr. award 1978). Democrat. Roman Catholic. Home: 5791 Sharon Dr Youngstown OH 44512-3725 Office: Dollar Savs & Trust Co Federal Pla Youngstown OH 44503

NURENBERG, DAVID, oil company executive; b. N.Y.C., Mar. 25, 1939; s. Abraham S. and Katherine G. N.; m. Brenda G. Schwait, Sept. 1960; children—Jill Suzanne, Brian Michael. B.S. in Marine Engring. U.S. Mcht. Marine Acad., 1960; M.S. in Indsl. Mgmt, Columbia U., 1963, Ph.D. in Mgmt. Sci., 1965. With Exxon Corp., 1963-67; employee relations mgr. Esso Pappas, Athens, Greece, 1968-72; labor relations and compensation mgr. Esso Europe, London, 1972-77; corp. sec. Esso Eastern Inc., Houston, 1977-82; mgr. exec. compensation Exxon Corp., N.Y.C., 1982-90; mgr. compensation and exec. programs Exxon Corp., Dallas, 1990—; mem. coun. exec. compensation Conf. Bd., past chmn.; adj. prof. Union Inst. Mem. Am. Compensation Assn. (bd. dirs., chmn., exec. comp. coun., bd. steering com.). Office: Exxon Corp 225 E John W Carpenter Frwy Dallas TX 75062-2298

NURHUSSEIN, MOHAMMED ALAMIN, internist, geriatrician, educator; b. Adwa, Ethiopia, Apr. 4, 1942; came to U.S., 1972; s. Hagos and Teberih

(Yusuf) N.; m. Zahra Said, June 10, 1972; children: Nadia, Siham, Safy. BS, Haile Selasie Mil. Acad., Harar, Ethiopia, 1961; MD, Zagreb (Yugoslavia) U., 1968. Intern, resident, then fellow Bklyn.-Cumberland Med. ctr., 1972-77; emergency rm. physician Cumberland Hosp., Bklyn., 1977-79; attending physician in medicine Kings County Hosp. Ctr., Bklyn., 1979—; faculty practice medicine, geriatrics SUNY Univ. Hosp., Bklyn., 1983—; instr., then asst. prof. SUNY Health Sci. Ctr., bklyn., 1979-92; med. cons., dir. drug abuse treatment Coney Island Hosp., Bklyn., 1982-84; adv. bd. Bklyn. Alzheimer's Disease Assistance Ctr., 1992—. Fellow ACP; mem. Am. Geriatric Soc., Am. Lung Assn., N.Y. Acad. Scis., Amnesty Internat., Physicians for Human Rights. Democrat. Moslem. Office: SUNY Health Sci Ctr 450 Clarkson Ave Brooklyn NY 11203

NURKIN, HARRY ABRAHAM, hospital administrator; b. Durham, N.C., Feb. 15, 1944; s. Leo and Nell Margaret (Webster) N.; m. Anne Jarleth Van Meter, Nov. 18, 1967; children—Matthew Harry, Bradley Kabat, Scott Webster, Patrick Christopher, Alexander Jeffrey. B.A., Duke U., 1966, M.H.A., 1968; Ph.D., U. Ala., 1983. Asst. dir. Meml. Mission Hosp., Asheville, N.C., 1971-74; assoc. administr., chief ops. officer U. Ala. Hosps., Birmingham, 1974-81; pres., chief exec. officer Carolinas Med. Ctr., Charlotte, N.C., 1981—, Charlotte Mecklenburg Hosp. Authority, 1983—. Bd. dirs. ARC, Charlotte, 1985, Arts and Sci. Council, Charlotte, 1985, Charlotte Symphony, 1984, Health Svcs. Found.; mem. bd. visitors Davidson Coll., N.C., 1983—, U. N.C., Charlotte, 1982—. Fellow Am. Coll. Hosp. Adminstrs.; mem. Am. Hosp. Assn., N.C. Hosp. Assn. (bd. trustees), United Way (div. chair 1990). Home: 3022 Chaucer Dr Charlotte NC 28210-4810 Office: Carolinas Med Ctr PO Box 32861 Charlotte NC 28232-2861

NUROCK, ROBERT JAY, investment analysis company executive; b. Phila., May 25, 1937; s. Abe and Sid (Smokler) N.; m. Doris L. Whitliff, Oct. 19, 1974 (div.); m. 2d, Bridget A. McManus, June 16, 1984; children: Megan, Andrew. BA, Pa. State U., 1958. Owner, pres. Md. Brake Alignment Service, Balt., 1959-67; v.p. investor support Merrill Lynch & Co., Inc., N.Y.C., 1967-79; 1st v.p. market strategy Butcher & Singer, Inc., Phila., 1979-82; pres., market strategist Investor's Analysis, Inc., 1982—; lectr. various ednl. and fin. orgns., 1973—. Panelist program Wall St. Week, Pub. Broadcasting System TV, 1970-89; author, pub. Bob Nurock's Advisory, Santa Fe, 1979—; contbg. editor The Hume Moneyletter, Atlanta, 1982—; creator ESP-Elves Shortterm Predictor, EMI-Elves Market Index, TMI-Tech. Market Index. Bd. dirs. Tredyffrin/Easttown Edn. Found., Wharton Esherick Mus., Paoli, 1989—, Penna. Trust Co. Mem. Market Technicians Assn. (chartered market technician, v.p 1977-78), N.Y. Soc. Security Analysis, Assn. for Investment Mgmt. and Rsch., Analysts Club (pres. 1979), Rolls Royce Owners Club (dir. Keystone region). Office: PO Box 460 Santa Fe NM 87504-0460

NUSBACHER, GLORIA W., lawyer; b. N.Y.C., July 22, 1951; d. Murray and Doris (Togman) Weinberg; m. Burton Nusbacher, Aug. 4, 1974; 1 child, Shoshana. BA, Barnard Coll., 1972; JD, Columbia U., 1975. Bar: N.Y. 1976. Assoc. Hughes Hubbard & Reed, N.Y.C., 1975-83, counsel, 1983-91, ptnr., 1991—; atty. specializing in exec. compensation and employee benefits; lectr. in field. Contbr. articles to profl. jours. Troop leader Girl Scouts Am. Mem. ABA (employee benefits and exec. compensation com. 1984—, fed. regulation securities com., subcom. employee benefits and exec. compensation 1983—, task force exec. compensation, chmn. subcom. fed. and state securities laws of com. employee benefits and exec. compensation 1994—), Phi Beta Kappa. Office: Hughes Hubbard & Reed 1 Battery Park Plz New York NY 10004

NUSIM, STANLEY HERBERT, chemical engineer, consultant; b. N.Y.C., Oct. 2, 1935; s. Seymour and Ranna T. (Weiner) N.; m. Marcia Anne Borsig, Feb. 21, 1960; children: David Mark, Jill Wendi. BSChemE, CCNY, 1957; MSChemE, N.Y. U., 1960, PhD, 1967. Rsch. engr. Battelle Meml. Inst., Columbus, Ohio, 1956; researcher, chem. engring. rsch. and devel. Merck Rsch. Labs. Div., Rahway, N.J., 1957-68; sect. mgr. Merck Rsch. Labs. Div., Rahway, 1968-70; tech. svcs. mgr. Merck Chem. Mfg. Div., Rahway, 1970-73, mfg. mgr., 1973-80; dir. subsidiary projects Merck Internat. Div., Rahway, 1981-82, exec. dir. Latin Am., Far East, Near East ops., 1982-88; exec. dir. licensee, Latin Am., Far East, Asia ops. Merck Pharm. Mfg. Div., Rahway, 1989-92; exec. dir. licensee ops. worldwide Merck mfg. divsn. Merck & Co. Inc., Whitehouse Station, N.J., 1992-94; chem. engr. S.H. Nusim Assocs., Hollywood, Fla., 1994—; v.p. mfg. Therics Inc., N.J., 1994—, v.p. mng., 1994—; adv. bd. CCNY Sch. Engring., 1982—. Author: Kinetic Studies on C4 Hydrocarbon Systems, 1967. V.p. men's club Temple Beth Shalom, Livingston, N.J., 1975-78; rep. to bd. edn. Livingston Home and Sch. Assn., 1982-83; bd. govs. Turnberry Isle Yacht and Racquet Club, Aventura, Fla., 1992-94. Mem. Am. Inst. Chem. Engrs. (bd. dir. N. Jersey sect. 1968-71, scholarship award 1955), Am. Chem. Soc., Tau Beta Pi, Garden State Yacht Club (bd. govs. 1987-88). Achievements include U.S. and foreign. patents on the continous manufacture of halogenated acetone, on the first commercial process, on the development of sophisticated recovery systems for complex organic compounds from catalytic processes. Home: 19355 Turnberry Way Aventura FL 33180 Office: SH Nusim Assocs 686 N Dixie Hwy Hollywood FL 33020 Office: Therics Inc 99 Hudson St New York NY 10013

NUSS, ELDON PAUL, casket manufacturer; b. Sumner, Iowa, Apr. 24, 1933; s. Paul John and Helen (Nolting) N.; m. Carolyn Ann Krug, June 6, 1959; children—Susan Elizabeth, Laurie Ann. Student, Grinnell Coll., 1950; B.S. with highest honors, U. Iowa, 1954; student, Harvard, 1971. With Arthur Young & Co. (C.P.A.'s), 1957-68; prin. Arthur Young & Co. (C.P.A.'s), Houston, 1967-68; v.p. Marathon Mfg. Co., Houston, 1969-71; exec. v.p., dir. Marathon Mfg. Co., 1972-75; pres., chief exec. officer PMI Industries, Houston, 1975-91, The York Group, Houston, 1991—. Served with USNR, 1955-57. Mem. Assn. for Corporate Growth, AICPA. Lutheran (council 1966-67). Club: Lakeside Country. Home: 327 Knipp Forest St Houston TX 77024-5030 Office: 9430 Old Katy Rd Houston TX 77055-6368

NUSSBAUM, ADOLF EDWARD, mathematician, educator; b. Rheydt, Fed. Republic Germany, Jan. 10, 1925; came to U.S. 1947; s. Karl and Franziska (Scheye) N.; m. Anne Ebbin, Sept. 1, 1957; children: Karl, Franziska. MA, Columbia U., 1950, PhD, 1957. Mem. staff electronic computer project Inst. Advanced Study, Princeton, N.J., 1952-53; mem. Inst. Advanced Study, 1962-63; instr. math U. Conn., Storrs, 1953-55; asst. prof. Rensselaer Poly. Inst., Troy, N.Y., 1957-58; vis. scholar Stanford U., Calif., 1967-68; asst. prof., then assoc. prof. Washington U., St. Louis, 1958-66, prof., 1966-95, prof. emeritus, 1995—. Contbr. articles to profl. jours. Grantee NSF, 1960-79. Mem. Am. Math. Soc. Home: 8050 Watkins Dr Saint Louis MO 63105-2517 Office: Washington U Dept Math Saint Louis MO 63130

NUSSBAUM, BERNARD J., lawyer; b. Berlin, Mar. 11, 1931; came to U.S., 1936; s. William and Lotte (Lauffurther) N.; m. Jean Beverly Enzer, Sept. 4, 1956; children—Charles, Peter, Andrew. A.B., Knox Coll., 1952; J.D., U. Chgo., 1955. Assoc. Proskauer Rose Goetz & Mendelsohn, N.Y.C., 1955-56; assoc. Sonnenschein Nath & Rosenthal, Chgo., 1959-65, sr. ptnr., 1965—; master bencher Am. Inns of Ct., 1986—; appointed to com. on civility 7th cir. U.S. Ct. Appeals, 1989-92. Editor U. Chgo. Law Rev., 1954-55; mem. nat. adv. bd. BNA Civil Trial Man., 1985—; contbr. articles to profl. jours. Mem. vis. com. U. Chgo. Law Sch., 1977-83. Served to capt. U.S. Army, 1956-59. Fellow Am. Bar Found., Ill. Bar Found. (charter); mem. ABA, Chgo. Bar Assn. (chmn. com. on fed. civil procedure 1968-69, mem. com. on judiciary 1970-76), Ill. Bar Assn. (council Antitrust sect. 1971-73, assembly del. 1972-80), U. Chgo. Law Sch. Nat. Alumni Assn. (pres. 1981-83), Law Club Chgo., Legal Club Chgo. Avocations: skiing, cycling. Office: Sonnenschein Nath & Rosenthal 8000 Sears Tower 233 S Wacker Dr Chicago IL 60606

NUSSBAUM, KAREN, federal agency administrator; b. Chgo., Apr. 25, 1950. BA, Goddard Coll., 1973. Exec. dir. 9 to 5 Nat. Assn. of Working Women, 1993; pres. dist. 925 Svc. Employees Internat. Union, 1993. Coauthor: Solutions for the New Work Force: Policies for a New Social Contract, 9 to 5: The Working Woman's Guide to Office Survival. Named to Ohio Women's Hall of Fame, 1984. Office: Dept of Labor Women's Bur 200 Constitution Ave NW Washington DC 20210

NUSSBAUM, LEO LESTER, retired college president, consultant; b. Berne, Ind., June 27, 1918; s. Samuel D. and Margaret (Mazelin) N.; m. Janet Nell Gladfelter, Nov. 25, 1942; children: Felicity Ann, Luther James, Margaret Sue. BS, Ball State U., 1942, MA, 1949; PhD, Northwestern U., 1952; Postgrad., U. Mich., 1963. Tchr. Monmouth High Sch., Decatur, Ind., 1946-48; dean men, asst. prof. bus. Huntington Coll., (Ind.), 1948-51; dean coll. liberal arts, assoc. prof. edn. and psychology U. Dubuque, (Iowa), 1952-60; dean coll., prof. edn. and psychology Austin Coll., 1960-67; dean coll., prof. psychology Coe Coll., 1967-70, pres., 1970-82, pres. emeritus, 1982—; dir. Acad. Sr. Profls. Eckerd Coll., 1983-87; dir. PEL-ASPEC Project, 1988-95; coord. faculty ASPEC Colleagues, St. Petersburg, 1992—; cons. pvt. practice St. Petersburg, Fla., 1982—; Fulbright lectr. U. Mysore (India), 1958-59; cons., evaluator So. Assn. Colls. and Schs., Atlanta, 1963-67, North Cen. Assn. Colls. and Schs., 1959-60, 67-82, dir. I.E. Industries and Iowa Electric Light and Power Co., Cedar Rapids, 1982-91, dir. emeritus, 1991-92. Contbr. articles to scholastic and profl. jours. and periodicals. Bd. dirs. Cedar Rapids Symphony, 1968-70; mem. cabinet Cedar Rapids United Way, 1980-82; elder Presbyn. Ch., moderator Presbytery of S.W. Fla., 1989. Recipient Disting. Alumnus award Ball State U., 1976, Alumni Merit award Northwestern U., 1977. Mem. Assn. Colls. Midwest (chmn. 1975-77), Iowa Assn. Ind. Colls. and Univs. (chmn. 1976-77), Danforth Assocs., Rotary (Cedar Rapids, pres. 1975-76), Phi Delta Kappa, Blue Key, Pi Gamma Mu. Home: 5819 3d St S Saint Petersburg FL 33705

NUSSBAUM, MARK STEPHEN, securities trader; b. Greenwich, Conn., Oct. 4, 1952; s. Philip Kaufman and Doris Elaine (Gross) N.; m. Patricia Ann Richardson, June 12, 1976; children: Stephen, Peter, Brian. Diploma, Ecole Hoteliere, Lausanne, Switzerland, 1975; BA in Econs. magna cum laude, Amherst Coll., 1976; MBA in Fin. with distinction, NYU, 1982. Trader Bankers Trust Co., N.Y.C., 1976-82; trading mgr., treas. Bankers Trust Co., Hong Kong, 1982-84; funding and risk mgr. Bankers Trust Co., N.Y.C., 1984-86, mem. staff global risk mgmt., 1986-87; mgr. propriety trading Paine Webber, Inc., N.Y.C., 1987-88, chief fin. officer, co-head fixed income div., 1988—. Mem. Forex. Office: PaineWebber Group Inc 1285 Ave Of The Americas New York NY 10019-6028

NUSSBAUM, MARTHA CRAVEN, philosophy and classics educator; b. N.Y.C., May 6, 1947; d. George and Betty (Warren) Craven; m. Alan Jeffrey Nussbaum, Aug., 1969 (div. 1987); 1 child, Rachel Emily. BA, NYU, 1969; MA, Harvard U., 1971, PhD, 1975; LHD (hon.), Kalamazoo Coll., 1988, Grinnell Coll., 1993. Asst. prof. philosophy and classics Harvard U., Cambridge, 1975-80, assoc. prof., 1980-83; vis. prof. philosophy, Greek and Latin Wellesley (Mass.) Coll., 1983-84; assoc. prof. philosophy and classics Brown U., Providence, R.I., 1984-85, prof. philosophy, classics and comparative lit., 1985-87, David Benedict prof. philosophy, classics and comparative lit., 1987-89, prof., 1989-95; prof. law and ethics U. Chgo., 1995—; rsch. advisor World Inst. Devel. Econs. Rsch., Helsinki, Finland, 1986-93; vis. prof. law U. Chgo., 1994. Author: Aristotle's De Motu Animalium, 1978, The Fragility of Goodness, 1986, Love's Knowledge, 1990, The Therapy of Desire, 1994; editor: Language and Logos, 1983; (with A. Rorty) Essays on Artistotle's De Anima, 1992, (with A. Sen) The Quality of Life, 1993, (with J. Brunschwig) Passions & Perceptions, 1993, (with J. Glover) Women, Culture, and Development, 1995. Soc. Fellows Harvard U. jr. fellow, 1972-75, Humanities fellow Princeton U., 1977-78, Guggenheim Found. fellow, 1983, NIH fellow, vis. fellow All Souls Coll., Oxford, Eng., 1986-87; recipient Brandeis Creative Arts award, 1990, Spielvogel-Diamondstein award, 1991; Gifford lectr. U. Edinburgh, 1993. Fellow Am. Acad. Arts and Scis. (membership com. 1991-93, coun. 1992—), Am. Philos. Soc.; mem. Am. Philos. Assn. (exec. com. Ea. divsn. 1985-87, chair com. internat. coop., ex-officio mem. nat. bd. 1989-92, chair com. on status of women 1994—), Am. Philol. Assn., PEN. Office: U Chgo Law Sch 1111 E 60th St Chicago IL 60637

NUSSBAUM, PAUL EUGENE, journalist; b. Upland, Ind., Aug. 30, 1952; s. Elmer N. and Ruth Ellen (Shugart) N.; m. Debra Stone, Oct. 31, 1987; children: Molly Elizabeth, Matthew Connor. Student, Taylor U., 1970-71; BS, Ball State U., 1974. Reporter Muncie (Ind.) Star, 1973-74, Indpls. Star, 1975, Anchorage Times, 1975-76; staff writer Anchorage Daily News, 1976-78, metro editor, 1978-80; staff writer L.A. Times, 1980-82; staff writer Phila. Inquirer, 1982-91, dep. fgn. editor, 1991-94; mng. editor Phila. Inquirer Mag., 1994—. Recipient Best Editorial award Alaska Press Club, 1978, Best News Story award Sigma Delta Chi, 1984, Best Mag. Story, Sigma Delta Chi Soc. of Profl. Journalists, 1991, 1st Pl. news reporting award Pa. AP Mng. Editors, 1985. Methodist. Office: Phila Inquirer 400 N Broad St Philadelphia PA 19130-4099

NUSSBAUM, STEPHEN, health care executive; b. Chgo., Aug. 2, 1948; s. Herbert and Edith (Wolf) N.; m. Ava Danziger, Feb. 25, 1973; children: Donny, Dafna, Orly. BHL Spertus Coll., 1971; BA, Roosevelt U., 1971; MBA, Loyola U., Chgo., 1979. Clinic coord. Dept. of Health, Chgo., 1975-79; dir. radiology Victory Meml. Hosp., Waukegan, Ill., 1979-81, v.p., 1981-88; sr. v.p. Victory Health Svcs., Waukegan, 1988-91; chief operating officer Greenberg Radiology Inst., Highland Park, Ill., 1991; instr. Coll. of Lake County, Grayslake, Ill., 1985-88; bd. dirs. J Blumberg Blood Bank, Waukegan. v.p. Hillel Toray Day Sch., Skokie, Ill., 1987-89, bd. dirs., 1977-87; v.p. Congregation Or Torah, Skokie, 1986-91; bd. dirs. radiology adv. com. Coll. of Lake County, Grayslake, 1980-85; com. mem. Am. Cancer Soc. Lake County, Ill., 1987-91. Fellow Am. Coll. Healthcare Execs.; mem. Am. Radiology Adminstrs., No. Ill. Health Execs. Coun. (pres. 1989-91). Jewish. Avocations: religious study, baseball, basketball, walking.

NUSSBAUM, V. M., JR., former mayor; b. Ft. Wayne, Ind., June 25, 1919; m. Terry O'Hayer, 1943; 9 children. Student, Holy Cross Coll., Univ. Pa., Harvard Univ. City councilman Greensboro, N.C., 1973-81; mayor City of Greensboro, Greensboro, 1987-93; founder, pres. So. Food Svc. Inc., 1954, So. Foods, 1960. Gen. chmn. united fund drive United Way, 1971, pres., 1972; former pres. United Arts Coun., Boy Scouts Am., Gen. Greene Coun. Lt. comdr. USN. Recipient Nat. Greene award Greensboro C. of C., 1983, Citizen of Yr. award, 1993. Home: 9 Saint Augustine Sq Greensboro NC 27408-3834

NUSSBAUMER, GERHARD KARL, metals company executive; b. Linz, Austria, Mar. 25, 1959; came to U.S., 1987; s. Franz and Stefanie (Hinternberger) N. MBA, U. Vienna, 1982. Jr. auditor Price Waterhouse, Vienna, 1983-85; corp. staff contr. Oesterreichische Industrieholding AG, Vienna, 1985-87; v.p. fin. Voest-Alpine Internat. Corp., N.Y.C., 1987-92, pres., 1993—; bd. dirs. Voest-Alpine Internat. Corp., N.Y.C., Voest-Alpine Svcs. and Technologies, Pitts., Voest-Alpine Tubular Corp., Houston, Voest-Alpine M.C.E. Corp., Berlin, Voest-Alpine Steel Products Corp., N.Y.C. Mem. U.S. Austrian C. of C., Am. Mgmt. Assn. Avocations: theatre, constitutional law, history, tennis, skiing. Office: Voest-Alpine Internat Corp 60 E 42nd St New York NY 10165

NUSSBAUM, SIEGFRIED FRED, chemistry educator; b. Vienna, Austria, Nov. 21, 1919; came to U.S., 1939; s. Marcus and Susan Sara (Rothenberg) N.; m. Celia Womark, Feb. 20, 1951; children; Deborah M., Evelyn R. BS in Chemistry, U. Calif., Berkeley, 1941, MS in Food Tech., 1948, PhD in Comparative Biochemistry, 1951. Analytical chemist Panam. Engring. Co., Berkeley, 1942-43; asst. chief chemist Manganese Ore Co., Las Vegas, 1943-45; rsch. assoc. U. Calif., Berkeley, 1951-52; dir. master clin. lab. sci. program U Calif., San Francisco, 1969-87; from instr. to prof. Calif. State U., Sacramento, 1952-90, chair dept. chemistry, 1958-65; cons. biochemist Sacramento County Hosp., 1958-70; lectr. U. Calif. Davis Med. Ctr., 1970-93, guest lectr., 1993—. Author: Organic Chem-Principles and Application, 1963; contbr. articles to profl. jours. Sgt. U.S. Army, 1945-47. Fellow AAAS; mem. Am. Chem. Soc., Am. Assn. Clin. Chemistry (Outstanding Contbn. in Edn. award no. sect. 1991), Nat. Acad. Clin. Biochemistry. Achievements include research in pectic enzymes, mechanism of amylopectin formation and differentiation from amylose, phenotyping of lipemias. Home: 2900 Latham Dr Sacramento CA 95864-5644

NUSSLE, JAMES ALLEN, congressman; b. Des Moines, June 27, 1960; s. Mark S. and Lorna Kay (Fisher) N.; m. Leslie J. Harbison, Aug. 23, 1986. BA, Luther Coll., Decorah, Iowa, 1983; JD, Drake U., 1985. Bar: Iowa 1985. Pvt. practice law Manchester, Iowa, 1986; states atty. Delaware County Atty., Manchester, 1986-90; mem. 102nd-104th Congresses from 2d Iowa dist., Washington, 1991—; mem. house ways and means com., budget com. 102nd-104th Congresses from 2d Iowa dist. Lutheran. Avocation: guitar. Office: US Ho of reps 303 Cannon Washington DC 20515-1502

NUTE, DONALD E., JR., philosophy educator; b. Maysville, Ky., Aug. 12, 1947; s. Donald E. Sr. and Virginia (Boyd) N.; m. Jane Greifenkamp, Aug. 17, 1968; 1 child, Achsa Lynn. BA, U. Ky., 1969; PhD, Ind. U., 1974. Assoc. instr. Ind. U., Bloomington, 1970-71; asst. prof. U. Ga., Athens, 1973-78, assoc. prof., 1978-83, prof. philosophy, 1983—; dir. MS in artificial intelligence program, 1987—; head dept. philosophy, 1989—; dir. artificial intelligence ctr., 1994—; vis. prof. U. Tubingen, Germany, 1985; pres. AI Assocs., Athens, 1987—; rsch. assoc. U. Antwerp, Belgium, 1989. Author: Topics in Conditional Logic, 1980, Essential Formal Semantics, 1981; co-author: Prolog Programming in Depth, 1988. Mem. Am. Philos. Assn., Am. Assn. Artificial Intelligence, So. Soc. for Philosophy and Psychology, Assn. for Symbolic Logic, Soc. for Exact Philosophy, Phi Beta Kappa. Office: U Ga Dept Philosophy Athens GA 30602

NUTT, FRED L., JR., retail store executive. Exec. v.p., sec., chief fin. officer Limited Strores Inc., Columbus, Ohio. Office: Ltd Stores Inc 1 Limited Pky Columbus OH 43230-1498

NUTT, JIM, artist; b. Pittsfield, Mass., Nov. 28, 1938. BFA, Sch. Art Inst., Chgo. 1965. One-man shows include Candy Store Gallery, Folsom, Calif., 1971, 72, 73, Mus. Contemporary Art, Chgo. 1974, Whitney Mus. Am. Art, N.Y.C., 1974, Walker Art Ctr., Mpls., 1974, San Francisco Art Inst., 1975, Portland (Oreg.) Ctr. for Visual Arts, 1975, Rotterdamse Kunststichting, Rotterdam, The Netherlands, 1980, James Mayor Gallery, London, 1983, Phyllis Kind Gallery, N.Y.C., 1976, 77, 80, 84, Chgo., 1970, 72, 75, 77, 79, 82, 85, 91, Gallerie Bonnier, Geneva, 1992; exhibited in group shows at Hyde Park Art Ctr., Chgo., 1966, 67, 68, Mus. Contemporary Art, Chgo., 1969, 72, 77, 82, 84, Corcoran Gallery Art, Washington, 1969, 85, U. Pa., Phila., 1969, E.B. Crocker Gallery, 1972, Whitney Mus. Am. Art, 1973, 77, 80, 81, 82, 83, John F. Kennedy Ctr., Washington, 1975, Art Inst. Chgo., 1976, 85, Sch. Art Inst. Chgo., 1976, U. Tex. at Austin, 1977, Soc. for Contemporary Art, Art Inst. Chgo., 1977, U. No. Iowa Gallery Art, Cedar Rapids, 1978, Smithsonian Instn., Washington, 1979, Bklyn. Mus., 1980, Chrysler Mus., Norfolk, Va., 1980, James Mayor Gallery, London, 1980, Meml. Art Gallery, U. Rochester, N.Y., 1980, Ackland Mus. U. N.C., Chapel Hill, 1980, Aldrich Mus., Ridgefield, Conn., 1981, Art Mus. South Tex., Corpus Christi, 1981, Pace Gallery, N.Y.C., 1982, U. Mass., Amherst, 1982, Coll. Fine Arts U. Nebr., Omaha, 1982, Butler Inst. Am. Art, Youngstown, Ohio, 1982, Milw. Art Mus., 1982, Ray Hughes Gallery, Brisbane, Australia, 1982, Roger Litz Gallery, N.Y.C., 1982, Ill. Wesleyan U., Bloomington, 1983, Galerie Bonnier, Geneva, 1983, U. Ohio at Athens, 1984, Phyllis Kind Gallery, Chgo., 1984, Hirshhorn Mus. and Sculpture Garden Smithsonian Instn., Washington, 1984-85, Morgan Gallery, Kansas City, Mo., 1985, No. Ill. U., DeKalb, 1987, Sch. Art Gallery Bowling Green State U., Ohio, 1987, Terra Mus. Am. Art, Chgo., 1987, Chgo. Pub. Library Cultural Ctr., 1987, David and Alfred Smart Gallery, U. Chgo., 1987, Milw. Art Mus., 1990-91, Kuntshalle Basel, 1992-93, Centro de Arte Reina Sofia, Madrid, 1992-93, Setagaya Art Mus., Tokyo, 1992-93, Art. Inst. Chgo., 1992; represented in permanent collections including Art Inst. Chgo., Meml. Art Gallery U. Rochester, N.Y., Met. Mus. Art, N.Y.C., Mus. Contemporary Art, Chgo., Mus. Modern Art, N.Y.C., Mus. Moderner Kunst, Vienna, Nat. Mus. Am. Art, Washington, New Orleans Mus. Art, Phila. Mus. Art, Scottish Nat. Mus., Glasgow, State Ill. Collection, Chgo., Weatherspoon Art Gallery U. N.C., Greensboro, Whitney Mus. Am. Art, N.Y.C. Office: care Phyllis Kind Gallery 313 W Superior St Chicago IL 60610-3515 also: Phyllis Kind Gallery 136 Greene St New York NY 10012

NUTT, ROBERT L., lawyer; b. New Castle, Pa., Mar. 30, 1945; s. James Earl and Dorothy (Cookson) N.; m. Virginia Anne Maurer, Aug. 16, 1969; children: David, Jonathan. BA, Grove City Coll., 1967; JD, U. Pa., 1970. Bar: N.Y., Mass. Law clerk U.S. Ct. Appeals (2d cir.), N.Y.C., 1970-71; assoc. Ropes & Gray, Boston, 1971-79, ptnr., 1979—; lectr. in law Boston U., 1989—. Contbr. articles to profl. jours. Trustee Shore County Day Sch., Beverly, Mass., 1986-94; moderator First Ch. of Christ, Marblehead, Mass., 1993—. Mem. ABA, Boston Bar Assn. (bus. law sect. chair 1990-93). Congregationalist. Avocations: skiing, golf, upland bird hunting. Office: Ropes & Gray One International Pl Boston MA 02110-2624

NUTT, WILLIAM JAMES, investment, management and mutual funds company executive; b. New Castle, Pa., Mar. 30, 1945; s. James Earl and Dorothy (Cookson) N.; m. Deborah Denison Stout, June 21, 1975; children: Caroline, Alexander, William. BA, Grove City Coll., 1967; JD, U. Pa., 1970. Ptnr. Ballard, Spahr, Andrews & Ingersoll, Phila., 1972-82; sr. exec. v.p. Boston Co., Boston, 1982-89, pres., COO, 1989-93; chmn., CEO Boston Safe Deposit & Trust Co., 1989-93; dir. Boston Co.; chmn. Boston Instnl. Svcs., Inc., 1993—; dir. Investment Co. Inst., Washington, 1986-94. Bd. dirs. Med. Coll. Pa., Phila., 1979-82; trustee New Eng. Aquarium, Boston, 1989—, The Tower Sch., Marblehead, Mass., 1986—. With U.S. Army, 1970-71. Fellow U. Pa. Ctr. for Study of Fin. Instns., 1971. Mem. ABA, Pa. Bar Assn., Eastern Yacht Club, Merion Cricket Club, Myopia Hunt Club. Avocations: skiing, squash, sailing, golf. Home: 20 Foster St APO AE 09145-5000 Office: Affiliated Mgrs Grop One Internat Pl Ste 820 1 Boston Pl Boston MA 02110

NUTTALL, GRANT, retired oil company executive; b. Toronto, Ont., Can., Nov. 20, 1932; s. Norman and Alcie M. (Eady) N.; m. Maureen L. Christie, Feb. 20, 1981; children: Wayne Norman, Jacqueline Ann, Virginia Marie. BS in Bus. Adminstrn., Mich. Tech. U., Houghton, 1959. With Imperial Oil Ltd., Toronto, 1959—, various mktg. positions, 1959-81, various mgmt. devel. position, then v.p. exec. devel. and orgn., 1981—; formerly chmn. organizing com. Fed. Govt. Exec. Exch. Program, Ottawa, 1989—, Human Resources Adv. Group Conf. Bd. Can., Ottawa, 1991—; mem. U. Toronto Task Force Women in Mgmt. Bd. dirs. Kinark Child and Family Svcs., Toronto, 1988—. Inducted into Mich. Tech.'s Acad. Bus., 1994. Mem. Granite Club (Toronto). Avocations: horology, golf. Home: 53 Gustav Crescent, Toronto, ON Canada M2M 4G9 Office: Imperial Oil Ltd, 111 St Clair Ave W, Toronto, ON Canada M2M 4G9

NUTTALL, RICHARD NORRIS, state agency administrator; b. Hamilton, Ont., Can., Feb. 7, 1940; s. James William and Margaret Gay (Walsh) N.; m. Ethel Jane Pickering, July 9, 1977; children: Andrew Richard, John Patrick. BSA, U. Toronto, 1961; MPA, Harvard U., 1964; MB, BS, U. London, Eng., 1974. Cert. Coll. Family Physicians Can., Mgmt. Cons. Zone dir. Health and Welfare Can., Prime Rupert, B.C., 1977-79; regional dir. Health and Welfare Can., Edmonton, Alta., 1980-82; pres. Rutland Consulting Group, Ltd., Vancouver, B.C., 1982-87, Richmond Assocs. Internat., Vancouver, 1988-90; med. health officer Govt. N.W. Ters., Yellowknife, B.C., 1990-93, Regina (Can.) Health Dist., 1993—. Mem. Can. Pub. Health Assn. (bd. dirs. 1991-93), Rotary Club North Regina. Office: Regina Health Dist, 1910 McIntyre St, Regina, SK Canada S4P 2R3

NUTTER, FRANKLIN WINSTON, lawyer; b. Charleston, W.Va., Apr. 17, 1946; s. Frank Hamilton and Marie Agnes (Ryle) N.; m. Linda Jean Davis, Sept. 2, 1972; children: Alycia Marie, Aaron Davis. BBA in Econs., U. Cin., 1968; JD, Georgetown U., 1974. Bar: D.C., Va., U.S. Dist. Ct. (no. dist.) Va., U.S. Ct. Appeals (9th and D.C. cirs.), U.S. Supreme Ct. 1993. Gen. counsel Nat. Flood Ins. Assn., Washington, 1975-78; gen. counsel Reins. Assn. Am., Washington, 1978-81, pres., 1981-84, 91—; pres. Alliance Am. Insurers, Schaumburg, Ill., 1984-91; bd. overseers Inst. Civil Justice subs. Rand Corp.; chair Natural Disaster Coalition. Bd. dirs. Advs. for Hwy. and Auto Safety; trustee Nat. Commn. Against Drunk Driving. Lt. (j.g.) USN, 1968-72. Mem. ABA (torts and injury practice sect., past chmn. internat. ins. law, excess and surplus lines and reins. com., coun. tort and ins. practice sect.), Va. Bar Assn., Ins. Inst. Hwy. Safety (bd. dirs.), Workers' Compensation Rsch. Inst., Industry Sector Adv. Coun. on Svcs. Home: 8458 Portland Pl McLean VA 22102 Office: 1301 Pennsylvania Ave NW Washington DC 20004-3807

NUTTER, WALLACE LEE, paper manufacturing executive; b. 1944. BA, U. Washington, 1967; grad. advanced mgmt. program, Harvard Coll., 1987. Ops. asst. N.W. timber div. ITT Rayonier Inc., Stamford, Conn., 1967-69, contract logging foreman, 1969-70, contract logging supt., 1970-71, mgr. log sales and purchases, 1971-78, mgr. wood resources sales and procurement, 1978-80, regional dir. forest and wood products N.W. regional ops., 1980-82, dir. timber and wood products N.W., 1982-84, dir. forest products ops., 1984-85, v.p. forest and wood products ops., from 1985, v.p. pulp mfg.; exec. v.p. Rayonier (no longer divsn. of ITT), Stamford, Conn., 1987—. Office: Rayonier 1177 Summer St Stamford CT 06905-5522

NUTTER, ZOE DELL LANTIS, public relations executive, retired; b. Yamhill, Oreg., June 14, 1915; d. Arthur Lee Lantis and Olive Adelaide (Reed) Lantis-Hilton; m. Richard S. West, Apr. 30, 1941 (div. Nov. 1964); m. Ervin John Nutter, Dec. 30, 1965. Assoc. in Bus., Santa Ana Jr. Coll., 1944. Cert. gen. secondary sch. tchr., Calif. Promoter World's Fair & Comml. Airlines Golden Gate Internat. Expn., San Francisco, 1937-39; pirate theme girl, official hostess Treasure Island's World Fair, San Francisco, 1939-40; prin. dancer San Francisco Ballet, 1937-41; artist, 1941-45; program dir. Glenn County High Sch., Willows, Calif., 1952-58; pub. rels. Monarch Piper Aviation Co., Monterey, Calif., 1963-65; pilot, pub. rels. Elano Corp., Xenia, Ohio, 1968-85; bd. dirs. Nat. Aviation Hall of Fame, Dayton, Ohio, pres., chmn., 1989-92, bd. trustees, 1976—, chmn. bd. nominations, 1992—; bd. trustees Ford's Theatre, Washington, Treasure Island Mus., San Francisco; charter mem. Friends of First Ladies, Smithsonian, Washington, 1990-93. Assoc. editor KYH mag. of Shikar Safari Internat., 1985-87; contbg. columnist Scripps Howard San Francisco News, 1938. Bd. dirs. Cin. May Festival, 1976-80; cen. com. Glenn County Rep. Party, Willows, 1960-64; state cen. com. Rep. Party, 1962-64; adv. bd. Women's Air & Space Mus., Dayton, 1987-94. Warrant officer, Civil Air Patrol, 1967-69. Recipient Civic Contbn. Honor award Big Brothers/Big Sisters, 1991, John Collier Nat. award Camp Fire Girls & Boys, 1988, Tambourine award Salvation Army, 1982, State of Ohio Gov.'s award for Volunteerism, 1992; named Most Photographed Girl in World, News Burs. & Clipping Svcs., 1938-39. Fellow Pres.'s Club U. Ky., Ohio State U., Wright State U.; mem. 99's Internat. Women Pilots Orgn. (life, hospitality chmn. 1968), Monterey Bay Chapter 99's (mem. chmn. 1964-65), Walnut Grove Country Club, Lost Tree Country Club, Windstar County Club (Naples, Fla.), Rotary (Paul Harris fellow 1987), Old Port Yacht Club, Shikar Safari Internat. (host com. 1976). Avocations: flying, horseback riding, hunting, shooting, fashion. Home: 986 Trebein Rd Xenia OH 45385-9534

NUTTING, GEORGE OGDEN, newspaper publisher; b. Washington, Oct. 21, 1935; s. George Kegley and Margaret Lawson (Ogden) N.; m. Betty S. Woods; children—William Ogden, Robert McLain. B.A., Williams Coll., 1956. With Martinsburg (W.Va.) Jour., 1956, Wheeling (W.Va.) News Register, 1957; with Ogden Newspapers, Inc., Wheeling, 1958—; pres., gen. mgr. Ogden Newspapers, Inc., 1970—; chmn. bd. United Nat. Bank North, Wheeling; bd. dirs. Stone & Thomas, United Bankshares. Bd. dirs. Bethany Coll.; mem. Wheeling Park Commn., Linsly Sch., Ohio Valley Indsl. and Bus. Devel. Corp., W.Va. U. Found. Mem. So. Newspaper Pubs. Assn. Republican. Episcopalian. Office: Wheeling News-Register 1500 Main St Wheeling WV 26003-2826

NUTZLE, FUTZIE (BRUCE JOHN KLEINSMITH), artist, author, cartoonist; b. Lakewood, Ohio, Feb. 21, 1942; s. Adrian Ralph and Naomi Irene (Rupert) Kleinsmith; children: Adrian David, Arielle Justine and Tess Alexandra (twins). Represented by The Pope Gallery, Santa Cruz, Calif. Author: Modern Loafer, Thames and Hudson, 1981, (autobiography) Futzie Nutzle, 1983, Earthquake, 1989, Run the World: 50 Cents Chronicle Books, 1991; illustrator: The Armies Encamped Beyond Unfinished Avenues (Morton Marcus), 1977, Box of Nothing, 1982, The Duke of Chemical Birds (Howard McCord), 1989, Book of Solutions, 1990, Fact and Friction, 1990, Managing for the 90s, 1992, Soundbites for Success, 1994; feature cartoonist Rolling Stone, N.Y.C., 1975-80, The Japan Times, Tokyo and L.A., 1986—, The Prague Post, Czechoslovakia, 1991—; contbr. exhbns. include Inaugural, 1966, Cupola, 1967, Rolling Renaissance, San Francisco, 1968, 100 Acres, O.K. Harris 1971, N.Y.C., San Francisco Mus. Art, 1972, Indpls. and Cin. Mus. Art, 1975, Leica, L.A., 1978, Santa Barbara Mus. Annex, Calif., 1978, Swope, Santa Monica, West Beach Cafe, Venice, Calif., 1985, Les Oranges, Santa Monica, Correspondence Art., 1970-78, 1st Ann. Art-A-Thon, N.Y.C., 1985, Am. Epiphany with Phillip Hefferton, 1986, Polit. Cartoon Show, Braunstein, San Francisco, Komsomolskaya Pravda, 1988, retrospective Eloise Packard Smith, 1990, exemplary contemporary, Cowell, U. Calif. Santa Cruz, 1991, Silicon Graphics Inc., Computer Graphics for NAB, Las Vegas, 1993, Prague Eco-Fair, 1991; represented in pvt. and pub. collections (complete archives) Spl. Collections, McHenry Libr., U. Calif., Santa Cruz, Mus. Modern Art, N.Y.C., San Francisco Mus. Modern Art, Oakland Mus., San Francisco Mus. Cartoon Art, Whitney Mus. Am. Art, N.Y.C. regular contbr. The Japan Times. Ltd., Tokyo. Address: PO Box 325 Aromas CA 95004-0325

NUZUM, JOHN M., JR., banker; b. Milw., Dec. 22, 1939; s. John M. and Helen (Ollis) N.; m. Margaret Bolway, Feb. 25, 1967; children: Kimberly, Courtney, Leah, Jonathan. AB, Princeton U., 1962; MBA, U. Pa., 1964. Sr. v.p. Chase Manhattan Bank, N.Y.C., 1965—. Project Reach Youth, Bklyn. 1977—, Park Slope Family Ctr., Bklyn., 1984-95. Mem. Montauk Club (bd. dirs. 1985-94), Heights Casino Club, Princeton Club. Office: Chase Manhattan Bank 1 Chase Manhattan Plz New York NY 10081-0001

NUZUM, ROBERT WESTON, lawyer; b. Evanston, Ill., Dec. 11, 1952; s. John Weston and Janet Marie (Talbot) N.; m. Julia Ann Abadie, Sept. 16, 1983. BS in Fin., La. State U., 1974, JD, 1977; LLM in Taxation, N.Y.U. 1978. Bar: La. 1977, D.C. 1979. Assoc. Office Chief Counsel, Washington, 1978-81, Jones, Walker, Waechter, Poitevent, Carrere & Denegre, New Orleans, 1981-85; ptnr. Jones, Walker, Waechter, Potevent, Carrere & Denegre, New Orleans, 1985-88, Deutsch, Kerrigan & Stiles, New Orleans, 1988-89, Phelps & Dunbar and predecessor firm, New Orleans, 1989—; adj. instr. Tulane U., New Orleans, 1984—. Editor La. Law Rev., 1977; contbr. articles to profl. jours. Wallace scholar N.Y.U., 1978. Mem. La. Bar Assn. (program chmn. tax sect. 1992-93, sec.-treas. 1993-94, vice chmn. 1994—), Tulane Tax Inst. (planning com. 1993—), Order of Coif. Republican. Roman Catholic. Avocations: golf, reading, fishing. Office: Phelps & Dunbar 400 Poydras St New Orleans LA 70130-3245

NUZZO, SALVATORE JOSEPH, defense, electronics company executive; b. Norwalk, Conn., Aug. 6, 1931; s. Rocco and Angelina (Ranzulli) N.; m. Lucille Cocco, Oct. 3, 1953; children—James, David, Thomas, Dana. B.S. in Elec. Engring, Yale U., 1953; M.S. in Bus, Columbia U., 1974. With Hazeltine Corp., Greenlawn, N.Y., 1953-88, v.p. govt. products and mktg., 1969-73, v.p. govt. products div., 1973-74, sr. v.p. ops., 1974-76, exec. v.p., chief oper. officer, 1976, pres., chief oper. officer, 1977-88, chief exec. officer, 1980-87, chmn., 1986-88, ret., 1988; chmn.; Technautics Corp., Cleve., 1991-94; chmn. Marine Mech. Corp., Cleve., 1994—; bd. dirs. Avnet Inc.; chmn. SL Industries, Bath Iron Works. Fellow Poly. Inst. N.Y. Mem. Yale Sci. and Engring. Assn. (former pres.). Home: 118 St Mellions Dr Pinehurst NC 28374 also: The Atriums IC-7 3400 S Ocean Blvd Palm Beach FL 33480-5692

NWE, KHIN MAY, physician, educator; b. Rangoon, Burma, Sept. 6, 1941; came to U.S., 1972; d. Unga Fawn and Shu Tin (Chan) Kyin; m. Maling Tin Aye, June 10, 1965 (div. 1972); 1 child, Timothy Maling Aye. BM, BS, Inst. Medicine, Rangoon, 1964. Asst. prof. Temple U., Phila., 1978-82; chief anesthesiologist VA Med. Ctr., Wilmington, Del., 1982—. Avocation: swimming. Office: VA Med Ctr 1601 Kirkwood Hwy Wilmington DE 19803

NYBERG, DONALD ARVID, oil company executive; b. Ridgewood, N.J., Aug. 23, 1951; s. Arvid H. and Rita T. (Tenwick) N.; m. Susan Radis, Feb. 16, 1985; children: Matthew D., Ryan T. Ba, St. Lawrence U., 1973; MBA, Harvard U., 1975. Mgr. marine ops. Standard Oil, L.A., 1982-83; mgr. ops. planning Standard Oil, Cleve., 1984-85, dir. strategic studies, 1986; divsn. mgr. Brit. Petroleum, Ltd., London, 1987-88; v.p., gen. mgr. U.S. gas bus. BP Exploration, Houston, 1989, v.p., gen. mgr. tech., 1990; v.p. BP Exploration, Anchorage, 1991—; pres., CEO BP Pipelines, Anchorage, 1991—; also bd. dirs. BP Pipelines; v.p. BP Exploration Inc. Mem. adv. bd. Providence Hosp. Anchorage. Avocations: running, weight lifting, reading. Office: B P Pipelines Inc 810 Oak Valley Houston TX 77024

NYBORG, LESTER PHIL, physician; b. Twin Groves, Idaho, May 4, 1925; s. Lester Thorsted and LaVernie Mildred (Hathaway) H.; m. LaWana Blanchard, Nov. 23, 1949; children: Jeffrey, Valeah, Vicki. BS, Utah State U., 1951; MD, Northwestern U., 1956; MPH, U. Calif., Berkeley, 1967. Diplomate Am. Bd. Preventive Medicine. Commd. med. officer, lt. USN, 1957, advanced through grades to lt. comdr., 1964; commd. major USAF, 1964, advanced through grades to col., 1970; intern LDS Hosp., Salt Lake City, 1957; resident USAF Sch. Aviation Medicine, 1968-69; chief profl. svcs. 9th Air Force, 1969-70; med. advisor Vietnamese USAF, Vietnam, 1970-71; ret. USAF, 1975; med. dir. Boise (Idaho) State U., 1976—. Decorated Bronze Star, Vietnamese Congressional medal Vietnamese Nat. Air Force, 1971. Mem. Ada County Med. Soc. Home: 660 Ballentine Ln Eagle ID 83616-4648 Office: Boise State U Boise ID 83725

NYCE, ROBERT EUGENE, state legislator, tax accountant; b. Allentown, Pa., Oct. 14, 1946; s. Preston Nyce and Flora Louise (Beck) Jones; m. Maria Irene Datta, Oct. 3, 1970; 1 child, Jennifer. BA in Acctg., Moravian Coll. Tax acct. Lehigh Portland Cement Co., 1970-72; mgr. credit, taxes & ins. Frick Co., 1973-75; sr. tax acct. Bethlehem Steel Corp., 1975-85; asst. v.p., tax dir. Chrysler First, Inc., 1985-90; mem. Ho. of Reps. Commonwealth of Pa., Harrisburg, 1990—; mem. edn. com., higher edn. & basic edn. subcoms., fin. com., game & fish, labor & industry, Gov.'s motor carrier adv. bd., 1991-92, 93-94, tuition acct. adv. program, 1991-92, 93-94. Mem. Northampton (Pa.) Sch. Bd., 1984-90, pres., 1987-89, v.p., 1986-87; ; mem. Bethlehem Area Vo-Tech Joint Com., 1984-90, chmn., 1986-87, vice chmn., 1985-86, 88-89; mem. East Allen Twp. Mcpl. Authority, 1979-84, former chmn. Served with U.S. Army, 1967-69. Mem. Masons, Star Grange, Am. Legion, Slate Belt C. of C., East Bath Rod & Gun Club, Pa. Fedn. Sportsmen. Republican. Lutheran. Avocations: fishing, tennis, skiing, cars. Home: 7416 Carol Ln Northampton PA 18067-9074 Office: House PO Box 147 Main Capitol Bldg Harrisburg PA 17120-0028

NYCKLEMOE, GLENN WINSTON, bishop; b. Fergus Falls, Minn., Dec. 8, 1936; s. Melvin and Bertha (Sumstad) N.; m. Ann Elizabeth Olson, May 28, 1960; children: Peter Glenn, John Winston, Daniel Thomas. BA, St. Olaf Coll., 1958; MDiv, Luther Theol. Sem., St. Paul, 1962; D of Ministry, Luth. Sch. Theology, Chgo., 1977. Ordained to ministry Am. Luth. Ch., 1962. Assoc. pastor Our Savior's Luth. Ch., Valley City, N.D., 1962-64; assoc. pastor Our Savior's Luth. Ch., Milw., 1964-67, co-pastor, 1967-73; sr. pastor Our Savior's Luth. Ch., Beloit, Wis., 1973-82, St. Olaf Luth. Ch., Austin, Minn., 1982-88; bishop Southeastern Minn. Synod, Evang. Luth. Ch. in am., Rochester, 1988—; bd. dirs. Luth. Social Svcs. of Minn., Mpls., Bd. of Social Ministries, St. Paul, Minn. Coun. Chs., Mpls. Mem. bd. regents St. Olaf Coll., Northfield, Minn., 1988—. Avocations: skiing, trap shooting, golf. Office: SE Minn Synod Evang Luth Ch Am Assist Heights Box 4900 Rochester MN 55903

NYCUM, SUSAN HUBBELL, lawyer. B.A., Ohio Wesleyan U., 1956; J.D., Duquesne U., 1960; postgrad., Stanford U. Bar: Pa. 1962, U.S. Supreme Ct. 1967, Calif. 1974. Sole practice law Pitts., 1962-65; designer, administr. legal research system U. Pitts., Aspen Systems Corp., Pitts., 1965-68; mgr. ops. Computer Ctr., Carnegie Mellon U., Pitts., 1968-69; dir. computer facility Computer Ctr., Stanford U., Calif., 1969-72, Stanford Law and Computer fellow, 1972-73; cons. in computers and law, 1973-74; sr. assoc. MacLeod, Fuller, Muir & Godwin, Los Altos, Los Angeles and London, 1974-75; ptnr. Chickering & Gregory, San Francisco, 1975-80; ptnr.-incharge high tech. group Gaston Snow & Ely Bartlett, Boston, NYC, Phoenix, San Francisco, Calif., 1980-86; mng. ptnr. Palo Alto office Kadison, Pfaelzer, Woodard, Quinn & Rossi, Los Angeles, Washington, Newport Beach, Palo Alto, Calif., 1986-87; sr. ptnr. Baker & McKenzie, Palo Alto, 1987—; trustee EDUCOM, 1978-81; mem. adv. com. for high tech. Ariz. State U. Law Sch., Santa Clara U. Law Sch., Stanford Law Sch., U. So. Calif. Law Ctr., law sch. Harvard U., U. Calif.; U.S. State Dept. del. OECD Conf. on Nat. Vulnerabilities, Spain, 1981; invited speaker Telecom, Geneva, 1983; lectr. N.Y. Law Jour., 1975—, Law & Bus., 1975—, Practicing Law Inst., 1975—; chmn. Office of Tech. Assessment Task Force on Nat. Info. Systems, 1979-80. Author:(with Bigelow) Your Computer and the Law, 1975, (with Bosworth) Legal Protection for Software, 1985, (with Collins and Gilbert) Women Leading, 1987; contbr. monographs, articles to profl. publs. Mem. Town of Portola Valley Open Space Acquisition Com., Calif., 1977; mem. Jr. League of Palo Alto, chmn. evening div., 1975-76. NSF and Dept. Justice grantee for studies on computer abuse, 1972—. Mem. ABA (sect. on sci. and tech. chmn. 1979-80, chmn. elect 1978-79), Internat. Bar Assn. (U.S. mem. computer com. of corps. sect.), Assn. Computing Machinery (mem. at large of council 1976-80, nat. lectr. 1977—, chmn. standing com. on legal issues 1975—, blue ribbon com. on rationalization of internat. proprietary rights protection on info. processing devel. in the '90s, 1990—), Computer Law Assn. (v.p. 1983-85, pres. 1986—, bd. dirs. 1995—), Calif. State Bar Assn. (founder first chmn. econs. of law sect., vice chmn. law and computers com.), Nat. Conf. Lawyers and Scientists (rep. ABA), Strategic Forum on Intellectual Property Issues in Software of NAS. Address: 35 Granada Ct Portola Valley CA 94028

NYDICK, DAVID, school superintendent; b. N.Y.C., Feb. 10, 1929; s. Irving and Minnie (Bilbom) N.; m. Gilda Pivnick, June 14, 1953; children: Leslie Ruth, Jay Scott. BA, NYU, 1950, MA, 1952, profl. Diploma, 1960, postgrad.—. Tchr. pub. schs., Great Neck, N.Y., 1954-60; prin. asst. supt. Princeton Pub. Schs., N.J., 1961-65; asst. supt. Jericho Pub. Schs. N.Y., 1965-68, supt., 1968-84; exec. dir. Guide Dog Found., Smithtown, N.Y., 1984-89; supt. Syosset (N.Y.) Pub. Schs., 1989-90, Bethpage (N.Y.) Pub. Schs., 1991—; assoc. prof. L.I. U., 1975—, Hofstra U., 1976—, Pace U., 1978—; asst. prof. Bklyn. Coll., 1979—; arbitrator Am. Arbitration Assn., Better Bus. Bur. Assn. Securities Dealers, N.Y. Stock Exchange, various N.Y. state agys. Syndicated columnist UPI, Copley News, DANY News, 1962—. Pres., East Plains Mental Health Ctr., 1964—. Served with U.S. Army, 1952-54. Recipient Edn. Achievement award NCCJ, 1975. Mem. N.Y.U. Alumni Assn. (pres. 1971-72), Am. Assn. Sch. Adminstrs., Ednl. Writers Assn., Overseas Press Club, Nat. Press Club, Masons. Home and Office: 22 Lesley Dr Syosset NY 11791-5298

NYDICK, ROBERT LINCOLN, JR., university educator; b. Phila., Mar. 28, 1957; s. Robert Lincoln Sr. and Christine (Papiro) N.; m. Susan Marie Karr; children: Robert Lincoln III, Gregory Streeper. BS, Phila. Coll. Textiles, 1978; MS, U. Pa., 1980; PhD, Temple U., 1985. Asst. prof. ops. rsch. Phila. Coll. of Textiles and Sci., Phila., 1980-87, MBA dir., 1986-87; asst. prof. mgmt. Villanova (Pa.) U., 1987—; cons. Quaker Constrn. Co., Montgomeryville, Pa., 1983-86, M.M.Reif & Co., Ivyland, Pa., 1983, Fraternal Order of Police, Phila., 1987. Author: (workbook) Production and Operations Management, 1989; contbr. articles to profl. jours. Explorer group leader Boy Scouts Am., Phila., 1985-86. Mem. Inst. Mgmt. Sci., Ops. Rsch. Soc. Am., Planning Forum (v.p. edn. 1986-87). Presbyterian. Avocation: softball. Home: 4003 Briar Ln Lafayette Hill PA 19444-1611 Office: Villanova U Bartley Hall Villanova PA 19085

NYE, EDWIN PACKARD, mechanical engineering educator; b. Atkinson, N.H., Jan. 29, 1920; s. Eben W. and Gertrude Florence (Dunn) N.; m. Persephone Fern Drumheller, Aug. 12, 1944; children: David Edwin, Sarah Leone, Benjamin Alfred. BS with high honor, U. N.H., 1941; ScM, Harvard U., 1947. Registered profl. engr., Conn. Service engr. Bailey Meter Co., Cleve., 1941-42; instr. mech. engring. U. N.H., 1942-44; project engr. NACA, 1944-46; from instr. to assoc. prof. mech. engring. Pa. State U., 1947-59; Halldon prof. Trinity Coll., Hartford, Conn., 1959-83; chmn. dept. engring. Trinity Coll., 1960-70, dean of faculty, 1970-79; pres. Charter Oak Coll., 1989; sec. Univ. Research Inst. Conn., 1964-68, pres., 1968-71, chmn., 1971-74; bd. dir. Hallden Machine Co.; chmn. coll. work Episcopal Diocese Conn., 1960-64. Co-author: Steam Power Plants, 1952, Power Plants, 1956, Thermal Engineering, 1959. Mem. bd. edn., Bloomfield, Conn., 1961-65; mem. State Bd. Acad. Awards, 1974—, dean faculty, 1979-83; corporator Hartford Public Library, 1978-82. Mem. ASME, Am. Soc. Engring. Edn. Conn. Acad. Sci. and Engring., Phi Kappa Phi, Pi Tau Sigma. Home: Bug Hill Rd Ashfield MA 01330

NYE, ERIC WILLIAM, English language educator; b. Omaha, July 31, 1952; s. William Frank and Mary Roberta (Lueder) N.; m. Carol Denison Frost, Dec. 21, 1980; children: Charles William, Ellen Mary. BA, St. Olaf Coll., 1974; MA, U. Chgo., 1976, PhD, 1983; postgrad., Queens' Coll.,

Cambridge, England, 1979-82. Tutor in coll. writing com. U. Chgo., 1976-79, teaching intern, 1978; supr., tutor in Am. Lit. Cambridge U., England, 1979-82; asst. prof. English U. Wyo., Laramie, 1983-89; assoc. prof. English U. Wyo., Laramie, Wyo., 1989—; v.p. bd. dirs. Plainview Tel. Co., Nebr.; hon. vis. fellow U. Edinburgh (Scotland) Inst. for Advanced Studies in the Humanities, 1987; guest lectr. NEH summer Inst., Laramie, Wyo., 1985, Carlyle Soc. of Edinburgh, 1987, Wordsworth summer Conf., Grasmere, Eng., 1988, cons. NEH. Contbr. articles and reviews to profl. jours. Mem. Am. Friends of Cambridge U.; elected mem. Wyo. Coun. for Humanities, 1992—, exec. com., 1993-94; mem. adv. bd. Wyo. Ctr. for the Book, 1995—. Named Nat. Merit Scholar St. Olaf Coll., 1970-74; recipient Grad. Fellowship, Rotary Found., 1979-80, grant U. Wyo., 1984-85, Am. Coun. of Learned Socs., 1988, Disting. Alumnus award, Lincoln (Neb.) E. High Sch., 1986. Mem. MLA (del. assembly 1991-93), Assn. for Documentary Editing, Bibliographical Soc. London, Assn. for Computers and the Humanities, Assn. for Literary and Linguistic Computing, Coleridge Soc. (life), Friends of Dove Cottage (life), Charles Lamb Soc., Carlyle Soc., Rsch. Soc. for Victorian Periodicals, The Victorians Inst., The Tennyson Soc., Penn Club (London), Queens' Coll. Club (Cambridge), Phi Beta Kappa (pres., v.p., sec. Wyo. chpt. 1988—). Home: 1495 Apache Dr Laramie WY 82070-6966 Office: U Wyo Dept English PO Box 3353 Laramie WY 82071-3353

NYE, ERLE ALLEN, utilities executive, lawyer; b. Ft. Worth, June 23, 1937; s. Ira Benjamen N.; m. Alice Ann Grove, June 5, 1959; children: Elizabeth, Pamela Nye Schneider, Erle Allen Jr., Edward Kyle, Johnson Scott. BEE, Tex. A&M U., 1959; JD, So. Meth. U., 1965. With Dallas Power & Light Co., 1960-75, v.p., 1975-80; exec. v.p. Tex. Utilities Co., Dallas, 1980-87, pres., 1987—; pres. Chaco Energy Co., Dallas, Tex. Utilities Mining Co., Dallas, Tex. Utilities Svcs., Inc., Dallas; chmn. bd., CEO Tex. Utilities Electric Co., Dallas, 1982—. Bd. dirs. Dallas Bar Found., 1980-83, Dallas Cen. Bus. Plan Com., 1980-83, Inroads/Dallas-Ft. Worth, Inc., 1984-88; trustee Baylor Dental Coll., Dallas, 1985—; mem. Dallas Together Forum, 1989—, Dallas Com. Fgn. Rels., 1991—. Served to 2d lt. U.S. Army, 1959-60. Mem. ABA, Dallas Bar Assn., Tex. State Bar Assn., Dallas C. of C. (bd. dirs. 1991—, vice chmn. 1992—). Methodist. Clubs: Engineers (pres. 1982-83), Northwood (Dallas). Home: 6924 Desco Dallas TX 75225-1716 Office: Tex Utilities Electric Co 2001 Bryan Tower Ste 1900 Dallas TX 75201-3005*

NYE, JOHN CALVIN, agricultural engineer, educator; b. Anthony, Kans., Mar. 24, 1945; s. Paul Everet and Alice Anna (Schmidt) N.; m. Gloria Tara Giese, Dec. 8, 1974; 1 child, Jaffe. BS in Agrl. Engring., Kans. State U., 1968; MS in Agrl. Engring., Purdue U., 1970, PhD, 1971. Registered profl. engr., La., Ind., Del. Asst. prof. Purdue U., West Lafayette, Ind., 1971-73, assoc. prof., then prof., 1975-84; chief agrl. permit team region V U.S. EPA, Chgo., 1974-75; prof., head agrl. engring. dept. La. State U., Baton Rouge, 1984-91; dean Coll. of Agrl. Scis. U. Del., Newark, 1991—; chair joint coun. food and agrl. sci. USDA; bd. dirs. Accreditation Bd. Engring. and Tech., Delmarva Poultry Industries, Inc. Bd. dirs. La. Sci. and Engring. Fair, Baton Rouge, 1986-91. 1st lt. U.S. Army, 1971. Recipient Disting. Svc. award La. Acad. Sci., 1990, Professionalism award La. Engring. Found., 1990. Mem. Am. soc. Engring. Educators, Am. Soc. Agrl. Engrs., Nat. Soc. Profl. Engrs. Home: 204 Wilson Rd Newark DE 19711-3629 Office: U Del Coll Agrl Scis 133 Townsend Hall Newark DE 19717-1303

NYE, SANDRA GAYLE, lawyer, psychiatric social worker, consultant; b. Chgo., Jan. 12, 1935; d. Harry A. and Mildred (Blumenthal) Iseberg; children: Elizabeth Robin, Jonathan Douglas. JD, DePaul U., 1962; MSW, Loyola U.-Chgo., 1974. Bar: Ill. 1963, U.S. Dist. Ct. (no. dist.) Ill. 1966, U.S. Supreme Ct. 1967. Ptnr., Nye and Nye, Chgo., 1962-74; dir. child and family law and psychiatry Inst. Juvenile Rsch., Chgo., 1974-78; dir. legal svcs. Jewish Family and Cmty. Svcs., Chgo., 1978-80; dir. Ill. Guardianship and Advocacy Commn., 1979-82; pres. Nye, Brent & Shoenberger, Ltd., Chgo., 1982-85, Law Offices of Nye & Assocs., Chgo., 1985—; asst. prof. psychiatry Abraham Lincoln Sch. Medicine, U. Ill., Chgo., 1978—; mem. faculty Inst. for Family Studies, Northwestern U. Sch. Medicine. Mem. com. on confidentiality Ill. Gov.'s Commn. to Revise the Mental Health Code, 1976-77; mem. Ill. Commn. on Children-Com. on Youth and the Law, 1975-79; mem. Oak Park (Ill.) Beautification Commn., 1969-73. Author: The Employee Assistance Law Answer Book. Mem. ABA (chmn. mental health law com., family law sect.), Ill. State Bar Assn., Chgo. Bar Assn. (chmn. juvenile law com., mental health law com.), Women's Bar Assn., Am. Soc. Law and Medicine, Am. Orthopsychiat. Assn., Am. Assn. Psychiat. Svcs. for Children. Home: 1150 N Lake Shore Dr Chicago IL 60611-1056 Office: 151 N Michigan Ave Ste 3314 Chicago IL 60601

NYE, THOMAS RUSSELL, retired drafting, reproduction and surveying company executive; b. Arlington, Mass., July 16, 1928; s. Russell Van Buren and Sibyl (Partridge) N.; m. Patricia Bentley, Dec. 14, 1951; children: Bradford V. B., Debra Nye Moran. AB, Brown U., 1950; MBA, Harvard U., 1952. Salesman Russell Nye Co., Inc., Boston, 1951-52; assignment dir., sr. assoc. Bruce Payne & Assocs., N.Y.C., 1953-59; with Keuffel & Esser Co., Morristown, N.J., 1959-84, exec. v.p., 1970, pres., 1970-82, chief exec. officer, 1971-82; bd. dirs. J.K. Adams Co., Inc.; arbitrator N.Y. Stock Exch., Nat. Assn. Securities Dealers. Author articles. Bd. dirs. United Way, Madison, N.J., 1968-73, Madison YMCA, 1970-72; mem. corp. United Way Morris County, 1973-91; mem. adv. bd. R & D Conn. N.J., 1980-88, Morristown Meml. Hosp. Corp., 1985-91. Lt. USAF, 1952-53. Mem. Assn. Reproduction Materials Mfrs. (pres. 1978, bd. dirs.), Am. Mgmt. Assn., NAM, Internat. Assn. Blueprinters and Allied Industries, Am. Congress Mapping and Surveying, Soc. Advancement Mgmt., Lake Sunapee Country Club, Boca Grande Club, Morris County Golf Club. Baptist. Home: PO Box 936 The Seasons New London NH 03257

NYE, W. MARCUS W., lawyer; b. N.Y.C., Aug. 3, 1945; s. Walter R. and Nora (McLaren) N.; m. Eva Johnson; children: Robbie, Stephanie, Philip, Jennifer. BA, Harvard U., 1967; JD, U. Idaho, 1974. Bar: Idaho 1974, U.S. Dist. Ct. Idaho 1974, U.S. Ct. Appeals (9th cir.) 1980. Ptnr. Racine, Olson, Nye, Cooper & Budge, Pocatello, Idaho, 1974—; vis. prof. law U. Idaho, Moscow, 1984; adj. prof. Coll. Engring. IDaho State U., 1993—. Recipient Alumni Svc. award U. Idaho, 1988. Fellow ABA (mem. ho. dels. 1988—, state chmn. ho. of dels. 1991—), Am. Bar Found. (stat. chmn. 1992—); mem. Am. Bd. Trial Advs., Am. Coll. Trial Lawyers, Idaho Bar Assn. (commr. 1985—, pres. bd. commrs. 1987-88), Idaho Def. Counsel Assn. (pres. 1982), Idaho State Centennial Found. (commr. 1985-90), 6th Dist. Bar Assn. (pres. 1982). Home: 173 S 15th Ave Pocatello ID 83201-4056 Office: Racine Olson Nye Cooper & Budge PO Box 1391 Pocatello ID 83204-1391

NYEMASTER, RAY, lawyer; b. Davenport, Iowa, Mar. 23, 1914; s. Jesse Ray and Clara Elva (Stucker) N.; children by previous marriage—Thomas Lee, Martha Merry; m. Martha Jane Backman Jaeger, Dec. 27, 1968; stepchildren—William John Jaeger, Judith Ann Jaeger Hand. Student, Cornell Coll., Mt. Vernon, Iowa, 1931-32; B.A., State U. Iowa, 1936, J.D., 1938. Bar: Iowa bar 1938. Since practiced in Des Moines; asso. partner firm Parrish, Guthrie, Colflesh & O'Brien, 1938-68; partner Nyemaster, Goode, McLaughlin, Emery & O'Brien, 1968—; dir. Vernon Co., Newton, Iowa, Central Life Ins. Co., Des Moines; Chmn. Iowa Aero. Commn., 1961-73. Bd. dirs. Des Moines Center Sci. and Industry; trustee Cornell Coll., Mt. Vernon, Iowa. Mem. Am., Iowa, Polk County bar assns., Des Moines C. of C. Clubs: Mason (Des Moines) (Shriner, 32 deg., Jester, royal impresario), Rotarian (Des Moines) (bd. dirs. Des Moines), Embassy (Des Moines), Wakonda (Des Moines). Home: 694 61st St Des Moines IA 50312-1226

NYERE, ROBERT ALAN, banker; b. Aberdeen, Wash., July 19, 1917; s. George Louis and Augusta (Draheim) N.; m. Jeanne Fortier, Nov. 8, 1941; children: Sharon L. Nyere Olson, Barbara J. Nyere Slevin. B.A., U. Wash. 1939; M.B.A., Harvard U., 1941; grad., Stonier Sch. Banking, Rutgers U., 1951. With First Nat. Bank of Boston, 1941-79, asst. mgr., mgr., v.p., 1948-58, v.p. 1958-69, sr. v.p., 1969-79; former dir. Mastercard Internat. Corp., FNBC Acceptance Corp., 1st La. Acceptance Corp., Boston Trust & Savs., Ltd.; cons. dir. Credit Card Services Corp., Springfield, 1981-83; mem. Sr. Corps Ret. Execs., SBA, 1980-85. Served from ensign to lt. USNR, 1942-46. Mem. Algonquin Club, The Lafayette Club, The Lexington Club, Masons (32 deg.), Shriners, Alpha Kappa Psi. Episcopalian. Home: 4922 Hartland Pky Lexington KY 40515-1109

NYERGES, ALEXANDER LEE, museum director; b. Rochester, N.Y., Feb. 27, 1957; s. Sandor Elek and Lena (Angeline) N.; 1 child, Robert Angeline. BA, George Washington U., 1979, MA, 1981. Intern The Octagon, Washington, 1976-79; archeol. asst. Smithsonian Instn., Washington, 1977, curatorial intern Nat. Mus. Am. History, 1978-79; adminstrv. asst. George Washington U., Washington, 1979-81; exec. dir. DeLand Mus. Art, Fla., 1981-85, Miss. Mus. Art, Jackson, 1985-92; dir. Dayton (Ohio) Art Inst., 1992—; grants panel Nat. Endowment for the Arts, 1988—; field surveyor Inst. Mus. Svcs., Washington, 1985-88, nat. review panel, 1990-92; treas., bd. dirs. Volusia County Arts Coun., Daytona Beach, Fla., 1983-85. Contbr. articles to profl. jours. Bd. dirs. West Volusia Hist. Soc., 1984-85; pres. Miss. Inst. Arts and Letters, 1987-88; trustee Cultural Arts Ctr., DeLand, 1984-85, Miami Valley Cultural Alliance, 1993—, Intermus. Conservation Lab., 1993—, Montgomery county arts and culture district, 1994—. U.S. Dept. Edn. scholar, 1973. Mem. DeLand Area C. of C. (bd. dirs., tourist adv. com. 1984-85), Assn. Art Mus. Dirs., Am. Assn. Mus. (SE regional rep. to non-print media com. 1983-85, nat. legis. com. 1986-93), Miss. Mus. Assn., Assn. Art Mus. Dirs., Southeastern Mus. Conf. (bd. dirs. 1991-92), Fla. Mus. Assn., Fla. Art Mus. Dirs. Assn., Cultural Roundtable (pres. 1993—), Ohio Mus. Assn. (trustee 1993—), Phi Beta Kappa. Republican. Presbyterian. Avocations: restoring old houses, gardening, music, writing, sports. Home: 113 1/2 Green St Dayton OH 45402 Office: Dayton Art Inst 456 Belmonte Park N Dayton OH 45405

NYGAARD, RICHARD LOWELL, federal judge; b. 1940. BS cum laude, U. So. Calif., 1969; JD, U. Mich. Mem. Orton, Nygaard & Dunlevy, 1972-81; judge Ct. Common Pleas, 6th Dist. Pa., Erie, 1981-88, U.S. Ct. Appeals (3d cir.) Pa., Erie, 1988—. Councilman Erie County, 1977-81. With USNR, 1958-64. Mem. Pa. Bar Assn., Erie County Bar Assn. Office: US Ct Appeals 3d Cir 500 First Nat Bank Bldg 717 State St Erie PA 16501-1341

NYGARD, HOLGER OLOF, English and folklore educator; b. Vasa, Finland, Feb. 24, 1921; came to U.S., 1953, naturalized, 1958; s. Victor N. and Maria (Bergman) Nygard; m. Margaret C. Rodger, Oct. 11, 1944; Jennifer K., Stephen V., Kerstin M., Karl Erik. B.A., U. B.C., Vancouver, 1944; M.A., U. Calif.-Berkeley, 1949, Ph.D., 1955. Instr. U. B.C., 1945-47; asst. prof. U. Kans., Lawrence, 1953-57; assoc. prof. U. Tenn., Knoxville, 1957-60; prof. English Duke U., Durham, N.C., 1960-90, prof. emeritus, 1990—. Author: (Chgo. Folklore prize 1959) The Ballad of Heer Halewijn, 1958. Fellow Am. Council Learned Socs., 1952; Guggenheim fellow, 1966; fellow Inst. Advanced Studies Humanities, U. Edinburgh, Scotland, 1979; NEH fellow, 1980. Mem. Am. folklore Soc., MLA. Home: 4015 Cole Mill Rd Durham NC 27712-2907

NYHAN, WILLIAM LEO, pediatrician, educator; b. Boston, Mar. 13, 1926; s. W. Leo and Mary (Cleary) N.; m. Christine Murphy, Nov. 20, 1948; children: Christopher, Abigail. Student, Harvard U., 1943-45; M.D., Columbia U., 1949; M.S., U. Ill., 1956, Ph.D., 1958; hon. doctorate, Tokushima U., Japan, 1981. Intern Yale U.-Grace-New Haven Hosp., 1949-50, resident, 1950-51, 53-55; asst. prof. pediatrics Johns Hopkins U., 1958-61, assoc. prof., 1961-63; prof. pediatrics, biochemistry U. Miami, 1963-69, chmn. dept. pediatrics, 1963-69; prof. U. Calif., San Diego, 1969—; chmn. dept. pediatrics U. Calif., 1969-86; mem. FDA adv. com. on Teratogenic Effects of Certain Drugs, 1964-70; mem. pediatric panel AMA Council on Drugs, 1964-70; mem. Nat. Adv. Child Health and Human Devel. Council, 1967-71; mem. research adv. com. Calif. Dept. Mental Hygiene, 1969-72; mem. med. and sci. adv. com. Leukemia Soc. Am., 1968-72; mem. basic adv. com. Nat. Found. March of Dimes, 1973-81; mem. Basil O'Connor Starter grants com., 1973-93; mem. clin. cancer program project rev. com. Nat. Cancer Inst., 1977-81; vis. prof. extraordinario U. del Salvador (Argentina), 1982. Author: (with E. Edelson) The Heredity Factor, Genes, Chromosomes and You, 1976, Genetic & Malformation Syndromes in Clinical Medicine, 1976, Abnormalities in Amino Acid Metabolism in Clinical Medicine, 1984, Diagnostic Recognition of Genetic Disease, 1987; editor: Amino Acid Metabolism and Genetic Variation, 1967, Heritable Disorders of Amino Acid Metabolism, 1974; mem. editorial bd. Jour. Pediatrics, 1964-78, King Faisal Hosp. Med. Jour., 1981-85, Western Jour. Medicine, 1974-86, Annals of Saudi Medicine, 1985-87, mem. editorial com. Ann. Rev. Nutrition, 1982-86; mem. editorial staff Med. and Pediatric Oncology, 1975-83. Served with U.S. Navy, 1944-46; U.S. Army, 1951-53. Nat. Found. Infantile Paralysis fellow, 1955-58; recipient Commemorative medallion Columbia U. Coll. Physicians and Surgeons, 1967. Mem. AAAS, Am. Fedn. Clin. Research, Am. Chem. Soc., Soc. Pediatric Research (pres. 1970-71), Am. Assn. Cancer Research, Am. Soc. Pharmacology and Exptl. Therapeutics, Western Soc. Pediatric Research (pres. 1976-77), N.Y. Acad. Sci., Am. Acad. Pediatrics (Borden award 1980), Am. Pediatric Soc., Am. Inst. Biol. Scis., Soc. Exptl. Biology and Medicine, Am. Soc. Clin. Investigation, Am. Soc. Human Genetics (dir. 1978-81), Inst. Investigaciones Citologicas (Spain; corr.), Biochem. Soc., Société Française de Pediatrie (corr.), Sigma Xi, Alpha Omega Alpha. Office: U Calif San Diego Dept Pediatrics # 0609A La Jolla CA 92093

NYHART, ELDON HOWARD, employee benefits consultant, lawyer; b. Lafayette, Ind., Jan. 17, 1927; s. Howard E. and Mabel (Keller) N.; m. Frieda Nyhart-Erni, Apr. 2, 1971; children: Maria, Malott, Sallie, Eldon Jr. AB cum laude, Princeton U., 1948; JD, Ind. U., 1952. Exec. v.p. The Nyhart Co., Inc., Indpls., 1953-55, pres., chief exec. officer, 1955-60, chief exec. officer, 1960-91, chmn. bd. dirs., 1991—; lectr. Purdue U., Lafayette, tchr. Ind. U. Grad. Sch. Bus., Bloomington, dir. Midwest Pension Conf. Contbr. articles to profl. jour. Life trustee Indpls. Mus. Art, bd. govs., 1990—; bd. dirs. Ind. Swiss Found., pres. 1991—, Ind. State Symphony Soc., 1990—, Eiteljorg Mus., 1990, Contemporary Art Soc., 1991—, Friends of Herron Gallery, 1990—; del. White House Conf. on Aging. Mem. ABA, Internat. Bar Assn., Ind. Bar Assn., Assn. Pvt. Pension and Welfare Plans, trustee 1987-91, Am. Judicature Soc., Pension Conf., Woodstock Club, Chgo. Racquet Club, Univ. Club (Indpls.), Princeton Club (N.Y.). Episcopalian. Home: 7468 Lions Head Dr Apt D Indianapolis IN 46260-3457 Office: Nyhart Co Inc 3515 N Washington Blvd Indianapolis IN 46205-3787

NYHUS, LLOYD MILTON, surgeon, educator; b. Mt. Vernon, Wash., June 24, 1923; s. Lewis Guttorm and Mary (Shervem) N.; m. Margaret Goldie Sheldon, Nov. 25, 1949; children: Sheila Margaret, Leif Torger. B.S., Pacific Luth. Coll., 1945; M.D., Med. Coll. Ala., 1947; Honoris Doctoris Causa, Aristotelian U., Thessalonika, Greece, 1968, Uppsala U., Sweden, 1974, U. Chihuahua, Mex., 1975, Jagallonian U., Cracow, Poland, 1980, U. Gama Filho, Rio de Janeiro, 1983, U. Louis Pasteur, Strasbourg, France, 1984, U. Athens, 1989. Diplomate Am. Bd. Surgery (chmn. 1974-76). Intern King County Hosp., Seattle, 1947-48; resident in surgery King County Hosp., 1948-55; practice medicine specializing in surgery Seattle, 1956-67, Chgo., 1967—; instr. surgery U. Wash., Seattle, 1954-56; asst. prof. U. Wash., 1956-59, assoc. prof., 1959-64, prof.; Warren H. Cole prof., head dept. surgery U. Ill. Coll. Medicine, 1967-89, emeritus head, 1989—, prof. emeritus, 1993; emeritus surgeon-in-chief U. Ill. Hosp.; sr. cons. surgeon Cook County, West Side VA, Hines (Ill.) VA hosps.; cons. to Surgeon Gen. NIH, 1965-69. Author: Surgery of the Stomach and Duodenum, 1962, 5th edit. (name changed to Surgery of the Esophagus, Stomach and Small Intestine), 1995, Abdominal Pain: A Guide to Rapid Diagnosis, 1969, 2d edit., 1995, Manual of Surgical Therapeutics, 1969, latest rev. edit., 1993, Mastery of Surgery, 1984, 2d edit., 1992, Surgery Ann., 1970-93, Treatment of Shock, 1970, 2d rev. edit., 1986, Surgrey of the Small Intestine, 1987; editor-in-chief Rev. of Surgery, 1967-77; editor-in-chief Current Surgery, 1978-90, emeritus editor, 1991—; assoc. editor Quar. Rev. Surgery, 1958-61; mem. editl. bd. Am. Jour. Digestive Diseases, 1961-67, Scandinavian Jour. Gastroenterology, 1966—, Am. Surgeon, 1967-89, Jour. Surg. Oncology, 1969—, Archives Surgery, 1977-86, World Jour. Surgery; contbr. articles to profl. jours. Served to lt. M.C. USNR, 1944-46, 50-52. Decorated Order of Merit (Poland); postdoctoral fellow USPHS, 1952-53; recipient M. Shipley award So. Surg. Assn., 1967, Rovsing medal Danish Surg. Soc., 1973; Disting. Faculty award U. Ill Coll. Medicine, 1983, Disting. Alumnus award Med. Coll. Ala., 1984, Disting. Alumnus award U. Wash., 1993; Guggenheim fellow, 1955-56. Fellow ACS (1st v.p. 1987-88), Royal Soc. Medicine, Assn. Surgeons Gt. Brit. and Ireland (hon.), Royal Coll. Surgeons Eng. (hon.), Royal Coll. Surgeons, Ireland (hon.), Royal coll. Surgeons Edinburgh (hon.); mem. Am. Gastroent. Assn., Am. Physiol. Soc., Pacific Coast Surg. Assn., Am. Surg. Assn. (recorder 1976-81, 1st v.p. 1989-90), Western Surg. Assn., Central Soc. Clin. Research, Chgo. Surg. Soc. (pres. 1974), Central Surg. Assn. (pres. 1984), Seattle Surg. Soc., St. Paul

Surg. Soc. (hon.), Kansas City Surg. Soc. (hon.), Inst. Medicine Chgo., Internat. Soc. Surgery (pres. U.S. sect. 1986-88, pres. 34th World Congress, 1991, internat. pres. 1991-93), Internat. Soc. of Surgery Found. (sec. treas. 1992—), Collegium Internat. Chirurgiae Digestivae (pres. III world congress Chgo. 1974, internat. pres. 1978-84), Soc. for Surgery Alimentary Tract (sec. 1969-73, pres. 1974), Soc. Clin. Surgery, Soc. Surg. Chairmen, Soc. U. Surgeons (pres. 1967), Deutschen Gesellschaft für Chirurgie (corr.), Polish Assn. Surgeons (hon.), L'Academie de Chirurgie (France) (corr.), Swiss Surg. Soc. (hon.), Brazilian Coll. Surgeons (hon.), Acad. Medicine France (hon.), Acad. Medicine Brazil (hon.), Asian Surg. Assn. (hon.), Surg. Biology Club, Warren H. Cole Soc. (pres. 1981), Japan Surg. Soc. (hon.), Assn. Gen. Surgeons of Mex. (hon.), Columbian Surg. Soc. (hon.), Internat. Fedn. Surg. Colls. (hon. treas. 1992—), Sigma Xi, Alpha Omega Alpha, Phi Beta Pi. Home: 310 Maple Row Winnetka IL 60093-1036 Office: M/C 958 840 S Wood St Chicago IL 60612-7317

NYIRJESY, ISTVAN, obstetrician, gynecologist; b. Budapest, Hungary, Nov. 14, 1929; came to U.S., 1954, naturalized, 1960; s. Sandor D. and Margit (Bertalan) N.; m. Michelle Shoepp, June 16, 1956; children—Francis, Paul, Christine. M.D., Catholic U. Louvain, Belgium, 1955. Diplomate: Am. Bd. Ob-Gyn. Intern Cath. U. Louvain and Little Co. Mary Hosp., Evergeen Park, Ill., 1954-55; resident in gynecology obstetrics, 1960-63; chief obstetrical research Nat. Naval Med. Center, Bethesda, Md., 1966-68; ret., 1968; practice medicine specializing in Ob-Gyn Bethesda, 1968—; clin. prof. Ob-Gyn Georgetown U., 1968—; cons. NIH, 1977-88, FDA, 1977-88. Lit. editor Breast Disease: contbr. articles to med. jours.; author: Prevention and Detection of Gynecologic and Breast Cancer, 1994. Pres., Internat. Found. for Gynecol. Cancer Detection and Prevention, 1993—. Officer M.C. USN, 1956-68; advanced through grades to comdr. Recipient Sword of Hope pin Am. Cancer Soc., 1973, Vicennial medal Georgetown U., 1988. Fellow ACOG (Host award 1964), Internat. Coll. Surgeons; mem. Montgomery County (Md.) Med. Soc. (chmn. profl. edn. com. 1971-72), Gynecol. Soc. Study of Breast Disease (past pres.), Assn. Profs. Ob-Gyn., Am. Fertility Soc., Washington Gynecol. Soc. (v.p. 1993-94, 1st v.p. 1994-95, pres.-elect). Office: 5301 Westbard Cir Ste 5 Bethesda MD 20816-1425

NYKROG, PER, French literature educator; b. Copenhagen, Nov. 1, 1925; came to U.S., 1979; s. Kai S. Nathanson and Karen E. (Olsen) Nykrog; m. Vibeke H. Rasmussen, 1951 (dec. 1977); children: Thomas, Jakob; m. Usha Saksena Nilsson, Jan. 2, 1981. Grad., U. Copenhagen, 1952; PhD, U. Aarhus, Denmark, 1957. Asst. prof. U. Aarhus, 1953-57, prof., 1957-79; prof. French lang. and lit. Harvard U., Cambridge, Mass., 1979—. Author: Les Fabliaux, 1957, La Pensée de Balzac, 1965, L'Amour et la Rose, 1986, La Recherche du Don perdu, 1987. Mem. Royal Soc. Scis. Denmark. Home: 243 Concord Ave Cambridge MA 02138-1360 Office: Harvard U Dept Romance Langs Boylston Hall Cambridge MA 02138

NYKVIST, SVEN VILHEM, cinematographer; b. Moheda, Sweden, Dec. 3, 1922; s. Gustaf Nathanael and Gerda Emilia (Nilson) N.; 1 son, Carl-Gustaf. Student, Stockholm Photog. Sch.; hon. doctorate, Am. Film Inst., 1991. Asst. cameraman Stockholm, 1941-44; co-owner film prodn. co. Josephson-Nykvist, Stockholm. Dir. photography over 100 feature films, including 22 films directed by Ingmar Bergman, 1945—; cinematographer: (films) Sawdust and Tinsel, 1953, The Virgin Spring, 1960, Winter Light, 1962, Karin Mansdotter, The Silence, 1963, Loving Couples, 1964, Persona, 1966, Hour of the Wolf, 1968, One Day in the Life of Ivan Denisovich, 1971, The Dove, 1973, Cries and Whispers, 1973, Scenes from a Marriage, 1973, Black Moon, 1975, The Magic Flute, 1975, Face to Face, 1976, The Tenant, 1976, The Serpent's Egg, 1977, Autumn Sonata, 1978, King of the Gypsies, 1978, Pretty Baby, 1978, Hurricane, 1979, Starting Over, 1979, Willie and Phil, 1980, The Postman Always Rings Twice, 1981, Cannery Row, 1982, Fanny and Alexander, 1983, Star 80, 1983, Swann in Love, 1984, Agnes of God, 1985, Dream Lover, 1986, The Sacrifice, 1986, The Unbearable Lightness of Being, 1988 (nominated Oscar award), Brothers, 1988, segment of film New York Stories, 1988-89, Crimes and Misdemeanors, 1989, Sleepless in Seattle, 1992, Him, 1993, Gilbert Grape, 1993, Him, 1993, Night Before Christmas, 1993, Kirsten Laviansdatter, 1994; (TV) Bergman, 1995; dir. film The Vine Bridge, 1965; dir., cinematographer The Ox, 1991, Charlie, 1992; dir. With Honors, 1993; author: Resan Till Lambarene. Recipient Acad. award Am. Acad. Motion Picture Arts and Scis. for Cries and Whispers, 1974, for Fanny and Alexander, 1984, Caesar French Acad. award, Swedish Acad. award, nominee for best fgn. film for the Ox, 1991, Doctorate Am. Film Inst., 1991. Mem. Swedish Film Acad., Am. Soc. Cinematographers, Svenska Teaterforbundet. Office: care Milton Forman 433 N Palm Dr Beverly Hills CA 90210

NYLANDER, JANE LOUISE, museum director; b. Cleve., Jan. 27, 1938; d. James Merritt and Jeannette (Crosby) Cayford; m. Daniel Harris Giffen, Nov. 30, 1963 (div. 1970); children: Sarah Louise, Thomas Harris; m. Richard Conrad Nylander, July 8, 1972; 1 child, Timothy Frost. AB, Brown U., 1959; MA, U. Del., 1961; postgrad., Attingham (Eng.) Summer Sch., 1970; PhD (hon.), New England Coll., 1994. Curator Hist. Soc. York (Pa.) County, 1961-62, N.H. Hist. Soc., Concord, 1962-69; instr. New England Coll., Henniker, N.H., 1964-65, Monadnock Community Coll., Peterborough, N.H., 1966-69; curator of textiles and ceramics Old Sturbridge (Mass.) Village, 1969-85; adj. assoc. prof. Boston U., 1978-85; sr. curator Old Sturbridge Vill., 1985-86; dir. Strawbery Banke Mus., Portsmouth, N.H., 1986-92, Soc. Preservation New England Antiquities, Boston, 1992-93; pres. Soc. for Preservation of New Eng. Antiquities, 1993—; adj. asst. prof. U. N.H., Durham, 1987-92; adj. prof. art history and Am. studies Boston U., 1993—; trustee Worcester (Mass.) Hist. Mus., 1978-84, Hist. Deerfield (Mass.), Inc., 1981-94, Hist. Mass. Inc., 1991-93, Decorative Arts Trust, 1991—, Portsmouth Athenaeum, 1988-90, Dublin Seminar Soc. N.H., 1988-92; mem. adv. bd. Concord (Mass.) Mus., 1986-94, Wentworth-Coolidge Commn., 1991—, John Nicholas Brown Ctr. for Am. Studies, Providence, 1995—; mem. adv. bd. dept. Am. decorative arts Mus. Fine Arts, Boston, 1971—; mem. coun. Colonial Soc. Mass., 1993—; cons. in field. Author: Fabrics for Historic Buildings, 4th edit., 1990, Our Own Snug Fireside: Images of the New England Home 1760-1860, 1993, paperback edit., 1994; mem. editorial bd. Hist. New Hampshire; 1993—; contbr. numerous articles to profl. jours. Mem. adv. bd. New Eng. Heritage Ctr., 1993—; active State House Adv. Com., Boston, 1984-85, Gov.'s Coun. for Wentworth Coolidge Mansion, Concord, 1964-66; mem. Com. for Preservation of N.H. State Flags, 1989-92. Recipient Charles F. Montgomery Prize Decorative Arts Soc., 1985. Mem. Am. Antiquarian Soc., Am. Assn. for State and Local History, Nat. Trust Hist. Preservation, Royal Oak Assn., Portsmouth Athenaeun, New Eng. Mus. Assn., Trustees of Reservations, Soc. Winterthur Fellows, Hist. Mass., Soc. Preservation of N.H. Forests, N.H. Audubon Soc., N.H. Humanities Coun., New Eng. Hist. Genealogy Soc., Hist. Houses Trust NSW, Costume Soc. Am. (bd. dirs. 1987-83); Dublin Seminar, Nat. Soc. Colonial Dames in N.H. (bd. dirs. 1967-73), Nat. Soc. Colonial Dames in Mass. (courtesy), Brown Club N.H. (trustee 1988-93). Episcopalian. Home: 17 Franklin St Portsmouth NH 03801-4501 Office: Soc Preservation New England Antiquities 141 Cambridge St Boston MA 02114

NYMAN, CARL JOHN, JR., university dean and official; b. New Orleans, Oct. 21, 1924; s. Carl John Sr. and Dorothy (Kraft) N.; m. Betty Spigelberg, July 15, 1950; children: Gail Katherine, John Victor, Nancy Kraft. B.S., Tulane U., 1944, M.S., 1945; Ph.D., U. Ill., 1948. Jr. technologist Shell Oil Co., Wilmington, Cal., 1944; instr. chemistry U. Ill., 1948, Wash. State U., Pullman, 1948-50; asst. prof. Wash. State U., 1950-55, assoc. prof., 1955-61, prof., 1961-88, prof. emeritus, 1988—, vice provost for rsch., 1981-86, acting dean grad. sch., 1968-69; dean, 1969-87; dean and vice provost emeritus for rsch. grad. sch. Wash. State U., 1988—; vis. asst. prof. Tulane U., summer, 1950, adj. prof., 1986-87; vis. fellow Cornell U., 1959-60, Imperial Coll. Sci. and Tech., 1966-67; vis. fellow Swiss Fed. Inst. Tech., Zurich, 1973; chmn. Acad. Coun. Ctr. Grad. Study, Richland Wash., 1968-70, N.W. Assn. Colls. and Univs. for Sci., 1969; mem. Gov.'s Adv. Coun. on Nuclear Energy, 1968-70, Washington State High Tech. Coord. Bd., 1984-86. Author: (with G.B. King and J.A. Weyh) Problems for General Chemistry and Qualitative Analysis, 4th edit, 1980, (with R.E. Homm) Chemical Equilibrium, 1967, (with W.E. Newton) Procs. of the 1st Internat. Conf. Nitrogen Fixation; Contbr. articles to profl. jours. Mem. Am. Chem. Soc. (chmn. Wash.-Idaho border sect. 1961-62), AAAS, Sigma Xi, Phi Lambda Upsilon, Alpha Chi Sigma, Omicron Delta Kappa. Home: East 1419 Cambridge Ln Spokane WA 99203

NYMAN, GEORGIANNA BEATRICE, painter; b. Arlington, Mass., June 11, 1930; d. Daniel Eugene Nyman and Irene Krans (Müller) Lombardi; m. David Aronson, June 10, 1956; children: Judith, Benjamin, Abigail. Diploma, Boston Mus. Sch. Art., 1952, student, 1952-54; postgrad., Longy Sch. Music, Cambridge, Mass., 1965-73. Portraits displayed in Brookline (Mass.) Hosp., Inst. Critical Care Medicine, U. Pitts., McClosky Inst. Voice Therapy, Boston, U.S. Supreme Ct., Washington, NewEng. Sch. of Law, Boston, 1991, Milton (Mass.) Acad., Boston Acad. Music; group exhbns. include Shore Studio Gallery, Boston, 1960, 61, Lee Nordness Gallery N.Y.C., 1963, Copley Soc. Boston, 1980, Nat. Acad. Design, N.Y.C., 1990; solo exhbns. include Nancy Lincoln Gallery, Brookline, 1990; represented in permanent collections Rose Art Mus., Brandeis U., U. Pitts. Sch. Medicine; commd. portraits include justice Sandra Day O'Connor, Mr. and Mrs. Pieh--headmaster Milton Acad., 1992, Justice Harry A. Blackmun, 1993, Julie Harris Am. actress, 1994, Hon. James R. Lawton, 1994, Richard Conrad, opera singer, dir. Boston Acad. Music, 1994, Justice Clarence Thomas, 1995, Justice Anthony M. Kennedy, 1995, David Leisner, 1995. Jurist Art and Mental Illness--An Itinerary Boston U., 1989; active in LeMoyne Found., Fla., 1989. Recipient Boit prize, 1951, cert. of merit NAD, 1992; Kate Morse fellow Boston Mus. Fine Arts, 1953. Mem. Women's Indsl. Inst. (life), Mass. Soc. Mayflower Descendants. Avocations: music, vocal recitals. Home and Studio: 137 Brimstone Ln Sudbury MA 01776-3203 also: RR 2, Cornwall, PE Canada C0A 1HO

NYMAN, MICHAEL LAWRENCE, composer; b. London, Eng., Mar. 23, 1944; s. Mark and Jeanette N.; m. Aet Toome, May 16, 1970; 2 children. Attended, King's Coll., London, 1964-67; B.Mus., Royal Acad. of Music, 1965; attended, Conservatoire and Folklore Inst., Bucharest, 1965-66. Music critic Spectator, New Statesman, The Listener, 1968-78; founder Michael Nyman Band, 1977. Music dir., composer, performer: (film scores) 1-100, 1977, A Walk Through H, 1977, Tom Philips, 1977, Vertical Features Remake, 1978, The Falls, 1980, Brimstone and Treacle, 1982, Frozen Music, 1983, Nelly's Version, 1983, The Draughtsman's Contract, 1983, The Cold Room, 1984, L'ange frenetique, 1985, A Zed and Two Noughts, 1985, Ballet Mechanique, 1986, The Disputation, 1986, Photographic Exhibits, 1987, Drowning By Numbers, 1988, La Traversee de Paris, 1989, The Cook, the Thief, His Wife, Her Lover, 1989, Monsieur, 1989, Prospero's Books, 1991, Les enfants volants, 1991, Le Mari de la Coiffeuse, 1991, The Piano, 1993; musical performer, composer: (theatre) The Masterwork/Award-Winning Fishknife, 1979, , (ballets) Portraits in Reflection, 1985, And Do They Do, 1986, (dance works) The Fall of Icarus, 1989, Garden Party, 1990; composer: (ballets) A Broken Set of Rules, 1984, Touch the Earth, 1987, (dance works) Miniatures, 1989, (operas) The Man Who Mistook His Wife for a Hat, 1986, La Princesse de Milan, 1991, Letters, Riddles and Writs, 1992, (TV spls.) Act of God, 1980, The Man Who Mistook His Wife for a Hat, 1987, Fairly Secret Army Series 2, 1987, Dancing in Numbers, 1988, Touch the Earth, 1988, Out of the Ruins, 1989, Death in the Seine, 1989, Men of Steel, 1990, Letters, Riddles and Writs, 1991, The Final Score, 1992, The Fall of Icarus, 1992; author: (music criticism) Experimental Music: Cage and Beyond, 1975; recs. include The Convertibility of Lute Strings, 1993, For John Cage, 1993, Goodbye Frankie, Goodbye Benny, 1993. Office: Gorfaine Schwartz Agency 3301 Barham Blvd Ste 201 Los Angeles CA 90068*

NYMAN, P. L., lawyer; b. Clermont, Iowa, May 18, 1924; s. Jens Christian and Minnie Amalia (Osmundson) N.; m. Charmaine Ann Petersen, Dec. 2, 1951 (div. 1979); children: Michel, Candace, Kimberly, Christopher, Jon (dec.); m. Anne Barrett McDermott, Feb. 15, 1992. BA, U. Iowa, 1949, JD, 1951. Bar: Iowa 1951. Assoc. Louis S. Goldberg, Sioux City, Iowa, 1951-57; ptnr. Goldberg, Nymann & Probasco, Sioux City, 1957-64; v.p., gen. counsel IBP, Inc., Dakota City, Nebr., 1964-72; pvt. practice Sioux City, 1972-74, 83-87; ptnr. Jacobs, Gaul, Nymann & Green, Sioux City, 1974-83, Nymann & Kohl, Sioux City, 1987—. Chmn., Civil Svc. Commn., 1977-79; bd. dirs. United Way Siouxland, 1979-85. With AUS, 1943-46. Mem. ABA, Iowa Bar Assn., Am. Arbitration Assn., Rotary. Republican. Avocations: travel, boating, music. Home: PO Box 1760 Lake Ozark MO 65049-1760 Office: Nymann & Kohl 383390 Orpheum Electric Sioux City IA 51101

NYQUIST, JOHN DAVIS, retired radio manufacturing company executive; b. Peoria, Ill., May 28, 1918; s. Eliud and Linnea (Widen) N.; m. Alice Schmidt, June 5, 1942; 1 child, Sarah Lynn. B.S. in Mech. Engring, U. Ill., 1941. With Collins Radio Co., Cedar Rapids, Iowa, 1941—; v.p., gen. mgr. Iowa region Collins Radio Co., Cedar Rapids, 1965-69; v.p. operations Collins Radio Co., 1969-70, sr. v.p., 1970-73, also dir.; ret., 1973; cons. Rockwell-Collins; dir. Norwest Bank Iowa N.A. (formerly Peoples Bank & Trust Co.), Cedar Rapids. Bd. dirs. Am. Cancer Soc., YMCA, St. Lukes Hosp. Recipient award for outstanding achievement Am. Inst. Indsl. Engrs., 1966, Indsl. Engring. award, 1969, Coll. Engring. Alumni Honor award, 1977; both U. Ill.). Mem. Iowa Mfrs. Assn., Am. Mgmt. Assn., Am. Inst. Indsl. Engrs., IEEE, Cedar Rapids C. of C. (dir.). Club: Cedar Rapids Country. Home: 3279 Jordans Grove Rd Springville IA 52336-9786

NYQUIST, ROBERT, sugar company executive. Vice chmn. Am. Crystal Sugar Co., Moonhead, Minn. Office: Am Crystal Sugar Co 101 3rd St N Moorhead MN 56560-1952

NYQUIST, THOMAS EUGENE, consulting business executive, mayor; b. Froid, Mont., June 20, 1931; s. Richard Theodore and Lydia (Baker) N.; m. Corinne Elaine Johnson, Dec. 22, 1956; children: Jonathan Eugene, Lynn Marie Nyquist Bergstrausser. BA, Macalester Coll., 1956; MA, U. Mont., 1958; PhD, Northwestern U., 1966. Prof. SUNY, New Paltz, 1968-76; adminstr. cen. div. SUNY, Albany, 1976-90; pres. Nyquist Assocs., New Paltz, N.Y., 1991—; mem. adv. bd. George Washington's Hdqrs., Newburgh, N.Y., 1980-92; acad. dir. N.Y. Edn. Dept., Kenya, 1982; head del. House of Peace and Friendship/Village of New Paltz delegation, St. Petersburg, Russia, 1992. Author: (monograph) Urban Africans in South Africa, 1977, (book) African Middle Class Elite, 1983. Mem. Ulster County Legislature, 1976-79; dep. mayor Village of New Paltz, 1983-87, mayor, 1987—; chmn. New Paltz Centennial Com., 1986-87; bd. dirs. Ulster Region Credit Union, Kingston, N.Y., 1976-87, Partnership in Svc. Learning, 1985—, Ulster Performing Arts Ctr., 1978-82, Friends of Cuttington Coll., Liberia, 1994—; treas. Lower Hudson Conf., 1988, 89-90, 91-92. With U.S. Army, 1952-54. Fellow SUNY, South Africa, 1975; Ford Found. grantee, 1986. Mem. African Studies Assn., N.Y. African Studies Assn. (exec. bd. dirs. 1973—, co-editor newsletter 1974—), Am. Polit. Sci. Assn. Democrat. Avocations: hiking, cross county skiing. Home: 62 S Chestnut St New Paltz NY 12561-1936 Office: Office of Mayor Village Hall 25 Plattekill Ave New Paltz NY 12561-1918

NYREN, NEIL SEBASTIAN, publisher, editor; b. Boston, June 13, 1948; s. Karl Edwin and Dorothy Elizabeth (Smith) N.; m. Lois Miriam Sharfman, Oct. 11, 1970; 1 child, Alexander. B.A., Brandeis U. Editor Random House Pubs., N.Y.C., 1974-77, Arbor House Pubs., N.Y.C., 1977-78; exec. editor Atheneum Pubs., N.Y.C., 1978-84; sr. editor G.P. Putnam's Sons Pub., N.Y.C., 1984-86, editor-in-chief, 1986—, pub., 1989—. Democrat. Jewish. Office: G P Putnam's Sons 200 Madison Ave New York NY 10016-3903

NYROP, DONALD WILLIAM, airline executive; b. Elgin, Nebr., Apr. 1, 1912; s. William A. and Nellie (Wylie) N.; m. Grace Cary, Apr. 19, 1941; children: Nancy, William, Karen, Kathryn. A.B., Doane Coll., 1934; LL.B., George Washington U., 1939. Bar: D.C. 1938. Atty. Gen. Counsel's Office, CAA, Washington, 1939-41; exec. officer to chmn. CAB, 1942, chmn., 1952; rep. U.S. airlines; mem. ofcl. U.S. delegations Internat. Civil Aviation Orgn. Assemblies, 1946, 47; dep. adminstr. for ops. CAA, 1948-50, adminstr., 1950-51; chmn. CAB, 1951-52; pres. Northwest Airlines, Inc., 1954-78. Served with Air Transport Command USAAF, 1942-46. Decorated Legion of Merit. Clubs: Minneapolis, Minnesota. Home: 4505 Golf Ter Minneapolis MN 55424-1510

NYSTRAND, RAPHAEL OWENS, university dean, educator; b. Maryville, Mo., Nov. 6, 1937; s. Phillip Owens and Emily (Martin) M.; m. Suzanne Rose Duval, Apr. 1, 1961; children: Kathryn Lee, Kristin Sue. B.A., Cornell Coll., 1959; M.A.T., Johns Hopkins U., 1960; Ph.D., Northwestern U., 1966. Tchr. Lyons Twp. High Sch., La Grange, Ill., 1960-64; research assoc. Research Council of Great Cities Program for Sch. Improvement, Chgo., 1965-66; asst. prof. Coll. Edn., Ohio State U., Columbus, 1967-69, assoc. prof., 1969-71, prof., chmn. dept., 1972-78; dean Sch. Edn., U. Louisville, 1978—, prof., 1978—; sec. edn. and humanities cabinet Commonweatlh of Ky., 1984 (on leave); postdoctoral fellow U. Chgo., 1966-67; vis. lectr., 1967; vis. prof. U. Victoria, B.C., Can., 1977; cons. various sch. dists., state agys.; v.p. Holmes Group, 1990—; mem. Nat. Policy Bd. for Ednl. Adminstrn., 1991-93, Nat. Coun. Accreditation Tchr. Edn. State Policy Bd., 1994—. Co-author: The Organization and Control of American Schools, 6th edit., 1990, Introduction to Educational Administration, 6th edit., 1983; co-editor: Educational Administration: The Developing Decades, 1977, Strategies for Educational Change, 1981. Trustee Columbus Met. Sch. 1974-78, Fairmount Fund, 1980—, Louisville Youth Choir, 1983-85, Louisville Art Gallery, 1985-87, Wesley Comty. House, 1986-90, Stage One, 1989-91, Ky. Derby Festival, 1990-92; adv. bd. Inst. Creative Learning, Inc. Louisville, 1980-90, Jr. League Louisville, 1984-87, Gov.'s Sch. for Arts, 1986-87; mem. Ky. Edn. Profl. Stds. Bd., 1993—. Mem. Am. Ednl. Rsch. Assn., Nat. Soc. Study Edn., Phi Delta Kappa. Methodist. Home: 3015 Springcrest Dr Louisville KY 40241-2755 Office: U Louisville Belknap Campus Louisville KY 40292

NYSTROM, HAROLD CHARLES, lawyer, labor consultant; b. White, S.D., Apr. 6, 1906; s. Charles Alfred and Augusta Cornelia (Olson) N.; m. Ruth Greenwood, Sept. 30, 1931 (dec. Jan. 1974); children: Nancy Ann Nystrom Railton, Erik Linfred; m. Martha Ann Harper Pattison, Oct. 13, 1980. Student, S.D. State Sch. Mines and Tech., 1922-23; AB cum laude, U. S.D., 1926; JD with honors, George Washington U., 1931. Bar: S.D. 1931, U.S. Supreme Ct. 1947. Asst. reading room Library of Congress, Washington, 1927-31; ptnr. Nystrom & Nystrom, Rapid City, S.D., 1931-35; editor Am. Jurisprudence Lawyers Coop. Pub. Co., Rochester, N.Y., 1935-41; br. and sect. chief, acting asst. solicitor for legis. and gen. legal services, asst. solicitor U.S. Dept. Labor, Washington, 1941-58, dep. solicitor, 1958-59, acting solicitor, 1959-61, dep. solicitor, 1961-62, assoc. solicitor, 1962-74; pvt. practice, cons. fed. labor standards Bethesda and Rockville, Md., 1975—; lectr. Labor Law Inst., Southwestern Legal Found., Dallas, 1960, Banking Law Inst., N.Y.C., 1967; speaker sect. labor law Assn. Bar City N.Y., 1967, Labor Relations Inst., Atlanta Lawyers Found., 1969, 73. Contbr. articles to legal publs. Atty. City of New Underwood, S.D., 1934; sec.-treas. Citizen's Com., Oakmont, Md., 1950-59; bd. dirs. Fenwick Island (Del.) Soc. Homeowners, 1974-75; deacon local Presbyn. Ch. Recipient cert. of appreciation Employment Standards Adminstrn., 1975. Mem. ABA (vice chmn. agy. liaison com. adminstrv. law sect. 1960-73), Fed. Bar Assn. (speaker BNA Labor Law briefing conf. 1967), Tenn. Bar Assn. (hon. life mem. labor law sect.), S.D. State Bar (50 Yr. award 1981), Old Georgetown Road Citizens Assn. (exec. bd. 1958-60), Phi Beta Kappa, Phi Alpha Delta. Home and Office: 11425 Luxmanor Rd Rockville MD 20852-3673

NYSTROM, JOHN WARREN, geographer, educator; b. Worcester, Mass. Nov. 22, 1913; s. John Walfred and Hulda Alfreda (Sundstrom) N.; m. Anne Hildegarde Carlson, Aug. 6, 1938; children—Jon Alfred, David Alan, Karen Elizabeth. A.B., Clark U., 1936, A.M., 1937, Ph.D., 1942. Instr. R.I. Coll. Edn., 1937-40, asst. prof. geography 1940-43; asst. prof. U. Pitts., 1943-45, asso. prof., 1945, prof., dept. head, 1947-53; head fgn. policy dept. U.S.C. of C., 1953-62, adminstrv. coordinator, 1956-62; partner firm Allen, Murden & Nystrom (internat. relations), Washington, 1962-64; mem. sr. staff Brookings Instn., 1964-66; exec. dir. Assn. Am. Geographers, Washington, 1966-79; prof. George Washington U., 1973-79; prof. geography U. Miami, 1980, Fla. Atlantic U., 1981—; exec. dir. Pitts. regional Inter-Am. Center, 1943-45, Fgn. Policy Assn. Pitts., 1945-53; cons. Dept. State, 1976-84; chmn. U.S. Nat. Com. Internat. Geog. Union; chmn. U.S. del. Internat. Geographic Congress, Stockholm, 1960, London, 1964, New Delhi, 1968, Budapest, 1971, Montreal, 1972, Moscow, 1976, Tokyo, 1980; mem. geography commn. NRC; chmn. Conf. of Secs., Am. Council Learned Socs. 1973-75; U.S. rep. Pan Am. Inst. Geography and History, 1973-77, ofcl. del., Panama, 1973, Quito, Ecuador, 1977; mem. U.S. Nat. Commn. for UNESCO, 1979-85. Author: A Geographic Study-Netherlands Information, 1942, Beyond Our Borders, 1954, Within Our Borders, 1957, Within The Americas, 1957, The Common Market, 1962, Alliance for Progress, 1966, The Common Market, 1976. Trustee Clark U. Mem. Nat. Council Geog. Edn., Assn. Am. Geographers, Am. Geog. Soc., AAUP, Sigma Xi. Club: Cosmos. Home: 783 SW 3d St Boca Raton FL 33486

NYTKO, EDWARD C., printing company executive; b. Chgo., Feb. 20, 1943; s. Edward Frank and Helen Nytko; m. Deborah Harriet Nytko, Nov. 21, 1980; children: Jeffrey Daniel, Christopher Edward. BBA in Mktg., U. Tex., 1965; MBA in Fin., Loyola U., Chgo., 1969. Mgmt. trainee W.F. Hall Printing Co., Chgo., 1965-67, group v.p. Gravure, 1980-81, pres., chief operating officer, 1981, pres., chief exec. officer, 1982-85; pres., chief exec. officer Ringier Am. (fomerly Krueger Ringier Inc., W.F. Hall Printing Co.), Itasca, Ill., 1985—. Mem. Gravure Assn. Am. (bd. dirs. 1987—). Office: Ringier Am 1 Pierce Pl Itasca IL 60143

NZEYIMANA, NOAH, bishop. Bishop Free Meth. Ch. N.Am., Winona Lake, Ind., 1987—. Office: Free Meth Ch N Am PO Box 535002 Indianapolis IN 46253-5002

OAK, CLAIRE MORISSET, artist, educator; b. St. Georges, Quebec, Can., May 31, 1921; came to U.S., 1945; d. Louis and Bernadette (Coulombe) Morisset; m. Alan Ben Oak, July 2, 1947. Student, Ecole des Beaux Arts, 1938-42, Parsons Sch. Design, N.Y.C., 1945, Art Students League, N.Y.C., 1945-46. Staff artist Henry Morgan & R. Simpson, Montreal, 1942-45; artist illustrator W.B. Golovin Advt. Agy., N.Y.C., 1947-49; freelance illustrator Arnold Constable & Advt. Agy., N.Y.C., 1948-50, Le Jardin des Modes, Paris, 1950-51, May & Co., L.A., 1956, Katten & Marengo Advt., Stockton, Calif., 1962-84; pvt. practice illustrator, designer San Joaquin Valley, Calif. 1984-92; art instr. San Joaquin Delta Coll., Stockton, 1973—; owner Fashion Illustrator's Workshop, N.Y.C., 1953-54; instr. Bauder Coll., Sacramento, 1975-76; painting workshop leader Lodi Art Ctr., 1991—; watercolor workshop leader D'Pharr Painting Adventures, Virginia City, Nev., 1992; ongoing watercolor workshop Galerie Iona, Stockton, Calif., 1993—. Named S.B. Anthony Woman of Achievement in the Arts, U. Pacific, 1982. Mem. Stockton Art League, Lodi Art Ctr., Ctrl. Calif. Art League, The League of Carmichael Artists, Delta Watercolor Soc. (bd. mem. 1988—). Avocations: outdoor painting, drawing from a model. Home: 2140 Waudman Ave Stockton CA 95209

OAKAR, MARY ROSE, former congresswoman; b. Cleve., Mar. 5, 1940; d. Joseph M. and Margaret Mary (Ellison) O. BA in English, Speech and Drama, Ursuline Coll., Cleve., 1962, LHD (hon.); MA in Fine Arts, John Carroll U., Cleve., 1966; LLD (hon.), Ashland U., 1978, Ursuline Coll., 1984, St. Mary's Notre Dame, 1989, Baldwin Wallace Coll., 1988; LHD (hon.), Trinity Coll., 1987. Instr. English and drama Lourdes Acad., Cleve., 1963-70; asst. prof. English, speech and drama Cuyahoga Community Coll., Cleve., 1968-75; mem. Cleve. City Council from 8th Ward, 1973-76; mem. 95th-102nd Congresses from 20th Dist. Ohio, 1977-92, mem. Pepper Commn. on Long Term Health Care; chair subcom. internat. devel., fin., trade and monetary policy;, chair task force on social security, elderly, women; chair subcom. on personnel and police, mem. banking, fin. and urban affairs com., select com. on aging, post office and civil service com., com. on house adminstrn., also numerous subcoms.; apptd. to Sec. Conf. to Establish Nat. Action Plan on Breast Cancer, 1994, by Pres. Clinton to bd. dirs. Bldrs., For Peace, 1994, to policy to White House Conf. on Aging. Founder, vol.-dir. Near West Side Civic Arts Center, Cleve., 1970; ward leader Cuyahoga County Democratic Party, 1972-76; mem. Ohio Dem. Central Com. from 20th Dist., 1974; trustee Fedn. Community Planning, Cleve., Health and Planning Commn. Cleve., Community Info. Service Cleve., Cleve. Soc. Crippled Children, Public Services Occupational Group Adv. Com., Cuyahoga Community Coll. Cleve. Ballet, Cleve. YWCA. Recipient Outstanding Service awards OEO, 1973-78, Community Service award Am. Indian Center, Cleve., 1973, Community Service award Nationalities Service Center, 1974, Community Service award Club San Lorenzo, Cleve., 1976, Cuyahoga County Dem. Woman of Yr., 1977, Ursuline Alumna of Yr. award, 1977, awards Irish Nat. Caucus, awards West Side Community Mental Health Center, awards Am. Lebanese League, awards Cleve. Fedn. Am.-Syrian Lebanese Clubs, Breast Cancer Awareness award Nat. Women's Health Resource Ctr., 1989, 1st lay recipient Barbara Bohen-Pfeiffer award Italian-Am. Found. Cancer Rsch., 1989, Disting. Svc. award Am. Cancer Soc., 1989, Myrl H. Shoemaker award Ohio Dem. Party, 1992, Philip Hart award Consumer Fedn. Am., 1987; cert. appreciation City of Cleve.; Woman

of Yr. award Cuyahoga County Women's Polit. Caucus, 1983; decorated Knight of Order of St. Ladislaus of Hungary, Women in Aerospace Outstanding Ach. award, Black Focus Woman of the Decade award. Office: 2621 Lorain Ave Cleveland OH 44113-3414

OAKES, JAMES L., federal judge; b. Springfield, Ill., Feb. 21, 1924; m. Evelena S. Kenworthy, Dec. 29, 1973; one son, two daus. by previous marriage. AB, Harvard U., 1945, LLB, 1947; LLD (hon.), New Eng. Coll., 1976, Suffolk U., 1980. Bar: Calif. 1949, Vt. 1950. Pvt. practice Brattleboro, Vt.; spl. counsel Vt. Pub. Service Commn., 1959-60; counsel Vt. Statutory Revision Commn., 1957-60; mem. Vt. Senate, 1961-65; atty. gen. Vt., 1967-69, U.S. dist. judge, 1970-71; U.S. cir. judge 2d Cir. Ct. Appeals, Brattleboro, 1971—; chief judge 2d Circuit Ct. Appeals, 1989-92; adj. faculty Duke U. Law Sch. 1985—, Iowa U. Coll. Law, 1993—. Office: US Ct Appeals PO Box 696 Brattleboro VT 05302-0696

OAKES, JOHN BERTRAM, writer, editor; b. Elkins Park, Pa., Apr. 23, 1913; s. George Washington Ochs Oakes and Bertie (Gans) Ochs; m. Margery C. Hartman, Oct. 24, 1945; children: Andra N., Alison H., Cynthia J., John G. H. A.B. magna cum laude, Princeton U. 1934; A.B., A.M. (Rhodes scholar), Queen's Coll., Oxford, 1936; LL.D. (hon.), U. Hartford, 1960; L.H.D. (hon.), Chatham Coll., 1969; Litt.D. (hon.), CUNY, 1976. Reporter Trenton (N.J.) State Gazette, Trenton Times, 1936-37; polit. reporter Washington Post, 1938-41; editor Rev. of the Week, Sunday N.Y. Times, 1946-49; mem. editorial bd. N.Y. Times, 1949-76; columnist on conservation environ., 1951-61, editor of edit. page, 1961-76; originator Op.-Ed. page N.Y. Times, 1970, contbg. columnist, 1977-90. Author: The Edge of Freedom, 1961; contbr.: Essays Today, 1955, Foundations of Freedom, 1958, Tomorrow's American, 1977, On the Vineyard, 1980, The March to War, 1991, Cast a Cold Eye, 1991. Mem. adv. bd. Nat. Parks Dept. Interior, 1955-62; Pres.'s Commn. White House Fellows, 1964-69; founding trustee Natural Resources Def. Coun., 1970—; adv. coun. U.S. Bur. Land Mgmt., 1980-81; mem. N.Y. State Commn. on Future of Adirondacks, 1989-90; trustee Nat. Parks Conservation Assn., bd. dirs. Com. to Protect Journalists; mem. com. Human Rights Watch; past trustee Fisk U., Chatham Coll., N.Y. Found., Sierra Club, Wilderness Soc., Nature Conservancy, Washington Journalism Ctr., Temple Emanu-El. Decorated Bronze Star, Order Brit. Empire, Croix de Guerre, Medaille de Reconnaissance (France); recipient Columbia-Catherwood award for disting. journalism, 1961, Dept. Interior Conservation award, 1963, George Polk Meml. award, 1965, Silurian Soc. award, 1969, Woodrow Wilson award Princeton U., 1970, Audubon medal Nat. Audubon Soc., 1976, UN Environ. award, 1982, Lawrenceville Sch. medal, 1994, others; Carnegie traveling fellow, 1959. Mem. Am. Philos. Soc., Coun. Fgn. Rels., Phi Beta Kappa, Century Assn. (N.Y.C.), Cosmos Club (Washington, D.C.). Jewish. Home: 1120 Fifth Ave New York NY 10128-0144

OAKES, LESTER CORNELIUS, retired electrical engineer, consultant; b. Knoxville, Oct. 11, 1923; s. Charles Vaughn and Maude Cornelia (Harrison) O.; m. Kathleen Clark, Dec. 27, 1947; children: Michael, Richard, Cynthia, Melissa. B.S. in E.E., U. Tenn., 1949, M.S., 1962. Registered profl. engr., Tenn. Engr. Fairchild Engring. and Aircraft, Oak Ridge, 1949-51; engr. I&C div. Oak Ridge Nat. Lab., 1951-68, dep. head I&C div., 1968—, asst. dir. I&C div., 1971-90; cons. Oak Ridge Nat. Lab., electric Power Rsch. Inst., Nuclear Regulatory Commn., 1990—. Contbr. articles to profl. jours.; patentee in field. Served with USAF, 1943-46. Martin Marietta Corp. fellow. Fellow IEEE. Presbyterian. Home: 710 Pleasant Hill Rd Maryville TN 37803-7337

OAKES, MELVIN ERVIN LOUIS, physics educator; b. Vicksburg, Miss., May 11, 1936; married, 1963; three children. Student, Fla. State U., 1958-64, PhD in Plasma Physics, 1964. Physicist USAR Guided Missile Agy., Redstone Arsenal, 1960; asst. in physics Fla. State U., Tallahassee, 1958-60, 60-64; asst. prof. physics U. Ga., Athens, 1964, rsch. assoc., 1964-65, from asst. prof. to assoc. prof., 1965-70; prof. of physics U. Tex., Austin, 1975—. Mem. Am. Phys. Soc., Am. Assn. Physics Tchrs. Achievements include rsch. on electromagnetic interaction with plasmas, plasma waves and radio frequency heating. Office: U Tex Dept Physics Austin TX 78712-1081

OAKES, ROBERT JAMES, physics educator; b. Mpls., Jan. 21, 1936; s. Sherman E. and Josephine J. (Olson) O.; children: Cindy L., Lisa A. B.S., U. Minn., 1957, M.S., 1959, Ph.D., 1962. NSF fellow Stanford U., 1962-64; asst. prof. physics, 1964-68; assoc. prof. physics Northwestern U., 1968-70, prof. physics, 1970-76, prof. physics and astronomy, 1976—; vis. staff mem. Los Alamos Sci. Lab., 1971—; vis. scientist Fermi Nat. Accelerator Lab., 1975—; faculty assoc. Argonne Nab. Lab., 1982—; U.S. scientist NSF-Yugoslav joint program, 1982—; panelist Nat. Rsch. Coun., 1990—. A.P. Sloan fellow 1965-68; Air Force Office Sci. Rsch. grantee, 1969-71, NSF grantee 1971, Dept. Energy grantee, 1987; named Fulbright-Hays Disting. prof. U. Sarajevo, Yugoslavia, 1979-80; recipient Natural Sci. prize China, 1993. Fellow Am. Phys. Soc., AAAS; mem. N.Y. Acad. Sci., Ill. Acad. Sci., Physics Club (Chgo.), Sigma Xi, Tau Beta Pi. Club: Physics (Chgo.). Office: Northwestern U Dept Physics 633 Clark St Evanston IL 60208-0001

OAKES, TIMOTHY WAYNE, tobacco import-export company executive; b. Chatham, Va., Nov. 27, 1938; s. John Averett and Edna Cora (Bolling) O.; m. Nancy Osborn Bunn, Mar. 19, 1965; children—Elizabeth, John. BA in Psychology, U. Va., 1961. With Imperial Tobacco Co., Ltd., 1961-68; asst. dir. internat. leaf purchase Philip Morris, Inc., Richmond, Va., 1968-75; with Dibrell Bros., Inc., Danville, Va., 1975—; sr. v.p., 1982—; also bd. dirs.; bd. dirs. Carolina Leaf Tobacco Co., Greenville, N.C. Mem. Leaf Tobacco Exporter's Assn. (pres. 1981-83, chmn. exec. com. Raleigh sect. 1984—), Tobacco Mchts. Assn. (chmn. Princeton, N.J. chpt. 1988—). Republican. Episcopalian. Avocations: golf, snow skiing. Home: 388 Hawthorne Dr Danville VA 24541-3516 Office: Dibrell Bros Inc 512 Bridge St Danville VA 24541-1406

OAKES, WALTER JERRY, pediatric neurosurgeon; b. De Soto, Mo., July 10, 1946; s. Marvin Melton and Mildred Florene (Link) O.; m. Linda Helen Maas (div. Jan. 1985); 1 child, Kathleen Suzanne; m. Jean Evans, Dec. 1988; children: Matthew Marvin, Peter Clifford. BA in Chemistry, U. Mo., 1968; MD, Duke U., 1972. Diplomate Am. Bd. Neurol. Surgeons. Neurosurgery resident Duke U., Durham, N.C., 1972-78, asst. prof. neurosurgery, 1979-90, assoc. prof. neurosurgery, 1991—, asst. prof. pediatrics, 1981-92; assoc. prof. pediatrics Duke U., 1992; pediatric neurosurgery resident U. Toronto Hosp. for Sick Children, Ont., Can., July-Dec., 1975; registrar pediatric neurosurgery U. London Hosp. for Sick Children, Eng., Sept., 1978-Feb., 1979; prof. neurosurgery and pediatrics U. Ala. Birmingham, 1992—. Fellow ACS. Office: Children's Hosp of Ala 1600 7th Ave S Ste 400 Birmingham AL 35233

OAKEY, JOHN MARTIN, JR., lawyer; b. Roanoke, Va., Jan. 29, 1935; s. John Martin and Mildred Hunter (Urquhart) O.; m. Jean Lindsey, May 7, 1966; children: John M. III, Daniel L., Christopher K. BA, U. Va., 1957, LLB, 1963. Law clk. U.S. Dist. Ct. (ea. dist.) Va., Richmond, 1963-64; assoc. McGuire, Woods & Battle, Richmond, 1964-69, ptnr., 1969-87; ptnr. McGuire, Woods, Battle & Boothe, Richmond, 1987—; mem. 4th Cir. Jud. Conf., Richmond, 1976—; chmn. Bar Com. on Unprofl. Conduct, 1977, Com. on Rules of Evidence, 1984-85. Chmn. Richmond Bd. Housing Appeals, 1975; pres. Richmond Tennis Patrons Assn., 1979. Served to lt. USN, 1958-61. Fellow Am. Coll. Trial Lawyers; mem. Va. Bar Assn., Richmond Bar Assn., Va. Assn. Def. Attys. (pres. 1994-95), Def. Rsch. Inst., Boyd Graves Conf. (chair 1991-94), Bull and Bear Club, Westwood Club, Phi Beta Kappa, Omicron Delta Kappa. Episcopalian. Avocations: tennis, travel. Home: 11 Roslyn Rd Richmond VA 23226-1609 Office: McGuire Woods Battle & Boothe 1 James Ctr Richmond VA 23219

OAKLEY, CAROLYN LE, state legislator, small business owner; b. Portland, Oreg., June 28, 1942; d. George Thomas and Ruth Alveta Victoria (Engberg) Penketh; m. Donald Keith Oakley, Jan 27, 1965; children: Christine, Michelle. BS in Edn., Oreg. State U., 1965. Educator Linn County (Oreg.) Schs., 1965-76; owner Linn County Tractor, 1965-90; mem. Oreg. Legis. Assembly, Salem, 1989—, asst. majority leader, 1993—, majority whip, 1994; mem. exec. bd. Oreg. Retail Coun., 1987-90. Chmn. Linn County Rep. Ctrl. Com., 1982-84; chmn. bd. dirs. North Albany Svc. Dist., 1988-90; chair Salvation Army, Linn and Benton Counties, 1987—;

vice chmn. bd. trustees Linn-Benton C.C. Found., 1987—; pres. Women for Agr., Linn and Benton Counties, 1984-86; mem. STRIDE Leadership Round Table, 1991—; state chair Am. Legis. Exch. Coun., 1991—, nat. bd. dirs., 1992—; mem. Edn. Commn. of the States, 1991—, com. policies and priorities, 1993—; hon. mem. Linn-Benton Compact Bd., 1993—; active Linn County Criminal Justice Coun., 1994—. Named Woman of Yr. Albany chpt. Beta Sigma Phi, 1970. Mem. Nat Conf. State Legislators (chmn. edn. com. 1992—), Albany C. of C. (bd. dirs. 1986-93), Linn County Rep. women (legis. chmn. 1982-91). Republican. Methodist. Avocations: gardening, camping. Home: 3197 NW Crest Loop Albany OR 97321-9627 Office: Oreg Legis Assembly State Capital Salem OR 97310

OAKLEY, DEBORAH JANE, researcher, educator; b. Detroit, Jan. 31, 1937; d. George F. and Kathryn (Willson) Hacker; m. Bruce Oakley, June 16, 1958; children: Ingrid Andrea, Brian Benjamin. BA, Swarthmore Coll., 1958; MA, Brown U., 1960; MPH, U. Mich., 1969, PhD, 1977. Dir. teenage and adult programs YWCA, Providence, 1959-63; editorial asst. Stockholm U., 1963-64; rsch. investigator, lectr. dept. population planning U. Mich. 1971-77; asst. prof. community health programs U. Mich., Ann Arbor, 1977-79, asst. prof. nursing rsch., 1979-81, assoc. prof., 1981-89, prof., 1989—, interim dir. Ctr. Nursing Rsch., 1988-90; prin. investigator NIH-funded Rsch. grants on family planning and women's health, mem. nat. adv. com. nursing rsch., 1993—; co-chair Mich. Initiative for Women's Health, 1993—. Author: (with Leslie Corsa) Population Planning, 1979; contbr. articles to profl. jours. Recipient Margaret Sanger award Washtenaw County Planned Parenthood, 1975; Outstanding Young Woman of Ann Arbor award by Jaycees, 1970, Dist. Faculty award, Mich. Assn. Gov. Bds., 1992. Mem. Am. Pub. Health Assn. (chmn. population sect. council), Internat. Union Sci. Study Population, Midwest Nursing Rsch. Soc., Population Assn. Am., Nat. Family Planning and Reproductive Health Assn. (nat. comms.), Delta Omega. Democrat. Home: 5200 S Lake Dr Chelsea MI 48118-9481 Office: U Mich Sch Nursing Ann Arbor MI 48109

OAKLEY, DIANE, insurance executive, benefit consultant; b. Teaneck, N.J., Dec. 27, 1953; d. Geard Joseph and Joan B. (Peterson) O.; m. John J. McCabe Jr., June 8, 1986. BS, Fairfield U., 1975; MBA, Fordham U., 1984. Actuarial asst. TIAA-CREF, N.Y.C., 1975-79, benefit plan counselor, 1979-82, adv. officer, 1982-85; branch mgr., 2nd v.p. TIAA-CREF, Bethesda, Md., 1985-89, v.p., assns. & govt. rels., 1989-95, v.p., 1995—. Mem. Am. Assn. Higher Edn., Am. Assn. Women in C.C.'s, Nat. Assn. Women in Edn., Washington EE Benefits Forum, Working in Employee Benefits. Roman Catholic. Home: 7823 White Cliff Trail Rockville MD 20855 Office: TIAA-CREF 601 13th St NW Ste 1100N Washington DC 20005

OAKLEY, FRANCIS CHRISTOPHER, history educator, former college president; b. Liverpool, Eng., Oct. 6, 1931; came to U.S., 1957, naturalized, 1968; s. Joseph Vincent and Siobean (NiCurean) O.; m. Claire-Ann Lamenzo, Aug. 9, 1958; children: Deirdre, Christopher, Timothy, Brian. BA, Corpus Christi Coll., Oxford U., 1953, MA, 1957; postgrad., Pontifical Inst. Medieval Studies, Toronto, 1953-55; MA, Yale U., 1958, PhD, 1960; LLD, Amherst Coll., 1986; Wesleyan U., 1989; LHD, Northwestern U., 1990, North Adams State Coll., 1993, Bowdoin Coll., 1993; LittD, Williams Coll., 1994. Mem. faculty Yale U., 1959-61; Mem. faculty Williams Coll., Williamstown, Mass., 1961—, prof. history, 1970—, dean faculty, 1977-84, Edward Dorr Griffin prof. history of ideas, 1984-85, 94—, pres., 1985-93, pres. emeritus, 1994—; hon. fellow Corpus Christi Coll., Univ. Oxford, 1991—; vis. lectr. Bennington (Vt.) Coll., 1967; mem. Inst. Advanced Study Princeton U., 1981-82; assoc. Nat. Humanities Ctr., 1991; guest scholar Woodrow Wilson Internat. Ctr. for Scholars, 1994; chair bd. dirs. Am. Coun. Learned Socs., 1993—; trustee Sterling and Francine Clark Inst., 1985—; mem. Mass. Cultural Devel. Commn., 1988—; trustee Williamstown Art Conservation Ctr., 1995—; sr. mem. The Conf. Bd. Author: The Political Thought of Pierre d'Ailly: The Voluntarist Tradition, 1964, Kingship and the Gods: The Western Apostasy, 1968, Council over Pope?, Towards a Provisional Ecclesiology, 1969, Medieval Experience: Foundations of Western Cultural Singularity, 1974, rev. England edit., The Crucial Centuries, 1979, Spanish edit., 1980, Medieval Acad. edit., 1988, 93, The Western Church in the Later Middle Ages, 1979, rev. edit. 1985, 88, 91, Natural Law, Conciliarism and Consent in the Middle Ages, 1984, Omnipotence, Covenant and Order: An Excursion in the History of Ideas, 1984, Community of Learning: The American College and the Liberal Arts Tradition, 1992; editor: (with Daniel O'Connor) Creation: The Impact of an Idea, 1969; contbr. articles to profl. jours. Served to lt. Brit. Army, 1955-57. Goldsmith's Co. London fellow, 1953-55, Social Sci. Rsch. Coun. fellow, 1963, Am. Coun. Learned Socs. fellow, 1965, 69-70, Weil Inst. fellow, 1965, Folger Shakespeare Libr. fellow, 1974, NEH fellow, 1976, 81-82. Fellow Medieval Acad. Am.; mem. Am. Hist. Assn., Am. Cath. Hist. Assn., Am. Ch. History Soc., New Eng. Medieval Conf., Am. Coun. Learned Socs. (chair bd. dirs. 1993—), The Century Assn. Democrat. Roman Catholic. Office: Williams Coll Dept History Williamstown MA 01267

OAKLEY, GARY WILLIAM, consulting company executive; b. Norfolk, Va., Dec. 29, 1942; s. Francis and Mabel (Waters) O.; m. Suzy Bridge Oakley, Apr. 3, 1982; div. 1980; children Gary W. Jr., Sara W. BA in Econs., Amherst Coll., 1960-64; MBA in Mktg., U. Pa., 1968. Assoc. N.W. Ayer & Sons, Inc., Phila., 1968-70; group. prodn. mgr. Lerner Bros., Inc., N.Y.C., 1970-73; mktg. dir. Am. Can Co., Greenwich, Conn., 1973-78; cons., chmn., chief exec. officer The Saugatuck Group, Westport, Conn., 1980—; chmn., chief exec. officer The Saugatuck Travel Co., Westport, Conn., 1987—; chmn., chief exec. officer Saugatuck Direct, Inc. Mem. Country Club New Canaan, Edgartown (Mass.) Yacht Club, The Mornings Club (Vero Beach, Fla.). Home: 243 White Oak Shade Rd New Canaan CT 06840-6833 Office: The Saugatuck Group 340 Pemberwick Rd Greenwich CT 06831-4240

OAKLEY, GODFREY PORTER, JR., health facility administrator, medical educator; b. Greenville, N.C., June 1, 1940; s. Godfrey Porter and Carrie O.; m. Mary Ann Bryant, Sept. 2, 1961; children: Martha Gray, Susan Herndon, Robert Bryant. Student, Duke U., 1958-61; MD, Bowman Gray Sch. of Medicine, 1965; MS in Preventive Medicine, U. Washington, 1972. Diplomate Am. Bd. Pediatrics, Nat. Bd. Med. Examiners, Am. Bd. Preventive Medicine, Am. Bd. Med. Genetics. Intern in straight pediatrics Cleve. Met. Gen. Hosp., 1965-66, resident in pediatrics, 1966-68; sr. fellow in teratology and human embryology U. Washington Sch. of Medicine, Ctrl. Lab. Human Embryology, Dept. of Pediatrics, Seattle, 1970-72; sr. fellow U. Washington Sch. Pub. Health and Community Medicine, Seattle, 1971-72; EIS officer leukemia sect. Ctrs. Disease Control and Prevention (CDC), Atlanta, 1968-70, chief etiology studies sect., bur. epidemiology, cancer and birth defects, 1972-81; chief birth defects br., choronic diseases divsn. Nat. Ctr. Environ. Health, Ctrs. Disease Control and Prevention, Atlanta, 1985—; clin. asst. prof. pediatrics divsn. med. genetics Emory U., Atlanta, 1968-70, 72—, clin. asst. prof. gynecology-obstetrics divsn. med. genetics, 1981—; mem. visiting med. staff Grady Meml. Hosp., Atlanta, 1974—; med. adv. bd. Ctrs. Disease Control & Prevention (CDC); mem. task force on predictors of hereditary desease or congenital defects NIH Consensus Conf., 1979; mem. genetics coordinating com. NIH/CDC; mem. adv. com. biometric and epidemiological methodology FDA/CDC; cons. bur. med. svcs. FDA; mem. Chronic Diseases Surveillance Working Group; mem. patient registry com. Cystic Fibrosis Found., med. adv. coun., 1978—; mem. drug experience coordinating com. Dept. Health, Edn. and Welfare; mem. genetics com. Ga. Dept. Human Resources, 1980—; ex-officio mem. genetic diseases rev. and adv. com. Health Svcs. Adminstrn., 1981; mem. master community health program, interdisciplinary faculty com., curriculum com. Emory U.; mem. working group on heart disease epidemiology Nat. Heart, Lung and Blood Insts., 1978; mem. ad hoc com. on Alpha-fetoprotein Pub. Health Svc.; mem. profl. adv. coun. Spina Bifida Assn. Am., 1981—; mem. WHO EURO-China Consultation, Beijing, China, 1983; lectr. in field. Mem. editorial bd. Pediatric & Perinatal Epidemiology, 1987-89; contbr. articles to profl. jours., chpts. to books. Nancy Lybrook Lasater scholar 1961-67; recipient Physician's Recognition award AMA, 1973-76, Outstanding Svc. medal Pub. Health Svc., 1981, Meritorious Svc. award, 1988, Spl. Recognition award, 1993, President's Excellence award Spina Bifida Assn. Am., 1988-89, Disting. Alumnus award U. Washington Sch. Pub. Health, 1990. Mem. Am. Acad. Pediatrics (past com. drugs/CDC liaison, com. genetics com. 1990, exec. com. 1990—, CDC rep. Ga. chpt. 1993), Am. Soc. Human Genetics, Am. Coll. Epidemiology, Am. Coll. Med. Genetics, Atlanta Genetics Soc., Greater

Atlanta Pediatric Soc., Atlanta Obstetrical and Gynecological Soc. (assoc.), Soc. Epidemiologic Rsch., Soc. Pediatric Rsch., Teratology Soc. (pres. elect 1983-84, pres. 1984-85, editorial bd. Teratology 1978-83, edn. com. 1988), Internat. Clearinghouse Birth Defects Monitoring Systems (chmn. 1981-82, vice chmn. 1982-83, chmn. 1983-84), Alpha Omega Alpha. Home: 2224 Kodiak Dr Atlanta GA 30345 Office: CDC NCEH BDDD 4770 Buford Hwy F34 Atlanta GA 30341-3724

OAKLEY, MARY ANN BRYANT, lawyer; b. Buckhannon, W.Va., June 22, 1940; d. Hubert Herndon and Mary F. (Deeds) Bryant; m. Godfrey P. Oakley, Jr., Sept. 2, 1961; children: Martha, Susan, Robert. AB, Duke U., 1962; MA, Emory U., 1970, JD, 1974. Tchr., Winston-Salem/Forsyth County Schs., N.C., 1961-65; assoc. Margie Pitts Hames, Atlanta 1974-80; ptnr. Stagg Hoy & Oakley, Atlanta, 1980-83, Oakley & Bonner, Atlanta, 1984-90; pvt. practice, 1990—; adj. prof. trial practice Ga. State U., 1986—; adj. prof. pretrial practice Emory U. Law Sch., 1991, 95; bd. dirs. Nat. Employment Lawyers Assn., 1989-94; founding coordr. NELA, Ga.; mem. Ga. Supreme Ct. Commn. on Racial and Ethnic Bias. Contbr. articles to law jours. Notes and Comments editor Emory Law Jour., 1973-74. Author: Elizabeth Cady Stanton, 1972; Bd. dirs. Atlanta chpt. YWCA, 1975-79, 1st v.p., 1978-79; mem. Leadership Atlanta, 1979; bd. dirs. Ga. chpt. ACLU, 1981-83; trustee Unitarian Universalist Congregation Atlanta, 1977-80, pres., 1979-80, mem. Unitarian Universalist Commn. Appraisal, 1987-85; bd. dirs. Unitarian Universalist Service Com., 1984-90, v.p., 1986-88, pres. 1988-90. Nat. Merit scholar, 1958. Mem. ABA, Am. Judicature Soc., State Bar Ga. (chmn. individual rights sect. 1979-81), Atlanta Bar Assn., Lawyers Club Atlanta, No. Dist. Bar Council, 1982-86, Ga. Assn. Women Lawyers, Ga. State Bar Disciplinary Bd. (investigative panel 1985-88, chmn., 1987-88), Gate City Bar Assn., Ga. Bd. Bar Examiners, Ga. Legal Svcs. Program Bd., LWV, Phi Beta Kappa, Order of Coif. Home: 2224 Kodiak Dr NE Atlanta GA 30345-4152 Office: 315 W Ponce De Leon Ave Ste 721 Decatur GA 30030-2441

OAKLEY, PHYLLIS ELLIOTT, diplomat; b. Omaha, Nov. 23, 1934; d. Thomas Myron Elliott and Elsa (Kerkow) Elliott Garabedian; m. Robert Bigger Oakley, June 8, 1958; children: Mary Oakley Kress, Thomas Elliott. B.A., Northwestern U., 1956; M.A., Fletcher Sch. Law and Diplomacy, 1957. Commd. fgn. svc. officer Dept. State, 1957-58, 74—, asst. cultural affairs officer, Kinshasa, Zaire, 1979-82, desk officer, Afghanistan, 1982-85, Pearson Exchange officer Senator Mathias, 1985-86; dep. spokesman, 1986-86, AID Afghan Humanitarian Assistance program, Islamabad, 1989-91, dep. asst. sec. INR Bur., 1993-94, asst. sec. PRM, 1994—. Mem. Coun. Fgn. Rels., Cosmos Club, Phi Beta Kappa. Office: Dept of State Bur Population Refugees & Migration 2201 C St NW Washington DC 20520-5824

OAKLEY, ROBERT LOUIS, law librarian, educator; b. N.Y.C., Nov. 6, 1945; s. Bert Tuttle Oakley and Allese (Duffin) Vestigo; m. Madeleine Cohen, Aug. 13, 1971; children: Esther Shulamit, Daniel Isaac-Meir. BA, Cornell U., 1968; MLS, Syracuse U., 1972; JD, Cornell U., 1976. Bar: N.Y. 1977, U.S. Dist. Ct. (no. dist.) N.Y. 1977. Assoc. dir. law libr. Cornell U., Ithaca, N.Y., 1976-79; dir., assoc. prof. law libr. Boston U. Law, 1979-82; dir., assoc. prof. law libr. Georgetown U., Washington, 1982-87, dir., prof. law libr., 1987—. Contbr. articles to profl. jours. Mem. Libr. of Congress, mem. Network Adv. Com., 1986-92, 95—; adv. nat. commn. on Preservation and Access, 1988-94; mem. AALL Exec. Bd., 1991-94; bd. dirs. Montgomery County (Md.) Pub. Libr., 1988-92. Mem. ABA, ALA, Am. Assn. Law Librarians, Assn. Am. Law Schs., Libr. of Congress Network Adv. Com. Avocations: photography, music, personal computers, amateur radio. Office: Georgetown U Law Ctr 111 G St NW Washington DC 20001-1489

OAKS, B. ANN, plant physiologist, educator; b. Winnipeg, Man., Can., June 4, 1929; d. H.A. and Bernice (Farlinger) O. BA with honors, U. Toronto, Ont., Can., 1951; MA, U. Sask., Can., 1954, PhD, 1959. Alexander von Humbolt assoc. Rsch. Inst. for Dairying, Freising, Fed. Republic Germany, 1958-60; rsch. assoc. Purdue U., West Lafayette, Ind., 1960-64, Oak Ridge (Tenn.) Nat. Lab., 1964-65; asst. prof. biology McMaster U., Hamilton, Ont., 1965-68, assoc. prof., 1968-74, prof., 1974-89; prof. emeritus McMaster U., Hamilton, 1989—; prof. U. Guelph, Ont., 1989—; vis. prof. Wash. State U., 1979-80, U. Nancy, France, 1980, Chiba U., Japan, 1984; adj. prof. U. Guelph, 1987-89; affiliated scientist NRC Lab., Saskatoon, Sask., 1988-92. Assoc. editor Biochemistry and Cell Biology, 1988-90; mem. editorial bd. Plant Physiology, 1970-89, Jour. Plant Physiology, 1984—, Plant and Cell Physiology, 1989-93; contbr. author various books; contbr. articles to profl. jours. Rsch. grantee in field. Fellow Royal Soc. Can.; mem. Can. Soc. Plant Physiologists (treas. 1974-76, Gold medal 1989); Am. Soc. Plant Physiologists. Avocations: skiing, hiking, naturalist, writing letters to members of parliament. Office: U Guelph, Dept Botany, Guelph, ON Canada N1G 2W1

OAKS, DALLIN HARRIS, lawyer, church official; b. Provo, Utah, Aug. 12, 1932; s. Lloyd E. and Stella (Harris) O.; m. June Dixon, June 24, 1952; children: Sharmon, Cheri Lyn, Lloyd D., Dallin D., TruAnn, Jenny June. B.A. with high honors, Brigham Young U., 1954, LL.D. (hon.) 1980; J.D. cum laude, U. Chgo., 1957; LL.D. (hon.), Pepperdine U., 1982; So. Utah U., 1991. Bar: Ill. 1957, Utah 1971. Law clk. to Supreme Ct. chief justice Earl Warren, 1957-58; with firm Kirkland, Ellis, Hodson, Chaffetz & Masters, Chgo., 1958-61; mem. faculty U. Chgo. Law Sch., 1961-71, assoc. dean and acting dean, 1962, prof., 1964-71, mem. vis. com., 1971-74; pres. Brigham Young U., Provo, Utah, 1971-80; also prof. law J. Reuben Clark Law Sch., 1974-80; justice Utah Supreme Ct., 1981-84; mem. Coun. of Twelve Apostles Ch. Jesus Christ of Latter Day Sts., 1984—; legal counsel Bill of Rights com. Ill. Constl. Conv., 1970. Author: (with G.G. Bogert) Cases on Trusts, 1967, 78, (with W. Lehman) A Criminal Justice System and The Indigent, 1968, The Criminal Justice Act in the Federal District Courts, 1969, (with M. Hill) Carthage Conspiracy, 1975, Trust Doctrines in Church Controversies, 1984, Pure in Heart, 1988, The Lord's Way, 1991; editor: The Wall Between Church and State, 1963. Mem. Wilson coun. Woodrow Wilson Internat. Ctr. for Scholars, 1973-80; trustee Intermountain Health Care Inc., 1975-80; mem. adv. com. Nat. Inst. Law Enforcement and Criminal Justice, 1974-76; bd. dirs. Notre Dame Ctr. for Constl. Studies, 1977-80, Rockford Inst., 1980—; bd. dirs. Pub. Broadcasting Svc., 1977-85, chmn., 1980-85; bd. dirs. Polynesian Cultural Ctr., 1987—, chmn., 1988—. Fellow Am. Bar Found. (exec. dir. 1970-71); mem. Am. Assn. Pres. Ind. Colls. and Univs. (pres. 1975-78, dir. 1971-78), Order of Coif. Mem. Ch. of Jesus Christ of Latter-day Saints (regional rep. 1974-80; past 1st counselor Chgo. South Stake). Address: 47 E South Temple Salt Lake City UT 84150

OAKS, MAURICE DAVID, retired pharmaceutical company executive; b. Everett, Pa., Jan. 22, 1934; s. Jacob Garvin and Hannah Alma (Young) O.; m. Judith Ann Rayne; 1 child, Kimberly. BS in Biology, Franklin and Marshall Coll., 1956. Sales rep. Squibb Pharm, Salisbury and Balt., Md., 1959-69; div. sales mgr. Squibb Pharm., Columbus, Ohio, 1969-71; product mgr. Squibb Pharm., Princeton, N.J., 1971-76, group product dir. antibiotics, cardiovasculars, and insulin, 1976-78, dir. product planning, U.S., 1979-80, v.p. world wide mktg. devel., 1980-82, v.p. mktg. svcs., 1983-85, pres. Princeton Pharm. Products, 1985-89; exec. v.p. Squibb Pharm. Group U.S., Princeton, N.J., 1989-90; v.p. worldwide ops. planning Bristol-Myers Squibb Pharms. Ops., Princeton, 1990-92; bd. dirs. Nat. Pharm. Coun., McLean, Va., 1985-90, mem. exec. com., 1988-90; bd. dirs. Penn Engring. Mfg., Danboro, Pa. Coun. mem. Franklin & Marshall Coll. Commn. on Found. and Corp. Support, Lancaster, Pa., 1987-90, ann. fund class capt., 1991-95; mem., pres. Mid-Atlantic regional adv. coun. Franklin & Marshall Coll.; active YMCA, Doylestown, Pa. With U.S. Army, 1956-58. Republican. Methodist. Avocations: tennis, golf, bicycling.

OAKS, ROBERT C., air force officer; b. L.A., Feb. 14, 1936; m. Gloria Unger; children: Perry, Barton, Derek, Brock, Keri, Kristie. BS, USAF Acad., 1959; MBA, Ohio State U., 1967; diploma, Naval War Coll., 1974. Enlisted Utah N.G., 1954-55; commd. 2nd lt. USAF, 1959, advanced through grades to gen., 1990; F-100 pilot, 524th Tactical Fighter Squadron Cannon AFB, N.M., 1961-63; F-100 pilot, 416th Tactical Fighter Squadron Misawa Air Base, Japan, 1963-64,; England AFB, La., 1964-65, Tan Son Nhut Air Base, South Vietnam, 1965-66; air officer commanding Cadet Squadron 23 USAF Acad., Colo., 1967-68, asst. exec. officer then exec. for honor and ethics, commandant of cadets, 1968-70; F-111 pilot, 430th Tactical Fighter Squadron Nellis AFB, Nev., 1970-71, ops. officer, 429th Tactical Fighter Squadron, 1971-72; comdr., 391st Tactical Fighter Squadron

Mountain Home AFB, Idaho, 1971-73; dep. chief Global Plans and Policy Div. Hdqrs. USAF, Washington, chief Joint Plans and Policy Branch, Joint Policy Divsn., chief Internat. Relations Div., chief Pacific-East Asia Div., chief Europe-NATO Div., dep. asst. for Nat. Security Counc. matters, 1974-77, chief Regular and Res. Gen. Officer Div., Office of the Dep. Chief of Staff for Personnel, asst. dep. chief of staff for Gen. Officer Matters; asst. dep. chief of staff readiness Hdqrs. USAF in Europe, Ramstein Air Base, Germany, asst. dep. chief of staff ops.; comdr., 86th Tactical Fighter Wing Ramstein Air Base, Germany; dir. personnel plans, Office of Dep. Chief of Staff, Manpower and Personnel Hdqrs. USAF, Washington, 1983-85, asst. dep. chief of staff, Manpower and Personnel, 1985-86; comdr. Allied Air Forces So. Europe, dep. comdr. in chief USAF in Europe for So. Area, Naples, Italy, 1986-88; comdr. Air Tng. Command Randolph AFB, Tex., 1988-90; comdr. in chief USAF in Europe, 1990—; comdr. Air Forces Cen. Europe, Ramstein Air Base, 1995. Decorated Def. Disting. Svc. medal, Disting. Svc. medal, Legion of Merit with oak leaf cluster, D.F.C., Meritorious Svc. medal with oak leaf cluster, Air medal with eight oak leaf clusters, Air Force Commendation medal, Air Force Outstanding Unit award with two oak leaf clusters, Nat. Def. Svc. medal with svc. star and others. Office: Comdr AIRCENT APO AE 09094-5001

OATES, ADAM R., professional hockey player; b. Weston, Ont., Can., Aug. 27, 1962. Attended, Rensselaer Polytech. Inst., 1985. With Detroit Red Wings, 1985-89, St. Louis Blues, 1989-92, Boston Bruins, 1992—; player NHL All-Star Game, 1991-94. Named NCAA All-American, 1984-85; named to Sporting News All-Star Team, 1990-91. Office: Boston Bruins 150 Causeway St Boston MA 02114-1310*

OATES, BART STEVEN, professional football player; b. Mesa, Ariz., Dec. 16, 1958; m. Michelle Oats. BA in Acctg., Brigham Young U.; JD, Seton Hall U. Bar: N.J. 1990. With Phila. Stars, USFL, 1983-85, N.Y. Giants, 1985-94, San Francisco 49ers, 1994-94; assoc. Ribis, Graham & Curtin, Morristown, N.J.; Player Super Bowl XXI, 1986, XXV, 1990, XXVIV, 1994. Named USFL All-Star Team Ctr. by Sporting News, 1983. Played in Pro Bowl, 1990-91, 93. *

OATES, CARL EVERETTE, lawyer; b. Harlingen, Tex., Apr. 8, 1931; s. Joseph William and Grace (Watson) O.; m. Eileen N. Hudnall; children: Carl William, Gregory Carl Hudnall, Patricia O. Chase, Matthew Noble Hudnall. BS, U.S. Naval Acad., 1955; LLB, So. Meth. U., 1962. Bar: Tex. 1962, D.C. 1977, Nebr. 1985. Assoc. Akin, Gump, Strauss, Hauer & Feld, Dallas, 1962-64, ptnr., 1965-91. Asst. atty. gen. State of Texas, 1992-94, spl. coun., Tex. Dept. Banking, 1994—. Chmn. bd. trustees S.W. Mus. Sci. and Tech., Dallas; v.p. S.W. Sci. Mus. Found., Dallas; bd. dirs. Kiwanis Wesley Dental Ctr., Inc., Dallas; pres. Wesley Dental Found., Dallas. Served to lt. USN, 1955-59. Mem. ABA, D.C. Bar Assn., Tex. Bar Assn., Dallas Bar Assn., Nebr. Bar Assn., Barristers, Northwood Club, Delta Theta Phi. Office: Tex Dept Banking 2601 N Lamar Blvd Austin TX 78705-4294

OATES, JAMES G., advertising executive; b. Kenton, Ohio, Apr. 2, 1943; m. Sue Ann Minter; 2 children. BS, Ohio State U. Trainee Leo Burnett USA, Chgo., 1966-68, asst. acct. exec., 1968-69, acct. exec., 1969-73, acct. supv., 1973-74, v.p., 1974-77, acct. supv. GM Olds acct., 1977-80, mgmt. dir. Philip Morris account, 1980-84, sr. v.p., 1984-86, exec. v.p., 1986-90, vice chmn., dir. client svcs., 1990-92, chmn., bd. dirs., mem. exec. com., 1992—, group pres. Asia/Pacific, 1993—; bd. dirs. The Advt. Coun. mem. MBA adv. bd. Ohio State U.; Kellogg Adv. Bd.; active Chgo. Crime Commn. Mem. Am. Assn. Advt. Agys. (bd. govs. Chgo. chpt.). Office: Leo Burnett Co Inc 17 Bougainvillea Ave Key West FL 33040-6226

OATES, JOHN FRANCIS, classics educator; b. Holyoke, Mass., Aug. 7, 1934; s. William Adrian and Lilian (Woods) O.; m. Rosemary Walsh, June 27, 1957; children: Elizabeth, Emily, John Francis, Sarah. B.A., Yale U., 1956, M.A., 1958, Ph.D., 1960; postgrad. (Fulbright fellow), Am. Sch. Classical Studies in Athens, Greece, 1956-57. Instr. classics Yale U., 1960-63, asst. prof., 1963-67; asso. prof. ancient history Duke U., 1967-71, prof., 1971—, chmn. dept. classical studies, 1971-80, chmn. Humanities Council, 1975-80, dir. database of documentary papyri, 1982—, dir. papyrus catalog project, 1992—; Hon. research asst., Morse fellow Univ. Coll. London (Eng.), 1965-66; vis. prof. Smith Coll., Northampton, Mass., 1967, 68; mem. mng. com. Intercollegiate Center Classical Studies in Rome, Italy, 1972-77, Am. Sch. Classical Studies in Athens, 1973—, mem. com on coms., 1975-77; mem. Council for Internat. Exchange of Scholars, 1974-77; v.p., trustee Triangle Univs. Center for Advanced Study, Inc.; 1975-90; trustee Nat. Humanities Center, 1977-90, trustee emeritus, 1990—; adv. council Sch. Classical Studies, Am. Acad. in Rome, 1976—; dir. summer seminar Nat. Endowment Humanities, 1978; dir. Nat. Fedn. State Humanities Councils, 1980-83; mem. N.C. Humanities Com., 1977-83, chmn. 1980-82. Author: The Status Designation, 1963, (with A.E. Samuel and C.B. Welles) Yale Papyri in the Beinecke Library, 1967, (with W.H. Willis and R.S. Bagnall) A Checklist of Papyrological Editions, 4th edit., 1992, (with Willis) Duke Data Bank of Documentary Papyri, 1991, The Basilikos Grammateus, 1995; mem. adv. bd. Greek, Roman and Byzantine Studies, 1977—, Humanities Report, 1981-83; dir. Hansa Reins. Co. Am., Tarrytown, N.Y., chmn. bd. Apple Syndicate Corp., Westport, Conn., 1983-85. Contbg. editor: Federal Income Taxation of Banks and Financial Institutions, 1968, Professional Responsibility in Federal Tax Practice, 1970; contbr. articles to law jours. Trustee Convent of Sacred Heart, Greenwich, Conn., 1979-83; mem. acctg. adv. bd. Columbia U. Grad. Sch. Bus., N.Y.C., 1982-86; mem. exec. com. Boston Coll. Wall St. Coun., 1989—; trustee Conn. Pub. Expenditure Coun., Inc., Hartford, 1984-85; mem. pres.'s adv. bd. Weston Sch. Theology, Cambridge, 1993—. Roman Catholic. Clubs: Union League (N.Y.C.); Landmark (Stamford); Country of New Canaan (Conn.). Office: Hargro Assocs One Landmark Sq Stamford CT 06901

OATES, JOHNNY LANE, professional baseball team manager; b. Sylva, N.C., Jan. 21, 1946. BS in Health and Phys. Edn., Va. Tech. U. Player minor league team Chgo. White Sox, 1967; player minor league team Balt. Orioles, 1967-71, player, 1970, 72, mgr. minor league team, 1988, coach, 1989-91, mgr., 1991-94; player Atlanta Braves, 1973-75, Phila. Phillies, 1975-76, L.A. Dodgers, 1977-79; player N.Y. Yankees, 1980, minor league coach, 1981-83; coach Chgo. Cubs, 1984-87; mgr. Texas Rangers, 1995—. Named Internat. League Mgr. of Yr., 1988. Office: The Ballpark in Arlington 1000 Ballpark Way Arlington TX 76011*

OATES, JOYCE CAROL, author; b. Lockport, N.Y., June 16, 1938; d. Frederic James and Caroline (Bush) O.; m. Raymond Joseph Smith, Jan. 23, 1961. BA, Syracuse U., 1960; MA, U. Wis., 1961. Instr. English U. Detroit, 1961-65, asst. prof., 1965-67; prof. English U. Windsor, Ont., Can., 1967-87; writer-in-residence Princeton (N.J.) U., 1978-81, prof., 1987—. Author: (short story collections) By the North Gate, 1963, Upon the Sweeping Flood, 1966, The Wheel of Love, 1970, Marriages and Infidelities, 1972, The Hungry Ghosts, 1974, The Goddess and Other Women, 1974, Where Are You Going, Where Have You Been?: Stories of Young America, 1974, The Poisoned Kiss and Other Stories From the Portuguese, 1975, The Seduction and Other Stories, 1975, Crossing the Border, 1976, Night-Side, 1977, All the Good People I've Left Behind, 1978, The Lamb of Abyssalia, 1980, A Sentimental Education: Stories, 1981, Last Days: Stories, 1984, Wild Nights, 1985, Raven's Wing: Stories, 1986, The Assignation, 1988, Heat: And Other Stories, 1991, Where is Here?. 1992, Haunted: Tales of the Grotesque, 1994; (novels) With Shuddering Fall, 1964, A Garden of Earthly Delights, 1967 (Nat. Book award nomination 1968), Expensive People, 1967 (Nat. Book award nomination 1969), them, 1969 (Nat. Book award for fiction 1970), Wonderland, 1971, Do With Me What You Will, 1973, The Assassins, 1975, Childwold, 1976, The Triumph of the Spider Monkey, 1976, Son of the Morning, 1978, Unholy Loves, 1979, Cybele, 1979, Bellefleur, 1980 (L.A. Times Book award nomination 1980), A Sentimental Education, 1981, Angel of Light, 1981, A Bloodsmoor Romance, 1982, Mysteries of Winterthorn, 1984, Solstice, 1985, Marya, 1986, You Must Remember This, 1987, (as Rosamond Smith) The Lives of the Twins, 1987, American Appetites, 1989, (as Rosamond Smith) Soul-Mate, 1989, Because It Is Bitter, and Because It Is My Heart, 1990, (as Rosamond Smith) Nemesis, 1990, I Lock My Door Upon Myself, 1990, The Rise of Life on Earth, 1991, Black Water, 1992, (as Rosamond Smith) Snake Eyes, 1992, Foxfire: Confessions of a Girl Gang, 1993, What I Lived For, 1994 (PEN/Faulkner award nomination 1995); (poetry collections) Women in Love, 1968, Expensive People, 1968, Anonymous Sins, 1969, Love and Its Derangements, 1970, Angel Fire, 1973, Dreaming America, 1973, The Fabulous Beasts, 1975, Season of Peril, 1977, Women Whose Lives are Food, Men Whose Lives are Money: Poems, 1978, The Stepfather, 1978, Celestial Timepiece, 1981, Invisible Women: New and

Selected Poems, 1970-1972, 1982, Luxury of Sin, 1983, The Time Traveller, 1987; (plays) The Sweet Enemy, 1965, Sunday Dinner, 1970, Ontological Proof of My Existence, 1970, Miracle Play, 1974, Three Plays, 1980, Daisy, 1980, Presque Isle, 1984, Triumph of the Spider Monkey, 1985, In Darkest America, 1990, I Stand Before You Naked, 1990; (essays) The Edge of Impossibility, 1972, The Hostile Sun: The Poetry of D.H. Lawrence, 1973, New Heaven, New Earth, 1974, Contraries: Essays, 1981, The Profane Art, 1984, On Boxing, 1987, (Woman) Writer: Occasions and Opportunities, 1988; editor, compiler: Scenes from American Life: Contemporary Short Fiction, 1973, (with Shannon Ravenel) Best American Short Stories of 1979, 1979, Night Walks, 1982, First Person Singular: Writer's on Their Craft, 1983, (with Boyd Litzinger) Story: Fictions Past and Present, 1985, (with Daniel Halpern) Reading and Fights, 1988, The Oxford Book of American Short Stories, 1992, The Sophisticated Cat: An Anthology, 1992; editor (with Raymond Smith) Ontario Rev.; contbr. to nat. mags. including N.Y. Times Book Rev., Nat. Quarterly Rev., Mademoiselle, Vogue, North Am. Rev., Hudson Rev., Paris Rev., Grand Street, Atlantic, Poetry, Esquire. Recipient O. Henry award, 1967, 73, Rosenthal award Nat. Inst. Arts and Letters, 1968, O. Henry Spl. award continuing achievement, 1970, 86, Award of Merit Lotos Club, 1975, St. Louis Lit. award, 1988, Rea award for the Short Story, 1990, Alan Swallow award for fiction, 1990, Nobel Prize i Lit. nomination, 1993; Guggenheim fellow, 1967-68, Nat. Endowment for the Arts grantee, 1966, 68. Mem. Am. Acad. and Inst. Arts and Letters. Office: care Ontario Review Press 9 Honey Brook Dr Princeton NJ 08540*

OATES, STEPHEN BAERY, history educator; b. Pampa, Tex., Jan. 5, 1936; s. Steve Theodore and Florence (Baer) O.; divorced; children: Gregory Allen, Stephanie; m. Marie Phillips. B.A. magna cum laude, U. Tex., 1958, M.A., 1960, Ph.D., 1968; Litt.D. (hon.), Lincoln Coll., 1981. Prof. history U. Mass., Amherst, 1971—; now also Paul Murray Kendall prof. biography U. Mass., adj. prof. English, 1980—. Author: Confederate Cavalry West of the River, 1961, Rip Ford's Texas, 1963, Republic of Texas, 1968, Visions of Glory, 1970, To Purge This Land With Blood: A Biography of John Brown, 1970, Portrait of America, 2 vols., 1973, rev. edits., 1976, 83, 86, 90, The Fires of Jubilee: Nat Turner's Fierce Rebellion, 1975, With Malice Toward None: The Life of Abraham Lincoln (Christopher award for outstanding lit.; Barondess/Lincoln award N.Y. Civil War Round Table 1977), Our Fiery Trial: Abraham Lincoln, John Brown, and the Civil War Era, 1979, Let the Trumpet Sound: The Life of Martin Luther King, Jr., 1982 (Christopher award, Robert F. Kennedy Meml. Book award), Abraham Lincoln, The Man Behind the Myths, 1984, Biography as High Adventure: Life Writers Speak on Their Art, 1986, William Faulkner: The Man and the Artist, 1987, A Woman of Valor: Clara Barton and the Civil War, 1994; contbr. articles and essays to periodicals; lectr. Recipient Chancellor's medal for outstanding scholarship U. Mass., 1976, Disting. Teaching award, 1981, Faculty fellowship award, 1981; Mayflower award, 1985; Master Tchr. award U. Hartford, 1985; Silver Medal award Case Council for Advance and Support of Edn., Prof. of Yr., 1986, 87, Kidger award New Eng. History Tchrs. Assn., Nevins-Freeman award Chgo. Civil War Round Table, 1993; Guggenheim fellow, 1972; sr. summer fellow NEH, 1978. Fellow Tex. State Hist. Assn.; mem. Tex. Inst. Letters, Soc. Am. Historians, Am. Antiquarian Soc., Phi Beta Kappa. Office: U Mass Dept History Amherst MA 01003

OATES, WILLIAM ARMSTRONG, JR., investment company executive; b. Pitts., July 27, 1942; s. William Armstrong and Margaret (Nichols) O.; m. Elizabeth Dick Macy, Sept. 7, 1968; children: Elizabeth N., Katherine M., Emily E.A. BA, Colby Coll., 1965; MBA, Harvard U., 1972. Asst. treas. Morgan Guaranty Trust, N.Y.C., 1966-70; trustee, dir. Northeast Investors Trust, Boston, 1972—; pres. Northeast Investors Growth Fund, Boston, 1980—; ptnr. Guild, Monrad & Oates, Inc., 1984—; dir. Horn Corp., Ayer, Mass., Furman Lumber Co., Boston, Clifford Inc., Bethel, Vt. Pres. bd. trustees Groton (Mass.) Sch., 1979; trustee, treas. Roxbury Latin Sch., West Roxbury, Mass., 1975—. Served to 2d lt. Army N.G., 1966-70. Republican. Episcopalian. Clubs: Harvard (Boston); Brookline Country (Brookline, Mass.); Somerset (Boston). Home: 201 Village Ave Dedham MA 02026-4230 Office: Guild, Monrad & Oates Inc 50 Congress St Boston MA 02109-4096

OATWAY, FRANCIS CARLYLE, lumber products, paper company executive; b. Bermuda, Nov. 29, 1936; s. Charles Y. and Josephine (McLellan) O.; m. Ann Thomason; children—Stephen F., Karen E., Andrew C., Christopher M. BSBA, Boston Coll., 1960. C.P.A., Mass., N.Y., others. With Deloitte Haskins & Sells, N.Y.C., 1960-80, ptnr., 1970-80; v.p. taxation Continental Group, Inc., Stamford, Conn., 1980-81, v.p. treasury and taxation, 1981-82, v.p. fin., 1982-83, v.p., chief fin. officer, 1983; exec. v.p., pres., dir. Continental Forest Industries, Inc., Stamford, Conn., 1984-85; pres. Hargro Assocs., Stamford, Conn., 1985—; pres., CEO, dir. Hargro Enterprises, Inc., Stamford, 1985—; chmn., bd. dirs. Hargro Packaging, Exton, Pa., 1985—; chmn. chief exec. officer, bd. dirs. NER Data Products, Glassboro, N.J., 1985—; pres., bd. dirs. Covent Ins. Co. Ltd., Hamilton, Bermuda, 1980-85; chmn. bd., mng. dir. CCC Finanz A.G., Zugi, Switzerland, 1980-85; mng. dir. Continental Group Overseas Fin. N.V., Curacao, Netherlands Antilles, 1981-85; dir. Hansa Reins. Co. Am., Tarrytown, N.Y., chmn. bd. Apple Syndicate Corp., Westport, Conn., 1983-85. Office: Hargro Assocs One Landmark Sq Stamford CT 06901

O'BANNON, FRANK LEWIS, state official, lawyer; b. Louisville, Jan. 30, 1930; s. Robert Pressley and Rosella Faith (Dropsey) O'B.; m. Judith Mae Asmus, Aug. 18, 1957; children: Polly, Jennifer, Jonathan. AB, Ind. U., 1952, JD, 1957. Ind. 1957. Pvt. practice Corydon; ptnr. firm Hays, O'Bannon & Funk, Corydon, 1966-80, O'Bannon, Funk & Simpson, Corydon, 1980—; mem. Ind. Senate, Corydon, 1970-89, minority floor leader, 1979-89, asst. minority floor leader, 1972-76; lt. gov. State of Ind., Corydon, 1989—; chmn., dir. O'Bannon Pub. Co., Inc. Served with USAF 1952-54. Mem. Ind. Dem. Editorial Assn. (pres. 1961), Am. Judicature Soc., Am. Bar Assn., Ind. Bar Assn. Democrat. Methodist. Office: Lt Govs Office 333 State House Indianapolis IN 46204

O'BARR, WILLIAM MCALSTON, anthropologist, educator; b. Sylvania, Ga., Dec. 1, 1942; s. William Jackson and Mary Walter (Clark) O'B.; m. Jean Ellen Fox, Sept. 4, 1965; children: Claire Anne, Emily Catherine. BA, Emory U., 1964; MA, Northwestern U., 1966, PhD, 1969. Research sociologist USPHS, 1964; research assoc. U. Dar-es-Salaam, Tanzania, 1967-68; asst. prof. anthropology Duke U., Durham, N.C., 1969-74; assoc. prof. Duke U., 1974-78, prof., 1978—; prof. sociology, 1988—, chmn. dept. anthropology, 1982-85, 92-93; vis. assoc. prof. Dalhousie U., 1976, Northwestern U., 1978; vis. fellow Wolfson Coll., Oxford U., 1983; adj. prof. law & anthropology U. N.C., Chapel Hill, 1989—; cons. in field. Author: Survey Research in Africa, 1973, Tradition and Identity in Changing Africa, 1973, Language and Politics, 1976, The Student Africanist's Handbook, 1974, Linguistic Evidence: Language, Strategy, and Power in the Courtroom, 1982, Language and Power, 1984, Rules versus Relationships: An Ethnography of Legal Discourse, 1990, Fortune and Folly: The Wealth and Power of Institutional Investing, 1992, Culture and the Ad: Exploring Otherness in the World of Advertising, 1994; author articles. Grantee NSF, 1966, 72-74, 86-89, NIMH, 1967-69, Wenner-Gren Found., 1966, 70; Social Sci. Rsch. Coun. fellow, 1967-69. Mem. Am. Anthrop. Assn., Linguistic Soc. Am., Law and Society Assn., Am. Ethnological Soc., Internat. African Inst., Royal Anthrop. Soc. Gt. Brit. and Ireland, African Studies Assn., U.S. Can. Studies Assn. Democrat. Office: Duke U Dept Cultural Anthropology 114 Social Sciences Bldg Durham NC 27706

OBATA, GYO, architect; b. San Francisco, Feb. 28, 1923; s. Chiura and Haruko (Kohaski) O.; m. Majel Chance, 1947 (div. 1971); children: Kiku, Nori, Gen; m. Courtney Bean, Nov. 28, 1984; 1 child, Max. BArch, Washington U., St. Louis, 1945; MArch in Urban Design, Cranbrook Acad. Art, 1946. Registered architect 39 states, D.C. Sr. designer Skidmore, Owings, & Merrill, Chgo., 1947-51; designer Hellmuth, Yamasaki & Leinweber, Detroit,

1951-55; pres., chmn. bd. dirs. Hellmuth, Obata & Kassabaum, Inc., St. Louis, 1955-93; affiliate prof. Washington U., 1971; frequent lectr. design and urban environment; serves on competition juries on design throughout country. Projects include Nat. Air and Space Mus., King Saud U., Riyadh, Saudi Arabia, Dalls and Houston Galleries, King Khaled Airport, Riyadh, hdqrs. Kellogg Co., hdqrs. BP America, World Bank, Washington, St. Louis Union Sta., Met. Sq., Dallas-Ft. Worth Airport, Squibb Corp. Rsch. Ctr., Lawrenceville, N.J., Burger King Corp. Hdqrs., numerous others. Fellow AIA; mem. Log Cabin Club, Noonday Club, St. Louis Club. Avocations: skiing, tennis. Office: Hellmuth Obata & Kassabaum Inc 211 N Broadway # 600 Saint Louis MO 63102-2733

OBEAR, FREDERICK WOODS, university chancellor; b. Malden, Mass., June 9, 1935; s. William Fred and Dorothea Louise (Woods) O.; m. Patricia A. Draper, Aug. 30, 1959 (dec. Dec. 1993); children: Jeffrey Allan, Deborah Anne, James Frederick. BS with high honors, U. Mass., Lowell, 1956, LHD, 1985; PhD, U. N.H., 1961. Mem. faculty dept. chemistry Oakland U., Rochester, Mich., 1960-81, prof., 1979-81, v.p. for acad. affairs, provost, 1970-81; chancellor U. Tenn., Chattanooga, 1981—; mem. nat. addv. panel Nat. Commn. on Higher Edn. Issues, 1981; mem. pres. commn. NCAA, 1991-94. Trustee Marygrove Coll., 1973-79. Am. Council Edn. fellow, 1967-68. Mem. AAAS, Am. Assn. State Colls. and Univs. (bd. dirs. 1992—, chairperson 1995), Am. Chem. Soc., Am. Assn. Higher Edn., Sigma Xi. Roman Catholic. Office: U Tenn Office of Chancellor 615 Mccallie Ave Chattanooga TN 37403-2504

OBEE, KENT, foreign service officer; b. Colorado Springs, Colo., May 13, 1942; s. Donald and Doli (Shaw) O.; m. Ruth Young, Aug. 10, 1963; children: Brock, Kiran. BSFS, Georgetown U., 1964. Joined U.S. Info. Agy., Washington, 1964; jr. officer trainee U.S. Info. Agy., New Delhi, 1964-65; asst. press officer U.S. Info. Agy., New Delhi, Lucknow, India, 1966-67; br. pub. affairs officer U.S. Info. Agy., Luchnow, India, 1967-70, INA dep. policy officer, 1970-73; pub. affairs officer U.S. Info. Agy., Kathmandu, Nepal, 1973-77, Dar es Salaam, Tanzania, 1977-81; chief of fast media guidance U.S. Info. Agy., Islamabad, Pakistan, 1982, Africa dep. dir., 1983-85, pub. affairs officer, 1985-89; pub. affairs officer U.S. Info. Agy., South Africa, 1989-92; dir. Office North African, Near Eastern and South Asian Affairs U.S. Info. Agy., Washington, 1992—. Office: US Info Agy 301 4th St SW Rm 866 Washington DC 20547-0009

OBENBERGER, THOMAS E., lawyer; b. Milwaukee, Wis., Nov. 29, 1942. AB, Marquette U., 1965, JD, 1967. Bar: Wis. 1967. Law clk. to Hon. E. Harold Hallows Wis. Supreme Ct., 1967-68; mem. Michael, Best & Friedrich, Milw. Mem. editorial bd. Marquette Law Rev., 1966-67. Mem. ABA. Office: Michael Best & Friedrich 100 E Wisconsin Ave Milwaukee WI 53202-4108*

OBENSCHAIN, STEPHEN PHILIP, physicist; b. Staunton, Va., 1949. BS, U. Va., 1971; PhD Physics, U. Calif., L.A., 1977. Recipient excellence in Plasma Physics Rsch. award Am. Physical Soc., 1993. Mem. Am. Physical Soc. Office: Naval Rsch Lab Code # 4730 Washington DC 20011*

OBER, DOUGLAS GARY, investment company executive; b. Balt., Apr. 15, 1946; s. Richard Francis and Caroline Fischer (Gary) O.; m. Rosina Bigham Huppman, July 17, 1971 (div. June 1986); children: Kenneth Houghton, Patrick Macgill; m. Francesmarie Kleinfelter, Aug. 2, 1986; children: William McDonald, Carlin DeLancey. BS in Engring., Princeton U., 1968; cert., U.S. Naval Test Pilot Sch., Patuxent River, Md., 1970; postgrad., Harvard U., 1971-72; M in Fin., Loyola Coll., Balt., 1979; cert., U. Pa., Phila., 1989. Chartered fin. analyst. Test project engr. U.S. Naval Air Test Ctr., Patuxent River, 1968-71; credit analyst First Nat. Bank of Md., Balt., 1972-78, v.p., 1978-80; securities analyst The Adams Express Co., Balt., 1980-86, exec. v.p., 1986-88, also bd. dirs., vice chmn., chief exec. officer, 1990-91, chmn., chief exec. officer, bd. dirs., 1991—; exec. v.p. Petroleum & Resources Corp., Balt., 1986-89, vice chmn., 1989-91, chmn., chief exec. officer, bd. dirs., 1991—; bd. govs. Investment Co. Inst., 1993—. Trustee Mary Byrd Wyman Meml. Assn., Balt. Mem. Princeton Alumni Assn. of Md. (bd. dir. 1989—), N.Y. Soc. Security Analysts, Balt. Security Analysts Soc., Md. Club, Elkridge Club, Sky Club. Republican. Episcopalian. Avocations: skiing, sailing, model trains. Home: 1915 Old Court Rd Ruxton MD 21204-1851 Office: Adams Express Co 7 St Paul St Baltimore MD 21202-1626

OBER, ERIC W., broadcasting executive. BA, Yale U.; Woodrow Wilson Fellow, Columbia U. With CBS, 1966—; newswriter, producer, exec. producer, asst. news dir., WCBS-TV N.Y.C.; news dir., WCAU-TV, Phila.; news dir. WBBM-TV Chgo.; v.p. news CBS TV stations, 1981-82; v.p., station mgr. WCBS-TV; v.p., gen. mgr. WBBM-TV Chgo., 1983-84; v.p. pub. affairs broadcasts CBS News, 1984-87; pres. CBS TV Stations, from 1987; now pres. CBS News Div. Served with U.S. Army. Office: CBS Inc 524 W 57th St New York NY 10019-2902

OBER, JOSIAH, history educator; b. Brunswick, Maine, Feb. 27, 1953; s. Nathaniel and Patricia Wilder (Stride) O. B.A., U. Minn., 1975, M.A., 1977; Ph.D., U. Mich., 1980. Asst. prof. history Mont. State U., Bozeman, 1980-84, assoc. prof., 1984-88, prof., 1988-90; prof. classics, Princeton U., 1990—; chmn. Dept. Classics, 1994—; vis. prof. U. Mich., Ann Arbor, 1986-87; sr. rsch. assoc. Am. Sch., Classical Studies, Athens, 1981, 83, 85, 88; vis. lectr. Archeol. Inst. Am., 1984-87; Martin Classical lctr. Oberlin Coll., 1994; Magie chair in Classics, 1994—; bd. dirs Princeton U. Press. Author: Fortress Attica, 1985, Mass and Elite in Democratic Athens, 1989. Contbr. articles to profl. jours. Grantee Am. Council Learned Socs., 1981, NEH, 1981, 89, Nat. Humanities Center N.C., 1983-84. Mem. Archaeol. Inst. Am., Am. Philol. Assn. (bd. dirs.), Am. Sch. Classical Studies, Classical Assn. Can., Phi Alpha Theta. Home: 55 Aiken Ave Princeton NJ 08540-5257 Office: Princeton U Dept Classics Princeton NJ 08544

OBER, RICHARD FRANCIS, JR., lawyer, banker; b. Balt., Dec. 12, 1943; s. Richard Francis and Caroline Fisher (Gary) O.; m. Carol Laycock Munger, Aug. 25, 1973; children: Julia Keyser, Margaret Delancey. A.B. cum laude, Princeton U., 1965; LL.B., Yale U., 1968. Bar: Md. 1968, Pa. 1970, N.J. 1977. Law clk. to chief judge Md. Ct. Apls., Annapolis, 1968; assoc. Ballard, Spahr, Andrews & Ingersoll, Phila., 1969-75; gen. counsel UJB Fin. Corp. Princeton, N.J., 1975—, sec., 1978—, sr. v.p., 1982-88, exec. v.p., 1988—; bd. dirs., sec. United Jersey Credit Life Ins. Co., UJB Credit Corp., N.J. Spl. Olympics; sec. United Jersey Bank, United Jersey Leasing Co., United Jersey Venture Capital, Inc.; fire commr. South Brunswick (N.J.) Fire Dist. 3, 1981-85; Republican county committeeman, 1975—; v.p. Republican Assn. Princeton; Princeton Day Sch., trustee, 1986-92, treas., 1988-92, vice chmn., 1990-92; trustee Yale Law Sch. Assn. N.J. Mem. ABA, Bank Corp. Counsel Com. (chmn. 1979-80), N.J. Bar Assn. (mem. gen. coun. 1982-85, 93-94, mem. exec. com. banking law sect. 1979-94, sec. sect. 1980-81, vice chmn. 1981-82, chmn. 1984-85), N.J. Corp. Counsel Assn. (exec. com. 1980—, 2d v.p. 1982-85, pres. 1985-86, chmn. banking and fin. instns. com. 1984-85), Am. Bankers Assn. (exec. com. bank counsel until 1990—, vice chmn. 1993—, chmn. 1994-95), N.J. Bankers Assn. (chmn. bank lawyers coun. 1993-94), N.J. Bus. and Industry Assn. (legal affairs com.), Pa. Bankers Assn. (Legal Affairs com.), Phila. Bar Assn., Assn. Corp. Counsel Am., Princeton Bar Assn., Bankers Roundtable, Lawyers Coun. Episcopalian. Club: Bedens Brook (Princeton).

OBER, RUSSELL JOHN, JR., lawyer; b. Pitts., June 26, 1948; s. Russell J. and Marion C. (Hampson) O.; m. Kathleen A. Stein, Apr. 8, 1972; children: Lauren Elizabeth, Russell John III. BA, U. Pitts., 1970, JD, 1973. Bar: Pa. 1973, U.S. Dist. Ct. (we. dist.) Pa. 1973, U.S. Tax Ct. 1982, U.S. Ct. Appeals (4th cir.) 1976, U.S. Ct. Appeals (3d cir.) 1979, U.S. Ct. Appeals (7th cir.) 1985, U.S. Ct. Appeals (2d cir.), 1990, U.S. Ct. Appeals (7th cir.) 1993, U.S. Supreme Ct. 1976. Assn. dist. atty. Allegheny County, Pitts., 1973-75; pvt. Wallace Chapas & Ober, Pitts., 1975-80, Rose, Schmidt, Hasley & DiSalle, Pitts., 1980-92, Meyer, Unkovic & Scott, Pitts., 1992—. Bd. dirs. Parent and Child Guidance Ctr., Pitts., 1983-90, treas., 1985-86, pres. 1986-88; bd. mgmt. South Hills Area YMCA, 1989-91; mem. Mt. Lebanon Traffic Commn., 1976-81; bd. dirs. Whale's Tale Youth Family Counseling Ctr., 1990—. Mem. ABA (discovery com. litigation sect. 1982-88, ho. of dels. young lawyers div. 1982-83), Pa. Bar Assn. (ho. of dels. 1983—), Allegheny

County Bar Assn. (chmn. young lawyers sect. 1983, bd. govs. 1984, fin. com. 1984-88, mem. coun. civil litigation sect. 1991-93), Nat. Bd. Trial Advocacy (diplomate), Acad. Lawyers Allegheny County (fellow 1983—, bd. govs. 1988-90) U. Pitts. Law Alumni Assn. (bd. govs. 1984-89, v.p. 1985-87, pres. 1987-88), Rivers Club, Chartiers Country Club. Home: 393 Parker Dr Pittsburgh PA 15216-1323 Office: Meyer Unkovic & Scott 1300 Oliver Bldg Pittsburgh PA 15222

OBER, STUART ALAN, investment consultant, book publisher; b. N.Y.C., Oct. 2, 1946; s. Paul and Gertrude E. (Stollerman) O.; m. Joanne Michaels, Sept. 20, 1981; 1 son, Erik Kenneth. BA, Wesleyan U., Middletown, Conn., 1968; postgrad., U. Sorbonne, Paris, 1970, CUNY, 1976-77. Pres., editor-in-chief, chmn. bd. Beekman Pubs. Inc., N.Y.C., 1972—; investment cons., 1972—; tax investment specialist Loeb, Rhoades & Co., 1976-77; div. dir. tax investment dept. Josephthal & Co., Inc., 1977; mgr. tax investment dept. Bruns, Nordeman, Rea & Co., 1978-80; pres. Ober Tax Investment Cons., 1980—, Securities Investigations, Inc., 1981—; sr. v.p. Cash Franchise Mgmt., Inc., 1988-89. Author: Everybody's Guide to Tax Shelters; editor-in-chief: Ober Income Letter, 1983-88; pub.: Tax Shelter Blue Book, 1983—. Bd. dirs., pres. Woodstock Playhouse Assn., 1985-87; trustee Maverick Concerts, 1986—; chmn. Woodstock Arts and Cultural Com., 1988. Mem. Inst. Cert. Fin. Planners (fin. standards product bd. 1986—, treas. 1988—, bd. dirs.). Office: PO Box 888 Woodstock NY 12498-0888

OBERDANK, LAWRENCE MARK, lawyer, arbitrator; b. Cleve., Nov. 1, 1935; s. Leonard John and Mary (Pavelich) O.; m. Arlene C. Baldini, Aug. 25, 1962; 1 child, Karen A. BA, Western Res. U., 1958, JD, 1965. Bar: Ohio 1965, U.S. Dist. Ct. (no. dist.) Ohio 1966, U.S. Ct. Appeals (6th cir.) 1968, U.S. Supreme Ct. 1970. Assoc. Law Offices Mortimer Riemer, Cleve., 1965-69; ptnr. Riemer and Oberdank, Cleve., 1969-76; prin. Lawrence M. Oberdank Co., L.P.A., Cleve., 1976—; arbitrator Ohio Employment Rels. Bd., 1985-89, Cleve. Civil Svc. commn. 1983—, FMHA, 1989—; chmn. mandatory arbitration panel Ct. Common Pleas; mem. Nat. Mediation Bd., 1986—; instr. indsl. rels. law Cleve. State U., 1982-85; instr. labor rels. Cuyahoga C. C., 1983; arbitrator/mediator U.S. Dist. Ct. (no. dist.) Ohio, ea. divsn. fee dispute panel Cleve. Bar Assn.; mem. securities arbitration panel Am. Stock Exchange. Lt. USNR, 1958-62. Mem. ABA (labor and employment sect., labor arbitration, law collective bargaining agreements, alternate dispute resolution sect., fed. ct. annexed/connected programs com.), Am. Arbitration Assn. (securities arbitrator, nat. labor panel 1973—, comml. arbitration panel, construction industry panel), Nat. Assn. Securities Dealers Inc., Bar Assn. Greater Cleve. (labor law com.), Cuyahoga County Bar Assn., Fed. Bar Assn., Am. Judicature Soc., Internat. Soc. Labor Law and Social Legislation, Ohio State Bar Assn. (chmn. labor law sect. 1970-73), Indsl. Rels. Rsch. Assn., Pub. Sector Labor Rels. Assn., Soc. Profls. in Dispute Resolution (bd. dirs. Southwest Ohio chpt.), Masons, Phi Gamma Delta. Roman Catholic. Avocations: golf, Civil War history. Home: 8051 Lakeview Ct N Royalton OH 44133-1214 Office: 815 Superior Ave E Cleveland OH 44114-2516

OBERDORFER, JEFF, architect, firm executive; b. Bronx, N.Y., May 8, 1947. BArch, Kent State U., 1970. Lic. arch., Calif. Instr. spatial design, lighting, multi-media Mus. Fine Arts, Boston, 1972-76; prin. Jeff Oberdorfer & Assocs. Archs., Cambridge, Mass., 1973-76, Jeff Oberdorfer & Assocs., Inc., Santa Cruz, Calif., 1980—; instr. Goodard/Cambridge Grad. Sch. for Social Change, 1975-76; vis. instr. comty. design U. Calif., Santa Cruz, 1979-80. Prin. works include North Cambridge Cmty. Ctr. (Quality of Life Competition award City of Cambridge, Mass.), Agassiz Cmty. Planning Process, Cambridge (City Spirit award NEH, 1979), Boulder Creek Libr. (Nat. Excellence award in libr. design ALA/AIA, 1987), Felton Covered Bridge (Renaissance 87 Design awards Nat. Assn. Home Builders Remodelers Coun., 1987, Ann. Design award for outstanding achievement in design preservation projects Calif. Preservation Found., 1987, Nat. Hist. Preservation award Adv. Coun. Hist. Preservation, 1988), Felton Town Plan (Outstanding Planning award Am. Planning Assn., 1988), Soquel Village Plan (Outstanding Planning award Am. Planning Assn., 1991), Washington St. Cooperative Apts., 1991, others. Active Lighthouse Field Adv. Commn., 1978-84, City of Santa Cruz (Calif.) Zoning Bd., 1980-84, Environ. Coun. Bd. Dirs., 1989-92. Mem. AIA, Am. Planning Assn., Internat. Conf. Bldg. Officials, Environ. Design Rsch. Assn. Office: Jeff Oberdorfer & Assoc Inc 303 Potrero St # 306 Santa Cruz CA 95060-2741

OBERDORFER, LOUIS F., federal judge; b. Birmingham, Ala., Feb. 21, 1919; s. A. Leo and Stella Maud (Falk) O.; m. Elizabeth Weil, July 31, 1941; children: John Louis, Kathryn Lee, Thomas Lee, William L. A.B., Dartmouth, 1939; LL.B., Yale, 1946. Bar: Ala. bar 1946, D.C. bar 1949. Law clk. to Justice Hugo L. Black, 1946-47; pvt. practice, 1947-51; mem. firm Wilmer, Cutler, & Pickering (and predecessors), 1951-61, 65-77; asst. atty. gen. tax div. Dept. of Justice, 1961-65; judge, now sr. judge U.S. Dist. Ct. (D.C. dist.), 1977—; vis. lectr. Yale Law Sch., 1966-71; adv. com. Fed. Rules Civil Procedure, 1962-84; co-chmn. lawyers com. Civil Rights Under Law, 1967-69; adj. prof. law Georgetown U., Washington, 1993—. Editor-in-chief Yale Law Jour., 1941. Served to capt. AUS 1941-46. Mem. ABA, D.C. Bar Assn. (bd. govs. 1972-77, pres. 1977), Ala. Bar Assns., Am. Law Inst., Yale Law Sch. Assn. (pres. 1971-73). Office: US Dist Ct US Courthouse 3d and Constitution Ave NW Washington DC 20001

OBERG, LARRY REYNOLD, librarian; b. Midvale, Idaho; s. Gustav Wilhelm and Esther Marie (Watkins) O.; m. Marilyn Ann Gow, Jan. 1, 1964 (div. 1985); 1 child, Marc Aurelien. AB in Anthropology, U. Calif., Berkeley, 1977, MLS, 1978. Reference librarian Stanford (Calif.) U., 1979-80, U. Calif., Berkeley, 1981-82; dir. library Lewis-Clark State Coll., Lewiston, Idaho, 1984-86, Albion (Mich.) Coll., 1986-92; univ. libr. Willamette U., Salem, Oreg., 1993—. Author: Human Services in Postrevolutionary Cuba, 1985 (named a Choice Outstanding Acad. Book, Choice Editors 1984-85); mem. editl. bd. College and Research Libraries; mem. adv. bd. Jour. Info. Ethics; contbr. articles to profl. jours. Mem. Am. Library Assn., Oreg. Library Assn., Phi Beta Kappa. Democrat. Office: Willamette U Mark O Hatfield Libr 900 State St Salem OR 97301

OBERG, ROGER WINSTON, management educator; b. Mpls., Oct. 5, 1919; s. Ezra Nathaniel and Adele Erika Wilhelmina (Boquist) O.; m. Pansy Jane Sherrill, June 29, 1957; children: Sherrill Katherine, Roger Winston, Keith Eric, Elizabeth Jane. Student, North Park Coll., 1937-38; B.B.A. with distinction, U. Minn., 1941; M.B.A., Ohio State U., 1947; Ph.D., M.I.T., 1955. Mgmt. trainee Sears Roebuck & Co., 1941-43; grad. asst. Ohio State U., 1946-47, M.I.T., 1947-50; human relations research analyst Prudential Ins. Co., Newark, 1950-51; personnel specialist Esso Research & Engring. Co., Linden, N.J., 1952-57; assoc. prof. mgmt. Mich. State U., 1957-65, prof. mgmt., 1965-86, prof. emeritus, 1986—; vis. prof. Leeds U., Eng., 1959, U. Rio Grande do Sul, Brazil, 1959-61, Stanford U., 1964, North European Mgmt. Inst., Norway, 1974-76; World Bank cons. to Bangladesh univs., 1985. Served to 2d lt. USAAF, 1943-46, PTO. Recipient Forensic medal U. Minn., 1941, Lit. Rev. prize, 1941. Mem. Beta Gamma Sigma, Delta Sigma Rho. Mem. Evangelical Covenant Ch. Clubs: University (Mich. State U.), Scandinavian Am. Home: 1585 Hillside Dr Okemos MI 48864-2319

OBERHELMAN, HARRY ALVIN, JR., surgeon, educator; b. Chgo., Nov. 15, 1923; s. Harry Alvin and Beatrice (Babel) O.; m. Betty Jane Porter, June 12, 1946; children: Harry Alvin III, James I., Robert P., Thomas L., Nancy L. Student, Yale U., 1942-43; B.S., U. Chgo., 1946, M.D., 1947. Diplomate: Am. Bd. Surgery. Intern U. Chgo. Clinics, 1947-48, resident in surgery, 1948-51, 52-57; asst. prof., then assoc. prof. surgery U. Chgo. Sch. Medicine, 1957-60; mem. faculty Stanford (Calif.) Sch. Medicine, 1960—, prof. surgery, 1964—; mem. div. licensing Calif. Bd. Med. Quality Assurance, 1970-82. Author papers in field. Served with USAF, 1951-53. Mem. AMA, Calif. Med. Assn., Soc. Univ. Surgeons, Am., Western, Pacific Coast surg. assns., Soc. Alimentary Tract, Halsted Soc., Fedn. State Med. Bds. U.S. (bd. dirs. 1979-82). Home: 668 Cabrillo St Stanford CA 94305

OBERHUBER, KONRAD JOHANNES, art museum curator, educator; b. Linz/Donau, Austria, Mar. 31, 1935. Ph.D., U. Vienna, Austria, 1959, Dozent, 1971. Asst. U. Vienna; delegated as research fellow to Austrian Inst. in Rome, 1959-61; asst., then curator Albertina, Vienna, 1961-71; research curator Nat. Gallery Art, Washington, 1971-74; guest lectr. Fogg Art Mus., Harvard U., Cambridge, Mass., spring 1974; curator of drawings,

prof. fine arts Fogg Art Mus., Harvard U., 1974-85, Ian Woodner curator of drawings, prof. fine arts, 1985-87; dir. Graphische Sammlung Albertina, Vienna, 1987—; T.A.O. prof. U. Vienna, 1991; Italian Ministry of Culture scholar, Rome, winter 1958; asst. prof. Smith Coll., 1964-65; Kress fellow Harvard Center for Renaissance Studies, Florence, Italy, 1965-66; guest prof. Cambridge (Eng.) U., 1968. Author: Raphael, Die Zeichnungen, 1983, Poussin, The Early Years in Rome, 1988; contbr. articles to profl. jours. fellow Inst. Advanced Study Princeton, N.J., 1974-75; Nat. Endowment Humanities grantee, 1979-80; Gerda Henkel Stiftung grantee, 1983-84. Mem. Print Council Am. Office: Graphische Sammlung Albertina, Augustinerstrasse 1, A-1010 Vienna Austria

OBERLANDER, CORNELIA HAHN, landscape architect; b. Muelheim-Ruhr, Germany, June 20, 1924; arrived in U.S., 1939; d. Franz and Lotte Beate (Jastrow) H.; m. H. Peter Oberlander, Jan. 2, 1953; children: Judith A., Timothy A., Wendy E. BA, Smith Coll., 1944; B of Landscape Architecture, Harvard U., 1947; LLD (hon.), U. British Columbia, 1991. guest prof. U. B.C. Dept. Landscape Architecture, 1992; lectr. for guided tour Renaissance Gardens of No. Italy, Smith Coll. Alumni Assn., 1988; mem. adv. com. on design Nat. Capital Commn., 1975-82; mem. adv. panel, co-founder Children's Play Resource Centre, Vancouver, 1978—; lectr. in field. Prin. works include Cathedral Place, Vancouver, B.C., 1991-93, New Pub. Library, 1992—, Asian Inst., U. B.C., 1993—, Thunderbird Housing, U. B.C., 1992—, Chan Shun Performing Arts Centre, 1992—, Kwantlen Coll., 1991—, Cariboo Coll., 1991—, N.W. Territories Legis. Bldg., 1991—, UN Peacekeeping Meml., 1990—, Ritsumeikan U. B.C. Ho., 1990—, Ottawa City Hall, 1989—, Environ. Sci. Bd., Ward Environ. Garden, Trent U., 1989—, Canadian Chancery, Washington D.C., 1983-89. Recipient medal Smith Coll., 1982, Regional Honor award and Nat. Merit award Christopher Phillips Landscape Architects, Inc., 1992, Cathedral Place, 1983-88, Nat. Gallery of Can., Ottawa, Ontario, Can. Chancery Am. Assn. of Nurseymen, 1990, Grand award for L'Ambassade du Can., Landscape Contractors Assn., 1989, Can. Architect award of Excellence, Matsuzaki Wright Architects, Inc., 1989, Amenity award City of Vancouver for Robson Square, 1986, Citation award Can. Soc. of Architects for Chancery & Nat. Gallery, 1990. Fellow Am. Soc. Landscape Architects, Can. Soc. Landscape Architects (pres. 1986-87, pres. elect. 1985-86, chair environ. com. 1987-88, Internat. Citation award 1991, Nat. and Regional Citation award 1989); mem. Order of Can., Royal Can. Acad. Arts. Home: 1372 Acadia Rd, Vancouver, BC Canada V6T 1P6

OBERLANDER, HERBERT, insect physiologist, educator; b. Manchester, N.H., Oct. 2, 1939 s. Solomon and Minnie (Shapiro) O.; m. Barbara Judith Marks, June 12, 1962; children: Jonathan, Beth. BA cum laude in Zoology, U. Conn., 1961; PhD in Biology, Western Res. U., 1965. Postdoctoral fellow U. Zurich (Switzerland), 1965-66; asst. prof. Brandeis U., Waltham, Mass., 1966-71; rsch. physiologist USDA, Agrl. Rsch. Svc., Gainesville, Fla., 1971-76, rsch. leader, physiology unit, insect attractants lab., 1976-84, lab. dir. insect attractants, behavior and basic biology rsch. lab., Gainesville, 1984—; prof. entomology U. Fla., Gainesville, 1979—. NSF fellow, 1961-65; NIH fellow, 1965-66; NSF Research grantee, 1966-71, 83; grantee U.S.-Israel BARD, 1989-93. Fellow Entomol. Soc. Am.; mem. Tissue Culture Assn., Entomol. Soc. Am., Phi Beta Kappa, Sigma Xi, Phi Kappa Phi. Contbr. chpts. to books, articles to profl. jours. Office: USDA Insect Attractant Behav Lab PO Box 14565 1700 SW 23rd Dr Gainesville FL 32604-2565

OBERLANDER, RONALD Y., paper manufacturing company executive. Past exec. v.p. Abitibi-Price Inc., Toronto, Ont., Can., now pres. and CEO. Office: Abitibi-Price Inc, Toronto-Dominion Ctr, Toronto, ON Canada M5K 1B3 Office: 45 Rockefeller Plz New York NY 10111*

OBERLIES, JOHN WILLIAM, construction company executive; b. Rochester, N.Y., June 9, 1939; s. Hubert H. and Martha (Voght) O.; m. Mary Theresa Sundholm, Sept. 29, 1962; children: Katie, Daniel. BCE, Villanova U., 1961; MBA, U. Rochester, 1978. From surveyor to purchasing agt. Rochester Gas & Electric Co., 1959-79, gen. mgr., 1979-82, v.p., 1982-87, sr. v.p., 1988-90; chief ops. officer Le Chase Constrn., Inc., Rochester, 1990—; bd. dirs. Transmation, Inc. Trustee Aquinas Inst., Rochester; Cath. Charities, Rochester, bd. dirs., 1984-85; chmn. bd. Preferred Care, Inc., Rochester, 1986—; mem. Diocesan Pastoral Coun., Health Futures of Rochester Commn.; bd. dirs. Rochester Area Found., 1984-85, Highland Hosp.; chmn. nominations com. United Way, Rochester; mem. Rochester Housing Partnership Commn. Served with U.S. Army, 1961-62. Mem. Rochester C. of C. (chmn. polit. action com. 1987). Republican. Avocation: fishing. Home: 242 Shoreham Dr Rochester NY 14618-4112 Office: Le Chase Constrn Inc 300 Trolley Blvd Rochester NY 14606-4209

OBERLY, CHARLES MONROE, III, state attorney general; b. Wilmington, Del., Nov. 9, 1946; s. Charles M. and Prudence Elizabeth (Curry) O.; children: Kimberly, Michael and Kristi-Lyn (twins). AA, Wesley Coll., 1966; BAA, Pa. State U., 1968; JD, U. Va., 1971. Bar: Del. Clk. U.S. Dist. Ct., 1971-72; assoc. Morris James Hitchens & Williams, Wilmington, Del., 1972-75; dep. atty. gen. Del. Dept. Justice, 1974-82, state prosecutor, 1976-78; atty. gen. State of Del., Wilmington, 1982—; instr. U. Del. Mem. Phi Beta Kappa, Phi Kappa Phi. Democrat. Lutheran. Office: Office of Atty Gen Justice Dept 820 N French St Wilmington DE 19801-3552

OBERMAN, MICHAEL STEWART, lawyer; b. Bklyn., May 21, 1947; s. Hyman Martin and Gertrude O.; m. Sharon Land, Oct. 8, 1975; 1 child, Abigail Land. AB, Columbia U., 1969; JD, Harvard U. 1972. Bar: N.Y. 1973, U.S. Dist. Ct. (so. and ea. dists.) N.Y. 1973, U.S. Ct. Appeals (2d cir.) 1973, U.S. Supreme Ct. 1976, Calif. 1981, U.S. Dist. Ct. (no. dist.) Calif. 1981, U.S. Ct. Appeals (9th cir.) 1981, U.S. Dist. Ct. (so. and cen. dists.) Calif. 1982, U.S. Ct. Appeals (5th cir.) 1989, D.C. 1992, U.S. Ct. Appeals (7th cir.) 1993. Law clk. to Hon. Milton Pollack U.S. Dist. Ct. (so. dist.) N.Y., 1972-73; assoc. Kramer, Levin, Naftalis, Nessen, Kamin & Frankel, N.Y.C., 1973-79, ptnr., 1980—. Contbr. articles to profl. jours. Recipient Nathan Burkan prize ASCAP, 1973. Mem. N.Y. State Bar Assn. (mem. ho. of dels. 1989-91, exec. com. comml. and fed. litigation sect.). Office: Kramer Levin Naftalis Nessen Kamin & Frankel 919 Third Ave New York NY 10022

OBERMAN, SHELDON ARNOLD, writer, educator; b. Winnipeg, Manitoba, Canada, May 20, 1949; s. Allan and Dorothy (Stein) O.; m. Lee Anne Block, Sept. 8, 1973 (div. Mar. 9, 1990); children: Adam, Mira; m. Lisa Ann Dveris, Sept. 2, 1990; 1 child: Jesse. BA in English, U. Winnipeg, Man., Can., 1972; BA in English with honors, U. Jerusalem, Israel, 1973; teaching cert., U. Man., Winnipeg, Can., 1974. tchr. W. C. Millar Collegiate, Altona, Man., Can., 1975-76, Joseph Wolinsky Collegiate, Winnipeg, Man., Can., 1976-95. Author: The Folk Festival Book, 1983, Lion in the Lake: A French English Alphabet Book, 1988, Julie Gerond and the Polka Dot Pony, 1988, TV Sal and the Game Show From Outer Space, 1993, This Business With Elijah, 1993, The Always Prayer Shawl, 1994, The White Stone in the Castle Wall, 1995; co-editor: A Mirror of a People: The Canadian Jewish Experience in Poetry and Prose, 1985. Nat. Jewish Book award Jewish Book Coun., 1995, Sydney Taylor award, 1995, Best Book of the Yr. A Child's Mag., 1994, Pick of the List award Am. Bookseller, 1994, Can. Author Short Story award Canadian Author's Assn., 1987; Bliss Carmen Poetry prize Banff Sch. of Fine Arts, 1980; various writer and film maker grants. Avocations: public address, acting, collage sculptor, canoing. Home: 822 Dorchester Ave, Winnipeg, MB Canada R3M 0R7

OBERMANN, C. ESCO, psychologist, rehabilitation consultant; b. Yarmouth, Iowa, July 31, 1904; s. Albert B. and Evalyne (Calloway) O.; m. Avalon F. Law, June 3, 1929. A.B., U. Iowa, 1926, M.A., 1931, Ph.D., 1938. Diplomate Am. Bd. Profl. Psychologists. Chief vocational edn. Rochester (Minn.) Schs., 1928-36; research fellow U. Iowa, Iowa City, 1938-40; asso. prof. psychology U. Iowa, 1966-70, U. Tex., Austin, 1946; dir. vocational rehab. VA, 1946-60; dir. Pa. Paul Rehab. Center, 1960-63; research fellow Vocational Rehab. Adminstrn., 1963-65; assoc. prof. psychology Iowa Wesleyan Coll., Mt. Pleasant, 1965-66; rsch. assoc. 1970—; adj. instr. Mankato (Minn.) State U., 1977—; mem. adv. com. Ctr. for Advance Studies, U. Iowa, 1979—; mem. com. handicapped People-to-People Program. Author: A History of Vocational Rehabilitation in America, 1965, Coordination of Services for Handicapped Children and Youth, 1963, (with others) Continuing Education for Rehabilitation Counselors, 1969; Editor: (with others) Basic Issues In Rehabilitation, 1972. Served to col. USAAF, 1940-46. Recipient Disting. Alumnus award U. Iowa, 1986, Merit award Nat. Iowa Lettermens Club, 1991. Fellow Am. Psychol. Assn., AAAS; mem. Nat. Rehab. Counseling Assn., Nat. Rehab. Assn. (pres. 1961-62), Minn. Rehab. Assn. (pres. 1954), Iowa Rehab. Assn. (pres. 1967), Am. Personnel and Guidance Assn., Am. Speech and Hearing Assn., Assn. Advancement of Psychology, Masons, Sigma Xi, Delta Upsilon. Episcopalian. Home: Cambridge Pl 1851 Melrose Ave Apt # 112 Iowa City IA 52246-1754 Office: U Iowa Obermann Ctr Advanced Study Iowa City IA 52246

OBERNAUER, MARNE, corporate executive; b. Pitts., Mar. 6, 1919; s. Arthur H. and Anna (Somerman) O.; m. Joan Strassburger, Aug. 1, 1941; children: Marne Jr., Wendy Damon. Grad., Cornell U. 1941. Chmn. exec. com. Devon Group, Inc., Stamford, Conn.; chmn. Beverage Distbrs. Corp. and BDH Inc., Aurora, Colo.; pres. Doric Securities Co.; bus. cons., pvt. investor. Pres., bd. dirs. The Obernauer Found., Inc. Served to lt. USNR, 1942-45. Mem. Hillcrest Country Club (L.A.), Concordia Club (Pitts.), Century Country Club (Purchase, N.Y.), Banyan Golf Club (Palm Beach, Fla.). Office: Devon Group In 281 Tresser Blvd #501 Stamford CT 06901-3227

OBERNAUER, MARNE, JR., investment company executive; b. Lakehurst, N.J., July 1, 1943; s. Marne and Joan Carolyn (Strassburger) O.; m. Marion Fleck Gislason, Aug. 22, 1976; children: Matthew Gene, Michael Sidney. BA, Yale U., 1965; MBA, Harvard U., 1972. With First Nat. City Bank (Citibank, N.A.), N.Y.C., 1965-70, Donaldson, Lufkin & Jenrette, N.Y.C., 1972-74; with Devon Group, Inc. N.Y.C. and Stamford, Conn., 1974—, pres., 1978, chief exec. officer, 1980—, chmn. bd., 1986—; bd. dirs. Devon Group Inc., Beverage Distbrs. Corp. Trustee Trinity Sch., The Obernauer Found., Inc.; bd. dirs. Com. for Responsible Fed. Budget, Assocs. of Harvard Bus. Sch. Mem. Am. Bus. Conf. (bd. dirs., vice chmn.), Yale Club of N.Y.C. Office: Devon Group Inc 450 Park Ave New York NY 10022-2605

OBERNDORF, MEYERA E., mayor; m. Roger L. Oberndorf; children: Marcie, Heide. BS in Elem. Edn., Old Dominion U., 1964. Broadcaster Sta. WNIS, Norfolk, Va.; mem. city coun. City of Virginia Beach, Va., 1976—, vice-mayor, 1986, mayor, 1988—. Mem. exec. bd. Tidewater coun. Boys Scouts Am.; bd. dirs. Virginia Beach Pub. Libr., 1966-76, chmn. bd., 1967-76. Mem. AAUW, U.S. Conf. Mayors, Va. Mcpl. League (exec. bd.), Nat. League Cities (vice-chmn.), Princess Anne Women's Club. Jewish. Home: 5404 Challedon Dr Virginia Beach VA 23462-4112 Office: Office of the Mayor Municipal Ctr City Hall Bldg Virginia Beach VA 23456*

OBERREIT, WALTER WILLIAM, lawyer; b. Paterson, N.J., Oct. 7, 1928; s. William and Gertrud (Limpert) O.; m. Anne-Marie Gohier, July 6, 1955; children: Stephan, Alexis, Jerome. BA, U. Mich., 1951; diploma, U. Paris Inst. Polit. Studies, 1955; JD, Yale U., 1958. Bar: N.Y. Assoc. Cleary, Gottlieb, Steen & Hamilton, N.Y.C., 1958-62, Paris, 1962-66; assoc. Cleary, Gottlieb, Steen & Hamilton, Brussels, 1966-67, ptnr., 1967—. Contbr. articles to profl. jours., chpts. to books. Lt. (j.g.) USN, 1953-55. Mem. ABA, Assn. of Bar of City of N.Y. (co-chmn. com. on rels. with European Bars 1981—), Am. Arbitration Assn., Ctr. European Policy Studies, Inst. Royal Rels. Internat., Union Internat. Des Avocats. Clubs: Cercle Royal Gaulois, Cercle Nations, Am. Common Market (Brussels). Avocations: sailing, tennis, skiing. Home: Ave Geo Bernier 7, 1050 Brussels Belgium Office: Cleary Gottlieb Steen & Hamilton, rue de la Loi 23, 1040 Brussels Belgium

O'BERRY, CARL GERALD, air force officer, electrical engineer; b. Lansing, Mich., Apr. 11, 1936; s. Gerald Ray and Edith Lenore (Watson) O'B.; m. Charlene Marice Bussche, June 21, 1958; children: Brian, Eileen, Kevin, Bradley, Kathleen. BSEE, N.Mex. State U., 1972; MS in Systems Mgmt., Air Force Inst. Tech., 1977. Commd. 2d lt. USAF, 1961, advanced through grades to lt. gen., 1993; comdr. 2019 Communications Squadron, Griffiss AFB, N.Y., 1974-76; project engr. Rome Air Devel. Ctr., Griffiss AFB, 1979-81; asst. dep. chief of staff requirements Air Force Systems Command, Andrews AFB, Md., 1982-84; comdr. Rome Air Devel. Ctr., Griffiss AFB, 1984-86; joint program mgr. WWMCCS info. system Hdqrs. USAF, Washington, 1986-88; dir. command, control and communications U.S. European Command, Stuttgart, Fed. Republic Germany, 1988-90; dir. command control systems and logistics U.S. Space Command, Peterson AFB, Colo., 1990-92; command control comm. and computers DCS, HQ USAF, Washington, 1992—. Mem. Air Force Assn., Armed Forces Communications-Electronics Assn., Soc. Logistics Engrs. Roman Catholic. Office: USAF HQ USAF/SC Washington DC 20330-5190

O'BERRY, PHILLIP AARON, veterinarian; b. Tampa, Fla., Feb. 1, 1933; s. Luther Lee and Marjorie Mae (Mahlum) O'B.; m. Terri Martin, July 31, 1960; children: Kelly, Eric, Holly, Danny, Andy, Toby, Michael Asefa. BS in Agr., U. Fla., 1955; DVM, Auburn U., 1960; PhD, Iowa State U., 1967. With Agrl. Rsch. Svc. USDA, 1956—; asst. to dir. vet. scis. rsch. div. USDA, Beltsville, Md., 1967-72; asst. dir. Nat. Animal Disease Ctr., Ames, Iowa, 1972-73, dir., 1973-88, nat. tech. transfer coord., 1988—; prin. scientist Office Agr. Biotech., USDA, Ames, 1988-90; adj. prof. Coll. Vet. Medicine, Iowa State U., 1973—; mem. expert panel livestock infertility FAO; sci. adv. com. Pan Am. Zoonosis Ctr., Buenos Aires; mem. Fed. Coun. Sci. and Tech.; mem. com. animal health, world food and nutrition study NRC; cons. Govt. of Italy, USDA; mem. nat needs grad. fellowship rev. panel USDA, 1989-91, cons. agr. biotech. rsch. adv. com.; mem. sci. adv. bd. Biotech. R&D Corp., 1992—; sci. review bd. Am. Bur. Vet. Rsch., 1990-92; mem. USDA Patent Review Com., 1988—. Author 27 research publs. Recipient Cert. of Merit, Agrl. Rsch. Svc., 1972, 84, Alumni Merit award Iowa State Club of Chgo., 1982, Cert. Appreciation, 1988, Tech. Transfer award, 1989, USDA, Disting. Alumnus award Auburn U., 1991. Mem. APHA, AVMA, AAAS, Nat. Assn. Fed. Vets., Iowa Vet. Med. Assn., N.Y. Acad. Scis., Conf. Rsch. Workers Animal Diseases, Am. Soc. Microbiology, Am. Assn. Lab. Animal Sci., U.s. Animal Health Assn., Am. Assn. Bovine Practitioners, Livestock Cons. Inst., Sigma Xi, Phi Zeta, Phi Kappa Phi, Gamma Sigma Delta (Alumni award Merit 1976), Alpha Zeta, Spades, Blue Key. Democrat. Home: 3319 Woodland St Ames IA 50014-3550 Office: Nat Soil Tilth Lab Rm 114 Ames IA 50011

OBERST, PAUL, law educator; b. Owensboro, Ky., Apr. 22, 1914; m. Elizabeth Durfee; children—Paul, James, George, Mary, John. A.B., U. Evansville, 1936; J.D., U. Ky., 1939; LL.M., U. Mich., 1941. Bar: Ky. 1938, Mo. 1942. Assoc. firm Ryland, Stinson, Mag & Thomson, Kansas City, Mo., 1941-42; asst. prof. law Coll. of Law, U. Ky., Lexington, 1946-47; prof. Coll. of Law, U. Ky., 1947-82; acting dean, 1966-67; emeritus prof. Coll. of Law, U. Ky., 1982—; vis. prof. of law U. Chgo., 1954-55, Duke U., 1980; prof., dir. civil liberties program N.Y. U., 1959-61; mem. Nat. Commn. on Acad. Tenure, 1971-73. Contbr. articles to legal jours. Mem. Ky. Commn. on Corrections, 1961-65; mem. Ky. Commn. on Human Rights, 1962-66, 80-90, chmn., 1966-70, 73-76; trustee U. Ky., Lexington, 1963-69, 72-75; mem. Ky. state adv. com. U.S. Civil Rights Commn., 1979-92, chmn., 1982-86. Served to lt. USNR, 1942-46. Mem. Assn. Am. Law Schs. (exec. com. 1970-72), Am., Ky. bar assns., Am. Law Inst., Order of Coif, Phi Delta Phi. Home: 829 Sherwood Dr Lexington KY 40502-2919

OBERSTAR, JAMES L., congressman; b. Chisholm, Minn., Sept. 10, 1934; s. Louis and Mary (Grillo) O.; m. Jo Garlick, Oct. 12, 1963 (dec. July 1991); children: Thomas Edward, Katherine Noelle, Anne-Therese, Monica Rose; m. Jean Kurth, Nov. 1993; stepchildren: Corinne Quinlan Kurth, Charles Burke Kurth, Jr. B.A. summa cum laude, St. Thomas Coll., 1956; postgrad. in French, Laval U., Que., Can.; M.S. in Govt. (scholar), Coll. Europe, Bruges, Belgium, 1957; postgrad. in govt. Georgetown U. Administrv. asst. Congressman John A. Blatnik, 1963-74; administr. Pub. Works Com. U.S. Ho. of Reps., 1971-74; mem. 94th-104th Congresses from 8th Minn. Dist., 1975—; ranking minority mem. transp. and infrastructure subcom. on aviation. Mem. Am. Polit. Sci. Assn. Office: US Ho of Reps 2366 Rayburn HOB Washington DC 20515-2308*

OBERT, CHARLES FRANK, banker; b. Cleve., Apr. 28, 1937; s. Carl William and Irene Frances (Urban) O.; m. Linda Marie Thoss, June 3, 1961; children—Lisa Marie, Charles David. Student, Ohio State U., 1955-57. With Ameritrust Corp., Cleve., 1958—, sr. v.p. affiliate bank div., 1975-80,

sr. v.p. corp. service div., 1980-87, sr. v.p. br. adminstrn., 1987-92, mgmt. cons., 1993—; pres. Acoustical Cleaning Systems Inc. Mem. Solon (Ohio) Recreation Commn., 1978-94, Solon Bd. Edn., 1986-94. Mem. Am. Inst. Banking, Am. Bankers Assn., Nat. Corp. Cash Mgmt. Assn., Ohio Bankers Assn., Bank Adminstrn. Inst., Internat. Assn. Laryngectomees, Cleve. Hearing and Speech Ctr., Greater Cleve. Growth Assn., Solon C. of C., Cleve. Athletic Club. Home and Office: 8270 Pebble Creek Ct Chagrin Falls OH 44023

OBERT, PAUL RICHARD, manufacturing company executive, lawyer; b. Pitts., Aug. 24, 1928; s. Edgar F. and Elizabeth T. (Buchele) O. B.S., Georgetown U., 1950; J.D., U. Pitts., 1953. Bar: Pa. 1954, D.C. 1956, Ohio 1972, Ill. 1974, U.S. Supreme Ct. 1970. Sole practice Pitts., 1954-60; asst. counsel H.K. Porter Co., Inc., Pitts., 1960-62, sec., gen. counsel, 1962-71; sec., gen. counsel Addressograph-Multigraph Corp., Cleve., 1972-74; v.p. law Marshall Field & Co., Chgo., 1974-82, sec., 1976-82; v.p., gen. counsel, sec. CF Industries, Inc., Long Grove, Ill., 1982—, also officer, dir. various subs. Served to lt. col. USAF. Mem. ABA (corp. gen. counsel com.), Pa. Bar Assn., Allegheny County Bar Assn., Ill. Bar Assn., Chgo. Bar Assn., Am. Soc. Corp. Secs., Am. Retail Fedn. (bd. dirs. 1977-80), Georgetown U. Alumni Assn. (bd. govs.), Pitts. Athletic Assn., Univ. Club, Delta Theta Phi. Office: CF Industries Inc 1 Salem Lake Dr Long Grove IL 60047-8402

OBEY, DAVID ROSS, congressman; b. Okmulgee, Okla., Oct. 3, 1938; s. Orville John and Mary Jane (Chellis) O.; m. Joan Therese Lepinski, June 9, 1962; children: Craig David, Douglas David. BS in Polit. Sci, U. Wis., 1960, MA, 1962. Mem. Wis. Gen. Assembly, 1963-69, asst. minority leader, 1967-69; mem. 91st-104th Congresses from 7th Wis. dist., 1969—; ranking minority mem. appropriations com., ranking minority mem. labor, HHS and edn. subcom., mem. joint econ. com.; mem. adminstrv. com. Wis. Dem. Com., 1960-62. Named Edn. Legislator of Yr., Rural div. NEA, 1968; recipient Legislative Leadership award Eagelton Inst. Politics, 1964, award of merit Nat. Council Sr. Citizens, 1976, citation for legis. statesmanship Council Exceptional Children, 1976. Office: US Ho of Reps 2462 Rayburn HOB Washington DC 20515*

OBLAD, ALEXANDER GOLDEN, chemistry educator, research chemist; b. Salt Lake City, Nov. 26, 1909; s. Alexander H. and Louie May (Brewster) O.; m. Bessie Elizabeth Baker, Feb. 23, 1933; children: Alex Edward, Elizabeth (Mrs. D. Sonne), Virginia Oblad Christensen, John R.B., Hayward B., Jean Rio B. (Mrs. S. Calder). BA in Chemistry, U. Utah, 1933, MA in Phys. Chemistry, 1934, DS (hon.), 1980; PhD in Phys. Chemistry, Purdue U., 1937, DS (hon.), 1959. Research chemist Standard Oil Co., Whiting, Ind., 1937-42; Magnolia Petroleum Co., Dallas, 1942-43; sect. leader Magnolia Petroleum Co., 1943-46, chief chem. research, 1946; head indsl. research Tex. Research Found., Dallas, 1947; dir. chem. research Houdry Process Corp., Marcus Hook, Pa., 1947-52; assoc. mgr. research and devel. Houdry Process Corp. 1952-55, mgr., 1955, v.p., dir., 1955-57; v.p. research and devel. M.W. Kellogg Co., N.Y.C., 1957-66, v.p. rsch. and engring. devel., patent and licensing, and process engring., 1966-69; v.p. IRECO Chems., Salt Lake City, 1969-70; prof. metallurgical and fuels engring. U. Utah, 1969-75, disting. prof. metallurgical and fuels engring., 1975-92, prof. chemistry, 1975—; assoc. dean U. Utah Coll. of Mines and Earth Scis., 1970-72, dean, 1972-75; disting. prof. dept. Chemical and Fuels Engring. Coll. Engring. U. Utah, Salt Lake City, 1992—; co-founder, dir. Ireco Chemicals Co., Salt Lake City, 1958-72, 74-75; mem. Sec. of Interior's Saline Water Conversion Adv. Com., Office of Saline Water, Washington, 1959-61; mem. fossil energy research working group Dept. Energy, 1980-82. Mem. editorial bd.: Catalysis Revs., Fuel Processing Tech, 1976—; mem. internat. adv. bd.: Ency. of Chem. Processing and Design, 1973—; contbr. numerous articles on phys. chemistry, catalysis, petroleum chemistry and chem. engring. to tech. and sci. jours.; patentee in field. Mem. alumni research council Purdue Research Found., Lafayette, Ind., 1960-63; chmn. sustaining membership campaign Orange Mountain council Boy Scouts Am., 1966-67; mem. nat. adv. council Sch. Bus., Brigham Young U., Provo, Utah, 1968-81, U. Utah, 1968-77, Dixie Coll., 1987—; bd. dirs. Internat. Congress on Catalysis, 1956-65. Recipient First Purdue Chemist's award, 1959, Distinguished Alumni award U. Utah, 1962. Mem. AAAS, Am. Chem. Soc. (mng. editor publs. div. petroleum chemistry 1957-69, sec./treas. div. petroleum chemistry 1952-54, chmn. petroleum chem. 1956, E.V. Murphree award 1969), Am. Inst. Chem. Engrs., Western States Catalysis Soc., Rocky Mountain Fuel Soc., Nat. Acad. Engring., Am. Inst. Chemists (Chem. Pioneer award 1972), Utility Shareholders Assn. Utah (trustee 1980-94), Sigma Xi, Phi Lambda Upsilon, Sigma Pi Sigma, Phi Kappa Phi, Tau Beta Pi. Mem. LDS Ch. Home: 1415 Roxbury Rd Salt Lake City UT 84108-2842 Office: U Utah 113 Energy Mineral Rsch Bu Salt Lake City UT 84112

OBLAK, JOHN BYRON, academic administrator; b. Little Falls, N.Y., June 1, 1942; s. Henry John Oblak and Lillian Ann (Walrath) Farber; m. Janiece Bacon, Nov. 12, 1966; children: Jeb, Jonathan, Jolynn, Jessica. BS in Speech Edn., State U. Coll. Arts & Scis., Geneseo, N.Y., 1964; MA in Speech/Theatre, U. Nebr., 1966; PhD in Theatre History, U. Kans., 1971. Tech. dir. U. Nebr., Lincoln, 1964-66; asst. instr. speech/theatre U. Kans., Lawrence, 1966-69; asst. prof. speech Ind. State U., Terre Haute, 1969-79, asst. dean student life, 1970-73, acting dir. theatre/acad. chmn., 1973-75, asst. dean summer and evening sessions, 1975-76, asst. dean acad. services and spl. programs, 1976-79; dir. summer sessions and continuing edn. Ithaca (N.Y.) Coll., 1979-80, assoc. dean summer sessions and continuing edn., 1980-82, dean sch. humanities and scis., assoc. prof., 1982-88, v.p. student affairs and campus life, 1988—; adminstrv. advisor to All-Univ. Ct. Appeals Ind. State U., mem. non-acad. com. Univ. Student Affairs, chmn. search com. for chmn. speech dept., adminstrv. advisor to interfraternity student ct., mem. univ. housing com.; mem. personnel tng. and devel. com. Ithaca Coll., calendar com., chmn. Greek Life Rev. Com. Author: Bringing Broadway to Maine: The History of Lakewood–1900-1969, 1971; contbr. articles to profl. jours. Committeeman Cub Scouts Am., Ithaca, 1979-80, den leader, 1980-82; committeeman Boy Scouts Am., Ithaca, 1981-85, Dems., 1990-93; chmn. publicity com., bd. dirs. Hangar Theatre, Ithaca, 1980-83; mem. allocations bd. United Way, Ithaca, 1979-82, chmn. Ithaca Coll. United Way fund raising campaign, 1981-83, campaign solicitor, Terre Haute, 1976-79; trustee Village of Lansing, N.Y., 1981-85; bd. dirs. Community Theatre Terre Haute, 1976-79, Cayuga Chamber Orch., 1988-90; adv. bd. Tompkins County Tourism Devel., 1991-94; chair Tompkins County United Way Campaign, 1993; pres. Bd. Tompkins County C. of C. (bd. dirs. 1985-88). Democrat. Roman Catholic. Home: 34 Highgate Cir Ithaca NY 14850-1484 Office: Ithaca Coll VP Student Affairs & Campus Life Ithaca NY 14850

OBLANDER, CHARLES P., university official; b. Augusta, Kans., Jan. 22, 1958; s. Charles J. and Frances M. (Hendricks) O.; m. Tamara J. Bervert; children: Shawna M., Shandy M. BS in Elec. Engring. Tech., Kans. State U., 1980; MS in Tech. Tchr. Edn., Pittsburg (Kans.) State U., 1991. Field svc. engr. Gen. Dynamics, Ft. Worth, 1981-82, Jostens Pub., Topeka, 1984-85; computer technician computer Topeka, 1983-84; instr. microprocessor sys. Kaw Area Tech. Sch., Topeka, 1985-91; adminstr. computer network Kans. State U., Manhattan, 1991—. Office: Kansas State U. 406 Trotter Hall Manhattan KS 66506

O'BLOCK, ROBERT PAUL, management consultant; b. Pitts., Mar. 9, 1943; s. Paul Joseph and Mary Elizabeth (Galicic) O'B.; m. Megan Marie. BSME, Purdue U., 1965; MBA, Harvard U., 1967. Rsch. and teaching fellow in fin., econs. and urban mgmt., Harvard U., 1967-70; assoc. in real estate mgmt. and fin. McKinsey & Co., Inc., Boston 1969-78, prin., 1979-84, dir., 1984—; gen. and mng. ptnr. Freeport Center, Clearfield, Utah, 1971—; vis. lectr. urban econs. Yale Law Sch., Princeton U.; cons. Mass., N.J. housing fin. agys., Rockefeller Assn.; HUD, 1968-76; chmn. mgmt. com. Snowbird Lodge (Utah), 1974-86. Mem. nat. adv. bd. Snowbird Arts Inst., 1977-83; mem. budget com. N.Y. Pub. Libr., 1977-79; mem. adv. bd. Internat. Tennis Hall of Fame, 1986-89, bd. dirs., 1989—; mem. bd. overseers Boston Symphony Orch., 1988—, vice-chmn. bd. overseers, 1992-95, chmn., 1995—; mem. bd. trustees U.S. Ski Ednl. Found., 1989—. Rsch. fellow Harvard U., 1967. Roman Catholic. Clubs: River (N.Y.C.), Devon Yacht, Maidstone (East Hampton, N.Y.), Nat. Golf Links Am. (Southampton, N.Y.), Alta (Salt Lake City), Ogden (Utah) Golf, The Country Club (Brookline, Mass.). Contbr. articles to profl. jours. Office: McKinsey & Co Inc 75 Park Pl 3d fl Boston MA 02116

OBNINSKY, VICTOR PETER, lawyer; b. San Rafael, Calif., Oct. 12, 1944; s. Peter Victor and Anne Bartholdi (Donston) O.; m. Clara Alice Bechtel, June 8, 1969; children: Mari, Warren. BA, Columbia U., 1966; JD, U. Calif., Hastings, 1969. Bar: Calif. 1970. Sole practice, Novato, Calif., 1970—; arbitrator Marin County Superior Ct., San Rafael, 1979—; superior ct. judge pro tem, 1988-90; lectr. real estate and partnership law. Author: The Russians in Early California, 1966. Bd. dirs. Calif. Young Reps., 1968-69, Richardson Bay San. Dist., 1974-75, Marin County Legal Aid Soc., 1976-78; baseball coach Little League, Babe Ruth League, 1970-84; mem. nat. panel consumer arbitrators Better Bus. Bur., 1974-88; leader Boy Scouts Am., 1970-84; permanent sec. Phillips Acad. Class of 1962, 1987—; mem. Phillips Acad. Alumni Council, 1991—; bd. community advisors Buck Ctr. for Rsch. on Aging. Mem. State Bar Calif., ABA, Marin County Bar Assn. (bd. dirs. 1985-91, treas. 1987-88, pres.-elect 1989, pres. 1990), Phi Delta Phi, Phi Gamma Delta. Republican. Russian Orthodox. Office: 2 Commercial Blvd Apt 103 Novato CA 94949-6121

OBOLENSKY, IVAN, investment banker, foundation consultant, writer, publisher; b. London, May 15, 1925; s. Serge and Alice (Astor) O. (parents Am. citizens); m. Claire McGinnis, 1949 (div. 1956); children—Marina Ava, Ivan Serge, David; m. Mary Elizabeth Morris, 1959; 1 child, Serge. AB, Yale U., 1947. Pres. Hotel Investments, Inc., N.Y.C., 1950-58; v.p., treas. Serge Obolensky Assocs., 1952-75; dir., chmn., pres. Ivan Obolensky Inc., pubs., 1956-65; dir. Silver Bear Inc., Atlanta; ptnr. A.T. Brod & Co., investment bankers, Dominick & Dominick Inc., investment bankers, 1965-70, Middendorf Colgate, investment bankers, 1970-73; v.p. C.B. Richard, Ellis/Moseley Hallgarten, investment bankers, 1974-81, Sterling Grace & Co., investment bankers, N.Y.C., 1982-87; sr. v.p. Jesup, Josephthal & Co., investment bankers, N.Y.C., 1987-90; gen. ptnr. Astor Capital Mgmt. Assocs., 1980—; v.p. Capital Mgmt. Assocs., N.Y.C., 1990—; v.p. Shields & Co., N.Y.C., 1990—; cons. and lectr. in field. Author: Rogues' March, 1956; contbr. to Nihon Keizai Shimbun, Tokyo, on precious metals, 1985—; program com. N.Y. Soc. of Security Analysts for pub., oil and gas; contbr. articles to profl. publs. Bd. dirs. Police Athletic League, N.Y.C., 1975-85, exec. com. 1980-85, U.S.O., 1987—, Audubon Canyon Ranch, Calif. 1989—, Tolstoy Found., 1994—, Soldiers', Sailors' and Airmen's Club, 1976—, pres., 1987—, Russian Nobility Assn. in Am., 1990—, treas., 1991—, Musicians Emergency Fund, 1985-93, pres., 1987-92, Children's Blood Found., N.Y. Hosp., 1952—, pres., 1981-95; pres., dir. Josephine Lawrence Hopkins Found., 1971—; pres. Whitemarsh Found., 1980-90. Lt. (j.g.) USNR, 1943-45, ret., 1980. Mem. Am. Legion, Mil. Order Loyal Legion U.S. (sr. vice-comdr. 1955, comdr. 1967-70), St. Elmo Soc., Met. Mus. Art (life), Knickerbocker Club, N.Y. Yacht Club, New Eng. Soc. N.Y., St. Georges Soc. N.Y., The Navy League, West Point Soc., Army and Navy Club, Explorers Club, Masons (Holland #8 master 1981, dist. dep. grand master 1st Manhattan 1983-84, grand treas. 1994—). Office: Shields & Co 71 Broadway New York NY 10006-2601

OBOLENSKY, MARILYN WALL (MRS. SERGE OBOLENSKY), metals company executive; b. Detroit, Aug. 13, 1929; d. Albert Fraser and Christine (Frischkorn) Wall; m. Serge Obolensky, June 3, 1971. Student, Duschesne Jr. Coll., 1947. Chmn. bd. Wall-Colmondy Corp., Detroit, 1959-61, exec. sec., 1961—; chmn. bd. Wall-Gases Inc., Morrisville, Pa., 1959-61; pres. Serge Obolensky Assocs. Bd. dirs. Heart and Lung Assn. N.Y.C., 1963—. Republican. Roman Catholic. Clubs: Bathing Corp. (Southampton, N.Y.), Southampton. Home: 45 Preston Pl Grosse Pointe Farms MI 48236

OBOMSAWIN, ALANIS, director, producer; b. Lebanon, N.H., Aug. 31, 1932; arrived in Can., 1933; d. Herman and Maria (Benedict) O.; 1 child Kisos. Dir., prodr. numerous filmstrips, 2 multimedia packages, 2 vignettes, 6 half hour 16mm films for ednl. TV; dir. 10 documentaries, short fiction film for children about racism; author, composer album Bush Lady, 1988. Chair bd. dirs. Native Women's Shelter Montreal; mem. Can. Coun.'s Native Adv. Com. Recipient several prizes for her films. Mem. Order of Can. Office: care Nat Film Bd CAN, CP 6100 Succ A, Montreal, PQ Canada H3C 3H5

O'BOYLE, ROBERT L., landscape architect; b. Alma, Mich., Oct. 26, 1935; s. Frederick and Ella (Keefer) O'B.; m. Kay Louise Wells, Dec. 18, 1954; children—Robert M., Brian P., Cathleen S., Andrew F. B.A., Alma Coll., 1958; B.S. in Landscape Architecture, Mich. State U., 1960. Registered landscape architect, Mich. Landscape designer Jane Smith Assocs., Lansing, Mich., 1959-61; park planner State of Mich., Lansing, 1961-62; landscape architect Light's Landscape, Richland, Mich., 1962-64; pres. O'Boyle, Cowell, Blalock & Assocs., Inc., Kalamazoo, 1964—; mem. Bd. Licensing and Registration, State of Mich., 1970-76. Contbr. articles to profl. jours. Bd. dirs. Kalamazoo Nature Ctr., 1971-76, Kalamazoo County Parks Commn., 1974-78; bd. dirs. Kalamazoo Flower Fest, Inc., 1983-89, pres., 1987-88; Parchment Downtown Devel. Authority, 1991—. Fellow Am. Soc. Landscape Architects (trustee Mich. chpt., awards 1980, 89, v.p. 1991-92); mem. Am. Forestry Assn., Kalamazoo County C. of C. (chair transp. com. 1993—), Rotary (editorian 1985-). Methodist. Avocations: sailing; photography; wood working. Home: 311 E Thomas Ave Kalamazoo MI 49004-1446 Office: O'Boyle Cowell Blalock & Assocs 521 S Riverview Dr Kalamazoo MI 49004-1230

O'BOYLE, THOMAS FRANCIS, editor, newspaper, writer; b. Newark, Nov. 12, 1955; s. Thomas Edward and Mae Vera (Redding) O'B.; m. Louise Mathews, Sept. 15, 1979; children: Brendan, Cara, Erin. BA, Allegheny Coll., 1978; MS in Journalism, Northwestern U., 1979. Journalist bus. Crain's Chgo. Bus., 1979-80, Pitts. Post-Gazette, 1980-81; journalist bus. fgn. corr., dep. bur. chief Wall St. Jour., Pitts., Bonn, 1981-92; author Pitts., 1992-94; editor bus. Pitts. Post-Gazette, 1994—. Presbyterian.

OBRAMS, GUNTA IRIS, research administrator; b. Düsseldorf, Germany, Sept. 2, 1953; came to U.S., 1961; d. Robert and Olga (Baltins) O.; m. Malcolm DeWitt Patterson, Dec. 22, 1975; 1 child, Andrew McDougal Patterson. BS in Biology cum laude, Rensselaer Poly. Inst., 1977; MD, Union U., Albany, N.Y., 1977; MPH, Johns Hopkins U., 1982, PhD, 1988. Resident in obstetrics and gynecology Ea. Va. Grad. Sch. Medicine, Norfolk, 1977-78; community physician Southampton Meml. Hosp., Franklin, Va., 1978-81; resident in gen. preventive medicine sch. hygiene and pub. health Johns Hopkins U., Balt., 1981-84, project dir., 1983-85, med. dir., 1985-86; med. officer divsn. cancer etiology Nat. Cancer Inst., Bethesda, Md., 1986-89, dep. chief, 1989-90, chief, 1990—. Editor: (with M. Potter): The Epidemiology and Biology of Multiple Myeloma, 1991; contbr. articles to profl. jours. With USPHS, 1987—. Recipient Nat. Cancer Inst. Nat. Rsch. Svc. award, 1981, Rsch. Career award Nat. Inst. Occupational Safety & Health; scholar Am. Med. Women's Assn., 1977. Mem. Phi Beta Kappa, Delta Omega, Alpha Omega Alpha. Office: National Cancer Institute 6130 Executive Blvd Ste 535 Bethesda MD 20892

O'BRIAIN, NIALL P., wood products company executive. Formerly sr. v.p. Fraser Inc., Edmundston, N. B., Canada, pres., 1988—; sr. v.p. Noranda Forest Inc., Toronto, Ont., 1988—. Office: Fraser Inc, 27 Rice St, Edmundston, NB Canada E3V 1S9

O'BRIAN, JACK, journalist; b. Buffalo, Aug. 16, 1921; s. Charles Joseph and Josephine Loretto (Kelleher) O'B.; m. Yvonne Johnston, Jan. 15, 1947; children—Bridget Mary, Kate Mary. D.Litt. (hon.), Niagara U., Niagara Falls, N.Y., 1966, St. John's (U., Wyndham, Maine, 1975, St. John's U., N.Y.C., 1978, Canisius Coll., Buffalo, 1979. With Buffalo Times, 1939, N.Y. World-Telegram, 1939-40, Buffalo News, 1940, Buffalo Courier-Express, 1940-43; drama critic, daily N.Y. columnist, movie and music critic Broadway columnist AP, 1943-49; columnist N.Y. Jour.-Am., 1949-67, Voice of Broadway, King Features Syndicate, N.Y.C., 1967—; host daily radio show Critics Circle, WOR, N.Y.C.; Bicentennial lectr. history of Am. theatre Columbia U., 1976; lectr. Fordham U., Caldwell Coll., Harvard Univ. Club, N.Y. U., New Sch. Social Research. (nominated for Pulitzer prize 1942, 61-62); Author: The Great Godfrey, 1953; Contbr. articles to popular mags. Bd. dirs. Damon Runyon-Walter Winchell Fund for Cancer Research. Named One of the Five Most Influential U.S. TV Critics, Ford Found.; recipient Christophers award, 1955, Deems Taylor award ASCAP, 1974, 76, 79, 81, United Jewish Appeal award, 1955, Am. Legion award 1955, Nat. Catholic War Vets. award, 1972, Morality in Media award, 1971, 73, World Mercy Fund award, 1975, George M. Cohan award Cath. Actors Guild,

1977, Theater award L.I.U., 1982; media sect. Buffalo Conv. Ctr. named in his honor, 1991. Mem. Cath. Actors Guild (nat. pres. 1978—). Home: 225 E 73d St New York NY 10021 Office: Sta WOR 1440 Broadway New York NY 10018-2301 also: King Features Syndicate 235 E 45th St New York NY 10018

O'BRIEN, ALBERT JAMES, management consultant; b. St. Louis, Oct. 30, 1914; s. James Daniel and Lydia Helena (Dreher) O'B.; m. Ruth Virginia Foster, Mar. 26, 1938 (dec. Jan. 1991); children: Denis James, James Douglas, Douglas Alan; m. Nancy Johnson Schuessler, Oct. 30, 1994. A.B., Washington U., St. Louis, 1935, A.M., 1940; LL.B., Mo. Inst. Law and Accountancy, 1944. Banking trainee, asst. mgr. indsl. service dept. First Nat. Bank, St. Louis, 1935-42; spl. asst. to gen. mgr. Atlas Powder Co., Weldon Springs, Mo., 1942-44; personnel mgr. prodn., mgr. prodn. staff dept. Ralston Purina Co., 1944-57, sec., 1957-59, v.p. finance, sec., 1959-61, exec. v.p., 1961-68, pres., 1968-69, vice chmn. bd., 1969-71; chmn. exec. com. R. Rowland & Co., St. Louis, 1972-74; bus. mgmt. cons., 1974—; chmn. bd. Union Bank of Ill., Union Ill. Co., State Bank of Jerysville, Ill. Mem. adv. bd. Salvation Army; bd. dirs. Met. YMCA, Boy Scouts Am., United Way Greater St. Louis; investment trustee St. Louis Pub. Sch. Retirement System; bd. dirs. Coll. of Ozarks. Presbyn. Clubs: Mo. Athletic (St. Louis), Algonquin Golf (Webster Groves, Mo.). Home: 5 Doubletree Ln Saint Louis MO 63131-3908

O'BRIEN, CHARLES G., furniture manufacturing company executive; b. 1931. BSIE, Va. Poly Inst. and State Univ. Served USN, 1948-52; with Armstrong World Industries Inc., from 1956; from v.p. to sr. v.p. to exec. v.p. Thomasville Furniture Industries Inc., 1975—. Office: Thomasville Furniture PO Box 339 Thomasville NC 27361-0339

O'BRIEN, CHARLES H., state supreme court chief justice; b. Orange, N.J., July 30, 1920; s. Herbert Rodgers and Agnes Sidman (Montanya) O'B.; m. Anna Belle Clement, Nov. 9, 1966; children: Merry Diane, Steven Shawn (dec.), Heather Lynn. LLB, Cumberland U., 1947. Rep. Tenn. Legislature, Memphis, 1963-65, senator, 1965-67; assoc. judge Tenn. Ct. Criminal Appeals, Crossville, 1970-87; assoc. justice Tenn. Supreme Ct., 1987-94, chief justice, 1994—; ret. Bd. dirs. Lake Tansi Village Property Owners Assn., 1984-89. With U.S. Army, 1938-45, ETO, 1950, UN Command, Tokyo. Decorated Bronze Star, Purple Heart with oak leaf cluster. Fellow Tenn. Bar Found.; mem. ABA, Tenn. Bar Assn., Cumberland County Bar Assn., Am. Legion, Lake Tansi Village Chowder and Marching Soc. (pres.). Democrat. Avocation: outdoor activities. Office: 403 Division St Crossville TN 38555

O'BRIEN, CHARLES O., chemical company executive; b. Albany, N.Y., Dec. 11, 1929; s. John E. and Ann (Drew) O'B.; m. Maureen T. Kenny, June 2, 1951; children: Ellen, Kenneth Charles, Christopher, Gail, Deirdre, Gregory. B.S. magna cum laude, Fordham U., 1955, LL.B. with honors, 1959; grad. Advanced Mgmt. Program, Harvard U., 1973. Bar: N.Y. State, 1959. Atty. CIBA-Geigy Corp., Ardsley, N.Y., 1962-66, v.p. mktg. agrl. div., 1966-70, exec. v.p., chief operating officer, 1986—; pres. agr. div. CIBA-Geigy Corp., Greensboro, N.C., 1970-82; pres. pharms. div. CIBA-Geigy Corp., Summit, N.J., 1982-86; bd. dirs. Summit and Elizabeth Trust. Bd. dirs. United Way, Greensboro, N.C. Mem. Pharms. Mfrs. Assn. (bd. dirs. 1982), Greensboro C. of C. Roman Catholic. Office: CIBA-GEIGY Corp 444 Saw Mill River Rd Ardsley NY 10502-2600

O'BRIEN, CONAN, writer, performer, talk show host; b. Brookline, Mass., Apr. 18, 1963. BA Am. Hist., Lit., Harvard U., 1981-85. staff mem. The Harvard Lampoon, 1981-85 (pres. 1983, 84). Stage appearances with: The Groundlings (L.A.) 1985-87; writer, performer The Happy Happy Good Show (L.A., Chgo.) 1988; writer (TV) Not Necessarily the News (HBO) 1985-87, Saturday Night Live, 1988-91 (NBC, Emmy Outstanding Writing in Comedy series 1989), Lookwell (NBC) 1991; writer, prodr. The Simpsons (Fox) 1991-93, The Wilton North Report (syndicated) 1987, Late Night with Conan O'Brien (NBC) 1993—. Office: Late Night with Conan O'Brien NBC 30 Rockefeller Ctr New York NY 10112*

O'BRIEN, DANIEL WILLIAM, lawyer, corporation executive; b. St. Paul, Jan. 6, 1926; s. Daniel W. and Kathryn (Zenk) O'B.; m. Sarah Ward Stoltze, June 20, 1952; children: Bridget Ann, Daniel William, Kevin Charles, Timothy John. Student, U. Dubuque, 1943, Ill. State U., 1944; B.S.L., U. Minn., 1948, LL.B., 1949. Bar: Minn. 1949. Practice in St. Paul, 1950—; partner Randall, Smith & Blomquist, 1955-65; of counsel Doherty, Rumble & Butler, 1965—; pres. F.H. Stoltze Land & Lumber Co., 1964—, Maple Island, Inc., 1968—; dir. Villaume Industries, Inc., Evercolor Corp. Served to ensign USNR, 1943-46. Mem. Minn., Ramsey County bar assns., World Pres's. Orgn., Chief Execs. Orgn. Home: 4734 Bouleau Rd White Bear Lake MN 55110 Office: 219 Main St N Stillwater MN 55082-5021

O'BRIEN, DARCY, English educator, writer; b. Los Angeles, July 16, 1939; s. George and Marguerite (Churchill) O'B.; m. Ruth Ellen Berke, Aug. 26, 1961 (div. 1968); 1 child, Molly; m. Suzanne Beesley, Feb. 27, 1987. A.B., Princeton U., 1961; postgrad., Cambridge (Eng.) U., 1963-64; M.A., U. Calif., Berkeley, 1963, Ph.D., 1965. Asst. prof. English Pomona Coll., Claremont, Calif., 1965-70, assoc. prof., 1970-75, prof., 1975-78; prof. English U. Tulsa, 1978—. Author: The Conscience of James Joyce, 1968, W.R.Rodgers, 1971, Patrick Kavanagh, 1975, A Way of Life, Like Any Other (Ernest Hemingway Found. award 1978), Moment By Moment, 1978, The Silver Spooner, 1981, Two of a Kind, 1985, Murder in Little Egypt, 1989, Margaret in Hollywood, 1991, A Dark and Bloody Ground, 1993. Woodrow Wilson fellow, 1961-62; U. Ill. Ctr. for Advanced Study fellow, 1969-70; Mellon Found. fellow, 1973-74; Guggenheim fellow, 1978-79. Mem. PEN, James Joyce Soc., Internat. Assn. Crime Writers, Authors Guild, Am. Irish Hist. Soc., Screen Writers Guild. Office: U Tulsa Dept English 600 S College Ave Tulsa OK 74104-3189

O'BRIEN, DAVID MICHAEL, political science educator, researcher; b. Rock Springs, Wyo., Aug. 30, 1951; s. Ralph Rockwell and Lucile (Resel) O'B.; m. Claudine Mendelovitz, Dec. 19, 1982; children: Benjamin Michael, Sara Ashley, Talia Michelle. BA, U. Calif.-Santa Barbara, 1973, MA, 1974, PhD, 1977. Lectr. U. Calif.-Santa Barbara, 1976-77; asst. prof. U. Puget Sound, Tacoma, Wash., 1977-79; chmn. polit. sci. dept., 1978-79; assoc. prof., prof. polit. sci., grad. advisor U. Va., Charlottesville, 1983-92; rsch. assoc. U.S. Supreme Ct., Washington, 1983-84; cons. Nat. Acad. Pub. Adminstrn., 1985; vis. fellow in Constn. studies Oxford U., 1987-88. Author: Privacy, Law and Public Policy, 1979 (Outstanding Book in Polit. Sci. award 1979), The Public's Right to Know, 1981 (Outstanding Book in Polit. Sci. award 1981), Storm Center: The Supreme Court in American Politics, 1986 (Silver gavel award ABA), What Process is Due?, 1987, Judicial Roulette, 1988, Constitutional Law and Politics, 2 vols., 1991, Abortion and American Politics, 1993, Supreme Court Watch; editor: (with others) Views from the Bench, 1985, The Politics of Technology Assessment, 1982. Fellow Russell Sage Found., 1981-82, U.S. Supreme Ct., 1982-83, Tom C. Clark Jud. Fellows Commn., 1983; Fulbright scholar, 1987-88, 1993-94. Mem. Am. Polit. Sci. Assn., Am. Soc. for Pub. Adminstrs., Internat. Polit. Sci. Assn., Supreme Ct. Hist. Soc. (editorial bd. 1986—), Pub. Adminstrn. Rev. (editorial bd. 1984-87). Avocations: oil painting; surfing. Office: U Va 232 Cabell Charlottesville VA 22901

O'BRIEN, DAVID PETER, oil company executive; b. Montreal, Que., Can., Sept. 9, 1941; s. John Lewis and Ethel (Cox) O'B.; m. Gail Baxter Corneil, June 1, 1968; children: Tara, Matthew, Shaun. B.A. with honors in Econs., Loyola Coll., Montreal, 1962; B.C.L., McGill U., 1965. Assoc. and ptnr. Ogilvy, Renault, Montreal, 1967-77; v.p., gen. counsel Petro-Can., Calgary, Alta., 1977-81; sr. v.p. Petro-Can., Calgary, 1982-85, sr. v.p. fin. and planning, 1982-85, exec. v.p., 1985-89; pres., chief exec. officer Noverco Inc., Montreal, 1989; chmn. bd. dirs., chief exec. officer PanCan. Petroleum Ltd., Calgary, Alta., Can., 1990-94; pres., COO Can. Pacific Ltd., Montreal, 1995—; bd. dirs. United Westburne Inc., Can. Pacific Ltd., PanCan. Petroleum Ltd., Marathon Realty Co. Ltd., Fording Coal Ltd., Laidlaw Inc.; chmn. bd. dirs. PanCan. Petroleum Ltd. Mem. Bus. Coun. on Nat. Issues, Glencoe Club, Calgary Petroleum Club, Calgary Golf and Country Club. Home: 906 Riverdale Ave SW, Calgary, AB Canada T2S 0Y6 Office: Can Pacific Ltd, PO Box 6042 Sta Centre-Ville, Montreal, PQ Canada H3C 3E4

O'BRIEN, DONAL CLARE, JR., lawyer; b. N.Y.C., May 16, 1934; s. Donal Clare and Constance (Boody) O'B.; m. Katharine Louise Slight, June 20, 1956; children: Donal Clare III, Constance Nancy O'Brien Ashforth, Katharine Louise O'Brien Rohn, Caroline Clare. BA, Williams Coll., 1956; LLB, U. Va., 1959. Bar: N.Y. 1961. Assoc. Milbank, Tweed, Hadley & McCloy, N.Y.C., 1959-67, ptnr, 1967-83, 91—; chief legal counsel Rockefeller Family & Assoc., N.Y.C., 1968-91; pres., CEO Rockefeller Trust Co., N.Y.C., 1986-91; bd. dirs. Winrock Farms, Inc., Little Rock, Greenacre Found., N.Y.C. Chmn. Nat. Audubon Soc., N.Y.C., Quebec Labrador Found., Ipswich, Mass.; chmn. bd. dirs. Atlantic Salmon Fedn., N.Y.C.; pres. BirdLife Internat., Cambridge, Eng.; trustee N.Am. Wildlife Found., Wendell Gilley Mus., Southwest Harbor, Maine, Waterfowl Rsch. Found., N.Y.C., Cornell Lab. Ornithology, Ithaca, N.Y., The JDR 3d Fund, N.Y.C., Trust for Mut. Understanding, Winthrop Rockefeller Charitable Trust, Little Rock; mem. coun. Rockefeller U.; commr. State of Conn. Bd. Fisheries and Game, 1971-72; mem. Coun. on Environ. Quality, Conn., 1971-76, 91—. Mem. Century Assn. Anglers Club of N.Y. Republican. Presbyterian. Home: 436 Trinity Pass Rd New Canaan CT 06840-2530 Office: Milbank Tweed Hadley & McCloy 1 Chase Manhattan Plz New York NY 10005

O'BRIEN, DONALD EUGENE, federal judge; b. Marcus, Iowa, Sept. 30, 1923; s. Michael John and Myrtle A. (Toomey) O'B.; m. Ruth Mahon, Apr. 15, 1950; children: Teresa, Brien, John, Shuivaun. LL.B., Creighton U., 1948. Bar: Iowa bar 1948, U.S. Supreme Ct. bar 1963. Asst. city atty. Sioux City, Iowa, 1949-53; county atty. Woodbury County, Iowa, 1955-58; mcpl. judge Sioux City, Iowa, 1959-60; U.S. atty. No. Iowa, 1961-67; pvt. practice law Sioux City, 1967-78, U.S. Dist. judge, 1978—; chief judge U.S. Dist. Ct. (no. dist.) Iowa, Sioux City, 1985-92; sr. judge U.S. Dist. Ct. (8th dist.) Iowa, Sioux City, 1992—; rep. 8th cir. dist. ct. judges to Jud. Conf. U.S., 1990—. Served with USAAF, 1943-45. Decorated D.F.C., air medals. Mem. Woodbury County Bar Assn., Iowa State Bar Assn. Roman Catholic. Office: US Dist Ct PO Box 267 Bldg Sioux City IA 51101

O'BRIEN, EDWARD IGNATIUS, lawyer, private investor; b. N.Y.C., Sept. 15, 1928; s. Edward I. and Marguerite (Malone) O'B.; m. Margaret M. Feeney, June 29, 1957; children: Edward Ignatius III, Margaret Mary, Thomas Gerard, John Joseph. AB, Fordham U., 1950; LLB, St. John's U., 1954; grad., Advanced Mgmt. Program, Cornell U., 1965. Bar: N.Y. 1954. With firm Hale, Kay & Brennan, N.Y.C., 1954-55; with Bache & Co., Inc., N.Y.C., 1955-74, gen. counsel, 1960, gen. ptnr., 1964, sec., 1968, v.p., 1965-68, sr. v.p., exec. com., 1969, exec. v.p., 1969, chmn. exec. com., 1971-74; pres. Securities Industry Assn., 1974-93; retired, 1993; bd. dirs. 8 corps.; lectr. Am. Law Inst., Practising Law Inst., Am. Mgmt. Assn.; exch. ofcl. Am. Stock Exch., 1972; mem. adv. bd., mem. exec. com. Securities Regulation Inst., U. Calif., 1975—. Mem. Cardinal's com. Laity Cath. Archdiocese N.Y., mem. Cardinal's com. for edn.; chmn. Fordham U. Coun., 1971-73; bd. dirs. 3 non-profit orgns.; chmn. corp. devel. com. Fordham U.; trustee, chmn. bd. trustees Fordham Prep. Sch., 1975-77, Capt. USAR. Mem. ABA, Assn. of Bar of City of N.Y., N.Y. State Bar Assn., Am. Arbitration Assn., Am. Soc. Internat. Law, Guild Cath. Lawyers, Securities Industry Assn. (chmn. publicly owned firms com. 1972), Nat. Assn. Securities Dealers (mem. dist. com. 1973-74), City Midday Club, Shenorock Shore Club (Rye, N.Y.), Town Club (Scarsdale, N.Y.), Met. Club (Washington). Home and Office: 12 Woods Ln Scarsdale NY 10583-6408

O'BRIEN, ELMER JOHN, librarian, educator; b. Kemmerer, Wyo., Apr. 8, 1932; s. Ernest and Emily Catherine (Reinhart) O'B.; m. Betty Alice Peterson, July 2, 1966. A.B., Birmingham So. Coll., 1954; Th.M., Iliff Sch. Theology, 1957; M.A., U. Denver, 1961. Ordained to ministry Methodist Ch., 1957; pastor Meth. Ch., Pagosa Springs, Colo., 1957-60; circulation-reference librarian Boston U. Sch. Theology, Boston, 1961-65; asst. librarian Garrett-Evang. Theol. Sem., Evanston, Ill., 1965-69; librarian, prof. United Theol. Sem., Dayton, Ohio, 1969—; abstractor Am. Bibliog. Center, 1969-73; dir. Ctr. for Evang. United Brethren Heritage, 1979—; chmn. div. exec. com. Dayton-Miami Valley Libr. Consortium, 1983-84; rsch. assoc. Am. Antiquarian Soc., 1990. Author: Bibliography of Festschriften in Religion Published Since 1960, 1972, Religion Index Two: Festschriften, 1960-69; contbg. author: Communication and Change in American Religious History, 1993; pub. Meth. Revs. Index, 1818-1985, 1989-91. Recipient theol. and scholarship award Assn. Theol. Schs. in U.S. and Can., 1990-91; Assn. Theol. Schs. in U.S. and Can. library staff devel. grantee, 1976-77, United Meth. Ch. Bd. Higher Edn. and Ministry research grantee, 1984-85. Mem. ALA, Acad. Libr. Assn. Ohio, Am. Theol. Libr. Assn. (head bur. personnel and placement 1969-73, dir. 1973-76, v.p. 1977-78, pres. 1978-79), Am. Antiquarian Soc. (rsch. assoc. 1990), Delta Sigma Phi, Omicron Delta Kappa, Eta Sigma Phi, Kappa Phi Kappa. Club: Torch Internat. (v.p. Dayton club 1981-82, pres. 1982-83). Home: 7818 Lockport Blvd Dayton OH 45459-5424

O'BRIEN, FRANCIS ANTHONY, lawyer; b. Albany, N.Y., Sept. 23, 1936; s. Francis Joseph and Helen Marie (Smith) O'B.; m. Maryanne Delia Mahoney, May 2, 1964; children—John, Dennis, Kathleen, Eileen. AB, Hamilton Coll., 1958; LLB, Cornell U., 1961. Bar: N.Y. 1962, D.C. 1968. Trial atty. FTC, Washington, 1962-68; assoc. Howrey & Simon, Washington, 1968-70, ptnr., 1971-86; prin. Francis A. O'Brien & Assocs., Washington. Alumni trustee Hamilton Coll., Clinton, N.Y., 1980-84; mem. Chesterbrook Woods Citizen Assn., McLean, Va., 1976—. Mem. ABA, Fed. Bar Assn., N.Y. Bar Assn., D.C. Bar Assn. Roman Catholic. Avocations: basketball; soccer; Civil War history. Home: 1600 Forest Ln Mc Lean VA 22101-3314 Office: Francis A O'Brien & Assocs Ste 900 1150 Connecticut Ave NW Washington DC 20036

O'BRIEN, FRANK B., manufacturing executive; b. Evanston, Ill., Dec. 5, 1946; s. Frank B. and Barbara (Greene) O'B.; m. Karen Eby, Oct. 12, 1974; children: Frank B. IV, Caroline Ann and Mary Karen, Margaret Greene, John Patrick, William Thomas. BSBA, Ohio State U., 1972. CPA, Ohio. Acct. Ernst & Whinney, Cleve., 1973-80; asst. to v.p. fin. The N.Am. Coal Corp., Cleve., 1980-82, mgr. corp. planning, 1982-87; v.p. corp. devel. NACCO Industries, Inc., Cleve., 1987-93, sr. v.p. corp. devel., chief fin. officer, 1994—; chmn. corp. planning coun. Mfrs.' Alliance for Productivity and Innovation, Washington, 1987—; dir. The Guidance Ctr., Boy Scouts of Am., Boys Hope, 1993; founder Children's Little Theater Endowment Fund, Cleve., 1987—. Sgt. U.S. Army, 1968-71. Mem. Assn. for Corp. Growth, Mayfield Country Club, Cleve. Playhouse Club, Pine Lake Trout Club. Republican. Roman Catholic. Office: NACCO Industries Inc 5875 Landerbrook Dr Mayfield Heights OH 44124-4017

O'BRIEN, GEOFFREY PAUL, editor; b. N.Y.C., May 4, 1948; s. Joseph Aloysius and Margaret Dorothy (Owens) O'B.; m. Carly Francis O'Brien, Mar. 18, 1977; 1 child, Heather. Student, Yale U., 1966-67, SUNY, Stony Brook, 1968-70. Editor Reader's Catalog, N.Y.C., 1987-91; exec. editor Libr. of Am., N.Y.C., 1992—. Author: Hardboiled America, 1981, Dream Time, 1988, A Book of Maps, 1989, The Phantom Empire, 1993, The Hudson Mystery, 1994; contbr. poetry, essays and revs. to profl. jours.; contbg. writer The Village Voice, 1982-90; editor: Frogpond, 1980-81; co-editor: Montemora, 1974-76. Recipient Writing award Whiting Found., 1988. Office: Libr of Am 14 E 60th St New York NY 10022-1006

O'BRIEN, GEORGE DENNIS, retired university president; b. Chicago, Ill., Feb. 21, 1931; s. George Francis and Helen (Fehlandt) O'B.; m. Judith Alyce Johnson, June 21, 1958; children: Elizabeth Belle, Juliana Helen, Victoria Alyce. AB in English, Yale, 1952; PhD in Philosophy, U. Chgo., 1961. Tchr. humanities, Carnegie rsch. fellow U. Chgo., 1956-57; successively instr., asst. prof., asst. dean coll. Princeton (N.J.) U., 1958-65; on leave in Athens, Greece, 1963-64; spl. honors seminars LaSalle Coll., spring 1963, fall 1964, spring 1965; assoc. prof. philosophy Middlebury (Vt.) Coll., 1965-71, prof., 1971-76, dean of men, 1965-67, dean of coll., 1973-74, dean faculty, 1975-76; pres. Bucknell U., 1976-84, U. Rochester, N.Y., 1984-94; ret., 1994; dir. Salzburg Seminar in Am. Studies. Author: Hegel on Reason in History, 1975, God and the New Haven Railway, 1986, What to Expect from College, 1991; contbr. articles to profl. jours. Trustee LaSalle Coll., Phila., 1965—; bd. dirs. Union Theol. Sem., 1985-90, Rsch. Librs. Group, 1994—; v.p. Commonwealth Found., 1994—. Fellow Am. Coun. Learned Socs., London, 1971-72. Mem. Am. Philos. Assn., Phi Beta Kappa. Home: Box 510 RD 3 Middlebury VT 05753

O'BRIEN, GEORGE DONOGHUE, JR., engineering consultant company executive; b. Detroit, Feb. 4, 1938; s. George Donoghue and Margaret (Foley) O'B.; m. Elise Maria Montilla, May 28, 1961; children: George III, Caroline, Kevin, Roseleen. BS, US Naval Acad., 1960; PhD, Naval Postgrad. Sch., 1970. Commd. ensign USN, 1960, advanced through grades to capt., 1982, naval aviator, test pilot, 1961-75, comdg. officer Attack Squadron 35, 1977-78, comdr. officer nuclear powered aircraft carrier, 1986-89, ret., 1989; pres., ceo Cygna Group, Oakland, Calif., 1990-92; chmn. infrastructure group ICF Kaiser Engrs., Oakland, 1991—. Chmn. Alameda County Bus. Devel. Com., Oakland, 1991-92. Decorated Legion of Merit, others. Mem. Bohemian Club San Francisco, St. Francis Yacht Club. Roman Catholic. Avocations: reading, running, sailing. Home: 1216 Paru St Alameda CA 94501-4038 Office: ICF Kaiser Engrs 1800 Harrison St Oakland CA 94612-3416

O'BRIEN, GERALD JAMES, utilities executive; b. St. Paul, May 1, 1923; s. Dewey Joseph and Henrietta Elizabeth O'B.; m. Patricia Margaret McCorison, Feb. 23, 1946; children: Kathleen, Thomas, John, Andrew. Student, St. Thomas Coll., 1940-41, 45-46; B.C.S., Drake U., 1948. Staff acct. Haskins & Sells, Mpls., 1948-50; with Donovan Cos., Inc., St. Paul, 1950-81; sec., asst. treas. Donovan Cos., Inc., 1977-81; utility rate cons., 1981-84; dir. Alumbaugh Coal Co., Donovan Constrn. Co., So. Tier Gas Corp., Gas Distbrs. Info. Service. Served with U.S. Army, 1942-45. Decorated Purple Heart. Address: 13313 Meeker Blvd Sun City West AZ 85375

O'BRIEN, J. WILLARD, lawyer, educator; b. N.Y.C., Oct. 19, 1930; s. J. Willard and Anna C. (Carroll) O'B.; m. Peggy J. O'Brien. B.S., Fordham U., 1952, J.D., 1957. Bar: N.Y. 1957. Assoc. Cahill, Gordon, Reindel & Ohl, N.Y.C., 1957-62; asst. prof. law Syracuse U. Coll. Law, 1962-65; prof. law Villanova (Pa.) U. Sch. Law, 1965—, dean, 1972-83, dir. Connelly Inst. Law and Morality, 1983—; mem. Pa. Law and Justice Inst., 1972-73, chmn. exec. com., 1973-75, pres., 1975-77. Editor-in-chief Fordham Law Rev, 1956-57. Bd. dirs. Nat. Inst. on Holocaust, 1984-85; bd. dirs. Phila. Coordinating Council on the Holocaust, 1983—. Served with USAF, 1952-54; Served with N.Y. Air N.G., 1954-58. Mem. ABA, N.Y. State Bar Assn., Pa. Bar Assn., Canon Law Soc. Am. Roman Catholic.

O'BRIEN, JACK GEORGE, artistic director; b. Saginaw, Mich., June 18, 1939; s. J. George and Evelyn (MacArthur Martens) O'B. A.B., U. Mich., 1961, M.A., 1962. Asst. dir. APA Repertory Theatre, N.Y.C., 1963-67; asso. dir. APA Repertory Theatre, 1967-69; worked with San Diego Nat. Shakespeare Festival, 1982, A.C.T., 1970-80, Loretto Hilton, 1975, Ahmanson, Los Angeles, 1978-80, San Francisco Opera, Houston Grand Opera, Washington Opera Soc., N.Y.C. Opera. Lyricist: Broadway prodn. The Selling of the President, 1972; dir.: on Broadway Porgy and Bess (Tony award nominee 1977), Most Happy Fella, Street Scene, Two Shakespearean Actors, 1993, Damn Yankees, 1994, Hapgood, 1994, others; artistic dir.: Old Globe Theatre, San Diego, 1981. Mem. Actors' Equity, Am. Soc. Composers and Performers, Soc. Stage Dirs. and Choreographers, Dirs. Guild Am.

O'BRIEN, JAMES ALOYSIUS, foreign language educator; b. Cin., Apr. 7, 1936; s. James Aloysius and Frieda (Schirmer) O'B.; m. Rumi Matsumoto, Aug. 26,1961. B.A., St. Joseph's Coll., 1958; M.A., U. Cin., 1960; Ph.D., Ind. U., 1969. Instr. English St. Joseph's Coll., Rensselaer, Ind., 1960-62; asst. prof. Japanese U. Wis.-Madison, 1968-74, assoc. prof., 1974-81, chmn. East Asia langs. and lit., 1979-80, 82-85, prof. Japanese, 1981—. Author: Dazai Osamu, 1975, Akutagawa and Dazai: Instances of Literary Adaptation, 1988; translator: Selected Stories and Sketches (Dazai Osamu), 1983, Three Works (Muro Saisei), 1985, Crackling Mountain and Other Stories (Dazai Osamu), 1989. Ford Found fellow, 1965-66; Fulbright-Hays and NDEA fellow, 1966-68; Social Sci. Research Council fellow, 1973-74; Japan Found. fellow, 1977-78. Mem. Assn. Asian Studies, Assn. Tchrs. of Japanese (exec. com. 1981-84, dir. devel. 1981-83, pres. 1984-90). Home: 2533 Branch St Middleton WI 53562-2812 Office: U Wis Dept East Asian Langs & Lit 1220 Linden Dr Madison WI 53706-1557

O'BRIEN, JAMES JEROME, construction management consultant; b. Phila., Oct. 20, 1929; s. Sylvester Jerome and Emma Belle Filer (Fulforth) O'B.; m. Carmen Hiester, June 10, 1952 (div. Aug. 1, 1984); children: Jessica Susan, Michael, David; m. Rita F. Gibson, Nov. 1, 1984. BCE, Cornell U., 1952; postgrad., U. Houston, 1957-58. Registered profl. engr., N.Y., N.J., Pa., Ga., Conn., Maine. Project engr. Rohm & Haas, Phila. and Tex., 1955-59, RCA Corp., Moorestown, N.J., Greenland and Alaska, 1959-62; cons. Mauchly Assocs., Fort Washington, Pa., 1962-65; founding ptnr., exec. v.p. Meridian Engring. Co., Phila., 1965-68; pres. MDC Systems, Cherry Hill, 1968-72; ptnr. James J. O'Brien P.E., Cherry Hill, 1972-77; pres. O'Brien-Kreitzberg & Assocs., N.Y.C., Pennsauken, San Francisco, 1977-80, chief exec. officer, 1980-89, chmn. bd. dirs., 1993, vice chmn., 1993—. Author: CPM in Construction Management-Scheduling by the Critical Path Method, 1965, CPM in Construction Management-Project Management with CPM, 4th edit., 1993, Management Information Systems-Concepts, Techniques and Applications, 1970, Management With Computers, 1972, Construction Inspection Handbook, 1974, 3d edit., 1989, Value Analysis in Design and Construction, 1976, Construction Delay-Risks, Responsibilities and Litigation, 1976, Preconstruction Estimating: Budget to Bid, 1994, Construction Documentation, 3d edit., 1995; co-author: Construction Management: A Professional Approach, 1974; editor: Recollections (L.D. Miles), 1987; author, editor: Scheduling Handbook, 1969, Contractor's Management Handbook, 1971, 2d edit., 1990, Standard Handbook of Heavy Construction, 3d edit., 1995; contbr. numerous articles to profl. jours. Lt. 1952-55, USN. Recipient Profl. Mgr. award N.Y. chpt. Soc. Advancement Mgmt., 1969. Fellow ASCE (Constrn. Mgmt. award 1976, v.p. 1985, pres. 1986 South Jersey Br., Disting. Engr. South Jersey br. 1986, pres. N.J. sect. 1987-89, mem. com. on quality in civil engring. profession 1990—), Project Mgmt. Inst. (sec. 1971, v.p. 1972, pres. 1973, chmn. bd. 1974-75, award for contbn. to project mgmt. 1983, Fellow award 1989), Constrn. Mgmt. Assn. Am. (bd. dirs. 1990-92, CM of Yr. award N.Y.-N.J. chpt. 1994), Cornell Soc. Engrs. (dean's adv. com. sch. civil and environ. engring. 1986-87); sr. mem. Am. Inst. Indsl. Engrs., Am. Assn. Cost Engring., Soc. Am. Value Engrs. (cert. value specialist, v.p. NE region 1986-87, Fallon Value-in-Life award 1993), Miles Value Found. (bd. dirs. 1987-90, trustee 1990—), Soc. Advancement Mgmt. (v.p. CPM divsn. 1970), Tau Beta Pi, Chi Epsilon. Home: 2 Linden Ave Riverton NJ 08077-1124 Office: 4350 Haddonfield Rd Pennsauken NJ 08109-5596

O'BRIEN, JAMES JOSEPH, meteorology and oceanography educator; b. N.Y.C., Aug. 10, 1935; s. Maurice J. and Beatrice (Cuddihy) O'B.; m. Sheila O'Keeffe, Nov. 29, 1958; children: Karen, Kevin, Sean, Dealyn, Denis. BS in Chemistry, Rutgers U., 1957; MS in Meteorology, Tex. A&M U., 1964, PhD in Meteorology, 1966. Meteorologist USAF, 1957-58; chemist E.I. duPont, 1958-62; mgr. office Naval Res., Washington, 1974-76; prof. Fla. State U., Tallahassee, 1972-82, sec. navy prof., 1982—, disting. rsch. prof., 1991—, pres. IAPSO, IUGG, 1987-91. Editor: The Sea, Vol. 6, 1976, Advanced Physical Modelling, 1986; contbr. over 100 papers to profl. jours. Mem. bd. advisors Naval Postgrad. Sch., Monterey, Calif., 1990—, capt. USAF, 1957-60. Recipient Liege Medal of Honor, Leige U., Disting. Ocean Educator award Office Naval Rsch., 1989, Disting. Rsch. Prof. award Fla. state U., 1991. Fellow AAAS, Am. Meteorol. Soc. (Sverdrups Gold medal); mem. Am. Geophys. Union, Royal Meteorol. Soc., Russian Acad. Sci. (fgn. mem.). Democrat. Roman Catholic. Achievements include expertise on Upper Ocean Modellings, forecasting; model to forecast El Nino; expertise in Ocean Models, climate models, physical oceanography, statistics. Office: Fla State U Dept Meteorology Tallahassee FL 32306

O'BRIEN, JAMES PHILLIP, lawyer; b. Monmouth, Ill., Jan. 6, 1949; s. John Matthew and Roberta Helen (Cavanaugh) O'B.; m. Laurene Reason, Aug. 30, 1969 (div. 1980); m. Lynn Florsheim, Sept. 5, 1987. BA, Western Ill. U., 1971; JD, U. Ill., 1974. Bar: Ill. 1974. Asst. atty. gen. State Ill., Springfield, 1974-75; jud. clerk Ill. Appellate Ct., Springfield, 1975-76; assoc. Graham & Graham, Springfield, 1976-81; corp. counsel Am. Hosp. Assn., Chgo., 1981-84; ptnr. co-chmn. health care dept. Katten, Muchin & Zavis, Chgo., 1984—; task force med. malpractice reform legislation Am. Hosp. Assn., 1983-84, tax adv. com., 1987-91, tax reporting and compliance com.,

1990-91; spkr. in field. Contbr. numerous articles to profl. jours. Recipient cert. recognition Ill. Dept. Children and Family Svcs., 1981; Edward Arthur Mellinger Found. scholar, Western Ill. U. 1971. Mem. Nat. Health Lawyers Assn., Am. Soc. Hosp. Attys., Am. Acad. Hosp. Attys., Am. Arbitration Assn. (Task Force Health Care Dispute Resolution 1982-84). Office: Katten Muchin & Zavis 525 W Monroe St Ste 1600 Chicago IL 60661-3693

O'BRIEN, JANE MARGARET, academic administrator; b. Washington, Nov. 17, 1953; d. Thomas and Edith (Pedersen) O'B; m. James A. Grube, June 28, 1975; children: William Howard Grube-O'Brien, Harold Thomas Grube O'Brien. BS in Biochemistry, Vassar Coll., 1975; PhD in Chemistry, U. Del., 1981. Rsch. asst. U. Vt., Burlington, 1978-79; asst. prof. chemistry Middlebury (Vt.) Coll., 1980-88, assoc. provost, 1988-89, assoc. prof. chemistry, 1988-91, dean of faculty, 1989-91; pres. Hollins Coll., Roanoke, Va., 1991—; ednl. chmn. biology task force New Eng. Consortium Undergraduate Sci., 1988-91; project mgr. H. Hughes Med. Inst. Instl. Awards, 1988-91; mem. steering com. Sloan New Liberal Arts Initiative, 1988-91. Implementation com. Vermont EPSCoR, 1989-91; bd. dirs. Coun. Ind. Colls. in Va., 1991—, Va. Found. for Ind. Colls., 1991—; ednl. adv. com. Rainforest All, 1991—. Grad. fellow U. Del., 1975-76, Kellogg fellow W.K. Kellogg Found., 1989-92, Internat. fellow Assoc. Am. Colls., 1990-91, Regional fellow finalist White House Fellowship, 1991. Home: PO Box 9625 Roanoke VA 24020 Office: Hollins Coll Office of the President Hollins College VA 24020*

O'BRIEN, JOHN CONWAY, economist, educator, writer; b. Hamilton, Lanarkshire, Scotland; s. Patrick and Mary (Hunt) O'B.; m. Jane Estelle Judd, Sept. 16, 1966; children: Kellie Marie, Kerry Patrick, Tracy Anne, Kristen Noël. B.Com., U. London, 1952, cert. in German lang., 1954; tchr.'s cert., Scottish Edn. Dept., 1954; AM, U. Notre Dame, 1959, PhD, 1961. Tchr. Scottish High Schs., Lanarkshire, 1952-56; instr. U. B.C., Can., 1961-62; asst. prof. U. Sask., Can., 1962-63, U. Dayton, Ohio, 1963-64; assoc. prof. Wilfrid Laurier U., Ont., Can., 1964-65; from asst. to full prof. Econs. and Ethics Calif. State U., Fresno, 1965—; vis. prof. U. Pitts., 1969-70, U. Hawaii, Manoa, 1984; keynote speaker Wageningen Agrl. U., The Netherlands, 1987; presenter papers 5th, eth, 10th World Congress of Economists, Tokyo, 1977, Mexico City, 1980, Moscow, 1992; presenter Schmoller Symposium, Heilbronn am Neckar, Fed. Republic Germany, 1988, paper The China Confucius Found. and "2540" Conf., Beijing, 1989, 6th Internat. Conf. on Cultural Econs., Univ. Umeå, Sweden, 1990, Internat. Soc. Intercommunication New Ideas, Sorbonne, Paris, 1990, European Assn. for Evolutionary Polit. Economy, Vienna, Austria, 1991; active rsch. U. Göttingen, Fed. Republic Germany, 1987; acad. cons. Cath. Inst. Social Ethics, Oxford; presenter in field. Author: Karl Marx: The Social Theorist, 1981, The Economist in Search of Values, 1982, Beyond Marxism, 1985, The Social Economist Hankers After Values, 1992; editor: Internat. Rev. Econs. Ethical Values and Social Economics, 1981, Selected Topics in Social Economics, 1981, Selected Topics in Social Economics, 1982, Festschrist in honor of George Rohrlich, 3 vols., 1984, Social Economics: A Pot=Pourri, 1985, The Social Economist on Nuclear Arms: Crime and Prisons: Health Care, 1986, Festschrift in honor of Anghel N. Rugina, Part I and II, 1987, Gustav von Schmoller: Social Economist, 1989, The Eternal Path to Communism, 1990, (with Z. Wenxian) Essays from the People's Republic China, 1991, Festschrift in Honor of John E. Elliott, parts I and II, 1992, Communism Now and Then, 1993, The Evils of Soviet Communism, 1994, Runimations on the USSR, 1994, Bradford, Eng.; translator econ. articles from French and German into English; contbr. numerous articles to profl. jours. With British Royal Army Service Corps, 1939-46, ETO, NATOUSA, prisoner of war, Germany. Recipient GE Corp. award Stanford U., 1966, Ludwig Mai Svc. award Assn. for Social Ecoupirat, Washington, 1994; ; named Disting. Fellow of Internat. Soc. for Intercommunication of New Ideas, Paris, 1990. Fellow Internat. Inst. Social Econs. (mem. coun., program dir. 3d World Cong. Social Econs. Fresno, Calif. 1983, keynote speaker 4th conf. Toronto 1986), Internat. Soc. for Intercommunication New Ideas (disting.); mem. Assn. Social Econs. (dir. west region 1977—, pres.-elect 1978-89, program dir. conf. 1989, pres. 1990, presdl. address, Washington 1990), Western Econ. Assn. (organizer, presenter 1977-93), History Econs. Soc., Soc. Reduction Human Labor (exec. com.), European Assn. Evolutionary Polit. Econ. Roman Catholic. Avocations: jogging, collecting miniature paintings, soccer, tennis, photography. Home: 2733 W Fir Ave Fresno CA 93711-0315 Office: Calif State U Econs And Ethics Dept Fresno CA 93740

O'BRIEN, JOHN F., insurance company executive. Pres., CEO State Mut. Life Assurance Co. Am., Worcester, Mass., also bd. dirs.; chmn., pres., CEO Allmerica Property & Casualty Cos. Inc., Worcester, also bd. dirs.; chmn., CEO Citizens Corp., Worcester, chmn., also bd. dirs.; chmn. The Hanover Ins. Co., Worcester; bd. dirs. Am. Coun. of Life Ins. Mem. Life Ins. Assn. Mass. (bd. dirs.). Office: Allmerica Fin 440 Lincoln St Worcester MA 01653

O'BRIEN, JOHN FEIGHAN, investment banker; b. Cleve., Aug. 8, 1936; s. Francis John and Ann (Feighan) O'B.; m. Regina Quaid Harahan, June 27, 1959 (div. 1976); children: Regina, Victoria, Julie, John Jr.; m. Marilyn E. Schreiner. BS, Georgetown U., 1958. Salesman Appliance Mart, Cleve., 1958-59, ptnr., 1960-66; investment broker McDonald & Co. Investments, Cleve., 1966-71, ptnr., 1971-83, exec. v.p., 1983-88, mng. dir., 1988-91, sr. mng. dir., 1993—. Bd. dirs. Hitchcock House, Cleve., 1978-89, St. John-St. John West Shore Devel. Bd., Cleve., 1987—; del. assembly United Way Cleve., 1987—; chmn. Alcoholism Svcs. of Cleve., 1989-92, Alcohol and Drug-Addiction Svcs. Bd. of Cuyahoga County, 1992—; bd. trustees St. Edward High Sch., Lakewood, Ohio, chmn. capital campaign, 1993-95. Mem. Leadership Cleve., Greater Cleve. Growth Assn., Georgetown U. Alumni Assn. (alumni bd. senator), Westwood Country Club, Cleve. Yacht Club, Catawba Island Club. Home: 1031 Brook Ln Cleveland OH 44116-2184 Office: McDonald & Co Investments 800 Superior Ste 2100 Cleveland OH 44114

O'BRIEN, JOHN M., newspaper publishing company executive; b. North Bergen, N.J., 1942. BA, Fairleigh Dickinson U., 1970. Sr. v.p. fin. and human resources The New York Times, now exec. v.p., dep. gen. mgr. Office: New York Times Co 229 W 43rd St New York NY 10036*

O'BRIEN, JOHN WILFRID, economist, university president emeritus, educator; b. Toronto, Ont., Can., Aug. 4, 1931; s. Wilfred Edmond and Audrey (Swain) O'B.; m. Joyce Helen Bennett, Aug. 4, 1956; children—Margaret Anne, Catherine Audrey. B.A., McGill U., 1953, M.A., 1955, Ph.D., 1962, LL.D., 1976; postgrad., Inst. Polit. Studies, Paris, France, 1954; D.C.L., Bishop's U., 1976. Lectr. econs. Sir George Williams U., Montreal, 1954-57; asst. prof. Sir George Williams U., 1957-61, assoc. prof., 1961-63, asst. dean U., 1961-63, dean arts, 1963-68, vice prin. acad., 1968-69, prof., 1965—, prin., vice chancellor, pres., 1969-74; rector, vice chancellor, pres. Concordia U., Montreal, 1974-84; rector emeritus Concordia U. 1984—; mem. Provincial Ednl. TV Com., Dept. Edn. Que., 1962-66, dep. chmn., 1965-66, mem. tchr. tng. planning com., 1964-66; mem. Gauthier Ad Hoc Com., Univ. Operating Budgets, 1965-68, Council Univs., 1969-76; pres. Conf. Rectors and Prins. Que. Univs., 1974-77; mem. council Assn. Commonwealth Univs., 1975-78; bd. dirs. Assn. Univs. and Colls., Can., 1977-79; mem. Conseil Consultatif sur l'Immigration, Que. Govt., 1977-79, Corp. Higher Edn. Forum, 1983-84; bd. govs. YMCA, 1969-89, Vanier Coll., 1975-79, Fraser-Hickson Inst., 1975—, pres. 1989-92, Que. div. Can. Mental Health Assn., 1977-79, Montreal World Film Festival, 1985—; sec., treas. Cinematheque Can., 1988—, World Film Fest. Found., 1989—; exec. mem. Alliance Que., 1989—; chmn. Alliance Que., 1990-91, 92—; hon. mem. Corp. Higher Edn. Forum, 1984—; hon. v.p. Que. Provincial council Boy Scouts Can., 1974-90; hon. councillor Montreal Mus. Fine Arts, 1969—. Author: Canadian Money and Banking, 1964, (with G. Lermer) 2d edit., 1969. Office: 1455 de Maisonneuve Blvd, Montreal, PQ Canada H3G 1M8

O'BRIEN, JOSEPH PATRICK, JR., apparel and textile company executive; b. Haverhill, Mass., May 25, 1940; s. Joseph P. and Helen M. (Atwood) O'B.; m. Gail E. Harris, May 19, 1962 (div. Apr. 1981); children: Michael, Pamela, Matthew, Amy; m. Phyllis L. Corso, July 12, 1981; children: Alicia, Jack. B.S.B.A., Northeastern U., Boston, 1963. CPA, N.J. Auditor Ernst & Ernst, 1972; acctg. mgr. Austenal div. Howmet Corp., Dover, N.J., 1965-68, controller Alloy div., 1969-71, budget dir., 1972-75; controller Pechiney Ugine Kuhlmann Co., Greenwich, 1976-80; v.p. fin. Howmet

Corp., Greenwich, 1980-93, Hart Holding and Reeves Industries, Darien, Conn., 1993—. Trustee King and Low-Heywood Thomas Schs. Mem. AICPA, Nat. Assn. Accts., Fin. Execs. Inst., Nat. Assn. Bus. Economists. Home: 66 Coachlamp Ln Stamford CT 06902-2005 Office: Hart Holding 120 Post Rd Darien CT 06820

O'BRIEN, KENNETH ROBERT, life insurance company executive; b. Bklyn., June 18, 1937; s. Emmett Robert and Anna (Kelly) O'B.; m. Eileen M. Halligan, July 1, 1961; children: Joan Marie, Margaret Mary, Kathy Ann. B.S. in Bus. Adminstrn, Coll. Holy Cross, Worcester, Mass., 1959. With N.Y. Life Ins. Co., N.Y.C., 1962—; 2d v.p. N.Y. Life Ins. Co., 1973-77, v.p. investments, 1977-82, sr. v.p. pensions, 1982-87, sr. v.p. individual products, 1987-89, exec. v.p., 1989-91; chief exec. officer Aurora Nat. Life Assurance Co., L.A., 1991—; founder, pres., CEO O'Brien Asset Mgmt., Inc., 1993—. Served to 1st lt. USAF, 1959-62. Mem. Nat. Consumer Fin. Assn., Fin. Forum, N.Y. Soc. Security Analysts. Home: 165 Loines Ave E Merrick NY 11566-3211

O'BRIEN, KEVIN J., lawyer; b. N.Y.C., Mar. 12, 1934; s. George and Kathleen (Fox) O'B.; m. Winifred Gallagher, Aug. 23, 1958; children: Karen A., Kevin J., Susan M. BS, Fordham U., 1959; LLB, Columbia U., 1962. Bar: N.Y. 1962, U.S. Ct. Appeals (2d cir.) 1971, U.S. Dist. Ct. (so. dist.) N.Y. 1972, U.S. Tax Ct. 1972. Law clk. to presiding justice U.S. Ct. Appeals (2d. cir.), N.Y.C., 1962-63; assoc. Paul, Weiss, Rifkind, Wharton & Garrison, N.Y.C., 1963-70, ptnr., 1970—. Contbr. articles to profl. jours. Trustee Convent of Sacred Heart, Greenwich, Conn., 1979-82; mem. Cardinal's Com. of Laity, N.Y.C., 1986—. Served with USN, 1952-55. Mem. ABA, N.Y. State Bar Assn. (exec. com. tax sect. 1979-83), Assn. of Bar of City of N.Y. Office: Paul Weiss Rifkind Wharton & Garrison 1285 Ave Of The Americas New York NY 10019-6028

O'BRIEN, KIMBERLY K., secondary education educator. Teacher White Rock H.S., Burr Oak, Kan. Recipient Sally Mae First Yr. Teacher awd., Am. Assn. of Sch. Administrators, 1992. Office: White Rock High Sch Burr Oak KS 66936

O'BRIEN, L. DOUGLAS, banking executive; b. Mineola, N.Y., Mar. 27, 1939; s. Leonard D. and Melda B. (Anderson) O'B.; m. Mary Jo McIntyre, Feb. 27, 1965 (div. May 1979); m. Ellen Mary Downs, June 8, 1979; children: Karin D., Kenneth D., Kristine D., Kimberly D., Kevin D. BA, Rutgers U., 1964. Cadet trainee Consol. Edison, N.Y.C., 1964; v.p. Bankers Trust Co., N.Y.C., 1965-77; sr. v.p. Midlantic Banks Inc., Edison, N.J., 1977-82; sr. exec. v.p. Nat. Westminster Bank U.S.A., N.Y.C., 1982-89; pres., chief exec. officer Nat. Westminster Bank N.J., Jersey City, 1990-92; sr. exec. v.p., dir. Nat. Westminster Bancorp., 1990-92; pres., CEO Bank of Ireland First Holdings Inc./First N.H. Bank, Manchester, 1992—; trustee N.J. Partnership, Princeton, 1990-92; bd. dirs. N.J. State C. of C., N.H. Bankers Assn. Bus. and Indsutry Assn., Currier Gallery of Art, N.H. Pub. T.V., N.H. Charitable Found., Optima Health, Greater Manchester C. of C. Trustee Stevens Inst. Tech., Hoboken, N.J., 1990—; bd. dirs. UNICEF, N.Y.C., 1987-88, Boy Scouts Am., N.Y.C., 1986-90. Sgt. U.S. Army, 1959-61. Recipient Norman Feldman award Goodwill Industries of N.J., 1990, Gimble award MS Care Ctr. Comprehensive, Holy Dame Hosp., 1990, Silver Beaver award Boy Scouts Am., 1990, Bus. Industry Expo Leadership award Middlesex County Regional C. of C., 1991. Mem. N.J. Bankers Assn. (exec. com. 1990-92), Westchester County Assn. (bd. dirs. 1987-90), Consumer Bankers Assn. Republican. Roman Catholic. Avocations: music, sports, tennis, golf, theatre. Office: Bank Ireland 1st Holdings/1st NH Bank 1000 Elm St Manchester NH 03101

O'BRIEN, LAWRENCE FRANCIS, III, lawyer; b. Springfield, Mass., Dec. 31, 1945; s. Lawrence Francis and Elva (Brassard) O'Brien; m. Helen Marie Powell; children: Lawrence L., Peter F. BA, Harvard U., 1967; JD, Columbia U., 1972. Bar: N.Y. 1973, D.C. 1979. Assoc. atty. Breed, Abbott & Morgan, N.Y.C., 1972-77; dep. tax. asst., sec. treas. U.S. Treas. Dept., Washington, 1977-79; ptnr. Breed, Abbott & Morgan, Washington, 1979-83, Dewey, Ballantine, Bushby, Palmer & Wood, Washington, 1983-93, O'Brien Calio, Washington, 1993—. Served to 1st lt. U.S. Army, 1968-70. Democrat. Roman Catholic. Club: River (N.Y.C.). Office: O'Brien Calio 35 Wisconsin Cir # 350 Bethesda MD 20815-7015

O'BRIEN, MARK STEPHEN, pediatric neurosurgeon; b. West New York, N.J., Jan. 2, 1933; s. Mark Peter and Hannah (Dempsey) O'B.; m. Mary Morris Johnson, June 3, 1961 (div.); children: David, Derek, Marcia; m. Karen-Marie Sampson, June 1, 1984; children: Blythe, Blake, Lauren-Blair, Connor. A.B. cum laude, Seton Hall U., 1955; M.D., St. Louis U., 1959. Intern St. John's Hosp., St. Louis, 1959-60; resident in surgery St. John's Hosp., 1960; resident in neurology Charity Hosp., New Orleans, 1962-63; resident in neurosurgery St. Vincent's Hosp., N.Y.C., 1963-64; resident in surgery St. Vincent's Hosp., 1965; sr. resident, chief resident Cin. Children's Hosp., U. Cin., 1965-68, research fellow in neurosurgery, 1966-67, 67-68; NIH spl. fellow in neuroradiology Albert Einstein Coll. Medicine, N.Y.C., 1968-69; mem. faculty dept. surgery Emory U. Sch. Medicine, Atlanta, 1969—; asst. prof. surgery, assoc. prof. pediatrics Emory U. Sch. Medicine, 1979—; chief neurosurgery Henrietta Egleston Hosp. for Children, Atlanta, 1971—; trustee Elaine Clark Center for Exceptional Children; mem. med. adv. bd. Nat. Found., March of Dimes; trustee Henrietta Egleston Hosp. for Children; mem. profl. adv. panel Spina Bifida Assn. Am. Editorial bd. Pediatric Neurosurgery; contbr. chpts. to books, articles to med. jours. Served with USNR, 1960-62. Mem. Am. Assn. Neurol. Surgeons, Soc. Neurol. Surgeons, Congress Neurol. Surgeons, Internat. Soc. Pediatric Neurosurgery, Greater Atlanta Pediatric Soc., Med. Soc. Atlanta, AMA, ACS, Ga. Neurosurg. Soc., Am. Acad. Pediatrics, Am. Soc. Pediatric Neurosurgery, Pediatric Oncology Group, Am. Bd. Pediatric Neurol. Surgery (sec.), Acad. Pediatric Neurosurgeons. Home: 350 Blackland Rd Atlanta GA 30342 Office: 1900 Century Blvd Ste 4 Atlanta GA 30345

O'BRIEN, MARY DEVON, communications executive, consultant; b. Buenos Aires, Argentina, Feb. 13, 1944; came to U.S., 1949, naturalized, 1962; d. George Earle and Margaret Frances (Richards) Owen; m. Gordon Covert O'Brien, Feb. 16, 1962 (div. Aug. 1982); children: Christopher Covert, Devon Elizabeth; m. Christopher Gerard Smith, May 28, 1983. BA, Rutgers U., 1975, MBA, 1976. Project mgmt. cert., 1989. Contr. manpower Def. Comm. dirsn. ITT, Nutley, N.J., 1977-80, adminstr. program, 1977-78, mgr. cost, schedule control, 1978-79, voice processing project, 1979-80; mgr. project Avionics div. ITT, Nutley, 1980-81, sr. mgr. projects, 1981-93, cons. strategic planning, 1983—; bd. trustees South Mountain Counseling Ctr., 1987—, chmn. bd. trustees, 1994—; bd. dirs. N.J. Eye Inst.; session leader Internet Conf., Florence, Italy, 1992; session moderator, panel mem. MES Conf., Cairo, Egypt, 1993; lectr. in field. Author: Pace: System Manual, 1979, Voices, 1982; contbr. articles to profl. jours. and Maplewood Community calendar. Chmn. Citizens Budget Adv. Com., Maplewood, N.J., 1984-87, chmn. recreation, litter, pub. svcs., 1982-83, 94—, chmn. pub. safety, emergency svcs., 1983-84, chmn. schs. and edn., 1984-85; bd. trustees United Way Essex and West Hudson Community Svc. Coun., 1988—; first v.p. Maplewood Civic Assn., 1987-89, pres., 1989-91, sec. 1993-94, bd. dirs., officer, 1984—; chmn. Maple Leaf Svc. award Com., 1987-89, 94—; Community Svc. Coun. of Oranges and Maplewood Homelessness, Affordable Housing, Shelter Com., 1988—; chmn. speaker's bur. United Way 1989-93; v.p. mktg. United Way Community Svc. Coun. of Orange and Maplewood, 1990-93; mem. Maplewood Zoning Bd. of Adjustment, 1983—; officer, mem. exec. bd. N.J. Project Mgmt. Inst., 1985—, pres., 1987-88, v.p. adminstrn., 1994—; bd. dirs. Performance Mgmt. Assn.; chmn. Charter Com.; chmn. Internat. Project Mgmt. Inst. Jour. and Membership survey, 1986-87, mktg. com., 1986-89, long range planning and steering com.; bd. dirs., vice chmn. Coun. Chpt. Pres. Interaction Com. 1986-90, chmn. 1991—, pres. Internat. Project Mgmt. Inst., 1991, chmn., 1992, v.p. Region II, 1989-90; adv. bd. Project Mgmt. Jour., 1987-90, N.J. PMI Ednl., 1987—; liaison officer; apptd. fellow Leadership N.J., 1993—, Internat. Project Mgmt. Inst. and Performance Mgmt. Assocs.; mem. MCA/N.J. Blood Bank Drive; chmn. Maplewood Community Calendar, 1990—; trustee community svc. coun. and edn. program United Way Essex and West Hudson, 1988—, also, chmn. leadership div., chmn. speakers bur., 1991— and mem. communications com., v.p. mktg. community svc. coun., Oranges and Maplewood, 1991-93. Recipient Spl. commendation for Community Svc. Twp. Maplewood, 1987; First Place

award Anti-Shoplifting Program for Distributive Edn. Club Am., 1981, N.J. Fedn. of Women's Clubs, 1981, 82, Retail Mchts. Assn., 1981, 82; Commendation and Merit awards Air Force Inst. Tech., 1981; Pres.'s Safety award ITT, 1983; State award 1st Pl. N.J. Fedn. of Women's Clubs Garden Show, 1982, Outstanding Pres. award Internat. Project Mgmt. Inst., 1988, Outstanding Svc. and Contbrn. award 1986-87; Cert. Spl. Merit award N.J. Fedn. of Women's Clubs, 1982, Disting. Contbr. award United Way, 1990, Pursuit of Exellence Cost Savings Achievement award ITT Avionics, 1990, Meritorious Svc. Recognition award Internat. Project Mgmt. Inst., 1989-90, Maple Leaf award for outstanding community svc., 1992, Phoebe and Benjamin Shackelford award United Way, 1992, U.S. Ho. Reps. citation, 1992, N.H. Gen. Assembly Senate resolution for Community Leadership and Svc., 1992, resolution of Appreciation Township of Maplewood; N.J. Leadership fellow, 1993, awarded fellow of Internat. Project Mgmt. Inst., 1995. Mem. Internat. Platform Speakers Assn., Grand Jury Assn., Telecommunications Group and Aerospace Industries Assn., Women's Career Network Assn., Nat. Security Indsl. Assn., Assn. for Info. and Image Mgmt., Internat. Project Mgmt. Inst. (liaison officerpresnce Mgmt. Assn., ITT Mgmt. Assn., NAFE, Rutger's Grad. Sch. Bus. Mgmt. Alumni Assn., Maplewood LWV (chair women and family issues com., bd. dirs.), Maplewood Women's Evening Membership Div. (pres. 1980-82), Lions (Maplewood dir. 1992-95, program chmn. 1991-92, treas. 1994-95, N.J. dist. 16E zone chmn. 1992-93, cabinet sec. internat. dist., region chmn. 1993-94, trustee Eye Bank N.J., internat. dist. 16-E cabinet sec. 1994-95). Home: 594 Valley St Maplewood NJ 07040-2616 Office: Ste 152 21 Madison Plaza Madison NJ 07940

O'BRIEN, MAURICE JAMES, business executive; b. Chgo., Aug. 30, 1925; m. Frances McDonald; children—Maureen, Martha, James M., Paula, Elizabeth, William, Martha, Timothy, John, Joe, Peter, Clare, Catherine, Jane. B.S., Northwestern U., 1947, J.D., 1949; LL.D., Coll. Great Falls, Mont., 1967. Asst. to pres. Robinson Bros. & Co., Chgo., 1950—; founder, pres. Chgo. Coke Co., (changed to Bulk Chems. Co., then Luria Bros., subs. Ogden & Co., N.Y.), 1951-61; v.p. sales Marblehead Lime Co., Chgo., subs. Gen. Dynamics Corp., St. Louis, 1961, pres., 1966-84, chmn., chief exec. officer, 1984-88, ret.; pres., chief exec. officer Arnel, Inc., Winnetka, Ill. 1988—; chmn. bd. subsidiaries Darlington Brick & Clay Products Co., Pa., Powell & Minnock Brick Works, Inc., Albany, N.Y.; dir. 1st Nat. Bank, Evanston, chmn. exec. com., 1970-85; dir. Pepper Constrn. Co., Chgo.; former dir. Advance Ross Corp., Chgo., Laidlaw Industries, Hinsdale, Ill., Miller Co., Chgo., Asbestos Corp., Ltd. Bd. dirs. former chmn. bd. St. Francis Hosp., Evanston. Served with U.S. Army, 1943-45. Recipient Merit award Northwestern U., 1968. Mem. Ill. Mfrs. Assn. (chmn. bd.), NAM (former dir.), Nat. Lime Assn. (chmn., merit award 1967). Clubs: John Henry Wigmore (former dir., past pres.) (Northwestern U. Sch. Law); Chgo., University (Chgo.); Econ., Bob O'Link Golf, Glen View, Riomar Golf Club (Vero Beach, Fla.). Home and Office: 33 Meadow View Dr Northfield IL 60093

O'BRIEN, NANCY PATRICIA, librarian, educator; b. Galesburg, Ill., Mar. 17, 1955; d. Leo Frederick O'Brien and Yvonne Blanche (Uhlmann) O'Brien Tabb; 1 child, Nicole Pamela. AB in English, U. Ill., 1976, MS in LS, 1977. Vis. instr. U. Ill., Urbana, 1977-78, asst. prof. libr. adminstrn., 1978-84, assoc. prof., 1984-91, prof., 1991—, serials bibliographer, 1977-78, social sci. bibliographer collection devel. div., 1979-81, project dir. Title II-C grant, 1987-88, acting libr. and info. sci. libr., 1989-90, head Edn. and Social Sci. Libr., 1994—, edn. subject specialist, 1981—; discussion leader Ill. White House Conf. on Libr. and Info. svcs., 1990; mem. nat. adv. bd. Office Ednl. Rsch. and Improvement, U.S. Dept. Edn., 1989-91; grant proposal reviewer NEH, 1991; mem. adv. bd. Ctr. for Children's Books, 1992—; cons. Ark. Coll., 1989; chmn. rev. team Instrnl. Materials Ctr., U. Wis., Madison, 1989; presenter in field. Author: Test Construction: A Bibliography of Resources, 1988, (with Emily Fabiano) Core List of Books and Journals in Education, 1991; co-editor Media/Microforms column Series Rev., 1979-82; mem. editl. bd. Bull. Bibliography, 1982-90; asst. editor Libr. Hi Tech., 1983-85; editor EBSS Newsletter, 1990-91; contbr. articles to profl. jours., chpts. to books. Mem. ALA (Whitney-Carnegie grantee 1990-91), Am. Ednl. Rsch. Assn. (spl. interest group on libr. resources and info. tech.), Assn. Coll. and Rsch. Librs. (access policy guidelines task force 1990—, vice chmn., chmn.-elect edn. and behavioral scis. sect. 1993—, chmn. 1994-95), Libr. Adminstrn. and Mgmt. Assn. (edn. and tng. com. pub. rels. sect. 1990-95), Resources and Tech. Svcs. Divsn.(micropub. com. 1982-85, chmn. 1983-85, cons. 1985-87). Office: U Ill Edn & Social Sci Libr 100 Main Libr 1408 W Gregory Dr Urbana IL 61801

O'BRIEN, NEAL RAY, geology educator; b. Newark, Ohio, May 25, 1937; s. Raymond and Eleanor (Pryor) O'B.; m. Kathryn Louise Gronberg, Sept. 15, 1962; children: Tyler, Rebecca, Amber. B.A., DePauw U., 1959; Ph.D., U. Ill., 1963. Prof. geology Coll. of Arts and Sci., SUNY, Potsdam, 1963—; chmn. dept. Coll. of Arts and Sci., SUNY, 1970-85. Contbr. articles to profl. jours. Postdoctoral research fellow Kyoto U., Japan, 1969-70, 77-78. Mem. Geol. Soc. Am., Clay Mineral Soc., Soc. Econ. Paleontology and Mineralogy. Research on clay sedimentology, electron microscope study of clay sediment. Home: PO Box 123 West Stockholm NY 13696-0123

O'BRIEN, ORIN YNEZ, musician, educator; b. Hollywood, Calif., June 7, 1935; s. George Joseph and Marguerite Graham (Churchill) O'Brien. Studied double bass with Frederick Zimmermann and Milton Kestenbaum; student, UCLA; diploma, The Juilliard Sch., 1957. Former double bassist N.Y.C. Ballet Orch., Saidenberg Little Symphony, Am. Symphony, 1956-66; double bassist N.Y. Philharm., N.Y.C., 1966—; former mem. faculty YMHA Sch. Music, 1967-71; mem. faculty Manhattan Sch. Music, N.Y.C., 1969—, Aronos Coll. Music; N.Y.C., 1988—, The Juilliard Sch., N.Y.C., 1990—; co-chair double bass dept., 1992—; participant numerous chamber music festivals, including Marlboro; featured in 1st performances of Gunther Schuller Quartet for 4 double basses; artist for GM, CBS and RCA Recording cos. Mem. Am. Fedn. Musicians, Internat. Soc. Bassists. Avocations: reading, writing, cooking. Office: Juilliard Sch Music 60 Lincoln Ctr Plz New York NY 10023-6588

O'BRIEN, PATRICK MICHAEL, library administrator; b. Newport, R.I., Mar. 17, 1943; s. Joseph Xavier and Laura (DeCotis) O'B.; m. Roberta Luther. Nov. 27, 1977; children—Megan MacRae, Brendan Watters. B.A. in Eng. Lit., Merrimack Coll., North Andover, Mass., 1964; M.L.S., U. R.I., Kingston, 1965; M.B.A., Case Western Res. U., Cleve., 1983. Reference libr. Newsweek mag., N.Y.C., 1965-72; asst. dir. rsch. FIND/SVP, N.Y.C., 1972-74; head cen. libr., cultural ctr. Chgo. Pub. Libr., 1974-79; dir. Cuyahoga County Pub. Libr., Cleve., 1979-84; dir. librs. Dallas Pub. Libr., 1984-92; dir. Alexandria (Va.) Libr., 1992—. Mem. editorial bd. Handel's Nat. Directory for Performing Arts; contbr. articles to profl. jours. Participant, alumnus Leadership Dallas Program, 1984-85, Leadership Cleve. Program, 1981; mem. nat. adv. com. to Libr. of Congress; mem. adv. coun. Tex. State Libr. Libr. Svcs. and Constrn. Act, 1986-89; co-chair, del. selection com. Tex. Conf. on Librs. and Info. Svcs.; mem. com. Goals for Dallas, 1985; mem. exec. bd. univ. librs. So. Meth. U., 1985—; bd. dirs. Urban Community Sch., Cleve., 1982-84, Mus. African-Am. Life and Culture, 1985-86; mem. client data base com. Dallas Assn. Svcs. to Homeless, 1988-90; mem. Latchkey Children's Task Force, 1985-90. Recipient Servant as Leader award City of Dallas, 1989, Disting. Alumnus award U. R.I. Grad. Sch. Libr. and Info. Studies, 1990. Mem. ALA (coun. mem. 1987—), Am. Libr. Trustee Assn. (bd. dirs.), Pub. Libr. Assn. (pres. 1985-86), Pub. Libr. Systems Sect. (pres. 1983), Tex. Libr. Assn. (legis. com. 1986-92), Tex. Women's Univ. Sch. Libr. and Info. Studies Vis. Com., Tex. Ctr. for Book Dallas Pub. Libr., Cleve. Area Met. Libr. Systems (pres. bd. 1980), Chgo. Libr. Club (pres. 1978), D.C. Libr. Assn., Va. Libr. Assn., Online Computer Libr. Ctr. (bd. trustees 1992—), The White House Conf. on Librs. and Info. Svcs. (del. 1991), Pub. Lib. Adminstrs. N.Tex. (pres. 1990-91), Dallas Rotary of Alexandria, Beta Gamma Sigma. Office: Alexandria Libr 717 Queen St Alexandria VA 22314-2420

O'BRIEN, PATRICK WILLIAM, lawyer; b. Chgo., Dec. 5, 1927; s. Maurice Edward and Ellen (Fitzgerald) O'B.; m. Deborah Bissell, July 2, 1955; children: Kathleen, Mariellen, Patrick, James, Patricia. BS in Mech. Engring., Northwestern U., 1947, JD, 1950. Bar: Ill. 1951, U.S. Dist. Ct. (no. dist.) Ill. 1954, U.S. Dist. Ct. (so. dist.)Ill. 1956, U.S. Ct. Appeals (7th cir.) 1955, U.S. Ct. Appeals (8th cir.) 1972, U.S. Supreme Ct. 1970. Assoc.

Bell, Boyd, Marshall & Lloyd, Chgo., 1950-51; assoc. Mayer, Brown & Platt, Chgo., 1953-62, ptnr., 1962-94, of counsel, 1995—. Served to capt. USAF, 1951-53. Fellow Am. Coll. Trial Lawyers; mem. ABA, Ill. Bar Assn., Chgo. Bar Assn. Republican. Roman Catholic. Clubs: Chgo., Attic, University, Westmoreland Country, Cliff Dwellers, Dairymen's Country. Home: 1119 Judson Ave Evanston IL 60202-1314 Office: Mayer Brown & Platt 190 S La Salle St Chicago IL 60603-3410

O'BRIEN, PAUL CHARLES, telephone company executive; b. N.Y.C., May 12, 1939; s. Charles Edward and Clare Mary (Becker) O'B.; m. Marie P. Moane, Dec. 30, 1961; children: Carolyn M., Deirdre M., Barbara M., Erin M. BEE, Manhattan Coll., 1960; MBA, NYU, 1968. Supervising engr. N.Y. Telephone Co., N.Y.C., 1964-67, div. engr., 1967-72, gen. staff supr., 1972-75, gen. planning engr., 1975-77, asst. v.p., 1977-83, pres. N.Y. New Eng. Exchange Enterprises, 1973-85, v.p. customer service, 1985-86; now chmn. exec. com., pres., CEO NYNEX Boston, 1987—, also dir.; bd. dirs. N.Y. New Eng. Exchange Systems Mktg. Co., N.Y.C., N.Y. New Eng. Exhange Info. Resources Co., Lynn, Mass., N.Y. New Eng. Exchange Service Co., White Plains, N.Y. Bd. dirs. NYNEX, 1986; Greater Boston Adult Literacy Fund, 1988, Jobs for Mass., Boston, 1988; assoc. chmn. United Way Ea. New Eng., 1988. Capt. USAF, 1961-64. Mem. AFCA, IEEE. Roman Catholic. Avocations: golf, musical shows. Office: NYNEX 185 Franklin St Boston MA 02110-1585*

O'BRIEN, PAUL HERBERT, surgeon; b. Evanston, Ill., Sept. 12, 1930; s. Maurice Edward and Nellie (Fitzgerald) O'B.; m. Ann Hope Miller, Aug. 28, 1965; children—Jennifer, Paul Edward. B.S., Northwestern U., 1950, M.D., 1954. Diplomate: Am. Bd. Surgery. Intern Northwestern U. Hosp., Chgo., 1954-55; asst. prof. surgery Northwestern U. Hosp., 1967-69; resident in surgery Cook County Hosp., Chgo., 1957-62; sr. resident Meml. Sloan Kettering Inst. Cancer and Allied Diseases, N.Y.C., 1962-65; also USPHS sr. fellow; assoc. prof. Med. U. S.C., Charleston, 1970-72, prof., 1972—, Am. Cancer Soc. clin. prof. oncology, 1974-79; chief Gold Surgery. Contbr. articles to profl. jours. Served to capt. AUS, 1955-57. Recipient career devel. award Schweppe Found. Mem. A.C.S., Soc. Surg. Oncology, Am. Cancer Soc. (past pres. profl. edn. com.), AMA, Halsted Soc., AAUP, Chgo. Surg. Soc. Anglo Catholic. Home: 1467 Burningtree Rd Charleston SC 29412-2602 Office: 171 Ashley Ave Charleston SC 29425-0001

O'BRIEN, RAYMOND FRANCIS, transportation executive; b. Atchison, Kans., May 31, 1922; s. James C. and Anna M. (Wagner) O'B.; m. Mary Ann Baugher, Sept. 3, 1947; children: James B., William T., Kathleen A., Christopher R. B.S. in Bus. Adminstrn., U. Mo., 1948; grad., Advanced Mgmt. Program, Harvard, 1966. Accountant-auditor Peat, Marwick, Mitchell & Co., Kansas City, Mo., 1948-52; contr., treas. Riss & Co., Kansas City, Mo., 1952-58; regional contr. Consol. Freightways Corp. of Del., Indpls., also Akron, Ohio, 1958-61; contr. Consol. Freightways, Inc., San Francisco, 1961—; v.p., treas. Consol. Freightways, Inc., 1962-63, bd. dirs., 1966, v.p. fin., 1967-69, exec. v.p., 1969-75, pres., 1975—, chief exec. officer, 1977-88, 90-91, chmn., 1988—; pres. CF Motor Freight subs. Consol. Freightways, Inc., 1973; dir. Transam. Corp., Watkins-Johnson, Inc.; past chmn. WesternHwy. Inst., Champion Road Machinery, Ltd. Former mem. bus. adv. bd. Northwestern U., U. Calif., Berkeley; bd. dirs., regent, former chmn. bd. trustees St. Mary's Coll.; bd. dirs., regent Charles Armstrong Sch., 1991—; mem. Pres.'s Adv. Herbert Hoover Boys and Girls Club; dir. Boy Scouts Am. Bay Area Coun.; adv. coun. Nat. Commn. Agaisnt Drunk Driving. Served to 1st lt. USAAF, 1942-45. Recipient Disting. Svc. Citation Automotive Hall Fame, 1991; named Outstanding Chief Exec. five times Financial World Mag. Mem. Am. Trucking Assn. Bd. dirs. Found., exec. com.), Pacific Union Club, World Trade Club, Commonwealth Club (San Francisco), Burning Tree Country Club, Menlo Country Club. Home: 26347 Esperanza Dr Los Altos CA 94022-2601 Office: Consol Freightways Inc 3000 Sand Hill Rd Menlo Park CA 94025-7116

O'BRIEN, RAYMOND VINCENT, JR., banker; b. Bronx, N.Y., Sept. 23, 1927; s. Raymond Vincent and Blanche (Harper) O'B.; m. Theresa Sweeney, Mar. 29, 1952 (dec. June 1981); children: Susan, Raymond, Christopher, Sean, Carol, Nancy Meisenzahl; m. Ellen Boyle, July 24, 1982. A.B., Fordham U., 1951, J.D., 1958; postgrad., Advanced Mgmt. Program, Harvard U., 1969. With Chase Manhattan Bank (N.A.), N.Y.C., 1953-74; chief exec. officer, chmn. bd. Emigrant Savs. Bank, N.Y.C., 1978-92; dir. Emigrant Savs. Bank, 1974—; bd. dirs. Emigrant Savs. Bank, Internat. Shipholding Corp. Trustee Fordham U., 1979-92; chmn. bd. trustees Regis High Sch., 1988-92; past chmn. Community Bankers Assn., N.Y., Nat. Assn. Community Bankers. Served with AUS, 1946-47, 51-53. Mem. N.Y. State Bar Assn., Guild Cath. Lawyers, Sky Club, Econ. Club, Navesink Country Club (Middletown, N.J.), Sawgrass Country Club (Ponte Vedra, Fla.), Plantation Country Club (Ponte Vedra), Knights of Malta, Friendly Sons St. Patrick. Republican. Roman Catholic. Home: 102 Lands End Ponte Vedra Beach FL 32082

O'BRIEN, RICHARD DESMOND, university administrator, neurobiologist; b. Sydenham, Eng., May 29, 1929; came to U.S., 1960, naturalized, 1966; s. Joseph Andrew and Louise (Stevens) O'B.; m. Ann Margaret Thom, Mar. 16, 1961; 1 child, Ian Richard; m. Susan Krauss Whitbourne, Sept. 19, 1981, 1 child, Jennifer Louise. B.Sc., Reading (Eng.) U., 1950; Ph.D. in Chemistry, U. Western Ont., Can., 1954, B.A. in Arts, 1956. Soil specialist Ont. Agrl. Coll., Guelph, 1950-51; chemist Pesticide Research Inst., London, Can., 1954-60; faculty Cornell U., 1960-78, prof. entomology, 1964-78, prof. neurobiology, 1965-78, chmn. dept. biochemistry, 1964-65, chmn. sect. neurobiology and behavior, 1965-70, dir. div. biol. scis., 1970-78, Richard J. Schwartz prof. biology and soc., 1977-78; provost U. Rochester (N.Y.), 1978-84; exec. vice chancellor, provost U. Mass., Amherst, 1984-91, chancellor, 1991—; NRC fellow Babraham, Cambridge, Eng., 1956-57; vis. assoc. prof. U. Wis., 1958-59; cons. Melpar Inc., 1960-65, Am. Cyanamid Co., 1960-69; dir. Lincoln First Bank, 1978-84. Author: Toxic Phosphorus Esters, 1960, (with L.S. Wolfe) Radiation, Radioactivity and Insects, 1964, Insecticides, Action and Metabolism, 1967, (with I. Yamamoto) Biochemical Toxicology of Insecticides, 1970, (with E.O. Wilson, others) Life on Earth, 1973, The Receptors, A Comprehensive Treatise, vol. I, 1979; also articles.; Founding editor: Pesticide Biochemistry and Physiology, 1971. Trustee Center for Govtl. Research, 1979-84, vice-chmn., 1980-84; trustee Rochester Mus. and Sci. Center, 1979-84, Donald Guthrie Found. Med. Research, Sayre, Pa., 1977-84; pres. Rochester Area Colls., 1982-84; bd. dirs. Five Colls. Inc., 1990—. Guggenheim fellow Naples, Italy, 1967-68. Fellow AAAS; mem. Am. Chem. Soc. (Internat. award pesticide chemistry 1971), Internat. Brain Rsch. Orgn., Phi Beta Kappa, Sigma Xi. Office: U Mass Office of Chancellor Amherst MA 01003

O'BRIEN, RICHARD FRANCIS, advertising agency executive; b. Everett, Mass., Aug. 3, 1942; s. James Raymond and Gertrude Lucille O'B.; m. Clare Lynch, Apr. 7, 1973; children: Catherine Lynch, Miles Edward. A.B. magna cum laude, Boston Coll., 1964; M.A., Ind. U., 1965; M.B.A., Columbia U., 1967. With Grey Advt. Inc., N.Y.C., 1967-83; v.p., mgmt. supr. Grey Advt. Inc., 1973-77, sr. v.p., mgmt. rep., 1977-80, exec. v.p., mgmt. 1980-83; exec. v.p., mgmt. dir. Dancer Fitzgerald Sample, Inc. (name changed to Saatchi & Saatchi Advt.), N.Y.C., 1983-88; vice chmn. Dancer Fitzgerald Sample, Inc. (became Saatchi & Saatchi Advt.), N.Y.C., 1988—; bd. dirs. Saatchi & Saatchi Advt. Worldwide, 1989—. Bd. dirs. Spl. Olympics Internat., 1983—. Office: Saatchi & Saatchi Advt 375 Hudson St New York NY 10014-3658

O'BRIEN, RICHARD L(EE), academic administrator, physician, cell biologist; b. Shenandoah, Iowa, Aug. 30, 1934; s. Thomas Lee O'B. and Grace Ellen (Sims) Parish; m. Joan Frances Gurney, June 29, 1957; children: Sheila Marie, Kathleen Therese, Michael James, Patrick Kevin. M.S. in Physiology, Creighton U., 1958, M.D., 1960. Diplomate: Nat. Bd. Med. Examiners. Intern and resident Columbia med. div. Bellevue Hosp., N.Y.C., 1960-62; postdoctoral fellow in biochemistry Inst. for Enzyme Research, U. Wis., 1962-64; asst. prof. to prof. pathology Sch. Medicine, U. So. Calif., Los Angeles, 1966-82, dep. dir. Cancer Ctr., 1975-80, dir. research and edn. Cancer Ctr., 1980-81; dir. Cancer Ctr. Sch. Medicine, U. So. Calif., 1981-82; dean Sch. Medicine Creighton U., Omaha, 1982-92; acting v.p. health scis. Creighton U., 1984-85, v.p. health scis., 1985—; vis. prof. molecular biology U. Geneva, 1973-74; cons. in field; mem. cancer control research grants rev. com. NIH, Nat. Cancer Inst.; mem. Cancer Ctr. Support grant rev. com.

Nat. Cancer Inst., 1984-88, chmn. 1987-88; co-chmn. United Way/CHAD Pacesetter campaign, 1988, 94. Contbr. articles; editor various profl. jours. Served to capt. U.S. Army, 1964-66. Spl. fellow Nat. Cancer Inst., 1967-69; Combined Health Agys. Drive—Health Citizen of Yr., 1986. Mem. ACP, Am. Assn. Pathologists, Am. Assn. Cancer Rsch., Am. Assn. Cancer Edn., AAAS, Am. Assn. Cancer Insts. (dir. 1982-83), Assn. Am. Med. Colls. (chmn. MCAT evaluation panel 1987-88, liaison com. on med. edn., 1988-93, co-chmn. 1989-93, adv. panel Strategic Planning Health Care Reform 1992—), Assn. Acad. Health Ctrs. (long-range planning com. 1986, nominating com. 1987, Task Force Health Care Delivery 1992, mem. task force on leadership and instl. values 1993—), Am. Cancer Soc. (adv. com. Inst. rsch. Grants 1977-80 Outstanding Leadership award, dir. Calif. div. 1980-82, dir. Nebr. divsn. 1992—), Am. Hosp. Assn. (com. on med. edn. 1986-89), Alpha Omega Alpha. Home: 142 N Elmwood Rd Omaha NE 68132-2714 Office: Creighton Univ VP Health Sci California at 24th Omaha NE 68178

O'BRIEN, ROBERT BROWNELL, JR., investment banker, consultant, savings bank executive, yacht broker; b. N.Y.C., Sept. 6, 1934; s. Robert Brownell and Eloise (Boles) O'B.; m. Sarah Lager, Nov. 28, 1958; children: Robert Brownell III, William Stuart, Jennifer. BA, Lehigh U., 1957; postgrad., NYU, Am. Inst. Banking. Asst. treas., credit officer, br. locations officer Bankers Trust Co., N.Y.C., 1957-63; with George A. Murray Co., gen. contractors, N.Y.C., 1964; also v.p. Bowery Savs. Bank, 1964-69; dir., chief exec. officer Fed. Savs. & Loan Ins. Corp., Washington, 1969-71; chmn. exec. com. Fed. Home Loan Bank Bd., 1969-71; v.p. Bowery Savs. Bank, N.Y.C., 1972; exec. v.p. First Fed. Savs. & Loan Assn., N.Y.C., 1973-75; chmn., chief exec. officer Carteret Savs. Bank, Morristown, 1975-91, also bd. dirs.; mng. dir. Printon Kane Group Inc., Short Hills, N.J., 1991-94; dir., former chief exec. officer Govs. Bank Corp., West Palm Beach, 1992—; bd. dirs. Fed. Home Loan Bank of N.Y., Govs. Bank Corp.; vice chmn. 1st Mortgage Capital Corp., Vero Beach, Fla.; chmn. Neighborhood Housing Svcs. Am., 1972—; vice-chmn. bd. dirs. U.S. League Savs. Instns., Washington, O'Brien Yacht Sales. Contbr. articles to trade mags. Trustee Trinity Pawling Sch., Palm Beach County Housing Partnership, Lehigh U.; chmn. Housing Opportunities Found.; trustee, past chmn. Cmty. Found. of N.J., 1987—; vice chmn., bd. dirs. Dalt Found.; chmn. adv. bd. Palm Beach Maritime Mus., Peanut Island, Fla.; active Nat. Commn. on Neighborhoods; past chmn., exec. dir. N.J. State Opera. Mem. Nat. Coun. Savs. Instns. (past chmn.), Essex County Savs. and Loan League (past chmn.), N.J. Savs. League (past chmn.), N.J. Hist. Soc. (past chmn.), Greater Newark C. of C. (bd. dirs.), N.J. C. of C. (bd. dirs.), Union League Club, Delray Beach Yacht Club, New York Yacht Club, Morris County Golf Club, Somerset Hills Golf Club, Palm Beach Yacht Club. Republican. Episcopalian. Home: 12 Banyan Rd Gulf Stream FL 33483 Office: 1400 Centerpark Blvd Ste 909 West Palm Beach FL 33401

O'BRIEN, ROBERT JOHN, JR., public relations executive, former government official, air force officer; b. Wheeling, W. Va., Apr. 16, 1935; s. Robert John and Martha Virginia (Hunter) O'B.; m. Margaret Eugenia Schultz. B.S. in Journalism, Northwestern U., 1957; M.A. in Journalism, U. Wis., 1970; grad., Indsl. Coll. Armed Forces, 1977. Comnd. officer U.S. Air Force, 1957, advanced through grades to col.; dir. pub. affairs N. Am. Air Def. Command, Colorado Springs, Colo., 1977-80, Air Force Systems Command, Camp Springs, Md., 1980-82; dir. def. info. Office Sec. Def., Washington, 1982-83, dep. asst. sec. def., 1983-86; dir. pub. rels., Washington McDonnell Douglas Corp., Arlington, Va., 1986—. Decorated D.S.M., Legion of Merit, Bronze Star, Air medal, Medal of Honor (Republic Vietnam). Mem. Air Force Assn., Pub. Rels. Soc. Am., Aviation/Space Writers Assn., U.S. Space Found., Ret. Officers Assn., U.S. C. of C. (bd. dirs.), Chincoteague Country Club (Reston, Va.), Nat. Aviation Club, Nat. Press Club. Republican. Methodist. Avocations: golf; stamp collecting; model railroading. Home: 13804 Leighfield St Chantilly VA 22021-2503

O'BRIEN, ROBERT KENNETH, insurance company executive; b. Worcester, Mass., Dec. 8, 1934; s. Robert Ivor O'Brien and Arline Mary (Lanois) Knight; m. Barbara Ann Hickey, Dec. 28, 1957; children: Kevin Robert, Brendan Robert. BS in Edn., Worcester State Coll., 1958. CLU. Group underwriter State Mut. of Am., Worcester, 1958-74, v.p. group underwriting, 1974-86, v.p. bus. unit, 1987, v.p. reins., 1988-90; pres. Health Reins. Mgmt., Inc., Salem, Mass., 1990—; v.p., bd. dirs. Bibliomania, Inc., West Yarmouth, Mass., 1982-87. Pres. Westboro PTA, 1965; chmn. Young Reps. Conv., Mass., 1960. Mem. Health Ins. Assn. Am., Life Office Mgmt. Assn., Am. Soc. CLUs, Self-Ins. Inst. Am., Am. Arbitration Assn. Avocations: boating, fishing, scuba diving, flying, golf. Office: Health Reinsurance Mgmt Inc 27 Congress St Salem MA 01970-5575

O'BRIEN, ROBERT S., state official; b. Seattle, Sept. 14, 1918; s. Edward R. and Maude (Ransom) O'B.; m. Kathryn E. Arvan, Oct. 18, 1941 (dec. June 1984). Student public schs. With Kaiser Co., 1938-46; restaurant owner, 1946-50; treas. Grant County, Wash., 1950-65, State of Wash., 1965-89; chmn. Wash. State Fin. Com., 1965-89, Wash. Public Deposit Protection Commn., 1969-89, Wash. Public Employees Retirement Bd., 1969-77, Law Enforcement Officers and Firefighters Retirement System, 1971-77, Wash. State Investment Bd., 1981-89; retired, 1989; mem. Wash. Data Processing Adv. Bd., 1967-73; Gov.'s Exec. Mgmt. and Fiscal Affairs Com., 1978-80, Gov.'s Cabinet Com. on Tax Alternatives, 1978-80; trustee Wash. Tchr.'s Retirement System, 1965-89; bd. dirs. Centennial Bank, Olympia, Wash. Recipient Leadership award Joint Council County and City Employees-Fedn. State Employees, 1970, Eagles Leadership award, 1967. Mem. Nat. Assn. State Auditors, Comptrollers and Treasurers (pres. 1977), Nat. Assn. Mcpl. Fin. Officers, Nat. Assn. State Treasurers, Western State Treasurers Assn. (pres. 1970), Wash. County Treas. Assn. (pres. 1955-56), Wash. Assn. Elected County Ofcls. (pres. 1955-58), Olympia Area C. of C., Soap Lake C. of C. (pres. 1948). Democrat. Clubs: Elks (hon. life); Moose, Eagles, Lions, Olympia Yacht, Olympia Country and Golf; Empire (Spokane); Wash. Athletic (Seattle). Address: 3613 Plummer St SE Olympia WA 98501-2126

O'BRIEN, ROBERT THOMAS, investment company executive; b. Phila., Oct. 7, 1941; s. James Francis Sr. and Mildred Anita (Gomez); m. Aurora Carol Forsthoffer, Nov. 7, 1964; 1 child, Michael Joseph. Cert., N.Y. Inst. Fin., 1963; BS, St. Joseph's U., 1971. Securities trader Brown Bros. Harriman, Phila., 1964-69, portfolio mgr., 1969-77, investment officer, 1977-80, asst. mgr., investment adv., 1980-83; v.p. Newbold's Asset Mgmt., Phila., 1983-85, sr. v.p., 1985-93, also bd. dirs., 1990-93; mng. dir. W.H. Newbold's Son & Co., Phila., 1993—. Bd. dirs. Cath. Philopatrian Literary Inst., 1973-76, Mary J. Drexel Home 1992—, treas. 1992—; mem. fin. and investment com. Neumann Coll., 1990—. Served with USAF and Pa. Air N.G., 1960-67. Mem. Phila. Securities Assn., Air Force Assn. (life), Confederate Air Force (life, wing fin. officer 1992). Republican. Roman Catholic. Clubs: Racquet of Phila., Sailing Assn. (commodore 1980-82); Lewes Yacht, Miles River Yacht, Avalon Yacht, Eastport Yacht, Aronimink Golf, Idle Hour Tennis. Avocations: tennis, squash, sailing, golf. Home: 665 Dodds Ln Gladwyne PA 19035-1514 Office: WH Newbold's Son & Co 1500 Walnut St Philadelphia PA 19102-3523

O'BRIEN, STEPHEN JAMES, geneticist; b. Rochester, N.Y., Sept. 30, 1944; s. Bernard Carroll and Kathryn Marie (O'Reilly) O'B.; m. Diane Louise Rockhill, Nov. 28, 1968; children: Mary Kirsten, Meghan Rockhill. BS, St. Francis Coll., Loretto, Pa., 1966; PhD, Cornell U., 1971. Postdoctoral fellow genetics-biochemistry Gerontology Rsch. Ctr., Balt., 1971-72; NIH postdoctoral fellow Nat. Cancer Inst., NIH, Bethesda, Md., 1972-73; staff fellow Lab. Viral Carcinogenesis, Nat. Cancer Inst., NIH, Frederick, Md., 1978-80; chief sect. of genetics Lab. Viral Carcinogenesis, Nat. Cancer Inst., NIH, Frederick, 1980—, acting chief, 1983-85, chief, 1986—; zoology and botany tchg. asst. St. Francis Coll., 1965-66; gen. genetics lab. instr. and lectr. Cornell U., 1966-71; biology and soc. tchg. asst., 1969-71; human genetics discussion leader, 1970-71; adj. prof. genetics Washington U., 1974—; adj. grad. advisor dept. biology Am. U., 1979—, Hood Coll., 1982—; adj. prof. zoology U. Md., 1982—, dept. biology Johns Hopkins U., 1982—; faculty affiliate dept. pathology Colo. State U., 1994—; affiliate prof. biology George Mason U., 1994—; apptd. rsch. fellow Smithsonian Instn., Washington, 1982—; bd. trustees Am. Type Culture Assn., Rockville, Md., 1983—; apptd. exec. bd.

Am. Type Culture Collection, Rockville, 1984—, sec.-treas. bd. trustees, 1987— ; founder, co-dir. New Opportunities in Animal Health Scis., Ctr. for Wildlife Scis., Smithsonian Instn., 1985—; mem. cat specialist group Internat. Union for Conservation of Nature, Geneva, 1985—, mem. captive breeding specialist group species survival commn., 1986—; lectr. in field. Editor Isozyme Bulletin, 1975-78, Genetic Maps, 1980—; exec. editor Jour. Heredity, Am. Genetics Assn., 1987—; assoc. editor Genomics, 1987-91, Mammalian Genome, 1990—, Molecular Phylogenetics and Evolution, 1990—; guest editor Current Biology, 1993; jour. adv. bd. Cosmos, 1994; contbr. numerous articles to profl. jours. Mem. AAAS, Genetics Soc. Am., Am. Soc. Naturalists, Tissue Culture Assn., Am. Genetics Assn. (bd. dirs. 1984—, chmn. long range planning com. 1985), Am. Assn. Zool. Pks. and Aquariums (advisor spl. survival plan-cheetah 1986—), N.Y. Acad. Sci., Cosmos Club. Achievements include research in molecular genetics, developmental and cell biology, genetics of oncology, viral oncology, immunology and reproductive physiology, molecular evolution, paleontology, cytology, populations genetics.

O'BRIEN, THOMAS FRANCIS, manufacturing company executive; b. Cambridge, Mass. Mar. 28, 1938; s. Thomas Francis and Ann (Deneen) O'B.; m. Elizabeth A. Coppinger, Sept. 3, 1960; children: Nancy Ann, Thomas F., Lisa Jean. B.S., Boston Coll., 1960; M.B.A., Boston U., 1965. Analyst Nat. Shawmut Bank Boston, 1964; fin. analyst Gen. Foods Corp., N.Y.C., 1965-66; asst. controller Hewitt Robins (Litton) Conn., Stamford, 1966-67; sec.-treas. controller Electra Motors (Litton) Calif., Anaheim, 1967-69; v.p., controller Power Transmission div. (Litton) Conn., Hartford, 1969-71, A-T-O, Inc., Willoughby, Ohio, 1971-74; v.p. Recreation Group, 1974-80; pres. Rawlings Sporting Goods, 1974-80; pres. men's and children's apparel group Kellwood Co., Chesterfield, Mo., 1980-83; sr. v.p. adminstrn. Sunmark Cos., St. Louis, 1983-90; pres., chief exec. officer Sumark Capital Corp., 1990—; bd. dirs. Sunmark Capital Corp., Pub. Safety Equipment, Inc., St. Louis, Dunmon Corp., St. Louis, Diagraph Corp., St. Louis, Overland Aviations Systems, Inc., St. Louis, ABC, Birmingham, Ala., Assn. Corp. Growth, St. Louis; chmn. bd. L-H Rsch., Tustin, Calif.; mem. faculty Westchester C.C., 1966-67. Bd. dirs. Cen. St. Louis County chpt. Am. Cancer Soc., 1977-80. Served with AUS 1960-63. Fellow Boston U., 1965. Home: 2821 Stonington Pl Saint Louis MO 63131-3417 Office: Sunmark Capital Corp 510 Maryville College Dr Saint Louis MO 63141

O'BRIEN, THOMAS GEORGE, III, lawyer; b. N.Y.C., Aug. 26, 1942; s. Thomas George Jr.and Margaret Patricia (Arctander) O'B.; m. Alison Marie Rich, Aug. 26, 1967; children: Christian Arctander, Kylin Stafford. AB magna cum laude, U. Notre Dame, 1964; LLB, Yale U., 1967. Bar: N.Y. 1967, Fla. 1988. Assoc. Carter, Ledyard & Milburn, N.Y.C., 1971-78; assoc. gen. counsel Frank B. Hall & Co. Inc., Briarcliff Manor, N.Y., 1978-79, v.p., sec., gen. counsel, 1979-86; exec. v.p., sec., gen. counsel Cen'Trust Savs. Bank, Miami, 1986-87; of counsel Steel Hector & Davis, Miami, 1987-88, ptnr., West Palm Beach, Fla., 1988—. Author: Florida Law of Corporations and Business Organizations, 1990, 92, 93, 94. Trustee Bus. Vols. for Arts, Miami, 1986-88, Fla. Repertory Theatre, West Palm Beach, 1989-91, chmn., 1990-91; mem. vestry Episcopal Ch. Bethesda-by-the-Sea, 1991-94, sr. warden, 1992-94; bd. dirs. Bus. Devel. Bd. Palm Beach County, 1991—, sec., 1992-93, chmn., 1993-94; bd. dirs. Palm Beach Fellowship Christians and Jews, 1993—. Lt. USNR, 1967-71, Vietnam. Mem. ABA (com. on legal opinions 1992—), N.Y. State Bar Assn., Fla. Bar (mem. corps./securities law com. 1988—, vice-chmn. 1989-90, chmn. 1990-91, chmn. com. on opinion standards 1988—, exec. coun. bus. law sect. 1989-93), Am. Soc. Corp. Secs. (sec. N.Y. regional group 1984-86), Govs. Club, PGA Nat. Club (Palm Beach Gardens). Home: 81 Sandbourne Ln Palm Beach Gardens FL 33418-8085 Office: 1900 Phillips Point W 777 S Flagler Dr West Palm Beach FL 33401-6198

O'BRIEN, THOMAS HENRY, bank holding company executive; b. Pitts., Jan. 16, 1937; s. J. Vick and Georgia (Bower) O'B.; m. Maureen Sheedy; children—Thomas Henry, Lauren C., Timothy B. BS in Commerce, U. Notre Dame, 1958; MBA, Harvard U., 1962. With Pitts. Nat. Bank, 1962—, v.p., 1967-73, sr. v.p., 1973-80, exec. v.p., 1980-83, vice chmn., 1983-84; pres., bd. dirs., chief exec. officer PNC Fin. Corp., 1984—; also chmn. PNC Fin. Corp., Pitts., 1988—; bd. dirs. Hilb, Rogal & Hamilton Co., Aristech Chem. Corp., Bell Atlantic Corp., Pvt. Export Funding Corp., Fed. Adv. Council, Internat. Monetary Conf. Bd. dirs. United Way Southwest Pa., Pitts. Symphony Soc., Children's Hosp., Pitts., Allegheny Trails council Boy Scouts Am., Pitts. Allegheny Conf. Community Devel., U. Pitts., World Affairs Council Pitts., Carnegie Inst. Res. City Bankers. Named Man of Yr. in fin. Vectors, Pitts., 1985. Mem. Assn. Res. City Bankers, Pa. Bankers Assn. Roman Catholic. Clubs: Duquesne, Allegheny (bd. dirs.), Pitts. Field, Rolling Rock, Laurel Valley Golf. Avocation: golf. Office: PNC Fin Corp 5th Wood St Pittsburgh PA 15274 also: Pitts Pirates 600 Stadium Cir Pittsburgh PA 15212-5731*

O'BRIEN, THOMAS HENRY, JR., banker; b. Middletown, Conn., Feb. 18, 1943; s. Thomas Henry and Maryanne (Kachinski) O'B.; m. Monica Mayer, July 26, 1969 (div. Oct. 1983); children: Kelly Ann, Timothy William; m. Sally May Saabye, June 27, 1987. BS in Edn., Villanova U., 1965. V.p., team leader, account officer corp. banking Chem. Bank, N.Y.C., 1979-80, v.p., chief credit officer fin. inst. group, 1980-83, sr. v.p., group head worldwide commodities, agribusiness and ship fin., 1983-86, mng. dir., chief credit officer capital markets, 1986-87, sr. v.p., sr. credit policy officer consumer banking group, 1987—. Contbr. to profl. jour. Chmn. Cranford (N.J.) Planning Bd., 1980-82, Downtown Mgmt. Corp., Cranford, 1985-87; trustee Cath. Community Services, Newark, 1984-87. 1st lt. N.Y. Nat. Guard, 1966-74. Recipient Community Service award C. of C., Cranford, 1987. Mem. Robert Morris Assocs. Avocations: teaching, political campaigns, reading.

O'BRIEN, THOMAS IGNATIUS, lawyer; b. Troy, N.Y., Dec. 24, 1925; s. Timothy F. and Catherine M. (McCarthy) O'B.; m. Barbara Lasher; children: Kathleen, Stephanie, Alicia. BAE, Rensselaer Poly. Inst., 1946; LLB, JD, Georgetown U., 1951. Bar: N.Y. 1951, U.S. Ct. Appeals (3d cir.) 1968, U.S. Dist. Ct. N.Y. (so. dist.) 1973, U.S. Ct. Appeals (9th cir.) 1973, U.S. Ct. Appeals (2d cir.) 1975, U.S. Ct. Appeals (fed. cir.) 1982, Conn. 1988. Patent examiner U.S. Patent Office, Washington, 1946-51; patent atty. North Am. Phillips, Irvington, N.Y., 1951, Pollard, Johnston, Smythe & Robertson, N.Y.C., 1952-54; patent atty. Union Carbide Corp., Danbury, Conn., 1954-90, chief patents counsel, 1969-90; counsel Morgan & Finnegan, N.Y.C., 1991—. Mem. ABA (chmn. coms.), Am. Intellectual Property Law Assn. (bd. dirs. 1986-89), Pacific Indsl. Property Assn. (pres.), Assn. Corp. Patent Counsel (pres.), Chem. Mfrs. Assn., Internat. Patent and Trademark Assn., Intellectual Property Orgn. (bd. dirs.), Assn. Bar City N.Y. Home: 58 Stonehenge Dr New Canaan CT 06840-3524 Office: Morgan & Finnegan 345 Park Ave New York NY 10154-0001

O'BRIEN, THOMAS JOSEPH, bishop; b. Indpls., Nov. 29, 1935. Grad., St. Meinrad Coll. Sem. Ordained priest Roman Catholic Ch., 1961. Bishop of Phoenix, 1982—. Office: 400 E Monroe St Phoenix AZ 85004-2336*

O'BRIEN, TIMOTHY ANDREW, writer, journalist, lawyer; b. N.Y.C., July 11, 1943; s. Timothy Andrew and Hildegarde J. (Schenkel) O'B.; m. Maria de Guadalupe Margarita Moreno, Jan. 15, 1971; children: Theresa Marie, Tim A. B.A. in Communications, Mich. State U., 1967; M.A. in Polit. Sci., U. Md., 1972; postgrad., Tulane U. Law Sch., 1974-75; J.D., Loyola U., New Orleans, 1976. Bar: La. 1976, D.C. 1977, U.S. Supreme Ct 1981. News writer, reporter, anchorman WKBD-TV, Detroit, 1968-69, WTOP-TV, Washington, 1969-72, WDSU-TV, New Orleans, 1972-74, WVUE-TV, New Orleans, 1974-77; law corr. ABC News, Washington, 1977—. Contbr. articles to profl. jours. Mem. bd. govs. Woodward Acad., College Park, Ga. Recipient AP award for outstanding reporting of extraordinary event, 1976; New Orleans Press Club award for non-spot news reporting, 1976; Emmy award for documentary on D.C., 1969; Am. Bar Assn. awards merit, 1979 (2), 80, 85, Gavel award for documentary, 1980, Nat. award for human rights reporting Women in Communications, 1981. Mem. Am. Law Inst., Radio-TV Corrs. Assn. Washington, Am. Judicature Soc. (bd. dirs. 1991—), Sigma Delta Chi, Pi Sigma Alpha, Phi Kappa Phi. Office: ABC News Washington Bur 1717 Desales St NW Washington DC 20036-4407

O'BRIEN, TIMOTHY JAMES, lawyer; b. Detroit, Nov. 4, 1945; m. Hyon Baek, Jan. 31, 1970; children: Jean, Jane. AB, Yale U., 1967; JD, Harvard U., 1976. Bar: N.Y. 1977, U.S. Dist. Ct. (so., ea. and we. dists.) N.Y. 1978. Assoc. Cleary, Gottlieb, Steen & Hamilton, N.Y.C., 1976-80; ptnr. Coudert Bros., N.Y.C., 1980—. Mem. Harvard Law Rev., 1975-76. Assoc. dir., vol. Peace Corps, Republic of Korea, 1967-73. Mem. ABA (co-chmn. conf. on Korea-U.S. trade and investment 1990-92), N.Y. Bar Assn., Assn. of Bar of City of N.Y. (internat. law com., Asian affairs com.). Office: Coudert Bros 1114 Avenue Of The Americas New York NY 10036-7703

O'BRIEN, WILLIAM DANIEL, oil industry executive; b. N.Y.C., Apr. 17, 1930; s. Joseph M. and Mary E. (Scott) O'B.; m. Sheila F. Flaherty, Dec. 26, 1955; children: M. Catherine Douglas, William D., Joseph Scott, Elizabeth, Carolyn. BS in Econs., Villanova U., 1952; LLB, Columbia U., 1955; LLM, NYU, 1959. Bar: N.Y. 1955, Tex. 1974. Tax atty. Esso Standard East, N.Y.C., 1963-66; tax mgr. Esso Standard Libya, 1966-69, Exxon Chem. Co. N.Y.C., 1969-73; tax mgr. Exxon Co. U.S.A., Houston, 1973-75, gen. tax counsel, 1975-80; assoc. gen. tax counsel Exxon Corp., N.Y.C., 1980-86; gen. tax counsel Exxon Co. Internat., Florham Park, N.J., 1986-89; v.p., gen. tax counsel Exxon Corp., Irving, Tex., 1989—. Mem. ABA, Tex., N.Y. bars, Internat. Fiscal Assn., Bus. Roundtable (tax com.). Tax Execs. Inst., Am. Petroleum Inst. (chmn. tax com. 1980), Tex. Mid-Continent Oil and Gas Assn. (chmn. tax com./leadership 1976-80), Northwood Club (Dallas), Loxahatchee Club (Jupiter, Fla.), Westhampton Country Club (Westhampton Beach, N.Y.). Roman Catholic. Avocations: golf, traveling, dancing. Office: Exxon Corp 225 E John W Carpenter Fwy Irving TX 75062-2298

O'BRIEN, WILLIAM JAMES, II, lawyer; b. Schenectady, Oct. 23, 1940; s. William V. and Dorothy T. O'B.; m. Shannon M. Collins, July 8, 1967; children—Shannon A., Ashley T., William J. A.B., Williams Coll., 1963; J.D., Northwestern U., 1966. Bar: Ill. 1966, N.Y. 1970, U.S. Dist. Ct. (no. dist.) Ill. 1967, U.S. Dist. Ct. (so. dist.) N.Y. 1971, U.S. Ct. Appeals (2d cir.) 1971, U.S. Ct. Appeals (7th cir.) 1968, U.S. Supreme Ct. 1977. Clk. to judge Appellate Ct. Ill., 1966-67; assoc. Peterson, Lowry, Rall, Barber & Ross, Chgo., 1967-69; assoc. Rogers & Wells, N.Y.C., 1969-73; assoc. Gould & Wilkie, N.Y.C., 1973-74, ptnr., 1974; successively staff counsel, sr. counsel, sr. lead counsel, asst. to gen. counsel ITT, N.Y.C., 1974-82, sr. group counsel, dep. dir. legal ops. internat. and worldwide, 1982-83, exec. asst. to pres. ITT Telecomm., exec. v.p. ITT Corp., 1983-85; counsel Seyfarth, Shaw, N.Y.C., 1986-90; capital ptnr. Keck, Mahin & Cate, Washington, 1990—. Mem. ABA, N.Y. State Bar Assn. Home: 3378 Lakeside Dr Falls Church VA 22041 Office: Keck Mahin & Cate 1201 New York Ave NW-PH Washington DC 20005

O'BRIEN, WILLIAM JEROME, II, lawyer; b. Darby, Pa., Oct. 22, 1954; s. Richard James O'Brien and Margaret (McGill) Hahn. BA in Econ. and Polit. Sci., Merrimack Coll., 1976; JD, Del. Law Sch., 1981. Bar: Pa. 1982, U.S. Dist. Ct. (ea. dist.) Pa. 1983, U.S. Supreme Ct. 1986. Law clk. Commonwealth Ct. of Pa., Harrisburg, 1982-83; assoc. Philips, Curtin and DiGiacomo, Phila., 1983-86, O'Brien & Assocs. PC, Phila., 1986—; bd. dirs. Mid-Atlantic Video Corp., Phila., New Manayunk Corp., Phila., counselo, 1987-94. Bd. dirs. North Light Inc., 1988-90, pres., 1990-92; bd. dirs. Manayunk Cmty. Ctr. for Arts, 1988-90, chmn. Chaminoux Mansion, 1989—, chmn., 1991—; spl. asst. to U.S. Senator H. John Heinz, 1976-78; Rep. candidate for Phila. City Coun., 1991. Mem. Phila. Bar Assn., Pa. Bar Assn., Del. Law Sch. Alumni Assn. (sec. 1985-87), Bus. Assn. Manayunk (bd. dirs. 1987-89). Republican. Roman Catholic. Club: Racquet (Phila.) (committeeman 1985-87). Avocations: squash, court tennis, scuba, golf. Office: O'Brien & Assocs PC 4322 Main St Philadelphia PA 19127-1421

O'BRIEN, WILLIAM JOSEPH, educator, consultant; b. N.Y.C., July 25, 1940; s. William P. O'Brien; divorced; children: Anne Marie, Matthew. BS, CCNY, 1958; MS, NYU, 1962; PhD, U. Mich., 1967. Assoc. dir. rsch. J.F. Jelenko Inc., N.Y.C., 1956-61; from asst. to assoc. prof. Marquette U., Milw., 1961-67; mech. engr., dir. Biomaterials Rsch. Ctr., Milw., 1967-70; prof. biologic and materials scis. U. Mich., Ann Arbor, 1970—, dir. Biomaterials Rsch. Ctr., 1994—; cons. WHO, N.Y.C., 1967-70, Johnson & Johnson, Inc., New Brunswick, N.J., 1970-83; chmn. rsch. com. Sch. Dentistry U. Mich., 1987-91. Editor: (book) Dental Materials, 1989; inventor Magnesia Ceramic, 1985. Recipient UN Cert., 1967, Disting. Contbn. award Mexican Prosthodontics Soc., 1991. Mem. Materials Rsch. Soc., Acad. Dental Materials, Adhesion Soc., Dental Materials Group (pres. 1985). Office: U Mich Biomaterials Rsch Ctr 1011 N University Ave Ann Arbor MI 48109-1078

O'BRIEN, WILLIAM K., accounting firm executive; b. 1945. With Coopers & Lybrand, 1967—, ptnr., 1975—, dep. chmn., 1991—. Office: Coopers & Lybrand 1251 Ave of the Americas New York NY 10020-1104

O'BRIEN, WILLIAM VINCENT, government educator; b. Washington, July 9, 1923; s. William Colombo and Theresa (Matthews) O'B.; m. Madge Laura Roberts, Sept. 19, 1951. BS in Fgn. Svc., Georgetown U., 1946, MS in Fgn. Svc., 1948, PhD Internat. Relations, 1953. Instr. dept. govt. Georgetown U., Washington, 1950-51; Fulbright fellow Faculte de droit, Sorbonne, Paris, 1951-52; asst. prof. dept. govt. Georgetown U., Washington, 1952-57; assoc. prof. dept. govt. Georgetown U., 1957-66, prof. dept. govt., 1966-89, chmn. dept. govt., 1974-77, 84-85; co-dir. summer institutes NEH, U. Mass., Amherst, 1979. Editor, co-author: World Polity, Vols. I-III, 1957, 60, 65, The Nuclear Dilemma and the Just War Tradition, 1986; author: War and/or Survival, 1969, The Conduct of Just and Limited War, 1981. Sgt. U.S. Army, 1943-46, PTO, lt. col. USAR, 1951-75. Research grantee U.S. Institutes of Peace, 1989. Mem. Am. soc. Internat. Law, Internat. Studies Assn. Roman Catholic. Avocations: collecting art, walking. Home: 1432 44th St NW Washington DC 20007-2001 Office: Georgetown Univ Dept Govt Washington DC 20057

O'BRYAN, WILLIAM HALL, insurance executive; b. Tulia, Tex., June 15, 1919; s. Barnett and Goldie (Hall) O'B.; m. Marjorie Mae Lewis, Apr. 14, 1962; children: Richard L., Clelie S. Student, Internat. Bus. Coll., El Paso, Tex., 1936-37, Hills Bus. U., Oklahoma City, 1937, Tulsa Law Sch., 1939. With Okla. Compensation Rating Bur., Oklahoma City, 1937; underwriter, v.p. Tri State Ins. Co., Tulsa, 1937-61; pres. Occidental Fire & Casualty Co., Denver, 1961-72; founder, owner Am. Underwriters, Denver, 1972-74; pres., chmn. bd. Prime Ins. Corp., 1973-74, exec. v.p., 1976-77; v.p. Assn. Internat. Mgmt., 1974-75; conservator Equity Educators Assurance Co. Denver, 1974-75; spl. dep. Colo. ins. commr. acting as receiver Equity Educators Assurance Co., 1975-77; receiver Mfrs. & Wholesalers Indemnity Exchange, 1975-77; pres. Mo. Profl. Liability Ins. Assn., Jefferson City, Mo., 1977-86; pres. subs. Providers Ins., 1981-86; dep. receiver Profl. Mut. Ins. Co., Kansas City, Mo., 1987—, Protective Casualty Ins. Co., Kansas City, Mo., 1991—. Capt. AUS, 1942-46. Episcopalian. Home: 5404 S Fulton Ct Englewood CO 80111-3660

O'BRYAN, WILLIAM MONTEITH, lawyer; b. Manning, S.C., Apr. 27, 1912; s. Samuel Oliver and Frances (Davis) O'B.; m. Jeane Barrett, Nov. 22, 1942; 1 dau., Donna. Student, U. Miami, Fla., 1931-32; LL.B., U. Fla., 1937. Bar: Fla. bar 1937. Practice in Miami, 1937-50, in Ft.Lauderdale, 1950—; partner firm Fleming, O'Bryan & Fleming (and predecessor), 1950—; Regional v.p. Def. Research Inst., 1963-65. Served to lt. USNR, 1942-45. Fellow Am. Coll. Trial Lawyers, Internat. Acad. Trial Lawyers; mem. Internat. Assn. Ins. Counsel (exec. com. 1964-67), Sigma Chi. Presbyn. Clubs: Mason (Shriner), Rotarian (pres. Ft. Lauderdale 1954-55). Home: 707 NE 26th Ave Fort Lauderdale FL 33304-3613 Office: 1415 E Sunrise Blvd Fort Lauderdale FL 33304-2339

O'BRYON, JAMES FREDRICK, defense executive; b. Schenectady, N.Y., Oct. 1, 1941; s. Frederick Stanley and Elizabeth Mary (Leppo) O'B.; m. Margaret Adina Bell, Oct. 23, 1965; children: Daniel, Douglas, Cris, Kera. BS in Math., King's Coll., Briarcliff, N.Y., 1964; MSA in Ops. Rsch., George Washington U., 1973; SM Through Elec. Engring. Dept., MIT, 1975. Mathematician Ballistics Rsch. Lab. Aberdeen (Md.) Proving Ground, 1966-74, asst. to dir. Ballistics Rsch. Lab., 1975-76, chmn. red-on-blue working group Joint Tech. Coord. Group, 1979-85, chief combat survivability and tech. U.S. Army Materiel Systems Analysis Activity, 1985-86; asst. dep. undersec. def. Office of Sec. of Def., Washington, 1986-88, dir. live-fire testing, 1988—; dir. Joint Live Fire Program, Washington, 1986—; mem. Conventional Systems Com., Washington, 1987—. Co-author: (manual) Red-on-Blue Weapons, Effects, 1983; contbr. over 50 articles to profl. jours. Active edn. coun. MIT, Cambridge, 1980—; trustee King's Coll., Briarcliff Manor, N.Y., 1988—. With U.S. Army, 1964-66. Named Outstanding Young Man in Am., Jaycees, 1970, Disting. Lectr., Def. Systems Mgmt. Coll., 1988. Fellow Ctr. Advanced Engring. Study MIT; mem. Am. Def. Preparedness Assn. (sr. adv. coun. 1989—), Internat. Test and Evaluation Assn., Assn. Governing Bds. of Univs. and Colls., Sigma Xi. Home: 1608 South Tolgate Rd Bel Air MD 21015 Office: The Pentagon Rm 3E 1060 Washington DC 20301-0001

O'BRYON, LINDA ELIZABETH, television station executive; b. Washington, Sept. 1, 1949; d. Walter Mason Ormes and Iva Genevieve (Batrus) Ranney; m. Dennis Michael O'Bryon, Sept. 8, 1973; 1 child, Jennifer Elizabeth. BA in Journalism cum laude, U. Miami, Coral Gables, Fla. News reporter Sta. KTVX, Salt Lake City, 1971-73; documentary and pub. affairs producer Sta. WPLG-TV, Miami, Fla., 1974-76; producer, reporter, anchor, news dir. then v.p. for news and pub. affairs, exec. editor, sr. v.p. The Nightly Business Report Sta. WPBT-TV (PBS), Miami, 1976—. Recipient award Fla. Bar, Tallahasse, 1977, 2 awards Ohio State U., 1976, 79, local Emmy award So. Fla. chpt. Nat. Acad. TV Arts and Scis., 1978, award Corp. for Pub. Broadcasting, 1978, Econ. Understanding award Amos Tuck Sch. Bus. Dartmouth Coll., Hanover, N.H., 1980, award Fla. AP, 1981, 1st prize Nat. Assn. Rea Hors, 1986, Bus. News Luminary award Bus. journalism Rev., 1990, Am. Women in Radio and TV award, 1995. Mem. Nat. Acad. TV Arts and Scis. (former So. Fla. chpt.), Radio-TV News Dirs. Assn., Sigma Delta Chi. Republican. Roman Catholic. Avocations: aerobics, tennis, golf. Office: Sta WPBT 14901 NE 20th Ave Miami FL 33181-1121

OBRZUT, TED, lawyer; b. Hatfield, Eng., May 26, 1949; came to U.S. 1956; naturalized, 1961; s. Stanley Jan Obrzut and Christel Maria (Achenbach) Obrzut Wenzel; m. Rochelle Marie Lindsey, Sept. 24, 1983. Student Columbia U., 1967-69; B.A., U. Calif.-Santa Barbara, 1969-71; LL.B., UCLA, 1974. Bar: Calif. 1974, N.Y., 1990. Assoc., O'Melveny and Myers, Los Angeles, 1974-82; ptnr. Lillick, McHose and Charles, Los Angeles, 1982-87; ptnr. Milbank Tweed Hadley & McCloy, L.A., 1987—. Mem. Calif. State Bar Assn. (uniform comml. code com. 1980-83), ABA, (com. commercial fin. services), Order of the Coif, Phi Beta Kappa. Office: Milbank Tweed Hadley & McCloy 601 S Figueroa St Los Angeles CA 90017

OBST, LYNDA ROSEN, film company executive, producer, screenwriter; b. N.Y.C., Apr. 14, 1950; d. Robert A. and Claire (Shenker) Rosen; m. David Obst (div.); 1 child, Oliver. BA, Pomona Coll., 1972; degree in philosophy, Columbia U., 1974. Editor Rolling Stone History of 60's, N.Y.C., 1974-76, New York Times mag., N.Y.C., 1976-79; exec. Polygram Pictures, Los Angeles, 1979-81, Geffen Films, Los Angeles, 1981-83; co-producer Paramount Pictures, Los Angeles, 1983-85, Disney Pictures, Los Angeles, 1986—. assoc. prodr. Flashdance, 1983; co-prodr. Adventures in Babysitting, 1987, Heartbreak Hotel, 1988; prodr. The Fisher King, 1991, This is My Life, 1992; exec. prodr. Sleepless in Seattle, 1993, Bad Girls, 1994; contbr. articles to mags. Mem. Writers Guild Am. Office: Lynda Obst Prodns care 20th Century Fox 10201 W Pico Blvd Los Angeles CA 90035

O'BYRNE, PAUL J., bishop; b. Calgary, Alta., Can., Dec. 21, 1922. Ordained priest Roman Catholic Ch., 1948; bishop of Calgary, 1968—. Office: Cath Pastoral Care Ctr, 1916 2nd Ave SW Rm 205, Calgary, AB Canada T2S 1S3

O'CALLAGHAN, JERRY ALEXANDER, government official; b. Klamath Falls, Oreg., Feb. 23, 1922; s. Jeremiah Patrick and Marie Jane (Alexander) O'C.; m. Florence Marie Sheehan, Aug. 6, 1949; children—Jane Mary, Susan Margaret. B.S. with honors, U. Oreg., 1943, M.A. with honors, 1947; Ph.D., Stanford, 1951. Acting instr. history Stanford, 1951-52, U. Wyo., 1952-53; oil editor Tribune-Herald, Casper, Wyo., 1953-55; acting asst. prof. U. Wyo., 1955-56; legis. asst. to Senator Joseph O'Mahoney (Wyo.), 1956-60; exec. asst. to Senator Joseph Hickey(Wyo.), 1961; asst. dir. lands and minerals mgmt. Bur. Land Mgmt., Dept. Interior, 1961-62, asst. dir. plans and legislation, 1962-64, chief legislation and office coop. relations, 1964-69, chief div. coop. relations, 1969-80, chief hist. studies, 1980-82, historian emeritus, 1982—. Author: Disposition of the Public Domain in Oregon, 1960, America 200—The Legacy of Our Lands, 1976. Bd. govs. St. Columba's Episc. Nursery Sch., Washington, 1959-71; vestryman Episc. Ch., 1964-68; lay ministry St. Columba's, 1990—. With AUS, 1943-46. Mem. Soc. of Forest History, Fed. Profl. Assn. (pres. 1972), Phi Kappa Psi. Home: 5607 Chesterbrook Rd Bethesda MD 20816-1301

O'CALLAGHAN, ROBERT PATRICK, lawyer; b. Mpls., Aug. 8, 1924; s. Robert Desmond and Claire Marie (Moe) O'C.; married Albina Julie Sepich, June 4, 1949; children: Michael, Edward, Catherine, Diana, Robert, Daniel. BA, Drake U., 1949; JD, U. Denver, 1951. Bar: Colo. 1951, U.S. Dist. Ct. Colo. 1956, U.S. Tax Ct. 1971, U.S. Ct. Appeals (10th cir.) 1978. Pvt. practice law Denver, 1952-53, Rangely, Colo., 1953-63; real estate broker Grand Junction, Colo., 1963-65; ptnr. Bellinger, Faricy, Tursi & O'Callaghan, Pueblo, Colo., 1965-73; pvt. practice law Pueblo, 1973-76; ptnr. Lattimer, O'Callaghan & Ware P.C., Pueblo, 1978-81; of counsel Quiet & Dice, Denver, 1981-83; pvt. practice law Pueblo, 1983—; atty. Town of Rangely, 1953-63; bd. atty. Pueblo Bd. Realtors, 1971-82; instr. real estate U. Colo., 1968-79; sr. cert. valuer Internat. Real Estate Inst. Pres. Homes for Sr. Citizens Inc., Pueblo, 1978-80; pres. Mt. Carmel Credit Union, 1972-74; adv. bd. dirs. Pueblo Salvation Army, 1987-91. With USNR, 1943-46. Mem. ABA, Colo. Bar Assn., Pueblo County Bar Assn., B.P.O., Elks (exalter ruler Rangley Lodge No. 1907). Republican. Roman Catholic. Avocation: photography. Address: Union Depot 132 W B St Ste 230 Pueblo CO 81003-3402

OCASIO-MELENDEZ, MARCIAL ENRIQUE, history educator; b. San Juan, P.R., Aug. 22, 1942; s. Manuel C. and Amparo (Melendez) Ocasio; m. Mimi Rivera, Apr. 15, 1973 (div. 1976). BA, U. P.R., 1964, MA, 1977; PhD, Mich. State U., 1988. Tchr. sci. P.R. Dept. Edn., San Juan, 1966-67; tchr. sci., history Nyack (N.Y.) Schs., 1967-71; instr. asst. prof. P.R. Jr. Coll., Rio Piedras, 1972-80; teaching asst. Mich. State U., E. Lansing, 1979-83; instr. history Caribbean U., Bayamon, P.R., 1983-85; instr. Inter Am. U., Bayamon, 1985-87, U.P.R., Rio Piedras, 1983-87; vis. asst. prof. Mich. State U., E. Lansing, 1987-88; asst. prof. history U. Mich., Flint, 1988-91; assoc. prof. history U. P.R., Rio Piedras, 1991—; dir. grad. program history, 1991-93, assoc. dean acad. affairs Coll. Humanities, 1994-95; bd. dirs. Spanish Speaking Info. Ctr., Flint; lectr. Universidad del Valle, Cali, Universidad de Los Andes, Bogota, Universidad Pedagogica Nacional, Tunja, U. del Norte Barranquilla, Colombia; dir. Rockefeller Found. Caribbean 2000 Project, U. P.R., 1994-95, Urban Preservation Project of Rio Piedras, P.R., 1994-95; mem. editorial bd. Caribbean Review, 1994—. Author: Rio Piedras Notas, 1985. Fulbright scholar (Colombia) 1989, 90; NEH fellow, 1973, 78-79, 91. Mem. U.S. Nexus, Social Sci. Studies Assn., Coun. Latin Am. History, Am. Hist. Assn., Latin Am. Studies Assn., Sociedad Historiadores de P.R., Joint Border Rsch. Inst., Assn. Caribbean Historians, Phi Alpha Theta. Office: U PR Dept History PO Box 22202 UPR Sta San Juan PR 00931-2202

OCCHIATO, MICHAEL ANTHONY, city official; b. Pueblo, Colo.; s. Joseph Michael and Joan Occhiato; m. Peggy Ann Stefonowicz, June 27, 1964 (div. Sept. 3, 1983); children: Michael, James, Jennifer; m. Patsy Gay Payne, June 2, 1984; children: Kim Carr, Jerry Don Webb. BBA, U. Denver, 1961; MBA, U. Colo., 1988; postgrad., U. So. Colo. Sales mgr. Tivoli Brewing Co., Denver, 1965-67, acting brewmaster, prodn. control mgr., 1967-68, plant mgr., 1968-69; adminstrv. mgr. King Resources Co., Denver, 1969-70; ops. mgr. Canners Inc., Pepsi-Cola Bottling Co., Pueblo, 1970-76; pres. Pepsi-Cola Bottling Co., Pueblo, 1978-82; gen. mgr. Pepsi-Cola Bottling Group div. PepsiCo., Pueblo, 1982, area v.p., 1982-83; ind. cons. Pueblo, 1983—; pres. Ethnic Foods Internat. dba Taco Rancho, Pueblo, Colo.; chmn. Weifang (China) Sister City del., 1991—; bd. dirs. HMO So. Colo. Health Plan, 1988-93; rancher, 1976—. Mem. coun. City of Pueblo, 1978-93, pres., 1986, 87, 90, 91; mem. bd. health, 1978-80, regional planning commn., 1980-81, Pueblo Action Inc., 1978-80, Pueblo Planning and Zoning Commn., 1985; chmn. Pueblo Area Coun. Govts., 1980-82; mem. Pueblo Econ. Devel.

OCHBERG, FRANK MARTIN, psychiatrist, health science facility administrator, author; b. N.Y.C., Feb. 7, 1940; s. Gerald Frank and Belle (Solomon) O.; m. Lynn Jeffie Wescott, July 1, 1962; children: Billie Jennifer, Jesse Frank, Abigail Kathryn. A.B., Harvard U., 1961; M.D., Johns Hopkins U., 1965; postgrad. in psychiatry, Stanford U., 1966-69. Diplomate: Am. Bd. Psychiatry and Neurology. Intern USPHS Hosp., San Francisco, 1965-66; resident in psychiatry Stanford (Calif.) U. Med. Ctr., 1966-69; with NIMH, 1969-79, dir. div. mental health service programs, 1973-76; dir. Mich. Dept. Mental Health, 1979-81; pres. Victimization Research and Tng. Inst., 1981—; med. dir. St. Lawrence Mental Health Center, Lansing, 1981-84; med. dir. Dimondale Stress Reduction Ctr., 1983-85; clin. prof. psychiatry and behavioral medicine, adj. prof. criminal justice, adj. prof. journalism, Mich. State U., East Lansing, 1979—; psychiat. adviser FBI, 1977—, U.S. Secret Service, 1978—. Co-editor: Violence and the Struggle for Existence, 1970, The Victim of Terrorism, 1982; editor: Post Traumatic Therapy and Victims of Violence, 1988. Fellow Am. Psychiat. Assn. (past chmn. coun. on nat. affairs 1979-87); mem. Internat. Soc. for Traumatic Stress Studies (founding bd. dirs.). Address: 4211 Okemos Rd Ste 6 Okemos MI 48864

OCHELTREE, RICHARD LAWRENCE, lawyer, retired forest products company executive; b. Springfield, Ill., Oct. 9, 1931; s. Chalmer Myerly and Helen Margaret (Camm) O.; m. Ann Maureen Washburn, Apr. 11, 1958; children: Kirstin Ann, Lorraine Page, Tracy Lynn. A.B., Harvard U., 1953, LL.B., 1958. Bar: Calif. 1959. Sec., gen. counsel Am. Forest Products Corp./Bendix Forest Products Corp., San Francisco, 1961-81; v.p. adminstrn., sec., gen. counsel Am. Forest Products Co., 1981-87. Served with USAF, 1953-55. Mem. Am. San Francisco bar assns. Home: 1446 Floribunda Ave Apt 102 Burlingame CA 94010-3810

OCHILTREE, NED A., JR., retired metals manufacturing executive; b. Omaha, Dec. 23, 1919; s. Ned A. and Garnett (Briggs) O.; m. Isabel Hayden, Oct. 25, 1946; 1 child, Judith Ann Ochiltree Herseth. B.S., Purdue U., 1942. Research engr. Gen. Motors Research Labs., 1942-47; with Ceco Industries, Inc., Oakbrook, Ill., 1947-86; exec. v.p. mfg. Ceco Industries, Inc., 1964-70, exec. v.p. sales and prodn., 1970-71, pres., 1971-80, Chief exec. officer, 1976-84, chmn. bd., 1979-86, chmn. exec. com., 1986-87, also bd. dirs., 1984-86; also bd. dirs. The Ceco Corp. Mem. Oak Park Country Club, University Club (Chgo.), DuPage Club. Home: 74 Briarwood Cir Hinsdale IL 60521-8709

OCHILTREE, STUART A., cosmetics company executive; b. Chgo., Sept. 17, 1941; s. Jaquin Anderson and Harriett (Randall) O.; m. Suzanne Howley, July 23, 1966; 1 child, Molly J. Ochiltree. BFA, U. Ill., 1964. Pres., CEO direct sales div. Avon Products, N.Y.C., until 1991; chmn. Finelle Acquisition Corp., Lawrence, Mass. Lt. USN, 1964-68. Democrat. Roman Catholic. Office: Finelle Acquisition Corp 137 Marston St Lawrence MA 01841*

OCHMANEK, DAVID ALAN, government official; b. Oak Park, Ill., Apr. 10, 1951; s. Edwin Joseph and Phyllis Jean (Strauss) O.; m. Barbara Jane Larson, June 16, 1973; children: James Edwin, Anne Skaaden. BS in Internat. Affairs, Polit. Sci., USAF Acad., 1973; MPA in Pub. Affairs and Internat. Rels., Princeton U., 1980. Tng. svc. officer U.S. Dept. State, 1980-85; profl. staff The Rand Corp., 1985-93; dep. assist. sec. of def. for strategy Washington, 1993—. Author: (with Edward L. Warner III) Next Moves: An Arms Control Agenda for the 1990's, 1989; contbr. articles to profl. jours., chpts. to books. Capt. USAF, 1973-78. Lutheran. Office: Office Sec of Def The Pentagon Rm 4B724 Washington DC 20301-2000

OCHS, CAROL REBECCA, philosophy and religion educator, writer; b. N.Y.C., May 7, 1939; d. Herman and Clara Florence (Michaels) Blumenthal; m. Michael Ochs, Sept. 27, 1959; children: Elisabeth Amy, Miriam Adina. BA, CUNY, 1960, MA, 1964; PhD, Brandeis U., 1968. Philosophy lectr. CUNY, 1964-65; from asst. prof. to prof. philosophy Simmons Coll., Boston, 1967-92, prof. emerita, 1992—; adj. faculty Grad. Sch., Union Inst., Cin., 1992—, Hebrew Union Coll.-Jewish Inst. Religion, N.Y.C., 1992—; cons. Inst. for Svc. to Higher Edn., Chestnut Hill, Mass., 1972, St. Mary's Coll., South Bend, Ind., 1980; scholar-in-residence Hollins Coll., Roanoke, Va., 1987, Temple Beth El, Rochester, N.Y., 1990; mem. selection com. Kent Postdoctoral Fellowships, Bunting Inst., Radcliffe Coll.; lectr. in field. Author: Behind the Sex of God: Toward a New Consciousness Transcending Matriarchy and Patriarchy, 1977, Women and Spirituality, 1983, An Ascent to Joy: Transforming Deadness of Spirit, 1989, The Noah Paradox: Time as Burden, Time as Blessing, 1991, Song of the Self: Biblical Spirituality and Human Holiness, 1994; contbr. articles to profl. jours. Mem. Jewish-Cath. Dialogue, Boston, 1989-93; mem. Cath.-Jewish com. Archdiocese of Boston, 1989-93. Fellow NEH, 1976, 88, Nat. Humanities Inst., U. Chgo., 1978-79, Danforth Found., 1981-86, Coolidge Rsch. Colloquium, 1985, Resource Theologian, 1995. Fellow Soc. for Values in Higher Edn. (bd. dirs. 1982-88, chair ctrl. com. 1985-87), Assn. for Religion and Intellectual Life (mem. editl. bd. 1986—). Office: 115 E 87th St #26A New York NY 10128

OCHS, MICHAEL, editor, librarian, music educator; b. Cologne, Germany, Feb. 1, 1937; came to U.S., 1939, naturalized, 1945; s. Isaac Julius and Claire (Baum) O.; m. Carol Rebecca Blumenthal, Sept. 27, 1959; children—Elisabeth Amy, Miriam Adina. B.A., CCNY, 1958; M.S., Columbia U., 1963; A.M., NYU, 1964; D.A., Simmons Coll., 1975. Cataloguer CCNY, 1963-65, lectr. in music, 1964; music libr. Brandeis U., Waltham, Mass., 1965-68; creative arts libr. Brandeis U., Waltham, 1968-74; asst. prof. libr. sci. Simmons Coll., Boston, 1974-78; libr. Eda Kuhn Loeb Music Libr., Harvard U., Cambridge, Mass., 1978-88; Richard F. French libr. Eda Kuhn Loeb Music Libr., Harvard U., Cambridge, 1988-92; lectr. music Harvard U., Cambridge, Mass., 1978-81, sr. lectr. music, 1981-92, also libr. cons., 1977-78; music editor W. W. Norton and Co., N.Y.C., 1992—; libr. cons. Biblioteca Berenson, Florence, Italy, 1983, Columbia U., 1987; project dir. U.S. Répertoire International des Sources Musicales Manuscript Inventory Ctr. at Harvard U., NEH, Cambridge, Mass., 1985-88. Editor Notes, Jour. Music Libr. Assn., 1987-92, Music Librarianship in America, 1991; contbr. articles to profl. jours., 1976—. Mem. Internat. Assn. Music Librs. (pres. rsch. librs. br. 1987-90), Music Libr. Assn. (new Eng. chpt. 1968-69, chmn. com. on bibliog. description 1971-73, chmn. music libr. adminstrn. com. 1975-76, chmn. fin. com. 1976-78, chmn. publs. com. 1983-87, pres. 1993-95). Office: W W Norton and Co 500 Fifth Ave New York NY 10110

OCHS, ROBERT DAVID, history educator; b. Bloomington, Ill., Mar. 27, 1915; s. Herman Solomon and Fannie Leah (Livingston) O. A.B., Ill. Wesleyan U., 1936; M.A., U. Ill., 1937, Ph.D., 1939; M.A., Oxford U. Eng., 1964. Research dir. Anti-Defamation League, 1939-41; mem. faculty U. S.C., 1946—; prof. history, 1957-76, disting. prof. emeritus, 1976—, chmn. dept., 1960-74; acting dean U. S.C. (Coll. Arts and Sci.), 1970-71; assoc. editor U. S.C. Press, 1950-53; vis. prof. Merton Coll., Oxford U., 1964. Mem. S.C. Archives Commn., 1960-74. U.S. cons.: History of The 20th Century, 1967. Bd. dirs. Columbia Music Festival assn., 1957-64, 77-85, v.p., 1961-62, pres., 1962-63; dir. Columbia Lyric Opera, Columbia Mus. Art, 1966-69, 74-77, McKissick Mus., 1991—. Major AUS, 1941-46; lt. col. Mem. Am. Hist. Assn., So. Hist. Assn. (exec. council 1973-76), S.C. Hist. Assn. (editor 1947-55, pres. 1956-57), Am. Studies Assn., Organ. Am. Historians, Southeastern Am. Studies Assn. (pres. 1960-61), Omicron Delta Kappa. Home: 100 Sunset Blvd # 401 West Columbia SC 29169

OCHS, SIDNEY, neurophysiology educator; b. Fall River, Mass., June 30, 1924; s. Nathan and Rose (Kniaz) O.; m. Bess Ratner; children—Rachel F., Raymond S. Susan B. Ph.D., U. Chgo., 1952. Research assoc. Ill. Neuropsychiat. Inst. Chgo. 1952-54; research fellow Calif. Inst. Tech., Pasadena, 1954-56; asst. prof. dept. physiology U. Tex. Med. Br., Galveston, 1956-58; assoc. prof. dept. physiology Ind. U. Indpls. 1958-61; prof. Ind. U. 1961-94, prof. emeritus, 1993—. Author: Elements of Neurophysiology, 1965; Axoplasmic Transport and Its Relation to Other Nerve Functions, 1982;

3110

founding editor, editor-in-chief Jour. Neurobiology, 1969-76; assoc. editor Jour. Neurobiology, 1977-86. Served with U.S. Army, 1943-45. Mem. Internat. Brain Research Orgn., Am. Physiol. Soc., Soc. Neurosci., Am. Soc. Neurochemistry. Democrat. Jewish. Office: Ind U Med Ctr Dept Physiology/Biophys 635 Barnhill Dr Indianapolis IN 46202-5126

OCHS, WALTER J., civil engineer, drainage adviser; b. Springfield, Minn., May 20, 1934; s. Walter Minrod and Cleo (Schultz) O.; m. Connie Mae Strate, Sept. 15, 1956; children: Julie, Brian. BS in Agrl. Engring., South Dakota U., 1957. Registered profl. civil engr., Mich. Engr. in training USDA, Soil Conservation Svc., Watertown, S.D., 1957-58; project engr. USDA, Soil Conservation Svc., Britton, S.D., 1958-61; area engr. USDA, Soil Conservation Svc., Sioux Falls, S.D., 1961-63; asst. state conservation engr. USDA, Soil Conservation Svc., East Lansing, S.D., 1963-66, state conservation engr., 1966-69; asst. state conservationist USDA, Soil Conservation Svc., Saint Paul, Minn., 1969-71; nat. drainage engr. USDA, Soil Conservation Svc., Washington, 1971-86; drainage adviser World Bank, Washington, 1986—; bd. dirs. Internat. Inst. for Land Reclamation and Improvement Postgrad Land Drainage Course, The Netherlands; cons. for over 25 countries; mem. Internat. Commn. Irrigation and Drainage. Contbr. to profl. jours. Named Federal Engr. Of The Year, Nat. Soc. Profl. Engrs., 1982; recipient Outstanding Alumnus award South Dakota State Univ., 1977, Outstanding Contributions award Corrugated Plastic Tubing Assn., 1981. Fellow Am. Soc. Agrl. Engrs., 1991; Mem. Am. Soc. Civil Engrs. (chmn. drainage com. 1975-76). Home: 6731 Fern Ln Annandale VA 22003 Office: The World Bank 1818 H St NW Washington DC 20433

OCHSNER, JOHN LOCKWOOD, thoracic-cardiovascular surgeon; b. Madison, Wis., Feb. 10, 1927; s. Edward William Alton and Isabel (Lockwood) O.; m. Mary Lou Hannon, Mar. 20, 1954; children: John L., Joby Hannon, Katherine Lockwood, Frank Hannon. MD, Tulane U., 1952. Diplomate Am. Bd. Thoracic Surgery (chmn.), Am. Bd. Surgery, Am. Bd. Vascular Surgery. Intern Univ. Mich. Hosp., Ann Arbor, 1952-53, resident, 1953-54; resident Baylor U. Affiliated Hosp., Houston, 1956-58, 1958-59; chief surg. resident Tex. Children's Hosp., 1959-60; instr. Baylor U., Houston, 1960-61; mem. staff Ochsner Clinic, New Orleans, 1961-66, chmn. dept. surgery, 1966-87, chmn. emeritus dept surgery, 1987—; clin. asst. prof. Tulane U. New Orleans, 1961-65, clin. assoc. prof., 1965-70, clin. prof., 1970—. Author: (with others) Coronary Artery Surgery, 1978. Pres. Tennis Patrons Assn. New Orleans, 1972; image amb. City of New Orleans, 1982; bd. dirs. Internat. Trade Mart, New Orleans, 1983. Capt. USAF, 1954-56. Recipient award Life Mag., 1961, Golden Plate Acad. Achievement award, 1962, medal of honor, Ecuador, 1981. Mem. Internat. Soc. Cardiovascular Surgery (pres. N.Am. chpt. 1983-84, internat. pres. 1989-91), Am. Assn. Thoracic Surgery (sec. 1979-83, pres. 1992-93), New Orleans Surg. Soc. (pres. 1977-78), So. Surg. Assn. (pres. 1991), So. Assn. for Vascular Surgery (pres. 1983), Boston Club, La. Club, New Orleans Country Club, City Club, Alpha Omega Alpha. Republican. Home: 84 Audubon Blvd New Orleans LA 70118-5540 Office: Ochsner Clinic & Hosp 1514 Jefferson Hwy New Orleans LA 70121-2483*

OCKENE, ALAN L., tire manufacturing executive; b. 1931. BA in Lit., Yale U.; MBA, NYU. With Studebaker Europe, 1953-57; various sales mgmt. positions Ford Motor Co., Carribean and S.Am., 1957-69; with Internat. Basic Economy Corp., 1969-74; v.p. Europe and Africa Goodyear Tire & Rubber Co., Akron, Ohio, 1974-91; pres. Gen. Tire Inc., Akron, 1991—. Office: General Tire Inc 1 General St Akron OH 44329-0001

OCKERBLOOM, RICHARD C., newspaper executive; b. Medford, Mass., Dec. 19, 1929; s. Carl F. and Helen C. (Haraden) O.; m. Anne Joan Torpey, Sept. 17, 1955; children: Catherine, Carl, Gail, Mark, John, Peter. BSBA, Northeastern U., 1952; D Pub. Svc. (hon.), Westfield State Coll., 1989. With Boston Globe, 1948—, salesman, 1955-63, asst. nat. advt. mgr., 1963-70, nat. advt. mgr., 1970-72, asst. advt. dir., 1972-73, advt. dir., 1973-77, v.p. mktg. and sales, 1977-81, exec. v.p., 1981—, gen. mgr., chief operating officer, 1984-86, pres., chief operating officer, 1986-93, vice chmn., 1993-94; ret.; retired; chmn. bd. Met. Sunday Newspapers. Bd. dirs. Greater Boston Conv. and Visitors Bur., Winchester Hosp., United Way Mass. Bay; trustee Northeastern U.; adv. bd. U. Mass., Boston. With U.S. Army, 1952-54. Mem. Algonquin Club (mem.), Winchester Country Club. Home: 80 Arlington St Winchester MA 01890-3735

OCKERMAN, HERBERT W., agricultural studies educator; b. Chaplin, Ky., Jan. 16, 1932; m. Frances Ockerman (dec.). BS with Distinction, U. Ky., 1954, MS, 1958; PhD, N.C. State U., 1962; postgrad., Air Univ., 1964-70, Ohio State U., 1974, 83, 87. Asst. prof. Ohio State U., Columbus, 1961-66, assoc. prof., 1966-71, prof., 1971—; former mem. Inst. Nutrition and Food Tech.; judge regional and state high sch. sci. fairs, 1965—, Ham Contest, Ky. State Fair, Sausage and Ham Contest, Ohio Meat Processing Groups; cons. various food companies, 1975—, Am. Meat Inst., 1977-88, USDA, 1977-88, CRC Press., Inc., 1988—; bd. examiners U. Calcutta, 1987-88; examiner U. Mysore, India, 1990—; expert witness, various firms, 1992—; presenter in field. Author: China Today: Contemporary Animal Husbandry (book award 1992), Quality Control of Post-Mortem Muscle Tissue, 1969, 14th rev. edit., 1986; contbr. chpts. to books, abstracts and articles to profl. jours, conf. proceedings. Comdr, USAF, 1955-58. Fisher Packing scholar; named Highest Individual in Beef Grading, Kansas City Meat Judging contest, 1952, Cert. Appreciation, Ohio Assn. Meat Processors, 1987-91, Profl. Devel. award Cahill faculty, Commendation for internat. work in agriculture Ohio Ho. Reps., Badge of Merit for svc. to agriculture Polish Govt., Plaque Argentina Nat. Meat Bd., veterinary faculty U. Cardoba, Spain, Nat. Chung-Hsing U., Veterinary Mus. Ciechanowcu, Poland, Animal Sci. award Roussel UCLAR, France, U. Assiut, Egypt, Silver Paltter Nat. Meat Bd. Sec. Agriculture, Livestock &Fishery, Argentina, Coun. of Graduate Studen Svc. award Pomerene, Enhancement Teaching award, Plaque from Argentina Soc. of Agrl., Presdl. Medallion award Achievement award Argentina Soc. Agrl., Vet. Faculty award U. Cordoba, Hall of Disting. Alumni award U. Ky., Pinkno award Brazil. Mem. NAS, NCR-19Am. Meat Sci. Assn., Am. Soc. Animal Sci. (rsch. award 1987), Am. Soc. Testing and Materials, Reciprocal Meat Conf., European Meeting of Meat Rsch. Workers, Polish Veterinary Soc. (hon.), Inst. Food Technologists (nat. and OVS chpts.), Can. Meat Sci. Assn., Internat. Congress Meat Sci. and Tech., Rsch. in Basic Sci., Phi Beta Delta (treas. 1987, pres. 1991, internat. scholar award 1991, internat. faculty award 1991), Gamma Sigma Delta (rsch. award 1977, award of merit 1988), Sigma Xi. Office: Ohio State U Meat Lab Animal Sci 2029 Fyffe Rd Columbus OH 43210-1007

OCKERSE, THOMAS, graphic design educator; b. Dutch Bandung, Java, Apr. 12, 1940; came to U.S., 1957, naturalized, 1964; s. Willem Fedor Pieter and Louise Johanna (Tideman) O.; m. Susan Carol Florence, Aug. 31, 1963; children: Kirsten Ingred, Eerin Irene, Tara Manisses. B.F.A., Ohio State U., 1963; M.F.A., Yale U., 1965. Sr. designer Fogleman Assos., Morristown, N.J., 1965-67; asst. prof. Ind. U., Bloomington, 1967-71; prof. graphic design R.I. Sch. Design, Providence, 1971—; head graphic design dept. R.I. Sch. Design, 1973-93, program head grad. studies in graphic design, 1993—; ptnr., prin. Ockerse Ltd. (design cons.); ptnr. Humanity Found.; mem. adv. bd. Visible Lang. and Design Issues; adj. faculty Jan van Eyck Acad., Maastricht, The Netherlands, 1992—. Artist, poet, freelance graphic designer, Providence, 1972—; author: SP-VII, 1968, Stamps-To, 1968, The A-Z Book, 1969, T.O.P., 1970, TV Demonstracing, 1974, Son of Fury, 1974, Time, 1974, 26 Poems 1, 1975, Word and Image Equations, 1975, Fact of Fiction, 1976, Stamps-USA, 1975, Graphic Design Education: An Exposition, 1977, Space Window, 1977, Semiotics and Graphic Design Education, Chance/Choice, 1988, Spirals, 1993. Recipient Edn. award Am. Ctr. for Design, 1991; faculty rsch. grantee Ind. U., 1969, RISD, 1992, Scottish Internat. Trust grantee for edn. and art, 1972. Mem. Am. Inst. Graphic Arts (v.p. 1980-85, chmn. edn. com.), Indsl. Design Soc. Am., Semiotic Soc. Am., Am. Ctr. for Design, Sigma Chi. Home: 37 Woodbury St Providence RI 02906-3509 Office: RI Sch Design Graphic Design Dept 2 College St Providence RI 02903-2784

OCKEY, RONALD J., lawyer; b. Green River, Wyo., June 12, 1934; s. Theron G. and Ruby O. (Sackett) O.; m. Arline M. Hawkins, Nov. 27, 1957; children: Carolyn S. Ockey Baggett, Deborah K. Ockey Christiansen, David Kathleen M. Ockey Hellewell, Valerie Ockey Sachs, Robert. B.A., U. Utah, 1959, postgrad. 1959-60; J.D. with honors, George Washington U., 1966.

Bar: Colo. 1967, Utah 1968, U.S. Dist. Ct. Colo. 1967, U.S. Dist. Ct. Utah 1968, U.S. Ct. Appeals (10th cir.) 1969, U.S. Ct. Claims 1987. Missionary to France for Mormon Ch., 1954-57; law clk. to judge U.S. Dist. Ct. Colo., 1966-67; assoc. ptnr., shareholder, v.p., treas., dir. Jones, Waldo, Holbrook & McDonough, Salt Lake City, 1967-91; pres., IntelliTrans Internat. Corp., 1992-95; mem. Utah Ho. Reps., 1989-90, Utah State Senate, 1991-94; lectr. in securities, pub. fin. and bankruptcy law. State govtl. affairs chmn. Utah Jaycees, 1969; del. state Rep. Convs., 1972-74, 1976-78, 1980-82, 84-86, del. Salt Lake County Rep. Conv., 1978-80, 88; sec. Wright for Gov. campaign, 1980; legis. dist. chmn. Utah Rep. Party, 1983-87; trustee Food for Poland, 1981—, pres., trustee, Unity to Assist Humanity Alliance, 1992—; bd. dirs. Utah Opera Co., 1991-94; trustee, mem. exec. com. Utah Info. Tech. Assn., 1991-94; bd. dir., mem. exec. com. Smart Utah, Inc., 1995—. Lt. U.S. Army, 1960-66; to capt. Judge Adv. Gen. USAR, 1966-81. Mem. Utah State Bar Assn. (various coms.), Nat. Assn. Bond Lawyers (chmn. com. on state legislation 1982-85), George Washington U. Law Alumni Assn. (bd. dirs. 1981-85), Order of Coif, Salt Lake Rotary, Phi Delta Phi. Contbr. articles on law to profl. jours.; mem. editorial bd. Utah Bar Jour., 1973-75; mem. staff and bd. editors George Washington Law Rev., 1964-66. Home: 4502 Crest Oak Cir Salt Lake City UT 84124-3825

OCKUN, ROBERT J., manufacturing executive. Sr. v.p., reinsurance divsn., no. am. Himont Inc., Wilmington, Del. Office: Himont USA Inc Box 15439 2801 Centerville Rd Wilmington DE 19850

O'CONNELL, ANTHONY J., bishop; b. Lisheen, County Clare, Ireland, May 10, 1938. Ed. Mt. St. Joseph Coll., Cork, Ireland, Mangret Coll., Limerick, Ireland, Kenrick Sem. Ordained priest Roman Cath. Ch., 1963. Bishop Diocese of Knoxville, 1988—. Office: Bishop of Knoxville 417 Erin Dr Knoxville TN 37919

O'CONNELL, BRIAN, community organizer, public administrator, writer, educator; b. Worcester, Mass., Jan. 23, 1930; s. Thomas J. and Mary (Carroll) O'C.; m. Ann C. Brown, July 11, 1953; children: Todd, Tracey, Matthew. B.A., Tufts Coll., 1953; postgrad., Maxwell Sch. Citizenship and Pub. Adminstrn., 1953-54; also numerous hon. degrees. Field rep. Am. Heart Assn., Pa., 1954-56; exec. dir. Am. Heart Assn., Md., 1956-61, Calif., 1961-66; exec. dir. Nat. Assn. Mental Health, 1966-78, dir. emeritus, 1978—; pres. Nat. Council on Philanthropy, 1978-80; exec. dir. Coalition of Nat. Vol. Orgns., 1978-80; pres. Independent Sector, 1980-95; founding pres. Tufts U., 1995—, prof. pub. svc., 1995—; mem. U.S. Pres.'s Com. Employment of Handicapped, 1966-68; chmn. Liaison Group Mental Health, 1969-72. Author: Effective Leadership in Voluntary Organizations, 1976, Finding Values That Work: The Search for Fulfillment, 1977, America's Voluntary Spirit, A Book of Readings, 1983, the Board Members Book, 1985, Philanthropy in Action, 1987, Our Organization, 1987, Volunteers in Action, 1989, People Power: Service Advocacy, Empowerment, 1994, The Cowboy of Boards, 1995. Mem. Alumni Coun. Tufts U., 1970-80, trustee, 1988—, chmn. pres. search com., 1992; trustee Point of Light Found., 1989-95; bd. dirs. Hogg Found., 1990-95; chmn. organizing com. co-chmn., chmn. exec. com. Civicus: World Alliance for Citizen Participation, 1992-95; bd. dirs. E.M. Kaufman Found., 1994—. Recipient outstanding sgr. prof. award United Way am., 1979, Lincoln Filene Citizenship award, 1985, John W. Gardner Leadership award, 1994, Gold Key award, 1994, Chmns. award, NSFBE, 1994. Fellow Am. Pub. Health Assn., Nat. Acad. Pub. Adminstrn. (trustee 1993—), Nat. Com. Patients' Rights (chmn. 1975-77). Home: 50 Chase St Chatham MA 02633 Office: Lincoln Filene Ctr Tufts U Medford MA 02155

O'CONNELL, BRIAN JAMES, academic administrator, priest; b. Hartford, Conn., Aug. 21, 1940; s. Jerry and Mary (Moloney) O'C. AB, Mary Immaculate Sem., 1964, MDiv, 1968; MA, St. John's U., Jamaica, N.Y., 1970; PhD, Ohio State U., 1974. Ordained priest Roman Cath. Ch., 1968. Social studies tchr. St. John's Prep. Sch., Bklyn., 1968-70; lectr. sociology St. John's U., Jamaica, 1970-71, asst. prof. sociology, 1974-79, assoc. prof., 1979-87, assoc. dean arts and scis., 1987-88, also bd. dirs., 1989—; exec. v.p. Niagara U., N.Y., 1988-89, pres., 1989—; bd. dirs. St. John's U., DePaul U., Niagara Cath. High Sch. Author: Blacks in White Collar Jobs, 1979; also articles. Cons. Bklyn. Ecumenical Coops., 1981-88. Mem. Niagara Falls C. of C. (bd. dirs. 1989—). Office: Office of the Pres Niagara U Niagara University NY 14109

O'CONNELL, CARMELA DIGRISTINA, appraisal executive, consultant; b. Johnstown, Pa., Nov. 8, 1925; d. Salvatore and Josephine (Riggio) Digristina; m. Maurice F. O'Connell, Sept. 21, 1974 (dec. Feb. 1984); children: Geraldine, John, Bernard. Diploma, Eastern Secretarial Sch., N.Y.C., Sch. Interior Design, N.Y.C. From typist to sec.-treas. Philip P. Masterson Co., N.Y.C., 1942-72; exec. v.p., bd. dirs Masterson & O'Connell Inc., N.Y.C., 1972-80, cons., 1981—; founder, pres. N.Y. Appraisal Corp., N.Y.C., 1971-80; co-founder, pres. Park Ave. Appraisal, N.Y.C., 1981—. Mem. N.Y. Rep. Com., 1974—, Met. Opera Guild, N.Y.C., 1986; chmn. Ch. of Our Saviour, N.Y.C., 1986; mem. ladies of charity Cath. Charities of the Archdiocese of N.Y., 1990. Recipient Amita award for Bus. Woman of Yr., 1977, Lena Madesin Phillips award N.Y. League/Fortune 500 Bus. and Profl. Women, 1989. Mem. Nat. Fedn. Bus. and Profl. Women's Clubs Inc. (2d v.p. 1964, 1st v.p. 1966). Roman Catholic. Home: 80 Park Ave New York NY 10016-2541

O'CONNELL, SISTER COLMAN, college president, nun. BA in English, Speech, Coll. St. Benedict, St. Joseph, Minn., 1950; MFA in Theater, English, Cath. U., 1954; PhD in Higher Edn. Adminstrn., U. Mich., 1979; student, Northwestern U., Birmingham U., Stratford, Eng., Denver U., Stanford U., Sophia U., Tokyo. Entered Order of St. Benedict. Tchr. English Pierz (Minn.) Meml. High Sch., 1950-53, Cathedral High Sch., St. Cloud, Minn., 1950-53; chairperson theater and dance dept. then prof. theater Coll. of St. Benedict, St. Joseph, 1954-74, dir. alumnae, parent relations, ann. fund, 1974-77, dir. planning, 1979-84, exec. v.p., 1984-86, pres., 1986—; cons. Augsburg Coll., Mpls., 1983-85, Assn. Cath. Coll. and Univs., 1982, Minn. Pvt. Coll. Council, 1982, SW (Minn.) State U., Marshall, 1980-82, Wilmar (Minn.) Community Coll., 1980-82, Worthington (Minn.) Community Coll., 1980-82, U. Minn., Morris, 1980-82; bd. dirs. St. Cloud Cmty. Found., 1991-94. Mem. Nat. Assn. Ind. Colls. and Univs (bd. dirs. 1993), St. Cloud Area C. of C. Roman Catholic. Office: Coll Saint Benedict 37 College Ave S Saint Joseph MN 56374-2001

O'CONNELL, DANIEL CRAIG, psychology educator; b. Sand Springs, Okla., May 20, 1928; s. John Albert and Letitia Rutherford (McGinnis) O'C. B.A., St. Louis U., 1951, Ph.L., 1952, M.A., 1953, S.T.L., 1960; Ph.D., U. Ill., 1963. Joined Soc. of Jesus, 1945; asst. prof. psychology St. Louis U., 1964-66, assoc. prof., 1966-72, prof., 1972-80, trustee, 1973-78, pres., 1974-78; prof. psychology Loyola U., Chgo., 1980-89; prof. psychology Georgetown U., Washington, 1990—, chmn., 1991—; vis. prof. U. Melbourne, Australia, 1972, U. Kans., 1978-79, Georgetown U., 1986; Humboldt fellow Psychol. Inst. Free U. Berlin, 1968; sr. Fulbright lectr. Kassel U., W. Ger., 1979-80. Author: Critical Essays on Language Use and Psychology, 1988; contbr. articles to profl. jours. Recipient Nancy McNeir Ring award for outstanding teaching St. Louis U., 1969; NSF fellow, 1961, 63, 65, 68; Humboldt Found. grantee, 1973; Humboldt fellow Tech. U. of Berlin, 1987. Fellow Am., Mo. psychol. assns., Am. Psychol. Soc.; mem. Midwestern, Southwestern, Eastern psychol. assns., Psychologists Interested in Religious Issues, Psychonomic Soc., Soc. for Scientific Study of Religion, N.Y., Mo. acads. sci., AAUP, AAAS, Phi Beta Kappa. Home and Office: Georgetown U Dept Psychology 37th & O Sts NW Washington DC 20057 *Were it over, it would have been more than my expected share already. The challenge of learning to serve others has moved it along at a quick pace, and I am grateful that I have always received more than I've been able to give in return—from the Lord and from many good people.*

O'CONNELL, DANIEL S., private investments and management buyouts; b. N.Y.C., Feb. 7, 1954; s. Daniel R. and Josephine (Morris) O'C.; m. Gloria Perri, Nov. 26, 1976; children: Carly, Evan, Jared, Jamie, Colin. AB, Brown U., 1976; M in Pub. and Pvt. Mgmt., Yale U., 1980. Assoc. Dillon, Read & Co., Inc., N.Y.C., 1980-82; assoc. The First Boston Corp., N.Y.C., 1982-84, v.p., 1984-87, pres., 1986-88, mng. dir., 1987-88; also bd. dirs. First Boston LBO, Inc., N.Y.C.; founding ptnr., chief exec. officer Vestar Capital Ptnrs.,

Inc., N.Y.C., 1988—; bd. dirs., Prestone Products Corp., Danbury, Conn., Hampshire Chem. Corp., Lexington, Mass., La Petite Acad., Inc., Kansas City, Mo., Anvil Knitwear, Inc., N.Y.C., Russell-Stanley Corp., Red Bank, N.J., Super D Drugs, Inc., Memphis, Pyramid Comms., Inc., Medford, Mass. Roman Catholic. Club: Field (Greenwich, Conn.). Avocation: athletics. Home: 16 Rock Ridge Ave Greenwich CT 06831-4401 Office: Vestar Capital Ptnrs Inc 245 Park 40th Ave New York NY 10167

O'CONNELL, DENNIS E., lawyer; b. Mo., 1944. BA, U. Notre Dame, 1966; JD, St. Louis U., 1969. Bar: Mo. 1969, U.S. Ct. Military Appeals. With Bryan Cave, St. Louis. Mem. ABA, Bar Assn. Met. St. Louis, Mo. Orgn. Defense Lawyers, Delta Theta Phi. Address: Bryan Cave 211 N Broadway Saint Louis MO 63102

O'CONNELL, EDWARD JAMES, JR., psychology educator, computer applications and data analysis consultant; b. Sterling, Ill., Aug. 15, 1932; s. Edward James and Elizabeth E. (Clapham) O.; m. Pamelia Canon Floyd, Aug. 21, 1959; children—Edward James III, John Matthew. B.S. in Psychology, Ill. Inst. Tech., 1958; M.A. in Psychology, Northwestern U., 1961, Ph.D. in Psychology, 1962. NSF postdoctoral fellow Carnegie Inst. Tech., Pitts., 1962-63; asst. prof. psychology Carnegie Inst. Tech., 1963-65; psychology faculty Syracuse (N.Y.) U., N.Y., 1965-93; prof. Syracuse (N.Y.) U., 1975-93, prof. emeritus, 1993—; cons. Rand Corp., Santa Monica, Calif., 1962-64, Abt Assocs., Boston, 1970-73, Marcy Psychiat. Hosp., N.Y., 1979-82. Served to cpl. U.S. Army, 1952-54. NSF predoctoral fellow, 1959-62; NSF postdoctoral fellow, 1962-63; Northwestern U. predoctoral fellow, 1958-59. Mem. Am. Psychol. Assn., Assn. Computing Machinery, Sigma Xi. Democrat. Avocations: billiards; computer programming. Home: 508 Halsted Rd Cashiers NC 28717 Address: PO Box 570 Cashiers NC 28717

O'CONNELL, EDWARD JOSEPH, III, financial executive, accountant; b. Evergreen Park, Ill., Aug. 9, 1952; s. Edward Joseph Jr. and Mary Jane O'C.; m. Mary M. Witt, May 30, 1976; children: Kelly, Edward IV, Molly, Kevin. BBA, U. Notre Dame, 1974. CPA, Ill. Mem. audit staff Coopers and Lybrand, Chgo., 1974-78, audit mgr., 1978-81; controller Union Spl. Corp., Chgo., 1981-83, v.p., treas., 1983-85, v.p. chief fin. officer, 1985-89, exec. v.p. fin. and adminstrn., chief. fin. officer, 1989-91; sr. v.p. fin., chief fin. officer GenDerm Corp., Lincolnshire, Ill., 1991—. Mem. Am. Inst. CPA's, Ill. Soc. CPA's, Fin. Execs. Inst., Machinery and Allied Products Inst. (fin. council II). Roman Catholic. Club: Notre Dame of Chgo. (bd. govs. 1984-86). Avocations: rugby, running, reading, golf. Home: 10420 Lamon Ave Oak Lawn IL 60453-4743 Office: GenDerm Corp 600 Knightsbridge Pky Lincolnshire IL 60069-3617

O'CONNELL, FRANCIS JOSEPH, lawyer, arbitrator; b. Ft. Edward, N.Y., Mar. 19, 1913; s. Daniel Patrick and Mary (Bowe) O'C.; m. Adelaide M. Nagro, Sept. 27, 1937; children: Chris, Mary Gaynor Lavonas. AB, Columbia U., 1934; JD, Fordham U., 1938; SJD summa cum laude, Bklyn. Law Sch., 1945. Bar: N.Y. 1938, U.S. Dist. Ct. (so. dist.) N.Y. 1942, U.S. Tax Ct. 1941. Counsel and asst. to chmn. exec. com. for labor law and litigation Allied Chem. Corp., N.Y.C., 1942-70; ptnr. Bill & O'Connell and predecessor, Garden City, N.Y., 1970-76; pvt. practice Garden City, N.Y., 1976-85, Cutchogue, N.Y., 1985—; arbitrator, fact-finder, mediator Fed. Mediation and Conciliation Svc., 1970—, N.Y. State Mediation Bd., Am. Arbitration Assn., N.Y. State, Nassau and Suffolk County pub. employment rels. bds., 1970—; adminstrv. law judge N.Y. State Dept. Health, 1979—; instr. labor law and labor rels. Cornell U.; U.S. del. ILO, Geneva, 1948, 59, 69, 72. Author: Labor Law and the First Line Supervisor, 1945, Restrictive Work Practices, 1967, National Emergency Strikes, 1968. Trustee Village of Garden City, 1948-50; mem. bd. edn. Diocese of Rockville Centre (N.Y.), 1972-80; pres. various civic orgns., 1942—. Mem. ABA (labor and internat. law sects.), N.Y. State Bar Assn. (labor com.), Bar Assn. Nassau County (labor and arbitration coms., former chmn. arbitration andlabor law coms.), Mfg. Chemists Assn. (chmn. indsl. rels. com.), U.S.C. of C. (indsl. rels. com.), Southold Indian Mus. (bd. dirs.). Republican. Roman Catholic. Office: PO Box 819 Cutchogue NY 11935-0819

O'CONNELL, FRANK JOSEPH, apparel company executive; b. Ithaca, N.Y., May 11, 1943; s. Daniel Michael and Virginia (Davidson) O'C.; m. Gail Young, 1961 (div. 1971); children: Lauren Beth, Kimberly; m. Barbara Jean Smith, Dec. 6, 1974; children: Shaun, Thomas. BS in Econs., Cornell U., 1965, MBA, 1966. Product mgr. Carnation Co., Los Angeles, 1966-71, Hunt-Wesson Foods, Fullerton, Calif., 1971-72; mktg. mgr. Archon Pure Products Co., Beverly Hills, Calif., 1972-73; dir. mktg. Oroweat Foods Co. div. Continental Grain Corp., San Francisco, 1973-80; gen. mgr., v.p. mktg. Arnold Baking Co. Seattle, Denver and Greenwich, Conn., 1980; sr. v.p. sales and mtkg. Mattel Toys, Hawthorne, Calif., 1980-82; pres., chief exec. officer Fox Video Games, San Jose, Calif., 1982-84, Optionware, Inc., Bloomfield, Conn., 1984-85, HBO Video, N.Y.C., 1986-88; pres. Reebok Brands and Apparel, Canton, Mass., 1988—. Mem. com. United Jewish Appeal, N.Y.C., 1986-87, People for the American Way, 1986-87. Roman Catholic. Avocations: skiing, motocycling. Home: 815 Park Ave New York NY 10021-3276 Office: Reebok Internat Ltd 150 Royall St Canton MA 02021-1031

O'CONNELL, GEORGE EDWARD, state official; b. Springfield, Mass., Feb. 20, 1940; s. George Edward and Delia Marie (Harper) O'C.; m. Joan Marie Cermak, Aug. 24, 1974; 1 child, George William. BA, U. Notre Dame, 1961, MA, 1966; MA, Niagara U., 1969; PhD, U. Minn., 1974. Dir. labor and urban affairs, mgr. prof. indsl. rels. U. Minn., Mpls., 1974-78; dir. assoc. prof. Labor Edn. Ctr. U. Conn., Storrs, 1978-84, ext. prof. labor edn., 1985-87; asst. commr. Minn. Dept. Labor and Industry, St. Paul, 1981-82; dep. commr. for labor and industry N.Y. State Dept. Labor, Albany, 1987—; pres. OHRD, Inc., Hebron, Conn., 1986-87; exec. bd. dirs. OSHA State Plan Assn.; v.p., pres. Nat. Assn. Govtl. Labor Ofcls., Washington, 1990-92, exec. bd. dirs. Nat. Apprenticeship Program, Washington, 1990-92; chair exec. com. N.Y. Labor Legacy Project, Troy, N.Y., 1989-95; exec. bd. dirs. Gov.'s Excelsior award, Albany, N.Y. Contbr. articles to profl. jours. Recipient Disting. Svc. as Pres. Nat. Assn. Govtl. Labor Ofcls., 1994. Mem. Am. Sociol. Assn. (nat. cert. orgnl. analysis 1991-95), Indsl. Rels. Rsch. Assn., Svc. Employees Internat. Union. Office: NY State Dept Labor Bldg 12 State Office Bldg Campus Albany NY 12240

O'CONNELL, HAROLD PATRICK, JR., banker; b. Chgo., Sept. 11, 1933; s. Harold P. and Charlotte Anne (Woodward) O'C.; m. Geraldine Taylor McLaughlin, 1979; children: Alexandra T. Close, Geraldine S. Kuchman, Peter B. McLaughlin Jr. AB, Dartmouth Coll., 1955; JD, U. Mich., 1958. V.p. Continental Ill. Nat. Bank and Trust Co., Chgo. 1958-83, No. Trust Co., Chgo., 1983-86; dir. Terra Mus. of Am. Art, Chgo., 1987-92; chmn. exec. com. Mid-Am. Nat. Bank, 1989-92, pres., CEO, dir., 1992-93, chmn. bd., 1993—. Trustee Better Govt. Assn. Chgo., 1974—, pres., 1979-83; governing mem. Chgo. Symphony Orchestra, 1979—; sustaining fellow Art Inst. Chgo., 1982—; bd. dirs. Rehab. Inst. Chgo., 1980—. Mem. Chgo. Club, Racquet Club, Econ. Club, Casino Club (pres. 1988-91), Owentsia Club (Lake Forest, Ill.), Shoreacres (Lake Bluff, Ill.), Old Elm Club (Highland Park, Ill.), Cypress Point Club (Pebble Beach, Calif.). Home: 132 S Green Bay Rd Lake Forest IL 60045-3054 Office: Mid-Am Nat Bank of Chgo 130 E Randolph St Chicago IL 60601

O'CONNELL, HUGH MELLEN, JR., architect, retired; b. Oak Park, Ill., Nov. 29, 1929; s. Hugh M. and Helen Mae (Evans) O'C.; m. Frances Ann Small, Apr. 13, 1957; children: Patricia Lynn, Susan Marie, Jeanette Maureen, Douglas, John Mackel. Student mech. engring., Purdue U., 1948-50; B.S. in Archtl. Engring, U. Ill., 1953. Registered architect, Ariz., Calif. La., Nev., Nat. Council Archtl. Registration Bds. Structural engr. Los Angeles, 1955-57; architect Harnish & Morgan & Causey, Ontario, Calif., 1957-63; self-employed architect Ventura, Calif., 1963-69; architect Andrews/O'Connell, Ventura, 1970-78; dir. engring. div. Naval Constrn. Bn. Center, Port Hueneme, Calif., 1978-91; supervisory architect Naval Constrn. Bn. Center, Port Hueneme, 1991-93; ret., 1993; mem. tech. adv. com. Ventura Coll., 1965-78; sec. Oxnard Citizens' Adv. Com., 1969-70, 1970-72, 1977—; chmn. Oxnard Beautification Com., 1969, 74, Oxnard Cmty. Block Grant adv. com., 1975-76; mem. Oxnard Planning Commn., 1978-86, vice chmn., 1978-79, chmn., 1980-81. Mem. Oxnard Art-in-Pub. Places Commn., 1988—. Served with AUS, 1953-55. Mem. AIA (emeritus, pres. Ventura chpt. 1973), Am. Concrete Inst., Soc. Am. Registered Architects

(Design award 1968, dir. 1970), Am. Legion, Soc. for Preservation and Encouragement of Barbershop Quartet Singing in Am. (chpt. pres. 1979, chpt. sec. 1980-83), Acad. Model Aeros. (#9190 1948—), Alpha Rho Chi. Presbyterian (elder 1963, deacon 1967). Lodges: Kiwanis (pres. 1969, div. sec. 1974-75), Elks. Home and Office: 520 Ivywood Dr Oxnard CA 93030-3527

O'CONNELL, JAMES JOSEPH, port official; b. Lockport, Ill., Feb. 7, 1933; m. Phyllis Ann Berard, Aug. 1, 1953; children: Lynn, Kathryn, Julie. BSBA, Lewis U., 1958. lic. pvt. pilot FAA. Recorder Will County, Joliet, Ill., 1976-88; dir., treas., corp. sec. Joliet Regional Port Dist., 1972-96, dir. Des Plaines Valley Enterprise Zone, Joliet. Precinct committeeman Will County, Joliet, 1962-72, exec. com. committeeman, 1965-70, dir. Will County Young Reps., Joliet, 1984, sec. Will County Econ. Affairs Commn., Joliet; candidate for U.S. Congress, 1994. With U.S. Army, 1953-54, Korea. Mem. Ill. Assn. Port Dists. (sec., treas. 1982—); Ill. Jaycees (senate pres. 1972-73, named to Hall of Fame 1993), Joliet Flying Club (sec.). Roman Catholic. Office: 1009 Western Ave Joliet IL 60435-6801

O'CONNELL, JOHN WILLIAM, health care facility administrator; b. Toledo, Feb. 24, 1943; married. B. Xaiver U., 1965, M, 1967. Adminstr. res. Cin. Gen. Hosp., Cin., 1966-67; adminstrv. asst. St. John Hosp., Detroit, 1969-70, asst. adminstr., 1970-75; asst. adminstr. St. John Hosp., Mount Clemens, Mich., 1975-78, assoc. adminstr., 1978-81, exec. v.p. 1981; pres. Franciscan Svcs. Corp., Sylvania, Ohio. Office: Franciscan Svcs Corp 6832 Convent Blvd Sylvania OH 43560-2891

O'CONNELL, KENNETH JOHN, state justice; b. Bayfield, Wis., Dec. 8, 1909; s. Daniel W. and Kathryn B. (Smith) O'C.; m. Evelyn L. Wachsmuth, June 2, 1938; children: Daniel, Thomas; m. Esther Erickson, July 3, 1964. LL.B., U. Wis., 1933, S.J.D., 1934; LL.D. (hon.), Williamette U., 1983. Bar: Wis. 1933, Oreg. 1944. Assisted preparation Restatement of Law of Property, Am. Law Inst.; asst. atty. Wis. Tax Commn., 1934; pvt. practice law Eugene, Oreg., 1944-47; mem. Oreg. Supreme Ct., 1958-77, chief justice, 1970-76; asst. prof. law U. Oreg. Law Sch., 1935-40, asso. prof., 1940-44, prof., 1947-58; Mem. faculty N.Y. U. Law Sch. Appellate Judges Seminar, 1966, 67; Disting. vis. prof. law U. Oreg., 1977; vis. prof. law Willamette U. Sch. Law, 1977-79, adj. prof., 1981-85; Chmn. Oreg. Statute Revision Council, 1950-54; mem. 2d Triennial Coif Award Com., 1965, Oreg. Jud. Reform Commn., 1971—; vice chmn. Constl. Revision Com., Oreg., 1961-63; mem. exec. com. Conf. Chief Justices.; Chmn. Oreg. Rhodes Scholarship Selection Com., 1969—; elector N.Y.U. Hall of Fame for Great Ams. Author article, monographs legal topics. Recipient Oreg. State Bar award of merit, 1953, Disting. Service award U. Oreg., 1967, Herbert Harley award Am. Judicature Soc., 1976, Cert. Distinction award U. Wis., 1983, E.B. McNaughton award ACLU, 1984, Legal Citizen of Yr., Oreg. Law Related Edn. Project, 1984, Disting. Service award U. Oreg. Law Sch., 1985. Center Advanced Study Behavioral Scis., 1965-66. Mem. Oreg. Jud. Council, Oreg. State Bar, Order of Coif, Omicron Delta Tau, Phi Delta Phi. Home: 3393 Country Club Rd S Salem OR 97302-9710

O'CONNELL, KEVIN, lawyer; b. Boston, Sept. 4, 1933; s. Michael Frederick and Kathryn Agnes (Kelley) O'C.; m. Mary Adams, July 14, 1990; children: Tiffany W., Elizabeth H., Dana A., Liesel E. A.B., Harvard, 1955, J.D., 1960. Bar: Calif. 1961. Assoc. firm O'Melveny & Myers, L.A., 1960-63; asst. U.S. atty. criminal div. Cen. Dist. Calif., L.A., 1963-65; staff counsel Gov. Calif. Commn. to Investigate Watts Riot, L.A., 1965-66; firm Tuttle & Taylor, L.A., 1966-70, Coleman & O'Connell, L.A., 1971-75; pvt. practice law L.A., 1975-78; of counsel firm Simon & Sheridan, L.A., 1978-89; ptnr. Manatt, Phelps & Phillips, L.A., 1989—. Bd. editors: Harvard Law Rev, 1958-60. Mem. Los Angeles County (Calif.) Democratic Central Com., 1973-74. Served to lt. USMCR, 1955-57. Mem. Am. Law Inst. Home: 426 N Mccadden Pl Los Angeles CA 90004-1026 Office: Manatt Phelps & Phillips Trident Ctr E Tower 11355 W Olympic Blvd Los Angeles CA 90064-1614

O'CONNELL, KEVIN GEORGE, priest, fundraiser, former college president; b. Boston, May 22, 1938; s. George Lawrence and Mary Margaret (Cohan) O'C. BA, Boston Coll., 1962, MA, 1963; PhD, Harvard U., 1968; MDiv, Weston Sch. Theology, Cambridge, Mass., 1969. Joined S.J., 1956; ordained priest Roman Cath. Ch., 1969. Asst. prof. Old Testament Weston Sch. Theology, Cambridge, 1971-77, dir. field edn., 1972-75, assoc. prof. Old Testament, 1977-80; assoc. prof., chmn. dept. religious studies John Carroll U., Cleve., 1981-87; pres., prof. Le Moyne Coll., Syracuse, N.Y., 1988-93; provincial asst. for capital devel. Soc. of Jesus of New Eng., Boston, 1994—; vis. prof. O.T., Woodstock Coll., Balt., 1969-70; vis. prof. theology U. San Francisco, 1970; William K. Warren Disting. vis. prof. Roman Cath. studies U. Tulsa, 1987; sabbatical John Carroll U., University Heights, Ohio, 1993-94; chmn. bd. Joint Archeol. Expdn. to Tell el-Hesi, Israel, 1982—. Author: The Theodotionic Revision of the Book of Exodus, 1972; editor: The Tell el-Hesi Field Manual, 1980, Tell el-Hesi: Modern Military Trenching and Muslim Cemetery, 1985, Tell el-Hesi: The Persian Period (Stratum V), 1989, Tell el-Hesi: The Site and the Expedition, 1989, Tell el-Hesi: The Muslim Cemetery in Fields V and VI/IX (Stratum II), 1993; mem. editorial adv. bd. Bible Rev., 1987—. Bd. dirs. Hiawatha coun. Boy Scouts Am., 1988-93, Syracuse Opera, 1991—; trustee Albright Inst. Archeol. Rsch., Jerusalem, Israel, 1982—, Am. Schs. Oriental Rsch., Balt., 1983—, vice chmn., 1993—, Boston Coll., 1988—, Loyola U., Chgo., 1990—, U. Scranton, 1992—. Kent fellow Danforth Found., 1965-67; Am. Coun. Learned Socs. study fellow, 1970-71, grantee, 1980-81; Grauel Faculty fellow John Carroll U., 1986-87. Mem. Cath. Bibl. Assn., Soc. Bibl. Lit., Internat. Fedn. Cath. Univs. (trustee, v.p., mem. coun. 1988-94). Office: Ignatius House PO Box 799 Back Bay Annex Boston MA 02117-0799

O'CONNELL, KEVIN MICHAEL, lawyer; b. N.Y.C., Sept. 10, 1948; s. George Francis and Marion O'Connor; m. Elizabeth Terlep, June 27, 1970; children: Brendan Matthew, Megan Lucy, Roderick George Francis, Daniel Victor, Patrick Vincent. AB, Providence Coll., 1970; JD, Am. U., 1973; LLM, Georgetown U., 1984. Bar: Md. 1974, D.C. 1975, U.S. Dist. Ct. D.C. 1975, U.S. Ct. Appeals (D.C. cir.) 1975, Va. 1984. Mem. legis. staff U.S. Senate, 1971-73, U.S. Ho. of Reps., 1973-76; assoc. Betts, Clogg & Murdock, Rockville, Md., 1976-80; assoc., then ptnr. Kenary, Tietz & Hogan, Rockville, Md., 1980-84; prosecuting atty. Loudoun County, Va., 1984-87; pvt. practice law Leesburg, Va., 1987-88; ptnr. Miles & Stockbridge, Rockville, Md., 1988-94, Semmes, Bowen & Semmes, Balt., 1994—; adj. prof. U. Md. Sch. of Law, 1991—. Contbg. author The Lessons of Victory, 1969. Cubmaster Boy Scouts Am., Leesburg, Va., 1986-87; chmn. bd. mgrs. Christ Child Inst. for Children, Rockville, 1977-81; bd. dirs. Christ Child Soc. of Washington, 1977-81; mem. Md. Anhui Province China Sisters Com., 1993—; bd. dirs., sec. Gonzaga Coll. High Sch., Washington, 1993—. Mem. ABA (People's Rep. China law com. sect. internat. law and practice, internat. investment and devel. com., subcoms. on infrastructure projects and power projects), Internat. Bar Assn. (Asia-Pacific forum), Montgomery County Bar Assn., Md. State Bar Assn., D.C. Bar, Va. State Bar, Bar Assn. Balt. City, Balt. Coun. Fgn. Affairs, South Africa Roundtable of Balt. Roman Catholic. Club: The Barristers. Home: 3700 N Charles St Baltimore MD 21218 Office: 250 W Pratt St Baltimore MD 21201-2423

O'CONNELL, MARY ANN, state senator, business owner; b. Albuquerque, Aug. 3, 1934; d. James Aubrey and Dorothy Nell (Batsel) Gray; m. Robert Emmett O'Connell, Feb. 21, 1977; children: Jeffery Crampton, Gray Crampton. Student, U. N.Mex., Internat. Coun. Shopping Ctrs. Exec. dir. Blvd. Shopping Ctr., Las Vegas, Nev., 1968-76, Citizen Pvt. Enterprise, Las Vegas, 1976; media supr. Southwest Advt., Las Vegas, 1977—; owner, operator Meadows Inn, Las Vegas, 1985—, 3 Christian bookstores, Las Vegas, 1985—; state senator Nev. Senate, 1985-93; chmn. gov. affairs; vice chmn. commerce and labor; mem. taxation com.; alt. Legis. Commn., 1985-86, mem., 1987-88, 91-93; commr. Edn. Commn. States; rep. Nat. Conf. State Legislators; past vice chair State Mental Hygiene & Mental Retardation Adv. Bd. Pres. explorer div. Boulder Dam Area coun. Boy Scouts Am., Las Vegas, 1979-80, former mem. exec. bd.; mem. adv. bd. Boy Scouts Am.; pres., bd. dirs. Citizens Pvt. Enterprise, Las Vegas, 1982-84, Secret Witness, Las Vegas, 1081-82; vice chmn. Gov.'s Mental Health-Mental Retardation, Nev., 1983—; past mem. community adv. bd. Care Unit Hosp., Las Vegas; past mem. adv. bd. Kidney Found., Milligan Coll., Charter Hosp.; tchr. Young Adult Sunday Sch. Recipient Commendation award Mayor O.

Grayson, Las Vegas, 1975, Outstanding Citizenship award Bd. Realtors, 1975, Silver Beaver award Boy Scouts Am., 1980, Free Enterprise award Greater Las Vegas C. of C., Federated Employers Assn., Downtown Breakfast Exch., 1988, Award of Excellence for Women in Politics, 1989, Legislator of Yr. award Bldg. and Trades, 1991, Legislator of Yr. award Nat. ASA Trade Assn., 1991, 94, Guardian of Liberty award Nev. Coalition of Conservative Citizens, 1991, Internat. Maxi Awards Promotional Excellence; named Legislator of Yr., Nev. Retail Assn., 1992. Mem. Retail Mchts. Assn. (former pres., bd. dirs.), Taxpayers Assn. (bd. dirs.), Greater Las Vegas C. of C. (past pres., bd. dirs., Woman of Achievement Politics women's coun. 1988). Republican. Mem. Christian Ch. Avocations: china painting, reading. Home: 7225 Montecito Cir Las Vegas NV 89120-3118 Office: Nev Legislature Senate 401 S Carson St Carson City NV 89701-4747

O'CONNELL, MAURICE DANIEL, lawyer; b. Ticonderoga, N.Y., Nov. 9, 1929; s. Maurice Daniel and Leila (Geraghty) O'C.; m. Joan MacLure Landers, Aug. 2, 1952; children: Mark M., David L., Ann M., Leila K., Ellen A. Grad., Phillips Exeter Acad., 1946; A.B., Williams Coll., 1950; LL.B., Cornell U., 1956. Bar: Ohio 1956. Since practiced in Toledo; assoc. Williams, Eversman & Black, 1956-60; ptnr. Robison, Curphey & O'Connell, 1961—; spl. hearing officer in conscientious objector cases U.S. Dept. Justice, 1966-68; mem. complaint rev. bd. Bd. Commrs. on Grievance and Discipline of Supreme Ct. Ohio, 1987. Mem. Ottawa Hills Bd. Edn., 1963-66, pres., 1967-69; former trustee Toledo Soc. for Handicapped; past trustee Woodlawn Cemetery; past trustee Toledo Hearing and Speech Center, Easter Seal Soc.; mem. alumni council Phillips Exeter Acad. Served to 1st lt. USMCR, 1950-53. Fellow Ohio State Bar Found.; mem. NW Ohio Alumni Assn. of Williams Coll. (past pres.), ABA, Ohio Bar Assn., Toledo Bar Assn. (chmn. grievance com. 1971-74), Kappa Alpha, Phi Delta Phi. Club: Toledo. Home: 3922 W Bancroft St Toledo OH 43606-2533 Office: Four SeaGate 9th Fl Toledo OH 43604

O'CONNELL, NEIL JAMES, priest, academic administrator; b. Buffalo, N.Y., May 21, 1937; s. Cornelius James and Marie Katherine (Schneider) O'C. BA, St. Bonaventure U., 1960; STB, Cath. U., Washington, 1964; MA, Siena Coll., 1967; PhD, U. Ga., 1970. Ordained priest Roman Cath. Ch. 1964. Instr. history and sociology St. Francis Coll., Rye Beach, N.H., 1965-67; asst. prof. history Prairie View (Tex.) A&M Coll., 1970-71; asst. assoc. prof. history Fisk U., Nashville, 1971-80, chmn. history, 1975-80, dir. div. fine arts and humanities, 1979-80; acad. dean Erie Community Coll., City Campus, Buffalo, 1980-86; dean faculty and instrn. Elizabeth Seton Coll., Yonkers, N.Y., 1986-89; dean Elizabeth Seton Sch. Assoc. Degree Studies of Iona Coll., Yonkers, N.Y., 1989-90; pres. St. Bonaventure U., St. Bonaventure, N.Y., 1990—. Contbr. articles to jours. in field. Trustee Archbishop Walsh High Sch., Olean, N.Y., 1990—, Bishop Timon High Sch., Buffalo, Trocaire Coll., Buffalo; bd. dirs. Econ. Devel. Zone, Olean, YMCA, Olean, 1990—; chair bd. dirs. Coll. Consortium for Internat. Studies. Mem. Olean C. of C. (bd. dirs. 1990—), Rotary, Phi Beta Kappa, Phi Kappa Phi, Phi Delta Kappa, Phi Beta Sigma. Democrat. Avocations: walking, theater, music. Home: Saint Bonaventure U Saint Bonaventure NY 14778 Office: Saint Bonaventure U Office of Pres Saint Bonaventure NY 14778 *Teaching/learning is an act of worship wherein we encounter divine wisdom. Faculty and students who engage in this act are responding to a vocation to be the ministers of this worship.*

O'CONNELL, PAUL EDMUND, publisher; b. Cambridge, Mass., Dec. 15, 1924; s. William Henry and Catherine O'C.; m. Phyllis B. Borgeson, July 18, 1970; children—Eileen Lucy, Brian Paul, Philip Bartlett, Douglas John, Donald Paul, Lori Ann, Stephanie Elizabeth, Kirsten Lynn. A.B. Harvard U., 1949. Salesman Am. Tobacco Co., 1949-50; sales rep. dept. coll. texts Prentice-Hall Co., 1950-58, editor, 1958-62, exec. editor, asst. v.p., 1963-68; chmn. Winthrop Pubs. Inc. subs. Prentice Hall Co., Cambridge, Mass., 1969-81; cons., 1981-82; sr. acquisition editor Bobbs-Merrill Ednl. Pubs., 1983-84; sr. editor Dorsey Press, 1985-88, Lexington Books, 1988-91; pub. cons., 1991—. Served with AC U.S. Army, 1943-47. Decorated Purple Heart. Mem. Am. Sociol. Assn., Am. Pyschol. Assn. Home: 60 Pleasant St #221 Arlington MA 02174

O'CONNELL, PHILIP RAYMOND, retired lawyer, paper company executive; b. N.Y.C., June 2, 1926; s. Michael Joseph and Ann (Blaney) O'C.; m. Joyce McCabe, July 6, 1957; children: Michael, Kathleen, Jennifer, David. AB, Manhattan Coll., 1949; LLB, Columbia U., 1956; grad. Advanced Mgmt. Program, Harvard U., 1967. Bar: N.Y. 1956, U.S. Supreme Ct. 1961, Conn. 1988. Assoc. Dewey, Ballantine, Bushby, Palmer & Wood, N.Y.C., 1956-61, 62-64; gen. counsel, sec. Laurentide Finance Corp., San Francisco, 1961-62; gen. counsel Wallace-Murray Corp., 1964-66, div. mgr., 1966-70; pres., chief exec. officer, dir. Universal Papertech Corp., Hatfield, Pa., 1970-71; sec. Champion Internat. Corp., Stamford, Conn., 1972-90, v.p., 1979-81, sr. v.p., 1981-90; mem. legal adv. com. N.Y. Stock Exch., 1985-88, corp. governance subcom., legal adv. com., 1985-94; chmn. lawyers steering com. corp. governance task force The Bus. Roundtable, 1981-87, mem., 1981-94. Mem. Champion Internat. Found., 1979-90; mem. bd. visitors Fairfield Univ. Sch. Bus., 1981-93, chmn., 1983-93; bd. dirs. Kearney-Nat. Corp., 1975-78. With USNR, 1951-54. Mem. Am. Law Inst., ABA, Am. Soc. Corp. Secs. (chmn. 1988-89).

O'CONNELL, QUINN, lawyer; b. Redfield, S.D., May 5, 1924; s. John Ignatius and Ann (Quinn) O'C.; m. Jane F. Salkeld, May 19, 1951; children—Quinn Jr., Jerome C., James S., John P., Maureen, Sharon Ann. A.B., Georgetown U., 1946, J.D., 1955; M.F.A., Catholic U., 1950. Bar: D.C. 1955. Instr. U. Md., 1948-50; asst. procurator Catholic U., Washington, 1952-55; assoc. Weaver & Glassie, Washington, 1957-64, ptnr., 1964-68; ptnr. Molloy & O'Connell, Washington, 1969-70, Connole and O'Connell, Washington, 1971-89, Holland & Hart, Washington, 1989-92; govt. affairs cons. Washington, 1992—. Served with USNR, 1943-46. Mem. ABA, D.C. Bar Assn. Roman Catholic. Clubs: Kenwood Golf and Country, (Washington). Home and Office: 5009 Sangamore Rd Bethesda MD 20816-2327

O'CONNELL, ROBERT FRANCIS, physics educator; b. Athlone, Ireland, Apr. 22, 1933; came to U.S., 1958; s. William and Catherine (O'Reilly) O'C.; m. Josephine Molly Buckley, Aug. 3, 1963; children: Adrienne Molly, Fiona Catherine, Eimear Kathleen. BSc, Nat. U. Ireland, Galway, 1953, DSc, 1975; PhD, U. Notre Dame, 1962. Telecommunications engr. Dept. Posts and Telegraphs, Dublin, Ireland, 1954-58; scholar Inst. Advanced Studies, Dublin, 1962-63; systems analyst IBM, Dublin, 1963-64; sr. rsch. assoc. Inst. Space Studies, N.Y.C., 1966-68; asst. prof. physics La. State U., Baton Rouge, 1964-66, assoc. prof., 1966-69, prof., 1969-86, Boyd prof., 1986—. Editor for theoretical physics Hadronic Jour.; bd. mem. Phys. Rev. A; contbr. articles to profl. jours. Named Disting. Rsch. Master, La. State U., 1975; NAS-NRC fellow, 1966-68, Sci. Rsch. Coun. (Eng.) sr. vis. fellow, 1976. Fellow Am. Phys. Soc.; mem. Am. Astron. Soc., Internat. Astronomy Union, Internat. Soc. Gen. Relativity and Gravitation. Republican. Roman Catholic. Avocation: tennis. Home: 522 Bancroft Way Baton Rouge LA 70808-4807 Office: La State Univ Dept Physics and Astronomy Baton Rouge LA 70803-4001

O'CONNELL, ROBERT JOHN, insurance company executive; b. N.Y.C., May 16, 1943; m. Claire M. Costantini; children: Kristin, Janet R. Bus. Fordham U., 1965; MA, U. Pa., 1966. With N.Y. Life Ins. Co., N.Y.C., 1970-89, v.p., 1983-86, sr. v.p., 1986-89; sr. v.p. group mgmt. divsn. AIG, 1989-91; sr. v.p. ALICO, 1989—, A.I. Life 1989-91; pres., CEO AIG Life Ins. Cos, 1991—; also bd. dirs. A.I. Life; bd. dirs. Am. Internat. Life Assn. N.Y., AIG Life Ins. Co., AIG Equity Sales Corp., Delam Life Ins. Co. Mem. Fin. Svcs. Vol. Corps Mission to Czechoslovakia, 1991. Mem. Am. Coun. of Life Ins., Life Ins. Mgmt. and Rsch. Assn. Home: 3040 North St Fairfield CT 06430-1624

O'CONNELL, WILLIAM EDWARD, JR., finance educator; b. N.Y.C., Sept. 16, 1937; s. William Edward and Helen Margaret (Brazel) O'C.; m. Janet Elinor Shields, Aug. 15, 1965; children: William Edward III, Cathleen Anne. AB, Manhattan Coll., 1959; MBA, Columbia U., 1961; D in Bus. Adminstrn. with honors, Ind. U., 1967; JD, Coll. William & Mary, 1974. Fin. analyst Pfizer, Inc., N.Y.C., 1962-64; asst. prof. U. Conn., Storrs, 1967-69; Morris prof. banking U. Va., Charlottesville, 1988; Chessie prof. bus. Coll. William and Mary, Williamsburg, Va., 1969—; mem. faculty Va.

Bankers Sch., Chrlottesville, 1975—, Stonier Grad. Sch. Banking, Newark, 1977—, Bank Adminstrn. Inst., Madison, Wis., 1978—; dir. Citizens & Farmers Bank. Author: Asset & Liability Management, 1979, Advanced Financial Planning, 1984, Financial Planning for Credit Unions, 1989, Strategic Financial Management for Commercial Banks, 1993. Mem. Am. Fin. Assn., Fin. Mgmt. Assn., Colonnade Club. Roman Catholic. Home: 102 Overlook Dr Williamsburg VA 23185-4434 Office: Coll William & Mary Sch Bus Williamsburg VA 23187-8795

O'CONNELL, WILLIAM RAYMOND, JR., college president; b. Richmond, Va., Jan. 4, 1933; s. William Raymond and Mary Helen (Wenenger) O'C.; m. Peggy Annette Tucker, June 29, 1957; 1 child, William Raymond III. BMusEd. Richmond Profl. Inst., 1955; MA, Columbia U., 1962, EdD, 1969. Asst. to provost Richmond (Va.) Profl. Inst., 1955-57, dean of men, 1957-59, dean of students, dean of men, 1959-61; asst. to provost, dir. student info. ctr. Tchrs. Coll. Columbia U., N.Y.C., 1962-65, rsch. asst. inst. of higher edn. Tchrs. Coll., 1965-66; rsch. assoc. So. Regional Edn. Bd., Atlanta, 1966-69, dir. spl. programs, 1969-73, project dir., undergrad. edn. reform, 1973-79; dir. curriculum and faculty devel. Assn. Am. Colls., Washington, 1979-80, v.p. for programs, 1980-82, v.p., 1982-85; pres. New Eng. Coll., Henniker, N.H., 1985—; cons. Coun. for Advancement Small Colls., 1975; mem. adv. com. project on instnl. renewal through improvement of teaching Soc. for Values in Higher Edn., 1975-78; mem., evaluator N.H. Postsecondary Edn. Commn., 1987—, vice chmn., 1990-92, chmn., 1992-94; evaluator Nat. Ctr. for Rsch. to Improve Postsecondary Teaching and Learning, 1987-90, New Eng. Assn. Schs. and Colls., 1988, 91; mem. higher edn. rev. panel awards for pioneering achievements in higher edn. Charles A Dana Found., 1988, 89. Author, editor articles in field. Pres. Richmond Cmty. Amb. Project, 1958-60, bd. dirs., 1960-61; bd. dirs. Alumni Assn. Acad. divsn. Va. Commonwealth U., 1970-73; trustee Atlanta Boys Choir, Inc., 1978-79, chmn. fundraising com., 1976-77; trustee Atlanta Coun. for Internat. Visitors, 1973-76, 78-79; pres. UN Assn., Atlanta, 1976, 77; mem. steering com. Nat. Coun. chpt. and divsn. pres. UN Assn. U.S., 1977-79, nat. coun., 1980-90; mem. steering com. Leadership Concord, 1992—, chmn., 1994-95. Named Community Amb. to Sweden Community Amb. Project of the Experiment in Internat. Living, 1956. Fellow Royal Soc. of the Arts (U.K.); mem. Am. Assn. Higher Edn., Newcomen Soc. U.S., N.H. Coun. on World Affairs (bd. dirs. 1993—), Greater Concord C. of C. (bd. dirs. 1989-93), Phi Delta Kappa. Methodist. Avocations: antiques, travel. Office: New Eng Coll 7 Main St Henniker NH 03242-3244

O'CONNOR, SISTER ANN PATRICIA, school system administrator. Supt. schs. Diocese of Santa Rosa, Calif. Office: Office Schs Supt PO Box 6654 Santa Rosa CA 95406-0654

O'CONNOR, CARROLL, actor, writer, producer; b. N.Y.C., Aug. 2, 1924; s. Edward Joseph and Elise Patricia (O'Connor) O'C.; m. Nancy Fields, July 28, 1951; 1 son, Hugh (dec.). B.A., Nat. U. Ireland, 1952; M.A., U. Mont., 1956, L.H.D. (hon.), 1985. Actor, Dublin, Cork, Limerick, Galway, London, Paris, Edinburgh, 1950-54; appeared in: Ulysses in Nightown, 1958, The Big Knife, 1959, Brothers, 1983, Home Front, 1984; TV appearance in The Sacco and Vanzetti Story, 1960; TV guest appearances on Armstrong Circle Theater; films include: Fever in the Blood, 1961, By Love Possessed, 1961, Lad a Dog, 1961, Lonely Are the Brave, 1962, Cleopatra, 1963, Not With My Wife, You Don't, 1966, Warning Shot, 1967, What Did You Do In The War Daddy?, 1968, Marlowe, 1969, Death of a Gunfighter, 1969, Kelly's Heroes, 1970, Doctors' Wives, 1971, Law and Disorder; TV film Brass, 1985; star TV series: All in the Family, 1971-79, Archie Bunker's Place, 1979-83, (also co-exec. producer) In The Heat of the Night, 1987-94; star TV spls. including: The Funny Papers, 1972, Of Thee I Sing, 1972, The Carroll O'Connor Special, 1973, The Last Hurrah, 1973. Recipient Emmy award for best actor, 1973, 77, 78, 79, 89; recipient George Foster Peabody award for broadcasting excellence, 1980; named to Hall of Fame Acad. TV Arts and Scis., 1990. Mem. The Players, Sigma Phi Epsilon. Office: Lionel Larner Ltd 130 W 57th St Ste 10A New York NY 10019 *Everyone should rid himself of the illusion that his fulfillments are of much interest to anyone else.*

O'CONNOR, CHARLES ALOYSIUS, III, lawyer; b. Providence, Apr. 7, 1942; s. Charles Aloysius Jr. and Mary Catherine (McGinn) O'C.; m. Wendy Law-Yone, Oct. 11, 1980; children: Charles Aloysius IV, Elisabeth. AB cum laude in Eng., Harvard U., 1964; JD, Georgetown U., 1967, MA, 1985. Bar: D.C. 1969. Assoc. Sellers, Conner & Cuneo, Washington, 1970-74; ptnr. McKenna & Cuneo, Washington, 1974—, ptnr., chmn. environ. dept., 1980—; adj. prof. Georgetown U., Washington, 1973-77; lectr. Cath. U. Am., Washington, 1975-77. Author: (with others) Consumer Product Safety Law, 1977, Pesticide Regulat Handbook, 1983, 2d rev. edit. 1991, TSCA Handbook, 1987, 2d rev. edit. 1991. Lt. USNR, 1967-69. Mem. ABA, Bar Assn. D.C., Univ. Club. Office: McKenna & Cuneo 1575 I St NW Washington DC 20005-1105

O'CONNOR, CHARLES P., lawyer; b. Boston, Sept. 29, 1940; m. Mary Linda Hogan; children: Jennifer, Amy, Austin, Catherine. Bachelors degree, Holy Cross Coll., Worcester, Mass., 1963; LLB, Boston Coll., 1966. Bar: Mass. 1966, D.C. 1968, U.S. Supreme Ct. 1974. Atty., gen. counsel's office NLRB, Washington, 1966-67; assoc. Morgan, Lewis & Bockius, Washington, 1968-71, ptnr., 1971—; gen. counsel Major League Baseball Player Rels. Com., N.Y.C., 1989-94. Contbr. numerous articles on labor and employment law to law jours. spl. counsel elections com. U.S. Ho. of Reps., Washington, 1968-69. Mem. ABA, D.C. Bar Assn., Belle Haven Country Club, N.Y. Athletic Club. Home: 6121 Vernon Ter Alexandria VA 22307-1152 Office: Morgan Lewis & Bockius 1800 M St NW Ste 800 Washington DC 20036-5869

O'CONNOR, DANIEL J., lawyer; b. Chgo., June 11, 1947. BA, Loyola U., 1969; JD, Georgetown U. 1974. Bar: Ill. 1974. Ptnr. Baker & McKenzie, Chgo. Office: Baker & McKenzie 1 Prudential Plz 130 E Randolph Dr Chicago IL 60601-6206

O'CONNOR, DANIEL WILLIAM, retired religious studies and classical languages educator; b. Jersey City, Mar. 17, 1925; s. Daniel William and Emma Pauline (Ritz) O'C.; m. Carolyn Lockwood, June 26, 1954; children—Kathlyn Forssell Beal, Daniel William III. B.A., Dartmouth Coll. 1945; M.A., Columbia U., 1956, Ph.D., 1960; M.Div., Union Theol. Sem., 1950. Ordained to ministry United Ch. of Christ, 1950. Mem. exec. com., bd. home missions Congl. Chs., 1946-51; pastor Paramus Congl. Ch., N.J., 1950-55; assoc. sec. Student Christian Movement YMCA, N.Y., 1947-48; exec. sec. Earl Hall Columbia U., N.Y.C., 1948-50; tutor asst., dept. N.T. Union Theol. Sem., N.Y.C., 1958-59; successively asst. prof., assoc. prof., prof. religious studies and classical langs. St. Lawrence U., Canton, N.Y., 1959-67, dir. summer session, 1966, assoc dean coll., 1967-68, Charles A. Dana prof. religious studies and classical langs., 1967-89, chmn. dept. religious studies and classical langs., 1974-89, Charles A. Dana emeritus prof., 1989—. Author: Peter in Rome, 1969; contbr. articles to Ency. Britannica and profl. jours., also revs. Trustee Silver Bay Assn. YMCA, N.Y., 1978-86, 86-92, Lit. Vols. Am., St. Lawrence County, N.Y., 1991-94; bd. dirs. U.S. Power Squadron, St. Lawrence Squadron, N.Y., 1972-75. With USNR, 1943-45. Grantee Lilly Found., Columbia U., 1969-70, Mellon Found., Am. Schs. Oriental Research, Jerusalem, 1979. Mem. AAUP, Am. Assn. Ret. Persons, Am. Soc. Oriental Rsch., Am. Soc. Bibl. Lit., Am. Acad. Religion (pres. Ea. Internat. region 1985-86), Nat. Audobon Soc., Adirondack Mountain Club, Rotary (pres. Canton Club 1972-73, Rotary Found. scholarship selection com. dist. 7040, 1983-87, dist. gov. 1987-88, dist. 7040 ext. com. 1988-89, youth exch. com. dist. 7040, 1990-93, lit. com. 1991-93). Home: 3 Hillside Cir Canton NY 13617-1409

O'CONNOR, DONALD THOMAS, lawyer; b. Lackawana, N.Y., Apr. 14, 1935; s. Thomas Joseph and Edna Mabel (Thomas) O'C.; children: Kevin M., David T., Donna M., Cheryl L. Grad., U. Buffalo, 1957; LLB, Boston Coll., 1966. Bar: Mass., Pa. Asst. pers. supr. Continental Can Co., Tonawanda, N.Y., 1957-62; pers. supr. Continental Can Co., Natick, Mass., 1962-65; asst. div. mgr. labor rels. Weyerhaeuser Co., Fitchburg, Mass., 1962-65; field atty. NLRB, Pitts., 1966-67; assoc. Berkman, Ruslander, Pohl, Lieber & Engel, Pitts., 1967-71; ptnr. Randall & O'Connor, Pitts., 1971-74; ptnr. Buchanan Ingersoll, P.C., Pitts., 1974—; chmn. labor sect., 1984-88, co-chmn. labor sect., 1988-90; speaker in field. Contbr. articles to profl.

jours. Solicitor Twp. of Penn Hills, Pa., 1971. Mem. ABA, Pa. Bar Assn., Allegheny County Bar Assn. (chmn. labor sect. 1971-73), St. Thomas More Soc. (treas. 1970-72), Rivers Club, Alcoma Golf Club (Penn Hills). Republican. Avocations: golf, sailing, water skiing, reading, dancing. Home: 1414 Towne Square Dr Allison Park PA 15101-1951 Office: Buchanan Ingersoll 600 Grant St Ste 57 Pittsburgh PA 15219

O'CONNOR, DORIS JULIA, non-profit fundraiser, consultant; b. N.Y.C. Apr. 30, 1930; d. Joseph D. and Mary (Longinotti) Bisagni; m. Gerard T. O'Connor, Oct. 8, 1950 (div. Dec. 1972); 1 dau., Kim C. BA cum laude in Econs., U. Houston, 1975. Adminstrv. asst. Shell Cos. Found., Inc., N.Y.C., 1966-71, asst. sec., Houston, 1971-73, sec., 1973-76, sr. v.p., dir., mem. exec. com., 1976-93; prin. Doris O'Connor & Co., 1993—; adj. prof. bus. adminstrn. U. Houston, 1994—. Corp. assoc. United Way of Am. Washington, 1976-93; corp. advisor Bus. Com. of Arts, N.Y.C., 1976-91; del. Bus. Com. of Arts, Houston, 1982-87; dir. Ind. Sector, Washington, 1981-89, vice chmn., 1983-87; mem. contbns. coun. Conf. Bd., N.Y.C., 1976-93; advisor Coun. of Better Bus. Burs., Washington, 1975—, vice chmn., 1983-87; commr. adv. commn. on work based learning Dept. Labor, 1991-93; mem. Houston/Harris County Arts Task Force, 1991-93, Houston Ind. Sch. Dist. Task Force, 1991-93; bd. trustees Houston Grand Opera, Houston Symphony Orch., Houston Symphony Soc., Soc. Performing Arts, Cultural Arts Coun., Greater Houston Coalition Edn. Excellence, 1993—; mem. adv. bd. Ctr. for Edn. Rice U., The Houston Zool. Soc., 1993—. Mem. Nat. Soc. Fundraising Execs. (Houston com. on fgn. rels. 1993—), Omicron Delta Epsilon. Club: Pla. (bd. govs. 1987-89).

O'CONNOR, EARL EUGENE, federal judge; b. Paola, Kans., Oct. 6, 1922; s. Nelson and Mayme (Scheetz) O'C.; m. Florence M. Landis, Nov. 3, 1951 (dec. May 1962); children: Nelson, Clayton; m. Jean A. Timmons, May 24, 1963; 1 dau., Gayle. B.S., U. Kans., 1947, LL.B., 1950. Bar: Kans. 1950. Practiced in Mission, Kans., 1950-51; asst. county atty. Johnson County, Kans., 1951-53; probate and juvenile judge, 1953-55; dist. judge 10th Jud. Dist., Olathe, Kans., 1955-65; justice Kans. Supreme Ct., 1965-71; judge U.S. Dist. Ct., Dist. of Kans., Kansas City, 1971—, chief judge, 1981-92; mem. Jud. Conf. U.S., 1988-91. Served with AUS, World War II, ETO. Mem. ABA, Nat. Conf. Fed. Trial Judges, Kans. Bar Assn., Phi Alpha Delta. Office: US Courthouse 500 State Ave Kansas City KS 66101-3037

O'CONNOR, EDWARD CORNELIUS, army officer; b. Middlesex County, Mass., June 22, 1931; s. Edward Denis and Gladys Marie (Devine) O'C.; m. Charlotte Hubble, June 1, 1958. A.B., Boston Coll., 1952; M.S., U. N.C., 1966; M.S. George Washington U., 1979. Commd. 2d lt. U.S. Army, 1952, advanced through grades to maj. gen., 1981; asst. for NATO Affairs, Office of Sec. Def., 1970-72; sec. Joint Staff, Vietnam, 1972; chief staff Joint Mil. Commn., Vietnam, 1973; arty. comdr. 1st Armored Div., Europe, 1973-74; Fed. exec. fellow Brookings Inst., Washington, 1975-76; chief Army Initiatives Group, Army Staff, Pentagon, 1976-77; dep. dir. ops. Nat. Mil. Command Center, Joint Chiefs of Staff, Washington, 1977-78; asst. div. comdr. (maneuver) 1st Armored Div., Europe, 1978-79; chief nuclear activities SHAPE, Belgium, 1979-82; dir. ops., readiness and mobilization ODCSOPS, Dept. Army, 1982-83; comdg. gen. Security Affairs Command Army Material Command, 1983-86; chief exec. officer, pres. Global Mktg. Corp. (doing bus. as GMA Internat., Inc.), 1986—; chmn. Contraves, Inc., Pitts., 1992—; mem. policy working group U.S. State Dept. Def. Trade Adv. Group, Washington, 1994—; internat. lectr. in field. Author: Performance Appraisal, 1966. Chmn. Harvard U. Grad. Sch. rels. com. Decorated D.S.M., Legion of Merit with 3 oak leaf clusters, Bronze Star, Air medal with 6 oak leaf clusters, Army Commendation medal with V device and 7 oak leaf clusters, Def. Meritorious Service medal, Def. Superior Service medal, Joint Service Commendation with oak leaf cluster, Identification Badges of Sec. Def. Office, Joint Chiefs of Staff and Army Gen. Staff. Mem. Harvard U. Alumni Assn. (bd. dirs. 1989-93). Address: 10202 Eagle Landing Ct Burke VA 22015

O'CONNOR, EDWARD GEARING, lawyer; b. Pitts., May 5, 1940; s. Timothy R. and Irene B. (Gearing) O'C.; m. Janet M. Showalter, June 17, 1972; children: Mark G., Susan M. BA, Duquesne U., 1962, JD, 1965. Bar: Pa. 1965, U.S. Dist. Ct. (we. dist.) Pa. 1965, U.S. Ct. Appeals (3d cir.) 1968, U.S. Supreme Ct. 1976. Assoc. Eckert, Seamans, Cherin & Mellott, Pitts., 1965-72, ptnr., 1973—; mem. adv. com. on appellate ct. rules Supreme Ct. Pa., 1986-92. Editor Duquesne U. Law Rev., 1964-65. Chmn. Hampton (Pa.) Twp. Planning Commn., 1986-87; bd. dirs. Pa. Health Choice Plan, St. Francis Health System; trustee Noble J. Dick Ednl. Found., 1989—. Recipient Disting. Alumni award Duquesne U. Law Rev., 1985, Disting. Law Alumni award Duquesne U. Sch. Law, 1991, Disting. Svc. award Hampton Twp., 1991, McAnurlty Svc. award Duquesne U., 1992; named Century Club Disting. Alumni, Duquesne U., 1985. Fellow Am. Bar Found., Pa. Bar Found.; mem. Pa. Bar Assn. (Ho. of Dels. 1985-90), Acad. Trial Lawyers Allegheny County (bd. govs. 1986-89), Duquesne U. Alumni Assn. (pres. 1980-82, 88-90, bd. govs. 1982-90, bd. dirs. 1988-89), Duquesne Club, Pitts. Athletic Assn., Harvard-Yale-Princeton Club of Pitts. Republican. Roman Catholic. Home: 4288 Green Glade Ct Allison Park PA 15101-1202 Office: Eckert Seamans Cherin & Mellott 600 Grant St Fl 42D Pittsburgh PA 15219-2702

O'CONNOR, FRANCINE MARIE, magazine editor; b. Springfield, Mass., Apr. 8, 1930; d. Wallace Harold and Celestine Margaret (Morrison) Provost; m. John Francis O'Connor, Dec. 27, 1951 (dec. Feb. 1992); children—Margaret Anne McGlynn, Kathryn Mary Boswell, Timothy John. Grad. high sch., Springfield. Editorial asst. Liguori Publs., Mo., 1975-76, assoc. editor, 1976-79, mng. editor, 1979-93; assoc. editor Parish Edn. Products, Mo., 1993—. Author: ABC's of Faith series, including The Stories of Jesus, 1982, The ABC's of the Rosary, 1984, The ABC's of the Mass, 1989, The ABC's of the Sacraments, 1989, The ABC's of the Old Testament, 1989, The ABC's of Prayer, 1989, Lessons of Love, 1991 (hon. mention Cath. Press Assn. 1992), God and You: The ABC's of Christmas, 1994. Religious edn. coord. Sts. Peter and Paul Roman Cath. Ch., St. Louis, 1978—. Mem. Cath. Press Assn. Avocations: bird watching; crossword puzzles; fishing. Home: 157 Crest Manor Dr House Springs MO 63051-1477 Office: Liguorian 1 Liguori Dr Liguori MO 63057-9999

O'CONNOR, FRANCIS X., financial executive; b. Bklyn., May 7, 1929; s. Richard B. and Mary (McCafferty) O'C.; m. Leona A. Windorf, June 30, 1951; children: Francis X., Edward K., Brendan T., Richard B. III, A. Bruce, Marianne, Margaret, Leona. BS, St. Peter's Coll., 1951. CPA, N.Y., N.J. Audit mgr. Coopers & Lybrand, N.Y.C., 1951-65; controller Ward Foods, Inc., N.Y.C., 1965-66, v.p. fin., CFO, 1966-72, also bd. dirs., 1968-73; v.p. fin., CFO UMC Industries, Inc., N.Y.C., 1973-76; v.p. fin. and corp. devel., CFO SKF Industries, Inc., King of Prussia, Pa., 1976-87; v.p. corp. fin. Moore & Schley Securities Corp., Morristown, N.J., 1987-89; mng. dir. Sterling Manhattan Corp. Investment Bankers, N.Y.C., 1989-93; adv. bd. Boyden Cons. Corp. Mem. AICPA, AIM, N.Y. State Soc. CPAs. Fin. Execs. Inst., Nat. Conf. on Power Transmission (trustee), Machinery and Allied Products Inst. Fin. Coun., St. Peter's Coll. Alumni Assn. (trustee, past pres. Monmouth chpt.), Navy League U.S., Spring Lake Golf Club (past pres., trustee), Seaview Country Club (N.J.), Green Gables Club (past pres.), Reserve Golf Club (Ft. Pierce, Fla.). Clubs: Spring Lake Golf and Country (pres., trustee); Seaview Country (Absecon, N.J.); Green Gables; Reserve Golf (Ft. Pierce, Fla.). Home: 2355 NE Ocean Blvd Stuart FL 34996-2945 Office: Boyden Cons Group Morristown NJ

O'CONNOR, SISTER GEORGE AQUIN (MARGARET M. O'CONNOR), college president, sociology educator; b. Astoria, N.Y., Mar. 5, 1921; d. George M. and Joana T. (Loughlin) O'C. B.A., Hunter Coll., 1943; M.A., Catholic U. Am., 1947; Ph.D. (NIMH fellow), NYU, 1964; LL.D. Manhattan Coll., 1983. Mem. faculty St. Joseph's Coll. (Bklyn.), 1966—; prof. sociology and anthropology St. Joseph's Coll., 1966—, chmn. social sci. dept., 1966-69, pres., 1969—; Fellow African Studies Assn., Am. Anthrop. Assn.; Bklyn. C. of C. (dir. 1973—), Alpha Kappa Delta, Delta Epsilon Sigma. Author: The Status and Role of West African Women : A Study in Cultural Change, 1964. Office: Saint Joseph's Coll Office of Pres 245 Clinton Ave Brooklyn NY 11205-3688

O'CONNOR, G(EORGE) RICHARD, ophthalmologist; b. Cin., Oct. 8, 1928; s. George Leo and Sylvia Johanna (Voss) O'C. AB, Harvard U. 1950;

MD, Columbia U., 1954. Resident in ophthalmology Columbia-Presbyn. Med. Center, N.Y.C., 1957-60; research fellow Inst. Biochemistry, U. Uppsala, Sweden, 1960-61, State Serum Inst., Copenhagen, 1961-62; asst. prof. ophthalmology U. Calif., San Francisco, 1962-68; prof. U. Calif., 1972-84; dir. Francis I. Proctor Found. for Research in Ophthalmology, 1970-84; mem. Nat. Adv. Eye Council NIH, 1974-78. Author: (with G. Smolin) Ocular Immunology, 1981; asso. editor: Am. Jour. Ophthalmology, 1976-81. Served with USPHS, 1955-57. Recipient Janeway prize Coll. of Physicians and Surgeons, Columbia U., 1954; Doyne medal Oxford U., 1984; NIH grantee, 1962-84. Mem. Am. Bd. Ophthalmology (examiner), Assn. for Rsch. in Vision and Ophthalmology (trustee 1979-83, pres. 1982-83, Weisenfeld award 1990), AMA, Am. Ophthal. Soc., Calif. Med. Assn., Frederic C. Cordes Eye Soc., Pan Am. Ophthal. Assn. Republican. Presbyterian. Club: Faculty. Home: 22 Wray Ave Sausalito CA 94965-1831 Office: U Calif Med Ctr 315-S San Francisco CA 94143

O'CONNOR, HAROLD J., wildlife research administrator. Dir. Patuxent Environ. Sci. Ctr., Laurel, Md. Office: Patuxent Enviorn Sci Ctr Laurel MD 20708-4039

O'CONNOR, JAMES JOHN, utility company executive; b. Chgo., Mar. 15, 1937; s. Fred James and Helen Elizabeth O'Connor; m. Ellen Louise Lawlor, Nov. 24, 1960; children: Fred, John (dec.), James, Helen Elizabeth. BS, Holy Cross Coll., 1958; MBA, Harvard U., 1960; JD, Georgetown U., 1963. Bar: Ill. 1963. With Commonwealth Edison Co., Chgo., 1963—, asst. to chmn. exec. com., 1964-65, comml. mgr., 1966, asst. v.p., 1967-70, v.p., 1970-73, exec. v.p., 1973-77, pres., 1977-87, chmn., 1980—, chief exec. officer, also bd. dirs.; bd. dirs. Corning, Inc., Chgo. Stock Exch., Tribune Co., United Air Lines, Scotsman Industries, Am. Nat. Can., First Chgo. Corp., First Nat. Bank Chgo., Am. Nuclear Energy Coun.; past chmn. Nuclear Power Oversight Com., Edison Electric Inst.; bd. dirs.; chmn. Advanced Reactor Corp. Mem. The bus. Coun.; bd. dirs. Assocs. Harvard U. Grad. Sch. Bus. Adminstrn., Lyric Opera, Helen Brach Found.; bd. dirs.; trustee Mus. Sci. and Industry; past chmn. Met. Savs. Bond Campaign; trustee Northwestern U.; bd. dirs., past chmn. Chgo. Urban League, Chicagoland C. of C.; bd. advisors Mercy Hosp. and Med. Ctr.; past chmn. bd. trustees Field Mus. Natural History; life trustee Adler Planetarium; exec. bd. Chgo. area coun. Boy Scouts Am.; chmn. Cardinal Bernardin's Big Shoulders Fund; exec. v.p. The Hundred Club Cook County; dir., past pres. Cath. Charities; past chmn., hon. dir. Am. Cancer Soc., Chgo. Conv. and Trourism Bur. With USAF, 1960-63. Mem. ABA, Ill. Bar Assn., Chgo. Bar Assn., Chgo. Assn. Commerce and Industry (bd. dirs., chmn.), Ill. Bus. Roundtable, Chicagoland C. of C. (dir., past chmn.). Home: 9549 Monticello Ave Evanston IL 60203-1119 Office: Commonwealth Edison Co PO Box 767 1 1st Nat Plz Chicago IL 60690-0767

O'CONNOR, JAMES JOSEPH, pathologist, educator; b. Blakely, Pa., Oct. 23, 1924; s. James J. and Mae G. (Kennedy) O'C.; m. Margaret Louise Terrill, Feb. 26, 1952; children: Patricia, Maureen, Karen, Susan, Erin, James III, Jeffrey, Ellen. Student, U. Scranton, 1942-44; MD, Jefferson Med. Coll., 1948. Bd. cert. Am. Bd. Pathology. Intern, pathology resident St. Francis Gen. Hosp., Pitts., 1948-52; resident pathology Med. Coll. Va., Richmond, 1954-55; dir. labs. Scranton (Pa.) State Gen. Hosp., 1955-61; chmn. dept. pathology Mercy Hosp., Scranton, 1958—; founder, pres. Pathology Assocs. of N.E. Pa. Ltd. and Clin. Labs., Scranton, 1958—; clin. assoc. prof. pathology Temple U. Sch. Medicine, Phila., 1958—; dir., sec. Pioneer Am. Bank, Carbondale, Pa., 1964—. Pres. Lacka Cancer Soc., Scranton, 1964-66; dir. Lacka Red Cross, Scranton, 1976-80, N.E. Philharm., Scranton and Wilkes-Barre, 1988—. Capt. USAF, 1952-54. Fellow Am. Soc. Clin. Pathologists, Coll. Am. Pathology; mem. AMA, Pa. Assn. Pathologists (exec. com. 1986-92), Lacka County Med. Soc., County Club Scranton. Republican. Roman Catholic. Avocations: golf, music. Office: Clin Labs Inc 441 Wyoming Ave Scranton PA 18503-1227

O'CONNOR, JENNIFER, public administrator; b. Somerville, Mass., Feb. 12, 1966; m. Paul J. Meyer, Nov. 13, 1993. BA in Govt. magna cum laude, Harvard U., 1987; MPA, Columbia U., 1992. Dep. press sec., econ. devel. assoc. Office of Manhattan Borough Pres Ruth Messenger, N.Y.C., 1990-92; budget specialist, N.E. regional polit. dir. Presdl. Transition Office, Little Rock, 1992-93; dep. dir. Office of Mgmt. and Adminstrn. The White House, Washington, 1993, spl. asst. to Pres. for Cabinet affairs, 1993-95, spl. asst. to Pres. Office Dep. Chief of Staff, 1995—; field. dir. N.Y. primary campaign, polit. dir. N.J. primary campaign, dep. mgr. at Dem. Nat. Conv., state dir. Vt. gen. election campaign Clinton for Pres./Clinton-Gore '92, 1992. Democrat. Roman Catholic. Office: Office of Chief of Staff 1600 Pennsylvania Ave NW Washington DC 20500-0001

O'CONNOR, JOHN DENNIS, chancellor, biology educator; b. Chgo., Mar. 20, 1942; married, 1964; 3 children. B.S., Loyola U. Chgo., 1963; M.S., DePaul U., 1966; Ph.D., Northwestern U., 1968. NIH fellow Mich. State U., East Lansing, 1968-70; asst. prof. biology UCLA, 1969-74, assoc. prof., 1974-77, prof. biology, 1977-81, chmn. biology, 1979-81, dean, life scis., 1981-87; vice chancellor for research, dean of grad. sch., prof. biology U. N.C.; previously U. N.C., Chapel Hill, 1987-91; chancellor, prof. biology U. Pitts., 1991—; vis. prof. Roman Catholic U., Nijmegan, Netherlands, 1975-76, Monash U., 1977; bd. dirs. PNC Bank, U. Pitts. Med. Ctr. Bd. dirs. Pitts. Symphony, Forging a New Freedom, Partnerships for Children, others; mem. exec. com. Allegheny Conf. Cmty. Devel. Mem. AAAS, Am. Soc. Zoology, Soc. Devel. Biology, Am. Soc. Biol. Chemistry, Pa. Assn. Colls. and Univs., Inst. Medicine (mem. com. on educating dentists for future), Pitts. C. of C. (bd. dirs.), Urban League (bd. dirs.), Pitts. Club, Duquesne Club, Univ. Club. Office: U Pitts Office of Chancellor 4200 Fifth Ave 107 CL Pittsburgh PA 15260-0001

O'CONNOR, JOHN E(DWARD), JR., association executive; b. Chgo., Oct. 9, 1942; s. John Edward Sr. and Marguerite (Naughton) O'C.; m. Judith M., Apr. 16, 1966; children: John, Barry, Ryan, Daniel. BBA, Loyola U., 1964. CPA, Ill. Fin. analyst Motorola, Inc., Franklin Park, Ill., 1965-66; sec./treas. Am. Coll. Hosp. Adminstrs., Chgo., 1966-79; exec. dir. Soc. Actuaries, Schaumburg, Ill., 1979—. Sgt. U.S. Army, 1964-70. Mem. AICPA, Ill. Soc. CPAs, Am. Soc. Assn. Execs., Chgo. Soc. Assn. Execs. (bd. dirs. 1988—, Shapiro award 1988). Roman Catholic. Avocation: raising show dogs. Office: Soc Actuaries 475 N Martingale Rd Ste 800 Schaumburg IL 60173-2226

O'CONNOR, JOHN JAY, III, lawyer; b. San Francisco, Jan. 10, 1930; s. John Jay and Sally (Flynn) O'C.; m. Sandra Day, Dec. 20, 1952; children: Scott, Brian, Jay. AB, Stanford U., 1951, LLB, 1953. Bar: Calif. 1953, Ariz. 1957, D.C. 1981. Mem. Fennemore, Craig, von Ammon & Udall, Phoenix, 1957-81, Miller & Chevalier, Washington, 1982-88; ptnr. Bryan Cave, Washington and Phoenix, 1988—; judge pro-tem Superior Ct. State of Ariz., 1979-81. Chmn. Ariz. Crippled Children's Services, 1968; Chmn. planning and zoning commn. Town of Paradise Valley, 1967; Chmn. Maricopa County Young Republicans, 1960, Ariz. Young Rep. League, 1962; bd. dirs. Ariz. Tax Research Assn., 1966-81; chmn. bd. dirs. Maricopa County Gen. Hosp., 1967-70; exec. com. bd. visitors Stanford Law Sch., 1976-80; pres. Stanford Law Fund, 1980-82; mem. nat. council Salk Inst. Biol. Studies, San Diego, 1977-90; pres. Phoenix-Scottsdale United Way, 1977-79; bd. dirs. World Affairs Council of Phoenix, 1970-81, Legal Aid Soc. Phoenix, Maricopa County Mental Health Assn.; trustee Meridian House Internat., Washington, 1982-88; mem. policy devel. com. Phoenix Community Service Fund, 1978; mem. exec. com. Valley Leadership, 1979-81; bd. dirs. Trusteeship for St. Luke's Hosp., 1979-81; mem. adv. com. Nat. Postal Mus., Washington, 1992—. Served to 1st lt. AUS, 1954-57. Mem. ABA, Stanford Assocs., Soc. Friendly Sons of St. Patrick, Paradise Rotary (pres. 1977-78), Paradise Valley Country Club (pres. 1979-81), Valley Field Riding and Polo Club, Stanford Club of Phoenix (pres.), Iron Springs Club (pres. 1974-76), Bohemian Club, Met. Club, Alfalfa Club, Alibi Club, Ariz. Acad. Delta Upsilon, Phi Delta Phi. Office: Bryan Cave 700 13th St NW Washington DC 20005-3960

O'CONNOR, JOHN JOSEPH CARDINAL, archbishop, former naval officer; b. Phila., Jan. 15, 1920; s. Thomas Joseph and Dorothy Magdalene (Gompie) O'C. M.A., St. Charles Coll., 1949, Catholic U. Am., 1954; Ph.D., Georgetown U., 1970; D.R.E., Villanova (Pa.) U., 1976. Ordained priest Roman Cath. Ch., 1945, elevated to monsignor, 1966, consecrated

bishop, 1979, created cardinal, 1985; served in Chaplain Corps U.S. Navy, 1952, advanced through grades to rear adm.; assigned to Atlantic and Pacific fleets U.S. Navy, Okinawa and Vietnam; sr. chaplain U.S. Naval Acad.; chief of chaplains U.S. Navy, Washington; aux. bishop, vicar gen. Mil. Vicariate, 1979-83; apptd. bishop of Scranton Pa., 1983-84; archbishop Archdiocese of N.Y., 1984—; Exec. bd. Nat. USO, Georgetown Center Strategic and Internat. Studies, Marine Corps Found. Author: Principles and Problems of Naval Leadership, 1958, A Chaplain Looks at Vietnam, 1969, In Defense of Life, 1981, (with Edward I. Koch) His Eminence and Hizzoner: A Candid Exchange, 1989, (with Elie Wiesel) A Journey of Faith, 1990. Decorated DMS, Legion of Merit (3), Meritorious Service medal. Mem. Am. Polit. Sci. Assn. Office: Archdiocese NY 452 Madison Ave New York NY 10022*

O'CONNOR, JOHN KILLEEN, lawyer; b. Buffalo, June 7, 1932; s. Raymond Aloysius and Bertha Elizabeth (Killeen) O'C.; m. Carol Cecelia Seguin, Aug. 21, 1954; children: Mary Ann, Maureen, Ellen, Thomas, Claire. BA, Holy Cross Coll., Worcester, Mass., 1953; LLB, Harvard U., 1956. Bar: Ill. 1956, U.S. Tax Ct. 1958, U.S. Dist. Ct. (no. dist.) Ill. 1956, U.S. Ct. Appeals (7th cir.) 1967, U.S. Ct. Appeals (2d cir.) 1968, U.S. Ct. Fed. Claims. Assoc. Lord Bissell & Brook, Chgo., 1956-64, ptnr., 1965-94, of counsel, 1995—; bd. dirs. various pvt. cos. Contbr. articles to tax publs. Pres. Wilmette (Ill.) Libr. Bd., 1975-79; trustee St. Joseph Ch., Wilmette, 1963-80. Avocations: tennis, golf. Office: Lord Bissell & Brook 115 S La Salle St Ste 3400 Chicago IL 60603-3903

O'CONNOR, JOHN MORRIS, III, philosophy educator; b. Evanston, Ill., Sept. 21, 1937; s. John Morris and Clare Evelyn (Merrick) O'C.; m. Mary Bittner, Dec. 31, 1960 (div.); 1 dau., Emily; m. Miranda E. P. Ind, Aug. 14, 1971 (div.); 1 dau., Amanda. Student, Georgetown U., 1955-56; B.A., Cornell U., 1959; M.A., Harvard U., 1962, Ph.D., 1965. Instr. Vassar Coll., 1964-66, asst. prof. philosophy, 1966-68; asst. prof. Case Western Res. U., Cleve., 1968-70, assoc. prof., 1970-77; exec. sec. Am. Philos. Assn. U. Del., Newark, 1977-84, assoc. prof., 1977-83; asst. dir. for programs Nat. Humanities Ctr., Research Triangle Park, N.C., 1983-87; dean Sch. Humanities William Paterson Coll., Wayne, N.J., 1987-91, dean Sch. Humanities, Mgmt. and Social Scis., 1991-92, coord. spl. projects Office of Provost, 1992-93, prof. philosophy, 1992—. Contbr. articles to profl. jours.; editor: (with others) Introductory Philosophy, 1967, Modern Materialism, 1969, Moral Problems in Medicine, 1976. Woodrow Wilson nat. fellow, 1959-60. Office: William Paterson Coll Wayne NJ 07470

O'CONNOR, JOHN T., civil engineering educator; b. N.Y.C., Feb. 11, 1933; married, 1966; 2 children. BCE, Cooper Union, 1955; MSCE, N.J. Inst. Tech., 1958; EngD, Johns Hopkins U., 1961. Sanitary engr. Elson T. Killam Sanit & Hydraulic Consulting Engrs., 1955-56; civil engr. George A. Fuller Constrn. Co., N.Y., 1956-57; sanitary engr. Parsons, Brinckerhoff, Quade & Douglas, 1957; from asst. assoc. prof. sanitary engr. U. Ill., Urbana, 1961-69, prof. civil engring., 1969-75; prof. civil engring. U. Mo., Columbia, 1975—, chmn. dept., 1975-89. Mem. ASCE, Am. Chem. Soc., Am. Water Works Assn., Am. Soc. Limnology and Oceanography, Water Pollution Control Fedn., Sigma Xi. Achievements include research on fate of radionuclides in natural waters; removal of iron and trace metals from ground waters; water and wastewater treatment; ozonation. Address: 2118 Robert Dr Champaign IL 61821-6535*

O'CONNOR, JOSEPH A., JR., lawyer; b. N.Y.C., Aug. 12, 1937; s. Joseph A. and Louise G. (Lucht) O'C.; m. Martha R. Schroeder, 1963; children: Joseph A. III, Edward W. BA, Yale U., 1959; LLB, Columbia U., 1962. Bar: N.Y. 1963, U.S. Supreme Ct. 1968, Pa. 1973, Fla. 1978. Assoc. Davis, Polk & Wardwell, N.Y.C., 1963-72; ptnr. Morgan, Lewis & Bockius, Phila., 1972—. Mem. ABA, N.Y. State Bar Assn., Pa. Bar Assn., Fla. Bar Assn., Phila. Bar Assn., Assn. of Bar of City of N.Y. Roman Catholic. Club: Racquet (Phila.). Office: Morgan Lewis & Bockius 2000 One Logan Sq Philadelphia PA 19103

O'CONNOR, KARL WILLIAM, lawyer; b. Washington, Aug. 1, 1931; s. Hector and Lucile (Johnson) O'C.; m. Sylvia Gasbarri, Mar. 23, 1951 (dec.); m. Judith Ann Byers, July 22, 1972 (div. 1983); m. Eleanor Celler, Aug. 3, 1984 (div. 1986); m. Alma Hepner, Jan. 1, 1987; children: Blair, Frances, Brian, Brendan. BA, U. Va., 1952, JD, 1958. Bar: Va. 1958, D.C. 1959, Am. Samoa 1976, Calif. 1977, Oreg. 1993. Law clk. U.S. Dist. Ct. Va., Abingdon, 1958-59; practice law Washington, 1959-61; trial atty. U.S. Dept. Justice, Washington, 1961-65; dep. dir. Men's Job Corps OEO, Washington, 1965-67; mem. civil rights div. Dept. of Justice, chief criminal sect., prin. dep. asst. atty. gen., 1967-75, spl. counsel for intelligence coordination, 1975; v.p.; counsel Assn. of Motion Picture and Television Producers, Hollywood, Calif., 1975-76; assoc. justice Am. Samoa, 1976, chief justice, 1977-78; sr. trial atty. GSA Task Force, Dept. Justice, 1978-81; insp. gen. GSA, 1982-83; spl. counsel Merit Systems Protection Bd., Washington, 1983-86; U.S. atty. for Guam and the No. Marianas, 1986-89, ret.; pvt. practice Medford, Oreg., 1989—; Am. counsel O'Reilly Vernier Ltd., Hong Kong, 1992-93; ptnr. O'Connor & Vernier, Medford, Oreg., 1993-94; pvt. practice Medford, 1994—. Served with USMC, 1952-55. Mem. ABA, Oreg. Bar Assn., D.C. Bar Assn., Va. Bar Assn., Calif. Bar Assn., Am. Samoa Bar Assn., Phi Alpha Delta, Sigma Nu. Home: 6853 Griffin Ln Box 112 Medford OR 97501-0008 Office: 916 W 10th St Medford OR 97501

O'CONNOR, KAY, state legislator; b. Everett, Wash., Nov. 28, 1941; d. Ernest S. and Dena (Lampers) Wells; m. Arthur J. O'Connor, Sept. 1, 1959; 6 children. Diploma, Lathrop H.S., Fairbanks, Alaska, 1959. Office mgr. Blaylock Chemicals, Bucyrus, Kans., 1981-84; store mgr. Copies Plus, Olathe, Kans., 1984-86; acct. Advance Concrete Inc., Spring Hill, Kans., 1986-92; mem. Kansas Ho. of Reps., 1993—; bd. dirs. Hometel Ltd. Republican. Roman Catholic. Avocations: choir dir., statue renovations, spkr. on sch. vouchers. Home: 1101 N Curtis Olathe KS 66061 Office: PO Box 2232 Olathe KS 66051

O'CONNOR, KEVIN JOHN, psychologist; b. Jersey City, N.J., July 18, 1954; s. John Lanning and Marilyn (Reynolds) O'C.; m. Ryan Michael, Matthew Benham. BA, U. Mich., 1975; PhD, U. Toledo, 1981. Clin. psychologist Blythedale Children's Hosp., Valhalla, N.Y., 1980-83; dir. Psychol. Svcs. Walworth Barbour Am. Internat. Sch., Kfar Shmaryahu, Israel, 1983-84; adjunct asst. prof. Dept. Psychology Iona Coll., New Rochelle, N.Y., 1984; clin. psychologist Northern Westchester Guidance Clinic, Mt. Kisco, N.Y. 1985; exec. dir., newsletter editor Assn. for Play Therapy, Fresno, Calif., 1982—; consulting psychologist Fresno (Calif.) Treatment Ctr., 1986-87, Diagnostic Sch. for Neurologically Handicapped Children, Fresno, Calif., 1986-90; adjunct faculty Pacific Grad. Sch. of Psychology, Palo Alto, Calif., 1987—; Calif. Sch. Profl. Psychology, Berkeley, Calif., 1988-89; prof., dir., 1985—. Contbr. numerous presentations in field. Named Psychologist of Yr. San Joaquin Psychol. Assn., 1994. Mem. APA, Assn. for Play Therapy, Mental Health Assn. Greater Fresno, San Joaquin Psychol. Assn., Western Psychol. Assn., Coun. for Nat. Register of Health Svc. Providers in Psychology. Democrat. Avocations: travel, art, ceramics. Office: Calif School Professional Psych 1350 M St Fresno CA 93721

O'CONNOR, LAWRENCE JOSEPH, JR., energy consultant; b. Tulsa, Dec. 29, 1914; s. Lawrence Joseph and Bess (Yarbrough) O'C. Student, Tulsa U., 1932-33; A.B. Rice U., 1936; M.B.A., Harvard U., 1938. With Haskins & Sells (C.P.A.s), Houston, 1938-45; v.p., treas. Goldston Oil Corp., Houston, 1945-58; oil and gas cons. Houston, 1958-59; asst. dir. Office Oil and Gas, Dept. Interior, 1959-60, adminstr. oil import adminstrn., 1960-61; commr. Fed. Power Commn., 1961-71; v.p. Standard Oil Co. (Ohio), Washington, 1971-74; energy cons. Houston, 1975—. Roman Catholic. Clubs: Congressional Country (Washington). Home: 846 Augusta Dr Houston TX 77057-2014 Office: PO Box 130505 Houston TX 77219-0505

O'CONNOR, MARY SCRANTON, public relations executive; b. New Haven, May 9, 1942; d. James T. and Mary E. (Scranton) O'C. BA, Manhattanville Coll., 1964. Women's editor Hartford Times, Conn., 1964-68; pub. relations. account exec. Wilson, Haight & Welch, Hartford, 1968-72, v.p., dir. pub. rels., 1972-75; pub. rels. cons. O'Connor/PR, Farmington, Conn., 1975-76; v.p. pub. rels. Lowengard & Brotherhood, Hartford, 1976-78, pres., 1978-83; pres. Harland O'Connor, Tine & White, Hartford, 1983-84; v.p. communications Conn. Mut. Life Ins. Co., Hartford, 1984-88; pres. Bradford Advt., Inc., Old Saybrook, Conn., 1988-90; prin. Strategic Communications,

Old Lyme, Conn., 1990—; instr. pub. rels. mgmt. Manchester Community Coll., 1975. Bd. dirs. Child and Family Svcs., Inc., Hartford, 1980-89, Better Bus. Bur., 1980-83, Criminal Justice Edn. Ctr., 1981; trustee The Mark Twain House, Hartford, 1994—. Recipient Woman of Yr. award YWCA, 1980. Mem. PRSA (Merit award 1992), Greater Hartford C. of C. Bus. 1983-86).

O'CONNOR, NANCY MORRISON, lawyer; b. Washington, Aug. 25, 1951; d. Paul Edward and Theresa Joan (Salmon) Morrison; m. Stephen Joseph O'Connor, Aug. 17, 1974; children: Bridget, Matthew, Caitlin. BA, Gettysburg Coll., 1973; JD, U. Notre Dame, 1976; postgrad., Univ. Coll. North Wales, 1972-73. Bar: Tex. 1977, U.S. Dist. Ct. (no., so., we. dists.) Tex. 1977, U.S. Ct. Appeals (5th cir.) 1977, U.S. Ct. Appeals (9th cir.) 1978, U.S. Ct. Appeals (11th cir.) 1981, U.S. Ct. Appeals (7th cir.) 1982, U.S. Supreme Ct. 1988, D.C. 1989, U.S. Dist. Ct. D.C. 1989, Md. 1990, U.S. Dist. Ct. Md. 1991. Bailiff, clk. St. Joseph County Superior Ct. South Bend, Ind., 1975-76; ptnr. Fulbright & Jaworski, Houston, 1976-88; ptnr. Fulbright & Jaworski, Washington, 1988-92, of counsel, 1992—; adj. prof. employment dispute resolution seminar Sch. Law U. Tex., Austin, 1986; med. jurisprudence lectr. Baylor Coll. Medicine, Houston, 1984-87. Bd. dirs. Montgomery County Rep. Club, 1989—, pres., 1992; mem. Sharon Pratt Dixon Transition Team, Washington, 1990; pres. Alumnae Assn., mem. bd. advisors Acad. Holy Cross, Kensington, Md., 1991—. Mem. ABA (vice chair sec. adminstrv. law and regulatory practice, labor and employment com., sec. labor and employment law devel. labor law com.), D.C. Bar (sects. on labor rels., litigation, health law), 5th Cir. Bar Assn., Fin. Women Internat., Houston Bar Assn., Am. Soc. Law and Medicine, Nat. Health Lawyers Assn., Tex. Bar Assn. Office: Fulbright & Jaworski Market Sq 801 Pennsylvania Ave NW Washington DC 20004-2604

O'CONNOR, NEAL WILLIAM, former advertising agency executive; b. Milw., Aug. 25, 1925; s. Arthur J. and Helen (Radell) O'C.; m. Nancy K. Turner, July 8, 1950; children: Robert W., Thomas N., David J. B.S. cum laude, Syracuse U., 1949. With N.W. Ayer Inc., N.Y.C., 1949-80; v.p., mgr. N.Y. service N.W. Ayer Inc., 1962-65, pres., 1965-73, chmn. bd., 1973-76, chief exec. officer, 1966-76, chmn. exec. com., 1976-80; Past dir. Advt. Council; past chmn. Am. Assn. Advt. Agys.; past pres. Consumer Research Inst. Pres. Found. for Aviation WWI, 1980—; past chmn. and pres. League of WWI Aviation Historians. With inf. AUS, 1943-45, ETO. Decorated Bronze Star, Combat Inf. badge. Mem. Beta Theta Pi, Alpha Delta Sigma. Clubs: Pretty Brook Tennis, Wings (N.Y.C.). Home: 10 Constitution Hl E Princeton NJ 08540-6749 Office: PO Box 212 Princeton NJ 08542-0212

O'CONNOR, PAUL DANIEL, lawyer; b. Paterson, N.J., Nov. 24, 1936; s. Paul Daniel and Anne Marie Christopher O'C.; children: Steven Paul, Sheryl Lynn, Laura Ann. B.S. in Engring, U.S. Naval Acad., 1959; LL.B., U. Va., 1965. Bar: N.Y. 1965. Assoc. firm Winthrop, Stimson, Putnam & Roberts, N.Y.C., 1965-72; partner Winthrop, Stimson, Putnam & Roberts, 1972-80; sr. v.p., gen. counsel Singer Co., Stamford, Conn., 1980-86; chief exec. officer Citation Builders, 1986—. 1st lt. USAF, 1959-62. Mem. Assn. of Bar of City of N.Y., Am. Horses Shows Assn., Fairfield County Hunt Club, Diablo Country Club. Home: 1150 Lombard StUnit 22 San Francisco CA 94109 Office: Citation Builders 3170 Crow Canyon Pl Ste 270 San Ramon CA 94583-1347

O'CONNOR, R. D., health care executive. BS Psychology, Sociology, U. So. Miss., 1960, MS Adminstrv. Personnel, 1961, PhD Mgmt., Orgnl. Communication, 1983. Asst. dean student affairs Holmes Jr. Coll. Goodman, Mo., 1961-64; spl. counselor vocat. rehab. divsn. Dept. Edn., Jackson, Mo., 1964-65; asst. adminstr. Hinds Gen. Hosp., Jackson, Mo., 1965-68; adminstr. Rankin Gen. Hosp., Brandon, Mo., 1968-76; v.p. Human Resources/ Mktg. Dental Mgmt. Systems, Metairie, La., 1976-79; asst. to exec. dir. Baptist Med. Ctr., Jacksonville, Fla., 1979-82; pres. RiverGroup Riverside Hosp., Rivercorp Inc., Riverside Found., Jacksonville, Fla., 1982-87; owner O'Connor & Assocs., Jacksonville, Fla., 1987-91; pres. Fla. 1st: Managed Health Care, Winter Haven, Orlando & Tampa, Fla., 1991-94; v.p. quality Mid Florida Med. Svcs. Inc., Winter Haven, Fla., 1994—; instr. U. So. Miss., Hattiesburg, Ms.; tchr., lectr. various univs., C.C.s, military acads.; grad. faculty coord. Webster U. Contbr. articles to profl. jours. Commr. Cleary Heights Sewer Dist., 1978-79; pres'. selective task force Induction Procedures, 1969; chmn. personnel com. San Jose Baptist Ch., 1981-86, strategic planning com., 1986-87; gov's. com. Statewide Planning Vocat. Rehab., 1968; bd. dirs. Rankin County C. of C., 1970-73, exec. com., chmn. health affairs com., 1970-72, chmn. highway com. 1970-74, fin. com. 1971-73), Family Blood Assurance Program, 1972-77, v.p. 1977, Vol. Action Coun., 1973-76, United Givers Fund, 1973-76. With Air Nat. Guard, Med. Svc. Corps., ret. Fellow Am. Coll. Healthcare Execs.; mem. Fla. Hosp. Assn. (com. chmn. 1984), Greater Jacksonville Area Hosp. Coun. (chmn. 1985), Jackson-Vicksburg Hosp. Coun. (chmn. 1974), Nat. Assn. Mental Health (bd. dirs. 1973-74), Miss. Assn. Mental Health (pres. 1972-74), Miss. Hosp. Assn. (bd. dirs .1973-74, exec. devel. com. 1972-75, mgmt. engring. adminstrv. bd. 1973, fin. com. 1972-74, chmn. nominating com. 1971, coord. divsn. profl. practice 1970). Home: 2 Casarena Court Winter Haven FL 33881

O'CONNOR, R. DENNIS, consumer products company executive. BSBA, U. Mo., 1964. Former audit mgr. Haskins & Sells; former v.p. fin. Builders Inc.; with Interstate Brands Corp., Charlotte, N.C., 1978—, dir. internal audit, 1978-81, v.p. planning & control, 1981-86, v.p. new bus. devel., from 1986, now exec. v.p. merita div. Office: Interstate Brands Corp Merita Div PO Box 669208 Charlotte NC 28266-9208

O'CONNOR, RALPH STURGES, investment company executive; b. Pasadena, Calif., Aug. 27, 1926; s. Thomas Ireland and Edith Masury (Sturges) O'C.; m. Alice Maconda Brown, Apr. 28, 1950; children—George Rufus, Thomas Ireland III, Nancy Isabel, John Herman. B.A., Johns Hopkins, 1951. With Highland Resources, Inc., Houston, 1951-87, exec. v.p., 1961-64; pres. Highland Resources, Inc., 1964-87; pres., chief exec. officer Ralph S. O'Connor and Assocs., 1987—; chmn. bd. Arnaud's Restaurant, New Orleans; bd. dirs. First City Bancorporation of Tex., Inc., Westheimer Transfer & Storage, Houston, Panhandle Eastern Corp. Trustee emeritus Rice U., Houston Oldfields Sch., Glencoe, Md., Nat. Found. Advancement in the Arts. With USAAF, 1943-46. Mem. NAS (Pres.'s Circle), Am. Petroleum Landmen, All Am. Wildcatters. Clubs: Bayou (Houston), Ramada (Houston), River Oaks Country (Houston). Home: 5627 Indian Cir Houston TX 77056-1006 Office: Ralph S O'Connor & Assocs 1001 Fannin Ste 622 Houston TX 77002

O'CONNOR, RICHARD DENNIS, lawyer; b. Worcester, Mass., Oct. 22, 1937. BS, Coll. of Holy Cross, 1959; LLB, Georgetown U., 1964. Bar: Conn. 1964, U.S. Dist. Ct. Conn. 1964, U.S. Ct. Appeals (2d cir.) 1969, U.S. Dist. Ct. D.C. 1971, U.S. Supreme Ct. 1973, U.S. Ct. Appeals (D.C. cir.) 1974, Mass. 1985, U.S. Dist. Ct. Mass. 1985. Law clk. to hon. judge Clarie U.S. Dist. Ct. Conn., Hartford, 1964-65; prin., founding ptnr. Siegel, O'Connor, Schiff, Zangari & Kainen, P.C., Hartford, 1965—; speaker on labor issues, Conn.; arbitrator Am. Arbitration Assn., Conn.; mem. Magistrate Reappointment Rev. Com., Conn.; arbitrator panel Gov.'s State Bd. of Edn., Conn., 1987—. Lt. USN, 1959-61. Mem. ABA, Conn. Bar Assn., Mass. Bar Assn., Assn. Trial Lawyers Am., Fed. Bar Coun. Assn., Conn. Hosp. Attys., Conn. Sch. Attys.' Coun. Office: Siegel OConnor Schiff Zangari & Kainen PC 370 Asylum St Hartford CT 06103-2003

O'CONNOR, RICHARD DONALD, advertising company executive; b. Nyack, N.Y., Dec. 29, 1931; s. James Patrick and Sophi Kathryn (Hensel) O'C.; m. Lucille Hartigan, Jan. 25, 1958 (div. 1986); children: Richard D., Kathryn Helen, Timothy Joseph, Meghan Mary, John Patrick; m. Katherine M. Unger, Apr. 7, 1989. B.A., U. Mich. 1954. With Lintas: Campbell-Ewald Co., Detroit, 1956—, v.p., chief operating officer, 1975-76, pres., 1976-79, vice chmn., chief exec. officer, 1979-82; chief exec. officer, vice chmn. Marschalk/Campbell-Ewald Worldwide, 1982-86, chmn. chief exec. officer, 1984-85; chmn., chief exec. officer Lintas: Campbell-Ewald Co., N.Y.C. and Warren, Mich., 1985—; bd. dirs. Lintas: Worldwide. Past trustee Walsh Coll., Troy, Mich., 1976-77; promotion chmn. United Found. Torch Drive, 1976; mem. adv. com. Mich. Cancer Found., 1976-77; past trustee Detroit Country Day Sch.; mem. Boys Clubs Am., past trustee; trustee Northwood Inst., Menninger Found.; adv. bd. Eton Acad.; dir. Boys

and Girls Clubs Southeastern Mich.; active Boys Clubs N.Y. With U.S. Army, 1954-56. Recipient Robert E. Healy award Interpub. Group Cos., 1974. Mem. Adcraft Club Detroit (past pres.), Am. Assn. Advt. Agys. (bd. dirs.), Am. Advt. Fedn. (bd. dirs. 1987—, chmn. 94-95), Advt. Coun. (bd. dirs. 1987-91), Advt. Ednl. Found. (bd. dirs.), Advt. Club of N.Y. (v.p. 1985-86, pres. 1987-89, chmn. 1989-91), Am. Ireland Fund (bd. dirs. 1985—), U.S. Space Found. (dir.), U. Mich. Alumni Assn., Bloomfield Hills Country Club, Detroit Athletic Club, Econ. Club Detroit (dir.), Grosse Pointe Club, Hundred Club, The Old Club (Mich.), Links, Friars Club. *. Republican. Roman Catholic.

O'CONNOR, ROBERT JAMES, publishing executive; b. Bklyn., Dec. 8, 1939; s. William Francis and Kathleen (Cruise) O. B.A., Bklyn., 1959. Midwest advt. mgr. Barron's Weekly, N.Y.C., 1959-62; midwest advt. mgr. Motor Boating, N.Y.C., 1962-70; advt. dir. Passengers Mag., N.Y.C. 1970-72, Chrysler Marine, N.Y.C., 1972-78, Motor Boating & Sailing Mag., N.Y.C., 1978-80; v.p., pub. Motor Boating & Sailing Mag., 1980—. Mem. Am. League Anglers and Boaters (adv. bd.). Republican. Roman Catholic. Club: N.Y. Athletic. Avocation: boating. Office: Motor Boating & Sailing Mag Hearst Mag Div The Hearst Corp 224 W 57th St New York NY 10019-3203

O'CONNOR, ROD, chemist, inventor; b. Cape Girardeau, Mo., July 4, 1934; s. Jay H. and Flora (Winters) O'C.; m. Shirley Ann Sander, Aug. 7, 1955; children: Mark Alan, Kara Ann, Shanna Suzanne, Timothy Patrick. BS, S.E. Mo. State Coll., 1955; PhD, U. Calif., Berkeley, 1958. Asst. prof. chemistry U. Omaha, 1958-60, Mont. State Coll., 1960-63; assoc. prof. chemistry Mont. State U., Bozeman, 1963-66; assoc. prof., coordinator gen. chemistry Kent (Ohio) State U., 1966-67; prof., dir. 1st year chemistry U. Ariz., Tucson, 1968-72; staff assoc. Adv. Council on Coll. Chemistry Stanford (Calif.) U., 1967-68; vis. prof. Wash. State U., Pullman, 1972-73; prof. chemistry Tex. A&M, College Station, 1973-86; pres. Texas ROMEC Inc., College Station, 1983—; cons. insect venoms Hollister-Stier Labs., Spokane, Wash., 1963-67; lab. separates editor W.H. Freeman Co., 1968-78; ednl. cons. TUCARA-4 Media Resources, Inc., 1971-74; mem. Coll. Chemistry Cons. Service; vis. scientist, tour lectr. Am. Chem. Soc., 1970—. Author: (with T. Moeller) Ions in Aqueous Systems, 1972, Fundamentals of Chemistry, 1981, (with C. Mickey and A. Hassell) Solving Problems in Chemistry, 1981, (with L. Peck and K. Irgolic) Fundamentals of Chemistry in The Laboratory, 1981, (with T.E. Taylor and P. Glenn) Toward Success in College, 1981; films Laboratory Safety, 1971; Contbr. articles to profl. jours.; patentee in field. Recipient nat. teaching award Mfg. Chemists Assn., 1978; 4 regional teaching awards. Fellow AAAS, Am. Inst. Chemists; mem. Internat. Soc. Toxinology, Am. Chem. Soc., Sigma Xi. Office: Tex ROMEC Inc Ste E 2900 Longmire Dr College Station TX 77845 *Only those who truly care can ever be hurt ... or know real joy.*

O'CONNOR, RUTH SUSAN, physician, educator; b. Augusta, Ga., Apr. 23, 1952; d. Henry and Margaret Adelire (Schreider) Wynstra; m. Thomas Joseph O'Connor, Apr. 23, 1977; children: Samuel, Grace, Anna, Rhoda. Student, Wheaton Coll., 1970-73; MD, Med. Coll. Wis., 1977; cert. family practice, Caraway Meth. Med. Ctr., 1980. Diplomate Am. Bd. Family Practice. Intern Carraway Meth. Med. Ctr., Birmingham, Ala. 1977-78, resident in family practice, 1978-80; fellow family practice Caraway Meth. Med. Ctr., Birmingham, Ala., 1980-81; instr. family practice, 1981-85; pvt. practice Greenville, Ill., 1986-88; instr. family practice Sch. Medicine So. Ill. U., Belleville, 1986-88; staff physician Student Health Ctr. Purdue U., West Lafayette, Ind., 1989—; instr. family medicine Ind. U., Indpls., 1989—. Recipient Achievement citation Am. Women's Med. Soc., 1977. Mem. Christian Med. Soc. Baptist. Avocation: caring for children. Home: 714 Kossuth St Lafayette IN 47905 Office: Purdue U 1826 Student Health Ctr West Lafayette IN 47907

O'CONNOR, SANDRA DAY, U.S. supreme court justice; b. El Paso, Tex., Mar. 26, 1930; d. Harry A. and Ada Mae (Wilkey) Day; m. John Jay O'Connor, III, Dec. 1952; children: Scott, Brian, Jay. AB in Econs. with great distinction, Stanford U., 1950, LLB, 1952. Bar: Calif. Dep. county atty. San Mateo, Calif., 1952-53; civil atty. Q.M. Market Ctr., Frankfurt am Main, Fed. Republic of Germany, 1954-57; sole practice Phoenix, 1959-65; asst. atty. gen. State of Ariz., 1965-69; Ariz. state senator, 1969-75, chmn. com. on state, county and mcpl. affairs, 1972-73, majority leader, 1973-74; judge Maricopa County Superior Ct., 1975-79, Ariz. Ct. Appeals, 1979-81; assoc. justice U.S. Supreme Ct., 1981—; referee juvenile ct., 1962-64; chmn. vis. bd. Maricopa County Juvenile Detention Home, 1963-64; mem. Maricopa County Bd. Adjustments and Appeals, 1963-64, Anglo-Am. Legal Exchange, 1980, Maricopa County Superior Ct. Judges Tng. and Edn. Com., Maricopa Ct. Study Com.; chmn. com. to reorganize lower cts. Ariz. Supreme Ct., 1974-75; faculty Robert A. Taft Inst. Govt.; vice chmn. Select Law Enforcement Rev. Commn., 1979-80. Mem. bd. editors Stanford (Calif.) U. Law Rev. Mem. Ariz. Personnel Commn., 1968-69, Nat. Def. Adv. Com. on Women in Services, 1974-76; trustee Heard Mus., Phoenix, 1968-74, 76-81, pres., 1980-81; mem. adv. bd. Phoenix Salvation Army, 1975-81; trustee Stanford U., 1976-80, Phoenix County Day Sch.; mem. citizens adv. bd. Blood Services, 1975-77; nat. bd. dirs. Smithsonian Assocs., 1981—; past Rep. dist. chmn.; bd. dirs. Phoenix Community Council, Ariz. Acad., 1970-75, Jr. Achievement Ariz., 1975-79, Blue Cross/Blue Shield Ariz., 1975-79, Channel 8, 1975-79, Phoenix Hist. Soc., 1977-87, Maricopa County YMCA, 1978-81, Golden Gate Settlement. Recipient Ann. award NCCJ, 1975, Disting. Achievement award Ariz. State U., 1980; named Woman of Yr., Phoenix Advt. Club, 1972. Lodge: Soroptimists. Office: US Supreme Ct Supreme Ct Bldg 1 First St NE Washington DC 20543

O'CONNOR, SINEAD, singer, songwriter; b. Dublin, Dec. 8, 1966; 1 child, Jake. Albums include The Lion and The Cobra, 1987, I Do Not Want What I Haven't Got (Grammy award for Best Alternative Performance), 1990, My Special Child, 1991, Am I Not Your Girl?, 1992, Universal Mother, 1994. Office: Chysalis Records 810 7th Ave 4th Fl New York NY 10017-5818*

O'CONNOR, THOMAS EDWARD, petroleum geologist, world bank officer; b. Boston, Dec. 16, 1936; s. John Stephen and Lucille (Arnold) O'C.; m. Jeannette Canuel, June 30, 1962 (dec. Mar. 1976); children: Kevin Patrick, David Andrew, Shelly Elizabeth; m. Moufida Banawi, Apr. 28, 1977; children: Tammer Thomas, Amr Adel Hammouda. BSc, Stanford U., 1958; MSc., U. Colo., 1961. Geologist Amoco Prodn. West, Denver, 1963-67, Amoco Netherlands, Utrecht, 1968-69, Amoco Europe, London, 1969-74; chief geologist Gulf of Suez Petroleum Co., Cairo, 1974-79; regional geologist Amoco Africa, Mid East, Houston, 1979-80; v.p. Aminoil, Houston, 1980-84; prin. petroleum engr. The World Bank, Washington, 1985—. Presenter numerous sci. confs., seminars, workshops in U.S. and abroad, 1976—. Lt. USNR, 1960-63. Mem. AAAS, Am. Assn. Petroleum Geologists (cert. petroleum geologist), Geol. Soc. Am., Houston Geol. Soc. Moslem. Home: 3637 Winfield Ln NW Washington DC 20007 Office: The World Bank 1818 H St NW Washington DC 20433

O'CONNOR, TOM, corporate executive, management consultant; b. Boston, June 11, 1942; s. Thomas Henry and Blanche (Cosgrove) O'C.; m. Mary Alice Kelly; 1 child, Michael Kelly O'Connor. BA in econs., U. Mass., 1971; postgrad., U. Wis., Milw., 1973. U. Del., 1978, Am. U., 1980. Economist Interstate Commerce Commn., Washington, 1973-74; mgr. planning U.S. Railway Assn., Washington, 1974-75; cons. transp. R.L. Banks & Assocs., Washington, 1975-77; asst. dir. Conrail, Phila., 1977-79; asst. v.p. econs. Assn. Am. R.R.'s, Washington, 1979-82; v.p. DNS Assocs., Inc., Washington, Lexington (Mass.), 1982-88; v.p., ptnr. Snavely, King & Assoc., Washington, 1988—; chmn. surface freight transport regulation com. Transp. Rsch. Bd., 1994—. Pres. Green Briar Civic Assn., Fairfax, Va., 1985, Greenbriar Dem. Club, Fairfax, 1984-89, Greenbriar Community Ctr., Fairfax, 1984; v.p. Greenbriar West PTA, Fairfax, 1986-88. Sgt. U.S Army, 1963-66. Mem. Am. Econ. Assn., Am. Statis. Assn., Coun. Logistics Mgmt., Transp. Rsch. Forum (pres. Washington chpt. 1987-88), Nat. Def. Assn. (bd. dirs. 1991-94), Air Force Assn., Phi Beta Kappa, Phi Kappa Phi. Democrat. Roman Catholic. Avocations: camping, reading, counseling. Home: 13222 Point Pleasant Dr Fairfax VA 22033-3515 Office: Snavely King & Assoc 1220 L St NW Washington DC 20005-4018

O'CONNOR, WILLIAM CHARLES, automobile agency finance executive; b. Poplar Bluff, Mo., July 19, 1943; s. Thomas Francis and Luella Darlene

(Davis) O'C.; m. Leigh Volkening, Dec. 21, 1975 (div. May 1992); children: Kelli, Megan, Katie. BA in English, Memphis State U., 1966. High rigger Boiler Makers Union, St. Louis, 1968-70; br. mgr. Pub. Fin. Corp., St. Louis, 1970-74; fin. specialist Pat Ryan & Assocs., Chgo., 1974-77; fin. mgr. Drew Ford, La Mesa, Calif., 1978-80; fin. dir. Honda of Pasadena, Calif., 1980-89, Goudy Honda, Alhambra, Calif., 1989-94, Scott Robinson Honda, Torrance, Calif., 1994—; cons. Am. Honda Fin. Corp., Torrance, 1987—. Contbr. articles to profl. jours. Mem. Fin. and Ins. Profls., KC, Jr. C. of C., Young Dems. Orgn. (pres. 1968-69). Avocations: L.A. marathon 1987, golf, fishing. Home: 613 E Camellia Dr Covina CA 91723-3608 Office: 20340 Hawthorne Blvd Torrance CA 90503

OCVIRK, OTTO GEORGE, artist; b. Detroit, Nov. 13, 1922; s. Joseph and Louise (Ekle) O.; m. Betty Josephine Lebie, June 11, 1949; children: Robert Joseph, Thomas Frederick, Carol Louise. B.F.A., State U. Iowa, 1949, M.F.A., 1950. Advt. artist apprentice Bass-Luckoff Advt. Agy., Detroit, 1941; engring. draftsman Curtiss-Wright Aircraft Corp., Buffalo, 1942; faculty Bowling Green (Ohio) State U., 1950—, assoc. prof., 1960-65, prof. art, 1965-85, prof. emeritus, 1985—. Exhibited in group shows at Denver Mus. Art, 1949, 50, 53, Detroit Inst. Art, 71948, 49, 50, 53, 56, Dayton (Ohio) Art Inst., 1950, 51, 56, Ohio State U., 1953, Walker Art Center, Mpls., 1948, 49, Library of Congress, Washington, 1949, Bklyn. Mus., 1949, Joslyn Mus., Omaha, 1949, Colorado Springs Fine Arts Center, 1949; represented in permanent collections, Detroit Inst. Arts, Dayton Art Inst., Friends of Am. Art, Grand Rapids, Mich., State U. Iowa, Iowa City, Bowling Green State U.; (Recipient 24 nat., regional juried art exhbn. awards 1947-57, others.); Author: (with R. Stinson, P. Wigg, R. Bone and David Cayton) Art Fundamentals—Theory and Practice, 1960-94, 7th edit., 1994. Scoutmaster Toledo Area council Boy Scouts Am., 1960-63, asst. scoutmaster, 1963-74, dist. commr., 1978-80. Served with AUS, 1943-46. Recipient Silver Beaver award Boy Scouts Am., 1976, Magnifico award Medici Circle, Bowling Green State U., 1987. Mem. Internat. Sculpture Center Washington, Coll. Art Assn. Am., Delta Phi Delta (hon.). Methodist. Home and Office: 231 Haskins Rd Bowling Green OH 43402-2206 *"Freedom for expression" keys creative thought into a productive whole.*

ODA, TAKUZO, biochemist, educator; b. Shinichicho, Japan, Oct. 20, 1923; s. Ryoichi and Misu Oda; M.D., Okayama U., 1947, Ph.D., 1953; m. Kazue Matsui, Dec. 8, 1946; children: Mariko, Yumiko. Intern, Okayama U. Hosp., 1947-48, mem. faculty, 1949—, prof. biochemistry, 1965—, dir. Cancer Inst., from 1969; dean Okayama U. Med. Sch., 1985-87; prof. Okayama U. Sci., 1989—; pres. and prof. Niimi Women's Coll., 1993—; postdoctoral trainee Inst. Enzyme Research, U. Wis., Madison, 1960-62. Fellow Rockefeller Found., 1959-60, grantee, 1964; USPHS grantee, 1963-68. Mem. Japanese Soc. Electron Microscopy (Seto prize 1966), Japanese Soc. Biochemistry, Am. Soc. Cell Biology, Japanese Soc. Cancer, Japanese Soc. Cell Biology, Japanese Soc. Histochemistry, Japanese Soc. Virology, Am. Soc. Microbiology. Author: Biochemistry of Biological Membranes, 1969, Mitochondria, Handbook of Cytology; editor, writer: Cell Biology series, 1979—; chief editor Acta Medica Okayama, 1975-85 . Home: 216-38 Maruyama, Okayama 703, Japan Office: Niimi Women's Coll, 1263-2 Nishikata, Niimi City Okayama 718, Japan

O'DAY, ANITA BELLE COLTON, entertainer, singer; b. Chgo., Oct. 18, 1919; d. James and Gladys (Gill) C. Student, Chgo. public schs. Singer and entertainer various Chgo. Music Clubs, 1939-41; singer with Gene Krupa's Orch., 1941-45, Stan Kenton Orch., 1944, Woody Herman Orch., 1945, Benny Goodman Orch., 1959; singing tours in U.S. and abroad, 1947—; rec. artist Polygram, Emily records, Verve, GNP Crescendo, Columbia, London, Signature, DRG, Pablo; million-seller songs include Let Me Off Uptown, 1941, And Her Tears Flowed Like Wine, 1944, Boogie Blues, 1945; appeared in films Gene Krupa Story, 1959, Jazz on a Summer's Day, 1960, Zigzag, 1970, Outfit, 1974; TV shows 60 Minutes, 1980; Tonight Show, Dick Cavett Show, Today Show, Big Band Bash, CBS Sunday Morning, CNN Showbiz Today, others. Author: High Times, Hard Times, 1981, rev. edit. 1989; performed 50 yr. anniversary concert Carnegie Hall, 1985, Avery Fisher Hall, 1989, Tanglewood, 1990, Town Hall, 1993, Rainbow and Stars, 1995, currently touring worldwide; albums include Drummer Man, Kenton Era, Anita, Anita Sings The Most, Pick Yourself Up, Lady is a Tramp, An Evening with Anita O'Day, At Mr. Kelly's, Swings Cole Porter, Travelin' Light, All The Sad Young Men, Waiter Make Mine Blues, With The Three Sounds, I Told Ya I Love Ya Now Get Out, Uptown, My Ship, Live In Tokyo, Anita Sings the Winners, Incomparable, Anita 1975, Live at Mingos, Anita O'Day/The Big Band Sessions, Swings Rodgers and Hart, Time for Two, Tea for Two, In a Mellowtone, At Vine St. Live, Mello'Day, Live at the City, Angel Eyes, The Night Has a Thousand Eyes, The Rules of The Road, 1993, Jazz Masters, others. Mem. AFTRA, Screen Actors Guild, BMI. Office: 1524 La Baig Ave Los Angeles CA 90028-6406 *From the time I was twelve or thirteen, my life was music. I never thought about being on top. I only wanted to be a part of the scene.*

O'DAY, DENIS MICHAEL, ophthalmologist, educator; b. Melbourne, Victoria, Australia, Dec. 10, 1935; came to U.S., 1967; s. Kevin John and Bernadette John (Hay) O'D.; m. Ann Georgina Despard, May 28, 1966; children: Luke Gerard, Simon Patrick, Edward Daniel. Diploma, Xavier Coll., 1953; MBBS, Melbourne U., 1960. Diplomate Am. Bd. Ophthalmology. Intern St. Vincent's Hosp./U. Melbourne, 1961; resident in internal medicine St. Vincent's Hosp., 1962-64, chief resident dept. medicine, 1964, clin. asst. medicine, 1965-66; 3d asst., mem. asst. Royal Victoria Eye & Ear Hosp., Melbourne, 1967-70; resident in ophthalmology U. Calif., San Francisco, 1970; Wellcome rsch. fellow in corneal disease Inst. Opthalmology, London, 1970-72; asst. prof. ophthalmology Vanderbilt U. Sch. Medicine, Nashville, 1972-74, assoc. prof. ophthalmology, 1974-77; prof. ophthalmology Vanderbilt U. Sch. Medicine, 1977; cons. ophthalmologist Royal Commonwealth Soc. of Blind, Nigeria, 1972; cons. VA Hosp., 1973-74, active staff, 74; mem. active staff Nashville Gen. Hosp., 1974, Park View Hosp., 1980, Vanderbilt Hosp. 1972; mem. cons. staff St. Thomas Hosp.; bd. dirs. Am. Bd. Ophthalmology, Phila., 1988—; proctor lectr. U. Calif., San Francisco 1993; co-med. dir. Lions Eye Bank and Sight Svc., 1973-86, med. dir. 1986—; bd. dirs. Lions Eye Bank Mid. Tenn. 1987—; ad-hoc mem. NIH Visual Sci. Study Sect., 1977. Author: Management of Functional Impairment due to Cataract, 1993; contbr. numerous articles, abstracts to profl. publs., chpts. to books. Chair ethics com. Cath. Pub. Policy Commn., Nashville, 1991—. Joyn Hayden rsch. fellow, 1965; recipent Felton Bequest and Potter Found. awards, 1967, recognition award Alcon Rsch. Inst., 1983, Sr. Sci. Investigator award Rsch. to Prevent Blindness, 1987, Health Profl. of Yr. award Tenn. chpt. Assn. for Edn. and Rehab. of Blind and Visually Impaired, 1990. Fellow ACS, Royal Australia Coll. Physicians, Royal Soc. Medicine, Am. Acad. Ophthalmology (sec. quality of care com. 1993—, Honor award for Ednl. Contbns. 1981-85, dir. clin. alert program, pub. health com. 1985-88); mem. AMA, AAUP, Am. Ophthalmol. Soc., Assn. for Rsch. in Vision and Ophthalmology, Nashville Acad. Medicine, Nashville Acad. Ophthalmology (v.p. 1980-81), Oxford Ophthalmol. Soc., Royal Australasian Coll. Physicians, Tenn. Acad. Medicine, Tenn. Acad. Ophthalmology. Avocation: sailing. Office: Vanderbilt U Med Ctr East Dept Ophthal and Vis Scis Nashville TN 37232

O'DAY, PAUL THOMAS, trade association executive; b. May 2, 1935; s. James Thomas and Jeannette Irene (Deschenes) O'D.; m. Nancy Frances Eitler, June 16, 1962; children: Kathleen, Maureen, Michael, Ellen. B.A., Am. Internat. Coll., Springfield, Mass., 1958; J.D., Georgetown U., 1963; MPA, Am. U., 1967. Bar: D.C. 1964, U.S. Supreme Ct. 1974. Patent examiner U.S. Patent Office, Washington, 1959-62; exec. sec. panel highspeed ground transp., auto. air poll. Dept. Commerce, Washington, 1965-66, staff asst. to sec., 1967-69, exec. asst. to sec., 1969-71, dep. dir. bur. domestic commerce, 1972-74; dep. dir. Nat. Bus. Coun. for Consumer Affairs, Washington, 1971-72; cons. to Gen. Counsel GE, Fairfield, Conn., 1974-75; asst. trade rep. Exec. Office of the Pres., Washington, 1975-77; dep. asst. sec. U.S. Dept. Commerce, Washington, 1978-84; pres. Am. Fiber Mfrs. Assn., Washington, 1984—; chmn. Fiber Econs. Bur., 1984—; pres. Eisenhower World Affairs Inst., 1993—. Corporator Am. Internat. Coll., 1974—; mem. governing coun. Shakespeare Theater Guild, 1989—; prin. Coun. for Excellence in Govt., 1988—; mem. bus. leadership coun. Dem. Nat. Com., 1990-93. Recipient Constl. Law award Georgetown U. Law Ctr., 1962; Alumni award Am. Internat. Coll., 1970; Pres.'s Meritorious Exec. award, 1984;

Nat. Inst. Pub. Affairs fellow Princeton U., 1964. Mem. AAAS, Am. Chem. Soc., Cosmos Club, Jefferson Islands Club (bd. dirs. 1993—), Federal City Club. Home: 8261 Private Ln Annandale VA 22003 Office: Am Fiber Mfrs Assn 1150 17th St NW Washington DC 20036-4603

O'DAY, ROYAL LEWIS, former banker; b. Avon, N.Y., Apr. 28, 1913; s. Roy Lyday and Winifred (Heath) O'D.; m. Elizabeth M. Fearon, Oct. 12, 1952; children: Margaret (Mrs. Thomas W. Wright), Patti (Mrs. Warner Blow), Timothy N. BS, Syracuse U., 1936. With Gen. Motors Acceptance Corp., 1936-42; sr. v.p. Mchts. Nat. Bank & Trust Co., Syracuse, N.Y., 1942-61; exec. v.p. Marine Midland Bank—Central, Syracuse, 1961-68; pres. Marine Midland Bank—Central, 1968-71, chmn. bd., 1971-76, chief exec. officer, 1973-76, cons., 1976—; bd. dirs. Syracuse Chiefs Baseball Club. Bd. dirs Syracuse Rsch. Corp.; past pres. Met. Devel. Assn., Syracuse, Syracuse Rep. Citizens Com.; past chmn. bd. trustees, now trustee Syracuse U.; past chmn. bd. N.Y. divsn. Am. Cancer Soc.; trustee Crouse Irving Meml. Hosp., Syracuse. Lt. USNR, WWII. Named Outstanding Man in Syracuse Area in Bus. and Fin. Syracuse Herald Jour., 1963; recipient Torch of Liberty award Anti-Defamation League of B'nai B'rith, 1974. Mem. Nat. Alumni Assn. Syracuse U. (pres. 1965-69), Automobile Club Syracuse (dir., vice chmn.) Hosp. Svcs. Assn. Cen. N.Y. (dir.), Greater Syracuse C. of C. (past pres.), Masons (33 deg., Shriner, Jester), Onondaga Golf and Country Club (Fayetteville, N.Y.), Royal Poinciana Golf Club (Naples, Fla.), Phi Gamma Delta. Mem. Dewitt Community Ch. (finance com.). Clubs: Mason (Fayetteville, N.Y.) (33 deg., Shriner, Jester), Onondaga Golf and Country (Fayetteville, N.Y.), Royal Poinciana Golf (Naples, Fla.). Home: 714 Scott Ave Syracuse NY 13224-2160 Office: 360 S Warren St Syracuse NY 13202-2017

ODDEN, ALLAN ROBERT, education educator; b. Duluth, Minn., Sept. 16, 1943; s. Robert Norman and Mabel Eleanor (Bjornnes) O.; m. Eleanor Ann Rubottom, May 28, 1966; children: Sarina, Robert. BS, Brown U., 1965; MDiv, Union Theol. Sem., 1969; MA, Columbia U., 1971, PhD, 1975. Tchr. N.Y.C. Pub. Schs., 1967-72; rsch. assoc. Teachers' Coll. Columbia U., N.Y.C., 1972-75; dir. policy Edn. Commn. of the States, Denver, 1975-84; prof. U. So. Calif., L.A., 1984-93, U. Wis., Madison, 1993—; rsch. dir. Sch. Fin. Commns. Conn., 1974-75, S.D., 1975-76, Mo. 1975-76, 93, 94, N.Y., 1978-81, N.J., 1991-92; dir. finance ctr. Consortium for Policy Rsch. in Edn.; cons. Nat. Govs. Assn., Nat. Conf. State Legislatures, U.S. Sec. Edn., U.S. Senate, U.S. Dept. Edn. and many state legislatures and govs. Co-author: School Finance: A Policy Perspective, 1992, Education Leadership for America's Schools, 1995; editor: Education Policy Implementation, 1991, Rethinking School Finance, 1992; contbr. articles to profl. jours., chpts. to books. Mem. L.A. Chamber Edn. & Human Resources Commm., 1986 Gov.'s Sch. Fin. Commn., Calif., 1987, Calif. Assessment Policy Com. Grantee Dept. Edn., Spencer Found., Ford Found., Mellon Found., Carnegie Corp., Pew Charitable Trusts. Mem. Am. Ednl. Rsch. Assn., Am. Ednl. Fin. Assn. (pres. 1979-80), Nat. Tax Assn., Politics of Edn. Assn., Nat. Soc. for Study of Edn. Democrat. Avocations: Lionel train collector, youth soccer and baseball coach. Home: 3128 Oxford Rd Madison WI 53705 Office: U Wis Sch Edn Wis Ctr Edn Rsch 1025 W Johnson St 753E Madison WI 53706-1796

ODDIS, JOSEPH ANTHONY, association executive; b. Greensburg, Pa., Nov. 5, 1928; s. Giacinto and Felicetta (D'Amico) O.; m. Jeanne Trevena, July 10, 1954; children—Joseph Michael, Marie Theresa. B.S., Duquesne U., 1950; D.Sc. (hon.), Mass. Coll. Pharmacy, 1975, Phila. Coll. Pharmacy and Sci., 1975, Albany Coll. Pharmacy, Union U., 1976, Duquesne U., 1989; LHD (hon.), L.I. U., 1991. Staff pharmacist Mercy Hosp., Pitts., 1950-51; asst. chief pharmacist Mercy Hosp., 1953-54; chief pharmacist Western Pa. Hosp., Pitts., 1954-56; staff rep. hosp. pharmacy Am. Hosp. Assn., Chgo., 1956-60; dir. div. hosp. pharmacy Am. Pharm. Assn., Washington, 1960-62; exec. v.p. Am. Soc. Hosp. Pharmacists, Washington, 1960—; pres. Am. Soc. Hosp. Pharmacists Research and Edn. Found., 1986—. Active Boy Scouts Am., Camp Fire Girls; Sec. Am. Soc. Hosp. Pharmacists Research and Edn. Found., 1970-86. Served with AUS, 1951-53. Recipient 1st cert. Honor award Duquesne U. Sch. Pharmacy, 1969, named Outstanding Alumnus, 1978; recipient Harvey A.K. Whitney award Am. Soc. Hosp. Pharmacists, 1970, Julius Sturmer Meml. Lecture award Rho Chi soc. Phila., 1971, Howard C. Newton Lecture award 1977, Samuel Melendy Lecture award, 1978, Hugo H. Schaefer award, 1983, Reed and Alice Henninger Lecture award, 1984, Donald E. Francke medal, 1986, Remington medal award, 1990. Fellow AAAS; mem. Am. Pharm. Assn., Am. Soc. Hosp. Pharmacists, Am. Inst. History Pharmacy, Internat. Pharm. Fedn. (pres. hosp. pharmacy sect. 1977-81, v.p. 1984-86, pres. 1986-90), Drug Info. Assn., Am. Soc. Assn. Execs., Can. Soc. Hosp. Pharmacists (hon.), Soc. Hosp. Pharmacists Australia (hon.), Pharm. Soc. Gt. Britain (hon.), Pharm. Soc. Nigeria (hon.), Nat. Coun. Patient Info. and Edn. (sec. 1982-85), Israel Pharm. Soc. (hon.), Rho Chi, Kappa Psi (hon.), Duquesne U. Century Club (charter). Home: 6509 Rockhurst Rd Bethesda MD 20817-1661 Office: Am Soc Hosp Pharmacists 4630 Montgomery Ave Bethesda MD 20814-3410

O'DEA, DENNIS MICHAEL, lawyer; b. Lowell, Mass., Nov. 1, 1946; s. James Lawrence and Carol Frances (Gibbons) O'D.; children: Emily C., Dennis C., Daniel P.; m. Mary Gail Frawley. BA in Govt., U. Notre Dame, 1968; JD magna cum laude, U. Mich., 1972. Bar: Mass. 1972, D.C. 1980, Ill. 1981. Assoc. Goodwin, Procter & Hoar, Boston, 1972-74, Fine & Ambrogne, Boston, 1974-77; assoc. prof. Syracuse U. Coll. Law, 1977-78; vis. assoc. prof.; co-dir. Gilmore Inst., 1995—. Nat. Law Ctr., George Washington U., 1978-80; prtnr. Keck, Mahin & Cate, N.Y.C., 1980—. Mem. Order of the Coif (Mich.), Univ. Club (Chgo.), Chgo. Literary Club (pres. 1993). Home: 75 N Broadway Nyack NY 10960-2624 Office: Keck Mahin & Cate 220 E 42nd St Fl 16 New York NY 10017-5806

ODEEN, PHILIP A., engineering company executive. V. chmn. BDM Internat., Inc., Mc Lean, Va., 1992—. Office: BDM International Inc 7915 Jones Branch Dr Mc Lean VA 22102°

ODEGAARD, CHARLES EDWIN, history educator; b. Chicago Heights, Ill., Jan. 10, 1911; s. Charles Alfred and Mary (Cord) O.; m. Elizabeth Jane Ketchum, Apr. 12, 1941 (dec. 1980); 1 child, Mary Ann Quarton. A.B, Dartmouth Coll., 1932; M.A., Harvard U., 1933, Ph.D., 1937; L.H.D. Lawrence Coll., 1951; LL.D., Miami U., Oxford, Ohio, 1955, U. B.C., Can., 1959, Gonzaga U., 1962, UCLA, 1962, Seattle U., 1965, U. Mich., 1969; Litt.D., U. Puget Sound, 1963. Asst. in history Radcliffe Coll., 1935-37; from instr. to prof. U. Ill., 1937-48; exec. dir. Am. Council Learned Soc., Washington, 1948-52; prof. history, dean Coll. Lit. Sci. and Arts U. Mich., Ann Arbor, 1952-58; pres. U. Wash., Seattle, 1958-73; pres. emeritus, prof. higher edn. U. Wash., 1974—, prof. biomed. history, 1975—; mem. U.S. Nat. Commn. UNESCO, 1949-55, advisor U.S. del. 5th Gen. Conf., Florence, Italy, 1950; chmn. Commn. Human Resources and Advanced Tng., 1949-53, pres. Internat. Council of Philosophy and Humanistic Studies, 1959-65; mem. adv. com. cultural info. USIA, 1955-62, Western Interstate Com. on Higher Edn., 1959-70, Citizens Com. on Grad. Med. Edn., 1963-66, Nat. Adv. Health Counci USPHS, 1964-68, Nat. Adv. Health Manpower, 1965-67, NEH, 1966-72, Study Commn. Pharmacy, 1973-75; mem. Macy Study Commn. on Acad. Psychiatry, 1978-79. Author: Fideles and Vassi in the Carolingian Empire, 1945; Minorities in Medicine, 1977, Area Health Education Centers, 1979, Dear Doctor: A Personal Letter to a Physician, 1986; contbr. articles on mediaeval history and higher edn. to profl. jours. bd. regents Uniformed U. Health Scis., 1973-80; chmn. Wash. State Bd. Continuing Legal Edn., 1976-79. Served from lt. (j.g.) to lt. comdr. USNR, 1942-46. Recipient Medal of Merit State of Wash., 1989. Mem. Am. Coun. on Edn. (dir., chmn. 1962-63), Am. Hist. Assn., NAS, Medieval Acad. Am., Tchrs. Ins. and Annuity Assn. (dir. 1963-69, trustee 1970-86, coll. retirement equity fund 1970-86), Inst. Medicine, Phi Beta Kappa, Phi Eta Sigma, Beta Theta Pi, Seattle Yacht Club, Univ. Club (Seattle), Cosmos Club (Washington), Bohemian Club (San Francisco), Rotary. Office: U Wash 222 Miller Hall DQ-12 Seattle WA 98195

ODEGARD, RICHARD ERWIN, banker; b. Snohomish, Washington, Apr. 30, 1940; s. Harold E. and Martha Jane (Crooker) O.; m. Kay Pepply Bonde, July 9, 1966; children: Cory, Mark, Eric. BA, Whitman Coll., 1962; cert., Pacific Coast Sch. Banking, Seattle, 1978. With Seattle 1st Nat. Bank, Spokane, Wash., 1965—, regional mgr., 1982—; sr. v.p., chmns. rep., 1984—, comml. div. mgr., 1988—, v.p., 1992—; mem. mayors task force on low income housing. Active Spokane Entertainment, Art, Conv. and Bus.; mem.

bd. overseers Whitman Coll.; mem. Momentum '95; chmn. blue ribbon com. Air Force Assn.; co-chair levy/bond issue Spokane Pub. Schs., 1990, 92, 94; hon. bd. dirs. Spokane Visitors and Conv. Bur., past chmn. Lt. (j.g.) USN, 1962-70, lt. comdr. Res. ret. Mem. Spokane Area C. of C. (bd. dirs. 1984-87, chmn. bd. 1989-90), Prosperity Club, Empire Club, Manito Golf and Country Club (Spokane). Clubs: Prosperity, Spokane, Empire, Manito Golf and Country (Spokane). Avocations: golf, tennis, fishing, cross country skiing. Office: Seattle 1st Nat Bank PO Box 1446 Spokane WA 99210-1608

O'DELL, CHARLES ROBERT, astronomer, educator; b. Hamilton County, Ill., Mar. 16, 1937; s. Herman and Madge (Allen) O'D.; m. Gail Sabanosh, July 6, 1991; children from previous marriage: Cynthia Dianne Rogers, Nicholle Ann Schreiber. Student, U. Ill., 1957; B.S. in Edn, Ill. State U., 1959; Ph.D., U. Wis., 1962. Carnegie fellow Mt. Wilson and Palomar Obs., Pasadena, Calif., 1962-63; asst. prof. U. Calif., at Berkeley, 1963-64; faculty U. Chgo., 1964-72, prof. astronomy, 1967-72, chmn. dept., 1967-72; dir. Yerkes Obs., Williams Bay, Wis., 1966-72; cons. Marshall Space Flight Center, Huntsville, Ala., 1968-70; project scientist Hubble Space Telescope, Marshall Space Flight Center, 1972-83, assoc. dir. sci., 1976-80, asso. dir. astronomy, 1972-76, 80-82; prof. space physics and astronomy Rice U., Houston, 1982-92, Buchanan prof. astrophysics, 1992—; mem. astronomy missions bd. NASA, 1967-70, space telescope Sci. Working Group NASA, 1983-91, presdl. adv. com. on space program, 1968-69, inter Halley watch steering group, 1981-89; astronomy adv. panel NSF, 1968-71, chmn., 1969-71; U.S. scientist Copernicus Astron. Ctr., Warsaw, Poland, 1972-78; team leader Hubble Space Telescope, 1989-95; lectr. U. Coll., London, 1970, U. Moscow, 1971. Mem. adv. com. Physics Today, 1986-92. Trustee Adler Planetarium, Chgo., 1967-75. Recipient Gold medal Order of Merit Polish Govt., 1977, Alumni Achievement award Ill. State U., 1981, Pub. Svc. Medal award NASA, 1991. Fellow AAAS; mem. Am. Astron. Soc. (treas. 1988—), Internat. Astron. Union, Internat. Aerobatic Club, Astron. Soc. Pacific, Soaring Soc. Am., U.S. Sailplane Aerobatics Team (pilot 1985, 87, 89, 93), Sailplane Aerobatics Assn. (pres. 1986-97), Internat. Astron. Union (chief U.S. del. 1973). Home: 540 W 18th St Houston TX 77008-3608 Office: Rice U Dept Space Physics & Astronomy PO Box 1892 Houston TX 77251-1892

O'DELL, EDWARD THOMAS, JR., lawyer; b. Lowell, Mass., Nov. 26, 1935; s. Edward Thomas and Helen Louise (Shaw) O'D.; m. Kerstin Lilly Sjoholm, Mar. 18, 1962; children: Edward Thomas III, Brian Patrick, Christine Marie. BA, Brown U., 1957; JD, U. Chgo., 1960. Bar: N.Y. 1961, Mass. 1968, U.S. Dist. Ct. Mass. 1968, U.S. Ct. Appeals (1st cir.) 1968. Ptnr. Goodwin, Procter and Hoar, Boston, 1966—; sec. Dynatech Corp., Burlington, Mass., 1977—. Trustee Gov. Dummer Acad., Byfield, Mass, 1982-87. Mem. ABA, Mass. Bar Assn., Internat. Bar Assn. (sec. 1986-88, chmn. investment cos. com. 1994—). Home: 96 Wildwood Rd Andover MA 01810-5126 Office: Goodwin Procter & Hoar Exchange Pl Boston MA 02109

O'DELL, FRANK HAROLD, banker; b. Hobart, N.Y., May 17, 1922; s. Harold E. and Naomi (Cole) O.; m. Elizabeth J. Hetherington, Dec. 29, 1946; children—Thomas A., Nancy E., Susan. A.B., U. Ala., 1943; M.B.A. Harvard U., 1949; postgrad., Stonier Grad. Sch. Banking, Rutgers U., 1958. With State Bank of Albany, N.Y., 1949-71; v.p. State Bank of Albany, 1963-69, sr. v.p. in charge bank's loan portfolio, 1969-71; exec. v.p. Norstar Bancorp Inc., Albany, 1971-72; also vice chmn. Norstar Bancorp Inc.; chmn., chief exec. officer Norstar Bank of Upstate N.Y., 1972-87, also bd. dirs. Active YMCA, Saratoga Performing Arts Ctr.; past bd. dirs.; bd. dirs. Albany Inst. History and Art, Robert Morris Assn., Capital Region Tech. Devel. Council, Mayor's Downtown Adv. Com., N.Y. State Banking Bd., Albany Med. Ctr., Albany chpt. ARC, United Way, Russell Sage Coll., Sta. WMHT-TV. Capt. C.E., AUS, 1943. Mem. Harvard Club (N.Y.C.), Harvard Club of Naples (pres.), Fort Orange Club (past pres.), Wyndemere C. of C., Forum Club of Collier County, Moorings Country Club, Masons. Republican. Presbyterian.

O'DELL, HERBERT, lawyer; b. Phila., Oct. 20, 1937; s. Samuel and Selma (Kramer) O.; m. Valerie Odell; children: Wesley, Jonathan, James, Sarah, Samuel. BS in Econs., U. Pa., 1959; LLB magna cum laude, U. Miami, 1962; LLM, Harvard U., 1963. Bar: Fla. 1963, Pa. 1968. Trial atty. tax div. U.S. Dept. Justice, Washington, 1963-65; assoc. Walton, Lantaff, Schroeder, Carson & Wahl, Miami, Fla., 1965-67; from assoc. to ptnr. Morgan, Lewis & Bockius, Phila., 1967-89; ptnr. Zapruder & Odell, Washington, 1989—; adj. prof. U. Miami, Villanova U.; lectr. various tax insts. Contbr. articles to profl. jours. Ford fellow, 1962-63. Mem. ABA, Fla. Bar Assn., Pa. Bar Assn., Phila. Bar Assn., Chester County Bar Assn., Phi Kappa Phi, Omicron Delta Kappa, Beta Alpha Psi. Clubs: Harvard, U. Pa. Avocations: sailing, running, tennis, scuba diving. Office: Zapruder & Odell 1235 Westlakes Dr Ste 385 Berwyn PA 19312-2414

O'DELL, JAMES E., newspaper publishing executive. V.p. ops. and techs. Chgo. Tribune. Office: Chgo Tribune 435 N Michigan Ave Chicago IL 60611

ODELL, MARY JANE, former state official; b. Algona, Iowa, July 28, 1923; d. Eugene and Madge (Lewis) Neville; m. John Odell, Mar. 3, 1967 (dec.); children: Brad Chinn, Chris Odell; m. Ralph Sigler, Nov. 22, 1987. B.A., U. Iowa, 1945; hon. doctorate, Simpson Coll., 1982. Host public affairs TV programs Des Moines and Chgo., 1953-79; with Iowa Public Broadcasting Network, 1975-79, host Assignment Iowa, 1975-78, host Mary Jane Odell Program, 1975-79; sec. of state State of Iowa, 1980-87; ret., 1987—; tchr. grad. classes in communications Roosevelt U., Chgo., Drake U., Des Moines. Chmn. Iowa Easter Seals campaign, 1979-83; mem. Midwest Com. Future Options; bd. dirs Iowa Shares; mem. exec. bd. Iowa Peace Inst.; 1985-92. Recipient Emmy award, 1972, 75; George Washington Carver award, 1978; named to Iowa Women's Hall of Fame, 1979. Republican. Address: 725 Hickman Rd Des Moines IA 50314-2935

ODELL, PATRICK LOWRY, mathematics educator; b. Watonga, Okla., Nov. 29, 1930; s. Max Vernon and Pamela (Massey) O.; m. Norma Lou Maddox, Aug. 16, 1958 (dec. May, 1980); children: James M., David L., Michael R.L., Julie K., Patricia L., Deborah L.; m. Dovalee Dorsett, Aug. 3, 1985. BS, U. Tex., 1952; postgrad., UCLA, 1953-54; MS, Okla. State U., 1958, PhD, 1962. Mathematician White Sands (N.Mex.) Proving Grounds, 1952-53, Kaman Nuclear, Albuquerque, 1958-59, U.S. Naval Nuclear Ordnance Evaluation Unit, 1959-62, Ling-Temco Vought Aeros., 1962; asst. prof. math. U. Tex., Austin, 1962-66; prof., chmn. dept. math. Tex. Technol. U., Lubbock, 1966-71, coordinator insts., dir. rsch., Coll. Arts and Sci., 1971-72; prof math. scis. and environ. scis. U. Tex., Dallas, 1972-88, prof. emeritus, 1988—, exec. dean grad. studies and rsch., 1972-75; prof. math. sci. Baylor U., Waco, Tex., 1988—; assoc. dir. Tex. Ctr. for Rsch., Austin, 1964-66; rsch. scientist Def. Rsch. Lab., 1963-65; cons. math statistician, 1962—. Capt. USAF, 1953-57. Fellow Tex. Acad. Sci. (Disting. Tex. Scientist award 1994), Am. Statis. Assn.; mem. Soc. Indsl. and Applied Math. Home: 3200 Windsor Ave Waco TX 76708-3113

ODELL, STUART IRWIN, lawyer; b. Phila., Jan. 1, 1940; s. P. Samuel and Selma Odell; m. Andrea L. Villegas; children: Stuart Irwin Jr., Benjamin Eaton, Manuela, Sebastian Patricio. BS in Econ., U. Pa., 1961; LLB cum laude, U. Miami, 1964; LLM in Tax, NYU, 1965. Bar: Fla. 1965, Pa. 1966, N.Y. 1982. Assoc., Morgan, Lewis & Bockius, 1966-70, ptnr. 1970-88; ptnr. Dewey Ballantine, 1988—; lectr. law NYU, 1965-66, adj. prof. law, 1966-80; adj. lectr. Temple U. Law Sch., 1972. Recipient Harry J. Ruddick award NYU. Mem. ABA, N.Y. State Bar Assn., Fla. Bar Assn., assoc. of Bar of City of N.Y., Univ. Assoc. editor U. Miami Law Rev., 1963-64. Office: Dewey Ballantine 1301 Avenue Of The Americas New York NY 10019-6092

ODELL, WILLIAM DOUGLAS, physician, scientist, educator; b. Oakland, Calif., June 11, 1929; s. Ernest A. and Emma L. (Mayer) O.; m. Margaret F. Reilly, Aug. 19, 1950; children: Michael, Timothy, John D., Debbie, Charles. AB, U. Calif., Berkeley, 1952; MD, MS in Physiology, U. Chgo., 1956; PhD in Biochemistry and Physiology, George Washington U., 1959. Intern, resident, chief resident in medicine U. Wash., 1956-60, postdoctoral fellow in endocrinology and metabolism, 1957-58; sr. investigator Nat. Cancer Inst., Bethesda, Md., 1960-65; chief endocrine service NICHD, 1965-66; chief endocrinology Harbor-UCLA Med. Center, Torrance, Calif., 1966-72; chmn. dept. medicine Harbor-UCLA Med. Center, 1972-79; vis. prof. medicine Auckland Sch. Medicine, New Zealand, 1979-80; prof. medicine

and physiology, chmn. dept. medicine U. Utah Sch. Medicine, Salt Lake City, 1980—. Mem. editorial bds. med. jours.; author 6 books in field; contbr. over 300 artilces to med. jours. Served with USPHS, 1960-66. Recipient Disting. Svc. award U. Chgo., 1973, Pharmacia award for outstanding contbns. to clin. chemistry, 1977, Gov.'s award State of Utah Sci. and Tech., 1988, also rsch. awards, Mastership award ACP, 1987. Mem. Am. Soc. Clin. Investigation, Am. Physiol. Soc., Assn. Am. PHysicians, Soc. Andrology (pres.), Endocrine Soc. (v.p. Robert Williams award 1991), Soc. Study of Reprodn. (bd. dirs.), Pacific Coast Fertility Soc. (pres.), Western Assn. Physicians (pres.), Western Soc. Clin. Rsch. (Mayo Soley award), Soc. Pediatric Rsch., Alpha Omega Alpha. Office: U of Utah Med Ctr 50 N Medical Dr Salt Lake City UT 84132-0002

O'DELL, WILLIAM FRANCIS, retired business executive, author; b. Detroit, Jan. 24, 1909; s. Frank Trevor and Garnett (Aikman) O'C.; m. Bess Baer, June 10, 1933 (dec. July 1986); m. Helen M. Porter, May 16, 1987; children: Peggy, David. B.S., U. Ill., 1930. With Penton Pub. Co., 1933-37; v.p. Ross Fed. Research Corp., 1937-44; mng. dir. Statis Research Co., 1944-45; pres. Market Facts, Inc., 1945-64, chmn., 1964-74; pres. ROC Internat., 1961-64; mem. census adv. bd. Dept. Commerce, 1963-73; prof. mktg. McIntire Sch. Commerce U. Va., 1965-78; vis. prof. Chinese U. of Hong Kong, 1969. Author: Marketing Decision, 1968, Marketing Decision Making, 1976, 4th edit., 1988, How to Make Lifetime Friends—With Peers and Parents, 1978, Twelve Families—An American Experience, 1981, Effective Business Decision Making and the Educated Guess, 1991; mem. editorial rev. bd. Jour. Mktg, 1964-73. Recipient Leader in Mktg. award, 1970, Jour. Mktg. Research editorial award, 1979; William F. O'Dell professorship in commerce named in his honor U. Va., 1983. Mem. Am. Mktg. Assn. (pres. 1960-61), Colonnade Club (Charlottesville), Univ. Club of Ft. Myers, Rotary, Delta Upsilon, Beta Gamma Sigma. Home: 5707 Junonia Ct Fort Myers FL 33908-1603

ODEN, JOHN TINSLEY, engineering mechanics educator, consultant; b. Alexandria, La., Dec. 25, 1936; s. John James and Sara Elizabeth (Lyles) O.; m. Barbara Clare Smith, Mar. 19, 1965; children: John Walker, Elizabeth Lee. BS, La. State U., 1959; MS, Okla. State U., 1960, PhD, 1962; doctorate in sci. (hon.), Tech. U. Lisbon, Portugal, 1986. Registered profl. engr., Tex., La. Teaching asst. La. State U., Baton Rouge, 1959; asst. prof. Okla. State U., Stillwater, 1961-63; sr. structures engr. Gen. Dynamics, Fort Worth, 1963-64; prof., head dept. engring. mechanics U. Ala., Huntsville, 1964-73; prof. U. Tex., Austin, 1973—; Carol and Henry Groppe prof. engring. U. Tex., Ernest and Virginia Cockrell chair in engring., 1987; prof. Coope U. Fed., Brazil, 1974; dir. Tex. Inst. Computational Mechanics, Austin, 1974-93, Tex. Inst. Computational and Applied Math., Austin, 1993—; Sci. Rsch. Coun. vis. scholar Brunel U., Eng., 1981; mem. com. on computational mechanics NRC; chmn. U.S. Nat. Com. on Theoretical and Applied Mechanics, 1992-94. Author, editor 38 books; contbr. numerous articles to profl. jours. Decorated medal Order de Palms Admique (France); recipient Rsch. award Southeastern Conf. on Theoretical and Applied Mechanics, 1978, Lohmann medal Okla. State U., 1991, Computational Mechanics medal Japan Soc. Mech. Engrs., 1993. Fellow ASCE (Outstanding Svc. award 1968, Walter Huber Rsch. award 1973, Theodore Von Karman medal 1992), ASME (Worcester Reed Warner medal 1990), Am. Acad. Mechanics (pres. 1990-94, Congress medal 1994), U.S. Nat. Acad. Engring.; mem. Soc. Engring. Sci. (pres. 1978, Eringen medal 1991), Soc. Indsl. and Applied Math., Internat. Assn. Computational Mechanics (pres., Congress-Gauss-Newton medal, 1994), U.S. Assn. Computational Mechanics (pres. 1990-92, John Von Neumann medal 1993), Soc. Natural Philosophy, Nat. Acad. Engring. Mem. Home: 7403 W Rim Dr Austin TX 78731-2044 Office: ASE-EM Dept U Tex WRW Bldg 305A Austin TX 78712

ODEN, WILLIAM BRYANT, bishop, educator; b. McAllen, Tex., Aug. 3, 1935; s. Charles Alva and Evea (Bryant) O.; m. Marilyn Brown, July 12, 1957; children: Danna Lee Oden Bowen, William Dirk, Valerie Lyn, Charles Bryant. BA, Okla. State U., 1958; MDiv, Harvard U., 1961, postgrad., 1974; ThD, Boston U., 1964; DD (hon.), Oklahoma City U., 1980; LHD (hon.), Centenary Coll., 1990. Ordained to ministry Meth. Ch., 1961. Pastor Aldersgate United Meth. Ch., Oklahoma City, 1963-69, St. Stephen's United Meth. Ch., Norman, Okla., 1969-76, Crown Heights United Meth. Ch., Oklahoma City, 1976-83; prof. Phillips Grad. Sem., Enid, 1976-88; pastor 1st United Meth. Ch., Enid, 1983-88; bishop United Meth. Ch., Baton Rouge, 1988—; assigned to La. area; pres. SCJ Coll. of Bishops, 1989-90; del. Gen. Conf., 1976, 80, 84, 88; chmn. Okla. Del. to Gen. and Jurisdictional Confs., 1984, 88; Jackson lectr. Perkins Sch. Theology, So. Meth. U., 1975, Wilson lectr. SCJ Bishop's Week, 1989; co-chair World Meth.-Anglican Dialogue, 1991—; bd. dirs. Wesley Works Project. Author: Oklahoma Methodism in the Twentieth Century, 1968, Liturgy as Life Journey, 1976, Wordeed: Evangelism in Biblical and Wesleyan Perspective, 1978; contbr.: Send Me: The Itineracy in Crisis, 1991. Trustee Oklahoma City U., 1980-88, Southwestern U., Winfield, Kans., 1983-88, Centenary Coll., 1988—, Dillard U., 1988—. Mem. Am. Acad. Homiletics. Avocations: writing, reading biographies, mountain climbing, backpacking. Home: 7344 Woodstock Dr Baton Rouge LA 70809-1136 Office: La United Meth Hdqrs 527 North Blvd Baton Rouge LA 70802-5720

ODENKIRCHEN, CARL JOSEF, Romance languages and literatures educator; b. Duisburg/Kaldenhausen, Germany, Jan. 28, 1921; came to U.S., 1929, naturalized, 1940; s. Apollinaris and Paula (Orth) O.; m. Stella Esther Behling, Sept. 6, 1948; children: David Michael, Susan Elizabeth. AB, Coll. Charleston, S.C., 1942; MA, U. Chgo., 1947; PhD, U. N.C., 1951; postdoctoral study, Sorbonne, Paris, 1953-54. Instr. Romance langs. U. N.C., 1947-49; instr. French and Spanish, Tchrs. Coll., SUNY-Albany, 1950-53; asst. prof. classical and modern langs. Lake Forest (Ill.) Coll., 1956-58; asso. prof. Romance langs. and humanities SUNY-Albany, 1958-61, prof. Romance langs. and comparative lit., 1961-76, prof. Romance langs. and lit., 1976-86, prof. emeritus, 1986—, chmn. dept. comparative lit., 1962-71; vis. prof. Boston U., 1966-68. Author: A Preliminary Chrestomathy of Old Catalan, 1949, The Play of Adam (Ordo Representacionis Ade), 1976, The Life of St. Alexius, 1978. Mem. Albany Symphony Orch., 1958-61. Served with AUS, 1942-45. Fulbright scholar U. Rome, 1950. Home: 47 Brookview Ave Delmar NY 12054-4425

ODENWELLER, ROBERT PAUL, philatelist, association executive, airline pilot; b. Colon, C.Z., Sept. 19, 1938; s. Charles Joseph and Robina Katharine (Watson, O.; m. Jane Blackistone Rawlings, June 24, 1965; 1 stepchild, Joy McCorriston; 1 child, Liesl Hasbrouck. BS U.S. Air Force Acad., 1960. Commd. USAF, 1956, advanced through grades to capt., 1963, resigned, 1956-66; mem. Collectors Club, Inc., N.Y.C., 1964—, gov. 1969—, program chmn., 1970-80, mem. editl. bd., 1975—, sec. 1979-82, v.p., 1983-86, pres. 1987-90, trustee, 1992—; trustee, vice chmn. then chmn. expert com. Philatelic Found., N.Y.C., 1970—. Author: The FIP Guide to Exhibiting and Judging Traditional and Postal History Exhibits, 1993; author, Editor: Philatelic Vocabulary in Five Languages, 1978 (Vermeil medal 1979); editor: Opinions VI, 1992; contbr. articles to profl. pubs. Recipient Grand Prix d' Honneur, Zeapex Orgn., 1980; selected to sign Roll of Disting. Philatelists, Brit. Philatelic Fedn., 1991, Alfred Lichtenstein Meml. award Philatelic Found., 1993. Fellow Royal Philatelic Soc. London, Royal Philatelic Soc. N.Z.; mem. Fedn. Internationale de Philatelie (pres. commn. traditional philately 1978—; Grand Prix d' Honneur 1980), Am. Philatelic Soc. (bd. dirs. 1981-84, 89-90, named Champion of Champions 1973), Assn. Internationale Des Experts Philateliques (expert 1980—, bd. dirs. 1987—), Fedn. New Zealand Philatelic Socs., Grand Prix Club Internat. (sec., treas. 1980-89, bd. dirs. 1989-92, 94—, v.p. 1994—), Soc. Australasian Specialists (pres. 1969-72), U.S. Chess Fedn. Republican. Episcopalian. Avocations: stamp collecting; photography; languages; chess; bridge. Home: Chalon Round Top Rd Bernardsville NJ 07924 Office: Collector's Club Inc 22 E 35th St New York NY 10016-3806

ODER, FREDERIC CARL EMIL, retired aerospace company executive, consultant; b. Los Angeles, Oct. 23, 1919; s. Emil and Katherine Ellis (Pierce) O.; m. Dorothy Gene Brumfield, July 2, 1941; children—Frederic E., Barbara Oder Debes, Richard W. B.S., Calif. Inst. Tech., 1940, M.S., 1941; Ph.D., UCLA, 1952. Commd. 2d lt. U.S. Army Air Force, 1941; advanced through grades to col. U.S. Air Force, 1960; ret., 1960; asst. dir. and program mgr. for research and engring. Apparatus and Optical div. Eastman Kodak Co., Rochester, N.Y., 1960-66; with Lockheed Missiles & Space Co.,

Sunnyvale, Calif., 1966-91; v.p. asst. gen. mgr. div. space systems Lockheed Missiles & Space Co., 1972-73, v.p., gen. mgr. div. space systems, 1973-84, exec. v.p., 1984-85; cons., 1985-91; mem. Def. Intelligence Agy. Sci. Adv. Com., 1972-76, assoc. mem., 1976-78; mem. Air Force Studies Bd., Assembly Engring., NRC, 1975-79, Def. Sci. Bd. Summer Study, 1975, Rev. Panel, 1979, Space Applications Bd., 1985-88. Contbr. articles to profl. publs. Decorated Legion of Merit. Fellow AIAA; mem. NAE, Masons, Sigma Xi. Episcopalian. Home: 400 San Domingo Way Los Altos CA 94022-2143

ODER, KENNETH WILLIAM, lawyer; b. Newport News, Va., July 9, 1947; s. Thomas William and Joy Reletta (McNeil) O.; m. Lucinda Ann Fox, July 20, 1969; children: Joshua, Devon, Chelsea. BA, U. Va., 1969, JD, 1975. Bar: Calif. 1975, U.S. Dist. Ct. (cen. dist.) Calif. 1975, U.S. Dist. Ct. (so. and no. dists.) Calif. 1977, U.S. Ct. Appeals (9th cir.) 1977, D.C. 1979. Assoc. Latham & Watkins, Los Angeles, 1975-77, 79-82, ptnr., 1982—; assoc. Latham & Watkins, Washington, 1978-79. Exec. editor U. Va. Law Rev., 1973-74. Coach San Marino Little League, Calif., 1983—, Am. Youth Soccer Orgn., Rosemeade, Calif., 1984—. Mem. Calif. Bar Assn. (employment law sect.), Los Angeles County Bar Assn., D.C. Bar Assn. Republican. Methodist. Avocations: jogging, hiking, fishing. Office: Latham & Watkins 633 W 5th St Ste 4000 Los Angeles CA 90071-2005

ODERMATT, ROBERT ALLEN, architect; b. Oakland, Calif., Jan. 3, 1938; s. Clifford Allen and Margaret Louise (Budge) O.; m. Diana Birtwistle, June 9, 1960; children: Kristin Ann, Kyle David. BArch, U. Calif., Berkeley, 1960. Registered architect, Calif., Oreg., Nev., Colo., Hawaii; cert. Nat. Coun. Archtl. Registration Bds. Draftsman Anderson Simonds Dusel Campini, Oakland, 1960-61; architect James R. Lucas, Orinda, Calif., 1961-62, ROMA Architects, San Francisco, 1962-76; architect, prin. ROMA Architects, 1976-84; prin. ROMA Design Group, San Francisco, 1962-92; pres. The Odermatt Group, Orinda, Calif., 1992—; prin. speaker Internat. Conf. on Rebuilding Cities, Pitts., 1988; mem. U.S. Design in Am. Program, Sofia, Bulgaria, Armenian Disaster Assn. Team, 1989; prin. State of Calif. Bay Area Facilities Plan, 1982; princ. Greece Resort Privatization Program, 1993. Prin. designer Grand Canyon Nat. Park, 1977, Yosemite Nat. Park, 1987; prin. planner hotel complex Westin Hotel, Vail, Colo., 1982, Kaanapali Resort, 1987, Las Montanas Resort, San Diego; master plan U. Calif., Berkeley, 1988, Kohanaiki and Mauna Lani resorts, 1989, Calif. State Strategic Real Estate Plan, 1992, Greek Resort/Marina Privatization Program, 1993, Tektronix Strategic Plan, 1994, United Labs, Manila Master Plan, 1995. Mem. Oakland Mayor's Com. on High Density Housing, 1982, Oakland Gen. Plan COngress, 1994; prin. charge Am. Embassy, Bahrain. Fellow AIA (dir. East Bay chpt. 1969-71, pres. 1980-81, dir. Calif. coun. 1979-81, Disting. Svc. award 1991, nat. dir. 1983-86, nat. v.p. 1986-87, chair AIA internat. steering com. 1993-94, graphic stds. adv. com. 1991-92, U. Calif. archtl. review commn. 1992-94). Office: The Odermatt Group 39 Drury Ln Berkeley CA 94705

ODGERS, RICHARD WILLIAM, lawyer; b. Detroit, Dec. 31, 1936; s. Richard Stanley and Elsie Maude (Trevarthen) O.; m. Gail C. Bassett, Aug. 29, 1959; children: Thomas R., Andrew B. AB, U. Mich., 1959, JD, 1961. Bar: Calif. 1962. Assoc. Pillsbury, Madison & Sutro, San Francisco, 1961-69, ptnr., 1969-87; exec. v.p., gen. counsel, sec. external affairs Pacific Telesis Group, 1987—. Served with USNR. Fellow Am. Bar Found.; Am. Judicature Soc., Am. Coll. Trial Lawyers; mem. ABA, Am. Law Inst., Legal Aid Soc. of San Francisco (bd. dirs.), Olympic Club, Pacific-Union Club, City Club (San Francisco). Office: Pacific Telesis Group 130 Kearny St Ste 3609 San Francisco CA 94108-4803*

ODHIAMBO, ATIENO E. S., history educator, researcher; b. Kisumu, Nyanza, Kenya, Sept. 11, 1946; came to U.S. 1988; s. Zablon and Rosbella (Akumu) Ogwamor; m. Jane Erose Audi, Mar. 15, 1968; children: Susan, Caroline, Michael, Samson. BA in History with first class honors, Makerere U., Kampala, Uganda, 1970; PhD in History, Nairobi (Kenya) U., 1973. Spl. asst. dept. history Nairobi U., 1970-71, tutorial fellow dept. history, 1971-73, lectr. dept. history, 1973-74; sr. lectr. dept. history, 1978-87, assoc. prof. dept. history, 1987; prof. history Egerton U., Njoro, Kenya, 1988, Rice U., Houston, 1989—; jr. rsch. assoc. St. Anthony's Coll., Oxford, England, 1971-72; vis. rsch. scholar Hoover Instn., Sanford, Calif., 1979-80; vis. lectr. dept. history Stanford U., 1980; rsch. scholar Cologne U., Germany, 1980; vis. prof. dept. history Johns Hopkins U., 1985, 86; vis. assoc. prof. dept. history Rice U., 1988-89; sr. rsch. fellow African Studies Ctr., U. Witwatersand, Johannesburg, South Africa, 1990; sr. fellow Harry S. Truman Inst. for Peace, Hebrew U. Jerusalem, 1990-91; vis. prof. dept. anthropology Witwatersand U., 1992. Author: The Paradox of Collaboration and Other Essays, 1974, A History of East Africa, 1977, Siasa: Politics and Nationalism in East Africa 1888-1939, 1982, (with Peter Wanyande) History and Government of Kenya, 1988, (with D. W. Cohen) Siaya: Historical Anthropology of an African Landscape, 1989, Burying S.M.: The Politics of Knowledge and the Sociology of Power in Africa, 1992; editor (with W. O. Oyugi et al) Democratic Theory and Practice in Africa, 1988; contbr. over 40 articles and book reviews to profl. jours. Grad. fellow Rockefeller Found., 1971-72; Fullbright scholar Syracuse U., 1978; grantee NEH, 1992. Office: Rice University PO Box 1892 6100 South Main Houston TX 77251

ODLAND, GERALD CLARK, association executive; b. Bellefonte, Pa., July 26, 1946; s. Martin Luther and Ethel Gladys (Wentzel) O.; m. Dianne Marlo DePue, May 29, 1969; children—Brian Martin, Kevin Michael. BS, U. Md., 1973, MS, 1976. Dir. services, computer mgr. Entomol. Soc. Am., College Park, Md., 1972-85; dep. exec. dir. Assn. for Childhood Edn. Internat., Wheaton, Md., 1985-91, exec. dir., 1991—. Editor: Directory of North American Entomologists, 1979; contbr. articles to profl. jours. Served as sgt. U.S. Army, 1967-70, Vietnam. Mem. Entomol. Soc. Am., Am. Soc. Assn. Execs. Republican. Lutheran. Avocations: hunting, fishing, boating, woodworking. Home: 13715 Oster Farm Rd West Friendship MD 21794 Office: Assn Childhood Edn Internat 11501 Georgia Ave Ste 315 Silver Spring MD 20902-1954

ODLE, ROBERT CHARLES, JR., lawyer; b. Port Huron, Mich., Feb. 15, 1944; s. Robert Charles and Elizabeth Dagmar (Lassen) O.; m. Lydia Ann Karpinol, Aug. 2, 1969. B.A., Wayne State U., Detroit, 1966; J.D., Detroit Coll. Law, 1969, LLD (hon.), 1992. Staff asst. to pres. of U.S., 1969-71; dir. adminstrn. Com. Re-election of President, 1971-73; dep. asst. sec. HUD, 1973-76; Washington corp. affairs rep. Internat. Paper Co., 1976-81; asst. sect. Dept. Energy, 1981-85; ptnr. Weil, Gotshal & Manges, 1985—. Mem. Mich. Bar Assn., D.C. Bar Assn., Delta Theta Phi. Republican. Roman Catholic. Club: University (Washington). Home: 219 S Lee St Alexandria VA 22314-3307 Office: Weil Gotshal & Manges 1615 L St NW Washington DC 20036-5608

ODLIN, RICHARD BINGHAM, retired banker; b. Olympia, Wash., Nov. 22, 1934; s. Reno and Edith Mary (Murphy) O.; m. 1963 (div. 1969); children: Julia Eleanor Odlin Lord, Tracy Edith; m. Barbara Ellen Button, Aug. 8, 1985. AB, Whitman Coll., 1957. With Wells Fargo Bank, San Francisco, 1957-63; various positions to sr. v.p., sec. Puget Sound Nat. Bank, Tacoma, Wash., 1963-92; pres. New Tacoma Parking Corp., 1969-91. Bd. dirs. Tacoma-Pierce County chpt. ARC, 1964-69, vice chmn., 1969; active Wash. State Hist. Soc., treas., 1971-92. Mem. Am. Contract Bridge League (life master), Tacoma Country and Golf Club, Tacoma Lawn Tennis Club, Columbia Tower Club (Seattle), Balboa Club (Mazatlan, Mex.), Kappa Sigma. Republican. Avocations: duplicate bridge, opera, old time radio. Home: 507 N 3d St Apt 301-A Tacoma WA 98403-2753

O'DOHERTY, BRIAN, writer, filmmaker; b. Ballaghadereen, County Roscommon, Ireland; came to U.S., 1957; m. Barbara Novak, 1960. M.D., Univ. Coll. Dublin, Nat. U. Ireland, 1952, D.P.H. with honors, 1955; MS in Hygiene, Harvard U., 1958; TV host programs Mus. Fine Arts, Boston, 1958-61; art critic N.Y. Times, 1961-64; vis. prof. Berkeley U., 1967; dir. visual arts Nat. Endowment for Arts, 1969-76, dir. media arts, 1976-94; dir. Millennium Project, 1994—; art and architecture critic Today Program, 1971-76; adj. prof. Barnard Coll., 1969—. Author: Object and Idea: A New York Art Journal 1961-67, 1967; Museums in Crisis, 1972; editor: American Masters, The Voice and the Myth, 1973 2d. revised edit., 1988, Inside the White Cube, 1986, The Strange Case of Mlle. P, 1992. Contbr. articles to profl. jours. Smith-Mundt fellow; recipient Mpls. Citizens award, 1961; Emmy nominations; Eire Soc. Gold medal for contbns. to Culture, 1963;

Mather award, 1964; Grand Prix Montreal Internat. Festival of Arts Film award, 1982; Sagittarius award London, 1993. Mem. Am. Irish Historical Soc., N.Y., Irish Mus. of Modern Art, Dublin, Coll. Art Assn. (life mem.). Office: NEA 1100 Pennsylvania Ave NW Washington DC 20506-0005

ODOM, ORIS LEON, II, finance educator, financial consultant; b. Amarillo, Tex., June 8, 1946; s. Oris Leon and Marjorie Avonne (Burch) O.; m. Cynthia Ann Chambless, June 15, 1968; children: Allison Noel, Travis Justin. AS, Amarillo Coll., 1966; BBA, U. Tex., 1968, MBA, 1970; DBA, U. Okla., 1979. Chartered fin. cons. Tax examiner IRS, Austin, Tex., 1969-70; teaching asst. U. Okla., Norman, 1970-73; asst. prof. Sam Houston State U., Huntsville, Tex., 1973-79; assoc. prof. Miss. State U., Starkville, 1979-83; prof. fin. U. Tex., Tyler, 1983—; forensic fin. cons., Tyler, 1983—. Mem. editorial rev. bd. Jour. Bus. Strategies, 1983—, Miss. Bus. Rev., 1982-83; contbr. articles to profl. jours. Avocations: reading, music, fishing. Office: U Tex 3900 University Blvd Tyler TX 75799

ODOM, WILLIAM E., automobile finance company executive; b. 1936; married. Student, U. S.C., U.S. Naval Acad., Wayne State U. With Ford Motor Credit Co., 1966—, dist. mgr. diversified financing ops., 1966-69, field ops. mgr., then mng. credit officer, then mgr. and sr. loan officer field ops. & real estate financing activities, 1969-79, ops. mgr. leasing truck & tractor financing, 1979-80, v.p. leasing truck and tractor financing ops., 1980-83, v.p. eastern U.S. and Canadian ops., 1983-85, exec. v.p N. Am. automotive financing ops., 1985-86, past pres., 1986—, now chmn., chief exec. officer, bd. dirs. Office: Ford Motor Credit Co American Rd Dearborn MI 48121

ODOM, WILLIAM ELDRIDGE, army officer, educator; b. Cookeville, Tenn., June 23, 1932; s. John Albert and Callie Frances (Everhart) O.; m. Anne Weld Curtis, June 9, 1962; 1 child, Mark Weld. BS, U.S. Mil. Acad., 1954; MA, Columbia U., 1962, PhD, 1970; DSc (hon.), Middlebury Coll., 1987. Commd. 2nd lt. U.S. Army, 1954, advanced through grades to lt. gen., 1984; mem. U.S. Mil. Liaison Mission to Soviet Forces, Germany, 1964-66; from asst. prof. to assoc. prof. govt. U.S. Mil. Acad., West Point, 1966-69, 74-76; asst. Army attache U.S. embassy, Moscow, 1972-74; nat. security staff mem. White House, 1977-81; asst. chief of staff for intelligence Dept. Army, Washington, 1981-85; dir. Nat. Security Agy., Fort Meade, Md., 1985-88; dir. nat. security studies Hudson Inst., 1988—; adj. prof. pol. sci. Yale U., 1989—. Author: The Soviet Volunteers, 1973, On Internal War, 1992, Trial After Triumph, 1992, America's Military Revolution, 1993, (with Robert Dujarric) Commonwealth or Empire? Russia, Central Asia and The Transcaucasus, 1995; contbr. articles to profl. jours. Decorated Def. Disting. medal with oak leaf cluster, DSM with oak leaf cluster, Legion of Merit, Nat. Security medal, Nat. Intelligence Disting. Svc. medal; grand cross Order of Merit with Star (Fed. Republic Germany); Order Nat. Security Merit (Republic of Korea), officer Nat. Order of Merit (France). Mem. Coun. on Fgn. Rels., Am. Assn. for Advancement of Slavic Studies, Internat. Inst. for Strategic Studies, Am. Polit. Sci. Assn., Acad. Polit. Sci. Conglist. Office: Hudson Inst 1015 18th St NW Ste 200 Washington DC 20036-5200

O'DONNELL, CHARLES PATRICK, retired newspaper executive, consultant; b. Cleve., Nov. 14, 1920; s. Charles Richard and Ella (Kilbane) O'D.; m. Mary Rita Monroe, May 17, 1944 (dec.); children: C. Patrick, Mary, Martha, Robert J. BBA, Case Western Res. U., 1942; IA, Harvard U., 1943. Salesman, research exec. IBM, 1946-52; mgmt. cons., partner Robert Heller & Assos., 1952-56, 59-64; pres. Electronic Tabulating Co. 1956-59; asst. controller East Ohio Gas Co., Cleve., 1964-66; v.p. Providence Gravure, Inc., 1966-69; v.p. Providence Journal Co., 1969-78, sr. v.p., 1978-85; pres. O'Donnell & Assocs., Providence, 1985—; bd. dirs. Charlotte Printing Co., Jackson Newspapers, Inc., Sun Coast Media Group, Inc., Manisses Communications Group, Inc. Treas. Pomenade Indsl. Center Assn., 1981; trustee Providence Preservation Soc., 1981—, v.p. 1986-87; trustee R.I. Philharm. Orch., 1979—, 1st v.p., 1985—, pres., 1987—; active R.I. Hist. Soc., 1984-87; vice chmn. Providence Off-Street Parking Commn., 1986—; trustee St. Joseph Hosp., 1973-77, Indsl. Found. R.I., 1973—. Served to lt. USNR, 1943-46. Mem. Providence C. of C. (dir. 1973-77), Am. Newspaper Publishers Assn., New England Newspaper Assn. (pres. 1985), Hope Club, Agawam Hunt Club (Providence), Dunes Club (Narragansett, R.I.), Knights of Malta, Phi Beta Kappa. Roman Catholic. Home and Office: 46 Cooke St Providence RI 02906-3102

O'DONNELL, CHRIS, actor; b. Winetka, Ill., 1970. Actor: (films) Men Don't Leave, 1990, Fried Green Tomatoes, 1991, Scent of a Woman, 1992 (Golden Globe award nomination best supporting actor 1992), School Ties, 1992, The Three Musketeers, 1993, Blue Sky, 1994, Circle of Friends, 1995, Mad Love, 1995, Batman Forever, 1995. Office: CAA 9830 Wilshire Blvd Beverly Hills CA 90212*

O'DONNELL, EDWARD JOSEPH, bishop, former editor; b. St. Louis, July 4, 1931; s. Edward Joseph and Ruth Mary (Carr) O'D. Student, Cardinal Glennon Coll., 1949-53; postgrad., Kenrick Sem., 1953-57. Ordained priest Roman Cath. Ch., 1957, consecrated bishop, 1984; asso. pastor in 5 St. Louis parishes, 1957-77; pastor St. Peter's Ch., Kirkwood, Mo., 1977-81; assoc. dir. Archdiocesan Commn. on Human Rights, 1962-70; dir. Archdiocesan Radio-TV Office, 1966-68, Archdiocesan Vocation Council, 1965; editor St. Louis Rev., 1968-81; vicar-gen. Archdiocese of St. Louis, 1981-84, aux. bishop 1984-94; bishop Diocese of Lafayette, Lafayette, LA, 1994—; bd. dirs. Nat. Cath. Conf. for Interracial Justice, 1980-85, NAACP, 1964-66, Urban League St. Louis, 1962-68; chmn. Interfaith Clergy Coun. Greater St. Louis, 1963-67. Named to Golden Dozen Internat. Soc. Weekly Newspaper Editors, 1970, 77. Mem. Cath. Press Assn., Nat. Assn. TV Arts and Scis. Office: PO Box 3387 Lafayette LA 70502

O'DONNELL, EUGENE J., department stores executive; b. 1946. BA, U. Vt.; MBA, Dartmouth Coll. V.p Hills Dept. Stores Inc., 1981-85, sr. v.p., gen. merchandise mgr., from 1985, now exec. v.p. Office: Hills Dept Stores Inc 15 Dan Rd Canton MA 02021-2847

O'DONNELL, F. SCOTT, banker; b. Brownsville, Pa., Sept. 20, 1940; s. Francis Horner and Rebecca (Warren) O'D.; m. Ann Bukmir, Dec. 30, 1976. BA, Grove City (Pa.) Coll., 1962; postgrad., U. Wis. Grad. Sch. Banking, 1970, Internat. Sch. Banking, U. Colo., 1972. Nat. bank examiner Comptroller of Currrency State of Ohio, Cleve., 1965-71; supt. of banks State of Ohio, Columbus, 1975-77; sr. v.p. First Nat. Bank, Steubenville, Ohio, 1971-75; exec. v.p. Heritage Bancorp, Steubenville, 1977-80; v.p. Society Corp., Cleve., 1980-86, sr. v.p., 1986—; mem. state banking bd. Div. of Banks, Columbus, 1979-85, govt. affairs com. Ohio Bankers Assn., 1982-84. Served with USCG, 1963-69. Clubs: Lakewood Country; Univ. (Pitts.). Lodge: Elks. Avocations: golfing, antiques. Home: 31830 Lake Rd Avon Lake OH 44012-2022 Office: Soc Corp 800 Superior Ave E Cleveland OH 44114-2601

O'DONNELL, BROTHER FRANK JOSEPH, principal; b. Phila., Aug. 6, 1942; s. Francis J. and Eleanor E. (Doney) O'D. BA, U. Dayton, 1963; MLS, Cath. U. Am., 1964; MEd, Loyola Coll., 1971; JD, U. Md. 1991. Faculty mem. Cardinal Gibbons High Sch., Balt., ednl. media coord., libr. 1964—, prin., 1969—; dir. tenant advocacy program Justice Ctr. Balt., 1991 N.Y. prov. dir. of edn., 1993. Mem. ABA, Nat. Assn. Secondary Sch. Prins., Nat. Cath. Edn. Assn.

O'DONNELL, G. DANIEL, lawyer; b. Scranton, Pa., 1951. BA summa cum laude, U. Notre Dame, 1973; JD, U. Pa., 1976. Bar: Pa. 1976. Ptnr., chmn. bus. dept. Dechert Price & Rhoads, Phila. Mem. Order of Coif. Office: Dechert Price & Rhoads 4000 Bell Atlantic 1717 Arch St Philadelphia PA 19103-2713

O'DONNELL, JAMES FRANCIS, health science administrator; b. Cleve., July 22, 1926; s. John Michael and Mary Louise (Hayes) O'D.; m. Winifred Locke, Sept. 10, 1955; children—Anne Catherine, Patrick John, Mary Elizabeth. B.S. in Biology, St. Louis U., 1949; Ph.D. in Biochemistry, U. Chgo., 1957. Asst., then assoc. prof. biol. chemistry and exptl. medicine Coll. Medicine, U. Cin., 1957-68; grants assoc., div. research grants NIH, Bethesda, Md., 1968-69; program dir. population and reprodn. grants br. Ctr. for Population Research, Nat. Inst. Child Health and Human Devel., NIH, 1969-71; asst. dir. div. research resources NIH, Bethesda, 1971-76, dep.

dir. div. research resources, 1976-90, acting dir. div. research resources, 1981-82, dir. Office of Extramural Programs, Office of the Dir., 1990— Served with U.S. Army, 1950-52. Home: 11601 Bunnell Ct S Rockville MD 20854-3603 Office: NIH 9000 Rockville Pike Ste 5b32 Bethesda MD 20892-0001

O'DONNELL, JOHN LOGAN, lawyer; b. Chgo., Mar. 6, 1914; s. William Joseph and Elizabeth (McLogan) O'D.; m. Mary Ellen Sipe, Sept. 2, 1939 (dec. Dec. 29, 1979); 1 son, John Logan; m. Michele G. Fischer, May 9, 1981. B.A., Williams Coll., 1934; J.D., Northwestern U., 1937. Bar: Ill. 1937, N.Y. 1943, D.C. 1977. Assoc. firm Defrees, Buckingham, Jones and Hoffman, Chgo., 1937-38; staff atty. Office Gen. Counsel, SEC, 1938-41; instr. Cath. U. Law Sch., 1938-41; assoc. Cravath, Swaine & Moore, N.Y.C., 1941-52; ptnr. Olwine, Connelly, Chase, O'Donnell & Weyher, N.Y.C., 1952-91, of counsel, 1991; of counsel Aron, Twomey, Hoppe & Gallanty, N.Y.C., 1991—. Bd. dirs. Near East Found., 1968-84. Fellow Am. Coll. Trial Lawyers; mem. Assn. Bar City N.Y., Am., Fed., bar assns., Beta Theta Pi, Phi Delta Phi. Roman Catholic. Clubs: Union, Univ., Williams, (N.Y.). Avocations: piano, sports. Home: 181 E 73d St New York NY 10021 Office: Aron Twomey Hoppe & Gallanty 757 3rd Ave New York NY 10017

O'DONNELL, KENDRA STEARNS, principal; b. July 1, 1943; d. Kendall Stearns; m. C. Patrick O'Donnell Jr.; children: Kendall Hamilton, Allegra Hamilton, Christopher. BA, Barnard Coll., 1965; MA, Columbia U., 1966, PhD, 1974; hon. degree, New Eng. Coll., 1988, Hamilton Coll., 1989. Lectr. in English Princeton (N.J.) U., 1971-73, asst. prof. English, 1973-76; program officer John and Mary R. Markle Found., 1977-78, cons., 1980—; cons. Arthur Vining Davis Found., 1979, 80—, program dir., 1980; spl. asst. to pres. Rockefeller Bros. Fund, 1984-87; prin. Phillips Exeter (N.H.) Acad., 1987—. Trustee N.H. Charitable Fund, Concord, 1989—, vice chair, 1991—. Mem. The Century Assn., The Headmasters Assn. Clubs: Harvard of N.Y.C., St. Botolph, Boston. Office: Phillips Exeter Acad Main St Exeter NH 03833-2438

O'DONNELL, KEVIN, retired metal working company executive; b. Cleve., June 9, 1925; s. Charles Richard and Ella (Kilbane) O'D.; m. Ellen Blydenburgh, Aug. 16, 1965; children: Kevin, Susan, Michael, John, Maura, Neil, Megan, Hugh. AB, Kenyon Coll., Gambier, Ohio, 1947, PhD in Law (hon.), 1980; MBA, Harvard U., 1947; PhD in Econs. (hon.), Pusan (Korea) Nat. U., 1970; Ph.D. in Humanities (hon.), Ohio Wesleyan U., 1972. Gen. sales mgr. Steel Improvement & Forge Co., Cleve., 1947-60; mgmt. cons. Booz, Allen and Hamilton, Cleve., 1960-62; gen. mgr., dir. Atlas Alloys-Rio Algom Corp., Cleve., 1963-66; dir. Peace Corps, Seoul, 1966-70; dir. adminstrn. and fin., then dep. acting dir. Peace Corps, 1970-71; assoc. dir. internat. ops. ACTION, 1971-72; exec. v.p. SIFCO Industries, Inc., Cleve., 1972-75; pres., chief oper. officer SIFCO Industries, Inc., 1976-83, pres., chief exec. officer, 1983-89, chief exec. officer, 1989-90, chmn., exec. comm., 1990-94; bd. dirs. Nat. Machinery, Tiffin, Ohio, Lamson and Sessions, Ferro Corp., R.P.M. Inc., Medina, Ohio. Trustee Alcohol Svcs. Cleve., 1993—, Cleve. Coun. World Affairs, Nat. Peace Corps Assn.; mem. Coun. Fgn. Rels., N.Y.C., Washington Inst. Fgn. Affairs, Cleve. Com. Fgn. Rels., chmn., 1979-82; chmn. CCWA, 1982-89; pres. Guest House, Inc., 1990-92. Decorated Order Civil Merit (Republic of Korea). mem. Harvard Bus. Sch. Club Cleve., Harvard Bus. Sch. Alumni Assn. (dir. Boston 1991-94), First Friday Club, 50 Club, Union Club, Pepper Pike Country Club, Westwood Country Club, Army-Navy Club (Washington), Knights of Malta (master knight). Republican. Roman Catholic. Avocations: golf, reading.

O'DONNELL, LAURENCE GERARD, newspaper editor; b. Bklyn., June 30, 1935; s. Thomas Edward and Dorothy (Clark) O'D.; m. Joan M. Coniglio, Jan. 9, 1960; children: Christopher, Carolyn, Jeffrey, Anthony. AB, Holy Cross Coll., 1957. Reporter Wall Street Jour., N.Y.C., 1958-66, chief Detroit Bur., 1966-74, asst. mng. editor, N.Y.C., 1974-77, mng. editor, 1977-83; assoc. editor Dow Jones & Co. Inc., N.Y.C., 1983-90; cons. Dow Jones & Co., Inc., 1991—; pres. Dow Jones Newspaper Fund, 1988-93; bd. dirs. Dow Jones Newspaper Fund, Inter Am. Press Assn. Trustee Holy Cross Coll., 1982-90; mem. journalism adv. bd. Queens Coll./CUNY, 1989—; juror Pulitzer Prize, 1982, 83. Mem. Am. Soc. Newspaper Editors. Office: Dow Jones Newspaper Fund PO Box 300 Princeton NJ 08543-0300

O'DONNELL, LAWRENCE FRANCIS, JR., legislative staff administrator, author; b. Boston, Nov. 7, 1951; s. Lawrence Frances and Frances Marie (Buckley) O'D.; m. Kathryn Hunter Harrold; 1 child, Elizabeth Buckley Harrold. AB, Harvard U., 1976. Writer self-employed, Boston and N.Y.C., 1976-84, 84-87; sr. advisor Senator Daniel Patrick Moynihan, Washington, 1988-92; chief of staff U.S. Senate Com. on Environment and Pub. Works, Washington, 1992-93, U.S. Senate Com. on Fin., Washington, 1993—. Author: Deadly Force, 1983; assoc. producer: A Case of Deadly Force, 1986. Mem. Writers Guild of Am. Home: 241 Central Park West New York NY 10024 Office: Committe on Finance 205 Dirksen Senate Bldg Washington DC 20510

O'DONNELL, LAWRENCE JAMES, architect; b. Oak Park, Ill., Jan. 16, 1929; s. George Edward and Sarah (Goonrey) O'D.; m. Alice Clare Lyons, Dec. 26, 1953; children: Michael, Maureen, Kerry, Kevin. BS in Architecture, U. Ill., 1951. Registered architect, Ill. Coll. architect Lake Forest (Ill.) Coll., 1963-71; founding prin., chmn. exec. bd. O'Donnell Wicklund Pigozzi and Peterson Architects, Inc., Deerfield, Ill., 1958—, prin. for mktg., 1971—. Bd. dirs. Glenkirk Sch., Northbrook, 1982-85, mem. found. bd., 1985—. Served to cpl. U.S. Army, 1951-53. Mem. AIA, Bus. Mobilized for Loyola U. Clubs: Econ. Club, Irish Fellowship, De Paul U. Pres.'s, Loyola U. Pres.'s. Lodge: Rotary (Lake Forest). Office: O'Donnell Wicklund Pigozzi & Peterson 570 Lake Cook Rd Deerfield IL 60015-4910

O'DONNELL, MICHAEL PAUL, restaurant executive; b. Phila., Mar. 17, 1956; s. John Gerald and Marjorie Ann (Wheeler) O'D.; m. Deane Jonas, Oct. 25, 1978. BA in English, Rollins Coll., 1978. Mgr. Saga Food Service, Winter Park, Fla., 1975-78; banker Kidder Peabody & Co., Phila., 1978-79; area supr. Pizza Hut Inc., Phila., 1979-81; franchise operator Mid-Atlantic region, 1981-82, dir. major franchise projects, 1982-84; pres. Pollo Food Service, Jacksonville, Fla., 1984-86; v.p. TGI Fridays, Dallas, 1986—; mem. franchise adv. bd. Grandy's Inc., Dallas, 1984-86; pres., chief exec. officer Ground Round Rest Co., Boston. Republican. Roman Catholic. Avocations: golf, running. Home: 109 Nichols Rd Cohasset MA 02025-1100 Office: Ground Round Restaurants Inc 35 BRaintree Hill Off Park Braintree MA 02184

O'DONNELL, PIERCE HENRY, lawyer; b. Troy, N.Y., Mar. 5, 1947; s. Harry J. and Mary (Kane) O'D.; m. Connie Casey, June 20, 1970; children: Meghan Maureen, Brendan Casey. BA, Georgetown U., 1969, LLD, 1972; LLM, Yale U., 1975. Bar: D.C. 1973, U.S. Supreme Ct. 1975, Calif. 1978. Assoc. Williams & Connolly, Washington, 1975-78; ptnr. Beardsley, Hufstedler & Kemble, L.A., 1978-81, Hufstedler, Miller, Carlson & Beardsley, L.A., 1981-82, O'Donnell & Gordon, L.A., 1982-88, Kaye, Scholer, Fierman, Hays & Handler, L.A., 1988—; exec. asst. U.S. Sec. Edn., 1979; spl. counsel Commn. Jud. Performance, San Francisco, 1979; chmn. Nat. Media, Inc., 1984-92. Co-author: Fatal Subtraction: The Inside Story of Buchwald v Paramount, 1992; contbr. articles to profl. jours. Chmn. Friends of Calif. Tech. YMCA, 1983-84, Verduga-San Rafael Urban Mountain Park Fund, 1980-84; bd. dirs. Friends of Altedena Libr., 1979-81, Pasadena-Foothill Urban League; bd. dirs. Foothill Family Svc., 1979-85, chmn., 1984-85; bd. dirs. Interfaith Ctr. To Reverse Arms Law, 1984-90, pres., 1987-88. Mem. Am. Law Inst., NAACP, Sierra Club, Univ. Club, Gridiron Club (Georgetown U.). Roman Catholic. Office: Kaye Scholer Fierman Hays & Handler 1999 Ave of Stars Ste 1600 Los Angeles CA 90067-1000

O'DONNELL, RICHARD WALTER, lawyer, accountant, brokerage company executive; b. Newark, Oct. 17, 1945; s. James Richard and Alice (Drep) O'D. BA, Rutgers U., 1967, MBA in Fin., 1969, MBA in Acctg., 1972, JD, 1985. Bar: N.J. 1985; CPA, N.J. Fin. analyst Allied Chem. Corp., Morristown, N.J., 1969-72; sr. audit mgr. Peat, Marwick, Mitchell & Co., Newark, 1972-80; asst. controller Crane Co., N.Y.C., 1980-81, controller, 1981-83; treas. Lehman Bros. Kuhn Loeb, Inc., N.Y.C., 1983-84; sr. v.p. Shearson Lehman Bros., Inc., N.Y.C., 1984-85; mng. dir. Kidder, Peabody & Co., Inc., N.Y.C., 1985—. Mem. AICPA, N.J. Soc. CPAs (chmn. community svcs. com. 1978-80), Nat. Assn. Accts., N.J. Bar Assn., Wayne C. of C.

(treas. 1979-80), Beta Gamma Sigma. Home: 12 Perrin Dr Wayne NJ 07470-4034 Office: Kidder Peabody & Co Inc 10 Hanover Sq New York NY 10005

O'DONNELL, ROBERT MICHAEL, electrical engineering executive; b. Lynn, Mass., Aug. 31, 1941; s. Michael Cornelius and Katherine (Niland) O'D.; m. Margaret Ann Connell, Aug. 20, 1968 (div. 1978); children: Michael, Meghan; m. Janice Elaine Nickerson, Aug. 1, 1983; children: Brian, Andrew. BS in Physics, MIT, 1963; MS in Physics, U. Pa., 1964, PhD in Physics, 1970. Mem. tech. staff MITRE Corp., Beford, Mass., 1969-73, MIT Lincoln Lab., Lexington, Mass., 1973-83; mgr. systems engring. RCA, Moorestown, N.J., 1983-86; v.p., chief scientist ISC Def. and Space Group, Lancaster, Pa., 1986-88; sr. staff MIT Lincoln Lab., Lexington, Mass., 1988—. Contbr. numerous articles to profl. jours. Mem. IEEE (sr., vice-chmn. radar panel 1983-84, chmn. 1985-86). Mem. United Ch. Christ. Avocations: sailing, amateur radio, classical music. Office: MIT Lincoln Lab 244 Wood St Lexington MA 02173-6499

O'DONNELL, ROSIE, comedienne, actress; b. Commack, N.Y., 1962; 1 adopted son: Parker Jaren. Attended. Dickinson Coll., Boston Univ. Appearances include (TV series) Gimme A Break, 1986-87, Stand By Your Man, 1992, Women Aloud, 1992, Stand-up Spotlight, VH-1 (American Comedy award nomination best female performer in a TV special 1994, Cable ACE award nomination best entertainment host 1994); (film) A League of Their Own, 1992, Sleepless in Seattle, 1993 (American Comedy award nomination best supporting female in a motion picture 1994), Another Stakeout, 1993 (American Comedy award nomination best actress in a motion picture 1994), Car 54, Where Are You?, 1994, The Flintstones, 1994, Exit to Eden, 1994; (theatre) Grease (Broadway prodn.), 1994. Office: Internat Creative Mgmt 8942 Wilshire Blvd Beverly Hills CA 90211

O'DONNELL, SCOTT RICHARD, aviation administrator; b. Pitts., Sept. 27, 1950; s. Robert Thomas and Corinne Ann (Phelps) O'D.; m. Patricia Lea Donnelly, Sept. 1, 1978; children: Ronald, Michael, Daniel. BA, Geneva Coll., 1972. Cert. secondary edn. teaching. Tchr. Montour High Sch., McKees Rocks, Pa., 1973-74; project administr. Allegheny County Law Dept., Pitts., 1974-76; adminstrv. asst. Allegheny County Police Dept., Pitts., 1976-77; exec. asst. Allegheny County Commr., Pitts., 1977-80; dir. adminstrn. Allegheny County, Pitts., 1980-88, dir. aviation, 1988-94, dir. property assessment appeals, 1994; v.p. airports Lockheed Air Terminals, 1994—; bd. dirs. Greater Pitts. (Pa.) Conv. and Visitors Bur., 1991—. Chmn. Higher Edn. Bldg. Authority, Pitts., 1983-90; dir. Allegheny West Authority, Pitts., 1988—; mem. Mediate, Moon Twp., Pa., 1991—. Recipient Disting. Alumni award Geneva Coll., Beaver Falls, Pa., 1988, Disting. Svc. award FAA, Jamaica, N.Y., 1992; named Man of Yr. in Law and Govt., Vectors, Pitts., 1992. Mem. Am. Soc. Pub. Adminstrn. (past pres., exec. bd.). Airport Area C. of C. (exec. bd. 1988—). Democrat. Presbyterian. Avocation: golf. Home: 20241 Ruston Rd Woodlawn Hills CA 91364 Office: PO Box 7229 Burbank CA 91510

O'DONNELL, TERRENCE, lawyer; b. N.Y.C., Mar. 3, 1944; s. Emmett and Lorraine (Muller) O'Donnell; m. Margaret Lynne Kidder; children: Stephanie T., Erin K., Victoria L. BS, U.S. Air Force Acad., 1966; JD, Georgetown Law Sch., 1971. Bar: D.C. 1971, U.S. Ct. Appeals (D.C. cir.) 1978, U.S. Ct. Appeals (4th cir.) 1987, U.S. Dist. Ct. Md. 1986, U.S. Ct. Mil. Appeals 1990. Commd. 2d lt. USAF, 1966, advanced through grades to capt.; various positions USAF, Washington and Republic of Vietnam, 1966-72; resigned USAF, 1972; spl. asst. Pres. of U.S., The White House, Washington, 1972-77; appointments sec. Pres. Ford, Washington, 1974-77; assoc. Williams & Connolly, Washington, 1977-82, ptnr., 1982-89; gen. counsel Dept. Def., Washington, 1989-92; ptnr. Williams and Connolly, Washington, 1992—; Presdl. appointee to bd. visitors U.S. Air Force Acad., Colorado Springs, 1982-87, chmn., 1985-86; U.S. corr. and rep. UN Program to Prevent Crime, Washington and N.Y.C., 1977-81; bd. dirs. IGI Inc. Trustee Gerald R. Ford Found., Grand Rapids, Mich., 1987—; mem. Adminstrv. Conf. U.S., 1991-92; mem. claims ct. adv. com., mem. code com. U.S. Ct. Mil. Appeals, 1993—; bd. dirs. Falcon Found., 1988—. Mem. ABA, D.C. Bar Assn., Fed. Bar Assn., Bar of U.S. Ct. Appeals, Bar of U.S. Dist. Ct. of Md., Bar of Mil. Ct. Appeals, Bar Fed. Ct. Claims. Home: 5133 Yuma St NW Washington DC 20016-4336 Office: Williams and Connolly 725 12th St NW Washington DC 20005-3901

O'DONNELL, THOMAS HOWARD, wheelchair manufacturing executive; b. Ft. Wayne, Ind., Aug. 18, 1943; s. Howard W. and Gwendolyn A. (Tillock) O'D.; m. Jo Anne Smith, Aug. 18, 1967 (div. Feb. 1974); m. Marilyn L. Jamroz, Dec. 21, 1974; adopted children: Steven, Sandra. BA, U. Mich., 1965, MBA, 1967. With sales, mktg., mgmt., corp. planning IBM, Detroit, Armonk, N.Y., White Plains, N.Y., 1967-79; dir. planning systems communications div. IBM, White Plains, 1979-81; product mgr. industry systems systems communications div. IBM, Raleigh, N.C., 1981-82; v.p product mgmt. entry systems div. IBM, Boca Raton, Fla., 1982-84; vice chmn., chief exec. officer Connecting Point of Am. Inc., Denver, 1984-86; chief operating officer Gen. Computer Co., Cambridge, Mass., 1986; exec. v.p. ops. Sunrise Med. Inc., Torrance, Calif., 1987-88; pres. Sunrise Med./Quickie Designs, Fresno, Calif., 1988—; bd. dirs. Fresno Bus. Coun., 1994—, The WOW Found., 1992—. Metro circle mem. Fresno Met. Mus., 1989—. Mem. Fresno C. of C. (bd. dirs.). Avocations: skiing, travel, reading, fishing. Home: 2557 Lake Van Ness Cir Fresno CA 93711 Office: Quickie Designs Inc 2842 N Business Park Ave Fresno CA 93727-1328

O'DONNELL, THOMAS LAWRENCE PATRICK, lawyer; b. Taunton, Mass., Aug. 12, 1926; s. Patrick Francis and Ellen Balfe (Brady) O'D.; m. Carol Hodgdon, Feb. 16, 1952; children—Ellen, Thomas, Janet Gael, Christopher Hodgdon. A.B. magna cum laude, Harvard U., 1947, LL.B., 1949. Bar: Mass. 1950. Assoc. Ropes & Gray, Boston, 1949-52, 54-61, ptnr., 1962—, chmn., 1984-90; dir. Rath & Strong, Inc. Trustee, Trustees of Reservations, 1970—, chmn. bd., 1975-76; bd. dirs. Mass. Land Conservation Trust, 1975—, chmn. bd., 1986—; bd. dirs. Mass. Taxpayers Found., 1972—, chmn. bd., 1977-79, 93-95, mem. exec. com., 1976—; bd. dirs. Boston Mcpl. Rsch. Bur., 1965—, chmn. bd., 1967-72; mem. pub. pension task force Mass. Bus. Roundtable, 1983-86; bd. dirs., sec. Jobs for Mass., Inc., 1981-83; moderator Town of Hingham, 1967—; del. Rep. Nat. Conv., 1972, all Rep. State convs., 1960-94; dir. Rep. Club of Mass., 1974—; overseer Harvard U., 1986-92; bd. dirs. United Way Mass. Bay, 1987—, mem. exec. com. 1993—. Lt. USNR, 1944-45, 52-54. Recipient Cushing award Labor Guild of Archdiocese Boston, 1973; Pub. Servant award Sons of Italy, Hingham, 1978; mem. Knights of Malta, 1983—. Fellow Am. Bar Found.; mem. ABA, Mass. Bar Assn., Boston Bar Assn., Am. Arbitration Assn., New England Legal Found. (Mass. adv. coun. 1980—), Indsl. Rels. Rsch. Assn. (pres. Boston chpt. 1980), Harvard Alumni Assn. (bd. dirs. 1978-81; 1st marshal class of 1947). Roman Catholic. Clubs: Harvard of Boston (bd. govs. 1985-91), Union of Boston; Hingham Yacht, Comml. Home: 7 South Ln Hingham MA 02043-2446 Office: Ropes & Gray 1 International Pl Boston MA 02110-2624

O'DONNELL, THOMAS MICHAEL, brokerage firm executive; b. Cleve., Apr. 9, 1936; s. John Michael and Mary L. (Hayes) O'D.; m. Nancy A. Dugan, Feb. 4, 1961; children—Christopher, Colleen, Julie. BBA, U. Notre Dame, 1959; MBA, U. Pa., 1960. Cert. Chartered Fin. Analyst. Fin. analyst Saunders Stiver & Co., Cleve., 1960-65; rsch. dir. McDonald & Co., Cleve., 1965-66, exec. v.p., 1967-83, gen. ptnr., 1968-83; pres. McDonald & Co. Investments, Inc./McDonald & Co. Securities, Cleve. 1984-88; chmn., chief exec. officer McDonald & Co. Securities, Cleve., 1988—; bd. dirs. Seaway Food Town; mem. regional firms adv. com. N.Y. Stock Exch., 1986-92, chmn., 1991-92; dir. C.I.D. Venture Funds. Author: The Why and How of Mergers, 1968. Trustee Cath. Charities, Cleve.; bd. dirs. Greater Cleve. Growth Assn., Inroads Northeast Ohio, PlayHouse Square Found.; adv. bd. Salvation Army; bd. regents St. Ignatius High Sch., Cleve.; steering com. Leadership Cleve. Mem. Nat. Soc. Security Analysts (cert.), Securities Industry Assn. (dir. 1988-94, chmn. 1993). Union Club, Westwood Country Club, 50 Club Cleve., Pepper Pike Club, Double Eagle Club. Roman Catholic. Avocation: golf. Home: 1325 Timber Lea Ct Cleveland OH 44145-2648 Office: McDonald & Co Securities Inc 800 Superior Ave Ste 2100 Cleveland OH 44114

O'DONNELL, WILLIAM DAVID, construction firm executive; b. Brockton, Mass., Aug. 21, 1926; s. John Frank and Agnes Teresa (Flanagan) O'D.; m. Dixie Lou Anderson, Jan. 31, 1951; children—Craig Patrick, Ginger Lynn. BS, U. N.Mex., 1953. Registered profl. engr., Ill., 1958. Engr. State of Ill., 1953-59; with Gregory-Anderson Co., Rockford, Ill., 1959—, gen. mgr., 1960-61, sec., 1961-81, pres., 1981—; bd. dirs. Growth Enterprise, Davis Meml. Park, BankOne, Rockford. Dir. St. Anthony Med. Ctr., Youth Svcs. Network; bd. dirs. Rockford YMCA, Rockford. Served with USN, 1943-47. Recipient Friend of the Boy award Optimist Club, 1966, Excalibur award for community service Rockford Register Star, 1971; named Titan of Yr., Boylan High Sch., 1974. Fellow ASCE, NSPE, Soc. Am. Mil. Engrs.; mem. No. Ill. Bldg. Contractors, Aircraft Owners and Pilots Assn., Balloon Fedn. Am., World Future Soc., Sigma Tau, Chi Epsilon, Tau Beta Pi. Clubs: Forest Hills Country (Rockford), Metropolitan Club (Chgo.); Adventurers (Chgo.). Lodges: Rotary (Service Above Self award 1972; v.p. Rockford chpt. 1983, pres. 1984). Home: 2004 Bradley Rd Rockford IL 61107-1258 Office: Gregory Anderson Co 2525 Huffman Blvd Rockford IL 61103-3900

O'DONNELL, WILLIAM HUGH, English educator; b. San Diego, June 17, 1940; s. William Henry and Ella (McMullen) O'D.; m. Gloria Roach, June 5, 1967; children: Kerry Susan, Clare Louise. BA, U. Wash., 1962; MA, Princeton U., 1969, PhD, 1971. Asst., then assoc. prof. English Pa. State U., University Park, 1971-86; prof. English, chmn. dept. U. Memphis, 1986-93, prof., 1986—. Author: Guide to Prose Fiction of Yeats, 1984, Poetry of W.B. Yeats, 1986; editor: Speckled Bird, 1977, Prefaces and Introductions by W.B. Yeats, 1989, Later Essays of W.B. Yeats, 1994. Served with USN, 1962-67. NEH grantee, 1973-74; fellow Am. Council of Learned Societies, 1977-78. Mem. MLA, Am. Conf. Irish Studies, Internat. Assn. Study Anglo-Irish Lit., South Atlantic MLA. Office: U Memphis English Dept Memphis TN 38152

O'DONNELL, WILLIAM JAMES, engineering executive; b. Pitts., June 19, 1935; s. William James and Elizabeth (Rau) O'D.; m. Joanne Mary Kusen, Jan. 31, 1959; children—Suzanne, Janice, William, Thomas, Kerry, Amy. B.S.M.E., Carnegie Inst. Tech., 1957; M.S.M.E., U. Pitts., 1959, Ph.D., 1962. Jr. engr. Westinghouse Research Lab., 1957-58, asso. engr., 1958; with Westinghouse Bettis Atomic Power Lab., West Mifflin, Pa., 1961-70, adv. engr., 1966-70; pres., chmn. bd. O'Donnell & Assos., Inc., Pitts. 1970—. Contbr. numerous articles on engring. and mechanics to profl. jours.; holder patents on processes and devices. Served with C.E. AUS, 1963-64. Recipient Machinery's Achievement award as outstanding mech. designer, 1957, Pi Tau Sigma Gold medal for achievements in engring., 1967. Fellow ASME (NAt. award for outstanding contbn. to engring. profession 1973, Internat. award for best publ. in pressure vessels and piping 1988, Engr. of Yr. 1988, Pressure Vessell and Piping medal 1994); mem. NSPE, AAAS, ASTM, Soc. Exptl. Mechanics, ASM Internat., Am. Nuclear Soc., Minerals, Metals & Materials Soc., Sigma Xi. Home: 3611 Maplevue Dr Bethel Park PA 15102-1423 Office: O'Donnell Consulting Engrs 3611 Maplevue Dr Bethel Park PA 15102

O'DONNELL, WILSON EDWARD, museum director; b. Sharon, Pa., Feb. 17, 1952; s. Charles John and Charlotte Jane (Magargee) O'D.; m. Carol Ann Brodeen, July 25, 1987. BA in Anthropology, Pa. State U., 1974; MA in History Mus. Studies, SUNY, Oneonta, 1982. Intern William Penn Meml. Mus., Harrisburg, Pa., 1975, Hist. Soc. York County, York, Pa., 1975; cons. Perry County Hist. Soc., Newport, Pa., 1978-79; curator of collections Cumberland County Hist. Soc., Carlisle, Pa., 1976-80; dir. Monmouth County Hist. Assn., Freehold, N.J., 1982-86; chief curator and mus. dir. N.J. Hist. Soc., Newark, 1986-88, dir., 1988-92; exec. dir. Mus. History and Industry, Seattle, 1993—; adj. faculty Mus. Am. Folk Art, N.Y.C., 1987. Author: (exhibit catalogues) It's in the Cards, 1976, Thus United Free: New Jersey in the Age of the Constitution, 1976. Mem. Monmouth County Heritage Com., Freehold, N.J., 1982-87; active Mountains to Sound, Greenway Trust. Mem. Am. Assn. Mus., Am. Assn. for State and Local History, Rotary (Puget Sound chpt.), Phi Beta Kappa (bd. trustees Puget Sound chpt. 1994-95). Avocations: decorative arts (particularly furniture), running, mandolin, fantasy, science fiction. Office: Mus of History & Industry 2700 24th Ave E Seattle WA 98112

O'DONOHUE, WALTER JOHN, JR., medical educator; b. Washington, Sept. 23, 1934; s. Walter John and Mavis Leota (Terry) O'D.; m. Cynthia Ann Halmintoller, Aug. 10, 1957 (div. 1978); 1 child, Diane Louise; m. Maria Theresa Sauer, Nov. 27, 1978; children: Walter John III, Mary Theresa. BA, Va. Mil. Inst., 1957; MD, Med. Coll. Va., 1961. Diplomate Am. Bd. Internal Medicine, Am. Bd. Pulmonary Medicine. Resident internal medicine Med. Coll. Va., Richmond, 1961-63, 65-66, chief med. resident, 1966-67, cardio-pulmonary fellow, 1967-69, asst. prof. medicine, 1968-73, assoc. prof., 1973-77; prof. Creighton U., Omaha, Nebr., 1977—, chief pulmonary medicine div., 1977—, chmn. dept. medicine, 1985—. Editor: Current Advances in Respiratory Care, 1984, Long-term Oxygen Therapy: Scientific Basis and Clinical Application, 1995; contbr. over 100 articles to med. jours., chpts. to books. Served to capt. M.C., U.S. Army, 1963-65. Fellow ACP, Am. Coll. Chest PHysicians (regent 1986-88, gov. for Nebr. 1982-88); mem. AMA (CPT adv. com. 1992—), Am. Lung Assn. (bd. dirs 1981-87), Nebr. Lung Assn. (bd. dirs., pres. 1979-81), Am. Assn. Respiratory Care (chmn. bd. med. advisors 1986-87), Assn. Profs. Medicine, Nat. Assn. Med. Dirs. on Respiratory Care (pres. 1995-97). Republican. Roman Catholic. Avocations: hunting, fishing. Home: 12773 Izard St Omaha NE 68154-1243 Office: Creighton U Sch Medicine 601 N 30th St Omaha NE 68131-2100

O'DONOVAN, LEO JEREMIAH, university president, theologian, priest; b. N.Y.C., Apr. 24, 1934; s. Leo J. Jr. O'D. AB, Georgetown U., 1956; Licentiate in Philosophy, Fordham U., 1961; STB, Woodstock Coll., 1966, Licentiate in Sacred Theology, 1967; ThD, U. Münster, Fed. Republic Germany, 1971. Joined S.J., 1957, ordained priest Roman Cath. Ch., 1966. Instr. philosophy Loyola Coll., Balt., 1961-63; asst. prof. Woodstock (Md.) Coll., 1971-74; assoc. prof. Weston Sch. Theology, Cambridge, Mass., 1974-81, prof., 1981-89; pres. Georgetown U., Washington, 1989—; provincial asst. formation Md. Province S.J., Balt., 1985-88; cons. Nat. Conf. Cath. Bishops, Washington, 1986-89; vis. fellow Woodstock Theol. Ctr.; bd. dirs. The Riggs Nat. Bank. Co-editor: The Society of Jesus and Higher Education in America, 1965; (author preface) Faithful Witness: Foundations of Theology for Today's Church, 1989; assoc. editor Jour. Am. Acad. Religion, 1985-89; mem. adv. bd. America mag., 1985-89; contbr. numerous articles to America, Washington Post, Theol. Studies, Communio, Cross Currents. Bd. dirs. U. Detroit Mercy, 1986-94; vice chair Consortium of Univs. of Washington Met. Area, 1993-94, chair, 1994—, trustee, 1989—; mem. campaign for communities com. Local Initiatives Support Corp., 1993—; mem. exec. com. Fed. City Coun., 1993-95; bd. dirs. Nat. Assn. Ind. Colls. and Univs., 1991-94, Consortium on Financing Higher Edn., 1990—; active Bus.-Higher Edn. Forum, 1989—. Nat. Coun. on Arts, 1994—. Fulbright scholar Fulbright Found., U. Lyon, France, 1956-57; Danforth fellow Danforth Found., 1956-71; Assn. Theol. Schs. grantee on teaching, 1978-79. Fellow Soc. for Values in Higher Edn.; mem. Boston Theol. Soc., University Club. Office: Georgetown U Office of President 37th O St NW Washington DC 20057*

O'DONOVAN, THOMAS RAPHAEL, professional association administrator; b. Detroit, Mar. 25, 1931; s. Patrick Gregory and Mary Laverne (Mitchell) O'D.; m. Gayle Marie O'Connell, Aug. 24, 1957; children: Patrick Gabriel, Lynda Mary, Julia Mary. BS in Mgmt., U. Detroit, 1954, MS, 1956; PhD in Mgmt., Corp. Fin., Mktg., Econs., Mich. State U., 1961. Tchr. mgmt. Mich. State U., East Lansing, U. Detroit, U. So. Calif., Los Angeles; adminstr., chief operating officer Mount Carmel Mercy Hosp. and Med. Ctr., Detroit, 1964-79; pres., chief exec. officer Am. Acad. Med. Adminstrs., Southfield, Mich., 1980—; adj. prof. hosp. adminstrn. Ohio State U., Columbus, U. Detroit, 1980-82; pres. Met. N.E. Detroit Hops. Inc., 1973-75; chmn. professions unit United Found. Drive, Detroit, 1976, com. emergency dept. coordination Regional Task Force on Emergency Health Care, Detroit, 1972-80, credentials com. Greater Detroit Area Hosp. Council, 1973-76, adminstrv. conf. com. Quadrangle, 1969-79; mem. ambulatory surgery panel Federal Health Services Criteria Project Dept. Health Services U. Wash., Seattle, 1975, fin. com. Eastern Mich. Regional Bd. Sisters of Mercy Health Corp., 1976-78, tech. adv. panel relative to ambulatory surgery criteria and standards Comprehensive Health Planning Council of Southeastern Mich.,

1979; bd. trustees Mich. Conf. Cath. Health Care Facilities, 1979; speaker in field. Author: Ambulatory Surgical Centers: Development and Management, 1976, Executive Administration in Hospitals, 1978; co-author: Managing Health Care Organizations, 1977, Management By Objectives for Hospitals, 1982; editor Jour. Ambulatory Care Mgmt., Rockville, Md., 1979-82; mem. editorial bd. Same-Day Surgery Newsletter, Atlanta, 1979—; contbr. chpts. to books, numerous articles to profl. jours. Recipient William Newcomer award Am. Acad. Med. Adminstrs., 1971, Hon. Mention award Hosp. Adminstrn. mag., 1975; named one of Outstanding Young Men Am., 1967. Fellow Am. Acad. Med. Adminstrs. (nat. chmn. edn. council, 1972-76), Am. Coll. Hosp. Adminstrs., Royal Soc. Health; mem. Met. N.W. Detroit Hosps. Inc. (pres. 1973-75), Am. Hosp. Assn., Cath. Hosp. Assn., Am. Coll. Hosp. Adminstrs. (book of yr. com. 1971-73, chmn. 1973, mem. editorial bd. jours. 1973-82, mem. com. self assessment 1980-82), Mich. Hosp. Assn. (chmn. com. edn. 1977-80, chmn. com. in-hosp. edn. and tng. 1973-76, mem. health manpower com. 1975-77, mem. com. on shared services 1978-79, alt. del. to Am. Hosp. Assn. 1976-79, chmn. ednl. services adv. com. 1978-79), Alpha Kappa Psi. Republican. Roman Catholic. Club: Detroit Golf. Home: 19541 Wilshire Birmingham MI 48009 Office: Am Acad Med Adminstrs 30555 Southfield Rd Southfield MI 48076-1221

O'DOR, RON, physiologist, marine biology educator; b. Kansas City, Mo., Sept. 20, 1944; s. Claude Marvin O'Dor and Opal LaMoyne (Sears) Mathes; m. Janet Ruth Spiller, Dec. 30, 1967; children: Matthew Arnold, Stephen Roderick. AA, El Camino Coll., 1965; AB, U. Calif., Berkeley, 1967; PhD, U. B.C., 1971. From asst. prof. to prof. Dalhousie U., Halifax, N.S., 1973—; dir. Aquatron Lab., Halifax, 1986-93; summer scientist Laboratoire Arago, Banyuls-sur-Mer, France, 1979-85; vis. scientist Pacific Biol. Sta., Nanaimo, B.C., 1980, U. Papua New Guinea, Motupore Island, 1989-91, Port Elizabeth Mus. South Africa, 1994; vis. prof. U. B.C., Vancouver, 1986-87; sessional prof. Bamfield, B.C. MArine Sta., 1987; cons. UN, Rome, 1987—; adv. space stas. Can. Space Agy., Ottawa, 1992—; mgmt. com. Ocean Prodn. Enhancement Network, Halifax, 1993-95. Author; editor: Cephalopod Fishery Biology, 1993, Physiology of Cephalopod Molluscs, 1995; contbg. author Cephalopod Life Cycles, Vol. I, 1983, Vol. II, 1987; contbr. articles, revs. to profl. jours. Scholar Meml. Rsch. Coun. Can., 1968; fellow MRC, Cambridge U., Eng., 1971-73, Stazione Zoologica, Naples, Italy, 1971-73; recipient Hon. Mention Rolex Awards Enterprise, 1987. Mem. Can. Soc. Zoologists (councillor 1989-92), Can. Fedn. Biological Socs.,Am. Soc. Zoologists, Am. Soc. Gravitational and Space Biology, Cephalopod Internat. Adv. coun. (councillor, pres. 1988-91), Phi Beta Kappa. Achievements include co-development of acoustic pressure transducer/transmitters and radio-linked tracking systems for monitoring cephalopod bioenergetics in nature, co-organization of projects in the Azores, South Africa, and Papua New Guinea to monitor squid and nautilus, first international cephalopod research conference in Japan, investigation for Aquatic Research Facility for Space Shuttle. Home: 1181 South Park St, Halifax, NS Canada B3H 2W9 Office: Dalhousie University, Biology Dept, Halifax, NS Canada B3H 4J1

O'DORISIO, THOMAS MICHAEL, internal medicine educator, researcher; b. Denver, May 29, 1943; s. Angelo Benedict and Olga Ester (Zarlengo) O'D.; m. M. Sue Wedemeyer; children: Joel, Rachelle, Nathan. BS, Regis Coll., 1965; MS in Anatomy, Creighton U., 1967, MD, 1971. Diplomate Am. Bd. Internal Medicine, Nat. Bd. Med. Examiners. Intern Creighton U., Omaha, 1971-72; resident Ohio State U., Columbus, 1972-74, fellow, 1974-77, asst. prof., 1977-79, assoc. prof., 1979-84, asst. program dir. clin. research ctr., 1984—, prof. medicine, 1984—, prof. physiology, 1985—, prof. pathology, 1993—, prof. human nutrition, 1993—, dir. div. endocrinology, diabetes and metabolism, 1989—; chmn. human subjects rev. bd. Ohio State U., 1987-89. Recipient Prof. of Yr. award Ohio State U. Class of 1983, teaching awards from sr. class of 1981, 82, 84, 85, 89, 90; grantee NIH, 1987—, Nat. Cancer Inst., 1974-77, 91, 92. Mem. ACP, Am. Fedn. Clin. Rsch., Am. Gastroenterology Assn., Ctrl. Soc. Clin. Rsch., Endocrinology Soc., Am. Assn. Clin. Endocrinology. Democrat. Roman Catholic. Club: St. Thomas Moore (Newman Ctr.). Avocation: golf, skiing. Office: Ohio State U Hosp 410 W 10th Ave Columbus OH 43210-1228

ODORIZZI, MICHELE L., lawyer; b. Chgo., July 12, 1952. BA, Northwestern U., 1973; JD cum laude, U. Chgo., 1976. Bar: Ill. 1976, U.S. Ct. Appeals (7th cir.) 1976, U.S. Dist. Ct. (no. dist.) Ill. 1977, U.S. Supreme Ct. 1980, U.S. Ct. Appeals (4th, 9th, 10th cirs.). Ptnr. Mayer, Brown & Platt, Chgo. Office: Mayer Brown & Platt 190 S La Salle St Chicago IL 60603

O'DOWD, DONALD DAVY, retired university administrator; b. Manchester, N.H., Jan. 23, 1927; s. Hugh Davy and Laura (Morin) O'D.; m. Janet Louise Fithian, Aug. 23, 1953; children: Daniel D., Diane K., James E., John M. BA summa cum laude, Dartmouth Coll., 1951; postgrad. (Fulbright fellow), U. Edinburgh, Scotland, 1951-52; MA, Harvard U., 1955, PhD, 1957. Instr., asst. prof. psychology, dean freshmen Wesleyan U., Middletown, Conn., 1955-60; assoc. prof., prof. of psychology, dean Univ. Oakland Univ., Rochester, Mich., 1960-65, provost, 1965-70; pres. Oakland U., Rochester, Mich., 1970-80; exec. vice chancellor SUNY, Albany, 1980-84; pres. U. of Alaska Statewide System, 1984-90. Chmn. U.S. Arctic Rsch. Commn.; sr. cons. Assn. Governing Bds. of Univs. and Colls. Carnegie Corp. fellow, 1965-66. Mem. Am. Psychol. Assn., AAAS, Phi Beta Kappa, Sigma Xi. Home and Office: 1550 La Vista Del Oceano Santa Barbara CA 93109-1739

O'DRISCOLL, PERRY R., archbishop. Archbishop of Ontario The Anglican Ch. Can. Office: The Anglican Ch of Can, 4-220 Dundas St, London, ON Canada N6A 1H3

ODRON, EDWARD ANDREW, supermarket executive; b. Chgo., Mar. 28, 1938; s. Edward John and Emily Mary (Rakicky) O.; m. Mary Jean Howe; children: Edward Russell, Scott Andrew. BS, Drake U., 1960. Produce buyer Atlantic and Pacific Tea Co., Chgo., 1960-65, Lucky Stores, Milan, Ill., 1965-71; produce buyer, merchandiser Lucky Stores, Annandale, Va., 1971-74, grocery buyer, merchandiser, 1974-76, dist. mgr., 1976-77; v.p., produce specialist Lucky Stores, Milan, 1977-85; corp. v.p., produce specialist Lucky Stores, Dublin, Calif., 1985-86; v.p. produce mktg. Lucky Stores, San Leandro, Calif., 1986—; bd. dirs. 5-a-Day Produce for Better Health. Mem. United Fresh and Vegetable Assn. (retail merchandising bd. 1985-87, chmn. retail merchandising bd. 1986-87), Produce Mktg. Assn. (bd. dirs. 1989-92). Avocation: showing purebred dogs. Home: 10367 Capewood Ln Stockton CA 95212-9447 Office: Lucky Stores Inc 1701 Marina Blvd San Leandro CA 94577-4230

OEHLER, RICHARD WILLIAM, lawyer; b. N.Y.C., Nov. 24, 1950; s. John Montgomery and Florence Mae (Jahn) O.; m. Linda Tyson. BA, Dartmouth Coll., 1972; JD, Harvard U., 1976. Bar: Calif. 1976, Wash. 1987, D.C. 1988, U.S. Dist. Ct. (no. dist.) Calif. 1976, U.S. Dist. Ct. Wash. 1987, U.S. Claims Ct. 1979, U.S. Ct. Appeals (fed. cir.) 1982, U.S. Ct. Appeals (9th cir.) 1976. Assoc. Pillsbury, Madison & Sutro, San Francisco, 1976-78; trial atty. U.S. Dept. Justice, Washington, 1978-87; of counsel Perkins Coie, Seattle, 1987-90, ptnr., 1990—. Mem. ABA, Nat. Contract Mgmt. Assn. (Spl. Achievement award 1990-92), Wash. State Bar Assn. Office: Perkins Coie 1201 Third Ave 40th Fl Seattle WA 98101

OEHLERT, WILLIAM HERBERT, JR., cardiologist, administrator, educator; b. Murphysboro, Ill., Sept. 11, 1942; s. William Herbert Sr. and Geneva Mae (Roberts) O.; m. L. Keith Brown, Mar. 14, 1976; children: Emily Jane, Amanda Elizabeth. BA, So. Ill. U., 1967; MD, Washington U., St. Louis, 1967. Diplomate Nat. Bd. Med. Examiners, Am. Bd. Internal Medicine, Am. Bd. Cardiovascular Disease, North Am. Soc. Pacing and Electrophysiology. Intern Union Meml. Hosp., Balt., 1967-68, resident, 1968-69; resident U. Iowa, Iowa City, 1969-70, cardiology fellow, 1970-72; asst. prof. medicine, dir. coronary care units U. Okla. Health Sci. Ctr., Oklahoma City, 1972-74, asst. clin. prof. medicine, 1974-82, assoc. clin. prof. medicine, 1982-88, clin. prof. medicine, 1988—; chmn. dept. cardiology Baptist Med. Ctr., 1992—; pvt. practice Oklahoma City, 1993—; med. dir. cardiovascular svcs. Bapt. Med. Ctr., 1993—; pres. Cardiovascular Clinic, Oklahoma City, 1987-91, chmn. exec. com., 1987-91; pres. med. dir. Cardiovascular Imaging Svcs. Corp., Oklahoma City, 1987-92; v.p. Plaza Med. Group, 1992-93; CEO W.H. Oehlert, MD, P.C., 1993—. Author: Arrhythmias, 1973, Cardiovascular Drugs, 1976; contbr. articles to profl. jours.

Fellow Am. Heart Assn. (nat. program com. 1979-82, pres. Okla. affiliate 1985-86, bd. dirs. 1974-88, ACLS nat. affiliate faculty 1987-90), Am. Coll. Cardiology; mem. AMA, ACP, Nat. Assn. Residents and Interns, Am. Soc. Internal Medicine, Am. Coll. Physician Execs., Okla. County Med. Assn. (chmn. quality of care com. 1990-91), Okla. State Med. Assn., Okla. City Clin. Soc., Okla. Cardiac Soc. (pres. 1978-79), Osler Soc., Soc. Nuclear Medicine, Wilderness Med. Soc., Stewart Wolf Soc., Phi Eta Sigma, Phi Kappa Phi. Home and Office: 3017 Rock Ridge Pl Oklahoma City OK 73120-5713

OEHME, FREDERICK WOLFGANG, medical researcher and educator; b. Leipzig, Germany, Oct. 14, 1933; came to U.S., 1934; s. Friedrich Oswald and Frieda Betha (Wohlgamuth) O.; m. Nancy Beth MacAdam, Aug. 6, 1960 (div. June 1981); children: Stephen Frederick, Susan Lynn, Deborah Ann, Heidi Beth; m. Pamela Sheryl Ford, Oct. 2, 1981; 1 child, April Virginia. BS in Biol. Sci., Cornell U., 1957, DVM, 1958; MS in Toxicology and Medicine, Kans. State U., 1962; DMV in Pathology, Justus Liebig U., Giessen, Germany, 1964; PhD in Toxicology, U. Mo., 1969. Diplomate Am. Bd. Toxicology, Am. Bd. Vet. Toxicology, Acad. Toxicological Scis. Resident intern, Large Animal and Ambulatory Clinic Cornell U., 1957-58; gen. practice vet. medicine, 1958-59; from asst. to assoc. prof. medicine Coll. Vet. Medicine Kans. State U., 1959-66, 69-73, dir. comparative toxicology labs., 1969—, prof. toxicology, medicine and physiology Coll. Vet. Medicine, 1974—; postdoctoral research fellow in toxicology, NIH U. Mo., 1966-69; cons. FDA, Washington, Ctr. for Vet. Medicine, Rockville, Md., Animal Care com. U. Kans., Lawrence, 1969-76, Syntex Corp., Palo Alto, Calif., 1976-77; mem. sci. adv. panel on PBB Gov.'s Office, State of Mich., 1976-77, Coun. for Agrl. Sci. and Tech. Task Force on Toxicity, Toxicology and Environ. Hazard, 1976-83; cons., mem. adv. group on pesticides EPA, Cin., 1977—; expert state and fed. witness; advisor WHO, Geneva; presenter more than 550 papers to profl. meetings; numerous other activities. Author over 650 books and articles on toxicoloty and vet. medicine; editor, pub. Vet. Toxicology, 1970-73, Vet. and Human Toxicology, 1977—; assoc. editor Toxicology Letters, mem. editorial bd. Am. Jour. Vet. Rsch., 1975-83, Toxicology, 1979-85, Clin. Toxicology, Jour. de Todicologie Medicale, Toxicology and Indls. Health, Poisindex, Jour. Analytical Toxicology, Companion Animal Practice; reviewer Toxicology and Applied Pharmacology, Jour. Agrl. and Food Chemistry, Spectroscopy. numerous others. Mem. council Luth. Ch. Am., sr. choir, numerous coms., adv. council Cub Scouts Am., Eagle Scouts, mgr., coach Little League Baseball; council rep., treas. area council, various coms. PTA; mem. Manhattan Civic Theatre; bd. trustees Manhattan Marlin Swim Team; dir. meet Little Apple Invitational Swim Meet, 1984. Recipient Disting. Grad. Faculty award Kans. State U., 1977-79, Dir.'s Letter of Commendation, FDA, 1983, Kenneth P. DuBois award Midwest Soc., Toxicology, 1991, Kenneth F. Lange Rsch. award Am. Acad. Clin. Toxicology, 1993, John Doull award Ctrl. States Soc. Toxicology, 1994, Azabu U. medallion, 1994, others; Morris Animal Found. Project fellow, 1967-69. Fellow Am. Acad. Clin. Toxicology (charter, past pres., numerous coms.), Am. Acad. Vet. and Comparative Toxicology (past sec.-treas., numerous coms.); mem. Soc. Toxicology (past pres., numerous coms.), World Fedn. Clin. Toxicology Ctrs. and Poison Control Ctrs. (past pres.), Soc. Toxicologic Pathologists, N.Y. Acad. Scis., Am. Vet. Med. Assn. (com. on environmentology 1971-73, adv. council on biol. and therapeutic agts. 1971-74, various others), Nat. Ctr. Toxicological Rsch. (vet. toxicology rep. sci. adv. bd.), Nat. Rsch. Coun. (subcom. on organic contaminants in drinking water, safe drinking water com., adv. ctr. on toxicology assembly life scis. 1976-77, panel on toxicology marine bd., assembly of engring. 1976-79, com. on vet. med. scis. assembly life scis. 1976-78), Nat. Ctr. for Toxicological Rsch. (grad. edn. subcom., sci. adv. bd. 1974-77), Cornell U. Athletic Assn, Omega Tau Sigma, Phi Zeta, Sigma Xi, numerous others. Republican. Clubs: Cornell U. Crew; Manhattan Square Dance. Avocations: hist. readings, sci. writings, nature tours and walks, travel. Home: 148 S Dartmouth Dr Manhattan KS 66502 Office: Comparative Toxicology Labs Kans State U Manhattan KS 66506

OEHME, REINHARD, physicist, educator; b. Wiesbaden, Germany, Jan. 26, 1928; came to U.S., 1956; s. Reinhold and Katharina (Kraus) O.; m. Mafalda Pisani, Nov. 5, 1952. Dr. rer. nat., U. Goettingen, Germany, 1951; Diplom Physiker, U. Frankfurt am Main, Germany, 1948. Asst. Max Planck Inst. Physics, Goettingen, 1949-53; research asso. Fermi Inst. Nuclear Studies, U. Chgo., 1954-56; mem. faculty dept. physics and Fermi Inst., 1958—, prof. physics, 1964—; mem. Inst. Advanced Studies, Princeton, 1956-58; vis. prof. Inst. de Física Teórica, São Paulo, Brazil, 1952-53, U. Md., 1957, U. Vienna, Austria, 1961, Imperial Coll., London, Eng., 1963-64, U. Karlsruhe, Fed. Republic Germany, 1974, 75, 77, U. Tokyo, 1976, 88; vis. scientist Internat. Centre Theoretical Physics, Miramare-Trieste, Italy, Brookhaven Nat. Lab., Lawrence Radiation Lab., U. Calif., Berkeley, CERN, Geneva, Switzerland, Max Planck Inst., Munich, Fed. Republic Germany, Rsch. Inst. for Fundamental Physics, Kyoto (Japan) U. Author articles in field, chpts. in books. Guggenheim fellow, 1963-64; recipient Humboldt award, 1974, Japan Soc. for Promotion of Sci. Fellowship awards, 1976, 88. Fellow Am. Phys. Soc. Office: Univ of Chicago Enrico Fermi Inst 5640 S Ellis Ave Chicago IL 60637-1433

OEHME, WOLFGANG WALTER, landscape architect; b. Chemnitz, Germany, May 18, 1930; came to the U.S., 1957; s. Walter Gustav and Elisabeth Elsa (Neumann) O.; 1 child, Roland. Degree in horticulture, Bitterfeld Trade Sch., 1950; degree in landscape architecture, U. Berlin, 1954. Exch. student Waterer & Sons Nurseries, Bagshot, United Kingdom, 1954-56; landscape architect Baltimore County Planning, Towson, Md., 1958-65, The Rouse Co., Columbia, Md., 1965-66; asst. prof. U. Pa., Phila., 1962-64, U. Ga., Athens, 1965; pvt. practice Balt., 1965-74; CEO Oehme, Van Sweden and Assocs., Inc., Washington, 1974—. Co-author: Bold Romantic Gardens, 1990, Gardening with Water, 1995. Fellow Am. Soc. Landscape Architects; mem. Perennial Plant Assn. (Disting. Svc. 1988), Garden Writers Assn. (Quill and Trowel award 1991). Home: 511 A W Joppa Rd Baltimore MD 21204 Office: 800 G St SE Washington DC 20003

OEHMLER, GEORGE COURTLAND, corporate executive; b. Pitts., May 6, 1926; s. Rudolph Christian and Virgia Sylvia (Stark) O.; B.S. in Indsl. Engring, Pa. State U., 1950; m. Martha Jane Swagler, July 3, 1954; children—Wendy Lynn, Christy Ann, Geoffrey Colin. Indsl. engr. Allegheny Ludlum Steel Corp., Pitts., 1953-54, salesman, 1954-60, mgr. export sales, 1960-67, mgr. flat rolled products, 1967-68, asst. to chmn., 1968-73, v.p. internat., 1973-75, v.p. internat. Allegheny Internat., Pitts., 1975-81, v.p. public and internat. affairs, 1981-86; pres., chief operating officer World Affairs Council, Pitts., 1987—; dir. Mathews Internat. Corp., 1982—; Mem. exec. bd. Pa. State U. Alumni Council, 1976-82; bd. dirs. United Way Allegheny County, 1982-84, Pitts. Ballet, 1982-89, Pitts. Pub. Theater, 1986-95, Mendelssohn Choir of Pitts., 1987—. With U.S. Army, 1944-46, 51-52. Mem. Am. Iron and Steel Inst., Assn. Iron and Steel Engrs., Machinery and Allied Products Inst. (internat. and pub. affairs councils), World Affairs Council Pitts. (chmn. 1980-82, dir.), Pitts. Council for Internat. Visitors (dir. 1975-87, pres. 1976-78), Greater Pitts. C. of C. Republican. Presbyterian. Clubs: Duquesne, Longue Vue (gov. 1982-84). Home: 321 Braddsley Dr Pittsburgh PA 15235-5302 Office: World Affairs Coun Pitts 400 Oliver Ave Pittsburgh PA 15219-1807

OELBAUM, HAROLD, lawyer, corporate executive; b. Bklyn., Jan. 9, 1931; s. Max and Betty (Molomet) O.; m. Nancy Rothkopf, June 28, 1968; children—Louise, Andrew, Jennifer. A.B., Franklin and Marshall Coll., 1952; J.D., Harvard, 1955; LL.M., N.Y.U., 1959. Bar: N.Y. 1955, Mass. 1960. Atty. Hellerstein & Rosner, Esqs., N.Y.C., 1955-59; gen. atty. Raytheon Co., Lexington, Mass., 1959-68; sr. atty. Revlon, Inc., N.Y.C., 1968-72; pres., dir., asst. treas. com. Kane-Miller Corp., Tarrytown, N.Y., 1972—. Home: 77 Chestnut Rd Bedford Corners NY 10549 Office: Kane-Miller Corp 555 White Plains Rd Tarrytown NY 10591-5109

OELGESCHLAGER, GUENTHER KARL, publisher; b. Jersey City, Apr. 19, 1934; s. Herman Wilhelm and Frieda Johanna (Onken) O.; m. Jacqueline L. Braley, July 16, 1962; children: Stacey, Lauren, Amy. BA cum laude, Princeton U., 1958; postgrad., Columbia U., 1959. Nat. sales mgr. Harper & Row Pubs., N.Y.C., 1959-67; dir. coll. div. F.A. Praeger Co., N.Y.C., 1968; v.p., gen. mgr. D.C. Heath & Co., Lexington, Mass., 1969-72; pres. Ballinger Pub. Co., Cambridge, Mass., 1973-78; v.p., dir. J.B. Lippincott Co., Phila., 1973-78; pres. Oelgeschlager, Gunn & Hain, Pubs., Inc., Cambridge,

1979—; pres. bd. dirs. Falcon Software Inc., Wentworth, N.H. With U.S. Army, 1954-56. Mem. Software Pubs. Assn. Democrat. Episcopalian. Home: 245 Merriam St Weston MA 02193-1350

OELMAN, ROBERT SCHANTZ, retired manufacturing executive; b. Dayton, Ohio, June 9, 1909; s. William Walter and Edith (Schantz) O.; m. Mary Coolidge, Oct. 17, 1936; children: Bradford Coolidge, Robert Schantz, Jr., Kathryn Peirce, Martha Forrer. A.B. summa cum laude, Dartmouth Coll., 1931, M.A., 1963, LL.D. (hon.), 1981; postgrad., U. Vienna, 1931-32; H.H.D. (hon.), U. Dayton, 1959; LL.D. (hon.), Miami U., Oxford, Ohio, 1960, Wright State U., 1976; L.H.D. (hon.), Wilmington Coll. (Ohio), 1965. With NCR Corp., Dayton, 1933-80; asst. to pres. NCR Corp., 1942-45, v.p., 1946-50, exec. v.p., 1950-57, pres., 1957-62, chmn., pres., 1962-64, chmn. 1962-74, chmn. exec. com., 1974-80, dir., 1948-80; ret., 1980; former dir. Koppers Co., Inc., Pitts. Winters Nat. Bank & Trust Co., Dayton, Citibank and Citicorp, N.Y.C., Ford Motor Co., Detroit, Ohio Bell Telephone, Cleve., Procter & Gamble, Cin. Trustee Dartmouth Coll., 1961-76; Mem. Bus. Council, 1965—; chmn. bd. trustees Wright State U., 1961-76; bd. dirs. Miami Conservancy, 1967-79, pres., 1975-79; chmn. Air Force Mus. Found., Dayton, 1970-80; trustee C.F. Kettering Med. Center, 1971-80; ind. dir. tournament policy bd. PGA Tour, Ponte Vedra, Fla., 1974-83, chmn., 1978-83. Mem. Phi Beta Kappa, Delta Kappa Epsilon. Clubs: Country of Fla., Ocean of Fla., Augusta (Ga.), Delray Beach Yacht.

OEMLER, AUGUSTUS, JR., astronomy educator; b. Savannah, Ga., Aug. 15, 1945; s. Augustus and Isabelle Redding (Clarke) O.; children: W. Clarke, Bryan S. AB, Princeton U., 1969; MS, Calif. Inst. Tech., 1970, PhD, 1974. Postdoctoral assoc. Kitt Peak Nat. Obs., Tucson, 1974-75; instr. astronomy Yale U., New Haven, 1975-77, asst. prof., 1977-79, assoc. prof., 1979-83, prof., 1983—, chmn. dept., 1988—. Contbr. articles to profl. jours. Alfred P. Sloan fellow, 1978-80. Mem. Am. Astronom. Soc., Internat. Astronom. Union. Republican. Roman Catholic. Home: 93 Water St Guilford CT 06437-2863 Office: Yale U Obs 260 Whitney Ave New Haven CT 06511-3748

OERTEL, GOETZ K. H., physicist, professional association administrator; b. Stuhm, Germany, Aug. 24, 1934; came to U.S., 1957; s. Egon F.K. and Margarete W. (Wittek) O.; m. Brigitte Beckmann, June 17, 1960; children: Ines M.H. Oertel Downing, Carsten K.R. Abitur, Robert Mayer, Heilbronn, Fed. Republic Germany, 1953; vordiplom, U. Kiel, Fed. Republic Germany, 1956; PhD, U. Md., 1963. Aerospace engr. Langley Ctr. NASA, Hampton, Va., 1963-68; chief solar physics NASA, Washington, 1968-75; analyst Office of Mgmt. and Budget, Washington, 1974-75; head astronomy div. NSF, Washington, 1975; dir. def. and civilian nuclear waste programs U.S. Dept. Energy, Washington, 1975-83; acting mgr. sav. river ops. office, Aiken, S.C., 1983-84; dep. mgr. ops. office, Albuquerque, 1984-85; dep. asst. sec. EH, Washington, 1985-86; pres. Assn. Univs. for Rsch. in Astronomy, Inc. (AURA, Inc.), Washington, 1986—, also bd. dirs.; cons. Los Alamos Lab., N.Mex., 1987-92, Westinghouse Electric, 1988—; bd. dirs. AURA, Inc., Inst. for Sci. and Soc., Ellensburg, Wash., IUE Corp., Inst. for Info., George Mason U. Patentee in field. Fulbright grantee, 1957. Fellow AAAS; mem. Am. Phys. Soc., Am. Astron. Soc., Internat. Astron. Union, N.Y. Acad. Scis., Internat. U. Exch., Inc. (bd. dirs.), Cosmos Club, Sigma Xi. Lutheran. Avocations: fitness, computing. Home: 9609 Windcroft Way Potomac MD 20854-2864 Office: Assn Univs for Rsch in Astronomy 1625 Massachusetts Ave NW Ste 701 Washington DC 20036-2212

OESTERLE, DALE ARTHUR, law educator; b. West Lafayette, Ind., Oct. 25, 1950; s. Eric Clark and Germaine Dora (Seelye) O.; m. Patricia Marie Pessemier, May 6,1972; children: Helen, Ann, William. BA, U. Mich., 1972, M in Pub. Policy, 1974, JD, 1975. Bar: N.Y., Va. Law clk. to Robert R. Merhige, Jr. U.S. Dist. Ct., Richmond, Va., 1975-76; assoc. Hunton & Williams, Richmond, 1976-79; prof. law Cornell U., Ithaca, N.Y., 1979-92; Monfort prof. comml. law U. Colo., Boulder, 1992—. Author: Mergers, Acquisitions and Reorganizations, 1991; contbr. articles to profl. jours. Sir William Henry Cooper fellow U. Auckland, New Zealand, 1992. Office: Univ Colo Law Sch Campus Box 401 Boulder CO 80309

OESTERLE, ERIC ADAM, lawyer; b. Lafayette, Ind., Dec. 2, 1948; s. Eric Clark and Germaine Dora (Seelye) O.; m. Carolyn Anne Scherer, Sept. 16, 1973; children: Adam Clark, Allison Margaret. BS, U. Mich., 1970, JD, 1973. Bar: Ill. 1973, U.S. Dist. Ct. (no. dist.) Ill. 1973, U.S. Ct. Appeals (7th cir.) 1987, U.S. Supreme Ct. 1986. Assoc. Sonnenschein, Carlin, Nath & Rosenthal, Chgo., 1973-80; ptnr. Sonnenschein Nath & Rosenthal, Chgo. 1980—. Mem. ABA, Ill. Bar Assn., Chgo. Bar Assn. Home: 645 Lake Rd Glen Ellyn IL 60137-4249 Office: Sonnenschein Nath & Rosenthal 8000 Sears Tower 233 S Wacker Dr Chicago IL 60606

OESTERLING, WENDY LEE, sales and marketing executive; b. Circleville, Ohio, Oct. 11, 1949; d. Victor K. and Mary R. (Young) O.; m. James S. Greene, Aug 7, 1979; children: Jennifer, Julie, Matthew. Student, Conn. Coll., 1967-68; MusB, Wittenberg U., 1972. Systems instr. Info. Control Systems, Ann Arbor, Mich., 1974-76; mktg. rep. Alphatext Ltd., Ottawa, Ontario, Can., 1976-78; edn. specialist Advanced Systems, Inc., Toronto, Ontario, 1978-79; mktg. rep. Advanced Systems, Inc., 1979-81, mgr. eastern Can., 1981-83, mgr. major accounts, 1983-84; dir. corp. communications Advanced Systems, Inc., Arlington Heights, Ill., 1984-85; v.p. sales ops. Advanced Systems, Inc., 1985-86; v.p. fed. systems div. Applied Learning, Arlington, Va., 1986-89; v.p. certification and testing Roach Orgn., Alexandria, Va., 1989-91; owner JJM Mktg. Assocs., Falls Church, Va., 1991—. Episcopalian. Avocation: music. Office: JJM Mktg Assocs Falls Church VA 22041-1117

OESTERREICHER, JAMES E., department stores executive; b. 1941. B.S., Mich. State U., 1964. With J. C. Penney Co. Inc., 1964—; pres. Western Region J. C. Penney Co. Inc., 1987-88, exec. v.p., 1988—. Office: J C Penney Co Inc 6501 Legacy Dr Plano TX 75024-3612

OESTMANN, IRMA EMMA, minister, artist, educator; b. Auburn, Nebr., May 6, 1930; d. Martin Edward and Magdalene Augusta (Volkman) O.; m. Allister Roland Behrends, July 29, 1948 (div. 1968); children: John Allan, Patricia, William, Michael, Russell, Kurt. BS in Edn., U. Nebr., 1972. Ordained min. United Ch., Unity Village, Mo., 1982. Dairy farm pvt. farmer Johnson, Nebr., 1948-68; art tchr. Burke High Sch., Omaha, 1972-73, L.A. (Calif.) Pub. Schs., 1974-77; mgr. U-Rent Furniture, Canoga Park, Calif., 1978-80; min. There Is A Way TV Ministry, Palm Springs, Calif., 1982-83, Unity Ch. of Truth, Pomona, Calif., 1983-85, Unity of Del Ray Beach, Fla., 1986-87, Unity of Jupiter, Fla., 1988-90, Unity Ch. of San Gabriel, Calif., 1991-94, United Fellowship of Grants Pass, Oreg., 1994—; cert. hypnotist, self-instr., therapist Encino, Calif., 1978-80; pvt. children's art tchr., Upland, Calif., 1986-87. Artist oil and watercolor paintings, 1968—; author, artist: (audio tapes) Self Help and Meditation, 1980—; producer, host: (tv panel series) The Truth Is, 1989; contbr. poems and articles to mags. Mem. San Gabriel (Calif.) Cmty. Coun., 1991-93. Avocations: visual arts, singing, hiking, traveling, photography. Home: Ste 846 233 Rogue River Hwy Grants Pass OR 97527 Office: Unity Fellowship Grants Pass Grants Pass OR 97526

OESTREICH, CHARLES HENRY, college president; b. Columbus, Ohio, June 8, 1932; s. Henry F. and Martha (Schwartz) O.; m. Rhoda J. Haseley, Aug. 26, 1957; children: Martha, Mary, David. BS, Capital U., 1954; MS, Ohio U., 1956, PhD, 1961; LLD, Capital U., 1986. Instr. chemistry Va. Military Inst., 1956-57; instr. Capital U., Columbus, 1960-62; asst. prof. chemistry Capital U., 1962-64, asso. prof. chemistry, 1965-69; acad. dean Tex. Luth. Coll., Seguin, 1969-76; interim pres. Tex. Luth. Coll., 1976-77, pres., 1977-94; area rep. Evang. Luth. Ch. Found., New Braunfels, Tex., 1994—; postdoctoral research fellow Vanderbilt U., 1965-66. Bd. dirs. Mid-Tex. Symphony; chmn. Seguin Citizens for Progress. Mem. Seguin Rotary Club (past prs.). Home: 2269 S Abbey Loop New Braunfels TX 78130

OETTER, BRUCE CHRISTIAN, lawyer; b. St. Louis, June 25, 1949; s. Donald L. and Joana (D'Arancha) O.; m. Rebecca P. Cullinane, May 20, 1973; 1 child, Ethan R. AB magna cum laude, Brown U., 1971; JD, Washington U., St. Louis, 1976. Bar: Mo. 1976. Assoc. Bryan, Cave, McPheeters & McRoberts, St. Louis, 1976-84, ptnr., 1985—. Mem. ABA, Mo. Bar

Assn., Bar Assn. Met. St. Louis, Mo. Athletic Club, Phi Beta Kappa. Avocations: tennis, squash. Office: Bryan Cave 211 N Broadway Saint Louis MO 63102

OETTGEN, HERBERT FRIEDRICH, physician; b. Cologne, Germany, Nov. 22, 1923; came to U.S., 1958; s. Peter and Minna (Kaul) O.; m. Trudi Hesberg, Feb. 16, 1957; children: Hans Christoph, Joerg Peter, Anne Barbara. MD, U. Cologne, 1951. Diplomate Bd. Internal Medicine, Fed. Republic of Germany. Resident in pathology City Hosp., Cologne, 1952-54, resident in medicine, 1955-58; fellow Meml. Sloan-Kettering Cancer Ctr., N.Y.C., 1958-62, assoc. to assoc. mem., 1963-69, mem., 1972—; attending physician, 1971—; prof. medicine Cornell U. Med. Coll., N.Y.C., 1972—; assoc. dir. Cancer Rsch. Inst., N.Y.C., 1985—. Author over 350 publs. in hematology, cancer rsch., immunology and clin. oncology. Recipient award for cancer rsch. Wilhelm Warner Found., Hamburg, Fed. Republic Germany, 1970, Lisec-Artz award for cancer rsch. Friedrich Wilhelm U., Bonn, Fed. Republic of Germany, 1982. Presbyterian. Avocations: violin, woodworking. Home: 48 Overlook Dr New Canaan CT 06840-6825 Office: Meml Sloan-Kettering Cancer Ctr 1275 York Ave New York NY 10021-6094

OETTINGER, ANTHONY GERVIN, mathematician, educator; b. Nuremberg, Germany, Mar. 29, 1929; came to U.S., 1941, naturalized, 1947; s. Albert and Marguerite (Bing) O.; m. Marilyn Tanner, June 20, 1954; children: Douglas, Marjorie. A.B., Harvard U., 1951, Ph.D., 1954; Henry fellow, U. Cambridge, Eng., 1951-52; Litt.D. (hon.), U. Pitts., 1984. Mem. faculty Harvard, 1955—, asso. prof. applied math., 1960-63, prof. linguistics, 1963-75, Gordon McKay prof. applied math., 1963—, chmn. program on info. resources policy, 1972—, mem. faculty of govt., 1973—, prof. info. resources policy, 1975—; mem. command control comm. and intelligence bd. Dept. Navy, 1978-83; mem. sci. adv. group Def. Comm. Agy., 1979-90; bd. visitors Joint Mil. Intelligence Coll., 1986—, chmn., 1995—; chmn., dir. Ctrl. Intelligence''s Advanced Tech. Panel, 1995—; cons. Arthur D. Little, Inc., 1956-80, Office Sci. and Tech., Exec. Office of Pres., 1960-73, Bellicomm, Inc., 1963-88, Sys. Devel. Corp., 1965-88, NSC, Exec. Office of Pres., 1975-81, President's Fgn. Intelligence Adv. Bd., 1981-90; chmn. computer sci. and engring. bd. NAS, 1968-73; mem. Nat. Rsch. Cmty. Antenna TV Commn., 1972-79, chmn., 1975-79; mem. rsch. adv. bd. Com. for Econ. Devel., 1975-79; trustee Babbage Inst., 1991—; penel mem. naval studies bd. NAS/NRC, 1993-95. Author: A Study for the Design of an Automatic Dictionary, 1954, Automatic Language Translation: Lexical and Technical Aspects, 1960, Run Computer Run: The Mythology of Educational Innovation, 1969, High and Low Politics: Information Resources for the 80s, 1977, Behind the Telephone Debates, 1988, Mastering the Changing Information World, 1993; editor: Proc. of a Symposium on Digital Computers and Their Applications, 1962. Fellow Am. Acad. Arts and Scis., AAAS, IEEE, Assn. Computing Machinery (mem. coun. 1961-68, chmn. com. U.S. Govt. Rels. 1964-66, editor computational linguistics sect. Commn. 1964-66, pres. 1966-68); mem. Soc. Indsl. and Applied Math. (mem. coun. 1963-67), Coun. on Fgn. Rels., Phi Beta Kappa, Sigma Xi. Clubs: Cosmos (Washington); Harvard (N.Y.C.). Home: 65 Elizabeth Rd Belmont MA 02178-3819 Office: Harvard U Program Info Resources Policy 200 Aiken Cambridge MA 02138-2901

OETTINGER, FRANK FREDERIC, electronics executive, researcher; b. N.Y.C., Aug. 6, 1940; s. Frank B. and Elizabeth (Leimer) O.; m. Kathleen Linda Johnson, Aug. 24, 1963; children: Meredith L., Melanie B., Megan M. BEE, Pratt Inst., 1963; MEE, NYU, 1966; postgrad., Columbia U., 1966-67. Electronics engr. U.S. Naval Applied Sci. Lab., N.Y.C., 1963-67; project leader Nat. Bur. Standards, Gaithersburg, Md., 1967-73, sect. chief, 1973-80, dep. div. chief, 1980-85; div. chief Nat. Inst. Standards & Tech. (formerly Nat. Bur. Standards), Gaithersburg, MD, 1985—. Contbr. articles to profl. jours.; author 15 standards in semiconductor metrology. Deacon Roman Cath. Ch. Recipient Silver medal Dept. Commerce, 1976, E.B. Rosa award Nat. Inst. Standards & Tech., 1990. Fellow IEEE; mem. Eta Kappa Nu. Office: Nat Inst Standards & Tech Semiconductor Elec Dv Gaithersburg MD 20899

OETTINGER, JULIAN ALAN, lawyer, pharmacy company executive. BS, U. Ill., 1961; JD, Northwestern U., 1964. Bar: Ill. 1964. Atty. SEC, 1964-67; atty. Walgreen Co., Deerfield, Ill., 1967-72, sr. atty., 1972-78, div. law, 1978-89, v.p., gen. counsel, corp. sec., 1989—. Office: Walgreen Co 200 Wilmot Rd Deerfield IL 60015-4620

OFFENBERGER, ALLAN ANTHONY, electrical engineering educator; b. Wadena, Sask., Can., Aug. 11, 1938; s. Ivy Viola (Hagglund) O.; m. Margaret Elizabeth Patterson, Apr. 12, 1963; children: Brian, Gary. BS, U. B.C., 1962, MS, 1963; PhD, MIT, 1968. Asst. prof. U. Alta., Edmonton, Can., 1968-70, assoc. prof., 1970-75, prof., 1975—; vis. prof. U.K. Atomic Energy Agy., Abingdon, Oxon, Eng., 1975-76; project dir. Laser Fusion Project, Edmonton, 1984-91; mem. strategic adv. com. Nat. Fusion Program, Atomic Energy of Can. Ltd., Chalk River, Ont., 1987—; vis. prof. U. Oxford, U.K., 1992. Mem. editorial bd. Laser and Particle Beams, 1987—; contbr. over 100 sci. articles on lasers and plasma physics. Killam Rsch. fellow Can. Coun., 1980-83. SERC rsch. fellow, Eng., 1992. Mem. Can. Assn. Physicists (exec. officer v.p. elect 1987-88, pres. 1989-90), Am. Phys. Soc., Sigma Xi. Home: 412 Lessard Dr, Edmonton, AB Canada T6M 1A7 Office: Dept Elec Engring, U Alta, Edmonton, AB Canada T6G 2G7

OFFENHARTZ, EDWARD, aerospace executive; b. Bklyn., Mar. 1, 1928; s. Hyman and Anna (Konecky) O.; m. Edith Enevoldsen, Nov. 4, 1951; children: Debra, Marc, Beth, Kay, David. BSME, Poly. Inst. Bklyn., 1948; postgrad., U. Va., 1949-50; student Program for Mgmt. Devel., Harvard U., 1970. Registered profl. engr., Mass. Aero. research scientist NACA, Langley, Va., 1948-56; with Avco Corp., Wilmington and Lowell, Mass., 1956-67, successively research engr., group leader, project engr., sr. project engr., project mgr., project dir., 1956-67; project dir. asst. gen. mgr. ops. Perkin-Elmer Corp., 1967-70; program dir. spl. projects Grumman Aerospace Corp., Bethpage, N.Y., 1970-73, program dir. Earth Limb Measurements Satellite program, 1973-75, mem. def. sci. bd. shuttle task force, 1974-75, program dir. internat. offset mgmt., 1975-82, program dir. mktg. planning, 1982-84; dir. strategic planning Grumman Data Systems Div., Woodbury, N.Y., 1984-90; pres. E.O. Assocs., 1991—; lectr. UCLA, 1965—. Contbr. articles to profl. jours. Mem. AIAA, Sci. Research Soc. Am., Am. Mgmt. Assn. Home: 4 Glen Ln Weston CT 06883-2308 Office: EO Assocs 4 Glen Ln Weston CT 06883-2308

OFFENSEND, DAVID GLENN, investment executive; b. Dayton, Ohio, June 16, 1953; s. Asa E. and Rhoda Q. (Lee) O.; m. Janet Lou Mawdsley, July 21, 1979; children: Rebecca Lee, Christopher David. BA magna cum laude, Princeton U., 1975; MBA, Harvard U., 1977. Assoc. Lehman Bros. Kuhn Loeb (name now Shearson Lehman Hutton), N.Y.C., 1977-80, v.p., 1980-83, prin., 1983-84, mng. dir., 1984-90; pres., chief exec. officer Shearson Lehman Hutton Mcht. Banking Ptnrs., 1989-90; mng. dir. Rosecliff Inc., N.Y.C., 1990-92, Oak Hill Ptnrs., Inc., N.Y.C., 1992—. Trustee Bklyn. Children's Mus., 1986—, pres., 1991-94; bd. govs. Bklyn. Heights Assn., 1991—; bd. dirs. Soho Rep Theatre, N.Y.C., 1985-90. Baker scholar Harvard U. 1977. Office: Oak Hill Ptnrs Inc 65 E 55th St New York NY 10022-3219

OFFER, DANIEL, psychiatrist; b. Berlin, Germany, Dec. 24, 1930; married; 3 children. Grad., U. Chgo., 1957. Intern Ill. Research and Ednl. Hosps., Chgo. 1957-58; resident Inst. Psychosomatics and Psychiat. Research and Tng. Michael Reese Hosp., Chgo., 1958-61; psychiatrist Chgo. Inst. Psychoanalysis, 1963-68; career investigator Nat. Inst. Mental Health, Psychosomatic and Psychiat. Inst., Michael Reese Hosp., 1961-64; asst. dir. Inst. Psychosomatics and Psychiat. Research and Tng., Chgo., 1961-64; assoc. dir. Inst. Psychosomatics and Psychiat. Research and Tng., 1965-74, co-dir., 1974-76, acting chmn., 1976-77, chmn., 1977-87; dir. Ctr. for Study of Adolescence, 1987-90; assoc. prof. psychiatry U. Chgo., 1969-73, prof., 1973-90, prof. psychiatry Northwestern U., 1991—; fellow Center for Advanced Studies in Behavioral Scis., Stanford, 1973-74. Author: Normality: Theoretical and Clinical Concepts of Mental Health, 1966, new edit., 1974, new edit., 1984, The Psychological World of the Teen-ager, 1969, From Teenage to Young Manhood: A Psychological Study, 1975, Psychological World of the Juvenile Delinquent, 1979, The Adolescent: A Psychological Self Portrait 1981, Patterns of Adolescent Self-Image, 1984, The Leader, 1985, The

Teenage World, 1988, The Diversity of Normal Behavior, 1991, Adolescent Suicide and Homicide, 1994; also numerous articles.; editor in chief Jour. Youth and Adolescence. Served with Israeli Army. Fellow Chgo. Inst. Medicine, Am. Soc. Adolescent Psychiatry (pres. 1972-73, Schonfeld Meml. award for rsch. 1985, John P. Hill Meml. award 1990). Office: Northwestern U Med Sch Dept Psychiatry & Behavioral Scis 303 E Ohio St Chicago IL 60611-3015

OFFER, STUART JAY, lawyer; b. Seattle, June 2, 1943; m. Judith Spitzer, Aug. 29, 1970; children: Rebecca, Kathryn. BA, U. Wash., 1964; LLB, Columbia U., 1967. Bar: D.C. 1968, U.S. Tax Ct. 1968, Calif. 1972. Atty., advisor U.S. Tax Ct., Washington, 1967-68; assoc. Morrison & Foerster, San Francisco, 1972-76, ptnr., 1976—. Mem. San Francisco Dir.'s Adv. Com 1985. Served as capt. U.S. Army, 1968-72. Mem. ABA (chmn. taxation sect. 1991-92, corp. tax com.), Internat. Fiscal Assn., Am. Coll. Tax Counsel. Office: Morrison & Foerster 345 California St San Francisco CA 94104

OFFICE, GERALD SIMMS, JR., restaurant chain executive; b. Dayton, Ohio, Oct. 22, 1941; s. Gerald Simms and Sarah (Lieberman) O.; m. Lynn Elise Isaacson, Aug. 26, 1972; children: Jeremy Simms, Marisa Lynn. B.B.A. with distinction, U. Mich., 1963; J.D. summa cum laude, Ohio State U., 1967; LLD, Westminster Coll. Bar: Ohio 1967. Ptnr. Office & Office, Dayton, 1967-69; chmn. bd. Ponderosa, Inc., Dayton, 1969—, chief exec. officer, from 1969, now also pres., dir.; dir. Bank One, Dayton, ChemLawn Corp., Columbus, Ohio. Trustee Dayton Devel. Council, Cin. Contemporary Art Center, Dayton Performing Arts Fund, U. Dayton, Hundred Club of Dayton; bd. overseers NYU Center for Study of Foodservice Mgmt.; mem. Bus. Com. for Arts, Inc.; hon. trustee Building Bridges Inc.; hon. mem. exec. com. Spl. Olympics Dayton and Montgomery County, Ohio.; mem. Dayton chpt. U.S. Olympic Com.; mem. adv. bd. Dayton Council on World Affairs; mem., past chmn. Area Progress Council-Dayton; trustee Dayton Free Enterprise Found., Wright State U. Found.; bd. mgrs. Air Force Mus. Found. Mem. Nat. Restaurant Assn. Office: Ponderosa Inc PO Box 578 Dayton OH 45401-0578

OFFIT, MORRIS WOLF, investment management executive; b. Balt., Jan. 22, 1937; s. Michael and Rhea (Wolf) O.; m. Nancy Silverman, Nov. 26, 1959; children: Ned S., Daniel W. BA in History, Johns Hopkins U., 1957; MBA in Fin., U. Pa., 1959. V.p. investment dept. Mercantile Safe Deposit and Trust, Balt., 1960-68; gen. ptnr. Salomon Bros. Inc., N.Y.C., 1970-80; pres. Julius Baer Securities, N.Y.C., 1980-82, Offit Assocs. Inc., N.Y.C., 1983—; bd. dirs. Merc. Bancshares Corp., Balt., Duty Free Internat. Chmn. bd. trustees Johns Hopkins U.; mem. adv. coun. Sch. Advanced Internat. Studies, Washington; trustee Jewish Mus., former chmn.; trustee Union Theol. Sem., Jewish Theol. Sem. Mem. Coun. Fgn. Rels. Office: Offitbank 520 Madison Ave New York NY 10022-4213

OFFIT, SIDNEY, writer, educator; b. Balt., Oct. 13, 1928; s. Barney and Lillian (Cohen) O.; m. Avodah Crindell Komito, Aug. 8, 1952; children: Kenneth, Michael Robert. B.A., Johns Hopkins U., 1950. Editorial staff Mercury Publs., N.Y.C., 1952-53, Macfadden Publs., N.Y.C., 1953-54; contbg. editor Baseball mag., Washington, 1955-58; mem. faculty N.Y. U., 1964—; adj. prof. creative writing, 1977—; asso. editor Intellectual Digest, 1970-72, sr. editor, 1972-74; lectr. creative writing New Sch. Social Research, 1965—; curator George Polk Awards for Journalism, 1977—; mem. nat. bd. Nat. Book Com., 1973-75; commentator Channel 5 TV, N.Y.C., 1975-85, Channel 11 TV, 1992. Author: He Had it Made, 1959, The Other Side of the Street, 1962, Soupbone, 1963, Topsy Turvey, 1965, the Adventure of Homer Fink, 1966, The Boy Who Made a Million, 1968; short stories Not All the Girls Have Million Dollar Smiles, 1971; Only a Girl Like You, 1972, What Kind of Guy Do You Think I Am?, 1977, Memoir of the Bookie's Son, 1995; series sports books for boys, 1961-65; also essays, revs., short stories; book editor: Politics Today, 1978-80. Mem. selection com. Dist. Sch. Bd., N.Y.C., 1968; Mem. exec. bd. Lexington Democratic Club, 1957-60, N.Y. Dem. County Com., 1966—; chmn. 19th Precinct Community Council of N.Y.C., 1964-80. Recipient Disting. Alumni award Valley Forge Mil. Acad., 1961, Otty Community Svc. award, 1975, Teaching Excellence award NYU, 1981, commendation for achievement as teacher, scholar, communicator N.Y. State Legislature, 1983, proclamation for contbns. to city, N.Y.C. Coun., 1983, Police Athletic League citation for svc. to children of N.Y.C., 1991, Honors Convocation award Marymount Manhattan Coll., 1994, Detlev W. Bronk award Johns Hopkins Alumni Assn., 1994. Mem. Tudor and Stuart Club, Authors Guild Found. (pres. 1993—), Authors League (coun. 1970-77, 79—, v.p. 1993-95), Authors League (nat. coun. 1976-79), Am. Ctr. PEN (exec. com. 1969-88, 89—, v.p. 1970-74, internat. del. 1971, 72, 74). Clubs: Century Assn. (N.Y.C.), Coffee House (N.Y.C.). Home: 23 E 69th St New York NY 10021-4919 *I have been guided by a strong devotion to my family and friends and moderate ambition. In both these priorities I have been influenced by my parents. With my writing I have tried to fulfill my own needs, and for the most I have been satisfied by the reception. I do not aspire to fame or great fortune, and this leaves me free to enjoy the sharing of experiences with my friends and family. I consider myself a lucky man and this keeps me grateful to whatever forces there are that contrive man's fortune.*

OFFNER, ERIC DELMONTE, lawyer; b. Vienna, Austria, June 23, 1928; came to U.S., 1941, naturalized, 1949; s. Sigmund J. and Kathe (Delmonte) O.; m. Julie Cousins, 1955 (dec. 1959); m. Barbara Ann Shotton, July 2, 1961; 1 son, Gary Douglas; m. Carol Sue Marcus, Jan. 12, 1980 (dec. 1983). B.B.A., CCNY, 1949; LL.B. in Internat. Affairs, Cornell U., 1952. Bar: N.Y. 1952. Assoc. Langner, Parry, Card & Langner, N.Y.C., 1952-57; ptnr. Haseltine, Lake, Waters & Offner, N.Y.C., 1957-77; sr. ptnr. Offner & Kuhn, 1978-83; pvt. practice N.Y.C., 1983—; instr. George Washington U. Law Sch., Cornell U. Law Sch.; spl. prof. law Hofstra Law Sch., 1974-92, Cornell Law Sch., 1979. Author: International Trademark Protection, 1964, Japanese edit., 1977, International Trademark Service, Vols. I-III 1970, Vol. IV, 1972, Vol. V, 1973, Vol. VI, 1976, Vol. VII, 1981, Vols. I-VII, 2d edit., 1981, Legal Training Course on Trademarks, 1982; editor in chief: Cornell Law Forum 1950-51; mem. editorial bd.: Trademark Reporter, 1961-64, 69-72; book reviewer Jour. Humanism and Ethical Religion; contbr. articles to profl. jours. V.p. Riverdale Mental Health Clinic, N.Y.C., 1966-67; pres. Riverdale Mental Health Assn., 1967-69, Ethical Culture Soc., Riverdale-Yonkers, 1964-67, Ethical Cultural Retirement Ctr., 1975-94; trustee Am. Ethical Union, 1967-73, Internat. Alliance of Holistic Lawyers; bd. dirs. Fit Kids. Mem. N.Y. Patent Law Assn. (editor Bull. 1961-66, gov. 1973-76), ABA, City N.Y. Bar Assn. (sec. 1962-64), U.S. Trademark Assn., World Peace Through Law (charter), Trademark Soc. Washington (charter), Inst. Trade Mark Agts. (London), Australian Patent Inst., Internat. Assn. Protection Indsl. Property, Nat. Coun. Patent Law Assn., Internat. Patent, Trademark Assn., Internat. Alliance of Holistic Lawyers, Phi Alpha Delta. Home: 20 Joy Dr New Hyde Park NY 11040-1109 *Do unto others so as to elicit the best in them and thereby the best in yourself.*

OFFUTT, GERALD M., lawyer; b. New Haven, Conn., Sept. 20, 1950. AB, Harvard U., 1973, JD, 1976. Bar: Ill. 1976. Ptnr. McDermott, Will & Emery, Chgo. Mem. ABA, Chgo. Bar Assn., Cook County Bar Assn., Nat. Bar Assn. Office: McDermott Will & Emery 3003 Van Ness St NW Apt S1105 Washington DC 20008-4708

O'FLAHERTY, LUCY LOUISE, secondary education educator; b. Bklyn., Dec. 13, 1941; d. Louis Charles and Carmela (De Luca) Aufiero; m. James Jerome O'Flaherty, May 26, 1973; children: Michael Sean, Alison Marie. BA in Edn., Social Studies, Fordham U., 1970; MS in Edn., Hofstra U., 1984; M in Social Work, Adelphi U., 1992. Cert. tchr., N.Y. Pers. recruiter Merrill, Lynch, Pierce, Fenner & Smith, Inc., N.Y.C., 1967-71, program adminstr., 1971-72; coord. and tchr. social studies St. Agnes Sch., Rockville Centre, N.Y., 1982-88; tchr. social studies Holy Trinity High Sch. Hicksville, N.Y., 1988—; psychiatric social worker Sunrise Psychiatric Clinic, 1990-91, 93—; med. social work intern Ctrl. Gen. Hosp., Plainview, 1990-91; pvt. practice counseling and psychotherapy. Bereavement counselor and group facilitator YWCA-YMCA, Plainview, N.Y., 1990-91, 92-94. Mem. NASW, Nat. Assn. Cath. Educators, N.Y. State Social Studies Assn., Kappa Delta Pi. Home: PO Box 113 Malverne NY 11565-0113 Office: 98 Cherry Ln Hicksville NY 11801

O'FLAHERTY, PAUL BENEDICT, lawyer; b. Chgo., Feb. 11, 1925; s. Benedict Joseph and Margaret Celestine (Harrington) O'F.; m. Catherine Margaret Bigley, Feb. 13, 1954; children: Paul, Michael, Kathleen, Ann, Neil. JD cum laude, Loyola U., Chgo., 1949. Bar: Ill. 1949, U.S. Dist. Ct. (no. dist). Ill. 1949, U.S. Ct. Appeals (7th cir.) 1956, U.S. Supreme Ct. 1959. Ptnr. Madden, Meccia, O'Flaherty & Freeman, Chgo., 1949-56; ptnr. Groble, O'Flaherty & Hayes, Chgo., 1956-63, Schiff Hardin & Waite, Chgo., 1963—; mem. adj. faculty Loyola U., 1959-65. Author: (with others) Illinois Estate Administration, 1983; contbr. articles to profl. jours. Bd. advisors Cath. Charities, Chgo., 1979-92; trustee Clarke Coll., Dubuque, Iowa, 1982—. Served to 2d lt. U.S. Army, 1943-46. Fellow Am. Coll. Trust and Estate Counsel; mem. ABA, Ill. Bar Assn. (past chmn. fed. taxation sect. council), Chgo. Bar Assn. (past chmn. trust law com.), Chgo. Estate Planning Council. Clubs: Union League, Metropolitan (Chgo.). Office: Schiff Hardin & Waite 7200 Sears Tower Chicago IL 60606

O'FLAHERTY, TERRENCE, journalist; b. What Cheer, Iowa, July 15, 1917; s. Leo J. and Lelia (Thomas) O'F. B.A., U. Calif. at Berkeley, 1939. Hist. researcher Metro-Goldwyn-Mayer Studios, 1940-42; columnist San Francisco Chronicle, 1949-86; writer nationally syndicated TV column, 1960-86; mem. bd. Peabody Awards for Radio and TV, 1952-84. Host: TV program PM West, San Francisco, 1961-62; created The Terrence O'Flaherty TV Collection for UCLA TV Archives and Theater Arts Library, 1987; contbr. articles to McCalls, Reader's Digest, TV Guide. Served as lt. USNR, 1942-46. Recipient Gov.'s award (Emmy) NATAS, 1988. Mem. Beta Theta Pi. Subject of UCLA oral history program. Home and Office: 4 Whiting St San Francisco CA 94133-2419

O'FLARITY, JAMES P., lawyer; b. Yazoo City, Miss., Oct. 15, 1923; s. James P. and Jessie E. (Marshall) O'F.; m. Betty Reichman, Apr. 9, 1955; children: Michael J., Deborah J. O'Flarity James, Steven M., Pamela G. BS, Millsaps Coll., 1950; postgrad., Miss. Coll. Sch. Law, 1948, 53-54; J.D., U. Fla., 1965. Bar: Miss. 1954, U.S. Dist. Ct. (so. dist.) Miss. 1954, U.S. Supreme Ct. 1957, U.S. Ct. Mil. Appeals (5th cir.) 1957, Fla. 1966, U.S. Dist. Ct. (so. and mid. dists.) Fla. 1966, U.S. Dist. Ct. (no. dist.) Fla. 1967, U.S. Ct. Appeals (11th cir.) 1981; state ct. cert. arbitrator. Assoc. law firm Cone, Owen, Wagner, Nugent & Johnson, West Palm Beach, Fla., 1966-69; sole practice law West Palm Beach, 1969—; mem. Supreme Ct. Matrimonial Law Commn. Fla., 1982-85; ABA observer family ct. proc. Nat. Jud. Coll., 1983; mem. U. Fla. Law Ctr. Coun., 1972—, mem. legal edn. com., 1973, chmn. membership and fin. com., 1977-78; lectr. on marital and family law; leader del. for legal exchange on family law to Ministry of Justice, Peoples Republic of China, 1984. Contbr. articles to profl. publs. Mem. U. Fla. Pres.'s Council; mem. U.S. Rep. Senatorial Inner Circle, 1988—; col. La. Gov.'s Staff, 1982—. With USAAF, 1942-45. Decorated Air medal with five oak leaf clusters. Fellow Royal Geog. Soc. (life), Am. Bar Found. (life), Roscoe Pound-Am. Trial Lawyers Found. (life), Am. Acad. Matrimonial Lawyers (nat. pres. 1985-86, nat. bd. of govs. 1977-88, founding pres. Fla. chpt. 1976-80, bd. mgrs. Fla chpt. 1976—, hon. permanent pres. emeritus 1982—), Internat. Acad. Matrimonial Lawyers (convenor, founder), Trusler Soc.; mem. Internat. Soc. Family Law, Internat. Bar Assn. (assoc.), Am. Law Inst. (consultative group law of family dissolution 1990—, Nat. Conf. Bar Pres' 1991), ABA (chmn. coms. 1973-75, 78-81, 82-83, editor Family Law Newsletter 1975-77, mem. council family law sect. 1976-85, vice-chmn. sect. 1981-82, chmn. sect. 1983-84, mem. conf. sect. chairmen 1982-85, mem. adv. bd. jour. 1978-80), Assn. Trial Lawyers Am. (Fla. State committeeman 1973-75, 1st chmn. family law sect. 1971-72, 72-73), Fla. Supreme Ct. Hist. Soc., Fla. Council Bar Assn. Presidents (life mem.), Fla. Bar Found. (life, exec. dir. screening com. 1976, chmn. projects com. 1976-77, asst. sect. 1973-79, dir. 1977-81), U. Fla. Law Ctr. Assn. (life), Acad Fla. Trial Lawyers (dir. 1974-77, coll. diplomates 1977), Fla. Bar Assn. (exec. council 1973-84, sec.-treas. family law sect. 1973-74, chmn. family law sect. 1974-75, 75-76, guest editor spl. issue jour. 1978, chmn. jour. and news editorial bd. 1978-79, mem. bd. legal specialization and edn. 1982-91, 92—, jud. nominating procedures com. 1992-93, Family Law Rules com. 1992—), Palm Beach County Bar Assn. (cir. ct. civil adv. com. 1981, mem. cir. ct. juvenile domestic rels. adv. com. 1971-80, 81-83, adv. com. chmn. 1974-78), Solicitor's Family Law Assn. (Eng.), Gov.'s Club of Palm Beach (founder, life, gov's. coun.), Explorers Club (life, vice chmn. South Fla. chpt. 1990—), Circumnavigators Club, Travelers Century Club (life), Phi Alpha Delta (life), Sigma Delta Kappa. Home: 908 Country Club Dr No Palm Beach FL 33408-3714 Office: 215 5th St Ste 100 West Palm Beach FL 33401-4026

O'FLINN, PETER RUSSELL, lawyer; b. Bklyn., Jan. 8, 1953; s. Russell William and Mary (Tavoulareas) O'F.; m. Kathleen Tracy, May 28, 1981; children: Peter Andrew, Michael Christopher. BA, Colgate U., 1974; JD, Columbia U., 1977. Bar: N.Y. 1978. Assoc. Dewey, Ballantine, Bushby, Palmer & Wood, N.Y.C., 1977-81; assoc. LeBoeuf, Lamb, Leiby & MacRae, N.Y.C., 1982-85, ptnr., 1986—. Office: LeBoeuf Lamb Leiby & MacRae 125 E 55th St New York NY 10022-3502

OFNER, J(AMES) ALAN, management consultant; b. East Orange, N.J., Mar. 23, 1922. Student, Newark U., 1941; B.A., Antioch Coll., 1949. Trainee, L. Bamberger & Co., Newark, 1941; asst. dept. mgr. Carson Pierie Scott Co., Chgo., 1949; sr. personnel rep. Argonne (Ill.) Nat. Lab., 1950-55; mgmt. cons. McKinsey & Co., Chgo. and San Francisco, 1955-60; mgr. orgn. planning J.C. Penney Co., Inc., N.Y.C., 1960-65; dir. orgn. devel. J.C. Penney Co., Inc., 1965-74, div. v.p., 1974-82, dir. corp. personnel planning, 1976-82; pres. Mng. Change, Inc., 1981—. Served with USAAF, 1941-44. Mem. Exec. Forum Group, Planning Forum, Human Resources Planning Soc., World Future Soc., Nat. Retail Fedn., Inst. Mgmt. Cons., N.C. Citizens for Bus. and Industry, Soc. for Human Resource Mgmt., Princeton Club. Office: Mng Change Inc PO Box 98387 Raleigh NC 27624-8387

OFTE, DONALD, environmental executive, former management consultant; b. N.Y.C., Aug. 23, 1929; s. Sverre and Ingeborg Ofte; m. Margaret Mae McHenney, July 23, 1955; children: Marc Christian, Nancy Carolyn Ofte Appleby, Kirk Donald Jr. BA in Chemistry, Dana Coll., 1952; postgrad. study metall. engring., Ohio State U., 1958-60. Jr. chemist Inst. Atomic Research, Ames, Iowa, 1952-53; sr. research chemist Monsanto Research Corp., Miamisburg, Ohio, 1958-66; ops. engr. AEC, Miamisburg, 1966-69; br. chief, div. dir. ops. office AEC, Albuquerque, 1969-73; mgr. Pinellas area office AEC, Largo, Fla., 1973-79; mgr. Rocky Flats area office Dept. Energy, Golden, Colo., 1979-82; asst. mgr. devel. and prodn. Dept. Energy, Albuquerque, 1982-83, dep. mgr. ops. office, 1983-84; prin. dep. asst. sec. Dept. Energy Defense Programs, Washington, 1984-87; mgr. ops. office Dept. Energy, Idaho Falls, Idaho, 1987-89; mgmt. cons. Idaho Falls, 1989-92; v.p. govt. ops. United Engrs. and Constructors, Denver, 1992-93; v.p. adv. Scis., Inc., Albuquerque, 1993-94; pres. FERMCO, Cin., 1994—; v.p. Fluor-Daniel, Inc., 1994—; affiliate prof. Idaho State U., 1990-92; bd. dirs. Denver Fed. Exec. Bd., 1979-82. Author: (with others) Plutonium 1960, 1965, Physicochemical; contbr. articles to profl. jours. on metallurgy and ceramics. Campaign chmn. United Way Pinellas, St. Petersburg, Fla., 1978; bd. dirs. Bonneville County United Way, Idaho Rsch. Found.; mem. adv. bd. Teton Peaks Council Boy Scouts of Am., 1987-92, Eastern Idaho Tech. Coll.; chmn. Excellence in Edn. Fund Com., 1990-92; vice chmn., bd. dirs. Rio Grande Ctr. ARC, Albuquerque, 1982-84. Served to lt. (j.g.) USN, 1953-57. Recipient citation AEC for Apollo 12 SNAP 27 Radioisotope Generator, 1969, High Quality Performance award AEC, 1968, Group Achievement award NASA, 1972; Meritorious Svc. award Dept. Energy, 1985, Disting. Career Svc. award, 1989. Mem. Am. Chem. Soc., Am. Nuclear Soc., Am. Soc. Metals, Nat. Contract Mgmt. Assn., Am. Soc. Pub. Adminstrs., Suncoast Archeol. Soc., Idaho Falls C. of C. (bd. dirs., cmty. svc. award 1990), Rotary Internat. Avocations: reading, bridge, hiking, gardening, golf. Home: 8820 Eagle Creek Ct West Chester OH 45069

OGAN, RUSSELL GRIFFITH, business executive, retired air force officer; b. Reading, Pa., Nov. 20, 1923; s. Russell John and Edna Gwendlyn (Griffith) O.; m. Gloria Mae Withers, Oct. 30, 1943; children: Susan Ann (Mrs. Greg Gunn), Russell Lee. Student, Wyomissing Polytech. Inst., 1942, Air Command Staff Coll., 1948, Nat. War Coll., 1963. Enlisted as pvt. U.S. Army, 1942; advanced through grades to brig. gen. USAF, 1970; fighter squadron comdr. Dover AFB, Del., 1951; dir. (Combat Operations (11th Air Div.), Ladd AFB, Alaska, 1951-53; dir. (Combat Operations Center), Hamilton AFB, Calif., 1953-56; with (Hdqrs. Air Def. Command), Ent AFB, Colo., 1956-60; dir. (Aerospace Def. Systems Office, Air Force Ballistic

Missile Div.), 1960-62; from dep. dir. plans to comdr. Sector Operation Ctr. NATO, Germany, 1963-66; dep. dir. personnel data and records (USAF Mil. Personnel Center), Randolph AFB, Tex., 1966-68; comdr. 71st Missile Warning Wing, then vice comdr. (14th Aerospace Force), Ent AFB, Colo., 1968-71; dep. dir. personnel programs Hdqrs. USAF, Washington, 1971-72; dir. Prisoner of War and Missing in Action Affairs, Office Sec. Def., Washington, 1972-74; former pres. Vacation Interval Mktg.; real estate broker Fishermen's Village, Punta Gorda, Fla. Decorated D.S.M., Legion of Merit with bronze oak leaf cluster, Air medal with 1 silver and 1 bronze oak leaf cluster. Mem. Daedalians, T.R.O.A., Venice Golf and Country Club. Home: 528 Cheval Dr Venice FL 34292-4605

O'GARA, PATRICK DENIS, editor; b. Hereford, Eng., Feb. 7, 1941; came to U.S., 1989; s. Terence Patrick and Eileen Mary (Heron) O'Gara; m. Loretta Eileen Momenee, Apr. 1, 1990 (div. Aug. 1992); children from previous marriage: Daniel James, Matthew John, Thomas Patrick. Student, Ealing Sch. of Art, London, 1958-62. Editorial artist Mirror Group Newspapers, London, 1962-70, art dir., 1970-78, asst. mng. editor, 1978-84; design editor Today Newspaper, London, 1984-86; dep. editor Hello Mag., London, 1986-88; asst. mng. editor Daily Star, London, 1988-89; asst. mng. editor graphics Toledo (Ohio) Blade, 1989-90, mng. editor, 1990—. Mem. Nat. Union Journalists Eng. Avocations: running, reading, writing. Office: Toledo Blade 541 N Superior Toledo OH 43660

OGATA, KATSUHIKO, engineering educator; b. Tokyo, Jan. 6, 1925; came to U.S., 1952; s. Fukuhei and Teruko (Yasaki) O.; m. Asako Nakamura, Sept. 6, 1961; 1 son, Takahiko. B.S., U. Tokyo, 1947; M.S., U. Ill., 1953; Ph.D., U. Calif., Berkeley, 1956. Research asst. Sci. Research Inst., Tokyo, 1948-51; fuel engr. Nippon Steel Tube Co., Tokyo, 1951-52; mem. faculty U. Minn., 1956—; prof. mech. engring., 1961—; prof. elec. engring. Yokohama Nat. U., 1960-61, 64-65, 68-69. Author: State Space Analysis of Control Systems, 1967, Modern Control Engineering, 1970, 2d edit. 1990, Dynamic Programming, 1973, Ingenieria de Control Moderna, 1974, 2d edit., 1993, Metody Przestrzeni Stanow w Teorii Sterowania, 1974, System Dynamics, 1978, 2d edit., 1992, Engenharia de Controle Moderno, 1982, 2d edit., 1993, Teknik Kontrol Automatik, 1985, Discrete-Time Control Systems, 1986, 2nd edit., 1995, Gendai Seigyo Riron, 1986, Dinamica de Sistemas, 1987, Solving Control Engineering Problems with MATLAB, 1994, Designing Linear Control Systems with MATLAB, 1994, Gendai Seigyo Kogaku, 1994. Recipient Outstanding Adv. award Inst. of Tech., U. Minn., 1981. Fellow ASME; mem. Sigma Xi, Pi Tau Sigma. Office: U Minn Dept Mech Engring Minneapolis MN 55455

OGAWA, DENNIS MASAAKI, American studies educator; b. Manzanar, Calif., Sept. 7, 1943; s. Frank M. and Alice T. (Tanaka) O.; m. Amy Ranko, Jan. 1, 1973; children: Quin, Owen, Autumn. BA, UCLA, 1966, MA, 1967, PhD, 1969. Prof. Am. studies U. Hawaii at Manoa, Honolulu, 1969—; dir. Nippon Golden Network, Honolulu, 1982—. Author: Jan Ken Po, 1973, Kodomo No Tame Ni, 1978; co-author: Ellison Onizuka: Remembrance, 1986. Dir. Japanese Cultural Ctr., Hawaii, 1992—. Danforth Found. assoc., 1975; named Disting. Historian Hawaiian Hist. Soc., 1992; fellow Japan Soc. Promotion of Sci., 1978, East West Ctr., Honolulu, 1979. Mem. Assn. Asian-Am. Scholars. Democrat. Office: Univ Hawaii Am Studies Dept 1890 East West Rd Honolulu HI 96822

OGAWA, MAKIO, physician; b. Otsu, Shiga, Japan, Jan. 22, 1940; s. Takeo and Yasuko (Sugata) O.; m. Mary-Jane Trevithick, June 21, 1969; children: Terry, Lesley. MD, Osaka U. Med. Sch., Japan, 1964; PhD, Toronto U., Can., 1973. Diplomate Am. Bd. Internal Medicine, Am. Bd. Hematology. Rotating intern U.S. Naval Hosp., Yokosuka, Japan, 1964-65; resident in Medicine Osaka U. Hosp., 1965-66; resident in Medicine Dartmouth Med. Sch. Affiliated Hosp., Hanover, N.H., 1966-68, fellow in Hematology, 1968-70; asst. prof. medicine Med. U. S.C., Charleston, 1973-77, assoc. prof., 1977-80, prof., 1980—, dir. div. exptl. hematology, 1984—; ACOS for R and D Va. Med. Ctr., Charleston, 1993—. Recipient W.S. Middleton award Dept. Vets. Affairs, 1989, William Dameshek prize Am. Soc. Hematology, 1991, Behring-Kitasato award in immunology, 1994; Leukemia Soc. Am. scholar, 1975-80; med. investigator Dept. Vets Affairs, 1980-85, 87-92. Fellow ACP; mem. Am. Soc. Clin. Investigation, Am. Soc. Clin. Investigation, Internat. Soc. Exptl. Hematology (pres. 1989-90), Assn. Am. Physicians. Office: VA Med Ctr 109 Bee St Charleston SC 29401-5703

OGBURN, CHARLTON, writer; b. Atlanta, Mar. 15, 1911; s. Charlton and Dorothy (Stevens) O.; m. Mary C. Aldis, June 6, 1945 (div. 1951); 1 child, William O. Aldis; m. Vera Weidman, Feb. 24, 1951; children: Nyssa, Holly. S.B. cum laude, Harvard, 1932; grad., Nat. War Coll., 1952. Writer Alfred P. Sloan Found., 1937-39; book reviewer Book-of-the-Month Club, 1940-41; with Div. Southeast Asian Affairs, Dept. of State, 1946-50, polit. adviser, acting U.S. rep. com. good offices on Indonesia UN Security Council, 1947-48, policy planning adviser Bur. Far Eastern Affairs, 1952-54, chief div. research for Near East, South Asia and Africa., 1954-57. Author: The White Falcon, 1955, The Bridge, 1957, Big Caesar, 1958, The Marauders, 1959, U.S. Army, 1960, The Gold of the River Sea, 1965, The Winter Beach, 1966, The Forging of Our Continent, 1968, The Continent in Our Hands, 1971, Winespring Mountain, 1973, The Southern Appalachians: A Wilderness Quest, 1975, The Adventure of Birds, 1976, Railroads: The Great American Adventure (Nat. Geog. Soc.), 1977, The Mysterious William Shakespeare: the Myth and the Reality, 1984, 2d edit., 1992, The Man Who Was Shakespeare, 1995; contbr. to mags. Served to capt. AUS, 1941-46, India-Burma. Recipient John Burroughs medal, 1967. Home: 403 Hancock St Beaufort SC 29902-4717

OGBURN, HUGH BELL, chemical engineer, consultant; b. Lexington, Va., July 13, 1923; s. Sihon Cicero Jr. and Bettie Mae (Bell) O.; m. Anne Wotherspoon, Mar. 2, 1946 (div.); children: Margaret Mathews Berenson, Scott A.; m. Nancy Wrenn Petersen, Sept. 5, 1974. B.S., Princeton U., 1944, M.S., 1947, Ph.D., 1954. Sect. dir. research and devel. dept. Atlantic Refining Co., Phila., 1950-61; mgr. process engring. M.W. Kellogg Co., N.Y.C., London, 1961-67; dir. research and engring. Union Carbide Corp., N.Y.C., 1967-69; dir. new bus. devel. Weyerhaeuser Co., Tacoma, 1969-72; pres. H.B. Ogburn Assoc., Greenwich, Conn. and Honolulu, 1971—; v.p., dir. Incontrade Inc. Stamford, Conn., 1973-78; v.p. Pacific Resources Inc., Honolulu, 1978-83; chmn. Pacific Oasis, Los Angeles, 1983-85; dir. Danmore Corp., Planning Research Corp.; cons. AEC; prof. chem. engring. Drexel U. Phila., 1951-61. Contbr. articles to profl. jours.; patentee in field. Pres. bd. trustees Woman's Hosp., Phila., 1954-62, Kapiolani Women's and Children's Med. Ctr., 1980-90; mem. adv. bd. Princeton U., 1960-70. Served to lt. j.g. USNR, 1942-46, PTO. Mem. Am. Inst. Chem. Engrs., Am. Chem. Soc., Research Engrs. Soc., Phi Beta Kappa, Sigma Xi, Tau Beta Pi. Republican. Presbyterian. Clubs: Pacific (Honolulu); Greenwich Field (Conn.); Merion Cricket (Haverford, Pa.); Princeton (N.Y.C.). Home and Office: 4340 Pahoa Ave Apt 16 A Honolulu HI 96816-5032

OGBURN, WAYNE LEE, health science facility administrator; b. Tulsa, July 23, 1947; s. Luther Calveston and LaDessa Malvina (Bohrer) O.; m. Kay McAdoo, Dec. 27, 1969 (div. July 1984); children: Vicki Elizabeth, Donna Marie; m. Cherry Lynn Manuel Roberts, Feb. 1, 1986; 1 child, Jared Brandon Roberts. BA, Tex. A&M U., 1970; MS, Trinity U., 1972. Adminstrv. resident St. Paul Hosp., Dallas, 1973; asst. adminstr. Tarrant County Hosp. Dist., Ft. Worth, 1973-75, assoc. adminstr., 1975, acting dep. adminstr., 1976; adminstr. Caney Valley Meml. Hosp., Wharton, Tex., 1976-79; v.p Hendrick Med. Ctr., Abilene, 1979-88, Hendrick Med. Devel. Corp., Abilene, 1979-88, Western Hosp. Affiliates, Inc., Abilene, 1985-88; sr. v.p. Dallas County Hosp. Dist.. Parkland Meml Hosp, Dallas, 1988-91; adminstr., CEO Titus County Meml. Hosp., Mt. Pleasant, Tex., 1991—; commmr. Houston/Galveston Area Hosp. System Agy., Houston, 1976-79; bd. mem. Group One, Inc., 1989-91; mem. Tex. State Bd. Vocat. Nurse Examiners, 1987-91, sec.-treas. 1988-89). Loaned exec. Abilene United Way, 1980-81, com. mem., 1986-87. Served with U.S. Army, 1970-71. Fellow Am. Coll. Healthcare Execs.; mem. Am. Hosp. Assn., Tex. Hosp. Assn. (div. sec. 1980-81), N.W. Tex. Hosp. Assn. (bd. dirs. 1985-88, pres. 1987-88), Wharton C. of C. (chmn. com. 1977), Mt. Pleasant C. of C. (bd. dirs. 1992—). Methodist. Avocations: antique autos, photography. Home: 213 Turnberry Cir Mount Pleasant TX 75455-6703 Office: Titus County Meml Hosp 2001 N Jefferson Ave Mount Pleasant TX 75455-2398

OGDEN, ALFRED, lawyer; b. Bklyn., Oct. 14, 1909; s. Alfred Trecartin and Sophronia (Wisner) O.; m. Mary Fell Jordan, June 25, 1938; 1 child, Alfred Trecartin II. Grad., Phillips Acad., 1928; B.A., Yale, 1932; LL.B. Harvard, 1935. Bar: N.Y. 1936. Since practiced N.Y.C.; partner Alexander & Green, 1955-75; of counsel firm Morgan, Lewis & Bockius, 1979-80, c/o Reboul, MacMurray, Hewitt, Maynard & Kristol, 1980—; Pres., dir. C. Tennant, Sons & Co., N.Y.C., 1952-54. Trustee Fay Sch. Southborough, Mass., 1950-70, Population Reference Bur., 1963-68, Daniel and Florence Guggenheim Found., 1972—, Lavenberg Found., 1986—; trustee Mystic Seaport Mus., Mystic, Conn., 1959—, chmn., 1982-83, chmn. emeritus, 1983—; bd. mgrs., bd. overseers Meml. Sloan Kettering Cancer Ctr., 1959—; trustee, exec. com. Robert Coll., Istanbul, Turkey, 1952-73, chmn., 1955-63; bd. dirs., v.p. English Speaking Union U.S., 1950-92, acting pres., 1983-84; bd. dirs., mem. exec. com. Winston Churchill Meml. Fund., 1966—; trustee Planned Parenthood N.Y.C., 1977-83; bd. dirs. Children's Mus. Manhattan, 1985-87. Served to lt. col. Gen. Staff Corps AUS, 1942-46. Decorated Legion of Merit. Mem. ABA, Internat. Law Assn., Soc. Colonial Wars, Pilgrims of U.S., Coun. on Fgn. Rels., Century Assn., Yale Club (N.Y.C.), Wadawanuck Club (Stonington, Conn.), Cosmopolitan Club, Thursday Evening Club. Home: 150 E 73d St New York NY 10021 Also: PO Box 214 Stonington CT 06378-0214 Office: 10th Fl 45 Rockefeller Plz Fl 10 New York NY 10111-0001 *There is nothing permanent except change.*

OGDEN, DANIEL MILLER, JR., government official, educator; b. Clarksburg, W.Va., Apr. 28, 1922; s. Daniel Miller and Mary (Maphis) O.; m. Valeria Juan Munson, Dec. 28, 1946; children: Janeth Lee Martin, Patricia Jo Hunter, Daniel Munson. BA in Polit. Sci., Wash. State U., 1944; MA, U. Chgo., 1947, PhD, 1949. From instr. to assoc. prof. Wash. State U., Pullman, 1949-61; staff asst. resources program U.S. Dept. Interior, 1961-64; asst. dir. U.S. Bur. Outdoor Recreation, 1964-67; dir. budget U.S. Dept. Interior, Washington, 1967-68; dean Coll. Humanities and Social Scis. Colo. State U., Ft. Collins, 1968-76; disting. vis. prof. Lewis and Clark Coll. and Portland (Oreg.) State U., 1977-78; dir. Office of Power Mktg. Coordination U.S. Dept. Energy, 1978-84; mgr. Pub. Power Coun., Portland, Oreg., 1984-88, ret., 1988; mem. profl. staff com. interstate and fgn. commerce U.S. Senate, 1956-57; spll. assst. to chmn. Dem. Nat. Com., 1960-61; lectr. Mgmt. Devel. Ctrs., U.S. Office Pers. Mgmt., 1966—. Co-author: Electing the President, rev. edit., 1968, American National Government, 7th edit., 1970, American State and Local Government, 5th edit., 1972, Washington Politics, 1960, How National Policy Is Made, 2d edit., 1994, Committeeman Wash. Dem. Cen. Com., 1952-56; chmn. Whitman County Dem. Cen. Com., 1958-60; chmn. 49th Legis. Dist. Dem. Com., 1990-94; chmn. Clark County Dem. Cen. Com., 1994—. With U.S. Army, 1943-46. Committeeman Wash. Dem. Ctrl. Com., 1952-56; chmn. Whitman County Dem. Ctrl. Com., 1958-60; chmn. 49th Legis. Dist. Dem. Com., 1990-94; chmn. Clark County Dem. Ctrl. com., 1994—. With inf. U.S. Army, 1943-46. Mem. Phi Beta Kappa, Phi Kappa Phi, Pi Sigma Alpha, Sigma Delta Chi. Mem. Unitarian Ch. Home: 3118 NE Royal Oak Dr Vancouver WA 98662-7435

OGDEN, DAVID WILLIAM, lawyer; b. Washington, Nov. 12, 1953; s. Horace Greeley and Elaine Celia (Condrell) O. BA summa cum laude, U. Pa., 1976; JD magna cum laude, Harvard U., 1981. Bar: D.C. 1983, Va. 1986, U.S. Dist. Ct. D.C. 1984, U.S. Dist. Ct. (ea. dist.) Va. 1988, U.S. Ct. Appeals (D.C. cir.) 1984, U.S. Ct. Appeals (4th cir.) 1986, U.S. Ct. Appeals (1st cir. 1989), U.S. Ct. Appeals (10th cir.) 1991, U.S. Supreme Ct. 1987. Law clk. to presiding judge U.S. Dist. Ct. (so. dist.) N.Y., N.Y.C., 1981-82; law clk. to assoc. justice Harry A. Blackmun U.S. Supreme Ct., Washington, 1982-83; assoc. atty. Ennis, Friedman, Bersoff & Ewing, Washington, 1983-85; atty., ptnr. Ennis, Friedman & Bersoff, Washington, 1986-88, Jenner & Block, Washington, 1988—. Mem. ABA, D.C. Bar Assn. Democrat. Office: Jenner and Block 601 13th St NW Fl 12 Washington DC 20005-3807

OGDEN, DAYTON, executive search consultant. CEO Spencer Stuart & Assocs., Stamford, Conn. Office: SpencerStuart & Assocs Fin Centre 695 East Main St Stamford CT 06901

OGDEN, MAUREEN BLACK, state legislator; b. Vancouver, B.C., Nov. 1, 1928; came to U.S., 1930; d. William Moore and Margaret Hunter (Leitch) Black; m. Robert Moore Ogden, June 23, 1956; children: Thomas, Henry, Peter. BA, Smith Coll., 1950; MA, Columbia U., 1963; M in City and Regional Planning, Rutgers U., 1977. Researcher, staff asst. Ford Found., N.Y.C., 1951-56; staff assoc. Fgn. Policy Assn., N.Y.C., 1956-58; mem. Millburn (N.J.) Twp. Com., 1976-81; mayor Twp. of Millburn, N.J., 1979-81; mem. N.J. Gen. Assembly, Trenton, 1982—; chmn. Assembly Environment Com., N.J. Gen. Assembly; chmn. Energy and Pub. Utilities Com., Coun. State Govts., 1991-92; mem. adv. bd. Sch. Policy and Planning, Rutgers Univ., New Brunswick, N.J., 1992—. Author: Natural Resources Inventory, Township of Millburn, 1974. Bd. govs. N.J. Hist. Soc., Newark, 1990—; trustee N.J. chpt. The Nature Conservancy; hon. trustee Paper Mill Playhouse, Millburn, 1990—; former trustee St. Barnabas Med. Ctr., Livingston, N.J.; former pres. N.J. Drug Abuse Adv. Coun. Recipient Citation award Nat. Assn. State Outdoors Recreation Liaison Officers, 1987, John F. Kennedy Ctr. for the Performing Arts cert. appreciation, The Alliance for Arts Edn., 1987, Disting. Svc. award Art Educators N.J., 1987, Annual Environ. Quality award EPA Region II, 1988, Citation, Humane Soc. of the U.S., 1989, N.J. Historic Sites Coun. award, 1989, award of merit N.J. Sch. Conservation, 1990, many others; named Legislator of Yr., Cogeneration Inst. Am. Elec. Engrs., 1990. Republican. Episcopalian. Home: 59 Lakeview Ave Short Hills NJ 07078 Office: 266 Essex St Millburn NJ 07041 Office: NJ State Senate State Capitol Trenton NJ 08625

OGDEN, PETER JAMES, investment banker; b. Rochdale, Lancashire, Eng., May 26, 1947; s. James Platt and Frances (Simmonds) O.; m. Catherine Rose Blincoe, Aug. 22, 1970; children—Tiffany, Cameron, Edward. B.S., U. Durham, Eng., 1968, Ph.D., 1971; M.B.A., Harvard U., 1973. Mng. dir. Merrill Lynch Capital Market, London, 1975-80; mng. dir. Morgan Stanley Internat., London, 1980-87, adv. dir., 1987—; chmn. Computacenter Ltd., 1981—, also bd. dirs.; mng. dir. MC & Cie Ltd. Home: 10 Upper Phillimore Gardens, London W8 7HA, England Office: Computacenter Ltd, 93-101 Blackfriars Rd, London SE1 8HW, England

OGDEN, RALPH LINDSEY, insurance company executive; b. Brunswick, Ga., May 12, 1941; s. Ralph W. Ogden and Audrey (Poppell) Ogden Cribbs; m. Lyric Padovani, Dec. 12; children—Jason, Jennifer. B.B.A. in Acctg., U. Ga., 1963; LL.B., Atlanta Law Sch., 1970. Vice pres. Daniel Constrn. Co., Greenville, S.C., 1972-82; vice pres. Fluor Corp., Irvine, Calif., 1982-83; exec. v.p. Liberty Life Ins. Co., Greenville, 1983-88, pres., 1988-93; dirs. Met. Arts Council, Greenville, 1985, Greenville Urban League, 1985, Greenville Literacy Assn., Life Insurers Conf. Mem. ABA, Ga. Bar Assn., Nat. Assn. Accts. Republican. Baptist. Office: Liberty Life Ins Co 2000 Wade Hampton Blvd Greenville SC 29615

OGDEN, SYLVESTER O., coal company executive; b. Paris, Mo., Oct. 29, 1935; s. Lester and Anastasia Ogden; m. Martha Jane Heterman, Feb. 15, 1964; children: Stasia, John. AA, Hannibal (Mo.) LaGrange Coll., 1957; BSChemE, U. Mo., 1961; MSChemE, U. Mo., Rolla, 1964; MBA, Gen. Mich. U., 1971. Various positions Dow Chem., Midland, Mich., 1964-71; v.p. planning and devel. Youghiogheny & Ohio, Cleve., 1971-75; pres., chief exec. officer Colorado Westermoreland; v.p. Westermoreland Coal, Colorado Springs, Colo., 1975-78, Panhandle Eastern Corp., 1978-81; pres., chief exec. officer Sunedco Co., Denver, 1981-84; v.p. Occidental Petrol, Lexington, Ky., 1984—; also chmn. bd., chief exec. officer Island Creek Coal Corp.; dir. Nat. Coal Coun., Washington, 1984-91; chmn. bd. Island Creek of China Coal, Ltd.; mem. joint ctrl. com. An Tai Bao Surface Mine, People's Republic China, 1986—. Founding chmn., dir. Alliance Clean Energy, Washington, 1983—. Mem. Nat. Coal Assn. (dir. 1978—), Ohio Mining and Reclamation Assn. (dir. 1978-81), Ky. Coal Assn. (dir. 1984—).

OGDEN, VALERIA JUAN, management consultant, state representative; b. Okanogan, Wash., Feb. 11, 1924; d. Ivan Bodwell and Pearle (Wilson) Munson; m. Daniel Miller Ogden Jr., Dec. 28, 1946; children: Janeth Lee Ogden Martin, Patricia Jo Ogden Hunter, Daniel Munson Ogden. BA magna cum laude, Wash. State U., 1946. Exec. dir. Potomac Coun. Camp Fire, Washington, 1964-68, Ft. Collins (Colo.) United Way, 1969-73, Designing Tomorrow Today, Ft. Collins, 1973-74, Poudre Valley Community Edn. Assn., Ft. Collins, 1977-78; pres. Valeria M. Ogden, Inc.,

Kensington, Md., 1978-81; nat. field cons. Camp Fire, Inc., Kansas City, Mo., 1980-81; exec. dir. Nat. Capital Area YWCA, Washington, 1981-84, Clark County YWCA, Vancouver, Wash., 1985-89; pvt. practice mgmt. cons. Vancouver, 1989—; mem. Wash. Ho. of Reps., 1991—; lectr. in field; adj. faculty pub. adminstrn. program Lewis and Clark Coll., Portland (Oreg.) State U., 1979—; mem. Pvt. Industry Coun., Vancouver, 1986. Author: Camp Fire Membership, 1980. County V chair Larimer County Dems., Ft. Collins, 1974-75; mem. precinct com. Clark County Dems., Vancouver, 1986-88; mem. Wash. State Coun. Vol. Action, Olympia, 1986-90; treas. Mortar Bd. Nat. Found., Vancouver, 1987—; chair Clark County Coun. Homeless, Vancouver, 1989—. Named Citizen of Yr. Ft. Collins Bd. of Realtors, 1975; recipient Gulick award Camp Fire Inc., 1956, Alumna Achievement award Wash. State U. Alumni Assn., 1988. Mem. Internat. Assn. Vol. Adminstrs. (pres. Boulder 1989-90), Nat. Assn. YWCA Exec. Dirs. Assn. (nat. bd. nominating com. 1988-90), Women in Action, Philanthropic and Ednl. Orgn., Phi Beta Kappa. Democrat. Avocation: hiking, travel. Home: 3118 NE Royal Oak Dr Vancouver WA 98662-7435 Office: John L O'Brien Bldg State Capitol Rm 342 Olympia WA 98504

OGDEN, WILLIAM MICHAEL, school system administrator; b. Wooster, Ohio, Oct. 29, 1944; s. Raymond Job and Vinnie Lena (Ensminger) O.; m. Norena Faith Parker, June 4, 1966 (div. 1978); children: Michele Rae, John Michael; m. Mary Ann Pusey, Oct. 6, 1978; 1 stepchild, Jeffrey Clare Applegate. BA, Coll. Wooster, 1968; MEd, LaVerne (Calif.) Coll., 1975; postgrad., Akron U., Ashland (Ohio) Coll. Cert. elem. tchr., prin., spl. edn. tchr. Tchr. Mansfield (Ohio) City Schs., 1968-77, adminstr., 1977—, dist. energy officer, 1980-83, dir. elem. summer reinforcement program, 1986-88. Martha Holden Jennings Found. scholar, 1977. Mem. ASCD, Ohio Assn. Elem. Sch. Prins., Mansfield Adminstrs. Assn., Ashland-Richland-Morrow County Assn. Elem. Sch. Prins. (pres. 1990-91), Mohican Assn. Edn. of Young Children, Mansfield Univ. Club, Jaycees, Elks, Phi Delta Kappa (Mohican Area Ohio chpt., area chpt. 1231, divsn. V). Republican. Presbyterian. Avocations: reading, travel, snow skiing, tennis, camping. Home: 79 Redwood Rd Mansfield OH 44907-2430 Office: Mansfield City Schs 53 W 4th St Mansfield OH 44902-1210

OGDON, WILBUR, composer, music educator; b. Redlands, Calif., Apr. 19, 1921; s. Alfred Benjamin and Ethel (Brooks) O.; m. Beverly Jean Porter, Aug. 22, 1958; children—Bethany, Benjamin, Erica. MusB, U. Wis., 1942; MA, Hamline U., 1947; postgrad., U. Calif., Berkeley, 1949-50; pvt. composition studies with René Leibowitz, Paris, 1952-53; composition studies Ph.D., Ind. U., 1955. Asst. prof. U. Tex., 1947-50; prof. Coll. St. Catherine, St. Paul, 1955-56; assoc. prof. Ill. Wesleyan U., 1956-65; dir. music Pacifica Found., KPFA, Berkeley, Calif., 1962-64; coordinator music programming U. Ill., 1965-66; prof. music U. Calif., San Diego, 1966-91, chmn. dept. music, 1966-71; research fellow Project for Music Expt., 1973-74. Author: (with Krenek and Stewart) Horizons Circled, 1974; mem. editorial bd. Perspective of New Music; composer: Three Sea Choruses, 1960-62, String Quartet, 1960, By the Isar, 1969, Un Tombeau de Cocteau, I, 1964, II, 1972, III, 1975, Sappho, The Awakening (chamber opera), 1976-80, Capriccio and Five Comments for Orch., 1980, Images, A Winter's Calendar (Soprano, piano and 3 winds), 1980, Six Small Trios for trumpet, marimba and piano, 1982, Five Preludes for violin and piano, 1982, Summer Images and Reflections, 1984-85, Five Preludes for Violin and Chamber Orchestra, 1985, Two Serenades for Wind Quintet, 1987, 90-94, Two Sea Chanteys for soprano, baritone and percussion, 1987-88, Seven Piano Pieces, 1987, 7 pieces and a Capriccio for violin and piano, 1988-89, Four D.H. Lawrence Songs for Soprano and Chamber Ensemble, 1989, 13 Expressions for solo violin and chamber ensemble, 1993, others. Bd. dirs. San Diego Opera Inc., 1967-70, La Jolla Civic Orch. and Chorus Assn., 1967-72, 80-82; hon. dir. N.C. Gov.'s Bd. Music, 1964—. Served with AUS, 1942-46. Nat. Endowment of Arts fellow, 1975. Mem. Anton Webern Soc. (charter), Music Execs. Calif., Calif. Profl. Music Tchrs. Assn. (hon.). Home: 452 15th St Del Mar CA 92014-2521 Office: U Calif at San Diego Dept Music La Jolla CA 92037 *As years pass, one becomes increasingly aware of an indebtedness to others: to those who taught, encouraged, tolerated and even sacrificed. That increasing sense of indebtedness serves to sustain one's own efforts to teach and encourage.*

OGG, GEORGE WESLEY, retired foreign service officer; b. Washington, June 13, 1932; s. William Raymond and Carrie (Blair) O.; m. Frances Zabilsky, Sept. 17, 1954; children: David Stuart, Carolyn Ogg Tripp. A.B., Colgate U., N.Y., 1954; M.A., George Washington U., Washington, 1970; postgrad., U. Md., College Park, 1968-69, Nat. Def. Coll., Can., 1977-78. Chief econ. sect. U.S. Embassy, San Jose, Costa Rica, 1974-77; chief commodities and developing countries div. State of State, 1978-80; dep. dir. Office Canadian Affairs, Dept. of State, 1980-82; consul gen. U.S. Consulate Gen., Vancouver, B.C., Can., 1982-86; prof. internat. rels. Nat. Defense U., Washington, 1986-91. Served to 1st lt. USAF, 1954-57. Recipient Superior Honor award U.S. Dept. State, 1974, Meritorious Honor award, 1980. Avocations: tennis, photography.

OGG, JAMES ELVIS, microbiologist, educator; b. Centralia, Ill., Dec. 24, 1924; s. James and Amelia (Glammeyer) O.; m. Betty Jane Ackerson, Dec. 27, 1948; children—James George, Susan Kay. B.S., U. Ill., 1949; Ph.D., Cornell U., 1956. Bacteriologist Biol. Labs., Ft. Detrick, Md., 1950-53; cons. Biol. Labs., 1953-56, med. bacteriologist, 1956-58; prof. microbiology Colo. State U., Ft. Collins, 1958-85, prof. emeritus, 1985—; asst. dean Grad. Sch., 1965-66, head dept. microbiology, 1967-77; dir. Advanced Sci. Edn. Program div. grad. edn. in sci. NSF, Washington, 1966-67; Fulbright-Hays sr. lectr. in microbiology, Nepal, 1976-77, 81; acad. adminstrn. advisor Inst. Agr. and Animal Sci., Tribhuvan U., Nepal, 1976-77, 81. Cons. NASA, 1968-69, NSF, 1968-73, Martin Marietta Corp., 1970-76; cons.-evaluator North Central Assn. Colls. and Secondary Schs., 1974-89; cons. Consortium for Internat. Devel., 1990—; Winrock Internat. Inst. for Agrl. Devel., 1992—. Contbr. articles to profl. jours. Served with AUS, 1943-46, 50-51. Fellow AAAS, Am. Acad. Microbiology; mem. Am. Soc. Microbiology (chmn. pub. service and adult edn. com. 1975-80). Home: 1442 Ivy St Fort Collins CO 80525-2348

OGG, WILSON REID, poet, lyricist, curator, publisher, lawyer, educator; b. Alhambra, Calif., Feb. 26, 1928; s. James Brooks and Mary (Wilson) O. Student Pasadena Jr. Coll., 1946; A.B., U. Calif. at Berkeley, 1949, J.D., 1952; Cultural D in Philosophy of Law, World Univ. Roundtable, 1983. Bar: Calif. Assoc. trust Dept. Wells Fargo Bank, San Francisco, 1954-55; pvt. practice law, Berkeley, 1955-78; adminstrv. law judge, 1974-93; real estate broker, cons., 1974-78; curator-in-residence Pinebrook, 1964—; owner Pinebrook Press, Berkeley, Calif., 1988—; rsch. atty., legal editor dept. of continuing edn. of bar U. Calif. Extension, 1988; instr. 25th Sta. Hosp., Taegu, Korea, 1954; English instr. Taegu English Lang. Inst., Taegu, 1954. Trustee World U., 1976-80; dir. admissions Internat. Soc. for Phil. Enquiry, 1981-84; dep. dir. gen. Internat. Biographical Centre, Eng., 1986—; dep. gov. Am. Biographical Inst. Research Assn., 1986—. Served with AUS, 1952-54. Cert. community coll. instr. Mem. VFW, AAAS, ABA, State Bar Calif., San Francisco Bar Assn., Am. Arbitration Assn. (nat. panel arbitrators), World Univ. Round Table, World Future Soc. (profl. mem.), Calif. Soc. Psychical Study (pres., chmn. bd. 1963-65), Parapsychol. Assn. (assoc.), Internat. Soc. Unified Sci., Am. Acad. Polit. and Social Sci., Artists Embassy Internat., Internat. Soc. Poets, (life), Internat. Platform Assn., Amnesty Internat., Am. Civil Liberties Union, Intertel, Mensa, Lawyers in Mensa, Triple Nine Soc., Wisdom Soc., Inst. Noetic Scis., Psychic Sci. Spl. Interest Group, Men's Inner Circle of Achievement, Truman Libr. Inst. (hon.), Am. Legion, Faculty Club (U. Calif.), City Commons Club (Berkeley), Commonwealth Club of California, Town Hall Club of Calif., Marines Meml. Club, Masons, Shriners, Elks. Unitarian. Contbr. numerous articles profl. jours; contbr. poetry to various mags. including American Poetry Anthology Vol. VI Number 5, Hearts on Fire: A Treasury of Poems on Love, Vol. IV, 1987, New Voices in American Poetry, 1987, The Best Poems of the 90's, Distinguished Poets of America, The Poetry of Life A Treasury of Moments Am. Poetry Anthology, Vol. VII, 1988, Nat. Libr. Poems, 1992, Disting. Poets Of Am., 1993. Home: Pinebrook 1104 Keith Ave Berkeley CA 94708-1607 Office: 8 Bret Harte Way Berkeley CA 94708-1611

OGIDA, MIKIO, history of religion educator; b. Akita, Japan, Jan. 20, 1938; s. Shigeji and Kiyono (Sato) O.; m. Noriko Yamamoto, May 3, 1966; 1 child, Satoshi. BD, Doshisha U., Kyoto, Japan, 1961; S.T.M., Doshisha U., 1963; ThM, Harvard U., 1969. Assoc. minister Heian Ch., United Ch. of

Christ in Japan, Kyoto, 1963-66; lectr. Kobe Jogakuin U., Nishinomiya, Hyogo, Japan, 1969-72; assoc. prof. Kobe Jogakuin U., 1972-81, prof., 1981—, dean students, 1989-93. Author: Religions of the World, 1981. Mem. Japan Soc. Christian Studies, Soc. Hist. Studies Christianity Japan, Classical Soc. Japan. Avocation: igo, skiing. Home: 4 11 1 108 Makami cho, Takatuki shi Osaka, Japan Office: Kobe Jogakuin U, 4 1 Okadayama, Nishinomiya Hyogo, Japan

OGIER, WALTER THOMAS, retired physics educator; b. Pasadena, Calif., June 18, 1925; s. Walter Williams and Aileen Vera (Polhamus) O.; m. Mayrene Miriam Gorton, June 27, 1954; children: Walter Charles, Margaret Miriam, Thomas Earl, Kathryn Aileen. B.S., Calif. Inst. Tech., 1947, Ph.D. in Physics, 1953. Research fellow Calif. Inst. Tech., 1953; instr. U. Calif. at Riverside, 1954-55, asst. prof. physics, 1955-60; asst. prof. physics Pomona Coll., Claremont, Calif., 1960-62, assoc. prof., 1962-67, prof. physics, 1967-89, prof. emeritus, 1989—, chmn. dept., 1972-89. Contbr. articles on metals, liquid helium, X-rays and proton produced X-rays to profl. jours. Served with USNR, 1944-46. NSF Sci. Faculty fellow, 1966-67. Mem. Am. Phys. Soc., Am. Assn. Physics Tchrs. (pres. So. Calif. sect. 1967-69), Tau Beta Pi. Home: 8555 San Gabriel Rd Atascadero CA 93422-4928

OGILVIE, DONALD GORDON, bankers association executive; b. N.Y.C., Apr. 7, 1943; s. John B. and Ann (Stephens) O.; m. Fan Staunton, Apr. 18, 1966; children: Jennifer B., Adam C. B.A., Yale U., 1965; M.B.A., Stanford U., 1967. Systems analyst Dept. of Def., Washington, 1967-68; pres., dir. ICF Inc., Washington, 1969-73; dep. assoc. dir. Office of Mgmt. and Budget, Washington, 1973-74, assoc. dir., 1974-76; assoc. dean Yale U., New Haven, 1977-80; v.p. Celanese Corp., N.Y.C., 1980-85; exec. v.p. Am. Bankers Assn., Washington, 1985—; dir. Colonial Bancorp, 1979-85, MacDermid Corp., 1986—, Marine Spill Response Corp., 1991—. Bd. dirs. N.Y.C. Ballet, 1981-88; bd. dirs. Hospice Edn. and Research, New Haven, 1978-81; mem. adv. bd. Yale Sch. Orgn. and Mgmt., 1992—; mem. Coun. Excellence in Govt., 1993—. Home: 1425 34th St NW Washington DC 20007-2804 Office: Am Bankers Assn 1120 Connecticut Ave NW Washington DC 20036-3902

OGILVIE, KELVIN KENNETH, chemistry educator; b. Windsor, N.S., Nov. 6, 1942; s. Carl Melbourn and Mabel Adelia (Wile) O.; m. Emma Roleen, May 7, 1964; children: Kristine, Kevin. B.Sc. with honors, Acadia U., 1964, D.Sc. honoris causa, 1983; Ph.D., Northwestern U., 1968; D.Sc. honoris causa, U. N.B., Can., 1991. Assoc. prof. U. Man., Winnipeg, 1968-74; prof. chemistry McGill U., Montreal, 1974-88, Can. Pacific prof. biotech., 1984-87; bd. dirs. St. Lawrence Sci. Adv. Bd., Biologicals, Toronto, Ont., 1979-84; dir. Office of Biotech. McGill U., 1984-87; v.p. acad. affairs, prof. chemistry Acadia U., Wolfville, N.S., 1987-93; pres., vice-chancellor, 1993—; invited lectr. on biotechnology Tianjin, People's Republic of China, 1985; Snider lectr. U. Toronto, 1991; Gwen Leslie Meml. lectr., 1991; mem. Nat. Adv. Bd. Sci. and Tech., 1994—; chair selection com. Indsl. Postgrad. Scholarship Program, NSERCC, 1994; mem. Coun. Nova Scotia U. Pres., 1993—; mem. Coun. of Applied Sci. and Tech. for N.S., 1988-93; mem. Nat. Biotech. Adv. Com., 1988—; mem. Fisher (Can.) Biotech. Adv. Ctr., 1989-92; bd. dirs. N.S. Rsch. Found. Corp. 1990-91; mem. sci. adv. bd. Allelix Biopharms., 1991-93; chair adv. bd. NRC Inst. for Marine Bioscis., 1990-93; mem. steering com. on biotech. labor Can., 1990-92; chair Atlantic regional com. Prime Min.'s Awards for Teaching Excellence in Sci., Tech. and Math., 1993—; chair regional planning forum for a pharm. industry, Atlantic, Can., 1993. Mem. editorial bd. Nucleosides and Nucleotides, 1981-92; contbr. over 150 articles to profl. jours.; holder 14 patents. Bd. dirs. Plant Biotech. Inst., 1987-90. Decorated Knight of Malta, 1985, Order of Can., 1991; recipient Commemorative medal for 125th Anniversary of Confedn. Can., 1992, Buck-Whitney medal, 1983, Manning Prin. award, 1992; named to McLean's Honor Roll of Canadians Who Made a Difference, 1988; E.W.R. Steacie Meml. fellow, 1982-84. Fellow Chem. Inst. Can.; mem. Am. Chem. Soc., Ordre des Chemists of Que., Assn. Canadienne Française pour l'Advancement des Scis., Assn. Univs. and Colls. Can. (standing com. on rsch. 1993—). Achievements include inventing of BIOLF-62 (ganciclovir), antiviral drug used worldwide; developed general synthesis of RNA; developed original 'gene machine'; developed complete chemical synthesis of large RNA molecules. Home: PO Box 307, Canning, NS Canada B0P 1H0 Office: Acadia U, Office of Pres, Wolfville, NS Canada B0P 1X0

OGILVIE, RICHARD IAN, clinical pharmacologist; b. Sudbury, Ont., Can., Oct. 9, 1936; s. Patrick Ian and Gena Hilda (Olson) O.; m. Ernestine Tahedl, Oct. 9, 1965; children—Degen Elisabeth, Lars Ian. M.D., U. Toronto, 1960. Intern Toronto (Ont.) Gen. Hosp., 1960-61; resident Montreal Gen. and Univ. Alta. hosps., 1962-66; fellow in clin. pharmacology McGill U., Montreal, 1966-68; asst. prof. medicine, pharmacology and therapeutics McGill U., 1968-73, assoc. prof., 1973-78, prof., 1978-83, chmn. dept. pharmacology and therapeutics, 1978-83; clin. pharmacologist Montreal Gen. Hosp., 1968-83, dir. div. clin. pharmacology, 1976-83; prof. medicine and pharmacology U. Toronto, 1983—; dir. div. cardiology Toronto Western Hosp., 1983-88, div. clin. pharmacology, 1983-91; mem. pharm. grants com. Med. Research Coun. Can., 1977-82, chmn. 1980-82; mem. med. adv. com. Que. Heart Found., 1976-82, chmn. 1977-81. Editor Hypertension Canada, 1989—. Bd. dirs. PMAC Health Care Found., 1986-92; hon. sec.-treas. Banting Research Found., 1984-87, chmn. grant rev. com., 1985-86. Decorated knight comdr. Sovereign Mil. Order St. John of Jerusalem, Knights of Malta, 1987, nat. chmn.; recipient prize in med. ethics, 1988—, sci. advisor to the prior, 1987—, Knight Grand Cross, 1990; jury mem. Can. Prix Galien, 1994—; grantee Can. Kidney Found., J.C. Edwards Found., Med. Rsch. Coun., Que. Heart Found., Can. Found. Advancement Therapeutics, Conseil de la recherche en sante du Que. Fellow ACP, Royal Coll. Physicians of Can.; mem. Can. Soc. Clin. Investigation (coun. 1977-80), Can. Hypertension Soc. (bd. dirs. 1979-81, 89—, v.p. 1991-92, pres. 1992-93), Can. Found. Advancement Clin. Pharmacology (dir. 1978-86), Canadian Soc. for Clin. Pharmacology (pres. 1979-82, Sr. Investigator award 1993), Internat. Union Pharmacology (coun. mem. clin. pharmacology sect. 1981-84, chmn. 1984-87), Pharm. Soc. Can., Can. Cardiovascular Soc., Am. Soc. Pharmacology and Exptl. Therapeutics, Am. Soc. Clin. Pharm., Am. Fedn. Clin. Rsch., Toronto Hypertension Soc. (pres. 1988—). Home: 79 Collard Dr, King City, ON Canada L7B 1E4 Office: Toronto Hosp Western Div, 399 Bathurst St, Toronto, ON Canada M5T 2S8

OGILVIE, T(HOMAS) FRANCIS, engineer, educator; b. Atlantic City, Sept. 26, 1929; s. Thomas Fleisher and Frances Augusta (Wilson) O.; m. Joan Husselton, Sept. 11, 1950; children: Nancy Louise, Mary Beth, Kenneth Stuart. B.A. in Physics, Cornell U., 1950; M.Sc. in Aero. Engring., U. Md., 1957; Ph.D. in Engring. Sci., U. Calif., Berkeley, 1960. Physicist, David Taylor Model Basin, Dept. Navy, Bethesda, Md., 1951-62, 64-67; liaison scientist Office of Naval Research, London, 1962-63; assoc. prof. naval architecture and marine engring. U. Mich., Ann Arbor, 1967-70; prof. fluid mechanics U. Mich., 1970-81, chmn. dept. naval architecture and marine engring., 1973-81; prof. ocean engring. MIT, Cambridge, 1982—, head dept., 1982-94; vis. prof. naval architecture Osaka (Japan) U., 1976; vis. prof. math. U. Manchester, Eng., 1976. Contbr. articles to profl. jours. Mem. Soc. Naval Architects and Marine Engrs. (mem. council 1977-82, mem. exec. com. 1978-80, 83-84), Soc. Naval Architects of Japan, Kansai Soc. Naval Architects, West Japan Soc. Naval Architects, Sigma Xi, Phi Beta Kappa. Home: 110 Gray St Arlington MA 02174-6337 Office: MIT Dept Ocean Engring Cambridge MA 02139

OGILVY, DAVID MACKENZIE, advertising executive; b. West Horsley, Eng., June 23, 1911; s. Francis John Longley and Dorothy (Fairfield) O.; m. Herta Lans, July 9, 1973; 1 son, David Fairfield. Ed., Fettes Coll., Edinburgh, 1924-29, Christ Church, Oxford U., 1929-31. Asso. dir. Audience Research Inst., Princeton, 1939-42; with Brit. Security Coordination, 1942-44; 2d sec. Brit. embassy, Washington, 1944-45; founder, later chmn. Ogilvy & Mather (advt. agy.), 1948-73; chmn. bd. Ogilvy & Mather (advt. agy.), 1961-75; chmn. WPP Group, London, 1988-92, consultant, 1992—. Author: Confessions of an Advertising Man, 1963, Blood, Brains and Beer, 1978, Ogilvy on Advertising, 1983, The Unpublished David Ogilvy, 1988. Chmn. pub. participation com. Lincoln Center, 1959; trustee Colby Coll., 1963-69; bd. dirs. N.Y. Philharmonic, 1957-67; chmn. United Negro Coll. Fund, 1968; mem. of honor World Wildlife Fund Internat. Decorated comdr. Order Brit. Empire; recipient Parlin award Am. Mktg.

Assn., 1972; elected to Advt. Hall of Fame, 1977, officier de L'Ordre des Arts et des Lettres, 1990. Office: Chateau De Touffou, 86300 Bonnes France

OGLE, EDWARD PROCTOR, JR., investment counseling executive; b. Inglewood, Calif., Dec. 20, 1935; s. Edward Proctor and Allene Emma (Blumenthal) O.; m. Elizabeth Lovejoy Myers, Mar. 28, 1958; children: Kathryn Ogle Nava, Terry Ogle Nelson, Wendy Ogle Reeves. BA, U. So. Calif., 1964; MA, Claremont Grad. Sch., 1980. Cert. fin. planning practitioner. Zone mgr. Investors Diversified Svcs., Pasadena, Calif., 1964-66; asst. mgr. Merrill Lynch Pierce Fenner Smith, Pasadena, 1966-72; mgr. Clark Dodge & Co-Capital Place Dept., L.A., 1972-74; sr. v.p. Security Pacific Bank - Pacific Century Group, L.A., 1974-86; mgr., registered prin. Brown Bros. Harriman & Co., L.A., 1986—. Author: (booklet) Role of Bank Trust Department, 1981; editor (booklet) Parade Operations Manual, 1992, 93. Sec. Tournament of Roses Assn., Pasadena, 1976—; mem. Town Hall of Calif., L.A., 1977—; mem. Rep. Presdl Task Force, Orange County, Calif., 1984—; mem. L.A. World Affairs Coun., 1985—; elder Presbyn. Ch. Recipient Corp. Fund Raising Cert. United Way, L.A., 1978-80, Exec. Mgmt. Cert. Claremont Grad. Sch., 1979, Mgmt. and Exec. Cert. Security Pacific Bank, L.A., 1981. Mem. Internat. Assn. Fin. Planners, Drucker Ctr. Mgmt. Assn., Claremont Grad. Sch. Alumni Assn. (pres. 1984-86), Pasadena Bond Club, Bond Club L.A., Jonathan Club. Republican. Avocations: photography, golf, basketball, music, travel. Office: Brown Bros Harriman & Co 355 S Grand Ave Ste 3250 Los Angeles CA 90071

OGLE, MARY ELLEN, nursing and surgical services executive; b. Waterbury, Conn., Oct. 11, 1944; d. William Joseph and Louise Jean (Brinche) Roach; m. William Henry Ogle, July 12, 1974; children: Patricia, Tracy. BSN, Syracuse U., 1969; MSN, Calif. State U., 1981. Staff nurse St. Joseph's Hosp., Syracuse, 1967-69; nursing supr. Meriden Wallingford Hosp., Meriden, Conn., 1969-71; nursing supr. ob-gyn clinic U.S. Army Hosp., Berlin, W. Germany, 1971-73; dir. home health, hosp. St. Agnes Med. Ctr., Fresno; unit dir. St. Agnes Med. Ctr., Fresno, 1979-81; asst. v.p. nursing St. Agnes Med. Ctr., 1981-83; v.p. nursing St. Agnes Med. Hosp. Fresno, 1983—; sec. Calif. Soc. Nsg. Administrn., Sacramento, 1988—; bd. mem. Calif. Soc. Nsg. Administrn., Sacramento, 1986-88. Author: Oncology Nsg Forum, 1982. Mem. Am. Orgn. Nurse Exec., Calif. Soc. Nursing (bd. mem. 1986-88), Service Administr. (sec. 1988–), Sigma Theta Tau Nursing, Alumni Assoc. Democrat. Roman Catholic. Office: St Agnes Med Ctr 1303 E Herndon Ave Fresno CA 93720-3309

OGLESBY, RAY THURMOND, aquatic science educator; b. Lynchburg, Va., Apr. 16, 1932; s. William Sterrett and Sadie (Thurmond) O.; m. Graciela Oglesby Rocha, July 4, 1955; children: Lisa, Scott, Karen; m. Janice Marie Ricardo, Aug. 20, 1982; stepchildren: William, Tamara, Christopher. B.S., U. Richmond, 1953; M.A., Coll. William and Mary, 1955; Ph.D., U. N.C. 1962. Fishery scientist U.S. Fish and Wildlife Service, Beaufort, N.C., 1957-58; asst. prof. U. Wash., Seattle, 1962-68, assoc. prof., 1968; assoc. prof. aquatic sci. Cornell U., Ithaca, N.Y., 1968-77, prof., 1977—, bd. dirs. Ctr. Environ. Research, 1981-84, chmn. natural resources, 1982-87, acting dir. lab. environ. applications remote sensing, 1990-91, acting dir. global environment program, 1991-92, dir. Biol. Field Sta., 1991-94; cons. FAO (UN), Rome, 1980—; mem. Cornell Univ. Assembly, 1992—, chmn., 1994—; mem. Cornell Univ. Health Bd., 1992-94. Editor: River Ecology and Man, 1972; contbr. chpts. to books. Pres. Wedgewood Comty. Assn., Seattle, 1966-67; advisor Ithaca Wastewater Treatment Comms., 1983; Basic EMT Varna Vol. Fire Dept., 1990-94. With USNR, 1955-57. Grantee EPA, 1964-68, 82-84, NSF, 1967-68, U.S. Dept. Interior, 1968-76, 91—, N.Y. State Electric and Gas, 1993-94, Rochester Gas & Electric, 1993-94, Hudson River Found., 1994-95. Home: 1776 Ellis Hollow Rd Ithaca NY 14850-9655 Office: Cornell U Dept Natural Resources Ithaca NY 14853

OGLESBY, SABERT, retired research institute administrator; b. Birmingham, Ala., May 14, 1921; s. Sabert Sr. and Myrtle (Dunn) O.; m. Carolyn Vance, Mar. 4, 1944; 1 child, Donald Thomas. B.S.E.E., Auburn U., 1943; M.S.E.E., Purdue U., 1951. Registered profl. engr., Ala. Research engr. So. Research Inst., Birmingham, 1946-48; various positions So. Research Inst., 1951-80, pres., 1980-87, pres. emeritus, 1987—; instr. Purdue U., West Lafayette, Ind., 1948-51. Author: Heat Pump Application; Electrostatic Precipitation. Mem. exec. bd. Birmingham Music Club, 1982—. 1st lt. Signal Corps, U.S. Army, 1943-46. Named to Ala. Engring. Hall of Fame, 1989. Mem. Internat. com. on Electrostatic Precipitation (steering com. 1978-85), Kiwanis (bd. dirs. 1982-83, 85-86), Vestavia Country Club, Sigma Xi, Tau Beta Pi, Eta Kappa Nu. Republican. Presbyterian. Avocations: golf; gem cutting; music. Home: 1348 Panorama Dr Birmingham AL 35216-3013

OGLETREE, THOMAS VINCENT, savings and loan association executive; b. Alva, Okla., Sept. 24, 1944; s. Lawrence Vincent and Thyra Lucille (Simms) O.; m. Lynda Beth Ogletree, Oct. 19, 1985; children: Robert, Cynthia, Colby. BSBA, U. Cen. Fla., 1972. CPA, Fla. Dep. sheriff Orange County Sheriff's Dept., Orlando, Fla., 1968-71; staff auditor Arthur Andersen & Co., Miami, 1972-75; chief fin. officer Landmark Banking Co., Ft. Lauderdale, Fla., 1975-86, Fla. Fed. Savs. and Loan, St. Petersburg, 1986—. Mem. Fla. Inst. CPA's, Am. Inst. CPA's. Republican. Methodist. Office: Fla Fed Savs & Loan Assn 360 Central Ave PO Box 1509 Saint Petersburg FL 33731 also: Unicorp Am Corp 99 Park Ave New York NY 10016-1503

OGLIARUSO, MICHAEL ANTHONY, chemist, educator; b. Bklyn., Aug. 10, 1938; s. Andrea and Anna (Bianco) O.; m. Basila Gallo, Apr. 2, 1961; 1 child, Michael Dana. B.S., Poly. Inst. Bklyn., 1960, Ph.D., 1965. Postdoctoral research asso. UCLA, 1965-67; asst. prof. chemistry Va. Poly. Inst. and State U., Blacksburg, 1967-72; assoc. prof. Va. Poly. Inst. and State U., 1972-78, prof., 1978—, assoc. dean Coll. Arts and Scis., 1984—. Contbr. articles to profl. jours. Served with C.E. U.S. Army, 1960-61. Mem. Am. Chem. Soc., Va. Acad. Sci., Sigma Xi, Phi Lambda Upsilon. Office: Coll Arts and Scis Williams Hall Va Poly Inst And State Blacksburg VA 24061 *I have been fortunate to be associated with the most personally rewarding profession available today, the professional education of young men and women. This career is best suited to persons who wish to remain young in spirit, since regardless of your age you are always surrounded with students who are between 18 and 22 years old. This is the best way I know to remain spiritually young.*

OGNIBENE, ANDRE J(OHN), physician, army officer, educator; b. N.Y.C., Nov. 18, 1931; s. Morris S. and Josephine C. (Macaluso) O.; m. Margaret A. Haug, Apr. 21, 1957; children: Judy, Andrea, Adrienne, Marc, Eric. B.A. cum laude, Columbia U., 1952; M.D., NYU, 1956. Diplomate Am. Bd. Internal Medicine, Am. Bd. Geriatrics, Am. Bd. Med. Mgmt. Intern in medicine Bellevue Hosp., N.Y.C., 1956-57; resident in medicine Bellevue Hosp., 1957-59; commd. capt. U.S. Army M.C., 1957, advanced through grades to brig. gen., 1978; resident in medicine Manhattan VA Hosp., N.Y.C. and chief resident in medicine, 1959-60; chief med. service U.S. Army Hosp., Nurnburg, Germany, 1961-62; chief dept. medicine U.S. Army Hosp., 1962-64; fellow in cardiology Walter Reed Gen. Hosp., Washington, 1964-65; asst. in cardiology Walter Reed Gen. Hosp., 1965-66, asst. chief dept. medicine, 1969-72; chief dept. medicine, chief profl. services U.S. Army Hosp., Ft. Meade, Md., 1966-68; cons. in medicine Hdqrs. U.S. Army, Vietnam, 1969; chief dept. medicine Brooke Army Med. Center, Ft. Sam Houston, Tex., 1972-76; dir. med. edn. Brooke Army Med. Center, 1976-78, dep. comdr. and chief profl. services, 1976-78, comdr., 1978-81; hosp. dir. San Antonio State Chest Hosp., 1981-85; program dir. internal medicine Canton, Ohio, 1985-95; assoc. dean for med. edn., med. dir. Timken Mercy Med. Ctr., Canton, 1995—; prof. medicine N.E. Ohio U., Rootstown, 1985—; chmn. dept. medicine N.E. Ohio U., 1989—; instr. medicine NYU, 1960; assoc. clin. prof. Georgetown U., 1972-77; adj. clin. prof. U. Tex. Health Sci. Center, San Antonio, 1973-85, mem. postgrad. adv. com., 1977-78; mem. Instl. Rev. Bd., 1981-85; pres. Bexar Met. unit Am. Cancer Soc., 1984; dir. Eisenhower Nat. Bank; bd. dirs. Cancer Therapy and Research Ctr.; chmn. South Tex. Epilepsy Found., 1985. Contbr. articles to med. publs.; editor, prin. author Internal Medicine in Vietnam, Vol. II, 1982; editor-in-chief Internal Medicine in Vietnam, vol. I, 1977. Bd. govs. S.W. Cancer Therapy Inst., 1982-85. Decorated Disting. Service medal, Legion of Merit, Meritorious Service medal, Army Commendation medal. Fellow ACP (laureate, master tchr.); Am. Coll. Physician Execs.; mem. N.Y. Acad. Scis., Am.

Fedn. Clin. Rsch., Bexar County Med. Soc., Stark County Med. Soc., Assn. Profs. Medicine, Alpha Omega Alpha. Home: 1409 Harbor Dr NW Canton OH 44708-3098 Office: 2600 6th St SW Canton OH 44710-1702 *Compassion must remain the universal prescription in medical practice. Technology can provide no solutions in the absence of humanity.*

O'GORMAN, JAMES FRANCIS, art educator, writer; b. St. Louis, Sept. 19, 1933; s. Paul Joseph and Dorothy Frances (Hogan) O'G.; m. Jean Baer, Feb. 9, 1957 (div. 1987); children—Christopher, Harold, Michael (dec.), Samuel. B.Arch., Washington U., St. Louis, 1956; M. Arch., U. Ill., 1960; Ph.D., Harvard U., 1966. Grace Slack McNeil prof. Am. art Wellesley Coll., Mass., 1975—. Author: H.H. Richardson and His Office: Selected Drawings, 1973; This Other Gloucester, 1976; H.H. Richardson. Architectural Forms for an American Society, 1987; ThreeAmerican Architects: Richardson, Sullivan, and Wright, 1865-1915, 1991; (with others) The Architecture of Frank Furness, 1974; editor, translator: Paul Frankl, Principles of Architectural History, 1968. Phila. Athenaeum fellow, 1985. Office: Wellesley Coll Dept Art 106 Central St Wellesley MA 02181-8203

O'GORMAN, KATHLEEN, newspaper editor. Education editor Detroit Free Press. Office: Detroit Free Press 321 W Lafayette Detroit MI 48226

O'GORMAN, PETER JOSEPH, retail company executive; b. Surbiton, Surrey, Eng., May 25, 1938; came to U.S., 1981; s. Peter and Noreen (O'Gorman) McCormack; m. Rosemary Anne Underhill, July 20, 1974; 1 child, Ruth. B in Nautical Sci., Nellists Nautical Coll., Gt. Britain, 1959; M in Nautical Sci., Auckland U., New Zealand, 1963. Cert. master mariner. Supermarket mgr., later sr. v.p. devel. Tesco Stores Ltd., London, 1964-81; pres. Doody Co., Columbus, Ohio, 1981-83; sr. v.p. devel. and mktg. Great Atlantic and Pacific Tea Co., Montvale, N.J., 1983-90, exec. v.p. real estate, store devel. and mktg., 1990—. Mem. Inst. Mktg. Gt. Britain. Office: Gt Atlantic & Pacific Tea Co Inc 2 Paragon Dr Montvale NJ 07645-1718

OGRA, PEARAY L., physician, educator; b. Srinagar, Kashmir, India, Mar. 19, 1939; came to U.S., 1961, naturalized, 1969; s. Govinda Kaul and Gunvati (Daftari) O.; m. Kathleen Marie Ogra; children: Sanjay, Monica. MB, Christian Med. Coll., Ludhiana, India, 1961. Intern Binghamton (N.Y.) Gen. Hosp., 1962-63; resident U. Chgo., 1963-64; resident N.Y. U.-Bellevue Med Center, 1964-66, fellow infectious diseases, 1966-68; asst. prof. pediatrics SUNY, Buffalo, 1968-71; assoc. prof. pediatrics and microbiology SUNY, 1972-74, prof., 1974-91; John Sealy disting. chair and prof., chmn. dept. pediatrics U. Tex. Med. Br., Galveston, 1991—; dir. div. virology Children's Hosp. Buffalo, 1969-81, chief dept. infectious diseases, 1970-91; dir. Clin. Labs. Children's Hosp., 1985-90; mem. study sect. NIH, 1979-85, maternal child health com., 1987-91; mem., chmn. bd. Internat. Pediat. Rsch. Found., Inc., 1984-89, respiratory diseases steering com. WHO. Recipient E. Mead Johnson award for Pediatric Research Am. Acad. Pediatrics, 1978; Kalhana award Kashmir Sci. Culture and Soc., 1984; Stockton Kimball award SUNY, 1985; Buswell fellow, 1968-71. Fellow Royal Soc. Medicine, Assn. Am. Physicians, Am. Acad. Pediatrics, Am. Acad. Microbiology; mem. Am. Soc. Clin. Investigation, Soc. Pediatric Rsch., Infectious Disease Soc. Am., Soc. Exptl. Biology and Medicine, Am. Assn. Immunologists, Am. Soc. Microbiology, AAAS, Am. Fedn. Clin. Rsch., Reticuloendothelial Soc., Am. Soc. Virology. Home: 8008 Channelview Dr Galveston TX 77554-9040

O'GRADY, DENNIS JOSEPH, lawyer; b. Hoboken, N.J., Nov. 16, 1943; s. Joseph A. and Eileen (Broderick) O'Grady; m. Mary Anne Amoruso, Sept. 9, 1966 (div. Apr. 1984); 1 child, Kara Anne. AB, Seton Hall Coll., 1965; MA, U. So. Calif., 1969; JD, Rutgers U., 1973. Bar: N.J. 1973, U.S. Ct. Appeals (3d cir.) 1975, U.S. Dist. Ct. N.J. 1984. Ptnr. Riker, Danzig, Scherer, Hyland & Perretti, Newark, Trenton and Morristown, N.J., 1974—; adj. asst. prof. of bus. law St. Peter's Coll., Jersey City, 1973—. Mem. ABA (bus./bankruptcy sect.), N.Y. State Bar Assn. (debtor/creditor sect.), Fed. Bar Assn., Am. Bankruptcy Inst. Democrat. Roman Catholic. Office: Riker Danzig Scherer Hyland & Perretti 1 Speedwell Ave Morristown NJ 07960-6838

O'GRADY, JOHN JOSEPH, III, lawyer; b. N.Y.C., Mar. 21, 1933; s. John Joseph and Terese (O'Rourke) O'G.; m. Mary E. McHugh, June 28, 1958; children—Glennon, Ellen, Carol, Paul. A.B., Holy Cross Coll., 1954; J.D., Harvard U., 1957. Bar: N.Y. 1958. Assoc. Cadwalader, Wickersham & Taft, N.Y.C., 1958-66, ptnr., 1966—. Mem. ABA, N.Y. State Bar Assn. Office: Cadwalader Wickersham & Taft 100 Maiden Ln New York NY 10038-4892

O'GRADY, WILLIAM M., manufacturing executive; b. Phila., 1939. Grad., Villanova U., 1961. Exec. v.p. adminstrn. CIT Group, Inc., N.Y.C. Office: CIT Group Holdings Inc 1211 Avenue Of The Americas New York NY 10036-8701

OGREN, CARROLL WOODROW, retired hospital administrator; b. Mpls., Mar. 22, 1927; s. Peter L. and Mabel (Wohleen) O.; m. Patricia Ann Sweeney. B.A., U. Minn., 1952; M.Hosp. Adminstrn., Washington U., St. Louis, 1958. Asst. adminstr. Washoe Med. Center, Reno, 1958-64; adminstr. Washoe Med. Center, 1964-80, Jean Hannah Clark Rehab. Center, Las Vegas, Nev., 1980-92. Served with USNR, 1944-46, 50-54, PTO. Mem. Am. Coll. Hosp. Adminstrs., Am. Hosp. Assn. (nat. com. state hosp. assn. 1967—), Nev. Hosp. Assn. (pres. 1961-62, sec. 1961-66). Club: Gourmet Toastmasters (Reno) (pres. 1960). Home: 5860 Via Manigua Las Vegas NV 89120-2348

OGREN, ROBERT EDWARD, biologist, educator; b. Jamestown, N.Y., Feb. 9, 1922; s. David Paul and Mary Gladys (Ahlstrom) O.; m. Jean Blose Jackson, Aug. 28, 1948; children: Paul Robert, Philip Edward. B.A., Wheaton Coll., 1947; M.S., Northwestern U., 1948; Ph.D., U. Ill., 1953. Asst. prof. biology Ursinus Coll., Collegeville, Pa., 1953-57, Dickinson Coll., Carlisle, Pa., 1957-63; mem. faculty Wilkes Coll., Wilkes-Barre, Pa., 1963—; prof. biology, 1981-86, prof. emeritus, 1986—. Contbr. articles to profl. lit. Bd. dirs. Northeastern Pa. chpt. Am. Heart Assn., 1971-88; chmn. bd. Northeastern Pa. chpt. Am. HeartAssn., 1973-76; bd. dirs. Wyo. Valley West Sch. Dis., 1973-79, pres., 1979. Served with AUS, 1943-46. Recipient Frank B. Shepela Meml. Vol. award Northeastern Pa. Heart Assn., 1977; NSF grantee, 1960, 63, 65. Fellow AAAS; mem. Am. Soc. Zoologists, Am. Soc. Parasitologists, Am. Micros. Soc., Soc. Protzoologists, Electron Micros. Soc. Am., Wyo. Commemorative Assn., Pa. Acad. Sci. (editor procs. 1961-62 Darbaker award 1989), Soc. Systematic Zoology, N.Y. Acad. Sci., Helminthological Soc. Washington, AAUP, Ecol. Soc. Am., Nat. Audubon Soc., Western N.Y. Geneol. Soc., Wyo. Hist. and Geol. Soc., Sigma Xi (chpt. pres. 1981-82). Republican. Presbyterian. Home: 88 Lathrop St Wilkes Barre PA 18704-4811 Office: Wilkes Univ S Franklin St Wilkes Barre PA 18701-1201 *To be involved as a citizen in some aspect of community life. To use academe as an opportunity to prepare scholarly works for publication advancing knowledge in your discipline. To work beyond your limitations. To recognize opportunities and use them for making progress. To be positive, honest, creative and persevering. To enjoy the fruits of your labor and the freedom of expression and movement in our great land.*

OGREN, WILLIAM LEWIS, physiologist, educator; b. Ashland, Wis., Oct. 8, 1938; m. Carolyn Schottland, June 24, 1967; children: Jason, Aaron, Susan. BS, U. Wis. 1961; PhD, Wayne State U., 1965. Research chemist Parker Rust Proof Co., Detroit, 1961-62; plant physiologist U.S. Dept. Agr., Urbana, Ill., 1965-79, research leader, 1979—; asst. prof. U. Ill., Urbana, 1966-72, assoc. prof., 1972-77, prof., 1977—. Recipient von Humboldt award Alexander von Humboldt Found., 1990. Fellow Crop Sci. Soc. Am. (Rsch. award 1979), Am. Acad. Arts and Scis., Am. Soc. Agronomy; mem. AAAS, NAS, Am. Soc. Plant Physiologists (sec. 1987-89, pres. 1990-91, Kettering award 1986), Am. Soc. for Biochemistry and Molecular Biology, Japanese Soc. Plant Physiologists. Office: USDA 1201 W Gregory Dr Urbana IL 61801-3838

OGUL, MORRIS SAMUEL, political science educator, consultant; b. Detroit, Apr. 15, 1931; s. Jack and Sarah (Zimmerman) O.; m. Eleanor Simon, Aug. 26, 1954. B.A., Wayne State U., 1952; M.A., U. Mich., 1953, Ph.D. 1958. Instr.. polit. sci. U. Pitts., 1957-59, asst. prof., 1959-64, assoc. prof., 1964-67, prof., 1967—; cons. U.S. Ho. of Reps., 1973, 83, U.S. Office Per-

sonnel Mgmt., Washington, 1975—, U.S. Senate, 1977. Author: (with William J. Keefe) American Legislative Process, 1964, 7th edit., 1989, 8th edit., 1993, Congress Oversees the Bureaucracy, 1976. Carnegie Corp. research grantee, 1965-68. Mem. Am. Polit. Sci. Assn., Midwest Polit. Sci. Assn. (council 1982-84), Pa. Polit. Sci. Assn. Democrat. Home: 1500 Cochran Rd Apt 814 Pittsburgh PA 15243-1068 Office: U Pitts Dept Polit Sci 4n25 Forbes Quadrangle Pittsburgh PA 15260-7454

OH, JOHN KIE-CHIANG, political science educator, university official; b. Seoul, Korea, Nov. 1, 1930; came to U.S., 1954, naturalized, 1971; s. Sung-Jun and Duk-Cho (Kim) O.; m. Bonnie Cho, Sept. 5, 1959; children: Jane J., Marie J., James J. B.S., Marquette U., 1957; postgrad., Columbia U., 1957-58; Ph.D., Georgetown U., 1962. Asst. prof. St. Thomas Coll., St. Paul, 1962-66; assoc. prof. Marquette U., Milw., 1967-71, prof., chmn., 1971-77, dean grad. sch., 1977-85; acad. v.p. Cath. U. Am., Washington, 1985-89, prof. politics dept., 1990—. Author: Korea: Democracy on Trial, 1968, (with Peter Cheng et. al.) Emerging Roles of Asian Nations in the 1980's, 1979, Democratization and Economic Development in Korea, 1990; contbr. articles to profl. jours. Chmn. scholarship com. World Affairs Council, 1976-78; mem. Wis. Gov.'s Commn. for UN, Madison, 1971-74; chmn. Korean Studies com., Assn. Asian Studies, 1975-76. Grantee Hill Found., 1963, Relm Found., 1968, Social Sci. Rsch Coun., 1973, Am. Coun. Learned Socs., 1973. Mem. Am. Polit. Sci. Assn., Assn. Asian Studies, Internat. Polit. Sci. Assn., Midwest Conf. Asian Affairs (pres. 1970-71, nat. chmn. China-Japan-Korea-The Philippines-Thailand sect.) Fulbright Hays Program, Assn. Cath. Colls. and Univs. (bd. dirs. 1983-87). Roman Catholic. Home: 8807 Maxwell Dr Potomac MD 20854-3123 Office: Cath U Am Politics Dept Washington DC 20064

OH, WILLIAM, physician; b. The Philippines, May 22, 1931; came to U.S., 1958, naturalized, 1970; s. Bun Kun and Chay Suat (Lim) O.; m. Mary Oh, June 4, 1960; children—Kenneth Albert, Kerstin Amy. M.D., U. Santo Tomas, Phillipines, 1958; M.A. (hon.), Brown U., 1974. Diplomate Am. Bd. Pediatrics, Am. Bd. Neonatal Perinatal Medicine. Intern Deaconess Hosp., Milw., 1958-59; resident in pediatrics Michael Reese Hosp., Chgo., 1959-63; fellow in neonatology Kavolinska Inst., Stockholm, 1963-65; dir. neonatology Michael Reese Hosp., Chgo., 1965-69; dir. neonatology, assoc. prof. pediatrics UCLA, 1969-73, prof., 1973-74; prof. pediatrics and obstetrics Brown U., Providence, 1974-88, Sylvia Hassenfeld prof. pediatrics, chmn. dept., 1989—; pediatrician-in-chief Women and Infants Hosp. of R.I., Providence, 1974—, R.I. Hosp.; prof., chmn. dept. pediatrics Brown U., 1989—; mem. NIH study sect. on human embryology and devel., chmn., 1985—; mem. pediatric test com. Bd. Med. Exam., 1985-89; mem. sub-bd. of neonatal-perinatal medicine Am. Bd. Pediatrics, 1982-88; chair com. on Fetus and Newborn, Am. Acad. Pediatrics; mem. Nat. Adv. Coun. for Child Health, 1995—. Author book in field; contbr. chpts. to books, numerous articles to profl. jours.; editor profl. jour. Adv. com. Nat. Found. of March of Dimes. NIH grantee. Mem. Am. Pediatric Soc., Am. Acad. Pediatrics (fetus and newborn com. 1986—), Soc. Pediatric Research, Perinatal Research Soc. (pres. 1981), Am. Inst. Nutrition, Fedn. Am. Socs. Exptl. Biology. Roman Catholic. Club: University. Home: 24 Robbins Dr Barrington RI 02806-2612 Office: 101 Dudley St Providence RI 02905-2401

O'HAGAN, JAMES JOSEPH, lawyer; b. Chgo., Dec. 29, 1936; s. Francis James and Florence Agnes (Dowgialo) O'H.; m. Suzanne Elizabeth Wiegand, June 28, 1958; children: Timothy, Karen, Peggy, Kevin. B in Commerce, De Paul U., 1958, JD, 1962. Law clk. Querrey & Harrow, Chgo., 1958-62, assoc., 1963-67, ptnr., 1968—, chmn. mgmt., 1985—; lawyer Chgo. Claim Mgrs. Assn., Chgo., 1992-93. Bd. dirs. Park Ridge (Ill.) Fine Arts Soc., 1984—, pres., 1992-94. Mem. ABA, Ill. Bar Assn. Chgo. Bar Assn. (mediator mediation program), Internat. Assn. Def. Coun., Trial Lawyers Club. Roman Catholic. Avocations: golf, tennis, physical conditioning, painting, reading. Office: Querrey & Harrow 180 N Stetson Ave Chicago IL 60601-6710

O'HAGAN, WILLIAM D., metal products executive; b. Bayonne, NJ, 1942. Graduate, Rutgers U., New Brunswick, N.J.; Post-Graduate, Harvard U., Cambridge, Mass. V.p.-gen. mgr., residental divsn. Nibco Inc., Elkhart, Ind.; coo Mueller Industries, Inc., Wichita, Kans. Office: Nibco Inc PO Box 1167 Elkhart IN 46515 Home: 50746 Andover Terr Granger IN 46530

O'HAIR, JOHN D., lawyer, county prosecuting attorney; b. Detroit, Sept. 29, 1929; s. Walter R. and Willis W. (Watts) O.; m. Barbara Stanton, Jan. 15, 1966; 1 child: John Dennis. B.A., DePauw U., 1951; J.D., Detroit Coll. Law, 1954. Bar: Mich. 1954. Asst. corp. counsel City of Detroit, 1957-65; judge Common Pleas Ct., Detroit, 1965-68; judge Wayne County Cir. Ct., 1968-83; Wayne County pros. atty., 1983—; Wayne County corp. counsel, 1983—; mem. Mich. Jud. Tenure Commn., 1977-82. Trustee, Detroit Coll. Law, 1982—. Served with Intelligence Corps, U.S. Army, 1955-56. Mem. ABA, Mich. Bar Assn. Democrat. Presbyterian. Office: 1441 St Antoine 12th fl F Murphy Hall of Justice Detroit MI 48226

O'HAIRE, KAREN A., lawyer; b. San Francisco, Jan. 14, 1953; d. Bernard Francis and Dorothy June O'Haire. BS, U. Calif., Davis, 1974; MPA, Calif. State U., Sacramento, 1980; cert. pub. sector labor rels., U. Calif. Extension, Davis, 1983; JD, McGeorge Sch. Law, Sacramento, 1989. Bar: Calif. 1989, U.S. Dist.t Ct. (ea. dist.) Calif. 1989, U.S. Dist. Ct. (so. dist.) Calif. 1990. Assoc. planner Sacramento Regional Area Planning Commn., 1974-80; sr. land use analyst Calif. Regional Water Quality Control Bd. Cen. Valley Region, Sacramento, 1980-89; staff counsel Calif. State Water Resources Control Bd., Sacramento, 1989—; arbitrator Am. Arbitration Assn., San Francisco. Commr. City of Davis Design Rev. Bd., 1973-75. Mem. ABA (chair and vice chair sect. natural resources, energy and environ. law 1989—), Commonwealth Club. Office: Calif St Wtr Rescs Ctl Bd 901 P St Sacramento CA 95814-6418

OHALA, JOHN JEROME, linguistics educator; b. Chgo., July 19, 1941; s. Stanley Andreas and Grace Marie (Mack) O.; m. Manjari Agrawal, Nov. 24, 1969. AB, U. Notre Dame, 1963; postgrad., U. Iowa, 1963-64; MA, UCLA, 1966, PhD, 1969; PhD (hon.), U. Copenhagen, 1992. Asst. prof. dept. linguistics U. Calif., Berkeley, 1970-72, assoc. prof., 1972-77, prof., 1977—; vis. lektor Inst. Phonetics, Copenhagen U., 1973; vis. prof. dept. linguistics UCLA, 1981; vis. prof. dept. hearing and speech sci. U. Md., College Park, 1982; vis. prof. dept. linguistics U. Alta. (Can.), Edmonton, 1991-92; pres. Permanent Coun. Internat. Conf. Spoken Lang. Processing, 1992—; chair Internat. Confs. Spoken Lang. Processing, Banff, 1992. Author; co-editor: Experimental Phonology, 1986, Sound Symbolism, 1994; author, guest co-editor vol. 3 Phonology Yearbook, 1986; N.Am. editor Phonetica, 1986-89; adv. editor Jour. Phonetics, 1985—; Speech Comm., 1993—, Edn., Speech Sci. and Phonetics Pergamon Ency. of Lang. and Linguistics, 1994; subject of Festschrift in Lang. and Speech, vol. 35, 1992. Grantee NSF, 1975-80, post doctoral fellow, 1969-70; grantee Harry Frank Guggenheim Found., 1981-82; sr. Fulbright lectureship Inst. Phonetics, Copenhagen U., 1985. Mem. Acoustical Soc. Am., Linguistic Soc. Am., N.Y. Acad. Scis., Internat. Phonetic Assn. (coun. 1985—), European Speech Comm. Assn. Democrat. Avocations: collecting rare books, bookbinding, photography. Home: 1149 Hillview Rd Berkeley CA 94708-1705 Office: Univ of Calif Dept Linguistics Berkeley CA 94720

O'HALLORAN, THOMAS ALPHONSUS, JR., physicist, educator; b. Bklyn., Apr. 13, 1931; s. Thomas Alphonsus Sr. and Nora (Sheehan) O'H.; m. Barbara Joyce Hug, June 4, 1954; children: Theresa Joyce, Maureen Ann, Kevin Thomas, Patrick Joseph. Student, San Jose State U., 1948-50; BS in Physics & Math., Oreg. State U., 1953, MS in Physics, 1954; PhD, U. Calif. Berkeley, 1963. Rsch. asst. Lawrence Berkeley Lab., U. Calif., 1963-64; rsch. fellow Harvard U., Cambridge, Mass., 1964-66; asst. prof. physics U. Ill., Urbana, 1966-68, assoc. prof., 1968-70, prof., 1970-93, prof. emeritus, 1993—; vis. scholar U. Utah, Salt Lake City, 1990-93, rsch. prof. physics, 1993—; mem. program adv. com. Argonne Nat. Lab., Lemont, Ill., Fermi Lab., Batavia, Ill., Brookhaven Nat. Lab., Upton, L.I.; vis. scientist Lawrence Berkeley Lab., U. Calif., 1979-80. Contbr. numerous articles on elem. particle physics to profl. jours. Lt. USN, 1954-58. Guggenheim fellow, 1979-80. Fellow Am. Phys. Soc. Home: 4614 Ledgemont Dr Salt Lake City UT 84124-4735 Office: U Utah Physics Dept 201 Jfb Salt Lake City UT 84112

OHAMA, YOSHIHIKO, architectural engineer, educator; b. Shimonoseki, Japan, Mar. 29, 1937; s. Yoshihiro and Kikuno O.; m. Ikuko Ohama, Mar. 24, 1966; children: Akiko, Noriko, Hiroshi. BE, Yamaguchi U., Japan, 1959; PhD, Tokyo Inst. Tech., 1974. Rsch. engr. cen. rsch. lab. Onoda Cement Co., Ltd., Koto-ku, Tokyo, 1959-66; rsch. engr. and dept. head Bldg. Rsch. Inst. Japanese Govt., Tokyo, 1966-76; from assoc. prof. to prof. Nihon U., Koriyama, Fukushima-ken, Japan, 1976—; rsch. engr. Inst. Indsl. Sci., U. Tokyo, 1972-81; adv. prof. Tongji U., Shanghai, 1990—; guest prof. Shandong Inst. Bldg. Materials, Jinan, China, 1991—; v.p. Internat. Congress on Polymers in Concrete, Detroit, 1987—; chmn. Polymers in Concrete Com., Japan Tech. Transfer Assn., Tokyo, 1987—. Author: Polymeric Waterproofing Work, 1972, Handbook of Polymer-Modified Concrete and Mortars, 1995; co-author: Plastics Concrete, 1965, Building Materials, 1981, Concrete Admixtures Handbook, 1984, Modern Construction Materials, 1990, Polymers in Concrete, 1994. Mem. ASTM, Am. Concrete Inst. Materials Rsch. Soc., Internat. Union Testing and Rsch. Labs. for Materials and Structures (chmn. tech. com. 113-CPT, 151-APC), Soc. for Advancement of Material and Process Engring. (Japan chpt., chmn. advanced constrn. tech. com.), Soc. Materials Sci. Japan, Archtl. Inst. Japan, Japan Concrete Inst. Avocations: travel, mountaineering, ham. Home: 14-10-402, Hiyoshi 2-chome, Kohoku-ku, Yokohama Kanagawa-ken 223, Japan Office: Nihon U, Coll Engring, Koriyama Fukushima-ken 963, Japan

OHANIAN, KREKOR See CONNORS, MIKE

OHANIAN, MIHRAN JACOB, engineering educator; b. Istanbul, Turkey, Aug. 7, 1933; came to U.S., 1956, naturalized, 1967; s. Mark and Mary Catherine (Sayabalian) O.; m. Sandra Jean Blair, Apr. 22, 1962; children: Heather Jean Allen, Holly Lynn. B.S.E.E. with high honors, Robert Coll. Engring. Sch., Istanbul, 1956; M.E.E., Rensselaer Poly. Inst., 1960, Ph.D. in Nuclear Engring. and Sci., 1963. Lectr. nuclear engring. Rensselaer Poly. Inst., 1963, instr., 1958-62; asst. prof. nuclear engring. U. Fla., Gainesville, 1964-67, assoc. prof., 1967-70, prof., 1970—, chmn. dept., 1969-79, assoc. dir. Engring. and Indsl. Expt. Sta., 1977—, assoc. dean for research, 1979-90, assoc. dean for adminstrn. and planning, 1990-91, assoc. dean for rsch. and adminstrn., 1991—; sabbatical leave Inst. Energy Analysis, Oak Ridge, 1976-77; on assignment Inst. Energy Analysis, 1977-78; cons. Fla. Power Corp., Batelle Meml. Inst., Fla. Nuclear Assos., Oak Ridge Nat. Lab., Inst. Energy Analysis, Argonne Nat. Lab., Savannah River Lab., U. Va., Tex. Higher Edn. Bd., NSF; U. Fla. rep. U.S. Nuc. Energy Inst., 1972—, mem. adv. council, 1972-80; U. Fla. rep. to Oak Ridge Associated Univs., 1972-76; mem. engring. accreditation commn. Accreditation Bd. Engring. and Tech., 1984-88; mem. rev. com. Reactor Analysis and Safety div. Argonne Nat. Lab, 1982-88, chmn. 1986-87, mem. rev. com. Reactor Engring. div., 1992—; mem. adv. com. Consol. Fuel Reprocessing Program Oak Ridge Nat. Lab., 1982-88; mem. com. on univ. research reactors Reactor Engring. Bd., NRC, 1986-88; mem. U.S. Dept. Energy's Adv. Com. on Nuclear Facility Safety (ACNFS), 1988-90; bd. dirs., chmn. Inst. Phosphate Rsch., 1990—. Contbr. articles to profl. jours. Trustee Fla. Defenders of the Environment, 1969-71, treas., 1969-70, mem., 1969—. Recipient valor medal Am. Legion, 1966, Disting. Faculty award Fla. Blue Key, 1984; Alumnus fellow Rensselaer Poly. Inst., 1994. Fellow AAAS, Am Nuclear Soc. (v.p., pres.-elect 1989-90, pres. 1990-91, bd. dirs. 1974-77, 84-93, vice chmn., chmn. edn. div. 1975-76, exec. com. nuclear fuel cycle div. 1978-81, mem. profl. devel. and accreditation com., chmn. tech. program of internat. conf. Washington 1980, mem. nominating com. 1980-81, 87-88, chmn. 1991-92, exec. com. 1986-92, Exceptional Service award 1980, adv. editor Nuclear Sci. and Engring. Jour. 1989—), Engrs.'s Council Profl. Devel. (dir. 1976-78), Am. Assn. Engring. Socs. (awards com. 1985-86, bd. dirs. 1990-91, exec. com. 1990-95, sec.-treas. 1992, chair-elect 1993, chair 1994, chair nominating com. 1995), Am. Soc. Engring. Edn. (adv. com. Ford Found. Resident Fellow Program 1971-79, sec./treas. nuclear engring. div. 1981-82, vice-chmn. 1982-83, chmn. 1983-84, projects bd. 1981-87, chmn. awards com. 1985-87); mem. Nat. Audubon Soc., Fla. Audubon Soc., Alachua Audubon Soc. (pres. 1965-66), Sigma Xi, Tau Beta Pi (eminent engr.), Alpha Nu Sigma (pres. 1981-83), Eta Kappa Nu, Phi Kappa Phi. Presbyterian. Lodge: Rotary (Paul Harris fellow). Home: 315 NW 28th St Gainesville FL 32607-2565

O'HANLON, JAMES BARRY, retired lawyer; b. Portland, Oreg., Sept. 27, 1927; s. James Emmett and Frances L. (Sullivan) O'H.; m. Theresa Emily Lamb, Aug. 25, 1951; children: James, Eileen, Patricia, Edwin, John, Timothy, Mary. BA, U. Portland, 1951; JD, U. Santa Clara, 1952. Bar: Oreg. 1952. From assoc. to sr. ptnr. Schwabe, Williamson & Wyatt, Portland, Oreg., 1952-94, ret., 1994. Mem. ABA, Oreg. State Bar Assn., Multnomah County Bar Assn. (chm. com. to determine possible consolidation of cir. and dist. cts, 1965, mem. coun. on ct. procedures 1979-81), Internat. Assn. of Def. Couns., Oreg. Assn. of Def. Couns. (pres. 1968), Def. Rsch. Inst., Multnomah Athletic Club, Riverside Golf Club. Republican. Roman Catholic. Home: 3216 NE Alameda Ter Portland OR 97212-1634

OHANNESSIAN, GRISELDA JACKSON, publishing executive; b. N.Y.C., Feb. 5, 1927; d. Schuyler Brinckerhoff and Katharine Savage (Townsend) Jackson; m. Garo Ohannessian, May 5, 1955 (dec.); children: Ani Maria, Lucia Victoria, Mary Margaret. BA, Barnard Coll., 1949; MA, Columbia U., 1951. Asst. to prodn. mgr. Scribners Pub. Co., N.Y.C., 1951-53; music and movie reviewer Al Nida, Beirut, Lebanon, 1955-56; promotion and prodn. mgr. New Directions Pub., N.Y.C., 1956-60, publicity dir., gen. asst., 1972-83, v.p., trustee, 1983-93, mng. dir., trustee, 1994—. Democrat. Episcopalian. Avocations: piano playing, reading, attending concerts. Office: New Directions Pub Co 80 8th Ave New York NY 10011-5126

O'HARA, ALFRED PECK, lawyer; b. Patterson, N.Y., Apr. 27, 1919; s. Peter and Anna L. (Peck) O'H.; m. Muriel A. Sandberg, Aug. 30, 1940 (dec.); children: Jane Ann O'Hara Toth, Margaret Kathleen O'Hara Duff, Peter James, John Edward; m. 2d Thelma deVries (div.); m. 3d Martha Stein, June 22, 1984. BA., Syracuse U., 1940; LL.B., Fordham U. 1942. Bar: N.Y. bar 1942, U.S. Supreme Ct 1956. Sec. to U.S. Dist. Ct., 1942-43; partner firm McLaughlin & Stickles, 1946-52; asst. U.S. atty., chief civil div. So. Dist. N.Y., 1953-56; cons. to atty. gen. N.Y. State, 1956; sr. ptnr. firm Rogers Hoge & Hills, N.Y.C., 1958-86; of counsel Kelley, Drye & Warren, N.Y.C., 1986—; counsel U.S. Trademark Assn., 1967-70; pres., chmn. bd. Bacardi Corp., 1976-87; bd. dirs. Guiding Eyes for the Blind, 1994—. Mem. ABA, NAM (bd. dirs. 1978-90), N.Y. State Bar Assn., Assn. Bar City N.Y., Fed Bar Coun., Am. Law Inst. (life), Internat. Patent adn Trademark Assn., Quaker Hill Club, Key Biscayne Yacht Club. Home: RR 4 Box 55 Birch Hill Rd Patterson NY 12563 Office: Kelley Drye & Warren 101 Park Ave New York NY 10178-0062

O'HARA, CATHERINE, actress, comedienne; b. Toronto, Mar. 4, 1954; m. Bo Welch, 1992. Actress, writer with Second City, Toronto, 1974; co-founder of SCTV, 1976 (Emmy award); films include After Hours, 1985, Heartburn, 1986, Beetlejuice, 1988, Dick Tracy, 1990, Betsy's Wedding, 1990, Home Alone, 1990, Little Vegas, 1990, There Goes The Neighborhood, 1992, Home Alone II: Lost In New York, 1992, The Nightmare Before Christmas, 1993 (voice), The Paper, 1994, Wyatt Earp, 1994, A Simple Twist of Fate, 1994, Tall Tale, 1995; TV, SCTV, Comic Relief, Dream On (dir.); co-writer SCTV, Cinemax, 1984, Really Weird Tales, HBO, 1986. Office: care ICM 8942 Wilshire Blvd Beverly Hills CA 90211*

O'HARA, JAMES THOMAS, lawyer; b. Hazleton, Pa., Oct. 11, 1936; s. Thomas James and Bridget Helen (Campbell) O'H.; m. Kathleen M. Shane, Aug. 3, 1963; children: Colleen, Michael, Brian. BS in Acctg., Kings Coll., 1958; LLB, Cath. U., 1962; LLM, Georgetown U., 1967. Bar: D.C. 1962. Ptnr. Casey, Tyre et al, N.Y.C., 1969-73, Jones, Day, Reavis & Pogue, Washington, 1973—; adj. prof. tax Georgetown U., Washington, 1976—; bd. advisers Corp. Taxation. Contbr. articles to profl. jours. Served with USAAF, 1959. Fellow Am. Bar Found.; mem. ABA (chmn. subcom. tax sect. 1982-86), Am. Coll. Tax Counsel. Democrat. Roman Catholic. Clubs: Metropolitan (Washington); Union (Cleve.). Home: 1610 44th St NW Washington DC 20007-2025 Office: Jones Day Reavis & Pogue 1450 G St NW Ste 600 Washington DC 20005-2088

O'HARA, PAUL M., clothing manufacturing company executive; b. 1946. BA, U. Santa Clara, 1968; MBA, U. Calif., 1971. 2nd v.p. Continental Ill. Nat. Bank & Trust Co., 1971-75; with Kimberly-Clark Co.,

1975-77; treas. Tiger Internat. Inc., 1977-81; v.p. fin. N.Am. Car Corp., 1981-84; v.p. corp. fin. IC Industries, 1984-88; with Farley Inc., 1988—; with Fruit of the Loom, Inc., Chgo., 1988—, now exec. v.p., chief fin. officer. Office: Farley Inc 233 S Wacker Dr Chicago IL 60606

O'HARA, ROBERT SYDNEY, JR., lawyer; b. Englewood, N.J., Apr. 26, 1939; s. Robert Sydney and Katharine (Drayton) O'H.; m. Elizabeth Crocker, June 17, 1961; children—Jennifer, Isabelle; m. 2d Bonnie Durkin, July 19, 1975. A.B., Princeton U., 1960; J.D., U. Pa., 1963. Bar: N.Y. 1964. Mem., Amer. Bar Assn. Ptnr. firm Milbank, Tweed, Hadley & McCloy, N.Y.C., 1965—. Served to capt. AUS 1963-65. Office: Milbank Tweed Hadley & McCloy 1 Chase Manhattan Plz New York NY 10005-1401*

O'HARA, THOMAS EDWIN, association executive; b. Springfield, Mo., July 28, 1915; s. Robert John and Olga Florence (Lindberg) O'H.; m. Eleanor McLennan Urquhart, May 6, 1950; children: Thomas Edwin, Robert Andrew, Shelley Janette. AB, Wayne State U., 1938. Accountant Nash-Kelvinator Corp., 1938-39, Gen. Electric Co., 1938-41, Ernst & Ernst, 1941-42; dir. payrolls Detroit Bd. Edn., 1942-58; chmn. bd. trustees Nat. Assn. Investment Clubs, Madison Heights, Mich., 1951—; treas. Sunshine Fifty, Inc., 1969-77; vice chmn. H.W. Rickel & Co., 1971-76; dir. N.Y. Stock Exch., 1973-75; mem. adv. com. individual investors, 1988—; dir. Investment Edn. Inst., 1962—; chmn. NAIC Growth Fund, Inc., 1990—. Bd. dirs. William Tyndale Coll.; chmn. N.Y. Stock Exch. Individual Investors Adv. Com., 1987-89; mem. U.S. Securities and Exch. Commn. Consumers Affairs Adv. Com. and Compensation Practices Com. With USAAF, 1942-45. Recipient Disting. Service award in investment edn., 1969, Disting. Alumni award Wayne State U. Sch. Bus. Adminstrn., 1987, Roalman award Nat. Investor Rels. Inst., 1987. Mem. World Fedn. Investment Clubs (dir., chmn. 1985-90), Arab Frat., Gamma Beta Phi. Presbyn. Home: 367 Sycamore Ct Bloomfield Hills MI 48302-1173 Office: National Assoc of Investors Corp 711 W 13 Madison Heights MI 48071

O'HARA, THOMAS PATRICK, managing editor; b. Phila., July 15, 1947; s. Hugh James and Agatha Mary (Gilroy) O'H.; m. Juliet Munro, 1970 (div. 1974); m. Pamela Smith, Oct. 8, 1977; children: Rachel Kathleen, Patrick Graham. BA in English, Rutgers South Jersey, 1972; MA in Communications, U. Fla., 1974. Sports reporter Gainesville SUN, 1972-74; reporter Orlando (Fla.) Sentinel, 1974-76, Daytona Beach (Fla.) News Jour., 1976-78; various editing and reporting positions Miami (Fla.) Herald, 1978-86, city editor Palm Beach ed., 1985-86; asst. met. editor Palm Beach Post, West Palm Beach, Fla., 1986-87; met. editor Palm Beach Post, West Palm Beach, 1987-88, asst. mng. editor, 1988-89, mng. editor, 1989—. Sgt. USAF, 1969-71. Home: 107 Seabreeze Ave Delray Beach FL 33483-7017 Office: Palm Beach Post PO Box 24700 2751 Dixie Hwy West Palm Beach FL 33416-4700*

O'HARE, DEAN RAYMOND, insurance company executive; b. Jersey City, June 21, 1942; s. Francis and Ann O'H.; m. Kathleen T. Walliser, Dec. 2, 1967; Dean, Jason. BS, NYU, 1963; MBA, Pace U., 1968. Trainee Chubb Corp., N.Y.C., 1963-64, tax advisor, 1964-67, asst. v.p., mgr. corp. fin. devel., 1968-72, sr. v.p., mgr. corp. fin. devel. dept., from 1979, chief fin. officer, 1979-94, pres., 1986-88, chmn., chief exec. officer, 1988—; chmn. Chubb Life Ins. Co. N.H., 1981—; chmn., pres. Fed. Ins. Co. 1988—, Vigilant Ins. Co., 1988—; chmn., dir. Bellemead Devel. Corp., 1973—; chmn. Colonial Life Ins. Co. Am., 1980—, Chubb Life Ins. Co. Am., 1980—; bd. dirs. Chubb Ins. Co. Can., Fed. Ins. Co., Vigilant Ins. Co. Dir. Coalition Svc. Industries, The N.J. Partnership; trustee com. for econ. devel. WDC. Mem. Am. Inst. Assn. (chmn. bd. dirs. 1991), Urban Land Inst., The Links Club (N.Y.C.), India House, Hanover Square Club, Halifax Club (Daytona Beach, Fla.), India House Club, Hanover Square Club. Home: 370 Lake Rd Far Hills NJ 07931-2314 Office: Chubb Corp PO Box 1615 15 Mountain View Rd Warren NJ 07059 also: Alliance Assurance Co Ltd 15 Mountainview Rd Warren NJ 07059-6711*

O'HARE, DON R., corporate executive; b. Joliet, Ill., 1922; married. B.S., U. Minn., 1943. Plant engr. Western Electric Co., 1946-47; sales engr. Wallace & Tiernan Co., 1947-50; sales trainee Falk Corp., Milw., 1950-51, sales engr., 1951-55, dist. office mgr., 1955-72, v.p., sales mgr., 1972-74, pres., 1974-76; with Sundstrand Corp., Rockford, Ill., 1976—, v.p. 1977-78, group v.p., 1977-79, vice chmn., 1980-88, chmn., 1989-94, chmn., chief exec., 1994—; also bd. dirs.; dir. M & I Corp., Modine Mfg. Corp. Served with USN, 1943-46. Office: Sundstrand Corp PO Box 7003 4949 Harrison Ave Rockford IL 61108-7987

O'HARE, JAMES RAYMOND, energy company executive; b. Evergreen Park, Ill., July 20, 1938; s. Raymond Clarence and Helen (Nickel) O'H.; m. Nan Jane Raleigh, Sept. 18, 1965; children: Joan, Daniel, Colleen, Patrick. B.S., Marquette U., 1960; M.B.A., U. Calif. at Los Angeles, 1961. C.P.A., Ill., Ill., Ky., Calif., Tex. Mgr. Peat, Marwick, Mitchell & Co., Chgo., 1961-68, South Bend, Ind., 1968-69; controller Essex Internat., Inc., Fort Wayne, Ind., 1969-76, Am. Air Filter Co., Inc., Louisville, 1976-80; fin. v.p. and treas. Petrolane Inc., Long Beach, Calif., 1980-85; treas. Tex. Eastern Corp., Houston, 1985-87, v.p., treas., 1987-88; sr. v.p. fin. and adminstrn. Texas Eastern Gas Pipeline Co., Houston, 1988-89; v.p., CFO Enclean Inc., Houston, 1991-93; fin. cons., 1993—. Served with USNR, 1962-68. Mem. AICPA, Evans Scholars, Fin. Execs. Inst., Houston Club, Beta Gamma Sigma.

O'HARE, JEAN ANN, lawyer; b. St. Louis, July 26, 1950; d. Eugene and Henrietta (Greenblatt) O'H. BS cum laude, U. Conn., 1972; MA magna cum laude, Fairfield U., 1976; JD, Fordham U., 1979. Bar: N.Y. 1980, Conn. 1980, U.S. Dist. Ct. (ea., so and no. dists.) N.Y. 1980. Assoc. Weil Gotshal & Manges, N.Y.C., 1979-82, Emmet Marvin & Martin, N.Y.C., 1982-83; atty. sole practice N.Y.C., 1983-86; atty. Crane Co., N.Y.C., 1986-88; corp. counsel Pfizer Inc., N.Y.C., 1988—. Vol. N.Y. chpt. Am. Heart Assn., N.Y.C., 1990; bd. dirs. United Neighbors East Midtown Manhattan, 1991—. Mem. ABA (litigation sect., tort and ins. practice sect., vice chair 1993—), Corp. Bar (co-chair N.Y.C. com. 1988-90), Internat. Assn. Defense Counsel, Product Liability Adv. Coun. Office: Pfizer Inc 235 E 42nd St New York NY 10017-5703

O'HARE, JOHN MITCHELL, lawyer; b. Oak Park, Ill., Apr. 9, 1946; s. John Mitchell Jr. and Doris Margaret (Lundblad) O'H.; m. Carole Beth Silver, Jan. 6, 1985; children: Rachele Olia, Suzanna Dee. AB, U. Ill., 1967, MS in Fin., 1969; JD, Harvard U., 1971. Bar: Ill. 1971, U.S. Dist. Ct. (no. dist.) Ill. 1971. Assoc. Sidley & Austin, Chgo., 1971-76, ptnr., 1977-85, 88—; resident ptnr. Sidley & Austin, Singapore, 1985-88. Mem. ABA, Chgo. Bar Assn., Phi Beta Kappa. Office: Sidley & Austin 1 First Nat Plz Chicago IL 60603

O'HARE, JOSEPH ALOYSIUS, university president, priest; b. N.Y.C., Feb. 12, 1931; s. Joseph Aloysius and Marie Angela (Enright) O'H. AB, Berchmans Coll, Cebu City, Philippines, 1954, MA, 1955; STL, Woodstock Coll., Md., 1962; PhD, Fordham U., 1968; DHL (hon.), Fairfield U., 1980, Rockhurst Coll., Kansas City, Mo., 1984, Ateneo de Manila U., 1990, CUNY, 1991; DLitt (hon.), Coll. New Rochelle, 1984. Joined S.J., 1948, ordained priest Roman Cath. Ch., 1961. Instr. Ateneo de Manila U., 1955-58, prof. philosophy, 1968-72; assoc. editor Am. Mag., N.Y.C., 1972-75, editor-in-chief, 1975-84; pres. Fordham U., Bronx, N.Y., 1984—. Author weekly column Of Many Things (Best Original Column award Cath. Press Assn. 1976, 78, 81, 84). Bd. dirs. Union Theol. Sem., The Seia Soc.; chmn. N.Y.C. Campaign Fin. Bd. Office: Fordham U Office of Pres New York NY 10458

O'HARE, LINDA PARSONS, management consultant; b. Robinson, Ill., Nov. 30, 1947; d. William Wayne and Silvetta (Simmons) Parsons; m. John M. O'Hare, Oct. 5, 1968 (div. May 1983). BS, U. Ill., 1965-68, 72; M in Mgmt., Northwestern U., 1984. Various positions Harvard U., Cambridge, Mass., 1968-71; mgr. employment dept. Leo Burnett Co., Inc., Chgo., 1972-75; various positions Booz, Allen & Hamilton, Inc., Chgo., 1975-81; pres. The Bridge Orgn., Inc., Chgo., 1981—; also bd. dirs.; bd. dirs. All Am. Bank Chgo.; former mem. adv. bd. human resources devel. Northeastern Ill. U., Chgo., 1980-93; mem. Kellogg Alumni Adv. Bd., 1989—. Mem. steering com. Kellogg Alumni Club Community Svcs. Project, Chgo., 1985-91; bd.

dirs., exec. com., long range planning com. chair YWCA Met. Chgo., 1986—; mem. governing bd. Ill. Coun. on Econ. Edn., 1992—. Mem. Inst. Mgmt. Cons. (bd. dirs., v.p. 1986-91), Chgo. Fin. Exch. (bd. dirs., sec. 1988-89, v.p. 1990-91, pres. 1991-92), Nat. Assn. Women Bus. Owners (bd. dirs. 1981-84), Chgo. Health Execs. Forum, Univ. Club Chgo. (bd. dirs. 1993—), Execs. Club Chgo. (bd. dirs. 1993—), Econ. Club Chgo., Chgo. Network, Wis. Arabian Horse Assn. Avocation: Arabian horses. Office: Bridge Orgn Inc 33 N Dearborn St Chicago IL 60602-3102

O'HARE, PATRICK K., lawyer; b. N.Y.C., Dec. 1, 1946. BA, Brown U., 1968; JD, Stanford U., 1971. Bar: D.C. 1973. Ptnr. McDermott, Will & Emery, Washington. Mem. Am. Acad. Hosp. Attys., Nat. Assn. Coll. & Univ. Attys. Office: McDermott Will & Emery 1850 K St NW Washington DC 20006-2296

O'HARE, SANDRA FERNANDEZ, secondary education educator; b. N.Y.C., Mar. 19, 1941; d. Ricardo Enrique and Rosario de Los Angeles (Arenas) Fernandez; m. S. James O'Hare, Oct. 12, 1963; children: James, Richard, Michael, Christopher. BA, Marymount Coll., 1962; MA, U. San Francisco, 1980. Cert. elem. and coll. tchr.; bilingual and lang. devel. specialist. Instr. adult edn. Guam, 1964-66, Spanish Speaking Ctr., Harrisburg, Pa., 1977-79; tchr. Colegio Salesiano, Rota, Spain, 1973, 84, Alisal Sch. Dist., Salinas, Calif., 1979-81, Liberty Sch., Petaluma, Calif., 1981-85, Cinnabar Sch., Petaluma, 1985—; instr. Chapman U., 1994—; also summer migrant edn. programs Cinnabar Sch., Petaluma, 1990, 91; instr. Santa Rosa (Calif.) Jr. Coll., 1982-83; mem. math. curriculum com. Sonoma County Office Edn., Santa Rosa, 1988; mem. Summer Sci. Connections Inst., Sonoma State U., 1994. Translator: Isabel la Catolica, 1962. Mem. Asian relief com. ARC, Harrisburg, 1975, Boy Scouts Am., Petaluma, 1983, Mechanicsburg, Pa., 1974, Monterey, Calif., 1971. Sarah D. Barder fellow Johns Hopkins U., 1990. Mem. NEA, AAUW (chair elem. founds. com. 1985-86), Calif. Assn. Bilingual Educators, Cinnabar Tchrs. Assn., Club Hispano-Americano Petaluma (pres. 1987-89). Roman Catholic. Avocation: travel. Home: 1289 Glenwood Dr Petaluma CA 94954-4326

O'HARE, THOMAS J(AMES), JR., federal commissioner; b. Balt., Oct. 13, 1937; s. Thomas James and Mary Irvin (Henthorn) O'H.; m. Rose Pauline Poleo, June 18, 1960 (div. Apr. 1980); 1 child, Thomas James III; m. Mary Margaret Vondersmith, Apr. 11, 1981; 1 child, James Matthew. BSBA, U. Balt., 1977. Computer systems analyst Bethlehem Steel Corp., Sparrows Point, Md., 1967-71; computer systems specialist Social Security Adminstrn., Balt., 1971-75, chief rsch. and planning br., 1976-79, dir. div. data communication ops., 1979-81, dep. dir. office data communications, 1981-82, dep. dir. office systems engring., 1982-84, dep. dir. office computer processing, 1984-87, sr. advisor to dep. commr., 1987-89, assoc. commr. for systems ops., 1989—. With USMCR, 1958-64. Mem. Coun. Fed. Data Ctr. Dirs. Roman Catholic. Office: Social Security Adminstrn Office Systems Ops Rm 543NCC 6401 Security Blvd Baltimore MD 21235-0001

O'HAREN, THOMAS JOSEPH, financial services executive; b. Shenandoah, Pa., Apr. 1, 1934; s. James Francis and Elizabeth Margaret (Sauer) O'H.; m. Virginia Ann Kobylinski, Mar. 4, 1957; children: Michelle, Timothy, Terrence, Anne, David, Mary. BS, Pa. State U., 1956. CLU, CHFC. Sales rep. Conn. Gen., Houston, 1957-62, asst. mgr., 1962-66; mgr. Conn. Gen., Atlanta, 1966-85, regional v.p., 1985—; regional v.p. Faculty Leadership Inst. Am. Coll., Atlanta, 1990—; adj. prof. mgmt. Am. Coll., Bryn Mawr, Pa., 1995, chmn. curriculum com., palnned Giving Com. Am. Coll., 1995; mem. pres.'s adv. coun., mentor program. Editor, contbr. Mgrs. Mag., 1987, Gen. Agts. & Mgrs. News, 1987. Fin. chmn. Mattingly Senate Campaign, 1980, Bell Gubernatorial Campaign, 1987; pres. Cobb County C. of C., 1980; co-chmn. Ga. Rep. Found.; chmn. bd. trustees Gama Found., 1990-95; Newt Gingrich Fin. Com., 1992-95, Millner Gubernatorial Campaign, 1994. Lt. (j.g.) USNR, 1956-58. Named to the Gama Hall of Fame, 1992, Cigna Fin. Advisors Hall of Fame, 1995; recipient Gordon Setchel award for Contbn. to Agy. Mgmt., 1994. Mem. Gen. Agts. and Mgrs. (Master Agy. award 1983-94, John W. Yates Meml. award 1990, chmn. GAMC Found. 1990-95), CLUs, Chartered Fin. Counsellors, Gen. Agts.-Assn. (pres. Atlanta, 1976-77, nat. bd. dirs., 1979-84, nat. pres. 1987-88), Advanced Assn. Life Underwriters (polit. involvement com.), Nat. Assn. Life Underwriters, Million Dollar Roundtable (Top of Table 1988), Atlanta Country Club (bd. dirs. 1986-92, pres. 1988-90), Georgian Club (bd. dirs 1985 pres.), Equestrian Order of the Holy Sepulchre (knight). Republican. Roman Catholic. Avocations: golf, tennis, reading. Home: 280 Pine Valley Rd Marietta GA 30067-4822 Office: Conn Gen 1800 Parkway Pl Marietta GA 30067-8237

OHE, SHUZO, chemical engineer, educator; b. Tokyo, Mar. 31, 1938; s. Kunio and Chizu (Tabata) O.; m. Nobuko Motegi, Oct. 31, 1975; 1 child, Kenzo. BS, Sci. U. Tokyo, 1962; D of Engring., Tokyo Met. U., 1971. Chem. engr. Ishikawajima-Harima Heavy Indsl. Co. Ltd., Tokyo, 1962-65, reseracher, then rsch. engr., 1966-80; assoc. prof. Tokai U., Tokyo, 1980-82; prof. chem. engring. Tokai U., 1982-91, Sci. U. of Tokyo, 1991—; vis. rsch.ir. Fractionation Rsch., Inc., South Pasadena, Calif., 1973; cons. Chiyoda Engring. Co. Ltd., 1986-89, NKK, Tokyo, 1988—; cons. Sibata Sci. Tech. Ltd., Siber Instrument Co. Ltd. Inventor angle tray distillation tower; author, editor: Computer-Aided Data Book of Vapor Pressure, 1976, Vapor-Liquid Equilibrium Data, 1988, Vapor-Liquid Equilibrium Data at High Pressure, 1990, Vapor-Liquid Equilibrium Data-Salt Effect, 1991; author: Chemical Engineering Design By P.C., 1985. Mem. AIChE, Kanagawa Micon Club (pres. 1988—), Japan Info. Ctr. Sci. and Tech., Japan Soc. Chem. Engineering. N.Y. Acad. Scis. Avocation: golf. Office: Sci Univ Tokyo, 1-3 Kagurazaka Shinjuku-ku, Tokyo 162, Japan

O'HEALY, QUILL, insurance company executive. With Parker Co., N.Y.C., 1964-1971; chb, ceo Sedgwick Group Inc., N.Y.C., 1971—. Office: Sedgwick Group Inc 1285 Ave of the Americas New York NY 10019

O'HEARN, JOHN HOWARD, publishing company executive; b. Black River Falls, Wis., June 14, 1937; s. Francis Jack O'Hearn and Opal Mae (McLaughlin) O'Hearn Overstreet; m. Carolyn Sue Marlow; children—Patrick John, Shannon. B.A. in Bus. Adminstrn., Midwestern U. Dispatch messenger Times Pub. Co., St. Petersburg, Fla., 1953-55, copy boy, 1960, apprentice printer, 1960-62, internal auditor, 1968-69, controller, 1974-76, treas., 1976-82, gen. mgr., 1982-84, exec. v.p., gen. mgr., 1984—; acct., office mgr. Electric Co., Wichita Falls, Wis., 1962-68; bus. mgr., controller Congl. Quar., Washington, 1969-74. Bd. dirs. United Way, Pinellas County, 1977, Com. of 100, 1984; mem. Suncoasters, 1985, Bayfront Ctr. Found. Clearwater Progress Fin.-Planning Com., Dali Mus; bd. trustees Fla. Orch. Exec. Com., St. Petersburg Progress Inc.; mem. adv. bd. Salvation Army. Served with USAF, 1955-60. Mem. Internat. Newspaper Fin. Execs. (pres. 1981-82), St. Petersburg C. of C. (bd. govs.), Pinellas Suncoast C. of C. (bd. govs., adv. council), Fla. C. of C. (bd. dirs.), U. South Fla. Bay Campus Adv. Bd. Republican. Clubs: Lakewood Country, Pres.' (bd. dirs. 1985); Tiger Bay. Office: Saint Petersburg Times PO Box 1121 Saint Petersburg FL 33731-1121

O'HEARN, ROBERT RAYMOND, stage designer; b. Elkhart, Ind., July 19, 1921; s. Robert Raymond, Sr. and Ella May (Stoldt) O'H. B.A., Ind. U., 1939-43; student, Art Students League, 1943-45. Designer Brattle Theatre, Cambridge, Mass. 1948-52; prof. stage design, chmn. design dept. Sch. Music Ind. U., 1989—; instr. Studio and Forum Scenic Design, 1968-88. Stage designer: Broadway shows The Relapse, 1950, Loves Labor's Lost, 1953, Othello, Festival, 1955, The Apple Cart, Child of Fortune, 1956; asst. designer: Broadway shows Kismet, 1953, Pajama Game, 1955, My Fair Lady, 1956, West Side Story, 1958; designer: for film A Clerical Error, 1955; designer prodns. Central City Opera House, 1959-63, Opera Soc. Washington, 1958-61, L'Elisir D'Amore at Met. Opera House, 1960, Die Meistersinger, 1962, Aida, 1963; stage designer: As You Like It, Stratford, Conn., 1961, Troilus and Cressida, Stratford, 1961, Kiss Me Kate, Los Angles Civic Light Opera, 1964, N.Y.C. Center, 1965, Samson and Delila, Met. Opera, 1964, La Sylphide, Am. Ballet Theatre, 1964, Italian Symphony, 1971, Adam Cochrane, Broadway, 1964, Pique Dame, Met. Opera, 1965, La Ventana, 1966, Die Frau Ohne Schatten, 1966, Porgy and Bess, Vienna Volksoper, 1965, Bregenzer Festspiele, 1971, Otello, Boston Opera, also Hamburg State Opera, 1967, Hansel and Gretel, Met. Opera, 1967, Nutcracker Ballet, San

Francisco Ballet, 1967, L.A. Ballet, 1979, La Traviata, Santa Fe Opera, 1968, Rosalinda, L.A. Civic Light Opera, 1968, Der Rosenkavalier, Met. Opera, 1969, Tallis Fantasia, N.Y.C. Ballet, 1969, Boris Godunov (unproduced), Met. Opera, 1970, Parsifal, Met. Opera, 1970, Porgy and Bess, Bregenz Festspiel, Austria, 1971, Falstaff, Marriage of Figaro, Gianni Schicci, Central City Opera House, 1972, Barber of Seville, 1973, The Enchanted, Kennedy Center, 1973, The Mind with the Dirty Man, Los Angeles, 1973, Midsummer Night's Dream, Central City Opera, 1974, Coppelia, Ballet West, 1974, Carmen, Strasbourg, 1974, The Pearl Fishers, Miami Opera, 1974, N.Y.C. Opera, 1980, Don Pasquale, Miami Opera, 1976, Scipio Africanus, Central City Opera, 1975, Swan Lake, Strasbourg, 1975, Marriage of Figaro, Met. Opera, 1975, Die Meistersinger, Karlsruhe, Germany, 1975, Girl of the Golden West, Houston Opera, 1976, N.Y.C. Opera, 1977, Vienna Staatsoper, 1976, Boris Godunov, Strasbourg, 1976, Der Rosenkavalier, Karlsruhe, 1976, Don Quixote, Ballet West, 1977, Die Meistersinger, Chgo. Lyric Opera, 1977, Adriana Lecouvreur, Miami Opera, 1978, La Boheme, 1978, Coppelia, Pacific N.W. Dance, Seattle, 1978, Andrea Chenier, N.Y.C. Opera, 1978, Der Rosenkavalier, Can. Opera Co., Toronto, 1978, Taming of the Shrew, Pa. State U., 1980, Die Fledermaus, Miami Opera 1980, Tosca, Miami Opera, 1981, West Side Story, Bregenz Festspiel, Austria, 1981, Mich. Opera Theatre, 1985; Pique Dame, San Francisco Opera, 1982, La Traviata, Miami Opera, 1982, Of Mice and Men, Miami Opera, 1982, Carousel, Annie Get Your Gun, Miami Opera, 1984, Lucia di Lammermoor, 1984, L'Italiana in Algeri, 1985, Porgy and Bess, Met. Opera, 1985, West Side Story, Mich. Opera Theatre, 1985, Aida, Don Giovanni, Opera Colo., 1986, My Fair Lady, Mich. Opera Theatre, 1986, Samson and Delilah, Manon Lescaut Opera Colo., 1987, Annie Get Your Gun, Paper Mill Playhouse, 1987, Peter Grimes, Ind. U., 1987, Madama Butterfly, N.J. State Opera, 1990. Mem. vis. com. Costume Inst., Met. Museum. Mem. United Scenic Artists. Home: 2604 E 2nd St Bloomington IN 47401-5371

O'HEARNE, JOHN JOSEPH, psychiatrist; b. Memphis, Feb. 5, 1922; s. John Joseph and Norma Rose (Ford) O'H.; children: Patricia Ann, Marilyn Eileen, John Stephen, Brian Donal. BS, Rhodes Coll. Memphis, 1944; MD, U. Tenn., 1945; MS in Psychiatry, U. Colo., 1951. Diplomate Am. Bd. Psychiatry and Neurology. Intern Denver Gen. Hosp., 1945-46; fellow U. Colo., Denver, 1948-51, instr., 1949-52; instr. U. Denver, 1951; clin. dir. psychiatry Kansas City (Mo.) Gen. Hosp. and Psychiat. Receiving Ctr., 1952-56; pvt. practice medicine specializing in psychiatry Kansas City, 1956—; adj. prof. sociology U. Mo., Kansas City, 1986—; Clin. Bapt. Theol. Sem., Kansas City, Kans.; mem. faculty Western Mo. Sch. for Ministry (Episc.); mem. staff St. Luke's Hosp., Menorah Hosp.; cons. Lifewise, Kansas City, 1984—; clin. prof. psychiatry U. Kans., 1972—, U. Mo., Kansas City, 1974—; pres. Transactional Analysis Inst., Kansas City, 1974—. Co-author: Practical Transactional Analysis in Management, 1977; contbr. articles to profl. jours. Priest Episcopal Ch.; coun. Friends of Art Nelson-Atkins Mus. Art, 1991—. Capt. AUS, 1942-45, 46-48. Recipient Bronze medal NASTAR, 1984. Fellow Am. Psychiat. Assn. (life), Am. Group Psychotherapy Assn. (disting., dir. 1970-78, pres. 1974-78)); Internat. Assn. Group Psychotherapy, Am. Orthopsychiat. Assn. (life); mem. Am. Psychiat. Assn. (pres. Western Mo. dist. br. 1960-61, 64-65), Mo. State Med. Assn. (chmn. mental health com. 1960-62, physicians rehab. com. 1979-89, chmn. 1987-88, chmn. impaired physicians' com. 1987-88), Jackson County Med. Soc. (chmn. mental health com. 1959-66, mem., family life com. 1989-90, mem., legal com. 1990-92, patient-physicians rels. com. 1992), Internat. Transactional Analysis Assn. (trustee 1972-83), Internat. Wine and Food Soc. of London (chmn. wine com. Kansas City chpt. 1989, dinner chmn. 1992, sec. 1993), Carriage Club. Republican. Episcopalian. Avocations: photography, wine, travel, herb gardening. Office: 4706 Broadway St Ste 103 Kansas City MO 64112-1961

O'HERN, DANIEL JOSEPH, state supreme court justice; b. Red Bank, N.J., May 23, 1930; s. J. Henry and Eugenia A. (Sansone) O'H.; m. Barbara Ronan, Aug. 8, 1959; children: Daniel J., Eileen, James, John, Molly. A.B., Fordham Coll., 1951; LL.B., Harvard U., 1957. Bar: N.J. 1958. Clk. U.S. Supreme Ct., Washington, 1957-58; assoc. Abramoff, Apy & O'Hern, Red Bank, N.J., 1966-78; commr. N.J. Dept. Environ. Protection, 1978-79; counsel to Gov. N.J. Trenton; justice N.J. Supreme Ct., Trenton, 1981—; former mem. adv. com. profl. ethics N.J. Supreme Ct. Past trustee Legal Aid Soc. Monmouth County, (N.J.); mayor Borough of Red Bank, 1969-78, councilman, 1962-69. Served as lt. (j.g.) USNR, 1951-54. Fellow Am. Bar Found.; mem. ABA, N.J. Bar Assn., Monmouth County Bar Assn., Harvard Law Sch. Assn. N.J. (past pres.). Office: NJ Supreme Ct Cn # 970 Trenton NJ 08625

O'HERN, ELIZABETH MOOT, microbiologist, writer; b. Richmondville, N.Y., Sept. 1, 1913; s. Carl Melvin and Margaret Esther (Dibble) Moot; B.A., U. Calif., Berkeley, 1945, M.A., 1947; Ph.D. (grad. fellow), U. Wash., 1956; m. William J. O'Hern, Jan. 4, 1952. Instr. SUNY, Bklyn., 1957-62; asst. prof. George Washington U., Washington, 1962-65; prin. investigator rsch. Bionetics Rsch. Lab., Kensington, Md., 1965-67; administr. rsch. grants in microbiology, genetics and anesthesiology NIH, Nat. Inst. Gen. Med. Scis., Bethesda, Md., 1968-75, spl. asst. to dir., 1975-77, administr. spl. programs, 1977-86, also programs adminstr. Mem. bd. examiners in basic scis. Commn. on Licensure to Practice Healing Arts in D.C., 1974-75; panel mem. Washington Area Office, U.S. Civil Svc. Commn., 1977-86; program cons. U. Calif., 1990. Fellow Am. Acad. Microbiology; mem. AAUW (pres. Washington br. 1967-69, trustee edn. found. 1976-81), AAAS, Am. Inst. Biol. Sci., Am. Public Health Assn., Am. Soc Cell Biology, Am. Soc. Microbiology (chmn. status of women in the profession 1975-78), Am. Soc. Tropical Medicine and Hygiene, Med. Mycology Soc. Am., Mycol. Soc. Am., N.Y. Acad. Sci., Wash. Acad. Sci., Assn. Women in Sci., Astron. Soc. Pacific, Planetary Soc., Grad. Women in Sci. (nat. sec. 1974-77, chpt. pres. 1979-80), Sigma Xi. Author: Profiles of Pioneer Women Scientists. Contbr. articles to profl. publs. Home: 633 G St SW Washington DC 20024-2451

O'HERN, JANE SUSAN, psychologist, educator; b. Winthrop, Mass., Mar. 21, 1933; d. Joseph Francis and Mona (Garvey) O'H. BS, Boston U., 1954, EdD, 1962; MA, Mich. State U., 1956. Instr. Mercyhurst Coll., 1954-55, Hofstra Coll., 1956-57, State Coll., Salem and Boston, 1957-60; asst. prof. Boston U., 1962-67, assoc. prof., 1967-75, prof. edn. and psychiat. (psychology), 1975-95, prof. emeritus, 1995—, chmn. dept. counseling psychology, 1972-75, 88-89, dir. mental health edn. program, 1975-81, dir. internat. edn., 1978-81, asst. v.p. internat. edn., 1981; pres. ASSIST Internat., Inc., 1989—; adv. bd. Internat. Study Cons., 1994—. Contbr. articles to profl. jours. Trustee Boston Ctr. Modern Psychoanalytic Studies, 1980-92. Recipient grants U.S. Office Edn., NIMH, Dept. of Def. Mem. Assn. Counselor Edn. and Supvrs., Am. Counseling Assn., North Atlantic Assn. Counselor Edn. and Supervision (past pres.), Mass. Psychol. Assn., Am. Psychol. Assn., Mortar Bd., Pi Lamda Theta, Sigma Kappa, Phi Delta Kappa, Phi Beta Delta. Home: 111 Perkins St Apt 287 Boston MA 02130-4324 Office: Boston U 605 Commonwealth Ave Boston MA 02215-1605

OHGA, NORIO, electronics executive; b. Numazu, Japan, Jan. 29, 1930; m. Midori Ohga. Grad. Tokyo Nat. U. Fine Arts and Music, 1953, Kunst U., Berlin, 1957. Cons., advisor Tokyo Tsushin Kogyo (later Sony Corp.), 1953-59; gen. mgr. tape recorder divsn., product planning divsn., indsl. design divsn. Sony Corp., Tokyo, 1959, bd. dirs., 1964-72, mng. dir., 1972-76, dep. pres., 1976-82, pres., chief oper. officer, 1982-89, pres., chief exec. officer, 1989—; sr. mng. dir. CBS/Sony Group, Inc., 1968-70, pres., 1970-80, chmn., 1980-91; chmn. Sony Corp. Am., 1988 — Sony Software Corp., 1991—. Decorated Medal of Honor with Blue Ribbon by J.M. the Emperor of Japan, 1988, Cmdrs. Cross First Class of the Order of Merit of the Rep. of Austria, 1987. Mem. Tokyo C. of C. and Industry (vice chmn.). Office: Sony Corp, 7-35 Kitashinagawa 6-chome, Shinagawa-ku Tokyo 141, Japan Office: Sony Corp Am 9 W 57th St 43 New York NY 10019*

OHINOUYE, TSUNEO, automobile manufacturing executive; b. Tokyo, Mar. 13, 1932; came to U.S., 1977; s. Tatsuo and Haru (Ito) O.; m. Tomie Murate, Oct. 23, 1958; children: Mariko Itoh, Yuko Ohinouye. B Mech. Engring., Kyoto (Japan) U., 1954; M Automobile Engring., Cranfield Inst. Tech., Bedford, Eng., 1964. Mgr. engine design Mitsubishi Heavy Industries, Kyoto, 1955-77; pres. Mitsubishi Motors Corp. Svcs., Southfield, Mich., 1977-80; chief coord. vehicle devel. passenger car ctr. Mitsubishi Motors Corp., Okazaki, Japan, 1980-85; corp. chief engr. export product planning Mitsubishi Motors Corp., Tokyo, 1985-87; pres. Mitsubishi Motors

Am., Southfield, 1987-91; pres., CEO Diamond-Star Motors (subs. Mitsubishi Motors Corp.), Normal, Ill., 1991—. UN fellow Cranfield Inst. Tech. Mem. Bloomington C. of C. (bd. dirs. 1993—). Office: Diamond-Star Motors Corp 100 Diamond Star Pky Normal IL 61761-8099

OHIRA, KAZUTO, theatre company executive, writer; b. Hiroshima, Japan, Jan. 5, 1933; s. Kitaro and Ryo (Sugimoto) O.; m. Evelyn Lanham, Sept. 3, 1964. BA, Waseda U., Tokyo, 1956. Theatre mgr. Toho's La Brea Theatre, L.A., 1961-63; gen. mgr. Toho Cinema, N.Y.C., 1963-64; publicity mgr. Towa Co., Ltd., Tokyo, 1965-69; rep., dir., mgr. Toho Internat. Inc., N.Y.C., 1969, chief exec. officer, 1988—; pres. Internat. Cultural Prodn. Inc., N.Y.C. Producer (dance performance and drama) Yasuko Nagamine's Musume Dojoji, 1982, Mandara, 1985, (drama) Yukio Ninagawa's Media, 1987, Takarazuka Show at Radio City Music Hall, N.Y., 1989, KanashibetsU: Furano Group at La Mama, Takarazuka Dance Concert at Joyce Theater, 1992, Sotoba Komachi, Yasuko Nagamine and Co., Beauty of Tokyo, Met. Tokyo, City Ctr., N.Y., 1993; author: Broadway parts I and II, 1982, 2d edit., 1987, Broadway, Broadway, 1987, Performing Arts of New York, 1989, Haiku Collection: Though The Travel is Short, The Charms of Broadway, 1994, Broadway Criticism, 1995. Bd. dirs. House Found. Meredith Monk, 1979, N.Y. Symphony Ensemble, Saeko Ichinohe Dance Co. Recipient 2d Fumiko Yamaji Cultural award, 1985. Mem. Internat. Theatre Critics Assn., UNESCO, N.Y. Waseda Univ. Alumni Assn. (hon. chmn.), Players Club. Avocations: playing the harp, golf. Home: Island House 555 Main St Rm 1204S New York NY 10044-0129 Office: Toho Internat Inc 1501 Broadway New York NY 10036-5502 also: ICP Inc 235 W 48th St Rm 33B New York NY 10036

OHKAWA, TIHIRO, physicist; b. Kanazawa, Ishikawa, Japan, Jan. 3, 1928; came to U.S., 1955; s. Ryoichi and Ryuko (Kitagawa) O.; m. Yoko Hitomi, June 2, 1959; children: Risa, Taro, Hana. B.S. in Physics, U. Tokyo, 1950, Ph.D., 1955, D.Sc., 1958. Research asso. Midwestern U. Research Assn., Madison, Wis., 1955-57; prof. physics U. Tokyo, 1958; with European Orgn. Nuclear Research, Geneva, 1959-60; vice chmn. Gen. Atomics, San Diego, 1960—; mem. joint high level adv. panel U.S.-Japan Agreement on Cooperation in R & D in Sci. and Tech., 1988-89; bd. councilors Nat. Inst. for Fusion Sci., Japan, 1989—; adj. prof. physics U. Calif., San Diego. Inventor doublet device, 2-beam FFAG accelerator, helical field stabilization of plasma devices; co-inventor multipole machine; contbr. articles to profl. publs. Mem. Am. Phys. Soc. (award 1979), Am. Nuclear Soc. (award 1984), Fusion Power Assn. (award 1984). Address: PO Box 85608 San Diego CA 92186-9784

OHL, RONALD EDWARD, academic administrator; b. Warren, Ohio, May 30, 1936; s. Howard Edward and Ella May (Van Auker) O.; m. Joan Ann Elizabeth Eschenbach, June 29, 1974. BA, Amherst Coll., 1958; MA, Columbia U., 1961; M in Divinity, Union Theol. Sem., N.Y.C., 1964; PhD, U. Pa., 1980. Ordained minister Congregationalist Ch., 1964. Counselor to grad. students Columbia U., N.Y.C., 1965-62; asst. dean students, asst. prof. history Elmhurst (Ill.) Coll., 1964-67; spl. asst. to dean of men Temple U., Phila., 1967-68; assoc. dean coll., asst. dean student affairs, instr. in edn. Colo. Coll., Colorado Springs, 1968-74; with Fairleigh Dickinson U., Rutherford, N.J., 1975-83, successively acting v.p. for external relations, asst. to pres., acting chmn. and cons. relations div. univ. resources and pub. affairs; pres. Salem (W.Va.)-Teikyo U., 1983—, trustee, 1989—, also bd. dirs. Contbr. articles to profl. jours. Bd. dirs. Clarksburg (W.Va.) YMCA, 1984-89, Sta. WNPB-TV, 1992—. Recipient Edward Poole Lay Traveling fellowship award Amherst Coll., 1958-59, Young Am. Artists' Dirs. award U.S. Embassy, Rome, 1959-60; Rockefeller Bros. Fund fellow, 1961-62; named Research Asst., U. Pa., 1967-68. Mem. W.Va. Assn. Ind. Colls. (pres. 1985-89), North Ctrl. Assn. Colls. and Schs. (cons.-evaluator 1987—), W.Va. Found. for Ind. Colls. (acad. vice chmn. 1992-94), Am. Humanics Bd. dirs. (bd. 1987-93), Clarksburg C. of C. (bd. dirs. 1985-91, 93—), Univ. Club (N.Y.C.), W.Va. Christopher Columbus Quincentenary Commn., Rotary (bd. dirs. Clarksburg club 1984-89). Avocations: reading, writing, aviation, skiing, backpacking. Home: 63 Terrace Ave Salem WV 26426-1124

OHLEN, ROBERT BRUCE, hospital executive; b. Pipestone, Minn., Feb. 26, 1943; s. Virgil Robert Ohlen and Mildred Loraine (Thiele) Skogmo; m. Gudrun Elfriede Umbach, Feb. 13, 1971; children: Christine Ann, Nicole Ann. Student, U. S.D., 1961-63; BS, Dakota Wesleyan U., 1965; MHA, Washington U., St. Louis, 1968. Adminstr. intern Anoka (Minn.) State Hosp., 1965-66; adminstrv. resident Hillsborough County Div. Hosps., Tampa, Fla., 1967-68, asst. adminstr., 1968-74; assoc. dir. Halifax Hosp. Med. Ctr., Daytona Beach, Fla., 1974-79; chief exec. officer Lawrence (Kans.) Meml. Hosp., 1979—. Chmn. campaign drive United Way, Lawrence, 1984, bd. dirs., 1985-88; bd. dirs. Kaw Valley coun. Girl Scouts U.S.A., 1983-89, Lawrence Hidden Valley Com., Inc., 1985-88. Named Young Alumnus of Yr., Dakota Wesleyan U., 1979. Fellow Am. Coll. Healthcare Execs., Royal Soc. Health; mem. Internat. Hosp. Fedn., Lawrence C. of C. (bd. dirs. 1987—), Kiwanis (appreciation award Lawrence 1985). Republican. Methodist. Avocation: travel. Home: RR 2 Box 336A Lawrence KS 66046-9590 Office: Lawrence Meml Hosp 325 Maine St Lawrence KS 66044-1393

OHLKE, CLARENCE CARL, public affairs consultant; b. Kansas City, Mo., Feb. 16, 1916; s. William Erdman and Amanda (Rubin) O.; m. Frances Woodley Nicholson, Oct. 9, 1954; children: Daniel N., Carl E., Amanda A. A.A., Kansas City Jr. Coll., 1935; B.S., U. Mo., 1940. Personnel examiner, rsch. asst. to city mgr. Mcpl. Govt., city of Kansas City, 1940-41; personnel specialist WPB, Washington, 1942; dir. civilian personnel Chief Naval Operations, Washington, 1946-47; successively personnel specialist, asst. dir. community ops., dir. contracts br., prodn. div. AEC, Washington, 1947-58, spl. asst. to chmn. and commr., 1959-61; asst. dir. operations div. contracts AEC, 1961, asst. to asst. gen. mgr. ops., 1962-63, dir. Office Econ. Impact and Conversion, 1964-66; spl. asst. to dir., head congl. and pub. affairs, govt. and pub. programs dir. NSF, Washington, 1966-73; cons. pub. affairs, 1976—. Served to lt. USNR, 1942-46. Recipient Disting. Service award NSF, 1973; resolution of commendation Pres.' Nat. Sci. Bd., 1973. Mem. AAAS (public understanding of sci. com. 1977-80). Home: Bear Branch Farms 7380 Ira Sears Rd Adamstown MD 21710-8501

OHLMEYER, DONALD WINFRED, JR., film and television producer; b. New Orleans, Feb. 3, 1945; s. Donald W. and Eva Claire (Bivens) O.; m. Adrian Perry, Feb. 11, 1978; 1 son, Kemper Perry; children by previous marriage: Justin Drew, Christopher Brett, Todd Bivens. BA in Communications, U. Notre Dame, 1967. Pres. Roadblock Prodns., 1977—; chmn. bd., chief exec. officer Ohlmeyer Communications, Los Angeles, 1982—. Assoc. dir. ABC Sports, N.Y.C., 1967-70, dir., 1971-72, producer, 1972-77; dir. Olympic Games, 1972, Walt Disney World's 4th of July Spectacular; producer dir. Summer and Winter Olympics, 1976; producer Monday Night Football, 1972-76; exec. producer NBC Sports, N.Y.C., 1977-82; exec. producer: 1980 Olympic Games, Crime of Innocence, Under Siege, Bluffing It, Right to Die; exec. producer: (movies) Special Bulletin, The Golden Moment: An Olympic Love Story; producer Battle of the Network Stars. Recipient 11 Emmy awards 1975-83, Cine Golden Eagle award, 1979, Miami Film Festival award 1979. Mem. Dirs. Guild Am., Acad. TV Arts and Scis. Clubs: Bel-Air (Calif.); Deepdale (N.Y.); Outrigger Canoe, Waialae Country (Honolulu). Office: NBC 3000 W Alameda Ave Burbank CA 91523-0002*

OHLROGGE, JOHN B., botany and plant pathology educator; b. June 7, 1949. BA in Chemistry, Earlham Coll., 1971; PhD in Biochemistry, U. Mich., 1975. Post doctoral fellow in biochemistry U. Calif., Davis, 1976-79; rsch. biochemist U.S. Dept. Agriculture, Peoria, Ill., 1980-86; assoc. prof. botany and plant pathology Mich. State U., East Lansing, 1987-91, prof., 1991—; mem. peer review panel USDA Competitive Grants Program. Mem. editorial bd. Archives Biochemistry and Biophysics, Plant Physiology; contbr. over 50 articles to sci. jours. Grantee Agrl. Rsch. Svc. Rsch. Assoc. Program, 1982-84, USDA 1984-86, 86-89, Am. Soybean Assn., 1987-89, DOE, 1987-90, 91—, USDA/DOE.NSF, 1988-93, 92—, NSF, 1989, 90—, Mich. State U. Rsch. Excellence Funds, 1993, Midwest Plant Pathology Consortium, 1993—. Achievements include research in plant fatty acid synthesis, organization of lipid metabolism in plant cells, molecular biology of genes controlling plant lipid synthesis. Office: Mich State U Dept Botany Plant Path East Lansing MI 48824

OHLSON, DOUGLAS DEAN, artist; b. Cherokee, Iowa, Nov. 18, 1936; s. Lloyd E. and Effie O. (Johnson) O. B.A., U. Minn., 1961. Prof. art Hunter Coll., N.Y.C., 1964—. One man shows include Fischbach Gallery, N.Y.C., 1964, 66-70, 72, Susan Caldwell Gallery, N.Y.C., 1974, 76, 77, 79, 81, 82, 83, Portland (Oreg.) Center for the Visual Arts, 1977, Ruth Siegel Gallery, N.Y.C., 1985, 87, Andre Zarre Gallery, N.Y.C., 1985, 90, 92, 93, Gallery 99, Miami, Fla., 1986, Nina Freidenheim Gallery, Buffalo, N.Y., 1986, Jaffe Gallery, Miami, 1989; group shows include, Mus. Modern Art, N.Y.C., 1968, Tate Gallery, London, 1969, Whitney Mus., N.Y.C., 1969, 71, Corcoran Gallery, Washington, 1972, 73, UCLA, 1975, Am. Acad. Arts and Letters, N.Y.C., 1994; represented in permanent collections Met. Mus. Art., N.Y.C., Nat. Gallery Art, Washington, Am. Fedn. Art, Mus. Modern Art, Frankfurt, Fed. Republic Germany, Mus. Contemporary Art, Helsinki; circulating exhbn. include Corcoran Gallery, Mpls. Inst. Art, Dallas Mus., Bklyn. Mus., Born in Iowa: The Homecoming, 1986-87; invitational Am. Acad. of Arts and Letters, N.Y.C., 1992. Served with USMC, 1955-58. Guggenheim fellow, 1968; Creative Artists Public Service grantee, 1974; Nat. Endowment for Arts grantee, 1976. Home and Studio: 35 Bond St New York NY 10012

OHLY, D. CHRISTOPHER, lawyer; b. N.Y.C., Nov. 7, 1950; s. Bobo Charles and Ellen Charlotte (Nekolla) O.; m. Karen Vanacek; 1 child, Sara Rebecca. AB, Johns Hopkins U., 1972; JD, U. Va., 1975. Bar: Md. 1975, U.S. Dist. Ct. Md. 1975, U.S. Ct. Appeals (1st, 2d and 4th cirs.), U.S. Tax Ct., U.S. Supreme Ct. Asst. U.S. Atty. U.S. Atty's Office, Balt., 1978-81; owner Hazel & Thomas, P.C., Balt., 1989-94; ptnr. Patton Boggs, LLP, Balt., 1994—. Contbr. articles to profl. jours. Mem. ABA (internat. law sect. 1973—), Md. Bar Assn. (internat. comml. law sect. 1978—), Am. Soc. Internat. Law, Phi Beta Kappa, Omicron Delta Kappa, Pi Sigma Alpha. Avocations: skiing, computers, amateur radio. Home: 5714 St Albans Way Baltimore MD 21212-2454 also: Village Chalet #5 Middle Ridge Rd Winhall VT 05155

OHM, HERBERT WILLIS, agronomy educator; b. Albert Lea, Minn., Jan. 28, 1945; s. Wilhelm Carl and Lena Ann (Finkbeiner) O.; m. Judy Ann Chrisinger, Aug. 8, 1964; children: Cari Lynn, David William. BS in Agrl. Edn., U. Minn., St. Paul, 1967; MS in Plant Breeding, N.D. State U., 1969; PhD in Plant Genetics and Breeding, Purdue U., 1972. Cert. agronomist. Asst. prof. Purdue U., West Lafayette, Ind., 1972-77, assoc. prof. agronomy, 1977-83, prof., 1983—; team leader Interdisciplinary Wheat and Oat Genetics and Breeding Program, West Lafayette, 1980—, Interdisciplinary Purdue/AID Devel. Program, Burkina Faso, West Africa, 1983-85; mgr. hard red winter wheat rsch. Pioneer Hi-Bred Internat., Inc., Hutchinson, Kans., 1980. Contbr. book chpts. Recipient Soils and Crops Merit award Ind. Crop Improvement Assn., 1988, Merit award Orgn. of African Unity, 1989, Meritorious Svc. award Sci., Tech. and Rsch. Commn., 1989. Fellow Crop Sci. Soc. Am. (chmn. divsn. 1991); mem. Am. Soc. Agronomy, Am. Oat Workers Conf. (chmn.), Nat. Oat Improvement Coun. (chmn.), Coun. Agrl. Sci. and Tech., Am. Registry Cert. Profls. in Agrl. Crops and Soils (cert.). Avocations: woodworking, music. Office: Purdue U Dept Agronomy Lilly Hall Life Scis West Lafayette IN 47907-7899

OHMAN, DIANA J., state official, former school system administrator; b. Sheridan, Wyo., Oct. 3, 1950; d. Arden and Doris Marie (Carstens) Mahin. AA, Casper Coll., 1970; BA, U. Wyo., 1972, MEd, 1977, postgrad., 1979—. Tchr. kindergarten Natrona County Sch. Dist., Casper, Wyo., 1971-72; tchr. rural sch. K-8 Campbell County Sch. Dist., Gillette, Wyo., 1972-80, rural prin. K-8, 1980-82, prin. K-6, 1982-84, assoc. dir. instrn., 1984-87; dir. K-12 Goshen County Migrant Program, Torrington, Wyo., 1988-89; prin. K-2 Goshen County Sch. Dist., Torrington, Wyo., 1987-90; state supt. pub. instrn. State of Wyo., Cheyenne, 1991-94, secretary of state, 1995—. Mem. Campbell County Mental Health Task Force, 1986-87; mem. Legis. Task Force on Edn. of Handicapped 3-5 Yr. Olds, 1988-89. State Committeewoman Wyo. Rep. Party, 1985-88. Recipient Wyo. Elem. Prin. of Yr. award, 1990; named Campbell County Tchr. of Yr. 1980, Campbell County Profl. Bus. Woman of Yr. 1984, Outstanding Young Woman in Am., 1983. Mem. Coun. of Chief of State Sch. Officers (Washington chpt.), Internat. Reading Assn., Wyo. Assn. of Sch. Adminstrs., Kappa Delta Pi, Phi Kappa Phi, Phi Delta Kappa. Republican. Lutheran. Office: Sec State Office State Capitol Cheyenne WY 82002-0020

OHMERT, RICHARD ALLAN, architect; b. Davenport, Iowa, Apr. 13, 1925; s. Richard George and Jeanette Marie (Ackerman) O.; m. Bonnie Lou Bruyere, June 26, 1948 (div. June 1964); children: Richard, Jennifer, Jan, Kenneth; m. Violet Maria Alto Holmes, Dec. 31, 1971; stepchildren: Candyce, Cynthia. Student, Gallery Fine Arts Sch. Design, 1940-41, UCLA, 1954-56. Registered architect Calif., Nev., accredited Nat. Coun. Archtl. Registration Bds. Assoc. Kistner Wright & Wright, L.A., 1950-71; asst. mgr. architecture Voorhis, Trindle, Nelson Corp., Irvine, Calif., 1971-74; assoc. Davis-Duhaime Assocs., Anaheim, Calif., 1974-89; firm assoc. Neptune-Thomas-Davis, Corona, Calif., 1989—; cons. architect E&O Corp., Irvine, 1985—. Pres. Groves Homeowners Assn., Irvine, 1981-82; bd. mgrs. YMCA, Irvine, 1988-89; pres. bd. dirs. Orange County Child Abuse Prevention Ctr., 1991. Mem. Soc. Am. Registered Architects (sec.-treas. 1990-92, pres. Orange County chpt. 1993—), Irvine Chpt. of Nat. Exch. Club (pres. 1983-84, dist. dir. 1986-87, Calif.-Nev. dist. pres. 1988-89, pres. Sunrise chpt. 1993-94, 94—, Exchangite of Yr. award 1990). Democrat. Episcopalian. Avocations: oil painting, astronomy, miniature car collecting, cooking. Home: 5200 Irvine Blvd Unit 18 Irvine CA 92720-2016 Office: Neptune-Thomas-Davis Architects 357 Sheridan St Ste 101 Corona CA 91720

OHNAMI, MASATERU, mechanical engineering educator; b. Kyoto, Japan, Apr. 6, 1931; s. Eijiro and Hisae O.; m. Hiroko Ohnami, Oct. 10, 1959; 1 child, Masahiro. B in Engring., Ritsumeikan U., Kyoto, Japan, 1954; D in Engring., Kyoto U., 1960; D Internat. Rels. honoris causa, American U., Washington, 1995. Assoc. prof. Kyoto U., 1955-61; assoc. prof. Ritsumeikan U., Kyoto, 1961-67, 1967—, dean acad. affairs, 1978-80, dean faculty sci. & engring., 1988-90, pres., 1991—; vis. rsch. prof. Columbia U., N.Y.C., 1963-64; mng. dir. Japan Assn. Pvt. Colls. and Univs., Tokyo, 1991—; dir. Japanese Univ. Accreditation Assn., Tokyo, 1991—; mem. Sci. Coun. Ministry Edn., 1984-86. 1989-91, mem. Univs. Formation Coun., 1993—. Author: Plasticity and High Temperature Strength of Materials, 1988, Fracture and Society, 1992. Mem. Deutscher Verband für Materialforschung und prüfung e.V. (hon. 1992—), Soc. of Materials Sci. Japan (bd. dirs. 1971-74, 81-84, 85-88, Prize 1971), Japanese Soc. for Strength and Fracture of Materials (bd. dirs. 1984—), Sci. Coun. Japan (material rsch. liaison com. 1988-94). Avocations: oil painting, reading. Home: 8-10 Hyugacho, Takatsuki Osaka Prefecture 569, Japan Office: Ritsumeikan Univ, 56-1 Tojiin Kitamachi, Kita Kyoto 603, Japan

OHNO, SUSUMU, research scientist; b. Seoul, Korea, Feb. 1, 1928; came to U.S., 1953; s. Kenichi and Yasuhiko (Saito) O.; m. Midori Aoyama, Jan. 7, 1951; children: Azusa, Yukali, Takeshi. DVM, Tokyo U. Agr. and Tech., 1949; PhD, Hokkaido U., 1956, DSc, 1961; DSc, U. Pa., 1984; HHD (hon.), Kwansei Gakuin U., 1983. Rsch. staff pathology Tokyo U., 1950-53; rsch. assoc. City of Hope, Duarte, Calif., 1953-63, mem. biology, 1966-81, disting. scientist, 1981—; vis. prof. Albert Einstein Med. Sch., Bronx, N.Y., 1969, Basel Inst. for Immunology, Switzerland, 1976; prof. at large Tohoku U., Japan, 1987—; bd. dirs. Beckman Rsch. Inst., Duarte, Calif. Author monographs. Recipient Kihara prize Genetic Soc. Japan, Tokyo, 1983. Fellow AAAS (Amory prize 1981); mem. NAS, Royal Danish Acad. Scis. and Letters (fgn.). Avocations: horsemanship, dressage, fishing, musical transformation of gene DNA sequences. Office: Beckman Rsch Inst City of Hope 1450 Duarte Rd Duarte CA 91010-3011

O'HOLLAREN, PAUL JOSEPH, former international fraternity administrator; b. Portland, Oreg., Dec. 24, 1927; s. Charles Edward and Helen Henrietta (McHugh) O'H.; m. Patricia Marie Foley, June 27, 1953; children: Mark T., Kevin J., Brian T., Patrick S., Kelly P. JD, Northwestern Coll. of Law, 1954. Bar: Oreg., 1954. Atty. Oreg. State Bar, 1954-83; mem. supreme coun. Moose Internat., Inc., Mooseheart, Ill., 1968-79; supreme gov. Loyal Order of Moose, Mooseheart, Ill., 1978-79; dir. gen., 1984-94, retired, 1994; chmn. exec. bd. Moose Internat., Inc., 1994—. Bd. dirs. Ill. Math. and Sci. Acad. Fund for the Advancement of Edn., Aurora, Ill., 1987—; chmn. Alliance for Drug Free Soc., Washington. With U.S. Army, 1945-46. Named Jr. First Citizen, U.S. Jr. C. of C., Portland, 1959; recipient Oreg.

State Bar award of Merit, 1979. Mem. Multnomah Athletic Club, Loyal Order of Moose. Republican. Roman Catholic. Avocation: golf. Office: 680 Benjamin Franklin Plz 1 SW Columbia Portland OR 97258

O'HORGAN, THOMAS FOSTER, composer, director; b. Chgo., May 3, 1924. BA, MA, DePaul U. Chgo. Debut performance in Fallout; off-Broadway revue, 1959; directing debut with month. The Maids, 1964; dir.: Hair (Tony award nominee 1968), Lenny (Drama Desk award 1971), Jesus Christ Super Star, Inner City, Six from La Mama, The Hessian Corporal, Futz (Obie award 1967, Drama Desk award 1968), Tom Paine (Drama Desk award 1968), Massachusetts Trust, Dude, The Leaf People, Sergeant Pepper's Lonely Hearts Club Band on the Road, Capitol Cakewalk, 1990, The Architect and The Emperor of Abyssinia; composer: music for numerous prodns. including Open Season at Second City Senator Joe (also dir.), 1989, The Body Builder's Book of Love, 1990; music for films including Futz, 1969, Alex in Wonderland, 1970, Rhinocerous, 1974; performer in: film All Men Are Apes, 1965. Recipient Creative Arts award Brandeis U., 1968. Office: care Dirs Guild Am 110 W 57th St New York NY 10019-3319*

OHRENSTEIN, MANFRED, state senator, lawyer; b. Mannheim, Germany, Aug. 5, 1925; came to U.S., 1938; s. Markus and Fannie (Hollander) O.; m. Marilyn Bacher, 1957; children: Nancy Ellen, David Jonathan. BA cum laude, Bklyn. Coll., 1948; JD (Harlan Fiske Stone scholar), Columbia U., 1951. Bar: N.Y. 1951, U.S. Ct. Mil. Appeals 1956, U.S. Dist. Ct. (so. dist.) N.Y. 1958, U.S. Ct. Appeals (2d cir.) 1977. Pvt. practice law N.Y.C., 1958—; counsel Cantor & Opper, 1958-61; ptnr. Karpatkin Ohrenstein & Karpatkin, 1961-74, Stein Simpson Rosen & Ohrenstein, 1974-81, Pincus Ohrenstein Bizar D'Alessandro & Solomony, 1981-83, Ohrenstein & Brown, 1983—; asst. dist. atty. New York County, 1954-58; mem. N.Y. State Senate, 1961-95, minority leader, 1975-95, chmn. N.Y. State delegation Dem. Nat. Conv., 1980. Mem. editorial bd. Present Tense Mag. Chmn. N.Y. State Holocaust Ctr. Albany; co-chmn. N.Y. State Holocaust Meml. Commn.; mem. exec. bd. N.Y.C. chpt. Am. Jewish Com. 1st lt. JAGC U.S. Army, 1952-54, capt. USAR, 1954-60. Mem. ACLU, Assn. of Bar of City of N.Y. (ins. com. 1977-83), N.Y. State Bar Assn., Am. Israel Pub. Affairs Com., N.Y. State Bar Assn. Office: Ohrenstein & Brown 230 Park Ave New York NY 10169-0103

OHRENSTEIN, ROMAN ABRAHAM, economics educator, economist, rabbi; b. Slomniki, Poland, June 12, 1920; came to U.S., 1951, naturalized, 1957; s. Joseph Barukh and Gena (Fiefkopf) O.; m. Ruth Silberstein, Aug. 30, 1953; children: Gena Ann, Ilana Rose. M.A. in Econs., U. Munich, 1948, Ph.D. cum laude in Econs., 1949, postgrad. in medicine, 1949-51; M.H.L., Jewish Theol. Sem. Am., 1955; postgrad., Columbia U., 1963-64. Ordained rabbi, 1955. Rabbi Auburn, N.Y., 1955-57, Pittsfield, Mass., 1957-60, Atlanta, 1960-62, N.Y.C., 1962-66; prof. econs. Nassau Coll. SUNY-Garden City, 1964—, chmn. econs. dept., 1976-78, 82-84, campus chaplain, 1970—; chaplain Nassau County Civic Preparedness, N.Y., 1965—; prof. econs. Am. Coll. Jerusalem, 1968-73, mem. Coll. Council, 1967-73; vis. prof. U. Newcastle, Australia, 1985, vis. rsch. prof., 1989; past chaplain Kiwanis, Police Dept. Cayuga County, N.Y., 1955-57, Mt. Sinai Hosp., N.Y.C., 1963-64; nat. dir. Jewish Rights Council; mem. Council of Orgns., U.S.A., 1978-85; mem. spl. com. on Jewish law Rabbinical Assembly, 1971; condr. seminars U. Queensland, Sydney U., Nat. Univ., all Australia, 1989, Sorbonne, Paris, 1990; lectr., guest speaker on radio, TV, Jewish civic and profl. orgns. Author: Economic Thought in Talmudic Literature (series), 1968, 70, 83, 86, 87, 89, 91-93, Inventories During Business Fluctuations, 1973, Inventory Control as an Economic Shock Absorber, 1975, Economic Analysis in Talmudic Literature, 1992; mem. editorial adv. bd. Internat. Rev. of Econs. and Ethics; contbr. articles to profl. jours. Mem. nat. exec. comm. Am. Profs. for Peace in the Middle East, 1971-73. Recipient 1st Faculty Disting. Achievement award Nassau Coll., SUNY, 1992, 95; SUNY fellow, 1968, 70. Mem. Nat. Assn. Jewish Chaplains, Rabbinical Assembly N.Y. Bd. Rabbis, Am. Econ. Assn., History of Econs. Soc., Assn. Social Econs. Learned Soc., N.Y. Acad. Scis., Internat. Soc. for Intercommunication New Ideas, Literati Club (Eng.). Home: 28-74 208 St Bayside NY 11360 Office: Nassau Coll Stewart Ave Garden City NY 11530 *I kept my faith in God coupled with loyalty to tradition, sharpened my mind while maintaining discipline of the heart; tenacity in the face of adversity, turning stumbling blocks into stepping stones while never losing sight of life's supreme purpose: to leave the world a little better than I found it.*

OHRN, NILS YNGVE, chemistry and physics educator; b. Avesta, Sweden, June 11, 1934; came to U.S., 1966; s. Nils E. and Gerda M. (Akerlund) O.; m. Ann M.M. Thorsell, Aug. 24, 1957; children: Elisabeth, Maria. M.S., Uppsala U., 1958, Ph.D., 1963, F.D. 1966. Research assoc. Uppsala (Sweden) U., 1963-66; assoc. prof. U. Fla., Gainesville, 1966-70, prof. chemistry and physics, 1971—, assoc. dir. Quantum Theory Project, 1976-77, dir. Quantum Theory Project, 1983—, chmn. dept. chemistry, 1977-83. Editor: Internat. Jour. Quantum Chemistry, 1970—. Fulbright grantee Com. for Internat. Exchange of Scholars, Washington, 1961-63; recipient Bicentennial Gold medal King of Sweden, 1980; Fla. Acad. Scis. medal, 1984. Fellow Am. Phys. Soc., Chaire Franqui Interuniversitaires im Belgium; mem. Am. Chem. Soc., Royal Acad. Scis. Sweden (fgn.), Finnish Acad. Scis. (fgn.), Royal Danish Acad. Scis. (fgn.), Sigma Xi, Phi Beta Kappa. Home: 1823 NW 11th Rd Gainesville FL 32605-5323 Office: U Fla Quantum Theory Project 362 Williamson Hall Gainesville FL 32611

OHSOL, ERNEST OSBORNE, consulting chemical engineer; b. Washington, May 28, 1916; s. Johann Gottfried and Klara Elizabeth (Karpowitz) O.; m. Mary Rosamond Montgomery, June 15, 1940 (div. Jan. 4, 1977); children: Frederick M., Richard B., Barbara Alison (Mrs. Layton S. Allen, Jr.), Elizabeth Anne; m. Barbara I. Handy, Mar. 24, 1977. Student, Fed. Polytech. Inst., Zurich, Switzerland, 1934-35; B.S., Coll. City N.Y., 1936; Sc.D., Mass. Inst. Tech., 1939. Registered profl. engr., N.J. Devel. engr. Standard Oil Devel. Co., Linden, N.J., 1939-50; mgr. process devel. chem. div. Gen. Elec. Co., Pittsfield, Mass., 1950-52; dir. research and devel. Pitts. Coke and Chem. Co., 1953-60; v.p. Haveg Industries, Inc. (plastics), Wilmington, Del., 1960-65, Chem. Constrn. Corp., N.Y.C., 1965-67, Escambia Chem. Co., N.Y.C., 1967; dir. chem. engring. dept. Am. Cyanamid Co. (central research div.), Stamford, Conn., 1967-72; cons. chem. engr. Plainfield, N.J., 1973; chief process engr. Eastern group Jacobs Engring. Co., Mountainside, N.J., 1973-75; corp. mgr. European fluid processing Selas Corp. Am., Munich, W. Ger., 1975-78; coordinator C.H. Dexter div. Dexter Corp., Windsor Locks, Conn., 1978-80; cons. Selastig Corp, Houston, Shell Nigerian Oil Co., Aramco, Tek-Rap, Petromin Shell, EnviroKinetics; chmn. emeritus Unipure Corp., 1993—; adj. prof. Grad. Sch., Stevens Inst. Tech., 1946-50. Patentee in field. Naumburg fellow CCNY, 1934-35; Arthur D. Little fellow Mass. Inst. Tech., 1937-38. Fellow Am. Inst. Chem. Engrs. (dir. 1973); mem. Am. Chem. Soc., Chemists Club N.Y.C., Sigma Xi. Episcopalian (vestryman 1963-65). Home and Office: 711 N Hyannis Port St Crosby TX 77532-5515

OHTAKE, YOSHITO, metal products executive. Exec. v.p. Nissho Iwai of the Americas, N.Y.C., 1988—. Office: Nissho Iwai American Corp 100 Galleria Officentre Ste 221 Southfield MI 48034

OHTSU, MASAKAZU, electronics executive; b. Osaka, Japan, Dec. 17, 1937; m. Yoshiko Asano, Feb. 4, 1962; children: Masashi, Ben. BE, Doshisha U., Kyoto, Japan, 1962. With Itochu Corp., 1962—; sr. v.ps, gen. mgr. Aerospace & Electronics Divsn. Itochu Internat., Inc., N.Y.C., 1988—; chmn. DX Comm., Inc., Hawthorn, N.Y., 1988—, VueScan, Inc., Deerfield Beach, Fla., 1994—, Telerent Leasing Corp., Raleigh, N.C., 1989—. Office: Itochu Internat Inc 335 Madison Ave New York NY 10017-4605

OHYAMA, HEIICHIRO, music educator, violist, conductor; b. Kyoto, Japan, July 31, 1947; came to U.S., 1970; s. Heishiro and Sumi (Ohara) O.; 1 child, Shinichiro Allen Ohyama. Assocs. degree, Guildhall Sch. Music and Drama, London, 1970. Instr. N.C. Sch. Arts, Winston-Salem, 1972-73; prof. music U. Calif., Santa Barbara, 1994—; prin. violist L.A. Philharm., 1979-91, asst. condr., 1987-90; music dir. Santa Barbara Chamber Orch., 1983—, Crossroads Chamber Orch., Santa Monica, Calif., 1981-93, Cayuga Chamber Orch., 1993—; music dir., condr. Japan Am. Symphony Orch., 1991—; artistic dir. La Jolla (Calif.) Chamber Music Festival, 1986—; condr. Round Top Music Festival, 1983—, N.W. Chamber Orch., 1985-87; vis. lectr. Ind. U., Bloomington, 1972-73; artistic dir. Santa Fe Chamber Music Festival,

1992—. Appearances at Marlboro Music Festival, Vt., 1972-76, Santa Fe Chamber Music Festival, 1977-85, Round Top Music Festival, Tex., 1983—, La Jolla (Calif.) Chamber Music Summer Fest., 1986—; various recordings. Recipient award Young Concert Artist N.Y., 1974, Calif. Artists Mgmt., 1991. Avocations: diving, kendo, photography. Home: 1643 Oramas Rd Santa Barbara CA 93103

OIKAWA, HIROSHI, materials science educator; b. Sakhalin, Japan, Oct. 15, 1933; s. Torao and Tomi (Kumagai) O.; m. Ayako Otomo, May 4, 1963; children: Makoto, Junko. BE, Tohoku U., Sendai, Japan, 1956, ME, 1958, D in Engring., 1961. Instr. Tohoku U., Sendai, 1961-63, lectr., 1963-64, assoc. prof., 1964-82; rsch. fellow U. Fla., Gainesville, 1966-68; prof. Tohoku U., Sendai, 1982—; councilor, 1993-95, dean faculty engring., 1995—. Co-editor: Metals Handbooks, 1990, Metals Databook, 1993. Mem. Engring. Acad. of Japan, Japan Inst. Metals (bd. dirs. 1992-94, bd. dirs Tohoku chpt. 1991-93), Iron and Steel Inst. of Japan (bd. dirs. 1990-92), Japan Inst. Light Metals (bd. dirs. 1989-95), Minerals, Metals and Materials Soc., ASM Internat., Inst. Materials. Office: Tohoku U Dept Materials Sci, Faculty Engring, Sendai 980-77, Japan

OINAS, FELIX JOHANNES, foreign language educator; b. Tartu, Estonia, Mar. 6, 1911; came to U.S., 1949, naturalized, 1955; s. Ernst and Marie (Saarik) O.; m. Lisbet Kove, July 10, 1935; children: Helina Oinas Piano, Valdar. MA, Tartu U., Estonia, 1938; postgrad., Budapest U., 1935-36, Heidelberg U., 1946-48; PhD, Ind. U., 1952. Lectr. Budapest U., 1938-40; lectr. Estonian Baltic U., Hamburg, 1946-49; lectr. Slavic langs. Ind. U., 1952-53, instr., 1953-55, asst. prof., 1955-61, assoc. prof., 1961-65, prof. Slavic langs. and Uralic and Altaic studies, 1965-81, prof. emeritus, 1981—; fellow Folklore Inst., 1955—. Author, editor 21 books in field, including Suremato Kalevipoeg (Immortal Kalevipoeg), 1994; contbr. articles to profl. jours. Guggenheim fellow, 1961, 66; Fulbright grantee, 1961; Fulbright-Hays grantee, 1964; Nat. Endowment for Humanities grantee, 1974; recipient Cultural award Found. Estonian Arts and Letters; 1st prize Dr. Arthur Puksow Found. Fellow Am. Folklore Soc., Finnish Literary Soc., Finno-Ugric Soc., Finnish Folklore Soc., Baltisches Forschungsinstitut (Bonn), Inst. Estonian Lang. and Lit. (Stockholm); mem. Finnish Acad. Scis. (gen. mem.), Estonian Learned Soc. Am. (hon.), Estonian Sci. Inst. in Sweden (hon.), Folklore Fellows Internat. Helsinki (hon.), Estonian Literatrure Soc. (hon.), Folklore Inst. Budapest U. (hon.), Folklore Fellows in Oral Epics, Estonian Writers League Abroad. Lutheran. Home: 2513 E 8th St Bloomington IN 47408-4214 Office: IN Univ Slavic Dept Bloomington IN 47405

OISHI, SATOSHI, architectural and engineering executive; b. Japan, Jan. 19, 1927; came to U.S., 1932, naturalized, 1954; s. Mitsuhei and Yei O.; m. Jeanette Corrine Allard, July 2, 1960; 1 dau., Michelle Yuki. B.S. in Civil Engring. with high honors, U. Conn., 1949. With Edwards & Kelcey, Inc., Newark and Livingston, N.J., 1949—; chief structural engr., assoc., 1958-65, ptnr., 1965—; pres., chief exec. officer Edwards & Kelcey, Inc., Livingston, 1987-90, chmn. bd., 1990-94, chmn. emeritus, 1994—. Prin. works include Round Valley Recreation Area, Hunterdon County, N.J., 1973-75, rehab. of Manhattan Bridge, 1979-83, also transit tunnels and sta. designs, Washington, Atlanta, Balt., Buffalo, bridges in N.J., N.Y., Conn., Minn., New Eng.; investigator bridges and structures/failures. Chmn. Berkeley Heights (N.J.) Planning and Zoning Bd., 1974, Fritz Medal Bd., 1990-91; trustee Summit Unitarian Ch.; mem. Engring. Found. Bd.; co-chair Journalism Award Com.; mem. alumni award and civil engring. adv. com. U. Conn. Fellow ASCE (v.p zone 1, dir. dist. 1, past pres. met. sect., Harland Bartholomew award 1992, Citizen Engr. award 1992), N.Y. Assn. Consulting Engrs. (bd. dirs.), Am. Cons. Engrs. Coun.; mem. AIA, Soc. Mil. Engrs. (sr. exec. com.), Internat. Assn. Bridge and Structural Engring., Am. Concrete Inst., Am. Pub. Transit Assn., N.Y. C. of C (transp. com.), Japan Soc., RPA N.J. Com., Sigma Xi, Chi Epsilon (hon.), Tau Beta Pi. Unitarian. Home: 67 River Rd Berkeley Heights NJ 07922-1006 Office: Edwards & Kelcey PO Box 1936 299 Madison Ave Morristown NJ 07962-1936

OJALVO, MORRIS, civil engineer, educator; b. N.Y.C., Mar. 4, 1924; s. Nissim and (Fanny) O.; m. Anita Beniou, Dec. 26, 1948; children—Lynne, Joseph, Howard, Isobel. B.C.E., Rensselaer Poly. Inst.; Troy, N.Y., 1944, M.C.E., 1952; Ph.D., Lehigh U., Bethlehem, Pa., 1960; J.D., Ohio State U., Columbus, 1978. Bar: Ohio bar 1979. Draftsman Am. Bridge Co., Elmira, N.Y., 1946-47; tutor civil engring. CCNY, 1947-49; instr. Rensselaer Poly. Inst., 1949-51; asst. prof. Princeton U., 1951-58; research instr. Lehigh U., 1958-60; mem. faculty Ohio State U., 1960—, prof. civil engring., 1964-82, prof. emeritus, 1982—; vis. prof. U. Tex.-Austin, 1982-83. Author: Thin-Walled Bars With Open Profiles, 1990; contbr. papers in field. Served with USNR, 1944-46. Mem. ASCE, Structural Stability Research Council. Patentee warp restraining device. Home: 2258 Wickliffe Rd Columbus OH 43221-1832 Office: Hitchcock Hall Ohio State Univ Columbus OH 43210

OJEMANN, GEORGE A., neurosurgeon, medical association executive; b. Iowa City, Feb. 25, 1935. MD, U. Iowa, 1959. Diplomate Am. Bd. Neurol. Surgery (dir. 1987, chmn. 1992). Intern in neurosurgery King County Hosp., Seattle, 1959-60; resident in neurosurgery U. Wash. Hosps., Seattle, 1960-64; attending neurosurgeon U. Hosp., Seattle, 1966—; prof. neurosurgery U. Wash., Seattle, 1979—. Author: (with William Calvin): Inside the Brain, Conversations with Neil's Brain. Office: U Wash Dept Neurol Surgery RI 20 Seattle WA 98195

OJEMANN, ROBERT GERDES, neurosurgeon; b. Iowa City, May 5, 1931; s. Ralph H. and Freda (Metzger) O.; m. Jean Munson; children: David, James, Michael, John. BA, U. Iowa, 1951, MD, 1955. Diplomate Am. Bd. Neurol. Surgery (chmn. 1982-83). Intern Cin. Gen. Hosp., 1955-56; resident in gen. surgery Baylor U. Coll. Medicine, Houston, 1956-57; resident in neurosurgery Mass. Gen. Hosp., Boston, 1957-61, mem. staff, 1961—, also vis. neurosurgeon, chmn. staff assocs., 1977-79, mem. exec. com., 1981-84; mem. staff Harvard Med. Sch., Boston, 1961—, now prof. surgery. Co-author: Operative Microneurosurgery, 1985, Surgical Management of Cerebrovascular Disease, 1983, 2d edit., 1988; contbr. numerous articles and book chpts. to profl. publs. Deacon Trinitarian Congl. Ch., Wayland, Mass., 1984-87, 93—. Recipient Disting. Alumni award U. Iowa, 1992. Mem. Congress Neurol. Surgeons (pres. 1975-76, honored guest 1992), Am. Acad. Neurol. Surgery (pres. 1989-90, Best Resident Rsch. Paper award 1960), Am. Assn. Neurol. Surgeons (pres. 1986-87), Soc. Neurol. Surgeons (pres. 1990-91), Harvard Club (Boston). Avocations: landscaping, carpentry, hiking, tennis, stamp collecting. Office: Mass Gen Hosp 32 Fruit St Boston MA 02114-2620

OJIMA, IWAO, chemistry educator; b. Yokohama, Japan, June 5, 1945; came to U.S., 1983; s. Masaharu and Sumiko (Takatsuki) O.; m. Yoko Ogino, Apr. 24, 1971. BS, U. Tokyo, 1968, MS, 1970, PhD in Organic Chemistry, 1973. Rsch. fellow Sagami Inst. for Chem. Rsch., Japan, 1970-76, sr. rsch. fellow, group leader, 1976-83; assoc. prof. chemistry SUNY, Stony Brook, 1983-84, prof., 1984-91, leading prof., 1991—; lectr. Tokyo Inst. Tech., 1978-79, 83, Tokyo U. Agrl. & Tech., 1983; prin. investor NSF, 1983, N.Y. Sci. Tech. Found., 1985—, NIH, 1986—, ACS-Prof., 1987—; vis. prof. U. Claude Bernard, Lyon (France) I, 1989; mem. editl. adv. bd. Elsevier Pubs., Lausanne, Switzerland, 1986-95; cons. Nippon Steel Corp., Yokohama, 1989—, Rhone-Poulenc Rorer, Vitry, France, 1991—. Editor: Catalytic Asymmetric Synthesis, 1993, Taxane Anticancer Agents, 1994; contbr. numerous articles to profl. jours.; numerous patents in field. Mem. AAAS, Am. Chem. Soc. (editl. adv. bd. 1985—, A.C. Cope scholar award 1994), Chem. Soc. Japan (Progress award 1976), N.Y. Acad. Scis., Sigma Xi. Research in homogeneous catalysis of transition metal complexes; asymmetric synthesis; organic synthesis by means of organometallic reagents; peptide syntesis; beta-lactam chemistry; organo flourine chemistry; medicinal chemistry, especially in regard to enzyme inhibitors and taxane anticancer agents. Home: 6 Ivy League Ln Stony Brook NY 11790 Office: State U New York Dept Chemistry Stony Brook NY 11794-3400

OKA, TAKESHI, physicist, chemist, astronomer, educator; b. Tokyo, June 10, 1932; arrived in Can., 1963, naturalized, 1973; s. Shumpei and Chiyoko O.; m. Keiko Nukui, Oct. 24, 1960; children: Ritsuko, Noriko, Kentaro, Yujiro. B.Sc., U. Tokyo, 1955, Ph.D., 1960. Research asso. U. Tokyo, 1960-63; fellow NRC Can., Ottawa, 1963-65; asst. NRC Can., 1965-68, asso. 1968-71, sr. research physicist 1971—; prof. U. Chgo., 1981—; Robert A. Millikan disting. prof., 1989—. Mem. editorial bd. Chem. Physics,

1972—, Jour. Molecular Spectroscopy, 1973—, Jour. Chem. Physics, 1975-77. Recipient Steacie prize, 1972; Earle K. Plyler prize, 1982. Fellow Royal Soc. Can., Royal Soc. London, Am. Phys. Soc., Optical Soc. Am., Am. Acad. Scis. and Arts; mem. Am. Astron. Soc. Office: U Chgo Dept Chemistry Astronomy & Astrophysics Chicago IL 60637

OKADA, TAKUYA, food service and retail executive; b. Sept. 19, 1925; m. Yasuko Okada. Student, Waseda U., Japan, 1948. Pres. Diamond City K.K.; chmn. Jusco Co. Ltd., N.Y.C. Office: Jusco USA Inc 525 Madison Ave Fl 4 New York NY 10022

OKAMURA, ARTHUR, artist, educator, writer; b. Long Beach, Calif., Feb. 24, 1932; s. Frank Akira and Yuki O.; m. Elizabeth Tuomi, Aug. 7, 1953 (div.); children: Beth, Jonathan, Jane, Ethan; m. Kitty Wong, 1991. Student, Art Inst. of Chgo., 1950-54, U. Chgo., 1951, SUNY, 1952; art seminar Yale, 1954. Faculty Central YMCA Coll., Chgo., 1956, 57, Evanston Art Center, 1956-57, Art Inst. Chgo., North Shore Art League, Winnetka, Ill., Acad. Art, San Francisco, 1957, Calif. Sch. Fine Arts, 1958, Ox Bow Summer Art Sch., Saugatuck, Mich.; faculty Calif. Coll. Arts and Crafts, 1958-59, prof. arts, 1966—; instr. watercolor painting, 1987; dir. San Francisco Studio Art, 1958; tchr. watercolor workshops, Bali, Indonesia, 1989, 92; lectr. in field. Author: (with Robert Creeley) 1, 2, 3, 4, 5, 6, 7, 8, 9, 0, 1971, (with Joel Weishaus) Ox-Herding, 1971, (with Robert Bly) Basho, 1972, (with Steve Kowit) Passionate Journey, 1984, Magic Rabbit, 1990, (with Robert Bly) Ten Poems by Issa, 1992; one-man shows include Charles Feingarten Galleries, Chgo., 1956, 58, 59, San Francisco, 1957, Santa Barbara Mus. Art, 1958, Oakland Mus. Art, 1959, Legion Honor, San Francisco, 1961, Dallas, 1962, LaJolla (Calif.) Mus., 1963, U. Utah, 1964, San Francisco Mus. Art, 1968, Hanssen Gallery, 1968, 71, Ruth Braunstein, San Francisco, 1981, 82, 84, 86-88, 90; exhibited in group shows including Pa. Acad. Fine Art, U. Chgo., U. Wash., U. Ill., Art Inst. Chgo., Los Angeles County Mus., Am. Fedn. Art, Denver Mus., NAD, De Young Mus., San Francisco, Knoedler Gallery, N.Y.C., Feingarten Galleries, Whitney Mus. Art, others; represented in permanent collections including Art Inst. Chgo., Borg-Warner Collection, Chgo., Whitney Mus. Art., N.Y.C., Santa Barbara Mus. Art, San Francisco Mus. Art, Ill. State Normal, Corcoran Mus., Nat. Collection Fine Arts. Smithsonian Instn., 1968, many others. Served as pvt. AUS, 1955-56. Recipient 1st prize religious art U. Chgo., 1953; Ryerson travelling fellow, 1954; Martin Cahn award contemporary Am. paintings Art Inst. Chgo., 1957; purchase award U. Ill., 1959; purchase award Nat. Soc. Arts and Letters, N.Y.C., 1960; Neysa McMein purchase award Whitney Mus. Art, 1960; Schwabacher-Frey award 79th Ann. of San Francisco Mus. Art, 1960. Mem. Commonweal (bd. dirs. 1993-94). Home: 210 Kale Rd Bolinas CA 94924 Office: Calif Coll Arts and Crafts 5212 Broadway Oakland CA 94618-1426

OKAY, JOHN LOUIS, information scientist; b. Emmett, Mich., Mar. 27, 1942; s. Stanley John and Mildred Isabell (Little) O.; m. Judith Ann Gerlach, Aug. 22, 1964; children: Stephen, Christopher, Douglas. BS in Agr., Mich. State U., 1964, MS in Agrl. Econs., 1967, PhD in Resource Econs., 1974. Agrl. economist U.S. Soil Conservation Svc., East Lansing, Mich., 1967-73; program analyst U.S. Soil Conservation Svc., Washington, Mich., 1974-83; dir. info. systems U.S. Soil Conservation Svc., Washington, 1983-85; assoc. dir. info. systems USDA, Washington, 1985-91, dir. info. systems, 1991—. Recipient Meritorious Exec. award Pres. of U.S., 1989. Mem. Sr. Execs. Assn. (bd. dirs. 1989—). Office: Dept of Agrl Info Resources Mgmt/USDA 14th & Independence Ave SW Washington DC 20250

OKE, JOHN BEVERLEY, astronomy educator; b. Sault Ste. Marie, Ont., Can., Mar. 23, 1928; s. Charles Clare and Lyla Jane (Partushek) O.; m. Nancy Sparling, Aug. 20, 1955; children—Christopher, Kevin, Jennifer, Valerie. B.A., U. Toronto, 1949, M.A., 1950; Ph.D., Princeton U., 1953. Lectr. U. Toronto, 1953-55, asst. prof. 1955-58; asst. prof. Calif. Inst. Tech., Pasadena, 1958-61, assoc. prof., 1961-64, prof., 1964-92; assoc. dir. Hale Observatories, 1970-78; vis. Dominion Astrophysical Observatory, 1992—. Mem. Astron. Soc. of the Pacific, Am. Astronomical Soc. (councillor 1969-72), Internat. Astronomical Union. Office: Dominion Astrophysical Obs, 5071 W Saanich Rd, Victoria, BC Canada V8X 4M6

O'KEEFE, DANIEL P., lawyer; b. Superior, Wis., 1952. BA cum laude, Coll. St. Thomas, 1974; JD magna cum laude, William Mitchell Coll. Law, 1978. Bar: Minn. 1978. Law clerk U.S. Dist. Ct., Minn., 1978; ptnr. Dorsey & Whitney, Mpls.; adj. prof. William Mitchell Coll. Law. Exec. editor William Mitchell Law Review, 1977-78. Office: Dorsey & Whitney 220 S 6th St Minneapolis MN 55402-4500

O'KEEFE, EDWARD FRANKLIN, lawyer; b. S.I., N.Y., June 9, 1937; s. Francis Franklin and Bertha (Hall) O'K.; m. Toni Lynne McGohan; children: Kira Kathleen, Douglas Franklin, Andrew Franklin, Alison Elizabeth, Theadore William, Nigel Francis. A.B., U. N.C., 1959; J.D., U. Denver, 1961. Bar: Colo. 1962. Law clk. Colo. Supreme Ct., Denver, 1962-63; assoc. gen. counsel Hamilton Mgmt. Corp., Denver, 1966-69; sec. Hamilton Mgmt. Corp., 1968-76, v.p. legal, gen. counsel, 1969-76; now mng. ptnr. Moye, Giles O'Keefe, Vermeire & Gorrell, Denver; assoc. gen. counsel, sec. ITT Variable Annuity Ins. Co., Denver, 1969, v.p. legal, gen. counsel, 1969-70; sec. Hamilton Funds Inc., Denver, 1968-76. Served with USNR, 1963-66. Mem. Nat. Assn. Security Dealers (dist. conduct com., chmn. 1976), Colo. Assn. Corporate Counsel (pres. 1974-75). Home: 6300 Montview Blvd Denver CO 80207-3947 Office: Moye Giles O'Keefe Vermeire 1225 17th St Fl 29 Denver CO 80202-5534

O'KEEFE, GERALD FRANCIS, bishop, retired; b. St. Paul, Mar. 30, 1918; s. Francis Patrick and Lucille Mary (McDonald) O'K. Student, St. Paul Sem., 1938-44; B.A., Coll. St. Thomas, 1945; LLD (hon.), St. Ambrose Coll., 1967, Loras Coll., 1967; LHD, Marycrest Coll., 1967. Ordained priest Roman Cath. Ch., 1944. Asst. St. Paul Cathedral, 1944, rector, 1961-67; chancellor Archdiocese of St. Paul, 1945-61, aux. bishop, 1961-67, vicar gen., 1962-67; bishop Diocese of Davenport, Iowa, 1967-93; ret., 1993; instr. St. Thomas Acad., St. Paul, 1944-45. Home: 2706 Gaines St Davenport IA 52804-1914

O'KEEFE, JAMES WILLIAM, JR., investment manager and banker; b. Troy, N.Y., Oct. 23, 1948; s. James William and Antoinnette (Shannon) O'K.; m. Ann Palmer Ghiglione, June 4, 1977; 1 child, Courtney Anne. BA, Georgetown U., 1970; MBA, Harvard U., 1972. Mng. dir. Morgan Stanley & Co. Inc., N.Y.C., 1972-87, Kidder, Peabody & Co. Inc., N.Y.C., 1987-92; CEO Aetna Realty Investors, Inc., 1993—; bd. dirs Fishers Island Devel. Co. Mem. bd. advisors Georgetown Univ. Coll., NYU Real Estate Inst. Mem. Urban Land Inst., Nat. Assn. Real Estate Investment Trusts, Nat. Realty Com., Real Estate Bd. N.Y., N.Y. Athletic Club, Fishers Island Club. Avocation: golf. Home: 1088 Park Ave New York NY 10128-1132 Office: Aetna Realty Investors Inc 242 Trumbull St Hartford CT 06103-1212

O'KEEFE, JOHN DAVID, investment specialist; b. N.Y.C., Nov. 16, 1941; s. Timothy J. and Agnes V. (Timlin) O.; m. Stefanie Carreau Keegan, Jan. 28, 1978; children: Douglas G., Hillary C., John M., Meredith B. BBA, Iona Coll., 1963; MBA, L.I. U., 1968. Analyst L.I. Lighting Co., Mineola, N.Y., 1965-69, Pershing and Co., N.Y.C., 1969-72; mng. dir. Kidder, Peabody and Co., Inc., N.Y.C., 1972-89; v.p. Smith Barney, N.Y.C., 1989—. Bd. dirs. Heisman Found. Sgt. USMC, 1963-65. Fellow Fin. Analysts Fedn.; mem. N.Y. Soc. Security Analysts, Securities Industry Assn. Republican. Club: Down Town Athletic (gov. 1986, 88, chmn. Heisman Trophy com. 1987, 88). Home: 31 Linden Tree Rd Wilton CT 06897-1613 Office: Smith Barney 1 Village Sq Westport CT 06880-3211

O'KEEFE, JOSEPH THOMAS, bishop; b. N.Y.C., Mar. 12, 1919. Ed. Cathedral Coll. N.Y.C., St. Joseph's Sem., Yonkers, N.Y., Cath. U., Washington. Ordained Roman Catholic priest, 1948; ordained titular bishop of Tre Taverse and aux. bishop of N.Y., 1982-87; apptd. and installed bishop of Syracuse, 1987. Office: PO Box 511 240 E Onondaga St Syracuse NY 13202-2608*

O'KEEFE, KAREN, health facility administrator; b. N.J., Mar. 11, 1942; d. William O'Keefe and Helena Czywski. RN, St. Joseph's Hosp., Paterson, N.J., 1962; BA in Health Sci., Jersey City State Coll., 1978, MHA, 1988.

RN, N.J.; cert. IV, neonatal critical care. Staff nurse, charge nurse St. Joseph Hosp.; head nurse, supr. Margaret Hague Maternity Hosp., Jersey City; asst. dir. to assoc. dir. speciality svcs. Jersey City Med. Ctr., v.p. nursing. Mem. ANA, N.J. One Nurse Execs., NACOOG, Hudson County Perinatal Soc., Tri-State Perinatal Soc..

O'KEEFE, KEVIN, public relations executive. BA, Washington Coll.; MA, U. Ill. Joined Adams Sandler, 1976; pres. The Sandler Group, 1986-89, Adams Group, 1989-90, Adams Sandler, A Shandwick Co., 1990. Office: Adams Sandler, Inc 1629 Thames Street Baltimore MD 21202

O'KEEFE, MICHAEL DANIEL, lawyer; b. St. Louis, Jan. 3, 1938; s. Daniel Michael and Hanoria (Moriarty) O'K.; m. Bonnie Bowdern, July 11, 1964; children: Collen Coyne, Daniel Michael. AB, St. Louis U., 1961, LLB, 1961; postgrad., George Washington U., 1963. Bar: Mo. 1961, U.S. Ct. Appeals (8th cir.) 1961, U.S. Dist. Ct. (ea. dist.) Mo. 1961, Ill. 1975, U.S. Dist. Ct. (so. dist.) Ill. 1975, U.S. Ct. Appeals (5th and 7th cirs.) 1983, (10th cir.) 1995. Asst. atty. U.S. Ct. Appeals, St. Louis, 1962-63, 64-65; pvt. practice St. Louis, 1964-67; ptnr. Lucas, Murphy & O'Keefe, St. Louis, 1967-74, Thompson & Mitchell, St. Louis, 1974—; adj. prof. trial practice Sch. of Law, St. Louis U., 1992—. Editor: American Maritime Cases, 1985—. Active Port Commn., St. Louis. Capt. USAF, 1962-64. Fellow Am. Coll. Trial Lawyers; mem. Internat. Assn. Def. Counsel, Fedn. Ins. and Corp. Counsel, Maritime Law Assn., USAZ, Nat. Assn. Railroad Trial Counsel, Am. Law Inst. Democrat. Roman Catholic. Avocations: reading, tennis, fencing, archaeology, microbiology. Home: 372 Walton Row Saint Louis MO 63108 Office: Thompson & Mitchell 1 Mercantile Ctr Ste 3300 Saint Louis MO 63101

O'KEEFE, PATRICK, transportation executive. With Rockware Internat., Oklahoma City, 1984-86, Burns & Roe Inc., Oradell, N.J., 1974-84; sr. v.p.-corporate operations Bath Iron Works Corp, Bath, Maine, 1986—. Office: Bath Iron Works Corp 700 Washington St Bath ME 04530-2556

O'KEEFE, ROBERT JAMES, retired banker; b. Boston, Dec. 30, 1926; s. James J. and Irene (Egan) O'K.; m. Mary U. Hughes, Oct. 12, 1951 (dec.); children—Mary F., Robert James; m. Simone A. Charbonneau, Apr. 3, 1976. A.B., Boston Coll., 1951; grad., Advanced Mgmt. Program, Harvard, 1968. Mem. staff Mass. Inst. Tech., Cambridge, 1951-55; cons. Arthur D. Little, Inc., Cambridge, 1955-58; with Chase Manhattan Bank, N.Y.C., 1958-79, v.p., 1964-69, sr. v.p., 1969-79; sr. v.p. Am. Security Bank, Washington, 1979-89; exec. v.p. MNC Info. Svcs., Balt., 1989-90, ret. Trustee Boston Coll., 1974-82, trustee assoc., 1982-86; mem. computer sci. and engring. bd. Nat. Acad. Sci., 1971-73. Served with AUS, 1945-46. Recipient Alumni medal Boston Coll., 1970. Mem. Boston Coll. Alumni Assn. (pres. 1973-74), Country Club at Jacaranda West, Woods Club. Home: 5136 Woods Resort Hedgesville WV 25427-9361

O'KEEFE, THOMAS JOSEPH, metallurgical engineer; b. St. Louis, Oct. 2, 1935; s. Thomas and Hazel (Howard) O'K.; m. Jane Gilmartin, Aug. 31, 1957; children—Thomas, Kathleen, Matthew, Daniel, Margaret, Robert. B.S., Mo. Sch. Mines, 1958; Ph.D., U. Mo., Rolla, 1965. Process control engr. Dow Metal Products Co., Madison, Ill., 1959-61; mem. faculty U. Mo., Rolla, 1965—, prof. metall. engring., 1972—, Curators metall. engring., 1985-86, Curators Disting. prof., 1986—; rsch. technologist NASA, Houston, summer 1965; rsch. metall. engr. Ames (Iowa) Lab., 1966-67; rsch. metall. engr., cons. Cominco Ltd., Trail, B.C., Can., 1970-71. Recipient Alumni Merit award U. Mo., Rolla, 1971, Outstanding Tchg. award, 1979, Silver medal paper award AESF, 1994; Jefferson-Smurfit fellow, 1984-85; named Disting. Hydrometallurgy lectr. U. B.C., 1992. Mem. AIME (dir. 1976-77, 79-81, EMD lectr. 1991), Testing Materials Soc., The Metall. Soc., Sigma Xi, Alpha Sigma Mu, Tau Beta Pi, Phi Kappa Theta (dir. 1965-77, cert. commendation 1970, pres. citation 1986). Home: 905 Southview Dr Rolla MO 65401-0904 Office: Material Research Center Univ Mo Rolla MO 65401

O'KEEFE, THOMAS MICHAEL, foundation executive; b. St. Cloud, Minn., Mar. 25, 1940; s. Thomas William and Genevieve B. (McCormick) O'K.; m. Kathleen Marie Gnifkowski, Aug. 20, 1966; children: Steven Michael, Ann Catherine. Student, Marquette U., 1961-65, BS, 1965; MS in Nuclear Physics, U. Pitts., 1968; DHL, Hamline U., 1989. Dir. edn. planning HEW, Washington, 1969-70, dep. asst. sec., 1977-80; v.p. Carnegie Found. for Advancement of Teaching, Washington, 1980-83; pres. Consortium for Advancement Pvt. Higher Edn., Washington, 1983-89; exec. v.p. McKnight Found., Mpls., 1989—; dir. Washington internships in edn. George Washington U., 1970-73; dir. policy analysis and evaluation U. Ill., Chgo., 1973-74, assoc. v.p. acad. affairs, 1974-77; head U.S. del. to Orgn. Econ. Coop. and Devel., 1979, 80; mem. Carnegie Forum on Edn. and the Economy, 1985-88; mem. N.J. Commn. on Ind. Higher Edn., 1986-88; mem. task force on ind. higher edn. Edn. Commn. States, 1987-89; cons. in field. Contbg. editor and contbr. articles on edn. programs, acad. policies, internships, and nuclear physics Change mag., 1985—; bd. dirs. Editl. Projects in Edn., 1984-93. Bd. dirs. The Edn. Resources Inst., Boston, 1987-94, Minn. Coun. on Founds., 1994—; trustee Buena Vista Coll., Storm Lake, Iowa, 1984-90. Mem. Minn. Club St. Paul, Mpls. Club. Democrat. Office: McKnight Found 121 S 8th St Ste 600 Minneapolis MN 55402-2825

O'KEEFE, VINCENT THOMAS, clergyman, educational administrator; b. Jersey City, Jan. 10, 1920; s. James and Sarah (Allen) O'K. A.B., Georgetown U., 1943; M.A., Woodstock Coll., 1945, Ph.L., 1944; Th.L., St. Albert de Louvain, Belgium, 1951; student, Muenster (Germany) U., 1951-52; S.T.D., Gregorian U., Rome, 1954. Ordained priest Roman Cath. Ch., 1950. Instr. Latin and math. Regis High Sch., N.Y.C., 1944-47; assoc. prof. fundamental theology Woodstock Coll., 1954-60; acad. v.p. Fordham U., Bronx, N.Y., 1960-62; exec. v.p. Fordham U., 1962-63, pres., 1963-65, rector Jesuit community, 1984-88; gen. asst. to superior gen. Soc. of Jesus, Rome, 1965-83; v.p. spl. projects Jesuit Conf. Soc. of Jesus, 1988-90; superior, writer provincial residence Soc. of Jesus, Bronx, 1990-94, superior; Mem. reagents exams. and scholarship center N.Y. State Dept. Edn.; pres., dir., mem. exec. com. Council Higher Edn. Instns. of N.Y.C. Author: The History and Meaning of Ex Attrito Fit Contritus, 1957; Contbr. articles to religious publs., also book reviews. Dir. N.Y. World's Fair, 1964-65; Corp. Bd. mgrs. New York Bot. Garden; dir., mem. bd. Center Intercultural Formation, Cuernavaca, Mexico; trustee Fordham U. Fellow Royal Soc. Encouragement Arts Mfrs. and Commerce (London); mem. Council Higher Edn. City N.Y., Religion Council Cath. Secondary Schs. Archdiocese of N.Y., Cath. Bibl. Assn., Cath. Theol. Assn. Am., Religion Edn. Assn., NEA, Jesuit Edn. Assn., Nat. Cath. Edn. Assn., Internat. Assn. Univs., Soc. Cath. Coll. Tchrs. Sacred Doctrine, Phi Beta Kappa. Office: 106 W 56 St New York NY 10019

O'KEEFFE, HUGH WILLIAMS, oil industry executive; b. Ft. Smith, Ark., May 23, 1905; s. Patrick Francis and Elizabeth Ann (Williams) O'K.; m. Lucylle Davis Durkee, Mar. 27, 1949 (dec. Dec. 1965); m. Josephine Helen Loughmiller, June 10, 1969 (dec. May 1980); m. Grace H. Freeny, Sept. 3, 1983 (dec. Jan. 1990). BS with honors, U. Ark., 1928. Jr. geologist Phillips Petroleum of Okla., Tex., Kans. Colo. and Okla., 1928-33; party chief on surface Phillips Petroleum of Okla., Shawnee, 1933, dist. geologist, 1934-37; div. geologist Phillips Petroleum of Okla., Bartlesville, 1937-40, asst. chief geologist, 1940-45; exploration mgr. Davon Oil Co., Oklahoma City, 1946-52; co-owner Davon Oil & Gas, Oklahoma City, 1952-55; pvt. practice cons. Oklahoma City, 1955-58; co-owner Wyant & O'Keeffe, Oklahoma City, 1930—. Mem. Am. Assn. Petroleum Geologists, Oklahome City Geol. Soc., Soc. Ind. Petroleum and Earth Scientists, Shawnee Geol. Soc. (v.p. 1936-37), Tulsa Geol. Soc., Petroleum Club of Oklahoma City (charter), Oklahoma City Golf and Country Club. Republican. Roman Catholic. Avocations: tennis, hunting, fishing. Home: 6511 Avondale Dr Oklahoma City OK 73116-6405 Office: Wyant & O'Keeffe 222 NE 50th St Oklahoma City OK 73105-1812

OKEH, SAMSON ENRUDJE, psychiatric nurse; b. Abraka, Nigeria, Nov. 5, 1943; s. Ovaguono Okeh; m. Pauline Okeh, Dec., 1969; children: Sunday, Debra, John, Amber. Diploma, Bapt. Sch. Nursing, Eku Sapele, Nigeria, 1967; BA, U. Ill., Chgo., 1979; MA in Pub. Admistrn., Northeastern Ill. U. 1981. RN Ill., Md., Calif. Asst. head nurse Loretto Hosp., Chgo.; nursing supr. Greater Laurel (Md.) and Beltsville Hosp.; charge nurse, part time supr. South Wood Hosp., Chula Vista, Calif.; asst. nurse mgr. Cedars Sinai

Med. Ctr., L.A., 1991—. Mem. United Nurses Assn. Calif., Nigerian Assn. San Diego (pres. 1990-91), URHOBO Assn. So. Calif. (pres. 1992-93). Home: PO Box 48151 Los Angeles CA 90048-0151 Office: Cedars Sinai Med Ctr 8700 Beverly Blvd Los Angeles CA 90048-1865

O'KEHIE, COLLINS EMEKA, lawyer, consultant; b. Aba, Nigeria, Apr. 4, 1952; came to U.S., 1976; s. Simon A. and Elizabeth Jane (Oledibe) O.; m. Justina Amuche Nnadi, Aug. 6, 1983; children: Pamela, Collins Emeka Jr., Stanley, Charles. Assoc. in Bus., Ellsworth Coll., 1977; BS, U. Tex., Richardson, 1979; MBA, N. Tex. State U., 1981; JD, Tex. So. U., 1984. Bar: Tex. 1985, U.S. Ct. Appeals (5th cir.) 1986, U.S. Dist. Ct. (so. dist.) Tex. 1987, Internat. Ct. of Trade 1990, U.S. Ct. Appeals (fed. cir.) 1990, U.S. Supreme Ct. 1992. Ptnr. Gregg, O'Kehie & Cashin, Houston, 1985-90; prin. O'Kehie & Assocs., Houston, 1990—; legal cons. various cos. and law firms in Eng., France, Belgium, Holland, Nigeria, 1985—. Mem. ABA, Tex. Bar Assn., Tex. Trial Lawyers Assn., Coll. of State Bar Tex., Assn. Trial Lawyers Am., Internat. Bar Assn., MBA Execs. Assn., Chartered Ins. Inst. London, Internat. Bar Assn., Internat. Platform Assn., Phi Delta Phi. Roman Catholic. Avocations: tennis, jogging. Office: O'Kehie and Assocs 1300 Main Bldg Ste 1930 Houston TX 77002-3126 *In my life I have found that one should use an opportunity to help less fortunate people and that the reward comes from sources other than the recipients.*

O'KELLEY, WILLIAM CLARK, federal judge; b. Atlanta, Ga., Jan. 2, 1930; s. Ezra Clark and Theo (Johnson) O'K.; m. Ernestine Allen, Mar. 28, 1953; children: Virginia Leigh O'Kelley Wood, William Clark Jr. AB, Emory U., 1951, LLB, 1953. Bar: Ga. 1952. Pvt. practice Atlanta, 1957-59; asst. U.S. atty. No. Dist. Ga., 1959-61; partner law firm O'Kelley, Hopkins & Van Gerpen, Atlanta, 1961-70; U.S. dist. judge No. Dist. Ga., Atlanta, 1970—, chief judge 1984-94; mem. com. on adminstrn. of criminal law Jud. Conf. U.S., 1979-82, exec. com., 1983-84, subcom. on jury trials in complex criminal cases, 1981-82, dist. judge rep. 11th cir., 1981-84, mem. adv. com. of fed. rules of criminal procedure, 1984-87; bd. dirs. Fed. Jud. Ctr., 1987-91, adv. com. history program, 1989—, com. on orientation of newly appointed dist. judges, 1985-88; mem. Com. Jud. Resources, 1990-94; mem. Jud. Coun. 11th Cir., 1990—, exec. com., 1990—; mem. Fgn. Intelligence Surveillance Ct., 1980-87; corp. sec., dir. Gwinnett Bank & Trust Co., Norcross, Ga., 1968-70. Mem. exec. com., gen. counsel Ga. Republican Com., 1968-70; mem. fin. com. Northwest Ga. Girl Scout Coun., 1958-70; trustee Emory U., 1991—. Served as 1st lt. USAF, 1953-57; capt. USAFR. Mem. ABA, Atlanta Bar Assn., Ga. State Bar, Dist. Judges Assn. 5th Cir. (pres. 1979-80, pres.-elect 1978-79, v.p. 1977-78, sec.-treas. 1976-77), Lawyers Club Atlanta, Nat. Lawyers Club, Sigma Chi, Phi Delta Phi, Omicron Delta Kappa. Baptist. Clubs: Kiwanian (past pres.), Atlanta Athletic, Lawyers of Atlanta. Home: 550 Ridgecrest Dr Norcross GA 30071-2158 Office: US Dist Ct 1942 US Courthouse 75 Spring St SW Atlanta GA 30303-3361

O'KELLY, BERNARD, university dean; b. Winnipeg, Man., Can., Aug. 10, 1926; came to U.S., 1954; s. Bartholomew Bernard and Cora (Beadle) O'K.; m. Marcia Herz Levin, Feb. 2, 1957; children: Christopher D.B. (dec.), Elizabeth S., Peter B.J. Student, U. Man., 1942-44; BA, Coll. de l'Immaculée Conception, Montreal, 1950, LPh, 1950; M.A., Harvard U., 1955, Ph.D., 1960. Lectr. classics St. Paul's Coll., U. Man., 1950-52; lectr. French and English Loyola Coll., Montreal, 1952-54; instr., then asst. prof. Ohio State U., 1957-66; research assoc. Yale U., 1964-65; prof. English, dean Coll. Arts and Scis., U. N.D., 1966—; Vice pres. Council Colls. Arts and Scis., 1972-73, pres., 1973-74; bd. dirs. Am. Conf. Acad. Deans, 1975—, sec.-treas., 1976-94; pres., chmn. exec. com. Fedn. Pub. Programs in the Humanities, 1977-79; mem. adv. panel U.S. Army, 1980-82; bd. dirs. Assn. Am. Colls., 1984-87. Editor: The Renaissance Image of Man and the World, 1966; (with C.A. Lartt) John Colet's Commentary on I Corinthians, 1985. Hart scholar classics U. Man., 1944; Dexter travelling fellow Harvard, 1956; research grantee Am. Philos. Soc. Mem. MLA, AAUP, Nat. Council Tchrs. English, Renaissance Soc. Am., Assn. for Canadian Studies in U.S. Office: U ND PO Box 8038 Grand Forks ND 58202-8038

OKEN, DONALD EDWARD, physician, educator; b. N.Y.C., Nov. 21, 1928; s. Harry and Deborah (Saperia) O.; m. Mary Lou Robinson, Sept. 26, 1952; children: Pamela A., Janet, Jacqueline, Gwendolyn, Keith R., Glenn B. BS, Columbia U., 1950, MD, 1954. Diplomate Am. Bd. Internal Medicine. Intern E.J. Meyer Meml. Hosp., Buffalo, 1954-55; resident Jackson Meml. Hosp., Miami, Fla., 1955-57; fellow Howard Hughes Inst., Miami, 1956-57; fellow Harvard Med. Sch., Boston, 1958-60, rsch. assoc., 1960-66, assoc. in medicine, 1966-68, asst. prof., 1968-71, assoc. prof., 1971-75; prof. medicine Med. Coll. Va., Richmond, 1975—, chmn. div. nephrology, 1975-84. Contbr. chpts. to books, articles to sci. and med. jours.; assoc. editor Nephron, 1964-72; mem. editorial bd. Kidney Internat. 1972-74, Am. Jour. Nephrology, 1980-88, Renal Failure, 1986—; cons. editor Am. Jour. Medicine, 1977-81. Mem. Am. Soc. Clin. Investigation, Am. Fedn. Clin. Rsch., Am. Heart Assn. (past chmn. Coun. on Kidney), Internat. Soc. Nephrology, Am. Soc. Nephrology, Australasian Soc. Nephrology (hon.), N.E. Salt and Water Club (emeritus), Old Wyggestonian. Home: 91 Maple Ave Richmond VA 23226-2339

OKERLUND, ARLENE NAYLOR, university official; b. Emmitsburg, Md., Oct. 13, 1938; d. George Wilbur and Ruth Opal (Sensenbaugh) Naylor; m. Michael Dennis Okerlund, June 6, 1959 (div. Apr. 1983); 1 dau., Linda Susan. B.A., U. Md., 1960; Ph.D., U. Calif.-San Diego, 1969. Instr. sci. Mercy Hosp. Nursing Sch., Balt., 1959-63; prof. English San Jose State U., Calif., 1969-80, 94—, dean humanities and arts, 1980-86, acad. v.p., 1986-93; cons. Ednl. Testing Service, Berkeley, Calif., 1976-80. Editor: San Jose Studies, 1975-80; contbr. articles on the humanities to profl. jours. Bd. dirs. World Forum Silicon Valley, Am. Beethoven Soc. Grantee NEH, 1979; grantee San Jose State U., 1971-72. Mem. Philol. Assn. Pacific Coast (sec.-treas. 1975-78), MLA (del. to assembly, west coast rep. 1976-77), Internat. Coun. Fine Arts Deans, Calif. Coun. Fine Arts Deans (pres. 1984-86), Am. Beethoven Soc. (bd. dirs.). Democrat. Office: San Jose State U Washington Sq San Jose CA 95192

OKEZIE, B. ONUMA, food scientist, nutritionist, educator; b. Obizi, Imo, Nigeria, Mar. 31, 1936; came to U.S., 1962; s. Chief Anyanwu and Lolo Ihuoma (Ogbediya) O.; m. Monique Chika Offurum, Sept. 4, 1971; children: Uchechi, Okezie II, Ihuoma, Oluchi. BS, U. Calif., Davis, 1966, MS, 1966; PhD, Cornell U., 1975. Sci. officer Ministry of Animal Health, Enugu, Biafra, 1967-68; advisor on nutrition Rehab. Commn., Okigwe, Biafra, 1968-70; rsch. fellow U. Ife, Ile-Ife, Nigeria, 1970; exec. advisor on nutrition Internat. Union for Child Welfare, Geneva, 1970-71; teaching and rsch. asst. Cornell U., Ithaca, N.Y., 1971-74, rsch. assoc., 1974; asst. prof. Howard U., Washington, 1975; assoc. prof. food sci. & nutrition Ala. A&M U., Huntsville, 1975-82, prof., 1982—; dir. internat. programs 1979—; spl. asst. to pres. Ala. A&M U., 1988-90; trustee S.E. Cons. for Internat. Devel., Washington, 1980—, v. chair bd. trustees 1992-93, chair 1993-94; bd. dirs. U.S. AID-Peanut-CRSP, Washington, also Griffin, Ga., 1982—, v. chair bd. dirs. 1993—, chair Assn. dirs. of Internat. Agr. Progs. 1992—; pres. Aries Enterprises, Inc., Huntsville, 1983—; disting. lectr. Berger Found. Cornell U., Ithaca, N.Y., 1993. Author: International Dimensions in Human Ecology, 1975, Effective Participation in Technical Assistance Programs, 1982; contbr. articles to profl. jours. NSF fellow, 1959-60, U.S. AID sci. fellow, 1962-66. Mem. Am. Dietetic Assn., Inst. Food Technologists (chair-elect internat. divsn., 1991-92, chair 1992-93, div. com. chair of two coms., 1990-93, mem. IFT awards com., 1993-95), Am. Assn. Cereal Chemists, Am. Chem. Soc., So., Assn. Agr. Scientists, Ala. Acad. Sci., Ala. Coun. for Internat. Programs (exec. com.), North Ala. Internat. Trade Assn., Huntsville C. of C. (small bus. com. 1985-87), Alpha Zeta. Avocations: tennis, jogging, photography. Home: 561 Hurricane Rd New Market AL 35761-8204 Office: Ala A&M U Office of Internat Programs Normal AL 35762

OKIISHI, THEODORE HISAO, mechanical engineering educator; b. Honolulu, Jan. 15, 1939; s. Clifford Muneo and Dorothy Asako (Tokushima) O.; m. Rae Wiemers, May 28, 1963; children: Christopher Gene, John Clifford, Mark William, Kenneth Edward. Student, U. Hawaii, 1956-57; BS, Iowa State U., 1960, MS, 1963, PhD, 1965. Registered profl. engr., Iowa, Ohio. From asst. prof. to assoc. dean coll. engring. Iowa State U., Ames, 1967—; cons. on fluid dynamics. Contbr. articles to profl. jours. Served to capt. C.E., U.S. Army, 1965-67. Decorated Joint Services Commendation award; named Outstanding Prof., Iowa State U. student sect. ASME, 1983,

Mech. Engring. Dept. Prof. of Yr., Iowa State U., 1977, 86, 90; recipient award for research NASA, 1975; Ralph R. Teetor award Soc. Automotive Engrs., 1976, Engring. Coll. Superior Teaching award Iowa State U., 1987, Cardinal Key Iowa State U., 1991. Fellow ASME (Melville medal 1989); mem. AIAA, Sigma Xi. Republican. Mem. Ch. of Jesus Christ of Latter-day Saints. Club: Osborn Research. Home: 2940 Monroe Dr Ames IA 50010-4362 Office: Iowa State U 104 Marston Hall Ames IA 50011

OKINAGA, LAWRENCE SHOJI, lawyer; b. Honolulu, July 7, 1941; s. Shohei and Hatsu (Kakimoto) O.; m. Carolyn Hisako Uesugi, Nov. 26, 1966; children: Carrie, Caryn, Laurie. BA, U. Hawaii, 1963; JD, Georgetown U., 1972. Bar: Hawaii 1972, U.S. Dist. Ct. Hawaii 1972, U.S. Ct. Appeals (9th cir.) 1976. Administrv. asst. to Congressman Spark Matsunaga, Honolulu, 1964, 1965-69; law clk. to chief judge U.S. Dist. Ct. Hawaii, Honolulu, 1972-73; assoc. Carlsmith, Ball, Wichman Murray and Ichiki, Honolulu, 1973-76, ptnr., 1976—; mem. Gov.'s Citizens Adv. Com. Coastal Zone Mgmt., 1974-79; sec. Hawaii Bicentennial Corp., 1975-77, chmn., 1985-87, vice chmn., mem. Jud. Selection Commn., State of Hawaii, 1979-87, vice chmn., 1986; mem. consumer adv. coun. Fed. Res. Bd., 1984-86; chmn. State of Hawaii Judicial Conduct Commn., 1991-94; apptd. mem. Fed. Savings and Loan Adv. Council, Washington, 1988-89; mem. nat. adv. coun. U.S. Small Bus. Adminstrn., 1994—; mem. adv. coun. on small bus. and agr. Fed. Reserve Bank of San Francisco, 1995—. Bd. dirs. Moiliili Community Ctr., Honolulu, 1965-68, 1973-86; bd. visitors Georgetown U. Law Ctr., 1993—; trustee Kuakini Med. Ctr., 1984-88, 1989—. Served to capt. USAFR, 1964-72, 1974-76. Mem. ABA (house of delegates 1991-94, mem. standing com. on judicial selection tenure and compensation, 1993—), Hawaii Bar Assn. (sec., bd. dirs. 1981), Res. Officers Assn., Am. Judicature Soc. (v.p. 1990-92, bd. dirs. 1986—, sec. 1993—), Georgetown U. Law Alumni Assn. (bd. dirs. 1986-91), Omicron Delta Kappa. Office: Carlsmith Ball Wichman Murray & Ichiki PO Box 656 Honolulu HI 96809-0656

OKITA, GEORGE T., pharmacologist educator; b. Seattle, Jan. 18, 1922; s. Kazuo and Fusao (Muguruma) O.; m. Fujiko Shimizu, Nov. 29, 1958; children—Ronald Hajime, Sharon Mariko, Glenn Torao. Student, U. Cin., 1943-44; B.A., Ohio State U., 1948, Ph.D., U. Chgo., 1951. Research asst., research assoc., instr., asst. prof. U. Chgo., 1949-63; asso. prof. Northwestern U., 1963-66, prof. pharmacology, 1966-90, prof. emeritus, 1990—, acting chmn. dept., 1968-70, 76-77. Contbr. articles to profl. jours.; Asst. editor: Jour. Pharmacology and Exptl. Therapeutics, 1965-68. Served with AUS, 1944-46. NIH Postdoctoral fellow, 1952. Mem. A.A.A.S., Am. Assn. U. Profs., Am. Soc. Pharmacology and Exptl. Therapeutics, Internat. Soc. Biochem. Pharmacology, Am. Heart Assn., Cardiac Muscle Soc., Sigma Xi. Research in med. field. Office: 8619 Vineyard Ridge Pl San Jose CA 95135-2153

OKO, ANDREW JAN, art gallery director, curator; b. London, Sept. 7, 1946; arrived in Can., 1948; s. Jan Kazimierz and Julia Helena (Suska) O.; m. Helen Marie Blanc, Dec. 21, 1972; children: Sonya Celeste, Michelle Kathleen. BA, U. Calgary, 1968; MA, U. Toronto, 1972. Preparator Glenbow Mus., Calgary, Alta., 1972-73, curatorial asst., 1973-74, asst. curator, 1974-77; curator Art Gallery of Hamilton, Ont., 1977-86; dir. MacKenzie Art Gallery, Regina, Sask., 1986—. Author: Country Pleasures: The Angling Art of Jack Cowin, 1984, (with others) Art Gallery Handbook 1982; author/curator: (exhbn. catalogue) The Frontier Art of R.B. Nevitt, 1974, T.R. MacDonald 1908-1978, 1980, The Society of Canadian Painter-Etchers and Engravers in Retrospect, 1981, The Prints of Carl Schaefer, 1983, Canada in the Nineteenth Century: The Bert and Barbara Stitt Family Collection, 1984, Jan Gerrit Wyers 1888-1973, 1989. Mem. Can. Mus. Assn., Can. Art Mus. Dirs.' Orgn., Sask. Arts Alliance (pres. 1991-93), Rotary. Avocations: flyfishing, swimming, music. Office: MacKenzie Art Gallery, 3475 Albert St, Regina, SK Canada S4S 6X6

OKRENT, DAVID, engineering educator; b. Passaic, N.J., Apr. 19, 1922; s. Abram and Gussie (Pearlman) O.; m. Rita Gilda Holtzman, Feb. 1, 1948; children—Neil, Nina, Jocelyne. M.E., Stevens Inst. Tech., 1943; M.A., Harvard, 1948, Ph.D. in Physics, 1951. Mech. engr. NACA, Cleve., 1943-46; sr. physicist Argonne (Ill.) Nat. Lab., 1951-71; regents lectr. UCLA, 1968, prof. engring., 1971-91, prof. emeritus, prof., 1991—; vis. prof. U. Wash., Seattle, 1963, U. Ariz., Tucson, 1970-71; Isaac Taylor chair Technion, 1977-78. Author: Fast Reactor Cross Sections, 1960, Computing Methods in Reactor Physics, 1968, Reactivity Coefficients in Large Fast Power Reactors, 1970, Nuclear Reactor Safety, 1981; contbr. articles to profl. jours. Mem. adv. com. on reactor safeguards AEC, 1963-87, also chmn., 1966; sci. to sec. gen. of Geneva Conf., 1958; mem. U.S. del. to all Geneva Atoms for Peace Confs. Guggenheim fellow, 1961-62, 77-78; recipient Disting. Appointment award Argonne Univs. Assn., 1970, Disting. Service award U.S. Nuclear Regulatory Commn., 1985. Fellow Am. Phys. Soc., Am. Nuclear Soc. (Tommy Thompson award 1980, Glenn Seaborg medal 1987), Nat. Acad. Engring. Home: 439 Veteran Ave Los Angeles CA 90024-1956

OKSAS, JOAN K., economist, educator; b. Chgo., Feb. 21, 1927; d. John Joseph and Antoinette (Pestinick) Kazanauskas; m. Casimir G. Oksas, Nov. 3, 1956; children: Stephen, Mary. BS, Northwestern U., 1944; MS in Edn., Chgo. State U., 1975, Northern Ill. U., 1981; EdD, Loyola U., Chgo., 1986. From instr. to assoc. prof. Chgo. State U., 1976-89, prof., 1989-93; ret., 1993; chair dept. libr. sci. and communication Chgo. State U., 1986-88; judge Am. Film and Video Festival, N.Y., Chgo., 1980-93, Chicagoland History Fairs, 1986—; mem. vis. com. North Ctrl. Assn. Accreditation, Chgo., 1980-93; cons. Adopt-a-Sch. program, 1984; bd. dirs. Mut. Fedn. Savs. and Loan, Chgo. Contbr. articles, revs. to profl. jours. Recipient Faculty Excellence award Chgo. State U., 1991. Mem. Ill. Libr. Assn., Phi Delta Kappa, Delta Kappa Gamma (Ill. Gamma Alpha chpt.) (bd. dirs. 1982—, pres. 1986-88). Republican. Roman Catholic.

OKUBO, TOSHITERU, health science facility administrator, educator; b. Tokyo, Japan, June 6, 1939; s. Michitada and Sumiko (Yamaguchi) O.; m. Tomoko (Ogura) Okubo, Feb. 15,1967; children: Junko, Toshitada. MD, Keio U., Tokyo, 1966, DMS, 1978. Asst. sch. medicine Keio U., 1967-77; assoc. prof. Jichi Med. Sch., Minamikawachi, Tochigi, Japan, 1977-83; vis. prof. sch. pub. health UCLA, 1981; prof. U. Occupational Environ. Health, Kitakyushu, 1983—; cons. Sony Corp., Tokyo, 1971-87, Ministry of Labor, Tokyo, 1984—, Japan Medical Assn., 1986—. Author: Introduction to Epidemiology, 1976, Protecting Worker's Health in the Third World, 1992. Mem. Japan Assn. Indsl. Health (bd. dirs.), Internat. Commn. Occupational Health (nat. sec. for Japan, chmn. sci. com. on edn. and tng.), Internat. Epidemiol. Assn., Japan Soc. for Occupational Health (bd. dirs.), Ramazzini Collegium. Home: 5-2-27 Takasuminami Wakamatsu, Kitakyushu Fukuoka 808-01, Japan Office: U Occupational Environ Health, 1-1 Iseigaoka Yahatanishi, Kitakyushu Fukuoka 807, Japan

OKUI, KAZUMITSU, biology educator; b. Ohta, Japan, July 8, 1933; s. Sadajiroh and Ume (Tanaka) O.; m. Mizue Aoki Okui, May 6, 1961; children: Teiichiroh, Ari. B Agr., Tokyo U. Agr., 1962, M Agr., 1964, D Agr., 1967. Lectr. biology Denki-Tsushin U., Tokyo, 1968-70; lectr. biology Kitasato U., Sagamihara, Japan, 1970-73, asst. prof. biology, 1973-82, prof. ethology, 1982—, dean ctr. libertal arts and scis., 1995—, councilor, 1995—; v.p. Internat. Centre of Wild Silkworm, 1990—; vis. rsch. prof. Waikato U., New Zealand, 1991; mem. book rev. com. Yomiuri Shimbun, Tokyo, 1981-85, Sankei Shimbun, Tokyo, 1990—. Author: Entomology, 1976, Ethology, 1976, General Zoology, 1984, General Zoology, 1985, General Entomology, 1992, Human Ethology, 1992, Essay of Insects, 1993, Textbook For Ethology, 1994. Mem. Internat. Soc. Wild Silkworm (sec. 1988—, v.p. 1990—), Japan Cosmo-Biol. Soc. (councilor 1987-89), Japan Wild Silkworm Soc. (v.p. 1994—), Sci. Coun. of Japan (mem. rsch. com. 1994—). Home: 972-7 Yumoto-machi, Kanagawa-ken 250-03, Japan Office: Kitasato U Ctr Liberal Arts and Scis, 1-15-1 Kitasato, Sagamihara, Kanagawa 228, Japan

OKULITCH, VLADIMIR JOSEPH, geologist, university administrator; b. St. Petersburg, Russia, June 18, 1906; came to Can., 1927, naturalized, 1932; s. Joseph Konstantin and Alexandra Andrea (Drozhilov) Okulitch-Oksha; m. Susanne Kouhar, Jan. 19, 1934 (dec. 1968); children—Andrew, Peter. B.Sc. in Geol. Engring., U. B.C., Vancouver, Can., 1931, M.Sc. 1932; Ph.D. in Geology, McGill U., Montreal, Can., 1934; D.Sc. (hon.), U. B.C., Vancouver, 1973. Research fellow Harvard U., Cambridge, Mass., 1934-36;

asst. prof. U. Toronto, Ont., Can., 1936-44; asst. prof. U. B.C., Vancouver, B.C., Can., 1944-46, assoc. prof., 1946-49, prof., 1949-64, head dept. geology, 1959-64, dean faculty sci., 1963-71; Mem. Can. Nat. Adv. Com. Research in Geol. Scis., 1958-61; Nat. Adv. Com. Astronomy, 1965—. Author: North American Pleosponia, 1943; (with Delaubenfels) Archaeocyatha and Porifera, Treatise on Invertebrate Palaeontology, 1955. Contbr. numerous articles to sci. jours. Fellow Royal Soc. Can., Geol. Soc. Am. (vice chmn. Cordilleran sect., research grants 1940, 41, 46, 55); Paleontological Soc. (v.p. 1954-55), Geol. Assn. Can.; mem. Royal Astron. Soc. Can. Club: Faculty (Vancouver). Avocations: photography; amateur astronomy. Home: 4504 49th St NW, Calgary, AB Canada T3A 1X4

OKULSKI, JOHN ALLEN, principal; b. Mineola, N.Y., July 28, 1944; s. John Joseph and Rose (Zebrowski) O.; m. Martina Carol Schoneboom, July 16, 1966; children: Richard, Peter, John. BS, Rutgers U., 1966; MS, C.W. Post Coll., 1972; postgrad., Hofstra U., 1975-76, Queens Coll., 1973. Social studies tchr. Long Beach (N.Y.) Jr. High Sch., 1966-67, Lynbrook (N.Y.) High Sch., 1967-69, Herricks High Sch., New Hyde Park, N.Y., 1969-72; guidance counselor Herricks Jr. High Sch., 1972-75; dept. chmn. sec. sch. guidance Herricks pub. schs., 1975-78; asst. prin. Herricks High Sch., 1978-87; prin. Bay Shore (N.Y.)High Sch., 1987-92, Garden City (N.Y.) High Sch., 1992—. Cubmaster Boy Scouts Am., New Hyde Park, 1975-83; v.p. New Hyde Park Little League, 1978-83. Mem. L.I. Pers. and Guidance Assn. (officer), Mid. States Accreditation Assn. (adv. com. N.Y. chpt.). Presbyterian. Home: 1505 Washington Ave New Hyde Park NY 11040-4332 Office: Garden City High Sch 170 Rockaway Ave Garden City NY 11530-1499

OKUN, DANIEL ALEXANDER, environmental engineering educator, consulting engineer; b. N.Y.C., June 19, 1917; s. William Howard and Leah (Seligman) O.; m. Elizabeth Griffin, Jan. 14, 1946; children: Michael Griffin, Tema Jon. BS, Cooper Union, 1937; MS, Calif. Inst. Tech., 1938; ScD, Harvard U., 1948. Registered prof. engr., N.Y.C. With USPHS, 1940-42; teaching fellow Harvard, 1946-48; with Malcolm Pirnie (cons. environ. engrs.), N.Y.C., 1948-52; assoc. prof. dept. environ. scis. and engring. U. N.C. at Chapel Hill, 1952-55, prof., 1955-73, Kenan prof., 1973-82, Kenan prof. emeritus, 1982—, head dept. environ. scis. and engring., 1955-73; bd. dirs. Water Resources Research Inst., 1965-84, chmn. faculty, 1970-73; vis. prof. Tech. U. Delft, 1960-61, Univ. Coll., London, 1964-67, 73-75, Tianjin U., 1981; editor environ. scis. series Acad. Press., 1968-75; cons. to industry, cons. engrs., govtl. agys. World Bank, WHO, UNDP, with spl. svc. in Switzerland, Israel, Jordan, Peru, Egypt, Colombia, Brazil, Venezuela, Thailand, Indonesia, Kenya, Zambia, Tunisia, Togo, Morocco, People's Republic China; mem. environ. adv. coun. Rohm & Haas Co., Inc., 1985-92; chmn. expert panel on N.Y.C. water supply EPA, 1992-93. Author: (with Gordon M. Fair and John C. Geyer) Water and Wastewater Engineering, 2 vols., 1966-68, Elements of Water Supply and Wastewater Disposal, 1971; (with George Ponghis) Community Wastewater Collection and Disposal, 1975; Regionalization of Water Management—A Revolution in England and Wales, 1977; editor: (with M.B. Pescod) Water Supply and Wastewater Disposal in Developing Countries, 1971; (with C.R. Schulz) Surface Water Treatment for Communities in Developing Countries, 1984; contbr. to publs. in field. Chmn. Chapel Hill Fellowship for Sch. Integration, 1961-63; mem. adv. bd. Ackland Meml. Art Mus., 1973-78; bd. dirs. Warren Regional Planning Corp., 1971-77, Inter-Ch. Council Housing Corp., 1975-83, N.C. Water Quality Council, 1975-77; adv. com. for med. research Pan Am. Health Orgn., 1976-79; chmn. Washington Met. Area Water Supply Study Com., 1976-80, NAS-NRC; bd. sci. and tech. for internat. devel. NRC, 1978-81, vice chmn. environ. studies bd., 1980-83, chmn. water sci. and tech. bd., 1991-94; mem. com. on human rights NAS, 1988-94; pres. Chapel Hill chpt. N.C. Civil Liberties Union, 1991-93. Served from lt. to maj. AUS, 1942-46. Recipient Harrison Prescott Eddy medal for research Water Pollution Control Fedn., 1950, Gordon Maskew Fair award Am. Acad. Environ. Engrs., 1973, Thomas Jefferson award U. N.C. at Chapel Hill, 1973, Gordon Y. Billard award N.Y. Acad. Scis., 1975, 1st Thomas R. Camp Meml. lectr. Boston Soc. Environ. Engrs., Gordon Maskew Fair medal Water Pollution Control Fedn., 1978, First Allen Hazen lectr. New England Water Works Assn., 1990, Donald R. Boyd award Assn. Met. Water Agys., 1993; Friendship medal Inst. Water Engrs. and Scientists (Gt. Britain), 1984; NSF fellow, 1960-61; Fed. Water Pollution Control Adminstrn. fellow, 1966-67; Fulbright-Hayes lectr., 1973-74. Mem. NAE, AAUP (U. N.C. chpt. pres. 1963-64), ASCE (chmn. environ. engring. divsn. 1967-68, 1st Simon W. Freese award 1977, hon. mem. 1995—), Am. Water Works Assn. (hon., N.C. Fuller award 1983, best paper award ednl. divsn. 1985, Abel Wolman award of Excellence 1991), Inst. Medicine Water Pollution Control Fedn. (hon., chmn. rsch. com. 1961-66, dir.-at-large 1969-72), Am. Acad. Engring. (pres. 1969-70, hon. diplomate), Assn. Environ. Engring. (Founders' award 1994), N.C. Pub. Health Assn. (Jarrett award), Order of Golden Fleece, Sigma Xi (U. N.C. chpt. pres. 1968-69). Home: 900 Linden Rd Chapel Hill NC 27514-9162

OKUN, HERBERT STUART, ambassador, international executive; b. N.Y.C., Nov. 27, 1930; s. Irving and Ida Muriel (Levine) O.; m. Lorraine Joan Price, Dec. 5, 1954 (div. 1985); children: Jennifer, Elizabeth, Alexandra; m. Enid Curtis Bok Schoettle, Dec. 27, 1990. AB with gt. distinction, Stanford U., 1951; postgrad., Syracuse U., 1951-52, Princeton U., 1952; Hochschule fuer Politische, Wissenschaft, Munich, Fed. Republic of Germany, 1956-57; MPA, Harvard U., 1959. Mem. U.S. Fgn. Service, 1955-91; vice consul U.S. Fgn. Service, Munich, Fed. Republic Germany, 1955-57, with bur. intelligence & research Office of Soviet Union Affairs, Dept. State, 1959-61, alt. dir., 1971-73; 2d sec. Am. embassy U.S. Fgn. Service, Moscow, 1961-63; consul, prin. officer U.S. Fgn. Service, Belo Horizonte, Brazil, 1964-65; 1st sec., prin. officer embassy U.S. Fgn. Service, Brasilia, Brazil, 1965-66, counsellor embassy, prin. officer, 1967-68; assigned Naval War Coll. U.S. Fgn. Svc., 1968-69; spl. asst. to Sec. of State U.S. Fgn. Service, 1969-71, dep. chmn. U.S. Del., U.S.-USSR Talks on Prevention Incidents at Sea, 1971-72; spl. asst. for internat. affairs to comdr.-in-chief NATO So. Command, Naples, Italy, 1973-74; minister-counsellor, dep. chief mission Am. Embassy, Lisbon, Portugal, 1975-78; dep. chmn. U.S. del. SALT, Geneva, 1978-79, U.S. del. to trilateral U.S.-U.K.-USSR Talks on comprehensive test ban treaty, Geneva, 1979-80; ambassador to German Democratic Republic East Berlin, 1980-83; ambassador-in-residence Aspen Inst., Washington, 1983-85; ambassador, dep. permanent rep. of U.S. to the UN N.Y.C., 1985-89; rep. of U.S. to 40th, 41st, 42d and 43d sessions of Gen. Assembly of UN, to UN Security Coun., 1985-89, to 29th and 30th sessions of Com. on Peaceful Uses of Outer Space, 1986, 87, to Disarmament Commn. of UN, 1985-89, to Commn. Human Rights, to 27th and 29th session of com. on program and coordination of Econ. and Social Coun., 1987, 89; amb. in residence Carnegie Corp. of N.Y., 1989-90; mem. UN sec. Gen.'s. Expert Group on Enhancing UN Structure for Drug Abuse Control, 1990; exec. dir. Fin. Svcs. Vol. Corps, N.Y.C., 1990—; vis. lectr. Yale Law Sch., New Haven, 1991—; spl. adviser to the personal envoy of the sec. gen. UN, Yugoslavia and Nagorno-Karabakh, 1991-92; spl. adviser, dep. to co-chmn. Internat. Conf. on former Yugoslavia, 1992-93; U.S. mem. UN Internat. Narcotics Control Bd., Vienna, Austria, 1992—; adv. bd. Chazen Inst. Internat. Bus. Grad. Sch. Bus., Columbia U.; bd. The European Inst.; mem. bd. dirs. World Rehab. Fund; mem. adv. bd. Minority Rights Group U.S.A.; spl. advisor Carnegie Commn. on Preventing Deadly Conflict. Commr. U.S.-Poland Action Commn. Served with AUS, 1952-54. Recipient Meritorious Honor award Dept. of State, 1972, Superior Honor award Dept. of State, 1980, Presdl. Meritorious Svc. award, 1983. Mem. Am. Fgn. Service Assn., Council Fgn. Relations, Am. Fgn. Policy (nat. com.), Washington Inst. Fgn. Affairs, Phi Beta Kappa. Home: 1133 Park Ave Apt 16E New York NY 10128-1246 Office: Fin Svcs Vol Corps 425 Lexington Ave New York NY 10017-3903

OKUN, JANICE, food editor; b. Buffalo, Dec. 3, 1932; d. Abraham I. and Berta Okun; m. Randolph J. Seidenberg Jr., Jan. 2, 1955; children: Jane Seidenberg-Lenk, Robert J. Seidenberg. BS, Cornell U., 1954. TV host WBEW-TV, Buffalo, 1954-55; asst. dir. Dairy Coun. of Niagara Frontier, Buffalo, 1962-79; food editor, restaurant critic Buffalo News, 1979—. Editor (with Eleanor Ostman): The Best Places to Eat in America, 1987. Mem. Assn. Food Journalists (pres. 1985, 86, v.p. 1974—). Office: Buffalo News 1 News Plz Buffalo NY 14240

OKUNIEFF, PAUL, radiation oncologist, physician; b. Chgo., Mar. 8, 1957; s. Michael and Beverly Okunieff; m. Debra Trione, Sept. 7, 1989. SB in Elec. Engring. & Biology, MIT, 1978; MD, Harvard U., 1982. Diplomate

Nat. Bd. Med. Examiners; cert. in therapeutic radiology Am. Bd. Radiology. Intern in medicine Beth Israel Hosp., Boston, 1982-83; resident in radiation oncology Mass. Gen. Hosp., Boston, 1983-86, fellow in radiation oncology, 1986-87, asst. prof. radiation oncology, 1987-93; chief dept. radiation oncology NIH, Bethesda, Md., 1993—; instr. in radiation medicine Harvard Med. Sch., Boston, 1987, asst. prof. radiation oncology, 1988-93; asst. radiation therapist Waltham (Mass.) Hosp. Med. Ctr., 1989-93, Mt. Auburn Hosp., Cambridge, Mass., 1989-93; assoc. radiation oncologist Univ. Hosp., Boston, 1990-93, co-dir. dept. radiation therapy, 1990-93; chief radiation neuro-oncology Mass. Gen. Hosp., Boston, 1991-93; chief radiation oncology br. Nat. Cancer Inst., Bethesda, 1993—; invited lectr. various med. schs., congresses & confs. Contbr. over 50 articles to profl. jours., also chpts. to books. Recipient Essay award IEEE, 1978, Young Oncologist Essay award Am. Radium Soc., 1987, travel award Am. Coll. Radiology, 1987, Young Investigator travel award VIth Internat. Meeting on Chem. Modifiers of Cancer Treatment, 1988, Basic Sci. travel grant ASTRO Ann. Meeting, 1989, USNC/UICC travel grant UICC Meeting, Hamburg, Germany, 1990, Melvin H. Knisely award Internat. Soc. Oxygen, 1991; grantee/fellow Am. Cancer Soc., 1985-86, 86-87, 89-92, Mass. Gen. Hosp., 1986, NIH, 1988-93. Office: NCI-Radiation Oncology Branch Bldg 10 B3B69 9000 Rockville Pike Bethesda MD 20892

OKWUMABUA, BENJAMIN NKEM, corporate executive; b. Issele-Uku, Nigeria, June 20, 1939; came to U.S., 1963; naturalized, 1978; s. Daniel Ikeduba and Nwaonogwu Emily O.; m. Constance Lee, Mar. 16, 1968; children: Benjamin Nkem, Oblamaka Patricia, Richard Ikeduba, Daniel Ikeduba. BS, Cen. State U., 1967; MBA, Mich. State U., 1969, M in Labor and Indsl. Relations, 1971, PhD, 1974. Prof. Saginaw (Mich.) Valley State Univ., 1971-75; dept. chmn., 1971-75; sales mgr. Oldsmobile div. Gen. Motors Corp., Buffalo, 1975-78; pres. chief exec. officer AFRO-LECON, Inc., Jamestown, N.Y., 1978-89, Watson Industries, Inc., Jamestown, N.Y., 1989—; N.Y. state del. White House Conf. Small Bus. Mem. gov.'s adv. council on minority bus. devel. State of N.Y., council on western N.Y. econ. devel.; pres. African-Am. Coalition, Jamestown. Researcher in field. Mem. Acad. Mgmt., Am. Mgmt. Assn., Am. Mktg. Assn., Indsl. Relations Research Assn., Beta Gammas Sigma, Sigma Iota. Democrat. Baptist. Lodge: Rotary. Home: 505 Chautauqua Ave Jamestown NY 14701-7615 Office: Watson Industries Inc 335 Harrison St Jamestown NY 14701-6903

OLAFSON, FREDERICK ARLAN, philosophy educator; b. Winnipeg, Man., Can., Sept. 1, 1924; s. Kristinn K. and Fredericka (Björnson) O.; m. Allie Lewis, June 20, 1952 (dec.); children—Peter Niel, Christopher Arlan, Thomas Andrew. A.B., Harvard U., 1947, M.A., 1948, Ph.D., 1951. Instr. philosophy and gen. edn. Harvard U., 1952-54; asst. prof. philosophy, then assoc. prof. Vassar Coll., 1954-60; assoc. prof. Johns Hopkins U., 1960-64; prof. edn. and philosophy Harvard Grad. Sch. Edn., 1964-71; prof. philosophy U. Calif., San Diego, 1971-91, chmn. dept., 1973-76, assoc. dean grad. studies and research, 1980-85. Author: Principles and Persons, 1967, Ethics and Twentieth Century Thought, 1973, The Dialectic of Action, 1979, Heidegger and the Philosophy of Mind, 1987. Served to lt. (j.g.) USNR, 1943-46. Mem. Nat. Acad. Edn. Home: 6081 Avenida Chamnez La Jolla CA 92037-7404

OLAFSSON, OLAFUR J., publishing company executive. Attended, Brandeis U. Researcher Sony, San Jose, Calif., 1984—; v.p., spl. projects Sony U.S.A., N.Y.C.; pres. Sony Electronic Pub. Corp., N.Y.C. Author: Marketplace of the Gods, Absolution. Office: Sony Electronics Pub Corp Sony USA 9 W 57th St New York NY 10019-2600

OLAH, GEORGE ANDREW, chemist, educator; b. Budapest, Hungary, May 22, 1927; came to U.S., 1964, naturalized, 1970; s. Julius and Magda (Rasznai) O.; m. Judith Agnes Lengyel, July 9, 1949; children: George John, Ronald Peter. PhD, Tech. U. Budapest, 1949, D honoris causa, 1989; DSc honoris causa, U. Durham, 1988, U. Munich, 1990, U. Crete, Greece, 1994, U. So. Calif., 1995, Case Western Res. U., 1995, U. Szeged, 1995, U. Veszprem, 1995. Mem. faculty Tech. U. Budapest, 1949-54; sci. scientist Dow Chem. Can. Ltd., 1957-64, Dow Chem. Co., Framingham, Mass., 1964-65; prof. chemistry Case-Western Res. U., Cleve., 1965-69, C.F. Mabery prof. rsch., 1969-77; Donald P. and Katherine B. Loker disting. prof. chemistry, dir. Hydrocarbon Rsch. Inst., U. So. Calif., L.A., 1977—; vis. prof. chemistry Ohio State U., 1963, U. Heidelberg, Germany, 1965, U. Colo., 1969, Swiss Fed. Inst. Tech., 1972, U. Munich, 1973, U. London, 1973-79, L. Pasteur U., Strasbourg, 1974, U. Paris, 1981; hon. vis. lectr. U. London, 1981; cons. to industry. Author: Friedel-Crafts Reactions, Vols. I-IV, 1963-64, (with P. Schleyer) Carbonium Ions, Vols. I-V, 1969-76, Friedel-Crafts Chemistry, 1973, Carbocations and Electrophilic Reactions, 1973, Halonium Ions, 1975, (with G.K.S. Prakash and J. Somer) Superacids, 1984; (with Prakash, R.E. Williams, L.D. Field and K. Wade) Hypercarbon Chemistry, 1987, (with R. Malhotra and S.C. Narang) Nitration, 1989, Cage Hydrocarbons, 1990, (with Wade and Williams) Electron Deficient Boron and Carbon Clusters, 1991, (with Chambers and Prakash) Synthetic Fluorine Chemistry, 1992, (with Molnar) Hydrocarbon Chemistry, 1995, also chpts. in books, numerous papers in field; patentee in field. Recipient Leo Hendrik Baekeland award N.J. sect. Am. Chem. Soc., 1966, Morley medal Cleve. sect., 1970, Alexander von Humboldt Sr. U.S. Scientist award, 1979, Pioneer of Chemistry award Am. Inst. Chemists, 1993, Mendeleev medal Russian Acad. Scis., 1992, Nobel Prize in Chemistry, 1994. Fellow AAAS, Chem. Inst. Can.; mem. NAS, Italian NAS, European Acad. Arts, Scis. and Humanities, Italy Chem. Soc. (hon.), Hungarian Acad. Sci. (hon.), Am. Chem. Soc. (award petroleum chemistry 1964, award Synthetic organic chemistry 1979, Roger Adams award in organic chemistry 1989), German Chem. Soc., Brit. Chem. Soc. (Centenary lectr. 1978), Swiss Chem. Soc., Sigma Xi. Home: 2252 Gloaming Way Beverly Hills CA 90210-1717 Office: U So Calif Labor Hydrocarbon Rsch Inst Los Angeles CA 90007 *America still is offering a new home and nearly unlimited possibilities to the newcomer who is willing to work hard for it. It is also where the "main action" in science and technology remains.*

OLAJUWON, HAKEEM ABDUL (THE DREAM), professional basketball player; b. Lagos, Nigeria, Jan. 21, 1963; s. Salaam and Abike O. Student, U. Houston, 1980-84. With Houston Rockets, 1984—. Named to Sporting News All-Am. First Team, 1984, NBA All-Rookie Team, 1985, All-Star team, 1985-90, 92-94, All-NBA First Team, 1987-89, 93-94, NBA All-Defensive First Team, 1987-88, 90, 93-94; named MVP 1993-94, 95, NBA Defensive Player of Yr., 1993-94, mem. NBA championship team, 1994; recipient award IBM, 1993. Holder NBA record for highest average of blocked shots per game (3.62). Office: Houston Rockets The Summit Ten Greenway Pl E Houston TX 77046*

OLAND, SIDNEY M., brewing and entertainment company executive; b. Halifax, NS, Can., Feb. 8, 1940. BA in Economics with honors, Dalhousie U., Halifax, Nova Scotia, 1960, MA, 1966; MBA, Harvard U., Cambridge, Mass., 1964. Asst. brewer Oland & Sons Ltd., 1960-65, v.p., asst. sec. treas., 1965-69, plant mgr., 1969-71; plant mgr. Oland's Breweries Ltd., 1971-72, v.p. spl. projects, 1972-73; sr. market rsch. analyst Labatt Breweries of Can. Ltd., 1973-74; v.p., gen. mgr. Labatt's Saskatchewan Brewery Ltd., 1974-76, Labatt's Ontario Breweries Ltd., 1976-79; exec. v.p. Can. ops. Labatt Brewing Co. Ltd., 1979-80, apptd. pres., 1980—; apptd. v.p. John Labatt Ltd., 1982—, apptd. bd. dirs., 1987—, apptd. pres., CEO, 1989—, apptd. vice chmn., group exec. of brewing, 1992—; past chmn. Brewers Assn. of Can. Mem. Gov. Coun., Shaw Festival; Can. Games (Halifax) v.p. sports, 1969. Served as capt. 1st Field Arty. Res., Halifax. Mem. Halifax Club, Royal Can. Yacht Club, Founders Club. Avocations: skiing, squash, tennis, sailing, scuba diving, reading. Office: John Labatt Ltd Labatt House, BCE Pl 181 Bay St PO Box 811, Toronto, ON Canada M5J 2T3 Home: 60 Russell Hill Rd, Toronto, ON Canada M4V 2T2

OLANDER, RAY GUNNAR, retired lawyer; b. Buhl, Minn., May 15, 1926; s. Olof Gunnar and Margaret Esther (Meisner) O.; m. Audrey Joan Greenlaw, Aug. 1, 1959; children: Paul Robert, Mary Beth. BEE, U. Minn., 1949, BBA, 1949; JD cum laude, Harvard U., 1959. Bar: Minn. 1959, Wis. 1962, U.S. Patent Office 1968. Elec. engr. M. A. Hanna Co., Hibbing, Minn., 1950-56; assoc. Leonard, Street & Deinard, Mpls., 1959-61; comml. atty. Bucyrus-Erie Co., South Milwaukee, Wis., 1961-70, dir. contracts, 1970-76, v.p. comml., 1976-78, gen. atty., 1978-80, corp. sec., 1978-88, gen. counsel, 1980-88; vice chmn., dir. Bucyrus-Erie Co., South Milwaukee, 1988-92; ret. Bd. dirs. Ballet Found. Milw., Inc., 1978-92. Pub. Expenditure Rsch. Found., Inc. Madison, Wis., 1978-94, Pub. Expenditure Survey Wis.,

Madison, 1978-82. With USN, 1944-46. Mem. ABA, Wis. Bar Assn., Wis. Intellectual Property Law Assn., Am. Soc. Corp. Secs., Inc., Am. Corp. Counsel Assn., VFW, Harvard Club (N.Y.C.), Harvard of Wis. Club, Bonita Bay Club. Republican. Roman Catholic. Home: 3708 Woodlake Dr Bonita Springs FL 33923-8605

OLAYAN, SULIMAN SALEH, corporate executive; b. Onaiza, Saudi Arabia, Nov. 5, 1918; s. Saleh and Heya (Al Ghanem) O.; student public schs., Bahrain Islands; m. Mary Perdikis, Feb. 22, 1974; children: Khaled, Hayat, Hutham, Lubna. Research specialist Arabian Am. Oil Co., 1937-47; founder and chmn. The Olayan Group, Saudi Arabia, 1947—, which includes Olayan Investments Co. Establishment and subs., Olayan Europe Ltd., Olayan Am. Corp., Crescent Holding GmbH, Competrol Real Estate Ltd.,; Competrol Establishment, Olayan Financing Co. and Affiliates, Olayan Saudi Holding Co. and Subs., Saudi Arabian Oil Co., Supreme Council (mem., 1989—); chmn. bd. The Saudi Brit. Bank, Riyadh, Saudi Arabia, 1977-89; adv. bd. Am. Internat. Group; mem. internat. council J.P. Morgan & Co. Inc. N.Y., 1979-90; internat. councillor, mem. adv. bd. Ctr. for Strategic and Internat. Studies, Washington, 1977-95; bd. dirs. C.S. First Boston Group, The Saudi Brit. Bank. Decorated Knight Comdr. of Brit. Empire, 1987, comdr. 1st class Royal Order of the Polar Star (Sweden), 1988; recipient Great Cross of the Order of Merit, Spain, 1985, Medal of Honor, Madrid C. of C., 1985. Mem. internat. adv. council SRI Internat., Menlo Park, Calif. Alumnus Mem. The Rockefeller U. Council, N.Y.C., 1978—; trustee Am. U. of Beirut, 1979-84; co-chmn. U.S.-Saudi Arabian Businessmen's Dialogue under the U.S.-Saudi Arabian Joint Commn. on Econ. Cooperation, 1980-92; Mem. Internat. Coun. Inst. Europeen de Adminstrn. des Affaires (INSEAD), Internat. Indsl. Conf., San Francisco (participant, internat. mem. 1985), Inst. for Internat. Econs., Washington (bd. dirs.), The Conf. Bd. of N.Y. (sr. mem., internat. counselor), Royal Inst. Internat. Affairs, 1979-91, London, Riyadh Handicapped Children Assn. (vice chmn., 1983-88). Islam. Clubs: Equestrian (Riyadh); Knickerbocker, N.Y. Athletic (N.Y.C.); Pacific-Union and Bohemian (San Francisco); Royal Automobile (London). Office: The Olayan Group, PO Box 8772, Riyadh 11492, Saudi Arabia

OLCOTT, JOHN WHITING, aviation executive; b. Orange, N.J., Oct. 20, 1936; s. Egbert Whiting and Marion Richmond (Braillard) O.; m. Hope Bennett Phillips, May 14, 1966 (div. Feb. 1987); children: David Whiting, Bradley Phllips, Carter Howell; m. Isobel Waxman Ritter, Nov. 25, 1989. BS in Aero. Engring., Princeton U., 1960, MS in Aero. Engring., 1964; MBA in Gen. Mgmt., Rutgers U., 1970. V.p. Linden (N.J.) Flight Svc., 1960-66; flight rsch. specialist Princeton (N.J.) U., 1966-68; v.p. corp. devel., sr. cons. Aero. Rsch. Assocs. Princeton, Inc., 1968-74; v.p. group pub., editorial dir. McGraw-Hill Aviation Week Group, Rye Brook, N.Y., 1973-92; pres. Nat. Bus. Aircraft Assn., Inc., 1992—; mem. R, E&D adv. com. FAA, 1990—; bd. govs. Flight Safety Found., 1992—. Crew chief, mem. New Vernon (N.J.) Vol. First Aid Squad, 1974-92; bd. dirs. Aviation Rsch. and Edn. Found., Washington, 1988-92; bd. visitors Aircraft Owner and Pilots Assn. Air Safety Found., Frederick, Md., 1988-93; trustee Embry-Riddle Aero. U., Daytona Beach, Fla., 1988-93; chmn. panel gen. aviation and commuter tech. NASA, Washington, 1974-86; chmn. panel gen. aviation safety FAA, Washington, 1983-88. Recipient Meritorious Svc. award Flight Safety Found., 1983, Dir.'s award FAA Ctral Region, 1984, Commendation cert. FAA, 1984, Gill Robb Wilson award Embry-Riddle Aero. U., 1986, Journalism award Helicopter Assn. Internat., 1990. Republican. Presbyterian. Office: NBAA 1200 18th St Washington DC 20036 also: 3808 N Richmond St Arlington VA 22207

OLCOTT, WILLIAM ALFRED, magazine editor; b. Bklyn., June 29, 1931; s. W. Alfred and Margaret Mary (Carr) O.; m. Anne Maria Gorman, Sept. 7, 1963; children: Christopher, James, Katharine, William, Terence. B.A. in Philosophy, Mary Immaculate Sem. and Coll., Northampton, Pa., 1957; postgrad., Columbia U. Reporter, writer AP, 1960-66; with McGraw-Hill Publs. Co., 1966-80, 81-84, chmn. editorial bd., 1976-77, editor in chief 26 Plus mag., 1977-81; editor in chief Nat. Petroleum News mag., 1977-81, editor in chief Office Adminstrn. and Automation mag., 1984; editor in chief Fund Raising Mgmt. mag., Garden City, N.Y., 1985—; publs. exec. editor Hoke Communications, Garden City, 1989—. Mem. adv. com. Garden City Bd. Edn., N.Y., 1976—; prin. religious edn. home program St. Joseph's Roman Cath. Ch., Garden City, 1976—, mem. pastoral coun., 1990-94. Recipient Jesse H. Neal Editorial Achievement award Am. Bus. Press, 1974, 80, Golden Mike award Nat. Religious Broadcasters, 1989. Home: 70 Greensboro Rd Hanover NH 03755 Office: 224 7th St Garden City NY 11530-5747

OLD, BRUCE SCOTT, chemical and metallurgical engineer; b. Norfolk, Va., Oct. 21, 1913; s. Edward H.H. and Eugenia (Smith) O.; m. Katharine G. Day, Oct. 7, 1939; children: Edward H., Randolph B., Lansing G., Ashlee Virginia, Barbara Stuart. B.S., U. N.C., 1935; Sc.D., M.I.T., 1938. Research engr. devel. and research dept. Bethlehem Steel Corp., 1938-41; with Arthur D. Little, Inc., Cambridge, Mass., 1946-78; v.p. Arthur D. Little, Inc., 1950-60, sr. v.p., 1960-78; pres. Bruce S. Old Assocs., Inc., 1979—; pres., chmn. Cambridge Corp., 1952-53; pres. Nuclear Metals, Inc., 1954-57; dir. Mass. Investors Trust and 13 other mut. funds in MFS group, 1973-85; chief metallurgy and materials br., div. research AEC, 1947-49; mem. Sci. Adv. Com. to Pres., 1952-56. Co-author: The Game of Singles in Tennis, 1962, Stroke Production in the Game of Tennis, 1971, The Game of Doubles in Tennis, 1956, Tennis Tactics, 1983; Contbr. articles to profl. publs.; patentee in field. Corporator Deaconess Hosp., Boston. Served to comdr. USNR, 1941-46. Fellow AAAS, Am Soc. Metals, Am. Inst. Chemists; mem. N.Y. Acad. Scis., Nat. Acad. Engring., Wianno (Mass.) Club, Sigma Xi, Tau Beta Pi. Address: PO Box 635 150 West St Osterville MA 02655-2242

OLD, LLOYD JOHN, cancer biologist; b. San Francisco, Sept. 23, 1933; s. John H. and Edna A. (Marks) O.; BA., U. Calif., Berkeley, 1955; MD, U. Calif., San Francisco, 1958; MD (hon.), Karolinskia Inst., 1994. Rsch. fellow Sloan-Kettering Inst. Cancer Rsch., N.Y.C., 1958-59, rsch. assoc., 1959-60, assoc., 1960-64, assoc. mem., 1964-67, mem., 1967—; rsch. assoc. biology Sloan-Kettering div. grad. sch. Med. Scis., Cornell U., N.Y.C., 1960-62, asst. prof. biology, 1962-66, assoc. prof. biology, 1966-69, prof. biology, 1969-81, prof. immunology, 1981—; acting assoc. dir. research planning Sloan-Kettering Inst. Cancer Rsch., N.Y.C., 1972, v.p., assoc. dir., 1973-76, v.p., assoc. dir. for sci. devel., 1976-83; assoc. dir. for research Meml. Sloan-Kettering Cancer Ctr. and Meml. Hosp., N.Y.C., 1973-83, William E. Snee Chair cancer immunology, 1983—; Harvey Soc. lectr., 1972, G.H.A. Clowes Meml. lectr., 1980; assoc. med. dir. N.Y. Cancer Rsch. Inst. Inc., 1970; med. dir. Cancer Rsch. Inst., Inc., 1971-74, dir. sci. adv. coun., 1974—; vis. prof. clin. investigation GM Cancer Rsch. Found., Dana-Farber Cancer Inst.; vis. prof. pathology Harvard U., 1986; fgn. adj. prof. med. faculty Karolinska Inst., 1994—; cons. in field. Adv. editor: Jour. Exptl. Medicine, 1971-76, 90—; Progress in Surface and Membrane Sci., 1972-74; assoc. editor: Virology, 1972-74; editl. adv. bd.: Cancer Rsch., 1967-70, Cancer, 1968-71, Recent Results in Cancer Rsch., 1972, editl. bd. Immunobiology, 1987—. Contbr. articles to profl. jours. Sci. dir., mem. Emeritus Sci. Com., 1973-86, chmn. sci. com. 1988—, bd. dirs. 1989—, CEO, 1995, dir. N.Y. unit, 1990; mem. rsch. coun. Pub. Health Rsch. Inst. City N.Y., 1978-80, sci. dir., 1979-89, vice chmn. exec. com. 1984-89; adv. bd. biology div. N.Y. Hall of Sci., 1985—; mem. med. and sci. adv. bd., trustee Leukemia Soc. Am., 1970-73; mem. sci. adv. bd. Jane Coffin Childs Meml. Fund for Med. Rsch., 1970-75. Recipient Roche award, 1957; Alfred P. Sloan award cancer research, 1962, Lucy Wortham James award James Ewing Soc., 1970, Louis Gross award, 1972, Founders Tumor Immunology award Cancer Research Inst., 1975, Rabbi Shai Shacknai Meml. award, 1976, Research Recognition award Noble Found., 1978; Robert Roesler de Villiers award, 1981; N.Y. Acad. Medicine medal, 1985, Robert Koch prize, 1990. Mem. NAS, AAAS, N.Y. Acad. Scis., Harvey Soc., Am. Acad. Arts and Scis., Am. Assn. Cancer Research (bd. dirs. 1980-83), Am. Assn. Immunologists, Inst. Medicine of Nat. Acad. Scis., Phi Beta Kappa, Sigma Xi, Alpha Omega Alpha. Office: Ludwig Inst Cancer Rsch 1345 Avenue Of The Americas New York NY 10105-0122

OLDBERG, CARL MALCOLM, public relations executive; b. Kansas City, Mo., Nov. 4, 1947; s. Philip Perry and Muriel (Swanson) O.; m. Linda Jane Swendson, Nov. 25, 1972; children: Elizabeth Ann, Katharine Allie. A.A., Met. Jr. Coll., 1967; B.A. in Journalism, U. Mo.-Columbia, 1970, M.B.A., 1972. With pub. relations dept. Motorola Inc., Schaumburg, Ill., 1972-77;

exec. v.p. Ruder Finn & Rotman, Chgo., 1977-89; pres. The Oldberg Group, 1989—. Recipient Best Ideas award ITT, 1981, 82, 83. Mem. Pub. Rels.Soc. (Silver Anvil award 1979), Publicity Club Chgo. (Golden Trumpet award, 1979, 82), Internat. Assn. Bus. Communicators (Silver Quill and Spectra awards 1984). Home: 1627 Portsmouth Ln Schaumburg IL 60194-3937

OLDEN, KENNETH, science administrator, researcher; b. Parrottsville, Tenn., July 22, 1938; s. Mack L. and Augusta (Christmas) O.; m. Sandra L. White; children: Rosalind, Kenneth, Stephen, Heather. BS, Knoxville Coll., 1960; MS, U. Mich., 1964; PhD, Temple U., 1970. Rsch. fellow, physiology instr. Harvard U., Cambridge, Mass., 1970-74; sr. staff fellow NIH, Nat. Cancer Inst., Bethesda, Md., 1974-77, biochemistry expert, 1977-78, rsch. biologist, 1978-79; assoc. dir. rsch. Howard U. Med. Sch. Cancer Ctr. Washington, 1979-82, dep. dir., 1982-85, dir., 1985-91; dir. Nat. Inst. Environ. Health Scis. and Nat. Toxicology Program NIH, Rsch. Triangle Park, N.C., 1991—. Author over 110 books; assoc. editor Cancer Rsch., 1990—, Jour. Nat. Cancer Inst., 1990—, Molecular Biology of the Cell, 1991-93, environ. Health Perspectives, 1992—; contbr. articles to profl. jours. Mem. awards bd. Gen. Motors Cancer Rsch. Found., Detroit, 1992—, Porter Devel. Postdoctoral fellow Am. Physiol. Soc., 1970, Postdoctoral fellow NIH, 1970-73, Macy Faculty fellow Macy Found., 1973-74. Mem. Am. Soc. Cell Biology, Am. Soc. Biol. Chemistry, Am. Assn. Cancer Rsch. (bd. dirs.), Soc. Biol. Response Modifiers, Metastasis Rsch. Soc., Inst. Medicine Internat. Soc. Study Comparative Incology, Inst. Medicine. Baptist. Avocations: tennis, hiking, cycling, cooking. Home: 19 Quail Ridge Rd Durham NC 27705-1870 Office: Nat Inst Environ Health Scis & Nat Toxicology Prog PO Box 12233 Research Triangle Park NC 27709-2233

OLDEN, PETER CARTER, healthcare administration educator; b. Trenton, N.J., Oct. 13, 1950; s. Walter Hart and Helen Elizabeth (Livingston) O.; m. Deborah Louise Kucher, Jan. 29, 1977; children: Ryan Hart, Alexander Carter. BS, Miami U., Oxford, Ohio, 1972; MHA, Duke U., 1975; PhD in Health Svcs. Orgn. and Rsch., Va. Commonwealth U., 1994. Asst. administr. Annie Penn Meml. Hosp., Reidsville, N.C., 1976-80; v.p. prof. svcs. Spartanburg (S.C.) Regional Med. Ctr., 1980-86; assoc. dir., COO Southside Regional Med. Ctr., Petersburg, Va., 1986-90; grad. asst., rsch. assoc. dept. health adminstrn. Va. Commonwealth U., Richmond, 1990-92, instr., 1992; instr. health adminstrn. programs U. Scranton, PA., 1993-94, asst. prof., 1994—; project leader Williamson Inst. for Health Studies, Va. Commonwealth U., 1992-93. Contbr. articles to profl. jours. Fellow Am. Coll. Healthcare Execs.; mem. Acad. of Mgmt. (orgn. and mgmt. theory and health care adminstrn. divs.), Assn. for Health Svcs. Rsch., Assn. Univ. Programs in Health Adminstrn., Duke U. Hosp. and Health Adminstrn. Alumni Assn., Va. Commonwealth U. Alumni Assn. Avocations: sports, music. Office: U Scranton Dept Health Adminstrn Scranton PA 18510

OLDENBURG, CLAES THURE, artist; b. Stockholm, Sweden, Jan. 28, 1929; s. Gosta and Sigrid Elisabeth (Lindforss) O.; m. Patricia Joan Muschinski, Apr. 13, 1960 (div. Apr. 1970); m. Coosje van Bruggen, July 22, 1977. B.A., Yale, 1951; student, Art Inst., Chgo., 1952-54. One-man shows include Reuben Gallery, N.Y.C., 1960, Green Gallery, N.Y.C., 1962, Sidney Janis Gallery, N.Y.C., 1964-70, Galerie Ileana Sonnabend, Paris, 1964, Robert Fraser Gallery, London, 1966, Moderna Museet, Stockholm, 1966, 77, Mus. Contemporary Art, Chgo., 1967, 77, Irving Blum Gallery, Los Angeles, 1968, Mus. Modern Art, N.Y.C., 1969, U. Calif. at Los Angeles Art Gallery, 1970, Stedelijk Mus., Amsterdam, 1970, 77, Tate Gallery, London, 1970, Nelson-Atkins Mus., Kansas City, 1972, Art Inst. Chgo., 1973, Leo Castelli Gallery, N.Y.C., 1974, 76, 80, 90, Kunstmus., Basel, 1992, Margo Leavin Gallery, Los Angeles, 1975, 76, 78, 88, Art Gallery of Toronto, Ont., 1976, Centre Georges Pompidou Musée National d'Art Moderne, Paris, 1977, Kröller-Muller Mus., 1979, Mus. Ludwig, Cologne, 1979, Wave Hill, Bronx, N.Y., 1984, Pace Gallery, 1992, 94, Nat. Gallery of Art, Washington, 1995, Mus. Contemporary Art, L.A., 1995, Solomon R. Guggenheim Mus., N.Y.C., 1995; group shows include Martha Jackson Gallery, N.Y.C., 1960, 61, Dallas Mus. Contemporary Art, 1961, 62, Sidney Janis Gallery, 1962, 64, Inst. Contemporary Arts, London, 1963, Art Inst. Chgo., 1962, 63, Allen Art Mus. Oberlin (Ohio) Coll., 1963, Mus. Modern Art, N.Y.C., 1963, 88, 90, 91, Washington Gallery Modern Art, 1963, Am. Pavilion, Venice, 1964, Moderna Museet, Stockholm, 1964, Gulbenkian Found. Tate Gallery, London, 1964, Rochester (N.Y.) Meml. Mus., 1964-65, Worcester (Mass.) Mus., 1965, Met. Mus. Art, N.Y.C., 1969, Walker Art Center, 1975, others, numerous commd. works, rep. permanent collections at, Guggenheim Mus., N.Y.C., Mus. Modern Art, Albright-Knox Art Gallery, Buffalo, Centre Georges Pompidou, Stedelijk Mus., Tate Gallery, Mus. Ludwig, Moderna Museet, Rose Art Mus. Brandeis U., Waltham, Mass., Oberlin Coll., Nat. Gallery Art, Canberra, Art Gallery Ont., Toronto, Art Inst. Chgo., Hirshorn Gallery and Sculpture Gorden, Whitney Mus. Modern Art, N.Y.C., Mus. Contemporary Art, L.A., many others; Numerous outdoor works in corporate and private collections. (Recipient Creative Arts citation Brandeis U. 1971, Sculpture award Am. Ann., Chgo. Art Inst. 1976, medal AIA 1977, Wilhelm Lehmbruck Sculpture award 1981); author: Store Days, 1967, Proposals for Monuments and Buildings, 1969, Notes in Hand, 1971, Raw Notes, 1973, Multiples in Retrospect, 1991, Claes Oldenburg Coosje van Bruggen: Large Scale Projects. Recipient Wolf Prize in Arts, 1989. Office: care Pace Gallery 32 E 57th St New York NY 10022-2513

OLDENBURG, RICHARD ERIK, auction house executive; b. Stockholm, Sept. 21, 1933; came to U.S., 1936, naturalized, 1959; s. Gösta and Sigrid Elisabeth (Lindforss) O.; m. Harriet Lisa Turnure, Dec. 17, 1960. A.B., Harvard U., 1954. Mgr. design dept. Doubleday & Co., Inc., N.Y.C., 1958-61; mng. editor trade div. Macmillan Co., Inc., N.Y.C., 1961-69; dir. publs. Mus. Modern Art, N.Y.C., 1969-72, dir., 1972-94, dir. emeritus, hon. trustee, 1995—; chmn. Sotheby's N.Am., N.Y.C., 1995—. Served with AUS, 1956-58. Home: 447 E 57th St New York NY 10022-3064 Office: Sotheby's Inc 1134 York Ave New York NY 10021-4806

OLDERSHAW, LOUIS FREDERICK, lawyer; b. New Britain, Conn., Aug. 30, 1917; s. Louis A. and Annie Louise (Bold) O.; m. Virginia Wakelin, Nov. 30, 1940; children: Peter W., Robert J., David L. A.B., Dartmouth Coll., 1939; LL.B., Yale U., 1942. Bar: Mass. 1946, Fed. 1947. Mem. legal staff Army Ordnance Dist., Springfield, Mass., 1942-43; with firm Lyon, Green, Whitmore, Doran & Brooks, Holyoke, Mass., 1947-49; partner firm Davenport, Millane & Oldershaw, Holyoke, 1949-64; treas. Nat. Blank Book Co., Inc., Holyoke, 1964-65; pres. Nat. Blank Book Co., Inc., 1965-78, chmn. bd., 1978-83; group v.p., dir. Dennison Mfg. Co., Framingham, Mass., 1967-82; counsel Bulkley, Richardson & Gelinas, Springfield, Mass., 1983—. Mem. editorial bd.: Yale Law Jour, 1941-42. Trustee Mt. Holyoke Coll., 1966-76, Greater Holyoke YMCA; bd. dirs. Holyoke Community Coll. Found., The Ctr. Redevel. Corp subs. Mt. Holyoke Coll., South Hadley, Mass., Sta. WGBY-TV. Lt. USNR, 1943-47. Republican. Mem. United Ch. Christ. Clubs: Longmeadow (Mass.) Country; Mill Reef (Antigua). Lodge: Rotary. Home: 1 Brookwood Rd Holyoke MA 01040 Office: Baybank Tower 1500 Main St Ste 2700 Springfield MA 01115-0001

OLDFATHER, CHARLES EUGENE, lawyer; b. Brady, Nebr., Oct. 7, 1927; s. Harold and Marcia (Hazlett) O.; m. Diane C. Harris, June 15, 1957; children: David H., Jane Oldfather Light. Student, U. Colo., 1945, Kearney (Nebr.) State Tchrs. Coll., 1946-48, U. Cal. at Berkeley, 1949; A.B., U. Nebr., 1950; J.D. with distinction, U. Mich., 1953. Bar: Nebr. bar 1953. Since practiced in Lincoln; asso. Cline, Williams, Wright & Johnson, 1953-58; partner Cline, Williams, Wright, Johnson & Oldfather, 1958-80, of counsel, 1980—. Bd. editors: U Mich Law Rev, 1952-53. Past pres. Family Svc. Assn., Lincoln; trustee U. Nebr. Found.; past pres. Nebr. State Hist. Soc. Found. Served with Adj. Gen. Div. AUS, 1946-48. Mem. Am. Nebr., Lincoln bar assns., Lincoln C. of C. (past dir.), Phi Kappa Psi, Phi Delta Phi. Republican. Presbyn. Club: Lincoln Country. Home: 6719 Old Cheney Rd Lincoln NE 68516-3561 Office: 1900 Firstier Bank Bldg Lincoln NE 68508

OLDFIELD, EDWARD CHARLES, JR., retired naval officer, communications company executive; b. Hampton, Va., July 21, 1919; s. Edward Charles and Alice Toomer (Parrish) O.; m. Lucy Garnett Jordan, Apr. 19, 1941; children: Edward Charles III, William Marshall, Henry Jordan. BS in Commerce, U. Va., 1940; MBA with distinction, Harvard U., 1950; grad., Naval War Coll., 1956. Commd. ensign USN, 1942, advanced through grades to capt., 1962, served in ships of Atlantic and Pacific fleets and major

naval installations, 1942-70; dep. comdr. Def. Indsl. Supply Ctr., Phila., 1966-68; comdg. officer Naval Supply Ctr., Newport, R.I., 1968-70; dir. U.S. Naval Audit Svc., S.E. U.S., 1970-71; ret. USN, 1971; asst. to pres. TeleCable Corp., Norfolk, Va., 1971-73; treas. TeleCable Corp., Norfolk, 1973-74, v.p. corp. devel., 1974-83; v.p., asst. to chmn. Landmark Communications Inc., Norfolk, 1983-88; ret., 1988. Mem. dean's adv. com., bd. dirs. ctr. for econ. edn., lectr. Old Dominion U. Sch. Bus. and Pub. Adminstrn., Norfolk, 1985-88. Baker scholar Harvard U., 1950. Mem. Tower Club-So. Cable TV Assn., Alpha Kappa Psi, Beta Gamma Sigma, Kappa Alpha, Harbor Club (Norfolk, bd. dirs. 1980-86, pres. 1986-88), Norfolk Yacht and County Club. Republican. Roman Catholic. Home: 4301 Lookout Rd Virginia Beach VA 23455-1520

OLDHAM, BILL W., mathematics educator; b. Paris, Tex., Oct. 30, 1934; s. H.H. and Margaret Irene (McDowna) O.; m. Monda Underwood, Jan. 30, 1954; children: Clifford, Brent, Bill. BA in Math., Abilene Christian U., 1956; MS in Math., Okla. State U., 1963; EdD in Math. Edn., U. No. Colo., 1972. Tchr. math. Mcpl. Sch., Ft. Summer, N.Mex., 1956-61; prof. math. Harding U., Searcy, Ark., 1961—. Mem. Math. Assn. Am., Nat. Coun. Tchrs. Math., Am. Coun. Tchrs. Math., Phi Delta Kappa. Ch. of Christ. Home: 1403 W Arch Ave Searcy AR 72143-5105 Office: Harding University PO Box 921 Searcy AR 72143-0921

OLDHAM, DALE RALPH, life insurance company executive, actuary; b. Topeka, May 31, 1943; s. Ralph W. and Anna Marie (Minch) O.; m. Marilyn D. Morris, June 5, 1965; children: Kent D., Kevin L. BS magna cum laude, Washburn U., 1965; am. U. Mich. 1967. Asst. actuary Nat. Res. Life, Topeka, Kans., 1967-72, assoc. actuary, 1972-74, v.p., assoc. actuary, 1974-76, v.p., chief actuary, 1976-84; also bd. dirs.; sr. v.p. adminstrn. Security Benefit Group, Topeka, 1984-88, sr. v.p. affiliated products, services, 1988-89; pres., COO, Savers Life Ins. Co. Am., 1989-90, pres., CEO, chmn. bd., 1990-94, pres., CEO 1994—. Bd. dirs., treas. United Way Greater Topeka, 1988-89; mem. adv. council Unified Sch. Dist., Topeka, 1981-84; trustee Meml. Hosp. Corp. Topeka, 1984-89, chmn., 1989; mem. adv. bd. Ctr. Ins. Edn., 1987-89. Fellow Soc. Actuaries; mem. Am. Acad. Actuaries, Kansas City Actuaries Club (pres. 1980-81), Adminstrv. Mgmt. Soc. (bd. dirs 1975-82, 84—, pres. 1981-82, Merit award 1980, Diamond Merit award 1987), Topeka Geneal. Soc. (pres. 1988-89). Republican. Club: Kiwanis (Topeka pres. 1980). Home: 12414 Wedd St Overland Park KS 66213-1841 Office: Savers Life Ins Co Am 9300 W 110th St Overland Park KS 66210-1403

OLDHAM, DARIUS DUDLEY, lawyer; b. Beaumont, Tex., July 6, 1941; s. Darius Saran and Mary Francis (Carraway) O.; m. Judy J. White, Jan. 23, 1965; children—Steven, Michael. BA, U. Tex., Austin, 1964; JD, U. Tex., 1966. Bar: Tex. 1966, U.S. Dist. Ct. (so., no., ea. and we. dists.) Tex. 1966, U.S. Supreme Ct. 1974, U.S. Ct. Appeals (5th and 11th cirs.) 1968. Assoc. Fulbright & Jaworski, Houston, 1966-74, ptnr., 1974—, mem. policy com., 1980—; mem. faculty grad. litigation program U. Houston; lectr. on corp. def. ins. and product liability. Mem. bd. editors Aviation Litigation Reporter, Personal Injury Def. Reporter; contbr. articles to profl. jours. Mem. Nat. Jud. Coll. Coun. for the Future; bd. dirs., former sec.-treas. FIC Found., 1979-87; past bd. dirs. Houston Pops Orch.; mem. liberal arts adv. coun. U. Tex. Fellow Am. Coll. Trial Lawyers, Tex. Bar Found. (life), Am. Bar Found. (life), Houston Bar Found. (life), Am. Bd. Trial Advs.; mem. ABA (vice chmn. aviation com. tips sect. 1980-82, chmn. aviation com. litigation sect. 1982-84, vice chmn. econs. law practice com. 1985-86, mem. coun. tort and ins. practice sect. 1988-91, vice chair 1991-92, chair-elect 1992-93, chmn. ann. meeting program com. 1987, chmn. professionalism com. 1990-91, fin. com. 1986-93, chmn. long range planning com. 1991-92, chair tort and ins. practice sect. 1994—, presdl. emissary), Tex. Bar Assn. (liaison with law schs. and law students com. 1983-86, PEER com. 1979-82, chmn. liaison with fed. jud. com. 1989-90, pattern jury charges Vol. IV com. 1988-92), Tex. Young Lawyers Assn. (bd. dirs., chmn.), Fedn. Ins. and Corp. Counsel (exec. v.p., pres.-elect 1988-89, pres. 1989-90, chmn. bd. 1990-91, exec. com. 1988-91, secretary 1984-87, chmn. continuing legal edn. com. 1984-87, chmn. aviation com. 1978-79, v.p. 1982-84, bd. dirs. 1984-87, sec./treas. 1987-88), Tex. Assn. Def. Counsel, Maritime Law Assn. U.S., Am. Counsel Assn. (bd. dirs. 1982-83, 89-94), Def. Rsch. Inst. (chmn. aerospace com. 1984-87, vice chmn. 1983-84, Presdl. Achievement award 1987, bd. dirs. 1989-92, exec. com. 1991-92), Lawyers for Civil Justice (bd. dirs. 1988-92, exec. com. 1990-92), River Oaks Country Club, Houston Ctr. Club, Sigma Chi, Phi Delta Phi. Office: Fulbright & Jaworski 51st Fl 1301 Mckinney St Fl 51 Houston TX 77010-3049

OLDHAM, JOE, editor; b. Bklyn., Aug. 1, 1943. B.S., NYU, 1965. Editor Car Model OLR Pub., North Arlington, N.J., 1966-68; assoc. editor Automobile Internat. Johnston Internat. Publs., N.Y.C., 1968-70; spl. projects editor Magnum-Royal Publs., N.Y.C., 1970-72; book devel editor Hearst Corp., N.Y.C., 1972-77; editor Motor Mag. Hearst Corp., 1977-81, exec. editor Popular Mechanics, 1981-85, editor-in-chief, 1985—; contbr. numerous articles to various mags. Recipient cert. of appreciation Nat. Inst. for Automotive Service Excellence, 1976; recipient cert. of appreciation Automotive Service Councils, 1979, cert. of appreciation Northwood Inst., 1981, cert. of appreciation Automotive Hall of Fame, 1981. Mem. Internat. Motor Press Assn. (pres. 1973-74, 81-82), Am. Soc. Mag. Editors, Soc. Profl. Journalists, Am. Auto Racing Writers and Broadcasting Assn. Club: Detroit Press. Office: Popular Mechanics The Hearst Corp 224 W 57th St New York NY 10019-3212*

OLDHAM, JOHN MICHAEL, physician, psychiatrist, educator; b. Muskogee, Okla., Sept. 6, 1940; s. Henry Newland and Alice Gray (Ewton) O.; m. Karen Joan Pacella, Apr. 24, 1971; children: Madeleine Marie, Michael Clark. BS in Engring., Duke U., 1962; MS in Neuroendocrinology, Baylor U., 1966, MD, 1967. Licensed physician N.Y., N.J., Tex.; diplomate in psychiat. Am. Bd. Psychiatry and Neurology. Intern pediatrics St. Luke's Hosp., N.Y.C., 1967-68; resident psychiat. Columbia U. Dept. Psychiat., N.Y.S. Psychiatric Inst., N.Y.C., 1968-70, chief resident in psychiat., 1970-71; auditor Washington Psychoanalytic Inst., 1971-72; candidate Columbia Psychoanalytic Ctr., N.Y.C., 1969-77; dir. psychiatric emergency svcs. Roosevelt Hosp., N.Y.C., 1973-74; dir. residency tng. dept. psychiat., 1974-77; dir. short term diagnostic and treatment unit N.Y. Hosp. Westchester Divsn., White Plains, 1977-80; dir. divsn. acute treatment svcs. N.Y. Hosp. Westchester Divsn., White Plains, 1980-84; deputy dir. N.Y. State Psychiatric Inst., N.Y.C., 1984-89, acting dir., 1989-90, dir., 1990—; assoc. chmn. dept. psychiatry Columbia U. Coll. Physicians & Surgeons, N.Y.C., 1986—; chief med. officer N.Y. State Office Mental Health, Albany, 1989—; instr. clin. psychiat. Columbia U. Coll. Physicians & Surgeons, 1974-76, assoc. clin. psychiat., 1976-77, lectr. psychiat., 1977-84, assoc. prof. clin. psychiat., 1984-88, prof. clin. psychiat., 1988—; asst. prof. psychiat. Cornell U. Med. Coll., N.Y.C., 1977-83, assoc. prof. clin. psychiat., 1983-84; attending staff dept. psychiat. Roosevelt Hosp., N.Y.C., 1973-77; assoc. attending psychiat., N.Y. Hosp., 1977-84, Presbyn Hosp., N.Y.C., 1984-88, attending psychiat., 1988—; tng., supervising psychoanalyst Columbia Psychoanalytic Ctr., N.Y.C., 1983—; coord. med. student edn., Cornell U. Med. Coll. Dept. Psychiat., Westchester Divsn., White Plains, N.Y., 1977-84; coord. clin. curriculum in psychiatr. Roosevelt Hosp., Columbia U. Coll. Physicians & Surgeons, N.Y.C., 1974-77; mem. acad. adv. com. Pfizer vis. professorship program in psychiat., 1990-92; mem. Sandoz Clozaril nat. adv. bd; spl. adv. bd. Freedom From Fear, Inc.; examiner Am. Bd. Psychiatry and Neurology; chmn. acute divisin rsch. group, Westchester Divsn., N.Y. Hosp., 1981-84, co-project dir. borderline rsch. group, 1982-84, co-prin. investigator familial transmission DSM III personality disorders, 1982-84; prin. investigator personality disorders in bulimia, N.Y.S. Psychiatric Inst., 1985-90, structured DSM III assessment psychoanalytic patients, Columbia Psychoanalytic Ctr., 1986-91; co-prin. investigator validity DSM III R personality disorders, N.Y. State Psychiatric Inst., 1987—. Author: (with L.B. Morris) The Personality Self-Portrait, 1990; contbg. editor Jour. Personality Disorders; sect. editor Psychiatry; mem. editl. adv. bd. Am. Psychiat. Press, Inc.; mem. exec. editl. bd. Psychiat. Quar.; reviewer Psychiat. Svcs., Jour. of Neuropsychiatry; contbr. numerous articles to profl. jours.; more than 100 presentations in field. Recipient John J. Weber prize Excellence in Psychoanalytic Rsch. Columbia Psychoanalytic Ctr., 1990. Fellow Am. Coll. Psychiatrists, Am. Psychiatric Assn. (pres. N.Y. County Dist. Branch 1989-90, com. rsch. psychiatric treatment 1987-93, coun. rsch., steering com. practice guidelines, chmn. sci. program com. 1992—coun. 1991-92, chmn. com. psychoanalytic liaison N.Y. County Dist. Branch 1986-87), Am. Psychopathological Assn., N.Y. Acad. Medicine; mem. Am. Psychoanalytic

Assn. (cert.), Assn. Facility Dirs. (N.Y. State Office Mental Health, coun. ethics), Assn. Psychoanalytic Medicine (pres. 1989-91), Internat. Psychoanalytical Assn., N.Y. Acad. Sci., N.Y. State Med. Soc., Assn. Rsch. Personality Disorders (bd. dirs.). Office: NY State Psychiatric Inst 722 W 168th St New York NY 10032-2603

OLDHAM, TODD, fashion designer; b. Corpus Christi, Tex., 1960; s. Jack and Linda Oldham. Alterations Ralph Lauren Polo Store, Dallas; founder Times 7, Dallas; founder, designer Todd Oldham, N.Y.C., 1989—; design dir. Escada, Munich, Germany, 1994—. Recipient Perry Ellis award New Fashion Talent Coun. Fashion Designers Am., 1992. Office: 499 Seventh 8th Floor South New York NY 10018 also: Todd Oldham Store 123 Wooster St New York NY 10012

OLDHAM, WILLIAM GEORGE, electrical engineering and computer science educator; b. Detroit, May 5, 1938; s. William D. and Freada (Howes) O.; m. Nancy Dereich; children: Katherine Ann, William James. B.S., Carnegie Mellon Inst., 1960, M.S., 1961, Ph.D., 1963. Staff scientist Siemens-Schuckert, Erlangen, W.Ger., 1963-64; mem. faculty elec. engring. and computer scis. dept. U. Calif., Berkeley, 1964—, prof., 1972—; dir. Electronics Research Lab., 1985-90; project mgr. Intel Corp., Santa Clara, Calif., 1974-75. Author: An Introduction to Electronics, 1972, Electrical Engineering, An Introduction, 1984. NSF fellow, 1970; Guggenheim fellow, 1985-86. Fellow IEEE; mem. Nat. Acad. Engring. Office: U Calif Berkeley Electronic Rsch Lab 509 Cory Hall Berkeley CA 94720

OLDMAN, GARY, actor; b. London, Mar. 21, 1958; m. Lesley Manville (div.); 1 child, Alfred; m. Uma Thurman (div.). BA, Rose Buford Coll. Speech and Drama, 1979. Appearances include (TV movies) Remembrance, 1982, Meantime, 1984, Honest, Decent and True, 1985, Fallen Angels: Dead End for Delia, 1993 (Cable Ace award, Actor in a Dramatic Series); (video) Since I Don't Have You by Guns n' Roses, 1994; (film) Sid and Nancy, 1986, Prick Up Your Ears, 1987 (Brit. Acad. Film and TV Arts nomination 1988), Track 29, 1988, We Think the World of You, 1988, Criminal Law, 1988, Paris by Night, 1989, Chattahoochee, 1990, State of Grace, 1990, Rosencrantz and Guildenstern Are Dead, 1991, JFK, 1991, Bram Stoker's Dracula, 1992, True Romance, 1993, Romeo is Bleeding, 1994, The Professional, 1994, Immortal Beloved, 1994, Murder in the First, 1995, The Scarlet Letter, 1995; (theatre) Massacre at Paris, 1980, Chinchilla, 1980, Desperado Corner, 1980, A Waste of Time, 1980, Summit Conference, 1982, Rat in the Skull, 1984, The Pope's Wedding, 1984 (Drama Mag. Best Actor award 1985, Fringe Best Newcomer award 1985-86), The War Plays, 1985, The Desert Air, 1985, Women Beware Women, 1986, Real Dreams, 1986, Serious Money, 1987. Office: c/o Douglas J Urbanski Douglas Mgmt Inc 8446 1/2 Melrose Pl Los Angeles CA 90029

OLDMAN, OLIVER, law educator; b. N.Y.C., July 19, 1920; s. Max and Rose (Meyers) O.; m. Barbara Lublin, May 2, 1943; children: Andrew, Margaret, Michele. Grad., Mercersburg Acad., 1938; S.B., Harvard, 1942, LL.B., 1953. Bar: N.Y. 1953, Mass. 1959. Jr. economist OPA, 1942; instr. econs. U. Buffalo, 1946-50; v.p. Lublin Constrn. Co., 1946-50; asso. firm Hodgson, Russ, Andrews, Woods & Goodyear, Buffalo, 1953-55; dir. tng. internat. tax program Law Sch. Harvard U., 1955-64, dir. internat. tax program Law Sch., 1964-89, prof. law, 1961-76, Learned Hand prof. law, 1976—, dir. East Asian Legal Studies Law Sch., 1981-90; cons. on taxation Govts. of Argentina, Bolivia, Chile, Colombia, Egypt, El Salvador, Ethiopia, Indonesia, Jamaica, Senegal, Venezuela, Mass., N.Y., N.H., N.Y.C., R.I. and, UN Secretariat; sr. advisor Lincoln Inst. of Land Policy, 1989—. Author: (with others) The Fiscal System of Venezuela, 1959, Financing Urban Development in Mexico City, 1967; Editor: (with R. Bird) Readings on Taxation in Developing Countries, 1964, rev. edit., 1967, 3d edit., 1975, 4th edit., 1990, (with P. Kelley) Readings on Income Tax Administration, 1973, (with F.P. Schoettle) State and Local Taxes and Finance, 1974. Served to 1st lt. AUS, 1943-46. Mem. ABA (vice chmn. com. on value added taxation 1990—, chmn. adv. bd. tax notes internat. 1989—), Nat. Tax Assn., Am. Econ. Assn., Pacific Community Legal Rsch. Seminar. Home: 15 Buckingham St Cambridge MA 02138-2219 Office: Harvard U Law Sch LW 332 Cambridge MA 02138

OLDS, ELIZABETH, dancer; b. Mpls.. Attended, SouthWest Ballet Ctr., Nat. Acad. of Arts, Ill., Royal Winnipeg (Man., Can.) Ballet Sch. Dancer Royal Winnipeg Ballet, 1982-85, soloist, 1985-89, prin. dancer, 1989—; various guest performances in U.S. and Can. Dance performances include Nuages, Symphony in D, Four Last Songs, Romeo & Juliet, Adagio Hammerklavier, Three Pieces, Giselle, Fall River Legend, Rodeo, Dark Elegies, Deuce Coupe, The Nutcracker, Tarantella, Apollo, Scotch Symphony, Roses, There is a Time, Lilac Garden, The Sleeping Beauty, Gâité Parisienne, many others. Master of ceremonies Western Can. Summer Games, 1990, Access Awareness Week, 1991; chairperson Easter Seals Campaign, 1994. Avocations: pottery, gardening. Office: Royal Winnipeg Ballet, 380 Graham Ave, Winnipeg, MB Canada R3C 4K2*

OLDS, JOHN THEODORE, banker; b. N.Y.C., Dec. 24, 1943; s. Richard J. and Barbara (Moses) O.; m. Candace Rose; children: Richard W., Samantha. Grad., Hill Sch., 1961; BA, U. Pa., 1965. With Morgan Guaranty Trust Co. N.Y., N.Y.C.; now mng. dir. J.P. Morgan & Co., N.Y.C. Mem. Univ. Club, Bedford Golf and Tennis Club, Mid-Ocean Club. Episcopalian. Home: 7 Plateau Ln Bedford NY 10506 Office: Morgan Guaranty Trust Co 60 Wall St New York NY 10005-2807

OLDS, SHARON, poet; b. San Francisco, Nov. 19, 1942. BA, Stanford U., 1964; PhD, Columbia U., 1972. Lectr.-in-residence on poetry Theodor Herzl Inst., 1976-80; Fanny Hurst chair Brandeis U., Waltham, Mass., 1986-87; dir. grad. program in creative writing NYU, 1988-91, assoc. prof. English, 1992—; vis. tchr. poetry Manhattan Theater Club, 1982, Poetry Ctr. for YMCA of N.Y.C., 1982. Poetry Soc. of Am., 1983, NYU, 1983, 85, Sarah Lawrence Coll., 1984, Goldwater Hosp., Roosevelt Island, N.Y., 1983-95, Columbia U., 1986, SUNY, Purchase, 1986; adj. prof. grad. program in creative writing NYU, 1983-92. Author: Satan Says, 1980 (San Francisco Poetry Ctr. award 1981), The Dead and Living, 1984 (Lamont Poetry Selection of the Am. Acad. Poets 1984, Nat. Book Critics Circle award 1985), The Gold Cell, 1987, The Matter of This World, 1987, The Sign of Saturn, 1991, The Father, 1992; contbr. poetry to numerous anthologies. Guggenheim fellow, 1981-82; Nat. Endowment for Arts grantee, 1982-83; recipient Madeline Sadin award N.Y. Quar., 1978, Poetry Miscellany Younger Poets award, 1979. Office: NYU Grad Program in Creative Writing 19 University Pl Rm 200 New York NY 10003

OLDSHUE, JAMES Y., chemical engineering consultant; b. Chgo., Apr. 18, 1925; s. James and Louise (Young) O.; m. Betty Ann Wiersema, June 14, 1947; children: Paul, Richard, Robert. B.S. in Chem. Engring., Ill. Inst. Tech., 1947, M.S., 1949, Ph.D. in Chem. Engring., 1951. Registered engr., N.Y. With Mixing Equipment Co., Rochester, N.Y., 1950-92, dir. research, 1960-63, tech. dir., 1963-70, v.p. mixing tech., 1970-92; pres. Oldshue Techs. Internat., Inc., Fairport, N.Y., 1992—; adj. prof. chem. engring. Beijing Inst. Chem. Tech., 1992—. Author: Fluid Mixing Technology, 1983; contbr. chpts. and articles to books and jours. Chmn. budget com. Internat. div. YMCA; bd. dirs. Rochester YMCA. Served with AUS, 1945-47. Recipient 1st Disting. Svc. award N.E. YMCA Internat. Com., 1979, J.E. Purkynje medal Czech Republic Acad. Sci.; named Rochester Engr. of Yr., 1980. Fellow AICE (pres. 1979, treas. 1983-89, Founders award 1981, Eminent Chem. Engr. award 1983, Svc. to Soc. award 1989, chmn. internat. activities com. 1987-92); mem. NAE, Am. Assn. Engring. Socs. (chmn. 1985, K.A. Roe award 1987), Am. Chem. Soc., Internat. Platform Assn., World Congress Chem. Engrs. (v.p. 1986, pres. 1994—), N.Am. Mixing Forum (chmn. 1990-93, Mixing Achievement rsch. award 1992), Interam. Confederation Chem. Engrs. (sec. gen. 1991-93, v.p. 1993-95, Victor Marquez award 1983), Rochester Engring. Soc. (pres. 1992-93). Mem. Reformed Ch. in Am. (gen. program coun.). Achievements include design and scale-up procedures in field of fluid mixing. Home: 141 Tyringham Rd Rochester NY 14617-2522 Office: 811 Ayrault Rd Fairport NY 14450

OLDSON, WILLIAM ORVILLE, history educator; b. Hampton, Va., Jan. 23, 1940; s. James Orville and Kathryn Francis (Zephir) O.; m. Judith Ann Kinsinger, June 11, 1967; children: Scott Ryan, Darren Randall. BA magna cum laude, Spring Hill Coll., Mobile, Ala., 1965; MA, Ind. U., 1966, PhD,

1970. Mem. Soc. of Jesus, 1959-65. Asst. prof. dept. history Fla. State U., Tallahassee, 1969-74; assoc. prof. history Fla. State U., 1974-79, assoc. chmn. undergrad. affairs, 1973-75, 83-84, dir. hist. adminstrn. and pub. history prog., 1987—, prof. history, 1979—, dir. history computer programs and rsch., 1993—, assoc. chmn. grad. affairs, 1994; dir. grievances and arbitration United Faculty of Fla., 1978-80, chief negotiator, 1980-81; dir. Social Sci. Interdisciplinary Program, Fla. State U., Panama City campus, 1986-90; charter mem. Pres.'s Coun. for Excellence in Coll. Teaching, 1990. Author: The Historical and Nationalistic Thought of Nicolae Iorga, 1973, A Providential Anti-Semitism: Nationalism and Polity in Nineteenth Century Romania, 1991; author numerous hist. manuals. Recipient Outstanding Tchr. award Phi Eta Sigma, 1990, John Frederick Lewis award Am. Philos. Soc., 1991, Univ. Teaching award, 1988, 95; NDEA fellow, 1966-67, Russian and East European Inst. fellow Ind. U., 1965-66, Fulbright fellow, 1967-68, Internat. Rsch. and Exch. Bd. fellow, 1973, Loyola U. of New Orleans honors fellow; Romanian State fellow, 1967-68, Holocaust Ednl. Found. fellow, 1994; Coun. Rsch. and Creativity Planning grantee, 1994-95. Mem. Sigma Pi Sigma, Delta Tau Kappa, Phi Alpha Theta (Prof. of Yr. 1988). Democrat. Roman Catholic. Home: 1116 Sandhurst Dr Tallahassee FL 32312-2530 Office: Fla State U History Dept Tallahassee FL 32306-2029

OLEARCHYK, ANDREW S., cardiothoracic surgeon, educator; b. Peremyshl, Ukraine, Dec. 3, 1935; s. Simon and Anna (Kravéts) O.; m. Renata M. Sharan, June 26, 1971; children: Christina N., Roman A., Adrian S. Grad., Med. Acad., Warsaw, Poland, 1961. Diplomate Am. Bd. Surgery, Am. Bd. Thoracic Surgery. Chief div. anesthesiology, asst. dept. surgery Provincial Hosp., Kielce, Poland, 1963-66; resident in gen. surgery Geisinger Med. Ctr., Danville, Pa., 1968-73; resident in thoracic, cardiac surgery Allegheny Gen. Hosp., Pitts., 1980-82; pvt. practice medicine specializing in cardiac, thoracic and vascular surgery Phila. and Camden, N.J., 1982—. Contbr. articles to med. jours., also 7 monographs. Achievements include grating of the internal thoracic to coronary arteries without touching the atherosclerotic ascending aorta, on cardiopulmonary bypass with a beating, warm and vented heart and bradycardia induced by beta-blocker; design of double occlusion clamps for the ascending aorta, Olearchyk R Triple Ringed Cannula Spring Clip to secure vein grafts over blunted cannulas in coronary artery bypass surgery; demonstration of safety of simultaneous use of fluothane and curare as gen. anesthesia; intro. of endarterectomy and external prosthetic grafting of ascending and transverse aorta under hypothermic circulatory arrest; pioneering promotion of grafting of the left anterior descending coronary artery sys. during resection of cardiac aneurysms, and of diffusely diseased coronary arteries with the internal thoracic artery; first to combine insertion of the inferior vena cava filter with iliofemoral venous thrombectomy. Home: 129 Walt Whitman Blvd Cherry Hill NJ 08003-3746

O'LEARY, DANIEL FRANCIS, university dean; b. Boston, Apr. 17, 1923; s. Dennis Joseph and Catherine Mary (O'Connell) O'L. BA, Oblate Coll., 1950; EdM, U. Buffalo, 1953, EdD, 1956. Tchr. gen. sci., biology Bishop Fallon High Sch., Buffalo, 1951-62, asst. prin., 1962-65; dir. edn. Oblate Fathers, Washington, 1963-68; prin. Bishop Fallon High Sch., Buffalo, 1968-74; dir. spl. programs Niagara U. (N.Y.), 1974-77, dean spl. programs, 1977-81, prof. edn., 1982—, dean edn. and continuing studies, 1982-88, prof., dean Coll. Edn., 1988—; adj. prof. Mt. St. Joseph's Tchrs. Coll., Buffalo, 1956-64, edn. evaluator reading clinic, 1956-64. Asst. dir. family life dept. Diocese of Buffalo, 1953-64. Mem. AAIP, ASCD, ATE, Am. Assn. Sch. Adminstrs., Nat. Coun. for Adminstrn. Tech. Edn., N.Y. State Assn. Tchr. Educators, Am. Assn. Colls. for Tchr. Edn., Phi Delta Kappa. Roman Catholic. Office: Niagara U Niagara University NY 14109-1930

O'LEARY, DANIEL J., retail trade executive; b. 1946. With Touche Ross & Co., 1969-87; ptnr., dir. audit ops. Touche Ross & Co., Rochester, N.Y., 1980-85; ptnr. Touche Ross & Co., Columbus, Ohio, 1985-87; with Fay's Inc., Liverpool, N.Y., 1987—, former chief fin. officer, v.p. fin., exec. v.p., now pres., chief operating officer, 1990—. Office: Fay's Inc 7245 Henry Clay Blvd Liverpool NY 13088-3523

O'LEARY, DANIEL VINCENT, JR., lawyer; b. Bklyn., May 26, 1942; s. Daniel Vincent and Mary (Maxwell) O'L.; m. Marilyn Irene Garrigan, June 1, 1968; children: Daniel, Katherine, Molly, James. AB cum laude, Georgetown U., 1963; LLB, Yale U., 1966. Bar: Ill. 1967. Assoc. Wilson & Mc Ilvaine, Chgo., 1967-75, ptnr., 1975-1987; ptnr. Peterson & Ross, Chgo., 1987-94, Schwartz & Freeman, Chgo., 1994—; bd. dirs. Atlantic Charter Ins. Co.; pres., bd. dirs. Jim's Cayman Co., Ltd. Lt. comdr. USNR, ret. Mem. Kenilworth Sailing Club (commodore 1985-87). Roman Catholic. Avocations: fishing, scuba diving. Office: Schwartz & Freeman 401 N Michigan Ave Ste 1900 Chicago IL 60611-4206

O'LEARY, DENIS JOSEPH, retired physician, insurance company executive; b. Ireland, Feb. 5, 1924; came to U.S., 1949, naturalized, 1954; s. Joseph and Mary Christine (Dennis) O'L.; m. Audrey Mary Ryan, Nov. 26, 1952; children: Michael, Brian, Denis, Kevin. M.D., Nat. U. Ireland, Cork, 1947. Intern St. Michael's Hosp., Toronto, Ont., Can., 1947-48; resident St. Michael's Hosp., 1948-49, St. Vincent's Hosp., N.Y.C., 1949-50, Triboro Hosp., Jamaica, N.Y., 1950-51; with N.Y. Life Ins. Co., N.Y.C., 1952-88; med. dir. employees' health N.Y. Life Ins. Co., 1961-70, v.p., 1970-82, sr. v.p., 1982-88; asst. attending physician Bellevue Hosp., N.Y.C., 1955-69; assoc. attending physician Bellevue Hosp., 1969-77, attending physician, 1977-84, sr. attending physician, 1984-87; instr. medicine, Columbia U. 1958-63, assoc. in medicine, 1963-68; asst. prof. clin. medicine NYU, 1968-86; sec. N.Y. Lung Assn., 1962-67, 69-71, v.p., 1967-69, dir., 1961-86, pres.-elect, 1983, pres., 1985-86. Bd. dirs. Nat. Council on Alcoholism, N.Y.C. 1979-86, pres. 1984-86. Served as capt. M.C. AUS, 1953-55. Fellow Am. Coll. Chest Physicians, Am. Occupational Med. Assn., Am. Pub. Health Assn.; mem. AMA, N.Y. State, New York County med. socs., Am. Thoracic Assn., Soc. Alumni Bellevue Hosp., N.Y. Occupational Med. Assn. (exec. com. 1967—, pres. 1973-74). Club: Scarsdale (N.Y.) Golf (gov. 1981-84), Rancho Bernardo Golf.

O'LEARY, DENNIS JOSEPH, lawyer; b. Phila., Jan. 11, 1941; s. Joseph P. and Catherine (Brannigan) O'L.; married; children: Dennis J., Terrance P., Patricia M., Maryann M. BS, Villanova U., 1963; JD, Temple U., 1972. Bar: Pa. 1972. Ptnr. White and Williams, Phila., 1972—. Mem. Pa. Bar Assn., Phila. Bar Assn., Defense Rsch. Inst., Pa. Defense Inst. Roman Catholic. Avocations: photography, travel, fishing, gardening. Office: White & Williams 1650 Market St Philadelphia PA 19103-7395

O'LEARY, DENNIS SOPHIAN, medical organization executive; b. Kansas City, Mo., Jan. 28, 1938; s. Theodore Morgan and Emily (Sophian) O'L.; m. Margaret Rose Wiedman, Mar. 29, 1980; children: Margaret Rose, Theodore Morgan. BA, Harvard U., 1960; MD, Cornell U., 1964. Diplomate Am. Bd. Internal Medicine, Am. Bd. Hematology. Intern U. Minn. Hosp., Mpls., 1964-65, resident, 1965-66; resident Strong Meml. Hosp., Rochester, N.Y. 1966-68; asst. prof. medicine and pathology George Washington U. Med. Ctr., Washington, 1971-73, assoc. prof., 1973-80, prof. medicine, 1980-86, assoc. dean grad. med. edn., 1973-77, dean clin. affairs, 1977-86; pres. Joint Commn. on Accreditation Healthcare Orgns., Chgo., 1986—; med. dir. George Washington U. Hosp., 1974-85, v.p. Univ. Health Plan, 1977-85; pres. D.C. Med. Soc., 1983. Chmn. editorial bd. Med. Staff News, 1985-86; contbr. articles to profl. jours. Founding mem. Nat. Capital Area Health Care Coalition, Washington, 1982; trustee James S. Brady Found., Washington, 1982-87; bd. dirs. D.C. Polit. Action Com., 1982-84. Maj. U.S. Army, 1968-71. Recipient Community Service award D.C. Med. Soc., 1981, Key to the City, Mayor of Kansas City, Mo., 1982. Fellow Am. Coll. Physician Execs.; mem. ACP, AMA (resolution commendation 1981), Am. Soc. Internal Medicine, Soc. Med. Adminstrs, Am. Hosp. Assn. (del. 1984-86, resolution commendation 1981), Internat. Club, DuPage Club (Chgo.). Avocation: tennis. Office: JCAHO 1 Renaissance Blvd Oak Brook Mall IL 60521

O'LEARY, EDWARD CORNELIUS, bishop; b. Bangor, Maine, Aug. 21, 1920; s. Cornelius J. and Annabel (McManus) O'L. B.A., Holy Cross Coll. Worcester, Mass., 1942; S.T.L., St. Paul's U. Sem., Ottawa, Can., 1946. Ordained priest Roman Cath. Ch., 1946, named monsignor, 1954, consecrated bishop, 1971; vice-chancellor, then chancellor of Diocese of Portland, Maine; diocesan consultor, pro-synodal judge of diocese, pres. priests

senate, mem. finance com. of diocese, also dir. Commodity Service Corp., 1969-75; titular bishop of Moglaena, aux. bishop Portland, 1971-74; bishop Roman Cath. Diocese Portland, 1974-89, bishop emeritus, 1989—; mem. Maine Office Religious Coop., from 1973. Mem. Nat. Conf. Cath. Bishops. Address: 307 Congress St Portland ME 04101-3638

O'LEARY, FRANK J., lawyer; b. Chgo., Aug. 27, 1953. BA, Colgate U., 1974; JD, Harvard U., 1978. Bar: Ill. 1978. Address: 916 W Armitage Ave Chicago IL 60614-4204

O'LEARY, HAZEL R., U.S. secretary of energy, former power company executive, lawyer; b. Newport News, Va., May 17, 1937; d. Russell E. and Hazel (Palleman) Reid; m. John F. O'Leary, Apr. 23, 1980; 1 child, Carl G. Rollins. BA, Fisk U., Nashville, 1959; JD, Rutgers U., Newark, 1966. Bar: N.J. 1967, D.C. 1985; cert. fin. planner. V.p., gen. counsel O'Leary Assocs., Inc., Washington, 1981-89; exec. v.p. corp. affairs No. States Power Co., Mpls., 1989-93, pres., 1993; sec. U.S. Dept. Energy, Washington, 1993—. Mem. Phi Beta Kappa. Office: US Dept Energy Office Sec 1000 Independence Ave SW Washington DC 20585-0001

O'LEARY, JAMES JOHN, economist; b. Manchester, Conn., May 7, 1914; s. James Henry and Helen Agnes (Hogan) O'L.; m. Rita Marie Phelps, May 31, 1941; children: James Phelps, Martha Ellen, Paul Howard, Mark Evans. B.A., Wesleyan U., 1936, M.A., 1937; Ph.D., Duke, 1941. Instr. econs. Wesleyan U., 1939-42, asst. prof., 1943-46, instr. air navigation U.S. Naval Flight Preparatory Sch., 1943-44; cons. Conn. Gen. Life Ins. Co., 1945-46; assoc. prof. econs. Duke, 1946-47; dir. investment research, economist Life Ins. Assn. Am., 1947-59, v.p., dir. econ. research, economist, 1959-67; chmn., chief economist Lionel D. Edie & Co., 1967-69; exec. v.p., economist U.S. Trust Co. of N.Y., 1969-70, vice chmn., 1970-80, econ. cons., 1980-91; bd. dirs. Bowery Savs. Bank, Guardian Life Ins. Co. Am., Atlantic Mut. Ins. Co.; dir. rsch. Com. on Pub. Debt Policy, 1946-47; mem. com. on rsch. in fin. Nat. Bur. Econ. Rsch.; alt. mem. nat. com. vol. credit restraint program Fed. Res. Bd., 1951-52. Author: Stagnation or Healthy Growth? The Challenge to the United States Economy in the Nineties, 1992; contbr. articles to profl. publs. Bd. dirs. Student Loan Mktg. Assn., Fed. Nat. Mortgage Assn., Kennecott/Copper Co., GAF/Corp., Excelsior Income Shares; mem. adv. com. Grad. Sch. Bus. NYU; trustee Wesleyan U.; bd. dirs. Nat. Bur. Econ. Rsch., chmn., 1976-80; trustee St. Joseph Coll. Recipient Silver Anniversary Sports Illustrated All Am. award, 1961, Disting. Alumnus award Wesleyan U., 1965, William Butler award for excellence in econs., 1985. Mem. Am. Soc. econs. assns., Am. Finance Assn., Am. Statis. Assn., Phi Beta Kappa, Pi Gamna Mu, Alpha Chi Rho. Club: University (N.Y.C.). Home: 8 Crooked Mile Rd Westport CT 06880-1123

O'LEARY, JOHN PATRICK, JR., packaging company executive; b. Pitts., Dec. 27, 1946; s. John P. Sr. and Beverly J. (Hagadorn) O'L.; m. Pamela J. Bailey, Dec. 27, 1969; children: Patrick, Christopher, David. BA in Econs., Gettysburg Coll., 1969; MBA, U. Pa., 1971. V.p. Tuscarora Plastics, Inc., New Brighton, Pa., 1971-83, pres. Western div., 1983-89, pres., CEO, 1990—; bd. dirs. 1st Western Bancorp, Inc., New Castle, Pa., Matthews Internat. Corp., Pitts. Bd. dirs. Beaver County Corp. for Econ. Devel., Beaver, Pa., 1986, Gateway Rehab. Ctr., Pitts., 1991, United Way of Beaver County, Aliquippa, Pa., 1991. 1st Lt. USAR, 1969-76. Mem. Assn. Foam Plastics Recyclers (chmn. 1991—), Polystyrene Packaging Coun. (bd. dirs. 1989—), Beaver County Country Club. Avocations: skiing, golf. Office: Tuscarora Inc 800 5th Ave New Brighton PA 15066-1922

O'LEARY, JOSEPH EVANS, lawyer; b. Newton, Mass., Sept. 17, 1945; s. Cornelius Joseph and Dorothy Mary (Evans) O'L.; m. Carolyn Brady, Aug. 16, 1969; children: Caryn, Kevin, David, Catherine. AB, Boston Coll., 1967, JD, 1970; LLM, Georgetown U., 1974. Bar: Mass. 1970, Ill. 1974, N.Y. 1979. Assoc. Seyfarth, Shaw, Fairweather & Geraldson, Chgo., 1974-78; ptnr. Seyfarth, Shaw, Fairweather & Geraldson, N.Y.C., 1978-82; of counsel Choate, Hall & Stewart, Boston, 1982-83, ptnr., 1983—. Lt. USN, 1971-74. Mem. ABA, Mass. Bar Assn., Boston Bar Assn. Home: 5 Penobscot St Medfield MA 02052-3008 Office: Choate Hall & Stewart Exchange Pl Boston MA 02109

O'LEARY, MARION HUGH, chemistry educator; b. Quincy, Ill., Mar. 24, 1941; s. J. Gilbert and Ruth Elizabeth (Kerr) O'L.; m. Sandra E. Eisemann, Sept. 5, 1964 (div. 1979); children—Catherine, Randall, Jessica; m. Elizabeth M. Kean, Jan. 24, 1981. B.S., U. Ill., 1963; Ph.D., MIT, 1966. Asst. prof. U. Wis., Madison, 1967-73, assoc. prof., 1973-78; prof. chemistry and biochemistry Coll. Letters and Scis. and Coll. Agrl. and Life Scis., Coll. Letters and Scis. and Coll. Agrl. and Life Scis., Madison, 1978-89; prof. and head dept. biochemistry U. Nebr., Lincoln, 1989—; cons. Institut Pertanian Bogor, Indonesia, 1983-84; vis. prof. Universitas Andalas, Padang, Indonesia, 1984-85, Australian Nat. U., 1982-83. Author: Contemporary Organic Chemistry, 1976. Editor: Isotope Effects on Enzyme-Catalyzed Reactions, 1977. Contbr. articles to sci. publs. Grantee, NSF, U.S. Dept. Agr., Dept. Energy, NIH; Guggenheim Found. fellow, 1982-83; Sloan Found. fellow, 1972-74. Fellow AAAS; mem. Am. Chem. Soc., Am. Soc. Biochemists and Molecular Biologists, Am. Soc. Plant Physiologists. Home: 8333 Horseshoe Dr Lincoln NE 68516-3926 Office: U Nebraska Dept Biochemistry Lincoln NE 68588

O'LEARY, PAUL GERARD, investment executive; b. Boston, June 22, 1935; s. Gerard Paul and Marie Agnes (Hennessey) O'L.; m. Elizabeth Jane Pollins. Oct. 14, 1961; children: Paul Hennessey, William Gerard, Mary Elizabeth, James Daniel. AB cum laude, Harvard U., 1956; MBA, U. Pa., 1958. Alumni dir. Wharton Grad. Sch., U. Pa., Phila., 1958-60; asst. sec. Empire Trust Co., N.Y.C., 1960-65; sr. investment analyst Blyth & Co., Inc., N.Y.C., 1965-70; v.p. William D. Witter, Inc., N.Y.C., 1970-76, also bd. dirs.; v.p. portfolio mgmt. Prudential Investment Corp., Newark, 1977—; instr. fin. U. Pa., 1957-60. V.p. Prudential Found., Newark, 1986—. Mem. Inst. Chartered Fin. Analysts, Am. Nuclear Insurers (chmn. investment com. West Hartford, Conn. 1989—), Assn. Ins. & Fin. Analysts (pres. 1973-74), Ins. Inst. for Hwy. Safety (investment com. 1983—), N.Y. Property Ins. Assn. (investment com. 1994—), N.Y. Soc. Security Analysts, Harvard Club of N.J. (pres. 1983-84), Boston Latin Sch. Alumni Assn., Indian Trail Club (Franklin Lakes, N.J.), Upper Ridgewood Tennis Club. Roman Catholic. Avocations: tennis, squash, philately, cartography, history. Home: 719 Belmont Rd Ridgewood NJ 07450-1300 Office: Prudential Investment Corp Gateway Ctr Two Newark NJ 07102

O'LEARY, ROBERT W., hospital operations company executive; b. 1944. Grad., U. Mass., Suffolk U. Law Sch., Boston. With Mass. Hosp. Assn., Boston, 1968-73, Ill. Hosp. Assn., Chgo., 1974-83, St. Joseph's Health Systems, Orange, Calif., 1983-89, Vol. Hosp. Group Am., Dallas, 1989-91; chmn. bd., CEO Am. Med. Holdings Inc., Dallas, 1991—. Office: Am Med Internat 8201 Preston Rd Ste 300 Dallas TX 75225

O'LEARY, THOMAS HOWARD, resources executive; b. N.Y.C., Mar. 19, 1934; s. Arthur J. and Eleanor (Howard) O'L.; m. Cheryl L. Westrum; children: Mark, Timothy, Thomas, Denis, Daniel, Mary Frances. A.B., Holy Cross Coll., 1954; postgrad., U. Pa., 1959-61. Asst. cashier First Nat. City Bank, N.Y.C., 1961-65; asst. to chmn. finance com. No. Pacific R.R. Co., 1966-70, v.p. finance, 1971-76, dir., 1972-82, chmn. finance com., 1976-82; treas. Mo. Pacific Corp., St. Louis, 1968-71; v.p. finance Mo. Pacific Corp., 1971-72, exec. v.p. 1972-74, dir., 1972-82, chmn. bd., chief exec. officer Mississippi River Transmission Corp., 1974-82; vice chmn. Burlington No., Inc., Seattle, 1982-89; bd. dirs. BF Goodrich, Kroger Co. Served to capt. USMC, 1954-58. Mem. Blind Brook Club (N.Y.C.), Chgo. Club. Office: Burlington Resources Inc 999 3rd Ave Ste 2810 Seattle WA 98104

O'LEARY, THOMAS MICHAEL, lawyer; b. N.Y.C., Aug. 16, 1948; s. James and Julia Ann (Conolly) O'L.; m. Luise Ann Williams, Jan. 13, 1978; 1 child, Richard Meridith. BA, CUNY, 1974; JD, Seattle U. Sch. of Law (formerly U. Puget Sound Law Sch.), 1977. Bar: Wash. 1977, U.S. Ct. Mil. Appeals 1978, U.S. Supreme Ct. 1983, U.S. Ct. Appeals (9th cir.). Dep. pros. atty. Pierce County, Tacoma, 1978; commd. 1st lt. U.S. Army, 1978, advanced through grades to capt., 1978; chief trial counsel Office of Staff Judge Adv., Fort Polk, La., 1978-79, trial def. counsel trial def. service, 1979-

81; chief legal advisor Office Insp. Gen., Heidelberg, Fed. Republic of Germany, 1981-82; sr. def. counsel Trial Def. Service, Giessen, W.Ger., 1982-84; asst. chief adminstrv. law U.S. Army Armor Ctr., Fort Knox, Ky., 1984-85, chief adminstrv law, 1985, chief legal asst., 1985-86; sr. trial atty. Immigration and Naturalization Svc., Phoenix, 1987; sector counsel, spl. asst. U.S. atty., U.S. Border Patrol, Tucson, 1987-90; enforcement counsel U.S. Immigration and Naturalization Svc., Tucson, 1990—. Decorated Purple Heart, Cross of Gallantry (Vietnam). Mem. ABA, Assn. Trial Lawyers Am., Judge Advs. Assn., Wash. State Bar Assn., Pierce County Bar Assn. Home: 9080 E 25th St Tucson AZ 85710-8675 Office: US Border Patrol Sector Hdqrs 1970 W Ajo Way Tucson AZ 85713-5605

OLECK, HOWARD LEONER, legal educator, writer; b. N.Y.C., Jan. 6, 1911; s. Richard and Yvette (Leoner) O.; m. Helen Eugenie Gemeiner, 1941; children: Mrs. Anabel Curtis, Joan Valerie. Grad., Townsend Harris Hall Prep. Sch., 1928; A.B., U. Iowa, 1933; J.D., N.Y. Law Sch., 1938; LL.D., Baldwin Wallace Coll., 1964; Litt.D. (hon.), J. Marshall U., 1967. Bar: N.Y. 1938, Ohio 1957, Fed. 1957. Assoc. prof. N.Y. Law Sch., 1947-56; prof. law, assoc. dean Cleve. State U., 1956-67, dean, 1967-68, 71, Disting. prof. law, 1968-74, Disting. prof. emeritus, 1974—; prof. law Wake Forest U., Winston-Salem, N.C., 1974-78, Stetson U., St. Petersburg, Fla., 1978-81; adj. prof. Stetson U., 1981-89, prof. emeritus, 1989—; asst. to editor N.Y. Law Jour., 1946-52; syndicated law columnist Cleve. Plain Dealer, 1959-75, Winston-Salem, Pinellas Rev., other newspapers, 1975-90; cons. to congl. coms. and presdl. commns. Am. Law Inst., pub. svc. groups, Calif., Ill. and Fla. Law Revision Commns., others. Author: Creditors' Rights, 1947, Creditors' Rights and Remedies, 1949, History of Allied Planning of Operations, E.T.O., 1939-45, 1945, Debtor-Creditor Law, 1953, Negligence Investigation Manual, 1953, Negligence Forms of Pleading, 1954, New York Corporations, 1954, Damages to Persons and Property, 1955, Non-Profit Corporations and Associations, 1956, Encyclopedia of Negligence, 2 vols, 1960, Modern Corporation Law, 6 vols, 1960, supplement, 1978, Cases on Damages, 1962, Eye Witness World War II Battles, 1963, Heroic Battles of World War II, 1963, Law for Living, 1967, A Singular Fury, 1968, Law for Everyone, 1971, Nonprofit Corporations, Organization and Associations, 6th edit. (with Stewart), 1994, supplementannually, Primer on Legal Writing, 1974, 4th edit., 1978, National Index to Insurance Laws, 1976, The Lion of Islam, 1977, Nonprofit Organizations Trends, 1977, (with Green and co-editor) Parliamentary Law and Practice for Non-Profit Organizations, 2d edit., 1991, Religious Non-profit Organizations' Problems, 1981, 4th edit., 1990, Oleck's Tort Law Practice Manual, 1982, also War Dept. histories, 1945-46; editor: Directors and Officers Ency. Manual, 1955, Negligence and Compensation Service, 1955-66; National Ins. Law Service, 1962-76, also various jours., 1956—; author: over 300 mag. articles, poems under own and various pen names. Served to maj., tanks AUS, 1942-45, ETO; War Dept. historian. Decorated U.S. and fgn. medals; recipient various bar assn. honors. Mem. St. Petersburg Bar Assn., Am. Trial Lawyers Assn., League Ohio Law Schs. (pres. 1963-64), Scribes (pres. 1972-73), Phi Alpha Delta. Democrat. Unitarian. Home: 5940 Pelican Bay Plz S Apt 301 Saint Petersburg FL 33707-3956

OLEEN, LANA, state legislator; b. Kirksville, Mo., Apr. 26, 1949; d. Robert James and Frances (Primm) Scrimsher; m. Kent E. Oleen; children: Brooke, Bentson. BS in Edn., Emporia State U., 1972, MS in Curriculum. Tchr. Council Grove, Kans., 1972-74, St. George, Kans., from 1978; communications coord. Woodward-Clyde Cons., San Francisco, 1974-75; dir. communication Kans. Dept. Human Resources; senator Kans. State Senate, 1988—; mem. Rep. Precinct Com., 1978—. Active Kans. Rep. Women, Riley County Rep. Women. Mem. NEA, Nat. Coun. Tchrs. of English. Lutheran. Home: 3000 Stagg Hill Rd Manhattan KS 66502-4035 Office: State Senate State Capitol Topeka KS 66612

OLEJAR, PAUL DUNCAN, former information science administrator; b. Hazelton, Pa., Sept. 13, 1906; s. George and Anna (Danco) O.; m. Ann Ruth Dillard, Jan. 6, 1933 (dec. Oct. 1978); 1 child, Peter; m. Martha S. Ross, Sept. 8, 1979. AB, Dickinson Coll., 1928. Dir. edn. W.va. Conservation Commn., 1936-41; coordinator U.S. Fish and Wildlife Service, 1941-42; chief press and radio Bur. Reclamation, Dept. Interior, 1946-47; editor Plant Industry Sta. AGRI, 1948-51; chmn. spl. reports Agrl. Research Adminstrn., 1951-56; dir. tech. info. Edgewood Arsenal, Md., 1956-63; chief, tech. info. plans and programs Army Research Office, Washington, 1963-64; chmn. chem. info. unit NSF, Washington, 1965-70; dir. drug info. program Sch. Pharmacy, U. N.C., Chapel Hill, 1970-73, ret., 1973. Author: A Taste of Red Onion, 1981, Sentinel at the Crossroads, 1991; newspaper columnist, editor AP, Pa. and W.va.; editor Hanover Record-Herald, Pa. Served with AUS, 1942-46. Decorated Army Commendation medal. Mem. Ravens Claw, Mil. Order of All World Wars (lt. col.), Masons (32 degree), Theta Chi, Omicron Delta Kappa. Methodist. Home: 724 Port Malabar Blvd NE Palm Bay FL 32905-4409

OLEKSIW, DANIEL PHILIP, former foreign service officer, consultant; b. Wilkes Barre, Pa., Feb. 5, 1921; s. Rev. Michael Nicholas and Maria Helena (von Kotzko) O.; m. Elizabeth Louise Hyatt, Aug. 21, 1948 (dec. 1990); children: Barbara Anne, Daniel Hyatt. BA, Pa. State U. 1940; student, Duke U.; postgrad., U. Mo., Princeton U., 1941-42; grad., Nat. War Coll., 1962. Reporter, editor small newspapers Mo. and Mich.; advt. copywriter Cleve.; info. specialist Civilian Prodn. Adminstrn., Washington, 1946-47; dep. chief press br. pub. rels. USAF Hdqrs., Washington, 1947, 48; pub. advt. newspapers Arlington and Alexandria, Va., 1948, 49; pub. rels. officer U.S. Mission for Aid to Turkey, 1949-50; attache Am. embassy, info. officer USIS, Ankara, 1951; press attache, chief info. officer Am. embassy, Cairo, 1952-55; 1st sec. Am. embassy, dep. pub. affairs officer USIS, Tehran, 1956-58; consul, pub. affairs officer consulate gen. Bombay, 1958-61; program coord. Africa USIA, 1962-63; dep. area dir. Africa, 1963-64, dir. media content, 1964-65; spl. asst. to permanent rep. U.S. mission to UN, 1966; area dir. for East Asia and Pacific USIA, 1966-70; minister-counselor pub. affairs Am. Embassy, New Delhi, 1970-73; dir. USIS, India; sr. faculty adviser Nat. War Coll., 1973; insp. gen. USIA, Washington, 1973-78; dir. ednl. programming Middle East Svcs., Washington, 1979-80; dir. Washington Export Info., Inc., 1980-89; program evaluation cons. Bur. Cultural and Ednl. Affairs, USIA, 1984-85; dir. Dan Oleksiw & Assocs., North Palm Beach, Fla.; cons. program evaluator Brit.-Am. Project Johns Hopkins U. Sch. Advanced Internat. Studies, 1986-95, Royal Inst. Internat. Affairs, Coun. for Internat. Devel. on Mercy Fund programs in Burkina Faso, Eselen Inst. San Francisco, 1988, U.S. Bus Leadership Exchange Program, USSR, 1988, Washington, 1987, Fgn. Svc. Inst., Dept. State, 1989-90. 2d lt. inf. AUS, 1942-45. Recipient Disting. Service award USIA, 1966. Roman Catholic. Home: 1208 Marine Way North Palm Beach FL 33408-6616

OLENDER, BEATRIJS TOBI, psychologist, marriage and family therapist; b. Wonosobo, Java, Dutch East Indies, July 30, 1941; came to U.S., 1966; d. Walther Frank Tobi and Ida (Leeuwe) Boehm; m. Irving William Olender, May 15, 1968; children: Derek Steven, Brian David. BA cum laude, Rijks U., Leiden, The Netherlands, 1961, MA cum laude, 1966; MA in Clin. Psychology, U. Mich., 1968, PhD Candidate, 1973. Lic. marriage, family and child counselor, Calif. Asst. Rijks U., Leiden, 1962-66, lectr., 1966; clin. intern U. Mich., Ann Arbor, 1966-68, 69-71, clin. teaching asst., 1971-73; staff psychologist Merced (Calif.) County Health Clinic, 1968-69; psychotherapy intern Midstream Counseling Ctr., Los Gatos, Calif., 1979-81; pvt. practice psychotherapy Los Gatos, 1981—. Bd. dirs. Santa Clara County Med. Soc. Aux., San Jose, 1976-78, ACLU Santa Clara County, San Jose, 1977-79; vol. dir., pres. bd. Parental Stress Hotline of Greater San Jose, 1976-79; bd. mem. San Jose Symphonic Choir, 1990—. Fulbright exch. grantee Inst. Internat. Edn., 1966; named Outstanding Vol. of Santa Clara County Vol. Action Ctr., San Jose, 1977; recipient Disting. Svc. award Santa Clara County Med. Soc. Aux., San Jose, 1978. Mem. Am. Assn. Marriage and Family Therapists (clin. mem.), Assn. Transpersonal Psychology, Assn. for Past-Life Rsch. and Therapies, Calif. Assn. Marriage and Family Therapists (clin. mem.). Avocations: music, theater, hiking. Office: 15810 Los Gatos Blvd Los Gatos CA 95032-3315

OLENDER, JACK HARVEY, lawyer; b. McKeesport, Pa., Sept. 8, 1935; m. Lovell Olender. BA, U. Pitts., 1957, JD, 1960; LLM, George Washington U., 1961. Bar: D.C. 1961, U.S. Supreme Ct. 1965, Md. 1966, Pa. 1985. Pvt. practice Washington, 1961-79; prin. Jack H. Olender & Assocs., P.C., Washington, 1979—. Contbr. articles to profl. jours. Active World

Peace through Law, Washington. Named to Hall of Fame Nat. Assn. Black Women Attys., 1987. Mem. Am. Bd. Profl. Liability Attys., Am. Coll. Trial Lawyers, Assn. Trial Lawyers Am., Inner Circle Advocates, Nat. Bd. Trial Advocacy, Internat. Acad. Trial Lawyers. Office: Jack H Olender & Assocs PC 1634 I St NW Fl 11 Washington DC 20006-4003

OLER, WESLEY MARION, III, physician, educator; b. N.Y.C., Mar. 8, 1918; s. Wesley Marion and Imogene (Rubel) O.; m. Virginia Carolyn Craemer, Dec. 8, 1951; children: Helen Louise (dec.), Wesley Marion IV, Stephen Scott. Grad., Phillips Andover Acad., 1936; AB, Yale U., 1940; MD, Columbia U., 1943. Intern Bellevue Hosp., N.Y.C., 1944; resident Bellevue Hosp., 1948-50; fellow Hosp. U. Pa., 1951; practice medicine specializing in internal medicine Washington, 1952-93; mem. emeritus staff, vice chmn. dept. medicine Washington Hosp. Ctr., 1962-64; v.p. med. bd. Washington Hosp. Center, 1971-72, trustee, 1973-81, emeritus, 1994; clin. prof. medicine emeritus Med. Sch. Georgetown U. Contbr. articles on old musical instruments to jours. Founder, past pres. Washington Recorder Soc.; bd. dirs. Am. Recorder Soc. Maj. M.C. U.S. Army (paratroops), 1944-47. Fellow ACP (gov. 1980-84); mem. Mensa, Osler Soc. Washington (past pres.), Met. Club, Cosmos Club, Chevy Chase Club. Republican. Episcopalian. Home: 8101 Connecticut Ave Apt 612N Chevy Chase MD 20815-2805

OLERUD, JOHN GARRETT, professional baseball player; b. Seattle, Aug. 5, 1968; s. John E. Olerud. Student, Washington State U. With Toronto Blue Jays, 1989—; mem. Am. League All-Star Team, 1993. Office: Toronto Blue Jays, 1 Blue Jay Way Ste 3200, Toronto, ON Canada MJV 1J1*

OLES, PAUL STEVENSON (STEVE OLES), architect, perspectivist, educator; b. San Antonio, Sept. 26, 1936; s. Paul Stevenson Sr. and Suda (Willis) O.; m. Carole Simmons, Oct. 11, 1963 (div. 1991); children: Brian Thomas, Julia Oles Carr; m. Susan Thompson, Sept. 26, 1992. BArch, Tex. Tech U., 1960; MArch, Yale U., 1963. Registered architect, Mass. Draftsman The Architects Collaborative, Cambridge, Mass., 1963-65, Cambridge Seven Assocs., Cambridge, 1965-67; architect MIT, Cambridge, 1968-70; prin. architect Interface Architects, Newton, Mass., 1971—; vis. faculty RISD, Providence, 1974-79; lectr. architecture Harvard Grad. Sch. Design, Cambridge, 1984-88, vis. scholar, 1989-91. Author: Architectural Illustration, 1979, Drawing the Future, 1988. Mem. vestry Episcopalian Ch. 1995—. Named Loeb fellow Harvard Grad. Sch. Design, 1982. Fellow AIA (inst. honor 1983, fellow 1989), Boston Soc. Architects, Am. Soc. Archtl. Perspectivists (founder, pres. 1986-90, bd. dirs. 1993—). Democrat. Avocations: music, painting, photography. Office: Interface Architects 1 Gateway Ctr Ste 501A Newton MA 02158-2882

OLESEN, DOUGLAS EUGENE, research institute executive; b. Tonasket, Wash., Jan. 12, 1939; s. Magnus and Esther Rae (Myers) O.; m. Michaele Ann Engdahl, Nov. 18, 1964; children: Douglas Eugene, Stephen Christian. B.S., U. Wash., 1962, M.S., 1963, postgrad., 1965-67, Ph.D., 1972. Research engr. space research div. Boeing Aircraft Co., Seattle, 1963-64; with Battelle Meml. Inst., Pacific NW Labs., Richland, Wash., 1967-84, mgr. water resources systems sect., water and land resources dept., 1970-71, mgr. dept., 1971-75, dep. dir. research labs., 1975, dir. research, 1975-79, v.p. inst., dir. NW div., 1979-84; exec. v.p., chief operating officer Battelle Meml. Inst., Columbus, Ohio, 1984-87, pres., chief exec. officer, 1987—. Patentee process and system for treating wast water. Trustees Capital Univ., Columbus Mus. of Art, Riverside Hosp., INROADS/Columbus Inc., Franklin County United Way; bd. dirs. Ohio State U. Found. Mem. Ohio C. of C. (trustee). Office: Battelle Meml Inst 505 King Ave Columbus OH 43201-2693

OLESKIEWICZ, FRANCIS STANLEY, retired insurance executive; b. Chicopee, Mass., Jan. 2, 1928; s. Francis and Agata (Gniady) O.; m. Ruth M. Ventrice, June 16, 1951; children—Francis H., Laurie. B.S., Am. Internat. Coll., Springfield, Mass., 1953; LL.B, Western New Eng. Coll., 1961. Bar: Mass. 1962. With Ins. Co. N.Am., Boston, 1953-67; property mgr. Employers-Comml. Union, Boston, 1967-69; pres., chmn. Lexington Ins. Co., Boston, 1969-86; v.p. Am. Internat. Group, N.Y.C., 1979-86; retired, 1986; limited sole practice law Framingham, Mass., 1986—; ins. arbitrator; chmn. bd. Risk Specialists Cos., Inc., Boston; vice chmn. Starr Assocs., N.Y.C., C.V. Starr & Co., Inc., Calif.; bd. dirs. Audubon Ins. Co., Baton Rouge, Union Atlantique d'Assurances S.A., Brussels; bd. trustees, mem. devel. com. We. New England Coll., Springfield, Mass., 1987—. Served as pfc. USMC, 1946-47, PTO. Mem. Mass. Bar Assn. (vol. law speaker, 1988—), Marine Corps League, Amvets, Am. Legion, Alpha Chi. Home: 19 Hickory Hill Ln Framingham MA 01701 also: 3328 Providence Plantation Ln Charlotte NC 28270-3719

OLESON, RAY JEROME, computer service company executive; b. Windom, Minn., June 20, 1944; s. Ray Jerome and Evah Oleson; m. Kathleen Ruth Johnson, July 2, 1966; children: Michelle Dawn, Carrie Elisabeth. BS in Math., Mankato State U., 1966; MS in Applied Stats., Villanova U., 1970. Mgr., dir. Sperry Univac, Egan, Minn., 1966-77; v.p. Computer Scis. Corp., Moorestown, N.J., 1977-84; from v.p. mktg. to pres. Systems and Applied Scis. Corp., Vienna, Va., 1984-87; pres. systems devel. and implementation div. CACI, Inc., Arlington, Va., 1987-90; pres., COO CACI Inc., Arlington, Ohio 1990—. Mem. Armed Forces Electronic and Comm. Assn. (pres. Phila. chpt. 1980-82), River Bend Country Club. Democrat. Lutheran. Avocations: golf, bridge, home computing. Home: 1312 Tulip Poplar Ln Vienna VA 22182-1340 Office: CACI 1100 N Glebe Rd Arlington VA 22201-4797

OLEXY, JEAN SHOFRANKO, English educator; b. Plymouth, Pa., Oct. 23, 1938; d. John Andrew and Elizabeth (Lawrence) Shofranko; m. Joseph P. Olexy Jr., Oct. 29, 1960; children: Lysbeth Olexy Kilcullen, Joseph P. Olexy III, Douglas L. Olexy. BA in English, Wilkes U., Wilkes-Barre, Pa., 1960; MEd in Teaching and Curriculum, Pa. State U., Harrisburg, 1992. Secondary English tchr. Wilkes-Barre (Pa.) City Schs., 1960-61, Brick Township Sch. Dist., Brick Town, N.J., 1964-66, Upper Merion Area Sch. Dist., King of Prussia, Pa., 1968—; lectr., cons. dept. fgn. langs. Šafarik U., Republic of Slovakia, 1992. Mem. Balch Inst. for Ethnic Studies, Phila., 1982-93; mem. N.E. Pa. Slovak Heritage Soc., Wilkes-Barre, Pa., 1982-94; sec. Valley Forge-Exch. Club, King of Prussia, Pa., 1985-89; bd. dirs. Francisvale Home for Smaller Animals, Wayne, Pa., 1987-88. Named Outstanding Educator of Yr. Beta Pi Chpt. Delta Kappa Gamma, King of Prussia, Pa., 1988; Nat. Faculty Acad. fellow Pa. State U., 1993. Mem. NEA, ASCD, Nat. Coun. Tchrs. English, Pa. Edn. Assn., N.E. Pa. Slovak Heritage Soc., Upper Merion Edn. Assn., Delta Kappa Gamma (pres. Beta Pi chpt. 1994-96). Lutheran. Avocations: music, reading, gardening, genealogy research, handcrafts. Home: 382 Maiden Ln King of Prussia PA 19406 Office: Upper Merion Area Sch Dist Crossfield Rd King Of Prussia PA 19406

OLIAN, JOANNE CONSTANCE, curator, art historian; b. N.Y.C., d. Richard Edward and Dorothy (Singer) Wahrman; m. Howard Olian; children: Jane Wendy, Patricia Ann. Student, Syracuse U.; BA, Hofstra U., 1969; MA, NYU/Inst. Fine Arts, 1972. Grad. internship Met. Mus., N.Y.C., 1973; asst. curator Mus. of City of N.Y., 1974, curator costume collection, 1975-91; cons. curator Costume Collection, 1992—; lectr. Parsons Sch. Design; vis. lectr. Musée des Arts Decoratifs, Paris, summer 1983, 84, 85. Author: The House of Worth: The Gilded Age, 1860-1918, 1982; editor: Authentic French Fashions of the Twenties, 1990, Everyday Fashions of the Forties, 1992, Children's Fashions from Mode Illustre 1860-1912, 1994; contbr. articles to profl. jours., chpts. to books. Mem. Internat. Council Mus. (costume com.), Costume Soc. Am. (dir. 1976-79, 83-86), Fashion Group (bd. dirs. 1985-86), Centre Internat. d'Etude des Textiles Anciens. Club: Cosmopolitan (N.Y.). Home: Shepherds Ln Port Washington NY 11050 Office: Mus City NY 1220 5th Ave New York NY 10029

OLIAN, ROBERT MARTIN, lawyer; b. Cleve., June 14, 1953; s. Robert Meade and Doris Isa (Hessing) O.; m. Terri Ellen Ruther, Aug. 10, 1980; children: Andrew Zachary, Alix Michelle, Joshua Brett. AB, Harvard U., 1973, JD, M in Pub. Policy, 1977. Bar: Ill. 1977, U.S. Dist. Ct. (no. dist.) Ill. 1977, U.S. Ct. Appeals (7th cir.) 1983, U.S. Dist. Ct. (no dist. trial bar) Ill. 1992, U.S. Dist. Ct. (we. dist.) Mich. 1994. Assoc. Sidley & Austin, Chgo., 1977-84, ptnr., 1985—. Editor: Illinois Environmental Law Handbook, 1988. Panel atty. Chgo. Vol. Legal Services, Chgo., 1983—; mem. regional strategic planning/mktg. com. Alexian Bros. Ill. Inc., Elk

Grove, 1985-88; trustee North Shore Congregation Israel, 1990—. Mem. ABA, Chgo. Bar Assn., Ill. Assn. Environ. Profls. (bd. dirs. 1984-85), Standard Club, Harvard Club (Chgo.). Jewish. Home: 85 Oakmont Rd Highland Park IL 60035-4111 Office: Sidley & Austin 1 First Nat Plz Chicago IL 60603

OLIANSKY, JOEL, author, director; b. N.Y.C., Oct. 11, 1935; s. Albert and Florence (Shaw) O.; children: Ingrid, Adam. M.F.A., Yale, 1962; B.A., Hofstra U., Hempstead, N.Y., 1959. Playwright-in-residence Yale, 1962-64; co-founder Hartford Stage Co., 1963; writer Universal Studios, 1974—. Author: Shame, Shame on the Johnson Boys!, 1966; writer, dir.: The Competition, 1980, The Silence at Bethany, 1987, Birds, 1988. Recipient Emmy award, 1971, Humanitas prize, 1975, Writers Guild award 1975. *I have, I think, used less than 1 percent of my talent. If I have achieved anything, it is because others have used even less of theirs.*

OLICK, ARTHUR SEYMOUR, lawyer; b. N.Y.C., June 15, 1931; s. Jack and Anita (Babsky) O.; m. Selma Ada Kaufman, June 27, 1954; children: Robert Scott, Karen Leslie. B.A., Yale U., 1952, LL.B., J.D., 1955. Bar: N.Y. 1956. Asst. instr. polit sci. Yale U., New Haven, Conn., 1953-55; instr. polit. sci.-bus. law U. Ga., 1955-57; assoc. atty. Casey, Lane & Mittendorf, N.Y.C., 1957-62; asst. U.S. atty. So. Dist. N.Y., 1962-68; chief civil div., 1965-68; partner Otterbourg, Steindler, Houston & Rosen, N.Y.C., 1968-71, Kreindler, Relkin, Olick & Goldberg, N.Y.C., 1971-74; officer, dir. Anderson, Kill Olick & Oshinsky, P.C. and predecessor firms, N.Y.C., 1974—; ptnr. Anderson, Kill, Olick & Oshinsky and predecessor firms, Washington, 1979—; ptnr. Anderson, Kill, Olick & Oshinsky, Phila., 1990—, Newark, 1991—, San Francisco, 1992—, Phila., 1994—, Phoenix, 1994—, New Haven, Conn., 1994—; lectr. Practicing Law Inst., N.Y.C., 1965—, Bklyn. Bar Assn., Comml. Law League, Nat. Jud. Coll.; lectr., CLE instr. Fordham Law Sch.; candidate N.Y. State Supreme Ct., 1971; counsel Tarrytown (N.Y.) Urban Renewal Agy., 1968-73, 75-77; town atty., Greenburgh, N.Y., 1974; spl. counsel, Town of New Castle, N.Y., 1979—; village atty., Tarrytown, N.Y., 1968-73, 75-77, Dobbs Ferry, N.Y., 1975-77, North Tarrytown, N.Y., 1978-81; dir. Westchester County (N.Y.) Legal Aid Soc., 1976-79. Pres. Hartsdale (N.Y.) Bd. Edn., 1968-72; bd. dirs. Westchester County Mcpl. Planning Fedn., 1976-78, Circle in the Sq. Theater, 1978—; trustee Calhoun Sch., N.Y.C., 1973-80. Served with U.S. Army, 1955-57. Fellow Am. Bankruptcy Coll.; mem. ABA (bus. bankruptcy com., chmn. sect. subcom., ad hoc com. on partnerships in bankruptcy), Am. Bar Found., N.Y. State Bar Assn., Assn. of Bar of City of N.Y. (com. on profl. responsibility), Fed. Bar Coun., Am. Arbitration Assn. (nat. panel arbitrators), Am. Law Inst., Bklyn. Soc. for Prevention Cruelty to Children (bd. dirs. 1994—), Yale Club, Merchants Club (N.Y.C.), Nat. Lawyers Club (Washington), Rockefeller Ctr. Club, Phi Beta Kappa. Home: 300 E 54th St New York NY 10022-5018 also: Lake Oscawana 7 Wildwood Ln Putnam Valley NY 10579 Office: 1251 Ave of the Americas New York NY 10020 also: 2000 Pennsylvania Ave NW Washington DC 20006-1812

OLICK, PHILIP STEWART, lawyer; b. N.Y.C., Oct. 2, 1936; s. Jack and Anita (Babsky) O.; m. Alice D. Chait, Mar. 25, 1961; children: Jonathan A., Jeffrey K., Diana M. B.A., Columbia U., 1957; LL.B., NYU, 1960. Bar: N.Y. 1961, Mo. 1966. Ptnr. Benjamin, Galton, Robbins & Flato, N.Y.C., 1961-65; gen. counsel, v.p., sec. Nat. Bellas Hess, Inc., Kansas City, Mo., 1965-69; dir. Nat. Bellas Hess, Inc., 1970-76; ptnr. Burke & Burke, N.Y.C., 1970-73, Townley & Updike, 1973-89, Moses & Singer, 1989—; bd. arbitrators N.Y. Stock Exch. Bd. dirs. Univ. Glee Club N.Y.C.; bd. dirs.; counsel Found. Interventional Cardiology, Inc., N.Y.C. With AUS, 1960-61. Mem. N.Y. Bar Assn., Assn. of Bar of City of N.Y., Univ. Club (N.Y.C.), Columbia Club. Home: 941 Park Ave New York NY 10028-0318 Office: 1301 Avenue Of The Americas New York NY 10019-6022 also: 4 Rosebud Ln East Quogue NY 11942-3627

OLIENSIS, SHELDON, lawyer; b. Phila., Mar. 19, 1922. AB with honors, U. Pa., 1943; LLB magna cum laude, Harvard U., 1948. Bar: N.Y. State 1949. With Kaye Scholer Fierman Hays & Handler, N.Y.C., 1960—; chair N.Y.C. Conflicts of Interest Bd., 1990—. Pres.: Harvard Law Rev., 1948. Trustee Harvard Law Sch. Assn., 1973-77, 1st v.p., 1980-82, pres., 1982-84, trustee, N.Y.C., 1962-65, v.p., 1972-73, pres., 1978-79; nat. chmn. Harvard Law Sch. Fund, 1973-75; mem. Harvard U. overseers com. to visit law sch., 1981-87; spl. master appellate divsn. 1st dept. N.Y. State Supreme Ct., 1983-89, 91—; bd. dirs. Legal Aid Soc., 1969-88, pres. 1973-75; vice chmn. N.Y.C. Cultural Coun., 1968-75; bd. dirs. Cultural Coun. Found., 1968-88, pres. 1968-72, v.p., 1972-82; bd. dirs. Park Assn. N.Y.C., Inc., 1963-73, exec. com., 1967-73, pres., 1965-67; bd. dirs. Gateway Sch. N.Y.C., 1968-83, chmn. bd. trustees, 1968-70; dir. officer Wiltwyck Sch. for Boys, Inc., 1951-71; bd. dirs. East Harlem Tutorial Program, 1972-80, Fund for Modern Cts., 1979-91, N.Y. Lawyers for Pub. Interest, 1980-85, 91-94; bd. dirs. Vols. of Legal Svc. Inc., pres., 1984-87; trustee Lawyers' Com. for Civil Rights Under Law, 1978-91. Fellow Am. Coll. Trial Lawyers; mem. N.Y. State Bar Assn., N.Y. County Lawyers Assn., Assn. of Bar of City of N.Y. (exec. com. 1961-65, v.p. 1974-75, 86-87, pres. 1988-90, chmn. com. state legis. 1959-61, com. revision of constn. and by-laws 1965-66, com. electric power and environ. 1971-74, com. on grievances 1975-78, com. on access to legal svcs. 1982-87, com. on free disputes and concilliation 1987-89, nominating com. 1991, Task Force on N.Y. State Constn. Conv. 1994—). Office: Kaye Scholer Fierman et al 425 Park Ave New York NY 10022-3506

OLIKER, DAVID WILLIAM, healthcare management administrator; b. Elkins, W.Va., Mar. 29, 1948; married; 3 children. BA in Sociology and Anthropology, East Carolina U., 1970; MA in Social Anthropology, Am. U., 1973; Cert. in Healthcare Adminstrn., George Washington U., 1977. Health svcs. specialist United Mine Workers Am. Health and Retirement Funds, 1976-78; health planner Health Sys. Agy. Western Md., Cumberland, 1978-79; ops. mgr. Md.-Individual Practice Assn., Inc., Rockville, 1979-81; project dir. N.Y. Health Maintenance Plan, Inc., N.Y.C., 1981-82; pres., CEO MVP Health Plan, Schenectady, N.Y., 1982—. Mem. APHA, Am. Managed Care and Res. Assn., N.Y. State HMO Conf. (bd. dirs.), Nat. Managed Care Inc. (bd. dirs.). Office: MVP Health Plan 111 Liberty St Schenectady NY 12305

OLIKER, VLADIMIR, mathematician, educator; b. Ulianovsk, Russia, Oct. 7, 1945; came to U.S. 1975, naturalized 1980; s. Yosef and Sonia (Bakelman) O.; m. Elena Matis, Mar. 20, 1969; children—Olga, Aviva, Josef Matis. M.S., Leningrad U., Russia, 1967; Ph.D., Leningrad U., 1971. Sr. researcher Hydrometeorological Inst., Leningrad, Russia, 1970-72; group leader Dept. Transportation, 1972-74; vis. prof. Temple U., Phila., 1975-77; assoc. prof. to prof. U. Iowa, Iowa City, 1977-80, 80-84; prof. math. Emory U., Atlanta, 1984—; vis. mem. Math Scis. Research Inst., Berkeley, Calif., 1983; vis. prof. U. Florence, Italy, 1983, Technische U., Berlin, 1982, U. Heidelberg, Fed. Republic Germany, 1981. Contbr. articles to profl. jours. Jewish. Home: 1565 Adelia Pl Atlanta GA 30329 Office: Emory U Dept Math and Computer Sci Atlanta GA 30322

OLIM, AUGUST SOUZA, counselor; b. Honolulu, Aug. 11, 1940; s. Frank Souza and Hilda Lucy (Leong) O; m. Sharon Jean Warren, Dec. 28, 1963; children: Warren Kalani Olim, Tamera Meilani Olim. BA, U. N. Colo., 1958-63; MS, Pepperdine U., 1973-75. Cert. Exceptional Children (Life), Educable Mentally Retarded Gen. Elem. (Life), Pupil Pers. Ryan Adminstrn. Clear, Learning Handicapped. Tchr. Educable Mentally Retarded Centennial Intermediate, Norwalk-LaMirada, Calif., 1963-65, Walton Intermediate, Garden Grove, Calif., 1965-67; tchr. Learning Handicapped Ralston Intermediate, Garden Grove, Calif., 1967-70; tchr. Learning Disability Group Chapman Jr. High Sch., Garden Grove, Calif., 1970-74, 9th grade English tchr., 1974-76, 7th, 8th, 9th grade counselor, 1976-81; project facilitator Clinton Elem. Sch., Garden Grove, Calif., 1981-84; counselor, co-adminstr. Lake Continuation High Sch., Garden Grove, Calif., 1984-95; prin. Cook Elem., Jordan Spl. Edn., Garden Grove, Calif., 1988, Lincoln Adult Edn. Ctr., Garden Grove, Calif., 1992; pres. Coun. for Exceptional Children, Orange County, Calif. 1976-80; regional dir. Pacific Am. Concerns HEW, Wash., 1977-81; treas. Asian/Pac/Islander Nat. Edn. Assn., Wash., 1977-81; v.p. Very Spl. Arts, So. Calif., 1989-90. Dir. Jr. Miss Pageant Fountain Valley (Calif.) Jaycees, 1970-72; treas., v.p. Fountain Valley (Calif.) Jaycees, 1972-74; state dir. Calif. Jaycees, 1975; dir. Jr. Miss Inc. Dist. Eight Jaycees Orange County, Calif., 1976; sch. bd. Speech Lang. Ctr., Buena Park, 1993—; bd. Crippled Children Soc. Orange County, 1995—. Recipient Life Hon. PTA Lampson, Garden Grove, Calif., 1967, Spoke award Fountain

Valley (Calif.) Jaycees, 1972; named Outstanding State Dir. Calif. Jaycees, 1976, Outstanding Bd. Mem. Asian Pacific Islander Dirs., HI, 1979. Mem. Calif. State Fedn. Coun. for Exceptional Children (mem. ethnic and multicultural concerns com.), Garden Grove Pupil Pers. Assn., Very Spl. Arts Calif., Spl. Olympics Beauty Pageant, Minority Affairs Commn. Nat. Edn. Assn., Interagy. for Legis. of Spl. Edn., Phi Delta Kappa. Roman Catholic. Avocations: music, tennis, cooking, gardening. Home: 9432 Flicker Ave Fountain Valley CA 92708

OLIN, KEN, actor; b. Evanston, Ill., July 30, 1955; m. Patricia Wettig, 1982; children: Clifford, Roxanne. Student, Putney Sch., Vt.; degree in English Lit., U. Pa.; studies with Warren Robertson, Stella Adler. Actor: (TV movies) Women at West Point, 1979, Flight 90: Disaster on the Potomac, 1984, There Must be a Pony, 1986, Tonight's the Night, 1987, A Stoning in Fulham County, 1988, Goodnight Sweet Wife: A Murder in Boston, 1990, Telling Secrets, 1993, Nothing But the Truth, 1995; (TV series) Bay City Blues, 1983, Hill Street Blues, 1984-85, Falcon Crest, 1985-86, thirtysomething, 1987-91; (films) Ghost Story, 1981, Queen's Logic, 1991; dir. TV films: The Broken Cord, 1992, Doing Time On Maple Drive, 1992, White Fang 2: Myth of the White Wolf, 1994. Avocations: spending time with family, basketball, baseball, distance running, weightlifting. Office: UTA 9560 Wilshire Blvd 5th fl Beverly Hills CA 90212*

OLIN, KENT OLIVER, banker; b. Chgo., July 27, 1930; s. Oliver Arthur and Beatrice Louise (Thompson) O.; m. Marilyn Louise Wood, Sept. 4, 1956. BS in Econs., Ripon Coll., 1955. Dist. sales rep. Speed Queen Corp., Ripon, Wis., 1955-57; v.p. United Bank, Denver, 1957-71; exec. v.p., pres. Bank One Boulder (formerly Affiliated First Nat. Bank), Boulder, Colo., 1971-74; pres., CEO Bank One Colo. Springs, Colorado Springs, 1974-86; pres., CEO Bank One Colo. (formerly Affiliated Bankshares of Colo.), Denver, 1986-91, vice chmn. bd., 1992-94, also bd. dirs. Trustee Colo. Coll., Colorado Springs, 1983-89, Falcon Found., Colorado Springs, 1983—, El Pomar Found., Colorado Springs, 1992—, Colorado Springs Fine Arts Ctr., 1992—; sec.-treas. Air Force Acad. Found., Colorado Springs, 1988; bd. dirs. Rocky Mountain Arthritis Found., Denver, 1989-94, Goodwill Industries, Colorado Springs, 1994. Staff sgt. USAF, 1950-54. Mem. Broadmoor Golf Club (dir. 1975-88, 93—). Office: El Pomar Found 10 Lake Cir Colorado Springs CO 80906

OLIN, LENA MARIA JONNA, actress; b. Stockholm, Mar. 22, 1955; d. Britta Alice Holmberg; 1 child, August. Actress Royal Dramatic Theatre, Stockholm, Bklyn. Acad. Music; performances include (theater) The Alchemist, Paradisbarnen, Juno and the Peacock, Gross and Klein, Servitore Di Due Padrone, Restoration, King Lear, Nattvarden, Summer, A Dream Play, The Master and Margerita, Miss Julie; (films) The Adventures of Picasso, 1978, Karleken, 1980, Fanny and Alexander, 1982, Grasanklingar, 1982, After the Rehersal, 1984, Friends, 1987, The Unbearable Lightness of Being, 1988, Enemies, A Love Story, 1989, Havana, 1990, Mr. Jones, 1993, Romeo is Bleeding, 1994. Office: care ICM/Martha Luttrell 8942 Wilshire Blvd Beverly Hills CA 90211*

OLIN, ROBERT FLOYD, mathematics educator and reseacher; b. Evanston, Ill., Oct. 8, 1948; s. Floyd Thomas and Anne Elanor (Knutson) O.; m. Linda Renee King, Aug. 23, 1969; children: Kristopher Robert, Susan Michelle. BSc, Ottawa U., 1970; PhD, Ind. U., 1975. Asst. prof. math. Va. Poly. Inst. and State U., Blacksburg, 1975-80, assoc. prof., 1980-87, prof., 1987—, dept. head, 1994—; vis. assoc. prof. Ind. U., Bloomington, 1985; rschr. NSF, 1975-94, grad. chmn., 1993-94; chmn. rsch. commn., 1993-94. Co-author: A Functional Calculus for Subnormal Operators II, 1977, Subnormal Operators, and Representations of Bounded Analytic Functions and Other Uniform Algebras, 1985. Pres. Southwestern Va. Soccer Assn., Blacksburg, 1989-90; tchr. Sunday Sch. Blacksburg Bapt. Ch., 1983—; treas. Margaret Beeks PTA, 1993-95; chmn. steering com. Southeastern Analysis Meeting, 1984—. Named Hon. Faculty Mem., Sichuan U., Chengdu, China, 1988; recipient cert. Math. Edn. Devel. Ctr., Ind. U., Bloomington, 1976. Mem. N.Y. Acad. of Scis., Va. Acad. Scis., Am. Math. Soc., Math. Assn. of Am., Sigma Xi, Pi Mu Epsilon. Avocations: racquetball, cooking, computers, soccer. Home: 707 Draper Rd SW Blacksburg VA 24060-4654 Office: Va Poly Inst and State U Math Dept Blacksburg VA 24061

OLIN, WILLIAM HAROLD, orthodontist, educator; b. Menominee, Mich., Mar. 7, 1924; s. Harold H. and Lillian (Hallgren) O.; m. Bertha Spitters, May 6, 1950; children—William Harold, Paul Scott, Jon Edward. D.D.S., Marquette U., 1947; M.S. U. Iowa, 1948. Asst. prof. orthodontics Univ. Hosps., U. Iowa, Iowa City, 1948, assoc. prof., 1963-70, prof., 1970-93; prof. emeritus, 1993; dir. Hills Bank, Iowa. Author: Cleft Lip and Palate Rehabilitation, 1960; contbr. articles on treatment of craniofacial deformities to profl. jours. Served to capt. U.S. Army, 1952-54. Mem. Angle Orthodontic Soc. Midwest (pres. 1982), Midwest Orthodontic Soc. (pres. 1968-69), Iowa Orthodontic Soc. (pres. 1959), Am. Cleft Palate Assn. (pres. 1970), Am. Acad. for Sports Dentistry (bd. dirs., sec./treas. 1989—). Republican. Methodist. Club: Univ. Athletic (bd. dirs.) (Iowa City). Lodge: Rotary (Iowa City). Avocations: coins, antique music boxes, sports, travel, political memorabilia. Home: 426 Mahaska Dr Iowa City IA 52246-1610 Office: University Hospitals Iowa City IA 52242

OLINGER, GLENN SLOCUM, entrepreneur, consultant, investor; b. New Castle, Ind., May 3, 1929; s. Glenn Arthur and Eva Lillian (Slocum) O.; m. Phyllis Lucille Roper, July 6, 1949 (div. Oct. 1981); children: Deborah Sue, Glenn Alan, Craig William, Gwen Gay; m. Diana Sue Hurst, Oct. 2, 1972. B.S., U. Chattanooga, 1952; M.B.A., Northwestern U., 1955. Various sales and gen. mgmt. positions Gen. Electric, Louisville, 1955-75; pres. Speed Queen Corp., Ripon, Wis, 1975-79; gen. mgr. Major Appliance Internat. div. Gen. Electric, Louisville, 1979-82; pres. Kitchen Aid Inc., Troy, Ohio, 1982-87; v.p. Whirlpool Corp., Benton Harbor, Mich., 1986-87; v.p. MII Inc., pres. Lundia Div., 1987-91; pres. Olinger Enterprises, Inc., 1991—. Trustee Ripon Coll., 1976-79; trustee Dayton Art Inst., 1984-85. Served with USN, 1946-49, 52-53. Northwestern U. scholar, 1954. Mem. Am. Mktg. Assn., Am. Mgmt. Assn., Mfrs. Agts. Nat. Assn., Jacksonville C. of C., Mensa, Masons, Rotary. Republican. Presbyterian. Avocations: golf; tennis; travel; reading. Home: 12 Westgate Cir Jacksonville IL 62650 Office: Olinger Enterprises Inc PO Box 947 Jacksonville IL 62651

OLINGER, SHEFF DANIEL, neurologist, educator; b. Olinger, Va., Oct. 23, 1930; s. Sheff Daniel and Ada Sue O.; m. Norma Lanier, June 25, 1953; children: Nancy, Sheff D. III, Amy. BS Va. Mil. Inst., 1949; MD, U. Va., 1953. Diplomate Am. Bd. Psychiatry and Neurology. Intern Tripler Army Hosp., Honolulu, 1953-54; resident in neurology U. Mich., Ann Arbor, 1956-59, clin. instr., 1958-59; instr. Southwestern Med. Sch., Dallas, 1960-82, assoc. prof. neurology, 1982—; pvt. practice in neurology Dallas, 1959-72; dir. dept. neurology Baylor U. Med. Ctr., Dallas, 1972-90, dir. stroke unit and EEG dept., 1972-90; cons. Presbyn. Hosp., Dallas, 1960—, Parkland Hosp., Dallas, 1960—, Timberlawn Psychiatric Hosp., 1960-90, also U.S. Dept. Labor, Dallas Mil. Entrance Processing Sta. Contbr. articles to profl. jours. Fellow Am. Acad. Neurology; mem. AMA, Tex. Med. Assn., Tex. Neurol. Soc. (founding pres. 1975), Dallas County Med. Soc., Dallas So. Clin. Soc. Home: 3564 Colgate Ave Dallas TX 75225

OLINS, ROBERT ABBOT, communications research executive; b. Cambridge, Mass., Sept. 25, 1942; s. Harry and Janice Olins; m. Irma Westrich, June 16, 1967; 1 son, Matthew Abbott. Student, Hobart Coll., 1961-62, San Francisco Art Inst., 1962; B.A. U. Mass., 1967; postgrad., U. Tampa, 1968; MA, U. Mo., 1969, PhD, 1972. With Marsteller, 1972, N.W. Ayer, 1972, Post, Keys & Gardner, Chgo., 1973; with Young & Rubicam, Chgo., 1973-76, mng. dir. communications research div., 1976-77; pres., chief exec. officer, subs. Communications Research Inc., Chgo., 1978—; owner, chmn. Communications Research Inc., 1979—; pres., chief exec. officer Insights, Chgo., 1976—. Contbr. articles to profl. jours. Recipient Chgo./4 award for creative excellence, 1974; overall winner Chgo. Mackinac race, 1981; Am. Assn. Advt. Agys. grantee, 1968-71. Mem. Am. Mktg. Assn., Lake Michigan Yachting Assn. U.S. Yacht Racing Union, Chgo. Yacht Club, Skyline Club. Avocations: skiing, sailing. Office: Communications Rsch Inc 233 E Wacker Dr Apt 2105 Chicago IL 60601-5110

OLIPHANT, BETTY, ballet school director; b. London, Eng., Aug. 5, 1918. Studied classical ballet under Tamara Karsavina and Laurent

Novikoff; student, Queen's and St. Mary's Colls.; LLD (hon.), Queen's U., 1978, Brock U., 1978, U. Toronto., 1980; DLitt, York U., 1992. Prin. dancer and arranger Prince & Emile Littler Prodns., London, 1936-46; dance arranger Howard & Wyndham, London, 1936-46; tchr. ballet London, 1936-40; dancer, dance arranger and ballet mistress Blue Pencils Concert Party, Eng., 1944-46; tchr. ballet Oliphant Sch., Toronto, Can., 1948-59; ballet mistress Nat. Ballet of Can., Toronto, 1951-62; prin. and dir. Nat. Ballet Sch., 1959; asso. artistic dir. Nat. Ballet of Can., 1969-75, artistic dir., 1975-89; founder Nat. Ballet Sch., 1991—; founder reorganized Ballet Sch. of Royal Swedish Opera, 1967, Royal Danish Theatre, 1978; mem. jury Internat. Ballet Competition, Moscow, 1977-81, III Internat. Ballet Competition, Jackson, MIss., 1986. Contbr. articles on dance and teaching to profl. publs. Decorated officer Order of Can., 1972, Companion Order of Can., 1985; recipient Centennial medal, 1967, Molson prize, 1978, Diplome d'Honneur Can. Conf. Arts, 1982, Lifetime Achievement award, Toronto Arts Awards Found., 1989, Order of Napoleon, France, 1990, Commemorative medal 125th Anniversary Can., 1992; fellow Ont. Inst. for Studies in Edn., 1985. Fellow Imperial Soc. Tchrs. of Dancing (examiner), Ont. Inst. Studies in Edn., 1985; mem. Can. Dance Tchrs. Assn. (founder, past pres.), Internat. Soc. of Tchrs. of Dancing, Can. Assn. Profl. Dance Orgns. (founding mem.). Office: Nat Ballet Sch, 105 Maitland St, Toronto, ON Canada M4Y 1E4

OLIPHANT, PATRICK, editorial cartoonist; b. Adelaide, Australia, July 24, 1935; came to U.S., 1964; s. Donald Knox and Grace Lillian (Price) O.; m. Hendrika De Vries, Jan. 11, 1958 (div. 1978); children: Laura Maria, Grant, Susan; m. Mary Ann Kuhn, Aug. 20, 1983 (div. 1994). L.H.D. (hon.), Dartmouth Coll., 1981. Copyboy, press artist Adelaide Advertiser, 1953-55, editorial cartoonist, 1955-64; world tour to study cartooning techniques, 1959; editorial cartoonist Denver Post, 1964-75, Washington Star, 1975-81, L.A. Times Syndicate, 1965-80, Universal Press Syndicate, 1980—; represented by Susan Conway Gallery, Washington. Author: The Oliphant Book, 1969, Four More Years, 1973, An Informal Gathering, 1978, Oliphant! A Cartoon Collection, 1980, The Jellybean Society, 1981, Ban this Book, 1982, But Seriously Folks, 1983, The Year of Living Perilously, 1984, Make My Day, 1985, Between a Rock and a Hard Place, 1986, Up to There in Alligators, 1987, Nothing Basically Wrong, 1988, What Those People Need Is A Puppy, 1989, Fashions for the New World Order, 1991, Just Say No, 1992, Why Do I Feel Uneasy?, 1993, Waiting for the Other Shoe to Drop, 1994. Recipient 2d place award as funniest cartoonist Internat. Fedn. Free Journalists in Fleet Street, London, 1958; 2d place award internat. cartoon competition Calif. Newspapers Pubs. Assn., 1960; Profl. Journalism award Sigma Delta Chi, 1966; Pulitzer prize for editorial cartooning, 1967; Cartoonist of Yr. award Nat. Cartoonist Soc., 1968, 72; Best in Bus. award Washington Journalism Rev., 1985, 87. Office: Universal Press Syndicate 4900 Main St 9 Kansas City MO 64112 also: care Susan Conway Gallery 1214 30th St NW Washington DC 20007

OLITSKI, JULES, artist; b. Snovsk, USSR, Mar. 27, 1922; came to U.S., 1923, naturalized, 1943; s. Jevel and Anna (Zarnitsky) Demikovsky; m. Gladys Katz, 1944 (div. 1951); 1 dau., Eve; m. Andrea Hill Pearce, Jan. 21, 1956 (div. 1974); 1 dau., Lauren; m. Kristina Gorby, Feb. 29, 1980. Student, Academie de la Grande Chaumiere, Paris, 1949-50; BA, NYU, 1952, MA, 1954; postgrad., Beaux Arts Inst., N.Y.C., 1940-42, Nat. Acad. Design, N.Y.C., 1947, Zadkine Sch. Sculpture, Paris, 1949. Assoc. prof. art SUNY, New Paltz, N.Y., 1954-55; curator Art Edn. Gallery, NYU, 1955-56; chmn. fine arts div. C.W. Post Coll. L.I. U., Greenvale, N.Y., 1956-63; tchr. Bennington Coll., 1963-67. Exhibited in many one-man shows including Galerie Huit, Paris, 1951, Iolas Gallery, N.Y.C., 1958, French & Co., N.Y.C., 1959-61, Poindexter Gallery, N.Y.C., 1961-68, Bennington (Vt.) Coll., 1962, Kasmin, Ltd., London, 1964-75, 89, Galerie Lawrence, Paris, 1964, David Mirvish Gallery, Toronto, Ont., Can., 1964-78, Nicholas Wilder, L.A., 1966, Corcoran Gallery, Washington, 1967, 74, Am. Pavillion, Venice Biennale Art Exhbn., 1966, 88, Andre Emmerich Gallery, N.Y.C., 1966-89, Zurich, Switzerland, 1973-78, Met. Mus. Art, N.Y.C., 1969, Inst. Contemporary Art, U. Pa., 1968, 86, Lawrence Rubin Gallery, N.Y.C., 1969, 71, 72, 73, Knoedler Contemporary Art, 1973-77, 79, 81, 83, 85, 87, Dart Gallery, Chgo., 1975, FIAL, Paris, 1976, Berlinische Galerie, 1977, Downstairs Gallery, Edmonton, Can., 1980, 82, Janus Gallery, L.A., 1981, Gallery One, Toronto, 1980-90, Yares Gallery, Scottsdale, Ariz., 1986-89, Galerie Wentzel, Hamburg and Cologne, Fed. Republic Germany, 1975, 77, 81, 89, Mus. Fine Arts, Boston, 1973, 77, Whitney Mus. Am. Art, 1973, Galleria Dell'Ariete, Italy, 1974, Corcoran Gallery Art, 1974-76, Waddington Gallery, London, 1975, Galerie Templon, Paris, 1984-85, Hirshhorn Mus., Washington, 1977, Edmonton (Alta., Can.) Art Gallery, 1979, Martha White Gallery, Louisville, 1982, Harcus/Krakow Gallery, Boston, 1978, 81, 82, Harcus Gallery, Boston, 1984, 86, Meredith Long, Houston, 1981, 82, 87, 90, (retrospective) Fondation du Chateau de Jau, Perpignon, France, 1984, La Musee de Valence, France, 1985, Hokin Gallery, Palm Beach, Fla., 1988, Associated Am. Artists, N.Y.C., 1989, (retrospective) Buschlen/Mowatt Gallery, Vancouver, B.C., Can., 1990, Salander-O'Reilly Galleries, N.Y.C., 1990, 92, 94, Gallery Camino Real, Boca Raton, Fla., 1987, 88, 90, 92, 94, Thorne-Sagendorf Art Gallery, Keene, N.H., 1993, Long Fine Arts, N.Y.C., 1994; exhibited in many group shows including Carnegie Internat., Pitts., 1961, 1965, Washington Gallery Modern Art, 1963, Los Angeles County Mus., 1964, Fogg Art Mus. Harvard, 1965, Pasadena Art Mus., 1965, Mus. Basel, Switzerland, 1965, 74, Whitney Mus. Am. Art, 1972, 73, Musée d'Art Contemporain, Montreal, 1973, Hirshhorn Mus., 1974, Corcoran Gallery Art, 1975, Everson Mus. Art, Syracuse, N.Y., 1976, Bass Mus., Miami, Am. Embassy, Madrid, 1984, Ft. Worth Art Mus., Mus. Art, Ft. Lauderdale, 1986, Joseloff Gallery, Hartford, Conn., 1994; represented in permanent collections including Mus. Modern Art, N.Y.C., Art Inst. Chgo., Whitney Mus., Corcoran Art Gallery, Nat. Gallery Can., Met. Mus. Art, N.Y.C., Bklyn. Mus., Hirshhorn Mus., Washington, Everson Mus. Art, Syracuse, N.Y., Mus. Fine Arts, Boston, Norman MacKensie Art Gallery, Regina, Can., also pvt. collections; subject book Jules Olitski by Kenworth Moffett, 1981, Nat. Acad. Design, N.Y., 1993. Recipient 2d prize Carnegie Internat. 1961, 1st prize Corcoran Biennial, Washington, 1967, Award for Distinction in the Arts Univ Union, U. S.C., 1975, The Milton and Sally Avery Disting. Professorship, Bard Coll., 1987; named Assoc. Nat. Academician Nat. Acad. of Design, 1993. Fellow AAAS, Nat. Acad. Arts and Scis. Office: PO Box 440 Marlboro VT 05344

OLIVA, TERENCE ANTHONY, marketing educator; b. Rochester, N.Y., Feb. 21, 1943; s. Anthony J. and Teresa (Savasta) O.; m. Diana Day, Jan. 15, 1981; children: Mark, Andrea. BA in Math. and Art, St. Mary's Coll., Calif., 1964; MBA with distinction, Fresno State U., 1971; PhD, U. Ala., 1974. Assoc. prof. mgmt. La. State U., Baton Rouge, 1974-82; vis. assoc. mktg. Columbia U., N.Y.C., 1982-83; assoc. prof. mktg. Rutgers U., Newark, 1983-88; vis. assoc. prof. Wharton Sch., U. Pa., Phila., 1985-87, assoc. prof., 1989-90; prof. Temple U., 1990—; mem. editl. bd. Org. Sci., 1993—. Author: Production Mgmt., 1981, editor, 1983; reviewer Behavioral. Sci., 1978—, Jour. Mktg., 1987—, Jour. Consumer Rsch., 1988—; assoc. editor Mgmt. Sci. Dept. Tech., 1989-91; editl. bd. mem. Org. Sci.; contbr. articles to profl. jours. Capt. USAF, 1965-69, Vietnam. Decorated Bronze Star; recipient Andrisani/Frank Undergrad Teaching award. Mem. Am. Mktg. Assn., Inst. for Mgmt. Sci. Avocation: restoring old Victorian homes. Office: Temple U Sch Bus Dept Mktg Philadelphia PA 19122

OLIVE, DAVID MICHAEL, magazine writer, magazine editor; b. Toronto, Ont., Canada, Nov. 9, 1957; s. Harold Leslie and Alison Linton (Black) O.; m. Margaret Anne O'Reilly, Feb. 13, 1982 (div. June 1992). B of Applied Arts in Journalism, Ryerson Polytech. U., 1979. Copy editor Toronto Life Mag., 1979-81; assoc. editor Can. Bus. Mag., Toronto, 1981-84; sr. writer Report on Bus. Mag., Toronto, 1984-87, Toronto Life Mag., 1988-90; editorial writer The Globe and Mail, Toronto, 1990-91; editor Report on Bus. Mag., 1991—; dir. Can. Ctr. for Ethics and Corp. Policy, 1988-91, Jessie's Ctr. for Teenagers, 1994—; pres. Jessie's Ctr. Non-Profit Homes Corp., 1994—; pres. Nat. Mag. Awards Found., 1988-90. Author: Just Rewards: The Case for Ethical Reform in Business, 1987, White Knights and Poison Pills: A Cynic's Dictionary of Business Jargon, 1990, Political Babble: The 1,000 Dumbest Things Ever Said by Politicians, 1992, Gender Babble: The Dumbest Things Men Ever Said About Women, 1993, Canadian Political Babble: A Cynic's Dictionary of Political Jargon, 1993. Recipient Nat. Mag. awards Silver, 1987, Gold, 1988, Nat. Bus. Writing awards, 1983, 85, Nat. Journalism award, 1983. Mem. Can. Soc. Mag. Editors. Office: The Globe and Mail, 444 Front St W, Toronto, ON Canada M5V 2S9

OLIVEIRA, ELMAR, violinist; b. Waterbury, Conn., June 28, 1950. Student, Hartt Coll. Music, Hartford, Conn., Manhattan Sch. Music; studied with Raphael Bronstein, Ariana Bronne, John Oliveira; MusD (hon.), Manhattan Sch. Music, 1985. Prof. violin Manhattan Sch. Music, N.Y.C., 1990-91; vis. prof. Harper Coll., Binghamton, N.Y.; guest artist Chamber Music Soc. Lincoln Ctr., N.Y.C., 1994-95. Debut with Hartford Symphony Orch.; appeared on nat. TV as soloist with Young People's Concert series of N.Y. Philharmonic; N.Y.C. debut in Town Hall, 1973; appeared in recitals at Alice Tully Hall, 1976, 77; appeared with orchs. of Atlanta, Balt., Chgo., Cin., Cleve., Dallas, Minn., Phila., Pitts., St. Louis, Denver, Portland (Oreg.), also appeared with Nat. Symphony, L.A. Chamber Orch., L.A. Philharmonic Orch., Boston Symphony Orch., Milw. Orch., Ton Halle Orch., Zurich, London Philharmonic Orch., Gewand Haus Orch., Leipzig, Casals Festival Orch., and in Europe, Far East, S. Am.; appeared TV CBS Sunday Morning, Good Morning Am.; appeared with Madeira Bach Festival, 1980; Carnegie Hall debut, 1979; honored by Pres. Carter, 1978; recs. include Elmar Oliveira; cs. for CBS, Angel, EMI, MMG, RCA, Delos, IMP, VOX Unique, Elan. Winner 1st prize G.B. Dealey-Dallas News award, 1975, 1st Naumberg Internat. Violin Competition, 1975, Gold medal in violin Tchaikovsky Internat. Competition, 1978, Avery Fisher prize, 1983. Office: care Shaw Concerts Inc 1900 Broadway 2nd fl New York NY 10023*

OLIVEIRA, NATHAN, artist, educator; b. Oakland, Calif., Dec. 19, 1928. Student, Mills Coll.; M.F.A., Calif. Coll. Arts and Crafts, 1952. Instr. San Francisco Art Inst., 1955-56, Calif. Coll. Arts and Crafts, 1955-56, U. Ill., 1961-62, UCLA, 1963-64, Cornell U., 1964; instr. Stanford U., 1964—, now Ann O'Day Maples prof. in the arts; prof. emeritus, 1992; instr. U. Colo., 1965, U. Hawaii, 1971, Cranbrook Acad. Art, Bloomfield Hills, Mich., 1972, Balt. Art Inst., 1972, John Herron Art Inst., Indpls., 1972, Kent State U., Ohio, 1973. One-man shows: U. Ill. 1961, Walker Art Ctr., Mpls., 1961, Stanford U., 1968, 71, San Francisco Mus. Modern Art, 1969, 84, Oakland Mus., 1973, 80, Galerie Veith Turske, Cologne, Germany, 1978, Carpenter Ctr. for Visual Arts, Harvard U., 1978, John Berggruen Gallery, San Francisco, 1979, 82, 83, 87, 90, 93, Newport Harbor Art Mus., 1980, Charles Cowles Gallery N.Y., 1980, 83, Honolulu Acad. Arts, 1983, 85; group shows: Library of Congress, Washington, 1957, 75, Whitney Mus. Am. Art, N.Y.C., 1958-62, 67-68, 77, 81, I Paris Biennial, 1959, Art Inst. Chgo., 1959, 61, 62, Mus. Modern Art, N.Y.C., 1959, 62-63, 66, Guggenheim Mus., N.Y.C., 1961, Bklyn. Mus., 1968, 72, 76, 84, 86, Corcoran Gallery, Washington, 1970, Met. Mus. Art, N.Y.C., 1980, Richard Gray Gallery, Chgo., 1981, Marilyn Pearl Gallery, N.Y.C., 1982; represented in permanent collections: Hirshhorn Mus. and Sculpture Garden, Washington, Mus. Modern Art, N.Y.C., Guggenheim Mus., N.Y.C., San Francisco Mus. Modern Art, Oakland Mus., Retrospective UCLA, 1963-64, Oakland Mus., 1973, San Francisco Mus. Modern Art, 1984-85, Campbell-Thiebaud Gallery, Salander-O'Reilly Galleries, 1991. Recipient Norman Wait Harris Bronze medal Art Inst. Chgo., 1960; Guggenheim Found. fellow, 1958, Tamarind fellow, 1964; NEA grantee, 1974; named acamadician Nat. Acad. Design, N.Y.C., 1988, Am. Acad. Arts & Letters, N.Y.C., 1994. Fellow Am. Acad. Arts and Scis. Home: 785 Santa Maria Ave Palo Alto CA 94305-8439 Office: John Berggruen Gallery 228 Grant Ave San Francisco CA 94108 also: Salander-O'Reilly Galleries 20 E 79th St New York NY 10021

OLIVELLA, BARRY JAMES, financial executive; b. Can., 1947. BA, York U., Toronto, Ont., Can., 1968. Chartered acct., Ont. Ptnr. Arthur Young Clarkson Gordon and Woods Gordon (name now Ernst & Young), Toronto, 1968-87; v.p. fin. Bombardier Inc., Montreal, Que., Can., 1987-89, v.p. planning and acquisitions, 1989-93, v.p. acquisitions and strategic alliances, 1993—. Pres. Uxbridge (Ont.) C. of C., 1986-87; chmn. Indsl. Adv. Com., Uxbridge, 1979. Mem. Inst. Chartered Accts. Ont. and Can., Nat. Club (Toronto). Office: Bombardier Inc Ste 2900, 800 Rene-Levesque Blvd W, Montreal, PQ Canada H3B 1Y8

OLIVER, ALEXANDER R., management consultant; b. Liverpool, Eng., Jan. 25, 1944; came to U.S., 1968; s. Cecil B. and Eileen F. O.; m. Lorraine S. Cooper, June 14, 1983. BA, Cambridge (Eng.) U., 1965; MBA, Stanford U., 1970. Mktg. cons. The J. Walter Thompson Co. Ltd., London, 1965-68; mgmt. cons. Boston Cons. Group, London and Boston, 1970-74; sr. v.p. M. Lowenstein & Sons Inc., N.Y.C., 1974-78; ptnr. Booz, Allen & Hamilton Inc., N.Y.C., 1980-84; mng. ptnr. Oliver, Wyman & Co. Inc., N.Y.C., 1984—. Harkness fellow Commonwealth Fund of N.Y., 1968-70. Home: 1016 Fifth Ave New York NY 10028 Office: Oliver Wyman & Co 666 Fifth Ave New York NY 10103

OLIVER, BERNARD MORE, electrical engineer, technical consultant; b. Soquel, Calif., May 27, 1916; s. William H. and Margaret E. (More) O.; m. Priscilla June Newton, June 22, 1946; children: Karen, Gretchen, Eric. AB in Elec. Engring., Stanford U., 1935; MS, Calif. Inst. Tech., 1936, PhD, 1940. Mem. tech. staff Bell Telephone Labs., N.Y.C., 1940-52; dir. R&D, Hewlett-Packard Co., Palo Alto, Calif., 1952-57, v.p R&D, 1957-81, dir. officer, 1973-81, tech. adviser to pres., 1981; now v.p. emeritus Hewlett-Packard Co., Palo Alto; lectr. Stanford U., 1957-60; cons. Army Sci. Adv. Com., from 1966; mem. sci. and tech. adv. com. Calif. State Assembly, 1970-76. Contbr. articles on electronic tech. and instrumentation to profl. jours.; patentee electronic circuits and devices. Mem. Pres.'s Commn. on the Patent System, 1966, State Senate Panel for the Bay Area Rapid Transit System, 1973; trustee Palo Alto Unified Sch. Dist., 1961-71. Recipient Disting. Alumni award Calif. Inst. Tech., 1972, Nat. Medal of Sci., 1986, Exceptional Engring. achievement medal, NASA, 1990, Pioneer award Internat. Found. Telemetering, 1990; ann. Symposium series est. in his name Hewlett-Packard Labs., 1991. Fellow IEEE (Lamme medal 1977); mem. AAAS, Astron. Soc., Nat. Acad. Sci., Nat. Acad. Engring., Palo Alto Club, Bohemian Club. Republican. Office: Hewlett-Packard Co Box 10490 Palo Alto CA 94303-0969*

OLIVER, DANIEL, foundation fellow, lawyer; b. N.Y.C., Apr. 10, 1939; s. Andrew and Ruth (Blake) O.; m. Anna Louise Vietor, Sept. 16, 1967; children: Anna Louise, Andrew II, Daniel Jr., Susan F., Peter A. AB, Harvard U., 1964; LLB, Fordham U., 1967. Bar: N.Y. 1967. Assoc. Hawkins, Delafield & Wood, N.Y.C., 1967-70; editorial asst. Nat. Rev. mag., N.Y.C., 1970-71, exec. editor, 1973-76; assoc. Alexander & Green, N.Y.C., 1971-73, 76-79; pvt. cons., 1980-81; gen. counsel U.S. Dept. Edn., Washington, 1981-83, USDA, Washington, 1983-86; chmn. FTC, Washington, 1986-89; disting. fellow The Heritage Found., Washington, 1989-91, Citizens for a Sound Economy Found., Washington, 1991-93; sr. fellow The Heritage Found., Washington, 1993—; coun. Administrv. Conf. U.S. 1983-89. Vestryman Christ Ch., Greenwich, Conn. 1972-75, St. Andrews Ch., Edgartown, Mass., 1985-87, Ch. of Ascension and St. Agnes, 1991—. Mem. Federalist Soc. Law Pub. Policy Studies (v.p. 1984, 86), Phila. Soc. (pres. 1991-92), Mont Pelerin Soc. Republican. Office: The Heritage Found 214 Mass Ave NW Washington DC 20002

OLIVER, DAVID ROGERS, JR., naval officer; b. Indpls., Sept. 17, 1941; s. David Rogers and Dorotha (Wallen) O.; m. Linda Bithell, July 3, 1965; children: David R. III, Morgan B. BS, USN Acad., 1963; MA, Am. U., 1974. Comd. ensign USN, 1963, advanced through grades to rear admiral; engr. officer USS Nautilus (SSN 571), New London, Conn., 1969-72; priority analyst Office of Chief of Naval Ops., Washington, 1972-74; exec. officer USS Haddo (SSN 604), San Diego, 1974-78; comdg. officer USS Plunger (SSN 595), Bremerton, Wash., 1978-81; dep. personnel Pacific Submarine Force, Pearl Harbor, Hawaii, 1981-83; comdr. Seventh Fleet Submarine Force Yokosuka, Japan, 1983-85; chief of staff Seventh Fleet, Yokosuka, 1985-86; dir. force levels Office of Chief of Naval Ops., Washington, 1986-88; comdr. Submarine Group Five, San Diego, 1988-90; programmer USN, Washington, 1990-93; acquisition dep. Washington, 1993—. Author: Lead On, 1992. Recipient disting. svc. medal USN. Mem. LDS Ch. Avocations: golf, jogging.

OLIVER, EDWARD CARL, state senator, retired investment executive; b. St. Paul, May 31, 1930; s. Charles Edmund and Esther Marie (Bjugstad) O.; m. Charlotte Severson, Sept. 15, 1956; children—Charles E., Andrew T., Peter A. B.A., U. Minn., 1955. Sales rep. Armstrong Cork Co., N.Y.C., 1955; registered rep. Piper, Jaffray & Hopwood, Mpls., 1958; mgr. Mut. Funds, Inc. subs. Dayton's, Mpls., 1964; mgr. NWNL Mgmt. Corp. subs. Northwestern Nat. Life Ins. Co., Mpls., 1968-72, v.p., 1972-81, pres., dir.,

1981-90; mem. Minn. Senate, 1992—; arbitrator, Nat. Assn. Securities Dealers, 1988—; bd. dirs. Minn. World Trade Ctr. Corp. Commr. Great Lakes Commn., 1993—. Served to capt. USAF, 1951-52. Mem. Internat. Assn. Fin. Planners (past pres. Twin City chpt. mem. nat. governing com.), Psi Upsilon. Presbyterian. Club: Mpls. Athletic. Home: 20230 Cottagewood Rd Deephaven MN 55331-9300 Office: Washington Sq Securities Inc 100 Washington Sq Ste 1639 Minneapolis MN 55401

OLIVER, ELIZABETH JEANNE, nurse, educator; b. Rahway, N.J., Mar. 11, 1940; d. George James and Marguerite Elizabeth (Perkins) Schaeffer; m. Gerald William Oliver, Sept. 29, 1960; children—Christopher William, David James. A.S., Rutgers U.-Newark, 1959, B.S., 1961; M.S.N., Tex. Woman's U., 1975. Registered nurse, N.J., Md., Tex., Maine. Staff nurse Morristown Meml. Hosp., N.J., 1959-62, Johns Hopkins Hosp., Balt., 1962-66; staff nurse Galveston County Meml. Hosp., Texas City, Tex., 1970-71; mem. faculty Alvin Community Coll., Tex., 1971-79, program dir. nursing, 1979—. Mem. adv. com. Houston ARC, 1978-81; bd. dirs. Brazoria County ARC, Tex., 1985—. Mem. Am. Nurses Assn., Nat. League Nursing, Tex. Jr. Coll. Tchrs. Assn., Southern Council on Collegiate Edn. in Nursing, Sigma Theta Tau. Republican. Presbyterian. Avocations: camping; furniture refinishing; reading. Home: 1626 Seagate Ln Houston TX 77062-4510 Office: Alvin Community Coll 3110 Mustang Rd Alvin TX 77511

OLIVER, ELIZABETH KIMBALL, writer, historian; b. Saginaw, Mich., May 21, 1918; d. Chester Benjamin and Margaret Eva (Allison) Kimball; m. James Arthur Oliver, May 3, 1941 (div. July 1967); children: Patricia Allison, Dexter Kimball. B.A. U. Mich., 1940. Tchr. Dexter (Mich.) High Sch., 1940-41; libr. Sherman (Conn.) Libr. Assn., 1966-75; pres. Sherman (Conn.) Libr. Assn., 1983-84; writer, historian, 1976—; reporter Sherman Sentinel, 1965-70; editor newsletter Sherman Hist. Soc., 1977-78; columnist Citizen News, Fairfield County, Conn., 1981-83. Author: History of Staff Wives-AMNH, 1961, Background and History of the Palisades Nature Association, 1964, History and Architecture of Grace United Methodist Church, 1990, Legacy to St. Augustine, 1993. Vol. N.Y. Hist. Soc., N.Y.C., 1961-65; treas. Coburn Cemetery Assn., Sherman, 1976-82; historian Greenbrook-Palisades Nature Assn., Tenafly, N.J., 1962-64; mem. St. Augustine Hist. Soc., Naromi Land Trust (life), Cedar Key Hist. Soc. Mem. AAUW, Friends of Libr. (life), Inst. for Am. Indian Studies, Marjorie Kinnan Rawlings Co. (charter), St. Augustine Woman's Club (archivist, cert. of appreciation 1990), Sherman Hist. Soc., Mandarin Hist. Soc. Republican. Congregationalist. Avocations: sacred choral music, research, reading, piano and dulcimer playing, botany. Home: 1500 Bishop Estates Rd 12-B Jacksonville FL 32259

OLIVER, EUGENE ALEX, speech and language pathologist; b. East Palatka, Fla., Apr. 18, 1938; s. John T. and Ida (McBride) O.; m. Barbara Ann Gainer, Apr. 20, 1963; 1 child, Zulika Bonita. BA, Fla. A&M Univ., 1962; MA (equiv.), Southern Conn. State Univ., 1983; cert. advanced studies (equiv.), Fairfield Univ., 1989. Cert. speech and language pathology, Conn., lic. speech pathologist, Conn. Speech and lang. pathologist Florence (S.C.) Pub. Schs., 1962-63, Baltimore Pub. Schs., 1963-66, Imerial County Supt.'s Office, El Centro, Calif., 1967-69, Dunbury (Conn.) Pub. Schs., 1969-80, Albuquerque Pub. Schs., 1980-81, Monzano H.S., Albuquerque, 1980-81; speech and lang. pathologist & coord. Cuba (N.Mex.) Pub. Schs., 1981-84; speech and lang. pathologist Waterbury (Conn.) Pub. Schs., 1985—; specialist comm. disorders on H.S. level Crosby H.S., Waterbury, 1986—, specialist Wilson Learning Ctr., Waterbury, 1985—. Founding mem. Black Congress, New Milford, Conn., 1969; cons. Kwanzaa Celebrations, Conn., 1993. Recipient Spl. Recognition, speech dept. Waterbury Pub. Sch., 1993, Wilson Learning Ctr., 1991. Mem. NEA, Conn. Speech Lang. Hearing Assn., Conn. Edn. Assn., Waterbury Tchrs. Assn. Avocations: tennis, horseback riding, archery, swimming, writing. Home: 3 Rolling Ridge Rd Monroe CT 06468 Office: Waterbury Pub Schs 236 Grand St Waterbury CT 06702-1930

OLIVER, G(EORGE) BENJAMIN, educational administrator, philosophy educator; b. Mpls., Sept. 17, 1938; s. Clarence P. and Cecile (Worley) O.; m. Paula Rae Foust, Sept. 15, 1963; children: Paul Benjamin, Rebecca Lee. B.A. with honors, U. Tex., 1960; M.Div., Union Theol. Sem., N.Y.C., 1963; M.A., Northwestern U., 1966, Ph.D., 1967. Lectr. Northwestern U., Evanston, Ill., 1966-67; asst. prof. Hobart & William Smith Coll., Geneva, N.Y., 1967-71, chmn. dept. philosophy, 1969-77, assoc. prof., 1971-77; prof., 1977; dean Southwestern U., Georgetown, Tex., 1977-89, provost, 1986-89; pres. Hiram (Ohio) Coll., 1989—; chmn. Coun. of Acad. Deans and V.P.s of Tex., 1987-88. Contbr. articles to profl. jours. Trustee John Cabot Univ., Rome, 1989—, Grand River Acad., Austinburg, Ohio, 1991—, Cleve. Commn. on Higher Edn., 1991—, Ohio Found. Ind. Colls., 1989—, Assn. Ind. Colls. and Univ. of Ohio, 1993—; chmn., bd. trustees, East Central Coll. Consortium, 1993-95. Rockefeller Found. fellow, 1960-61, Internat. fellow Columbia U., 1962-63; research grantee NEH, 1973-74. Mem. Am. Coun. Edn. (mem. commn. on govtl. rels.), Soc. for Values in Higher Edn., Assn. Indep. Coll. and Univ. of Ohio (treas. 1993-94), East Ctrl. Colls. Consortium (chair, bd. trustees, 1993-95, exec. com. Ohio Found. Ind. Colls. 1994—), Am. Assn. Higher Edn., AAUP. Episcopalian. Office: Hiram Coll Office of Pres Hiram OH 44234

OLIVER, GERALD CLIFFORD, hospital administrator; b. Decatur, Ala., May 20, 1940; s. Melvin Roland and Odessa (Creel) O.; m. Betty Lou Harland, Dec. 20, 1960; children—Phillip, Nicole. B.S., U. N. Ala., 1962; M.S. in Hosp. Adminstrn., Baylor U., 1973. Exec. officer 58th Med. Battalion, U.S. Army, Vietnam, 1970-71; assoc. adminstr. U.S Army Med. Dept, Fort Campbell, Ky., 1973-76, health facilities project officer, Fort Knox, Ky., 1976-79; exec. officer Health Facilities Planning Agy., Washington, 1979-81; dir. med. activities adminstrn. Walter Reed Med. Ctr., Washington, 1981-82; hosp. adminstr. U.S. Army Med. Dept., Fort Campbell, Ky., 1982-85; Chief of Staff William Beaumont Army Med. Ctr., El Paso, Tex., 1985-87; adj. prof., Park Coll., Ft. Bliss, Tex.; preceptor George Washington U., Dept. Health Services Adminstrn., Washington, 1981-82, U. Ala., Birmingham, 1982-83, Austin Peay State U., Clarksville, Tenn., 1982—, U.S. Army-Baylor U. Health Care Adminstrn., Fort Sam Houston, Tex., 1982-87. Mem. Fort Campbell Community Civilian Awards Council, 1982-85, Community Health Care Consumer Com., Fort Campbell, 1982-85, Med., Dental Equal Opportunity Council, Fort Campbell, 1982—. Decorated Order Mil. Med. Merit award U.S. Army Health Services Command, 1984. Fellow Am. Coll. Hosp. Adminstrs.; mem. Am. Hosp. Assn., Assn. Mil. Surgeons U.S., Assn. U.S. Army, Fed. Health Care Exec. Inst., Am. Coll. of Health Care Execs., Fed. Health Care Execs. Inst., El Paso Hosp. Council, ARC, Tenn. Hosp. Assn. (1982-85), Hopkinsville-Clarksville Area Hosp. Adminstrs. Assn., Pennyrile Pilots Assn. (pres. 1984-85). Mem. Ch. Christ. Home: Rt One Box 126 Cherokee AL 35616

OLIVER, HARRY MAYNARD, JR., retired brokerage house executive; b. Kansas City, Mo., Jan. 21, 1921; s. Harry Maynard and Marie (Curtin) O. BA, Williams Coll., 1943. Pres. M.A. Gesner & Co., Marsh & McLennan Co., Chgo., 1947-88. Chmn. Chgo. Commn. for Sr. Citizens, 1960-69; mem. Chgo. Bd. Edn., 1966-69; pres. Vol. Agys. Chgo., 1956-86; mem. vis. com. Sch. Edn. and div. of social scis., U. Chgo.; pres., bd. dirs. Benton House Settlement, 1953-58; bd. dirs. Adult Edn. Council Greater Chgo., Nat. Fedn. Settlements and Community Centers, 1961-67; trustee Old Peoples Home Chgo., Pub. Sch. Tchrs. Pension and Retirement Fund Chgo., 1966-69, George M. Pullman Edn. Found., Field Mus. Natural History, 1971-75. Served to lt. (j.g.) USNR, World War II. Mem. Chgo. Club, Racquet Club, Commonwealth Club, Tavern Club, Onwentsia Club (Lake Forest, Ill.), Chi Psi. Home: 1948 N Lincoln Ave Chicago IL 60614-5476 also: PO Box 1319 Big Pine Key FL 33043 also: New Richmond PO Box 100 Fennville MI 49408

OLIVER, JACK ERTLE, geophysicist; b. Massillon, Ohio, Sept. 26, 1923; s. Chester L. and Marie (Ertle) O.; m. Gertrude van der Hoeven, Apr. 16, 1964; children: Cornelia Oliver, Amy Oliver. AB, Columbia U., 1947, MA, 1950, PhD, 1953; DSci (hon.), Hamilton Coll., 1988. Rsch. asst., then rsch. assoc. Columbia, 1947-55, mem. faculty, 1955-73, prof. geology, 1961-71, chmn. dept., 1969-71, adj. prof., 1971-73; Irving Porter Church prof. engring. dept. geol. scis. Cornell U., 1971-93, prof. emeritus, 1993—, chmn. dept., 1971-81; chmn. exec. com. COCORP; terrestrial physicist USAF Cambridge (Mass.) Rsch. Labs., 1951; dir. Inst. for Study of the Continents, 1981-88; cons. AEC, 1969-72, ACDA, 1962-74, USAF Tech. Applications Ctr., 1959-

65; mem. Polar Rsch. Com., 1959-71, also nat. commn. uppermantle program, 1963-71; mem. panel solid earth problems NAS, 1962; mem. adv. com. U.S. Coast and Geodetic Survey, 1962-66, on seismology, 1960-72, chmn., 1966-70; mem. Geophysics Rsch. Bd., 1969-70; U.S. earth sci. panel NSF, 1962-65; mem. USAF Sci. Adv. Bd., 1960-63, 64-69; mem. geophysics adv. panel Office Sci. Rsch., USAF, 1961-74, chmn., 1966-68; U.S. del. Test Ban Conf., Geneva, Switzerland, 1958-59; intergovtl. meeting seismology and earthquake engring., mem. exec. com. IASPEI, 1968-71; mem. governing com. Internat. Seismol. Summary Commn., 1963-67, 75-76; mem. exec. com. UNESCO, Paris, France, 1964, U.S.-Japan Earthquake Prediction Conf., Tokyo, 1964; mem. UNESCO Joint Com. on Seismology and Earthquake Engring., 1965-71; chmn. exec. com. Office Earth Scis., NRC, 1976-79, Internat. Seismol. Centre, 1976-78; mem. U.S. Geodynamics Com., 1979-87, chmn. 1984-87; mem. Geol. Scis. Bd., Assembly of Math. and Phys. Scis., NRC, 1981-84; Cabot Disting. vis. scholar U. Houston, 1985-86; commn. on phys. scis., math. and resources NRC, 1987-90, commn. on geoscis., environ. and resources, 1990—. Served with USNR, 1943-46. Recipient Hedberg award Inst. for Study of Earth and Man, So. Meth. U., 1990. Fellow Am. Geophys. Union (pres. seismology sect. 1964-68, Walter H. Bucher medal 1981), Geol. Soc. Am. (coun. 1970-73, v.p. 1986, pres. 1987, Woollard medal 1990), Geol. Soc. London (hon.); mem. AAAS (chmn. geol. geog. sect. 1993), NAS, Seismol. Soc. Am. (pres. 1964-65, bd. dirs. 1961-70, 72-76, Eighth medal 1984), Soc. Exploration Geophysicists (Virgil Kauffman Gold medal 1983), European Union Geoscis. (hon. fgn. fellow), Sigma Xi. Home: 125 Cayuga Park Rd Ithaca NY 14850-1405

OLIVER, JOHN PRESTON, chemistry educator, academic administrator; b. Klamath Falls, Oreg., Aug. 7, 1934; s. Robert Preston and Agnes May (McCornack) O.; m. Elizabeth Ann Shaw, Aug. 12, 1956; children: Karen Sue Oliver Vernon, Roy John, Gordon Preston. BA, U. Oreg., 1956; PhD, U. Wash., 1959. Asst. prof. chemistry Wayne State U., Detroit, 1959-64, assoc. prof., 1964-67, prof., 1967—, assoc. dean R&D, Coll. Liberal Arts, 1987-91, acting dean, 1991-92, interim dean Coll. Sci., 1992-93; chmn. organizing com. XIV Internat. Conf. on Organometallic Chemistry. Mem. Ferndale (Mich.) Bd. Edn., 1984-88. Mem. Am. Chem. Soc., Detroit sect. Am. Chem. Soc., Sigma Xi. Office: Wayne State Univ Rm 135 Chemistry Bldg Detroit MI 48202-3489

OLIVER, JOHN THOMASON, JR., commercial bank executive; b. Birmingham, Ala., Apr. 19, 1929; s. John Thomason and Sara (Crumpton) O.; m. Barbara Bankhead, Nov. 4, 1952; children: Melissa, Beth, Rebecca, John III, Will. BS, U. Ala., 1949, LLB, 1952; cert. in banking, La. State U., 1962. V.p. 1st Nat. Bank, Jasper, Ala., 1955-59, pres., chief exec. officer, 1959-89, chmn., chief exec. officer 1st Comml. Bancshares, Inc., Jasper, 1983—; pres. Bankhead Found., Jasper, 1987—; bd. dirs. mem. exec. com. Synovus Fin. Corp., 1993—. Pres. Jasper Area C. of C., 1960-67, United Appeal, Jasper, 1961; trustee U. Ala. System, Tuscaloosa, 1971—, pres. pro-tempore bd. trustees, 1985-87; trustee Ala. Dept. Archives and History, Montgomery, 1990—, Walker Coll., Jasper. 1st lt. JAGC, U.S. Army, 1952-54. Episcopalian. Office: First Commercial Bancshares 200 18th St W Jasper AL 35501

OLIVER, JOHN WILLIAM POSEGATE, minister; b. Vincennes, Ind., Apr. 9, 1935; s. Dwight L. and Elizabeth (Posegate) O.; m. Cristina Shepard Hope, Oct. 19, 1968; children: John William Posegate Jr., Sloan Christian Shepard. BA, Wheaton Coll., 1956; BD, Fuller Theol. Sem., 1959; ThM, So. Bapt. Theol. Sem., 1963. Ordained to ministry Presbyn. Ch. in Am., 1962. Asst. pastor Covenant Presbyn. Ch., Hammond, Ind., 1964-66, Trinity Presbyn. Ch., Montgomery, Ala., 1966-69; pastor 1st Presbyn. Ch., Augusta, Ga., 1969—; moderator Cen. Ga. Presbytery, Presbyn. Ch. in Am., 1976. Founder, trustee Westminster Schs., Augusta, 1972—; chmn. clergy Augusta United Way Campaign, 1974; mem. exec. bd. clergy staff Univ. Hosp., Augusta, 1975-76; mem. bd. commrs. Augusta Housing Authority, vice-chmn., 1976-93; trustee, chmn. bd. Columbia Internat. U., 1978—; mem. ministerial adv. bd. Reformed Theol. Sem., 1978-85, 89-93; bd. dirs. Mission to the World, Presbyn. Ch. in Am., 1984-89, 92—; dir. Bailey Manor Retirement Ctr., Clinton, S.C., 1992—. Mem. Evang. Theol. Soc., Nassau Club of Princeton, Augusta Country Club. Home: 3205 Huxley Dr Augusta GA 30909-3128 Office: 642 Telfair St Augusta GA 30901-2325

OLIVER, JOSEPH J., consumer products company executive. With R J Reynolds Foods, Winston-Salem, N.C., 1978-79; ceo Ken J. Pezrow Corp., Ramsey, N.J., 1979—. Office: Ken J Pezrow Corp 535 E Crescent Ave Ramsey NJ 07446

OLIVER, KATHERINE C., museum director. Office: Mid Ga Hist Soc Inc 935 High St Macon GA 31201-2034

OLIVER, MARY, poet; b. Maple Heights, Ohio, Sept. 10, 1935; d. Edward William and Helen May (Vlasak) O. Student, Ohio State U., 1955-56, Vassar Coll., 1956-57. Chmn. writing dept. Fine Arts Work Ctr., Provincetown, 1972-73, mem. writing com., 1984; Banister poet in residence Sweet Briar Coll., 1991-95; William Blackwood vis. prof. creative writing Duke U., 1995. Author: No Voyage and Other Poems, 1963, enlarged edit., 1965, The River Styx, Ohio, 1972, The Night Traveler, 1978, Twelve Moons, 1979, American Primitive, 1983, Dream Work, 1986, House of Light, 1990, New and Selected Poems, 1992, A Poetry Handbook, 1994, White Pine, 1994, Blue Pastures, 1995; contbr. to Yale U. Rev., Kenyon Rev., Poetry, Atlantic, Harvard mag., others. Recipient Shelley Meml. award, 1970, Alice Fay di Castagnola award, 1973; Cleve. Arts prize for lits., 1979; Achievement award Am. Acad. and Inst. Arts and Letters, 1983; Pulitzer prize for poetry, 1984; Christopher award, 1991, L.L. Winship award, 1991, Nat. Book award, 1992; Nat. Endowment fellow, 1972-73; Guggenheim fellow, 1980-81. Mem. PEN, Authors Guild. Home: care Molly Malone Cook Lit Agy PO Box 338 Provincetown MA 02657

OLIVER, MARY WILHELMINA, law librarian, educator; b. Cumberland, Md., May 4, 1919; d. John Arlington and Sophia (Lear) O. AB, Western Md. Coll., 1940; BS in Library Sci, Drexel Inst. Tech., 1943; JD, U. N.C. 1951. Bar: N.C. 1951. Asst. circulation librarian N.J. Coll. Women, 1943-45; asst. in law library U. Va., 1945-47; asst. reference, social sci. librarian Drake U., 1947-49; rsch. asst. Inst. Govt., U. N.C., Chapel Hill, 1951-52, asst. law librarian, 1952-55, asst. prof. law, law librarian, 1955-59, asso. prof. law, law librarian, 1959-69, prof. law, law librarian, 1969-84, prof. law and law librarian emeritus, 1984—. Mem. ABA, N.C. Bar Assn., Am. Assn. Law Librs. (pres. 1972-73, Marion Gould Gallagher Disting. Svc. award 1992), Assn. Am. Law Schs. (exec. com. 1971-83), Law Alumni Assn. U. N.C., Order of Coif. Home: 157 Carol Woods Chapel Hill NC 27514 Office: U NC Law Libr Van Hecke Wettach Hall # 064A Chapel Hill NC 27514

OLIVER, ROBERT BRUCE, retired investment company executive; b. Brockton, Mass., Aug. 1, 1931; s. Stanley Thomas and Helen (Sabine) O.; m. Sylvia E. Bell, Feb. 17, 1954; children: Susan Pamela, Robert Bruce. A.B., Harvard U., 1953; postgrad., Bus. Sch., 1971, Boston U. Law Sch., 1955-57; M.A., Mich. State U., 1958. Ret. chmn., pres., chief exec. officer John Hancock Income Securities Trust, Boston, 1989; ret. chmn., pres. chief exec. officer John Hancock Investors Trust, John Hancock Bond Trust, John Hancock Growth Trust, John Hancock Tax Exempt Cash Mgmt. Trust, John Hancock Govt. Securities Trust, John Hancock Tax Exempt Income Trust, John Hancock Cash Mgmt. Trust, John Hancock Spl. Equities Trust, John Hancock Global Trust, John Hancock World Trust, John Hancock High Income Trust, John Hancock Tax Exempt Series Trust; chmn., dir. John Hancock Distbrs.; vice chmn., chief exec. officer John Hancock Advisers, Inc.; chmn., mng. dir. John Hancock Advisers Internat. Ltd. 1st lt. USMCR, 1953-55. Mem. Marine Corps League, Club at Pelican Bay. Home: 6619 Trident Way Naples FL 33963-8243

OLIVER, ROBERT WARNER, economics educator; b. L.A., Oct. 26, 1922; s. Ernest Warner and Elnore May (McConnell) O.; m. Darlene Hubbard, July 1, 1946 (dec. Mar. 1987); children: Lesley Joanne Oliver McClelland, Stewart Warner; m. Jean Tupman Smock, July 15, 1989. AB, U. So. Calif. 1943, AM, 1948; AM, Princeton U., 1950, PhD, 1958. Teaching asst. U. So. Calif., 1946-47; instr. Princeton U., 1947-50, Pomona Coll., L.A., Calif. 1950-52; asst. prof. U. So. Calif., Los Angeles, 1952-56; economist Stanford Research Inst., South Pasadena, Calif., 1956-59; mem. faculty dept. econs.

Calif. Inst. Tech., 1959-88, prof. econs., 1973-88, prof. emeritus, 1988—; urban economist World Bank, Washington, 1970-71; cons. Brookings Instn., 1961, OECD, Paris, 1979; vis. prof. U. So. Calif., 1985; vis. scholar Pembrook Coll., Cambridge U., Eng., 1989-90. Author: An Economic Survey of Pasadena, 1959, International Economic Cooperation and the World Bank, 1975, Bretton Woods: A Retrospective Essay, 1985, Oral History Project: The World Bank, 1986; contbg. author: Ency. of Econs., 1981, 94, George Woods and the World Bank, 1995. Mem. Human Rels. Com. City of Pasadena, 1964-65, Planning Commn., 1972-75, 91—; bd. dirs. Pasadena City Coun., 1965-69; mem. Utilities Adv. Commn., 1984-88, Strategic Planning Com., 1985; pres. Pasadena Beautiful Found., 1972-74; bd. dirs. Pasadena Minority History Found., 1984—, Jackie Robinson Meml. Found., 1994—; trustee PAsadena Hist. Soc., 1992-94. Lt. (j.g.) USN, 1942-46. Social Sci. rsch. fellow London Sch. Econs., 1954-55; Rockefeller Found. fellow, 1974, 91; Danforth assoc., 1981; recipient Outstanding Teaching award, 1982, Master of the Student Houses, 1987; Hon. Alumnus, 1987. Mem. Am. Econs. Assn., Royal Econs. Assn., Com. on Fgn. Rels., Phi Beta Kappa, Phi Kappa Phi, Delta Tau Delta. Democrat. Methodist. Club: Athenaeum. Home: 3197 San Pasqual St Pasadena CA 91107-5330 Office: 1201 E California Blvd Pasadena CA 91125-0001 *The world is so full of beauty, natural and man-made, that human intelligence should seek to comprehend and enjoy it. Observation and reflection which lead to understanding are more important than performance, and the most important performance is service to others. The greatest human virtue is love, which is why family is important. If there be a God, I believe He works His will amongst civilized men through love, and He manifests His works through beauty.*

OLIVER, RUFUS W., III, lawyer; b. Port Sulphur, La., Aug. 13, 1947. BA with high honors, U. Tex., 1969, JD with high honors, 1972. Bar: Tex. 1972. Ptnr. Baker & Botts LLP, Houston. Mem. ABA (chmn. antitrust sect. subcom. fuel and energy inds. 1989), State Bar Tex. (coun. mem. antitrust and bus. litigation sect. 1990—), Houston Bar Assn. (chmn. antitrust and trade regulation sect. 1990-92). Office: Baker & Botts 1 Shell Plz 910 Louisiana Houston TX 77002

OLIVER, SAMUEL WILLIAM, JR., lawyer; b. Birmingham, Ala., Apr. 18, 1935; s. Samuel William and Sarah Pugh (Coker) O.; m. Anne Holman Marshall, Aug. 26, 1961; children: Sarah Bradley Oliver Crow, Samuel William III, Margaret Nelson. BS, U. Ala., 1959, JD, 1962. Bar: Ala. 1962, U.S. Dist. Ct. (no. dist.) Ala. 1963. Law clk. Supreme Ct. Ala., Montgomery, 1962-63, U.S. Dist. Ct. (no. dist.) Ala., Birmingham, 1963; assoc. Burr & Forman (formerly Thomas, Taliaferro, Forman, Burr), Birmingham, 1964-65, ptnr., 1966—, also chmn. bus./corp. law sect., 1990-93; dir. Metalplate Galvanizing Inc., Birmingham; mem. panel arbitrators commercial Am. Arbitration Assn., Atlanta and Nashville, 1981—. Chmn. bd. govs. The Relay House, Birmingham, 1985-89; mem. Leadership Birmingham, 1990; mem. adv. bd. Jr. League Birmingham, 1975-77; bd. dirs. Jr. Achievement Greater Birmingham, Inc., 1975—; sr. warden St. Stephen's Episcopal Ch., Birmingham, 1979; mem. diocese coun. Episcopal Diocese Ala., Birmingham, 1981-85; chmn. bd. trustees Highlands Day Sch. Found., Inc., Birmingham, 1980-81; bd. dirs. Ala. Kidney Found., Birmingham, 1990-95. With U.S. Army, 1956-58. Mem. ABA (bus. law sect. 1965—, negotiated acquisitions com. 1990—, task force on joint venture agreements 1994—, sect. internat. law and practice), Internat. Bar Assn. (bus. law sect.), Ala. Bar Assn. (corp. law sect.), Birmingham Bar Assn., Country Club Birmingham, Summit Club (bd. govs.), Monday Morning Quarterback Club, Rotary Club. Episcopalian. Avocations: fishing, golf, investments. Office: Burr & Forman 3000 S Trust Tower 420 20th St N Birmingham AL 35203-3202

OLIVER, STEPHANIE STOKES, magazine editor; b. Seattle; m. Reginald Oliver; 1 child, Anique. BA in Journalism cum laude, Howard U., 1974. Former fashion & beauty merchandising editor Glamour Mag.; editor contemporary living sect. Essence Mag., N.Y.C., 1978-80, sr. editor, 1980-84; West Coast editor Essence Mag., Seattle, 1984-85; editor of mag. Essence Mag., N.Y.C., 1986-94; editor-in-chief Heart & Soul Mag., N.Y.C., 1994—. Recipient Outstanding Alumnae award Howard U., 1986. Mem. Am. Soc. Mag. Editors (sec. bd. dirs.), Nat. Assn. Black Journalists, Fashion Group Internat., Black Women in Publishing, Women's Media Group. Office: Heart & Soul 733 Third Ave 15th Floor New York NY 10017

OLIVER, STEVEN WILES, banker; b. Los Angeles, May 27, 1947; s. Frank Wiles and Hazel Gloria (Patton) O.; m. Susan Elizabeth Peace, Nov. 27, 1971; children: Andrew Wells, Elizabeth Patton, Laura Rice. AB cum laude, Claremont Men's Coll., 1969; JD, Vanderbilt U., 1972. Officer Citibank, N.A., S.E. Asia, 1972-79; mng. dir. Lazard Asia Ltd., Hong Kong, 1980-88, Lazard Freres & Co. Ltd., London, 1988-90; gen. ptnr. Lazard Frères & Co., N.Y.C., 1988-94; mng. dir. Lazard Asia Ltd., Singapore, 1995; non-exec. dir. Lazard Bros. & Co. Ltd., London, 1989; mng. dir. Lazard Freres K.K., Tokyo, 1991. Mem. president's coun. The Asia Soc. Mem. Tokyo Lawn Tennis Club, Tokyo Am. Club, Hong Kong Country Club, Penang Club, Leland Country Club. Presbyterian. Office: Lazard Freres & Co One Rockefeller Plz New York NY 10020 also: Lazard Asia Ltd, # 22-20 UOB Plz II, 80 Raffles, Singapore 0104, Singapore also: Lazard Freres & Co 1 Rockefeller Plz New York NY 10020-2001

OLIVER, THOMAS WILLIAM, lawyer; b. Dallas, Nov. 10, 1939; s. Frank Gillespie and Eloise (Adams) O.; m. Susan Jane Kahn, Mar. 19, 1966; children: Marion Adams, Thomas William Jr. BBA, U. Tex., 1963, LLB, 1964. Bar: Tex. 1964. From assoc. to ptnr. McCulloch, Ray, Trotti & Hemphill, Dallas, 1965-77; ptnr. Winstead, Sechrest & Minick, Dallas, 1977—. Mem. bd. editors Accounting for Law Firms, 1987—; contbr. to legal jours. and newsletters. Bd. dirs. The Dallas Opera, 1983—, Am. Lung Assn., Dallas, pres., 1977-79; mem. adv. coun. to Sec. Labor William Brock on pension and welfare plans, Washington, 1985-88. With USAR, 1964-70. Mem. ABA (employee benefits com. sect. taxation), Tex. Bar Assn., Dallas Bar Assn., Park Cities Rotary (bd. dirs. 1979-81), Brook Hollow Golf Club, City Club, Tower Club. Office: Winstead McGuire Sechrest 5400 Renaissance Tower 1201 Elm St Dallas TX 75270-2014

OLIVER, THORNAL GOODLOE, health care executive; b. Memphis, Aug. 26, 1934; s. John Oliver and Evelyn Doris (Goodloe) Mitchell; m. Pauline Reid, Oct. 1, 1959. B.S., Tenn. State U., Nashville, 1956; M.H.A., Washington U., St. Louis, 1973. Cert. nursing home adminstr., Mo. Asst. dir., King Meml. Hosp., Kansas City, Mo., 1973-75; evening mgr. Truman Med. Ctr., Kansas City, Mo., 1975-77; asst. adminstr. Mid-Am. Radiation Ctr. U. Kans. Coll. Health Sci., Kansas City, Kans., 1977-81; dir. CHS, Inc., Leawood, Kans., 1981-82; adminstr. Poplar Bluff Hosp., Mo., 1982-83; adminstr. The Benjamin F. Lee Health Ctr., Wilberforce, Ohio, 1983-86; asst. clin. prof. Dept. Community Medicine, Wright State U., Dayton, 1986-89; asst. patent adminstr. Munson Army Hosp., Ft. Leavenworth, Kans., 1987—; cons. Urban Health Assocs., Nashville, 1986-87, others. Contbr. articles to profl. jours. Served with U.S. Army, 1957-59, USAR, 1959-63. Fellow Am. Coll. Hosp. Adminstrs.; mem. Am. Hosp. Assn., Nat. Assn. Health Services Execs., Am. Med. Record Assn., Mo. League of Nursing Home Adminstrs. Home: 10641 N Grand Ave Kansas City MO 64155-1655 Office: Munson Army Hosp Fort Leavenworth KS 66027

OLIVER, WILLIAM ALBERT, JR., paleontologist; b. Columbus, Ohio, June 26, 1926; s. William Albert and Mary-Maud (Thompson) O.; m. Johanna L. Kramer, Sept. 1, 1948 (dec.); children: Robert A., James A. B.S., U. Ill., 1948; M.A., Cornell U., 1950, Ph.D., 1952. Instr., then asst. prof. geology Brown U., Providence, 1952-57; research geologist-paleontology U.S. Geol. Survey, Washington, 1957-93, emeritus scientist, 1993—; mem. U.S. Nat. Com. on Geology, 1975-79, chmn., 1979; U.S. rep. Internat. Subcommn. on Devonian Stratigraphy, 1973-92; chmn., 1984-89; rsch. assoc. dept. paleobiology U.S. Nat. Mus. Natural History-Smithsonian Instn., Washington, 1993—. Contbr. articles to profl. jours. Fellow AAAS (coun. 1971-73), Geol. Soc. Am.; mem. Paleontol. Soc. (councilor 1964-69, 73-76, editor Jour. 1964-69, pres. 1974-75), Paleontol. Assn. Soc. (London), Paleontol. Rsch. Inst. (trestee 1976-89, pres. 1984-86, Harris award, 1994), Am. Geol. Inst. (dir. 1974-77, v.p. 1975-76, pres. 1976-77), Internat. Assn. for Study of Fossil Cnidaria (coun. 1971-88, pres. 1983-88), Internat. Palaeontological Assn. (sec. gen. 1984-89). Home: 4203 McCain Ct. Ken-

sington MD 20895-1321 Office: Natural Hist Bldg MRC137 Smithsonian Inst E-305 Washington DC 20560

OLIVER, WILLIAM JOHN, pediatrician, educator; b. Blackshear, Ga., Mar. 30, 1925; s. John Wesley and Katherine (Schalwig) O.; m. Marguerite Bertoni, May 28, 1949; children: Ralph Scott, Catherine, Susan. Student, Ga. Southwestern Coll., 1942-43, Mercer U., 1943-44; MD cum laude, U. Mich., 1948. Diplomate Am. Bd. Pediatrics (examiner), Subsplty. Bd. Pediatric Nephrology. Intern, resident U. Mich. Med. Center, 1948-53, dir. pediatric labs., 1953-67; pvt. practice medicine specializing in pediatrics Ann Arbor, Mich., 1953—; instr. dept. pediatrics U. Mich., 1953-56, asst. prof., 1956-61, assoc. prof., 1961-65, prof., 1965, chmn. dept. pediatrics, 1967-79; chief pediatric service Wayne County Hosp., 1958-61; co-chmn. task force on recent advances of coordinating com. on continuing edn. and recertification Am. Bd. Pediatrics and Am. Acad. Pediatrics, 1977-80, mem. task force for pediatric rev. edn. program, 1980-88; mem. com. program for renewal certification in pediatrics Am. Bd. Pediatrics, 1989-91; mem. exam. writ. com. for cert. pediatric nephrology Am. Bd. Pediatrics, 1989—, PRCP pilot test com., 1993—, mem. rev. and question writ. com. for pediatrics in Rev. Am. Acad. Pediatrics, 1991—; cons. U. Riyadh, Saudi Arabia, 1980, Rsch. Rev. Com. on Pediatrics, 1989; ednl. cons. dept. pediatrics Stanford U. Hosps., 1991—; mem. self-assessment program for Pediatrics in Rev., 1990—; investigator adaptation primative So. Ams. Indiand, 1976—, African Pygmies, 1987—. Mem. editorial bd.: IRCS Jour. Med. Sci., 1975—. Pres. Mich. Kidney Disease Found., 1969, Washtenaw County br. Mich. Childrens Aid Soc., 1964; trustee Ann Arbor Hands-On Mus., 1983-88; pres. bd. trustees Perry Nursery Sch., Ann Arbor, 1989-90. With USNR, 1950-52. Fellow Am. Acad. Pediatrics (chmn. com. med. edn. 1974-80, chmn. council on pediatric edn. 1975-80, chmn. task force oversight of pediatric rev. and edn. program 1984-88, Clifford G. Grulee award 1979); mem. Soc. Pediatric Research, Midwest Soc. Pediatric Research (pres. 1968), Am. Soc. Nephrology, Assn. Med. Sch. Pediatric Dept. Chairmen (mem. council 1977-79), Soc. for Exptl. Biology and Medicine, Am. Pediatric Soc., Alpha Omega Alpha, Gamma Sigma Epsilon. Home: 2892 Bay Ridge St Ann Arbor MI 48103

OLIVER-WARREN, MARY ELIZABETH, library science educator; b. Hamlet, N.C., Feb. 23, 1924; d. Washington and Carolyn Belle (Middlebrooks) Terry; m. David Oliver, 1947 (div. 1971); children: Donald D., Carolyn L.; m. Arthur Warren, Sept. 14, 1990. BS, Bluefield State U., 1948; MS, South Conn. State U., 1958; student, U. Conn., 1977. Cert. tchr., adminstr. and supr., Conn. Media specialist Hartford (Conn.) Pub. Schs., 1952-86; adj. teacher So. Conn. State U., New Haven, 1972-86, asst. prof. Sch. Libr. Sci. and Instructional Tech., 1987—, mem. dept. curriculum com., 1987—. Author: My Golden Moments, 1988, The Elementary School Media Center, 1990, Text Book Elementary School Media Center, 1991, I Must Fight Alone, 1991, (textbook) I Must Fight Alone, 1994. Mem. ALA, Conn. Ednl. Media Assn., Assn. Ret. Tchrs. Conn., Black and Hispanic Consortium, So. Conn. State U. Women's Assn., Cicuso Club (v.p.), Friends Club (v.p.), Delta Kappa Gamma. Avocations: reading, music, piano, walking. Home: 6 Freeman Rd Somerset NJ 08873-2925 Office: So Conn State U 501 Crescent St New Haven CT 06515-1330

OLIVETO, FRANK LOUIS, recreation consultant; b. Bellaire, Ohio, Oct. 9, 1956; s. Donald Albert and Patricia Edna (Pezdriz) O.; m. Ann Marie Mongelli, Mar. 13, 1982; children: Leah Marie, Hannah Emily. BS, Pa. State U., 1980. Intern, then asst. dir. recreation Kiawah Island Resort, Charleston, S.C., 1980; dir. recreation Seabrook Island Resort, Charleston, 1981-85, Innisbrook Resort, Tampa, Fla., 1985-88; pres., owner Recreation Mgmt. Assn., Tampa, 1988—. Contbr. articles to mags. Elder, home group leader In the Name of Jesus World Outreach Ctr., Odessa, Fla., 1989. Mem. Resort and Comml. Recreation Assn. (founding mem., pres. 1983, exec. dir. 1988—), Fla. Recreation and Park Assn., Nat. Recreation and Park Assn. Republican. Avocations: travel, public speaking, racquetball, photography. Home: 6850 Larchmont Ave New Port Richey FL 34653-5921 Office: Recreation Mgmt Assn PO Box 215 New Port Richey FL 34656-0215

OLIVO, MARGARET ELLEN ANDERSON (MARGARET ELLEN ANDERSON), physiologist, educator; b. Omaha, June 17, 1941; d. Clarence Lloyd and Anita Emma (Kruse) Anderson; m. Richard F. Olivo, Sept. 4, 1971. BA, Augustana Coll., Sioux Falls, S.D., 1963; PhD, Stanford U., 1967. NIH postdoctoral fellow Harvard U., 1968-70; research assoc. Lab. of Neuro-biology U. P.R., 1970-71; vis. asst. prof. Clark U., 1972; asst. prof. Bennington (Vt.) Coll., spring 1973; asst. prof. Smith Coll., Northampton, Mass., 1973-79, assoc. prof. dept. biol. scis., 1979-85, prof., 1985—, dean sr. class, 1993—; mem. Bingham award selection com. Transylvania U., Lexington, Ky., 1987-94. Assoc. editor Advances in Physiology Edn., 1988-92; contbr. articles to Tissue and Cell, Jour. Gen. Physiology, other jours. Predoctoral fellow NSF, Stanford U., 1967; rsch. grantee NIH, 1974-86, NSF, 1989-90. Mem. Am. Physiol. Soc. (assoc. editor jour. 1988-92), Soc. for Neurosci., Soc. Gen. Physiologists, Biophys. Soc. Office: Smith Coll Dept Biol Sci Northampton MA 01063

OLKINETZKY, SAM, artist, retired museum director and educator; b. N.Y.C., Nov. 22, 1919; s. Isidor and Jennie O.; m. Sammie Lee Sturdevant, Dec. 20, 1959; children: Jov Shan, Tova Shana. B.A., Bklyn. Coll., 1942; postgrad., Inst. Fine Arts, N.Y.U., 1946-47. Asst. prof. art and humanities Okla. A&M U., Stillwater, 1947-57; vis. asst. prof. art U. Okla., Norman, 1957-58; assoc. prof. art Mus. of Art, 1959—; dir. Mus. Art U. Okla., Norman, 1959-83; vis. prof. art and humanities U. Ark., Fayetteville, 1962-63, 67-68, Langston (Okla.) U., 1969-70; art cons. Kerr-McGee Industries, Inc.; advisor State of Okla. Visual Arts; mem. State Art Collection Com.; Mem. Norman Arts and Humanities Council. One-man exhbns. include Arts Place II, Okla. Art Ctr., Firehouse Art Ctr., Norman, 1989; other exhbns. include Mus. Non-Objective Art, N.Y.C., Mus. Modern Art, N.Y.C.; 50-yr. Retrospective Exhbn., 1942-92, Norick Art Ctr., Oklahoma City, 1992; represented in permanent collections Philbrook Art Ctr., Tulsa, Okla. Art Ctr., Mus. Art. U. Okla. Served with USAAF, 1942-45. Recipient Gov.'s Art award, 1981. Mem. Okla. Museums Assn. (pres. 1978-79), Internat. Council Museums, Mountain-Plains Museums Assn., Am. Assn. Museums, Art Mus. Assn.

OLLEMAN, ROGER DEAN, industry consultant, former metallurgical engineering educator; b. Cornelia, Ga., Nov. 25, 1923; s. Faye Erlando and Esther (Perkins) O.; m. Elizabeth Ann Deutsch, May 24, 1947; children—Esther Jean, Ruth Ellen, Mark Charles. B.S. in Mech. Engring, U. Wash., 1948; M.S. in Metall. Engring. Carnegie Inst. Tech., 1950; Ph.D., U. Pitts., 1955. Group leader Westinghouse Research Labs., Pitts., 1950-55; asst. br. head, dept. metall. research Kaiser Aluminum & Chem. Corp., Spokane, Wash., 1955-59; mem. faculty dept. mech. and metall. engring. Oreg. State U., Corvallis, 1959-76, now courtesy prof.; pres. Accident and Failure Investigations, Inc., 1974—; cons. to industry, also Lawrence Radiation Lab., 1965-66, U.S. Bur. Mines Metallurgy Research Ctr., Albany, 1962-72. Bd. dirs. Benton Assn. Retarded Children. Served with AUS, 1944-46. Recipient Lloyd Carter award outstanding teaching Sch. Engring., Oreg. State U., 1962. Mem. ASTM (Templin award 1953), ASME (past sec., nonferrous subcom. boiler and pressure vessle code), Am. Soc. Engring. Edn., Am. Soc. Metals Internat., Am. Inst. Mining, Metall. and Petroleum Engrs., Sigma Xi, Tau Beta Pi, Pi Tau Sigma. Home: 1005 NW 30th St Corvallis OR 97330-4441

OLLER, WILLIAM MAXWELL, retired energy company executive, retired naval officer; b. Lancaster, Pa., Apr. 7, 1924; s. John Secrist and Mabel Margaret (Coffman) O.; m. Doris Seitz Greenleaf, June 15, 1946; children: Arthur G., J. Richard. BS, U.S. Naval Acad., 1946; MBA, George Washington U., 1960. Commd. ensign U.S. Navy, 1946, advanced through grades to rear adm., 1972; svc. in Samoa, Philippines and Italy; exec. officer Naval Supply Ctr., Newport, R.I., 1966-67, Ships Parts Control Ctr., Mechanicsberg. Pa., 1970-72; comdr. Def. Fuel Supply Ctr., Alexandria, Va., 1972-76; comdg. officer Naval Supply Ctr., Norfolk, Va., 1976-77; gen. mgr. corp. supply and distbn. Champlin Petroleum Co., Houston, 1977-79, Ft. Worth, 1979-81; sr. v.p. Petroleum Ops. and Support Svcs., Inc., New Orleans, 1981-82, pres., 1982-84; spl. asst. to pres., chief exec. officer Kaneb Svcs., Inc., Houston, 1984-85; exec. v.p. Tex. Ea. Products Pipeline Co., Houston, 1986-90; pres. Maxwell Woodworks Inc., Sugar Land, Tex., 1991—. Pres. Am. Leadership Forum, Houston, 1986. Decorated Legion of Merit with gold star, Meritorious Svc. medal with gold star, Joint Svc. Commendation medal. Mem. Sugar Creek Country Club (Sugar Land, Tex.), Army Navy Country Club (Arlington, Va.). Home: 1238 Sugar Creek Blvd Sugar Land TX 77478-3926

OLLEY, ROBERT EDWARD, economist, educator; b. Vendun, Que., Can., Apr. 16, 1933; s. Edwin Henry and Elizabeth (Reed) O.; m. Shirley Ann Dahl, Jan. 19, 1957; children—Elizabeth Anne, George Steven, Susan Catherine, Maureen Carolyn. B.A., Carleton U., Can., 1960; M.A., Queen's U., Can., 1961, Ph.D in Econs., 1969. Vis. asst. prof. Queen's U., Kingston, Ont., Can., 1967-68; asst. prof. econs. U. Sask., Saskatoon, Can., 1963-67, 68-69, assoc. prof., 1969-71, 73-75, prof., 1975-93, prof. emeritus, 1993—; pres. Gen. Econs. Ltd., 1993—; dir. rsch. Royal Commn. on Consumer Problems and Inflation, 1967-68; econ. advisor Bell Can., Montreal, Que., 1971-73, 78-79, Can. Telecom. Carriers Assn., 1978-85, Sask. Power Corp., 1980-83; econ. advisor AT&T, 1980-90, Weste Mgmt., Inc., 1990-92, SaskTel, 1989-93; chmn. adv. com. on consumer stds. Stds. Coun. Can., 1992-93; Can. rep. to ISO/COPOLCO, Geneva, 1992-93. Author, editor: Consumer Product Testing, 1979; Consumer Product Testing II, 1981; Consumer Credit in Canada, 1966; Economics of the Public Firm: Regulation, Rates, Costs, Productivity Analysis, 1983, Total Factor Productivity of Canadian Telecommunications, 1984; Consumer Reps. Conf. Procs., 1st-4th, 1982-91. Bd. dirs. Can. Found. for Econ. Edn., 1974-82, Can. Gen. Standards Bd., 1977-81. Recipient Her Magesty The Queen Silver Jubilee medal, 1977. Mem. Royal Econ. History Soc., Royal Econs. Assn., Econ. History Assn., Am. Econ. Assn., Can. Econ. Assn., Consumers Assn. Can. (v.p. 1967-75, chmn. 1975-77), Can. Stds. Assn. (bd. dirs., exec. com. 1971-93, vice chmn. 1985-87, chmn. 1987-89), Consumer's Assn. Found. Can. (v.p. 1989-95), Can. Comm. Rsch. Ctr. (bd. dirs. 1992—), Internat. Telecom. Soc. (bd. dirs. 1986—), Shaw Guild. Home and office: PO Box 1040, 374 Queen St, Niagara on the Lake, ON Canada L0S 1J0

OLLING, EDWARD HENRY, aerospace engineer, consulting firm executive; b. Zion, Ill., Feb. 18, 1922; s. Edward and Lydia Ester (Amstudz) O.; children—Linda L., Charles R., Carole. B.S.M.E., Purdue U., 1949; postgrad., UCLA, 1952-54, U. Houston, 1963-66. Registered profl. engr., Tex. Sr. thermodynamics engr. Lockheed Aircraft Corp., Burbank, Calif., 1954-56; project mgr. NASA Project Mercury, Garret Airesearch Corp., Los Angeles, 1956-60; dep. asst. Apollo project mgr., chief Future Projects Office chief advanced earth orbital missions office and space sta. office NASA, Houston, 1960-70; dir. Galaxy Engring. Inc., Captiva Island, Fla., 1971-90; cons. in oceanography, energy, environment, conservation. Pres. Captiva Island Wildlife Sci. Research Found.; pres. Satellite-TV Communications Enterprises; surrogate astronaut, 1962-69; cons.-dir. Orbita Space Sta., 1985-94, revised space sta., 1990-94; pres. Seaboard Stamp Soc., 1980-94; leader Hong Kong-China Progress Studios; cons. People to People Ambassadors, China Space Progress Tour and Survey; delaer rare books and antiques, big band era records; pres. Nouveaux Terra Electic Motion Corp., Generator Electrics. Contbg. author: Enciclopedia Mondadori, Italy; Contbr. articles to profl. jours.; Inventor, developer auto rsch. engring. devel. patent applications; inventor, patentee and devel. APU Electric Car. Bd. dirs. Captiva Seaside Flora and Fauna Research Found. Center; bd. dirs. Concerned Captiva Citizens.; mem. exec. com. Lee County (Fla.) Democratic Party; campaign worker John Glenn for Pres., 1984 Dem. State Conv.; campaign worker Frank Mann for Fla. Gov., 1986; founder, dir. Restoration of Mars Found., 1975-94; CEO Les Nouveaux Mars Found.; dir. Found. for Restoration Pyramids, Stonehenge. Served with USAAC, 1942-46. Recipient Sustained Superior Performance awards NASA, Inventions and Contbns. awards. Mem. Nat. Space Inst., Nat. Aerosp. Inst., Nat. Audubon Soc. (pres. Theodore Roosevelt chpt.), Am. Assn. Concerned Scientists, Sanibel Captiva Conservation Assn., Captiva Civic Assn., Am. Fla. Stamp Dealers Assns., Am. Topical Assn., Rocket Mail Soc., Tex. Profl. Engring. Soc., Am. Legion, LBJ Space Center Stamp Club, Jack Knight Aerospace Philatelic Assn., Am. Soc. Polar Philatelists, Strengthen Am. Def. Assn., Support Nuclear Energy Soc. (pres.), Purdue Club S. W. Fla., Danish Am. Genealogy Rsch. Assn., High Flight Soc. (search for Noah's Ark divsn.), Scientists So. Fla., Imaginarium Ft. Meyers, Conquest Space Philatelic Soc., Orbital Space Covers, Lea. Co. Edison Philatelic Soc., Alligator Deltrology Soc., Sunshine Postcard Club, Tropical Postcard Club, Edison Inventor Assn. (dir.). Address: 2581 Palm Ave Fort Myers FL 33916-5347

OLLINGER, W. JAMES, lawyer; b. Kittanning, Pa., Apr. 5, 1943; s. William James and Margaret Elizabeth (Reid) O.; m. Susan Louise Gerspacher, Oct. 20, 1979; children: Mary Rebecca, David James. BA, Capital U., Columbus, Ohio, 1966; JD, Case Western Res. U., 1968. Bar: Ohio 1968, U.S. Dist. Ct. (no. dist.) Ohio 1971. Ptnr. Baker & Hostetler, Cleve., 1968—; bd. dirs. Parts Assocs., Inc., Cleve., 1975—. Mem. Bentleyville (Ohio) Village Coun., 1990-93. Mem. Wembley Club, Order of Coif, Phi Delta Phi. Office: Baker & Hostetler 3200 Nat City Ctr 1900 E 9th St Cleveland OH 44114-3303

OLLIVER, DENIS G., transportation company executive; b. 1940. Mng. dir. Nat. Freight Consortium plc, 1961—; vice chmn. Allied Van Lines Inc., 1988—. Office: Allied Van Lines Inc 251 W Diehl Rd Naperville IL 60563-1278

OLLWERTHER, WILLIAM RAYMOND, newspaper editor; b. Neptune, N.J., Jan. 1, 1950; S. William Frederick and Daphne Marie (Hawkins) O.; m. Arlene Judith Newman; children: Geoffrey Vaughan, Alyssa Irene. BA, Princeton U., 1971; MS, Northwestern U., 1972. Reporter Asbury Park (N.J.) Press, 1972-76, bur. chief, 1977-78, night suburban editor, 1979-82, asst. to editor, 1982-84; asst. mng. editor Asbury Park (N. J.) Press, Neptune, 1985-87, exec. editor, 1988—, v.p. news, 1994—; adj. prof. Rutgers U., New Brunswick, N.J., 1988. Editor: The Shore Catch, 1987. Commr. Ocean County Cultural & Heritage Commn., Toms River, N.J., 1977-78. Mem. Am. Soc. Newspaper Editors. Unitarian. Office: Asbury Park Press PO Box 1550 3601 Hwy 66 Neptune NJ 07754-1550*

OLMER, LIONEL HERBERT, lawyer; b. New Haven, Nov. 11, 1934; s. Abraham and Gertrude (Jacobs) O.; m. Jody R. Westby, 1992; children from a previous marriage: Stuart A., Sally A. BA, U. Conn., 1956; JD, Am. U., 1963; postgrad., Nat. War Coll., 1972-73. Bar: Conn. 1963, D.C. 1975. Commd. ensign U.S. Navy, advanced through grades to capt., 1977; sea duty and shore assignments in Japan, Philippines, Hawaii, and the Atlantic; staff of chief of naval ops., 1969-72; staff exec. Pres.'s Fgn. Intelligence Adv. Bd., 1973-77; ret., 1977; dir. internat. programs Motorola Corp., Washington, 1977-81; undersec. internat. trade U.S. Dept. Commerce, Washington, 1981-85; ptnr. Paul, Weiss, Rifkind, Wharton & Garrison, Washington, 1985—; bd. dirs. Dresser Industries. Bd. dirs. Internat. Rescue Com., 1980-85. Mem. Conn. Bar Assn., Fed. Bar Assn., D.C. Bar Assn. Home: 1615 L St NW # 1300 Washington DC 20036-5610 Office: Paul Weiss Rifkind Wharton & Garrison 1615 L St NW Ste 1300 Washington DC 20036-5694

OLMOS, EDWARD JAMES, actor; b. Los Angeles, Calif., Feb. 24, 1947; m. Kaija Keel; m. Lorraine Bracco, Jan. 28, 1994; 2 children. AA in Sociology, East Los Angeles City Coll.; postgrad., Calif. State U., Los Angeles. Performed in exptl. theater, Los Angeles; actor (play) Zoot Suit (Tony nominee, Los Angeles Drama Critics Circle award, Theatre World award), Broadway and Los Angeles, 1978-80; actor, producer film The Ballad of Gregorio Cortez, 1982, Triumph of the Spirit, 1989; actor, co-producer film Stand and Deliver, 1988 (nominee best actor Acad. Awards 1988); actor films Wolfen, 1981, Zoot Suit, 1981, Blade Runner, 1982, (also assoc. prodr., composer, music adapter) The Ballad of Gregorio Cortez, 1983, Saving Grace, 1986 (also co-prodr.) Stand and Deliver, 1988, Triumph of the Spirit, 1989, Talent for the Game, 1991, (also dir., co-prodr.) American Me, 1992, A Million to Juan, 1994, My Family, 1995; TV series Miami Vice, 1984-89 (Emmy award for best supporting actor in drama series 1985, Golden Globe award 1986), TV miniseries The Fortunate Pilgrim, 1988, Menendez: A Killing in Beverly Hills, 1994; prodr., dir. TV documentary Lives in Hazard, 1994. Office: The Artists Agency 10000 Santa Monica Blvd Ste 305 Los Angeles CA 90067*

OLMSTEAD, CECIL JAY, lawyer; b. Jacksonville, Fla., Oct. 15, 1920; s. Cecil Jay Sr. and Bessie (Irby) O.; m. Frances Hughes; children: Cecil Jay III, Frank Hughes, Jane Olmstead Murphy, Amy Olmstead Vanecek. B.A., U. Ga., 1950, LL.B., 1951; Sterling Grad. fellow, Yale Law Sch., 1951-52;

LL.D. (hon.), U. Hull, Eng., 1978. Bar: Ga. 1950, U.S. Supreme Ct 1964, D.C. 1978. Asst. to legal adviser Dept. State, counsel Mut. Security Agy., counsel Hoover Commn. on Orgn. Exec. Br. of Govt., 1952-55; prof. N.Y. U. Sch. Law, 1953-61; dir. Inter-Am. Law Inst., 1958-61, adj. prof. law, 1961-69; atty. Texaco, Inc., N.Y.C., 1961-62; asst. to chmn. bd. Texaco, Inc., 1962-70, v.p., asst. to chmn. bd., 1970, v.p., asst. to chmn. 1970-71, v.p., asst. to chief exec. officer, 1971-73; exec. dept., v.p., 1973-80; mem. firm Steptoe & Johnson, Washington, 1980—; Wang Disting. vis. prof. St. Johns U., 1987-90; mem. adv. panel on internat. law to sec. state; adv. com. law of sea State Dept.; also adv. com. transnat. enterprise; U.S. del. UN Com. on Law of Sea, 1972-73; U.S. del. UN Conf. on Law of Sea, 1974-76; Eisenhower lectr. Nat. War Coll., 1973; mem. U.S. del. UN Conf. on Code of Conduct for Transnat. Corps., ann. 1984-90; mem. World Bank's panel of conciliatiors of the Internat. Ctr. for Settlement of Investment Disputes, 1988-95; vis. fellow All Souls Coll., Oxford U., 1988; vis. scholar Yale Law Sch., 1990-91. Recipient Gold medal City of Brussels (Belgium), 1973, Gold medal City of Paris (France), 1984; named Commdr. Brit. Empire (hon.), 1990. Mem. Internat. Law Assn. (pres. Am. br. 1966-73, pres. 1972-75, vice chmn. exec. council 1975-86, chmn. exec. council, 1986-88, patron 1989), Am. Law Inst. (assoc. reporter Restatement of the Fgn. Relations Law of the U.S., 2d edit. 1964 adviser, 3d edit.), Council on Fgn. Relations, Washington Inst. Fgn. Affairs, Nat. Fgn. Trade Council (dir.), Am. Council on Germany (hon. dir.), Council on Ocean Law (dir.). Clubs: Knickerbocker, Yale (N.Y.C.); Fairfield County Hunt (Westport); 1925 F Street, Cosmos (Washington). Home: 4 Sprucewood Ln Westport CT 06880-4021 Office: 1330 Connecticut Ave NW Washington DC 20036-1704

OLMSTEAD, CLARENCE WALTER, JR., lawyer; b. Alexandria, Va., Jan. 24, 1943; s. Clarence Walter and Rhea Nancy (Donnelly) O.; m. Kathleen Frances Heenan, Sept. 7, 1973; children: Nicholas Heenan, Jonathan Heenan, Caitlin Heenan. AB, Stanford U., 1965; LLB, Columbia U., 1968. Bar: N.Y. 1970, U.S. Dist. Ct. (so. and ea. dists.) N.Y. 1970, U.S. Ct. Appeals (2d cir.) 1970, U.S. Supreme Ct. 1986. Law clk. to presiding judge U.S. Dist. Ct. (we. dist.) Wis., 1968-69; assoc. Shearman & Sterling, N.Y.C., 1969-76, ptnr., 1976—. Bd. dirs. West Side Montessori Sch., N.Y.C., 1983-89, pres., 1985-87; mem. sch. com. Cathedral Sch., N.Y.C., 1992—; trustee North Country Sch. Camp Treetops, 1992—. Mem. ABA, N.Y. State Bar Assn., Assn. Bar City of N.Y., Phi Beta Kappa. Home: 470 West End Ave New York NY 10024-4933 Office: Shearman & Sterling 153 E 53rd St New York NY 10022-4611

OLMSTEAD, FRANCIS HENRY, JR., plastics industry executive; b. Corning, N.Y., June 21, 1938; s. Francis Henry and Josephine (Andolino) O.; B.S., Detroit U., 1960; M.S., Purdue U., 1962; postgrad. program for mgmt. devel. Harvard, 1976; m. Mary Helen Nelson, Sept. 2, 1961; children: Kathleen, Ann, John. Foreman, Corning Glass Works, 1962, sect. foreman, 1963-64, dept. foreman, 1965-66, prodn. supt., 1967-69, plant mgr., 1970-71, mgr. mktg., 1972-73, gen. sales and mktg. mgr., 1973-75, bus. mgr. lighting products, 1976-79, bus. mgr. TV products, 1979-80, v.p., gen. mgr. TV products, 1981—, gen. mgr. elec. products div., 1982-83 ; exec. v.p. N.Am. Philips Lighting Corp., Bloomfield, N.J., 1984-86, exec. v.p., gen. mgr. Somerset, N.J., 1986-88; pres., chief operating officer Anchor Advanced Products, Inc., Morristown, Tenn., 1988-90, chmn., pres., chief exec. officer, 1990—; instr. bus. adminstrn. Elmira Coll., 1972-73; vis. lectr. Purdue U., 1973. Mem. exec. bd. Steuben area council Boy Scouts Am., 1975—, v.p. fin., 1977-79, coun. pres., 1979-84, bd. dirs. N.E. region, 1984-88, pres. N.J. Area, 1985-88, pres., bd. dirs. South region Boy Scouts Am., 1988-91, v.p. S.E. region, 1991-93, pres. Southeast region, 1993—, pres. Southern region, mem. nat. bd. dirs.; mem. dean's adv. coun. Krannert Sch. Purdue U., Coll. Engring. U. Detroit; bd. dirs. Knoxville Symphony, 1994—; Served to capt. U.S. Army, 1961-62. Recipient Silver Beaver award, Silver Antelope award, St. George Catholic award, Boy Scouts Am., Disting. Alumni award Purdue U. Mem. ASME, Am. Soc. Plastics Engrs., Am. Brush Mfg. Assn., Cosmetics, Toiletry and Fragrance Assn., Corning C. of C., Krannert Sch. Alumni Assn. Purdue U. (pres.), Corning Country Club, Cherokee Country Club, Tau Beta Pi, Pi Tau Sigma. Republican. Roman Catholic. Home: 7328 Misty Meadow Pl Knoxville TN 37919-7219 Office: Anchor Advanced Products 1111 Northshore Dr Ste N-600 Knoxville TN 37919-4048

OLMSTEAD, LAURENCE DANIEL, journalist; b. Bronx, N.Y., July 31, 1957; s. John Napoleon and Miriam Priscilla (Randolph) O.; m. Michele Renee Chandler, May 29, 1983; 1 child, Nyasha Chandler. Student, George Washington U., 1974-78. Reporter Balt. Evening Sun, 1978-80; successively copy editor, asst. city editor, city desk reporter Detroit Free Press, 1980-84, Africa corr., 1985-88, dep. city editor, 1989-90, city editor, 1991—. Recipient citation Overseas Press Club, 1988. Mem. Nat. Assn. Black Journalists (Internat. Reporting award 1986, 88). Avocation: tennis. Office: Detroit Free Press 321 W Lafayette Blvd Detroit MI 48226

OLMSTEAD, MARJORIE ANN, physics educator; b. Glen Ridge, N.J., Aug. 18, 1958; d. Blair E. and Elizabeth (Dempwolf) O. BA in Physics, Swarthmore Coll., 1979; MA in Physics, U. Calif., Berkeley, 1982, PhD, 1985. With research staff Palo Alto (Calif.) Research Ctr. Xerox Corp., 1985-86; asst. prof. physics U. Calif., Berkeley, 1986-90; asst. prof. physics U. Wash., Seattle, 1991-93, assoc. prof., 1993—; prin. investigator materials sci. divsn. Lawrence Berkeley Lab., 1988-93; mem. exec. com. Stanford (Calif.) Synchroton Radiation Lab., 1986-90, chmn., 1988-89. Contbr. articles to profl. jours. Named Presdl. Young Investigator, Nat. Sci. Found., 1987; recipient Devel. awards IBM, 1986, 87. Mem. Am. Assn. Physics Tchrs., Am. Phys. Soc., Am. Vacuum Soc. (Peter Mark Meml. award 1994), Materials Rsch. Soc., Assn. Women in Sci., Phi Beta Kappa, Sigma Xi. Office: Univ Washington Dept Physics FM 15 Seattle WA 98195*

OLMSTEAD, WILLIAM EDWARD, mathematics educator; b. San Antonio, June 2, 1936; s. William Harold and Gwendolyn (Littlefield) O.; m. Adele Cross, Aug. 14, 1957 (div. 1967); children: William Harold, Randell Edward. BS, Rice U., 1959; MS, Northwestern U., 1962, PhD, 1963. Mem. research staff S.W. Research Inst., San Antonio, 1959-60; Sloan Found. postdoctoral fellow Johns Hopkins, 1963-64; prof. applied math. Northwestern U., Evanston, Ill., 1964—, chmn. dept. engring. scis. and applied math., 1991-93; vis. mem. Courant Inst. Math. Scis., NYU, 1967-68; faculty visitor Univ. Coll. London, Eng., 1973, Calif. Inst. Tech., 1987, 90. Contbr. articles to profl. jours. Named Technol. Inst. Tchr. of Yr., 1980; recipient Award for Tchg. Excellence, Northwestern Alumni Assn., 1993; appointed Charles Deering McCormick prof., 1994. Mem. Am. Acad. Mechanics, Am. Math. Soc., Am. Phys. Soc., Soc. Indsl. and Applied Math., Am. Contract Bridge League, (Silver Life master), John Evans Club (Northwestern U.), Sigma Xi, Tau Beta Pi, Sigma Tau. Episcopalian. Home: 141 Lockerbie Ln Wilmette IL 60091-2947 Office: Northwestern U Dept Engring Scis and Applied Math Evanston IL 60208

OLMSTED, JERAULD LOCKWOOD, telephone company executive; b. Des Moines, Aug. 26, 1938; s. George Hamden and Virginia (Camp) O.; m. Mary Karen Autenrieth, June 20, 1962 (div. Dec. 1986); children: Scott H., Victoria L., Jerauld; m. Gisele A. Child, June 17, 1988. B.S., Iowa State U., 1961; M.B.A., George Washington U., 1979; Cert. mgmt. accountant. Vicepres. First Nat. Bank of Washington, 1969; v.p., dir. Intermediate Credit Corp., 1969-73; v.p., dir. Internat. Gen. Industries, Inc., 1974-79, pres., dir., 1980-82; pres., dir. IB Credit Corp., 1982-85, N.Am. Communications, Inc., Bethesda, Md., 1985—; sr. v.p., dir. Internat. Bank, 1978-85. Bd. govs. Iowa State U. Found., 1980—; mem. corporate adv. bd. div. arts and humanities U. Md., 1982—; sec.-treas. George Olmsted Found., 1970— Served with U.S. Army, 1961-63. Decorated Knight of Malta, Order of St. John. Mem. Fin. Execs. Inst., Mensa, Soc. Cincinnati, Beta Alpha Psi., Beta Gamma Sigma. Republican. Episcopalian. Clubs: Metropolitan, City, Georgetown (Washington). Home & Office: 7735 Arrowood Ct Bethesda MD 20817-2821

OLMSTED, JOANNA BELLE, cell biology educator; b. Chgo., Mar. 8, 1947; d. Charles Edward and Hazel (Wiggers) O.; m. Douglas Hugh Turner, Aug. 27, 1977; 1 child, Richard. BA, Earlham Coll., 1967; PhD, Yale U., 1971; postgrad., U. Wis., 1971-74. Asst. prof. cell biology U. Rochester, N.Y., 1975-81, assoc. prof., 1981-87, prof., 1987—; mem. Cellular and Molecular Basis of Disease Study Sect., NIH, 1992—. Fellow NIH, 1968-74. Mem. Am. Soc. for Cell Biology (councillor 1980-82, publs. com. 1983-85, edn. com. 1989-91). Office: U Rochester Dept Biology Rochester NY 14627

OLMSTED, PATRICIA PALMER, educational researcher; b. Chgo., Sept. 19, 1940; d. Richard O. and Marion E. (Huffman) Palmer. BA in Psychology, Mich. State U., 1962; postgrad. Stanford U., 1962-63; MA, Columbia U., 1965; PhD, U. Fla., 1977. Grad. research asst. Columbia U., N.Y.C., 1964, pub. health trainee psychopathology, 1964-65; assoc. rsch. scientist dept. med. genetics Psychiat. Inst., N.Y.C., 1965-66; asst. rsch. coord. Merrill-Palmer Inst., Detroit, 1966-68, instr., 1966-69, rsch.coord., 1966-69; instr. Coll. Edn. U. Fla., Gainesville, 1969-71, asst. in edn., 1971-73, assoc. in edn., 1973-77; clin. assist. prof. Sch. Edn. U. N.C., Chapel Hill, 1977-82, clin. assoc. prof., 1982-86, dir. parent edn. follow-through program, 1977-86; rsch. assoc. High/Scope Ednl. Rsch. Found., 1986-91, sr. rsch. assoc., 1991—, dep. coord. internat. child care study, 1986—; grantee, 1977-86, cons. various pub. schs., 1969—. Contbr. articles on rsch. in edn. to profl. jours., chpts. to books. Recipient Edn. grantee, 1977-84. Mem. APA, Soc. Rsch. Child Devel., Am. Ednl. Rsch. Assn., Nat. Assn. Edn. Young Children, Phi Delta Kappa. Office: High/Scope Ednl Rsch Found 600 N River St Ypsilanti MI 48198-2898

OLMSTED, RONALD DAVID, foundation executive, consultant; b. Portland, Oreg., June 27, 1937; s. Clifford Wolford and Ruth Emily (Driesner) O.; m. Susan Mary Spare, Dec. 27, 1961 (div. June 1972); 1 child, Craig William. Student, Lewis & Clark Coll., 1955-57, U. So. Calif., L.A., 1959-62. V.p., exec. dir. L.A. Ctr. for Internat. Visitors, 1961-67; assoc. dir. devel. U. Chgo., 1967-71; v.p. devel. and pub. affairs Northwestern Meml. Hosp., Chgo., 1971-79; dir. devel. Marimed Found., Honolulu, 1989-93; dir. devel., protection Advocacy Agy. of Hawaii, Honolulu, 1994—; cons. on health, edn. and human svc. orgns., Mich., Oreg., Hawaii, 1979—. Contbr. articles on African travels and African affair to profl. publs. Co-founder, treas. Civil Found. of Chelsea, Mich., 1982-83; treas. Chelsea Area C. of C., 1981-83; trustee Harris Sch., Chgo., 1972-73, Ogden Dunes (Ind.) Town Bd.; bd. dirs. United Way Porter County, Ind., 1969-71; mem. L.A. Com. on Fgn. Rels., 1965-69; bd. dirs. Am. Friends of Africa, 1965-68, Nat. Coun. for Cmty. Svcs. to Internat. Visitors, 1965-67; mem. exec. com. L.A. Mayor's Coun. for Internat. Visitors and Sister Cities, 1964-68; vice chmn. Greater L.A. Com. Internat. Student Svcs., 1966. Recipient Koa Anvil award Pub. Rels. Soc. Am.-Honolulu, 1992, multiple awards Assn. Am. Colls., 1975-79, multiple MacEachern awards Am. Acad. Hosp. Pub. Rels., 1974-79, multiple awards Nat. Assn. for Hosp. Devel., 1975-79. Mem. Nat. Soc. Fund Raising Execs. Presbyterian. Avocations: cooking, gardening, sailing, wines. Home and Office: 469 Ena Rd Apt 1506 Honolulu HI 96815

OLNEY, JAMES, English language educator; b. Marathon, Iowa, July 12, 1933; s. Norris G. and Doris B. (Hawk) L.; 1 child, Nathan. B.A., U. Iowa, 1955; M.A., Columbia U., 1958, Ph.D, 1963. Asst. prof. Drake U., Des Moines, 1963-67; Fulbright lectr. Cuttington Coll., Liberia, 1967-69; prof. English N.C. Central U., Durham, 1970-83; Voorhies prof. English La. State U., Baton Rouge, 1983—; vis. prof. Northwestern U., 1974, Amherst Coll., 1978-79. Author: Metaphors of Self, 1972, Tell Me Africa, 1973, the Rhizome & the Flower, 1980, The Language(s) of Poetry, 1993; editor: Autobiography, 1988; editor So. Rev., 1983—. Fellow NEH, 1975-76, Guggenheim Found., 1980-81, Nat. Humanities Ctr., Research Triangle Park, N.C., 1980-81. Mem. MLA (exec. council 1983-87). Home: 1744 Pollard Pky Baton Rouge LA 70808-8854 Office: La State U Southern Review 43 Allen Hall Baton Rouge LA 70803

OLNEY, PETER BUTLER, JR., retired management consulting firm executive; b. N.Y.C., Nov. 29, 1924; s. Peter Butler and Amy (Cruger) O.; m. Elinor Ann Bowman, Sept. 10, 1949; children: Peter B., Ann B., Stephen R. AB, Harvard U., 1949; MA, Boston U., 1951. Cert. mgmt. cons. Credit investigator Shawmut Bank, Boston, 1949-51; tchr. social studies Cohasset (Mass.) Sch., 1951-53; mgmt. trainee Corn Exch. Bank, N.Y.C., 1953-55; job analyst Allied Chem., N.Y.C., 1955-56; pers. adminstr. Avco Corp., Lawrence, Mass., 1956-58; dir. pers. Avco Corp., Cin., 1958-61; dir. human resources United Shoe Corp., Beverly, Mass., 1961-64; mgmt. cons. Frank C. Brown Co., Boston, 1964-66; founder, pres. of mgmt. cons. corp. Olney Assocs., Inc., Boston, 1966-89. Author: (periodical) Meeting the Challenge of Comparable Worth, 1987. Pres. West Andover PTA, Andover, Mass., 1963; bd. dirs. Unitarian Universalist Ch., Andover, 1964-70, Interfaith Counseling, Andover, 1986-93. Named one of Top 100 Cons. Firms in U.S. by Inst. Mgmt. Cons., 1987. Mem. North Andover Country Club (bd. dirs. 1970-74). Democrat. Avocations: traveling, water color painting. Home: 18 Royal Crest Dr Apt 10 North Andover MA 01845

OLNEY, ROBERT C., diversified products manufacturing executive; b. Bklyn., Aug. 19, 1926; s. Herbert Mason and Martha L. (Otten) O.; m. Wanda G. Olney, July 17, 1948 (dec. 1988); children: Robert C. Jr., Thomas J., Douglas P.; m. Ann Waters Bell, Mar. 14, 1992. BA in Econs., Cornell U., 1946. With Chem. Bank, N.Y.C., 1946-48; various mgmt. positions 3M Co., from 1948; v.p., gen. mgr. 3M-Nat. Adv. Co., Bedford Pk., Ill., 1976-80; chmn., mng. dir. 3M UK plc, Bracknell, Eng., 1980-86; dir. Yale-Valor plc, Chiswick, London, Eng., 1986-91; chmn. Nutone Inc., Cin., 1987-91; bd. dirs. Revere Holdings Inc., Balt., Merton Assocs. Ltd. Mem. Hinsdale (Ill.) Golf Club, Worshipful Co. of Upholders (London), Royal Automobile Club (London). Avocation: skiing. Home: Oatlands Park, 32 Lakeside Grange, Weybridge Surrey KT139ZE, England KT139ZE also: PO Box 1764 Avon CO 81620-1764 also: PO Box 223 Montchanin DE 19710

OLOFSON, ROY LEONARD, financial executive, accountant; b. Kenmore, N.Y., Jan. 13, 1939; s. Eric Leonard and Karin (Smith) O.; m. Lillian Dimich, Apr. 28, 1962; children—Eric Leonard, Erin Diane, Roy Andrew. B.S., UCLA, 1965; A.M.P., Harvard U., 1980. C.P.A., Calif. Mgr. Price Waterhouse, Los Angeles, 1965-70; v.p., Carter, Hawley, Hale Stores, Inc., Los Angeles, 1970-82; chief fin. officer Fedco, Inc., Santa Fe Springs, Calif., 1982—; pres., dir. Fedco Credit Corp., Santa Fe Springs, 1983—. Served with USMC, 1956-59. Mem. Fin. Execs. Inst., Am. Inst. C.P.A.s, Calif. Soc. C.P.A.s. Clubs: Jonathan (Los Angeles), Los Angeles Athletic. Office: Federal Employees Distrg Co 9300 Santa Fe Springs Rd Springs CA 90670

OLOFSON, TOM WILLIAM, business executive; b. Oak Park, Ill., Oct. 10, 1941; s. Ragnar V. and Ingrid E. Olofson; BBA, U. Pitts., 1963; m. Jeanne Hamilton, Aug. 20, 1960; children: Christopher, Scott. Various mgmt. positions Bell Telephone Co. of Pa., Pitts., 1963-67; sales mgr. Xerox Corp., Detroit, 1967-68, nat. account mgr., Rochester, N.Y., 1968, mgr. govt. planning, Rochester, 1969, mgr. Kansas City (Mo.) br., 1969-74; corp. v.p. health products group Marion Labs., Inc., Kansas City, Mo., 1974-78, sr. v.p., mem. Office Pres. 1978-80; exec. v.p., dir. Electronic Realty Assocs., Inc., 1980-83; chmn. bd., CEO Emblem Graphic Systems, Inc., 1983-88, Electronic Processing, Inc., 1988—; dir. DemoGraFX, Wordenglass & Electricity, Inc., Elinco Internat., Access Industries, Inc., Saztec Internat., Capital Ptnrs. Bd. visitors U. Pitts. Joseph M. Katz Grad. Sch. Bus.; past trustee Barstow Sch.; past chmn. bd. trustees Village United Presbyn. Ch.; bd. dirs. Mid.-Am. Immunotherapy and Surg. Research Found., Inc. Mem. Omicron Delta Kappa, Sigma Chi. Republican. Presbyterian. Club: Kansas City. Home: 4808 W 87th St Shawnee Mission KS 66207-1848 Office: Electronic Processing Inc 501 Kansas Ave Kansas City KS 66105-1309

O'LOUGHLIN, JOHN KIRBY, retired insurance executive; b. Bklyn., Mar. 31, 1929; s. John Francis and Anne (Kirby) O'L.; m. Janet R. Tag, July 5, 1952; children: Robert K., Steven M., Patricia A., John A. BA in Econs., St. Lawrence U., Canton, N.Y., 1951. State agt. Royal Globe Ins. Group, 1953-58; with Allstate Ins. Co., 1958—, mktg. v.p. group v.p., then exec. v.p., 1972—; pres. Allstate Life Ins. Co., 1977—; chmn. bd. Allstate Ins. Co. and Life Co. Can., 1976—; sr. exec. v.p., chief planning officer, 1980-90; ret.; ret.; pres., CEO JKO Cons. Ltd., Lake Forest, Ill., 1991—; bd. dirs. all cos. in Allstate Ins. Group and Allstate Enterprises, Inc.; former pres. Allstate Enterprises, Inc., ret. 1990; pres., CEO Royal Links Ventures Ltd., Small Coll. Ins. Cons. Inc. Trustee St. Lawrence U.; VS MArine Staff and Command Coll. Found. Bd.; bd. dirs. Marine Corps Assn., Am. Ireland Fund, USMC Scholarship Found. Inc., Coun. on Ind. Colls.; past chmn. No. Suburban Chgo. chapter, elder 1st United Presbyn. Ch., Lake Forest, Ill. Capt. USMCR, 1951-53. Mem. Sales and Mktg. Execs. Internat. (bd. dirs., past chmn., pres.), Marine Corps Assn. (bd. dirs.), Met. Club (Chgo.), Knollwood Club, Whispering Woods GolfClub (N.C.), Pinehurst (N.C.) Country Club, Lahinch Club (Ireland). Office: JKO Cons Ltd 133 E Laurel Ave Lake Forest IL 60045-1205

OLPIN, OWEN, lawyer; b. July 10, 1934; m. Jan Cummings. BS with honors, Brigham Young U., 1955; JD, Columbia U., 1958. Bar: U.S. Supreme Ct. 1973. Assoc. O'Melveny & Myers, Los Angeles, 1958-66, ptnr., 1966-69, 76—; adj. prof. Loyola U., Los Angeles, 1967-69; prof. law U. Utah, Salt Lake City, 1970-76, Farr presdl. endowed chair, 1973-76; Baker vis. prof. law U. Tex., Austin, 1969-70; lectr. in field. Contbr. articles to profl. jours. Bd. dirs Environ. Law Inst., Sierra Club Legal Def. Fund; sr. conf. fellow Adminstrv. Conf. U.S., past pub. mem., past chmn. com. interagy. coordination. Mem. ABA (adminstrv. law and natural resources sects., coun. adminstrv. law sect.), Calif. Bar Assn., D.C. Bar Assn., L.A. County Bar Assn., Am. Law Inst. Office: O'Melveny & Myers 400 S Hope St Los Angeles CA 90071-2899

OLPIN, ROBERT SPENCER, art history educator; b. Palo Alto, Calif., Aug. 30, 1940; s. Ralph Smith and Ethel Lucille (Harman) O.; m. Mary Florence Catharine Reynolds, Aug. 24, 1963; children: Mary Courtney, Cristin Lee, Catharine Elizabeth, Carrie Jean. BS, U. Utah, 1963; AM, Boston U., 1965, PhD, 1971. Lectr. art history Boston U., 1965-67; asst. prof. U. Utah, Salt Lake City, 1967-72, assoc. prof., 1972-76, prof., 1976—, chmn. dept., 1975-82, dir. art history program, 1968-76, 83-84, dean Coll. Fine Arts, 1987—; cons. curator Am. and English art Utah Mus. Fine Arts, 1973—. Grantee U. Utah, 1972, 85, Utah Mus. Fine Arts 1975, Utah Bicentennial Commn., 1975, Ford Found., 1975, Utah Humanities Coun., 1984, Stat Utah, 1989, Christensen Found., 1993, Eccles Found, 1994, 95; trustee Pioneer State Theatre Found., 1988—. Mem. NASULGC (commn. on the arts, 1989-93), Utah Arts Coun., Utah Sci. Authority, Archives Am. Art Smithsonian Instn., Coll. Art Assn. Am., Utah Acad. Scis. Arts Letters, Assn. Historians Am. Art, Internat. Coun. Fine Arts Deans, Phi Kappa Phi, Sigma Nu. Republican. Mormon. Author: Alexander Helwig Wyant, 1836-92, 1968, Mainstreams/Reflections-American/Utah Architecture, 1973, American Painting Around 1850, 1976, Art-Life of Utah, 1977, Dictionary of Utah Art, 1980, A Retrospective of Utah Art, 1981, Waldo Midgley: Birds, Animals, People, Things, 1984, A Basket of Chips, 1985, The Works of Alexander Helwig Wyant, 1986, Salt Lake County Fine Arts Collection, 1987, Signs and Symbols...Utah Art, 1988, J.A.F. Everett, 1989, George Dibble, 1989, Utah Art, 1991; contbd. articles to profl. jours. including Utah, State of the Arts, 1993, Utah History Encyclopedia, 1994. Home: 687 Woodshire Ave Salt Lake City UT 84107-7639 Office: U Utah Coll Fine Arts 250 Art & Architecture Ctr Salt Lake City UT 84112 *Personal philosophy: Not to reduce what I think about life to a motto.*

OLSAK, IVAN KAREL, civil engineer; b. Nitra, Czechoslovakia, Apr. 30, 1933; came to the U.S., 1970; s. Innocenc and Jolana (Rutkovska) O.; m. Renata Gabriela Franclova, Sept. 26, 1959; children: Ruth E., Patricia L. Degree in civil and sanitary engring., Slovak Tech. U., 1958. Registered profl. engr., Pa., Fla. Chief engr. Keramoproject, Bratislava, Czechoslovakia, 1961-63; chief of commune hygien Slovak Dept. Health, Bratislava, 1963-68; draftsman Crippen Acres Ltd., Winnipeg, Canada, 1969-71; design engr. Bouguard & Assocs., Harrisburg, Pa., 1971-72; chief dept. engring. Adair & Brady, Inc., West Palm Beach, Fla., 1972-74; profl., engr., ptnr. Weimer & Co., Inc., West Palm Beach, 1974-75; pvt. practice Olsak & Assocs., West Palm Beach, 1975—. Active Rep. Cen. Com., Tallahassee, Fla., 1984—, Rep. Presdl. Task Force, Washington, 1986—, Rep. Nat. Com., Washington, 1989—, Citizens Against Govt. Waste, Washington, 1988—; hon. mem. Fla. Sherrif's Assn., 1992. Recipient Cert. of Appreciation Palm Beach County Bar Assn., 1990, Fla. Assn. State Troopers, 1987. Mem. NSPE, Fla. Engring. Soc., Profl. Engrs. in Pvt. Practice. Roman Catholic. Achievements include research in oil refinery construction, influence of oil exfiltration on ground water system. Home: 308 Greymon Dr West Palm Beach FL 33405 Office: PO Box 6727 West Palm Beach FL 33405

OLSCAMP, PAUL JAMES, academic administrator; b. Montreal, Que., Can., Aug. 29, 1937; s. James J. and Luella M. (Brush) O.; m. Ruth I. Pratt, Dec. 2, 1978; children by previous marriage: Rebecca Ann, Adam James. BA, U. Western Ont., 1958, MA, 1960; PhD, U. Rochester, 1962. Instr. Ohio State U.; Columbus, 1962, asst. prof., 1963-66, assoc. prof., 1966-69, assoc. dean humanities, 1969; dean faculties, prof. philosophy Roosevelt U., Chgo., 1970-71, v.p. acad. affairs, 1971-72; prof. philosophy Syracuse (N.Y.) U., 1972-75, exec. asst. to chancellor, 1972, vice chancellor student programs, 1972-75; pres. Western Wash. U., Bellingham, 1975-82, Bowling Green (Ohio) State U., 1982—; Grad. fellow in humanities U. Western Ont., 1959. Author: Descartes: The Discourse, Optics, Geometry and Meteorology, 1965, The Moral Philosophy of George Berkeley, 1970, An Introduction to Philosophy, 1971, Malebranche: The Search After Truth, 1980; contbr. articles to profl. jours. Mem. Nat. Coun. on the Humanities, 1988-92, NCAA Pres.'s Commn., 1989-91; bd. dirs., treas. Inter-Am. Univ. Coun. for Econ. and Social Devel. 1991—. Recipient Mackintosh Pub. Speaking and Lecturing award U. Western Ont., 1959-60, Alfred J. Wright award Ohio State U., 1970; Grad. fellow in humanities U. Western Ont., 1959, Grad. Studies fellow U. Rochester, 1960, 61-62; Danforth Found. assoc., 1966—. Mem. Am. Assn. State Colls. and Univs. (mem. com. undergrad. edn. 1982-90, com. confs. and profl. 1989-92), Am. Philos. Assn. Office: Bowling Green State U McFall Ctr Bowling Green OH 43403

OLSCHWANG, ALAN PAUL, lawyer; b. Chgo., Jan. 30, 1942; s. Morton James and Ida (Ginsberg) O.; m. Barbara Claire Miller, Aug. 22, 1965; children: Elliot, Deborah, Jeffrey. B.S., U. Ill., 1963, J.D., 1966. Bar: Ill. 1966, N.Y. 1984, Calif. 1992. Law clk. Ill. Supreme Ct., Bloomington, 1966-67; assoc. Sidley & Austin, and predecessor, Chgo., 1967-73; with Montgomery Ward & Co., Inc., Chgo., 1973-81, assoc. gen. counsel, asst. sec., 1979-81; ptnr. Seki, Jarvis & Lynch, Chgo., 1981-84; exec. v.p., gen. counsel, sec. Mitsubishi Electric Am., Inc., N.Y.C., 1983-91, Cypress, Calif., 1991—. Mem. ABA, Am. Corp. Counsel Assn., Calif. Bar Assn., Ill. Bar Assn., Chgo. Bar Assn., N.Y. State Bar Assn., Bar Assn. of City of N.Y., Am. Arbitration Assn. (panel arbitrators). Office: Mitsubishi Electric Am 5665 Plaza Dr Cypress CA 90630-5023

OLSEN, ALFRED JON, lawyer; b. Phoenix, Oct. 5, 1940; s. William Hans and Vera (Bearden) O.; m. Susan K. Smith, Apr. 15, 1979. B.A. in History, U. Ariz., 1962; MS in Acctg., Ariz. State U., 1964; J.D., Northwestern U., 1966. Bar: Ariz. 1966, Ill. 1966; C.P.A., Ariz. Ill. cert. tax specialist. Acct Arthur Young & Co., C.P.A.s, Chgo., 1966-68; dir. firm Ehmann, Olsen & Lane (P.C.), Phoenix, 1969-76; dir. Streich, Lang, Weeks & Cardon (P.C.), Phoenix, 1977-78; v.p. Olsen-Smith, Ltd., Phoenix, 1978—. Bd. editors: Jour. Agrl. Law and Taxation, 1978-92, Practical Real Estate Lawyer, 1983-95. Mem. Phoenix adv. bd. Salvation Army, 1973-81. Fellow Am. Coll. Trust and Estate Counsel, Am. Coll. Tax Counsel; mem. State Bar Ariz. (chmn. tax sect. 1977-78), ABA (chmn. com. on agr. sect. taxation 1976-78, chmn. CLE com. sect. taxation 1982-84), Am. Law Inst. (chmn. tax planning for agr. 1973-84), Cen. Ariz. Estate Planning Coun. (pres. 1972-73), Nat. Cattlemen's Assn. (tax com. 1979-88), Internat. Acad. Estate and Trust Law (exec. coun. 1994—), Sigma Nu Internat. (pres. 1986-88). Office: 3300 Virginia Financial Pla 301 E Virginia Ave Phoenix AZ 85004-1215

OLSEN, ARTHUR MARTIN, physician, educator; b. Chgo., Aug. 29, 1909; s. Martin I. and Aagot (Rovelstad) O.; m. Yelena Pavlinova, Sept. 16, 1936; children: Margaret Ann (Mrs. Frank A. Jost), David Martin, Karen Yelena (Mrs. Dori Kanellos), Mary Elizabeth. AB, Dartmouth Coll., 1930; MD, U. Chgo., 1935; MS, U. Minn., 1938. Diplomate Am. Bd. Internal Medicine. Intern Cook County Hosp., Chgo., 1935-36; fellow in medicine, resident Mayo Found., U. Minn., 1936-40, from instr. to prof. medicine, 1950-57, prof., 1957—; cons. medicine Mayo Clinic, Rochester, Minn., 1940-76, chmn. divsn. thoracic diseases, 1968-71. Author numerous publs. on diseases of the lungs and esophagus. Mem. nat. heart and lung adv. coun. NIH, 1970-71; trustee Mayo Found., 1961-68, mem. subsplty. bd. pulmonary diseases, 1958—, chmn., 1961-63. Recipient Alexander B. Vishnevski medal Inst. Surgery, Moscow, 1966, Andres Bello medal Govt. of Venezuela, 1987, Disting. Alumnus award Rush Med. Coll., U. Chgo., 1989. Fellow ACP, Am. Coll. Chest Physicians (master, regent 1955—, chmn. 1959-66, pres. 1970, Disting. Fellow award 1978, dir. internat. activities 1976-83, cons. internat. activities 1983-85); mem. AMA (Billings gold meadl for exhibit on esophagitis 1955), Am. Soc. Gastrointestinal Endoscopy (pres. 1962-63), Minn. Respiratory Health Assn. (pres. 1964-68), Minn. Med. Assn., Am. Assn. Thoracic Surgery, Am. Thoracic Soc., Minn. Thoracic Soc. (pres. 1952), Am. Bronchoesophagol. Assn. (pres. 1969-70, Chevalier Jackson

award 1973), Internat. Bronchoesophagol. Soc. (pres. 1979-81), Minn. Soc. Internal Medicine, Brit. Thoracic Soc. (hon.), Nat. Acad. Medicine of Buenos Aires (hon.), Portuguese Soc. Respiratory Pathology (corr.), Sigma Xi, Alpha Omega Alpha. Episcopalian. Home: 211 2nd St NW Apt 2002 Rochester MN 55901-3101 Office: Mayo Clinic Rochester MN 55901

OLSEN, CLIFFORD WAYNE, retired physical chemist; b. Placerville, Calif., Jan. 15, 1936; s. Christian William and Elsie May (Bishop) O.; m. Margaret Clara Gobel, June 16, 1962 (div. 1986); children: Anne Katherine Olsen Cordes, Charlotte Marie; m. Nancy Mayhew Kruger, July 21, 1990 (div. 1994). AA, Grant Tech. Coll., Sacramento, 1955; BA, U. Calif.-Davis, 1957, PhD, 1962. Physicist, project leader, program leader, task leader Lawrence Livermore Nat. Lab., Calif., 1962-93; ret., 1993; mem. Containment Evaluation Panel, U.S. Dept. Energy, 1984—, mem. Cadre for Joint Nuclear Verification Tests, 1988; organizer, editor procs. for 2nd through 7th Symposiums on Containment of Underground Nuclear Detonations, 1983-93. Contbr. articles to profl. jours. Mem. bd. convocators Calif. Luth. U., 1976-78; pres. Livermore Amateur Radio Club, 1994-96. Recipient Chevalier Degree, Order of DeMolay, 1953. Mem. AAAS, Am. Radio Relay League, Seismol. Soc. Am., Livermore Amateur Radio Klub (pres. 1994-95), Sigma Xi, Alpha Gamma Sigma, Gamma Alpha. Democrat. Lutheran. Avocations: gardening, amateur radio, music, cooking.

OLSEN, DAVID ALEXANDER, insurance executive; b. Bklyn., Nov. 29, 1937; s. Alexander and Meile (Anderson) O.; m. Roberta Ruth Garverick, May 11, 1963; children: Bradford, Amy. BA, Bowdoin Coll., 1959. With marine dept. Gt. Am. Ins. Co., N.Y.C. and Chgo., 1959-62; acct. exec. Johnson & Higgins, San Francisco, 1966-71; v.p., mgr. marine dept. Johnson & Higgins, Chgo., 1971-78, exec. v.p. Ill. br., 1978-79; br. mgr., exec. v.p. Johnson & Higgins, Houston, 1979-80, chmn., bd. dirs. Tex. br., 1980-85; exec. v.p. Johnson & Higgins, N.Y.C., 1985-87, pres., COO, 1987-93, CEO, 1990—, chmn., 1991—; trustee Am. Inst. Chartered Property Casualty Underwriters, Ins. Inst. Am., Coll. of Ins., N.Y.C., 1994—, U.S. Coun. Internat. Bus., N.Y.C., 1995. Vice chmn., South St. Seaport Mus., N.Y.C.; v.p. bd. overseers Bowdoin Coll., Brunswick, Maine; bd. dirs. United Way, N.Y.C., N.Y.C. Partnership; bd. dirs. corp. congress N.Y. Pub. Libr. 1st lt. U.S. Army, 1960-62. Mem. India House (bd. dirs.), The Links Club, Econ. Club N.Y., Psi Upsilan. Republican. Avocations: art, photography, antiques, scuba diving, tennis, skiing. Home: 1120 Park Ave New York NY 10128-1242 Office: Johnson & Higgins 125 Broad St New York NY 10004-2400

OLSEN, DAVID MAGNOR, science educator; b. Deadwood, S.D., July 23, 1941; s. Russell Alvin and Dorothy M. Olson; m. Muriel Jean Bigler, Aug. 24, 1963; children: Chad, BS, Luther Coll., 1963; MS in Nat. Sci., U. S.D., 1967. Instr. sci., math. Augustana Acad., Canton, S.D., 1963-66; instr. chemistry Iowa Lakes Community Coll., Estherville, Iowa, 1967-69; instr. chemistry Merced (Calif.) Coll., 1969—, instr. astronomy, 1975—, div. chmn., 1978-88, coord. environ. hazardous materials tech., 1989—. Trustee Merced Union High Sch. Dist., 1969—, pres., 1986-87. Mem. NEA, Am. Chem. Soc., Astron. Soc. of the Pacific, Calif. Tchrs. Assn., Planetary Soc., Calif. State Mining & Mineral Mus. Assn. (bd. dirs. 1988—, sec. 1990-93), Nat. Space Soc., Merced Coll. Faculty Assn. (pres. 1975, 93-94, treas. 1980-90, bd. dirs. 1986—, sec. 1990-91), Castle Challenger Learning Ctr. Found. (bd. dirs. 1991—), Merced Track Club (mem. exec. bd. 1981), M Star Lodge, Sons of Norway (v.p. 1983), Rotary Internat. Democrat. Lutheran. Home: 973 Idaho Dr Merced CA 95340-2513 Office: Merced Coll 3600 M St Merced CA 95348-2806

OLSEN, DONALD BERT, biomedical engineer, experimental surgeon, research facility director; b. Bingham, Utah, Apr. 2, 1930; s. Bertram Hansen and Doris (Boad) O.; m. Joyce Cronquist; children: Craig, Kathy, Debbie, Jeff, Gary. BS, Utah State U., 1952; DVM, Colo. State U., 1956. Gen. practice vet. medicine Smithfield, Utah, 1956-63; extension veterinarian U. Nev., Reno, 1963-65, researcher Deseret Rsch. Inst., 1965-68; postdoctoral fellow U. Colo. Med. Sch., Denver, 1968-72; researcher U. Utah, Salt Lake City, 1972—, rsch. prof. surgery, 1973—, dir. artificial heart lab., 1976—, rsch. prof. pharmaceutics, 1981—, rsch. prof. biomed. engring., 1986—, dir. Inst. Biomed. Engring., 1986—, prof. surgery, 1986—; mem. sci. adv. bd. Link Resources, Inc., 1987. Contbr. articles to profl. jours.; patentee in field. Recipient Clemson award Soc. Biomaterials, N.Y.C., 1987, Centennial award for outstanding alumni Utah State U., Logan, 1988, Gov.'s medal for Sci. and Tech., 1988; named Alumnus of Yr. Colo. State U., 1986. Mem. Am. Soc. Artificial Internal Organs (trustee 1985—, mem. fellowship rev. com. 1983, chmn. program com. 1988-89, sec., treas. 1989-90, pres. elect. 1990-91, pres. 1991-92), Internat. Soc. Artificial Organs (v.p. 1987—), Am. Coll. Vet. Surgeons (hon.), Utah Vet. Med. Assn. (trustee 1985-88), Alpha Zeta. Mem. LDS Ch. Avocations: fishing, hunting, camping, hiking. Office: U Utah Inst Biomed Engring 803 N 300 W Salt Lake City UT 84103-1414

OLSEN, DOUGLAS H., superintendent. Supt. Southfield Christian Schs., Mich. Recipient Blue Ribbon award, 1990-91. Office: Southfield Christian Sch 28650 Lahser Rd Southfield MI 48034

OLSEN, EDMUND GUSTAVE, education educator emeritus; b. Portland, Oreg., Mar. 26, 1908; s. Gustav Adolph and Emma Maria (Bush) O.; m. Faith Theresa Elliott, June 25, 1931 (dec. died 1947); children: Marvin Elliott, Marcia Evelyn; m. Pauline Marie Walsh, Sept. 11, 1948; 1 son, Douglas Walsh. AB, Pacific U., Forest Grove, Oreg., 1930; BD, Union Theol. Sem., N.Y.C., 1933; AM, Columbia U., 1932, EdD, 1937. Instr. acting chmn. dept. edn. Colgate U., 1935-41; assoc. prof., dir. sch. edn. Russell Sage Coll., 1941-45; dir. sch. and community relations Wash. State Office of Pub. Instrn., 1945-50; assoc. prof. edn. adminstrn. U. Tex., 1950-51; edn. dir. NCCJ, Chgo. region, 1951-66; prof. edn. Calif. State U. at Hayward, 1966-73, emeritus, 1973—; formerly vis. prof. Ga. Tchrs. Coll., U. Wash., William and Mary, Western Wash. Coll. Edn., U. Maine, Wash. State U., Stanford; cons. Phila. Teachers Workshop; dir. Kitsap County Teachers' Workshop; dir. workshop on community resources U.Tex., Mont. State U.; dir. workshop on human relations Northwestern U., Nat. Coll. Edn., U. Oreg., Roosevelt U., U. Chgo., Pacific U., Pacific Lutheran U.; dir. Curry County (Oreg.) Ednl. Service Dist. Prin. author: School and Community; co-author: Life Centering Education; compiler: School and Community Programs; compiler, editor: The School and Community Reader; editor: The Modern Community School; editor, prin. author: Then Till Now: A Social History of the Brookings-Harbor Community; contbr. numerous articles to profl. jours. Exec. sec. Wash. State Coordinating Council for UNESCO; pres. Park Ridge Council Human Relations. Recipient Thomas H. Wright award City of Chgo., 1957; Distinguished Service award Nat. Community Edn. Assn., 1969; Fulbright scholar U. Coll. Rhodesia and Nyasaland, 1958. Mem. NEA (life), Oreg. Community Edn. Assn. (life membership award 1987), Nat. Community Edn. Assn. (life mem. award 1977), Blue Key, Kappa Delta Pi, Phi Delta Kappa. Unitarian. Lodge: Rotary. Home: 317 Memory Ln Brookings OR 97415-9031 *The goal of education should be to improve the quality of human living, both as individuals and in group life on this planet. The school curriculum should be centered in the enduring life concerns of human kind, oriented to the future yet ever aware of the relevant past in relation to present human needs.*

OLSEN, EDWARD JOHN, geologist, educator; b. Chgo., Nov. 23, 1927; s. Edward John and Elizabeth (Bornemann) O.; children—Andrea, Erick-a. A.B., U. Chgo., 1951, M.S., 1955, Ph.D., 1959. Geologist Geol. Survey Can., 1953, U.S. Geol. Survey, 1954—; Canadian Johns-Manville Co. Ltd., 1956, 57, 59; asst. prof. Case Inst. Tech., also Western Res. U., 1959-60; curator mineralogy Field Mus. Natural History, 1960-91, chmn. dept. geology, 1974-78; research assoc. prof. dept. geophys. scis. U. Chgo., 1977—; adj. prof. U. Ill., Chgo. Circle, 1970-91. Assoc. editor Geochim. et Cosmochim. Acta., 1985-91. Fellow Mineral. Soc. Am.; mem. Mineral. Assn. Can., Geochem. Soc., Meteoritical Soc. Spl. research stability relations of minerals in earth's mantle and meteorites. Office: U Chgo Dept Geophys Sci Chicago IL 60637

OLSEN, FRANCES ELISABETH, law educator, theorist; b. Chgo., Feb. 4, 1945; d. Holger and Ruth Mathilda (Pfeifer) O.; m. Harold Irving Porter, June 8, 1984. Cert., Roskilde (Denmark) Højskole, 1967; BA, Goddard Coll., 1968; JD, U. Colo., 1971; SJD, Harvard U., 1984. Bar: Colo. 1972, U.S. Dist. Ct. Colo. 1972. Law clk. hon. Arraj U.S. Dist. Ct. Colo., Denver,

1972; lawyer Am. Indian Movement, Wounded Knee, S.D., 1973; pvt. practice Denver, 1973-74; law prof. U. Puget Sound, Tacoma, Wash., 1975-79, St. John's U., Jamaica, N.Y., 1982-83, UCLA, 1984—; vis. fellow New Coll., Oxford, Eng., 1987; vis. prof. U. Mich., Ann Arbor, 1988, Harvard U., Cambridge, Mass., 1990-91; Fulbright prof. U. Frankfurt, Germany, 1991-92. Contbr. articles to law revs. Named Outstanding Alumnus U. Colo., 1989. Mem. Assn. Am. Law Schs. (chair jurisprudence sect. 1987-88, exec. com. women in law teaching sect. 1986-89), European Conf. Critical Legal Studies, Conf. Critical Legal Studies. Avocations: wind-surfing, sailing, bicycling, mountain climbing, harpsichord. Office: UCLA Sch Law 405 Hilgard Ave Los Angeles CA 90024-1722

OLSEN, GORDON, retired lawyer; b. Pitts., July 5, 1927; s. ALvin Gordon and Alma (Wollbrandt) O.; m. Nancy Smith, Dec. 26, 1955; children: Lars Andrew, Lisa Olsen Lerch (dec.). Student, Duquesne U., 1947-48; B.A., Pa. State U., 1951; LL.B., Fordham U., 1957; student, Ariz. State U., 1986. Bar: Ariz. 1958. Sr. asst. furniture buyer Macy's, N.Y.C., 1957-58; practice law Phoenix, until 1986, ret.; law clk. to justice Ariz. Supreme Ct., 1957-58; assoc. Lewis & Roca, 1958-63, ptnr., 1963-86. Bd. dirs. Family Svc. Phoenix, 1962-68, pres., 1966-67; bd. dirs. Ariz. Assn. for Health and Welfare, 1967-70, 1st v.p., 1967-68; bd. dirs. Community Coun., 1969-75; commr. LEAP Commn., Phoenix Community Action Agy., 1971-75, chmn., 1972-73; mem. plan steering com. Comprehensive Health Planning Coun., 1973-75; mem. CETA Manpower Adv. Coun., 1974-76, chmn., 1974-75, vice chmn., 1975-76; bd. dirs. Planned Parenthood Cent. and No. Ariz., 1975-81, pres., 1977-78; pres. Trinity Luth. Ch. of Maricopa County, 1989-91. Seaman 1st cl. USNR, 1945-46; 1st lt. USAF, 1951-53. Home: 232 W Frier Dr Phoenix AZ 85021-7233

OLSEN, HANS PETER, lawyer; b. Detroit, May 21, 1940; s. Hans Peter and Paula M. (Olsen) O.; m. Elizabeth Ann Gayton, Sept. 14, 1968; children: Hans Peter, Heidi Susanne, Stephanie Elizabeth. BA, Mich. State U., 1962; JD, Georgetown U., 1965; LLM, NYU, 1966. Bar: Mich. 1967, Pa. 1969, R.I. 1974. Law clk. firm Monaghan, McCrone, Campbell & Crawmer, Detroit, 1964; law clk. U.S. Ct. of Claims, Fed. Appellate Ct., Washington, 1966-68; assoc. firm Pepper, Hamilton & Scheetz, Phila., 1968-72; ptnr. firm Hinckley, Allen, & Snyder, Providence, 1972—; adv. planning com. U. R.I. Fed. Taxation Inst.; continuing legal edn. adv. bd., tax symposium adv. bd. Bryant Coll.; mem. Gov.'s State Task Force, R.I. Pub. Expenditure Coun.; cons. Bur. Nat. Affairs; liaison Bar Assn. and North Atlantic region IRS; tax adminstrs. adv. com. R.I.; lectr. tax insts. and other profl. groups N.Y., L.A., Phila., Boston, R.I. Contbr. numerous articles on taxation to legal jours. Fellow Am. Bar Found.; mem. ABA (sect. taxation, exempt orgns. com., subcom. healthcare, corp.-shareholders rels. com., partnerships com.), R.I. Bar Assn. (sect. taxation, sec.-treas. 1977-80, liaison with CPAs, specialization com., mem. various coms.), Providence C. of C., R.I. C. of C. (chmn. com. on bus. taxes and public spending, mem., past chmn. legis. action council), Mich. State Bar, Pa. State Bar. Home: 274 Olney St Providence RI 02906-2305 Office: 1500 Fleet Ctr Providence RI 02903

OLSEN, HAROLD FREMONT, lawyer; b. Davenport, Wash., Oct. 17, 1920; s. Oscar E. and Dorothy (Sprowls) O.; m. Jeanne L. Rounds, Aug. 30, 1942; children: Eric O., Ronald R., Margaret Ruth. B.A., Wash. State U., 1942; LL.B., Harvard U., 1948. Bar: Wash. 1948, U.S. Ct. Claims 1970, U.S. Supreme Ct. 1982; C.P.A., Wash. Instr. Oxford Bus. Sch., Cambridge, Mass., 1946-47; examiner Wash. State Dept. Pub. Utilities, 1948; with firm Perkins Coie (and predecessors), Seattle, 1949—, ptnr., 1954-88, of counsel, 1989—; bd. dirs. Exotic Metals Forming Co.; v.p., dir. Barker Ranch, Inc.; trustee Exec. Svcs. Corp. of Wash. Bd. dirs. Northwest Hosp. Found., Northwest Hosp., 1980-90; trustee Wash. State U. Found., chmn. 1986-88; mem. adv. coun. Wash. State U. Sch. Bus. and Econs., 1978-90; trustee, mem. exec. com., pres. Mus. of Flight, 1991-92, chmn. 1993. Served to maj. USAAF, 1942-45. Decorated Silver Star. Mem. ABA, Wash. Bar Assn., Seattle Bar Assn., Aircraft Industry Assn. (chmn. legal com. 1957), Nat. Contract Mgmt. Assn., Alumni Assn. Wash. State U. (pres. 1956), Mcpl. League Seattle and King County, Seattle C. of C., Internat. Law Soc., Am. Judicature Assn., Phi Beta Kappa, Phi Kappa Phi, Tau Kappa Epsilon, Rainier Club, Seattle Golf Club (pres. 1986-87), Sr. N.W. Golf Assn. Congregationalist. Home: 8875 Overlake Dr W Bellevue WA 98004-5347 Office: 1201 3rd Ave Ste 4500 Seattle WA 98101-3099

OLSEN, JACK, writer; b. Indpls., June 7, 1925; s. Rudolph O. and Florence (Drecksage) O.; m. Su Peterson, 1966; children: John Robert, Susan Joyce, Jonathan Rhoades, Julia Crispin, Evan Pierce, Barrie Elizabeth, Emily Sara Peterson, Harper Alexander Peterson. Student, U. Pa., 1946-47. Newspaper reporter San Diego Union Tribune, 1947-48, San Diego Jour., 1949-50, Washington Daily News, 1950- 51; TV news editor and broadcaster sta. WMAL-TV, Washington, 1950-51; newspaper reporter New Orleans Item, 1952-53, Chgo. Sun-Times, 1954-55; corr. Time mag., 1956-58, Midwest chief, 1959-59. Author: The Mad World of Bridge, 1960, (pseudonym Jonathan Rhoades) Over the Fence is Out, 1961, The Climb up to Hell, 1962, (with Charles Goren) Bridge Is My Game, 1965, Black is Best: The Riddle of Cassius Clay, 1967, The Black Athlete: A Shameful Story, 1968, Silence on Monte Sole, 1968, Night of the Grizzlies, 1969, The Bridge at Chappaquiddick, 1970, Aphrodite: Desperate Mission, 1970, Slaughter the Animals, Poison the Earth, 1971, The Girls in the Office, 1971, The Girls on the Campus, 1972, Sweet Street, 1973, The Man with the Candy, 1974, Alphabet Jackson, 1974, Massy's Game, 1976, The Secret of Fire Five, 1977, Night Watch, 1979, Missing Persons, 1981, Have You Seen My Son?, 1982, Son: A Psychopath and His Victims, 1983, Give a Boy a Gun, 1985, Cold Kill, 1987, Doc: The Rape of the Town of Lovell, 1990, Predator, 1991, The Misbegotten Son, 1993, Charmer: A Ladies Man and his Victims, 1994; work included in numerous anthologies. Served with OSS AUS, 1943-44. Recipient Edgar award Mystery Writers Am., Page One award Chgo. Newspaper Guild; Nat. Headliners award; Wash. Gov.'s award; citations U. Ind., Columbia U.

OLSEN, KATHIE LYNN, neuroscientist, administrator; b. Portland, Oreg., Aug. 3, 1952; d. Roland Berg and Gladys Elizabeth (Eldreth) O. BS, Chatham Coll., 1974; PhD, U. Calif., Irvine, 1979. Postdoct. fellow Harvard Med. Sch., Boston, 1979-80; rsch. scientist Long Island Rsch. Inst., Stony Brook, N.Y., 1980-83; rsch. asst. prof. SUNY, Stony Brook, 1982-85, asst. prof., 1985-89; assoc. program dir. NSF, Washington, 1984-86, program dir., 1988—, leader neurosci., 1991—; adj. assoc. prof. George Washington U., Washington, 1989—; cons. editor Hormones and Behavior, 1988—. Contbr. articles to profl. jours, chapters to books. Mem. Soc. Neurosci., Endocrine Soc., Women in Neurosci., Sod. Study of Reproduction, Internat. Acad. Sex Rsch. Office: Nat Sci Found 1800 G St NW Washington DC 20550-0001

OLSEN, KENNETH HARRY, manufacturing company executive; b. Bridgeport, Conn., Feb. 20, 1926; s. Oswald and Svea (Nording) O.; m. Eeva-Liisa Aulikki Valve, Dec. 12, 1950. B.S in Elec. Engring. MIT, 1950, M.S., 1952. Elec. engr. Lincoln Lab., MIT, 1950-57; founder Digital Equipment Corp., Maynard, Mass., 1957, pres. emeritus; bd. dirs. Polaroid Corp., Ford Motor Co. Patentee magnetic devices. Mem. Pres.'s Sci. Adv. Com., 1971-73; trustee, v.p. Joslin Diabetes Found.; mem. corp. Wentworth Inst., Boston, MIT, Cambridge; trustee Gordon Coll., Wenham, Mass. Served with USNR, 1944-46. Named Young Elec. Engr. of Year Eta Kappa Nu, 1960; recipient of Nat. Medal of Tech., Nat. Sci. Found., 1993. Mem. Nat. Acad. Engring. Office: Digital Equipment Corp 40 Old Bolton Rd Stow MA 01775-1299

OLSEN, KURT, investment company executive, adviser; b. Astoria, Oreg., Nov. 2, 1924; s. Matt J. and Irene (Lindholm) O.; m. Lois Helen Giberson, Mar. 23, 1947; children: Kurt F., Eric J., Mark C. BS, U. Oreg., 1949. RR mgr. and ptnr. Foster & Marshall, Eugene, Oreg., 1948-61; mgr., v.p., dir. Harris, Upham Inc., Portland, Oreg., 1961-70; v.p., dir. Foster & Marshall Inc., Portland, 1971-76; pres. Alpen Securities, Inc., Portland, 1977—. mem. adv. bd. Columbia Pacific coun. Boy Scouts Am.; mem. nat. coun., 1966-73; bd. dirs. United Way Columbia and Willamette, 1973-77, Oreg. Law Found, 1986-89. With USNR, 1944-46. Mem. Nat. Assn. Securities Dealers (chmn. dist. 1 1967), Investment Bankers Assn. Am. (bd. govs. 1968-70), Sigma Alpha Epsilon, Rotary. Home: 1127 SW Myrtle Dr Portland OR 97201-2270 Office: Alpen Securities Inc 1425 Yeon Bldg Portland OR 97204

OLSEN, MERLIN JAY, sports analyst, former professional football player, actor; b. Logan, Utah, Sept. 15, 1940; s. Lynn Jay and Merle (Barrus) O.; m. Susan Wakley, Mar. 30, 1962; children: Kelly Lynn, Jill Catherine, Nathan Merlin. B.S. in Fin., Utah State U., 1962, M.S. in Econs, 1970. Profl. football player Los Angeles Rams, 1962-76; with Allied Chem. Corp., 1962-67; motivational cons. Liggett & Myers, 1971-72, Consol. Cigar, 1972-73; pub. relations exec. Combined Communications Corp., 1972-73; owner Merlin Olsen Porsche Audi, 1969—; TV spokesman Florists' Transworld Delivery. Sports analyst, NBC, 1977-93; numerous other TV performances; regular in: Little House on the Prairie; star: TV series Father Murphy, 1981, Fathers & Sons (NBC-TV), Aaron's Way; co-host Children's Miracle Network Telethon, 1983—; TV movies: A Fire in the Sky, The Golden Moment, An Olympic Love Story, Time Bomb; TV Specials: The Juggler of Notre Dame, 1982, (host, narrator) Lifequest, 1987-89, The Sleeping Beauty, 1987, The Nutcracker, 1990, Fantastic Facts, 1991-92; co-producer: films include: All Pro, Mitchell, Something Big, One More Train to Rob, The Undefeated. Grand marshall 94th Tournament of Roses Parade; v.p. So. Calif. Multiple Sclerosis Soc. Recipient Numerous football awards including MVP (Maxwell Trophy), 1974, Coll. Football Hall of Fame, 1980; named to Pro Football of Fame, 1982, NFL-AFL Quarter Century Team. Mem. Sigma Chi, Phi Kappa Phi. *

OLSEN, REX NORMAN, trade association executive; b. Hazeltown, Idaho, Apr. 9, 1925; s. Adolph Lars and Pearl (Robbins) O. B.J., B.A. in English, U. Mo., 1950. Editor Clissold Pub. Co., Chgo., 1950-54; copy editor Am. Peoples Ency., Chgo., 1955; asst. editor Am. Hosp. Assn., Chgo., 1956-59; mng. editor Am. Hosp. Assn., 1959-64, dir. jours. div., 1964-69, dir. publs. bur., 1969-75, exec. editor, asso. pub., 1975-79; v.p., treas. Am. Hosp. Pub., Inc., 1980-85; pres. Words Ltd., 1985—. Served with USNR, 1943-46. Mem. Am. Pub. Health Assn., Am. Med. Writers Assn., Soc. Nat. Assn. Pubs. (sec. 1975-76, 2d v.p 1976-77, 1st v.p. 1977-78, pres. 1978-79), Chgo. Bus. Publs. Assn. (dir. 1974-78, 4th v.p 1978-79), Sigma Delta Chi. Home and Office: 3845 N Alta Vista Ter Chicago IL 60613-2907

OLSEN, RICHARD GALEN, biomedical engineer, researcher; b. Colorado Springs, Colo., Aug. 10, 1945; s. Floyd Edwin and Ruth Elizabeth (Robinson) O.; m. Karen Fidler Brubaker, June 17, 1973; children: Kathryn Elizabeth, Nickolas Robert. BSEE, U. Mo., Rolla, 1968; MS, U. Utah, 1970, PhD, 1975. Registered profl. engr., Fla. Engr. Bendix Corp., Kansas City, Mo., 1968-69; elec. engr. Naval Aerospace Med. Rsch. Lab., Pensacola, Fla., 1975-79, chief engring. systems div., 1979-82, head bioengring. divsn., 1982-94; head bioengring. dept. Naval Med. Rsch. Inst. Detachment, Brooks AFB, Tex., 1994—; tech. cons., Armstrong Lab., USAF, 1991—, German Ministry of Def., Mannheim, 1994, Naval Surface Warfare Ctr., Dahlgren, Va., 1989-91, Naval Sea Sys. Command, Arlington, Va., 1989-91. Contbr. articles to profl. jours. and books. With U.S. Army, 1970-72. Recipient NDEA fellowship U. Utah, 1969, Fred A. Hitchcock award Aerospace Physiologist Soc. of Aerospace Med., 1987; named Engr. of the Yr., N.W. Fla. Engrs. Coun., 1991. Mem. IEEE (sr., chmn. Pensacola sect. 1982-83, mem. radio frequency and microwave measuring methods 1982—, nionizing radiation hazards com. 1983—, SCC-28 com., cert. of appreciation 1983), Bioelectromagnetics Soc. (charter, editl. bd. 1990—), Aerospace Med. Assn. (editl. cons. 1986—), Fla. Engring. Soc., Rotary (bd. dirs. Suburban West 1980-81), Sigma Xi, Eta Kappa Nu, Tau Beta Pi, Phi Kappa Phi. Republican. Adventist. Achievements include conducting the first shipboard measurements of specific absorption rate (SAR) and of electromagnetic pulse (EMP) induced body current; patents in RF coil for hypothermia resuscitation, RF dosimetry system and RF warming of submerged extremities. Home: 1503 N Baylen St Pensacola FL 32501-2101 Office: Naval Med Rsch Inst Detach 8308 Hawks Rd Brooks AFB TX 78235-5423

OLSEN, ROBERT JOHN, savings and loan association executive; b. N.Y.C., July 8, 1928; s. Christian Marinius and Agnes Geraldine (Jensen) O.; m. Eleanor Marion Peters, June 19, 1951; 1 child, Philip John. BS, Strayer Coll., 1956. Supervisory agt. Fed. Home Loan Bank Bd., N.Y.C., 1956-65; pres., dir. Keystone Savs. & Loan Assn., Asbury Park, N.J., 1965-82; chmn. bd., pres. Rapid Money Svcs., Inc., Deal, N.J., 1977-82, Elmora Savs. and Loan Assn., Elizabeth, N.J., 1982-88; pres. Ramsey (N.J.) Savs. and Loan Assn., 1988-90; pres. mng. agt. Resolution Trust Corp., 1990—; also bd. dirs. Ramsey (N.J.) Savs. and Loan Assn.; pres. 2d Century Corp., Asbury Park, 1980-82; dir. Central Corp. of Savs. & Loans, Newark, 1976-82, Fed. Home Loan Bank N.Y., 1974-77. Councilman, Borough of Oceanport, N.J., 1971-73, 77-80, pres., 1979; police commr. Oceanport, N.J., 1972-80; v.p. Econ. Devel. Corp., Asbury Park, N.J., 1972-81, Oceanport, N.J., 1974-77; mem. Zoning Bd. of Adjustment, Oceanport, 1969-70; mem. Citizens Adv. Coun., Oceanport, 1975-76; dir. Monmouth and Ocean Devel. Coun., Eatontown, N.J., 1974-82; trustee Savs. and Loan Found. of Washington, 1978-82; chmn. N.J. Electronic Funds Transfer Com., 1971-82; mem. Monmouth County Fair Housing Task Force, 1980-82, Monmouth County Vocat. Sch. Bd., 1981-83; pres. Paulinskill Lake Assn., 1987-90, chpt. 56 Heart Assn., Morristown, N.J., 1989. Served with USMC, 1946-48, 1950-56. Mem. N.J. Savs. League (pres. chpt. 1966-67), U.S. Savs. League (vice chmn. com. on internal ops., chmn. ATM com.), Nat. Assn. Review Appraisers and Mortgage Underwriters, Fin. Mgrs. Soc. (adv. coun.), Nat. Assn. Savs. and Loan Suprs., Nat. Soc. Fin. Examiners, Monmouth County, Eastern Union County Realtors Assn., Sussex County Realtors Assn., Internat. Union Bldg. Socs. and Savs. Assns., Navy League, Assn. U.S. Army., World Trade Club (N.Y.C.), Channel Club (Monmouth Beach, N.J.), Provost Marshals Guild Club (Ft. Monmouth, N.J.), Wheelman's Club (Asbury Park). Home: 51 Vail Dr Newton NJ 07860 Office: Resolution Trust Corp 10 Waterview Blvd Parsippany NJ 07054

OLSEN, ROGER MILTON, lawyer; b. San Jose, Calif., 1942. AB, U. Calif., Berkeley, 1964; postgrad. in Am. Govt., U. So. Calif., 1964-65; JD, Boalt Hall, 1968; LLM in Taxation, George Washington U., 1977. Bar: Calif. 1969, D.C. 1977. Dept. dist. atty. Alameda County Dist. Atty.'s Office, Oakland, Calif., 1969-72; trial atty. tax div. Dept. Justice, Washington, 1972-76; asst. atty. gen. criminal div., 1981-83, dep. asst. atty. gen. tax div., 1983-85, asst. atty. gen. tax div., 1985-87. Author: Criminal Tax Procedure I, 1989, and II, 1990. Mem. U. Calif. Alumni Assn., Boalt Hall Alumni Assn., Big C Soc. Office: Roger M Olsen PC 445 S Figueroa St Ste 2400 Los Angeles CA 90071-1628

OLSEN, STANLEY SEVERN, minister; b. Denver, Mar. 10, 1944; s. Olaf S. and Margaret Ruth (Hook) O.; m. Patricia Joy Wahlen, Sept. 17, 1966; children: Nathaniel S, Nisse J. BA, Bethel Coll., 1966; postgrad., U. Minn., 1968; MA in Christian Edn., Bethel Theol. Sem., 1969; Theol. Orientation, North Park Theol. Sem., 1984; D of Ministry, Trinity Divinity Sch., 1995. Ordained to ministry, 1985. Minister of Christian Edn. Aldrich Ave. Presbyn. Ch., Mpls., 1969-71; minister of children, dir. children's ctr. Grace Community Ch., Tempe, Ariz., 1972; minister of Christian Edn. Bethel Reformed Ch., Bellflower, Calif. 1973-77; assoc. pastor First Covenant Ch., Mpls., 1977-85; exec. pastor Hillcrest Covenant Ch., Prairie Village, Kans., 1985—; adj. prof. Bethel Theol. Sem., St. Paul, 1980-85; chmn. N.W. Covenant Conf. Bd. of Christian Edn., Mpls., 1980-84, Nat. Bd. of Christian Edn. and Discipleship, 1987-93; pres. Nat. Assn. Dirs. Christian Edn., 1981-85; vis. prof. AIM Pastors Conf., Nairobi, Kenya, 1995. Pub., editor (mag.) Infocus, 1981-83; author: (with others) Introduction to Christian Education, 1991, Adult Education in the Church, 1992; keynote speaker Christian Edn. Meeting of Seminarians, Dallas, 1992. Mem. Young Reps., Mpls., 1966-69; pres. Bellflower (Calif.) Ministerial Assn., 1974-77; sec. Downtown Pastors Ministerial Assn., Mpls., 1981-84. Mem. Profl. Assn. Christian Educators (bd. dirs., v.p. 1986-93). Republican. Avocations: hist. fiction, antique fishing gear. Office: Hillcrest Covenant Ch 8801 Nall Ave Shawnee Mission KS 66207

OLSEN, T. FRED, timing instruments manufacturing company executive. Chmn., chief exec. officer Timex Group Ltd., Waterbury, Conn. Office: Timex Group Ltd PO Box 2126 Waterbury CT 06722-2126

OLSEN, THOMAS RICHARD, SR., air force officer; b. Houston, June 28, 1934; s. Oscar Leonard and Catherine (Byers) O.; m. Dorothy Kendrick Taylor, July 7, 1956; children: Thomas Richard Jr., Lisa Kendrick Olsen Wesolick. BSME, Tex. A&M U., 1956; MS in Internat. Affairs, George Washington U., 1968. Mech. engr. Tex. Gas Corp., Houston, 1956; commd.

2d lt. USAF, 1957, advanced through grades to maj. gen., 1986; pilot trainee Greenville AFB, Miss., 1957-58; fighter pilot 326 FIS/526 FIS, U.S. and Fed. Republic Germany, 1958-65, 614 TFS/615 TFS, England AFB, La., 615 TFS, Phan Rang AB, Vietnam, 1966-67; instr. U.S. Naval Amphibious Sch., Coronado, Calif., 1968-71; fighter pilot 391 TFS, Mt. Home AFB, Idaho, 1971-72; squadron ops. officer, squadron comdr. 391 TFS, Mt. Home AFB, 1972-74; chief rated officer Mgmt. Hdqrs. AFMPC, Randolph AFB, Tex., 1975-78; chief of staff Hdqrs. 9th Air Force, Shaw AFB, S.C., 1978-79; dep. comdr. Hdqrs. 314th Air Div., Seoul, Republic of Korea, 1979-81; dir. ops. Hdqrs. 5th Air Force, Yokota AFB, Japan, 1981-82; wing comdr. 51 TFW, Osan AB, Republic of Korea, 1982-83; dep. dir. ops. Hdqrs. Pacific Command, Camp Smith, Hawaii, 1983-85; asst. chief of staff ops. Hdqrs. AFCENT, NATO, Brunsuum, The Netherlands, 1985-87; dep. comdr., chief of staff Hdqrs. 4 ATAF, NATO, Heidelberg, Fed. Republic Germany, 1987-89; vice comdr. Hdqrs. 9th Air Force, Shaw AFB, S.C., 1989-91; dep. comdr. U.S. Cen. Command Air Forces (Desert Shield/Desert Storm), Riyadh, Saudi Arabia, 1990-91; ret., 1991. Mem. Optimist Club, Coronado, 1969-71. Mem. Air Force Assn., Ret. Officers Assn., Daedalians, Kiwanis, Rotary. Presbyterian. Home: 1006 Golfcrest Rd Sumter SC 29154-6179

OLSEN, TILLIE, author; b. Omaha, Nebr., Jan. 14, 1912; d. Samuel and Ida (Beber) Lerner; m. Jack Olsen; children: Karla, Julie, Kathie, Laurie. LittD (hon.), U. Nebr., 1979, Knox Coll., 1982, Hobart and William Smith Coll., 1984, Clark U., 1985, Albright Coll., 1986, Wooster Coll., 1991, Mills Coll., 1995. Writer-in-residence Amherst Coll., 1969-70; vis. faculty Stanford U., 1972; Writer-in-residence, vis. faculty English M.I.T., 1973-74, U. Mass., Boston, 1974; internat. vis. scholar Norway, 1980; Hill prof. U. Minn., spring 1986; writer-in-residence Kenyon Coll., 1987—; Regents lectr. U. Calif. at San Diego, 1977—, UCLA, 1987; commencement spkr. English dept. U. Calif., Berkeley, 1983, Hobart and William Smith Coll., 1984 Bennington Coll., 1986. Author: Tell Me A Riddle, 1961 (title story received First prize O'Henry award 1961), Rebecca Harding Davis: Life in the Iron Mills, 1972, Yonnondio: From the Thirties, 1974, Silences, 1978, The Word Made Flesh, 1984; editor: Mother to Daughter, Daughter to Mother, 1984, Mothers and Daughters, That Special Quality: A Exploration in Photographs, 1989; short fiction published in 173 anthologies; books translated in 11 langs. Recipient Am. Acad. and Nat. Inst. of Arts and Letters award for distinguished contbn. to Am. letters, 1975, Ministry to Women award Unitarian Universalist Fedn., 1980, Brit. Post Office and B.P.W. award, 1980, REA award Dungannon Found., 1994; Ford Found. grantee, 1959, Nat. Endowment for Arts grantee, 1968, MacDowell Colony grantee; Stanford Univ. creative writing fellow, 1956-57, Radcliffe Inst. fellow, 1962-64, Guggenheim fellow, 1975-76, Bunting Inst. Radcliffe Coll. fellow, 1985; Tillie Olsen day designated in San Francisco, 1981. Mem. Authors Guild, PEN, Writers Union. Home: 1435 Laguna St # 6 San Francisco CA 94115

OLSHAN, KENNETH S., advertising agency executive; b. Evansville, Ind., July 15, 1932; s. Harry and Ethel (Hamburg) O.; m. Patricia E. Shane, Aug. 25, 1954; children: Margot E., Mathew S., John K. BA, Ind. U., 1954; postgrad., Grad. Sch. Bus. Washington U., 1955. Trainee, TV-radio buyer Batten Barton Durstine & Osborn (Advt.), N.Y.C., 1958-60; v.p., account exec. Doherty, Clifford, Steers & Shenfield, N.Y.C., 1960-64; v.p., account mgmt. supr. McCaffrey & McCall, N.Y.C., 1964-67; pres. Olshan, Smith & Gould, N.Y.C., 1967-69, Doherty, Mann & Olshan, N.Y.C., 1969-76; exec. v.p. Wells, Rich, Greene, N.Y.C., 1976-80; pres. Wells, Rich, Greene/East, 1980-81; chmn. Wells, Rich, Greene/USA, 1981-82, also dir.; chmn. Wells, Rich, Greene/World Wide, 1982-90, chmn. bd. dirs.; chief exec. officer Wells Rich Greene BDDP Inc., 1990—; vice-chmn. BDDP Advt. Agy. Group, 1990—; lectr. journalism Miriam Meloy Sturgeon Ind. U., 1981; mem. dean's adv. coun. Ind. U. Sch. Bus., 1988—; mem. Advt. Coun. Campaigns Rev. Com., 1994. Trustee Westport Pub. Libr., 1976-83; bd. dirs. Nat. Multiple Sclerosis Found., 1984—, Poly. U. Promise Bd., 1988—; trustee Central Park Conservancy, 1992—, chmn. mktg. com., 1992—. With U.S. Army, 1954-56. Mem. Am. Assn. Advt. Agys. (bd. dirs. 1992-95, ops. com. 1993-95), Blue Key, Sigma Alpha Mu. Office: Wells Rich Greene BDDP Inc 9 W 57th St New York NY 10019-2600

OLSHAN, RICHARD A., statistician, educator; b. Portland, Oreg., May 17, 1942; s. A.C. and Dorothy (Olds) O.; m. Susan Abroff, 1979. AB, U. Calif., Berkeley, 1963; PhD, Yale U., 1966. Rsch. staff statistician, lectr. Yale U., New Haven, 1966-67; asst. prof. of statistics Stanford (Calif.) U., 1967-72; assoc. prof. of statistics and math. U. Mich., Ann Arbor, 1972-75; assoc. prof. of math. U. Calif., San Diego, 1975-77, prof. of math., 1977-89, dir. lab. for math. and statistics, 1982-89; prof. of biostatistics U. Sch. Medicine Stanford U., 1989—, prof. by courtesy dept. statis., 1990—. Office: Stanford U Sch Medicine Hrp Bldg Stanford CA 94305

OLSHIN, SAMUEL E., architect. BA in Design of the Environment, U. Pa., 1982, MArch, 1986. Registered architect, Pa. Project arch. Tony Atkin & Assocs., Phila., 1986-95, Atkin, Olshin, Lawson-Bell & Assocs., Phila., 1995—; Juror Temple U., U. Pa., Drexel U., Bryn Mawr Coll., Villanova U., Phila. Coll. Textiles and Sci.; participant Architecture in Edn., 1985—; asst. prof. U. Pa., fall 1988; lectr. Bryn Mawr Coll., 1990—. Prin. works include Jaffe History of Art Bldg. at U. Pa., Wenger Residence, Hitchings Residence (Merit award Cedar Shake and Shingle Bur. 1989, 1st prize Sympathetic Additions category Nat. Trust Hist. Preservation, 1990), Mitchell Residence (Merit award Builder Mag. 1991), Kesher Israel Synagogue renovation, Pensacola St. Beach Pavilion, Seaside, Fla.; one man shows include AIA, Phila., 1995. Phila. Chpt. scholar Victorian Soc., summer 1991. Office: Atkin Olshin Lawson Bell & Assocs Architects 125 S 9th St Fl 900 Philadelphia PA 19107-5122

OLSINSKI, PETER KEVIN, international outplacement executive; b. N.Y.C., Aug. 27, 1942; s. Peter Andrew and Mary Lucinda (O'Connor) O.; m. Joan Mary Mahon; children: Marybeth, Peter John. BA, Cathedral Coll., 1964; MS, St. John's U., Jamaica, N.Y., 1971; PhD, St. John's U., 1979. Dir. pers. Bklyn. Diocese, 1968-84; dir. Mainstream Access, N.Y.C., 1984-85; v.p. Fuchs Cuthrell & Co., N.Y.C., 1985-88; sr. v.p. Fuchs Cuthrell & Co., 1988, exec. v.p., 1989-91, sr. exec. v.p., 1991-94; vice chmn. Fuchs Cuthrell & Co., N.Y.C., 1994—; also bd. dirs., 1991-94, vice chmn., 1994—. Mem. Somerset Hills Hist. Soc., N.J. Mem. Am. Psychol. Assn., Soc. for Indsl. & Orgnizational Psychology, Am. Soc. for Tng. and Devel., Soc. Human Resource Mgmt. Roman Catholic. Avocation: Civil War research. Office: Fuchs Cuthrell & Co Inc 555 Madison Ave New York NY 10022-3301

OLSON, BETTY-JEAN, elementary education educator; b. Camas, Wash., Apr. 26, 1934; d. Earl Raymond and Mabel Anna (Burden) Clemons; m. Arthur H. Geda, Dec. 31, 1957; children: Ann C. Geda-Wall, Scott A. Geda; m. Conrad A. Olson, June 14, 1980. AA, Clark Coll., 1954; BA in Edn., Cen. Wash. Coll. Edn., 1956; MEd, No. Monn. Coll., 1975. Cert. elem. tchr. class I, Mont., supr. K-9 class III. Supervising tchr., demo. teaching No. Mont. Coll.; kindergarten, 1st grade instr. Glasgow, Mont.; supervisor, head tchr. Reading Lab, Glasgow AFB, Mont.; 1st grade instr., kindergarten tchr., elem. adminstr. K-7 Medicine Lake (Mont.) Dist. 7; certification stds. and practices Adv. Coun. to the State Bd. Pub. Edn.; mem. bd. examiners Nat. Coun. for Accred. of Tchr. Edn., adv. com. Western Mont. Coll., U. Mont.; workshop leader and presenter in field. Mem. Sheridan County Community Protective Svcs. Com., Mid-Lake Scholarship Com. Mem. NEA, ASCD, Internat. Reading Assn., Nat. Coun. for Social Studies, Nat. Elem. Prin. Assoc., Medicine Lake Edn. Assn. (past pres.), Mont. Edn. Assn. (officerships), Mont. Elem. Prin., Delta Kappa Gamma (chpt. pres., exec. bd., Alpha Mu, State pres., mem. various coms., internat. exec. bd.). Home: 108 E Antelope Rd Antelope MT 59211-9607

OLSON, BOB MOODY, marketing executive; b. Memphis, June 18, 1934; s. Nels Antone and June Esther (Hogan) O.; m. Sandra Holmes, Oct. 2, 1956; children: Jeffrey, Sandra Leigh, Karen Louise. AB in Econs., Princeton (N.J.) U., 1955; postgrad., U. Va., 1974; MBA in Bus. Fordham U., 1977. With IBM Corp., 1955-80, industry dir. ins., 1969-74; account exec. IBM Corp., N.Y.C., 1974-80; sr. v.p. sales and mktg. div. ITT World Communications, Inc., N.Y.C., 1980-83; v.p. sales and mktg. div. Siemens/Databit, Hauppauge, N.Y., 1983-85, Amdahl Communications, Richardson, Tex., 1985-86; v.p. U.S. div. Gandalf Techs., Inc., Nepean, Ont., Can., 1986-88; sr. dir. Motorola Info. Systems Group, King of Prussia, Pa., 1988—.

Capt. USAF, 1956-59. Mem. Charter Club (bd. govs. 1968-85), Princeton Club of N.Y. Republican. Avocations: tennis, golf. Home: 222 Nevin Ln Lower Gwynedd PA 19002 Office: Motorola ISG 660 Am Ave Ste 105 King Of Prussia PA 19406

OLSON, CAL OLIVER, golf architect; b. Grindstone, S.D., Oct. 18, 1939; s. Harold John and Maxine Lorraine (Knutson) O.; m. Paula Lavon Hancock, Dec. 27, 1971. BSCE, Calif. Poly., Pomona, 1974. Prin. Peridian Group, Irving, Calif., 1966-78; v.p. L.D. King Engring., Ontario, Calif., 1978-79; prin. Cal Olson Golf Architect, Costa Mesa, Calif., 1979—. Author: Turftgrass Science, 1983. Mem. ASCE, Am. Soc. Landscape Architects. Republican. Lutheran. Avocation: golf. Office: Cal Olson Golf Architect 3070 Bristol St # 460 Costa Mesa CA 92626

OLSON, CAROL LEA, lithographer, educator, photographer; b. Anderson, Ind., June 10, 1929; d. Daniel Ackerman and Marguerite Louise Olson. AB, Anderson Coll., 1952; MA, Ball State U., 1976. Pasteup artist Warner Press, Inc., Anderson, 1952-53, apprentice lithographic stripper, 1953-57, journeyman, 1957-63, lithographic dot etcher, color corrector, 1959-73, prepres coord. art dept., 1973-81, prepres tech. specialist, 1981-83, color film assembler, 1983—; part-time photography instr. Anderson Univ.; tchr. photography Anderson Fine Arts Ctr., 1976-79; instr. photography, photographics Anderson U., 1979—; mag. photographer Bd. Christian Edn. of Ch. of God, Anderson, 1973-86; freelance photographer. One person show Anderson U., 1979; exhibited in group shows Anderson U., 1980-90, Purdue U., 1982. Instr. 1st aide ARC, Anderson, 1969-79; sec. volleyball Anderson Sunday Sch. Athletic Assn., 1973—. Recipient Hon. mention, Ann Arbor, Mich., 1977, Anderson Fine Arts Ctr., 1977, 78, 83, 1st Pl., 1983, Hon. Mention, 1983, 2d Pl., 1988, Hon. Mention, 1988, 93, Best of Show, 1983, 91, 92, Best Nature Catagory Anderson Fine Arts Ctr., 1994. Mem. AAUW, Associated Photographer Internat., Nat. Inst. Exploration, Profl. Photographers Am. Mem. Ch. of God. Avocations: camping, travel, canoeing. Home: 2604 E 6th St Anderson IN 46012-3725

OLSON, CHARLES ERIC, economist; b. Wausau, Wis., June 2, 1942; s. Roland Anthony and Lois (Erickson) O.; student U. Wis., Marathon County, 1960-62; B.B.A. with honors, U. Wis., Madison, 1964, M.S., 1966, Ph.D. (Vilias fellow), 1968; m. Pamela Ann Templin, July 1, 1967 (div. Oct. 1973), children—Sonja Anne, Erika Christine; m. 2d, Carole Emily Collesian, Dec. 1, 1973 (div. Oct. 1990); children—Cora Elizabeth, Sarah Emily; m. 3d, Jeanne Esther Katz, Apr. 14, 1991. Instr., U. Wis., Madison, 1966-68; asst. prof. U. Md., College Park, 1968-71, assoc. prof. bus. adminstrn., 1971-76; sr. economist H. Zinder & Assocs., Washington, 1976—, v.p., 1977-79, sr. v.p., 1979—; pres. Olson & Co., Inc., 1980-86, pres. H. Zinder and Assocs., 1986—; cons. Devel. Adv. Service, atty. gens. N.C., Minn., Ky., Mass., Va. U.S. Postal Rate Commn., Dept. Def., numerous electric and gas utilities in U.S. and Can. Testified numerous pub. utility rate cases, before Senate Subcom. on Inter-govtl. Relations; mem. advisory com. research and devel. and energy conservation Fed. Power Commn., 1973-74, vice chmn. rate design task force, 1976—. Mem. Prince Georges County (Md.) Citizens Airpark Advisory Com., 1970-71. Inst. Pub. Utilities grantee, 1967-68; U. Md. grantee, 1970, 76. Mem. Am. Econ. Assn., Transp. and Pub. Utilities Group, Beta Gamma Sigma, Delta Sigma Pi. Author: Cost Considerations for Efficient Electricity Supply, 1970. Contbr. chpts. to books, articles to profl. jours. Home: 10822 Alloway Dr Rockville MD 20854-1503 Office: 1828 L St NW Washington DC 20036

OLSON, CLARENCE ELMER, JR., newspaper editor; b. Edgerton, Wis., July 1, 1927; s. C. Elmer and Helen (Turnbull) O.; m. Arielle North, Sept. 4, 1954; children: Randall Jack, Christina North, Jens Sterling Elmer. B.S., U. Wis., 1950. News editor Edgerton Reporter, 1953; photographer, writer Madison (Wis.) Capital Times, 1953-59; writer St. Louis Post-Dispatch Pictures mag., 1959-65, asst. editor, 1965-68; asst. mng. editor Careers Today mag., Delmar, Calif., 1968-69; book editor St. Louis Post-Dispatch, 1969-91, ret., 1991. Served with USNR, 1945-46. Home: 236 N Elm Ave Saint Louis MO 63119-2240

OLSON, CLIFFORD LARRY, management consultant, entrepreneur; b. Karlstad, Minn., Oct. 11, 1946; s. Wallace B. and Lucille I (Pederson) O.; m. B.A. Blue Blodgett, March 18, 1967; children: Derek, Erin. B in Chemical Engring., U. Minn., 1969, B in Physics, 1969; MBA, U. Chgo., 1972; Licence en Sciences Economiques, U. de Louvain, Brussels, 1972. CPA, Cert. mgmt. cons. Project engr. Procter & Gamble, Chgo., 1969-71; engagement mgr. McKinsey & Co., Chgo., 1972-75; ptnr., midwest regional dir. mgmt. consulting Peat, Marwick, Mitchell, St. Louis, 1976-87; chmn. Casson Industries Inc., Mpls., 1987—; bd. dirs. Castlerock Group, Inc., Chevron, Inc. Mem. AICPA, Inst. Mgmt. Cons., Union League Club Chgo., Tavern Club. Episcopalian. Avocations: skiing, carpentry. Office: 5804 Schaefer Rd Minneapolis MN 55436-1116

OLSON, CLINTON LOUIS, foreign service officer, former ambassador; b. S.D., Mar. 31, 1916; s. William H. and Allie (Sparling) O.; m. Ethel Hoover, June 14, 1943; children: Merilee, Peter, David, Steven. B.S., Stanford U., 1939, M.B.A., 1941. Petroleum engr. with Robert S. Lytle, 1939-40; partner Chino Homes, Inc. (realtors), 1946- 47; pres. EXIM of Calif. 1946-48; with U.S. Fgn. Service, 1948-75; 2d sec. U.S. legation, Vienna, Austria, 1948-52; consul. French West Indies, 1953-55; budget examiner State Dept., 1956; exec. dir. bur. Inter-Am. Affairs, 1957-59; assigned Nat. War Coll., 1959-60; counselor of embassy London, Eng., 1960-62; counselor econ. affairs Am. embassy, Vienna, 1962-66; charge d'affaires, minister-counselor Am. embassy, Lagos, Nigeria, 1966-70; sr. fgn. service insp., 1970-72; U.S. ambassador to Sierra Leone, 1972-75; internat. cons., 1975—. Served to lt. col., ordnance AUS, 1941-46, Russia, Iran. Fellow Explorers Club; mem. Fgn. Service Assn., Theta Xi. Clubs: Rolling Rock (Ligonier, Pa.); Ross Mountain (Pa.); Mill Reef (Antigua, W.I.). Home: Ross Mountain Club New Florence PA 15944

OLSON, DALE C., public relations executive; b. Fargo, N.D., Feb. 20, 1934; s. Arthur Edwin and Edith (Weight) Olson Neubauer. Sr. v.p., prin., prs. motion picture div. Rogers and Cowan, Inc., Beverly Hills, Calif., 1967-85; prin. Dale C. Olson & Assocs., Beverly Hills, 1985—; cons. Filmex, Los Angeles, 1972-83; U.S. del. Manila Film Festival, Manila, Philippines, 1982-83. Editor: Los Angeles edit. Theatre ann. Best Plays, 1963-67. Vice pres. Diamond Cirle City of Hope, Duarte, Calif., 1980-83; adv. bd. Calif. Mus. of Sci. and Industry, Los Angeles, 1975-81; bd. govs. Film Industry Workshops, Inc., 1965-80; pres. Hollywood Press Club, 1963-66; assoc. Los Angeles County Art Mus., 1981-83. Recipient Golden Key Pub. Relations News, 1982; recipient Les Mason and pub. service awards Publicists Guild. Mem. Acad. Motion Picture Arts and Scis. (chmn. pub. rels. coordinating com. 1982—), NATAS, Actors Fund Am. (chmn. Western Coun. 1991, trustee 1992), Pres.' Club, Thallions. Lutheran. Office: 6310 San Vincente Blvd #340 Los Angeles CA 90048

OLSON, DAVID JOHN, political science educator; b. Brantford, N.D., May 18, 1941; s. Lloyd and Alice Ingrid (Black) O.; m. Sandra Jean Crabb, June 11, 1966; 1 dau., Maia Kari. B.A., Concordia Coll., Moorhead, Minn., 1963; Rockefeller fellow Union Theol. Sem., N.Y.C., 1963-64; M.A. (Brookings Instn. predoctoral research fellow 1968-69), U. Wis., Madison, 1966, Ph.D. (univ. fellow 1967), 1971. Community planner Madison Redvel. Authority, 1965-66; lectr. U. Wis., 1966-67; from lectr. to asso. prof. polit. sci. Ind. U., Bloomington, 1969-76; prof. polit. sci. U. Wash., Seattle, 1976—; chmn. dept. U. Wash., 1983-88, Harry Bridges endowed chairlabor studies, 1992-94; bd. dirs. Harry Bridges Inst.; dir.Ctr. Labor Studies U. Wash., 1992-94; Disting. lectr. in labor studies San Francisco State U., 1994; vis. prof. U. Bergen, 1987, Harvard U., 1988-89, U. Hawaii, 1989. Co-author: Governing the United States, 1978, Commission Politics, 1977, To Keep the Republic, 1975, Black Politics, 1971; co-editor: Theft of the City, 1974. Recipient Disting. Teaching award U., 1973, faculty fellow, 1973. Mem. Am. Polit. Sci. Assn., Western Polit. Sci. Assn. (v.p. 1984, pres. 1985), Midwest Polit. Sci. Assn., So. Polit. Sci. Assn. Democrat. Lutheran. Home: 6512 E Green Lake Way N Seattle WA 98103-5418 Office: Univ Wash Dept Polit Sci Seattle WA 98195

OLSON, DAVID MARK, college dean, physical education educator; b. St. Paul, Dec. 13, 1934; s. Vendel W. and Helme D. (Engman) O.; m. Arvis Joyce Garberg, Aug. 7, 1957; children: Jana, Mark, Julie, Michael. BA,

Concordia Coll., Moorhead, Minn., 1956; MA, U. Minn., 1957; PhD, U. Iowa, 1966. Tchr. Nicolet High Sch., Milw., 1958-60, Wartburg Coll., Waverly, Iowa, 1960-66; tchr. Pacific Luth. U., Tacoma, 1968—, dean sch. phys. edn., dir. athletics; dir. N.W. regional clinic Pres.' Coun. on Phys. Fitness and Sports, 1979, 84; speaker in field. Lay pastor Emmanuel Luth. Ch., Yelm, Wash., 1988—; v.p. Trinity Luth. Ch., Parkland, Wash., 1972, pres., 1973; mem. adminstrv. team North Univ. Games, Sofia, Bulgaria, 1988, Poland, 1991, Japan, 1993, Spain, 1995; mem. steering com. U.S. Olympic Acad. XIII, Olympia, Wash., 1988-89; del. U.S. Olympic Com., L.A., 1986, 88. Mem. Am. Assn. Health, Phys. Edn., Recreation and Dance (pres. N.W. dist. 1981-82), Nat. Assn. Intercollegiate Athletics (dist. chmn. 1970-75, nat. exec. com. 1975-87, nat. pres. 1985-86, award of merit 1979, mem. Hall of Fame), Wash. Assn. Health, Phys. Edn., Recration and Dance (pres. 1975), Nat. Assn. Coll. Athletic Dirs., Rotary (local v.p. 1970-71, pres. 1971-72), Phi Delta Kappa, Phi Epsilon Kappa. Home: 15810 Lawrence Pl Yelm WA 98597-9103 Office: Sch of Phys Edn Pacific Luth U Tacoma WA 98597

OLSON, DAVID R., lawyer; b. Mpls., May 21, 1938; s. Russell M. and Lenore E. (Goulet) O.; m. m. Judith A., Sept. 23, 1966; children: Mary, Stephen, Kathleen, Jennifer, Kristin. BBA, U. Minn., 1960, JD, 1963. Bar: Wis. 1963. Assoc. Michael, Best & Frederich, Milw., 1963-70, ptnr., 1970—. Mem. bd. editors U. Minn.Law Review 1962-63. Mem. ABA, Milw. Bar Assn. (pres. 1991-92). Roman Catholic. Avocations: tennis, landscaping, history. Office: Michael Best & Friedrich 100 E Wisconsin Ave Milwaukee WI 53202-4108

OLSON, DONALD ERNEST, retired physician; b. Portland, Oreg., June 22, 1921; s. Ernest S. and Edith (Swanman) O.; m. Alice Curtis Bergh, July 7, 1951; children—Julie Rene, Reid Martin, Kathy Ruth, Marc Ernest. B.A., Reed Coll., 1943; M.S., U. Oreg., 1947, M.D., 1947, Ph.D., 1948. Diplomate: Am. Bd. Internal Medicine (chmn. subsplty. pulmonary disease 1968-70; mem. bd. 1972-79). Intern U. Hosps., Madison, Wis., 1948-49; resident U. Hosps., 1949-51; research fellow dept. medicine U. Wis., 1952-53; staff physician VA Hosp., Madison, 1952-53, Portland Clinic, 1955-92; mem. staff VA Hosp., Portland; assoc. clin. prof. medicine U. Oreg., now clin. prof. medicine emeritus. Served with M.C., AUS, 1953-55. Fellow ACP (master 1992); mem. Am., Oreg. thoracic socs., Am. Coll. Chest Physicians, North Pacific Soc. Internal Medicine, Am., Ore. med. assns., Am. Clin. and Climatol. Assn., Multnomah County Med. Soc., Phi Beta Kappa, Alpha Omega Alpha. Home: 8375 SW Crestwood Ln Portland OR 97225-2227

OLSON, DONALD RICHARD, mechanical engineering educator; b. Sargent, Nebr., Dec. 26, 1917; s. Harry T. and Gyneth E. (Wittemyer) O.; m. Nancy Walker Benton, June 17, 1944; children: Walter H., Sally, Timothy W. B.S., Oreg. State U., 1947; M.Engring., Yale U., 1944, D.Engring., 1951. Profl. engr., Conn. Asst. prof., assoc. prof. mech. engring. Yale U., New Haven, 1951-62; prof. mech. engring. Pa. State U., University Park, 1962-83; prof. emeritus Pa. State U., 1983—; head underwater power plants Applied Research Lab., 1962-72, head dept. mech. engring., 1972-83; mem. engring. accreditation commn., 1979-82. Contbr. tech. papers in field to publs. Mem. ASME, Soc. Automotive Engrs. (dir. 1968-71), Sigma Xi. Home: 621 Glenn Rd State College PA 16803-3475

OLSON, DONALD W., transportation executive; b. 1932. BA, De Paul U., 1958, MBA, 1960. Audit mgr. Ernst. & Whinney, Chgo., 1958-68; exec. v.p. Std. Alliance Industries, Inc., Chgo., 1968-81; v.p. fin. Evangelical Health Systems, Inc., Hinsdale, Ill., 1981-88; chmn. bd. NFC Internat. Holdings USA, Naperville, Ill., 1988—. Office: NFC International Holdings USA 215 W Diehl Rd Naperville IL 60563-8457

OLSON, FRANK ALBERT, car rental company executive; b. San Francisco, July 19, 1932; s. Alfred and Edith Mary (Hazeldine) O.; m. Sarah Jean Blakely, Oct. 19, 1957; children—Kimberly, Blake, Christopher. AA, City Coll. San Francisco, 1961. V.p. and gen. mgr. Barrett Transp. Inc., San Francisco, 1950-64; v.p., gen. mgr. Valcar Co. subs. Hertz Corp., San Francisco, 1964-68; mgr. N.Y. zone Hertz Corp., N.Y.C., 1968-69, v.p., mgr. eastern region, v.p. gen. mgr. rent-a-car div., exec. v.p. rent-a-car div., gen. mgr., also bd. dirs., 1973-77, pres., chief exec. officer, 1977-80, chmn. bd., 1980, also dir., chief exec. officer, from 1982; chmn., chief exec. officer Allegis Corp., 1987; pres., chief exec. officer United Airlines, 1987; chmn., chief exec. officer Hertz Corp., Park Ridge, N.J., 1987—; bd. dirs. Becton Dickinson & Co., Cooper Industries, Commonwealth Edison, Found. Health Corp. Bd. dirs. World Travel & Tourism Coun., (mem. exec. com.). Mem. Am. Assn. Sovereign Mil. Order of Malta, Olympic Club (Calif.), Pine Valley Golf Club (N.J.), Royal and Ancient St. Andrews (Scotland), Arcola Country Club (Paramus, N.J.), Metropolitan Club (N.Y.C.). Republican. Roman Catholic. Office: Hertz Corp 225 Brae Blvd Park Ridge NJ 07656-1870

OLSON, FRANK L., electrical power industry executive. With Crisp County Power Commission, Cordele, Ga., 1964-91; pres., gen. manager Municipal Electric Auth of Ga., Atlanta, 1992—. Office: Municipal Electric Auth of Ga 1470 Riveredge Pky NW Atlanta GA 30328-4640

OLSON, FREDERICK IRVING, retired history educator; b. Milw., May 30, 1916; s. Frank and Clara (Hansen) O.; m. Jane Marian Correll, June 8, 1946; children: David Frederick, Donald Frank, Roger Alan. B.A. magna cum laude, Harvard U., 1938, M.A. (George W. Dillaway fellow 1938-39), 1939, Ph.D. in History, 1952. Mem. faculty U. Wis., Milw., 1946-85, prof. history, 1956-85, chmn. on univ. future, 1959-60, chmn. dept. history, 1960-62, 67-70, assoc. dean Coll. Letters and Sci., 1971-76, acting dean Sch. Library Sci., 1977-79; exec. dir. Milw. Humanities Program, 1979-84; vis. prof. history U. Wis.-Madison, summer 1957; assoc. dean U. Wis. extension-Milw., 1960-68; dir. M & I Wauwatosa State Bank. Author: (with Harry H. Anderson) Milwaukee: At the Gathering of the Waters, 1981, 2d edit., 1984, (with Frank Cassell and J. Martin Klotsche) The University of Wisconsin-Milwaukee: A Historical Profile, 1985-92, 1992, (with Jane Correll Olson) Dear Jane: A Soldier's Letters from Africa and the Middle East, 1942-1945, 1994; contbr. articles and book revs. to profl. jours. Trustee Milw. Pub. Mus., 1951-52; bd. dirs. Milw. County Hist. Soc., 1947-85, pres. 1953-57, 72-75; bd. curators State Hist. Soc. Wis., 1961-91; mem. Milw. Landmarks Commn., 1964-71, Milw. County Landmarks Commn., 1976—, chmn. 1976-82; mem. rev. bd. Wis. Hist. Preservation, 1978-89; bd. dirs. Wis. Heritages, Inc., 1983-93, pres., 1989-90; v.p., bd. dirs. Wauwatosa Hist. Soc., 1984—. With AUS, 1942-45. Mem. Orgn. Am. Historians, Wis. Acad. Scis., Arts and Letters, Lincoln Group (Boston), North Hills Country Club (Waukesha, Wis.), Phi Beta Kappa, Phi Alpha Theta, Phi Kappa Phi. Lutheran. Home: 2437 N 90th St Milwaukee WI 53226-1809

OLSON, GARY, lawyer; b. Harper, Kans., June 30, 1943. BS, Kans. State Coll., 1965; JD, U. Kans., 1968. Bar: Calif. 1969. Ptnr. Latham & Watkins, L.A. Editor in chief U. Kans. Law Review, 1967-68. Mem. ABA (fed. regulation securities com.), State Bar Calif. (vice chair com. corps. and business law sect.), L.A. County Bar Assn. (exec. com. bus. and corp. law sect.), Order of Coif, Omicron Delta Kappa. Office: Latham & Watkins Bldg 48 Ste 2200 1900 Avenue Of The Stars Los Angeles CA 90067-4503

OLSON, GARY MONROE, psychology educator; b. L.A., Dec. 24, 1944; s. Harold M. and Delaine E. (Huseth) O. BA, U. Minn., 1967; MA, Stanford U., Palo Alto, Calif., 1968, PhD, 1970. Asst. prof. psychology Mich. State U., E. Lansing, 1973-75; asst. prof. to prof. psychology U. Mich., Ann Arbor, 1975—; dir. Cognitive Sci. and Machine Intelligence Lab, Ann Arbor, 1985—. Editor: Empirical Studies of Programmers; contbr. articles to profl. jours. Lt. USN, 1970-73. Recipient Career Devel. award, NIH, 1976-81; rsch. grantee, NSF, NIH, others. Mem. APA, ACM, IEEE, Cognitive Sci. Soc., Midwestern Psychol. Assn., Psychonomic Soc. Office: U Mich 701 Tappan Ave Ann Arbor MI 48109-1217*

OLSON, GARY ROBERT, banker; b. Milw., May 9, 1946; s. Ward Louis and Mary Jane (Brown) O.; m. Mia Kristina Sohn, Feb. 26, 1972; children: Kristin Anne, Brian Ward. Student, Loyola U., Rome, 1966-67; AB, Marquette U., 1968; M Internat. Mgmt., Am. Grad. Sch. Internat. Mgmt., Glendale, Ariz., 1973. Instr. Sogang Jesuit U., Seoul, 1968-70, Hankuk U.

Fgn. Studies, Seoul, 1971-72; grad. asst. Am. Grad. Sch. Internat. Mgmt., 1972; credit analyst Chase Manhattan Bank, N.A., N.Y.C. and Tokyo, 1973-75; asst. treas. Chase Manhattan Bank, N.A., N.Y.C., 1975-77; 2d v.p. Chase Manhattan Bank, N.A., Madrid, 1977, Paris, 1977-80; v.p., mgr. Regional Banking Office Chase Manhattan Bank, N.A., Chgo., 1980-83; v.p., regional mgr. Case Nat. Corp. Svcs., San Francisco, 1983-87; sr. v.p. Chase Bank Ariz., Phoenix, 1987-90; v.p. Bklyn. and S.I. commercial mgr. Chase Manhattan Bank, N.A., Bklyn., 1990-93; v.p. Chase Manhattan Bank, N.A., Melville, L.I., 1993—. Advisor English program USIS, Seoul, 1969; alumni domestic counselor Am. Grad. Sch. Internat. Mgmt. Marquette U., 1990—; vol. Spl. Olympics, Phoenix, 1988-89; fund drive capt. Phoenix Econ. Growth Corp., 1988; trustee, bd. dirs. Variety Pre-schooler's Workshop, 1994—; bd. dirs. L.I. chpt. Robert Morris Assocs., 1994—, chmn., 1995—; mem. devel. com. Hocksher Mus., Huntington, N.Y., 1995—. Mem. Robert Morris Assocs. (assoc.), Econ. Club Phoenix, World Trade Club. Republican. Roman Catholic. Avocations: reading, skiing, swimming, golf. Office: Chase Manhattan Bank NA 135 Pinelawn Rd Melville NY 11747

OLSON, GREGORY BRUCE, materials science and engineering educator, academic director; b. Bklyn., Apr. 10, 1947; s. Oscar Gustav Fritz and Elizabeth Rose (Dorner) O.; m. Jane Ellen Black, May 10, 1980; 1 child, Elise Marie. BS, MS in Materials Sci. and Engring., MIT, 1970, ScD in Materials Sci. and Engring., 1974. Rsch. assoc. dept. materials sci. and engring. MIT, Cambridge, 1974-79, prin. rsch. assoc., 1979-85, sr. rsch. assoc., 1985-88; prof. materials sci. and engring. Northwestern U., Evanston, Ill., 1988—; cons. Army Materials Tech. Lab., Watertown, Mass., 1975-88, Lawrence Livermore (Calif.) Nat. Lab., 1983-89; Jacob Kurtz Exchange Scientist Technion-Israel Inst. Tech., 1979; SERC vis. prof. U. Cambridge, 1992; now assoc. chmn. dept. materials sci. and engring. Northwestern U., dir. materials rsch. ctr.-steel rsch. group, 1985—. Editor: Innovative UHS Steel Technology, 1990, Martensite, 1992; contbr. over 135 papers and articles to jours., encyclopedias and symposia; inventor hydrogen-res. UHS steel, stainless bearing steel. Fellow AMAX Found., 1972-74; named N.Mex. Disting. lectr. in Materials, 1983; recipient Creativity Extension award NSF, 1983-85; Wallenberg grantee Jacob Wallenberg Found., Sweden, 1993; recipient Tech. Recognition award NASA, 1994. Fellow ASM (chmn. phase transformation com. 1987-90, Boston chpt. Sauveur Meml. lectr. 1986), ASM Internat.; mem. AAAS, Materials Rsch. Soc., Internat. Com. Martensitic Transformation, Internat. Conf. Martensitic Transformation (co-chmn. 1992), TMS-AIME, ISS-AIME (M.R. Tenenbaum award 1993), TMS-AIME (student affairs com.). Lutheran. Avocations: sports cars, jazz trumpet. Office: Northwestern U Dept Materials Sci and Engring 2225 N Campus Dr Evanston IL 60208-3108

OLSON, HERBERT THEODORE, trade association executive; b. Bridgeport, Conn., Feb. 9, 1929; s. Herbert Theodore and Inez Evelyn (Lindahl) O.; children: Christina, Victoria; m. Kathleen A. Harrison, Dec. 27, 1988. Student Heidelberg Coll., 1947-49; A.B., Ohio U., 1951, postgrad., 1951-52. Asst. to dean of men Ohio U., Athens, 1951-52; with Union Carbide Corp., 1952-71, mgr. employee relations, coordinator pub. affairs, N.Y.C., 1969-71; exec. v.p. Am. Assn. for Aging, Washington, 1971-75; dir. spl. projects Am. Health Care Assn., Washington, 1975-79; pres. Promotional Products Assn. Internat., Irving, Tex., 1979—; exec. bd. Allied Bank. Mem. long-term care for elderly research rev. and adv. com. Dept. Health, 1972-77; mem. Longterm Care grant rev. com. HEW, 1972-77; mem. planning commn. City of Torrance, Calif., 1962-64, city councilman, 1964-67; mem. nat. exploring com., vice chmn. nat. events com., ann. meetings com., mem.-at-large nat. council Boy Scouts Am.; chmn. Gov's Operation Leegit; treas. U.S. Found. for Internat. Scouting, 1988—, chmn. audit com. 1984-87; adv. bd. Irving Hosp.; bd. dirs. Irving Cancer Soc. Served with USAR. Lord Baden Powell fellow, 1986; recipient Disting. Eagle award Boy Scouts Am., 1974, Silver Beaver award, 1968. Mem. Meeting Planners Internat. (charter), Am. Soc. Assn. Execs., U.S.C. of C., Washington Soc. Assn. Execs., Nat. Assn. Exhibit Mgrs., Small Bus. Legal Council (chmn. bd. 1993-95), Dallas Ft. Worth Soc. Assn. Execs. (v.p. 1985-87), Irving C. of C. (past bd. dirs.), Am. Advt. Fedn., Tex. Soc. Assn. Execs. Lutheran. Club: Las Colinas Country. Lodges: Rotary (past bd. dirs.), Masons, Shriners. Home: 2910 Pacific Ct Irving TX 75062-4624 Office: 3125 Skyway Cir N Irving TX 75038-3541

OLSON, HILDING HAROLD, surgeon, educator; b. Burlington, Wash., Apr. 30, 1916; s. Adolph and Gerda (Gerdin) O.; m. Donna D. Anderson, Aug. 14, 1943; children: Sheila K. Richardson, Susan L. LeClerq, Daniel L. BS, U. Wash., 1939; MD, U. Oreg., 1943. Diplomate Am. Bd. Surgery. Intern King County Hosp., Seattle, 1944-45, resident, 1945-51, attending surgeon, 1951—; clin. prof. surgery U. Wash. Seattle, 1964-87, emeritus, 1987—; mem. staff Providence Med. Ctr., Harborview Med. Ctr., Swedish Hosp. Med. Ctr., Univ. Hosp.; teaching fellow Dept. Anatomy, U. Oreg., 1940-43; dir. surgical clerkship program U. Wash. Dept. Surgery, 1954-73; dir. residency program Providence Med. Ctr., U. Wash. Dept. Surgery, 1976-87. Author: A Retrospective View of Northwest Medicine: The Early History of the Department of Surgery and the Health Sciences of the University of Washington, 1989; co-author: Saddlebags to Scanners: The First 100 Years of Medicine in Washington State, 1989; contbr. numerous articles to profl. jours. Served with U.S. Army, 1941-43, 46. recipient Most Outstanding Tchr. award U. Wash. Sch. Medicine, 1958, 68, 85. Fellow Am. Coll. Surgeons; mem. AMA, Western Surg. Assn., Pacific Coast Surg. Assn. (pres. 1982-83), North Pacific Surg. Assn., Seattle Surg. Soc. (pres. 1975), Internat. Soc. Surgeons, King County Med. Assn., Pan Pacific Surg. Assn. Avocations: piano, pipe organ. Home and Office: 401 100th Ave NE Apt 317 Bellevue WA 98004-5456

OLSON, JAMES CLIFTON, historian, university president; b. Bradgate, Iowa, Jan. 23, 1917; s. Arthur Edwin and Abbie (Anderson) O.; m. Vera Blanche Farrington, June 6, 1941; children: Elizabeth, Sarah Margaret. AB, Morningside Coll., 1938, LLD, 1968; MA, U. Nebr., 1939, PhD, 1942, LittD, 1980; LittD, Chonnam Nat. U., Korea, 1978. Instr. Northwest Mo. State Tchrs. Coll., summers 1940-42; dir. Nebr. State Hist. Soc., 1946-56; lectr. U. Omaha, 1947-50; lectr. U. Nebr., 1946-54, part-time assoc. prof., 1954-56, prof., chmn. dept. history, 1956-65, Bennett S. and Dorothy Martin prof. history, 1962-65; dean Grad. Coll., univ. research adminstr., 1966-68, vice chancellor, 1968; chancellor U. Mo.-Kansas City, 1968-76; interim pres. U. Mo. System, 1976-77, pres., 1977-84, pres. emeritus, 1984—; OAS prof. Am. history El Colegio de Mexico, Mexico City, 1962; vis. prof. U. Colo., summer 1965; commr. N. Cen. Assn. Colls. and Schs.; bd. dirs. Uhlmann Co. Author: J. Sterling Morton, 1942, The Nebraska Story, 1951, History of Nebraska, 1955, (with Vera Farrington Olson) Nebraska is My Home, 1956, This is Nebraska, 1960, Red Cloud and the Sioux Problem, 1965, paper edit., 1975, 79, (with Vera Farrington Olson) The University of Missouri: An Illustrated History, 1988, Serving the University of Missouri: A Memoir of Campus and System Administration, 1993; contbg. author: The Army Air Forces in World War II, 1951, 53; editor: Nebraska History, 1946-56; contbr. articles to profl. jours., encys. Bd. dirs. Harry S. Truman Libr. Inst., Mid-Am. Arts Alliance; chmn. Mo. Arts Coun.; trustee Midwest Rsch. Inst., Kansas City. Mem. Am. Assn. State and Local History, Coun. Basic Edn., Am. Hist. Assn., Orgn. Am. Historians, State Hist. Soc. Mo. (exec. com.), Nebr. State Hist. Soc., We. Hist. Assn., Cosmos Club, Phi Beta Kappa, Omicron Delta Kappa, Phi Kappa Phi, Pi Gamma Mu.

OLSON, JAMES RICHARD, transportation company executive; b. Alexandria, Minn., Mar. 11, 1941; s. Orie D. and Theresa Marie (Erickson) O.; m. Ronna Lee, Feb. 1, 1969 (dec.); 1 child, Trevor James. BS, N.D. State U., 1963; LLD, U. Minn., 1966; MBA, Harvard U., 1968. Asst. to v.p. finance Cargill Inc., Mpls., 1968-69; with Graco Inc., Mpls., 1969-75; v.p. finance Graco Inc., 1972-75; exec. v.p. finance Ponderosa System, Inc., Dayton, Ohio, 1975-77; v.p. planning Pillsbury Co., Mpls., 1977-79; v.p. restaurant group Pillsbury Co., 1979-80; group v.p.-restaurants The Carlson Cos., Inc., Mpls., 1981-83; exec. v.p., chief fin. and adminstrv. officer Schneider Nat., Inc., 1983-87, pres. van group, 1987-92, pres. transp. sector, 1992—. Mem. Financial Execs. Inst., Citizens League Mpls.-St. Paul, Harvard Bus. Sch. Club Minn. (past pres.). Lutheran. Home: 2512 Riverside Dr Green Bay WI 54301-1950 Office: PO Box 2545 Green Bay WI 54306-2545

OLSON, JAMES ROBERT, consulting engineer; b. Columbus, Nebr., Nov. 23, 1940; s. Robert August and Jean Elizabeth O.; 1 child, Eric Robert.

Student, U.S. Naval Acad., 1962; BA, U. Nebr., 1965; MA, Cen. Mich. U., 1977; diploma Nat. Def. U., 1981. Commd. ensign USN, 1965, advanced through grades to comdr., 1980; svc. in S.W. Pacific, Philippines and Vietnam; designated Space Systems Ops. Subspecialist, 1982; ret., 1983; sr. systems engr. G.E. Space Systems Div., Valley Forge, Pa., 1983-92; mem. faculty Def. Intelligence Sch., 1970-71; mem. Naval Insp. Gen. Staff, 1982. Decorated Bronze Star with combat V, Air medal (5), Republic of Vietnam Cross of Gallantry, numerous others. Mem. NRA, Inst. Navigation, Fla. Gulf Coast R.R. Mus., Rlwy. and Locomotive Hist. Soc. (life), Colo. R.R. Hist. Found. (life), Am. Swedish Hist. Found., VASA Order of Am., Phi Alpha Theta, Army-Navy Country Club (Washington). Methodist. Home: 1356 Nathan Hale Dr Phoenixville PA 19460-2777

OLSON, JAMES WILLIAM PARK, architect; b. St. Louis, Oct. 6, 1940; s. James William Park; s. Louis Garfield and Gladys Helen (Schuh) O.; m. Katherine Fovargue, June 11, 1971; children: Park, Reed. BArch, U. Wash., 1963. Registered architect, Wash., Oreg., Calif., Ill. Ptnr. Olson/Sundberg Architects, Seattle, 1985—; assoc. architect New Seattle Art Mus., 1991. Prin. works include Pike and Virginia Bldg. (AIA Honor award 1989), Seattle's Best Coffee Retail Locations (AIA Honor award 1984), Hauberg Residence Complex, 1992, Olympic Block Bldg. (Outstanding Merit award Wash. Trust Hist. Preservation 1986), numerous residences nationwide. Bd. dirs. On The Bds., Ctr. Contemporary Art, Seattle, 1982-86, Artist Trust, Seattle, 1986-90, U. Wash. Henry Art Gallery, Seattle, 1986-92; active Seattle Art Mus., Allied Arts. Recipient Best Architect award Seattle Mag., 1985. Fellow AIA; mem. IFRAA, NEA (juror). Avocation: art. Work published in numerous mags, jours., including The AD 100 Architects, N.Y. Times, Archtl. Digest, Archtl. Record, Global Architecture and others. Office: Olson/Sundberg Architects 108 1st Ave S 4th fl Seattle WA 98104

OLSON, JARLE, clergy member, Church administrator. Exec. dir. World Missions of the Church of the Lutheran Brethren of America, Fergus Falls, Minn. Office: Ch Luth Brethren Am Box 655 Fergus Falls MN 65537

OLSON, JOHN FREDERICK, lawyer; b. Santa Monica, Calif., Dec. 24, 1939; s. Paul Frederick and Helen Elizabeth (Evans) O.; m. Elizabeth H. Callard, Feb. 22, 1966; children: Timothy Cooley, Peter Jacobus, Matthew Evans, Emily Merrell, Nicholas Porter. AB, U. Calif., Berkeley, 1961; LLB, Harvard U., 1964. Bar: Calif. 1965, U.S. Dist. Ct. (cen. dist.) Calif. 1965, D.C. 1977, U.S. Dist. Ct. (D.C.) 1977. Assoc. Gibson, Dunn & Crutcher, Los Angeles, 1964-71, ptnr., 1971-90, sr. ptnr., 1990—. Author: (with Josiah O. Hatch III) Officer and Director Liability: Indemnification and Insurance, 1990; mem. adv. bd. Securities Regulation & Law Report and Insights, The Corporate and Securities Law Advisor; contbr. articles to profl. jours. Vestryman St. John's Ch., Lafayette Sq., Washington, 1981-86, chmn. Triennial fund drive, 1984; v.p. Combined Health Appeal Nat. Capital Area, 1985-88, pres., 1988-90; chmn. Lawyers Com. for Performing Arts, 1986-90; mem. adv. com. Senate Banking Com. on Insider Trading Legislation, 1987-90, U. Calif. San Diego Securities Regulation Inst., 1990—; trustee Washington Opera, 1986-91; trustee Stone Ridge Country Day Sch. of Sacred Heart, 1990—, exec. com., 1991—; dir. Washington Performing Arts Soc. Mem. ABA (chmn. task force regulation of insider trading 1983-87, chmn. subcom. civil liabilities and litigation 1985-87, com. on fgn. claims 1982-86, chmn. com. on fed. regulation securities 1991—), Fed. Bar Assn. (exec. coun. securities com. 1985—), Am. Law Inst., D.C. Bar Assn. (gen. counsel 1983-85), Am. Coll. Investment Counsel (founding trustee 1981-85), Nat. Assn. Securities Dealers (legal adv. bd. 1990—), N.Y. Stock Exchange (legal adv. com. 1990—), Met. Club, Univ. Club. Democrat. Episcopalian. Home: 3719 Bradley Ln Bethesda MD 20815-4256 Office: Gibson Dunn & Crutcher 1050 Connecticut Ave NW Ste 90 Washington DC 20036-5303

OLSON, JOHN MARSHALL, lawyer; b. Milw., Feb. 16, 1949; s. John Robert and Helen (Linder) O.; m. Lynde Bradley Uihlein, Jan. 6, 1973 (div. Dec. 1986); children: Sarah Lynde, John Uihlein. BA summa cum laude, Princeton U., 1971; postgrad., Oxford (Eng.) U., 1971-72; JD, Yale U., 1976. Bar: Wis. 1976, U.S. Dist. Ct. (ea. dist.) Wis. 1981, U.S. Ct. Appeals (7th cir.) 1981. Assoc. Whyte & Hirschboeck, S.C., Milw., 1976-82, ptnr., 1982-89; ptnr. Foley & Lardner, Milw., 1989—; bd. dirs. Banner Welder, Inc., Germantown, Wis., Phoenix Products Co., Inc., Milw., Schroeder-Manatee Ranch, Inc., Sarasota, Fla. Contbr. articles to profl. jours. Trustee David Uihlein Racing Mus. Found., Cedarburg, Wis., 1978, Univ. Sch. Milw., 1979-85, Lakeland Coll., Sheboygan, Wis., 1984-86; bd. dirs. AWARE Inc., Ft. Atkinson, Wis., 1991—, Tympanuchus Soc., Milw., 1992—. Mem. State Bar Wis. (chmn. bus. law sect. 1992-93), Univ. Club, Milw., Coleman Lake Club (bd. dirs., Goodman, Wis.), Milw. Club, Milw. Country Club. Avocations: grouse hunting, fly fishing, tennis. Office: Foley & Lardner 777 E Wisconsin Ave Milwaukee WI 53202-5302

OLSON, JOHN MICHAEL, lawyer; b. Grafton, N.D., Feb. 9, 1947; s. Clifford Inguold and Alice M. (Schwandt) O.; children: Dana Michel, Kirsten Lee. BA, Concordia Coll., Moorhead, Minn., 1969; JD, U. N.D., 1972. Bar: N.D. 1972. Asst. atty. gen. N.D. Atty. Gen.'s Office, Bismarck, 1972-74; state's atty. Burleigh County, Bismarck, 1974-82; pvt. practice Bismarck, 1983—; mem. 49th dist. N.D. Senate, Bismarck, 1983-91, minority leader, 1987-91; ptnr. Wheeler Wolf, Bismarck, 1990—. Recipient Disting. Svc. award N.D. Peace Officers Assn., 1981, Outstanding Bismarcker award Bismarck Jaycees, 1981. Mem. N.D. Bar Assn. Republican. Lutheran. Office: 115 N 4th St Bismarck ND 58501-4001

OLSON, JUDY MAE, geography, cartography educator, consultant; b. Waupaca, Wis., May 15, 1944; d. Leonard A. and Hilma R. (Johnson) O. B.S., Wis. State U., Stevens Point, 1966, M.S., U. Wis., Madison, 1968, Ph.D., 1970. Asst. prof. U. Ga., Athens, 1970-74; asso. prof. Boston U., 1974-83; prof. geography Mich. State U., East Lansing, 1983—; vis. asst. prof. U. Minn., Mpls., 1973, vis. assoc. prof.; cons. U.S. Bur. Census, Washington, 1975, U.S. Army Engr. Topog. Labs., Washington, 1983, U.S. Dept. Transp., Boston, 1980. Editor: The Am. Cartographer, 1977-82; U.S. Nat. Report to ICA, 1984; co-editor Geography's Inner Worlds, 1988-91; contbr. articles to profl. jours. Recipient Presdl. citation Am. Congress Surveying and Mapping, 1979, 80, 84, 85; AAG hon., 1990. Fellow Am. Congress Surveying and Mapping (dir. 1976-79, 81-82); mem. Am. Cartographic Assn. (pres. 1981-82), Assn. Am. Geographers councillor 1990-93, sec. 1991-93, pres. 1995—), U.S. Nat. Com. for ICA (chmn. 1985-88), Internat. Cartographers Assn. (v.p. 1992—). Office: Mich State Univ 315 Natural Sci Bldg East Lansing MI 48824

OLSON, KATY, state legislator, farmer; b. Rock Rapids, Iowa, Oct. 24, 1928; d. Cornelius and Cornelia (Bakker) Gaalswyk; m. Robert R. Olson, Nov. 13, 1948; children: Cynthia, Shirley, Roberta, Kent, Amy. Student, Luther Coll. Bd. mem. PTA Minn. State, 1968-84; mem. Trimont Sch. Bd. Minn., 1976-86; bd. mem. Edn. Coop. Svc. Unit, Mankato, Minn., 1980-86; commr. Region 9 Devel. Commn., 1982-86; rep. Minn. State Govt., St. Paul, 1986-94; vice chair Edn. Com. in House, St. Paul, 1986-94; asst. maj. leader Minn. House of Reps., 1992-94; ret. Avocations: golf, fishing, family activities. Home: R R 2 Box 115 Sherburn MN 56171 Office: Minn State Senate State Capitol Saint Paul MN 55155

OLSON, KAY MELCHISEDECH, magazine editor; b. Mpls., Nov. 16, 1948; d. John William and Carol Louise (Born) Melchisedech; m. John Addison Olson, Sept. 5, 1970 (div. 1988); children: Jennifer Marie, Nathan John. BA, U. Minn., 1971. News editor New Hope-Plymouth Post, Crystal, Minn., 1971-73; features editor Sun Newspapers, Bloomington, Minn., 1973-75; with pub. rels. dept. Nat. Car Rental, Bloomington, Minn., 1975-77; free-lance pub. rels. profl. Mpls., 1977-82; mag. editor Miller Pub., Minnetonka, Minn., 1982-90; exec. editor Flower & Garden mag., Workbasket mag. Easy-Does-It Needework & Crafts mag. KC Pub. Inc., Kansas City, Mo., 1990—. Mem. Garden Writers Assn. Am. Roman Catholic. Avocation: fiction writing. Home: 4726 W 78th Ter Shawnee Mission KS 66208-4413 Office: KC Pub Inc 700 W 47th St Ste 310 Kansas City MO 64112

OLSON, KEITH WALDEMAR, history educator; b. Poughkeepsie, N.Y., Aug. 4, 1931; s. Ernest Waldemar and Elin Ingeborg (Rehnstrom) O.; m. Marilyn Joyce Wittschen, Sept. 10, 1955; children—Paula, Judy. B.A., SUNY-Albany, 1957, M.A., 1959; Ph.D., U. Wis., 1964. Mem. history faculty Syracuse U., N.Y., 1963-66; mem. history faculty U. Md., College

Park, 1966—; prof. history U. Md.; Fulbright prof. U. Tampere, Finland, 1986-87, U. Oulu, 1993, U. Jyväskylä, 1994. Author: The G.I. Bill, the Veterans and the Colleges, 1974; Biography of a Progressive: Franklin K. Lane, 1979. Pres. Am. Scandinavian Found., Washington, 1977-79. Served with U.S. Army, 1952-54. U.S. Office Edn. grantee, 1965-66; U. Md. grantee, 1971, 76, 78. Mem. Am. Hist. Assn., Orgn. Am. Historians, Wis. Hist. Soc., Swedish Am. Hist. Soc., Finnish Hist. Soc., Soc. Historians of Am. Fgn. Rels., Cen. Study of Presidency. Unitarian. Home: 10746 Kinloch Rd Silver Spring MD 20903-1226 Office: Dept History U Md College Park MD 20742

OLSON, KENNETH HARVEY, computer company executive; b. Souris, N.D., May 7, 1927; s. Oscar L. and Clara (Haugen) O.; m. Darlene R. Gronseth, Aug. 19, 1950 (div. 1987); children: Kenneth David, Martha C., Marie K. BA, Concordia Coll., Moorhead, Minn., 1950; MS, U. N.D., 1953; postgrad., U. Minn., 1955. Instr. math U. N.D., Grand Forks, 1952-54; programming supr. Convair, San Diego, 1955-59; mgr. software Control Data Corp., Mpls., 1959-61, product mgr., 1961-62; sales mgr. Control Data Corp., San Diego, 1962-70; v.p. Automated Med. Analysts, San Diego, 1970-90; pres., dir. Focus 010 Group, San Diego, 1975—; pres., dir. Health Care Svcs. Corp., San Diego, 1971-74, H.C.S. Corp., San Diego, 1972-75; v.p., trustee Calif. Prepaid Health Plan Coun., 1971-74; trustee HMO Assn. Am., 1974-75; bd. dirs. Touch Techs., Inc., San Diego. Editor: Approximations for the 1604 Computer, 1960; contbr. papers to Computer Applications, 1957-61. Pres. Lemon Grove (Calif.) Luth. Ch., 1957-59; treas. St. Luke's Luth. Ch., La Mesa, Calif., 1992-93; founder San Diego Nat. Bank, 1980, mem. bus. adv. com., 1981-85. Named Subcontractor of Yr., Small Bus. Assn. and SAI Corp., 1985; day proclaimed in his honor Mayor of San Diego, 1986; recipient Pres.'s award for disting. svc. Concordia Coll., 1991. Mem. Assn. for Computing Machinery, Sons of Norway. Republican. Avocations: photography, travel, classical concerts.

OLSON, LEROY CALVIN, retired educational administration educator; b. Kane, Pa., Mar. 7, 1926; s. Vernon Reinhold and Gertrude Viola (Hutchins) O.; m. Miriam Marie Vogler, June 19, 1954; children—David Lee, Thomas Edward, Steven Andrew. B.S., Clarion State Coll., 1949; M.Ed., Pa. State Coll., 1950; Ed.D., Pa. State U., 1962; postgrad., U. Del., 1964-65. Tchr.-counselor Boiling Springs (Pa.) High Sch., 1950-52, Gordon Jr. High Sch., Coatesville, Pa., 1952-54; guidance dir. Cen. Dauphin Sch. Dist., Harrisburg, Pa., 1954-57; coordinator pupil personnel services, asst. supt. for instrn. and personnel, acting supt. Alfred I. duPont Sch. Dist., Wilmington, Del., 1957-65; prof. ednl. administrn. Temple U., Phila., 1965-92, prof. emeritus, 1992—; cons. to schs. bds. and dists., also Nat., Wis., Pa. sch. bds. assns. Contbr. articles to profl. jours. Trustee Luth. Ch., 1963-66, chmn. bd., 1974-78, chmn. various coms., discussion groups. Served with USNR, 1944-46, PTO. Recipient Disting. Alumni award Clarion State Coll., 1972. Mem. Am. Personnel and Guidance Assn., AAUP, Am. Assn. Sch. Personnel Administrs., Assn. Supervision and Curriculum Devel., Council Profs. Instrn. Supervision, Nat. Staff Devel. Council, Am. Legion, Phi Delta Kappa, Phi Kappa Phi. Republican. Home: 231 Prospect Dr Wilmington DE 19803-5331 *God's gift of life is a marvelous thing. My attempt to make the best use of that gift is to try to live an integrated and balanced life. This means that active attention must be paid to the physical, social, spiritual, and recreational aspects as well as to the work or career dimension. It also means we must share that gift through loving and caring about others.*

OLSON, LUTE, university athletic coach; b. Mayville, N.D., Sept. 22, 1934; s. Albert E. and Alinda E. (Halvorson) O.; m. Roberta R. Russell, Nov. 27, 1953; children: Vicki, Jodi, Gregory, Christi, Steven. B.A., Augsburg Coll., Mpls., 1956; M.A., Chapman Coll., Orange, Calif., 1964. Cert. counselor. Head basketball coach Mahonomen High Sch., Minn., 1956-57, Two Harbors High Sch., Minn., 1957-61; dean of boys Baseline Jr. High Sch., Boulder, Colo., 1961-62; head basketball coach Loara High Sch., Anaheim, Calif., 1962-64, Marine High Sch., Huntington Beach, Calif., 1964-69, Long Beach City Coll., 1969-73, Long Beach State U., 1973-74, U. Iowa, Iowa City, 1974-83; head basketball coach U. Ariz. Wildcats, 1983—, head coach NCAA Divsn. 1A basketball, ranked #10, 1992, head coach NCAA Tournament winner West Region, semifinalist (overall), 1994. Author: Passing Game Offense, 1980, Multiple Zone Attack, 1981, Pressure Defense, 1981, Match-up Zone, 1983. Crusade chmn. Am. Cancer Soc., Iowa, 1982. Named Coach of Yr. Orange League, 1964; named Coach of Yr. Sunset League, 1968, Coach of Yr. Met. Conf. Calif., 1970-71, Coach of Yr. PCAA, 1974, Coach of Yr. Big Ten Conf., 1979, 80. Mem. Nat. Assn. Basketball Coaches (Coach of Yr. 1980). Lutheran. Office: U Ariz Mckale Ctr Tucson AZ 85721*

OLSON, LYNDON LOWELL, JR., insurance executive; b. Waco, Tex., Mar. 7, 1947; s. Lyndon Lowell and Frances (McLaughlin) O.; m. Nancy Swenson, Mar. 6, 1970 (div. Dec. 1980); m. Kathleen Woodward, Nov. 2, 1982. BA in Polit. Sci. and Religion, Baylor U., 1969, postgrad. Mem. Tex. Legislature, 1973-78; apptd. chmn. Tex. State Bd. Ins., Austin, 1979-81, 83-87, apptd. mem., 1981-83; pres. and chief exec. officer Nat. Group Ins. Cos., Waco, Tex., 1987—; lectr. UN Conf. on Trade and Devel., Phillipines, 1985; mem. Expert Com. on Reinsurance for UN, Geneva, 1986-87; negotiator U.S.-Israeli Free Trade Agreement, 1986-87. leader trade delegation People to People for Russia and People's Republic of China, 1985; chmn., bd. dirs. Tex. Arts Alliance, Austin, 1984, chmn. and pres. Tex. Opera Theater, Houston, 1980-82; mem. exec. com. Houston Grand Opera, 1985—; pres. Tex. Lyceum, The Woodlands, 1987; chmn. Baylor U. Honors Council, 1969; bd. dirs. Am. Income Life Ins., Behrens Drug Inc., Gulf Life Ins. Co. United Bank of Waco, Tex. Mcpl. League Ins. Trust, Paul Quinn Coll., 1987. Recipient Disting. Alumni award Baylor U., 1985, Distinguished Pub. Servant award Tex. Med. Assn., 1986, Gates of Jerusalem award State of Israel, 1986; named Outstanding Pub. Ofcl. Tex. Mcpl. League, 1986. Mem. Nat. Assn. Ins. Commrs., Profl. Liability Ins. com. of the State Bar of Tex., Omicron Delta Kappa. Democrat. Presbyterian. Lodge: Masons. Home: 3800A Greenleaf Dr Waco TX 76710-1416 Office: The Nat Group Ins Cos. 900 Austin Ave Waco TX 76701-1933

OLSON, MANCUR LLOYD, economics educator; b. Grand Forks, N.D., Jan. 22, 1932; s. Mancur L. and Clara Lenore (Fuglesten) O.; m. Alison Gilbert, Aug. 29, 1959; children: Ellika L.P., Mancur Severin, Sander Brandt. B.S., N.D. State U., 1954; M.A., Oxford U., 1960; Ph.D., Harvard U., 1963. Lectr. Princeton U., 1960-61, asst. prof., 1963-67; dep. asst. sec. U.S. Dept. HEW, Washington, 1967-69; faculty mem. U. Md., College Park, 1969—, prof., 1970—, Disting. prof. econs., 1979-95; chair, prin. investigator Ctr. for Instl. Reform and the Informal Sector, 1990—; Disting. U. prof. U. Md., College Park, 1995—. Author: Logic of Collective Action, 1965, Rise and Decline of Nations, 1982; prin. author: Toward a Social Report, 1969; co-editor: The No-Growth Society, 1974; mem. editorial bd. Challenge, 1985—. Vice chmn. Health Services Cost Commn., Balt., 1971-77. 1st lt. USAF, 1961-63. Fellow Woodrow Wilson Internat. Ctr. for Scholars, 1974, Lehrman Inst., 1977, Am. Acad. Arts Scis., 1985—; Disting. fellow U.S. Inst. of Peace, 1990-91; Rhodes scholar, 1954-56; recipient Kammerer Book award Am. Polit. Sci. Assn., 1983, Social Issues Divsn. Book award Am. Acad. Mgmt., 1993. Fellow Univ. Coll., U. Oxford (hon.); mem. Am. Econ. Assn. (v.p. 1986), So. Econ. Assn. (pres. 1981-82), Pub. Choice Soc. (pres. 1972-74), AAAS (editorial bd. 1980-81, pres. sect. K social, econ. and polit. scis. 1989), Ea. Econ. Assn. (pres. 1993-94). Club: Cosmos (Washington). Home: 4316 Clagett Pineway Hyattsville MD 20782 Office: U Md Dept Econs College Park MD 20742

OLSON, MARIAN KATHERINE, emergency management executive, consultant, publisher, information broker; b. Tulsa, Oct. 15, 1933; d. Sherwood Joseph and Katherine M. (Miller) Lahman; m. Ronald Keith Olson, Oct 27, 1956, (dec. May 1991). BA in Polit. Sci., U. Colo., 1954, MA in Elem. Edn., 1962; EdD in Ednl. Adminstrn., U. Tulsa, 1969. Tchr. public schs. Wyo., Colo., Mont., 1958-67; teaching fellow, adj. instr. edn. U. Tulsa, 1968-69; asst. prof. edn. Eastern Mont. State Coll., 1970; program assoc. research adminstrn. Mont. State U., 1970-75; on leave with Energy Policy Office of White House, then with Fed. Energy Adminstrn., 1973-74; with Dept. Energy, and predecessor, 1975—, program analyst, 1975-79, chief planning and environ. compliance br., 1979-83; regional dir. Region VIII Fed. Emergency Mgmt. Agy., 1987-93; exec. dir., Search and Rescue Dogs of the U.S., 1993—; pres. Western Healthclaims, Inc., Golden, Co.; pres. Marian Olson Assocs., Bannack Pub. Co.; mem. Colo. Nat. Hazards Mitigation

Coun., Colo. Urban Search and Rescue Task Force. Contbr. articles in field. Grantee Okla. Consortium Higher Edn., 1969, NIMH, 1974. Mem. Am. Soc. for Info. Sci., Am. Assn. Budget and Program Analysis, Internat. Assn. Ind. Pubs., Nat. Inst. Urban Search and Rescue (bd. dirs.), Nat. Assn. for Search and Rescue, Colo. Search and Rescue, Search and Rescue Dogs of U.S., Colo. Emergency Mgmt. Assn., Front Range Rescue Dogs, Colo. State Fire Chiefs Assn., Kappa Delta Pi, Phi Alpha Theta, Kappa Alpha Theta. Republican. Home: 203 Iowa Dr Golden CO 80403-1337 Office: Western Healthclaims Inc 203 Iowa Dr Ste B Golden CO 80403

OLSON, MARTEEN LESLIE, nurse; b. Oct. 12, 1948; d. Margaret Holcombe; m. Larry Wood Olson, Aug. 23, 1968; children: Tiffany, Lisa. BS in Nursing, U. Pa., 1972, MS in Nursing, 1974; EdD, U. Houston, 1982. Instr. Parkland Coll., Champaign, Ill., 1974-75, Bethany Gynecologists and Obstetricians, Phoenix, 1975-80; mem. faculty Ariz. State U., Tempe, 1975-80; dean, prof. Grand Canyon Coll., Phoenix, 1981-88, Samaritan Coll. Nursing, Phoenix, 1981—; instr. Grand Canyon Coll., summers 1978-80; cons. Baylor U., Waco, Tex., 1986, Samaritan Health Service, Phoenix, 1986. Contbr. articles to profl. jours. Mem. Am. Nurses' Assn., Nat. League for Nursing (cons. 1986), Ariz. Nurses' Assn. (cons. 1987), Ariz. Coun. on Nursing Edn., Ariz. Statewide Coun. on Nursing (chairperson 1987—). Baptist.

OLSON, NORMAN FREDRICK, food science educator; b. Edmund, Wis., Feb. 8, 1931; s. Irving M. and Elva B. (Rhinerson) O.; m. Darlene Mary Thorson, Dec. 28, 1957; children: Kristin A., Eric R. BS, U. Wis., 1953, MS, 1957, PhD, 1959. Asst. prof. U. Wis.-Madison, 1959-63, assoc. prof., 1963-69, prof., 1969—, dir. Walter V. Price Cheese Research Inst., 1976-93; dir. Ctr. Dairy Research, 1986-93; disting. prof. U. Wis., 1993—. Author: Semi-soft Cheeses; inventor enzyme microencapsulation. Served to lt. U.S. Army, 1953-55. Fellow Inst. Food Technologists (Macy award 1986); mem. Am. Dairy Sci. Assn. (v.p. 1984-85, pres. 1985-86, Pfizer award 1971, Dairy Research Fedn. award 1978, Borden Found. award 1988), Inst. Food Technologists. Democrat. Lutheran. Avocation: cross-country skiing. Home: 114 Green Lake Pass Madison WI 53705-4755 Office: U Wis Dept Food Sci Babcock Hall Madison WI 53706

OLSON, PAUL RICHARD, Spanish literature educator, editor; b. Rockford, Ill., Nov. 2, 1925; s. Oscar Wilhelm and Jenny Ingeborg (Taube) O.; m. Phyllis Elizabeth Edwards, Jan. 10, 1953; children: Thomas Jeremy, John Stephen, Carl Philip, Paul Andrew. A.B., U. Ill., 1948, A.M., 1950; Ph.D., Harvard U., 1959. Instr. Dartmouth Coll., Hanover, N.H., 1956-59, asst. prof., 1959-61; asst. prof. modern Spanish lit. Johns Hopkins U., Balt., 1961-63, assoc. prof., 1963-67, prof., 1967-91, prof. emeritus, 1991—. Author: Circle of Paradox, 1967, Unamuno: Niebla, 1984, Unamuno and the Primacy of Language, 1989; editor: Unamuno: Como se hace una novela, 1977; gen. editor: Modern Lang. Notes, 1983-86. Guggenheim Found. fellow, 1964; Fulbright grantee, 1964-65; Am. Council Learned Socs. grantee, 1969. Mem. MLA, Acad. Lit. Studies, Asociacion Internacional Hispanistas.

OLSON, PHILLIP DAVID LEROY, agriculturist, chemist; b. Anchorage, Feb. 3, 1940; s. Marvin Willard and Bernadette (McName) O.; m. Deborah Andreé Butler, Apr. 10, 1982; children from a previous marriage: Jamie Kay, Samuel Phillip, Jill Andre. BS, U. Idaho, 1963; MS, Oreg. State U., 1972. Technician U. Calif., Riverside, 1963-65; rsch. staff Oreg. State U., Corvallis, 1965-75; r & d mgr. Hoechst-Roussel Agri-Vet Co., Somerville, N.J., 1975-91; pres. Profl. Agrl. Cons., Hayden Lake, Idaho, 1991—; rsch. and devel. cons., investigator Atochem NA, Bryan, Tex., 1991—, Dupont, Wilmington, Del., 1991—, Ciba-Geigy, Greensboro, N.C., 1991—, BASF, Research Triangle Park, N.C., 1991, ISK-Bioscis., Fresno, Calif., 1992—, Rhône-Poulenc, Durham, N.C., 1992—, Sandoz Agro, Inc., Des Plaines, Ill., 1992—, Zeneca, Inc., Richmind, Calif., 1992—, Stewart AG, 1995—; cons. in field rsch. and devel. Mem. Soc. Quality Assurance, Pacific Regional Quality Assurance Soc., Elks. Avocations: reading, fishing, RC model building, rose gardening. Office: Profl Agricultural Cons Rt 3 Box 125 Hayden Lake ID 83835

OLSON, PHILLIP ROGER, naval officer; b. Elmhurst, Ill., June 23, 1939; s. Willard Clarence and Carol (Schulz) O.; m. Marsha Andrea Lippert, July 10, 1966; children: Christine Carole, Phillip Roger Jr. B in Naval Sci., U.S. Naval Acad.; M in Physics, Naval Postgrad. Sch. Commd. ens. USN, advanced through grades to rear adm., 1991—; instr. ship material readiness group USN, Idaho Falls, 1978-81; commdg. officer USS Pharris (FF 1094) USN, Norfolk, Va., 1981-82; commdg. officer USS Mississippi (CGN 40) &, Norfolk, 1983-86; sr. instr. ship material readiness group &, Newport, R.I., 1986-87; dep. dir. ops. Joint Staff &, Washington, 1987-88, dep. dir. strategy & policy Joint Staff, 1988-89; comdr. logistics group two &, Norfolk, 1989-90; comdr. cruiser-destroyer group one &, San Diego, 1990-92; pres. bd. inspection & survey &, Norfolk, 1992—. Decorated Legion of Merit (3). Mem. Surface Navy Assn. Lutheran. Avocations: golf, tennis. Office: Bd of Inspection & Survey 2600 Tarawa Court Ste 250 Norfolk VA 23521-3295

OLSON, RICHARD DAVID, psychology educator; b. Reading, Pa., Oct. 10, 1944; s. Milton Stuart and Sarah Ellen (Moyer) O.; m. M. Gayle Augustine, Aug. 26, 1967. B.A., U. Redlands, 1966; M.S., St. Louis U., 1968, Ph.D., 1970. Lic. psychologist. La. Asst. prof. psychology U. New Orleans, 1970-74, chmn. dept. psychology, 1974-79, prof., chmn. dept., 1979-81, assoc. dean Grad. Sch., 1981-82, dean, 1982-88, vice chancellor, 1984-88, rsch. prof., 1988—; cons. psychologist, New Orleans, 1973—; pres. Statis. Cons. of New Orleans, 1977-82. Editor: Learning in the Classroom, 1971, The Comma After Love, The Selected Poems of Raeburn Miller; contbr. articles to profl. jours. Grantee HEW, 1976-81. Fellow APA, Am. Psychol. Soc.; mem. Soc. for Neuroscis., Animal Behavior Soc., Am. Statis. Assn. Home: 103 Doubloon Dr Slidell LA 70461-2715 Office: U New Orleans Lake Front New Orleans LA 70148

OLSON, RICHARD DEAN, researcher, pharmacology educator; b. Rupert, Idaho, June 22, 1949; s. Emerson J. and Thelma Maxine (Short) O.; m. Carol Ann Dyba, Jan. 5, 1974; children: Stephan Jay, David Richard, Jonathan Philip. BS, Coll. Idaho, 1971; postgrad., Idaho State U., 1972-74; PhD, Vanderbilt U., 1978. Instr. Vanderbilt U., Nashville, 1980-81, asst. prof., 1982, head pediatric clin. pharmacology unit, 1982; asst. prof. U. S. Ala., Mobile, 1982-83; acting asst. prof. U. Wash., Seattle, 1984-85, research assoc. prof., 1985-95; cardiovascular sect. head Mountain States Med. Rsch. Inst., Boise, Idaho, 1995—; v.p. Olson, Wong and Walsh Labs., Inc., Lindenhurst, Ill., 1987-90; pres. Olson, Mushlin and Walsh Labs., Inc., Birmingham, Ala., 1990—; chief cardiovascular pharmacology rsch. VA Med. Ctr., Boise, Idaho, 1984—; hon. dir. cardiovascular rsch. lab. Capital Inst. Medicine Beijing, People's Republic of China, 1986; investigator Am. Heart Assn., Nashville, 1981, NIH, Mobile, 1982; bd. dirs. Idaho Affailiate Am. heart Assn.; pres. JB Internat. Inc., Boise, 1990; sr. cons. Longwood Cons. Group, Boston, 1990—; rsch. adv. bd. mem. PhytoMed. Inc., Rockville, Md.; adj. assoc. prof. pharmacology Sch. Medicine U. South Alabama, Mobile, 1995—. Contbr. articles to profl. jours. Pres. Fellowship Crusade for Christ, Inc., Nampa, Idaho, 1986—. Grantee Am. Heart Assn., 1981, 83, 84, 86, 88, Am. Fedn. Aging Research, Inc., Boise, 1985; VA Merit Review grantee, 1985, 88, 91; NIH trainee, 1975-78; NIH New Investigator 1982; fellow, Am. Fedn. Aging Research, Inc. 1985—, NIH U. Colo, Denver, 1978-80. Mem. AAAS, N.Y. Acad. Scis., Am. Soc. Pharmacology and Exptl. Therapeutics, Am. Assn. Am. Fedn. for Clin. Research, Sigma Xi. Avocations: camping, radio-controlled model airplanes. Home: 605 Crocus Ct Nampa ID 83651-6549 Office: VA Med Ctr # 151 500 W Fort St Boise ID 83702-4501

OLSON, RICHARD EARL, lawyer, state legislator; b. Elmhurst, Ill., Apr. 24, 1953; s. Earl Leroy and Helen Ellen (Wanamaker) O.; m. Patricia Michelle McKinney, May 16, 1976; children: Shelley, Rachel, Eric. BA, U. Miss., Oxford, 1975; Jd, So. Meth. U., 1978. Bar: N.Mex. 1978. Ptnr. Hinkle, Cox, Eaton, Coffield & Hensley, Roswell, N.Mex., 1978—; mem. N.Mex. Ho. of Reps., 1989-95, mem. various coms. Mem. Roswell City Coun., 1986-88, chmn. sts. and alleys com., mem. various other coms.; past chmn. pastor-parish rels. com. 1st United Meth. Ch., Roswell; bd. dirs. Roswell Econ. Forum, Roswell Mus. and Art Ctr. Found., city coun. liaison; bd. dirs Assurance Home, 1980—, former v.p.; mem. N.Mex. 1st, former bd. dirs. Mem. ABA, Am. Legis. Exec. Coun. (civil justice task force), Def. Rsch. Inst., Noon Optimist Club, Order of Coif, Phi Kappa Phi.

Republican. Home: 5003 Thunderbird Lane Roswell NM 88201 Office: Hinkle Cox Eaton Coffield & Hensley PO Box 10 Roswell NM 88202

OLSON, RICHARD GEORGE, historian, educator; b. St. Paul, Minn., Nov. 4, 1940; s. George Henry and Lenore Marie (Dickhudt) O. BS, Harvey Mudd Coll., 1962; MA, Harvard U., 1963, PhD, 1967. Instr. Tufts U., 1966-67; asst. prof., then assoc. prof. U. Calif., Santa Cruz, 1967-76; prof. history, J. Willard Kieth fellow in humanities Harvey Mudd Coll., Claremont, Calif., 1976—. Author: Science as Metaphor, 1970, Scottish Philosophy and British Physics, 1975, Science Deified and Science Defied, 1982, vol. 2, 1990, The Emergence of the Social Sciences: 1642-1792, 1992. Nat. Endowment Humanities Younger Humanist fellow; recipient Graves award. Mem. History of Sci. Soc. (sec.-treas. West Coast br. 1977-79, chair com. on honors and prizes 1994—). Office: Harvey Mudd Coll 301 E 12th St Claremont CA 91711-5994

OLSON, ROBERT EDWARD, coal mining executive; b. Phila., Aug. 5, 1927; s. Oscar E. and Marie B. (Kilgallen) O.; m. Jean Emilie Wadsworth, Dec. 31, 1955; children: Grace Olson Carmichael, Nancy Olson Ashcraft, Karen Olson Culbertson. Student U. Richmond, 1945, Duke, 1945-46, U. Pa., 1946; BS in Mining Engring., Pa. State U., 1952. Registered profl. engr., Pa., W.Va. Indsl. engr. Island Creek Coal Co., Holden, W.Va., 1952-55; dir., treas., sr. assoc. Coal Standards, Inc., mgmt. cons., Charleston, W.Va., 1955-61; v.p. adminstrn. Rochester & Pitts. Coal Co., Indiana, Pa., 1961-81; pres., chief operating officer, Valley Camp Coal Co., Oil City, Pa., 1981-86, vice chmn., dir., mem. exec. com., 1986-88, ret., 1988; past pres., dir. Kanawha and Hocking Coal & Coke Co., Kelley's Creek and Northwestern R.R. Co., Valley Camp Coal Sales Co.; pres., chief exec. officer Gt. Lakes Coal & Dock Co.; chmn., dir. Donaldson Mine Co., Elm Grove Coal Co., Shrewsbury Coal Co., Helen Mining Co., Valley Camp of Utah Inc.; chmn., CEO Pa. and W.Va. Supply Co.; bd. dirs. Strickland Constrn. Co. Bd. dirs. United Way of Venango County, 1983-88; pres. bd. trustees Venango County Community Area Found., 1988-94, former dir.; mem. Ind. County C. of C. 1973-81, pres. 1976-77; mem. vestry Christ Episc. Ch., Oil City, 1989-92. With USN, 1945-47. Mem. Wanango Country Club, One Hundred Club, Univ. Club, Franklin Club, Rotary Internat., Theta Delta Chi, Sigma Phi Sigma. Home: 8 Glenwood Dr Oil City PA 16301-2104

OLSON, ROBERT EUGENE, physician, biochemist, educator; b. Minn., Jan. 23, 1919; s. Ralph William and Minnie (Holtin) O.; m. Catherine Silvoso, Oct. 21, 1944; children: Barbara Lynn, Robert E., Mark Alan, Mary Ellen, Carol Louise. A.B., Gustavus Adolphus Coll., 1938; Ph.D., St. Louis U., 1944; M.D., Harvard, 1951; M.D. (hon.), Chiang Mai U., Thailand, 1983. Diplomate: Nat. Bd. Med. Examiners, Am. Bd. Nutrition (pres. 1962-63). Postgrad. research asst. biochemistry St. Louis U. Sch. Medicine, 1938-43, asst. biochemistry, 1943-44, Alice A. Doisy prof. biochemistry, chmn. dept. biochemistry, 1945-82, assoc. prof. medicine, 1966-72, prof. medicine, 1972-82; vis. prof. (sabbatical) dept. biochemistry U. Freiburg, Breisgau, West Germany, 1970-71; also Hoffman-La Roche Co., Basel, Switzerland, 1970-71; instr. biochemistry and nutrition Harvard Sch. Pub. Health, 1946-47; research fellow Nutrition Found., 1947-49; research fellow Am. Heart Assn., 1949-51, established investigator, 1951-52; house officer Peter Bent Brigham Hosp., Boston, 1951-52; prof., head dept. biochemistry and nutrition Grad. Sch. Pub. Health U. Pitts.; lectr. medicine Sch. Medicine, 1952-65; mem. panel malnutrition Japan-U.S. Med. Scis. Program, 1965-69; dir. Nutrition Clinic, Falk Clinic, 1953-65; mem. sr. staff Presbyn. Hosp., dir. metabolic unit, 1960-65; mem. staff St. Louis U. Hosp., 1965-81; prof. biochemistry, prof. medicine, assoc. dean acad. affairs U. Pitts. Sch. Medicine, 1982-84; prof. medicine, prof. pharm. scis. SUNY-Stony Brook, 1984-90, prof. emeritus, 1990-94; prof. pediatrics U. South Fla., Tampa, 1994—; cons. Mercy Hosp., U. Pitts. Med. Center; assoc. in medicine St. Margaret's Meml. Hosp., Pitts.; dir. metabolic unit, 1954-60; cons. div. research grants USPHS, 1954-69, 72-76; dir. Anemia and Malnutrition Center, Chiang Mai, Thailand, 1967-77; vis. scholar dept. biochemistry Oxford (Eng.) U., 1961-62; vis. prof. dept. biochemistry U. Freiburg, West Germany, 1970-71; mem. food and nutrition bd. NRC, 1977-83; mem. adv. council Nat. Inst. Arthritis, Diabetes, Digestive and Kidney Diseases, 1981-85; William A. Noyes lectr. U. Ill., Urbana, 1980. Assoc. editor Nutrition Revs., 1954-56, editor, 1978-88; assoc. editor Am. Jour. Medicine, 1956-63, Circulation Rsch., 1956-76, Am. Heart Jour., 1958-65, Am. Jour. Clin. Nutrition, 1960-66, Methods in Med. Rsch., 1963-70, Biochem. Medicine, 1967-90, Molecular and Cellular Cardiology, 1967-78; assoc. editor Ann. Rev. Nutrition, 1979-84, editor, 1984-94; co-editor: Vitamins and Hormones, 1975-81. Bd. dirs. Nat. Nutrition Consortium, 1977-81, Am. Council on Sci. and Health, 1984-91. Served as lt. (j.g.) USNR, 1944-46. Recipient Fulbright award, 1961-62; Guggenheim Found. award, 1961-62, 70-71; McCollum award, 1969; Joseph Goldberger award, 1974; Atwater Meml. lectr., 1978; Geiger Meml. lectr., 1979, William A. Noyes lectr. U. Ill., 1980, H. Brooks James lectr. N.C. State U., 1981, Virginia Beal lectr. U. Mass., 1990. Fellow ACP, Am. Pub. Health Assn. (chmn. food and nutrition sect. 1960-61), Am. Inst. Nutrition (pres. 1981-82), Assn. Am. Physicians; mem. AAAS (sec. med. scis. N. sect. 1965-67), Am. Assn. Cancer Research, Am. Heart Assn., AMA (mem. council food and nutrition 1959-67, vice chmn. 1962-67), Royal Soc. Health (London), N.Y. Acad. Scis., Am. Fedn. Clin. Research, Am. Soc. Clin. Investigation, Boylestop Med. Soc., Am. Chem. Soc. (pres. biochemistry group Pitts. sect. 1960-61), Am. Soc. Biol. Chemists, Soc. Exptl. Biology and Medicine, Am. Soc. Clin. Nutrition (pres. 1961-62, McCollum award 1965), Assn. Med. Sch. Depts. Biochemistry (pres. 1979-80), Pa., St. Louis, Allegheny County med. socs., Am. Soc. Study Liver Diseases, Phi Beta Kappa, Sigma Xi, Phi Lambda Upsilon, Alpha Omega Alpha, Alpha Sigma Nu. Clubs: Cosmos (Washington), Countryside Country Club (Tampa). Home: 2673 Camille Dr Palm Harbor FL 34684 Office: U South Fla Dept Pediatrics 1 Davis Blvd Ste 307 Tampa FL 33606

OLSON, ROBERT GOODWIN, philosophy educator; b. Mpls., May 8, 1924; s. Goodwin Carl and Mary Helen (Hutchins) O. B.A., U. Minn., 1943; Docteur (French Govt. scholar 1951), U. Paris, 1953; Ph.D., U. Mich., 1957. Staff editor Grolier Soc., N.Y.C., 1946-48; historian Office Mil. Govt., Berlin, Germany, 1948-49; asst. prof. philosophy Ripon (Wis.) Coll., 1953-56; instr. philosophy U. Mich., 1956-58; asst. prof. Columbia U., 1958-61; asso. prof., chmn. dept. philosophy Rutgers U., 1961-65, prof., chmn. dept. philosophy, 1965-69; prof., chmn. dept. philosophy L.I. U., Bklyn., 1969—. Author: An Introduction to Existentialism, 1962, The Morality of Self-Interest, 1965, A Short Introduction to Philosophy, 1967, Meaning and Argument, 1969, Ethics: A Short Introduction, 1977. Contbr. articles to profl. jours. Served with USAAF, 1943-46. Mem. Am., L.I. philos. assns., AAUP, United Fedn. Coll. Tchrs. Home: 2 Cornelia St New York NY 10014 Office: Long Island U Bklyn Ctr Brooklyn NY 11201

OLSON, ROBERT GRANT, lawyer; b. Ft. Dodge, Iowa, Mar. 29, 1952; s. Grant L. and R. June (Pohlman) O.; m. Cynthia Lynn Murray, Sept. 7, 1978; children: Brendon, Elisabeth, Jeffrey, Daniel. BS, Iowa State U., 1973; JD, U. Iowa, 1976. Bar: Mo., 1976, Ill. 1977. Ptnr. Thompson & Mitchell, St. Louis, 1976-92, Riezman & Blitz, P.C., St. Louis, 1992—. Editor Jour. Corp. Law, 1975-76. Vol. Gephardt for Pres. Campaign, 1988, Carnahan for Lt. Gov. Campaign, 1988, Carnahan for Gov. Campaign, 1992. Mem. ABA, Mo. Bar Assn., Ill. Bar Assn., Met. St. Louis Bar Assn., Downtown St. Louis Lions Club (pres. 1990-91). Home: 424 E Jackson Rd Saint Louis MO 63119-4128 Office: Riezman & Blitz PC 120 S Central Ave Saint Louis MO 63105-1705

OLSON, ROBERT HOWARD, lawyer; b. Indpls., July 6, 1944; s. Robert Howard and Jacqueline (Wells) O.; m. Diane Carol Thorsen, Aug. 13, 1966; children: Jeffrey, Christopher. BA in Govt. summa cum laude, Ind. U., 1966; JD cum laude, Harvard U., 1969. Bar: Ohio 1969, Fla. 1980, U.S. Dist. Ct. (no. dist.) Ohio 1970, U.S. Dist. Ct. (no. Dist.) Ind. 1970, U.S. Dist. Ct. (so. Dist.) Ohio 1971, U.S. Supreme Ct. 1973, Ariz. 1985. Assoc. Squire, Sanders & Dempsey, Cleve., 1969, 70-71, 76-81, ptnr., 1981—, ptnr., Phoenix, 1985—; sr. law clk. U.S. Dist. Ct., No. Dist. Ind. 1969-70; chief civil rights div. Ohio Atty. Gen.'s Office, Columbus, 1971-73, chief consumer protection, 1973-75, chief counsel, 1975, 1st asst. (chief of staff), 1975-76; instr. Law Sch., Ohio State U., Columbus, 1974; mem. Cen. Phoenix com. to advise city council and mayor, 1987-89; bd. dirs., sec. Orpheum Theater Found., 1989-90, pres., 1990—; bd. dirs. The Ariz. Ctr. for Law in the Pub. Interest, 1988—, mem. exec. com., 1990—, treas. 1992-93, v.p., 1993-95; mem. Ariz. Ctr. for Disability Law, 1994—, treas. 1994—; mem. Valley Leadership Class

XIV. Author monograph on financing infrastructure, 1983; also law rev. articles on civil rights, consumer protection. Bd. dirs. 1st Unitarian Ch. Phoenix, v.p., 1987-89; bd. dirs. 1st Unitarian Ch. Found., 1987-93, pres., 1990-93. Mem. Am. Acad. Hosp. Attys., Ariz. State Bar Assn., Nat. Assn. of Healthcare Lawyers, Phi Beta Kappa. Democrat. Home: 5201 E Paradise Dr Scottsdale AZ 85254-4746 Office: Squire Sanders & Dempsey 40 N Central Ave Ste 2700 Phoenix AZ 85004-4441

OLSON, ROBERT LEONARD, retired insurance company executive; b. Auburn, Mass., Aug. 11, 1930; s. Henry Leroy and Marie Albertina (Holquist) O.; m. Muriel E. Storms, Mar. 22, 1958; children: Cynthia L., Mark W., Keith E. AAS, Becker Jr. Coll., 1956; BBA, Clark U., 1958; grad. exec. program, Dartmouth Coll., 1986. Supr. payroll and expense acctg. State Mut. Life Assurance Co. Am., Worcester, 1958-66, asst. mgr. budget fiscal planning, 1966-68; mgr. cost acctg. State Mut. Life Assurance Co. Am., Worcester, Mass., 1968-72, asst. contr., 1972-75, asst. v.p., 1975-82, 2d v.p. fin. planning and reporting, 1982-85, v.p. fin. planning and reporting, 1985-87, v.p., contr., 1987-90, also bd. dirs. Asst. treas. Mass. affiliate Am. Heart Assn., Needham, 1982-90, mem. budget, fin. and audit com., 1983-90; treas. Auburn Dist. Nursing Assn., 1972—. With U.S. Army, 1952-54. Mem. Inst. Mgmt. Accts., Fin. Execs. Inst., Bus. Planning Bd., Am. Mgmt. Assn. (cert. mgmt. course 1982). Avocations: antique and classic cars. Home: 7 Ridgewood Dr Auburn MA 01501-2316 Office: State Mut Life Assurance Co 440 Lincoln St Worcester MA 01653-0002

OLSON, ROBERT WYRICK, lawyer; b. Madison, Wis., Dec. 19, 1945; s. John Arthur and Mary Katherine (Wyrick) O.; m. Carol Jean Duane, June 12, 1971; children: John Hagan, Mary Catherine Duane. BA, Williams Coll., 1967; JD, U. Va., 1970. Assoc. Cravath, Swaine & Moore, N.Y.C., 1970-79; asst. gen. counsel Penn Cen. Corp., Cin., 1979-80, assoc. gen. counsel, 1980-82, v.p., dep. gen. counsel, 1982-87; sr. v.p., gen. counsel, sec. Am. Premier Underwriters, Inc. (formerly Penn Cen. Corp.), Cin., 1987—. Mem. ABA. Office: Am Premier Underwriters Inc 1 E 4th St Cincinnati OH 45202-3717

OLSON, ROBERTA JEANNE MARIE, art historian, author, educator; b. Shawano, Wis., June 1, 1947; d. Robert Bernard Olson and Emma Pauline (Dallmann) Hoops; m. Alexander Buchanan Vance Johnson, June 15, 1980; 1 child, Allegra Alexandra Olson Johnson. BA, St. Olaf Coll., 1969; MA, U. Iowa, 1971; MFA, Princeton U., 1973, PhD, 1976. Preceptor Princeton (N.J.) U., 1972-74; contbg. editor Arts Mag., 1973-75; art news editor The Soho Weekly News, N.Y.C., 1976-78; asst. prof., assoc. prof. Wheaton Coll., Norton, Mass., 1975-88, prof., 1988—, chmn. art dept., 1987-89, 92-93; A. Howard Meneely chair Wheaton Coll., 1990-92; cons. Smithsonian Instn., Washington, 1984-86; bd. dirs. The Drawing Soc., N.Y.C., 1989-94, The Friends of Art; bd. advisers Halley's Comet Soc., 1986—; mem. vis. com. drawing and print dept. Met. Mus. Art, 1993—. Author: Italian Nineteenth Century Drawings and Watercolors: An Album, 1976, Italian Drawings 1780-1890, 1980 (N.Y. Times Best Art Book award 1981, Whole Earth Book award), Fire and Ice: A History of Comets in Art, 1985, Italian Renaissance Sculpture, 1992, French edit., 1993, Ottocento: Romanticism and Revolution in 19th Century Italian Painting, 1993; contbr. articles to profl. jours., including Burlington mag., Art Bull., Master Drawings, Artibus et Historiae, Sci. Am., Gazette des Beaux-Arts, Antologie di Belle Arti, Astronomy and Astrophysics, Art Jour., Studies in History of Art; contbr. articles to art exhbn. catalogs, including Six Centuries of Sculptors Crawings, The Drawing Ctr., N.Y.C., 1981, Disegni de Tommaso Minardi, 2 vols., 1982, Old Master Drawings from the Mus. Art, RISD, 1983; guest curator Art Mus. Princeton U., 1974, Nat. Gallery Art, 1980 N.Y. Hist. Soc., 1990. Fellow Samuel H. Kress Found., 1973-74, Whiting Found. for Humanities, 1974-75, NEH, 1982-83; grantee NEH, 1987-88, Am. Philos. Soc., 1989, Am. Coun. Learned Socs., 1990-91, Getty sr. rsch. grantee, 1994-95. Mem. Coll. Art Assn. Am., Am. Assn. Univ. Profs. Italian, Drawing Soc., Phi Beta Kappa (pres. 1980-82, Kappa chpt.). Avocations: running, squash, collecting. Home: 35 Howard St Norton MA 02766 Office: Wheaton Coll Watson Hall Norton MA 02766

OLSON, ROGER NORMAN, health service administrator; b. Spokane, July 3, 1936; s. Harry Leonard and Evelyn Helen (Pearson) O.; m. Joyce Marlene Markert, June 28, 1959; children: Leonard Mark, Brent Norman. BA, Pacific Luth. U., 1958; MDiv, Augustana Theol. Sem., 1962; MSW, U. Wash., 1970. Pastor Christ Luth. Ch., Des Moines, 1962-64; asst. pastor First Immanuel Luth. Ch., Portland, Oreg., 1964-68; planner Tri-County Community Coun., Portland, 1970-71; project coord. City-County Commn. on Aging, Portland, 1971-73; evaluation coord. Portland Bur. of Human Resources, 1973-74; asst. dir. Multnomah County Project Health Div., 1974-83; interim pastor Augustana Luth. Ch., 1984-85; dir. family support svcs. Met. Family Svc., 1985-91, dir. planning and rsch., 1992-94; coord. spl. programs Luth. Family Svc. Rockefeller Bros. fellowship Rockefeller Fund for Theol. Edn., 1958-59, fellowship NIMH, 1968-69, Adminstn. on Aging, 1969-70. Democrat. Lutheran. Avocations: music, reading, theatre. Home: 3939 NE 21st Ave Portland OR 97212-1432 Office: Luth Family Svc 605 SE 39th Ave Portland OR 97214-3298

OLSON, RONALD DALE, grain company executive; b. Ft. Dodge, Iowa, Oct. 22, 1947; s. Albert Dale and Gladys Marie (Peters) O.; m. Lynn Diane Rustwick, Nov. 22, 1969; children: Jenna, Jill. BS in Agr. Bus., Iowa State U., 1969, MS in Econs., 1971. Instr. econs. Iowa State U., Ames, 1969-71; various merchandising and mgmt. positions Continental Grain Co., Portland, Oreg., San Francisco, Fairmont, Minn. and Mpls.; regional mgr., v.p. N.W. region Continental Grain Co., 1971-90; pres. Atwood-Kellogg Co., Mpls., 1990—; bd. dirs. Mpls. Grain Exchange, chmn. bd., 1985-87. Mem. ch. council Mt. Olivet Luth. Ch., Mpls., 1975—. Avocations: sports; music; woodworking. Home: 3510 Beard Curve Minneapolis MN 55431-2724 Office: Atwood Kellogg Co 876 Grain Exchange Minneapolis MN 55415

OLSON, RONALD LEROY, lawyer; b. Carroll, Iowa, July 9, 1941; s. Clyde L. and Delpha C. (Boyens) O.; m. Jane Tenhulzen, June 21, 1964; children—Kristin, Steven, Amy. B.S., Drake U., 1963; J.D., U. Mich., 1966; Diploma in Law, Oxford U., Eng., 1967. Bar: Wis. 1966, Calif. 1969, U.S. Dist. Ct. (cen. dist.) Calif. 1969, U.S. Dist. Ct. (so. dist.) Calif. 1973, U.S. Ct. Appeals (9th cir.) 1974, U.S. Ct. Appeals (10th cir.) 1980, U.S. Ct. Appeals (5th cir.) 1982, U.S. Supreme Ct. 1976, U.S. Dist. Ct. Alaska 1983. Atty. U.S. Dept. Justice, 1967; clk. to chief judge U.S. Ct. Appeals (D.C. cir.), Washington, 1967-68; ptnr. Munger, Tolles & Olson, Los Angeles, 1968—; ; lawyer del. Ann. 9th Cir. Conf., 1984-89; lectr. in field. Mem. editorial bd. Alternatives, 1983—. Contbr. numerous articles to legal jours. Mem. adv. com. Los Angeles and Orange Counties chpt. Lawyers Alliance for Nuclear Arms Control; trustee Drake U., 1977—; Sequoia Nat. Park Natural History Assn., 1983—; bd. dirs., pres. Fraternity of Friends of Music Ctr., 1978—; chmn. bd. fellows Claremont U. Ctr. and Grad. Sch., 1984—; bd. dirs. Legal Aid Found. L.A., 1975-86, pres., 1984-85; bd. dirs. Salzburg Seminar; com. visitors U. Mich. Law Sch., 1986—, sec. L.A. Arts Festival, 1985—; mem. Skid Row Housing Trust of L.A., 1986—; mem. editorial bd. Alternatives, 1983-88. Burton scholar U. Mich.; Ford Found. fellow Oxford U., 1967. Fellow Am. Coll. Trial Lawyers, Am. Bar Found.; mem. ABA (litigation sect. council 1976—, chmn. 1981-82, chmn. spl. com. on dispute resolution 1976-86, litigation sect. Soviet Exchange Program com. 1983—; editorial bd. Human Rights publ. sect. ind. rights and responsiblities, 1986—, task force on tng. the advocate 1986—, standing com. fed. judiciary), Am. Judicature Soc., L.A. Bar Found. (bd. dirs. 1977—), Am. Arbitration Assn. (bd. dirs. 1983—, comml. panel 1983—), L.A. County Bar Assn., State Bar Calif. (bd. dirs. 1985—, v.p. 1986-87), Assn. Bus. Trial Lawyers (mem. adv. com. trial ct. improvement fund for dist. jud. coun. 1988—), L.A. County Barristers (pres. 1976), 9th Cir. Jud. Conf. (exec. com. 1984-89), Chancery. Democrat. Episcopalian. Office: Munger Tolles & Olson 355 S Grand Ave Fl 35 Los Angeles CA 90071-1560

OLSON, RUSSELL L., pension fund administrator; b. Elizabeth, N.J., Jan. 3, 1933; s. Harold B. and Edythe M. (Roberts) O.; m. Jeanette A. Sanderson, Aug. 9, 1958; children: Tracy, Stephen, Heather. BA, Rutgers U., 1954; MBA, Harvard U., 1977. Trainee Eastman Kodak Co., Rochester, N.Y., 1954-56, with pub. rels. dept., 1957-69, coordinator internt. info. svcs., 1964-69, treas. staff, 1971-74; adminstrv. asst. pension investments Eastman Kodak Co., Rochester, 1974-82, dir. pension investments worldwide, 1982—.

With USAF, 1954-56. Presbyterian. Office: Eastman Kodak Co 343 State St Rochester NY 14650-0249

OLSON, SIGMUND LARS, corporate finance executive; b. Green Bay, Wis., Feb. 7, 1935; s. Edwin Louis and Marjorie Magdelene (Miller) O.; m. Diana Lynn Armentrout, Mar. 15, 1961 (div. 1974); children: Eric L., Lafe S., Britta C., Gunnar A.; m. Linda Marie Larson, Sept. 25, 1976. BS, Calif. State U., Long Beach, 1963; MBA, U. Iowa, 1964. With fin. staff Ford Motor Co., Detroit, 1964-69; with mgmt. staff Mattel, Inc., Los Angeles, 1969-72, Allen Group, Los Angeles, 1972-77; dir. planning Internat. Harvester Co., Chgo., 1977-78, dir. fin. German div., Düsseldorf, 1978-79, v.p. fin. European div., Paris, 1979-82, asst. controller, Chgo., 1982-84, asst. treas., 1984-85; v.p. treas. Ecolab, Inc., St. Paul, 1985-86, v.p., controller, 1986-88, sr. v.p. fin., 1988-90; CFO Henkel-Ecolab Joint Venture, Dusseldorf, Fed. Republic Germany, 1990-94; v.p. fin. Internat. Ecolab., Inc., St. Paul, 1995—. Bd. dirs. YMCA, St. Paul, 1986-90, chmn., 1989-90. Served to cpl. USMA, 1957-60. Mem. Fin. Execs. Inst., Planning Execs. Inst., Am. Mgmt. Assn., Nat. Assn. Corp. Treas. Lutheran. Club: Univ. (St. Paul). Avocations: sailing, reading, skiing, investments. Office: Ecolab Inc 370 Wabosha Saint Paul MN 55102

OLSON, STANLEY WILLIAM, physician, educator, medical school dean; b. Chgo., Feb. 10, 1914; s. David William and Agnes (Nelson) O.; m. Lorraine Caroline Lofdahl, June 26, 1936; children: Patricia Ann, Richard David, Robert Dean. BS, Wheaton Coll., 1934, LLD (hon.), 1956; MD, U. Ill., 1938; MS in Medicine (fellow), U. Minn., 1943; ScD, U. Akron, 1979, N.E Ohio U., 1985, Morehouse Sch. Medicine. Diplomate: Am. Bd. Internal Medicine. Intern Cook County Hosp., Chgo., 1938-40; asst. dir. Mayo Found., from 1947; cons. medicine Mayo Clinic, 1947—; instr. medicine grad. sch. U. Minn., 1947-50; dean and prof. coll. medicine, dir. Rsch. and Ednl. Hosp. U. Ill., 1950-53; dean and prof. Coll. Medicine Baylor U., Tex. Med. Ctr., Houston, 1953-66; prof. medicine Vanderbilt U.; clin. prof. medicine Meharry Med. Coll., 1966-68; dir. Tenn. Mid-South Regional Med. Program, 1967-68; dir. Div. Regional Med. Programs Svc. USPHS, 1968-70; pres. S.W. Found. for Rsch. and Edn., San Antonio, 1970-73; provost Coll. Medicine N.E. Ohio U., 1973-79, cons. med. edn. Morehouse Coll. Medicine, 1980-81; dean Morehouse Sch. Medicine, Atlanta, 1985-87; past chmn. med. bd., chief staff Ben Taub Hosp., Jefferson Davis Hosp., Houston; nat. adv. council for health research facilities NIH, 1963-68; rev. panel constrn. med. schs. USPHS, 1964-65; spl. cons. div. Regional Med. Programs NIH, 1966-68; med. cons. bd. trustees SUNY, 1949; cons. to Hoover Commn., 1954; mem. bd. trustees. Wheaton Coll., Ill., 1953-68. Contbr. articles to profl. jours. Capt., M.C. AUS, 1943-46. Mem. AMA, Houston Philos. Soc. (pres. 1962-63), Tex. Philos. Soc., Assn. Am. Med. Colls., Alumni Assn. Mayo Found., Sigma Xi, Alpha Kappa Kappa, Alpha Omega Alpha. Baptist. Home: 5901 Churchview Dr Unit 25 Rockford IL 61107

OLSON, STEPHEN M(ICHAEL), lawyer; b. Jamestown, N.Y., May 4, 1948; s. Charles R. and Marilyn (Dietzel) O.; m. Linda C. Hanson, Aug. 24, 1968; children: Kevin, Darren. AB cum laude, Princeton U., 1970; JD, U. Chgo., 1973. Bar: Pa. 1973, U.S. Dist. Ct. (we. dist.) Pa. 1973, U.S. Ct. Appeals (3d cir.) 1975, U.S. Ct. Appeals (1st and D.C. cirs.) 1986, U.S. Ct. Appeals (7th cir. and 8th cir. 1988), U.S. Supreme Ct. 1986. Assoc. Kirkpatrick & Lockhart, Pitts., 1973-81, ptnr., 1981—. Mem. bd. editors HealthSpan. Sec. bd. trustees Chatham Coll.; bd. dirs. Competitive Employment Opportunities. Mem. ABA (rlwy./airline labor law com.), Pa. Bar Assn., Allegheny County Bar Assn., Princeton Alumni Assn. West Pa., Duguesne Club, Edgeworth Club. Avocations: photography, music, tennis. Office: Kirkpatrick & Lockhart 1500 Oliver Building Bldg Pittsburgh PA 15222-2312

OLSON, SYLVESTER IRWIN, government official; b. Herman, Minn., Apr. 2, 1907; s. Jacob John and Theresia Mary (Kremer) O.; m. Virginia Varney Culbert, Aug. 19, 1948; children—Karen Therese, Eric Sylvester. Student, Marquette U., 1925-26; B.A., U. Minn., 1929, J.D., 1931. Bar: Minn. bar 1931, Wash. bar 1949, Republic of Korea bar 1954, D.C. bar 1962. Asso. Ewing & Lehmann, St. Paul, 1931-33, Harold E. Stassen, Elmer J. Ryan, Farmington, Minn., 1933-34; mem. firm Stassen, Olson, Kelly & LeVander, South St. Paul, Minn., 1935-39; asst. county atty. Dakota County, Minn., 1933-39; dep. chief counsel Dept. Rural Credit Minn., 1939-42; chief counsel div. adminstrv. mgmt. Minn., 1942-43, atty. and pub. relations counsel, 1944-48; mem. firm Brown, Olson & Clarke, Yakima, Wash.; asso. counsel Graves, Kizer & Graves, Spokane, 1949-54; legal cons. UN Econ. Coordinator, Korea, 1954; minister embassy, dir. U.S. Operations Mission to, Portugal, U.S. Operations Mission to (FOA), 1954-55; dep. dir. U.S. Operations Mission, ICA, also attache Am. Embassy, Tokyo, Japan, 1956-58; asst. dir. office Territories, Dept. Interior, 1959-61; practiced in Washington, 1962-66; program adviser Fed. Water Pollution Control Adminstrn., 1967-68; dir. enforcement div. EPA, 1969-76, spl. asst. dir. water enforcement, 1976-77; Pres. Wells Olson Co., Herman, 1946-78; dir. Pacific N.W., Trans-N.W. Gas, Inc., 1951-55. Chmn. Citation Crusade for Freedom, Central Wash., 1951. Mem. Yakima C. of C. (dir. 1951-53), Fed., Wash. Minn., D.C. bar assns., Tau Kappa Epsilon, Phi Alpha Delta. Home: Heatheridge 356 Pikes Peak Dr Grand Junction CO 81503-1740

OLSON, THEODORE ALEXANDER, former environmental biology educator; b. Oakes, N.D., Sept. 12, 1904; s. Henry Martin and Anna R. (Anderson) O.; m. Grace Myrtle Lundberg, Jan. 5, 1929; children—Theodore A., R. Thomas, Robert C. B.S., U. Minn., 1926; M.A., Harvard, 1938, Ph.D., 1958. Econ. entomologist U. Wis., 1926; instr. entomology U. Minn., 1926-28; prof. environmental biology Sch. Pub. Health, 1938-73, prof. emeritus, 1973—; biologist Minn. Dept. Health, 1928-38; Cons. health depts., Minn., N.Y., Wash.; Cons. health depts. Ohio River Valley Sanitation Commn., WHO, Norwegian Inst. Water Research, NIH; participant internat. study rodent control, Europe, Mid East, Pacific WHO, 1965, Internat. Conf., Munich, 1966. Author 1 book and over 100 profl. pubis. Served from 1st lt to lt. col. San. Corps AUS, 1942-46. Rockefeller fellow, 1947; WHO fellow Caribbean, 1955; USPHS fellow N. Europe, 1962. Mem. AAAS, Am. Pub. Health Assn. (sect. vice chmn., chmn. lab. sect., governing council 1960-70), Am. Soc. Limnology and Oceanography, Am. Micros. Soc., Entomol. Soc. Am., State and Territorial Lab. Dirs. Assn., Sigma Xi, Internat. Assn. Great Lakes Research (dir., pres. 1968—). Clubs: University Minnesota, Harvard. Research on basic limnology of Lake Superior. Home: 4752 16th Ave S Minneapolis MN 55407-3607

OLSON, THEODORE BEVRY, lawyer, government official; b. Chgo., Sept. 11, 1940; 2 children. B.A., U. Pacific, 1962; LL.B., U. Calif.-Berkeley, 1965. Bar: Calif. 1965, D.C. 1982. Assoc. Gibson, Dunn & Crutcher, Los Angeles, 1965-71, ptnr., 1972-81; asst. atty. gen. Dept. Justice, Washington, 1981—. Mem. Calif. Commn. on Uniform State Laws, 1972-74; del. Republican Nat. Conv., 1976, 80. Mem. ABA (chmn. com. on pleadings, motions and pre-trial litigation sect. 1973-74), Los Angeles County Bar Assn. Office: Gibson Dunn & Crutcher 1050 Connecticut Ave NW Ste 90 Washington DC 20036-5303

OLSON, THOMAS FRANCIS, II, communications company executive; b. Chgo., July 31, 1948; s. Thomas Francis and Nora Theresa (Shaw) O.; m. Maureen Eunice Walsh, July 28, 1972; children: Amy Michelle, Danielle Renee. B in Bus. Mktg., Western Ill. U., 1970. TV time salesman Sta. WQAD-TV, Moline, Ill., 1970-73; computer salesman Honeywell, Inc., Springfield, Ill., 1973; project mgr. Olson Bros. and Sons Constrn. Co., Chgo., 1973-75; TV time salesman Katz Communications, Chgo., 1975-77, sales team mgr., 1977-81; nat. sales mgr. Katz Communications, N.Y.C., 1981-83, gen. sales mgr., 1983-84, div. pres., 1984-90, exec. v.p. TV group, 1991-92; pres. Katz TV Group, N.Y.C., 1992—; pres. chief exec. officer Katz Media Corp., 1994—. Mem. Nat. Assn. Broadcasters, TV Bur. Advt. Roman Catholic. Avocations: running, skiing, hiking, sailing, scuba diving. Office: Katz Media Corp Inc 125 W 55th St New York NY 10019

OLSON, WALTER GILBERT, lawyer; b. Stanton, Nebr., Feb. 2, 1924; s. O.E. Olson and Mabel A. Asplin; m. Gloria Helen Bennett, June 26, 1949; children: Clifford Warner, Karen Rae Olson. BS, U. Calif., Berkeley, 1947, JD, 1949. Bar: Calif. 1950, U.S. Dist. Ct. (no. dist.) Calif. 1950, U.S. Tax Ct. 1950, U.S. Ct. Appeals (9th cir.) 1950. Assoc. Orrick, Herrington and Sutcliffe (formerly Orrick, Dahlquist, Herrington and Sutcliffe), San Francisco, 1949-54, ptnr., 1954-88, of counsel, 1989—; bd. dirs. Alltel Corp.,

Little Rock, 1988-94; mem. Commn. to Revise Calif. Corp. Securities Law, 1967-69, Securities Regulatory Reform Panel, 1978-80; mem. corp. security adv. com. Calif. Commr. of Corps, 1975—. Editor-in-chief Calif. Law Review, 1948-49. Bd. dirs. Internat. Ho., Berkeley, 1981-86. With U.S. Army, 1943-46, ETO. Fellow Am. Bar Found.; mem. ABA (trust divsn. nat. conf. of lawyers and reps. of Am. Bankers Assn.), Calif. Bar Assn. (chmn. corps com. 1975-76, exec. com. bus. law sect. 1977-78), San Francisco Bar Assn., U. Calif. Alumni Assn., Boalt Hall Alumni Assn. (bd. dirs. 1982-90, sec. 1985, v.p. 1987, pres. 1988), Order of Coif, Menlo Country Club (Woodside, Calif.), Pacific-Union Club. Office: Orrick Herrington & Sutcliffe 400 Sansome St San Francisco CA 94111

OLSON, WALTER JUSTUS, JR., management consultant; b. Paterson, N.J., July 27, 1941; s. Walter Justus and Viola (Trautvetter) O. BS, BA, Brown U., 1964; MBA, Columbia U., 1967. CPA, Va. Design engr. Rockwell Internat., Inc., Downey, Calif., 1964-65; mgmt. officer CIA, Washington, 1969-73; sr. cons. Booz, Allen and Hamilton, Inc., Washington, 1973-78; corp. planning coordinator Washington Gas Light Co., Washington, 1978-82; prin. Walter J. Olson and Assoc., McLean, Va., 1982-83; dep. asst. sec. for export adminstrn. U.S. Dept. Commerce, Washington, 1983-86; prin. Walter J. Olson & Assoc., Washington, 1986—. Vice-chmn. fin. com. Fairfax County (Va.) Reps., 1982-83. Served to 1st lt., USAF, 1967-69. Mem. AICPA, D.C. Inst. CPAs, Washington Internat. Trade Assn., The Planning Forum (pres. Washington chpt. 1990-91). Republican. Episcopalian. Home: 7348 Dartford Dr Mc Lean VA 22102-7348 Office: 1815 H St NW Ste 600 Washington DC 20006-3604

OLSON, WALTER THEODORE, research scientist, consultant; b. Royal Oak, Mich., July 4, 1917; s. Oscar Thomas and Edith Margaret (Ketcham) O.; m. Ruth Elisabeth Barker, Oct. 28, 1943; 1 child, David Paul. AB, DePauw U., 1939; MS, Case Inst. Tech., 1940, PhD, 1942. Instr. Case Inst. Tech., 1941-42; research scientist Lewis Research Center, NASA, Cleve., 1942-45; chief combustion br. Lewis Research Center, NASA, 1945-50, chief chemistry and energy conversion research div., 1950-63, asst. dir., 1963-72, dir. tech. utilization and public affairs, 1972-81, disting. research assoc., 1981-82; pvt. cons., 1981—; mem. numerous govt. adv. coms. Editor: (with W.R. Hawthorne) Design and Performance of Gas Turbine Power Plants, 1960; editorial bd.: Combustion and Flame, 1955-65; contbr. articles to profl. jours. Dir. Build Up Greater Cleve. Program, 1981-91; vice chmn. United Appeal Greater Cleve., 1973-83; chmn. legis. affairs Ohio Assn. Gifted Children, 1969-76; trustee Blue Cross N.E., Ohio, 1972-84, N.E. Ohio Transit Coalition, 1992—; mem. industry adv. com. Coll. Engrs., Cleve. State U., 1975-85, chmn., 1975-76; mem. Ohio Pub. Works Commn., 1988-89. Recipient Career Service award Greater Cleve. Growth Assn., 1972, Exceptional Contbns. award NASA, 1981, Excellence award Am. Soc. Assn. Execs., 1987. Fellow AIAA (dir. 1969-75, Disting. Svc. award Cleve.-Akron sect. 1966, 75, Exceptional Svc. award 1981, other awards), AAAS; mem. Combustion Inst. (dir. 1954—), Am. Chem. Soc., Sigma Xi, Phi Gamma Delta. Methodist. Clubs: Cosmos (Washington); City (Cleve.). Patentee in field. Home and Office: 18960 Coffinberry Blvd Cleveland OH 44126-1602

OLSON, WANDA JEAN, lawyer; b. Ft. Meade, Md., Sept. 4, 1957; d. Donald Leslie and Wanda Ardeen (Phillips) O.; m. Robert Selnick Silverstein, June 6, 1981; children: Joshua Olson Silverstein, Erica Olson Silverstein. BA, Johns Hopkins U., 1978; JD, NYU, 1981. Bar: N.Y. 1982, N.J. 1983. Assoc. Cleary, Gottlieb, Steen & Hamilton, N.Y.C., 1981-89, ptnr., 1990—. Editor Ann. Survey Am. Law, 1979-80, mng. editor, 1980-81. Mem. ABA, Order of Coif, Phi Beta Kappa, Omicron Delta Epsilon. Office: 1 Liberty Plz New York NY 10006-1401

OLSON, WARREN KINLEY, operations research analyst, engineer, physicist; b. Minot, N.D., Aug. 11, 1943; s. Arthur Conrad and Dorothy Elenor (Kinley) O.; m. Colleen Kay Ude, Dec. 18. 1965; children: Christine Kay, Cynthia Dorine. BA in Physics and Math., St. Olaf Coll., 1965; MS in Stats., U. Del., 1974. Mathematician Ballistics Rsch. Lab., Aberdeen Proving Ground, Md., 1962-68; ops. rsch. analyst Army Material Systems Analysis Agy., Aberdeen Proving Ground, 1969-76; br. chief USA TRADOC Systems Analysis Activity, White Sands Missile Range, N. Mex., 1976-85; dir. rsch. USA TRADOC Ops. Rsch. Activity, White Sands Missile Range, 1985-86; div. chief USA TRADOC Analysis Command, White Sands Missile Range, 1986, dir. rsch., 1986-87; sr. staff engr. Honeywell Defense Systems Group, Edina, Minn., 1987-90, Alliant Techsystems, Inc., Hopkins, Minn., 1990-93; rsch. mem. Inst. for Def. Analysis, Alexandria, Va., 1993—; mem. sci. staff NATO Joint Field Trials, Munich, Germany, 1973-74; chmn. U.S. Army ABCA QWG/AOR Spl. Work Group, White Sands, 1979-87; mem. def. sci. bd. MOBA Study, 1994. Co-author: (with others) (text) Military Strategy and Tactics, 1975, (handbook) Military Operations Research, 1994; contbr. tech. reports to profl., military pubs., 1965-95. Elder Peace Luth. Ch., El Paso, Tex., 1985-87. Recipient Citizenship award, DAR, 1956, Civilian Svc. Commander's award, U.S. Army, Washington, 1979. Mem. Soc. for Preservation and Encouragement of Barber Shop Quartet Singing (bd. dirs. El Paso 1977-79, Internat. medalist 1991, 92, 93, Gt. No. Union Chorus), Mil. Ops. Rsch. Soc., Am. Def. Preparedness Assn., Sigma Pi Sigma. Avocations: music, skiing, scuba diving, photography, model railroading, chess. Home: 4657 Longstreet Ln # 302 Alexandria VA 22311-4912 Office: Inst Defense Analyses 1801 N Beauregard St Alexandria VA 22311-1733

OLSON, WILLIAM CLINTON, international affairs educator, author, lecturer; b. Denver, Aug. 19, 1920; s. Albert Merrill and Frances (Murray) O.; m. Mary Elizabeth Matthews, Aug. 16, 1943; children—Jon Eric, Peter Murray, Elizabeth Ann. A.B. (Outstanding Sr. award), U. Denver, 1942; Ph.D., Yale U., 1953; DHL (hon.), U. Denver, 1992. Staff officer Social Sci. Found., Denver, 1947-49; chmn. com. internat. relations Pomona Coll., 1953-61; sr. mem. St. Antonys Coll., Oxford (Eng.) U., 1959-60; assoc. dean sch. internat. affairs Columbia U., 1965-67; assoc. dir. for social scis. Rockefeller Found., N.Y.C., 1967-79; prof. Sch. Internat. Service, Am. U., Washington, 1979-90, prof. emeritus, 1990—, dean, 1979-86; visiting research fellow Royal Inst. Internat. Affairs, London, 1986-87; dir. The Bellagio Study and Conf. Ctr. of The Rockefeller Found., Villa Serbelloni, Italy, 1970-79; prof. Grad. Inst. Internat. Studies, Geneva, Switzerland, 1976-78; life fellow Clare Hall, Cambridge; cons. to vice chancellor U. Colomb, Sri Lanka, 1983. Author, editor: The Theory and Practice of International Relations, 1960, 9th edit., 1994; contbr.: International Relations: British and American Perspectives, 1985, The Aberystwth Papers, 1972, Jahrbuch des offentlichen Rechts der gegenwart, 1972, 74, 78, 80, Internat. Affairs, 1976, 91; co-author: Internat. Relations Then and Now: Origins and Trends in Interpretation, 1991. Trustee Expt. in Internat. Living, 1959-65; trustee Social Sci. Found. and Grad. Sch. Internat. Studies, U. Denver, 1967-76, 80-92, 94—; co-founder Am. Friends Wilton Park, Inc., 1986. Recipient Disting. Alumnus award Grad. Sch. Internat. Studies, 1986; recipient medal and named Hon. Ancien, NATO Def. Coll., 1989. Mem. Coun. Fgn. Rels., Washington Inst. Fgn. Affairs, Internat. Studies Assn. (nat. pres. 1968-69), British Internat. Studies Assn., Cosmos Club (Washington), Phi Beta Kappa (pres. Gamma of Calif. 1957-58), Sigma Iota Rho (founder).

OLSSON, ANN-MARGRET See ANN-MARGRET

OLSSON, BJÖRN ESKIL, railroad supply company executive; b. Kristianstad, Sweden, Oct. 7, 1945; came to U.S. 1990; m. Cecilia Lindblad, July 6, 1968; children: Fredrik, Karin, Eva. M Bus. and Adminstrn., U. Lund, Sweden, 1968. Internal auditor Kockums Mek. Verkstad, Malmö, Sweden, 1969-71, mgr. acctg., 1971-74; v.p. fin. analysis and adminstrn. Kockums Industri, Söderhamn, Sweden, 1974-76, Linden Alimak, Skellefteå, Sweden, 1976-81, Sonessons, Malmö, 1981-82; pres. Sab-Nife, Malmö, 1982-87; v.p. corp. devel. Investment AB Cardo, Malmö, 1987-90; pres., CEO Harmon Industries Inc., Blue Springs, Mo., 1990—; bd. dirs. Deve Schindler, Stockholm, Green & Co., Malmö; mem. adv. bd. Ctrl. Mo. State U. Bus. Sch., Warrensburg, 1991—. Staff sgt. Swedish Army, 1964-65. Avocations: golf, skiing. Office: Harmon Industries Inc 1300 NW Jefferson Ct Blue Springs MO 64015-7265

OLSSON, CARL ALFRED, urologist; b. Boston, Nov. 20, 1938; s. Charles Rudolph and Ruth Marion (Bostrom) O.; m. Mary DeVore, Nov. 4, 1962; children: Ingrid, Leif Eric. Grad., Bowdoin Coll., 1959; M.D., Boston U., 1963. Diplomate Am. Bd. Urology (trustee 1988—, pres. 1993-94). Asst.

prof. urology Boston U. Sch. Medicine, 1971-72, assoc. prof., 1972-74, prof., chmn. dept., 1974-80; dir. urology dept. Boston City Hosp., 1974-77; chief urology dept. Boston VA Med. Ctr., 1971-75; urologist-in-chief Univ. Hosp., Boston, 1971-80; John K. Lattimer prof., chmn. dept. urology Coll. Phys. and Surgs., Columbia U., N.Y.C., 1980—; dir. Squier Urol. Clinic, urology service Presbyn. Hosp., N.Y.C.; lectr. surgery Tufts U. Sch. Medicine. Boston Interhosp. Organ Bank, 1976-79; mem. working cadre Nat. Prostate Cancer Project, Nat. Cancer Inst., 1979-84; mem. adv. coun. Nat. Inst. Diabetes, Digestive Disease and Kidney. Editl. bd. Jour. Prostate, World Jour. Urology, Jour. Urodynamics and Neurourology, Jour. Urology; asst. editor Jour. Urology, 1978-89; contbr. chpts. to books, articles to med. jours. Recipient Disting. Alumnus award Boston U., 1985. Fellow ACS; mem. Am. Urol. Assn. (coord. continuing med. edn. New Eng. sect. 1977-80, del. rsch. com., Gold Cystoscope award 1979, Grayson-Carroll award 1971, 73), Boston Surg. Soc. (exec. com. 1976-80), Am. Assn. Clin. Urologists, Am. Surg. Assn., Am. Assn. Genitourinary Surgeons, Clin. Soc. Genitourinary Surgeons, Transplantation Soc., Soc. Urologic Oncology (pres. 1993), Soc. Univ. Urologists (pres. 1990), N.Y. Sect. Am. Urol. Assn., Am. Fertility Soc., AMA, Assn. Acad. Surgery, Am. Soc. Artificial Internal Organs, Am. Soc. Transplant Surgeons, Assn. Med. Colls., Can. Urol. Assn., Societe Internationale d'Urologie, Internat. Urodynamics Soc., Mass. Med. Soc., Soc. Govt. Urologists, Australasian Urol. Soc. (hon.), New Eng. Handicapped Sportsmen's Assn. (exec. com. 1977-81), U.S. Yacht Racing Union, Yacht Racing Union L.I. Sound Club, N.Y. Yacht Club, Cottage Park Yacht Club, Larchmont Yacht Club, Storm Trysail Club, Alpha Omega Alpha. Episcopalian. Home: 18 Elm Ave Larchmont NY 10538-3649 Office: Columbia-Presbyn Hosp P&S Box 44 630 W 168th St New York NY 10032-3702

OLSSON, NILS WILLIAM, former association executive; b. Seattle, June 11, 1909; s. Nils A. and Mathilda (Lejkell) O.; m. Dagmar T. Gavert, June 15, 1940; children: Karna B., Nils G. and Pehr C. (twins). Student, North Park Coll., Chgo., Northwestern U., U. Minn., 1929-34; A.M., U. Chgo., 1938, Ph.D., 1949; Ph.D., U. Uppsala, Sweden, 1968; LHD, North Park Coll., Chgo., 1990. Admissions counselor, instr. Swedish North Park Coll., 1937-39; asst. Scandinavian U. Chgo., 1939-42, instr., 1945-50, asst. prof., 1950; mem. U.S. diplomatic service, 1950-67; 2d sec., pub. affairs officer Am. legation, Reykjavik, Iceland, 1950-52; attache, pub. affairs officer Am. embassy, Stockholm, Sweden, 1952-55; 1st sec., consul Am. embassy, 1955-57; pub. affairs adviser Dept. State, 1957-59; chief Am. sponsored schs. abroad, 1959-62; 1st sec. Am. embassy, Oslo, Norway, 1962-64; counselor for polit. affairs Am. embassy, 1964-66; diplomat in residence Ind. U., 1966-67; dir. Am. Swedish Inst., Mpls., 1967-73; exec. dir. Swedish Council of Am., 1973-84. Author: Swedish Passenger Arrivals in New York 1820-1850, 1967, Swedish Passenger Arrivals in U.S. Ports (except New York) 1820-1850, 1979, Tracing Your Swedish Ancestry, 1974, (with Erik Wiken) Swedish Passenger Arrivals in the U.S. 1820-1850, 1995; editor: A Pioneer in Northwest America, 1841-1858, vol. I, 1950, vol. II, 1959, Veckobladet, 1934-35; editor, pub: Swedish American Genealogist, 1981—; editor: A Swedish City Directory of Boston 1881, 1986; contbr. to hist. and ednl. jours. Mem. bd. Evang. Covenant Hist. Commn., Chgo., 1958; asst. naval attache Am. legation, Stockholm, 1943-45. Served from lt. (j.g.) to lt. comdr. USNR, 1942-45. Decorated knight Order Vasa 1st class, knight comdr. Order North Star, Sweden; recipient Swedish Pioneer Centennial medal, 1948; King Carl XVI Gustaf Bicentennial Gold medal, Carl Sandburg medal Swedish Pioneer Hist. Soc., 1982, Charlotta medal Emigrant Inst. Växjö, Sweden; named Swedish Am. of Yr. Stockholm, 1969; recipient Hans Mattsson Plaque, Önnestad, Sweden, 1992; Victor Örnberg prize, Sweden, 1994. Fellow Geneal. Soc. (Finland), Geneal. Soc. (Sweden), Am. Soc. Genealogists; mem. Wermländska Sällskapet Stockholm (hon.), Nat. Geneal Soc., Carl Johan Soc. Sweden, Swedish-Am. Hist. Soc. (exec. sec. 1949-50, 57-68, pres. 1986-88), Royal Acad. Belles Lettres, History and Antiquities (Sweden, fgn. corr.), Pro Fide et Christianismo (Sweden, hon.), Royal Soc. Pub. Manuscripts Dealing with Scandinavian History (Sweden, fgn.). Clubs: Skylight (Mpls.); Grolier (N.Y.C.); Cosmos (Washington); Explorers (Central Fla.); Univ. (Winter Park, Fla.). Lodge: Rotary. Home: Winter Park Gardens Apt # G-21 700 Melrose Ave Winter Park FL 32789

OLSSON, STURE GORDON, manufacturing executive; b. Richmond, Va., July 1, 1920; s. Elis and Signe (Granberg) O.; m. Anne Shirley Carter, June 8, 1957; children—Lisa Maria, Anne Carter, Inga Maja, Charles Elis. B.S., U. Va., 1942. Service engr. Sperry Gyroscope Co., Inc., 1943-44; plant engr. Chesapeake Corp., Va., 1946-51; v.p. charge mfg. Chesapeake Corp., 1952, exec. v.p., gen. mgr., 1952, pres., dir., 1968—; dir. Citizens & Farmers Bank. Mem. Business-Industry Polit. Action Com., Boy Scouts of Am.; trustee Episc. High Sch.; bd. dirs. Va. Forests Ednl. Fund; trustee St. Margaret's Sch. Found.; chmn. Va. Equine Edn. Found.; sponsor Ducks Unlimited. Served as lt. (j.g.) USNR, 1944-46. Decorated Swedish Royal Order North Star. Mem. Va. Mfrs. Assn. (past pres.), Am. Legion, Am. Horse Council, Raven Soc. of U. Va. Clubs: Capitol Hill (Washington); West Point Country, Country of Virginia, Commonwealth. Home: Romancoke West Point VA 23181 Office: Chesapeake Corp PO Box 2350 1021 E Cary St Richmond VA 23219-4000

OLSTAD, ROGER GALE, science educator; b. Mpls., Jan. 16, 1934; s. Arnold William and Myra (Stroschein) O.; m. Constance Elizabeth Jackson, Aug. 20, 1955; children: Karen Louise, Kenneth Bradley. B.S., U. Minn., 1955, M.A., 1959, Ph.D., 1963. Instr., U. Minn., Mpls., 1956-63; asst. prof. U. Ill., Urbana, 1963-64; mem. faculty U. Wash., Seattle, 1964—; asso. prof. sci. edn. U. Wash., 1967-71, prof., 1971—, asso. dean grad. studies Coll. Edn., 1969-81. Fellow AAAS; mem. NSTA (bd. dirs.) Wash. Sci. Tchrs. Assn. (pres. 1973-74), Nat. Assn. Rsch. Sci. Teaching (pres. 1977-78, bd. dirs.), N.W. Sci. Assn. (chmn. 1966-68), Assn. Edn. Tchrs. in Sci. (regional pres. 1966-68, pres. 1991-92), Nat. Assn. Biology Tchrs., Biol. Scis. Curriculum Study (chmn., bd. dirs. 1989-94), U. Wash. Faculty Club, Phi Delta Kappa. Home: 20143 53d Ave NE Seattle WA 98155 Office: U Wash Coll Edn Seattle WA 98195

OLSTEN, STUART, personnel services company executive; s. William O. Exec. v.p. Olsten Corp., Westbury, N.Y. Office: Olsten Corp 1 Merrick Ave Westbury NY 11590-6612

OLSTOWSKI, FRANCISZEK, chemical engineer, consultant; b. N.Y.C., Apr. 23, 1927; s. Franciszek and Marguerite (Stewart) O.; A.A., Monmouth Coll., 1950; B.S. in Chem. Enging., Tex. A. and I. U., 1954 (name now Tex. A&M U.); m. Rosemary Sole, May 19, 1952; children: Marguerita Antonina, Anna Rosa, Franciszek, Anton, Henryk Alexander. Research and devel. engr. Dow Chem. Co., Freeport, Tex., 1954-56, project leader, 1956-65, sr. research engr., 1965-72, research specialist, 1972-79, research leader, 1979-87; dir. Tech. Cons. Services, Freeport, 1987—. Lectr. phys. scis. elementary and intermediate schs., Freeport, 1961-85. Vice chmn. Freeport Traffic Commn., 1974-76, chmn., 1976-79, vice-chmn. 1987-89, chmn., 1989-92. With USNR, 1944-46. Fellow Am. Inst. Chemist; mem. AAAS, Am. Chem. Soc., Electrochem. Soc. (sec. treas. South Tex. sect. 1963-64, vice chmn. 1964-65, chmn. 1965-67, councillor 1967-70), N.Y. Acad. Sci, Velasco Cemetery Assn. (sec.-treas. 1992-95). Patentee in synthesis of fluorocarbons, natural graphite products, electrolytic prodn. magnesium metal and polyurethane tech.

OLSZEWSKI, EDWARD JOHN, art history educator; b. Detroit, Jan. 7, 1937; s. John Peter and Mary Catherine (Kaminski) O.; m. I. Monica Foltarz. BS, U. Detroit, 1958, MS, 1962; PhD, U. Ill., 1964, U. Minn., 1974. Rsch. assoc. prof. U. South Fla., Tampa, 1964-65; rsch. chemist Archer Daniels Midland, Mpls., 1965-68; asst. prof. art history Case Western Res. U., Cleve., 1971-77, assoc. prof., 1977-89, prof., 1989—. Author: Art of Painting, 1977, Draftsman's Eye, 1981. Fellow NEH, 1979, Fulbright-Hays fellow, 1980, fellow Gladys Kriebl Delmas Found., 1986. Mem. Coll. Art Assn., Midwest Art History Soc. (pres. 1981-84), Renaissance Soc. Am. Avocation: travel. Office: Case Western Res U University Cir Cleveland OH 44106

OLTHOF, MEINT, engineering company executive consultant. Exec. v.p., gen. mgr. Killam Assoc., Inc., Warrendale, Pa. Office: Killam Assoc Inc 100 Allegheny Dr Warrendale PA 15086*

OLTMAN, C. DWIGHT, conductor, educator; b. Imperial, Nebr., May 27, 1936; s. George L. and Lois Beryl (Wine) O.; m. Shirley Jean Studebaker,

May 30, 1966; children—Michelle Leigh, Nicole Alicia. B.S., McPherson Coll., 1958; M.Mus., Wichita State U., 1963; postgrad., U. Cin., 1967-70; student, Nadia Boulanger, Paris, 1960, Pierre Monteux, 1963. Asst. prof. music Manchester Coll., North Manchester, Ind., 1963-67; prof. of conducting, music dir. symphony orch. and Bach Festival Baldwin-Wallace Coll., Berea, Ohio, 1970—; music dir. Ohio Chamber Orch., Cleve., 1972-92, laureate conductor, 1992—; music dir., prin. condr. Cleve. Ballet, 1976—; music dir. Cullowhee Music Festival, N.C., 1977-79; guest conductor Europe, Can., U.S.A. Mem. Am. Symphony Orch. League, Conductor's Guild. Democrat. Avocations: reading; walking; theater; spectator sports. Home and Office: 21631 Cedar Branch Trl Strongsville OH 44136-1287

OLTMAN, HENRY GEORGE, JR., retired engineering executive; b. Brookhaven, Miss., Oct. 6, 1927; s. Henry George Oltman and Eunice Zelma (Yawn) Oltman Hoyland; m. Dorothy Carolyn Howard, Oct. 19, 1947 (div. 1949); 1 child, Carolyn Ann; m. Loretta Marie Nemes, Mar. 27, 1954; children: Joan Marie Oltman-Shay, David Lee, Brian George, Neil Robert. BS in Physics, U. N.Mex., 1950, MS in Physics, 1954. Registered profl. engr., N.Mex. Mem. tech. Sandia Corp., Albuquerque, 1947-57; group head Electronic Specialty Co., L.A., 1957-58; sr. engr. Rantec Corp., Calabasas, Calif., 1958-61; mem. tech. staff TRW Systems, Redondo Beach, Calif., 1961-67; sr. scientist Hughes Aircraft Co., Canoga Park, Calif., 1967-86; v.p., dir. engring. Tecom Industries, Chatsworth, Calif., 1986-93; cons. TRW Systems, Redondo Beach, 1967-68. Contbr. articles to profl. jours.; assoc. editor: IEEE Transactions on Microwave Theory and Techniques, 1974-82; inventor 11 patents in field. Cubmaster/scoutmaster Boy Scouts Am. Recipient L.A. Hyland Patent award Hughes Aircraft Co., 1981. Fellow IEEE (vice chmn. L.A. coun. 1976, tech. activities bd. 1983-84, fellow com. 1990-92), Inst. Advancement Engring.; mem. Microwave Theory and Techniques Soc. (pres. 1984, Disting. Svc. award 1990), Antennas and Propagation Soc. (profl. chmn. 1956, 62, antenna standard com. 1986—), Automatic RF Technique Group (pres. 1982-83, Disting. Svc. award 1983, hon. life 1989, Automated Measurement Career award 1990), Sigma Xi, Kappa Mu Epsilon. Republican. Home: 23411 Dolorosa St Woodland Hills CA 91367-4125 Creativity and participation are the essence of life. Through them come the most meaningful personal rewards. Through them come the contributions to society that are the basis for these personal rewards. Any contributions that I have made have come naturally; I did not overtly work toward such objectives. I can only thank my parents for instilling me with a measure of creativity and participation as a child that has provided me with the rewards I have.

OLTZ, RICHARD JOHN, publishing executive, minister; b. Duluth, Minn., Sept. 20, 1945; s. Donald F. and Helen J. (Richardson) O.; m. Mary Jane Willman, June 1969; children: Shawn Richard, Jennifer Marie. Student, Olivet Coll., 1963-64; pastorial ministries, Berean Coll., 1980-83, counseling, 1984. Sr. pastor First Missionary Ch., Bad Axe, Mich., 1985-87; exec. dir. Bethel Pub., Elkhart, Ind., 1987—; sr. pastor Grace Chapel, N. Liberty, Ind., 1990—; pastor Oslo Missionary Ch., Elkhart, 1995. Mem. Christian Booksellers Assn., Anabaptist Pubs., Christian Mgmt. Assn., Evang. Christian Pubs. Assn., Am. Assn. Christian Counselors. Office: Bethel Pub Co 1819 S Main St Elkhart IN 46516-4299 No matter how successful life may appear to be, no matter what you may have accomplished, God must get all the glory or you will have labored in vain.

OLUM, PAUL, mathematician, former university president; b. Binghamton, N.Y., Aug. 16, 1918; s. Jacob and Rose (Citlen) O.; m. Vivian Goldstein, June 8, 1942 (dec. Mar. 1986); children—Judith Ann (dec.), Joyce Margaret, Kenneth Daniel. A.B. summa cum laude, Harvard, 1940, Ph.D. (NRC predoctoral fellow 1946-47), 1947; M.A., Princeton, 1942. Theoretical physicist Manhattan Project, Princeton, 1941-42, Los Alamos Sci. Lab., 1943-45; Frank B. Jewett postdoctoral fellow Harvard, 1947-48, instr. Advanced Study, 1948-49; mem. faculty Cornell U., Ithaca, N.Y., 1949-74, prof. math., 1957-74, chmn. dept., 1963-66, trustee, 1971-75; prof. math., dean Coll. Natural Scis. U. Tex. at Austin, 1974-76; prof. math., v.p. for acad. affairs, provost U. Oreg., Eugene, 1976-80, acting pres., 1980-81, pres., 1981-89, pres. emeritus, 1989—, prof. math. emeritus, 1989—; mem. Inst. Advanced Study, 1955-56; on leave at U. Paris (France) and Hebrew U., Jerusalem, 1962-63; vis. prof. U. Wash., 1970-71. Author monograph, research articles on algebraic topology. Mem. adv. com. Office Ordnance Research, NRC, 1958-61. NSF fellow Stanford, 1966-67. Mem. AAAS, Am. Math. Soc., AAUP, Math Assn. Am., Phi Beta Kappa, Sigma Xi. Home: 156 Massapoag Ave Sharon MA 02067

OLVER, JOHN WALTER, congressman; b. Honesdale, Pa., Sept. 3, 1936; s. Helen Fulleborn Olver; m. Rose Alice Richardson, Sept. 12, 1959; children: Martha, Jane. BS, Rensselaer Poly. Inst., 1955; MS, Tufts U., 1956; PhD, MIT, 1961. Asst. prof. chemistry, U. Mass., Amherst, 1962-68; mem. Mass. Ho. of Reps., Boston, 1969-72, Mass. Senate, 1973-91; mem. 101st-104th Congresses from 1st Mass. dist., 1991—, mem. com. on budget and sci. Contbr. articles to profl. jours. Democrat. Avocations: hiking; gardening; tennis. Office: US Ho of Reps 1027 Longworth HOB Washington DC 20515-2101*

OLWIN, JOHN HURST, surgeon; b. Robinson, Ill., May 28, 1907; s. Charles Hurst and Etta (Campbell) O.; m. Betty Smothers, Apr. 17, 1943; children: Holly Corinne, Barbara Hurst. BA, U. Ill., 1929; MD, U. Chgo., 1934. Diplomate: Am. Bd. Surgery. Intern Presbyn. Hosp., Chgo., 1935-36, surg. resident, 1937-39; practice in Chgo., 1938—; clin. prof. surgery Rush Med. Coll., 1942—; attending surgeon Presbyn.-St. Luke's Hosp., Chgo., Rush North Shore Med. Ctr.; clin. prof. surgery U. Ill. Coll. Medicine, 1959-71; chmn., dir. TEI Analytical Inc., 1970—; bd. dirs. Wm. Blair Mut. Funds Inc. Contbr. over 155 articles to profl. jours. Bd. dirs. Vascular Disease Rsch. Found., 1963—. Lt. col. M.C., AUS, 1940-46. Decorated Bronze Star. Mem. AMA, Chgo., Western, Central surg. assns., Soc. Vascular Surgery (recorder 1960-66), Internat. Cardiovascular Assn., Internat. Surg. Soc. Episcopalian (warden). Home: 1508 Hinman Ave Evanston IL 60201-4664 Office: 9631 Gross Point Rd Skokie IL 60076-1264

O'MAHONEY, ROBERT M., lawyer; b. Indpls., Jan. 4, 1925; s. Joseph Francis and Evelyn (O'Connor) O'M.; m. Mary C. Mitchell, Sept. 12, 1953; children: Terrance M., Patrick J., Mary E., Susan M., Sharon A. B.S., Purdue U., 1948; J.D., Georgetown U., 1954. Bar: D.C. 1954, Ind. 1954, U.S. Supreme Ct. 1959. Assoc. Ross McCord, Ice and Miller, Indpls., 1954-55; dep. atty. gen. Ind., 1954-59; gen. counsel Def. Air Transp. Adminstrn., 1959; dep. asst. gen. counsel for transp. Dept. Commerce, 1959-66; adviser to dep. asst. sec. state for transp. and communications, 1966-67; asst. gen. counsel Fed. Hwy. Adminstrn., 1968-69; commr. transp. and telecommunications service GSA, 1969-73; transp. cons. EPA, 1973; atty. Fed. Power Commn., Washington, 1973-77, Fed. Energy Regulatory Commn., Washington, 1977-80; sales assoc. Shannon & Luchs, Potomac, Md., 1980-83, Merrill Lynch Realty, Potomac, Md., 1983-85, Long & Foster Realtors, Rockville, Md., 1985-86. Co-author: Great Lakes Pilotage Act, 1960. Served with USAAF, 1943-45; Served with USAF, 1950-52. Decorated Air medal with oak leaf cluster. Mem. Phi Alpha Delta. Roman Catholic.

O'MALLEY, BERT WILLIAM, cell biologist, educator, physician; b. Pitts., Dec. 19, 1936; s. Bert Alloysius O'M.; m. Sally Ann Johnson; children: Sally Ann, Bert A., Rebecca, Erin K. BS, U. Pitts., 1959, MD summa cum laude, 1963; DSc (hon.), N.Y. Med. Coll., 1979, Nat. U. Ireland, 1985; MD (hon.), Karolinska Inst., Stockholm, 1984. Intern, resident Duke U., Durham, N.C., 1963-65; clin. assoc. Nat. Cancer Inst., NIH, Bethesda, Md., 1965-67, head molecular biology sect., endocrine br., 1967-69; Lucius Birch prof., dir. Reproductive Biology Ctr. Vanderbilt U. Sch. Medicine, Nashville, 1969-73; Tom Thompson prof., chmn. dept. cell biology Baylor Coll. Medicine, Houston, 1973—. Disting. Svc. prof., 1985, dir. Baylor Ctr. for Reproductive Biology, 1973—; mem. endocrine study sect., NIH, 1970-73, chmn. 1973-74; chmn. CETUS-UCLA Symposium on Gene Expression 1982; coun., mem. coun. rsch. and clin. investigation awards Am. Cancer Soc., 1985-87. Author (with A.R. Means) Receptors for Reproductive Hormones, 1973, (with L. Birnbaumer) Hormone Action, vols. I and II, 1977, vol. III, 1978, (with A.M. Gotto) The Role of Receptors in Biology and Medicine, 1986; co-author: Methods in Enzymology: Hormone Action; Calmodulin and Calcium-Binding Proteins, 1983, Mechanism of Steriod Hormone Regulation of Gene Transcription, 1994; editor: Gene Regulation: UCLA Symposium on

Molecular Cellular Biology, 1982; contbg. author to over 400 publs. Lt. comdr. USPHS, 1965-69. Recipient Ernst Oppenheimer award Am. Endocrine Soc., 1975, Gregory Pincus medal, 1975, Lila Gruber Cancer award, 1977, Disting. Achievement in Modern Medicine award, 1978, Borden award Assn. Am. Med. Colls., 1978, Dickson prize for Basic Med. Rsch., 1979, Philip S. Hench award U. Pitts., 1981, Axel Munthe Reproductive Biology award, Capri, Italy, 1982, Bicentennial Medallion of Distincton U. Pitts., 1987. Mem. AAAS, NAS, Inst. Med. NAS, am. Soc. Biol. Chemists, Endocrine Soc. (pres. 1985—, Fred Conrad Koch medal 1988), Am. Soc. Clin. Investigation, Am. Inst. Chemists, Fedn. Clin. Rsch., Harvey Soc., Alpha Epsilon Delta, Phi Beta Kappa, Alpha Omega Alpha. Democrat. Roman Catholic. Office: Baylor Coll Medicine Dept Neuroscience One Baylor Pla Houston TX 77030-3411*

O'MALLEY, CARLON MARTIN, judge; b. Phila., Sept. 7, 1929; s. Carlon Martin and Lucy (Bol) O'M.; m. Mary Catherine Lyons, Aug. 17, 1957; children: Carlon Martin III, Kathleen B., Harry Tighe, John Todd, Cara M. B.A., Pa. State U., 1951; LL.B., Temple U., 1954. Bar: Pa. 1955, Fla. 1973, U.S. Supreme Ct. 1973. Practiced law, 1957-61; asst. U.S. atty. for Middle Dist. Pa., Dept. Justice, 1961-69, U.S. atty., 1979-82; ptnr. O'Malley & Teets, 1970-72, O'Malley, Jordan & Mullaney (and predecessor firms), 1976-79; pvt. practice Pa. and Fla., 1972-79, 82-87; judge Ct. Common Pleas of Lackawanna County (45th Judicial Dist.), 1987—; dir. pub. safety City of Scranton, 1983-86; lectr. Lackawanna Jr. Coll., 1982-86. Editorial bd.: Temple Law Rev, 1952-53. Pres. Lakawanna County (Pa.) unit Am. Cancer Soc., 1966-67; bd. dirs. Pa. Cancer Soc., 1967-68, Lackawanna County chpt. ARC, 1967-69; mem. solicitation team, govtl. divsn. Lackawanna United Fund, 1963-68, B.P.O.E. Jud. Com., 1985-89, 94-95, justice Grand Forum Elks of U.S.A., 1995—, chief justice, 1992-93; chmn. profl. divsn. Greater Scranton (Pa.) YMCA Membership Drives; trustee Everhart Mus., Scranton, 1987. Pilot USAF, 1955-57, Pa. NG, 1957-59. Mem. Am. Judges Assn., Nat. Assn. Former U.S. Attys., Pa. Bar Assn., Lackawanna County Bar Assn., Fla. Bar Assn., Country Club of Scranton, Elks (pres. Pa. chpt. 1978-79), K.C., Phi Kappa (pres.), Delta Theta Phi (pres.). Democrat. Office: Judges Chambers Lackawanna County Courthouse Scranton PA 18503

O'MALLEY, EDWARD, physician, consultant; b. Hudson, N.Y., May 30, 1926; s. Thomas Patrick and Helen Mary (Cornell) O. BS, St. John's U., Bklyn., N.Y., 1949; MS, Loyola U., Chgo., 1952, PhD, 1954; MD, SUNY, Bklyn., 1958. Psychiat. cons. dept. of corrections N.Y.C., 1962-68; psychiatrist Cath. Charities, N.Y.C., 1963-68; dir. of mental health Suffolk County Govt., Hauppauge, N.Y., 1968-70; commr. of mental health Orange County, Goshen, N.Y., 1970-72; dir. drug abuse services State of N.Y., Bronx, 1972-78; lic. sch. psychiatrist N.Y.C. Bd. of Edn., 1962-82; chief psychiatry services VA, Huntington, W.Va., 1982-86; med. cons. State of Calif., San Diego, 1986—, psychiat. cons. dept. of corrections, 1987—; asst. prof. psychiatry N.J. Med. Sch., Newark, 1975—; examiner Am. Bd. of Psychiatry and Neurology, Los Angeles, 1980; assoc. prof. psychiatry U. Calif., San Diego, 1980—; prof. psychiatry Marshall U. Sch. of Medicine, Huntington, 1982-86; dir. com. on sea cadets Navy League, San Diego, 1987—; cons. HHS, Social Security Adminstrn., Office of Hearings and Appeals, 1989—. Contbr. articles to profl. jours. Bd. dirs. Suffolk Community Council, Hauppauge, 1968-70, United Fund of Long Island, Huntington, 1968-70. Served to capt. USN, 1978-81. Scholar N. Y. State Coll., 1946-49, SUNY Joseph Collins Med. Sch., 1955-58; Teaching and Research fellow Loyola U., 1952-54. Fellow Am. Psychiat. Assn.; mem. San Diego Psychiat. Soc., Soc. of Med. Cons. to the Armed Forces, Soc. of Mil. Surgeons of U.S.A., N.Y. Celtic Med. Soc., Union Am. Physicians and Dentists (steward 1990—), State Employed Physicians Assn. (bd. dirs. 1993—). Roman Catholic. Home: 3711 Alcott St San Diego CA 92106-1212

O'MALLEY, JAMES TERENCE, lawyer; b. Omaha, Nov. 24, 1950; s. John Austin and Mayme Bernice (Zentner) O'M.; m. Colleen L. Kiser, May 22, 1972; children: Erin C., Michael B., James P. BA magna cum laude, U. Notre Dame, 1972; JD, Stanford U., 1975. Bar: Calif. 1975. Ptnr. Gray, Cary, Ames & Frye, San Diego, 1975-87, of counsel, 1987-91, ptnr., 1991—; vice chmn., exec. v.p., gen. counsel Noble Broadcast Group, Inc., San Diego, 1987-91. Bd. dirs. Children's Mus., San Diego, 1986-87, Am. Ireland Fund. Mem. Am. Judicature Soc., San Diego Taxpayers Assn. (pres. 1986-87), Order of Coif. Avocation: jogging, music. Office: Gray Cary Ware & Freidenrich PC 401 B St San Diego CA 92101-4297

O'MALLEY, JOHN DANIEL, legal educator, banker; b. Chgo., Dec. 18, 1926; s. William D. and Paula A. (Skaugh) O'M.; m. Caroline Tyler Taylor, July 12, 1958; children: John Daniel, Taylor John. Grad., St. Thomas Mil. Acad., 1945; B.S., Loyola U., Chgo., 1950, M.A., 1952, J.D., 1953; grad. U.S. Army Intelligence Sch., 1962, Command & Gen. Staff Coll., 1965. Bar: Ill. 1953, Mich. 1954, U.S. Supreme Ct. 1962. Asst. prof. law Loyola U., 1953-59, asso. prof., 1959-65; formerly spl. counsel and bond claims mgr. Fed. Ins. Co.; prof. law Loyola U. Grad. Sch. Bus., 1965—, chmn. dept. law, 1968-86; trust officer, v.p. First Nat. Bank Highland Park (Ill.), Marina City Bank, Chgo., Hyde Park Bank & Trust Co., 1970-75; exec. v.p. Harris Bank Winnetka, Ill., 1975-95. Author: Subrogation Against Banks on Forged Checks, 1967, Common Check Frauds and the Uniform Commercial Code, 1969; Contbr. articles to profl. jours. and law revs. Served to maj. AUS, 1945-47, 61-62. Decorated Army Commendation medal; knight grand officer Papal Order of Holy Sepulchre, knight with star Constantinian Order of St. George (Italy), knight Order of St. Maurice and St. Lazarus (Italy). Mem. ABA, Chgo., Ill., Mich. bar assns., Chgo. Crime Commn., French Nat. Hon. Soc., Am., Chgo. bus. law assns., Mil. Govt. Assn. Home: 1040 Chestnut Ave Wilmette IL 60091-1732 Office: Loyola U 820 N Michigan Ave Chicago IL 60611

O'MALLEY, JOHN EDWARD, medical association administrator, physician; b. Detroit, Oct. 27, 1942; s. Jack Patrick and Anne C. (Jones) O'M.; m. Carol Ann Dellicolli, Aug. 22, 1963; children: Dawn, April. BS, U. Mich., 1963, MD, 1967. Diplomate Am. Bd. Psychiatry and Neurology, diplomate Am. Bd. Med. Mgmt. Pediatric intern Johns Hopkins Hosp., Balt., 1967-68; resident child psychiatry I Hawthorn Ctr., Northville, Mich., 1968-69; resident adult psychiatry II, III Mass. Gen. Hosp., Boston, 1969-71, resident child psychiatry IV, 1971-72; sr. assoc. Children's Hosp., Boston, 1974-85; asst. prof. Harvard Med. Sch., 1974-85; psychiatrist Sidney Farber Cancer Inst., Boston, 1975-81; attending psychiatrist McLean Hosp., Belmont, Mass., 1985-86; med. dir. Greenville (S.C.) Hosp. System, 1985-87, Meml. Hosp. South Bend, Ind., 1987-88; v.p. clin. affairs The Devereux Found., Devon, Pa., 1988—; clin. assoc. prof. Jefferson Med. Coll., 1990—, U. Pa. Sch. of Med., 1990—; mem. com. Psychiat. Hosp. of Children/ Adolescents, Washington, 1988—; panelist Nat. Assn. Pvt. and Psychiat. Hosps., Washington, 1989; chief investigator Psychosocial Sequelae of Surviving Childhood Cancer, Sidney Farber Cancer Inst., Boston, 1975-81; clin. assoc. prof. Jefferson Med. Coll., 1990—, U. of Pa. Sch. of Med., 1990—. Author: Massachusetts General Hospital Handbook of Psychiatric Consultation, 1979, The Damocles Syndrome, 1981; contbr. articles to profl. jours. Bd. dirs. Thom Clinic, Boston, 1977-84, Concord (Mass.) Assabett Sch., 1979-85. Maj. U.S. Army, 1972-74. Fellow Am. Psychiat. Assn., Am. Acad. Child and Adolescent Psychiatry (com. on hospitalization), Am. Orthopsychiat. Assn., Regional Coun. of Child/Adolescent Psychiatry; mem. Am. Coll. Physician Execs. Office: The Devereux Found 19 S Waterloo Rd Devon PA 19333-1533

O'MALLEY, JOSEPH JAMES, lawyer; b. Wilkes-Barre, Pa., Oct. 24, 1923; s. Edward Leo and Mary Catherine (Moran) O'M.; m. Helen Alberta Hyde, Mar. 21, 1952 (div. Jan. 1979); children—Patricia, Katherine, Sharon, Edward, Joseph James; m. Theresa Hernandez, Jan. 20, 1979; 1 child, James Christopher. B.A., U. Scranton, 1946; J.D., Georgetown U., 1956. Bar: D.C. 1956, Calif., 1977, U.S. Supreme Ct. 1967. Sr. trial atty. antitrust div. Dept. Justice, Washington, 1957-65; assoc. chief counsel Comptroller of Currency, Washington, 1965-68; asst. dir. FTC, Washington, 1968-76; ptnr. Paul, Hastings, Janofsky & Walker, Los Angeles, 1976—; guest lectr. Georgetown U., 1966-68. Mem. ABA, L.A. County Bar Assn. (exec. com. antitrust sect. 1990-93), KC (grand knight 1963-64, state dep. 1971). Office: Paul Hastings Janofsky & Walker 555 S Flower St Los Angeles CA 90071-2300

O'MALLEY, KEVIN FRANCIS, lawyer, writer, educator; b. St. Louis, May 12, 1947; s. Peter Francis and Dorothy Margaret (Cradick) O'M.; m.

Dena Hengen, Apr.2, 1971; children: Kevin Brendan, Ryan Michael. AB, St. Louis U., 1970, JD, 1973. Bar: Mo. 1973, U.S. Ct. Appeals D.C. 1974, U.S. Ct. Appeals (8th cir.) 1979, Ill. 1993. Trial lawyer U.S. Dept. Justice, Washington, 1973-74, Los Angeles, 1974-77, Phoenix, 1977-78; asst. U.S. atty. U.S. Dept. Justice, St. Louis, 1978-83; adj. prof. law St. Louis U., 1979—. Author: (with Devitt, Blackmar, O'Malley) Federal Jury Practice and Instruction, 1990, 92; contbr. articles to law books and jours. Community amb. Expt. in Internat. Living, Prague, Czechoslovakia, 1968; bd. dirs. St. Louis-Galway (Ireland) Sister Cities. Capt. U.S. Army, 1973. Recipient Atty. Gen.'s Disting. Service award U.S. Dept. Justice, 1977, John J. Dwyer Meml. Scholarship award, 1967-70. Mem. ABA (chmn. govt. litigation counsel com. 1982-86, chmn. jud. com. 1986-87, chmn. com. on ind. and small firms, chmn. trial practice com. 1991-94, health care litigation 1994—), Am. Law Inst., Met. Bar Assn. St. Louis (chmn. criminal law sect.), Nat. Inst. Trial Advocacy, Mo. Athletic Club. Roman Catholic. Office: 10 S Brentwood Blvd Ste 102 Saint Louis MO 63105-1694

O'MALLEY, MARJORIE GLAUBACH, health care executive; b. Orange, N.J., Apr. 28, 1950; d. Robert M. and Joanne (Weil) Glaubach; m. Charles A. O'Malley III, Dec. 27, 1969; children: Gregory, Ashley. BA in Econs., U. Pa., 1969. With Old Stone Bank, Providence, 1970-75, v.p., 1975-76; sr. v.p., treas. Old Stone Bank and Old Stone Corp., Providence, 1976-80; dir. corp. fin. Conn. Gen. Corp., Hartford, 1980-81; 2d v.p., dept. head mktg. pensions Cigna Corp., Hartford, 1981-85, v.p. fin. employee benefit group, 1985-89; v.p. corp. acctg. and planning Cigna Corp., 1989-90; v.p., contr. employee benefits div. Cigna Corp., Hartford, 1990-92, pres. Rx Prime, 1993—. Mem. health Planning Coun. R.I., 1976-79, Statewide Planning Coun. R.I., 1978; mem. bd. Health Sys. Agy.-North Cen. Conn., Hartford, 1980. Mem. Life Ins. Mktg. and Rsch. Assn. (chmn. group and pension com. 1989), New Eng. Econ. Project (bd. mem. 1976-79, treas. 1978-79). Home: 23 Henley Way Avon CT 06001-4067 Office: Cigna Corp Hartford CT 06152

O'MALLEY, PETER, professional baseball club executive; b. N.Y.C., Dec. 12, 1937; s. Walter F. and Kay (Hanson) O'M.; m. Annette Zacho, July 10, 1971; children: Katherine, Kevin, Brian. B.S. in Econs, U. Pa., 1960. Dir. Dodgertown, Vero Beach, Fla., 1962-64; pres., gen. mgr. Spokane Baseball Club, 1965-66; v.p. Los Angeles Dodgers Baseball Club, 1967-68, exec. v.p., from 1968; pres. Los Angeles Dodgers, Inc., 1970—, also bd. dirs.; bd. dirs. Tidings newspaper. Bd. dirs. L.A. Police Meml. Found., L.A. World Affairs Coun., Jackie Robinson Found., L.A.-Gungzhou (Republic of China) Sister City Assn., Amateur Athletic Found.; pres. Little League Found.; active L.A. County Bd. Govs., Music Ctr., So. Calif. Com. for the Olympic Games. Mem. Korean-Am. C. of C. of L.A. Office: LA Dodgers 1000 Elysian Park Ave Los Angeles CA 90012-1112

O'MALLEY, ROBERT EDMUND, JR., mathematics educator; b. Rochester, N.H., May 23, 1939; s. Robert E. and Jeanette A. (Dubois) O'M.; m. Candace G. Hinz, Aug. 31, 1968; children: Patrick, Timothy, Daniel. B.S. in Elec. Engring., U. N.H., 1960, M.S., 1961; Ph.D. Stanford U., 1966. Mathematician Bell Labs., Gen. Electric Research Co., RCA, summers 1961-63; asst. prof. U. N.C., Chapel Hill, 1965-66; vis. mem. Courant Inst., NYU, 1966-67; research mem. Math. Research Ctr., Madison, Wis., 1967-68; asst. prof., assoc. prof. NYU, N.Y.C., 1968-73; prof. math. U. Ariz., Tucson, 1973-81, chmn. applied math. program, 1976-81; prof. math. Rensselaer Poly. Inst., Troy, N.Y., 1981-90, chmn. dept. math. scis., 1981-84, Ford Found. prof., 1989-90; prof., chair applied math. U. Wash., Seattle, 1990-93, prof., 1993—; sr. vis. fellow U. Edinburgh, (Scotland), 1971-72; guest prof. Tech. U. Vienna, 1987-88. Author: Introduction to Singular Perturbations, 1974; editor: Asymptotic Methods and Singular Perturbations, 1976, Singular Perturbation Methods for Ordinary Differential Equations, 1991, ICIAM 91 procs.; contbr. numerous articles to profl. jours. Mem. Soc. for Indsl. and Applied Math. (pres. 1991-92), Am. Math. Soc. Roman Catholic. Home: 3415 W Laurelhurst Dr NE Seattle WA 98105-5345 Office: U Wash Dept Applied Math Fs # 20 Seattle WA 98195

O'MALLEY, SEAN, bishop; b. Lakewood, Ohio, June 29, 1944. Ed., St. Fidelis Sem., Herman, Pa., Capuchin Coll. and Cath. U., Washington. Ordained priest Roman Cath. Ch., 1970. Espiscopal vicar of priests serving Spanish speakin Washington archdiocese, 1978-84; exec. dir. Spanish Cath. Ctr., Washington, from 1973; bishop Roman Cath. Ch., St. Thomas, V.I., 1985-92, Fall River, MA, 1992—. Office: Bishop of Fall River PO Box 2577 47 Underwood St Fall River MA 02722

O'MALLEY, SHAUN F., accounting firm executive; b. 1935; m. Julie O'Malley; 3 children. BS in Econ., U. Pa. Mem. staff Price Waterhouse, Phila., 1959, Tokyo, Osaka, 1966; mem. nat. office rsch. dept. Price Waterhouse, N.Y.C., 1968-70, mem. nat. office acctg. and auditing svc. dept., 1979; ptnr. Price Waterhouse, Phila., 1970-80, ptnr. in charge, 1980-88; elected to World Firm Coun. of Ptnrs. Price Waterhouse, 1982, elected to Policy Bd., 1984; chmn., sr. ptnr. Price Waterhouse, N.Y.C., 1988—; co-CEO Price Waterhouse World Firm, N.Y.C., 1990-92, chmn., 1993—; mem. emerging markets adv. com. SEC; past pres. Fin. Acctg. Found. Mem. exec. com. N.Y.C. Mayor's Pvt. Sector Survey; ptnr. N.Y.C. Partnership; vice chmn. N.Y.C. Internat. Bus. Initiative; adv. bd. Nat. Ctr. on Ednl. Quality of Workforce; bd. dirs. Curtis Inst. Music, SEI Ctr. Advanced Studies in Mgmt.; past chmn. bd. Young Audiences Ea. Pa.; bd. govs. Pa. Economy League; ea. div. bd. dirs. Greater Phila. Internat. Network, chmn. Com. of Seventy, Phila. Inst. CPAs com. on acctg. and auditing; bd. overseers Wharton Sch., others. Mem. AICPA. Office: Price Waterhouse 1251 Ave Of The Americas New York NY 10020-1104*

O'MALLEY, SUSAN, professional basketball team executive. Degree in Bus. and Finance, Mt. St. Mary's, 1983. Dir. advt. Washington Bullets, 1986-87, dir. mktg., 1987-88, exec. v.p., 1988-91, pres., 1991—. Avocations: tennis, vacations. Office: Washington Bullets USAir Arena Landover MD 20785*

O'MALLEY, THOMAS D., diversified company executive; b. N.Y.C., 1941. Grad., Manhattan Coll., 1963. Vice chmn., dir. Salomon, Inc. (formerly Phibro-Salomon, Inc.). N.Y.C.; former chmn., chief exec. officer, pres. Phibro Energy Inc., Greenwich, Conn.; chmn. Argus Investments (formerly Argus Resources), Stamford, Conn., from 1987; now chmn., chief exec. officer Tosco Corp., Conn. Office: Tosco Corp Hdqrs 72 Cummings Point Rd Stamford CT 06902-7919*

O'MALLEY, THOMAS PATRICK, university president; b. Milton, Mass., Mar. 1, 1930; s. Austin and Ann Marie (Feeney) O'M. BA, Boston Coll., 1951; MA, Fordham U., 1953; STL, Coll. St.-Albert de Louvain, 1962; LittD, U. Nijmegen, 1967; LLD (hon.), John Carroll U., 1988. Entered Soc. of Jesus, 1952. Instr. classics Coll. of Holy Cross, Worcester, Mass., 1956-58; asst. prof., chmn. dept. classics Boston Coll., 1967-69, assoc. prof., chmn. dept. theology, 1969-73; dean Boston Coll. (Coll. Arts and Scis.), 1973-80; pres. John Carroll U., Cleve., 1980-88; vis. prof. Cath. Inst. W. Africa, 1988-89; assoc. editor AMERICA, N.Y.C., 1989-90; rector Jesuit Com. Fairfield U., 1990-91; pres. Loyola Marymount U., L.A., 1991—. Author: Tertullian and the Bible, 1967. Trustee Boston Theol. Inst., 1969-73, Fairfield U., 1971-82, 89-91, John Carroll U., 1976-88, Xavier U., 1980-86, U. Detroit, 1982-88, Boston Coll. High Sch., 1986-88, Boys Hope, 1986-88. Mem. AAUP, Soc. Bibl. Lit., N.Am. Patristic Soc.

OMAN, RICHARD GEORGE, museum curator; b. Salt Lake City, Oct. 15, 1945; s. Dorse Miles and Margaret (Call) O.; m. Susan Staker, May 31, 1970 (div. 1983); children: Sarah Elizabeth, Nathan Bryan, Bevin Marie; m. Pamela Fillmore, Oct. 4, 1984; children: Emily Anne, Lisa Meleana. AB, Big Bend Community Coll., 1965; BA in History, Brigham Young U., 1970; BA in Art History, U. Wash., 1971, postgrad., 1971-75. Dir. audio-visual sect. Seattle Art Mus., 1973-75; mgr. mus. sect., hist. dept. Ch. of Jesus Christ of Latter-day Saints, Salt Lake City, 1975-86; curator acquisitions Mus. Ch. History and Art, Salt Lake City, 1986—; high priest missionary to Quebec and Ontario, 1965-67; v.p., Import Broker, Salt Lake City, 1984—; instr. Brigham Young U., Provo, 1979; cons., Utah State Hist. Soc., Salt Lake City, 1980—; Utah Endowment for Humanities, Salt Lake City, 1981; bd. dirs., Utah Children's Mus., Salt Lake City, 1981-83. Original author: Arts and Inspiration, 1980, Utah Folk Art, 1980; contbr. articles to numerous publs. Asst. commr., Salt Lake City area Boy Scouts Am., 1979-

82; chmn. Cen. City Parks Com., Salt Lake City, 1980-83; cons. L.D.S. Hosp. Found., Salt Lake City, 1984; cons., judge, Dixie Coll. Ann. Art Exhbn., St. George, Utah, 1987-89, Springville (Utah) Mus. Art; cons. art mus., Brigham Young U., 1984-87; mem. sesquicentennial com., Mormon Ch., Salt Lake City, 1980. Mem. Utah Mus. Assn. (pres. 1979-81), Am. Assn. State and Local History, Am. Assn. Mus., Mormon History Assn. Republican. Mormon. Avocations: skiing, camping, gardening, sailing, gourmet cooking. Home: 3266 Bonview Dr Salt Lake City UT 84109-3704 Office: Mus Ch History and Art 45 N West Temple Salt Lake City UT 84150

OMAN, RICHARD HEER, lawyer; b. Columbus, Ohio, Jan. 4, 1926; s. B. R. Oman and Marguerite H. (Oman) Andrews; m. Jane Ellen Wert, Oct. 5, 1963; children: Sarah M., David W. B.A., Ohio State U., 1948, J.D., 1951. Bar: Ohio 1951. Atty. Ohio Nat. Bank, Columbus, 1951-55; partner firm Isaac, Postlewaite, O'Brien & Oman, Columbus, 1955-71; dir. Columbus Found., 1955-77, counsel, 1955—; partner firm Porter, Wright, Morris and Arthur (and predecessor firm), Columbus, 1972-89; of counsel Vorys, Sater, Seymour and Pease, Columbus, 1990; ptnr. Vorys, Sater, Seymour and Pease, 1991—. Mem. Columbus Airport Commn., 1960-64; trustee Reinberger Found., Cleve., 1980—, Columbus Acad., 1981-87, Grant Hosp., 1978-86, Harding Hosp., 1978-86; sr. warden Trinity Epsic. Ch., 1985-88. Fellow Ohio State Bar Found.; mem. ABA, Am. Coll. Trust and Estate Counsel, Ohio State Bar Assn. (past mem. bd. govs. probate and trust law sect.), Columbus Bar Assn., Columbus Club, Rocky Fork Hunt and Country Club, Nantucket (Mass.) Yacht Club, Kit Kat Club. Republican. Episcopalian. Office: Vorys Sater Seymour & Pease PO Box 1008 52 E Gay St Columbus OH 43216

O'MARA, ARTHUR JAMES, civil engineer; b. Trenton, N.J., Sept. 28, 1920; s. Arthur James and Esther Isabelle (Yeoman) O'M.; m. Lois Marion Johnson, Dec. 26, 1943; children: Thomas R., Michael R., Marc J., Dennis A., Brian K. BA, Dartmouth Coll., 1942, CE, 1943. Registered profl. engr., Md., Va., Del., Pa., W.Va., D.C. Engr. Turner Constrn. Co., Phila., 1946-47, Malcolm Pivnie Engrs., White Plains, N.Y., 1947-48, Robert Sawyer Engrs., Hyattsville, Md., 1948-50; ptnr. Greenhorne & O'Mara, Hyattsville, 1950-65; chmn. chief exec. officer Greenhorne & O'Mara, Inc., Greenbelt, Md., 1965—. Lt. (s.g.) USN, 1943-46, PTO. Office: Greenhorne & O'Mara Inc 9001 Edmonston Rd Greenbelt MD 20770-1083*

O'MARA, JOHN ALOYSIUS, bishop; b. Buffalo, Nov. 17, 1924; s. John Aloysius and Anna Theresa (Schenck) O'M. Student, St. Augustine's Sem., Toronto, Ont., Can., 1944-51; J.C.L., St. Thomas U., Rome, 1953. Ordained priest Roman Catholic Ch., 1951; mem. chancery Archdiocese of Toronto, 1953-69; pres., rector St. Augustine's Sem., Toronto, 1969-75; pastor St. Lawrence Parish, Scarboro, Ont., 1975-76; bishop Diocese of Thunder Bay, Ont., 1976-94, Diocese of St. Catharines, Ont., 1994—; St. Catharines, 1994—; pres. Ont. Conf. Cath. Bishops, 1986-92. Bd. dirs. Ont. Hosp. Assn., 1961-65, Cath. Ch. Extension Soc. Can.; mem. Ont. Hosp. Services Commn., 1964-69. Named hon. prelate of Papal Household with title monsignor, 1954. Address: 122 Riverdale Rd, Saint Catharines, ON Canada L2R 4C2

O'MARA, ROBERT EDMUND GEORGE, radiologist, educator; b. Flushing, N.Y., Dec. 8, 1933; s. George Harold and Leonora (Potter) O'M.; m. Brenda Mae Millard, Feb. 15, 1964; children—Robert, Susan, Bridget. B.S., U. Rochester, 1955; M.D., Albany Coll. Medicine, 1959. Diplomate: Am. Bd. Radiology, Am. Bd. Nuclear Medicine (sec. 1982—, chmn. 1983-84). Resident in radiology St. Vincent's Hosp., N.Y.C., 1963-66; fellow in nuclear medicine Upstate Med. Center SUNY, Syracuse, 1966-67; instr. radiology Upstate Med. Center SUNY, 1967-68, asst. prof. radiology, 1968-71; assoc. prof. radiology, dir. nuclear medicine U. Ariz., Tucson, 1971-74; prof., dir. nuclear medicine U. Ariz., 1974-75; prof. radiology, chief div. nuclear medicine U. Rochester Sch. Medicine and Dentistry, 1975—; acting chmn. dept. radiology U. of Rochester, 1987-88, chmn. dept. radiology, 1988—; med. dir. nuclear medicine tech. program Rochester Inst. Tech., 1976-89. Contbr. articles to med. jours. Pres. Clover Hills Assn., Rochester, N.Y., 1978-79; pres. Fruchtendler Parent Tchr. Assn., Tucson, 1974-75. Served with M.C. USAF, 1960-62. Fellow Am. Coll. Radiology (councillor 1983-89), Am. Coll. Nuclear Physicians (pres. 1980, trustee 1972-80), N.Y. State Radiol. Soc. (pres. 1989-90); mem. Soc. Nuclear Medicine (trustee 1978-82, v.p. 1985-86, Gold medal for sci. exhibit 1977), Radiol. Soc. N.Am., Assn. Univ. Radiologists. Office: 601 Elmwood Ave Rochester NY 14642

O'MARA, THOMAS PATRICK, manufacturing company executive; b. St. Catharine's, Ont., Can., Jan. 17, 1937; s. Joseph Thomas and Rosanna Patricia (Riordan) O'M.; m. Nancy Irene Rosevear, Aug. 10, 1968; children: Patricia Catharine, Tracy Irene, Sara Megan. B.S., Allegheny Coll., 1958; M.S., Carnegie Inst. Tech. 1960. Mktg. analyst U.S. Steel Corp., Pitts., 1960-65; dir. info. systems AMPCO Pitts. (formerly Screw & Bolt Corp.), Pitts., 1965-68; v.p., gen. mgr. Toy div. Samsonite Corp., Denver, 1968-73; regional mgr. Mountain Zone, Hertz Corp., Denver, 1973-75; asst. to chmn. Allen Group, Melville, N.Y., 1975-76; corp. exec. v.p. fin. and adminstrn. Bell & Howell Co., Chgo., 1976-77; corp. controller Bell & Howell Co., 1977-78, corp. v.p., 1978-85, pres. visual communications, 1978-85; chief operating officer, dir. Bridge Product Inc., Northbrook, Ill., 1985-87; chmn., chief exec. officer Micro Metl Corp., Indpls., 1987-91; chmn. Omara Ptnrs., 1992—; bd. dirs. Loyola U. Press; trustee Barat Coll., 1994—. Mem. Lake Forest High Sch. Bd., 1989—, pres., 1993—. With USAR, 1961-66. Mem. Econs. Club Chgo., Fin. Execs. Inst., Newcomen Soc. U.S., Sigma Alpha Epsilon. Club: Knollwood. Home: 1350 Inverleith Rd Lake Forest IL 60045-1540

O'MEALLIE, KITTY, artist; b. Bennettsville, S.C., Oct. 24, 1916; d. Earle and Rosa Estelle (Bethea) Chamness; m. John Ryan O'Meallie, June 27, 1939 (dec. Apr. 26, 1974); children—Sue Ryan, Kathryn Bethea; m. Lee Harnie Johnson, Aug. 21, 1976. BFA Tulane U., 1937; postgrad., 1954-59. One-woman shows include Masur Mus., Monroe, La., 1979, Marlboro County Mus. of S.C., 1975, Meridian Mus. Art, Miss., 1981, 85; exhibited in group shows at New Orleans Mus. Art, Contemporary Art Ctr., Meadows Mus., Cushing Gallery, SE Ctr. of Contemporary Art, Art 80, Art Expo West, Art Expo 81. Represented in permanent collections New Orleans Mus. Art, Tulane U. Pan-Am. Life Ctr., Masur Mus. Art, Meridian Mus. Art. Nat. officer Newcomb Coll. Alumnae Assn., 1964-66; lectr. exhibitor for many charitable orgns. Recipient award WYES-TV, 1979, Hon. Invitational New Orleans Women's Caucus, 1986, numerous awards and prizes in competitive exhibitions. Mem. Womens Caucus for Art, New Orleans Womens Caucus for Art, Chi Omega Alumnae Assn. (pres. mothers' club 1964), Town and Country Garden Guild (pres. 1970, 1986). Avocations: birdwatching; bridge. Home and Office: 211 Fairway Dr New Orleans LA 70124-1018

O'MEARA, DAVID COLLOW, retired banker; b. Cin., Apr. 21, 1929; s. Joseph Gibson (Jr.) and Jean (Collow) O'M.; m. Marnell Jackson; children: Shawn Kathleen, Scott Matthew, Patrick Michael. B.A., U. Ariz., 1951. Sr. v.p. Security Pacific Nat. Bank, Los Angeles, 1955-84. Served with USMC, 1951-53. Home: 541 Calle De La Paz Escondido CA 92029-7949

O'MEARA, JOHN CORBETT, federal judge; b. Hillsdale, Mich., Nov. 4, 1933; s. John Richard and Karolyn Louise (Corbett) O'M.; m. Penelope Reingier Appel, June 9, 1962 (div. Feb. 1975); children: Meghan Appel, John Richard, Corbett Edge, Patrick Fitzpatrick, Tighe Roberts; m. Julia Donovan Darlow, Sept. 20, 1975; 1 child, Gillian Darlow. AB, U. Notre Dame, 1955; LLB, Harvard U., 1962. Bar: Mich. 1962. Assoc. Dickinson, Wright, Moon, Van Dusen & Freeman, Detroit, 1962-70; mem. faculty U. Detroit, 1965-70; ptnr. Dickinson, Wright, Moon, Van Dusen & Freeman, Detroit, 1970-94, head of labor group, 1985-94; judge U.S. Dist. Ct., Detroit, 1994—; bd. dirs. Spectrum Human Svcs., Livonia, Mich., Mich. Opera Theatre, Detroit. Contr. articles to profl. jours. Fin. chmn. Dem. Party Mich., 1968-70; chmn. U.S. Cts. Comn State Bar Mich. 1984-94. Lt. USN, 1955-59. Fellow Am. Coll. Trial Lawyers, Am. Bar Found.; mem. ABA, U.S. Supreme Court Bar, Am. Judicature Soc., Mich. State Bar Assn., 6th Cir. Court Appeals Bar (life mem., 6th Cir. Jud. Conf. 1986). Democrat. Office: US Dist Ct 231 Lafayette Blvd Detroit MI 48226

O'MEARA, ONORATO TIMOTHY, academic administrator, mathematician; b. Cape Town, Republic of South Africa, Jan. 29, 1928; came to U.S., 1957; s. Daniel and Fiorina (Allorto) O'M.; m. Jean T. Fadden, Sept. 12, 1953; children—Maria, Timothy, Jean, Kathleen, Eileen. B.Sc., U. Cape Town, 1947, M.Sc., 1948; Ph.D., Princeton U., 1953; LLD (hon.), U. Notre Dame, 1987. Asst. lectr. U. Natal, Republic South Africa, 1949; lectr. U. Otago, New Zealand, 1954-56; mem. Inst. for Advanced Study, Princeton, N.J., 1957-58, 62; asst. prof. Princeton, 1958-62; prof. math. U. Notre Dame, Ind., 1962-76; chmn. dept. U. Notre Dame, 1965-66, 68-72, Kenna prof. math., 1976—, provost, 1978—; vis. prof. Calif. Inst. Tech., 1968; Gauss prof. Göttingen Acad. Sci., 1978; mem. adv. panel math. scis. NSF, 1974-77, cons., 1960—. Author: Introduction to Quadratic Forms, 1963, 71, 73, Lectures on Linear Groups, 1974, 2d edit., 1977, 3d edit., 1988, Russian translation, 1976, Symplectic Groups, 1978, 82, Russian translation, 1979, The Classical Groups and K-Theory (with A.J. Hahn), 1989; contbr. articles on arithmetic theory of quadratic forms and isomorphism theory of linear groups to Am. and European profl. jours. Mem. Cath. Commn. Intellectual and Cultural Affairs, 1962—; bd. govs., trustee U. Notre Dame Australia, 1990—. Recipient Marianist award U. Dayton, 1988; Alfred P. Sloan fellow, 1960-63. Mem. Am. Math. Soc., Am. Acad. Arts and Scis., Collegium (bd. dirs. 1992—). Roman Catholic. Home: 1227 E Irvington Ave South Bend IN 46614-1417 Office: U Notre Dame Office of Provost Notre Dame IN 46556

O'MEARA, PATRICK O., political science educator; b. Cape Town, South Africa, Jan. 7, 1938; came to U.S., 1964; s. Daniel and Fiorina (Allorto) O'M. B.A., U. Capetown, 1960; M.A., Ind. U., 1966, Ph.D., 1970. Dep. dir. African studies program, asst. prof. polit. sci. Ind. U., Bloomington, 1970-72, dir. African studies program, 1972—, assoc. prof. polit. sci. and pub. and environ. affairs, 1972-81, prof. polit. sci. and pub. and environ. affairs, 1981—, dean office of internat. programs, 1993—; cons. in field. Author: Rhodesia: Racial Conflict or Coexistence?, 1975; editor: (with Gwendolen M. Carter) Southern Africa in Crisis, 1977, African Independence: The First Twenty-Five Years, 1985, Southern Africa: The Continuing Crisis, 1979, International Politics in Southern Africa, 1982, (with Phyllis M. Martin) Africa, 1977, 3d edit., 1995, (with C.R. Halisi and Brian Winchester) Revolutions of the Late Twentieth Century, 1991; contbr. chpts. to books, articles to profl. jours. Mem. African Studies Assn., Pi Alpha Alpha. Roman Catholic. Office: Ind U Woodburn Hall # 211 Bloomington IN 47405

O'MEARA, SARA, foundation administrator; b. Knoxville, Tenn., Sept. 9; m. Robert O'Meara (dec.); children: John Hopkins, Charles Hopkins (dec.); m. Robert Sigholtz, Nov. 1986; stepchildren: Taryn, Whitney. Chmn., CEO, co-founder Childhelp USA/Internat., Woodland Hills, Calif., 1960—; bd. dirs. Internat. Alliance of Child Abuse and Neglect, Children to Children, Inc. Past pres., sustaining mem. Spastic Children's League; past recording sec. Assistance League of Calif. Recipient Outstanding Achievement award YWCA, 1986, Internat. Collaboration to Prevent Child Abuse awarded by HRH Queen of England, 1989, Living Legacy award Women's Internat. Ctr., 1989, Kiwanis World Svc. medal, 1991, Family Circle award Family Circle Mag., 1992, Chancellor's Founders award U. Calif., 1993, Outstanding Woman from Tenn. award Nat. Mus. Women in Arts, 1993, Nat. Caring award Nat. Caring Inst., 1993, Hubert Humphrey award Touchdown Club, 1994 and numerous others. Mem. World Fund of Successful Women. Office: Childhelp USA Inc 6463 Independence Ave Woodland Hills CA 91370

O'MEARA, THOMAS FRANKLIN, priest, educator; b. Des Moines, May 15, 1935; s. Joseph Matthew and Frances Claire (Rock) O'M. MA, Aquinas Inst, Dubuque, Iowa, 1963; PhD, U. Munich, Germany, 1967. Ordained priest Roman Cath. Ch., 1962. Assoc. prof. Aquinas Inst. of Theology, Dubuque, Iowa, 1967-69; prof. U. Notre Dame, South Bend, Ind., 1981-84, William K. Warren prof. of theology, 1985—. Author 14 books, including: Romantic Idealism and Roman Catholicism, 1983, Theology of Ministry, 1985, Church and Culture, 1991. Mem. Catholic Theol. Soc. Am. (pres. 1980). Office: U Notre Dame Dept Of Theology Notre Dame IN 46556

OMENS, SHERWOOD, cinematographer. Prodr.: (documentary) Somebody Waiting, 1971 (Academy award nomination best documentary short subject 1971); cinematographer: (TV movies) Ishi, the Last of His Tribe, 1978, The Man in the Santa Claus Suit, 1979, Stone, 1979, Madame X, 1981, The Facts of Life Goes to Paris, 1982, Fire on the Mountain, 1982, Policewoman Centerfold, 1983, Grace Kelly, 1983, The Red Light Sting, 1984, Why Me?, 1984, An Early Frost, 1985 (Emmy award outstanding cinematography 1986), Blade in Hong Kong, 1985, Evergreen, 1984 (Emmy award nomination outstanding cinematography 1988), (TV series) Magnum P.I., 1981 (Emmy award nomination outstanding cinematography 1982), Alfred Hitchcock Presents ("Road Hog"), 1985 (Emmy award nomination outstanding cinematography 1986), (TV pilots) Lime Street, 1985, Heart of the City, 1986 (Emmy award outstanding cinematography 1987), (films) History of the World, Part I, 1981, Coming to America, 1988, Harlem Nights, 1989, Boomerang, 1992. Office: 6647 Morella Ave North Hollywood CA 91606*

OMER, GEORGE ELBERT, JR., orthopaedic surgeon, hand surgeon, educator; b. Kansas City, Kans., Dec. 23, 1922; s. George Elbert and Edith May (Hines) O.; m. Wendie Vilven, Nov. 6, 1949; children: George Eric, Michael Lee. B.A., Ft. Hays State U., 1944; M.D., Kans. U., 1950; M.Sc. in Orthopaedic Surgery, Baylor U., 1955. Diplomate Am. Bd. Orthopaedic Surgery, 1959, re-cert. orthopaedics and hand surgery, 1983 (bd. dirs. 1983-92, pres. 1987-88), cert. surgery of the hand, 1989. Commd. 1st lt. U.S. Army, 1949; advanced through grades to col., 1967; ret. U.S. Army, 1970; rotating intern Bethany Hosp., Kansas City, 1950-51; resident in orthopaedic surgery Brooke Gen. Hosp., San Antonio, 1952-55, William Beaumont Gen. Hosp., El Paso, Tex., 1955-56; chief surgery Irwin Army Hosp., Ft. Riley, Kans., 1957-59; cons. in orthopaedic surgery 8th Army Korea, 1959-60; asst. chief orthopaedic surgery, chief hand surgeon Fitzsimons Army Med. Center, Denver, 1960-63; dir. orthopaedic residency tng. Armed Forces Inst. Pathology, Washington, 1963-65; chief orthopaedic surgery and chief Army Hand Surg. Center, Brooke Army Med. Center, 1965-70; cons. in orthopaedic and hand surgery Surgeon Gen. Army, 1967-70; prof. orthopaedics, surgery and anatomy, chmn. dept. orthopaedic surgery, chief div. hand surgery U. N.Mex., 1970-90, med. dir. phys. therapy, 1972-90, acting asst. dean grad. edn. Sch. Medicine, 1980-81; mem. active staff U. N.Mex. Hosp., Albuquerque, chief med. staff, 1984-86; cons. staff other Albuquerque hosps.; cons. orthopaedic surgery USPHS, 1966-85, U.S. Army, 1970-92, USAF, 1970-78, VA, 1970—; cons. Carrie Tingley Hosp. for Crippled Children, 1970—; interim med.dir., 1970-72, 86-87, mem. bd. advisors, 1972—, chair, 1994-95. Mem. bd. editors Clin. Orthopaedics, 1973-90, Jour. AMA, 1973-74, Jour. Hand Surgery, 1976-81; trustee Jour. Bone and Joint Surgery, 1993—, sec., 1993—; contbr. more than 200 articles to profl. jours., numerous chpts. to books. Decorated Legion of Merit, Army Commendation medal with 2 oak leaf clusters; recipient Alumni Achievement award Ft. Hays State U., 1973, Recognition plaque Am. Soc. Surgery Hand, 1989, Recognition plaque N.Mex. Orthopaedic Assn., 1991. Fellow ACS, Am. Orthopaedic Assn. (pres. 1988-89, exec. dir. 1989-93), Am. Acad. Orthopaedic Surgeons, Assn. Orthopaedic Chmn., N.Mex. Orthopaedic Assn. (pres. 1979-81), La. Orthopaedic Assn. (hon.), Korean Orthopaedic Assn. (hon.), Peru Orthopaedic Soc. (hon.), Caribbean Hand Soc., Am. Soc. Surgery Hand (pres. 1978-79), Am. Assn. Surgery of Trauma, Assn. Bone and Joint Surgeons, Assn. Mil. Surgeons U.S., Riordan Hand Soc. (pres. 1967-68), Sunderland Soc. (pres. 1981-83), Soc. Mil. Orthopaedic Surgeons, Brazilian Hand Soc. (hon.), S.Am. Hand Soc. (hon.), Groupe D'Etude de la Main, Brit. Hand Soc., Venezuela Hand Soc. (hon.), Western Orthopaedic Assn. (hon.), Western Orthopaedic Assn. (pres. 1981-82), AAAS, Russell A. Hibbs Soc. (pres. 1977-78), 38th Parallel Med. Soc. (Korea) (sec. 1959-60); mem. AMA, Phi Kappa Phi, Phi Sigma, Alpha Omega Alpha, Phi Beta Pi. Home: 316 Big Horn Ridge Rd NE Sandia Heights Albuquerque NM 87122 Office: U N Mex Dept Orthopaedic Surgery 2211 Lomas Blvd NE Albuquerque NM 87106-2745

OMER, ROBERT WENDELL, hospital administrator; b. Salt Lake City, Feb. 10, 1948; s. Wayne Albert and Melva Bernice (Thunell) O.; m. Deborah Jackson, May 4, 1972;children: Melinda, Carmen, Creighton, Preston, Allison. BS in Biology, U. Utah, 1972; MHA, Washington U., St. Louis, 1975.

V.p. St. Luke's Hosp., Cedar Rapids, Iowa, 1974-80; asst. adminstr. Franciscan Med. Ctr., Rock Island, Ill., 1980-82, Latter Day Saints Hosp., Salt Lake City, 1982-85; asst. adminstr. Clarkson Hosp., Omaha, 1985-93, v.p., COO, 1993—; bd. dirs. ARC, Heartland chpt. Omaha; bd. dirs. Nebr. Scanning Svcs. Lt. col. USAR, 1972. Fellow Am. Coll. of Healthcare Execs. 1975; mem. Nebr. Hosp. Assn., Omaha C.C. (leadership Omaha award 1978), Omaha Healthcare Execs. Group (pres. 1989-90), Rotary (bd. dirs. 1990). Republican. Mem. LDS Ch. Avocations: jogging, history, cycling, backpacking, racquetball. Home: 14111 Cedar Cir Omaha NE 68144-2120

OMINSKY, HARRIS, lawyer; b. Phila., Sept. 14, 1932; s. Joseph and Lillian (Herman) O.; m. Rosalyn Rita Rutenberg, June 4, 1961; children—Michelle, David. B.S. in Econs., U. Pa., 1953, LL.B., 1956. Bar: Pa. 1956. Ptnr. Ominsky & Ominsky, Phila., 1958-64; ptnr. Blank, Rome, Comisky & McCauley, Phila., 1964—; mem. mgmt. com. Blank, Romme, Comisky & McCauley, Phila., 1981-84, 88-92, co-chmn. real estate dept., 1988-93; lectr. Temple U. Law Sch., Phila., 1969-71; lectr. and planner Pa. Bar Inst., Harrisburg, 1969—. Contbr. numerous articles to profl. jours. Pres. bd. Phila. Singing City Choir, 1984-88; chmn. zoning com. Merion Civic Assn., Pa., 1984-91. Mem. ABA (Harrison Tweed Spl. Merit award 1988), Pa. Bar Assn. (ho. of dels. 1984—), Pa. Bar Inst. (bd. dirs. 1981—, exec. com. 1986-93, v.p. 1988-89, pres. 1989-90), Phila. Bar Assn. (chmn. real estate taxes subcom. 1984-85, chmn. real property sect. 1991-92, Leon J. Obermayer Edn. award 1989), Am. Coll. Real Estate Lawyers (chmn. publs. com. 1987-91, bd. govs. 1993—), Order of Coif. Home: 526 Baird Rd Merion Station PA 19066-1302 Office: Blank Rome Comisky & McCauley 4 Penn Center Plz Philadelphia PA 19103-2521

OMLOR, JOHN JOSEPH, management consultant; b. Ashland, Pa., Mar. 15, 1935; s. Victor S. and Mary C. (Keller) O.; m. Shirley A. Sich, Aug. 30, 1958; children: John V., David J., Marlene Kane, Sarah Jane, Shannon Kane. B.S., Pa. State U., 1960; M.B.A., Drexel Inst., 1971. C.P.A. Acct. Peat, Marwick, Mitchell & Co., Phoenix, 1960; chief acct. Honeywell Corp., Ft. Washington, Pa., 1961-63; chief acct., div. controller, corp. controller SPS Techs., Newtown, Pa., 1963—; group v.p. material handling SPS Techs.; pres. Hallowell div. SPS Techs.; pres., chief exec. officer SPSAS, Tulsa; pres. John J. Omlor Assocs. Ltd., Southhampton, Pa.; exec. v.p., chief fin. officer, dir. Paper Mfrs. Co., Phila., FGC Corp., "C" Cor Electronics Corp.; tchr. evening faculty Pa. State U. Contbr. articles to mags. Chmn. Holy Redeemer, VNA. Served with AUS, 1954-56. Mem. AICPA, Pa. Inst. CPAs, Fin. Execs. Inst., Nat. Assn. Corp. Dirs., Acad. Sr. Profls. at Eckard Coll., The Planning Forum. Home and Office: 1260 Mill Rd Southampton PA 18966

OMMAYA, AYUB KHAN, neurosurgeon; b. Pakistan, Apr. 14, 1930; came to U.S., 1961, naturalized, 1968; s. Sultan Nadir and Ida (Counil) Khan; children: David, Alexander, Shana, Aisha, Iman, Sinan. M.D., U. Punjab, Pakistan, 1953; M.A., Oxford U., Eng., 1956. Intern Mayo Hosp., Lahore, Pakistan, 1953-54; resident in neurosurgery Radcliffe Infirmary, Oxford, Eng., 1954-61; vis. scientist NIH, Bethesda, Md., 1963-63, assoc. neurosurgeon, 1963-68, head sect. applied research, 1968-74, chief neurosurgery, 1974-79; clin. prof. George Washington U. Med. Sch., 1970; cons. VA Armed Forces Radiobiology Rsch. Inst.; chmn. Inter-Agy. Com. for Protection Human Rsch. Subjects of Fed. Coordinating Coun. for Sci., Engring. and Tech., NAS; chmn. biomechanics adv. com. com. Nat. Hwy. Traffic Safety Adminstrn.; mem. adv. com. Nat. Ctr. Injury Control & Prevention, Atlanta; inaugural Lewin Meml. lectr. U. Cambridge, Eng., 1983; mem. adv. coun. CDC; Shively lectr. Am. Assn. Auto. Medicine, 1988; Ibn-Sina lectr. Islamic Med. Assn. N.Am. Contbr. articles to profl. jours.; inventor, patent holder spinal fluid flow driven analytical organs for diabetes and degenerative diseases of the nervous system. Pres. Found. for Fundamental and Applied Neurosci., Bethesda, Cyborgan, Inc., Bethesda. Recipient J. W. Kirkdaldy prize Oxford U., 1956; recipient Sitara-i-Imtiaz for Achievements in Neurosurgery Govt. Pakistan, 1981; Hunterian prof. Royal Coll. Surgeons, 1968; Rhodes scholar, 1954-60. Fellow Third World Acad. Scis. (assoc., mem. med. scis. com.); mem. APA, ASME, So. Neurosci., Am. Assn. Neurol. Surgeons, Rsch. Soc. Neurosurgeons, Brit. Soc. Neurol. Surgeons, Am. Assn. Pakistani Physicians (pres.), Internat. Brain Rsch. Orgn. (life), Pan-Am. Med. Assn. Home: 8901 Burning Tree Rd Bethesda MD 20817-3007 Office: 8006 Glenbrook Rd Bethesda MD 20814-2608 *My research on how consciousness is disrupted and restored after brain injuries is serving as a paradigm for my current investigations into the mind-body problem. In this work my scientific training as well as experiential work in both Eastern and Western modes are useful.*

OMMODT, DONALD HENRY, dairy company executive; b. Flom, Minn., July 7, 1931; s. Henry and Mabel B. (Kvidt) O.; m. Evelyn Mavis Blilie, June 15, 1957; children—Linette, Kevin, Lee, Jodi. Student, Interstate Bus. Coll., Fargo, N.D. Acct. Farmers State Bank, Waubun, Minn., 1950-53; chief acct. Cass-Clay Creamery, Inc., Fargo, 1953-61, office mgr., 1961-65, gen. mgr., 1965-83, pres., 1983—. Pres. Messiah Luth. Ch., Fargo, 1976-78; mem. Minn. Dairy Task Force Com., 1988-90; bd. dirs. Communicating for Agr., Fergus Falls, Minn., 1977-80, Blue Cross of N.D., Fargo, 1971-88. Recipient Builder of the Valley award Minn. Red River Valley Devel. Assn., 1991, N.D. Milky Way award, 1993. Mem. N.D. Dairy Industries Assn. (bd. dirs., past pres.), Am. Dairy Assn. (bd. dirs. N.D. 1970-80), N.D. Dairy Product Promotion Commn. (bd. dirs. 1970-80), Messiah Found. Christian Communications (pres. 1987—), Moorhead C. of C. Office: Cass-Clay Creamery Inc 1220 Main Ave Box 2947 Fargo ND 58108

O'MORCHOE, CHARLES CHRISTOPHER CREAGH, administrator, anatomical sciences educator; b. Quetta, India, May 7, 1931; came to U.S., 1968; s. Nial Francis C. and Jessie Elizabeth (Joly) O'M.; m. Patricia Jean Richardson, Sept. 15, 1955; children: Charles Eric Creagh, David James Creagh. B.A., Trinity Coll., Dublin (Ireland) U., 1953, M.B., B.Ch., B.A.O. 1955, M.A., 1959, M.D., 1961, Ph.D., 1969, Sc.D., 1981. Resident Halifax Gen. Hosp., U.K., 1955-57; lectr. in anatomy Sch. Medicine Trinity Coll., Dublin (Ireland) U., 1957-61, 63-65, lectr. in physiology, 1966-67, assoc. prof. in physiology, 1967-68; instr. in anatomy Harvard Med. Sch., Boston, 1962-63; vis. prof. physiology U. Md. Sch. Medicine, Balt., 1961-62, assoc. prof. anatomy, 1968-71, prof. anatomy, 1971-74; chmn. anatomy bd. State of Md., 1971-73; prof., chmn. dept. anatomy Stritch Sch. Medicine Loyola U., Maywood, Ill., 1974-84; dean Coll. Medicine, U. Ill., Urbana-Champaign, 1984—, prof. anat. scis. and surgery, 1984—; WHO cons., vis. prof. physiology Jaipur, India, 1967, S.M.S. Med. Coll., U. Rajasthan, vis. prof. anatomy, 1971. Assoc. editor: Anatomical Record, 1978—; Am. Jour. Anatomy, 1987-92; contbr. articles to profl. jours. Elected fellow Trinity Coll., Dublin U., 1966; named faculty mem. of yr. Loyola U., Chgo., 1982. Mem. AMA, Am. Soc. Nephrology, N.Am. Soc. Lymphology (v.p. 1982-84, pres. 1984-86, Cecil K. Drinker award 1992), Am. Assn. Anatomy Chairmen (emeritus), Am. Assn. Anatomists (dir. placement svc. 1981-91), Internat. Soc. Lymphology (exec. com. 1987—, pres. 1993—), Ill. State Med. Soc., Champaign County Med. Soc., Alpha Omega Alpha. Mem. Church of Ireland. Home: 2709 Holcomb Dr Urbana IL 61801-7724 Office: U Ill Coll Medicine 190 Med Scis Bldg 506 S Mathews Urbana IL 61801

O'MORCHOE, PATRICIA JEAN, pathologist, educator; b. Halifax, Eng., Sept. 15, 1930; came to U.S., 1968; d. Alfred Eric and Florence Patricia (Pearson) Richardson; m. Charles Christopher Creagh O'Morchoe, Sept. 15, 1955; children: Charles E.C., David J.C. BA, Dublin U., Ireland, 1953, MB, Bch., BAO, 1955, MA, 1966, MD. Intern Halifax (Yorkshire) Gen. Hosp., Eng., 1955-57; instr., lectr. physiology Dublin U., 1957-61, 63-68; instr. pathology Johns Hopkins U., Balt., 1961-62, 68-72, asst. prof. pathology, 1972-74; rsch. assoc. surgery, pathology Harvard U., Boston, 1962-63; asst. prof. anatomy U. Md., 1970-74; assoc.prof., prof. pathology, anatomy Loyola U. Chgo., 1974-84; prof. pathology, cell and structural biology U. Ill., Urbana, 1984—; head dept. pathology coll. medicine U. Ill. Urbana-Champaign, 1994—; staff pathologist VA Hosp., Danville, Ill., 1989—; assoc. head dept. pathology U. Ill., 1991-95; courtesy staff pathologist Covenant Hosp., Urbana, 1984—, Carle Clinic, Urbana, 1990—. Contbr. numerous articles to profl. jours. Recipient Golden Apple Tchg. award, 1985. Mem. Internat. Acad. Cytology, Internat. Soc. Lymphology (auditor 1989-91, exec. com. 1991-93), N.Am. Soc. Lymphology (sec. 1988-90, treas. 1990-92, v.p. 1992-94, pres. 1994—), Am. Soc. Cytology, Am. Assn. Anatomists, Ill. Soc. Cytology. Avocations: boating, needlework. Home:

2709 Holcomb Dr Urbana IL 61801-7724 Office: U Ill Coll Med 506 S Mathews Ave Urbana IL 61801-3618

O'MORE, ELOISE PITTS, designer; b. Fayetteville, Tenn., June 7, 1911; d. William Woodruff and Josephine Martin (Diemer) Pitts; student Ward-Conley Art Sch., 1928-30, Ward-Belmont Coll., 1930-32; Baccalaureat d'Art Decoratif, Le College Feminin, Paris, 1937; m. James Robert Muratta, Oct. 4, 1929; 1 child, Donna Maria; m. Rory O'More, IV, Dec. 26, 1940; 1 child, Rory V. Self-employed designer and muralist, 1938-60; dir. design Stoddards Office Designs, Nashville, 1960-66; partner Mitchell & O'More, designers, Nashville, 1966-69; founder, dir. O'More Sch. of Design, Franklin, Tenn. 1970—; executed historic murals 3d Nat. Bank, Nashville, 1963, First Franklin Fed., 1964, First Nat. Bank, Centerville, 1972, United Am. Bank, Nashville, 1972, Harpeth Nat. Bank, Franklin; lectr. design and decoration for various schs., clubs and bus. orgns. Mem. Heritage Found. Franklin; mem. Cheekwood Fine Arts Center, Nashville; mem. Nashville Hist. Commn. Mem. Interior Design Educators Council, Am. Soc. Interior Designers, Nat. Trust Historic Preservation, Williamson County Hist. Soc., Societe des Arts, Alliance Francaise. Roman Catholic. Office: O'More Sch of Design PO Box 908 Franklin TN 37065-0908

OMORI, MORIO, lawyer; b. Maui, Hawaii, Oct. 15, 1921; m. Rachel T. Tanaka, June 29, 1946; children: Sharyn, Colleen. BE, U. Hawaii, 1942, 5th yr. cert., 1943; LLB, U. Colo., 1954. Bar: Hawaii 1955, U.S. Dist. Ct. Hawaii 1955, U.S. Supreme Ct. 1959. Law clk. to chief justice Supreme Ct. Hawaii, Honolulu, 1954-55, spl. dep. atty. gen., 1956-68; pvt. practice law, 1957—; gen. counsel Pacific Savs. & Loan, Honolulu, 1968-76, chmn. bd., 1972-76; gen. counsel Halekulani Corp., Honolulu, 1985—, also bd. dirs. Campaign coord. for U.S. Senator Daniel Inouye, Hawaii, 1959, 62, state rep., 1959-70. With U.S. Army, 1944-46, ETO. Mem. ABA, Hawaii Bar Assn., 442d Vets. Club, Phi Delta Phi. Avocations: golf, landscaping, travel. Home: 1031 Waiiki St Honolulu HI 96821-1234

O'MORROW, DIANNE MARIE, nursing administrator; b. Yankton, S.D., Aug. 14, 1955; d. Gerald Stephen and Mary Joan (Hans) O'M. BSN, Med. Coll. Ga., 1978; MS in Nursing Adminstrn., Ind. U., 1983. RN, N.C., Ind. Asst. patient care coord. Winona Meml. Hosp., Indpls., 1981-82, patient care coord., 1982-84, dir. emergency dept. ambulatory care and investigation drug program, 1984-85, asst. adminstr. nursing svcs., 1986-89; v.p. patient care svcs. Cabarrus Meml. Hosp., Concord, N.C., 1989—; nurse cons. SunHealth, Charlotte, N.C., 1989. Mem. ANA, Am. Orgn. for Nurse Execs., Am. Coll. Healthcare Execs., N.C. Orgn. Nurse Execs., Rotary (Concord chpt. 1989—), Sigma Theta Tau (Mu Psi chpt.). Roman Catholic. Avocations: scuba diving, skiing, swimming, tennis. Office: Cabarrus Meml Hosp 920 Church St N Concord NC 28025-2983

OMURA, GEORGE ADOLF, medical oncologist; b. N.Y.C., Apr. 30, 1938; s. Bunji K. and Martha (Pilger) O.; m. Emily Fowler, Dec. 27, 1962; children: June Ellen, Susan, Ann, George Fowler. B.A. magna cum laude, Columbia U., 1958; M.D., Cornell U., 1962. Intern Bellevue Hosp., N.Y.C., resident, 1965-67; fellow Meml. Sloan Kettering Cancer Ctr., N.Y.C., 1967-70; asst. prof. medicine U. Ala., Birmingham, 1970-73, assoc. prof. medicine, 1973-78, prof. medicine, 1978—, prof. ob-gyn., 1991—; cons. Nat. Cancer Inst., 1975—; chmn. Southeastern Cancer Study Group, 1983-87; cons. to FDA, 1994—. Contbr. articles to profl. jours. Served with USNR, 1963-65. Am. Cancer Soc. jr. faculty clin. fellow, 1971-74. Fellow A.C.P.; mem. Gynecol. Oncology Group (co-prin. investigator for Ala. 1988, prin. investigator cancer and leukemia Group B for Ala. 1986), Am. Soc. Clin. Oncology, Am. Soc. Hematology, Am. Assn. Cancer Research, Phi Beta Kappa, Alpha Omega Alpha. Home: 3621 Crestside Rd Birmingham AL 35223-1514 Office: U Ala University Sta Birmingham AL 35294

OMURA, JIMMY KAZUHIRO, electrical engineer; b. San Jose, Calif., Sept. 8, 1940; s. Shomatsu and Shizuko Dorothy (Takesaka) O.; divorced; children: Daniel, Dawn. B.S., MIT, 1963, M.S., 1963; Ph.D. (NSF fellow 1963-66), Stanford U., 1966. Research engr. Stanford Research Inst., 1966-69; mem. faculty UCLA, 1969-85; founder, chmn. bd. Cylink Corp., Sunnyvale, Calif., 1983—; cons. to industry and govt. Co-author: Principles of Digital Communication and Coding, 1979, Spread Spectrum Communications Handbook, 1994; contbr. articles to profl. jours. NSF grantee, 1970-78. Fellow IEEE (info. theory group). Office: Cylink Corp 910 Hermosa Ct Sunnyvale CA 94086

OMURTAG, YILDIRIM (BILL), engineering educator; b. Istanbul, Turkey, May 27, 1939; came to U.S., 1956; s. Ahmet Hikmet and Emine O.; m. Janet Rich, June 24, 1964 (div. Apr. 1980); children: Tijen, Meral; m. Ferda Calis, Dec. 2, 1980; 1 child, Kenan. BS, Iowa State U., 1962, PhD, 1971; MS, Middle East Tech. U., Ankara, Turkey, 1968. Registered profl. engr., Iowa, Mo. Lectr. Calif. State U., Sacramento, 1973-74; prof. U. Mo., Rolla, 1974-84, chmn. dept. engring. mgmt., prof., 1986—; chmn. dept. indsl. engring. Wichita (Kans.) State U., 1984-85; cons. Calif. State U. System, Long Beach, 1973-83, UN, OECD, NATO, Calif., Hawaii, Oreg., N.C., Turkey, Saudi Arabia, China, Chile, Taiwan, Oman, Australia, Japan, Peru, The Philippines, Venezuela. Contbr. over 100 articles to profl. jours. Served to lt. Turkish Army, 1966-68. Recipient various grants. Mem. NSPE, Am. Soc. Engring. Edn., Inst. Indsl. Engrs., Am. Soc. Engring. Mgmt. (founder) Soc. Mfg. Engrs., Inst. Mgmt. Scis., Rotary. Mem. Unitarian Ch. Avocations: music, travel. Home: 1613 Lincoln Ln Rolla MO 65401-2613 Office: U of Mo Rolla 227 E Mgmt Rolla MO 65401

ONAK, THOMAS PHILIP, chemistry educator; b. Omaha, July 30, 1932; s. Louis Albert and Louise Marie (Penner) O.; m. Sharon Colleen Neal, June 18, 1954. B.A., Calif. State U., San Diego, 1954; Ph.D., U. Cal. at Berkeley, 1957. Research chemist Olin Mathieson Chem. Corp., Pasadena, Calif., 1957-59; asst. prof. Calif. State U., Los Angeles, 1959-63, assoc. prof., 1963-66, prof. chemistry, 1966—. Author: Organoborane Chemistry, 1975; Contbr. articles to profl. jours., chpts. to books. Recipient Rsch. Career award NIH, 1973-78, Nat. award Am. Chem. Soc., 1990; Fulbright rsch. fellow U. Cambridge, Eng., 1965-66, Outstanding Prof. award Calif. State U. System, 1993-94. Home: PO Box 4177 South Pasadena CA 91031-1477 Office: Calif State U Dept Chemistry 5151 State U Dr Los Angeles CA 90032

O'NAN, MARTHA, foreign language educator; b. Shelbyville, Ky., June 28, 1921; d. Samuel Gross and Mary S. (Mays) O'N. B.A., Agnes Scott Coll. 1941; M.A., U. Ky., 1942; Ph.D., Northwestern U., 1952; diploma, U. Paris, 1953; cert. univ. adminstrn., U. Wis., 1977. Instr. Spanish Pikeville Coll., 1942-44, Jacksonville Coll., 1944-46; asst. prof. Centre Coll., 1946-48; chmn. French Elmhurst Coll., 1951-54; assoc. prof. to chmn. modern langs. Millikin U., 1956-63; assoc. prof., then prof. modern langs. Ohio U., 1964-69, asst. chmn. modern langs., 1964-69; prof. SUNY, Brockport, 1969—; chmn. fgn. langs. SUNY, 1969-77; dir. of overseas program SUNY, Tours, France, 1986; vis. prof. Ind. U., 1987; evaluator Middle States Assn. Colls. and Schs., 1978—; owner Dutch Creek Hereford and Angus cattle. Author: The Role of Mind in Hugo, Faulkner, Beckett and Grass, 1967; gen. editor: Folio, 1970—, Papers on Romance Literary Relations, 1987; editor: Papers on Romance Literary Relations, 1987; co-editor: Romance Literary Studies, 1979, 87; contbr.: French Rev, 1954, 58, Ky. Fgn. Lang. Quar, 1957, Symposium, 1958, Hispania, 1959, Instants: Poems, 1964, Names, 1982, CELFAN, 1983, Ency. Contemporary Literary Theory, 1993; also numerous book revs.; corr.: Littératures, 1983. Master conservationist Commonwealth of Ky., 1988. French Govt. fellow, 1952-53; SUNY grantee, 1976, 80, 81; Bibliothèque Nationale grantee, 1981; named Col. of Commonwealth of Ky., 1986. Mem. ACLU, NOW, United U. Professions (v.p. polit. action com. 1989), SCOPE (bd. dirs. 1991), Great Meadows Angus Assn., Am. Angus Assn., Am. Polled Hereford Assn., Eta Sigma Phi, Phi Sigma Iota, Phi Kappa Phi. Home: 1059 Magruder Ln Pleasureville KY 40057-9610

ONA-SARINO, MILAGROS FELIX, physician, pathologist; b. Manila, May 8, 1940; came to U.S., 1965, naturalized, 1983; d. Venancio Vale Ona and Fidela Torres Felix; m. Edgardo Formantes Sarino, June 11, 1966; children: Edith Melanie, Edgar Michael, Edenn Michele. AA, U. Santo Tomas, Manila, 1959, MD meritissimus cum laude 1964. Diplomate Am. Bd. Pathology; med. licensure N.Y., N.J., W.Va. Rotating intern N.Y. Infirmary, pediatrics, Roosevelt Hosp., N.Y.C., 1965-66; resident in anatomic and clin. pathology Lenox Hill Hosp., N.Y.C., 1966-71, asst. adj. pathologist, 1972-

74; assoc. pathologist St. Francis Med. Ctr., Trenton, N.J., 1974-84, Hamilton Hosp., N.J., 1974-84; pathologist, chief pathology and lab. medicine svc. Louis A. Johnson VA Med. Ctr., Clarksburg, W.Va., 1984—; clin. instr. pathology Columbia U. Coll. Physicians and Surgeons, N.Y.C., 1973-85; clin. assoc. prof. pathology, W.Va. U. Sch. Medicine. Fellow Am. Soc. Clin. Pathologists, Coll. of Am. Pathologists; mem. Internat. Acad. Pathology, N.Y. Acad. Scis. (life). Office: Louis A Johnson VA Med Ctr Clarksburg WV 26301

ONASCH, DONALD CARL, business executive; b. New Castle, Pa., July 5, 1927; m. Ruth Ellen Widman; children: Gregory W., Jay W., David R. BA, Washington and Jefferson Coll., 1950; MS in Retailing, U. Pitts., 1952. Div. mgr. mdse. Higbee Co., Cleve., 1953-65, Sibley, Lindsay & Curr, Rochester, N.Y., 1965-70; v.p., gen. mgr. mdse. Liberty House of Hawaii, Honolulu, 1970-72, pres., 1973-77; v.p. Amfac, Inc., Honolulu, 1977-78, exec. v.p., 1978—; bd. dirs. Associated Merchandising Corp. Served with USCG, 1945-46. Club: Oahu Country. Office: Amfac Inc 900 N Michigan Ave # 2860 Chicago IL 60611-1542 Also: Liberty House Inc 1450 Ala Moana Blvd Honolulu HI 96814-4603

ONCKEN, HENRY KUCK, lawyer; b. Shiner, Tex., Sept. 17, 1938; s. William Otto and Stella Helen (Kuck) O.; m. Jacqueline Ann Mansker, Aug. 6, 1960; 1 child, Leah Ann. BBA, U. Houston, 1965, JD, 1966. Bar: Tex. 1966, U.S. Dist. Ct. (so. dist.) Tex. 1968. Ptnr. Mabry & Oncken, Houston, 1966-69; asst. dist. atty. Harris County, Houston, 1969-81; judge Texas Dist. Ct. (248th jud. dist.), 1981-82; assoc. Gardner, Wald & Evans, Houston, 1983-84; U.S. Atty. so. dist. Tex. U.S. Dept. Justice, Houston, 1985-90; with firm Butler, Ewalt & Hailey, Houston, 1990-91. Mem. Mcpl. Utility Dist., Houston, 1976-81. Served with USNG, 1956-63. Republican. Avocations: hunting, fishing, pistol shooting, automobiles. Home: 9303 Godstone Ln Spring TX 77379-6510 Office: Oncken & Oncken PC 12907 Veterans Meml Dr Houston TX 77014

ONDAATJE, (PHILIP) MICHAEL, author, educator; b. Colombo, Ceylon, Sept. 12, 1943; came to Can., 1962; s. Philip Mervyn and Enid Doris (Gratiaen) O.; children: Quintin, Griffin. Student, St. Thomas Coll., Colombo, Dulwich Coll., London, Bishop's U., Lennoxville, Que.; BA, U. Toronto, Can., 1965; MA, Queen's U., Kingston, Ont., Can., 1967. Mem. faculty U. Western Ont., London, 1967-71; vis. prof. U. Hawaii, 1979, Brown U., 1990. Author: (poems) The Dainty Monsters, 1967, The Man with Seven Toes, 1969, The Collected Works of Billy the Kid: Left Handed Poems, 1970 (Canadian Governor-General's award for literature 1970), Rat Jelly, 1973, Elimination Dance, 1978, There's a Trick with a Knife I'm Learning to Do: Poems, 1963-1978, 1979 (Canadian Governor-General's award for literature 1979), Secular Love, 1984, All along the Mazinaw: Two Poems, 1986, The Cinnamon Peeler: Selected Poems, 1989; (novels) Coming Through the Slaughter, 1976, In the Skin of a Lion, 1987, The English Patient, 1992 (Canadian Governor-General's award for literature 1992, Booker McConnell prize 1992); (plays) The Collected Works of Billy the Kid, 1974, In the Skin of a Lion, 1987; (non-fiction) Leonard Cohen, 1970, Claude Glass, 1979, Tin Roof, 1982, Running in the Family, 1982; editor: The Broken Ark, 1971, Personal Fictions: Stories by Munro, Wiebe, Thomas, and Blaise, 1977, The Long Poem Anthology, 1979, Brushes with Greatness, 1989, The Brick Anthology, 1989, From Ink Lake: An Anthology of Canadian Short Stories, 1990, The Faber Book of Contemporary Canadian Short Stories, 1990; dir: (films) Sons of Captain Poetry, 1970, Carry on Crime and Punishment, 1972, Royal Canadian Hounds, 1973, The Clinton Special, 1974, Inventor of Dragland Hog Feeder, 1975. Recipient Ralph Gustafson award, 1965, Epstein award, 1966, E.J. Pratt medal, 1966, President's medal U. Western Ont., 1967. *

ONDETTI, MIGUEL ANGEL, chemist, consultant; b. Buenos Aires, Argentina, May 14, 1930; came to U.S., 1960, naturalized, 1971; s. Emilio Pablo and Sara Cecilia (Cerutti) O.; m. Josephine Elizabeth Garcia, June 6, 1958; children: Giselle Christine, Gabriel Alexander. Licensiate in Chemistry, U. Buenos Aires, 1955, D.Sc., 1957. Prof. chemistry Inst. Tchrs., Buenos Aires, 1957-60; instr. organic chemistry U. Buenos Aires, 1957-60; rsch. scientist Squibb Inst. Med. Rsch., Buenos Aires, 1957-60; rsch. investigator Squibb Inst. Med. Rsch., Princeton, N.J., 1960-66; rsch. supr. Squibb Inst. Med. Rsch., 1966-73, sect. head, 1973-76, dir. biol. chemistry, 1976-79; assoc. dir. Squibb Inst., 1980-82, v.p. rsch. cardiopulmonary disease, 1982-86, sr. v.p. cardiovascular rsch., 1987-91; pharm. cons., 1991—; ad-hoc cons., sculptor NIH; mem. adv. com. dept. chemistry Princeton U., 1982-86. Patentee in field (115); contbr. articles to sci. jours. Served with Argentine Army, 1950-51. Recipient Thomas Alva Edison Patent award R&D Coun. N.J., 1983, Ciba award for hypertension rsch. Am. Heart Assn., 1983, Perkins medal Soc. Chemistry Industry, 1991, Warren Alpert Found. award, 1991; scholar Brit. Coun., 1960, Squibb, 1956. Mem. AAAS, Am. Chem. Soc. (Alfred Burger award 1981, Creative Invention award 1992, Perkin medal 1992), Am. Soc. Biol. Chemists. Home: 79 Hemlock Circle Princeton NJ 08540-5405

ONDRICEK, MIROSLAV, cinematographer. Cinematographer: (films) If..., 1969, Slaughterhouse Five, 1971, Taking Off, 1971, O Lucky Man!, 1973, Hair, 1979, Ragtime, 1981 (Academy award nomination best cinematography 1981), The World According to Garp, 1982, Silkwood, 1983, The Divine Emma, 1983, Amadeus, 1984 (Academy award nomination best cinematography 1984), Heaven Help Us, 1985, F/X, 1986, Big Shots, 1987, Funny Farm, 1988, Valmont, 1989, Awakenings, 1990, A League of Their Own, 1992. Office: The Gersh Agency 232 N Canon Dr Beverly Hills CA 90210*

O'NEAL, BOB H., utilities company executive; b. 1934. BBA, East Tex. State U., 1955. With Stewart & Stevenson Power Inc., Denver, 1978-81, pres.; with Stewart & Stevenson Svcs. Inc., 1964—, v.p. from 1981, now pres., also bd. dirs. Office: Stewart & Stevenson Svcs Inc Box 1637 2707 N Loop W 8th Fl Houston TX 77251

O'NEAL, EDGAR CARL, psychology educator; b. St. Louis, Apr. 30, 1939; s. Clarence Edgar O'Neal and Alyce (Mullins) Redwine; m. Ellen Rose Luther, Aug. 31, 1963; children—Colleen Ruth, Patrick Blaine. B.A., Duke U., 1961; M.Div., Drew U., 1964; M.A., U. Mo., 1968, Ph.D., 1969. Ordained to ministry United Meth. Ch., 1964. Minister Community Meth. Ch., Cold Spring Harbor, N.Y., 1962-65; NIMH fellow U. Mo., Columbia, 1966-69; asst. prof., assoc. prof. psychology Tulane U., New Orleans, 1969-76, chmn. dept. psychology, 1978-84, prof. psychology, 1977—. Editor: Perspectives on Aggression, 1976; mem. editl. bd. Jour. Personality and Social Psychology, 1991—, Jour. Non-verbal Behaviour, 1991-94, Aggressive Behavior, 1995—; contbr. articles to profl. jours. Fellow APA (coun. 1982-85); mem. Sigma Xi, Sigma Chi. Democrat. Home: 7219 Oneil Dr Harahan LA 70123-4844 Office: Tulane U Dept Psychology 2007 Stern Hall New Orleans LA 70118

O'NEAL, HANK, entertainment producer, business owner; b. Kilgore, Tex., June 5, 1940; s. Harold Lee and Sarah (Christian) O'N.; m. Shelley M. Shier, May 14, 1985. BA, Syracuse U., 1962. With CIA, Washington and N.Y.C., 1963-76; exec. v.p. Hammond Music Enterprises, N.Y.C., 1980-83; pres., owner Chiaroscuro Records Co./Downtown Sound recording studio, N.Y.C., 1970-80, 85—; exec. v.p. HOSS, Inc., N.Y.C., 1983—; instr., dept. head New Sch. for Social Rsch., N.Y.C., 1970—; bd. dirs. Composer's and Choreographer's Theater, N.Y.C.; pres. SOS Prodns., Wilkes Barre, Pa., 1987—. Author: Eddie Condon Scrapbook of Jazz, 1973, A Vision Shared, 1976, Berenice Abbott-American Photographer, 1982, Djuna Barnes 1978-81, 1990, Charlie Parker/The Funky Blues Date, 1995; author/photographer: The Floating Jazz Festival, 1985; photographer: (books) Allegra Kent's Water Beauty Book, 1976, All the King's Men, 1990; producer, cover photographer/designer numerous record albums, 1967—. Capt. U.S. Army, 1963-67. Recipient various awards and prizes for books. Mem. Phi Gamma Delta. Home: Glenside Box 101 River Rd Thornhurst PA 18424 Office: Chiaroscuro Records 830 Broadway New York NY 10003-4827

O'NEAL, LILLIANA BELARDO DE, territory senator; b. St. Croix, V.I., Jan. 11, 1944; d. Gil and Paula (Mendez) Belardo; m. Humberto O'Neal, Jan. 30, 1981; 1 child, Carlos G. Ortiz. BA, Inter Am. U., San German, P.R., 1966; MSW, U. Mich., 1969; postgrad., U. Miami, 1988. Social worker V.I. Dept. Social Welfare, Christiansted, V.I., 1966-67, 70-72; counselor, social worker Youth Authority, L.A., 1972-73; guidance counselor V.I. Dept. Edn., Christiansted, 1975-81; mem. V.I. Senate, Frederiksted, 1987-87, 89—. Candidate for lt. gov. of V.I., 1996; committeewoman Rep. Nat. Com., Washington, 1987—. Capt. V.I. N.G., 1978-88. Mem. ASCD, Bus. and Profl. Women Frederiksted (Woman of Achievement award), Phi Delta Kappa. Republican. Home: PO Box 3383 Christiansted VI 00820 Office: Legislature of VI Lagoon St Complex Frederiksted VI 00840

O'NEAL, MICHAEL RALPH, state legislator, lawyer; b. Kansas City, Mo., Jan. 16, 1951; s. Ralph D. and Margaret E. (McEuen) O'N.; m. Tammy E. Miller, Dec. 30, 1978 (div.); children: Haley Anne, Austin Michael. BA in English, U. Kans., 1973, JD, 1976. Bar: Kans. 1976, U.S. Dist. Ct. Kans. 1976, U.S. Ct. Appeals (10th cir.) 1979. Intern Legis. Counsel State of Kans., Topeka, 1975-76; assoc. Hodge, Reynolds, Smith, Peirce & Forker, Hutchinson, Kans., 1976-77; ptnr. Reynolds, Peirce, Forker, Suter, O'Neal & Myers, Hutchinson, 1980-88, Gilliland & Hayes, P.A., Hutchinson, 1988—; mem. Kans. Ho. of Reps.; chmn. jud. com., 1989-90, 93—; minority whip Kans. Ho. of Reps., 1991-92, majority whip, 1995—; instr. Hutchinson C.C., 1977-88. Vice-chmn. Rep. Com., Reno County, Kans., 1982-86; bd. dirs. Mental Health Assn., Reno County, Hutchinson, 1984-89, YMCA, 1984-86, Crime Stoppers (ex-officio), Hutchinson; chmn. adv. bd. dirs. Wesley Towers Retirement Comty., 1984—; mem. Kans. Travel and Tourism Commn., 1990-94; bd. govs. Kans. U. Law Sch., 1991—. Recipient Leadership award Kans. C. of C. and Industry, 1985; named one of Outstanding Young Men Am., 1986. Mem. ABA, ATLA, Nat. Conf. State Legislatures (criminal justice com.), Kans. Assn. Def. Counsel, Def. Rsch. Inst., Kans. Bar Assn. (prospective legis. com., Outstanding Svc. award), Hutchinson C. of C. (ex-officio bd. dirs., Leadership award 1984), Am. Coun. Young Polit. Leaders (del. to Atlantic conf. biennial assembly), Kans. Jud. Coun., Commn. on Uniform State Laws. Avocations: basketball, tennis, golf. Home: 8 Windemere Ct Hutchinson KS 67502 Office: Gilliland & Hayes PA 335 N Washington St Ste 2977 Hutchinson KS 67501-4861

O'NEAL, MICHAEL SCOTT, SR., lawyer; b. Jacksonville, Fla., Dec. 22, 1948; s. Jack Edwin and Lucille (Colvin) O'N.; m. Barbara Louise Hardie, Jan. 30, 1971 (div. Sept. 1974); 1 child, Jennifer Erin; m. Helen Margaret Joost, Mar. 18, 1985; children: Mary Helen, Angela Marie, Michael Scott O'Neal Jr. AA, Fla. Jr. Coll., 1975; BA in Econs. summa cum laude, U. No. Fla., 1977; JD cum laude, U. Fla., 1979. Bar: Fla. 1980, U.S. Dist. Ct. (mid. dist.) Fla. 1980, U.S. Dist. Ct. (no. dist.) Fla. 1981, U.S. Ct. Appeals (5th and 11th cirs.) 1981, U.S. Supreme Ct. 1986. Assoc. Howell, Liles, Braddock & Milton, Jacksonville, Fla., 1980-83; ptnr. Commander, Legler, Werber, Dawes, Sadler & Howell, Jacksonville, 1983-91, Foley & Lardner, Jacksonville, 1991-93, Howell O'Neal & Johnson, Jacksonville, 1993—; pro bono atty. Legal Aid Soc., Jacksonville, 1980—; practicing atty. Lawyers Reference, Jacksonville, 1980—; pres.-elect N.E. Fla. Med. Malpractice Claims Coun., 1995. Pres. Julington Landing Homeowners Assn., Jacksonville, 1980-83. Served to staff sgt. USAF, 1968-74. Mem. ABA, Jacksonville Bar Assn., Fed. Bar Assn., Jacksonville Bar Assn. Trial Lawyers Am., Fla. Def. Lawyers Assn., Jacksonville Def. Lawyers Assn., Internat. Assn. Def. Counsel. Republican. Methodist. Clubs: University, San Jose Country (Jacksonville). Avocations: golf, music. Home: 1299 Norwich Rd Jacksonville FL 32207-7525 Office: Howell O'Neal & Johnson 200 N Laura St Ste 1100 Jacksonville FL 32202-3518

O'NEAL, RYAN (PATRICK RYAN O'NEAL), actor; b. Los Angeles, Apr. 20, 1941; s. Charles and Patricia (Callaghan) O'N.; m. Joanna Moore, Apr. 1963 (div. Feb. 1967); children: Tatum Beatrice, Griffin Patrick; m. Leigh Taylor-Young, Feb. 1967; 1 child, Patrick; 1 child (with Farrah Fawcett), Redmond James Fawcett. Grad. high sch. Appeared in several TV series in early 1960s including Dobie Gillis, Two Faces West, Perry Mason, Gen. Electric Theatre, The Virginian, This Is the Life, The Untouchables, My Three Sons, Bachelor Father, June Allyson Show, Empire, Peyton Place, 1964-69; actor: (films) The Big Bounce, 1969, The Games, 1970, Love Story, 1970 (David of Donatello award), The Wild Rovers, 1971, What's Up, Doc?, 1972, The Thief Who Came to Dinner, 1973, Paper Moon, 1973, Barry Lyndon, 1975, Nickelodeon, 1976, A Bridge Too Far, 1977, Oliver's Story, 1978, The Main Event, 1979, The Driver, 1978, So Fine, 1981, Partners, 1982, Irreconcilable Differences, 1984, Green Ice, The Fever Pitch, 1984, Tough Guys Don't Dance, 1987, Chances Are, 1989, (TV movies) Love, Hate, Love, 1971, Small Sacrifices, 1989; (TV series) Empire, 1962-63, Peyton Place, 1964-69, Good Sports, 1991. •

O'NEAL, SHAQUILLE RASHAUN, professional basketball player; b. Newark, Mar. 6, 1972; s. Philip A. Harrison and Lucille O'Neal. Student, La. State U. Center Orlando Magic, 1992—. Appeared in movie Blue Chips, 1994. Named to Sporting News All-American first team, 1990-91; recipient Rookie of the Yr. award NBA, 1993; mem. NBA All-Star team, 1993, 94, Dream Team II, 1994; first pick overall, 1992 draft. Office: Orlando Magic 1 Magic Pl Orlando FL 32801-1114*

O'NEAL, TATUM, actress; b. Nov. 5, 1963; d. Ryan and Joanna (Moore) O'N.; m. John McEnroe, Aug. 1, 1986; 3 children: Kevin, Sean, Emily. Ed., pvt. schs. and tutors. Appearances include (films) Paper Moon, 1973 (Acad. award for best supporting actress), The Bad News Bears, 1976, Nickelodeon, 1976, International Velvet, 1978, Little Darlings, 1979, Circle of Two, 1981, Certain Fury, 1985, Little Noises, 1992; (TV movies) Woman on the Run: The Lawrencia Bambenek Story, 1993. Office: care Erwin Stuff 7920 Sunset Blvd Ste 350 Los Angeles CA 90046*

O'NEAL, TIMOTHY D., church administrator. Dir. of computer and info. svcs. Ch. of God. Office: Church of God PO Box 2430 Cleveland TN 37320

O'NEIL, CHLOE ANN, state legislator; m. John G.A. O'Neil (dec.); children: Beth Ann Rice, John A.S. BS in Psychology, SUNY, Potsdam, 1967, MS in Edn. Tchr. Hermon-DeKalb Ctr. Sch.; Canton, N.Y., Potsdam; elem. tchr. Parishville (N.Y.)-Hopkinton Ctrl. Sch.; mem. N.Y. State Assembly, 1993—. Past mem. St. Mary's Sch. Bd. Edn.; active St. Michael's Ch. in Parishville, N.Y. Mem. N.Y. State United Tchrs. Home: Cassidy Rd Hopkinton NY 12940 Office: NY State Assembly State Capitol Albany NY 12224

O'NEIL, DANIEL JOSEPH, science research executive, university consultant; b. Boston, June 5, 1942; s. Daniel Joseph and Grace Veronica (Francis) O'N.; m. Elizabeth Noone, Nov. 14, 1964; children: Elizabeth Grace, Daniel Joseph, Dara Veronica. BA, Northeastern U., 1964; MS, So. Conn. State U., 1967; PhD, U. Dublin, 1972. Sr. rsch. chemist Raybestos-Manhattan Advanced Rsch. Lab., Stratford, Conn., 1964-67; unit leader Hitco Materials Sci. Ctr., Gardena, Calif., 1967-68; tech. dir. Euroglas Ltd., Middlesex, Eng., 1970-72, Kildare, Ireland, 1970-72; founding faculty mem., dir. external liaison and coop. edn., lectr. polymer sci. U. Limerick, Ireland, 1972-75; chief exec. European Rsch. Inst. Ireland, Limerick, 1981-83; sr. rsch. scientist Ga. Tech. Rsch. Inst., Atlanta, 1975-78, prin. rsch. scientist, 1978-91, dir. energy and materials sci. lab., 1988-90, group dir. office of dir., 1990-91; v.p. and dean grad. coll. U. Okla., Norman, 1991-93, prof. chemistry, 1991-93; pres., dir. Sarkeys Energy Ctr. Univ. Okla. Rsch. Corp., Norman, 1992-93; founder, mng. dir. Okla. Energy Rsch. Ctr., Atlanta, 1992-93; chmn., pres. CRADA Corp., Atlanta, 1993, pres., 1993—; bd. dirs. U. Okla. Rsch. Corp., Okla. Ctr. for Advancement of Sci. and Tech., Okla. Exptl. Program Stim. Comp. Res.; mem. adv. bd. Gov.'s Energy Coun., Okla. Higher Edn. State Regents Coun. on Rsch. and Grad. Edn. NAS/NRC, Washington, 1978-79, 86-87; pres. com. EEC, Brussels, 1982, 87, 89, U.S. rep., 1989; mem. nat. policy rev. panel U.S. Dept. Energy, Washington, 1986; witness, cons. energy R & D com. U.S. Senate, Washington, 1986-88; reviewer small bus. innovation rsch. program U.S. Dept. Energy, Washington, 1988-90; active Israel Tech. Project Com., Atlanta Jewish Fedn., Jewish Agy for Israel, 1990-91; rep., sect. Fedn. Arab. Sci. Rsch. Coun., Arab Bur. Edn. for Gulf States, 1987. Author, co-author of 100 reports and publs. including University Strategic Planning, 1993, High Flux Materials Treatment, 1990, USDOE Solar Thermal Tech., 1989, Energy from Biomass and Wastes XIII, 1989, Internat. Conf. Pyrolysis/Gasification, 1989, Energy Initiative and Competitive Strategies, 1991, Research Innovation and the University, 1992, University Research and Economic Development, 1992. Pres. U. Okla Res. Corp., 1992-93, bd. dirs., 1992-93; mng. dir., Okla. Energy Res. Ctr., 1992-93; expert evaluator NBS Office Energy-Related Inventions, Gaithersburg,

Md., 1978-86; adv. bd. dirs. tech. utilization USDOC Office Minority Bus. Enterprises, Washington, 1977-86; U.S. del. U.S.-Brazil energy workshop U.S. Dept. State, Washington, Brazil, 1980; active Okla. Higher Edn. State Regents Coun. on Rsch. and Grad. Edn., 1991-93, Okla. Ctr. Advancement of Sci. and Tech., 1991-94. Fellow Am. Inst. Chemists; mem. AAAS, Com. Grad. Rsch., Oak Ridge Associated Univs., Univ. Rsch. Assn., Midwest Assn. Grad. Schs., Nat. Assn. State Univs. and Land Grant Colls., Nat. Coun. Univ. Rsch. Adminstrs., Am. Chem. Soc., Assn. Big Eight Univs., Biomass Energy Res. Assn. (bd. dirs. 1990—), Coun. on Rsch., Edn. and Tech., Ga. Acad. Sci. (councillor 1990-91), Ga. Inst. Chem. (pres 1988-90), Internat. Club of Atlanta (founder), Japan-Okla. Soc., Petroleum Club of Okla., Assn. Western U. (bd. dirs. 1991-93), Husky Club, Northeastern U., Univ. Okla. Assn., Trinity Coll. Dublin Alumni Assn., Sigma Xi. Office: CRADA Corp Atlanta HQ 2660 Goodfellows Rd Tucker GA 30084

O'NEIL, JAMES PETER, financial printing company executive; b. Bloomfield, N.J., Dec. 8, 1944; s. John F. and Mary (Kane) O'N.; m. Jo Anne Elizabeth Schweitzer, Oct. 10, 1970; children: Pamela, James, Kathleen. BBA, Seton Hall U., 1966. CPA, N.J. Ptnr. J.H. Cohn and Co., N.Y.C., 1968-84; v.p. fin. Bowne and Co., Inc., N.Y.C., 1984—. Served as sgt. U.S. Army, 1966-68, Vietnam. Decorated twice Bronze Star with Valor. Office: Bowne & Co Inc 345 Hudson St New York NY 10014-4502

O'NEIL, J(AMES) PETER, elementary education educator, computer software designer; b. Rockville Center, N.Y., Apr. 2, 1946; s. Clement Lee and Frances Rita (Theis) O'N.; m. Carol Ann Sypniewski, June 8, 1968; children: Kelly Ann, Thomas Joseph. BA in Psychology, Loyola U., Chgo., 1968; M in Sci. Edn., Webster Coll., St. Louis, 1972. Cert. elem. tchr. K-8, Mo., elem. tchr. K-8, Wis., dir. instruction, Wis. Tchr., student tchr. Sacred Heart Sch., Florissant, Mo., 1968-73; tchr. sci. Waunakee (Wis.) Mid. Sch., 1973—, chmn. K-8 sci. dept., 8 yrs., chmn. K-12 dept., 1984-92; dir. Waunakee Summer Sci. Program, 1975-91; designer sci. curriculum computer program Science CAP and elementary science CAP, 1990—; Sunday store mgr. H.C. Prange Corp., 1975-83. Editor: Science Scope, 1989—; contbr. over 30 activities and articles to profl. jours. Group worker settlement houses Chgo., St. Louis; mem. Parish Coun.; dir. Waunakee Area Edn. Found. Named Master Tchr. NSF, Waunakee, 1986—; recipient Tchr. of Yr. award Waunakee, 1984, 90, 92, Kohl Found. award, 1992, Mid. Sch. Tchr. of Yr. award Wis., 1992-93. Mem. Nat. Sci. Tchrs. Assn., Wis. Soc. Sci. Tchrs., Wis. Elementary Sci. Tchrs., NEA, Wis. Ednl. Assn. Roman Catholic. Avocations: computers, sports, writing, jogging. Home: 119 Simon Crestway Waunakee WI 53597-1721 Office: Waunakee Mid Sch 1001 South St Waunakee WI 53597-1651

O'NEIL, JOHN, artist; b. Kansas City, Mo., June 16, 1915; s. Michael and Emma (Harms) O'N. BFA, U. Okla., 1936, MFA, 1939; student, Taos Sch. Art, 1942, U. Florence, Italy, 1951. Dir. U. Okla. Sch. Art, 1951-65; chmn. dept. fine arts Rice U., Houston, 1965-70; dir. Sewall Art Gallery, 1972-77, Joseph and Joanna Nazro prof. art and art history, 1979-81; vis. lectr. NYU, U. Mich., U. Mass., l'Accademia di Belle Arti, Rome, Moana Olu Coll., Hawaii. One-man show, Mus. Art, U. Okla., Sask. (Can.) Art Centers, Seattle Art Mus., M-59 Galleries, Copenhagen, Denmark, Los Robles Galleries, Calif., La. Gallery, Houston, Philbrook Art Ctr., Tulsa, Firehouse Art Ctr., Norman, Okla.; works exhibited, Carnegie Inst., Artists West of Mississippi at Colorado Springs, Denver Art Mus., San Francisco Mus., Art Inst. of Chgo., U. Ill., Dallas Mus., Cin. Mus., Sadeer Gallery, Kuwait, Kauffman Galleries, Houston, Graham Gallery, Houston, Wierzbowski Gallery, Houston, N.Y. World's Fair, Pickard Gallery, Oklahoma City, U.S. Art Expo, San Francisco; rep. collections, Philbrook Art Center, U. Mich., Denver Art Mus., Dallas Mus., Am. Arts., Kansas City, Chgo., others. Recipient 30 painting and graphics awards. Painting fellow Huntington Hartford Found., MacDowell Colony, Montalvo Assn. Mem. Coll. Art Assn., Southwestern, Mid-Am. art confs., Delta Phi Delta. Home: 1701 Hermann Dr #901 Houston TX 77004

O'NEIL, JOHN JOSEPH, lawyer; b. Detroit, July 20, 1943; s. John J. and Dora J. (Collins) O'N.; children: Meghan, Kathryn; m. Bettina Drummond, July 17, 1992. BA, Trinity Coll., 1965; LLB, U. Va., 1968. Bar: N.Y. 1969, U.S. Ct. Appeals (2d cir.) 1969, Fla. 1979, D.C. 1982. Assoc. Jackson & Nash, N.Y.C., 1968-71; assoc. Paul, Weiss, Rifkind, Wharton & Garrison, N.Y.C., 1971-77; ptnr., 1977—. Fellow Am. Coll. Trusts and Estates Counsel; mem. ABA (com. on spl. problems of aged), N.Y. State Bar Assn. (com. on taxation, trusts and estates sect.), Assn. Bar City N.Y. (com. on trusts and estates), Pi Gamma Mu. Office: Paul Weiss Rifkind Wharton & Garrison 1285 Ave of the Americas New York NY 10019-6064

O'NEIL, JOHN P(ATRICK), athletic footwear company executive; b. Malden, Mass., 1921; s. Jeremiah James and Elizabeth Agnes (McMahon) O'N.; m. nancy Hodgkins, Dec. 21, 1944; children: John W., Michael P., Martha E., Timothy P. B.S., Tufts U., 1943. Vice pres. prodn. Granite State div. Converse Inc., Berlin, N.H., 1946-66; v.p. mfg. Converse Rubber Co., Malden, Mass., 1966-70; v.p. ops. Converse Rubber Co., Wilmington, Mass., 1970-73, exec. v.p., 1974; pres. Converse Inc., Wilmington, 1974-87, vice chmn., 1987—; dir. Footwear Industries Am., Washington; chmn. Athletic Footwear Council, North Palm Beach, Fla., 1981-90; trustee Mass. Bank for Savs., Reading, 1982-87. Served to 1st lt. U.S. Army, 1943-46. Named Businessman of Yr. Dr. I. Fund Found., N.Y.C., 1982. Mem. Internat. Athletic Footwear and Apparel Mfg. Assn. (pres.), Rubber and Plastics Footwear Mfg. Assn. (pres.), Internat. Athletic Footwear Assn. (pres. worldwide). Roman Catholic. Clubs: Lanam (Andover, Mass.), Meadow Brook Golf (Reading, Mass.) bd. dirs. 1980-86), Country Club of New Seabury (Mass.), Mariner Sands Country (Stuart, Fla.); Tufts of Boston. Office: Converse Inc 1 Fordham Rd North Reading MA 01864-2619

O'NEIL, JOSEPH FRANCIS, association executive; b. Chicopee, Mass., Oct. 3, 1934; s. Joseph Francis and Mary Agnes (Sheehan) O'N.; m. Carol Marie Quindlen, June 12, 1975; 1 child, Anne Lyons. B.A., Holy Cross Coll., 1956; M.S. in Theology, St. Mary's Coll., Balt., 1960; M.S. in Journalism, Columbia U., 1965. Mem. editorial staff Cath. Observer, Springfield, Mass., 1961-64; asst. editor Cath. Observer, 1965-69, editor, 1969-74; editor Child Devel. Asso. Consortium, Washington, 1975-77; asst. exec. sec. Am. Council Independent Labs., Washington, 1977-80; exec. dir. Am. Council Independent Labs., 1981—. Chmn. Bus. Coalition for Fair Competition, 1983-90; sec., treas. Bus. Coalition for Fair Competition, 1990-92; chmn., cons. coun. Nat. Inst. Bldg. Scis., 1992-93; bd. dirs. Small Bus. Legis. Coun. Mem. Am. Nat. Standards Inst. (bd. dirs.). Home: 1712 N Jefferson St Arlington VA 22205-2817 Office: Am Coun Ind Labs 1629 K St NW Washington DC 20006-1604

O'NEIL, LEO E., bishop; b. Holyoke, Mass., Jan. 31, 1928. Ed. Mary-knoll Sem., St. Anselm's Coll., Manchester, N.H., Grand Sem., Montreal, Que., Can. Ordained Roman Cath. priest, 1955; ordained titular bishop of Bencenna and aux. bishop of Springfield (Mass.), 1980-89, co-adjutor bishop Manchester, N.H., 1989-90, bishop, diocese of Manchester, 1990—. Office: Bishop of Manchester 657 N River Rd Manchester NH 03104*

O'NEIL, MARY AGNES, health science facility administrator; b. Bridgeport, Conn., Sept. 26, 1926. Diploma in nursing, St. Vincent's Hosp., Bridgeport, 1947; BS, St. Joseph's Coll., Emmitsburg, Md., 1952; MS in Nursing Services Adminstrn., Boston Coll., 1960; LLD (hon.), Sacred Heart U., Bridgeport, 1974. Nurse St. Vincent's Hosp., 1947-48, dir. nursing, 1961-63, assoc. adminstr., 1969, adminstr., 1969-74, chmn. bd. dirs., 1969-76, coordinator constrn., in-residence chmn. bd. dirs., 1973—; 3d directress Sisters of Charity Sem., Emmitsburg, 1949-54; supr. nursing services Carney Hosp., Boston, 1954-57, dir. nursing svcs., 1957-60, adminstrv. asst. patient care svcs., 1960-61, asst. to pres., 1981-83; assoc. adminstr. St. Mary's Hosp., Troy, N.Y., 1963, 'adminstr., 1963-69, pres., chief exec. officer, chmn. bd. dirs., ex-officio lay adv. bd., 1976—; sr. v.p./chmn. bd. dirs. Good Samaritan Hosp., Pottsville, Pa., 1983-86, chmn. bd. dirs., v.p. corp. affairs, 1986, chmn. corp. reorgn., chmn. bd. dirs., Lay liaison, 1986—; acting bd. chair Sisters of Charity Hosp., Buffalo, N.Y., 1991-92; mem. Upper Hudson subarea council, mem. project rev. com. Health Systems Agy. of Northeastern N.Y.; mem. regional bd. Nat. Comml. Bank and Trust Co., N.Y., 1979; bishop's rep., mem. legis. com. N.Y. State Council Cath. Hosps., 1980; rep. governing bd. Iroquois Hosp. Consortium, Inc., N.Y., 1980; mem. Green Island Bridge Task Force Com., Troy, 1981; mem. Northeast Province

Health Commn., 1987, Devel. Corp. Good Samaritan Hosp., Pottsville, Pa., 1989-90, chmn. bd. dirs., 1983-90; provincial health councillor Dau. of Charity Northeast Province De Paul Provincial House, Albany, N.Y., 1990-93, provincial asst., 1991-93; acting bd. chairperson Sisters of Charity Hosp., Buffalo, N.Y., 1991-92; bd. dirs. Carney Hosp., Boston, St. Vincent's Med. Ctr., Bridgeport, Conn., Sisters of Charity Hosp., Buffalo, N.Y., Dau. of Charity of St. Vincent de Paul, Northeast Province, Inc.; sec. regional corp. DCNHS-NE, bd. dirs., treas., Daus. of Charity Nat. Health System; bd. dirs. St. Mary's Hosp., Troy, N.Y., chair, 1993; chair Our Lady Lourdes Meml. Hosp., Binghamton, N.Y; chmn. bd. Seton Health Sys., Inc. V.p. Greater Bridgeport C. of C., 1975; mem. mayor's human rights commn. City of Troy, 1976; bd. dirs. Northeastern/Southeastern Shared Services of Daus. of Charity, 1977, treas. Eastern Coop. Services, 1980, chmn. investment com., 1981, mem. health adv. commn. N.E. Province, 1986; v.p. govtl. relations City of Troy, 1978; hon. chmn. Upper Hudson area chpt. Am. Diabetes Assn., Inc., 1978-79; bd. dirs. Blue Cross of Northeastern N.Y., 1977; bd. dirs. Lourdes Hosp., Binghamton, N.Y., 1985, chmn. evaluation com., 1987; mem. adv. bd. Jr. League, Troy, 1979; mem. St. Mary's Hosp. Found. Bd., 1981; provincial asst. Daus. of Charity, Buffalo, 1991. Recipient Community Services award City of Troy, 1968, Leadership and Service cert. Conn. Hosp. Assn., 1973, Community Service and Accomplishment award Sta. WICC-FM, 1974, Community Service award Sta. WNAB-FM, 1975, Key to City Mayor of Brideport, 1975; named one of Outstanding Women of State of Conn., Gov. Ella Grasso, 1976; Sister Mary Agnes Day proclaimed by City of Bridgeport, 1976, Sister Mary Agnes Day proclaimed by City of Troy, 1981. Fellow Am. Coll. Hosp. Adminstrs.; mem. Hosp. Assn. Northeastern N.Y. (mem. program com. 1978, chmn. bylaws com. 1979). Democrat. Avocations: music, walking, swimming. Home: Sacred Heart Sisters' Residence 76 Adams Ave Cohoes NY 12047-3502 Office: St Mary's Hosp 1300 Massachusetts Ave Troy NY 12180-1695

O'NEIL, MICHAEL JOSEPH, opinion survey executive, marketing consultant; b. Springfield, Mass., June 22, 1951; s. James Francis and Mary Helen (Apolis) O'N.; m. Catherine Mary Zirkel, Sept. 10, 1983; children: Heather Rose, Sean Michael, Ryan Joseph. BA, Brown U., 1974, MA, 1975; PhD, Northwestern U., 1977. Mem. faculty U. Ill., Chgo., 1977; mem. faculty U. Mich., Ann Arbor, 1977-79, postdoctoral fellow Survey Rsch. Ctr., Inst. Social Rsch., 1977-79; dir. Pub. Opinion Rsch. Ctr. Ariz. State U., Tempe, 1979-81; pres. O'Neil Assocs., Tempe, 1981—; reviewer grant proposals NSF, Washington, 1977—; mem. nktg. com. Phoenix Art Mus., 1992—; mem. bd. dirs. Phoenix Children's Hosp. Found., 1993—. Manuscript reviewer Social Problems, 1977—, Pub. Opinion Quar., 1977—, Urban Affairs Quar., 1977—, Jour. Ofcl. Statistics, 1990—, Sociological Methods and Rsch., 1993; contbr. articles to profl. jours. Chmn. Tempe Union High Sch. Dist. Bus. Edn. adv. com., 1986-88; mem. mktg. com. Mesa Assn. Retarded Citizens, 1985-87; bd. dirs. East Valley Camelback Hosp., Mesa, 1985-90, v.p. 1988-90; active Valley Leadership, Class X, Ariz. Acad., Maricopa County Citizens' Jud. Adv. Coun.; mem. Phoenix Pride Commn., 1991-94. Mem. Am. Mktg. Assn., Am. Assn. Pub. Opinion Rsch., Alumni Assn. Brown U. (bd. dirs. 1985-90), Brown U. Club of Phoenix (pres. 1984—), Phoenix City Club (bd. dirs. 1987-93, pres. 1990-91), East Valley Partnership (mem. bd. dirs. 1993—), Phi Beta Kappa. Democrat. Avocation: tennis. Home: 418 E Erie Dr Tempe AZ 85282-3711 Office: O'Neil Assocs 412 E Southern Ave Tempe AZ 85282-5203

O'NEIL, ROBERT MARCHANT, university administrator, law educator; b. Boston, Oct. 16, 1934; s. Walter George and Isabel Sophia (Marchant) O'N.; m. Karen Elizabeth Elson, June 18, 1967; children—Elizabeth, Peter, David, Benjamin. A.B., Harvard U., 1956, A.M., 1957, LL.B., 1961; LL.D., Beloit Coll., 1985, Ind. U., 1987. Bar: Mass. 1962. Law clk. to justice U.S. Supreme Ct., 1962-63; acting assoc. prof. law U. Calif.-Berkeley, 1963-66, prof., 1966-67, 1969-72; exec. asst. to pres., prof. law SUNY-Buffalo, 1967-69; provost, prof. law U. Cin., 1972-73, exec. v.p., prof. law, 1973-75; v.p., prof. law Ind. U., Bloomington, 1980-; pres. U. Wis. System, 1980-85; prof. law U. Wis.-Madison, 1980-85; prof. law U. Va., Charlottesville, 1985—, pres., 1985-90; gen. counsel AAUP, 1970-72, 91-92. Author: Civil Liberties: Case Studies and the Law, 1965; Free Speech: Responsible Communication Under Law, 2d edit., 1972; The Price of Dependency: Civil Liberties in the Welfare State, 1970; No Heroes, No Villians, 1972; The Courts, Government and Higher Education, 1972; Discrimination Against Discrimination, 1976; Handbook of the Law of Public Employment, 1978, 2nd rev. edit., 1993; Classrooms in the Crossfire, 1981; co-author: A Guide to Debate, 1964; The Judiciary and Vietnam, 1972, Civil Liberties Today, 1974. Trustee Carnegie Found. Advancement Teaching; trustee Tchrs. Ins. and Annuity Assn., bd. dirs. Ednl. Testing Svc., Johnson Found., Commonwealth Fund, James River Corp. Home: 1839 Westview Rd Charlottesville VA 22903-1632 Office: Thomas Jefferson Ctr 400 Peter Jefferson Pl Charlottesville VA 22901

O'NEIL, THOMAS MICHAEL, physicist, educator; b. Hibbing, Minn., Sept. 2, 1940; married; 1 child. BS, Calif. State U., Long Beach, 1962; MS, U. Calif., San Diego, 1964, PhD in Physics, 1965. Rsch. physicist Gen. Atomic, 1965-67; prof. physics U. Calif., San Diego, 1967—; mem. adv. bd. Inst. Fusion Studies, 1980-83, Inst. Theoretical Physics, 1983-86. Assoc. editor Physics Review Letters, 1979-83; correspondent Comments Plasma Physics & Controlled Fusion, 1980-84. Alfred P. Sloan fellow, 1971. Fellow Am. Phys. Soc. (Plasma Physics Rsch. award 1991). Achievements include research in theoretical plasma physics with emphasis on nonlinear effects in plasmas and on non-neutral plasmas. Office: Univ of California Dept of Physics 9500 Gilman Dr La Jolla CA 92093-5003

O'NEIL, WAYNE, linguist, educator; b. Kenosha, Wis., Dec. 22, 1931; s. L.J. and Kathryn (Obermeyer) O'N.; married; children: Scott Leslie, Patrick Sean, Elizabeth Erla. AB, U. Wis., 1955, AM, 1956, PhD, 1960; AM (hon.), Harvard U., 1965. Asst. prof. linguistics and lit. U. Oreg., 1961-65; prof. linguistics and edn. Harvard U., 1965-68, lectr. edn., 1968-72; vis. prof. edn. 1978-86; prof. linguistics and humanities MIT, 1968—, chmn. lit. faculty, 1969-75, chmn. linguistics program, 1986—, head dept. linguistics and philosophy, 1989—; lectr. bilingualism Wheelock Coll., Boston, 1991—; lectr. Beijing Normal U., 1980, Beijing and Shanghai Fgn. Lang. Insts., 1981; lectr. linguistics Shandong (China) U., 1982-83, prof., 1984—; prof. Summer inst. on Lang. Change, NEH, 1978; vis. prof. Tsuda Coll., Tokyo, 1983. Mem. editorial group Radical Teacher, 1975—; author: (in Chinese) English Transformational Grammar, 1981, Linguistics and Applied Linguistics, 1983, (with S.J. Keyser) Rule Generalization and Optionality in Language Change, 1985, (with S. Flynn) Linguistic Theory in Second Language Acquisition, 1988; contbr. articles to profl. jours. Mem. steering com. Resist, 1967—; Peoples Coalition for Peace and Justice, 1970-72; cofounder, mem. Linguistics for Nicaragua, 1985—. With U.S. Army, 1952-54. Fulbright fellow in Iceland, 1961; Am. Council Learned Socs. study fellow M.I.T., 1964-65. Mem. AAAS, Linguistic Soc. Am., Nat. Coun. Tchrs. English, Native Am. Langs. Inst., Soc. Pidgin and Creole Linguistics. Office: MIT Dept Linguistics and Philosophy Cambridge MA 02139

O'NEIL, WILLIAM FRANCIS, academic administrator; b. Worcester, Mass., Mar. 26, 1936; s. John J. and Mary A. (Trahant) O'N.; m. Mary Elizabeth Dillon, Aug. 22, 1959; children: Kathleen, Mary Elizabeth. BS, Boston U., 1960; MEd, Worcester State Coll., 1963; diploma, U. Conn., 1970; EdD, Wayne State U., 1972. Tchr. Worcester Pub. Schs., 1960-68, community sch. dir., 1968-73; assoc. prof., dir. community edn. devel. ctr. Worcester State Coll., 1973-75, dir. community svc., 1975-77, dean grad. and continuing edn., 1977-83, exec. v.p., 1983-85; exec. v.p. Mass. Coll. Art, Boston, 1985-86, acting pres., 1986-87, pres., 1987—. Contbr. articles to profl. jours. Mem. Worcester Dem. City Com., Ward I Dem. Com., 1980—; pres., trustee Worcester Pub. Libr., 1977-82; mem. Mass. Bd. Libr. Commrs., 1984-89. Recipient citation Mass. Ho. of Reps., 1977, key City of Worcester, 1982; Mott fellow Charles Stewart Mott Found., 1971. Mem. Mass. Pub. Colls., Univs. Pres. and Chancellors Assn. (chair 1991-92), Assn. Ind. Colls. Art and Design (bd. dirs.), Mass. Community Edn. Assn. (life mem., bd. dirs. 1972-77), Mass. State Colls. Pres. Assn. (chair 1992-93), Profl. Arts Consortium (v.p. Boston, pres. 1993—), Emerald Club. Roman Catholic. Office: Mass Coll Art Office Pres 621 Huntington Ave Boston MA 02115-5801

O'NEIL, WILLIAM FRANCIS, financial executive; b. Cambridge, Mass., Oct. 30, 1929; s. George Francis and Alice L. (Denehy) O'N.; m. Gloria T.

Blouin, Dec. 18, 1927; children: Marcia E., Carol A., William W. BBA, Boston U., 1962; Advanced Mgmt. Program, Harvard U., 1979. Staff analyst Exxon, Boston, 1953-63; acctg. mgmt. staff Arthur D. Little, Inc., Cambridge, 1963-74; fin. project mgr. Arthur D. Little, Inc., Rio de Janeiro, Brazil; internat. controller Arthur D. Little, Inc., Cambridge, 1977-81, controller, 1981-85; v.p., chief fin. officer, 1985—; mgr. fin. projects Arthur D. Little, Ltd., Rio de Janeiro, Brazil, 1974-77; 1974-77; bd. dirs. Opinion Research Corp., Princeton, N.J., Cambridge Cons. Ltd., Eng. Served with USAF, 1951-53. Mem. Fin. Execs. Inst.(profl. devel. com.), Treas.' Club Boston. Roman Catholic. Club: Harvard (Boston). Office: Arthur D Little Inc 25 Acorn Park Cambridge MA 02140-2301

O'NEIL, WILLIAM J., aerospace engineer. Galileo project mgr. NASA. Recipient Laurels award-Space/Missiles Aviation Week & Space Tech., 1991. Home: 2081 Liliano Dr Sierra Madre CA 91024-1537*

O'NEILL, ALBERT CLARENCE, JR., lawyer; b. Gainesville, Fla., Nov. 25, 1939; s. Albert Clarence and Sue Virginia (Henry) O'N.; m. Vanda Marie Nigels, Apr. 26, 1969; 1 child, Heather Marie. B.A. with high honors, U. Fla., 1962; LL.B. magna cum laude, Harvard U., 1965. Bar: Fla. bar 1965. Law clk. to judge U.S. Dist. Ct. (mid. dist.) Fla., Jacksonville, 1965-66; assoc. Fowler, White, Collins, Gillen, Humkey & Trenam, Tampa, Fla., 1966-69; ptnr. Trenam, Simmons, Kemker, Scharf & Barkin, Tampa, 1970-77; mem. firm Trenam, Kemker, Scharf, Barkin, Frye, O'Neill & Mullis (P.A.), Tampa, 1977—, also bd. dirs.; vis. lectr. law Stetson Law Sch., 1970-73. Exec. editor: Harvard Law Rev, 1964-65; contbr. articles to profl. jours. Bd. dirs. Fla. Gulf Coast Symphony, Inc., 1975-86, U. Fla. Found., Inc., 1976-84, Fla. Orch., 1989—. Mem. ABA (chmn. tax sect. 1992-93), Am. Law Inst., Am. Coll. Tax Counsel, Fla. Bar (chmn. tax sect. 1975-76), Phi Beta Kappa. Office: Trenam Kemker Scharf Barkin Frye O'Neill & Mullis 2800 Barnett Plz Tampa FL 33602

O'NEILL, ARTHUR JULIUS, state legislator, lawyer; b. Waterbury, Conn., Apr. 27, 1952; s. Arthur Eugene and Leona (Urban) O'N. BA, U. Conn., 1974; JD, Rutgers U., 1978. Bar: Conn., D.C. Atty. Prescott W. May Law Office, Seymour, Conn., 1979-80; pvt. practice Southbury, Conn., 1980—; mem. Conn. Ho. of Reps., 1988—. Town com. chmn. Southbury Rep. Com., 1988; dir. Southbury Tsp. Sch. Found., 1991—. Mem. Conn. Bar Assn. Roman Catholic. Home: 1468 Bucks Hill Rd Southbury CT 06488 Office: 2 Pomperaug Office Park Southbury CT 06488

O'NEILL, BEVERLY LEWIS, mayor, former college president; b. Long Beach, Calif., Sept. 8, 1930; d. Clarence John and Flossie Rachel (Nicholson) Lewis; m. William F. O'Neill, Dec. 21, 1952. AA, Long Beach City Coll., 1950; BA, Calif. State U., Long Beach, 1952, MA, 1956; EdD, U. So. Calif., 1977. Elem. tchr. Long Beach Unified Sch. Dist., 1952-57; instr., counsellor Compton (Calif.) Coll., 1957-60; curriculum supr. Little Lake Sch. Dist., Santa Fe Springs, Calif., 1960-62; women's advisor, campus dean Long Beach City Coll., 1962-71, dir. Continuing Edn. Ctr. for Women, 1969-75, dean student affairs, 1971-77, v.p. student svcs., 1977-88, supt.-pres., 1988—, exec. dir. Found., 1983—; mayor City of Long Beach, Calif. Advisor Jr. League, Long Beach, 1976—, Nat. Coun. on Alcoholism, Long Beach, 1979—, Assistance League, Long Beach, 1982—; bd. dirs. NCCJ, Long Beach, 1976—, Meml. Hosp. Found., Long Beach, 1984-92, Met. YMCA, Long Beach, 1986-92, United Way, Long Beach, 1986-92. Named Woman of Yr., Long Beach Human Rels. Commn., 1976, to Hall of Fame, Long Beach City Coll., 1977, Disting. Alumni of Yr., Calif. State U., Long Beach, 1985, Long Beach Woman of Yr. Rick Rackers, 1987, Assistance League Aux., 1987; recipient Hannah Solomon award Nat. Coun. Jewish Women, 1984, Outstanding Colleague award Long Beach City Coll., 1985, NCCJ Humanitarian award, 1991, Woman of Excellence award YWCA, 1990, Community Svc. award Community Svcs. Devel. Corp., 1991, Citizen of Yr. award Exch. Club, 1992, Pacific Regional CEO award Assn. Community Coll. Trustees, 1992. Mem. Assn. Calif. Community Coll. Adminstrs. (pres. 1988-90), Harry Buttimer award 1991), Calif. Community Colls. Chief Exec. Officers Assn., Rotary, Soroptomists (Women Helping Women award 1981, Hall of Fame award 1984). Democrat. Office: Office of the Mayor 333 W Ocean Blvd Long Beach CA 90802

O'NEILL, BRIAN, research organization administrator; b. Bristol, Eng., Sept. 20, 1940; s. Raymond and Phyllis Mary (Marshall) O'N.; m. Alayne O'Neill, Aug. 31, 1969 (div. Sept. 1987); children: Allison Sarah, Stuart Douglas, Lesley Alexandra; m. Karen O'Neill, Feb. 20, 1988. BSc in Math. and Stats., Bath. U. Tech., 1965. Cons. in stats. and ops. research Unilever Ltd., London, 1965-66; research assoc. Tech. Ops. Inc., Ft. Belvoir, Va., 1966-67; mgr. applied math. dept. Wolf Research & Devel. Corp., Riverdale, Md., 1967-69; v.p., sr. v.p., exec. v.p. Ins. Inst. for Hwy. Safety, Washington, 1969-85, pres., 1985—; v.p., sr. v.p., exec. v.p. Hwy. Loss Data Inst., Washington, 1969-85, pres., 1985—; witness at numerous fed. and state hearings on hwy. safety and transp. Contbr. numerous articles to profl. jours.; also presentations at profl. confs. Mem. Am. Pub. Health Internat. Com. on Alcohol Drugs and Traffic Safety, Royal Statis. Soc. Assn. Automotive Engrs. Office: Ins Inst for Hwy Safety 1005 N Glebe Rd Ste 800 Arlington VA 22201-4751

O'NEILL, BRIAN BORU, lawyer; b. Hancock, Mich., June 7, 1947; s. Brian Boru and Jean Anette (Rimpela) O'N.; m. Ruth Bohan Sept. 18, 1991; children: Brian Boru, Maggie Byrne, Phelan Boru, Ariel Margaret. B.S., U.S. Mil. Acad., 1969; J.D. magna cum laude U. Mich., 1974. Bar: Mich. 1974, U.S. Ct. Mil. Appeals 1975, U.S. Ct. Appeals (6th cir.) 1975, Minn. 1977, U.S. Dist. Ct. Minn. 1977, U.S. Ct. Appeals (8th cir.) 1977. U.S. Ct. Claims, 1981, U.S. Supreme Ct. 1981, U.S. Ct. Appeals (fed. cir.) 1983, U.S. Ct. Appeals (7th cir.) 1985, U.S. Ct. Appeals (10th cir.) 1986, U.S. Ct. Appeals (9th cir.) 1990. Asst. to gen. counsel Dept. Army, Washington, 1974-77; assoc., ptnr. Faegre & Benson, Mpls., 1977—; mem. com. vis. Mich. Law Sch., 1994—; counsel Defenders of Wildlife, Washington, 1977—, also bd. dirs; counsel Sierra Club, Audubon Soc. Mng. editor Mich. Law Rev., 1973-74; contbr. articles to law jours. Served to capt. U.S. Army, 1969-77. Named Environmentalist of Yr. Sierra Club North Star, 1982; recipient William Douglas award Sierra Club, 1985. Fellow Am. Coll. Trial Lawyers; mem. Order Coif. Clubs: Mpls. Golf, Mpls. Athletic. Office: Faegre & Benson 2200 Norwest Tower 90 S 7th St Minneapolis MN 55402

O'NEILL, BRIAN DENNIS, lawyer; b. Phila., Feb. 21, 1946; s. Harry William and Margaret Elizabeth (Miller) O'N.; m. Bonnie Anne Ryan, Aug. 17, 1968; children: Aimee Kathleen, Catherine Margaret. BA, Fla. State U., 1968, JD, 1971. Bar: Fla. 1971, D.C. 1975, U.S. Ct. Appeals (D.C. cir.) 1978, U.S. Ct. Appeals (5th and 11th cirs.) 1981, U.S. Ct. Appeals (10th cir.) 1985. Trial atty. Fed. Power Commn., Washington, 1972-75; assoc. Farmer, Shibley, McGuinn & Flood, Washington, 1975-80; ptnr. LeBoeuf, Lamb, Greene & MacRae, Washington, 1980—; lectr. in field. Editorial bd. Energy Law Jour., Washington, 1983-84; contbr. articles to profl. jours. Bd. dirs. Immaculata Coll., Rockville, Md., 1989-91; bd. advisors Acad. of the Holy Cross, Kensington, Md., 1994—; bd. visitors Fla. State U. Coll. of Law, 1994—. 2d lt. USAF, 1971-72. Mem. Fla. Bar Assn. (pub. utilities com. 1985-90), Fed. Energy Bar Assn. (chmn. coms. 1983-84), Montgomery Village Golf Club (Gaithersburg, Md.) (bd. dirs. 1984-88), Congl. Country Club (Bethesda, Md.), Phi Alpha Delta. Democrat. Roman Catholic. Office: LeBoeuf Lamb Green & MacRae 1875 Connecticut Ave NW Washington DC 20009-5728

O'NEILL, BRIAN FRANCIS, professional hockey executive; b. Montreal, Que., Can., Jan. 29, 1929; s. Stafford John and Jean (Ferry) O'N.; m. Jean Yates, Aug. 20, 1955; children: Sean, Darcy, Nancy, Patrick, Sandra. B.A., Loyola Coll., Montreal, 1949; B.Com., McGill U., Montreal, 1951. Publisher Wallace Pub. Co., Montreal, 1953-62; bus. mgr. Fin. Times Can. Montreal, 1961-66; with Nat. Hockey League, Montreal, 1966—; now exec. v.p. Nat. Hockey League. Bd. dirs., past pres. St. Mary's Hosp. Found.; bd. dirs. St. Mary's Hosp. Found., Loyola Coll. Found., Que. Student Intra Exchange Program; pres. Loyola High Sch. Found. Mem. Montreal Amateur Athletic Assn. Roman Catholic. Office: Nat Hockey League, Sun Life Bldg, Ste 960, Montreal, PQ Canada H3B 2W2

O'NEILL, CHARLES KELLY, marketing executive, former advertising agency executive; b. Springfield, Mo., Apr. 2, 1933; s. Charles Chester and Frances (Kelly) O'N.; m. Kyoko Hirano, June 2, 1981. B.J., U. Mo., 1955.

With Galvin-Farris-Alvine, Kansas City, Mo., 1957-58; copy chief Galvin-Farris-Alvine, 1958; with Potts-Woodbury, Inc., Kansas City, 1958-61; chief time buyer Potts-Woodbury, Inc., 1960-61; with Gardner Advt. Co., St. Louis, 1962-88; assoc. media dir. Gardner Advt. Co., 1964-65, media dir., 1965-69, v.p., 1966-76, copy chief media dir., dir. co. 1969-88, sr. v.p., 1976-78, pres., 1978-88; gen. mgr. Advanswers div., 1971-72; pres. Advanswers Media/Programming, Inc., 1973-78, chmn., 1978-88; v.p. Wells, Rich, Greene, N.Y.C., 1974-88; exec. v.p. Wells, Rich, Greene, 1979-88, dir., 1978-88; vice chmn. WRG-USA, 1981-88; chmn. O'Neill Mktg., Honolulu, 1988—; exec. v.p. Kyoko O'Neill, Inc., 1993—; dir. Colony Surf Ltd., Honolulu, 1990-94, chmn., bd. dirs., 1994. Bd. dirs. Waialae Iki Ridge Cmty. Assn., Honolulu, 1991—, 1st v.p., 1993-94. Lt. (j.g.) USN, 1955-57. Mem. St. Louis Advt. Club (gov. 1981-83), Outrigger Canoe Club (Honolulu), N.Y. Athletic Club, St. Louis Club, St. Louis Racquet Club, Labrador Retriever Club of Hawaii, Sigma Chi, Alpha Delta Sigma. Episcopalian. Home: 1594 Hoaaina St Honolulu HI 96821-1345

O'NEILL, DANIEL JOSEPH, lawyer; b. N.Y.C., Apr. 15, 1937; s. Daniel and Catherine (Early) O'N.; m. June Marie Kelly, July 9, 1960; children—Daniel J., Kerry Marie, Elizabeth Ann, William, Brian, Peter. A.B., Coll. of the Holy Cross, Worcester, Mass., 1959; J.D., Fordham U. Sch. Law, 1962. Bar: N.Y. 1962. Asst. staff judge advocate 52d Fighter Wing, USAF, Westhampton Beach, NY, 1963-65; assoc. Chadbourne, Parke, Whiteside & Wolff, N.Y.C., 1965-72, ptnr., 1972—. Served to capt. USAF, 1963-65. Mem. ABA. Democrat. Roman Catholic. Avocations: fishing; golf. Home: 118 Hilton Ave Garden City NY 11530-3000 Office: Chadbourne & Parke 30 Rockefeller Plz New York NY 10112-0002

O'NEILL, DONALD EDMUND, health science executive; b. Port Angeles, Wash., Feb. 10, 1926; s. Edward I. and Christine (Williamson) O'N.; m. Violet Elizabeth Oman, June 12, 1948; children: Shelly O'Neill Lane, Erin O'Neill Kennedy, Shawn O'Neill Hoffman. B.S., U. Wash., 1949. With G.D. Searle & Co., 1950-71, regional sales dir., 1962-64, dir. med. service, 1964-68, dir. mktg., 1968-71; with Warner-Lambert Co., 1971—, v.p., 1974-77, exec. v.p. pharm. group, 1977, exec. v.p.; chmn. Internat. profl. group, 1974-76; pres. Parke-Davis & Co., 1976-78; pres., exec. dir. Warner-Lambert/Parke Davis Research Div., 1978, pres. Health Care Group, 1978-81; pres. Parke-Davis Group, 1981, Health Techs. Group, 1982-86, Internat, Ops., 1986-89; exec. v.p., chmn. internat. ops. Warner-Lambert Co, 1989-91; ret., 1991; bd. dirs. Fujisawa U.S.A., N.J. Resources, Alliance Pharm. Immunogen Co., Scios/Nova Pharm., M.D.L. Info. Sys., Targeted Genetics. Served with USAF, 1944-46. Mem. John's Island and Bent Pine Golf Clubs, Morris County Golf Club, Elk River Country Club.

O'NEILL, EDWARD, actor; b. Youngstown, Ohio, Apr. 12, 1946; s. Edward Philip and Ruth Ann (Quinlan) O'N.; m. Cathy Rusoff, Feb., 1986. Student, Ohio State U., Youngstown State U. Appearances include (theatre) Knockout (Broadway debut), 1979, Androcles and the Lion, 1986, Lakeboat, 1983, Elm Circle, 1984, Of Mice and Men, 1984; (films) Cruising, 1980, Dogs of War, 1981, Disorganized Crime, 1989, K-9, 1989, Sibling Rivalry, 1990, The Adventures of Ford Fairlane, 1990, Dutch, 1991, Wayne's World, 1992, Blue Chips, 1993, Little Giants, 1994; (TV episodes) Miami Vice, Spencer for Hire; (TV series) Married...with Children, 1987—; (TV movies) The Day the Women Got Even, 1980, Farrell for the People, 1982, When your Lover Leaves, 1983, Popeye Doyle, 1986, A Winner never Quits, 1986, Right to Die, 1987, The Wherabouts of Jenny, 1991. Avocations: handball, history, literature. Office: 2607 Grand Canal Venice CA 90291*

O'NEILL, EUGENE FRANCIS, communications engineer; b. N.Y.C., July 2, 1918; s. John J. and Agnes (Willmeyer) O'N.; m. Kathryn M. Walls, Oct. 24, 1942; children—Kathryn Anne, Kevin, Jane A., Andrew Thomas. B.S. in Elec. Engring, Columbia U., 1940, M.S., 1941; D.Sc. (hon.), Bates Coll.; D.Engring. (hon.), Politecnico di Milano; D.Sc. (hon.), St. John's U., N.Y.C. With Bell Telephone Labs., Holmdel, N.J., until 1983, engaged in radar devel., 1941-45, coaxial and submarine cable and microwave radio relay, 1945-56, headed devel. of speech interpolation terminals which doubled capacity submarine telephone cables, 1956-60, dir. Telstar satellite projects, 1960-66, exec. dir. network projects, 1966-83. Pulitzer prize; scholar Columbia, 1936-40. Fellow IEEE; mem. Nat. Acad. Engring., Sigma Xi, Tau Beta Pi. Home: 17 Dellwood Ct Middletown NJ 07748-3010

O'NEILL, EUGENE MILTON, mergers and acquisitions consultant; b. Richmond, Calif., Nov. 4, 1925; s. John Milton and Vivian Elda (Vogel) O'N.; m. Jane Prigmore; children: Karen, Kay, Mary. B.S. in Bus. and Pub. Adminstrn., Washington U. St. Louis, 1949. CPA, Mo. Acct., Jeff K. Stone & Co., St. Louis, 1948-52; controller Campbell Holton & Co. (div. Gen. Grocer Co.), Bloomington, Ill., 1953-54; pres. Campbell Holton & Co. (div. Gen. Grocer Co.), 1955-57; v.p. Gen. Grocer Co., St. Louis, 1957-60, pres., 1960-74, chmn. bd., pres., 1974-83. Treas., trustee Food Industry Crusade Against Hunger. With Army Air Corp, 1943-45. Mem. Nat. Wholesale Am. Grocers Assn. (past chmn.). Home: 8 Deacon Dr Saint Louis MO 63131-4803

O'NEILL, FRANCIS XAVIER, III, marketing executive; b. Hampton, Va., June 25, 1953; s. Francis Xavier Jr. and Elizabeth Theresa (Javorsky) O'N. Student, U. Md., 1974; BA in History cum laude, So. Conn. State U. 1980. Clk. FBI, Washington, N.Y.C., 1975-78; rsch. analyst McGavren Guild Radio, N.Y.C., 1981; rsch. mgr. McGavren Guild Radio, 1982, rsch. dir., 1982-84; v.p. mktg. rsch. div. Interep, 1984-90; mgr. mktg. devel. The Arbitron Co., N.Y.C., 1990-93, coms. mktg. comm. and joint ventures, 1994-95; dir. rsch. Sports Programming CBS, 1995—. Author (booklets) Radio's Got Rhythm, 1984, Flying to Succeed: Frequent Business Air Travelers, 1988, The Vital Link: Adults 35-54 in American Society, 1988, On The Air: American Team Sports and the Media, 1989, Seasonal Listening Trends, 1991, Frequent Moviegoers, 1994, Reaching The Non-Prescription Drug Consumer, 1994. Campaigner Francis O'Neill Jr. for State Rep., Conn., 1980-92. Avocations: writing, music, biking, tennis. Home: 47 Valley Shore Dr Guilford CT 06437-2151 Office: 51 West 52nd St New York NY 10019

O'NEILL, GEORGE DORR, business executive; b. N.Y.C., Dec. 27, 1926; s. Grover and Catharine (Porter) O'N.; m. Abby Milton, June 22, 1949; children: George D. Jr., Abby Caulkins, David M., Catharine Broderick, Wendy Wang, Peter M. BA, Harvard Coll., 1950. Registered rep. Harris Upham & Co., N.Y.C., 1949-53; with Chase Manhattan Bank, N.Y.C., 1953-58; chmn. exec. com. Equity Corp., N.Y.C., 1959-63, Train Cabot & Assocs., N.Y.C., 1963-76; chmn. Meriwether Capital Corp., N.Y.C., 1977—; chmn., bd. dirs. Chemstone Corp., Strasburg, Va., 1984-94, Victoreen Inc., Cleve., 1990—. Trustee Colonial Williamsburg (Va.) Found., 1966-94, Inc. Village of Oyster Bay (N.Y.) Cove, 1989—, Ednl. Broadcasting Corp., N.Y.C., 1991—; commr. The Port Authority of N.Y. and N.J., N.Y.C., 1991—. With U.S. Merchant Marine Cadet Corps, 1945-46. Office: Meriwether Capital Corp 30 Rockefeller Plz Ste 5432 New York NY 10112-0245

O'NEILL, HARRY WILLIAM, survey research company executive; b. Atlantic City, Jan. 30, 1929; s. Harry William and Marian Elizabeth (Kuhl) O'N.; m. Carmel Gullo, Sept. 21, 1952; children: Sharon Ruth, Randal Bruce. B.A., Colgate U., 1950; M.S., Pa. State U., 1951. Lic. practicing psychologist, N.J. Research analyst Prudential Ins. Co., Newark, 1957-62; with Opinion Research Corp., Princeton, N.J., 1962-87; sr. v.p. Opinion Research Corp., 1970-73, exec. v.p., 1973-80, pres., 1980-85, vice chmn., 1985-87; vice chmn. Roper Starch Worldwide, N.Y.C., 1988—; mem. coadj. faculty Rutgers U., 1959-64; vis. lectr. Woodrow Wilson Sch., Princeton U., 1980-82;. Editor Marketing Research: A Magazine of Management & Applications, 1988-93. Pres. Nat. Coun. Pub. Polls, 1984-94, trustee, 1994—; bd. dirs. Roper Ctr. for Pub. Opinion Rsch., 1984-94, chmn., 1994—; bd. dirs. Coun. Am. Survey Rsch. Orgns., 1981-83, chmn., 1982-83; vice chmn. Rsch. Industry Coalition, 1993-94, chmn., 1994-95; mem. Highland Park (N.J.) Human Rights Commn., 1973-77; bd. dirs. Del-Raritan Lung Assn., 1974-88, v.p., 1977-82, chmn., 1982-84; fin. chmn. Highland Park Rep. Orgn., 1977-89. Served with USAF, 1951-54. Recipient Maroon citation Colgate U., 1975. Mem. Am. Psychol. Assn., Ea. Psychol. Assn., Am. Assn. Pub. Opinion Rsch., Am. Assn. Consumer Rsch., Am. Mktg. Assn., Market Rsch. Coun., Highland Park Rep. Club, Masons, Elks. Presbyterian. Office: Roper Starch Worldwide 205 E 42d St New York NY 10017

O'NEILL, J. NORMAN, JR., lawyer; b. L.A., Nov. 12, 1943; s. J. Norman and Helen (Mueller) O'N.; m. Rebecca Wylie, Apr. 19, 1975; children: Kathleen, Taryn, J. Norman III. BA, U. So. Calif., L.A., 1966, MBA, 1969; JD, Southwestern U., L.A., 1974. Bar: Calif. 1977, U.S. Dist. Ct. (cen. dist.) Calif. 1978. Corp. trust adminstr. Title Ins. and Trust Co., L.A., 1971-77; v.p. adminstrn. Nat. Am. Title Ins. Co., L.A., 1977-78; asst. to pres. Hydril Co., L.A., 1978-79; gen. counsel System Parking, Inc., Pasadena, Calif., 1979—. Bd. dirs. Hathaway Home for Children, L.A., 1982-88, Queen of Angeles Med. Ctr., L.A., 1987—, St. Josephs Hosp., San Francisco, 1978—. Mem. ABA, Calif. Bar Assn., L.A. County Bar Assn. (exec. com. corp. law depts. sect. 1990—), Calif. Club (L.A.), Bel Air Bay Club (Pacific Palisdes, Calif.), Santa Ana Turf Club (Arcadia, Calif.). Republican. Roman Catholic. Avocations: tennis, stamps. Home: 1368 Bedford Rd San Marino CA 91108 Office: System Parking Inc 918 E Green St Pasadena CA 91106-2907

O'NEILL, JAMES ANTHONY, JR., pediatric surgeon, educator; b. N.Y.C., Dec. 7, 1933; m. Susan Pokorny; children: James Anthony III, Elizabeth, Kathryn S. BS, Georgetown U., 1955; MD, Yale U., 1959. Diplomate Am. Bd. Surgery (bd. dirs. 1981-87, sec. 1988—), Am. Bd. Thoracic Surgery; lic. surgeon, Ohio, La., Tenn., Pa.; cert. instr. advanced trauma life support. Intern Vanderbilt U. Hosp., 1959-60, asst. resident, 1960-64, resident, instr. surgery, 1964-65; chief burn study divsn. U.S.A. Surgl Rsch. Unit Brooke Army Med. Ctr., 1965-67; resident, USPHS fellow in pediatric oncology Columbus Children's Hosp., 1967-68; instr. pediatric surgery Coll. Medicine Ohio State U., 1967-68; asst. prof. surgery and pediatrics, chief pediatric surg. svc. Sch. Medicine La. State U., 1968-70, assoc. prof. surgery, chief sect. pediatric surgery, 1970-71; prof. surgery, chmn. dept. pediatric surgery Sch. Medicine Vanderbilt U., 1971-81; chief med. bd. Med. Ctr., 1976-77; prof. pediatric surgery Sch. Medicine U. Pa., Phila., 1981-95, C.E. Koop prof. pediatric surgery, 1988-95; surgeon-in-chief Children's Hosp. Phila., 1981-95; chmn. Vanderbilt U. Med. Ctr., Nashville, 1995—; site visitor residency rev. com. for surgery AMA; mem. trauma care subcom. med. adv. com. Phila. Emergency Med. Svcs. Coun.; surg. cons. U.S. Army Inst. Surg. Rsch., Ft. Sam Houston, Tex. Mem. editorial bd. Jour. Burn Care and Rehab., Jour. Enteral and Parenteral Nutrition, Jour. Surg. Rsch., Pediatrics, 1984—, Pediatric Emergency Care, 1984—, Pediatric Surgery, Pediatrics Surgery Internat., 1988; mem. assoc. editorial bd. Jour. Pediatric Surgery; editorial cons. Jour. Trauma, 1983—, Jour Vascular Surgery, 1992; contbr. 250 articles to med. jours. Mem. med. adv. bd. Hope Found.; mem. adv. bd. James Whitcomb Riley Rsch. Found., 1986-89; mem. standards com. State Pa. Found. for Trauma Care. Fellow Am. Acad. Pediatrics (surg., pediatric trauma care coord. Pa. chpt., sect. on oncology-hematology chmn. surg. sect. program com. 1975-77, adv. com. postgrad. 1979-81, exec. com. surg. sect. 1977-80, chmn. 1980-81); mem. ACS (founding, cancer liason physician, Met. Phila. chpt., exec. com. trauma com. 1975-77, adv. coun. pediatric surgery 1977-83, 86-88, 90—, postgrad. edn. com. 1979-82, continuing edn. com. 1981-88, nominating com. 1986, regental ad hoc com. on legis issues in trauma in emergency med. svcs. 1987—, bd. govs. 1990—, com. to study fiscal affairs coll. 1992-93, subcom. on burns, spl. soc. gov. from. AM Pediatric Surg. Assn. 1992—, coun. on acad. surgery 1993—, v.p. Phila chpt. 1993-94), Am. Assn. for Surgery Trauma, Am. Trauma Soc. (bd. dirs. 1974-78), Am. Burn Assn., Am. Pediatric Surg. Assn. (sec. 1976-79, chmn. edn. com. 1984-87, pres.-elect 1987-88, pres. 1988-89, manpower, trauma and issues and ethics coms.), Am. Surg. Assn., Assn. for Acad. Surgery (membership com. 1973-74), Soc. for Surgery Alimentary Tract, Soc. Univ. Surgeons (edn. com. 1974-75), Assn. Program Dirs. in Surgery (steering com. 1990-94), Internat. Soc. for Burn Injuries, Internat. Soc. Parenatal Nutrition, Brit. Assn. Pediatric Surgeons, S.E. Surg. Congress (program com. 1979-82), So. Gut Club, So. Soc. for Pediatric Rsch., So. Surg. Assn., Tenn. Med. Assn. (del. 1976, 77), Tenn. Pediatric Soc., New Orleans Surg. Soc., Phila. Acad. Surgery, Phila Peduatric Soc., Coll. Physicians Phila. (coun. 1988-91), Portland Surg. Soc. (hon.), Nashville Surg. Soc., Davidson County Med. Assn., James D. Rives Surg. Soc., Halsted Soc. (bd. govs. 1986-89), Alpha Omega Alpha. Office: Vanderbilt Univ Med Ctr Dept of Surgery T 2116 MCN Nashville TN 37232

O'NEILL, JOHN H., JR., lawyer; b. Bainbridge, Md., Oct. 20, 1946; s. John Hardin and Lois May (Schnepfe) O'N.; m. Vivian Lidwina Gemelli, Nov. 29, 1969; children: Eric Michael, David Christopher, Sean Timothy, Daniel Ryan. BS with distinction Naval Engring., U.S. Naval Acad., Annapolis, Md., 1968; Nuclear Power Tng., U.S. Navy, Bainbridge, 1969; JD, Yale U., 1976. Bar: Md. 1976, D.C. 1977, U.S. Supreme Ct., U.S. Dist. Ct. D.C.; lic. to supervise operation, maintenance naval nuclear propulsion power plants AEC. Officer nuclear submarines USN, 1968-73; ptnr. Shaw, Pittman, Potts & Trowbridge, Washington, 1976—; gen. counsel various nuclear industry cos.; cons. in field to fgn. govs. Mem. ABA, Internat. Bar Assn., Internat. Nuclear Law Assn. Republican. Roman Catholic. Avocations: squash, tennis, skiing. Office: Shaw Pittman Potts & Trowbridge 2300 N St NW Washington DC 20037-1122

O'NEILL, JOHN JOSEPH, speech educator; b. De Pere, Wis., Dec. 6, 1920; s. John Joseph and Elizabeth (Murray) O'N.; m. Dorothy Jane Arnold, Dec. 28, 1943; children—Katherine, Thomas, John, Philip. B.S., Ohio State U., 1947, Ph.D., 1951. From instr. to assoc. prof. speech Ohio State U., 1949-59; prof. emeritus U. Ill. at Champaign, 1959-91, prof. emeritus, 1991—; prof. audiology U. Ill. Coll. Medicine, Chgo., 1965-79, head speech and hearing sci. dept., 1973-79; research assoc. U.S. Naval Sch. Aviation Medicine, summers 1953, 54; cons. in field. Co-author: Visual Communication, 1961, 81;, Hard of Hearing, 1964, Applied Audiometry, 1966. Pres. Columbus Hearing Soc., 1956-58; Bd. dirs. Champaign County Assn. Crippled-United Cerebral Palsy, 1961-63. Served with inf. AUS, 1942-46. Decorated Purple Heart, Bronze Star with oak leaf cluster; recipient Distinguished Alumnus award Dept. Speech, Ohio State U., 1969, honors, 1979. Fellow Am. Speech and Hearing Assn. (pres. 1969), Ohio Psychol. Assn.; mem. Am. Bd. Examiners Speech Pathology and Audiology (pres. 1967-68), Acad. Rehabilitative Audiology (pres. 1969). Home: 1203 W University Ave Champaign IL 61821-3224

O'NEILL, JOHN JOSEPH, JR., business consultant, former chemical company executive; b. N.Y.C., Sept. 13, 1919; s. John Joseph and Margaret (Patterson) O'N.; m. Irene Ray, Apr. 18, 1940; children—Anne, Mary (Mrs. George Schuler). B.S. in Chem. Engring. Mo. Sch. Mines, 1940, Chem. Engr., 1951. Research engr. Western Cartridge Co., 1940-49; with Olin Industries, Inc., 1949-60, dir. prodn. explosives operations, energy div., 1959-60; with Olin Mathieson Chem. Corp., 1960-71, asst. to pres., 1963-64, staff v.p. planning, 1964-65, v.p. comml. devel., chems. group, 1965-67, corporate v.p. plastics, 1967-70, corporate v.p. product diverification, 1970-71; cons., 1971-72; exec. v.p., chief operating officer Kleer-Vu Inc., N.Y.C., 1972-76; v.p. planning and devel. Vertac Consol., 1976-77; pres., chief exec. officer Vertac, Inc., 1977-78, cons., 1979-80, vice chmn. bd., chief oper. officer, 1980-81; cons., 1981—; pres. Jonco, Inc., 1986-89. Contbr. articles to profl. jours.; patentee explosives, chemicals, ordnance items. Emeritus trustee St. Mary-of-Woods Coll., Terre Haute, Ind. Fellow Am. Inst. Chemists; mem. Am. Inst. Chem. Engring. Club: Chemists (N.Y.C.). Home and Office: 7 Castlewood Ln PO Box 429 Pinehurst NC 28374-0429

O'NEILL, JOHN ROBERT, airline executive; b. Bronxville, N.Y., Feb. 13, 1937; s. John R. and Hazel (Edwards) O'N.; m. Laura M. Bellmer, May 25, 1962; children: Amy, Wendy. B.A., Hamilton Coll., 1958. Various positions in scheduling Eastern Airlines, Miami, Fla., 1961-71, dir. schedule planning, 1971-74, systems dir. schedule planning, 1974-75, dir. current schedules, 1975-80, dir. schedules, 1980-81, v.p. schedules, 1981-87; v.p. scheduling TWA Airlines, 1987—. Mem. Phi Beta Kappa. Presbyterian. Office: TWA Airlines 515 N 6th St Saint Louis MO 63101

O'NEILL, JOHN T., toy company executive; b. N.Y.C., Oct. 25, 1944; s. John and Rhoda (Dillon) O'N.; m. Lois E. McGarry, Oct. 8, 1966; children: John, Margaret, Gregory, Brian. BS in Acctg., Providence Coll., 1962-66. Acct. Arthur Andersen & Co., Providence, 1966-67; ptnr. Peat Marwick, KPMG, Providence, 1970-84; mng. ptnr. Peat Marwick KPMG, 1984-87; sr. v.p. fin. Hasbro, Inc., Pawtucket, R.I., 1987-88; v.p., chief fin. officer Hasbro, Inc., 1988-89, cons. v.p., chief fin. officer, 1990—; mem. bd. dirs. coun. Providence Coll.; bd. dirs., past pres. Jr. Achievement R.I.; pres., bd. dirs. Galaxy Funds. Trustee Women and Infants Hosp. R.I., Providence; treas., bd. dirs. R.I. Philharmonic Orch., Providence, C. of C.; chmn. Catholic

Charity Fund, Providence. Capt. Med. Svc. Corps, U.S. Army, 1967-70. Decorated Bronze Star. Mem. AICPA, R.I. CPA Soc., Inst. Mgmt. Accts., Fin. Execs. Inst., Warwick Country Club, Hope Club, Dunes Club, Univ. Club. Avocations: golf, outdoors, art. Office: Hasbro Inc 200 Narragansett Park Dr Pawtucket RI 02861-4342

O'NEILL, JOSEPH PATRICK, retail association executive; b. Boston, July 18, 1947; s. John Matthew and Mary Elisabeth (Connolly) O'N.; m. Linda Ann Quelle, Nov. 3, 1948; children: Susannah, Patrick, Kathleen. AB in Internat. Relations cum laude, Harvard U., 1969; M in Pub. Affairs, U. Tex., 1973. Planner City of Dallas, 1971-73; econ. cons. NASA, Houston, 1973; exec. asst. to Sen. Lloyd Bentsen, Austin, 1973-80; adminstrv. asst. to Sen. Lloyd Bentsen, Washington, 1980-84; pres. Am. Retail Fedn., Washington, 1985—; instr. LBJ Sch. U. Tex., Austin, 1974-75; advisor on U.S. cleared trade to Multilateral Trade Negotiations, Washington, 1986-87; dir. Retail Industry Trade Action Coalition, Washington, 1985-87; bd. dirs. Cranston Bank, Washington; chief of staff for v.p. campaign Sen. Lloyd Bentsen, summer 1988. Editor: Social Services in Texas, 1973. Mem. Bus. Roundtable Dem. Senatorial Campaign com., 1987; bd. dirs. Am. Retail Edn. Found., 1985-87; chief of staff vice-presdl. campaign Senator Lloyd Bentsen, 1988. Roman Catholic. Club: Harvard (Washington) (Austin) (treas. 1977-78), Avenel (Potomac, Md.), Army-Navy (Washington). Avocations: golf, tennis. Office: Am Retail Fedn 1616 H St NW Washington DC 20006-4903

O'NEILL, JUNE ELLENOFF, economist; b. N.Y.C., June 14, 1934; d. Louis and Matilda (Liebstein) Ellenoff; m. Sam Cohn, 1955 (div. 1961); 1 child, Peter; m. David Michael O'Neill, Dec. 24, 1964; 1 child, Amy. BA, Sarah Lawrence Coll., Bronxville, N.Y., 1955; PhD, Columbia U., 1970. Econs. instr. Temple U., Phila., 1965-68; rsch. assoc. Brookings Instn., Washington, 1968-71; sr. economist Pres.'s Coun. Econ. Advisors, Washington, 1971-76; chief human resources budget Congl. Budget Office, Washington, 1976-79; sr. rsch. assoc. The Urban Inst., Washington, 1979-86; dir. Office Policy and Rsch. U.S. Commn. Civil Rights, Washington, 1986-87; prof. econs. and fin., dir. Ctr. for Study Bus. and Govt. Baruch Coll., CUNY, 1987-95; dir. Congl. Budget Office U.S. Congress, Washington, 1995—; mem. Nat. Adv. Com., The Poverty Inst., U. Wis., 1988-95. Contbr. articles to profl. jours. Rsch. grantee, U.S. Dept. Labor, NICHD, Dept. Health & Human Svcs., others. Mem. Am. Econs. Assn. (bd. dirs. com. on status of women). Republican. Jewish. Home: 420 Riverside Dr New York NY 10025-7773 Office: Baruch College CUNY 17 Lexington Ave Box 348A New York NY 10010

O'NEILL, LAWRENCE DANIEL, lawyer, consultant, entrepreneur; b. Granite City, Ill., May 16, 1946; s. Lawrence Frederick and Dorthy Lee (Breckenridge) O'N.; m. Feena MacLaverty, Oct. 28, 1989; children: Olsin Miceal, Lorćan Shane, Jaishri Erin, Tara Breckenridge. Student U. Mo., 1964-66; BA, U. Md., 1970; postgrad. Georgetown U., 1970; JD, U. Balt., 1975. Bar: Md. 1975, D.C. 1978, U.S. Supreme Ct. 1980, U.S. Ct. Claims 1982. Cryptologist/linguist Nat. Security Agy., Fort Meade, Md., 1966-70; fgn. svc. officer U.S. Info. Agy., Washington, New Delhi (India), 1970-73; budget officer U.S. Consumer Product Safety Commn., Washington, 1973-75; asst. to dir. then dir. policy White House Office Telecommunication Policy, 1975-78; assoc. chief counsel Nat. Telecommunications and Info. Adminstrn., U.S. Dept. Commerce, 1978-81; chmn., chief exec. Technology Analysis Group, Washington, 1981-87; Washington counsel Fenwick, Stone, Davis & West, Palo Alto, Calif., 1982-86; ptnr. Winston & Strawn, Washington, 1986-88, counsel, 1988-89; sec. gen. Internat. Soc. Aero. Telecommunications, Paris, 1988-91; ptnr. O'Neill & Co., Internat. Legal Advisers, Dublin and Paris; chmn. Pan Am Tech. Policy Forum, Miami, Fla., 1982—; bd. dirs. Teleport Internat., Washington, 1984-90; bd. dirs. In-Flight Phone Europe, Dublin, Virtual Comm. Internat. Ltd., Dublin. Author: The Telecommunications Revolution, 1981, Five Top Technologies 1984-1995, 1982. Contbr. chpt. to Media Privacy, 1984. Mem. legis. adv. bd. Md. Senate, 1983-84. Sgt. U.S. Army, 1966-70. Mem. ABA (mem. coun. 1984—), AAAS, Md. Bar Assn., D.C. Bar Assn., Nat. Conf. Lawyers and Scientists. Democrat. Roman Catholic. Lodge: Order of Hibernians. Home: Le Bailliage, 12 Rue du Dr Rochefort, Chatou France also: Killadreenan Grange, Newcastle County, Wicklow Ireland Office: Internat Soc Aero Telecommunications, 112 Ave Charles de Gaulle, 92522 Neuilly-sur-Seine France

O'NEILL, MICHAEL JAMES, editor, author; b. Detroit, Nov. 19, 1922; s. Michael J. and Ellen Mary (Dacey) O'N.; B.A., U. Detroit, 1946, L.H.D. (hon.), 1977; postgrad. Fordham U., 1946-47; m. Mary Jane Kilcoyne, May 31, 1948; children: Michael, Maureen, Kevin, Kathryn. Writer Standard News Assn., N.Y.C., 1946-47; with UPI, 1947-56; Washington corr. N.Y. Daily News, 1956-66, asst. mng. editor, 1966-68, mng. editor, 1968-74, exec. editor, 1974-75, editor, 1975-82, v.p., 1971-79, exec. v.p., 1979-82, also dir.; freelance writer, lectr., 1983—. Mem. Nat. Adv. Coun. Health Professions Edn., 1967-71. Served with U.S. Army, 1943-45; ETO. Decorated Bronze Star. Recipient Nat. Affairs Reporting award Nat. Headliner's, 1956. Mem. Overseas Writers (pres. 1965), Am. Soc. Newspaper Editors (pres. 1981-82), Council Fgn. Relations. Club: Century (N.Y.C.). Author: (with L. Tanzer) The Kennedy Circle, 1961; China Today, 1976, Terrorist Spectaculars: Should TV Coverage Be Curbed, 1986, The Roar of the Crowd, How TV and People Power are Changing the World, 1993. Address: 23 Cayuga Rd Scarsdale NY 10583-6941

O'NEILL, PATRICK HENRY, consulting mining engineer; b. Cordova, Alaska, Aug. 11, 1915; s. Harry I. and Florence (Leahy) O'N.; m. Sandra Dorris, Dec. 5, 1967; children: Kevin Reddy, Erin Dorris, Patrick Henry, Timothy Hazleton, Frederick Leahy. B.S., B.Min.E., U. Alaska, 1941, E.M. 1953, D.Sc. (hon.), 1976. Engr. and supt. U.S. Smelting Refining & Mining Co., Fairbanks, Alaska, 1939-41, 46-53; chief engr. Compañia Minera Choco Pacifico, Colombia, 1953-54; v.p. South Am. Gold & Platinum Co., N.Y.C., 1954-57; exec. v.p. Internat. Mining Corp. (formerly SAG&P Co.), 1957-70; chmn. Frontino Gold Mines Ltd., London, 1958-76; pres. S.Am. Placers, Bolivia, 1960-76; chmn. Pato Consol. Gold Dredging Ltd., Can., 1961-76, Consol. Purchasing and Designing, San Francisco, 1961-77; pres. Internat. Mining Corp., 1970-76; sr. v.p. Rosario Resources Corp., N.Y.C., 1977-80; exec. v.p. Rosario Resources Corp., 1981-82; mining cons., 1982—; bd. dirs. Zemex Corp., Toronto, Ont. Chmn. bd. trustees Joslin Diabetes Ctr., Boston, 1981-94. Served to maj. USAAF, 1941-46. Mem. Mining and Metall. Soc. Am., Am. Inst. Mining, Metall. and Petroleum Engrs., Can. Inst. Mining and Metallurgy, Arctic Inst., NAM (gov., chmn. 1972-73), Pioneers of Alaska, Instn. Mining and Metallurgy London, Am. Geog. Soc. (councilor), Ireland-U.S. Coun. for Commerce and Industry (dir.), Explorers Club, Mining Club, Wings Club, Met. Club (N.Y.C.), Darien Country Club, Woodway Country Club. Home and Office: 42 Dunning Rd New Canaan CT 06840-4008

O'NEILL, PAUL HENRY, aluminum company executive; b. St. Louis, Dec. 4, 1935; s. John Paul and Gaynald Elsie (Irvin) O'N.; m. Nancy Jo Wolfe, Sept. 4, 1955; children—Patricia, Margaret, Julie, Paul Henry. A.B., Fresno State Coll., 1960; Haynes Found. fellow, Claremont Grad. Sch., 1960-61; postgrad., George Washington U., 1962-65; M.P.A., Ind. U., 1966. Site engr. Morrison-Knudsen, Inc., Anchorage, 1955-57; systems analyst VA, Washington, 1961-66; budget examiner Bur. of Budget, Washington, 1967-69; chief human resources program div. U.S. Govt. Office of Mgmt. and Budget, Washington, 1969-70; asst. dir. U.S. Govt. Office of Mgmt. and Budget, 1971-72, assoc. dir., 1973-74, dep. dir., 1975-77; v.p. Internat. Paper Co., N.Y.C., 1977-81, sr. v.p., 1981-85, pres., dir., 1985-87; chmn., CEO Aluminum Co. Am., Pitts., 1987—; also bd. dirs.; bd. dirs. GM, Rand Corp.; chmn. Pres.'s Edn. Policy Adv. Com., 1989-92. Mem. JFK bd. visitors Harvard U. 1983-87; mem. adv. com., 1982—; bd. dirs. Gerald R. Ford Found., 1984—; dir. Manpower Demonstration Rsch. Corp., 1981—. Recipient Nat. Inst. Pub. Affairs Career Edn. award, 1965, William A. Jump Meritorious award, 1971; Fellow Nat. Inst. Pub. Affairs, 1966. Mem. Am. Enterprise Inst. (trustee), Bus. Coun., Bus. Roundtable (policy com.), Hudson Inst. (mem. edn. policy com.), Nat. Acad. Social Ins. (founding mem.), Inst. Internat. Econs. (bd. dirs.), Inst. Rsch. on Econs. of Taxation, Internat. Primary Aluminum Inst. (former chmn.), Mgmt. Exec. Soc. Methodist. Office: Aluminnum Co Am 1501 Alcoa Bldg Pittsburgh PA 15219-1850

O'NEILL, PHILIP DANIEL, JR., lawyer, educator; b. Boston, Sept. 19, 1951; s. Philip Daniel Sr. and Alice Maureen (Driscoll) O'N.; m. Lisa G.

Arrowood, June 25, 1983; children: Alexander Edwin, Sean Matthew, Madeleine Clarice. BA, Hamilton Coll., 1973; JD cum laude, Boston Coll., 1977. Bar: Mass. 1977, N.Y. 1985, R.I. 1988. Assoc. Hale and Dorr, Boston, 1977-83, ptnr., 1983-87; ptnr. Edwards & Angell, Boston, 1987—; adj. rsch. fellow John F. Kennedy Sch. of Govt., Ctr. for Sci. and Internat. Affairs Harvard U., 1983-86; adj. prof. of law Boston Coll., 1988—; adj. prof. law Boston U., 1992; cons. Arms Control and Disarmament Agy. U.S. Dept. Def., 1983-84; guest lectr., commentator Boston Coll. Law Sch., Harvard U. Bus. Sch., Kennedy Sch. of Govt., 1985, Boston U. Law Sch., 1990-91, Harvard Law Sch., 1994-95; internat. and domestic comml. arbitrator Am. Arbitration Assn., Hong Kong Ctr. for Internat. Arbitration, U.S.-Can. Free Trade Agreement, Internat. C. of C. Ct. of Arbitration of Paris, Inter-Am. Comml. Arbitration Commn., Japanese Comml. Arbitration Assn., Cario Regional Centre, Euro-Arab C. of C; panlist in a number of internat. and domestic legal programs. Contbr. chpts. to books and articles to profl. jours. Fellow Chartered Inst. Arbitrators; mem. ABA, Internat. Law Assn. (chmn. Am. br. arbitration com. 1985-89, rep. internat. arbitration com. 1989—), R.I. Bar Assn., Mass Bar Assn., Boston Bar Assn. (chmn. internat. law sect. 1994-96, past chmn. internat. litigation and arbitration com.), Am. Soc. Internat. Law. Home: 11 Blackburnian Rd Lincoln MA 01773-4317 Office: Edwards & Angell 101 Federal St Boston MA 02110-1800

O'NEILL, ROBERT CHARLES, consultant, inventor; b. Buffalo, Dec. 3, 1923; s. Albert T. and Helen (Lynch) O'N.; m. Agnes Balischak; 1 dau., Eileen Anne. BS in Chemistry, Rensselaer Poly. Inst., 1945; PhD in Organic Chemistry, Mass. Inst. Tech., 1950. Sr. chemist Merck & Co., Inc., Rahway, N.J., 1950-56, marketing devel. specialist, 1956-58; v.p. Stauffer Pharms. div. Stauffer Chem. Co., N.Y.C., 1958-61; v.p., dir. R & D Cooper Labs., Inc., 1961-70, exec. v.p., 1970-76, gen. mgr., 1975-76, pres., 1976-77, also dir.; cons., inventor, 1977—. Contbr. articles to profl. jours. Served with USNR, 1943-46. Mem. Am. Chem. Soc., Chemists Club N.Y. Patentee in field. Home: 10 Whitlaw Close Chappaqua NY 10514-1008

O'NEILL, ROBERT EDWARD, business journal editor; b. N.Y.C., Aug. 30, 1925; s. Joseph Michael and Ethel Agnes (Seymour) O'N.; m. Phyllis Ann Schreck, Apr. 19, 1952; children: Keith, Kathy, Kim, Karen. B.A. in Journalism, Syracuse (N.Y.) U., 1950. Reporter Southeasterner, Long Island, N.Y., 1950-51; rep. Bklyn. Daily, 1952; asso. editor Progressive Grocer, N.Y.C., 1952-62; sr. editor Progressive Grocer, 1962-69, exec. editor, 1970-86; editor in chief Monitor mag., Stamford, Conn., 1986—; editorial dir. Progressive Grocer; dir. Sopro Foods, Inc. Contbg. author/editor: Foodtown Study, 1954, Super Valu Study, 1957, Dillon Study, 1959, Colonial Study, 1961, Outstanding New Super Markets, 1961, Consumer Dynamics, 1963, A & P Study, 1970, Merchandising in Action, 1972, Consumer Behavior Study, 1976, Brand Power Study, 1977. Served with USN, 1944-47. Mem. Am. Bus. Press (editorial com. 1974-75, co-winner, Jesse H. Neal award 1961, 66, 74, 89, 90, Points of Light award 1991), Glacier Hills Assn. (pres. 1964-66), Sigma Delta Chi. Club: Overseas Press. Home: 67 Moraine Rd Morris Plains NJ 07950-2752 Office: Monitor Four Stamford Forum Stamford CT 06901

O'NEILL, RUSSELL RICHARD, engineering educator; b. Chgo., June 6, 1916; s. Dennis Alyssious and Florence Agnes (Mathurin) O'N.; m. Margaret Bock, Dec. 15, 1939; children: Richard A., John R.; m. Sallie Boyd, June 30, 1967. BSME, U. Calif., Berkeley, MSME, 1940; PhD, UCLA, 1956. Registered profl. engr., Calif. Design engr. Dowell, Inc., Midland, Mich., 1940-41; design engr. Dow Chem. Co., Midland, 1941-44, Airesearch Mfg. Co., Los Angeles, 1944-46; lectr. engring. UCLA, 1946-56, prof. engring., 1956, asst. dean engring., 1956-61, assoc. dean, 1961-73, acting dean, 1965-66, dean, 1974-83, dean emeritus, 1983—; staff engr. NAS-NRC, 1954; dir. Data Design Labs., 1977-81, dir. emeritus, 1986—; mem. engring. task force Space Era Edn. Study Fla. Bd. Control, 1963; mem. regional Export Expansion Coun. Dept. Commerce, 1964-66, Los Angeles Mayor's Space Adv. Com., 1964-69; mem. Maritime Transp. Rsch. Bd., 1974-81; bd. advisers Naval Postgrad. Sch., 1976-84; mem. Nat. Nuclear Accreditation Bd., 1983-88; mem. accrediting bd. Dept. Energy, 1992—. Trustee West Coast U., 1981-90; bd. dirs. Western region United Way, 1982-90. Mem. NAE, Am. Soc. Engring. Edn., Sigma Xi, Tau Beta Pi. Home: 15430 Longbow Dr Sherman Oaks CA 91403-4910 Office: 405 Hilgard Ave Los Angeles CA 90095-1595

O'NEILL, SHEILA, principal. Prin. Cor Jesu Acad., St. Louis. Recipient Blue Ribbon award U.S. Dept. Edn., 1990-91. Office: Cor Jesu Acad 10230 Gravois Rd Saint Louis MO 63123

O'NEILL, THOMAS J., engineering company executive; b. 1952. AB, Dartmouth Coll., 1973, BE, 1974. With Parsons Brinckerhoff/Tudor, Atlanta, 1977-78, Tudor Engring. Co., Atlanta, 1978-92; pres., COO Parsons, Brinckerhoff, Quade, N.Y.C., 1992—. Office: Parsons Brinckerhoff Quade 1 Penn Plz Fl 5 New York NY 10119-0001*

O'NEILL, THOMAS NEWMAN, JR., federal judge; b. Hanover, Pa., July 6, 1928; s. Thomas Newman and Emma (Cornpropst) O'N.; m. Jeanne M. Corr., Feb. 4, 1961; children: Caroline Jeanne, Thomas Newman, III, Ellen Gitt. A.B. magna cum laude, Catholic U. Am., 1950; LL.B. magna cum laude, U. Pa., 1953; postgrad. (Fulbright grantee), London Sch. Econs., 1955-56. Bar: Pa. 1954, U.S. Supreme Ct. 1959. Law clk. to Judge Herbert F. Goodrich U.S. Ct. Appeals (3d cir.), 1953-54; to Justice Harold H. Burton U.S. Supreme Ct., 1954-55; assoc. firm Montgomery, McCracken, Walker & Rhoads, Phila., 1956-63; ptnr. Montgomery, McCracken, Walker & Rhoads, 1963-83; judge U.S. Dist. Ct. (ea. dist.) Pa., 1983—; counsel 1st and 2d Pa. Legis. Reapportionment Commns., 1971, 81; lectr. U. Pa. Law Sch., 1973. Articles editor: U. Pa. Law Rev, 1952-53. Former trustee Lawyers Com. for Civil Rights Under Law; former mem. Gov.'s Trial Ct. Nominating Commn. for Phila. County; former mem. bd. overseers U. Pa. Mus. Fellow Am. Coll. Trial Lawyers; mem. Am. Law Inst. (life), Phila. Bar Assn. (chancellor 1976), Pa. Bar Assn. (gov. 1978-81), U. Pa. Law Alumni Soc. (pres. 1976-77), Pa. Conf. County Bar Officers (pres. 1981-82), Order of Coif (pres. U. Pa. chpt. 1971-73), Merion Cricket Club, Edgemere Club, Broadacres Trouting assn., Phi Beta Kappa, Phi Eta Sigma. Office: US Dist Ct 14613 US Courthouse 601 Market St Philadelphia PA 19106-1723

O'NEILL, TIMOTHY P., lawyer; b. Shotts, Scotland, Sept. 23, 1940; came to U.S., 1953; s. Thomas P. and Catherine (O'Connor) O'N.; m. Maria E. Karagianis, May 19, 1982; children: Katherine, Elizabeth. STB, Gregorian U., Rome, 1965; MA, Brandeis U., 1970; JD, Boston U., 1971. Bar: Mass. 1972, U.S. Dist. Ct. Mass. 1982, U.S. Ct. Appeals (1st cir.) 1982. Asst. dist. atty. Suffolk County, Mass., 1981-83; ptnr. Murphy, DeMarco & O'Neill, Boston, 1983-93, Hanity & King P.C., Boston, 1993—; clin. supr. Sch. Law Harvard U., Cambridge, Mass., 1976-81; lectr. Mass. Continuing Legal Edn., 1988—. Chmn. fin. com. City of Boston, 1984-86. Recipient Disting. Prosecutor award Citizens for Decency Through Law, Phoenix, 1981. Mem. ABA, Internat. Assn. Defense Coun., Mass. Bar Assn. Avocations: skiing, reading, classical music. Home: 145 Dudley Ln Milton MA 02186-4013 Office: Hanify & King PC One Federal St Boston MA 02110

O'NEILL, WILLIAM LAWRENCE, history educator; b. Big Rapids, Mich., Apr. 18, 1935; s. John Patrick and Helen Elizabeth (Marsh) O'N.; m Elizabeth Carol Knollmueller, Aug. 20, 1960; children: Cassandra Leigh, Catherine Lorraine. A.B., U. Mich., 1957; M.A., U. Calif., Berkeley, 1958, Ph.D., 1963. Asst. prof. history U. Colo., 1964-66; asst. prof. U. Wis., 1966-69, asso. prof., 1969-71; prof. Rutgers U., New Brunswick, N.J., 1971—; vis. asst. prof. U. Pitts., 1963-64; vis. asso. prof. U. Pa., 1969-70. Author: Divorce in the Progressive Era, 1967, Everyone Was Brave: The Rise and Fall of Feminism in America, 1969, rev. and repub. as: Feminism in America: A History, 1989, Coming Apart: An Informal History of America in the 1960's, 1971, The Last Romantic: A Life of Max Eastman, 1978, 2d edit., 1991, A Better World: The Great Schism: Stalinism and the American Intellectuals, 1982, repub. as: A Better World: Stalinism and the American Intellectuals, 1989, American High: The Years of Confidence, 1945-60, 1986, A Democracy at War: America's Fight at Home and Abroad in World War II, 1993. Nat. Endowment Humanities fellow, 1979-80. Mem. Am. Hist. Assn. Office: Rutgers U Dept History New Brunswick NJ 08903

O'NEILL, WILLIAM PATRICK, lawyer; b. Joplin, Mo., Sept. 14, 1951; s. Fred Charles and Dorothy Isabel (Snyder) O'N.; m. Mary Louise Richardson, June 17, 1989. BA, U. Kans., 1973; JD, U. Mich., 1976. Bar: Ill. 1976, U.S. Dist. Ct. (no. dist.) Ill. 1976, U.S. Dist. Ct. D.C. 1982. Assoc. Kirkland & Ellis, Chgo., 1976-81, Sidley & Austin, Chgo., 1982-85, Skadden, Arps, Slate, Meagher & Flom, N.Y.C., 1986-87; assoc. Crowell & Moring, Washington, 1987-88, ptnr., 1988—; gen. counsel Ill. Common Cause, Chgo., 1979-81. Editor, author: (with others) Successfully Acquiring A U.S. Business, 1990; editorial chmn. Antitrust Law Jour., 1984-89. Mem. University Club of Chgo. Office: Crowell & Moring 1001 Pennsylvania Ave NW Washington DC 20004-2505

O'NEILL, WILLIAM ROBERT, lawyer; b. Rahway, N.J., Aug. 8, 1950; s. Philip Thomas and Mary Ellen O.; m. Kathleen Kenney, Feb. 17, 1973; children: William, Garrett, Elizabeth. BA, Boston Coll., 1972; MA, U. Va., 1974, JD, 1977; LLM, NYU, 1983. Bar: Conn. 1977, Fla. 1978, U.S. Tax Ct. 1980. Assoc. Cummings & Lockwood, Stamford, Conn., 1977-85, pntr., 1985-89; ptnr. Cummings & Lockwood, Naples, Fla., 1989—. Contbr. articles Conn. Bar Jour., 1980, Bus. Lawyer, 1987. Mem. St. Joseph Med. Ctr. Found., Stamford, 1980-89, Bus. Press Ednl. Found., N.Y.C., 1984-89, S. Fla. Chpt. Nat. Multiple Sclerosis Soc., 1991—; econ. devel. coun. Coller County, 1993—. Mem. ABA (subcom. exec. compensation, corps. sect. 1986-88), Conn. Bar Assn. (exec. com., taxation sect. 1983-85), Rotary (bd. dirs. 1988-89). Roman Catholic. Avocations: gardening, choral singing, boating. Home: 263 Ridge Dr Naples FL 33963-2902 Office: Cummings & Lockwood 3001 Tamiami Trail N PO Box 413032 Naples FL 33941-3032

O'NEILL BIDWELL, KATHARINE THOMAS, fine arts association executive, performing arts executive; b. Dayton, Ohio, Mar. 2, 1937; d. Charles Allen and Margaret Stoddard (Talbott) Thomas; children: Margaret, Stephen, Thomas; m. J. Truman Bidwell. B.A., Sarah Lawrence Coll., Bronxville, N.Y., 1959. Mng. dir. Met. Opera Assn., 1977-86, v.p., 1979-86; first v.p. Met. Opera Guild, N.Y.C., 1978-79, pres., chief exec. officer, 1979-86; dir. spl. projects Lincoln Ctr., N.Y.C., 1986—; dir. Norlin Corp. Bd. dirs. Lincoln Ctr. for Performing Arts, N.Y.C., Assn. of Mentally Ill Children, 1975-76, Valerie Bettis Sch. of Theater/Dance, 1976-79, Salisbury Sch., Conn., 1982-84; trustee Sarah Lawrence Coll., 1977-86; Westminster Choir Coll., 1986-91, Greenwall Found., 1986, Vol. Cons. Group, 1986. Mem. Assn. Sarah Lawrence Coll. (pres. 1975-77). Republican. Episcopalian. Home: 455 E 57th St New York NY 10022-3065 Office: Lincoln Center 70 Lincoln Center Plz New York NY 10023-6548

ONEK, JOSEPH NATHAN, lawyer; b. N.Y.C., Jan. 9, 1942; s. Jacob J. and Doris (Aaronson) O.; m. Margot Debra Piore, June 29, 1963; children: David, Matthew. A.B. magna cum laude, Harvard Coll., 1962; M.A., London Sch. Econs., 1964; LL.B. magna cum laude, Yale Law Sch., 1967. Bar: D.C. 1968. Law clk. to chief judge David L. Bazelon, U.S. Ct. Appeals (D.C. cir.), 1967-68; law clk. Justice William J. Brennan, U.S. Supreme Ct., 1968-69; staff Senate Adminstrv. Practice and Procedure Subcom., Senate Labor and Pub. Welfare Commn., 1969-71; dir., atty. Ctr. for Law and Social Policy, 1971-76; adj. prof. U. Md. Law Sch., Health Care Law, 1976-77; dir. health policy analysis Carter-Mondale Transition Planning Group, 1976-77; assoc. dir. for health and human resources Domestic Policy Staff, White House, 1977-79; dep. counsel to Pres., White House, 1979-81; ptnr. Onek, Klein & Farr, Washington, 1981-91; ptnr. Crowell & Moring, 1991—; presdl. appointee to D.C. Jud. Nominating Com., 1994—. Marshall scholar, 1962. Mem. ABA, Phi Beta Kappa. Home: 3723 Ingomar St NW Washington DC 20015-1819 Office: Crowell & Moring 1001 Pennsylvania Ave NW Washington DC 20004-2595

ONESTI, SILVIO JOSEPH, psychiatrist; b. San Francisco, Jan. 3, 1926; s. Silvio Joseph and Johanna (Kristoffy) O.; m. Jean Thomas, May 12, 1956; children: Sally Joanna, Stephen Thomas. BS, Stanford U., 1947; MD, McGill U., 1951. Diplomate Am. Bd. Psychiatry and Neurology. Instr. pediatrics Yale Med. Sch., New Haven, 1956-58; career tchr. psychiatry NIMH, Harvard Med. Sch., Beth Israel Hosp., Boston, 1963-65; head child psychiatry unit Beth Israel Hosp., Boston, 1965-73; dir. child and adolescent psychiatry McLean Hosp., Belmont, Mass., 1973-91; dir. Hall-Mercer Ctr. for children and adolescents McLean Hosp., Belmont, 1973-91; dir. child and adolescent psychiat. tng., 1973-92; dir. clin. svcs. McLean Hosp., Belmont, 1981-83; asst. prof. psychiatry Harvard Med. Sch., Boston, 1969—; faculty Boston Psychoanalytic Soc. and Inst. Inc., Boston, 1971-81. Contbr. articles to profl. jours. With USN 1944-46. Fellow Am. Psychiat. Assn., Am. Acad. Child and Adolescent Psychiatry, Am. Coll. Psychiatrists; mem. Group for Advancement of Psychiatry (fellow 1959-61, bd. dirs. 1987-89), Boston Psychoanalytic Soc. and Inst. Inc., Mass. Med. Soc., Alpha Omega Alpha. Home: 4 Gray Gdns W Cambridge MA 02138-2312 Office: McLean Hosp 115 Mill St Belmont MA 02178-9106

ONET, VIRGINIA C(ONSTANTINESCU), research scientist, educator, writer; b. Sarmasag, Salaj, Romania, Mar. 17, 1939; came to U.S., 1986; naturalized, 1991.; d. Virgil and Eugenia (Marinescu) Constantinescu; m. Gheorghe Emil Onet, Sept. 3, 1981. DVM, U Agriculture Scis., Cluj-Napoca, Romania, 1966; PhD, Coll. Vet. Med., Bucharest, Romania, 1974. From asst. to assoc. prof. Coll. Vet. Medicine, Cluj-Napoca, 1966-81, lectr., 1981-85; pvt. researcher Fed. Republic Germany, 1985-86; ind. cons. Detroit, 1986-88; rsch. group leader Grand Labs., Inc., Larchwood, Iowa, 1988-92, mgr. R&D dept. parasitology, 1992—; mem. profl. bd. Coll. Vet. Medicine, Cluj-Napoca, 1970-72, mem. faculty com., 1980-81; mem. Exam. Bd. for Screening Vet. Medicine Candidates, Cluj-Napoca, 1974-85. Author: Diagnosis Guide for Parasitic Disease, 1983; co-author: Laboratory Diagnosis in Veterinary Medicine, 1978; author 7 textbooks; contbr. over 45 articles to profl. jours. Merit scholar Coll. Vet. Medicine, Bucharest, 1964. Mem. AAAS, Am. Soc. Parasitologists, Am. Vet. Med. Assn., Am. Assn. Vet. Parasitologists, World Vet. Poultry Assn., World Assn. for Advancement Vet. Parasitology, Romanian Vet. Medicine Soc., Romanian Soc. Biologists, World Assn. Buiatrics, N.Y. Acad. Scis. Avocations: music, poetry, travel, crocheting, reading. Home: 4509 Mountain Ash Dr Sioux Falls SD 57103-4959 Office: Grand Labs Inc PO Box 193 Larchwood IA 51241-0193

ONG, CHEE-MUN, engineering educator; b. Ipoh, Perak, Malaysia, Nov. 23, 1944; came to U.S., 1969; s. Chin-Kok Ong and Say-Choo Yeoh; m. Penelope Li-Lok, July 17, 1971; children: Yi-Ping, Yi-Ching, Chiew-Jen. BE with honors, U. Malaysia, 1967; MS, Purdue U., 1968, PhD, 1974. Registered profl. engr. Ind., Eng. Plant engr. Guinness Brewery, Malaysia, 1967; asst. lectr. U. Malaysia, 1968-73, lectr., 1976-78; rsch. asst. Purdue U., West Lafayette, Ind., 1973-74, vis. asst. prof., 1975-76, asst. prof., 1978-81, assoc. prof., 1985-; cons. SIMTECH, West Lafayette, 1978-85, L.A. Water and Power Co., 1986-88. Contbr. articles to jours. in field. Fulbright-Hayes scholar, 1967-68; UNESCO fellow, 1969-70. Fellow Inst. Elec. Engrs. (U.K.); mem. IEEE (sr.). Avocations: gardening, fishing, reading. Office: Purdue U Dept Elec Engring 1285 Elec Engring Bldg West Lafayette IN 47907

ONG, JOHN DOYLE, lawyer; b. Uhrichsville, Ohio, Sept. 29, 1933; s. Louis Brosee and Mary Ellen (Liggett) O.; m. Mary Lee Schupp, July 20, 1957; children: John Francis Harlan, Richard Penn Blackburn, Mary Katherine Caine. BA, Ohio State U., 1954, MA, 1954; LLB, Harvard, 1957; LHD, Kent State U., 1982. Bar: Ohio 1958. Assoc. counsel B.F. Goodrich Co., Akron, 1961-66, group v.p., 1972-73, exec. v.p., 1973-74, vice chmn., 1974-75, pres., dir., 1975-77, pres., chief operating officer, dir., 1978-79, chmn. bd., pres., chief exec. officer, 1979-84, chmn. bd., chief exec. officer, 1984—; asst. to pres. Internat. B.F. Goodrich Co., Akron, 1966-69, v.p., 1969-70, pres., 1970-72; bd. dirs. Cooper Industries, Ameritech Corp., The Kroger Co., Asarco Inc., Geon Co. V.p. exploring Great Trail coun. Boy Scouts Am., 1974-77; bd. dirs. Nat. Alliance of Bus., 1981-94; trustee Mus. Arts Assn., Cleve., Bexley Hall Sem., 1974-81, Case Western Reserve U., 1980-92, Kenyon Coll., 1983-85, Hudson (Ohio) Libr. and Hist. Soc., Pres. 1971-72, Western Res. Acad., Hudson, 1975—; pres. bd. trustees, 1977—; nat. trustee Nat. Symphony Orch., 1975-83; mem. bus. adv. com. Transp. Ctr. Northwestern U., 1975-78, Carnegie-Mellon U. Grad. Sch. Indsl. Adminstrn., 1978-83; trustee U. Chgo. 1991—; chmn. Ohio Bus. Roundtable, 1994—. Mem. Ohio Bar Assn. (bd. govs. corp. counsel sect. 1962-74, chmn. 1970), Rubber Mfrs. Assn. (bd. dirs. 1974-84), Chem. Mfrs. Assn. (bd. dirs. 1988-91), Conf. Bd., Bus. Roundtable (chmn. 1992-94), Bus. Coun., Portage Country Club, Union Club, Links, Union League, Ottawa

Shooting Club, Met. Club, Rolling Rock Club, Castalia Trout Club, Phi Beta Kappa, Phi Alpha Theta. Episcopalian. Home: 230 Aurora St Hudson OH 44236-2941 Office: The B F Goodrich Co 3925 Embassy Pky Akron OH 44333-1799

ONG, TONG-MAN, microbiologist, educator; b. Tainan, Taiwan, June 9, 1935; came to U.S., 1965; s. Kar and Tsai (Tsai) Ong.; m. Shu-hui Huang, Jan. 14, 1967; children: Fiona, Kara. BS, Taiwan Normal U., Taipei, 1960; MS, Ill. State U., 1967, PhD, 1970. Faculty asst. Taiwan Normal U., Taipei, Taiwan, 1961-64; rsch. asst. Ill. State U., Normal, Ill., 1965-70; postdoctoral fellow Oak Ridge (Tenn) Nat. Lab., 1970-72; fellow Nat. Inst. Environ. Health, Rsch. Triangle Pk., N.C., 1972-77; geneticist Nat. Inst. Environ. Health, Rsch. Triangle Pk., 1977-78; vis. prof. Shanghai Med. U., China, 1986-92; adj. prof. West Va. U., Morgantown, 1985—; disting. vis. prof. Guanzhou Med. Coll., China, 1988—; microbiology sect. chief Nat. Inst. Occup. Safety & Health, Morgantown, W. Va., 1979—. Contbr. over 250 articles to profl. jours. Recipient Rsch. Fellowship Damon Runyon Rsch. Inc., 1971, '72, Achievment award Ill. State U. Alumni Assn., Normal, Ill., 1988. Mem. AAAS, Environ. Mutagen Soc., Environ. Health Inst., Sigma Xi, Phi Sigma Soc. (outstanding grad. student Ill. State U. 1968). Home: 149 Lamplighter Dr Morgantown WV 26505-8649 Office: Nat Inst Occupational Safety Health 1095 Willowdale Morgantown WV 26505-2888

ONG, WALTER JACKSON, priest, English educator, author; b. Kansas City, Mo., Nov. 30, 1912; s. Walter Jackson and Blanche Eugenia (Mense) O. AB, Rockhurst Coll., 1933; PhL, St. Louis U., 1940, AM, 1941, STL, 1948; PhD, Harvard U., 1955; various hon. degrees. Joined S.J., Roman Cath. Ch., 1935, ordained priest, 1946. Newspaper, comml. positions until, 1935; instr. English and French Regis Coll., Denver, 1941-43; asst. English St. Louis U., 1944-47, instr., 1953-54, asst. prof., 1954-57, assoc. prof., 1957-59; prof., 1959—, prof. humanities in psychiatry Sch. Medicine, 1970—, Univ. prof. humanities, 1981—, prof. emeritus, 1984—; mem. Fulbright nat. selection com., France, 1957-58, chmn., 1958; regional asso. Am. Coun. Learned Socs., 1957-66; mem. White House Task Force on Edn., 1966-67, Nat. Coun. on Humanities, 1968-74, vice chmn., 1971-74; co-chmn. adv. com. on sci., tech. and human values NEH, 1974-78; mem. Rockefeller Found. Commn. on Humanities, 1978-80; vis. prof. U. Calif., 1960; Terry lectr., Yale, 1963-64; vis. lectr. U. Poitiers, 1962; Berg prof. English N.Y. U., 1966-67; McDonald lectr. McGill U., 1967-68; Willett vis. prof. humanities U. Chgo., 1968-69; nat. Phi Beta Kappa vis. scholar, 1969-70; Lincoln lectr. Central and West Africa, 1973-74; Messenger lectr. Cornell U., 1979-80; Alexander lectr. U. Toronto, 1981; vis. prof. comparative lit. Washington U., 1983-84; Wolfson Coll. lectr. Oxford U., 1985. Author: Frontiers in American Catholicism, 1957, Ramus, Method, and the Decay of Dialogue, 1958, Ramus and Talon Inventory, 1958, Am. Cath. Crossroads, 1959, The Barbarian Within, 1962, In the Human Grain, 1967, The Presence of the Word, 1967, Rhetoric, Romance and Technology, 1971, Why Talk?, 1973, Interfaces of the Word, 1977, Fighting for Life: Contest, Sexuality, and Consciousness, 1981, Orality and Literacy, 1982, Hopkins, the Self and God, 1986, Faith and Contexts, 1992; co-author, editor: Darwin's Vision and Christian Perspectives, 1960, Knowledge and the Future of Man, 1968; editor: Petrus Ramus and Audomarus Talaeus, Collectaneae praefationes epistolae, orationes, 1969, Petrus Ramus, Scholae in liberales artes, 1970; co-editor, translator: Logic (John Milton), 1982; mem. editorial bd.: Studies in English Literature, 1962—; editorial adv. bd.: Philosophy and Rhetoric, 1967—, The English Literary Renaissance, 1969—, Manuscripta, 1957—; others; contbr. articles, chpts. learned and popular publs. Mem. adv. bd. John Simon Guggenheim Meml. Found., 1962-84; trustee Nat. Humanities Faculty, 1968-76, chmn., 1974-76. Decorated chevalier l'Ordre des Palmes Académiques (France); Guggenheim fellow, 1949-50, 51-52; fellow Ctr. Advanced Studies, Wesleyan U., Middletown, Conn., 1961-62; fellow Sch. Letters, Ind. U., 1965—; fellow Ctr. for Advanced Study in Behavioral Scis., Stanford, 1973-74. Fellow Am. Acad. Arts and Scis.; mem. AAUP, MLA (pres. 1978), Renaissance Soc. Am. (adv. coun. 1957-59), Modern Humanities Rsch. Assn., Nat. Coun. Tchrs. English, Cambridge Bibliog. Soc. (Eng.), Catholic Commn. Intellectual and Cultural Affairs (exec. com. 1962-63), Milton Soc. Am. (pres. 1967), Phi Beta Kappa, Alpha Sigma Nu. Office: Saint Louis University Saint Louis MO 63103

ONGERT, STEVEN WALTER, lawyer, mediator; b. Palm Springs, Calif., Aug. 9, 1945; m. Kathy D. Dean, July 4, 1991. BA, Hastings (Nebr.) Coll., 1972; JD, South Tex. Coll. Law, 1988. Bar: Tex. 1989, U.S. Dist. Ct. (so. dist.) Tex. 1990. Assoc. Bill De La Garza & Assocs., Houston, 1988-90; ptnr. Dean & Ongert, P.C., Houston, 1990—. Sgt. USAF, 1965-69. Mem. ABA, Houston Bar Assn., Galveston Family Law Bar Assn. (pres. 1993, 94), Assn. Trial Lawyers Am., Tex. Assn. Mediators, Coll. State Bar Tex. Avocations: fishing, collecting antiques. Office: 1000 Bay Area Blvd Ste 200 Houston TX 77058-2631

ONGMAN, JOHN WILL, lawyer; b. Chgo., July 19, 1951; s. John Warner and Helen Will (Dunbar) O.; m. Joanne Patricia Sawicki, Oct. 17, 1981. BS, Purdue U., 1972; MS, U. Ill., 1973; JD, Northwestern U., 1976. Bar: Ill. 1976, D.C. 1984, N.Y. 1990. Law clk. to Hon. Walter J. Cummings U.S. Ct. Appeals 7th cir., Chgo., 1976-77; assoc. Sidley & Austin, Chgo. and Washington, 1977-83; ptnr. Pepper, Hamilton & Scheetz, Washington, 1983—. Contbr. numerous articles to law jours. Mem. University Club of Chgo., Metropolitan Club of Washington. Office: Pepper Hamilton & Scheetz 1300 19th St NW Washington DC 20036-1609

ONKEN, GEORGE MARCELLUS, lawyer; b. Bklyn., Aug. 15, 1914; s. William Henry and Lillian Charlotte (Dawe) O.; m. Mildred Ann Tausch, Dec. 13, 1958; children: Jane Elizabeth, Nancy Catherine. AB, Princeton U., 1936; LLB, Columbia U., 1948; LLM, NYU, 1952. Bar: N.Y. 1949. Asst. to pres. Welsbach Engring. and Mgmt. Corp., Phila., 1939-43; mem. legal staff L.I. R.R., 1949-78, gen. counsel, 1963-78, v.p., 1966-78, sec., 1968-78. Bd. dirs. Orphan Asylum Soc., Bklyn., 1958—; YMCA Greater N.Y., 1963-80, Pop Warner Little League, 1976-78; bd. mgrs. Pa. R.R. br. YMCA, N.Y.C., 1957-80, chmn., 1967-80; trustee Bklyn. YWCA, 1976-92. Lt. (j.g.) USNR, 1943-46. Recipient Man of Year award YMCA, 1977; Outstanding Svc. award Bklyn. Chpt. ARC Greater N.Y., 1994. Mem. Newcomen Soc. N.Am. Republican. Episcopalian (vestry 1958-64, 76-85). Clubs: Union League (N.Y.C.), Univ. (N.Y.C.), Church (N.Y.C.), Rembrandt (Bklyn.), Heights Casino (Bklyn.), Ihpetonga (Bklyn.). Home: 215 Adams St Brooklyn NY 11201-2856

ONO, MASATOSHI, tire manufacturing executive; b. 1937. BS in Elec. Engring., Kumamoto U., 1959. With Bridgestone Tire Co. (now Bridgestone Corp.), 1959-87, dir., 1987-90, v.p., plant mgr. Kurume Plant, 1990; exec. v.p. mfg. and tech. Bridgestone/Firestone, Inc., 1991-93, CEO, 1993—. Office: Bridgestone Firestone Inc 50 Century Blvd Nashville TN 37214

ONORATO, NICHOLAS LOUIS, program director, economist; b. South Barre, Mass., Feb. 24, 1925; s. Charles and Amalia (Tartaglia) O.; m. Elizabeth Louise Settergren, July 19, 1947; children—Gary, Deborah, Nicholas, Jeffrey, Glenn, Charles, Lisa. B.S. in Pub. Relations, Boston U., 1951; M.A. in Econs, Clark U., 1952, Ph.D., 1959. Mem. faculty Becker Jr. Coll., Worcester, Mass., 1952-54; prof. econs. Worcester Poly. Inst., 1955-68, chmn. dept. econs., govt., bus., 1968-74, dir. Sch. Indsl. Mgmt., 1972-94; prof. emeritus Worcester (Mass.) Poly Inst., 1994; vis. prof. Clark U., Worcester, 1964-66; financial cons. Coz Chem. Co., Northbridge, Mass., 1959—. Contbr. to newspapers and mags. Trustee Bay State Savs. Bank, Worcester. Served with USNR, 1943-46. Mem. Am. Finance Assn., Am. Econ. Assn., Am. Accounting Assn., Phi Kappa Theta. Club: Torch (pres. Worcester 1967, 87). Home: 39 Knollwood Dr Shrewsbury MA 01545-3329 Office: Institute Rd Worcester MA 01609

ONSAGER, JEROME ANDREW, research entomologist; b. Northwood, N.D., Apr. 8, 1936; s. Alfred and Anne Marie (Kielbauch) O.; m. Bette Lynn Stanton, Aug. 16, 1958. B.S., N.D. State U., 1958, M.S., 1960, Ph.D., 1963. Research entomologist USDA Agrl. Research Service, Bozeman, Mont., 1963—. Contbr. articles on biology, ecology, population dynamics of rangeland grasshoppers to profl. jours. Fellow NSF, 1960. Mem. Entomol. Soc. Am., Entomol. Soc. Can., Orthopterist Soc., Sigma Xi, Alpha Zeta. Lutheran. Avocations: fishing; big game hunting; equestrian activities. Home: 4141 Blackwood Rd Bozeman MT 59715-9130 Office: USDA ARS Rangeland Insect Lab Bozeman MT 59717

ONSLOW FORD, GORDON MAX, painter; b. Wendover, Buckinghamshire, Eng., Dec. 26, 1912; came to U.S., 1947, naturalized, 1952; s. Max and Maud Elizabeth (Woollerton) Onslow Ford; m. Jacqueline Marie Johnson, May 5, 1941. Grad., Royal Naval Coll., Dartmouth, Eng., 1929; grad., Royal Naval Coll., Greenwich, Eng., 1930. Mem. Surrealist Group, Paris, London, N.Y.C. 1938-43. One-man shows include New Sch. for Social Rsch., N.Y.C., 1940, Nierendorf Gallery, N.Y.C., 1946, San Francisco Mus. Art, 1948, M.H. DeYoung Mus., San Francisco, 1962, San Francisco Mus., 1951, 59, 70, Oakland (Calif.) Mus., 1977, Art Gallery Greater Victoria, B.C., 1971, Samy Kinge Gallery, Paris, 1985; group shows: Paris, 1983, London, 1940, N.Y.C., 1943, L.A. County Mus., 1950, 61, 70, 87, Newport Harbor Mus., 1986, Mus. Rath, Geneva, 1987, Centro Atlantico De Arte Moderno, Gran Canaica, Spain, 1989, Laguna Art Mus., 1990, U. Calif.-Berkeley Art Mus., 1990, Pepperdine U. Art Mus., 1992, Harcourt Gallery, San Francisco, 1993, Pavillion Gallery, Munich, 1993, Brochier Gallery, Munich, 1993, Mus. Bochum, Ger., 1994, Museo de Arte Contemporáneo, Santiago, Chile, 1995; permanent collections: San Francisco Mus. Modern Art, Tate Gallery, London, M.H. deYoung Mus., Oakland Mus., Guggenheim Mus., N.Y.C., Whitney Mus. Modern Art, N.Y.C., Denver Mus., Fogg Mus., U. Mass., U. Calif-Davis, L.A. County Mus. Art, Chgo. Art Inst.; author: Toward A New Subject in Painting, 1947, Painting in the Instant, 1964, Creation, 1978, Yves Tanguy and Automatism, 1983, Insights, 1991, Ecomorphology, 1993.

ONSTEAD, RANDALL, consumer goods company executive. Pres. Randall's Food & Drug Inc., Houston, 1976—. Office: Randall's Food & Drug Inc 3663 Briarpark Dr Houston TX 77042

ONSTEAD, ROBERT R., consumer goods company executive; b. 1931. Student, North Tex. State Tchrs. Coll., 1952-54. With IBM Co., Dallas, 1954-55, Randall's Super Valu, Houston, 1955-57; v.p. Randall's #1, Inc., Houston, 1957-64, pres., 1964-66; with Randall's Food Markets, Inc., Houston, 1966—, now chmn. bd., CEO. With USAF, 1951-52. Office: Randalls Food Markets Inc 3663 Briar Park Houston TX 77042*

ONTJES, DAVID AINSWORTH, medicine and pharmacology educator; b. Lyons, Kans., July 19, 1937; s. Max S. and Elizabeth (Ainsworth) O.; m. Sherri James, Aug. 27, 1960; children: Linden F., Sarah E., Ethan A., Jason A. B.A., U. Kans., 1959; M.A., Oxford U., 1961; M.D., Harvard U., 1964. Am. Bd. Internal Medicine, sub-board endocrinology. Intern, resident Boston City Hosp., 1964-66; research assoc. NIH, Besthesda, Md., 1966-69; asst. prof. dept. medicine and pharmacology U. N.C., Chapel Hill, 1969-72, assoc. prof., 1972-76, prof., 1976—, Eunice Bernhardt Disting. prof., 1982—. Contbr. articles in field to profl. jours. Served with USPHS, 1966-69. Rhodes scholar Oxford U., 1959-61; USPHS grantee Nat. Ints. Arthritis and Metabolic Diseases, NIH, 1969-82; recipient Basic Sci. Teaching award U. N.C., 1978. Fellow ACP; mem. Endocrine Soc., Am. Soc. Clin. Investigation, Am. Soc. Pharmacology and Exptl. Therapeutics, Assn. Profs. Medicine. Republican. Presbyterian. Office: U NC Sch Medicine Dept Medicine Chapel Hill NC 27514

ONTO, JOHN, think-tank executive. Dir. Ctr. for International Business Education and Research, Washington, D.C. Office: Ctr Internat Bus Edn & Rsch Georgetown U Sch Bus Washington DC 20057-1008

ONUFROCK, RICHARD SHADE, pharmacist, researcher; b. Colorado Springs, Colo., July 5, 1934; s. Frank and Winifred Joy (Overstreet) O.; m. Karen Faye Larson, June 15, 1958 (div. 1980); children: Richard Alan (dec.), Amy Mildred. BS in Pharmacy, U. Colo., 1961; diploma, Famous Artists Schs., 1963. Registered pharmacist, Colo., Ariz., South Africa. Pharmacist Aley Drug Co., Colorado Springs, 1961-75, St. Joseph Hosp., Denver, 1976-77, Navajo Nation Health Found., Ganado, Ariz., 1977-81, Kearny (Ariz.) Kennecott-Samaritan Hosp., 1984-85, NIH, Warren G. Magnuson Clin. Ctr., Bethesda, Md., 1988—; dir. pharmacy, chief pharmacist Tintswalo Hosp., South Africa, 1981-84; pharmacist, chief pharmacist Miami (Ariz.)-Inspiration Hosp., 1985-88; instr. Coll. of Ganado, 1979-80; asst. in textbook revision and illustration U. Colo., 1961; cons. Heritage Health Care Ctr., Globe, Ariz., 1988. Illustrator Pharmacy for Nurses, 1961, Colo. Jour. of Pharmacy, 1962-64; illustrations exhibited Colo. Springs Fine Art Ctr., 1964-66, Gilpin County Art Assn., Central City, Colo., 1968-74, 1st Nat. Space Art Show, Denver, 1969. dem. precinct committeeman, 1974-76; den leader Boy Scouts Am., com. mem., 1975-76; fireman, lt. Ganado Vol. Fire Dept., 1977-81; compassionate med. missionary Nazarene Ch., Tintswalo Hosp. Gazankulu, South Africa, 1981-84;bd. dirs. Friends of Libr., Kearny, 1985-87; active Grace Episcopal Ch. Mem. Am. Pharm. Assn., Am. Soc. Hosp. Pharmacists, Washington Met. Soc. Hosp. Pharmacists, Phi Delta Chi, Delta Sigma Phi. Avocations: traveling, bicycling, hiking, skiing, computers. Home: 4831 36th St NW 202 Washington DC 20008 Office: NIH Clin Ctr Pharm Dept Bldg 10 Rm 1N257 9000 Rockville Pike Bethesda MD 20892

OOLIE, SAM, investment company executive; b. N.Y.C., Aug. 11, 1936; s. Bernadt S. and Rose (Moyel) O.; m. Marjorie R. Oolie, Dec. 3, 1961; children: Janis, Caroline, Tara. BS in Metallurgy, MIT, 1958; MBA, Harvard U., 1961. Chmn. Food Concepts, Inc., Rutherford, N.J., 1962-85; pres. CFC Venture Capital Corp., Fairfield, N.J., 1984-90; chmn. Oolie Enterprises, Fairfield, 1985—; vice chmn. Am. Mobile, Inc., Secaucus, N.J., 1986-89; chmn. The Nostalgia Network, N.Y.C., 1987-90, New Thermal Corp., Keasbey, N.J., 1991—; chmn.; CEO NoFire Tech., Inc., Upper Saddle River, N.J., 1995—; bd. dirs. Avesis, Inc., Phoenix, Comverse Tech., N.Y.C., Noise Cancellation Tech., Stamford, Conn., PNF Inds., Inc. Saddle Brook, N.J., Wayfinder, Inc., Chestnut, N.Y. Mem. exec. com. State of N.J.-Israel Commn., 1989—; commr. Essex County Improvement Authority, 1987-88; trustee Coun. Jewish Fedns., 1986—; bd. govs. Haifa U., 1986-90, 93—; trustee Garden State Cancer Ctr., 1989—, Beth Israel Med. Ctr., 1990—, Assn. Reform Zionists Am., 1990—, Am. Joint Distbn. Com., 1990—; pres. United Jewish Fedn. Met. West N.J., 1988-90; vice chmn. United Jewish Appeal, 1986—; chmn. Beth Israel Health Care Found., 1993—. Recipient Gates of Jerusalem award Boys Town of Jerusalem, 1990, Israel 40th Ann. medal State of Israel Bonds, 1988. Mem. World Bus. Coun., Harvard Club of N.Y., Greenbrook Country Club. Avocations: golf, numismatics. Office: One Passaic Ave Fairfield NJ 07004-3815

OOMMEN, GEORGE, architect, painter, athletic facilities planning consultant, educator; b. Munnar, India, Feb. 27, 1942; came to U.S., 1968; s. George and Achy (Abraham) O.; m. Laurie Jeanne; children—Mia, Christie, Sarah. B.Arch., Delhi U., 1964; M. Arch. in Urban Design, Harvard U., 1970. Registered architect, planner. Prin., Khanna, Oommen, Jain, New Delhi, India, 1964-65, George Oommen & Assocs., Mepral, Kerala, India, 1964-67; archtl. designer Ewing Miller Assocs., Terre Haute, Ind., 1967-68; project planner Harvard U., Cambridge, Mass., 1972-79; planning officer, 1972-79, adj. asst. to v.p. adminstrn., 1979-84, critic Grad. Sch. Design, 1973-74, faculty Grad. Sch. Design and Continuing Edn., 1983—, sr. property check. officer Planning Group, 1984—; faculty Boston Archtl. Ctr., 1970-73, Babson Exec. Edn. Program, 1985-86; cons. infield. author: Program for Athletic Facilities, 1975; urban designer various jours., Eng., Greece, Italy, India, Japan, U.S.A.; creator first outdoor fine tuned track McCurdy Track, Harvard U., 1984. Exec. council Harvard/Radcliffe Child Care Council, Cambridge, 1974; mem. Gov.'s Task Force Commonwealth of Mass., 1975; athletic cons. Long Island U., Franklin & Marshall Coll., Drew U., Babson Coll., Western Mont. Sports Medicine & Fitness Ctr., DePaul U., Assumption Coll., St. Marks Sch., Mansfield U., The Nutrasweet Co., Hamline U., Adelphi U. Exhbns. include Wellbridge Ctr., Boston, 1994, Harvard Club of Boston, 1994, Dru Arstark, N.Y.C., 1994, Kresge Gallery, Boston, 1994, Rocco's Charles St. South, Boston, 1994. Recipient award of distinction for exhibit Internat. Conf. Architects, India, 1964, Cert. of Merit, Winthrop Housing Design Competition, Boston, 1975, Athletic Bus. Facility of Merit Award, 1987, 88 89, 90, Preservation Honor award Nat. Trust Hist. Preservation, 1987; John D. Rockefeller III Found. grantee, 1969. Mem. AIA (assoc.), Am. Inst. Cert. Planners, Am. Planning Assn., Am. Inst. Planners, Boston Soc. Architects, Mass. State Assn. Architects, Indian Inst. Architects (assoc.). Clubs: Harvard (Boston) Harvard Varsity (hon.) (Cambridge). Office: Harvard Planning Group 912 Holyoke Ctr 1350 Massachusetts Ave Cambridge MA 02138-3846

OOMS, VAN DOORN, economist; b. Chgo., Oct. 29, 1934; s. Casper William and Ruth P. (Miller) O.; m. Theodora J. Parfit, June 17, 1961; children: Katrina, Alex, Tamara. BA summa cum laude, Amherst Coll., 1956, LHD (hon.), 1981; BA with 1st class honors, Oxford (Eng.) U., 1958, MA, 1962; M.A., Yale U., 1960, Ph.D., 1965. Lectr. Yale U., 1962, asst. prof. econs. to 1968; assoc. prof. Swarthmore Coll., 1968, prof., to 1978; chief economist U.S. Senate Budget Com., Washington, 1977-78; asst. dir. for econ. policy U.S. Office Mgmt. and Budget, Washington, 1978-81; chief economist U.S. House Budget Com., Washington, 1981-91, exec. dir. for policy, 1989-91; sr. v.p., dir. rsch. Com. for Econ. Devel., Washington, 1991—. Rhodes scholar, Oxford U., 1958; Ford Found. Dissertation fellow Yale U., 1965. Office: 2000 L St NW Ste 700 Washington DC 20036-4907

OORT, ABRAHAM HANS, meteorologist, researcher, educator; b. Leiden, The Netherlands, Sept. 2, 1934; came to U.S., 1961; s. Jan Hendrik and Johanna Maria (Graadt Van Roggen) O.; m. Bineke Pel, May 20, 1961; children: Pieter Jan, Michiel, Sonya. MS, MIT, 1963; PhD in Meteorology, U. Utrecht, The Netherlands, 1964. Rsch. meteorologist Koninklyk Nederlands Meteorological Instituut, De Bilt, The Netherlands, 1964-66; rsch. meteorologist Geophysical Fluid Dynamics Lab/NOAA, Washington, 1966-68; rsch. meteorologist Geophysical Fluid Dynamics Lab/NOAA, Princeton, N.J., 1968-77, sr. rsch. meteorologist, 1977—; prof. dept. geological and geophysical scis., Princeton U., 1971—. Author: Physics of Climate, 1992; contbr. monographs in field. 2nd lt. Netherlands Air Force, 1959-61. NATO sci. fellow MIT, Cambridge, 1961-63; 10th Victor P. Starr Meml. lectr. MIT, 1988; recipient Gold medal U.S. Dept. Commerce, Washington, 1979. Fellow N.Y. Acad. Scis., Am. Meteorol. Soc. (Jule G. Charney award 1993), Royal Meteorol. Soc.; mem. Am. Geophys. Union. Democrat. Avocations: sculpture, shiatsu, meditation. Office: Princeton U NOAA Box 308 Princeton NJ 08542

OPALA, MARIAN P(ETER), state supreme court justice; b. Lódz, Poland, Jan. 20, 1921. BSB in Econs., Oklahoma City U., 1957, JD, 1953, LLD, 1981; LLM, NYU, 1968; HHD, Okla. Christian U. Sci. & Arts, 1981. Bar: Okla. 1953, U.S. Supreme Ct. 1970. Asst. county atty. Oklahoma County, 1953-56; practiced law Oklahoma City, 1956-60, 65-67; referee Okla. Supreme Ct., Oklahoma City, 1960-65; prof. law Oklahoma City U. Sch. Law, 1965-69; asst. to presiding justice Supreme Ct. Okla., 1967-68; administrv. dir. Cts. Okla., 1968-77; presiding judge Okla. State Indsl. Ct., 1977-78; judge Workers Compensation Ct., 1978; justice Okla. Supreme Ct., 1978—, chief justice, 1991-93; adj. prof. law Okla. City U., 1962—, U. Okla. Coll. Law, 1969—; prof. law U. Tulsa Law Sch., 1982—; mem. permanent faculty Am. Acad. Jud. Edn., 1970—; mem. NYU Inst. Jud. Adminstrn.; mem. faculty Nat. Jud. Coll., U. Nev., 1975—; chmn. Nat. Conf. State Ct. Adminstrs., 1976-77; mem. Nat. Conf. Commrs. on Uniform State Laws, 1982—. Co-author: Oklahoma Court Rules for Perfecting a Civil Appeal, 1969. Recipient Herbert Harley award Am. Judicature Soc., 1977, Disting. Alumni award Oklahoma City U., 1979, NSDAR Americanism medal, 1984, ABA/Am. Law Inst. Harrison Tweed Spl. Merit award, 1987, Humanitarian award Nat. Conf. of Christians and Jews, 1991; named Outstanding Okla. Pub. Adminstr., Am. Soc. Pub. Adminstrn., 1978. Mem. ABA (edn. com. appellate judges conf. 1984-93), Okla. Bar Assn (Earl Sneed Continuing Legal Edn. award 1988), Okla. County Bar Assn. Am. Soc. Legal History, Oklahoma City Title Lawyers Assn., Am. Judicature Soc. (bd. dirs. 1988-92), Am. Law Inst. (elected), Order of Coif, Phi Delta Phi (Oklahoma City Alumni award), Adminstrn. Conf. U.S. Office: Okla Supreme Ct State Capitol Rm 238 Oklahoma City OK 73105

OPARA, EMMANUEL CHUKWUEMEKA, biochemistry educator; b. Lagos, Nigeria, July 4, 1951; came to U.S., 1984; s. Eugene Uba and Caroline (Adanma) O.; m. Clarice Adaku Njemanze, Mar. 28, 1980; children: Ogechi, Chiedu, Chukwuka, Ikenna. BS with honors, U. Nigeria, 1976; MS, U. Surrey, Eng., 1980; PhD, U. London, 1983. Assoc. Royal Coll. of Pathologists. Inspecting officer Food and Drug Adminstrn., Lagos, 1977-78; clin. biochemist Epsom (Eng.) Hosp. Labs., 1978-81; teaching asst. Chelsea Coll., London, 1981-83; rsch. fellow Mayo Clinic, Rochester, Minn., 1984-86; vis. fellow NIH, Bethesda, Md., 1986-88; rsch. assoc. Duke U. Med. Ctr., Durham, N.C., 1988-89; asst. prof. Duke U. Med. Ctr., 1989—. Contbr. articles to numerous scientific and med. jours. Com. chairperson Holy Cross Ch., Durham, 1992. WHO fellow, Geneva, 1984; Fogarty Internat. fellow, Bethesda, 1986; recipient Cystic Fibrosis Found. grant, 1990, Am. Diabetes Assn. grant, 1993. Mem. Am. Fedn. for Clin. Rsch., Am. Diabetes Assn., Am. Pancreatic Assn., Assn. Clin. Biochemists (U.K.), Biochemistry Soc. Democrat. Roman Catholic. Avocations: tennis, walking, current affairs, reading, television. Home: 2 Scarsdale Pl Durham NC 27707 Office: Duke U Med Ctr Dept of Surgery PO Box 3065 Durham NC 27710

OPARIL, SUZANNE, cardiologist, educator, researcher; b. Elmira, N.Y., Apr. 10, 1941; d. Stanley and Anna (Penkova) O. AB, Cornell U., 1961; MD, Columbia U., 1965. Diplomate Am. Bd. Internal Medicine. Intern in medicine Presbyn. Hosp., N.Y.C., 1965-66; sr. asst. resident in medicine Mass. Gen. Hosp., Boston, 1967-68, clin. and rsch. fellow in medicine, cardiac unit, 1968-71; asst. prof. medicine Med. Sch., U. Chgo., 1971-75, assoc. prof., 1975-77; assoc. prof. dept. medicine U. Ala., Birmingham, 1977-81, asst. prof. physiology and biophysics, 1980-81, assoc. prof., 1981—, prof. medicine, 1981—, dir. vascular biology and hypertension program, 1985—; mem. vis. faculty Nat. High Blood Pressure Edn. Program, 1974—, Joint Nat. Com. on Detection, Evaluation and Treatment High Blood Pressure, 1991; mem. bd. sci. advisors Sterling Drug Inc., 1988-91; lectr. in field; Selkurt lectr. Ind. U. Sch. Medicine, 1994; hon. prof. Peking Union Med. Coll., 1994. Author books on hypertension; editor Am. Jour. Med. Scis., 1984-94; associate editor Hypertension, 1979-83, mem. editl. bd., 1984—; assoc. editor Am. Jour. Physiology-Renal, 1989-91; mem. editl. bd. Jour. Hypertension, 1989—; contbr. over 300 articles to profl. jours., chpts. to books. Recipient Young Investigator award Internat. Soc. Hypertension, 1979, ann. award Med. Coll. Pa., 1984; fellow Am. Coll. Cardiology, 1992. Fellow Am. Coll. Cardiology; mem. Am. Heart Assn. (council Nat. Com. on human rights 1992, chmn. com. advise Dept. Def. 1993 Breast Cancer Rsch. Program), AAAS, Endocrine Soc., Inter-Am. Soc. Hypertension, Am. Soc. Hypertension (pub. policy com. 1990—, sci. program com. 1990-92), Assn. for Women in Sci., Am. Heart Assn. (coun. for high blood pressure rsch., 1973—, exec. com. 1985-90, vice chmn. 1986, coun. on basic scis. 1978—, mem.-at-large, exec. com. 1979-81, mem.-at-large bd. dirs. 1992, chmn. Louis B. Katz Prize com. 1984-86, chmn., 1988-90, chmn. budget com. 1990-91, v.p. Ala. affiliate 1986-87, pres.-elect Ala. affiliate 1987-88, 93-94, pres. Ala. affiliate 1988-89, nat. pres.-elect 1993-94, nat. pres. 1994—, Lewis K. Dahl Meml. Lectr. 1993), Am. Physiol. Soc. (clin. physiology sect. 1990—), Am. Soc. for Clin. Investigation (sec.-treas. 1983-86), Soc. Exptl. Biology and Medicine (councillor 1993—), So. Soc. for Clin. Investigation (Founder's award 1995), Assn. Am. Physicians, Am. Fedn. for Clin. Rsch. (midwest councillor 1974-75, nat. councillor 1975-78, sec.-treas. 1978-80, pres. 1981-82), Phi Beta Kappa, Sigma Xi, Alpha Omega Alpha (mem. nat. bd. dirs., dir.-at-large 1991, treas. 1993). Avocations: horseback riding, tennis, hiking, cooking. Office: U Ala Sch Medicine 1034 Zeigler Research Bldg Birmingham AL 35294

OPDYCKE, LEONARD EMERSON, educator, publisher; b. Boston, May 22, 1929; s. Leonard and Frances (Prescott) O.; m. Susan Wolcott, 1951 (div.); children: Susan, Deborah, Margot; m. Jeanne Bernhard, 1968 (div.); children: Sarah, Frances; m. Sandra S. Auchincloss, 1976. BA, Harvard U., 1951; MA, U. Rochester, 1965. Tchr. Southfield Sch., Shreveport, L.A., 1952-53, Dedham County Day, Dedham, Mass., 1953-56, Harley Sch., Rochester, N.Y., 1956-64; dir. Poughkeepsie (N.Y.) Day Sch., 1965-72; chair English dept. Rhinebeck (N.Y.) High Sch., 1974-77; adj. prof. of English i Marist Coll., Poughkeepsie, N.Y., 1977-84, 93-95. Editor, pub. WWI Aero, 1961—; pub. Skyways, 1987—. Mem. Phi Beta Kappa. Avocations: building aircraft, linguistics, education. Home and Office: 15 Crescent Rd Poughkeepsie NY 12601

OPEKA, JOHN FRANK, utility executive, electrical engineer; b. Forest City, Pa., Nov. 9, 1940; s. Frank Carl and Albina (Chodorwski) O.; m. Jacqueline Marie Fiorillo, Oct. 25, 1969; children—Jennifer, Janel. B.S.E.E., Pa. State U., 1967; M.B.A., Rensselaer Poly. Inst., 1982; P.M.D., Harvard Bus. Sch., 1984. Project engr. Combustion Engring., Windsor, Conn., 1967-70; asst. sta. supt. Millstone Point, Northeast Utilities, Waterford, Conn., 1977-78, sta. supt., 1978-80, systems supt. nuclear ops. Northeast Utilities, Berlin, Conn., 1980-81, v.p. nuclear ops., 1981-85, sr. v.p. nuclear engring and ops., 1985-86, exec. v.p. engring ops., 1986—; chmn. NEIL Engring.

Adv. Commn., Bermuda, 1984-86; chmn. Analysis and Engring. Industry Rev. Group, Inst. Nuclear Power Ops., Atlanta, 1984-86. Bd. dirs. Thames Sci. Ctr., New London, Conn., 1984—, pres. bd. 1988—, Opportunities Industrialization Ctr., New London, 1984. Mem. Am. Nuclear Soc. Served to lt. USN, 1962-67. Republican. Roman Catholic. Club: Christ the King Men's (Old Lyme, Conn.). Office: NE Utilities PO Box 270 Hartford CT 06141-0270

OPEL, JOHN R., business machines company executive; b. Kansas City, Mo., Jan. 5, 1925; s. Norman J. and Esther (Roberts) O.; m. Julia Carole Stout, Dec. 28, 1953; children: Robert, Nancy, Julia, Mary, John. AB, Westminster Coll., 1948; MBA, U. Chgo., 1949. With IBM Corp., Armonk, N.Y., 1949—, salesman, various mgmt. positions, 1949-66, v.p. 1966-68, mem. mgmt. com., 1967, v.p. corp. finance and planning, 1968-69, sr. v.p. finance and planning, 1969-72, group exec. data processing group, 1972-74, dir., 1972-94, pres., 1974-83, chief exec. officer, 1981-85, chmn., 1983-86, chmn. exec. com., 1986-93, ret. chmn., 1993; bd. dirs. Prudential Ins. Co. Am. Trustee, Westminster Coll. Served with U.S. Army, 1943-45. Mem. Bus. Coun., Coun. on Fgn. Rels. Office: IBM Corp 590 Madison Ave New York NY 10022-2505

OPELA, MARIAN MEADE, principal, consultant; b. Sharon, Conn., July 5, 1941; d. Jerry Roselle and Ruth Bean (Wills) Meade; m. H. Terry Opela, July 1, 1967; children: Stephen, Glenn, H. Kevin. BA, Middlebury Coll., 1962; MEd, SUNY, Buffalo, 1968; postgrad., Coll. of St. Rose, 1993—. Cert. tchr. social studies, N.Y.; cert. SAS. Tchr. Cheektowaga (N.Y.) Ctrl. High Sch., 1963-67; nursery sch. dir. Magic Dragon Pre-Sch., Stockport, N.Y., 1979-81; tchr. Acad. of the Holy Names, Albany, N.Y., 1981-84; tchr. Ichabod Crane Ctrl. Sch., Valatie, 1984-94, strategic planning coord., 1991-94; asst. prin. Ravena (N.Y.)-Coeymans-Selkirk Mid. Sch., 1994—; cons. N.Y. State Ed. Dept., Albany, 1990, 92, 94. Lay leader, speaker North Chatham (N.Y.) Meth. Ch., 1990—; del. Columbia County Environ. Mgmt. Coun., Hudson, N.Y., 1984-92; candidate for Kinderhook Town Bd., 1991. Mem. N.Y. State Coun. for Social Studies, Kinderhook Rep. Club, Nat. Campers and Hikers Assn. (exec. bd. 1968-93, Nat. plaque 1980), Delta Kappa Gamma, Phi Delta Kappa. Avocations: camping, hiking, reading, mentoring. Home: 309 Rt 28 B Valatie NY 12184-9782

OPHULS, MARCEL, film director and producer; b. Frankfurt, Germany, Nov. 1, 1927; came to U.S., 1947, naturalized, 1950; s. Max and Hilda (Wall) Oppenheimer; m. Regine Ackermann, Aug. 21, 1956; children: Catherine Julie, Danielle, Josane Dorothee. Student, Occidental Coll., Los Angeles, 1946-49; Licencie es Letters, U. Paris, 1950; DArts (hon.), Columbia Coll., Chgo., 1983. Asst. dir. films France, 1951-56; tchr. film Princeton U., 1973-74, also sr. vis. fellow council humanities and mem. adv. council sociology dept. Program dir. TV and radio plays, Sudwestfunk, Fed. Republic of Germany, 1956-60; dir. feature films, Paris, 1961-65; producer, dir. documentary films, 1966—; dir.: (sketch) Love at Twenty, 1961, (films) including Banana Peel, 1963, Fire at Will, 1964, Munich, or Peace in Our Time, 1966, The Sorrow and The Pity, 1971, America Revisited, 1972, A Sense of Loss, 1972, The Memory of Justice, 1976, Kortner Geschichten, 1980, Yorktown, The Sense of A Battle, 1982, Hotel Terminus: The Life and Times of Klaus Barbie, 1988 (Acad. award best documentary feature 1989), November Days, 1990; The Troubles We've Seen, 1993, contbg. editor Am. Film. Served with AUS, 1946-47. Decorated knight of arts and letters French Ministry Culture; recipient film and TV awards including Best Documentary award, 1988, award Brit. Acad., 1972, 88, Best Documentary French Authors' Soc., 1994, Achievement award Acad. of Motion Pictures, 1995; MacArthur fellow, 1991. Mem. German Acad. Arts, French Authors Guild, French Dirs. Guild, Am. Acad. Arts and Scis. Address: 10 Rue Ernest Deloison, Neuilly-sur-Seine France *I believe that individuals shape history, but are also shaped by it.*

OPIE, WILLIAM ROBERT, retired metallurgical engineer; b. Butte, Mont., Apr. 3, 1920; s. Ellison Stuart and Myrtle (Williams) O.; m. Constance E. Kickuth, Oct. 14, 1944; children: Lyle Margaret, Guy William. B.S. Mont. Sch. Mines, 1942, M.E. (hon.), 1965; S.c.D., MIT, 1949, student, Advanced Mgmt. Program, Harvard U., 1967; S.c.D. (hon.), Mont. Coll. Mineral Sci. and Tech., 1980. Foundry metallurgist Wright Aero Corp., Paterson, N.J., 1942-45; research asso. MIT, Cambridge, 1946-48; research metallurgist Am. Smelting and Refining, Perth Amboy, N.J., 1948-50; research supr. Nat. Lead Co., Sayreville, N.J., 1950-60; pres. Amax Base Metals Research & Devel., Inc., Carteret, N.J., 1960-85; cons., 1985—. Contbr. articles to profl. jours. Served with U.S. Navy, 1945-46. Fellow AIME, Am. Soc. Metals; mem. Nat. Acad. Engring. Patentee in field. Home: 119 Crawfords Corner Rd Holmdel NJ 07733-1947

OPITZ, JOACHIM LUDWIG, physiatrist; b. Gottingen, Germany, 1927. MD, Georg August U., Gottingen, 1953. Diplomate Am. Bd. Physical Medicine and Rehabilitation (exec. dir., sec.). Intern Rochester Gen. Hosp., 1954-55, resident in internal medicine, 1955-56; resident in internal medicine Mayo Clin., Rochester, 1957-60, resident in phys. and rehab. medicine, 1961-63, cons. in phys. and rehab. medicine, 1963-68, instr., 1968-73, asst. prof., 1973-79, assoc. prof., 1979-89, prof., 1989-92, prof. emeritus, 1992—. Office: Norwest Ctr 21 1st St SW Ste 674 Rochester MN 55902*

OPITZ, JOHN MARIUS, clinical geneticist, pediatrician; b. Hamburg, Germany, Aug. 15, 1935; came to U.S., 1950, naturalized, 1957; s. Friedrich and Erica Maria (Quadt) O.; m. Susan O. Lewis; children: Leigh, Teresa, John, Chrisanthi, Emma. BA, State U. Iowa, 1956, MD, 1959; DSc (hon.), Mont. State U., 1983; MD (hon.), U. Kiel, Fed. Republic of Germany, 1986. Diplomate Am. Bd. Pediatrics, Am. Bd. Med. Genetics. Intern, State U. Iowa Hosp., 1959-60, resident in pediatrics, 1960-61; resident and chief resident in pediatrics U. Wis. Hosp., Madison, 1961-62; fellow in pediatrics and med. genetics U. Wis., 1962-64, asst. prof. med. genetics and pediatrics, 1964-69, assoc. prof., 1969-72, prof., 1972-79; dir. Wis. Clin. Genetics Ctr., 1974-79; clin. prof. med. genetics and pediatrics U. Wash., Seattle, 1979—; adj. prof. medicine, biology, history and philosophy, vet. rsch. and vet. sci. Mont. State U., Bozeman, 1979-94, McKay lectr., 1992, Univ. prof. med. humanities MSU. Bozeman, 1994—; adj. prof. pediatrics, med. genetics U. Wis., Madison, 1979—, Class of 1947 Disting. prof., U. of Wis., 1992; coordinator Shodair Mont. Regional Genetic Svcs. Program, Helena, 1979-82; chmn. dept. med. genetics Shodair Children's Hosp., Helena, 1983-94; dir. Found. Devel. and Med. Genetics, Helena, Mont.; Farber lectr. Soc. Pediatric Pathology, 1987; Joseph Garfunkel lectr. So. Ill. U., Springfield, 1987, McKay lectr. Mont. State U., 1992; Warren Wheeler vis. prof. Columbus (Ohio) Children's Hospital, 1987. Editor, author 13 books; founder, editor in chief Am. Jour. Med. Genetics, 1977—; mng. editor European Jour. Pediatrics, 1977-85; contbr. numerous articles on clin. genetics. Chair Mont. Com. for Humanities, 1991. Recipient Found of Bethesda award for excellence in mental retardation rsch. Bethesda Luth. Home, 1988, Med. Alumni Citation U. Wis., 1989, Col. Harlan Sanders Lifetime Achievement award for work in the field of genetic scis. March of Dimes. Fellow Am. Coll. Med. Genetics (founder); mem. German Acad. Scientists Leopoldina, Am. Soc. Human Genetics, Am. Pediatric Soc., Soc. Pediatric Rsch., Am. Bd. Med. Genetics, Birth Defects Clin. Genetic Soc., Am. Inst. Biol. Scis., Am. Soc. Zoologists, AAAS, Teratology Soc., Genetic Soc. Am., European Soc. Human Genetics, Soc. Study Social Biology, Am. Acad. Pediatrics, German Soc. Pediatrics (hon.), Western Soc. Pediatrics Rsch., Italian Soc. Med. Genetics, Israel Soc. Genetics (hon.), Russian Soc. Med. Genetics (hon.), So. Africa Soc. Med. Genetics (hon.), Japanese Soc. Human Genetics (hon.), Sigma Xi. Democrat. Roman Catholic. Home: 2180 Lime Kiln St Helena MT 59601-5871

OPOTOWSKY, MAURICE LEON, newspaper editor; b. New Orleans, Dec. 13, 1931; s. Sol and Fannie (Latter) O.; m. Madeleine Duhamel, Feb. 28, 1959 (dec.); children: Didier Sol Duhamel, Joelle Duhamel, Arielle Duhamel (dec.); m. Bonnie Feibleman, May 4, 1991. Student, Tulane U., 1949-51; B.A. cum laude, Williams Coll., 1953. Reporter Berkshire Eagle, Pittsfield, Mass., 1951-53; pub. Sea Coast Echo, Bay St. Louis, Miss., 1953-54; reporter U.P.I., 1956-62; feature editor Newsday, Ronkonkoma, N.Y., 1962-64; Suffolk day editor Newsday, 1964-65, Nassau night editor, 1965-67, nat. editor, 1967-70, Suffolk editor, 1970-72; dir. L.I. Mag., 1972; day editor Press-Enterprise, Riverside, Calif., 1973-84, mng. editor features/adminstrn., 1984-87, sr. mng. editor, 1987-92, mng. editor, 1992—; chief N.Y. State

Syndicate Service, 1961-74; mem. Calif. Freedom of Info. Exec. Com., sec., 1979-80, treas., 1980-81, v.p., 1981-82, pres., 1982-83. Trustee Harbor Country Day Sch., 1970-72; bd. dirs. Calif. Newspaper Editor Conf. Bd., 1978-83; mem. Smithtown (N.Y.) Hunt, 1970-73, West Hills Hunt, 1976-80, Santa Fe Hunt, Whip, 1985—; co-chmn. Calif. Bench-Bar Media Com.; mem. adv. coun. dept. comm. Calif. State U., Fullerton, 1995—. Served with AUS, 1954-56. Mem. AP News Execs. Calif. (chmn. 1986-87), Calif. 1st Amendment Coalition (pres., treas.), Calif. Soc. Newspaper Editors (bd. dirs., vice chmn. steering com. 1983), AP Mng. Editors Assn., Am. Soc. Newspaper Editors. Office: Press Enterprise Co 3512 14th St Riverside CA 92501-3878

OPOTOWSKY, STUART BERGER, holding company executive; b. N.Y.C., Feb. 23, 1935; s. Rubin S. and Rebecca (Sapolin) O.; m. Enid Berk, June 27, 1959 (div. Apr. 1972); children: Peter, Catherine; m. Barbara Berger, Aug. 3, 1972; 1 child, Sasha. BBA, Wayne State U., 1957, LLB, 1962. Bar: Mich. 1963, Calif. 1965, N.Y. 1972; CPA, Mich. Gen. tax counsel Norton Simon Inc., N.Y.C., 1964-76; ptnr. Phillips Nizer Benjamin Krim & Ballon, N.Y.C., 1976-80; gen. tax counsel The Penn Cen. Corp., N.Y.C., 1980-82; ptnr. Feit & Ahrens, N.Y.C., 1982-87; v.p. tax Loews Corp., N.Y.C., 1987—; adj. prof. law NYU, N.Y.C., 1975-85. Mem. ABA, N.Y. State Bar Assn. Office: Loews Corp 1 Park Ave New York NY 10016

OPPEDAHL, JOHN FREDRICK, newspaper editor; b. Duluth, Minn., Nov. 9, 1944; s. Walter H. and Lucille (Hole) O.; m. Alison Owen, 1975 (div. 1983); m. Gillian Coyro, Feb. 14, 1987; 1 child, Max. B.A., U. Calif., Berkeley, 1967; M.S., Columbia U., 1968. Reporter San Francisco Examiner, 1967; reporter, asst. city editor Detroit Free Press, 1968-75, city editor, 1975-80, exec. city editor, 1981, exec. news editor, 1981-82, asst. mng. editor, 1983; nat. editor Dallas Times Herald, 1983-85, asst. mng. editor, 1985-87; mng. editor/news L.A. Herald Examiner, 1987-89; mng. editor Ariz. Republic, Phoenix, 1989-93; exec. editor Phoenix Newspapers, 1993—. Mem. Am. Soc. Newspaper Editors, AP Mng. Editors. Office: Phoenix Newspapers Inc 120 E Van Buren St Phoenix AZ 85004-2227

OPPEL, RICHARD ALFRED, newspaper executive; b. Newark, Jan. 30, 1943; s. Alfred William and Jane Genevieve (Owen) O.; m. Carol Freeman Van Aken, Apr. 1, 1967; children: Richard Alfred, Shelby Reid. B.A. in Polit. Sci., U. South Fla. Reporter Tampa Tribune, Fla., 1963-65; newsman, corr., chief bur. AP, Tallahassee, Tampa, Miami and Detroit, 1965-76; assoc. editor Detroit Free Press, 1976-77; exec. editor, v.p. Tallahassee Democrat, 1977-78; v.p. Charlotte (N.C.) Observer, 1978-93; editor Charlotte News, 1985-87; chief Washington bur. Knight-Ridder Newspapers, Washington, 1993—. Pres. N.C. First Amendment Found. Served with USMCR, 1960-65. Recipient Disting. Alumni award U. South Fla.; named Editor of Yr. Nat. Press Found., 1987, Ralph McGill Lectr. U. Ga., 1992. Mem. N.C. Press Assn. (pres. 1992-93), Am. Soc. Newspaper Editors. Episcopalian. Avocations: long distance running, hunting, fishing. Office: Knight-Ridder 529 14th St NW Washington DC 20045-1000

OPPENHEIM, ALAN VICTOR, electrical engineering educator; b. N.Y.C., Nov. 11, 1937; s. Sydney and Dorothy (Arenz) O.; m. Phyllis Arnold, June 20, 1964; children: Justine Ruth, Jason Philip. S.B., MIT, 1961, S.M., 1961, S.c.D., 1964; D (hon.), Tel Aviv U., 1995. Asst. prof. elec. engring. MIT, 1964-69, assoc. prof. dept. elec. engring. and computer scis., 1969-76, prof. dept. elec. engring. and computer sci., 1976-90, Disting. prof. elec. engring., 1990—; staff scientist Lincoln Lab., 1967-69, assoc. head data systems div., 1978-80; cons. Lincoln Lab., Atlantic Aerospace Inc., Sanders Assocs., Inc. Co-author: Digital Signal Processing, 1975, Signals and Systems, 1983, Discrete-Time Signal Processing, 1989, others; editor: Applications of Digital Signal Processing, 1978, (with others) Advanced Topics in Signal Processing, 1988; contbr. articles to profl. jours. Guggenheim fellow, 1972-73. Fellow IEEE (Edn. medal 1988, other awards); mem. Nat. Acad. Engring., Sigma Xi, Eta Kappa Nu, Tau Beta Pi. Office: MIT Dept Electric Engring & Computer Sci 50 Vassar St Cambridge MA 02139-3594

OPPENHEIM, ANTONI KAZIMIERZ, mechanical engineer; b. Warsaw, Poland, Aug. 11, 1915; came to U.S., 1948, naturalized, 1954; s. Tadeusz and Zuzanna (Zuckerwar) O.; m. Lavinia Stephens, July 18, 1945; 1 dau., Terry Ann. Diploma in Engring., Warsaw Inst. Tech., London, 1943; PhD in Engring., U. London, 1945; diploma of Imperial Coll., 1945; DSc, U. London, 1976; Dr. Honoris Causa, U. Poitiers, France, 1981, Tech. U., Warsaw, 1989. Registered profl. engr., Calif. Research asst. City and Guilds Coll., 1942-48, lectr., 1946-48; asst. prof. mech. engring. Stanford U., 1948-50; faculty U. Calif. at Berkeley, 1950—, prof. mech. engring., 1958-86, Miller prof., 1961-62, prof. emeritus, 1986—; vis. prof. Sorbonne, Paris, 1960-61, U. Poitiers, France, 1973, 80; staff cons. Shell Devel. Co., 1952-60. Editor-in-chief: Acta Astronautica, 1974-79; contbr. articles to profl. jours., also monographs. Chmn. Heat Transfer and Fluid Mechanics Inst., 1958; IAA Com. on Gasdynamics of Explosions 1968—; organizer Internat. Colloquia on Gas Dynamics of Explosions and Reactive Systems, 1967, 69, 71, 73, 75, 77, 79, 81, 83; mem. NASA, adv. com. fluid mechanics, 1963-69. Fellow Imperial Coll., 1995; recipient Water Arbitration prize Inst. Mech. Engrs., 1948, Numa Manson medal Inst. for Dynamics of Explosions and Reactive Sys., 1981, Dioniz Smolenski medal Polish Acad. Scis., 1987, Alfred C. Egerton medal The Combustion Inst., 1988, citation U. Calif., Berkeley, 1988. Fellow Am. Rocket Soc. (nat. dir. 1963-62, founder, pres. No. Calif. sect. 1957), ASME (hon. mem.1989, chmn. profl. conf. 1958, program chmn. San Francisco 1959-60, hon. 1989), Am. Inst. Aeros. and Astronautics (Pendray award 1966); mem. AIAA, Soc. Automotive Engrs., Internat. Acad. Astronautics, Nat. Acad. Engring., Am. Phys. Soc., Sigma Xi, Psi Tau Sigma, Tau Beta Psi. Spl. research compressible fluid flow, gas turbines and internal combustion engines, heat transfer, combustion, detonation and blast waves. Home: 54 Norwood Ave Berkeley CA 94707-1119

OPPENHEIM, DAVID JEROME, musician, educational administrator; b. Detroit, Apr. 13, 1922; s. Louis and Julia (Nurko) O.; m. Judy Holliday, 1948; 1 child, Jonathan; m. Ellen Adler, Apr. 14, 1957; children: Sara, Thomas; m. Pat Jaffe, June 13, 1987. Student, Julliard Sch. Music, 1939-40; MusB, U. Rochester, 1943. Dir. Masterwork div. Columbia Records, N.Y.C., 1950-59; producer, dir., writer network news CBS-TV, N.Y.C., 1962-68; exec. producer Pub. Broadcasting Lab., N.Y.C., 1968-69; dean Tisch Sch. of the Arts NYU, N.Y.C., 1969-92, dean emeritus, 1992—; adv. com. Sta. WNCN; mem. Tony awards com., 1983-88. Clarinet soloist Casals Festival, Prades, France, 1955, San Juan, P.R., 1959, recs. include Budapest Quartet, Brahms Clarinet Quintet, Opus 115 and Mozart Clarinet Quintet in A Maj., (Stravinsky conducting) L'Histoire du Soldat, Octet, Septet, Bernstein Sonata, Leonard Bernstein, piano (dedicated to David Oppenheim), (with Julliard Quartet) Copland Sextet, (with New Music Quartet) Douglas Moore Quintet; co-producer (play) Saul Whose Last Analysis on Broadway, 1962; producer documentary films on Stravinsky and Casals, CBS News. Bd. dirs. emeritus Film Soc. Lincoln Center, Inc., Town Hall Found.; bd. dirs. Am. Theatre Wolpe Soc.; bd. advisors New Sch. Concerts. With AUS, World War II, ETO. Recipient Prix Italia Radiotelevisione Italiana, 1964. Mem. Nat. Soc. Lit. and Arts, Internat. Council Fine Arts Deans, N.Y. State Arts Deans, Town Hall Found., Soc. of Fellows (charter), Am. Fedn. Arts (film program). Avocations: camping, reading, gardening, hiking.

OPPENHEIM, ELLEN W., media director, advertising executive; married; 2 children. BA in Journalism with honors in regional planning, U. N.C., 1975. Media rsch. and media planning exec. Young & Rubicam, N.Y.C., 1975-83, group supr., v.p., 1983-88; worldwide promotion dir. Time Mag., N.Y.C., 1988-89, U.S. mktg. dir., 1989; mng. dir. custom media Am. Express Pub., N.Y.C., 1989-90; sr. v.p., media dir. FCB/Leber Katz Ptnrs., N.Y.C., 1990—. Mem. Am. Assn. Advt. Agys. (mag. com. 1991-92, newspaper com. 1992-94, direct mktg. com. 1994—). Office: FCB Leber Katz Ptnrs 150 E 42d St New York NY 10017

OPPENHEIM, IRWIN, chemical physicist, educator; b. Boston, June 30, 1929; s. James L. and Rose (Rosenberg) O.; m. Bernice Buresh, May 18, 1974; 1 child, Joshua Buresh. A.B. summa cum laude, Harvard U., 1949; postgrad., Calif. Inst. Tech., 1949-51; Ph.D., Harvard U., 1956. Physicist Nat. Bur. Standards, Washington, 1953-60; chief theoretical physics Gen. Dynamics/Convair, San Diego, 1960-61; assoc. prof. chemistry MIT, Cambridge, 1961-65; prof. MIT, 1965—; lectr. physics U. Md., 1953-60; vis. assoc. prof. physics U. Leiden, 1955-56, Lorentz prof., 1983; vis. prof. Weizmann Inst.

Sci., 1958-59, U. Calif., San Diego, 1966-67; Van der Waals prof. U. Amsterdam, 1966-67. Author: (with J.G. Kirkwood) Chemical Thermodynamics, 1961; editor: Phys. Rev. E, 1992—. Fellow Am. Phys. Soc., Am. Acad. Arts and Scis., Washington Acad. Sci.; mem. Phi Beta Kappa, Sigma Xi. Research in quantum statis. mechanics, statis. mechanics of transport processes, thermodynamics. Home: 140 Upland Rd Cambridge MA 02140-3623 Office: MIT 77 Massachusetts Ave Cambridge MA 02139-3594

OPPENHEIMER, FRANZ MARTIN, lawyer; b. Mainz, Germany, Sept. 7, 1919; s. Arnold and Johanna (Mayer) O.; m. Margaret Spencer Foote, June 17, 1944; children: Martin Foote, Roxana Foote, Edward Arnold. B.S., U. Chgo., 1942; student, U. Grenoble, France, 1938-39; LL.B. cum laude note editor Law Jour. 1945) Yale U., 1945. Bar: N.Y. 1946, D.C. 1955. Rsch. asst. com. human devel. U. Chgo., 1942-43; law clk. to Judge Swan, U.S. Circuit Ct. of Appeals, N.Y., 1945-46; assoc. atty. Chadbourne, Wallace, Parke & Whiteside, N.Y.C., 1946-47; atty. IBRD, Washington, 1947-57; individual practice law, 1958-59; ptnr. firm Leva, Hawes, Symington, Martin & Oppenheimer, 1959-83, Fort & Schlefer, Washington, 1984-94; pvt. practice Washington, 1995—. Contbr. articles to The Am. Spectator and other jours. Bd. dirs. Internat. Student House; founding mem. Company of Christian Jews; hon. trustee Com. 100 on Fed. City, Washington. Decorated officer's cross Order of Merit (Fed. Republic Germany), chevalier Nat. Order of Merit (France). Mem. ABA, Fed. Bar Assn., Am. Soc. Internat. Law (treas. 1964-76), Coun. Fgn. Rels., Yale Club, Century Assn. (N.Y.), City Tavern, Met. Club (Washington). Episcopalian. Home: 3248 O St NW Washington DC 20007-2847 Office: 3000 K St NW Ste 300 Washington DC 20007-5116

OPPENHEIMER, JACK HANS, internist, scientist, educator; b. Egelsbach, Hesse, Germany, Sept. 14, 1927; came to U.S., 1937; s. Julius and Elsa (Reis) O.; m. Ann Ehrlich, Dec. 20, 1953; children: Mark, Lawrence, Adele Oppenheimer Brown. BA, Princeton U., 1949; MD, Columbia U., 1953. Diplomate Am. Bd. Internal Medicine. Intern Boston City Hosp., 1953-54; fellow Sloan Kettering Inst., N.Y.C., 1954-55, Columbia Presbyn. Hosp., N.Y.C., 1959-60; resident Duke U., 1957-59; asst. prof. to prof. medicine Albert Einstein Coll. Medicine, Bronx, N.Y., 1964-76; prof. medicine U. Minn., Mpls., 1976—, Cecil J. Watson prof., 1986—; staff physician Montefiore Hosp. Med. Ctr., Bronx 1960-76. Contbr. over 200 articles to profl. jours.; editor 2 books. Capt. U.S. Army, 1955-57. Fellow ACP; mem. Endocrine Soc. (coun. 1974-78, Astwood award 1978), Am. Thyroid Assn. (pres. 1985-86, Van Meter award 1965, Parke-Davis award 1984), Am. Soc. Clin. Investigation, Assn. Am. Physicians. Home: 4100 Kerry Ct Hopkins MN 55345-1825 Office: U Minn 520 Delaware St SE Minneapolis MN 55455-0356

OPPENHEIMER, JAMES RICHARD, lawyer; b. St. Paul, July 27, 1921; s. William Henry and Marion Louise (Joslin) O.; m. Mary Ensign Dunning, Jan. 14, 1944 (div. 1957); m. Christine Kurth White, Oct. 14, 1960 (dec. 1979); 1 child, Susan. BA, Dartmouth Coll., 1942; JD, Yale U., 1948. Bar: Minn. 1948, U.S. Dist. Ct. Minn., 1950, U.S. Ct. Appeals (8th cir.) 1963. Assoc. Oppenheimer Wolff & Donnelly and predecessor firm, St. Paul, 1948-54, ptnr., 1954-91, of counsel, 1992—. Trustee Charles K. Blandin Found., Grand Rapids, Minn., 1958—, pres. and chair, 1972-89; trustee Charles K. Blandin Residuary Trust, Mpls., 1968—, Tozer Found., St. Paul, 1978—. Lt. (j.g.) USN, 1943-46, PTO and Atlantic. Mem. ABA, Minn. Bar Assn., Ramsey County Bar Assn., St. Paul C. of C. (bd. dirs. 1978-81), Rotary (St. Paul club pres. 1957-58), White Bear Yacht Club (commodore 1988-89). Unitarian. Office: Oppenheimer Wolff & Donnelly 1700 1st Bank Bldg Saint Paul MN 55101

OPPENHEIMER, JANE MARION, biologist, historian, educator; b. Phila., Sept. 19, 1911; d. James Harry and Sylvia (Stern) O. B.A., Bryn Mawr Coll., 1932; Ph.D., Yale U., 1933, postgrad. (Sterling fellow), 1935-36, Am. Assn. U. Women fellow, 1936-37; Sc.D. (hon.), Brown U., 1976. Research fellow embryology U. Rochester, 1937-38; faculty Bryn Mawr (Pa.) Coll., 1938—, prof., 1953-80, prof. emeritus, 1980—, acting dean grad. sch., 2d semester, 1946-47; Vis. prof. biology Johns Hopkins, 1966-67; exchange prof. U. Paris, 1969. Author: New Aspects of John and William Hunter, 1946, Essays in History of Embryology and Biology, 1967; editor: Autobiography of Dr. Karl Ernst von Baer, 1986; co-editor: Founds. Exptl. Embryology, 1964, editor 2d edit., 1974; assoc. editor: Jour. Morphology, 1956-58, Quar. Rev. Biol, 1963-64; mem. editorial bd.: Am. Zoologist, 1965-70, Jour. History Biology, 1967-75, Quar. Rev. Biology, 1968-75; sect. editor developmental biology: Biol. Abstracts, 1970-73. Mem. history life scis. study sect. NIH, 1966-70. Recipient Lucius Wilbur Cross medal Yale Grad. Alumni Assn., 1971, K. E. von Baer medal Estonian Acad. Scis., 1992; Guggenheim Mem. Found. fellow, 1942-43, 52-53; Rockefeller Found. fellow, 1950-51; NSF postdoctoral fellow, 1959-60. Fellow AAAS (sect. L 1955-58, coun. del. sect. G 1980-83, com. on coun. affairs 1981-82), Am. Acad. Arts & Scis., Phila. Coll. Physicians (hon.); mem. Am. Soc. Zoologists (treas. 1957-59, chmn. div. devel. biology 1967, pres. 1973), Am. Assn. Anatomists, History of Sci. Soc. (mem. coun. 1975-77), Am. Assn. History Medicine (mem. coun. 1971-74), Am. Soc. Naturalists, Soc. for Developmental Biology, Internat. Soc. for Developmental Biology, Am. Inst. Biol. Scis. (mem. at large governing bd. 1974-77), Internat. Soc. History Medicine, Internat. Acad. History of Sci. (Paris) (corr.), Internat. Acad. History Medicine (Paris), Am. Philos. Soc. (coun. 1982-92, exec. com. 1984-92, sec. 1987-92). Home: 241 S 6th St Apt # 304 Philadelphia PA 19106-3728

OPPENHEIMER, JERRY L., lawyer; b. Birmingham, Ala., Feb. 22, 1937; s. Jerome H. and Mina (Loveman) O.; m. Joan H. Chadwick-Collins, Feb. 23, 1963; children: Julia Cole, James Chadwick. BS, U. N.C., 1958; LLB, U. Va., 1961. Bar: D.C. 1961, Va. 1961. Assoc. Covington & Burling, Washington, 1961-69; atty., advisor U.S. Treasury Dept., Washington, 1969-70, assoc. tax legis. counsel, 1970-71, dep. tax legis. counsel, 1971-73; ptnr. Mayer, Brown & Platt, Washington, 1973—. Home: 4655 Garfield St NW Washington DC 20007-1026 Office: Mayer Brown & Platt 2000 Pennsylvania Ave NW Washington DC 20006-1812

OPPENHEIMER, JOSEPH, infosystems consultant, television producer; b. Wurzburg, Germany, June 27, 1927; came to U.S., 1936; s. Ludwig E. and Mary (Schwarzenberger) O.; divorced. BA, Washington U., 1948. Reporter Wichita (Kans.) Eagle, 1948-49; corr. Internat. News Service, St. Louis, 1949-55; corr., fin. editor N.Y.C., 1955-59; account exec. AA Schechter, N.Y.C., 1959-62; editor, pub. Outlook, Standard and Poor's Corp., N.Y.C., 1962-78, v.p. mktg., 1978-80, v.p. mktg. and advt., 1980-82, gen. mgr. electronic info. services, 1982-89, sr. v.p., 1982-89, ret.; info. cons., lectr. U. Calif., San Diego, 1989—; cons. in field; att. Am. Jour. Nursing Co., 1986—, chair fin. and audit com., 1987-91, corp. sec. 1994—; elected to Del Mar TV Adv. Commn., 1991-94, chmn. 1992-94. TV producer Coffee in Del Mar interview program for 3 San Diego area cable systems, 1992—; founder, bd. dirs. Lenox Hill Dems., N.Y.C., 1957-60; bd. dirs., v.p. YMHA Washington Heights, 1965-87; trustee Fedn. of Jewish Philanthropies, N.Y.C., 1983-86. Served to master sgt. U.S. Army, 1950-52. Founder, bd. dirs. Lenox Hill Dems., N.Y.C., 1957-60; bd. dirs., v.p. YMHA Washington Heights, 1965-87; trustee Fedn. Jewish Philanthropies, N.Y.C., 1983-86; bd. dirs. San Diego Agy. Jewish Edn., 1994—. Avocations: tennis, travel, bible study, politics.

OPPENHEIMER, MARTIN J., lawyer; b. Apr. 11, 1933; s. Julius and Sylvia (Haas) O.; m. Suzanne Rosenhirsch, July 3, 1958; children: Marcy, Evan, Joshua, Alexandra. BS with honors, U. Pa., 1953; LLB, Yale U., 1956. Assoc. Hays, Sklar & Hertzberg, Mendes & Mount; ptnr. Proskauer Rose Goetz & Mendelsohn, N.Y.C., 1958—. Contbr. articles to profl. jours. Chmn. City Ctr. of Music and Drama, Lincoln Ctr., N.Y., 1984—; vice chmn. N.Y.C. Opera, 1985—; bd. dir. 92nd St. YWCA, N.Y., 1985—, Lincoln Ctr. for Performing Arts, 1987—. Fulbright scholar Goethe U., Frankfurt, Fed. Republic Germany, 1956-57. Home: 400 Claflin Ave Mamaroneck NY 10543-3999 Office: Proskauer Rose et al 1585 Broadway New York NY 10036-8200

OPPENHEIMER, MAX, JR., foreign language educator, consultant; b. N.Y.C., July 27, 1917; s. Max and Louise (Pourfuerst) O.; m. Christine Backus, Oct. 14, 1942; children: Edmund Max, Christine Oppenheimer Burns. Bachelier ès Lettres, U. Paris, 1935; BA cum laude, NYU, 1941; MA, UCLA, 1942; PhD, U. So. Calif., 1947. Instr. fgn. langs. San

Diego State Coll., 1947-49; asst. prof. Romance langs. Washington U., St. Louis, 1949-51; assoc. prof. modern langs. Fla. State U., Tallahassee, 1958-61; prof., chmn. dept. Russian U. Iowa, Iowa City, 1961-67; prof. SUNY, Fredonia, 1967-76, prof. emeritus, 1976—, chmn. dept. fgn. langs., 1967-74; prof. Englsh Yunnan Normal U., Kunming, Peoples Republic of China, 1985-86; intelligence officer CIA, 1956-58. Author: Outline of Russian Grammar, 1962; translator: Theory of Molecular Excitons (Davydov), 1962, Theory of Ship Waves and Wave Resistance (Kostyukov), 1968, The Fake Astrologer (Calderón de la Barca), 1976, 94, The Lady Simpleton (Lope de Vega), 1976, Don Juan (Tirso de Molina), 1976, Swim First and Last, 1981; contbr. articles to scholarly and profl. jours. Active YMCA, 1936—. Served to lt. col., MI, AUS, 1942-46, lt. col. Res., ret. Decorated Bronze Star; Fla. State U. grantee, 1961, Office Naval Rsch. grantee, 1965, SUNY grantee, 1973. Mem. MLA, Am. Soc. Geolinguistics (pres. 1975-76), Am. Soc. Dowsers, Ariz. Soc. for Profl. Hypnosis, Dobro Slovo, Am. Mensa Ltd., Elks, Phi Beta Kappa, Sigma Delta Pi, Pi Delta Phi (nat. pres. 1946-51), Alpha Mu Gamma. Avocation: swimming. Home: 11619 97th Ave Sun City AZ 83351-3608 *When you speak, always say what you think, not what you think you should say for the sake of expediency. Steadfastly, stubbornly, cling to your ideals, principles and beliefs, but be flexible enough to change whenever changing them reflects wisdom, not weakness or compromise. Avoid ego trips or being awed by your own alleged accomplishments.*

OPPENHEIMER, MICHAEL, physicist; b. Bklyn., Feb. 28, 1946; s. Harry and Shirley (Meyer) O.; m. Leonie Haimson, Dec. 31, 1986; 1 child, Chloe. S.B., MIT, 1966; Ph.D., U. Chgo., 1970. Research fellow Harvard Coll., 1971-73; lectr. astronomy Harvard U., 1973-81; physicist Harvard-Smithsonian Center for Astrophysics, Harvard U., 1973-81, Environ. Def. Fund, N.Y.C., 1981—; mem. adv. com. on atmospheric effects of aviation NASA; chmn. adv. panel on global warming Am. Mus. Natural History, 1990-93; mem. environ. adv. com. to N.Y. Gov. Cuomo, 1991-94. Author: Dead Heat: The Race Against the Greenhouse Effect, 1990; contbr. articles to profl. jours. Union Carbide fellow, 1969-70; A.F. Morrison fellow, 1979; Guggenheim fellow, 1978-79. Mem. AAAS, Am. Phys. Soc., Am. Geophys. Union, Am. Meteorol. Soc. Office: Environ Def Fund 257 Park Ave S New York NY 10010-7304

OPPENHEIMER, PAUL EUGENE, English comparative literature educator, poet, author; b. N.Y.C., May 1, 1939; s. Fred R. Oppenheimer and Gertrude Samuels; children: Julie Sarah, Ben. BA, Princeton U., 1961; MA, Columbia U., 1963, PhD, 1970. Lectr. Hunter Coll. CUNY, 1964-67, lectr., poet-in-residence City Coll., 1967-70, from asst. prof. to assoc. prof. City Coll., 1970-84, prof. City Coll., 1984—; exch. prof., dir. CUNY student exch. program Sorbonne nouvelle, Paris, 1984-85; exch. prof. U. North London, Eng., 1989-90, Univ. Coll. London, 1993, German Dept., 1993, 95; Fulbright prof. U. Osnabrück, Germany, 1993-94. Author: Before a Battle and Other Poems, 1967, The Birth of the Modern Mind: Self, Consciousness, and the Invention of the Sonnet, 1989, Beyond the Furies, New Poems, 1985; author, translator: Till Eulenspiegel: His Adventures, 1972, 91, 95. Woodrow Wilson fellow, 1961-62, Alfred Hodder fellow, 1969-70, Fulbright sr. fellow, Germany, 1993-94. Mem. Dante Soc. Am. Home: 50 W 67th St New York NY 10023 Office: Coll English and Comparative Lit NAC 138 St and Convent Ave New York NY 10031

OPPENHEIMER, STEVEN BERNARD, biology educator; b. Bklyn., Mar. 23, 1944; s. Hugo and Irma (Schellenberg) O.; m. Carolyn Roberta Weisenberg, May 23, 1971; 1 child, Mark. BS magna cum laude, Bklyn. Coll., 1965; PhD, Johns Hopkins U., 1969. Am. Cancer Soc. postdoctoral fellow U. Calif., San Diego, 1969-71; asst. prof. biology Calif. State U., Northridge, 1971-74, assoc. prof., 1974-77, prof., 1977—, dir. Sch. Sci. and Math. Ctr. for Cancer and Devel. Biology; speaker in field; panel mem. NSF, Washington, 1985, NIH, 1987, 94; prin. investigator NIH, Northridge, 1972-84, 86—, NSF, Northridge, 1981—; cons. Northridge Hosp., 1984-92. Author: Introduction to Embryonic Development, 1980, 2d rev. edit., 1986, Cancer, Biological and Clinical Introduction, 1982, 2d rev. edit., 1985, Cancer Prevention Guidebook, 1984, 2d rev. edit., 1991, Atlas of Embryonic Development, 1984; editor: Cancer, Longevity Letter, 1984-85, Jour. Student Rsch. Abstracts, 1995—; writer: (film) Cancer Prevention, A Way of Life, 1986; contbr. articles to profl. jours. Grantee Nat. Cancer Inst., 1972-84, Am. Cancer Soc., 1977-86, NSF, 1981—, Nat. Inst. Child Health and Human Devel., 1986-88, Nat. Inst. Health, 1993—, Joseph Drown Found., 1988—, NASA, 1988—, Eisenhower Program, 1990—, Urban Cmty. Svc. Program, 1992—; fellow Exxon, 1982, Thomas Eckstrom Trust, 1982—; recipient Disting. Prof. award Calif. State U., 1977, Statewide Outstanding Prof. award Bd. Trustees of 19 Campuses, 1984, Excellence in Sci. Edn. award Calif. Sci. Tchrs. Assn., 1988. Fellow AAAS; mem. Am. Soc. Zoologists (nat. program chmn., devel. biology and nat. membership chmn. 1983-85), Am. Soc. Cell Biology, Soc. Devel. Biology, Am. Cancer Soc. (bd. dirs. San Fernando Valley chpt. 1985-89, Pub. Edn. award 1985), Sigma Xi (Disting. Rsch. award 1984), Phi Kappa Phi. Home: 8933 Darby Ave Northridge CA 91325-2706 Office: Calif State U Dept Biology 18111 Nordhoff St Northridge CA 91330-8303

OPPENHEIMER, SUZI, state senator; b. N.Y.C., Dec. 13, 1934; d. Alfred Elihu Rosenhirsch and Blanche (Schoen) O.; m. Martin J. Oppenheimer, July 3, 1960; children: Marcy, Evan, Josh, Alexandra. BA in Econs., Conn. Coll. for Women, 1956; MBA, Columbia U., 1958. Security analyst McDonnell & Co., N.Y.C., 1958-60, L.F. Rothschild Co., N.Y.C., 1960-63; mayor Village of Mamaroneck, N.Y., 1977-85; mem. N.Y. State Senate, Albany, 1985—; ranking mem. transp. com., mem. fin., edn., environ. conservation, consumer protection, vets., and drugs com., chmn. Senate Minority Task Force on Women's Issues, treas. Legis. Women's Caucus. Former pres. Mamaroneck LWV, Westchester County Mcpl. Ofcls. Assn., Westchester Mcpl. Planning Fedn. Recipient Humanitarian Svc. award Am. Jewish Com., 1988, Legis. Leadership award Young Adult Inst., 1988, Legis. award Westchester Irish Com., 1988, Hon. Svc. award Vis. Nurses Svcs., 1989, Humanitarian Svc. award Project Family, 1990, Meritorious Svc. award N.Y. State Assn. Counties, 1990, Friend of Edn. award N.Y. State United Tchrs., 1991; honoree Windward Sch. Ann. Dinner, 1992; named Legislator of Yr., N.Y. State Women's Press Club. Democrat. Jewish.

OPPENLANDER, ROBERT, retired airline executive; b. N.Y.C., May 20, 1923; s. Robert and Lillian (Ahrens) O.; m. Jessie I. Major, Sept. 30, 1950; children: Kris Oppenlander Austin, Robert Kirk, Tenley Oppenlander Norman. B.S., MIT, 1944; M.B.A., Harvard U., 1948. With Metals & Controls Corp., Attleboro, Mass., 1948-53; prin. Cresap, McCormick & Paget, N.Y.C., 1953-58; comptroller, treas. Delta Air Lines, Inc., Atlanta, 1958-88; v.p. fin. Delta Air Lines, Inc., 1964-67, sr. v.p. fin., treas., 1967-78, sr. v.p. fin., 1978-83, vice chmn. bd., chief fin. officer, 1983-88, ret., 1988, also adv. dir. Served to lt. USNR, 1944-46. Club: Capital City. Home: 3944 Powers Ferry Rd NW Atlanta GA 30342-4026

OPPER, JOHN, painter, retired educator; b. Chgo., Oct. 29, 1908; m. Jospeh and Mary (Milstein) O.; m. Estelle Hausman, Mar. 24, 1934; children: Jane, Joseph. Grad., Cleve. Sch. Art, 1931; Masters, Case Western Reserve U., 1931; EdD, SUNY, 1952. Prof. art Wyoming U., Laramie, 1945-47, Columbia U., 1947, 1947-52, U. N.C. Greensboro, 1952-57, NYU, N.Y.C., 1957-74. One man shows include Artists' Gallery, N.Y.C., 1937, 40, 42, Feragil Gallery, N.Y.C., 1945, Ten Thirty Gallery, Cleve., 1945, San Francisco Mus., 1947, Egan Gallery, N.Y.C., 1955, Stable Gallery, N.Y.C., 1959, 60, 62, Grace Borgenicht Gallery, 1966, 68, 71, 73, 78, 79, 84, Vered Gallery, East Hampton, N.Y., 1989, 90; exhibited in group shows including Nat. Acad. Design, 1933, Met. Mus. Art, N.Y.C., 1941, Art Inst. Chgo., 1941, 42, 44, 47, 48, Pa. Acad. Fine Arts, 1941, 62, Bklyn. Mus., 1941, 42, San Francisco Mus. Art, 1945, 46, 47, Weathersport Gallery, Greensboro, 1945, Colo. Springs. Fine Art Gallery, 1946, 47, Denver Art Mus., 1946, Calif. Palace Legion Honor, 1947, Nat. Acad., Washington, 1947, Sacramento Mus. Art, 1947, Corcoran Gallery Art, 1948, 53, Toledo Mus., 1948, Whitney Mus. Am. Art, 1952, Carnegie Inst., 1961, Yale U., 1961, 62, Santa Barbara Calif. Mus., 1964, Guild Hall, East Hampton, N.Y., 1970, Ball State U., 1971, Montclair Art Mus., 1977, Cleve. Mus. Art, 1982, Cleve. Inst. Art, 1990 (Disting. Alumnus award 1990); represented in permanent collections including Mus. Modern Art, N.Y., Whitney Mus. Am. Art, N.Y., Met. Mus. Art, N.Y., Nat. Mus. Am. Art, Washington. Recipient Earnst award Acad. Arts and Letters, 1990, Spath award Guild Hall Mus., 1991; fellow Guggenheim Found., 1968—. Home: PO Box 347

102 Schellinger Rd Amagansett NY 11930 Studio: 222 Bowery New York NY 10019

OPPERMAN, DANNY GENE, packaging professional, consultant; b. Fostoria, Ohio, June 29, 1938; s. Roy and Iva Ann (Dotson) O.; m. Dorothy Rae Bugner, Dec. 30, 1957; children: Carrie Rae Opperman Hammond, Melissa Ann Opperman Lee, Jon Aaron, Christopher Douglas. Assoc., ICS, 1960. Tool engr. Ford Motor Co., Fostoria, 1957-68; packaging engr. Allied-Signal Corp., Fostoria, 1968-86; machine designer Interconnect, Inc., Toledo, 1987; prodn. engr. TRW, Elyria, Ohio, 1987-88; pres. packaging consulting firm Opperman/Assocs., Inc., Fostoria, 1988—. Pres. Fostoria Jaycees, 1970-71; advisor Fostoria Teen Ctr., Inc., 1968-88; mem. ASTM (D-10 packaging com), Inst. Packaging Profls. (cert., chpt. bd. dirs. 1984-92), Packaging Cons. Coun., Elks (exalted ruler 1984-85), Masons.

OPPERMAN, DWIGHT DARWIN, publishing company executive; b. Perry, Iowa, June 26, 1923; s. John H. and Zoa L. Opperman; m. Jeanice Wifvat, Apr. 22, 1942 (dec.); children: Vance K., Fane W. JD, Drake U., 1951. Bar: Iowa 1951, U.S. Supreme Ct. 1976, U.S Ct. Internat. Trade, 1988. Editor, asst. editorial counsel West Pub. Co., St. Paul, Minn., 1951-64, mgr. reporters and digest depts., 1964-65; v.p. West Pub. Co., 1965-68, pres., 1968-93, CEO, 1978—, chmn., 1993—; dir. Inst. Judicial Adminstrn. Vice pres., trustee Supreme Ct. Hist. Soc.; dir. Inst. of Judicial Adminstrn.; bd. govs., mem. nat. task force Drake U., Des Moines; dir. Minn. D.A.R.E. Inc. With U.S. Army, 1942-45. Recipient Herbert Harley award Am. Judicature Soc., 1984, Justice award, 1992, 1st George Wickersham Founder's award Friends of Law Libr. of Congress, 1993. Fellow Am. Bar Found.; mem. ABA (coalition for justice), Fed. Bar Assn., Am. Judicature Soc., Am. Law Inst., Jud. Fellows Commn., Drake U. Nat. Alumni Assn. (disting. svc. award 1974, Centennial award 1981, Outstanding Alumni award 1988), Minn. Club (pres. 1975-76). Office: West Pub Co 610 Opperman Dr Eagan MN 55123

OPPERMANN, JOSEPH KAY, architect; b. Galveston, Tex., Apr. 15, 1949; s. Gustav John and Katherine (Shuberg) O.; m. Langdon Edmunds, Oct. 24, 1987; children: Joseph Sjöberg, Frances Edmunds. BA in Liberal Arts, U. Tex., 1971, BArch, 1975, MArch, 1975, cert. in mus. conservation, 1986. Registered architect, N.C., S.C., Ga., Ky., La., D.C. Grants mgr. Tex. Hist. Commn., Austin, 1976-79, dir. tech. svcs., 1979-81, dep. state hist. preservation officer, 1981-87; prin. C. Phillips & Co., Winston-Salem, N.C., 1987; pres. Phillips & Oppermann, P.A., Winston-Salem, 1988—; mem. hist. Am. bldgs. survey team Winedale Inst., 1975; architect mem. nat. register adv. com. N.C. Dept. Cultural Resources; lectr. in field. Contbr. articles to profl. publs. Architect mem. task group to prepare mandatory growth plan City of Austin, 1986; architect mem. rev. panel for hist. facade grants City of Winston-Salem, 1990-91; bd. advisors Hist. Preservation Found. N.C.; bd. advisors grad. archtl. program in hist. preservation Tex. A&M U., 1986-89; bd. dirs. Preservation Action, 1984-87; bd. dirs. Nat. Conf. State Hist. Preservations Officers, 1984-86, chmn. grants appropriations com.; pres. Tex. chpt. Soc. Archtl. Historians, 1980-83. Recipient Tower award for Outstanding Restoration, 1992, 93, 94. Mem. AIA (mem. hist. resources com. N.C. chpt.), Assn. for Preservation Tech., Soc. Archtl. Historians (pres. Tex. chpt. 1980-82), Am. Inst. Conservation of Hist. and Artists Works, Vernacular Archtl. Forum. Office: Phillips & Oppermann PA 1134-A Burke St Winston Salem NC 27101

OPPLT, JAN JIRI, clinical pathologist, educator; b. Czechoslovakia, Nov. 25, 1921; came to U.S., 1969; s. Jan Opplt and Anna (Vochocova) O.; m. Marie A. Koudelkova, Dec. 22, 1960. MD, Charles U., Prague, Czechoslovakia, 1949, PhD in Biochemistry, 1952, PhD in Med. Scis., 1966, Docent Habilit, 1969. Asst. prof. med. and clin. chemistry Charles U., 1948-51, dir., chmn. dept. clin. chemistry, 1951-69; vis. prof. rsch. fellow lab. medicine Clev. Clinic Found., 1969-70; dir. clin. chemistry Cleve. Met. Gen. Hosp., 1971-88; asst. prof. Case Western Res. U., Cleve., 1971-72, assoc. prof. pathology, 1973—; clin. prof. chemistry Cleve. State U., 1970-92. Co-author: Diabetic Nephropathy, 1969, Diabetes Mellitus, 1970, Handbook of Electrophoresis, 1980; patentee in field. Recipient Gold award Am. Soc. Clin. Pathologists, 1971, Svc. award Am. Heart Assn., 1978, Internat. Recognition award IFCC, Holland, 1987; Fellow WHO, 1959, Cleve. Clinic Found., 1970. Fellow Nat. Acad. Clin. Biochemistry, Coun. on Atherosclerosis; mem. Am. Assn. Clin. Chemsitry, N.Y. Acad. Sci., Cleve. Acad. Medicine, Czechoslovak Soc. Arts and Scis. Achievements include development of courses in differential diagnostic procedures and clinico-pathologic correlations as well as in clinical chemical pathology, used in therapeutic and preventative medicine, photometric analytical scanning of proteinograms, lipoproteinograms, permanent standard for electrophoretic analyses, isolation and description of medium-density lipoprotein, anti-atherogenic anti-hypertensive drug Quanadrel, correlations of metabolic and conformational changes in lipoproteins, ultra centrifugal determination of natural subclasses of serum lipoproteins, molecular phoresis, new screening project for atherosclerosis, research of physiological and pathological metabolism of plasma proteins and lipoproteins. Home: 17364 Falling Water Rd Strongsville OH 44136-4202

OPPMANN, ANDREW JAMES, newspaper editor; b. Hopkinsville, Ky., Apr. 3, 1963; s. Patrick George Oppmann and Elizabeth Anne (Freeman) Peace; m. Emily Elise Wey, Oct. 8, 1988. BA in Journalism, U. Ky., 1985. Staff writer The Orange County Register, Santa Ana, Calif., 1985-86; copy editor, staff writer Lexington (Ky.) Herald-Leader, 1986-87, bur. chief, asst. metro editor, 1988-91; urban affairs writer The Knoxville (Tenn.) News-Sentinel, 1987-88; asst. city editor The Houston Post, 1991-92, dep. met. editor, 1992, asst. to mng. editor, 1992, met editor, 1992-94; Ky. editor The Cin. (Ohio) Enquirer, Covington; supervising editor The Ky. Enquirer, Covington, 1994—. Bd. vis. U. Ky. Sch. Journalism, 1994—. Fellow U. Ky., 1984. Office: The Ky Enquirer 309 Garrard St Covington KY 41011

OPRE, THOMAS EDWARD, magazine editor, film company executive, corporate travel company executive; b. Evansville, Ind., Nov. 6, 1943; s. William Jennings and Ruth (Strouss) O.; children: Thomas Andrew, William Hartley. A.B. in Journalism, Ind. U., 1965. Writer sports and outdoors Decatur (Ill.) Herald and Rev., 1965-66; outdoor editor Detroit Free Press, 1966-90; field editor Midwest div. Field and Stream mag., 1971-81; editorial dir. Gt. Lakes Sportsman mag., 1972-75; editor-at-large and sports vehicles editor Outdoor Life mag., 1981-93; pres. Tom Opre Prodns., 1967—; pres. TOP Safaris, Inc., 1986—. Author numerous articles in outdoor and travel fields. Recipient James Henshall award Am. Fish Tackle Mfrs. Assn., 1969, Teddy award Internat. Outdoor Travel Film Festival, 1973, Environ. award EPA, 1977, Nat. Writer's award Safari Club Internat., 1977, Deep Woods Writing award OWAA, 1977, Conservation Service award Ducks Unltd., 1977; World Wildlife Found. award, 1981; named to Internat. Fishing Hall of Fame, 1968, Conservation Communicator of Yr., 1985. Mem. Outdoor Writers Assn. Am. (past dir., pres., v.p., chmn. bd.), Assn. Gt. Lakes Outdoor Writers (past dir., chmn. bd., pres., v.p.), Mich. Outdoor Writers Assn. (v.p., pres., chmn. bd. dirs.), Alpha Tau Omega. Home and Office: PO Box 156 Northville MI 48167-0156

O'QUINN, JOHN M., lawyer; b. 1941. JD magna cum laude, U. Houston, 1967. Bar: Tex. 1967, U.S. Dist. Ct. (so. and ea. dists.) Tex., 1967, U.S. Appeals (5th cir.) 1971, U.S. Supreme Ct. 1972. Founding ptnr. O'Quinn, Kerensky, McAninch & Laminack, Houston, 1981—; mem. adv. com. Tex. State Supreme Ct., 1984-94; trustee U. Houston Law Found., 1985—. Editor-in-chief Houston Law Rev., 1966-67. Regent U. Houston, 1993—. Named Disting. Alumnus U. Houston, 1993; honored by Nat. Law Jour. as one of 100 Most Influential Lawyers in U.S. Mem. Trial Lawyers Assn., Tex. Trial Lawyers Assn. (dir.), Houston Trial Lawyers Assn. (dir.), State Bar Tex., U. Houston Law Alumni Assn. (pres. 1978). Office: O'Quinn Kerensky McAninch & Laminack PC 2300 Lyric Centre 440 Louisiana Houston TX 77002

ORAM, JOHN L., chemical company executive; b. 1944. With Deloitte Haskins & Sells, 1968-72, CIT Container Transport Inc., 1972-78; with ICC Industries Inc., N.Y.C., 1978—, former exec. v.p., pres., 1986—, also bd. dirs. Office: ICC Industries Inc 720 5th Ave New York NY 10019-4107

ORAM, ROBERT W., library administrator; b. Warsaw, Ind., June 11, 1922; s. George Harry and Lottie Mae (Gresso) O.; m. Virginia White, June

16, 1949; 1 child, Richard W. B.A., U. Toledo, 1949; M.S. in Library Adminstrn., U. Ill., 1950. Asst. to librarian U. Mo.-Columbia, 1950-56; circulation librarian U. Ill.-Urbana, 1956-67, dir. pub. service, 1968-71, assoc. univ. librarian, 1971-79, acting univ. librarian, 1975-76; dir. Central Univ. Libraries So. Meth. U., Dallas, 1979-89, dir. emeritus, 1989; mem. adv. com. Ill. State Library, Springfield, 1975-79. Contbr. articles to profl. jours. Exec. sec. Friends of So. Meth. U. Libs., 1989-89; former mem. bd. dirs. Urbana Free Libr., Lincoln Trails Libr. Sys., Champaign, Ill.; trustee Friends Austin (Tex.) Pub. Libr., 1994—. Mem. ALA (life, pub. com. 1975-79), Friends of Libraries U.S.A. (exec. bd. 1980-86), Ill. Library Assn. (treas. 1972-73),. Democrat. Avocations: reading; music. Home: 8410 Lone Mesa Austin TX 78759-8025

ORAN, ELAINE SURICK, physicist, engineer; b. Rome, Ga.; d. Herman E. and Bessye R. (Kolker) Surick; m. Daniel Hirsh Oran, Feb. 1, 1969. AB, Bryn Mawr Coll., 1966; MPh, Yale U., 1968, PhD, 1972. Rsch. physicist Naval Rsch. Lab., Washington, 1972-76, supervisory rsch. physicist, 1976-88, sr. scientist reactive flow physics, 1988—; head Ctr. for Reactive Flow and Dynamical Systems, 1985-87; mem. adv. bd. NSF; cons. to U.S. govt., agys., NATO. Author: Numerical Simulation of Reactive Flow, 1987, Numerical Approaches to Combustion Modeling, 1991. Assoc. editor Jour. Computational Physics; mem. adv. bd. Computers in Physics; editl. bd. Prog. Ener. Comb. Sci., Combustion and Flame; contbr. numerous articles to profl. jours., chpts. to books. Recipient Arthur S. Flemming award, 1979, Women in Sci. and Engring. award, 1988; grantee USN, NASA, USAF, Advanced Rsch. Projects Agy. Fellow AIAA (pubs. com. 1986—, v.p. pubs. 1993), Am. Phys. Soc. (exec. com. fluid dynamics divsn. 1986, 88, exec. com. computer physics 1989—, chmn. 1991-92); mem. AAAS, Am. Inst. Aeronautics and Astronautics, Am. Phys. Soc., Am. Geophys. Union, Combustion Inst. (bd. dirs. 1990—), Internat. Colloquium Dynamic Energy Systems (bd. dirs. 1989—), Sigma Xi. Office: Naval Rsch Lab Code 6404 # 6004 Washington DC 20011

ORBACH, JERRY, actor, singer; b. N.Y.C., Oct. 20, 1935; s. Leon and Emily (Olexy) O.; m. Marta Curro, June 21, 1958 (div. 1975); children: Anthony Nicholas, Christopher Ben; m. Elaine Cancilla, Oct. 7, 1979. Student, U. Ill., 1952-53, Northwestern U., 1953-55; studied acting with, Herbert Berghof, Mira Rostova, Lee Strasberg, N.Y.C.; studied singing with, Hazel Schweppe, N.Y.C. Actor various films, on and off-Broadway prodns., 1956—. Profl. stage debut: Room Service, 1952; resident actor: Show Case Theatre, Evanston, Ill., summers 1953-54; N.Y.C. stage debut: Three Penny Opera, 1955; actor: (stage) Chicago, 3 Penny Opera, The Fantasticks, Carnival, Scuba Duba, Promises Promises, The Rose Tattoo, 6 Rums Riv Vu, The King and I, Guys and Dolls, The Student Prince, Annie Get Your Gun, The Trouble With People ... And Other Things, 42d Street, 1980; (films) Cop Hater, 1958, Mad Dog Coll, 1961, John Goldfarb Please Come Home, 1965, The Gang That Couldn't Shoot Straight, 1971, A Fan's Notes, 1974, Sentinel, 1977, The Prince of the City, 1982, Brewster's Millions, 1985, F/X, 1986, The Image Maker, 1986, Dirty Dancin', 1987, Someone to Watch Over Me, 1988, Crimes and Misdemeanors, 1989, Last Exit to Brooklyn, 1990, Out for Justice, 1991, Toy Soldiers, 1991, Delusion, 1991, Delirious, 1991, Beauty and the Beast, 1991 (voice only), Straight Talk, 1992, Universal Soldier, 1992, Mr. Saturday Night, 1992, The Cemetary Club, 1993; (TV episodes) including Love American Style, Murder She Wrote; (TV series) The Law and Harry McGraw, 1987-88, Law and Order, 1992—; (TV movies) An Invasion of Privacy, 1983, Out on a Limb, 1987, Love Among Thieves, 1987, In Defense of a Married Man, 1990, Broadway Bound, 1992, Quiet Killer, 1992; (TV miniseries) Dream West, 1986. Recipient New March of Dimes Horizon award, 1961, award of merit Actors Fund, 1961, Tony award Antoinette Perry Com., 1968. Mem. AFTRA, Screen Actors Guild, Actors Equity Assn. Club: Lone Star Boat. Avocations: poker, pool, golf, tennis.

ORBACH, RAYMOND LEE, physicist, educator; b. Los Angeles, July 12, 1934; s. Morris Albert and Mary Ruth (Miller) O.; m. Eva Hannah Spiegler, Aug. 26, 1956; children: David Miller, Deborah Hedwig, Thomas Randolph. BS, Calif. Inst. Tech., 1956; PhD, U. Calif., Berkeley, 1960. NSF postdoctoral fellow Oxford U., 1960-61; asst. prof. applied physics Harvard U., 1961-63; prof. physics UCLA, 1963-92, asst. vice chancellor acad. change and curriculum devel., 1970-72, chmn. acad. senate L.A. divsn., 1976-77, provost Coll. Letters and Sci., 1982-92; chancellor U. Calif., Riverside, 1992—; Cons. Aerospace Corp., 1965-70; mem. physics adv. panel NSF, 1970-73; mem. vis. com. Brookhaven Nat. Lab., 1970-74; mem. materials rsch. lab. adv. panel NSF, 1974-77; mem. Nat. Commn. on Rsch., 1978-80; chmn. 16th Internat. Conf. on Low Temperature Physics, 1981; Joliot Curie prof. Ecole Superieure de la Physique et Chimie Industrielle de la Ville de Paris, 1982, chmn. Gordon Rsch. Conf. on Fractals, 1986; Lorentz prof. U. Leiden, Netherlands, 1987; Raymond and Beverly Sackler lectr. Tel Aviv U., 1989; faculty rsch. lectr. UCLA, 1990; Andrew Lawson lectr. U. Calif., Riverside, 1992. Author: (with A.A. Manenkov) SpinLattice Relaxation in Ionic Solids, 1966; Div. assoc. editor Phys. Rev. Letters, 1980-83, Jour. Low Temperature Physics, 1980-90, Phys. Rev., 1983—; contbr. articles to profl. jours. Alfred P. Sloan Found. fellow, 1963-67; NSF sr. postdoctoral fellow Imperial Coll., 1967-68; Guggenheim fellow Tel Aviv U., 1973-74. Fellow Am. Phys. Soc. (chmn. nominations com. 1981-82, counselor-at-large 1987-91, chmn. divsn. condensed matter 1990-91); mem. AAAS (chairperson steering group physics sect.), NSF (mem. rsch. adv. com. divsn. materials 1992-93), Phys. Soc. (London), USN Rsch. Assn. (chair coun. pres. 1993), Sigma Xi, Phi Beta Kappa, Tau Beta Pi. Home: 4171 Watkins Dr Riverside CA 92507 Office: U Calif Riverside Chancellor's Office Riverside CA 92521-0101

ORBAN, EDMOND HENRY, political science educator; b. Heron, Liege, Belgium, Apr. 25, 1925; emigrated to Can., 1961; s. Edmond and Maria (Jamar) O.; m. Anne Marie Anciaux, May 10, 1955; children: Margaret, Christine, Yvon, Francois, Benoit. Ph.D. in Polit. Sci., U. Louvain, Belgium, 1967. Asst. adminstr. Province of Kasaï Govt. of Belgium, 1951-59, adminstr. Province of Kasaï, 1961; prof. polit. sci. U. Montreal, Que., Can., 1961—. Author: La Presidence moderne, 1974, Le Conseil legislatif, 1967, Le Conseil nordique, 1978; author-editor: Mecanisms constitutionnels, 1982, Dynamique de la Centralisation dans l'Etat Fédéral, 1984, Le Systeme politique des Etats-Unis, 1987, Federalism and Supreme Courts, 1991, Federalism, 1992, Système Politique Américain, 1994. Served as info.-commando Belgium Army, 1950-51. Decorated Medal of the Resistance, 1945; chevalier de l'Ordre de la Couronne, Belgium, 1960,. Mem. Can. Polit. Sci. Assn. (v.p.). Roman Catholic. Home: 337 Lac des chats, Saint-Sauveur, PQ Canada J0R 1R1 Office: U Montreal Dept Sci Politique, 2900 Boul Edouard Montpetit, Montreal, PQ Canada H3C 3J7

ORBAN, KURT, foreign trade company executive; b. S.I., N.Y., Aug. 6, 1916; s. Kurt and Gertrude (Astfalck) Orbanowski; children: Robert Arnold, Robin Ann, Kurt-Matthew, Jonathan; m. 2d, Ann Norris, Oct. 1986. Grad. steel fgn. trade course, Stahlunion-Export GmbH, Duesseldorf, Germany, 1938. Fgn. trade corr. Stahlunion, Duesseldorf, 1938; rep. Stahlunion, Bulgaria, 1939-40; steel export trader Steel Union Sheet Piling Co., N.Y.C., 1941; v.p. North River Steel Co., N.Y.C., 1941; chmn., pres. Kurt Orban Co., Inc., Wayne, N.J., from 1946; now sr. ptnr. Kurt Orban Ptnrs. Mem. field hockey games com. U.S. Olympic Com., 1948-61; playing mgr. U.S. Field Hockey Team, London, Eng., 1948, playing coach, Melbourne, Australia, 1956; U.S. rep. Bur. Internat. Hockey Fedn., Brussels, 1954-62. Served to 1st lt. USAAF, 1943-45. Field Hockey Assn. Am. named its cup for each yrs. men's team competition for him. Mem. Am. Inst. Imported Steel (pres. 1966-68, 78-80, bd. dirs. N.Y.C.), Am. Exporters and Importers Assn. (pres. 1972-73, bd. dirs.), West Coast Metal Importers Assn. (bd. dirs.), Wire Assn. Internat. Climbed Mt. Shasta, Calif. (14, 203') and Mt. Kilimanjaro (20, 103'), 1987. Avocation: sr. tennis, skiing, photography, languages. Address: 450 Kings Rd Brisbane CA 94005-1650

ORBEN, JACK RICHARD, investment company executive; b. Bklyn., June 16, 1938; s. Stanley Souza and Helena Emily (Hall) O.; A.A., Valley Forge, 1956; B.A., Tufts U., 1960; m. Patricia Wells, Dec. 17, 1960; children—Stacey Souza, Stephanie Anne, Bradford Richard. Sales mgr. nat. accounts N.Y. Telephone Co., 1960-66; founder, exec. v.p. Facts, Inc., 1966-69; with Orben Assocs., Inc., N.Y.C., 1970—, pres., 1979—; chmn. CEO Associated Family Svcs., Inc., Econ. Analysts, Inc. Starwood Corp.; pres. Venturevest, Inc.; chmn. Fiduciary Counsel, Inc., Estate Mgmt. Co., Seward,

Groves, Richard & Wells; bd. dirs. Unified Holdings, Vintage Funds, Unified Advisers, Inc. Chmn. White Plains Charter Revision Commn.; mem. Fin. Com. City of White Plains; past pres. White Plains Child Day Care Assn., Thomas Slater Ctr.; past chmn., bd. dirs. YMCA of Cen. and No. Westchester. Served with N.G., 1960-66. Clubs: Larchmont Yacht, N.Y. Yacht, City Midday, Union League, Windemere Island, University, Down Town Assn. Home: 177 Soundview Ave White Plains NY 10606-3825 Office: The AFS Group 40 Wall St New York NY 10005-1302

ORBEN, ROBERT, editor, writer; b. N.Y.C., Mar. 4, 1927; s. Walter August and Marie (Neweceral) O.; m. Jean Louise Connelly, July 25, 1945. Humor and speech writer for entertainment personalities, bus. execs., politicians, 1946—; writer Jack Paar Show, N.Y.C., 1962-63, Red Skelton Hour, Hollywood, Calif., 1964-70; editor Orben's Current Comedy, Wilmington, Del., 1971-89; cons. to Vice Pres. Gerald R. Ford, Washington, 1974; speechwriter Pres. Gerald R. Ford, Washington, 1974-75; spl. asst. to pres., dir. White House speechwriting dept., Washington, 1976-77; speaker on uses of humor in communication, 1977—. Author: 2500 Jokes to Start 'Em Laughing, 1979, 2100 Laughs for All Occasions, 1983, 2400 Jokes to Brighten Your Speeches, 1984, 2000 Sure-Fire Jokes for Speakers, 1986; numerous other books of humor for performers and public speakers. Recipient World Humor award Workshop Libr. on World Humor, 1992. Mem. Writers Guild Am. Unitarian. Club: Nat. Press (Washington). Avocations: travel, theater. Home: # 205 E 3709 S George Mason Dr Falls Church VA 22041 I have spent most of my lifetime creating laughter and consider it a lifetime well spent. Laughter is one of the glories of the human experience. It warms, amuses, instructs, and opens emotional doors. For me, laughter has been a living and a loving as well.

ORBEN, ROBERT ALLEN, engine company executive; b. Bklyn., Aug. 18, 1936; s. Stanley Souza and Helena Emily (Hall) O.; m. Mary West Foster, May 7, 1960; children: Christopher Riis, Janet Hyde, Virginia Hamilton, William Robert. BA in Fin., Lehigh U., 1958; MBA in Acctg., Rutgers U., 1960. CPA, N.Y. Audit mgr. Price Waterhouse & Co., N.Y.C., 1958-73; asst. controller NCR Corp., Dayton, Ohio, 1973-74, corp. controller, 1974-76; v.p., controller Cummins Engine Co., Columbus, Ind., 1976-91; gen. mgr. Columbus (Ind.) Container Inc., 1992—; bd. dirs. Fin. Execs. Inst., Morristown, N.J, Hamilton Foundry and Machine Co.; pres. Fin. Execs. Research Found., Morristown, 1985-86. Pres. Columbus Arts Coun., 1980-81; pres. Bartholomew Consol. Sch. Found., Columbus, 1989-90; adv. council Beta Alpha Psi; bd. dirs. Sans Souci, Inc., Columbus, 1985-86. Served to 1st lt. U.S. Army, 1960-62. Mem. Am. Inst. CPA's, Fin. Execs. Inst. (bd. dirs., pres. com. corp. reporting 1985-86), Am. Inst. CPAs, Ohio State Acctg. Hall Fame (mem. adv. com.). Presbyterian. Clubs: Harrison Lake Country (Columbus). Home: 1080 Pintail Ct Columbus IN 47201-8535 Office: Columbus Container Inc 3460 Commerce Dr Columbus IN 47201

ORBON, MARGARET J., lawyer; b. Chgo., Jan. 21, 1951. BA cum laude, St. Mary's Coll., 1973; JD, Loyola U., 1976. Bar: Ill. 1976, U.S. Dist. Ct. (no. dist.) Ill. 1976. Pvt. practice Clausen Miller, Chgo.; lectr. Loyola U., 1976-87. Mem. ABA, Def. Rsch. Inst., Chgo. Bar Assn. Office: Clausen Miller 10 S LaSalle St Chicago IL 60603

ORCE, KENNETH W., lawyer; b. Yonkers, N.Y., Apr. 3, 1943; s. Edmund John and Helen (Mulcahy) O.; m. Helene Mary Sparti, Aug. 20, 1966; children: Kenneth W., Kimberley J., Brian C. B.S. with honors, Manhattan Coll., 1965; LL.B. cum laude, Harvard U., 1968. Bar: N.Y. 1969. Assoc. Cahill Gordon & Reindel, N.Y.C., 1968-76, ptnr. 1976—; bd. dirs. La. Land and Exploration Co. Mem. ABA, Assn. Bar City N.Y., Down Town Assn. (N.Y.C.), Scarsdale (N.Y.) Golf Club, Met. Opera Club. Editor: Harvard Law Rev. 1966-68. Home: 220 Highland Rd Scarsdale NY 10583-1227 Office: Cahill Gordon & Reindel 80 Pine St New York NY 10005-1701

ORCHARD, HENRY JOHN, electrical engineer; b. Oldbury, Eng., May 7, 1922; came to U.S., 1961, naturalized, 1973; s. Richard John and Lucy Matilda O.; m. Irene Dorothy Wise, Sept. 13, 1947; 1 child, Richard John; m. Marietta Eugenie Gayet, Aug. 2, 1971. B.Sc., U. London, 1946, M.Sc., 1951. Prin. sci. officer Brit. Post Office, London, 1947-61; sr. staff GTE Lenkurt Inc., San Carlos, Calif., 1961-70; mem. faculty UCLA, 1970—, prof. elec. engring., 1970-91, prof. emeritus, 1991—, vice chmn. dept., 1982-91. Author. Fellow IEEE (Best Paper award group circuit theory 1968). Republican. Home: 828 19th St Unit E Santa Monica CA 90403 Office: UCLA Elec Engring Dept Los Angeles CA 90095-1594

ORCHARD, ROBERT JOHN, theater producer, educator; b. Maplewood, N.J., Dec. 3, 1946; s. Robert Orchard and Beatrice (Gould) Todd; m. Pamela Marcy Pritchard, Sept. 6, 1969; children: Christopher, Katherine. Student, The Lawrence Acad., 1965; BA, Middlebury Coll., 1969; MFA, Yale U., 1972. Gen. mgr. Peterborough (N.H.) Players, 1967-70; asst. mng. dir. Yale Repertory Theatre, 1971-72, artistic admistr., 1972-73; instr. Yale Sch. Drama, 1972-73; mng. dir. Yale Repertory Theatre and Sch. Drama, 1973-79, Am. Repertory Theatre, Cambridge, Mass., 1979—; assoc. prof., cochmn. Theatre Adminstrn. Tng. Program Yale Sch. Drama, 1975-79; mng. dir. Loeb Drama Ctr., Inst. for Advanced Theatre Tng. Harvard U., 1979—. Bd. dirs. Theatre Commn. Group; pres. bd. Mass. Cultural Edn. Collaborative; former bd. dirs. Am. Arts Alliance, Peterborough Players, Cambridge Multi-Cultural Arts Ctrs.; former exec. com. League of Residents Theatres; chmn. NEA, Profl. Theatre Cos. Panel. Office: Am Repertory Theatre 64 Brattle St Cambridge MA 02138-3443

ORCUTT, DANIEL C., airport terminal executive. Dir. Oklahoma Airport, 1965-1970; exec. dir. Indpls. Airport Authority, 1970—. Office: Indpls Ind Airport Authority PO Box 100 2500 S High School Rd Indianapolis IN 46241-4943

ORCUTT, JOHN ARTHUR, geophysicist; b. Holyoke, Colo., Aug. 29, 1943; married, 1967; 2 children. BS, U.S. Naval Acad., 1966; MSc, U. Liverpool, 1968; PhD in Earth Scis., U. Calif., San Diego, 1976. Fellow Scripps Inst. Oceanography, La Jolla, Calif., 1976-77, rsch. geophysicist, 1977—, assoc. prof., 1982-84, prof. geophysics, 1984—; dir. geophysics & planetary physics divsn., 1984—. Recipient Newcomb Cleveland prize AAAS, 1980. Mem. Am. Geophys. Union (Maurice Ewing award 1994), Soc. Exploration Geophysicists. Office: U Calif Inst Geophys & Planetary Physics UCSD 0225 La Jolla CA 92093*

ORD, ROBERT L., III, military officer; b. Phila., May 12, 1940. BS, U.S. Mil. Acad., 1962; grad., Infantry Officer Advanced Crs., 1969, Command and Gen. Staff Coll., 1974, Army War Coll., 1980. Commd. 2d lt. U.S. Army, 1962, advanced through grades to lt. gen., 1992; with 25th Infantry Divsn., Schofield Barracks, Hawaii, 1962-66; rifle co. comdr. 25th Infantry Divsn., Vietnam, 1966-67; ground liaison officer 516th Tactical Airlift Wing, Dyess AFB, Tex., 1967-68; aide-de-camp to comdg. gen. 1st U.S. Army, Ft. Meade, Md., 1969-72; Vietnamese ranger command sr. advisor Vietnam, 1972-73; chief of plans and ops. Mil. Region IV, Four Party Joint Mil. Commn., Vietnam, 1973; pers. mgmt. officer U.S. Army Mil. Pers. Ctr. (MILPERCEN), Alexandria, Va., 1974-76; comdr. 2d Bn., 1st Infantry Tng. Brigade, Ft. Benning, Ga., 1976-77; from chief inf. br. and officer pers. mgmt. directorate to chief of joint and staff activities br. MILPERCEN; G3, chief of staff, comdr. 9th Inf. Regiment 7th Inf. Divsn., Ft. Ord, Calif.; exec. officer to dep. chief of staff for pers. Dept. Army; chief of staff Combined Field Army, Camp Red Cloud, Korea, 1987-88; asst. divsn. comdr. 7th Inf. Divsn., 1989-90; commdg. gen. U.S. Total Army Pers. Command, Alexandria, Va., 1990-92; comdr. 25th Inf. Divsn. and U.S. Army Hawaii, Schofield Barracks, 1992-93, U.S. Army Pacific, Ft. Shafter, Hawaii, 1993—. Decorated Combat Infantry Badge, D.S.M., Silver Star, Def. Superior Svc. medal, Legion of Merit with oak leaf cluster, Bronze Star with v device with two oak leaf clusters, Air medal with v device and oak leaf cluster, Meritorious Svc. medal with three oak leaf clusters. Office: Department of the Army Chief of Public Affairs office Washington DC 20310

ORDAL, CASPAR REUBEN, business executive; b. Martell, Wis., May 5, 1922; s. Zakarias John and Sina Carlovna (Wulfsberg) O.; m. Ann Elizabeth Brady, June 7, 1947; Christopher Rolf, Peter Stuart. B.S., Harvard Coll., 1946; M.P.A., Harvard U. 1947. Supr. central indsl. relations staff Ford Motor Co., Dearborn, Mich., 1947-53; dir. orgn. planning and mgmt. devel.

Colgate-Palmolive Co., N.Y.C., 1953-65; v.p., gen. mgr. New Holland div. Sperry Rand Corp., (Pa.), 1965-76; corp. v.p. personnel Norton Simon Inc., N.Y.C., 1976-78; sr. v.p. adminstrn. Max Factor & Co., Hollywood, Calif., 1978-85. Served to 1st lt. USAAF, 1943-46. Mem. Personnel Round Table (chmn. 1983-84), Am. Mgmt. Assn. (Adv. council 1977-82), Phi Beta Kappa. Republican. Lutheran. Club: Lancaster (Pa.) Country.

ORDEN, TED, gasoline service stations executive; b. 1920. With Thrifty Oil Co., Inc., Downey, Calif., 1959—, now pres., also bd. dirs. Office: Thrifty Oil Co Inc 10000 Lakewood Blvd Downey CA 90240-4020

ORDIN, ANDREA SHERIDAN, lawyer; m. Robert Ordin; 1 child, Maria; stepchildren: Allison, Richard. AB, UCLA, 1962, LLB, 1965. Bar: Calif. 1966. Dep. atty. gen. Calif., 1965-72; So. Calif. legal counsel Fair Employment Practices Commn., 1972-73; asst. dist. atty. Los Angeles County, 1975-77; U.S. atty. Central Dist. Calif. Los Angeles, 1977-81; adj. prof. UCLA Law Sch., 1982; chief asst. atty. gen. Calif. L.A., 1983-90; ptnr. Morgan, Lewis & Bockius, L.A., 1993—. Mem. Los Angeles County Bar Assn. (past pres., past exec. dir.). Office: Morgan Lewis & Bockius 801 S Grand Ave Fl 22 Los Angeles CA 90017-4613

ORDONEZ, NELSON GONZALO, pathologist; b. Bucaramanga, Santander, Colombia, July 20, 1944; came to U.S., 1972; s. Gonzalo and Itsmenia Ordonez; m. Miranda Lee Ferrell, Dec. 18, 1976 (div. June 1983); 1 child, Nelson Adrian; m. Catherine Marie Newton, Nov. 6, 1987; 1 child, Sara Catherine Itsmenia. BA and Sci., Instituto Daza Dangond, Bogota, Colombia, 1962; MD, Nat. U. Colombia, Bogota, 1970. Resident pathology U. N.C., Chapel Hill, 1972-73; resident pathology U. Chgo., 1974-76, asst. prof. pathology, 1977-78; asst. prof. pathology U. Tex. M.D. Anderson Cancer Ctr., Houston, 1978-82, assoc. prof., 1983-85, prof., 1985—, dir. immunocytochemistry sect., 1981—. Author: (with others) Renal Biopsy Pathology and Diagnostic and Therapeutic Implications, 1980, Tumors of the Lung, 1991; contbr. chpts. to books, numerous articles to med. jours. Nat. Kidney Found. fellow, 1977-78. Mem. AMA, Am. Assn. Pathologists, Internat. Acad. Pathology, Am. Soc. Clin. Pathologists, Am. Soc. Cytology, Am. Soc. Investigative Pathology, Internat. Acad. Cytology, Arthur Purdy Stout Soc. Surg. Pathologists, Latin-Am. Soc. Pathology. Office: U Tex MD Anderson Cancer Ctr 1515 Holcombe Blvd Houston TX 77030-4009

ORDOVER, ABRAHAM PHILIP, lawyer; b. Far Rockaway, N.Y., Jan. 18, 1937; s. Joseph and Bertha (Fromberg) O.; m. Carol M. Ordover, Mar. 23, 1961; children: Andrew Charles, Thomas Edward. BA magna cum laude, Syracuse U., 1958; JD, Yale U., 1961. Bar: N.Y. 1961, U.S. Dist. Ct. (so. and ea. dists.) N.Y., U.S. Ct. Appeals (2d cir.), U.S. Supreme Ct. Assoc. Cahill, Gordon & Reindel, N.Y.C., 1961-71; prof. law Hofstra U., Hempstead, N.Y., 1971-81; L.Q.C. Lamar prof. law Emory U., Atlanta, 1981-91; CEO Resolution Resources Corp., Atlanta, 1991—; mediator and arbitrator; vis. prof. Cornell U., Ithaca, N.Y., 1977; vis. lectr. Tel Aviv U., 1989, Am. Law Inst.; team leader nat. program Nat. Inst. Trial Advocacy, Boulder, Colo., 1980, 82, 84, 86, 89, tchr. program Cambridge, Mass., 1979-84, 88, adv. program Gainesville, Fla., 1978-79, northeast regional dir., 1977-81; team leader SE regional program, 1983; team leader Atlanta Bar Trial Tech. Program, 1981-91; lectr. in field. Author: Argument to the Jury, 1982, Problems and Cases in Trial Advocacy, 1983, Advanced Materials in Trial Advocacy, 1988, Alternatives to Litigation, 1993, Cases and Materials in Evidence, 1993, Art of Negotiation, 1994; producer ednl. films; contbr. articles to profl. jours. Bd. dirs. Atlanta Legal Aid Soc., 1984-91. Recipient Gumpert award Am. Coll. Trial Lawyers, 1984, 85, Jacobsen award Roscoe Pound Am. Trial Lawyer Found., 1986. Mem. ABA, N.Y. State Bar Assn., Assn. Am. Law Schs. (chair litigation sect.), Atlanta Lawyers Club, Am. Law Inst. Avocations: photography, scuba diving, jogging. Office: Resolution Resources Corp Ste 2850 Marquis One 2960 One Peachtree Cir Atlanta GA 30308

ORDWAY, ELLEN, biology educator, entomology researcher; b. N.Y.C., Nov. 8, 1927; d. Samuel Hanson and Anna (Wheatland) O. B.A., Wheaton Coll., Mass., 1950; M.S., Cornell U., 1955; Ph.D., U. Kans., 1965. Field asst. N.Y. Zool. Soc., N.Y.C., 1950-52; research asst. Am. Mus. Natural History, N.Y.C., 1955-57; teaching asst. U. Kans., Lawrence, 1957-61, research asst. 1959-65; asst. prof. U. Minn., Morris, 1965-70, assoc. prof. biology, 1970-85, prof., 1986—; cooperator and cons. U.S. Dept. Agr. Bee Research Lab., Tucson, Ariz., 1971, 1983. Contbr. articles to sci. jours. Mgr. preserves Nature Conservancy, Mpls., 1975—; lectr. Morris area service clubs, 1972—. Mem. Ecol. Soc. Am., Entomol. Soc. Am., Soc. Systematic Biology, Soc. Study Evolution, Kans. Entomol. Soc., Internat. Bee Research Assn., AAAS, AAUP (v.p. 1975-76, sec.-treas. 1971-73 Morris chpt.), Sigma Xi, Sigma Delta Epsilon. Episcopalian. Avocations: travel, photography, raquetball, exploring natural environments, wilderness, areas, etc. Office: U Minn Div Sci And Math Morris MN 56267

ORDWAY, FREDERICK IRA, III, educator, consultant, researcher, author; b. N.Y.C., Apr. 4, 1927; s. Frederick Ira and Frances Antoinette (Wright) O.; m. Maria Victoria Arenas, Apr. 13, 1950; children: Frederick Ira IV, Albert James, Aliette Marisol. S.B., Harvard, 1949; postgrad., U. Alger, 1950, U. Paris, France, 1950-51, 53-54, U. Barcelona, Spain, 1953, U. Innsbruck, Austria, 1954, Air U., 1952-63, Alexander Hamilton Bus. Inst., 1952-58, Indsl. Coll. Armed Forces, 1953, 63; DSc (hon.), U. Ala., 1992. Various ocel., engring. positions Mene Grande Oil Co., San Tome, Venezuela, 1949-50, Orinoco Mining Co., Cerro Bolivar, Venezuela, 1950, Reaction Motors, Inc., Lake Denmark, N.J., 1951-53; with guided missiles div. Republic Aviation Corp., 1954-55; pres. Gen. Astronautics Research Corp., Huntsville, Ala., 1955-59, 65-66; v.p. Nat. Research & Devel. Corp., Atlanta, 1957-59; asst. to dir. Saturn Systems Office, Army Ballistic Missile Agy., Huntsville, 1959-60; chief space information systems br. George C. Marshall Space Flight Center NASA, 1960-64; prof. sci. and tech. applications Sch. Grad. Studies and Research, U. Ala. Research Inst., 1967-73; cons. Sci. and Tech. Policy Office, NSF, 1974-75, Ops. Analysis div. Gen. Research Corp., 1974-75; asst. to adminstr. ERDA, 1975-77; Dept. Energy, 1977-80, dir. spl. projects, 1981-94; aerospace cons., 1994—; also participant internat. energy devel. program Office of Asst. Sec. Internat. Affairs, Dept. Energy, 1978-79; cons. to industry, Ency. Britannica, Am. Coll. Dictionary of English Lang., M.G.M. film 2001: A Space Odyssey, 1965-66, Paramount Picture Corp., The Adventurers , 1968-69; internat. lectr. space flight and energy programs. Author: (with C.C. Adams) Space Flight, 1958, (with Ronald C. Wakeford) International Missile and Spacecraft Guide, 1960, Annotated Bibliography of Space Science and Technology, 1962, (with J.P. Gardner, M.R. Sharpe, Jr.) Basic Astronautics: An Introduction to Space Science, Engineering and Medicine, 1962, (with Adams, Wernher von Braun) Careers in Astronautics and Rocketry, 1962, (with Gardner, Sharpe, R.C. Wakeford) Applied Astronautics: An Introduction to Space Flight, 1963, (with Wakeford) Conquering the Sun's Empire, 1963, Life in Other Solar Systems, 1965, (with Roger A. MacGowan) Intelligence in the Universe, 1966, (with W. von Braun) History of Rocketry and Space Travel, 1966, 1969, 75, L'Histoire Mondiale de l'Astronautique, 1968, 70, Rockets Red Glare, 1976, (with C.C. Adams, M.R. Sharpe) Dividends from Space, 1972, Pictorial Guide to Planet Earth, 1975, (with W. von Braun) New Worlds, 1979, (with M.R. Sharpe) The Rocket Team, 1979, (with F.C. Durant and R.C. Seamans) Between Sputnik and the Shuttle, 1981, (with E.M. Emme) Science Fiction and Space Futures, 1982, (with von Braun, Dave Dooling) Space Travel: A History, 1985, (with Ernst Stuhlinger) Wernher von Braun: Aufbrach in den Weltraum, 1992, Wernher von Braun: Crusader for Space (2 vols.), 1994, Passion for Spaceships, 1995; (with Randy Liebermann) Blueprint for Space, 1992; editor: Advances in Space Science and Technology, vols. I-XII, 2 supplements, 1959-72, (with R.M.L. Baker, N.W. Makemson) Introduction to Astrodynamics, 1960, (with others) From Peenemünde to Outer Space, 1962, Astronautical Engineering and Science, 1963; mem. editorial bd.: (with others) IX Internat. Astronautical Congress procs., 2 vols, 1959, Xth Congress procs, 2 vols, 1960; guest editor: Acta Astronautica, 1985, 94, History of Rocketry and Astronautics, Vol. IX, 1989; contbr. (with others) numerous articles to profl. jours., U.S. and fgn. encys., chpts. to books, sects. to others; organizer Blueprint for Space exhbn. 1991-95, U.S. Space and Rocket Ctr., IBM Gallery of Sci. and Art, NASA Vis. Ctr., Houston, Spaceport USA, Cape Canaveral, Fla., Nat. Air and Space Mus., Washington, Va. Air and Space Ctr., Hampton. Served with USNR, 1945. Recipient (with W. von Braun) diplôme d'honneur French Commn. d'Histoire, Arts et Lettres, Paris, 1969; commended for contbns. to

U.S. Space and Rocket Ctr., Ala. Space Sci. Exhibit. Fellow AAAS, Brit. Interplanetary Soc., AIAA (history com. 1975—, internat. activities com. 1980-89, Pendray award 1974, Hermann Oberth award 1977); mem. Internat. Acad. Astronautics (history of astronautics com. 1983—,chmn. 1989—, space activities and soc. com. 1986—, peer review com. 1985—, co-recipient Luigi Napolitano Literature award, 1992), Am. Astronautical Soc. (Emme award 1994), Brit. Interplanetary Soc., Nat. Space Soc. (bd. dirs. 1986—, mem. publs. com. 1987-88, nominating com. 1990-92), Cosmos Club (bd. mgmt. 1986-91, v.p. 1988-90), Harvard Club N.Y. Home: 3423 Lookout Dr Huntsville AL 35801 Office: Dept Energy Forrestal Bldg 4a107 Washington DC 20585

ORDWAY, JOHN DANTON, pension administrator, lawyer, accountant; b. Mpls., Mar. 19, 1928; s. John Dunreath Ordway and Inez Adelaide (Stahl) Larson; m. Mary E. Bateman, June 16, 1951(div. 1978); 1 child, David. BBA, Am. U., 1963, JD, 1965. Bar: U.S. Dist. Ct. D.C. 1966; CPA, Minn. Dir. ins. Nat. Automobile Dealers Assn., Washington, 1957-69; v.p. Edward H. Friend and Co., Washington, 1969-74; exec. v.p. and CEO Pension Bds. United Ch. of Christ, N.Y.C., 1974—. Alt. mem. Planning Bd., Stamford, Conn., 1982-86. With U.S. Army, 1946-47. Mem. AICPAs. Republican. Mem. United Ch. of Christ. Club: Westwood Country (Vienna, Va.); Quail Run Golf Club (Naples, Fla.). Lodge: Kena Temple. Home: 304 River W Greenwich CT 06831-4164

O'REAR, EDGAR ALLEN, III, chemical engineering educator; b. Jasper, Ala., Feb. 24, 1953; s. Edgar Allen Jr. and Edith (Idzorek) O'R. BSChemE., Rice U., 1975; SM in Organic Chemistry, MIT, 1977; PhD, Rice U., 1981. Rsch. engr. Exxon Rsch. and Engring., Baytown, Tex., 1975; asst. prof. U. Okla., Norman, 1981-86, assoc. prof., 1986-91, prof., 1991—, Conoco Distng. lectr., 1987-92; vis. sr. researcher Hitachi Cen. Rsch. Lab., Kokubunji, Japan, 1988; vis. scientist RIKEN-Inst. for Phys. and Chem. Rsch., Wakoshi, Japan, 1992; cons. Kerr-McGee Corp., Oklahoma City, Boehringer-Mannheim Corp., Indpls., Baxter-Travenol, Inc., Deerfield, Ill., Associated Metallurgists, Norman. Contbr. articles to profl. jours.; co-author books; inventor, patentee producing polymeric films from a surfactant template, method and composition for treatment of thrombosis in a mammal; reviewer for sci. pubs. and funding agencies. Mentor Big Bros./Big Sisters, Norman, 1984-86; usher, mem. parish coun. St. Thomas More Cath. Ch., Norman; mem. Japan-Okla. Soc., Oklahoma City, U. Okla. Faculty Senate, Norman, 1984-86. Recipient Sigma Xi Faculty Rsch. award U. Okla. chpt. Sigma Xi, 1986. Mem. AAAS, NSF (separations and purification program dir. 1993-94), Internat. Soc. Biorheology (sec. gen.), North Am. Soc. Biorheology (charter, membership com.), Am. Chem. Soc., Biomed. Engring., Soc., Soc. Rheology, Okla. Acad. Scis., MIT Chemists' Club, Tau Beta Pi, Sigma Xi, Phi Lambda Upsilon. Roman Catholic. Office: U Okla Dept Chem Engring 100 E Boyd St Rm 335T Norman OK 73069-5816

OREAR, JAY, physics educator, researcher; b. Chgo., Nov. 6, 1925; s. Leslie and Edna (Tragnitz) O.; m. Jeanne Bliven, Mar. 10, 1951; children—Scott, Robin, Wendy; m. Virginia Watts, Sept. 6, 1974. Ph.B., U. Chgo., 1944, Ph.D., 1953. Research assoc. U. Chgo., 1953-54; instr. to asst. prof. Columbia U., N.Y.C., 1954-58; assoc. prof. Cornell U., Ithaca, N.Y., 1958-64, prof. physics, nuclear studies, 1964—; Chmn. Fedn. Am. Scientists, 1967-68. Author: Nuclear Physics, 1951, Fundamental Physics, 1961, Programmed Manual, 1963, Statistics for Physicists, 1958, 82, Physics, 1979. Served with USNR, 1944-46. Fellow AAAS, Am. Phys. Soc. (editor Forum Newsletter 1972-74); mem. Phi Beta Kappa, Sigma Xi. Home: 20 Sun Path Ithaca NY 14850-9781

OREFFICE, PAUL FAUSTO, retired chemical company executive; b. Venice, Italy, Nov. 29, 1927; came to U.S., 1945, naturalized, 1951; s. Max and Elena (Friedenberg) O.; m. Franca Giuseppina Ruffini, May 26, 1956; children: Laura Emma, Andrew T. B.S. in Chem. Engring., Purdue U., 1949. With Dow Chem. Co., various internat. locations, 1953-92; assigned to Switzerland, Italy, Brazil and Spain to 1969; pres. Dow Chem. Latin Am., Coral Gables, Fla., 1966-70; corporate fin. v.p. Dow Chem. Co., Midland, Mich., 1970-75, pres. Dow Chem. U.S.A., 1975-78, pres., chief exec. officer, 1978-86, chmn., pres., chief exec. officer, 1986-87, chmn. bd., 1987-92; ret., 1992; bd. dirs. Morgan Stanley Group Inc., Inc., CIGNA Corp., No. Telecom Ltd., Coca Cola Co. Chmn. bd. trustees Am. Enterprise Inst.; trustee Morehouse Coll.; bd. govs. Nat. Parkinson Found.; chmn. bd. overseers Inst. Civil Justice; mem. sr. adv. bd. Arthritis Found. Decorated Encomienda del Merito Civil Spain, 1966. Mem. Chem. Mfrs. Assn., Bus. Coun. (mem. adv. com. for trade policy and negotiations). Office: The Dow Chem Co 2030 Willard H Dow Ctr Midland MI 48674

O'REGAN, RICHARD ARTHUR, editor, retired foreign correspondent; b. Boston, July 15, 1919; s. Arthur R. and Amelia H. (Egbers) O'R.; m. Elizabeth A. Hill, Mar. 23, 1946; children—John K., Michael L. Student. Temple U., 1940-41, Vienna U., Austria, 1953-54. With London Daily Mail and London Daily Sketch, 1938-39; reporter, night city editor Phila. Bull., 1939-43; writer Russian-German war specialist UPI, 1943-45; fgn. corr. AP, 1945-84; assigned AP, London, Paris, Germany, 1945-50; chief bur. AP, Vienna, 1950-55, Germany, 1956-66, London, 1966-77; dir. gen. for AP, Europe, Africa and Middle East, 1977-84; mng. dir., editor-in-chief Oriole Internat. Publs., Geneva, 1987—; bd. dirs. A.P. Ltd. Co-author: International Geneva (ann.). Mem. Assn. Am. Corrs. in London (pres. 1969). Clubs: Overseas Press (N.Y.C.); Press (Frankfurt, Germany) (past pres.); London Press, London Directors. Home: 33 Chemin de Grange Canal, 1208 Geneva Switzerland

O'REILLY, ANTHONY JOHN FRANCIS, food company executive; b. Dublin, Ireland, May 7, 1936; s. John Patrick and Aileen (O'Connor) O'R.; m. Susan Cameron, May 5, 1962 (div.); children: Susan, Cameron, Justine, Gavin, Caroline, Tony; m. Chryss Goulandris, Sept. 14, 1991. Student, Belvedere Coll., Dublin, Univ. Coll., Dublin, Wharton Bus. Sch. Overseas, 1965; B.C.L.; D.C.L. (hon.), Ind. State U.; Ph.D. in Agrl. Mktg, U. Bradford, Eng.; LL.D. (hon.), Wheeling Coll., 1974, Trinity Coll., Dublin, 1978, Allegheny Coll., 1983, De Paul U., Chgo., 1988; D in Bus. Studies (hon.), Rollins Coll., 1978; D in Civil Law honoris causa, Ind. State U., 1980; DBA (hon.), Boston Coll., 1985; D in Econ. Sci. (hon.), Nat. U. Ireland, 1989. Indsl. cons. Weston Evans, 1958-62; personal asst. to chmn. Suttons Ltd., Cork, Ireland, 1960-62; lectr. dept. applied psychology Univ. Coll., Cork, 1960-62; dir. Robert McCowen & Sons Ltd., Tralee, Ireland, 1961-62; mng. dir. An Bord Bainne/Irish Dairy Bd., 1962-66; dir. Agrl. Credit Corp. Ltd., 1965-66, Nitrigin Eireann Teoranta, 1965-66; mng. dir., chief exec. officer Comhlucht Siuicre Eireann Teo. (Irish Sugar Co.) and Erin Foods Ltd., Dublin, 1966-69; joint mng. dir. Heinz-Erin Ltd., 1967-70; mng. dir. H.J. Heinz Co. Ltd., Eng., 1969-71; sr. v.p. N.Am. and Pacific H.J. Heinz Co., 1971-72; exec. v.p., chief operating officer H.J. Heinz Co., Pitts., 1972-73, pres., chief operating officer, 1973-79, pres., chief exec. officer, 1979—, also chmn., 1978—, also bd. dirs.; chmn. Fitzwilton Plc., Independent Newspapers Plc., Atlantic Resources, Dublin, Am. Ireland Fund.; ptnr. Cawley Sheerin Wynne and Co., solicitors, Dublin; bd. dirs. Bankers Trust N.Y. Corp., Bankers Trust N.Y. Corp., Washington Post Co. London Tablet Found. Inc., Starkist Foods Inc., Ore-Ida Foods Inc. Author: Prospect, 1962, Developing Creative Management, 1970, The Conservative Consumer, 1971, Food for Thought, 1972. Bd. govs. Hugh O'Brian Found., L.A.; mem. counc. Rockefeller U., N.Y.C.; bd. dirs. Assocs. Grad. Sch. Bus. Adminstrn. of Harvard U., Cambridge, Mass.; sr. bd. dirs. The Conf. Bd.; trustee U. Pitts., Com. for Econ. Devel.; mem. Nat. Com. Whitney Mus. Am. Art. Named Hon. Officer Order of Australia, 1988. Fellow Brit. Inst. Mgmt., Royal Soc. Arts; mem. Inst. Dirs., Inc., Law Soc. Ireland (treas.), Grocery Mfrs. Am. (sec., bd. dirs.), Am. Irish Found., Internat. Life Scis. Inst. Nutrition Found. (chmn., chief exec. officer council), Irish Mgmt. Inst. (council), Exec. Council Fgn. Diplomats (bd. dirs.). Clubs: St. Stephens Green, Kildare St., University (Dublin); Annabels, Les Ambassadeurs, Marks (London); Union League, The Links, The Bd. Room (N.Y.C.); Duquesne, Allegheny, Pitts. Golf, Fox Chapel Golf, Pitts. Press, Pitts. Golf (Pitts.); Rolling Rock (Ligonier) (bd. govs.); Lyford Cay (Bahamas). Office: H J Heinz Co PO Box 57 600 Grant St Pittsburgh PA 15219-2857 also: Mobil Corp 150 E 42nd St New York NY 10017-5612*

O'REILLY, CHARLES TERRANCE, university dean; b. Chgo., May 30, 1921; s. William Patrick and Ann Elizabeth (Madden) O'R.; m. Rosella Catherine Neilland, June 4, 1955; children—Terrance, Gregory, Kevin, Joan

Bridget, Kathleen Ann. B.A., Loyola U., Chgo., 1942, M.S.W., 1948; post-grad., U. Cattolica, Milan, Italy, 1949-50; Ph.D., U. Notre Dame, 1954. Instr. DePaul U., Chgo., 1948-49; asst. in psychology U. Cattolica, 1949-50; caseworker Cath. Charities, N.Y.C., 1953-54; exec. dir. Family Service, Long Branch, N.J., 1954-55; asst. prof. Loyola U., 1955-59; vis. lectr. Ensiss Sch. Social Work, Milan, 1959-60; asso. prof. U. Wis.-Milw., 1961-64; prof., asso. dir. U. Wis. Sch. Social Work, Madison, 1965-68; dean social welfare, v.p. acad. affairs SUNY-Albany, 1969-76; dean social work Loyola U., Chgo., 1976-92; vis. prof. sch. social work SS Maria Asunta, Rome, 1992-93. Author: OAA Profile, 1961, People of Inner Core North, 1965, Men in Jail, 1968; contbr. articles to profl. jours. Pres. Community Action Commn. Dane County, Wis., 1967-68; bd. dirs. Council Community Services, Albany, Family and Children's Service, Albany; mem. adv. bd. Safer Found.; vice chmn. Ill. Pub. Aid Citizens Council. Served with AUS, 1942-46, 51-52. Fulbright scholar, 1949-50; fellow, 1959-60. Mem. AAUP, Nat. Assn. Social Workers. Roman Catholic. Home: 4073 Bunker Ln Wilmette IL 60091-1001 Office: Sch Social Work Loyola Univ Chicago IL 60611

O'REILLY, DENIS, aluminum company executive, lawyer; b. Pointe Gatineau, Que., Can., Feb. 9, 1950; s. Florian D. and Marielle O'R.; B.A. with honors, Three Rivers U., 1969; LL.L., Montreal U., 1973; postgrad. Ecole des Hautes Etudes Commerciales, Montreal, 1976; m. Jocelyne Ryter, Aug. 16, 1980; children: Marianne, Patrick. Called to Que. bar, 1975; research worker Sec. of State, Ottawa, Ont., Can., 1971; analyst Datum Sedoj, Montreal, Que., Can., 1972; assoc. firm Lette & Assocs., Montreal, 1973-76; legal officer Aluminum Co. of Can., Ltd., Montreal, 1977-80; chief legal officer, sec. Alcan Smelters and Chems. Ltd., Montreal, 1981-82, also dir. adminstrn.; pres., gen. mgr. Vic Metal Corp., Victoriaville, Que., 1982—; pres., Vic West Steel, Oakville, Ont., 1986—. Mem. Bd. Trade (Que.), Quebec Bar Assn., Can. Bar Assn., Can. Constrn. Assn. (dir.). Office: 1296 So Svc Rd W, Oakville, ON Canada L6L 5M7

O'REILLY, DON, reporter, writer, photographer; b. Attleboro, Mass., May 1, 1913; s. Dennis Charles and Helen Louise (Barden) O'R.; m. Edith Lillian Macomber, July 9, 1938; 1 child, Howard (dec.). Owner, operator Eagle Press, 1930-37; reporter, photographer Attleboro (Mass.) Sun, 1937-39, N. Attleboro Chronicle, 1939-40, New London (Conn.) Day, 1940-42, Washington Post, 1945-47; editor, pub. Speed Age Mag., Washington, 1947-53; mgr. NASCAR News Bur., Daytona Beach, Fla., 1953-56; sports broadcaster NBC Radio Monitor, various locations, 1956-59, Stas. WESH-TV, WROD, Daytona Beach, 1956-59; dir. pub. rels. Atlanta Internat. Raceway, 1959-64; mgr. automotive divsn., writer, prodn. asst., unit mgr. sports documentaries Dynamic Films, Inc., 1964-68; pub. rels. Am. Motor Corp., 1971-75; broadcaster Mutual, ABC, NBC, 1968-80; writer Popular Mechanics, Sat. Evening Post, Stock Car Racing, Argosy, Small Cars, Illustrated Speedway News, others, 1968-80; bur. chief, reporter, photographer News-Jour., Daytona Beach, 1976-80; feature writer Circle Track Mag., Speed Age, Stock Car Racing, Racing Pictorial, others, 1980-90; columnist various newspapers, 1980-90; feature writer newspapers, mags., books, 1991—; stringer Boston Post, Globe, Herald-Traveler, 1937-39; dir. press rels. U.S. Grand Prix; self-syndicated columnist Inside Auto Racing, Motorcade USA, 1956-85. Author: Mr. Hockey: The World of Gordie Howe, The Complete Book of Motor Camping, Sports Review-Motorspeed, Auto Racing Guide, (with Curtis Crider) The Road to Daytona. Chief photographers mate U.S. Coast Guard, 1942-45. Elected to Nat. Auto Racing Hall of Fame by Nat. Old Timers Auto Racing Club, Flemington, N.J., 1988; named Living Legend of Auto Racing by Living Legends, Port Orange, Fla., 1993, Hon. Order of Ky. Cols., Louisville, 1990. Mem. Nat. Motorsports Press Assn., Ea. Motorsports Press Assn. (1st pl. award in feature writing 1991), Nat. Press Club, Am. Assn. Auto Racing Writers (v.p.), Nat. Press Photographers Assn. (charter, life), Am. Auto Racing Writers and Broadcasters Assn. (Best Column of Yr. 1989), Nat. Sportswriters and Sportscasters Assn., Soc. Profl. Journalists, Nikon Profl. Svcs., Fla. Freelance Writers Assn., Halifax Hist. Soc., Bay State Old Timers Racing Assn., Williams Grove Old Timers, Indpls. 500 Old Timers Club (charter, life). Home and Office: 198 Sea Pines Cir Indigo Lakes Daytona Beach FL 32114-1166

O'REILLY, HUGH JOSEPH, restaurant executive; b. Emporia, Kans., July 20, 1936; s. Henry Charles and Mary Esther (Rettiger) O'R.; m. Eileen Ellen Browne, Feb. 11, 1961; 1 child, Hugh Jr. Student, St. Benedicts Coll., Atchison, Kans., 1954-57, Kansas City Conservatory of Music, 1957-58. Banquet mgr. Stouffer Corp., N.Y.C., 1958-61; gen. mgr. Howard Johnsons, L.I., N.Y., 1961-65; regional mgr. Malt Village Corp., St. Louis, 1965-68; ops. cons. McDonald's Corp., Chgo., 1968-78; pres., chief exec. officer O'Reilly Mgmt. Corp., Emporia, Kans., 1978—; nat. advt. cons. McDonalds Operators Assn., Oak Brook, Ill., 1980-84. Republican. Roman Catholic. Lodge: Shriner. Avocations: golf, fishing. Office: 907 Commercial St Emporia KS 66801-2916

O'REILLY, JAMES THOMAS, lawyer, educator, author; b. N.Y.C., Nov. 15, 1947; s. Matthew Richard and Regina (Casey) O'R.; m. Rosann Tagliaferro, Aug. 26, 1972; children: Jean, Ann. BA cum laude, Boston Coll., 1969; JD, U. Va., 1974. Bar: Va. 1974, Ohio, 1974, U.S. Supreme Ct. 1979, U.S. Ct. Appeals (6th cir.) 1980. Atty. Procter & Gamble Co., Cin., 1974-76, counsel, 1976-79, sr. counsel for food, drug and product safety, 1979-85, corp. counsel, 1985-93, assoc. gen. counsel, 1993—; adj. prof. in adminstrv. law U. Cin., 1980—; cons. Adminstrv. Conf. U.S., 1981-82, 89-90; arbitrator State Employee Relations Bd.; mem. Ohio Bishops Adv. Council, Mayor's Infrastructure Commn, Cin. Environ. Adv. Coun. Author: Federal Information Disclosure, 1977, Food and Drug Administration Regulatory Manual, 1979, Unions' Rights to Company Information, 1980, Federal Regulation of the Chemical Industry, 1980, Administrative Rulemaking, 1983, Ohio Public Employee Collective Bargaining, 1984, Protecting Workplace Secrets, 1985, Emergency Response to Chemical Accidents, 1986, Product Defects and Hazards, 1987, Toxic Torts Strategy Deskbook, 1989; Protecting Trade Secrets Under SARA, 1988, Complying With Canada's New Labeling Law, 1989, Solid Waste Mgmt., 1991, Ohio Products Liability Handbook, 1991, Toxic Torts Guide, 1992, ABA Product Liability Resource Manual, 1993, RCRA and Superfund Practice Guide, 1993, Clean Air Permits manual, 1994, United States Environmental Liabilities, 1994, Elder Safety, 1994; contbr. articles to profl. jours.; editorial bd. Food and Drug Cosmetic Law Jour. Mem. Hamilton County Dem. Central Com. Served with U.S. Army, 1970-72. Mem. Food and Drug Law Inst. (chair program com.), ABA (chmn. AD law sect.), Fed. Bar Assn., Leadership Cin. Democrat. Roman Catholic. Office: Procter & Gamble Co PO Box 599 Cincinnati OH 45201-0599

O'REILLY, RICHARD BROOKS, journalist; b. Kansas City, Mo., Feb. 19, 1941; s. Charles Alfred and Wilma Faye (Brooks) O'R.; m. Anne Pustmeuller, June 27, 1974 (div. 1978); children—Kathleen Marie, Randall Charles; m. Joan Marlene Sweeney, Jan. 1, 1981. B.A., U. Denver, 1966. Reporter Washington Park Times, Denver, 1963-64; mng. editor Aurora Advocate, Colo., 1964; police reporter Rocky Mountain News, Denver, 1964-66, night rewrite reporter, 1966, city hall reporter, 1966-67, statehouse reporter, 1967-68, investigative reporter, 1971-74; minority affairs reporter Denver Post, 1968-70; freelance writer St. Georges, Grenada, 1970; investigative reporter Orange County edition Los Angeles Times, 1974-78, chief county bur., 1978, asst. met. editor, 1978-80, environ. reporter, 1980-84; computer columnist, syndicated columnist, 1983—, coord. tech. resources, 1984-89, dir. editorial computer analysis, 1989—; adj. prof. journalism U. So. Calif., 1990-92. Named Colo. Journalist of Yr., Sigma Delta Chi, 1972; recipient Pub. Svc. award U.S. Justice Dept., 1973, McWilliams award Denver Press Club, 1974, Investigative Reporting award Orange Country Press Club, 1977, 95, Los Angeles Times, 1977, Nat. Journalism award Soc. Profl. Engrs., 1983, Clean Air award Am. Lung Assn., 1985. Democrat. Avocations: flying; sailing; camping. Office: Los Angeles Times Times Mirror Sq Los Angeles CA 90012

O'REILLY, THOMAS EUGENE, human resources consultant; b. Wichita, Kans., Sept. 7, 1932; s. Eugene William and Florence Irene (Gustner) O'R.; m. Lorraine Bryant, Feb. 9, 1957; children: Thomas Jr., Patricia, Susan, Gregory, Pamela. BA, Iona Coll., 1954; MBA, NYU, 1958. Mem. human resources staff Chase Manhattan Bank, N.Y.C., 1957-69; dir. employee rels. Chase Manhattan Bank, 1969-71, mgr. internat. personnel, 1971-75, dir. internal staffing, 1976-77, dir. mgmt. resources, 1978-80; dir. exec. resources

Chase Manhattan Bank, N.Y.C., 1980-87; v.p., sr. cons. Lee Hecht Harrison, Inc., N.Y.C., 1988-93. Spl. agt. counter-intelligence corps, U.S. Army, 1954-57. Mem. Nat. Fgn. Trade Coun., Exec. Issues Forum. Republican. Roman Catholic. Home and Office: 6200 E Cielo Run Cave Creek AZ 85331-7645

O'REILLY, THOMAS PATRICK, state senator, lawyer; b. N.Y.C., Sept. 2, 1938; B.E.E., U. Md., 1968, J.D., 1972; m. Barbara E. Smith. Admitted to Md. bar, 1972; law clk. Circuit Ct. Prince George's County; ptnr. firm Thomas Patrick O'Reilly; mem. Md. State Senate, 1975—. Mem. ABA, Md. Bar Assn., Prince George's County Bar Assn., Md. Trial Lawyers Assn. Am. Legion. Democrat. Clubs: Elks, Irish-American. Office: 5707 E West Hwy Riverdale MD 20737-2165 Address: PW James Senate Office Bldg 110 College Ave Annapolis MD 21401

O'REILLY, TIMOTHY PATRICK, lawyer; b. San Lorenzo, Calif., Sept. 12, 1945; s. Thomas Marvin and Florence Ann (Ohlman) O'R.; m. Susan Ann Marshall, July 18, 1969; children: T. Patrick Jr., Sean M., Colleen K. BS, Ohio State U., 1967; JD, NYU, 1971. Bar: Pa. 1971, U.S. Dist. Ct. (ea. dist.) Pa. 1971, U.S. Dist. Ct. (mid. dist.) Pa. 1972, U.S. Ct. Appeals (3d cir.) 1977, U.S. Supreme Ct. 1988. Ptnr. Morgan, Lewis & Bockius, Phila., 1978—. Editor: Developing Labor Law, 1989; contbr. articles to profl. jours. V.p. Chester Valley Bd. Govs., Malvern, Pa., 1980-85. Mem. ABA (chmn. com. on devel. of the law under the Nat. Labor Relations Act., editor-in-chief The Developing Labor Law jour.), Pa. Bar Assn., Phila. Bar Assn., Ohio State U. Alumni Assn. Avocation: golf. Home: 1127 Cymry Dr Berwyn PA 19312-2056 Office: Morgan Lewis & Bockius 2000 One Logan Sq Philadelphia PA 19103

O'REILLY, VINCENT M., accounting firm executive; b. 1937. BS, Boston Coll., 1959; MBA, U Pa., 1961. With Coopers & Lybrand, N.Y.C., 1961—, dep. chmn., 1988—. Office: Coopers & Lybrand 1251 Ave of the Americas New York NY 10020-1104

OREL, HAROLD, literary critic, educator; b. Boston, Mar. 31, 1926; s. Saul and Sarah (Wicker) O.; m. Charlyn Hawkins, May 25, 1951; children: Sara Elinor, Timothy Ralston. BA cum laude, U. N.H., 1948; MA, U. Mich., 1949, PhD, 1952; postgrad., Harvard U., 1949. Teaching fellow U. Mich., 1948-52; instr. dept. English, U. Md., 1952-54, 55-56; overseas program U. Md., Germany, Austria, Eng., 1954-55; tech. editor Applied Physics Lab., Johns Hopkins U., Balt., 1953-56; flight propulsion lab. dept. Gen. Electric Co., Cin., 1957; asso. prof. U. Kans., Lawrence, 1957-63; prof. U. Kans., 1963-74, Disting. prof. English, 1974—; asst. dean faculties and research adminstrn., 1964-67; cons. to various univ. presses, scholarly jours., Can. Coun. Arts, Nat. Endowment of Humanities, Midwest Rsch. Inst., 1958—; lectr., Japan, 1974, 88, India, 1985. Author: Thomas Hardy's Epic-Drama: A Study of The Dynasts, 1963, The Development of William Butler Yeats, 1885-1900, 1968, English Romantic Poets and the Enlightenment: Nine Essays on a Literary Relationship in Studies in Voltaire and the Eighteenth Century, vol. CIII, 1973, The Final Years of Thomas Hardy, 1912-1928, 1976, Victorian Literary Critics, 1984, The Literary Achievement of Rebecca West, 1985, The Victorian Short Story: Development and Triumph of a Literary Genre, 1986, The Unknown Thomas Hardy: Lesser-Known Aspects of Hardy's Life and Career, 1987, A Kipling Chronology, 1990, Popular Fiction in England, 1914-1918, 1992, The Historical Novel from Scott to Sabatini, 1995; contbg. author: Thomas Hardy and the Modern World, 1974, The Genius of Thomas Hardy, 1976, Budmouth Essays on Thomas Hardy, 1976, Twilight of Dawn: Studies in English Literature in Transition, 1987; contbr. numerous articles on English lit. history and criticism to various mags.; co-editor: The Thomas Hardy Rev., 1975—; editor: The World of Victorian Humor, 1961, Six Essays in Nineteenth-Century English Literature and Thought, 1962, Thomas Hardy's Personal Writings: Prefaces, Literary Opinions, Reminiscences, 1966, British Poetry 1880-1920: Edwardian Voices, 1969, The Nineteenth-Century Writer and his Audience, 1969, Irish History and Culture, 1976, The Dynasts (Thomas Hardy), 1978, The Scottish World, 1981, Rudyard Kipling: Interviews and Recollections, 2 vols., 1983, Victorian Short Stories: An Anthology, 1987, Critical Essays on Rudyard Kipling, 1989, Victorian Short Stories 2: The Trials of Love, 1990, Sir Arthur Conan Doyle: Interviews and Recollections, 1991, Critical Essays on Sir Arthur Conan Doyle, 1992, Gilbert and Sullivan: Interviews and Recollections, 1994, Critical Essays on Thomas Hardy's Poetry, 1995; delivered orations Thomas Hardy ceremonies, Westminster Abbey, 1978, 90. With USN, 1944-46. Recipient Higuchi Endowment Rsch. Achievement award, 1990; grantee Am. Coun. Learned Socs., 1966, NEH, 1975, Am. Philos. Soc., 1964, 80. Fellow Royal Soc. Literature; mem. Thomas Hardy Soc. (v.p. 1966—), Am. Com. on Irish Studies (v.p. 1967-70, pres. 1970-72). Unitarian. Home: 713 Schwarz Rd Lawrence KS 66044-4507 Office: U Kans Dept English Lawrence KS 66045

OREM, JOSEPH CLIFTON, sales professional; b. Kimberly, Nev., Jan. 3, 1944; s. Clifton Monroe and Lola Mae (Russell) O.; m. Margaret Elizabeth Tarte, June 25, 1966; children: Margaret Kathryn, Andrew Joseph, Teresa Marie Werner. BBA, U. Wash., 1968. Lab. technician U. Wash., Seattle, 1962-68; salesman Bellingham (Wash.) Sash & Door Co., 1968-74, v.p., 1974-80, pres., 1980—. Mem. Western Bldg. Materials Assn. (pres. 1988, Disting. Dealer award 1989), Nat. Lumber and Bldg. Materials Assn. (1st v.p. 1993), Bellingham Yacht Club (commodore 1977), Corinthian Yacht Club, Rotary (Paul Harris fellow, pres. 1991-92). Republican. Episcopalian. Home: 1524 Maple Ln Bellingham WA 98226-5242 Office: Bellingham Sash & Door Co 3801 Hannegan Rd Bellingham WA 98226-9103

OREN, BRUCE CLIFFORD, newspaper editor, artist; b. Mineola, N.Y., Aug. 31, 1952; s. Ralph and Bernice (Lands) O.; 1 child, Adam Nathaniel; m. Angela Malone Williams, Mar. 4, 1990. Student, U. Md., College Park, 1970-74. Archtl. sculptor Universal Restoration Inc., Washington, 1974-76; tech. illustrator Tex. Instruments, Stafford, Tex., 1976-77; graphic artist Houston Chronicle, 1977-79, photo editor, 1979-86, artist, 1986—; artist L.A. Times Syndicate, 1987-91. Recipient Bronze medal Soc. Newspaper Design, 1992. Jewish. Office: 801 Texas St Houston TX 77002-2907

OREN, JOHN BIRDSELL, retired coast guard officer; b. Madison, Wis., Dec. 27, 1909; s. Arthur Baker and Lucile Grace (Comfort) O.; m. Harriet Virginia Prentis, Feb. 9, 1934; children—Virginia Joan (Mrs. Luther Warren Strickler II), John Edward. B.S., USCG Acad., 1933; M.S. in Marine Engring, MIT, 1942. Commd. ensign USCG, 1933, advanced through grades to rear adm., 1964; chief engring. div. (11th Coast Guard Dist.), 1957-59, (12th Coast Guard Dist.), 1960-61; dep. chief (Office Engring.), Washington, 1962-63; chief Office of Engring. (Office Engring.), 1964-68; now ret.; Mem. Mcht. Marine Council, 1964—; chmn. ship structures com. Transp. Dept., 1964—; exec. dir. Maritime Transp. Research Bd., Nat. Acad. Scis. 1968—; mem. nat. adv. bd. Am. Security Council. Recipient Legion of Merit. Mem. Soc. Am. Mil. Engrs. (pres. 1966), Am. Soc. Naval Engrs. (pres. 1965), Internat. Inst. Welding (vice chmn. Am. council 1964), Ret. Officers Assn. (dir. 1978), Pan Am. Inst. Naval Engring., Masons. Republican. Episcopalian. Home: 5539 Columbia Pike Apt 215 Arlington VA 22204-5805

ORENSTEIN, (IAN) MICHAEL, philatelic dealer, columnist; b. Bklyn., Jan. 6, 1939; s. Harry and Myra (Klein) O.; m. Linda Turer, June 28, 1964; 1 child, Paul David. BS, Clemson U., 1960; postgrad., U. Calif., Berkeley, 1960-61. Career regional mgr. Minkus Stamp & Coin Co., Calif., 1964-70; mgr. stamp div. Superior Stamp & Coin Co., Inc., Beverly Hills, Calif., 1970-90; dir. stamp divsn. Superior Galleries, Beverly Hills, Calif., 1991-94; dir. space memorabilia Superior Stamp and Coin. Co., Inc., Beverly Hills, Calif., 1992-94; dir. stamp and space divsn. Superior Stamp & Coin an A-Mark Co., Beverly Hills, 1994—; stamp columnist L.A. Times, 1965-93; bd. Adelphi U. N.Y. Inst. Philatelic and Numismatic Studies, 1978-81. Author: Stamp Collecting Is Fun, 1990; philatelic advisor/creator The Video Guide To Stamp Collecting, 1988. With AUS, 1962-64. Mem. Am. Stamp Dealers Assn., C.Z. Study Group, German Philatelic Soc., Confederate Stamp Alliance, Am. Philatelic Soc. (writers unit 1975-80, 89-93), Internat. Fedn. Stamp Dealers, Internat. Soc. Appraisers: Stamps, Space Memorabilia. Republican. Avocation: fishing. Office: Superior Stamp & Coin An A-Mark Co 9478 W Olympic Blvd Beverly Hills CA 90212

ORENSTEIN, THEODORE PAUL, lawyer; b. Malden, Mass., Feb. 8, 1943; s. Louis and Lillian G. (Fruit) O.; divorced; children: Nathaniel

Van. BA, U. Bridgeport, 1964; JD, U. Tex., 1967. Bar: Tex. 1967, Mass. 1970, U.S. Dist. Ct. Mass. 1971, U.S. Ct. Appeals (1st cir.) 1971, U.S. Supreme Ct. 1979. Pvt. practice Boston, 1970-80; assoc. Hochberg & Schultz, Boston, 1980-86; ptnr. Aresty, Levin & Orenstein, Boston, 1986-90; prin. Hale, Sanderson, Byrnes & Morton, 1990—. Co-author: Flying Solo, 1984, When a Lawyer Divorces, 1985; contbr. numerous articles to legal publs. With U.S. Army, 1967-69. Recipient citation Mass. Lawyers, 1976. Fellow Am. Acad. Matrimonial Lawyers (bd. mgrs. Mass. chpt. 1985-88); mem. ABA (coun. sect. econs. of law practice 1983-89, Achievement award 1977), Mass. Bar Assn. (chmn. young lawyers sect. 1976-77, chmn. law practice sect. 1981-83, bd. dels. 1983-85, Pres.'s award 1985). Office: Hale Sanderson Byrnes & Morton 1 Center Plz Boston MA 02108-1801

ORENSTEIN-BELLIA, JESSICA, publishing company manager; b. Levittown, N.Y., July 8, 1959; d. Martin and Lorraine (Peffer) Orenstein; m. Leonard Mitchell Bellia, Apr. 26, 1987. BS cum laude, C.W. Post Coll., Greenvale, N.Y., 1981, MBA, 1991. Mgr. customer svc. Channel Home Ctrs., Jericho, N.Y., 1978-81; credit collections analyst, then corp. billing mgr. Superior Care Inc., Great Neck, N.Y., 1981-84; supr., now dept. mgr. CMP Pubs., Inc., Manhasset, N.Y., 1984—. Mem. Delta Mu Delta. Avocations: animals, gardening, cooking. Home: 17 Chase Ln Levittown NY 11756-1046 Office: CMP Publs Inc 600 Community Dr Manhasset NY 11030-3847

ORESKES, IRWIN, biochemistry educator; b. Chgo., June 30, 1926; s. Herman and Clara (Rubenstein) O.; m. Susan E. Nagin, June 18, 1949; children: Michael, Daniel, Naomi, Rebecca. B.S. in Chemistry, CCNY, 1949; M.A. in Phys. Chemistry, Bklyn. Coll., 1956; Ph.D. in Biochemistry, CUNY, 1969. Cert. clin. lab. dir. N.Y.C., N.Y. State. Chemist Tech. Tape Co., Bronx, N.Y., 1949; technician NYU Sch. Medicine, 1950-51; phys. chemist Kingsbrook Jewish Med. Ctr., 1951-56; research fellow Poly. Inst., N.Y., 1957-58; research assoc. Mt. Sinai Hosp., N.Y., 1959-68, dir. arthritis lab., 1961-90; rsch. asst. prof. Mt. Sinai Sch. Medicine, 1969-74, rsch. assoc. prof., 1974-91; assoc. prof. Hunter Coll. Sch. Health Scis., CUNY, 1970-74, prof., 1974—, dean, 1977-80; mem. doctoral faculty in biochemistry Grad. Center, CUNY, 1970—; vis. prof. Johns Hopkins U. Sch. Health Services, 1976-77; cons to diagnostic reagent and instrument mfrs., 1953—; mem. Internat. Sci. Council, Albert Einstein Research Inst., Buenos Aires, Argentina, 1969-79; mem. bd. examiners for clin. labs. N.Y.C. Dept. Health, 1973-75; sr. cons. Biotech. Rev. Assocs., 1983—. Co-editor: Rheumatology for the Health Care Professional, 1991; contbr. numerous articles to profl. jours. Served with U.S. Army, 1944-46. Nat. Inst. Arthritis and Metabolic Diseases grantee, 1961-69; Arthritis Found. grantee, 1961-65, 69, 72; Lupus Found. grantee, 1975-76; CUNY Found. grantee, 1982-83. Mem. Am. Chem. Soc., Am. Coll. Rheumatology, AAAS, N.Y. Acad. Scis., Am. Assn. Immunologists, Am. Assn. Clin. Chemistry, Harvey Soc., Nat. Acad. Clin. Biochemistry, Acad. Clin. Lab. Physicians and Scientists, Clin. Immunology Soc., Sigma Xi, Phi Lambda Upsilon. Home: 670 West End Ave New York NY 10025-7313 Office: Hunter Coll Sch Health Sci 425 E 25th St New York NY 10010-2547 I have always tried to live and work by the idea that strength is not harshness, caring is not sentimentality, and honesty is not vulnerability.

ORESMAN, DONALD, entertainment and publishing company executive, corporate lawyer; b. 1925. BA, Oberlin Coll., 1946; LLB, Columbia U., 1957. Ptnr. Simpson, Thacher & Bartlet, N.Y.C., 1957-83; exec. v.p., sec., gen. counsel, chief adminstrv. officer Paramount Communications Inc., N.Y.C., 1983—, also bd. dirs., mem. exec. com. Office: Paramount Comm Inc 15 Columbus Cir New York NY 10023-7706

ORFIELD, MYRON WILLARD, JR., state legislator, educator; b. Mpls., July 27, 1961. BA summa cum laude, U. Minn., 1983; grad., Princeton U., 1983-84; JD, U. Chgo., 1987. Bar: Minn. 1988. Law clk. Judge Gerald W. Heaney, U.S. Ct. Appeals, 8th Cir., 1987-88; rsch. assoc. Ctr. for Studies in Criminal Justice, U. Chgo., 1988-89; assoc. Faegre & Benson, 1989; asst. atty. gen. Minn. Atty. Gen.'s Office, 1989—; Bradley fellow Ctr. for Studies in Criminal Justice, U. Chgo., 1990-91; rep. Minn. Ho. of Reps. Dist. 60B, Mpls., 1991—; adj. prof. law U. Minn., 1991—, Hamline U., 1991—; prin. Met. Area Project, Mpls. Contbr. articles to profl. jours. Office: 521 State Office Bldg Saint Paul MN 55155

ORGAN, DENNIS MICHAEL, English educator; b. Shreveport, La., Dec. 2, 1944; s. Fred Marshall and Mary Ellen (Maddox) O.; m. Sherry Lee Balthrop, Aug. 12, 1967; children: Michael, David, Philip. BA, Harding U., Searcy, Ark., 1966; MA, U. Mo., 1968; PhD, Tex. Tech. U., Lubbock, 1974. Instr. journalism Harding U., Searcy, 1967-72, asst. prof. English, 1972-79, assoc. prof. English, 1979-84, chair dept. English, 1981—, prof. English, 1984—. Author: Tennyson's Dramas, 1979; editor The Recorder, 1976—; contbr. articles to profl. jours. Recipient Disting. Tchr. award Harding U., Searcy, 1977, 84. Mem. Nat. Coun. Tchrs. English, Conf. on Christianity and Lit. (regional program chair 1990), Alpha Chi (editor publs. 1976—, assoc. exec. dir. 1992-93, exec. dir. 1994—). Mem. Ch. of Christ. Home: 105 River Oaks Ct Searcy AR 72143-4532 Office: Harding U PO Box 2248 Searcy AR 72143-2248

ORGAN, JOSEPH B., lawyer; b. Oak Park, Ill., Oct. 28, 1951. BA, Rollins Coll., 1974; JD, Northwestern U., 1977; LLM Taxation, NYU, 1983. Bar: Ill. 1977. Ptnr. Mayer Brown & Platt, Chgo. Office: Mayer Brown & Platt 190 S La Salle St Chicago IL 60603-3441

ORGANSKI, ABRAMO FIMO KENNETH, political scientist, educator; b. Rome, May 17, 1923; came to U.S., 1939, naturalized, 1944; s. Menasce and Anna (Feinstein) O.; m. Katherine Davis Fox, May 29, 1947 (dec. Feb. 1973); children: Eric Fox, Elizabeth Anna; m. Patricia Joan Bard, June 14, 1986. BA, NYU, 1947, MA, 1948, PhD, 1951; student, Ginnasio Liceo Torquato Tasso, Rome, 1933-38. From asst. prof. to prof. polit. sci. Bklyn. Coll., CUNY, 1952-64; prof. polit. sci. U. Mich., Ann Arbor, 1965—, James Orin Murfin prof. polit. sci., 1985-87, sr. scientist, program dir. Ctr. Polit. Sci., Inst. Social Research, 1969—; adj. research prof. polit. sci. Grad. Sch. Pub. Adminstrn., NYU, 1960; vis. assoc. prof. pub. law and govt., Columbia U., N.Y.C., 1961-62; vis. prof. Fletcher Sch. Law and Diplomacy, 1963-66, Dartmouth Coll., 1963-64, U. Pa., 1983, U. Catania, 1975, 77, U. Florence, 1990, U. Turin, 1991; sr. cons., bd. dirs. Policon Corp., 1982—, Decision Insight, 1991—; lectr., cons. to various pvt. and govtl. instns., U.S. and abroad, 1960—, European Inst., Florence, 1993; vis. scholar The Hoover Instn., Stanford U., 1991, 92, 93; vis. scholar in residence Agnelli Found., 1991. Author: World Politics, 1958, 68, (with Katherine Organski) Population and World Power, 1961, Stages of Political Development, 1965, (with Jacek Kugler) The War Ledger, 1980, (with Kugler, Y. Cohen and T. Johnson) Births, Deaths and Taxes: The Political and Demographic Transition, 1984, The 36 Billion Dollar Bargain: Strategy and Politics in U.S. Assistance to Israel, 1990; bd. editors: Affari Sociali Internazionali, Comparative Politics, International Interactions. Served with U.S. Army, 1943-45. Decorated Cavaliere della Repubblica Italiana; recipient Disting. Faculty Achievement award U. Mich., 1983, Lifetime Achievement award ASPA conflict processes sect., 1992; Social Sci. Research Council fellow, 1976, Fulbright fellow, 1977. Mem. Am. Polit. Sci. Assn. (council 1969), Internat. Polit. Sci. Assn. Avocations: skiing, tennis. Home: 460 Hillspur Rd Ann Arbor MI 48105-1049 Office: U Mich Ctr Polit Studies Inst Social Rsch Ann Arbor MI 48106-1248

ORGEBIN-CRIST, MARIE-CLAIRE, biology educator; b. Vannes, France, Mar. 20, 1936. License Natural Scis., License Biology, Sorbonne, U. Paris, 1957; D. Scis., Lyons U., France, 1961. Stagiaire dept. biochemistry faculty medicine Paris, France, 1957-58; stagiaire Centre Nat. de la Recherche Scientifique, Paris, 1958-60, attachee de recherche, 1960-62; research assoc. Population Council (Med. Div.), N.Y.C., 1962-63; research assoc. dept. ob/gyn Vanderbilt Sch. Medicine, 1963-64, research instr., 1964-66, asst. prof., 1966-70, assoc. prof., 1970-73, Lucius E. Burch prof. reproductive biology, 1973—, prof. dept. anatomy, 1975—; dir. Vanderbilt Sch. Medicine (Center Reproductive Biology Research), 1973—; Editor-in-Chief Jour. Andrology, 1983-89. Recipient Career Devel. award NIH, 1968-73, NIH Merit award, 1986, Disting. Andrologist award Am. Soc. Andrology, 1990; Fogarty Internat. sr. fellow, 1977. Mem. Am. Assn. Anatomists, Am. Soc. Cell Biology, Am. Soc. Andrology (v.p. 1994-95, pres. 1995-96), Internat. Com. on Andrology, Endocrine Soc., Soc. for Study Fertility (Eng.), Soc. for Study

Japan Sea Grant Inst.

Reprodn., N.Y. Acad. Scis. Office: Vanderbilt U Sch Med Ctr Reproductive Biology Rsch Rm D-2303 MCN Nashville TN 37232

ORI, KAN, political science educator; b. Osaka, Japan, Jan. 28, 1933; s. Tazo and Tamaji (Moriki) O.; m. Teruko Horie, Apr. 27, 1961; children: Akemi, Harumi, Noriko. BA cum laude, Taylor U., Upland, Ind., 1956; MA, Ind. U., Bloomington, 1958; PhD, Ind. U., 1961. Instr. Jochi (Sophia) U., Tokyo, 1965-67; assoc. prof. Jochi (Sophia) U., 1967-70, prof. polit. sci., 1970—, mem., faculty Inst. Internat. Relations, 1969—, dean grad. sch. Faculty Fgn. Studies, 1985-87; vis. prof. U. Malaya, Kuala Lumpur, Malaysia, 1974-75, U. Mo., Columbia, 1975-76 (winter semester), U. Minn., Mpls., summer 1978, 88, Princeton (N.J.) U., 1982-83 (fall semester). Author (with Roger Benjamin): Tradition and Change in Postindustrial Japan, 1981; editor Jour. Internat. Studies, 1978-82; editorial bd. Internat. Studies Quar., 1980-84. Ind. U. fellow, 1960; Matsunaga Sci. Found. grantee, 1970; Japan Found. grantee, 1974-75. Mem. Japanese Polit. Sci. Assn., Japanese Assn. Internat. Relations (councilor 1975—), Japanese Assn. Am. Studies (councilor 1986—). Office: Sophia U Inst Internat Rel, 7-1 Kioi-cho Chiyoda-ku, Tokyo 102, Japan

ORIANI, RICHARD ANTHONY, metallurgical engineering educator; b. El Salvador, July 19, 1920; came to U.S., 1929, naturalized, 1943; s. Americo and Berta (Siguenza) O.; m. Constance Amelia Gordon, June 26, 1949; children—Margaret, Steven, Julia, Amelia. B. Chem.Engring, CCNY, 1943; M.S., Stevens Inst. Tech., 1946; M.A., Princeton U., 1948, Ph.D., 1949. Lab. asst. CCNY, 1943; chemist Bakelite Corp., Bloomfield, N.J., 1943-46; instr. physics Miss Fine's Finishing Sch., Princeton, N.J., 1946-47; research asso. Gen. Electric Corp. Research Lab., Schenectady, 1949-59; asst. dir. U.S. Steel Corp. Research Lab., Monroeville, Pa., 1959-80; prof. U. Minn., Mpls., 1980-89, dir. Corrosion Rsch. Ctr., 1980-87, prof. and dir. emeritus, 1989—; cons. in field. Contbr. chpts. to books, articles to profl. jours. Founder, mem. Foxwood Civic Assn., Monroeville, 1959-80; founder, v.p. Monroeville Public Library, 1960-80. Recipient Alexander von Humboldt Sr. Scientist award, 1984, W.R. Whitney award, 1987. Fellow Am. Soc. for Metals, Am. Inst. Chemists, N.Y. Acad. Scis.; mem. Nat. Assn. Corrosion Engrs., Electrochem. Soc.; mem. AAAS, Am. Phys. Soc., Am. Inst. Metall. Engrs. Republican. Home: 4623 Humboldt Ave S Minneapolis MN 55409-2264 Office: U Minn 112 Amundson Hall 221 Church St SE Minneapolis MN 55455-0152

ORIANS, GORDON HOWELL, biology educator; b. Eauclaire, Wis., July 10, 1932; s. Howard Lester and Marion Meta (Senty) O.; m. Elizabeth Ann Newton, June 25, 1955; children: Carlyn Elizabeth, Kristin Jean, Colin Mark. BS, U. Wis., 1954; PhD, U. Calif., Berkeley, 1960. Asst. prof. zoology U. Wash., Seattle, 1960-64, assoc. prof., 1964-68, prof., 1968—, dir. Inst. for Environ. Studies, 1976-86, 89-90; active Wash. State Ecol. Commn., Olympia, 1970-75, ecology adv. com. EPA, Washington, 1974-79; assembly life scis. NAS/NRC, Washington, 1977-83; environ. studies and toxicology bd., 1991—. Author: Some Adaptations of Marsh Nesting Blackbirds, 1980, Blackbirds of the Americas, 1985, Life: The Science of Biology, 1995; editor: Convergent Evolution in Warm Deserts, 1968. 1st lt. U.S. Army, 1955-56. 1st lt. U.S. Army, 1955-56. Mem. AAAS, NAS, Am. Inst. Biol. Scis. (Disting. Svc. award 1994), Am. Ornithologists Union (Brewster award 1976), Am. Soc. Naturalists, Animal Behavior Soc., Royal Netherlands Acad. Arts and Scis., Orgn. for Tropical Studies (pres. 1988-94), Ecol. Soc. Am. (v.p. 1975-76, pres.-elect 1994—). Avocations: hiking, opera. Office: U Wash Dept Zoology Seattle WA 98195

ORIHEL, THOMAS CHARLES, parasitology educator, research scientist; b. Akron, Ohio, Feb. 10, 1929; s. Joseph Andrew and Mary Susannah (Barno) O.; m. Dorothy Lila Williams, Dec. 27, 1952; children—Timothy Stewart, Charles Theodore, Susan Ethra, Adrianne Louise. B.S., U. Akron, 1950; M.S., U. Wash., 1952; Ph.D., Tulane U., 1959. Sr. scientist Tulane Delta Primate Ctr., Covington, La., 1963-85; prof. parasitology Tulane Med. Ctr., New Orleans, 1972—; William Vincent prof. tropical diseases Tulane Med. Ctr., 1982—; dir. Tulane U. Internat. Collaboration Infectious Diseases Rsch. Program, New Orleans, 1976-89; cons. NIH, Bethesda, Md., 1973-77; mem. expert panel WHO, Geneva, 1973-83; mem. U.S.-Japan Cooperative Med. Sci. Program, Bethesda, 1974-78; external examiner U. Queensland, Australia, U. Guelph, Ont., Can., U. Claude Bernard, Lyon, France, U. Malaya, Kuala Lumpur, Malaysia. Author books on subject of medical parasitology, 1976, 81, 84, 90, 94, 95; contbr. articles to Am. and internat. jours. Served to 1st lt. Med. Service Corps, U.S. Army, 1953-56, Korea. Mem. Am. Soc. Tropical Medicine and Hygiene (councilor 1975-78), Royal Soc. Tropical Medicine and Hygiene, Am. Soc. Microbiology, Southwestern Assn. Parasitologists (v.p. 1972-73), Am. Soc. Parasitologists, Sigma Xi. Avocations: gardening; woodworking. Home: 115 Bertel Dr Covington LA 70433-4815 Office: Tulane Med Ctr Dept Tropical Medicine 1430 Tulane Ave New Orleans LA 70112-2699

ORING, STUART AUGUST, visual information specialist, writer/photographer; b. Bronx, N.Y., Aug. 28, 1932; s. Irving and Helen Flora (Greenhut) O.; m. Mary Carolyn Barth, Aug. 22, 1957; children: Carlene Marie Oring, Sheri Alyce Oring. AAS, Rochester Inst. Tech., 1957; BFA, R.I. Tech., 1959; MA, Am. U., 1970. Photo lab asst. Nat. Geographic, Washington, summer 1957; photography asst. Nepo-Nuss, I.J. Becker Studio Assocs., N.Y.C., 1959-61; freelance photographer pvt. practice, Washington, 1961; indsl. photographer Vitro Corp., Rockville, Md., 1962-64; health photographer Nat. Ctr. Radiol. Health, Rockville, Md., 1964-67; visual info. specialist ARS Info. Ctr. USDA, Washington, 1967-69; audio visual specialist Nat. AV Ctr., Washington, 1969-71; photojournalist Office of Econ. Opportunity, Washington, 1971-74; visual info. specialist ASCS, U.S. Dept. Agr., Washington, 1974-94; ret., 1994; mgr., owner ISIS Visual Comms.; photography tchr. Prince George's C.C., Largo, Md., 1975—; guest lectr. U. Md. Balt. County, Towson, Md., Corcoran Gallery of Art, Washington; program speaker Conf. Internat. Soc. Psychopathology of Expression. Author, editor and pub.: (textbook/gallery text) Understanding Pictures-A Teacher's Planning Guide, 1994, Understanding Pictures-Theories, Exercises and Procedures, 1990, rev. 1992, rev. 1995; contbr. numerous articles to profl. jours.; photos published in books, mags., brochures, pamphlets. Pub. rels. Calvert County Humane Soc., 1990. Photographer with U.S. Army, 1952-55. Recipient Cert. Recognition award Eastman Kodak Co., 1973, Nat. Ctr. Radiol. Health, Rockville, Md., 1965. Mem. Soc. Photographic Edn., Am. Soc. Psychopathology of Expression. Avocations: chess, swimming, classical music, oriental philosophy, art. Home and Office: 2570 Redbud Ln Owings MD 20736

O'RIORDAN, WILLIAM HUGH, lawyer; b. Chgo., June 3, 1947; s. Francis Joseph and Mary Elvera (McHugh) O'R.; m. Kaye L. Zimmerman, Sept. 28, 1969; 1 child, Moira Anne. BA, U. Ariz., 1969, JD, 1972; LLM, George Washington U., 1978. Bar: D.C. 1972, Idaho, Ariz. Atty. U.S. Dept. Interior, Washington, 1972-76, Pacific Legal Found., Washington, 1976-78; dep. atty. gen. State of Idaho, Boise, 1978-80; ptnr. Runft, Leroy, Coffin & O'Riordan, Boise, 1980-85, Lindsay Hart Neil & Weigler, Boise, 1985-87, Davis Wright Tremaine, Boise, 1987-93, Givens Pursley & Huntley, Boise, 1993—; bd. dirs. Washington Legal Found., 1978—; mem. subcom. NAS, Washington, 1992—. Contbr. articles to legal jours. Trustee, pres. Boise Pub. Libr., 1987-91. Republican. Roman Catholic. Avocations: skiing, fly fishing, photography, outdoor activities. Home: 1750 Shaw Mountain Rd Boise ID 83712-6634 Office: Givens Pursley & Huntley 277 N 6th St Boise ID 83702-7720

ORKAND, DONALD SAUL, management consultant; b. N.Y.C., Mar. 2, 1936; s. Harold and Sylvia (Wagner) O.; children: Dara Sue, Katarina Day. BS summa cum laude, NYU, 1956, MBA, 1957, PhD, 1963. Statistician, Western Electric Co., N.Y.C., 1956-58; group v.p. Ops. Rsch., Inc., Silver Spring, Md., 1960-69; pres. Ops Rsch. Industries, Ltd., Ottawa, Ont., Can., 1968-69; pres., chief exec. officer The Orkand Corp., Silver Spring, 1970—; bd. dirs. U. Md. Found., Inc., College Park, 1993—. Contbr. articles to profl. jours. Bd. visitors coll. of bus. and mgmt. U. Md., College Park, 1985—; trustee Suburban Hosp., 1994—. 1st lt. Ordnance Corps, USAR, 1958-60. Mem. Am. Econs. Assn., Am. Statis. Assn., Ops. Rsch. Soc. Am. Republican. Jewish. Avocations: reading, theater, travel, exercise. Office: The Orkand Corp 8484 Georgia Ave Silver Spring MD 20910

ORKAND, RICHARD KENNETH, neurobiologist, researcher, educator; b. N.Y.C., Apr. 23, 1936. BS, Columbia U., 1956; PhD, U. Utah, 1961; MA, U. Pa., 1974. Fellow U. Coll. London, 1961-64, Harvard U., Boston, 1964-66; asst. prof. U. Utah, Salt Lake City, 1966-68; prof. UCLA, 1968-74; prof., chmn. U. Pa., Phila., 1974-86; dir. Inst. Neurobiology U. P.R., San Juan, 1986—; Benjamin Meaker prof. U. Bristol, 1993; adj. prof. biology Calif. Poly. U., San Luis Obispo, 1993—; exec. dir. Caribbean Neurosci. Found., 1987—; mem. adv. coun. Conservation Trust of P.R., 1990-94; councilor AAAS, Caribbean, 1990-95. Co-author: Introduction to Nervous Systems, 1977; contbr. over 80 articles to profl. jours. Mem. com. Dem. Party, Phila., 1981. Fellow AAAS. Achievements include research in studies of physiology of neuroglia and neuron-glia interaction. Office: U PR Inst Neurobiology 201 Calle Blvd Del Vly San Juan PR 00901-1123

ORKIN, LEONARD, lawyer; b. N.Y.C., 1932. AB, Harvard U., 1954; LLB, Columbia U., 1957. Bar: N.Y. 1958, U.S. Supreme Ct. 1964. Ptnr. Winston & Strawn, N.Y.C. Mem. N.Y. State Bar Assn. (chmn. advt. and mktg. standing com. 1988, sec. entertainment, arts and sports law sect. 1991), Assn. Bar City N.Y., Am. Arbitration Assn. (panel arbitrators). Office: Winston & Strawn 175 Water St New York NY 10038-4918

ORKIN, LOUIS RICHARD, physician, educator; b. N.Y.C., Dec. 23, 1915; s. Samuel David and Rebecca (Rish) O.; m. Florence Fine, Mar. 5, 1938; 1 dau., Rita. B.A., U. Wis., 1937; M.D., N.Y. U., 1941; AAS in Marine Tech., Kingsborough Coll., 1992. Intern Bellevue Hosp., N.Y.C., 1942; resident anesthesiology Bellevue Hosp., 1946-48; practice medicine specializing in anesthesiology Bronx, N.Y., 1946—; dir. anesthesiology Backus Hosp., Norwich, Conn., 1948-50; asst. prof. anesthesiology N.Y. U. Coll. Medicine, 1950-55; prof., chmn. dept. anesthesiology Albert Einstein Coll. Medicine, 1955-82, Disting. univ. prof., 1982-86, dist. univ. prof. emeritus, 1986—; vis. prof. depts. bioengring., anesthesiology U. Calif., San Diego, 1971; Cons. VA, USPHS, USN; mem. com. anesthesiology Nat. Acad. Scis., 1964-69; mem. com. anesthetic drugs FDA, Dept. Health, Edn. and Welfare, 1970—. Author: Patient in Shock, 1965, Physiology of Obstetrical Anesthesia, 1969; Contbr. articles to profl. jours. Vice pres., trustee Wood Library Mus. Served to capt. M.C. AUS, 1942-45. Decorated Bronze Star. Fellow Am. Coll. Chest Physicians, N.Y. Acad. Sci., N.Y. Acad. Medicine, Am. Coll. Anesthesiology (past chmn. bd. govs.); mem. N.Y. State Soc. Anesthesiologists (past pres.). Home: 11 Stuyvesant Oval New York NY 10009-2001 Office: Albert Einstein Coll Medicine Bronx NY 10461

ORLAND, FRANK, oral microbiologist, educator; b. Little Falls, N.Y., Jan. 23, 1917; s. Michael and Rose (Dorner) O.; m. Phyllis Therese Mrazek, May 8, 1943; children: Frank R., Carl P., June Rose, Ralph M. AA, U. Chgo., 1937, SM, 1945, PhD, 1949; BS, U. Ill., 1939, DDS, 1941. Diplomate Am. Bd. Med. Microbiology. With U. Chgo., 1941—; intern Zoller Meml. Dental Clinic, U. Chgo., 1941-42; Zoller fellow, asst. in dental surgery U. Chgo., 1942-49, instr., asst. prof., assoc. prof., of dental sci., 1949-88, prof. emeritus, 1988—, from instr. to assoc. prof. microbiology, 1950-58, rsch. assoc. prof., 1958-64; dir. Zoller Meml. Dental Clinic, 1954-66; prof. Fishbein Ctr. for Study History Sci. and Medicine, 1980-88, prof. emeritus, 1988—; attending dentist Country Home for Convalescent Children; past cons. Nat. Inst. Dental Rsch., NIH, Bethesda, Md.; mem. panel on dental drugs The Nat. Formulary; past chmn. dental adv. bd. Med. Heritage Soc. Author: The First Fifty-Year History of the International Association for Dental Research, 1973, Microbiology in Clinical Dentistry, 1982, William John Gies-His Contributions to the Advancement of Dentistry, 1992; editor: Jour. Dental Rsch., 1958-69, (Centennial brochure) Loyola U. Sch. Dentistry, 1983; editor, contbr. Microbiology in Clinical Dentistry, 1982; writer, prodr. 50th anniversary booklet Zoller Meml. Dental Clinic U. Chgo., 1987; contbr. articles to profl. jours. Past chmn. adv. coun. Forest Park (Ill.) Bd. Edn.; mem. Forest Park Citizens Com. for Better Schs.; past pres. Garfield Sch. PTA, 1953-55; chairperson heritage com. Bicentennial Commn. on Forest Park, 1983-85; editor Chronicles of Forest Park, 1976—. Recipient Rsch. Essay award Chgo. Dental Soc., 1955, Cook County Sheriff Medal of Honor award, 1993; named Citizen of Yr., Forest Park, 1989. Fellow AAAS, Inst. Medicine Chgo. (chmn. com. publ. comms.), Am. Acad. Microbiology (William Gies award 1994), Am. Coll. Dentists; mem. ADA (past chmn. coun. dental therapeutics), Internat. Assn. Dental Rsch. (pres. 1971-72, past councilor Chgo. sect., past chmn. program com., past chmn. com. on history), Am. Assn. Dental Schs. (past chmn. conf. oral microbiology, past chmn. com. on advanced edn.), Am. Assn. Dental Editors (William Gies Editl. award 1968), Ill. State Dental Soc. (chmn. com. on history), Fedn. Dentaire Internat. (Commn. on History Rsch.), Am. Acad. History Dentistry (pres. 1976-77, Hayden-Harris award 1989), Hist. Soc. Forest Park (pres.), Soc. Med. History Chgo. (past pres.), Chgo. Lit. Club, Sigma Xi. Home: 519 Jackson Blvd Forest Park IL 60130-1896 Office: 521 Jackson Blvd Forest Park IL 60130-1896

ORLANDO, CARL, medical research and development executive; b. Palermo, Italy, Sept. 26, 1915; came to U.S., 1928; s. Peter and Maria (Bongiorno) O.; m. Ann Bove, May 29, 1943; children: Ann Marie, Francine, Patricia, Charleen, Joan. BS, Columbia U., 1941; postgrad., Rochester U., 1943. Chief photo optics U.S. Army Elec. Commd., Ft. Monmouth, N.J., 1945-75; cons. pvt. practice, New Shrewsbury, N.J., 1975-79; v.p. rsch. & devel. Analytical R&D Inc., Eatontown, N.J., 1979-88; cons. rsch. & devel. Engring. Devel. Co., Tinton Falls, N.J., 1986-88; pres., rsch. & devel. dir. Sens-O-Tech Industries Inc., Eatontown, N.J., 1988—; chmn. bd. dirs. Sens-O-Tech Industries, 1988-92. Contbr. articles to profl. jours. Bd. dirs. Monmouth Regional High Sch., Tinton Falls, 1974; com. mem. Tinton Falls Environ. Unit, 1984; chmn. Entertainment Activities St. Dorothaas Ch., Eatontown, 1983. With USN, 1945. Recipient Monetary Suggestion award Signal Corp. Engring. Lab., 1948. Mem. Soc. Photographic Scientist & Engrs. (sr. mem.), Soc. Imaging Sci. & Tech., Elks, Battle Ground Country Club. Republican. Roman Catholic. Achievements include over 20 patents in various fields: non-invasive heart and breathing alarm monitors, moving target indicator, photographic reproduction in 0.2 second, one step photographic technic, image stabilization system, perk-type automatic-drip coffee maker, military tactical image interpretation facility, production and reconstruction of holograms, device for intensifying photoelectrostatic images, bandwidth compression of photographic images, Natinol photographic high speed shutter. Home and Office: 47 Willow Rd Tinton Falls NJ 07724-3135

ORLANDO, DANIELLE, opera company administrator. Artistic adminstr. Opera Co. of Phila., until 1994; voice coach The Curtis Inst. of Music, Phila., 1995—. Office: The Curtis Inst of Music 1726 Locust St Philadelphia PA 19103*

ORLANDO, GEORGE (JOSEPH), union executive; b. N.Y.C., Nov. 27, 1944; s. Joseph and Anita O.; m. Joan Perrotta, Nov. 5, 1967; children: Gregory, Valerie, Dana, Christopher, Lauren. B.A. in Polit. Scis., St. John's U., Bklyn., 1966. Adminstrv. asst. Distillery, Wine and Allied Workers Internat., Englewood, N.J., 1966-67; internat. v.p. Distillery, Wine and Allied Workers Internat., 1968-74, gen. sec.-treas., 1974-85, gen. pres., 1985—; labor trustee Distillery, Wine and Allied Workers Internat.-Social Security Fund, 1974, chmn. bd. trustees, 1985; mem. exec. bd. dept. food and allied service trades AFL-CIO, 1975; mem. Wine, Liquor & Distillery Workers Union-Local 1, 1985—, also trustee pension fund. Office: Internat Union Wine & Allied Workers Distillery PO Box 567 66 Grand Ave Englewood NJ 07631

ORLEANS, JEFFREY HOWARD, lawyer; married; one child. BA in Polit. Sci. cum laude, Yale U., 1967, JD, 1971. Bar: D.C. 1971, U.S. Supreme Ct. 1980. Mem. staff Office Gen. Counsel div. civil rights HEW, 1971-74, advisor, supr. Office Gen. Counsel, 1974-75; spl. asst. to pres. U. N.C., Chapel Hill, 1975-84; exec. dir. Coun. Ivy Group Pres.'s, Princeton, N.J., 1984—. Contbr. articles to sports jours. Mem. Amateur Athletic Found. of L.A., 1987. Nat. Merit scholar; Cono Found. fellow in Pub. Affairs, San Francisco, 1967-68. Mem. Nat. Assn. Coll. and Univ. attys. (exec. bd. 1981-84, contbg. editor Jour. Coll. and Univ. Law 1980-81, chmn./co-chmn. editorial adv. bd. and publs. com. 1979-83, ann. conf. program coms. 1979-84, com. on mem. svcs. and continuing legal edn. 1980-83, athletics, affirmative action, mus. and collections sects. 1985—), NCAA (spl. com. on amateurism and fin. aid standing 1987—), Am. Coun. on Edn. (task force on affirmative action 1982), Nat. Assn. Coll. and Univ. Bus.

Officers (sect. 504 task force 1979-80), Assn. Yale Alumni (law sch. del. 1977-80), Nat. Assn. State Univs. and Land-Grant Colls. (legal affairs com. 1979-84). Home: 107 Meadowbrook Dr Princeton NJ 08540-3664 Office: Coun Ivy Group Presidents 70 Washington Rd Rm 22 Princeton NJ 08540-6409

ORLEN, JOEL, association executive; b. Holyoke, Mass., Aug. 1, 1924; s. Barnet and Fannie (Fuchs) O.; m. Yana Sorra Edmundson, Nov. 24, 1963; 1 stepson, Charles. BA, U. Chgo., 1950, MA, 1952. Fgn. svc. officer U.S. Dept. State, Washington, 1952-56; fgn. affairs officer AEC, Washington, 1956-58; officer NAS, Washington, 1958-63; asst. dir. Desert Rsch. Inst., Reno, 1963-65; exec. officer, provost MIT, Cambridge, 1965-80; v.p. Sci. Mus. Minn., St. Paul, 1980-86; exec. officer Am. Acad. Arts and Letters, Cambridge, 1986—; dir. Mounds Park Acad., St. Paul, 1983-86; cons. MIT, 1980-82; exec. sec. Mass. Tech. Devel. Corp., 1980-84; advisor U.S. del. to UN, N.Y.C. and Geneva, 1952-63. Contbr. chpts. to several books. Staff sgt. U.S. Army, 1943-46, ETO. Home: 130 Mt Auburn St Cambridge MA 02138-5757 Office: Am Acad Arts and Scis 136 Irving St Cambridge MA 02138-1996

ORLIK, PETER BLYTHE, media educator, author, musician; b. Hancock, Mich., Sept. 30, 1944; s. Harry Victor and Ruth Estelle (Blythe) O.; m. Christina Grace Bear, Aug. 18, 1967; children: Darcy Anne, Blaine Truen. BA with distinction, Wayne State U., 1965, MA, 1966, PhD, 1968. Copywriter Robin Prodns., Huntington Woods, Mich., 1962-63; announcer Sta. WQRS-FM, Detroit, 1963; copywriter Campbell-Ewald Advt., Detroit, 1965; asst. music dir. Sta. WDET-FM, Detroit, 1965-66; instr. Wayne State U., Detroit, 1966-69; from asst. prof. to assoc. prof. to prof. Cen. Mich. U., Mt. Pleasant, Mich., 1969—; univ. Merit prof. Cen. Mich. U., Mt. Pleasant, 1988, 92, also founder, head dept. Broadcast and Cinematic Arts, 1969-79; freelance copywriter Mt. Pleasant, 1979—; profl. clarinetist various Mich. ensembles, Detroit, Saginaw, 1965—; asst. dir. creative svcs. Sta. WXYZ-TV, Detroit, 1982; coord. prior learning assessment external degree program Ctrl. Mich. U., 1978-85; cons. various univs., 1980—; judge Thomas Jefferson Broadcast Awards, Dept. Def., 1994. Author: Broadcast/Cable Copywriting, 5th edit., 1994, Mass Media Description and Performance, 1979, Critiquing Radio and Television Content, 1988, The Electronic Media: An Introduction to the Profession, 1992, Electronic Media Criticism, 1994; mem. editl. bd. Media Mgmt. Rev.; contbr. articles to profl. jours. Lectr., liturgical clarinet soloist, eucharistic minister Sacred Heart Parish, Mt. Pleasant, 1969—, mem. religious edn. bd., 1978-84; adjudicator various H.S. speech and drama competitions, Mich., 1971-80; vice chmn. Zoning Bd. Appeals, Mt. Pleasant, 1974-78, 89-91, chmn., 1978-82, 91—; mem. faculty adv. com. Mus. Broadcast Comms. Named one of Outstanding Young Men Am. Nat. Jaycees, 1979; Nat. Assn. TV Program Execs. Faculty fellow, 1982. Mem. Broadcast Edn. Assn. (chmn. courses and curricula divsn. 1974-76, 80-82, bd. dirs. 1989-93, chmn. faculty internship com. 1990-91, chmn. nat. scholarship com. 1991—), Assn. for Edn. in Journalism and Mass Comms., Nat. Assn. TV Program Execs., Alpha Epsilon Rho (nat. v.p. profl. alumni rels. 1976-77, legis. coord. 1979-82), Phi Kappa Phi. Avocation: writing half-time show scripts for college and profl. football games. Home: 613 Kane St Mount Pleasant MI 48858-1949 Office: Cen Mich U 343 Moore Hall Mount Pleasant MI 48859

ORLIN, JAMES BERGER, mathematician, management scientist, educator; b. Buffalo, Apr. 19, 1953; s. Albert Norman and Roslyn Louise (Berger) O.; m. Donna Lynn Hogan, Jan. 3, 1982; children: Jennifer Robin, Benjamin Aaron, Caroline Anne. BA, U. Pa., 1974; MS, Caltech, 1976; MMath, U. Waterloo, Ont., Can., 1976; PhD, Stanford U., 1981. Asst. prof. MIT, Cambridge, Mass., 1979-83, assoc. prof., 1983-87, prof., 1987—; vis. prof. Erasmus U., Rotterdam, The Netherlands, 1984-85; vis. sci. Collaborative Rsch. Inc., Waltham, Mass., 1992-93, Whitehead Inst., 1993—. Co-author: Network Flows: Theory, Algorithms and Applications, 1993; assoc. editor Networks, 1992—; contbr. over 50 articles to profl. jours. Fulbright Rsch. grantee, 1984-85, UPS fellow, 1991-94; recipient Presdl. Young Investigator award NSF, 1985-90. Mem. Ops. Rsch. Soc. Am. (Co-recipient Lanchester prize 1993), Assn. Computing Machinery, Math. Programming Soc., Soc. Indsl. and Applied Math. Home: 10 Taft Dr Winchester MA 01890-3748 Office: MIT E53-357 77 Massachusetts Ave Cambridge MA 02139-3594

ORLOFF, CHET, cultural organization administrator; b. Bellingham, Wash., Feb. 22, 1949; s. Monford A. and Janice (Diamond) O.; m. Wendy Lynn Lee, Sept. 20, 1970; children: Callman Labe, Hannah Katya, Michele Alison. BA, Boston U., 1971; MA, U. Oreg., 1978; postgrad., Portland State U. Tchr. Peace Corps, Afghanistan, 1972-73; asst. dir. Oreg. Hist. Soc., Portland, 1975-86, dir., 1991—; dir. Ninth Cir. Hist. Soc., Pasadena, Calif., 1987-91. Editor: Western Legal History, 1987-91, Law for the Elephant, 1992; sr. editor: Oreg. Hist. Quar.; contbr. articles to profl. jours. Commr. Met. Arts Commn., Portland, 1981-84, Portland Planning Commn., 1989-92. Mem. Phi Alpha Theta. Avocations: reading, tennis. Office: Oregon Historical Society 1200 SW Park Ave Portland OR 97205-2483

ORLOFF, GARY W(ILLIAM), lawyer, former energy company executive; b. Des Moines, June 7, 1946; s. Bernard M. and Beatrice (Silverman) O.; m. Marsha Jo Forman, Aug. 2, 1970; children: Denise Lynn, Julie Shannon. BBA, U. Tex., 1969; JD, U. Houston, 1973. Atty. Houston Natural Gas Corp., 1973-75, asst. gen. counsel, 1975-79, sr. asst. gen. counsel, 1979-81, v.p., asst. gen. counsel, 1981-85; v.p., asst. gen. counsel Enron Corp., Houston, 1985-87, sr. v.p., gen. counsel, 1987-91; ptnr. Bracewell & Patterson, L.L.P., Houston, 1991—. Contbr. articles to law rev. Mem. ABA, Tex. Bar Assn. (chair corp. counsel sect. 1993-94), Houston Bar Assn. (chair corp. counsel sect. 1992-93), Houston Club, Brae-Burn Country Club. Office: Bracewell & Patterson LLP 2900 South Tower Penzoil Pl Houston TX 77002

ORLOFF, NEIL, lawyer; b. Chgo., May 9, 1943; s. Benjamin R. and Annette (Grabow) O.; m. Jan Krigbaum, Oct. 9, 1971 (div. 1979); m. Gudrun Mirin, Oct. 2, 1992. BS, MIT, 1964; MBA, Harvard U., 1966; JD, Columbia U., 1969. Bar: D.C. 1969, N.Y. 1975, Calif. 1989, Utah 1993. Ops. officer World Bank, Washington, 1969-71; dir. regional liaison staff EPA, Washington, 1971-73; legal counsel Pres.'s Council on Environ. Quality, Washington, 1973-75; prof. dept. environ. engring. Cornell U., Ithaca, N.Y., 1975-88, sch. law UCLA, 1992; dir. Ctr. for Environ. Research, 1984-87, Am. Ecology Corp., 1986-88; of counsel Morgan, Lewis & Bockius, N.Y.C., 1986-87; ptnr. Irell & Manella, Los Angeles, 1986-92, Parsons, Behle & Latimer, Salt Lake City, 1992—; vice chmn. bd. dirs. S.W. Research and Info. Ctr., Albuquerque, 1975-84; vice chmn. air quality commn. ABA, Chgo., 1983-92, co-chmn. intensive short course in environ. law ABA, 1994—. Author: The Environmental Impact Statement Process, 1978, The National Environmental Policy Act, 1980, Air Pollution-Cases and Materials, 1980, Community Right-to-Know Handbook, 1988; mem. editorial bd. Natural Resources and Environment, 1984-87. Adviser Internat. Joint Com. Can., 1979-81; governing bd. N.Y. Sea Grant Inst., 1984-87; vice chmn. City of Ithaca Environ. Commn., 1976-77; adviser N.Y. Dept. Environ. Conservation, 1984-87.

ORLOWSKI, RONALD JOSEPH, wood preserving company executive; b. Buffalo, Jan. 19, 1936; s. Joseph Bronislaus and Bernice (Mycek) O.; m. Veronica Rose Paluma, July 16, 1960; children: Joseph R., Gary J., Sheryl A., DAna A. BS, Canisius Coll., Buffalo, 1958. Acct. Firewel Co./ARO, Cheektowaga, N.Y., 1958-66; treas., v.p. Osmose Wood Preserving Inc., Buffalo, 1966—, also bd. dirs. With U.S. Army, 1958. Recipient various scouting awards Boy Scouts Am., Erie County, N.Y., various youth award Cath. Diocese of Buffalo. Mem. Am. Acctg. Soc. Office: Osmose Wood Preserving Inc 980 Ellicott St Buffalo NY 14209

ORLOWSKY, MARTIN L, retail company executive; b. N.Y.C., Dec. 7, 1941; s. Solomon and Sylvia (Levine) O.; m. Carolyn Louise Brady, Mar. 25, 1973; children—Daniel, Keith, Matthew. B.A., Long Island U., N.Y.C., 1963. Media planner Compton Advertising, N.Y.C., 1968-69; media planner Young & Rubicam Inc., N.Y.C., 1969-71; v.p. media Grey Advertising, N.Y.C., 1971-76; sr. v.p., media and mktg. services Needham, Harper & Steers, N.Y.C., 1976-77; media dir. R.J. Reynolds Tobacco Co., Winston-Salem, N.C., 1977-80, dir. mktg. services, 1980-82; v.p. brand mktg., 1982-84, sr. v.p. mktg., 1984-85, exec. v.p., 1986; pres. Grocery div. Nabisco

Brands, U.S.A., Parsippany, N.J., 1986—, Planters and Life Savers div. Nabisco Brands, U.S.A., Parsippany, N.J., 1987—. Vol., Peace Corps, Bolivia, 1963-65. Served to sgt. U.S. Army, 1966-68. Avocations: fishing; tennis. Home: 15 Manette Rd Morristown NJ 07960-6345 Address: 666 Fifth Ave New York NY 10103-0001

ORLY, ELVIRA JOLAN, lawyer; b. Berkeley, Calif., Nov. 22, 1948; d. Cyrill Vladimir and Elvira Maria (Erni) O.; m. Joseph A. Jeffrey, Aug. 17, 1979 (dec. June 1990). BS, U. Calif., Berkeley, 1970; MBA, JD, U. Calif., 1975. Bar: Calif. 1976, D.C. 1878. Tax atty. Pettit & Martin, San Francisco, 1975-76; legis. dir. for Senator S.I. Hayakawa, Washington, 1976-80; dir. legis. and regulatory affairs Edison Electric Inst., Washington, 1980-82, Getty (Texaco), Washington, 1982-85, Allied Signal, Washington, 1985-88; Washington counsel Browning-Ferris Industries, 1988-89; v.p. market devel. Browning-Ferris Industries, The Netherlands, 1989-90; v.p. external affairs Browning-Ferris Industries Europe, 1990-93; cons. in pub. and govt. affairs, 1993—. Bd. dirs. Codornices coun. Camp Fire Girls, 1973-75. Mem. U.S. Fencing Team to World Championships, 1974, 75; mem. U.S. Olympic Fencing Squad, 1976. Mem. ABA, Calif. Bar Assn., D.C. Bar Assn., U.S. Fencing Assn. (treas. 1987-92), European Environ. Lawyers Assn., Tax Coalition (bd. dirs. 1983-86, chmn. 1985), Behind the Tree Tax Group (chmn. 1985), Nat. Women's Econ. Alliance, Women in Govt. Rels., Assn. Former Senate Employees, Prytanean Club, Jr. League, Beta Gamma Sigma, Alpha Xi Delta. Home: Avenue de Tervueren 48, 1040 Brussels Belgium

ORMAN, LEONARD ARNOLD, lawyer; b. Balt., June 15, 1930; s. Samuel and Bertie (Adler) O.; m. Barbara Gold, June 9, 1978; children: Richard Harold, Robert Barton. AB summa cum laude, U. Md., 1952, JD, 1955. Bar: Md. 1955, U.S. Ct. Appeals (4th cir.) 1956, U.S. Dist. Ct. Md. 1955, Ct. Appeals Md. 1955, U.S. Supreme Ct. 1977, U.S. Ct. Claims 1990, D.C. Ct. Appeals 1987; cert. civil trial advocate by Nat. Bd. Trial Advocacy. Law clk. Hon. Frederick W. Brune, Chief Judge Md. Ct. of Appeals, 1955-56; mem. dept. legis. reference Md. Legislature, 1957-58; mem. Gov's Commn. to Revise Criminal Code, 1958-59; pvt. practice law Balt., 1956—; lectr. trial tactics. Mem. editorial bd.: Md. Law Rev, 1953-55; Contbr. articles to profl. jours. Pres. Young Dems. 2d Dist., Balt., 1960-63. With AUS, 1948-49; lt. col. USAF Res. ret. Rosco Pound Found. fellow, trustee. Mem. Md. State Bar Assn. (various coms. Balt. City Bar Assn. (various coms.), Nat. Coll. Trial Advocacy (trustee), Assn. Trial Lawyers Am. (nat. committeeman 1976-80, bd. govs. 1985—, exec. com. 1988-90, chmn. corp. rev. com., home office and budget com., orgn. and home office com., election com., key man com., past mem. steering com., past mem. publi. com., past mem. edit. adv. group 1989-90, co-chair hall of fame com., past vice chair ABA-ATLA liaison com., M Club, co-chair conv. site planning com., co-chairpolit. insight com., long range planning com., auto-hwy. adv. com., toy safety conf., med. malpractice adv. com., product liability adv. com., co-chair home office capital improvements adv. com., election com., co-chmn. conv. planning com. Washington), Md. Trial Lawyers Assn. (bd. govs., pres. 1988), Order of Coif, Masons. Home: 2 Celadon Rd Owings Mills MD 21117-3010 Office: 5 Light St Ste 1100 Baltimore MD 21202-1224

ORME, ANTONY RONALD, geography educator; b. Weston-Super-Mare, Somerset, Eng., May 28, 1936; came to U.S., 1968; s. Ronald Albert and Anne (Parry) O.; m. Amalie Jo Brown, Nov. 18, 1984; children: Mark Antony, Kevin Ronald, Devon Anne. B.A. with 1st class honors, U. Birmingham, 1957, Ph.D., 1961. Lectr. Univ. Coll., Dublin, Ireland, 1960-68; mem. faculty UCLA, 1968—, prof. geography, 1973—, dean social scis., 1977-83; cons. geomorphology various orgns., throughout U.S., 1968—. Editor-in-chief Phys. Geography; mem. editorial bd. Catena, Springer-Verlag, Berlin, U. Calif. Press. Recipient Award of Merit Am. Inst. Planners, 1975; recipient Outstanding Service award USAF, 1977-80. Mem. Geol. Soc. Am., Assn. Am. Geographers, Assn. Geography Tchrs. Ireland (pres. 1964-68), Inst. Brit. Geographers, Internat. Geog. Union. Home: 5128 Del Moreno Dr Woodland Hills CA 91364-2426 Office: UCLA Dept Geography Los Angeles CA 90095-1524

ORME, DENIS ARTHUR, management consultant; b. Auckland, New Zealand, Jan. 24, 1946; came to U.S., 1981; BA in Mgmt. and Econs., Victoria U., 1975; BA in Organizational Devel., Massey U., 1976. Insp. mgmt. svcs. New Zealand Police Dept., Wellington, 1963-77; bus. mgr. Russell McVeagh et al, Auckland, 1977-79; chief exec. officer, receiver Comml. Svcs., Inc., Auckland, 1979-81; mgr., cons. Price Waterhouse, Houston, 1981-82; pres., mgmt. cons. Orme Assocs. Inc., Houston, 1982—; pres. Distribution Sys. Tex., Inc.; pres., mgmt. cons. Med. Bus. Systems Inc., Houston, 1983-85; pres. Mighty Auto Parts, Houston. Contbr. articles to profl. jours. Mem. tech. adv. com. Tex. Healthcare Found., 1987-88. Mem. Am. Abritation Assn., Health Svcs. Mktg. Soc. (bd. dirs., treas. 1986), ABA (strategic planning for mktg. com. 1987, 88) Houston C. of C. (chmn. bus. group 1985-86), Tex. Bar Assn. (peer com.), Kiwanis (chmn. internat. com. 1986-87, vice chmn. internat. com. 1989). Anglican. Home: 12227 Briar Forest Dr Houston TX 77077-2501 Office: Orme Assocs Inc PO Box 440546 Houston TX 77244-0546

ORME-JOHNSON, WILLIAM HENRY, III, chemist, educator; b. Phoenix, Apr. 23, 1938; s. William Henry and Jean Mary (McGhee) O.; m. Nanette Roberts, May 27, 1957 (div. 1982); m. Carol Chamberlain, Aug. 3, 1983; children: Doris Helen, Ruth David, McGhee Charles. Student, Rice U., 1955-57; BS, U. Tex., 1959, PhD, 1964. Postdoctoral fellow U. Wis., Enzyme Inst., Madison, 1965-67, asst. prof., 1967-70; asst. prof. U. Wis., Dept. Biochemistry, Madison, 1970-71, assoc. prof., 1971-73, 1973-79, prof., 1973-79; prof. MIT, Dept. Chemistry, Cambridge, Mass., 1979—; sci. cons. BioTechnica Ltd., Cambridge, 1983—. Contbr. over 150 articles to sci. jours. V.p. The Lyric Stage, Boston, 1990-92. Grantee NIH, 1967—. Fellow AAAS; mem. Am. Chem. Soc., Am. Soc. Biol. Chemists. Episcopalian. Avocations: choral singing, acting, sailing. Home: 48 Massachusetts Ave Cambridge MA 02139-4322 Office: MIT 77 Massachusetts Ave Cambridge MA 02139-3594

ORMES, JONATHAN FAIRFIELD, astrophysicist, science administrator, researcher; b. Colorado Springs, Colo., July 18, 1939; s. Robert Manly and Suzanne (Viertel) O.; m. Karen Lee Minnick, Dec. 26, 1960 (div.); 1 child, Laurie Kylee; m. Janet Carolyn Dahl, Sept. 12, 1964; children: Marina, Nicholas. BS, Stanford U., 1961; PhD, U. Minn., 1967. NRC assoc. Goddard Space Flight Ctr., NASA, Greenbelt, Md., 1967-69, astrophysicist, 1969, head cosmic radiations br., 1981-82, head nuclear astrophysics br., 1983-87, assoc. chief lab. for high energy astrophysics, 1987-90, chief lab. for high energy astrophysics, 1990—; acting head high energy physics NASA hdqrs., Washington, 1982-83, mem. high energy astrophysics mgmt. ops. working group, 1975-83, mem. cosmic ray program working group, 1984-91; mem. com. on space and solar physics, com. on cosmic ray physics Nat. Acad. Sci., Washington, 1991-94. Editor: Essays in Space Science, 1987; assoc. editor astrophysics Phys. Rev. Letters, 1991-93; contbr. Astrophysics Jour., Phys. Rev. Letters, Astronomy and Astrophysics. Trustee Paint Br. Unitarian Universalist Ch., Adelphi, Md., 1987-88, chair bd. trustees, 1989, numerous positions, 1972-91. Fellow Am. Phys. Soc. (various div. offices); mem. Internat. Astron. Union, Am. Astron. Soc. (sec.-treas. High Energy Astrophysics div. 1985-87), Am. Geophys. Union. Achievements include discovery of unusual isotopic abundance of Ne in galactic cosmic rays; research on high energy spectra of cosmic rays, on anti-protons in galactic cosmic rays. Office: NASA Code 660 Goddard Space Flight Ctr Greenbelt MD 20771

ORMISTON, PATRICIA JANE, elementary education educator; b. Flint, Mich., Aug. 22, 1938; d. Elmer A. and Katheryn Lucille (Day) Knudson; m. Lester Murray Ormiston, June 13, 1964; 1 child, Brian Todd. BS, Minot State U., 1962; postgrad., U. Mont., 1963—, Mont. State U., 1963—, Western Mont. Coll., 1987. Elem. tchr. Lowell Sch., Gt. Falls, Mont., 1958, Webster Sch., Williston, N.D., 1958-59, Plaza (N.D.) Pub. Sch., 1959-61, Cen. Sch. Helena, Mont., 1962-63, Elrod Sch., Sch. Dist. 5, Kalispell, Mont., 1963—; core team Onward to Excellence, Sch. Dist. 5, Kalispell, 1989-92; participant Rocky Mountain Nat. Outcome-Based Edn. Conf., Greeley, Colo., 1990; presenter Kendall Hunt Lit. Reading Unit, Phi Delta Kappa, Kalispell, 1991, Mont. Assn. Gifted Talented Edn., 1991, Word Conf., Seattle, 1993; inst. presenter, symposium spkr. Utah Coun. Internat. Reading Assn. 28th Ann. State Reading Conf., Salt Lake City, 1994; univ. supr. student tchrs. Mont. State U., Bozeman, 1994—; mem. adv. bd. Kendall Hunt Pub. Co.,

Dubuque, Iowa, 1991—; symposium spkr., mem. reading coun., coun. tchrs. English S.D. State Conf., Mitchell, 1994; symposium spkr. Five Valleys Reading Conf. U. Mont., Missoula, 1994; invis. presenter South Whidbey Intermediate Sch., Langley, Wash., 1994. Contbr. author lit. based reading units 2d grade level Kentall Hunt Pub. Co., Dubuque, Iowa, 1989—; author: PEGASUS Integrating Themes in Literature and Language Correlated to Gages Lake, Illinois State Goals for Learning Language Arts, Grades K-6, 1993, PEGASUS Integrating Themes in Literature and Language Correlated to State of Georgia Quality Core Curriculum for English and Language Arts, Grades K-6, 1994, PEGASUS Integrating Themes in Literature and Language Correlated to State of Indiana Essential Skills English/Language Arts, Grades K-6, 1994, PEGASUS Integrating Themes in Literature and Language Correlated to Dade County Public Schools Competency-Based Curriculum for Language Arts, Grades K-5, 1994. Vol. Conrad Mansion Restoration, Kalispell, 1976—; presenter 34th ann. conv. Lit. Base Reading Internat. Reading Assn., New Orleans, 1989. Named Tchr. of Yr., Kalispell Sch. Dist. 5, 1986; Chpt. 2 grantee, 1987-88; Gertrude Whipple Profl. Devel. grantee IRA, 1988. Mem. NEA, Internat. Reading Assn. (symposium speaker 38th ann. conv. San Antonio 1993), Nat. Coun. Tchrs. English, Kalispell Edn. Assn. (bldg. rep. 1987-88, chmn. profl. acknowledgement com. 1988-93), Nat. Hist. Preservation, Phi Delta Kappa, Delta Kappa Gamma. Avocations: reading, writing, hiking, skiing, golf. Home: PO Box 64 Kalispell MT 59903-0064 Office: Elrod Sch 3rd Ave W Kalispell MT 59901-4426

ORMS, HOWARD RAYMOND, dramatics educator; b. Keota, Iowa, Oct. 25, 1920; s. Emmett Hartwell and Anna Marie (Fry) m. Vivian MacDowell, Feb. 6, 1914; children: Vivian Evans, Russell H., Kenneth A. BA, Cornell Coll., Mt. Vernon, 1947; MFA, Yale Drama Sch., New Haven, 1950. Asst. prof. Howard Coll., Birmingham, 1950-51; mng. dir. Nashville Community Playhouse, 1951-53, Des Moines Community Playhouse, 1953-61; mng. dir. Tulsa Little Theatre, Tulsa, 1961-66; Springfield, 1966—; prof. Southwest Mo. State U., Springfield, 1966-93, prof. emeritus, 1993—, performance coach, 1993—; owner, mng. dir. Merry-Go-Round Summer Theatre, 1949-62; cons. St. Johns Regional Hosp. Springfield, 1988; voice cons. St. Johns Personel, Springfield, 1988, Pub. Defenders Office, Springfield, 1986-88. Guest dir. Cornell Coll. of Iowa, 1993. Staff sgt. AAA, 1942-45. Recipient Southwest Mo. State U. Found. Outstanding Tchr. award, 1987-88. Mem. Am. Assn. of Community Theatre (Founding Fellow 1987), Nat. Theatre Conf. Republican. Presbyterian. Avocations: golfing, film, flower gardening, acting. Home: 3363 S Winton Pl Springfield MO 65804-6415 Office: Southwest Mo State U Dept Theatre & Dance 901 S National Ave Springfield MO 65804-0027

ORMSBEE, ALLEN IVES, aeronautical and astronautical engineering educator, researcher, consultant; b. Reno, Nev., Aug. 20, 1926; s. Randall Holden and Nelle Carolyn (Greene) O.; m. Geraldine Wilma Bartlett, Aug. 24, 1946; children: Pamela, Marilyn, Patricia. BS in Aero. Engring., U. Ill., 1946, MS in Math., 1949; PhD in Aeros., Calif. Inst. Tech., 1955. Instr. U. Ill., Urbana, 1946-51, asst. prof. aero. and astron. engring., 1951-55, assoc. prof., 1955-57, prof., 1957-92, prof. aviation, 1972-92, head aviation rsch. lab., 1977-79, acting assoc. dir. Inst. Aviation, 1982-88, assoc. dir. Inst. Aviation, 1988-92, prof. emeritus, 1992—; rsch. physicist Hughes Aircraft Co., Culver City, Calif., 1952-54; vis. prof. UCLA, 1964; mem. Engring. Accreditation Commn., 1985-94, vice chmn. ops., 1990-91, vice chmn. policy, chmn.-elect, 1991-92, chmn., 1992-93, past chmn., 1993-94; cons. in field; bd. dirs. Accreditation Bd. for Engring. and Tech., 1994—; mem. panel on causes and prevention grain elevator explosions Nat. Materials Adv. Bd., 1980-83; mem. Citizens Transp. Adv. Com., Champaign County, Ill., 1975-83, chmn., 1979-83. Contbr. articles on aerodynamics to tech. jours.; assoc. editor Jour Aircraft, 1976-80. Recipient Effective Teaching award U. Ill., 1951, Disting. Alumnus award, 1974; TWA scholar, 1945-46; Howard Hughes fellow, 1952-54. Fellow AIAA (assoc.); mem. AAUP, Am. Soc. Engring. Edn., Sigma Xi. Office: U Ill 306 Talbot Lab 104 S Wright St Urbana IL 61801-2935

ORMSBY, ERIC LINN, library administrator, researcher; b. Atlanta, Oct. 16, 1941; s. Robert and Virginia (Haire) O.; m. Dorothy Louise Hoffmann, July 22, 1967; children: Daniel Paul, Charles Martin. BA summa cum laude, U. Pa., 1971; MA, Princeton U., 1973, PhD, 1981; MLS, Rutgers U., 1978. Near East bibliographer libr. Princeton U., N.J., 1975-77; Near East curator libr. Princeton U., 1977-83; libr. dir. Cath. U. Am., Washington, 1983-86, McGill U., Montreal, Can., 1986—; assoc. prof. Inst. Islamic Studies, McGill U., 1986—; cons. NYU, 1981-82; mem. libr. com. Middle East Inst., Washington, 1985—; chmn. continuing edn. com. Washington Consortium, 1983-86; mem. bd. Ctr. Rsch. Librs., 1989—. Author: Theodicy in Islamic Thought, 1984 (Choice Mag. award 1984), Bavarian Shrine and Other Poems, 1990 (QSPELL award for poetry 1991), (poems) Coastlines, 1992, (with others) Handlist of Arabic Manuscripts, 1986; editor: Moses Maimonides and His Time, 1989; contbr. articles and book revs. to profl. jours., poetry to various mags. including The New Republic, The New Yorker, Grand Street, Shenandoah, The Souther Rev. and Chelsea. Instr. Princeton Adult Sch., 1978-80. DAAD fellow German Acad. Exch., 1973-74; recipient Ingram Merrill award, 1993. Mem. Middle East Librs. Assn. (v.p. 1981-82, pres. 1982-83), Hoelderlin Gesellschaft, Can. Assn. Rsch. Librs. (v.p. 1988-89), Can. Libr. Assn., Assn. pour l'Avancement des Scis. et des Techniques de la Documentation, Conseil des recteurs et des principaux des univs. du Québec, Sous-Comité des Bibliotheques (pres. 1989-91). Roman Catholic. Avocations: natural history, writing, cooking, photography. Office: McGill U Librs, 3459 McTavish St, Montreal, PQ Canada H3A 1Y1

ORNAUER, RICHARD LEWIS, retired educational association administrator; b. Bklyn., Oct. 19, 1922; s. Edwin L. and Emma (Handler) O.; m. Jane Robb, May 15, 1955 (div. Jan. 7, 1976); children: David S., Michael J., SaraJo; m. J. Rexene Ashford, Nov. 24, 1985. BJ, U. Mo., 1947. Wire editor Coastal Georgian, Brunswick, Ga., 1947-48; reporter copyreader, night editor, city editor Nassau Daily Rev.-Star, Rockville Centre, N.Y., 1948-53; city editor L.I. Press, Jamaica, N.Y., 1953-71; asst. commr. Nassau County Dept. Social Services, Mineola, 1971-74; pub. health info. program officer Nassau County Dept. Health, Mineola, 1974-87; adminstr. Bur. Epidemiology, 1979-84; dir. communications N.Y. State Sch. Bds. Assn., Albany, 1987-89; instr. Queens Coll., Flushing, N.Y., 1955-59; instr., mentor 55/ Alive mature driving program AARP, Dover, Del., 1994—; mem. exec. bd. Hofstra U. Sch. Bd. Forum, 1969-87; chmn. Merrick Planning Com., 1959-61; mem. publs. com. N.Y. State Sch. Bds. Assn., 1961-64, cons. to com., 1980-81, mem. BOCES com. 1971-74; vice chmn. State Sch. Bd. Leaders Com., 1975-79, cons. to com., 1980, bd. dirs., 1979-87, v.p., 1981, 84, 85, 86, 87, mem. exec. com., 1981-87, cons. to disting. service com., 1984, 85; cons. cities com., 1986, cons. grants com., 1987; del. L.I. Edn. Conf. Bd., 1967-86; trustee Merrick Bd. Edn., 1962-87, pres., 1966-71; trustee Bd. Coop. Ednl. Services Nassau County, 1967-87, v.p., 1967-71, pres., 1971-87; mem. exec. com. Nassau-Suffolk Sch. Bds. Assn., 1962-87, v.p., 1974-77, pres., 1977-79; mem. exec. com. Merrick Citizens Com. for Pub. Schs., 1959-87; mem. fed. relations network 4th Congl. dist. Nat. Sch. Bds. Assn., 1973-87, study com. on career edn., 1976-78, sub-chmn. for N.E. region presdl. task force on edn. of handicapped children, 1977-78, presdl. task force on critical viewing of TV by children, 1979-80; del. Northeast Region, Nat. Sch. Bds. Assn., 1980-87, vice chmn., 1985-87, chmn., 1987; adv. com. N.Y. State Senate Standing Com. on Civil Service and Pensions, 1978-79; mem. Instructional Service Television Com. WLIW-TV/Channel 21, pres., 1973-82; mem. Com. for Better Schs. of Merrick, 1975-87, Hist. Soc. Merricks, 1976-88; bd. dirs. L.I. Coalition Fair Broadcasting, 1977-82; mem. commr.'s adv. council N.Y. State Edn. Dept., 1980-87; mem. City of Dover Pub. Safety Issues Implementation Studies Commn., 1993—. Mem. citizens adv. com. Dover Met. Planning Orgn., 1993—, vice chmn., 1994—; Planned Parenthood Del., United Way Del., Spl. Olympics Ptnr., Medic Alert Internat. With AUS, 1942-45, PTO. Recipient citations N.Y. State Police Conf., 1949, citations Rockville Centre Police Benevolent Assn., 1953, citations Nassau Div. Am. Cancer Soc., 1961, citations Nassau Am. Legion, 1963, citations Nassau Library System, 1964, citations Firemen's Assn. of Nassau County, 1964, citations Nassau County Scholastic Press Assn., 1965, citations United Fund of L.I., 1970, citations Kiwanis Clubs Internat., 1971, citations Jewish War Vets., 1972, citations WLIW-TV, 1982; Educator of Yr. award Hofstra U. chpt. Phi Delta Kappa, 1973; Educator of Yr. award Assn. for the Help of Retarded Children, Nassau County chpt., 1977; Disting. Service award Nassau-Suffolk Sch. Bds. Assn., 1979, 87, Spl. Merit award Nassau-Suffolk Sch. Bds. Assn., 1987; named Educator of Yr. U.S. Congress, 1987, County

of Nassau, 1987, Town of Hempstead (N.Y.), 1987, Merrick Bd. Edn., 1987, various depts. Nassau County Bd. Coop. Ednl. Services, 1987, Merrick Sch. Dist. Faculty Assn., 1987; named Man of Yr. L.I. Spl. Edn. Adminstrs. Assn., 1979, Man of Yr. Merrick C. of C., 1980. Man of Yr. N.Y. State Legislature, 1980, 87, Man of Yr. Nassau-L.I. dist. N.Y. State Congress Parents and Tchrs., 1980. Mem. Nat. Sch. Pub. Rels. Assn. (exec. com. N.Y. State chpt., Capital Dist. chpt.), Edn. Writers Assn., Am. Newspaper Guild, Nat. Congress Parents and Tchrs. (life), N.Y. State Congress Parents and Tchrs. (life), N.Y. State Pub. Health Assn., Assn. Emotionally Haapped Children, Assn. to Help Retarded Children, Assn. Children With Learning Abilities, N.Am. Assn. Environ. Edn., N.Y. Citizens Com. Pub. Schs., Nat. Soc. Autistic Children, Am. Assn. Career Edn., Ad Hoc Planning Com. Mobilized Community Resources, L.I. Sch.-Community Relations Assn., N.Y. Civil Svc. Employees Assn., N.Y. State Outdoor Edn. Assn., Nat. Parks and Conservation Assn., Nat. Arbor Day Found., Conf. Sch. Bds. Assn. Communicators, Am. Assn. Retired Persons (Greater Dover area chpt., bd. dirs. 1995—), Ednl. Press Assn. U. Mo. Alumni Assn., Boise State U. Alumni Assn., Albany Inst. History and Art (charter mem.), N.Y. State Mus. Assocs., Smithsonian Inst. Assocs., Libr. Congress Assocs. (charter), U.S. Holocaust Meml. Mus. Assocs. (charter), Newtonville Neighborhood Assn., Mifflin Rd. Neighborhood Assn. (gov. rels. chmn., exec. com.), Deerfield Civ. Assn., Consumer Union Assocs., Common Cause, Nat. Com. to Preserve Social Security and Medicare, Soc. Profl. Journalists, Sigma Delta Chi (life, Empire State chpt.), Alpha Epsilon Pi (life). Jewish. Home: 17 Mifflin Rd Dover DE 19904-3316

ORNDUFF, ROBERT, botany educator; b. Portland, Oreg., June 13, 1932; s. Robert and Kathryn (Davis) O. B.A., Reed Coll., 1953; M.Sc., U. Wash., 1956; Ph.D. U. Calif.-Berkeley, 1961. Asst. prof. Reed Coll., 1962, Duke U., 1963; asst. prof. botany U. Calif., Berkeley, 1963-66, assoc. prof., 1966-69, prof., 1969-93, prof. emeritus, 1993—, dir. Jepson Herbarium, 1968-83, dir. Univ. Herbarium, 1975-83, exec. dir. Miller Inst. for Basic Research in Sci., 1984-87, chmn. dept. botany, 1986-89. Dir. Stanley Smith Hort. Trust, 1992—. Fellow AAAS, Calif. Acad. Scis.; mem. Calif. Native Plant Soc. (pres. 1972-73), Am. Soc. Plant Taxonomists (pres. 1975). Home: 490 Arlington Ave Berkeley CA 94707-1609 Office: Dept Integrative Biology U Calif Berkeley CA 94720-3140

ORNITZ, RICHARD MARTIN, lawyer, business executive; b. Annapolis, Md., July 4, 1945; s. Martin Nathaniel and Beatrice Cynthia (Swick) O.; m. Margareth Adams, June 15, 1971 (div. Apr. 1977); m. Janet Alma Steen, Dec. 5, 1981; children—Alexandra, Zachary, Darren, Erik, Nicholas. B.S. in Metall. Engring., Cornell U., 1967; J.D., NYU, 1970; grad. sr. exec. program, MIT, 1985. Bar: N.Y. 1971, U.S. Dist. Ct. (ea. dist.) 1972, U.S. Supreme Ct. 1984. Assoc. Cravath, Swaine & Moore, N.Y.C., 1972-77; v.p., gen. counsel, sec. Degussa Corp., Teterboro, N.J. 1977-90, mem. mgmt. com., 1987-90; of counsel, Hughes, Hubbard & Reed, N.Y.C., 1985-92; dir. Degussa Corp. subs., 1980-92; ptnr. Stroock, Stroock & Lavan, 1991—; dir. Metal Products Internat., Inc., Greenwich, Conn; speaker Risk Ins. Mgmt. Soc., 1984, 85, 86, IBA, 1986, ACCA, 1986, European Co. Lawyers Assn., 1986; Swiss Co. Lawyers Assn., 1987; Norwegian Co. Lawyers Assn., 1988; mem. pvt. law adv. com. Office of Legal Adv. U.S. Dept. State, adv. bd. Nat. Inst. Preventive Maintenance, adv. bd. corp. counsel Am. Arbitration Assn. Assoc. editor Am. Survey of Law, NYU, 1970. Fin. com. Conn. Spl. Olympics; bd. dirs. Old Greenwich Civic Assn. Served to 1st lt. U.S. Army, 1970-72. Mem. ABA (chmn. European law sect., human relations and labor law, 1987-90), N.Y. State Bar Assn., Internat. Bar Assn., Am. Corp. Counsel Assn. (chmn. of internat. sect. com., 1986-90) European Am. Gen. Counsels Group (chmn. 1986-87), N.J. Gen. Counsels Group, Cornell Soc. Engrs. Republican. Jewish. Clubs: Old Greenwich Republican (Conn.), Innis Arden, Rocky Point. Home: 18 Meadowbank Rd Old Greenwich CT 06870-2312 Office: Stroock Stroock & Lavan 7 Hanover Sq New York NY 10004-2616

ORNSTEIN, DONALD SAMUEL, mathematician, educator; b. N.Y.C., July 30, 1934; s. Harry and Rose (Wisner) O.; m. Shari Richman, Dec. 20, 1964; children—David, Kara, Ethan. Student, Swarthmore Coll., 1950-52; Ph.D., U. Chgo., 1957. Fellow Inst. for Advanced Study, Princeton, N.J., 1955-57; faculty U. Wis., Madison, 1958-60; faculty Stanford (Calif.) U., 1959—, prof. math., 1966—; faculty Hebrew U., Jerusalem, 1975-76. Author: Ergodic Theory Randomness and Dynamical Systems, 1974. Recipient Bocher prize Am. Math. Soc., 1974. Mem. NAS, Am. Acad. Arts and Sci. Jewish. Office: Dept Math Stanford U Stanford CA 94305

ORNSTEIN, NORMAN JAY, political scientist; b. Grand Rapids, Minn., Oct. 14, 1948; s. Joseph and Dorothy (Latz) O.; m. Judith Linda Harris, May 29, 1977; children—Matthew, Daniel. BA, U. Minn., 1967; MA, U. Mich., 1968, PhD, 1972. Asst. prof. Johns Hopkins U., Bologna, Italy, 1971-72; prof. Cath. U. Am., Washington, 1972-84; staff mem., staff dir. Senate Com. on Com. System, Washington, 1976-77; fellow Ctr. for Advanced Study in Behavioral Scis., Palo Alto, Calif., 1979-80; resident scholar Am. Enterprise Inst., Washington, 1980—; co-dir. Renewing Congress Project, Washington, 1992—, Times Mirror-Gallup Study: The People, the Press and Politics, 1987-90, Times Mirror Ctr. for the People and the Press, 1991—; columnist Roll Call newspaper, 1993—; polit. editor Lawmakers program Sta. WETA-TV, Washington, 1980-84; cons. CBS News Election Unit, N.Y.C., 1982—; commentator, cons. MacNeil/Lehrer News Hour, Washington and N.Y.C., 1983—; moderator Calif. Congl. Report, Sta. KCET-TV, L.A., 1983; lectr. USIA. Author: Interest Groups Lobbying and Policy, 1978; (with others) The New Congress, 1981, Vital Statistics on Congress, 1993, Debt and Taxes, 1994; writer, editor, co-host: (tv series) Congress: We the People, 1984 (cert. of merit ABA 1985). Fortieth Anniversary Fulbright Disting. fellow, 1986-87. Mem. Coun. on Fgn. Rels., Am. Polit. Sci. Assn. (coun. 1984-86, Congl. fellow 1969-70), Nat. Commn. Pub. Svc. (bd. dirs., Volcker commn. 1987-90), Phi Beta Kappa (vis. scholar 1986-87). Jewish. Home: 5818 Surrey St Bethesda MD 20815-5419 Office: Am Enterprise Inst 1150 17th St NW Washington DC 20036-4603

ORNSTEIN-GALICIA, JACOB LEONARD (JACK ORNSTEIN-GALICIA), foreign language educator, linguist, author; b. Cleve., Aug. 12, 1915; s. Joseph and Bertha (Schwartz) Ornstein; m. Janet Ann Eaton, Dec. 25, 1962 (div. Nov. 1977); 1 child, Dena Hayden. BS in Edn., Ohio State U., 1936, MA, 1937; PhD, U. Wis., 1940. Cert. tchr., Ohio. Instr. Spanish and Portuguese U. Wis., Madison, 1940-41; asst. prof. Washington U., St. Louis, 1941-42; intelligence officer Office Strategic Svcs., Washington, North Africa and Italy, 1942-45; assoc. prof. Waldorf Coll., Forest City, Iowa, 1947-49, N.Mex. State U., Las Cruces, 1949-51; intelligence officer, sci. linguist CIA, Washington, 1951-68; prof. linguistics and langs. U. Tex., El Paso, 1968—, now emeritus prof.; lectr. Sch. Langs. and Linguistics, Georgetown U., Washington, 1964-68; cons. U.S. Office Edn., Washington, 1968-74, S.W. Coop. Ednl. Lab., Albuquerque, 1970, Ednl. Testing Svc., Princeton, N.J., 1974; reader proposals NSF, Washington, 1975—; faculty mem. U. Ctr. for Lifelong Learning, 1992—; prof. 1993—. Author: Slavic and East European Studies: Their Development in the Western hemisphere, 1957, A Sociolinguistic Study of Mexican-American and Anglo Students in a Border University, 1975, Sociolinguistic Foundations of Language Assessment, 1983; also articles; co-author: Elements of Russian, 1964, Programmed Instruction and Educational Technology in the Language Teaching Field, 1971, The New ABC's of Language and Linguistics, 1977, A Problem-Solving Model for Integrating Science and Language in Bilingual-Bicultural Education, 1983; editor: Repetición de amores (Luis de Lucena), 1954, Form and Function in Chicano English: New Insights, 1984, rev. edit., 1988; co-editor: Studies in Language and Linguistics, 1969-70, Studies in Language and Linguistics II, 1970-71, College English and the Mexican-American, 1976, Problems of Standard vs. Non-Standard: Dimensions of Foreign Language Teaching, 1977, Problems in Applied Educational Sociolinguistics: Readings on Language and Cultural Problems of U.S. Ethnic Groups, 1978, Bilingualism and Bilingual Education: New Readings and Insights, 1979, Sociolinguistic Studies in Language Contact: Methods and Cases, 1979, Problems of Loyalty and Accomodation Among Minority Languages and Dialects, 1980, Social and Educational Issues in Bilingualism and Biculturalism, 1981, Politics and Society in the Southwest: Ethnicity and Chicano Pluralism, 1982, Chicano English: An Ethnic Contact Dialect, 1985, Mexican-American Language: Usage, Attitudes, Maintenance, Instruction and Policy, 1986, Chicano Speech in the Bilingual Classroom, 1988, Research Issues and Problems in U.S. Spanish, 1988, Mexican-American Spanish in its Societal and Cultural Context, 1989, Jewish Farmer in America, The Unknown Chronicle, 1992. Adviser Armadillo orgn., Disabled Students'

Orgn., U. Tex., El Paso, 1969-81; organizer Town and Gown forum, El Paso, 1975-85. Recipient A. G. Solalinde award U. Wis., 1938, Outstanding Alumnus award Ohio State U. Stadium Scholarship Alumni Assn., 1989. Mem. MLA, Linguistic Soc. Am., Am. Assn. Tchrs. Spanish and Portuguese, Assn. Lingistica y Filologia de America Latina Linguistica. Home: 315 W Schuster Ave Apt 4 El Paso TX 79902-3434 Office: U Tex Dept Langs and Linguistics University and Hawthorne El Paso TX 79968

ORNSTON, DARIUS GRAY, JR., psychiatrist; b. Phila., Sept. 13, 1934; s. Darius Gray and Marie Elizabeth (Wallace) O. BA, U. Pa., 1955, MD, 1959. Psychiatrist Dept. Student Mental Hygiene, New Haven, 1967-74; pvt. practice Greenville, S.C., 1974—; clin. prof. U.S.C., Columbia, 1988, Med. U. S.C., Charleston, 1988; assoc. clin. prof. Yale U., New Haven, 1983. Editor: Translating Freud, 1993. Office: 880 S Pleasantburg Dr 4C Greenville SC 29607

ORONSKY, ARNOLD LEWIS, scientific research company executive, medical educator; b. N.Y.C., Oct. 22, 1940; s. Isaac Albert and Rosalind (Siegel) O.; m. Paula Renee Kirschner, Aug. 19, 1964; children: Bryan Todd, Neil Charles. AB, NYU, 1961; PhD, College of Physicians and Surgeons, Columbia U., 1968. Postdoctoral fellow Harvard Med. Sch., Boston, 1968-70, King Trust Found. fellow, 1970-71, asst. prof. dept. medicine, 1971-72; sr. scientist CIBA-GEIGY, Ardsley, N.Y., 1972-74, dir. immunology, 1974-76; dir. Lederle Labs., Pearl River, N.Y., 1977-79, v.p. rsch., 1980-94; gen. ptnr. Interwest Venture Ptnrs., Menlo Park, Calif., 1994—; CEO Coulter Pharm., Palo Alto, Calif.; adj. prof. Mt. Sinai Sch. Medicine, N.Y.C., 1980-94; sr. lectr. Johns Hopkins Sch. Medicine, Balt., 1983-94. Contbr. articles to profl. jours. and chpts. to books; editor 2 books. Mem. Am. Physiol. Soc., Othopedic Rsch. Soc., N.Y. Acad. Scis., Am. Soc. Microbiology. Office: Interwest Ptnrs 3000 Sandhill Rd Bldg 3 Ste 255 Menlo Park CA 94025

OROPALLO, DEBORAH, artist, educator; b. Hackensack, N.J., Nov. 29, 1954. BFA, Alfred (N.Y.) U., 1979; MA, U. Calif., Berkeley, 1982, MFA, 1983. Teaching asst. Alfred (N.Y.) U., 1979, U. Calif., Berkeley, 1982-83; instr. San Francisco Art Inst., 1984-85, San Francisco Art Acad. Coll., 1986, 87-92; vis. prof. San Francisco Art Inst., 1993; artist C. O. Stephen Wirtz Gallery, San Francisco, 1994—. One-woman shows include Media Gallery, N.Y., 1979, Stephen Wirtz Gallery, San Francisco, 1986, 88, 90, 93, Meml. Union Art Gallery, Davis, Calif., 1987, Raab Gallerie, Berlin, 1987, Inst. Contemporary Art, Boston, 1990, Artspace, San Francisco, 1990, Greenville County Mus. Art, Greenville, S.C., 1991, Germans van Eck Gallery, N.Y.C., 1991, Weatherspoon Gallery, Greensboro, N.C., 1992, Ann Jaffee Gallery, Bay Harbor Island, Fla., 1992, Kate Block Fine Arts, Boston, 1993, Stephen Wirtz Gallery, San Francisco, 1993, 95, San Jose Mus. Art, 1994; exhibited in group shows at Fosdick Nelson Gallery, Alfred, N.Y., 1979, Albright Knox Mus., Buffalo, 1980, Richmond (Calif.) Art Ctr., 1980, Civic Ctr., San Francisco, 1981, Calif. State Fair Art Exhbn., Sacramento, 1981, San Jose Inst. Contemporary Art, 1981, Worth Ryder Gallery, Berkeley, Calif., 1981, 1982, Annual Conf. of Mus. Assn. Am., 1983, Berkeley Art Mus., 1983, San Francisco Art Inst., 1984, San Francisco Arts Commn. Gallery, 1985, Acad. Art Gallery, San Francisco, 1986, Freson (Calif.) Art Ctr., 1987, Allport Gallery, San Francisco, 1988, Whitney Mus. Am. Art, N.Y.C., 1989, Stephen Wirtz Gallery, San Francisco, 1989, 91, 95, Am. Acad. and Inst. Arts and Letters, N.Y.C., 1989, Cleve. Ctr. Contemporary Art, 1990, Milw. Art Mus., 1990, Okla. Mus. Art, Oklahoma City, 1990, Contemporary Art Mus., Houston, 1990, Oakland Mus., 1991, Molica Guidarte Gallery, N.Y.C., 1991, Susan Cummins Gallery, Mill Valley, Calif., 1992, Calif. Coll. Arts and Crafts, Oakland, 1992, Krakow Gallery, Boston, 1992, Kate Block Fine Art, Boston, 1992, Corcoran Gallery of Art, Washington, 1993, San Jose Mus., 1993, Galleria de Arte, Sao Paulo, Brazil, 1994, Palo Alto (Calif.) Cultural Ctr., 1994, Michael Kohler Arts Ctr., Sheboygan, Wis., 1994, Okeanos Press, Berkeley, Calif., 1994, CAPP Street Project, San Francisco, 1994, The Artists Contemporary Gallery, Hyatt Regency Plz., Sacramento, 1995, Gallery Concord, Concord, Calif., 1995, others. Recipient F.C.-J.C. Fine Art award Alfred U., 1977, Michael Cory Levins Sculpture award Alfred U., 1978, N.Y. Coll. Register Cert. of Recognition, 1977, Hon. mention Calif. State Fair Art Exhbn., 1981, Second Pl. award, 1981, Richmond (Calif.) Art Ctr. award, 1982, Ann Bremer award U. Calif., 1982, 22nd Ann. Art Exhibit Second Pl. award, 1983, Engelhard award Inst. Contemporary Art, Boston, 1987, Art Space Support grant, 1988, 90, NEA award, 1991, Fleishhacker award, 1993. Office: C O Stephen Wirtz Gallery 49 Geary 3rd Fl San Francisco CA 94108-5707

OROPEZA, MARK, airport director; b. Tallahassee, Fla., Dec. 29, 1955; s. Oscar and Dorothy Ann (Miller) O.; m. Terry Lee Bradford, Feb. 14, 1981; children: Christopher, Andrew. AS in Aviation Adminstrn., Miami (Fla.) Dade Community Coll., 1975; B of Aviation Mgmt., Auburn U., 1978. Cert. flight instr. Flightsafety Internat., Vero Beach, Fla., 1978; asst. dir. Dekalb Peachtree Airport, Atlanta, 1979-86; dir. Columbus (Ga.) Metro Airport, 1986—; instr. aviation Dekalb Community Coll., Atlanta, 1984. Active Leadership Columbus, 1988-89. Mem. Southeastern Airport Mgrs. Assn. (program com. 1985-88), Am. Assn. Airport Execs., Kiwanis. Methodist. Avocations: flying, scuba diving, boating. Office: Columbus Metro Airport 1000 Airport Thruway Columbus GA 31909-5381

O'RORKE, JAMES FRANCIS, JR., lawyer; b. N.Y.C., Dec. 4, 1936; s. James Francis and Helen (Weber) O'R.; m. Carla Phelps, Aug. 6, 1964. A.B., Princeton U., 1958; J.D., Yale U., 1961. Bar: N.Y. 1962. Assoc. Davies, Hardy & Schenck, 1962-69; ptnr. Davies, Hardy, Ives & Lawther, 1969-72, Skadden, Arps, Slate, Meagher & Flom, N.Y.C., 1972—; dir. Clinipad Corp.; mem. adv. bd. Chgo. Title Ins. Co. N.Y. Trustee Mus. Am. Indian-Heye Found., 1977-80. Mem. ABA, N.Y. State Bar Assn., Assn. Bar City N.Y., Am. Coll. Real Estate Lawyers, Princeton Club N.Y.C. Office: Skadden Arps Slate Meagher & Flom 919 3rd Ave New York NY 10022-3903

O'ROURKE, ANDREW PATRICK, lawyer, county official; b. Plainfield, N.J., Oct. 26, 1933; s. Andrew Patrick and Helene (Anderson) O'R.; children: Alice T., Andrew Patrick, Alleen B. BS, Fordham Coll., 1954, LLD, 1962; LLM, NYU, 1965; LLD, Mercy Coll., 1988, Pace U., 1987, Manhattanville Coll., 1986, Marymount Coll., 1986. Bar: N.Y. 1962, U.S. Dist. Ct. (so. and ea. dists.) N.Y., U.S. Ct. Appeals (2d cir.) 1964, U.S. Supreme Ct. 1970. Assoc. Kreindler & Kreindler, N.Y.C., 1963-68; sole practice, Westchester County, N.Y., 1968-82; county exec. Westchester County, White Plains, N.Y., 1983—. Author: Red Banner Mutiny, 1985, Hawkwood, 1989; contbr. articles to profl. jours. Mem. Yonkers (N.Y.) City Coun., 1966-73; mem. Westchester County Bd. Legislators, 1973-82, chmn., 1978-82; del. Rep. Nat. Convention, New Orleans, 1988. Served to capt. USNR. Recipient Seth Lowe award L.I. U., 1984, Tree of Life award Jewish Nat. Fund, 1984, Coun. for Arts award Westchester County Council Arts, 1984, Hispanic Coun. Westchester award, 1985, Disting. Svc. award Putnam Affirmative Action Program Inc., Westchester, 1991. Office: County Office Bldg 148 Martine Ave White Plains NY 10601-3311

O'ROURKE, C. LARRY, lawyer; b. Colusa, Calif., Dec. 10, 1937; s. James Harold and Elizabeth Janice (Jenkins) O'R.; m. Joy Marie Phillips, May 22, 1965; children: Ryan, Paula. BSEE, Stanford U., 1959, MBA, 1961; JD, George Washington U., 1972. Bar: Va. 1971, D.C. 1974, U.S. Ct. Appeals (fed. cir.) 1973, U.S. Patent and Trademark Office 1971, U.S. Supreme Ct. Patent atty. Westinghouse Elec., Washington, 1969-70, Pitts., 1970-73; assoc. Finnegan, Henderson, Farabow, Garrett & Dunner, Washington, 1974-79, ptnr., 1979—; dir. Zest Inc., Md., 1988, chmn. bd. dirs., 1990—; elec. practice group leader Finnegan, Henderson, Farabow, Garrett & Dunner, 1993—. Mem. ABA, Am. Intellectual Property Law Assn. Democrat. Presbyterian. Office: Finnegan Henderson Farabow Garrett & Dunner 1300 Eye St NW Ste 700 Washington DC 20005-3315

O'ROURKE, DENNIS, lawyer; b. Whiteclay, Nebr., Oct. 31, 1914; s. Frank L. and Jerene (Rebbeck) O'R.; m. Ruth Rouss, Jan. 21, 1940; children: Susan, Kathleen, Brian, Dennis, Ruth, Dolores. A.B. cum laude, Nebr. Tchrs. Coll., 1935; J.D. with distinction, George Washington U., 1939; LLD (hon.), Chadron State Coll., 1993. Bar: D.C. 1939, U.S. Supreme Ct 1945, Colo. 1946. Typist, auditor GAO, Washington, 1935-39; lawyer solicitor's office U.S. Dept. Agr., Washington, 1939-45; chief basic commodity div. U.S. Dept. Agr., 1945; gen. counsel Group Health Assn., Washington, 1943, Holly Sugar Corp., Colorado Springs, Colo., 1945; v.p. Holly Sugar Corp.,

Colorado Springs, 1953-63, pres., 1963-67, chmn. bd., 1967-69, dir., 1983-88; vice chmn. bd., mem. exec. com. Holly Sugar Corp. (merged with Imperial Sugar Co.), Colorado Springs, 1986-88; v.p., gen. counsel Holly Oil Co., 1955-63; sr. ptnr. Rouss & O'Rourke, Colorado Springs and Washington; U.S. counsel Union Nacional de Productores de Azucar, Mexico, 1970-82; pres. Man Exec., Inc., Colorado Springs and Washington; chmn. examining com. 1st Nat. Bank Colorado Springs, 1983-84. Contbr. articles financial and bus. jours. Bd. dirs. Colo. Pub. Expenditure Coun., vice chmn., exec. com., 1968-76; dir. Nat. C. of C. of the U.S., 1968-70; trustee, pres. Colorado Springs Fine Arts Center, 1961-62, 68-71, 73, chmn. adv. com., 1981-84, hon. trustee, 1988; founder, 1st chmn. Colo. Com. (now Coun.) on Arts and Humanities, 1963; Mem. Bus. and Industry Adv. Com. OECD, Paris, France, 1969-71; adviser U.S. dels. Internat. Sugar Confs., Geneva, 1965, Mexico City, 1959; chmn. Colorado Springs-El Paso County Citizens' Task Force on Local Govt. Reorgn., 1976-77. Mem. Am. Soc. Sugar Beet Technologists, Internat. Soc. Sugar Cane Technologists, Fed. Bar Assn., Colo. Bar Assn., El Paso County Bar Assn, Order of Coif, Cheyenne Mountain Country Club, El Paso Club, Garden of Gods Club, Sugar Club, Met. Club (Washington), Rotary, Phi Delta Phi. Home: 8 Heather Dr Broadmoor Colorado Springs CO 80906 Office: PO Box 572 Colorado Springs CO 80901-0572 also: 1614 20th St NW Washington DC 20009-1001

O'ROURKE, J. TRACY, manufacturing company executive; b. Columbia, S.C., Mar. 14, 1935; s. James Tracy and Georgia Adella (Bridges) O'R.; m. Lou Ann Turner, Mar. 19, 1954; 1 son, James Tracy. BSME, Auburn U., 1956. Teflon specialist duPont Co., Wilmington, Del., 1957-62; pres., chief exec. officer LNP Corp., Malvern, Pa., 1962-72; v.p. Carborundum, Niagara Falls, N.Y., 1972-76; exec. v.p. Chemetron, Chgo., 1976-78; sr. v.p. Allen Bradley Co. subs. Rockwell Internat. Corp., Milw., 1978-81, pres., chief oper. officer, 1981-86, also chief exec. officer, dir., 1986-90; chmn., chief exec. officer Varian Assocs., Palo Alto, Calif., 1990—. Served as 1st lt. USAF, 1957-59. Office: Varian Assocs PO Box 10800 3050 Hansen Way Palo Alto CA 94304

O'ROURKE, JACK, financial company administrator; b. Newark, Mar. 13, 1937; s. John and Mary (Cook) O'R.; m. Patricia Ann Beyer; children: Suzanne P., John, Christine J. Student, Boston U., 1967. CLU, Chfc. Gen. mgr. ManuLife Fin., Toronto, Ont., Can., 1962—. Bd. dirs. Metro Bank Dade County, Miami, Fla., 1984—. With USN, 1955-58. Mem. Miami Assn. Life Underwriters (bd. dirs. 1986—, pres. 1993-94), Miami Gen. Agts. and Mgts. Assn. (bd. dirs. 1981—), Fla. Gen. Agts. and Mgrs. Assn. (bd. dirs. Tallahassee 1989-91), Miami chpt. CLU and ChFC (pres. 1990-91), Coral Reef Yacht Club (commodore 1994— Coconut Grove, Fla. chpt.), Com. of 100, Beach Colony Club, Falls Racquet Club. Republican. Roman Catholic. Avocations: boating, fishing, snow skiing, photography. Office: ManuLife Fin The Colonnade 2333 Ponce De Leon Blvd Ste 303 Miami FL 33134-5418

O'ROURKE, JOANNE A., state legislator; b. Manchester, N.H., Sept. 4, 1939; m. Thomas F. O'Rourke; 3 children. Attended, N.H. Coll. Formerly with New Eng. Telephone and Telegraph Co.; mem. N.H. Ho. of Reps.; asst. minority leader, 1990; Dem. whip N.H. Ho. of Reps., 1990—; mem. appropriations com.; mem. rules com.; mem. state-fed. rels. com. Selectman ward three City of Manchester, 1972-77; bd. dirs. Greater Manchester Mental Health, 1985-91, So. N.H. Svcs., 1985—; co-chmn. State Dem. Policy Coun., 1985-87; chmn. Manchester Legis. Del., 1986-92, Dem. City Com., 1992—; mem. exec. com. Hillsborough County, 1986; vice chmn. Coun. State Govt. Intergovtl. Affairs, 1988, chmn., 1989. Democrat. Roman Catholic. Home: 91 Harrison St Manchester NH 03104-3611 Office: NH Ho of Reps State Capitol Concord NH 03301

O'ROURKE, P. J. (PATRICK JAKE O'ROURKE), writer, humorist; b. Toledo, Ohio, Nov. 14, 1947; s. Clifford Bronson and Delphine (Loy) O'R. BA, Miami U. of Ohio, 1969; MA, Johns Hopkins U., 1970. Writer Nat. Lampoon mag., from 1973, former prin. editor; freelance writer, writer screenplays, 1980s; writer Rolling Stone mag., 1981—, now fgn. affairs desk chief. Author: Modern Manners: An Etiquette Book for Rude People, 1983, The Bachelor Home Companion: A Practical Guide to Keeping House Like a Pig, 1987, Republican Party Reptile, 1987, Holidays in Hell, 1988, Parliament of Whores: A Lone Humorist Attempts to Explain the U.S. Government, 1991, Give War a Chance: Eyewitness Accounts of Mankind's Struggle Against Tyranny, Injustice and Alcohol-Free Beer, 1992, All the Trouble in the World: The Lighter Side of Overpopulation, Famine, Ecological Disaster, Ethnic Hatred, Plague and Poverty, 1994. Office: care Rolling Stone 1290 Ave of the Americas New York NY 10104

O'ROURKE, THOMAS DENIS, civil engineer, educator; b. Pitts., July 31, 1948; s. Lawrence Robert and Adel Mildred (Moloski) O'R.; m. Patricia Ann Lane, Aug. 12, 1978; B.S.C.E., Cornell U., Ithaca, N.Y., 1970, M.S.C.E., U. Ill., 1973, Ph.D., 1975. Soils engr. Dames & Moore, N.Y.C., 1970; research asst. U. Ill., Urbana, 1970-74, asst. prof., 1975-78; asst. prof. Cornell U., 1978-80, assoc. prof., 1981-87, prof., 1987—. Elected to Nat. Acad. Engring., 1993. Mem. ASCE (pres. Ithaca sect. 1981-82, Collingwood prize 1983, Huber prize 1988, C. Martin Duke award 1995), ASME, ASTM (C.A. Hogentoger award 1976), Earthquake Engring. Research Inst., Internat. Soc. Engring. Geology, Internat. Soc. Rock Mechanics, U.S. Nat. Com. on Tunnelling Tech. (chmn. 1987-88). Home: 10 Twin Glens Rd Ithaca NY 14850-1041 Office: Cornell U Sch Civil Environ Engring 265 Hollister Hall Ithaca NY 14853-3501

O'ROURKE, WILLIAM ANDREW, English language educator, author; b. Chgo., Dec. 4, 1945; s. William Andrew and Elizabeth (Kompare) O'R.; m. Marion Teresa Ghilarducci, July 9, 1986; 1 child, Joseph Ghilarducci. B.A., U. Mo. at Kansas City, 1968; M.F.A., Columbia U., 1970. Instr. journalism Kean Coll., Union, N.J., 1973; asst. prof. English Rutgers U., 1975-78, Mount Holyoke Coll., 1978-81; asst. prof. English U. Notre Dame, Ind., 1981-87, assoc. prof., 1987-94, prof., 1994—; writer-in-residence Thurber House, Columbus, Ohio, fall 1984. Author: The Harrisburg 7 and the New Catholic Left, 1972, The Meekness of Isaac, 1974, Idle Hands, 1981, Criminal Tendencies, 1987, Signs of the Literary Times: Essays, Reviews, Profiles 1970-92, 1993; editor: On the Job, 1977. Fine Arts Work Ctr. fellow, Provincetown, Mass., 1970-72; recipient Creative Artists Pub. Svc. award N.Y. State Coun. on Arts, 1975; Nat. Endowment for Arts creative writing fellow, 1981-82, 90-91. Mem. Nat. Emergency Civil Liberties Com. (nat. coun.), Authors Guild, PEN Am. Ctr., Nat. Book Critics Cir. Office: U Notre Dame Dept English Notre Dame IN 46556

OROZCO, RAYMOND E., protective services official; b. Chgo., Dec. 17, 1933; m. Patricia King; children: Linda Orozco Stinson, Raymond II, Maripat Orozco Lannin, Michael. Cert. in firefighting and fire instrn. State of Ill. Br. chief Chgo. Fire Dept., 1970-80, dep. dist. chief, 1980-81, exec. asst. to fire commr., 1981-82, dist. chief, 1982-86, asst. dep. fire commr., 1986-88, dep. fire commr., 1988-89, fire commr., 1989—. With USN, 1953-57. Office: Fire Department City Hall Rm 105 121 N La Salle St Chicago IL 60602-1202

ORR, BOBBY (ROBERT GORDON ORR), former hockey player; b. Parry Sound, Ont., Can., Mar. 20, 1948; m. Peggy Orr; children: Darren, Brent. With Boston Bruins, 1966-76; with Chgo. Black Hawks, 1976-77, asst. coach, 1976-77; spokesman Nabisco Brands, Inc., N.Y.C., Bay Banks, Inc., Boston; asst. to the pres. Pandick New Eng.; host Hockey Legends program CBC; bd. dirs. numerous cos. Winner Calder Meml. trophy, 1967, Art Ross trophy, 1970-75, James Norris Meml. trophy, 1968-75, Hart Meml. trophy, 1970-72, 2 Conn Smythe trophies, Lou Marsh trophy, 1970; named Male Athlete of Yr., Can. CP Poll, 1970, Athlete of Yr., Sport Mag. and Sports Illustrated, Most Valuable Player, Can. Cup, 1976. Address: 647 Summer St Boston MA 02210-2189*

ORR, CAROL WALLACE, book publishing executive; b. Newton, Mass., Dec. 17, 1933; d. Barton Stuart Wallace and Mary (Blanthorne) Stigler; children: Brett Amanda, Ross Wallace. Student, Boston U., 1951-53; BA, Douglass Coll., 1966. Successively permissions mgr., paperback editor, reprint editor, asst. to assoc. dir. Princeton (N.J.) U. Press, 1966-75, exec. asst. to dir. then asst. dir., 1975-78; dir. U. Tenn. Press, Knoxville, 1978-82, aerobics instr.; freelance editor, 1992—. Mem. editorial bd. Book Rsch. Quar., 1988-92; contbr. articles to Scholarly Pub. jour., 1974-86. Recipient

Book Woman award Women's Nat. Book Assn., 1987. Mem. Assn. Am. Univ. Presses (pres. 1987-88), Internat. Assn. Scholarly Pubs. (sec.-gen. 1980-83), Women in Scholarly Pub. (first pres. 1980-81), AAUP Lang. Task Force (chair 1989-91), AAUP Golden Fluke Award Com. (chair 1984-91), Phi Beta Kappa, Phi Kappa Phi. Avocations: jogging, aerobics, gardening, travel, music.

ORR, DANIEL, educator, economist; b. N.Y.C., May 13, 1933; s. Robert Connell and Lillian (Nagle) O.; m. Mary Lee Hayes, Oct. 12, 1957; children—Rebecca, Matthew, Sara. A.B., Oberlin Coll., 1954; Ph.D., Princeton, 1960. Ops. analyst Procter & Gamble Co., 1956-58; instr. econs. Princeton U., 1959-60; asst. prof. econs. Amherst Coll., 1960-61, Grad. Sch. Bus., U. Chgo., 1961-65; mem. faculty U. Calif. at San Diego, 1965-78, chmn. econs. dept., 1969-72; prof. econs., cons. in field; prof., head dept. econs. Va. Poly. Inst. and State U., 1978-89; prof. econs. U. Ill., Champaign-Urbana, 1989—, dept. head, 1989-94; vis. prof. U. Nottingham, Eng., 1972, U. Calif., 1988, U. Warsaw, 1992. Author: Cash Management and the Demand for Money, 1970, Property, Markets and Government Intervention, 1976. Trustee Oberlin (Ohio) Coll., 1993—. Served with AUS, 1958. Mem. Am. Econ. Assn., Crystal Downs Country Club. Home: 515 S Willis Ave Champaign IL 61821-3917 Office: U Ill 330 Commerce Bldg W 1206 S 6th St Champaign IL 61820-6915

ORR, DAVID E., electronics executive; b. Pitts., Sept. 10, 1951; s. Lewis E. and Betty (Bauer) O.; m. Kathleen Ann Engist, Mar. 23, 1979; children: Michael, Kristen. BS in Indsl. Engring., Gannon U., 1973; MBA, U. Chgo., 1986. Bus. rels. mgr. GTE Svc. Corp., Indpls., 1982-83; engring. and constrn. dir. GTE Wis., Madison, 1983-85; mktg. dir. Rockwell Internat., Richardson, Tex., 1985-89; v.p. mktg. and sales network transmission systems Rockwell Internat., Richardson, 1989-90, v.p., gen. mgr., 1990-92; pres., CEO, Alcatel Network Systems Inc., Dallas, 1992—. Mem. IEEE, Inst. Indsl. Engrs. Avocations: golf, biking. Office: Alcatel Network Systems Inc PO Box 568842 1225 Alma Rd Richardson TX 75081

ORR, DAVID L., lawyer; b. Oklahoma City, Oct. 16, 1946. BS with spl. honors, West Tex. State U., 1969; JD with honors, U. Tex., 1972. Bar: U.S. Dist. Ct. (no., so., ea. and we. dists.) Tex., U.S. Ct. Appeals (5th cir.), U.S. Supreme Ct. Briefing atty. Supreme Ct. Tex., Austin, 1972-73; ptnr. McGinnis, Lochridge & Kilgore, Austin, 1973-90; shareholder Johnson & Gibbs, P.C., Austin, 1990—. Fellow Tex. Bar Found.; mem. Alpha Chi. Office: Johnson & Gibbs Ste 1400 100 Congress Ave Austin TX 78701

ORR, FRANKLIN MATTES, JR., petroleum engineering educator; b. Baytown, Tex., Dec. 27, 1946; s. Franklin Mattes and Selwyn Sage (Huddleston) O.; m. Susan Packard, Aug. 30, 1970; children: David, Katherine. BSChemE, Stanford U., 1969; PhDChemE, U. Minn., 1976. Sanitary engr. EPA, Washington, 1970-72; research engr. Shell Devel. Co., Houston, 1976-78; sr. engr. N.Mex. Petroleum Recovery Research Ctr., Socorro, 1978-84; assoc. prof. petroleum engring. Stanford (Calif.) U., 1985-87, prof., 1987—, interim dean Sch. Earth Scis., 1994-95, dean Sch. Earth Scis., 1995—. Contbr. articles to profl. jours. Bd. dirs. Wolf Trap Found. for the Performing Arts, 1988-94, Monterey Bay Aquarium Rsch. Inst., 1987—; chair sci. adv. com. David and Lucile Packard Found. Fellowships for Sci. and Engring. With USPHS, 1970-72. Mem. Soc. Petroleum Engrs. (named Distin. Lectr. 1988-89, Disting. Achievement award for petroleum engring. faculty 1993), AIChE, AAAS, Soc. Indsl. and Applied Math. Home: 927 Cottrell Way Stanford CA 94305-1057

ORR, GREGORY SIMPSON, English educator, poet; b. Albany, N.Y., Feb. 3, 1947; s. James Wendall and Barbara Ruth (Howe) O.; m. Trisha Lynn Winer, Mar. 3, 1973; children: Eliza Simpson, Sophia Katherine. Student, Hamilton Coll., 1964-66; BA, Antioch Coll., 1969; MFA, Columbia U., 1972. Asst. prof. English, U. Va., Charlottesville, 1975-81, assoc. prof., 1981-88, prof., 1988—; poetry cons. Va. Quar. Rev., 1978—. Author: (poetry) Burning the Empty Nests, 1973, Gathering the Bones Together, 1975, The Red House, 1980, We Must Make a Kingdom of It, 1986, New and Selected Poems, 1987, City of Salt, 1995, (criticism) Stanley Kunitz: An Introduction to the Poetry, 1985, Richer Entanglements, 1993. Jr. fellow U. Mich. Soc. Fellows, 1972-75, fellow Nat. Endowment for Arts, 1977, 88, Guggenheim fellow 1978. Mem. Poetry Soc. Am. Office: U Va Wilson Hall Charlottesville VA 22903

ORR, J. SCOTT, newspaper correspondent. Coor., wash. bur. The Star-Ledger, Newark, N.J. Office: Wash Bur 2000 Pennsyvania Ave NW Ste 3900 Washington DC 20006

ORR, JAMES F., III, insurance company executive; b. Mpls., 1943. BA, Villanova U., 1962; MA, Boston U., 1969. With New Eng. Mchts. Bank, Boston, 1965-67, Bache & Co., N.Y.C., 1967-69; ptnr. Cardinal Mgmt. Co., Boston, 1969-75; exec. v.p., treas. Conn. Bank and Trust Corp., 1975-86; with UNUM, 1986—, formerly pres. COO; chmn. bd., CEO UNUM Corp.; also pres., chmn., CEO UNUM Life Ins. Co. (subs.). Office: UNUM Corp 2211 Congress St Portland ME 04122-0001

ORR, JIM (JAMES D. ORR), columnist, writer; b. Buffalo, Feb. 7, 1960; s. David James and Doris Kathleen (Wolos) O.; m. JoEllen Black, June 4, 1994. B in Journalism, Ind. U. of Pa., 1982, M in Comm., 1987. Station mgr. Sta. WIUP-TV, Ind., Pa., 1983-84; sports writer, news writer Ind. (Pa.) Gazette, 1984-88; edn. reporter Stuart (Fla.) News, 1988-89; staff writer, columnist Gannett Rochester (N.Y.) Newspapers, 1989—. Columnist Orrdinary People, 1994—. Moderator polit. debate Edu-Cable Corp., Greece, N.Y., 1993. Recipient Agrl. Writing 1st Place award Penn-Ag Industries, 1985, 2d place Keystone State Press award Pa. Newspaper Pub. Assn., 1987. Home: 1035 Edgemere Dr Rochester NY 14612-1503 Office: Gannett Rochester Newspapers 55 Exchange Blvd Rochester NY 14614-2001

ORR, JOEL NATHANIEL, computer graphics consultant; b. Bklyn., June 19, 1947; s. Martin J. and Esther B. Filler; m. Gail Naomi Smith, June 15, 1973; children—David, Anne, John, Thomas, Stephen, Shir. Ph.D. in Math., SUNY, 1972. Editor, translator Israel Program Sci. Translations, Jerusalem, 1967-68; tech. writer, editor then analyst Compat, Westbury, N.Y., 1969-72; system mgr. Met. Nashville, 1973-74; pres. Jerusalem Systems; pub. Computer Graphics newsletter; pres., prin. cons. Orr Assocs. Inc., Great Falls, Va., 1975—; mem. seminar faculty, lab. computer graphics and spatial analysis Harvard U., 1979—; dir. CAD-CAM Inst., 1982—. Author: Computer Graphics Extravaganza, 1977; co-editor: The CAD/CAM Handbook, 1985, The CIM Handbook, 1986, Thoughts on Engineering Automation, 1994; contbg. editor: Windows Sources, 1992—, NextWorld; contbr. articles to profl. jours.; contbr. editor: Harvard Newsletter on Computer Graphics, 1979-80, Computer Graphics Today, 1984—, Computer Graphics World, 1985—; series editor McGraw-Hill, 1989—; host Computer Talk. Exec. dir. Virtual Worlds Soc., 1992—; chmn. bd. Xanadu Operating Co., 1992-94; bd. dirs. Macscitech, Virtus Corp., Ithaca Software Corp., COB Agorics, Inc., 1993—. With Israeli Army, 1964-67. Named Disting. Fellow, Autodesk Inc., 1990; recipient Orthogonal medal N.C. State U. 1991. Mem. IEEE, Assn. Computing Machinery, Nat. Computer Graphics Assn. (pres. 1988-89, directory editor, interim pres. 1990), Urban and Regional Info. Systems Assn., Am. Congress Surveying and Mapping Land Info. Inst. (pres.), Inst. Modernization Land Data System, League for Engring. Automation Productivity (founder), Soc. Mfg. Engrs., Soc. Mfg. Engrs./Computers and Automated Systems Assn. Jewish. Office: Orr Assocs Inc 261 Marsh Island Dr Chesapeake VA 23320

ORR, KENNETH BRADLEY, college president; b. Charlotte, N.C., Mar. 15, 1933; s. Frank Wylie and Kark Harriett O.; m. Janice Jarrett, July 15, 1960; children: Kevin, Jeffrey, Jonathan. BA, Duke U., 1954; MDiv, Union Theol. Sem., 1960, ThM, 1961; PhD, U. Mich., 1978; LittD, Carroll Coll. 1990. Ordained to ministry, Presbyn. Ch., 1961. Minister West End Presbyn. Ch., Roanoke, Va., 1961-64; asst. to pres. Union Theol. Sem., Richmond, Va., 1964-68; v.p. Union Theol. Sem., 1968-74; pres. Presbyn. Sch. Christian Edn., Richmond, 1974-79, Presbyn. Coll., Clinton, S.C., 1979—; past mem. coun. presidents Nat. Assn. Intercollegiate Athletics, Kansas City, Mo.; chmn. South Atlantic Conf., 1989-91. Contbr. to religious and ednl. publs. Mem. Nat. Adv. Com. on Instnl. Quality and

Integrity, 1994—. Capt. USAF, 1955-57. Mem. Assn. Presbyn. Colls. and Univs. (pres. 1994, exec. com.), Coun. Ind. Colls. (bd. dirs. 1993—), Laurens County C. of C. (past pres.), Kiwanis. Democrat. Avocations: reading, camping, travel, tennis, classical music. Office: Presbyn Coll S Broad St Clinton SC 29325

ORR, L. GLENN, JR., banker; b. Charlotte, N.C., Apr. 28, 1940; s. Laney G. and Mildred Rice O.; m. Ruthlee Phillips, June 15, 1962; children: Mildred Ruth, Laney G., Virginia DeArmon. AB, Wofford Coll., 1962; MBA, U. S.C., 1963; PhD (hon.) Pembroke (N.C.) State U., 1993. V.p. Wachovia Bank & Trust Co., Winston-Salem, N.C., 1965-72; pres. Community Bank, Greenville, S.C., 1972-73, Forsyth Bank & Trust, Winston-Salem, 1973-82; sr. exec. v.p. So. Nat. Bank, Winston-Salem, 1982-83, vice-chmn., Lumberton, N.C., 1983—; chmn., CEO So. Nat. Bank N.C., 1985—; chmn., pres., CEO So. Nat. Corp., 1990—; chmn. So. Nat. Bank S.C., 1990—; mem. Charlotte br. Fed. Res. Bd. of Richmond, Va., Econ. Devel. N.C. Deacon, supt. Sunday sch. Knollwood Baptist Ch., 1965; div. head United Fund, 1966; adv. bd. treas. Salvation Army, 1965; mem. adv. bd. Boys' Club, 1970, Amos Cottage, 1973; bd. dirs. Goodwill Industries, 1975, Forsyth Country Day Sch., 1975, 79, Sch. Pastoral Care, 1979, Winston-Salem Industries for the Blind, 1980-81, Industries for the Blind, Carolina Civic Ctr. Lumberton, Brennen Children's Hosp., Old Salem, Inc.; trustee Wake Forest U., 1982-83, 88—, vice chmn. bd. trustees 1985-86; bd. trustees U. N.C., Greensboro, 1993—; bd. dirs. Lineberger Cancer Research Ctr. U. N.C., Chapel Hill, 1985—, Alumni Bd. Wofford Coll., 1981-85; Winston-Salem Nat. Little League, 1979, chmn. fin. com., 1979-80; mem. long range planning com. United Way, 1982-83; bd. dirs., mem. fin. com. Better Bus. Bur., 1979; chmn. bd. dirs. Goodwill Industries, 1979; mem. endowment com. Converse Coll., 1972. Served to 1st lt. U.S. Army, 1963-65. Mem. C. of C. (dir. 1965), N.C. Bankers Assn. (group chmn. 1979, pres. 1987), Am. Bankers Assn., Kappa Alpha. Republican. Baptist. Lodge: Rotary. Office: So Nat Corp 500 N Chestnut St # 1489 Lumberton NC 28358-5551

ORR, PARKER MURRAY, former lawyer; b. Cleve., Mar. 29, 1927; s. Stanley Lutz and Katherine (Murray) O.; m. Joan Luttrell, June 8, 1946; children: Kathleen Orr Guzowski, Parker Murray, Louise Orr Black, Kevin J. B.A., Western Res. U., 1948, LL.B., 1950. Bar: Ohio 1950. Atty. Leckie, McCreary, Schlitz, Hinslea & Petersilge, Cleve., 1950-51; owner Orr Constrn. Co., Cleve., 1951-57; assoc. firm Baker & Hostetler, Cleve., 1957-67, ptnr., 1967-88; ret. Chmn. City of Willoughby Hills Planning Commn., Ohio, 1964-78. Mem. ABA, Ohio Bar Assn., Greater Cleve. Bar Assn. Republican. Club: Mayfield Country (Cleve.). Home: 37801 Rogers Rd Willoughby OH 44094-9485 Office: Baker & Hostetler 3200 National City Ctr Cleveland OH 44114

ORR, RICHARD TUTTLE, journalist; b. Springfield, Ill., Feb. 19, 1915; s. Thomas Edward and Anna Maude (Tuttle) O.; m. Lois Marie Hollesen, June 3, 1939. B.S. in Journalism, U. Ill., 1937. Reporter City News Bur., Chgo., 1941-42; reporter Chgo. Tribune, 1941-49, farm editor, 1949-83, editorial writer, 1961-72, rural affairs writer, 1983—. Served with USAF, 1943-46. Recipient Edward Scott Beck award Chgo. Tribune, 1962, Oscar in Agr. award DeKalb Agrl. Research Inc., 1969, Pfizer Agr. Communications award Pfizer Genetics Inc., 1969, Champion Media award Dartmouth Coll., 1982, Hall of Fame award Saddle and Sirloin club, 1972. Mem. Nat. Assn. Agrl. Journalists (pres. 1958, J.S. Russell Meml. award 1965, Nat. Farm Features award 1977, 79, Nat. Farm Column award 1981), Chgo. Press Club (pres. 1966), Chgo. Press Vets. Assn. (chmn. 1968). Republican. Methodist. Avocations: photography; watercolor painting; jazz records; western Americana. Home: 2933 N Sheridan Rd Apt 809 Chicago IL 60657-5938 Office: Chgo Tribune PO Box 25340 Chicago IL 60625-0340

ORR, ROBERT DUNKERSON, diplomat, former governor; b. Ann Arbor, Mich., Nov. 17, 1917; s. Samuel Lowry and Louise (Dunkerson) O.; m. Joanne Wallace, Dec. 16, 1944; children: Robert Dunkerson, Susan Orr Jones, Marjorie R. Orr Hail. A.B., Yale U., 1940; postgrad., Harvard Bus. Sch., 1940-42; hon. degrees, Ind. State U., 1973, Hanover Coll., 1974, Butler U., 1977, U. Evansville, 1985, U. So. Ind., 1986, Ind. U., 1986; hon., Tri-State U., 1986, Purdue U., 1987. Officer, dir. Orr Iron Co., 1946-60, Sign Crafters, Inc., 1957-74, Hahn, Inc., 1957-69, Indian Industries, Inc., 1962-73; mem. Ind. Senate, 1968-72; lt. gov. Ind., 1973-81; gov., 1980-89, U.S. ambassador to Singapore, 1989—; dir. Nat. Passenger Rail Co. (Amtrak), 1981—. Leader Fgn. ops. Adminstrn. evaluation team to Vietnam, 1954; Pres. Buffalo Trace council Boy Scouts Am., 1957-58; v.p. Evansville's Future, Inc., 1958-62; Chmn. Vanderburgh County Republican Com., 1955-71; alternate del. Rep. Nat. Conv., 1956, 76, del. 1984, 88; Trustee Hanover Coll., Willard Library, Evansville YMCA, 1950-70; trustee, elder, deacon Presbyn. Ch. Served to maj. AUS, 1942-46. Decorated Legion of Merit. Mem. Scroll and Key Soc., Meridian Hills Club, Columbia Club, Rotary, Delta Kappa Epsilon. Presbyn. (elder, trustee, deacon).

ORR, RONALD STEWART, lawyer; b. L.A., Nov. 19, 1946; s. Ashley S. and Nancy (McKenna) O.; m. Regina McConahay, Dec. 5, 1980; children: Justin, Hailey. BSEE, Leland Sanford Jr. U., 1968; JD, U. So. Calif., 1972, MBA, 1987. Bar: Calif. 1973, U.S. Dist. Ct. (so. dist.) Calif. 1973, U.S. Ct. Appeals (9th cir.) 1974, U.S. Supreme Ct. 1983. Mem. tech. staff Hughes Aircraft Co., L.A., 1968-72; ptnr. Shutan and Trost, L.A., 1972-80, Gibson, Dunn and Crutcher, L.A., 1980—. Co-author: Secured Creditors Under the New Bankruptcy Code, 1979, Entertainment Contracts, 1986. Trustee U. So. Calif., L.A., 1986-91; exec. com. Nancy Regan Ctr., L.A., 1988-89. Mem. U. So. Calif. Alumni Assn. (bd. dirs. 1984-89), Order of Coif. Office: Gibson Dunn & Crutcher 333 S Grand Ave Los Angeles CA 90071

ORR, SAN WATTERSON, JR., lawyer; b. Madison, Wis., Sept. 22, 1941; s. San Watterson and Eleanor Augusta (Schalk) O.; m. Joanne Marie Ruby, June 26, 1965; children: San Watterson III, Nancy Chapman. BBA, U. Wis., 1963, JD, 1966. Bar: Wis. 1966; CPA, Wis. Sec., tres., bd. dirs. Yawkey Lumber Co., Wausau, Wis., 1971—; chmn. exec. com. Wausau Paper Mills Co., 1977—, chmn. bd., 1989—; pres. Woodson Fuduciary Corp., Wilmington, Del., 1979—, also bd. dirs.; pres. Forewood, Inc., Wausau, 1979—, also bd. dirs.; chmn. Marathon Electric Mfg. Corp., Wausau, 1982—, also bd. dirs.; chmn. Mosinee (Wis.) Paper Corp., 1987—, also bd. dirs.; dir. M&I First Am. Nat. Bank, Wausau, 1988—, Marshall & Ilsley Corp., 1994—; bd. dirs. Wausau Ins. Cos., M&I Marshall & Ilsley Bank, Milw., MDU Resources Group, Inc., Bismark, N.D. Editor: U. Wis. Law Rev., 1962-63. Bd. dirs. The Aytchmonde Woodson Found., Inc., Wausau, 1966—, The Leigh Yawkey Woodson Art Mus., Inc., Wausau, 1981—, Wis. Taxpayers Alliance, Madison, 1983—, Competitive Wis., Inc., Milw., 1989—, U. Wis. Found., Madison, 1991—; mem. adv. bd. Wis. Policy Rsch. Inst., Milw., 1990—; bd. regents U. Wis. Sys., Madison, 1993—; v.p., bd. dirs. Wausau YMCA Found., 1979—; trustee U. Wis. Hosp. and Clinics, 1980—, chair, 1993—. Mem. Wis. Bar Assn., Am. Law Inst., Wausau Club. Office: Yawkey Lumber Co 500 3rd St Ste 602 Wausau WI 54403-4857

ORR, STEVEN R., health facility administrator; b. 1947. Undergrad. degree, Macalester Coll.; M in Hosp. Adminstrn., U. Minn., 1973. Tchr., coord. master's degree program in hosp. adminstrn. U. Minn., 1974-76; v.p. corp. planning, v.p managed and affiliated hosp. divsn. Fairfield Community Hosps., Mpls., 1976-81; COO Mid-Atlantic Health Group, 1981-83; adminstr. Monmouth Med. Ctr. Mid-Atlantic Health Group, Long Branch, N.J., 1981-83; ptnr., cons. Peat, Marwick, Main & Co., Mpls., 1984-88; pres., CEO Lutheran Health Systems, Fargo, N.D., 1988—. Office: Luth Health System PO Box 6200 Fargo ND 58106

ORR, TERRENCE S., dancer; b. Berkeley, Calif., Mar. 12, 1943; m. Cynthia Gregory (div.). m. Marianna Tcherkassky. Student, San Francisco Ballet Sch. With San Francisco Ballet, 1959-65; with Am. Ballet Theatre, N.Y.C., 1965—, soloist, 1967-72, rehearsal asst., 1973-78, prin. dancer, 1972-78, assoc. ballet master, 1973-78, ballet master, 1978—; Mounted prodns. for the royal Winnipeg Ballet, The National Ballet of Mexico, Teatro alla Scala in Millan, National ballet of Nancy in France, Teatro Colon in Buenos Aires, Pittsburgh Ballet Theatre, Boston Ballet, West, Dance theatre of Harlem, New York City Ballet, the Cleveland/San Jose Ballet, the San Francisco Ballet and Ballet Arizona. Repertoire includes (with San Francisco Ballet) The Nutcracker, Fantasma, Divertissement d'Auber, Jeu des Cartes, Con Amore, (with Am. Ballet Theatre) Billy the Kid, Coppelia, La Fille Mal Gardee, Petrouchka, The River, Rodeo, Don Quixote, (leading

roles) At Midnight, Dark Elegies, Fancy Free, Graduation Ball, Harbinger, Variations for Four, Pulcinella Variations, Brahms Quintet, Schubertiade, Mendelssohn Symphony, Polyandrion, (featured roles) Giselle, Swan Lake, La Sylphide, Gartenfest, Ontogeny; prodr., dir. Gala Performance, 1984, 86; stage prodns. La Sylphide, Rodeo, Fancy Free, Graduation Ball, Etudes, Billy the Kid, Fall River Legend, Giselle. Office: care Am Ballet Theatre 890 Broadway New York NY 10003-1211*

ORR, T(HOMAS) J(EROME) (JERRY ORR), airport terminal executive; b. Charlotte, N.C., Feb. 25, 1941; m. Marcia Mincey; 3 children. BS in Civil Engring., N.C. State U., 1962. Registered profl. engr., N.C. Pvt. practice land surveyor Charlotte, 1962-75; with Charlotte/Douglas Internat. Airport, 1975—, asst. mgr. airport ops., until 1989, aviation dir., 1989—. Mem. pers. com. Park Rd. Bapt. Ch.; chmn. employees campaign United Way of Ctrl. Carolinas, 1990; active Neighborhood Task Force, Charlotte's Cities in Schs. Program. Recipient Outstanding Support award N.C. Air Nat. Guard, 1989, Spirit award Charlotte-Mecklenburg Spirit Sq. Ctr. for Arts, 1990, Design award Precast/Prestressed Concrete Inst. Jour., 1990, Continuing Contbg. award N.C. Dept. Transp., 1990. Mem. Am. Assn. Airport Execs., N.C. Airports Assn. (past pres.), Airport Operators Coun. Internat., Charlotte Chamber Aviation Com., Airport Adv. Com. Office: Charlotte/Douglas Internat Airport PO Box 19066 Charlotte NC 28219

ORR-CAHALL, CHRISTINA, art gallery director, art historian; b. Wilkes-Barre, Pa., Apr. 12, 1947; d. William R.A. and Anona (Snyder) Boben; m. Richard Cahall. BA magna cum laude, Mt. Holyoke Coll., 1969; MA, Yale U., 1974, MPhil, 1975, PhD, 1979. Curator of collections Norton Gallery Art, West Palm Beach, Fla., 1975-77; asst. prof. Calif. Poly. State U., San Luis Obispo, 1978-81, Disting. prof., 1981; dir. art div., chief curator Oakland (Calif.) Mus., 1981-88; chief exec. officer Corcoran Gallery Art, Washington, 1988-90; dir. Norton Gallery of Art, West Palm Beach, 1990—. Author: Addison Mizner: Architect of Dreams and Realities, 1974, 2d printing, 1993, Gordon Cook, 1987, Claude Monet: An Impression, 1993; editor: The Art of California, 1984. Office: Norton Gallery of Art 1451 S Olive Ave West Palm Beach FL 33401-7162

ORREGO-SALAS, JUAN ANTONIO, composer, retired music educator; b. Santiago, Chile, Jan. 18, 1919; came to U.S., 1961; s. Fernando M. and Filomena E. (Salas) Orrego-S.; m. Carmen Benavente, Apr. 17, 1943; children: Juan Cristian, Francisca, Juan Felipe, Juan Miguel, Juan Matias. Bachillerato, Liceo AlemAn, Santiago, 1938; MusM, State U., 1942; MusD, Conservatorio Nacional de Música, Santiago, 1942; architect diploma, Cath. U. Chile, 1943; postgrad., Columbia U., 1944-45, Princeton U., 1945-46; MusD, U. Chile, Santiago, 1953; D Honoris Causa, Cath. U., Santiago, 1973. Condr. Cath. U. Choir, Santiago, 1938-57; prof. composition and musicology U. Chile, Santiago, 1942-61; editor Revista Musical Chilena, 1949-53; music critic El Mercurio, Santiago, 1950-61; dir. Instituto de Extension Musical, 1957-59; founder, chmn. dept. music Cath. U., Santiago, 1959-61; prof. music, dir. Latin Am. Music Center, Sch. Music, Ind. U., Bloomington, 1961-87, now prof. emeritus; chmn. composition dept. Latin Am. Music Center, Sch. Music, Ind. U., 1975-79; mem. Contemporary Music Panel, NEA, Washington, 1978-80. Composer Canciones Castellanas, 1948, Concertos for piano and orch., 1950, 85, Sextet, 1954, 4 symphonies, 1949, 54, 61, 66, String Quartet, 1957, The Tumbler's Prayer Ballet, 1960, Sonata a Quattro, 1964, Missa, 1968, The Days of God, 1976, The Celestial City, 1992, Concerto for violin and orch., 1983, Riley's Merriment, 1986, Partita, 1988, (operas) The Dawn of the Poor King, 1952, Widows, 1990, Concerto for cello and orch., 1992, (cantata) The Heavenly City, 1992; chamber music, ballet, choral and solo instrumental; contbr. articles to profl. jours. and encys. Mem. Frei Found. 5th Centennial of Discovery Commn., 1992. Served with Army of Chile, 1938. Recipient Olga Cohen prize Cohen Found., 1955, 58, Biennial Chilean Music Festival awards, 1948, 50, 54, 58, 60, InterAm. Mistral Cultural prize OAS, 1987, de National Prize Chilean Gov't., 1992; fellow Rockefeller Found., 1944, Guggenheim Found., 1945, 54; grantee Nat. Endowment for the Arts, 1975, 87. Mem. Am. Soc. Univ. Composers, Latin Am. Studies Assn., Interam. Music Council, Nat. Acad. Art (Chile), Broadcast Music Inc. Roman Catholic. Avocations: gardening, water coloring. Home: 490 Serena Ln Bloomington IN 47401-9226

ORRICK, WILLIAM HORSLEY, JR., federal judge; b. San Francisco, Oct. 10, 1915; s. William Horsley and Mary (Downey) O.; m. Marion Naffziger, Dec. 5, 1947; children: Mary-Louise, Marion, William Horsley III. Grad., Hotchkiss Sch., 1933; B.A., Yale, 1937; LL.B., U. Calif. Berkeley, 1941. Bar: Calif. 1941. Partner Orrick, Dahlquist, Herrington & Sutcliffe, San Francisco, 1941-61; asst. atty. gen. civil div. Dept Justice, 1961-62, antitrust div., 1963-65; dep. under sec. state for adminstrn. Dept. State, 1962-63; practice law San Francisco, 1965-74; former partner firm Orrick, Herrington, Rowley & Sutcliffe; U.S. dist. judge No Dist. Calif., 1974—. Past pres. San Francisco Opera Assn., Trustee, World Affairs Council; former trustee San Francisco Law Library, San Francisco Found., Children's Hosp. San Francisco, Grace Cathedral Corp. Served to capt. M.I. AUS, 1942-46. Recipient Alumnus of Yr. award Boalt Hall Alumni Assn., U. Calif., 1980. Fellow Am. Bar Found.; mem. Bar Assn. San Francisco (past trustee, treas.). Office: US Dist Ct PO Box 36060 450 Golden Gate Ave San Francisco CA 94102

ORRINGER, MARK B., thoracic surgeon; b. Pitts., Apr. 19, 1943; s. Harry B. and Alta M. (Moses) O.; m. Susan Michaels, June 20, 1964; children: Jeffrey Scott, Lisa Jill. BA magna cum laude, U. Pitts., 1963, MD, 1967. Diplomate Am. Bd. Surgery, Am. Bd. Thoracic Surgery. Intern The Johns Hopkins Hosp., Balt., 1967-68, asst. resident in surgery, 1968-72, chief resident in surgery, 1972-73; registrar in Thoracic surgery Frenchay Hosp., Bristol, Eng., 1970; asst. prof. surgery, sect. thoracic surgery U. Mich., Ann Arbor, 1973-76, assoc. prof., 1976-80, prof., 1980—, head of sect. thoracic surgery, 1985. Contbr. articles to surg. jours. Mem. editorial bd. Annals of Thoracic Surgery, 1989; author: numerous chpts. in surgical textbooks, 1977—. Capt. M.C., U.S. Army, 1974-76. Fellow Am. Coll. Chest Physicians, ACS; mem. Am. Bd. Thoracic Surgery, Soc. Thoracic Surgeons, Am. Assn. Thoracic Surgery, Soc. Univ. Surgeons, Central Surg. Assn. Am. Surg. Assn., Phi Beta Kappa, Phi Eta Sigma, Alpha Epsilon Delta, Alpha Omega Alpha, Phi Delta Epsilon. Office: U Mich Med Ctr 1500 E Medical Center Dr Ann Arbor MI 48109-0999

ORRMONT, ARTHUR, writer, editor; b. Albany, N.Y., July 3, 1922; m. Lora Orenstein, Oct. 6, 1956 (div. 1965). Student, U. Ala., 1941, U. Mich., 1942-45, Cornell U., 1945; BA, U. Mich., 1945. Editl. dept. head Farrar, Straus & Co., N.Y.C., 1945-51; sr. editor Popular Libr., N.Y.C., 1951-55; exec. editor Fawcett Books, N.Y.C., 1955-57; pres., editl. dir. Author Aid Assocs., N.Y.C., 1967—; v.p. Rsch. Assocs. Internat., N.Y.C., 1980—; lectr. in writing CCNY, N.Y.C., 1961, Columbia U., N.Y.C., 1967. Author: Love Cults and Faith-Healers, 1961, (with Capt. Marion Aten) Last Train Over Rostov Bridge, 1962, Brit. edit., 1962, Indestructible Commodore Matthew Perry, 1962, Japaneese edit., 1963, Amazing Alexander Hamilton, 1964, Portuguese edit., 1965, Master Detective: Allan Pinkerton, 1965, Chinese Gordon: Hero of Khartoum, 1966, Fighter Against Slavery: Jehudi Ashmun, 1966, Mr. Lincoln's Master Spy: Lafayette Baker, 1966, Diplomat in Warpaint: Chief Alexander Gillivray of the Creeks, 1967, Richard Burton, 1969, Brit. edit., 1969, James Buchanan Eads: The Man Who Mastered The Mississippi, 1970, (with Fr. Joseph Lauro) Action Priest, 1970, French edit., 1970, Requiem for War: The Life of William Owen, 1972; editor: (with Leonie Rosenstiel) Literary Agents of North America, 1984, 5th edit., 1994; editor Nat. Hall of Fame Biography series, 1970-72. With U.S. Army, 1942. recipient Avery Hopwood award for short story 1943-45. Office: Author Aid Assocs 340 E 52nd St New York NY 10022

ORSATTI, ALFRED KENDALL, organization executive; b. Los Angeles, Jan. 31, 1932; s. Alfredo and Margaret (Hayes) O.; m. Patricia Decker, Sept. 11, 1960; children: Scott, Christopher, Jean. B.S. in Bus. U. So. Calif., 1956. Assoc. prodr., v.p Sabre Prodns., L.A., 1957-58; assoc. prodr. Ror Vic Prodns., L.A., 1958-59; bus. rep. AFTRA, L.A., 1960-61; Hollywood exec., sec. SAG L.A., 1961-81, nat. exec. dir., 1981—; trustee Pension Welfare Plan SAG, 1971—; del. Los Angeles County Fedn. Labor, Los Angeles, Hollywood Film Council, Los Angeles; v.p., mem. exec. Calif. Fedn. Labor; v.p. Calif. Theatrical Fedn.; chmn. arts, entertainment and media com. dept. profl. employees AFL-CIO. Mem. Mayor's Film Devel. Com., Los Angeles.

Mem. Hollywood C. of C. (bd. dirs.), Actors and Artists Am. Assn. (1st v.p.). Office: SAG 5757 Wilshire Blvd Los Angeles CA 90036

ORSBON, RICHARD ANTHONY, lawyer; b. North Wilkesboro, N.C., Sept. 23, 1947; s. Richard Chapman and Ruby Estelle (Wyatt) O.; m. Susan Cowan Shivers, June 13, 1970; children: Sarah Hollingsworth, Wyatt Benjamin, David Allison. BA Disting. mil. grad. ROTC, Davidson Coll., 1969; JD, Vanderbilt U., 1972; honor grad. Officers Basic Course, U.S. Army, 1972. Bar: N.C. 1972, U.S. Dist. Ct. (we. dist.) N.C., 1972; cert. specialist in probate and fiduciary law. Assoc. Kennedy, Covington, Lobdell & Hickman, Charlotte, N.C., 1972-75; assoc. Parker, Poe et al, Charlotte, 1975-77, ptnr. 1978—; lectr. on estate planning, probate. Assoc. editor, contbr. Vanderbilt Law Rev., 1971-72. Pres. ECO, Inc., Charlotte, 1982—; bd. dirs. Charlotte United Way, 1983—; mem. planning bd. Queens Coll. Estate Planning Day, 1978—, chmn., 1991; active Myers Park United Meth. Ch., chmn. adminstrv. bd., 1994—; trustee Davidson Coll., 1990-91, Camp Tekoa, Hendersonville, N.C.; mem. YMCA basketball com., Dem. precinct chmn., 1980-86; mem. Dem. state exec. com., 1980; bd. dirs. law explorer program Boy Scouts Am., Charlotte, 1976-78; bd. vis. Johnson C. Smith Univ., 1986-89. 1st lt. U.S. Army, 1972-73. Named Outstanding Vol., Charlotte Observer/United Way, 1984; Patrick Wilson Merit scholar Vanderbilt U. Law Sch., 1969-72. Mem. ABA (real property probate sect.), N.C. State Bar (cert. specialist estate planning and probate, 1987), N.C. Bar Assn. (probate and fiduciary law sect., author, speaker 1987-92), N.C. Bar Assn. Coll. of Advocacy, Mecklenburg County Bar Assn. (law day com., vol. lawyers program, bd. dirs., chmn. 1988-89, grievance com. 1987-88), Deans Assn. of Vanderbilt U. Law Sch. (bd. dirs.), Davidson Coll. Alumni Assn. (bd. dirs. 1983, class alumni sec. 1986—, pres.-elect 1989-90, pres. 1990-91, bd. dirs. Wildcat Club 1989—, pres. 1993—), Charlotte Estate Planning Coun. (exec. com., 1992—, sec. 1994—), Foxcroft Swim and Racquet Club (pres. 1986-87, bd. dirs. 1985-88), Omicron Delta Kappa. Home: 2819 Rothwood Dr Charlotte NC 28211-2623 Office: Parker Poe Thompson 2600 Charlotte Plz Charlotte NC 28244

ORSER, EARL HERBERT, insurance company executive; b. Toronto, Ont., Can., July 5, 1928; s. Frank Herbert and Ethel Marjorie (Cox) O.; m. Marion Queenie Ellis, Aug. 4, 1951; children: Darlene, Barbara, Beverley, Nancy. B in Comm., U. Toronto, 1950, Chartered Acct., 1953. bd. dirs. DMR, Inc., London, Ont.; chmn. bd. dirs. SPAR Aerospace Ltd., Inter-Provincial Pipe Line Ltd. With Clarkson Gordon, 1950-61, ptnr., 1958-61; treas. Anthes Imperial Ltd., 1961-63, v.p. fin., 1963-68, also bd. dirs.; sr. v.p. Molson Industries Ltd., 1968-70, also bd. dirs.; v.p. fin. Air Can., Montreal, Que., 1970-73; with T. Eaton Co. Ltd., Toronto, 1973-77, pres., CEO, 1975-77; exec. v.p., COO Lonvest Life Ins. Co. subs. Lonvest Corp., Ont., 1978-80; pres. London Life Ins. Co. subs. London Ins. Group, 1980-81, COO, 1980-81, CEO, 1981-89, chmn. bd. dirs., 1994—; mem. univ. coll. com. U. Toronto, Ont., Can., Geneva Assn., Brit.-N.Am. Com. Mem. London Club (Ont.), Granite Club, St. James' of Montreal Club, Toronto Club, Nat. Toronto Rosedale Golf Club, London Hunt and Country Club. Mem. Can. Life and Health Ins. Assn. (chmn. 1987-88), London Club (Ont.), Granite Club, St. James' of Montreal Club, Toronto Club, Nat. Toronto Rosedale Golf Club, London Hunt and Country Club. Office: London Life Ins Co, 255 Dufferin Ave, London, ON Canada N6A 4K1

ORSILLO, JAMES EDWARD, computer systems engineer, company executive; b. Elmira, N.Y., Oct. 30, 1939; s. Giacomo and Irene (Heppy) O.; 1 child, June Lynne. BEE, RCA Insts., 1962; BS in Elec. Engring. and Math., Ind. Inst. Tech., 1964; MS, Rensselear Poly., 1968; BS in Nuclear Engring., Capital Radio Electronic Inst., 1974. Communications engr. Bell Telephone Labs., Holmdel, N.J., 1962-63; video engr. Westinghouse, Elmira, N.Y., 1965-66; computer engr. GE, Pittsfield, Mass., 1966-67; systems specialist Control Data Corp., Mpls., 1968-70; software specialist Computer Sci. Corp., Morristown, N.Y., 1970-72; prin. cons. Computer Cons. Assocs., Elmira 1972-78; pres. ORTHSTAR, Inc., Elmira, 1974—; owner, pres. O-K Properties Co., Elmira, 1984—, Thundering Hooves Stables, Elmira, 1985—. Mem. IEEE, Am. Nuclear Soc., Soc. Indsl. and Applied Math., Am. Helicopter Soc., Army Aviation Assn. Am., Internat. Flying Engrs., USAF Assn., U.S. Naval League, U.S. Polo Assn. Republican. Achievements include invention of Integrated Data Acquisition System (IDAS), of Thread Algebra used in simulation development, of Extended Sentient Non-linear Ensemble (ESNE). Office: ORTHSTAR Inc PO Box 3430 1864 W Water St Elmira NY 14905-0430

ORSINI, ERIC ANDREW, army official; b. Lodi, N.J., Jan. 7, 1918; s. Serafine and Valentina Lena (Dinino) O.; m. Mildred Jean Andre, Feb. 7, 1947; children: Donna Jean, Debra Jane. BS, GED, Fort Knox, Ky., 1948; student, Def. Sys. Mgmt. Coll., Ft. Belvoir Va., 1978, Harvard U., 1982, George Washington U., 1986. Registered mech. engr. Commd. 2d lt. U.S. Army, 1943, advanced through grades to col., 1965; ret., 1971; appt. dep. asst. sec. for logistics U. S. Army, 1971—. Developer policy guidance mil. identification symbology technologies LOGMARS, 1982; policy developer mil. ordnance/maintenance policies and procedures. Decorated Purple Heart, Silver Star, Bronze Star, Legion of Merit; named to Ordnance Hall of Fame, 1991. Avocations: golf, fishing. Office: Office Asst Sec Army Installations Logistics 110 Army The Pentagon Washington DC 20310-0110

ORSZAG, STEVEN ALAN, applied mathematician, educator; b. N.Y.C., Feb. 27, 1943; s. Joseph and Rose (Siegel) O.; m. Reba Karp, June 21, 1964; children—J. Michael, Peter Richard, Jonathan Marc. B.S., M.I.T., 1962; postgrad. (Henry fellow), St. John's Coll., Cambridge (Eng.), U., 1962-63; Ph.D., Princeton U., 1966. Mem. Inst. Advanced Study, Princeton, N.J., 1966-67; prof. applied math. M.I.T., 1967-84; prof. applied and computational math. Princeton U., 1984—, dir., 1990-92, Hamrick prof. engring., 1989—; chmn. CHI, Inc. 1975—; cons. in field. Author: Studies in Applied Mathematics, 1976, Numerical Analysis of Spectral Methods, 1977, Advanced Mathematical Methods for Scientists and Engineers, 1978; editor: Springer Series in Computational Physics, 1977—, AIP Lecture Series Computational Physics, 1993—, Jour. Sci. Computing, 1986—; numerous research publs. in field. A.P. Sloan Found. fellow, 1970-74, Guggenheim fellow, 1989-90. Fellow Am. Inst. Physics (Otto Laporte award 1991), AIAA (Fluid and Plasmadynamics award, 1986), Soc. Indsl. and Applied Math., Soc. Engring. Sci. (G.I. Taylor medal, 1995). Office: 206 Fluid Dynamics Rsch Ctr Princeton NJ 08544

ORTEGA, JAMES McDONOUGH, mathematician, educator; b. Madison, Wis., June 15, 1932; s. Joaquin and Margaret (McDonough) O.; m. Sara Angell Martin, Nov. 27, 1957; 1 son, Scott. BS, U. N.Mex., 1954; PhD, Stanford U., 1962. With U. Md., College Park, 1964-73; prof. math. and computer sci. U. Md., 1969-73; dir. Inst. Computer Applications in Sci., Engring., NASA Langley Research Center, Hampton, Va., 1973-77; head dept. mathematics N.C. State U., Raleigh, 1977-79; Charles Henderson prof. applied math. and computer sci. U. Va., Charlottesville, 1979—; chmn. dept. U. Va., 1979-84, assoc. dean Sch. Engring and Applied Sci., 1980-82, chmn. applied math., 1984-89, spl. advisor to dean, 1989-90, dir. Inst. for Parallel Computation, 1990—; chmn. dept. Computer Sci. U. Va., Charlottesville, 1993—. Author: Iterative Solution of Nonlinear Equations in Several Variables, 1970, Numerical Analysis: A Second Variables, 1970, Numerical Analysis: A Second Course, 1972, Introduction to Numerical Solution to Differential Equations, 1981, Matrix Theory: A Second Course, 1986, Introduction to Parallel and Vector Solution o f Linear Systems, 1988, (with G.H. Golub) Scientific Computing and Differential Equations, 1991, (with G.H. Golub) Scientific Computing, 1992, Intro to Fortran for Scientific Computing, 1993, Intro to Fortran 90 for Scientific Computing, 1994; editor Mathematics of Computation, 1966-71, Soc. Indsl. Applied Mathematics Jour. on Numerical. Served with U.S. Navy, 1954-56. Mem. Assn. Computing Machinery (editor Trans. on Math. Software 1979), Am. Math. Soc., Soc. Indsl., Applied Math. (editor Jour. Sci. and Statis. Computing 1979—). Home: 12 Rivanwood Dr Charlottesville VA 22901 Office: U Va Dept Computer Sci Thornton Hall Charlottesville VA 22903-2442

ORTEGA, RAFAEL CLEMENTE, English language educator; b. San Diego, Oct. 3, 1935; s. Rafael O. and Santos (Clemente) O.; m. Carol, Dec. 6, 1961 (div. 1969); children: Zerina, Rafael Rossano, Lance Sterling. BA, San Diego State U., 1971, MA, 1972; ABD in Grad. Studies, U. So. Calif., L.A., 1977; EdD, Calif. Coast U., L.A., 1987. Head wrestling coach San Diego State U., 1971-74; asst. prof. Cerritos Coll., Norwalk, Calif., 1976-81; dir.

Avco Saudi Arabia, Jeddah, 1981-86; asst. prof. Miramar Coll., San Diego, 1986-89; supr. USAIR, Charlotte, 1987—; lectr. English-as-second-lang. Winthrop U., Rock Hill, S.C., 1992—; tech. advisor Mexican Olympic Com., Mexico City, 1968. Author: Barrio Language, 1977, How to Win American Football, 1986, Anthology of Mexican-American Literature, 1993. With USN, 1953-55. Dept. Spanish and Portuguese, U. So. calif. academs, 1975-77. Mem. Tchrs. of English as Second Land. Assn. Avocations: pre-Colombian art, polo, horse racing.

ORTEGO Y GASCA, FELIPE DE, education educator; b. Blue Island, Ill., Aug. 23, 1926; s. Luis Darragh Ortego and Anita (Campos) Gasca; m. Gilda Baeza Ortego, Dec. 21, 1986. BA, Tex. Western Coll., 1959; MA, U. Tex., 1966; PhD, U. N.Mex., 1971; cert. mgmt. and planning studies, Columbia U., 1973. Asst. prof. of English N.Mex. State U., Las Cruces, 1964-70; dir. Chicano studies U. Tex., El Paso, 1970-72; asst. to pres. Met. State, Denver, 1972-74; vice chancellor, acad. devel. Hispanic U. of Am., Denver, 1974-78; dir. Inst. for Intercultural Studies and Rsch. Our Lady of the Lake U., San Antonio, Tex., 1978-82; chmn. bd. Hispanic Found., Washington, 1982-86; dean Hispanic Leadership Inst., prof. English Ariz. State U., Phoenix, 1986-90; prof. libr. and info. studies Tex. Woman's U., Denton, 1990-93; prof. of edn. Sul Ross State U., Alpine, Tex., 1993—; bd. dirs. Ctr. for Big Bend Studies, Sul Ross State U.; pub. Nat. Hispanic Reporter, Washington, 1983-92; assoc. pub. La Luz mag., Denver, 1972-82; cons. info. mgmt. Exec. Office of Pres. of U.S., Washington, 1985-86. Author: Stamp of One Defect: Study of Hamlet, 1966, Backgrounds of Mexican American Literature, 1971, The Broken Arcs: Essays in the Quest for Human Dignity, 1989; editor: We Are Chicanos: Anthology of Mexican American Literature, 1973; editor The Hispanic Scholar; editor-in-chief Reforma Newsletter. Bd. dirs. Pub. TV, El Paso, 1970-72; del. White House Conf. on Libr. and Info. Svcs., Washington, 1991; chmn. Nat. Commn. on Status of Hispanics in DOD, Washington, 1984-85, Com. on Svc. to Hispanics, Am. Cancer Soc., N.Y., 1980-82. Recipient Presidio La Bahia award Sons of Rep. of Tex., Austin, 1980, NEA-Reader's Digest award for fiction, 1968; Lilly fellow for comty. leadership NACL, Indpls., 1990; Sr. Fulbright scholar Agy. for Internat. Edn., 1971. Mem. MLA, Am. Libr. Assn., Nat. Coun. Tchrs. of English, Tex. Libr. Assn., Tex. Assn. Chicanos in Higher Edn., Kiwanis (bd. dirs. 1993—). Methodist. Avocations: swimming, jogging, songwriting, community theater. Home: 503 Hendryx Dr Alpine TX 79830-2107 Office: Sul Ross State U PO Box 6031 Alpine TX 79832

ORTENBERG, ELISABETH CLAIBORNE See CLAIBORNE, LIZ

ORTENZIO, ROCCO ANTHONY, health care executive; b. Steelton, Pa., Nov. 28, 1932; s. Rocco and Minnie O.; m. Nancy Miller, Jan. 29, 1955; children—John, Robert, Martin. B.S., West Chester U., 1955; postgrad. in phys. therapy U. Pa., 1955-56. Pvt. practice phys. therapy, Harrisburg, Pa., 1957-69; founder, pres., chief exec. officer Rehab. Corp., Harrisburg, 1969-77, Pa. Health Corp., Mechanicsburg, 1977-79, Rehab. Hosp. Service Corp., Mechanicsburg and Camp Hill, Pa., 1979-85; pres. chief exec. officer Continental Med. Systems, Inc., Mechanicsburg, 1986—; bd. dirs. Continental Med. Systems, Inc., PNC, N.A., AMSCO Internat., Quorum Health Group, Inc. Mem. World Pres.'s Orgn. Republican. Roman Catholic. Home: 3428 Lisburn Rd Mechanicsburg PA 17055-6714 Office: Continental Med Systems Inc PO Box 715 Mechanicsburg PA 17055-0715

ORTH, DAVID NELSON, physician, educator; b. East Orange, N.J., Mar. 5, 1933; s. John Joseph and Marjorie Adelaide (Wauters) O.; m. Linda Diana D'Errico, June 9, 1979; children by previous marriage: John Randall (dec.), Jennifer Stewart, Julie Thomas. Sc.B. in Chemistry, Brown U., 1954; M.D., Vanderbilt U., 1962. Intern, Osler med. service Johns Hopkins Hosp., Balt., 1962-63; fellow in medicine Johns Hopkins Hosp., 1962-65; asst. resident John Hopkins Hosp., 1963-65; mem. faculty dept. medicine Vanderbilt U. Sch. Medicine, Nashville, 1965—; prof. Vanderbilt U. Sch. Medicine, 1975—; joint dir. endocrinology div. dept. medicine, 1968-81, dir. cancer research and treatment ctr., 1972-77, dir. div. endocrinology, 1984—; scholar-in-residence Rockefeller Found. Bellagio (Italy) Study and Conf. Ctr., 1989; vis. scientist Vollum Inst. for Advanced Biomed. Rsch., Oreg. Health Scis. U., Portland, 1993-94. Contbr. numerous articles in field of endocrinology to med. jours. Served with U.S. Navy, 1954-57. John and Mary R. Markle scholar, 1968-73; Howard Hughes Med. Inst. investigator, 1969-75. Mem. AAUP, AAAS, A.C.P., Assn. Am. Physicians, Am. Soc. Clin. Investigation, Endocrine Soc., N.Y. Acad. Scis., Am. Fedn. Clin. Research, So. Soc. Clin. Investigation. Office: Vanderbilt U Med Ctr North 715 A MRB II Nashville TN 37232-6303

ORTHWEIN, WILLIAM COE, mechanical engineer; b. Toledo, Ohio, Jan. 27, 1924; s. William Edward and Millie Minerva (Coe) O.; m. Helen Virginia Poindexter, Feb. 1, 1948; children—Karla Frances, Adele Diana, Maria Theresa. B.S., M.I.T., 1946; M.S., U. Mich., 1951, Ph.D., 1959. Registered profl. engr., Ill., Ind., Ky. Aerophysicist Gen. Dynamics Co., Ft. Worth, 1951-52; research asso. U. Mich., 1952-59; adv. engr. IBM Corp., Owego, N.Y., 1959-61; dir. computer centers U. Okla., Norman, 1961-63; research scientist Ames Lab., NASA, Moffett Field, Calif., 1963-65; mem. faculty So. Ill. U., Carbondale, 1965—; prof. engring. So. Ill. U., 1967—; cons. in field. Author: Clutches and Brakes, 1986, Machine Component Design, 1990; papers, revs., books in field. Pres. Jackson County (Ill.) Taxpayers Assn., 1976. Served with AUS, 1943-46. Mem. ASME (Outstanding Svc. award 1972), Am. Gear Mfrs. Assn., Am. Acad. Mechanis, Soc. Automotive Engrs., Ill. Acad. Sci., Ill. Soc. Profl. Engrs. (chmn. salary and employment com. 1974, chmn. ad hoc com. continuing edn. 1975), NRA, Aircraft Owners and Pilots Assn., Sigma Xi. Mormon. Home: Rt 1 PO Box 879 Carbondale IL 62902 Office: So Ill Univ Carbondale IL 62901 *Success in engineering is, I believe, contingent upon one's ability to see the world as it really is, to quickly gain insight enough to detect fundamental parameters that determine behavior of the system in question, to conduct a straightforward check of one's analysis, and to simply synthesize a means of modifying and/or controlling the parameters to obtain the desired results. These ingredients apply to both physical mechanisms and to human organizations—only the means of implementation differ.*

ORTINO, HECTOR RUBEN, chemical company executive; b. Buenos Aires, July 23, 1942; came to U.S., 1983; s. Miguel and Maria Julia (Moauro) O.; m. Beatriz Monica Mayantz, Dec. 14, 1972; children: Nicolas Martin, Gabriela Andrea. B in Acctg. and Adminstrn., Buenos Aires U., 1971. Mng. dir. Ferro Argentina, Buenos Aires, 1976-81, also bd. dirs.; mng. dir. Ferro Mexicana, Mexico City, 1982-83, also bd. dirs.; asst. to v.p. Ferro Corp., Cleve., 1983-84, v.p. fin., 1984—, chief fin. officer, 1987-93, exec. v.p., chief fin.-adminstrv. officer, 1993—. Mem. Fin. Exec. Inst. Roman Catholic. Clubs: Cleve. Skating, Cleve. Athletic. Avocations: tennis, swimming, hunting. Home: 32100 Meadow Lark Way Pepper Pike OH 44124-5523 Office: Ferro Corp 1000 Lakeside Ave E Cleveland OH 44114-1147

ORTIQUE, REVIUS OLIVER, JR., city official; b. New Orleans, June 14, 1924; s. Revius Oliver and Lillie Smith (Long) O.; m. Miriam Marie Victorianne, Dec. 29, 1947; children—Rhesa Marie (Mrs. Alden J. McDonald), AB, Dillard U., 1947; MA, Ind. U., 1949; JD, So. U., 1956; LLD (hon.), Campbell Coll., 1960; LHD (hon.), Ithaca Coll., 1971; LLD (hon.), Ind. U., 1983, Morris Brown Coll., 1992, Loyola U. South, 1993. Bar: La. 1956, U.S. Dist. Ct 1956, Eastern Dist. La 1956, U.S. Fifth Circuit Ct. of Appeals 1956, U.S. Supreme Ct 1956. Practiced in New Orleans, 1956-79; judge Civil Dist. Ct. for Orleans Parish, 1979-92; assoc. justice La. Supreme Ct., 1993-94; chmn. New Orleans Aviation Bd., 1994—; lectr. labor law Dillard U., 1950-52, U. West Indies, 1986-94; formerly assoc. gen. counsel Cmty. Improvement Agy.; gen. counsel 8th Dist. A.M.E. Ch.; mem. Fed. Hosp. Coun., 1966, Pres.'s Commn. on Campus Unrest, 1970, Bd. Legal Svcs. Corp., 1975-83; chief judge civil cts. Orleans Parish, 1986-87; spkr. in field. Contbr. articles to profl. jours. Former pres. Met. Area Com.; former mem. Bd. City Trusts, New Orleans, New Orleans Legal Assistance Corp. Bd., Ad Hoc Com. for Devel. of Civil. Bus. Dist. City of New Orleans; bd. dirs. Cmty. Rels. Coun., Am. Lung Assn.; trustee Antioch Coll. Law, New Orleans chpt. Operation PUSH, 1981—; pres. Louis A. Martinet Soc., 1959; active World's Fair, New Orleans, 1984, Civil Rights Movement, 1960-79; bd. dirs., mem. exec. com. Nat. Sr. Citizens Law Ctr., L.A., 1970-76, Criminal Justice Coordinating Com., UN Assn. New Orleans, 1980—; former mem. exec. bd. Nat. Bar Found.; mem. exec. com. econ. Devel. Coun.

Greater New Orleans; past chmn. Health Edn. Authority of La.; trustee, mem. exec. com. Dillard U.; former mem. bd. mgmt. Flint Goodridge Hosp.; mem. adv. bd. League Women Voters Greater New Orleans; mem. men's adv. bd. YWCA; trustee AME Ch., aldo connectional trustee; chancellor N.O. Fedn. Chs.; bd. dirs. Nat. Legal Aid and Defender Assn.; bd. trustees Civil Justice Found.; served on over 50 bds., commns. 1st It. AUS, 1943-47, PTO. Recipient Arthur von Briesen medal Disting. Svcs. Disadvantaged Ams. NLADA, 1971, Weiss award NCCJ, 1975, Brotherhood award NCCJ, 1976, Nat. Black Achievement award, 1979, Poor People's Banner award, 1979, William H. Hastie award, 1983, Outstanding Citizen award Kiwanis of Pontchartrain, 1986, Civil Justice award, 1989, Daniel E. Byrd award NAACP, 1991, A.P. Tureaud Meml. medal La. State NAACP, 1993; Revius O. Ortique Jr. Law Libr. named in his honor, Lafayette, La., 1988; named Outstanding Young Man Nat. Urban League, 1958, Outstanding Person in La. Inst. Human Understanding, 1976, Citizen of Yr. Shreveport, 1993. Mem. ABA (del., Legal Svcs. program, Nat. adv. coun., 1964-71, jud. divsn.), Nat. Bar Assn. (pres. 1965-66, exec. bd., Raymond Pace Alexander award, jud. coun. 1987, William Hastie award 1982, Gertrude E. Rush award 1991), La. State Bar Assn. (former mem. ho. of dels., Lifetime Achievement award 1986), Nat. Legal Aid and Defender Assn. (past pres., mem. exec. bd.), La. District Judges Assn., Am. Judicature Soc. (bd. dirs. 1975-79), Civil Justice Found. (trustee), Louis A. Martinet Legal Soc., World Peace Through Law (charter mem.), Blue Key Honor Soc., Phi Delta Kappa, Alpha Kappa Delta. In 1989 the National Black Law Journal in cooperation with the UCLA Law Center published: Struggle: A Power Reserved to the People, which was distrubted nationwide; in commemoration of Black History Month, the State of Louisiana thru the office of the Secretary of State has permanently installed a life size portrait of Justice Orique in the gallery of the State Archives, 1992, "With little or no effors on our part, life unfolds with opportunities and rewards, except that we permit our frailties to enslave our ambitions. I am grateful that there are only horizons." Home: 10 Park Island Dr New Orleans LA 70122-1229 Office: New Orleans Aviation Bd PO Box 20007 New Orleans LA 70141 *In 1989 the National Black Law Journal in cooperation with the UCLA Law Center published: Struggle: A Power Reserved to the People, which was distributed nationwide in commemoration of Black History month, the State of Louisiana thru the office of the Secretary of State has permanently installed a life size portrait of Justice Ortique in the gallery of the State Archives the Law Day Celebration on college campuses, 1992. "With little or no effort on our part, life unfolds with opportunities and rewards, except that we permit our frailties to enslave our ambitions. I am grateful that there are only horizons."*

ORTIZ, ANGEL VICENTE, church administrator; b. L.A., Nov. 9, 1956; s. Benjamin and Petra (Santiago) O.; m. Michele Annette Gaunt, May 5, 1979; children: Angela Nicole, Michael David. BS in Bibl. Studies, Ft. Wayne (Ind.) Bible Coll., 1982. Ordained to ministry Christian and Missionary Alliance, 1987. Pastor, ch. planter Christian and Missionary Alliance, Chula Vista, Calif., 1983-90; supt. Spanish western dist. Christian and Missionary Alliance, Escondido, Calif., 1991—, also nat. conf. speaker, evangelist. Republican. Avocations: camping, woodworking, refinishing, travel, teaching. Home: 334 Springtree Pl Escondido CA 92026-1417

ORTIZ, DANIEL ROY, law educator; b. Pitts., Aug. 29, 1956; s. Daniel S. and Retha Lois (Vinson) O. BA, Yale U., 1978, JD, 1983; MPhil, Oxford (England) U., 1980. Bar: Va. 1988. Asst. prof. law U. Va., Charlottesville, 1985-90, prof., 1990—; vis. prof. law ctr. U. So. Calif., L.A., 1991. Office: U Va Sch Law 580 Massie Rd Charlottesville VA 22903-1738

ORTIZ, FRANCIS VINCENT, JR., retired ambassador; b. Santa Fe, Mar. 14, 1926; s. Francis Vincent and Margaret Mary (Delgado) O.; m. Dolores Duke, May 2, 1953; children: Christina, Francis, Stephen, James. BS, Georgetown U., 1950, postgrad., 1951-53; postgrad., U. Madrid, Spain, 1950, Am. U. Beirut, Lebanon, 1952; MS, George Washington U., 1967; LLD (hon.), U. N.Mex., 1980. Joined U.S. Fgn. Service, 1951; asst. officer charge Egyptian affairs State Dept., 1951-53; 3d sec. embassy Addis Ababa, Ethiopia, 1953-55; 2d sec. Am. embassy, Mexico City, 1955-57; spl. asst. to ops. coordinator Office Undersec. State, 1957-60, staff asst. to asst. sec. interam. affairs, 1960-61; spl. asst. Am. ambassador to Mexico, 1961-63; officer charge Spanish affairs State Dept., 1963-66; assigned Nat. War Coll., 1966; chief polit. sect. Am. embassy, Lima, Peru, 1967-70; dep. chief of mission Am. embassy, Montevideo, Uruguay, 1970-72; charge' d'affairs Am. embassy, 1973; country dir. for Argentina, Uruguay and Paraguay, 1973-75; dep. exec. sec. Dept. State, 1973-77; ambassador to Barbados and Grenada, spl. rep. to Antigua, Dominica, St. Christopher-Nevis-Anguilla, St. Lucia & St. Vin, 1977-79; U.S. ambassador to Guatemala, 1979-80; spl. advisor for polit. affairs U.S. So. Command, Panama, 1980-81; U.S. ambassador to Peru, 1981-83, to Argentina, 1983-86; diplomat-in-residence U. N.Mex., Santa Fe, 1986-88; spl. asst. to under sec. of state for mgmt., 1988-90, ret., 1990. With USAAF, 1944-46. Decorated Air medal; Knight of Malta; recipient Honor award Dept. State, 1952, Superior Service award, 1964, Unit Superior Service award, 1973, Meritorious Civilian Svc. award U.S. Sec. of Def. 1981; Orden del Quetzal (Guatemala), 1980; Gran Cruz Merito Civil award (Spain), 1980; Gran Cruz Orden de Mayo (Argentina), 1991; U.S. Mexican Presdl. Chamizal Commemorative medals, 1964. Mem. Am. Fgn. Service Assn., Sigma Chi. Roman Catholic.

ORTIZ, RAPHAEL MONTAÑEZ, performance artist, educator; b. Bklyn., Jan. 30, 1934; s. Joseph H. and Eusabia (Velazquez) O. BS, Pratt Inst., 1964, MFA, 1964; MEd, Columbia U., 1974, EdD, 1982. Instr. grad. art faculty Tchr. Coll. Columbia U., N.Y.C., 1967; instr. art NYU, N.Y.C., 1968; adj. prof. art Fordham U., N.Y.C., 1971, C. W. Post Coll., L.I., N.Y., 1971; adj. prof. art Livingston Coll. Rutgers U., New Brunswick, N.J., 1971, assoc. prof. art Livingston Coll., 1972; assoc. prof. grad. and undergrad. faculty Mason Gross Sch. Arts Rutgers U., 1972, prof. I Mason Gross Sch. Arts, 1991—; lectr.; panelist Sch. of Visual Arts 4th Ann. Nat. Conf. on Edn. of Artist, 1990, Cleve. Ctr. Contemporary Art, 1994, Internat. Exposition: Art Miami Art and Tech., 1995; panelist, moderator The Artist in Multiculturalism and Art History, Alternative Mus., Soho, N.Y.C., 1992 numerous others; The Robert Flaherty seminar spkr. Its All Digital, Wells Coll., Aurora, N.Y., 1993, The Mus. of Modern Art panalist the Artist as Activist, 1993, Cleve. Ctr. for Contemporary Art panalist Performance is Dead Long Live Performance, 1994; presenter in field. Numerous one-man performances including Piano Destruction concert, BBC, London, 1966, Mother Father, Mercury Theater, London, 1966, Paper Bag and Piano Destruction concert, Fordham U., N.Y.C., 1967, Ecce Homo Gallery, N.Y.C., 1967, Piano Destruction concert, Bitter End Cafe, N.Y.C., 1967, Piano Destruction concert, Johnny Carson Show, 1968, Riverside Ch., N.Y.C., 1968, Theater Ritual, Middle Atlantic States regional meeting Am. Theater Assn., Temple U., Phila., 1970, Crossing, Mime Theater, N.Y.C., 1976, physio-psycho-alchemy San Francisco Art Inst., 1982, UCLA, 1985, Twin Palms Gallery, San Francisco, 1985, Museo del Barrio, N.Y.C., 1988, Piano Destruction duet Hommage to Huelsenbeck, Conz Archival Gallery, Verona, Italy, 1986, Atelier Sommering, Ko, 1990, Antiteatro U. P.R., Snug Harbor Cultural Ctr.; co-exec. dir. and participant in Art and the Invisible Reality Internat. Symposium, Munich, 1988; organizer, participant Internat. Symposium of Art and the Invisible-Reality, U.S.A., Franklin-Furnace Mus., N.Y.C., Rutgers U., New Brunswick, N.J., 1989, Vision Quest Gallery Rem, Vienna, Austria, 1988, Vision Quest II Bloomfield Coll., N.J., 1989, Piano Destruction concert Hommage to Huelsenbeck, Soul Release project, Alternative Mus., N.Y.C., 1989, Kölnischer Kunstverein, Köln, computer-laser-video, Köln, Fed. Republic Germany, Soul Release-Ritual Kunst Müller Köln, 1989, Soul Release project Piano Sacrifice concert, Atelier Eva Ohlaw Bildskulpturenaktionmusik, Köln, 1990, Decade Show Dance Theater Workshop, N.Y.C., performance-ritual sponsored by the New Mus., N.Y.C., The Mus. of Contemporary Hispanic Art, N.Y.C., The Harlem Mus. of Contemporary Art, N.Y.C., 1990, Alternative Mus., Soho, N.Y.C., 1992, Mus. Modernerkunst, Stiftung Ludwig, 1992, performance-installation, Vienna, 1992, I.S.D.N. Video Conf. interactive audience participation between Köln and Kassel Germany, The Electronic Cafe Gallery at Documenta, Kassel, 1993, Grand Prix, Regime Lomabdia, Prix Lago Maggiore XIV Festival Internat. de la video et des arts electroniques, Dance Number 22, computer-laser-video, Locarno, Switzerland, 1993, Cleve. Ctr. Contemporary Art, 1994, Museo del Barrio, N.Y.C., 1994, Whitney Mus. of Am. Art, N.Y.C., 1995; one-person sculpture exhbn. Fordham U., N.Y.C., 1967, Museo del Barrio, N.Y.C., 1988, Francesco Conz Archival Gallery, Verona, Italy, 1986, DiMaggio Mus., Milan, Italy, 1989, Ateliér Sommering, Kô, 1990, (sculpture with text) Galerie David, Bielefeld, Germany, 1992, works

Children of Treblinka in Memorium, Archaelogical Find No. 3, Estacion Plaza de Armas, Seville, Spain, 1992, Kunsthalle, Kôlin, 1993, Mus. Modern Art, N.Y.C., 1993, Johnson Mus. at Cornell U., Ithaca, N.Y., 1993, Whitney Mus. Am. Art, N.Y.C., 1993; group shows include Whitney Mus. Am. Art, N.Y.C., 1965, 95, The Object Transformed, sculpture, Mus. Modern Art, N.Y.C., 1966, Franklin Furnace Mus., N.Y.C.; participated in Internat. Destruction in Art Symposium, London, 1966, Finch Coll. Mus. Art Destruction in Art Symposium Sculpture, 1968, sculpture, Everson Mus. Art, Syracuse, N.Y., 1973, sculpture, Chgo. Mus. Comtemporary Art, 1979, Ancient Roots New Visions, sculpture, Palacio de Mineria Mus., Mexico City, 1980, Rutgers Computer Art Group, Walters Gallery, Rutgers U., 1982, computer animation, Paul Robeson Gallery, Rutgers U., 1983, computer art, The Salem Syndrome, Tamasulo Gallery, N.J., 1985, computer graphics and sound, computer-laser-video, Bonnefanten Mus., Maastricht, Holland, 1986, computer-laser-video, De-Haag, Fed. Republic Germany, 1986, computer-laser-video Bridge Game, Mülheim Mus., Fed. Republic Germany, 1986, computer-laser-video, Berlin Internat. Video and Film Festival, Coll. of Art, Gwent, Wales, Eng., 1986, 87, computer-laser-video Techno-Bop 87, The Kitchen, N.Y.C., El Museo del Barrio, 1995; numerous one-man exhbns. including Rene Gallery Video Installation, Music Reconstruction, Amsterdam, Holland, 1988, computer-laser-video, Museo del Barrio, N.Y.C, 1988, Infermental 9, Internat., Video Mag., Dance No. 6, 1989, computer-laser-video, Barcelona Biennale, Spain, 1989, Beograd, Yugoslavia, 1989, Kriens Videodrom, Switzerland, 1989, computer-laser-video, Vienna, Austria, 1990, computer-laser-video, The Internat. Berlin Video and Film Festival, Berlin, 1990, computer-laser-video, Leningrad, Riga-Cine Fantom, USSR, 1990, Video Presentation Series I and II Median Werk Statt, Vienna, 1991, computer-laser-video, Stadtisches Kunstmus., Bonn, 1990, Median Operative, Juried Internat. Video Festival, Berlin, 1992, 6th Juried Internat. Video and TV Festival Montbeliard, France, 1992, Videonale 5 Juried Internat. Video Festival, Bonn, 1993, Video Arco 93 Juried Internat. Video Festival, Madrid, 1993, Mus. Modern Art, Video Works of Latin Am. Artists, Filmreferet Forum Stadpark, Graz, Austria, 1994, Berlin Internat. Film and Video Festival, 1994, Associazione Italiana Cinema d'Essai, 1995; represented in mus. collections: sculpture Mattress destructed by the artist, Mus. Modern Art, 1963, sculpture Disassembled Sofa, Whitney Mus. Am. Art, 1964, sculpture Shoe Construct-Destruct, Memorial to Buchenwald Holocaust Victims, Menil Mus., Houston, 1965, sculpture Disassembled Upholstered Chair, Chrysler Mus., Va., 1965, sculpture Disassembled Sofa, Everson Mus., Syracuse, N.Y., 1972, sculpture Feather Pyramids Museo del Barrio, 1982, computer-laser-video, Museo del Barrio, 1985, computer-laser-video, Everson Mus., Syracuse, N.Y., 1985, computer-laser-video, Friedricheshof Mus., Zurndorf, Austria, 1986, computer-laser-video, Mus. Modern Art, Brussels, 1987, Piano Destruction Fragments, Museo del Barrio, N.Y.C., 1988, Ludwig Mus., Cologne, Fed. Republic Germany, 1988, Centre Georges Pompidou, Paris, 1989, Stadishces Kunst Mus., Bonn, Germany, 1990, Neuer Belriner Kunstverein, Berlin, 1994. Recipient Cert. of Outstanding Achievement in Multicultural Edn., N.J. Dept. Higher Edn., 1993. Mem. Mus. Computer Art (founder, pres. 1984), Hispanic Assn. Higher Edn. (N.J.), Art Educators N.J., Coll. Art Assn., Assn. Rsch. and Enlightenment. Office: Rutgers U Berru Cir Livingston Coll Campus Piscataway NJ 08855

ORTIZ, SOLOMON P., congressman; b. Robstown, Tex., June 3, 1937; children: Yvette, Solomon P. Student, Del Mar Coll., Corpus Christi, Tex.; cert., Inst. Applied Sci., Chgo.; student, Nat. Sheriff's Tng. Inst., Los Angeles. Constable Neuces County, Tex., 1965-68, comm'r., 1969-76, sheriff, 1977-82; mem. 98th-104th Congresses from 27th Tex. dist., Washington, D.C., 1983—; mem. armed svcs. com., military installations and facilities subcom., readiness subcom., mcht. marine and fisheries com., subcoms.-environ. & natural resources, oceanography, Gulf of Mex., outer continental shelf, mcht. marine. Served with U.S. Army, 1960-62. Named Man of Yr., Internat. Order Foresters, 1981. Mem. Nat. Sheriff's Assn., Sheriff's Assn. Tex. Office: US Ho Reps 2136 Rayburn Washington DC 20515*

ORTIZ, VÍCTOR RAÚL, parochial school educator; b. Barranquitas, P.R., Feb. 25, 1959; s. Wilfredo and Gladys (Ortiz) O. ThM summa cum laude, St. Vicente de Paul Seminary, Fla., MDiv summa cum laude; MEd summa cum laude, U. Pheonix, Ariz, P.R.; postgrad., Catholic U., Santo Domingo, Dominican Republic. Tchr. theology, history Colegio Valvanera, Coamo, P.R., 1980-83; asst. prin. Colegio Valvanera, Coamo, 1981-83, tchr. Spanish, 1982-83; supt. catholic schs. Diócesis de Caguas, 1986-89; vicario cooperador-párroco San Andrès Apóstol, Barranquitas, 1986-89; vicario episcopal de educaciÓn Diócesis de Caguas, 1989—. Author (with P. Victor) Concepto del Pecado, 1987, Desarrollo de la Conciencia Moral, 1992. Mem. Alianza Pro-Ley de Cierre, San Juan, P.R. 1991; v.p. grupo civico contra El Crimen Naranjito, P.R., 1992. Recipient Primer Alto Honor Escuela Superior Dr. Jose N Gandara, 1977, Cuadro Alto Honor del Decano Univ. Pontificia Catholica, 1982. Mem. Assn. Tchrs. of P.R. Office: Superintendencia de Escuelas Catolicas PO Box 8699 Caguas PR 00726-8699

ORTIZ VELAZQUEZ, ROLANDO, territory legislator, lawyer; b. Cayey, P.R., Apr. 7, 1960; s. Pablo Ortiz Berrios and Ana Luz Velazquez Rivera; m. Carmen L. Rivera Berrios, May 17, 1985; children: Carol Marie Ortiz Rivera, Karla Maria Ortiz Rivera. BBA in Criminology magna cum laude, U. Turabo, Gurabo, P.R., 1988; JD, Interam. U., Hato Rey, P.R., 1992. Bar: P.R. Pres. Cayey Mcpl. Assembly, 1989-92; mem. P.R. Ho. of Reps., San Juan, 1992—, alt. minority speaker, 1992-93, mem. govt. affairs and internal affairs coms., 1992—, mem. Juvenile Commn., com. for devel. ctrl. region, 1992—. Coord. youth affairs Office of Gov., San Juan, 1985-89; coord. interagys. P.R. Senate, 1989; campaign coord. Popular Dem. Party, Cayey, Cidra, Comerio, 1994. Mem. Coun. State Govt. (participant ea. regional conf. 1993). Roman Catholic. Avocations: cycling, scouting. Office: House of Reps PO Box 2268 San Juan PR 00901 also: Ho of Reps Dist Office 105 E Nuñez Rumeu St Cayey PR 00736

ORTLIEB, ROBERT EUGENE, sculptor; b. San Diego, July 4, 1925; s. William Martin and Ruth Lina (Powers) O.; m. Donna Lynn Forman, Dec. 28, 1976. B.F.A., U. So. Calif., 1950, M.F.A., 1951. Instr. sculpture Riverside (Calif.) Art Center and Mus., 1960-85, Village Ctr. for the Arts, Palm Springs, Calif., 1966-90, U. So. Calif. Idyllwild Arts Found., 1964-76, Palos Verdes Community Arts Assn., 1970—, Instituto Professionale Stato Industria Artigianato, Marmo, Carrara, Italy, 1972; mem. art juries. Sculptor stone, plexiglas, wood, terra cotta, bronze, exhbns. in over 100 museums, galleries, including, Creative Galleries, N.Y.C., Cin. Art Mus., Denver Art Mus., Dallas Mus. Fine Arts, Oakland (Calif.) Art Mus., Santa Barbara (Calif.) Mus. Art, San Diego Fine Arts Gallery, Pasadena (Calif.) Art Mus., Los Angeles County Mus., San Francisco Mus. Art, Palm Springs Desert Mus.; represented in permanent collections, including, Met. Mus., N.Y.C., Achenbach Found. Graphic Arts Calif. Palace Legion Honor, San Francisco, Riverside Art Mus., Laguna Beach Art Mus., U. So. Calif., U. Calif. Riverside, Loma Linda (Calif.) U., Lawson Products, Inc., Chgo., City of Costa Mesa (Calif.) Community Center; represented by Miranda Galleries, Laguna Beach, Calif., Gallery La Jolla, Calif. Recipient numerous awards. Address: 11111 Jerry Ln Garden Grove CA 92640-3320 *To create a totality of expression, sensitivity to dynamics and a comprehensive aliveness is indispensable to the nature of my work. In a broader sense, sculpture is life, disciplined, balancing on a knife edge between the emotional and intellectual forces. Art is like a religion, requiring a spiritual equilibrium from physical to etheric.*

ORTLIP, PAUL DANIEL, artist; b. Englewood, N.J., May 21, 1926; s. Henry Willard and Aimee (Eschner) O.; m. Mary Louise Krueger, June 1981; children from previous marriage: Carol, Kathleen, Sharon (dec.), Danielle (dec.), Michelle. Diploma, Houghton Acad., 1944; student, Art Students League, 1947-49; diploma, Acad. la Grande Chaumiere, Paris, 1950; DFA (hon.), Houghton Coll., 1988. Tchr. Fairleigh Dickinson U., Teaneck, N.J., 1956-68; artist in residence, curator Fairleigh Dickinson U. Rutherford, N.J., 1968-72; official USN artist on assignment, Cuban missile crisis, Fla., 1963, Gemini 5 Recovery, Atlantic Ocean, 1965, Vietnam, 1967, Apollo 12 recovery, Pacific Ocean, 1969, Apollo 17 recovery, Pacific Ocean, 1972, Internat. Naval Rev., N.Y. harbor, 1976, USCG Sta., Key West, Fla., 1985; mem. USN Art Coop. and Liason Com. Exhbns. include Salonde L'Art Libre, Paris, 1950, Nat. Acad. Design, 1952, Allied Artists of Am., N.Y.C., Acad. Sci., Nunnald Gallery, Rochester, N.Y., Monclair Art Mus., Hist. Mus, Lima, Ohio, Butler Art Inst., Youngstown, Ohio, Fine Arts Gallery, San Diego, State Capitol Bldg., Sacramento, Calif., Capitol Mus.,

Olympia, Wash., Mus. Gt. Plains, Lawton, Okla., Witte Meml. Mus., San Antonio, Nimitz Meml. Mus., Fredericksberg, Tex., Pentagon Collection of Fine Arts, James Hunt Barker Galleries, Palm Beach, Fla., Nantucket, Mass, N.Y.C., Smithsonian Inst., Gallerie Vollem Breuse, Biarritz, France, Galerie Mouffe, Paris, Guggenheim Gallery, London, Wickersham Gallery, N.Y.C., Soc. Illustrators, N.Y.C.; retrospective exhbn. Bergen Community Mus., Paramus, N.J. 1970, The Curzon Gallery, 1987, 88, 89, 93, Ardennes et de l'Eifel, Charleville Mézières, France, June-Sept. 1990; represented permanent collections including Salmagundi Club N.Y.C., Houghton (N.Y.) Coll., Portrait Meml. J.F. Kennedy Library, Fairleigh-Dickinson U., Nat. Air and Space Mus., Smithsonian Inst., Intrepid Sea-Air Space Mus., N.Y.C., Hist. Mural Visitors Ctr., Palisades Interstate Pk., Ft. Lee, N.J., Vets. Med. Ctr., East Orange, N.J., USN Exhbn. Ctr., Washington Navy Yard, Am. Coll. Clin. Pharmacology, N.Y.C., N.J. U. Dentistry & Medicine, Newark, Bergen County Ct. House, Hackensack, N.J., Dickinson Coll., Carlisle, Pa., George Washingtogn Meml Pk., Paramus, N.J., Marietta (Ohio) Coll., Mcpl. Bldg., Ft. Lee, N.J., Navy League U.S., Arlington, Va., Nat. Archives and Records Adminstrn., Washington, (mural) Pub. Libr., Fort Lee, N.J. Served to sgt. U.S. Army, 1944-47, ETO, PTO, 1946-47. Recipient 1st prize Am. Artists Profl. League State Exhibit N.J. chpt., Paramus, 1960, 1st prize U.S. Armed Forces Exhibit Far East, Seoul, Korea, Tokyo, 1946, Franklin Williams award, Salmagundi Club, N.Y., 1967, Outstanding Achievement award for oil painting, USN, 1968, Artist of Yr. award, Hudson Artists, Jersey City (N.J.) Mus., 1970, Statue of Victory World Culture prize, Academia Italia, Parma, 1982, Men of Achievement medal Cambridge, Eng., 1990, Connaissance de Notre Europe Gold medal Charleville-Mézières, France, 1990. Mem. Allied Artists Am. (art coop. and liaison com. with USN), Nat. Soc. Mural Painters, Nat. Soc. Arts and Letters, Bergen County Artists Guild (pres. 1960-62), Am. Portrait Soc., Artists Fellowship, Inc., U.S. Coast Guard Art Program, Art Students League N.Y. (life), Navy League U.S., VFW (life), Am. Legion. Clubs: Salmagundi (N.Y.C.) (art assn.); Gov.'s of the Palm Beaches (Fla.). Home: 588 Summit Ave Hackensack NJ 07601-1547 Office: care The Curzon Gallery 501 E Camino Real Boca Raton FL 33432-6127

ORTLOFF, GEORGE CHRISTIAN, SR. (CHRIS ORTLOFF), journalist, state legislator; b. Lake Placid, N.Y., Sept. 20, 1947; s. Carl Jacob and Lillian Grace (Travis) O.; m. Ruth Mary Hart, Jan. 28, 1978; children: George Christian Jr., Jonathan Hart. BS, Rensselaer Poly. Inst., 1969; MA, U. Mich., 1975. Reporter, producer Sta. WUOM-FM, Ann Arbor, Mich., 1973-75; reporter Nat. Pub. Radio, 1973-75, Adirondack Daily Enterprise, Saranac Lake, N.Y., 1976-77, Sta. WNBZ-Am, Saranac Lake, 1975-76; pub. rels. dir. Ctr. for Music, Drama and Art, Lake Placid, 1975-76; pres. Macromedia, Inc., Lake Placid, 1976-82; anchor, mng. editor Sta. WPTZ-TV, Plattsburgh, N.Y., 1981-85; mem. N.Y. State Assembly, Albany, 1986—, ranking minority mem. Legis. Commn. on Sci. and Tech., 1987—; chmn. Rep. program com., 1993—; mem. health care reform task force Am. Legis. Exch. Coun., 1994—. Author: Lake Placid, The Olympic Years: 1932-80, 1976, A Lady in the Lake, 1985; reporter, producer (TV news series) "Special Segment", 1981-85 (N.Y. State Broadcasters Best Series award 1982, 83, 84, 85), (TV documentary) "A Time to Choose", 1985 (N.Y. State Broadcasters Best award 1986). Chief ceremonies 1980 Olympic Winter Games, Lake Placid, 1978-80; field asst. to Congressman, David O'B. Martin, Plattsburgh, 1981; committeeman Essex County Rep. Com., 1980-81; trustee Lake Placid Village, 1977-81; lay reader Episcopal Ch., Lake Placid and Plattsburgh, 1976-92. Recipient Disting. Eagle award Adirondack coun. Boy Scouts Am., 1991. Mem. VFW, AMVETS, Am. Legion, North Country Vietnam Vets. Assn., Elks, Kiwanis (pres. Lake Placid 1980-81). Avocations: skiing, piano, trumpet, painting, woodworking. Home: 23 Morrison Ave Plattsburgh NY 12901 Office: NY State Assembly 450 Legislative Office Bldg Albany NY 12248

ORTMAN, ELDON E., entomologist, educator; b. Marion, S.D., Aug. 11, 1934; s. Emil and Kathryn (Tieszen) O.; m. Margene Adrian, June 27, 1957; children—Karen, Connie, Nancy. A.B., Tabor Coll., 1956; M.S., Kansas State U., 1957, Ph.D., 1963. Research entomologist USDA, No. Grain Insects Research Lab., Brookings, S.D., 1961-68; dir., leader investigations USDA, No. Grain Insects Research Lab., Brookings, 1968-72; asst. prof. entomology S.D. State U., Brookings, 1961-63; assoc. prof. S.D. State U., 1963-68, prof., 1968-72; asst. Entomology Research Div. Office, Beltsville, Md., 1971; head dept. entomology Purdue U., West Lafayette, Ind., 1972-89; head dept. entomology Purdue U., 1972-89; assoc. dir. Ind. Agrl. Rsch. Programs, 1989—. Fellow AAAS; mem. Entomol. Soc. Am., Phi Kappa Phi, Gamma Sigma Delta, Sigma Xi. Research in plant resistance to insects and pest mgmt. Home: 3615 Capilano Dr West Lafayette IN 47906-8870 Office: Purdue U Agrl Rsch AGAD West Lafayette IN 47907

ORTMAN, GEORGE EARL, artist; b. Oakland, Calif., Oct. 17, 1926; s. William Thomas and Anna Katherine (Noll) O.; m. Conni Whidden, Aug. 5, 1960 (dec.); 1 stepson, Roger Graham Whidden. Student, Calif. Coll. Arts and Crafts, 1947-49, Atelier Stanley William Hayter, 1949, Acad. Andre L'Hote, Paris, 1949-50, Hans Hoffman Sch. Art, 1949-50. Instr. painting and drawing NYU, 1962-65; co-chmn. fine arts Sch. Visual Arts N.Y.C., 1963-65; artist-in-residence Princeton U., 1966-69, Honolulu Acad. Art, 1969; head painting dept. Cranbrook Acad. Art, Bloomfield Hills, Mich., 1970-92. One-man exhbns. include Tanager Gallery, 1954, Wittenborn Gallery, 1955, Stable Gallery, 1957, 60, Howard Wise Gallery, 1962, 63, 64, 66, 69, Gimpel-Weitzenhoffer Gallery, 1972 (all N.Y.C.), Swetzoff Gallery, Boston, 1961-62, Fairleigh Dickinson U., 1962, Mirvish Gallery, Toronto, Can., 1964, Walker Art Center, Mpls., 1965, Milw. Art Center, 1966, Dallas Mus. Art, 1966, Portland Mus. Art, 1966, Akron Inst. Art, 1966, U. Chgo., 1967, Princeton U. Art Mus., 1967, Honolulu Acad. Art, 1969, Reed Coll. 1970, Cranbrook Acad. Art, 1970, 92, Indpls. Mus. Art, 1971, J.L. Hudson Gallery, Detroit, 1971, Gimpel-Weitzenhoffer, N.Y.C., 1972, 73, Gertrude Kasle Gallery, Detroit, 1976, Lee Hoffman Gallery, Detroit, 1977, Flint (Mich.) Mus. Art, 1977; other one-man exhbns. include Cranbrook Mus. Art, 1982; exhibited numerous group shows including Whitney Mus. Am. Art Annual, 1962, 63, 64, 65, 67, 73, Carnegie Internat., Pitts., 1964, 67, 70, Jewish Mus., N.Y.C., 1964, Corcoran Mus., Washington, 1964, others; represented permanent collections, Walker Art Center, Mpls., Mus. Modern Art, Whitney Mus. Am. Art, (both N.Y.C.), Guggenheim Mus., N.Y.C., Albright-Knox Mus., Buffalo, NYU, Christian Theol. Sem., Indpls., Indpls. Mus. Art, Cleve. Mus. Art, Mus. Am. Art, Washington, Honolulu Acad. Art, Newark Mus. Art, Container Corp. Am., Chgo. Ind. U. Music Bldg., Wausau (Wis.) Hosp. Center, Unitarian Ch., Princeton, Mfr. Hanover Trust Bldg., Albert Kahn & Assos., Detroit, Renaissance Center, Detroit, Mich. State Univ. Performing Arts Ctr., East Lansing, Detroit Inst. Arts. Guggenheim fellow, 1965-66; Ford Found. grantee, 1966; One of five Am. artists selected for 1965 Japanese Bi-ann.; recipient Gov. N.J.'s Purchase award 2d ann. exhbn. art, 1967; Best of Show Religion in Art Exhbn., Birmingham, Ala., 1966. Office: Tim Hill Gallery 163 Townsend St Birmingham MI 48009-6001

ORTMANN, JEFFREY, theater producer, director; b. Chgo., June 2, 1954; s. Robert Thomas and Lorraine Rose (Charpentier) O. BFA in Theatre Adminstrn., U. Ill., 1976. Mng. dir. Great Am. People Show, Petersburg, Ill., 1975-76; mgr. audience ops. U. Ill. Krannert Ctr. for Performing Arts, Urbana, 1976-77; dir. ops. St. Louis Symphony Orchestra, 1977-79; exec. dir. Wisdom Bridge Theatre, Chgo., 1979-88, producing dir., 1989—; part-time faculty Roosevelt U., Chgo., 1991—. Producer Hamlet, 1985 (Joseph Jefferson award), Kabuki Macbeth, 1982 (Joseph Jefferson award), Getting Out, 1980 (Joseph Jefferson award). Treas., chmn. Howard/Paulina Devel. Corp., Chgo., 1984—; mem. adv. bd. Artists Abroad, 1986-88; trustee, v.p., pres. Chgo. Theatre Found, 1983—; bd. dirs., pres. League of Chgo. Theatres, 1980-86; co-founder, pres. Centre East for the Arts, 1978—. Mem. Am. Arts Alliance, Ill. Arts Alliance, Theatre Communications Group. Democrat. Roman Catholic. Office: Wisdom Bridge Theatre PO Box 608019 Chicago IL 60660-8019

ORTNER, DONALD J., biological anthropologist, educator; b. Stoneham, Mass., Aug. 23, 1938; s. A.W. and Marie B. (Schweizer) O.; m. Joyce E. Walker, April 9, 1960; children: Donald J. Ortner Jr.,' Allison A. May, Karen L. Ortner. BA, Columbia Union Coll., 1960; MA, Syracuse U., 1967; PhD, U. Kans., 1970; DSc (hon.), U. Bradford, England, 1995. Asst. curator Smithsonian Instn., Washington, 1969-71, assoc. curator, 1971-76, curator, 1976—; chmn. anthropology, 1988-92; acting dir. Nat. Mus. Natural History, Washington, 1994—; vis. prof. U. Bradford, 1988—; mem. editl. bd. Jour. Paleopathology, 1988—; Internat. Jour. Osteoarch., 1990—. Author: (book) Identification of Pathological Conditions in Human Skeletal Remain, 1981; editor: How Humans Adapt, 1983. Mem. Am. Assn. Phys. Anthropology (mem. exec. com. 1987-90), Internat. Skeletal Soc., Paleopathology Assn. Office: Smithsonian Inst Nat Mus Natural History 10th & Constitution Ave NW Washington DC 20560

ORTNER, DONALD RICHARD, psychology and sociology educator; b. Bay City, Mich., Sept. 2, 1922; s. Richard John and Caroline Dorothea Elisabeth (Deuring) O.; m. Gertrude Martha Stoekli, June 29, 1947; 1 child, Stephen Richard Edward. BA, Northwestern Coll., Watertown, Wis., 1944; BMus, Ill. Wesleyan U., Bloomington, 1946; MA, Eastern Mich. U., Ypsilanti, 1957; Candidatus Reverendi Ministerii, Wis. Evang. Luth. Sem., 1947; PhD, Mich. State U., 1964; MS, Va. Commonwealth U., 1980. Lic. profl. counselor, Va.; ordained to ministry Luth. Ch., 1947. Asst. pastor St. John's Luth. Ch., Toronto, Ont., Can., 1947-49; pastor Ch. of the Redeemer, Winnipeg, Man., Can., 1949-52, Christ Ch., St. Catharines, Ont., 1952-54, St. John's Ch., Waltz, Mich., 1954-57; Latin tchr., guidance counselor Rodney B. Wilson High Sch., St. Johns, Mich., 1957-60; asst. prof. to prof. counseling Morningside Coll., Sioux City, Iowa, 1960-61; asst. prof. to prof. emeritus psychology and sociology Hampden Sydney (Va.) Coll., 1961—, dean students, 1963-70, coll. psychologist, 1970—, chmn. dept. psychology, 1964-90; pastor St. John's Luth. Ch., Farmville, Va., 1985—; sociol. researcher Evangelical-Luth. State Ch. Iceland, 1985—. Mem. com. troop 6516 Boy Scouts Am., 1980—. Mem. APA (assoc.), ACA, Soc. for Sci. Study Religion, So. Soc. Philosophy and Psychology, Sigma Nu. Democrat. Home: 1421 Gilliam Dr Farmville VA 23901-2353 Office: Hampden-Sydney Coll 221 Bagby Hall Hampden Sydney VA 23943

ORTNER, EVERETT HOWARD, magazine editor, writer; b. Lowell, Mass., Aug. 25, 1919; s. Herman and Anne (Ehrenhaus) O.; m. Evelyn Francis Gelbman, Jan. 1, 1953. B.A., U. Ark., 1939. Editor Popular Publs. N.Y.C., 1946-52; assoc. editor Popular Sci., N.Y.C., 1953-56, copy chief, 1956-70, group editor, 1970-76, mng. editor, 1976-80, editor, 1980-85. Pres. Brownstone Revival Com. N.Y., 1968-76, chmn., 1986—; founder, pres. Back to the City, Inc., N.Y.C., 1974-83, chmn. bd., 1983—; v.p. L.I. Hist. Soc., Bklyn., 1979-83. Lt. U.S. Army, 1942-46, ETO. Recipient Cinderella award Bklyn. Union Gas Co., 1978, Honor citation Borough Pres. Bklyn., 1983, Disting. Citizen award City Louisville, 1979, Quality of Life award Kings County Hosp. Ctr., Bklyn., 1976, Spirit of Life award N.Y. Congl. Home, 1994. Mem. Overseas Press Club, Montauk Club, Ft. Hamilton Officers Club.

ORTOLANI, MINOT HENRY, zoo director; b. Buffalo, Aug. 7, 1929; s. Joseph and Sylvia (Jacobi) O.; m. H. Anne Sweeney, June 30, 1956; children—Timothy, John, Terrence. B.S., Canisius Coll., 1951; postgrad., Stonier Grad. Sch. Banking Rutgers U., 1962. With M&T Trust Co., Buffalo, 1957-79; v.p. corp. banking M&T Trust Co., 1969-79; exec. dir. Buffalo Zool. Gardens, 1979—; bd. dirs. Carton Craft Corp. Bd. dirs. Arboretum Soc.; chmn. gen. bus. div. United Fund; bd. dirs. pres. Psychiat. Clinic for Children; v.p., treas. United Negro Coll. Fund; bd. dirs. St. Ritas Home for Children, Nottingham Sch. Sacred Heart, Niagara Frontier Rehab. Center, United Health Found.; chmn. corp. gift div. Catholic Charities. Served with USN, 1951-56; lt. comdr. USNR, 1951-89, ret. Recipient Pres.'s award Daemen Coll., 1989, Disting. Alumnus award Canisius Coll., 1990, Comty. Svc. award Harmonic Lodge of Free and Accepted Masons. Fellow Am. Assn. Zool. Parks and Aquariums; mem. Buffalo C. of C. (chmn. Boost Buffalo com., Small Bus. Com.), U.S. Navy League (v.p., dir.), Buffalo Exec. Assn. (past pres.). Clubs: Park Country, Rotary (dir.). Home: 81 Huntington Ct Buffalo NY 14221-5309 Office: Buffalo Zool Gardens 300 Parkside Ave Buffalo NY 14214-1999

ORTOLANO, LEONARD, civil engineering educator, water resources planner; b. Bklyn., Sept. 26, 1941; s. Salvatore Thomas and Anna (Salerno) O. B.S. in Civil Engring., Poly. Inst. Bklyn., 1963; M.S. in Engring., Harvard U., 1966, Ph.D., 1969. Sanitary engr. USPHS, Denver, 1963-65; research scientist Ctr. for the Environment and Man, Hartford, Conn., 1969-70; prof. civil engring. Stanford U., Calif., 1970—, dir. program on urban studies, 1980—; vis. prof. Inst. Ricerca sulle Acqua, Rome, 1979, South China Environ. Inst. Sci., Guanzhou, 1987, Ecole Nat. des Ponts et Chaussées, Paris, 1987-88; vis. scholar Kyoto (Japan) U., 1992; vis. lectr. Nat. Sci. Coun. China, 1991. Author: Environmental Planning and Decision Making, 1984 (Chinese edit. 1989). Resources for the Future Natural Resources fellow, 1968-69; Fulbright-Hays grantee, 1979, 87. Mem. ASCE, Internat. Water Resources Assn., Internat. Assn. for Impact Assessment. Office: Stanford Univ Dept Civil Engring Stanford CA 94305

ORTOLANO, RALPH J., engineering consultant; b. Phila., Apr. 12, 1931. BS in Marine Engring., U.S. Mcht. Marine Acad., 1954; MBA, Santa Clara U., 1969. Registered profl. engr., Calif. Engring. watch officer USN, 1954-56; sr. design engr. marine divsn. Westinghouse, Lester, Pa., 1956-64, Sunnyvale, Calif., 1964-69; mgr. project engring. corp. cost recovery dept. Litton Ship Systems, Inc., L.A., 1969-72; consulting engr.; scientist So. Calif. Edison Co., Rosemead, Calif., 1978-92, chief cons., 1993—; formed Turbine RESCUE, 1984. Contbr. more than 100 articles to profl. jours.; holder 21 U.S. patents in field. Recipient William R. Gould award SCE, 1992. Mem. ASME (past dir. ASME-SCAC power chpt., past chmn. steam turbine com., past chmn. power divsn., mem. exec. com., co-chmn. steam turbine course 1984—, George Westinghouse Gold medal 1991).

ORTON, COLIN GEORGE, medical physicist; b. London, Essex, England, June 4, 1938; came to U.S., 1966; s. Frederick G. and Audrey V. (Sewell) O.; m. Barbara G. Scholes, July 25, 1964; children: Nigel, Susanne, Philip. BS in Physics with honors, Bristol U., 1959; MS in Radiation Physics, London U., 1961, PhD in Radiation Physics, 1965; MA (hon.), Brown U., 1976. ABR, ABMP. Instr. London U. St. Barts' Hosp., 1961-66; assoc. prof. NYU Med. Ctr., 1966-75, Brown U., R.I., 1975-81; prof., chief physicist Wayne State U., Harper Hosp., Detroit, 1981—; dir. grad program, Wayne State U., 1981—. Author: Radiation Physics Review Books I, 1971, II, 1978; editor: Electron Treatment Planning, 1978, Progress in Medical Physics I, 1982, II, 1985, Radiation Dosimetry, 1986. Marie Curie Gold Medal, Health Physics Soc., 1987. Fellow Am. Assn. Physicists in Am. (pres. 1981, William D. Coolidge award 1993), Am. Coll. Med. Physics (chmn. 1985), Inst. Physics London, Internat. Orgn. for Med. Physics (sec. gen. 1988-94, v.p. 1994—), Am. Coll. Radiology. Avocations: golf, badminton, tennis, running, squash. Home: 8 Lakeside Ct Grosse Pointe MI 48230-1906 Office: Harper Hosp 3990 John R St Detroit MI 48201-2097

ORTON, GEORGE FREDERICK, aerospace engineer; b. Flushing, N.Y., Aug. 8, 1941; s. Harry and Evelyn (Brostrom) O.; m. Susan K., Dec. 21, 1962; children: Karen, Kevin, Kristen. BS in Aeron. Engring., U. Md., 1964; MS in Engring. Mechanics, St. Louis U., 1971. Engr. propulsion McDonnell Douglas, St. Louis, 1964-73, sr. engr. propulsion, 1973-77, unit chief propulsion, 1977-81, sect. chief propulsion, 1981-86, br. chief nat. aerospace plane, 1986-90, staff dir. nat. aerospace plane, 1990-92, dir. space programs, 1992-93, program mgr. Hypersonics Ctr. Excellence, 1993—. Contbr. articles to profl. jours. Advisor Explorer Post 9005, St. Louis, 1980-87; sci. advisor University City (Mo.) Schs. Fellow AIAA (assoc., liquid propulsion tech. com. 1980-84, 91-95, best paper award 1986), St. Louis Head Injury Assn. Methodist. Achievements include patent for propellant acquisition device for zero-g engine starts, patent for propellant resupply system, NASA technology cash award for work on shuttle auxiliary propulsion. Office: McDonnell Douglas Corp Mailcode 1067250 PO Box 516 Saint Louis MO 63166

ORTON, STEWART, retail company executive, merchant; b. Cin., Nov. 19, 1915; s. Henry S. and Helen (Block) O.; m. Hanni Stern, Nov. 16, 1946; children: Judith, John. B.A., U. Mich., 1937. With Shillito's Dept. Store, Cin., 1937-57; v.p.; gen. mdse. mgr. Shillito's Dept. Store, 1954-57; pres. J.N. Adam & Co. (dept. store), Buffalo, 1957-60; v.p. parent co. Assoc. Dry Goods Corp., N.Y.C., 1957-60; exec. v.p. Boston Store, Milw., 1960-63; v.p. Federated Dept. Stores, Cin., 1963-76; exec. v.p. Foley's Houston, 1964-68, pres., 1968-78, chmn., chief exec. officer, 1979-82; exec. v.p. Federated Dept Stores Inc. Found., 1982-88. Campaign chmn. Houston United Fund, 1968, pres., 1969; trustee U. Houston Found., Mus. Fine Arts, Houston, 1980-88; bd. dirs. Alley Theatre, Consumer Credit Conseling Svc., 1988—, chmn., 1990-92; bd. dirs. St. Joseph Hosp. Found., chmn., 1978-80; bd. dirs. Houston Com. for Pvt. Sector Initiatives, co-chmn., 1981-86; bd. dirs., v.p. Communities in Schs., 1986—; pres. Houston Econ. Devel. Coun., 1984-85; bd. dirs. Houston Symphony Orch., 1988—, chmn., 1990-91. Maj. Q.M.C., AUS, 1942-45. Mem. Houston C. of C. (dir., chmn vice chmn. 1979-80, chmn. 1981-82). Clubs: Forum of Houston (pres. 1983, chmn. 1984); Heritage. Home: 3711 San Felipe St Apt 11J Houston TX 77027-4040 Office: 2360 Citicorp Ctr 1200 Smith St Houston TX 77002

ORTON, WILLIAM H. (BILL ORTON), congressman, lawyer; b. North Ogden, Utah, Sept. 22, 1948. BS, Brigham Young U., 1973, JD, 1979. Adj. prof. Portland Portland C.C., 1974-76, Brigham Young. U., Provo, Utah, 1984-85; tax auditor IRS, 1976-77; atty., 1980-90; mem. 103rd-104th Congresses from 3rd Utah dist., 1990—; mem. budget com., mem. banking and fin. svcs. com. Democrat. Mormon. Office: US Ho of Reps 440 Cannon HOB Washington DC 20515-4403•

ORTTUNG, WILLIAM HERBERT, chemistry educator; b. Phila., June 16, 1934; s. Elmer Herbert and Rosalind Orttung; married; children: Robert W., Mark. H. SB, MIT, 1956; PhD, U. Calif., Berkeley, 1961. Asst. prof. chemistry Stanford (Calif.) U., 1960-63; asst. prof. chemistry U. Calif., Riverside, 1963-69, assoc. prof., 1969-79, prof., 1979-94; emeritus prof., 1994—. Mem. AAAS, Am. Chem. Soc., Am. Phys. Soc.

ORULLIAN, B. LARAE, bank executive; b. Salt Lake City, May 15, 1933; d. Alma and Bessie (Bacon) O.; cert. Am. Inst. Banking, 1961, 63, 67; grad. Nat. Real Estate Banking Sch., Ohio State U., 1969-71. With Tracy Collins Trust Co., Salt Lake City, 1951-54; sec. to exec. sec. Union Nat. Bank, Denver, 1954-57; exec. sec. Guaranty Bank, Denver, 1957-64, asst. cashier, 1964-67, asst. v.p., 1967-70, v.p., 1970-75, v.p., 1975-77, also bd. dirs.; pres., CEO, dir. The Women's Bank N.A., Denver, 1989—, Equitable Bankshares of Colo., 1980—; vice chmn. Equitable Bank Littleton; chmn. bd., dir. Colo. Blue Cross/Blue Shield, lectr.; bd. dirs. Rocky Mountain Life Ins. Co., Frontier Airlines. Treas. Girl Scouts U.S.A., 1981-87, 1st. nat. v.p., chair exec. com., 1987-90, nat. pres., 1990—; bd. dirs., chair Rocky Mountain Health Care Corp.; bd. dirs. Ams. Clean Water Found., Denver Improvement Assn.; bd. dirs. Commn. Savings in Am. Recipient Woman Who Made a Difference award Internat. Women's Forum, 1994; named to Colo. Women Hall of Fame, 1988, Colo. Entrepreneur of Yr., Inc. Mag. and Arthur Young and Co., 1989, Woman of the Yr., YWCA, 1989. Mem. Bus. and Profl. Women Colo. (3d Century award 1977), Colo. State Ethics Bd., Denver C. of C., Am. Inst. Banking, Am. Bankers Assn. (adv. bd. edn. found.), Nat. Assn. Bank Women, Internat. Women's Forum (Woman Who Makes a Difference award 1994), Com. of 200. Republican. Mormon. Home: 10 S Ammons St Lakewood CO 80226-1331

ORVICK, GEORGE MYRON, church denomination executive, minister; b. Hanlontown, Iowa, Jan. 9, 1929; s. George and Mabel Olina (Mandsager) O.; m. Ruth Elaine Hoel, Aug. 25, 1951; children: Daniel, Emily, Mark, Kirsten. AA, Bethany Luth. Coll., Mankato, Minn., 1948, candidate of theology, 1953; BA, Northwestern Coll., Watertown, Wis., 1950. Ordained to ministry Evang. Luth. Synod, 1953. Pastor Our Saviour Luth. Ch., Amherst Junction, Wis., 1953-54, Holy Cross Luth. Ch., Madison, Wis., 1954-86; cir. visitor Evang. Luth. Synod, Mankato, 1964-69, pres., 1970-76, 1980—. Author: Our Great Heritage, 1966; columnist: The Luth. Sentinel, 1982—. Home: 1117 Lori Ln Mankato MN 56001-4728 Office: Evang Luth Synod 447 N Division St Mankato MN 56001-6138

ORVILLE, RICHARD EDMONDS, atmospheric science educator; b. Long Beach, Calif., July 28, 1936; s. Howard Thomas and Lillian (Duvall) O.; m. Barbara Isabel Pierce, Jan. 25, 1964; children—Richard Edmonds (dec.), John Keith. AB, Princeton U., 1958; MS, U. Ariz., 1963, PhD in Meteorology, 1966. Mfg. mgr. Procter & Gamble Co., 1959-60; rsch. asst. physics Johns Hopkins U., 1960-61; rsch. asst. meteorology U. Ariz., 1961-64; rsch. assoc. Westinghouse Electrical Corp., 1964-66; sr. rsch. scientist Westinghouse Electric Corp., Pitts., 1966-68; assoc. prof. atmospheric sci. SUNY, Albany, 1968-81; prof. SUNY, 1981-91, chmn. dept. atmospheric sci., 1983-88, trustee univ. corp. for atmospheric research, 1984-90; rsch. scientist Coop. Inst. for Applied Meteorol. Studies, dept. meteorolv Tex. A&M U., College Station, 1991-93; dir. Coop. Inst. for Applied Meteorol. Studies, dept. meteorology, 1993—; bd. dirs. Thunderstorm Analysis Ctr., SUNY, Albany, assoc. program dir. NSF, Washington, 1970-71; vis. sr. scientist Nat. Center Atmospheric Research, Boulder, Colo., 1976; vis. scientist Swiss Inst. Tech., Zurich, 1967, 69, 70; vis. prof. U. Wis., Madison, 1979. Contbr. articles to profl. jours. Mem. environ. adv. com. City of Niskayuna, N.Y., 1972-74. Served to 2d lt. U.S. Army, 1958-59. Research grantee Office Naval Research, 1967-69, NSF, 1968—, USAF, 1977-82, NASA, 1979-89, Electric Power Research Inst., 1983-90; recipient Sackler medal for Geophysics, Tel Aviv U., 1987, First Suomi Lecture U. Wis., 1989. Fellow Am. Meteorol. Soc. (chmn. publs. Commn. 1985-92, Charles Franklin Brooks award 1994), Am. Geophys. Union (atmospheric sci. sect., pres. 1988-90); mem. AAAS, Royal Meteorol. Soc., Am. Soc. Physics Tchrs., Optical Soc., Sigma Xi. Office: Texas A&M Univ Dept Meteorlogy 1204 Eller O & M Bldg College Station TX 77843-3150•

ORWOLL, ROBERT ARVID, chemistry educator; b. Mpls., Aug. 28, 1940; s. Arvid Lyder and Agnes Gertrude (Christiansen) O.; m. Betty Lou Magers, Feb. 24, 1972; children: Katherine Sonja, Karen Elizabeth. BA, St. Olaf Coll., Northfield, Minn., 1962; PhD, Stanford U., 1967. Postdoctoral fellow Dartmouth Coll., Hanover, N.H., 1967-68; rsch. instr., 1967-68; postdoctoral fellow U. Conn., Storrs, 1968-69; asst. prof. Coll. William and Mary, Williamsburg, Va., 1969-72, assoc. prof., 1972-82, prof., 1982, dir. applied sci., 1988-92. Bd. dirs. Williamsburg Hospice, 1989-94; bd. dirs. Wesley Found., treas., 1976-80. Recipient Alumni fellow teaching award Soc. Alumni William and Mary, 1985. Methodist. Home: 202 Buford Rd Williamsburg VA 23188-1509 Office: Coll William and Mary Williamsburg VA 23187

ORY, MARCIA GAIL, social science researcher; b. Dallas, Feb. 8, 1950; d. Marvin Gilbert and Esther (Levine) O.; m. Raymond James Carroll, Aug. 13, 1972. BA magna cum laude, U. Tex., 1971; MA, Ind. U., 1972; PhD, Purdue U., 1976; MPH, Johns Hopkins U., 1981. Rsch. asst. prof. U. N.C., Chapel Hill, 1976-77; from adj. asst. prof. to assoc. prof. sch. pub. health U. N.C., 1978-88; rsch. fellow U. Minn., Mpls., 1977-78; asst. prof. Sch. Pub. Health U. Ala., Bham, 1978-80; program dir. biosocial aging and health Nat. Inst. on Aging, Bethesda, Md., 1981-86; chief social sci. rsch. on aging Nat. Inst. on Aging, Bethesda, 1987—. Contbr. articles, editor vols. profl. jours. Mem. several nat. task forces on aging and health issues. Recipient Dept. of Health and Human Svcs. award, 1984, 85, 88, Am. Men and Women of Sci., 1989-90. NIH Dir.'s award NIH, 1995; named Disting. Alumna by Purdue U. Fellow Gerontol. Soc. Am.; mem. APHA (gov. coun. 1986-88, program chmn. 1986, chmn.-elect 1989-91, chmn. 1992-93), Am. Sociol. Assn. (regional reporter 1984—, program com. 1986, nominations com. 1987, councilor-at-large 1992-93), Soc. Behavioral Medicine (program chmn. pub. health track 1988-89, program com. 1991-92), Assn. Health Svcs. Rsch., Phi Kappa Phi, Omicron Nu. Avocations: biking, birding, travel. Office: Nat Inst Aging Gateway Bldg Ste 533 7201 Wisconsin Ave MSC 9205 Bethesda MD 20892-9205

ORYSHKEVICH, ROMAN SVIATOSLAV, physician, physiatrist, dentist, educator; b. Olesko, Ukraine, Aug. 5, 1928; came to U.S., 1955, naturalized, 1960; s. Simeon and Caroline (Deneszczuk) O.; m. Oksana Lishchynsky, June 16, 1962; children: Marta, Mark, Alexandra. DDS, Ruperto-Carola U., Heidelberg, Ger., 1952, MD, 1953, PhD cum laude, 1955. Cert. electromyography and electrodiagnosis. Diplomat Am. Bd. Physical Medicine & Rehab. Research fellow in cancer Esptl. Cancer Inst., Rupert-Charles U., 1953-55; rotating intern Coney Island Hosp., Bklyn., 1955-56; resident in diagnostic radiology NYU Bellevue Med. Ctr.-Univ. Hosp., 1956-57; resident, fellow in phys. medicine and rehab. Western Res. U. Highland View Hosp., Cleve., 1958-60; orthopedic surgery Met. Gen. Hosp., Cleve., 1959; asst. chief rehab. medicine service VA West Side Med. Ctr., Chgo., 1961-74, acting chief, 1974-75, chief, 1975—; dir. edn. integrated residency tng. program U. Ill. Affiliated Hosp., 1974-89; clin. instr. U. Ill., 1962-65, asst. clin. prof., 1965-70, asst. prof., 1970-75, assoc. clin. prof., 1975-94, clin. prof., 1994—. Author and editor: Who and What, 1978; contbr. articles to profl. jours; splty. cons. in phys. medicine and rehab. to editorial bd. Chgo. Med. Jours., 1978-89. Founder, pres. Ukrainian World Med. Mus., Chgo.,

1977; founder, 1st pres. Am. Mus. Phys. Medicine and Rehab., 1980-91. Fellow AAUP, Am. Acad. Phys. Medicine and Rehab.; mem. Assn. Acad. Physiatrists, Am. Assn. Electromyography and Electrodiagnosis, Ill. Soc. Phys. Medicine and Rehab. (pres., dir. 1979-80), Ukrainian Med. Assn. N.Am. (dir., pres. chpt. 1977-79, fin. mgr. 17th med. conv. and congress Chgo. 1977, adminstr. and conv. chmn. 1979), World Fedn. Ukrainian Med. Assns. (co-founder and 1st exec. sec. research and sci. 1977-79), Internat. Rehab. Medicine Assn., Rehab. Internat. U.S.A., Nat. Assn. VA Physicians, AAAS, Assn. Med. Rehab. Dirs. and Coordinators, Nat. Rehab. Assn., Nat. Assn. Disability Examiners, Am. Med. Writers Assn., Biofeedback Research Soc. Am., Chgo. Soc. Phys. Medicine and Rehab. (pres., founder 1978-79), Ill. Rehab. Assn., Ukrainian Acad. Med. Scis. (founder, pres. 1979-80), Gerontol. Soc., Internat. Soc. Electrophysiol. Kinesiology, Internat. Soc. Prosthetics and Orthotics, Fedn. Am. Scientists. Ukrainian Catholic. Home: 1819 N 78th Ct Chicago IL 60635-3502 Office: 820 S Damen Ave Chicago IL 60612-3740

OSBALDESTON, GORDON FRANCIS, business educator, former government official; b. Hamilton, Ont., Can., Apr. 29, 1930; s. John Edward and Margaret (Hanley) O.; m. Geraldine Keller, Oct. 3, 1953; children—Stephen, David, Robert, Catherine. B.Commerce, U. Toronto, Ont., Can., 1952; M.B.A., U. Western Ont., London, 1953, LL.D., 1984; LL.D., York U., Toronto, 1984, Dalhousie U., Halifax, N.S., 1985, Carleton U., Ottawa, Ont., Can., 1987. Fgn. service officer Dept. Trade and Commerce, Ottawa, 1953-54; vice consul, asst. trade commr. Dept. Trade and Commerce, Sao Paula, Brazil, 1954-57, Chgo., 1957-60; consul, trade commr. Dept. Trade and Commerce, Los Angeles, 1960-64; asst. dir., personnel trade commr. service Dept. Trade and Commerce, Ottawa, 1964-66, asst. dir. ops. trade commr. service, 1966-67, exec. dir. trade commr. service, 1967-68; asst. dep. minister Dept. Consumer and Corp. Affairs, Ottawa, 1968-70, dep. minister, 1972-73; dep. sec. Treasury Bd. Secretariat, Ottawa, 1970-72, sec., 1973-76; dep. minister Dept. Industry, Trade and Commerce, Ottawa, 1976-78; sec. Ministry of State for Econ. Devel., Ottawa, 1977-82; undersec. of state Dept. External Affairs, Ottawa, 1982; clk. privy council, sec. to cabinet Privy Council Office, Ottawa, 1982-86; mem. Queen's Privy Coun. for Can., 1986; prof. emeritus Western Bus. Sch. U. Western Ont., 1986—; bd. dirs. Molson Cos., Ltd., DuPont of Can. Inc., Nat. Bank of Can., Bell Can., Ellis Don Can., NatCan Trust Co. Author: Keeping Deputy Ministers Accountable, 1989, Organizing to Govern, 1990. Decorated officer Order of Can.; recipient Outstanding Achievment award Can. Govt., 1981, Vanier medal Inst. Pub. Adminstrn., 1990. Mem. Psi Upsilon. Roman Catholic. Avocations: philately; golf. Home: 1353 Corley Dr N, London, ON Canada N6G 4L4 Office: U Western Ont Sch Bus, London, ON Canada N6A 3K7

OSBERG, TIMOTHY M., psychologist, educator, researcher, clinician; b. Buffalo, Aug. 11, 1955; s. John Carlton and Adeline Rose (Weichsel) O.; m. Debra A. Morreale, July 14, 1990; children: John Peter, Erika Evelyn. BA, SUNY, Buffalo, 1977, MA, 1980, PhD, 1982. Lic. psychologist, N.Y. Intern VA Med. Ctr., Buffalo, 1981-82; from asst. prof. to prof. Niagara U. N.Y., 1982—; pvt. practice Niagara Falls, N.Y., 1985—; psychologist Optifast Weight Loss Program, Niagara Falls, 1989-92; editorial bd. Jour. Personality and Social Psychology, 1988-92, Teaching of Psychology, 1991—, Jour. Correctional Edn., 1993—; instr. Attica Correctional Facility, 1980—; presenter in field. Contbr. articles to profl. jours. Vol. group leader prerelease program Attica (N.Y.) Correctional Facility, 1984-90, exec. com. Psychol. Assn. Western N.Y., Buffalo, 1982-87. Recipient Feldman-Cohen Meml. award SUNY, Buffalo, 1977. Fellow APA; mem. Am. Psychol. Soc., Eastern Psychol. Assn., Soc. for Personality Assessment, Assn. Advancement Behavior Therapy, Phi Beta Kappa. Democrat. Roman Catholic. Avocations: spectator sports, running, golf, tennis. Home: 2652 David Dr Niagara Falls NY 14304-4619 Office: Niagara U Dept Psychology Niagara University NY 14109

OSBORN, ANN GEORGE, retired chemist; b. Nowata, Okla., Aug. 1, 1933; d. David Thomas and Alice Audrey (Giles) George; m. Charles Wesley Osborn, Nov. 8, 1958 (dec. Dec. 1977); 1 child, Charles David. BA in Chemistry, Okla. Coll. Women, 1955. Rsch. chemist thermodynamics rsch. lab. Bartlesville (Okla.) Energy Rsch. Ctr., U.S. Dept. Energy, 1957—; ret., 1983. Contbr. articles to profl. jours. Mem. AAAS (emeritus), Am. Chem. Soc. Republican. Mem. Christian Ch. (Disciples of Christ). Home: 647 S Pecan St Nowata OK 74048-4015

OSBORN, DONALD ROBERT, lawyer; b. N.Y.C., Oct. 9, 1929; s. Robert W. and Ruth C. (Compton) O.; m. Marcia Lontz, June 4, 1955; children: David, Judith, Robert; m. Marie A. Johnson, Sept. 11, 1986. BA, Cornell U., 1951; LLB, Columbia U., 1957. Bar: N.Y. 1957, U.S. Ct. 1958, U.S. Ct. Claims 1961, U.S. Ct. Appeals (2d cir.) 1974, U.S. Ct. Appeals (8th cir.) 1974, U.S. Dist. Ct. (so. and ea. dists.) N.Y. 1975, U.S. Supreme Ct. 1975. Assoc. Sullivan & Cromwell, N.Y.C., 1957-64, ptnr., 1964—. Trustee Hamilton Coll., 1978-88, Mus. of Broadcasting, 1975-80; trustee, treas. Kirkland Coll., 1969-78; mem. coun. White Burkett Miller Ctr. Pub. Affairs, 1976-82; bd. dirs., pres. Stevens Kingsley Found., 1967—; sec., treas. Dunlevy Milbank Found., 1974—; bd. dirs. Spanel Found., 1978-88, CBS, Inc., 1975-80. Served with USN, 1951-54. Mem. ABA, N.Y. State Bar Assn., Assn. of Bar of City of N.Y., Am. Bar Found., Scarsdale Golf Club, India House, World Trade Ctr. Club (N.Y.C.), Regency Whist Club, Country Club of the Rockies. Presbyterian. Home: 1049 Park Ave New York NY 10028-1061 Office: Sullivan & Cromwell 125 Broad St New York NY 10004

OSBORN, ELBURT FRANKLIN, former geochemistry educator, research scientist; b. Winnebago County, Ill., Aug. 13, 1911; s. William Franklin and Anna (Sherman) O.; m. Jean Thomson, Aug. 12, 1939; children: James Franklin, Ian Charles. BA, DePauw U., 1932, DSc (hon.), 1972; MS, Northwestern U., 1934, DSc (hon.), 1972; Ph.D., Calif. Inst. Tech., 1938; D.Sc. (hon.), Alfred U., 1965, Ohio State U., 1972. Teaching fellow geology Northwestern U., 1932-34, instr. geology, 1937; teaching fellow Calif. Inst. Tech., 1934-37; geologist Que-on-Gold Mines, Ltd., Que., 1936, Val d'Or, Que., 1938; petrologist geophys. lab. Carnegie Instn., Washington, 1938-42; phys. chemist div. I Nat. Def. Research Com., 1942-45; research chemist Eastman Kodak Co., Rochester, N.Y., 1945-46; prof. geochemistry Pa. State U., 1946-70; chmn. div. earth sci. Pa. State U. (Coll. Mineral Industries), 1946-52, asso. dean coll., 1952-53, dean, 1953-59, v.p. research, 1959-70, prof. emeritus geochemistry, v.p. research emeritus, 1971—; dir. U.S. Bur. Mines, 1970-73; disting. prof. Carnegie Instn. Washington, 1973-77, emeritus, 1977—; NSF sr. postdoctoral fellow Cambridge U., 1958; Com. adviser geophysics br. Office Naval Research, 1947-50; adviser panel mineral products div. Nat. Bur. Standards, 1958-62, chmn., 1958-59, adviser panel metallurgy div., 1958-64; adviser to com. basic research U.S. Army Research Office in Ceramics, 1960-63; mem. earth sci. panel NSF, 1953-55, div. com. math., phys. and engring. scis., 1955-59, chmn., 1957-58, adv. panel phys. scis. facilities, 1960-64; exec. com. earth scis. div. Nat. Acad. Sci., 1969-72; cons. Sci. and Tech. Policy Office, NSF, 1974-76; mem. materials adv. com. Office Tech. Assessment, U.S. Congress, 1975-80; chmn. adv. com. on mining and mineral resources research U.S. Dept. Interior, 1978-83; mem. geoscis. adv. panel Los Alamos Sci. Lab., Dept. Energy, U. Calif-Berkeley, 1975-78. Contbr. articles to profl. jours. Mem. bd. Univ. Corp. Atmospheric Research, Pa. Health Research Inst., Geisinger Med. Center; mem. adv. bd. Coll. Engring. U. Calif-Berkeley, 1974-78; mem. earth sci. adv. bd. Stanford U., 1969-72. Recipient Tech. Meeting award Am. Iron and Steel Inst., 1954. Fellow Geol. Soc. Am. (council 1959-62), Mineral. Soc. Am. (pres. 1960-61, assoc. editor Am Mineralogist 1953-55, Roebling medal 1972), Geochem. Soc. (pres. 1967-68), AAAS (council), Am. Ceramic Soc. (disting. life mem., pres. 1964, chmn. basic scis. 1951-52, tech. adv. com. Nat. Bur. Standards 1954-58, chmn. 1957-58, chmn. publ. com. 1960-63, 70-71, Jeppson award 1973, Bleininger award 1976), Am. Geophys. Union; mem. Am. Chem. Soc., Geol. Soc. Washington, Am. Inst. Mining, Metall. and Petroleum Engrs. (Hardinge award 1974, Disting. mem. 1975), Soc. Econ. Geologists (v.p. 1965, pres. 1972-73), Am. Geol. Inst. (dir. 1956-59), Nat. Acad. Engring. (mem. engring. aspects environ., quality com.), NRC (chmn. mineral sci. and tech. com. 1966-69, mem. materials adv. bd. 1965-69, chmn. bd. mineral resources 1974-77, mem. commn. natural resources 1974-77, geophysics research bd. 1974-77, chmn. workshop on continental drilling sci. purposes 1978, chmn. com. geol. aspects of indsl. waste disposal 1980-82, panel on geochemistry fibrous materials related to health risks 1979-81, chmn. panel on volcanic studies at Katmai, Alaska 1989), Internat. Union Geol. Sci. (nat. com. 1961-64, 73-77, chmn. 1975-77,

hon. mem. Internat. Geol. Congress 1989), Can. Ceramic Soc. (hon.), Internat. Assn. Volcanologists, Nat. Assn. State Univs. and Land Grant Colls. (chmn. com. mineral resources 1969, mem. water resources com. 1965-71, council research policy adminstrn. 1965-71), Phi Beta Kappa, Sigma Xi (nat. exec. com. 1961-64, com. nat. lectureships 1969-71), Phi Lambda Upsilon, Delta Tau Delta, Phi Kappa Phi, Keramos. Club: Cosmos. Home: 330 E Irvin Ave State College PA 16801-5415 Office: Deike Bldg Pa State U University Park PA 16802

OSBORN, FREDERICK HENRY, III, fundraiser, investment advisor; b. Phila., Dec. 31, 1946; s. Frederick Henry Osborn Jr. and Anne de Witt (Pell) O.; m. Anne Hampton de Peyster Todd, July 10, 1971; children: Frederick Henry IV, Elisabeth Van Cortlandt, Graham Livingston. Student in Econs., Princeton U., 1964-66; BA in Bus. Adminstrn., Colby Coll., 1971; postgrad., Nat. Planned Giving Inst., 1987, Philanthropy Tax Inst., 1988. Registered investment advisor. Pres. Call-Us, Inc., Edgartown, Mass., 1969-72; exec. v.p. Hall Labs., Boston, 1972-74; fin. officer Episcopal Diocese Mass., Boston, 1972-76; diocesan adminstr. Episcopal Diocese Maine, Portland, 1976-80; dir. adminstrn. Episcopal Diocese Conn., Hartford, 1980-86; dir. planned giving Nat. Episcopal Ch., N.Y.C., 1987-94; dir. of devel. Episcopal Ch. Found., N.Y.C., 1995—; bd. dirs. Living Music, Inc., Ulysees Co., William O. Benson Co., FAN Trusts, Oslands, Inc., Boscobel Restoration, Inc., Garrison Sta. Plz., Inc.; prin. Cat Rock Counsel, Garrison, N.Y., 1990—. Co-author: Planned Giving for the Episcopal Parish, 1989. Bd. dirs. The Giraffe Project, chmn. 1989-93, Alice Desmond & Hamilton Fish Libr., Harvest with Heart; chmn. bd. dirs. Hudson Highlands Land Trust; v.-chair., bd. dirs. Scenic Hudson, Berkeley Divinity Sch. Yale U., Nature Conservancy (lower Hudson chpt. chair 1994—); trustee Tabor Acad., Cathedral Ch. St. John the Divine; chair devel. com. Soc. Promoting Christian Knowledge, chair Hudson Highlands Music Festival; With U.S. Army, 1966-68, Vietnam. Mem. Nat. Assn. Fund Raising Execs., Nat. Planned Giving Assn., Nat. Environ. Leadership Coun., Planned Giving Group Greater N.Y., Social Investment Forum, Coun. Econ. Priorities, Social Venture Network, Century Assn., St. Andrews Soc. of N.Y., Highlands Country Club, N.Y. Yacht Club, Portland Yacht Club, Dauntless Club, Garrison Yacht Club, Princeton Club (N.Y.), Internat. Platform Assn. Avocations: sailing, music, photography. Home: PO Box 347 Cat Rock Rd Garrison NY 10524 Office: Episcopal Church Found 815 2nd Ave New York NY 10017-4565

OSBORN, GUY A., food products company executive; b. 1936. BSBA, Northwestern U., 1958. Group mktg. mgr. Pillsbury Co., Mpls., 1958-65; with Universal Foods Corp., Milw., 1971—, dir. mktg., 1971-73, v.p. spl. products, 1973-78, group v.p. 1978-82, exec. v.p., 1982-84, past pres., chief operating officer, 1984-88, chief exec. officer, 1988—, also chmn. bd., dir. Office: Universal Foods Corp 433 E Michigan St Milwaukee WI 53202-5106*

OSBORN, JOHN SIMCOE, JR., lawyer; b. Louisville, Jan. 14, 1926; s. John S. and Ruby (Pinnell) O.; m. Mary Jo Fishback, Sept. 6, 1947; children—Robert, John, Donna. LL.B., U. Louisville, 1949. Bar: Ky. 1949, U.S. Dist. Ct. (ea. and we. dists.) Ky. 1954. Exec. v.p., gen. counsel Louisville Title Ins. Co., 1954-72; ptnr. Tarrant Combs & Bullitt (name changed to Wyatt Tarrant & Combs 1980), Louisville, 1972—; chmn. bd. Beargrass Corp. Served to capt. JAGC, U.S. Army, 1952-54. Fellow Am. Bar Found.; mem. Ky. Bar Assn., Louisville Bar Assn., ABA, Am. Land Title Assn., Am. Coll. Real Estate Lawyers. Democrat. Presbyterian. Lodge: Rotary (Louisville). Office: Wyatt Tarrant & Combs Citizens Plz Ste 2800 Louisville KY 40202

OSBORN, JUNE ELAINE, pediatrician, microbiologist, educator; b. Endicott, N.Y., May 28, 1937; d. Leslie A. and Dora W. (Wright) O.; divorced; children: Philip I. Levy, Ellen D. and Laura A. Levy (twins). BA, Oberlin (Ohio) Coll., 1957; MD, Western Res. U., 1961; DSc (hon.), U. Med. Dental Sch. N.J., 1990; DMS (hon.), Yale U., 1992; DSc (hon.), Emory U., 1993, Oberlin Coll., 1993; LHD (hon.), Med. Coll. Pa., 1994; DSc (hon.), Rutgers U., 1994. Intern, then resident in pediatrics Harvard U. Hosp., 1961-64; postdoctoral fellow Johns Hopkins Hosp., 1964-65, U. Pitts. Hosp., 1965-66; practice medicine specializing in pediatrics Madison, Wis., 1966-84; dean Sch. Pub. Health U. Mich., 1984-93; prof. epidemiology, pediatrics and communicable diseases, 1984—; mem. faculty U. Wis. Med. Sch., 1966-84, prof. pediatrics and microbiology, 1975-84, asso. dean Grad. Sch., 1975-84; mem. rev. panel viral vaccine efficacy FDA, 1973-79, mem. vaccines and related biol. products adv. com., 1981-85; mem. exptl. virology study sect. Div. Research Grants, NIH, 1975-79; bd. dirs. Stetler Research Fund Women Physicians, 1971-75; mem. med. affairs com. Yale U. Council, 1981-86; chmn. life scis. associateships rev. panel NRC, 1981-84; mem. U.S. Army Med. Research and Devel. Adv. Com., 1983-85; chmn. working group on AIDS and the Nation's Blood Supply, NHLBI, 1984-89; chmn. WHO Planning Group on AIDS and the Internat. Blood Supply, 1985-86. Contbr. articles to med. jours. Mem. task force on AIDS, Inst. of Medicine, 1986; mem. adv. com. Robert Wood Johnson Found. Health Svcs. Program, 1986-91; mem. nat. adv. com. on health of pub. program Pew and Rockefeller Founds.; mem. health promotion and disease prevention bd. IOM, 1987-90, Global Commn. on AIDS, WHO, 1988-92; chmn. Nat. Commn. on AIDS, 1989-93; trustee Kaiser Found., 1990—; trustee Case Western Res. U., Cleve., 1993—; mem. coun. Inst. Medicine, 1995—; mem. Nat. Vaccine Adv. Ctr., HHS, 1995—. Grantee NIH, 1969, 72, 74-75, Nat. Multiple Sclerosis Soc., 1971; recipient Scientific Freedom award, Am. Assn. for Advancement of Science, 1994. Fellow Am. Acad. Arts and Scis., Am. Acad. Pediat., Am. Acad. Microbiology, Infectious Diseases Soc. Am.; mem. Am. Assn. Immunologists, Soc. Pediat. Rsch., Inst. Medicine. Office: U Mich Dept Epidemiology Sch Pub Health Ann Arbor MI 48109

OSBORN, LESLIE ANDREWARTHA, psychiatrist; b. Warrnambool, Victoria, Australia, Aug. 10, 1906; came to U.S., 1931, naturalized, 1938; s. Andrew Rule and Annie (Delbridge) O.; m. Dora Wright, June 12, 1931 (dec.); children: Anne L. Osborn Krueger Henderson, June E.; m. Gwen F. Arnold, Aug. 13, 1960 (dec. Mar. 12, 1976); m. Corinne H. Kirchmaier, June 7, 1985. Student, Wesley Coll., Melbourne, 1920-23; M.B., B.S., Melbourne Med. Sch., 1929; M.D., U. Buffalo, 1945. Diplomate: Am. Bd. Psychiatry and Neurology, 1944. Intern Melbourne Gen. Hosp., 1930-31; postgrad. Post Grad. Hosp., N.Y.C., 1934; in chest diseases Trudeau Sch. Tb, Saranac Lake, 1937; in neurology and psychiatry Columbia U., 1940; gen. practice medicine, physician Endicott-Johnson Med. Dept., Binghamton, N.Y., 1932-38; asst. physician Willard (N.Y.) State Hosp., 1938-41; psychiatrist Meyer Meml. Hosp.; assoc. psychiatry U. Buffalo, 1941-45; attending psychiatrist, dir. psychiatry Edward J. Meyer Meml. Hosp., psychiat. service, 1946-49; prof. psychiatry U. Buffalo Sch. Medicine, 1946, acting dir. dept. psychiatry, 1946-49, head dept., 1949-50; dir. Wis. Psychiat. Inst.; prof. psychiatry U. Wis. Med. Sch., 1950-60; dir. div. mental hygiene Wis. Dept. Pub. Welfare, 1950-60; dir. Walworth County Family Counseling Center, 1960; prof. psychiatry dept. neurology and psychiatry U. Nebr., 1960-66; dir. Swanson Clinic for Multiply Handicapped Children, Nebr. Psychiat. Inst., Omaha, 1960-64; med. dir. Winnebago County Mental Health Clinic, Rockford, Ill., 1966; dir. Mental Health Services, Tompkins County, 1967-68; pvt. practice psychiatry Seneca Falls, N.Y., 1968-74, Scottsdale, Ariz., 1974—. Author: Psychiatry and Medicine, 1952, Prognosis, A Guide to the Study and Practice of Clinical Medicine, 1966, Foundation Learning and Innumeracy, 1977, King of the Hill: Chess for Children: 1981, Preventing War: A Doctor's Trilogy: Vol. 1 Living in a Changed World, 1994. Fellow Am. Psychiat. Assn. (life). Presbyterian. Address: 4800 N 68th St #110 Scottsdale AZ 85251 *Within 200 years a changed medical approach brought the Health Age. World War I troubled my childhood and another holocaust was coming as I began my practice. Homo sapiens was now the main cause of mortality and morbidity, and war spread like pestilence. The work of a country doctor began the control of pestilence; I have tried to apply the powerful principle that he discovered to contribute to ultimate control of War. "Human history becomes more and more a race between education and catastrophe" (H. G. Wells). My 50-plus years of research have sought clues to the sense in which education may avert impending catastrophe. "Living in a Changed World" proposes a redesign of educating at all levels and prevention of schooling, personality and social problems leading ultimately to control and prevention of aggression.*

OSBORN, MARVIN GRIFFING, JR., educational consultant; b. Baton Rouge, Sept. 7, 1922; s. Marvin Griffing and Mamie (Hester) O.; m. Sarah Fleming, Aug. 3, 1945; children: Jane Fleming, Charles Porter. BA, La. State U., 1942, MA, 1946; LLD. St. Xavier U., 1971; DHum, Phillips U., 1977. Pub. relations counsel La. State U., 1945-47, acting dir. bur. pub. service, 1947; assoc. prof., chmn. dept. journalism and dir. pub. relations Howard Coll. (now Frank Samford U.), 1947-49; dir. pub. relations, lectr. journalism Miss. State Coll. (now Miss. State U.), 1949-53; dir. information Washington U., 1953-58, pub. relations adviser, 1955-58, dir. Devel. Funds, 1958-61; cons. coll. and univ. adminstrn., 1961—, including Drake, Duke, Phillips, Tampa, Tex. Christian univs., Atlantic Christian Coll. (now Barton Coll.), Bethany (W.Va.), Eckerd, Loretto Heights, St. Xavier U., Tenn. Wesleyan, Webster U., Hendrix, Mercy (Detroit), Bethel (Tenn.), McMurry U., St. Scholastica, Coker Coll., Christian Ch. Found., Nat. Meth. Found. Christian Higher Edn., Lexington Theol. Sem., Memphis Theol. Sem., Nat. Benevolent Assn. Christian Ch., Sisters of Loretto; interim pres. St. Xavier Coll., now St. Xavier U., 1968-69; mem. planning com. Conf. for Advancement Understanding and Support Higher Edn., White Sulphur Springs, W.Va., 1958; mem. exec. com. program and arrangements com. Gen. Assembly Christian Ch., 1977, 87-89. Bd. dirs. St. Louis Heart Assn., 1969-75, Fla. Christian Ctr., 1986-88; trustee Nat. City Christian Ch. Corp., 1981-85; mem. Christian Ch. bd. dirs., exec. com., sec. divsn. of higher edn., 1973-77, mem. panel to study fin. procedures of Christian Ch. (Disciples of Christ), 1987-89, Cypress Village Devel. Coun., Jacksonville, Fla., 1992—. Served from lt. to capt. 28th Inf. Divsn. AUS, 1942-45, ETO. Recipient Harry T. Ice award Christian Ch. Found., 1991. Mem. Am. Coll. Pub. Rels. Assn. (v.p. dists. 1951-52, v.p. membership 1952-53, sec.-treas. 1953-55, pres. 1959-60), Nat. Benevolent Assn. (amb. 1992—), Soc. Profl. Journalists, Omicron Delta Kappa, Sigma Chi. Home: 13655 Myrica Ct Jacksonville FL 32224-6626 also: PO Box 1639 Cashiers NC 28717

OSBORN, MARY JANE MERTEN, biochemist; b. Colorado Springs, Colo., Sept. 24, 1927; d. Arthur John and Vivien Naomi (Morgan) Merten; m. Ralph Kenneth Osborn, Oct. 26, 1950. B.A., U. Calif., Berkeley, 1948; Ph.D., U. Wash., 1958. Postdoctoral fellow, dept. microbiology N.Y. U. Sch. Medicine, N.Y.C., 1959-61; intern N.Y. U. Sch. Medicine, 1961-62, asst. prof., 1962-63; asst. prof. dept. molecular biology Albert Einstein Coll. Medicine, Bronx, N.Y., 1963-66; assoc. prof. Albert Einstein Coll. Medicine, 1966-68; prof. dept. microbiology U. Conn. Health Center, Farmington, 1968—; head U. Conn. Health Center, 1980—; mem. bd. sci. counselors Nat. Heart, Lung and Blood Inst., 1975-79; mem. Nat. Sci. Bd., 1980-86; adv. coun. Nat. Inst. Gen. Med. Sci., 1983-86, divsn. rsch. grants NIH, 1989-94, chair, 1992-94; trustee Biosci. Info. Systems, 1986-91; mem. German Am. Acad. Coun., 1994—; mem. space scis. bd. NRC, 1994—, chair com. space biology and medicine, 1994—. Assoc. editor Jour. Biol. Chemistry, 1978-80; contbr. articles in field of biochemistry and molecular biology to profl. jours. Mem. rsch. com. Am. Heart Assn., 1972-77, chair, 1976-77. NIH fellow, 1959-61; NIH grantee, 1962—; NSF grantee, 1965-68; Am. Heart Assn. grantee, 1968-71. Fellow Am. Acad. Arts and Scis. (coun. 1988-91), NAS (coun. 1990-93, com. sci. engring. and pub. policy 1993—); mem. Am. Chem. Soc. (chmn. divsn. biol. chemistry 1975-76), Am. Fedn. Soc. Exptl. Biology (pres. 1982-83), Am. Soc. Biol. Chemists (pres. 1981-82), Am. Soc. Microbiology. Democrat. Office: U Conn Health Ctr Dept Microbiology Farmington CT 06030

OSBORN, RONALD EDWIN, minister, church history educator; b. Chgo., Sept. 5, 1917; s. George Edwin and Alma Edith (Lanterman) O.; m. Naomi Elizabeth Jackson, Sept. 10, 1940 (dec.); 1 dau., Virginia Elizabeth (dec.); m. Nola L. Neill, Aug. 29, 1986. Student, Lynchburg Coll., 1934-35, Union Theol. Sem. in Va., 1936; A.B., Philips U., 1938, M.A., 1939, B.D., 1942, Litt. D., 1969; postgrad., U. Okla., 1940-41; Ph.D., U. Oreg., 1955; D.D., Bethany Coll., 1989. Ordained to ministry Christian Ch. (Disciples of Christ), 1940. Min. Christian Ch., Lahoma, Okla., 1936-38, 1st Christian Ch., Geary, Okla., 1938-42, First Christian Ch., Jonesboro, Ark., 1942-43; editor youth publs. Christian Bd. Publ., St. Louis, 1943-45; prof. ch. history Northwest Christian Coll., Eugene, Oreg., 1946-50; min . Ch. of Christ, Creswell, Oreg., 1946-50; assoc. prof. ch. history Christian Theol. Sem. (formerly Butler U. Sch. Religion), Indpls., 1950-53, prof., 1953-73, dean, 1959-70; dir. ecumenical study Council Christian Unity, Disciples of Christ, Indpls., 1954-57; vis. prof. ch. history and ecumenics Union Theol. Sem., Manila, Philippines, 1965; vis. prof. ch. history Sch. Theology, Claremont, Calif., 1970-71; prof. Sch. Theology, 1973-82; lectr. Grad. Sch. Ecumenical Studies, Chateau de Bossey, Switzerland, 1954-55; Del. World Conf. on Faith and Order, 1952, 63, 4th Assembly World Council Chs., Sweden, 1968; pres. Internat. Conv. Christian Chs., 1967-68; 1st moderator Christian Ch. (Disciples of Christ), 1968; staff Assembly World Council Chs., Evanston, Ill., 1954. Author: Toward the Christian Church, 1964, A Church for These Times, 1965, In Christ's Place, 1967, Experiment in Liberty, 1978, The Faith We Affirm, 1979, The Education of Ministers for the Coming Age, 1987, Creative Disarray: Models of Ministry in a Changing America, 1991; editor: Seeking God's Peace in a Nuclear Age, 1985, symposium The Reformation of Tradition, 1963, Encounter (formerly Shane Quar.), 1952-63. Mem. Disciples of Christ Hist. Soc. (trustee emeritus, past pres.), Am. Hist. Assn., Am. Soc. Ch. History, ACLU, Phi Kappa Phi, Theta Phi. Home: 85647 Bradbury Ln Eugene OR 97405-9683 *A person who doesn't think is a slave; a person who won't imagine is a prisoner.* — Daniel Dyer from "Imagine the world without imagination," Cleve. Plain Dealer, Jan. 3, 1986.

OSBORN, TERRY WAYNE, biochemist, executive; b. Roswell, N.Mex., May 17, 1943; s. Woodrow Edward and Wilma Marie (Meador) O. AA, Ventura Coll., 1967; BS, U. Calif., Riverside, 1969; PhD, U. Calif.-Riverside, 1975; MBA, Pepperdine U., 1981. Research scientist McGaw Labs., Irvine, Calif., 1976, research scientist-project leader, 1976, research scientist, project team leader, 1976-77, group leader, sr. research scientist, 1978-79, mgr. clin. research, 1979-81, mktg. product mgr., 1981-82, mktg. group product mgr., 1982-83, dir. mktg., 1983-84; mktg. dir. IVAC Corp., San Diego, 1984-87; v.p. sales/mktg., officer Nichols Inst., Calif., 1987-89, v.p., asst. to chmn., 1990-91; v.p., gen. mgr. regional labs. Nichols Inst., 1991-93; pres., CEO Health Advance Inst., 1993—; 010 dirs. Med. Mktg. Assn., Peoria Med. Rsch. Corp.; mem. chemistry faculty Riverside City Coll., 1974-76, San Bernardino Valley Coll., 1974-76; asst. prof. clin. pharmacology U. Ill. Coll. Medicine. Served with U.S. Army, 1962-65. Recipient Agnes M. Toland Meml. Trust award, 1966; recipient Ventura Emblem Club award, 1967; Environ. Sci. fellow, 1970-73; Dean's Spl. fellow, 1974-75. Mem. Am. Chem. Soc., Am. Oil Chemists Soc., Am. Med. Mktg. Assn. (bd. dirs.), Inst. Food Technologists, U.S. Ski Assn., One Mile Soc., Sigma Xi, Chi Gamma Iota, Alpha Gamma Sigma. Club: Tyrolean Ski (pres. 1972-73). Office: PO Box 1466 1 Illini Dr Peoria IL 61655-1466 *Nothing would be done at all if a man waited till he could do it so well that no one could find fault with it.*

OSBORN, WILLIAM C., personnel organization executive. Pres. Human Resources Rsch. Orgn., Alexandria, Va. Office: Human Resources Research Org 66 Canal Center Plz Ste 400 Alexandria VA 22314-1591

OSBORN, WILLIAM GEORGE, savings and loan executive; b. Alton, Ill., Dec. 9, 1925; s. Ralph A. and Pauline J. (Horn) O.; m. Hilda M. Alexander, Aug. 12, 1950; children: Barbara K., David A., Robert W., James A. B.S. in Math., Shurtleff Coll., 1947; certificate, Grad. Sch. Savs. and Loan, Ind. U., 1946-48; A.M. in Econs., St. Louis U., 1962. With Germania Fed. Savs. and Loan Assn., Alton, 1946-90; exec. officer Germania Fed. Savs. and Loan Assn., 1955-86, pres., 1964-86, chmn., 1981-86, chmn. trust com., 1982-86; pres. Fin. Service Assocs., Ft. Lauderdale, Fla., 1986—; pres. Germania Fin. Corp., 1970-86; owner Fin. Guidance, Alton, 1951—; mem. Opportunities Unltd., 1954-58; instr. Am. Savs. and Loan Inst.; bd. dirs. Nat. Coun. Savs. Instns., Washington, 1984-86. Author: Savings and Loan Operating Policies Manual, 1960, Economic Factors Influencing Savings and Loan Interest Rates, 1962. Pres. Alton Wood River Community Chest, 1959; bd. dirs. Piasa Bird coun. Boy Scouts Am., 1945-88, Mississippi Valley Jr. Achievement, Alton Area United Fund, 1961-63; founder, bd. dirs., treas. New Piasa Chautauqua Ch. Assembly, 1982-86; treas. Lewis and Clark Community Coll. Found., 1976-86; bd. dirs., sec. Riverbend Civic Progress, 1984-86. Served to lt. (j.g.) USNR, 1943-46, 50-51. Mem. Nat. Assn. Bus. Economists, Nat. Economists Club, St. Louis Economists Club, Am. Inst. Mgmt. Presbyterian (elder). Clubs: Masons (Alton); Shriners; Lockhaven Country (Alton); Chautauqua (Ill.) Yacht.

OSBORNE, BURL, newspaper publisher, editor; b. Jenkins, Ky., June 25, 1937; s. Oliver and Juanita (Smallwood) O.; m. Betty S. Wilder, Feb. 14, 1974; 1 son, Burl Jonathan. Student, U. Ky., 1955-57; B.A. in Journalism, Marshall U., 1960; M.B.A., L.I. U. Sch. Bus., 1984; A.M.P., Harvard Bus. Sch., 1984. Reporter Ashland (Ky.) Daily Ind., 1957-58; reporter, editor Sta. WHTN-TV, Huntington, W.Va., 1958-60; corr. AP, Bluefield, W.Va., 1960-62; statehouse corr. AP, Charleston, W.Va., 1963-64; corr. AP, Spokane, Wash., 1964-67; news editor AP, Denver, 1967-70; chief of bur. AP, Ky., 1970-72, Ohio, 1972-74; asst. chief of bur. AP, Washington, 1974-76; mng. editor AP, N.Y.C., 1977-80; exec. editor Dallas Morning News, 1980-83, v.p., 1981, sr. v.p., editor, 1983-84, pres., editor, 1985-90, pub., editor, 1991—; bd. dirs. A.H. Celo Corp., Owensboro (Ky.) Pub. Co., AP; bd. dirs. Pulitzer Prize Com., 1986-95; co-chair, bd. mem. adv. com. Nieman Found., Harvard U.; mem. journalism adv. com. Knight Found. Named Newspaper Exec. of Yr., Nat. Press Found., 1992; inducted to Ky. Journalism Hall of Fame, 1994. Mem. Orgn. Profl. Journalists, Am. Soc. Newspaper Editors (bd. dirs., v.p. 1989—, pres. 1990-91), Am. Newspaper Pubs. Assn., Assn. Press Inst. (chmn. 1988-93), Tex. Daily Newspaper Assn. (bd. dirs. 1982-92, pres. 1993), So. Newspaper Pub. Assn. (bd. dirs.). Home: 7609 Southwestern Blvd Dallas TX 75225-7927 Office: Dallas Morning News Communications Ctr PO Box 655237 Dallas TX 75265-5237

OSBORNE, CHARLES WILLIAM, transportation executive; b. Dungannon, Va., Nov. 9, 1942; s. David Doyle and Lula Cordelia (Gillenwater) O.; m. Sandra Jean Elliot, Oct. 6, 1968; children: Jennifer, Michael, William. BS, Va. Tech., 1965; MA, West Ga. Coll., 1975. Mktg. planner Union Oil Co., Schaumburg, Ill., 1974-75, mgr. mktg. planning, 1981-82, mgr. purchasing, 1983-84, divsn. mktg. mgr., 1984-86; gen. mgr. mktg. Union Oil Co., Schaumburg, 1986-89; dist. sales mgr. Union Oil Co., Atlanta, 1975-78, mgr. divsn. svc., 1978-81; v.p. mktg. Uno-Ven Co., Arlington Heights, Ill., 1989-93; pres., CEO, bd. dirs. Nat. Auto/Truckstops, Inc., Nashville, 1992—; spl. asst. to chmn. U.S. Internat. Trade Commn., Washington, 1982-83. bd. dirs. Northwest Community Hosp., Arlington Heights, 1989-94; active bus. adv. bd. Roosevelt U., Arlington Heights, 1989-94, adult edn. Presbyn. Ch., Barrington, Ill., 1991-93, bldg. com., 1991-93. 1st lt. U.S. Army, 1966-68. Mem. Am. Trucking Assn., Nat. Assn. Truckstop Operators, Petroleum Marketers Assn. Am., Petroleum Marketers Edn. Found. (bd. dirs.), Soc. Ind. Gasoline Marketers. Avocations: golf, racquetball, reading. Home: 6201 Belle Rive Dr Brentwood TN 37027 Office: National Auto/Truckstops Inc 3100 W End Ave Ste 200 PO Box 76 Nashville TN 37202

OSBORNE, DEE S., banker; b. Winters, Tex., Dec. 14, 1930; s. M.S. and Lillie (Hambright) O.; m. Patricia Anne Seeley; children: Cynthia Anne Osborne Beckham, Shelley Elizabeth Osborne Allen. BBA, West Tex. State U., 1952; LLB, U. Tex., 1955. Bar: Tex. 1955. Assoc. Price, Veltmann & Skelton, Houston, 1957-63; v.p., treas. South Coast Life Ins. Co., Houston, 1963-66; exec. v.p. fin. Quintana Petroleum Corp., Houston, 1966-78; co-chmn. bd. Cullen Ctr. Bank & Trust Co., 1969-78; chmn. bd. Cullen Savs. Assn., 1972-78, Cullen Ctr., Inc., 1974-78, Cullen Bankers, Inc., 1975-78; vice chmn. bd. Citizens Nat. Bank-Dallas, 1973-77; co-chmn., pres. Finial Investment Corp., Houston, 1978—; pres., dir. internat. Bank of Fin. Cayman Island, B.W.I., 1977—, also bd. dirs.; chief exec. officer, pres. Magnesium Internat. Corp., Ltd.; chmn. Uniteg Investment Co.; bd. dirs. Seagull Energy Corp., EnCap/Tenneco Joint Venture, Bogan Aerotech, Inc., EOTT Energy Corp., Jacintoport Terminal Co., Legacy Trust Co. Trustee Scott and White Meml. Hosp., Vivian L. Smith Found., Sherwood and Brindley Found., Temple, Tex., Ralph A. Johnston Found. Endowment; mem. adv. com. U. Houston System; fin. com. St. Luke's Meth. Ch.; mem. devel. bd. U. Tex. Health Sci. Ctr., Houston; mem. tech. investment and licensing com. Pres. Adv. Coun. Houston Advanced Rsch. Ctr. With U.S. Army, 1955-57. Mem. Tex. Bar Assn., Houston Bar Assn., Houston Country Club, Coronado Club (bd. dirs.). Home: 3860 Olympia Dr Houston TX 77019-3032 Office: 6800 Texas Commerce Tower Houston TX 77002

OSBORNE, FREDERICK SPRING, JR., academic administrator, artist; b. Phila., Sept. 10, 1940; s. Frederick Spring and Katherine (Mitchell) O.; m. Deborah H. Cooper, June 30, 1964 (div. June 1979); children: Thomas, Sophia, Jessica; m. Judith K. M. Barbour, Feb. 15, 1986. BFA in Sculpture, Temple U., 1963; MFA in Sculpture, Yale U., 1965. From instr. to asst. prof. Grad. Sch. Fine Arts U. Pa., Phila., 1966-77; dir. continuing edn. Phila. Coll. Art, 1977-85; co-founder, dir., trustee Vt. Studio Ctr., Johnson, 1983—; dean, dir. Pa. Acad. Fine Arts, Phila., 1985—; lectr. Smith Coll., 1966, Phila. Coll. Art, 1976-85, U. Maine, 1980; cons. Inst. Internat. Edn., N.Y.C., 1984, Jury for Korean War Vet. Meml., Washington, 1989. Sculpture exhbns., 1962-82. Trustee Mantua-Powelton Edn. Fund, 1978-81, Assn. Ind. Coll. Art & Design, 1991—, Grass Roots Art and Comm. Effort, 1990—; mem. Phila. Redevel. Authority Fine Arts Com.; co-chmn. Internat. Sculpture Conf., Phila., 1991. Mem. Nat. Assn. Sch. Art and Design (bd. dirs. 1989—), Coll. Art. Assn., Nat. Art Edn. Assn., Nat. Assn. Art Administrs. Home: 3621 Hamilton St Philadelphia PA 19104-2327 Office: Pa Acad Fine Arts 118 N Broad St Philadelphia PA 19102-1598

OSBORNE, GEORGE DELANO, performing arts company director; b. Ft. Worth, Aug. 25, 1938; s. Hugh and Eula Catherine (Trent) O.; children from previous marriage: David Warren, Hugh Philip, George Douglas. B in Mus, Oklahoma City U., 1960; M in Mus, Ind. U., 1964; postgrad. in Arts Mgmt., Hartford Grad. Ctr., 1978. Mem. faculty Tex. Tech. U., Lubbock, 1962-64, S.W. Mo. State U., Springfield, 1964-66, Memphis State U., 1966-76, W.Va. U., Morgantown, 1976-78; gen. dir. Memphis Opera, Morgantown, 1971-76, Hartford (Conn.) Chamber Orch., Morgantown, 1978-79, Conn. Opera, Hartford, 1979—; Hartford Chamber Orch., 1979-88, Hartford Ballet, 1982-88; dir. opera prodns. Hartt Sch. Music, U. Hartford, 1993—. Mem. Hartford Cultural Affairs Commn., 1980. Fulbright scholar, Rome, 1960; Am. Leadership Forum fellow, 1986-87. Mem. Cen. Opera Svc. (regional dir.), Nat. Opera Assn. Home: 144 Pond Cir Glastonbury CT 06033 Office: Conn Opera Assn 226 Farmington Ave Hartford CT 06105-3501

OSBORNE, HAROLD WAYNE, sociology educator, consultant; b. Eldorado, Ark., Sept. 5, 1930; s. Carl Clinton and Mary Eunice (Peace) O.; m. Alice June Williams, Feb. 15, 1953; children—Michael, Van, Samuel. B.A. in History, Ouachita Bapt. Coll., 1952; M.A. in Sociology, La. State U., 1956, Ph.D. in Sociology, 1959. Research assoc. dept. rural sociology La. State U., 1954-56; social sci. analyst USDA, Baton Rouge, 1956-58; asst. prof. sociology Baylor U., Waco, 1958-60; assoc. prof. Baylor U., 1960-63, prof., 1963—, dir. grad. studies dept. sociology, 1963-87, chair dept. sociology, anthropology, social work and gerontology, 1988—; cons. in field; dir. workshops on crime and delinquency. Co-editor: Research Methods: Issues and Insights, 1971; co-author: Sociology: A Pragmatic Approach, 1981; assoc. editor for sociology Social Sci. Quar., 1965-75. Bd. dirs. Mclennan County Mental Health Assn., Tex., 1970-80. Served with inf. U.S. Army, 1952-54. Named Outstanding Baylor Prof., Baylor U., 1976, Master Tchr., 1993. Mem. Am. Sociol. Assn., Southwestern Sociol. Assn. (v.p. 1985-87, pres. 1987-88), Southwestern Social Sci. Assn., Population Assn. Am., Population Reference Bur., Am. Social Health Assn. (bd. dirs. Southwestern region). Democrat. Baptist. Home: 2717 Braemar St Waco TX 76710-2118 Office: Baylor U Dept Sociology Waco TX 76798

OSBORNE, JAMES ALFRED, religious organization administrator; b. Toledo, July 3, 1927; s. Alfred James and Gladys Irene (Gaugh) O.; m. Ruth Glenrose Campbell, Nov. 26, 1945; 1 child, Constance Jean (Mrs. Donald William Canning). Grad., Salvation Army Coll., 1947; student, U. Chattanooga, 1954-55; 1989-93, ret., 1993. Corps officer Salvation Army, Magness, Nashville, 1947, Southside, Memphis, 1948, Owensboro, Ky., 1949-54; comdg. officer Salvation Army, Chattanooga, 1954-61; city comdr. Salvation Army, Miami, Fla., 1961-65; divisional sec. Ky.-Tenn. Div. Salvation Army, 1965-68, gen. sec. N.C. and S.C. Div., 1968-70, pub. rels. sec. 15 so. states, D.C. and Mex., 1970-71, divisional comdr. Md. and No. W.Va. Div., 1971-73; divisional comdr. Nat. Capital and Virginias Div. Salvation Army, Washington, 1973-78; divisional comdr. Fla. Div. Salvation Army, 1978-80, chief sec. Western Ter., 1980-84; nat. chief sec. Salvation Army, Verona, N.J., 1984-86; territorial comdr. so. states Salvation Army, Atlanta, 1986-89; nat. comdr., Republic of Marshall Islands, Guam, P.R., Virgin Islands Salvation Army USA, 1989-93; chmn. Salvation Army Nat. Planning and Devel. Commn., 1974-76, 84-86; exec. bd. Vision Interfaith Satellite

Network, Nat. Assn. Evangelicals, Christian Children's Fund Inc.; chmn. bd. Christian Mgmt. Assn., 1993-94; exec. com. religious alliance Against Pornography; rep. Salvation Army to numerous orgns. sec. Tenn. Conf. on Social Welfare, 1959, v.p., 1960; pres. Fla. Conf. on Social Welfare, 1965; pres. Ky. Welfare Assn., 1970. Mem. Chattanooga Pastors Assn. (pres. 1958), Va. and W. Va. Welfare Confs., Rotary.

OSBORNE, JAMES WILLIAM, radiation biologist; b. Pana, Ill., Jan. 17, 1928; s. Samuel Frederick and Ruby Clascena (Irel) O.; m. Marilyn Corrine Shaw, July 1, 1950; children—Walter, David. B.S., U. Ill., Champaign-Urbana, 1949, M.S., 1951, Ph.D., 1955. Research asst. dept. physics U. Ill., 1949-51; research asso. Control Systems Lab., 1951-55; asst. prof. Radiation Research Lab., U. Iowa, 1955-61, asso. prof., 1961-67, prof., 1967—, dir. lab., 1978-93. Served with USAAF, 1946-47. Mem. Am. Soc. Therapeutic Radiology and Oncology, Radiation Rsch. Soc., Am. Physiol. Soc., Cell Kinetics Soc., Soc. Exptl. Biology and Medicine, Am. Assn. for Cancer Rsch., Sigma Xi. Methodist. Research, studies on biol. effects of radiation and kinetics of cell populations. Home: 815 14th Ave Coralville IA 52241-1742 Office: Radiation Research Lab 14 Med Labs U Iowa Iowa City IA 52242

OSBORNE, JOHN WALTER, historian, educator, author; b. Bklyn., Aug. 19, 1927; s. Douglas Walter and Margaret Ann (Purcell) O.; m. Frances Patricia Hannon, Aug. 2, 1958; 1 son, David. B.A., U. Rutgers U., 1957, M.A. (Louis Bevier fellow), 1959, Ph.D., 1961. Asst. prof. history Kean Coll. of N.J., 1961-63, N.J. Inst. Tech., 1963-64; asst. prof. Rutgers U., New Brunswick, N.J., 1964-66; assoc. prof. Rutgers U., 1966-69, prof., 1969—. Author: William Cobbett-His Thought and His Times, 1966, The Silent Revolution: The Industrial Revolution in England as a Source of Cultural Change, 1970, John Cartwright, 1972; co-author: Cobbett in His Times, 1990; editor: Jour. of Rutgers U. Libraries, 1975-80; co-editor: A Grammar of the English Language, 1983; contbr. articles to profl. jours. Recipient Henry Browne award for disting. teaching Rutgers U., 1988; Am. Philos. Soc. grantee, 1966, 75. Home: 16 Townwoods Rd Ivoryton CT 06442

OSBORNE, MARY POPE, writer; b. Ft. Sill, Okla., May 20, 1949; d. William Perkins and Barnette (Dickens) Pope; m. William R. Osborne, May 16, 1976. BA in Religion, U. N.C., 1971. Author: Favorite Greek Myths, 1988, American Tall Tales, 1990, Moon Horse, 1991, Spider Kane Mystery Series, 1992, 93, Magic Tree House Series, 1992-95, Haunted Waters, 1994, Molly and the Prince, 1994. Recipient Disting. Alumna award U. N.C., Chapel Hill, 1994. Mem. PEN, Authors Guild (pres. 1993—, dir. found.), Authors League Fund (bd. dirs.), Author's Registry (founder). Office: Brandt & Brandt Lit Agy 1501 Broadway #2310 New York NY 10036

OSBORNE, PAUL DOUGLAS, hospital administrator; b. Blackwater, Va., Apr. 29, 1943; s. Paul James and Addie Mae (Bledsoe) O.; m. Susan Henry, Apr. 23, 1966; children: Karen D. Bennett, Amy Lynn. BA, Lynchburg Coll., 1965; MHA, Ga. State U., 1971. Health planner Ctrl. Va. Health Planning Coun., Lynchburg, Va., 1971-72; assoc. administr. N.E. Ga. Reg. Med. Ctr., Gainesville, Ga., 1972-76; administr. Mary Black Meml. Hosp., Spartanburg, S.C., 1976-80; v.p. Spartanburg (S.C.) Regional Med. Ctr., 1980-90; dep. supt. Ctrl. State Hosp., Milledgeville, Ga., 1990—. Bd. dirs. United Way Ctrl. Ga., 1993—, Regional Girl Scout Coun., 1987-90, Salvation Army, 1986-88; sr. warden St. Christopher's Episc. Ch., Spartanburg, 1983. Capt. U.S. Army, 1966-69, Vietnam. Fellow Am. Coll. Healthcare Execs., Milledgeville Country Club, Rotary. Avocations: tennis, photography. Home: 218 Pine Knoll Ln SE Eatonton GA 31024 Office: Ctrl State Hosp Milledgeville GA 31062

OSBORNE, REED E., library executive. MLS, Univ. Western Ont., Can., 1973. Chief libr. St. Thomas (Ont.) Pub. Libr., 1976-80, Markham (Ont.) Pub. Libr., 1980-84; CEO London Pub. Libr., 1984—. Office: London Pub Libr, 305 Queens Ave, London, ON Canada N6B 3L7

OSBORNE, RICHARD DE JONGH, mining and metals company executive; b. Bronxville, N.Y., Mar. 19, 1934; s. Stanley de Jongh and M. Elizabeth (Ide) O.; m. Cheryl Anne Archibald, Dec. 14, 1957; children: Leslie Anne, Lindsay Ide, Nicholas de J., Stanley de J. A.B. in Econs., Princeton U., 1956. With Cono Engring. Corp., Meriden, Conn., 1956-60; fin., planning and mktg. exec. IBM Corp., Armonk, N.Y., 1960-69; investment adviser Sherman M. Fairchild, N.Y.C., 1969-70; exec. v.p. fin. and bus. devel., dir. Fairchild Camera & Instrument Corp., Mountain View, Calif. 1970-74; v.p. fin. ASARCO Inc. (formerly Am. Smelting & Refining Co.), N.Y.C., 1975-77, exec. v.p., 1977-81, pres., 1981-85, chmn., pres., chief exec. officer, 1985—, also bd. dirs.; bd. dirs. Schering-Plough Corp., The Continental Corp., E.T. & H.K. Ide, Inc., Am. Mining Congress; chmn. Copper Devel. Assn. Mem. Conf. Bd. Ams. Soc., U.S.C. of C., Coun. on Fgn. Rels., Coun. of Ams. (bd. dirs.), Am. Australian Assn. (pres., bd. dirs.), Internat. Copper Assn. (bd. dirs.), Down Town Assn. Club, Econ. Club, River Club, Brook Club, City Midday Club, Bedens Brook Club, Sakonnet Golf Club. Mem. Ams. Soc. (bd. dirs.), U.S.C. of C. (bd. dirs.), Coun. on Fgn. Rels., Coun. of Ams. (bd. dirs.), Am. Australian Assn. (pres., bd. dirs.), Internat. Copper Assn. (bd. dirs.), Conf. Bd. Clubs: Down Town Assn., Economic, River, Brook, City Midday; Bedens Brook; Sakonnet Golf. Home: 40 E 94th St Apt 32B New York NY 10128-0709 Office: Asarco Inc 180 Maiden Ln New York NY 10038-4925

OSBORNE, RICHARD HAZELET, anthropology and medical genetics educator; b. Kennecott, Alaska, June 18, 1920; s. Clarence Edward and Margaret Jerenne (Hazelet) O.; m. Barbara White, Oct. 14, 1944; children: Susan, Richard, David; m. Barbara Teachman, Sept. 1, 1970. Student, U. Alaska, 1939-41; BS, BA, U. Wash., 1949; postgrad., Harvard U., 1949-50; PhD (Viking Fund Pre-doctoral fellow, Spl. fellow Inst. for Study Human Variation), Columbia, 1956; hon. doctor odontology, U. Oulu, Finland, 1994. Research asso. Columbia U., 1953-58; asst. Sloan-Kettering Inst. N.Y.C., 1958-60; asso. Sloan-Kettering Inst., 1960-62, asso. mem. head sect. human genetics, 1962-64; prof. anthropology and med. genetics U. Wis., Madison, 1964-86, prof. emeritus, 1986—; asso. prof. preventive medicine Cornell Med. Coll., 1962-64; clin. geneticist Meml. Hosp. for Cancer, N.Y.C., 1963-65; vis. scientist Forsyth Dental Center, Boston, 1969-71; cons. human genetics Newington (Conn.) Childrens Hosp., 1971-73; Mem. com. on epidemiology and vets. follow-up studies NRC, 1969-73; mem. perinatal research com. Nat. Inst. Neurol. Diseases and Stroke, NIH, 1970-72; mem. cultural anthropology fellowship and rev. NIMH, 1969-73. Author: Genetic Basis of Morphological Variation, 1959, Biological and Social Meaning of Race, 1971; Editor: Social Biology, 1961-77, 81—; contbr. articles to profl. jours. Served to maj. USAAF, 1942-46. Decorated D.F.C., Air medal with 3 oak leaf clusters; Named Health Research Council Career Scientist City N.Y., 1962-64. Fellow Explorers Club; Mem. Am. Assn. Phys. Anthropology (exec. com. 1965-67, v.p. 1968-70), Am. Soc. for Human Genetics (dir. 1960-61, 67-69), Behavior Genetics Assn. (pres. pro-tem 1970-71), Soc. for Study Social Biology (dir. 1981-83, 86—), Pioneers of Alaska (life), Sigma Xi. Office: PO Box 2349 Port Angeles WA 98362

OSBORNE, RICHARD JAY, electric utility company executive; b. N.Y.C., Feb. 16, 1951; s. Victor and Evelyn Celia (Sweetbaum) O. B.A., Tufts U., 1973; M.B.A., U. N.C., 1975. Fin. analyst Duke Power Co., Charlotte, N.C., 1975-78; sr. fin. analyst, 1978-80, mgr. fin. rels., 1980-81, mgr. treasury activities, 1981, treas., 1981-88, v.p. fin., CFO, 1988-94, sr. v.p., CFO, 1994—. Active Charlotte Jewish Fedn.; pres. Hist. Elizabeth Neighborhood Found. Mem. Fin. Execs. Inst., Edison Electric Inst. (fin. & regulatory sect.), Found. for the Carolinas (chmn. investment com.), N.C. Coun. Edn. (chair). Democrat. Jewish. Office: Duke Power Co 422 S Church St Charlotte NC 28242-0001

OSBORNE, RONALD WALTER, communications executive; b. Eng., 1946; m. Grace Snead; 3 children. Degree in French and German, Cambridge U., 1968. Chartered acct., 1972. Ptnr. Arthur Young, Clarkson Gordon & Co., Rio de Janeiro, 1976-79; Clarkson Gordon, Toronto, Ont., Can., 1979-81; v.p. fin., chief fin. officer Maclean Hunter Ltd., Toronto, 1981-82, v.p broadcasting, 1982-84, pres., chief oper. officer, 1984-86, pres., chief exec. officer—; bd. dirs. Royal Bank Can., Sun Life Ins. Co., Toronto Sun Pub. Corp., CTV TV Network; mem. adv. bd. Fin. Post; part-time lectr. York U., Toronto. Apptd. Internat. Trade Adv. Com.; chmn. Sectoral Adv. Group on Internat. Trade; bd. dirs. Roy

Thomson Hall; mem. Bus. Coun. Nat. Issues. Fellow Inst. Chartered Accts. Ont.; mem. Toronto Club, United Oxford and Cambridge U. Club. Office: Maclean Hunter Limited, 777 Bay St, Toronto, ON Canada M5W 1A7

OSBORNE, STANLEY DE JONGH, investment banker; b. San Jose, Costa Rica, Mar. 21, 1927; s. Claude H. and Marguerite S. (Cramer) O.; m. Geraldine Smith, May 9, 1950; children—James, Michael. B.S. with honors, U. Man., 1948, M.S., 1949; postgrad., U. Ariz., 1949-50. Exploration geologist, mgr. Internat. Nickel Co., Asarco and others, Can., U.S., Mex., Cuba, 1944-80; exec. v.p. Asarco Inc., 1980-92; chmn. Asarco Australia Ltd., 1986-92; mineral industry cons., 1992—. Mem. AIME, Can. Inst. Mining and Metallurgy. Home and Office: 7887 N La Cholla Apt 3168 Tucson AZ 85741

OSBORNE, THOMAS CRAMER, mineral industry consultant; b. Winnipeg, Man., Can., Mar. 21, 1927; s. Claude H. and Marguerite S. (Cramer) O.; m. Geraldine Smith, May 9, 1950; children—James, Michael. B.S. with honors, U. Man., 1948, M.S., 1949; postgrad., U. Ariz., 1949-50. Exploration geologist, mgr. Internat. Nickel Co., Asarco and others, Can., U.S., Mex., Cuba, 1944-80; exec. v.p. Asarco Inc., 1980-92; chmn. Asarco Australia Ltd., 1986-92; mineral industry cons., 1992—. Mem. AIME, Can. Inst. Mining and Metallurgy. Home and Office: 7887 N La Cholla Apt 3168 Tucson AZ 85741

OSBORNE, TOM, college football coach; b. Feb. 23, 1937; m. Nancy Tederman; children: Mike, Ann, Susie. B.A., Hastings Coll., 1959; M.A., U. Nebr., 1963, Ph.D. in Ednl. Psychology, 1965. Flankerback Washington Redskins, NFL, 1959-61, San Francisco 49ers, NFL, 1961-62; asst. football coach U. Nebr., 1962-73, head football coach, 1973—; coach team U. Nebr. (Cotton Bowl), 1974, U. Nebr. (Sugar Bowl), 1971, U. Nebr. (Astro-Bluebonnet Bowl), 1976, U. Nebr. (Liberty Bowl), 1977, U. Nebr. (Sun Bowl), 1980, U. Nebr. (Orange Bowl), 1979, 83, 84, 89, 92-95. Served in U.S. Army. Named Big Eight Coach of Yr., 1975, 78, 80; named Bobby Dodds Nat. Coach of Yr., 1978. Coached team to NCAA Divsn. IA Nat. Championship, 1994. Office: care Nebr Sports Info 116 South Stadium Lincoln NE 68588*

OSBORNE-POPP, GLENNA JEAN, health services administrator; b. East Rainelle, W.Va., Jan. 5, 1945; d. B.J. and Jean Ann (Haranac) Osborne; m. Thomas Joseph Ferrante Jr., June 11, 1966 (div. Nov. 1987); 1 child, Thomas Joseph Osborne; m. Brian Mark Popp, Aug. 13, 1988. BA cum laude, U. Tampa, 1966; MA, Fairleigh Dickinson U., 1982; cert., Kean Coll., 1983. Cert. English, speech, dramatic arts tchr., prin./supr. Tchr. Raritan High Sch., Hazlet, N.J., 1966; tchr. Keyport (N.J.) Pub. Schs., 1968-86, coord. elem. reading and lang. arts, 1980-84, supr. curriculum and instrn., 1984-86; prin. Weston Sch., Manville, N.J., 1986-88, The Bartle Sch., Highland Park, N.J., 1988-91, Orange Ave. Sch., Cranford, N.J., 1991-92; dir. The Open Door Youth Shelter, Binghamton, N.Y., 1992-94; child protective investigator supr. Dept. Health and Rehab. Svcs., Orlando, Fla., 1994-95; program supr. Children's Home Soc., Sanford, Fla., 1995—; program supr. Children's Home Soc., 1995—; regional trainer Individualized Lang. Arts, Weehawken, N.J., 1976-86; cons. McDougal/Little Pubs., Evanston, Ill., 1982-83. Contbr. chpt. to: A Resource Guide of Differentiated Learning Experiences for Gifted Elementary Students, 1981. Sunday sch. tchr. Reformed Ch., Keyport, 1975-80, supt. Sunday sch., 1982-84. Mem. Order Ea. Star (Tampa, Fla.), Phi Delta Kappa. Republican. Methodist. Avocation: writing. Office: Ste 100 520 W Lake Mary Blvd Sanford FL 32773

OSBOURN, GORDON CECIL, materials scientist; b. Kansas City, Mo., Aug. 13, 1954; 2 children. BS, U. Mo., 1974, MS, 1975; PhD in Physics, Calif. Inst. Tech., 1979. Tech. staff Sandia Nat. Labs., 1979-83, divsn. supr., 1983—. Recipient E.O. Lawrence award Dept. Energy, 1985; Internat. prize For New Materials Am. Physical Soc., 1993. Fellow Am. Physical Soc. Home: 5851 Lost Dutchman Albuquerque NM 87111 Office: Sandia Nat Labs MS 1423 Albuquerque NM 87185-1423

OSBOURNE, OZZY (JOHN OSBOURNE), vocalist; b. Birmingham, Eng., Dec. 3, 1948. Vocalist Black Sabbath band, 1969-78, solo career, 1978—. Albums include Blizzard of Ozz, 1980, Diary of a Madman, 1981, Bark at the Moon, 1983, The Ultimate Sin, 1986, No Rest for the Wicked, 1989, Just Say Ozzy, 1990 (EP), No More Tears, 1991, Live & Loud, 1993, (with Black Sabbath) Black Sabbath, 1969, Paranoid, 1970, Master of Reality, 1971, Sabotage, 1975, Technical Ecstasy, 1976, Never Say Die, 1978; singles: So Tired, 1984, (with Black Sabbath) Paranoid, 1970. Grammy award, Best Heavy Metal Performance 1994 for "I Don't Want to Change the World". *

OSBURN, CHARLES BENJAMIN, librarian, university dean; b. Pitts., May 25, 1939; s. C. Benjamin and Lydia (Harmon) O.; divorced; 1 child, Christopher Bart; m. Sharon Tuffendsam, June 12, 1987; 1 stepchild, Bradley Alan Tuffendsam. B.A., Grove City Coll., 1961; M.A., Pa. State U., 1963; M.S., U. N.C., 1971; Ph.D., U. Mich., 1978. Instr. French Pa. State U., University Park, 1963-66; assoc. prof. libr. U. Wis-Whitewater, 1966-69; humanities bibliographer U. N.C., Chapel Hill, 1969-74; asst. dir. libraries SUNY-Buffalo, 1974-76; asst. univ. librarian Northwestern U., Evanston, 1976-80; dean, univ. librarian U. Cin., 1980-86; dean libraries U. Ala., Tuscaloosa, 1986—; prof. library sci. U. Ala., 1986—; bd. dirs. Ctr. for Research Libraries, Chgo., SOLINET, Atlanta, Assn. Rsch. Librs., 1987-93; mem. rsch. libr. adv. counc. to Online Computer Library Ctr., Dublin, Ohio. Author: Academic Research and Library Resources: Changing Patterns in America, 1979 (award ALA 1980); compiler: Research and Reference Guide to French Studies, 2d edit., 1981; mem. editorial bd. Literary Research: A Journal of Scholarly Method and Technique, 1986—; co-editor: (with R. W. Atkinson) Collection Management: A New Treatise, 2 vols., 1991. Mem. ALA, MLA, Assn. Rsch. Librs., Phi Sigma Iota, Beta Phi Mu. Office: University of ALabama Library Office of the Librarian Tuscaloosa AL 35487

OSBY, LARISSA GEISS, artist; b. Artemowsk, Russia, June 7, 1928; came to U.S., 1951, naturalized, 1958; d. Andrew Frank and Valentine G. (Pogoreloff) Geiss; m. Howard M. Osby, June 7, 1952; children: Erik Andrew, Karin Marian. Student, U. Goettingen (Germany), 1947, 48, 49, Acad. Art, 1949-50, U. Munich, 1949-50; postgrad., U. Goettingen, Germany, 1951. Rsch. asst., translator, med. illustrator U. Pitts. Med. Sch., 1952-53; artist Pitts. Ctr. for Arts, 1961-64, 88-90; pvt. art tchr. Pitts., 1961-64; adv. artist Pitts. Bd. Edn., 1964-66; instr. anatomy, drawing and painting High Sch. for Creative and Performing Arts, Pitts., 1984—. One woman shows at, AAP Gallery, Pitts., 1960, Pitts. Plan for Art Gallery, 1961, 63, 65, 68, 71, 79, Carnegie Inst., Pitts., 1972, Pa. State U., 1973, Duquesne U., Pitts., 1980, Pitts. Ctr. for Arts, 1983, St. Vincent Coll., 1983, others; exhibited in group shows at, Butler Inst., Youngstown, Ohio, 1958, 59, 79, 86, Chautauqua Nat. Anns., 1964, 73, St. Paul Art Center, 1963, Marietta Coll., 1968, Walker Art Center, Mpls., 67, William Penn Meml. Mus., Harrisburg, Pa., 1971, also museums in Germany, France, Scotland, numerous others; represented in permanent collections at, Carnegie Inst., U. Pitts., Pitts. Bd. Edn., Am. Cancer Soc., Alcoa, U.S. Steel, Westinghouse, Koppers Co., others; comms. include, Koppers Co., First Fed. Savings & Loan Assn., U.S. Steelworkers Am., others. Recipient Citation as Woman of Distinction, Gov. Pa., 1972; named Artist of Yr., Pitts. Center for Arts, 1983, 19 Jury awards, others. Mem. Abstract Group Pitts. (pres. 1964-65), Associated Artists Pitts. (bd. dirs. 1965-68, 80-83), Pitts. Ctr. for Arts, Concept Gallery. Democrat. Address: 4218 Maple Ln Allison Park PA 15101-3017

OSBY, ROBERT EDWARD, protective services official; b. San Diego, Oct. 29, 1937; s. Jesse William and Susie Lillian (Campbell) O.; m. Clydette

Deloris Mullen, Apr. 11, 1961; children: Daryl Lawrence, Gayle Lorraine. AA in Fire Sci., San Diego Jr. Coll., 1970; BA in Mgmt., Redlands U., 1985. Recreation leader San Diego Parks and Recreation Dept., 1955-58; postal carrier U.S. Postal Service, San Diego, 1958-59; fire fighter San Diego Fire Dept., 1959-67, fire engr., 1967-71, fire capt., 1971-76, fire bn. chief, 1976-79; fire chief Inglewood (Calif.) Fire Dept., 1979-84, San Jose (Calif.) Fire Dept., 1985—. Served to 2d lt. Calif. NG, 1960-65. Mem. Calif. Met. Fire Chiefs (chmn. 1986-87—), Internat. Assn. Black Firefighters (regional dir. 1974-77), Brothers United (pres. 1972-75). Democrat. Avocations: fishing, jogging, landscaping. Home: 5240 Fiore Ter # J206 San Diego CA 92122-5636 Office: San Diego Fire Dept 1010 2nd Ave Ste 300 San Diego CA 92101

O'SCANNLAIN, DIARMUID FIONNTAIN, federal judge; b. N.Y.C., Mar. 28, 1937; s. Sean Leo and Moira (Hegarty) O'S.; m. Maura Nolan, Sept. 7, 1963; children: Sean, Jane, Brendan, Kevin, Megan, Christopher, Anne, Kate. BA, St. John's U., 1957; JD, Harvard U., 1963; LLM, U. Va., 1992. Bar: Oreg. 1965, N.Y. 1964. Tax atty. Standard Oil Co. (N.J.), N.Y.C., 1963-65; assoc. Davies, Biggs, Strayer, Stoel & Boley, Portland, Oreg., 1965-69; dep. atty. gen. Oreg., 1969-71; public utility commr. of Oreg., 1971-73; dir. Oreg. Dept. Environ. Quality, 1973-74; sr. ptnr. Ragen, Roberts, O'Scannlain, Robertson & Neill, Portland, 1978-86; judge, U.S. Ct. Appeals (9th cir.), San Francisco, 1986—, mem. exec. com., 1988-89, 1993-94, mem. Jud. Coun. 9th Cir., 1991-93; mem. U.S. Judicial Conf. Com. on Automation and Tech., 1990—; cons. Office of Pres.-Elect and mem. Energy Transition Team (Reagan transition), Washington, 1980-81; chmn. com. adminstrv. state Bar, 1980-81. Mem. council of legal advisers Rep. Nat. Com., 1981-83; mem. Rep. Nat. Com., 1983-86, chmn. Oreg. Rep. Party, 1983-86; del. Rep. Nat. Convs., 1976, 80, chmn. Oreg. del., 1984; Rep. nominee U.S. Ho. of Reps., First Congl. Dist., 1974; team leader Emerge Task Force, Pres.'s Pvt. Sector Survey on Cost Control, 1982-83, trustee Jesuit High Sch.; mem. bd. visitors U. Oreg. Law Sch., 1988—; mem. citizens adv. bd. Providence Home, 1986-92. Maj. USAR, 1955-78. Mem. Fed. Bar Assn., ABA (sec. Apellate Judges Conf. 1989-90, exec. com. 1990—, chmn.-elect 1994—), Arlington Club, Multnomah Club. Roman Catholic. Office: US Ct Appeals 313 Pioneer Courthouse 555 SW Yamhill St Portland OR 97204-1336*

OSCHMANN, JOAN EDYTHE, gifted and elementary education educator; b. N.Y.C., July 27, 1936; d. Jesse Melchior and Edythe Martha (Fritsche) Budacz; m. Herbert V. Oschmann, Dec. 14, 1957 (div. Dec. 1971); children: Penney Joan Werner, John Peter. BA in Early Childhood Edn., Queens Coll., 1957; MS in Edn., Hofstra U., 1975, CAS, 1980, postgrad. Cert. tchr., adminstr., N.Y. Tchr. kindergarten East Meadow (N.Y.) Schs., 1957-59; tchr., dir. nursery sch. Wesleyan Sch., Smithtown, N.Y., 1962-67; tchr. gifted, elem. edn., home-based enrichment program Three Village Schs., Setauket, N.Y., 1967-92; mem. writing inst. Three Village Schs., 1976—, kindergarten com., 1984, gifted adv. com., 1986. Mem. Ea. Star, Amaranth Orgn. Triangles (jr. dep. 1974-80). Avocations: ceramics, crewel stitchery, writing. Home: 6 Clifford Blvd Hauppauge NY 11788

OSENTON, THOMAS GEORGE, publisher; b. Boston, Apr. 9, 1953; s. George Thomas and Helen (Curran) O.; m. Mary Ellen Dalzell, Aug. 16, 1975; children: Curran Lynn, Matthew. BA, U. New Hampshire, 1976. Pub. relations dir. USA Hockey, Colorado Springs, Colo., 1976-78; exec. dir. Blue Line Club Wis., Madison, 1978-81; writer WCVB-TV Ch.5 ABC Affil., Boston, 1981-82; dir. olympic pub. ABC TV Network, N.Y.; dir. mktg. ABC Pub., N.Y., 1983-86; pub. Sports Mktg. News, Conn., 1986-88; pub. Am. Artist Billboard Pubs. Inc., N.Y.C., 1988-89; pres., chief exec. officer Sporting News Pub. Co., St. Louis, 1989-93; exec. v.p., chief mktg. officer Courier Corp., Lowell, Mass., 1993—; chmn. Altered States, Inc. Avocation: golf. Home: 7 Reimer Rd Westport CT 06880-2733 Office: 165 Jackson St Lowell MA 01852-2131

OSEPCHUK, JOHN MOSES, engineering physicist, consultant; b. Peabody, Mass., Feb. 11, 1927; s. Moses Nicholas and Mary (Sukoff) O.; m. Shirley Greenwood Small; children: Jonathan Greenwood, Lauren Ann, Janet Miriam. AB, Harvard U., 1949, AM, 1950, PhD, 1957. Devel. engr. power tube div. Raytheon, Waltham, Mass., 1950-56, liaison engr. at CSF, 1956-57; devel. engr. microwave and power tube div. Raytheon Co., Burlington, Mass., 1957-62; prin. rsch. engr. rsch. div. Raytheon Co., Waltham, 1964-74; cons. scientist Raytheon Co., Lexington, Mass., 1974—; chief microwave engr. Sage Labs., Natick, Mass., 1962-64; mem. accredited standards com. C95 Am. Nat. Standards Inst., N.Y.C., 1968—. Editor: Biological Effects of Electromagnetic Radiation, 1983; contbr. over 80 articles to profl. jours.; patentee in field. Clk. Park St. Ch., Boston, 1958-65, trustee, 1965-72; mem. Rep. Town Com., Concord, Mass., 1974—. With U.S. Army, 1945-46. Fellow IEEE (chmn. com. on man and radiation, exec. sec. stds. coord. com. 1991—), Internat. Microwave Power Inst. (pres. 1992-95), Am. Scientific Affiliation; mem. Microwave Soc. of IEEE (nat. lectureship 1977-78), Electromagnetic Energy Policy Alliance (v.p. sci. and tech., bd. dirs.), Bioelectromagnetics Soc., Sigma Xi, Phi Beta Kappa. Republican. Congregationalist. Avocations: tennis, music, tree work, writing. Home: 248 Deacon Haynes Rd Concord MA 01742-4712 Office: Raytheon Rsch Div 131 Spring St Lexington MA 02173-7803

OSER, ROMAN BERNARD, manufacturing company executive; b. Huntinburg, Ind., June 16, 1930; s. Roman N. and Alene J. (Sumner) O.; m. Barbara Brown, May 28, 1960; children: Debra, Nancy, Mary. Student, Ind. U., 1954, Lockyears Coll., 1956. Credit mgr. Austin Powder Co., 1956-59; comptroller Kimball Internat. Inc., Jasper, Ind., 1959-64, exec. v.p. raw materials div., 1965—. Served with U.S. Army, 1952-53. Mem. Forest Products Research Soc., Am. Mgmt. Assns., Am. Forestry Assn., Nat. Hardwood Lumber Assn., Am. Legion, Jasper C. of C. Roman Catholic. Home: RR 4 Box 56 Jasper IN 47546-9322 Office: Kimball Internat Inc 1600 Royal St Jasper IN 47549-1001

OSGOOD, CHARLES, news broadcaster, journalist; b. N.Y.C., Jan. 8, 1933; s. Charles Osgood and Mary F. (Wilson) Wood; m. Jean Crafton, Dec. 5, 1973; children: Kathleen, Winston, Anne Elizabeth, Emily Jean, James Edward. B.S., Fordham U., 1954; L.H.D. (hon.), St. Bonaventure U., 1977; PhD (hon.), Fordham U.; LLD, St. John's U. Program dir. Sta. WGMS, Washington, until 1963; gen. mgr. Sta. WHCT, Hartford, Conn., 1963-64; reporter ABC Radio News, 1964-67; anchorman Sta. WCBS, 1967-72; corr. television and radio CBS, N.Y.C., 1972—; host CBS Sunday Morning, 1994—. Author: Nothing Could be Finer Than A Crisis That Is Minor in the Morning, 1979, There's Nothing That I Wouldn't Do If You Would Be My POSSLQ, 1981, Osgood on Speaking, 1988, The Osgood Files, 1991. Mem. AFTRA. Office: CBS Radio Network 524 W 57th St New York NY 10019-2902

OSGOOD, RICHARD M., JR., applied physics and electrical engineering educator, research administrator; b. Kansas City, Mo., Dec. 28, 1943; s. Richard Magee and Mary Neff (Russell) O.; m. Alice Rose Dyson, June 25, 1966; children—Richard Magee, III, Nathaniel David, Jennifer Anne. B.S. in Engring., U.S. Mil. Acad., 1965; M.S. in Physics, Ohio State U., 1968; Ph.D., MIT, 1973. Rsch. assoc. dept. physics MIT, Cambridge, 1969-72, mem. rsch. staff Lincoln Lab., 1973-80, project leader Lincoln Lab., 1980-81; assoc. prof. physics and elec. engring. Columbia U., N.Y.C., 1981-82, prof., 1982-91, Higgins prof., 1989—, dir., 1984-90; bd. dirs. Microelectronics Scis. Labs.; mem. Army Sci. and Tech., Basic Energy Scis. Adv. Com. Materials Rsch. Coun.-ARPA; cons. Los Alamos Nat. Lab. Editor: Laser Diagnostics and Photochemical Processing of Semiconductor Devices, 1983; assoc. editor: Applied Physics; contbr. articles to profl. jours.; patentee in field. Served to capt. USAF, 1965-69. Recipient Samuel Burka award USAF Avionics Lab., 1968, Leos Travelling Lectr. award, 1986-87, Disting. Travelling Lectr. APS, R.W. Wood Prize, 1991, Optical Soc. Am. Lectr., John Simon Guggenheim fellowship, 1989. Fellow IEEE, Optical Soc. Am. (R.W. Wood award, 1991); mem. Am. Chem. Soc., Materials Rsch. Soc. (councillor 1983-86), Optical Device Assn. (Japanese hon. lectr. 1990), Am. Phys. Soc. (travelling lectureship 1992). Home: 345 Quaker Rd Chappaqua NY 10514-2615 Office: Columbia U Radiation Laboratory New York NY 10027

OSGOOD, ROBERT MANSFIELD, lawyer; b. Elmira, N.Y., Jan. 27, 1942; s. Roland Lorenzo and Isabelle (Mansfield) O.; m. Janice Deakin, 1992; children: Christopher, Elisabeth, Abigail. BA, Syracuse U., 1963, JD,

1968; postgrad. diploma in EC law, Kings Coll., London, 1994. Bar: N.Y. 1968, U.S. Dist. Ct. (no. dist.) N.Y. 1969, U.S. Dist. Ct. (so. dist.) N.Y. 1970, U.S. Ct. Appeals (2d cir.) 1971, U.S. Dist. Ct. (ea. dist.) N.Y. 1974, U.S. Ct. Appeals (D.C. cir.) 1976, U.S. Supreme Ct. 1977. Ptnr. Sullivan & Cornwell, N.Y.C. and London, 1968—. Fellow Am. Coll. Trial Lawyers; mem. Am. Law Inst. Office: Sullivan & Cromwell 125 Broad St New York NY 10004-2498 also: 27 Pembroke Sq, London W8 6PB, England

OSGOOD, RUSSELL KING, law educator; b. Fairborn, Ohio, Oct. 25, 1947; s. Richard Magee and Mary (Russell) O.; m. Paula Haley, June 6, 1970; children: Mary, Josiah, Micah, Iain. BA, Yale U., 1969, JD, 1974. Bar: Mass. 1974, U.S. Dist. Ct. Mass. 1976. Assoc. Hill & Barlow, Boston, 1974-78; assoc. prof. Boston U., 1978-80; prof. Cornell U., Ithaca, N.Y., 1980-88, dean law sch., 1988—. Served to lt. USNR, 1969-71. Mem. Am. Soc. for Legal History (editor Law and History Rev. 1982-87), Osgoode Soc., Stair Soc., Selden Soc. Office: Cornell U Sch Law Myron Taylor Hall Ithaca NY 14853-4901

O'SHAUGHNESSY, GARY WILLIAM, military officer; b. N.Y.C., Feb. 6, 1939; s. William Eugene and Anne Elizabeth O'Shaughnessy; m. Diane Gertrude Gavin, May 8, 1971; children: Kim Gavin, Karen Anne. BA in English, Fordham U., 1960; MEd, Manhattan Coll., 1970. Commd. 2d lt. USAF, 1960, advanced through grades to maj. gen., 1989; adminstrv. officer Air Flight Test Ctr., Edwards AFB, Calif., 1960-62; student Communication Intelligence Officer Course, Goodfellow AFB, Tex., 1962-63; dir. ops. 6923RSM and OL, Vietnam, 1963; intelligence officer 6922ESG, Clark AB, P.I., 1963-65, Nat. Security Agy., Ft. Meade, Md., 1965-67; instr., comdt. of cadets Manhattan Coll., N.Y.C., 1967-70; intelligence officer Pacific Security Region, Wheeler AFB, Hawaii, 1970-72; asst. ops. officer 6921ESW, Misawa AB, Japan, 1972; intelligence officer USAF Security Svc., San Antonio, 1972-73; rep. to air staff Nat. Security Agy., Ft. Meade, 1974-77; comdr. 6903ESS, Korea, 1977-78, Electronic Security Command Units in Pacific, Hickam AFB, Hawaii, 1979-82, Electronic Security Command Units in Europe, Ramstein AB, Germany, 1982-85; assoc. dep. dir. for ops. Nat. Security Agy., Ft. Meade, 1985-87; dep. chief of staff, intelligence Hdqrs. U.S. Forces in Europe, Ramstein AB, Germany, 1987-88; dir. intelligene Hdqrs. U.S. European Command, Stuttgart-Vaihingen, Germany, 1988-89; comdr. Air Force Intelligence Command, San Antonio, 1989-93. Contbr. articles to profl. jours. Decorated Def. Superior Svc. medal, Legion of Merit, Bronze Star, Meritorious Svc. medal, Joint Svc. Commendation medal. Mem. Air Force Assn., USAF Security Svc./Electronic Security Command Assn. (pres. Potomac chpt.), Armed Force Comm. and Electronics Assn., Nat. Mil. Intelligence Assn., Assn. Old Crows, World Affairs Coun. Avocations: reading, carpentry, tennis, exercise. Home: 17808 Stoneridge Dr North Potomac MD 20878 Office: Oracle Govt Corp 3 Bethesda Metro Ctr Bethesda MD 20814

O'SHAUGHNESSY, JAMES PATRICK, lawyer; b. Rochester, N.Y., Mar. 3, 1947; s. John Andrew and Margaret May (Yaxley) O'S.; m. Terry Lee Wood. BS cum laude, Rensselaer Poly. Inst., 1972; JD, Georgetown U., 1977. Bar: Va. 1977, Ohio 1979, Wis. 1987. Assoc. Squire, Sanders & Dempsey, Cleve., 1978-81; ptnr. Hughes & Cassidy, Sumas, Wash., 1981-84; patent counsel Kimberly-Clark Corp., Neenah, Wis., 1984-85; ptnr. Foley & Lardner, Milw., 1986—; mem. adv. bd. Licensing Econs. Rev.; frequent lectr., chmn. seminars to legal and bus. groups. Contbr. articles to chpts. to profl. publs. Bd. dirs. Skylight Opera Theatre, 1991-92. With USN, 1964-68. mem. Ctr. for Pub. Resources (mediation/arbitration panel), Lic. Execs. Soc., Am. Intellectual Property Law Assn., Disabled Am. Vets., Tau Beta Pi, Alpha Sigma Mu. Home: 10021 N Waterleaf Dr Mequon WI 53092 Office: Foley & Lardner Firstar Ctr 777 E Wisconsin Ave Milwaukee WI 53202

O'SHAUGHNESSY, JOSEPH A., restaurant company executive. Sr. exec. v.p. Friendly Ice Cream Corp., Wilbraham, Mass., 1957—. Office: Friendly Ice Cream Corp 1855 Boston Rd Wilbraham MA 01095-1098

O'SHEA, JOHN P., insurance executive; b. Poughkeepsie, N.Y., May 1, 1930; s. John P. and Mildred A. (Galbraith) O'S.; m. Nancy Ann Shaw; m. Michael, Patricia, Stephen, Sandra. BS, Fordham U., 1951. Various positions Marshall & Sterling Inc., Poughkeepsie, 1955-70, v.p. 1970-80, pres., 1980—; bd. dirs. Crabapple Ins. Co., vice chmn., 1992—; Bermuda, Riverside Bank, Poughkeepsie, 1987—, chmn. of bd., 1993—; chmn. bd. VBH Ins. Co., Barbados. Trustee Area Fund Dutchess County, Poughkeepsie, 1983-89, Marist Coll., 1994—, Mid-Hudson Med. Ctr., 1991—, Bardavon Opera House, 1990-94; chmn. bd. Vassar Bros. Hosp. and VGH Corp., Poughkeepsie, 1986-88l bd. dirs. Poughkeepsie Partnership, 1993—. Lt. USNR, 1952-55, Korea; comdr. 1955-76. Mem. Poughkeepsie Area C. of C. (chmn. 1982-83), Dutchess Golf and Country Club, Amrita Club, Rotary (pres. Poughkeepsie 1968-69). Avocation: golf. Office: 110 Main St Poughkeepsie NY 12601-3080

O'SHEA, LYNNE EDEEN, advertising executive, educator; b. Chgo. Oct. 18, 1945; d. Edward Fisk and Mildred (Lessner) O'S. B.A., B.J. in Polit. Sci. and Advt, U. Mo., 1968, M.A. in Communications and Mktg. Research, 1971; PhD in Consumer Cultures, Northwestern U., 1977; postgrad., Sch. Mgmt. and Strategic Studies, U. Calif., 1988. Tchr. U. Mo. Advt. Agy., Dallas, 1968-69; congl. asst. Washington, 1969-70; brand mgr. Procter & Gamble Co., Cin., 1971-73; v.p. Foote, Cone & Belding, Inc., Chgo., 1973-79; v.p. corp. communications Internat. Harvester Co., Chgo., 1979-82; dir. communications Arthur Andersen & Co., Chgo., 1983-86; v.p. strategic planning Campbell-Ewald, Detroit and Los Angeles, 1986; v.p. bus. devel. Gannett Co., Inc., Chgo., 1987-94; group strategic planning dir. DDB Needham Worldwide, Inc., Chgo., 1995—; prof. mktg. U. Chgo. Grad. Sch. Bus., 1979-80, Kellogg Grad. Sch. Mgmt., 1983-94; disting. vis. prof. Syracuse U., 1982—. Bd. dirs. Off-the-Street Club, Chgo., 1977-86; mem. adv. bd. U. Ill. Coll. Commerce, 1980—, Ctr. for Mature Industries, 1982—, Girl Scouts Am., 1985—, Chgo. Crime Commn., 1987—, Stephenson Rsch. Ctr., 1987—, DePaul U., 1989—, Roosevelt U., 1994—. Recipient numerous Eagle Fin. Advt. awards, Silver medalist Am. Advt. Fedn., 1989; named Advt. Woman of Yr. Chgo. Advt. Club, 1989; named Glass Ceiling Commn., 1992-95, Com. 21st Century, 1992—. Mem. Internat. Women's Forum (v.p. devel., exec. com., bd. dirs.), Chgo. Network, Women's Forum Chgo., Women's Forum Mich., Tarrytown Group, Social Venture Network, Execs. Club Chgo, Mid-Am. Club (bd. govs. 1990—). Office: DDB Needham Worldwide Inc 303 E Wacker Dr Chicago IL 60601-5282

O'SHEA, PATRICIA A., physician, educator; b. Syracuse, N.Y., June 14, 1944; d. John Daniel and Mildred (Olbeter) Allen; m. John S. O'Shea, July 5, 1969. BS summa cum laude, Le Moyne Coll., 1966; MD, Johns Hopkins U., 1970. Diplomate Am. Bd. Pathology, Am. Bd. Anatomic, Clin. and Pediat. Pathology. From intern to resident Duke U. Med. Ctr., Durham, N.C., 1970-74; from asst. to assoc. prof. pathology Brown U., Providence, 1974-90; assoc. prof. pathology Emory U., Atlanta, 1990—; mem. faculty Armed Forces Inst., Washington, 1989; short-course faculty U.S. and Can. Acad. Pathology, Augusta, Ga., 1992—. Contbr. articles to profl. jours. Fellow Am. Acad. Pedits., Coll. Am. Pathologists; mem. Soc. Pediat. Pathology (mem. coun.). Avocations: tennis, opera, baseball, travel. Office: Egleston Children's Hosp Emory U 1405 Clifton Rd NE Atlanta GA 30322

OSHEROFF, DOUGLAS DEAN, physicist, researcher; b. Aberdeen, Wash., Aug. 1, 1945; s. William and Bessie Anne (Ondov) O.; m. Phyllis S.K. Liu, Aug. 14, 1970. B.S. in Physics, Calif. Inst. Tech., 1967; M.S., Cornell U., 1969, Ph.D. in Physics, 1973. Mem. tech. staff Bell Labs., Murray Hill, N.Y., 1972-82, head solid state and low temperature physics research dept., 1982-87; prof. Stanford (Calif.) U., 1987—, J.G. Jackson and C.J. Wood prof. physics, 1992—; chair physics, 1993-96. Researcher on properties of matter near absolute zero of temperature; co-discoverer of superfluidity in liquid 3He, 1971, nuclear antiferromagnetic resonance in solid 3He, 1980. Co-recipient Simon Meml. prize Brit. Inst. Physics, 1976, Oliver E. Buckley Solid State Physics prize, 1981; John D. and Catherine T. MacArthur prize fellow, 1981. Fellow Am. Phys. Soc., Am. Acad. Arts and Scis., Nat. Acad. Scis. Office: Stanford U Dept Physics Stanford CA 94305-4060

OSHEROW, JACQUELINE SUE, poet, English language educator; b. Phila., Aug. 15, 1956; d. Aaron and Evelyn Hilda (Victor) O.; m. Saul Korewa, June 16, 1985; children: Magda, Dora, Mollie. AB Magna cum

laude, Radcliffe Coll., Harvard U., 1978; postgrad., Trinity Coll., Cambridge U., 1978-79; PhD in English and Am. Lit., Princeton U., 1990. Asst. prof. English U. Utah, Salt Lake City, 1989—. Author: (poetry) Looking for Angels in New York, 1988, Conversations with Survivors, 1994. Recipient Witter Bynner prize Am. Acad. and Inst. Arts and Letters, 1990, Lucille Medwick Meml. award, 1995; Ingram Merrill Found. grantee, 1990. Mem. Poetry Soc. Am. (John Masefield Meml. award 1993). Jewish. Home: 1148 E 100 S Salt Lake City UT 84102-1640 Office: U Utah Dept English 3500 LNCO Salt Lake City UT 84112

O'SHIELDS, RICHARD LEE, retired natural gas company executive; b. Ozark, Ark., Aug. 12, 1926; s. Fay and Anna (Johnson) O'S.; m. Shirley Isabelle Washington, Nov. 8, 1947; children: Sharon Isabelle O'Shields Boles, Carolyn Jean, Richard Lee Jr. B.S. in Mech. Engring, U. Okla., 1949; M.S. in Petroleum Engring. La. State U., 1951. Registered profl. engr., Kans., Tex. Instr. petroleum engring. La. State U., 1949-51; prodn. engr. Pure Oil Co., 1951-53; sales engr., chief engr., v.p. Salt Water Control, Inc., Ft. Worth, 1953-59; cons. engr. Ralph H. Cummins Co., Ft. Worth, 1959-60; with Anadarko Prodn. Co. and parent co. Panhandle Eastern Pipe Line Co., 1960-88; pres. Anadarko Prodn. Co., 1966-68; exec. v.p. Panhandle Eastern Pipe Line Co., 1968-70, pres., chief exec. officer, 1970-79, chmn., chief exec. officer, 1979-83, chmn., 1983-88, also bd. dirs., 1969-93; pres., CEO Trunkline Gas Co., 1970-79, chmn., CEO, 1979-83, chmn., 1983-88; bd. dirs. Daniel Industries, chmn., 1995—, Petrolite Corp. With USAAF, 1945. Mem. Am. Petroleum Inst., Soc. Petroleum Engrs., Ind. Natural Gas Assn. Am., Gas Research Inst., Ind. Petroleum Assn. Am., So. Gas Assn., Tau Beta Pi. Republican. Baptist. Lodge: Masons. Home: 3130 Camels Ridge Ln Colorado Springs CO 80904-1032

OSHITA, KOJI, advertising executive; b. Hiroshima, Japan, Jan. 11, 1928; s. Haruo and Katsumi O.; m. Yukie Kawasaki, May 23, 1958; children: Shotaro, Shintaro. BA in Law, Tokyo U., 1954; postgrad., Harvard U., 1967. Internat. media dir. Hakuhodo Inc., Tokyo, 1960, bd. dir., 1973—; exec. asst. McCann-Erickson Hakuhodo Inc., Tokyo, 1961, exec. v.p., 1969, rep. dir. and exec. v.p., 1973, rep. dir., pres. and chief exec. officer, 1981-91, chmn., rep. dir., 1991—; bd. dirs., exec. v.p. Worldwide/Asia Pacific McCann-Erickson Worldwide, N.Y., 1984-91, exec. v.p., dep. regional dir. 1991—. Bd. dir. Nice Heart Found. Orgn., Japan, 1982—; trustee Am. Sch. in Japan, 1984—; councillor Japan Fedn. Econ. Orgn., Keidanren, 1982—. Mem. Internat. Advt. Assn. (Global Commn. on the Media 1984—), Am. C. of C. in Japan (nominating com. 1988—), Japan Advt. Agys. Assn. (bd. dirs. 1989—), Am.-Japan Soc., Tokyo Am. Club, Rotary (Tokyo South, Japan). Avocations: golf, fishing, reading. Office: Shin Aoyama Bldg E, 1-1-1 Minami-Aoyama, Minato-ku Tokyo 107, Japan

O'SHONEY, GLENN, church administrator. Exec. dir. Mission Services of the Lutheran Church NO Synod International Ctr., St. Louis. Office: Luth Ch Mo Synod Internat Ctr 1333 S Kirkwood Rd Saint Louis MO 63122-7226

OSIAS, RICHARD ALLEN, international financier, investor, real estate investment executive, corporate investor; b. N.Y.C., Nov. 13, 1938; s. Harry L. and Leah (Schenk) O.; m. Judy Delaine Bradford, Oct. 26, 1984; children: Kimberly, Alexandra Elizabeth. Grad., Columbia U., 1963; postgrad., David Lipscomb U., 1988—. Founder, chmn., CEO Osias Enterprises, Inc., numerous locations, 1953—; mem. bus. cabinet David Lipscomb U.; bd. dirs. Am. 21. Prin. works include city devel., residential and apt. units, founder City North Lauderdale, Fla., co-founder City of Lauderhill, Fla., complete residential housing communities, shopping centers, country clubs, golf courses, hotel chains, comprehensive housing communities; contributed Greystone Raquet and Tennis Club to Nolensville, Tenn.; owner, operator Coolsprings Exec. Plz., landmark office bldg., Internat. Common Market Shopping Complex and other office bldgs., shopping ctrs. in mid-southern region; co-author: South Florida Uniform Building Code. Mem. North Lauderdale City Coun., 1967—, mayor, 1968, police and fire commr., 1967—; mem. Gold Cir., Atlanta Ballet; benefactor Atlanta Symphony Soc.; founder Boys Clubs Broward County, Tower coun. Pine Crest Prep. Sch., Ft. Lauderdale; mem. condr.'s cir. Nashville Symphony; mem. bd. advisors Williamson-Davidson County chpt. MADD, 1990; mem. univ. bus. adv. cabinet David Lipscomb U., Nashville, 1988—; bd. dirs. Rape, Nashville chpt. Cystic Fibrosis, Citizens Against Sexual Exploitation, N.Y.C., Queens County Assn. for Prevention Cruelty to Children, 1963—, Easter Seal Soc. Tenn.; bd. dirs. Tenn. Children's Home, mem. adv. coun., 1993—; hon. police commr., N.Y.C.; mem. Children's Abuse and Sexual Exploitation; mem. Ft. Lauderdale Better Bus. Bur., N.Y.C. Better Bus. Bur., Nashville Better Bus. Bur. Recipient Best Am. House award Am. Home mag., 1962, Westinghouse award, 1968, Cert. of Merit for outstanding achievement and contbn. to City of Atlanta by Mayor Andrew Young, 1982; named Builder of Yr., Sunshine State Info. Bur., Fla. and Sunshine State Sr. Citizen, Fla., 1967-70, Builder of Month, Builder/Arch. Mag., 1992; profiles on nat. and internat. media, including CBS TV and Fuji Network. Mem. Ft. Lauderdale BBB, N.Y. BBB, Nashville BBB, Offshore Power Boat Racing Assn., Fraternal Order Police Assn. (pres.), U.S. C. of C., Fla. C. of C., Margate C. of C., Ft. Lauderdale C. of C., Smithsonian Instn., Soc. Founders U. Miami, Tower Coun., Columns Soc. Pinecrest Prep. Sch. (founder), Nat. Assn. Home Builders, Bankers Club (Miami, Fla.), Bankers Top of First Club, Quarter Deck Club (Galveston, Tex.), Boca Raton (Fla.) Yacht and Country Club, Maunalua Bay Club (Honolulu), Tryall Golf and Country Club (Jamaica), Top of the Home Club, Svc. Plus Club (France), Ensworth Red Gables Soc., Cannes Island Yacht Club, Canary Islands Yacht Club, Venitian Bay Yacht Club, The Club Pelican Bay. Home: Club Le Ciel #1401 3991 Gulf Shore Blvd N Naples FL 33940 also: The Hillsborough 505 Almonte Ct Nashville TN 37215

OSIER, WILLIAM RICHARD, school administrator; b. Randolph, Vt., July 23, 1938; s. Seward E. and Corolyn (Wood) O.; m. Catherine Stone, June 19, 1976; children—Hannah, William. B.A., U. Md., 1961; M.A., St. John's Coll., 1972. Tchr. Rumsey Hall Sch., Washington, Conn., 1965-67; English tchr. Moses Brown Sch., Providence, 1967-69, Thacher Sch., Ojai, Calif., 1969-79; chmn. dept. English, Marin County Day Sch., Corte Madera, Calif., 1970-72; tchr. English, dir. students Dexter Sch., Brookline, Mass., 1972-78; headmaster Lower Sch., Cin. Country Day Sch., 1978-82; headmaster Highland Sch., Warrenton, Va., 1982—. Vestryman, Leeds Episcopal Ch., Markham, Va., 1984. Mem. Elem. Sch. Heads Assn. Republican. Episcopalian. Club: Prouts Neck Country (Maine), Fauquier, Old Dominion Hunt, Ashland Bassets (bd. dirs.). Avocations: running, tennis. Office: Highland Sch 597 Broadview Ave Warrenton VA 22186-2007

OSIMITZ, DENNIS VICTOR, lawyer; b. Racine, Wis., May 28, 1951; s. Victor and Julianna (Wiernasz) O.; m. Mary Carol Rindt, June 5, 1976; children: Jeffrey Allen, Kevin James. BA, U. Wis., 1973, JD, 1976. Bar: Wis. 1976, Ill. 1976. U.S. Dist. Ct. (no. dist.) Ill. 1976. Assoc. Sidley & Austin, Chgo., 1976-83, ptnr., 1983—. Mem. ABA, Ill. Bar Assn., Chgo. Bar Assn., Union League Club, Chgo. Club. Roman Catholic.

OSIPOW, SAMUEL HERMAN, psychology educator; b. Allentown, Pa., Apr. 18, 1934; s. Louis Morris and Tillie (Wolfe) O.; m. Sondra Beverly Feinstein, Aug. 26, 1956; children: Randall A., Jay I., Reva S., David S. B.A., Lafayette Coll., Easton, Pa., 1954; M.A., Columbia U., 1955; Ph.D., Syracuse U., 1959. Lectr. U. Wis., Madison, 1961; psychologist, asst. prof. Pa. State U., 1961-67; mem. faculty Ohio State U., Columbus, 1967—; prof. psychology Ohio State U., 1969—, chmn. dept., 1973-86; vis. prof. Tel-Aviv U., 1972, U. Md., 1980-81; vis. research assoc. Harvard U., 1965; cons. to govt. Author: Strategies in Counseling for Behavior Change, 1970, Theories of Career Development, 1983, Handbook of Vocational Psychology, 2 vols., 1983, A Survey of Counseling Methods, 1984; editor: Jour. Vocat. Behavior, 1970-75, Jour. Counseling Psychology, 1975-81, Applied and Preventative Psychology, 1993—. Served to 1st lt. U.S. Army, 1959-61. Mem. APA (bd. dirs. 1985-88), Nat. Register Health Svc. Providers in Psychology (bd. dirs. 1982-89, chmn. 1986-89). Home: 330 Eastmoor Blvd Columbus OH 43209-2022 Office: Ohio State U Psychology Dept Columbus OH 43210

OSIYOYE, ADEKUNLE, obstetrician/gynecologist, educator; b. Lagos, Nigeria, Jan. 5, 1951; came to U.S., 1972; s. Alfred and Grace (Apena) Oshiyoye; m. Toyin Osinowo Oshiyoye, Dec. 28, 1991; children: Adekunle

Jr., Adedayo Justice. Student, Howard U., 1972-73; BS, U. State of N.Y., 1974; postgrad., Columbia U., 1974-78; MD, Am. U., Montserrat, West Indies, 1979. Intern South Chgo. Community Hosp., 1980-81; intern dept. obstetrics-gynecology Cook County Hosp., Chgo., 1981-82, resident physician, 1982-84, chief resident physician dept. obstetrics-gynecology, 1984-85; assoc. adjunct dept. obstetrics-gynecology Chgo. Osteo. Coll. Medicine, 1986—; health physician, cons. physician City of Chgo. Dept. Health, 1989—; attending physician St. Bernard Hosp., Chgo., 1985—, Hyde Park Hosp., Chgo., 1986—, Mercy Hosp., Chgo., 1987—, Roseland Hosp., Chgo., 1985—, Columbus Hosp., Chgo., 1985—, Jackson Park Hosp., Chgo., 1985—; coord. emergency rm. Cook County Hosp., 1983-85. Med. editor African Connections, 1990—; med. columnist Newsbreed Mag., 1990—; founding mem. Ob-Gyn Video Jour. Am. Organizer Harold Washington Coalition, Chgo., 1983-87; operation mem. Operation P.U.S.H., Chgo., 1987—; active Chgo. Urban League, 1988—, Cook County Dem. Party, 1988—; mem. Mayor's Commn. on Human Rels., Chgo., 1990—, State of Ill. Inaugaural Com., 1991. Shell scholar, 1965-69; recipient Fed. Govt. scholarship award, 1972, Howard Univ. scholarship award, 1973, Fed. Govt. Nigeria grad. med. scholarship award, 1975-79, Cerebral Palsy rsch. award, 1977, Ob-gyn. Video Jour. award, 1989, Role Model award Chgo. Police Dept., 1991, 92, Chgo. Bd. Edn., 1991, Chgo. 100 Black Men, 1991, Gov.'s Recognition award, 1992; named one of Best Dressed Men in Chgo. Chgo. Defender, 1990, 91. Fellow Am. Coll. Internat. Physicians, Am. Coll. Obstetricians & Gynecologists; mem. AMA (physician recognition award 1986), Am. Coll. Glegal Medicine (edn. com.), Am. Soc. Law Medicine, Am. Pub. Heart Assn., Nat. Med. Assn., Ill. Med. Soc., Chgo. Med. Assn., Chgo. Gynecol. Soc., Cook County Physician Assn., Nigerian Am. Forum (chmn. health com., chmn. election com.), Cook County Hosp. Surg. Alumni Assn., Howard U. Alumni Assn. (regent, chmn. scholarship com. Chgo. chpt.), Eureka Lodge (investigating com.), Masons, Shriners, Order of Eastern Star, Alpha Phi Alpha (life mem., mem. Labor Day com., dir. ednl. programs Xi Lambda chpt. 1990—, co-chmn. courtesy Black & Gold com. 1989, 90, Recognition award 1991), Pan Hellenic Action Coun. (chmn. pub. rels. com.), Ill. Maternal and Child Health Coalition, Beta Kappa Chi. Apostolic. Avocations: ping pong, fishing, golf, basketball, swimming. Home: PO Box 15187 Lansing MI 48901-5187 Office: Dept Health 37 W 47th St Chicago IL 60609-4657

OSKEY, D. BETH, banker; b. Red Wing, Minn., Dec. 23, 1921; d. Alvin E. and Effie D. (Thompson) Feldman; m. Warren B. Oskey, Sept. 27, 1941; children: Jo Cheryl, Warren A., Peter (dec.), Jeffery L.; student U. Wis., River Falls, 1939-41; B.A., Met. State U. Minn., 1975; grad. degree in banking, U. Wis., 1973, M in banking, 1977; student in interior decorating LaSalle Extension U., Chgo., 1970. Officer Hiawatha Nat. Bank, Hager City, Wis., 1959-91, cashier, 1978-79, pres., 1979, chmn. bd., 1984—, exec. v.p., dir., sec. bd. dirs, 1959—, sec., mem. discount com.; with First Nat. Bank of Glenwood, Glenwood City, Wis., 1965—, pres., exec. v.p., 1979—, dir., sec. bd., 1965—, chmn. bd., 1984—, sec., mem. discount com.; ret., 1991; speaker on women in banking. Mem. banking com. Vo-Tech Sch., Red Wing; former officer civic orgns.; mem. Leisurettes, L.W. Barbershop Belles. Mem. AAUW, Ind. Bankers Am., Wis. Bankers Assn., Am. Bankers Assn., Gen. Fedn. Women's Clubs Internat., Inc. (bd. dirs., pres. 1988-90), Minn. Fedn. Women's Clubs (v.p. 1983-85, pres. dist. III 1988-90, pres. elect 1986-88, pres. 1988-90; Leisure World (in charge of comm., mem. mixed chorus), Mesa, Ariz. (pres. Wis. Club, 1991-92). Republican. Lutheran. Home: 1022 Hallstrom Dr Red Wing MN 55066-3819 also: 1561 Leisure World Mesa AZ 85206 Office: Hiawatha Nat Bank Hager City WI 54014

OSKI, FRANK ARAM, physician, educator; b. Phila., June 17, 1932; s. Aram P. and Sarah (Koshgerian) O.; m. Barbara Fassett, June 22, 1957; children: Jonathan, Jane, Jessica. BA, Swarthmore Coll., 1954; MD, U. Pa., 1958; DSc (hon.), SUNY, 1991. Diplomate Am. Bd. Pediatrics. Intern Hosp. U. Pa., 1958-59, resident, 1959-61; practice medicine specializing in pediatrics Phila., 1962-72; mem. faculty Sch. Medicine, U. Pa., 1963-72, asso. prof. pediatrics, 1968-72; prof. pediatrics, chmn. dept. Upstate Med. Center, SUNY-Syracuse, 1972-85; chmn. dept. pediatrics Johns Hopkins U. Sch. Medicine, Balt., 1985—; former mem. staff State Univ. Hosp., Crouse-Irving Meml. Hosp., Syracuse; physician-in-chief Children's Ctr., Johns Hopkins Hosp., 1985—. Author: Hematologic Problems of the Newborn, 3d edit., 1982, Hematology of Infancy and Childhood, 3d edit., 1987, The Whole Pediatrician Catalog, Vol. 1, 1977, Vol. 2, 1979, Vol. 3, 1981, Don't Drink Your Milk, 1977, Core Textbook of Pediatrics, 1978, 2d edit., 1982, Principles and Practice of Pediatrics, 1994; editor Year Book of Pediatrics, 1979-81, Contemporary Pediatrics, 1984—, Current Opinion in Pediatrics, 1992—; also articles. Recipient E. Mead-Johnson award Am. Acad. Pediatrics, 1972, St. Geme award, 1990, Disting. Grad. award. U. Pa. Sch. Medicine, 1990; named Scientist of Yr., Am. Students Assn., 1972. Mem. Soc. Pediatric Rsch. (pres. 1977-78), Am. Pediatric Soc., Am. Soc. Clin. Investigation, Am. Soc. Clin. Nutrition, Red Cell Club, Am. Soc. Hematology-Oncology (Disting. Career award 1993), Assn. Am. Med. Sch. Pediatric Dept. Chairmen (pres. 1992-93). Home: 1610 Park Ave Baltimore MD 21217-4305 Office: Johns Hopkins Hosp Baltimore MD 21205

OSKIN, DAVID WILLIAM, businesss executive; b. Clairton, Pa., Aug. 30, 1942; s. David L. and M. Catherine (Nicodemus) O.; m. JoEllen Ross, Sept. 5, 1964; 1 child, David W., Jr. B.A., Pa. Mil. Coll., 1964. Dir. employee relations Davol, Inc., Cranston, R.I., 1975-76, dir. U.K. ops., 1976-77, v.p. ops., 1977-79; dir. compensation and benefits Internat. Paper, Purchase, N.Y., 1979-81, v.p. human resources, 1981-88, sr. v.p., 1988-90; sr. v.p. distribution Timber and Wood, 1990—. Mem. Fgn. Policy Com., N.Y.C., 1984-85; chmn. internat. adv. bd. U. Ill.-Chgo., 1984—; mem. Bus. Roundt-able-Employee Relations Com., Washington, 1984-90; trustee Nat. 4-H, 1991—; vice chmn. bd. dirs. Nat. Forest Products Assn., 1990—. Served to capt. U.S. Army, 1964-65, Vietnam. Republican. Methodist. Avocations: golf, tennis. Home: 2 Manhattanville Rd Purchase NY 10577-2118

OSKOLKOFF, GRASSIM, Indian tribal chief; b. Ninilchik, Alaska, Oct. 14, 1926; s. Michael and Zoya (Darien) O.; m. Marine Emma Encelewski, Oct. 30, 1952; children: Debra, Maria, Bruce, Gary, Becky. Grad. high sch., Ninilchik. With Alaska R.R., Anchorage; commnl. fisherman, Ninilchik; pres., dir. Ninilchik Native Assn., Inc., 1971-82; chief, pres. Ninilchik Traditional Coun., 1982—; former rep. Alaska Fedn. Natives, Anchorage; rep. Alaska Inter-Tribal Coun., Anchorage, Cook Inlet Treaty Tribes, Alaska; mem. Alaska Sea Otter Common., Fairbanks. Bd. dirs. Russian Orthodox Ch., Ninilchik; environ. adv. Promotion of Peace Among People and Nations. With inf. AUS, WWII, PTO. Avocations: fishing, hunting. Office: Ninilchik Traditional Coun PO Box 39070 Ninilchik AK 99639-0070

OSLER, DOROTHY K., state legislator; b. Dayton, Ohio, Aug. 19, 1923; d. Carl M. and Pearl A. (Tobias) Karstaedt; BS cum laude in Bus. Adminstrn., Miami U., Oxford, Ohio, 1945; m. David K. Osler, Oct. 26, 1946; children: Scott C., David D. Mem. Conn. Ho. of Reps., 1973-92. Mem. Greenwich (Conn.) Rep. Town Meeting, 1968—, Eastern Greenwich Women's Rep. Club, 1970—; sec. Conn. Student Loan Found., 1973-83, v.p., 1983-84; mem. Spl. Edn. Cost Commn., 1976-77, Sch. Fin. Adv. Panel, 1977-78, Edn. Equity Study Com., 1980-81, Commn. on Goals for U. Conn. Health Ctr., 1975-76; bd. dirs. ARC, 1975. Mem. Nat. Order Women Legislators (sec. 1987-89), Conn. Order of Women Legislators (sec. 1983-84, pres. 1985-86), LWV (pres. Greenwich chpt. 1965-67, sec. Conn. chpt. 1967-72), AAUW (dir. 1971-73), Mortar Board, Phi Beta Kappa, Alpha Omicron Pi. Republican. Christian Scientist. Bi-weekly columnist local newspaper, 1973-83.

OSLER, GORDON PETER, retired utility company executive; b. Winnipeg, Man., Can., June 19, 1922; s. Hugh Farquarson and Kathleen (Harty) O.; m. Nancy A. Riley, Aug. 20, 1948; children: Sanford L., Susan Osler Matthews, Gillian Osler Fortier. Student, Queen's U., Kingston, Ont., Can., 1940-41. Pres. Osler, Hammond & Nanton Ltd., Winnipeg, 1952-64; UNAS Investments Ltd., Toronto, Ont., Can., 1964-72; chmn. Slater Steel Industries, Hamilton, Ont., Can., 1972-86, N.Am. Life Assurance Co., Toronto, 1986-95; chmn. TransCan. Pipelines, Toronto, 1983-89, ret., 1993; bd. dirs. Co-Steel Inc., Toronto. Lt. Can. Army, 1942-45, ETO. Mem. Toronto Club, York Club (Toronto), Everglades Club (Palm Beach, Fla.). Avocation: golf. Home: 17 Lamport Ave, Toronto, ON Canada M4W 1S7 Office: TransCan Pipelines, 55 Yonge St 8th Flr, Toronto, ON Canada M5E 1J4

OSLER, HOWARD LLOYD, controller; b. Camden, N.J., Nov. 24, 1927; s. Howard B. and Miriam (Locke) O.; m. Barbara C. Skufca, 1987; children by previous marriage: Carol, Peter, Andrew, Bruce. B.A., Antioch Coll., 1951. CPA, D.C. Pub. acct. Peat, Marwick Mitchell & Co., Boston, 1949-55; staff asst. to corp. contr. Gillette Co., Boston, 1957-59; gen. mgr. Panamanian subs. Gillette Co., 1959-61; asst. to pres. Gillette Co. Argentine subs., 1961-63; asst. to corp. contr. Gillette Co., Boston, 1963-65; contr. mil. Far East div. Gillette Co., 1965-67; contr. U.S. div. Foxboro Co., Mass., 1967-68; corp. contr. Foxboro Co., 1968-87, sec., clk., 1976-86, v.p., contr., 1981-87, ret., 1987. Trustee Gilman Cemeteries, 1988—, Trust Funds, 1990-91, 94—; commr. Gilmanton Corner Precinct, 1989—; mem. Gilmanton Budget Com., 1990—, Sch. Bldg. Com., 1988, 90, Zoning Bd. Adjustment, 1990-91; mem. Bd. Selectmen, 1991-94. With USAAF, 1945-46. Home: PO Box 413 Gilmanton NH 03237-0413

OSLIN, GEORGE POER, writer, retired telegraph official; b. West Point, Ga., Aug. 5, 1899; s. Reuben Jefferson and Mary (Poer) O.; m. Louise Love, Jan. 31, 1922; children: Louise, Jeanne, Catherine; m. Susanna Meigs, Dec. 22, 1956. Student, Duke U., 1915-19; AB, Mercer U., 1920; postgrad. in journalism, Columbia U., 1921. Reporter Macon (Ga.) Daily Telegraph, 1920-21; fin., real estate and auto editor Newark (N.J.) Ledger, 1922; reporter, feature writer Newark Evening News, 1922-29; dir. pub. rels. Western Union, 1929-64. Author: Talking Wires, 1942, The Story of Telecommunications, 1993, also monograph; contbr. chpts. and sects. to books, artles to profl. jours. and mags.; creator singing telegram.

OSLIN, K. T. (KAY TOINETTE OSLIN), country singer; b. Crossett, Ark.. Student, Lon Morris Jr. Coll. Sang in folk trio; professional singing debut at Purple Onion, 1962; mem. road co. Hello, Dolly, also N.Y.C.; mem. cast Promise, Promises, revival West Side Story; songwriter; songs include Do Ya?, Round the Clock Lovin, Where Is A Woman To Go, Come Next Monday, Younger Men, others; albums: 80's Ladies (Grammy 1987, Country-Best Vocal Perfomance, Female), Hold Me (Grammy 1988, Country-Best Song, Country-Best Vocal Performance, Female), This Woman, 1988, Love in a Small Town, 1990, Songs From An Aging Sex Bomb; K.T. Oslin's Greatest Hits, 1993, New Way Home, 1993. Recipient Top Female Vocalist award Acad. Country Music, 1988. Office: Moress Nanas Shea c/o Stan Moress 1209 16th Ave S Nashville TN 37212-2901*

OSMAN, EDITH GABRIELLA, lawyer; b. N.Y.C., Mar. 18, 1949; d. Arthur Abraham and Judith (Goldman) Udem; children: Jacqueline, Daniel. BA in Spanish, SUNY, Stony Brook, 1970; JD cum laude, U. Miami, 1983. Bar: Fla. 1983, U.S. Dist. Ct. (so. dist.) Fla. 1984, U.S. Dist. Ct. (mid. dist.) Fla. 1988, U.S. Ct. Appeals (11th cir.) 1985, U.S. Supreme Ct. 1987, U.S. Ct. Mil. Appeals 1990. Assoc. Kimbrell & Hamann, P.A., Miami, 1984-90, Dunn & Lodish, P.A., Miami, 1990-93; pvt. practice in law Miami, 1993—; spkr. in field. Mem. adv. com. for Implementation of the Victor Posner Judgement to Aid the Homeless, 1986-89; spkr. small firm and solo practitioner Town Hall Meetings, 1993; spkr. Bridge the Gap Seminar, Comml. Litigation, 1994. Mem. ABA (product liability com., corp. counsel com.), Fla. Bar Assn. (budget com. 1989-92, voluntary bar liaison com. 1989-90, spl. com. on formation of All-Bar Conf. 1988-89, chmn. mid-yr. conv. 1989, mem. long range planning com. 1988-90, bd. govs. 1991—, spl. commn. on delivery of legal svcs. to the indigent 1990-92, chair program evaluation com. bd. govs., mem. exec. com. 1992-93, rules & bylaws com. 1993-94, dipcilnary rev. com. 1994—, investment com., 1994—, vice chair rules com., 1994—), Dade County Bar Assn. (fed. ct. rules com. 1985-86, chmn. program com. 1988-89, 90-91, exec. com. 1987-88), Fla. Assn. of Bar Assn. Pres.'s (bd. dirs. 1989-90, v.p. 1990-91, pres. 1991-92), Fla. Assn. Women Lawyers (bd. dirs. 1985-86, v.p. Dade County chpt. 1986-87, pres. 1987-88, pres-elect Fla. chpt. 1988-89, pres. 1989-90), Nat. Coun. of Women's Bar Assn. (dir. nat. conf. 1990-91), Dade County Trial Lawyers Assn. Office: Edith G Osman PA Internat Place 100 SE 2nd St Ste 3920 Miami FL 33131-2148

OSMAN, STEPHEN EUGENE, historic site administrator; b. Berkeley, Calif., Aug. 8, 1949; s. Eugene Lee and June Elizabeth (Claus) O.; m. Wendy Kay Holmberg, June 21, 1975; children: Rachel Ann, Austin Thomas, Laurel Suzanne. BA in History and Edn. cum laude, St. Olaf Coll., 1971. Program mgr. Historic Ft. Snelling, St. Paul, 1971-85, dir., 1985—; program mgr. Legis. Commn. on Minn. Resources, 1985; mem. Coun. on Am.'s Mil. Past, Midwest Open Air Mus. Coord. Coun.; lectr. in field. Author: The Soldiers Handbook, 1825, 1972; contbr. articles to profl. jours. Fellow Co. Mil. Historians; mem. Assn. Living History Farms and Agrl. Mus., Living History Soc. Minn. Republican. Lutheran. Avocations: 19th Century military uniforms and equipment, historic crafts. Office: Minn Hist Soc Ft Snelling History Ctr Saint Paul MN 55111

OSMER, PATRICK STEWART, astronomer; b. Jamestown, N.Y., Dec. 17, 1943; s. William Proudfit Jr. and Jane Briggs (Stewart) O.; m. Anita Amanda Bauza, Jan. 5, 1973; children—Katherine, Charlotte. B.S., Case Inst. Tech., 1965; Ph.D., Calif. Inst. Tech., 1970. Research assoc. Cerro Tololo Inter-Am. Obs., La Serena, Chile, 1969-70, asst. astronomer, 1970-73, assoc. astronomer, 1973-76, astronomer, 1977-85, dir., 1981-85; astronomer Kitt Peak Nat. Obs., 1986-93; dep. dir. Nat. Optical Astronomy Observatories, 1988-93; scientist 8-M telescope project Nat. Optical Astronomy Observatories, 1988-92, interim gemini project scientist, 1991-92; prof., chmn. astronomy dept. Ohio State U., 1993—. Contbr. articles to profl. jours. Chmn. telescope allocation com. Hubble Space Telescope, 1991. Fellow Woodrow Wilson Found., 1965, NSF, 1965-67. Mem. Am. Astron. Soc. (councillor 1985-88), Internat. Astron. Union, Astron. Soc. of Pacific, Tau Beta Pi. Avocations: running; tennis. Office: Ohio State U Dept Astronomy 174 W 18th Ave Columbus OH 43210-1106

OSMER-MCQUADE, MARGARET, business executive, broadcast journalist; b. N.Y.C.; d. Herbert Bernard and Margaret Normann (Brunjes) O.; m. Lawrence Carroll McQuade, Mar. 15, 1980; 1 son, Andrew. B.A., Cornell U., 1960. Assoc. producer UN Bur., CBS News, N.Y.C., 1962-69; producer 60 Minutes, N.Y.C., 1969-72; reporter, producer Bill Moyer's Jour., Pub. Broadcasting Service, N.Y.C., 1972-73, Reasoner Report, ABC News, N.Y.C., 1973-75; corr., anchor person Good Morning Am., ABC Morning News, Washington, 1975-77; corr. ABC TV News, Washington, 1977-79; v.p., dir. programs Council on Fgn. Relations, 1979-93; pres., CEO Qualitas Internat., N.Y.C., 1994—; dir. Dime Savs. Bank, 1980—; cons. pub. broadcasting; mem. program com. Ditchley Found. Producer, reporter: TV news shows Come Fly A Kite (Nat. Press Photographer's award 1974), Kissinger, 1970, No Tears for Rachel, 1972, Calder: Master of Mobiles, 1975; moderator, producer World in Focus, publ. TV series for Coun. Fgn. Relations/ Sta. WNYC, PBS, Worldnet, 1988-93. Mem. U.S. delegation World Conf. on Cambodian Refugees, Geneva, 1980; mem. Def. Adv. Com. on Women in the Service, 1978-82; trustee Cornell U.; mem. bd. overseers Cornell U. Med. Coll., pres.'s coun. Cornell Women; mem. program com. The Ritchley Found., 1994—, task force N.Y. Sch. Vols., 1994—; vol. Nat. Svc. Learning, 1994—. Recipient Peabody award Staff of 60 Minutes, 1970. Mem. NATAS, Coun. Fgn. Relations, program comm. The Mitching Found., Task Force N.Y. Sch. Vol., Nat. Press Club, Mid. Atlantic Club., vol. Nat. Svc. Learning. Club: Cosmopolitan, Century.

OSMOND, DENNIS GORDON, medical educator, researcher; b. N.Y.C., Jan. 31, 1930; s. Ernest Gordon and Marjorie Bertha (Milton) O.; m. Anne Welsh, July 30, 1955; children: Roger Gordon, Martin Henry, David Richard. B.Sc. with first class honors, U. Bristol, Eng., 1951, M.B., Ch.B., 1954, D.Sc., 1975. House surgeon Royal Gwent Hosp., Newport, Eng., 1954-55; house physician Bristol Royal Infirmary, 1955; demonstrator, lectr. anatomy U. Bristol, 1957-60, 61-64; instr. anatomy U. Wash., Seattle, 1960-61; assoc. prof. anatomy McGill U., Montreal, Que., Can., 1965-67; prof. McGill U., 1967-74, Robert Reford prof. anatomy, 1974—, chmn. dept. anatomy and cell biology, 1985-95; vis. scientist Walter and Eliza Hall Inst. Med. Research, Melbourne, Australia, 1972-73; hon. sr. research fellow U. Birmingham, Eng., 1979; vis. scientist Basel Inst. Immunology, Switzerland, 1980. Contbr. numerous articles to profl. jours. Served with Royal Army Med. Corps, 1955-57. Fellow Royal Soc. Can.; mem. Am. Assn. Anatomists, Can. Assn. Anatomists, Anat. Soc. Gt. Britain and Ireland, Am., Can. assns. for immunology, Am. Assn. Immunology, Internat. Soc. for Exptl. Hematology. Home: 116 rue de Touraine, St Lambert, PQ

Canada J4S 1H4 Office: Dept Anatomy McGill Univ, 3640 University St, Montreal, PQ Canada H3A 2B2

OSMOND, GORDON CONDIE, playwright; b. Washington, Nov. 9, 1934; s. Harvard Reginald and Melba (Condie) O. A.B., Columbia U., 1956, J.D., 1959. Bar: N.Y. 1959. Assoc. firm Donovan Leisure Newton & Irvine, N.Y.C., 1969-94, ptnr., 1969—. Author: (plays) A Matter of Tone, Fertile Deception, Full House, Lunch in the Afternoon, Cut, The Scales.

OSNES, LARRY G., academic administrator; b. Scottsbluff, Nebr., Oct. 30, 1941; s. Earl E. and Rose (DeRock) O.; m. Susan C.; 1 child, Justin. BA in History, Anderson Coll., 1963; MA in History, Wayne State Coll., 1965; PhD in History, U. Cin., 1970. Asst. prof. history and govt. U. Cin., 1967-69; dir. Am. studies Anderson (Ind.) Coll., 1970-75, chmn. dept. history, 1975-76, dean acadmeic devel., 1975-78, asst. corp. sec., dean academic devel. and pub. affairs, 1978-83; pres. Minn. Pvt. Coll. Coun., St. Paul, 1983-88, Hamline U., St. Paul, 1988—. Mem. Assoc. Colls. Twin Cities (chmn. 1988-90), Mpls. Club, St. Paul Athletic Club. Office: Hamline Univ 1536 Hewitt Ave Saint Paul MN 55104-1284

OSNOS, DAVID MARVIN, lawyer; b. Detroit, Jan. 10, 1932; s. Max and Florence (Pollock) O.; m. Glenna DeWitt, Aug. 10, 1956; children: Matthew, Alison. A.B. summa cum laude, Harvard U., 1953, J.D. cum laude. 1956. Bar: D.C. 1956. Assoc. Arent, Fox, Kintner, Plotkin & Kahn, Washington, 1956-61, ptnr., 1962—, chmn. exec. com., 1978—; bd. dirs. EastGroup Properties, Jackson, Miss., VSE Corp., Alexandria, Va., Washington Real Estate Investment Trust, Kensington, Md., Washington Bullets Basketball Club, Landover, Md., Washington Capitals Hockey Club, Landover. Trustee Mt. St. Mary's Coll., Emmitsburg, Md., 1981-90; bd. dirs. Greater Washington Jewish Community Found., Rockville, Md., Jewish Community Ctr. Greater Washington, 1964-75. Avocations: tennis, music, enology. Office: Arent Fox Kintner 1050 Connecticut Ave NW Washington DC 20036-5339

OSNOS, GILBERT CHARLES, management consultant; b. Detroit, Nov. 23, 1929; s. Herman Sol and Helen (Yudkoff) O.; m. Margaret N. Paysner, Aug. 18, 1957; children: Steven, Elisabeth. BA, U. Mich., 1951; MBA, Harvard U., 1953. Dept. mgr. Sams, Inc., Detroit, 1956-57, asst. buyer, 1957-58, dir. store ops., 1958, buyer, 1958-59, mdse. buyer, 1959-62; buyer Topps Divsn. Interstate Dept. Stores, N.Y.C., 1962-65; mdse. mgr. Arlans Dept. Stores, N.Y.C., 1965-68; pres. Nazareth Mills divsn. Kayser Roth, N.Y.C., 1968-73, Rosenau Bros., Phila., 1973-75, Warnaco Men's Sport-swear, 1975-78; with Grisanti and Galef, 1979-81, ptnr., 1981—; pres. Grisanti, Galef & Osnos, N.Y.C., 1983—; bd. dirs. Mrs. Field's; bd. dirs. Turnaround Mgmt. Assn., chmn., 1990-91. Lt. j.g. USNR, 1953-56. Mem. Am. Apparel Assn. (consumer affairs com.), Am. Bankruptcy Inst., Bus. Execs. for Nat. Security, Harvard Club, Holloween Yacht Club. Avocations: sailing, opera, classical music, photography, reading. Office: Osnos & Company Inc 230 Park Ave Ste C-301 New York NY 10169

OSNOS, PETER LIONEL WINSTON, publishing executive; b. Bombay, India, Oct. 13, 1943; s. Joseph Lionel and Marta (Bychowski) O.; m. Susan R. Sherer, Aug. 18, 1973; children: Katherine Mason, Evan L.R. Ba, Brandeis U., Waltham, Mass., 1964; MS in Journalism with honors, Columbia U., 1965. Editorial asst. I.F. Stone's Weekly, Washington, 1964-65; corr., editor The Washington Post, 1966-84; v.p, assoc. pub. Random House Trade Books and pub. Times Books, Random House, Inc., N.Y.C., 1984—. Contbr. articles to profl. publs. Bd. dirs. Human Rights Watch; vice chmn. Free Expression Project. Fellow NEH, 1973-74. Mem. Assn. Am. Pubs. (chmn. gen. pub. div.), Coun. on Fgn. Rels., Century Club. Office: Random House 201 E 50th St New York NY 10022-7703

OSRIN, RAYMOND HAROLD, retired political cartoonist; b. Bklyn., Oct. 5, 1928; s. Elkan and Amelia (Boll) O.; divorced 1968; children: Caren, Glenn Elliot; m. Stephanie Hearshen, Aug. 23, 1981; stepchildren: Calanit, Orli. Student, Art Students League, 1945-47. Free-lance cartoonist, comic book illustrator, comic strip ghost artist and TV animator, W.R. Smith Inc., Pitts., 1957-58, staff artist, Pitts. Press, 1958-63, Cleve. Plain Dealer, 1963-66, polit. cartoonist, 1966-93. Recipient Freedom award, 1966, 67, Nat. Headliners award, 1970, 3d pl. award Internat. Salon de Cartoon, Montreal, Que., Can., 1975, award for excellence in journalism Press Club Cleve., 1978, 82, Disting. Service award Sigma Delta Chi, 1983. Excellence in Journalism 1st pl. award Cleve. Press Club, 1991; inducted into Cleve. Press Club Hall of Fame, 1986.

OSSERMAN, ROBERT, mathematician, educator; b. N.Y.C., Dec. 19, 1926; s. Herman Aaron and Charlotte (Adler) O.; m. Maria Anderson, June 15, 1952; 1 son, Paul; m. Janet Adelman, July 21, 1976; children—Brian, Stephen. B.A., NYU, 1946; postgrad., U. Zurich, U. Paris; M.A., Harvard U., 1948, Ph.D., 1955. Teaching fellow Harvard U., 1949-52, vis. lectr., research assoc., 1961-62; instr. U. Colo., 1952-53; mem. faculty Stanford U., 1955—, prof. math., 1966—, chmn. dept. math., 1973-79, Mellon Prof. Interdisciplinary Studies, 1987-90; dep. dir. Math. Scis. Rsch. Inst., Berkeley, Calif., 1990—; mem. NYU Inst. Math. Scis., 1957-58, Math. Scis. Rsch. Inst., Berkeley, 1983-84, head math. br. Office Naval Rsch., 1960-61; researcher and author publs. on differential geometry, complex variables, differential equations, especially minimal surfaces, Laplace operator, isoperimetric inequalities, ergodic theory. Author: Two-Dimensional Calculus, 1968, A Survey of Minimal Surfaces, 1969, 2d edit., 1986, Poetry of the Universe, 1995. Fulbright lectr. U. Paris, 1965-66; Guggenheim fellow, 1976-77; vis. fellow U. Warwick, Imperial Coll., U. London. Fellow AAAS; mem. Am. Math. Soc., Math. Assn. Am. Office: Math Scis Rsch Inst Berkeley CA 94720

OSSOFF, ROBERT HENRY, otolaryngological surgeon; b. Beverly, Mass., Mar. 25, 1947; s. Michael Max and Eve Joan (Kladky) O.; m. Lynn Spilman, 1984; 1 child, Leslin; 1 child by previous marriage, Jacob. BA, Bowdoin Coll., 1969; DMD, Tufts U., 1973, MD, 1975; MS in Otolaryngology, Northwestern U., 1981. Intern Northwestern Meml. Hosp., Chgo., 1975-76; resident in otolaryngology Northwestern Med. Sch., Chgo., 1976-80, NIH Rsch. fellow dept. otolaryngology, 1977-78, Am. Cancer Soc. clin. fellow, 1980-81, jr. faculty clin. fellow, 1981-84; pvt. practice medicine specializing in head and neck surgery, laryngology and care of the profl. voice, Chgo., 1975-86, Nashville, 1986—; chmn. dept. otolaryngology Vanderbilt U. Hosp., Nashville, 1986—, med. dir. Vanderbilt Voice Ctr., 1991—; mem. staff Children's Meml. Hosp., Chgo., 1980-81, Nashville VA Hosp., 1986—; chmn. div. otolaryngology Evanston (Ill.) Hosp. 1983-86; chief div. otolaryngology VA Lakeside Hosp., Chgo., 1982-86; mem. staff Northwestern Meml. Hosp., Chgo., 1981-86, Children's Meml. Hosp., Chgo., 1981-84; asst. prof. otolaryngology Vanderbilt U. Sch. Medicine, 1986—; assoc. dir. Vanderbilt Free-Electron Laser Ctr. Med. and Materials Rsch., 1992—. Trustee Midwest Biolaser Inst., Chgo., 1981-86; bd. dirs. Laser Inst. Am., 1984-90, Am. Bd. Otolaryngology, 1995. Recipient Lederer-Pierce award Chgo. Laryngol. and Otol. Soc., 1978. Fellow ACS, Am. Coll. Chest Physicians; mem. AMA, Am. Acad. Oral Medicine, Am. Acad. Oral Pathology, Am. Acad. Otolaryngology-Head and Neck Surgery (chmn. laser surgery com. 1983-89, chmn. self instl. package com. 1990—, Cert. of Honor 1984, bd. dirs. 1992-95), Am. Soc. Laser Medicine and Surgery (bd. dirs. 1985-88, pres.-elect 1988-89, pres. 1989-90, recipient William B. Mark award 1992), Soc. Head and Neck Surgeons, Am. Soc. Head and Neck Surgery (sec. 1991-94), Am. Broncho-esophagological Assn. (treas. 1980-84, pres.-elect 1994-95, pres. 1995—), Soc. Ear, Nose and Throat Advances in Children, The Triological Soc., Am. Laryngol. Assn., Cartesian Soc. Mem. editl. rev. bd. Otolaryngology-Head and Neck Surgery, 1988—; sr. editor Lasers in Surgery and Medicine, 1987-94, editor in chief-elect, 1994—, editor in chief 1995—; co-editor Complications in Head and Neck Surgery W.B. Saunders Co., 1993; mem. editl. bd. Jour. of Voice, 1987—, The Laryngoscope, 1988—, Operative Techniques in Otolaryngology-Head and Neck Surgery, 1989—, Jour. of Laser Applications, 1989—; contbr. chpts. to books, articles to profl. jours. Office: Vanderbilt U Med Ctr Dept Otolaryngology S-2100 Med Ctr N Nashville TN 37232-2559

OSTAR, ALLAN WILLIAM, higher education consultant; b. East Orange, N.J., Sept. 4, 1924; s. William and Rose (Mirmow) O.; m. Roberta Hutchison, Sept. 10, 1949; children: Karen, Rebecca, John. Cert. engring., U. Denver, 1943; B.A., Pa. State U., 1948; postgrad., U. Wis., 1949-55; LL.D., U. No. Colo., 1968, Eastern Ky. U., 1972, Whittier Coll., 1973; L.H.D., U. Maine, 1975; D.Letters, Central Mich. U., 1975; D.P.S., Bowling Green State U., 1975, R.I. Coll., 1983; D.Higher Edn., Morehead State U., 1977; L.H.D., Appalachian State U., 1977, No. Mich. U., 1978, Dickinson State Coll., N.D., 1979, Towson State U., 1980, Salem State Coll., 1980, Mont. Coll. Mineral Sci. and Tech., 1983, Ball State U., 1984; LL.D., U. Alaska, 1978, Ill. State U., 1983, Western Mich. U., 1984; D. Polit. Sci., Kyung Hee U., Korea, 1984; L.H.D., Fitchburg State Coll., 1986, Bridgwater State Coll., 1988, No. State Coll., 1988, Harris-Stowe State Coll., 1986; LLD, Edinboro U. Pa., 1987, Loch Haven U., Pa., 1989; LHD, No. Ariz. U., 1990, Shepherd (W.Va.) Coll., 1992, SUNY, 1993. Dir. nat. pub. relations U.S. Nat. Student Assn., 1948-49; exec. asst. Commonwealth Fund, N.Y.C., 1952-53; asst. to dean extension div. U. Wis., 1949-52, dir. office communications services, 1954-58; dir. Joint Office Instnl. Research, Nat. Assn. State Univs. and Land Grant Colls., Washington, 1958-65; pres. Am. Assn. State Colls. and Univs., Washington, 1965-91; pres. emeritus Am. Assn. State Colls. and Univs., 1991—; sr. cons. Acad. Search Consultation Svc., 1991—; adj. prof. edn. Pa. State U., 1990—; mem. N.Y. Regents Commn. on Higher Edn.; bd. advisors Bowie State U., Pa. State U. Alumni Coun. Co-author: Colleges and Universities for Change, 1987; contbr. chpts. in books. Bd. visitors Air Univ. With U.S. Army 42d divsn., 1943-46. Decorated 2 Bronze Stars; recipient Centennial award for disting. svcs. to edn. U. Akron, 1970, Fogelsanger award Shippensburg (Pa.) State Coll., 1974, World Peace Through Edn. medal Internat. Assn. U. Pres., 1975, Disting. Achievement award, U. So. Colo., 1979, Chancellor's award U. Wis., 1985, Chancellor's medal CUNY, 1986, Disting. Alumnus award Pa. State U., 1989, svc. award Coun. on Internat. Ednl. Exch., 1990, Chancellor's medal Internat. Svc. U. Ark., Little Rock, 1990, Disting. Pub. Svc. medal Dept. of Def., 1991; Alumni fellow Pa. State U., 1975. Unitarian-Universalist. Home: 5500 Friendship Blvd Chevy Chase MD 20815 Office: Acad Search Cons Svc 1818 R St NW Washington DC 20009-1604

OSTASHEK, JOHN, government leader. Leader Govt. of Yukon Territory, Whitehorse, YT. Office: Office of Govt Leader, PO Box 2703, Whitehorse, YK Canada Y1A 2C6

OSTBERG, HENRY DEAN, corporate executive; b. Bocholt, Germany, July 21, 1928; came to U.S., 1939, naturalized, 1945; s. Fred and Lotte (Hertz) O.; m. Sydelle Burns, Dec. 13, 1987; 1 child, Neal; stepchildren: Elysa Bari, Brent Adam, Ross Jay. LLB, N.Y. Law Sch., 1950; MBA, Ohio State U., 1953, PhD, 1957. Pres. H.D. Ostberg Assocs., N.Y.C., 1950—; chmn. bd. Admar Research Co., Inc., N.Y.C., 1960; dir. Self-Instructional Devel. Corp., Amherst Group, Porter Industries, Inc.; pres. Eastman Enterprises, Inc.; assoc. prof. mktg. NYU, 1954-63. Trustee Ostberg Found. Capt. USAF, 1950-53. Jewish. Contbr. articles to profl. jours. Home: 278 Fountain Rd Englewood NJ 07631-4403 Office: Admar Rsch Inc 225 Park Ave S New York NY 10003

OSTBY, RONALD, dairy and food products company executive; b. 1937. BS, U. S.D., 1959. With Pillsbury Co., 1961-84, v.p. fin. planning; v.p., chief fin. officer AG Processing, 1984-86; group v.p., chief fin. officer Land O'Lakes, 1986—. Office: Land O'Lakes Inc 4001 Lexington Ave N Saint Paul MN 55126-2934

OSTEEN, CAROLYN MCCUE, lawyer; b. Spartanburg, S.C., June 3, 1943; d. Howard McDowell Jr. and Carolyn Hartwell (Moore) McCue; m. Robert Tilden Osteen, Dec. 21, 1963; children: Carolyn Willingham Moore, Sarah Lloyd. Student, Wellesley Coll., 1960-63; LLB, Duke U., 1966, LLM, 1970. Bar: N.C. 1966, Mass. 1971. Assoc. Robinson O. Everett, Durham, N.C., 1967-68, Cox, Smith, Smith, Hale & Guenther, San Antonio, 1969-70; assoc. Ropes & Gray, Boston, 1970-79, ptnr., 1979—; tchr. taxes Tex. Asns. Realtors, 1969-70. Co-author: Harvard Manual-Tax Aspects of Charitable Givine, 6 edits., 1980—; contbr. articles to legal publs. Bd. dirs., clk. Historic Boston, Inc., 1978—; Trustees of Reservations, Boston, 1983-87. Mem. ABA, Boston Bar Assn. (vice-chmn. exempt orgns. com. 1987-92). Republican. Episcopalian. Office: Ropes & Gray 1 International Pl Boston MA 02110-2624

OSTEEN, H(OWARD) KENNETH, JR., real estate developer, hotel management executive; b. Jacksonville, Fla., June 25, 1954; s. Howard Kenneth and Grace (Todd) O.; m. Linda M. Montemayor, Mar. 31, 1958; children: Trey Howard III, Cameron. Student, Valdosta (Ga.) State U. Salesman Coggin-Osteen Investments, Inc., Jacksonville, 1976-79; v.p. O-Wax, Inc., Houston, 1979-81, Coggin-Osteen Investments, Inc., Jacksonville, 1981-83; exec. v.p. Landcom, Inc., Jacksonville, 1983-87; pres. Landcom Hospitality Mgrs., Inc., Jacksonville, 1987—; exec. v.p. Landcom-Orange Park Ltd., Jacksonville, Landcom-Bay Meadows Ltd., Jacksonville, Riverside Hotel Ltd., Palatka, Fla., Landcom-North Dallas Ltd., Landcom-Ocala (Fla.) Ltd.; founding bd. dirs. Ft. Caroline Bank. Bd. dirs. Jacksonville County Day Sch., Jacksonville Conv. Vis. Bur. Mem. Internat. Assn. Holiday Inns, Kappa Alpha Alumni (v.p. Jacksonville 1985). Republican. Methodist. Avocations: golf, scuba diving, skiing. Home: 8139 Sabal Oak Ln Jacksonville FL 32256-7386

O'STEEN, SAM, film editor, director; b. Nov. 6, 1923. Asst. editor: (film) The Wrong Man, 1956; editor: (films) Youngblood Hawke, 1964, Kisses for My President, 1964, Robin and the Seven Hoods, 1964, Marriage on the Rocks, 1965, None But the Brave, 1965, Who's Afraid of Virginia Woolf?, 1966 (Academy award nomination best film editing 1966), Cool Hand Luke, 1967, The Graduate, 1967, Rosemary's Baby, 1968, The Sterile Cuckoo, 1969, Catch-22, 1970, Carnal Knowledge, 1971, Portnoy's Complaint, 1972, The Day of the Dolphin, 1973, Chinatown, 1974 (Academy award nomination best film editing 1974), (with Randy Roberts) Straight Time, 1978, Hurricane, 1979, Amityville II: The Possession, 1982, Silkwood, 1983 (Academy award nomination best film editing 1983), Heartburn, 1986, Nadine, 1987, Biloxi Blues, 1988, Frantic, 1988, Working Girl, 1988, (with Glenn Cunningham) A Dry White Season, 1989, Postcards from the Edge, 1990, Regarding Henry, 1991, Consenting Adults, 1992, Wolf, 1994; dir.: (films) Sparkle, 1976, (TV movies) A Brand New Life, 1973, I Love You, Goodbye, 1974, Queen of the Stardust Ballroom, 1975 (Emmy award nomination outstanding director of spl. program 1975), High Risk, 1976, Look What's Happened to Rosemary's Baby, 1976, The Best Little Girl in the World, 1981, Kids Don't Tell, 1985. Office: care Motion Picture Editors 7715 Sunset Blvd #220 Los Angeles CA 90046*

O'STEEN, WENDALL KEITH, neurobiology and anatomy educator; b. Meigs, Ga., July 3, 1928; s. Wellna Hubert and Lillian (Powell) O'S.; m. Sandra Lynn Kraeer, July 30, 1983; children: Lisa Diane, Kerry Keith, Buckley Powell. BA, Emory U., 1948, MS, 1950; PhD, Duke U., 1958. Asst. prof. Jr. Coll. Emory U., Valdosta, Ga., 1948-49; instr. Emory U., Atlanta, 1950-51, prof. Sch. Medicine, 1968-77; from asst. prof. to prof. med. br. U. Tex., 1958-67; asst. prof. Wofford Coll., Spartanburg, S.C., 1951-53; prof., chmn. dept. neurobiology and anatomy, Bowman Gray Sch. Med. Wake Forest U., Winston-Salem, N.C. 1977-93, prof. emeritus, 1993—; mem. anatomy com. Nat. Bd. Med. Examiners, Phila., 1982-87. Contbr. over 150 articles to books, nat. and internat. jours. Served to lt. col. USAR. Recipient Golden Apple teaching award Med. Br. U. Tex., Galveston, 1967, Outstanding Tchr. award Emory U., 1973, Williams Disting. Teaching award Emory U., 1974, award for teaching excellence Bowman Gray Sch. Medicine, Wake Forest U., 1978. Mem. Am. Assn. Anatomists (exec. com. 1980-84, v.p. 1990-92), Assn. Anatomy Chairmen (exec. com. 1982-84, pres. 1990-91), So. Soc. Anatomists (pres. 1975-76), Soc. for Neurosci., N.C. Soc. Neurosci. (pres. 1980-81), Western N.C. Soc. Neurosci. (pres. 1987-88), Assn. Rsch. in Vision and Ophthalmology, Alpha Omega Alpha. Republican. Methodist. Avocations: gardening, music. Office: Bowman Gray Sch of Medicine Wake Forest Univ Dept of Neurobiology & Anatomy Winston Salem NC 27157-1010

OSTEEN, WILLIAM L., SR., federal judge; b. 1931. BA, Guilford Coll., 1953; LLB, U. N.C., 1956. With Law Office of W.H. McElwee, Jr., North Wilkesboro, N.C., 1956-58; pvt. practice Greensboro, N.C., 1958-59; with Booth & Osteen, Greensboro, 1959-69; U.S. atty. U.S. Attys. Office, Greensboro, 1969-74; ptnr. Osteen, Adams & Osteen, Greensboro, 1974-91; fed. judge U.S. Dist. Ct. (mid. dist.) N.C., Greensboro, 1991—. With USAR,

1958-51. Fellow Am. Coll. Trial Lawyers; mem. ABA, N.C. State Bar, N.C. Bar Assn. (mem. and chair subcom. N.C. sentencing commn.), U. N.C. Law Alumni Assn. Office: US Dist Ct PO Box 3485 Greensboro NC 27402-3485

OSTENSO, NED ALLEN, oceanographer, government official; b. Fargo, N.D., June 22, 1930; s. Nels Andres and Estella (Temple) O.; m. Grace Elaine Laudon, June 29, 1963. BS, U. Wis., 1952, MS, 1953, PhD, 1962; postgrad., Johns Hopkins U., 1975. Scientist Arctic Inst. N.Am., Washington, 1956-66; asst. prof. geology and geophysics U. Wis., Madison, 1962-66; dir. marine geol. and geophys. programs Office Naval Rsch., Washington, 1966-69, sr. oceanographer, 1970-77; asst. Presdl. sci. advisor White House, Washington, 1969-70; dir. nat. sea grant coll. program NOAA, Washington, 1977-83, dir. Office Oceanic Rsch. 1983-89, chief scientist, 1989-90, asst. adminstr. for rsch., 1990—; founder Joy/Mac Petroleum, Madison, 1963-65; fellow Fed. Execs. Inst., Charlottesville, Va., 1974, Am. Polit. Sci. Assn., Washington, 1975-76. Contbr. over 60 articles on polar regions, oceanography and geophysics to sci. jours., chpts. to books. 1st lt. Signal Corps, U.S. Army, 1953-56. Recipient Antarctic Svc. medal Dept. of Def., 1958, Meritorius Svc. citation NAS, 1959, Superior Accomplishment award USN, 1968; Mt. Ostenso named in his honor, 1963, Ostenso Seamount (Arctic Ocean) named in his honor, 1978. Fellow Geol. Soc. Am., Arctic Inst. N.Am., Marine Tech. Soc., Explorers Club; mem. Acad. Polit. Sci., Am. Geophys. Union, UN Assn. U.S.A., Cosmos Club. Home: 2871 Audubon Ter NW Washington DC 20008-2309 Office: Dept of Commerce Oceanic & Atmospheric Rsch 1335 East-West Hwy Silver Spring MD 20910

OSTER, JEFFREY WAYNE, marine corps officer; b. Milw., Nov. 11, 1941; s. Richard Alexander and Isabel Aagut (Jacobson) O.; m. Sherry Christine Holt, Feb. 1, 1969; children: Allison Brett, Jennifer Alexandria. BS in Geology, U. Wis., 1963, MBA, 1976; postgrad., Nat. War Coll., Washington, 1982-83. Commd. 2d lt. USMC, 1964, advanced through grades to major gen., 1992; various assignments USMC, U.S., Vietnam, Japan, 1964-81; exec. officer 4th marine rgt. 3d Marine Div., Okinawa, Japan, 1981-82; sec. gen. staff Hdqrs. USMC, Washington, 1983-86; ops. officer 1st Marine Div., Camp Pendleton, Calif., 1986-87, comdr. officer 7th marine rgt., 1987-89; comdg. gen. 9th Marine Expeditionary Brigade, Okinawa, 1989-90; comdr. Def. Electronics Supply Ctr., Dayton, Ohio, 1990-92; deputy chief of staff for Resources Hqrs. USMC, 1992—. Decorated Legion of Merit. Mem. Am. Def. Preparedness Assn. (bd. dirs. Tri-State chpt. 1990-92), Marine Corps Assn., Vietnam Vets. Am., U.S. Naval Inst., Dayton C. of C. (bd. dirs., vets. affairs com. 1990-92). Lutheran. Avocations: golf, running, computers. Home: 9367 Tartan View Dr Fairfax VA 22032-1209 Office: DCS For Programs & Resorces HQ MC Washington DC 20380-0001

OSTER, LEWIS HENRY, manufacturing executive, engineering consultant; b. Mitchell, S.D., Jan. 18, 1923; s. Peter W. and Lucy (Goetsch) O.; m. Mary Mills, Aug. 17, 1948; children—David, Lewis, Nancy, Susan. B.S. in Engring., Iowa State U., 1948; M.B.A., Syracuse U., 1968. Registered profl. engr., Iowa. Mgr., Maytag Co., Newton, Iowa, 1953-59; sr. staff engr., mgr. Philco-Ford Corp., Phila., 1959-62; mgr. mech. and indsl. engring. Carrier Corp., Syracuse, N.Y., 1962-75; v.p. Superior Industries Internat., Van Nuys, Calif., 1981—; v.p., gen. mgr. Superior/Ideal, Inc., Oskaloosa, Iowa, 1975—; engring. cons., Louisville, 1951-53. Author: MTM Application Manual, 1957. Leader, Boy Scouts Am., Syracuse, 1965-73; fund chmn. United Fund, Syracuse, 1965-73. Served to lt. col. USAFR, 1942—; ETO. Mem. Am. Inst. Indsl. Engrs. (pres. 1951-53). Club: Oskaloosa Country. Lodge: Elks.

OSTER, LUDWIG FRIEDRICH, physicist; b. Konstanz, Ger., Mar. 8, 1931; came to U.S. 1958, naturalized, 1963; s. Ludwig Friedrich and Emma Josefine (Schwarz) O.; m. Cheryl M. Oroian, Oct. 10, 1987; children from previous marriage: Ulrika, Mattias. B.S., U. Freiburg, 1951, M.S., 1954; Ph.D., U. Kiel, 1956. Fellow German Sci. Council, U. Kiel, 1956-58; research asso. Yale U., 1958-60, asst. prof., then asso. prof. physics, 1960-67; mem. faculty U. Colo., Boulder, 1967-83; prof. physics and astrophysics U. Colo., 70-83; program mgr. Nat. Radio Astronomy Obs., NSF, 1983—; fellow Joint Inst. Astrophysics, Boulder, 1967-83; NRC Sr. assoc., 1981-82; vis. prof. U. Bonn, W.Ger., 1966, Johns Hopkins, 1981; cons. to govt. and industry. Author: Modern Astronomy, 1973 (also Spanish and Polish edits); editor: Scripta Technica, 1960-70; contbr. articles profl. jours. Recipient Humboldt Stiftung, 1974. Mem. Am. Phys. Soc., Am. Astron. Soc., Internat. Astron. Union, German Astron. Soc., Sigma Xi.

OSTER, MERRILL JAMES, entrepreneur, publisher, author, lecturer; b. Cedar Falls, Iowa, May 30, 1940; s. Harland James and Pearl Rosetta (Smith) O.; m. Carol Jane Dempster, June 1, 1962; children: David, Leah Jane. BS, Iowa State U., 1961; MS, U. Wis., 1962. Asst. radio-TV farm dir. Sta. WKOW, Madison, Wis., 1961-62; asst. editor Crops and Soils mag., Madison, 1962, Ford Farming and Ford Almanac mags., 1964-67; editor Top Farmer Intelligence, Woodstock, Ill., 1967-69; pres. Communication Cons., Cedar Falls, 1969—, Oster Farms and Pork Pro, Inc., Cedar Falls, 1971—; founder, pres. Profl. Farmers of Am., Inc., 1973—; pub. Futures Mag., Inc., 1975—; pres. Hometowner, Inc., 1976-84, Cedar Terrace Developers, Inc., 1977-91; Greenhill Estates, Inc., 1991—; pres. Oster Communications, Inc., 1981—; Greenhill Estates, Inc., 1991—; chmn. Future Source Inc., Lombard, Ill., 1981—; bd. dirs. Danish Mut. Ins. Co., Western Home Inc.; instr. U.S. Small Bus. Banking, 1976-82, Land Buying Strategies Seminar, 1977-86; mem. Nat. Yr. of the Bible Com., 1983. Author: How Farmers Use Futures for Profit, 1978, Multiply Your Money Through Commodity Trading, 1979, Multiply Your Money Trading Soybeans, 1981, Farmland Buying Strategies, 1983, Becoming a Man of Honor, 1986, Becoming a Woman of Purpose, 1989, Vision-Driven Leadership, 1991; also booklets and articles on future of agr.; contbg. editor: AgriFinance, Banking mag., Successful Farming, Soybean Digest, 1969-75. Mem. Young Pres.'s Orgn., 1983-90, chmn. Iowa chpt., 1989. Named Outstanding Young Iowa State U. Alumnus, 1975, Iowa Entrepreneur of Yr. Inc. Mag., 1989, Cedar Falls Personality of Yr., 1991; recipient Blue Chip Enterprise Initiative award, 1992. Mem. Am. Assn. Agrl. Editors, Nat. Assn. Agrl. Marketers Assn., Mag. Pubs. Assn., Chief Execs. Orgn. World Pres. Orgn., Cedar Falls C. of C. (bd. dirs. 1975-76, v.p. 1989, pres. 1990-91), Athletic Congress of U.S., Beaver Hills Country Club, Alpha Zeta, Sigma Delta Chi. Republican. Home: RR 4 Cedar Falls IA 50613-9803 Office: 219 Parkade Cedar Falls IA 50613-2773

OSTER, ROSE MARIE GUNHILD, foreign language professional, educator; b. Stockholm, Feb. 26, 1934; came to U.S. 1958; d. Herbert Jonas and Emma Wilhelmina (Johnson) Hagetorn; m. Ludwig F. Oster, May 17, 1956; children: Ulrika, Mattias. Fil. mag., U. Stockholm, 1956; D. Phil., Kiel (Germany) U., 1958. Postdoctoral research fellow linguistics Yale U., 1958-60, research fellow Germanic langs., 1960-64; 71780Pojeta; lectr. Swedish Yale U., 1964-66; mem. faculty U. Colo., Boulder, 1966-80; assoc. prof. Germanic langs. and lits. U. Colo., 1970-77, prof., 1977-80, chmn. dept., 1972-75; assoc. dean U. Colo. (Grad. Sch.), 1975-79, assoc. vice chancellor for grad. affairs, 1979-80; dean for grad. studies and research U. Md., College Park, 1980-83; prof. Germanic langs. and lits. U. Md., 1980—; mem. Fulbright Nat. Screening Com. Scandinavia, 1973, 83-87, chair, 1986-87; mem. selection com. Scandinavia Internat. Exch. of Scholars, 1982-86; cons. panelist Nat. Endowment for Humanities, 1975—; mem. bd. cons., 1980—; state coord. Am. Coun. on Edn., Colo., 1978-80, Md., 1981-83, dir. dept. leadership program, 1986-91; mem. exec. com. Assn. Grad. Schs., 1980-83; mem. dean's exec. com. African-Am. Inst., 1981-85; interim dir. Washington Sch. Psychiatry, 1994—; cons. in field. Contbr. articles and revs. to profl. publs. Bd. dirs. Washington Sch. Psychiatry, Am.-Swedish Hist. Mus., Phila., Open Theatre, Washington. Carnegie fellow, 1974; grantee Swedish Govt., Am. Scandinavian Found.; grantee German Acad. Exchange Service. Mem. NOW, MLA (mem. Del. Assembly 1995—), AAUP, Soc. Advancement Scandinavian Studies (pres. 1979-80), Am. Scandinavian Assn. of Nat. Capital Area (pres. 1983-86), Am.-Scandinavian Found., Am. Assn. Higher Edn. Home: 4977 Battery Ln Bethesda MD 20814-4931 Office: U Md Dept Germanic & Slavic College Park MD 20742

OSTERBERG, CHARLES LAMAR, marine radioecologist, oceanographer; b. Miami, Ariz., June 15, 1920; s. Arthur Edward and Grace Viola (Johnson) O.; m. Betty Peltier, Nov. 10, 1945; children: Cheryl Ann Osterberg Cheek, David Arthur, John Charles. BS, No. Ariz. U., 1948, MS, 1949; postgrad., Purdue U., 1958, U. Wash., 1960; PhD, Oreg. State U., 1962. Rsch. assoc. Lowell Obs., Flagstaff, Ariz., 1949-53; asst. scientist Atmospheric Rsch.

Lab., No. Ariz. U., Flagstaff, 1953-56; tchr. high sch. Flagstaff, 1956-59; successively instr., asst. prof., assoc. prof., prof. oceanography Oreg. State U., 1942-67; asst. dir. vis. biomed. and environ. programs AEC, Washington, 1967-74; program mgr. environ. programs ERDA, Washington, 1974-76; dir. Internat. Lab. Marine Radioactivity, Mus. Océanographique, Monaco, 1976-79; marine scientist U.S. Dept. Energy, Washington, 1979-86, chmn. oceanography subcom., nuclear safety, Galileo and solar polar space project, ret., 1986; co-founder EnRad, Inc./Radon Testing and Engring., Inc., Gaithersburg, Md., 1986—; cons. Internat. Atomic Energy Agy., Vienna, Austria; participant NSF Acad. Yr. Inst., 1959-60. Contbr. numerous articles on radioecology to profl. jours. With AC, U.S. Army, 1940-45; PTO. Recipient Alumni Achievement award No. Ariz. U., 1983; USPHS fellow, 1962. Mem. Am. Soc. Limnology, Oceanography, Health Physics Soc., Am. Assn. Radon Scientists and Technologists (bd. dirs. 1988), Sigma Xi. Home: 14525 N Crown Point Dr Tucson AZ 85737-9322

OSTERBERG, JAMES NEWELL See POP, IGGY

OSTERBROCK, DONALD E(DWARD), astronomy educator; s. William Carl and Elsie (Wettlin) O.; m. Irene L. Hansen, Sept. 19, 1952; children: Carol Ann, William Carl, Laura Jane. Ph.B., U. Chgo., 1948, B.S., 1948, SM, 1949, Ph.D., 1952; DSc (hon.), Ohio State U., 1986, U. Chgo., 1992. Postdoctoral fellow, mem. faculty Princeton, 1952-53; mem. faculty Calif. Inst. Tech., 1953-58; faculty U. Wis.-Madison, 1958-73, prof. astronomy, 1961-73, chmn. dept. astronomy, 1966-67, 69-72; prof. astronomy & astrophys. U. Calif., Santa Cruz, 1972-92, prof. emeritus, 1993—; dir. Lick Obs., 1972-81; mem. staff Mt. Wilson Obs., Palomar Obs., 1953-58; vis. prof. U. Chgo., 1963-64, Ohio State U., 1980, 86; Hill Family vis. prof. U. Minn., 1977-78. Author: Astrophysics of Gaseous Nebulae, 1974, James E. Keeler, Pioneer American Astrophysicist and the Early Development of American Astrophysics, 1984, (with John R. Gustafson and W.J. Shiloh Unruh) Eye on the Sky: Lick Observatory's First Century, 1988, Astrophysics of Gaseous Nebulae and Active Galactic Nuclei, 1989, Pauper and Prince: Ritchey, Hale, and Big American Telescopes, 1993; editor: (with C.R. O'Dell) Planetary Nebulae, 1968, (with Peter H. Raven) Origins and Extinctions, 1988, (with J.S. Miller) Active Galactic Nuclei, 1989; Stars and Galaxies: Citizens of the Universe, 1990; letters editor Astrophys. Jour., 1971-73. Served with USAAF, 1943-46. Recipient Profl. Achievement award U. Chgo. Alumni Assn., 1982; Guggenheim fellow Inst. Advanced Studies, Princeton, N.J., 1960-61, 82-83, Ambrose Monnell Found. fellow, 1989-90; NSF Sr. Postdoctoral Rsch. fellow U. Coll., London, 1968-69, Antoinette de Vancouleurs Meml. Lectr. and medal, U. Tex., 1994. Mem. NAS (chmn. astronomy sect. 1971-74, sec. class math. and phys. sci. 1980-83, chmn. class math and phys. sci. 1983-85, councilor 1985-88), Am. Acad. Arts and Scis., Internat. Astron. Union (pres. commn. 34 1967-70), Royal Astron. Soc. (assoc.), Am. Astron. Soc. (councilor 1970-73, v.p. 1975-77, pres. 1988-90, vice chmn. hist. astronomy div. 1985-87, chmn. 1987-89, Henry Norris Russell lectr. 1991), Astron. Soc. Pacific (chmn. history com. 1982-86, Catherine Wolfe Bruce medal 1991, bd. dirs. 1992-95), Wis. Acad. Scis. Arts and Letters, Am. Philos. Soc. Congregationalist. Home: 120 Woodside Ave Santa Cruz CA 95060-3422

OSTERGARD, PAUL MICHAEL, bank executive; b. Akron, Ohio, Apr. 1, 1939; s. Paul and Janette Beryl (Laube) O.; m. Elizabeth K. McCombs, Jan. 1965 (div. Nov. 1971). A.B. magna cum laude, Case-Western Res. U., 1961; J.D., U. Mich., 1964; M.P.A., Harvard U., 1969; student, U. Madrid, Spain, 1959-60. Bar: Ohio 1964. Atty. U.S. Steel Corp., Pitts., 1967-69; gen. atty. TWA Inc., N.Y.C., 1969-71; v.p adminstrn., sec., counsel Pa. Co. (now Penn Cen. Corp.), 1971-74, and subs. Buckeye Pipe Line Co., N.Y.C., 1972-74; pub. affairs exec. GE, Fairfield, Conn., 1974-84; pres. GE Found., Fairfield, Conn., 1984-90, Citicorp Found., N.Y.C., 1990—; bd. dirs. Clearfeld Bituminous Coal Corp., Penn Towers, Inc., Pullman Co. Mem. Nat. Hispanic Scholarship Bd., Am. Coun. on the Arts Bd., Inst. Ednl. Leadership Bd., Jr. Achievement of N.Y.; trustee U. Bridgeport, 1991; corp. adv. coun. ARC. Capt. USAF, 1965-68, Vietnam. Decorated Bronze Star, Legion of Merit (Vietnam); Univ. scholar, 1957-61; Littauer fellow, 1968-69. Mem. Ohio Bar Assn., Phi Beta Kappa, Omicron Delta Kappa. Episcopalian. Clubs: Harvard, Atrium (N.Y.C.). Home: 146 W 57th St # 39-c New York NY 10019-3323 Office: Citibank 850 3rd Ave Fl 13 New York NY 10022-6222

OSTERGREN, GREGORY VICTOR, insurance company executive; b. Mpls., May 27, 1955; s. Theodora Carl and Donna Marie (Williams) O.; m. Diane Jane Schaller, Oct. 12, 1985; children: Patrick, Cynthia. BS in Math., BA in Econs., U. Minn., 1977. Actuarial analyst Allstate Ins. Co., Northbrook, Ill., 1977-79; actuary MSI Ins. Co., Arden Hills, Minn., 1979-84, dir. actuarial dept., 1984-86, v.p. ops., 1986-90; pres., CEO Am. Nat. Property and Casualty Ins. Co., Springfield, Mo., 1990—, also bd. dirs.; mem. governing bd. Minn., S.D. and N.D. Auto Assigned Risk, Mpls., 1984-90. Bd. dirs. United Way of Ozarks, Springfield, 1990—; mem. cert. com. S.W. Mo. State U., Springfield, 1992-93; mem. steering com. Salvation Army, Springfield, 1992-93. Mem. Casualty Actuarial Soc., Am. Acad. Actuaries, Internat. Actuarial Assn., Midwest Actuarial Forum, Ins. Fraternity. Baptist. Avocations: golf, boating, scuba diving, reading, travel. Home: 1951 E Buena Vista St Springfield MO 65804-4326 Office: Am Nat Property Casualty 1949 E Sunshine St Springfield MO 65899-0001

OSTERHAUS, WILLIAM ERIC, television executive; b. N.Y.C., July 31, 1935; s. Eric Hugo and Helen (McAuliff) O.; m. Nancy Jean Heinemann, June 19, 1960 (div.); children: Eric Frank, Marc Andrew; m. Annemarie Clark, Dec. 28, 1985. Student, Fordham U., 1953-54, Harvard U. Bus. Sch., summer 1970. Broadcast news and spl. events dept. Sta. WNBC-AM-TV, N.Y.C., 1956-61; exec. producer Sta. KYW-TV, Cleve., 1961-64; exec. producer Sta. KPIX, San Francisco, 1964-67, gen. mgr., 1969-73; program mgr. Sta. KYW-TV, Phila., 1967-69; pres., gen. mgr. Sta. KQED Inc., San Francisco, 1973-78; pres. Varitel Communications Inc., San Francisco, 1979—; chmn. bd. VariCom Inc., San Francisco, 1982-86, Myriad Communications Inc., San Francisco, 1985—; chmn. TV adv. com. Calif. Pub. Broadcasting Commn., 1977-78; mem. joint com. on film and broadcasting Indo-U.S. Subcomm. on Edn. and Culture., 1975-85; chmn. TV com. San Rafael Redevel. Agy., Calif., 1977-78; mem. citizens adv. com. CATV, San Rafael, 1976-77, Dominican Coll., San Rafael, 1972-80. Bd. dirs., chmn. facilities com. The Ctr. for the Arts, San Francisco, 1985—. 1st lt. U.S. Army, 1958-60. Recipient Peabody award and Hillman award for One Nation Indivisible documentary, 1968. Office: 1 Union St San Francisco CA 94111

OSTERHELD, R(OBERT) KEITH, chemistry educator; b. Bklyn., Apr. 19, 1925; s. Albert Henry and Hilda Pearl (Heatlie) O.; m. Jean Drake Evans, June 28, 1952; children: Robert Keith, Albert Laighton, James Evans, Thomas Heatlie. BS in Chemistry, Poly. Inst. Bklyn., 1945; PhD in Inorganic Chemistry, U. Ill., 1950. Instr. Cornell U., Ithaca, N.Y., 1950-54; asst. prof. chemistry U. Mont., Missoula, 1954-58, assoc. prof., 1958-65, prof., 1965-90; prof. emeritus U. Mont., 1990—; chmn. dept. U. Mont., Missoula, 1973-90. Contbr. articles to profl. jours. Mem. Florence (Mont.) Sch. Bd., 1969-75, chmn., 1972-73, 74-75; bd. dirs. Mont. Sch. Bd. Assn., Helena, 1973-75; council mem. Florence-Carlton Community Ch., 1965-90, treas., 1965-90. Served to sgt. USAAF, 1945-47. Mem. Am. Chem. Soc., N.Am. Thermal Analysis Soc., Sigma Xi. Home: 524 Larry Creek Loop Florence MT 59833-6705 Office: U of Montana Dept of Chemistry Missoula MT 59812

OSTERHOFF, JAMES MARVIN, telecommunications company executive; b. Lafayette, Ind., May 18, 1936; s. Abel Lyman and Mildred Paulene (Post) O.; m. Marilyn Ann Morrison, Aug. 24, 1958; children—Anne Michelle Bitsie, Amy Louise Olmsted, Susan Marie. B.S.M.E., Purdue U., 1958; M.B.A., Purdue U., 1963. Staff asst. FMC Corp., San Jose, Calif., 1963-64; with Ford Motor Co., Dearborn, Mich., 1964-84; v.p. fin. Ford Motor Credit Co., Dearborn, 1973-75; controller car ops. N. Am. Automotive Ops., Ford Motor Co., Dearborn, 1975-76; asst. controller N. Am. Automotive Ops., Ford Motor Co., 1976-79; controller tractor ops. Ford Motor Co., Troy, Mich., 1979-84; v.p. fin., CFO Digital Equipment Corp., Maynard, Mass., 1985-91; exec. v.p., CFO U.S.West Inc., Englewood, Colo., 1991—; bd. dirs. GenCorp, Inc., FSA Holdings, Ltd., Pvt. Sector Coun.; mem. Conf. Bd. Fin. Coun. Served to lt. (j.g.) USN, 1958-61. Recipient Disting. Engring. Alumnus award Purdue U.; named Outstanding Mech. Engring. Alumnus,

Purdue U. Mem. Fin. Execs. Inst. Office: US West Inc 7800 E Orchard Rd Englewood CO 80111-2533

OSTERHOLM, J(OHN) ROGER, humanities educator; b. Worcester, Mass., Nov. 24, 1936; s. Walfred Anders and Ellen Olivia (Hendrickson) O.; m. Jo-Ann M. Doiron, Dec. 22, 1962 (div. 1981); children: Doreen, Jon R., Don J.; m. Diane Jane Ungerer, May 1, 1982. BA, Upsala Coll., 1959; MA, CCNY, 1966; PhD, U. Mass., 1978; postgrad., Tex. Tech U., 1961-62, Worcester (Mass.) State Coll., 1965-66, Clark U., 1972. Instr. Worcester Jr. Coll., 1962; tchr. Aetna Life Ins. Co., N.Y.C., 1963-65; tchr. Wachusett Regional High Sch., Holden, Mass., 1965-66; assoc. prof. Cen. NE Coll., Worcester, 1966-79; prof. Embry-Riddle Aero. U., Daytona Beach, Fla., 1979—; chmn. humanities Cen. NE Coll., Worcester, 1977-79; speaker on aviation films and Bing Crosby. Author: Literary Career of Isaiah Thomas, 1978, Bing Crosby, 1994; editor: The Riddle Reader, 1988; contbr. articles to profl. jours. Dirs. Daytona Playhouse, Daytona Beach, 1980-83; lector Grace Luth. Ch., Ormond Beach, Fla., 1989—. With USAF, 1960-62. Recipient Best Supporting Actor award Daytona Playhouse, 1981. Mem. Popular Culture Assn., Air Force Assn., Soc. Collegiate Journalists, Internat. Crosby Circle. Republican. Avocations: acting, airplane models, computer simulations. Home: 303 Timberline Trl Ormond Beach FL 32174-8505 Office: Embry-Riddle Aero U Humanities Dept Daytona Beach FL 32114

OSTERHOUT, DAN RODERICK, insurance executive; b. Sharon, Pa., May 12, 1950; s. Donald Glenn and Phyllis Irene (Ellison) O.; m. D. Catherine Dear, July 26, 1970; children: Jason Ryan, Brandon Lee, Jordan Shane. BS in Fin., U. Balt., 1976; MBA, Loyola Coll., 1980. Various positions Alexander & Alexander, Balt., 1970-84; chief fin. officer Alexander & Alexander Europe, PLC, London, 1985-88; sr. v.p. Alexander & Alexander Svcs., Inc., N.Y.C., 1988—; pres., COO, Alexander & Alexander Inc., N.Y.C., 1993—; chmn., CEO Alexander Underwriting Svcs., Inc., N.Y.C., 1994-95; pres., CEO Alexander Howden N.Am. Inc., N.Y.C., 1995—. Office: Alexander Howden NAm 1185 6th Ave New York NY 10036

OSTERHOUT, SUYDAM, physician, educator; b. Bklyn., Nov. 25, 1925; s. Howard and Edna Cornell (Davison) O.; m. Shirley Elizabeth Kirkman, Sept. 17, 1960; children—Mark, Martin, Ann. B.A., Princeton, 1945; M.D. (Hanes fellow), Duke, 1949; Ph.D., Rockefeller U., 1959. Diplomate: Am. Bd. Internal Medicine. Intern pathology Cleve. City Hosp., 1950; intern internal medicine Mass. Meml. Hosp., Boston, 1950-51; resident Duke Hosp., 1953-56; faculty Duke Med. Sch., Durham, N.C., 1959—; now prof. medicine, prof. microbiology, assoc. dean. Duke Med. Sch. Contbr. articles to profl. jours. Served with M.C. USAF, 1951-53. Recipient NIH Career Devel. award, 1960-65; Markle scholar in medicine, 1959-64. Fellow A.C.P.; mem. Am. Soc. Micro-Biology, Am. Fedn. Clin. Research, Sigma Xi, Alpha Omega Alpha. Home: 5133 N Willowhaven Dr Durham NC 27712-1956 Office: PO Box 3007 Durham NC 27715-3007

OSTERLOH, EVERETT WILLIAM, county official; b. Luxemburg, Mo., June 7, 1919; s. Fred and Esther (Miller) O.; m. Eunice Gramann, Oct. 20, 1940 (dec. Apr. 1983); m. Herta Anna Emery, Oct. 25, 1987. BSME, Washington U., St. Louis, 1958. Registered profl. engr., Mo.; cert. code ofcl. Plant engr. Jasper-Blackburn Corp., St. Louis, 1958-60; equipment engr. Monsanto Chem. Co., St. Louis, 1960-68; pres. Caribean Beach Club, Antigua, West Indies, 1968-73; dep. dir. pub. works St. Louis County Govt., Clayton, Mo., 1973-93; assoc. dir. emergency preparedness pub. works St. Louis County Govt., St. Louis, 1993—; engring. instr. St. Louis Community Coll., 1986-91; exec. sec. Profl. Code Com. St. Louis, 1975—, Met. Area Code Com., St. Louis, 1982—. Staff sgt. USAF, 1942-53. Mem. Mo. Soc. Profl. Engrs. (emergency response task force 1990-92, pres. St. Louis chpt. 1991-92, chmn. disaster response com. 1992—, Outstanding Engr. in Govt. 1987). Lutheran. Home: 283 Spring Oaks Dr Ballwin MO 63011-3835 Office: St Louis County Govt Emergency Ops Ctr 14847 Olive St Rd Saint Louis MO 63103

OSTERMAN, CONSTANTINE ELAINE, Canadian legislator; b. Acme, Alta., Can., June 23, 1936; m. Joe Osterman, Oct. 30, 1954; children: Theo, Kurt, Kim, Kelly, Joe Jr. MLA representing Three Hills constituency Alta. Legis. Assembly, 1979-92, party whip, mem. edn. caucus and agr. caucus coms., 1982-86, minister of consumer and corp. affairs, mem. social planning com. of cabinet, cabinet/caucus com. on legis. rev., agr. caucus com., 1986, minister of social svcs. and community health, 1986-89, minister career devel. and employment, chair econ. devel., 1989-92; retired Alta. Legis. Assembly, Three Hills, 1992; served select legis. com. to rev. surface rights issue, lead role in passing of Surface Rights Act, 1983. Active exec. bds. local ch., home and sch. assns., Carstairs, Alta., 1958—, varied surface rights area; commr., charter mem. Alta. Human Rights Commn., 1973-78; pres. Can. Assn. Statutory Human Rights Agys. Address: RR # 1, Carstairs, AB Canada

OSTERN, WILHELM CURT, retired holding company executive; b. Geisenheim am Rhein, Germany, Sept. 29, 1923; came to U.S., 1956, naturalized, 1970; s. Wilhelm A. and Margarete R. (Seul) O.; m. Beatrice Atkin, Jan. 3, 1992; children from previous marriage: Karen, Ellen, Wilhelm. Grad., Staatliches Realgymnasium, Geisenheim, 1941. With Bayer AG, and predecessor, 1941-88, officer and/or dir. subsidiaries and affiliates, 1956-89; vice chmn., chief fin. officer Mobay Corp., Pitts., 1974-86; vice chmn. Bayer USA, Inc., Pitts., 1986-88; bd. dirs. Schott Corp., Inc., Carl Zeiss, Inc., CDS Internat. Inc.; mem. compensation com. Henkel Corp. With German Army, 1942-45. Hon. Consul Fed. Republic of Germany. Mem. CDS Internat. Inc. (dir. 1974—). Clubs: Brook (N.Y.C.); Duquesne (Pitts.). Home: Hartle Rd Sewickley PA 15143 Office: Bayer Corp 500 Grant St One Mellon Ctr Pittsburgh PA 15219-2502

OSTERTAG, ROBERT LOUIS, lawyer; b. N.Y.C., June 21, 1931; s. Frederick C. and Lillian (Bishop) O.; m. Ann Mary Flynn, Aug. 28, 1954; children—Thomas J., Daniel V., Debra A. B.A., Fordham U., 1953; LL.B., St. John's U., Bklyn., 1956; LL.M., Georgetown U., 1960. Bar: N.Y. 1957, U.S. Dist. Ct. (so. dist.) N.Y. 1969, U.S. Tax Ct. 1965, U.S. Ct. Mil. Appeals 1959, U.S. Supreme Ct. 1960. Atty. office chief counsel IRS, Washington, 1958-60; ptnr. Guernsey, Butts & Walsh, Poughkeepsie, N.Y., 1963-90, Guernsey, Butts, Ostertag & O'Leary, Poughkeepsie, N.Y., 1991—; adj. prof. paralegal studies Marist Coll., Poughkeepsie, 1975-91; adj. prof. Fordham U. Sch. of Law, N.Y.C., 1993—; counsel Agr. Com., N.Y. State Assembly, 1967-68; mem. Gov.'s Jud. Screening Com., 1987-93; counsel to cons. and draftsman of proposed county charters and adminstrv. codes for Sullivan, Fulton, Orange and Onondaga Counties, N.Y.; mem. 9th Jud. Dist. Grievance Com., 1975-79, 9th Jud. Dist. Med. Malpractice Panel, 1975-91, mem. 9th Jud. Dist. Arbitration Panel, 1980—. Mem. adv. coun. Pace U. Sch. Law, 1975-84, paralegal adv. coun. Marist Coll., 1975—; bd. dirs. Com. for Modern Cts., 1975—; trustee Joseph F. Barnard Meml. Law Libr., Poughkeepsie, 1979—; mem. Dutchess County Charter Commn., N.Y., 1966-67, Dutchess County Bd. of Health, 1964-70, pres., 1966-70; chmn. Dutchess County Charter Revision Task Force, 1979-88; dir. Hudson Valley Philharm. Soc., 1973-76; v.p.; dir. High Tor Opera Co., 1967-70; dir. United Fund of Dutchess County, 1973-78, Dutchess County chpt. Am. Heart Assn., 1975-81, 84-89; trustee Sports Mus. Dutchess County, 1983-93, chmn., 1989-90; dep. supr. Town of Poughkeepsie, 1976; dir. Standard Gage Co., 1972-88. Served to capt. JAGC, USAF, 1956-58. Recipient Recognition award Cen. Poughkeepsie Exch. Club, 1967, Marist Coll. Pres.'s award, 1991. Mem. Hudson Valley Estate Planning Council (pres. 1965-66, dir. 1969-74), ABA (chmn. conf. of state bar gen. practice leaders of gen. practice sect. 1980-87, mem. coun. 1982-86, chmn. by-laws com. 1988-89, chmn. litigation com. 1989-90, ho. of dels. 1985—, Gavel awards com. 1989—, spl. com. on solo and small firm practitioners 1992—), Am. Bar Found., N.Y. Bar Found., N.Y. State Bar Assn. (exec. com. 1983-85, 1986-93, ho. of dels. 1973-79, 80—, pres. 1991-92, chmn. unlawful practice of law com. 1977-81, chmn. com. on profl. econs. and efficiency rsch. 1982, chmn. sect. on gen. practice of law 1980-82, com. profl. ethics, 1986-90, chmn. long range planning com. 1992—), Dutchess County Bar Assn. (sec. 1969-79, pres. 1984-85), Delta Theta Phi. Home: 5 Pat Dr Poughkeepsie NY 12603-5626 Office: 75 Washington St PO Box G Poughkeepsie NY 12602

OSTFELD, ADRIAN MICHAEL, physician; b. St. Louis, Sept. 2, 1926; s. Simon and Margaret (Fisman) O.; m. Ruth Vogel, Dec. 31, 1950; children: Barbara Horowitz, Richard, Robin. Student, Washington U., St. Louis, 1943-44, 46-47, MD cum laude, 1951. Instr. Cornell U. Med. Coll., 1955-56;

faculty U. Ill. Coll. Medicine Chgo., 1956-68, prof. preventive medicine, 1963-66, head dept., 1966-68; staff Research and Edn. Hosps., 1956-68; chmn. dept. epidemiology and pub. health Yale U., 1968-70, Anna Lauder prof. epidemiology and pub. health, 1970-94; prof. emeritus, 1994—; head div. chronic disease epidemiology Yale U., dir. med. student edn. Sch. Pub. Health, 1971-75; spl. cons. Surgeon Gen. USPHS, 1964—; chmn. ad hoc com. on life prolonging drugs NIH, 1973-76, mem. nat. adv. council on aging; cons. council on drugs AMA, 1964—; cons. human experimentation Nat. Inst. on Aging, 1977, cons., 1979, mem. overall program planning panel, 1981—; mem. Mayor's Com. on Elderly, New Haven, vice chmn., 1972, chmn., 1977-80; co-chmn. Nationwide Study Precursors of Stroke; dir. Conn. High Blood Pressure Program; cons. Am. Inst. Biol. Scis., Population Lab.; nat. cons. White House Conf. on Aging, 1981; mem. research rev. com. B Nat. Heart, Lung and Blood Inst., NIH, 1976—; mem. exec. com. Yale Center for Behavioral Medicine, 1977—; v.p. Conn. Heart Assn., 1978-80, pres., 1980-82; mem. nat. policy bd. on health and phys. fitness YMCA, 1979-81; chmn. Commrs. Council on Hypertension Conn.; mem. Interagy. Planning Group on Coronary Heart Disease Prevention, 1981; cons. Robert Wood Johnson Found., Commonwealth Found; mem. cardiac adv. com. N.Y. State Health Dept., 1989; mem. com. on drug use in the workplace NRC, 1991. Author: The Common Headache Syndromes, 1962, Epidemiology of Aging, 1975, Psychosocial Variables in Epidemiological Studies of Cardiovascular Disease, 1985, Established Populations for Epidemiologic Studies of Elderly, 1986, Stress, Crowding and Blood Pressure in Prisons, 1987; assoc. editor The Black American Elderly, 1989; editor Am. Jour. Epidemiology, 1979-91; mem. editorial bd. 5 med. jours.; also numerous articles. Mem. panel on nat. health care survey Nat. Rsch. Coun., 1989. Recipient Wisdom Soc. award, 1970; fellow Morse Coll., Yale U.; named one of Conn.'s most Disting. Citizens, Hartford Courant, 1985. Fellow Royal Soc. Health, Soc. Clin. Investigation, Royal Soc. Medicine; mem. NAS (com. on rsch. in the prevention of addiction 1989), Inst. Medicine (com. to evaluate artificial heart program Nat. Heart, Lung and Blood Inst., coord. health promotion and disease prevention for the second fifty 1990, com. on epidemiology and vets. studies 1991), Am. Epidemol. Soc., Am. Coll. Epidemiology, Am. Heart Assn. (fellow couns. on stroke and epidemiology, chmn. com. risk edn. in heart attack and stroke, Disting. Vol. award 1976, C-E. A. Winslow award 1976, Ivy award 1987), Am. Soc. for Pharmacology and Exptl. Therapeutics, Am. Coll. Preventive Medicine, Gerontol. Soc., Internat. Platform Assn., Am. Pub. Health Assn., Am. Coll. Preventive Medicine, Inst. of Medicine (program com.), Conn. Acad. Sci. and Engring., Am. Soc. Clin. Investigation, AAUP, Sigma Xi, Alpha Omega Alpha. Research on relevant social and psychol. factors in cardiovascular disease and high blood pressure, risk factors for stroke, health and social problems of aging. Home: 17 Marlborough Rd North Haven CT 06473-2928 Office: 60 College St New Haven CT 06510-8034

OSTFELD, ALEXANDER MARION, advertising agency executive; b. St. Louis, Feb. 13, 1932; s. Simon and Margaret (Fishmann) O.; B.S., Washington U., St. Louis, 1953; postgrad. St. Louis U., 1953-56. Mktg. mgr. lighting div. Emerson Electric Co., St. Louis, 1955-59; dir. research and media Frank Block Assos., St. Louis, 1959-61; research and media supr. Compton Advt., Chgo., 1961-65; media and mktg. supr. Leo Burnett Advt., Chgo., 1965-68; dir. mktg. and account planning, v.p. McCann-Erickson, Chgo., 1968-72, Kenyon & Eckhardt, Chgo., 1972; dir. Canadian and internat. ops. A. Eicoff & Co., Chgo.; owner Alex Ostfeld Co. Advt. and Mktg., Woodbridge, Conn. and Can. Cons. Am. Assn. Advt. Agys., Yale/New Haven Sci. Park. Mem. Am. Mktg. Assn. (sec. St. Louis 1956-57), Internat. Platform Assn., Broadcast Advt. Club, Am. Research Found. Clubs: Chgo. Exec., Woodbridge Hunt (Conn.). Home: 4 Ledge Rd Woodbridge CT 06525-1802 Office: 6 Ledge Rd Woodbridge CT 06525-1802

OSTFELD, LEONARD S., computer company executive; b. Passaic, N.J., Oct. 1, 1942; s. Edward and Anne (Grossman) O.; m. Barbara Molen, Aug. 22, 1965; children: Robert, Scott. BS in Acctg., NYU, 1964; MBA, Fairleigh Dickinson U., 1968. Sr. acct. Coopers & Lybrand, Newark, 1965-68, Ward Foods, N.Y.C., 1968-69; mgr. acctg. Reliance Group Inc., N.Y.C., 1969-78; v.p. acctg., treas. Ampal Am. Israel Corp., N.Y.C., 1978-81; v.p. controller CGA Computer Assocs., Holmdel, N.J., 1982-84; v.p., CFO, AGS Computers Inc., Mountainside, N.J., 1985-93. Mem. Am. Inst. CPAs, N.J. Soc. CPAs, Fin. Execs. Inst.

OSTHEIMER, GERARD WILLIAM, anesthesiology educator; b. Poughkeepsie, N.Y., Feb. 9, 1940; s. Gerard William and Margaret Amelia (Theil) O. BS, St. Francis Coll., Loretto, Pa., 1961; MD, U. Pa., 1965; MS (hon.), Harvard U., 1992. Diplomate Am. Bd. Anesthesiology. Rotating intern Misericordia Hosp., Phila., 1965-66; resident in anesthesiology Hosp. of U. Pa., Phila., 1966-68; instr. U. Pa., 1966-69; fellow in cardiovasc. anesthesiology Mayo Clinic, Rochester, Minn., 1968-69; rsch. fellow dept. anesthesia Mass. Gen. Hosp., Boston, 1969-70; instr., 1970, 72-76, asst. prof., 1976-83, assoc. prof., 1983-91, prof., 1991—; anesthesiologist Brigham and Women's Hosp., Boston, 1972—, dir. obstetric anesthesia, 1982-88, vice chmn. dept. anesthesia, 1988-91, 92—; vis. prof. numerous univs., 1974— including U. Md., U. Wis., UCLA, 1990, U. Rochester, Columbia U., 1991, U. Ill., Chgo., 1992, 93, 94, Rush Med. Sch., Chgo., 1992, U. Cin., U. Conn., U. Colo., Denver, Med. Coll. Pa., Cornell U. 1993, Wake Forest U., Med. Coll. Wis., 1994; editl. reviewer Anesthesiology, Anesthesia and Analgesia, Ob-Gyn., Am. Jour. Ob-Gyn.; Astra Pharm. vis. prof.; Australia and New Zealand, 1989; 1st Benjamin G. Covino lectr. Maimonides Med. Ctr., 1992, U. Mass. Sch. Medicine, 1992; Henry Ruth lectr. Hahnemann U., Phila., 1993; med. projects advisor Internat. Coun. on Edn., 1977-82; mem. ednl. materials project appraisal panel Assn. Am. Med. Colls., 1977-82; profl. cons. Internat. Childbirth Edn. Assn., 1980-82. Editor: Manual of Obstetric Anesthesia, 1984, 2d edit., 1992, (with S. Datta) Common Problems in Obstetric Anesthesia, 1987, (with Ferrante and Covino) Patient-Controlled Analgesia, 1989, Pain Relief and Anesthesia in Obstetrics, 1995; editor-in chief Regional Anesthesia, 1988—, Internat. Monitor, 1990—, also others; contbr. numerous articles, revs. and abstracts to med. jours., chpts. to books. Maj. M.C., U.S. Army, 1970-72. Fellow Am. Coll. Anesthesiologists; mem. AMA, Am. Soc. Anesthesiologists, Internat. Anesthesia Rsch. Soc., Soc. for Obstetric Anesthesia and Perinatology (bd. dirs. 1973-81, pres. 1980-81), Mass. Soc. Anesthesiologists, New Eng. Soc. Anesthesiologists, Obstetric Anaesthetists Assn., Mass. Med. Soc. (com. on perinatal welfare 1977—, com. on maternal welfare 1981—), Norfolk Dist. Med. Soc., New Eng. Perinatal Soc., Assn. Univ. Anesthetists, World Fedn. Scocs. Anaesthesiologists (com. on obstetric anaesthesia and analgesia 1984-92), Am. Soc. Regional Anesthesia (bd. dirs. 1985-94, pres. 1991-92), European Soc. Regional Anesthesia, L.Am. Soc. Regional Anesthesia, Phi Rho Sigma. Avocations: fly fishing, weight training. Office: Brigham and Women's Hosp Dept Anesthesia 75 Francis St Boston MA 02115

OSTLER, SCOTT, newspaper sports columnist. Sports columnist San Francisco Chronicle. Office: San Francisco Chronicle 901 Mission St San Francisco CA 94103-2905

OSTLING, PAUL JAMES, lawyer; b. Jamaica, N.Y., Sept. 22, 1948; s. John Carl and Margaret Ruth (Reilly) O.; m. Jane B. Mahler, June 1, 1974 (div. 1980); m. Julie Eileen Boyum, Feb. 20, 1982 (div. 1988); m. Danita Kay Hoover, May 3, 1991. BS in Math. and Philosophy, Fordham U., 1969, JD, 1973. Bar: N.Y. 1974, U.S. Dist. Ct. (so. and ea. dists.) N.Y. 1974, U.S. Ct. Appeals (2d cir.) 1974, U.S. Ct. Appeals (4th, 5th, 9th, 10th, 11th cirs.) 1978. Assoc. Chadbourne Parke, N.Y.C., 1973-77; asst. gen. counsel Authur Young & Co., N.Y.C., 1977-79, assoc. gen. counsel, 1979-82, ptnr., assoc. gen. counsel, 1982, nat. dir. human resources, 1985-90; vice chmn. Ernst & Young, N.Y.C., 1990-94, assoc. gen. counsel, 1994—. Office: Ernst & Young 787 7th Ave New York NY 10019-6018

OSTLING, RICHARD NEIL, journalist, author, broadcaster; b. Endicott, N.Y., July 14, 1940; s. Acton Eric Sr. and Christine Cathryn (Cumins) O.; m. Joan Elaine Kerns, July 8, 1967; children: Margaret Anne, Elizabeth Anne. BA, U. Mich., 1962; MS in Journalism, Northwestern U., 1963; MA in Religion, George Washington U., 1970; MA (hon.), Gordon (Mass.) Coll., 1989. Reporter, copyreader Morning News and Evening Jour., Wilmington, Del., 1963-64; asst. news editor Christianity Today mag., Washington, 1965-67, news editor, 1967-69; staff corr. Time mag., N.Y.C., 1969-

74, religion writer, 1975-94, sr. corr., 1994—; broadcaster Report on Religion, CBS Radio Syndication, Washington, 1979—; religion corr. MacNeil/Lehrer Newshour, PBS, 1991—; adv. bd. Ctr. for Religion and the News Media, Northwestern U., 1994—. Author: Secrecy in the Church, 1974; co-author: Aborting America, 1979. Served with USNG, 1964-70. McCormick Found. fellow, 1962-63. Mem. Religion Newswriters Assn. (pres. 1974-76), Phi Beta Kappa. Mem. Christian Reformed Ch. Home: 280 Hillcrest Rd Ridgewood NJ 07450-2400 Office: care Time Magazine and Life Bldg 1271 Avenue of the Americas New York NY 10020

OSTLUND, H. GOTE, atmospheric and marine scientist, educator; b. Stockholm, June 26, 1923; came to U.S., 1963; s. Sven and Ruth (Lundin) O.; m. Doris Beck, Sept. 30, 1950; children: Stellan, Goran. Fil Kand., U. Stockholm, 1949, Fil Lic., 1958; hon. doctorate, U. Gothenburg, 1984. Research asst. U. Stockholm, 1944-46; tchr. Technol. Night Coll., Stockholm, 1946-51; research asst. Royal Inst. Tech., Stockholm, 1947; asst. instr. Royal Inst. Tech., 1948-52; head of lab. Swedish Nitrogen Fertilizer Works, Ltd., 1952-54, Radioactive Dating Lab., Stockholm, 1954-63; asst. instr. Royal Inst. Tech., Stockholm, 1956-57; vis. research asso. prof. Inst. Marine Scis., U. Miami (Fla.), 1960-61, asso. prof. geochemistry, 1963-67, prof. marine and atmospheric chemistry Rosenstiel Sch. Marine and Atmospheric Sci., 1967—, chmn. div. chem. oceanography, 1970-72, coordinator Geochem. Oceans Sects., 1976-86, mem. exec. com. Geochem. Oceans Sects., 1973-86, coordinator Transient Tracers in Ocean, 1977-85. Assoc. editor: Revs. of Geophysics and Space Physics, 1974-76; mem. editorial bd.: Marine Chemistry, 1974-93; mem. adv. bd.: Tellus B; contbr. articles to profl. jours. Served in Royal Swedish Air Force, 1943-44, 46. Mem. Am. Geophys. Union, Am. Meteorol. Soc., AAAS, Swedish Chem. Soc., Swedish Geophys. Soc., Fla. Acad. Scis. Office: U Miami 4600 Rickenbacker Cswy Miami FL 33149-1031

OSTMAN, ELEANOR A., food writer; b. Hibbing, Minn., May 14, 1940; d. Ero Victor and Ellen Ina (Lapinoja) O.; m. Ronald Thomas Aune, June 20, 1965; 1 child, Aric Bruce. BA in Journalism, Macalester, 1962. Staff writer St. Paul Dispatch-Pioneer Press (now St. Paul Pioneer Press), 1962-65, home furnishings writer, 1965-70, food writer, 1967—. Chmn. residential crusade Am. Cancer Soc., St. Paul, 1985-86; chmn. St. Paul Jr. League 60th Anniversary, 1968. Recipient 6 Golden Carnation Nutrition writing awards Carnation Co., James Beard Journalism award, 1994, others. Mem. Assn. Food Journalists (founder, pres. 1976-78, Food Writing awards)), Internat. Food Media Conf. (bd. dirs. 1990—). Republican. Presbyterian. Avocations: travel, reading. Home: 853 Lincoln Ave Saint Paul MN 55105 Office: St Paul Pioneer Press 345 Cedar St Saint Paul MN 55101

OSTRACH, SIMON, engineering educator; b. Providence, Dec. 26, 1923; s. Samuel and Bella (Sackman) O.; m. Gloria Selma Ostrov., Dec. 31, 1944 (div. Jan. 1973); children: Stefan Alan, Louis Hayman, Naomi Ruth, David Jonathan, Judith Cele; m. Margaret E. Stern, Oct. 29, 1975. B.S. in Mech. Engring. U. R.I., 1944, M.E., 1949; Sc.M., Brown U., 1949, Ph.D. in Applied Math, 1950; D.Sci. (h.c.) Technion, Israel Inst. Tech., 1986; D.Eng. (hon.), Fla. State U., 1994. Rsch. scientist NACA, 1944-47; rsch. assoc. Brown U., 1947-50; chief fluid physics br. Lewis Rsch. Ctr. NASA, 1950-60; prof. engring., head div. fluid, thermal and aerospace scis. Case Western Res. U., Cleve., 1960-70; Wilbert J. Austin Distinguished prof. engring. Case Western Res. U., 1970—; home sec. Nat. Acad. Engring., 1992—; disting. vis. prof. City Coll. CUNY, 1966-67, Fla. A&M U., Fla. State U. Coll. Engring., 1990; Lady Davis fellow, vis. prof. Technion-Israel Inst. Tech., 1983-84; cons. to industry, 1960—; mem. rsch. adv. com. fluid mechanics NASA, 1963-68, mem. space applications adv. com., 1985—; hon. prof. Beijing U. Aeronautics and Astronautics, 1991; mem. space studies bd. Nat. Rsch. Coun., 1992, bd. govs., 1993—. Contbr. papers to profl. lit. Fellow Japan Soc. for the Promotion of Sci., 1987; recipient Cont. award for best paper Nat. Heat Transfer Conf., 1963, Richards Meml. award Pi Tau Sigma, 1964, Disting. Svc. award Cleve. Tech. Socs. Coun., 1987, Disting. pub. svc. medal NASA, 1993. Fellow AIAA (Space Processing award 1993), ASME (hon., Heat Transfer Meml. award 1975, Freeman scholar 1982, Thurston lectr. 1987, Max Jacob meml. award 1983, Heat Transfer divs. 50th Anniversary award 1988), Am. Acad. Mechanics; mem. NAE (chmn. com. on membership 1986, chmn. nominating com. 1989, chmn. awards com. 1990, sec., mem. space studies bd. 1992), Univs. Space Rsch. Assn. (trustee 1990), Soc. Natural Philosophy, Sigma Xi (nat. lectr. 1978-79), Tau Beta Pi. Home: 28176 Belcourt Rd Cleveland OH 44124-5618 Office: Case Western Res U Cleveland OH 44106

OSTRAGER, BARRY ROBERT, lawyer; b. N.Y.C., July 14, 1947; m. Pamela Goodman, Apr. 18, 1972; children: Anne Elizabeth, Katie, Jane. BA, CCNY, 1968, MA, 1973; JD, NYU, 1972. Bar: N.Y. 1973. Sr. ptnr., trial lawyer Simpson Thacher & Bartlett, N.Y.C., 1973—. Co-author: Handbook on Insurance Coverage Disputes, 7th edit., 1994. Mem. Am. Law Inst., Assn. of Bar of City of N.Y. Office: Simpson Thacher & Bartlett 425 Lexington Ave New York NY 10017-3954

OSTRANDER, THOMAS WILLIAM, investment banker; b. Detroit, July 20, 1950; s. Roland J. and Sybil (Swartout) O.; m. Mary Ellen Gallagher, Mar. 17, 1979; children: John Charles, Elizabeth Ann, Brian Thomas. AB, U. Mich., 1972; MBA, Harvard U., 1976. CPA, Mich. Staff acct. Ernst & Whinney, Detroit, 1972-74, sr. acct., 1974; sr. acct. Ernst & Whinney, Cleve., 1975; assoc. Kidder, Peabody & Co., N.Y.C., 1976-78, asst. v.p., 1978-80, v.p., 1980-86, mng. dir. Salomon Bros., Inc., N.Y.C., 1989—; mem. adv. bd. Paton Sch. Accountancy U. Mich., 1984-87, mem. vis. com. Literature, Sci. and Arts Sch., 1988-90, 95—. Mem. AICPAs, Metropolitan Club, Harvard Club, Hasty Pudding Club, The Creek, Bond Club (N.Y.), Theta Delta Chi. Home: 60 E End Ave Apt 25B New York NY 10028-7906 Office: Salomon Bros Inc 7 World Trade Ctr New York NY 10048-1100

OSTRIKER, ALICIA SUSKIN, poet; b. N.Y.C., Nov. 11, 1937; d. David and Beatrice (Linnick) Suskin; m. Jeremiah P. Ostriker, 1958; children: Rebecca, Eve, Gabriel. BA, Brandeis U., 1959; MA, U. Wis., 1961, PhD, 1964. Asst. prof. Rutgers U., New Brunswick, N.J., 1965-68, assoc. prof., 1968-72, prof. English, 1972—. Author: Vision and Verse in William Blake, 1965, Songs, 1969, Once More Out of Darkness, and Other Poems, 1974, A Dream of Springtime, 1979, The Mother/Child Papers, 1980, A Woman Under the Surface: Poems and Prose Poems, 1982, Writing Like a Woman, 1983, The Imaginary Lover, 1986 (William Carlos Williams prize Poetry Soc. Am. 1986), Stealing the Language: The Emergence of Women's Poetry in America, 1986, Green Age, 1989, Unwritten Volume: Rethinking the Bible, 1993, Feminist Revision and the Bible, 1993, The Nakedness of the Fathers: Biblical Visions and Revisions, 1994; editor: William Blake: Complete Poems, 1977. Nat. Coun. on Humanities grantee, 1968; Nat. Endowment for Arts fellow, 1976-77; N.J. Arts Coun. fellow, 1980-81; Rockefeller Found. fellow, 1982; Guggenheim Found. fellow, 1984-85; recipient Strousse Poetry prize Prairie Schooner, 1986. Office: Rutgers Univ Dept of English New Brunswick NJ 08903*

OSTRIKER, JEREMIAH PAUL, astrophysicist, educator; b. N.Y.C., Apr. 13, 1937; s. Martin and Jeanne (Sumpf) O.; m. Alicia Suskin, Dec. 1, 1958; children—Rebecca, Eve, Gabriel. A.B., Harvard, 1959; Ph.D. (NSF fellow), U. Chgo., 1964; postgrad., U. Cambridge, Eng. 1964-65; hon. degree, U. Chgo., 1992. Rsch. assoc., lectr. astrophysics Princeton (N.J.) U., 1965-66, asst. prof., 1966-68, assoc. prof., 1968-71, prof., 1971—; chmn. dept. astronomy, dir. obs., 1979—, Charles A. Young prof. astronomy, 1982—. Editorial bd., trustee Princeton U. Press; Contbr. articles to profl. jours. Alfred P. Sloan Found. fellow, 1970-72. Fellow AAAS; mem. NAS (bd. govs. 1993—, councilor 1992—), Am. Astron. Soc. (councilor 1978-80, Warner prize 1972, Russell prize 1989), Internat. Astron. Union, Royal Astron. Soc. (assoc.), Am. Philos. Soc., Am. Acad. Arts and Scis. (Bappu award Indian Nat. Sci. Acad. 1993). Home: 33 Philip Dr Princeton NJ 08540-5409 Office: Princeton Univ Obs Dept Astrophysics Peyton Hall Princeton NJ 08544

OSTROFF, ALLEN J., insurance company executive; b. Bklyn., Mar. 19, 1936; s. Irving and Sally (Cassoff) O.; m. Lenore, Oct. 29, 1967; children: Bruce, Gary, Stephen. BS, NYU, 1957. Ops. analyst N.Y. Hilton, 1964-66, corp. asst/ v.p., 1967-68, gen. mgr., 1972; mgr. Statler Hilton, N.Y.C., 1969-71; group v.p. Americana Hotel, N.Y.C., 1974-75; v.p. The Prudential,

Newark, 1976-93, sr. v.p., 1993—; chmn. bd. Prime Hospitality Corp., Fairfield, N.J., Newark Meadowlands Convention and Visitors Bur.; co-chair Am. Hotel Found. Inc., Newark; univ. lectr. in field. Mem. Cornell Soc. Hotelmen (chmn.), NYU Real Estate (chmn., inst. bd. exec. com.), Inst. Masters in Hospitality Program (chmn.), Ah & MA Mgmt. (adv. com., co-chair Irefac, Washington). Avocations: teaching, boating. Office: The Prudential Realty Group 751 Broad St Newark NJ 07102-3777

OSTROFF, PETER I., lawyer; b. Washington, Dec. 15, 1942. BA, Washington U., 1964; JD, U. Chgo., 1967. Bar: Ill. 1967, Calif. 1970. Law clk. to Hon. Shirley M. Hufstedler U.S. Ct. Appeals (9th cir.), 1969-70; teaching fellow in law Monash U., Melbourne, Australia; ptnr. Sidley & Austin, L.A. Mem. ABA (dir. divsn. substantive law 1982-83, chmn. comml. transations litigation com. 1976-80, coun. mem. 1980-83, chmn. computer litigation com. 1985—, dir. programs divsn. 1990—), State Bar Calif. (mem. exec. com. intellectual property sect. 1988-89, litigation sect. 1990—), L.A. County Bar Assn. (bd. trustees 1974-76, chair human rights sect. 1975-76, mem. ethics com. 1982-84), Assn. Bus. Trial Lawyers (pres. 1988-89, mem. exec. com. litigation sect. 1990—). Office: Sidley & Austin 555 W 5th St 40th Fl Los Angeles CA 90013-1010

OSTROFSKY, BENJAMIN, business and engineering management educator, industrial engineer; b. Phila., July 26, 1925; s. Eli and Edith (Segal) O.; m. Shirley Marcia Welcher, June 2, 1956; children: Keri Ellen Pearlson, Marc Howard. BSME, Drexel U., 1947; M in Engring., UCLA, 1962, PhD in Engring., 1968. Registered profl. engr., Tex., Calif. Lectr. Engring. Systems Design, UCLA, L.A., 1962-68; dir. ctr. mgmt. studies and analyses Coll. Bus. Adminstrn., Houston, 1970-72, prof. prodn. and logistics mgmt., 1969-73, chmn. dept., 1972-74; prof. indsl. engring. Cullen Coll. Engring., Houston, 1970—; prof. ops. mgmt. Coll. of Bus. Adminstrn., Houston, 1973—; lectr. Army Rsch. Inst. and various govt. and indsl. agys., also engring. industry, 1964-76; v.p. Tech. Soc. Logistics Engrs., 1974-76; nat. dir. Logistics Edn. Found., 1980—, acad. advisor, 1990—. Author: Design, Planning and Development Methodology, 1977; co-author: Manned Systems Design: Methods, Equipment and Applications, 1981. Program mgr. USAF Office of Sci. Rsch. project, 1977-86. Lt. U.S Army, 1943-45, USAF, 1950-53. Fellow AAAS, Soc. Logistics Engrs. (cert. profl. logistician, chmn. nat. edn. com. 1972-74, sr. editor Annals 1986—, mng. editor 1986—, Armitage medal 1978, Eccles medal 1988, Founders medal 1993); mem. NSPE, Inst. Indsl. Engrs., Ops. Rsch. Soc. Am., Decision Scis. Inst., Am. Soc. for Engring. Edn., IEEE Engring. Mgmt. Soc., Blue Key, Sigma Xi, Tau Beta Pi, Phi Kappa Phi, Alpha Iota Delta, Alpha Pi Mu. Home: 14611 Carolcrest Dr Houston TX 77079-6405

OSTROM, CAROL MARIE, reporter; b. Seattle, June 27, 1947; d. Cameron Walthew and Eula Marie (Curry) O. BA in English Lit., U. Wash., 1970. Program asst. Sch. Medicine U. Wash., Seattle, 1970-73; asst. mgr. circulation Seattle Sun, 1974-75, reporter, asst. editor, 1974-77, editor, 1978-79; reporter, assoc. editor Willamette Week, Portland, Oreg., 1979-80; reporter features and news Seattle Times, 1980-83, reporter religion, 1983—. Recipient Excellence in Journalism award Sigma Delta Chi, 1988-89; John S. Knight fellow Stanford U., 1984-85. Mem. Religion Newswriters Assn. (Supple award 1988). Office: Seattle Times Fairview Ave N & John St PO Box 70 Seattle WA 98111-0070

OSTROM, DON, state legislator, political science educator; b. Chgo., Mar. 9, 1939; s. Irving and Margaret (Hedberg) O.; m. Florence Horan, Jan. 13, 1972; children: Erik, Rebecca, Katherine. BA, St. Olaf Coll., Northfield, Minn., 1960; MA, Washington U., 1970, PhD, 1972. Prof. polit. sci. Gustavus Adolphus Coll., St. Peter, Minn., 1972—; state rep. Minn. Ho. of Reps., St. Paul, 1988—. Democrat. Home: 405 N 4th St Saint Peter MN 56082

OSTROM, ELINOR, political science educator, researcher; b. Los Angeles, Aug. 7, 1933; d. Adrian and Leah (Hopkins) Awan; m. Charles Scott, Aug. 8, 1954 (div. 1961); m. Vincent Ostrom, Nov. 23, 1963. A.B. with honors, UCLA, 1954, M.A., 1962, Ph.D., 1965. Vis. asst. prof. dept. polit. sci. Ind. U., Bloomington, 1965-66, asst. prof., 1966-69, assoc. prof., 1969-74, prof., 1974-91, Arthur F. Bentley prof., 1991—, prof., chmn. dept., 1980-84, 89-90, co-dir. Workshop in Polit. Theory and Policy Analysis, 1973—; adv. bd. Nat. Evaluation Program Law Enforcement Assistance (Adminstrn.), Washington, 1975-76; mem. task force on criminal justice rsch. and devel. Nat. Adv. Com. on Criminal Justice Standards and Goals, 1975-76; adv. panel Div. Policy Rsch. and Analysis, NSF, Washington, 1977-78; rev. panel Polit. Sci. div. NSF, 1982-83; adv. com. nat. urban policy NAS, 1985-88, rsch. adv. com. U.S. AID, 1989-91. Co-author: Policing Metropolitan America, 1978, Local Government in the United States, 1988, Institutional Incentives and Sustainable Development: Infrastructure Policies in Perspective, 1993, Rules, Games, and Common-Pool Resources, 1994; author: Governing the Commons, 1990, Crafting Institutions for Self-Governing Irrigation Systems, 1992; editor: Strategies of Political Inquiry, 1982; co-editor Jour. Theoretical Politics, 1987—; contbr. articles to profl. jours. Grantee NSF, 1974-85, 87—, NIMH, 1977-81, U.S. Dept. Justice, 1978-82, AID, 1984-94, U.S. Geol. Survey, 1987-89, Ford Found., 1991—. Fellow Am. Acad. Arts. and Scis.; mem. Pub. Choice Soc. (pres. 1982-84), Am. Polit. Sci. Assn. (v.p 1976-76), Midwest Polit. Sci. Assn. (pres. 1984-85), Internat. Polit. Sci. Assn., Am. Econ. Assn., Internat. Assn. for Study Common Property (pres. 1990-91). Democrat. Home: 5883 E Lampkins Ridge Rd Bloomington IN 47401-9726 Office: Ind Univ Workshop in Polit Theory and Policy Analysis 513 N Park Ave Bloomington IN 47408-3829

OSTROM, JOHN H., vertebrate paleontologist, educator, museum curator; b. N.Y.C., Feb. 18, 1928; s. William C. and Norma (Beebe) O.; m. Nancy Grace Hartman, June 14, 1952; children: Karen Ann Williams, Alicia Jane. BS in Geology, Union Coll., Schenectady, 1951, DSc (hon.), 1991; PhD in Vertebrate Paleontology, Columbia U., 1960. Lectr. Bklyn. Coll. 1955-56; instr. Beloit (Wis.) Coll., 1956-58, asst. prof. geology, 1958-61; asst. prof. geology Yale U., 1961-66; assoc. prof., 1966-71, prof., 1971-93; asst. curator vertebrate paleontology Peabody Mus. Natural History, 1961-66, assoc. curator, 1966-71, curator, 1971-93; research asst. vertebrate paleontology Am. Mus. Natural History, N.Y.C., 1951-56; research assoc. Am. Mus. Natural History, 1965—. Author: The Strange World of Dinosaurs, 1964, (with John McIntosh) Marsh's Dinosaurs: The Collections from Como Bluff, 1966; editor: Bull. Soc. Vertebrate Paleontology, 1962-74, Am. Jour. Sci., 1970—, Bull. Peabody Mus., 1993; co-editor: Tectonics and Mountain Ranges, 1975, The Beginnings of Birds, 1985, Proterozoic Evolution and Environments, 1990; contbr. articles on new fossil vertebrates, particularly Mesozoic reptiles to profl. jours. Recipient Alexander von Humboldt U.S. Sr. Scientist award, 1976-77, F.V. Hayden medal, 1986; Guggenheim fellow, 1966-67, Am. Acad. Arts & Scis. fellow, 1994. Mem. AAAS, Soc. Vertebrate Paleontology (pres. 1969-70, Romer-Simpson medal 1994), Soc. Study Evolution, Soc. Systematic Zoology (coun. 1975-78, 83-85), Paleontol. Soc., Soc. Earth Sci. Editors, Sigma Xi (pres. Yale chpt. 1972-73). Home: 198 Towpath Ln Cheshire CT 06410-3356 Office: Yale U Dept Geology & Geophysics New Haven CT 06520

OSTROM, MEREDITH EGGERS, retired geologist; b. Rock Island, Ill., Nov. 16, 1930; s. Meredith Louis Hult and Alma (Eggers) O.; m. Ann Carolyn Postels, Aug. 1, 1953; children—Michael Eric, Craig Alan, Terry Scott. B.S., Augustana Coll., Rock Island, Ill., 1952; M.S., U. Ill., 1954, Ph.D., 1959. Geologist Ill. Geol. Survey, Urbana, 1955-59; geologist Wis. Geol. and Natural History Survey, Madison, 1959-62; asso. state geologist Wis. Geol. and Natural History Survey, 1962-72, state geologist, dir., 1972-90. Fellow Geol. Soc. Am.; mem. Am. Geol. Inst. (mem. governing bd. 1979-82), Am. Inst. Profl. Geologists (Pub. Svc. award 1991), Assn. Am. State Geologists (pres. 1982-83), Wis. Acad. Scis., Arts and Letters (pres. 1989), Masons. Unitarian. Home: 6802 Forest Glade Ct Middleton WI 53562-1711

OSTROM, PHILIP GARDNER, computer company executive; b. New Haven, Aug. 8, 1942; s. David McKellar and Barbara (Kingsbury) O.; m. Toni Hammons, Dec. 21, 1965; n. Nancy Jean Kahl, Apr. 2, 1983; children: Eric Craig, Paige Lynne. BS, UCLA, Ariz., 1965; postgrad., U. Calif., 1992-94. Cert. sr. examiner quality control, Calif. Sales mgr. Proctor & Gamble Co., Louisville, 1968-70, Dun & Bradstreet, L.A., 1970-71; internat. sales mgr. Memorex Corp., Santa Clara, Calif. 1971-82; dir. ops. Memtek Products,

Campbell, Calif., 1982-86, Victor Techs., Scotts Valley, Calif., 1986-88; ops. mgr. Apple Computer, Cupertino, Calif., 1988-93; pres./CEO Ostrom & Assocs., San Jose, Calif., 1993—; Malcolm Baldrige examiner, 1993, 94, 95; ISO9000 lead assessor, 1992—; CCQS sr. examiner, judge State of Calif., 1994-95. Capt. USMC, 1965-68, Vietnam. Recipient Malcolm Baldrige Nat. Quality award U.S. Govt. Examiner, 1993, 94, 95, ISO 9000 Lead Assessor award Neville-Clarke, U.K., others. Home: 1099 Maraschino Dr San Jose CA 95129 Office: Ostrom & Assocs 1099 Maraschino Dr M/S 07PG0 San Jose CA 95129-3317

OSTROM, VINCENT A(LFRED), political science educator; b. Nooksack, Wash., Sept. 25, 1919; s. Alfred and Alma (Knudson) O.; m. Isabell Bender, May 20, 1942 (div. 1963); m. Elinor Awan, Nov. 23, 1963. BA in Polit. Sci., UCLA, 1942, MA in Polit. Sci., 1945, PhD in Polit. Sci., 1950. Tchr. Chaffey Union High Sch., Ontario, Calif., 1943-45; asst. prof. polit. sci. U. Wyo., Laramie, 1945-48; asst. prof. polit. sci. U. Oreg., Eugene, 1949-54, assoc. prof. polit. sci., 1954-58; assoc. prof. polit. sci. UCLA, 1958-64; prof. polit. sci. Ind. U., Bloomington, 1964-90, Arthur F. Bentley prof emeritus polit. sci., 1990—; Hooker disting. vis. scholar McMaster U., 1984-85; rsch. assoc. Bur. Mcpl. Rsch., 1950, Resources for Future, Inc., 1962-64; assoc. dir. Pacific NW Coop. Program in Ednl. Adminstrn., 1951-58; co-dir. Workshop in Polit. Theory and Policy Analysis, Ind. U., Bloomington, 1973—; cons. and lectr. in field. Author: Water and Politics, 1953, The Political Theory of a Compound Republic, 1971, 2d rev. edit., 1987, The Intellectual Crisis in American Public Administration, 1974, 2d edit., 1989, The Meaning of American Federalism, 1991; co-author: Understanding Urban Government, 1973, Local Government in the United States, 1988; author numerous monographs on polit. sci.; co-editor: Comparing Urban Service Delivery Systems, 1977, Guidance, Control and Evaluation in the Public Sector, 1986, Rethinking Institutional Analysis and Development, 1988, 2nd. edit. 1993; mem. bd. editors Publius, 1972—; mem. edit. bd. Constitutional Political Economy, 1989—; mem. founding bd. Committee on the Political Economy of the Good Society, 1990—; contbr. articles to profl. jours. Program coord. Wyo. Assessors' Sch., 1946-48, Budget Officer's Sch., 1947-48; exec. sec. Wyo. League of Municipalities, 1947-48; cons. Wyo. Legis. Interim Com., 1947-48, Nat. Resources, Alaska Constitutional Convention, 1955-56, Tenn. Water Policy Commn., 1956. Grantee and fellowships from numerous govt. and profl. agys. including Social Sci. Research Council, 1954-55, Ctr. Advanced Study in Behavioral Scis., 1955-56, Ctr. Interdisciplinary Rsch., 1981-82. Mem. Am. Polit. Sci. Assn. (special achievement award significant contbns. to study of federalism, 1991), Am. Econ. Assn., Am. Soc. Pub. Adminstrn., AAAS, Pub. Choice Soc., Internat. Polit. Sci. Assn. Home: 5883 E Lampkins Ridge Rd Bloomington IN 47401-9726 Office: Ind U Workshop in Polit Theory 513 N Park Bloomington IN 47408-3895

OSTROW, JAY DONALD, gastroenterology educator, researcher; b. N.Y.C., Jan. 1, 1930; s. Herman and Anne Sylvia (Epstein) O.; m. Judith Fargo, Sept. 9, 1956; children: George Herman, Bruce Donald, Margaret Anne. B.S. in Chemistry, Yale U., 1950; M.D., Harvard U., 1954; M.Sc. in Biochemistry, Univ. Coll., London, 1970. Diplomate Am. Bd. Internal Medicine, Am. Bd. Gastroenterology. Intern Johns Hopkins Hosp., Balt., 1954-55; resident Peter Bent Brigham Hosp., Boston, 1957-58; NIH trainee in gastroenterology, 1958-59; NIH trainee in liver disease Thorndike Mem. Lab. Boston City Hosp., 1959-62; instr. in medicine Harvard U., Boston, 1959-62; asst. prof. medicine Case-Western Res. U., Cleve., 1962-70; assoc. prof. U. Pa., Phila., 1970-76, prof., 1977-78; Sprague prof. medicine Northwestern U., Chgo., 1978-89, prof. medicine, 1989-95, prof. emeritus, 1995—, chief gastroenterology sect., 1978-87; vis. prof. gastrointestinal and hepatology dept. Acad. Med. Ctr., U. Amsterdam, The Netherlands, 1995—; med. investigator VA Hosp., Phila., 1973-78, VA Med. Ctr. Lakeside, Chgo., 1990-95. Editor, contbg. author: Bile Pigments and Jaundice, 1986. Asst. scoutmaster Valley Forge council Boy Scouts Am., Merion, Pa., 1972-78; asst. scoutmaster Northeast Ill. council Boy Scouts Am., 1978-81; vestryman St. Matthew's Episcopal Ch., Evanston, Ill., 1979-82; treas. Classical Children's Chorale, Evanston, 1982. Served to lt. comdr. M.C. USN, 1955-57. Recipient Gastroenterology Rsch. award Beaumont Soc., El Paso, 1979, Sr. Disting. Scientist award Alexander von Humboldt Found., Germany, 1989-90; NIH fellow, 1958-62, grantee, 1962-92; VA grantee, 1970-95. Mem. Am. Assn. Study Liver Diseases (councillor 1983-85, v.p. 1985-86, pres. 1987), Am. Gastroent. Assn. (chmn. exhibit com. 1969-72, mem. undergrad teaching project 1972-88), Am. Soc. Clin. Investigation, Am. Physiol. Soc. (asst. editor 1974), Internat. Assn. Study Liver, Am. Soc. Photobiology. Club: Peripatetic (Bethesda, Md.). Office: U Amsterdam Acad Med Ctr, Meibergdreef 9 Rm C2-111, 1105 AZ Amsterdam The Netherlands

OSTROW, JOSEPH W., advertising executive; b. N.Y.C., Feb. 22, 1933; s. Meyer H. and Helen (Small) O.; m. Francine Lee Goldberg, Sept. 4, 1955; children: Elizabeth Sara, Peter Mathew, William Nathan. B.S. in Mktg., NYU, 1955. Researcher W.R. Simmons, N.Y.C., 1954-55; with Young & Rubicam, N.Y.C., 1955-87; sr. v.p., dir. communication planning Young & Rubicam, 1972-73, exec. v.p., dir., dir. communications services, 1973-87, mem. N.Y. exec. com., U.S.A. bd. dirs.; pres., chief operating officer worldwide Direct Mktg. Group of Cos., 1983-84; exec. v.p., dir. media worldwide Foote, Cone & Belding Co., N.Y.C., 1987-94; pres., CEO Cabletelevision Advt. Bur., N.Y.C., 1994—; lectr. in field; past chmn. Traffic Audit Bur.; dir. Audit Bur. Circulations; bd. dirs., past mem. exec. com. Advt. Info. Svcs., Advt. Rsch. Found. Mem. nat. coun. Boy Scouts Am. Mem. Media Dirs. Council (past pres.), Am. Assn. Advt. Agys. (past vice chmn. media policy com.), Internat. Radio and TV Found. (bd. dirs.). Office: Cable TV Advt Bur 757 3rd Ave New York NY 10017 *It is important that one continue to set goals that seem unachievable and at the same time live by standards that remain consistently high. The maintenance of integrity and adherence to principles which support it, are especially critical when dealing with consumer commercial persuasion. Anything less would be detrimental to the proper pursuit of both personal and business achievements.*

OSTROW, SAMUEL DAVID, public relations executive; b. Chgo., Nov. 6, 1945; s. Herbert Harold and Rose (Brown) O.; m. Toby Michelle Gurewitz, Mar. 23, 1969 (div. May 1976); m. Judith Ann Platt, May 11, 1980; children: Adam, Rachel. AB, Dartmouth Coll., 1967; JD with honors, John Marshall Law Sch., 1975. Bar: Ill. 1975, U.S. Dist. Ct. (no. dist.) Ill. 1975. V.p. Pub. Communications, Inc., Chgo., 1971-76; sr. v.p. Manning, Selvage & Lee, N.Y.C., 1977-84; exec. v.p. Rowland Worldwide (formerly The Rowland Co.), N.Y.C., 1984—; gen. mgr. internat. div., 1988—; Pres. U.S. Corp. Pub. Affairs div., 1990. Contbr. articles to profl. jours. Sec. Pound Ridge (N.Y.) Assn. Inc., 1986, trustee, 1985-87, pres., 1988—; trustee Harold Parmington Found., Hanover, N.H., 1970—. Mem. Nat. Investor Rel. Inst. (pres. Chgo. chpt. 1975-76, v.p. programs, bd. dirs. N.Y.C. chpt. 1988—). Office: Rowland Co Worldwide 1675 Broadway New York NY 10019

OSTROW, STUART, theatrical producer, educator; b. N.Y.C.; m. Ann Elizabeth Gilbert; children: Julie Elizabeth, Katherine Ann, John Stuart. Cynthia Woods Mitchell chair, theatre prof. U. Houston; Pres. Stuart Ostrow Found., Inc., Musical Theatre Lab.; former mem. operamusical theatre panel NEA; mem. bd. overseers com. to visit Loeb Drama Ctr., Harvard U. Producer: We Take the Town, 1961, The Apple Tree, 1966, 1776, 1969, Scratch, 1971, Pippin, 1972, The Moony Shapiro Songbook, 1981, American Passion, 1983, M. Butterfly, 1988, La Bête, 1991, Face Value, 1993; producer, dir.: Here's Love, 1963, Swing, 1980; author, producer: Stages, 1978; assoc. dir.: Chicago, 1975. Served with USAF, 1952-55. Office: PO Box 188 Pound Ridge NY 10576-0188

OSTRUM, DEAN GARDNER, actor, writer, calligrapher; b. Russell, Kans., Jan. 2, 1922; s. Oscar and Helen Mae (Gross) O.; m. Sarepta Pierpont, Dec. 25, 1943 (div. Sept. 1980); children: Karna Hanna, John Pierpont, Daniel Gross, Peter Gardner. A.B. with honors in Polit. Sci, U. Kans., 1947; J.D.; Yale U., 1950. Bar: Kans. 1950, Mo. 1954, Tex. 1955, Oreg. 1958, Wash. 1961, Ohio 1964, N.Y. 1975. Ptnr. Ostrum & Qstrum, Russell, 1950-54; asst. atty. gen. Kan., 1953-54; atty. Southwestern Bell Telephone Co., St. Louis, 1954-55; asst. gen. atty. Southwestern Bell Telephone Co., Dallas, 1955-57; area. atty. Pacific Tel.&Tel. Co., Portland, Oreg., 1957-60; gen. atty. Pacific Tel.&Tel. Co., Seattle, 1960-61; v.p., gen. counsel Pacific N.W. Bell Telephone Co., Seattle, 1961-62, gen. comml. mgr., 1962-63; v.p., gen. counsel Ohio Bell Telephone Co., Cleve., 1963-74; v.p., regulatory matters Western Electric Co., Inc., N.Y.C., 1974-81; v.p., counsel

AT&T Techs., Inc., 1981-85; now actor, writer, and calligrapher N.Y.C. Former trustee AT&T Found., Cleve. Playhouse, Cleve. Orch.; dir. Nat. Corp. Theatre Fund; support care vol. St. Vincent's Hosp. Served with AUS, 1943-46, 50-52. Mem. AFTRA, SAG, Actors Equity Assn., Actors' Fund of Am. (life mem.), Phi Beta Kappa, Sigma Nu. Episcopalian (past vestryman). Home and Office: 45 Christopher St Ph A New York NY 10014

OSTRY, BERNARD, broadcasting executive; b. Wadena, Sask., Can., June 10, 1927; s. Abraham and Tobie (Goldman) O.; m. Sylvia Knelman; children: Adam, Jonathan. BA with honors, U. Man., 1948; postgrad., U. London, 1948-52. Rsch. assoc. U. Birmingham, Eng., 1951-55; spl. asst. and advisor to leader of Indian del. to UN, 1951-52; David Davies fellow in internat. history U. London, London Sch. of Econs. and Polit. Sci., 1956-58; exec. sec.-treas. Commonwealth Inst. Social Rsch., 1959-61; moderator Nightline, CBC, 1960-63; sec.-treas. Social Sci. and Humanities Rsch. Couns. Can., 1961-63; supr. dept. pub. affairs radio and TV CBC, 1963-68; chief cons. to chmn. Can. Radio TV Commn., 1968-69; commr. Prime Min.'s Task Force on Govt. Info., 1968-70; asst. under-sec. of state Dept. of Sec. of State, Ottawa, Can., 1970-73; dep. min., sec.-gen. Nat. Mus. of Can., Ottawa, 1974-78; dep. min. of communications Govt. of Can., 1978-80; spl. adv. sec. state and min. of communications Paris, 1980-81; dep. min. of industry and tourism Govt. of Can., 1981-82, dep. min. of industry and trade, 1982-84; dep. min. of citizenship and culture Govt. of Can., Ont., 1984-85; chmn., chief exec. officer TVOnt., Toronto, 1985—; mem. adv. coun. Elgin and Winter Garden Project, 1988—; moderator, commentator CBC, radio and TV programs; mem. Can. Videotex Adv. Com. Author: Research in the Humanities and in the Social Sciences of Canada, 1962, The Cultural Connection, 1978; co-author: The Age of Mackenzie King: The Rise of the Leader, 1955, To Know and Be Known, 1969; also articles on Canadian social, labor, polit. and cultural history. Bd. govs. Heritage Can., 1975-80, Can. Conf. of Arts, 1977-82, 86—, U. Guelph, 1986—, Shaw Festival, 1986—; mem. adminstrv. coun. Internat. Fund for Promotion of Culture, UNESCO, Paris, 1975-80; mem. adv. com. on cultural policy Govt. of Can., 1979-80; hon. patron Wedge Entomol. Rsch. Found., McClellandville, S.C., 1975-80; bd. dirs. Festival of Festivals, 1982-84, Agy. for Instructional TV, 1985—, vice chmn., 1990; bd. dirs. Can. Native Arts Found., 1990—, Nat. Ballet Sch., 1990—; patron Bicentennial N.Am. Indian Art Exhibit; mem. nat. adv. coun. Can. Friends of Tel Aviv U., Inc.; mem. bd. advisors Festival Music of Can.; trustee Inst. for Jewish Learning, 1990—. Decorated officer Order of Can.; recipient Can. Film award for best documentary for The Style is Man Himself, 1968, numerous other awards for Twenty Million Questions. Mem. Canadian Hist. Assn. (life), Assn. Can. TV and Radio Artists (v.p. 1963), Can. Writer's Found., Assn. for Tele-Edn. in Can. (bd. dirs. 1985—), Internat. Inst. Communications (trustee 1979-85, founding mem. Can. chpt. 1980, chmn. of bd. nominating com. 1986-89), Can. Mediterranean Inst. (bd. dirs. 1986—), Children's Broadcast Inst. (bd. dirs. 1987—), Inst. Pub. Adminstrn. Can. Avocations: reading, travelling. Home: 44 Charles St W Apt 4111, Toronto, ON Canada M4Y 1R8 Office: TVOnt, PO Box 200 Stn Q, Toronto, ON Canada M4T 2T1

OSTRY, SYLVIA, academic administrator, economist; b. Winnipeg, Man., Can.; d. Morris J. and B. (Stoller) Knelman; m. Bernard Ostry; children: Adam, Jonathan. BA in Econs., McGill U., 1948, MA, 1950; PhD, Cambridge U. and McGill U., 1954; also 17 hon. degrees. Lectr., asst. prof. econs. McGill U.; research officer Inst. Stats. U. Oxford, Eng.; assoc. prof. U. Montreal, Can.; with dept. stats. Econ. Coun. Can., Ottawa, 1964-72, chmn., 1978-79; chief statistician Stats. Can., Ottawa, 1972-75; dep. minister consumer and corp. affairs Govt. Can., Ottawa, 1975-78, dep. minister internat. trade, coordinator internat. econ. relations, 1984-85, ambassador for multilateral trade negotiations, personal rep. of Prime Minister for Econ. Summit, 1985-88; chancellor U. Waterloo, 1991-97; head dept. econs. and stats. OECD, Paris, 1979-83; chmn. U. Toronto, Ont. Can., 1990—; lectr. Per Jacobssen Found., 1987; chmn. nat. coun. Can. Inst. Internat. Affairs, 1990—; western co-chmn. Blue Ribbon Commn. for Hungary's Econ. Recovery, 1990—; chmn. internat. adv. bd. Bank of Montreal; bd. dirs. Power Fin. Corp., mem. internat. adv. coun. UN U. World/World Inst. Devel. Econs. Rsch., Helsinki; expert advisor Commn. Transnat. Corps., UN; mem. internat. com. InterAm. Devel. Bank/Econ. Commn. L.Am.-Carribbean Project; mem. acad. adv. bd. World Orgn. Rehab. through Tng., London. Author: Governments and Corporations in a Shrinking World: The Search for Stability, 1990, The Threat of Managed Trade to Transforming Economies; co-author: (with Richard Nelson) Technonationalism and Technoglobalism: Conflict and Cooperation, 1995; co-editor: Rethinking Federalism: Citizens, Markets and Governments in a Changing World, 1995; contbr. articles on empirical and policy-analytic subjects to more than 90 profl. publs. Decorated companion Order of Can.; recipient Outstanding Achievement award Govt. of Can., 1987, Hon. Assoc. award Conf. Bd. of Can., 1992; Disting. vis. fellow Volvo, 1989-90. U. Toronto fellow, 1989-90. Fellow Royal Soc. Can., Am. Statis. Assn.; mem. Am. Econ. Assn., Can. Econ. Assn., Royal Econ. Soc. (founding), Ctr. for European Policy Studies (internat. adv. coun.), Group of Thirty, Inst. for Internat. Econs. (adv. bd.). Avocations: films, theatre, contemporary reading. Office: U Toronto Ctr Int Studies, 170 Bloor St W 5th Fl, Toronto, ON Canada M5S 1T9

OSTWALD, MARTIN, classics educator emeritus; b. Dortmund, Germany, Jan. 15, 1922; came to U.S., 1946, naturalized, 1956; s. Max and Hedwig (Strauss) O.; m. Lore Ursula Weinberg, Dec. 27, 1948; children: Mark F., David H. B.A., U. Toronto, 1946; A.M., U. Chgo., 1948; Ph.D., Columbia U., 1952. Instr. classics and humanities Wesleyan U., Middletown, Conn., 1950-51; from lectr. to asst. prof. Greek and Latin, Columbia U., 1951-58; mem. faculty Swarthmore Coll., 1958—, prof. classics, 1966-92; prof. classical studies U. Pa., 1968-92, prof. emeritus, 1992—; vis. assoc. prof. Princeton, spring 1964; vis. prof. U. Calif. at Berkeley, summer 1969; vis. fellow Balliol Coll., Oxford (Eng.) U., 1970-71, Wolfson Coll., Oxford, 1987, 91; dir. fellowships-in-residence in classics NEH 1976-77, d'etudes, EHESS, Paris, 1991. Author: Autonomia, Its Genesis and Early History, 1982, From Popular Sovereignty to the Sovereignty of Law, 1987, Ananke in Thucydides, 1988, (with T.G. Rosenmeyer and J.W. Halporn) The Meters of Greek and Latin Poetry, 2d edit., 1980, Nomos and the Beginnings of the Athenian Democracy, 1969; also articles; translaator with intro., notes and glossary Nicomachean Ethics (Aristotle), 1962; mem. editl. bd. Cambridge Ancient History, 1976-94. Fulbright research fellow Greece, 1961-62; fellow Am. Council Learned Socs., 1965-66; fellow Nat. Endowment Humanities, 1970-71, 90-91; mem. Inst. for Advanced Study Princeton, 1974-75, 81-82, 90-91, Inst. Advanced Studies, Tel Aviv, 1994; Guggenheim fellow, 1977-78; Lang. fellow Swarthmore Coll., 1986-87. Fellow AAAS; mem. Am. Philos. Soc., Am. Philol. Assn. (pres. 1986-87), Classical Assn. Sec. Am. Soc. Promotion Hellenic Studies (hon.), Classical Assn. Atlantic States, Soc. Ancient Philosophy. Home: 408 Walnut Ln Swarthmore PA 19081-1137

O'SULLIVAN, BRENDAN PATRICK, lawyer; b. N.Y.C., May 26, 1930; s. Patrick Joseph and Rosaleen (McQuillan) O'S.; m. Maria Teresa Conlosa, Sept. 8, 1957; children: Leslie, Laurie, James. Bar: N.Y. 1958, Fla. 1961, U.S. Dist. Ct. (so. mid. and no. dists.) Fla. 1961, U.S. Ct. Appeals (5th and 11th cirs.) 1961, U.S. Ct. Internat. Trade 1980, U.S. Supreme Ct. 1975. Staff atty. Maritime Administrn., Washington, 1958-60; assoc. Fowler, White, Gillen, Boggs, Villareal & Banker, P.A., Tampa, Fla., 1960-63, ptnr., 1963—, Coach; mgr. Tampa Bay Little League, Tampa, 1973-78. Lt. Comdr USNR-R, 1953-75. Mem. ABA, Fla. Bar Assn. (chmn. admiralty law com. 1979-80), Hillsborough County Bar Assn., Maritime Law Assn. (sec. marine ins. com. 1988—, bd. dirs. 1993—), Fed. Bar Assn., Def. Rsch. Inst. (chmn. admiralty law com., 1988-91, editor newsletter, 1987—), Civil Trial Lawyers (bd. cert.), Nat. Bd. Trial Advocates, Tampa Bay Mariners Club (skipper 1979-80, speakers trophy, 1976), Gray-Gables-Bon Air Civic Club (pres. 1964-65), Southeastern Admiralty Law Inst. (bd. govs. 1974-77), University Club, Centre Club. Democrat. Roman Catholic. Avocations: tennis, swimming, jogging. Office: Fowler White Gillen Boggs Villareal & Banker PA 501 E Kennedy Blvd Tampa FL 33602-5200

O'SULLIVAN, EUGENE HENRY, retired advertising executive; b. Plainfield, N.J., June 8, 1942; s. Patrick J. and Helen (Callahan) O'S.; 1 child, Meredith. B.B.A., U. Notre Dame, 1964. Media buyer Foote Cone Belding, N.Y.C., 1967-68; account exec., mgmt. supr. Group Dtr, N.Y.C., 1968-84; exec. v.p., dir. client svcs. Young & Rubicam, N.Y.C., 1968-84; sr. v.p., group dir. Ogilvy & Mather, N.Y.C., 1984-86, 87; exec. v.p. Hill, Holliday, Boston, 1986-87; exec. v.p., gen. mgr. McCann Erickson, N.Y.C.,

1988-90; ret., 1990. Served to lt. (j.g.) USN, 1964-66. Mem. Lotos Club. Democrat. Home: 21 E 10th St New York NY 10003

O'SULLIVAN, GERALD JOSEPH, association executive; b. Chgo., Dec. 9, 1941; s. Gerald Thomas and Norine Rita (Herbert) O'S.; m. Joan Griffin, June 14, 1992; children from previous marriage: Stacey Marie, Lauren Ann; 1 stepchild, Kelly. Student, Chgo. Tchrs. Coll., Roosevelt U.; MPA, Roosevelt U., 1974. Cert. tchr., Ill.; cert. law enforcement officer, Ill. Pub. health adminstr. Chgo. Dept. Health, 1968-76, dir. fiscal svcs., 1976-78, dir. mgmt. and ops., 1978-81, adminstrv. dir., 1981-83; dir. personnel Ill. Atty. Gen. Office, Chgo., 1983-86, dir. ops., 1986-91; dir. program devel. Genesis Schs., Inc., Chgo., 1991—; sr. v.p. ops. World Trade Ctr. Chgo. Assn., 1994—; community officer Gov. State U., Chgo., 1986-88; prof. grad. program Roosevelt U., Chgo., 1974-81; cons E.W. Lynch Vocat. Sch., Chgo. Mem. steering com. Ill. Juvenile Justice Inst., 1992-93; bd. dirs Apple Canyon Lake Property Owners' Assn., Apple River, Ill., 1988-90. Staff sgt. U.S. Army, 1964-70. Mem. Soc. Human Resource Mgmt., Ill. Juvenile Justice Inst. (steering com. 1992-93), Chgo. Bar Assn. (justice for youth com. 1992—), Ill. C. of C., Sierra Club. Roman Catholic. Office: World Trade Ctr Chgo Assn 1 World Trade Ctr 929 The Merchandise Mart Chicago IL 60654

O'SULLIVAN, JUDITH ROBERTA, state administrator, author; b. Pitts., Jan. 6, 1942; d. Robert Howard and Mary Olive (O'Donnell) Gallick; m. James Paul O'Sullivan, Feb. 1, 1964; children: Kathryn, James. BA, Carlow Coll., 1963; MA, U. Md., 1969, PhD, 1976; postgrad. in law, Georgetown U., 1992—. Editor Am. Film Inst., Washington, 1974-77; assoc. program coord. Smithsonian Resident Assocs., Washington, 1977-78; dir. instl. devel. Nat. Archives, Washington, 1978-79; exec. dir. Md. State Humanities Coun., Balt., 1979-81, 82-84, Ctr. for the Book, Libr. of Congress, Washington, 1981-82; dep. asst. dir. Nat. Mus. Am. Art, Washington, 1984-87, acting asst. dir., 1987-89; pres., CEO The Mus. at Stony Brook, N.Y., 1989-92; exec. dir. Nat. Assn. Women Judges, Washington, 1993; clk. Office Legal Advisor U.S. Dept. of State, Washington, 1994—; summer assoc. Piper & Marbury, Balt., 1995; chair Smithsonian Women's Coun., Washington, 1988-89; mem. editorial advisory bd. Am. Film Inst., 1979—. Author: The Art of the Comic Strip, 1971 (Gen. Excellence award Printing Industry Am.), Workers and Allies, 1975, (with Alan Fern) The Complete Prints of Leonard Baskin, 1984, The Great American Comic Strip, 1991; editor Am. Film Inst. Catalogue: Feature Films, 1961-70, 1974-77. Trustee Child Life Ctr., U. Md., College Pk., 1971-74; chair Smithsonian Women's Coun., 1988-89. Univ. fellow U. Md., 1967-70, Mus. fellow, 1970-71; Smithsonian fellow Nat. Collection Fine Arts, Washington, 1972-73. Mem. Assn. Assn. Art Mus. Dirs., Am. Assn. Mus., Mid-Atlantic Mus. Conf., AAUW. Avocations: mystery writing. Home: 17 Ridge Rd # F Greenbelt MD 20770-1749

O'SULLIVAN, LYNDA TROUTMAN, lawyer; b. Oil City, Pa., Aug. 30, 1952; d. Perry John and Vivian Dorothy (Schreffler) Troutman; m. P. Kevin O'Sullivan, Dec. 15, 1979; children: John Perry, Michael Patrick. B.A., Am. U., 1974; J.D., Georgetown U., 1978, postgrad; Bar: D.C. 1978; assoc. firm Chapman, Duff & Paul, Washington, 1978-82, Gadsby & Hannah, Washington, 1983-85; ptnr. Perkins Coie, Washington, 1985-92, Fried, Frank, Harris, Shriver & Jacobson, Washington, 1993—; mem. adv. bd. Fed. Contracts Report; mem. faculty govt. contracts program George Washington U.; lectr. Contbr. articles to profl. jours. Mem. ABA (chair truth in negotiations com. 1991-94, vice chair 1985-93, coun. rep. 1994—, acctg., cost and pricing com., coun. sect. pub. contract law 1993—, chair membership com. 1994—). Office: Fried Frank Harris Shriver and Jacobson 1001 Pennsylvania Ave NW Washington DC 20004

O'SULLIVAN, PAUL KEVIN, business executive, management and instructional systems consultant; b. Syracuse, N.Y., May 10, 1938; s. John Hugh and Helen Troy (Smith) O'S.; m. Lynda Troutman; children: Mary Kathleen and Karin Jennifer (twins), John Perry, Michael Patrick. A.B., Dartmouth Coll., 1960. Communications specialist Gen. Electric Co., Schenectady, N.Y., 1963-66; nat. inst. dir. Gen. Learning Corp., Washington, 1966-67; sr. con. ednl. systems. Aries Corp., McLean, Va., 1967-69; dir. profl. devel. Nat. Audio-Visual Assn., Fairfax, Va., 1969-74; exec. dir. Am. Soc. Tng. and Devel., Madison, Wis., 1974-80; sr. v.p. Sterling Inst., Washington, 1980-87, nat. account mgr. Orgnl. Dynamics, Inc., 1987-94; account exec. Zenger Miller, 1995—; staff dir. Nat. Audio-Visual Inst. for Effective Communications Ind. U., 1969-74; chief adminstr. Internat. Fedn. Tng. and Devel. Orgns., 1974-80; dir. Internat. Symposia for Tng. Communications in Switzerland, Australia and Middle East. Producer and dir. films and multimedia presentations; author communications and tng. courses, textbooks; contbr. articles to profl. jours. Served to lt. (j.g.), USNR, 1956-63. Recipient Honor medal for Literature Freedoms Found., 1963; Writers Gold Cup award Gen. Electric, 1966; Resolution for Outstanding Achievement Nat. Audio-Visual Assn., 1974, Pres.'s award for bus. achievement, 1989, 90, 91, 92, 93. Mem. Nat. Soc. for Performance and Instrn. (Presdl. citation 1977), Am. Soc. Assn. Execs. (Grand award for mgmt. achievement 1978), Am. Soc. Tng. and Devel. (hon. life).

O'SULLIVAN, THOMAS J., lawyer; b. New Haven, Apr. 7, 1940; s. Thomas J. and Marjorie (Hession) O'S.; m. Anita Brady, Aug. 10, 1968; children: Kathleen, Margaret, Mary Tess, Anne Elizabeth. BA in History, Yale U., 1961; LLB, Harvard U., 1966. Bar: Conn. 1966, U.S. Dist. Ct. Conn. 1967, N.Y. 1967, U.S. Dist. Ct. (so. and ea. dists.) N.Y. 1967, U.S. Ct. Appeals (2d cir.) 1971, U.S. Supreme Ct. 1971, U.S. Dist. Ct. (no. dist.) N.Y. 1976. Assoc. White & Case, N.Y.C., 1966-74, ptnr., 1974—. Served to 1st lt. U.S. Army, 1961-63. Mem. ABA, N.Y. State Bar Assn., Assn. of Bar of City of N.Y. Clubs: Milbrook (Greenwich, Conn.); Yale (N.Y.C.). Home: 56 Hillside Rd Greenwich CT 06830-4835 Office: White & Case 1155 Ave Of The Americas New York NY 10036-2787

OSUMI, MASATO, utility company executive; b. Osaka, Japan, Aug. 20, 1942; s. Masahiro and Sachiko Osumi; m. Masako Nakajima, Apr. 21, 1968; children: Masanori, Koji, Yuko. BS, Yokohama Nat. U., 1966; MS, NYU, 1971; D in Engring., Kyoto U., 1978. Engr. Sanyo Elec. Co. Ltd., Hirakata, Osaka, 1966-71, chief researcher rsch. ctr., 1978-85, mgr., 1985-86, mgr. control systems rsch. ctr., 1987-89, div. mgr., 1989-92; gen. mgr. Sanyo Elec. Co. Ltd., 1992—; engr. Tokyo Sanyo Elec. Co. Ltd., Ohizumi-Cho, Gunma, Japan, 1971-73. Contbr. articles to profl. jours. Mem. Japanese Soc. Mech. Engrs. (bd. dirs. 1986-87), Japanese Soc. Precision Engrs, Heat Transfer Soc. of Japan. Avocation: golfing. Home: 3-10-8 Takiimotomachi, Moriguchi Osaka 570, Japan Office: Sanyo Elec Co Ltd 1-18-13, Hashiridani, Hirakata, Osaka 573, Japan

OSVER, ARTHUR, artist; b. Chgo., July 26, 1912; s. Harry and Yetta (Woodrov) O.; m. Ernestine Betsberg, Aug. 12, 1940. Student, Northwestern U., 1930-31, Art Inst. Chgo., 1931-36. Instr. art Washington U., St. Louis, 1960-83. Works exhbtd., Art Inst. Chgo., Pa. Acad. Art, Carnegie Inst., Whitney Mus., St. Louis Art Mus., Nelson Gallery, Atkins Mus., Corcoran Art Gallery, U. Ill. Ann., Mus. Modern Art, Met. Mus., others, works in permanent collections, Whitney Mus., Toledo Mus., Isaac Delgado Mus., Peabody Mus., Rio de Janeiro Mus.; artist in residence, U. Fla., 1954-55; trustee emeritus Am. Acad Rome, 1993, artist in residence, 1957-58, one man shows, Wilson Gallery, Chgo., 1940, Grand Central Moderns, N.Y.C., 1947, 49, 51, 56, U. Tenn., 1948, Syracuse U., 1949, Hamline U., 1950, U. Fla., 1951, 55, Fairweather-Hardin Gallery, Chgo., 1953, 55, 69, others. Recipient John Barton Payne medal Va. Mus., 1944, purchase prize U. Ill., 1949, Temple gold medal and purchase prize Pa. Acad., Prix de Rome, 1952, 53, J. Henry Schiedt prize Pa. Acad. Fine Arts, award Am. Acad. and Inst. Arts and Letters, 1991, Arts & Edn. Excellence in Painting award, Arts and Edn. Coun. Greater St. Louis, 1994; James Nelson Raymond traveling fellow, 1936-38; Guggenheim fellow, 1950-51; sabbatical leave grantee Nat. Endowment Arts. Mem. Audubon Artists, Artists Equity. Address: 465 Foote Ave Webster Groves MO 63119

OSWALD, GEORGE CHARLES, advertising executive, management and marketing consultant; b. Springfield, Ill.; s. William A. and Lucille (Harrison) O.; m. Wanda Lillian Hartmann, Sept. 6, 1938; children: William Allan, Suzanne Mae, George Charles, Nanette Marie. B.S., U. Ill., 1936. Copywriter J. Stirling Getchell, Inc., 1936-37; Washington corr. Popular Sci. Picture Mag., 1937-38; copywriter, account exec. William Esty Co., Inc., 1942-50; v.p., account supr. Cecil & Presbrey, Inc., 1950-52; v.p., dir. re-

gional offices and internat. div. Kenyon & Eckhardt, 1952-61; exec. v.p., dir. Geyer, Morey, Ballard, Inc., N.Y.C., 1961-65; pres., chief exec. officer Geyer, Morey, Ballard, Inc., 1965-67; pres., chief exec. officer Geyer-Oswald, Inc., 1967-69, chmn. bd., chief exec. officer, 1969-70; vice chmn. bd. Lennen & Newell, Inc., 1970-72; chief exec. officer, dir. Bailey-Oswald, Inc., Dannemora, N.Y., 1972-75; dir. mgmt. assoc. Quadrant Mktg. Counselors, Ltd., N.Y.C., 1976-80; chmn. Mgmt. Assocs., N.Y.C., 1980—; bd. dirs. Farm Products Labs., Matrix, Inc., Satellite Beach, Fla., Realtime Assocs., Inc., Satellite Beach, Fla., Technocraft, Inc., McElhattan, Pa., Ameratec Corp.; pres., dir. Realmar, Inc.; dir. Piper Indsl. Complex, Inc. Mem. Am. Assn. Advt. Agys. (gov. Eastern region 1964-66, nat. gov. 1966-69), Nat. Outdoor Advt. Bur. (dir.), Am. Arbitration Assn., Delta Chi. Clubs: N.Y. Athletic, Adirondack League, Camp Fire Am., Winged Foot Golf (N.Y.C.). Home: 38 Edgewood Rd Scarsdale NY 10583-6421 also: Old Forge NY 13420

OSWALD, ROBERT BERNARD, science administrator, nuclear engineer; b. Detroit, May 25, 1932; s. Robert Bernard and Leona Virginia (LeFave) O.; m. Judith Ann Dick, Feb. 3, 1964; children: Robert Vernon, Susan Marie. BSME, U. Mich., 1957, BS in Math., 1957, MSME, 1958, PhD in Nuclear Engring., 1964. Rsch. physicist Harry Diamond Labs., U.S. Army, Washington, 1964-69, chief radiation, phys. br., 1970-72, chief rsch. lab., 1972-76; assoc. tech. dir. Harry Diamond Labs., U.S. Army, Adelphi, Md., 1976-79; asst. to dep. dir. sci. and tech. Def. Nuclear Agy., Alexandria, Va., 1979-81; tech. dir. Electronic R&D Command, U.S. Army, Adelphi, 1981-85; corp. v.p. Sci. Application Internat. Corp., McLean, Va., 1985-87; dir. R&D C.E. Washington, 1987—; exec. dir. strategic environ. R&D program, 1992-94; vis. prof. dept. nuclear engring. U. Mich., Ann Arbor, 1986-70. Contbr. articles to profl. jours. With USAF, 1950-53. Recipient Louis J. Hamilton award U. Mich., 1973, Disting. Exec. award Pres. of U.S., 1983, Meritorious Exec. Pres. award, 1991; Boeing fellow, 1957-58, Atomic Energy Spl. fellow, 1961-63. Fellow IEEE; mem. Am. Phys. Soc., Soc. Mil. Engrs., Cath. Acad. Scis., Cosmos Club. Republican. Roman Catholic. Avocations: sailing, woodworking, gardening. Office: USA CE 20 Massachusetts Ave NW Washington DC 20314-0002

OSWALD, RUDOLPH A., economist; b. Milw., Aug. 4, 1932; s. Carl J. and Anne O.; m. Mary Louise Hurney. B.A., Holy Cross Coll., 1954; postgrad. (Fulbright scholar), U. Munich, W. Ger., 1954-55; M.S., U. Wis., Madison, 1958; Ph.D. in Econs, Georgetown U., 1965. Research and edn. dir. Internat. Assn. Fire Fighters, Washington, 1959-63; economist research dept. AFL-CIO, Washington, 1963-72; asst. dir. edn. dept. AFL-CIO, 1975-76, dir. research dept., 1976—; rsch. dir. Svc. Employees Internat. Union, Washington, 1972-75; adj. teaching of econs. George Washington U.; mem. Fed. Employees Pay Coun., 1970-72, Sec. Navy's Adv. Bd. Edn. and Tng., 1975-78, Nat. Commn. Employment and Unemployment Stats., Fgn. Investment Adv. Com.; mem. adv. coun. Indsl. Labor Rels. Sch., Cornell U., 1981-85; mem. Labor Rsch. Adv. Coun. to Bur. Labor Stats., mem. adv. com. on trade; mem. adv. com. Ex-Im Bank, 1989-92. Bd. dirs. Nat. Industries for the Blind, 1965-71. Served with U.S. Army, 1956-57. Mem. Am. Econ. Assn., Am. Statis. Assn., Indsl. Rels. Rsch. Assn. (past pres.), Nat. Bur. Econ. Rsch. (dir.). Nat. Planning Assn. (dir.), Joint Coun. on Econ. Edn. (dir.). Home: 11804 Devilwood Dr Rockville MD 20854-3407 Office: AFL-CIO Dept Econ Rsch 815 16th St NW Ste 504 Washington DC 20006-4104

OSWALD, STANTON S., lawyer; b. Phila., Oct. 15, 1927; s. Sylvan J. and Myra (Steiger) O.; m. Bernice Boorstein, June 17, 1951; children: Jane Mitchell, Eve Robbins, David Oswald, Beth Oswald. BA, U. Pa., 1949; LLB magna cum laude, Harvard U., 1952. Bar: Pa., 1953. Law clk. to Judge William L. Hastie U.S. Ct. Appeals Third Circuit, Phila., 1952-53; assoc. Wolf, Block, Schorr & Solis-Cohen, Phila., 1953-63, ptnr., 1963—. Trustee Peirce Coll., Phila. Jewish Fedn. Greater Phila.; trustee, hon. dir. Congregation Adath Jeshurun, Melrose Park; chmn. bd. dirs Pa. affiliate Am. Diabetes Assn., immediate past chmn. bd. dirs. Phila. chpt. With USAAF, 1946-47. Mem. ABA, Pa. Bar Assn., Phila. Bar Assn. Democrat. Jewish. Office: Wolf Block Schorr & Solis-Cohen 12th Fl Packard Bldg 15th & Chestnut Sts Philadelphia PA 19102

OSWALD, WILLIAM H., lawyer; b. Chgo., Oct. 3, 1938; married, June 1964; 1 child, Andrew. BA in Polit. Sci. with distinction, Northwestern U., 1960, JD, 1963. Bar: Ill. 1963, U.S. Supreme Ct. 1972, U.S. Dist. Ct. (no. dist.) Ill. 1973, U.S. Ct. Appeals (7th cir.) 1973. Asst. univ. counsel Northwestern U., 1963-70, univ. atty., 1971-73; gen. counsel, corp. sec. Loyola U., Chgo., 1973-81, v.p., gen. counsel corp. sec., 1981—; speaker, panelist various institutionally oriented profl. groups. Mem. ABA, Ill. Bar Assn., Chgo. Bar Assn., Am. Soc. Hosp. Attys., Nat. Health Lawyers Assn. Nat. Assn. Coll. and Univ. Attys. (sec. treas 1968-73, exec. bd. 1973—, 2d v.p. 1979-80, 1st v.p., chmn. program com. 1980-81, pres.-elect 1981-82, pres. 1982-83), Nat. Orgn. Legal Problems Edn., Phi Beta Kappa. Home: 426 South Ave Glencoe IL 60022-1606 Office: Loyola U Chgo 820 N Michigan Ave Chicago IL 60611-2103

OSWEILER, GARY DOUGLAS, veterinary medicine educator, toxicologist; b. Sigourney, Iowa, Sept. 8, 1942; s. James Burke and Ruth Mildred (House) O.; m. Sue Ann Miller, July 2, 1966; children: Julie, John, Jeff, Jill. DVM, Iowa State U., 1966; MS in Pathology, Iowa Staate U., 1968, PhD in Toxicology, 1973. Diplomate Am. Bd. Vet. Toxicology (pres. 1992-94). Assoc. prof. U. Mo., Columbia, 1974-79, prof., 1979-82; instr. Iowa State Vet. Clinic, Ames, 1967-69; instr. vet. medicine Iowa State U., Ames, 1966-67, asst. prof., 1969-74, prof., 1983—; interim assoc. dean Coll. Vet. Medicine, 1992-93; dir. vet. diag. lab., 1994—; chmn. vet. medicine adv. com. FDA, Washington, 1988-91; mem. Nat. Organic Stds. Bd., USDA, Washington, 1992—. Author: Clinical and Diagnostic Veterinary Toxicology, 1985, (autotutorial slide-tape set) Aflatoxins, 1990. Mem. Boone County Disasteer Com., Columbia, 1979-82; pres. Rock Bridge Sch. PTA, Columbia, 1980-82; mem. Iowa Gov.'s Task Force on Toxicology, Des Moines, 1985-89; mem. bd. Coun. for Agrl. Sci. and Tech., Ames, 1990-93. Area grantee NIH, 1990. Fellow Soc. Toxicology; mem. Am. Soc. Animal Sci., Kiwanis, KC (recorder 1976-77). Roman Catholic. Avocations: jogging, gardening and landscaping, music, history, carpentry. Office: Iowa State U Coll Vet Medicine Vet Diagnostic Lab Ames IA 50011 Address: 1251 Quill Ave Boone IA 50036-7574

OTEY, ORLANDO, music executive, educator, pianist, theorist; b. Mexico City, Mexico, Feb. 1, 1925; s. Ponciano O. and Dolores (Olin) O.; D. Mus., U. Mexico, 1945; student Curtis Inst. Music, Phila., 1945-48; also studied with Luis Moctezuma, Vladimir Sokoloff, Walter Gieseking, Manuel M. Ponce, Gian-Carlo Menotti; m. Diane E. McAnney, Feb. 22, 1974; 1 son, Nathaniel; children by previous marriage—Olivia, Alexander. Pianist appearing in Mexico, U.S., recitals and with orchs., 1929—; mem. faculty Nat. Sch. Music, U. Mex., 1941-45, Jenkintown Music Sch.; faculty Wilmington (Del.) Mus. Sch., 1957-60, exec. dir., 1966-70; musical dir. Brandywine Pops Orch., 1969-74, Jewish Community Ctr. Orch., 1974-78; dir. Otey Music Sch., 1970—. Gen. mgr. Am. Trade Export Corp., 1964-63; tech. translator export dept. S.S. White Co. (Pennwalt), 1957-60; one of 3 U.S. pianists at Chopin Centennial Festival, Warsaw, Poland, 1949; organist, choirmaster St. John's Episcopal Ch., Bala-Cynwyd, Pa., 1962-64, Christ Episcopal Ch., Media, Pa., 1965-67, Mt. Salem United Meth. Ch., Wilmington, Del., 1973-84. Composer: Mexican Fantasy, 1941, Etudes for Piano, 1941, Sonata Tenochtitlan, 1948, Arabesque, 1950, (songs) Sinfonia Breve, 1956, Suite for Strings, 1957, Tzintzuntzan for strings, 1958, Poetica for Soprano and orch., 1958; Poetica for solo trumpet and orch., 1970; Sonata Adelita, 1982. Program chmn. Tri-County Concerts Assn., Wayne Pa., 1955-57; v.p. Main Line Symphony Orch., 1956-58; mem. steering com. Cultural Center Commn. Wilmington. Bd. dirs. Del. Symphony Orch. Mem. Nat. Assn. Composers U.S.A. (pres. Phila. chpt. 1959-61), Nat. Edn. Assn. Jazz Educators, Am. Guild Organists, Am. String Tchrs. Assn. (life), Pan-Am. Assn., Curtis Inst. Music Alumni Assn. (life), Postal Commemorative Soc., Am. Symphony Orch. League (life), Nat. Music Tchrs. Assn., Phila., Nat. Music Tchrs. Assn. (Del. Music Tchr. of Yr. 1982), Phila. Music Tchrs. Assn., Del. Music Tchrs. Assn. Advancement Mus. Edn., Smithsonian Assos., Nat. Hist. Soc. (charter), Del. Classical Guitar Soc., Wilmington Soc. Fine Arts, Del. Art Mus., Phila. Franklin Inst., Salem County (N.J.) Valley Forge (life) hist. socs., Music Educators Nat. Conf., Internat. Platform Assn. Club: Rotary (pres. local club 1973). Author: Otey Music Teaching Method, 1973; discoverer formula of natural, exotic and non-septonic musical keys,

1978; rec. (albums) Sea of Galillee, Alacrán, 1992. Home and Office: 2391 Limestone Rd Wilmington DE 19808-4100

OTHERSEN, HENRY BIEMANN, JR., pediatric surgeon, physician, educator; b. Charleston, S.C., Aug. 26, 1930; s. Henry and Lydia Albertine (Smith) O.; m. Janelle Lester, Apr. 4, 1959; children: Megan, Mandy, Margaret, Henry Biemann III. B.S., Coll. Charleston, 1950; M.D., Med. Coll. S.C., 1953. Diplomate: Am. Bd. Surgery, Am. Bd. Thoracic Surgery, Am. Bd. Pediatric Surgery. Intern Phila. Gen. Hosp., 1953-54; postgrad. U. Pa., 1956-57; resident in gen. surgery Med. Coll. S.C., Charleston, 1957-62; resident in pediatric surgery Ohio State U. and Columbus Children's Hosp., 1962-64; research fellow Harvard U., Mass. Gen. Hosp., Boston, 1964-65; asst. prof. pediatric surgery Med. U. S.C., Charleston, 1965-68; assoc. prof. Med. U. S.C., 1968-72, prof., 1972—; chief pediatric surgery, 1972—; med. dir. Med. U. S.C. Hosp., 1981-85, Children's Hosp., 1985—. Editor The Pediatric Airway; mem. editorial bd. Jour. Pediatric Surgery, Jour. Parenteral and Enteral Nutrition; contbr. articles on pediatric oncology, esophageal, tracheal strictures to profl. jours. Bd. dirs., pres. S.C. div. Am. Cancer Soc., 1977-79. Served with USN, 1954-56, Korea. Fellow ACS, Am. Acad. Pediat.; mem. Am. Pediatic Surg. Assn. (bd. govs. 1986-89), Brit. Assn. Pediatric Surgeons (overseas coun.), Am. Trauma Soc., So. Surg. Assn., Charleston County Med. Soc. (pres. 1980), Alpha Omega Alpha (councillor 1978-94). Home: 171 Ashley Ave Charleston SC 29425 Office: MUSC Children's Hosp 171 Ashley Ave Charleston SC 29425-0001 *A man ought to do what he thinks is right.*

OTHMER, DAVID ARTMAN, television and radio station executive; b. West Medford, Mass., Mar. 18, 1941; s. Murray Eade and Mary (Artman) O.; m. Nancy Trumbull, Sept. 12, 1965 (div. Dec. 1982); 1 child, Rachel; m. Maureen Barden, June 4, 1983; 1 child, Matthew. BA, Harvard Coll., 1963; MBA, Harvard U., 1966. Asst. to pres. Sta. WNET, N.Y.C., 1974-75, dir. broadcasting, 1975-82, dir. telecommunications, 1982-83; v.p. sta. mgr. Sta. WHYY, Phila., 1983—. Exec. producer (TV show) Science Spots, 1985 (Ohio State award 1985); producer (TV show) Who is Red Grooms?, 1986 (Emmy 1986), various other TV shows, 1980— (Emmy nominations). Avocations: growing grapes and making wine. Home: 4220 Spruce St Philadelphia PA 19104-4040 Office: Sta WHYY 150 N 6th St Philadelphia PA 19106-1508

OTHS, RICHARD PHILIP, hospital administrator, insurance firm executive; b. N.Y.C., July 3, 1935; s. Philip John and Florence Violet (Kraus) O.; m. Eleanor Fuerst, May 11, 1957; children—Philip, Lisa, Eleanor, Richard. BS in Pharmacy, Fordham U., 1956; MBA in Health Care Adminstrn., CUNY, 1976. Field sales rep. E.R. Squibb & Sons, N.Y.C., 1960-63; hosp. rep. E.R. Squibb & Sons, 1963-65; div. mgr. E.R. Squibb & Sons, Manhattan, 1965-68; adminstr. operating room Mt. Sinai Hosp., N.Y.C., 1968-69, dir. admitting, 1969-71, asst. dir. hosp., 1971-76; v.p. mgr. Bethesda Hosp. Oak, Cin., 1976-84; pres. Am. Health Capital HIBI Mgmt., Inc., N.Y.C., 1984-88; pres., chief exec. officer Morristown (N.J.) Meml. Hosp., 1988—; Goldwater fellow in hosp. adminstr. Mt. Sinai Hosp., N.Y.C., 1973; cons. Physicians Protective Trust Fund-Fla. Served with USAF, 1957-60. Recipient award E.R. Squibb-AMA, 1964. Mem. APHA, ACHA, Am. Hosp. Assn. Republican. Roman Catholic. Home: 26 Glen Gary Dr Mendham NJ 07945-3030 Office: Morristown Meml Hosp PO Box 1956 Morristown NJ 07962-1956

OTIS, ARTHUR BROOKS, physiologist, educator; b. Grafton, Maine, Sept. 11, 1913; s. Will Howe and Carrie (Brooks) O.; m. Eileen Macomber, Aug. 24, 1942; 1 son, Chandler Brooks. A.B., U. Maine, 1935; M.Ed., Springfield Coll., 1937; Sc.M., Brown U., 1939, Ph.D., 1941. Research assoc. cellular physiology State U. Iowa, 1941-42; instr. physiology U. Rochester Sch. Medicine, 1942-46, assoc. physiology, 1946-47, asst. prof. physiology, 1947-51; assoc. prof. physiology and surgery Johns Hopkins Sch. Medicine, 1952-56; prof. physiology U. Fla. Coll. Medicine, Gainesville, 1956-86; prof. emeritus U. Fla. Coll. Medicine, 1986—, head dept., 1956-80; civilian scientist OSRD, 1944; mem. physiology com. Nat. Bd. Med. Examiners, 1981-84. Author sci. papers; editor respiration sect.: Am. Jour. Physiology and Jour. Applied Physiology, 1962-64; editorial bd.: Respiration Physiology, 1970-81. Fulbright research scholar, 1950-51, 64-65. Mem. Am. Physiol. Soc., Soc. Gen. Physiologists, Phi Beta Kappa, Sigma Xi. Home: 2123 NW 4th Pl Gainesville FL 32603-1515

OTIS, DENISE MARIE, editor, writer; b. Detroit, July 25, 1927; d. J. Hawley and Florence Ruth O. AB cum laude, Radcliffe Coll., Cambridge, Mass., 1949. English tchr. Cambridge Sch., Weston, Mass., 1949-50; asst. to feature editor House and Garden, N.Y.C., 1952-53, assoc. decorating editor, 1953-56, editor, entertaining dept., 1956-66, assoc. editor, 1966-80, deputy editor, 1980-87; sr. editor and cons. Condé Nast Pubs., N.Y.C., 1987-93; consulting editor Vogue Decoration, Paris, 1989-91. Author: Decorating with Flowers, 1978; contbr. articles to profl. jours. Fulbright scholar Inst. Internat. Edn., France, 1950-51. mem. Internat. Dendrology Soc., Decorators Club, Phi Beta Kappa. Episcopalian. Avocations: cooking, photography, gardening.

OTIS, GLENN KAY, retired army officer, research and engineering company executive; b. Plattsburgh, N.Y., Mar. 15, 1929; s. Glenn Kirk and Violet Lucy (Hart) O.; m. Barbara Davies, June 6, 1953; children: Caren Otis, Nancee Otis Groh, Peter. BS, U.S. Mil. Acad., 1953; MS in Math., Rensselaer Poly. Inst., 1960; M in Mil. Sci., U.S. Army Command and Gen. Staff Coll., 1965. Commd. 2d lt. U.S. Army, 1953; gen.; dep. chief staff for ops. and plans Hdqrs. Dept. Army; comdg. gen. U.S. Army Tng. and Doctrine Command, Ft.Monroe, Va.; comdr. in chief U.S. Army Europe, Heidelberg, Federal Republic of Germany, 1983-88; ret. U.S. Army Europe, Heidelberg, 1988; corp. v.p. Coleman Rsch. Corp., 1989—. Decorated D.S.C., Silver Star, Legion of Merit, Purple Heart. Roman Catholic. Home: 97 Normandy Ln Newport News VA 23606-1533 Office: 9302 Lee Hwy Fairfax VA 22031-1214

OTIS, JACK, social work educator; b. N.Y.C., Feb. 13, 1923; s. Abraham and Esther (Goldberg) O.; children: Elisabeth H., Erich R., Greta M., Marcus H., Alicia. A.B., Bklyn. Coll., 1946; M.S. in Social Work, U. Ill., 1948, M.Ed., 1955, Ph.D., 1957. Social worker Jewish Social Svc. Bur. Dade County, 1948-49; Psychiat. social worker Free Synagogue Social Service, N.Y. U., 1949-50; assoc. prof. U. Ill., 1950-61; dep. dir. Office Juvenile Delinquency and Youth Devel., Dept. Health, Edn. and Welfare, 1961-65; dean Grad. Sch. Social Work U. Tex., 1965-77, prof. emeritus, 1993—; cons. to govt., 1961—; presenter Internat. Coun. on Social Welfare, Inter-Univ. Consortium for Internat. Social Devel., Internat. Assn. Schs. Social Work, 1994; mem. President's Com. Juvenile Delinquency and Youth Crime, 1961-65; spl. cons. for Am. social work edn. and rsch. European Ctr. for Social Welfare Tng. and Rsch., Vienna, Austria, 1976—. Author: (with George Barnett) Corporate Society and Education, 1961; contbr. article on child labor to Ency. Social Work, 1995. Bd. overseers Ctr. for Study Violence, Brandeis U., 1966-70. With AUS, 1943-46, PTO. Fulbright-Hays research fellow Austria, 1977-78. Mem. AAUP, Coun. on Social Work Edn. (commn. on accreditation), Philosophy of Edn. Soc., Nat. Assn. Social Workers, Am. Acad. Polit. and Social Sci., N.Y. Acad. Sci., Johannesburg Child Welfare Soc. (rsch. cons. South Africa chpt. 1990-91), Phi Kappa Phi (pres.). Office: Univ of Tex Sch Social Work Austin TX 78712 *The meaning of my life is whether I have added to the meaning of another's.*

OTIS, JAMES, JR., architect; b. Chgo., July 8, 1931; s. James and Edwina (Love) O.; m. Diane Cleveland, Apr. 9, 1955; children: James III, Julie C., David C. BArch cum laude, Princeton U., 1953; postgrad., U. Chgo., 1955-57. Registered architect, Ill., Ariz., Colo., Ind., Iowa, Wis. Designer Irvin A. Blietz Co., Wilmette, Ill., 1955-57; pres. Homefinders Constrn. Corp., Wilmette, 1957-59, O & F Constrn. Co., Northbrook, Ill., 1959-61; chmn. bd., chief exec. officer Otis Assocs., Inc., Northbrook, Ill., 1960-89; pres. Otis Co., 1981—; bd. dirs. Pioneer Bank, Chgo.; So. Mineral Corp. Prin. works include GBC Corp. Hdqrs., Zurich Towers Office Complex, Schaumburg, Ill., Combined Ins. Co. Corp. Hdqrs., Performing Arts Ctr., Northbrook Ill., All State Regional Hdqrs, Skokie, Ill. Trustee Evanston (Ill.) Hosp., 1971-93, Better Govt. Assn., Chgo., Graham Found.; chmn. bd. trustees North Suburban YMCA, Northbrook, 1990—; governing mem. Shedd Aquarium; bd. govs. Chgo. Zool. Soc.; mem. adv. bd. Cook County Forest Preserve Dist.; mem. founder's coun. Field Mus., Chgo. Lt. USNR, 1953-55. Mem.

AIA, Nat. Coun. Archtl Registration Bds., Urban Land Inst., Northwestern U. Assocs., Chgo. Coun. Fgn. Rels. (assoc.), Internat. Wine and Food Soc., Princeton Club (pres. 1971-72), Econ. Club, Commonwealth Club, Chgo. Club, Comml. Club, Glenview (Ill.) Club, coleman Lake Club, Angler's Club. Republican. Episcopalian. Office: 310 Happ Rd Northfield IL 60093

OTIS, JOHN JAMES, civil engineer; b. Syracuse, N.Y., Aug. 5, 1922; s. John Joseph and Anna (Dey) O.; m. Dorothy Fuller Otis, June 21, 1958; children: Mary Eileen Dawn, John Leon. B of Chem. Engring., Syracuse U. 1943, MBA, 1950, postgrad., 1951-55. Registered profl. engr., Ala., Tex.; cert. profl. for hazardous waste opns. and emergency response. Jr. process engr. GM, Syracuse, 1951-53, prodn. engr., 1954-58, process control engr. 1958-59, process engr., 1960-61; engr., writer GE, Syracuse, 1961-63; configuration control engr. GE, Phila., 1969; assoc. research engr. Boeing Co. Huntsville, Ala., 1963-65; assoc. Planning Rsch. Corp., Huntsville, 1965-67; prin. engr. Brown Engring. Co. subs. Teledyne Co., Huntsville, 1967-69; mech. designer Drever Co., Beth Ayres, Pa., 1970-71; civil engr. U.S. Army Corps Engrs., Mobile, Ala., 1971-74, Galveston, Tex., 1974—. Lector, lay minister Roman Cath. Ch. Served with USNR, 1944-50. Mem. Am. Inst. Indsl. Engrs. (past v.p. Syracuse and Huntsville chpts.), Tex. Soc. Profl. Engrs. (dir. Galveston County chpt. 1976-79, sec.-treas. 1979-80, v.p. 1980-81, pres. 1982-83), Am. Legion, Tau Beta Pi, Phi Kappa Tau, Alpha Chi Sigma, Chi Eta Sigma. Home: 2114 Yorktown Ct N League City TX 77573-5056 Office: US Army Corps Engrs Jadwin Bldg 2000 Fort Point Rd Galveston TX 77550-3038

OTIS, LEE LIBERMAN, lawyer, educator; b. N.Y.C., Aug. 19, 1956; d. James Benjamin and Deen (Freed) L.; m. William Graham Otis, Oct. 24, 1993. BA, Yale U., 1979; JD, U. Chgo., 1983. Bar: N.Y. 1985, D.C. 1994. Law clk. U.S. Ct. Appeals (D.C. cir.), Washington, 1983-84; spl. asst. to asst. atty. gen., civil div. U.S. Dept. Justice, Washington, 1984-86; dep. assoc. atty. gen. U.S. Dept. Justice, 1986, assoc. dep. atty. gen., 1986; law clk. to Justice Antonin Scalia U.S. Supreme Ct., Washington, 1986-87; asst. profl. law George Mason U., Arlington, Va., 1987-89; assoc. counsel to the Pres. Exec. Office of the Pres., Washington, 1989-92; assoc. Jones, Day, Reavis & Pogue, Washington, 1993-94; chief judiciary coun. U.S. Sen. Spence Abraham, 1995—; adj. prof. law Georgetown Law Sch., 1995. Mem. Federalist Soc. for Law & Pub. Policy (founder, dir., nat. co-chmn.). Republican. Jewish. Avocations: sailing, computers.

O'TOOLE, ALLAN THOMAS, electric utility executive; b. Waterloo, Iowa, Dec. 22, 1925; s. Delmar C. and Elsie M. (Winkelman) O'T.; m. Barbara Joyce Boyd, Sept. 2, 1947; children: Kathy Lynn, Timothy Allan. BA, Westminster Coll., Fulton, Mo., 1948; postgrad., U. Mich., 1965. With Pub. Svc. Co. Okla., 1953-88, asst. treas., 1967-70, treas., 1970-73, v.p., contr., 1973-76, v.p. adminstrn., 1976-80, v.p. materiel and property mgmt., 1980-85, v.p. corp. svcs., 1985-88; ret. 1988. Bd. dirs., chmn. bd. Tulsa Area chpt. ARC, 1975—, regional chmn. midwestern ops. hdqrs., 1989-92; bd. dirs., pres. Tulsa Sr. Svcs. Inc., 1990—. Lt. USNR, 1943-46, 51-53. Mem. Tulsa C. of C, Adminstrv. Mgmt. Soc. (bd. dirs., pres.), Westminster Coll. Alumni Assn. (pres., bd. trustees), K.C., Cedar Ridge Country Club, Kappa Alpha. Roman Catholic. Home: 8442 S Florence Ave Tulsa OK 74137-1435

O'TOOLE, AUSTIN MARTIN, lawyer; b. New Bedford, Mass., Oct. 5, 1935; s. John Brian, Jr. and Helen Veronica O'T.; m. Kay Murphy, Nov. 27, 1982; children: Erin Ann, Austin Martin 2d. BBA, Coll. Holy Cross, 1957; JD, Georgetown U., 1963. Bar: N.Y. 1965, D.C. 1963, Tex. 1975. Law clk. to judge U.S. Ct. Appeals, Washington, 1962-63; assoc. White & Case, N.Y.C., 1963-74; sr. v.p., sr. counsel, sec. Coastal Corp., Houston, 1974—; bd. dirs. A.A. White Dispute Resolution Inst. Bd. editors Georgetown Law Jour., 1962-63. Bd. dirs. Houston Coun. on Alcoholism and Drug Abuse, Houston, 1986-91; com. mem. Houston-Tenneco Marathon. Officer USMCR, 1957-60. Mem. ABA, Am. Soc. Corp. Secs. (bd. dirs. 1982-85), Tex. Bar Assn., Houston Bar Assn. (past chmn. corp. counsel sect. 1979-80), Am. Arbitration Assn. (comml. com.). Home: 2008 Timberlane Houston TX 77027 Office: Coastal Corp 9 E Greenway Plz Houston TX 77046-0995

O'TOOLE, DENNIS ALLEN, museum director; b. Scott AFB, Ill., Mar. 12, 1941; s. Roger Leslie and Emily May (Fisher) O'T.; m. Gertrude Lenore Probsting, July 10, 1965; children: Kara, Anne, Aaron. BA, Princeton U., 1963; MAT, Harvard U., 1965; PhD, Brown U., 1973; cert. exec. program, Dartmouth Coll., 1989. Tchr. Belmont (Mass.) H.S., 1965-67; curator of edn. Nat. Portrait Gallery, Washington, 1972-78; dir. group visits and ednl programs Colonial Williamsburg (Va.), 1979; dep. dir. mus. ops. Colonial Williamsburg Va.) Farm, 1982-88; v.p., chief edn. officer Colonial Williamsburg (Va.), 1988-92; assoc. dir. Strawbery Banke, Inc., Portsmouth, N.H., 1992—; at-large coun. mem. Am. Assn. Mus., Washington, 1988-91; mem. coun. Am. Assn. State and Local History, Nashville, 1992—; mem. coun., exec. com. Inst. Early Am. History and Culture, Williamsburg, 1988-92. House minority clk. R.I. Ho. of Reps., Providence, 1968; bd. dirs. Friends of Williamsburg Regional Libr., 1990-92; mem. Portsmouth Advocates, 1993—. Mem. Rotary. Avocations: tennis, hiking, cross-country skiing, biking, reading. Office: Strawbery Banke Mus PO Box 300 Portsmouth NH 03802

O'TOOLE, FRANCIS J., lawyer; b. Dublin, Ireland, Feb. 10, 1944; came to U.S., 1960; s. Francis Herbert and Josephine (McCarthy) O'T.; m. Carole Ann Leland, Apr. 11, 1977; children: Kathleen, Kirra. AB, Harvard U., 1967; JD, U. Maine, 1970. Bar: Maine 1970, U.S. Supreme Ct. 1977, U.S. Dist. Ct. D.C., U.S. Dist. Ct. (ea. dist.) Va., U.S. Ct. Appeals (1st, 2d, 4th, 5th, 7th, 8th, 9th and 10th cirs.). Assoc. Fried, Frank, Harris, Shriver & Jacobsen, Washington, 1971-78, ptnr., 1978-92; ptnr. Sidley & Austin, Washington, 1992—. Editor-in-chief U. Maine Law Rev., 1969-70; contbr. articles to profl. jours. Reginald Heber Smith fellow Calif. Indian Legal Services, 1970-71. Mem. ABA. Avocations: horse breeding and racing. Home: 1214 Vinita Ln Mc Lean VA 22102-1716 Office: Sidley & Austin 1722 I St NW Washington DC 20006-3705

O'TOOLE, JAMES JOSEPH, business educator; b. San Francisco, Apr. 15, 1945; s. James Joseph and Irene (Nagy) O'T.; m. Marilyn Louise Burrill, June 17, 1967; children: Erin Kathleen, Kerry Louise. BA, U. So. Calif., L.A., 1966; DPhil, Oxford (Eng.) U. (Eng.), 1970. Corr. Time-Life News Service, L.A., 1967-68, Nairobi, Kenya, 1967-68; mgmt. cons. McKinsey & Co., San Francisco, 1969-70; coordinator field investigations Pres.'s Comm. on Campus Unrest, Washington, 1970; spl. asst. to sec. HEW, Washington, 1970-73; prof. mgmt. U. So. Calif.-Los Angeles, 1973-93, Univ. Assocs. Chair of Bus., 1982-93; chmn. sec.'s com. work in Am. HEW, Wshington, 1971-72; exec. dir. The Leadership Inst., 1990-93; v.p. Aspen Inst., 1994—; bd. dirs. Radica Games. Prin. author: Work in America, 1973, Energy and Social Change, 1976; author: Work, Learning and the American Future, 1977, Making America Work, 1982 (Phi Kappa Phi prize 1982), Vanguard Management, 1985, The Executive's Compass, 1993, Leading Change, 1995; bd. editors: Ency. Britannica, Chgo., 1981-87; editor: New Management, Los Angeles, 1983-89. Mem. Project Paideia, Chgo., 1981-83. Rhodes scholar, 1966; recipient Mitchell prize Woodlands Conf., 1979. Mem. Phi Beta Kappa. Home: 19912 Pacific Coast Hwy Malibu CA 90265-5423 Office: The Aspen Inst 1000 N 3rd St Aspen CO 81611

O'TOOLE, JOHN DUDLEY, retired utility executive, consultant; b. N.Y.C., Sept. 16, 1921; s. Lawrence Patrick and Mary Gertrude (Casey) O'T.; m. Constance Telfair, Jan. 17, 1952; children: John D. Jr., Paul L., Mary C., Michelle E. Hair, Jane C. Keating. M.E. with honors, Stevens Inst. Tech., 1949; postgrad., Poly. Inst. Bklyn., 1949-51. Registered profl. engr., Conn. Engr. Gibbs & Cox Inc., N.Y.C., 1949-54; engring. mgr. Union Carbide Nuclear Co., Paducah, Ky., 1954-55, Combustion Engring. Inc., Windsor, Conn., 1955-62, Westinghouse Electric Co., Pitts., 1962-66; engring. mgr., v.p. United Nuclear Corp. and Gulf United Nuclear Corp., Elmsford, N.Y., 1966-72; asst. to v.p., then v.p. Consol. Edison Co. of N.Y., N.Y.C., 1973-86; cons. Power Mgmt. Assocs., 1986—; nuclear div. com. Electric Power Research Inst., Palo Alto, Calif., 1980-86; vice chmn. Welding Research Council, N.Y.C., 1984-86; mem. vis. com. Lehigh U., Bethlehem, Pa., 1982-86. Contbr. tech. papers and articles to profl. jours. Mgmt. com. Nature Preserve, Nature Conservancy, Katonah, N.Y., 1970 nominating Katonah-Lewisboro Sch. Bd., 1970. Served with USN,

1943-46. N.Y. State War Service scholar N.Y. Dept. Edn., 1949. Home: 7 Thomas St Barrington RI 02806-4824

O'TOOLE, JOHN E., advertising executive; b. Chgo., Jan. 17, 1929; m. Phyllis Treadway, 1955; children: Sally, Ellen. BJ, Northwestern U., 1951. With Batten, Barton, Durstine & Osborn, 1953-54, Foote, Cone & Belding, 1954-85; successively copy writer, copy supr., v.p., creative dir. Foote, Cone & Belding, L.A. and Chgo.; pres. Foote, Cone & Belding, N.Y.C., 1969; pres. Foote, Cone & Belding Communications, Inc., N.Y.C., 1970-81, chmn. 1981-85; dir. Am. Assn. Advt. Agys., Washington, 1986-88, pres., 1988—; dir. Nat. Advt. Rev. Coun.; bd. dirs. John Nuveen Mut. Funds. Author: The Trouble with Advertising, 1981. Served with USMCR, 1951-53; ret. Res. 1956. Office: Am Assn Advt Agys 666 3d Ave New York NY 10017-4011

O'TOOLE, LAWRENCE WILLIAM, lawyer, educational finance professional; b. Bklyn., Sept. 23, 1950; s. Vincent P. and Rita (Ryan) O'T.; m. Nancy Fay Partridge, Sept. 6, 1975; children: Matthew V., James W. BBA, Adelphi U., 1972; JD, Union U., 1975. Bar: N.Y. 1976, 79, U.S. Dist. Ct. (no. dist.) N.Y. 1976, U.S. Dist. Ct. (we. and ea. dists.) N.Y. 1978, U.S. Dist. Ct. (so. dist.) N.Y. 1979, U.S. Ct. Appeals (2d cir.) 1979, U.S. Supreme Ct. 1980, Mass. 1982. Of counsel com. on higher edn. N.Y. State Assembly, Albany, 1975-76; of counsel com. on corps. and authorities, 1977; gen. counsel N.Y. State Higher Edn. Services Corp., Albany, 1977-80; v.p., gen. counsel Mass. Higher Edn. Assistance Corp., Boston, 1980-82; pres., chief exec. officer New Eng. Edn. Loan Mktg. Corp., Braintree, Mass., 1982—; mem. adv. com. Mass. Industrial Fin. Agy., Boston, 1985; bd. dirs. Secondary Sch. Admission Test Bd., Princeton, N.J., 1985—, Nat. Council Higher Edn. Loan Programs, Washington, 1987—. Democrat. Episcopalian. Office: New Eng Edn Loan Mktg Corp 50 Braintree Hill Office Park Suite 300 Braintree MA 02184*

O'TOOLE, MARIE THERESA, rehabilitation nursing educator; b. Phila., Sept. 12, 1950; d. Edmond Francis and Margaret Mary (McKee) O'Donnell; m. Kevin Francis O'Toole, June 3, 1972; children: Timothy, Michael, Daniel, Kevin Patrick. Diploma, Hosp. U. Pa., 1971; BSN, U. Pa., 1974, MSN, 1977; EdD, Rutgers U., 1992. RN, N.J., Pa.; cert. rehab. nurse. Staff devel. instr. Hosp. U. Pa., Phila.; instr. U. Pa., Phila.; asst. prof. rehab. nursing Rutgers U., Camden, N.J., Thomas Jefferson U., Camden; participant bd. rev. courses Med. Coll. Pa. Author: (with others) Rehabilitation Nursing: Concepts and Practice, 1987; editor: Miller-Keane Dictionary of Medicine, Nursing and Allied Health, 1992; co-author monthly continuing edn. units RN Mag. Recipient Thomas B. McCabe Achievement award, 1969, 70, 71; Alumni scholar Hosp. U. Pa., 1974. Mem. ANA, ARN, N.J. State Nurses Assn., Sigma Theta Tau, Kappa Delta Pi. Home: 318 2d Ave Haddon Heights NJ 08035

O'TOOLE, PETER, actor; b. County Galway, Ireland, Aug. 2, 1932; s. Patrick Joseph and Constance (Ferguson) O'T.; m. Sian Phillips, 1959 (div. 1979); children: Kate, Pat; m. Karen Brown, 1983 (div.); 1 child, Lorcan. Student, Royal Acad. Dramatic Arts. Actor Bristol Old Vic Co., 1955-58; London stage debut in Major Barbara, 1956; other stage appearances include Present Laughter, The Apple Cart, 1986, Pygmalion, 1987, Jeffrey Bervard is Unwell, 1989; films include Kidnapped, 1960, The Day They Robbed the Bank of England, 1960, Savage Innocents, 1961, Lawrence of Arabia, 1962, Becket, 1964, Lord Jim, 1965, What's New, Pussycat?, 1965, How to Steal a Million, 1966, The Bible... in the Beginning, 1966, The Night of the Generals, 1967, Great Catherine, 1968, The Lion in Winter, 1968, Goodbye Mr. Chips, 1969, Murphy's War, 1971, Under Milk Wood, 1971, Brotherly Love, The Ruling Class, 1972, Man of LaMancha, 1972, Rosebud, 1975, Man Friday, 1975, Foxtrot, 1976, Coup d'Etat, 1977, Zulu Dawn, 1978, Power Play, 1978, Caligula, 1979, Stuntman, 1980, The Antagonists, 1981, My Favorite Year, 1981, Supergirl, 1984, Creator, 1985, Club Paradise, 1985, The Last Emperor, 1987, High Spirits, 1988, On a Moonlit Night, 1989, Helena, Wings of Fame, The Pit and the Pendulum, King Ralph, 1991, Rebecca's Daughters, 1992, The Seventh Coin, 1993; appeared in: Rogue Male, BBC-TV, 1976, Strumpet City, RTE-TV, 1979; TV mini-series Masada, 1981, Svengali, 1982; TV film: Kim, 1983, The Dark Angel, BBC TV, 1988, Crossing to Freedom, 1990; autobiography Loitering with Intent, 1993. Decorated Comdr. des Arts et des Lettres, 1988. Office: William Morris Agy, 31/32 Sotto Sq, London W1V 5DG, England*

O'TOOLE, ROBERT JOSEPH, manufacturing company executive; b. Chgo., Feb. 22, 1941; s. Francis John O'Toole; children: William, Patricia, Timothy, Kathleen, John. BS in Acctg., Loyola U., Chgo., 1961. Fin. analyst A.O. Smith Corp., Milw., 1963-66, mgr. corp. fin. analysis and planning, 1966-68; contr. electric motor div. A.O. Smith Corp., Tipp City, Ohio, 1968-71; mng. dir. Bull Motors, Ipswich, Eng., 1971-74; gen. plant mgr. electric motor div. A.O. Smith Corp., Tipp City, 1974-79, v.p., gen. mgr., 1979-83; v.p. A.O. Smith Corp., Milw., 1984-85, pres., chief oper. officer, 1986-89, pres., chief exec. officer, 1989—; also bd. dirs., now chmn. bd. dirs., 1992—; bd. dirs. 1st Wis. Nat. Bank, Milw.; mem. exec. com. TEC XIV, Milw., Mfrs. Alliance for Productivity and Innovation, Bus. Roundtable, Greater Milw. Com., Competitive Wis., Inc. Mem. Wis. Mgrs. and Commerce Assn. (exec. com.), Met. Milw. Assn. Commerce (bd. dirs.), Milw. Country Club, Univ. Club. Office: A O Smith Corp 1 Park Plz 11270 W Park Pl Milwaukee WI 53224-3623*

O'TOOLE, TARA J., federal official; d. Harold J. and Jeanne (Whalen) O'T. BA, Vassar Coll., 1974; MD, George Washington U., 1981; MPH, Johns Hopkins U., 1988. Diplomate Am. Bd. Internal Medicine, Am. Bd. Preventive/Occupational Medicine. Rsch. asst. Sloan-Kettering Cancer Inst., N.Y.C., 1974-77; resident in internal medicine Yale New Haven (Conn.) Hosp., 1981-84; physician Balt. Cmty. Health Ctrs., 1984-87; fellow in occupational medicine Johns Hopkins U., Balt., 1987-89; sr. analyst Office Tech. Assessment, Washington, 1989-93; asst. sec. energy for environ., safety and health Dept. Energy, Washington, 1993—. Democrat. Office: Dept of Energy Environ Safety & Health 1000 Independence Ave SE Washington DC 20585

O'TOOLE, TERRENCE J., lawyer; b. Mo., 1946. AB, St. Louis U., 1968; JD, U. Mo., 1972. Bar: Mo. 1973, U.S. Ct. Appeals (5th cir.) 1984, U.S. Ct. Appeals (3d cir.) 1988, U.S. Ct. Appeals (8th cir.) 1991. Asst. cir. atty. City St. Louis, 1973-76, 1st asst. cir. atty., 1977-78; ptnr. Bryan Cave, St. Louis. Mem. ABA. Office: Bryan Cave 211 N Broadway Saint Louis MO 63102-2733

OTSTOTT, CHARLES PADDOCK, army officer; b. Ft. Worth, June 2, 1937; s. Daniel Dushane and Sarah May (Paddock) O.; m. Candice Lee Curley, Nov. 6, 1982; 1 child, Kelley Ann; 1 child from previous marriage, James Boyd. BS, U.S. Mil. Acad., West Point, N.Y., 1960; MS, Purdue U., 1967. Commd. 2d lt. U.S. Army, 1960, advanced through grades to lt. gen., 1990; bn. advisor Republic of Vietnam, 1964-65; co. cmdr., S-3, 2d bn. 502 Inf. (Airborne) 101st Airborne Div., 1967-68; comdr. 1st bn. 46 Inf., 1st Armored Div., Erlangen, Fed. Republic Germany, 1976-78; student Nat. War Coll., Ft. McNair, D.C., 1978-79; comdr. 2d brigade 9th High Tech. Light Div., Ft. Lewis, Wash., 1979-82; chief of staff 9th High Tech. Light Div., Ft. Lewis, 1982-83; exec. to SACEUR Supreme Hdqrs. Allied Powers Europe, Belgium, 1983-85; asst. div. comdr. 1st Armored Div., Bamberg, Fed. Republic Germany, 1985-86; comdg. gen. Combined Arms Combat Devel. Activity, Ft. Leavenworth, Kans., 1986-88, 25th Inf. Div. (Light), Schofield Barracks, Hawaii, 1988-90; dep. chmn. NATO Mil. Com., Brussels, 1990-92; ret. from active svc., 1992—, pvt. cons. strategic planning, 1992—; instr., then asst. prof. dept. physics U.S. Mil. Acad., West Point, 1968-71. Chmn. adv. com. Resolution Am. Sch., 1990-92. Decorated Def. D.S.M., Army D.S.M., Def. Superior Svc. medal, Silver Star, Legion of Merit. Avocations: handball, jogging, picture framing, woodworking.

OTT, DAVID MICHAEL, engineering company executive; b. Glendale, Calif., Feb. 24, 1952; s. Frank Michael and Roberta (Michie) O.; m. Cynthia Dianne Bunce. BSEE, U. Calif., Berkeley, 1974. Electronic engr. Teknekron Inc., Berkeley, 1974-79; chief engr. TCI, Berkeley, 1979-83; div. mgr. Integrated Automation Inc., Alameda, Calif., 1983-87, Litton Indsl. Automation, Alameda, 1987-92; founder, chmn. Picture Elements Inc., Berkeley, 1992—. Inventor method for verifying denomination of currency, method for processing digited images, automatic document image revision. Mem.

IEEE, AAAS, Assn. Computing Machinery, Union of Concerned Scientists. Office: Picture Elements Inc 777 Panoramic Way Berkeley CA 94704-2538

OTT, GEORGE WILLIAM, JR., management consulting executive; b. Chgo., May 5, 1932; s. George William and Isabelle (Salkeld) O.; m. Joan Virginia Vasseur; June 20, 1954; children: Lisa Joan, George William III, Robert Alexander. BSBA, U. So. Calif., L.A, 1954, MBA, 1960. CPA, Tex. Engr. adminstr. Douglas Aircraft, El Segundo, Calif., 1956-59; adminstrv. engr. Lear Corp., Santa Monica, Calif., 1959-61; co. adminstr. Plasmadyne Corp., Santa Ana, Calif., 1961-63; ptnr. Peat Marwick Mitchell & Co., L.A. and Houston, 1963-71; v.p. Korn/Ferry Internat., L.A., 1971-76; founder., pres., chief exec. officer Ott and Hansen, Inc., Pasadena, Calif., 1976—; bd. dirs. Vireo Mfg. Co.; mem. adv. bd. Compensation Resource Group Inc. 1988—. Pres., bd. dirs. Career Encores, 1989—; chmn., bd. dirs. Salvation Army, L.A. metro, 1989—. Lt. (j.g.) USN, 1954-56. Mem. Nat. Assn. Corp. Dirs., Calif. Exec. Recruiters Assn. (pres. 1992), Jonathan Club (L.A.), Annandale Golf Club, Rotary. Avocations: golf, model railroading. Office: Ott & Hansen 136 S Oak Knolls Ave Ste 300 Pasadena CA 91101-2624

OTT, GILBERT RUSSELL, JR., lawyer; b. Bklyn., Apr. 15, 1943; s. Gilbert Russell Sr. and Bettina Rose (Ferrel) O.; m. Lisa S. Weatherford, Apr. 12, 1986; children: Gilbert R. III, Laura Elisabeth. BA, Yale U., 1965; JD, Columbia U., 1969, MBA, 1969. Bar: N.Y. 1970. Assoc. Chadbourne, Parke, Whiteside & Wolff, N.Y.C., 1969-72, LeBoeuf, Lamb, Leiby & MacRae, N.Y.C., 1972-78; assoc. gen. counsel Kidder, Peabody & Co., Inc., N.Y.C., 1978—, asst. sec. 1978-91, asst. v.p., 1978-79, v.p., 1979-86, mng. dir., 1986-91, sr. v.p., sec., 1992—; v.p. Kidder, Peabody Group Inc., N.Y.C., 1989—; asst. sec., 1986—; bd. dirs. various subs. of Kidder, Peabody Group, Inc. Mem. Assn. of Bar of City of N.Y., Piping Rock Club, Down Town Assn., Univ. Club. Home: 260 Highwood Cir Oyster Bay NY 11771-3205 Office: Kidder Peabody & Co Inc 10 Hanover Sq New York NY 10005-3516

OTT, JACK M., mathematics educator; b. Albion, Ind., June 30, 1931; s. William Cleon and Alice Ann (Shew) O.; m. Melvia June Day, Dec. 24, 1952; children: Barbara Jean Ott Babb, Debra Ann Ott Miller, Gregory C. AB, Marion (Ind.) Coll., 1956; MA, Ball State U., 1962; PhD, Ohio State U., 1967. Mathematics tchr. Harrison Twp. Sch., Amboy, Ind., 1956-58; mathematics, physics tchr. Marion High Sch., 1958-59; asst. prof. Tri State Coll., Angola, Ind., 1959-62, Montclair (N.J.) State Coll., 1962-63; tchng. asst., dir. test devel. ctr. Ohio State U., Columbus, 1963-68; asst. prof. Ontario (Can.) Inst. for Study in Edn., Toronto, 1968-70; assoc. prof. U. S.C., Columbia, 1970-74, prof., 1974—; adv. bd. Columbia Bible Coll. 1986—; bd. dirs. S.C. Ind. Schs. Assn., Columbia, 1980. Author: A Decision Process and System for Planning Educational Change, 1967, Geometry, 1969, Merrill Mathematics, 1985, Building Skills in Mathematics Workbooks, 1988, Mathematics Application and Connections, 1993, 2d edit., 1995. Sgt. U.S. Army, 1952-54. S.C. Commn. of Higher Edn. grantee, 1971, 72, U.S. Office of Edn. grantee 1974; named one of Disting. Alumni Marion Coll., 1987. Mem. Nat. Council Tchrs. of Mathematics, Am. Ednl. Research Assn., Phi Delta Kappa. Republican. Baptist. Avocations: gardening, athletics. Home: 785 Garden Dr Columbia SC 29210 Office: U SC Coll Edn Columbia SC 29208 *Intelligence is about 99% the results of hard work and integrity. Work and experience are great teachers, but integrity is needed to assure that what one learns is productive rather than destructive.*

OTT, JAMES FORGAN, finance company executive; b. Chgo., Oct. 22, 1935; s. John Nash and Emily (Fentress) O.; m. Edna Cassinerio, July 8, 1961; children: Jeffery, Edna, Michael, Emily. A.B., Brown U., 1958; M.B.A., Northwestern U., 1961. C.P.A., Ill. Asso. investment banking White Weld & Co., Chgo., 1961-65; v.p. corp. fin. Eastman Dillion Union Securities & Co., Inc., Chgo., 1966-70; ptnr. Blunt Ellis & Simmons, Chgo., 1970-73; v.p. and treas., chief fin. officer The L.E. Myers Co., Chgo., 1973-83; sr. v.p., chief fin. officer Chgo. Title and Trust Co., 1983-86; v.p. fin., chief fin. officer, sec., treas. Middleby Corp., Chgo., 1987-93; sr. account mgr. Fin. Rels. Bd., Inc., Chgo., 1994. Mem. Ill. Soc. CPAs, Investment Analyst Soc. Chgo., Fin. Execs. Inst. Home: 25 Warrington Dr Lake Bluff IL 60044-1322

OTT, JOHN HARLOW, museum administrator; b. Ottawa, Ont., Can., Jan. 29, 1944; s. Thomas Gordon and Lois Elizabeth (Wright) O.; m. Lili Reineck, May 20, 1972; children—Jennie Elizabeth, Michael James Hutchins. B.A., Eastern Bapt. Coll., St. David's, Pa., 1966; M.A., SUNY-Oneonta, 1975; postgrad. Mus. Mgmt. Inst. U. Calif., Berkeley, 1987. Curator Hancock Shaker Village, Inc., Pittsfield, Mass., 1970-72, dir., 1972-83; exec. dir. Atlanta Hist. Soc., 1983-91, B&O R R Mus., Inc., Balt., 1991—; curator Ga. Hist. Soc., Savannah, 1983-87; mem. adv. bd. Concord (Mass.) Mus. Author: Hancock Shaker Village, 1976. Mem., chmn. arts com. Berkshire Hills Conf., Pittsfield, Mass., 1979-83; chmn. Pittsfield Civic Ctr. Commn., 1980-82; active Leadership Atlanta, 1984—; bd. dirs. Buckhead Bus. Assn. 1985-91, New Lebanon Shaker Heritage Found., N.Y.C., Hist. Ellicott City Restoration Found., 1992—; grad. 1993 Class of Leadership Blat.; mem. Mayor's Task Force on Greenways; mem. bd. dirs., exec. com. Balt. City C. of C., 1994—. Decorated Bronze Star; named Mus. Profl. of Yr. in Ga., 1991. Mem. Am. Assn. Mus. (accrediting officer 1982—), Am. Assn. for State and Local History, Mid-Atlantic Mus. Assn., Ga. Soc. Assn. Execs., Nat. Hist. Communal Socs. Assn. (pres. 1983-84), Nat. Soc. Fund Raising Execs. (bd. dirs. Ga. chpt. 1985-91, bd. dirs. Md. chpt. 1993). Republican. Episcopalian. Office: B&O Railroad Mus 901 W Pratt St Baltimore MD 21223-2644

OTT, JURG, geneticist, educator; b. Schaffhausen, Switzerland, Apr. 11, 1939; came to U.S., 1970; s. Heinrich Paul and Anna Ida (Prag) O.; m. Susanne Rohr, 1968 (div. 1978); m. Salome Agathe Looser, Aug. 23, 1986. PhD. U. Zurich, Switzerland, 1968; MS, U. Wash., 1972. Asst. prof. U. Wash., Seattle, 1975-78; asst. dir. City Statistics Office, Zurich, 1979-85, dir., 1986; prof. Columbia U., N.Y.C., 1986—; research scientist N.Y. State Psychiat. Inst., 1986—. Author: Analysis of Human Genetic Linkage, 1991; (computer program) LIPED for Genetic Linkage, 1974; editor: American Journal of Human Genetics, 1988—, Human Genetics, 1988—. NIMH grantee, 1989. Fellow Am. Psycho-Pathological Assn.; mem. Am. Soc. Human Genetics. Democrat. Avocation: piano. Office: Columbia U Box 58 722 W 168th St New York NY 10032-2603

OTT, KARL OTTO, nuclear engineering educator, consultant; b. Hanau, Germany, Dec. 24, 1925; came to U.S., 1967, naturalized, 1987; s. Johann Josef and Eva (Bergmann) O.; m. Gunhild G. Göring, Sept. 18, 1958 (div. 1986); children: Martina, Monika; m. Birgit Fehse, May 1, 1995. BS, J. W. von Goethe U., Frankfurt, Germany, 1948; MS, G. August U., Göttingen, Fed. Republic Germany, 1953, PhD, 1958. Physicist Nuclear Rsch. Ctr., Karlsruhe, Fed. Republic Germany, 1958-67, sect. head, 1962-67; prof. Sch. Nuclear Engring. Purdue U., West Lafayette, Ind., 1967—; cons. Argonne (Ill.) Nat. Lab., 1967—. Author: Nuclear Reactor Statics, 1983, 2nd edit., 1989, Nuclear Reactor Dynamics, 1985. Fellow Am. Nuclear Soc. Office: Sch Nuclear Engring Purdue U Lafayette IN 47907

OTT, MICHAEL DUANE, lawyer; b. San Bernardino, Calif., June 9, 1948; s. Thomas Russell and Beverly Louise (Pentland) O.; m. Karen Hiroko Matsumoto, Dec. 23, 1967 (div. Jan. 1989); children: Jonathan Thomas, Steven Michael; m. Cynthia Lee Fontana, July 15, 1989. BA in History, U. Calif.-San Diego, 1971; JD, U. Iowa, 1974. Bar: Calif., Oreg. Law clk. Hon. A. Andrew Hank, U.S. Dist. Ct., L.A., 1974-75; assoc. Mulvaney, Kahan, Dysart and Fraser, San Diego, 1975-77, 78-79; atty. Union Pacific R.R., Portland, Oreg., 1977; sr. dep. county counsel County of Lake, Lakeport, Calif., 1979-81, County of Fresno, Calif., 1981-83; county counsel County of Madera, Calif., 1983-88; ptnr. Borton, Petrini and Conron, Fresno, 1988—; judge protem Madera County Superior Ct., 1986-88; jud. arbitration panel Fresno County, 1990—; paralegal adv. com. Fresno City Coll., 1992—. Editor Iowa Law Review, 1973-74; contbr. articles to profl. jours. Mem., vice chmn. Lake County Dem. Cen. Com., Lakeport, 1979-81; mem. Madera County Action Com., 1987-88. Mem. State Bar of Calif. (exec. com., Rep. sect. 1986-88), Fresno County Bar Bulletin (editorial bd. 1986-88), Madera County Bar Assn. (sec. 1986, treas. 1987), U. Calif. San Diego Alumni Assn. (bd. dirs. 1976-77, gen. counsel 1978-79). Avocations: tennis, golf. Office: Borton Petrini and Conron 2014 Tulare St # 830 Fresno CA 93721-2011

OTT, WALTER RICHARD, academic administrator; b. Bklyn., Jan. 20, 1943; s. Harold Vincent and Mary Elizabeth (Butler) O; children: Regina Winter Burrell, Christina W., Walter R. Jr. BS in Ceramic Engring., Va. Poly. Inst. and State U., 1965; MS in Ceramic Engring., U. Ill., 1967; PhD in Ceramic Engring., Rutgers U., 1969. Registered profl. engr., Pa. Process engr. Corning Inc. Buckhannon, W.Va., 1965-66; staff research engr. Champion Spark Plug Co., Detroit, 1969-70; prof. engring. Rutgers U., New Brunswick, N.J., 1970-80; dean, assoc. provost N.Y. State Coll. Ceramics, Alfred, 1980-88; provost, chief acad. officer Alfred U., Alfred, 1988—; rsch. assoc. Atomic Energy Commn.-E.I. duPont de Nemours, Aiken, S.C., 1971; cons. Haight & Hofeldt Inc., Chgo., 1984-88, Pillsbury, Mpls., 1977-79, Ctr. for Profl. Advancement, New Brunswick, 1971-79, Hammond (Ind.) Lead Products, 1970-80; bd. dirs. Victor (N.Y.) Insulator Inc., UNIPEG, 1987-88; chmn. bd. dirs. Alfred Tech. Resources N.Y. Contbr. articles to profl. jours.; patentee in field. Recipient Ralph Teetor award Soc. Automotive Engrs., 1973, PACE award Nat. Inst. Ceramic Engrs., 1975, Ann. award Ceramic Assn. N.J., 1980; named to Greaves Walker Roll, Keramos, 1991. Fellow Am. Ceramic Soc. (trustee 1980-83, v.p. 1988-89); mem. Am. Soc. Engring. Educators, Ceramic Ednl. Coun. (pres. 1976-77), Ceramic Assn. N.Y. (treas. 1980-88, bd. dirs.) Ceramic Assn. N.J. (bd. dirs. 1974-80), Keramos (pres. 1982-84, Greaves-Walker Roll of Honor 1991), Tau Beta Pi. Avocations: tennis, reading. Home: 86 Maple Ave Wellsville NY 14895-1043 Office: Alfred U Provost Office Alfred NY 14802

OTT, WAYNE ROBERT, environmental engineer; b. San Mateo, Calif., Feb. 2, 1940; s. Florian Funstan and Evelyn Virginia (Smith) O.; m. Patricia Faustina Bertuzzi, June 28, 1967 (div. 1983). BA in Econs., Claremont McKenna Coll., 1962; BSEE, Stanford U., 1963, MS in Engring. 1965, MA in Comm., 1966, PhD in Environ. Engring., 1971. Commd. lt. USPHS, 1966, advanced to capt. 1986; chief lab. ops. br. U.S. EPA, Washington, 1971-73, sr. systems analyst, 1973-79, sr. rsch. engr., 1981-84, chief air toxics and radiation monitoring rsch. staff, 1984-90; vis. scientist dept. stats. Stanford (Calif.) U., 1979-81; vis. scholar Ctr. for Risk Analysis and dept. stats., civil engring., 1990-93; sr. environ. engr., EPA Atmospheric Rsch. and Exposure Assessment Lab, 1993-95; consulting prof. in civil engring. Stanford (Calif.) U., 1995—; dir. field studies Calif. Environ. Tobacco Smoke Study, 1993-95; cons. prof. civil engring. Stanford U., 1995—. Author: Environmental Indices: Theory and Practice, 1976, Environmental Statistics and Data Analysis, 1995; contbr. articles on indoor air pollution, total human exposure to chems., stochastic models of indoor exposure, motor vehicle exposures, personal monitoring instruments, and environ. tobacco smoke to profl. jours. Recipient Nat. award outstanding contrbn. EPA, Jerome J. Weselowski Internat. award; decorated Commendation medal; recipient Nat. Statistician award for outstanding contribution to environ. statistics EPA, 1995, Jerome J. Weselowski Internat. award for career achievement in exposure assessment, 1995. Mem. Internat. Soc. of Exposure Analysis (v.p. 1989-90), Am. Statis. Assn., Am. Soc. for Quality Control, Air and Waste Mgmt. Assn., Phi Beta Kappa, Sigma Xi, Tau Beta Pi, Kappa Mu Epsilon. Democrat. Clubs: Theater, Jazz, Sierra. Avocations: hiking, photography, model trains, jazz recording. Developer nationally uniform air pollution index, first total human exposure activity pattern models. Home: 1008 Cardiff Ln Redwood City CA 94061-3678 Office: Stanford U Dept Stats Sequoia Hall Stanford CA 94305

OTT, WENDELL LORENZ, art museum director, artist; b. McCloud, Calif., Sept. 17, 1942; s. Wendell and Rose (Jacob) O. Student, San Francisco Art Inst., 1960-61, 62-63; B.A. Trinity U., San Antonio, 1968; M.F.A., U. Ariz., 1970; postgrad., Mus. Mgmt. Inst., U. Calif., 1984. Asst. dir. Roswell (N.Mex.) Mus. and Art Center, 1970-71, dir., 1971-86; dir. Tacoma (Wash.) Art Mus., 1986-92, Mus. of the Southwest, Tex., 1992-94, Tyler (Tex.) Mus. Art., 1995—; chmn. Roswell Humanities Series, 1972-73; instr. N.Mex. Mil. Inst., Roswell; mem. visual arts adv. com. Coll. of Santa Fe, 1985; grant reviewer Inst. Mus. Services, Washington, 1983. One man exhbns. include, Trinity U., 1967, 68, Men of Art Guild, San Antonio, 1967, 68, David Orr's Gallery, Roswell, 1976, G.W.V. Smith Art Mus., Springfield, Mass.; group exhbns. include Tex. Painting and Sculpture, Dallas Mus. Fine Arts, 1966, Witte Meml. Mus., San Antonio, 1967, 68, 1st ann. S.W. Arts Festival, Tucson, 1969, Graphics 69, Western N.Mex. U., 1969, 11th Ariz. ann. Phoenix Art Mus., 1969 (purchase award), 9th ann. Security, Colo., 1969, 5th invitational Yuman Art Center, Yuma, Ariz., 1970, Juarez (Mexico) Mus. Art and History, 1973. Served with AUS, 1964-66. Mem. Am. Assn. Museums (MAP surveyor mus. assessment program 1984, pres. Washington arts consortium 1989—), Rotary. Home: PO Box 4881 Midland TX 79704

OTTAWAY, JAMES HALLER, JR., newspaper publisher; b. Binghamton, N.Y., Mar. 24, 1938; s. James Haller and Ruth Blackburne (Hart) O.; m. Mary Warren Hyde, June 16, 1959; children—Alexandra, Christopher, Jay. Grad., Phillips Exeter Acad., 1955; B.A., Yale U., 1960; D.Journalism (hon.), Suffolk U., Boston, 1970; D.B.A. (hon.), Southeastern Mass. U., 1984. Reporter, mgmt. trainee New-Times, Danbury, Conn., 1960-62, Times Herald-Record, Middletown, N.Y., 1962-63; editor Pocono Record, Stroudsburg, Pa., 1963-65; publisher New Bedford (Mass.) Standard-Times, 1965-70; pres. Ottaway Newspapers, Inc., Campbell Hall, N.Y., 1970-85, chief exec. officer, 1976-88, chmn. bd., 1979—; v.p. Dow Jones & Co. 1980-86, sr. v.p., 1986—, also bd. dirs.; dir. Associated Press, 1982-91. Past v.p. bd. trustees Phillips Exeter Acad.; trustee Am. Sch. Classical Studies at Athens, StormKing Art Ctr., Cornwall, N.Y.; trustee World Wildlife Fund USA, 1993—; past pres., bd. dirs. Arden Hill Hosp. Found., Goshen, N.Y. Mem. Am. Newspaper Pubs. Assn., Am. Soc. Newspaper Editors. Episcopalian. Office: PO Box 401 Campbell Hall NY 10916-0401 also: Dow Jones & Co Inc 200 Liberty St New York NY 10281-1003

OTTE, CARL, political consultant, lobbyist, retired state senator; b. Sheboygan, Wis., June 24, 1923; s. John and Magdalena (Verconteren) O.; m. Ethel Dorothy Braatz, Nov. 1, 1949; children—Allen Carl, Jane Karen, Julie Beth, Lynn Carol. Mem. Wis. State Assembly, 1967-82; mem. Wis. Senate from 9th Dist., 1983-86. Mem. Sheboygan County Bd. Suprs., 1962-68; mem. Democratic Party of Wis.; mem. VFW. Served with U.S. Army, 1943-45. Mem. Am. Fedn. Musicians. Lutheran. Lodge: Am. Legion.

OTTE, CLIFFORD, state legislator; b. Wis., Jan. 15, 1933; m. Haleta Riel, Oct. 9, 1953; children: Gregory, Timothy, Bruce, Brian, Barbara, Charles. Clk., supr. Town of Sheboygan Falls, Wis., 1977-84; county supr. Sheboygan County, Wis., 1982-93; farmer Sheboygan, 1957—; legis. State of Wis., Madison, 1993—. bd. dirs. Sheboygan Falls Sch. Dist., 1973-84. With USN, 1952-56, Korea. Republican. Home: N5385 Bridgewood Rd Sheboygan Falls WI 53085-2406 Office: Wis State Assembly PO Box 8953 Madison WI 53708-8953

OTTE, PAUL JOHN, college administrator, consultant, trainer; b. Detroit, July 10, 1943; s. Melvin John Otte and Anne Marie (Meyers) Hirsch; children: Deanna, John. BS, Wayne State U., 1968, MBA, 1969; EdD, Western Mich. U., 1983. With Detroit Bank and Trust Co., 1965-68; teaching fellow Wayne State U., Detroit, 1968-69; auditor, mgr. Arthur Young & Co., Detroit, 1969-75; contr., dir. Macomb Community Coll., Warren, Mich., 1975-79, v.p. bus., 1979-86; pres. Franklin U. Columbus, Ohio, 1986—; owner, mgmt. trainer Otte and Assocs., Warren, then Westerville, Ohio, 1976—. Author various tng. manuals, 1982. Bd. dirs. Ohio Found. Ind. Colls., Mt. Carmel Coll. Nursing, Cen. Ohio Med. Group. Served to cpl. USMC, 1961-65. Teaching fellow Wayne State U., 1968-69. Mem. AICPA, Mich. Assn. CPAs (chmn. continuing profl. edn. com. 1980-82, leadership com. 1981-83), Nat. Assn. Coll. and Univ. Bus. Officers (acctg. prins. com. 1986), Assn. Ind. Colls. and Univs. Ohio (bd. dirs.), Mich. Community Colls. Bus. Officers Assn., Greater Detroit C. of C. (leadership award 1983), Columbus C. of C. (info. svc. com.) Roman Catholic. Club: Breakfast (Detroit) (pres. 1980-81). Avocations: travel, speaking engagements. Office: Franklin U 201 S Grant Ave Columbus OH 43215-5301

OTTE, RUTH L., cable television executive. V.p. mktg. MTV Networks Inc.; pres., COO Discovery Channel, 1986—. Office: Discovery Channel 7700 Wisconsin Ave Bethesda MD 20814-3578

OTTEN, ARTHUR EDWARD, JR., lawyer, corporate executive; b. Buffalo, Oct. 11, 1930; s. Arthur Edward Sr. and Margaret (Ambrusko) O.; m. Mary Therese Torri, Oct. 1, 1960; children: Margaret, Michael, Maureen Staley,

Suzanne, Jennifer. BA, Hamilton Coll., 1952; JD, Yale U., 1955. Bar: N.Y. 1955, Colo. 1959. Assoc. Hodges, Silverstein, Hodges & Harrington, Denver, 1959-64; ptnr. Hodges, Kerwin, Otten & Weeks (predecessor firms), Denver, 1964-73, Davis, Graham & Stubbs, Denver, 1973-86; pres., mem. Otten, Johnson, Robinson, Neff & Ragonetti, P.C., Denver, 1986—; rec. sec. Colo. Nat. Bankshares, Inc., Denver, 1983-93. Lt. USN, 1955-59. Mem. ABA, Colo. Bar Assn., Denver Bar Assn., Am. Arbitration Assn. (panel arbitrators, large complex case panel, mediator panel), Law Club, Univ. Club, Denver Mile High Rotary (pres. 1992-93), Phi Delta Phi. Republican. Roman Catholic. Avocations: hiking, biking, church activities. Home: 3774 S Niagara Way Denver CO 80237-1248 Office: Otten Johnson Robinson Neff & Ragonetti PC 1600 Colorado National Bldg Denver CO 80202-1056

OTTEN, THOMAS, zoological park director. Student, El Camino Coll., 1965-68, Brigham Young U., 1969. Animal keeper, aquarist Marineland, Rancho Palos Verde, Calif., 1969-70, lead dolphin trainer, 1970-73, curator of mammals, 1973; gen. curator, dep. dir. Point Defiance Zoo & Aquarium, Tacoma, Wash., 1981, zoo dir., 1985—; mem. adj. faculty U. Puget Sound, Tacoma, 1985-90. Contbr. articles to profl. jours. Mem. Am. Assn. Zool. Parks and Aquariums, Internat. Assn. Aquatic Animal Medicine, Internat. Soc. Zooculturalists, Marine Mammal Interest Group (chmn. 1990). Office: Point Defiance Zoo & Aquarium 5400 N Pearl St Tacoma WA 98407-3218*

OTTENBACHER, KENNETH JOHN, dean, educator; b. Missoula, Mont., Apr. 5, 1950; s. John and Florence (LaCasse) O.; m. Margaret E. Vaughn, May 7, 1975; children: Heather, Allison. BS, U. Mont., 1972, U. Ctrl. Ark., 1975; MS, U. Tenn., 1976; PhD, U. Mo., 1982. Registered occupational therapist. Prof. U. Wis., Madison, 1990—; assoc. dean SUNY, Buffalo, 1990—. Author: Evaluating Clinical Change, 1986; editor Occupational Therapy Jour. Rsch., 1987-91. Mem. Am. Acad. Sci., Am. Occupational Therapy Found. (charter), Acad. Rsch. (charter), Congress Rehab. Medicine. Home: 172 Rambling Rd East Amherst NY 14051-2126 Office: SUNY 232 Parker Hall Buffalo NY 14214

OTTENBERG, JAMES SIMON, hospital executive; b. N.Y.C., Feb. 28, 1918; s. Irving Simon and Madeleine (Hirsh) O.; m. Margaret Anne Davies, May 10, 1941; children: Jeffrey, Betsy (Mrs. Michael Cherkasky), Jill (Mrs. Joshua Muscat). A.B., Swarthmore Coll., 1939; J.D., Harvard, 1942; M.Pub. Adminstrn., N.Y. U., 1963, postgrad., 1963-65. Bar: N.Y. bar 1945. Pvt. practice N.Y.C.; sec. to judge Gen. Sessions Ct., N.Y.C., 1955-58; exec. asst. commr. Marine and Aviation, N.Y.C., 1958-62; dep. commr. Mental Health Dept., N.Y.C., 1962-67; grant adminstr. Addiction Services Agy., N.Y.C., 1967-68; asst. dir. Child Study Assn. Am., N.Y.C., 1968-69, exec. dir., 1969-72; exec. dir. Edn. and Research Found. Better Bus. Bur. Met. N.Y., 1973-77; adminstr. Crotona Park Community Mental Health Center, N.Y.C., 1977-89; dir. med. adminstrn. Bronx-Lebanon Hosp., N.Y.C., 1989-92, adminstr. alcohol programs, 1992—; lectr. sch. continuing edn. NYU, 1969. Author: (with Rachele Thomas) You, Your Child and Drugs, 1971; annotated bibliography Political Reform, Machines and Big City Politics 1950-62, 1962. Active campaigns N.Y. Citizens for Stevenson, 1956, Kennedy and Johnson, 1960, Wagner, 1961, Robert F. Kennedy, 1964; bd. dirs. Lenox Hill Neighborhood Assn., N.Y.C., 1954-68, Union Settlement, 1968-70. Served with USAAC, 1942-45. Recipient Lepesqueur award for highest scholarship Grad. Sch. Pub. Adminstrn., N.Y. U., 1963. Fellow Am. Pub. Health Assn. Home: 145 E 92nd St New York NY 10128-2431 Office: 321 E Tremont Ave Bronx NY 10457-5304

OTTENFELD, MARSHALL, marketing research company executive; b. Chgo., Jan. 15, 1937; s. Leo and Sadie (Patt) O.; B.A., U. Chgo., 1959; M.A., Roosevelt U., 1968; m. Gloria Jean Zilke, Dec. 28, 1960; children—David Joel, Jonathan Lawrence, Jennifer Lynn, Heather Anne. Study dir. Chgo. Tribune, 1962-64; project dir. Gardner Advt. Co., N.Y.C., 1964-65; research asso. Advt. Research Found., N.Y.C., 1965-66; research asso. pharm. products div. Abbott Labs., North Chicago, Ill., 1966-70; sr. v.p., dir. mktg. research D'Arcy-MacManus & Masius, Inc., Chgo., 1970-83; pres. Mid-Am. Research, Chgo., 1970—; pres., chief exec. officer Mid-Am. Research, Inc., 1983—; ptnr. Market Shares Corp., 1986—; lectr. mktg. Roosevelt U.; assoc. editor Jour. Data Collection. Scout master Boy Scouts Am., Deerfield, Ill., 1980—. Served with AUS, 1961-62. Mem. Am. Mktg. Assn., Advt. Research Found., Research Practices Council, Qualitative Research Council, Am. Assn. Public Opinion Research, Midwest Assn. Public Opinion Research, Am. Assn. Advt. Agys., N.Y. Acad. Sci., Am. Acad. Polit. and Social Sci., Mktg. Research Assn., Zeta Beta Tau. Jewish. Club: Internat. Home: 1050 Summit Dr Deerfield IL 60015-1823 Office: Mid-America Rsch Inc 999 N Elmhurst Rd Mount Prospect IL 60056

OTTENSMEYER, DAVID JOSEPH, neurosurgeon, health care executive; b. Nashville, Tenn., Jan. 29, 1930; s. Raymond Stanley and Glenda Jessie (Helpingstine) O.; m. Mary Jean Langley, June 30, 1954; children: Kathryn Joan, Martha Langley. BA, Wis. State U., Superior, 1951; MD, U. Wis., Madison, 1959; MS in Health Svcs. Adminstrn., Coll. St. Francis, 1985. Diplomate Am. Bd. Neurological Surgery. Intern then resident in gen. surgery Univ. Hosps., Madison, Wis., 1959-61; resident in neurol. surgery Univ. Hosps., 1962-65; staff neurosurgeon Marshfield Clinic, Wis., 1965-76; from instr. of neurol. surgery to clin. asst. prof. U. Wis. Med. Sch., Madison, 1964-77; CEO Lovelace Med. Ctr., Albuquerque, 1976-86, chmn., 1986-91; clin. prof. community medicine U. N.Mex., Albuquerque, 1977-79, clin. prof. neurol. surgery, 1979—; exec. v.p., chief med. officer Equicor, 1986-90; v.p. Marshfield Clinic, 1970-71, pres., CEO, 1972-75; pres., CEO The Lovelace Insts., 1991—; sr. v.p., chief med. officer Travelers Ins. Co., 1990-91; served on numerous adv. and com. posts. Contbr. articles to profl. jours. Col. USAR, 1960-90. Fellow ACS, Am. Coll. Physician Execs. (pres. 1985-86); mem. Am. Group Practice Assn. (pres. 1983-84), Am. Bd. Med. Mgmt. (bd. dirs. 1989-93). Republican. Episcopalian. Avocations: flying; golf; travel. Home: 2815 Ridgecrest Dr SE Albuquerque NM 87108-5132

OTTER, CLEMENT LEROY, lieutenant governor; b. Caldwell, Idaho, May 3, 1942; s. Joseph Bernard and Regina Mary (Buser) O. m. Gay Corinne Simplot, Dec. 28, 1964; children: John Simplot, Carolyn Lee, Kimberly Dawn, Corinne Marie. BA in Polit. Sci., Coll. Idaho, 1967; PhD, Mindanao State U., 1980. Mgr. J.R. Simplot Co., Caldwell, Idaho, 1971-76, asst. to v.p. adminstrn., 1976-78, v.p. adminstrn., 1978-82, internat. pres., from 1982, now v.p.; lt. gov. State of Idaho, Boise, 1987—. Mem. Presdl. Task Force-AID, Washington, 1982-84; com. mem. invest tech. devel. State Adv. Council, Washington, 1983-84; mem. exec. council Bretton Woods Com., 1984—; mem. U.S.C. of C., Washington, 1983-84. Mem. Young Pres.' Orgn., Sales and Mktg. Execs., Idaho Assn. Commerce and Industry, Idaho Agrl. Leadership Council, Idaho Ctr. for Arts, Idaho Internat. Trade Council, Pacific N.W. Waterways Assn., N.W. Food Producers, Ducks Unltd. Republican. Roman Catholic. Clubs: Aid, Hillcrest Country. Lodge: Moose, Elks. Avocations: jogging, music, art collecting, horse training, fishing. Office: Office of the Lt Gov State House Rm 225 Boise ID 83702

OTTER, JOHN MARTIN, III, television advertising consultant, retired; b. Pottsville, Pa., Nov. 26, 1930; s. John Martin and Ruth A. (Knipe) O.; m. Susan Morgan Eaves, May 21, 1960; children—John Martin, IV, Robert Marshal. B.A., Cornell U., 1953. Comml. producer Arlene Frances Home Show, 1953-55; program sales NBC-TV, 1959-61, v.p. nat. sales, 1962-64, v.p. charge sales, 1965-73; cons. sta. WNET-TV, Practising Law Inst., also Dragonwk Prodns., 1973-75; v.p., dir. network programming SSC&B Inc., 1975-78; sr. v.p., dir. network programming SSC&B Lintas Worldwide, N.Y.C., 1978-84; sr. v.p. dir. nat. broadcast McCann-Erickson U.S.A., N.Y.C., 1984-88; sr. v.p. spl. projects McCann-Erickson Worldwide, N.Y.C., 1988; pres. RETTO Internat. Inc., N.Y.C., 1989-94; retired, 1994. Republican. Episcopalian. Home: Four Seafarer's Cir Savannah GA 31411

OTTERBOURG, ROBERT KENNETH, public relations consultant, writer; b. N.Y.C., Jan. 26, 1930; s. Albert Marcus and Frances (Roset) O.; m. Susan Delman, Apr. 14, 1957; children—Laura Ann, Kenneth Douglas. BA, Colgate U., 1951; MS, Columbia U., 1954. Reporter, editor Fairchild Publs., N.Y.C., 1953-57; editor McGraw-Hill Pub. Co., 1957-59; v.p. pub. rels. Charles Mathieu & Co., 1959-61; pres. pub. rels. Otterbourg & Co., 1962-69, 71—; sr. v.p. Daniel J. Edelman, 1970. Author: It's Never Too Late, 1993; contbr. articles to profl. and consumer jours. Legis. asst. N.Y.

State Senate, 1962-64; mem. exec. com. Columbia U. Sch. Journalism, N.Y.C., 1980-93, pres. exec. com., 1985-87; trustee Flat Rock Nature Ctr., pres., 1991-92; trustee Planned Parenthood Bergen County, 1985-88, v.p., 1986-88; trustee Urban League for Bergen County, 1988—; bd. dirs. Colgate U. Alumni Corp., 1969-93. 1st lt. USAF, 1951-53. Mem. Pub. Rels. Soc. Am., Columbia U. Grad. Sch. Journalism Alumni Assn. (pres. 1985-87). Democrat. Jewish. Home and Office: 68 Beverly Dr Durham NC 27707-2224

OTTERHOLT, BARRY L., technology management consultant; b. Richland, Wash., Aug. 15, 1953; s. Ernest D. and Jean T. Otterholt; m. Nancy L. Musgrave, Dec. 13, 1985; children: Casey J., Kris K., Cody M.E. BA in Computer Sci. Acctg., Western Wash. U., 1980; MBA in Bus. Administrn., Seattle Pacific U., 1982. Mgr. Robinson's, Wenatchee, Wash., 1971-75; purchasing agt. Sound Ctrs., Inc., Bellingham, Wash., 1975-79; chief oper. officer Speakerlab/Compulab, Seattle, 1979-82; mgmt. cons. Deloitte & Touche, Seattle, 1982-88; founder, prin. Solutions Consulting Group LLC, Bellevue, Wash., 1988—. Mem. Inst. Mgmt. Cons. (cert.). Office: Solutions Consulting Group 1400 112th Ave SE Bellevue WA 98004-6901

OTTESON, SCHUYLER FRANKLIN, former university dean, educator; b. Mondovi, Wis., July 17, 1917; s. Hans and Elizabeth (Meyer) O.; m. Marie Lila Rothering, 1940; children: Judith Marie, Martha Jean, Karn Wilma, John Christian. Student, Eau Claire State Tchrs. Coll., 1935-37; Ph.B., U. Wis., 1939; M.B.A., Northwestern U., 1940; Ph.D., Ohio State U., 1948. Research asst. exec. com. Fair Store, Chgo., 1940-42; asst. buyer Montgomery Ward & Co., 1942-43; instr. econs. and bus. adminstrn. Ohio Wesleyan U., 1943-44, asst. prof., 1944-46; asst. prof. mktg. Ind. U., 1946-48, assoc. prof., 1948-52, prof., 1952—, assoc. dir. Bur. Bus. Research, 1947-49, dir. Bur. Bus. Research, 1954-60, chmn. of mktg. dept., 1960-65, chmn. Dr. Bus. Adminstrn. Program, 1965-71, acting dean Sch. Bus., 1971-72, dean, 1972-82, also dir. Internat. Bus. Research Inst.; bd. dirs. Circle Income Shares, Inc.; mem. ednl. adv. com. Chgo. Bd. Trade, 1952-55, chmn. com., 1954-55; bd. dirs. Am. Assembly Coll. Schs. of Bus., 1978-82, pres., 1981; chmn. Ctr. for Leadership Devel., 1976—. Author: (with T.N. Beckman) Cases in Credits and Collections, 1949, (with William G. Panschar and James M. Patterson) Marketing: The Firm's Viewpoint, 1964; Editor: Marketing—Current Problems and Theories, 1952, Business Horizons, 1957-66; Contbr. articles profl. publs. Recipient leather medal Sigma Delta Chi, 1960; named Sagamore of Wabash, gov. Ind., 1956. Mem. Am., Midwest econs. assns., Ind. Acad. Social Scis. (pres. 1969-70), Am. Marketing Assn. (pres. 1965-66), Alpha Delta Sigma, Beta Gamma Sigma (bd. govs.). Home: 512 S Jordan Ave Bloomington IN 47401-5120

OTTH, EDWARD JOHN, JR., retired marine systems executive, retired naval officer; b. Chgo., Mar. 16, 1925; s. Edward John and Gladys (Chamberlin) O.; m. Marilyn Knappenbuch Patjens, Aug. 16, 1950; children: John Andreas, Annabel, Hilde Otth McEwan. Student, Northwestern U., 1943-45; B.S., U.S. Naval Acad., 1949; Profl. degree in Naval Engring, Mass. Inst. Tech., 1955. Served as enlisted man U.S. Navy, 1943-45, commd. ensign, 1949, advanced through grades to rear adm., 1976; with (U.S.S. New), 1949-52; docking officer (Phila. Naval Shipyard), 1955-56, asst. planning and estimating supt., 1956-58; engring. officer (U.S.S. Newport News), 1958-60; at cruiser desk (Bur. Ships, Navy Dept.), Washington, 1960-62; ship installation and test mgr. (Terrier Missile project), Washington, 1962-64; staff comdr. (Cruiser Destroyer Force Atlantic), 1964-67; planning and estimating supt. (Long Beach (Calif.) Naval Shipyard), 1967-71; project mgr. (Guided Missile Frigate FFG-7 Ship Acquisition Project, Naval Ship Systems Command), Washington, 1971-76; spl. asst. for shipbldg. to comdr. (Naval Sea Systems Command), Washington, 1976-78, prin. dep. comdr. for acquisition, 1978-79, 80-81; dep. chief naval material acquisition (Naval Material Command), 1979-80 ret., 1981; mgr. marine systems dept. Field Service and Support Div., Hughes Aircraft Co., 1981-83, mgr. tech. staff, Test and Tng. Systems Div., 1983-86, mgr. program mgmt. support equipment programs, 1986-89, ret., 1989. Decorated Legion of Merit, Meritorious Service medal, Navy Commendation medal. Mem. Soc. Naval Architects and Marine Engrs., Am. Soc. Naval Engrs., Sigma Xi, Phi Eta Sigma. Republican. Home: 5 Valley Vw Irvine CA 92715-3211

OTTINO, JULIO MARIO, chemical engineering educator, scientist; b. La Plata, Buenos Aires, Argentina, May 22, 1951; came to U.S., 1976; naturalized, 1990; s. Julio Francisco and Nydia Judith (Zufriategui) O.; m. Alicia I. Löffler, Aug. 20, 1976; children: Jules Alessandro, Bertrand Julien. Diploma in Chem. Engring., U. La Plata, 1974; PhD in Chem. Engring., U. Minn., 1979. Instr. in chem. engring. U. Minn., Mpls., 1978-79; asst. prof. U. Mass., Amherst, 1979-83, adj. prof. polymer sci., 1979-91, assoc. prof. chem. engring., 1983-86, prof., 1986-91; Chevron vis. prof. chem. engring. Calif. Inst. Tech., Pasadena, 1985-86; sr. rsch. fellow Ctr. for Turbulence Rsch. Stanford (Calif.) U., 1989-90; Walter P.Murphy prof. chem. engring. Northwestern U., Evanston, Ill., 1991—, chmn. dept. chem. engring., 1992—; cons. in field; William N. Lacey lectureship Calif. Inst. Tech., 1994, Allan P. Colburn Meml. lectr. U. Del., 1987; Merck Sharp & Dohme lectr. U. P.R., 1989, Stanley Corrsin lectr. Johns Hopkins U., 1991; Centennial lectr. U. Md., 1994. Author: The Kinematics of Mixing: Stretching, Chaos and Transport, 1989; contbr. articles to profl. jours.; assoc. editor Physics Fluids A, 1991—; mem. editl. bd. Internat. Jour. Bifurc. Chaos, 1991—; cons. editor Am. Chem. Engring. Jour., 1991-95, assoc. editor., 1995—; one man art exhibit, La Plata, 1974. Recipient Presdl. Young Investigator award NSF, 1984; Univ. fellow U. Mass., 1988, Alpha Chi Sigma award AIChE, 1994. Fellow Am. Phys. Soc.; mem. AAAS, Soc. for Natural Philosophy (selection com. 1993—), Am. Chem. Soc., Soc. Rheology, Am. Soc. Engring. Edn., Sigma Xi, Pau Beta Pi. Avocations: research in fluid dynamics, chaos, mixing and turbulence, complex systems, polymers. Home: 1182 Asbury Ave Winnetka IL 60093-1402 Office: Northwestern U Dept Chem Engring 2145 Sheridan Rd Evanston IL 60208-0834

OTTLEY, JEROLD DON, choral conductor, educator; b. Salt Lake City, Apr. 7, 1934; s. Sidney James and Alice (Warren) O.; m. JoAnn South, June 22, 1956; children: Brent Kay, Allison. B.A., Brigham Young U., Provo, Utah, 1961; M.Mus., U. Utah, 1967; Fulbright study grantee, Fed. Republic Germany, 1968-69; D.M.A. (grad. teaching fellow), U. Oreg., 1972. Tchr. public schs. Salt Lake City area, 1961-65; mem. faculty U. Utah, Salt Lake City, 1967—; asst. prof. music, 1971-78, adj. assoc. prof. music, 1978-81, adj. prof. music, 1981—; assoc. conductor Salt Lake Mormon Tabernacle Choir, 1974-75, conductor, 1975—; also guest conductor throughout U.S. Conducted Mormon Tabernacle Choir in 12 concert tours U.S., 24 fgn. countries, Utah Phila. and Milw. Orchestra in performance; rec. artist CBS Masterworks, London/Decca Records, Bonneville Records and Laserlight; prepared choirs for Eugene Ormandy, Maurice Avravanel, Stanislaw Skrowaczewski, Michael Tilson Thomas, Robert Shaw, Julius Rudel, Sir David Willcocks, Ling Tung. Past mem. gen. music coms. Mormon Ch., cultural arts com. Salt Lake City C. of C. (Honors in the Arts award), past bd. advs. Barlow Endowment Music Composition; v.p., past bd. dirs., com. chair Chorus Am. Served with U.S. Army, 1957-59. Faculty Study grantee U. Utah, 1971-72; recipient Brigham Young U. Alumni Achievement award, 1990. Mem. Am. Choral Dirs. Assn., Am. Choral Found., Master Tchr. Inst. Arts (past trustee), Great Music West Festival. Office: Mormon Tabernacle Choir 50 E North Temple Fl 20 Salt Lake City UT 84150-0001

OTTLEY, WILLIAM HENRY, professional association director, consultant; b. N.Y.C., Mar. 7, 1929; s. James Henry and Margaret (Deeble) O. BA, Yale U., 1950; spl. cert., Georgetown U., 1953; D of Aero. Sci. (hon.), Embry Riddle Aero. U., 1979. Dir. pub. rels. Thomas A. Edison Co., West Orange, N.J., 1953-56; exec. v.p. Career Publs., Inc., N.Y.C., 1956-60; dir. spl. exhibits N.Y. World's Fair, 1960-65; exec. dir. Nat. Pilots Assn., Washington, 1965-77, U.S. Parachute Assn., Washington, 1978-92, Nat. Aero. Assn., Washington, 1992-93; pres. Internat. Gen. Aviation Commn., Paris, 1994—; v.p. Fedn. Aero. Internat., Paris, 1994—. Editor: Wall Street 20th Century, 1959; publ. Parachutist, 1978-92; editor/publ. Nat. Pilots Assn. News, 1965-77. 1st lt. USAF, 1951-53. Mem. Am. Mus. Sport Parachuting (pres.), Met. Club Washington, Soc. of Cin. Republican. Episcopalian. Avocations: skydiving (world record holder 1982), flying (world record holder 1985), scuba diving, waterskiing, snow skiing. Home and Office: 2627 Woodley Pl Washington DC 20008

OTTMANN, PETER, choreographer, ballet dancer; b. Renfrew, Ont., Can.; m. Karen Ottman. Grad., Nat. Ballet Sch.; postgrad., Benesh Inst., London, 1993. Mem. Nat. Ballet of Can., Toronto, Ont., 1976—, 1st soloist, 1983-93, resident choreologist, ballet master, 1993—; mem. dancer exch. program Australian Ballet Co. Created roles of Reginald Hargreaves and Caterpillar in Glen Tetley's Alice, and for Café Dances, 1991; debuted as Lewis Carrol at Met. Opera House, N.Y.C., 1986; performed in The Nutcracker, Giselle, Romeo and Juliet, Don Quixote, The Miraculous Mandarin, La Ronde, 1987, Dream Dances, 1989, The Leaves Are Fading, 1990, the second detail, 1991, The Strangeness of a Kiss, 1991, Musings, 1991, The Taming of the Shrew, 1992, The Merry Widow, 1992, (in films) Alice, 1989, La Ronde, 1989, (TV prodn.) A Moving Picture; guest appearances at Spoleto Festival, Italy, Toronto Symphony Orch., 1986, Houston Ballet, 1993. Office: Nat Ballet Can, 157 King St E, Toronto, ON Canada M5C 1G9

OTTO, CHARLES EDWARD, health care administrator; b. Somerville, N.J., Nov. 12, 1946; s. Hans and Virginia (Hegeman) O.; m. Wendy Ann Halsey; June 26, 1971; children: Eric, C. Halsey, Robert. BA, Hobart Coll., Geneva, N.Y., 1968; MBA, U. Pa., 1973. Adminstrv. asst. Mass. Gen. Hosp., Boston, 1970-71; adminstrv. resident Hosp. of U. of Pa., Phila., 1973; adminstrv. asst. Norwalk (Conn.) Hosp., 1974-76; exec. dir. Waveny Care Ctr., New Canaan, Conn., 1977-93; adminstr. Avery Heights Retirement Village, Hartford, Conn., 1994—; bd. chmn. Conn. Assn. of Non-Profit Facilities for the Aged, Wallingford, 1984-86; chmn. regional adv. group Conn. Community Care, Inc., Norwalk, 1983-85. Bd. chmn. S.W. Fairfield Am. Cancer Soc., Norwalk, 1985-87. Served to lt. (j.g.) USNR, 1968-70. Mem. Wharton Healthcare Alumni Assn. (bd. dirs. 1993-94), Rocky Point Club. Episcopalian. Home: 12 Lake Dr S Riverside CT 06878-2016

OTTO, FRED DOUGLAS, chemical engineering educator; b. Hardisty, Alta., Jan. 12, 1935. BSc, U. Alta, 1957, MSc, 1959; PhD chem. engr., U. Mich., Ann Arbor, 1963. Asst. prof. to assoc.prof. U. Alta, Edmonton, 1962-70, acctg. chmn. dept., 1970-72, prof. chem. engr., 1970—; dean engr. U. Alta, 1985—. Recipient Centennial award Assn. of Profl. Engrs., Geologists and Geophysicists of Alberta, 1993. Mem. Can. Soc. Chem. Engr. (pres. 1986-87), Am. Inst. Chem. Engr., Am. Soc. Eng. Edu. Office: U Alta, 5-1 Mechanical Engr Bldg, Edmonton, AB Canada T6G 2G8*

OTTO, GEORGE JOHN, investment banker; b. San Francisco, June 8, 1904; s. Paul O. and Emma (Shanstrum) O.; m. Marie Kendrick, Oct. 10, 1933; children—Marie L., Elizabeth A., Susan. A.B., U. Calif. at Berkeley, 1926. Bond salesman Mitchum Tully & Co., 1926-35; partner Irving Lundborg & Co., San Francisco, 1935-70; vice chmn. bd. dirs. Clark Dodge Co., Inc., San Francisco, 1970-74; v.p. Kidder Peabody & Co., 1974—; dir. Schlage Lock Co.; gov. Stock Exchange Firms; pres. Pacific Coast Stock Exchange, chmn. San Francisco div. Active local council Girl Scouts U.S.A.; trustee World Affairs Council; bd. dirs. Internat. Hospitality Center, Columbia Park Boys Club, Golden Gate Coll., No. Calif. Soc. for Prevention Blindness, San Francisco Ladies Protection and Relief Soc., Palace Fine Arts League. Mem. Investment Bankers Assn. Am. (v.p., gov. Calif. group; past gov.), Brit. Am. C. of C. (dir.). Clubs: Bond (San Francisco) (pres. 1947), Bohemian (San Francisco) (sec., dir. 1956-57), San Francisco Golf (San Francisco), Pacific Union. Home: 2701 Pierce St San Francisco CA 94123-4632 Office: 555 California St San Francisco CA 94104-1502

OTTO, JEAN HAMMOND, journalist; b. Kenosha, Wis., Aug. 27, 1925; d. Laurence Cyril and Beatrice Jane (Slater) Hammond; m. John A. Otto, Aug. 22, 1946; children: Jane L. Rahman, Mary Ellen Takayama, Peter J. Otto; m. Lee W. Baker, Nov. 23, 1973. Student, Ripon Coll., 1944-46. Women's editor Appleton (Wis.) Post-Crescent, 1960-68; reporter Milw. Jour., 1968-72, editorial writer, 1972-77, editor Op Ed page, 1977-83; editorial page editor Rocky Mountain News, Denver, 1983-89, assoc. editor, 1989-92, reader rep., 1992—; Endowed chair U. Denver, 1992—. Founder, chmn. bd. trustees First Amendment Congress, 1979-85, chmn. exec. com., 1985-88, 89-91, pres. 1991—, mem. bd. trustees, 1979—; founding mem. Wis. Freedom of Info. Council. Recipient Headliner award Wis. Women in Communications, 1974; Outstanding Woman in Journalism award YWCA, Milw., 1977; Knight of Golden Quill Milw. Presss Club, 1979; spl. citation in Journalism Ball State U., 1980; James Madison award Nat. Broadcast Editorial Assn., 1981; spl. citation for contbn. to journalism Nat. Press Photographers Assn., 1981; Ralph D. Casey award, 1984; U. Colo. Regents award, 1985; John Peter Zenger award U. Ariz., 1988; Paul Miller Medallion award Okla. State U., 1990; Colo. SPJ Lowell Thomas award, 1990, Disting. Alumna award Ripon Coll., 1992, Hugh M. Hefner First Amendment Lifetime Achievement award Playboy Found., 1994. Mem. Colo. Press Assn. (chmn. freedom of info. com. 1983-89), Assn. Edn. in Journalism and Mass Communications (Disting. Svc. award 1984), Am. Soc. Newspaper Editors (bd. dirs. 1987-92), Soc. Profl. Journalists (nat. treas. 1975, nat. sec. 1977, pres.-elect 1978, pres. 1979-80, First Amendment award 1981, Wells Key 1984, pres. Sigma Delta Chi Found. 1989-92, Gold Found. 1992—), Milw. Press Club (mem. Hall of Fame 1993). Office: Rocky Mountain News 400 W Colfax Ave Denver CO 80204-2694

OTTO, KLAUS, physicist, physical chemist; b. Friedrichroda, Fed. Republic of Germany, Sept. 18, 1929; came to U.S., 1960, naturalized, 1967; s. Theodor M.W.A. and Gertrud (Gohla) O.; m. Christa Thomsen, Nov. 16, 1962; children: Ina N., Peter N. Vordiplom, U. Hamburg, Fed. Republic of Germany, 1954, Diplom, 1957, D of Natural Scis., 1960. Rsch. asst. U. Hamburg, 1959-60; postdoctoral fellow Argonne (Ill.) Nat. Lab., 1960-62; sr. rsch. scientist Ford Motor Co., Dearborn, Mich., 1962-73, prin. rsch. scientist assoc., 1973-81, staff scientist, 1981—; adj. prof. Mich. State U., 1986—. Contbr. articles to profl. jours. Recipient Parravano award for excellence in catalysis rsch. and devel., 1986. Mem. AAAS, Am. Chem. Soc., German Bunsen Soc. of Electrochemistry, Mich. Catalysis Soc. (pres. 1980-81), N.Y. Acad. Scis., Sigma Xi (pres. Ford chpt. 1985-86). Home: 35173 6 Mile Rd Livonia MI 48152-2976 Office: Sci Rsch Staff Ford Motor Co Dearborn MI 48121

OTTO, MARGARET AMELIA, librarian; b. Boston, Oct. 22, 1937; d. Henry Earlen and Mary (McLennan) O.; children—Christopher, Peter. A.B., Boston U., 1960; M.S., Simmons Coll., 1963, M.A., 1970; M.A. (hon.), Dartmouth Coll., 1981. Asst. sci. librarian M.I.T., Cambridge, 1963; Lindgren librarian M.I.T., 1964-67, acting sci. librarian, 1967-69, asst. dir., 1969-75, asso. dir., 1976-79; librarian of coll. Dartmouth Coll., Hanover, N.H., 1979—; pres., chmn. bd. Universal Serials and Book Exch., Inc. 1980-81; bd. dirs. Rsch. Libr. Group; trustee Howe Libr., Hanover, 1988—, chair 1992—; mem. Brown Libr. Com., rsch. librs. adv. com. OCLC, 1991—, ARL Com. on Preservation of Rsch. Librs., Materials, 1993—; Colby Coll. Overseers Visiting Com., 1993—; editorial com. U. Press New Eng., 1993—; Council on Library Resources fellow, 1974; elected to Collegium of Disting. Alumnus Boston U., 1980. Mem. ALA (task force on assn. membership issues 1993—, ad hoc working group on copyright issues), Assn. Rsch. Librs. (chair preservation com. 1983-85, bd. dirs. 1985-88, mem. stats. com., chair membership com. 1992—), Coun. on Libr. Resources (proposal rev. com. 1992—), Dartmouth Club (N.Y.C.), St. Botolph Club (Boston), Sloane Club (London). Home: 16 Dresden Rd Hanover NH 03755-1322 Office: Dartmouth Coll 115 Baker Meml Libr Hanover NH 03755

OTTO, TERRE A., real estate executive and developer, interior designer; b. N.Y.C., Aug. 8, 1941; d. Sigfried S. and Ethyl (Goldstein) Alper; children—Regan Alexis, Tiffany Ariana, Dylan Richard. BA, Bennington Coll., 1963; postgrad., Columbia U., 1964, U. Geneva, 1960. Pres. Primiterre Assocs., Port Washington; dir. Nassau County Family Ct. Nursery. Office: Primiterre Assocs PO Box 1030 Port Washington NY 11050-0204

OTTOSON, HOWARD WARREN, agricultural economist, former university administrator; b. Detroit Lakes, Minn., Sept. 18, 1920; s. John Henry and Hilma Marie (Johnson) O.; m. Margaret Jane Featherstone, Oct. 22, 1944; children—Keith Richard, John Howard, David Thomas. B.S., U. Minn., 1942, M.S., 1950; Ph.D., Iowa State U., 1952. Chmn. dept. agrl. econs. U. Nebr., Lincoln, 1956-66, Bert Rodgers prof., 1965, dir., dean, 1966-79, asst. vice chancellor, 1979-81, vice chancellor, 1981-82, exec. v.p., provost, 1982-85, prof. agrl. econs. emeritus, 1985—; cons. USDA, Washington, 1961, 64, AID, Buenos Aires, Argentina, 1962, Colombian Inst. Agr., Bogota, 1970; mem. USDA Policy Adv. Com. on Feed Grains, Washington, 1966-68; mem. Gt. Plains Agrl. Council, Lincoln, Nebr., 1971, 79;
bd. dirs. Farm Found. Bd., Chgo., 1977-85. Sr. author: Land and People in the Northern Plains Tranition Area, 1966; sr. author Agrl. Land Tenure Research bull., 1962; editor: Land Use Problems and Policies in the U.S., 1963; co-editor: Transportation Problems and Policies in the Trans Missouri West, 1967. Pres. Lincoln Coun. Chs., Nebr., 1958-59, Nebr. divsn. UN Assn.-U.S.A., Lincoln, 1977-78; chmn. Mayor's Adv. Com. on Taxation, Lincoln, 1991; bd. dirs. LWV Nebr., 1993—. Served to lt. USNR, 1944-46, PTO. Mem. LWV (bd. dirs. Nebr. 1993—), Am. Agrl. Econs. Assn., Internat. Assn. Agrl. Economists (travel fellow 1958, 64), Open Forum (pres. 1991-92), Fifty-Fifty Club, Norden Club (pres. 1985-87), Farm House, Sigma Xi, Phi Kappa Phi, Gamma Sigma Delta, Phi Delta Kappa. Democrat. Presbyterian. Avocations: golf; skiing; woodwork; Civil War history; gardening. Home: 5811 Margo Dr Lincoln NE 68510-5029

OTTWEIN, MERRILL WILLIAM GEORGE, real estate company executive, veterinarian; b. Troy, Ill., Apr. 24, 1929; s. Oscar J. and Hilda (Bardelmeier) O.; m. Grace Marie Schmidt, Jan. 22, 1932; children: Ann Marie, Amy Sue, Paul John, Emily Carol. BS with highest honors, U. Ill., 1951, MS in Agrl. Econs., 1952, BS in Vet. Medicine, 1954, DVM with honors, 1956. Lic. veterinarian, Ill.; real estate broker, Ill. Pvt. practice Edwardsville, Ill., 1956-66; dir. Diakonia, Ch. World Svc., Honduras, 1967; mem. Ill. Senate, Springfield, 1968-70; real estate developer Cottonwood Sta. Corp., 1970-81; real estate broker Coldwell Banker, Edwardsville, 1981-91; buying-broker Home Relocation Svcs., Edwardsville, 1991—; mem. vet. med. adv. com. U. Ill., Urbana, 1960-64; treas. Nat. Assn. Exclusive Buyer Agents, 1995. Pres. Cahokia Mounds coun. Boy Scouts Am., 1969-71; mem. bd. for world ministries United Ch. of Christ, N.Y.C., 1970-74; active local Rep. politics. Mem. Ill. Assn. Realtors, Edwardsville-Glen Carbon C. of C., Edwardsville-Collinsville Bd. Realtors, Land of Goshen C. of C. (pres. 1974-75), U. Ill. Vet. Medicine Alumni Assn. (pres. 1960-61), Rotary (pres. Edwardsville 1976), Phi Kappa Phi, Alpha Zeta. Avocations: vocal and instrumental music, photography. Home: 34 Lilac St Edwardsville IL 62025-2706 Office: Home Buyers Relocation Svc 2888 Hwy 159 S Edwardsville IL 62025-4300

OTUS, SIMONE, public relations executive; b. Walnut Creek, Calif., Jan. 10, 1960; d. Mahmut and Alexa (Artemenko) O. BA, U. Calif., Berkeley, 1981. Account exec. Marx-David Advt., San Francisco, 1981-82; freelance writer Mpls. and San Francisco, 1982-83; account exec. D'Arcy, MacManus & Masius, San Francisco, 1983; account supr. Ralph Silver Assocs., San Francisco, 1984-85; ptnr., co-founder Blanc & Otus Pub. Relations, San Francisco, 1985—. Office: Blanc & Otus Pub Rels Ste 425 100 Spear St San Francisco CA 94105

OTWELL, RALPH MAURICE, retired newspaper editor; b. Hot Springs, Ark., June 17, 1926; s. Walter Clement and Pearl Oda (Tisdale) O.; m. Janet Barbara Smith, July 18, 1953; children—Brian Thornton, Douglas Keith, David Smith. Student, U. Ark., 1947-48; B.S., Northwestern U., 1951; postgrad. (Nieman fellow), Harvard, 1959-60. Reporter, telegraph editor So. Newspapers, Inc., Hot Springs, 1943-44, 47; asst. city editor Chgo. Sun-Times, 1953-59, news editor, 1959-63, asst. mng. editor, 1963-65, asst. to editor, 1965-68, mng. editor, 1968-76, editor, 1976-80, exec. v.p., editor, 1980-84; Mgmt. bd. newspaper div. Field Enterprises, Inc., 1967-84; lectr. Medill Sch. Journalism, Northwestern U., 1955—; charter mem. Nat. News Council, 1973-80. Trustee Garrett-Evang. Theol. Sem., 1965-79; Mem. nat. bd. Christian Social Concerns, United Meth. Ch., 1968-72; mem. bd. Community Renewal Soc., 1987-90, Chgo. Reporter, 1987-90, student publs. Northwestern U., 1968-72. Served to 1st lt. AUS, 1944-47, 51-53. Recipient Page One award Chgo. Newspaper Guild, 1964; named Ill. Journalist of Year No. Ill. U., 1974. Mem. Am. Soc. Newspaper Editors (chmn. ethics com. 1976-77), AP Mng. Editors Assn., Soc. Profl. Journalists (dir. 1966-71, sec. 1971-72 v.p. 1972-73, pres. 1973-74), Northwestern U. Alumni Assn. (dir. 1965-68, 91-93, sec. 1993-94, Merit award 1969, Svc. award 1995), Sigma Delta Chi (pres. 1987-89), Kappa Tau Alpha, Econ. Club, Headline Club (pres. Chgo. chpt. 1965-66), Harvard Club Chgo., Chgo. Press Club (dir. 1968-77), Northwestern Club. Home: 2750 Hurd Ave Evanston IL 60201-1268

OUDENS, GERALD FRANCIS, architect, architectural firm executive; b. Manchester, N.H., May 18, 1934; s. John and Louise Esther (Wagner) O.; m. Monica Elizabeth Wohlfert, June 16, 1962; children: Elizabeth Marian, Matthew Thomas, Katherine Frances. BA in Architecture cum laude, Yale U., 1956, MArch, 1958. Registered arch., D.C., Va., Md., Pa., Ind., Nat. Coun. Archtl. Registration Bds. Intern architect Koehler & Isaak, Manchester, 1955-58; staff architect Office Surgeon Gen. USAF, Washington, 1958-61; assoc. Metcalf & Assocs., Washington, 1961-69; prin. Oudens & Knoop Architects, PC, Chevy Chase, Md., 1970—; vis. critic, thesis advisor dept. architecture Cath. U. Am., 1968-88; mem. adv. com. acad. med. ctr. study sch. architecture Rice U., 1975; mem. ambulatory care adv. panel U.S. VA, 1974-75; mem. adv. panel No. Ind. Health Systems Agy., 1977-81, AIA Rsch. Corp., 1978, Nat. Inst. Bldg. Scis., 1982-88; mem. design award juries Modern Healthcare Ann. Design Awards, 1992, Soc. for Critical Care Medicine/AACN/AIA ICU Design Awards, 1992-94, AIA Health Facilities Rev. Jury, 1995; presenter in field. Principal works include NIH Master Plan, Bethesda, Md., Sibley Meml. Hosp., Washington, D.C., Washington Adventist Hosp., Takoma Park, Md., Martha Jefferson Hosp., Charlottesville, Va., Marion (Ind.) Gen. Hosp., Humana Lucerne Hosp., Orlando, Fla., Hosp. de Pedregal, Mexico City, Fairfax Hosp., Falls Church, Va., Humana Audubon Hosp. and Heart Inst., Louisville, Ky., Humana Greensboro (N.C.) Hosp., Centre Universitaire des Sciences de la Sante, Yaounde, Cameroon, Washington Home and Hospice, Washington, D.C., Stoddard Bapt. Home, Washington, D.C., Cuttington U. Coll., Suakoko, Liberia, Escuela Agricola Panamericana, El Zamorano, FM, Honduras, others; contbr. articles to profl. jours. Recipient Nat. Capital Architecture award D.C. Coun. Engring. and Archtl. Scis./Washington Acad. Scis., 1961. Mem. AIA (acad. on architecture for health 1971—, past pres. and dir., nat. healthcare policy task force 1993—, mem. adv. com. AIA Collegiate Schs. Architecture coun. on archtl. rsch. 1994—), Henry Adams award 1958, Honor award Ky. chpt., 1980, Outstanding Leadership and Commitment to Healthcare Design award 1987, Merit award Washington Met. chpt. 1989, Citations for Design Excellence 1988, 1990, Am. Hosp. Assn. Grad. Fellowship Rev. Panel), Am. Hosp. Assn. (mem. faculty continuing edn. insts. 1972-76, adv. panel 1978), Internat. Hosp. Fedn., Forum for Health Care Planing. Office: Oudens & Knoop Architects PC 2 Wisconsin Cir Chevy Chase MD 20815-7003

OUELLET, ANDRÉ, Canadian government official; b. St. Pascal, Quebec, Canada, Apr. 6, 1939; s. Albert and Rita (Turgeon) O.; m. Edith Carmichael, July 17, 1965; children: Sonia, Anna, Olga, Pierre. Sec. to min. external affairs Canadian Parl., 1970, sec. to min. nat. health and welfare, 1971; postmaster gen. Canada, 1972; min. consumer and corp. affairs Canadian Parl., 1974, min. state urban affairs, 1974, min. public works, 1978, acting min. labor, 1978; min. consumer and corp. affairs, postmanster gen. Canada, 1980, min. resp. for Can. Post Corp., 1981, min. labor, 1983, min. resp. Crown Corps., 1984, min. foreign affairs, 1993—; various political coms. Office: Fgn Affairs & Internat Trade, 125 Sussex Dr, Ottawa, ON Canada K1A 0G2

OUELLETTE, BERNARD CHARLES, pharmaceutical company executive; b. Windsor, Ont., Can., July 8, 1936; s. Edouard and Alice (Parent) O.; m. Mary Catherine Robert, Sept. 8, 1962; children: Timothy, Michelle, Maureen, Catherine, Suzanne. B.A., U. Windsor, 1964; M.B.A., Wayne State U., 1968; AMP, Harvard U., 1987. Pres. North York (Toronto) Cancer Soc., 1975-77; v.p. bus. devel. Connaught Biosciences Inc., 1975-78; exec. v.p. Winthrop Labs. Ltd., Toronto, Ont., Can., 1978-79; pres. Winthrop Labs. Ltd., 1979-80; exec. v.p. Winthrop Labs., N.Y.C., 1981-82, pres. 1982-83; pres. Pharm. Group Sterling Drug, Inc., N.Y.C., 1983-88, group v.p., 1984-88; pres., chief exec. officer Praxis Biologics Inc., Rochester, N.Y., 1988-89, also bd. dirs.; chief exec. officer Horus Therapeutics (formerly Biocare, Inc.), Rochester, 1989-90, chmn., pres., chief exec. officer, 1990—. Mem. Am. Mgmt. Assn. Roman Catholic. Home: 15 Merrycreek Xing Pittsford NY 14534-1881

OUGHTON, JAMES HENRY, JR., corporate executive, farmer; b. Chgo., May 14, 1913; s. James H. and Barbara (Corbett) O.; student Dartmouth Coll., 1931-35; m. Jane Boyce, Jan. 23, 1940 (dec.); children: Diana (dec.),
Carol Oughton Biondi, Pamela Oughton Armstrong, Deborah Oughton Callahan. Pres., dir. L.E. Keeley Co., Dwight, Ill., 1936—, Nev. Corp.; past adminstr. The Keeley Inst., Dwight, 1938-66; dir. 1st Nat. Bank of Dwight, Ill., 1939—, Ill. Valley Investment Co., 1945-89; farmer, farm mgr., livestock feeder, Ill.; sec., dir. Dwight Indsl. Assn., 1958-93; past mem. Ill. Ho. of Reps. Co-chmn. 1st Indsl. Conf. on Alcoholism, 1948; chmn. Midwest Seminar on Alcoholism for Pastors, 1957, 58, 59, 60; chmn. adv. bd. Ill. Dept. Corrections; chmn. Gov.'s Task Force on Mental Health Adminstrn., 1971-72; mem. adv. bd. Ill. Dept. Mental Health; dir., mem. exec. bd. W.D. Boyce council Boy Scouts Am.; del. 31st Internat. Congress on Alcoholism and Drug Dependence, Bangkok, 1975; mem. Internat. Council on Alcohol and Addictions, Lausanne, Switzerland, 1977; mem. Ill. Trade and Investment Mission to Japan and Korea, 1985; mem. adv. council Small Bus., Fed. Reserve Bank Chgo., 1985-86. Served as lt. (j.g.) USNR, 1944-46; PTO. Republican. Episcopalian. Clubs: Univ., Union League (Chgo.). Address: 103 W South St Dwight IL 60420-1329

OURANT, EDWIN L., fast food restaurant chain executive; b. 1933. With Food Plex Inc., 1967-81, pres.; pres. Casa Lupita, 1981-84; exec. v.p. ops. Rax Restaurants Inc., 1985-86; sr. v.p. spl. projects Wendy's Internat. Inc., Dublin, Ohio, 1986-87, exec. v.p., 1987—. Office: Wendy's Internat Inc 4288 W Dublin Granville Rd Dublin OH 43017-2093

OURS, MARIAN LEAH, elementary education educator; b. Tallmansville, W.Va., Apr. 6, 1937; d. Mayford Thaddeus and Leila Joy (Tenney) O. BS, W.Va. U., 1960, MA, 1965. Tchr., libr. Monongalia County Schs., Morgantown, W.Va., 1960-68; tchr., dept. head Fremont (Calif.) Unified Sch. Dist., 1968—; mem. libr. task force Fremont Unified Sch. Dist., 1989-90, dist. and secondary math. com., 1980—, tech. task force, 1992, 93. Chair Santa Clara County Libr. Commn., San Jose, Calif., 1989-90, mem., 91, 92, 93; treas. Friends of Milpitas (Calif.) Libr., 1990, 92, 93, pres., 1987-89. Recipient Ednl. Leadership award Fremont Sch. Adminstrs. Assn., 1985, Cert. of Appreciation PTA, 1984, Tchr. of Month Fremont Bd. Edn., 1988. Mem. Nat. Coun. Tchrs. Math., Calif. Math. Coun., Computer Using Educators, Fremont Unified Dist. Tchrs. Assn., Calif. Tchrs. Assn. Methodist. Home: 115 Poppy Ct Milpitas CA 95035-5011 Office: Walters Jr High 39600 Logan Dr Fremont CA 94538-1999

OURSLER, FULTON, JR., editor-in-chief, writer; b. West Falmouth, Mass., June 27, 1932; s. Fulton and Grace (Perkins) O.; m. Anne Noel Nevill, Nov. 29, 1954; children: Theresa Noel, Fulton III, Mark Nevill, James Randall, Carroll Grace. B.A., Georgetown U., 1954. With Reader's Digest, Pleasantville, N.Y., 1956-87, book editor, 1968-70, sr. staff editor, 1970-72, asst. mng. editor, 1973, mng. editor, 1974-82, exec. editor, 1982-85, dep. editor-in-chief, 1986-87; editor-in-chief Guideposts mag., 1992—; editor-in-chief, founder Angels on Earth mag., 1995—. Established: Fulton Oursler Meml. Collection, Georgetown U. Library.; editor: (commentary) Behold This Dreamer, 1964. Bd. dirs. Georgetown U. Library Assocs. Served with U.S. Army, 1954-56. Mem. Friends of the Nyacks, Cath. Actors Guild, Univ. Club. Home: 2 Laveta Pl Nyack NY 10960-1604 Office: Reader's Digest Pleasantville NY 10570 *Man makes two journeys in life: one in matter, the other in spirit. The first journey is outward and manifest; it leads to family, society, and career. The second journey is inward and invisible; it leads to the kingdom of God. The first journey is limited by logic, flesh, and time. The second is infinite, and its pathway is paradox. Self-preservation is the strongest instinct on the first journey; freedom, maturity, self-knowledge, power, and abundance seem to be important goals. But on the second journey, one learns that to find our truest selves, we must lose the sense of self; that to grow we must become as a child; that freedom is won by surrender, that the one counts for more than the many, that the meek are powerful, and the poor are rich. On both journeys, to gain life one must lose it, and be reborn.*

OUSLEY, JAMES E., systems integrator. Pres., CEO, Control Data Sys., Inc., Arden Hills, Minn. V.p., marketing & sales Control Data Corp., St. Paul; pres., ceo Ceridian Corp., St. Paul. Office: Control Data Sys Inc 4201 Lexington Ave N Arden Hills MN 55126

OUSSANI, JAMES JOHN, stapling company executive; b. Bklyn., Jan. 3, 1920; s. John Thomas and Clara (Tager) O.; m. Lorraine G. Tutundgy, Apr. 25, 1954; children: James J., Gregory P., Rita C. B.M.E., Pratt Inst., 1938-42; J.D. (hon.), Coll. Boca Raton, Lynn U.; LLD. Dir. research, mfg. Supertronic Co., N.Y.C., 1943-46; sr. partner Perl-Oussani Machine Mfg. Co., N.Y.C., 1946-49; founder The Staplex Co., Bklyn., 1949, pres., 1949—; exec. dir. Lourdes Realty Corp.; dir. Junios Corp.; producer air sampling equipment for radioactive fallout AEC, 1951—. Mem. Bur. Research Air Pollution Control, Pres.'s Council on Youth Opportunity, Cardinal's Com. for Edn.; trustee Ch. of Virgin Mary; bd. dirs. St. Joan Arc Found., Boca Raton; founding mem. Lumen Christi-Palm Beach Diocese; founder, bd. dirs. Oussani Found.; founder James J. & Lorraine G. Oussani Scholarship Fund, Coll. Boca Raton; mem. cardinal's com. of laity, bishop's com. of laity; mem. Lumen Christi Found.; chmn. bd. overseers Lynn U., Boca Raton. Recipient Blue Ribbon Mining award, Sch. Mgmt. award, Aerospace Pride Achievement award; installed Knight of Jerusalem. Mem. Adminstrv. Mgmt. Soc., Office Adminstrn. Assn., Nat. Stationery and Office Equipment AssOffice Equipment Assn., Office Execs. Assn., Nat. Office Machine Mfg. Assn., Nat. Office Machine Dealers Assn., Nat. Office Products Assn., Bus. Equipment Mfrs. Assn., Our Lady Perpetual Help Holy Name Soc., Knights of Holy Sepulchre, Knights of St. Gregory, Knights of Malta, Rotary, Salaam Club, Mahopac Golf Club (Lake Mahopac, N.Y.), Internat. Club of Boca Raton, Boca Raton Hotel and Resort Club. Inventor automatic electric stapling machine. Patentee in field. Office: 777 5th Ave Brooklyn NY 11232-1695

OUTCALT, DAVID LEWIS, academic administrator, mathematician, educator; b. Los Angeles, Jan. 30, 1935; s. Earl Kinyon and Alberta Estes Ferguson O.; m. Marcia Lee Beach, July 1, 1956; children—Jeffrey David, Kevin Douglas, Gregory Mark, Eric Matthew. B.A. in Math., Pomona Coll., 1956; M.A. in Math., Claremont Grad. Sch., 1958; Ph.D. in Math., Ohio State U., 1963; D.Pub. Adminstrn. (hon.), Kyung Hee U., Korea, 1984. Asst. prof. math. Clarement McKenna Coll., 1962-64; asst. prof. to prof. math. U. Calif.-Santa Barbara, 1964-80, chmn. dept. math., 1969-72, dean instrnl. devel., 1977-80; vice chancellor acad. affairs U. Alaska, Anchorage, 1980-81, prof. math., 1980-86, chancellor, 1981-86; prof. natural and applied sci. U. Wis., Green Bay, 1986-93, chancellor, 1986-93, Hendrickson prof. econ. devel., 1994—; pres. Mid-Continent athletic conf. 1990-91. Author math. textbooks; contbr. articles on math. and higher edn. to profl. jours. Moderator bd. trustees Humana Hosp. Anchorage, 1982-83; mem. exec. bd. Western Alaska coun. Boy Scouts Am., 1982-86, Bay-Lakes coun., 1987—; v.p. exploring 1988-92, v.p. ops., 1992-93, pres., 1993-94; mem. Anchorage Symphony bd., 1986, Green Bay Symphony Bd., 1988—, mem. Weidner Ctr. Presents Bd., 1994—. Grantee USAF Office Sci. Research, 1964-71, U. Calif., 1975-78, NSF, 1976-79. Mem. Math. Assn. Am. (mem. Assn. Univ. Pres.'s (exec. com. 1988—, vice chair N.Am. coun. 1988-94, newsletter editor 1994—), Greater Green Bay C. of C. (advance bd. 1987—, bd. dirs. 1991-94), Brown County Industrial Devel. (pres. bd. dirs. 1994—), Rotary, Sigma Xi. Mem. Congregational Ch.

OUTEN, DAWN, secondary education educator; b. L.A., Mar. 4, 1942; d. Jesse Lee and Joe Anna (Joshua) Williams; m. Wilbert Outen Jr., Sept. 1, 1964; children: JohAnna, Clarence, Christy. B of Human Studies, Dominguez Hills U., Carson, Calif., 1976; MEd, U. LaVerne, Calif., 1986; postgrad., Nova U., Ft. Lauderdale, Fla., 1992—. Tchr. L.A. Unified Sch. Dist., 1977-81, Compton (Calif.) Unified Sch. Dist., 1981-86; multi-cultural coord. Chino (Calif.) Unified Sch. Dist., 1986—; part-time faculty Calif. Poly. State U., Pomona, 1990-92; mem. steering com. Los Angeles County Bd. Edn., L.A., 1984—; lectr. multi cultural, child and youth studies and tech. in edn. Contbr. articles to profl. jours. Mem. steering coun. on interracial unity YWCA, Pomona, 1992—; v.p. Parents Against Violence in Edn., Chino, 1992. Recipient Outstanding Contbns. award Consl. Rights Found., L.A., 1987, Recognition of Svc. award County of Los Angeles, 1992. Mem. ASCD, Calif. Tchrs. Assn., Chino Valley C. of C., Notary Assn., Coun. of Negro Women, Univ. Women, Phi Delta Kappa. Republican. Christian. Avocations: music, theater, reading, computer. Office: Chino Unified Sch Dist 5130 Riverside Dr Chino CA 91710-4130

OUTERBRIDGE, CHERYL, lawyer; b. Monte Vista, Colo., July 11, 1943; d. George Herbert and Gladys Mae (Walker) Hazard; m. J. Robert Outerbridge, June 4, 1961 (div. 1984); 1 child, Grant Hazard; m. Carl F. Nagy, Nov. 16, 1985; B.A., U. Denver, 1968; J.D., U. Colo., 1975. Bar: Colo. 1975, U.S. Dist. Ct. Colo. 1975. Assoc., Gorsuch, Kirgis, Campbell, Walker & Grover, Denver, 1975-79; staff atty. Amax Inc., Golden, Colo., 1979-81; editor-in-chief American Law of Mining, 2d edit., Rocky Mountain Mineral Law Found., Boulder, Colo., 1981-85; sr. atty. AMAX Inc., Golden, Colo., 1985—. Contbr. articles to profl. jours. Mem. ABA, Order of Coif, Colo. Bar Assn., Denver Bar Assn., The Alliance of Profl. Women, Phi Beta Kappa. Office: AMAX Inc 1707 Cole Blvd Golden CO 80401-3214

OUTKA, GENE HAROLD, philosophy and Christian ethics educator; b. Sioux Falls, S.D., Feb. 24, 1937; s. Harold Irvin and Gertrude Anne (Elliott) O.; m. Carole Lee DeVore, June 26, 1960 (div. 1982); children: Paul Harold, Elizabeth Noelle; m. Susan Jane Owen, Dec. 29, 1984; 1 child, Jacqueline Elliott. B.A., U. Redlands, 1959; B.D., Yale U., 1962, M.A., 1964, Ph.D., 1967; L.H.D., U. Redlands, 1978. Instr. Princeton U., N.J., 1965-66, lectr., 1966-67, asst. prof., 1967-73, assoc. prof., 1973-75; assoc. prof. Yale U., New Haven, 1975-81, Dwight prof. philosophy and Christian ethics, 1981—; chair dept. religious studies, 1992—; dir. resdl. seminar for coll. tchrs. NEH, New Haven, 1977-78; Mary Farnum Brown lectr. Haverford Coll., Pa., 1977; mem. faculty workshop on teaching of ethics Hastings Inst. of Soc., Ethics and Life Scis., Princeton, N.J., 1979; Merrick lectr. Ohio Wesleyan U., Delaware, Ohio, 1983; Williamson Meml. lectr. Meth. Theol. Sch. in Ohio, 1986. Author: Agape: An Ethical Analysis, 1972; co-editor, contbr.: Norm and Context In Christian Ethics, 1968, Religion and Morality, 1973, Prospects for a Common Morality, 1992; editorial bd. Jour. Religious Ethics. Service fellow office of spl. projects Health Services and Mental Health Adminstrn., HEW, Washington, 1972-73; mem. adv. com. social ethics Inst. Medicine Nat. Acad. Scis., 1975-77. Fellow Am. Council Learned Socs., 1968-69; fellow NEH, 1979-80, Woodrow Wilson Internat. Ctr. for Scholars, 1983; vis. scholar Kennedy Inst. of Ethics, Georgetown U., 1972-73. Mem. Am. Acad. Religion, Soc. Christian Ethics (bd. dirs.). Office: Yale U Dept Religious Studies 320 Temple St New Haven CT 06520

OUZOUNIAN, ARMENUHI, dentist; b. Mosul, Iraq, Feb. 17, 1942; came to U.S., 1974; d. Yervant and Warda (Efram) O. DDS, U. Baghdad, Iraq, 1962, degree in anesthesiology, 1966. Cert. U.S. Bd. Dentistry; lic. dentist, Ill. Resident Fed. Teaching Hosp., Baghdad, 1963-66; anesthesiologist Maternity Hosp., Baghdad, 1966-73; gen. practice dentistry Baghdad, 1967-73; asst. various offices, Chgo., 1975-83; gen. practice dentistry Chgo., 1984—. Active Smithsonian Inst., Washington. Mem. ADA, Internat. Platform Assn., Am. Women Dentists Assn., Ill. Dental Soc., Chgo. Dental Soc., Acad. Polit. Sci., U.S. Naval Acad. Avocations: painting, reading, writing, research. Home: 9346 N Greenwood Ave Niles IL 60714-5748 Office: 3647 W 26th St Chicago IL 60623-3823

OUZTS, DALE KEITH, broadcast executive; b. Miami, Fla., Aug. 26, 1941; s. Jacob C. and Edna P. (Sloan) O.; m. Judy Olcott, June 11, 1964 (div. Mar. 1980); children: Dale Keith Jr., Karen J. Frost; m. Kathleen Gross, Mar. 15, 1982 (div. Nov. 1991); m. Suzanne Kasavage, June 18, 1993; 1 child, Ryan Keith. BJ, U. Ga., 1965, MA, 1966; postgrad. advanced mgmt. seminar, Harvard U., 1977. Mgr. Sta. WSJK-TV, Knoxville, Tenn., 1966-69; exec. v.p., gen. mgr. Sta. KPTS-TV, Wichita, Kans., 1969-72; gen. mgr. Sta. WSSR-FM, Springfield, Ill., 1972-77; sr. v.p. Nat. Pub. Radio, Washington, 1977-79; gen. mgr. Sta. WOSU-AM-FM and Sta. WOSU-TV Ohio State U., Columbus, Ohio, 1979—; gen. mgr. WPBO-TV, Portsmouth, Ohio, 1979—, WOSV-FM, Mansfield, Ohio, 1988—, WOSP-FM, Portsmouth, 1993—; assoc. prof. communications Ohio State U., Columbus, Ohio, 1979—, assoc. prof. journalism, 1983—; adminstrv. dir. Ohio State Awards, 1979—; mem. Ohio Ednl. TV Stas., v.p., 1983-84, pres., 1988-90; pres. Ohio Pub. Radio, 1995-96; chmn. Nat. Pub. Radio, 1990-92; pres. Pub. Radio in Mid-Am., 1976-77, 85-87. Bd. dirs. Ctr. of Vocat. Alts. in Mental Health, 1985-93, sec.-treas., 1986-88, chmn., 1988-90, Pub. Radio Expansion Task Force, 1989-90; bd. dirs. Brule Conservation Trust, 1985-94, Columbus Zoo, 1984—, Mental Health Assn., Franklin County, 1987-93, Ohio China Coun., 1982-93, v.p., 1984-85, pres., 1987-89; advisor Chinese Student and Scholar Soc. at Ohio State U., 1987-91; program rev. panel Nat. Telecomms., 1988; mgmt. cons. Corp. for Pub. Broadcasting, 1975—. Recipient Disting. Service award Nat. Pub. Radio, 1986, Disting. Service award Nat. Black Program Consortium, 1985, Disting. Service award PRIMA, 1977, 87, award for fundraising and promotion Corp. Pub. Broadcasting, 1971, Outstanding Broadcaster award Wichita (Kans.) Chpt. of Kappa Mu Psi, 1970, OEBIE award Ohio Ednl. Broadcasting Network Commn., 1987, Emmy award nomination Acad. TV Arts and Scis., 1987. Mem. Nat. Assn. Broadcasters, Ohio Assn. Broadcasters, Nat. Assn. State Univs. and Land Grant Colls. (mem. telecomms. com. 1980-93), Columbus Ducks Unltd. (bd. dirs. 1982-93), Scioto Valley Skeet Club (bd. dirs. 1982-92), Grand Hotel Hunt Club, Sawmill Athletic Club, Ohio-Rocky Mountain Elk Found., Rotary (Dublin-Worthington, v.p. 1988-89, pres. 1990-91). Avocations: racquetball, softball, golf, hunting, tennis. Home: 2038 Michelle Dr Grove City OH 43123-4019 Office: Sta WOSU 2400 Olentangy River Rd Columbus OH 43210-1027

OVERALL, JAMES CARNEY, JR., pediatrics laboratory medicine educator; b. Nashville, Sept. 27, 1937; s. James Carney and Evelyn Byrd (Duncan) O.; m. Marie Kathryn Pauli, Aug. 14, 1965; children: David, Paul. BS, Davidson Coll., 1959; MD, Vanderbilt U., 1963. Cert. pediatrics infectious diseases. Intern Vanderbilt U. Hosp., Nashville, 1963-64; resident Columbia Presbyn. Med. Ctr., N.Y.C., 1964-66; research assoc. Nat. Inst. Child Health, Bethesda, Md., 1966-68; instr. pediatrics Rochester, N.Y., 1968-70; asst. prof. pediatrics, microbiology U. Utah Sch. Med., Salt Lake City, 1970-74, assoc. prof. pediatrics, microbiology, 1974-79, prof. pediatrics, 1979—, prof. pathology, 1981—; chief pediatrics infectious diseases Univ. Utah Sch. Medicine, 1970-93, dir. virology course, 1980—, vice chmn. pediatrics dept., 1982-92, med. dir. diagnostic virology lab., 1981—; bd. govs. Primary Children's Med. Ctr., Salt Lake City, 1976-78; mem. sub-bd. infectious disease Am. Bd. Pediatrics, 1992—. Contbr. chpts. to textbooks, articles to profl. jours. vice moderator Holladay United Ch. Christ, Salt Lake City, 1982-85. Served to lt. comdr. USPHS, 1966-68. Recipient Investigator award Howard Hughes Med. Inst., 1974-80. Mem. Am. Pediatric Soc., Soc. Pediatric Rsch., Am. Soc. Virology, Infectious Diseases Soc. Am., Pan Am. Soc. for Clin. Virology (mem. coun.), Rapid Viral Diagnosis, Am. Bd. Pediatrics (sub-bd. for infectious diseases 1992-96), Am. Acad. Pediatrics (commn. on infectious diseases 1993—). United Ch. of Christ. Home: 896 18th Ave Salt Lake City UT 84103-3721 Office: Univ Utah Sch Med Dept Pediatrics Salt Lake City UT 84132

OVERBECK, GENE EDWARD, retired airline executive, lawyer; b. St. Louis, June 16, 1929; s. Harry C. and Edna (Kessler) O.; m. Patricia June Bay, Oct. 5, 1957; children: Richard, Thomas, Elizabeth, Katherine. B.A., U. Mich., 1951, J.D., 1953. Bar: Mich. 1953, Mo. 1954, N.Y. 1958, Tex. 1980. Asso. firm Sullivan & Cromwell, N.Y.C., 1957-59; gen. atty. Am. Airlines, 1959-67, v.p., gen. counsel, 1967-72, sr. v.p., 1972-90; dir. Stevens Graphics Corp. Served with AUS, 1954-57. Home: 4634 Charleston Ter NW Washington DC 20007-1900

OVERBECK, JAMES A., library director, educator; b. Eau Claire, Wis., Sept. 11, 1940; s. Arwin Kubel O.; m. Lois Ellen More, June 11, 1966; children: Kristen, Andrew, Jonathan. BA, CArthage Coll., 1963, MDiv, 1967, MLS, 1975; PhD, U. Chgo., 1975. Ordained elder Presbyn. Ch. 1983. Instr. Ch. hist. Luth. Sem., Phila., 1969-71; dir. libr. Sch. Theol., Claremont, Calif., 1975-80, Columbia Theol. Sem., Campbell Libr., Decatur, Ga., 1980-93; dir. libr. svcs. Shorter Coll., Rome, Ga., 1993—; bd. dirs. U. Ctr. Ga. Libr. Group, Atlanta, 1990-91. Mem. Am. Theol. Libr. Assn. (bd. dirs. 1983-86), Am Soc. Ch. Hist., Am. Acad. Religion. Office: Shorter Coll 315 Shorter Ave Rome GA 30165-4298

OVERBY, OSMUND RUDOLF, art historian, educator; b. Mpls., Nov. 8, 1931; s. Oscar Rudolph and Gertrude Christine (Boe) O.; m. Barbara Ruth Spande, Mar. 20, 1954; children: Paul, Katherine, Charlotte. B.A., St. Olaf Coll., 1953; B.Arch., U. Wash., 1958; M.A., Yale U., 1960, Ph.D, 1963. Asst. in instruction dept. of history of art Yale U., 1959-60, 61-62; architect Hist. Am. Bldgs. Survey, U.S. Nat. Park Service, 1960-61, summers 1959, 62, 63, 65, 68, 69, 70, 73, 85; lectr. dept. fine arts U. Toronto, Ont., Can., 1963-64; faculty dept. art history and archaeology U. Mo., Columbia, 1964—;

dept. chmn. U. Mo., 1967-70, 75-77, prof. art history, 1979—; dir. Mus. of Art and Archaeology, 1977-83; vis. prof. dept. architecture U. Calif., Berkeley, 1980; Morgan prof. U. Louisville, 1989; bd. advisors Nat. Trust for Hist. Preservation, 1974-83; cons., panelist Nat. Endowment for Humanities, 1974—; bd. Mo. Mansion Preservation Commn., 1974-87; advisor Heritage/St. Louis Survey, 1974-76; counsellor to St. Louis Landmarks Assn., 1977—; chmn. Task Force on Hist. Preservation City of Columbia, 1977-78; cons. on hist. preservation; active Mo. Adv. Council on Hist. Preservation, 1967-82; lectr., exhibitor profl. confs. in field. Author: Historic American Buildings Survey, Rhode Island Catalog, 1972; co-author: Laclede's Landing, a History and Architectural Guide, 1977, The Saint Louis Old Post Office, A History and Architectural Guide to the Building and Its Neighborhood, 1979; co-author, editor: Illustrated Museum Handbook, A Guide to the Collections in the Museum of Art and Archaeology, University of Missouri-Columbia, 1982; editor in chief Buildings of the United States series; contbr. sects. to books, articles to profl. publs. in field. Served with U.S. Army, 1953-55. Recipient various fellowships and grants in field. Mem. Soc. Archtl. Historians (bd. dirs. 1968-73, 78-81, Jour. editor 1968-73, dir. Mo. Valley chpt., session chmn. ann. meeting 1976, v.p. 1982-86, pres. 1986-88, chmn. coms.), Mid-Continent Am. Studies Assn. (editorial bd. American Studies 1965-70), Midwest Art History Soc. (bd. 1975-78, gen. chmn. annual meeting 1977), Mid-Am. Coll. Art Assn. (session chmn. annual meeting 1975), Mo. Heritage Trust (pres. 1976-79, 81-83, bd. dirs. 1979—), Coll. Art Assn., Landmarks Assn. St. Louis, Soc. for Hist. Archaeology. Lutheran. Home: 1118 W Rollins Rd Columbia MO 65203-2221 Office: U Mo Dept Art History & Archaeology Columbia MO 65211

OVERCASH, MICHAEL RAY, chemical engineering educator; b. Kannapolis, N.C., July 17, 1944; s. Ray Leonard and Ruth (Crabbe) O.; m. Mary C.N. Yoong; 1 child, Rachael. BS, N.C. State U., 1966; MS, U. New South Wales, Sydney, Australia, 1967; PhD, U. Minn., 1972. Prof. biol. and agrl. engring. N.C. State U., Raleigh, 1972—, prof. chem. engring. dept., 1981—, ctr. dir. process improvement and pollution prevention ctr., 1989—. Author: Design Industrial Land Treatment Systems, 1979, Industrial Pollution Prevention, 1986, Prevention, Management and Compliance for Hazardous Wastes, 1987. Com. mem. N.C. Govs. Waste Mgmt. Bd., 1984-88, Air Force Sci. Adv. Bd., 1984-86. Fulbright scholar, 1966-67; disting. vis. scientist EPA, 1986-89. Mem. Am. Inst. Chem. Engrs., Am. Soc. Agrl. Engrs. (young researcher award 1984), Inst. Chem. Engrs., N.C. Acad. Scis., History of Sci. Soc., Nat. Acad. of Sci. Office: Pollution Prevention Rsch Ctr NC State U Dept Chem Engring PO Box 7905 Raleigh NC 27695-7905

OVERCASH, REECE A., JR., financial services company executive; b. Charlotte, N.C., June 15, 1926; s. Reece A. and Mary Louise (Daniel) O.; m. Christa Lee Anderson; children: Susan Kay Overcash-Jenkins, Mary Ann Austin, Sarah Lee, Alex. BBA, U. N.C., 1950. With Am. Credit Corp., Charlotte, 1952-75, pres., 1970-75; pres. Assocs. Corp. N.Am., Dallas, 1975-81, chmn., chief exec. officer, 1978—; dir. Assocs. Corp. N.Am. (The Associates), Dallas; chmn. Assocs. First Capital Corp.; sr. exec. v.p. Gulf & Western Inc., N.Y.C., 1983-87; bd. dirs. Duke Power Co., Charlotte, Belo Corp., Dallas, Nat. Gypsum Co., Charlotte. Bd. dirs. Dallas Citizens Council, 1986-88, 1990-92, Sammons Dallas Found., Sammons Found., 1994—; campaign chmn. United Way Met. Dallas, 1979, exec. com., 1979—, pres. exec. com., 1981, ; so. cen. regional chmn. United Way Am., 1988—; v.p. Met. Dallas, 1980-81, pres., from 1981, bd. dirs., 1978—; bd. dirs. Dallas County Community Coll. Dist. Found., 1977—, vice chmn., 1978-79, chmn., 1979-81; mem. consumer adv. council Fed. Res. Bd., 1976-78; bd. trustees Dallas Baptist U., 1986-90; bd. dirs. Circle Ten Council Boy Scouts Am., 1978-86, North Tex. Commn., 1977—, Better Bus. Bur. Met. Dallas, 1979—, Community Council Greater Dallas, 1981; mem. devel. council U Dallas Campaign, 1980; vice chmn. patron gifts com. Dallas Mus. Fine Arts, 1980; adv. council Credit Research Ctr., Purdue U., 1980; mem. bus. devel. com. So. Meth. U., 1985; mem. strategic planning com. United Way Am., 1985; chmn. bd. Dallas United Adv. Coun., 1986-88; exec. bd. Cox Sch. Bus. of So. Meth. U., 1983—; adv. com. Dallas County Treasurer's Office, 1987. Served with inf., AUS, World War II. Recipient Disting. Bus. Leadership award U. Tex., Arlington, 1988, Statesman award Harvard Bus. Sch. Club of Dallas, 1990; named Man of Yr., Charlotte, 1972. Mem. Dallas C. of C. (bd. dirs. 1977-80, 86-89, chmn. adv. com. Leadership Dallas prog. 1979-80, Dallas United prog. 1986), Am. Fin. Svcs. Assn. (bd. dirs., exec. com. 1966-83, Disting. Svc. award 1973), Myers Park Country Club, City Club (Charlotte), Brookhollow Country Club, Petroleum Club (Dallas). Baptist.

OVERFELT, CLARENCE LAHUGH, lawyer; b. Big Timber, Mont., Apr. 15, 1935; s. Leo and Clara (Drivdahl) O.; m. Joyce Overfelt, Feb. 15, 1959 (div. 1977); children: Kent Leo, Reed Allen; m. Allyce Overfelt, Nov. 21, 1977. BA, U. Mont., 1958, JD, 1968. Bar: Mont. 1968, U.S. Dist. Ct. Mont. 1968. Ptnr. Randono Overfelt & Gianotti, Great Falls, Mont., 1968-73; pvt. practice Overfelt Law Firm, Great Falls, Mont., 1973-91, pres., sr. mem., 1980—; tchr. Cut Bank (Mont.) Pub. Schs., 1959-60, Helena (Mont.) Pub. Schs., 1960-65. mem. Assn. Trial Lawyers Am., Mont. Trial Lawyers Assn., Civil Justice Found., Meadowlark Country Club, Elks, Kiwanis. Democrat. Episcopalian. Avocations: golf, skiing, music, woodworking, gardening. Home: 128 Lower River Rd Great Falls MT 59405-8203 Office: Overfelt Law Firm PC 121 4th St N Rm 2E Great Falls MT 59401-2552

OVERFIELD, RONALD EDWIN, radiologist; b. Henderson, Ky., Apr. 22, 1938; s. Covington and Helena Gertrude (Whelan) O.; m. Kathryn Hamilton Jones, Oct. 19, 1963; children: Laura Lee, John Covington. BS, U. Ky., 1960; MD, Vanderbilt Med. Sch., 1963. Diplomate Am. Bd. Radiology, Am. Bd. Nuclear Medicine. Radiology resident Vanderbilt U., Nashville, 1963-67, chief radiology resident, 1966-67; radiologist Radiol. Assocs. Nashville, 1969—; bd. dirs. Clin. Ethics Guild, Nashville, Canby Robinson Soc. Vanderbilt, Nashville; chmn. dept. med. imaging Bapt. Hosp., Nashville, 1977-93, pres. med. staff, 1981, vice chief of staff, 1993-94, chief of staff, 1994—; assoc. clin. prof. dept. radiology Vanderbilt U., Nashville, 1979—; exec. com. Mid. Tenn. Health Systems Agy., Nashville, 1981-84. Capt. USAF, 1967-69. Recipient Svc. award AMA, 1977. Fellow Am. Coll. Nuclear Medicine (bd. dirs., editor 1992—, v.p. 1994), Am. Coll. Radiology (counsilor 1980-94); mem. AMA (del. 1994—), Tenn. Med. Assn. (bd. dirs. 1994—), Tenn. Radiol. Soc. (pres. 1976-77), Mid. Tenn. Radiol. Soc. (pres. 1973-74), Nashville Acad. Medicine (bd. dirs., chmn. 1983, pres. 1982, Pres. award 1979). Methodist. Avocations: southern history, photography.

OVERGAARD, MITCHELL JERSILD, lawyer; b. Chgo., Jan. 9, 1931; s. Kristen Mikkelsen and Rose Eunice (Jersild) O.; m. Joan Marquardt, Aug. 2, 1958; children: Wade, Kristin, Neil. B.A., U. Chgo., 1950, J.D., 1953. Bar: Ill. 1957, U.S. Supreme Ct. 1975. Assoc. Dale, Haffner & Grow, Chgo., 1957-63; ptnr. Overgaard & Davis, Chgo., 1963—; Dir. Community Bank of Homewood-Flossmoor, Homewood, Ill., 1973-83. Trustee Village of Homewood, 1965-69, 85—; commr. Homewood-Flossmoor Park Dist., 1969-77; past pres., bd. dirs. Family Services and Mental Health Center of South Cook County, Homewood Youth Council; bd. dirs. Ill. Philharm. Orch. Served with U.S. Army, 1953-56. Mem. Ill. Bar Assn., Chgo. Bar Assn. Mem. Reformed Ch. in America (elder). Home: 19137 Loomis Ave Homewood IL 60430-4431 Office: Overgaard & Davis 134 N La Salle St Chicago IL 60602-1086

OVERGAARD, ROBERT MILTON, religious organization administrator; b. Ashby, Minn., Nov. 6, 1929; s. Gust and Ella (Johnson) O.; m. Sally Lee Stephenson, Dec. 29, 1949; children: Catherine Jean Overgaard Thuleen, Robert Milton, Elizabeth Dianne Overgaard Almendinger, Barbara, Craig, David (dec.), Lori Overgaard Noack. Cert., Luth. Brethren Sem., 1954; BS, Mayville (N.D.) State U., 1959; MS, U. Oreg., 1970. Ordained to ministry Ch. Luth. Brethren am., 1954. Pastor Elim Luth. Ch., Frontier, Sask., Can., 1954-57, Ebenezer Luth. Ch., Mayville, 1957-60, Immanuel Luth. Ch., Eugene, Oreg., 1960-63, 59th Street Luth. Ch., Bklyn., 1963-68, Immanuel Luth. Ch., Pasadena, Calif., 1969-73; exec. dir. world missions Ch. Luth. Brethren Am., Fergus Falls, Minn., 1973-86, 1986—; editor Faith and Fellowship, 1967-75. Home: 806 W Channing Ave Fergus Falls MN 56537-3221 Office: Ch Luth Brethren Am PO Box 655 Fergus Falls MN 56538-0655

OVERGAARD, WILLARD MICHELE, retired political scientist, jurisprudent; b. Montpelier, Idaho, Oct. 16, 1925; s. Elias Nielsen and Myrtle LaVerne (Humphrey) O.; m. Lucia Clare Cochrane, June 14, 1946; children:

Eric Willard, Mark Fredrik, Alisa Claire. B.A. U. Oreg., 1949; Fulbright scholar, U. Oslo, 1949-50; M.A. (non-resident scholar 1954-55), U. Wis., Madison, 1955; Ph.D. in Polit. Sci. (adminstrv. fellow 1955-56, research fellow 1962-64), U. Minn., 1969. Instr., Soviet and internat. affairs Intelligence Sch., U.S. Army, Europe, 1956-62; dir. intelligence rsch. tng. program Intelligence Sch., U.S. Army, 1958-61; asst. prof. internat. affairs George Washington U., 1964-67; sr. staff polit. scientist Ops. Research Inst., U.S. Army Inst. Advanced Studies, Carlisle, Pa., 1967-70; assoc. prof. polit. sci., chmn. dept., dir. Internat. Studies Inst., Westminster Coll., New Wilmington, Pa., 1970-72; prof. polit. sci. and pub. law Boise (Idaho) State U., 1972-94, chmn. dept., 1972-87, acad. dir. M.P.A. degree program, personnel adminstr., mem. humanities council interdisciplinary studies in humanities, 1976-87, prof. of pub. law emeritus, 1994—, dir. Taft Inst. Seminars for Pub. Sch. Tchrs., 1985-87, coord. Legal Asst. Program, 1990—; mem. comml. panel Am. Arbitration Assn., 1974—; mem. Consortium for Idaho's Future, 1974-75; adv. com. Idaho Statewide Tng. Program Local Govt. Ofcls., 1974-78; adv. group Gov. Idaho Task Force Local Govt., 1977; co-dir. Idaho State Exec. Inst., Office of Gov., 1979-83; grievance hearing officer City of Boise, 1981-85; arbitrator U.S. Postal Svc., 1988-90; cons. in field. Author: The Schematic System of Soviet Totalitarianism, 3 vols, 1961, Legal Norms and Normative Bases for the Progressive Development of International Law as Defined in Soviet Treaty Relations, 1945-64, 1969; co-author: The Communist Bloc in Europe, 1959; editor: Continuity and Change in International Politics, 1972; chief editor: Idaho Jour. Politics, 1974-76. Served with USAAF, 1943-45; with AUS, 1951-54; ret. maj. USAR. Named Disting. Citizen of Idaho Idaho Statesman, 1979; named Outstanding Prof. of Sch. Social Scis. and Pub. Affairs, Boise State U., 1988. Mem. ABA (assoc.). Home: 2023 S Five Mile Rd Boise ID 83709-2316

OVERHAUSER, ALBERT WARNER, physicist; b. San Diego, Aug. 17, 1925; s. Clarence Albert and Gertrude Irene (Pehrson) O.; m. Margaret Mary Casey, Aug. 25, 1951; children—Teresa, Catherine, Joan, Paul, John, David, Susan, Steven. A.B., U. Calif. at Berkeley, 1948, Ph.D., 1951; D.Sc. (hon.), U. Chgo., 1979. Research assoc. U. Ill., 1951-53; asst. prof. physics Cornell U., 1953-56, assoc. prof., 1956-58; supr. solid state physics Ford Motor Co., Dearborn, Mich., 1958-62; mgr. theoret. scis. Ford Motor Co., 1962-69, asst. dir. phys. scis., 1969-72, dir. phys. scis., 1972-73; prof. physics Purdue U., West Lafayette, Ind., 1973-74; Stuart disting. prof. physics Purdue U., 1974—. With USNR, 1944-46. Recipient Alexander von Humboldt sr. U.S. scientist award 1979, Nat. Medal of Sci., Pres. of U.S., 1994. Fellow Am. Phys. Soc. (Oliver E. Buckley Solid State Physics prize 1975), Am. Acad. Arts and Scis.; mem. NAS. Home: 236 Pawnee Dr West Lafayette IN 47906-2115 Office: Purdue U Dept Of Physics West Lafayette IN 47907

OVERHOLT, HUGH ROBERT, lawyer, retired army officer; b. Beebe, Ark., Oct. 29, 1933; s. Harold R. and Cuma E. (Hall) O.; m. Laura Annell Arnold, May 5, 1961; children: Sharon, Scott. Student, Coll. of Ozarks, 1951-53; B.A., U. Ark., 1955, LL.B., 1957. Bar: Ark. 1957. Commd. 1st lt. U.S. Army, 1957, advanced through grades to maj. gen., 1981; chief Criminal Law Div., JAG, U.S. Army, Washington, 1971-73; chief personnel, plans and tng. Office of JAG, U.S. Army, Washington, 1973-75; staff judge adv. XVIII Airborne Corps, Ft. Bragg, N.C., 1976-78; spl. asst. for legal and selected policy matters Office of Dep. Asst., 1978-79; asst. judge adv. gen. for mil. law Office of JAG, Washington, 1979-81; asst. judge adv. gen. Office of JAG, 1981-85, judge adv. gen. 1985-89. Notes and comment editor Ark. Law Rev, 1956-57. Decorated Army Meritorious Service medal with oak leaf cluster, Army Commendation medal with 2 oak leaf clusters., Legion of Merit, Def. Meritorious Service medal, D.S.M. Mem. ABA, Ark. Bar Assn., Assn. U.S. Army, Delta Theta Phi, Omicron Delta Kappa, Sigma Pi. Presbyterian. Office: McNair & Sanford 3810 Washington Woods Dr Alexandria VA 22309-2734

OVERHOLT, MILES HARVARD, III, management consultant, family therapist; b. L.A., July 7, 1948; s. Miles Harvard and Jessie Louise (Foster) O.; m. Deborah Jean Robinson, Nov. 22, 1970; 1 child, Rebecca Robinson. BA, Lafayette Coll., 1970; MSW, U. Pa., 1976, D in Social Work, 1979. Cert. social worker; lic. marriage and family therapist, N.J.; cert. mgmt. cons.; cert. clin. hypnotherapist. Youth dir. Camden County YMCA, Haddonfield, N.J., 1970-71; dir. multi-service ctr. Community YMCA, Red Bank, N.J., 1972-74; indsl. cons. NE Community Mental Health/Mental Retardation, Phila., 1977; therapist Marriage and Family Therapy Assns., Wilingboro, Marlton, N.J., 1976-82; mgmt. cons., owner Ambler and Overholt Cons., Inc., Cherry Hill, N.J., 1979-85; therapist, ptnr. Affiliated Counseling and Therapy Assocs., Moorestown, N.J., 1982—; owner, cons. Applied Orgnl. Devel., Inc., Palmyra, N.J., 1985-90; instr. Burlington County Coll., Willingboro, 1978-80; mem. co-adj. faculty Rutgers U., 1978-80; prin. Riverton Mgmt. Cons. Group (formerly Comm. Link Co.). Contbr. articles to profl. jours. Mott scholar YMCA, 1974-75. Mem. NASW, Inst. Mgmt. Cons. (bd. dirs. Phila. chpt. 1987, nat. bd. dirs. 1988-91), Assn. Mgmt. Cons. (bd. dirs. 1985—, nat. conf. chmn. 1985, regional v.p. 1986-88, pres. 1988-90), Am. Assn. Marriage and Family Therapy (editor N.J. newsletter 1989), Coun. Cons. Orgns. (bd. dirs. 1989-93, sec., officer 1991-93). Avocations: running, model trains. Office: Riverton Mgmt Cons Group 303 E Broad St Palmyra NJ 08065-1607

OVERLOCK, WILLARD JOSEPH, JR., investment banker; b. Norwalk, Conn., Apr. 15, 1946; s. Willard Joseph and Frances (Frost) O.; m. Katharine Smith, Dec. 31, 1977; children—Emily, Willard, Garret. A.B. in Econs., U. N.C., Chapel Hill, 1968; M.B.A., Columbia U., N.Y.C., 1973. Ptnr. Goldman, Sachs & Co., N.Y.C., 1982—. mem. mgmt. com., co-head investment banking divsn., 1990. Bd. dirs. Phoenix House, N.Y.C., 1984-93; bd. dirs. Juvenile Diabetes Found. Internat., pres., 1995; bd. overseers Columbia Grad. Sch. Bus. 1st lt. U.S. Army, 1968-71, Vietnam. Office: Goldman Sachs & Co 85 Broad St New York NY 10004-2434

OVERMAN, DEAN LEE, lawyer, investor, author; b. Harvey, Ill., Oct. 9, 1943; s. Harold Levon and Violet Claire (True) O.; m. Linda Jane Olsen, Sept. 6, 1969; children: Elisabeth True, Christiana Hart. BA, Hope Coll., 1965; student, Princeton Sem. and U., 1965-66; JD, U. Calif., Berkeley, 1969; postgrad. in bus., U. Chgo., 1974, U. Calif. Bar: Ill. 1969, D.C. 1977. Assoc. to ptnr. D'Ancona, Pflaum et al., Chgo., 1970-75; White House fellow, asst. to v.p. Nelson Rockefeller, Washington, 1975-76; assoc. dir. Domestic Council The White House, Washington, 1976-77; sr. ptnr. Winston & Strawn, Washington, 1977—; cons. White House; spl. counsel to Gov. James Thompson, Springfield, Ill.; adj. faculty in secured financing U. Va. Law Sch., Charlottesville; vice chmn. J.F. Forstmann Co.; chmn. Holland Investment Co.; co-founder Multi Media Communicators, Inc.; adj. fellow Ctr. for Strategic and Internat. Studies, 1993-95; vis. scholar, officer Harvard U. 1994-95. Author: Toward a National Policy on State and Local Government Finance, 1976, Effective Writing Tecniques, 1980, (with others) Financing Equipment, 1973, Sales and Financing Under the Revised UCC, 1975; monthly newspaper column Chgo. Daily Law Bull.; contbr. articles to profl. jours. Commencement speaker Hope Coll., Holland, Mich., 1978; bd. dirs. Internat. Bus. Inst., White House Fellows Assn., Cities in Schs., Inc.; former bd. dirs. U. Decathlon Assn. Mem. Mensa, Intertel, ABA, Ill. Bar Assn., D.C. Bar Assn., Chgo. Bar Assn., Met. Club (D.C.), Burning Tree Club (Bethesda, Md.), Country Club (Bethesda), Harvard Club of Washington, Macatawa (Mich.) Bay Yacht Club. Office: Winston & Strawn 1400 L St NW Washington DC 20005-3509

OVERMAN, GLENN DELBERT, college dean emeritus; b. Camden, Ark., Apr. 23, 1916; s. George D. and Mattie D. (Scott) O.; m. Roberta Marie Thomas, May 20, 1939; children—Priscilla Ann, George Dan. B.S., Central State U., Edmond, Okla., 1937; M.S., Okla. State U., 1946; D.B.A., Ind. U., 1954. Cert. for labor arbitration Fed. Mediation and Conciliation Service, also Am. Arbitration Assn. Tchr. bus. high sch. Fairfax, Okla., 1937-39; Okla. rep. South-Western Publishing Co., 1939-42; dir. Sch. Intensive Bus. Tng., Okla. State U. Coll. Bus., 1946-50; dean Oklahoma City U. Sch. Bus., 1952-56; dean Ariz. State U. Coll. Bus. Adminstrn., 1956-85, dean emeritus, 1985—; hon. prof. Autonomous U. Guadalajara, Mex., 1990—. Author: Economics Concepts Everyone Should Know, 1956. Mem. lay adv. bd. S.W. Found. Med. Research and Edn.; mem. U.S. Officer Edn. Appeal Bd., 1985—. Served from ensign to lt. (s.g.), Supply Corps USNR, 1942-46. Mem. Soc. Advancement Mgmt., Financial Execs. Inst., Systems and Procedures Assn. Am., Am. Marketing Assn., Newcomen Soc. Am., Red

Red Rose, Am. Right of Way Assn., Beta Gamma Sigma, Delta Sigma Pi, Pi Sigma Epsilon, Lambda Chi Alpha, Phi Kappa Phi, Delta Pi Epsilon, Phi Delta Kappa, Alpha Phi Sigma, Kappa Delta Pi, Delta Nu Alpha. Methodist. Home: 512 E Fairmont Dr Tempe AZ 85282-3723

OVERMAN, LARRY EUGENE, chemistry educator; b. Chgo., Mar. 9, 1943; s. Lemoine Emerson and Dorothy Jane (Riggin) O.; m. Joanne Louise Dewey, June 5, 1966; children: Michael, Jackie. BA in Chemistry, Earlham Coll., 1965; PhD in Organic Chemistry, U. Wis., 1969. Asst. prof. chemistry U. Calif., Irvine, 1971-76, assoc. prof. chemistry, 1976-79, prof. chemistry, 1979—, chair dept. chemistry, 1990-93, disting. prof. chemistry, 1994—; bd. dirs. Organic Reactions, 1993—; mem. sci. adv. bd. Pharmacopeia, Inc., 1993—. Bd. editors Organic Reactions, 1984, Organic Synthesis, 1986-94; mem. editl. adv. bd. Ann. Reports in Hetero Chem., 1989—, Synlett, 1989—. NIH fellow, 1969-71, A.P. Sloan Found. fellow, 1975-77; Arthur C. Cope scholar, 1989; Guggenheim fellow, 1993-94; recipient Sr. Scientist award Alexander von Humboldt Found., 1985-87, Jacob Javits award Nat. Inst. Neurol. Sci., 1985-91. Mem. AAAS, Am. Chem. Soc. (exec. com. organic divsn., award for creative work in synthetic organic chemistry 1995), Japanese Chem. Soc., Swiss Chem. Soc., German Chem. Soc., Royal Soc. Chemistry. Achievements include research in new methods for organic synthesis, natural products synthesis, medicinal chemistry. Office: U Calif Irvine Dept Chemistry Irvine CA 92717-2025*

OVERMYER, DANIEL LEE, Asian studies educator; b. Columbus, Ohio, Aug. 20, 1935; s. Elmer Earl and Bernice Alma (Hesselbart) O.; m. Estella Velazquez, June 19, 1965; children—Rebecca Lynn, Mark Edward. B.A., Westmar Coll., LeMars, Iowa, 1957; B.D., Evang. Theol. Sem., Naperville, Ill., 1960; M.A., U. Chgo., 1966, Ph.D., 1971. Pastor Evangel. United Brethren Ch., Chgo., 1960-64; asst. prof. dept. religion Oberlin Coll., Ohio, 1970-73; prof. Asian studies U.B.C., Vancouver, Can., 1973—, acting head religious studies, 1984-85, head Asian studies, 1986-91; vis. prof. U. Heidelberg, 1993. Author: Folk Buddhist Religion, 1976; Religions of China, 1986; (with David Jordan) The Flying Phoenix, 1986. Contbr. articles to encys. and profl. jours. Chmn. Sch. Consultative Com., Vancouver, 1976-77; coord. Vancouver Boys Soccer League, 1979-81; adult edn. coord. United Ch. Can., Vancouver, 1981-84; co-chmn. Endowment Lands Regional Park Com., 1987-90; co-chair China and Inner Asia Coun., Assn. Asian Studies, 1992—. With USNR, 1953-61. Recipient Killam faculty rsch. prize U. B.C., 1986; NEH fellow, 1978, 79, China Rsch. fellow, 1981, sr. fellow coun. humanities Princeton U., 1983, Wang Inst. Grad. Studies fellow, 1985-86. Fellow Royal Soc. Can.; mem. Soc. Study Chinese Religions (pres. 1985-88), Am. Soc. Study Religion, Assn. Asian Studies, Can. Asian Studies Assn. Democrat. Methodist. Avocations: photography, swimming, hiking, gardening. Home: 3393 W 26th Ave V, Vancouver, BC Canada V6S 1N4 Office: U BC, Dept Asian Studies, Vancouver, BC Canada V6T 1Z2

OVERMYER, JOHN EUGENE, manufacturing company executive; b. Ft. Wayne, Ind., Mar. 16, 1933; s. Arthur N. and Gladys M. (Fry) O.; m. Shirley A. Johnson, Dec. 27, 1956; children: Patrick T., Michael E., Kathleen M. Wiley, Andrew V., Thomas V., John J., Anne I., Maureen R., Mary. BS, Ind. U., 1957. Mem. acct. specialty budget tax and spl. projects Gen. Tel., Ft. Wayne, 1957-62; sales planning Magnavox, Ft. Wayne, 1962; budget dir. Tokheim Corp., Ft. Wayne, 1962-68, contr., 1968-74, treas., 1974-79, v.p., treas., 1979-86, pres., 1986—, chmn. bd. dirs., 1988—; bd. dirs. Nat. Controls Corp., West Chicago, Ill., Tokheim Automation Corp., Houston, William M. Wilson's Sons, Inc., Lansdale, Pa., Tokheim of Can., Ltd., Brighton, Ont., Tokheim B.V. Leiderdorp, The Netherlands, Tokheim Investment Corp., Houston, Tokheim Ltd., Glenrothes, Scotland, Tokheim South Africa Pty, Ltd., Johannesburg. Treas., bd. dirs. United Way Allen County, Ft. Wayne, 1976-87, chmn. 1987-88, pres., 1987-88; active fin. commn. Ancilla Systems, Chgo.; trustee St. Francis Coll., Ft. Wayne, 1984—. Cpl. U.S. Army, 1953-55. Named to Acad. Alumni Fellows Sch. Bus. Ind. U., 1988. Mem. NAM (bd. dirs.), Fin. Execs. Inst. (v.p. 1972, pres. 1987), Nat. Assn. Accts. (v.p. 1964, pres. 1976, bd. dirs., Stuart Cameron McClead Soc. award 1975), Ind. Mfrs. Assn. (bd. dirs.), Lions (pres. Leo, Ind. club 1970). Republican. Roman Catholic. Office: Tokheim Corp PO Box 360 Fort Wayne IN 46801-0360

OVERSETH, OLIVER ENOCH, physicist, educator; b. N.Y.C., May 11, 1928; s. Oliver Enoch and Ione (Johnson) O.; m. Anneke deBruyn, Aug. 28, 1954 (divorced); children—Alison, Tenley. B.S., U. Chgo., 1953; Ph.D., Brown U., 1958. Instr. physics Princeton, 1957-60; mem. faculty U. Mich., Ann Arbor, 1961—; prof. physics U. Mich., 1968—; assoc. physicist Cern, Geneva, 1983—. Office: Cern PPE Div, CH-1211 Geneva Switzerland

OVERSTREET, JAMES WILKINS, obstetrics and gynecology educator, administrator. BA in Biology magna cum laude, U. South, 1967; BA in Natural Scis., U. Cambridge, Eng., 1970, PhD in Reproductive Physiology, 1973, MA in Natural Scis., 1974; MD, Columbia U., 1974. Diplomate Nat. Bd. Med. Examiners; lic. physician, Calif. NIH Med. Scientist Tng fellow dept. anatomy coll. physicians ans surgeons Columbia U., 1970-72, NIH Med. Scientist Tng. fellow Internat. Inst. for Study Human Reproduction, 1972-74; asst. resident in ob-gyn. Presbyn. Hosp., N.Y.C., 1974; Ford Found. Postdoctoral Rsch. fellow dept. ob-gyn. Cornell U. Med. Coll., 1975-76; asst. prof. human anatomy and ob-gyn. sch. medicine U. Calif., Davis, 1976-80, assoc. prof. human anatomy, 1980-84, assoc. prof. ob-gyn. sch. medicine, 1980-85, prof. ob-gyn. sch. medicine, 1985—, chief divsn. reproductive biology and medicine dept. ob-gyn. sch. medicine, 1983-86, dir. lab. for energy-related health rsch., 1985-88, dir. Inst. Toxicology and Environ. Health, unit based and reproductive biology Primate Rsch. Ctr., 1988—; mem. sci. rev. panel for health rsch., reviewer test rules dept. and reproductive abd devel. toxicology brs. U.S. EPA; mem. ad hoc study sect., cons. Nat. Inst. for Occupational Safety and Health; chair AIDS and related rsch. rev. group NIH; chmn. spl. study sect., site visit team, mem. ad hoc reproductive endocrinology study sect. Nat. Inst. Child Health and Human Devel.; reviewer, mem. site visit team Nat. Inst. Environ. Health Scis./NIH, Med. Rsch. Coun. Can.; mem. tech. adv. com. and site visit team contraceptive rsch. and devel. project Agy. for Internat. Devel./Ea. Va. Med. Sch.; temp. advisor spl. program rsch. devel. and rsch. tng. in human reproduction WHO; mem. reproductive and devel. toxicology program rev. panel Chem. Industry Inst. Toxicology; mem. exec. com. systemwide toxic substances rsch. and tng. program U. Calif.; reviewer NSF, Office Health and Environ. Rsch., U.S. Dept. Energy, March of Dimes Reproductive Hazards in the Workplace Rsch. Grants Program, Mt. Sinai Hosp., Alta. Heritage Cancer Grants, U.S.-Israel Binational Agrl. Rsch. and Devel. Fund; clin. cons. lab. surveys program Coll. Am. Pathologists; cons. Ctr. for Drugs and Biologics, U.S. FDA, Inst. for Internat. Studies in Natural Family Planning, Georgetown U., Internat. Devel. Rsch. Ctr. Assoc. editor Molecular Reproduction and Devel.; mem. editorial bd. Biology of Reproduction, 1983-86, Jour. In Vitro Fertilization and Embryo Transfer, 1984-89, Reproductive Toxicology, Fertility and Sterility, 1984-92, Jour. Andrology, 1990-92; referee Jour. Reproduction and Fertility, Jour. Exptl. Zoology, Am. Jour. Physiology, Am. Jour. Ob-Gyn., Jour. Urology, Science, Jour. Clin. Endocrinology and Metabolism, Archives Internal Medicine, Internat. Jour. Andrology, Reproduction, Nutrition, Devel., Western Jour. Medicine, Contraception, Human Reproduction, Proceedings Royal Soc. Series B.; invited lectr. in field. Georgia Fulbright scholar, 1967-68; recipient Rsch. Career Devel. award NIH, 1978-83, Disting. Career in Clin. Investigation award Columbia Presbyn. Med. Ctr., 1992; grantee Syntex Rsch. Divsn., 1978-81, NIH, 1978-81, 78-83, 79-90, 81-90, 85-88, 86—, 87—, 88—, 89—, 90—(two grants), 91—, 92—, 93—, U. Calif., 1981-82, U.S. EPA, 1981-84, 82-84, Nat. Inst. for Occupational Safety and Health, 1982-84, U.S. Dept. Energy, 1985-88, Georgetown U., 1987-89, 92—, Merck Rsch. Labs., 1988-90, 92, 92—, March of Dimes, 1988-90, Semiconductor Industry Assn. 1989-92, Tobacco Related Disease Rsch. Program, 1990-93, Andrew W. Mellon Found., 1993—. Mem. Am. Fertility Soc., Am. Soc. Andrology (exec. coun. 1986-89), Soc. for Study Fertility, Soc. for Study Reproduction, Phi Beta Kappa. Achievements include research in physiology of mammalian spermatozoa, sperm transport in the female reproductive tract, in vivo and in vitro mammalian fertilization, diagnosis and therapy of human male infertility, reproducti, environmental and occupational hazards to male and female fertility, contraceptive development, reproductive endocrinology. Office: U Calif Davis Inst Toxicology & Enviro Health Rsch Office Davis CA 95616*

OVERSTREET, JIM, public relations executive; b. Savannah, Ga., Dec. 11, 1947. Reporter Atlanta Constitution, 1967-69; asst. sports editor Marietta Daily Jour., 1969-73; mktg. dir. Lake Lanier Islands Resorts, 1973-77; gen. mgr. Harlequin Theatre, 1977-78; acct. exec. Cohn & Wolfe, 1978-80, acct. supr., 1980-83, dir. acct. svc., 1983-84, exec. v.p., gen. mgr., 1984-92, vice chmn., gen. mgr., 1993—. Office: Cohn & Wolfe 225 Peachtree St NE Atlanta GA 30303-1701

OVERSTROM, GUNNAR S., JR., banker; b. Buffalo, 1942. BSBA, Babson Coll.; MA, Trinity Coll.; LLB, Suffolk U., 1968. With Travelers Ins. Co., 1969-73; fin. cons. B.L. McTeague & Co., 1973-75; with Conn. Nat. Bank, Hartford, 1975—, chief fin. officer, exec. v.p., 1979-88, pres., chief oper. officer, bd. dirs., 1988—; also chief oper. officer Shawmut Nat. Corp. (formerly Hartford Nat. Corp.). Office: Shawmut Bank 777 Main St Hartford CT 06115-2001

OVERTON, BENJAMIN FREDERICK, state supreme court justice; b. Green Bay, Wis., Dec. 15, 1926; s. Benjamin H. and Esther M. (Wiese) O.; m. Marilyn Louise Smith, June 9, 1951; children: William Hunter, Robert Murray, Catherine Louise. B.S. in Bus. Adminstrn., U. Fla., 1951, J.D., 1952; LL.D. (hon.), Stetson U., 1975, Nova U., 1977; LL.M., U. Va., 1984. Bar: Fla. 1952. With Office Fla. Atty. Gen., 1952; with firms in St. Petersburg, Fla., 1952-64; city atty. St. Petersburg Beach, Fla., 1954-57; circuit judge 6th Jud. Circuit Fla., 1964-74, chief judge, 1968-71; chmn. Fla. Conf. Circuit Judges, 1973; justice Supreme Ct. Fla., Tallahassee, 1974—; chief justice Supreme Ct. Fla., 1976-78; past adj. faculty Stetson U. Coll., Law and Fla. St. U. Coll. Law; bd. dirs. Nat. Jud. Coll., 1976-87; mem. Fla. Car Continuing Legal Edn. Com., 1963-74, chmn., 1971-74; 1st chmn. Fla. Inst. Judiciary, 1972; mem. exec. com. Appellate Judges Conf.; chmn. Appellate Structure Commn., 1978-79, Article Rev. Commn., 1983-84, Matrimonial Law Commn., 1982-85; chmn. Jud. Coun. Fla., 1985-89.; chmn. adv. com. for LLM program for appellate judges U. Va., 1985-94. Contbr. legal publs. Past reader, vestryman, sr. warden St. Albans Episcopal Ch., St. Petersburg; chmn. U.S. Constn. Bicentennial Commn. Fla. 1987-91; ch. Family Ct. Commn., 1990-91; ch. Death Case Postconviction Relief Proceeding 1990-91. Fellow Am. Bar Found.; mem. ABA (chmn. criminal justice task force to rev. trial and discovery standards 1991—), Fla. Bar Assn., Am. Judicature Soc. (dir., sec.). Democrat. Lodge: Rotary. Office: Fla Supreme Ct Supreme Ct Bldg Tallahassee FL 32399

OVERTON, BRUCE, personnel executive, consultant; b. Caldwell, N.J., June 27, 1941; s. E.F. and V.B. Overton; m. Charlene Gayle Overton; children: Julie, Diane, Sharon. BS, Widener U., 1963. Personnel mgr. Xerox Corp., Rochester, N.Y., 1965-71; prin. cons. Sibson and Co., Princeton, N.J., 1971-77; v.p. compensation RJR Nabisco, Inc., Atlanta, 1977-87, v.p. pers., 1987-89; ptnr. Ernst and Young, Atlanta, 1989-90; pres. Overton & Assocs., 1990-93; prnt. HR Mgmt. Inc., 1993—. Author articles on compensation and personnel mgmt., 1979—. Bd. dirs. Cobb County YMCA; bd. trustees Kennesaw Coll. Served to 1st lt. U.S. Army, 1963-65. Mem. Am. Compensation Assn. (chmn. bd. 1986-87). Republican. Presbyterian. Avocation: boating. Office: 3901 Roswell Rd Ste 330 Marietta GA 30062-6277

OVERTON, GEORGE WASHINGTON, lawyer; b. Hinsdale, Ill., Jan. 25, 1918; s. George Washington and Florence Mary (Darlington) O.; m. Jane Vincent Harper, Sept. 1, 1941; children—Samuel Harper, Peter Darlington, Ann Vincent. A.B., Harvard U., 1940; J.D., U. Chgo., 1946. Bar: Ill. 1947, U.S. Dist. Ct. (no. dist.) Ill. 1947, U.S. Supreme Ct. 1951. Assoc. Pope & Ballard, Chgo., 1946-48; ptnr. Overton & Babcock, Chgo., 1948-51, Taylor, Miller, Busch & Magner, Chgo., 1951-60; pvt. practice Chgo., 1960; sr. prin. Overton, Schwartz & Fritts and predecessor cos., Chgo., 1961-81; of counsel Wildman Harrold Allen & Dixon, Chgo., 1981—; bd. dirs. Ill. Inst. Continuing Legal Edn., 1974-81, chmn. 1980-81; mem. com. on profl. responsibility of Ill. Supreme Ct., 1986—, chmn., 1990-93. Contbr. articles to profl. jours. Bd. dirs. Open Lands Project, 1961—, pres. 1978-81; bd. dirs. Canal Corridor Assn., 1981—, chmn., 1981-84. 1st lt. U.S. Army, 1942-45. Mem. ABA (mem. com. on counsel responsibility 1985—, com. on nonprofit corps.), Ill. Bar Assn., Chgo. Bar Assn. (bd. mgrs. 1981-83), Assn. of Bar of City of N.Y., Am. Law Inst., Univ. Club (bd. dirs. 1981-83). Office: Wildman Harrold Allen & Dixon 225 W Wacker Dr Chicago IL 60606-1229

OVERTON, JANE VINCENT HARPER, biology educator; b. Chgo., Jan. 17, 1919; d. Paul Vincent and Isabel (Vincent) Harper; m. George W. Overton, Sept. 1, 1941; children: Samuel, Peter, Ann. AB, Bryn Mawr Coll., 1941; PhD, U. Chgo., 1950. Rsch. asst. U. Chgo., 1950-52, mem. faculty, 1952-89, prof. biology, 1972-89; prof. emeritus, 1989. Author articles embryology, cell biology. NIH, NSF research grantee, 1965-87. Home: 1700 E 56th St Apt 2901 Chicago IL 60637-1935 Office: U Chgo 1103 E 57th St Chicago IL 60637-1572

OVERTON, JOHN BLAIR, lawyer; b. Newburgh, N.Y., Dec. 23, 1949; s. Jesse Woodhull and Joan (Blair) O. BA, Columbia U., 1972; JD, Golden Gate U., 1979. Bar: Calif. 1981, U.S. Dist. Ct. (no. dist.) Calif. 1981, U.S. Dist. Ct. (cen. dist.) Calif. 1985, U.S. Ct. Appeals (9th cir.) 1986. Sole practice Sausalito, Calif., 1981—; bd. dirs. Ind. Feature Project of No. Calif. Author: Oregon Clean Water Handbook, 1975. Mem. ABA (chmn. subcom. copyright legis. com. 1985—), Phi Beta Kappa. Avocations: fly fishing, playing music. Office: 2401 Marinship Way Sausalito CA 94965-2854

OVERTON, MARCUS LEE, performing arts administrator, actor, writer; b. Calhoun, Ga., Aug. 13, 1943; s. Marcus Burl Jr. and Eva Mae (Greene) O. BS in Speech and Theatre, Northwestern U., 1965. Actor, tchr. Southeastern Shakespeare Festival, Atlanta, summer 1965; actor, company mgr. Eagles Mere Assocs. Repertory Co., Chgo., 1966; prodn. stage mgr. Lyric Opera of Chgo., 1966-72; mgr. Ravinia Festival, Highland Park, Ill., 1973-77; performing arts program mgr. Smithsonian Instn., Washington, 1983-92; exec. dir. Spoleto Festival U.S.A., Charleston, S.C., 1992-94; narrator talking books Libr. Congress, Washington, 1982-83; adv. panelist Nat. Endowment for Arts, 1977-79, D.C. Commn. on Arts and Humanities, 1989, 90; bd. dirs. Nat. Cultural Resources, 1989-90, Performing Arts Assistance Corp., 1992—; cons. in field. Producer Falstaff (J.A. Philharm.), 1981-82. Northwestern U. scholar, 1961-65. Avocations: travel, prehistoric cave art, motorcycle touring, linguistics, French culture. Office: 210 Little Oak Dr Folly Bch SC 29439

OVERTON, STANLEY DIXON, banking executive; b. Dickson, Tenn., May 2, 1928; s. Dallas Stanley and Ova (Dixon) O.; m. Carolyn Ruane, Feb. 14, 1976; children—Stanley D. Jr., James Stanton; 1 stepchild, Cecelia Halter. Student Fall's Bus. Coll., Nashville, 1948-49; Acctg. degree Internat. Accts. Soc., 1952; student Savs. & Loan Grad. Sch. Ind. U., 1961-63. With Fidelity Fed. Bank, FSB, Nashville, 1950-92, exec. v.p., 1963-67, pres., 1967-74, chmn., pres., 1974-84, chmn., chief exec. officer, 1983-92; chmn., chief exec. officer, Union Planters Bank of Middle Tenn., 1992-94, chmn., 1994—, also bd. dirs. Union Planters Corp.; past bd. dirs. Fed. Home Loan Bank Bd., Cin. United Way, Nashville; bd. dirs. YMCA, Nashville, Fellowship of Christian Athletes, Nashville. Served with USNR, 1946-48. Mem. C. of C. (past bd. govs.), Tenn. League Savs. Assns. (pres. 1969-70), U.S. League Savs. Assns., Am. Savs. and Loan Inst. (past pres.), Found. for Savs. Instns. (trustee). Clubs: Hillwood Country, Nashville City. Lodges: Masons, Shriners, Kiwanis. Home: 7 Warwick Ln Nashville TN 37205 Office: Union Planters Bank of Middle Tenn 401 Union St Nashville TN 37219

OVESON, W(ILFORD) VAL, state official, accountant; b. Provo, Utah, Feb. 11, 1952; s. Wilford W. and LaVon Oveson; m. Emilee Nebeker, Sept. 1, 1973; children: Polly, Libby, Peter, Benjamin. Student, U. Utah, 1973-74; BS in Acctg., Brigham Young U., 1976. CPA, Utah. Acct. Squire and Co. Orem, Utah, 1975-79; pvt. practice acctg. Squire and Co., Orem, 1979-80; state auditor State of Utah, Salt Lake City, 1981-84, lt. gov., 1985-93; sr. mgr. KPMG Peat Marwick, 1993; chmn. Utah Tax Commn., Salt Lake City, 1993—; mem. dist. export coun. U.S. Dept. Commerce, 1985—, mem. bd. examiners, State of Utah, 1981-84; chmn. State Records Com., 1981-84. Bd. dirs., unit campaign dir. United Way of Greater Salt Lake, 1985-86; trustee Travis Found., 1985-88; treas. Utah Republican Party; mem. State Platform Com., 1982, 84; mem. exec. com. Utah State Rep. Party, 1981—. Mem. AICPA (mem. governing coun. 1986), Utah Assn. CPAs (Pub. Svc. award 1984). Republican. Mem. LDS Ch. Avocations: skiing, personal finance,

computers, house plants, fishing. Home: 2125 S 900 E Bountiful UT 84010-3105

OVITSKY, STEVEN ALAN, musician, symphony orchestra executive; b. Chgo., Oct. 12, 1947; s. Martin N. and Ruth (Katz) O.; m. Camille Levy; 1 child, David Isaac. MusB, U. Mich., 1968; MusM, No. Ill. U., 1975. Fine arts dir. Sta. WNIU-FM Pub. Radio, Dekalb, Ill., 1972-76; program mgr. Sta. WMHT-FM Pub. Radio, Schenectady, N.Y., 1976-79; gen. mgr., artistic dir. Grant Park Concerts, Chgo., 1979-90; v.p., gen. mgr. Minn. Orch., Mpls., 1990-95; exec. dir. Milw. Symphony Orch., 1995—; panelist Ill. Arts Coun., 1986, 87, 88, Chgo. Artists Abroad, 1987-91. Nat. Endowment for the Arts, 1987-89; bd. dirs. Ill. Arts Alliance, Chamber Music Chgo.; hon. dir. Chgo. Sinfonietta. With U.S. Army, 1968-71, Korea. Mem. NARAS, Am. Symphony Orch. League. Jewish. Avocations: audio, record collecting, softball. Office: Milw Symphony 330 E Kilbourn Ave Ste 900 Milwaukee WI 53202

OVITZ, MICHAEL S., artists agency executive; b. 1946; m. Judy Reich, 1969; 3 children. Grad., UCLA, 1968. With William Morris Agy., 1968-75; co-founder, chmn. Creative Artists Agy., L.A., 1975—; mem. bd. advisors Med. Sch. UCLA, bd. dirs. Sch. Theatre, Film and TV. Trustee St. John's Hosp. and Health Ctr., Santa Monica, Calif., Mus. Modern Art, N.Y.C.; bd. govs. Cedars-Sinai Hosp., L.A.; mem. exec. adv. bd. Pediatric AIDS Found.; bd. dirs. Calif. Inst. Arts, Sundance Inst. Mem. Zeta Beta Tau. Avocations: contemporary art, African antiques, Chinese furniture. Office: Creative Artists Agy 9830 Wilshire Blvd Beverly Hills CA 90212-1825

OVSHINSKY, STANFORD ROBERT, physicist, inventor, energy and information company executive; b. Akron, Ohio, Nov. 24, 1922; s. Benjamin and Bertha T. (Munitz) O.; m. Iris L. Miroy, Nov. 24, 1959; children—Benjamin, Harvey, Dale, Robin Dibner, Steven Dibner. Student public schs., Akron; DSc (hon.), Lawrence Inst. Tech. 1980; DEng (hon.), Bowling Green State U. 1981; DSc (hon.), Jordan Coll., Cedar Springs, Mich., 1989. Pres. Stanford Roberts Mfg. Co., Akron, 1946-50; mgr. centre drive dept. New Britain Machine Co., Conn., 1950-52; dir. research Hupp Corp., Detroit, 1952-55; pres. Gen. Automation, Inc., Detroit, 1955-58, Ovitron Corp., Detroit, 1958-59; pres., chmn. bd. Energy Conversion Devices, Inc., Troy, Mich., 1960-78; pres., chief exec. officer, chief scientist Energy Conversion Devices, Inc., 1978—; adj. prof. engring. scis. Coll. Engring., Wayne State U.; hon. advisor for sci. and tech. Beijing (China) Inst. Aeronautics and Astronautics (name changed to Beijing U. Aeros. and Astronautics); chmn. Inst. for Amorphous Studies. Contbr. articles on physics of amorphous materials, neurophysiology and neuropsychiatry to profl. jours. Recipient Diesel Gold medal German Inventors Assn., 1968, Coors Am. Ingenuity award, 1988; named to Mich. Chem. Engring. Hall of Fame, 1983, Mich. Scientist of Yr., Impression 5 Sci. Mus., 1987. Fellow AAAS, Am. Phys. Soc.; mem. IEEE (sr.), Soc. Automotive Engrs., N.Y. Acad. Scis., Electrochem. Soc., Engring. Soc. Detroit, Cranbrook Inst. Sci. (bd. govs. 1981). Office: Energy Conversion Devices Inc 1675 W Maple Rd Troy MI 48084-7118

OWEISS, IBRAHIM MOHAMED, economist, educator; b. Egypt, Sept. 25, 1931; came to U.S., 1960; s. Mohamed Zaki and Warda (Zeiden) O.; m. Celine M. J. Lesuisse, July 19, 1975; children: Yasmeen, Kareem. B.Com., Alexandria U., Egypt, 1952; M.A., U. Minn., 1961, Ph.D., 1969. Tchr., 1953-55; econ. dir. indsl. projects Cairo, 1958-60; mem. faculty U. Minn., Mpls., 1961-67; mem. faculty Georgetown U., Washington, 1967—, prof. econs., 1973—; mem. faculty Johns Hopkins U., 1971-74; first undersec. state econ. affairs Govt. Egypt, Cairo, 1977; coord. Egyptian Econ. Mission to U.S., 1977-79; cons. econs., 1971—. Author: Pricing of Oil in World Trade, 1974, The Israeli Economy, 1974; editor: The Dynamics of U.S.-Arab Economic Relations, 1980, Economic Development of Egypt, 1982, Arab Civilization, Challenges and Responses, 1988, Political Economy of Contemporary Egypt, 1990. Pres. Assn. Egyptian-Am. Scholars, 1984-88; chmn. bd. dirs. Arab-Am. Bus. and Profl. Assn.; Howard and Georgeanna Jones Inst. for Reproductive Medicine, 1984-90, Egyptian Am. Cultural Assn., 1975-77, Faith and Hope Project, 1975-77. Officer Egyptian Army, 1955-58. Decorated Egyptian Order Merit decoration 1st Order, Order of St. John; Ford Found. fellow, 1979-80. Mem. Am. Econ. Assn. Moslem. Club: University (N.Y.C.). Home: 4017 Glenridge St Kensington MD 20895-3708 Office: Georgetown University Dept Econs Washington DC 20057

OWEN, AMY, library director; b. Brigham City, Utah, June 26, 1944; d. John Wallace and Bertha (Jensen) O. BA, Brigham Young U., 1966, MLS, 1968. Systems libr. Utah State Libr., Salt Lake City, 1968-72, dir. reference svcs., 1972-74, dir. tech. svcs., 1974-81, dep. dir., 1981-87; dir., 1987—; serials com. chmn. Utah Coll. Libr. Coun., Salt Lake City, 1975-77, exec. sec., 1978-84, coun. mem. 1987—; mem. staff Gov.'s Utah Systems Planning Task Force, Salt Lake City, 1982; staff liaison Utah Gov.'s Conf. on Libr. and Info. Svcs., 1977-79, chair exec. planning com., 1990-91; mem. pres.'s adv. panel Baker & Taylor Co., Somerville, N.J., 1977-78; panelist U.S. Dept. Edn., 1992; mem. rsch. project adv. com. U. Wis. Sch. Libr. and Info., Madison, 1992-94; mem. adv. panel Nat. Commn. Libr. and Info. Svcs., 1985; Alumni Honor lectr. Coll. Humanities, Brigham Young U., 1990. Contbr. chpts. to books, also contbg. author various manuals; cons. and trainer in field. Coun. mem. Utah Endowment for Humanities, 1986-91, vice chmn., 1987-88, chair, 1988-90; trustee Bibliographic Ctr. for Rsch., 1987—, pers. com., 1988-89, chmn. pers. com., 1989-90, nominating com., 1984, v.p. bd. trustees, 1989-91, pres, 1991-93; active Chief Officers of State Libr. Agys., 1987—, stats. com. 1988, mem. network com., 1993—, state info. policy workshop com., 1988, bd. dirs., 1992—; mem. conf. program com. Fedn. of State Humanities Couns., 1988; mem. coop. pub. libr. data system task force Nat. Commn. on Libr. and Info. Svcs., 1988-90; grant rev. panelist NEH, 1988, 92, panel mem. reading and discussion groups, 1988; regional project mgmt. bd. mem. Intermountain Community Learning and Info. Ctr. Project, 1987-90; mem. midcontinental regional adv. com. Nat. Libr. Medicine 1991-94; mem. adv. com. Brigham Young U. Sch. Libr. and Info. Svcs. Named Libr. of Yr., Libr. Jour., 1990. Mem. Utah Libr. Assn. (pres. 1978-79, exec. bd. 1976-80, Spl. Svc. award 1989), Mountain Plains Libr. Assn. (rec. sec. 1979-80, fin. com. 1982-84, Disting. Svc. award 1989), ALA (bd. dirs. ASCLA divsn. 1984-86, 93—, pres. ASCLA divsn. 1994-95, fin. com. 1984-86, 89-92, 93—, planning, orgn. and bylaws com. 1981-85, SLAS program com. 1984-86, pres. program com. 1986, exec. bd. mem. 1993, 93-94; clene roundtable mem. 1984-86, nominations com. 1986-87, nat. adv. bd. office communications svcs., voices and visions project 1988-89; LITA div. Satellite Conf. Task Force mem. 1982; PLA div. editor column 1987-89, PLA div. goals, guidelines and standards com. 1987-90, chair, 1990-91, PLA pub. libr. data svc. com. 1988-91, PLA Kellogg Phase III EIC project adv. com. chair 1990-92, PLA strategic issues and directions com., 1991-92, PLA non MLIS involvement com., 1990-91, ALA Office for Rsch. coop. pub. libr. data system adv. com. 1985-89), Dynix Snowbird Leadership Inst. coll. adv. bd. 1990—), Phi Kappa Phi, Alpha Lambda Delta. Home: 7453 Lost Canyon Cir Salt Lake City UT 84121-4624 Office: Utah State Libr 2150 S 300th W Ste 16 Salt Lake City UT 84115

OWEN, CHRISTINA L., lawyer; b. Oakland, Calif., Sept. 22, 1946. BS, U. Calif., Berkeley, 1968; JD, U. So. Calif., 1971. Bar: Calif. 1972. Ptnr. Baker & Hostetler, Long Beach, Calif. Mem. State Bar Calif., Maritime Law Assn. U.S. Office: Baker & Hostetler 300 Oceangate Ste 620 Long Beach CA 90802-6801

OWEN, CLAUDE BERNARD, JR., tobacco company executive; b. Danville, Va., June 12, 1945; s. Claude Bernard and Mildred Carter (Fulton) O.; m. Mary Lamar Lewis, Aug. 14, 1965; children: Christopher E., Jennifer L. BA in Econs., Davidson Coll., 1967; MBA in Fin., U. N.C., 1969. Fin. analyst Dibrell Bros., Inc., Danville, 1971-73, asst. v.p., 1973-76, v.p., 1976-81, sr. v.p., 1981-84, exec. v.p., 1984-86, pres., 1986-89, chmn., CEO, 1990-95; chmn., CEO Dimon Inc., 1995—; bd. dirs. Am. Nat. Bankshares, Danville; chmn. bd. Richfood Holdings Inc., Richmond. Trustee Averett Coll., Danville, 1985, chmn. bd. trustees, 1991; pres. Danville-Pittsylvania County United Way, 1989. Served to 1st lt. U.S. Army, 1969-71. Mem. Va. C. of C. (bd. dirs. 1992—), Va. Mfg. Assn. (vice chmn. 1992, chmn. 1995—), Danville Golf Club (v.p. 1984-86), Commonwealth Club (Richmond), Country Club of Va. (Richmond), Rotary. Methodist. Avocations: golfing, raquetball, skiing. Office: Dibrell Bros Inc 512 Bridge St Danville VA 24541-1406

OWEN, DUNCAN SHAW, JR., physician, medical educator; b. Fayetteville, N.C., Oct. 24, 1935; s. Duncan S. and Mary Gwyn (Hickerson) O.; m. Irene Lacy Rose, Oct. 22, 1966; children: Duncan Shaw III, Robert Burwell, Frances Gwyn. BS, U. N.C., 1957, MD, 1960. Diplomate Am. Bd. Internal Medicine. Intern Med. Coll. Va., Richmond, 1960-61; jr. asst. resident in medicine N.C. Meml. Hosp., Chapel Hill, 1961-62; asst. resident in medicine Med. Coll. Va., Richmond, 1964-65, fellow in rheumatic diseases, 1965-66; practice medicine specializing in internal medicine and rheumatology Richmond, Va., 1966—; instr. in medicine Med. Coll. Va., Richmond, 1966-67, asst. prof., 1967-71, assoc. prof., 1971-78, prof. dept. internal medicine, 1978—; Taliaferro/Scott Disting. prof. internal medicine Med. Coll. Va., U. Commonwealth U., 1999—; mem. staff Med. Coll. Va. Hosp., McGuire VA; bd. dir. clin. tng. div. rheumatology, allergy, immunology, chmn. clin. activities comm., dept. internal medicine; chmn. med. adv. com. Richmond Br. Arthritis Found., 1966-75, bd. dirs., 1966—, mem. nat. patient edn. com., 1979-80; med. adv. Social Security Adminstrn., HHS, 1967—; bd. dirs Blue Shield Va., 1975-77; co-chmn. Arthritis Project Va. Regional Med. Program, 1975-76; bd. dirs. Internal Medicine Found., 1979—; producer Your Health TV Series, Va. Ednl. TV, 1978-79; producer Update in Medicine, Good Morning Virginia TV Show, 1980; mem. various coms. in field; proctor Am. Bd. Internal Medicine, 1977—. Contbr. numerous papers, chpts. in books, articles to profl. jours.; assoc. editor: Va. Med., 1978—; editorial reviewer Jour. AMA, 1979—, Arthritis Rheumatism, 1981—, Jour. Rheumatology, 1984—. Mem. usher's guild First Presbyn. Ch., Richmond, Va., 1966-70, deacon, 1974-77, chmn. of diaconate, 1976-77, elder, 1978—, chmn. witness com., 1978-80; co-chmn. physicians statewide capital funds campaign Va. Commn. U., 1986-87; bd. dirs. Mooreland Farms Assn., 1971-73, 77-81, Va. chpt. Arthritis Found., 1970-85; mem. Va. Mus., Richmond Symphony; bd. dirs. Richmond Area Health Care Coalition, 1980-84. Served to capt. MC, 1962-64. Recipient Army Commendation medal, 1964. Nat. Inst. Arthritis and Metabolic Diseases fellow, 1965-66; recipient Gerard B. Lambert award, 1974-75, Disting. Service award Arthritis Found., 1971. Fellow ACP, Am. Coll. Rheumatology; mem. AMA (expert on diagnostic and therapeutic tech. assessment program), Am. Rheumatism Assn. (exec. com. 1979-80), Richmond Acad. Medicine (pres. 1982, chmn. bd. 1983, parliamentarian 1988—), Med. Soc. Va. (mem. com. on aging 1980-89, v.p. 1973, 75, del. 1972—, scholarship com. 1980-89), Richmond Soc. Internal Medicine (bd. dirs 1971-73), Jr. Clin. Club (emeritus), Met. Richmond C. of C. (bd. dirs. 1981-84), Country Va. Club, Alpha Omega Alpha. Avocations: hunting, fishing, photography, amateur radio. Home: 8910 Brieryle Rd Richmond Va 23229-7704 Office: Med Coll Va Nelson Clinic Rm 742 PO Box 980647 Richmond VA 23298-0647

OWEN, FRED WYNNE, lawyer; b. Oroville, Calif., Jan. 12, 1928; s. Robert Wynne and Hazel (Illingworth) O.; m. Mary Carmen Lujan, May 28, 1988; children from previous marriage: Fred Wynne, Kathleen Marie, Debra Jean, Teresa Maureen. A.B., U. of Pacific, 1950; J.D., U. Calif. at Berkeley, 1953. Bar: Calif. bar 1953. Since practiced in Bakersfield; with contract div. Standard Oil Co. of Calif., 1953-55; asst. dist. atty. Kern County, 1955-63; sec.-treas. King, Eyherabide, Owen, Anspach & Jenkins, 1963-72; prin. Fred W. Owen Law Office, 1972—. Mem. Am., Calif. bar assns., Calif. Def. Attys. Assn., Am. Arbitration Assn. (life), Calif. Scholarship Fedn., Phi Delta Phi. Home: Star Rt 4 14500 Las Palmas Dr # 24 Bakersfield CA 93306-9509 Office: 323 18th St Bakersfield CA 93301-4715

OWEN, H. MARTYN, lawyer; b. Decatur, Ill., Oct. 3, 1929; s. Honore Martyn and Virginia (Hunt) O.; m. Candace Catlin Benjamin, June 21, 1952; children—Leslie W., Peter H., Douglas P. A.B., Princeton U., 1951; LL.B., Harvard U., 1954. Bar: Conn. 1954. Assoc. Shipman & Goodwin, Hartford, Conn., 1958-61, ptnr., 1961-78, of counsel, 1995—. Mem. Simsbury (Conn.) Zoning Bd. Appeals, 1961-67, Simsbury Zoning Commn., 1967-79; sec. Capitol Region Planning Agy., 1965-66; bd. dirs Symphony Soc. Greater Hartford, 1967-73; trustee Renbrook Sch., West Hartford, Conn., 1963-72, treas., 1964-68, pres., 1968-72, hon. life trustee, 1972—; trustee Simsbury Free Library, 1970-84; pres. Hartford Grammar Sch., 1987—, trustee; corporator Hartford Hosp., Inst. Living, Hartford. Lt. USNR, 1954-57. Mem. ABA, Conn. Bar Assn., Hartford County Bar Assn., Am. Law Inst. Republican. Episcopalian. Clubs: Princeton (N.Y.C.); Ivy (Princeton, N.J.); Dauntless (Essex, Conn.). Home: 44 Pinnacle Mountain Rd Simsbury CT 06070-1809 Office: One American Row Hartford CT 06103-2819

OWEN, HENRY, former ambassador, consultant; b. N.Y.C., Aug. 26, 1920. A.B., Harvard U., 1941. Economist Dept. State, Washington, 1946-55, mem. policy planning staff, 1955-62, dep. counselor, vice chmn. policy planning coun., 1962-66, chmn. coun., 1966-69; dir. fgn. policy studies Brookings Instn., 1969-77; personal rep. of Pres. U.S. with rank of ambassador to participate in preparations for summit meetings, 1977-81; cons. Salomon Bros., 1981—. Editor: Next Phase of U.S. Foreign Policy, 1971, (with Charles Schultze) Setting National Priorities, 1976. Served to lt. USN, 1942-46. Office: 1616 H St NW Washington DC 20006-4903

OWEN, HOWARD WAYNE, journalist, writer; b. Fayetteville, N.C.; Mar. 1, 1949; s. E.F. and Roxie Geddie (Bulla) O.; m. Karen Lane Van Neste, Aug. 18, 1973. BA in Journalism, U. N.C., 1971; MA in English, Va. Commonwealth U., 1981. Sports writer Martinsville (Va.) Bulletin, 1971-73; sports editor Gastonia (N.C.) Gazette, 1974-76, Chapel Hill (N.C.) Newspaper, 1974-77; exec. sports editor Tallahassee Dem., 1977-78; asst. sports editor Richmond (Va.) Times-Dispatch, 1978-83, sports new editor, 1983-92, sports editor, 1992-95, dep. mng. editor, 1995—; founder Scholar/Athlete Awards, Richmond, 1986—. Author: Littlejohn, 1992, Fat Lightning, 1994. Recipient Ark. Traveler award State of Ark., 1993. Mem. AP Sports Editors (regional chmn. 1986-87), Va. Writers Club, Met. Richmond Sports Backers, PEN Am. Ctr., 2300 Club. Democrat. Avocations: travel, reading, cooking, sports, jogging. Home: 12836 Ashtree Rd Midlothian VA 23113-3095 Office: Richmond Newspapers Inc 333 E Grace St Richmond VA 23293-1000

OWEN, JACK WALDEN, retired hospital association administrator; b. Union City, Pa., Sept. 21, 1928; s. Wallace A. and Rosamond (Walden) O.; m. Charlotte Keller Owen, Sept. 14, 1957; children: Linda, Lisa, Jack II. BS, Western Mich. U., 1951, BA, 1953; MBA, U. Chgo., 1957. Chmn., CEO Princeton (N.J.) Ins. Co., 1975-83; pres. N.J. Hosp. Assn., Princeton, 1962-82; exec. v.p. Am. Hosp. Assn., Washington, 1982-89; pres. Am. Hosp. Assn., Chgo., 1991; pres. Am. Hosp. Assn. Svcs., Chgo., 1988-94, ret., 1994; bd. dirs. Robert W. Johnson Found., Princeton; chmn. Nat. Com. Prot. S.S., Washington, 1989—; assoc. trustee Suburban Hosp., Bethesda, Md., 1993—. Contbr. articles to profl. jours. Mem. Rocky Hill (N.J.) Sch. Bd., 1974-82. Cpl. U.S. Army, 1953-55. Recipient medal of honor U. Med. and Dentistry, Newark, 1980. Mem. City Tavern Club (Georgetown). Lutheran. Avocations: fishing, golf, woodworking. Home: 7301 Loch Edin Ct Potomac MD 20854

OWEN, JAMES CHURCHILL, JR., lawyer; b. Beverly, Mass., July 30, 1926; s. James Churchill and Alice Wright (Mann) O.; m. Garvene Hales, Feb. 3, 1950 (div. Feb. 1963); children: James Churchill III, Taylor Mann. Student, Yale U., 1944-47; BS, JD, U. Denver, 1956. Bar: Colo. 1957, U.S. Dist. Ct. Colo. 1957. Reporter Oklahoma City Times, 1947-50; writer Phila. Bull., 1951-54; assoc. Holme Roberts & Owen, Denver, 1957-60, ptnr., 1961—; mem. faculty Colo. Grad. Sch. Banking, Boulder, 1975-86; bd. dirs. Norwest Colo., Inc., Denver. Mem. com. on acquisitions Denver Pub. Libr. Friends Found., 1991—; trustee Denver Bot. Gardens, 1976-81, Denver Bot. Gardens Endowment, Inc., 1994—, Denver Zool. Found., 1992—; chmn. law alumni fund U. Denver Coll. Law, 1988-89, chmn. law alumni coun., 1989-91, mem. centennial planning com.; former mem. Colo. Gov.'s Coun. Advisors on Consumer Credit; bd. dirs. Rocky Mountain chpt. Juvenile Diabetes Found., 1993—. Mem. ABA, Colo. Bar Assn. (past chmn. banking com. corp., banking and bus. law sect.), Denver Bar Assn., Colo. Bar Found., Econ. Club Colo. (co-founder, bd. dirs., sec.), Assn. Bank Holding Cos. (past chmn. lawyers' com.), Denver Country Club, Univ. Club, Law Club, Denver Club. Republican. Episcopalian. Avocation: classic cars. Office: Holme Roberts & Owen 1700 Lincoln Ste 4100 Denver CO 80203

OWEN, JOHN, retired newspaper editor; b. Helena, Mont., June 10, 1929; s. John Earl and Ella Jean (McMillian) O.; m. Alice Winnifred Kesler, June 9, 1951; children—David Scott, Kathy Lynn. B.A. in Journalism, U. Mont., 1951. Sports editor Bismarck (N.D.) Tribune, 1953-55; wire editor Yakima

(Wash.) Herald, 1956; with Seattle Post-Intelligencer, 1956-94, sports editor, 1968-80, assoc. editor, 1980-94, columnist. Author: Intermediate Eater Cookbook, 1974, Gourmand Gutbusters Cookbook, 1980, Seattle Cookbook, 1983, Great Grub Hunt Cookbook, 1989, Press Pass, 1994; also short stories. Served with AUS, 1951-52. Named Top Sports Writer in Wash. Nat. Sportswriters Orgn., 1966, 68, 69, 71, 74, 85, 88. Home: 611 Bell Apt 4 Edmonds WA 98020

OWEN, JOHN ATKINSON, JR., physician, educator; b. South Boston, Va., Sept. 24, 1924; s. John Atkinson and Mary Helen (Carrington) O.; m. Wanda Earle Reamy, Nov. 29, 1952; children—John Atkinson III, Ryland R. B.S., Hampden-Sydney Coll., 1944; M.D., U. Va., 1948. Intern Cin. Gen. Hosp., 1948-49; resident, fellow U. Va. Hosp., 1950-52; rsch. fellow Duke Med. Center, 1954-56; asst. prof. medicine Med. Coll. Ga., 1956-58, George Washington U. Med. Sch., 1958-60; mem. faculty U. Va. Sch. Medicine, 1960—, prof., 1970—, vice chmn. dept. internal medicine, 1972-74; mem. Va. Vol. Formulary Bd.; Mem. exec. com. U.S. Pharmacopeia, 1970-75, pres., 1975-80, trustee, 1975-85. Mem. editorial bd.: Jour. Clin. Pharmacology, 1971-84; editor-in-chief: Hosp. Formulary, 1974-83. Served with USNR, 1942-45, 48-50, 52-53; capt. M.C. Res. Recipient Raven award U. Va., 1948; co-recipient Horsley Research prize, 1962. Mem. AMA, Am. Fedn. Clin. Rsch., So. Soc. Clin. Investigation, Med. Soc. Va. (pres. 1990-91), Am. Diabetes Assn., Endocrine Soc. Presbyterian (elder 1965—). Home: 106 Tally Ho Dr Charlottesville VA 22901-2034 Office: U Va Sch Medicine PO Box 242 Charlottesville VA 22908-9999

OWEN, JOHN LAVERTY, human resources executive, consultant; b. Mayfield, Ky., July 28, 1923; s. John Clarence and Lydia (Laverty) O.; m. Marjory Clara Wallace, June 29, 1946; children: John Wallace, David William, Jeffrey Daniel. BA magna cum laude, Westminster (Mo.) Coll., 1944; postgrad., Purdue U., 1945; MS in Psychology, Pa. State U., 1951. Lic. psychologist, Pa. With Hamilton Watch Co., Lancaster, Pa., 1946-70, staff pers. svcs. dir., 1963-70; dir. corp. employee rels. HMW Industries, Inc., Lancaster, Pa., 1970-77; dir. human resources Hamilton Tech., Inc., Lancaster, Pa., 1977-80, v.p. human resources and public rels., 1980-84, sec., v.p. human resources and pub. rels., 1984-85; v.p. human resources Gen. Def. Corp., York, Pa., 1985-88; pres. Performance Systems Internat., 1984—, cons., 1984—; v.p., cons. Greenfield Assocs., Lancaster, 1988-91. Bd. dirs. Lancaster County United Way, 1972-78, 84-86, Lancaster chpt. Nat. Urban League, 1972-81, Assocs. in Downtown Lancaster, 1981-86, Lancaster YMCA, 1984-86, Lancaster Area Arts Coun., 1987-89; bd. dirs. Lancaster Guidance Clinic, 1959-63, pres., 1961-63. Mem. Am. Psychol. Assn., Pa. Psychol. Assn., Ea. Psychol. Assn., Am. Mgmt. Assn., Soc. Human Resource Mgmt. (cert. sr. profl. human resources), Am. Soc. Tng. and Devel., Lancaster Chamber Commerce and Industry, Omicron Delta Kappa, Psi Chi, Phi Kappa Phi, Delta Tau Delta. Republican. Presbyterian.

OWEN, MICHAEL, ballet dancer; b. Carlisle, Pa.. Studied with Marcia Weary; student, Pa. Ballet Sch., Sch. Am. Ballet, Am. Ballet Theatre Sch. Mem. Ballet Repertory Co.; with Am. Ballet Theatre, 1974—, soloist, 1977-87, prin. dancer, 1987—. Appeared in ballets including La Bayadere, Coppelia, Fall River Legend, Giselle, Jardin aux Lilas, The Leaves are Fading, Manon, Pillar of Fire, Romeo and Juliet, The Sleeping Beauty, Swan Lake, Undertow. Office: Am Ballet Theatre 890 Broadway New York NY 10003-1211*

OWEN, MICHAEL LEE, lawyer; b. L.A., Aug. 17, 1942; s. Richard M. Owen and Betty Hamilton; m. Esperanza Bolivar. AB in Econ. with distinction, Stanford U., 1964; LLB, Harvard U., 1967. Bar: Calif., 1968, N.Y. 1968. Assoc. Reid & Priest, N.Y.C., 1967-69; mem. legal dept. Bank of Am. NT&SA, San Francisco, 1969-81; v.p., assoc. gen. counsel Bank of Am. NT&SA, L.A., 1980-81; ptnr. & chair of Latin Amer. practice group Paul, Hastings, Janofsky & Walker, L.A., 1981—; corp. sec. BRE Corp., San Francisco, 1970-75. Contbr. articles to profl. jours. regarding legal issues affecting financing and investment in Latin Amer. Office: Paul Hastings Janofsky & Walker 555 S FLower St 24th fl Los Angeles CA 90071

OWEN, NATHAN RICHARD, manufacturing company executive; b. Burnt Hills, N.Y., May 3, 1919; s. George H. and Mildred T. (Sharpley) O.; m. Janet M. Smith, Sept. 26, 1942; children: Patricia O. Smith, David G., Lorinda O. Clauson. B.S. in Mech. Engring. Mass. Inst. Tech., 1941, M.S., 1942; D.Sc., Clarkson Coll., 1979. With Chase Brass & Copper Co., 1946-47; with J.H. Whitney & Co., N.Y.C., 1947-62, ptnr., 1951-62; chmn. bd. Gen. Signal Corp., 1962-84, chmn. exec. com., 1980-95; chmn. emeritus, 1995—; bd. dirs. TechnoServe, Inc., Braille Internat., Inc., Enabling Techs. Inc. Served to lt. USN, 1942-46. Home: 18 Simara St Stuart FL 34996-6324 Office: PO Box 10351 Stamford CT 06904-2351

OWEN, PHILIP WALTER, mayor, business owner; b. Vancouver, B.C., Can., Mar. 11, 1933; s. Walter Stewart and Jean Margaret (Dowler) O.; m. Brita Johanne Busch, Dec. 6, 1957; children: Lise, Christian, Andrea. Store mgr. T. Eaton Co. Ltd., Vancouver, 1964-66; pres. Elysee Fabrics Ltd. N.Y.C., 1967-71, Elle Fabrics Ltd., Vancouver, 1972—, Manhasset Inv. Ltd., Vancouver, 1974—; v.p. L. Walker Industries Inc., Surrey, B.C., 1988—; commr. Bd. of Parks and Recreation, Vancouver, 1978-80; councillor City Coun., Vancouver, 1985-93; mayor City of Vancouver, 1993-96; chmn. Standing Com. on City Svcs. and Budgets; coun. rep. Downtown Parking Corp.; bd. dirs. Pacific Nat. Exhbn.; mem. Standing Com. on Planning and Environment, Vancouver Arts Initiative, Vancouver Liquor Licensing Commn. Mem. adv. com. B.C. Festival of the Arts; chmn. B.C. divsn. Nat. Fundraising Campaign, Can. Paraplegic Assn.; chmn. B.C. Paraplegic Found.; B.C. Transit Pkwy. Com., The Bishop's Men; chmn. bd. variance Greater Vancouver Regional Dist.; chmn. transp. com. Independence '92, dir. Vancouver Art Gallery & the Endeavour Soc.; gov. St. George's Sch.; patron. dir. Rick Hansen Man in Motion World Tour; treas. Diocese New Westminster; pres. Downtown Vancouver Assn.; patron Internat. Found. of the Arts. Decorated Knights St. John, The Sovereign Order of St. John of Jerusalem-Knights Hospitaller, 1990. Mem. The Vancouver Club, The Arbutus Club. Anglican. Home: 3850 Marguerite St, Vancouver, BC Canada V6J 4E9 Office: City of Vancouver, 453 W 12th Ave, Vancouver, BC Canada V5Y 1V4

OWEN, RAY DAVID, biology educator; b. Genesee, Wis., Oct. 30, 1915; s. Dave and Ida (Hoeft) O.; m. June J. Weissenberg, June 24, 1939; 1 son, David G. B.S., Carroll Coll., Wis., 1937, Sc.D., 1962; Ph.D., U. Wis., 1941, Sc.D., 1979; Sc.D., U. of Pacific, 1965. Asst. prof. genetics, zoology U. Wis., 1944-47; Gosney fellow Calif. Inst. Tech., Pasadena, 1946-47; assoc. prof. div. biology Calif. Inst. Tech., 1947-53, prof. biology, 1953-83, also chmn., v.p. for student affairs, dean of students, prof. emeritus, 1983—; research participant Oak Ridge Nat. Lab., 1957-58; Cons. Oak Ridge Inst. Nuclear Studies; mem. Pres.'s Cancer Panel. Author: (with A.M. Srb) General Genetics, 1952, 2d edit. (with A.M. Srb, R. Edgar), 1965; Contbr. articles to sci. jours. Recipient Gregor Mendel medal Czech Acad. Scis., 1965. Fellow AAAS; mem. Genetics Soc. Am. (pres., Thomas Hunt Morgan medal 1993), Am. Assn. Immunologists, Am. Soc. Human Genetics, Western Soc. Naturalists, Am. Soc. Zoologists, Am. Genetics Assn., Nat. Acad. Scis., Am. Acad. Arts and Scis., Am. Philos. Soc., Am. Acad. Allergy and Immunology (hon.), Internat. Soc. Animal Genetics (hon.), Sigma Xi. Home: 1583 Rose Villa St Pasadena CA 91106-3524 Office: Calif Inst Tech 156-29 Pasadena CA 91125

OWEN, RAYMOND HAROLD, minister; b. Gleason, Tenn., Apr. 21, 1932; s. Charlie Emerson and Lula (Page) O.; m. Lavell Coburn, Oct. 4, 1952; children: Dana (dec.), Darryl R., Dyton L. BA in Religion, Oklahoma City U., 1966; ThM, So. Meth. U., 1967; MA in Evangelism, Scarritt Coll., Nashville, 1972; DD (hon.), Oklahoma City U., 1979. Ordained to ministry United Meth. Ch., 1967. Pastor 1st United Meth. Ch., Hugo, Okla.; dist. supt. Meth. Ch., Bartlesville Dist., Okla., 1977-82; sr. min. Epworth United Meth. Ch., Oklahoma City, 1971-73, New Haven United Meth. Ch., Tulsa, 1973-77, 1st United Meth. Ch., Bartlesville, Okla., 1982—; del. Jurisdictional Conf. S.W. United Meth. Ch., 1976, 80, 84, 88—, Gen. Conf., 1980, 84, 88, 90; mem. exec. com. World Meth. Coun. 1986—; bd. dirs. Green Co. Retirement Villa, Bartlesville. Author: Probingins in Prayer, 1975, Seedtime and Harvest, 1980, Questions That Shape Destiny, 1983, Listening To Life, 1987. 2d lt. U.S. Army, 1954-60. Mem. Rotary. Office: First United Meth Ch 500 S Johnstone Ave Bartlesville OK 74003-6621 It is never very far from the mediocre to the exceptional; it is just more painful.

OWEN, RICHARD, federal judge; b. N.Y.C., Dec. 11, 1922; s. Carl Maynard and Shirley (Barnes) O.; m. Lynn Rasmussen, June 6, 1960; children: Carl R., David R., Richard. AB, Dartmouth Coll., 1947; LLB, Harvard U., 1950; MusD (hon.), Manhattan Sch. Music, 1989. Bar: N.Y. 1950. Practiced in N.Y.C., 1950-74; assoc. Willkie Owen Farr Gallagher & Walton, 1950-53, Willkie Farr Gallagher Walton & Fitzgibbon, 1958-60; pvt. practice, 1960-65; ptnr. Owen & Aarons, 1965-66, Owen & Turchin, 1966-74; asst. U.S. atty. So. Dist. N.Y., 1953-55; trial atty. antitrust div. U.S. Dept. Justice, 1955-58; U.S. dist. judge So. Dist. N.Y., 1974—; asst. prof. N.Y. Law Sch., 1951-53; assoc. counsel N.Y. State Moreland Com. on Alcoholic Beverage Control Laws, 1963-64. Composer, librettist operas A Moment of War, 1958, A Fisherman Called Peter, 1965, Mary Dyer, 1976, The Death of the Virgin, 1980, Abigail Adams, 1987, Tom Sawyer, 1989. Trustee Manhattan Sch. Music, N.Y.C.; founder, bd. dirs Maine Opera Assn., 1975-85; pres., bd. dirs. N.Y. Lyric Opera Co. 1st N.Y.C. USAAF, 1942-45. Decorated D.F.C. with oak leaf cluster, Air medal with 3 oak leaf clusters. Mem. ASCAP, Century Assn., Metropolitan Opera Club, Pine Pond Yacht Club (commodore 1967-70), Chelsea Yacht Club. Republican. Mem. Soc. of Friends. Office: US Dist Ct US Courthouse Foley Sq New York NY 10007-1501

OWEN, ROBERT HUBERT, lawyer, real estate broker; b. Birmingham, Ala., Aug. 3, 1928; s. Robert Clay and Mattie Lou (Hubert) O.; m. Mary Dane Hicks, Mar. 14, 1954; children: Mary Kathryn, Robert Hubert. B.S. U. Ala., 1950; J.D., Birmingham Sch. Law, 1956. Bar: Ala. 1957, Ga. 1965. Methods and procedures analyst, supr. Ala. Power Co., Birmingham, 1952-58; assoc. Martin, Vogtle, Balch & Bingham, Birmingham, 1958-63; asst. sec. So. Services, Atlanta, 1963-69; sec. Southern Co., Atlanta, 1969-71; sec., asst. treas. Southern Co., 1971-77; exec. v.p., sec., gen. counsel, dir. Proverbs 31 Corp., Atlanta, 1978-81, 90—; broker Bob Owen Realty, Atlanta, 1990—; pvt. practice law Marietta, 1978-85; v.p., gen. counsel Hubert Properties, 1985-86. Atlanta area rep. Inst. Basic Youth Conflicts, 1970-80. Served to maj. USAF, 1951-52, 61-62. Mem. Jasons, Delta Chi, Omicron Delta Kappa, Beta Gamma Sigma, Delta Sigma Pi, Phi Eta Sigma. Baptist. Home and Office: 6590 Bridgewood Valley Rd NW Atlanta GA 30328-2906

OWEN, ROBERT RANDOLPH, accountant; b. Ardmore, Okla., June 24, 1939; s. Buford Randolph and Ruth Marie (Cleeton) O.; m. Patra Malinda Randolph, June 20, 1958; children: Stacy Malinda Owen Hodges, Mindy Carol Owen Long. BBA with high honors, So. Meth. U., 1961; postgrad., Harvard U., 1985. CPA, Tex. Various positions Alford, Meroney & Co., Dallas, 1961-80, mgr., 1967-69, ptnr., 1969-73, mng. ptnr. Dallas office, 1975-78, firm mng. ptnr., 1978-80; dep. regional mng. ptnr. S.W. region Arthur Young & Co., Dallas, 1980-83, ptnr., nat. dir. entrepreneurial svcs., 1983-86, ptnr., nat. dir. indsl. specialization, 1986-89; ptnr., nat. dir. industry svcs. Ernst & Young, 1990—. Author, editor: The Arthur Young Guide to Financing for Growth, 1986, The Ernst & Young Guide to Raising Capital, 1991. Capt. USAF, 1961-64. Mem. Tex. Soc. CPAs (pres. 1994-95, pres. Dallas chpt. 1988-89, bd. dirs. 1986—), AICPA. Baptist. Office: Ernst & Young LLP 2121 San Jacinto St Ste 500 Dallas TX 75201-6706

OWEN, ROBERT ROY, manufacturing company executive; b. Somerton, Ariz., Aug. 29, 1921; s. Wilbur Parker and Flossye Bell (White) O.; m. Barbara Dean Burton, Apr. 3, 1943; children—Melinne, Claudia, Christina, Rebecca, Jennifer. B.S., U. Calif. at Davis, 1942. Plantation engr. Del Monte, Hawaii, 1946-49; tech. rep. E.I. duPont de Nemours & Co., 1949-50; head engring. Pineapple Research Inst. of Hawaii, 1950-56; farm implement planning mgr., product planning and programming mgr., asst. chief engr., gen. mgr. equipment operations Tractor and Implement div. Ford Motor Co., Birmingham, Mich., 1956-68; pres. Gt. Western Sugar Co., Denver, 1968-71, Gt. Western Producers Coop., Englewood, Colo., 1971-76, Eversman Mfg. Co., Denver, 1976—; dir. Ivancie Cellars, Inc.; Gen. chmn. Birmingham Arts Festival, 1960; pres. Evergreen Homes Assn., 1969-71; mem. U.S. Dept. Agr. Joint Council Food and Agrl. Scis., 1983-86. Contbr. articles to profl. jours. Served with AUS, 1942-46; brig. gen. Res. Recipient Centennial citation U. Calif., 1968, Distinguished Service award Colo. State U., 1971. Fellow Am. Soc. Agrl. Engrs.; mem. Newcomen Soc., Internat. Wine and Food Soc., Denver Club, Hiwan Country Club. Patentee in field. Office: Eversman Mfg Co 7475 W 5th Ave Ste 214 Lakewood CO 80226-1674

OWEN, ROBERT VAUGHAN, financial company executive; b. No. Adams, Mass., June 2, 1920; s. William and Lucy Anne (Morgan) O.; m. Jean Ann Gebauer, Dec. 6, 1946; children: Robert, Nancy, Bruce, Elizabeth. BA cum laude, Dartmouth Coll., 1946; MBA, Amos Tuck Sch., 1947. Fin. mgr. Gen. Electric Co., various locations, 1950-62; sr. budget dir. Citibank, N.Y.C., 1962-68, v.p., 1968-78, mng. dir., 1978-83; pres., chief exec. officer Bob Owen Assocs., Inc., Darien, Conn., 1984—. Contbr. articles to profl. jours. With USNR, 1943-45. Mem. N.Y. Fin. Execs. Inst. (pres. 1976). Republican. Roman Catholic. Office: Bob Owen Assocs Inc 10 Haskell Ln Darien CT 06820-3301

OWEN, ROBERTS BISHOP, lawyer; b. Boston, Feb. 11, 1926; s. Roberts Bishop and Monica Benedict (Burrell) O.; m. Kathleen Comstock von Schrader, Aug. 27, 1966; children—David Roberts, Lucy Leffingwell, William Atreus. Student, Dartmouth Coll., 1943-44; A.B. cum laude, Harvard U., 1948, LL.B. cum laude, 1951; Dip.C.L.S., Cambridge U., Eng., 1952. Bar: D.C. 1952, U.S. Ct. Appeals (D.C. cir.) 1953, U.S. Supreme Ct. 1958. Assoc. Covington & Burling, Washington, 1952-60; ptnr. Covington & Burling, 1960-79, 81—; the legal advisor U.S. Dept. State, Washington, 1979-81; mem. Permanent Ct. Arbitration, The Hague, Netherlands, 1980-86, 93—; mem. arbitration panel Internat. Ctr. for Settlement of Investment Disputes, 1995—. Served to ensign USN, 1943-46. Recipient Disting. Honor award Dept. State, 1981; Fulbright scholar, 1951-52. Fellow Am. Coll. Trial Lawyers; mem. ABA, Council Fgn. Relations, Am. Soc. Internat. Law (exec. council 1981-85). Clubs: Royal Ocean Racing (London); Metropolitan, City (Washington). Office: Covington & Burling Po Box 7566 1201 Pennsylvania Ave NW Washington DC 20044

OWEN, SALLY ANN, gifted and talented education educator; b. Columbus, Wis., Aug. 14, 1932; d. Willard Ervin and Marian (Thomas) O.; m. Thomas. BS, U. Wis., 1955; MA, Pepperdine U., L.A., 1978; postgrad., U. Calif., La Jolla, San Diego State U. Cert. gifted edn. tchr., Calif. Tchr. humanities Am. Community Schs., Athens, Greece; tchr. English, counselor Dept. Def., Tokyo; secondary tchr. English history and phys. edn., counselor San Diego Unified Sch. Dist.; tchr. gifted and talented edn. ind. study seminar Point Loma High Sch., San Diego; tchr. interdisciplinary team, tchr. gifted and talented edn. ind. study seminar Standley Jr. High Sch.; mentor tchr., 1983—; presenter in lang. arts field. Recipient svc. award PTA, Latin Am. studies award. Mem. Assn. San Diego Educators for the Gifted (Tchr. of Yr. award 1991, Excellence in Gate Edn. award 1993, Gate New Voices in the Humanities award 1994-95), Calif. Assn. Tchrs. English, Nat. Coun. Tchrs. English (Lit. Mags. Excellence award). Home: 7285 Charmant Dr Apt 222 San Diego CA 92122-4357

OWEN, STEPHEN, Chinese literature educator; b. St. Louis, Mo., Oct. 30, 1946; s. George Ernest and Deha (Gursey) O.; m. Phyllis Anne Leffingwell, Nov. 25, 1967; children—Rustem Gruffudd, Leigh Morgan. B.A., Yale U., 1968, Ph.D., 1972; M.A. (hon.), Harvard U., 1983. Asst. prof. Yale U., New Haven, Conn., 1972-82; assoc. prof., 1979-81, prof. 1981-82; prof Chinese lit. Harvard U., Cambridge, Mass., 1982—. Author: The Poetry of Meng Chiao and Han Yu, 1975, The Poetry of the Early Tang, 1978, The Poetry of the High Tang, 1980, Traditional Chinesr Poetry and Poetics, 1985, Remebrances the Experience of the Past in Classical Chinese Literature, 1986, Mi-lou Poetry and The Lebyrinth of Desire, 1989, Readings in Chinese Literary Thought, 1992. Office: Harvard U 2 Divinity Ave Cambridge MA 02138-2020

OWEN, STEPHEN LEE, lawyer; b. Danville, Va., Mar. 25, 1952; s. L.F. Davis and Ann (Brodie) O.; m. Catherine Bryan Mapery; children: Hillary Brodie, Stephen Grayson. BA, Hampden-Sydney Coll., Va., 1974; JD, Coll. of William and Mary, Williamsburg, Va., 1977. Bar: Va. 1977, Md. 1977, U.S. Tax Ct. 1978, U.S. Dist. Ct. Md., D.C. 1990. Assoc. Venable, Baetjer

& Howard, Balt., 1977-84, ptnr., 1985-93; ptnr. Piper & Marbury, Balt., 1993—. Co-author: Federal Taxation of Estates, Gifts & Trusts, 1988; co-author newsletter Real Estate Tax Ideas, 1985--; contbr. articles to profl. jours.; editorial bd. Jour. Partnership Taxation, 1984--, The Practical Tax Lawyer, 1985--. Bd. dirs. Balt. City Found., 1979-89. Mem. Am. Law Inst., Md. Bar Assn. (chmn. sect. of taxation 1989-90), Balt. Country Club, Caves Valley Golf Club. Avocation: golf. Office: Piper & Marbury 36 S Charles St Baltimore MD 21201

OWEN, SUZANNE, retired savings and loan executive; b. Lincoln, Nebr., Oct. 6, 1926; d. Arthur C. and Hazel E. (Edwards) O. BSBA, U. Nebr., Lincoln, 1948. With G.F. Lessenhop & Sons, Inc., Lincoln, 1948-57; with First Fed. Lincoln, 1963-91; v.p., dir. personnel, 1975-81, 1st v.p. 1981-87, sr. v.p., 1987-91, ret., 1991; mem. pers. bd. City of Lincoln, 1989—. Mem. Lincoln Human Resources Mgmt. Assn., Lincoln Mgmt. Soc., Phi Chi Theta. Republican. Christian Scientist. Clubs: Wooden Spoon, Exec. Women's Breakfast Group, Community Women's. Lodges: Pi Beta Phi Alumnae, Order of Eastern Star (Lincoln).

OWEN, SYLVIA, interior design executive; d. Manfred and Maria Curry; grad. in Interior Design, U. Munich, 1963, N.Y. Sch. Interior Design, 1965; m. Christopher Owen, Oct. 9, 1965; 1 dau., Tjasa. With Internat. Knoll Planning Unit, N.Y.C., 1968-71; sr. interior designer, assoc. John Carl Warnecke and Assocs., N.Y.C., 1971-78; ptnr. Innerplan, N.Y.C., 1978-82; founder, operator Owen & Mandolfo, Inc., 1982—. Mem. Am. Soc. Interior Designers, AIA (assoc.). Projects include Chase Manhattan Bank, Chemical Bank, Republic Nat. Bank, AT&T Hdqrs., Bedminster, N.J., Sun Co. Hdqrs., Radnor, Pa., Globtik Tankers' exec. offices, N.Y.C. (first prize for corp. interiors Interior Design mag. 1976), Am. Hosp. in Paris expansion, CCNY, Commerzbank, N.Y.C., Restoration Villard Houses for Capital Cities Communications, Inc., N.Y.C., Beneficial Mgmt. Corp., Peapack, N.J., David Murdock Assocs., N.Y.C.; developing Gen. Telephone Electric hdqrs. bldg., Stamford, Conn., Dime Savings Banks, L.I., Christian Dior stores, N.Y.C. and Bal Harbour, Fla., tower stes. Waldorf Astoria Hotel, Trump Tower stores, numerous others; redesigning Neiman-Marcus store, San Francisco; developing new image Charles Jourdan stores, Davidoff of Geneva, L.A.; designing numerous pvt. residences. Works pub. in Archtl. Record, Interior Design, Interiors, N.Y. Mag., N.Y. Times, Archtl. Digest. Named one of 100 Best Interior Designers Worldwide, Archtl. Digest; recipient Outstanding Achievement award and 1st prize best of competition by Inst. Bus. Designers and Interior Design Mag., 1992, 1st prize for best design Am. Soc. Interior Designers, 1992; featured in Women of Design by Rizzoli. Office: Owen & Mandolfo Inc 192 Lexington Ave New York NY 10016-6823

OWEN, THOMAS BARRON, retired naval officer, space company executive; b. Seattle, Mar. 19, 1920; s. Thomas Barron and Ruth (Deane) O.; m. Rosemary Stolz, Dec. 24, 1944; children—Catherine Adams, Thomas Barron, James Rowell, Nancy Deane. B.S. cum laude, U. Wash., 1940; postgrad., U.S. Naval Postgrad. Sch., 1946-47; Ph.D. in Chemistry, Cornell U., 1950; postgrad., U. Amsterdam, 1950-51, Indsl. Coll. Armed Forces, 1961-62, Harvard Grad. Sch. Bus. Adminstrn., 1964. Commd. ensign U.S. Navy, 1940, advanced through grades to rear adm., 1967, combat duty with Pacific Fleet, 1940-45; officer distbn. div. Bur. Naval Personnel, 1945-46; with armaments br. and mil. operations br. Office Naval Research, 1951-53; asst. repair supt. (hull) and prodn. analysis supt. Long Beach (Calif.) Naval Shipyard, 1953-57; dir. applied scis. div., dir. research and devel. planning div. Navy Bur. Ships, 1957-61; mil. asst. to dep. dir. def. research and engring. engring. and chemistry, 1962-63; assigned Office Asst. Sec. Navy Research and Devel., 1963; dir. support services Naval Research Lab., 1963-65, dir., 1965-67; chief naval research, 1967-70, ret., 1970; asst. dir. nat. and internat. programs NSF, 1970-74; assoc. dean grad. affairs and rsch. Am. U., Washington, 1974-76; asst. provost Am. U., 1976-79; asst. administr. NOAA, Dept. Commerce, Rockville, Md., 1979-81; mgr. program planning Fairchild Space & Electronics Co., Germantown, Md., 1981-83; sr. dir. systems effectiveness Fairchild Space Co., Germantown, 1983-84, v.p. procurement, 1984-86. Author profl. papers. Decorated D.S.M., Silver Star, Bronze Star. Fellow AAAS; mem. Am. Chem. Soc., U.S. Naval Inst., Philos. Soc. Washington, Sigma Xi, Phi Kappa Phi, Phi Lambda Upsilon, Tau Beta Pi, Chi Psi. Club: Cosmos (Washington). Home: 8409 Magruder Mill Ct Bethesda MD 20817-2746 *Demand high standards of excellence for self and others. Achieve respect of others through own performance. Be direct; avoid circumspection. Develop empathy; listen; consider feelings and rights of others. Maintain philosophy of "Onward and Upward!".*

OWEN, THOMAS LLEWELLYN, SR., investment executive; b. Patchogue, N.Y., June 24, 1928; s. Griffith Robert and Jeanette Roberts (Hatfield) O.; A.B. in Econs., Coll. William and Mary, 1951; postgrad. Columbia U., 1952, N.Y. Inst. Fin., 1960-62; M.B.A., N.Y. U., 1966. Exec. trainee Shell Oil Co., N.Y.C. and Indpls., 1951-59, supr., 1958-59; petroleum and chem. investment analyst Paine, Webber, Jackson & Curtis, N.Y.C., 1959-62; sr. oil investment analyst DuPont Investment Interests, Wilmington, Del., N.Y.C., 1962-66, dir. research, 1964-66; v.p., sr. investment officer, mem. policy, investment coms. Nat. Securities and Research Corp., N.Y.C., 1966-75; sr. investment exec., v.p., portfolio mgr. F. Eberstadt & Co. and Eberstadt Asset Mgmt., Inc., N.Y.C., 1975-85, mem. policy com., 1979-85, also dir. portfolio rev. com.; sr. investment exec., portfolio mgr. Brown Brothers Harriman, N.Y.C., 1985-89; pres., CEO Owen Capital Mgmt., N.Y.C., 1989—. Mem. N.Y. Soc. Security Analysts, Assn. of Investment Mgmt. and Rsch., Oil Analysts Group N.Y., Am. Econ. Assn., Investment Assn. N.Y., Am. Petroleum Inst., Nat. Assn. Petroleum Investment Analysts, Internat. Assn. Energy Economists. Contbr. chpt. "Oil and Gas Industries" to Financial Analysts Handbook, 1975. Home and Office: 251 E 32d St New York NY 10016

OWEN, THOMAS WALKER, banker, broker; b. Everett, Wash., June 7, 1925; s. Thomas Walker and Frances (Yantis) O.; m. Barbara May Neils, Oct. 20, 1951; children: Thomas W., Gerhard, Caroline, Jeffrey; m. Ingrid Lundgren, June 7, 1975. B.A., U. Wash., 1949; postgrad., Pacific Coast Banking Sch., 1956. Adminstrv. trainee Seattle Trust & Savs. Bank, 1949-54, asst. br. mgr., 1954-56, trust investment officer, 1956-57, mgr. investment dept., chmn. investment com., 1957-59; v.p., mgr. investment dept. Nat. Bank Wash., Tacoma, 1959-66, vice chmn., 1967-71; exec. v.p. bank adminstrn. Pacific Nat. Bank Wash., 1971-73; v.p. Reeder, Owen & Co., Inc., 1975-92; pres., chmn. Owen, Reeder, Inc., Merrill Lynch, 1991-92; bd. dirs. West One Bank Wash., Tacoma, 1981-93. Served with AUS, 1943-45. Decorated Bronze Star, Purple Heart. Mem. Tacoma C. of C., N.W. Forum, Phi Gamma Delta. Clubs: Wash. Athletic, Tacoma (past pres.), Tacoma Country and Golf. Home: 10819 Evergreen Ter SW Tacoma WA 98498-6701

OWEN, WADSWORTH, oceanographer, consultant; b. N.Y.C., Sept. 4, 1932; S. George Wadsworth and Helen (Hammett) O.; m. Elaine M. Brewster, Oct. 26, 1955 (div. 1973); children: Leslie Shore, Victoria Rand, Samantha; m. Margaret W. Emslie, May 31, 1975 (div. July 22, 1992); 1 child, Joanna W. BS in Physics and Math., U. Mass., 1961; MA in Phys. Oceanography, Johns Hopkins U., 1969. Asst. scientist Avco R&D, Wilmington, Mass., 1956-61; rsch. asst. Johns Hopkins U., Balt., 1961-64; engr. sonar devices Westinghouse-Undersea, Balt., 1964-66; sr. engr. Sikorski Aircraft, Stratford, Conn., 1966-67; mgr. marine tech. Raytheon Subsig, New London, Conn., 1967-69; divsn. mgr. marine sci. and v.p. underwater vehicles VAST, Inc., Waterford, Conn., 1969-73; divsn. dir. phys. sci. divsn. Normandeau Assocs., Bedford, N.H., 1973-77; dir. marine ops. Coll. Marine Studies, U. Del., Lewes, 1977-94. Contbr. articles to profl. jours.; patentee in field. Adv. bd. New Eng. Marine Rsch. Info. Program, R.I., 1970-73. Sgt. USMC, 1952-55, PTO. U. Mass. scholar, 1958-61; NDEA fellow, 1961-64. Mem. So. N.E. Marine Scis. Assn. (chmn. exec. bd. 1970-73), Marine Tech. Soc., Acad. of Modeel Aeronautics, Nat. Free Flight Soc. Avocations: model aircraft design and construction, art, history, boats, diving. Home: PO Box 268 Friendship ME 04547

OWEN, WALTER SHEPHERD, materials science and engineering educator; b. Liverpool, Eng., Mar. 13, 1920; s. Walter L. and Dorothea (Lunt) O. B.Engring., U. Liverpool, 1940, M.Engring., 1942, Ph.D., 1950, D.Eng.,

1972. Metallurgist English Electric Co., 1940-46; mem. research staff MIT, 1951-57; prof. metallurgy U. Liverpool, 1957-66; prof., dir. materials sci. and engring. Cornell U., 1966-70; dean Tech. Inst., 1967-70; v.p. sci. and research Northwestern U., Evanston, Ill., 1971-73; prof. and head materials sci. and engring. MIT, 1973-82, prof. phys. metallurgy, 1982-85, prof. emeritus, sr. lectr. materials sci. and engring., 1985—; Cons. to industry. Author research papers. Commonwealth Fund fellow, 1951. Fellow ASM; mem. NAE, AIME, Instn. Metallurgists, N.Y. Acad. Scis., Inst. Metals, Materials Rsch. Soc., Japan Inst. Metals (hon.). Office: MIT Rm 13-5114 Cambridge MA 02139

OWEN, WARREN HERBERT, utility executive; b. Rock Hill, S.C., Jan. 8, 1927; s. Warren Herbert and Margaret Elizabeth (White) O.; m. Virginia Lea Boulware, Oct. 22, 49; children: Virginia Ann, Carol Elizabeth, Susan Laine. B.M.E., Clemson (S.C.) U., 1947; JD (hon.), Clemson U., 1988. With Duke Power Co., Charlotte, 1948-92, prin. mech. engr., design engring. dept., 1966-71, v.p. design engring., 1971-78; sr. v.p. engring. and constrn., 1978-82, exec. v.p. engring. and constrn., 1982-84, exec. v.p. engring., constrn. and prodn., 1984-88, exec. v.p. Power Group, 1988-92, also bd. dirs., 1978-92. Recipient Robinson award Duke Power Co., 1968, Philip T. Sprague award Instrument Soc. Am., 1970. Fellow ASME (James L. Landis medal 1987); Mem. Am. Nuclear Soc., Atomic Indsl. Forum (Clyde Lilly award 1981), N.C. Soc. Engrs. (Engr. of Yr. award 1984), Profl. Engrs. N.C., Charlotte Engrs. Club (Disting. Service award 1981), Nat. Acad. Engring. Episcopalian. Home: 43 Oyster Reef Dr Hilton Head Island SC 29926-2622

OWEN, WILLIAM CONE, lawyer; b. Tallahassee, Fla., Jan. 21, 1942; s. George Everett and Nellie (Cone) O.; m. Patricia Moss Wash, Nov. 24, 1969; children: Robert Davis, William Cone. BSBA, U. Fla., 1964; JD, U. Nebr., 1967. Bar: Fla. 1967, U.S. Dist. Ct. (no. and mid. dists.) Fla. 1967, U.S. Ct. Appeals (11th cir.) Fla. 1967. Rsch. clk. Fla. Supreme Ct., Tallahassee, 1968-70; pvt. practice Tallahassee, 1970-72; ptnr. Carswell, McKenzie, Dean & Owen, Tallahassee, 1972-74, McClure, Wigginton & Owen, Tallahassee, 1974-81, Calton, Fields, Ward, Emmanuel, Smith & Cutler, P.A., Tallahassee, 1981—; bd. dirs. Woodmen of World Life Ins. Soc., Omaha. Contbr. articles to legal jours. Mem. Exchange Club. Democrat. Presbyterian. Avocation: golf. Office: PO Box 190 Tallahassee FL 32302-0190

OWEN, WILLIAM HAROLD, JR., academic administrator; b. Stilwell, Okla., Aug. 2, 1933; s. William Harold Sr. and Nellie (Whiteside) O.; m. Mary Ann Fryar, Mar. 10, 1956; children: David G., John F. AA, Jr. Agrl. Coll., Beebe, Ark., 1953; BS, Ark. State Tchrs. Coll., 1957, MS in Edn., 1960. Tchr. Beebe Pub. Schs., 1957-59; asst. prof. social scis. Ark. State U., Beebe, 1959-69, dean students, registrar, 1969-81, chancellor, 1981—; bd. dirs. Beebe Indsl. Devel. Corp. Corp. sec. White County Meml. Hosp., Searcy, Ark., 1987—. With USAF, 1953-55. Mem. Ark. Assn. Two-Yr. Colls. (chmn. bd. dirs. 1989-90), Ark. Higher Edn. Coun., Beebe C. of C. (bd. dirs. 1985—), Beebe Kiwanis (past pres.). Presbyterian. Avocations: hunting, fishing, woodworking. Office: Ark State Univ PO Drawer H Beebe AR 72012

OWENS, ALBERT HENRY, JR., oncologist, educator; b. Staten Island, N.Y., Aug. 27, 1926; married, 1949; 4 children. BA, MD, Johns Hopkins U., 1949. Diplomate Am. Bd. Internal Medicine. Staff internal medicine Johns Hopkins U. Hosp., 1949-50, 52-53, 55-56; from instr. to assoc. prof. medicine Johns Hopkins U. Sch. Medicine, 1956-68, instr. pathobiology sch. hygiene and pub. health, 1957-76, prof. oncology and medicine, 1968—, dir. oncology ctr., 1976—; fellow pharmacology and exptl. therapeutics, sch. medicine Johns Hopkins U., 1953-55; vis. physician Balt. City Hosp., 1957—. Fellow ACP; mem. Am. Soc. Pharmacology and Exptl. Therapeutics, Am. Soc. Clin. Oncology, Am. Assn. Cancer Insts., N.Y. Acad. Sci. Achievements include research in neoplastic diseases. Office: Johns Hopkins Oncology Ctr Ross Rsch Bldg Rm 361 720 Rutland Ave Baltimore MD 21205-2196

OWENS, A(RNOLD) DEAN, lawyer; b. Visalia, Calif., June 14, 1943; s. Clarence Cecil and Eula Mae (Boaz) O.; m. Marilyn Joyce Hatfield, Sept. 16, 1967; children: Eric, Rachel. BS, U. Calif., Berkeley, 1966; JD, U. Oreg., 1969. Bar: Oreg. 1969. Assoc. O'Reilly, Anderson, Richmonds & Adkins, Eugene, Oreg., 1969-71; ptnr. Anderson, Richmond & Owens, Eugene, 1971-74, Owens & Loomis, Eugene, 1975-79, Owens & Platt, Eugene, 1982-85; pvt. practice, Eugene, 1979-82, 85—; atty. City of Coburg, Oreg., 1971-79, City of Lowell, Oreg., 1973-79; hearings officer Lane County, Eugene, 1972—. Author: Advising Oregon Business Chpter 13, 1979; editor Lane County Bar News, 1980-87; also articles. Pres. Lane County Muscular Dystrophy Assn., Eugene, 1969-71; chmn. Eugene Human Rights Commn., 1969-71; bd. dirs. Asian Counseling Ctr., Eugene, 1991—; mem. exec. com. Lane County Rep. Party, Eugene, 1993—; mem. Eugene econ. devel. City of Eugene, 1989—; bd. dirs. Eugene-Springfield Met. Partnership, Inc., 1989-90; mem. exec. com. Eugene/Springfield Community Partnership, 1991—. Recipient cert. of appreciation Lane County Law Libr. Adv. Com., 1976-78, Bd. Lane County Legal Aid and Sr. Law Svcs., 1987, 90, spl. award and recognition of vol. svc. Eugene Sports Program, 1982. Mem. Eugene Area C. of C. (bd. dirs. 1986-90, pres. 1989, Disting. Svc. award 1986, 88), Emerald Exec. Assn. (pres. 1984), Eugene Swim and Tennis Club (pres. 1982), Eugene Country Club (chmn. tennis com. 1975-79), Downtown Athletic Club, Tri-Pass Water Ski Club, Eugene Active 20-30 Club (hon. life, editor newsletter 1969-72). Republican. Avocations: tennis, basketball, running, reading, water and snow skiing. Home: 2160 Oakmont Way Eugene OR 97401-2372 Office: 933 Pearl St Eugene OR 97401-2741

OWENS, BUCK (ALVIS EDGAR, JR.), singer, musician, songwriter; b. Sherman, Tex., Aug. 12, 1929; s. Alvis Edgar and Maicie A.; m. Bonnie Owens, 1947 (div. 1955); children: Buddy, Mike; m. Phyllis Owens (div. 1972); 1 son, John; m. Jennifer, 1978. Attended pub. schs., Mesa, Ariz. Pres. Buck Owens Prodns.; owner stas. KUZZ-FM, KCWR-AM, Bakersfield, Calif., stas. KCWW-AM, KNIX-FM, Phoenix, sta. KUZZ-TV, Bakersfield, Owens Enterprises, Bakersfield, Home Preview and Camera Ads Publs. Rec. artist, Capitol Records, 1958-76, 88—, Warner Bros. Records 1976-80; star syndicated TV shows Buck Owens Ranch Show; leader, Buck Owens' Buckaroos Band, 1960—; star of TV show Hee Haw, 1969-86. Records include Under Your Spell Again, Above and Beyond, Excuse Me, I Think I've Got a Heartache, Fooling Around, Under the Influence of Love, My Heart Skips a Beat, Act Naturally, Waitin' in the Welfare Line, Sam's Place, How Long Will My Baby Be Gone, Tall Dark Stranger, Too Old to Cut the Mustard, Rollin' in My Sweet Baby's Arms, The Kansas City Song, We're Gonna Get Together, albums include All Time Greatest Hits Vol. 1, 1990, vol. 2, 1992, vol. 3, 1993, The Buck Owens Collection (1959-90), 92; others. Recipient Instrumental Group of Year award Country Music Assn., 1967-68; named Artist of Decade Capitol Records, Country Artist of Year for 5 consecutive years Billboard, Cash Box and Record World; awarded 28 consecutive No. 1 records. Office: Buck Owens Prodns 3223 Sillect Ave Bakersfield CA 93308*

OWENS, CHARLES VINCENT, JR., diagnostic company executive and consultant; b. Kansas City, Mo., May 15, 1927; s. Charles Vincent and Helen (Barrett) O.; m. Cheryl Kreighbaum, Feb. 12, 1955; children: Melody, Kevin, Michael, John, Barbara. B.S., U. Notre Dame, 1948; M.S. (Univ. fellow), U. N.C., 1949. Public health educator Richmond County (N.C.) Health Dept., 1949-51; with Miles Labs., Inc., Elkhart, Ind., 1951-82; pres. Ames Co. div. Miles Labs., Inc., 1967-71, group v.p. profl. products group, 1971-77, exec. v.p. internat. ops., 1977-82; chmn., chief exec. officer Kyoto Diagnostics, Inc., 1983-85; bd. dirs. Genesis Labs., Inc., St. Jude Med. Inc., Chronimed Inc.; chief exec. officer Genesis Inc., 1985-88, chmn., 1988—. Bd. dirs. Elkhart YWCA, 1972-76; vice chmn. Elkhart County Bd. Health, 1973-77; chmn. Child Abuse Task Force, Elkhart County, Ind., 1977-78. Served with M.C., USAAF, 1945-47. Mem. Am. Public Health Assn. Health Industry Mfg. Assn. (dir.), Pharm. Mfrs. Assn., Nat. Pharm. Council (pres. 1970-71, dir. 1965-73), Am. Mgmt. Assn., Am. Diabetes Assn., Am. Assn. Diabetes Educators, Internat. Diabetes Fedn., Am. Soc. Med. Tech. Republican. Roman Catholic.

OWENS, DONALD D., church officer; m. Adeline Owens; children: Donna Bean, Debbi Bohi, Darlene Conyers. MA in Religion, Bethany Nazarene Coll.; MA and PhD in Cultural Anthropology, U. Okla. Established Ch. of

the Nazarene, Korea, 1954-66; tchr. Nazarene Theol. Sem., Kansas City, Mo., 1975-81, Bethany (Okla.) Nazarene Coll., 1966-74; founding pres. Asia Pacific Nazarene Theol. Sem., Manila, 1981-84; regional dir. Asia Pacific World Mission Divsn., Manila, 1981-85; pres. MidAm. Nazarene Coll., Olathe, 1985—; mem. bd. gen. supnts. Ch. of the Nazarene, Indpls., 1989—; founder Korea Nazarene Theol. Coll. Author: Challenge in Korea, Church Behind the Bamboo Curtain, Revival Fires in Korea, Sing Ye Islands. Office: Church of Nazarene 6401 The Paseo Kansas City MO 64131

OWENS, FREDRIC NEWELL, animal nutritionist, educator; b. Baldwin, Wis., Sept. 1, 1941; s. Fred Newell and Stella Elvera (Jorstad) O.; m. Christa F. Hanson, Dec. 1983; children: Gwen, Eric, Crystal. Student, Wis. State U., River Falls, 1959-61; B.S., U. Minn., 1964, Ph.D., 1968. Asst. prof. animal sci. U. Ill., Urbana, 1968-74; prof. animal sci. Okla. State U., Stillwater, 1974-86, Regents prof., 1986-90, Regents prof., Sarkeys Disting. prof., 1990—; lectr. Sigma Xi, 1990, numerous other invted lectures; mem. com. on animal nutrition NRC, 1985-88. Contbr. chpts. to 13 books, more than 180 articles to profl. jours.; sect. editor Jour. Animal Sci., 1975-78, editor-in-chief, 1987-90. Recipient Tyler award Okla. State U., 1980, Am. Feed Industry Nutrition Rsch. award, 1986, Elmo Baumann Prof. award Okla. State U., 1990; NSF fellow, 1966-68. Mem. Am. Soc. Animal Soc. (pres. 1992), Am. Inst. Nutrition, Am. Dairy Sci. Assns., Nutrition Soc. Lutheran. Home: RR 5 Box 507 Stillwater OK 74074-9340 Office: Okla State U 208 Animal Science Bldg Stillwater OK 74078

OWENS, GARLAND CHESTER, accounting educator; b. Wilson, N.C., Dec. 12, 1922; s. James F. and Leona (Owens) O.; m. Mary Elizabeth Wade, June 19, 1948; 1 dau., Lynn Carol. B.S., U. Richmond, 1947; M.S., Columbia U., 1948, Ph.D., 1956. C.P.A., N.Y. State. Acct. Arthur Young & Co. (C.P.A.s), N.Y., 1950-53; mem. faculty Columbia Grad. Sch. Bus., N.Y.C., 1956-86; prof. Columbia Grad. Sch. Bus., 1964-86, assoc. dean, 1962-70; prof. Mercer U. Sch. Bus., 1986-93; program dir. Mgmt. Devel. Center, Belo Horizonte Minas Gerais, Brazil, 1973-75; Controller Arctic Inst. N.Am., 1957-77. Author: Cost Basis in Business Combinations, 1956, (with James A. Cashin) Auditing, 1963; current reading editor: Jour. Accountancy. Mem. bd. edn. Union Free Sch. Dist. 5, Greenburgh, N.Y., 1964-69, v.p. 1965-68, pres., 1968-69; mem. N.E. Regional Postmaster Selection Bd., U.S. Postal Service, 1969-75. Served to capt. USAAF, 1942-45. Decorated D.F.C., Air medal. Mem. Am. Inst. C.P.A.s, N.Y. State Soc. C.P.A.s, Ga. State Soc. C.P.A.'s, Am. Acctg. Assn., Beta Gamma Sigma. Methodist. Home: 4923B Rivoli Dr Macon GA 31210-4139 Office: Mercer U Sch Bus and Econs 1400 Coleman Ave Macon GA 31207-0003

OWENS, GARY, broadcast personality, entrepreneur, author; b. Mitchell, S.D., May 10; s. Bernard and Vennetta O.; m. Arleta Lee Markell, June 26; children: Scott, Christopher. Student (speech and psychology scholar), Dakota Wesleyan U., Mitchell; student, Mpls. Art Inst. With Sta. KMPC, L.A., 1962-82; with Sta. KPRZ, L.A., 1982—, Sta KFI, L.A., 1986-90; pres. Foonman & Sons, Inc., 1987—; v.p., creative dir. GoldenWest Broadcasters, 1981-82; v.p., nat. creative dir. Gannett Broadcasting, 1984; TV performer, 1963—. writer Jay Ward Prodns., 1961-62; syndicated radio show The G.O. Spl. Report, from 1969; host: world-wide syndicated show Soundtrack of the 60's, 1981—, Biff Owens Sports Exclusive, 1981—; USA Today, Mut. Broadcasting System, 1982-83; radio host Gary Owens Music Weekend, Lorimar Telepictures, 1987—; performer, writer: world-wide syndicated show Sesame St, 1969—, Electric Co, 1969—, Dirkniblick (Mathnet) CTW, 1988; performer over 2500 animated cartoons including Dyno-Mutt, ABC-TV, 1975, Roger Ramjet, 1965, Space Ghost, 1968, Perils of Penelope Pitstop, 1970, Square One, 1987, Godzilla's Power Hour, 1979, Space Heroes, 1981, Mighty Orbots, 1984, World's Greatest Adventures, 1986, Garfield, Cops, Bobby's World, 1990, The 3 Musketeers, Return of Roger Ramjet, Alice in Wonderland, The Count of Monte Cristo, 20,000 Leagues Under the Sea, Godzilla, Mickey Mouse, Donald Duck, Goofy Chip N'Dale, Bill & Ted's Great Adventure, Tom & Jerry Jr., Eek the Cat, Swat Kats, Two Stupid Dogs, Ren & Stimpy, Bonkers, Dirk Niblick, numerous others, 1990; appeared: in films The Love Bug, 1968, Prisoner of Second Ave., 1975, Hysterical, 1982, Nat. Lampoon's European Vacation, 1985, I'm Gonna Get You Sucka, 1988, Kill Crazy, 1988, How I Got Into College, 1988, Say Bye Bye, 1989, Green Hornet, 1966 Regular on series; performer on camera more than 1000 nat. TV shows; performer: Rowan and Martin's Laugh-in, 1968-73; TV host: Gong Show, ABC-TV, 1976, Monty Pythons Flying Circus, 1975; regular performer: TV Games People Play, 1980-81, Breakaway, 1983; TV spls. include Bob Hope Spls., Like Hep, The Muppets Go Hollywood, Perry Como Visits Hollywood, The Gary Owens All-Nonsense News Network, Jonathan Winters & Friends, NBC's 50 Years, CBS's 50 Years, Battle of Beverly Hills, America's Choice. The American Comedy Awards, 1986—, Flip Wilson's Spls., Saturday Night at the Superbowl, Mickey Mouse's 50th Birthday; author: Elephants, Grapes and Pickles, 1963; 12 printings The Gary Owens What To Do While You're Holding the Phone Book, revised edit., 1973, A Gary Owens Chrestomathy, 1980; host Encore Pay TV, 1992; author: (screenplay) Three Caraway Seeds and an Agent's Heart, 1979; columnist: Radio and Records newspaper, 1978—, Hollywood Citizen-News, 1965-67, Hollywood mag., 1983—, The Daily News, 1981—; rec. artist MGM, ABC, Epic, Warner Bros., RCA, Reprise, Decca; TV announcer NBC, 1968-80, ABC, 1980—; host many top video's in U.S. including Dinosaurs, More Dinosaurs, Son of Dinosaurs, TV's Greatest Bits; host: How to Collect Comic Books, Aliens, Dragons, Monsters and Me, Gone Fishing, 1993, The Gary Owens All-Nonsense News Network. Chmn. Multiple Sclerosis dr. L.A., 1972; chmn., grand marshall So. Calif. Diabetes Dr. 1974—; mayor City of Encino, Calif., 1972-74; bd. govs. Grammy Awards, 1968—, Emmy Awards, 1972; mem. adv. bd. Pasadena (Calif.) City Coll., 1969—, Sugar Ray Robinson Youth Found., 1971—; mem. nat. miracle com. Juvenile Diabetes Found., 1981—; nat. com. for Carousel Ball Children's Diabetes Found. Denver; radio adv. bd. U. So. Calif., 1980—; hon. chmn. Goodwill Industries Sporting Goods Dr., 1986, chmn., 1986; active telethons Cerebral Palsy, 1980, DARE program, 1985—, S.A.N.E. program, 1985—, comic relief to help U.S. Homeless, 1986. Named outstanding radio personality in U.S., 1965-79, top Radio Personality in World, Internat. Radio Forum, Toronto, 1977, Man of Yr. All-Cities Employees Assn., City of Los Angeles, 1968, Top RadAssn. Broadcasters, 1986, Radio Man of Yr. Nat. Assn. Broadcasters, 1986; recipient Distinguished Service award Hollywood Jaycees, 1966, David award, 1978, Hollywood Hall of Fame award, 1980, Am. award Cypress Coll., 1981, Carbon Mike award Pacific Broadcasters, 1987, 5 Grammy nominations, Emmy award for More Dinosaurs, 1986; Star on Hollywood Walk of Fame, 1981; honored by U.S. Dept. Treasury, 1985, Am. Diabetes Assn., 1990, Variety Clubs Internat., 1990; inducted into Nat. Broadcasters Hall of Fame, 1994, Radio Hall of Fame, 1994, Nat. Assn. Broadcasters Hall of Fame, 1995. Mem. Nat. Cartoonists Soc., So. Calif. Cartoonists Assn., Cartoonists and Artists Profl. Soc. Office: 2444 Wilshire Blvd Ste 506 Santa Monica CA 90403-5893 *Without sounding like a coffee break Voltaire, the apothegm that "Everyman is his own Pygmalion" may be correct. I have tried to enrich my life by performing, reading, writing, creating, and helping others whenever possible. I try to stand up for what I believe, for it is better to give ulcers than to receive! Humor has helped protect me from the bruises of life, in addition to a daily supply of fantasy and illusion.*

OWENS, GARY STEVEN, architect; b. Mansfield, Ohio, May 25, 1953; s. Everett Edward and Verniece Lucille (Anderson) O.; m. Luana Marie Jones, Aug. 18, 1991; children: Lauren A., Camille V., Caitlin L. B in Environ. Design, Tex. A & M U., 1975, MArch, 1976. Registered architect, Tex.; registered interior designer, Tex. Staff architect 3D/Internat., Houston, 1977; project design architect Koether, Tharp, Cowell, Houston, 1977-80, Lockwood, Andrews, Newnam, Houston, 1980-83; sr. design architect Page, Southerland, Page, Houston, 1984-89; assoc. Falick/Klein Partnership, Houston, 1983-84, sr. project designer, 1989—. Prin. works include Ambulatory Care Facility St. Joseph's Hosp., Orange, Calif., Laureat Psychiatric Hosp., Tulsa, Outpatient Facility and Office Bldg. S.E. Bapt. Hosp., San Antonio, Stafford (Tex.) Meadows Hosp., Psychiatric Facility Huntington Meml. Hosp., Pasadena, Calif., Children's Hosp., Galveston, Tex. (1st Place Interior Design award Am. Soc. Interior Designers 1993). Mem. Walnut Bend PTO, Houston, 1992—. Mem. AIA (com. health care design 1990—, Houston chpt.), Tex. Soc. Architects, Former Students Assn. Tex. A & M U., Willowisp Country Club, Men's Golf Assn. Office: The Falick/Klein Partnership Inc 8 E Greenway Plz Ste 300 Houston TX 77046-0801

OWENS, GREGORY RANDOLPH, physician, medical educator; b. Glendale, W. Va., Oct. 3, 1948; s. Elmer Herman and Anne Elizabeth (Kroggel) O.; m. Jane Marie Fleming, June 1, 1974; children: Gregory R. Jr., Allison Fleming. AB cum laude, Princeton U., 1970; MD, U. Pa., 1974. Diplomate Am. Bd. Internal Medicine, Am. Bd. Pulmonary Medicine, Am. Bd. Critical Care Medicine. Intern in internal medicine Hosp. U. Pa., Phila., 1974-75, residency in internal medicine, 1975-77, fellowship pulmonary disease, 1977-78, chief med. resident, 1978-79, fellowship pulmonary disease, 1979-80; asst. prof. medicine U. Pitts., 1980-86, assoc. prof. medicine, 1986-93, prof. medicine, 1993—, assoc. chief div. pulmonary medicine, 1984—; chief Montefiore U. Hosp., Pitts, 1991—; dir. Pulmonary Exercise Physiology Lab., Presbyn.-Univ. Hosp., Pitts, 1980—, co-dir. Pulmonary Function Lab., 1980—; co-dir. Occupational Lung Clinic, Falk Clinic, Pitts., 1983—. Contbr. articles to New Eng. Jour. Medicine, Am. Jour. Medicine, Jour. Lab. Clin. Medicine and others, presenter at profl. confs. Coach Oakmont (Pa.) Athletic Assn., 1988—, bd. dirs. Am. Lung Assn. Named awardee Future Leaders of Pulmonary Medicine, Chgo., 1984, Preventive Pulmonary Acad. award NIH, 1988-93; grantee Health Rsch. and Svc. Found., 1980-82, 83-85, NIH Lung Health Study P.I., 1984-89, 87-94, NIH Lung Health Study II P.I., 1994—. Mem. ACP, Am. Coll. Chest Physicians (Pa. gov. 1993—), Am. Thoracic Soc., Am. Fedn. for Clin. Rsch., Pa. Thoracic Soc. (pres. 1993-96). Avocations: golfing, gardening. Office: U Pitts Sch Medicine 1117 Kaufman Bldg 3471 5th Ave Pittsburgh PA 15213-3221

OWENS, HILDA FAYE, management/leadership development consultant, human resource trainer; b. Fountain, N.C., Mar. 23, 1939; d. Floyd Curtis and Essie Lee (Gay) O. BS in Edn. and Psychology, East Carolina U., 1961, MA in Edn., 1965; PhD in Higher Edn., Fla. State U., 1973; postgrad., Western Carolina U., 1962, U. Louisville, 1967, U. N.C., 1968. Tchr. New Bern (N.C.) City Schs., 1961-65; dir. counseling svcs., prof. Mt. Olive (N.C.) Coll., 1965-71, dean students, prof., 1973-77; coord. student affairs, rsch. assoc. bd. regents State Univ. System Fla., Tallahassee, 1971-73; assoc. prof. higher edn. U. S.C., Columbia, 1977-83; v.p. acad. affairs, prof. Spartanburg (S.C.) Meth. Coll., 1985-90; exec. asst. to pres. for planning and rsch., cons. Spartanburg (S.C.) Meth. Coll., 1990-91; pres. Excel Resource Assocs., Spartanburg, 1991—; mem. bd. dirs. The Haven; numerous presentations in field; speaker bus., ednl., civic and ch. meetings, confs. and workshops. Editor: Risk Management and the Student Affairs Professional, 1984, (with Witten and Bailey) College Student Personnel Administration: An Anthology, 1982; mem. editorial bd. Jour. sTaff, Orgn. and Program Devel., Assn. Student Pers. Adminstrs. Jour., Nat. Assn. Student Pers. Adminstrs. Monograph Bd., Coll. Student Affairs Jour.; contbr. articles to profl. jours.; chpts. to books. Grad. Leadership Spartanburg, 1987; adminstrv. bd. Bethel United Meth. Ch.; mem. exec. bd. Tuscarora coun. Boy Scouts Am. Honored by Seymour Johnson AFB, 1976; S.C. Coll. Pers. Assn. named Rsch. and Writing award in her honor, 1995; named One of 45 Outstanding S.C. Women, 1980, Disting. Grad. award Fla. State U., 1981, Outstanding Bus. and Profl. Woman of Yr. Spartanburg Bus. and Profl. Women, 1986, Capital Bus. and Profl. Women, 1982, Mt. Olive Bus. and Profl. Women, 1977; recipient Meritorious Svc. award S.C. Coll. Pers. Assn., 1990. Mem. AMA, ASTD, NAFE, Nat. Assn. Student Pers. Adminstrs. (adv. bd. region III, Disting. Svc. award), Am. Assn. Higher Edn., Carolinas Soc. Tng. and Devel., S.C. Coll. Pers. Assn. (pres.), bus. and Profl. Women U.S., Bus. and Profl. Women S.C. (pres., bd. dirs. Ednl. Found.), Internat. Platform Assn., Rotary Internat., Spartan West Rotary (bd. dirs.), Delta Kappa Gamma, Phi Delta Kappa (Greenville/Spartanburg chpt., pres. U.S.C. chpt.). Democrat. Avocations: coin collecting, golf, movies, basketball, reading. Home: 230 Old Towne Rd Spartanburg SC 29301-3555 Office: Excel Resource Assocs PO Box 17248 Spartanburg SC 29301-0103

OWENS, JACK BYRON, lawyer; b. Orange, Calif., Oct. 14, 1944; s. Jack Byron and Lenna Mildred (Gobar) O.; children: John Byron, David Harold, James Paul, Alexandra Grace. A.B., Stanford U., 1966, J.D., 1969. Bar: Calif. 1970, D.C. 1970. Law clk. U.S. Ct. Appeals 9th Circuit, 1969-70; asso. firm Wilmer, Cutler & Pickering, Washington, 1970-71, 74-75; atty. adv. Dept. Air Force, 1971-73; law clk. U.S. Supreme Ct., 1973-74; prof. law Boalt Law Sch., U. Calif., Berkeley, 1975-79; partner firm Orrick, Herrington & Sutcliffe, San Francisco, 1978-81; exec. v.p., gen. counsel E & J Gallo Winery, 1981—; adj. prof. Georgetown U. Law Sch. Contbr. articles legal publns. Served with USAF, 1971-73. Mem. Am. Law Inst., Am. Bar Assn., Phi Beta Kappa, Order of Coif. Office: E & J Gallo Winery PO Box 1130 600 Yosemite Blvd Modesto CA 95353

OWENS, JOHN MURRY, dean; b. Livermore, Calif., Feb. 13, 1942; s. John Stephen and Hazel Mae (Murry) O.; m. Diane Davis, June 12, 1971; children: John, Jennifer, Mark. AA, Orange Coast Coll., 1961; BSEE, U. Calif., Berkeley, 1963; MSEE, Stanford U., 1964, PhD, 1968. Registered profl. engr., Tex. Prof. elec. engring. U. Tex., Arlington, 1979-87, dir. bur. engring., 1983-85, asst. dean rsch. coll. engring., 1983-85, dir. ctr. for advanced electron devices, 1984-87; prof., chmn. elec. engring. dept Santa Clara (Calif.) U., 1987-89; program dir. NSF, Washington, 1989-91; prof. dir. engring. exptl. sta., assoc. dean for rsch. Auburn (Ala.) U., 1991—; cons. Microwave and Electronic Systems Ltd., Edinburgh, United Kingdom, Ivory and Sime Ltd., Edinburgh, Herbies Foods, Fort Worth, Tex. Instruments, Dallas, Rockwell Internat., Anaheim, Calif., Westinghouse Electric, Pitts., E.W. Communication Inc., Palo Alto, Calif., Telsar, Inc., Campbell, Calif., ITT Aerospace and Optical, Ft. Wayne, Ind., SMA, Inc., Florence, Italy, many others. Patentee in field. Bd. dirs Arlington Swim Club; dist. chmn. boy Scouts Am., Auburn; bd. dirs. Arlington Gifted and Talented Assn.; pres. Masters of Upper Tex. Swimmers. Fellow IEEE; mem. Am. Soc. Engring. Edn., Kiwanis (bd. dirs. Arlington club), Tau Beta Pi, Eta Kappa Nu, Sigma Xi. Avocations: swimming, water skiing, camping, hiking, airplanes. Office: Auburn U 108 Ramsay Hall Auburn AL 36849

OWENS, JOSEPH, clergyman; b. Saint John, N.B., Can., Apr. 17, 1908; s. Louis Michael and Josephine (Quinn) O. Student, St. Mary's Coll., 1922-27, St. Anne's Coll., Montreal, Que. Can., 1928-30, St. Alphonsus Coll., Woodstock, Ont., Can. 1930-34; M.S.D., Pontifical Inst. Mediaeval Studies, Toronto, 1951. Ordained priest Roman Cath. Ch., 1933; parish asst. St. Joseph's Ch., Moose Jaw, Sask., Can. 1934-35, St. Patrick's Ch., Toronto, 1935-36, Maria-Hilf Ch., Tomslake, B.C., Can., 1940-44; instr. philosophy St. Alphonsus Sem., Woodstock, Ont., Can., 1936-40, 48-51, 53, Assumption U., Windsor, Ont., Can., 1954; with Pontifical Inst. of Mediaeval Studies, Toronto, 1954—; prof. Pontifical Inst. of Mediaeval Studies, 1960—; instr. mediaeval moral doctrine Accademia Alfonsiana, Rome, Italy, 1952-53; mem. faculty dept. philosophy Sch. Grad. Studies, U. Toronto. Mem. editorial bd.: The Monist, 1961—; Contbr. numerous articles to religious and profl. jours. Mem. Canadian Philos. Assn. (pres. 1981-82), Am. Catholic Philos. Assn. (pres. 1965-66), Metaphys. Soc. Am. (councillor 1965-67, pres. 1971-72), Soc. Ancient Greek Philosophy (pres. 1971-72), Catholic Commn. Intellectual and Cultural Affairs, Royal Soc. Can. Home: 141 McCaul St, Toronto, ON Canada M5T 1W3 Office: 59 Queen's Park Crescent, Toronto, ON Canada M5S 2C4

OWENS, LEWIS E., newspaper executive; b. Knoxville, Tenn., Mar. 11, 1934; m. Janetta Owens. B.S., Gainesville Coll. Retail advt. salesman Fort Worth Press, 1956-59; advt. dir. Gainesville Daily Register, 1959-62; asst. retail advt. mgr. Charlotte Observer and News, N.C., 1962-66; retail advt. mgr. Tallahassee Democrat, Fla., 1966-68, Charlotte Observer and News, 1968-75; advt. dir. Lexington Herald-Leader, Ky., 1975-78, v.p. sales and mktg., 1978-82, then v.p. and gen. mgr., now pres., pub. Soc. bd. dirs. Lexington Arts Council; v.p. Central Ky. Blood Ctr.; pres. United Way of the Bluegrass, 1978, 79, campaign chmn., 1977. Mem. Greater Lexington Area C. of C. (pres.-elect), Ky. Press Assn. (v.p.). Avocations: golf; racquetball; travel; sports. Office: Lexington Herald-Leader Co 100 Midland Ave Lexington KY 40508-1999*

OWENS, LUVIE MOORE, association executive; b. Cleve., July 26, 1933; d. Dan Tyler and Elizabeth (Oakes) Moore; m. Lloyd H. Owens, Jan. 1, 1955; children: Luvie Owens Myers, Elizabeth, Lloyd H. Student, Smith Coll., Northampton, Mass., 1956. Tchr. Howard Jr. High Sch., Wilmette, Ill., 1971-75; U.S. ops. mgr. Frank T. Ross & Co., Evanston, Ill., 1976-86; dir. Internat. Platform Assn., Winnetka, Ill., 1972—, chief exec. officer, 1986—. Treas., mem. jr. coun. Cleve. Mus. Art, 1964-65; commr. Police and Fire Commn., Winnetka, 1980-86; chmn. bd. Lake Shore Unitarian Ch., Winnetka, 1986-87; mem. alumnae bd. Madeira Sch., Greenway, Va., 1984-88.

Mem. Jr. League Club (Chgo.), Rotary. Office: Internat Platform Assn PO Box 250 Winnetka IL 60093-0250

OWENS, MAJOR ROBERT ODELL, congressman; b. Memphis, June 28, 1936; m. Marie Cuprill; children: Christopher, Geoffrey, Millard, Carlos, Cecilia. Grad. with high honors, Morehouse Coll., 1956; M.S., Atlanta U., 1957. Mem. Internat. Commn. on Ways of Implementing Social Policy to Ensure Maximum Pub. Participation and Social Justice for Minorities, The Hague, Netherlands, 1978; 98th-104th Congresses from 12th (now 11th) N.Y. dist., 1983—; chmn. select edn. & civil rights subcom., edn. and labor com., 1987, ranking minority mem. econ. and ednl. opportunity subcom. on worker protections, mem. govt. reform and oversight com.; featured speaker White House Conf. on Librs., 1979. Pub. author and lectr. on library sci. Chmn. Bklyn. Congress Racial Equality; v.p. Met. Coun. on Housing, 1964; community coord. Bklyn. Pub. Library, 1964-66; exec. dir. Brownsville Community Coun., 1966-68; commr. N.Y.C. Community Devel. Agy., 1968-73; bd. dirs. community media program Columbia U., N.Y.C., 1973-75; mem. N.Y. State Senate, 1975-82, chmn. Dem. Ops. Com. Major R. Owens Day, named in his honor, City Bklyn., 1971. Office: US Ho of Reps 2305 Rayburn HOB Washington DC 20515-2311

OWENS, MARILYN MAE, art educator; b. Poland, Ohio, Nov. 17, 1932; d. S. Reed and Vernice Mae (Flickinger) Johnson; m. J. Edward Owens, July 23, 1953; children: Charlene, Preston, Lorraine. BS in Art Edn., Millersville State U., 1970, elem. cert., 1983; MEd in Art, Towson U., 1975; elem. prin. cert., Western Md. U., 1984. Cert. elem. and secondary tchr. art, elem. tchr., Pa.: art supr. elem. and secondry, prin. elem., Md. Tchr art. k-12 Northeastern Sch. Dist., Manchester, Pa., 1970—; adj. instr. humanities, art appreciation York Coll. of Pa., 1977-81; mem. long range planning com., Northeastern Sch. Dist., Manchester, 1988-90, supt.'s adv. bd., 1990-91, elem. adv. bd. Orendorf Sch., 1990-92, dist. budget com., 1991-92, elem. budget com. Conewago Elem. Sch., 1993-94, 94-95, computer tech. elem. com., 1993-94, 94-95, instrnl. and profl. devel. com., 1994-95; calligraphy tchr. Northeastern Adult Comty. Edn., 1988-90. Leader Girl Scouts of U.S., Penn Laurel, York, Pa., 1963-67; mem. Northeastern Art Out-Reach program, Northeastern Edn. Assn. Comty. Rels. Com., Northeastern Sch. Dist.'s Portfolio Com. Recipient scholarship Ind. (Pa.) State Coll., 1950; grantee Northeastern Sch. Dist., Manchester, 1989-90. Mem. AAUW, Nat. Art Edn. Assn., Northeastern Edn. Assn. (v.p. 1987-88, pres. 1988-89, community rels. program 1993-95), Pa. Art Edn. Assn., Pa. Guild of Craftsmen (Yorktowne chpt.), Pa. Inst. CPA (Women's Aux. S. Ctrl. chpt.), York Art Assn., Phi Delta Kappa (scholarship com. 1990-94). Avocations: painting, crafts, hiking, camping, sewing. Home: 2505 Schoolhouse Ln York PA 17402-3918 Office: Northeastern Sch Dist 48 Harding St Manchester PA 17345-1100

OWENS, MARVIN FRANKLIN, JR., oil company executive; b. Oklahoma City, Feb. 20, 1916; s. Marvin Franklin and Levis (Coley) O.; m. Jessie Ruth Hay, June 15, 1941; children: Marvin Franklin III, William Earl, Jack Hay. B.S., U. Okla., 1937; postgrad., Stonier Grad. Sch. Banking Rutgers U., 1960-62. Petroleum engr. Brit. Am. Oil Producing Co., Oklahoma City, 1937-41; chief petroleum engr. Bay Petroleum Corp., Denver, 1946-54; sr. v.p. Cen. Bank of Denver, 1954-81; now mng. ptnr. Allison Owens Resources, Denver. Elder Presbyn. Ch., Denver. With U.S. Army, 1941-46; col. Res. ret. Mem. Cherry Hills Country Club. Home: 3899 S Glencoe St Denver CO 80237-1024 Office: Allison Owens Resources 1275 Sherman St Denver CO 80203-2212

OWENS, MARY JO, electronic guidance services company executive; b. Asheville, N.C., Nov. 26, 1936; d. William James and Mamie Laura (Simms) O.; children: Lolita Omaria, Ionita. BS, N.C. State U., 1963; MS in Edn., Iona Coll., 1973; DLitt, Knightsbridge U., Copenhagen, 1995; PhD (hon.), World Acad., Germany, England, 1995, Australian Inst. Coord. Rsch., 1995, London Inst. Applied Rsch., 1995. Prof. English N.C. State U., Greensboro, 1961-62, prof. French, 1962-63; instr. French Phillips Sr. High Sch., Battleboro, N.C., 1963-64, Farmville (N.C.) Sr. High Sch., 1964-65; instr. French, English Jordan Sellars Sr. High Sch., Burlington, N.C., 1965-66; program coord. Project Aware, Fed. Grant Program, Greensboro, 1966-67; instr. French, English Westchester County Schs., Mt. Vernon, N.Y., 1967-88; instr. Spanish evening sch. Bedford Park Acad., Bronx, N.Y., 1976-79; realty broker, owner M.J. Howell and Co. Inc., Stanfordville, N.Y., 1982—; founder, owner Electronic Guidance Svcs. Corp., Hunns Lake, N.Y., 1988—. Author: An No Clouds Over My Sun, 1973 (Demale Writers award 1975), Native American Images and Resipes, 1991, Through the Glass, Clearly a Character Study of the "Half-Breed" in America, 1992. Founder Children of Profls. Orgn., Westchester County, N.Y., 1991—; pres. New Rochelle (N.Y.) Assn. Women Voters, 1981-89. Recipient Ludwig von Beethoven Medal of Honor, 1995, Albert Einstein Medal of Honor, 1995, Henri Dunant Medal of Honor, 1995; am. Sch. Honors scholar, 1959; City of Mt. Vernon grantee, 1982-84. Mem. Internat. Culture Club (pres. 1982—), N.Y. Profl. Women (pres. 1990-92), N.Y. State Tchrs. Fedn., N.Y. State Retired Tchrs. Assn., Westchester County Minority Bus. Assn. (pres. 1982—), Westchester County Minority Real Estate Bd. (bd. dirs. 1982—), Cherokee Child Orgn. (chmn. 1988-92, Native Am. Visionary award 1992, Inner Man award 1991). Avocations: writing, drama, art, piano, voice. Home: PO Box 310 Hunns Lake NY 12581 Office: Electronic Guidance Svcs PO Box 27 Stanfordville NY 12581

OWENS, MICHAEL, camera graphics expert, executive. Student fil prodn., history, criticism. Freelance editor, prodn. mgr., asst. cameraman, gaffer, grip L.A. area, 1975-81; asst. cameraman, effects cameraman Indsl. Light & Magic, San Rafael, Calif., 1981—; freelance photography dir. 1981—. Asst. cameraman (films) ET: The Extraterrestrial, 1982, Star Trek II: The Wrath of Kahn, 1982; effects cameraman (films) Return of the Jedi, 1983, Indiana Jones and the Temple of Doom, 1984, Young Sherlock Holmes, 1985, Witches of Eastwick, 1987 (Brit. Acad. award); visual effects supr. The Burbs, 1989, Skin Deep, 1989, Switch, 1990, The Doors, 1990; dir. Robin Williams trailer for Mill Valley Film Festival. Office: Indsl Light & Magic PO Box 2459 San Rafael CA 94912-2459

OWENS, ROCHELLE, poet, playwright; b. Bklyn., Apr. 2, 1936; d. Max and Molly (Adler) Bass; m. George Economou, June 17, 1962. Fellow, Yale Sch. Drama, 1968. writer-in-residence, Brown U., 1989; tchr. U. Calif. 1982, U. Okla., 1985, 87, 88. Author: plays The String Game, 1965, Istanboul, 1965, Futz, 1967, Homo, 1966, Beclch, 1966, Futz and What Came After, 1968, He Wants Shih, 1969, Farmers Almanac, 1969, The Queen of Greece, 1969, Kontraption, 1970, The Karl Marx Play, 1971, O.K. Certaldo, 1975, Emma Instigated Me, 1976, The Widow and the Colonel, 1977, Mountain Rites, 1977, Who Do You Want, Peire Vidal, 1978, Chucky's Hunch, 1981, Who Do You Want, Peire Vidal, 1982; poetry Not be Essence That Cannot Be, 1961, Salt and Core, 1968, I am the Babe of Joseph Stalin's Daughter, Poems from Joe's Garage, The Joe 82 Creation Poems, The Karl Marx Play & Others, The Joe Chronicles, Part 2, Four Young Lady Poets, 1962, Shemuel, 1979, French Light, 1984, Constructs, 1985, Anthropologists at a Dinner Party, 1985, Who Do You Want Peire Vidal, 1986, W.C. Fields in French Light, 1986, How Much Paint Does the Painting Need, 1988, Selected Poems: 1961-1994, Black Chalk, 1992, Rubbed Stones: Poems from 1960-1992, 1994; (radio play) Sweet Potatoes, 1979 (Obie award 1982); (feature film) Futz, 1969; editor: (plays) Spontaneous Combustion; (Obie award 1967), Cimmarron Rev.; recs. include: From a Shaman's Notebook, 1968, The Karl Marx Play, 1974, Totally Corrupt, 1976, Black Box 17, 1979, (play) Three Front, 1990; (radio play) A Guerre Trois, 1991; reading performances at St. Mark's Poetry Project, Mus. Modern Art, Guggenheim, Whitney Mus., Oxford U., Am. Coll., Paris; host of The Writer's Mind; producer radio show, U. Okla.; (video) Oklahoma Too, 1987, How Much Paint Does The Painting Need, 1992; translator Festival Franco-Anglais, 1991, The Passersby, 1993; (video) Black Chalk, 1994. Founding mem. N.Y. Theatre Strategy, Women's Theatre Council. Ford Found. grantee, 1965; Guggenheim fellow, 1971; Creative Arts Pub. Svc. grantee, 1973; Nat. Endowment for Arts grantee, 1974; Rockfeller Found. grantee, 1974; honors N.Y. Drama Critics Circle; Rockefeller Found. Bellagio resident, 1993. Mem. Dramatists Guild, ASCAP. Included in anthologies. Address: 1401 Magnolia St Norman OK 73072-6827 *Creativity, idealism and mental concentration have enabled me to pursue the world of ideas, transforming itself always into art.*

OWENS, STEPHEN THOMAS, lawyer; b. San Jose, Calif., Aug. 2, 1948; s. Thomas Cunnane and Patricia Ann (Howie) O.; m. Joyce Barbara, June 15, 1970 (div. Dec. 1972); 1 child, Eric Albert; m. Janet Lynn Gattuccio, Aug. 28, 1977; 1 child, Monica Lisa Cali. Diplôme des Etudes Franç, Université de Provence, Aix-en-Provence, France, 1973; BA, San Jose State U., 1974; JD, UCLA, 1978. Bar: Calif. 1978, U.S. Ct. Appeals (9th cir.) 1980, U.S. Dist. Ct. (no, cen., ea. & so. dists.) Calif., U.S. Dist. Ct. (ea. dist.) Ark. Assoc. Graham & James, L.A., 1978-84, ptnr., 1985—. Vol. atty. Pub. Counsel, L.A., 1990—, bd. dirs., 1992—. Recipient Pro Bono Svc. award State Bar of Calif., 1992, John Minor Wisdom Profl. and Pub. Svc. award ABA, 1993. Avocations: sailing, skiing, sea kayaking. Office: Graham & James 801 S Figueroa St Fl 14 Los Angeles CA 90017-2573

OWENS, WILBUR DAWSON, JR., federal judge; b. Albany, Ga., Feb. 1, 1930; s. Wilbur Dawson and Estelle (McKenzie) O.; m. Mary Elizabeth Glenn, June 21, 1958; children: Lindsey, Wilbur Dawson III, Estelle, John. Student, Emory U., 1947-48; JD, U. Ga., 1952. Bar: Ga. 1952. Mem. firm Smith, Gardner & Owens, Albany, 1954-55; v.p., trust officer Bank of Albany, 1955-59; sec.-treas. Southeastern Mortgage Co., Albany, 1959-65; asst. U.S. atty. Middle Dist. Ga., Macon, 1962-64; assoc., then ptnr. Bloch, Hall, Hawkins & Owens, Macon, 1965-72; judge U.S. Dist. Ct. for Mid. Dist. Ga., Macon, 1972—, now sr. U.S. dist. judge. Served to 1st lt., JAG USAF, 1952-54. Mem. State Bar Ga., Assn. Trial Lawyers Am., Macon Bar Assn., Am. Judicature Soc., Phi Delta Theta, Phi Delta Phi. Republican. Presbyterian. Clubs: Rotarian, Idle Hour Golf and Country. Office: US Dist Ct PO Box 65 Macon GA 31202-0065

OWENS, WILLIAM ARTHUR, military officer; b. Bismarck, N.D., May 8, 1940; s. Earl and Ruth (Arthur) O.; m. Monika Bastian, Sept. 30, 1967; 1 child, Todd. BS, U.S. Naval Acad., 1962; BA, MA, U. Oxford, Eng., 1974; MBA, George Washington U., 1976. Registered profl. engr., Commd. ensign USN, 1962, advanced through ranks to admiral, 1994, multiple assignments in nuclear submarines, 1962-77; comdg. officer USS Sam Houston (SSBN609), Honolulu, 1977-80, USS Corpus Christi (SSN705), New London, Conn., 1980-81, Submarine Squadron 4, Charleston, S.C., 1984-85, Submarine Group 6, Charleston, S.C., 1987-88; dir. USN Strategic Think Tank Washington, 1988, sr. mil. asst. to Sec. Def., 1988-90; comdr. 6th Fleet, Gaeta, Italy, 1990-92; dep. chief naval ops. Resources, Warfare Requirements & Assessments, Washington, 1992-94; vice-chmn. Joint Chiefs of Staff The Pentagon, Washington, 1994—. Author: Future of the Maritime Strategy, 1988, High Seas, 1994. Mem. Submarine League, U.S. Naval Acad. Alumni Assn., Oxford Soc., Coun. Fgn. Rels. Republican. Episcopalian. Avocations: golf, tennis.

OWENS, WILLIAM DON, anesthesiology educator; b. St. Louis, Dec. 12, 1939; s. Don and Caroline Wilhemena (Raaf) O.; m. Patricia Gail Brown, Dec. 12, 1964; children: Pamela, David, Susan. AB, Westminster Coll., 1961; MD, U. Mich., 1965. Diplomate Am. Bd. Anesthesiology. Resident and fellow Mass. Gen. Hosp. and Harvard Med. Sch., Boston, 1969-72; instr. Harvard Med. Sch., Boston, 1972-73; asst. prof. anesthesiology Washington U. Sch. Medicine, St. Louis, 1973-76, assoc. prof., 1976-82, prof., 1982—, chmn. dept., 1982-92; trustee Barnes Hosp., St. Louis, 1987-89; bd. dirs. Am. Bd. Anesthesiology, Hartford, Conn., Found. for Anesthesia Edn. and Rsch., Anesthesia Found. Assoc. editor Survey of Anesthesiology, 1977-92; contbr. 50 articles to profl. jours., 7 chpts. to books. Served to lt. comdr. USN, 1966-69. Fellow Am. Coll. Anesthesiology; mem. Am. Soc. Anesthesiologists (bd. dirs. 1989—), Internat. Anesthesia Rsch. Soc., Acad. Anesthesiology, Assn. Univ. Anesthesiologists. Office: Washington U Sch Med Dept Anesthesiology 660 S Euclid Ave Saint Louis MO 63110-1010 also: Am Bd of Anesthesiology 100 Constitution Plz Hartford CT 06103-1701

OWEN-TOWLE, CAROLYN SHEETS, clergywoman; b. Upland, Calif., July 27, 1935; d. Millard Owen and Mary (Baskerville) Sheets; m. Charles Russell Chapman, June 29, 1957 (div. 1973); children: Christopher Charles, Jennifer Anne, Russell Owen; m. Thomas Allan Owen-Towle, Nov. 16, 1973. BS in Art and Art History, Scripps Coll., 1957; postgrad. in religion, U. Iowa, 1977. Ordained to ministry Unitarian-Universalist Ch., 1978. Minister 1st Unitarian Universalist Ch., San Diego, 1978—; pres. Ministerial Sisterhood, Unitarian Universalist Ch., 1980-82; mem. Unitarian Universalist Svc. Com., 1979-85, pres., 1983-85. Bd. dirs. Planned Parenthood, San Diego, 1980-86; mem. clergy adv. com. to Hospice, San Diego, 1980-83; mem. U.S. Rep. Jim Bates Hunger Adv. Com., San Diego, 1983-87; chaplain Interfaith AIDS Task Force, San Diego, 1988—. Mem. Unitarian Universalist Ministers Assn. (exec. com. 1988, pres. 1989-91). Avocations: freedom of choice, reading, walking, designing environments. Office: 1st Unitarian Universalist Ch 4190 Front St San Diego CA 92103-2098

OWERS, BRIAN CHARLES, holding company executive; b. London, 1934. Grad., U. of London, 1955. Sec. The Rank Orgn. Plc; sec., bd. dirs. Rank RX Holdings Ltd.; sec. A. Kershaw & Sons Plc; bd. dirs. Rank Holdings (UK) Ltd., Rank Overseas Holdings Ltd. Office: The Rank Organisation Plc, 6 Connaught Pl, London W2 2EZ, England

OWETT, ADAM THOMAS, advertising creative director, writer; b. N.Y.C. Sept. 16, 1957; s. Bernard S. and Trudy (Hilsenrad) O. BA, U. Pa., 1979. Freelance producer N.Y.C., 1979-81; sr. copywriter Laurence, Charles, Free & Lawson, N.Y.C., 1981-86; sr. copywriter, supr. Grey Advt. Inc., N.Y.C., 1986—; creative supr. various bus., N.Y.C., 1983-86, Polygram Records, N.Y.C., 1984-85. Recipient Gold Clio award N.Y.C., 1983. Democrat. Jewish. Avocations: writing, songwriting, surfing, theater, dance, reading. Office: Grey Advt Inc 777 3rd Ave New York NY 10017-1301

OWINGS, DONALD HENRY, psychology educator; b. Atlanta, Dec. 7, 1943; s. Markley James and Loyce Erin (White) O.; m. Sharon Elizabeth Calhoun, Jan. 29, 1966; children: Ragon Matthew, Anna Rebekah. BA in Psychology, U. Tex., 1965; PhD, U. Wash., 1972. Asst. prof. psychology U. Calif., Davis, 1971-78, assoc. prof., 1978-83, prof., 1983—, chair dept., 1989-93. Contbr. articles to profl. jours., book chpts. NSF rsch. grantee, 1978-80, 82-84. Mem. Animal Behavior Soc., Internat. Soc. for Ecol. Psychology, Internat. Soc. for Behavioral Ecology, Internat. Soc. for Comparative Psychology. Democrat. Avocations: hiking, music, bird watching, reading. Home: 815 Oeste Dr Davis CA 95616 Office: U Calif Dept Psychology Davis CA 95616-8686

OWINGS, FRANCIS BARRE, surgeon; b. McColl, S.C., Mar. 9, 1941; s. Ralph Seer and Antoinette (Moore) O.; B.S., U. Miss., 1963, M.D., 1966; m. Judith Myers, Feb. 14, 1976; children—F. Patterson, Caroline C. Intern, San Francisco Gen. Hosp., 1966-67; resident in surgery U. Calif., San Francisco, 1969-74; surg. registrar Norfolk and Norwich Hosp., Norwich, Eng., 1971-72; practice medicine specializing in surgery, Atlanta, 1974—; mem. staff Crawford Long Hosp., pres. med. staff, 1981-82; mem. staff Piedmont Hosp.; clin. instr. surgery Emory U. Served to capt. USAF, 1967-69. Diplomate Am. Bd. Surgery. Fellow ACS, Southeastern Surg. Congress; mem. Med. Assn. Atlanta, Med. Assn. Ga., Naffziger Surg. Soc., Alpha Epsilon Delta, Sigma Chi, Phi Chi. Republican. Methodist. Home: 3400 Wood Valley Rd NW Atlanta GA 30327 Office: 478 Peachtree NE Atlanta GA 30308

OWINGS, MALCOLM WILLIAM, retired management consultant; b. Cin., Feb. 5, 1925; s. William Malcolm and Margaret (Benvie) O.; m. Margie M. Gehiker, Sept. 4, 1948; children: Lynn A., Sandra S., Wendy K., Cheryl M. B.S. in Bus. Adminstrn., Miami U., Oxford, Ohio, 1950, LL.D., 1976, A.M.P., Harvard U., 1975. With Continental Can Co., 1950-83, corp. v.p., from 1971; v.p., gen. mgr. pub. affairs Continental Packaging Co (Continental Group, Inc.) 1982-83; owner, pres. Owings Assocs., Inc., Pinehurst, N.C., 1983-92; dir. First Bank, Pinehurst, N.C.; adviser to Am. del. Internat. Tin Council, 1978-82. Dean's assoc. exec. in residence Miami U. Sch. Bus., 1973; village trustee Village of Thiensville, Wis., 1956-59; mem. alumni coun. Miami U., 1958-65, mem. pres.'s devel. coun., 1965—; mem. resource devel. bd. Miami U., 1982; mem. N.C. Clean, 1985—; chmn., 1986-93; bd. dirs. Barrington Area Devel. Coun., 1974-79, Sales Mgmt. Execs. Grad. Sch., Am. Soc. Environment, 1976, Keep Am. Beautiful, 1980-81, also chmn., 1990; chmn. Keep N.C. Beautiful Coun., Raleigh, 1986-92, Moore Meml. Hosp. Found., Pinehurst, N.C., 1986-89; chmn. Moore County (N.C.) Rep. Party; co-funder Rep. Presdl. Task Force; mem. U.S. Senate Bus. Adv. Bd., 1981-91; commr. Moore County, N.C., 1988—, re-elected 1992, Youth Svcs., 1993-95; apptd. to N.C. Watershed Protection Adv. Com. by N.C. Environ.

Mgmt. Commn., 1990-92; bd. dirs. Pub. Edn. Found., 1994—, Ptnrs. for Children and Family, 1994—, Drug-Free Moore County Inc., 1995—; Dispute Settlement Ctr. of Moore County, 1995—; mem. Moore County Bd. of Health. Recipient Cert. of Meritorious Svc. Miami U., 1967, Meritorious Svc. award Keep Moore County Beautiful, Inc., 1993-94; named Alumnus of Yr. Miami U., 1970; 1st Am. recipient Order of Apteryx Earth Awareness Found., 1971. Mem. Ill. C. of C. (bd. dirs. 1976-78), Miami U. Alumni Assn. (nat. pres. 1964-65), Omicron Delta Kappa, Sigma Chi, Delta Sigma Pi. Clubs: Pinehurst Country, Country of N.C. (Pinehurst). Home and Office: 805 Diamond Head Dr S Pinehurst NC 28374-9773 *The Golden Rule - "treating others as thyself" is not only a cornerstone for success, it is the foundation of personal happiness. However, it is well to remember that none of this is possible without political freedom and the contingent responsibilities that freedom requires.*

OWINGS, MARGARET WENTWORTH, conservationist, artist; b. Berkeley, Calif., Apr. 29, 1913; d. Frank W. and Jean (Pond) Wentworth; m. Malcolm Millard, 1937; 1 child, Wendy Millard Benjamin; m. Nathaniel Alexander Owings, Dec. 30, 1953. A.B., Mills Coll., 1934; postgrad., Radcliffe Coll., 1935; LHD, Mills Coll., 1993. One-woman shows include Santa Barbara (Calif.) Mus. Art, 1940, Stanford Art Gallery, 1951, stitchery exhbns. at M.H. De Young Mus., San Francisco, 1963, Internat. Folk Art Mus., Santa Fe, 1965. Commr. Calif. Parks, 1963-69, mem., Nat. Parks Found. Bd. 1968-69; bd. dirs African Wildlife Leadership Found., 1968-80, Defenders of Wildlife, 1969-74; founder, pres. Friends of the Sea Otter, 1969-90; chair Calif. Mountain Lion Preservation Found., 1987; trustee Environmental Def. Fund, 1972-83; Regional trustee Mills Coll., 1962-68. Recipient Gold medal, Conservation Svc. award U.S. Dept. Interior, 1975, Conservation award Calif. Acad. Scis., 1979, Am. Motors Conservation award, 1980, Joseph Wood Krutch medal Humane Soc. U.S., Nat. Audubon Soc. medal, 1983, A. Starker Leopole award Calif. Nature Conservancy, 1986, Gold medal UN Environment Program, 1988, Conservation award DAR, 1990, Disting. Svc. award Sierra Club, 1991. Home: Grimes Point Big Sur CA 93920

OWNBY, CHARLOTTE LEDBETTER, anatomy educator; b. Amory, Miss., July 27, 1947; d. William Moss and Anna Faye (Long) Ledbetter; m. James Donald Ownby, Sept. 6, 1969; children: Holly Ruth, Mary Faye. BS in Zoology, U. Tenn., 1969, MS in Zoology, 1971; PhD in Anatomy, Colo. State U., 1975. Instr. Okla. State U., Stillwater, 1974-75, asst. prof., 1975-80, assoc. prof., 1980-84, prof., 1984—, dept. head, 1990—, dir. Electron Microscope Lab., 1977-87. Editor Proc. 9th World Congress Internat. Soc. Toxicology, 1989; editorial bd. Toxion, 1984—. Recipient SmithKline-Beecham award for rsch. excellence, 1992; NIH, USPHS grantee, 1984—. Mem. Okla. Soc. for Electron Microscopy (pres. 1977-78), Pan Am. Soc. on Toxinology (pres. 1984-85), Internat. Soc. on Toxinology (pres. elect 1992), Phi Beta Kappa, Sigma Xi, Phi Kappa Phi. Avocations: butterfly photography, bird watching, hiking, camping. Office: Okla State U Dept Physiol Scis 264 Vet Medicine Stillwater OK 74078

OWNBY, DENNIS RANDALL, pediatrician, allergist, educator, researcher; b. Athens, Ohio, July 14, 1948; s. Dillard Ralph and Miriam (Lee) O.; m. Helen Louise Engelbrecht, May 24, 1970; children: David Randall, Kathryn Louise. BS, Ohio U., 1969; MD, Med. Coll. Ohio, 1972. Diplomate Am. Bd. Allergy and Immunology, Am. Bd. Pediatrics, Nat. Bd. Med. Examiners. Intern and resident Duke U. Sch. Medicine, Durham, N.C., 1972-74, asst. prof., 1977-80; staff physician Henry Ford Hosp., Detroit, 1980—, dir. Allergy Rsch. Lab., 1986—; clin. asst. prof. pediatrics U. Mich., Ann Arbor, 1980-86, clin. assoc. prof., 1986—. Contbr. articles to med. jours., chpts. to books. Recipient Young Investigator award Nat. Allergy and Infectious Disease, 1978. Fellow Am. Acad. Pediatrics, Am. Acad. Allergy. Office: Henry Ford Hosp Dept Allergy & Clin Immunology 2799 W Grand Blvd Detroit MI 48202-2689

OWNBY, JERRY STEVE, landscape architect, educator; b. Shawnee, Okla., Jan. 25, 1939; s. Hugh H. and N. Lorraine (Hopkins) O.; children by previous marriage: Gregory Steve, Mitchell Hugh; m. Arnola Colson, Dec. 19, 1971; 1 child, Steven Cory. BS, Okla. State U., 1961; MS in Landscape Architecture, Kans. State U., 1964, M in Landscape Architecture, 1970. Coun. Landscape Archtl. Registration Bds. cert. and registered landscape architect, Ariz., Kans., Okla., Mo., Tex. Extension landscape architect Kans. State U., Manhattan, 1963-64, instr., 1969-70; landscape architect Beardsley & Talley, Seattle, 1964-65; extension specialist Okla. State U., Stillwater, 1965-69, from asst. prof. to prof. landscape architecture and coordinator landscape architecture, 1970-85; pvt. practice, 1985—; chmn. Okla. Landscape Architect Registration Bd., 1980-85; mem. 1985 Expert Panel for Uniform Nat. Exam., 1984-85; gov.'s appointee Mo. Coun. Landscape Architects, 1991—. Designs include Las Laderas residence, 1978 (Merit award 1981), Student Union courtyard Okla. State U., 1981 (Honor award 1983). Chmn. Oklahomans for Landscape Architecture, 1979-80; chmn., vice chmn. Stillwater Park and Recreation Adv. Bd., Okla., 1971-79. Recipient Outstanding Prof. award Okla. State U. chpt. Alpha Zeta, 1974-75, Svc. award Stillwater City Commn., 1980, Springfield Planning and Zoning Commn. design awards, 1988, 89, 90, Design award Springfield Environ. Adv. Bd., 1990, Gov.'s Landscape design award for Andy Williams' Moon River Theatre, Branson, Mo., 1992, Design award Watershed Com., 1993; Kans. Stae U. Alumni fellow, 1995. Fellow Am. Soc. Landscape Architects (v.p. 1983-85, Okla. chpt. Svc. award 1980); mem. Nat. Coun. State Garden Clubs (accredited instr. 1964—), Nat. Coun. of Educators in Landscape Architecture, Mo. Assn. of Landscape Architects, Coun. Landscape Archtl. Registration Bds. (cert.), Phi Kappa Phi, Sigma Lambda Alpha. Republican. Baptist. Avocations: travel; photography; fishing. Home and Office: 1161 S Virginia Ave Springfield MO 65807-1727

OWSIA, NASRIN AKBARNIA, pediatrician; b. Babol, Iran, Dec. 5, 1940; came to U.S., 1968; d. Ahmad and Hoora O.; m. Behrooz A. Akbarnia, Mar. 19, 1968; children: Halleh, Ladan, Ramin. MD, Tehran (Iran) U., 1966. Intern in pediatrics Berkshire Med. Ctr. Hosp., Pittsfield, Mass., 1968-69; resident in pediatrics Albany (N.Y.) Med. Ctr. Hosp., 1969-72; pediatric gastroenterologist St. Christopher Hosp. for Children, Phila., 1972-73; asst. prof. Albany Med. Coll., 1973-76, Tehran U., 1976-80; asst. prof. St. Louis U. Med. Ctr., 1981-89, clin. assoc. prof., 1989-90; pvt. practice San Diego, 1990—. Bd. mem. Persian Cultural Ctr., San Diego, 1993—. Recipient award AMA. Fellow Am. Acad. Pediatrics; mem. Allergy and Asthma Found., Calif. Med. Soc., San Diego Med. Soc. Avocations: knitting, downhill skiing. Office: 8010 Frost St No 414 San Diego CA 92123-4284

OWSLEY, ALVIN, manufacturing executive, lawyer; b. Dallas, Feb. 9, 1926; s. Alvin Mansfield and Lucy (Ball) O.; m. Barbara Ann Robinson, June 23, 1950; children: Michael M., Carol McFadden, Steven A. A.B., Princeton U., 1949; J.D., U. Tex., 1952. Bar: Tex. 1952. Assoc. Baker & Botts, Houston, 1952-63; ptnr. Baker & Botts., Houston, 1964-87, sr. ptnr.; chmn. Ball Corp., Muncie, Ind., 1991—; dir. Ball Corp.; prin. mgr. Alvin & Lucy Owsley Found. Mem. centennial commn. U. Tex., Austin, 1981-83; assoc. bd. visitors M.D. Anderson Cancer Ctr., Houston. Served with arty. AUS, 1944-46, ETO. Fellow Am. Coll. Trial Lawyers; mem. ABA, Houston Bar Assn., Soc. Mayflower Desc., Houston Country Club, Ramada Club, Tejas Club, Leland Country Club, Order of St. Lazarus, Malta. Republican. Presbyterian. Home: 65 Briar Hollow Ln Houston TX 77027-9315 Office: Ball Corp 345 S High St Muncie IN 47305-2326°

OWSLEY, DAVID THOMAS, art consultant, appraiser, lecturer, author; b. Dallas, Aug. 20, 1929; s. Alvin Mansfield and Lucy (Ball) O. Grad., Phillips Andover Acad., 1947; A.B., Harvard, 1951; M.F.A. N.Y. U., 1964; fellow, Met. Mus. Am. Wing, 1964. Asst. curator dept. decorative arts and sculpture Boston Mus. Fine Arts, 1965-66; visitor Victoria and Albert Mus. London, Eng., 1966-68; curator antiquities, Oriental and decorative arts Mus. Art, Carnegie Inst., Pitts., 1968-78; mem. acquisition com. Dallas Mus. Art, 1994—; mem. adv. coun. Inst. Asia Studies, N.Y.C. Served to 1st lt. USAF, 1952-54. Recipient Pres.' medal of Distinction Ball State U., 1989, Westmoreland Soc. Gold medal, 1991. Clubs: D.U. (Harvard Coll.); Leland Country (Mich.); Knickerbocker (N.Y.C.). Home: 116 E 68th St New York NY 10021-5956 *I have tried to pursue beautiful and significant works of art and to encourage others to share my love and respect for them.*

OWSLEY, NORMAN LEE, electrical engineer, educator; b. Cleve., June 24, 1941; s. Joseph and Mildred R. (Johnson) O.; m. Judith Reuter, Aug. 28, 1965; children: Lane M., Kara K. BSEE, Lehigh U., 1963; MSEE, Duke U., 1965, PhD, 1968. Engr. in tng. Westinghouse Electric Corp., Pitts., 1962; constrn. trainee Am. Bridge Corp., Pitts., 1961-63; teaching intern NSF, Duke U., Durham, N.C., 1963-64; rsch. assoc. NASA, Duke U., Durham, N.C., 1965-68; rsch. elect. engr. Naval Underwater Sound Lab., New London, Conn., 1968—; adj. prof. U. Conn., Storrs, 1973—; instr. Advanced Tech. Inst., Clarksville, Md., 1990—, Continuing Edn. Inst., Linkoping, Sweden, 1990—. Author: Array Signal Processing, 1985; patentee in field. NATO Sci. Exch. scholar, Horten, Norway, 1976-78. Fellow IEEE, Rotary (Paul Harris fellow, bd. dirs. Ledyard, Conn. club), Sigma Xi, Eta Kappa Nu, Pi Mu Epsilon. Home: 29 Hemlock Cir Gales Ferry CT 06335-1024 Office: Naval Underwater Systems Ctr New London Lab Code 3211 New London CT 06320

OWSLEY, WILLIAM CLINTON, JR., radiologist; b. Austin, Tex., Oct. 6, 1923; s. William Clinton and Lois (Lamar) O.; B.A., U. Tex., 1944; M.D., U. Pa., 1946; m. Betty Pinckard, 1949; 2 children. Intern, Hermann Hosp., Houston, 1946-47; resident Hosp. of U. Pa., Phila., 1949-52; instr. radiology U. Pa., 1950-52; practice medicine specializing in radiology, Houston, 1952—; mem. staff Hermann Hosp., Twelve Oaks Hosp., Bellville Hosp., St. Elizabeth Hosp., Brazos Valley Hosp.; assoc. clin. prof. radiology U. Tex. Served with USNR, 1947-48. Diplomate Am. Bd. Radiology. Fellow Royal Soc. Medicine (U.K.), Am. Coll. Radiology; mem. Am. Roentgen Ray Soc., Radiol. Soc. N.Am., Interam. Coll. Radiology, AMA. Republican. Baptist. Office: Ste 230 4710 Greeley St Houston TX 77006

OWYOUNG, STEVEN DAVID, curator; b. San Francisco, Jan. 14, 1947; s. Fay and Ethel (Woo) O.; m. Diana Lee Wong, Aug. 29, 1971; children: Christopher Mark, Todd Alexander. BA, U. Hawaii, 1973; MA, U. Mich., 1977, postgrad., 1978. Lectr., editor Nat. Palace Mus., Taipei, Taiwan, 1971-72; curatorial assoc. Fogg Art Mus., Harvard U., Cambridge, Mass., 1980-82, asst. curator, 1982-83; curator Asian arts St. Louis Art Mus., 1983—; sec. commn. bd. commrs. St. Louis Art Mus., 1991-93; vis. Washington U., St. Louis, 1990—; cons. Getty Art History Info. Program, 1993. Bd. dirs. World Affairs Coun. St. Louis, 1984-86, Nanjing-St. Louis Sister Cities, 1989-90; del. Chinese painting historians to People's Republic China, 1980. Charles L. Freer fellow Freer Gallery Art, 1976, 77, Horace H. Rackham predoctoral fellow, 1978, Louise W. Hackney fellow Am. Oriental Soc., 1978-79, Fulbright-Hays fellow, 1978-79, Social Sci. Rsch. Coun. and Am. Coun. Learned Socs. fellow, 1978-80; Samuel H. Kress Found. grantee, 1980, Horace H. Rackham grantee, 1980, Asian Cultural Coun. grantee, 1990. Mem. Asian Art Soc. Washington U. (bd. dirs. 1983—). Office: St Louis Art Mus Forest Pk Saint Louis MO 63110

OXENBURY, HELEN, children's writer, illustrator; b. Suffolk, Eng., June 2, 1938; d. Thomas Bernard and Muriel (Taylor) O.; m. John Burningham, Aug. 15, 1965; children: Lucy, William Benedict. Stage designer Colchester, Eng., 1960, Tel-Aviv, 1961; TV designer London, 1963. Author, illustrator: Number of Things, 1967, ABC of Things, 1971, Pig Tale, 1973, The Queen and Rosie Randall, 1979, 729 Curious Creatures, 1980, 729 Merry Mix-ips, 1980, 729 Puzzle People, 1989, 729 Animal Allsorts, 1980, Crazy Creatures, 1980, Assorted Animals, 1980, Bill and Stanley, 1981, Bedtime, 1982, Monkey See, Monkey Do, 1982, Holidays, 1982, Helping, 1982, Mother's Helper, 1982, Animals, 1982, Bearch Day, 1982, Shopping Trip, 1982, Good Night, Good Morning, 1982, The Birthday Party, 1983, The Dancing Class, 1983, Eating Out, 1983, The Car Trip, 1983, The Drive, 1983, The Checkup, 1983, First Day of School, 1983, First Day at Playschool, 1983, Playschool, 1983, Grandma and Grandpa, 1984, Our Dog, 1984, The Important Visitor, 1984, Helen Oxenbury Nursery Story Book, 1985, Tom and Pippo Go Shopping, 1988, Tom and Pippo's Day, 1988, Tom and Pippo in the Garden, 1988, Tom and Pippo Go for a Walk, 1988, Tom and Pippo Make a Mess, 1988, Tom and Pippo Read a Story, 1988, Tom and Pippo See the Moon, 1988, Tom and Pippo and the Washing Machine, 1988, Pippo Gets Lost, 1989, Tom and Pippo and the Dog, 1989, Tom and Pippo in the Snow, 1989, Tom and Pippo Make a Friend, 1989, Tom and Pippo on the Beach, 1993, It's My Birthday, 1994, First Nursery Stories, 1994; (with Fay Maschler): A Child's Book of Manners: Verses, 1978; illustrator: The Great Big Enormous Turnip, 1968, The Quangle-Wangle's Hat, 1969, Letters of Thanks, 1969, The Dragon of an Ordinary Family, 1969, The Hunting of the Snark, 1970, Meal One, 1971, Cakes and Custard: Children's Rhymes, 1974, Balooky Klujypop, 1975, Animal House, 1976, Tiny Tim: Verses for Children, 1981, We're Going on a Bear Hunt, 1989, Farmer Duck, 1992, The Three Little Wolves and the Big Bad Pig, 1993, So Much, 1994. Office: care Greene and Heaton Ltd, 37 Goldhawk Rd, London W12 8QQ, England also: 5 E Heath Rd Hampstead, London NW3 1BN, England

OXENHANDLER, NEAL, language educator, writer; b. St. Louis, Feb. 3, 1926; s. Joseph and Billie (Lutsky) O.; m. Jean Romano (div. Nov. 1975); children: Noelle, Daniel, Alicia; m. Judith I. Josel, Dec. 12, 1979. AB, U. Chgo., 1948; MA, Columbia U., 1951; PhD, Yale U., 1955; MA (hon.), Dartmouth Coll., 1973. Lectr. French St. Louis U., 1951-52; asst. instr. Yale U., New Haven, Conn., 1952-54, instr., 1954-57; asst. prof. UCLA, 1957-60, assoc. prof., 1960-65; assoc. prof. U. Calif., Santa Cruz, 1965-66, prof., 1966-69; prof. Dartmouth Coll., Hanover, N.H., 1969—, Edward Tuck prof., 1987—, chmn. dept. French and Italian, 1987-91; dir. NEH Summer Seminar in Comparative Lit., 1981. Author: Scandal and Parade: Theater of Jean Cocteau, 1957, Aspects of French Literature, 1961, French Literary Criticism: The Basis of Judgment, 1966, Max Jacob and Les Feux de Paris, 1964, (novel) A Change of Gods, 1962, Looking for Heroes in Post-War France, 1995; adv. editor Film Quar., Berkeley, 1958-91; mem. editl. com. U. Calif. Press, Berkeley, 1966-69; asst. editor French Rev., 1969-73; contbr. articles, revs., poetry and translations to profl. jours. With U.S. Army, 1941-43, ETO, PTO. Fulbright scholar, Italy, 1953; Cross-Disciplinary fellow Soc. for Values in Higher Edn., France, 1966, Guggenheim fellow, France, 1962, Inst. for Shipboard Edn., 1995. Mem. MLA (adv. editor proc. 1977-80), Internat. Assn. Philosophy and Lit., Internat. Comparative Lit. Assn. Democrat. Roman Catholic. Avocations: skiing, fly-fishing. Home: 468 Monroe Dr Sarasota FL 34236-1715 Office: Dartmouth Coll Dept French Hanover NH 03755

OXENREITER, MAURICE FRANK, chemical engineer; b. Pitts., Oct. 26, 1924; s. Maurice Fallert and Helen Alberta (Miller) O.; m. Jean Gertrude Bailey, Nov. 25, 1950; children: Richard David, Karen Ann, Gayle Diane, Janice Marie, Suzanne Elizabeth. BSChemE, U. Pitts., 1948, MSChemE, 1949, PhD, 1952; MBA, U. Chgo., 1970. Rsch. engr., supr. Standard Oil Co., Whiting, Ind., 1952-67; rsch. dir. AMOCO Corp., Whiting, 1967-75; rsch. mgr. AMOCO Corp., Naperville, Ill., 1975-84, gen. mgr. rsch. svcs., 1984-89; cons., 1990—. Contbr. articles to profl. jours.; patentee in field. Governing mem. DuPage County (Ill.) Conservation Found., 1985—; mem. pres.'s adv. com. No. Ill. U., DeKalb, Ill., 1987—. With U.S. Army, World War II. Decorated Bronze Star with two oak leaf clusters; recipient Am. Theater Svc. medal; European, African, Middle Eastern medal with three bronze stars, Combat Medic badge. Mem. Am. Inst. Chem. Engrs., Am. Mgmt. Assn., Sigma Xi, Phi Lamda Epsilon, VFW, Rotary, Am. Legion.,. Roman Catholic. Home: 6S166 New Castle Rd Naperville IL 60540

OXFORD, CHARLES WILLIAM, university dean, chemical engineer; b. Texarkana, Tex., Nov. 16, 1921; s. Charles Edward and Ellen (Alphin) O.; m. Mary Rae Mauzy, Dec. 24, 1946; children—Constance Susan, Catherine Ellen. BS, U. Ark., 1944, LLD (hon.), 1992; postgrad., U. Minn., 1946-48; PhD, U. Okla., 1952; DSc (hon.), U. Ark., Little Rock. Asst. chemist Koppers Co., 1941; control chemist W.S. Dickey, 1942; asst. prof. chem. engring. U. Ark., 1948-50, asso. prof., 1952-57, prof., 1957—; asso. dean U. Ark. (Coll. Engring.), 1960—; asso. dir. U. Ark. (Engring. Expt. Sta.), 1964—, adminstrv. v.p. univ., 1968-73; exec. v.p., 1973-79, v.p. acad. affairs, 1979-88, v.p. emeritus, 1987—; exec. dir. U. Ark. Found., Inc., 1989-91; research participant Union Carbide Co., 1952; research engr. Boeing Airplane Co., 1955; cons. to industry. Exec. dir. U. Ark. Found., 1988-91. Served with USNR, 1944-46. Mem. Am. Inst. Chem. Engrs., Am. Soc. Engring. Edn., Am. Soc. Profl. Engrs., Sigma Xi, Tau Beta Pi, Alpha Chi Sigma, Omicron Delta Kappa. Club: Lion. Home: 110 Cydnee Fayetteville AR 72703

OXFORD, SHARON M., insurance company executive; b. Ekalaka, Mont., Aug. 30, 1939; d. Price S. and Myrtle I. (Wilkoski) Purdum; m. James L. Oxford Jr., Sept. 7, 1958 (div. May 1973); children: James L. III, Dana Renee, Monica Lynn Oxford Jones; m. Ronald Butts, Jan. 1, 1990. Degree in bus. adminstrn., Nat. Coll. Bus., Rapid City, S.D., 1958; student, Mesa (Ariz.) Community Coll., 1979-80. CPCU; cert. ins. counselor. Office mgr. Foster Fritchle Ins. Co., Colorado Springs, Colo., 1968-71, Mikes Ives Ins./ Profl. Ins. Exchange, Colorado Springs, 1971-73; asst. to pres. Tolley-Weidman Ins. Co., Colorado Springs, 1973-76; rater Home Ins. Co., Phoenix, 1976-78; mgr. adminstrn. Fred S. James & Co. Ariz., Phoenix and Tempe, 1978-84; v.p. Sedgwick James, Tempe, 1984-85; sr. v.p. Fred S. James & Co. Ariz., Tempe, 1985—. Vol. MADD, store monitor Red Ribbon campaign; corr. sec. Young Reps., Colo. Springs, 1967; v.p. Colorado Springs chpt. Parents Without Ptnrs., 1975. Mem. Am. Inst. for Property and Liability Underwriters, Soc. Cert. Ins. Counselors, Jaycee Wives (pres. Colorado Springs chpt. 1970), Assoc. of Automated Mgmt. Republican. Avocations: dancing, square dancing. Office: Sedgwick James 1414 W Broadway Rd Ste 200 Tempe AZ 85282-1122

OXLEY, DWIGHT K(AHALA), pathologist; b. Wichita, Kans., Dec. 2, 1936; s. Dwight K. Jr. and Ruth Erdene (Warner) O.; m. Patricia Warren, June 18, 1961; children: Alice DeBloois, Thomas Oxley. AB, Harvard U., 1958; MD, U. Kans., 1962. Diplomate Am. Bd. Pathology (trustee 1992—), Am. Bd. Nuclear Medicine. Pathologist Wesley Med. Ctr., Wichita, 1969-74, Eisenhower Med. Ctr., Rancho Mirage, Calif., 1974-78, St Joseph Health Ctr., Kansas City, Mo., 1978-88; chmn. dept. pathology Wesley Med. Ctr., 1988—. Bd. editors Archives of Pathology and Lab. Medicine, Chgo., 1984—, Clinica Chimica Acta, Amsterdam, 1980-86, Am. Jour. Clin. Pathology, Chgo., 1974-80. Sr. warden St Stephens Episcopal Ch., Wichita, 1994. Lt. commdr. USN, 1964-69. Fellow Am. Soc. Clin. Pathologists (various offices), Coll. Am. Pathologists (various offices); mem. Am. Pathology Found. (bd. dirs. 1979-89), Kans. Soc. Pathologists (pres. 1993—). Republican. Avocations: music, athletics. Office: Wesley Med Ctr 550 N Hillside Wichita KS 67214

OXLEY, JOHN THURMAN, ranching and investments executive, former petroleum company executive; b. Bromide, Okla., July 26, 1909; s. Moses E. and Sallie E. (Cochran) O.; m. Mary K. Yetter, Aug. 17, 1935; children: John C., Mary J., Thomas E. Student, East Central Coll., Okla., Tulsa Bus. Coll., Tulsa Law Sch., U. Tulsa. With Amerada Petroleum Corp., 1927-35; with Warren Petroleum Corp., 1935-48; sec. and mgr. gasoline div., pres., dir. Tex. Natural Gasoline Corp., Tulsa, 1948-60; exec. v.p., dir. Union Tex. Petroleum Corp., 1960-63; cons. Union Tex. Petroleum (merged with Allied Chem. Corp.), 1963; part owner Oxley Petroleum Co., 1963—; chmn., pres., chief exec. officer, dir. Arkansas Valley Industries, Inc., 1964-69; dir. Apco Oil Corp. Mem. So. Hills Country Club, Royal Palm Polo Sports Club, Boca Raton, Fla. Office: Williams Center Tower I Ste 1305 Tulsa OK 74103

OXLEY, MICHAEL GARVER, congressman; b. Findlay, Ohio, Feb. 11, 1944; s. George Garver and Marilyn Maxine (Wolfe) O.; m. Patricia Ann Pluguez, Nov. 27, 1971; 1 child, Michael Chadd. BA, Miami U., Oxford, Ohio, 1966; JD, Ohio State U., 1969. Bar: Ohio 1969, U.S. Supreme Ct. 1985. Agt. FBI, 1969-71; mem. Ohio Ho. of Reps., 1973-81, 97th-103rd Congresses from 4th Ohio dist., Washington, D.C., 1981—; mem. commerce com., chmn. subcom. commerce, trade and hazardous materials, vice chmn. subcom. telecomm. and fin. Mem. ABA, Ohio Bar Assn., Findlay Bar Assn., Soc. Former Spl. Agts. FBI, Ohio Farm Bur., Sigma Chi. Lodges: Rotary, Elks. Office: US Ho Reps 2233 Rayburn House Bldg Washington DC 20515

OXMAN, DAVID CRAIG, lawyer; b. Summit, N.J., Mar. 10, 1941; s. Jacob H. and Kathryn (Grear) O.; m. Phyllis Statter; children—Elena, Lee. A.B., Princeton U., 1962; LL.B., Yale U., 1969. Bar: N.Y. 1970, N.J. 1974, U.S. Dist. Ct. (so. and ea. dists.) N.Y. 1974, U.S. Ct. Appeals (2d cir.) 1974, U.S. Tax Ct. 1977, U.S. Supreme Ct. 1974. Assoc. Davis Polk & Wardwell, N.Y.C., 1970-76, ptnr., 1977—. Served with USN, 1962-66. Fellow Am. Coll. Trust and Estate Counsel; mem. ABA, N.Y. State Bar Assn., Assn. of Bar of City of N.Y., N.J. Bar Assn., N.Y. County Lawyers Assn. Office: Davis Polk & Wardwell 450 Lexington Ave New York NY 10017-3911

OXMAN, STEPHEN A., federal official; b. Summit, N.J., 1945; m. Patricia Jo Hedlund; children: Stephen, Gavin, Matthew. BA magna cum laude, Princeton U., 1967; DPhil, Oxford U., Eng., 1973; JD, Yale U., 1972. Assoc. Cravath, Swaine & Moore, 1973-77; spl. asst. to dep. sec. of state, 1977-78, exec. asst. to dep. sec. state, 1978-79; ptnr. Shearman & Sterling, 1980-88; mng. dir., dep. chmn. Wasserstein Perella & Co., 1988-93; asst. sec. state for European and Can. affairs Dept. State, Washington, 1993—. Bd. editors: Yale Law Jour. Rhodes scholar, 1967-69. Office: Dept State European & Canadian Affairs 2201 C St NW Rm 6228 Washington DC 20520-0001

OXNARD, CHARLES ERNEST, anatomist, anthropologist, human biologist, educator; b. Durham, Eng., Sept. 9, 1933; arrived in Australia, 1987; s. Charles and Frances Ann (Golightly) O.; m. Eleanor Mary Arthur, Feb. 2, 1959; children: Hugh Charles Neville, David Charles Guy. B.Sci. with 1st class honors, U. Birmingham, Eng., 1955, M.B., Ch.B. in Medicine, 1958, Ph.D., 1962, D.Sc., 1975. Med. intern Queen Elizabeth Hosp., Birmingham, 1958-59; rsch. fellow U. Birmingham, 1959-62, lectr., 1962-65, sr. lectr., 1965-66, court govs., 1958-66; assoc. prof. anatomy, anthropology and evolutionary biology U. Chgo., 1966-70, prof., 1970-78, gov. biology collegiate div., 1970-78, dean coll., 1973-77; dean grad. sch. U. So. Calif., Los Angeles, 1978-83; univ. rsch. prof. biology and anatomy U. So. Calif., 1978-83, univ. prof., prof. anatomy and cell biology, prof. biol. scis., 1983-87; prof. anatomy and human biology, head dept. of anatomy and human biology U. Western Australia, 1987-90, 93-95, dir. ctr. for human biology, 1989—, head div. agr. and sci., 1990-92; rsch. assoc. Field Mus. Natural History, Chgo., 1967—; overseas assoc. U. Birmingham, 1968—; Lo Yuk Tong lectr. U. Hong Kong, 1973, 94, hon. prof., 1978—, Chan Shu Tzu lectr., 1980, Octagon lectr. U. Western Australia, 1987, Latta lectr. U. Nebr., Omaha, 1987; Stanley Wilkinson orator, 1991; rsch. assoc. L.A. County Natural History Mus., 1984—, George C. Page Mus., L.A., 1986—; bd. dirs. U. Western Australia Press, 1993—; advisor on human biology World Sci. Pub. Co., 1993—; editor-in-chief, 1994—. Author: Form and Pattern in Human Evolution, 1973, Uniqueness and Diversity in Human Evolution, 1975, Human Fossils: The New Revolution, 1977, The Order of Man, 1983, Humans, Apes and Chinese Fossils, 1985, Fossils, Teeth and Sex, 1987, Animal Anatomies and Lifestyles, 1990; editor-in-chief Recent Advances in Human Biology Series World Sci. Pub., vol. 1, 1995, vol. 2, 1995; mem. editl. bd. Annals of Human Biology; cons. editor: Am. Jour. Primatology, Jour. Human Biology, Jour. Human Evolution; Australia com. mem. Ency. Britannica, 1991—; contbr. articles to anat. and anthrop. jours. Mem. Pasteur Found., 1988; bd. dirs. West Australian Inst. for Child Health, 1991—; mem. electoral bd. Freemantle Hosp., 1991-94. Recipient Book award Hong Kong Coun., 1984, S.T. Chan silver medal U. Hong Kong, 1980; grantee USPHS, 1960-71, NIH, 1974-87, NSF, 1971-87, Raine Found., 1988-91, Viertel Found., 1993-94, Australian Acad. Scis., 1995. Fellow N.Y. Acad. Sci., AAAS, So. Calif. Acad. Sci. (bd. dirs. 1985); mem. Chgo. Acad. Soc. (hon. life), Australasian Soc. for Human Biology (pres. 1987-90), Australia and New Zealand Anat. Soc. (pres. 1989-90), Anat. Soc. Gt. Britain and Ireland (councillor 1992-94), Nat. Health and Med. Rsch. Coun. (grantee 1988—), Australian Rsch. Coun. (grantee 1988—), Soc. for Study Human Biology (treas. 1967-66), Sigma Xi (pres. nat. lectr. 1990—), Phi Beta Kappa (pres. chpt.), Phi Kappa Phi (pres., Book award 1984). Office: U Western Australia, Nedlands WA 6009, Australia

OXTOBY, DAVID WILLIAM, chemistry educator; b. Bryn Mawr, Pa., Oct. 17, 1951; s. John Corning and Jean (Shaffer) O.; m. Claire Bennett, Dec. 17, 1977; children: Mary-Christina, John, Laura. BA, Harvard U., 1972; PhD, U. Calif., Berkeley, 1975. Asst. prof. U. Chgo. 1977-82, assoc. prof., 1982-86, prof., 1986—, Mellon prof., 1987-92, dir. James Franck Inst., 1992—. Co-author: Principles of Modern Chemistry, 1986, Chemistry: Science of Change, 1990. Trustee Bryn Mawr Coll., 1989—. Recipient Quantrell award U. Chgo., 1986; Alfred P. Sloan Found. fellow, 1979, John Simon Guggenheim Found. fellow, 1987; Camille and Henry Dreyfus Found. tchr.-scholar, 1980. Fellow Am. Phys. Soc.; mem. Am. Chem. Soc. Physical Chemistry (Marlow medal 1983), Phi Beta Kappa. Office: James Franck Inst U Chgo 5640 S Ellis Ave Chicago IL 60637-1433

OXTOBY, ROBERT BOYNTON, lawyer; b. Huron, S.D., May 8, 1921; s. Frederic Breading and Frieda (Boynton) O.; m. Carolyn Barthof; children: Michael, Thomas, Susan. Student, Ill. Coll.; B.A., Carleton Coll., 1943; J.D., Northwestern U., 1949. Bar: Ill. 1949. Mem. firm Van Meter, Oxtoby & Funk, 1949—; asst. U.S. atty., 1953-57, spl. asst. atty. gen., 1970—. Mem., now chmn. Ill. Capital Devel. Bd.; bd. dirs. Downtown Park, Inc., Springfield Bd. Edn. Served to 1st lt. USMCR, 1943-46, PTO. Home: 1933 Outerpark Dr Springfield IL 62704 Office: First Am Ctr 1 Old Capitol Pla N Springfield IL 62701

OYE, KENNETH A., political scientist, educator; BA in Polit. Sci. and Econs. with highest honors, Swarthmore Coll., 1971; PhD in Polit. Sci., Harvard U., 1983. Lectr. polit. sci. U. Calif., Davis, 1976-79; asst. prof. politics Princeton U., 1980-89, faculty assoc. ctr. internat. studies, 1982-89; assoc. prof. polit. sci. Swarthmore Coll., 1989-90; assoc. prof. polit. sci. MIT, Cambridge, 1990—, dir. ctr. internat. studies, 1992—; lectr. summer program quantitative methods Kennedy Sch. Harvard U., 1974, 75; guest scholar The Brookings Instn., 1979-80; co-dir. seminar XXI program MIT, 1993—, mem. coun. global environment, 1994—; presenter in field. Author: Economic Discrimination and Political Exchange: World Political Economy in the 1930s and 1980s, 1993; editor: Cooperation under Anarchy, 1986, (with Robert J. Lieber and Donald Rothchild) Eagle Entangled: U.S. Foreign Policy in a Complex World, 1979, Eagle Defiant: United States Foreign Policy in the 1980s, 1983, Eagle Resurgent? The Reagan Era in United States Foreign Policy, 1987, Eagle in a New World: American Grand Strategy in the Post Cold War Era, 1992; mem. editorial com. World Politics, 1982-89, mem. editorial bd., 1989—; contbr. chpts. to books and articles to profl. jours. Econs. and Security grantee Pew Charitable Trusts, 1986; Grad. fellow Woodrow Wilson Found., 1971, NSF, 1971-74. Mem. Am. Econs. Assn., Am. Polit. Sci. Assn., Phi Beta Kappa. Office: MIT Ctr Internat Studies 292 Main St E38-648 Cambridge MA 02139

OYLER, GREGORY KENNETH, lawyer; b. Moses Lake, Wash., Sept. 16, 1953; s. Eugene Milton and Annetta Diane (Williams) O.; m. Evelyn Hartwell Wright, Oct. 18, 1986; 1 child, Elizabeth Atwood. AB, Princeton U., 1975; JD, Georgetown U., 1978; LLM, NYU, 1981. Bar: Pa. 1978, U.S. Tax Ct. 1978, U.S. Ct. Appeals (D.C. cir.) 1979, D.C. 1981, U.S. Supreme Ct. 1982, U.S. Ct. Claims 1983, U.S. Ct. Appeals (fed. cir.) 1987. Law clk. to judges U.S. Tax Ct., Washington, 1978-80; assoc. Hamel & Park, Washington, Washington, 1981-85; ptnr. Hopkins & Sutter, Washington, 1985—. Mem. adv. com. IRS Info. Reporting Program, 1993-94. Mem. ABA (tax sect., ins. and govt. submissions coms.), D.C. Bar Assn. (tax sect.), Soc. Preservation Md. Antiquities (bd. dirs. 1991—). Office: Scribner, Hall & Thompson 1850 K St NW Ste 1100 Washington DC 20006-2201

OYLER, JAMES RUSSELL, JR., manufacturing executive; b. Gettysburg, Pa., Mar. 18, 1946; s. James Russell and Gail Louise (Dinwiddie) O.; m. Clare Marie Walther, Sept. 16, 1967; children: Catherine Meredith, Amanda Christine, Margaret Anne. BSEE magna cum laude, Cambridge U., 1967; MA in Econs. with honors, Cambridge U., Eng., 1969. Cert. mgmt. acct. Assoc. Booz, Allen & Hamilton, N.Y.C., 1967-76; product dir. Harris Corp., Dallas, 1976-79; v.p. Harris Corp., Ft. Lauderdale, Fla., 1979-82; gen. mgr. Harris Corp., Melbourne, Fla., 1982-86, sr. v.p., 1986-90; also bd. dirs. Harris Iberica, Madrid; pres. Am. Mfg. Group Inc., Vero Beach, Fla., 1990-93, AMG Inc., Harvard, Mass., 1993-94; pres., CEO Evans & Sutherland Computer Corp., Salt Lake City, 1994—; bd. dirs. Ikos Systems, Inc., sec. audit com., 1992—. 1st lt. U.S. Army, 1969-72. Fellow Am. Chem. Soc.; mem. IEEE, Nat. Am. Electronics Assn. (bd. dirs. 1984-87, nat. bd. dirs. 1988), Corp. for Open Systems (bd. dirs. 1986-88), Tau Beta Pi. Republican. Episcopalian. Avocations: tennis, photography. Home: PO Box 639 Harvard MA 01451 Office: PO Box 58700 600 Komas Dr Salt Lake City UT 84158

OZ, FRANK (FRANK RICHARD OZNOWICZ), puppeteer, film director; b. Hereford, Eng., May 25, 1944; s. Isidore and Frances Oznowicz. Student, Oakland City Coll., 1962. Puppeteer with the Muppets, N.Y.C., 1963—; characters performed include The Mighty Favag (Saturday Night Live 1975-76), Miss Piggy, Fozzie Bear, Animal, Sam the Eagle; now v.p. Jim Henson Prodns., N.Y.C.; creative cons. feature film The Great Muppet Caper; appeared in films The Blues Brothers, 1980, Trading Places, 1983, Labyrinth, 1986; voice of Yoda in films The Empire Strikes Back, 1980, Return of the Jedi, 1983; dir. films The Dark Crystal (with Jim Henson), 1982, The Muppets Take Manhattan, 1984, Little Shop of Horrors, 1986, Dirty Rotten Scoundrels, 1988, What About Bob?, 1991, Housesitter, 1992, The Indian in the Cupboard, 1995. Recipient 4 Emmy awards for outstanding performance. Mem. AFTRA, Dirs. Guild Am., Writers Guild Am., Screen Actors Guild, Acad. TV Arts and Scis. Office: Jim Henson Prodns 117 E 69th St New York NY 10021-5004*

OZANNE, JAMES HERBERT, financial services executive; b. Oak Park, Ill., Aug. 23, 1943; m. Susan Shennan; children: Timothy, Jill, Jeanne Marie, William. BS, DePaul U., Chgo., 1967. Pres. North American Car Corp., Chgo., 1975-83, Gen. Electric Railcar Services Corp., Chgo., 1983-84; v.p., gen. mgr. Gen. Electric Credit Corp., Stamford, Conn., 1984-86, exec. v.p., 1986-89; pres., chief exec. officer U.S. West Capital Corp., Stamford, Conn., 1989—. Office: US West Capital Corp 1 Canterbury Green 200 Stamford CT 06912 also: US West Fin Svcs 6300 S Syracuse Englewood CO 80111

OZAWA, MARTHA NAOKO, social work educator; b. Ashikaga, Tochigi, Japan, Sept. 30, 1933; came to U.S., 1963; d. Tokuichi and Fumi (Kawashima) O.; m. May 1959 (div. May 1966). BA in Econs., Aoyama Gakuin U., 1956; MS in Social Work, U. Wis., 1966, PhD in Social Welfare, 1969. Asst. prof. social work Portland (Oreg.) State U., 1969-70, assoc. prof. social work, 1970-72; assoc. rsch. prof. social work NYU, 1972-75; assoc. prof. social work Portland State U., 1975-76; prof. social work Washington U., St. Louis, 1976-85, Bettie Bofinger Brown prof. social policy, 1985—. Author: Income Maintenance and Work Incentives, 1982; editor: Women's Life Cycle: Japan-U.S. Comparison in Income Maintenance, 1989, Women's Life Cycle and Economic Insecurity: Problems and Proposals, 1989; editorial bd. Social Work, Silver Spring, Md., 1972-75, 85-88, New Eng. Jour. Human Svcs., Boston, 1987—, Encyc. of Social Work, Silver Spring, 1974-77, 91—, Jour. Social Svc. Rsch., 1977—, Children and Youth Svcs. Rev., 1991—, Social Work Rsch., 1994—. Grantee Adminstrn. on Aging, Washington, 1979, 84, Nat. Inst. Mental Health, 1990-93. Mem. Nat. Assn. Social Workers, Nat. Acad. Social Ins., Nat. Conf. on Social Welfare (bd. dirs. 1981-87), The Gerontol. Soc. Am., Coun. Social Work Edn., Washington U. Faculty Club (bd. dirs. 1988-91). Avocations: photography, tennis, swimming, gardening. Home: 13018 Tiger Lily Ct Saint Louis MO 63146-4339 Office: Washington U Campus PO Box 1196 Saint Louis MO 63130-4899

OZAWA, SEIJI, conductor, music director; b. Shenyang, People's Republic of China, Sept. 1, 1935; s. Kaisaku and Sakura Ozawa; m. Vera Motoki-Ilyin; children: Seira, Yukiyoshi. Student, Toho Sch. Music, Tokyo, Japan, 1953-59; studies with Hideo Saito, Eugene Bigot, Herbert Von Karajan, Leonard Bernstein; student at the invitation of Charles Munch, Tanglewood, 1959; DMus (hon.), U. Mass., New England Conserv. Music, Wheaton Coll. Music dir. Boston Symphony Orch., 1973—. One of three asst. condrs., N.Y. Philharm., 1961-62 season, music dir. Ravinia Festival, 1964-68, music dir. Toronto Symphony Orch., 1965-69, San Francisco Symphony Orch., 1970-76, appointed artistic advisor Tanglewood Festival, 1970, condr. Boston Symphony Orch. Evening at Symphony (Emmy award); music advisor Boston Symphony Orch., 1972-73, Saito Kinen Orch., Japan, 1992, internat. tour and Dvorak Gala, Prague, 1993; guest condr. major orchs. Recipient 1st prize Internat. Competition Orch. Condrs., 1959, Koussevitzky prize Tanglewood Music Ctr., 1960, Inouye award for Lifetime Achievement, 1994; conducting fellow Tanglewood Music Ctr., summer 1959; named Laureate Fondation du Japon, 1988; Seiji Ozawa Hall named for him Tanglewood Music Ctr., 1994. Office: Columbia Artists Mgmt Inc care Ronald A Wilford 165 W 57 St New York NY 10019-2201*

OZAWA, TED, electronics executive; b. 1937. V.p. Maxell Corp. of Am. Fair lawn, N.J.; treas. Battery Engring., Inc., Boston. Office: Maxell Corp of Am 22-08 State Rt 208 Fair Lawn NJ 07410 also: Battery Engring Inc 1636 Hyde Park Ave Boston MA 02136*

OZBUN, JIM L., academic administrator. Dean agr. and home econs. Wash. State U., Pullman, until 1988; pres. N.D. State U., Fargo, 1988—. Office: ND State U Office of Pres PO Box 5167 Fargo ND 58105-5167

OZELLI, TUNCH, economics educator, consultant; b. Ankara, Turkey, May 18, 1938; came to U.S., 1962; s. Sufyan and Saziye (Ozmorali) O.; m. Lale A. Baymur, Dec. 30, 1960 (div. Mar. 1972); children: Selva, Kerem; m. Nancy Ann Goldschlager, Feb. 3, 1974 (div. Dec. 1984); m. Meral Ozdemir, May 9, 1992. MBA, Fla. State U., 1963; PhD, Columbia U., 1968. Rsch. fellow Harvard U., Cambridge, Mass., 1969-70; econ. advisor Office Prime Minister, Ankara, 1970-72; prof. mgmt. N.Y. Inst. Tech., N.Y.C., 1972—; spl. advisor State Planning Orgn., Ankara, 1989-91. Contbr. articles to profl. jour. Ford Found. scholar, 1963-64, Found. for Econ. Edn. fellow, 1968. Mem. Am. Econ. Assn., Middle East Studies Assn., Turkish Mgmt. Assn., Delta Mu Delta. Avocation: equestrian activities. Office: NY Inst Tech Old Westbury NY 11568

OZERNOY, LEONID MOISSEY, astrophysicist; b. Moscow, May 19, 1939; came to U.S., 1986, naturalized citizen; m. Marianne Rosen; 2 children. BS in Physics, Moscow State U., 1961, MS in Astronomy, 1963; PhD in Astrophysics, Shternberg Astron. Inst., Moscow, 1966; DSc in Astrophysics, Lebedev Phys. Inst., USSR Acad. Scis., Moscow, 1971. Rsch. scientist, dept. theoretical physics Lebedev Phys. Inst., 1966-71, sr. rsch. scientist, 1971-86; asst. then assoc. prof. Moscow Physics and Tech. Inst., 1968-79, fired after applying for emigration from USSR; prof. astrophysics, disting. vis. scientist Ctr. for Astrophysics, Harvard Coll. Obs. and Smithsonian Astrophys. Obs., Cambridge, Mass., 1986-89; prof. astrophysics, disting. vis. scholar Inst. Geophysics and Planetary Physics, Los Alamos (N.Mex.) Nat. Lab., 1989-91; sr. assoc. Nat. Rsch. Coun. NAS Goddard Space Flight Ctr., NASA, Greenbelt, Md., 1991-92, sr. rsch. scientist Univ. Space Rsch. Assn., cons., 1993—; cons. Goddard Space Flight Ctr., NASA, 1993—; prof. computational sci. and space sci. Inst. Computation Sci. and Informatics, George Mason U., Fairfax, Va., 1993—, prof. physics and astron. dept., 1994—; vis. prof. Boston U., 1986-87, Harvard U., 1987; mem. sci. coun. on plasma astrophysics, Presidium of USSR Acad. Scis., 1971-75. Co-editor: Astrophysics and Space Scis. mag., 1976-86; author several books; contbr. over 220 sci. papers in theoretical astrophysics and related fields. Recipient Silver medal USSR Exhbn. of Achievements in Nat. Economy, 1988; NRC/NAS fellowship, 1991. Fellow Am. Phys. Soc. (com. on internat. freedom of scientists 1988-90); mem. AAAS, Internat. Astron. Union, N.Y. Acad. Scis., Am. Astron. Soc. (exec. com. high energy astrophysics div. 1989-90), Astron. Soc. Pacific, COSPAR (Com. Space Rsch., Internat. Coun. Sci. Unions), The Planetary Soc., Internat. Platform Assn. Achievements include establishment of mass-radius and mass-angular momentum relationships for galaxies, of methods for measuring/constraining the black hole mass at the center of the galaxy; research on theory for evolution of cosmological turbulence; and on theory for structure and evolution of supermassive, rotating, magnetized bodies (magnetoids). Office: George Mason U Inst Computat Sci & Informatics Sci and Tech Bldg I Fairfax VA 22030-4444 Office: NASA Code 685 Astronomy Solar Physics Goddard Space Flight Ctr Lab Greenbelt MD 20771

OZERO, BRIAN JOHN, chemical engineer; b. Winnipeg, Manitoba, Can., Dec. 14, 1932; came to U.S., 1963; s. Daniel and Mary (Karpiuk) O.; m. Ila Atlas, Dec. 14, 1985. BS in Chem. Engring., Queens U., Kingston, Ontario, Can., 1954; MS in Chem. Engring., NYU, 1968. Technologist Shell Oil Co., Montreal, Quebec, Can., 1954-60; design engr. Chem. Constrn. Co., London, 1960-63; sr. process engr. Sci. Design Co., N.Y.C., 1963-65, process mgr., 1965-75; tech. dir. Halcon SD Group Inc., N.Y.C., 1976-85; sr. process mgr. Tech. Evaluation and Devel. Assocs., Hoboken, N.J., 1986; pres., prin. cons. Scientech Assocs. Inc., N.Y.C., 1986—. Recognized expert in ethylene oxide/ethylene glycol; contbr. articles and chpts. to tech. jours. and encyclopedias in field; patentee in field. Pres. Barrier Beach Preservation Assn., Westhampton, N.Y., 1985-88. Mem. Am. Inst. Chem. Engrs., Rotary. Republican. Roman Catholic. Avocations: reading, tennis, skiing. Home: PO Box 1524 Westhampton Beach NY 11978-7524 Office: Scientech Assocs Inc 225 E 36th St Apt 19A New York NY 10016-3628

OZICK, CYNTHIA, author; b. N.Y.C., Apr. 17, 1928; d. William and Celia (Regelson) O.; m. Bernard Hallote, Sept. 7, 1952; 1 dau., Rachel Sarah. BA cum laude with honors in English, NYU, 1949; MA, Ohio State U., 1950; LHD (hon.), Yeshiva U., 1984, Hebrew Union Coll., 1984, Williams Coll., 1986, Hunter Coll., 1987, Jewish Theol. Sem. Am., 1988, Adelphi U., 1988, SUNY, 1989, Brandeis U., 1990, Bard Coll., 1991, Spertus Coll., 1991, Skidmore Coll., 1992. Author: Trust, 1966, The Pagan Rabbi and Other Stories, 1971, Bloodshed and Three Novellas, 1976, Levitation: Five Fictions, 1982, Art and Ardor: Essays, 1983, The Cannibal Galaxy, 1983, The Messiah of Stockholm, 1987, Metaphor and Memory: Essays, 1989, The Shawl, 1989, Epodes: First Poems, 1992, What Henry James Knew, and Other Essays on Writers, 1994, Portrait of the Artist as a Bad Character, and Other Essays on Writing, 1995, (play) Blue Light, 1994; also poetry, criticism, revs., transls., essays and fictions in numerous periodicals and anthologies. Phi Beta Kappa orator, Harvard U., 1985. Recipient Mildred and Harold Strauss Living award Am. Acad. Arts and Letters, 1983, Rea award for short story, 1986; Lucy Martin Donnelly fellow, Bryn Mawr Coll., 1992, Guggenheim fellow, 1982. Mem. PEN, Authors League, Am. Acad. of Arts and Scis., Am. Acad. of Arts and Letters, Dramatists Guild, Académie Universelle des Cultures (Paris), Phi Beta Kappa. Office: care Alfred A Knopf Co 201 E 50th St New York NY 10022-7703

OZIER, IRVING, physicist, educator; b. Montreal, Que., Can., Sept. 7, 1938; s. Harry and Peppi (Schwartzwald) O.; m. Joyce Ruth Weinstein, July 4, 1963; children: Elizabeth, David, Douglas. B.A., U. Toronto, 1960; A.M., Harvard U., 1961, Ph.D., 1965. Research fellow Harvard U., Cambridge, Mass., 1965-67, MIT, Cambridge, Mass., 1966-67; mem. tech. staff Sci. Ctr. Rockwell Internat., Thousand Oaks, Calif., 1966-70; assoc. prof. physics U. B.C., Vancouver, B.C., Can., 1970-77, prof., 1977—; vis. rsch. officer Katholieke Universiteit, Nijmegen, The Netherlands, 1976-77; vis. rsch. officer Nat. Rsch. Coun. Can., Ottawa, 1982-83; vis. prof. Eidgenossische Technische Hochschule, Zurich, Switzerland, 1988-89. Author research articles in molecular spectroscopy. Alfred P. Sloan research fellow, 1972-74; Izaak Walton Killiam Meml. Sr. fellow B.C., 1982-83. Mem. Am. Phys. Soc., Can. Assn. Physicists. Office: Dept Physics Univ BC, 6224 Agriculture Rd, Vancouver, BC Canada V6T 1Z1

OZIO, DAVID, professional bowler. Winner Firestone Tournament of Champions, 1991. Office: c/o Profl Bowlers Assn 1720 Merriman Rd Akron OH 44313-5252

OZMENT, STEVEN, historian, educator; b. McComb, Miss., Feb. 21, 1939; s. Lowell V. and Shirley M. (Edgar) O.; m. Andrea Todd Foster, Apr. 30, 1977; children: Amanda, Emma; children by previous marriage: Joel, Matthew, Katherine. B.A., Hendrix Coll., 1960; B.D., Drew Theol. Sch., 1964; Ph.D., Harvard U., 1967; M.A. (hon.), Yale U., 1975. Asst. prof. Inst. Late Medieval and Reformation Studies, U. Tübingen, Fed. Republic Germany, 1966-68; asst. prof. history and religious studies Yale U., New Haven, 1968-72; assoc. prof. Yale U., 1972-75, prof., 1975-79; prof. history Harvard U., 1979—, McLean prof. ancient and modern history, 1991—, assoc. dean undergrad. edn., 1984-87; Bonsall vis. prof. Stanford U., 1991. Author: Homo Spiritualis, 1969, The Reformation in Medieval Perspective, 1971, Mysticism and Dissent, 1973, The Reformation in the Cities, 1975, (with others) The Western Heritage, 1979, 5th edit., 1994, The Age of Reform, 1980; winner Schaff prize (Am. Book Award nominee 1980), Reformation Europe: A Guide to Research, 1982, When Fathers Ruled: Family Life in Reformation Europe, 1983, (with others) The Heritage of World Civilizations, 1985, 3d edit., 1993, Magdalena and Balthasar: An Intimate Portrait of Life in 16th Century Europe, 1986, Three Behaim Boys: Growing Up in Early Modern Germany, 1990, Protestants: The Birth of a Revolution, 1992; mem. editorial bd. Archive for Reformation History, 1976-93, Sixteenth Century Jour., 1976—, Jour. Am. Acad. Religion, 1972-77, Jour. Hist. Ideas, 1986—, Netherlands Archive for Church History, 1987—, Morse fellow, 1970-71, Guggenheim fellow, 1978, Cabot fellow, 1992. Mem. Am. Soc. Reformation Rsch. (dir. 1979-83). Home: 69 High Rd Newbury MA 01951-1725 Office: Harvard Univ Robinson Hall Cambridge MA 02138

OZMON, KENNETH LAWRENCE, university president, educator; b. Portsmouth, Va., Sept. 4, 1931; emigrated to Can.; s. Howard Augustine and Anna Josephine (Lynch) O.; m. Elizabeth Ann Morrison, July 6, 1968; children: Angela Francene, Kendi Elizabeth. BA in Philosophy and History magna cum laude, St. Bernard Coll., Ala., 1955; MA in Psychology, Cath. U., 1963; PhD in Psychology, U. Maine, 1968. Lic. psychologist, N.S. Instr. U. Maine, Orono, 1966-68; vis. lectr. St. Dunstan's U., P.E.I., Can., 1967; asst. prof. Calif. State U., Chico, 1968-69; chmn. dept. psychology U. P.E.I., Charlottetown, 1969-72, dean of arts, 1972-79; pres. St. Mary's U., Halifax, N.S., 1979—; chmn. Pres.' Council N.S.U., 1982-85; chmn. Met. Halifax U. Pres.' Com., 1982-84, 86-87, 92—; co-chmn. coordinating com. Nat. U. Week, 1983, 86-87. Contbr. numerous articles to psychol. jours. Bd. dirs. United Way Halifax-Dartmouth, 1980-82, Interuniv. Svcs., Inc., 1987-94, chmn., 1992—; provincial bd. dirs. Can. Assn. Mentally Retarded, 1980-82; co-chmn. Found. for Irish and Can. Studies, 1993; bd. dirs. Friends Nova Scotia Mus. Industry Soc., 1993—; mem. nat. coun. Can. Human Rights Found., 1976; mem. selection com. J.H. Moore Awards for Excellence, Toronto, 1983-92; hon. chmn. ann. campaign N.S. div. Can. Paraplegic Assn., 1985-86; mem. fundraising com. Phoenix House, 1986-88, Charitable Irish Soc. Halifax; chmn. Human Rights Commn., 1990—; mem. adv. coun. Order of Can., 1991-94; area chair for Nova Scotia Internat. Coun. Psychologists, 1992-93. Recipient Gov. Gen. of Can. award, 1993; named hon. prof. U. Internat. Bus. and Econs., Beijing, People's Republic of China; trustee scholar U. Maine, 1965-67; NDEA fellow, 1967-68. Mem. Assn. Atlantic Univs. (vice chmn. 1983-85, chmn. 1985-87), Assn. Commonwealth Univs (governing coun. 1988-91), Assn. Univs. and Colls. Can. (exec. coun. 1985-89, vice chmn. 1990-91, chmn., 1991-93, mem. audit com. 1991—, chmn. exec. com. 1991—, vice-chmn. nominating com. 1990-91), Can. Psychol. Assn. (Nat. Univ. Week coordinating com. 1983, co-chmn. 1986-87, audit com. 1985—, co-chmn. steering com. Halifax Met. Econ. Summit II 1994), Halifax Bd. Trade (internat. trade com. 1985-91, bd. dirs. 1989-91), Halifax Press Club, Halifax Club, Ashburn Golf Club, Saraguay Club. Roman Catholic. Avocations: fishing, golf, running. Home: 5895 Gorsebrook Ave, Halifax, NS Canada B3H 1G3 Office: St Mary's U, Halifax, NS Canada B3H 3C3

OZNOWICZ, FRANK RICHARD See OZ, FRANK

OZOG, EDWARD J., lawyer; b. Chgo., June 13, 1948. BA, DePaul U., 1970, JD, 1973. Bar: Ill. 1973, U.S. Supreme Ct. 1980. Asst. state's atty. Cook County Attys. Office, Ill., 1973-80; ptnr. Clausen Miller Gorman Caffrey & Witous, P.C., Chgo.; mem. faculty Loss Execs. Assn. Claims Coll., 1991; speaker in field. Bus. mgr. DePaul U. Law Rev., 1971-73; spl. asst. atty. gen./editor Arson Prosecution and Tng. Manual, 1987; contbr. articles to law jours. Mem. ABA (vice chmn. property law com., tort and ins. practice sect. 1988—), Ill. State Bar Assn., Chgo. Bar Assn., Internat. Assn. Def. Counsel, Advocates Soc., Internat. Assn. Arson Investigators (mem. Ill. chpt., Disting. Svc. award 1992). Office: Clausen Miller Gorman Caffrey & Witous PC 10 S LaSalle St Chicago IL 60603

PAALZ, ANTHONY L., beverage company executive; b. Louisville, Apr. 18, 1924; s. Leon A. and Rose M. (Westendick) P.; m. Elaine Wolf, Feb. 11, 1956 (dec. Dec. 1981); children: Teresa Dawson, Eileen Baldwin, Anthony L. Jr.; m. Alison Kerr, May 3, 1986. BS, U. Ind., 1949. Chief acct. J.E. Seagram & Sons Inc., N.Y.C., 1959-69, asst. controller, 1969-72, dir. of taxes, 1972-84, v.p. taxes, 1984—. Served with USN, 1943-45, PTO. Decorated numerous battle stars. Mem. Tax Execs. Inst. Avocation: golf. Home: 29 Treeview Dr Melville NY 11747-2413 Office: Joseph E Seagram & Sons Inc 800 3rd Ave New York NY 10022-7699

PAANANEN, VICTOR NILES, English educator; b. Ashtabula, Ohio, Jan. 31, 1938; s. Niles Henry and Anni Margaret (Iloranta) P.; m. Donna Mae Jones, Aug. 15, 1964; children: Karl, Neil. AB magna cum laude, Harvard U., 1960; MA, U. Wis., 1964, PhD, 1967. Instr. English Wofford Coll., Spartanburg, S.C., 1962-63; asst. prof. Williams Coll., Williamstown, Mass., 1966-68; asst. prof. Mich. State U., East Lansing, 1968-73, assoc. prof., 1973-82, prof., 1982—, asst. dean Grad. Sch., 1977-82, chmn. dept. English, 1986-94; vis. prof. Roehampton Inst., London, 1982, hon. fellow, 1992. Author: William Blake, 1977; contbr. articles to profl. and scholarly jours. Univ. fellow U. Wis., 1962, 63-64, Roehampton Inst. hon. fellow, London, 1992—; Harvard Nat. scholar, 1956-60. Mem. MLA, AAUP, Labor Party Advocates, Harvard Club of Washington, D.C., Phi Beta Kappa. Office: 152 Orchard St East Lansing MI 48823-4536 Office: Mich State Univ Dept of English Morrill Hall East Lansing MI 48824-1036

PAAS, JOHN ROGER, German language educator; b. Chgo., Mar. 14, 1945; s. Walter V. and Doris (Marinoff) P.; m. Martha Clem White, Aug. 24, 1968; children: Emily, Anne. BA summa cum laude, Hamilton Coll., Clinton, N.Y., 1967; PhD, Bryn Mawr Coll., 1973. Part-time asst. prof. Bryn Mawr (Pa.) Coll., 1973-74; prof. German Carleton Coll., Northfield, Minn., 1974—, dept chair, 1985-88. Author: The German Political Broadsheet, 1600-1700, 4 vols., 1985—, Effigies and Poesis: An Illustrated Catalogue of Printed Portraits with Laudatory Verses by German Baroque Poets, 2 vols., 1988; editor: Unbekannte Gedichte und Lieder des Sigmund von Birken, 1990, Hollstein's German Engravings Etchings and Woodcuts, 1400-1700, vols. 38-41, 1994-95, Der Franken Rom: Nuünbergs Blütezeit in der zweiten Hältle des 17 Jhs, 1995; (with Wolfgang Harms, Michael Schilling and Andreas Wang) Illustrierte Flugblätter des Barock: Eine Auswahl, 1983; contbr. articles to profl. jours. Sgt. U.S. Army, 1969-71. Summer grantee German Acad. Exch. Svc., 1975, 78, 83, Andrew W. Mellon Found., 1976, Faculty Devel. grantee Bush Found., 1978, Carleton Coll., 1985, NEH grantee, 1990, 92-93; vis. fellow Beinecke Libr., Yale U., 1991, IREX fellow, 1978, Fulbright sr. rsch. fellow, 1988-89. Mem. MLA, AATG, Soc. German Renaissance and Baroque Literature, Internationaler Arbeitskreis für Barockliteratur, Frühe Neuzeit Interdisziplinär. Home: 107 College St Northfield MN 55057 Office: Carleton College 1 N College St Northfield MN 55057

PAASWELL, ROBERT EMIL, civil engineer, educator; b. Red Wing, Minn., Jan. 15, 1937; s. George and Evelyn (Cohen) P.; m. Rosalind Snyder, May 31, 1958; children: Judith Marjorie, George Harold. B.A. (Ford Found. fellow), Columbia U., 1956, B.S., 1957, M.S., 1961; Ph.D., Rutgers U., 1965. Field engring. asst. Spencer White & Prentis, Washington, 1954-56; engr. Spencer White & Prentis, N.Y.C., 1957-59; rsch. scientist Davidson Lab., N.J., 1964; rsch. fellow Greater London Council, 1971-72; rsch. and teaching asst. Columbia U., 1959-62; asst. prof. civil engring. SUNY, Buffalo, 1964-68; chmn. bd. govs. Urban Studies Coll., 1973-76, assoc. prof., 1968-76, prof. civil engring., 1976-82; dir. Center for Transp. Studies and Research, 1979-82, chmn. dept. environ. design and planning, 1980-82; prof. transp. engring. U. Ill., Chgo., 1982-86, 89-90, dir. Urban Transp. Ctr., 1982-86; exec. dir. Chgo. Transit Authority, 1986-89; dir. transp. rsch. consortium, prof. civil engring. CCNY, 1990—, disting. prof., 1991—; faculty-on-leave Dept. Transp., 1976-77, cons., 1981—; v.p. Faculty Tech. Cons., Inc., Midwest Systems Scis., Inc., 1982-86; dir. Urban Mass Transp. Adminstrn. Summer Faculty Workshop, 1980, 81, Tel Aviv Transit Authority Project; cons. transp. planning, energy and soil mechanics; spl. cons. to Congressman T. Dulski, 1973; vis. expert lectr. Jilin U. Tech., Changchun, Peoples Republic of China, 1985, hon. prof. transp., 1986—; bd. dirs. D'Escuto Architects & Engrs., Chgo., Hickling Co., Ottawa, Can. Transit Devel. Corp.; chmn. transp. steering com. Sustainable Devel. Inst., 1994—; mem. adv. bd. Office of Tech. Assessment for Infrastructure and the Urban Core Project, 1994—; mem. faculty Lincoln Inst. Land Policy, 1994—; vis. prof. Tel Aviv U., 1995—. Author: Problems of the Carless, 1977; editor: Site Traffic Impact Assessment, 1992; contbg. author: Decisions for the Great Lakes, 1982, World Book Encyclopedia, 1992, 93, 94; mem. bd. editors Jour. Environ. Systems, 1974—, Transp., 1978—, Jour. Urban Tech., 1992—; contbr. articles to profl. jours. Mem. Buffalo Environ. Mgmt. Commn., 1972-74; mem. Area Com. for Transit, Mayor's Energy Adv. Bd., 1974, Block Grant Rev. Com., City of Buffalo; chmn. com. on transp., mem. rev. adv. bd. Rsch. and Planning Coun. Western N.Y.; mem. transp. com. Chgo. 1992 Worlds Fair; mem. citizens' adv. bd. Chgo. Transit Authority, 1985—; mem. strategic planning com. Regional Transp. Authority, 1985; mem. steering com. Nat. Transit Coop. Rsch. Program, 1991—, Borough pres. (Manhattan) Trans. Adv. Bd.; Bronx Ctr. Devel. Project; bd. dirs. Transit Devel. Corp., 1992—. Recipient Dept. Transp. award, 1977; SUNY faculty fellow, 1965-66. Fellow ASCE (past pres. Buffalo sect., chmn. steering com. 1992 specialty conf. traffic impact analysis); mem. AAAS, Transp. Rsch. Bd.

(chmn. com. on transp. disadvantaged, mem. exec. com., peer rev. com. nat. transp. ctrs. 1988—), Inst. Transp. Engrs. (transit coun., exec. com., chmn. legis. policy com.), Sigma Xi. Office: CCNY Inst Transp Systems Rm 220-Y 135th St and Convent Ave New York NY 10031

PABST, EDMUND G., retired insurance company executive, lawyer; b. Chgo., Apr. 22, 1916. Student, U. Calif-Berkeley; LL.D., B.S.L., Northwestern U., 1940. Bar: Ill., D.C. Mem. firm Leonard & Leonard, Chgo., 1940-41; atty. FTC, Washington, 1941-42; civilian lawyer U.S. Army, 1942-43; trial atty. OPA, Chgo., 1946-47; atty. Combined Ins. Co. Am., Chgo., 1947, v.p., asst. gen. counsel, 1954-59, sec., 1959-62, exec. v.p. adminstrn., 1962-76, W.Ger. Ops., 1976-78, v.p., gen. counsel, 1978-81, dir., 1952-83, mem. exec. com., 1958-76; officer, dir., mem. exec. com. Combined Am. Ins. Co., 1960-76; officer, dir.,mem. exec. com. Combined Ins. Co. Wis., 1953-76; officer, dir., mem. exec. com. Combined Life Ins. Co. N.Y., 1971-76; pres. Combined Opportunities, 1972-76. Bd. dirs. Uptown Chgo. Commn., pres., 1959-61; pres. S.E. Evanston Assn., 1968-70, 87-88; founding mem. Dewey Community Orgn., Evanston; mem. Evanston Zoning Bd. Appeals, 1969-76; mem. Evanston Zoning Amendment Com., 1980-88; bd. dirs. St. Francis Hosp., Evanston, 1980-89; trustee Mundelein Coll., 1971-88; mem. Commonwealth Edison Task Force City of Evanston, 1988-93; chmn. Foster Reading Ctr., 1992—. Mem. ABA, Ill. Bar Assn., Chgo. Bar Assn. (civil rights com. 1959-70, chmn. 1966-67, ins. law com. 1947-60, chmn. 1951-52), Health Ins. Assn. Am. (sec. bd. dirs. 1969-73), U.S. C. of C. (internat. ins. adv. council 1978-81), ACLU (dir. Ill. div., treas. 1969-76). Home: 425 Grove St Apt 7C Evanston IL 60201-4632

PACALA, LEON, retired assocation executive; b. Indpls., May 3, 1926; s. John and Anna (Ferician) P.; m. Janet Lefforge, Dec. 28, 1947 (dec. July 1987); children: Mark, Stephen, James; m. Virginia Strasenburgh, Mar. 10, 1990. AB, Franklin (Ind.) Coll., 1949; BD, Colgate Rochester Div. Sch., 1952; PhD, Yale U., 1960; LLD (hon.), Nazareth Coll., 1980; LHD (hon.), Franklin Coll., 1987. Ordained to ministry Baptist Ch., 1952. Asst. prof. philosophy and religion DePauw U., 1956-61; participant study religion undergrad. coll. Lilly Found., 1957-59; assoc. prof. religion Bucknell U., 1961-68, prof., 1968-73, chmn. dept., 1961-64, dean, 1962-73; pres. Colgate Rochester (N.Y.) Div. Sch.; also Bexley Hall, Crozer Theol. Sem., 1973-80; exec. dir. Assn. Theol. Schs. in U.S. and Can., 1980-91; cons. acad. adminstrn. Beirut Coll. Women, 1972. Contbr. articles to profl. jours. Exec. com. Christian Faith in Higher Edn. Projects, 1965-68; trustee Franklin Coll., 1967-73; bd. dirs. Rohesters Jobs, Inc., 1973-80; trustee Rochester Area Colls., 1973-80; dir. Nat. Housing Ministries, Am. Bapt. Chs., 1976-80. With USAAF, 1944-45. Internat. Rotary scholar, Louvain U., Belgium, 1952-53. Mem. Am. Conf. Acad. Deans (exec. com., treas., chmn., presiding officer 1973-74), Am. Assn. Higher Edn., Assn. Am. Colls. (commn. religion higher edn.), Assn. Theol. Schs. (com. accreditation), World Conf. Assns. Theol. Instns. (v.p. 1988—), Am. Bapt. Assn. Sem. Adminstrs. (chmn 1975-80). Home: 3515 Elmwood Ave Rochester NY 14610-3464

PACE, CAROLINA JOLLIFF, communications executive, commercial real estate investor; b. Dallas, Apr. 12, 1938; d. Lindsay Gafford and Carolina (Juden) Jolliff; student Holton-Arms Jr. Coll., 1956-57; BA in Comparative Lit., So. Meth. U., 1960; m. John McIver Pace, Oct. 7, 1961. Promotional advisor, dir. season ticket sales Dallas Theatre Ctr., 1960-61; exec. sec. Dallas Book and Author Luncheon, 1959-63; promotional and instl. cons. Henry Regnery-Reilly & Lee Pub. Co., Chgo., 1962-65; pub. trade rep. various cos., instl. rep. Don R. Phillips Co., Southeastern area, 1965-67; Southwestern rep. Ednl. Reading Svc., Inc.-Troll Assocs., Mahwah, N.J., 1967-72; v.p., dir. multimedia div. Melton Book Co., Dallas, 1972-79; v.p. mktg. Webster's Internat., Inc., Nashville, 1980-82; pres. Carolina Pace Inc., 1982—; mem. adv. bd. Nat. Info. Ctr. of Spl. Edn. Materials; mem. materials rev. panel Nat. Media Ctr. for Materials of Severely-Profoundly Handicapped, 1981; mem. mktg. product rev. bd. LINC Resources, 1982, 83, 84, mktg. task force, 1983, adv. bd., 1987; reviewer spl. edn. U.S. Dept. Edn., 1975-79, 85; rev. cons. Health and Humas Svcs., 1982, 83, 84, 86; product rev. task force CEC, 1984, 85, 86; cons. Ednl. Cable Consortium, Summit, N.J., 1982-87. Mem. adv. coun. Grad. System Sch. Libr. and Info. Sci. Found., U. Tex., 1987—; co-vice chair Friends Highland Park Libr., 1989; mem. focus group City Dallas Growth Policy Plan; mem. art and design com. West Downtown Ctrs.; active Dallas City Wide Parking Task Force, Ctrl. Transp. Forum Ctrl. Bus. Dist., Union Sta. Art & Design Com., Downtown Transfer Ctrs., Art and Design Com., West End Task Force, Ctrl. Bus. Dist. Task Force; co-founder Operation TexRec, 1990-91. Mem. Ctrl. Dallas Assn. (transportation com.), Dallas Plan (focus com.), Nat. Audio Visual Assn. (conf. panelist 1979), Internat. Comm. Industries Assn., Assn. Ednl. and Comm. Tech., Assn. Spl. Edn. Tech. (nat. dir., v.p. publicity 1980-82), Women's Nat. Book Assn, Women in Comm., Dallas Founders, Ctrl. Dallas Assn., Friends of the West End (pres. 1988—), West End Assn. Dallas (alums. subcom. on traffic and parking 1986-87, com. demographic study 1987-88), Pub. Rels. Soc. Am., Coun. Exceptional Children (art exhibitors com., chmn. public. com. 1979 conf., conf. speaker 1981), Downtown Transp. Mgmt. Assn. (adv. bd., chmn. vanpools subcom.), DAR (Jane Douglas chpt.), Dallas Zool. Soc., Dallas West End Hist. Dist. Assn., Dallas Mus. of Art, Dallas Southern Meml. Tex. Parking Assn., Kimball Art Mus., Alpha Delta Pi. Presbyterian. Producer ednl. videos; contbr. articles to profl. jours. Home: 4524 Lorraine Ave Dallas TX 75205-3613

PACE, CHARLES ROBERT, psychologist, educator; b. St. Paul, Sept. 7, 1912; s. Charles N. and Lenore (Lee) P.; m. Rosella Gaarder, Dec. 18, 1937; children: Rosalind, Jenifer. B.A., De Pauw U., 1933; M.A., U. Minn., 1935, Ph.D., 1937. Instr. in gen. coll. U. Minn., 1937-40; research asso. Am. Council Edn., 1941-42; research psychologist Bur. Naval Personnel, Navy Dept., 1943-47; mem. faculty Syracuse U., 1947-61, asso. dir., then dir. evaluation service center, 1947-52, asst. to chancellor, 1948-52, prof. psychology, chmn. dept., dir. psychol. research center, 1952-61; prof. higher edn. UCLA, 1961-82, prof. emeritus, 1982—; Mem. adv. cons. Am. Council Edn., Coll. Entrance Exam. Bd., Social Sci. Research Council. Author: They Went to College, 1941, (with M. E. Troyer) Evaluation in Teacher Education, 1944, (with F.H. Bowles and J.C. Stone) How to Get Into College, 1968, College and University Environment Scales, 2d edit, 1969, Education and Evangelism, 1972, The Demise of Diversity?, 1974, Measuring Outcomes of College, 1979, Measuring the Quality of College Student Experiences, 1984, The Undergraduates, 1990. Post-doctoral fellow Rockefeller Found., 1940-41; fellow Center Advanced Study Behavioral Scis., 1959-60; recipient citation for meritorious civilian service Navy Dept., 1946, E.F. Lindquist award Am. Ednl. Research Assn. and Am. Coll. Testing Program, 1984, Suslow award for outstanding svc. Assn. for Instl. Rsch., 1989. Mem. Am. Psychol. Assn., Am. Ednl. Research Assn., Assn. for Study Higher Edn. (Disting. Career award 1989), Am. Assn. Pub. Opinion Research.

PACE, ERIC DWIGHT, journalist; b. N.Y.C., Oct. 13, 1936; s. Eric and Eleanor Marguerite (Jones) Paepcke; m. Suzanne Monique Wiedel, June 12, 1976 (div. Jan. 1987); children: Christine, Lydia. Grad., Phillips Exeter Acad., 1953; student, U. Heidelberg, Germany, 1955-56; B.A. magna cum laude, Yale, 1957; M.A., Johns Hopkins, 1959. Reporter San Angelo (Tex.) Standard Times and Evening Standard, 1957-58; mem. staff Life mag. N.Y.C., 1959-61; assigned to Life mag., Bonn, 1961, Paris, 1961-62; corr. Time mag., Bonn, 1962-63, Hong Kong, 1963-65; mem. staff New York Times, N.Y.C., 1965-66; assigned to New York Times, Saigon, 1966, Cairo, 1966-69, Paris, 1969-70, Beirut, 1970-71, N.Y.C., 1971-74, Teheran, 1974-77, N.Y.C., 1977—. Author: novels Saberlegs, 1970, Any War Will Do, 1973, Nightingale, 1979; contbr. articles to Fgn. Affairs among others. Served with AUS, 1957. Recipient George Polk Meml. award Overseas Press Club, 1968, Page One award N.Y.C. Newspaper Guild, 1968. Mem. Mystery Writers Am., Authors Guild, Crime Writers Assn. (Gt. Britain), Am. P.E.N. Unitarian. Clubs: Century (N.Y.C.), Squadron A (N.Y.C.). Office: New York Times 229 W 43rd St New York NY 10036-3959

PACE, LEONARD, retired management consultant; b. Torrington, Conn., Oct. 24, 1924; s. Anthony and Maria G. P.; m. Maureen Therese Murphy, Sept. 15, 1956; children: Leonard Anthony, Susan Maria, Daniel Graham, Thomas William, Mary Macaire, Cathleen Anne. Student, Syracuse U., 1943; B.S.M.E., U. Conn., 1949; postgrad, N.Y. U., 1951-52, Wayne U., 1955. Cert. mgmt. cons. With GAF, 1949-57, asst. to div. controller, 1954-57; with Deloitte Haskins and Sells, N.Y.C., 1957—, head N.Y. mgmt. adv. services, 1965-67, head Eastern region, 1967-76, nat. dir. mgmt. adv. services,

1976-85, chmn. internat. mgmt. adv. svcs. com. Served as officer, pilot USAAF, 1943-45. Mem. Am. Mgmt. Assn., Inst. Mgmt. Cons. (dir., chmn. profl. standards com.). Clubs: Baltusrol Golf, Union League, Circumnavigators. Home: 35 Little Wolf Rd Summit NJ 07901-3112

PACE, NORMA, economist, consulting firm executive. Grad., Hunter Coll., 1941; grad. study, Columbia U.; Ph.D. (hon.), Mich. Tech. U., 1975, Poly. Inst.; N.Y., 1976, Cedar Crest Coll., 1977, Grove City Coll., 1980, City U. N.Y., 1981. Staff Econometric Inst.; with U.S. Economics Corp. (bus. adv. cons. service), 1944-71, pres., 1969-71; v.p., dir. indsl. econs. Lionel D. Edie & Co., N.Y.C., 1971-73; sr. v.p. Am. Paper Inst.; pres. ECAP (cons. firm), 1987-92; dir. WEPA Group, 1992-95, Paper Analytics Assn., 1995—; asst. devel. visual aids for teaching econs. Columbia Visual Lab.; dir. Sears, Roebuck & Co., Ga. Pacific Corp., Englehard Corp., Hasbro Co., 3M Co., A. O. Smith Co.; gov. U.S. Postal Svc. Trustee Com. for Econ. Devel. Named to Hunter Coll. Hall of Fame, 1973. Mem. U.S.C. of C. Address: 100 E 42d St New York NY 10017

PACE, R(ALPH) WAYNE, organizational behavior educator; b. Wanship, Utah, May 15, 1931; s. Ralph W. and Elda (Fernelius) P.; m. Gae Tueller, Mar. 19, 1953; children: Michael, Rebecca, Lucinda, Gregory, Angela, Lavinia. BS, U. Utah, 1953; MS, Brigham Young U., 1957; PhD, Purdue U., 1960. Assoc. prof. Parsons Coll., Fairfield, Ia., 1960-62; vis. prof. Bowdoin Coll., Brunswick, Maine, 1961; asst. prof. Calif. State U., Fresno, 1962-66; prof., chmn. dept. speech communication U. Mont., 1966-72; lectr. Sch. Adminstrv. Leadership, 1966-72; prof., chmn. dept. speech communication U. N.Mex., 1972-78; prof. dept. communication, dir. Communication Research Ctr., coordinator human resource devel. program Brigham Young U., 1978-85, prof. orgnl. behavior Sch. Mgmt., 1986—; prof. human resource devel. Brigham Young U., Laie, Hawaii, 1987-88; sr. ptnr. Organizational Assocs., 1970—; cons. editor HRD series Prentice Hall Pub. Co., 1989—; disting. vis. prof. Boise State U., 1992; faculty rsch. fellow So. Cross U., Lismore, N.S.W., Australia, 1995. Author: (with R.R. Boren) The Human Transaction: Facts, Functions and Forms of Interpersonal Communication, 1973, (with Boren and B.D. Peterson) Communication Behavior: A Scientific Approach, 1975, Communication Experiments: A Manual for Conducting Experiments, 1975; co-editor: (with B.D. Peterson and T.R. Radcliffe) Communicating Interpersonally: A Reader, 1973, (with B.D. Peterson and G.M. Goldhaber) Communication Probes, 3d edit, 1982, (with B.D. Peterson and M.D. Burnett) Techniques for Effective Communication, 1979, Organizational Communication, 1983, (with G.E. Mills) Bibliography of Management Development Literature, 1987, Supplement, 1990, (with G.E. Mills and B.D. Peterson) Analysis in Human Resource Training and Organizaton Development, 1989, (with D.F. Faules) Organizational Communication, 1989, 2d edit., 1994, (with E. Stephan) The Perfect Leader, 1990, (with P.C. Smith and G.E. Mills) Human Resource Development, 1991, (with D. F. Faules) Organizational Communication, 3d edit., 1994, (with E. Stephan) Me Mum Sez, 1994. Served with AUS, 1953-55. Fellow AAAS, Acad. Human Resource Devel. (pres. 1993); mem. ASTD (Mgmt. Devel. award of Excellence 1987, Profs. Human Resource Devel. Disting. Scholar award 1992), Internat. Com. Assn. (pres. 1970-71, Divsn. IV Outstanding Mem. award 1986), Western States Comm. Assn. (pres. 1978), Internat. Soc. Gen. Semantics, Am. Bus. Comm. Assn., Speech Comm. Assn., Acad. Mgmt., Sons Utah Pioneers (nat. v.p. 1986-87, pres. Brigham Young chpt. 1986, Disting. Svc. award 1987). Republican. Mem. LDS Ch.

PACE, RICHARD RANDALL, lawyer, educator; b. Chgo., Dec. 19, 1940; s. John Gordon and Marie Chewning (Doherty) P.; m. Janet Yvonne Davis, Aug. 1, 1965 (div. Nov. 1970); children: Terrence Randall, John Douglas; m. May (Nmn) Yee, Nov. 7, 1987. BS in Engring., U.S. Naval Acad., 1963; JD, U. Ill., 1970. Bar: Ill. 1970, Calif. 1971. Assoc. Schiff, Hardin & Waite, Chgo., 1970-73, Pope Ballard, Shepard & Fowle, Chgo., 1974-76; assoc., ptnr. Hill, Farrer & Burrill, L.A., 1976-85; ptnr. Carlsmith Ball Wichman Murray Case Mukai & Ichiki (formerly Carlsmith Wichman Case Mukai & Ichiki), L.A., 1986-95, Preston Gates & Ellis, L.A., 1995—; vis. lectr. sch. indsl. rels. UCLA, 1979-82, sch. bus. adminstrn. U. So. Calif., 1985—; lectr. employment law. Co-author: Advising California Employers, 1980. Lt. USN, 1963-67. Mem. ABA, Calif. Bar Assn., Ill. Bar Assn. Republican. Roman Catholic. Avocation: golf. Office: Preston Gates & Ellis 601 S Figueroa St Ste 3450 Los Angeles CA 90017

PACE, STANLEY CARTER, retired aeronautical engineer; b. Waterview, Ky., Sept. 14, 1921; s. Stanley Dan and Pearl Eagle (Carter) P.; m. Elaine Marilyn Cutchall, Aug. 21, 1945; children: Stanley Dan, Lawrence Timothy, Richard Yost. Student, U. Ky., 1939-40; B.S., U.S. Mil. Acad., 1943; M.S. in Aero. Engring., Calif. Inst. Tech., 1949; LLD (hon.), Maryville Coll., 1987. Commd. 2d lt. USAAF, 1943, advanced through grades to col., 1953; pilot, flight leader B-24 Group, 15th Air Force, 1943-44; chief power plant br., procurement div. Hdqrs. Air Materiel Command Wright-Patterson AFB, Ohio, 1945-48; assignments, procurement div. Hdqrs. Air Materiel Command, 1949-53; dep. chief prodn. Hdqrs. Air Materiel Command, 1952-53, resigned, 1954; with TRW, Inc., Cleve., 1954-85, successively sales mgr., asst. mgr.; mgr. West Coast plant; mgr. jet div. Tapco plant, Cleve.; asst. mgr. Tapco group, 1954-58, v.p., gen. mgr., 1958-65, exec. v.p. co., 1965-77, pres., 1977-85, vice chmn., 1985, dir., 1965-85; vice chmn., dir. Gen. Dynamics Corp., St. Louis, 1985, chmn., chief exec. officer, 1985-90, also bd. dirs. Head United Way drive, Cleve., 1984; former council commr., pres. Great Cleve. Council Boy Scouts Am.; former trustee Nat. Jr. Achievement, Denison U., Washington U., Judson Park; former chmn. Greater Cleve. Roundtable, Cleve. Found. Distbn. Com., Nat. Assn. Mfrs. Decorated Air medal with oak leaf clusters. Mem. AIAA, Aerospace Industries Assn. (chmn.), Soc. Automotive Engrs., Union Club, Country Club, Chagrin Valley Hunt Club, Pepper Pike Club, Eldorado Club, Rolling Rock Club, St. Louis Country Club, Delta Tau Delta. Home: 75-735 Topaz Ln Indian Wells CA 92210-8666

PACE, STEPHEN SHELL, artist, educator; b. Charleston, Mo., Dec. 12, 1918; s. John C. and Ora K. (Reeves) P.; m. Palmina Natalini, Feb. 26, 1949. Student, Inst. Fine Arts, San Miguel, 1945-46, Art Students League, N.Y.C., 1948-49, Grande Chaumiere, Paris, 1950, Inst. D'Arte Statale, Florence, Italy, 1951, Hans Hofmann Sch., N.Y.C., 1951-52. Artist in residence Washington U., 1959; instr. painting Pratt Inst., N.Y.C., 1961-69; artist in residence Des Moines Art Ctr., 1970; vis. artist U. Calif., 1968; assoc. prof. Bard Coll., 1969-71, Am. U., 1975-83. One-man shows include Hendler Gallery, 1953, Artists Gallery, 1954, Poindexter Gallery, 1956, 57, Washington U., St. Louis, 1959, Holland-Goldowsky Gallery, Chgo., 1960, Howard Wise Gallery, Cleve., 1960, N.Y., 1960, 61, 63, 64, Dilexi Gallery, San Francisco, 1960, HCE Gallery, 1956-59, 61-63, 66, Dwan Gallery, Los Angeles, 1961, Hayden Gallery, Cambridge, Mass., 1961, Ridley Gallery, Evansville, Ind., 1966, U. Calif. at Berkeley, 1968, Graham Gallery, N.Y.C., 1969, Des Moines Art Center, 1970, U. Tex., Austin, 1970, Kansas City Art Inst., 1973, A.M. Sachs Gallery, N.Y.C., 1974, 76, 77, 78, 79, 81, 83, 85, Drew U., 1975, Bard Coll., 1975, Am. U., 1976, Roberto Polo Gallery, Washington, 1976, New Harmony (Ind.) Gallery, 1977, Farm Gallery, Far Hill, N.J., 1978, Barbara Fiedler Gallery, Washington, 1980, Chastenet Gallery, Washington, 1981, Katherina Rich Perlow Gallery, N.Y.C., 1987, 89, 91, 94, Vanderwoude-Tananbaum Gallery, N.Y.C., 1991, U. N.C., Greensboro, 1991, Evansville Mus., 1992, Maine Coast Artists, Rockport, 1994, Bates Coll. Mus., Lewiston, Maine, 1994; exhibited in group shows in U.S., Europe, Japan, Middle East, India, Burma, Australia, N.Z., Hawaii, Central and S.Am.; represented in permanent collections, Whitney Mus., Chrysler Mus., Norfolk, Va., Provincetown (Mass.) Mus., Evansville (Ind.) Mus., U. So. Ill., Michener Found., Walker Art Center, U. Calif., CIBA-Geigy Collection, Hallmark Collection, Bundy Art Gallery, U. N.C., Greensboro, Chase Manhattan Bank, Munson-Williams-Procter Inst., Utica, N.Y., Des Moines Art Center, Boston Mus. Fine Arts, Met. Mus., N.Y.C., Phillips Collection, Washington, Am. U. Washington, Corcoran Gallery, Washington, J. Patrick Lannan Mus., Venice, Calif., Curie Inst., Paris, Hirshhorn Mus., Washington, Bristol Myers Collection, Indpls. Mus., Portland (Maine) Mus., Bowdoin Coll. Mus., U. So. Ill., Carbondale, Brown U., Providence, Oberlin (Ohio) Coll. Mus. Served with AUS, 1941-45, ETO. Recipient Dolian Lorian award for promising Am. painters, 1954; Hallmark award, 1961; Guggenheim fellow, 1980; Creative Artists Pub. Service Program grantee, 1973. Mem. Nat. Acad. of Design (Benjamin Altman prize 1993). Office: 164 11th Ave New York NY 10011-1005

PACE, THOMAS M., lawyer; b. Mesa, Ariz., Feb. 5, 1952; s. Lemuel Max and Ann (Green) P.; m. Vi Garrett Pace, Jan. 24, 1981; children: Melanie, Brittany. BA, Stanford U., 1973; JD, U. Ariz., 1976. Bar: Ariz.; cert. real estate specialist. Assoc. Martin, Feldhacker & Freidl, Phoenix, 1976-77, Trew & Woodford, Phoenix, 1977-78; ptnr. Hecker, Phillips & Hooker, Tucson, 1978-88; sr. ptnr. O'Connor Cavanagh, Tucson, 1988-95. Mem. Mayor's Housing Task Force, Tucson, 1993; bd. dirs. Tucson Urban League, 1986—; chmn. So. Ariz. Homebuilders Polit. Action Com., 1995. Mem. So. Ariz. Homebuilders (tech. com.), Pima County Real Estate Rsch. Coun., Tucson C. of C. (bus. devel. com. 1991—), Stanford Club of So. Ariz. Democrat. Office: 3443 N Campbell Ave Ste 145 Tucson AZ 85719-2379

PACELLA, BERNARD LEONARDO, psychiatrist; b. Toronto, Ont., Can., July 25, 1912; m. Theresa Rita Domalesky; children: Karen Pacella Oldham, Richard B., Madelyn Joyce Nichols, Bernard Leonard Jr. BS, U. Colo., 1931, MD, 1935; post doctoral, N.Y. Psychoanalytic Inst., 1946-51. Cert. child, adolescent, and adult psychoanalyst; Diplomate Am. Bd. Psychiatry and Neurology. Intern Kings County Hosp., Bklyn., 1935-37, resident in pediatrics, 1937-38; resident in psychiatry Dept. Psychiatry Columbia U. and N.Y. State Psychiat. Inst., N.Y.C., 1938-40; rsch. fellow in psychiatry Columbia Presbyn. Med. Ctr., N.Y.C., 1940-41, instr. mil. psychiatry, 1943-46; lectr. clin. psychiatry Coll. Physicians and Surgeons Columbia U., 1942-44, assoc. clin. psychiatry, 1944-45, instr., 1945-47, asst. clin. prof., 1947-55, assoc. clin. prof., 1955-72, clin. prof., 1972-84, spl. lectr., mem. faculty Ctr. Psychoanalytic Tng. and Rsch., 1984—, clin. prof. emeritus, 1990—. Contbr. articles to profl. jours.; reviewer Psychoanalytic Quar. Pres. Margaret S. Mahler Psychiat. Rsch. Found., 1970-88, bd. dirs.; sec.-treas., bd. dirs. Sigmund Freud Archives; pres. Psychoanalytic Assistance Fund, 1974-89, bd. dirs.; bd. dirs. Freud London Mus.; co-trustee Mary S. Sigourney award, 1990. With Colo. N.G., 1930-35, M.C. USAR, 1935-40. Decorated Cavaliere Officiale dell Ordine al Merito (Italy), 1958. Fellow Am. Coll. Psychoanalysis, Am. Acad. Child and Adolescent Psychiatry, N.Y. Acad. Medicine, Am. Psychiat. Assn.; mem. AMA, Am. Orthopsychiat. Assn., Am. Soc. Adolescent Psychiatry, Am. Psychoanalytic Assn. (reviewer jour., pres.-elect 1990, pres. 1992—, treas. 1983—), Assn. Child Psychoanalysis, Group Advancement Psychiatry, Assn. Psychoanalytic Medicine, N.Y. Psychoanalytic Soc. and Inst. (bd. dirs.), Internat. Psychoanalytic Assn. N.Y. Coun. Child and Adolescent Psychiatry, Alpha Omega Alpha. Home and Office: 115 E 61st St New York NY 10021

PACH, PETER BARNARD, newspaper columnist and editor; b. Bklyn., Aug. 3, 1951; s. Stewart Warner and Constance (Barnard) P.; m. Kathleen Ann Megan, Sept. 7, 1985; children: Nell, Samuel. BA in English, Union Coll., 1973. Reporter Record Jour., Meriden, Conn., 1974-78, Wallingford bur. chief, 1978-83; Middletown bur. chief Hartford Courant, Conn., 1983-84, columnist, 1984-95; mem. editorial bd. Hartford (Conn.) Courant, 1992—; vis. instr. Wesleyan U., Middletown, Conn., 1985—. Recipient First Bus. and Econ. Reporting award New England Press Ass., 1977. Mem. Dedham County and Polo Club. Avocations: running, skiing, golf, gardening, reading. Home: PO Box 46 Middle Haddam CT 06456-0046 Office: Hartford Courant 285 Broad St Hartford CT 06115-2510

PACHECO, MANUEL TRINIDAD, university president; b. Rocky Ford, Colo., May 30, 1941; s. Manuel J. and Elizabeth (Lopez) P.; m. Karen M. King, Aug. 27, 1966; children: Daniel Mark, Andrew Charles, Sylvia Lois Elizabeth. BA, N.Mex. Highlands U., 1962; MA, Ohio State U., 1966, PhD, 1969. Prof. edn., univ. dean Tex. A&I U., Laredo, 1972-77, exec. dir. Bilingual Edn. Ctr., Kingsville, 1980-82 prof. multicultural edn., chmn. dept. San Diego State U., 1977-78; prof. Spanish and edn. Laredo State U., 1978-80, pres., 1984-88; assoc. dean Coll. Edn. U. Tex., El Paso, 1982-84, exec. dir. for planning, 1984; chief policy aide for edn. to gov. N.Mex., 1984; pres. U. Houston-Downtown, 1988-91, U. Ariz., Tucson, 1991—; cons. lang. div. Ency. Britannica, 1965-72; bd. dirs. Valley Nat. Bank Corp., Nat. Security Edn. Program.; mem. exec. com. Bus-Higher Edn. Forum. Co-editor: Handbook for Planning and Managing Instruction in Basic Skills for Limited English Proficient Students, 1983; producer: (videotapes) Teacher Training, 1976. Treas. nat. com. U.S. Commn. on Civil Rights, L.A., 1987-91; trustee United Way of Houston, 1988-91; chmn. pub. rels. Buffalo Bayou Partnership, Houston, 1988-91; bd. dirs. Ctr. for Addiction and Substance Abuse, Greater Tucson Econ. Coun., Ariz. Econ. Coun., Ariz. Town Hall. Recipient Disting. Alumnus award Ohio State U., Columbus, 1984; named Most Prominent Am.-Hispancis Spanish Today mag., 1984, one of 100 Outstanding Hispanics Hispanic bus., 1988, Man of Yr. Hispanic Profl. Action Com., 1991; Fulbright fellow U. de Montepellier, France, 1962. Mem. Am. Assn. State Colls. and Univs., Nat. Assn. of Pub. Adminstrn., Hispanic Assn. Colls. and Univs., Tex. Assn. of Chicanos in Higher Edn., Rotary, Phi Delta Kappa. Office: U Ariz Office of Pres Tucson AZ 85721

PACHECO-RANSANZ, ARSENIO, Hispanic and Italian studies educator; b. Barcelona, Spain, Feb. 8, 1932; s. Arsenio Pacheco and Jacoba Ransanz-Alvarez; m. Mercedes Olivella-Sole, Sept. 1, 1956; children: Arsenio-Andrew, David-George. MA, U. Barcelona, 1954, PhD, 1958. Tutor Colegio Mayor Hispanoamericano Fray Junipero Serra, Barcelona, 1954-56; lectr. Hochschüle für Wirtschaft und Sozialwissenschaften, Nurnberg, 1956; asst. lectr. U. Glasgow, Scotland, 1957-59; lectr. U. St. Andrews, Scotland, 1960-70; vis. prof. U. Pitts., 1966; prof. Hispanic and Italian studies U. B.C., Vancouver, Can., 1970—. Editor: Historia de Xacob Xalabin, 1964, Testament de Bernat Serradell, 1971, Varia fortuna del soldado Pindaro, 1975; contbr. articles to profl. jours. Bd. dirs. Can. Fedn. Humanities, 1981-84. Fellow Royal Soc. Can.; mem. Can. Assn. Hispanists (pres. 1978-81), Asociacion Internacional de Hispanists, MLA, Assn. Hispanists Gt. Britain and Ireland, N.Am. Catalan Soc. (v.p. 1984-87, 1988-90), Anglo Catalan Soc., Associacio Internacional de Llengua i Literatura Catalana. Roman Catholic. Office: U BC, Hispanic and Italian Studies, Vancouver, BC Canada V6T 1Z1

PACHMAN, DANIEL J., physician, educator; b. N.Y.C., Dec. 20, 1911; s. Louis and Ann (Kleinman) P.; m. Vivian Allison Futter, Nov. 8, 1935; children—Lauren Merle, Grace Allison. A.B., U.N.C., 1931; M.D., Duke U., 1934. Diplomate Nat. Bd. Med. Examiners, Am. Bd. Pediatrics. Intern pediatrics U. Chgo., 1934-35, instr. pediatrics, 1937-40; intern pediatrics N.Y. Hosp., 1935-36; resident pediatrics, attending pediatrician Duke Hosp., Durham, N.C., 1936-37; instr. Duke U., 1936-37, Northwestern U., 1940-42; practice medicine specializing in pediatrics Chgo., 1940—; clin. asst. prof. pediatrics U. Ill., 1950-59, clin. assoc. prof., 1960-67, clin. prof., 1967-81, emeritus prof., 1981—; attending pediatrician Ill. Research and Edn. Hosp., 1950-81; cons. Presbyn-St. Luke's Hosp., Chgo., 1971-81, South Shore Hosp., 1955-60, Ill. Central Hosp., 1970-72, chmn. dept. pediatrics, 1962-70; attending pediatrician Trinity Hosp., 1971—; prof. pediatrics Rush Med. Coll., 1971-81, emeritus prof., 1981—; staff Children's Meml. Hosp.; courtesy staff Chgo. Lying-in Hosp; Med. cons. Bd. Edn., S. Shore High Sch., 1954-56; mem. advisory com. on sch. health Chgo. Bd. Health, 1962—, Chgo. Bd. Edn., 1962-66; pediatric cons. Ill. Council for Mentally Retarded Children, 1960-66; chmn. subcom. on sch. health Chgo. Med. Sch., 1961-67; chmn. Ill. Pediatric Coordinating Council, 1969-76. Contbr. numerous articles to profl. jours. Mem. com. on rights of minors Ill. Commn. on Children, 1975-77; mem. Mayor's Com. on Sch. Bd. Nominations, 1965-68; mem., co-chmn. Ill. Bd. for Opinions on Profl. Nursing, 1980—. Served to lt. col. M.C. U.S. Army, 1942-46. Recipient Archibald L. Hoyne award Chgo. Pediatric Soc., 1977. Fellow Am. Acad. Pediatrics (mem. exec. com. Ill. 1961-69, rep. to adv. council on child health Nat. Congress Parents and Tchrs., chmn. sci. exhibits com. 1964-72), Am. Cancer Soc. (pub. edn. com. 1967-69), Chgo. Inst. Medicine (mem.-at-large jt. com. on sch. services 1961-64), Chgo. Med. Soc. (past chmn. child health com.), Chgo. Pediatric Soc., AMA (med./edn. com. on sch. and coll. health), Phi Beta Kappa, Sigma Xi. Club: Quadrangle (bd. dirs. 1969-72), Carlton. Home: 1212 N Lake Shore Dr Chicago IL 60610-2371 Office: 2315 E 93rd St Chicago IL 60617-3948 *Knowledge, perception and an outlook of acceptance and encouragement make the life of a pediatrician an interesting and disciplined adventure.*

PACHOLSKI, RICHARD FRANCIS, retired securities company executive, financial advisor, consultant; b. Seattle, June 18, 1947; s. Theodore Francis and Nellie (Tarabochia) P.; m. Dorothy Irene Nelson, May 25, 1974; children: Nicolas, Tara. BA cum laude, U. Wash., 1969, MBA summa cum laude, 1970. CPA, Wash. Mgr. Arthur Andersen & Co., Seattle, 1970-76; v.p., contr. SNW Enterprises, Seattle, 1976-82; sr. v.p., treas., sec., dir.

Seattle N.W. Securities, 1982-93; cons. Carl & Co., Portland, Oreg., 1984-88, Ellis & Carl Inc., Portland, 1979-83; CPA cons. and advisory practice, 1979—; adj. prof. U. Wash., Seattle, 1976-80; bd. dirs. Seattle N.W. Securities. Mem. AICPA, Wash. Soc. CPAs, Nat. Assn. Securities Dealers (past bd. dirs. local dist.), Wash. Athletic Club, PacWest Club (Redmond, Wash.). Roman Catholic. Home and Office: 5060 164th Ct NE Redmond WA 98052-5294

PACHTER, IRWIN JACOB, pharmaceutical consultant; b. N.Y.C., July 15, 1925; s. Nathan and Ethel Lillian (Thomases) P.; m. Elaine Anna White, Aug. 23, 1953; children: Wendy, Jonathan. B.S., UCLA, 1947; M.S., U. N.Mex., 1949; Ph.D., U. So. Calif., 1951; postgrad., U. Ill., 1951-52, Harvard U., 1952-53. Research chemist Ethyl Corp., 1953-55; asso. research chemist Smith Kline & French, 1955-62, asst. sec. head, 1962; dir. medicinal chemistry Endo Labs., 1962-66; dir. research Endo div. du Pont Co., 1967-70; v.p. research and devel. Bristol Labs. div. Bristol-Myers Co., 1970-82; lectr. Adelphi U., 1963-69. Contbr. articles to profl. jours.; patentee in field. Trustee Gordon Research Conf., 1972-75; chmn. medicinal chemistry study group Walter Reed Inst. Research, 1975-77. Served with USN, 1944-46. Mem. Am. Chem. Soc. (chmn. div. medicinal chemistry 1974-76), Pharm. Mfrs. Assn. (chmn. research and devel. sect. 1975-76). Home: 101 Woodberry Ln Fayetteville NY 13066-1745

PACIFICO, ALBERT DOMINICK, cardiovascular surgeon; b. Bklyn., Sept. 24, 1940; s. Dominick Vincent and Amelia Catherine (Jannelli) P.; m. Vicki Lynne Overton, May 16, 1980; children—Albert D., Nicole M., Paul V. B.S., St. Johns U., 1960; M.D., N.J. Coll. Medicine, 1964. Diplomate Am. Bd. Surgery, Am. Bd. Thoracic Surgery. Med. intern Jersey City Med. Ctr., Seton Gall Coll. Medicine, 1964-65; asst. resident in surgery Mayo Clinic, Rochester, Minn., 1965-67; research fellow in surgery U. Ala., Birmingham, 1967-69, sr. resident, then chief resident surgery, resident in thoracic and cardiovascular surgery, 1968-72, mem. faculty dept. surgery, 1970—, prof. surgery, 1978-83, John W. Kirklin prof. cardiovascular surgery, 1983—, vice chmn. dept. surgery, 1990, dir. cardiothoracic surgery, 1984—, dir. Congenital Heart Disease Diagnosis and Treatment Ctr., 1985—; mem. staff gen., thoracic and cardiovascular surgery Univ. Hosp., Birmingham, 1972—, VA Hosp., Birmingham, 1972—; mem. staff Children's Hosp., Birmingham, 1971—, chief gen., thoracic and cardiovascular surgery, 1984—. Author: (with others) Pediatric Cardiac Surgery, 1985, Cardiology, 1985, Textbook of Surgery, 13th edit., 1986, The Treatment of Congenital Cardiac Anomalies, 1986, Perspectives in Pediatric Cardiology, 1988, Current Therapy in Cardiothoracic Surgery, 1989, Decision Making in Surgery of the Chest, 1989, Cardiac Surgery: Cyanotic Congential Heart Disease, 1989, Reoperation in Cardiac Surgery, 1989, others; mem. editorial bd. Am. Jour. Cardiology, 1983—, Heart and Vessel, 1985—, Jour. Cardiac Surgery, 1985—; cons. editorial referee Ala. Jour. Med. Scis., 1974-75; contbr. articles to med. jours. Fellow ACS, Am. Coll. Cardiology, Am. Surg. Assn.; mem. AMA, Ala. State Med. Soc., Jefferson County Med. Soc., Am. Heart Assn. (Paul Dudley White Internat. Svc. Citation 1977), Am. Assn. Thoracic Surgery, Soc. Thoracic Surgeons, Am. Surg. Soc., Internat. Coll. Pediatrics, John Kirklin Soc., Congentital Heart Surgeons Soc., Assn. Acad. Surgery, Ala. chpt. Mayo Clinic Alumni Assn., Panamanian Soc. Cardiology (hon.), Peruvian Soc. Thoracic and Cardiovascular Surgery (hon.), Soc. Nat. Inst. Cardiology Mex. (hon.), Cardiac Soc. Australia and New Zealand (corr.), Peruvian Soc. Cardiology (corr.), Alpha Omega Alpha. Republican. Roman Catholic. Office: Univ Ala UAB Station Birmingham AL 35294

PACINO, AL (ALFREDO JAMES PACINO), actor; b. N.Y.C., Apr. 25, 1940; s. Salvatore and Rose P. Student, High Sch. of Performing Arts, N.Y.C., Actors Studio, from 1966. Formerly mail deliverer editorial offices Commentary Mag.; formerly messenger, movie theatre usher, bldg. supt.; co-artistic dir. The Actors Studio, Inc., N.Y.C., 1982-84. Served subsequently as actor, dir. and comedy writer in Off-Off Broadway theatres, Elaine Stewart's Cafe La Mama, Julian Beck & Judith Malina's Living Theatre; appeared in New Theatre Workshop prodn. of The Peace Creeps, Dec., 1966; joined Charles Playhouse, Boston, fall, 1967, and performed in New Theatre Workshop prodn. of America Hurrah and Awake and Sing; appeared in a one-act play Off Broadway The Indian Wants the Bronx, opened Astor Pl. Theater on Jan. 17, 1968 (Obie as best actor in Off-Broadway prodn. 1967-68); made Broadway debut in Does A Tiger Wear A Necktie?, 1969 (Tony award as best dramatic actor in a supporting role, named most promising new Broadway actor in a Variety poll of metropolitan drama critics); appeared in The Local Stigmatic at Actors Playhouse, N.Y.C., opening 1969; joined Repertory Theater of Lincoln Center, N.Y.C.; other plays include The Basic Training of Pavlo Hummel, Boston Repertory Theater, 1972, Camino Real, Richard III, 1973, 79, Jungle of Cities, 1979, The Connection, Hello Out There, Tiger at the Gates, American Buffalo, Julius Caesar, 1988, Salome, Chinese Coffee, Circle in the Square, 1992; (films) debut in Me, Natalie, 1969, Panic in Needle Park, 1971, The Godfather, 1972 (Best Actor award Nat. Soc. Film Critics, Acad. award nominee), Scarecrow, 1973, Serpico, 1973 (Acad. award nominee), The Godfather, Part II, 1974 (Acad. award nominee), Dog Day Afternoon (Acad. award nominee), 1975, Bobby Deerfield, 1977, And Justice for All, 1979 (Acad. Award nomination), Cruising, 1980, Author! Author!, 1982, Scarface, 1983, Revolution, 1985, Sea of Love, 1990, Dick Tracy, 1990 (Acad. award nominee), The Godfather Part III, 1990, Frankie and Johnny, 1991, Glengarry Glen Ross, 1992 (Acad. award nominee), Scent of a Woman, 1992 (Acad. award for Best Actor), Carlito's Way, 1993, Two Bits, 1994, City Hall, 1995, Heat, 1995. Recipient Am. Comedy award film Dick Tracy, 1991. Office: Chal Productions 301 W 57th St New York NY 10019*

PACIOCCO, C. ANTHONY, banker; b. Williamsport, Pa., Oct. 11, 1944; s. Thomas Sr. and Theresa (Cardelli) P.; m. Pamela Garnett, Dec. 18, 1972; children: Scott Anthony, Matthew Garnett Paciocco. Student, U. Richmond, 1973; grad., U. Va., 1979, La. State U., 1983. Mgmt. assoc. NationsBank, Richmond, Va., 1973-74, asst. mgr., 1975-76, first level officer, 1976, dept. head, asst. v.p., 1982-89, gen. mgr., 1990—; mgr. NationsBank, Vienna, Va., 1977. Contbr. articles to profl. jours. Pres. Pemberton PTA, Richmond, 1989, bd. dirs. 1989-90; bd. dirs. Tuckahoe Little League, Richmond, 1989-92, v.p. 1989—; bd. dirs. U. Richmond, 1983-88, v.p. 1983; com. mem. United Way of Greater Richmond, Godwin High Sch. Community Coun.; nominating com. Boy Scouts Am.; fund raiser Tuckahoe YMCA, others; With U.S. Army, 1968-70, Vietnam. Decorated by U.S. Army, Vietnam; recipient Disting. Sales award Sales and Mktg. Execs. Mem. Rotary (com. chmn. West Richmond chpt.). Republican. Baptist. Avocations: reading, music, sports, family. Home: 1800 Windingridge Dr Richmond VA 23233-4137 Office: Hand Craft Svcs 5705 Patterson Ave Richmond VA 23226

PACK, ALLEN S., retired coal company executive; b. Bramwell, W.Va., Dec. 11, 1930; s. Paul Meador and Mable Blanche (Hale) P.; m. Glenna Rae Christian, June 21, 1952; children: Allen Scott Jr., David Christian, Mark Frederick, Andrew Ray. B.S., W.Va. U., 1952. Gen. mgr. Island Coal Co., Holden, W.Va., 1969-70, pres., 1970-73; v.p administrn. Island Coal Co., Lexington, Ky., 1973-75; exec. v.p. Cannelton Holding Co., Charleston, W.Va., 1975-77, pres., chief ops. officer, 1977-80, pres., chief exec. officer, 1980-91; chmn., 1991-93, ret., 1993. Bd. dirs. Buckskin coun. Boy Scouts Am., Charleston, 1976—, pres., 1980, chmn., 1994, 95; bd. dirs. W.Va. Univ. Found., Morgantown, 1978—; trustee Davis and Elkins Coll., W.Va. Served to capt. USMC, 1952-54. Recipient Silver Beaver award Boy Scouts Am., 1981. Presbyterian.

PACK, EMILY LLOYD See LLOYD, EMILY

PACK, LEONARD BRECHER, lawyer; b. Seattle, Feb. 7, 1944; s. Howard David and Vivian (Brecher) P.; m. Barbara-Jane Lunin (div. Sept. 1978); children: Jesse, Justin; m. Adele Susan Weisman, Jan. 7, 1979; 1 child, Anna Rae. BA, Columbia U., 1966, JD, 1970, MIA, 1970. Bar: N.Y. 1971. Law clk. to judge U.S. Ct. Appeals D.C. Circuit, 1970-71; assoc. Fried, Frank, Harris, Shriver & Jacobson, N.Y.C., 1971-78; sec., assoc. gen. counsel Metromedia, Inc., Secaucus, N.J., 1979-86; sr. v.p., gen. counsel Orion Pictures Corp., N.Y.C., 1986-90; ptnr. Berger Steingut & Stern, N.Y.C., 1990-93; pvt. practice N.Y.C., 1993—. Bd. dirs., v.p. Dance Theatre Workshop. Mem. ABA. Democrat. Jewish. Avocation: music. Office: 1271 Ave of Americas Ste 4500 New York NY 10020

PACK, RICHARD MORRIS, broadcasting executive; b. N.Y.C., Nov. 22, 1915; s. Charles and Bertha (Gross) P.; m. Laura Lipkin, June 27, 1940; children: Robert N., Judith (dec.). A.B., NYU, 1938. Dir. publicity and continuity Sta. WNYC, N.Y.C., 1938-40; dir. publicity Sta. WOR, N.Y.C., 1942-47; dir. programming Sta. WNEW, N.Y.C., 1949-52; dir. programming and ops. Sta. WNBC and WNBT-TV, N.Y.C., 1952-54; v.p. programming Westinghouse Broadcasting Co. Inc., N.Y.C., 1955-65, sr. v.p. programming and prodn., 1965-72; pres. Group W Films, 1966-72; exec. adviser to chmn. Westinghouse Broadcasting Co., 1972-76; creative cons. Post-Newsweek Stas., Washington, 1972-76; disting. vis. lectr. telecommunications and film San Diego State U., 1988. Exec. producer film: One Day in the Life of Ivan Denisovich; author: (with Jo Ranson) Opportunities in Radio, 1948, Opportunities in Television, 1950; editor TV Quar., 1981—. Mem. pres.'s coun. social work edn. NYU, 1963-73. With USAAF, 1943-46.

PACK, ROBERT M., American literature educator, poet; b. N.Y.C., May 19, 1929; s. Carl and Henrietta (Langbert) P.; m. Patricia Powell, June 7, 1961; children: Erik, Pamela, Kevin. B.A., Dartmouth Coll., 1951; M.A., Columbia U., 1953. Abernathy prof. Am. Lit., Middlebury (Vt.) Coll., 1970—; dir. Bread Loaf Writers' Conf., 1973—. Author poetry: The Irony of Joy, 1955, A Stranger's Privilege, 1959, Guarded By Women, 1963, Home from the Cemetery, 1969, Nothing But Light, 1972, Keeping Watch, 1976, Waking to My Name: New and Selected Poems, 1980, Faces in a Single Tree: A Cycle of Monologues, 1984, Affirming Limits: Essays on Morality, 1985, A Swquence of Poems, 1987. Fulbright fellow, 1956-57; recipient awards Nat. Council of Arts, awards Nat. Arts and Humanities. Home: RR 2 Middlebury VT 05753-9802 Office: Middlebury Coll Middlebury VT 05753

PACK, RUSSELL T, theoretical chemist; b. Grace, Idaho, Nov. 20, 1937; s. John Terrell and Mardean (Izatt) P.; m. Marion Myrth Hassell, Aug. 21, 1962; children: John R., Nathan H., Allen H., Miriam, Elizabeth, Quinn R., Howard H. BS, Brigham Young U., 1962; PhD, U. Wis., 1967. Postdoctoral fellow U. Minn., Mpls., 1966-67; asst. prof. Brigham Young U., Provo, 1967-71; assoc. prof. Brigham Young U., 1971-75, adj. prof., 1975-88; staff scientist Los Alamos (N.Mex.) Nat. Lab., 1975-83, fellow, 1983—, assoc. grp. leader, 1979-81; vis. prof. Max Planck Institut, Gottingen, 1981; chmn. Gordon Rsch. Conf., 1982; lectr. in field. Contbr. articles to profl. jours. Named Sr. U.S. Scientist, Alexander Vol Humboldt Found., 1981. Fellow Am. Phys. Soc. (sec.-treas. div. Chem. Physics 1990-93); mem. Am. Chem. Soc., Sigma Xi. Mem. Ch. of Jesus Christ of Latter Day Saints. Home: 240 Huberty Ln Los Alamos NM 87544-3526 Office: Los Alamos National Lab T-12 Ms # B268 Los Alamos NM 87545

PACK, SUSAN JOAN, art consultant; b. N.Y.C., June 15, 1951; d. Howard Meade and Nancy (Buckley) P. BA summa cum laude, Princeton U., 1973. Copywriter Laurence Charles & Free, N.Y.C., 1978-83, Warwick Advt., N.Y.C., 1983-85; sr. copywriter Saatchi & Saatchi Compton, N.Y.C., 1985-88; pres. The Pack Collection, 1989—. Author: Film Posters of the Russian Avant-Garde, 1995. Mem. Princeton (N.J.) U. Libr. Coun., 1985-93; trustee Pack Found. for Med. Rsch., N.Y., 1983—; bd. dirs. The Poster Soc., N.Y., 1985-87. Recipient 4 Clio awards, 1981, 1 Clio award, 1982; named one of top art collectors under 40 Art and Antiques Mag., 1985. Mem. Phi Beta Kappa.

PACKARD, BARBARA BAUGH, science institute administrator, physician, physiologist; b. Uniontown, Pa., Mar. 10, 1938; d. Walter Ray and Yolande (Ciarlo) Baugh; m. Lawrence Arthur Krames, Nov. 24, 1963 (div. 1971); m. John E. Packard III, July 14, 1979. B.S., Waynesboro Coll., 1960; M.S., W. Va. U., 1961, Ph.D., 1964; M.D., U. Ala.-Birmingham, 1974. Rsch. assoc. Boston U., 1966; instr. biology, rsch. assoc. in medicine U. Chgo., 1966-67; physiologist myocardial infarction br. Nat. Heart Inst., Bethesda, Md., 1967-71; rsch. assoc. U. Ala., Birmingham, 1971-74; Osler med. intern Johns Hopkins Hosp., Balt., 1974-75; sr. med. scientist administr. cardiac disease br. div. heart and vascular disease Nat. Heart, Lung, and Blood Inst., Bethesda, Md., 1975-79, assoc. dir. cardiology, 1979-82, dir. div. heart and vascular diseases, 1980-86, assoc. dir. for sci. program operation, 1986—; Trustee Waynesburg Coll., 1991—. Served with USPHS, 1975—. Decorated USPHS Commendation Medal, Outstanding Svc. medal, 1986, Meritorious Svc. medal, 1988, Disting. Svc. medal 1991; recipient Disting. Pa. Coll. Alumni citation, 1991. Fellow Am. Coll. Cardiology (bd. govs. 1992—); mem. Am. Physiol Soc., Am. Heart Assn., Johns Hopkins Med. and Surgical Soc., Assn. Military Surgeons, Sigma Xi. Office: Nat Heart Lung & Blood Inst Bldg 31 Rm 5A03 9000 Rockville Pike Bethesda MD 20892-0001

PACKARD, BONNIE BENNETT, state legislator; b. Concord, N.H., Nov. 9, 1946; d. James Oliver and Caro Lucia (Arsenault) Bennett; m. David Bartlett Packard, Oct. 1, 1983. Mem. N.H. Ho. of Reps., Concord, 1981-82, 85—, vice chair ho. econ. devel. com., 1992, chair ho. commerce com., 1993—; v.p., treas. Dodd Ins. Agy., Contoocook, N.H., 1984-85; bd. dirs. Bus. Fin. Authority. State pres. N.H. Fedn. Rep. Women, 1982-83; chmn. Merrimack County (N.H.) Rep. Com., 1979-80; mem. Hillsborough County Rep. Com., 1995, chair Hillsborough County Del., 1995—; mem. Bd. Selectmen, New Ipswich, N.H., 1989-90; nat. del. trustee Nat. Kidney Found., 1990-91, 1st v.p. N.H. chpt., 1990-91. Mem. New Ipswich Hist. Soc., Greenville Women's Club. Episcopalian. Avocations: sketching, antiques, political campaigns. Home: 6 Joy Ln New Ipswich NH 03071-3610 Office: NH Ho of Reps Legis Office Building Rm 302 Concord NH 03301

PACKARD, DAVID, manufacturing company executive, electrical engineer; b. Pueblo, Colo., Sept. 7, 1912; s. Sperry Sidney and Ella Lorna (Graber) P.; m. Lucile Salter, Apr. 8, 1938 (dec., 1987); children: David Woodley, Nancy Ann Packard Burnett, Susan Packard Orr, Julie Elizabeth Stephens. B.A., Stanford U., 1934, EE, 1939; LLD (hon.), U. Calif., Santa Cruz, 1966, Catholic U., 1970, Pepperdine U., 1972; DSc (hon.), Colo. Coll., 1964; LittD (hon.), So. Colo. State Coll., 1973; D.Eng. (hon.), U. Notre Dame, 1974. With vacuum tube engring. dept. Gen. Electric Co., Schenectady, 1936-38; co-founder, ptnr. Hewlett-Packard Co., Palo Alto, Calif., 1939-47, pres., 1947-64, chief exec. officer, 1964-68, chmn. bd., 1964-68, 72-93, chmn. emeritus, 1993—; U.S. dep. sec. defense Washington, 1969-71; dir. Genetech, Inc., 1981-92; bd. dirs. Beckman Laser Inst. and Med. Clinic; chmn. Presdl. Commn. on Def. Mgmt., 1985-86; mem. White House Sci. Coun., 1982-88. Mem. President's Commn. Pers. Interchange, 1972-74, President's Coun. Advisors on Sci. and Tech., 1990-92, Trilateral Commn., 1973-81, Dirs. Coun. Exploratorium, 1987-90; pres. bd. regents Uniformed Svcs. U. of Health Scis., 1975-82; mem. U.S.-USSR Trade and Econ. Coun., 1975-82; mem. bd. overseers Hoover Instn., 1972—; bd. dirs. Nat. Merit Scholarship Corp., 1963-69, Found. for Study of Presdl. and Congl. Terms, 1978-86, Alliance to Save Energy, 1977-87, Atlantic Coun., 1972-83, vice chmn., 1972-80, Am. Enterprise Inst. for Public Policy Rsch., 1978—, Nat. Fish and Wildlife Found., 1985-87, Hitachi Found. Adv. Coun., 1986—; vice chmn. The Calif. Nature Conservancy, 1983-90; trustee Stanford U., 1954-69, pres., 1958-60, Hoover Instn., The Herbert Hoover Found., David and Lucile Packard Found., pres., chmn. Found 1964—; Herbert Hoover Found., 1974—; Monterey Bay Aquarium Found., chmn., 1978—, The Ronald Reagan Presdl. Found. 1986-91, Monterey Bay Aquarium Rsch. Inst., chmn., pres. 1987—. Decorated Grand Cross of Merit Fed. Republic of Germany, 1972, Medal Honor Electronic Industries, 1974; numerous other awards including Silver Helmet Def. award AMVETS, 1973, Washington award Western Soc. Engrs., 1975, Hoover medal ASME, 1975, Gold Medal award Nat. Football Found. and Hall of Fame, 1975, Good Scout award Boy Scouts Am., 1975, Vermilye medal Franklin Inst., 1976, Internat. Achievement award World Trade Club of San Francisco, 1976, Merit award Am. Cons. Engrs. Council Fellows, 1977, Achievement in Life award Ency. Britannica, 1977, Engring. Award of Distinction San Jose State U., 1980, Thomas D. White Nat. Def. award USAF Acad., 1981, Disting. Info. Scis. award Data Processing Mgmt. Assn., 1981, Sylvanus Thayer award U.S. Mil. Acad., 1982, Environ. Leadership award Natural Resources Def. Council, 1983, Dollar award Nat. Fgn. Trade Council, 1985, Gandhi Humanitarian Award, 1988, Roback Award Nat. Contract Mgmt. Assn., 1988, Pub. Welfare Medal NAS, 1989, Chevron Conservation Award, 1989, Doolittle Award Hudson Inst., 1989, Disting. Citizens Award Commonwealth Club San Francisco, 1989, William Wildback award, Nat. Conf. Standards Labs., Washington, 1990, Terrance Keenan Leadership award Grantmakers in Health, 1994, John Martin Excellence in Marine Scis. medal Stanford U., 1994, Nat. Disting. Svc. award Nat. Acads. Practice, 1994, Disting. Grantmakers award Coun. on Founds., 1994, Am. Philanthropy award Columbus Found., 1994, Lifetime Achieve-

ment award Lemelson-MIT, 1995; named to Silicon Valley Engring. Hall of Fame, Silicon Valley Engring. Coun., 1991, Pueblo (Colo.) Hall of Fame, 1991. Fellow IEEE (Founders medal 1973); mem. Nat. Acad. Engring. (Founders award 1979), Instrument Soc. Am. (hon. lifetime mem.), Wilson Council, The Bus. Roundtable, Bus. Council, Am. Ordnance Assn. (Crozier Gold medal 1970,) Henry M. Jackson award 1988, Nat. Medal Tech. 1988, Presdl. Medal of Freedom 1988, Sigma Xi, Phi Beta Kappa, Tau Beta Pi, Alpha Delta Phi (Disting. Alumnus of Yr. 1970). Office: Hewlett-Packard Co PO Box 10301 Palo Alto CA 94304-1112 also: Monterey Bay Aquarium Rsch Inst 160 Central Ave Pacific Grove CA 93950-3067 also: David and Lucile Packard Found 300 2nd St Ste 200 Los Altos CA 94022-3621

PACKARD, ELEANOR GOULD See GOULD, ELEANOR LOIS

PACKARD, GEORGE RANDOLPH, journalist, educator; b. Phila., May 27, 1932; s. George Randolph and Anita Porter (Clothier) P.; m. Mary Biddle Lloyd, June 26, 1954 (div. Aug. 1978); children: Frank Randolph, Mary Wingate, William Clothier, Andrew Lloyd, Benjamin Wood, Alexander Barnes, Kent Elizabeth Davis-Packard; m. Lavinia Fletcher Plumley, July 1990. A.B., Princeton U., 1954; Ph.D., Fletcher Sch. Law and Diplomacy, 1963; research scholar, Tokyo U., 1961-62. Spl. asst. to U.S. ambassador to Japan, 1963-65; chief diplomatic corr. Newsweek mag., Washington, 1965-67; mng. editor Phila. Bull., 1969-73, exec. editor, 1973-75; dep. dir. Woodrow Wilson Internat. Center for Scholars, Smithsonian Instn., Washington, 1976-79; prof. Sch. Advanced Internat. Studies Johns Hopkins U., 1967-68, 94—, dean Sch. Advanced Internat. Studies, 1979-93; vis. pres. Internat. U. Japan, 1994—. Author: Protest in Tokyo: The Security Treaty Crisis of 1960, 1966, Japan, Korea and China, 1979, also articles. Candidate for U.S. Senate from Pa., 1975-76; bd. dirs. Asia Found., San Francisco, Atlantic Council U.S. Served to 1st lt. AUS, 1956. Ford fellow, 1960-62. Mem. Assn. Asian Studies, Japan Soc. N.Y., Council Fgn. Relations N.Y., Phi Beta Kappa. Club: Metropolitan (Washington). Home: 4425 Garfield St NW Washington DC 20007-1143 Office: Johns Hopkins U Sch Advanced Internat Study 1619 Massachusetts Ave NW 1740 Massachusetts Ave NW Washington DC 20036

PACKARD, JOHN MALLORY, physician; b. Saranac Lake, N.Y., Sept. 25, 1920; s. Edward Newman and Mary Bissell (Betts) P.; m. Ann Maurine Schoonover, June 15, 1944; children: Michael David, John Mallory, Ann Maurine, Mary Betts, Charles Edward, Kris Asvananda, Frank Schoonover, Charlotte Mellen. B.A., Yale U., 1942; M.D., Harvard U., 1945. Diplomate Am. Bd. Internal Medicine. Intern Presbyn. Hosp., N.Y.C., 1945-46; resident in internal medicine Peter Bent Brigham Hosp., Boston, 1948-49; practice medicine specializing in internal medicine and cardiology Pensacola, Fla., 1954-68; prof. medicine, asso. dean Med. Sch. U. Ala., Birmingham, 1968-76; exec. dir. Ala. Regional Med. Program, Birmingham, 1968-73; corp. v.p. med. edn. Bapt. Med. Centers, Birmingham, 1976-92; ret. Contbr. articles to med. jours. Served with USN, 1946-54. Fellow ACP, Am. Coll. Cardiology, Council Clin. Cardiology; mem. Jefferson County Med. Soc., Med. Assn. Ala., AMA, Am. Soc. Internal Medicine, Ala. Soc. Internal Medicine (pres. 1981-82), Alpha Omega Alpha. Republican. Episcopalian.

PACKARD, JULIE, aquarium administrator; d. David and Lucile P. Exec. dir. Monterey Bay Aquarium, Monterey, Calif., 1984—. Recipient Edward H. Bean Awd., Am. Assn. Zoological Parks and Aquariums, 1993. Office: Monterey Bay Aquarium 886 Cannery Row Monterey CA 93940-1085*

PACKARD, P. KIM, diversified products company executive; b. Rome, N.Y., Dec. 23, 1938; s. Walter E. and Gretchen (Kauth) P.; m. Evelyn A. Stumphauzer, Apr. 28, 1962; children: Laurel A. Springer, David J., Brian K. BSEE, Pa. State U., 1960; MS in Mgmt., MIT, 1971. With GT Sylvania, 1960-80; various mktg. and sales positions, 1960-71; ops. mgr. picture tubes Seneca Falls, N.Y., 1971-72; gen. mgr. Cable TV div. RL Tex., 1972-74; v.p. Western Switch Gear div. Los Angeles, 1974-77; v.p. Engineered Products div. St. Louis, 1977-80; v.p., group exec. Warner & Swasey div. Bendix Corp., Cleve., 1980-82, pres., 1984-85; v.p., group exec. Allied/ Bendix, Cleve., 1982-84; pres., chief operating office Hobart Bros. Co., Troy, Ohio, 1985-92; pres., CEO Prestolite Electric Inc., 1992—; also bd. dirs.; bd. dirs. 1st Nat. Bank of Dayton, PEI Holding Inc., Columbus Jack Corp. & Kurz Kasch. Mem. exec. com. labor mgmt. forum Greater Cleve. Roundtable, 1984-85; mem. adv. bd. Ohio State U. Coll. Engring., 1987—; various offices United Way Cleve., 1980-84; trustee Arts Dayton; mem. St. Leonard Bus. Devel. Com.; active parish activities Roman Cath. Ch.; mem. Dayton Area Progress Coun.; bd. dirs. Dayton Art Inst., 1991-93. Sloan fellow MIT, 1970-71; named one of Outstanding Young Men Am., 1972. Mem. IEEE, Nat. Electrical Mfrs. Assn. (bd. govs. 1986—, chmn. indsl. automation div. 1987-88), Nat. Machine Tool Builders Assn., Am. Welding Soc., Dayton C. of C. (bd. dirs., steering com./regulatory planning), Electrical Mfrs. Club. Avocations: skiing, tennis, golf. Home: # 230 3000 Glazier Way Ann Arbor MI 48105 Office: Prestolite Electric Inc Ste 300 2100 Commonwealth Blvd Ann Arbor MI 48105

PACKARD, ROBERT CHARLES, lawyer; b. Los Angeles, Sept. 21, 1919; s. Charles W. and Gertrude (Vern) P.; m. Nanette Taylor, Dec. 21, 1973. B.S., U. So. Calif., 1941, J.D., 1947. Bar: Calif. 1948. Sr. ptnr. Kirtland & Packard, L.A., 1948—. Fellow Am. Coll. Trial Lawyers; mem. ABA, L.A. Bar Assn. (substantive law com.), Intreanat. Bar Assn., Los Angeles County Bar Assn., Lawyer Pilots Bar Assn., Internat. Assn. Ins. Counsel (aviation com.), Am. Bd. Trial Advs., Am. Judicature Soc., Internat. Soc. Barristers, Calif. Club, Los Angeles Country Club, La Quinta Country Club, Phi Delta Phi. Home: 11445 Waterford St Los Angeles CA 90049-3438 Office: 1900 Avenue Of The Stars Los Angeles CA 90067

PACKARD, RONALD, congressman; b. Meridian, Idaho, Jan. 19, 1931; m. Jean Sorenson, 1952; children: Chris, Debbie, Jeff, Vicki, Scott, Lisa, Theresa. Student, Brigham Young U., 1948-50, Portland State U., 1952-53; D.M.D., U. Oreg., Portland, 1953-57. Gen. practice dentistry Carlsbad, Calif., 1959-82; mem. 98th-104th Congresses from 43rd (now 48th) Dist. Calif., 1983—; chmn. appropriations legis. subcom., former mem. pub. works and transp. com., sci., space, tech. Mem. Carlsbad Sch. Dist. Bd., 1960-72; bd. dirs. Carlsbad C. of C., 1972-76; mem. Carlsbad Planning Commn., 1974-76, Carlsbad City Coun., 1976-78; Carlsbad chmn. Boy Scouts Am., 1977-79; mayor City of Carlsbad, 1978-82; mem. North County Armed Svcs. YMCA, North County Transit Dist., San Diego Assn. Govts., Coastal Policy Com., Transp. Policy Com.; pres. San Diego div. Calif. League of Cities. Served with Dental Corps USN, 1957-59. Republican. Mem. Ch. LDS. Office: US Ho of Reps 2162 Rayburn HOB Washington DC 20515*

PACKARD, SANDRA PODOLIN, association administrator; b. Buffalo, Sept. 13, 1942; d. Mathew and Ethel (Zolte) P.; m. Martin Packard, Aug. 2, 1964; children: Dawn Esther, Shana Fanny. B.F.A., Syracuse U., 1964; M.S.Ed., Ind. U., 1966, Ed.D., 1973. Cert. tchr. art K-12, N.Y. Asst. prof. art SUNY-Buffalo, 1972-74; assoc. prof. art Miami U., Oxford, Ohio, 1974-81, spl. asst. to provost, 1979-80, assoc. provost, spl. programs, 1980-81; dean Coll. Edn. Bowling Green State U., Ohio, 1981-85; provost and vice chancellor for acad. affairs U. Tenn., Chattanooga, 1985-92; pres. Oakland U., Rochester, Mich., 1992-95; sr. fellow, dir. tech. in edn. Am. Assn. State Colls. and Univs., 1995—; art therapist, Ohio, 1973-78; cons. Butler County Health Ctr., Hamilton, Ohio, 1976-78; vis. prof. art therapy Simmons Coll., 1979, Mary Mount Coll., Milw., 1981; bd. dirs. SE Ctr. for Arts in Edn., 1994—; mem. corp. adv. com. Detroit Mag., 1994—. Sr. editor Studies in Art Edn. jour., 1979-81; editorial adv. bd. Jour. Aesthetic Edn., 1984-90; editor: The Leading Edge, 1986; contbr. articles to profl. jours., chpts. to conf. papers. Chmn. com. Commn. on Edn. Excellence, Ohio, 1982-83, Tenn. State Performance Funding Task Force, 1988, Tenn. State Task Force on Minority Tchrs., 1988; reviewer art curriculum N.Y. Bd. Edn., 1985; mem. supt. search com. Chattanooga Pub. Schs., 1987-88; mem. Chattanooga Met. Coun., 1987-88, Chattanooga Ballet Bd., 1986-88, Fund for Excellence in Pub. Edn., 1986-90, Tenn. Aquarium Bd. Advisors, 1989-92, Team Evaluation Ctr. Bd., 1988-90; mem. Strategic Planning Action Team, Chattanooga City Schs., 1987-88, Siskin Hosp. Bd., 1989-92, Blue Ribbon Task Force Pontiac 2010: A New Reality, City of Pontiac Planning Divsn., 1992—; steering com., cultural action bd. Chattanooga, planning com. United Way, 1987; Jewish Fedn. Bd. 1986-91; mem. coun. for policy studies Art Edn. Adv. Bd. 1982-91; ex-officio mem. Meadow Brook Theatre Guild, 1992—; bd. chair Meadow Brook Performing Arts Co., 1992—; chair

World Cup Soccer Edn. Com./Mich. Host Com., 1993—; bd. dirs. Partners for Preferred Future, Rochester Community Schs., 1992—, Traffic Improvement Assn. Oakland County, 1992—, Oakland County Bus. Roundtable, 1993—; Rochester C. of C. host comm. chair on edn. World Cup, 1992—; bd. dirs. United Way Southeastern Mich.; active United Way Oakland County, Pontiac 2010: A New Reality, mayor's transition team/city sch. rels. task force; team evaluation leader Dept. of State Am. Univ. Bulgaria, 1995. Am. Coun. on Edn. and Mellon fellow Miami U., 1978-79; recipient Cracking the Glass Ceiling award Pontiac Area Urban League, 1992. Fellow Nat. Art Edn. Assn. (disting.); mem. Am. Assn. Colls. for Tchr. Edn. (com. chair 1982-85), Am. Art Therapy Assn. (registered), Nat. Art Edn. Women's Caucus (founder, pres. 1976-78, McFee award 1986), Am. Assn. State Colls. and Univs. (com. profl. devel. 1993-95, state rep. 1994-95), Econ. Club Detroit (bd. dirs. 1992-95), Rotary Club, Phi Delta Kappa (Leadership award 1985). Avocation: sailing. Home: 300 S Adams Rd Rochester MI 48309-1902 Office: Oakland U 204 Wilson Hall Rochester MI 48309

PACKARD, VANCE OAKLEY, writer; b. Granville Summit, Pa., May 22, 1914; s. Philip Joseph and Mabel (Case) P.; m. Mamie Virginia Mathews, Nov. 25, 1938; children: Vance Philip, Randall Mathews, Cynthia Ann. B.A., Pa. State U., 1936; M.S., Columbia U., 1937; Litt.D., Monmouth Coll., 1975. Reporter Centre Daily Times, State College, Pa., 1936; columnist Boston Record, 1937-38; writer, editor Asso. Press Feature Service, 1938-42; editor, staff writer Am. mag., 1942-56; staff writer Collier's mag., 1956; lectr. reporting, mag. writing Columbia, 1941-44, N.Y.U., 1945-57; guest lectr. several hundred colls. and univs., U.S. and 13 other countries. Author: Animal IQ, 1950, The Hidden Persuaders, 1957, The Status Seekers, 1959, The Waste Makers, 1960, The Pyramid Climbers, 1962, The Naked Society, 1964, The Sexual Wilderness, 1968, A Nation of Strangers, 1972, The People Shapers, 1977 (Notable Book of 1977, ALA), Our Endangered Children, 1983, The Ultra Rich, 1988; Mem. planning commn., New Canaan, Conn., 1954-56; pres. Chappaquiddick Island Assn., 1977-78; mem. nat. bd. Nat. Book Com.; Trustee Silvermine Coll. Art. Recipient Distinguished Alumni award Pa. State U., 1961; Outstanding Alumni award Grad. Sch. Journalism, Columbia, 1963. Mem. Soc. Mag. Writers (pres. 1961); mem. Am. Sociol. Assn., Authors' Guild, Am. Acad. Polit. and Social Sci., Population Resource Ctr. (bd. dirs.), Ctr. for Study of Commercialism (bd. advisors). Home: 87 Mill Rd New Canaan CT 06840-4305

PACKER, BOYD K., church official. Mem. Quorum of the Twelve, Ch. of Jesus Christ of Latter-Day Saints. Office: LDS Church 50 E North Temple Salt Lake City UT 84150

PACKER, KATHERINE HELEN, retired library educator; b. Toronto, Ont., Can., Mar. 20, 1918; d. Cleve Alexander and Rosa Ruel (Dibblee) Smith; m. William A. Packer, Sept. 27, 1941; 1 dau., Marianne Katherine. B.A., U. Toronto, 1941; A.M.L.S., U. Mich., 1953; Ph.D., U. Md. 1975. Cataloguer William L Clements Library, U. Mich., 1953-55, U. Man. (Can.) Library, Winnipeg, 1956-59; cataloguer U. Toronto Library, 1959-63; asst. prof. Faculty Library Sci., 1967-75, asso. prof., 1975-78, prof., dean, 1979-84, prof. emeritus, 1984—; head cataloguer York U. Library, Toronto, 1963-64; chief librarian Ont. Coll. Edn., Toronto, 1964-67. Author: Early American School Books, 1954. Mem. property tax working group Ont. Fair Tax Commn., 1991-92; mem. assessment reform working group City of Toronto, 1992—. Recipient Disting. Alumnus award U. Mich., 1981. Mem. Can. Library Assn. (Howard Phalin award 1972), Phi Kappa Phi. Home: 53 Gormley Ave, Toronto, ON Canada M4V 1Y9 Office: U Toronto, Faculty Library and Info Sci, 140 Saint George St, Toronto, ON Canada M5S 1A1

PACKER, MARK BARRY, lawyer, financial consultant, foundation official; b. Phila., Sept. 18, 1944; s. Samuel and Eve (Devine) P.; m. Donna Elizabeth Ferguson (div. 1984); children: Daniel Joshua, Benjamin Dov, David Johannes. AB magna cum laude, Harvard U., 1965, LLB, 1968. Bar: Wash. 1969, Mass. 1971. Assoc. Ziontz, Pirtle & Fulle, Seattle, 1968-70; pvt. practice, Bellingham, Wash., 1972—; bd. dirs., corp. sec. BMJ Holdings (formerly No. Sales Co., Inc.), 1977—; trustee No. Sales Profit Sharing Plan, 1977—; bd. dirs., corp. sec., gen. counsel Dr. Cookie, Inc., 1981-92. Mem. Bellingham Planning and Devel. Commn., 1975-84, chmn., 1977-81, mem. shoreline subcom., 1976-82; pres. Congregation Beth Israel, Bellingham, 1980-82; mem. Bellingham Mcpl. Arts Commn., 1986-91, landmark rev. bd., 1987-91; chmn. Bellingham campaign United Jewish Appeal, 1979-90; bd. dirs. Whatcom Community Coll. Found., 1989-92; lit. tutor Whatcom Lit. Coun., 1988-90; trustee, chmn. program com. Bellingham Pub. Sch. Found., 1991—; discussion leader, short story/novella reading group, 1988-92; active Heavy Culture classic lit. group, 1991—; Jewish studies group, 1993—; mng. trustee Bernard M. & Audrey Jaffe Found. Recipient Blood Donor award ARC, 1979, 8-Gallon Pin, 1988, Mayor's Arts award City of Bellingham, 1993. Mem. ABA (sec. real property probate and trust), Wash. State Bar Assn. (sec. environ. and land use law, com. law-related edn. 1990-92, sec. bus. law, sec. real property, probate and trust, com. law examiners 1992-94). Office: PO Box 1151 Bellingham WA 98227-1151

PACKER, REKHA DESAI, lawyer; b. N.Y.C., Apr. 20, 1955; d. Rajanikant C. and Santosh (Nagpaul) Desai; m. Michael Benjamin Packer, Aug. 11, 1979. AB magna cum laude, Harvard U., 1976, JD, 1979. Bar: Mass. 1979, U.S. Dist. Ct. Mass. 1979, U.S. Tax. Ct. 1980. Assoc. Gaston & Snow, Boston, 1979-87, ptnr., 1987-91; sr. ptnr. Hale and Dorr, Boston, 1991—; speaker Fed. Tax Inst., 1987—, World Trade Inst., 1986—. Mem. Internat. Bar Assn. (mem. com. on investment cos., funds and trusts 1989—), ABA (mem. com. on regulated investment cos., labor law sect. 1986—, com. on U.S. activities of foreigners 1988—), Boston Bar Assn. (labor law sect. 1987—, co-chmn. internat. tax. com. 1987-89), Phi Beta Kappa. Office: Hale and Dorr 60 State St Boston MA 02109-1803

PACKER, RUSSELL HOWARD, automotive company executive; b. Santa Fe, Sept. 8, 1951; s. Russell Howard Thorwaldsen and Florence (Bullis) Bryant; m. Melanie Lea Martell, Aug. 31. 1974; children: Lindsey Anne, Andrew Thomas. BS, U. So. Calif., 1973, MBA, 1975. Research analyst Automobile Club of So. Calif., Los Angeles, 1973-75, sr. fin. analyst, 1975-81, mgr. fin. and investment analysis, 1982-83; dir. planning and devel. Coca Cola Bottling Co. of Los Angeles, 1983-87; v.p. planning, adminstrn. Coca Cola Bottling Co. of San Diego, 1987-88; contr. Sunroad Capital Corp., San Diego, 1988-89; v.p., dir. contr. Sunroad Enterprises, San Diego, 1989-90; v.p., treas., CFO Geometric Results Inc, Escondido, Calif., 1990—; lectr. fin. Calif. State U., Los Angeles, 1977-87, San Diego State U., 1988-90. Mem. Fin. Execs. Inst., Beta Gamma Sigma. Republican. Home: 12519 Shropshire Ln San Diego CA 92128-1016 Office: Geometric Results Inc 800 La Terraza Blvd Escondido CA 92025-3800

PACKHAM, MARIAN AITCHISON, biochemistry educator; b. Toronto, Ont., Can., Dec. 13, 1927; d. James and Clara Louise (Campbell) A.; m. James Lennox Packham, June 25, 1949; children: Neil Lennox, Janet Melissa. BA, U. Toronto, 1949, PhD, 1954. Sr. fellow dept. biochemistry U. Toronto, 1954-58, lectr. dept. biochemistry, 1958-63, 66-67; rsch. assoc. dept. physiol. scis. Ont. Vet. Coll., U. Guelph, 1963-65; rsch. assoc. blood and cardiovascular disease rsch. unit U. Toronto, 1965-66; asst. prof. U. Toronto dept. biochemistry, 1967-72, assoc. prof., 1972-75, prof., 1975-89, acting chmn. dept. biochemistry, 1983, univ. prof., 1989—. Contbr. articles to profl. jours. Royal Soc. Can. fellow, 1991; recipient Lt. Govs. Silver medal Victoria Coll., 1949; co-recipient J. Allyn Taylor Internat. prize in Medicine, 1988. Mem. Can. Biochem. Soc., Am. Soc. Hematology, Can. Soc. Hematology, Am. Assn. Pathologists, Can. Soc. Clin. Investigation, Coun. Thrombosis of Am. Heart Assn., Internat. Soc. Thrombosis and Haemostasis, Can. Atherosclerosis. Avocation: skiing. Office: U Toronto, Dept Biochemistry, Toronto, ON Canada M5S 1A8

PACKWOOD, BOB, senator; b. Portland, Oreg., Sept. 11, 1932; s. Frederick William and Gladys (Taft) P.; children: William Henderson, Shy-la. BA, Willamette U., 1954; LLB, NYU, 1957; LLB (hon.), Yeshiva U., 1982, Gallaudet Coll., 1983. Bar: Oreg. Law clerk to Justice Harold J. Warner Oreg. Supreme Ct., 1957-58; pvt. atty. 1958-68; Chmn. Multnomah County Rep. Cen Com., 1960-62; mem. Oreg. Legislature, 1963-69; U.S. senator from Oreg., 1969—, chmn. small bus. com., 1981-84, chmn. commerce com., 1981-85, chmn. fin. com. 1985-86, ranking min. mem. fin. com. 1987-94, chmn. fin. com. 1995—. Mem. Internat. Working Group of Par-

liamentarians on Population and Devel., 1977; mem. Pres.'s Commn. on Population Growth and the Am. Future, 1972; chmn. Nat. Rep. Senatorial Com., 1977-78, 81-82; bd. dirs. NYU, 1970; bd. overseers Lewis and Clark Coll., Portland, 1966. Named One of Three Outstanding Young Men of Oreg., 1967; Portland's Jr. 1st Citizen, 1966; Oreg. Speaker of Yr., 1968; recipient Arthur T. Vanderbilt award NYU Sch. Law, 1970; Anti-Defamation League Brotherhood award, 1971; Torch of Liberty award B'nai B'rith, 1971; Richard L. Neuberger award Oreg. Environ. Coun., 1972; Conservation award Omaha Woodmen Life Ins. Soc., 1974; Monongahela Forestry Leadership award, 1976; Solar Man of Yr., Solar Energy Industries Assn. 1980; Guardian of Small Bus. award Nat. Fedn. Ind. Bus., 1980; Forester of Yr., Western Forest Industries Assn., 1980; Am. Israel Friendship award B'nai Zion, 1982; Grover C. Cobb award Nat. Assn. Broadcasters, 1982; Religious Freedom award, Religious Coalition for Abortion Rights, 1983; 22d Ann. Conv. award, Oreg. State Bldg. and Constrn. Trade Council, 1983; United Cerebral Palsy Humanitarian award, 1984; Am. Heart Assn. Pub. Affairs award, 1985; Margaret Sanger award Planned Parenthood Assn., 1985; Worth his Wheat in Gold award for leadership on tax reform Gen. Mills., 1986; Am. Assn. Homes for the Aging for Outstanding Svc. in cause of elderly, 1987; NARAL award for congrl. leadership, 1987; James Madison award Nat. Broadcast Editorial Assn., 1987; Pub. Excellence award First Ann. Jacob K. Javits, 1987; Golden Bulldog award Watchdogs of Treasury, Inc., 1988, 90; Sound Dollar award, 1989; Golden Eagle award Nurse Anesthetists, 1990; John. F. Hogan Disting. Svc. award Radio-TV News Dirs. for def. of First Amendment, 1991; Nat. Conf. Soviet Jewry recognition, 1992, Space Shuttle Endeavor recognition, 1993, Spirit of Enterprise award U.S. C. of C., 1994, numerous others. Mem. Oreg. Bar Assn., D.C. Bar Assn., Beta Theta Pi. Office: US Senate 259 Russell Senate Bldg Washington DC 20510-3702

PACTER, PAUL ALLAN, accounting educator; b. N.Y.C., Jan. 26, 1943; s. Bernard David and Hilda Libby (Margolies) P. B.S., Syracuse U., 1964; Ph.D., Mich. State U., 1967. C.P.A., N.Y. Asst. prof. N.Y.U., 1967-69; rsch. mgr. Peat Marwick, N.Y.C., 1969-73; exec. dir. Fin. Acctg. Standards Bd., Stamford, Conn., 1973-84; commr. fin. City of Stamford, 1984-90; prof. acctg., MBA program U. Conn., Stamford, 1990—, adj. prof., 1982-84; adj. prof. NYU, 1982-84; project cons. Fin. Acctg. Standards Bd., 1990—, Internat. Acctg. Standards Com., London, 1993-94. Consulting editor The Jour. of Accountancy, 1968-73. Chmn. Stamford Commn. on Human Rights, 1977-84, Stamford Film Commn., 1984-90; mem. Charter Revision Commn., Stamford, 1979-80, Gov.'s Tourism Coun., Conn., 1984-90, acctg. adv. coun. U. Conn., 1984-90; pres. N. Stamford Dem. Club, 1983-84, treas., 1987—; dir. Stamford Citizen Authority, 1984-90; vice chmn. govtl. acctg. stds. adv. coun., 1984-91; treas. Conn. Tourism Assn., 1987-90, North Stamford Assn., 1993-94; bd. dirs. Stamford Ctr. for the Arts, United Way Stamford, Stamford Theatre Works, Stamford Community Fund, Housing Devel. Fund of Fairfield County. Earhart Found. fellow Mich. State U., 1966-67; U.S. Office of Edn. grantee, 1967. Mem. AICPA, Am. Acctg. Assn. (coun.), N.Y. State Soc. CPA's, Beta Gamma Sigma, Beta Alpha Psi. Jewish. Home: 247 Chestnut Hill Rd Stamford CT 06903-3925 Office: U Conn 641 Scofieldtown Rd Stamford CT 06903-2899

PACUN, NORMAN, lawyer; b. Bklyn., Mar. 1, 1932; s. Joseph J. and Tillie (Demburg) P.; m. Carol Yvonne Anderson, June 8, 1957; children: Catherine Elizabeth, David Edward. A.B. magna cum laude, U. So. Calif., 1953; LL.B., Harvard U., 1958. Bar: N.Y. 1959. With firm Kirlin, Campbell & Keating, N.Y.C., 1958-61; with Crane Co., 1961-76, sec., gen. counsel, 1964-68, v.p., sec., gen. counsel, 1968-76; v.p., gen. counsel Ingersoll-Rand Co., Woodcliff Lake, N.J., 1977-82, cons., 1982-83; cons. corporate devel. Crane Co., 1985-86; dir. Huttig Sash and Door Co., 1971-76, CF&I Steel Corp., 1974-76. Sec.-treas. Mid-Atlantic Legal Found., 1977-81, bd. dirs., 1980-85, treas., vice-chmn., 1981-84; mem. com. Ctr. for Pub. Resources Legal Program, 1981-82; mem. Scarsdale Vol. Ambulance Corps, 1983-87, treas., 1985-87; emergency med. technician, N.Y., 1986-89; call firefighter and emergency med. technician Chatham Fire Rescue, 1989—; mem., chmn. Chatham Hist. Commn., 1989—; mem. Chatham Long-Range Planning Commn., 1993-94. Served with AUS, 1953-55. Mem. ABA, Assn. of Bar of City of N.Y., Am. Soc. Internat. Law, Harvard Club, Beach and Tennis Club (trustee 1994—), Chatham Platform Paddle Club (bd. govs. 1993—), Phi Beta Kappa. Home and Office: 14 Sunset Ln Chatham MA 02633-2461

PACY, JAMES STEVEN, political science educator; b. Caldeonia, Ont., Can., Aug. 17, 1930; s. James and Elizabeth (Fonagy) P.; m. Ruth Eleanor West, May 22, 1955; children: Laura Jeanne Echevarria, Benjamin West Pacy. BA, Lebanon Valley Coll., 1952; MA, U. Mo., 1956; PhD, Am. U., 1969. Exec. asst. Nat. Wildlife Fedn., Washington, 1957-58; rsch. prof. Spl. Ops. Rsch. Office Am. U., 1960-65; asst. prof. polit. sci. Westminster Coll., Fulton., Mo., 1965-67; prof. polit. sci. U. Vt., Burlington, 1967-93, prof. emeritus, 1993—. Co-editor: Perspectives on the Holocaust: Essays in Honor of Raul Hilberg, 1994; contbr. articles on internat. rels. and diplomacy to Fgn. Svc. Jour., World Affairs, Polish Rev., East European Quar., Asian Affairs, Diplomacy and Statecraft. With USAF, 1952-56. Summer Rsch. grant U. Vt.; scholar Harvard U., 1959. Mem. Am. Fgn. Svc. Assn., Am. Polit. Sci. Assn., Internat. Studies Assn. (past mem. governing bd. New Eng. chpt.), UN Assn. of the USA. Avocation: philately. Home: 34 Robinson Pky Burlington VT 05401-3516

PACZYNSKI, BOHDAN, astrophysicist, educator; b. Wilno, Poland, Feb. 8, 1940; came to U.S., 1981; s. Jan and Helena (Milkowska) P.; m. Hanna Adamska, Aug. 25, 1965; children—Agnieszka, Marcin. M.A., Warsaw U., 1962, Ph.D., 1964. Prof. astrophysics Polish Acad. Sci., Warsaw, 1976-82; Lyman Spitzer Jr. prof. theoretical physics Princeton (N.J.) U., 1982—. Recipient State prize in Sci., Govt. of Poland, 1980, Alfred Jurzykowski Found. award, 1982, Dannie Heineman prize for astrophysics Am. Astron. Soc., 1992. Mem. Polish Acad. Sci. (corr.), U.S. Nat. Acad. Sci. (fgn. assoc.), Deutsche Academie Leopoldina, Royal Astron. Soc. (U.K., Eddington medal 1987), Internat. Astron. Union (invited lectr. 1979). Office: Princeton U 124 Peyton Hall Princeton NJ 08544

PADBERG, HARRIET ANN, mathematics educator; b. St. Louis, Nov. 13, 1922; d. Harry J. and Marie L. (Kilgen) P. AB with honors, Maryville Coll., St. Louis, 1943; MMus, U. Cin., 1949; MA, St. Louis U., 1956, PhD, 1964. Registered music therapist; cert. tchr. math. and music, La., Mo. Tchr. elem. math. and music Kenwood Acad., Albany, N.Y., 1944-46; tchr. secondary math. Acad. of Sacred Heart, Cin., 1946-47; instr. math. and music Acad. and Coll. of Sacred Heart, Grand Coteau, La., 1947-48; secondary tchr. music Acad. Sacred Heart, St. Charles, Mo., 1948-50; instr. math. and music Acad. and Coll. Sacred Heart, Grand Coteau, 1950-55, Maryville Coll., St. Louis, 1955-56; tchr. elem. and secondary math. and music Acad. Sacred Heart, St. Louis, 1956-57; asst. prof. Maryville Coll., St. Louis, 1957-64, assoc. prof., 1964-68, prof. math., 1968-92, prof. emeritus, 1992—; music therapist Emmaus Homes, Marthasville, Mo., 1992—. Recipient Alumni Centennial award Maryville Coll., St. Louis 1986; grantee Danforth Found., Colorado Springs, 1970, Tallahassee, 1970, Edn. Devel. Ctr., Mass., 1975, U. Kans., 1980. Mem. Assn. Women in Math., Am. Math. Soc., Math. Assn. Am., Nat. Coun. Tchr. Math., Mo. Acad. Sci., Delta Epsilon Sigma (sec. local chpt. 1962), Pi Mu Epsilon (sec. local chpt. 1958), Sigma Xi. Avocations: computer music, organist, knitting.

PADBERG, MANFRED WILHELM, mathematics educator, researcher; b. Bottrop, North-Rhine, Westphalia, Fed. Republic Germany, Oct. 10, 1941; came to U.S., 1968; s. Fritz Georg and Franziska (Grosse-Wilde) P.; m. Brigitte Anna Trager, July 7, 1967 (div. 1980); children:Britta, Marc Oliver. Diploma in mathematics Westfalische Wilhelms U., 1967; M.S. in Industrial Adminstrn., Carnegie-Mellon U., 1971, Ph.D., 1971. Scientific asst. Universitat, Mannheim, Fed. Republic Germany, 1967-68; rsch. fellow IIM, Berlin, 1971-74; assoc. prof. NYU, N.Y.C., 1974-78, prof. ops. rsch., 1978—, rsch. prof. ops. rsch., 1988—; vis. prof. Bonn (Fed. Republic Germany) U., 1974, IBM Rsch., Yorktown Heights, N.Y., 1975-76, Westfalische Wilhelms U., Münster, Fed. Republic Germany, 1978, Inst. Nat. de Recherche en Informatique et d'Automatique, Rocquencourt, France, 1980-81, Univ. Cath. de Louvain, Belgium, 1981-82, Centro Nat. di Ricorche Roma, 1982, U. Scientifique et Med. de Grenoble, France, 1984, SUNY, Stony Brook, 1987, Cen. Nat. de la Recherche Sci., Paris, 1988, others; vis. distr. rsch. Ecole Poly., Paris, 1989-90; vis. disting. rsch. prof. George Mason U., 1990—; vis. prof. Augsburg U., Germany, 1990-91; cons. in field. Author: Linear Optimiza-

tion and Extensions, 1995; editor: Combinatorial Optimization, 1980; co-editor: Polyhedra and Discrete Optimization, 1989, Algorithms and Discrete Optimization, 1989; contbr. numerous articles to profl. jours. Recipient Alexander-von-Humboldt Rsch. award, 1990-91. Mem. Ops. Research Soc. (Lanchester prize 1983), Math. Programming Soc. (G.B. Dantzig prize 1985). Avocation: traveling. Office: NYU Washington Sq New York NY 10003

PADDOCK, ANTHONY CONAWAY, financial consultant; b. Paris, July 9, 1935; came to U.S., 1940; s. H. Watson and Mildred V. (Decker) P.; m. Wendy E. Brewer, Apr. 24, 1971. AB, Harvard U., 1957, JD, 1960; MBA, Columbia U., 1961. Bar: N.Y. 1961. Assoc. investment bank Merrill Lynch & Co., N.Y.C., 1961-69; v.p. Chase Manhattan Bank, N.Y.C., 1970-78, Standard Rsch. Cons., N.Y.C., 1978-84; mng. dir. Benchmark Valuation Cons., N.Y.C., 1978-84; prin. KPMG Peat Marwick, N.Y.C., 1984—; adj. prof. NYU, 1979-90. Mem. Assoc. for Corp. Growth, Inst. Mgmt. Cons. (cert.). Episcopalian. Home: 25 East End Ave New York NY 10028 Office: KPMG Peat Marwick 345 Park Ave New York NY 10154

PADDOCK, AUSTIN JOSEPH, engineering executive; b. Washington Court House, Ohio, July 18, 1908; s. Leon A. and Nellie (Hare) P.; m. Janet Nevin, Aug. 3, 1934 (dec. Aug. 1964); children: Larry C. and Linda M. (twins), Jane M.; m. JoAnn Rourke, May 1966; 1 child, Jennifer Jo. BSCE, U. Mich., 1929. With Am. Bridge div. U.S. Steel Corp., 1929-61; from timekeeper constrn. dept., through ops. and sales to pres.; corp. adminstrv. v.p. fabrication and mfg. U.S. Steel Corp., 1961-69; chmn. bd., pres., chief exec. officer Blount, Inc., 1969-75; exec. v.p., chief oper. officer Pa. Engring. Corp., Pitts., 1975-78; vice chmn. bd., dir. Pa. Engring. Corp., 1978-87; dir., mem. exec. com. Pitts.-Des Moines Corp.; past dir. bldg. research adv. bd. Nat. Acad. Sci.; past dir. Am. Standards Inst., Steel Structures Paint Council; past dir. constrn. affairs com. U.S. C. of C.; past chmn. research tech. com. Am Iron and Steel Inst. Past bd. dirs. Allegheny council Boy Scouts Am. Past dir. NAM. Clubs: Duquesne (Pitts.), Longue Vue Country (Pitts.); Montgomery Country, Men of Montgomery, Capital City. Home: 3875 Taylor Rd Montgomery AL 36116-6514 Office: 421 S Mcdonough St Montgomery AL 36104-4262

PADDOCK, JOHN, professional hockey team head coach; b. Oak River, Man., Can.; m. Jill Paddock; children: Jenny, Sally, Anna. Coach Maine Mariners, 1983-84, Hershey Bears, 1988-89; asst. gen. mgr. Phila. Flyers, 1989-90; coach Binghamton Rangers, 1990-91; head coach Winnipeg (Man.) Jets, 1991—; also gen. mgr. Twice named Am. League Coach of Yr. Office: care Winnipeg Jets, 15-1430 Maroons Rd, Winnipeg, MB Canada R3G 0L5*

PADDOCK, ROBERT YOUNG, publisher; b. Palatine, Ill., Apr. 4, 1917; s. Stuart Ransom and Margaret (Young) P.; 1 child, Robert Y. Jr. BA, Knox Coll., 1939. With prodn. dept. Daily Herald/Paddock Publs., Arlington Heights, Ill., 1939-42, asst. editor, sports editor, 1942-48, v.p., 1948-86, vice-chmn. bd. dirs., 1986—. Past area chmn. Am. Cancer Soc.; past sec. Econ. Devel. Commn., Arlington Heights; mem. Adv. Com. Roosevelt U.; past treas. Wynstone Children's Charities; chmn. Arlington Heights 125th Anniversary celebration; chmn. bus. and profl. com., celebrity sports dinner, bd. govs. Northwest Community Health Svcs. Found.; past chief crusader Northwest Suburban United Way; past expediter Downtown Arlington Heights Merchants Assn.; sec. Cen. Bus. Dist. Assn. Arlington Heights; pres. Paddock Publs. Jr. Miss Found.; Gerald A. McElroy Meml. Scholarship Fund; past co-chmn. Arlington Heights Plaza Com.; active Northwest Suburban Coun. Boy Scouts; past bd. dirs. Northwest Community Hosp.; past gen. chmn. Arlington Heights United Fund; past chmn. bd. dirs. 1st Meth. Ch. Arlington Heights; one of three mayors Herald City. Recipient Outstanding Community Svc. award Clearbrook Ctr., 1978, Silver Beaver award Northwest Suburban Coun. Boy Scouts, 1975, Good Scout award Northwest Suburban Coun. Boy Scouts, 1978, Community Svc. award Northwest Suburban Coun. Boy Scouts, 1984, Community Svc. award Palatine Jaycees, Outstanding Grad. award Palatine High Sch., 1986; named Rotarian of Yr. Arlington Heights Rotary Club, 1979. Mem. Suburban Press Found. Inc. (charter, dir., pres., treas.). Methodist. Avocations: dancing, swimming. Home and Office: Daily Herald Paddock Pub PO Box 280 Arlington Heights IL 60006-0280

PADDOCK, STUART R., JR., publishing executive. Bd. chmn. Daily Herald/Sunday Herald, Arlington Heights, Ill. Office: Daily Herald/Sunday Herald Paddock Publs PO Box 280 Arlington Heights IL 60006-0280

PADEREWSKI, CLARENCE JOSEPH, architect; b. Cleve., July 23, 1908. B.Arch., U. Calif., 1932. Chief draftsman Sam W. Hamill, 1939-44; with Heitschmidt-Matcham-Blanchard-Gill & Hamill (architects), 1943; then practiced as C.J. Paderewski, 1944-48; pres. Paderewski, Dean & Asso., Inc. (and predecessor), San Diego, 1948-78; instr. adult edn. San Diego city schs., 1939-44, U. Calif. extension div., 1945, 56; Lectr. in field. Prin. works include Characron Labs, Gen. Dynamics Corp., Convair, S.D., 1954, South Bay Elem. Schs., S.D., 1948-74; additions to El Cortez Hotel; including first passenger glass elevator in the world and New Travolator Motor Hotel, S.D., 1959, Palomar Coll. San Marcos, 1951-80, San Diego County U. Gen. Hosp., San Diego Internat. Airport Terminal Bldgs., Fallbrook Elem. Schs., 1948-74, Silver Strand Elem. Sch., Coronado, Tourmaline Terrace Apt. Bldg., San Diego Salvation Army Office Bldg. Mem. adv. bd. Bayside Social Service Center, 1953-75, San Diego Internat. Airport Terminal, Honor award for Portland Cement Co., Golden Trowel award Plastering Inst., 1958-60, 4 awards Masonry Inst., 1961, award Prestressed Concrete Inst., 1976, Outstanding Community Leadership award San Diego Downtown Assn., 1963, 64, 65, 80. Fellow AIA (pres. San Diego chpt. 1948, 49, bd. dirs. 1947-53, chmn. several coms., spl. award 1977, Calif. Coun. Spl. award 1979, Calif. Coun. Disting. Svc. award 1982); mem. San Diego C. of C. (bd. dirs. 1959-62, 64-67), Am. Arbitration Assn. (San Diego adv. coun. 1969—), Sister City Soc. (bd. dirs.), Lions (past pres. Hillcrest Club, Lion of Yr. 1990, fellow internat. found. 1991), Father Serra Club (charter, past pres.), Outboard Boating Club San Diego, Chi Alpha Kappa, Delta Sigma Chi.*. Home: 2837 Kalmia Pl San Diego CA 92104-5418

PADGETT, GEORGE ARTHUR, retired lawyer; b. N.Y.C., Feb. 17, 1932; s. Arthur Samuel and Marion Louise (Schramm) P.; m. Ann M. Padgett; children: Ann Linton, James Dunbar. AB, Hamilton Coll., 1954; JD, Georgetown U., 1960. Bar: D.C. 1960, N.J. 1961. Assoc. Covington & Burling, Washington, 1959-60, Pitney, Hardin & Kipp, Newark, 1961-65; asst. sec., corp. counsel Lionel Corp., N.Y.C., 1965-70; sec., corp. counsel Lionel Corp., Edison, N.J., 1970-82, sr. v.p., counsel, corp. sec., 1983-93; also bd. dirs. Lionel Corp., Edison, ret., 1993. Mem. planning bd. Hopewell Boro, N.J., common coun., 1993-94, mayor, 1994—. Mem. ABA, Am. Corp. Counsel Assn., N.J. Bar Assn., Am. Soc. Corp. Secs.

PADGETT, JOY, state legislator; m. Don Padgett; 1 child, Walter. BS, Kent State U. Mem. Ohio Ho. of Reps.; owner Main Off Supply. Mem. YWCA. Recipient Don K. Wales award CORC Joint Policy Bd., 1990, Tchr. of Yr. award Southwestern Ohio, 1992. Mem. Coshocton, Holmes and Muskingum C. of C., Farm Bur., Coshocton Area Personnel Assn. Republican. Home: 871 Walnut St Coshocton OH 43812-1649 Office: OH Ho of Reps State House Columbus OH 43215

PADGETT, NANCY WEEKS, law librarian, consultant, lawyer; b. Newberry, S.C., June 3, 1932; d. Price James and Caroline (Weeks) P.; m. David Lazar, Aug. 6, 1953 (div. Feb. 1994). BS, Northwestern U., 1953; MLS, U. Md., 1972; JD, Georgetown U., 1977. Bar: D.C. 1977. Asst. law libr. U.S. Ct. Appeals for D.C. Dist., Washington, 1972-74, supervisory law libr., 1974-84, circuit libr. 1984—. Mem. ALA, D.C. Bar Assn., Am. Assn. Law Librs. (profl. law libr. cert.). Home: 5301 Duvall Dr Bethesda MD 20816 Office: US Ct Appeals for DC Cir Judges' Libr 3518 US Court House Washington DC 20002-5618

PADGETT, SHELTON EDWARD, lawyer; b. San Marcos, Tex., June 9, 1948; s. Sidney Curtis and Sybil (Dobie) P.; 1 child, Shelton Edward Jr. BS in Edn., S.W. Tex. U., 1970; JD, St. Mary's U., San Antonio, Tex., 1973. Bar: Tex. 1973. Briefing atty. Supreme Ct. Tex., Austin, 1973-74; assoc. Bracewell & Patterson, Houston, 1974-76; ptnr. Manitzas, Harris & Padgett, San Antonio, 1976-87, Kaufman, Becker, Clare & Padgett, San Antonio, 1987-89, Akin, Gump, Strauss, Hauer & Feld, San Antonio, 1989—. Bd. dirs. Bexar County Vol. Ctr., 1982-85, Beeville (Tex.) Meml. Hosp., 1982-85, Tex. Lyceum, Austin, 1984-86, Luth. Gen. Hosp., San Antonio, 1984-87; mem. labor law adv. com. to Tex. Bd. Legal Specialization, 1987—; mem. S.W. Tex. State U. Devel. Found., 1978—; mem. adv. commn. City of San Antonio Baseball Stadium, 1992—. Roman Catholic. Avocation: baseball. Office: Akin Gump Strauss Hauer & Feld 1500 Nationsbank Plz 300 Convent St San Antonio TX 78205-3701

PADILLA, JAMES EARL, lawyer; b. Miami, Fla., Dec. 28, 1953; s. Earl George and Patricia (Bauer) P. BA, Northwestern U., 1975; JD, Duke U., 1978. Bar: Ill. 1978, U.S. Ct. Appeals (5th and 7th cir.) 1978, U.S. Supreme Ct. 1981, Colo. 1982, U.S. Ct. Appeals (10th cir.) 1982, D.C. 1985, N.Y. 1989. Assoc. Mayer, Brown & Platt, Chgo. and Denver, 1978-84; ptnr. Mayer, Brown & Platt, Denver, 1985-87, N.Y.C., 1988—. Contbg. author: Mineral Financing, 1982, Illinois Continuing Legal Education, 1993. Mem. ABA, Ill. Bar Assn., D.C. Bar Assn., Colo. Bar Assn., N.Y. Bar Assn., Denver Bar Assn., Denver Club. Avocation: golf. Office: Mayer Brown & Platt 1675 Broadway New York NY 10019-5820

PADOS, FRANK JOHN, JR., trust company executive; b. Easton, Pa., Feb. 9, 1944; s. Frank John and Mary Helen (Pokrifscak) P.; m. Barbara Janselwitz, July 6, 1968; children—Frank John (dec.), Kelly Ann, Kristin, Matthew John, Kaitlyn. B.A. cum laude in Econs, Boston Coll., 1966; M.B.A., U. Pa., 1968. Securities analyst Tchrs. Ins. and Annuity Assn., N.Y.C., 1971-77; investment officer Tchrs. Ins. and Annuity Assn., 1975-77, v.p., 1977-78, sr. v.p., mgr. securities div., 1978-83; mng. dir. Trust Co. of the West, 1983—; dir. Broadcasting Ptnrs., Inc. Served with U.S. Army, 1969-70. Decorated Bronze Star. Mem. Wharton Club, Sky Club. Roman Catholic. Home: 57 Thornley Dr Chatham NJ 07928-1360 Office: 200 Park Ave New York NY 10166-0001

PADOVA, JOHN R., federal judge; b. 1935. AB, Villanova U., 1956; JD, Temple U., 1959. With Marcu & Marcu, 1960; ptnr. Solo, Bergman & Trommer, 1962-65, Solo, Abrams, Bergman, Trommer & Padova, 1965-71, Solo, Bergman, Trommer, Padova & Albert, 1971-74, Solo, Bergman & Padova, 1974-75, Solo & Padova, 1975-77, 84-86, Solo, Padova & Lisi, 1977-84, Padova & Hinman, 1986-91, Padova & Lisi, 1991-92; fed. judge U.S. Dist. Ct. (ea. dist.) Pa., 1992—. With USNGR, 1959-64, USAR, 1964-68. Mem. ABA, Am. Trial Lawyers Assn., Phila. Bar Assn., Nat. Bd. Trial Advocacy, Pa. Trial Lawyers Assn., Phila. Trial Lawyers Assn. Office: US Dist Ct 601 Market St # 7614 Philadelphia PA 19106-1723

PADOVANO, ANTHONY THOMAS, theologian, educator; b. Harrison, N.J., Sept. 18, 1934; s. Thomas Henry and Mary Rose (Cierzo) P.; m. Theresa Lackamp, 1974; children—Mark, Andrew, Paul, Rosemarie. B.A. magna cum laude, Seton Hall U., 1956; S.T.B. magna cum laude, Pontifical Gregorian U., Rome, Italy, 1958, S.T.L. magna cum laude, 1960, S.T.D. magna cum laude, 1962; Ph.L. magna cum laude, St. Thomas Pontifical Internat. U., Rome, 1962; M.A., NYU, 1971; Ph.D., Fordham U., 1980. Ordained priest Roman Cath. Ch., 1959. Asst. chaplain Med. Center, Jersey City, 1960; asst. St. Paul of the Cross Ch., Jersey City, 1962, St. Catharine Ch., Glen Rock, N.J., 1963; prof. systematic theology Darlington Sem., Mahwah, N.J., 1962-74; prof. Am. lit. Ramapo Coll., N.J., 1971—; founding faculty mem., adj. prof. theology/religious studies Fordham U., 1973-93; mem. Archdiocesan Commn. Ecumenical and Interreligious Affairs, 1975, Commn. Instrn. Clergy in Documents Vatican II, 1966; del. dialogue group Luth.-Roman Cath. Theol. Conversations, 1969; del.-at-large senate of priests Archdiocese of Newark; Danforth assoc., 1975—; Cath. pastor inclusive cmty. World Coun. Chs., 1986—; lectr. in field, also appearances on radio and TV; parish min. St. Margaret of Scotland, Morristown, N.J. Author: The Cross of Christ, the Measure of the World, 1962, The Estranged God, 1966, Who is Christ, 1967, Belief in Human Life, 1969, American Culture and the Quest for Christ, 1970, Dawn Without Darkness, 1971, Free to be Faithful, 1972, Eden and Easter, 1974, A Case for Worship, 1975, America: Its People, Its Promise, 1975, Presence and Structure, 1975, The Human Journey, 1982, Trilogy, 1982, Contemplation and Compassion, 1984, Winter Rain: A Play, 1985, His Name is John: A Play, 1986, Christmas to Calvary, 1987, Love and Destiny, 1987, Summer Lightening: A Play, 1988, Conscience and Conflict, 1989, Reform and Renewal, 1990, A Celebration of Life, 1990, The Church Today: Belonging and Believing, 1990, Scripture in the Streets, 1992, A Retreat with Thomas Merton, 1995; editor: Centenary Issue Roman Echoes, 1959; mem. editl. bd. The Advocate, 1966-73; contbr. articles to mags.; Padovano Collection, personal and profl. papers, Archives, U. Notre Dame. Active Diocese Paterson Ecumenical Commn.; founding pres. Justice and Peace Commn., Diocese of Paterson, active Resigned Priests Com. Mem. Cath. Theol. Soc. Am., Mariological Soc. Am., Nat. Fedn. Priests Councils (ofcl. rep. to Constl. Conv., Chgo. 1968), Corpus (pres.), Fedn. Christian Ministries, Internat. Fedn. of Married Cath. Priests (v.p. for N.Am.). Home: 9 Millstone Dr Morris Plains NJ 07950-1536 Office: Ramapo Coll New Jersey Mahwah NJ 07430 *People rather than ideas have been most formative in my life. More accurately, people, as they embodied certain ideals have proved most decisive. There is nothing more persuasive than an idea which becomes so vital that it transforms the person who proclaims it.*

PADULA, FRED DAVID, filmmaker; b. Santa Barbara, Calif., Oct. 25, 1937; s. Fred and Mary (Adams) P.; married; 1 child. B.A. in Music, San Francisco State U., M.A. in Art, 1965. Adj. faculty U. Calif., San Francisco Art Inst., San Francisco State U.; artist-in-residence U. Minn., Mpls. Filmmaker: Ephesus, 1965 (1st pl. award San Francisco Internat. Film Festival, awards N.Y. Film Festival, Chgo. Internat. Film Festival, others), The Artist Speaks, Two Photographers: Wynn Bullock and Imogen Cunningham, Little Jesus (Hippy Hill), Anthology of Books, David and My Porch, Salmon River Run, El Capitan (awards: Grand Prize Festival Internat. de Film D'Aventure Uecue, La Plagne, France, Grand Prize Film Festival Internat. Montagna Esplorazione, Trento, Italy, Grand Prize Banff Festival of Mountain Films, Can., Grand Prize Mountain Film, Telluride, Colo., Gold medal Festival Internat. du Film Alpine, Les Diablerets, Switzerland); electronic music compositions include: Barking Dogs, Charnet Loops, others; one-man shows (photography) include aerial photographic survey of Mayan Indian Ruins, Yucatan, Mex., 1989, San Francisco Internat. Airport, San Francisco Mus. Modern Art, Kalamazoo Inst. Arts, DeYoung Mus., San Francisco, San Fernando Valley State Coll., Bekersfield Coll., Wash. State U., George Eastman House, represented in permanent collections, Kalamazoo Inst. Arts, State of Calif., George Eastman House, San Francisco Internat. Airport, Crocker Art Mus., Oakland Mus. Art, 1004 Gallery, Port Towsend, Wash., New Horizons Nat. Bank Hdqs., San Rafael, Calif. Address: 47 Shell Rd Mill Valley CA 94941-1551

PADULO, LOUIS, university administrator; b. Athens, Ala., Dec. 14, 1936; s. Louis and Helen (Yarbrough) P.; m. Katharine Seamans, Jan. 28, 1963; children: Robert, Joseph. BSEE, Fairleigh Dickinson U., 1959; MSEE, Stanford U., 1962; PhD, Ga. Inst. Tech., 1966. Engr. design and devel. Radio Corp. Am., 1959-60; asst. prof. elec. engring. San Jose State Coll., 1962-63; asst. prof. math. Ga. State U., 1966-67; assoc. prof. Columbia U., summer 1969, Harvard U., summer 1970; asst. prof. Morehouse Coll., 1967-68, assoc. prof., chmn. dept. math., 1968-71; dir. exchange student program Stanford U., 1969-71, assoc. prof. elec. engring. 1971-75, assoc. prof. math., summers 1971-75, dir. MITE program, 1975; prof. elec. engring. and math., dean Coll. Engring. Boston U., 1975-88, assoc. v.p., 1986-87; pres. U. Ala., Huntsville, 1988-90; pres., chief exec. officer Univ. City Sci. Ctr., Phila., 1991—; vis. assoc. prof. Stanford U., 1969-71; vis. prof. U. Tokyo, 1986-88, MIT, 1987-88; program dir. Inst. on Computers, Logic and Automata

Theory, NSF, 1969; founder, dir. dual degree program Atlanta U. Ctr. and Ga. Inst. Tech., 1968-70;l numerical analyst Airesearch Corp., L.A., 1969; vis. scientist MIT, 1990-91; dir. Cartermill, Inc. Nemawashi, Inc. Author: System Theory, 1973, Minorities in Engineering, 1974; contbr. chpts. to books. Pres. Valley Found., Huntsville, Ala., 1988-89, Ala. Engring. Found., Huntsville, 1989; mem. task force Vision 2000, Huntsville, 1989; bd. dirs. North Ala. Internat. Trade Assn., 1989, Ala. Supercomputer Network, 1989, Vision 2000, Am. Poetry Ctr., 1992, Benjamin Franklin Tech. Ctr. 1991; pres. Higher Edn. Congress, 1992—; bd. dirs. U.S. Japan Soc., 1990—; trustee Fairleigh Dickinson U., 1989—, Presbyn. Med. Ctr. Phila., 1993—; vis. com. sch. engring. Tuskegee U., Coll. Engring. Drexel U., 1993—; mem. Huntsville Army Community Rels. Com. Recipient Excellence in Sci. and Engring. Edn. award Nat. Consortium for Black Profl. Devel., 1977, Reginald H. Jones Disting. Svc. award GE Found. and Nat. Action Coun. Minorities in Engring., 1983. Fellow IEEE, Am. Soc. Engring. Edn. (Western Electric Fund Excellence in Teaching award 1973, Vincent Bendix award 1984); mem. AAAS, ACM, Mass. Engrs. Coun., Math. Assn. Am., Union League of Phila., NAACP (life). Office: Univ City Sci Ctr 3624 Market St Philadelphia PA 19104

PAEZ, CAROLYN JEAN, secondary education educator; b. Wapanucka, Okla., Dec. 14, 1946; d. John Franklin and Etna Ethel (King) Eacret; m. Rudy R. Paez, Nov. 25, 1977; 1 child, Eric Richard. BA, Western N.Mex. U., 1970, MA, 1984. Tchr. Mountainair (N.Mex.) Pub. Schs., 1970-73, St. Mary's Acad., Silver City, N.Mex., 1973-74, Deming (N.Mex.) Pub. Schs., 1974-78, Silver Consolidated Schs., Silver City, N.Mex., 1978—. Bd. dirs., v.p. N.Mex. Teen Coalition, 1988-91; mentor Future Homemakers Am., 1989-93; cons. So. Area Health Edn. Ctr., Las Cruces, N.Mex., 1989-91. Named champion Future Homemakers Am., 1990; recipient Thanks to Tchr. award Apple Computers, 1990, Tchr. of Yr. award N.Mex. State, 1991, Home Econs. Exemplary Program award, 1989-90, Exemplary Tchrs program Burger King. Mem. NEA, SCEA (bldg. rep. 1987-89, 93), N.Mex. Am. Home Econ. Assn. (bd. dirs. 1989-93), N.Mex. Vocat. Assn., Nat. Assn. Vocat. Home Econs. Tchrs., Home Econ. Edn. Assn., Am. Home Econ. Assn., N.Mex. Vocat. Home Econs. Tchrs. Assn. (2d v.p. 1991, 1st v.p. 1992, pres. 1993), Silver Consol. Edn. Assn. Democrat. Avocations: camping, reading, needlecrafts, Irish blessings, cooking. Home: 61 Coleman Dr Silver City NM 88061-8954 Office: Silver High Sch 3200 N Silver St Silver City NM 88061-7283

PAEZ, RAFAEL ROBERTO, holding company executive; b. Monterrey, Nuevo Leon, Mex., May 20, 1931; s. Rafael Páez Margain and Maria Garza Guerra; m. Maria Teresa Yrigoyen y Diaz González, May 14, 1955; children: Maria de Lourdes, Maria de los Angeles, Maria Teresa, Martha Cecilia, Maria Eugenia, Lucia, Maria del Carmen, Rafael Roberto. Degree in mech. and elec. engring., Inst. Tech. Estudios Superior, Monterrey, 1953, M Adminstrn., 1966. Mgr. finishing dept. Hojalata y Lamina, S.A. Monterrey, 1953-57, asst. supt., 1957-59, supt. gen., 1959-68; dir. ops. steel div. HYLSA, Monterrey, 1968-69, dir. gen. steel div., 1969-78; dir. gen. steel div. Alfa, Monterrey, 1978-81; pres., chief exec. officer Grupo Indsl. Alfa, S.A. de C.V. Monterrey, 1981-94; cons. Vitro Envases, Monterrey, 1980—, Gas Indsl. de Monterrey, 1980, Grupo Financiero Serafin, 1986—, Conek, S.A. de Capital Veriable, Monterrey, 1989—, Bancomer S.A., Monterrey, 1992, Grupo Financiero GBM Atlántico, 1992, Korn/Ferry Internat., L.A., 1994. Roman Catholic. Avocations: tennis, swimming. Office: ALFA SA de CV, Av Gomez Morin 1111 Sur, 66254 Garza Garcia Nuevo Leon, Mexico

PAFFENBARGER, RALPH SEAL, JR., epidemiologist; b. Columbus, Ohio, Oct. 21, 1922; s. Ralph Seal and Viola Elizabeth (Link) P.; m. Mary Dale Higdon, Sept. 19, 1943 (dec.); children—Ralph, James, Ann, Charles, John (dec.), Timothy; m. Jo Ann Schroeder, July 20, 1991. A.B., Ohio State U., 1944; M.B., Northwestern U., 1946, M.D., 1947; M.P.H., Johns Hopkins U., 1952, Dr.P.H., 1954. Intern Evanston (Ill.) Hosp., 1946-47; research asst. pediatrics La. State U. and Charity Hosp., New Orleans, 1949-50; practice medicine, specializing in geriatrics Framingham, Mass., 1960-68; clin. asst. prof. preventive medicine U. Cin., 1955-60; lectr. biostatistics Sch. Pub. Health, Harvard U., 1961-62, clin. assoc. preventive medicine Med. Sch., 1963-65; lectr. epidemiology Sch. Pub. Health, 1965-68, vis. lectr., 1968-83, vis. prof. epidemiology, 1983-85, vis. lectr., 1986-88, adj. prof. epidemiology, 1988—; prof. epidemiology in-residence U. Calif. Sch. Pub. Health, Berkeley, 1968-69, adj. prof., 1969-80; prof. epidemiology Stanford U., 1977-93, prof. emeritus, 1993—; rsch. epidemiologist U. Calif., Berkeley, 1993—; commd. officer USPHS, 1947, med. dir. Atlanta, Ga., 1947-53, Bethesda, Md., 1953-55, Cin., 1955-60, Framingham, 1960-68, ret., 1968; mem. epidemiology and disease control study sect. NIH, 1972-76. Assoc. editor: Am. Jour. Epidemiology, 1972-75, 80—, editor, 1975-79; contbr. articles to profl. publs. Served with AUS, 1943-47. Mem. AAAS, AMA, APHA, Am. Epidemiol. Soc., Am. Heart Assn., Internat. Epidemiol. Assn., Soc. Epidemiol. Rsch., Rsch. Soc. Am., Internat. Soc. Cardiology, Am. Assn. Suicidology, Marcé Soc., Am. Coll. Sports Medicine, Am. Acad. Sports Physicians, Nat. Fitness Leaders Assn., Royal Soc. Medicine, Phi Eta Sigma, Pi Kappa Epsilon, Delta Omega. Home: 892 The Arlington Berkeley CA 94707 Office: Stanford U Sch Medicine Stanford CA 94305

PAGALA, MURALI KRISHNA, physiologist; b. Sri Kalahasti, Andhra, India, Oct. 2, 1942; came to U.S., 1970; s. Lakshmaiah and Radhamma (Bhimavaram) P.; m. Vijaya Bhimavaram, Dec. 12, 1969; children: Sobhan, Suresh. PhD in Zoology, S. V. Univ., Tirupati, A.P., India, 1969; MS in Computer Sci., Pratt Inst., N.Y., 1985. Postdoctoral fellow Inst. for Muscle Disease, N.Y.C., 1970-73, asst. mem., 1974; assoc. rsch. scientist NYU, N.Y.C., 1974-75; asst. to dir. Neuromus Disease Div. Maimonides Med. Ctr., Bklyn., 1975-89, dir. neuromuscular rsch., 1990—; vis. scientist II Physiol. Inst., U. Saarlandes, Hamburg, Germany, 1981, 82; sci. cons. UNDP/TOKTEN Program, Calcutta, India, 1990, NIGMS/FASEB MARC Program Grambling State U., La., 1992, 95; chair sci. confs., participated in Sci. Congress, Germany, 1990, Israel, 1992, Japan, 1994, 95. Reviewed and contbr. articles to profl. jours. Life mem. Telugu Assn. of North Am., 1989; sci. fair judge N.Y. Acad. Scis., N.Y.C., 1986—. Named Best speaker Zool. Soc. of S. V. Univ., 1964, Best Basic Rsch. paper Maimonides Med. Ctr., 1983, 88, 94; Fatigue Rsch. grantee Maimonides Rsch. Devel. Found., 1986—, Drug Rsch. grantee Maimonides Rsch. Devel. Found., 1989—, Aging Rsch. grantee Maimonides Rsch. Devel. Found., 1995—. Mem. N.Y. Acad. Scis., Am. Physiol. Soc., Assn. Scientists of Indian Origin in Am. (pres. 1993-94). Democrat. Hindu. Achievements include devel. in vitro electromyographic, electrocardiographic and multi-muscle chambers to evaluate the function of skeletal muscle, heart and smooth muscule preparations from experimental animals and human subjects; and development of consumer products. Home: 82 Dudley Ave Staten Island NY 10312 Office: Maimonides Med Ctr 4802 Tenth Ave Brooklyn NY 11219

PAGAN, JOHN RUSTON, law educator; b. Little Rock, Aug. 4, 1951; s. John Frank and Betty (Hardin) P. BA, Coll. of William and Mary, 1973; MLitt, Oxford U., 1975; JD, Harvard U., 1978. Bar: Ark. 1979, Va. 1982, D.C. 1984. From asst. to assoc. prof. Randall-Whyte Sch. of Law Coll. of William and Mary, Williamsburg, Va., 1979-84; assoc. prof. Sch. of Law U. Ark., Little Rock, 1984-86, prof. Sch. of Law, 1986—. Contbr. articles to profl. jours. Ark. state senator, Little Rock, 1991-92; legislator Pulaski County Quorum Ct., Little Rock, 1987-90. Mem. Assn. of Marshall Scholars, Phi Beta Kappa. Democrat. Avocation: historical research. Home: 6907 Lucerne Dr Little Rock AR 72205 Office: U Ark Sch Law 1201 McAlmont Dr Little Rock AR 72202

PAGAN MARTINEZ, JUAN, administrative corps officer; b. Cartagena, Murcia, Spain, Apr. 6, 1938; arrived in U.S., 1979; s. Juan and Rosa (Martinez) Pagan Lopez; m. Josefina Serrano Botella, Mar. 19, 1964; children: Rosa, Juan Carlos, Cristina. Degree, Escuela Pericial de Comercio, Cartagena, Spain, 1963. Warehouse, acctg. chief Almirante Bastarreche Profl. Sch., Cartagena, 1956-77; adminstrv. corps officer Spanish Navy, Cartagena, 1961-79, Embassy of Spain, Washington, 1979—. Contbr. articles to profl. jours. Centurion Franco's Youth Front, Cartagena, 1955; bandurria player Spanish Dance Soc., Washington, 1991—; sec. Sports and Phys. Edn. Coun., Cartagena, 1972-79. Recipient Golden Poet award World of Poetry, 1990, 91, Honorable mention, 1990, Blue Ribbon award So. Poetry Assn., 1990. Mem. Washington Spanish Club (sec. 1992-94, pres. 1994—). Avocations: poetry, music composer, bandurria, lute, guitar, sax player. Home: 1009 1st St Rockville MD 20850-1451

PAGANO, JOSEPH STEPHEN, physician, researcher, educator; b. Rochester, N.Y., Dec. 29, 1931; s. Angelo Pagano and Marian (Vinci) Signorino; m. Anna Louise Reynolds, June 8, 1957; children: Stephen Reynolds, Christopher Joseph. A.B. with honors, U. Rochester, 1953; M.D., Yale U., 1957. Resident Peter Bent Brigham Hosp. Harvard U., Boston, 1960-61; fellow Karolinska Inst., Stockholm, 1961-62; mem. Wistar Inst., Phila., 1962-65; asst. prof., then assoc. prof. U. N.C., Chapel Hill, 1965-73, prof. medicine, 1974—, dir. div. infectious diseases, 1972-75; dir. U. N.C. Lineberger Comprehensive Cancer Ctr., Chapel Hill, 1974—; attending physician N.C. Meml. Hosp., Chapel Hill; vis. prof. Swiss Inst. Cancer Rsch., Lausanne, 1970-71, Lineberger prof. cancer rsch., 1986—; mem. virology study sect. NIH, Bethesda, Md., 1973-79; cons. Burroughs Wellcome Co., Research Triangle Park, N.C., 1978—; mem. Recombinant DNA adv. com. USPHS, 1986-90; mem. chancellor's adv. com. U. N.C., 1985-91, chair 1990-91; bd. dirs. AACI, Burroughs Wellcome Fund; adv. com. N.C. Cancer Coord. and Control, 1993—; mem. N.C. planning commn. for N.C. Inst. of Medicine to organize Research!America, 1993. Mem. editorial bd. Jour. Virology, 1974-90; bd. assoc. editors Cancer Rsch., 1976-80; assoc. editor Jour. Gen. Virology, 1979-84, Antimicrobial Agts. and Chemotherapy, 1984-93; contbr. numerous articles to profl. publs., chpts. to books. Bd. dirs. Am. Cancer Soc., N.C., 1980—; mem. Carolina Fedn. of Environtl. Programs, 1994-96. Recipient Sinsheimer award, 1966-68, USPHS Research Career award NIH, 1968-73; named Harry F. Dowling lecturer, 1991. Mem. AAAS (Newcomb Anderson prize selection com. 1984-88), Infectious Disease Soc., Am. Soc. Microbiology, Am. Soc. Clin. Investigation, Am. Soc. Virology, Am. Assn. Physicians, Internat. Assn. for Rsch. in Epstein-Barr Virus and Associated Diseases (pres. 1991-94, First Gertrude & Werner Henle Lectureship in Viral Oncology 1990), Chapel Hill Country Club, Chapel Hill Tennis (pres. 1980-82), Carolina (Baldhead Island). Episcopalian. Avocations: tennis, squash. Home: 114 Laurel Hill Rd Chapel Hill NC 27514-4323 Office: U NC Lineberger Comp Cancer Ctr U NC Chapel Hill NC 27599-7295

PAGANUCCI, PAUL DONNELLY, banker, lawyer, former college official; b. Waterville, Maine, Apr. 18, 1931; s. Romeo J. and Martha (Donnelly) P.; m. Marilyn McLean, Sept. 10, 1966; children: Thomas Donnelly, Elizabeth Mary. A.B., Dartmouth Coll., 1953; M.B.A., Amos Tuck Sch. Bus. Adminstrn., 1954; J.D., Harvard U., 1957. Bar: N.Y. 1958, N.H. 1972. Staff asst. to pres. W.R. Grace & Co., N.Y.C., 1958-61, vice chmn., bd. dirs., 1986-89, chmn. exec. com., bd. dirs., 1989-91; pres., treas., bd. dirs. Lombard, Vitalis, Paganucci & Nelson, Inc., N.Y.C., 1961-72; prof. bus. adminstrn. Amos Tuck Sch. Dartmouth Coll., Hanover, N.H., 1972-77, assoc. dean, 1972-76, sr. investment officer, 1976-77, v.p., 1977-84, v.p. and treas., 1984-85; chmn. Ledyard Nat. Bank, Hanover, 1991—; bd. dirs. W.R. Grace Found., N.Y.C., Filene's Basement, Inc., Meriden-Stinehour, Inc., Allmerica Securities Trust, HRE Properties, Hypertherm, Inc.; allied mem. N.Y. Stock Exch., 1961-72. Chmn. bd. trustees Dartmouth Cath. Student Ctr., 1973-85, overseer, 1973—; trustee Colby Coll., 1975-85, 87—; Casque and Gauntlet; mem. Pres.'s Pvt. Sector Survey on Cost Control. Served with AUS, 1956-62. Mem. Inst. Chartered Fin. Analysts. Clubs: Dartmouth of N.Y. (dir., v.p., pres.); Union (Boston); Knights of Malta. Home: 33 Ropeferry Rd Hanover NH 03755-1404 Office: 38 S Main St Hanover NH 03755-2015

PAGE, ALAN CEDRIC, judge; b. Canton, Ohio, Aug. 7, 1945; s. Howard F. and Georgianna (Umbles) P.; m. Diane Sims, June 5, 1973; children: Nina, Georgianna, Justin, Khamsin. BA, U. Notre Dame, 1967; JD, U. Minn., 1978; LLD (hon.), U. Notre Dame, 1993; student, St. John's U., 1994, Westfield State Coll., 1994, Luther Coll., 1995. Bar: Minn. 1979, U.S. Dist. Ct. Minn. 1979, U.S. Supreme Ct. 1988. Profl. athlete Minn. Vikings, Mpls., 1967-78, Chgo. Bears, 1978-81; assoc. Lindquist & Vennum, Mpls., 1979-85; former atty. Minn. Atty. Gen.'s Office, Mpls., 1985-92; assoc. justice Minn. Supreme Ct., St. Paul, 1993—; cons. NFL Players Assn., Washington, 1979-84. Commentator Nat. Pub. Radio, 1982-83. Founder Page Edn. Found., 1988. Named NFL's Most Valuable Player, 1971, one of 10 Outstanding Young Men Am., U.S. Jaycees, 1981; named to NFL Hall of Fame, 1988, Coll. Football Hall of Fame, 1993. Mem. ABA, Minn. Bar Assn., Hennepin County Bar Assn., Minn. Minority Lawyers Assn. Avocations: running, biking. Office: 245 Minnesota Judicial Ctr 25 Constitution Ave Saint Paul MN 55155-1500

PAGE, ALBERT LEE, soil science educator, researcher; b. New Lenox, Ill., Mar. 19, 1927; s. Thomas E. and Hattie O. (Pease) Pugh; m. Shirley L. Jessmore, Sept. 14, 1952; children—Nancy, Thomas. BA in Chemistry, U. Calif.-Riverside, 1956; PhD in Soil Sci., U. Calif.-Davis, 1960. Prof. soil sci. U. Calif.-Riverside, 1960—; dir. Kearney Found., Univ. Calif.-Riverside, program of excellence in energy research. Editor: Methods of Soil Analysis, 1983, Utilization of Municipal Wastewater and Sludge on Land, 1983, Heavy Metals in the Environment, 1977. Served as QMQ1 USN, 1945-52. Recipient Environ. Quality Research award Am. Soc. Agronomy, 1984, Disting. Teaching award U. Calif., Riverside, 1976, Disting. Svc. award USDA, 1991; Fullbright scholar, 1966-67; Guggenheim Meml. Found. fellow, 1966-67. Fellow Am. Soc. Agronomy, Soil Sci. Soc. Am.; mem. Internat. Soil Sci. Soc., Western Soil Sci. Soc., Soc. Environ. Geochemistry and Health, Sigma Xi. Lodge: Elks. Home: 5555 Canyon Crest 1F Riverside CA 92507 Office: Univ of Calif Dept Soil & Environ Sci Riverside CA 92521

PAGE, ANN, stock brokerage executive; b. Carbondale, Ill., Apr. 12, 1958; d. Richard Frank and Marilyn Kay (Bays) P. BFA in Theatre, S.W. Mo. State U., 1990. V.p. individual retirement products Paine Webber, N.Y.C., 1984-86; v.p. bank trust products Paine Webber, 1986-88, v.p. equity sales, 1988-91; asst. br. mgr. Paine Webber, Inc., Chesterfield, Mo., 1991-92; br. mgr. Paine Webber, Inc., Houston, 1992—. Sponsor March of Dimes, N.Y.C., 1982-88, Symphony Space, N.Y.C., 1988; bd. dirs. Greater Greenspoint Mgmt. Dist., 1993—. Mem. NAFE, Soc. for Parapsychol. Rsch., Internat. Found. Employee Benefit Plans, Internat. Assn. Fin. Planners., North Greenspoint Co. of C. (bus. and econ. devel. coms. 1992—). Avocations: parapsychology, French, skiing, singing jazz/blues. Office: Paine Webber Inc 16945 Northchase Dr Ste 100 Houston TX 77060-2199

PAGE, ANNE RUTH, gifted education educator, education specialist; b. Norfolk, Va., Apr. 13, 1949; d. Amos Purnell and Ruth Martin (Hill) Bailey; m. Peter Smith Page, Apr. 24, 1971; children: Edgar Bailey, Emmett McBrannon. BA, N.C. Wesleyan Coll.; student, Fgn. Lang. League; postgrad., N.C. State U.; student, Overseas Linguistic Studies, France, Spain, Eng., 1978, 85, 86. Cert. tchr., N.C. Tchr. Cary (N.C.) Sr. High Sch., 1971-72; tchr., head dept. Danesk Mid. Sch., Raleigh, N.C., 1978-83; chmn. fgn. lang. dept. Martin Mid. Gifted and Talented, Raleigh, N.C., 1983—; leadership team Senate Bill 2 Core co-chair; student group Overseas Studies, Am. Coun. for Internat. Studies, France, Spain, Eng. 1982, 84, 86, 88; bd. dirs. N.T.H., Inc., Washington; cert. mentor tchr. Wake County Pub. Schs., 1989; dir. student exchs. between Martin Mid. Sch. and Sevigné Inst. of Compiegne, France. Sunday sch. tchr. Fairmont United Meth. Ch., Raleigh, 1983-85. Mem. Alpha Delta Kappa. Democrat. Home: 349 Wilmot Dr Raleigh NC 27606-1232 Office: Martin Mid Sch GT 1701 Ridge Rd Raleigh NC 27607-6737

PAGE, AUSTIN P., construction technology and property development company executive; b. Sherbrooke, Que., Can., 1936. Grad., Sir George Williams U., 1966. Exec. v.p., CFO Tridel Enterprises Inc., Toronto; pres., CEO Aluma Systems Corp., Toronto; bd. dirs. Tridel Equities Ltd., Banca Commerciale Italiana of Can. Office: Tridel Enterprises Inc, 4800 Dufferin St, Downsview, ON Canada M3H 5S9

PAGE, BENJAMIN INGRIM, political science educator, researcher; b. Los Angeles, Sept. 17, 1940; s. Benjamin Markham and Virginia Claire (Ingrim) P.; m. Mary Herbert Robertson, Dec. 30, 1964; children: Benjamin R., Alexandra C., Timothy M., Eleanor St. J. AB in History, Stanford U., 1961, PhD in Polit. Sci., 1973; LLB, Harvard U., 1965. Asst. prof. govt. Dartmouth Coll., 1971-73; asst. prof. polit. sci. U. Chgo., 1973-77, assoc. prof., 1978-82, prof., 1982-83; assoc. prof. U. Wis.-Madison, 1977-78; Frank C. Erwin Jr. Centennial chair in govt. U. Tex., Austin, 1983-88; Gordon Scott Fulcher prof. of decision making Northwestern U., 1988—; rsch. assoc. Nat. Opinion Rsch. Ctr., Chgo., 1978-82; bd. overseers Nat. Election Studies, Ann Arbor, Mich., 1975-81; cons. in field. Author: (with Sullivan,

Pressman and Lyons) The Politics of Representation, 1974, Choices and Echoes in Presidential Elections, 1978, (with Petracca) The American Presidency, 1983, Who Gets What from Government, 1983, (with Shapiro) The Rational Public, 1992, (with Greenberg) The Struggle for Democracy, 1993; contbr. articles to numerous jours. Recipient Law Week award Bur. of Nat. Affairs, 1965; fellow Social Sci. Research Council, 1972-73, Hoover Instn., 1981-82. Mem. AAAS, Am. Polit. Sci. Assn. (governing coun. 1984-86), Midwest Polit. Sci. Assn. (v.p. 1991-93), Pub. Choice Soc., Am. Assn. Pub. Opinion Rsch., Am. Econs. Assn., Phi Beta Kappa. Democrat. Episcopalian. Home: 1633 Asbury Ave Evanston IL 60201-4101 Office: Northwestern U Polit Sci Dept Evanston IL 60208

PAGE, CLARENCE E., newspaper columnist; b. Dayton, Ohio, June 2, 1947; m. Lisa Johnson Cole, May 3, 1987. BS in Journalism, Ohio U., 1969. Reporter, asst. city editor Chgo. Tribune, 1969-80; dir. community affairs dept. Sta. WBBM-TV, 1980-82, reporter, planning editor, 1982-84; columnist, mem. editorial bd. Chgo. Tribune, 1984—. Frequent guest Sta. WTTW-TV, Chicago Tonight, Chicago in Review; contbr. articles to profl. jours. Participant 1972 Chgo. Tribune Task Force Series on Vote Fraud which won the Pulitzer Prize. Recipient Community Svc. award Ill. UPI, 1980, James P. McGuire award CLU, 1987, Pulitzer Prize for commentary, 1989. Office: Tribune Media Svcs 435 N Michigan Ave Ste 600 Chicago IL 60611*

PAGE, DAVID RANDALL, hospital administrator; b. Plainfield, N.J., Oct. 30, 1940; married;. BA, Davidson Coll., 1962; MA, Duke U., 1964. Administrv. resident Durham County Gen. Hosp., Durham, N.C., 1964; administrv. resident Duke U. Hosp., Durham, N.C., 1963-64, administrv. asst., 1964-65; asst. dir. Children's Mercy Hosp., Kansas City, 1968-69; asst. dir. Meml. Mission Hosp., Asheville, N.C., 1969-71, assoc. dir., 1971-81; exec. v.p., dir. Ochsner Fedn. Hosp., New Orleans, 1981-93; pres. Hermann Hosp., Houston, 1993—. Mem. AHA, ACHE. Office: Hermann Hosp 6411 Fannin Houston TX 77030*

PAGE, ELLIS BATTEN, behavioral scientist, educator; b. San Diego, Apr. 29, 1924; s. Frank Homer and Dorothy (Batten) P.; m. Elizabeth Latimer Thaxton, June 21, 1952; children: Ellis Batten (Tim), Elizabeth Page Sigman, Richard Leighton. A.B., Pomona Coll., 1947; M.A., San Diego State U., 1955; Ed.D., UCLA, 1958; postdoctoral (NSF fellow), U. Mich., 1959; postdoctoral (IBM fellow), MIT, 1966-67. Tchr. secondary schs. Calif., 1952-56; mem. psychology dept. San Diego City Coll., 1957-58; dir. guidance and testing Eastern Mich. U., 1958-60; dean Coll. Edn., prof. edn. and psychology Tex. Woman's U., 1960-62; dir. Bur. Ednl. Rsch. U. Conn., 1962-70, prof. ednl. psychology, 1962-79; prof. ednl. psychology and research Duke U., 1979—; vis. prof. U. Wis., 1960, 62, Harvard U., 1968-69, U. Javeriana, Bogotá, 1975; leader Ford Found. rsch. adv. team Venezuelan Ministry Edn., Caracas, 1969-70; vis. prof. Spanish Ministry Edn., 1972, 80, 82-85; rsch. cons. U.S. Office Edn., USN, Nat. Inst. Edn., Bur. Edn. Handicapped; chmn. nat. planning com. Nat. Ctr. Edn. Stats.; adviser Brazilian Ministry Edn., 1973, 80; chief Ministerial Commn. Edn., Bermuda, 1983-85; mem. Adv. Coun. for Edn. Stats., U.S. Dept. Edn., 1987-90; pres. TruJudge, Inc., 1993—. Author, editor in field. Capt. USMCR, 1943-46. Recipient Disting. Alumnus award San Diego State U., 1980. Fellow AAAS (life), APA (pres. ednl. psychology 1976-77), Am. Psychol. Soc., John Dewey Soc., Am. Assn. Applied & Preventive Psychology, Nat. Conf. Rsch. English, Philosophy Edn. Soc.; mem. Am. Coun. Assn., Am. Ednl. Rsch. Assn. (pres. 1979-80), Am. Statis. Assn. (officer N.C. chpt.), Behavior Genetics Assn., Assn. Computational Linguistics, Nat. Assn. Scholars, N.C. Assn. Rsch. Edn. (Disting. Rsch. award 1981, 91, pres. 1984-85), Rhetoric Soc. Am. (dir.), Psychometric Soc., Sociedad Española de Pedagogía (hon.), Sigma Xi, Phi Kappa Phi, Phi Gamma Delta, Psi Chi, Kappa Delta Pi, Phi Delta Kappa (life; svc. key). Anglican. Home: 110 Oakstone Dr Chapel Hill NC 27514-9585 Office: Duke U 213 W Duke Bldg Durham NC 27708

PAGE, ERNEST, medical educator; b. Cologne, Germany, May 30, 1927; came to U.S., 1936, naturalized, 1942; s. Max Ernest and Eleanor (Kohn) P.; m. Eva Veronica Gross, June 5, 1967; 1 son, Thomas J. A.B., Calif., Berkeley, 1949; M.D., Calif., San Francisco, 1952. Intern Peter Bent Brigham Hosp., Boston, 1952-53; resident Peter Bent Brigham Hosp., 1953-54, 57-58; research assoc. Harvard Med. Sch., 1957-65; assoc. prof. medicine and Physiology U. Chgo. Med. Sch., 1965-69, prof., 1969—. Editor: Am. Jour. Physiology: Heart and Circulatory Physiology, 1981-86. Served with AUS, 1945-46. Established investigator Am. Heart Assn., 1959-65. Mem. Am. Physiol. Soc., Biophys. Soc., Am. Soc. Cell Biology, Soc. Gen. Physiologists, Assn. Am. Physicians. Home: 5680 S Harper Ave Chicago IL 60637-1832 Office: U Chgo Med Sch 5841 S Maryland Ave Chicago IL 60637-1470

PAGE, FREDERICK WEST, business consultant; b. East Orange, N.J., Oct. 19, 1932; s. Frederick West and Dorothy (Donham) P.; m. Miriam Lowell Jones, Feb. 14, 1959; children: William, Janet, Thomas, James. A.B., Dartmouth Coll., 1954; postgrad., Wharton Grad. Sch. Bus., U. Pa., 1956-57; M.B.A., NYU, 1960. With Schering Corp. (now Schering-Plough), 1957-91, various mktg. positions, 1957-73, gen. mgr. animal health products, 1973-80, pres. U.S. Animal Health Products Div., 1980-83, v.p. pharm. ops., 1983-91; pres. Bus. Cons. Svcs., 1991—. Served with U.S. Army, 1954-56. Mem. Animal Health Inst. (exec. com. 1978-81, chmn. 1979-80). Republican. Club: Phi Kappa Psi. Home and Office: 22 Martin Rd West Caldwell NJ 07006-7419

PAGE, GEORGE KEITH, banker; b. Rolling Prairie, Ind., July 7, 1917; s. Glenn Keith and Ruth (Mansfield) P.; m. Carmen Bailey; children: Kay, Susan, John Michael. Ed., U. Ala. Coll. Commerce and Bus. Adminstrn. Asst. cashier Baldwin County Bank, Bay Minette, Ala., 1938-43; pres., dir. Baldwin County Savs. & Loan Assn., Robertsdale and Fairhope, Ala., 1943-58; chmn. bd., chief exec. officer United First Fed. Savs. & Loan Assn. (merger Barnett Bank S.W. Fla.), Sarasota, Fla., 1958-86; sr. chmn. Barnett Bank S.W. Fla., 1986-89; also bd. dirs. Barnett Bank S.W. Fla., Sarasota, Fla.; ret., 1989; trustees Found. for Savs. Instns., 1984-86. Pres. Ala. Savs. and Loan League, 1956; past pres., gen. campaign chmn., bd. dirs., mem. adv. coun. Sarasota United Way; past chmn. Sarasota Housing Authority; past bd. dirs. Met. YMCA Sarasota-Manatee Counties; past bd. dirs., treas. Sarasota County Libr. Bldg. Fund; trustee Sarasota Meml. Hosp. Found., 1986-92, 93-94, chmn. endowment com., 1987-92; bd. dirs. Sarasota Opera Assn., Inc., 1992—; mem. adv. bd. Sunny Land coun. Boy Scouts Am.; past trustee Argus Found.; past bd. dirs. Indsl. Devel. Corp. Fla.; gen. chmn. capital campaign funds Sarasota YMCA, 1969. With USN, WWII. Recipient cert. of honor City Commn. and C. of C., Fairhope, 1958, Silver Beaver award Boy Scouts Am., Mobile, 1949, named Disting. Eagle Scout, 1982, Outstanding Citizen award Sarasota Jaycees, 1978, recipient Brotherhood award NCCJ, 1979. Mem. Fla. Savs. and Loan League (pres. 1970-71), Sarasota County C. of C. (past treas., bd. dirs.), Sarasota U. Club (past pres., bd. dirs.), Oaks Country Club, Field Club (bd. dirs. 1968-71), Masons (32d degree), Shriners. Avocation: golf. Office: Ste 808 1800 2nd St Sarasota FL 34236

PAGE, HARRY ROBERT, business administration educator; b. Milw., Mar. 22, 1915; s. Harry Allen and Lydia (Rosendahl) P.; m. Jeanne Tompkins, Apr. 1, 1945; children: Patricia Jeanne, Margaret Berenice. A.B., Mich. State U., 1941; postgrad., U.S. Army Command and Staff Coll., 1945-46, Indsl. Coll. Armed Forces, 1958-59; M.B.A., Harvard, 1950; Ph.D. Am. U., 1966. Served from 2d lt. to lt. col. U.S. Army, 1941-46; from lt. col. to col. USAF, 1947-61; exec. officer logistics directorate U.S. Joint Chiefs of Staff, Washington, 1959-61; asst. prof. bus. adminstrn. George Washington U., Washington, 1961-65; assoc. prof., chmn. dept. George Washington U., 1965-69, prof., chmn. dept. bus. adminstrn., 1970-74, assoc. dean, 1975-80, prof. emeritus, 1981—; cons. Advanced Study program Brookings Instn., Washington, 1966-70, Ednl. Svcs. Inst., U.S. Postal Svc., 1985-92. Author: Church Budget Development, 1964, An Analysis of the Defense Procurement Program Decision-Making Process, 1966, Public Purchasing and Materials Management, 1980, rev. edit., 1989; co-author: Federal Contributions to Management, 1972. Chmn. task force edn. and tng. Commn. Govt. Procurement, 1972-73; bd. dirs., treas. Coun. Chs., Greater Washington, 1963-68; bd. dirs. Hunter Assocs. Lab., Inc.; deacon Rock Spring Congregational Ch., 1994—. Decorated Air medal, Purple Heart, Legion of Merit. Fellow Nat. Contract Mgmt. Assn.; mem. Acad. mgmt., Nat. Assn.

Purchasing Mgmt., Internat. Fedn. Purchasing and Materials Mgmt., Harvard Bus. Sch. Assn., Air Force Assn., Nat. Parks and Conservation Assn. (trustee), Air Force Sgts. Assn. (trustee, chmn. scholarship bd. 1971—), Harvard Bus. Club, Sch. of Wash. Club (dir., pres. 1980-81), Alpha Phi Omega, Lambda Chi Alpha Alpha Kappa Psi, Pi Sigma Alpha, Beta Gamma Sigma. Home: 3612 N Glebe Rd Arlington VA 22207-4317 Office: 710 21st St NW Washington DC 20052-0001

PAGE, JAKE (JAMES K. PAGE, JR.), writer, editor; b. Boston, Jan. 24, 1936; s. James Keena Page and Ellen Van Dyke (Gibson) Kunath; m. Aida de Alva Bound, Nov. 28, 1959 (div. 1976); children: Dana de Alva Page, Lea Gibson Page Kuntz, Brooke Bound Page; m. Susanne Calista Stone, Mar. 10, 1974; stepchildren: Lindsey Truitt, Sally Truitt, Kendall Barrett. BA, Princeton U., 1958; MA, NYU, 1959. Asst. sales promotion mgr. Doubleday & Co., 1959-60; editor Doubleday Anchor Books, 1960-62, Natural History Press, Doubleday, N.Y.C., 1962-69; editorial dir. Natural History Mag. N.Y.C., 1966-69; editor-in-chief Walker & Co., N.Y.C., 1969-70; sci. editor Smithsonian Mag., Washington, 1970-76; founder, dir. Smithsonian Books, Washington, 1976-80; start-up editor Smithsonian Air & Space Mag., Washington, 1985; pvt. practice as writer Waterford, Va., Corrales, N.Mex., 1980—; mag. cons. Denver Mus. Nat. History, 1989-90; contract text editor Doubleday, 1992. Author: (with Richard Saltonstall Jr.) Brown Out & Slow Down, 1972, (with Larry R. Collins) Ling-Ling & Hsing Hsing: Year of the Panda, 1973, Shoot the Moon, 1979, (with Wilson Clark) Energy, Vulnerability and War: Alternatives for America, 1981, Blood: River of Life, 1981, (with Susanne Page) Hopi, 1982, Forest, 1983, Arid Lands, 1984, Pastorale: A Natural History of Sorts, 1985, Demon State, 1985, Navaho, 1995, (with Eugene S. Morton) Lords of the Air: The Smithsonian Book of Birds, 1989, Smithsonian's New Zoo, 1990, Zoo: The Modern Ark, 1990, Animal Talk: Science and the Voice of Nature, 1992, The Stolen Gods, 1993, Songs to Birds, 1993 (with Chalres B. Officer) Tales of the Earth, 1993, The Deadly Canyon, 1994 (with David Leeming) Goddess: Mythology of the Female Divine, 1994, The Knotted Strings, 1995, Smithsonian Guides to Natural America: Arizona and New Mexico, 1995, God: Mythology of the Male Divine; editor: (with Malcolm Baldwin) Law and the Environment, 1970; contbg. editorships Science Mag., 1980-86, Oceans Mag., 1987, Mother Earth News, 1990, National Geographic Traveler, 1990-93, TDC (now Destination Discovery), 1991—; contbg. author to numerous books and mags. Mem. nat. bd. advisors Futures for Children, Albuquerque, 1980—. Democrat. Avocation: Arab horses. Home and Office: PO Box 78 345 Chimaja Rd Corrales NM 87048

PAGE, JANICE ELLEN, retail executive; b. Phila., Nov. 6, 1948; d. Richard F. and Helen M. (Faerber) Koecher; m. Verner L. Page, Dec. 10, 1977. BA, Pa. State U., 1970. Exec. trainee Sears, Roebuck and Co., St. Davids, Pa., 1970-71, field mgr., 1971-74; asst. buyer children's apparel and home fashions Sears, Roebuck and Co., Chgo., 1974-77, buyer toys, 1977-80, sr. buyer sporting goods, 1980-82, group buying coord. automotive and recreation, 1982, nat. mgr. direct mktg., 1982-87, nat. mdse. mgr. sporting goods, 1987-88, nat. mdse. mgr. intimate apparel, nightwear and hosiery, 1988—. Named one of Chgo.'s Most Powerful Women, Chicago Tribune, 1987, 100 Best and Brightest Women in Mktg. and Advt., Advertising Age mag., 1988, New Am. Woman, Time mag., 1990. Mem. Direct Mktg. Assn., Am. Mktg. Assn., Chgo. Coun. Fgn. Rels. Lutheran. Office: Sears Roebuck & Co Sears Tower 18th Fl Chicago IL 60684

PAGE, JOHN ARTHUR, professional association executive, educator; b. New Rochelle, N.Y., Sept. 23, 1957; s. Arthur John and Yolanda Gloria (Malzone) P.; m. Patricia Alta Marsh, June 18, 1984. BA in Sci., Pa. State U., 1980, BS in Health Planning and Adminstrn., 1980; MS in Health Sys., Ga. Inst. Tech., 1982. Strategic planner Gnaden Huetten Meml. Hosp., Lehighton, Pa., 1980; grad. tchg. and rsch. asst. Ga. Inst. Tech. Sch. Health Sys., Atlanta, 1981-82; mgmt. sys. engr. Good Shepherd Med. Ctr., Longview, Tex., 1982-84; dir. mgmt. engring. U. Nebr. Med. Ctr., Omaha, 1984-88; dir. mgmt. svcs. Children's Hosp., Inc., Columbus, Ohio, 1988-90; pres., CEO, Innovative Healthcare Assocs., Inc., Columbus, 1990—, PAGE Techs., Inc., Columbus, 1990—; exec. dir., CEO, Healthcare Info. and Mgmt. Sys. Soc., Chgo., 1991—; mem. grad. program adv. bd. U. Ill., Chgo., 1991—; adj. asst. prof., 1994—; mem. grad. program adv. bd. U. Ala., Birmingham, 1991—; pres., chmn. bd. Healthcare Info. and Mgmt. Sys. Soc. Found., 1995—. Contbg. author: Patients and Purse Springs, 1987, Productivity and Performance Management in Healthcare Institutions, 1989, An Orientation for Management Engineers New to Health Care, 1992, The Emergency Department: A Guide to Operational Excellence, 1992, Clinical Administration of Audiology and Speech Language Pathology, 1994, Guide to Effective Health Care Informaton and Management Systems and the Role of the CIO, 1994; mem. editl. adv. bd. Report on Health Care Info. Mgmt., 1993—. Advisor Med. Explorers, 1988-90, Jr. Achievement, 1988-90; alumni admissions counselor Pa. State U., 1986—; campaign chmn. United Way, 1988, 89, 90; vol. Am. Heart Assn., 1991, March of Dimes, 1991-93, Am. Cancer Soc., 1990. Recipient Tech. Paper of Yr. award Healthcare Info. and Mgmt. Sys. Soc., 1989. Mem. Masons (chmn. blood drive 1990—). Avocations: computers, music, photography, football. Home: 3123 N Orchard St Chicago IL 60657 Office: Healthcare Info and Mgmt Sys Soc 230 E Ohio St Ste 600 Chicago IL 60611

PAGE, JOHN BOYD, physics educator; b. Columbus, Ohio, Sept. 4, 1938; s. John Boyd and Helen (Young) P.; m. Norma Kay Christensen, July 28, 1966; children: Rebecca, Elizabeth. BS, U. Utah, 1960, PhD, 1966. Rsch. assoc. Inst. for Theoretical Physics U. Frankfurt/Main, Fed. Republic of Germany, 1966-67; rsch. assoc. Cornell U., Ithaca, N.Y., 1968-69; asst. prof. physics Ariz. State U., 1969-75, assoc. prof., 1975-80, prof., 1980—; vis. prof. dept. physics Cornell U., 1989. Contbr. articles to profl. jours. Recipient Humboldt Rsch. award, 1991; NSF grantee, 1972-77, 77-80, 80-82, 82-86, 90-92, 91—. Fellow Am. Phys. Soc.; mem. Am. Assn. Physics Tchrs., Phi Beta Kappa, Sigma Xi, Phi Kappa Phi, Phi Eta Sigma. Office: Ariz State U Physics Dept Tempe AZ 85287-1504

PAGE, JOHN HENRY, JR., artist, educator; b. Ann Arbor, Mich., Jan. 18, 1923; s. John Henry and Lucille (Bennett) P.; m. Mary Lou Franks, July 22, 1945; children: Jonathan, Marilyn, Jeremy. Student, Mpls. Sch. Art, 1940-42; B.Design, U. Mich., 1948; M.F.A., U. Iowa, 1950. Instr. Mankato (Minn.) State Coll., 1950-54; asst. prof. art U. No. Iowa, Cedar Falls, 1954-55; asst. prof. U. No. Iowa, 1955-59, assoc. prof., 1959-64, prof., 1964-87, acting head dept. art, 1984-85; head art dept. U. Omaha, 1959-60. One-man exhbns. include Luther Coll., Decorah, Iowa, 1981, Laura Musser Mus., Muscatine, Iowa, 1978, Coe Coll., Cedar Rapids, Iowa, 1975, Sheldon Gallery, Lincoln, Nebr., 1974, Creighton U., Omaha, 1969, Augustana Coll., Rock Island, Ill., 1964, Muskegon (Mich.) Mus. Art, 1983, retrospective (in three parts) Gallery of Art U. No. Iowa, Hearst Ctr. for the Arts, Cedar Falls, Iowa, Waterloo (Iowa) Mus. of Art, 1992; group exhbns. include 10th Nat. Print Show Bklyn. Mus., 1956, 9 Iowa Artists Gov. Exhbn., 1971-72, Walker Art Ctr., Mpls., 1973, Regional Invitational Exhbn., U. Omaha, 1978, Fragile Giants, Brunner Gallery, 1994—; represented in permanent collections, Library of Congress, Walker Art Center, Des Moines Art Center, Joslyn Art Mus., Omaha, Carnegie Inst., Pitts. Served with U.S. Army, 1943-45. Nat. Endowment Arts grantee, 1974. Unitarian. Home: 114 Los Arcos Green Valley AZ 85614

PAGE, JONATHAN ROY, investment analyst; b. Harrisburg, Pa., Sept. 10, 1946; s. John and Ellen (Smith) P.; m. Patrice Marie Margerm, May 17, 1975; children: Elizabeth, Gregory, Richard, Brian. B.A., Dartmouth Coll., 1968; M.B.A., Tuck Sch. Dartmouth, 1969. Chartered fin. analyst. Investment officer Irving Trust Co., N.Y.C., 1970-75; sr. v.p., portfolio mgr. Dean Witter Intercapital Funds, N.Y.C., 1975—. Vestry person St. John's Ch., Ramsey, N.J., 1984-88. Mem. N.Y. Soc. Security Analysts, Fin. Analysts Fedn. Republican. Episcopalian. Avocations: tennis, golf, skiing, landscaping. Home: 36 Sturbridge Dr Saddle River NJ 07458-1742 Office: Dean Witter Intercapital Funds 2 World Trade Ctr Fl 72 New York NY 10048-0203

PAGE, JOSEPH ANTHONY, law educator; b. Boston, Apr. 13, 1934; s. Joseph E. and Eleanor M. (Santosuosso) P.; m. Martha Gil-Montero, May 18, 1984. AB, Harvard U., 1955, LLB, 1958, LLM, 1964. Asst. prof. coll. law U. Denver, 1964-67, assoc. prof., 1967-68; assoc. prof. law ctr. Georgetown U., 1968-73, prof., 1973—; bd. dirs. Pub. Citizen, Inc., Wash-

ington. Author: The Revolution that Never Was, 1972, The Law of Premises Liability, 1976, Peron: A Biography, 1984; The Brazilians, 1995; co-author: Bitter Wages, 1973. Lt. USCGR, 1959-67. Office: Georgetown U Law Ctr Law Ctr 600 New Jersey Ave NW Washington DC 20001

PAGE, LARRY KEITH, neurosurgeon, educator; b. Rayville, La., July 7, 1933; s. Ardie Lee and Edris Estelle (Chaney) P.; m. Joan Marie Doherty, Aug. 27, 1960; children: Matthew, Elizabeth, Jennifer. BS, La. State U., 1955, MD, 1958. Diplomate: Am. Bd. Neurol. Surgery. Intern Grad. Hosp., U. Pa., Phila., 1958-59; resident Children's Hosp. and Peter Bent Brigham Hosp., Boston, 1962-66; assoc. neurosurgeon Children's Hosp., assoc. surgeon Peter Bent Brigham Hosp., 1966-71; cons. Beverly Hosp., Mass., Robert Breck Brigham Hosp., Boston, Pondville Hosp., Boston, West Roxbury VA Hosp., Boston VA Hosp.; clin. instr. neurosurgery Harvard U., Boston, 1966-71; prof., vice chmn. dept. neurosurgery U. Miami, Fla., 1971—, chief div. pediatric neurosurgery, 1971—; neurosurgeon VA Hosp., Miami, 1971-88; neurosurgeon Jackson Meml. Hosp., Miami, 1971—, dir. neurosurgery, 1994—; chief neurosurgery Mt. Sinai Hosp., Miami, 1990-94; neurosurg. cons. FDA; neurosurg. cons. NASA. Mem. editorial bds., contbr. articles to profl. jours. Served to lt. USN, 1959-62. Mem. ACS, Am. Acad. Pediatrics, Am. Assn. Neurol. Surgeons, Internat. Soc. Pediatric Neurosurgery, Am. Soc. Pediatric Neurosurgery, Congress Neurol. Surgeons, Fellowship of Acad. Neurosurgeons, Internat. Neurosurg. Forum, Royal Soc. Medicine, Soc. for Research in Hydrocephalus and Spina Bifida, New Eng. Neurosurg. Soc., Fla. Neurosurg. Soc. (pres. 1989-90), Mass. Med. Soc., Dade County Med. Assn., Alpha Omega Alpha. Roman Catholic. Home: 13845 SW 73rd Ct Miami FL 33158-1213 Office: U Miami Sch Medicine PO Box 16960 Miami FL 33101-6960

PAGE, LESLIE ANDREW, disinfectant manufacturing company executive; b. Mpls., June 5, 1924; s. Henry R. and Amelia Kathryn (Steinmetz) P.; m. DeEtte Abernethy Griswold, July 6, 1952 (div. Sept. 1975); children: Randolph, Michael, Kathryn, Caroline; m. Mary Ellen Decker, Nov. 26, 1976. BA, U. Minn., 1949; MA, U. Calif., Berkeley, 1953; PhD, U. Calif., 1956. Asst. microbiologist, lectr. U. Calif., Davis, 1956-61; cons. San Diego Zoological Soc. Zoo Hosp., 1957-60; microbiologist, research leader Nat. Animal Disease Ctr., USDA, Ames, Iowa, 1961-79; ret., 1979, specialist in Chlamydial nomenclature and disease; med. text cons. Bay St. Louis, Miss., 1979-85; founder, pres., chmn. bd. Steri-Derm Corp., Escondido, Calif., 1987—; specialist in Chlamydial nomenclature and disease. Editor: Wildlife Diseases, 1976, Jour. Wildlife Diseases, 1965-68; contbr. chpts. to med. texts, more than 70 articles to profl. jours.; patentee Liquid Antiseptic Composition, 1989. Pres. Garden Island Community Assn., Bay St. Louis, 1980-81; chief commr. East Hancock Fire Protection Dist., Bay St. Louis, 1982-83; sec., treas. Woodridge Escondido Property Owners Assn., 1986-88. With AUS, 1943-46, ETO. Fellow Am. Acad. Microbiology (emeritus); mem. Wildlife Disease Assn. (pres. 1972-73, Disting. Svc. award 1980), Am. Soc. for Microbiology, Sigma Xi, Phi Zeta (hon.). Home and Office: 1784 Deavers Dr San Marcos CA 92069

PAGE, LINDA KAY, banking executive; b. Wadsworth, Ohio, Oct. 4, 1943; s. Frederick Meredith and Martha Irene (Vance) P. Student Sch. Banking, Ohio U., 1976-77; cert. Nat. Pers. Sch., U. Md.-Am. Bankers Assn., 1981; grad. banking program U. Wis., Madison, 1982-84; BA Capital U. Asst. v.p., gen. mgr. Bancohio Corp., Columbus, Ohio, 1975-78, v.p., dist. mgr., 1979-80, v.p., mgr. employee rels., 1980-81, v.p., divsn. mgr., 1982-83; commr. of banks State of Ohio, Columbus, 1983-87, dir. Commerce, 1988-90; pres., CEO Star Bank Cen. Ohio, Columbus, 1990-92; state dir. FMHA-USDA, 1993—. Bd. dirs. Clark County Mental Health Bd., Springfield, Ohio, 1982-83, Springfield Met. Housing, 1982-83; bd. advisers Orgn. Indsl. Standards, Springfield, 1982-83; trustee League Against Child Abuse, 1986-90; treas. Ohio Housing Fin. Agy., 1988-90; vice chair Fed. Reserve Bd.-Consumer Adv. Coun., 1989-91. Bd. dirs. Pvt. Industry Coun. Franklin County, 1990—, Ohio Higher Edn. Facilities Commn., 1990-93; trustee, treas. Columbus State Community Coll. Found., 1990—; bd. dirs. Columbus Urban League, 1992—. Recipient Leadership Columbus award Sta. WTVN and Columbus Leadership Program, 1975, 82, Outstanding Svc. award Clark County Mental Health Bd., 1983. Mem. Nat. Assn. Bank Women (pres. 1980-81), Am. Bankers Assn. (govt. rels. coun. 1990-92), Women Execs. in State Govt., LWV, Conf. State Bank Suprs. (bd. dirs., sec./treas. 1985-90), dist. chmn. 1984-85), Ohio Bankers Assn. (bd. dirs. 1982-83, 91-92), Internat. Womens Forum, Zonta. Democrat. Avocations: tennis, animal protection, reading, golf. Home: 641 Mirandy Pl Reynoldsburg OH 43068-1602 Office: 200 N High St Columbus OH 43215-2408

PAGE, LORNE ALBERT, physicist, educator; b. Buffalo, July 28, 1921; s. John Otway and Laura (Stewart) P.; m. Muriel Emily Jamieson, Sept. 7, 1946; children: J. Douglas, Kenneth L., James F., Donald S., David K. B.Sc., Queen's U., Can., 1944; Ph.D., Cornell U., 1950. Faculty U. Pitts., 1950—, prof. physics, 1958-86, prof. emeritus, 1987—. Contbr. articles to profl. jours. Served to lt. Royal Canadian Navy, 1944-45. Guggenheim fellow Upsala U., Sweden, 1957-58; Alfred P. Sloan research fellow, 1961-63. Fellow Am. Phys. Soc. Episcopalian. Achievements include measurement of the positron's mass; identification of positronium in condensed matter; devel. of method for analyzing circular polarization of high energy x-rays; first measurement of inherent polarization of positive beta partic. Home: 157 Lloyd Ave Pittsburgh PA 15218-1645

PAGE, LYMAN ALEXANDER, JR., physicist; b. San Francisco, Sept. 24, 1957; s. Lyman Alexander and Gillet (Thomas) P.; m. Elizabeth Olson, Feb. 12, 1990; children: William, James. BA with high honors, Bowdoin Coll., 1978; PhD, MIT, 1987. Rsch. technician Bartol Rsch. Found., Newark, Del., 1978-80; postdoctoral rsch. fellow MIT, 1989-90; instr. physics Princeton (N.J.) U., 1990-91, asst. prof. physics, 1991-95, assoc. prof., 1995—. Contbr. numerous sci. papers on cosmic microwave background Astrophys. Jour., 1979—. Surdna fellow Bowdoin Coll., 1978, NASA grad. student rschrs. program fellow MIT, 1987-89, David and Lucile Packard fellow Princeton U., 1994; Rsch. Corp. Cottrell scholar Princeton U., 1994. Mem. Am. Phys. Soc., Am. Astron. Soc. Achievements include measurement of tiny spatial variations in the temperature of the radiation thought to be the afterglow of the big-bang. Office: Princeton U Dept Physics Jadwin Hall Princeton NJ 08544-1019

PAGE, MARCUS WILLIAM, federal official; b. Washington, Sept. 20, 1937; s. Marcus William and Edna May (Horner) Pugh; m. Mary Jane Bitting, Dec. 10, 1989; 1 child from previous marriage, David Stephen. BA, Duke U., 1959; postgrad., George Washington U., 1961-65. Chief fin. svcs. FDA, Washington, 1965-68; chief fin. mgmt. br. Environ. Health Svcs., Washington, 1968-70; chief acctg. ops. EPA, Washington, 1970-77, dir. fin. mgmt., 1977-81; dir. govt. acctg. systems Fin. Mgmt. Svc., Washington, 1981-83, dir. systems devel., 1983-84, dep. commr., 1984-87; dep. fiscal asst. sec. U.S. Treasury, Washington, 1987—. Columnist Govt. Computer News, Washington, 1984-86; contbr. articles to various jours. Recipient Fin. Mgmt. Improvement award Joint Fin. Mgmt. Improvement Program, Washington, 1980, Disting. Leadership award No. Va. Assn. Govt. Accts., 1986, Commrs. award Fin. Mgmt. Svc., 1987. Mem. Assn. Govt. Accts. (bd. dirs. 1981-85, pres. 1992-93), Planning Execs. Inst. (pres. 1973-74), Treasury Hist. Assn. (sec. 1990—), Fed. Exec. Inst. Alumni Assn., C&O Canal Assn., Theta Chi. Avocations: hiking, science fiction, historic building restoration. Office: US Treasury 1500 Pennsylvania Ave Washington DC 20220-0001

PAGE, MICHEL, biochemist; b. Quebec, Que., Can., Feb. 18, 1940; s. Hector and Alma (Dussault) P.; m. Marthe Boudreau, Dec. 17, 1966; children: Brigitte, Marie, Charles, Madeleine. B.A., Laval U., 1960; B.Sc., Ottawa U., 1965, Ph.D., 1969. Nat. Cancer Inst. postdoctoral fellow U. Colo., Boulder, 1968-70; research fellow Mt. Sinai Sch. Medicine, N.Y.C., 1970-71; clin. biochemist Hotel Dieu Hosp., Quebec, 1971-81; research scholar Nat. Cancer Inst. Can., 1975-81; with U. Laval, Quebec City; mem. grant panels Med. Rsch. Coun., Nat. Cancer Inst.; pres. BCH Biotech Inc., BCH Devel. Inc. Author: La cuisine sans cholesterol, 1975, Cancer, 1983, Cancérologie expérimentale, 1993; contbr. over 125 articles to sci. publs. Mem. Ordre des Chimistes du Que., AAAS, Canadian Biochem. Soc., Canadian Immunol. Soc., Am. Soc. Cell Biology., Am. Assn. Clin. Research. Roman Catholic. Home: 9175 Pl Lavallière, Charlesbourg, PQ Canada G1G 3J9 Office: Faculty of Medicine, U Laval, Quebec, PQ Canada G1K 7P4

PAGE, OSCAR C., college administrator; b. Bowling Green, Ky., Dec. 22, 1939; s. Oscar H. and Elizabeth (Dearing) P.; m. Anna Laura Hood, June 12, 1965; children: Laura Kristen, Matthew Dearing. BS in Social Science Edn., Western Ky. U., 1963; MA in History, U. Ky., 1962, PhD, 1967. Asst. prof. U. Ga., Athens, 1967-71; acad. dean Wesleyan Coll., Macon, Ga., 1971-78; v.p. acad. affairs Lander Coll., Greenwood, S.C., 1978-88; pres. Austin Peay State U., Clarksville, Tenn., 1988-94, Austin Coll., Sherman, Tex., 1994—. Mem. Greenwood C. of C. (pres. 1984), Clarksville C. of C. (pres. 1992), Rotary (bd. dirs. 1983-88). Baptist. Home: 921 N Grand Ave Sherman TX 75090 Office: Austin Coll Office of the President Sherman TX 75090-4440

PAGE, PATRICIA M., health science association administrator; b. Boston; d. Frank William and Anna Loretta (Murphy) P. BA, Boston State Coll., 1976; M in Urban Planning, Hunter Coll., 1978. Dir. govt. affairs Quality Care Inc., Rockville Ctr., N.Y., 1978-82; regional dir. govt. affairs Squibb, Lawrenceville, N.J., 1983-84; exec. dir. N.Y. State Assn. Health Care Providers, Bellrose Manor, N.Y., 1985-87, Home & Health Care Assn. Mass., Inc., Boston, 1987—; Pres. Mass. Health Coun., Boston, 1992—. Mem. Am. Soc. Assn. Execs., Forum State Assns. (chmn. 1991—), Nat. Assn. Homecare (bd. dirs. 1991—), New England Soc. Assn. Execs. Office: Home & Health Care Assn Mass 20 Park Plz Ste 620 Boston MA 02116-4300

PAGE, ROBERT HENRY, engineer, educator, researcher; b. Phila., Nov. 5, 1927; s. Ernest Fraser and Marguerite (MacFarl) P.; m. Lola Marie Griffin, Nov. 12, 1948; children: Lola Linda, Patricia Jean, William Ernest, Nancy Lee, Martin Fraser. BS in Mech. Engring, Ohio U., 1949; MS, U. Ill., 1951, PhD, 1955. Instr., research assoc. U. Ill., 1949-55; research engr. fluid dynamics Esso Research & Engring. Co., 1955-57; vis. lectr. Stevens Inst. Tech., 1956-57, dir. fluid dynamics lab., prof. mech. engring., 1957-61; prof. mech. engring., chmn. dept. mech., indsl. and aerospace engring. Rutgers-The State U., 1961-76, prof., research cons., 1976-79; dean engring. Tex. A&M U., 1979-83, Forsyth prof., 1983-93, prof. emeritus mech. engring., 1994—; spl. research base pressure and heat transfer, wake flow and flow separation. Author papers in field. Served with AUS, 1945-47, Pacific Theatre of Operations. Recipient Western Electric Fund award for excellence in engring. edn. Am. Soc. Engring Edn., 1968; Lindback Found. award for distinguished teaching, 1969; Disting. Alumnus award U. Ill., 1971; Disting. Service award, 1973; Life Quality Engring. award, 1974, James Harry Potter Gold medal, 1983, Ohio U. medal, 1983; named hon. prof. Ruhr U., Buchum, Fed. Republic Germany, 1984. Fellow AAAS, AIAA (assoc.), ABET, Am. Astron. Soc. (chmn. nat. space engring. com. 1969-70, 72-76), Am. Soc. Engring. Edn. (Centennial medal 1993); mem. ASME (hon. mem. award 1988), Am. Phys. Soc. Home: 1905 Comal Cir College Station TX 77840-4818

PAGE, ROBERT WESLEY, engineering and construction company executive, federal official; b. Dallas, Jan. 22, 1927; s. Arch Cleo and Zelma (Tyler) P.; m. Nancy Ann Eaton, Sept. 17, 1952; children: Robert W. Jr., David, Mark, Margaret. BS in Archtl. Engring., Tex. A&M U., 1950. Asst. prof. Am. Univ., Beirut, Lebanon, 1952-54; project mgr. Aramco, The Hague and Saudi Arabia, 1954-56; dir. constrn. and devel. Internat. Coll., Beirut, N.Y.C., 1956-58; internat. mgr. Bechtel Co., N.Y.C., 1958-64; v.p. Rockresorts Co., N.Y.C., 1964-71; pres., chief exec. officer George A. Fuller Co., N.Y.C., from 1971; corp. v.p. Northrop Corp., N.Y.C., from 1971; pres., chief exec. officer Rust Engring. Co., Birmingham, Ala., 1976-81; pres., chief exec. officer Kellogg Rust Inc., Houston, 1981-85, chmn., chief exec. officer, dir., 1985-86; pres., chief exec. officer PM Co., Houston, 1986; asst. sec. U.S. Dept. of Army, Washington, 1987-90; chmn. Panama Canal Commn., 1989-90; exec. v.p. McDermott Internat., Washington, 1990—; sr. lectr. MIT, 1993; adj. prof. Georgetown U.; bd. dirs. I.C.F./Kaiser Internat.; bd. dirs. Thormatrix, Inc., San Jose, Calif. Trustee Internat. Coll. Beirut; mem. Pres.'s Coun., U. Ala.; bd. dirs. Coll. Football Hall of Fame. With USNR, 1944-46, PTO. Trustee Am. U. in Cairo; trustee Wortham Theatre Ctr., Houston, Internat. Coll. Beirut; mem. Pres.'s Council, U. Ala.; mem. adv. bd. John E. Gray Inst., Lamar U.; bd. dirs. Coll. Football Hall of Fame. Served with USNR, 1944-46, PTO. Mem. ASME, ASCE, Rolling Rock Club (Ligoner, Pa.), Internat. Club (Washington), Army-Navy Club (Washington), Georgetown Club (Washington), Sakonnet Country Club (Little Compton, R.I.), Tau Beta Pi. Home: 3025 P St NW Washington DC 20007-3054 Office: 1850 K St NW Ste 950 Washington DC 20006-2213

PAGE, ROY CHRISTOPHER, periodontist, educator; b. Campobello, S.C., Feb. 7, 1932; s. Milton and Anny Mae (Eubanks) P. B.A., Berea Coll., 1953; D.D.S., U. Md., 1957; Ph.D., U. Wash., 1967; Sc.D. (hon.), Loyola U., Chgo., 1983. Cert. in periodontics. Pvt. practice periodontics Seattle, 1963—; asst. prof. U. Wash. Schs. Medicine and Dentistry, Seattle, 1967-70, prof., 1974—, dir. Ctr. Research in Oral Biology, 1976—; dir. grad. edn. U. Wash. Sch. Dentistry, 1976-80, dir. research, 1976—; dir. clin. dental tech. ctr., 1990—; vis. scientist MRC Labs., London, 1971-72; cons., lectr. in field. Author: Periodontal Disease, 1977, 2d edit., 1990, Periodontitis in Man and Other Animals, 1982. Recipient Gold Medal award U. Md., 1957; recipient Career Devel. award NIH, 1967-72. Fellow Internat. Coll. Dentists, Am. Coll. Dentists, Am. Acad. Periodontology (Gies award 1982); mem. ADA, Am. Asssn Dental Rsch. (pres. 1982-83), Am. Soc. Exptl. Pathology, Internat. Assn. Dental Rsch. (pres. 1987, basic periodontal rsch. award 1977). Home: 8631 Inverness Dr NE Seattle WA 98115-3935

PAGE, TERRY LEE, biology educator; b. Sept. 25, 1947. BA, U. Tex., 1970, MA, 1971, PhD, 1974. NIH postdoctoral trainee Stanford U., 1974-76, rsch. assoc. dept. biology, 1976-80; from asst. to assoc. prof. biology Vanderbilt U., Nashville, 1980-91, prof., 1991—; scientist John F. Kennedy Ctr. Rsch. Edn. and Human Devel., 1983—; mem. organizing com. timberline symposium Biol. Clocks, 1984; vice-chmn. Gordon Conf. Chronobiology, 1986-87, chmn., 1988-89; mem. grad. faculty assembly Vanderbilt U., 1986-88, mem. various coms., 1986—, dir. honors and ind. study biology, 1987-95, mem. grad. faculty coun., 1989-90, 92-95; mem. neurosciences rsch. rev. com. NIMH, 1988-92; vis. scholar NSF sci. and tech. ctr. biol. timing U. Va., 1990; co-organizer US-Japan Conf. Biol. Clocks, 1992; mem. Alcohol, Drug Abuse and Mental Health Adminstrn. Reviewers Res., 1992-93; ad hoc reviewer various funding agys., jours.; presenter in field. Contbr. chpts. to books and articles to profl. jours.; assoc. editor Jour. Biol. Rhythms, 1985-94; mem. adv. bd. Jour. Comparative Physiology, 1993—. Recipient Honma prize Honma Found., 1988; grantee NIH, 1981—, NSF, 1987—. Mem. Soc. Neuroscience (pres. mid. Tenn. chpt. 1984-85), Soc. Rsch. Biol. Rhythms (mem. adv. bd. 1986-92, nominating com. 1991, publs. com. 1992-94). Office: Vanderbilt U Dept Biology Nashville TN 37235

PAGE, THOMAS ALEXANDER, utility executive; b. Niagara Falls, N.Y., Mar. 24, 1933; m. Evelyn Rainnie, July 16, 1960; children: Christopher, Catherine. B.S. in Civil Engring, Purdue U., 1955, M.S. in Indsl. Adminstrn, 1963. Registered profl. engr., N.Y. C.P.A., Wis., Tex. Comptroller, treas. Wis. Power & Light Co., Madison, 1970-73; treas. Gulf States Utilities Co., Beaumont, Tex., 1973-75; sr. v.p. fin., 1975, exec. v.p., 1975-78, also bd. dirs.; exec. v.p., chief operating officer San Diego Gas & Electric Co., 1978-81, pres., chief exec. officer, 1981-92, chmn., 1983-92, chmn., chief exec. officer, 1992—, also pres., also bd. dirs. Mem. Dane County Bd. Suprs., Wis., 1968-72. Served to capt. USAF, 1955-57. Home: 1904 Hidden Crest Dr El Cajon CA 92019-3653 Office: San Diego Gas & Electric Co PO Box 1831 San Diego CA 92112*

PAGE, THORNTON LEIGH, astrophysicist; b. New Haven, Aug. 13, 1913; s. Leigh and Mary Edith Cholmondeley (Thornton) P.; m. Helen Ashbee, Aug. 28, 1938 (div. 1944); 1 dau., Tanya; m. Lou Williams, Aug. 28, 1948; children—Mary Anne, Leigh II. B.S., Yale U., 1934; D.Phil. in Astrophysics (Rhodes scholar for Conn. 1934-37), Oxford (Eng.) U., 1938; M.A. (hon.), Wesleyan U., Middletown, Conn., 1959; D.H.C. (hon.) U. Cordoba, Argentina, 1969. Chief asst. Oxford U. Obs., 1937-38; from instr. to asst. prof. astronomy U. Chgo., 1938-50; physicist Naval Ordnance Lab., 1941-43; dep. dir. Ops. Research Office, Johns Hopkins, 1950-58; prof. astronomy Wesleyan U., Middletown, 1958-71; dir. Van Vleck Obs., 1959-71; research assoc. Manned Spacecraft Center, NASA, 1968-70, E.O. Hulburt Center Space Research, Naval Research Lab., Washington, 1970-76; contract astrophysicist Johnson Space Center, NASA, 1976-93; part-time instr. U. Houston, Clear Lake, 1982-88; mem. for Ops. Research Soc. Am. to NRC, 1960-62; mem. research adv. com. United Aircraft Corp., 1959-72; Smith-

sonian research asso. Harvard Obs., 1965-67; Nat. Acad. Scis. sr. research asso., 1968-70. Author: Stars and Galaxies, 1962, Wanderers in the Sky, 1965, Neighbors of the Earth, 1965, Origin of the Solar System, 1966, Telescopes, 1966, Starlight, 1967, Evolution of Stars, 1967, Stars and Clouds of the Milky Way, 1968, Beyond the Milky Way, 1969, UFO's, A Scientific Debate, 1972, Far-UV Preliminary Science Report, Apollo 16, 1973, Space Science and Astronomy, 1976, Apollo-Soyuz Experiments in Space, 1977, S201 Catalogue of Far-UV Objects, 1977, S201 Far-UV Atlas of the Large Magellanic Cloud, 1978, S201 Catalogue of Far-UV Objects, 1978, Space Telescope, 1983. Served to comdr. USNR, 1943-46. Decorated Bronze Star, Legion of Merit. Fellow Royal Astron. Soc., AAAS (v.p. sect. D astronomy 1967-68), Am. Astronautical Soc.; mem. Operations Research Soc. Am. (charter, editor, council, v.p.), Astron. Soc. Pacific., Am. Assn. Physics Tchrs., Internat. Astron. Union, Am. Astron. Soc., Internat. Statis. Inst., Sigma Xi. Clubs: Cosmos (Washington); Appalachian Mountain, Explorers. Home: 18639 Point Lookout Dr Houston TX 77058-4038 Office: NASA Johnson Space Ctr Code Sn # 3 Houston TX 77058 *I have lived through a remarkable period in the history of astronomy, from spectroscopy through radio, X-ray, and gamma-ray detection, to the space telescope launched in 1990. We astronomers have learned a lot, and hope to learn much more with the space telescope.*

PAGE, TROY EDWARD, health care administrator; b. Tulsa, June 19, 1938; m. Marvis Oneita Fisher; children: Amelia, Kimberly M., Troy, Julia D., Jennifer L., Sylvia A. BA, U. Tulsa, 1962; MSW, U. Ill., 1965; MPH, U. Mo., 1973. Dir. day treatment program VA Med. Ctr., Oklahoma City, 1969-71; trainee health care adminstrn. VA Med. Ctr., Columbia, Mo., 1971-73; staff asst. VA Med. Ctr., Marion, Ill., 1973-75, asst. dir. trainee, 1975-76; asst. dir. VA Med. Ctr., Bath, N.Y., 1976-77, Coatesville, Pa., 1977-80, Indpls., 1980-83; dir. VA Med. Ctr., Chillicothe, Ohio, 1986—, VA Outpatient Clinic, Columbus, Ohio, 1983-86; social worker U.S. Dept. Interior, Miami, Okla., 1965-66; specialist correctional treatment U.S. Dept. Justice, El Reno, Okla., 1966-69. Asst. field dir. ARC, Chanute AFB, Ill., 1964-65; bd. dirs. Chief Logan coun. Boy Scouts Am., 1988—. With USMC, 1960-66. Mem. Am. Hosp. Assn., Ohio Hosp. Assn., So. Ohio Hosp. Coun., Inst. Indsl. Engrs., Fed. Exec. Assn., Chillicothe/Ross C. of C., Rotary (com. chmn. Chillicothe chpt.). Adventist. Office: Vets Med Ctr 17273 State Route 104 Chillicothe OH 45601-8608

PAGE, WILLIAM CANDLER, JR., career officer; b. Tupelo, Miss., Feb. 26, 1939; s. William C. and Venola A. (Rankin) P.; m. Gayle Louis Baker, June 29, 1957; children: William C. III, Alison D. Page Carpenter. Student, Ark. State U., 1957-59, Miss. State U., 1959-60; BS, U. Nebr., 1971. Commd. 2d lt. U.S. Army, 1960, advanced through grades to maj. gen., 1990; exec. officer 1st bn., 7th Cav. (Tank) U.S. Army, Fort Hood, Tex., 1974-76; insp. gen. U.S. Army, Washington, 1976-78; comdg. officer 52d aviation bn. U.S. Army, Seoul, Korea, 1978-80; dep. comdr. 6th air cav. combat brigade U.S. Army, Fort Hood, 1980-81, ops. officer (G3) 2d armored div., 1981-83; comdg. officer 17th aviation group U.S. Army, Seoul, 1983-85; dir. ops. HQ Forces Command U.S. Army, Atlanta, 1985-87; asst. div. comdr. 24th inf. div. (Mech.) U.S. Army, Fort Stewart, Ga., 1987-89; comdg. gen. test and experimentation command U.S. Army, Fort Hood, 1989-91. Decorated Legion of Merit with two oak leaf clusters, D.F.C., Bronze Star with one oak leaf cluster, Meritorious Svc. medal. Mem. Assn. U.S. Army, Assn. Army Aviators (chpt. pres. 1983-85). Republican. Avocations: golf, fishing. Home: 12 Masters Place Dr Maumelle AR 72113-7019 Office: Department of the Army Chief of Public Affairs Office Washington DC 20310

PAGE, WILLIAM MARION, lawyer; b. Columbus, Ga., July 31, 1917; s. Roger McKeene and Louise Olivia (Seals) P.; m. Lucy Quillian Page, Feb. 8, 1941 (dec. 1982); children: John Roger, Jane Quillian Page McCamy, William Franklin; m. Barbara Brown Waddell, May 10, 1985. LLB, U. Ga., 1939, JD. Bar: Ga. 1938, U.S. Supreme Ct. 1955. Ptnr. Page & Scranton P.C., Columbus, Ga., 1939—. Bd. visitors U. Ga. Law Sch., 1969-74. With U.S. Army, 1941-46. Fellow Am. Coll. Trial Lawyers; mem. State Bar Ga. (bd. govs. 1964-71), ABA, Chattahoochee Circuit Bar Assn. (pres. 1948-49), Columbus Lawyers Club (pres. 1946-47), Am. Judicature Soc., Big Eddy Club, Kiwanis. Home: 916 Overlook Dr Columbus GA 31906-3029 Office: PO Box 1199 Columbus GA 31902-1199

PAGE, WILLIS, conductor; b. Rochester, N.Y.. Grad. with distinction, Eastman Sch. Music, Rochester. Prof. conducting Eastman Sch. Music, 1967-69; prof. conducting, dir. orchestral activities Drake U., Des Moines, 1969-71; guest condr. Sony concerts, Chiba, Japan, 1992. Mem. Boston Symphony Orch., 1940-55; prin. bass, Boston Pops, 1947-55, condr., Cecilia Soc. of Boston, organizer, New Orchestral Soc. of Boston (name now Boston Festival Orch.); music dir.-condr., Nashville Symphony Orch., 8 years; assoc. condr., Buffalo Philharm., 5 years; music dir. Linwood Summer Music Sch.; first condr., Yomiuri Nippon Symphony, Tokyo, Japan, 1962-63, Des Moines Symphony, 1969-71, Jacksonville (Fla.) Symphony Orch., from 1971-83; guest condr. with, Boston Pops, Toronto, Richester Civic, Eastman-Rochester, Denver, Muncie, Kol Israel, St. Louis, Colorado Springs, Memphis, Hartford orchs., Yomiuri Nippon, Tokyo, 1992, Kay Choir, Messiah, Tokyo, 1988, Vanderbilt Chamber Orch., 1991, Jacksonville Symphony, 1993; founding condr. St. Johns River City Band, 1985; founder, condr., exec. dir. First Coast Pops Orch., 1989; condr. all-state orchs. of, N.Y., Ia., Ky., Tenn., Fla., also regional festivals; condr. recordings including Symphony of the Air (Roger Williams soloist), Boston Festival Orch., Cook, Nashville Symphony. Interpreter for comdr. gen. 95th inf. div. U.S. Army, World War II. Decorated Bronze Star medal; Ford Found. European travel award, 1967.

PAGELS, JÜRGEN HEINRICH, balletmaster, dance educator, dancer, choreographer, author; b. Lübeck, Fed. Republic Germany, Apr. 16, 1925; came to U.S., 1955; s. Heinrich and Margret (Haas) P. Artists diploma, Hamburg (Fed. Republic Germany) State Exam Bd., 1947; advanced soloist exam. with honors, Assn. Russian Ballet, London, 1952, advanced tchrs. exam. with honors, 1961, sr. tchrs. exam. with honors, 1969; DFA, Pacific Western U., 1988. Ballet soloist Atlantic Theater, Lübeck, 1945-46, Stadt-Theater, Lübeck, 1946-47; prin. dancer Dortmund, Fed. Republic Germany, 1947-48, Operette and Stattl. Schauspielhaus Theater, Hamburg, 1949-50; ballet soloist Ballet Theater Co., Hamburg, 1950-51; prin. dancer Ballet Legat, London, 1951-52, Ballet Legat and Yugoslav Nat. Ballet, touring throughout Europe, 1952-53; ballet soloist Ballet Etoile, Paris Opera, Paris, 1954; dir., owner Pagels Legat Sch. Ballet, Dallas, 1955-62; guest tchr. ballet numerous dance acads. and ballet cos., worldwide, 1962-70; prof. dance Ind. Univ., Bloomington, 1970-90; prof. emeritus Ind. U., Bloomington, 1990—; guest tchr. ballet numerous orgns. including Vaganova Choreography Inst., Leningrad, USSR, Ballet do Rio de Janeiro, Egypt Nat. Ballet of Cairo, Ballet Intezet, Hungary, Nat. Ballet, Istanbul, Turkey, Royal Danish Ballet, Tex. Christian Univ., Ft. Worth, Nat. Ballet, Nicaragua; condr. master classes for Ballet Guatemala, Escuela Nacional de Danza, San Salvador, Academia de Danza Classica, Costa Rica, Nat. Ballet Venezuela, T.W. Univ. Nat. U. Costa Rica, Bellas Artes, Honduras; co-founder, dir. Dallas Civic Ballet; art dir. Ballet Guatemala, 1978-79, Nat. Ballet Salvador, Ulm Theatre, Germany, Ballet Co., 1995, Artemis, Amsterdam, Holland; Internat. Ballet Competition Managuq, Nicaragua, 1999. Author of character dance books in English, German and Spanish, 1984, 85, and ballet dance books; collaborator and coach to Dame Margot Fonteyn. U.S. judge Internat. Ballet Competition, Trujillo, Peru, 1989, 90. Served as sgt. German Army, 1942-45. Research grantee Ind. Univ., 1977. Avocations: exhibited sculptor, tennis, deep-sea fishing. Home: 934 E Maxwell Ter Apt A Bloomington IN 47401-5278 Office: Ind U Sch Music Ballet Dept Bloomington IN 47405 also: Curtius Str 6, 23568 Lübeck Germany

PAGENKOPF, ANDREA LESUER, university official; b. Hamilton, Mont., July 28, 1942; d. Andrew and Martha Gail (Thompson) LeSuer; m. Gordon Kyle Pagenkopf, June 12, 1964 (dec. Feb. 1987); 1 child, Sarah Lynn. BA, U. Mont., 1964; PhD, Purdue U., 1968. Registered dietitian; lic. nutritionist. Asst. prof. Purdue U., West Lafayette, Ind., 1968, U. Ill., Champaign, 1968-69; asst. prof. Mont. State U., Bozeman, 1969-76, assoc. prof., 1976-86, prof. nutrition, 1986-91, dir. extension, 1991—, vice provost for outreach, 1993—. Author: (with others) Grow Healthy Kids, 1980. Worship commn. chair United Meth. Ch., Bozeman, 1989-90; cons. Gallatin Hospice, Bozeman, 1986-91. Recipient Excellence in Nutrition Edn. award

Western Dairy Coun., 1987, Silver Buffalo award Mont. Extension, 1989, Mid-Career award Extension Hon., 1988; named Home Econs. Leader, Mont. Home Econs. Assn., 1990. Mem. Am. Dietetic Assn., Soc. Nutrition Edn. (interest group chair 1990-91), Am. Home Econs. Assn. Avocations: fly fishing, racquet ball, jogging. Office: Mont State U Extension 211 Montana Hall Bozeman MT 59717

PAGLIA, CAMILLE, writer, humanities educator; b. Endicott, N.Y., 1947; d. Pasquale John and Lydia (Colapietro) P. BA in English summa cum laude with highest honors, SUNY, Binghamton, 1968; MPhil, Yale U., 1971, PhD in English, 1974. Mem. faculty Bennington (Vt.) Coll., 1972-80; prof. humanities U. Arts, Phila., 1984—; vis. lectr. Yale U., New Haven, 1980-84. Author: Sexual Personae: Art and Decadence from Nefertiti to Emily Dickinson, 1990, Sex, Art, and American Culture, 1992, Vamps and Tramps: New Essays, 1994. Office: Univ Arts 320 S Broad St Philadelphia PA 19102

PAGLIARINI, JAMES, broadcast executive. AB, Princeton U., 1975; MEd, Temple U., 1976. Asst. to gen. mgr. Sta. KTEH-TV, San Jose, Calif., 1976-80; co-founder Sta. KNPB-TV, Reno, Nev., 1980—, sta. mgr., 1982-83, gen. mgr., CEO, 1983—; bd. dirs. Agy. Instrnl. T.V., Pub. Broadcasting, Western Indsl. Nev.; chmn. bd. govs. Pacific Mountain Network, 1987—; mem. Cable Access Bd., Reno, PBS assessment policy com., 1988-89, funding task force, 1991, task force on nat. prodns., 1992-93. Chmn. community adv. com. U. Nev. Sch. Engring., Reno; past bd. dirs. Planned Parenthood No. Nev., Boy Scouts Am., We. Nev. Clean Cities Com. Mem. Nev. Pub. Broadcasting Assn. (pres.), Small Sta. Assn. (pres. 1991-92). Office: Station KNPB PO Box 14730 Reno NV 89507

PAGLIARO, HAROLD EMIL, English language educator; b. N.Y.C., June 19, 1925; s. Harry E. and Linda (Ricci) P.; m. Judith Marie Egan, Sept. 16, 1966; children: Blake, Robert, Susanna, John. AB, Columbia U., 1947, MA, 1948, PhD, 1961. Instr. English, Columbia U., N.Y.C., 1956-60; asst. prof. Columbia U., 1961-63, faculty fellow, 1962, dir. honors sch. gen. studies, 1962-64; asst. prof. Swarthmore (Pa.) Coll., 1964-65, asso. prof., 1966-69, prof., 1970—, Alexander Griswold Cummins prof. English lit., 1982—, chmn. dept. English lit., 1970-74, 86-91, provost, 1974-79, Alexander Griswold Cummins prof. emeritus English, provost emeritus, 1992—; mem. sr. common room St. Edmund Hall, Oxford (Eng.) U., 1973-74, 79-80; assoc. Columbia U. Seminar 18th Century European Culture, 1982—. Author: Selfhood and Redemption in Blake's "Songs", 1987; editor: Fielding's Journal of a Voyage to Lisbon, 1963, Major English Writers of the Eighteenth Century, 1969, Studies In Eighteenth Century Culture, Vol. 2, 1972, Vol. 3, 1973, Vol. 4, 1974; contbr. articles to profl. jours. Mem. coll. evaluation fed. Middle States Assn., 1966—. Served with AUS, 1943-45. Decorated Purple Heart; NEH sr. fellow, 1983-84; George Becker fellow, 1988-89. Mem. MLA, Am. Soc. for Eighteenth-Century Studies (editor Proc. 1971-75), Am. Soc. Eighteenth-Century Studies (mem. publs. com. 1974-76). Home: 536 Ogden Ave Swarthmore PA 19081-1129

PAGLIARO, JAMES DOMENIC, lawyer; b. Phila., Aug. 18, 1951; s. Domenic A. and Nancy I. (D'Amore) P.; m. Susan B. Boag, Aug. 25, 1973; children: Jamie C., Justin A. BA cum laude, LaSalle U., 1973; JD, Dickinson Law Sch., 1976. Bar: Pa. 1976, U.S. Dist. Ct. (ea. dist.) Pa. 1977, U.S. Ct. Appeals (3d, 8th, 9th and 10th cirs.) 1989, U.S. Supreme Ct. 1989. Regional atty. Gov. of Pa., Phila., 1976-79; sr. trial atty. office regional solicitor U.S. Dept. Labor, Phila., 1979-85; assoc. Morgan, Lewis & Bockius, Phila., 1985-88, ptnr. litigation, 1988—. Mem. Home & Sch. Bd. Norwood Acad., Chestnut Hill, Pa., 1983-87; vestry Hist. St. Paul's Ch., Elkins Park, Pa., 1993-94. Mem. ABA, Pa. Bar Assn. (speaker continuing legal edn. 1987—), Phila. Bar Assn., Woolsach Honors Soc., Pyramid Club. Avocations: history, swimming, numismatics. Home: 404 Westview Rd Elkins Park PA 19027 Office: Morgan Lewis & Bockius 2000 One Logan Sq Philadelphia PA 19103

PAGLIO, LYDIA ELIZABETH, editor; b. Providence; d. Victor and Lydia Anne (DiPrete) P. BA, NYU. Researcher Young Pres. Orgn., 1970-71; editorial asst. Sport mag., N.Y.C., 1971-72; assoc. editor True Experience, also True Love mags., N.Y.C., 1972-73; editor True Experience mag., 1973-81; assoc. editor Dell Pub., N.Y.C., 1983; editor Dell Pub., 1983-84, sr. editor, 1984-87, dir. Candlelight Ecstasy Romances, 1987; sr. editor Zebra Books, Pinnacle Books, 1987-89; pres. Sutton Press, Inc., N.Y.C., 1989—; pub. cons., N.Y.C., 1989—; dir. publicity Dancer's World, Springfield, Mass., 1978-80. Author articles. Pres., sec., mem. exec. com. West Side Community Recycling Corp., 1979-81; pres. #1 W 82 St. Tenants, 1989—. Mem. Editl. Free-lance Assn. (bd. dirs. 1984).

PAGNI, PATRICK JOHN, mechanical and fire safety engineering science educator ;. b. Chgo., Nov. 28, 1942; s. Frank and Helen Boyle Pagni; m. Carol DeSantis, Dec. 26, 1970; children: Christina Marie, Catherine Ann, Patrick John Jr. B in Aeronautical Engring. magna cum laude, U. Detroit, 1965; SM, MIT, 1967, ME, 1969, PhD, 1970. Registered profl. mechanical engr., Calif., fire protection engr., Calif. Research asst. MIT, Cambridge, 1965-70; asst. prof. Mech. Engring. Dept. U. Calif., Berkeley, 1970-76, assoc. prof., 1976-81, prof., 1981—, vice chmn. grad. study, 1986-89; acting assoc. dean Coll. Engring. U. Calif., 1990; assoc. faculty scientist Lawrence Berkeley Lab., 1976—; vis. scientist Factory Mut. Research Corp., Norwood, Mass., 1980; cons. on fire safety sci. various orgns., 1972—. Editor: Fire Science for Fire Safety, 1984, Fire Safety Science--Procs. of the First Internat. Symposium, 1986, Procs. of the Second Internat. Symposium, 1989; contbr. articles to profl. jours. Grantee NSF, NASA, Nat. Bur. Standards, Nat. Inst. Standards and Tech., 1971—; Applied Mechanics fellow Harvard U., 1974, 77; Pullman Found. scholar, 1960. Mem. ASME, Am Phys. Soc., Combustion Inst., Internat. Assn. Fire Safety Sci. (exec. com., chmn. awards com.), Tau Beta Pi, Pi Tau Sigma, Alpha Sigma Nu. Democrat. Roman Catholic. Home: 1901 Ascot Dr Moraga CA 94556-1412 Office: Univ of Calif Coll of Engring Mech Engring Dept Berkeley CA 94720-1740

PAGNOZZI, AMY, columnist. Columnist The N.Y. Post, until 1993, The Daily News, N.Y.C., 1993—; also contbr. Mirabella, Elle, N.Y.C. Office: The Daily News 220 E 42nd St New York NY 10017

PAGONIS, WILLIAM GUS, retired army officer; b. Charleroi, Pa., Apr. 30, 1941; s. Constantinos V. and Jennie (Kontos) P.; m. Cheryl Elaine Miller, June 4, 1964; children: Gust, Robert. BS, Pa. State U., 1964, MBA in Bus. Logistics, 1970. Commd. 2d lt. U.S. Army, 1964, advanced through grades to lt. gen., 1991; comdr. 109th Transp. Co., Vietnam, 1968; div. transp. officer, then exec. officer 2d bn., 501st inf., 101st Airborne Div., Vietnam, 1970-71; pers. staff officer U.S. Army Mil. Pers. Ctr., Alexandria, Va., 1973-75; staff office Office Chief of Legis. Liaison, Washington, 1975-76; comdr. 10th transp. bn. 7th Transp. Group, Ft. Eustis, Va., 1977-78; dep. chief of staff, then ops. and rsch. systems analyst U.S. Army Transp. Sch. and Ctr., Ft. Eustis, 1978-79; dir. logistics, dir. indsl. ops., then chief of staff 193d Inf. Brigade, Panama, 1980-81, comdr. Logistics Support Command, 1981-82; comdr. Div. Support Command, 4th Inf. Div., Ft. Carson, Colo., 1982-85; spl. asst. to dep. comdg. gen. 21st Support Command, U.S. Army Europe, 1985-86, dep. comdg. gen., 1986-88; dir. plans and ops. Office Dep. Chief of Staff for Logistics, Washington, 1988-89; dir. transp., energy and troop support, 1989-90; comdg. gen. 22d Support Command, Dhahran, Saudi Arabia, 1990-91, U.S. Cen. Command/22d Support Command, Dhahran, 1991-92; comdr. 21st Theater Army Command, Germany, 1992-93; lt. gen., ret. U.S. Army, 1993; exec. v.p. logistics Sears & Roebuck Merchandising Group, Hoffman Estates, Ill., 1993—. Author: Moving Mountains (Logistics Leadership and Management of the Gulf War), (one of top 30 best bus. books of 1992, top leadership book 1992 Soundview Exec. Book Summaries, 1992), 1992. Decorated D.S.M., Silver Star, Legion of Merit with oak leaf cluster, Bronze Star with 3 oak leaf clusters, Air medal with 2 oak leaf clusters, Meritorious Svc. medal with 4 oak leaf clusters, King Abdul Aziz 2d Class award Chief of Staff, Saudi Arabian Army, 1991, Kuwait Liberation medal Chief of Staff, Kuwait Army, 1992; recipient Merit and Honor award Govt. of Greece, 1991, Joseph C. Scheleen award Am. Soc. Transp. and Logistics, 1991, Man of Yr. award Modern Materials Handling, 1991, Grad. Man of Yr. award Alpha Chi Rho, 1991, AHEPA Man of Yr., 1992, Disting. Alumni award Pa. State U., 1994; named Hellenic Man of Yr., 1992; Pa. State U. fellow, 1992. Mem. Soc. Logistics Engrs. (hon.), Am. Legion, Am. Vets. Home: 25190 North Pawnee Rd Barrington

IL 60010-1354 Office: Sears Merchandising Group Sears Roebuck & Co 3333 Beverly Rd Hoffman Estates IL 60179

PAGTER, CARL RICHARD, lawyer; b. Balt., Feb. 13, 1934; s. Charles Ralph and Mina (Amelung) P.; m. Judith Elaine Cox, May 6, 1978; 1 child by previous marriage: Corbin Christopher. AA, Diablo Valley Coll., 1953; BA, San Jose State U., 1956; LLB, U. Calif., Berkeley, 1964. Bar:Calif. 1965, D.C. 1977, U.S. Supreme Ct. 1976. Law clk. Kaiser Industries Corp., Oakland, Calif., 1963-64, counsel, 1964-70; assoc. counsel Kaiser Industries Corp., Washington, 1970-73; counsel Kaiser Industries Corp., Oakland, Calif., 1973-75; dir. govt. affairs Kaiser Industries Corp., Washington, 1975-76; v.p., sec., gen. counsel Kaiser Cement Corp., Oakland, Calif., 1976-88; cons., gen. counsel Kaiser Cement Corp., Oakland, Calif., 1988—. Author: (with A. Dundes) Urban Folklore from the Paperwork Empire, 1975, More Urban Folklore from the Paperwork Empire, 1987, Never Try to Teach a Pig to Sing, 1991, Sometimes the Dragon Wins, 1995. Served with USNR, 1957-61, to comdr., 1978. Mem. ABA, Fed. Bar Assn., Contra Costa County Bar Assn., Am. Folklore Soc., Calif. Folklore Soc., Calif. Bluegrass Assn. (founder), Oakland Athletic Club, University Club. Republican. Home: 17 Julianne Ct Walnut Creek CA 94595-2610 Office: Kaiser Cement Corp Ste 445 Box 8018 1333 N California Blvd Walnut Creek CA 94596-1209

PAI, ANANTHA MANGALORE, electrical engineering educator, consultant; b. Mangalore, Karnataka, India, Oct. 5, 1931; came to U.S., 1979; s. Ramachandra M. and Janaki (Kamath) P.; m. Nandini Kamath, Nov. 25, 1956; children: Sunanda, Sujata, Shona, Gurudutt. BS, Madras U., India, 1953; MS, U. Calif., Berkeley, 1958, PhD, 1961. Elec. engr. Bombay Electric Supply Co., 1953-57; prof. Indian Inst. Tech., India, 1963-81, dean R&D, 1976-78; prof. U. Ill., Urbana, 1981—. Author: Computers in Power System, 1979, Power System Stability, 1981, Energy Functions, 1989. Recipient Bhatnagar award Govt. of India, 1974. Fellow IEEE, Indian Nat. Sci. Acad., NAE (India), Instn. Engrs. (India). Hindu. Office: U Ill Dept Elec Engring 1406 W Green St Urbana IL 61801-2918

PAI, DAVID H(SIEN)-C(HUNG), research engineer; b. Kweilin, China, Jan. 7, 1936; came to U.S.; m. Anna Chao, 1959; children: Benjaman, Michael. BS, Va. Military Inst., 1958; MS, Lehigh U., 1960; ScD in Engring. Sci., N.Y.U., 1965. Devel. engr. rsch. divsn., 1960-63, sr. engr., 1964-65, rsch. assoc. creep anal & plasticity theory, 1966-68, asst. head solid mechanics dept., 1969-73, chief engr. nuclear dept., 1973-77, mgr. engring. tech. dept., 1977-80; v.p. Foster Wheeler Application, Inc., 1980-84, sr. v.p., 1984-88; pres. Foster Wheeler Devel. Corp., 1988—; mem. steering com. high temperature structure design tech. U.S. Atomic Energy Commn., 1970-84; cons. China Nat. Standards Com. Pressure Vessels; sr. adv. Chinese Mechancial Engring. Soc., 1988—. Mem. Nat. Acad. Engring.; ASME (v.p. 1981-83), ASCE, Sigma Xi. Research in creep and plastic behavior of structural and machine components; metal fatigue; pressure vessel design and analysis. Office: Foster Wheeler Development Corp 12 Peach Tree Hill Rd Livingston NJ 07039 also: Perryville Corporate Pk Clinton NJ 08809 Address: 223 W Hobart Gap Rd Livingston NJ 07039*

PAI, SHIH I., aeronautical engineer, educator; b. Tatung, Anhwei, China, Sept. 30, 1913; s. Hsi Chuan and Swe Lin (Cha) P.; B.S. in Elec. Engring., Nat. Central U. China, 1935; M.S., MIT, 1938; Ph.D., Calif. Inst. Tech., 1940; Dr. Tech. h.c., Tech. U. Vienna, 1968; m. Alice Jen-Lan Wang, July 2, 1960; children—Stephen Ming, Sue Yang, Robert Yang, Lou Lung. Prof. aerodynamics Nat. Central U., China, 1940-47; vis. prof. Cornell U., 1947-49; research prof. Inst. Phys. Sci. and Tech., U. Md., College Park, 1949-83, prof. emeritus, 1983—; vis. prof. Tokyo U., 1966, Tech. U. Vienna, 1967, Tech. U. Denmark, 1974, U. Karlsruhe (Germany), 1980-81, U. Paris, 1981; hon. prof. Northwestern Poly. U., Peoples Republic China, 1980—, Zhejiang U., Peoples Republic China, 1985—; cons. Gen. Electric Co., N. Am. Aviation, Boeing Co., Martin Co. Served with Chinese Air Force, 1937-40. Guggenheim fellow, 1957-58; recipient Alexander von Humboldt award, 1980, Centennial medal A. James Clark Sch. Engring. U. Md., 1994. Fellow Academia Sinica; mem. AIAA, Am. Phys. Soc., German Soc. Applied Math. and Mechanics, Internat. Acad. Astronautics (corr.). Author: 13 tech. books in fluid dynamics, latest being Two-Phase Flows, 1977; Modern Fluid Mechanics, 1981, (with Shijin Lu) The Theroetical and Computational Dynamics of a Compressible Flow, 1991; contbr. numerous articles to profl. jours.; first to experimentally show the importance of coherent structure in turbulent flow, the authority of jet flow from low speed aerodynamics to hyperionic flow; contbr. modern fluid mechanics including magnetic fluid dynamics, radiation gas dynamics and two phase flows. Home: 4301 Sarasota Pl Beltsville MD 20705-2755 Office: U Md Inst Phys Sci Tech College Park MD 20742

PAIDOUSSIS, MICHAEL PANDELI, mechanical engineering educator; b. Nicosia, Cyprus, Aug. 20, 1935; emigrated to Can., 1953, naturalized, 1976; s. Pandelis Aristeidis and Parthenope (Leptou) P. B. Eng., McGill U., 1958; Ph.D. in Engring, U. Cambridge, 1963. Overseas fellow Gen. Electric Co., Erith, Kent, Eng., 1958-60; research officer Atomic Energy of Can., Chalk River, Ont., 1963-67; with McGill U., Montreal, 1967—, prof., dept. mech. engring., 1976—, chmn, 1977-86, Thomas Workman prof., 1986—; cons. and research in field. Editor Jour. Fluids and Structures; contbr. articles in field. Pres. Hellenic-Canadian Solidarity Com. for Cyprus, 1974-80, Comite Pan-Canadien de Solidarite pour Chypre, 1978-83; hon. consul Republic of Cyprus, Montreal, 1983—. Recipient Brit. Assn. medal for high distinction in mech. engring., 1958, George Stephenson prize Inst. Mech. Engrs., 1976, Commemorative medal for 125th Anniversary of Confedn. of Can., 1993. Fellow Instn. of Mech. Engrs., ASME, Can. Soc. Mech. Engring., Royal Soc. Can., Am. Acad. Mechanics; mem. Internat. Assn. Hydraulic Rsch., Internat. Assn. Structural Mechanics in Reactor Tech., Order Engrs. Que. Home: 2930 Edouard Montpetit #PH2, Montreal, PQ Canada H3T 1J7 Office: 817 Ouest Rue Sherbrooke, Montreal, PQ Canada H3A 2K6

PAIER, ADOLF ARTHUR, computer software and services company executive; b. Branford, Conn., Oct. 27, 1938; s. Adolf Arthur and Margaret Mary (Almond) P.; m. Geraldine Shnakis, Sept. 17, 1966; children: Nathaniel Jason, Andrew Joseph, Alena Catherine. A.A., Quinnipiac Coll., 1958; B.S. in Econs, U. Pa., 1960. Audit mgr. Touche Ross & Co., Phila., 1960-67; pres., dir. Safeguard Scientifics, Inc., Wayne, Pa., 1967-92; chmn., CEO Healthworks Alliance, Inc., Wayne, Pa., 1992—; pres., CEO Novus Corp., Radnor, Pa., 1992—; bd. dirs. Deltapaper, Croydon, Pa., ERM Computer Svcs., Inc., Exton, Pa.. Bd. dirs. Univ. of Arts, Phila., Lincoln Ctr. Family and Youth, Bridgeport, Pa.; mem. adv. bd. Sol C. Snider Entrepreneurial Ctr., Phila., Analytical Graphics, Inc., King of Prussia, Pa. Mem. AICPA, Chief Execs. Orgn., Phila. Pres. Orgn. Office: Novus Corp 259 Radnor Chester Rd Ste 145 Radnor PA 19087-5240

PAIGE, EUGENE CARROLL, JR., mathematics educator, consultant; b. Dallas, Sept. 9, 1929; s. Eugene Carroll and Kate (Moore) P.; m. Ora Nell Henniger, Sept. 14, 1951; children—Richard Carroll, Sharon Lynn. B.A., Rice Inst., 1950; M.S., U. Chgo., 1952, Ph.D., 1954. Mathematician Nat. Security Agy., Washington, 1954-56; mem. math faculty U. Ill., Champaign, 1956-57; mem. math. faculty U. Va., Charlottesville, 1957-68, asst. provost, 1968-71, mem. math. faculty, 1971-83, prof., 1983—, chmn. dept. math., 1983-86; cons. U.S. Dept. Def., Washington, 1956-60; mathematician Inst. for Def. Analyses, Princeton, N.J., 1965-67. Contbr. articles to profl. jours. Rockefeller Found. fellow, 1950-52; Air Force Grad. fellow, 1952-54. Mem. Am. Math. Soc., Math. Assn. Am., Phi Beta Kappa, Sigma Xi (chpt. pres. 1969). Lutheran. Avocations: electronics; computer science. Home: 1610 Rickey Rd Charlottesville VA 22901-2614 Office: Univ Va Dept Math Math-Astronomy Bldg Charlottesville VA 22903

PAIGE, GLENN DURLAND, political scientist, educator; b. Brockton, Mass., June 28, 1929; s. Lester Norman and Rita Irene (Marshall) P.; m. Betty Gail Grenier, Jan. 2, 1949 (div.); children: Gail, Jan, Donn, Sean, Sharon, Van; m. Glenda Hatsuko Naito, Sept. 1, 1973. Grad., Phillips Exeter Acad., 1947; A.B., Princeton U., 1955; M.A., Harvard U., 1957; Ph. D., Northwestern U., 1959; PhD (hon.), Soka U., 1992. Asst. prof. pub. adminstrn. Seoul Nat. U., 1959-61; asst. to assoc. prof. politics Princeton U., 1961-67; prof. polit. sci. U. Hawaii, Honolulu, 1967-92, prof. emeritus, 1992—. Author: The Korean Decision, 1968, The Scientific Study of Political Leadership, 1977, To Nonviolent Political Science, 1993; editor: Political Leadership, 1972, (with George Chaplin) Hawaii 2000, 1973, (with Sarah Gilliatt) Nonviolence in Hawaii's Spiritual Traditions, 1991, Buddhism and Nonviolent Global Problem-Solving, 1991, (of Petra K. Kelly) Nonviolence Speaks to Power, 1993, (with Chaiwat Satha-Anand) Islam and Nonviolence, 1993; social sci. editor: Biography, 1977—. Program chmn. Hawaii Gov.'s Conf. on Yr. 2000, 1970; leader U.S. Group 103, Amnesty Internat., 1977-78; cons. UN Univ., 1980-86; coord. planning project Ctr. for Global Nonviolence, U. Hawaii Spark M. Matsunaga Inst. for Peace, 1988-95; pres. Ctr. for Global Nonviolence, 1994—; mem. nat. adv. group Martin Luther King Jr. Inst. for Nonviolence, State of N.Y., 1989-90. With U.S. Army, 1948-52. Decorated Commendation medal; recipient Seikyo Culture prize, 1982, Dr. G. Ramachandrn award for internat. understanding, 1986, Anuvrat award for internat. peace, 1987; named Woodrow Wilson nat. fellow, 1955-56, Princeton U. Class of 1955 award, 1987, 3d Gandhi Meml. lectr., New Dehli, 1990, Disting. life fellow Delhi Sch. Nonviolence, 1992, Jai Tulsi Anuvrat award, 1995. Mem. Internat. Peace Rsch. Assn. (co-convenor nonviolence study group 1989-91), Internat. Polit. Sci. Assn., World Future Studies Fedn., Phi Beta Kappa. Home: 3653 Tantalus Dr Honolulu HI 95822-5033 *Political science is a science that can liberate humankind from violence. To do so, it must first liberate itself. This will require five related transformations: normative, empirical, theoretical, institutional, and educational. The tasks of political scientists at the end of the 20th century are to begin these transformations. Twenty-first century successors must carry them forward, consolidate them, and extend their influence throughout global society.*

PAIGE, HILLIARD WEGNER, corporate director, consultant; b. Hartford, Conn., Oct. 2, 1919; s. Joseph Wegner and Ruth (Hill) P.; m. Dorothea Magner, Dec. 8, 1945; children—Elizabeth, Deborah, Hilliard, Jr. BSME, Worcester Poly. Inst., 1941, D Engring. (hon), 1971. Sr. v.p. Gen. Electric N.Y.C., 1941-71; pres. Gen. Dynamics, St. Louis, 1971-73; chmn., chief exec. officer Satellite Bus. Systems, Inc., Washington, 1973-76; vice chmn. bd. Internat. Energy Assocs., Ltd., Washington, 1976-85; chmn. bd. H.A. Knott, Ltd., Silver Spring, Md., 1984-89; dir. The Atlantic Coun. of U.S., 1987—; Computer Data Systems, Inc., Videoconferencing Systems, Inc., Gen. Environ. & Energy, Inc., Gallager Marine Systems, Inc. Patentee in field; contbr. articles to profl. jours. Mem. Def. Sci. Bd. U.S. Dept. Def., Washington, 1973-78; trustee Worcester Poly. Inst., Mass., 1974—. Recipient Pub. Service award NASA, 1969, Order of Merit Italy, 1970, Engr. of Year award Greater Phila. Engring Council, 1960. Fellow AIAA; mem. Nat. Acad. Engring. Republican. Congregationalist. Clubs: Metropolitan, Chevy Chase (Washington); Conquistadores del Cielo. Avocations: skiing, tennis, scuba diving, golf. Home and Office: 5163 Tilden St NW Washington DC 20016-1961

PAIGE, JEFFERY MAYLAND, sociologist, educator; b. Providence, June 15, 1942; s. Charles Warren and Dorothy Frances (Rice) P.; m. Karen Ericksen, Apr. 30, 1966 (div. 1980). AB summa cum laude, Harvard U., 1964; PhD, U. Mich., 1968. Asst. prof. U. Calif., Berkeley, 1968-76; assoc. prof. U. Mich., Ann Arbor, 1976-82, prof., 1982—, dir. ctr. for rsch. on social orgn., 1992—; vis. lectr. U. Ctrl. Am., San Salvador, El Salvador, 1990, Fla. Internat. U., Miami, 1992; internat. observer Nicaraguan Nat. Adv. Commn. on Atlantic Coast, Managua, 1986. Author: Agrarian Revolution, 1975 (Sorokin award 1976); co-author: The Politics of Reproductive Ritual, 1981. Fulbright fellow, 1990, Kellog fellow, 1991; rsch. grantee NSF, 1990-92. Mem. Am. Sociol. Assn. (coun. chair polit. econ. of world sys. sect. 1987-89), Latin Am. Studies Assn., Sociol. Rsch. Assn. Democrat. Avocations: hiking, Nordic and alpine skiing, sailing. Office: U Mich Dept Sociology Ann Arbor MI 48109

PAIGE, NORMA, lawyer, corporate executive; b. Lomza, Poland, Oct. 11, 1922; came to U.S., 1927; d. Morris and Edith (Kachourek) Zelaso; children: Holly Paige Russek, Madelyn Paige Givant. BA, NYU, 1944, JD, 1946; postgrad. in bus. adminstrn., CCNY, 1953, NYU, 1969. Bar: N.Y. 1946, U.S. Supreme Ct. 1951. Ptnr. Paige and Paige, N.Y.C., 1948—; v.p., bd. dirs. Astronautics Corp. Am., Milw., 1959—, chmn. bd., 1984—; exec. v.p., bd. dirs. Kearfott Guidance & Navigation Corp., Wayne, N.J., 1988—; bd. dirs. Astronautics C.A., Ltd., Israel. Recipient Jabotinsky Centennial medal Prime Minister of Israel, 1980, Tribute to Women in Indsl. Industry Twin II award YWCA, 1981, NYU Sch. Law Outstanding Alumnus of Yr. award, 1991. Mem. N.Y. Women's Bar Assn. (pres. 1958-59). Office: Astronautics Corp Am 4115 N Teutonia Ave Milwaukee WI 53209

PAIGE, RICHARD BRUCE, financial information executive; b. Phila., Apr. 21, 1949; s. Frederick Osgood and Helen (Symons) P.; m. Constance Ellen Horton, June 16, 1973; children: Christine, Jennifer, Stephanie, Michael. BS in Mgmt. Sci., Fla. Inst. Tech., 1972; MS in Systems Mgmt., U. So. Calif., 1975. Info. analyst Army Security Agy., Okinawa, Japan, 1973-76; salesman Dun & Bradstreet, Hartford, Conn., 1976-77; products mgr. Dun & Bradstreet, N.Y.C., 1977-78; dir. database mgmt. Dun & Bradstreet, Parsippany, N.J., 1978-84, v.p. database mgmt. and devel., 1985-88, v.p. pub., 1988-89; gen. mgr. book div. Jour. Commerce, Phillipsburg, N.J., 1990—. Contbr. articles to Purchasing World Mag., 1978. Mem. Info. Resources Coordinating Com., Info. Industry Assn. Republican. Methodist. Avocations: marathon running, sailing, cross country skiing, bicycle racing. Home: RR 3 Box 3736 East Stroudsburg PA 18301-8806 Office: The Journal of Commerce 445 Marshall St Phillipsburg NJ 08865-2665

PAIGE, WOODROW WILSON, columnist; b. Memphis, June 27, 1946; s. Woodrow Wilson and Billie (Montgomery) P.; m. Virginia Hunt, Oct. 28, 1973; 1 child, Shannon Hunt. Student, U. Tenn., 1964-68. Columnist/reporter Whitehaven Press, Memphis, 1963-64, Knoxville (Tenn.) Jour., 1966; columnist The Comml. Appeal, Memphis, 1968-74; The Rocky Mountain News, Denver, 1974-81, The Denver (Colo.) Post, 1981—; talk show host Variety Radio Sta., Denver, 1975-95; commentator KMGH-TV, Denver, 1989-90; tv talk show host KNBD-TV, Denver, 1993-94. Author: Orange Madness, 1978, Blitz, 1987, Sudden Death, 1995. Named Sportswriter of Yr., Nat. Assn. Sportswriters and Sportscasters, 1992, 93, 94, Best Column, Colo. Press Assn., 1979, 81, 84, 86, 88, 89, 91, 92, 93, 94.

PAIGEN, KENNETH, geneticist, educator; b. N.Y.C., Nov. 14, 1927; s. Alexander and Ida (Kantor) P.; m. Beverly Vandermolen, June 14, 1970; children: Susan, Gina, Mark, David, Jennifer. A.B., Johns Hopkins U., Balt., 1946; Ph.D., Calif. Inst. Tech., Pasadena, 1950. Staff mem. Roswell Park Meml. Inst., Buffalo, 1955-72, dept. head, 1972-82; prof. dept. genetics U. Calif., Berkeley, 1982-89; dir., sr. staff scientist Jackson Lab., Bar Harbor, Maine, 1989—. Mem. AAAS, Am. Assn. for Cancer Rsch., Internat. Mammalian Genome Soc., Human Genome Orgn., Genetics Soc. Am., Am. Soc. for Biochemistry and Molecular Biology, Sigma Xi, Phi Beta Kappa. Democrat. Jewish. Avocation: sailing. Home: Old Farm Rd Bar Harbor ME 04609 Office: Jackson Lab 600 Main St Bar Harbor ME 04609-1523

PAIKOWSKY, SANDRA ROSLYN, art historian; b. St. John, N.B., Can., Dec. 29, 1945; d. Morton Ernest and Bessie Frances (Rabkin) P.; m. John Richard Fox, Dec. 11, 1982. B.A., Sir. George Williams U., Montreal, Que., Can., 1967; M.A., U. Toronto, 1969. Curatorial asst. Royal Ont. Mus., Toronto, 1967-68; prof. art history Concordia U., Montreal, 1969—; curator Concordia Art Gallery, Montreal, 1981-93. Editor: Jour. Can. Art, 1991—; co-editor: Jour. Can. Art History, 1972—, co-pub. 1981-92, pub.; author exhbn. catalogues. Mem. Can. Mus. Assn., Univ. Art Assn. Can. Office: Concordia U Fine Arts BC 210-4, 1455 de Maisonneuve Blvd W, Montreal, PQ Canada H3G 1M8

PAIN, BETSY M., lawyer; b. Albertville, Ala., Aug. 29, 1950; d. Charles Riley and Jean Faye (Rains) Stone; m. William F. Pain, Nov. 18, 1977; children: Taylor Holland, Emily Anne Pain. AA, Northeastern Okla. A&M, Miami, Okla., 1970; BA, U. Okla., 1974, JD, 1976. Bar: Okla. 1977; U.S. Dist. Ct. (we. dist.) 1979. Staff atty. Okla. Dept. Corrections, Oklahoma City, 1978-79; gen. counsel Okla. Pardon and Parole Bd., Oklahoma City, 1979-84, exec. dir., 1984-88; corp. counsel Roberts, Schornick & Assocs., Inc., Norman, Okla., 1990—. Editor: (newsletter) RSA Environmental Report, 1991—. With extended family program Juvenile Svcs., Inc. Cleveland County, Okla., 1983-91. Mem. Okla. Bar Assn. (environ. law sect. 1977—), Am. Corp. Counsel Assn. Democrat. Methodist. Avocations: reading, needlework, church activities. Office: Roberts Schornick & Assoc Inc 3700 W Robinson Ste 200 Norman OK 73072

PAIN, CHARLES LESLIE, lawyer; b. Austin, Tex., Apr. 26, 1913; s. William Francis and Ruby (Gates) P.; m. Roberta Wilmoth, Mar. 27, 1942; children—Charles Laurence, William Francis, Glenn David. B.A., LL.B., U. Okla., 1935. Bar: Okla. 1935. Asst. atty. Southwestern Light & Power Co., 1935-40; practice in Anadarko, 1956—; partner Pain & Garland, 1956—; Exec. sec. to Congressman Toby Morris, 1951-53; Mem. Okla. Bd. Bar Examiners, 1969-78. Pres. Black Beaver council Boy Scouts Am., 1971-72; bd. dirs. Okla. Baptist Found., Inc., 1984-85, vice chmn., 1985-87. Served with AUS, 1940-46; col. Res. (Ret.). Recipient Silver Beaver award Boy Scouts Am. Mem. Am., Okla., Caddo County bar assns., Am. Legion, Res. Officers Assn., Order of Coif, Phi Beta Kappa, Phi Eta Sigma, Phi Alpha Delta, Sigma Chi. Democrat. Baptist. Club: Lion (past dist. gov.). Office: 111 SW 2nd St Anadarko OK 73005

PAINE, ANDREW J., JR., banker; b. Chgo., Oct. 18, 1937; s. Andrew J. and Louise (Kelley) P.; m. Jane Medaris, June 25, 1960; children: Linda, Stephanie, Andrew. B.A., DePauw U., 1959; M.B.A., Ind. U., 1967; grad. Stonier Grad. Sch. Banking, 1969. Asst. cashier Ind. Nat. Bank, Indpls., 1964-66; asst. v.p. Ind. Nat. Bank, 1966-68, v.p., 1968-72, sr. v.p., 1972-76, exec. v.p. corp. devel., 1976-77, exec. v.p. corp. banking, 1977-79, pres., 1979—, chief oper. officer; also vice chmn. Ind. Nat. Corp.; vice chmn. Ind. Nat. Corp., 1981—; dir. Indpls. Life Ins. Co., Hammond Co., Newport Beach, Calif. Mem. past pres.'s council Jr. Achievement Central Ind.; nat. bd. dirs. Jr. Achievement Inc.; trustee Children's Mus., DePauw U.; bd. dirs. Community Service Council Met. Indpls.; bd. govs. United Way, chmn. campaign, 1983. Recipient Key Man award Indpls. Jaycees, 1972; Alumni citation DePauw U., 1978. Mem. Am. Bankers Assn. (chmn. govt. relations council), Young Presidents Orgn., Ind. U. Sch. Bus. Alumni Assn. (past pres.). Methodist. Club: Columbia, Meridian Hills Country. Office: Ind Nat Bank 1 Indiana Sq # 501 Indianapolis IN 46266

PAINE, JAMES CARRIGER, federal judge; b. Valdosta, Ga., May 20, 1924; s. Leon Alexander and Josie Carriger (Jones) P.; m. Ruth Ellen Bailey, Sept. 8, 1950; children: James Carriger, Jonathan Jones, JoEllen. B.S., Columbia U., 1947; LL.B., U. Va., 1950, J.D., 1970. Bar: Fla. 1950. Mem. firm Earnest, Lewis, Smith & Jones, West Palm Beach, Fla., 1950-54, Jones Adams Paine & Foster, 1954-60, Jones Paine & Foster, 1960-79; judge U.S. Dist. Ct. (so. dist.) Fla., West Palm Beach, 1979—. Bd. dirs., pres. Children's Home Soc. Fla., 1978-80; mem. bd. Episcopal Diocese S.E. Fla. Served to lt. USNR, 1943-47. Mem. Greater West Palm Beach C. of C. (pres. 1973-74), Palm Beach County Bar Assn. Democrat. Office: US Dist Ct 701 Clematis St West Palm Beach FL 33401-5197

PAINE, LOUIS BURR, JR., lawyer; b. Dallas, Dec. 22, 1932; s. Louis Burr and Winifred (Baker) P.; m. Lynne Murphy, July 23, 1960; children: Louis, Preston, Jeffrey. BA, U. Tex., 1954, LLB, 1956. Bar: Tex. 1956. Assoc. Butler & Binion, Houston, 1960-70, ptnr., 1970—, mng. ptnr., 1985-95. Lt. USN, 1956-60. Fellow Am. Bar Found., Am. Law Inst., Tex. Bar Found., Houston Bar Found., Houston Country Club. Presbyterian. Home: 107 Glynn Way Dr Houston TX 77056-1111 Office: Butler & Binion LLP 1600 1st Interstate Bank Plz Houston TX 77002

PAINE, ROBERT TREAT, zoology educator; b. Cambridge, Mass., Apr. 13, 1933; s. Robert Treat and Barbara (Birkhoff) P.; m. Alice E. Coleman, Jun. 11, 1959 (div. 1972); children: Susan M., Nancy C., Anne E. AB, Harvard U., 1954; MS, U. Mich., 1958, PhD, 1961. Asst. prof. zoology U. Wash., Seattle, 1962-67, assoc. prof., 1967-71, prof., 1971—; Tansley lectr. Brit. Ecol. Soc., 1979. With U.S. Army, 1955-56. Sverdrup fellow Scripps Inst. Oceanography, La Jolla, Calif., 1961-62; Guggenheim fellow, 1982. Mem. NAS, Ecol. Soc. Am. (v.p. 1979, pres. 1981-82, McArthur award 1983, ECI prize 1990), Am. Soc. Limnology and Oceanography (editorial bd. 1974-76). Avocations: gardening, stamp collecting. Office: U Wash NJ-15 Dept Zoology Seattle WA 98195

PAINO, RONALD THOMAS, education consultant; b. Passaic, N.J., July 10, 1945; s. Eugene Joseph and Josephine Ann (Cellini) P. BS, Monmouth Coll., 1969; cert., Newark State Coll., 1974, Georgian Ct. Coll., 1982, 85, Princeton U., 1993. Cert. tchr., N.J. Tchr. math. and sci. Freehold Twp. (N.J.) Bd. Edn., 1969-80; math. content specialist East Windsor Bd. Edn., Hightstown, N.J., 1982-88; edn. cons. Control Data Corp., Mpls., 1988-89; edn. specialist Roach Orgn., Inc., Atlanta, 1989-93; tchr., dir. Coop. Math. Lab. East Windsor Bd. Edn., Hightstown, N.J., 1993—; edn. cons. in devel. studies Richmond Community Coll., Hamlet, N.C., 1990-91, Morris Brown Coll., Atlanta, 1990-92, Sampson C.C., Clinton, N.C., 1990-91; sch.-based cons. N.J. Dept. Edn., Trenton, 1986; edn. specialist TVA, 1992. Mem. ASCD. Avocations: sailing, gardening, swimming.

PAINTER, CARL ERIC, manufacturing company executive; b. Balt., Aug. 1, 1946; s. Walter Savery and Eleanor (Johnson) P.; m. Roxann Dawn Caprio. BSEE, Lehigh U., 1968; MBA, Harvard U., 1975. With Phelps Dodge Cable & Wire Co., Yonkers, N.Y., 1975-79; plant mgr. Phelps Dodge Cable & Wire Co., DuQuoin, Ill., 1979-83; dir. mktg. Phelps Dodge Cable & Wire Co., Greenwich, Conn., 1983-84; v.p. ops. & mktg. Cablec Corp., New City, N.Y., 1984-87; pres. Cablec Utility Cable Co. divsn. BICC Cables Corp., West Nyack, N.Y., 1987-93; exec. v.p. BICC Cables Corp., West Nyack, N.Y., 1990-92, pres., COO, 1992-93, pres., chmn., CEO, 1993—; bd. dirs. BICC plc, Phillips Cables. Lt. USN, 1968-72. Office: BICC Cables Corp 1 Crosfield Ave West Nyack NY 10994-2221

PAINTER, JACK TIMBERLAKE, civil engineer; b. Kincaid, W.Va., July 23, 1930; s. Troy Earl and Nannie Bell (Proffit) P. BSCE, W.Va. U., 1950, MSCE, 1956. Instr. civil engring. W.Va. U., 1950-51, 53-55; mem. faculty La. Tech U., Ruston, 1955—; prof. civil engring. La. Tech. U., 1962-92, prof. emeritus, 1992—; Alumni Found. prof. La. Tech U., 1977-78; vis. lectr. Manhattan Coll., Coll. Forestry, SUNY, Syracuse, Cornell U., U. Wis., summers 1954-60. Nat. pres. Circus Fans Assn. Am., 1967; lic. layreader Episcopal Ch. Served with USNR, 1951-52. Faculty fellow NSF, 1958-59; named Man of Year Omicron Delta Kappa, 1972. Fellow ASCE; mem. Am. Congress Surveying and Mapping, La. Engring. Soc. (Charles M. Kerr Pub. Rels. award 1990), Am. Soc. Engring. Edn., Tau Beta Pi (Outstanding Prof. award 1963, 68, 74, 78), Chi Epsilon (Excellent Teaching award 1985). Address: 1303 Hodges Ave Ruston LA 71270

PAINTER, JOHN CECIL, library director; b. Oswald, W.Va., July 21, 1943; s. Cecil Ule and Daphna Pearl (O'Neal) P.; m. Dana Lynn Abbott, July 20, 1986; children: Laura Elaine, John Russell, Natalie Ryan. BE, Concord Coll., Athens, W.Va., 1965; MS in Libr. Sci., Drexel U., 1972. Head libr. Millsboro (Del.) Sch. Dist., 1965-69; reference libr. Del. Tech. and Community Coll., Georgetown, 1969-72, dir. libr., 1972—; mem. planning com. to White House on librs.; def. Del. Gov.'s Conf., 1991. Mem. ALA, Mid-Atlantic Regional Libr. Assn. (exec. bd. 1979-82), Del. Acad. Librs. Coun., Del. Libr. Assn. (pres. 1976-79, com. legis. lobby 1982, editor newsletter 1979), Del. Tech. and Community Coll. Faculty Assembly (pres. 1990-91). Democrat. Methodist. Avocations: woodworking, golf. Home: 102 Marjorie Rd Seaford DE 19973-3639 Office: Del Tech & Community Coll PO Box 160 Georgetown DE 19947-0160

PAINTER, JOHN HOYT, electrical engineer; b. Winfield, Kans., Mar. 27, 1934; s. John Paul and Marjorie Marietta (Slack) P.; m. Joy Lou Vaughan, June 7, 1955; children—John Mark, Paul Burton, William Vaughan, Joy Lynn. B.S., U. Ill., Urbana, 1961; Gen. Electric Found. fellow, M.S., 1962; Ph.D., So. Meth. U., 1972; postgrad., Calif. Inst. Tech., 1967-69. Communications engr. NASA Manned Spacecraft Center, Houston, 1962-65; sr. engr. Motorola Govt. Electronics div., Scottsdale, Ariz., 1965-67; research engr. NASA Langley Research Center, Hampton, Va., 1967-74; asso. prof., elec. engring. Tex. A&M U., College Station, 1974-79, prof., 1979—; pres. ALTAIR Corps. cons., College Station, 1980—; tchr. Christian seminars. Served with USAF, 1953-58. Recipient Recognition cert. NASA, 1975. Mem. IEEE (sr.). Patentee digital communications processing. Home: 119 Merry Oaks Dr College Station TX 77840-2606 Office: Tex A&M U Dept Elec Engring College Station TX 77843

PAINTER, LINDA ROBINSON, physics educator, dean; b. Lexington, Ky., May 4, 1940; d. J. Kenneth and Juanita Marie (Crosier) R.; m. Roy Allen Painter, May 6, 1967; children: Holly Suzanne, Brent Allen. BS in

Physics, U. Louisville, 1962; MS in Physics, U. Tenn., 1963, PhD in Physics, 1968. Asst. prof. physics U. Tenn., Knoxville, 1968-75, assoc. prof. physics, 1975-82, prof. physics, 1982—, asst. dean, Grad. Sch., 1985-88; assoc. dean, 1988—; cons. Health Physics Div., Oak Ridge (Tenn.) Nat. Lab., 1967-77; adj. rsch. and devel. participant, Health and Safety Rsch. Div., Oak Ridge Nat. Lab., 1977-83, part-time employee, 1983-89; bd. dirs. Consultec Scientific, Inc. Contbr. numerous articles to profl. jours. Named Outstanding Young Woman of the Yr., Tenn., Outstanding Young Women of Am., 1974; recipient grants, U.S. Atomic Energy Commn., U.S. Energy Rsch. and Devel. Agy., U.S. Dept. Energy, 1968-89. Fellow Am. Phys. Soc.; mem. Tenn. Conf. Grad. Schs. (pres. 1990-91, editor 1985—), Radiation Rsch. Soc. (assoc. editor 1984-88), Coun. So. Grad. Schs. (publs. com. 1988-90, com. issues and planning 1991—). Baptist. Home: 7708 Devonshire Rd Knoxville TN 37919-8019

PAINTER, MICHAEL ROBERT, landscape architect, urban designer; b. L.A., Jan. 27, 1935; s. John Guy and Lillias (Armour) P.; m. Susan Margaret Collins, Jan. 3, 1959; children: Melissa Ann, Joshua Michael. BS, U. Calif., Berkeley, 1956; M Landscape Architecture in Urban Design, Harvard U., 1966. Registered landscape architect, Calif., N.Y., Nev., Pa., Tex. Jr. designer Lawrence Halprin & Assoc., San Francisco, 1956-58; ptnr. John Carl Warnecke & Assoc., San Francisco, 1958-69; pres. Michael Painter & Assoc., San Francisco, 1969-87, MPA Design, San Francisco, 1987—. Maj. archtl. works include Kennedy Gravesite, Arlington, Va., 1968 (honor award Am. Soc. Landscape Architects 1970), Lafayette Pk., Washington, 1970 (merit award Am. Soc. Landscape Architects 1972), corp. campus PacBell Adminstrn. Ctr., San Ramon, Calif., 1988 (merit award Am. Soc. Landscape Architects 1989), waterfront restoration Gt. Hwy./Ocean Beach, San Francisco, 1989 (honor award Am. Soc. Landscape Architects 1989), Doyle Drive Scenic Pkwy. Plan (merit award Am. Soc. Landscape Architects, Cmty. Svc. award San Francisco chpt. AIA, 1993). Pres., bd. dirs. Friends of Recreation and Pks., San Francisco, 1969—; bd. dirs, advisor San Francisco Planning and Urban Rsch., 1972—; bd. dirs. Exploratorium, San Francisco, 1974—; coun. Grad. Sch. Design, Harvard U., 1983-86; chmn. Citizens Adv. Com., San Francisco. Fellow Am. Soc. Landscape Architecture (com. chair 1968-69, v.p. No. Calif. chpt. 1970-72, honor awards 1978, 82, merit awards 1981, 84); mem. Urban Land Inst. (assoc.), Calif. Coun. Landscape Architecture (design jury 1991), U. Calif. Coll. Environ. Design Alumni Assn. (bd. dirs. 1990—), Mill Valley Tennis Club, Lambda Alpha. Avocations: gardening, hiking, swimming, historical research. Office: MPA Design 414 Mason St San Francisco CA 94102-1719

PAINTER, NELL IRVIN, historian, educator; b. Houston, Aug. 2, 1942. BA, U. Calif., Berkeley, 1964; student, U. Bordeaux, France, 1962-63, U. Ghana, 1965-66; MA, UCLA, 1967; PhD, Harvard U., 1974. Teaching fellow Harvard U., Cambridge, Mass., 1969-70, 72-74; asst. prof. history U. Pa., Phila., 1974-77, assoc. prof., 1977-80; prof. history U. N.C., Chapel Hill, 1980-88; prof. history Princeton (N.J.) U., 1988-91, acting dir. Afro-Am. Studies Program, 1990-91, Edwards Prof. Am. History, 1991—; Russell Sage vis. prof. history Hunter Coll., CUNY, N.Y.C., 1985-86. Author: Exodusters: Black Migration to Kansas After Reconstruction, 1976, The Narrative of Hosea Hudson: His Life as a Negro Communist in the South, 1979, Standing at Armageddon: The United States 1877-1919, 1987; co-editor: Gender and Am. Culture Series; mem. editorial bd. Jour. Women's History, Encyclopedia Americana; contbr. articles to profl. jours. Ford Found. fellow, 1971-72, Am. Coun. Learned Soc. fellow, 1976-77, Charles Warren Ctr. Studies in Am. History fellow, 1976-77, Radcliffe/Bunting Inst. fellow, 1976-77, Nat. Humanities Ctr. fellow, 1978-79, Guggenheim fellow, 1982-83, Ctr. Advanced Study in Behavioral Scis. fellow, 1988-89, Kate B. and Hall J. Peterson fellow Am. Antiquarian Soc., 1991, NEH fellow, 1992-93; recipient Coretta Scott King award AAUW, 1969-70, Grad. Soc. medal Radcliffe Coll. Alumnae, 1984, Candace award Nat. Coalition One Hundred Black Women, 1986; named U. Calif. at Berkeley Alumnae of Yr., 1989. Mem. Am. Coun. Learned Soc., Am. Antiquarian Soc., Am. Hist. Assn. (mem. program com. 1976-78, J. Franklin Jameson fellowship com. 1978-79, Beveridge and Dunning prizes com. 1985-87, mem. coun. 1991-93), Am. Studies Assn. (mem. internat. com. 1983-88, mem. nat. coun. 1989-92, mem. adv. coun. 1991-92), Assn. Study Afro-Am. Life and History (mem. program com. 1976), Assn. Black Women Historians (mem. rsch. com. 1980—, nat. dir. 1982-84, chair Brown pub. prize com. 1983-86, 88-91), Berkshire Conf. Women Historians (mem. program com. 1976), Inst. So. Studies (mem. exec. com. 1987-88), Orgn. Am. Historians (mem. com. status women 1975-77, mem. program com. 1977-79, 83-85, Frederick Jackson Turner award com. 1983, mem. exec. bd. 1984-87, chair ad hoc com. on minority historians 1985-87, chair Avery O. Craven award 1994-95), Nat. Book Found. (chair non-fiction jury, Nat. Book awards 1994), Social Sci. Rsch. Coun. (mem. com. social sci. pers. 1977-78), So. Hist. Assn. (chair Syndor prize com. 1991-92), So. Regional Coun. (mem. Lillian Smith Book prize com. 1986, mem. exec. com. 1987), Soc. Am. Historians (chair Parkman prize com. 1993—). Office: Princeton U History Dept Princeton NJ 08544-1017

PAINTER, PAUL WAIN, JR., lawyer; b. Cleveland, Tenn., Aug. 10, 1945; s. Paul Wain and Juanita (Davis) P.; m. Judith Ann Babine, Aug. 28, 1971; 1 child, Paul Wain III. BS, Ga. Tech., 1968; JD, U. Ga., 1974. Bar: Ga. 1974, U.S. Dist. Ct. (so dist.) Ga., U.S. Ct. Appeals (11th cir.). Assoc. Bouhan, Williams & Levy, Savannah, Ga., 1974-79; ptnr. Karsman, Brooks, Painter & Callaway, Savannah, 1979-88, Painter, Ratterree & Bart, Savannah, 1988—; faculty mem. Nat. Inst. Trial Advocacy Emory U. Sch. Law, 1982-90; mem. ct. adv. com. U.S. Dist. Ct. (so. dist.) Ga., 1992—; mem. Gov.'s Adv. Com. on Tort Reform, Atlanta, 1986. Trustee Ga. Inst. Continuing Legal Edn., Athens, 1992—; pres. Savannah Arthritis Found., 1982-83; bd. dirs. Ga. Arthritis Found., Atlanta, 1983; grad. Leadership Savannah, 1986-88. Lt. (j.g.) USN, 1968-71. Fellow Am. Coll. Trial Lawyers; mem. ABA, State Bar Ga. (chair trial sect. 1992-93), Def. Rsch. Inst. (Ga. state chmn. 1988-91), Savannah Bar Assn. (pres. 93), Ga. Def. Lawyers Assn. (pres. 1986-87). Roman Catholic. Avocations: reading history and fiction, hunting, fishing. Office: Painter Ratterree & Bart PO Box 9946 Savannah GA 31412

PAINTER, WILLIAM HALL, law educator; b. Pitts., May 2, 1927; s. John Littleton Dawson and Eleanor Cramer (Hall); m. Marion Symmes Homer, July 9, 1955; children: Richard William, Edward Homer. A.B., Princeton U., 1950; J.D., Harvard U., 1954. Bar: N.Y. 1955. Assoc. Debevoise, Plimpton & McLean, N.Y.C., 1954-58; teaching fellow Harvard U.Law Sch., Cambridge, Mass., 1958-59; prof. Villanova U. Law Sch., Phila., 1959-65; vis. prof. U. Mich. Law Sch., Ann Arbor, 1965; prof. U. Mo., Kansas City, 1965-71; spl. counsel, dir. study securities industry U.S. Ho. Reps., Washington, 1971-72; prof. U. Ill. Coll. Law, Champaign, 1972-81, Albert E. Jenner Jr. prof., 1981-87; Theodore Rinehart prof. law George Washington U., Washington, 1987—. Author: Federal Regulation of Insider Trading, 1968, Corporate and Tax Aspects of Closely Held Corporations, 1971, 2d edit., 1981, Problems and Materials in Business Planning, 1975, 3d edit., 1994, The Federal Securities Code and Corporate Disclosure, 1979, Painter on Close Corporations, 1991; contbr. articles to legal publs. Mem. Ill. Bus. Corp. Act Revision Com., 1981-83. Mem. ABA (fed. securities comm. sect. corp., banking and bus. law, chmn. subcom. on legis. 1974-81), Assn. Am. Law Schs. (chmn. sect. bus. assn. 1976), Am. Law Inst., Phi Beta Kappa. Home: 6652 32nd St NW Washington DC 20015-2310 Office: George Washington U Nat Law Ctr 720 20th St NW Washington DC 20052-0001

PAINTON, IRA WAYNE, retired securities executive; b. Longdale, Okla., Nov. 3, 1917; s. Ira W. and Leatha (Ball) P.; m. Jane Tiffin, Apr. 9, 1941; children: Ann Painton Anderson, Scott N. A.B., Northwestern State U., Okla., 1940; postgrad., So. Meth. U., 1953. C.L.U. Mng. ptnr. Waynoka Motor Co., Okla., 1946-50; br. mgr. Am. Nat. Ins. Co., Omaha, 1953-57; dir. tng. Pacific Mut. Life Ins. Co., Los Angeles, 1957-61; dir. recruiting and tng. Fin. Programs, Inc., Denver, 1962-66; v.p. Securities Mgmt. & Research, Inc., Galveston, Tex. 1967; pres. Securities Mgmt. & Research, Inc., 1967-83; pres., dir. Am. Nat. Growth, Income and Bond Funds. Served to capt. Signal Corps, AUS, 1940-46, 50-52, Korea. Decorated Bronze Star. Mem. Am. Assn. CLUs, Northwestern Okla. State U. Alumni Assn. (Outstanding Bus./Profl. award 1992, chmn. foun. bd. 1993—). Home: 12004 Dahoon Dr Oklahoma City OK 73120 *I believe real success, like beauty, is in the mind of the beholder. And as long as we persist in trying there can be no final failure, since success is usually a series of failures that turn out all right.*

PAINTON, RUSSELL ELLIOTT, lawyer, mechanical engineer; b. Port Arthur, Tex., Dec. 5, 1940; s. Clifford Elliott and Edith Virginia (McCutcheon) P.; m. Elizabeth Ann Mullins, July 2, 1965 (div. Dec. 1977); 1 child, Todd Elliott; m. Mary Lynn Weber, May 9, 1981. BS in Mech. Engring., U. Tex.-Austin, 1963, JD, 1972. Bar: Tex. 1972; registered profl. engr., Tex. Engr. Gulf States Utilities, Beaumont, Tex., 1963-66; engr. Tracor, Inc., Austin, Tex., 1966-70, corp. counsel, 1973-83, v.p., gen. counsel, 1983—, corp. sec., 1991—; atty. Brown, Maroney, Rose, Baker & Barber, Austin, 1972-73, Childs, Fortenbach, Beck & Guyton, Houston, 1973; corp. sec. Westmark Systems, Inc., Austin, 1990-91. Gen. counsel Paramount Theatre for Performing Arts, 1977-83, 2d vice chmn. 1978-80, 1st vice chmn., 1980-82, chmn. bd., 1982-84, retiring chmn., 1984-85; mem.Centex chpt. ARC; adv. bd. Austin Sci. Acad., 1985-88, 93—; adv. coun. Austin Transp., 1985-88; bd. dirs. Tex. Industries for the Blind and Handicapped, 1988—, vice chmn., 1990-91. Named Boss of Yr. Austin Legal Secs. Assn., 1981. Mem. ABA, Tex. Bar Assn. (treas. corp. counsel sect. 1982-83), Travis County Bar Assn., Nat. Chamber Litigation Ctr., Better Bus. Bur. (arbitrator 1983—), Am. Electronics Assn. (chmn. Austin coun. 1985-86), Austin Yacht Club (race comdr. 1968-69, treas. 1970-71, sec. 1972, 75, vice commodore 1980, commodore 1981, fleet comdr. 1986), Order Blue Gavel, Delta Theta Phi. Republican. Episcopalian. Office: Tracor Inc 6500 Tracor Ln Austin TX 78725-2151

PAIS, ABRAHAM, physicist, educator; b. Amsterdam, Holland, May 19, 1918; s. Jesaja and Kaatje (van Kleeff) P.; m. Lila Atwill, Dec. 15, 1956 (div. 1962); 1 child, Joshua; m. Agnes Ida Benedicte Nicolaisen, Mar. 15, 1990. B.Sc., U. Amsterdam, 1938; M.Sc., U. Utrecht, 1940, Ph.D., 1941. Research fellow Inst. Theoretical Physics, Copenhagen, Denmark, 1946; prof. Inst. Advanced Study, Princeton, N.J., 1950-63; prof. physics Rockefeller U., N.Y.C., 1963-81, Detlev Bronk prof., 1981—, prof. emeritus, 1988—; Balfour prof. Weizmann Inst., Israel, 1977. Author: Subtle is the Lord (Am. Book award 1983, Am. Inst. Physics award 1983) Inward Bound, 1986, Niels Bohr's Times, 1991, Einstein Lived Here, 1994. Decorated officer Order of Oranje Nassau (The Netherlands); recipient J.R. Oppenheimer Meml. prize, 1979, Physica prize The Netherlands, 1992, Gemant award Am. Inst. Physics, 1993, Lewis Thomas prize, 1995; Guggenheim fellow, 1960. Fellow Am. Phys. Soc.; mem. Royal Acad. Scis. Holland (corr., medal of sci. 1993), Royal Acad. Scis. and Letters, Denmark, Am. Acad. Arts and Scis., Am. Philos. Soc., Nat. Acad. Scis., Council on Fgn. Relations. Home: 1161 York Ave New York NY 10021 Office: Rockefeller Univ Dept of Physics New York NY 10021

PAISANT, SISTER IMMACULATA, school system administrator. Supt. Cath. schs. Diocese of Houma-Thibodaux, La. Office: Office Supt Cath Schs PO Box 9077 Houma LA 70361-9077

PAISLEY, KEITH W., state senator, small business owner; b. Mpls., Dec. 29, 1928; s. Manley G. and Maxine Alice (Watkins) P.; m. Jean Clare Robson, Sept. 23, 1950; children: Mark, Susan, Julie, Jeanne. BA, Hamline U., 1950. Rep. State of S.D., Pierre, 1981-84, senator, 1985—; owner Robson Hardware, Sioux Falls, S.D. Lutheran. Home: 2409 S Elmwood Ave Sioux Falls SD 57105-3315 Office: Robson Hardware 2322 W 12th St Sioux Falls SD 57104-3898

PAISNER, BRUCE LAWRENCE, lawyer, television and film executive; b. Providence, July 4, 1942; s. Isadore and Reva Josephine (Novogroski) P.; m. Nicole Pilotaz, Sept. 12, 1971; children: Jennifer Ann, Michael Sylvain. A.B. cum laude, Harvard U., 1964, J.D. cum laude, 1968. Corr., Life mag., 1964-65; asst. to chmn. bd. Time Inc., N.Y.C., 1968-70, v.p., 1975-80; gen. mgr. Time-Life Video, N.Y.C., 1970-73; pres. Time-Life Films Inc., N.Y.C., 1973-80, Novacom, Inc., N.Y.C., 1980-81, King Features Entertainment, Inc. subs. Hearst Corp., N.Y.C., 1981—; chmn., chief exec. officer King Features Entertainment, Inc. subs. Hearst Corp., 1989; v.p. The Hearst Corp., N.Y.C., 1989—; dep. group head Entertainment & Syndication Group The Hearst Corp., 1989—; pres. CEO Hearst Entertainment, Inc., N.Y.C., 1989—; bd. dirs. Columbia Media & Soc. Seminars. Bd. dirs. Schepen's Eye Rsch. Inst. Harvard Med. Sch., 1993—. Mem. Univ. Club, The Players Club, The Century Assn. Home: 1021 Park Ave New York NY 10028-0959 Office: Hearst Entertainment 235 E 45th St New York NY 10017-3305

PAIVIO, ALLAN URHO, psychology educator; b. Thunder Bay, Ont., Can., Mar. 29, 1925; s. Aku and Ida Julia (Hanninen) P.; m. Kathleen Laura Blanche Austin, Jan. 9, 1946; children—Sandra, Anna Lee, Heather, Eric, Karina. B.Sc., McGill U., 1949, M.Sc., 1957, Ph.D., 1959. Lectr. Sir George Williams U., Montreal, 1957; research psychologist Cornell U., Ithaca, N.Y., 1958-59; asst. prof. psychology U. New Brunswick, Can., 1959-62; asst. prof. U. Western Ont., London, Can., 1962-63, assoc. prof., 1963-67, prof., 1967-92; prof. emeritus U. Western Ont., London, 1992—. Author: Imagery and Verbal Processes, 1971, Mental Representations: A Dual Coding Approach, 1986, Images in Mind: The Evolution of a Theory, 1991. Served with Royal Can. Navy, 1944-45. Recipient Queen's Silver Jubilee medal Can., 1977. Fellow Am. Psychol. Assn., Can. Psychol. Assn. (Disting. Contbns. to Psychology award 1982), Royal Soc. Can.; mem. Psychonomic Soc. Home: 919 Waterloo St, London, ON Canada N6A 3X2 Office: Univ of Western Ont, Dept Psychology, London, ON Canada

PAJOR, ROBERT E., paint and plastics company executive; b. 1936. BS, Roosevelt U., 1958; MBA, U. Calif., Berkeley, 1964. With The Richardson Co., Melrose Park, Ill., 1959, De Soto Chems., 1959-69; v.p. Valspar Corp., Mpls., 1959-69, v.p., 1974-81, pres., COO, 1981-94, vice chmn., 1994—; also bd. dirs. With U.S. Army, 1959. Office: Valspar Corp 1101 S 3rd St Minneapolis MN 55415-1211*

PAK, HYUNG WOONG, foundation executive, educator; b. Ham-Hoong, Korea, Nov. 6, 1932; came to U.S., 1955, naturalized, 1968; s. Kyung-Koo and Myung-Sook (Lee) P.; m. Diana Lee Stenen Woodruff, 1975; children: Jonathan Tong-Hee, Michelle Hyun-Hi Lee. A.B., U. Chgo., 1958. Editor and publisher Chgo. Rev., 1958-63, cons., 1963-65; assoc. editor Ency. Britannica Press, Chgo., 1963-64; sr. editor social scis. and humanities Ency. Britannica Press, Hmea-book, 1964-66; ednl. dir. Bantam Books, Inc., N.Y.C., 1966-69; gen. mgr. sch. dept. Appleton-Century-Crofts/New Century, N.Y.C., 1970-72; v.p., editorial dir. D. Van Nostrand Co., N.Y.C., 1972-74; pres. D. Van Nostrand Co., 1974-76, Chatham Sq. Press, N.Y.C., 1976-83; pub. Urizen Books, Inc., N.Y.C., 1978-81; exec. v.p. Bus. Software Mag., Palo Alto, Calif., 1983-84; pub., editor Asian High-Tech. Report, 1984-90; pres. Korean Publs. Co., Phila., 1988-92; exec. dir. The Philip Jaisohn Meml. Found., Inc., Phila., 1990—; fellow Hoover Instn., Stanford, Calif., 1984-85. Author: The Pacific Rim, 1990; columnist The Phila. Bus. Rev., 1993—. Mem. Bd. Sch. Dirs. Cheltenham Twp., Pa., 1987-94, Asian Task Force, Phila. Sch. Dist., 1988—; co-chmn. Bus. Adv. Com. Montgomery County, Pa., 1991-93; del. Citizens' Assembly for a Greater Phila., 1991-95; chmn. Pan Asian Assn. Greater Phila., 1992—, mem. bd. fellowship commn., 1992—; mem. bd. Asian Am. Congress, 1993-95. With Republic of Korea Army, 1950-54. Mem. ACLU (life), Phila. Mus. Art. Home: 1015 Sharpless Rd Philadelphia PA 19027-3040 also: Philip Jaisohn Meml Found 6705 Old York Rd Philadelphia PA 19126-2841

PAKE, GEORGE EDWARD, research executive, physicist; b. Jeffersonville, Ohio, Apr. 1, 1924; s. Edward Howe and Mary Mabel (Fry) P.; m. Marjorie Elizabeth Semon, May 31, 1947; children—Warren E., Catherine E., Stephen G., Bruce E. BS., M.S., Carnegie Inst. Tech., 1945; Ph.D., Harvard U., 1948. Physicist Westinghouse Research Labs., 1945-46; mem. faculty Washington U., 1948-56, 62-70; prof. physics, provost Washington U., 1962-69, exec. vice chancellor, 1965-69, Edward Mallinckrodt prof. physics, 1969-70; v.p. Xerox Corp.; mgr. Xerox Palo Alto (Calif.) Research Center, 1970-78, v.p. corp. research, 1978-83, group v.p., 1983-86; dir. Inst. for Research on Learning, Palo Alto, Calif., 1987-91, dir. emeritus, 1991—; prof. physics Stanford U., 1956-62. Author: (with E. Feenberg) Quantum Theory of Angular Momentum, 1953, Paramagnetic Resonance, 1962, (with T. Estle) The Physical Principles of Electron Paramagnetic Resonance, 1973. Mem. gov. bd. Am. Inst. Physics, 1957-59; bd. dirs. St. Louis Research Council, 1964-70; mem. physics adv. panel NSF, 1958-60, 63- 66; chmn. physics survey com. Nat. Acad. Sci.-NRC, 1964-66; Mem. St. Louis County Bus. and Indl. Devel. Commn., 1963-66; chmn. bd. Regional Indsl. Devel. Corp., St. Louis, 1966-67, St. Louis Research Council, 1967-70; mem. President's Sci. Adv. Com., 1965-69; Bd. dirs. St. Louis Country Day Sch., 1964-70,

Central Inst. for Deaf, 1965-70; trustee Washington U., 1970—, Danforth Found., 1971—, U. Rochester, 1982—; trustee Ctr. for Advanced Study in Behavioral Scis., Palo Alto, 1986-92, The Exploratorium, San Francisco, 1987—; bd. overseers Superconducting Super Collider, Univ. Rsch. Assn., 1984-89. Fellow Am. Phys. Soc. (pres. 1977); mem. Am. Assn. Physics Tchrs., AAUP, AAAS, Am. Acad. Arts and Sci., Nat. Acad. Sci., Sigma Xi, Tau Beta Pi. Home: 2 Yerba Buena Ave Los Altos CA 94022-2208 Office: Inst for Rsch on Learning 2550 Hanover St Palo Alto CA 94304-1115

PAKISER, LOUIS CHARLES, JR., geophysicist; b. Denver, Feb. 8, 1919; s. Louis C. and Lila E. (Hanson) P.; m. Helen L. Meineke, Oct. 9, 1939. Geol. Engr., Colo. Sch. Mines, 1937-42; postgrad., U. Nancy, France, 1945, Stanford, U. Colo. 1958-60. Geophysicist Carter Oil Co., 1942-49; first nat. exec. dir. Am. Vets. Com., 1949-52; also mng. editor AVC Bull.; mem. nat. planning com.; geophysicist U.S. Geol. Survey, 1952-92; rep. geophysics br. U.S. Geol. Survey, Denver, 1958-60; chief maj. crustal studies U.S. Geol. Survey, 1960-61, chief br. crustal studies, 1961-65; acting chief Nat. Center Earthquake Research, 1965-67, chmn. exec. com. of center, 1967-68; chief Office Earthquake Research and Crustal Studies, 1967-70, research geophysicist, 1970-79, annuitant research geophysicist, 1979-92, chief br. seismicity and earth structure and nat. earthquake info. service, 1975-77; ad hoc panel on earthquake prediction OST, 1964-68; disting. lectr. Soc. Exploration Geophysicists, 1964; spl. lectr. U. New Orleans, 1982-83; chmn. interagy. staff group on minority participation in sci. and engring. U.S. Dept. Interior, 1972-74; adv. com. Am. Indian Ednl. Opportunity Program U. Colo., 1981-84; vis. com. geophysics dept. Colo. Sch. Mines, 1986-94. Chmn. land use adv. com. Douglas County, Colo., 1975-76, chmn. mineral extraction planning task force, 1989-90; mem. sci. standards com. Douglas County Sch. Dist.; bd. dirs. Nat. Consortium for Black Profl. Devel., 1976-79; mem. adv. coun. Am. Vets. Com., 1960-61; mem. steering com. Nat. Civil Liberties Clearing House, 1950-52. Recipient Distinguished Service award U.S. Dept. Interior, 1970. Mem. NAACP (exec. com. Tulsa br. 1949, co-chmn. membership com. 1949), Am. Indian Sci. and Engring. Soc., Am. Geophys. Union, Soc. Advancement Chicanos and Native Ams. in Sci., Am. Geol. Inst. (chmn. adv. com. to minority participation program 1973-75), Geol. Soc. Am. (chmn. com. on minority participation in geol. scis. 1975-80), AAAS. Mem. United Ch. Christ (state social action bd. 1964-66). Home: 111 Emerson St Apt 1142 Denver CO 80218

PAKULA, ALAN J., producer, director; b. N.Y.C., Apr. 7, 1928; m. Hannah Cohn Boorstin, 1973. BA, Yale U., 1948. Producer's apprentice Metro Goldwyn-Mayer, Los Angeles, 1950; producer's asst. Paramount Pictures, Los Angeles, 1951; producer various studios, 1955—; founder, co-owner Pakula-Mulligan Prodns., Inc., Los Angeles; owner Pakula Prodns., Inc., N.Y.C. Producer: (play) There Must Be a Pony, (films) Fear Strikes Out, 1957, To Kill a Mockingbird, 1963, Love With the Proper Stranger, 1963, Baby, the Rain Must Fall, 1965, Inside Daisy Clover, 1965, Up the Down Staircase, 1967, The Stalking Moon, 1968; dir., producer: (films) The Sterile Cuckoo, 1969, Klute, 1971 (London Film Critics Best Dir. award), Love and Pain and the Whole Damned Thing, 1972, The Parallax View, 1974, (with James L. Brooks) Starting Over, 1979, (with Jon Boorstin) Dream Lover, 1986 (grand prize Avoriaz Film Festival), (with Susan Solt), Orphans, 1987; dir.: (films) All The President's Men, 1976 (Best Dir. award N.Y. Film Critics, Best Dir. award Nat. Bd. Rev.), Comes A Horseman, 1978, Rollover, 1981; dir., screenwriter, producer: (film) (with Keith Barish) Sophie's Choice, 1982, See You in the Morning, 1989, Presumed Innocent, 1990, The Pelican Brief, 1993. Office: Pakula Prodns Inc 330 W 58th St # 508 New York NY 10019-1819

PAL, PRABIR KUMAR, aluminium company executive; b. Chittagong, Bengal, India, Feb. 17, 1936; arrived in Can., 1969; s. Niranjan and Renuka (Mitter) P.; m. Nandinee Majumdar, Dec. 13, 1960; 1 child, Nobina. BA with honors in law, Cambridge U., 1958, MA, 1972; Diploma in Indsl. Mgmt., Geneva U., Geneva, 1964. Legal asst. Indian Aluminium Co. Ltd. (subs. Alcan), Calcutta, India, 1959-69, sec., 1972-76; fin. analyst Alcan Aluminium Ltd., Montreal, Que., Can., 1969-72; sr. legal and fin. officer, 1976-82, v.p., chief legal officer, 1987-88, v.p., chief legal officer, sec., 1988—; chief legal officer, treas. Alcan Europe, Geneva, 1982-84; chief legal and fin. officer Alcan Pacific, Vancouver, B.C., Can., 1984-86. Fellow Inst. Chartered Secs. and Adminstrs.; mem. Internat. Bar Assn., Univ. Club Montreal. Avocations: photography, rowing. Office: Alcan Aluminium Ltd, 1188 Sherbrooke St W, Montreal, PQ Canada H3A 3G2

PAL, PRATAPADITYA, museum curator; b. Bangladesh, Sept. 1, 1935; came to U.S., 1967; s. Gopesh Chandra and Bidyut Kana (Dam) P.; m. Chitralekha Bose, Apr. 20, 1968; children—Shalmali, Lopamudra. M.A., U. Calcutta, 1958, D.Phil., 1962; Ph.D. (U. K. Commonwealth Scholar), U. Cambridge, Eng., 1965. Research assoc. Am. Acad. of Benares, India, 1966-67; keeper Indian collections Mus. Fine Arts, Boston, 1967-69; sr. curator Indian and Southeast Asian art Los Angeles County Mus. Art, Los Angeles, 1970—, acting dir., 1979; adj. prof. fine arts U. So. Calif., 1971-89; vis. prof. U. Calif., Santa Barbara, 1980; William Cohn lectr. Oxford U., 1983; Catherine Mead Meml. lectr. U. Wis., 1985; Franklin Jasper Walls lectr. Pierpont Morgan Libr., N.Y., 1986; Ananda K. Coomaraswamy Meml. lectr. Prince of Wales Mus., Bombay, 1987; D.J. Sibley Pre-Historic Art lectr. U. Tex-Austin, 1989; mem. IRS Commr.'s Art Adv. Panel, Washington. Author: The Arts of Nepal, vol. 1, 1974, vol. 2, 1979, The Sensuous Immortals, 1977, The Ideal Image: Gupta Sculptures and its Influence, 1978, The Classical Tradition in Rajput Painting, 1978, Elephants and Ivories, 1981, A Buddhist Paradise: Murals of Alchi, 1982, Art of Tibet, 1983, Tibetan Painting, 1984, Art of Nepal, 1985, From Merchants to Emperors, 1986, Indian Sculpture, vol. 1, 1986, Icons of Piety, Images of Whimsey, 1987, Indian Sculpture, vol. 2, 1988, Buddhist Book Illuminations, 1988, Romance of The Taj Mahal, 1989, Art of the Himalayas, 1991, Pleasure Gardens of the Mind, 1993; Indian Painting, vol.1, 1993, The Peaceful Liberators: Jain Art from India, 1994. Bd. dirs. Music Circle, Pasadena, Calif. John D. Rockefeller III Fund fellow, 1964, 69; NEA fellow, 1974. Fellow Asia Soc. (hon., Bombay); mem. Asiatic Soc. (Calcutta). Office: Los Angeles County Mus Art 5905 Wilshire Blvd Los Angeles CA 90036-4523

PALACIO, JUNE ROSE PAYNE, professor of nutritional science; b. Hove, Sussex, Eng., June 14, 1940; came to U.S., 1949; d. Alfred and Doris Winifred (Blanch) P.; m. Moki Moses Palacio, Nov. 30, 1968. A.A, Orange Coast Coll., Costa Mesa, Calif., 1960; BS, U. Calif., Berkeley, 1963; PhD, Kans. State U., 1984. Registered dietitian. Asst. dir. food svc. and res. halls Mills Coll., Oakland, Calif., 1964-66; staff dietitian Servomation Bay Cities, Oakland, 1966-67; commissary mgr. Host Internat., Inc., Honolulu, 1967-73; dir. dietetics Straub Clinic and Hosp., Honolulu, 1973-80; instr. Kans. State U., Manhattan, 1980-84; prof. and program dir. Calif. State U., L.A., 1984-85; prof., program dir. Pepperdine U., Malibu, Calif., 1985—; instr. Kapiolani Community Coll., Honolulu, 1973-79, U. Hawaii, Honolulu, 1975-80, Ctr. for Dietetic Edn., Woodland Hills, Calif., 1986—; cons. Clevenger Nutritional Svcs., Calabasas, Calif., 1985—, Calif. Mus. Sci. and Industry, L.A., 1989—, Calif. State Dept. Edn., Sacramento, Calif., 1985—. Author: Foodservice in Institutions, 1989, Introduction to Foodservice, 1992. Mem. Am. Dietetic Assn. (del. 1977-80, 86-89, reviewer 1986—), Calif. Dietetic Assn. (pres. 1992-93), L.A. Dist. Dietetic Assn., Foodsvc. Systems Mgmt. Edn. Coun., Dietetic Educators of Practitioners, Gamma Sigma Delta, Omicron Nu, Phi Upsilon Omicron. Republican. Episcopalian. Avocations: tennis, running, reading, traveling. Home: 24319 Baxter Dr Malibu CA 90265-4728 Office: Pepperdine U 24255 Pacific Coast Hwy Malibu CA 90263-0001

PALACIOS, RONALD, immunologist; b. Sucre, Bolivia, Jan. 11, 1953; came to U.S., 1992; s. Enrique and Leddy (Castrillo) P.; m. Patricia Ibarra, June 4, 1977; children: Catherine, Patricia. B Humanities, Colegio Sagrado Corazon, Sucre, 1970; MD with distinction, U. Nat. Autonoma de Mex., Mexico City, 1976, degree in internal medicine splty., 1979. Cert. Mexican Bd. Internal Medicine. Instr. histology U. Nat. Mexico, Mexico City, 1973, asst. prof. introduction to medicine; fellow immunology Inst. Nat. Nutrition, Mexico City, 1979-80; mem. Basel (Switzerland) Inst. Immunology, 1982-92; prof., dep. chmn. dept. immunology U. Tex. M.D. Anderson Cancer Ctr., Houston, 1992—. Contbr. articles to profl. jours., chpts. to books. Fellow Swedish Inst., Stockholm, 1980-82, WHO, 1980-81. Fellow Mexican Bd. Internal Medicine; mem. AAAS, Am. Assn. Hematology, Assn. Medicos Internistas Mexico, Assn. Medicos Instituto Nat. Nutrition, Am. Assn.

Immunology, Am. Assn. Microbiology, Scandinavian Soc. Immunology, U. Tex. M.D. Anderson Assocs., N.Y. Acad. Scis. Office: MD Anderson Cancer Ctr U Tex Dept Immunology 1515 Holcombe Blvd Houston TX 77030-4009

PALADE, GEORGE EMIL, biologist, educator; b. Jassy, Romania, Nov. 19, 1912; came to U.S., 1946, naturalized, 1952; s. Emil and Constanta (Cantemir) P.; m. Irina Malaxa, June 12, 1941 (dec. 1969); children—Georgia Teodora, Philip Theodore; m. Marilyn G. Farquhar, 1970. Bachelor, Hasdeu Lyceum, Buzau, Romania, M.D., U. Bucharest, Romania. Instr., asst. prof., then assoc. prof. anatomy Sch. Medicine, U. Bucharest, 1935-45; vis. investigator, asst. assoc., prof. cell biology Rockefeller U., 1946-73; prof. cell biology Yale U., New Haven, 1973-83; sr. research scientist Yale U., 1983-89; prof.-in-residence, dean sci. affairs Med. Sch., U. Calif., San Diego, 1990—. Author sci. papers. Recipient Albert Lasker Basic Research award, 1966, Gairdner Spl. award, 1967, Horwitz prize, 1970, Nobel prize in Physiology or Medicine, 1974, Nat. Medal Sci., 1986. Fellow Am. Acad. Arts and Scis.; mem. Nat. Acad. Sci., Pontifical Acad. Sci., Royal Soc. (London), Leopoldina Acad. (Halle), Romanian Acad., Royal Belgian Acad. Medicine. Research interests correlated biochem. and morphological analysis cell structures.

PALADINO, ALBERT EDWARD, venture capitalist; b. N.Y.C., Aug. 4, 1932; s. Albert E. and Jennie (Fiato) P.; m. Dorothy M. Hayes (div. June 1979); children: Thomas A., Robert E. Catherine J., Paul F.; m. Susan Flynn, June 11, 1983. BS in Ceramic Engring., Alfred U., 1954, MS in Ceramic Engring., 1956; ScD in Materials Sci., MIT, 1962. Registered profl. engr., Mass. Staff mem. Raytheon Co. Rsch. Div., Waltham, Mass., 1955-59; mgr. materials and crystal growth lab. Raytheon Co. Rsch. Div., Waltham, 1962-69; mgr. materials and techniques group Raytheon Co. Microwave & Power Tube Div., Waltham, 1969-72; mgr. electronics materials group, 1972-75; program mgr. materials Office of Tech. Assessment U.S. Congress, Washington, 1975-78; asst. dir. telephone ops. tech. ctr. GTE Labs., Waltham, 1978-79; dep. dir. Office Energy Programs U.S. Dept. Commerce, Nat. Inst. Standards and Tech., Washington, 1979-81; mng. ptnr. Advanced Tech. Ventures, Boston, 1981—; chmn. bd. dirs. Millitech Corp., South Deerfield, Mass., 1988—, Electro-Scan Corp., Billerica, Mass., 1990-95; bd. dirs. TranSwitch Corp., Shelton, Conn., 1988—, Microwave Networks, Houston, 1990-95, Integrated System Assemblies, Woburn, Mass., 1991-95F Micro Devices, Greensboro, N.C., 1992—, Thunderbird Techs., Morrisville, N.C., 1992—. Contbr. articles profl. jours.; patentee in field. Pres. West Needham (Mass.) Civic Assn., 1967-69; bd. trustees Alfred U., 1991—; mem. Needham Town Meeting, 1973-74, Rep. Nat. Com., 1988—. Recipient Disting. Svc. resolution Office of Tech. Assessment U.S. Congress, 1978. Fellow Am. Ceramic Soc. (chmn. basic sci. div. 1968-69, chmn. New Eng. sect. 1969-70, Disting. New Eng. Ceramic award), Nat. Venture Capital Assn. Avocations: painting, music, physical fitness, hiking, tennis, reading. Office: Advanced Tech Ventures 10 Post Office Sq Boston MA 02109-4603

PALADINO, DANIEL R., lawyer, beverage corporation executive; B.S., Fordham U., 1965; J.D., NYU, 1968. Associate Simpson Thacher & Bartlett, 1969-76; ptnr. Davis & Cox, 1976-79; v.p., sec., gen. counsel Joseph E. Seagram & Sons Inc., N.Y.C., 1979-86, v.p., gen. counsel, sec., dir., 1986—. Office: Joseph Seagram & Sons Inc 375 Park Ave New York NY 10152

PALADINO, JOSEPH ANTHONY, clinical pharmacist; b. Utica, N.Y., May 5, 1953; s. Paul Francis and Jacqueline Ann (Monaco) P.; m. Carol Ann Jenny, June 5, 1976; children: Nicholas Joseph, Matthew Jerome, Kathryn Elizabeth. BS in Biology, Siena Coll., Loudonville, N.Y., 1975; BS in Pharmacy, Mass. Coll. Pharmacy, 1977; D Pharmacy, Med. U. S.C., 1982. Acting dir. pharmacy Utica (N.Y.) Psychiat. Ctr., 1978-80; decentralized pharmacist Med. U. Hosp., Charleston, S.C., 1980-82; asst. dir. pharmacy Rochester (N.Y.) Gen. Hosp., 1982-87, adj. med. staff, 1986-87; clin. instr. pediatrics U. Rochester Sch. Medicine, 1985-87; clin. asst. prof. pharmacy SUNY, Buffalo, 1989-93, clin. assoc. prof., 1994—; dir. pharmacokinetics Millard Fillmore Suburban Hosp., Williamsville, N.Y., 1987—; dir. clin. outcomes and econs. rsch. Millard Fillmore Health System, Buffalo; editorial adv. bd. Jour. of Infectious Disease Pharmacotherapy, 1993—; mem. adv. bd. several major pharm. cos.; 1st vis. prof. pharmacy Tayside Health Bd., Dundee, Scotland, 1992. Big Bro., Big Bros. and Big Sisters, Albany, N.Y., 1972-80; bd. mem., den leader Cub Scouts, Clarence, N.Y., 1989-91; founding bd., coach Clarence Little League Football, 1992-94. Mem. Am. Coll. Clin. Pharmacy (founder, 1st chmn. Outcomes and Econs. Practice and Rsch. Network), Am. Soc. Microbiology, Soc. Infectious Diseases Pharmacists, N.Y. Acad. Scis. Achievements include pioneering a method of treating certain infectious diseases with an early switch from intravenous to oral antibiotics; co-development of a standardized format for dosing charts for critical intravenous medications; discovery of drug interaction between secobarbital and theophylline; integration of switch therapy with pharmacology, outcomes therapy, and health care economics. Office: Millard Fillmore Suburban Hosp 1540 Maple Rd Williamsville NY 14221-3698

PALAIMA, THOMAS GERARD, classics educator, researcher; b. Cleve., Oct. 6, 1951; s. Michael Aloysius and Ann Dolores (Schulz) P. BA in Math. and Classics, Boston Coll., 1973; PhD in Classics, U. Wis., 1980; HHD (hon.), U. Uppsala, 1994. Asst. prof. Classics Fordham U., Bronx, N.Y., 1980-86; assoc. prof. U. Tex., Austin, 1986-91, Dickson Centennial prof. # 2, 1991—, chair dept., 1994—; dir. summer session Am. Sch. Classical Studies, Athens, 1984; dir. Aegean scripts and prehistory program U. Tex., Austin, 1986—; mem. mng. com. Am. Sch. Classical Studies, 1980—; mem. Mycenaean com. Austrian Acad. Scis., 1993—. Author: The Scribes of Pylos, 1988; editor: Pylos Comes Alive, 1984, Texts, Tablets and Scribes, 1988, Problems in Decipherment, 1989, Studia Mycenaea 1988, 1989, Aegean Seals, Sealings and Administration, 1990; book rev. editor Minos, 1989—. Fulbright fellow, Greece, 1979-80, Austria, 1992-93, Am. Coun. Learned Socs. fellow, 1983, MacArthur Found. fellow, 1985-90; NEH grantee, 1984, 89. Mem. Archaeol. Inst. Am., Am. Philolog. Assn. Democrat. Home: 706 Harris Ave Austin TX 78705-2518 Office: U Tex Dept Classics Wag 123 Austin TX 78712-1181

PALANCE, JACK, actor; b. Lattimer, Pa., Feb. 18; s. John and Anna (Gramiak) Palahnuik; m. Virginia Baker, Apr. 21, 1949 (div. 1969); children: Holly Kathleen, Brook Gabrielle, Cody John; m. Elaine Rochelle Rogers, May 6, 1987. Student, U. N.C., Stanford U. Appeared in stage plays The Big Two, 1947, Temporary Island, 1948, The Vigil, A Street Car Named Desire, 1948, The Silver Tassie, 1949, Darkness at Noon, 1950, Julius Caesar, The Tempest, 1955; motion pictures include Panic in the Streets, 1950, Halls of Montezuma, Sudden Fear (Acad. award nominee best supporting actor 1952), Shane (Acad. award nominee best supporting actor 1953), Arrowhead, Flight to Tangier, The Silver Chalice, Kiss of Fire, Attack!, Ten Seconds to Hell, The Big Knife, Man in the Attic, Warriors Five, Barabbas, I Died A 1000 Times, The Lonely Man, House of Numbers, Contempt, Torture Garden, Kill a Dragon, They Came to Rob Las Vegas, The Desperadoes, The Mercenary, Justine, Legion of the Damned, A Bullet for Rommel, The McMasters, The Professionals, Chato's Land, Companeros, Che, Oklahoma Crude, Craze, The Four Deuces, The Diamond, Hawk the Slayer, Gor, Bagdad Cafe, Young Guns, The Getaway, The Horsemen, The Shape of Things to Come, Hawk the Slayer, Without Warning, Tango & Cash, Solar Crisis, 1990, City Slickers, 1991 (Acad. award for Best Supporting Actor 1991), Cops and Robbersons, 1994, City Slickers II: The Legend of Curley's Gold, 1994, Natural Born Killers, 1994, (voice) The Swan Princess, 1994, others; appeared on TV: Requiem for a Heavyweight (Sylvania award), Dr. Jekyll and Mr. Hyde, Dracula, (series) Bronk, 1975-76, (series host) Ripley's Believe It Or Not, (miniseries) Buffalo Girls, 1995. With AC, U.S. Army. Named Most Prominent Newcomer Theatre World, Best Screen Newcomer Look mag. Office: PO Box 223 Drums PA 18222-0223*

PALANS, LLOYD ALEX, lawyer; b. St. Louis, Aug. 6, 1946; s. Hyman Robert and Mae (Sherman) P.; m. Deborah Regn, Aug. 5, 1972; children: Emily Rebecca, Samantha Jane. BS, Tulane U., 1968; JD, U. Mo., 1972. Bar: Mo. 1972, U.S. Dist. Ct. (ea. and we. dists.) Mo. 1972, U.S. Ct. Appeals (8th cir.) 1972, U.S. Ct. Appeals (5th cir.) 1974, U.S. Supreme Ct. 1975, U.S. Ct. Appeals (9th cir.) 1992. Ptnr. Kramer, Chused, Kramer, Shostak & Kohn, St. Louis, 1972-77, Blumenfeld, Marx & Tureen, P.C., St. Louis, 1978-8l, Gallop, Johnson & Neuman, St. Louis 1981-90, Bryan Cave, St. Louis,

1990—; adj. prof. Washington U. Sch. Law, St. Louis, 1989—. Bd. dirs. St. Louis Chpt. ARC, 1987—, St. Louis Chpt. Leukemia Soc., 1988—, Combined Health Appeal Greater St. Louis, 1988—, Combined Health Appeal of Am., 1990. Mem. ABA, Mo. Bar, St. Louis Met. Bar Assn. Office: Bryan Cave 1 Metro Sq 211 N Broadway Saint Louis MO 63102

PALAST, GERI D., federal agency administrator. BA in Polit. Sci., Stanford U., 1972; JD, NYU, 1976. Atty., legis. program analyst Am. Fedn. State County and Mcpl. Employees, Washington, 1976-77; legal counsel, field rep. Nat. Treasury Employers Union, Washington, 1977-79; dir., supervising atty. Nat. Employment Law Project, Washington, 1979-81; dir. politics and legislation Svc. Employees Internat. Union, AFL-CIO, Washington, 1981-93; asst. sec. congrl. and intergovtl. affairs Dept. Labor, Washington, 1993—. Office: Dept Labor Congl & Intergovtl Affairs 200 Constitution Ave NW Washington DC 20210-0001

PALAY, GILBERT, temporary help services company executive; b. 1927. BBA, U. Wis. CPA. Ptnr. Zetley and Palay, 1960-76; with Manpower Inc., 1976—, v.p., 1976-77, v.p. planning and devel., from 1977, since exec. v.p., now sr. exec. v.p. Office: Manpower Inc Box 2053 5301 N Ironwood Ln Milwaukee WI 53217-4910

PALAY, SANFORD LOUIS, retired scientist, educator; b. Cleve., Sept. 23, 1918; s. Harry and Lena (Sugarman) P.; m. Victoria Chan Curtis, 1970 (div. Nov. 1990); children: Victoria Li-Mei, Rebecca Li-Ming. A.B., Oberlin Coll., 1940; M.D. (Hoover prize scholar 1943), Western Res. U., 1943. Teaching fellow medicine, rsch. assoc. anatomy Western Res. U., Cleve., 1945-46; NRC fellow med. scis. Rockefeller Inst., 1948, vis. investigator, 1953; from instr. anatomy to assoc. prof. anatomy Yale U., 1949-56; chief sect. neurocytology, lab. neuroanatomical scis. Nat. Inst. Neurol. Diseases and Blindness, NIH, Washington, 1956-61; chief lab. neuroanatomical scis. Nat. Inst. Neurol. Diseases and Blindness, NIH, 1960-61; Bullard prof. neuroanatomy Harvard, Boston, 1961-89, prof. emeritus, 1989—; Linnean Soc. lectr., London, 1959; vis. investigator Middlesex Hosp. (Bland-Sutton Inst.), London, Eng. 1961; Phillips lectr. Haverford Coll., 1959; Ramsay Henderson Trust lectr. U. Edinburgh, Scotland, 1962; George H. Bishop lectr.. Washington U., St. Louis, 1990; Disting. Scientist lectr. Tulane U. Sch. Medicine, 1969, 75; vis. prof. U. Wash., 1969; Rogowski Meml. lectr. Yale, 1973; Disting. lectr. biol. structure U. Miami, 1974; Disting. Scientist lectr. U. Ark., 1977; Disting. scholar-in-residence dept. biology Boston Coll., Chestnut Hill, Mass., 1994—; other Disting. lectureships; vis. prof. U. Osaka, Japan, 1978, Nat. U. Singapore, 1983; spl. vis. prof. U. Osaka, 1988; chmn. study sect. on behavioral and neural scis. NIH, 1984-86; mem. fellowship bd. NIH, 1958-61, cell biology study sect., 1959-65, adv. com. high voltage electron microscope resources, 1973-80, mem. rev. com. behavioral and neurol. scis. fellowships, 1979-86; chmn. Gordon Research Conf. Cell Structure and Metabolism, 1960; assoc. Neuroscis. Research Program, 1962-67, cons. assoc., 1975—; mem. anat. scis. rng. com. Nat. Inst. Gen. Med. Scis., 1968-72; mem. sci. adv. com. Oreg. Regional Primate Research Center, 1971-76. Author: The Fine Structure of the Nervous System, 1970, 3d edit., 1991, Cerebellar Cortex, Cytology and Organization, 1974; editor: Frontiers of Cytology, 1958, The Cerebellum, New Vistas, 1982; mem. sci. coun. Progress in Neuropharmacology and Jour. Neuropharmacology, 1961-66; mem. editorial bd. Exptl. Neurology, 1959-76, Jour. Cell Biology, 1962-67, Brain Research, 1965-71, Jour. Comparative Neurology, 1966—, Jour. Ultrastructure Research, 1966-86, Jour. of Neurocytology, 1972-87, Exptl. Brain Research, 1965-76, Neurosci, 1975—, Anatomy and Embryology, 1968; co-mng. editor, 1978-88; editor in chief Jour. Comparative Neurology, 1981-93, editor emeritus, 1994—; mem. adv. bd. editors Jour. Neuropathology and Exptl. Neurology, 1963-82, Internat. Jour. Neurosci, 1969-74, Tissue and Cell, 1969-86; contbr. articles to profl. jours. Served to capt. M.C. AUS, 1946-47. Recipient 50 Best Books of 1974 award Internat. Book Fair, Frankfurt, Fed. Republic Germany, Best Book in Profl. Readership award Am. Med. Writers Assn., 1975, Biomed. Rsch. award Assn. Am. Med. Colls., 1989, Lashley award Am. Philos. Soc., 1991, Camillo Golgi award Fidia Rsch. Found., 1992; Guggenheim fellow, 1971-72; Fogarty scholar-in-residence NIH, Bethesda, 1980-81. Fellow Am. Acad. Arts and Scis.; mem. NAS, Am. Assn. Anatomists (chmn. nominating com. 1964, mem. exec. com. 1970-74, anat. nomenclature com. 1975-78, pres. 1980-81, Henry Gray award 1990), Histochem. Soc., Electron Microscope Soc. Am., AAAS, Am. Soc. Cell Biology (program com. 1975), Internat. Soc. Cell Biology, Soc. for Neurosci. (Gerard award 1990), Washington Soc. Electron Microscopy (organizing com., sec.-treas. 1956-58), Soc. Francaise de Microscopie Electronique (hon.), Royal Microscopical Soc. (hon.), Golgi Soc. (hon.), Anat. Soc. Gr. Britain and Ireland (hon.), Cajal Club (pres. 1973-74), Phi Beta Kappa, Sigma Xi, Alpha Omega Alpha. Home: 78 Temple Rd Concord MA 01742-1520

PALAZZI, JOSEPH L(AZARRO), manufacturing executive; b. New Haven, July 5, 1947; s. Joseph Anthony and Helen (Volosovich) P.; m. Lorna May Mickiewicz, May 27, 1978. BS, Quinnipiac Coll., 1969; MBA, U. New Haven, 1973. Mgr. budgets The Stanley Works, New Britian, Conn., 1972-76; mgr. planning Bangor Punta Corp., Greenwich, Conn., 1976-79; asst. corp. controller Pepperidge Farm, Norwalk, Conn., 1979-81, dir. fin. services, 1981-82, group controller, 1982-83; corp. controller Plessey, Inc., White Plains, N.Y., 1983-84; v.p. finance, 1984-86, chief fin. officer, 1986-89; v.p. fin., chief fin. officer BTR Inc., Stanford, Ct., 1990-92; pres. Fasco Industries Inc., Chesterfield, Mo., 1992—. Mem. Rep. Town Com., Newtown, Conn., 1981; bd. dirs. Danbury Hosp., 1987-92. Served with U.S. Army, 1969-76. Mem. AICPA, Nat. Assn. Accts., Sigma Six Flying Club. Episcopalian. Avocations: sailing, tennis, golf, flying. Home: 39 Villa Coublay Saint Louis MO 63131-2730 Office: Fasco Industries Inc 500 Chesterfield Ctr Ste 200 Chesterfield MO 63017-4827

PALDUS, JOSEF, mathematics educator; b. Bzi, Czechoslovakia, Nov. 25, 1935; emigrated to Can., 1968; s. Josef and Ludmila (Danicek) P.; m. Eva Zdena Bajer, Jan. 26, 1961; 1 dau., Barbara Alice. M.Sc., Charles U., Prague, 1958; Ph.D., Czechoslovak Acad. Sci., Prague, 1961. Research scientist Czechoslovak Acad. Scis., Prague, 1961-62, 64-68; postdoctoral fellow NRC, Ottawa, Can., 1962-64; assoc. prof. applied math. U. Waterloo, Ont., Can., 1968-75, prof., 1975—; assoc. dir. Fields Inst., 1992—; vis. prof. Cath. U., Nijmegen, Holland, 1981; vis. prof. U Rheims, 1973, U. Louis Pasteur, Strasbourg, France, 1975-76, 82-83, Technion, Haifa, Israel, 1983; vis. scientist Free U. Berlin, 1981, NRC, Ottawa, 1966-68; fellow Inst. for Advanced Study, Berlin, 1986-87. Mem. editl. bd. Comtex Sci., 1981-83, Jour. Chem. Physics, 1987-89; mem. adv. editl. bd. Internat. Jour. Quantum Chemistry, 1977-88, Advances in Quantum Chemistry, 1986, Theoretica Chimica Acta, 1988-94, Jour. Math. Chemistry, Switzerland, 1989, Can. Jour. Chemistry, 1994; contbr. numerous articles to profl. jours., chpts. to books. Killam Rsch. fellow, 1987-89; recipient prize Chemistry div. Czechoslovak Acad. Scis., 1962, 67, J. Heyrovsky Gold medal Czechoslovak Acad. Sci., 1992, Gold medal Faculty of Math and Physics, Comenius U., Slovakia, 1994. Fellow Royal Soc. Can.; mem. Internat. Acad. Quantum Molecular Sci., Internat. Soc. Theoretical Chemical Physics (bd. dirs.), European Acad. Scis., Arts and Letters (corr.), Am. Inst. Physics, N.Y. Acad. Sciences; applied Math. Soc. Can., Can. Soc. for Chemistry, Chem. Inst. Can. Roman Catholic. Office: U Waterloo Dept Applied Math, University Ave, Waterloo, ON Canada N2L 3G1

PALERMO, ANTHONY ROBERT, lawyer; b. Rochester, N.Y., Sept. 30, 1929; s. Anthony C. and Mary (Palvino) P.; m. Mary Ann Coyne, Jan. 2, 1960; children: Mark Henry, Christopher Coyne, Peter Stuart, Elisabeth Megan McCarthy, Julie Coyne Lawther, Gregg Anthony. BA, U. Mich., 1951; JD, Georgetown U., 1956. Bar: D.C. 1956, N.Y. 1957, U.S. Supreme Ct. 1961. Trial atty. U.S. Dept. Justice, Washington, 1956-58; asst. atty. U.S. Dept. Justice, N.Y.C., 1958-60; asst. U.S. atty. in charge U.S. Dept. Justice, Rochester, N.Y., 1960-61; ptnr. Brennan, Centner, Palermo & Blauvelt, Rochester, 1962-81, Harter, Secrest & Emery, Rochester, 1981-94, Hodgson, Russ, Andrews, Woods & Goodyear, Rochester, 1994—. Note editor Georgetown Law Jour., 1956. Bd. dirs. McQuaid Jesuit High Sch., Rochester, 1978-84, St. Ann's Home for Aged, Rochester, 1974—; bd. dirs. sec. St. Ann's Home Found., Rochester, 1985—; trustee, charter chmn. Clients' Security Fund N.Y., 1981-90; chmn. Govs. Jud. Screening Com. 4th Jud. Dept., mem. statewide com., 1987-89. Fellow Am. Bar Found., N.Y. State Bar Found. (bd. dirs. 1978-91), Am. Coll. Trial Lawyers; mem. ABA (ho. dels. 1980—, state del. 1982-85, bd. govs. 1985-88, 1989-93, sec. 1990-

93), N.Y. State Bar Assn. (pres. 1979-80, ho. dels. 1973-75, 77—), Monroe County Bar Assn. (pres. 1973), Oak Hill Country Club. Roman Catholic. Avocation: golf. Home: 38 Huntington Rochester NY 14625

PALERMO, DAVID STUART, retired psychology educator and administrator. BS in Psychology and Edn., Lynchburg Coll., 1951; MS in Psychology, U. Mass., 1953; PhD, U. Iowa, 1955. Rsch. assoc. Iowa Child Welfare Rsch. Sta. U. Iowa, 1955; asst. prof. psychology So. Ill. U., Carbondale, 1955-58; asst. prof. Inst. Child Devel. U. Minn., Mpls., 1958-63; vis. prof. dept. psychology U. Edinburgh, Scotland, 1969-70; sr. Fulbright scholar dept. psychology U. Sydney, Australia, 1975; prof. Inst. Advanced Psychol. Studies Adelphi U., Garden City, L.I., N.Y., 1978-79; assoc. prof. Pa. State U., University Park, 1963-66, prof., 1966—, assoc. dir. Ctr. for the Study of Child, Adolescent Devel., 1984-88, assoc. dean for rsch. and grad. studies, Coll. Liberal Arts, 1988-92; assoc. The Behavioral and Brain Scis., 1982—. Editor Child Development Abstracts and Bibliography, 1971-74; editor Jour. Exptl. Child Psychology, 1973-83, mem. editorial bd., 1966—; mem. editorial bd. Jour. Verbal Learning and Verbal Behavior, 1964-77, Metaphor and Symbolic Activity, 1983—, Cognitive Devel., 1990—; contbr. numerous articles to profl. jours. Recipient Career Devel. award Nat. Inst. of Child Health and Human Devel. award, 1965-70. Fellow APA, AAAS; mem. Soc. for Rsch. in Child Devel., Psychonomic Soc., Ea. Psychol. Assn., Jean Piaget Soc., Am. Psychol. Soc.,1976-79, Internat. Soc. for the Study of Behavioral Devel., Sigma Xi.

PALERMO, GREGORY SEBASTIAN, architect; b. Westfield, N.Y., Oct. 28, 1946; s. Sebastian and Frances Joan (Ciminella) P.; divorced; children: Mark Sebastian, Christopher Anthony. BArch, Carnegie Mellon U., 1969; MArch in Urban Design, Wash. U., 1976. Registered architect, Mo., Calif., N.Y., Iowa. Architect PGAV Inc., St. Louis, 1976-79; sr. v.p. HOK, Inc. St. Louis, 1980-87; sr. assoc. Mackey Assocs., St. Louis 1987-89; v.p., prin. Stone Marraccini Patterson, St. Louis, 1989-91; affiliate asst. prof. Washington U. Sch. Architecture, 1984-90; vis. assoc. prof. Iowa State U. Dept. Architecture, 1992—. Editorial bd. Iowa Architect mag., 1992—, assoc. ed., 1995—. Mem. Light Rail Transit Rev. Com., 1985, St. Louis Mayoral Task Force, 1986; exec/coun. Arts in Transit Com., St. Louis, 1987—; chmn. design rev. com.,St. Louis Metrolink Transit System, 1989-91; chair Nat. AIA Edn. Task Force, 1990; mem. Leadership St. Louis, 1990-91, Archtl. Adv. Commn. city of Des Moines, 1992—. Fellow AIA (bd. dirs., nat. v.p.); mem. Nat. Archtl. Accreditation Bd (pres. 1993-94). Office: Iowa STate U Rm 156 Dept Architecture Ames IA 50011-3093

PALERMO, JOSEPH, language educator; b. Trenton, N.J., Sept. 9, 1917; s. Joseph Robert and Margaret (Zoda) P.; m. Eileen Viola Wilcox, Apr. 4, 1943; children: Margaret Ann, Eleanor (Mrs. Francis A. Roxby), Richard Alan. A.B. (William J. Bickett Meml. scholar), Temple U., 1940; A.M. (Herbert Montgomery Bergen fellow), Princeton U., 1948, PhD, 1950; postgrad., Poitiers, France, 1960. Asst. editor Merriam-Webster Dictionaries, 1940-43; instr. Mass. div. Univ. Extension, 1941-45, Temple U., Phila., 1945-51, U. Conn., Storrs, 1951-52; asst. prof. U. Conn., 1952-57, assoc. prof., 1957-61, prof., 1961-72; now emeritus, chmn. Grad. Admissions Com. for Mediaeval Studies, 1969-72; prof. Va. Poly. Inst. and State U., Blacksburg, 1974-86, prof. emeritus, 1986; head dept. fgn. langs. Va. Poly. Inst. and State U. 1974-75; Vis. lectr. Ecole Libre des Hautes Etudes, N.Y., 1961-64; vis. prof. U. Laval, Que., summers 1962, 63; vis. lectr. Nat. Def. Edn. Act Summer Inst. French, U. Mass., 1963; vis. prof. Ecole Française, Middlebury Coll., summers 1966-68; vis. prof. French, Yale, 1968; vis. prof. linguistics U. Palermo, Italy, 1973-74. Author: Le Roman de Cassidorus, 2 vols., 1963, 64, Le Roman d'Hector et Hercules, 1972, Le Nouveau Gargantua, 1982; mem. editorial bd. Mountain Interstate Fgn. Lang. Conf. Rev., 1991—; contbr. articles to profl. jours. Princeton Grad. scholar in modern langs., 1946; Am. Philos. Soc. grantee, 1954, 60, 65, 82; Belgian-Am. Ednl. Found. fellow, 1958; Am. Council Learned Socs. grantee, 1962, 63, 65, 67; U. Conn. Research Council grantee, 1968, 69, 70, 72; Va. Tech. Ednl. Found. grantee, 1982. Mem. MLA, Mediaeval Acad. Am., Am. Assn. Tchrs. French, Am. Assn. Tchrs. Italian, Mountain Interstate Fgn. Language Conf. (editorial bd. MIFLC Rev. 1991—), Société de Linguistique Romane, Société Internationale Arthurienne, Société des Professeurs Français en Amérique, Assn. Internationale de Littérature Comparée, Assn. Déf. de la Langue Française, Fédn. Internationale des Langues et Littératures Modernes, Alliance Française des Monts de Virginie (founder 1973, pres. 1973-74)/. Home: 4386 Summertree Rd Venice FL 34293

PALERMO, JUDY HANCOCK, elementary school educator; b. Longview, Tex., Sept. 7, 1938; d. Joseph Curtis and Bennie Lee (Deason) Hancock; m. Donald Charles Palermo, Apr. 1, 1961; 1 child, Donald Charles Jr. (dec.). BS in Secondary Edn., 1960. Cert. secondary and elem. edn. tchr., Tex. Art tchr. Dallas Ind. Sch. Dist., 1960-62, 65-67; asst. dir. freshmen orientation program North Tex. State U., Denton, summer 1969, dormitory dir. Oak St. Hall, 1968-71, tchr. part-time, 1970-77; substitute tchr. Denton Ind. Sch. Dist., 1975-78, tchr. 5th grade, 1979-87, art tchr., 1987—; tchr. kindergarten Kiddie Korral Pre-Sch., Denton, 1978-79; trained gifted tchr. Woodrow Wilson Elem. Sch., Denton, 1980, grade level chmn.; 1980; grade level chmn. Eva S. Hodge Elem. Sch., Denton, 1988-89, 92-93; mem. rsch. bd. advisors Am. Biog. Inst., 1991—. Active Denton Humane Soc., 1982—; Denton Educators Polit. Action Com., 1984-85; Eva S. Hodge historian PTA, 1992—. Mem. NEA, NAFE, Tex. State Tchrs. Assn., Denton Classroom Tchrs. Assn. (faculty rep. 1984-85), Denton Edn. Assn., Denton Area Art Edn. Assn. (program chmn. 1990-91), Greater Denton Arts Coun., Numismatic Assn. (sec. Greater Denton chpt.), Denton Sq. Athletic Club, Denton Greater Univ. Dames Club (treas. 1970), Bus. and Profl. Women's Assn. (treas. 1990-91, chair audit com. 1992-93, chmn. 1993—), Delta Kappa Gamma (treas. 1986-88, comms. com. 1994—). Democrat. Avocations: painting, ceramics, drawing, calligraphy, photography. Home: 1523 Pickwick Ln Denton TX 76201-1290

PALERMO, NICHOLAS J., banker; b. Jersey City, Feb. 9, 1937; s. Joseph Anthony and Agostina (Tosto) P.; m. Josephine Davino, Apr. 30, 1960; children: Jennifer Lee, Cristina Nicole. B.A. in Polit. Sci., Rutgers U., 1958; M.B.A. in Bus. Mgmt., Fairleigh Dickinson U., 1967. V.p. personnel ops. Citibank, N.Y.C., 1973-75; v.p. div. exec. ops. Europe Chase Manhattan Bank, N.Y.C., 1975-76; v.p. internat. ops, and systems, 1976-78, sr. v.p., group exec. customer services, 1978-81, sr. v.p., group exec. human resources and customer services, 1981-82, sr. v.p., group exec. internat. ops. and systems, 1982-84; sr. v.p. Chase AMP Bank, Sydney, Australia, 1984-85; sr. v.p., customer svc. exec. Chase Individual Banking, 1986-88; pres., chief exec. officer Amalgamated Bank of N.Y., 1989—, chief exec. Disting lectr.: oral thesis The Management Process, 1979—. Commr. recreation Borough of Oradell Mcpl. Govt., N.H., 1980—; founder, past pres. Oradell chpt. Unico Nat., 1981—; trustee, chmn. memberships com. Columbus Citizens House, Inc., 1983—. 1st lt. U.S. Army, 1958-61; maj. USAR, ret. 1979. Named Mgr. of Yr. Fla. A&M U., Tallahassee, 1982. Mem. Am. Bankers Assn., Com. on Internat. Banking, Rutgers U. Alumni Assn., Fairleigh Dickinson Univ. Grad. Sch. Alumni Assn., Delta Mu Delta. Republican. Roman Catholic. Home: 385 Chapin Ct Oradell NJ 07649-2034 Office: Amalgamated Bank NY 11-15 Union Sq New York NY 10003

PALERMO, PETER M., JR., photography equipment company executive; b. Rochester, N.Y., Aug. 21, 1941; s. Peter M. and Adeline M. (Bruno) P.; m. Marcia G. Hendershott, Aug. 25, 1962; children: Peter M., Lisa M., Michelle A. B.A., Bowling Green U., 1963; M.B.A., U. Rochester, 1973. Mgr. mktg. Kodak Caribbean, Ltd., San Juan, P.R., 1976-79; gen. mgr. Kodak Philippines Ltd., Manila, 1979-81; gen. mgr. Mexican Ops. Eastman Kodak Co. Internat. Photo div., Mexico City, 1983-84; corp. v.p., gen. mgr. Eastman Kodak Co. Health Scis. div., Rochester, N.Y., 1984-86; corp. v.p., gen. mgr. consumer products div. Eastman Kodak Co., Rochester, 1986—, corp. v.p., gen. mgr. consumer imaging, 1991-93, v.p. dir. mktg., sr. v.p. imaging, 1993—; pres. Ultra Technis div. Eastman Tech., Inc. (subs. Eastman Kodak Co.), 1989—; adj. faculty mem. Rochester Inst. of Tech., 1965-69. Contbr. articles to profl. jours. Bd. dirs. Spl. Olympics, 1990. Recipient Catholic Media award Pope John Paul II, Manila, 1981; named one of Outstanding Young Men of Am., 1973. Fellow Profl. Photog. Soc. of Philippines; mem. Health Industry Mfrs. Assn. (corp. mem., trustee 4-H com. 1990), Internat. Mgmt. Assn. (corp. mem.), Photo Mktg. Assn. Internat. (corp. mem.), Assn. Photog. Mfrs. Mex. Republican. Roman Catholic. Clubs: Manila Polo,

Dorado Beach Country P.R. Lodge: Rotary (dir. Manila, 1979-81). Avocations: scuba diving; writing; photography; tennis. Office: The Jason Found for Edn 40A Grove St Pittsford NY 14534

PALERMO, STEVE, sportscaster, color analyst, former umpire; b. Worcester, Mass., Oct. 9, 1949; m. Debbie, 1991. Attended, Norwich U., Worcester State Coll. Umpire N.Y. Penn League, 1972; umpire winter baseball P.R., Fla., and, Dominican Republic, 1972-74; umpire, single A baseball Carolina League, 1973; umpire, double A baseball Ea. League, 1973-74; umpire, triple A baseball Am. Assn., 1975-76; umpire Am. League Baseball, 1977-91; sports caster Seattle Mariners, 1992-94; sports caster MSG Network, 1994—, back-up color analyst, 1994—; sports analyst The Baseball Network, 1994—; umpire Am. League Championships, 1980, 82, 84, 89, World Series, 1983, Baseball All-Star Game, 1986; spl. asst. Major League Baseball Exec. Coun., 1994—. Co-founder Steve Palermo Found. for Spinal Cord Injuries, Overland Park, Kans. Recipient over 25 awards for courage and dedication, Arthur Ashe Courage award, 1994; named Sporting News # 1 Rated Am. League Umpire, 1991. Office: MSG Network 2 Penn Plz 14th fl New York NY 10121*

PALEVSKY, MAX, industrialist; b. Chgo., July 24, 1924; s. Isadore and Sarah (Greenblatt) P.; children: Nicholas, Madeleine, Alexander, Jonathan, Matthew; m. Ellen Hemming. Ph.B., B.S., U. Chgo., 1948; postgrad., U. Calif.-Berkeley, UCLA, 1951-52. Mathematician Computer div. Bendix Corp., Los Angeles, 1952-56; v.p., gen. mgr., dir. Packard Bell Electronics, Los Angeles, 1957-61; pres., chmn. bd. Sci. Data Systems; chmn. bd. Xerox Data Systems, Inc., El Segundo, Calif., 1961-72; dir. Xerox Corp., 1969-72, chmn. exec. com. of bd., 1969-72; bd. dirs. Intel Corp., Santa Clara, Calif., Komag, Inc., Milpitas, Calif. Organized George McGovern's campaign for Pres. of U.S., 1972; organized and ran Tom Bradley's campaign for Mayor of L.A., 1973; mem. Folger com. Folger Shakespeare Libr., Washington, 1977—; mem. Dem. Adv. Com., 1968—; bd. dirs. ACLU, Constl. Rights Found.; trustee The Inst. for Advanced Study, Princeton U., 1988—. With USAAF, 1943-46. Office: 924 Westwood Blvd Los Angeles CA 90024-2910

PALEY, ALBERT RAYMOND, art educator, sculptor; b. Phila., Mar. 28, 1944; s. Albert Raymond and Dorothy (Appelgran) P.; B.F.A., Temple U., 1966, M.F.A., 1969; PhD (hon.), U. Rochester, 1989. Instr. art Tyler Sch. Art, Temple U., Phila., 1962-66; asst. prof. Sch. Am. Craftsmen, Rochester Inst. Tech., N.Y., 1969-72, prof. Coll. Fine and Applied Arts, 1984—; Morris Endowed Chair Coll. Fine and Applied Arts Sch. Am. Crafts, Rochester Inst. Tech., 1985-87; prof. art SUNY-Brockport, 1972-84; cons. Rochester Inst. Tech., 1978, Haystack Sch. Crafts, Deer Isle, Maine, 1979, Pa. Ave. Devel. Corp., Washington, 1979, Margaret Woodbury Strong Mus., Rochester, N.Y., 1980. Prin. works include portal gates Renwick Gallery, Smithsonian Instn., Washington, sculpture court enclosure Hunter Mus. Art, Chattanooga, portal gates N.Y. State Senate, Albany, exterior sculpture Margaret Woodbury Strong Mus., Rochester, 800 tree grates & 30 benches, Pa. Ave. Devel. Corp., Washington, poster cases Port Authority of Allegheny County, Pitts., exterior sculpture Harro Theatre East, Rochester, N.Y., gates Va. Mus. Fine Arts, Richmond, sculpture The Willard, Washington, sculptures Wortham Theater Ctr., Houston, Milk Street Sta., Boston, Mus. of Fine Arts, Boston, Hartford, Conn. City Courthouse, Marco Philharmonic, Naples, Fla., Birmingham (Ala.) Mus. of Fine Art, Cornell U., Lasdon Biomed. Rsch. Ctr., N.Y.C., Washington Hebrew Congregation, Main Street Bridge Railings, Rochester; exterior sculpture Olympia at Promenade Two Bldg., The Landmarks Group, 1990, sculpture Aurora at Roanoke (Va.) Regional Airport, 1990, Ceremonial Gates at Ariz. State U., 1991; jewelry exhbn. at Renwick Gallery, Washington, Nat. Mus. Am. Art, 1992; exterior sculpture Criss Cross, Silver Spring, Md., 1992, interior sculpture screens for Fed. Courthouse, Camden, N.J., 1993. Nat. Endowment for Arts grantee, 1975, 76, 79, 84; recipient award of excellence Rochester chpt. AIAA, 1982; design in steel award Iron and Steel Inst., 1975, Artists fellow N.Y. Found. Arts, 1991; Lillian Fairchild award, U. Rochester, 1975; certificate of honor Tyler Sch. Art, Temple U., 1981. Mem. Artist and Blacksmith Assn. N.Am., Am. Craftsman Council. Office: Paley Studio Ltd 25 N Washington St Rochester NY 14614-1110

PALEY, ALFRED IRVING, value engineering and consulting company executive, lecturer; b. Monticello, N.Y., Apr. 12, 1927; s. Max and Dora (Gutkin) P.; m. Sylvia Tiffel, June 26, 1949; children: Maureen, Howard, Doreen. BEE, Poly. Inst. Bklyn., 1949. Sr. engr. W.L. Maxson Corp., N.Y.C., 1950-58; chief engr. Acoustica Assocs., Mineola, N.Y., 1958-60; staff scientist in acoustics Am. Bosch Arma Corp., Garden City, N.Y., 1960-62; chief engr. in elec. acoustics Janus Products, Syosset, N.Y., 1962-63; mgr. Anti-Submarine Warfare systems Gyrodyne Co. of Am., St. James, N.Y., 1963-67; mgr. cost and value control Loral Electronic Systems, Yonkers, N.Y., 1967-80; v.p. program mgmt. FEL Corp., Farmingdale, N.J., 1980-84; pres. NRI Assocs., Oceanport, N.J., 1984—; value engring. program mgr. CECOM, U.S. Army, Ft. Monmouth, N.J., 1985-95, ret. 1995; assoc. prof. Poly. Inst. Bklyn., 1955-65, Hofstra U., Hempstead, N.Y., 1974-79; lectr. Am. Mgmt. Assn., N.Y.C., 1973-80. Contbr. articles to profl. jours. Patentee in field. Bd. dirs. Suburban Temple, Wantagh, N.Y., 1964-80, Monmouth Reform Temple, Tinton Falls, N.J., 1983-91. Served with USN, 1945-46. Mem. Project Mgmt. Inst., Soc. Info. Display, (sec. 1978), Nat. Mgmt. Assn. (pres. chpt. 1975-76), Soc. Am. Value Engrs. (fellow, cert. tech. v.p. svcs. 1993—, pres. mem. N.Y. chpt. 1986-91, Value Engr. of Yr. 1985-86, 88-89, Disting. Svc. award 1991). Democrat. Jewish. Home and Office: 5442 N Whitethorn Pl Tucson AZ 85704-2634

PALEY, GERALD LARRY, lawyer; b. Albany, N.Y., Sept. 11, 1939; s. Arthur and Mary (Peckner) P.; m. Joyce R., June 25, 1961 (div. June 1985); children: Jonathan, Eric, Suzanne; m. Sheryl Gae, Aug. 14, 1985. BA, Union Coll., 1961; JD with distinction, Cornell U., 1964. Bar: N.Y. 1964. Assoc. Nixon, Hargrave, Devans & Doyle, Rochester, N.Y., 1964-69; assoc. solicitor Dept. Labor, Washington, 1969-71; ptnr. Nixon, Hargrave, Devans & Doyle, Rochester, 1971-87, Phillips, Lytle, Hitchcock, Blaine & Huber, Rochester, 1987—. Author: Handbook of Federal Labor Relations Laws, 1981, Understand Employee Regulations, 1984. Mem. ABA. Republican. Jewish. Office: Phillips Lytle Hitchcock et al 1400 First Federal Pla Rochester NY 14614

PALEY, GRACE, author, educator; b. N.Y.C., Dec. 11, 1922; d. Isaac and Mary (Ridnyik) Goodside; m. Jess Paley, June 20, 1942; children: Nora, Dan.; m. Robert Nichols, 1972. Ed. Hunter Coll., NYU. Formerly tchr. Columbia, Syracuse U.; ret. mem. lit. faculty Sarah Lawrence Coll., Stanford, Johns Hopkins, Dartmouth. Author: The Little Disturbances of Man, 1959, Enormous Changes at the Last Minute, 1974, Leaning Forward, 1985, Later the Same Day, 1985, Long Walks and Intimate Talks, 1991, New and Collected Poems, 1992, The Collected Stories, 1994 (Nat. Book award nomination 1994); stories published in Atlantic, Esquire, Ikon, Genesis West, Accent, others. Sec. N.Y. Greenwich Village Peace Center. Recipient Literary award for short story writing Nat. Inst. Arts and Letters, 1970, Edith Wharton award N.Y. State, 1988, 89, Rea award for short story, 1993, Vt. Gov.'s award for Excellence in the Arts, 1993, award for contbn. to Jewish culture Nat. Found. Jewish Culture; Guggenheim fellow. Mem. Am. Acad. and Inst. Arts and Letters. Office: Box 620 Thetford Hill VT 05074*

PALIHNICH, NICHOLAS JOSEPH, JR., retail chain executive; b. Montclair, N.J., Nov. 9, 1939; s. Nicholas Joseph and Lucille (Pflugh) P.; m. Diane Lorraine Parise, Nov. 12, 1966; children: Nicholas, Kristin, Danielle. B.B.A., U. Notre Dame, 1961. Retail buyer R.H. Macy, N.Y.C., 1961-66, Korvettes Inc., N.Y.C., 1966-69; retail v.p., gen. mdse. mgr. Mangurians Inc., Ft. Lauderdale, Fla., 1970-72; sr. v.p. retail mgmt. Korvettes Inc., N.Y.C., 1973-79; pres. Korvettes Inc., 1979-81; sr. v.p. retail mgmt. Lane Bryant, 1981-83; pres. retail mgmt. Dan Inc., 1984-86; exec. v.p. retail Bally U.S.A. 1987-93; dir. retail The Rockport Co., Marlborough, Mass., 1994—. Served with U.S. Army, 1962. Republican. Roman Catholic. Office: 220 Donald J Lynch Blvd Marlborough MA 01752

PALIN, MICHAEL EDWARD, actor, screenwriter, author; b. May 5, 1943; s. Edward and Mary P.; m. Helen M. Gibbons, 1966; 3 children. BA, U. Oxford, Eng., 1965. Writer, performer BBC Corp., 1965-69. Actor, writer: (TV shows) Monty Python's Flying Circus, 1969-74, Ripping Yarns, 1976-80; (films) And Now for Something Completely Different, 1970, Monty Python and the Holy Grail, 1974, Monty Python's Life of Brian, 1978, Time

Bandits, 1980, Monty Python's The Meaning of Life, 1982, American Friends, 1991; TV presenter, writer Around the World in 80 Days, 1989, Pole to Pole, 1993, Palin's Column, 1994; actor: (TV shows) Three Men in a Boat, 1975, GBH, 1991; (films) Jabberwocky, 1976, A Private Function, 1984, Brazil, 1985, A Fish Called Wanda (Best Supporting Actor Brit. Acad. Film and TV Arts, 1989); actor, writer and co-producer: The Missionary, 1982; writer (stage play) The Weekend, 1994; author: Monty Python's Brand New Book, 1973, Dr. Fegg's Encyclopaedia of All World Knowledge, 1984, Limericks, 1985, Around the World in 80 Days, 1989, Pole to Pole, 1993, Pole to Pole: The Photographs, 1994, Hemingway's Chair 1995; (children's books) Small Harry and the Toothache Pills, 1981, The Mirrorstone, 1986, The Cyril Stories, 1986. Co-recipient (with Monty Python) Michael Balcon award for outstanding contribution to cinema British Academy of Film and TV Arts, 1987. Avocations: reading, running, railways. Office: 68 A Delancey St, London NW1 7RY, England

PALISCA, CLAUDE VICTOR, musicologist, educator; b. Rijeka, Croatia, Nov. 24, 1921; came to U.S., 1930; s. Matthew and Gisella (Fleischhacker) P.; m. Jane Agnes Pyne, June 12, 1960 (div. Feb. 1987); children: Carl Pyne, Madeline Grace; m. Elizabeth Ann Keitel, Apr. 4, 1987. B.A., Queens Coll., 1943; M.A., Harvard U., 1948, Ph.D., 1954; M.A. (hon.), Yale U., 1964. Instr., then asst. prof. music U. Ill. at Urbana, 1953-59; asso. prof. history music Yale U., New Haven, 1959—, prof., 1964-80, Henry L. and Lucy G. Moses prof. music, 1980-92, emeritus, 1992—, dir. grad. studies music, 1967-69, 87-92, chmn. music dept., 1969-75, chmn., dir. grad. studies in Renaissance studies, 1977-80; chmn. council on humanities Yale U., 1977-79, fellow Silliman Coll., 1963—; sr. fellow council humanities Princeton U., 1961; cons. U.S. Office Edn., 1963—, NEH, 1967—; dir. Nat. Seminar Music Edn., 1963. Author: Girolamo Mei: Letters on Ancient and Modern Music, 1960, 2d edit., 1977, (with others) Musicology, 1963, Baroque Music, 1968, 3d edit., 1991, (with Donald Grout) History of Western Music, 4th edit., 1988, Humanism in Italian Renaissance Musical Thought, 1985 (Internat. Musicol. Soc. award 1987), The Florentine Camerata, 1989, Studies in the History of Italian Music and Music Theory, 1994; translator: (with Guy Marco) Zarlino, The Art of Counterpoint, 1968; editor: Hucbald, Guido and John on Music: Three Medieval Treatises, 1978, Norton Anthology of Western Music, 1980, 2d edit., 1988, (with D. Kern Holloman) Musicology in the 1980's, 1982, Zarlino, On the Modes, 1983, Yale Music Theory Translation Series, Boethius, Fundamentals of Music, 1989, The Theory of Music (Franchino Gaffurio) 1993; mem. editorial and adv. bds. Studies in Music (Western Australia); mem. exec. com.: New Grove Dictionary, Jour. History of Ideas, Jour. Music Theory; contbr. articles to publs. Bd. dirs., exec. com. Arts Council Greater New Haven, 1964-77, Neighborhood Music Sch., 1966-69; mem. exec. com. Ednl. Center for Arts, New Haven, 1973-83, chmn., 1979-80; bd. dirs., chmn. edn. com. New Haven Symphony Soc., 1966-72, v.p., 1968-72; mem. ednl. adv. bd. J.S. Guggenheim Meml. Found., 1983-92. Served with AUS, 1943-46. John Knowles Paine traveling fellow, 1949-50; Fulbright fellow, 1950-52; Guggenheim fellow, 1959-60, 81-82; Nat. Endowment for the Humanities sr. fellow, 1972-73; Misha Strassberg sr. fellow in creative arts U. Western Australia, summer, 1984. Fellow AAAS, Am. Council Arts in Edn. (pres. 1967-69); mem. Internat. Musicol. Soc. (dir., v.p. 1977-82), Am. Musicol. Soc. (hon., pres. 1970-72), Coll. Music Soc. (council), Renaissance Soc. (council 1973-74, exec. com. 1978-87), ACLS-Soviet Union of Composers Commn. on Music Composition and Musicology (co-chmn. 1986—). Office: Yale Univ PO Box 208310 New Haven CT 06520-8310

PALISI, ANTHONY THOMAS, psychologist, educator; b. Rahway, N.J., Mar. 8, 1930; s. Anthony Francis and Marianne Catherine (Picone) P.; m. Dyane Cassidy, Apr. 19, 1954; children: Jane, Anthony Francis II, Phyllis, Damian-Marie. BS, Seton Hall U., 1947, MA, 1958; EdD, Temple U., 1973. Cert. secondary tchr., elem. prin., psychologist, rehab. counselor, N.J. Tchr., coach pub. schs. Rahway, 1953-60; sports editor Rahway News-Record, 1950-60; prin. elem. pub. sch. Franklin Twp., N.J., 1960-65; asst. prof. edn. Seton Hall U., 1965-73, assoc. prof., 1974-77, prof., 1977-82, acting grad. dean, 1976-77, dir., 1969-80, indsl. cons. group dynamics, 1967—. Contbr. articles and short stories to profl. jours. and popular periodicals. Mem. Rahway Bd. Edn. 1961-62; trustee Rahway Libr., 1961-68, pres. 1967-68. Recipient award N.J. Sportswriters' Assn., 1953. Mem. APA, ACA, Am. Mgmt. Assn. (co-author video tng. program), N.J. Psychol. Assn., Assn. for Specialists in Group Work (mem. rsch. com. 1980-82), N.Y. Acad. Scis., Nat. Acad. Counselors and Family Therapists (chmn., exec. dir. 1988-93). Roman Catholic. Home: 810 Riverview Dr Brielle NJ 08730-1718

PALITZ, BERNARD G., finance company executive; b. N.Y.C., Aug. 21, 1924; s. Clarence Y. and Ruth (Krummas) P.; m. Louise Beringer; children: Bernard G. Jr., Anne L. BS, MIT, 1947. Chmn. bd. Comml. Alliance Corp., N.Y.C., 1963-88, Credit Alliance Corp., N.Y.C., 1963-88, Leasing Svc. Corp., N.Y.C., 1963-88, Fin. Guaranty Ins. Co., Wilmington, Del., 1975—, Colonial Surety Co., Pitts., 1976—, Fin. Fed. Corp., 1989—; pres. Am. Credit Mgmt., Inc., N.Y.C. Trustee Coun. for Arts, MIT, 1979—, Haverford Coll., Pa., 1979-82, Rockefeller U. Coun.; incorporator Worcester (Mass.) Art Mus. Mem. Harmonie Club (N.Y.C.), Quaker Ridge Club (Scarsdale, N.Y.), Beach Point Club (Mamaroneck, N.Y.). Home: PO Box 287 221 E 70th St New York NY 10021-5203 Office: Am Credit Mgmt Inc 400 Park Ave New York NY 10022

PALITZ, CLARENCE YALE, JR., commercial finance executive; b. N.Y.C., Jan. 21, 1931; s. Clarence Yale and Ruth (Kromnes) P.; m. Muriel Dobson (div. Nov., 1988), children: Michael, Suzanne; m. Anka Kriser. B.A., Dartmouth Coll., 1952; M.B.A., NYU, 1953. With Bankers Trust Co., N.Y.C., 1952-53; v.p., dir. Credit Am. Corp., N.Y.C., 1956-58; asst. sec. James Talcott, Inc., N.Y.C., 1958-60; v.p., mng. dir. Shopper's Park-Westmount, Ltd., Edmonton, Alta., Can., 1958-74; pres., dir. 140 E 72d St Corp., N.Y.C., 1962-65, Comml. Alliance Corp., N.Y.C., 1963-88, Credit Alliance Corp., N.Y.C., 1963-88, Leasing Service Corp., N.Y.C., 1963-88, Colonial Surety Co., Pitts., 1976—, Fin. Guaranty Ins. Co., Wilmington, Del., 1976—, Kidde Credit Corp., N.Y.C., 1976-80, First Interstate Comml. Alliance Corp., 1984-88, Fin. Fed. Corp., 1989—; pres., chmn. bd. dirs. First Land Devel. Inc., Allamuchy, N.J., 1987—; chmn. bd. Fin. Fed. Credit Inc., Houston; bd. dirs. City & Suburban Fin. Corp. Served to lt. (j.g.) USN, 1955-59. Office: Fin Fed Credit Inc 300 Frank W Burr Blvd Teaneck NJ 07666-6703

PALIZZI, ANTHONY N., lawyer, retail corporation executive; b. Wyandotte, Mich., Oct. 27, 1942; s. Vincenzo and Nunziata (Dagostini) P.; m. Bonnie Marie Kirkwood, Mar. 11, 1966; children—A. Michael, Nicholas A. PhB, Wayne State U., 1964, JD, 1966; LLM, Yale U., 1967. Bar: Mich. 1967. Prof. law Fla. State U., Tallahassee, 1967-69; prof. law Tex. Tech U., Lubbock, 1969-71; atty. Kmart Corp., Troy, Mich., 1971-74, asst. sec., 1974-77, asst. gen. counsel, 1977-85, v.p., assoc. gen. counsel, 1985-91, sr. v.p., gen. counsel, 1991-92, exec. v.p., gen. counsel, 1992—. Editor law rev. Wayne State U., 1964-66. Chmn. Brandon Police and Fire Bd., Mich., 1982-87. Mem. ABA, Am. Corp. Counsel Assn., Mich. State Bar Assn. Roman Catholic. *

PALKO, MICHAEL JAMES, finance company executive; b. Passaic, N.J., Sept. 4, 1936; s. Michael and Josephine Marie (Jasper) P.; m. Alexandra S. Palko; children: Timothy, Christopher. Student, Upsala Coll., 1955, BSBA, U. Denver, 1963. CPA, Calif., Colo., Mich., N.J. Acct. Ernst & Young, Denver, 1963-66, Marquette, Mich., 1966-69, Trenton, N.J., 1969-72; v.p. First Interstate Bancorp., Los Angeles, 1972-74, H.F. Ahmanson & Co., Los Angeles, 1974-80; sr. v.p. Gt. Western Fin. Corp., Chatsworth, Calif., 1980—. Chmn. United Fund, Marquette, 1969; pres. Trenton, N.J. chpt. ARC, 1972; fin. chmn. Diocese of Marquette, Roman Cath. Ch., 1968-69. Served with USAF, 1955-59. Mem. AICPA, Calif. Soc. CPAs, Savs. and Cmty. Bankers of Am. (chair, tax com. 1993-94), Am. Fin. Svcs. Assn. (chair tax com. 1990-92), Western League of Savs. Instns. (former chair tax com.), Tax Execs. Inst., L.A. Taxpayers Assn. (bd. dirs. 1984-89), Kiwanis (past officer), Beta Gamma Sigma. Republican. Office: Gt Western Fin Corp 9200 Oakdale Ave Chatsworth CA 91311-6519

PALL, DAVID B., manufacturing company executive, chemist; b. Ft. William, Ont., Can., Apr. 2, 1914; came to U.S., 1939, naturalized, 1942; s. Adolph and Mary (Donner) P.; m. Josephine H. Blatt, Feb. 4, 1940 (dec.

1959); children: Stephanie (Mrs. Wendel Kincaid, Jr.), William, Ellen, Abigail; m. Helen R. Stream, July 10, 1960; 1 stepchild, Jane Block. B.Sc. in Chemistry, McGill U., 1936, Ph.D. in Phys. Chemistry, 1939, D.S. (hon.), 1987; postgrad., Brown U., 1936-37; DSc (hon.), L.I. U., 1985. Group leader research labs. Interchem. Corp., 1939-44; founder Pall Corp. (successor to Micrometallic Corp.), Glen Cove, N.Y., 1944; past pres., and chmn. bd. Pall Corp. (successor to Micrometallic Corp.), now dir. Inventor bio-medical filters. Trustee North Shore Hosp., Manhasset, N.Y., cold Spring Harbor Lab., 1987. Recipient Nat. medal Tech. U.S. Dept. Commerce Tech., 1990. Mem. Am. Chem. Soc., Am. Soc. Metals, AAAS. Home: 5 Hickory Hl Roslyn NY 11576-1713 Office: Pall Corp 2200 Northern Blvd Greenvale NY 11548-1289*

PALLADINO, NUNZIO JOSEPH, retired nuclear engineer; b. Allentown, Pa., Nov. 10, 1916; s. Joseph and Angelina (Trentalange) P.; m. Virginia Marchetto, June 16, 1945; children: Linda Susan, Lisa Anne, Cynthia Madaline. B.S., Lehigh U., 1938, M.S., 1939, D.Eng. (hon.), 1964. Registered profl. engr., Pa. Engr. Westinghouse Electric Co., Phila., 1939-42; nuclear reactor designer Oak Ridge Nat. Lab., 1946-48; staff asst. to div. mgr. Argonne Nat. Lab., Lemont, Ill., 1948-50; mgr. PWR reactor design subdiv. Westinghouse Electric Corp., Pitts., 1950-59; head nuclear engring. dept. Pa. State U., University Park, 1959-66, dean Coll. Engring., 1966-81; chmn. Nuclear Regulatory Commn., Washington, 1981-86; past mem. Pa. Gov.'s Sci. Adv. Com., Gov.'s Energy Coun., Pa.'s Commn. To Investigate Three Mile Island; mem. Nat. Nuclear Accrediting Bd., 1989-92. Contbr. tech. articles to profl. jours. Served to capt. AUS, 1942-45. Recipient Order of Merit Westinghouse Electric Corp. Fellow ASME (Prime Movers award), Am. Nuclear Soc. (past pres., A.H. Compton award, W. Zinn award), Am. Soc. Engring. Edn.; mem. NAE, NSPE, Argonne Univs. Assn. (past interim pres., past bd. dirs.). Roman Catholic. Club: Rotary. *Do it right the first time.*

PALLADINO, VINCENT NEIL, lawyer; b. Phila., Dec. 5, 1950; s. Vincent Salvatore and Agnes (Ludwig) P.; m. Laurel Ruth Tanner, Apr. 15, 1984; children: Alissa Kathryn, Samantha Leigh. BA, Yale U., 1972; JD, Columbia U., 1975. Bar: N.Y. 1976. Atty. Nims, Howes, Collison & Isner, N.Y.C., 1975-77; atty. Fish & Neave, N.Y.C., 1977—, ptnr., 1987—; Editor-in-chief The Trademark Reporter, N.Y.C., 1986-88, mem. adv. bd., 1988—. Mem. ABA, Assn. Bar City of N.Y., N.Y. Intellectual Property Law Assn., Internat. Trademark Assn., Copyright Soc. U.S.A. Avocations: reading, running. Office: Fish & Neave 1251 6th Ave New York NY 10020

PALLADINO-CRAIG, ALLYS, museum director; b. Pontiac, Mich., Mar. 23, 1947; d. Stephan Vincent and Mary (Anderson) Palladino; m. Malcolm Arnold Craig, Aug. 20, 1967; children—Ansel, Reed, Nicholas. BA in English, Fla. State U., 1967; grad., U. Toronto, Ont., Can., 1969; MFA, Fla. State U., 1978, ABD, 1993. Editorial asst. project U. Va. Press, Charlottesville, 1970-76; instr. English Inst. Franco Americain, Rennes, France, 1974; adj. instr. Fla. State U., Tallahassee, 1978-79, dir. Four Arts Ctr., 1979-82, dir. U. Mus. of Fine Arts, 1982—. Curator, contbg. editor various articles and exhbn. catalogues, 1982—, including Nocturnes and Nightmres, Monochrome/Polychrome, and Chroma; gen. editor Athanor I-XIII, 1980—; represented in permanent collection Fla. Ho. of Reps., Barnett Bank, IBM. Individual artist fellow Fla. Arts Coun., 1979. Mem. Am. Assn. Mus., Fla. Art Mus. Dirs. Assn. (sec. 1989-91), Phi Beta Kappa. Democrat. Avocation: antique American fountain pen collecting. Home: 1410 Grape St Tallahassee FL 32303-5636 Office: Fla State U Mus of Fine Arts 250 Fine Arts Bldg Tallahassee FL 32306-2055

PALLASCH, B. MICHAEL, lawyer; b. Chgo., Mar. 30, 1933; s. Bernhard Michael and Magdalena Helena (Fixari) P.; m. Josephine Catherine O'Leary, Aug. 15, 1981; children: Bernhard Michael III and Madeline Josephine (twins). B.S.S., Georgetown U., 1954; J.D., Harvard U., 1957; postgrad., John Marshall Law Sch., 1974. Bar: Ill. 1957, U.S. Dist. Ct. (no. dist.) Ill. 1958, U.S. Tax Ct. 1961, U.S. Ct. Claims 1961, U.S. Ct. Appeals (7th cir.) 1962. Assoc. Winston & Strawn, Chgo., 1958-66; resident mgr. br. office Winston & Strawn, Paris, 1963-65; ptnr. Winston & Strawn, Chgo., 1966-70, sr. capital ptnr., 1971-91; sr. ptnr. B. Michael Pallasch & Assocs., 1991—; dir., corp. sec. Tanis, Inc., Calumet, Mich., 1972—, Greenbank Engring. Corp., Dover, Del., 1976-91, C.B.P. Engring. Corp., Chgo., 1976-91, Chgo. Cutting Svcs. Corp., 1977-88; corp. sec. Arthur Andersen Assocs., Inc., Chgo., 1976—, L'hotel de France of Ill., Inc., Chgo., 1980-85, Water & Effluent Screening Co., Chgo., 1988-91; dir. Bosch Devel. Co., Longview, Tex., 1977-87, Lor Inc., Houghton, Mich., 1977-87, Rana Inc., Madison, Wis., 1978-87, Woodlak Co., Houghton, 1977-87, Zipatone, Inc., Hillside, Ill., 1975-82, Keco Inc., Madison, 1977-81. Bd. dirs. Martin D'Arcy Mus. Medieval and Renaissance Art, Chgo., 1975—; bd. dirs. Katherine M. Bosch Found., 1978—; asst. sec. Hundred Club of Cook County, Chgo., 1966-73, bd. dirs., sec., 1974—. Served with USAFR, 1957-63. Decorated knight Merit Sacred Mil. Constantinian, Order St. George of Royal House of Bourbon of Two Sicilies, Sovereign Mil. Order of Temple Jerusalem; recipient Oustanding Woodland Mgmt. Forestry award Monroe County (Wis.) Soil and Water Conservation Dist., 1975, Youth Mayor of Chgo. award, 1950. Mem. Ill. Bar Assn. (tax lectr. 1961), Advs. Soc., Field Mus. Natural History (life), Max McGraw Wildlife Found., English Speaking Union. Roman Catholic. Clubs: Travellers (Paris); Saddle and Cycle (Chgo.). Home: 737 W Hutchinson St Chicago IL 60613-1519 Office: 35 W Wacker Dr Ste 4700 Chicago IL 60601-1614 *Personal philosophy: We define and measure success in various ways: achievement, position, wealth: and attribute it to the application of various attributes but is there any degree of success that we can attribute that is worthier than the knowledge that we have faithfully served those who depend upon and trust in us?.*

PALLENIK, CHRISTINE M., lawyer; b. Cleve., Mar. 9, 1957; d. Joseph and Marie Theresa (Kubik) P. BA in History, Seton Hall Coll., 1979; JD, Gonzaga Sch. of Law, 1982. Bar: Tex. Gas buyer United Gas Pipeline Co., Houston, 1984-85; sr. gas buyer Tex. Gas Transmission, Houston, 1985-88; sr. atty. United Gas Pipeline Co., Houston, 1988-93; sr. counsel Panhandle Eastern Corp., Houston, 1993—. Mem. Am. Assn. Corp. Counsel, Fed. Energy Bar Assn. Office: Panhandle Ea Corp 5400 Westheimer Ct Houston TX 77056-5310

PALLIN, IRVING M., anesthesiologist; b. Boston, Feb. 11, 1910; s. Abraham and Lillian (Stoler) P.; m. Ann Gertrude Lear; children: Samuel Lear, Mary Jane, Carol Sue, Jonathan Jacob. B.S., Tufts U., 1932, M.D., 1937. Diplomate: Am. Bd. Anesthesiology. Intern W.W. Backus Hosp., 1937-39; resident anesthesiology N.Y. Postgrad. Med. Sch. and Hosp., 1939-41; practice medicine specializing in anesthesiology N.Y.C., 1941-70, Sun City, Ariz., 1970-80; attending anesthesiologist Jewish Hosp. Bklyn., 1942-54, sec. med. bd., 1951-70, pres. med. bd., 1962-63, dir. dept. anesthesiology, 1954-70; cons. anesthesiologist VA Hosp., Bklyn., 1950-65; dir. anesthesiology Cumberland Hosp., 1948-55; dir. dept. anesthesiology Queens Gen. Hosp., 1955-66; former prof. clin. anesthesiology SUNY Coll. Medicine, Bklyn.; chief anesthesia Boswell Meml. Hosp., Sun City, Ariz., 1970-77; dir. Asso. Med. Service (Blue Cross) Greater N.Y.; chmn. advisers of AMA to Am. Assn. Med. Assts., 1968-70. Contbr. articles to profl. publs. Co-chmn. Bklyn. physicians div. United Jewish Appeal, 1953-56; pres. Sun City unit Am. Cancer Soc., 1981-85, bd. dirs. Ariz. div. 1982—; pres. Beth Shalom Congregation of Sun City, 1976-78, Brotherhood, 1980, 81, pres. 1982-83; bd. dirs. Ariz. Endowment of Jewish Welfare, 1982-85. Recipient Heritage award State of Israel Bonds, 1983. Fellow Am. Coll. Anesthesiologists, N.Y. Acad. Medicine, N.Y. Acad. Scis.; mem. AMA (del. 1964—), Kings County Med. Soc. (pres. 1960-61, hon.), N.Y. Med. Soc. (ho. dels. 1952-54, sec. sect. anesthesiology 1952057), Acad. Medicine Bklyn. (pres. 1961), Am. Soc. Anesthesiologists (pres. 1957), N.Y. Soc. Anesthesiologists (pres. 1949-50, chmn. jud. com. 1951-56, hon.), Tam O'Shanter Golf Club (pres. 1960-63, Union Hills Country Club. Home: 10358 Highwood Ln Sun City AZ 85373

PALLISER, CHARLES, writer, educator; b. Holyoke, Mass., Dec. 11, 1947. BA, Oxford U., 1970, BLitt, 1975. Lectr. Strathclyde U., Scotland, 1974-90. Author: The Quincunx, 1989, The Sensationist, 1991, Betrayals, 1995. Recipient Sue Kaufman 1st fiction prize Am. Acad. & Inst. Arts and Letters, N.Y.C., 1991.

PALLMEYER, REBECCA RUTH, federal judge; b. Tokyo, Sept. 13, 1954; came to U.S., 1957; d. Paul Henry and Ruth (Schrieber) P.; m. Dan P. McAdams, Aug. 20, 1977; children: Ruth, Amanda. BA, Valparaiso (Ind.) U., 1976; JD, U. Chgo., 1979. Bar: Ill. 1980, U.S. Ct. Appeals (7th cir.) 1980, U.S. Ct. Appeals 11th and 5th cirs.) 1982. Jud. clk. Minn. Supreme Ct., St. Paul, 1979-80; assoc. Hopkins & Sutter, Chgo., 1980-85; judge administrv. law Ill. Human Rights Commn., Chgo., 1985-91; magistrate judge U.S. Dist. Ct., Chgo., 1991—; mem. jud. resources com. Jud. Conf. of U.S., 1994—. Bd. govs. Augustana Ctr., 1990-91. Mem. Fed. Bar Assn., Nat. Assn. Women Judges, Fed. Magistrate Judge's Assn. (bd. dirs. 1994—), Chgo. Bar Assn. (past chair devel. of law com. 1992-93, David C. Hilliard award 1990-91), Valparaiso U. Alumni Assn. (bd. dirs. 1992-94). Lutheran. Avocations: choral music, sewing, running. Office: US Dist Ct Rm 2414 219 S Dearborn St Chicago IL 60604-1802

PALLONE, ADRIAN JOSEPH, research scientist; b. Lille, France, Apr. 8, 1928; came to U.S., 1946; s. Giovanni and Laurina (Caccia) P.; m. Teresa Maria Violino, June 12, 1954; children—John M., Anne Marie, Janet M., Joan L. B.S. in Aero. Engring., Poly Inst. Bklyn., 1952, M.S. in Aero. Engring., 1953, Ph.D. in Applied Mechanics, 1959; cert., Sloan Sch. Mgmt., MIT, 1984. Research assoc. Poly. Inst. Bklyn., 1955-59; mgr. Avco Systems Div., Wilmington, Mass., 1959-63; mem. faculty NYU, N.Y.C., 1963-67; dir. Avco Systems Div., Wilmington, 1967-78; chief scientist Avco Systems Div., 1978-87; aerospace cons. Textron Def. Systems, Wilmington, 1987-91; pres. Aerophysics Systems & Tech., Inc., Silver Lake, N.H., 1992—. Patentee in field. Contbr. articles to sci. jours. Fellow AIAA; mem. N.Y. Acad. Scis., Sigma Xi, Sigma Gamma Tau. Roman Catholic. Avocations: skiing; sailing; hiking. Office: Aerophysics Systems & Tech Inc PO Box 189 Silver Lake NH 03875

PALLONE, FRANK, JR., congressman; b. Long Branch, N.J., Oct. 30, 1951. Grad. cum. laude, Middlebury Coll., 1973; MA, Tufts U., 1974; JD, Rutgers U., 1978. Councilman City of Long Branch, 1982-88; mem. N.J. Senate, 1984-88, 101st-104th Congresses from 3d (now 6th) N.J. dist., 1988—; ranking minority mem. commerce subcom. on energy and power. Democrat. Roman Catholic. Office: US Ho of Reps 420 Condon Ter SE Washington DC 20032-3710 Address: 540 Broadway Ste 118 Long Branch NJ 07740-5905*

PALLOTTI, MARIANNE MARGUERITE, foundation administrator; b. Hartford, Conn., Apr. 23, 1937; d. Rocco D. and Marguerite (Long) P. BA, NYU, 1968, MA, 1972. Asst. to pres. Wilson, Haight & Welch, Hartford, 1964-65; exec. asst. Ford Found., N.Y.C., 1965-77; corp. sec. Hewlett Found., Menlo Park, Calif., 1977-84, v.p., 1985—; bd. dirs. Overseas Devel. Network. Bd. dirs. N.Y. Theatre Ballet, N.Y.C., 1986—; Consortium for Global Devel., 1992, Miramonte Mental Health Svcs., Palo Alto, Calif., 1989, Austin Montessori Sch., 1993. Mem. Women in Founds., No. Calif. Grantmakers, Peninsula Grantmakers. Avocations: running, skiing, hiking. Home: 532 Marine World Pky # 6203 Redwood Shores CA 94065 Office: William & Flora Hewlett Found 525 Middlefield Rd Ste 200 Menlo Park CA 94025-3495

PALM, CHARLES GILMAN, university official; b. Havre, Mont., Apr. 25, 1944; s. Victor F. and Laura (McKinnie) P.; m. Miriam Willits, Sept. 15, 1968. AB, Stanford U., 1966; MA, U. Wyo., 1967; MLS, U. Oreg., 1970. Asst. archivist Hoover Instn., Stanford (Calif.) U., 1971-74, dep. archivist, 1974-84, archivist, 1984-87, head libr., 1986-87, assoc. dir., 1987-90, dep. dir., 1990—. Co-author: Guide to Hoover Institution Archives, 1980, Herbert Hoover, Register of His Papers in the Hoover Institution Archives, 1983. Mem. Calif. Heritage Preservation Commn., Sacramento, 1988—, vice chmn., 1993—; mem. Nat. Hist. Records and Publs. Commn., Washington, 1990—. Fellow Soc. Am. Archivists; mem. Am. Hist. Assn., Soc. Calif. Archivists (pres. 1983-84). Republican. Office: Hoover Instn Stanford CA 94305

PALM, GARY HOWARD, lawyer, educator; b. Toledo, Sept. 2, 1942; s. Clarence William, Jr. and Emily Marie (Braunschweiger) P. AB, Wittenberg U., 1964; JD, U. Chgo., 1967. Bar: Ill. 1967, U.S. Dist. Ct. (no. dist.) Ill. 1967, U.S. Ct. Appeals (7th cir.) 1970, U.S. Supreme Ct. 1974. Assoc. Schiff Hardin & Waite, Chgo., 1967-70; dir. Edwin F. Mandel Legal Aid Clinic, Chgo., 1970-91, atty., 1991—; asst. prof. law U. Chgo., 1970-75, assoc. prof., 1975-83, prof., 1983-91, clin. prof., 1991—; peer rev. reader, clin. edn. grants U.S. Dept. Edn., Washington, 1980, 81, 83, 84, 86, 87, Legal Svcs. Corp., 1986-87; chairperson-elect, chairperson sect. clin. legal edn. Assn. Am. Law Schs., 1985, 86. Vol. ACLU, Chgo. 1968-75. Mem. ABA (clin. edn. com. 1974-80, membership com. 1984-85, skills tng. com. 1985-90, accreditation for Law Schs., 1987-94, mem. coun. sect. on legal edn. and admissions to the bar 1994—), Chgo. Bar Assn., Chgo. Council Lawyers, Ill. State Bar Assn. (legal edn., admission and competence com. 1985-91, 93—), Am. Trial Lawyers Assn., Assn. Am. Law Schs. (clin. teaching conference 1985, 86, 87, 89, recipient Award for Outstanding Contbn. to Clin. Edn., sect on clin. legal edn., 1989, co-recipient of the award, 1994), Inter Univ. Consortium on Poverty Law, Ill. Task Force on Child Support. Democrat. Home: 2800 N Lake Shore Dr Apt 3706 Chicago IL 60657-6250 Office: Mandel Legal Aid Clinic 6020 S University Ave Chicago IL 60637-2798 Notable cases include: Logan vs. Zimmerman Brush Co.; Buckhalter vs. Pepsi-Cola Gen. Bottlers, Inc.; Scott vs. Ill.; Slate vs. McFetridge.

PALM, GERALD ALBERT, lawyer; b. Seattle, Nov. 4, 1942; s. Albert Nels and Gladys Elizabeth (Danberg) P.; m. Nancy Lee Himes, Dec. 6, 1969; children: Jason E., Kimberly A. BA, Dartmouth Coll., 1964; LLB, Harvard U., 1967. Bar: Wash. 1967, U.S. Dist. Ct. (we. dist.) Wash. 1967, U.S. Ct. Appeals (9th cir.) 1981, U.S. Dist. Ct. (ea. dist.) Wash. 1982. Assoc. Jones, Grey, Bayley, Kehoe, Hooper & Olsen, Seattle, 1967-68; assoc. Williams, Kastner and Gibbs, Seattle, 1968-74, ptnr., 1974-95. Youth basketball coach Jewish Community Ctr., Mercer Island, Wash., 1988; deacon, youth commn. Mercer Island Covenant Ch., 1988—. Mem. Am. Bd. Trial Advocates (pres. Wash. chpt. 1989), Def. Rsch. Inst., Wash. Def. Trial Lawyers Assn. (trustee 1971), Wash. State Bar Assn., King County Bar Assn., East King County Bar Assn., Fed. Bar Assn., Dartmouth Lawyers Assn., Mercer Island Country Club (trustee 1991-94, pres. 1993-94), Wash. Athletic Club, Mercer Island Kiwanis (pres. 1986-87). Republican. Mem. Covenant Ch. Avocations: tennis, water skiing, snow skiing, running, attending musicals and theatre. Home: 7400 E Mercer Way Mercer Island WA 98040-5819 Office: Two Union Sq 601 Union St Ste 4100 Seattle WA 98101-2322

PALM, MARY EGDAHL, mycologist; b. Mpls., Jan. 27, 1954; d. Lauren Ingman and Mary (Tanner) E.; m. children: Natalie Elizabeth Palm, Christopher Steven Palm. BA in Biology, St. Olaf Coll., Northfield, Minn., 1976; MS in Plant Pathology, U. Minn., 1979, PhD in Plant Pathology, 1983. Lab. asst. Biology Dept. St. Olaf Coll., 1974; field supr. Rsch. Divsn. Northup, King, and Co., 1974; teaching asst. Biology Dept. St. Olaf Coll., 1975-76; rsch. asst. in Plant Pathology Dept. U. Minn., 1976-83; rsch. assoc. in Plant Pathology Dept., 1983-84; mycologist in Biological Assessment and Support Staff USDA/APHIS, 1984-1991, mycologist in Biological Assessment and Taxonomic Support, 1991—; teaching asst. in Plant Physiology, St. Olaf Coll., 1975, U. Minn., 1977, Lake Itasca Forestry and Biological Station, 1977; co-instructor U. Minn., 1978; instr./coord. USDA/APHIS, 1988, Nat. Mycological Soc. Am. Meeting, 1989. Contbr. numerous articles and book reviews to profl. jours. Tutor Fgn. Born Info, Referral Network, Columbia, Md., 1995. Recipient Cert. Merit 1986, 88, 90, 91, 93, 95, U.S. Dept. Agr., St. Olaf Coll. Honorary Biology scholarship, 1976, U. Minn. Computer Ctr., 1979-82. Mem. Am. Phytopathological Soc., Latin Am. Mycological Assn., Mycological Soc. Am. Office: USDA BARC-WEST 10300 Baltimore Ave Beltsville MD 20705-2350

PALM, WILLIAM JOHN, mechanical engineering educator; b. Balt., Mar. 1, 1944; s. William John Jr. and Lillian Mary (Hartmann) P.; m. Mary Louise Palm, Aug. 17, 1968; children: Aileen, William IV, Andrew. BS in Engring. Physics, Loyola Coll., Balt., 1966; PhD in Mech. Engring. and Astron. Sci., Northwestern U., 1971. Engr. Ballistic Rsch. Labs., Aberdeen, Md., 1966-67; prof. mech. engring. U. R.I., Kingston, 1971—; dir. Robotics Rsch. Ctr., 1985—; cons. Analysis and Tech. Inc., North Stonington, Conn., 1977—, Vitro Inc., Silver Spring, Md., 1989—. Author: Modeling, Analysis and Control of Dynamic Systems, 1983, Control Systems Engineering, 1986; patentee in field. Asst. cubmaster Boy Scouts Am., Kingston, 1986-89, asst.

scoutmaster, 1989—. Mem. ASME, IEEE, AIAA, Tau Beta Pi, Pi Tau Sigma. Avocations: cycling, sailing. Office: U RI Wales Hall Kingston RI 02881

PALMA, DOLORES PATRICIA, urban planner, consultant, lecturer, author; b. Bklyn.; d. Anthony Michael Resse and Eleanor Dorothea (Palma) Graffeo; m. Doyle G. Hyett, Apr. 12, 1986. BA, CUNY, Bklyn., 1972; M of Urban Planning, U. Mich., 1974. Student intern Mich. Mcpl. League, Ann Arbor, 1973-74; park planner Metro Bd. Parks and Recreation, Nashville, 1975; preservation planner Metro. Hist. Commn., Nashville, 1976; sr. community planner Metro Planning Commn., Nashville, 1977-79; exec. dir. Metro Hist. Zoning Commn., Nashville, 1980-82; asst. dir. Mid-Atlantic Regional Office, Nat. Trust for Hist. Preservation, Washington, 1983, dir. Office of Neighborhood Conservation, 1984, project dir. Urban Demonstration Program Nat. Main St. Ctr., 1985-87; pres. Hyett-Palma Inc. 1985—, Hyett-Palma Publs. 1988—; del. Nat. Assn. Neighborhoods Platform Conv., 1979. Founder Neighborhood Reinvestment Corp., Nashville, 1978; mayoral appointee Neighborhood Housing Services, Nashville, 1979-82; dir. Restore the U.S. Capitol Campaign, 1983. Author: Salaries, Wages and Fringe Benefits in Michigan Cities and Villages, 1973; Nashville: Conserving a Heritage, 1977; Neighborhood Commercial Buildings: A Survey and Analysis of Metropolitan Nashville, 1983; Business Enhancement Plan for Downtown Poughkeepsie, N.Y., 1987; Future Directions for Seward, Alaska, 1987; Action Agenda for Gay Street, Knoxville, 1987; Agenda for Economic Enhancement of Haymarket Lincoln, Nebraska, 1987; Management of Downtown Palmer, Alaska, 1988; Successful Business Recruitment Strategies in the U.S., 1988, Business Clustering: How to Leverage Sales, 1988, Business Plans for Business Districts, 1988, Office Tenant Recruitment for Pittsfield, Mass., 1989, Business Plan for the Heart of Corpus Christi, Tex., 1989, Retail Recruitment Strategies for Reading, Pa., 1989, Seward 2000: Comprehensive Plan, Seward, Alaska, 1989, Business Plan for Downtown Rocky Mount, N.C., 1990, Retail and Restaurant Audit for Rosslyn, Va., 1990, Market Analysis and Enhancement Strategies for Liberal, Kans., 1990, Market Analysis and Enhancement Strategies for Geneva, N.Y., 1990, Building the Vision: Washington Street Corridor, Falls Church, Va., 1990, The Magnetic Mile Vision, Glendale, Ariz., 1990, Downtown Hopkinsville (Ky.) Business Plan, 1990, Downtown Denton (Md.) Devel. Plan, 1991. East Downtown Dearborn (Mich.) Bus. Plan, 1991, Leavenworth/Lansing Market Analysis, 1991; (with Nat. League of Cities) City Commercial Centers Reborn: Building Commercial District Dynamism, 1990, Downtown Visions, 1992, Focus Groups for Downtown, 1992, Business Retention and Expansion, 1993, Winning Ways, 1993, Downtowns and Utilities, 1994, Downtown Safety: Addressing the Myths and the Realities, 1994; project dir.: A Market and Design Study for the Broadway National Register Historic District, 1982; author studies, pamphlet, articles; contbr. newsletters; editor Edgefield News, Nashville, 1978-80. Publicity dir. Hist. Edgefield, Inc., 1979; ptnr. Nat. League of Cities The Rebirth of Am's. Downtowns Pilot Program, 1993-94; hon. mem. Tenn. State Legislature, 1980. Woodlawn scholar Nat. Trust for Hist. Preservation, 1976; named one of Outstanding Young Women of Am., 1985, award of excellence Va. Downtown Devel. Assn., 1990, Am. Planning Assn., 1991. Office: Hyett-Palma Inc Ste 110 1600 Prince St Alexandria VA 22314

PALMANTEER, EDDIE ADRIAN, JR., tribal government administrator; b. Okanogan, Wash. July 5, 1932; s. Eddie Adrian and Agnes (Whistocken) P.; m. Edith Oppenheimer, 1958 (div. 1967); children: Loni, Dale, Audrey; m. Mary Ann Quill, Aug. 9, 1968; 1 child, Eddie Adrian III. Student, Wenatchee (Wash.) Jr. Coll., 1952-53; AA in Acctg., Merrit-Davis Sch. Commerce, Salem, Oreg., 1960. Supt. Colville Indian Agy., Nespelem, Wash., 1974-78; pres., CEO, CTEC, Nespelem, 1985-87; dir. phys. resources Colville Confederated Tribes, Nespelem, 1979-84, chmn., councilman, 1987—. Troop leader Boy Scouts Am., Nespelem, 1970-71; bd. dirs. Wenatchee Intermediate Sch. Dist., 1971-72; leader Disautel Eagles 4-H Club, Omak, Wash., 1972-74; coach Omak Little League, 1972-73; chmn. parents com. JOM, Omak, 1975, PSIS Sch. Bd., Omak, 1979. With U.S. Army, 1953-55. Mem. Am. Legion, Moose. Democrat. Roman Catholic. Avocations: golf, horseshoes, pool, reading, walking. Home: Rt 2 Box 5070 Omak WA 98841 Office: Colville Confederated Tribes PO Box 150 Nespelem WA 99155

PALMER, ALAN KENNETH, lawyer; b. Bradford, Pa., Feb. 9, 1941; s. James Kenneth and M. Mae (Gore) P.; m. Carole Ellen Mancha, Sept. 14, 1963 (Dec. 1981); m. M. Shelley Buck, Jan. 24, 1987. AB, Dartmouth Coll., 1963; postgrad., Oxford U., 1963-64; JD, Harvard U., 1967. Bar: D.C. 1970, U.S. Ct. Appeals (D.C., fed. and 10th cirs.), U.S. Supreme Ct. Law clk. to presiding justice U.S. Ct. Appeals (9th cir.), Los Angeles, 1967-68; law clk. to Justice Potter Stewart U.S. Supreme Ct., Washington, 1968-69; assoc. Covington & Burling, Washington, 1969-74; dep. assoc. solicitor Dept. Interior, Washington, 1974-76; bur. competition FTC, Washington, 1976-77, dep. dir. bur. competition, 1977-81, acting dir. bur. competition, 1981; ptnr. Morrison & Foerster, Washington, 1981—; vis. fellow Inst for Social and Policy Studies, Yale U., New Haven, Conn., 1979-80. Contbr. articles to profl. jours. Victor Kramer fellow, 1979. Mem. ABA, Fed. Bar Assn. Home: 2108 Bancroft Pl NW Washington DC 20008-4020 Office: Morrison & Foerster Ste 5500 2000 Pennsylvania Ave NW Washington DC 20006-1888

PALMER, ALICE EUGENIA, retired physician, educator; b. Chgo., Sept. 17, 1910; d. Charles Grover and Eugenia Marie (Sundquist) P.; m. Lawrence A. Pratt, 1935; m. Clyde K. Bowles, 1973; children: Lawrene Alice Porter, Dorothy Jane Pratt (Mrs. John D. Shilling). BSc, U. Chgo., 1932, MS in Physiology, 1937; MD, Wayne State U., 1938. Diplomate Am. Bd. Dermatology (preceptor 1956—). Resident pathology Detroit Receiving Hosp., 1938, resident physician dermatology, 1939-42; practice medicine specializing in dermatology Detroit, 1942-61, 65-71, Sun City, Ariz., 1971-90; instr. pathology Sch. Medicine, Wayne State U., Detroit, 1938, assoc. clin. prof. medicine, 1964-61, 65-68, adj. clin. prof., 1968-71; chmn. dept. dermatology Grace Hosp., Detroit, 1956-61, 68-71; sr. cons. dermatology Jennings Hosp., Detroit, 1954-71; med. educator U.S. AID, 1961, chief med. edn. project, Vietnam, 1961-65, med. cons., Vietnam and East Asia, 1965-68; mem. 3-man team for Survey S.E. Asian Med. Rsch. Instns., 1966; vis. prof. dermatology faculty medicine U. Saigon, 1961, 62, 63, 64, 71-73; mem. Nat. Program Dermatology, 1969-75; served Clinica Adelante, Surprise, Ariz. Assoc. editor Detroit Med. News, 1959-60. Bd. dirs., exec. bd. YWCA, Detroit, 1965-70. Recipient Disting. Alumni award Wayne State U., 1987, Disting. Svc. award Sch. Medicine, Key to the City of Detroit, 1959, U.S. Civilia Svc. medal Vietnam; named one of 10 Top Women in Detroit, 1959; Julius Stieglitz fellow in chemistry U. Chgo., 1932. Mem. AMA, Ariz. Med. Soc., Mich. Med. Soc. (chmn. dermatology 1959), Pacific Dermatol. Soc., Detroit Dermatol. Soc. (pres. 1959), Phoenix Dermatol. Soc. (v.p. 1977), Am. Acad. Dermatology (mem. internat. com., mem. internat. task force 1971-75), Maricopa County Med. Soc., Internat. Soc. Tropical Dermatology, Am. Soc. Dermatologic Surgery, Am. Geriatric Soc., Am. Acad. Cosmetic Surgery, Am. Soc. Lipo-Suction Surgery, Am. Acad. Facial Plastic and Reconstructive Surgery, S.W. Derm. Soc. (sec.-treas. 1978—), Women's Econ. Club Detroit (bd. dirs.), Pilot Club (pres.), Sigma Xi, Alpha Omega Alpha. Home and Office: 18170 N 91st Ave Apt 1155 Peoria AZ 85382-0868

PALMER, ARNOLD DANIEL, professional golfer; b. Youngstown, Pa., Sept. 10, 1929; s. Milfred Jerome and Doris M. Palmer; m. Winnie Walzer, Dec. 20, 1954; children: Peggy Palmer Wears, Amy Palmer Saunders. Student, Wake Forest Coll., LLD, 1970. Profl. golfer, 1954—, businessman, entrepreneur, 1960—; nat. spokesman Pennzoil Petroleum Products, Lanier Worldwide, Sears Can., Rolex, Lofts Seed, Cadillac Motor Car, PaineWebber, GTE, Golf mag., Rayovac, Textron; designer numerous golf courses. Author: Arnold Palmer's Golf Book, 1961, Portrait of a Professional Golfer, 1964, My Game and Yours, 1965, rev. edit., 1983, Situation Golf, 1970, Go for Broke, 1973, Arnold Palmer's Best 54 Holes of Golf, 1977, Arnold Palmer's Complete Book of Putting, 1986, Play Great Golf, 1987. With USCGR, 1951-54. Winner over 90 major golf tournaments, 1955— including Masters Championship 1958, 60, 62, 64; recipient numerous golf awards including Bob Jones award U.S. Golf Assn., William D. Richardson award Golf Writers Assn. Am., Herb Graffis award Nat. Golf Found.; named Athlete of Decade AP, 1969, Sportsman of Yr. Sports Illustrated mag., 1960, Player of Yr. Profl. Golfers Assn., 1960, 62; Profl. Golfers Assn. Tour Money Leader, 1958, 60, 62, 63; elected to World Golf

Hall of Fame, Profl. Golfers Assn. Hall of Fame. Mem. Latrobe (Pa.) Country Club, Laurel Valley Golf Club, Rolling Rock Club (Ligonier, Pa.), Bay Hill Club, Duquesne Club (Pitts.). Avocation: aviation. Home and Office: PO Box 52 Youngstown PA 15696-0052

PALMER, BARBARA JEAN, special education administrator; b. Louisiana, Mo., Dec. 14, 1939; d. Charles Mountjoy and Mary Margaret (Barnett) Crank; m. Lewis William Palmer, Nov. 23, 1961; children: Sidney Justin, Nathan Randolph. BA, Phillips U., 1961; MS, Ft. Hays State U., 1987, EdS, 1989; EdD, Kans. State U., 1992. Cert. tchr. secondary sci., tchr. spl. edn., adminstr., Kans. Tchr. sci. North Kansas City (Mo.) Pub. Schs., 1961-63, kindergarten (Mo.) Pub. Schs., 1963-64, Ottowa (Kans.) Pub. Schs., 1966-67, Hugoton (Kans.) Unified Sch. Dist., 1968-69; dir. Grant County Day Care Ctr., Ulysses, Kans., 1969-74; tchr. behavior disorders High Plains Ednl. Coop., Ulysses, 1985-88, asst. dir., 1988—. Mem., past pres. Unified Sch. Dist. 214 Bd. Edn., Ulysses, 1979-87; mem., past pres. bd. dirs. High Plains Ednl. Coop., 1980-86. Mem. ASCD, Coun. for Exceptional Children, Kans. Assn. for Spl. Edn. Administrs., Kans. Coun. for Children with Behavior Disorders (state sec. 1988-90), Phi Kappa Phi. Democrat. Methodist. Avocations: candle making, travel, hiking, reading, church activities. Office: High Plains Ednl Coop 621 E Oklahoma Ave Ulysses KS 67880-2897

PALMER, BARBARA LOUISE MOULDEN, elementary education educator; b. Winchester, Va., Nov. 20, 1941; d. Howard Kemper and Mary Elethia (Jones) Moulden; m. Staymon Eli Palmer, Aug. 9, 1958; children: Mark Eli, Nancy Louise. AB in Elem. Edn., Shepherd Coll., 1972; MA in Edn. Adminstrn., W.Va. U., 1992. Cert. tchr., W.Va. Tchr. Gerrardstown (W.Va.) Elem. Sch., 1972-90; tchr. lang. arts, computer edn. Pikeside Learning Ctr., Martinsburg, W.Va., 1991-94; computer skills tchr. Musselman Middle Sch., Bunker Hill, W.Va., 1995; demonstrator use of computers in edn. Gerrardstown Homemakers' Club; tchr. computer skills to youth orgns.; designer computer programs Gerrardstown Men's Club, presenter computer learning experience sessions. Past adult leader 4-H Club; past sec., past pres. Gerrardstown PTA; past mem. Musselman High Sch. Band Boosters Assn. Musselman High Sch. Athletic Booster Club; parent mem. Sch. Improvement Coun. Musselman Middle Sch., 1993, 94. Named lifetime mem. Gerrardstown PTA, 1990. Mem. NEA, ASCD, W.Va. Edn. Assn., Berkeley County Edn. Assn., Gerrardstown Elem. Faculty Senate (chair 1990-91), Pikeside Learning Ctr. Faculty Senate (vice-chair 1992-93, chair 1993-94, 94-95), Phi Delta Kappa. Avocations: reading, computer technology, travel. Home: Rt 1 Box 31 A Gerrardstown WV 25420 Office: Musselman Middle Sch Rte 2 Box 119 Bunker Hill WV 25413

PALMER, BEVERLY BLAZEY, psychologist, educator; b. Cleve., Nov. 22, 1945; d. Lawrence E. and Mildred M. Blazey; m. Richard C. Palmer, June 24, 1967; 1 child, Ryan Richard. PhD in Counseling Psychology, Ohio State U., 1972. Lic. clinical psychologist, Calif. Adminstrv. assoc. Ohio State U., Columbus, 1969-70; research psychologist Health Services Research Ctr. UCLA, 1971-77; commr. pub. health Los Angeles County, 1978-81; pvt. practice clin. psychology Torrance, Calif., 1985—; prof. psychology Calif. State U., Dominguez Hills, 1973—. Reviewer manuscripts for numerous textbook pubs; contbr. numerous articles to profl. jours. Recipient Proclamation County of Los Angeles, 1972, Proclamation County of Los Angeles, 1981. Mem. Am. Psychol. Assn. Office: Calif State U Dominguez Hills Dept Psychology Carson CA 90747

PALMER, BRIAN EUGENE, lawyer; b. Mpls., May 16, 1948; s. Eugene Philip and Virginia Breeze (Rolfshus) P.; m. Julia Washburn Morrison, Dec. 29, 1972; 1 child, Julia Hunter. AB, Brown U., 1970; JD, William Mitchell Coll. of Law, 1974. Bar: Minn. 1974, U.S. Dist. Ct. Minn. 1975, U.S. Ct. Appeals (8th cir.) 1980, U.S. Supreme Ct. 1980, U.S. Ct. of Fed. Claims 1984. Asst. pub. defender Hennepin County Pub. Defender, Mpls., 1974-78; assoc. Dorsey & Whitney, Mpls., 1978-82, ptnr., 1983—. Home: 1190 Lyman Ave Wayzata MN 55391-9671 Office: Dorsey & Whitney Pillsbury Ctr S 220 S 6th St Minneapolis MN 55402-4500

PALMER, CRUISE, newspaper editor; b. Kansas City, Kans., Apr. 9, 1917; s. Thomas Potter and Margaret Scroggs (McFadden) P.; m. Dorraine Humphreys, Sept. 7, 1946; children: Thomas Cruise, Martha D. Sprague. B.S. in Journalism, Kans. State U., 1938. With Kansas City (Mo.) Star, 1938—, news editor, 1963-64, mng. editor, 1965-66; exec. editor and bd. Star and Times, 1967-77, cons., 1978—; dir. Purtec Systems, Inc. Mem. bd. govs. Am. Royal Live Stock and Horse Show Assn., 1967-91; bd. dirs. ARC, 1978-91, Kansas City Mayor's Corps Progress, 1978-91; found. trustee Kans. State U.; trustee Kansas City Sister Cities Commn., 1978-91. Served to lt. (j.g.) USNR, 1943-46. Recipient Distinguished Service award Kans. State U., 1967; First Place award Pro-Am. Southgate Open Golf Tournament, 1973; Second Place award Pro-Am. Hawaiian Open, 1973, 85; Third Place, 1981; First Place award Jim Colbert Celebrity Tournament, 1981, First Place Team award Kansas City area Am. Cancer Soc. Golf Tournament, 1986. Mem. Am. Soc. Newspaper Editors, Mo.-Kans. A.P. Editors and Pubs., Soc. Profl. Journalists, Kansas City Sr. Golf Assn., Mo. Sr. Golf Assn., Kansas City Press Club (pres. 1953-54, 64-65, permanent trustee, pres. scholarship found. 1989), Kansas City Club, Chiefs Red Coat Club, Milburn Gold and Country Club, Waialae Country Club, Beta Theta Pi (Greater Kansas City Beta of Yr. 1980). Episcopalian (former vestryman and lay reader). Home: 4900 W 64th Ter Shawnee Mission KS 66208-1340 Office: 1729 Grand Ave Kansas City MO 64108-1413

PALMER, CURTIS HOWARD, diversified company executive, lawyer; b. Oakland, Calif., 1908; s. Howard H. and Catherine May (Larkin) P.; m. Helen Hayes, Apr. 8, 1936. LL.B., U. Calif., 1932. Sole practice, 1932-35; tax counsel Calif. Bd. of Equalization, 1935-43; gen. counsel Alfred Hart, Los Angeles, 1943-60; exec. officer City Nat. Bank, Beverly Hills, Calif., 1960-75, chmn. bd., 1975; chmn. bd. Arden Group, Inc., Beverly Hills, 1976—; dir. Internat. Aluminum Corp.; chmn. bd. dirs. Arden Group Inc. Office: Arden Mayfair Inc 2020 S Central Ave Compton CA 90220*

PALMER, DAVE RICHARD, educator, military officer; b. Ada, Okla., May 31, 1934; s. David Furman and Lorena Marie (Clardy) P.; m. LuDelia Clemmer, Apr. 13, 1957; children: Allison, J. Kersten. BS, U.S. Military Acad., 1956; MA in History, Duke U., 1966; postgrad., Army War Coll., 1972-73; PhD (hon.), Duke U., 1990. Commd. U.S. Army, 1956, advanced through grades to lt. gen.; mem. faculty dept. history U.S. Mil. Acad., 1966-69; mem. staff (Pentagon), 1973-76, Joint Chiefs of Staff, 1979-81; comdr. Baumholder Mil. Community, W.Ger., 1981-83; dep. comdt. Command and Gen. Staff Coll., Ft. Leavenworth, Kans., 1983-85; comdg. gen. 1st Armored Div., W.Ger., 1985-86; supt. U.S. Mil. Acad., 1986-91, 1991; pres. Walden U., 1995—. Author: The River and the Rock, 1969, The Way of the Fox, 1975, Summons of the Trumpet, 1978, 1794-America, Its Army, and The Birth of the Nation, 1994. Bd. dirs. Walden U., 1992-94. Decorated Legion of Merit (3); Bronze Star (2), D.S.M.(2). Mem. Assn. U.S. Army, Armor Assn., Am. Mil. Conflict Inst., Coun. on America's Mil. Past, Soc. Mil. History, Soc. Cin.

PALMER, DAVID, dancer; b. Cairns, Australia. Attended, Saill Acad. of Dance, Sydney, Australia; studied with Janice Breen. Dancer Australian Ballet, Joffrey Ballet, Miami City Ballet, Royal Ballet of Flanders; prin. dancer San Francisco Ballet, 1994—; guest artist Sydney Dance Co., Ballet du Nord, France, Pact Ballet of South Africa, Queensland Ballet, Australian Ballet, Ballet Theatre of Miami. Dance performances include Prodigal Son, Apollo, Scotch Symphony, Rubies, Donizetti Variations, La Source, Bugaku, Divertimento No. 15, Tchaikovsky Pas de Deux, Minkus Pas de Trois, Sylvia Pas de Deux, Stars and Stripes, Diana and Acteon, Taming of the Shrew, Romeo & Juliet, Jeu Des Cartes, Lady and the Fool, La Fille mal gardée, Illuminations, Valentine, Jamboree, Kettantanz, Suite Saint-Säens, Trinity, Light Rain, Forgotten Land, Return to a Strange Land, Dream Dances, Arden Court, Aureole, Cloven Kingdom, Reus, Transtangos, Movillisimanoble, Caoticos, Contropical, Concerto for La Donna, The Moor's Pavane, Threshold, Resolucia, La Bayadere, Nutcracker, Beyond Twelve, Surfacing, Aerial, The Hunchback of Notre Dame, Le Corsaire Pas de Deux, The Three Muscateers, Valses Poeticos, Maestrom, In the Night, The Concert, Company B, Rodeo, others; (film) To Dream of Roses, 1990; choreographer Aerial, Memories, Beauty and the Beast, Intimacy Pas de Deux, Collage. Office: San Francisco Ballet 455 Franklin St San Francisco CA 94102*

PALMER, DAVID BRENT, lawyer; b. Des Moines, Oct. 19, 1946; s. Martin S. and Jean P.; children: Jed, Miles. BA, U. Wash., 1972; JD, Syracuse U., 1975. Bar: D.C. 1975. Atty. health care fin. divsn. Dept. Health & Human Svcs., Balt., 1975-82; ptnr. Akin, Gump, Strauss, Hauer & Feld, LLP, Washington, 1984—. Vol. VISTA, Marietta, Wash., 1966; area dir. Am. Cancer Soc., New Orleans, 1972. Mem. Nat. Health Lawyers Assn. Office: Akin Gump Strauss et al Ste 11 1333 New Hampshire Ave NW Washington DC 20036-1500

PALMER, DAVID GILBERT, lawyer; b. Lakewood, N.J., Jan. 10, 1945; s. Robert Dayton and Lois (Gilbert) P.; m. Susan Edmundson Walsh, Aug. 17, 1968; children: Jonathan, Megan. AB, Johns Hopkins U., 1967; JD, U. Colo., 1970. Bar: Colo. 1970, U.S. Dist. Ct. Colo. 1970, U.S. Ct. Appeals (9th and 10th cirs.) 1970, U.S. Supreme Ct. 1970. Ptnr., chmn. litigation dept. Holland & Hart, Denver, 1970-87, Gibson, Dunn & Crutcher, Denver, 1987—. Chmn. N.W. region Am. Heart Assn., Dallas, 1986—, bd. dirs., 1986—, sec., 1990—, chmn. elect, 1991-92, chmn., 1992-93; pres., bd. dirs. Colo. Heart Assn., Denver, 1974; bd. dirs. C. H. Kempe Nat. Ctr. for Prevention of Child Abuse, Denver, 1984-90, pres., 1989-90; bd. dirs. Goodwill Industries, Denver, 1981-84. Mem. ABA, Colo. Bar Assn., Denver Law Club. Clubs: University, Mile High (Denver). Home: 7271 S Pontiac Way Englewood CO 80112-1633 Office: Gibson Dunn & Crutcher 1801 California St Ste 4200 Denver CO 80202-2694

PALMER, DAVID SCOTT, political scientist, educator; b. Boston, July 16, 1937; s. Walter S. and Jean (Stuart) P.; m. Sarah Crawford, 1955 (dec. Nov. 1985); children: Walter Scott, Henry Crawford, Asa MacAdam. BA in Internat. Rels. cum laude, Dartmouth Coll., 1959; MA in Hispanic Am. Studies, Stanford U., 1962; PhD in Comparative Govt., Cornell U., 1973. Vol. leader Peace Corps, Peru, 1962-64; asst. dean freshmen, asst. to dir. admissions Dartmouth Coll., Hanover, N.H., 1964-68; from instr. to asst. prof. dept. govt. Bowdoin Coll., 1972-76; professorial lectr. Sch. Advanced Internat. Studies Johns Hopkins U., Washington, 1977-88; assoc. dean for programs Fgn. Svc. Inst., Dept. State, 1984-88, chair Latin Am. and Caribbean studies, 1976-88; prof. polit. sci. Boston U., 1988—, prof. internat. rels., 1990—, dir. Latin Am. studies, 1991-94; vis. lectr. Princeton U., 1978-79, Georgetown U., 1985. Author: Peru: The Authoritarian Tradition, 1980, (with Kevin Middlebrook) Military Government and Political Development: Lessons from Peru, 1975, (with Robert Wesson and others) The Latin American Military Institution, 1985; editor, 2d contbr.: Shining Path of Peru, 1992, 2d edit., 1994; contbr. chpts. to books, articles and revs. to profl. jours. Recipient Meritorious Honor award U.S. Dept. of State, 1981; Daniel Webster nat. scholar, 1955-59; Edward John Noble Found. leadership grantee 1959-62. Mem. Latin Am. Studies Assn. (exec. com. 1983-86), New Eng. Coun. Latin Am. Studies (exec. com. 1989-91, pres. 1993-94), Interam. Coun. of Washington (pres. 1978-79), Phi Beta Delta, Phi Kappa Phi, Sigma Delta Pi. Home: 69 Waverley St Belmont MA 02178-1958 Office: Boston U 152 Bay State Rd Boston MA 02215-1501

PALMER, DEBORAH JEAN, lawyer; b. Williston, N.D., Oct. 25, 1947; d. Everett Edwin and Doris Irene (Harberg) P.; m. Kenneth L. Rich, Mar. 29, 1980; children: Andrew, Stephanie. BA, Carleton Coll., 1969; JD cum laude, Northwestern U., 1973. Bar: Minn. 1973, U.S. Dist. Ct. Minn. 1973, U.S. Ct. Appeals (8th cir.) 1975, U.S. Supreme Ct. 1978. Econ. analyst Harris Trust & Savs. Bank, Chgo., 1969-70; assoc. Robins, Kaplan, Miller & Ciresi, Mpls., 1973-79, ptnr., 1979—. Trustee Carleton Coll., 1984-88; mem. bd. religious edn. Plymouth Congl. Ch., 1992-95. Mem. ABA, Minn. Bar Assn., Minn. Women Lawyers Assn. (sec. 1976-78), Hennepin County Bar Assn., Hennepin County Bar Found. (bd. dirs. 1978-81), Carleton Coll. Alumni Assn. (bd. dirs. 1978-82, sec. 1980-82), Women's Assn. of Minn. Orch. (bd. dirs. 1980-85, treas. 1981-83). Home: 1787 Colfax Ave S Minneapolis MN 55403-3008 Office: Robins Kaplan Miller & Ciresi 800 Lasalle Ave Minneapolis MN 55402

PALMER, DENNIS DALE, lawyer; b. Alliance, Nebr., Apr. 30, 1945; s. Vernon D. Palmer and Marie E. (Nelson) Fellers; m. Rebecca Ann Turner, Mar. 23, 1979; children: Lisa Marie, Jonathan Paul. BA, U. Mo., 1967, JD, 1970. Bar: Mo. 1970, U.S. Dist. Ct. (we. dist.) Mo. 1970, U.S. Ct. Appeals (8th and 10th cirs.) 1973, U.S. Supreme Ct. 1980. Staff atty. Legal Aid Soc. Western Mo., Kansas City, 1970-73; assoc. Shughart, Thomson & Kilroy, P.C., Kansas City, 1973-76, ptnr., bd. dirs., 1976—. Contbr. articles on franchise and employment law to legal jours. Bd. dirs., chmn. legal assts. adv. bd. Avila Coll., Kansas City, 1984-87. 2d lt. U.S. Army, 1970. Mem. ABA (litigation com. 1980, forum com. on franchising 1987), Mo. Bar Assn. (antitrust com. 1975—, civil practice com. 1975—), Kansas City Bar Assn. (chmn. franchise law com. 1987—), Univ. Club. Avocations: jogging, golf, tennis, outdoor activities, reading. Home: 3000 W 120th Ter Leawood KS 66209-1003 Office: Shughart Thomson & Kilroy 12 Wyandotte Plz 120 W 12th St Fl 16 Kansas City MO 64105-1917

PALMER, DONALD CURTIS, interdenominational missionary society executive; b. Nelson, Minn., Oct. 8, 1934; s. Roy August Adn Cora (Bergner) P.; m. Dorothy Mae Nordquist, Mar. 16, 1962; children: Jean Marie, John Eric. Student, U. Minn., 1952-55; BS in Bible, Briercrest Bible Coll., Caronport, Can., 1958; MA in Missions, Trinity Divinity Sch., Deerfield, Ill., 1967; D in Ministry, Trinity Divinity Sch., 1989. Missionary Colombia GMU Internat., Kansas City, Mo., 1959-71; dir. evangelism GMU Internat., 1969-71, field sec. Latin Am., 1971-73, v.p. field ministries for Latin Am. 1973-85, v.p. research and strategy, 1985-92; gen. dir. Am. Missionary Fellowship, Villanova, Pa., 1992—; vis. prof. Grace Coll. of the Bible, Omaha, 1982-92; mem. Frontier People's Com., 1985-92, Evang. Missiological Soc., 1991—. Author: Explosion of People Evangelism, 1974; (with others) Dynamic Religious Movements, 1978, Managing Conflict Creatively, 1990. Republican. Baptist. Avocations: golf, tennis, hiking. Home: 200 Cohasset Ln West Chester PA 19380-6504 Office: Am Missionary Fellowship 672 Conestoga Rd Villanova PA 19085 *The greatest inner quality that a person can possess is a thankful, grateful spirit.*

PALMER, EDWARD L., social psychology educator, television researcher, writer; b. Hagerstown, Md., Aug. 11, 1938; s. Ralph Leon and Eva Irene (Brandenburg) P.; children: Edward Lee, Jennifer Lynn. BA, Gettysburg Coll., 1960; BD, Luth. Theol. Sem., Gettysburg, 1964; MS, Ohio U., 1967, PhD, 1970. Asst. prof. Western Md. Coll., Westminster, 1968-70; asst. prof. Davidson Coll., N.C., 1970-77, assoc. prof., 1977-86, chair, 1985—, prof., 1986—, Watson prof., 1991—; guest rschr. Harvard U. Cambridge, Mass., 1977; vis. scholar UCLA, 1984; coms. Council on Children, Media, Merchandising, 1978-79, 1st Union Bank Corp., Charlotte, N.C., 1975-79; NSF proposal reviewer, 1978—. Editl. reviewer Jour. Broadcasting and Electronic Media, 1978—; editor: Children and the Faces of TV, 1980, Children in the Cradle of TV, 1987; contbr. to Wiley Ency. of Psychology, 1984; author jour. articles. Sec. A. Mecklenburg Child Devel. Assn., Davidson and Cornelius, N.C., 1974-78; bd. mem. pub. radio sta. WDAV, 1970-90. Telecommunications task force Rutgers U., 1981. Recipient Thomas Jefferson Teaching award Robert Earll McConnell Found., 1993. Mem. Am. Psychol. Assn., Soc. Rsch. in Child Devel., Am. Psychol. Soc., Assn. Heads Depts. Psychology (pres. 1994—), Southeastern Psychol. Assn., Southeastern Soc. Social Psychologists, So. Assn. Pub. Opinion Rsch., Phi Beta Kappa (pres. Davidson chpt. 1985-86). Avocations: sunrise and sunset walks; writing poetry; music composition and performance. Office: Davidson Coll PO Box 1719 Davidson NC 28036

PALMER, EDWARD LEWIS, banker; b. N.Y.C., Aug. 12, 1917; s. William and Cecelia (Tierney) P.; m. Margaret Preston, Jan. 5, 1940; children: Edward Preston, Jane Lewis. A.B., Brown U., 1938. With N.Y. Trust Co., 1941-59, v.p., 1952-59; with Citibank, N.A., N.Y.C., 1959-82; sr. v.p. Citibank, N.A., 1962-65, exec. v.p. 1965-70, dir., chmn. exec. com., 1970-82; pres. Mill Neck Group, Inc., 1982; bd. dirs. Devon Group, Inc., Lanxide Corp., SunResorts Ltd., Holmes Protection Group Inc., Phoenix Home Funds Inc.; dir. emeritus Cornign Inc.; trustee emeritus Mut. N.Y. Trustee emeritus Met. Mus. Art, Brown U. Served to lt. comdr. USNR, 1942-46. Mem. Phi Gamma Delta. Home: Horseshoe Rd Mill Neck NY 11765 Office: 399 Park Ave New York NY 10022-4614

PALMER, FORREST CHARLES, librarian, educator; b. Burlington, Wis., Oct. 17, 1924; s. Forrest Blaire and Marie Florence (Rubach) P.; m. Lois Mae Davis, June 12, 1946; children: Forrest Charles, Beth Elaine, Janet

Lorrayne. Student, U. Pitts., 1943-44; B.A., Valparaiso U., 1948; B.S. in L.S, George Peabody Coll., 1949, M.S. in L.S, 1953. Head catalog dept. Janesville (Wis.) Pub. Library, 1949-50; serials cataloger N.C. State U., Raleigh, 1950-51; head serials dept. N.C. State U., 1951-55; dir. libraries Miss. State U., State College, 1955-62; librarian, head dept. library sci. James Madison U., Harrisonburg, Va., 1962-70, head librarian, 1970-74, prof. library sci., documents librarian, 1973-89, ret., 1989, prof. emeritus, 1990—, mem. faculty senate, 1982-86, faculty marshall, 1983-85, treas. senate, 1985-86; mem. library com. Va. Higher Edn. Study Commn.; sec. joint law library com. Laird L. Conrad Meml. Library, Harrisonburg, 1974-89; adv. com. Va. Council Higher Edn.; Madison Coll. rep. Library Affairs Va. U. Center. Editor: Virginia Librarian, 1963-65. Contbr. articles and book revs. to profl. publs. Mem. edn. com. Starkville (Miss.) Youth Ctr., 1956; chmn. adv. bd. YMCA, State College, Miss., 1957-59; vice-chmn. Rep. city com., Harrisonburg, 1979-81; mem. land use adv. com. Ctrl. Shenandoah Planning Dist. Commn., 1979; mem. Bd. Zoning Appeals, Harrisonburg, 1981-91, vice chmn., 1983-85, chmn., 1985-91; visiting elder Presbyn. Ch. U.S., clk. of session, 1982-84; mem. task force on maintenance Synod of Mid-Atlantic, Presbyn. Ch., Massanetta Springs, 1991; mem. Ft. Delaware Soc., 1992, life mem., 1995—. With Signal Corps AUS, PTO, 1943-46. Recipient Golden Triangle award YMCA. Mem. ALA (liaison com. Library Instrn. Round Table 1978-80, com. on instrn. in use of libraries 1977-79, mem. Govt. Documents Round Table 1983-89), Southeastern Library Assn. (chmn. coll. sect. 1960-62, treas., mem. exec. bd. 1975-76, budget com. 1974-80, hdqrts. liason com., 1987-91), Miss. Library Assn. (chmn. standards and planning com. 1958-59, chmn. coll. sect. 1959-60), Va. Library Assn. (activities com. 1962-65, chmn. publs. com. 1963-65, 1st v.p. 1968, pres. 1969-70), Pi Gamma Mu, Alpha Beta Alpha (adviser 1962-70), Beta Phi Mu. Republican. Presbyterian. Home: 60 E Weaver Ave Harrisonburg VA 22801-3041 *Long-lasting and meaningful contributions to society are those made out of consideration for others, not those where another individual is harmed.*

PALMER, GARY ANDREW, portfolio manager; b. Stamford, Conn., Dec. 30, 1953; s. Andrew and Edna Balz (Brogan) P.; m. Suzanne Branyon, Oct. 10, 1981; children: Gregory Allen, Kimberly Lynn. BS in Bus. Adminstrn., U. Vt., 1977; MBA, U. N.C., 1979. Sr. fin. analyst Carolina Power and Light Co., Raleigh, N.C., 1979-80; dir. fin. planning and analysis Fed. Home Loan Mortgage Corp., Washington, 1980-85; sr. v.p. capital markets Imperial Corp. of Am., San Diego, 1985-90; sr. v.p., treas. Pacific 1st Fin. Corp., Seattle, 1990-92, Gentra Capital Corp., Seattle, 1993-95.

PALMER, GARY STEPHEN, health services administrator; b. Murphy, N.C., Jan. 19, 1949; s. Bruce and Mary Frances (Patterson) P.; m. Kathleen Hart Middleton, June 12, 1976; children: Eric S., Brian S. BS in Bus. Adminstrn., U. N.C., 1971; MHA, Baylor U., 1982. Commd. U.S. Army, 1972, advanced through grades to lt. col., 1990; dir. program budget Letterman Army Med. Ctr., San Francisco, 1979-80; adminstrv. resident Womack Community Hosp., Fayetteville, N.C., 1981-82, ambulatory healthcare adminstr., 1982-83, asst. adminstr. profl. svcs., 1983-85; ambulatory healthcare adminstr. USA Health Svcs., San Antonio, 1985-88; COO U.S. Army Den Rl Activity, Killeen, Tex., 1988-91; inspector gen. Womack Army Med. Ctr., Ft. Bragg, N.C., 1993-94; assoc. dir. exec. master's program Sch. Pub. Health U. N.C., Chapel Hill, 1994—. Fellow Am. Coll. Healthcare Execs. (army regent's adv. coun. 1988-92, Elua Alii chpt. Honolulu 1991-92); mem. Tex. Hosp. Assn., Med. Group Mgmt. Assn. Home: 103 William White Ct Carrboro NC 27510 Office: U NC Sch Pub Health CB 7400 Dept Health Policy/Adminstn Chapel Hill NC 27599-7400

PALMER, HANS CHRISTIAN, economics educator; b. N.Y.C., Sept. 21, 1933; s. Hans P. and Dagny E. (Stockel) P.; m. Beverly Wilson, June 28, 1963; children: Margaret D., David E. B.A., U. Calif.-Berkeley, 1954, M.A., 1955, Ph.D., 1965. Instr. econs. Pomona Coll., Claremont, Calif., 1962-65, asst. prof., 1965-70, assoc. prof., 1970-77, prof. econs., 1977—. Co-author: Financial Barrier to Higher Education in California, 1965; co-author, co-editor: Long-Term Care: Perspectives from Research and Demonstrations, 1983. Served to 1st lt. U.S. Army, 1955-57. Grantee NSF, 1975-76. Mem. Am. Econs. Assn., Assn. Health Services Research, Econ. History Assn., Econ. History Soc. (U.K.), Gerontol. Soc., History of Econs. Soc., Assn. Comparative Econ. Studies. Office: Dept Econs Pomona Coll Claremont CA 91711

PALMER, HARVEY JOHN, chemical engineering educator, consultant; b. N.Y.C., Apr. 3, 1946; s. Harvey Anthony and Pearl Edna (Weber) P.; m. Donna Mary Partigan, July 11, 1966; children—Harvey D., Angeline, Thomas. B.S.C.E., U. Rochester, 1967; Ph.D. in Chem. Engring., U. Wash. 1971. Lic. profl. engr., N.Y. Asst. prof. chem. engring. U. Rochester, N.Y., 1971-77, assoc. prof., 1977-84, prof., 1984—, assoc. dean for grad. studies, 1983-89, chair dept. chem. engring., 1990—; cons. Pfaudler Co., Rochester, 1978-79, Eastman Kodak Co., Rochester, 1982-92, Helios Corp., Mumford, N.Y., 1983-91, Boehringer Mannheim Corp., Indpls., 1993; bd. dirs. Transmation Inc., Rochester. Contbr. articles to profl. jours. Mem. sch. bd. Honeoye Falls-Lima Central Schs., N.Y., 1983-92, pres., 1988-90. Recipient Undergrad. Teaching award Coll. Engring., U. Rochester, 1979, 82. Mem. Am. Inst. Chem. Engrs. (sec. Rochester sect. 1976-77), Sigma Xi. Office: Univ Rochester Dept Chem Engring Rochester NY 14627

PALMER, IRENE SABELBERG, university dean and educator emeritus, nurse, researcher, historian; b. Franklin, N.J., May 28, 1923; d. John Joseph and May (Heiser) Sabelberg; 1 son, Andrew C. B.S., N.J. State Tchrs Coll., 1945; diploma, Jersey City Med. Center Sch. Nursing, 1945; M.A., N.Y. U., 1951, Ph.D., 1963. Edn. dir. Diploma Schs. Nursing, N.J., Mass., 1948-52; ednl. dir. Glenn Dale (Md.) Hosp., D.C. Dept. Pub. Health, 1956, dir. nursing svc. and edn., 1956-61; assoc. clin. prof. nursing Georgetown U., 1960-61; USPHS trainee, 1961-62; assoc. chief nursing svc. for rsch. VA Hosp., San Francisco, 1963-64; rsch. nurse cons. HEW, USPHS, Div. Nursing, Nursing Rsch. Field Center, San Francisco, 1964-66; asst. dean, assoc. prof. nursing U. Colo. Sch. Nursing, Denver, 1966-68; dean, prof. nursing Boston U. Sch. Nursing, 1968-74; prof. Hahn Sch. Nursing, U. San Diego, 1974-91, prof. emeritus, 1991—, dean, 1974-87, dean emeritus, 1988—. Editor: Nursing Clinics of North America, 1970; Contbr. articles to profl. jours. Served to capt. Nurse Corps U.S. Army, 1953-56. Internat. Nightingale scholar; Nat. Health Svc. fellow; recipient Excellence in Nursing Scholarship award Orgn. Nurse Execs., 1993. Fellow Nat. League Nursing (bd. visitors 1977-87); mem. Am. Acad. Nursing; mem. ANA, Am. Assn. History Nursing, Am. Assn. Colls. Nursing (hon.), Boston U. Nursing Archives, Sigma Theta Tau (Leadership award Zeta Mu chpt. 1986, Excellence in Nursing award 1991).

PALMER, JAMES ALVIN, baseball commentator; b. N.Y.C., Oct. 15, 1945; children: Jamie, Kelly. Student, Ariz. State U., Towson (Md.) State Coll. Pitcher Balt. Orioles, 1966-84; commentator ABC Sports, 1984—; also appears in TV and print advertisements. Author: (with Jack Clary) Jim Palmer's Way to Fitness, 1985. Recipient Cy Young Meml. award Am. League, 1973, 75, 76; named Am. League Pitcher of Year The Sporting News, 1973, 75, 76; elected to Baseball Hall of Fame, 1990. Played All-Star Game, 1970, 71, 72, 77, 78. Office: care ABC-TV Sports 1330 Ave Of The Americas New York NY 10019-5422*

PALMER, JAMES DANIEL, information technology educator; b. Washington, Mar. 8, 1930; s. Martin Lyle and Sarah Elizabeth (Hall) P.; m. Margret Kupka, June 21, 1952; children: Stephen Robert, Daniel Lee, John Keith. AA, Fullerton Jr. Coll., 1953; BS (Alumni scholar), U. Calif. Berkeley, 1955, MS, 1957; PhD, U. Okla., 1963; DPS (hon.), Regis Coll., Denver, 1977. Chief engr. Motor vehicle and Illumination Lab. U. Calif., Berkeley, 1955-57; assoc. prof. U. Okla., Norman, 1957-63; prof. U. Okla., 1963-66, asst. to dir. Rsch. Inst., 1960-63, cons. Rsch. Inst., 1966-69, dir. Sch. Elec. Engring., 1963-66, dir. Systems Rsch. Center, 1964-66; dean sci. and engring., prof. elec. engring. Union Coll., Schenectady, 1966-71; ptnrs. Met. State Coll., Denver, 1971-78; rsch. and spl. programs adminstr. Dept. Transp., Washington, 1978-79; v.p., gen. mgr. rsch. and devel. div. Mech. Tech., Inc., Latham, N.Y., 1979-82; exec. v.p. J.J. Henry Co., Inc., Moorestown, N.J., 1982-85; BDM internat. prof. info. tech. George Mason U., Fairfax, Va., 1985—; bd. dirs. J.J Henry Co., Inc. cons. Sym Mgmt. Co., Boston, Higher Edn. Exec. Assocs., Denver, PERI, Princeton; adj. prof. U. Colo. Co-author: (with A.P. Sage) Software Systems Engineering, (with

Aseltine, Beam and Sage) Introduction to Computer Systems, Analysis, Design and Application. Bd. dirs., exec. v.p. adv. com. U.S.A. Vols. for Internat. Tech. Assistance, 1967-83, exec. v.p., 1970-71, chmn. exec. com.; trustee, vice chmn. Nat. Commn. on Coop. Edn.; mem. exec. policy bd. Alaska Natural Gas Pipeline, 1978-79; trustee Auraria Higher Edn. Program, Denver; mem. Fulbright fellow Selection Com., Colo.; bd. mgrs., mem. exec. com. Hudson-Mohawk Assn. Colls. and Univs., trustee, chmn. bd., 1970-71; adv. com. USCG Acad., 1972-82, chmn. adv. com., 1979-82; mem. Colo. Gov.'s Sci. and Tech. Adv. Council; pres. Denver Cath. Community Services Bd.; mem. Archdiocesan Catholic Charities and Community Services; mem. bd. U. Okla. Rsch. Inst.; mem. adv. com. Mile-Hi Red Cross. With USMC, 1950-51. Case-Western Res. Centennial scholar, 1981; recipient U.S. Coast Guard award and medal for meritorious pub. service, 1983. Fellow IEEE (exec. and adminstrv. coms., v.p. long-range planning and finance, chmn. com. on large scale systems, Joseph E. Wahl Outstanding Career Achievement award 1993); mem. Systems, Man and Cybernetics Soc. (pres., Outstanding Contbns. award 1981), alumni assns. U. Calif. and U. Okla., Inst. Internat. Edn. (bd. dir. Rocky Mt. sect.). Soc. Naval Architects and Marine Engrs., Am. Soc. Engring. Edn., Am. Mil. Engrs., N.Y. Acad. Sci., Navy League, Sigma Xi, Eta Kappa Nu, Pi Mu Epsilon, Alpha Gamma Sigma. Home: 12903 New Parkland Dr Herndon VA 22071-2646 Office: George Mason U Sch of Info Tech & Engring Fairfax VA 22030

PALMER, JAMES DANIEL, inspector; b. Oklahoma City, Okla., Aug. 11, 1936; s. Athol Ford and Marjorie Lorraine (Ward) P.; m. Gloria Jean Myers, June 1954 (div. Sept. 1956); 1 child, James Douglas; m. Gloria Jean West, Dec. 14, 1963; children: Diana Lorraine, Elana Louise, Sheri Francis. AB in Police Sci. with honors, San Jose (Calif.) State U., 1963, AB in Psychology, 1964; MPA, Golden Gate U., 1972. Cert. Calif. police officers standards and tng. Asst. foreman Hunts Foods, Inc. Hayward, Calif., 1959-64; spl. investigator Dept. A.B.C. State of Calif., Oakland, 1964-67; criminal inspector Contra Costa County Dist. Atty., Martinez, Calif., 1967-72, lt. of inspectors, 1972-92; ret., 1992; pres. Contra Costa County Peace Officers, Richmond, 1974-75; past v.p. Contra Costa County Dist. Atty's Inv. Assn., Martinez, 1971, tng. officer, 1990-92. Contbr. articles to profl. jours. Past pres. South Hayward (Calif.) Dem. Club, 1976, 77, San Leandro (Calif.) Dems., 1975; mem. Gov's Law Enforcement Adv. Commn., Sacramento, Calif., 1972-76, Calif. Dem. Coun., 1972-73; rev. Am. Fellowship Protestant Ch., 1990—, min., 1990—. With USAF, 1955-58. Avocations: stocks, bonds, real estate, family, church. Home: 2788 Sydney Way Castro Valley CA 94546-2738

PALMER, JAMES EDWARD, public relations executive; b. Evansville, Ind., July 30, 1935; s. James Edward and Verble (Hearin) P. B.A. in English, N.Y.U., 1955. Reporter Evansville Courier, 1955-59; non-fiction editor Cosmopolitan mag., N.Y.C., 1959-61; exec. editor Cosmopolitan mag., 1961-65; editor Mag. Mgmt. Co., Inc., 1971-72; editor-in-chief Liberty mag., N.Y.C., 1972-73; dir. mag. and book dept. Carl Byoir & Assos., N.Y.C., 1973-76; corp. public relations dir. Macmillan, Inc., N.Y.C., 1977-80; pres. James Palmer Assos., N.Y.C., 1980-88, The Palmer Group, Houston, 1988—. Mem. Sigma Chi. Office: PO Box 90422 Houston TX 77290-0422

PALMER, JAMES RUSSWORTH, theoretical physicist, high energy laser optics researcher; b. Madera, Calif., Oct. 12, 1936; s. James Russworth Palmer and Georgella (Battmann) Palmer Irelan; m. Nancy Diane Byrne, Jan. 21, 1988. BSChemE, Calif. State U., 1963, MSChemE, 1966; PhD, UCLA, 1973; JD, Western State U., 1990. Project scientist Aerospace Controls, Los Angeles, 1963-66; project engr. Electroptical Systems, Pasadena, Calif., 1966-70; pres.-cons. Doc Jim Enterprises, Orange, Calif., 1970—; chief scientist Comarco, Inc., Ridgecrest, Calif., 1983-87; adj. sr. research scientist U. Ala. Ctr. for Applied Optics, Huntsville, 1987—; vis. rsch. prof. Trinity Coll., Ireland, 1991-92; cons. Seven Engring., Santa Monica, Calif., 1980—, Super Computing Surfaces, 1992, Fiat Rsch., Italy. Author: Laser Damage in Optical Thin Films, 1985,High Power Laser Optics, 1990, Transient Heat Transfer in Flat Plates, Vol. I, 1993; also numerous articles, 1963—. Served to lt. (j.g.) USN, 1955-59. Mem. Optical Soc. Am., Am. Inst. Physics, N.Y. Acad. Scis., Internat. Soc. Optical Engring. (Rudolf Kingslake Silver medal 1984), Sigma Xi.

PALMER, JEFFRESS GARY, hematologist, educator; b. Bklyn., Oct. 7, 1921; s. William Ware and Margaret Lee (Boswell) P.; m. Jane Ann Cartwright, Feb. 2, 1951; children: Kristin Cartwright, Julie Mitchell. BS, Emory U., 1942, MD, 1944. Intern N.C. Bapt. Hosp., 1944-45; resident in medicine Emory U., Atlanta, 1947-49; fellow hematology U. Utah, Salt Lake City, 1949-52; from asst. prof. to prof. medicine U. N.C., Chapel Hill, 1952—. Capt. M.C. AUS, 1945-47. Mem. AAAS, AAUP, AMA, Am. Fedn. for Clin. Rsch., So. Soc. for Clin. Investigation, N.Y. Acad. Scis., Am. Soc. Hematology. Home: Morgan Creek Rd Chapel Hill NC 27514

PALMER, JOHN BERNARD, III, lawyer; b. Ft. Wayne, Ind., May 18, 1952; s. John Bernard and Dorothy Alma (Lauer) P. B.A., Mich. State U., 1974, J.D. U. Mich., 1977. Bar: Ill. 1977, U.S. Dist. Ct. (no. dist) Ill. 1977, U.S. Tax Ct. 1979. Assoc. Mayer Brown & Platt, Chgo., 1977-80; assoc. Hopkins & Sutter, Chgo., 1980-83, ptnr., 1983—; adj. prof. Ill. Inst. Tech.-Kent Coll. of Law, Chgo., 1984—. Mem. ABA. Office: Hopkins & Sutter Three First Nat Plaza Chicago IL 60602

PALMER, JOHN L., social sciences researcher, educator; b. Upper Darby, Pa., Apr. 10, 1943; s. Richard Sidwell and Helen (Logan) P.; m. Nancy Hetenyi, June 29, 1968 (div. Dec. 1984); 1 child, Georgina; m. Stephanie Graham Gould, June 21, 1986; 1 child, Joanna. BA in Math., Williams Coll., 1965; PhD in Econs. Stanford U., 1970. Asst. prof. econs. Stanford U., Calif., 1969-71; dir. office income security policy HEW, Washington, 1971-75; asst. sec. HHS, Washington, 1979-81; sr. fellow The Brookings Instn., Washington, 1975-79, The Urban Inst., Washington, 1981-88; dean Maxwell Sch. Syracuse U., 1988—; adj. faculty Harvard U., Cambridge, Mass., 1982-84; cons. numerous govt. agys. and pvt. founds., 1975-79, 81—. Author, editor 12 books; contbr. numerous articles on econs., social and budgetary concerns and policies. Woodrow Wilson fellow, 1965, NDEA scholar, Stanford U. Fellow Nat. Acad. Pub. Adminstrn.; mem. Am. Econ. Assn., Assn. Pub. Policy Analysis and Mgmt., NAS (various coms.), Nat. Acad. Social Ins. Home: 680 Woodchuck Hill Rd Fayetteville NY 13066-9760 Office: Syracuse U 200 Eggers Hall Syracuse NY 13244-1090

PALMER, JOHN M., medical administrator. AB, William Jewell Coll., 1967; MDiv, Gen. Sem. of Episcopal Ch., 1970. Ordained priest Episcopal Ch. Asst. to bishop Diocese of S.E. Fla., 1973-77; rector Ch. of the Transfiguration, 1977-79; dir. spl. parish ministries Trinity Ch., N.Y.C., 1979-86; exec. dir. Helen Keller Inst., N.Y.C., 1986—. Bd. dirs. Roosa Sch. Music, 1984-86, Village Nursing Home, 1984-86, Nat. Inst. Tng. 1982-86; chair Diocesan Com. on World Peace and Disarmament, 1988-86; chmn. bd. dis. Wyatt Cmty. Trust, 1977-79; mem. adv. com. WHO, 1986—; sec. Found. for Integrative Studies, 1990—; exec. com. World Blind Union, 1989—; exec. com. Interaction, 1986-91, Prvt. Agys. Collaborating Together, 1987-91; chmn. Partnership of Internat. Non-Govtl. Orgns. to Prevent Blindness, 1990—.

PALMER, JOHN MARSHALL, lawyer; b. Fairmont, Minn., June 5, 1906; s. John Earl and Winnifred Ann (Ibertson) P.; m. Mary Louise Arntsen, June 28, 1934 (div.); children: Loring Swift, John Edward, Marsha; m. Dorothy Mae Bright, July 27, 1984. B.A., U. Minn., 1928, LL.B., 1931. Bar: Minn. 1931. Assoc. Sweet, Johnson & Sands, Mpls., 1931-32, Stinchfield, Mackall, Crounse, McNally & Moore, Mpls., 1932-42; chief enforcement atty. OPA, St. Paul, 1942-44; ptnr. Stinchfield, Mackall, Crounse & Moore, Mpls., 1944-51, Mackall, Crounse, Moore, Helmey & Palmer, Mpls., 1951-57, Levitt and Palmer, 1957-60, Levitt, Palmer & Bearmon, 1961-65, Levitt, Palmer, Bowen & Bearmon, 1965-68, Levitt, Palmer, Bowen, Bearmon & Rotman, 1968-79; ptnr. Levitt, Palmer, Bowen, Rotman & Share, 1979-82, of counsel, 1982-83; of counsel Briggs & Morgan, 1983-92; sec., dir. Triangle Devel. Co. Mem. ABA, Minn. Bar Assn. (pres. 1955-56), Law Alumni Assn. U. Minn. (past pres., dir.), Am. Coll. Trial Lawyers, Mpls. Club, Phi Gamma Delta, Phi Delta Phi. Congregationalist. Home: 10401 S Cedar Lake Rd Apt 219 Minnetonka MN 55305

PALMER, LANGDON, banker; b. Montclair, N.J., Mar. 4, 1928; s. Lubin and Marjorie (Maxfield) P.; m. Millicent M. Lott, June 27, 1954; children—Jennifer Leigh, Langdon Jr., Christopher Lott. B. in Comml. Sci., Dartmouth Coll., 1951; M.B.A., NYU, 1959; postgrad. in advanced mgmt., Harvard Bus. Sch., 1968. Sr. v.p. Chase Manhattan Bank, N.Y.C., 1953-83; chmn., chief exec. officer Horizon Bank, Morristown, N.J., 1984-89; ret., 1989; bd. dirs. Chem. Bank N.J., N.A., 1989-92, now mem. adv. bd. Exec. v.p. Greater N.Y. coun. Boy Scouts Am., until 1983, Morris Sussex coun., 1984—; trustee African Am. Inst., N.Y.C., until 1983; bd. dirs. N.J. Conservation Found., Nature Conservancy (chmn. N.J. chpt.), Morris County Agrl. Devel. Bd., until 1993, Morris County Park Commn.; chmn. bd. Morris 2000; trustee Morris County Parks and Conservation Found. Sgt. U.S. Army, 1951-53, Korea. Decorated Bronze Star; named Knight Great Commander of Liberian Humane Order of African Redemption, 1983; Ordre National Republic of Guinee, 1982; recipient Silver Beaver award Boy Scouts Am., 1977, Disting. Eagle award, 1989. Mem. Morris County C. of C. (bd. dirs.—vice chmn. 1987—, chmn. 1988). Republican. Episcopalian. Clubs: Morristown (N.J.); Anglers (N.Y.C.). Avocation: fly fishing.

PALMER, LARRY ISAAC, lawyer, educator; b. 1944. AB, Harvard U., 1966; LLB, Yale U., 1969. Bar: Calif. 1970. Asst. prof. Rutgers U., Camden, N.J., 1970-73, assoc. prof., 1973-75; assoc. prof. Cornell U., Ithaca, N.Y., 1975-79, prof., 1979—, vice provost, 1987-91, v.p. acad. programs, 1987-91, v.p. acad. program and campus affairs, 1991—; vis. fellow Cambridge U., 1984-85. Mem. Am. Law Inst. Office: Cornell U Acad Programs-Campus Affairs 311 Day Hall Ithaca NY 14853-2801

PALMER, LESTER DAVIS, minister; b. Augusta, Ga., Oct. 6, 1929; s. Lawton Evans and Gwendolyn (Ramsbotham) P.; m. Janelle Griffin, May 6, 1951; children: Gwen Palmer Chandler, Kathy, Sandra Palmer Wood, Leslie. BA, Johnson Bible Coll., 1952; MDiv, Lexington Theol. Sem., 1958; postgrad., Boston U., 1961-63; DD, Bethany Coll., 1989. Ordained to ministry Christian Ch. (Disciples of Christ), 1951; CLU, 1981, ChFC, 1984. Assoc. gen. min. Christian Ch. Ky., Lexington, 1957-61; assoc. prof. ch. adminstrn. Lexington Theol. Sem., 1963-66; v.p. Pension Fund of Christian Ch., Indpls., 1966-83, pres., 1983—. Editor Promotional and Interpretive Bull., 1984—; contbr. articles to profl. jours. Home: 5953 Manning Rd Indianapolis IN 46208-1082 Office: Pension Fund of Christian Ch 155 E Market St Indianapolis IN 46204-3294

PALMER, MELVILLE LOUIS, retired agricultural engineering educator; b. Dobbinton, Ont., Can., Aug. 30, 1924; came to U.S., 1953, naturalized, 1960; s. Louis Grange and Laura Lavina (Peacock) P.; m. Shirley Adams, Aug. 2, 1952; children: Laura, Melanie, Bradley. B.S., U. Toronto, 1950; M.S., Ohio State U., 1955. Asst. dean men Ont. Agrl. Coll., Guelph, 1950-52; asst. mgr. farm machinery United Coop., Toronto, 1952-53; research asst. Ohio Agrl. Expt. Sta., Wooster, 1953-55; extension agrl. engr. Ohio State U., Columbus, 1955-87, prof. agrl. engring., 1970-87, prof. emeritus, 1987—; cons. Ford Found., 1967. Contbr. numerous articles to tech. jours. Served with RCAF, 1943-46. Inducted into Internat. Drainage Hall of Fame, 1987. Fellow Am. Soc. Agrl. Engrs. (chmn. Ohio sect. 1979, recipient Hancor Soil and Water Engring. award, Gunlogson Countryside Engring. award 1986), Soil and Water Conservation Soc. (pres. All-Ohio chpt. 1973); mem. Ohio Extension Profs. Assn. (pres. 1964), Water Mgmt. Assn. Ohio (Disting. Svc. award 1985), Ohio Land Improvement Contractors (hon. mem., ednl. advisor 1956-87), Gamma Sigma Delta, Epsilon Sigma Phi (Disting. Svc. award 1989). Home: 4731 Goose Lane Rd Alexandria OH 43001-9730

PALMER, MICHAEL PAUL, lawyer, mediator, educator; b. San Francisco, Mar. 7, 1944; s. Coy Cornelius and Fay Janetta (Conley) P.; m. Gisela Schultz, Jan. 8, 1969; children: Eva Rebecca, Esther Marie. BA, McMurry Coll., Abilene, Tex., 1967; MA, Freie U., Berlin, 1971, PhD, 1976; JD, Georgetown U., 1980. Bar: Ill. 1980, U.S. Dist. Ct. (no. dist.) Ill. 1980, U.S. Ct. Appeals (7th and 11th cirs.) 1981, U.S. Dist. Ct. Vt. 1987. Asst. prof. Freie U., Berlin, 1971-76; assoc. Jenner & Block, Chgo., 1980-87; pres. Palmer Legal Svcs., Middlebury, 1987—; adj. prof. Kent U., Ill. Inst. Tech., Chgo., 1983; pres. Conflict Mgmt. Systems, Inc., Legal Access. Author: Das Problem der Technik, 1976, The Art of a Just Peace, 1995; contbr. articles to profl. jours. Active Amnesty Internat.; bd. dirs. Sheldon Mus. Hon. mention Amnesty award Am. Lawyer, 1982. Mem. ACLU, Vt. Bar Assn., SPIDR. Office: Palmer Legal Svcs Marble Works Office Bldg PO Box 528 Middlebury VT 05753-0528

PALMER, MILTON MEADE, landscape architect; b. Washington, May 13, 1916; s. Estler Milton and Helen Louise (Vietch) P.; m. Isabelle Sasules, Apr. 9, 1948; 1 child, Sara Meade. B. Landscape Arch., Cornell U., 1939. Asst. county planning engr. Arlington County, Va., 1939-40; asst. Charles F. Gillette (Landscape Architect), Richmond, Va., 1940-41; landscape architect Basil M. Delashmutt (C.E.), Arlington, Va., 1941-42; sr. site planning engr. Pacific Islands Engrs., Guam, 1946-48; pvt. practice landscape architect Warrenton, Va., 1948—; lectr. U. Va., 1961-86, 87—, mem. 5th ann. symposium landscape architecture; cons. Washington Cathedral, Dumbarton Oaks, Colonial Williamsburg Found., 1969—; mem. design rev. com. Colonial Williamsburg, Kings Mill, 1986—; jury mem., hon. mention Md. Vietnam Vets. Meml. Competition, 1986; juror Peace Garden Design Competiion, 1992. Prin. works include Washington Cathedral, 1969—, Lyndon B. Johnson Meml. Grove on Potomac, 1973, James Madison U. campus, 1968—, Carter's Grove Country Rd. at Williamsburg, Va., Darden Meml. Garden, Richmond, Va. Pres. Va. Citizens Planning Assn., 1959-60; chmn. Fauquier County (Va.) Planning Commn., 1950-55; mem. Va. Outdoor Recreation Study Commn., 1964-65, Fauquier County Park and Recreation Study Commn., 1970-71. Served with USNR, 1942-46; lt. comdr. Res. ret. Fellow Am. Soc. Landscape Architects (chpt. pres. 1953-54, nat. 1st v.p. 1969-71, chmn. coun. fellows 1973-75, trustee Va. chpt. 1984—, ASLA medal 1991). Clubs: Fauquier, Casanova Hunt. Home: Greenview Warrenton VA 22186 Office: 57 Culpeper St Warrenton VA 22186-3320

PALMER, NORMAN DUNBAR, political scientist, educator, author; b. Hinckley, Maine, June 25, 1909; s. Walter Elmer and Gertrude (Dunbar) P.; m. Evelyn Florence Kalal, Oct. 28, 1944; 1 child, Patricia Lee; m. Gurina McIlrath, Feb. 8, 1992. AB summa cum laude, Colby Coll., 1930, LHD (hon.), 1955; MA (Currier fellow), Yale U., 1932, PhD, 1936. From instr. to assoc. prof. history and govt., chmn. dept. Colby Coll., Maine, 1933-42, 46-47; assoc. prof. polit. sci. U. Pa., Phila., 1947-51; prof. U. Pa., 1951-79, prof. emeritus, 1979—, chmn. dept., 1949-52, chmn. internat. rels. grad. program, 1959-66; coordinator U. Pa.-U. Karachi project, 1954-59; sr. assoc. Fgn. Policy Research Inst., Phila., 1955-82; dir. Phila. Transnat. Project, 1974-82; vis. prof. internat. relations Columbia U., summer 1950; Fulbright prof. polit. sci. and internat. affairs U. Delhi, India, 1952-53; vis. prof. Swarthmore (Pa.) Coll., 1955; vis. prof. Sch. Advanced Internat. Studies Johns Hopkins U., 1958; vis. prof. Bombay U., 1966-67, U. Hawaii, 1967, Am. U. in Cairo, 1971, Duke U., 1974, Naval Postgrad. Sch., 1976, Grad. Inst. Peace Studies, Kyung Hee U., Seoul, Republic of Korea, 1984, 89, 92; sr. specialist East-West Center, Honolulu, 1966-67; cons. Dept. State, Research Analysis Corp. Author: The Irish Land League Crisis, 1940, 78, (with H.C. Perkins) International Relations: The World Community in Transition, 3d edit., 1969, (with Shao Chuan Leng) Sun Yat-Sen and Communism, 1961, (with others) Studies in Political Science, 1961, The Indian Political System, rev. edit., 1971, (with others) The Indian Ocean: Its Political, Economic and Military Importance, 1972, Elections and Political Development: The South Asian Experience, 1975, The United States and India: The Dimensions of Influence, 1984, (with others) The Art and Science of Politics, 1985, (with others) Fundamentals of Political Science, 1952, (with others) The Idea of Colonialism, 1958, (with others) Leadership and Political Institutions in India, 1958, (with others) Major Governments of Asia, rev. edit., 1963, (with others) The United States and the United Nations, 1964, South Asia and United States Policy, 1966, (with others) Problems of Defense of South and East Asia, 1969; (with others) The Foreign Policy of China, 1972, (with others) Pakistan-The Long View, 1977, (with others) Dynamics of Development: The International Perspective, 1977, (with others) The Subcontinent in World Politics, 1978, 82, (with others) Asian Studies III, 1979; (with others) Changing Patterns of Security and Stability in Asia, 1980, (with others) Great Power Relations, World Order and the Third World, 1981, (with others) South Asian Regional Cooperation, 1985, Westward Watch: The United States and the Changing Western Pacific, 1987, (with others) New Tides in the Pacific, 1987, The New Regionalism in Asia and the Pacific, 1991; contbr. editor Current History, 1949—; editor, contbr.: A Design for International Relations Research, 1970; mem. editorial bd. Orbis,

1957-88, South Asian Studies, 1966—, Asian Affairs, 1974-85, Global Futures Digest, 1980—; contbr. articles to profl. jours. Mem. Citizens Com. for Hoover Report, also Phila. Citizens Charter Com., 1950-51; chmn. Friends of India Com., 1961-68; trustee Princeton in Asia, 1978-82; mem. San Juan County Centennial Com., 1987-88, Bill of Rights Bicentennial Com., 1991. Served to lt. comdr. USNR, 1942-46. Decorated Bronze Star medal; recipient Honor award award of Indians in Am., 1988, Citizen of Yr. award San Juan County, 1991; Carnegie Endowment Internat. Peace fellow, 1959-60; Coun. Fgn. Rels. rsch. fellow, 1961-62, Guggenheim fellow, 1961-62, Am. Coun. Learned Socs. fellow, 1961-62, 71-72, Am. Inst. Indian Studies fellow, 1966-67, 71-72. Mem. ASPA (internat. com.), Internat. Polit. Sci. Assn., Am. Polit. Sci. Assn. (Council 1954-56), Indian Polit. Sci. Assn. (life), Global Futures Soc., Am. Acad. Polit. and Social Sci. (dir., sec.), Interdependence Council (dir.), Council on Fgn. Relations, Phila. Com. Fgn. Relations, World Affairs Council (dir.), Phila. Council Internat. Visitors (dir.), Assn. Asian Studies, Pa. Polit. Sci. and Pub. Adminstrn. Assn. (exec. council), Fgn. Policy Assn., Nat. Coun. Asian Affairs (pres., Phila.), Am. Vets. Com., Am. Legion, Res. Officers Assn., Peace Sci. Soc., Internat. Studies Assn. (pres. 1970-71, life), Internat. Study and Research Inst. (v.p., dir.), Am.-Asian Ednl. Exchange (dir.), Elks, Phi Beta Kappa, Pi Kappa Delta, Alpha Tau Omega. Home: 485 Friday Ave Friday Harbor WA 98250-9688 *I have always been conscious of wider horizons, physical and intellectual, of the lure and challenge of the unknown, of commonalities as well as differences among peoples and nations, of the potentialities of human beings and the factors that hamper the realization of these potentialities. My life has been a full one, personally and professionally. But I have seldom been able to measure up to the standards that I have set for myself. There has always been something beyond, something I could not fully conquer or even grasp. Perhaps this is due to my Puritan background.*

PALMER, PATRICK EDWARD, radio astronomer, educator; b. St. Johns, Mich., Dec. 6, 1940; s. Don Edward and Nina Louise (Kyes) P.; m. Joan Claire Merlin, June 9, 1963; children—Laura Katherine, Aidan Edward, David Elijah. S.B., U. Chgo., 1963; M.A., Harvard U., 1965, Ph.D, 1968. Radio astronomer Harvard U., Cambridge, Mass., 1968; asst. prof. astronomy and astrophysics U. Chgo., 1968-70, assoc. prof., 1970-75, prof., 1975—; vis. assoc. prof. astronomy Calaaif. Inst. Tech., Pasadena, 1972; vis. radio astronomer Cambridge (Eng.) U., 1973; vis. rsch. astronomer U. Calif., Berkeley, 1977, 86; vis. scientist Nat. Radio Astronomy Obs., 1980-94. Contbr. articles on radio astron. investigations of comets and interstellar medium to tech. jours. Recipient Bart J. Bok prize for contbns. to galactic astronomy, 1969, Alfred P. Sloan Found. fellow, 1970-72, Helen B. Warner prize, 1975. Fellow AAAS (Chmn. sect. D astronomy 1984); mem. Am. Astron. Soc. (chmn. nominating com. 1981, publs. bd. 1985-86, Warner Prize selection com. 1977-78), Royal Astron. Soc., Internat. Astron. Union, AAUP. Club: U. Chgo. Track. Home: 5549 S Dorchester Ave Chicago IL 60637-1720 Office: Univ Chgo Astronomy & Astrophysics Ctr 5640 S Ellis Ave Chicago IL 60637-1467

PALMER, PHILIP EDWARD STEPHEN, radiologist; b. London, Apr. 26, 1921. Ed., Kelly Coll., Tavistock, Eng., 1938; M.B., B.S., U. London, 1944, D.M.R., 1946, D.M.R.T., 1947. Intern, then resident Westminster Hosp.; cons. radiologist West Cornwall (Eng.) Hosp. Group, 1947-54; sr. govt. radiologist Matabeleland, Rhodesia-Zimbabwe, 1954-64; prof. radiology U. Cape Town, South Africa, 1964-68; prof. U. Pa., 1968-70; prof. diagnostic radiology and vet. radiology U. Calif., Davis, 1970—; WHO cons. in field. Author: The Radiology of Tropical Diseases, 1980; contbr. articles to profl. jours. Recipient German Röentgen award, 1993. Fellow Calif. Radiol. Assn., Royal Coll. Physicians (Edinburgh), Royal Coll. Radiologists (Eng.), Romanian Soc. Radiol. and Nuclear Med.; mem. Brit. Inst. Radiology, Brit. Med. Assn., Calif. Med. Assn., Internat. Skeletal Soc., Assn. Univ. Radiologists, Radiol. Soc. N. Am., Kenya Radiol. Soc., South African Coll. Medicine, Egyptian Soc. Radiology and Nuclear Medicine, Yugoslav Assn. for Ultrasound, West African Assn. Radiologists. Address: 821 Miller Dr Davis CA 95616

PALMER, RAYMOND A., medical association administrator, librarian; b. Louisville, May 8, 1939. BA in Biology, U. Louisville, 1961; MLS, U. Ky., 1966. Adminstrv. asst. Johns Hopkins Med. Libr., Balt., 1966-69; asst. librarian Harvard Med. Libr., Boston, 1969-74; health scis. librarian Wright State U., Dayton, Ohio, 1974-82; assoc. prof. library adminstrn., 1974-82; exec. dir. Med. Libr. Assn., Chgo., 1982-92, Am. Assn. Immunologists, Bethesda, Md., 1992—; cons. Acad. Mil. Med. Scis. Libr., Beijing, 1990, Alzheimer's Assn., Chgo., 1991. AUthor: Management of Library Associations; mng. editor: Jour. Immunology, 1992—; contbr. articles to profl. jours. Mem. ALA, Am. Soc. Assn. Execs., Greater Washington Soc. Assn. Execs., Spl. Librs. Assn., Biomed. Communication Network (chmn. 1980-82), Am. Mgmt. Assn. (strategic planning adv. coun. 1987-91), Coun. Biology Editors, Friends of Nat. Libr. Medicine (bd. dirs. 1989-92, 94—), Internat. Fedn. Libr. Assns. and Instns. (exec. com. Round Table for Mgmt. of Libr. Orgns. 1989-92), Med. Libr. Assn., Spl. Libr. Assn.

PALMER, RICHARD ALAN, chemistry educator; b. Austin, Tex., Nov. 13, 1935; s. Ernest Austin and Eugenia Rosalie (Robey) P.; m. Janice Leah Boyce, June 30, 1961; children: William D., Leah D., Sarah L., Benjamin C. BS, U. Tex., 1957; MS, U. Ill., 1962, PhD, 1965. Asst. prof. chemistry Duke U., 1966-71, assoc. prof., 1971-78, prof., 1978—; dir. grad. studies dept. chemistry, 1979-82, dir. Chemistry for Executives Program, 1992—. Author: Problems in Structural Inorganic Chemistry, 1971; mem. editorial bd. Applied Spectroscopy, 1990—. Served with USN, 1957-60. NIH fellow, 1965-66; NSF Internat. Study grantee, 1980-81. Mem. Am. Chem. Soc. (nat. coun. 1993—), Soc. Applied Spectroscopy, Coblentz Soc. (bd. mgrs. 1992—), Phi Beta Kappa, Sigma Xi, Phi Lambda Upsilon. Home: 126 Pinecrest Rd Durham NC 27705-5813 Office: Duke U Chemistry Dept Durham NC 27706

PALMER, RICHARD N., judge; b. Hartford, Conn., May 27, 1950. BA, Trinity Coll., 1972; JD with high honors, U. Conn., 1977. Bar: Conn. 1977, U.S. Dist. Ct. Conn. 1978, D.C. 1980, U.S. Ct. Appeals (2nd cir.) 1981. Law clk. to Hon. Jon O. Newman U.S. Ct. Appeals (2nd cir.), 1977-78; assoc. Shipman & Goodwin, 1978-80; asst. U.S. atty. Office U.S. Atty. Conn., 1980-83, 87-90, U.S. atty. dist. Conn., 1991, chief state's atty. Conn., 1991-93; ptnr. Chatigny and Palmer, 1984-86; assoc. justice Conn. Supreme Ct., Hartford, 1993—. Mem. Phi Beta Kappa. Office: 231 Capitol Ave Hartford CT 06106-1537

PALMER, RICHARD WARE, lawyer; b. Boston, Oct. 20, 1919; s. George Ware and Ruth French (Judkins) P.; m. Nancy Fernald Shaw, July 8, 1950; children: Richard Ware Jr., John Wentworth, Anne Fernald. A.B., Harvard U., 1942, J.D., 1948. Bar: N.Y. State 1950, Pa. 1959. Sec., dir. N. Am. Mfg. Co., Natick, Mass., 1946-48; assoc. Burlingham, Veeder, Clark & Hupper, Burlingham, Hupper & Kennedy, N.Y.C., 1949-57; ptnr. Rawle & Henderson, Phila., 1958-79, Palmer, Biezup & Henderson, Phila., 1979—; sec., bd. dirs. Underwater Technics, Inc., Camden, N.J., 1967-85; adv. on admiralty law to U.S. del. Inter-Govtl. Maritime Consultative Orgn., London, 1967; mem. U.S. Shipping Coordinating Com., Washington legal sub com., 1967—; U.S. del. 30th-35th internat. confs. Titular mem. Comité Maritime International; v.p., sec., bd. dirs. Phila. Belt Line R.R.; bd. dirs. Mather (Bermuda) Ltd. Editor: Maritime Law Reporter. Mem. permanent adv. bd. Tulane Admiralty Law Inst., Tulane U. Law Sch., New Orleans, 1975—; trustee Seamen's Ch. Inst., Phila., 1967—, pres., 1972-84; bd. dirs. Haverford (Pa.) Civic Assn., 1978-79; consul for Denmark in State of Pa., 1980-91. Lt. comdr. USNR, 1942-46. Fellow World Acad. Art and Sci. (treas. 1986—); mem. ABA (former chmn. standing com. on admiralty and maritime law 1978-79), N.Y.C. Bar Assn., Phila. Bar Assn., Am. Judicature Soc., Maritime Law Assn. (chmn. limitation liability com. 1977-83, 2d v.p. 1984-86, 1st v.p. 1986-88, pres. 1988-90, immediate past pres. 1990-92), Internat. Bar Assn., Internat. Assn. Def. Counsel., Assn. Average Adjusters USA and Gt. Britain, Port of Phila. Maritime Soc., Danish Order of Dannebrog, Phila. Club, Union League Club, Rittenhouse Club, Downtown Club, Merion Cricket Club, Union League Club, Harvard Club N.Y.C. and Phila. (v.p., mem. exec. com. 1983-86, 94—). Republican. Episcopalian. Home: 318 Grays Ln Haverford PA 19041-1907 Office: Palmer Biezup & Henderson Pub Ledger Bldg 620 Chestnut St Philadelphia PA 19106-3409

PALMER, ROBERT B., computer company executive; b. 1941. BS, Tex. Tech U., MS. V.p. semiconductor ops. Digital Equipment Corp., v.p. mfg., pres., CEO, 1992—, now also chmn., 1995—. Office: Digital Equipment Corp 146 Main St Maynard MA 01754-2504*

PALMER, ROBERT BAYLIS, librarian; b. Rockville Centre, N.Y., Apr. 5, 1938; s. John Frederick and Marion (Baylis) P.; divorced; 1 child, Michele Palmer Fracasso. A.B., Kenyon Coll., Gambier, Ohio, 1960; M.S. in LS, Simmons Coll., Boston, 1965; M.A. in English, Middlebury (Vt.) Coll., 1965. Tchr. Brooks Sch., North Andover, Mass., 1960-65; librarian Brooks Sch., 1961-65; acting librarian Columbia Coll., 1965-66; asst. to dir. libraries Columbia U., 1965-67; dir. Barnard Coll. Library, 1967-81; Fulbright lectr. Tribhuvan U. Library, Kathmandu, Nepal, 1972-73, Kathmandu, 1980; vol. lectr. USIS, library cons., Asia, 1976; Fulbright lectr. Wuhan, Peoples Republic China, 1984-85; library cons., advisor, Peoples Republic China, 1986-87, Zanzibar, Tanzania, 1988; lectr., cons. Kenya, Ethiopia, Zimbabwe, 1988; English lang. escort officer U.S. Dept. State, 1989—. Mem. ALA. Address: 190 Riverside Dr New York NY 10024-1008 *Viewing one's country through the eyes of international guests, one can be both amazed and appalled by our human progress. Such experiences reconfirm the belief that there is much more to life than accumulating wealth.*

PALMER, ROBERT BITTS, banker; b. Gorman, Tex., 1940. Grad., Tex. Tech U., 1962. Formerly pres., CEO Phila. Nat. Bank; now chief retail svcs. officer CoreStates Fin. Corp.; chmn. CoreStates First Pa. Bank. Office: CoreStates Fin Corp NE Corner Broad Chestnut St Philadelphia PA 19107 also: First Pa Bank NA 16th Market St Philadelphia PA 19101

PALMER, ROBERT BLUNDEN, newspaper, printing executive; b. Port Huron, Mich., Nov. 25, 1917; s. Joseph Frank and Hazel Quinn (Blunden) P.; m. Mary Bellatti (dec.), Feb. 11, 1946; children: Robert L. Palmer, Frances Lobpries, Barbara Caldwell. Office mgr. Palmer Circulation Co., Midwest, 1933-41; reporter, bus. mgr. Titus County Tribune, Mt. Pleasant, Tex., 1941-42, editor, 1946-57; pub. editor Daily Tribune, Mt. Pleasant, Tex., 1957-88; pres. Palmer Media, Inc., Mt. Pleasant, Tex., 1972—, NorTex Press, Inc., Mt. Pleasant, Tex., 1973—, F.V.P. Network, Inc., Mt. Pleasant, Tex., 1989; owner Palmer Real Estate, 1968—. Capt. U.S. Army, 1942-46, ETO. Presbyterian. Avocations: reading, golf, travel, music. Office: Palmer Media Inc. 1705 Industrial Mount Pleasant TX 75455

PALMER, ROBERT ERWIN, association executive; b. Texarkana, Ark., Feb. 6, 1934; s. Burgess Prince and Ruth (Erwin) P. BJ, U. Tex., 1961. Reporter Texarkana Gazette, 1961; editor Southwestern Bell Telephone, Houston, 1961; info. specialist Southwestern Bell Telephone, St. Louis, 1961-63; editor Shell Oil Co., Houston and Chgo.; head office pub. relations Shell Oil Co., N.Y.C.; dir. pub. relations Nat. PTA, Chgo., 1969-74; program dir. Nat. Assn. Realtors, Chgo., 1974-76; corp. communications mgr. The Milw. Rd., Chgo., 1976-78; staff v.p. Soc. Real Estate Appraisers, Chgo., 1978-83, exec. v.p., 1983-90; sr. v.p. communications, 1991—; co. assoc., v.p Appraisal Inst., Chgo., 1992-93; v.p. mem. svcs. Appraisal Inst., 1993—; bd. dirs. Tower Advt., Chgo., Costumes Unltd. Inc., Chgo. Founding mem. Chgo. Crime Commn., 1967. Served to staff sgt. USAF, 1953-57. Recipient Award of Merit, Chgo. Internat. Film Festival, 1970, 71, Spl. Corrs. Pring Feature award, 1971, 72, Golden Trumpet award Realtor Week promotion, 1975, Golden Trumpet award Pvt. Property Week promotion, 1977, Golden Trumpet award Realtor bicentennial program, 1977, Gold Circle award Chpt.-by-Chpt. program, 1982. Mem. Pub. Relations Soc. Am., Am. Soc. Assn. Execs., Sigma Delta Chi. Methodist. Club: Chgo. Headline. Office: Appraisal Inst 875 N Michigan Ave Ste 2400 Chicago IL 60611-1980

PALMER, ROBERT J(OSEPH), advertising executive, winery owner; b. N.Y.C., July 16, 1934; s. Patrick S. and Irene M. Palmer; m. Lorraine E. Wittmer; children: Linda, Katherine, Lori-Ann, Barbara. Media dir. Cunningham and Walsh Advt., N.Y.C., 1950-67; pres. Kelly Nason, Inc., N.Y.C., 1968-76, R.J. Palmer, Inc., N.Y.C., 1977—; exec. v.p. Kornhauser and Calene, Inc., N.Y.C., 1980-85; pres. Palmer Vineyards, Inc., N.Y.C., 1983—; chmn. R.J. Palmer Media Svc., 1985—. Office: R J Palmer Inc 156 W 56th St Ste 1801 New York NY 10019-4701

PALMER, ROBERT R., performing arts administrator; b. Chicago, Sept. 8, 1950; s. Marvin R. and Martha A. Palmer. BA cum laude, Augustana Coll., Rock Island, Ill., 1973; MA in Arts Adminstrn., U. Wis., 1975. Mgr., U. Wis.-Madison Symphony Orchs., 1974-75, Madison Civic Music Assn., 1975—; tchr. music appreciation U. Wis. Extension, Madison Area Tech. Coll. Bd. dirs. Am. Symphony Orch. League, 1991-92; treas., mem. exec. com. of bd. dirs. Dane County Arts Coun., 1979-80; chair Madison Com. for the Arts, 1987-89; narrator Madison Symphony Orch. Mem. Beta Gamma Sigma, Omicron Delta Kappa, Phi Mu Alpha, Alpha Phi Omega. Office: Madison Symphony Orch 211 N Carroll St Madison WI 53703-2285

PALMER, ROBERT ROSWELL, historian, educator; b. Chgo., Jan. 11, 1909; s. Roswell Roy and Blanche (Steere) P.; m. Esther Howard, Dec. 19, 1942; children: Stanley, Richard, Emily. Ph.B., U. Chgo., 1931, LL.D., 1963; Ph.D., Cornell U., 1934; Litt.D., Washington U., St. Louis, 1962; L.H.D., Kenyon Coll., 1963, U. New Haven, 1980; Dr. honoris causa, U. Toulouse, France, 1965, U. Uppsala, Sweden, 1977. Mem. faculty Princeton U., 1936-63, 66-69, prof. history, 1946-63, Dodge prof. history, 1952-63; dean faculty arts and sci., prof. history Washington U., St. Louis, 1963-66; prof. history Yale U., 1969-77, emeritus, 1977; adj. prof. U. Mich., 1977-80; vis. prof. U. Chgo., summer 1947, U. Colo. summer 1951, U. Calif. at Berkeley, summer 1962, U. Mich., 1969, 75. Author: Catholics and Unbelievers in 18th Century France, 1939, Twelve Who Ruled, 1941, A History of the Modern World, 1950, (with Joel Colton) A History of the Modern World, 8th edit., 1994, also in Swedish, Italian, Finnish, Spanish and Chinese, The Age of the Democratic Revolution, 1959, vol. II, 1964, also German, Italian edits., World of the French Revolution, 1971, also in French, School of the French Revolution, 1975, The Improvement of Humanity: Education and the French Revolution, 1985, The Two Tocquevilles, Father and Son on the Coming of the French Revolution, 1987; co-author: Organization of Ground Combat Troops, 1947, Procurement and Training of Ground Combat Troops, 1948; editor: Rand McNally Atlas of World History, 1957. Served hist. div. U.S. Army, 1943-45. Recipient of ACLS Spl. prize, 1960, Bancroft prize, 1960, Antonio Feltrinelli Internat. prize, Rome, 1990. Mem. Am. Acad. Arts and Scis., Mass. Hist. Soc., Am. Philos. Soc., Am. Hist. Assn. (pres. 1970), Soc. French Hist. Studies (pres. 1961), Acad. Naz. dei Lincei. Home: Pennswood Village # K205 Newtown PA 18940-2401

PALMER, ROBERT TOWNE, lawyer; b. Chgo., May 25, 1947; s. Adrian Bernhardt and Gladys (Towne) P.; m. Ann Therese Darin, Nov. 9, 1974; children: Justin Darin, Christian Darin. BA, Colgate U., 1969; JD, U. Notre Dame, 1974. Bar: Ill. 1974, D.C. 1978, U.S. Supreme Ct. 1978. Law clk. Hon. Walter V. Schaefer, Ill. Supreme Ct. 1974-75; assoc. McDermott, Will & Emery, Chgo. 1975-81, ptnr., 1982-86; ptnr. Chadwell & Kayser, Ltd., 1987-88, Connelly, Mustes, Palmer & Schoendorf, 1988-89; of counsel Garfield & Merel Ltd., 1990—; mem. adj. faculty Chgo. Kent Law Sch., 1975-77, Loyola U., 1976-78; mem. adv. com. Fed. Home Loan Mortgage Corp., 1988-89; bd. dir. Lincoln Legal Found., Cen. Fed. Savs. & Loan Assn. of Chgo.; mem. Chgo. Ct. Adv. Bd. Voyageur Outward Bound Sch., 1988-91. Mem. ABA, Ill. State Bar Assn. (Lincoln award 1983), Chgo. Bar Assn., Internat. Assn. Def. Counsel, Chgo. Club, Dairymen's Country Club, Lambda Alpha. Contbr. articles to legal jours. and textbooks. Office: Garfield & Merel Ltd 211 W Wacker Dr Ste 1500 Chicago IL 60606-1217

PALMER, R(OBIE MARCUS HOOKER) MARK, banker; b. Ann Arbor, Mich., July 14, 1941; s. Robie Ellis and Katherine (Hooker) P.; m. Sushma Palmer. BA, Yale U., 1963. Copy asst. N.Y. Times, N.Y.C., 1963; asst. to producer WNDT-TV, N.Y.C., 1963-64; entered U.S. Fgn. Service, 1964; third sec. U.S. Embassy, New Delhi, India, 1964-66; internat. relations officer NATO affairs, Dept State, Washington, 1966-68; second sec. U.S. Embassy, Moscow, 1968-71; prin. speechwriter Sec. of State Rogers, Kissinger, Washington, 1971-75; counselor for polit. affairs U.S. Embassy, Belgrade, Yugoslavia, 1975-78; dir. office disarmament and control of arms Bur. of Polit.-Mil. Affairs Dept. State, Washington, 1978-81, dep. to undersec. for polit. affairs, 1981-82, dep. asst. state for European affairs, 1982-86; amb. U.S. Embassy, Budapest, Hungary, 1986-90; pres., chief exec. officer

Cen. European Devel. Corp., 1990—; chmn. bd. NOVA TV. Czech Republic Berlin-Brandenburg TV; Gen. Banking and Trust, Budapest. Author: speeches for five Secs. of State and three Presidents. Recipient Superior Honor award Dept. State, 1980, Presdl. Meritorious Service award, award, 1984. Mem. Council Fgn. Relations, Am. Fgn. Service Assn., Phi Beta Kappa. Episcopalian. Avocation: tennis. Home: Gelfertstr 17A, D-14195 Berlin-Dahlem Germany Office: Mauerstrasse, 10117 Berlin 93, Germany

PALMER, ROGER FARLEY, pharmacology educator; b. Albany, N.Y., Sept. 23, 1931; m. Nelida Santiago, Apr. 1994. B.S. in Chemistry, St. Louis U., 1953; postgrad., Fla. State U., 1955-56, Woods Hole Marine Biology Lab., 1956; M.D., U. Fla., 1960. Intern Johns Hopkins Hosp., 1960-61, resident in medicine, 1961-62; asst. dept. biochemistry U. Fla., Gainesville, 1957; asst. medicine Osler Med. Service, 1960-62; instr. pharmacology and therapeutics U. Fla., 1962, asst. prof. pharmacology, therapeutics and medicine, 1964-67, assoc. prof. pharmacology and medicine, 1967-69, prof. medicine, chief div. clin. pharmacology, 1969-70, 81-82; prof., chmn. dept. pharmacology, prof. medicine U. Miami, Fla., 1970-81; clin. prof. medicine U. Miami, 1982—; chmn. pharmacology sect. Nat. Bd. Med Examiners, 1977-81; cons. Nat. Acad. Scis.; chmn. pharmacology sect. Nat. Bd. Med. Examiners, 1977-81. Editorial bd. Pharmacol. Revs.; assoc. editor Advances in Molecular Pharmacology; ad hoc editor Am. Heart Jour.; editor Horizons in Clinical Pharmacology, 1976; author abstracts; contbr. articles to profl. jours. Served with USAR. Mosby scholar, 1957-60; Markle scholar in acad. medicine, 1965-70; recipient Basic Sci. Teaching award U. Miami, 1975-76; Meritorious Service medal Am. Heart Assn., 1972; citation for meritorious Service So. Region Am. Heart Assn., 1979; Visitante Distinguido award, Costa Rica, 1979; Outstanding Tchr. award U. Miami, 1982. Mem. Am. Coll. Clin. Pharmacology, Am. Fedn. Clin. Research, Am. Therapeutic Soc. (prize essay award 1970), Am. Soc. Pharmacology and Exptl. Therapeutics, N.Y. Acad. Sci., AAAS, So. Soc. Clin. Investigation, U.S. Pharmacopeia Revision Com., Internat. Study Group Research Cardiac Metabolism, Royal Soc. Health, Sigma Xi. Office: 24 W Enid Dr Key Biscayne FL 33149-2009

PALMER, ROGER RAYMOND, accounting educator; b. N.Y.C., Dec. 31, 1926; s. Archibald and Sophie (Jarnow) P.; m. Martha West Hopkins, June 7, 1986; children by previous marriage: Kathryn Sue, Daniel Stephen, Susan Jo. B.S., U. Wis., 1949; M.B.A., Cornell U., 1951; student, NYU Grad. Sch. Bus. Adminstrn., 1951-54. Auditor, Ernst and Ernst (C.P.A.s), N.Y.C., 1953-54; auditor Gen. Dynamics Corp., 1956-60; mgr. corp. audits Tex. Instruments, 1960-64; auditor First National Bank, St. Paul, 1964-68; v.p. planning First National Bank, 1968-69, v.p., comptroller, 1969-75, sr. v.p., controller, 1975-82; asst. prof. fin. and acctg. Coll. St. Thomas, 1982—; dir. First Met. Travel, Inc.; guest lectr. U. Minn., 1966; conf. leader, speaker, 1959—. Contbr. articles to publs. Bd. dirs. Waterford (Conn.) Civic Assn., 1959-60, Friends of St. Paul Pub. Library, 1967, Mpls. Citizens League; chmn. bd. dirs. Film in the Cities, 1983-85; mem. acctg. adv. council U. Minn.; trustee Hazelton Found. Served with U.S. Maritime Service, 1945-47; with AUS, 1954-56. Mem. Inst. Internal Auditors (pres. So. New Eng chpt. 1957-60, edn. chmn. Dallas 1961, Twin City chpt. 1965-66), Nat. Assn. Accts. (dir. Norwich, Conn. chpt. 1958-60), Nat. Assn. Accountants (St. Paul chpt. 1967), Assn. Bank Audit, Control and Operation, Am. Inst. Banking, Fin. Execs. Inst.; Planning Forum (pres. Twin Cities chpt. 1984-85), Univ. Club (St. Paul). Club: St. Paul Athletic. Home: 1411 Lincoln Ave Saint Paul MN 55105-2217 Office: Univ Saint Thomas Saint Paul MN 55105

PALMER, RONALD DEWAYNE FAISAL, retired diplomat, educator, consultant; b. Uniontown, Pa., May 22, 1932; s. Wilbur Fortune and Ethel Danya (Roberts) P.; m. Tengku Intan Badariah Abubakar; children: Derek Ronald, Alyson Cecily, Natasha Elina, Nadiah Raha. B.A., Howard U., 1954; MA in Internat. Studies, Johns Hopkins U., 1957. Assigned to U.S. Mil. Acad., Indonesia, Denmark, Malaysia, The Philippines, prior to 1976; amb. to Togo, 1976-78; dep. dir. gen. Fgn. Service State Dept., 1978-81; amb. to Malaysia Kuala Lumpur, 1981-83; sr. scholar, mem. adv. bd. Ctr. Strategic and Internat. Studies, Washington, 1983-86; amb. to Mauritius Port Louis, 1986-89; ret., 1989; prof., diplomatic con. internat. studies George Washington U., 1990—. Author: Building Cooperation - 20 Years of ASEAN, 1987. Decorated Order of Mono, Togo, Most Hon. Order of Johor Sultan of Johor Bahru, Malaysia; recipient Sr. Fgn. Svc. Performance award U.S. Dept. State, 1985. Mem. Am. Fgn. Svc. Assn., Coun. on Fgn. Rels., Wash. Inst. Fgn. Affairs, Asia Soc., Inst. Strategic Studies, Royal Asia Soc., Advisory Bd. of U.S. Indonesia Soc. Office: George Washington U Elliott Sch Internat Affairs 2013 G St NW 4600 Washington DC 20052 also: care State Dept Fgn Soc Mailroom 2201 C St NW Washington DC 20520-0001

PALMER, RONALD LEIGH, lawyer; b. Blossburg, Pa., Feb. 22, 1939; s. Leigh Judson and Henrietta (Stevens) P.; m. Deanna Ruth Doss, Nov. 22, 1962; 1 child, Ashley Christine. BSME, U. Cin., 1962; LLB, So. Meth. U., 1966. Bar: Tex. 1966, U.S. Dist. Ct. (all dists.) Tex. 1968, U.S.C. Appeals (5th cir.) 1968. Law clk. to Judge Joe Ingraham, Houston, 1966-68; assoc. Baker & Botts, Houston, 1968-75, ptnr., 1975-85, sr. ptnr., 1985—; speaker numerous seminars, 1977—. Contbr. articles to profl. jours. Bd. councillors U. Dallas, 1990—; mem. exec. bd. So. Meth. U. Law Sch., 1992—. Republican. Presbyterian. Avocations: archeology, golf, computers. Home: 3301 Hanover Ave Dallas TX 75225-7642 Office: Baker & Botts 2001 Ross Ave Dallas TX 75201

PALMER, RUSSELL EUGENE, investment executive; b. Jackson, Mich., Aug. 13, 1934; s. Russell E. and Margarite M. (Briles) P.; m. Phyllis Anne Hartung, Sept. 8, 1956; children: Bradley Carl, Stephen Russell, Russell Eugene, III, Karen Jean. BA with honors, Mich. State U., 1956; D in Comml. Sci. (hon.), Drexel U., 1980; MA (hon.), U. Pa., 1984; PhD (hon.), Chulalongkorn U., 1988, Free U. of Brussels, 1989, York Coll., 1989. With Touche Ross & Co., N.Y.C., 1956-83, mng. ptnr., CEO, 1972-82, also bd. dirs., exec. coms.; mng. dir., CEO Touche Ross Internat., 1974-83; dean, Reliance prof. mgmt. and pvt. enterprise Wharton Sch. U. Pa., 1983-90, CEO; bd. dirs. Contel Cellular Inc., GTE Corp., The May Dept. Stores Co., Bankers Trust Co., Allied-Signal, Inc., Imasco Ltd.; corp. bd. Safeguard Scientifics, Inc., Fed. Home Loan Mortgage Corp. Mem. pub. bds. Dirs. & Bds., Mergers & Aquisitions, Directory Corp. Affiliations, Directory Leading Pvt. Cos. Pres. Fin. Acctg. Found., 1979-82; trustee Acctg. Hall of Fame; bd. dirs. Joint Coun. Econ. Edn., 1978-83, United Fund Greater N.Y., 1980-83, UN Assn. U.S.A.; mem. Bus. Com. Arts, 1977-83; mem. Pres.'s Mgmt. Improvement Coun., 1979-80; mem. N.Y. adv. bd. Salvation Army, past mem. nat. adv. bd.; former mem. adv. coun. Sch. Internat. and Pub. Affairs Columbia U., Grad. Sch. Bus. Stanford U., Womens Way; mem. assocs. coun. Bus. Sch. Oxford U.; mem. adv. panel Comptr. Gen. U.S.; mem. U.S. Sec. Labor's Commn. on Workforce Quality and Labor Market Efficiency; pub. mem. Hudson Inst., mem. adv. bd. Radnor Venture Ptnrs.; bd. dirs. SEI Ctr. for Advanced Studies in Mgmt. Recipient Gavin Meml. award Beta Theta Pi, 1956, Disting. Community Svc. award Brandeis U., 1974, Outstanding Alumnus award Mich. State U., 1978, Humanitarian award Fedn. Jewish Philanthropies, 1979, Disting. Aux. Svc. award Salvation Army, 1979, LEAD Bus. award, 1984, Good Scout award Phila. coun. Boy Scouts Am., 1987. Mem. Cts. of Phila. Club, Merion Cricket Club, Merion Golf Club, Round Hill Club, Lost Tree Country Club, Conf. Bd. (bd. dirs.), Beta Gamma Sigma (mem. bd. govs.). Presbyterian. Office: The Palmer Group 3600 Market St Fl 530 Philadelphia PA 19104-2646

PALMER, SAMUEL COPELAND, III, lawyer; b. Phila., June 9, 1934; s. Samuel Copeland Jr. and Vivian Gertrude (Plumb) P.; divorced; children: Samuel C. IV, Sarah Anne, Bryan Douglas. Grad., Harvard Sch., Los Angeles, 1952; student, Yale U., 1953; A.B., Stanford U., 1955; JD, Loyola-Marymount U., Marymount, 1958. Bar: Calif. 1959, U.S. Dist. Ct. (cen., ea. and so. dists. Calif.) 1959, U.S. Ct. Appeals (9th cir.) 1970, U.S. Supreme Ct. 1971. Dep. city atty. Los Angeles, 1959-60; assoc. firm Pollock & Deutz, Los Angeles, 1960-63; ptnr. firm Pollock & Palmer, Los Angeles, 1963-70, Palmer & Bartenetti, Los Angeles, 1970-81, Samuel C. Palmer III, P.C. 1981-85; ptnr. Thomas, Snell, Jamison, Russell & Asperger, 1985—; adj. prof. Calif. State U., Fresno, 1993. Trustee Western Ctr. Law and Poverty; bd. dirs. Big Bros./Big Sisters, Fresno, Lively Arts Found., Nat. Sleep Found., Vols. in Parole; pres., bd. dirs. Poverello House; founder, pres. Fresno Crime Stoppers. Mem. ABA, State Bar Calif. (disciplinary subcom., bar examiners subcom.), Fresno County Bar Assn. (pres., bd. dirs. 1988-93), Pickwick Soc., Am. Bd. Trial Advocates, Chancery Club, Downtown Club,

Calif. Club, Fig Garden Tennis Club, Rotary, Delta Upsilon, Phi Delta Phi. Home: 4607 N Wilson Fresno CA 93704 Office: 2445 Capitol St Fresno CA 93721-2224

PALMER, STANTON DEAN, newspaper editor; b. Evanston, Ill., Sept. 15, 1920; s. Paul Lester and Irma Leafy (Macklin) P.; m. Alice LaNeave Boroughs, May 19, 1951; children: Susan Palmer Pierce, David William. BS in Chemistry, U. Chattanooga, 1941. Civilian ordnance insp. U.S. Army Ordnance Dist., Chattanooga, 1941-42; copy editor Chattanooga Free Press, 1948-66, news editor, 1966—. Trumpet player Chattanooga Symphony Orch., 1938-74, Chattanooga Opera Orch., 1950-77. Lt. (s.g.) USN, 1942-46, PTO. Recipient Dedicated Svc. citation Chattanooga Symphony Orch., 1972. Mem. Am. Fedn. Musicians (hon. life, Chattanooga local chpt.). Baptist. Home: 4300 Evergreen Dr Chattanooga TN 37411-2201 Office: Chattanooga Free Press 400 E 11th St Chattanooga TN 37403-4203

PALMER, STEPHEN, trucking company executive; b. 1954. Fuel coordinator J.B. Hunt Transport Svcs. Inc., 1980-82; mgr.human resources J.B. Hunt Transport Svcs. Inc., 1982-83; v.p. J.B. Hunt Transport Svcs. Inc., 1983-89, exec. v.p., 1989—. Office: J B Hunt Transport Svcs Inc PO Box 130 Lowell AR 72745-0130

PALMER, STEPHEN EUGENE, JR., government official; b. Superior, Wis., July 31, 1923; s. Stephen Eugene Sr. and Katharine (Greenslade) P.; m. Nancy Jane Swan, July 26, 1947 (div. 1986); children: Katharine Caldwell, Susan Greenslade, Stephen Eugene III; m. Patsy Elaine Simmons Lee, Sept. 7, 1989. A.B., Princeton U., 1944; postgrad., Columbia U., 1947-48, M.A., 1971; postgrad. Serbo-Croatian lang. and Balkan area, Ind. U., 1953-54; postgrad. in French Fgn. Service Inst., 1982-83. Tchr. Am. Community Sch., Tehran, Iran, 1946-47; with U.S. Govt., 1949-51; joined U.S. Fgn. Service, 1951; vice consul Nicosia, Cyprus, 1951-53; 3d sec., vice consul Belgrade, Yugoslavia, 1954; 2d sec., 1954-56, consul, 1956-57; consul, prin. officer Sarajevo, Yugoslavia, 1957-59; fgn. affairs officer Office UN Polit. Affairs, State Dept., 1959-63; 1st sec., chief polit. sect. Tel Aviv, Israel, 1963-66; 1st sec. polit. div. Middle Eastern and North African affairs Am. embassy, London, 1966-68; counselor for polit. affairs Am. embassy, Rawalpindi, Islamabad, Pakistan, 1968-71; consul gen. Madras, India, 1971-73; fellow Center for Internat. Affairs, Harvard, 1973-74; dir. Office Near Eastern and South Asian Regional Affairs, State Dept., 1974-78; also staff dir. interdepartmental group for Near East and South Asia NSC, 1974-78; project dir. country reports on human rights and practices Dept. State, 1978; minister-counselor for refugee and humanitarian affairs U.S. Mission to Geneva, 1979, prin. dep. asst. sec. of state for human rights and humanitarian affairs, 1980-81, acting asst. sec., 1981; Dept. State mem. Congl. Commn. on Security and Cooperation in Europe, 1981-82; chmn. Fgn. Service Selection Bd., 1983, Project for Dissemination of the Laws of Armed Conflict, 1983-84; sr. advisor mgmt. systems and programs Dept. State, 1984-88, sr. cons., 1988-91, insp., 1991-93; cons. Booz, Allen & Hamilton, 1992—; mem. editorial team for country reports on human rights practices, 1993-94. Co-author: Yugoslav Communism and the Macedonian Question, 1971. Served to 1st lt. USMCR, 1943-46. Recipient Superior Svc. awards U.S. Dept. of State, 1966, 82, Meritorious Honor award, 1971, John Jacobs Rogers award, 1988. Mem. Fgn. Svc. Res. Corps. Office: 2813 Bolling Rd Falls Church VA 22042-2012

PALMER, STEVEN O., federal official; b. Bowdle, S.D., Feb. 1, 1956; s. Richard James and Beverly Ann (Barlund) P.; m. Laurel Beach, July 17, 1982; children: Kristin Michelle, Lindsay Ann. BA in Polit. Sci., Kalamazoo Coll., 1978; MPA, U. Tex., Austin, 1980. Rschr. U. Tex., Austin, 1979-80; presdl. mgmt. intern Dept. Transp., 1980-82; mem. profl. staf com. budget U.S. Senate, Washington, 1982-83, sr. mem. staff subcom. on aviation, 1983-90, sr. mem. profl. staff subcom. sci., tech and space, com. commerce , sci. and transp., 1990-93; asst. sec. govtl. affairs U.S. Dept. Transp., Washington, 1993—; team leader Clinton-Gore Presdl. Transition, 1992. Office: Dept Transp Govtl Affairs 400 7th St SW Rm 10408 Washington DC 20590

PALMER, STUART HUNTER, academic dean, sociology educator; b. N.Y.C., Apr. 29, 1924; s. Herman G. and Beatrice (Hunter) P.; m. Anne Barbara Scarborough, June 22, 1946; 1 dau., Catherine. B.A., Yale U., 1949, M.A., 1951, Ph.D., 1955. Asst. to dean Yale Coll., New Haven, 1949-51; instr. sociology New Haven Coll., 1949-51, 53-55; faculty U. N.H., Durham, 1955—; prof. U. N.H., 1964—, chmn. dept. sociology and anthropology, 1964-69, 79-82, dean Coll. Liberal Arts, 1982—; disting. vis. prof. SUNY, Albany, 1970-71; vis. behavioral scientist N.H. Div. Mental Health; vis. prof. U. Sussex, Eng., 1976, U. Ga., 1977; cons. U.S. Office Edn., USPHS, U.S. Office Delinquency and Youth Devel., Dept. Justice; mem. adv. com. for sociology Com. on Internat. Exchange of Persons; mem. exec. com. N.H. Gov.'s Commn. on Crime and Delinquency; co-chmn. Internat. Symposium on Univs. in Twenty-First Century; co-chmn. Internat. Confs. on Stress Rsch., Nat. Commn. Arts and Scis. Author: Understanding Other People, 1955, A Study of Murder, 1960, (with Brian R. Kay) The Challenge of Supervision, 1961, Deviance and Conformity, 1970, (with Arnold S. Linsky) Rebellion and Retreat, 1972, The Violent Society, 1972, The Prevention of Crime, 1973, (with John A. Humphrey) Deviant Behavior, 1980, Role Stress, 1981, Deviant Behavior: Patterns, Sources, and Controls, 1990; also articles. Chmn. bd. trustees Daniel Webster Coll., New Eng. Aero. Inst. Served to lt. AC AUS, 1942-45; Served to lt. AC USAF, 1951-53. Decorated Air medal with 3 oak leaf clusters; Henry Page fellow, 1953-55. Mem. Am. Sociol. Assn., Eastern Sociol. Soc., Internat. Sociol. Soc., Internat. Soc. Criminology, Internat. Soc. Forecasters, Am. Assn. Colls., Council for Liberal Learning, Am. Assn. Higher Edn., Council Colls. Arts and Scis., Nat. Assn. State Univs. and Land-Grant Colls., AAAS, Am. Acad. Polit. and Social Scis., N.Y. Acad. Scis., Am. Assn. Suicidology, Soc. Cross-Cultural Research, Am. Soc. Criminology, Assn. Gov. Bds. Univs. and Colls., Phi Beta Kappa (hon.), Sigma Xi, Alpha Kappa Delta. Home: Riverview Dr Durham NH 03824-3304 Office: U NH Coll Liberal Arts Murkland Hall Durham NH 03824

PALMER, TIMOTHY JACKSON, bank executive; b. Albany, Ga., Dec. 22, 1946. BA in History, Ga. So. Coll., 1969, MBA in Fin., 1983. Loan officer First Nat. Bank, Vidalia, Ga., 1972-75; asst. registrar, data processing Ga. So. Coll., Statesboro, 1975-79; data processing/ops. officer Sea Island Bank, Statesboro, 1979-84; sr. v.p. Citizen's Bank, Gainesville, Ga., 1984-88; pres. Bank South, Douglas, Ga., 1988-90; pres., CEO FNC Bancorp, Inc., Douglas, 1990—, First Nat. Bank, Douglas, 1992—. With U.S. Army, 1969-72. Office: FNC Bancorp Inc PO Box 1699 Douglas GA 31533-7699

PALMER, WILLIAM JOSEPH, accountant; b. Lansing, Mich., Sept. 3, 1934; s. Joseph Flammin Lacchia and Henrietta (Yagerman) P.; m. Judith Pollock, Aug. 20, 1960 (div. Nov. 1980); children: William W., Kathryn E., Leslie A., Emily J.; m. Kathleen Francis Booth, June 30, 1990. BS, U. Calif., Berkeley, 1963. CPA. With Coopers and Lybrand, 1963-80, mng. ptnr., Sacramento, 1976-80; ptnr. Arthur Young & Co., San Francisco, 1980-89; ptnr. Ernst & Young, San Francisco, 1989-94; guest lectr. Stanford U. Engring. Sch., 1976; lectr. Golden Gate Coll., 1975; prof. U. Calif., Berkeley, 1994—. Author: (books) Businessman's Guide to Construction, 1981, Construction Management Book, 1984, Construction Accounting & Financial Management 5th Edition, 1994, Construction Litigation-Representing The Contractor, 1992, Construction Insurance, Bonding and Risk Management, 1995. Bd. dirs. Sacramento Met. YMCA, 1976-82, v.p., 1979-82; bd. dirs. Sacramento Symphony Found., 1977-80; asst. state fin. chmn. Calif. Reagan for Pres., 1980. Served to lt. USN, 1953-59. Mem. AICPA (vice chmn. com. constrn. industry, 1975-81), Nat. Assn. Accts. (pres. Oakland/East Bay chpt. 1972, Man of Yr. 1968), Calif. Soc. CPAs., Assn. Gen. Contractors Calif. (bd. dirs. 1971-74), World Trade Club, Commonwealth Club (San Francisco), Del Paso Country Club, Sutter Club, Comstock Club (Sacramento), Lambda Chi Alpha. Presbyterian. Avocations: antique boats, sailing, tennis, book collecting, pipe collecting. Home: 6 Heather Ln Orinda CA 94563-3508 Office: Ernst & Young 555 California St San Francisco CA 94104

PALMERTREE, RUTH GODRON, counselor; b. Baldwyn, Miss., Aug. 1, 1942; d. Charles Murray and Virginia (Barnett) G.; m. Hiram Douglas Palmertree, Nov. 28, 1964; children: Virginia Delese, Jason Murray. BS, Miss. State U., 1965, MS, 1972. Tchr. spl. edn. Wheeler (Miss.) Sch., 1969-

71; tchr. pub. sci. musicci. Ward Elem. Sch., Starkville, Miss., 1973-74; ednl. TV Cordinator Oktibbeha County Sch., Starkville, Miss., 1974-77; media specialist Chickasaw County Sch., Houlka, Miss., 1979-82; vocat. counselor Oktibbeha County Schs., Starkville, Miss., 1988—. Author: newspaper article Starkville Daily News, 1991-93. Mem. adv. bd. Drug Free Schs., Starkville, 1992-93. Mem. Hosp. Aux., Pilot Club. Avocations: reading, music, art. Home: Heritage Colony RR 5 Box 60 Starkville MS 39759-9805

PALMETER, N. DAVID, lawyer; b. Elmira, N.Y., Jan. 29, 1938; s. Neal Henry and Elizabeth Jane (McHale) P.; m. Mary Lee Morken, 1964 (div. 1979); m. Mary Faith Tanney, Jan. 15, 1983; children: Stephen Michael, John David, Elizabeth Jane, James Martin. AB, Syracuse U., 1960; JD, U. Chgo., 1963. Bar: N.Y. 1963, D.C. 1969. Trial atty. U.S. Dept. Justice, Washington, 1966-68; assoc. Daniels & Houlihan, Washington, 1969-73, ptnr., 1973-75; ptnr. Daniels, Houlihan & Palmeter, Washington, 1975-84, Mudge, Rose, Guthrie, Alexander & Ferdon, Washington, 1984—. Contbr. articles to profl. publs. Mem. ABA, Internat. Bar Assn. (chmn. internat. trade and customs law com. 1989-93), Fed. Bar Assn., N.Y. State Bar Assn., D.C. Bar Assn., Washington Fgn. Law Soc. (pres. 1992-93), Am. Soc. Internat. Law, Can. Coun. on Internat. Law, British Inst. Internat. and Comparative Law. Home: 2804 29th St NW Washington DC 20008-4112 Office: Mudge Rose Guthrie Alexander 1200 19th St NW Washington DC 20036

PALMIERI, VICTOR HENRY, lawyer, business executive; b. Chgo., Feb. 16, 1930; s. Mario and Maria (Losacco) P.; children: Victor Henry, Matthew B., John W.; m. Cathryn Connors, July 6, 1990. AB in History, Stanford U., 1951, JD, 1954. Bar: Calif. 1954. Assoc. O'Melveny & Myers, L.A., 1955-59; exec. v.p. Janss Investment Corp., L.A., 1959-63, pres., 1963-68; chmn. Pa. Co. and its subs. Great S.W. Corp., 1969-77; chmn. bd. Palmieri Co., N.Y.C., 1969—; chmn. bd. PHL Corp. Inc. (formerly Baldwin-United Inc.), Phila., 1983-87; trustee, CEO Colo.-Ute Electric Assn. Inc., 1990-92; spl. dep. rehabilitator Confedn. Life Inst. Co., 1994—; rehabilitator, CEO Mut. Benefit Life Inst. Co., 1991-94; pres., CEO MBL Life Assurance Corp., 1994-95; dir. Ernst Home Ctr., Inc., 1992—, William Carter Corp., 1992—, Outlet Comms., Inc., 1993—, Broadcasting Ptnrs., Inc., 1994—, Mgmt. Compensation Group, 1990—. Chmn. Am. Learning Corp., 1970-85; dep., exec. dir. Nat. Adv. Commn. on Civil Disorders, 1967-68; ambassador-at-large, U.S. coord. Refugee Affairs, Dept. State, 1979-81; trustee Rockefeller Found., 1979-89; pres., bd. dirs. Lincoln Ctr. Theater, 1985-89; chmn. Overseas Devel. Coun., 1985-91; mem. Coun. on Fgn. Rels. Office: Palmieri Co 35th Fl 245 Park Ave Fl 35 New York NY 10167-0001

PALMINTERI, CHAZZ, actor; b. Bronx, N.Y., May 15, 1951. Actor: (theatre) The Guy in the Truck, 1982, Broadway, 1983, The King's Men, 22 Years, The Flatbush Faithful, 1985, (TV movies) Peter Gunn, 1990, (films) Oscar, 1991, Bullets Over Broadway, 1994 (Academy award nomination best supporting actor 1994), The Perez Family, 1994; playwright, actor: (theatre) A Bronx Tale, 1989; screenwriter, actor: (film) A Bronx Tale, 1993. Office: William Morris Agency 151 El Camino Beverly Hills CA 90212*

PALMISANO, SISTER MARIA GORETTI, principal; b. Balt., Nov. 6, 1929; d. Theodore Michael and Agnes Marie (Wheeler) P. BS in Edn. Duquesne U., 1966; MEd in Adminstrn. and Supervision, Towson State U., 1974; postgrad., Loyola Coll., 1976-83. Cert. advanced profl., Md. Tchr. St. Michael Sch., Forstburg, Md., 1952-59; music tchr. Holy Name Sch., Pitts., 1959-64; music tchr., tchr. jr. high St. Margaret Mary Sch., Harrisburg, Pa., 1964-69; prin. St. Brigid Sch., Balt., 1969-73, Bishop John Neumann Sch., Balt., 1973-83; adminstr. SSND Motherhouse, Balt., 1983-91; prin. St. Mary Sch., Hagerstown, Md., 1991—; mem. St. Maria Goretti Recruitment, Hagerstown, 1992—. Named Woman of Yr., Highlandtown Exch. Club, 1983. Mem. ASCD, Nat. Cath. Prins. Assn., Elem. Sch. Prins. Assn.-Archdiocese of Balt. (v.p. 1979-83). Avocations: reading, playing piano/organ, walking, crossword puzzles. Home: 218 W Washington St Hagerstown MD 21740 Office: Saint Mary Sch 218 W Washington St Hagerstown MD 21740

PALMORE, JOHN STANLEY, JR., lawyer; b. Ancon, C.Z., Aug. 6, 1917; s. John Stanley and Antoinette Louise (Gonzalez) P.; m. Eleanor Anderson, July 31, 1938 (dec. 1980); 1 child, John Worsham (dec.). Student, Western Ky. State Coll., 1934-36; LL.B. cum laude, U. Louisville, 1939. Bar: Ky. 1938. Practice law Henderson, 1939-42, 47-59; judge Ct. Appeals Ky. (name changed to Supreme Ct. Ky. 1975), 1959-82, chief justice, 1966, 73, 77-82; practice law Frankfort, Ky., 1983-84; ptnr. Palmore & Sheffer, Henderson, 1984-86; sr. counsel Jackson & Kelly, Lexington, Ky., 1986-92, of counsel, 1992—; city pros. atty., Henderson, 1949-53, city atty., 1953-55; commonwealth's atty. 5th Circuit Ct. Ky., 1955-59. Served to lt. USNR, 1942-46, 51-52. Mem. Ky. Bar Assn., Am. Legion, Ky. Hist. Soc., Frankfort Country Club, Lexington Club, Frankfort Rotary Club (pres. 1993-94), Masons, Shriners, Elks, Phi Alpha Delta. Episcopalian (past vestryman, sr. warden). Home: 2310 Peaks Mill Rd Frankfort KY 40601-9437

PALMORE, RODERICK ALAN, lawyer; b. Pitts., Feb. 14, 1952; s. Jefferson and Sophie (Spencer) Palmore; m. Lynne Avril Janifer, June 3, 1978; children: Jordan, Adam. BA, Yale U, 1974; JD, U. Chgo., 1977. Bar: Pa. 1977, Ill. 1982. Assoc. atty. Berkman Ruslander Pohl Lieber & Engel, Pitts., 1977-79; asst. U.S. atty. U.S. Atty's Office, Chgo., 1979-82; assoc. atty. Wildman Harrold Allen & Dixon, Chgo., Ill., 1982-86, ptnr., 1986-93; ptnr. Sonnenschein Nath & Rosenthal, Chgo., 1993—. Commr. Oak Park Plan Commn., 1988—, chair, 1994—; lectr. Youth Motivation Program Chgo. Coun. Commerce & Industry, 1989—; bd. govs. Am. Heart Assn. Met. Chgo., 1993-94; bd. dirs. Pub. Interest Law Initiative, Legal Assistance Found. Chgo. Named one of Outstanding African-Am. Businessmen, Dollars & Sense mag., Chgo., 1991. Mem. ABA (monirity ptnrs. com. 1993—), Nat. Bar Assn., Cook County Bar Assn., Chgo. Bar Assn. (bd. dirs. 1992-94, co-chmn. minority clerkshop program 1991-92), Chgo. Com. on Minorities in Law Firms (bd. dirs. 1990-92), Chgo. Bar Found. (bd. dirs. 1993-94). Baptist. Avocations: running, biking, tennis, reading. Home: 507 N Euclid Ave Oak Park IL 60302 Office: Sonnenschein Nath & Rosenthal 8000 Sears Tower Chicago IL 60606-6404

PALMQUIST, LOWELL ELDON, health administrator; b. Taylors Falls, Minn., Nov. 25, 1929; s. Roy Leonard and Gladys Hermina (Hyland) P.; m. Ramona Cecilia Kienitz, May 21, 1955; children: David, Nancy Gifford, John. BA, St. Olaf Coll., 1952; MHA, U. Minn., 1958. Bus. mgr. Redwood Falls (Minn.) Mcpl. Hosp., 1955-56; asst. adminstr., adminstr. Fairview Hosp., Mpls., 1958-69; pres., CEO Swedish Med. Ctr., Englewood, Colo., 1969-87; pres. VHA Mountain States, Englewood, 1987-92; sr. v.p. VHA Inc., Washington, 1992—. Chmn. Colo. Hosp. Assn., Denver, 1981-82, Assn. Western Hosps., San Francisco, 1982-83; regent Am. Coll. Healthcare Execs., 1986-91. Staff sgt. U.S. Army, 1952-54. Fellow Am. Coll. Healthcare Execs.; mem. Am. Hosp. Assn. (del. 1984-86). Avocations: skiing, jogging, biking, reading, travel. Office: VHA Eastern Divsn 5904 Mt Eagle Dr Alexandria VA 22303

PALMREUTER, KENNETH RICHARD LOUIS, principal; b. Vassar, Mich., Feb. 8, 1939; s. Clarence L. and Louise M. (Koch) P.; m. Martha Marie Zoellick, June 16, 1962; children: Pauline, Karen, Joel. BS in Edn. Concordia Tchrs. Coll., 1962; MA in Elem. Sch. Adminstrn., U. Mich., 1967; postgrad., Wayne State U., 1978-79. Colo. 1988-89; LLD, Concordia Tchrs. Coll., Seward, Nebr., 1993. Tchr. Grace Luth. Sch., River Forest, Ill., 1960-61; tchr. Calvary Luth. Sch., Lincoln Park, Mich., 1962-63, prin., tchr. jr. high, 1963-76; asst. prin. Luth. High Sch. West, Detroit, 1976-78, prin., 1978-87; exec. dir., prin. Luth. High Sch., Denver, 1987—. Planning coun. for mission and ministry Luth. Ch.-Missouri Synod, 1988-90, mgmt. team Luth. High Schs., 1984-88, 94—, Concordia Centennial adv. com., 1992; day sch. com. Rocky Mountain Dist., 1990-94, tchrs. conf. chmn., 1990-94, dist. conv. com., 1988, 91; nominations com. Mich. Dist., 1987, bd. social ministry, 1980-84, dist. conv. com., 1972, student aid com., 1974-78; conf. program com. Mich. Assn. Non-Pub. Schs., 1984-85; adv. coun. Wayne County Community Coll., 1986-87. Named Outstanding Young Educator, Lincoln Park Jaycees, 1973; nominated Nat. Disting. Luth. Prin., 1992. Mem. NASSP, ASCD, Assn. Luth. Secondary Schs., Luth. Edn. Assn. Lutheran. Home: 2783 S Depew St Denver CO 80227-4106 Office: Lutheran High Sch 3201 W Arizona Ave Denver CO 80219-3941

PALMS, JOHN MICHAEL, university president; b. Rijswijk, The Netherlands, June 6, 1935; naturalized, 1956; s. Peter Joannes and Mimi Adele (DeYong) P.; m. Norma Lee Cannon, June 2, 1958; children: John Michael, Daniele Maria, Lee Cannon. BS in Physics, The Citadel, 1958, DSc (hon.), 1980; MS in Physics, Emory U., 1959; PhD, U. N.Mex., 1966. Commd. 2d lt. USAF, 1958, retired capt. Res., 1970; lectr. physics dept. U. N.Mex., 1959-62; instr. physics dept. USAF Acad., 1961-62; staff mem. Western Electric Sandia Lab., 1961-62, U. Calif. Los Alamos Sci. Lab., 1962-66, Oak Ridge Nat. Lab., 1966; asst. prof. Emory U., Atlanta, 1966-69; assoc. prof. Emory U., 1969-73, chmn., assoc. prof. dept. physics, assoc. prof. radiology dept. Med. Sch., 1973-74, prof., chmn. dept. physics, 1973-74, dean Coll. Arts. and Scis., 1974-80, acting chmn. dept. math. and computer sci., 1976-77, v.p. arts and scis., 1979-82, acting dean Emory Coll., 1979-80, acting dir. Emory U. Computing Ctr., 1980-82, v.p. acad. affairs, interim dean Grad. Sch., 1985-86, Charles Howard Candler prof. nuclear, radiation and environ. physics, 1988-90; pres., prof. physics Ga. State U., Atlanta, 1989-91, U. S.C., Columbia, 1991—; bd. dirs Phila. Electric Co., Fortis Inc., N.Y.C., Source Techs., Inc., Atlanta, NationsBank S.C., N.C., Columbia, Policy Mgmt. Systems Corp., Columbia, Citizens and So. Bank S.C.; mem. adv. com. Oak Ridge Nat. Lab., 1984-89; mem. Nat. Nuclear Accrediting Bd. Inst. Nuclear Power Ops., 1985-91—; mem. Nat. Acad. Sci., NRC Panel for Semiconductor Detectors, 1963-74; cons. Acad. Natural Scis., Phila., EG&G, Inc., Santa Barbara, Calif., Tennelec, Inc., radiology dept. U. S.C. Med. Sch., Three Mile Island Environ. Study, Phila. Health Fund's, ORTEC, Inc., Oak Ridge, Allied-Gulf Nuclear Services, Barnwell, S.C., TRW Space Systems Div., Los Angeles, AEC, Harshaw Chem. Co., Canberra Industries, dept. radiol. health Ga. Dept. Human Resources, Nat. Cancer Inst.; mem. high tech. task force Atlanta C. of C. Contbr. articles on nuclear, atomic, med. and environ. physics to profl. jours. Mem. adv. bd. The Citadel, Oak Ridge Nat. Lab.; mem. exec. bd. Atlanta Area Coun. Boy Scouts of Am., 1989-90; mem. community rels. bd. U.S Penitentiary, Atlanta; trustee Inst. for Def. Analyses, Wesleyan Coll., 1984-89, Pace Acad., 1984-89, St. Joseph's Hosp., Atlanta, 1987-89, Ga. Rsch. Alliance, 1988-89; mem. S.C. Univs. Rsch. and Ednl. Found. Bd., S.C. Rsch. Authority Bd.; bd. dirs. Civic-Atlanta Partnership Bus. and Edn., Inc., 1988-90. Mem. AAAS, Am. Phys. Soc., Am. Assn. Physics Tchrs., IEEE (Nuclear Sci. Group), Am. Nuclear Soc., Am. Coun. Edn., Coun. Provosts and Acad. V.P.s, Am. Conf. Acad. Deans, Soc. Nuclear Medicine, Health Physics Soc., Columbia C. of C. (bd. dirs.), Rotary, Phi Beta Kappa, Sigma Xi, Phi Kappa Phi, Omicron Delta Kappa, Sigma Pi Sigma. Home: U SC President's House Columbia SC 29208 Office: U SC Office of President Columbia SC 29208

PALMS, ROGER CURTIS, religious magazine editor, clergyman; b. Detroit, Sept. 13, 1936; s. Nelson Curtis and Winifred Jessie (Bennett) P.; m. Andrea Sisson, Aug. 22, 1959; children—Grant Curtis, Andrea Jane. B.A., Wayne State U., 1958; B.D., Eastern Baptist Sem., Phila, 1961, M.Div., 1971, D.D., 1977; M.A., Mich. State U., 1971. Ordained to ministry Am. Bapt. Chs., 1961. Pastor Ronceverte Bapt. Ch., W.Va., 1961-64; pastor 1st Bapt. Ch., Highland Park, N.J., 1964-67; chaplain Am. Bapt. Student Found., Mich. State U., East Lansing, 1967-73; assoc. editor Decision mag. Billy Graham Evang. Assn., Mpls., 1973-76, editor, 1976—; guest lectr. at schs of evangelism and writers' confs. Author 12 books including: Living on the Mountain, 1985, Enjoying the Closeness of God, 1989, Let God Help You Choose, 1989; speaker nationally syndicated radio program Something for You. Trustee No. Bapt. Theol. Sem., 1973—. Mem. Evang. Press Assn. (pres. 1991-93). Office: Decision Mag Billy Graham Evang Assn 1300 Harmon Pl Minneapolis MN 55403-1925 *Investing in people's spiritual lives, giving time and counsel, will bring multiplied results for generations. It is one of the most far-reaching ways I can put faith to work.*

PALO, NICHOLAS EDWIN, professional society administrator; b. Waukegan, Ill., Nov. 18, 1945; s. Edwin Arnold and Eevi Kustaava (Hukkala) P.; m. Lauren M. Reynolds, Aug. 18, 1990 (dec.). BA, U. Wis., Eau Claire, 1971; MS, U. Mo., 1975. Instr., coordinator U Mo. Extension, Columbia, 1974-85; exec. officer Am. Bd. Profl. Psychology, Columbia, 1984—. Pres. Columbia Community Band, 1987; chmn. Arts Resources Coun., Columbia, 1988; adv. bd. Columbia Art League. Mem. Am. Soc. Assn. Execs., Psychology Execs. Roundtable, Mensa, Windjammers Unltd. Club, Am. Assn. Concert Bands Club, Internat. Trombone Assn., Phi Delta Kappa (hon.), Phi Mu Alpha (hon.). Democrat. Lutheran. Avocation: music. Home: 608 Spring Valley Rd Columbia MO 65203-2261 Office: Am Board of Profl Psychology 2100 E Broadway Ste 313 Columbia MO 65201-6082

PALOMO, JUAN RAMÓN, columnist; b. Grafton, N.D., July 7, 1946; s. Domingo L. and Martina (López) P. AA, S.W. Tex. Jr. Coll., Uvalde, 1967; BS, S.W. Tex. State U., 1970; MA, Am. U., 1979. Cert. secondary tchr., Tex. Instr. art San Marcos (Tex.) High Sch., 1970-72; editor, pub. La Otra Voz, San Marcos, 1972; editor Hays County Citizen, San Marcos, 1972-76; gen. assignment/polit. reporter Houston Post, 1979-82; nat. reporter USA Today, Arlington, Va., 1982-83; Latin Am. and Caribbean corr. Houston Post, Barbados, 1984; Washington corr. Houston Post, 1985-90, columnist, editorial writer, 1990—; press asst. Carter-Mondale Tex. Hdqs., Austin, 1976; speech writer, press aide Warren Harding for State Treas., Austin, 1978. Mem. Tex. Dem. Exec. Com., Austin, 1976-78. Recipient 1st Pl. for Column Writing, Press Club Houston, 1989, 1st Pl. for Editorial Writing, Press Club Dallas, 1992, Tex. Associated Press Mng. Editors, 1992, Charles E. Green award Headliners Club Tex., 1992. Mem. Nat. Lesbian and Gay Journalists Assn. (bd. dirs. 1991-93, chair elections com. 1991), Nat. Assn. Hispanic Journalists, Nat. Conf. Editl. Writers, Houston Assn. Hispanic Media Profls., Parents, Family and Friends Lesbians and Gays. Avocations: painting, sketching. Home: 1636 Castle Ct Houston TX 77006-5708 Office: Houston Post PO Box 4747 Houston TX 77210-4747

PALOYAN, EDWARD, physician, educator, reseacher; b. Paris, Mar. 19, 1932; s. Michael and Renee (Palaian) P.; m. Geraldine Richveis, July 7, 1957; children—Vivian, Regina, Edmund, Grace. M.D., U. Chgo., 1956. Intern U. Chgo. hosps. and clinics, 1956-57; resident in surgery, 1957-58, 1960-65, asst. prof. surgery, 1965-68; assoc. prof. surgery U. Chgo. Hosps. and Clinics, Pirtzker Sch. Medicine, 1968-73; prof. surgery Loyola U. Stritch Sch. Medicine, Maywood, Ill., 1973—; chief endocrine surgery Loyola and Hines, Ill., 1980—; assoc. chief of staff for rsch. VA Hosp., Hines, 1973—; assoc. staff Hinsdale (Ill.) Hosp., 1991—. Author: (with A.M. Lawrence) Endocrine Surgery, 1976, (with A.M. Lawrence, F.H. Straus) Hyperparathyroidism, 1973. Served with USN, 1958-60. Recipient McClintock award U. Chgo. Med. Sch., 1971. Mem. Am. Surg. Assn., Soc. Univ. Surgeons, Endocrine Soc., Central Surg. Assn., Am. Assn. Endocrine Surgeons (pres. 1987). Home: 827 Taft Rd Hinsdale IL 60521-4836 also: 40 S Clay St Ste 220W Hinsdale IL 60521-3257

PALSER, BARBARA F., botany researcher, retired educator; b. Worcester, Mass., June 2, 1916; d. G. Norman and Cora A. (Munson) P. A.B., Mt. Holyoke Coll., 1938, A.M., 1940, D.Sc. (hon.), 1978; Ph.D., U. Chgo., 1942. From instr. to prof. botany U. Chgo., 1942-65; from assoc. prof. to prof. botany Rutgers U., New Brunswick, N.J., 1965-83, dir. grad. program in botany, 1973-80; adj. prof. botany U. Mass., Amherst, 1991—; Erskine fellow U. Canterbury, Christchurch, N.Z. 1969; vis. prof. Duke U., Durham, N.C., fall 1962; vis. research fellow U. Melbourne, Australia, fall 1984-85. Author lab. manual Principles of Botany, 1973, also numerous research papers in bot. jours.; bot. adviser Ency. Brit., Chgo., 1958-59; editor Bot. Gazette, Chgo., 1960-65. Named Outstanding Tchr., Rutgers Coll., 1977. Mem. Bot. Soc. Am. (sec. 1970-74, v.p. 1975, pres. 1976, Merit award 1985), Torrey Bot. Club (pres. 1968), Internat. Soc. Plant Morphologists, N.J. Acad. Scis. (pres. elect 1987-88, pres. 1988-89, Outstanding Svc. award 1985, 90), Am. Inst. Biol. Scis. Avocations: mountain hiking and climbing; stamp collecting; photography. Home: 1 Spencer Dr Apt 330 Amherst MA 01002-3367 Office: U Mass Dept Biology Morrill (South) PO Box 35810 Amherst MA 01003-5810

PALSHO, DOROTHEA COCCOLI, information services executive; b. Phila., June 9, 1947; d. John Charles and Dorothy Lucille (Decker) C.; m. Edward Robert Palsho; children: Christopher, Ryan, Erica (stepchild). BS, Villanova U., 1976; MBA, Temple U., 1977. V.p. info. svcs Dow Jones & Co., Princeton, N.J., 1977—. Named one of Class of Women Achievers YWCA Acad. of Women Achievers, 1985. Avocation: sports with the boys. Office: Dow Jones & Co Inc PO Box 300 Princeton NJ 08543-0300

PALTER, ROBERT MONROE, philosophy and history educator; b. N.Y.C., June 19, 1924; s. Meyer and Mildred (Gilder) P.; m. Ruth Rappeport, July 15, 1945; 1 child, Alixe Daphne Cielo; m. Toni Ann Inmam, Apr. 5, 1955; children: Geoffrey Meyer, Jennifer Thorn, Nicholas Trask, Adam Finch; m. Annette B. Weiner, May 21, 1979 (div. 1982). AB, Columbia U., 1943; PhD, U. Chgo., 1952. From instr. to asso. prof. phys. scis. and philosophy U. Chgo., 1949-64; prof. philosophy and history U. Tex., Austin, 1964-82; Dana prof. history of sci. Trinity Coll., Hartford, Conn., 1983-91, prof. emeritus, 1991—. Author: Whitehead's Philosophy of Science, 1960; editor: Toward Modern Science, 1961, The Annus Mirabilis of Sir Isaac Newton, 1971. Served with AUS, 1944-46. Mem. Phi Beta Kappa.

PALTIEL, A. ROBERT, engineering consulting company executive. Sr. v.p., CFO Synetics Corp., Wakefield, Mass. Office: Synetics Corp 540 Edgewater Dr Wakefield MA 01880*

PALUCK, ROBERT JOHN, electronics executive; b. Chgo., Dec. 23, 1947; s. John J. and Evelyn (Kaminski) P.; m. Michelle Deknock, June 28, 1969. BSEE, U. Ill., 1969; MBA, So. Meth. U., 1980. V.p product devel. and mktg. Mostek Corp., Carrollton, Tex., 1971-82; pres., chief exec. officer, chmn. bd. CONVEX Computer Corp. Richardson, Tex., 1982—. Mem. adv. bd. Coll. Engring. U. Ill., 1986—, U. Tex. Dallas, 1987—. Recipient Outstanding Entrepreneur award So. Meth. U., 1987, Disting. Alumnus award U. Ill., 1988; named Tex. Hi-Tech. Entrepreneur, 1989. Mem. Am. Electronics Assn. (bd. dirs.), Coun. Competitiveness. Office: Convex Computer Corp 3000 Waterview Pky Richardson TX 75080-1400

PALUMBO, BENJAMIN LEWIS, public affairs consulting company executive; b. Boston, Mar. 4, 1937; s. Guido Americo and Stella Marie (Lombardo) P.; m. Magdalene Julia Palinczar, Nov. 18, 1961; children: Matthew, Jason, Guy. BA, Rutgers U., 1959, MA, 1961. Adminstrv. asst. to Gov. Richard J. Hughes, N.J., 1963-65; dir. rsch. N.J. Dem. Com., Trenton, 1965-66; asst. to commr. N.J. Dept. Transp., Trenton, 1966-70; asst. dean Woodrow Wilson Sch., Princeton (N.J.) U., 1970-7l; adminstrv. asst. to Senator Harrison Williams, U.S. Senate, Washington, 1971-73, staff dir. Dem. caucus, 1975-77, subcom. on govt. activities and transp., 1977-78; nat. campaign dir. Bentsen for Pres., Washington, 1973-75; dir. fed. govt. rels. Phillip Morris, Inc., Washington, 1978-83; pres. Palumbo & Cerrell, Inc., Washington, 1983—. Bd. dirs. Washington Performing Arts Soc. Mem. Nat. Press Club, Rutgers Club Washington (chmn. bd. dirs. 1990—), Econ. Club Washington, Am. League Lobbyists, KC, Nat. Dem. Club. Democrat. Roman Catholic. Office: Palumbo & Cerrell Inc Ste 500 1717 K St NW Washington DC 20036-5302

PALUMBO, DONALD R., metal products executive; b. 1936. Pres. Gold Coast Engring. Inc., Chula Vista, Calif., 1980—. Office: Gold Coast Engring Inc 1891 Nirvana Ave Chula Vista CA 91911*

PALUSZEK, JOHN L., public relations firm executive; b. Bklyn., Nov. 3, 1933. BA in Mgmt., Manhattan Coll, 1955. Assoc. editor Petroleum Week, 1955-59; v.p., then sr. v.p., exec. v.p. Basford Pub. Rels., 1960-71; pres. Paluszek & Leslie Assocs., 1971-84; exec. v.p. Ketchum Pub. Rels., from 1984; now pres for pub. affairs Ketchum Pub. Rels., N.Y.C.; pres-elect Pub. Rels. Soc. Am., past pres. N.Y. chpt., past chmn., N.E. dist. Author articles in profl. jours. Office: Ketchum Pub Rels 1133 Ave Of The Americas New York NY 10036-6710

PALVINO, JACK ANTHONY, broadcasting executive; b. Rochester, N.Y., May 28, 1934; s. John Charles and Mary Aurelia P.; m. Joyce Ann Vilkaitis, Oct. 8, 1960; children: John Charles, Jill Marie, Jason Allen. B.S., St. John Fisher Coll., 1955. Broadcaster, program dir. Sta. WGVA, Geneva, N.Y., 1958-60, Sta. WBBF, Rochester, N.Y., 1965-70; pres. Sports and Spls. TV, 1970-73; exec. v.p. Lincoln Group Ltd., 1978—; gen. mgr. Stas. WHAM, WVOR, WHTK, WPXY, Rochester, 1978—. Chmn. bd. trustees St. John Fisher Coll. Served with U.S. Army, 1957-58. Mem. St. John Fisher Alumni Assn., Nat. Assn. Broadcaster, Rochester Radio Broadcasters Assn. (pres. 1987—), N.Y. State Broadcasters Assn., Rochester C. of C. Roman Catholic. Clubs: University, Rochester Press Radio (pres. 1974), Rotary. Office: 207 Midtown Plz Rochester NY 14604-2016

PAMPEL, JOSEPH PHILIP STEVENSON, investment executive; b. Findlay, Ohio, Feb. 11, 1932; s. William Sumner and Helen (Stevenson) P.; m. Georgia Anne Hertzman, June 23, 1963; children: Joseph P.S. Jr., Martha Anne. BS in Chem. Engring., Case Inst. Tech., 1954; MBA in Prodn., Fin., Harvard U., 1960. Faculty Harvard Bus. Sch., Cambridge, Mass., 1961; various banking and investment positions, 1962-79; group controller Charterhouse Group Internat., Inc., N.Y.C., 1979-81; v.p. fin. Charterhouse Group Internat., Inc., 1981-82, v.p., treas., CFO to v.p. banking and investment mgmt., 1982-87; owner, chief exec. J.P. Pampel & Co., N.Y.C., 1987-89; founder, dir. Carpenter Enterprises Ltd., Fenton, Mich., 1987-89; treas. Charterhouse Automotive, N.Y.C., 1987—, Tex. Tech Industries Inc., N. Monmouth, Maine, 1988—; ptnr. Wier & Pampel, Inc., N.Y.C., 1989—; bd. dirs. Charterhouse Automotive, N.Y.C., Carpenter Enterprises, Ltd., Fenton.; chmn. bd., treas. Blair Industries, Inc., Scott City, Mo., 1987—. Pres., alumni assn. Case Inst. Tech., N.Y.C.; past pres. Case Western Res. Alumni in Greater Metro Area, N.Y.C. Lt. (j.g.) USNR, 1954-58. Mem. Harvard Club, Quechee Country Club. Avocations: skiing, gardening, golf, old cars. Office: Wier & Pampel Inc 780 3rd Ave New York NY 10017-2024

PAMPEL, ROLAND D., computer company executive; b. Mystic, Conn., Nov. 16, 1935; s. Alban and Doris (Denison) P.; m. Carol Patricia Clay, Apr. 5, 1958; children: Lynne Pampel Albertini, Jean Pampel Losier, Sandra. BSEE, U. Conn., 1956. Product mgr., then gen. mgr. IBM Corp., 1961-82; gen. mgr., lab dir. IBM Corp., Kingston, N.Y., until 1982; v.p. research and devel. Prime Computer, Natick, Mass., 1982-85; sr. v.p. mktg. and devel. AT&T Computer Div., Morristown, N.J., 1985-86; pres. Apollo Computer Inc., Chelmsford, Mass., 1986-87, CEO, 1987-90; CEO Bull HN Onformation Systems, Inc., Billerica, Mass., 1990-91; pres., CEO Nicolet Instrument Corp., Madison, Wis., 1991—. Lt. USN, 1956-59. Mem. Nat. Computer Graphics Assn. (vice chmn. 1988—), Braeburn Country Club (Newton, Mass.). Office: Nicolet Instrument Corp 5225 Verona Rd Madison WI 53711

PAMPLIN, ROBERT BOISSEAU, SR., textile manufacturing executive; b. Sutherland, Va., Nov. 25, 1911; s. John R. and Pauline (Beville) P.; m. Mary K. Reese, June 15, 1940; 1 child, Robert Boisseau Jr. BBA, Va. Poly. Inst. & State U., 1933; postgrad., Northwestern U., 1933-34; LLD (hon.), U. Portland (Oreg.), 1972; LHD (hon.), Warner Pacific Coll., 1976. With Ga.-Pacific Corp., Portland, 1934-76, sec., from 1936, adminstrv. v.p., 1952-55, exec. v.p., 1955-57, pres., 1957-67, chmn. bd., chief exec. officer, from 1967; ret., 1976; with R.B. Pamplin Corp., 1977—, chmn. bd., chief exec. officer; also chmn. bd., chief exec. officer Mt. Vernon Mills Inc. (subs. R.B. Pamplin Corp.), Greenville, S.C. Office: R B Pamplin Corp 900 SW 5th Ave Ste 1800 Portland OR 97204-1259 also: Mt Vernon Mills Inc PO Box 3478 1 Insignia Fin Plz Greenville SC 29602

PAMPLIN, ROBERT BOISSEAU, JR., agricultural company executive, minister, writer; b. Augusta, Ga., Sept. 3, 1941; s. Robert Boisseau and Mary Katherine (Reese) P.; m. Marilyn Joan Hooper; children: Amy Louise, Anne Boisseau. Student Va. Poly. Inst., 1960-62; BSBA, Lewis and Clark Coll., 1964, BS in Acctg., 1965, BS in Econs., 1966, LHD (hon.), 1995; MBA, U. Portland, 1968, MEd, 1975, LLD (hon.), 1972, Western Bapt. Coll., 1989; MCL, Western Conservative Bapt. Sem., 1978, DMin, 1982, PhD, Calif. Coast U., DHL (hon.), Warner Pacific Coll., 1988, LLD (hon.), Western Bapt. Coll., 1989; cert. in wholesale mgmt. Ohio State U., 1970; cert. in labor mgmt., U. Portland, 1972; cert. in advanced mgmt., U. Hawaii, 1975; DD (hon.), Judson Baptist Coll., 1984; DBA (hon.), Marquis Giuseppe Scicluna Internat. U. Found., 1986; LittD (hon.), Va. Tech. Inst. and State U., 1987, LHD (hon.); D of Sacred Letter (hon.) Western Conservation Bapt. Sem., 1991; DD, Western Evangelical Sem., 1994. Pres., also dir. R.B. Pamplin Corp., Portland, Oreg., 1964—; chmn. bd. Columbia Empire Farms, Inc. Lake Oswego, Oreg., 1976—; vice chmn., also dir. Mt. Vernon Mills Inc.; pres., also dir. Ross Island Sand & Gravel Co.; lectr. bus. adminstrn. Lewis and Clark Coll., 1968-69, trustee, 1989—; adj. asst. prof. bus. adminstrn., U. Portland, 1973-76; pastor Christ Community Ch., Lake Oswego, Oreg. lectr.

in bus. adminstrn. and economics, U. Costa Rica, 1968, Va. Tech. Found., 1986; chmn. bd. dirs. United Tile Co., Christian Supply Ctrs., Inc. Author: Everything is Just Great, 1985, The Gift, 1986, Another Virginian: A Study of the Life and Beliefs of Robert Boisseau Pamplin, 1986, (with others): A Portrait of Colorado, 1976, Three in One, 1974, The Storybook Primer on Managing, 1974. One Who Believed, Vol. I, 1988, Vol. II, 1991, Climbing the Centuries, 1993, Heritage The Making of an American Family, 1994, American Heroes, 1995, Prelude to Surrender, 1995; editor Oreg. Mus. Sci. and Industry Press, 1973, trustee, 1971, 74—; editor Portrait of Oregon, 1973, (with others) Oregon Underfoot, 1975; hon. life pres. Western Conservative Baptist Seminary. Mem. Nat. Adv. Coun. on Vocat. Edn., 1975—; mem. Western Interstate Comm. for Higher Edn., 1981-84; co-chmn. Va. Tech. $50 million Campaign for Excellence, 1984-87, Va. Tech Found., 1986—, Va.-Oreg. State Scholarship Commn., 1974—, chmn., 1976-78; mem. Portland dist. adv. council SBA, 1973-77; mem. rewards rev. com., City of Portland, 1973-78, chmn., 1973-78; mem. bd. regents U. Portland, 1971-79, chmn. bd., 1975-79, regent emeritus, 1979—; trustee Oreg. Episc. Schs., 1979, Linfield Coll., U. Puget Sound, 1989—, chmn. bd. trustees Lewis and Clark Coll., 1991. Recipient Disting. Alumnus award Lewis and Clark Coll., 1974, Air Force ROTC Disting. Svc. award, USAF, 1974, Albert Einstein Acad. Bronze medal, 1986, Disting. Leadership medal Freedoms Found., Disting. Bus. Alumnus award U. Portland, 1990, Nat. Caring award Caring Inst., 1991, Pride of Portland award Portland Lions Club, Hero Athlete award, 1994; Va. Tech Coll. of Bus. Adminstrn. renamed R.B. Pamplin Coll. of Bus. Adminstrn. in his honor; Western Conservative Bapt. Sem. Lay Inst. for Leadership, Edn., Devel. and Rsch. named for R.B. Pamplin, Jr., 1988. Mem. Acad. Mgmt., Delta Epsilon Sigma, Beta Gamma Sigma, Sigma Phi Epsilon, Waverley Country Club, Arlington, Multnomah Athletic Club, Capitol Hill Club, Greenville Country Club, Poinsett Club, Eldorado Country Club, Rotary. Republican. Episcopalian. Office: Mt Vernon Mills Inc Box 3478 1 Setter Ln Greenville SC 29607-4200

PAMPUSCH, ANITA MARIE, academic administrator; b. St. Paul, Aug. 28, 1938; d. Robert William and Lucille Elizabeth (Whaley) P. BA, Coll. of St. Catherine, St. Paul, 1962; MA, U. Notre Dame, 1970, PhD, 1972. Tchr. St. Joseph's Acad., St. Paul, 1962-66; instr. philosophy Coll. of St. Catherine, St. Paul, 1970-76, assoc. acad. dean, 1979, acad. dean, 1979-84, pres., 1984—; Am. Council Edn. fellow Goucher Coll., Balt., 1976-77; bd. dirs. St. Paul Cos.; head Women's Coll. Coalition, 1988-91. Author: (book rev.) Philological Quarterly, 1976; contbr. articles to profl. jours. Mem. adv. com. Instl. Leadership project, Columbia U., 1986—; dist. chmn. Rhodes Scholarship Selection com., Mo., Neb., Minn., Kans., N.D., S.D., 1987—; exec. com. Women's Coll. Coalition, Washington, 1985—. Mem. Coun. for Ind. Colls. (bd. dirs. 1987—, chair 1991—), Am. Philos. Assn., St. Paul C. of C. (bd. dirs. 1986—), St. Paul's Athletic Club, Mpls. Club, Phi Beta Kappa. Roman Catholic. Avocations: swimming, camping, reading, music. Office: Coll of St Catherine Office of the President 2004 Randolph Ave Saint Paul MN 55105-1789

PAN, CODA H. T., mechanical engineering educator, consultant, researcher; b. Shanghai, China, Feb. 10, 1929; came to U.S., 1948; s. Ming H. Pai and Chih S. Ling; m. Vivian Y.C. Chang, June 2, 1951; children—Lydia Codetta, Philip Daniel. Student, Tsing Hwa U., Beijing, China, 1946-48; B.S. in Mech. Engring., Ill. Inst. Tech., 1950; M.S. in Aero. Engring., Rensselaer Poly. Inst., 1958, Ph.D., 1961. Engr. Gen. Electric Co., Schenectady, 1950-61; dir. research Mech. Tech. Inc., Latham, N.Y., 1961-73; tech. dir. Shaker Research Corp., Ballston Lake, N.Y., 1973-81; prof. mech. engring. Columbia U., N.Y.C., 1981-87; sr. cons. engr. Digital Equipment Corp., Shrewsbury, Mass., 1987-92; adj. prof. Rensselaer Poly. Inst., 1961-81; vis. prof. Tech. U. Denmark, Copenhagen, 1971, U. Poitiers, France, 1987; mem. adv. panel nand Corp., 1974; engring. cons., 1992—, v.p. Indsl. Tribology Inst., Troy, N.Y., 1982—; co-prin. investigator Spacelab I, 1984. Contbg. author: Tribology, 1980, Structural Mechanical Software Series 3, 1980; contbr. articles to profl. jours.; patentee in field. Recipient IR-100 award, 1967; NIH fellow, 1972. Fellow ASME, Soc. Tribologists and Lubrication Engrs.; mem. AAAS, Am. Phys. Soc., Am. Acad. Mechanics. Home and Office: 5 Pinehurst Cir Millbury MA 01527-3361

PAN, ELIZABETH LIM, information systems company executive; b. Manila, Dec. 6, 1941; came to U.S., 1961, naturalized, 1967; d. Lim Hu and Maria (Ramos) Lim; m. Jeff T. S. Pan, Jan. 17, 1962 (dec. 1978); children: Jeffrey, James. Student, U. Philippines, Quezon City, 1959-61; B.A., U. Ill., 1963, M.S., 1966; Ph.D., Rutgers U., 1974. Pres. Trulim, Inc., Inst. Info. Studies, Inc., PSI Internat. Editor: (with others) Collection Mgmt., 1977-80; editor: Annual Rev. Rehab., 1980-83; contbr. articles to profl. publs. Pres. Nat. Fedn. 8(a) Cos. (pres.). Home: 3220 Lake Edge Way Oakton VA 22124-2028 Office: 10306 Eaton Pl Fairfax VA 22030-2201

PAN, HENRY YUE-MING, clinical pharmacologist; b. Shanghai, China, Dec. 27, 1946; came to U.S. 1969; s. Chia-Liu and Siu-Ging (Sung) P.; m. Mary Agnes Tse; children: Lincoln Jonathan, Gregory Kingsley. BSc (hon.), McGill U., Montreal, 1969; MS in Toxicology, U. Hawaii, 1973, PhD in Pharmacology, 1974; MD, U. Hong Kong, 1979. Rsch. asst. U. Hawaii, Honolulu, 1969-74, teaching asst., 1970-74; med. officer Queen Mary Hosp., Hong Kong, 1979-81; asst. prof. medicine U. Hong Kong, 1981-85; vis. asst. prof. Stanford (Calif.) U., 1983-85; asst. clin. pharmacology dir. Squibb Inst. Med. Rsch., Princeton, N.J., 1985-87, assoc. clin. pharmacology dir., 1987-88, clin. pharmacology dir., 1988-89, exec. dir. clin. rsch., 1989-91; v.p. clin. rsch. Bristol-Myers Squibb Pharm. Rsch. Inst., Princeton, 1991-92; v.p. clin. rsch. and devel. DuPont Merck Pharm. Co., Wilmington, Del., 1992-93; sr. v.p. drug devel. Du Pont Merck Pharm. Co., Wilmington, Del., 1993—. Contbr. articles to profl. jours. Stanford Asian Med. Fund grantee, 1983-85. Fellow Am. Coll. Clin. Pharmacology, Am. Heart Assn. Coun., Am. Coll. Cardiology; mem. AAAS, Am. Soc. Clin. Pharmacology and Therapeutics, Am. Soc. for Pharmacology and Exptl. Therapeutics, Am. Fedn. Clin. Rsch. Roman Catholic. Avocations: tennis, golf, distance running, cycling, baseball, classical music, plays. Office: DuPont Merck Pharm Co DuPont Merck Plaza Centre Rd Wilmington DE 19805

PAN, HUO-HSI, mechanical engineer, educator; b. Fuzhou, Peoples Republic of China, Nov. 11, 1918; came to the U.S., 1948; s. Bai-ming and Won-ching (Chen) P.; m. Chao Pan, June 4, 1960; children: Lillian, Nina. BS in Mech. Engring., Nat. S.W. Associated U., Kunming, Peoples Republic of China, 1943; MS in Mech. Engring., Tex. A&M U., 1949; MS in Applied Mechanics, Kans. State Coll., 1950; PhD, U. Calif., Berkeley, 1954. Asst. engr. Yunnan Smelting Plant, Peoples Republic of China, 1942-43; from mem. tech. staff to head inspection dept. 21st Arsenal, Peoples Republic of China, 1943-47; from teaching asst. to assoc. mech. engring. U. Calif., Berkeley, 1950-53; rsch. engr. Portland Cement Assn., 1954; asst. prof. U. Toledo, 1954-55, U. Ill., Champaign, 1955-57; asst. prof. engring. mechanics NYU, 1957-59, from asst. prof. to prof. applied mechanics, 1957-73; prof. applied mechanics, mech. engring. Poly. U., 1973-90, prof. emeritus, 1990—; cons. Frankford Arsenal, Picatinny Arsenal, Petro-Chem Devel. Co.; referee Jour. Applied Mechanics, AIAA Jour., Internat. Jour. Mech. Sci., Internat. Jour. Solid and Structures, NSF; reviewer Applied Mechanics Revs.; sect. chmn. Internat. Modal Analysis Confs.; lectr. Kunming Inst. Tech., Tsinghua U., Jilin U. Tech., Jilin U. 1984. Contbr. numerous articles to Jour. Applied Mechanics, AIAA Jour., Jour. Mechanique, Jour. Engring. Mechanics, Jour. Applied Math. and Physics, Quar. Jour. Mechanics and Applied Math., Quar. Applied Math., Internat. Jour. Mech. Sci., Bull. Acad. Polonaise des Scis., Jour. Sound and Vibration, many others. Grantee NSF, 1964-67, NASA, 1966-68. Mem. ASME, AIAA, Am. Acad. Mechanics, Soc. Engring. Sci., Soc. for Indsl. and Applied Math., U.S. Assn. for Computational Mechanics, Internat. Assn. for Computational Mechanics, Phi Kappa Phi, Sigma Xi, Tau Beta Pi, Pi Tau Sigma, Pi Mu Epsilon. Achievements include development of method for reduction of vibrational systems, general method of modal analysis, solution for ordinary differential equation containing symbolic functions, eigenfunction expansion method in vibration problems of viscoelestic bodies. Home: 76 Edgars Ln Hastings-on-Hudson NY 10706-1122 Office: Poly U Dept Mech Engring 6 Metrotech Ctr 333 Jay St Brooklyn NY 11201-2990

PANARESE, WILLIAM C., civil engineer; b. Framingham, Mass., Mar. 6, 1929; s. Angelo and Stephanie (De Profilo) P. B.S. in Civil Engring., Purdue U., 1952. Structural research engr. Assn. Am. Railroads, Chgo., 1952-55; with Portland Cement Assn., Chgo. and Skokie, Ill., 1957-76, 80-94; mgr.

concrete tech. sect. Portland Cement Assn., 1973-76, assoc. mgr. bldg. constrn. sect., 1980-83, mgr. bldg. tech. dept., 1983-86, mgr. constrn. info. services dept., 1987-94. Author, editor Design and Control of Concrete Mixtures, Concrete Masonry handbook for Architects, Engineers, Builders, High Strength Concrete, Concrete Floors on Ground, Fiber Reinforced Concrete, Cement Mason's Guide, other bldg. guides and handbooks; editor: Concrete Constrn. mag., 1976-80, Concrete Technology Today newsletter, 1980-94. Served with C.E. U.S. Army, 1955-57. Fellow Am. Concrete Inst. (coms. 302 on constrn. of concrete floors, 332 on residential concrete work, chmn. 332 1984-88). Roman Catholic. Home: 942 Washington St Glenview IL 60025-4273

PANARO, VICTOR ANTHONY, radiologist; b. Buffalo, Aug. 7, 1928; s. Anthony and Teresa P.; m. Virginia Spann, Dec. 4, 1954; children: Denise, Lynn, Stephen. BA summa cum laude, U. Buffalo, 1948, MD, 1952. Diplomate Am. Bd. Radiology, Am. Bd. Nuclear Medicine, Am. Bd. Med. Examiners. Intern E. J. Meyer Meml. Hosp., Buffalo, 1952-53; resident E. J. Meyer Meml. Hosp., 1953-54, 56-58, Roswell Park Meml. Hosp. Cancer Inst., Buffalo, 1956-57; practice medicine specializing in radiology and nuclear medicine Buffalo, 1961—; mem. staff Erie County Med. Center, Buffalo, 1961—; assoc. dir. radiology dept. Erie County Med. Center, 1972—; mem. staff Westfield (N.Y.) Meml. Hosp., 1959-81, dir. radiology dept., 1959-81; mem. staff Buffalo Psychiat. Inst., 1974—, dir. radiology dept., 1974—; cons. nuclear medicine and radiology Brooks Meml. Hosp., 1970—; cons. VA Hosp., Buffalo; prof. radiology and nuclear medicine SUNY, Buffalo. Served as capt. M.C. U.S. Army, 1954-56. Fellow Am. Coll. Radiology; mem. AMA, N.Y. State Med. Soc., Erie County Med. Soc., Radiol. Soc. N.Am., Assn. Univ. Radiologists, Buffalo Radiol. Soc., Radiologists Bus. Mgrs. Assn., N.Y. State Radiol. Soc., Gibson Anatomical Soc., Cath. Physicians Guild Western N.Y., Phi Beta Kappa, Phi Chi. Republican. Roman Catholic. Clubs: Baccelli Med, Holy Name Soc, Knights of Jerusalem Malta. Home: 25 Elmhurst Rd Buffalo NY 14226-3539 Office: Erie County Med Center 462 Grider St Buffalo NY 14215-3021

PANATIER, M. J., gas industry executive. Sr. v.p., coo Phillips 66 Natural Gas Co., Houston, 1986—. Office: Phillips 66 Natural Gas Co 1300 Post Oak Blvd Houston TX 77056

PANAYIOTOU, GERGIOS KYRIAKOU See MICHAEL, GEORGE

PANCAKE, EDWINA HOWARD, science librarian; b. Butte, Mont., Nov. 10, 1942; d. Robert Evan and Edwina Howard (Handfield) P. Student, Miami U., 1960-63; BS in Biology, Baylor U., 1967; MLS, U. Tex., 1969. Sci. info. specialist U. Va., Charlottesville, 1969-73, acting dir. sci. and tech. info. ctr., dir. sci. and engring libr., 1974-93, assoc. prof. emeritus, 1994—. NDEA fellow U. Tex., 1967-68. Fellow Spl. Libraries Assn. (bd. dirs. 1979-81, 83-84, 85-88, pres. 1994-95), Mensa. Episcopalian. Avocations: travel, theater, costuming, science fiction, editing newsletters.

PANCAKE, JOHN, newspaper editor. State news editor, environ. editor Miami Herald. Office: Miami Herald Pub Co One Herald Plz Miami FL 33132-1693*

PANCOAST, EDWIN C., retired foreign service officer, writer, researcher; b. Stratford, N.J., Aug. 20, 1925; m. Eunice Billings, June 12, 1948; children: Laurence E., Karen L., Joanne L. B.A., Maryville Coll., 1949; M.S., George Washington U., 1971; grad., Nat. War Coll., Washington, 1971. Served U.S. Fgn. Svc., Dept. State, 1949-53, USIA, 1953-86; sr. policy officer USIA, Washington, 1984-86; chief of policy Voice of Am., 1975-79; U.S. consul, dir. Amerika Haus, Munich, 1979-84; 1986; writer, researcher Chevy Chase, Md., 1986—. 1st lt. AUS, 1943-46, ETO. Address: 4813 Drummond Ave Chevy Chase MD 20815-5428

PANCOAST, SCOTT R., distribution company executive; b. Jacksonville, FL, June 5, 1958; s. John Wily Pancoast and Mary Virginia Gregg Reynolds; m. Ann Ruth Young; 1 child, Zachary Aaland. BA in Econs. summa cum laude, U. Va., 1980; MBA, Harvard U., 1983. With Chemed Corp. and its subsidiaries, 1978—; v.p., chief fin. officer Chemed Corp. and its subsidiaries, L.A., 1986-88, v.p., dir. ops., 1988-90; sr. v.p. ops., gen. mgr. Midwest div. Chemed Corp. and its subsidiaries, Cin., 1991—, bd. dirs. Nat. San. Supply Co., 1986—; dir administrn. and fin. Formica Corp., Cin., 1990-91. Author: The Business Grammar Handbook, 1986. Mem. Delta Kappa Epsilon (pres. 1979-80), Phi Beta Kappa. Office: Nat San Supply Co 255 E 5th St Cincinnati OH 45202-4700

PANCZENKO, RUSSELL, museum director; b. Frille, Fed. Republic Germany, Mar. 23, 1947; came to U.S., 1950; s. Stanislaw Panczenko and Jaroslawa (Lysaniuk) Horiatshou; m. Paula McCarthy, Mar. 14, 1980. BA, Fairfield (Conn.) U., 1969; Dr. Lettere, Università degli Studi di Firenze, Florence, Italy, 1979. Tchr. Latin Notre Dame High Sch., Bridgeport, Conn., 1969-71; asst. dir. Williams Coll. Mus. Art, Williamstown, Mass., 1980-84; dir. Elvehjem Mus. Art, Madison, Wis., 1984—. Bd. dirs. Upper Midwest Conservation Assn., Mpls., 1986—, Wis. Citizens for Arts Inc., Madison, 1986—. Fellow NEH, 1984. Mem. Assn. Art Mus. Dirs., Coll. Art Assn., Am. Assn. Mus., Wis. Fedn. Mus., Midwest Mus. Assn. Lodge: Rotary. Home: 160 N Prospect Ave Madison WI 53705-4073 Office: Elvehjem Mus Art 800 University Ave Madison WI 53706-1479

PANDEY, DHIRENDRA KUMAR, mechanical engineer,scientist; b. Jaunpur, India, July 1, 1951; came to U.S., 1978; s. Ram Raj and Ram Patti Pandey; m. Snehlata Pandey, Jan. 27, 1981; children: Nirnimesh, Nisheeth, Niket. BS, Banaras Hindu U., Varanasi, India, 1972, MS, 1974; PhD, U. Ill., Chgo., 1982. Asst. prof. H.B. Technol. Inst., Kanpur, India, 1976-78, Banaras Hindu U., 1975-76; teaching and rsch. asst. U. Ill., 1978-82; rsch. asst. prof. Old Dominion U., Norfolk, Va., 1982-85; rsch. scientist Info. & Control Systems, Hampton, Va., 1986-89; prin. scientist Hughes STX Corp., Hampton, Va., 1989-92; atmospheric scientist Sci. Applications Internat. Corp., Hampton, Va., 1992—. Contbr. articles to profl. jours.; patentee high temperature directional emissivity measurement system. Mem. Am. Meteorol. Soc., Am. Geophys. Union. Avocations: reading, writing. Home: 1 Carlisle Ct Hampton VA 23666-6024 Office: SAIC One Enterprise Pky Ste 250 Hampton VA 23666

PANDOLFI, FRANCIS P., publishing executive; s. Frank and Carmela P.; m. Joyce Verhalen, June, 1973; children: Jonathan, Christopher, Nicholas. BSCE, Princeton U., 1965; MBA Mktg., Harvard U., 1967. Pres. MBA Comm., 1969-78; v.p group pub. CBS Publs., 1978-82; pres., CEO Lifeboat Assocs., 1982-88, Times Mirror Mags., 1988—; bd. dirs. Cornell Lab. Orinthology, Trout Unlimited, Neversink Assn., Advt. Coun. (campaigns review com.); founding bd. mem. Software Pub. Assn. Vice chair Recreation Roundtable; coach Am. Youth Soccer Orgn. program; bd. trustees Nat. Environ. Edn. and Tng. Found. (treas., chair fin. com., mem. devel. com.). Recipient Chevron Conservation award, 1993, Annual Disting. Svc. award South Street Seaport Mus., Pres'. award Colo. Ski County, 1993. Mem. Mag. Pub. Am. (sec., bd. dirs., exec com., chmn. mem. com., chair Am. Mag. Conf. 1990, Pub. Mgmt. Conf. 1992). Avocations: fishing, skiing, hunting, boating. Office: Times Mirror Mag 2 Park Ave New York NY 10016-5603

PANE, REMIGIO UGO, Romance languages educator; b. Scigliano, Italy, Feb. 5, 1912; s. Michele Antonio and Carmela (Gigliotti) P.; m. Philomena Pascale, Apr. 13, 1941 (Jul. aug. 1959); children: Michael A., Elissa A.; m. Josephine R. Bruno, Aug. 15, 1964. B.A., Rutgers U., 1938, M.A., 1939; student, Middlebury Spanish Sch., Italian Sch., summers 1937-38, Columbia U., 1939-41. From instr. to assoc. prof. Romance langs. Rutgers U., 1939-57, prof., 1957-81, chmn. dept., 1952-71; dir., founder Rutgers Jr. Year in Italy, 1971-73; assoc. dean Rutgers Coll., 1977-80, prof. emeritus, 1981—; State coord. Am. Assn. Tchrs. Spanish and Portuguese, also Am. Assn. Tchrs. Italian, 1958; chmn. N.E. Conf. Teaching Fgn. Langs., 1960; chmn. examining com. Italian achievement test Coll. Entrance Exam. Bd., 1964-71; mem. selection com. Center 20th Century Studies, U. Wis.-Milw., 1970-71; v.p. Nat. Fedn. Modern Lang. Tchrs. Assns., 1969, pres., 1970, exec. coun., 1976-87; mem. nat. scholarship com. Internat. Ladies Garment Workers Union, 1964—; dir. NDEA Fgn. Lang. Inst., Rutgers U., summers 1963, 64, 65, 66, 67; cons. fgn. langs. U.S. Office Edn.; chmn. evaluating bd. Italian

program Def. Lang. Inst. Author: English Translations from the Spanish, 1484-1943, A Bibliography, 1944, (with J.G. Fucilla) Annual Bibliography of Italian Language and Literature, 1961-70; editor: Italian Americans in the Professions, 1983; Asst. editor: Modern Lang. jour., 1965-71; Contbr. to: The Literatures of the World in Translation, 1970, The Italian Americans, 1987; Contbr. articles to profl. jours. Mem. Italian contbrn. sect. nat. com. U.S.A. Bicentennial; mem. Italian heritage com. 41st Internat. Eucharistic Congress, 1976; mem. Middlesex County Cultural and Heritage Commn., 1984-94, chmn., 1990-93; vice chmn. N.J. Christopher Columbus Quincentennial Observance Commn., 1989-93; chair Friends of the Rutgers Librs. Adv. Coun., 1989—; mem. N.J. Hist. Commn., 1991—. Decorated Latern Cross Vatican, 1954, Commendatore, 1955, Grande Ufficiale, 1970, dell'Ordine della Stella della Solidarietà Italiana, 1976, Sovereign Order St. John of Jerusalem Knights Malta; named Man. of Yr. Columbus Civic League, Trenton, 1962, Italian Am. Club, N. Brunswick, N.J., 1963; recipient award Leonardo da Vinci Soc., Ft. Lee, N.J., 1966, Presdl. plaque Am. Inst. Italian Culture, 1970, Disting. Svc. plaque Unico Nat., 1981, Immigrant of Yr. award Italians Found. of Miami, 1982; Grand Marshall N. Brunswick, N.J., Columbus Day Parade, 1984; inducted into Italian Am. Hall of Fame, 1985, Rutgers U. Hall of Disting. Alumni, 1992. Mem. MLA (life), AAUP, Am. Assn. Tchrs. Italian (life, pres. 1968-72, exec. coun. 1976—, hon. life pres., Leonard Covello Educator of Yr. award Italian Tchrs. chpt. 1991), Am. Assn. Tchrs. Spanish and Portuguese (life), Am. Coun. Teaching Fgn. Langs., N.J. Modern Lang. Tchrs. Assn. (life, pres. 1962-64, award 1979), Am. Italian Hist. Assn. (exec. coun. 1978-93, coord. nat. conf. 1979), Deputazione di Storia Patria per la Calabria (hon.). Home: 69 Lincoln Ave Highland Park NJ 08904-1823 *When I was leaving home at the age of seventeen to emigrate to the United States I asked my mother if she had any advice to give me and she replied, "The world will teach you, but be sure to always associate with people who are better than you, even if you have to pay their meals." Upon arrival in the United States I found that indeed I had a great deal to learn from the world, but associating with people 'better' than myself made the learning easier.*

PANEK, JAN, electrical power engineer, consultant; b. Benesov, Czechoslovakia, Aug. 10, 1930; came to U.S., 1971; s. Ludvik and Marie (Holzerova) P.; m. Eva Soukupova, Aug. 16, 1957; children: Hana, Paul. BSEE, Czech U. Engring., Prague, 1953, MSEE, 1956; PhD in Elec. Engring. Sci., Czechoslovak Acad. Scis., Prague. Rsch. engr. Rsch. Inst. Elec. Engring., Prague, 1953-65; elec. engring. expert UNESCO, Paris, 1965-71; chief tech. advisor UNESCO, Mexico City, 1969-71; cons. engr. GE, Phila., 1971-72, mgr. High Power Lab. switchgear div., 1972-74, cons. elec. power group tech. resources, 1975-78; mgr. transmission studies, elec. utility systems div. GE, Schenectady, 1978-85, mgr. transmission and distbn. studies system devel. engring. dept., 1985-87, sr. cons. dept. power systems engring., 1987-94; adj. prof. Rensselear Poly. Inst., Troy, N.Y., 1994—; Pres. Electric Power Cons. Group, Inc., 1995—. Contbr. over 40 articles to profl. jours. Bd. dirs. Mental Health Orgn., Schenectady, 1985-92. Fellow Nat. Poly. Inst., Mexico City, 1971. Fellow IEEE (various offices 1971—, prize paper awards 1984, 85, 92), Conf. Internat. Grands Reseaux Electriques. Office: 711 Plank Rd Clifton Park NY 12065-2016

PANELLA, ELIZABETH M., secondary school principal. Prin. Fair Lawn (N.J.) High Sch. Recipient Blue Ribbon award U.S. Dept. Edn., 1990-91. Office: Fair Lawn High Sch Berdan Ave Fair Lawn NJ 07410

PANES, JACK SAMUEL, publishing company executive; b. N.Y.C., Apr. 6, 1925; s. Max S. and Sophie (Levine) P.; m. Pearl Shaine, Dec. 25, 1949; children—Stephanie Jill, Michael Jonathan. B.A., Bklyn. Coll., 1947; M.S. in Journalism, Northwestern U., 1949. Editor, pub. The Howe Service, Inc. N.Y.C., 1949-54; founder, pub. Publs. for Industry, N.Y.C., 1955—, Panes Publs., Inc., N.Y.C., 1959—; owner Drug Products Display Service Advt. Co., N.Y.C., 1955—, Supplies for Industry Co., N.Y.C., 1956—; pres. Senap Devel. Corp., Great Neck, N.Y., 1972—. Pres. Russell Woods Civic Assn. Great Neck; trustee Great Neck Symphony Soc., Inc. Served with inf. AUS, 1942-45, ETO. Decorated Silver Star medal, Bronze Star medal. Mem. Deadline Club, Sigma Delta Chi. Home: 21 Russell Woods Rd Great Neck NY 11021-4699 Office: Panes Publications Inc Great Neck NY 11021

PANETH, DONALD J., editor, writer; b. N.Y.C., Feb. 28, 1927; s. Irving and Maud (Kramer) P.; m. Elma Olans, Apr. 10, 1949 (dec. 1987); children: Thea, Ira. BBA, CCNY, 1948; postgrad., Columbia U., 1949-50. Reporter N.Y. Times, 1947-49; free-lance journalist N.Y.C., 1950-56, 73-75, 77-83, 94—; rewriteman Daily Mirror, N.Y.C., 1956-63; copy editor The Morning Telegraph, N.Y.C., 1964-65; staff writer Med. Tribune, N.Y.C., 1966-72; copy editor L.I. Press, Queens, N.Y., 1975-77; editor-in-chief News Dictionary: People, Places and Events, 1977-80; editor, writer Yearbook of the UN, N.Y.C., 1986-93; documents editor UN Office Conf. Svcs., N.Y.C., 1993-94; adj. lectr. English York Coll., CUNY, 1983-86. Author: William Baziotes: A Literary Portrait, 1961, Current Affairs Atlas, 1979, The Ency. of American Journalism, 1983; contbr. articles to Commentary mag., The Nation, Village Voice, Peacework, WorldPaper, others; work included in anthologies Commentary on the American Scene, 1953, New York City Folklore, 1956. Mem. The Authors Guild, Willa Cather Pioneer Meml. Democrat. Avocation: reading. Home and Office: 240 Cabrini Blvd Apt 1E New York NY 10033

PANETTA, LEON EDWARD, federal official, former congressman; b. Monterey, Calif., June 28, 1938; s. Carmelo Frank and Carmelina Maria (Prochilo) P.; m. Sylvia Marie Varni, July 14, 1962; children: Christopher, Carmelo, James. B.A. magna cum laude, U. Santa Clara, Calif., 1960, LL.B., J.D., 1963. Bar: Calif. bar 1965, U.S. Supreme Ct. 1965, U.S. Dist. Ct. (no. dist.) Calif. 1965, U.S. Ct. Appeals 1965. Legis. asst. to U.S. Sen. Thomas Kuchel, Washington, 1966-69; dir. U.S. Office Civil Rights, HEW, Washington, 1969-70; exec. asst. to Mayor of N.Y.C., 1970-71; ptnr. Panetta, Thompson & Panetta, Monterey, 1971-76; mem. 95th-103d Congresses from 17th Calif. dist., 1977-93, chmn. budget com., mem. agr. com., adminstrn. com., also com. dep. majority whip for budget issues, mem. select com. on hunger; dir. U.S. Office Mgmt. and Budget, Washington, 1993-94; chief of staff The White House, Washington, 1994—. Author: Bring Us Together, 1971. Counsel Monterey Regional Park Dists.; counsel NAACP, 1971-76; bd. trustees U. Santa Clara Law Sch.; founder Monterey Coll. Law; mem. Monterey County Dem. Cen. Com., 1972-74; v.p. Carmel Valley Little League, 1974-75. Served with AUS, 1964-66. Recipient Lincoln award NEA, 1970, Disting. Svc. award NAACP, 1972, Bread for World award, 1978, Nat. Hospice Orgn. award, 1984, Golden Plow award Am. Farm Bur. Fedn., Pres.'s award Am. Coun. on Tchr. of Fgn. Langs., 1991, Coastal and Ocean Mgmt. award Coastal Zone Found., 1991, Food Rsch. and Action Ctr. award, 1991; named Lawyer of Yr., Law Sch. U. Santa Clara, 1970. Mem. Calif. Bar Assn. Roman Catholic. Office: Office Mgmt Budget Dir 252 Old Executive Off Bldg Washington DC 20503

PANETTI, RAMON STANLEY, investment company executive, consultant, lawyer; b. Akron, Ohio, Sept. 18, 1931; s. Augustine and Margaret Ruth (Sirdefield) P.; m. Bernadette S. Browne, Oct. 21, 1967; 1 child, Robert Lincoln. BBA, John Carroll U., 1954; MBA, U. Pa., 1958; JD, Cleve. State U., 1964. Bar: Ohio 1964. Fin. exec. Standard Oil Co. (Ohio), Cleve., 1957-65; mgmt. cons. Alspaugh & Co., Cleve., 1965-66; CEO, bd. dirs. Intersvc. Corp., Cleve., 1966-73; fin. cons., Cleve., 1973-77; CEO, investment cons. Capital Res. Advisors Inc., Newport Beach, Calif., 1978—; lectr. econs., fin. and bus. policy John Carroll U., Cleve., 1965-67. 1st lt. U.S. Army, 1954-56. Mem. Chancellor's Club (U. Calif., Irvine), Univ. Athletic Club. Office: Capital Res Advisors Inc 1500 Quail St Ste 470 Newport Beach CA 92660-2736

PANEYKO, STEPHEN HOBBS, banker; b. N.Y.C., June 30, 1942; s. Mirko and Leonore (Lane) P. Student, U. Pa., 1961-65. With Phila. Nat. Bank, 1965-66; v.p. Citibank, N.A., N.Y.C., 1970-82; exec. v.p. UJB Fin. Inc., Princeton, N.J., 1982-87, sr. exec. v.p., 1987—; chmn. bd. dirs. Gibraltar Corp., N.Y.C.; bd. dirs. UJB Mortgage Corp., Hackensack, N.J. Served to lt. USNR, 1966-70. Mem. Bankers Roundtable Assn. Republican. Congregationalist. Clubs: University (N.Y.C.); Baltusrol, Nassau, Bedens Brook. Home: 30 Duncan Ln Skillman NJ 08558-2313 Office: UJB Fin Corp 301 Carnegie Ctr Princeton NJ 08540-6227

PANG, FREDERICK F. Y., federal official; b. Honolulu, Nov. 16, 1936; s. Henry Kam and Constance Yu (Kyau) P.; m. Brenda W. I. Tom, Aug. 18, 1962; 2 children. BEd, U. Hawaii, 1959, MBA, 1972. Commd. 2d lt. USAF, 1959, advanced through grades to col., 1986, ret., 1986, adjudant 790th Aircraft Control and Warning Squadron, 1959-60; adjutant 1980th Aircraft Control and Warning Squadron USAF, Resolution Island, N.W.T., Can., 1960-61; dep. chief consolidated base pers. office USAF, 1961-62, dir. assignments hdqs. Pacific comm. area, 1964-65; dir. pers. 1964th Comm. Group USAF, Vietnam, 1965-68; dir. pers. plans hdqs. Pacific comm. area USAF, 1969-72, chief total officer force programs hdqs., 1972-77, asst. dir. office force structures, office asst. sec. def. manpower, res. affairs and logistics, 1977-80, dir.officer and enlisted pers. mgmt., 1980-84, dir. compensation, 1984-86, cons. office asst. sec. defense force mgmt. and pers., 1986-87; profl. mem. staff com. armed fordes U.S. Senate, Washington, 1987-93; asst. sec. Navy manpower and res. affairs The Pentagon, Washington, 1993—. Decorated Bronze Star USAF. Mem. Alpha Phi Omega. Office: Dept Navy Office Manpower & Res Affairs The Pentagon Rm 4E788 Washington DC 20350-1000

PANG, HERBERT GEORGE, ophthalmologist; b. Honolulu, Dec. 23, 1922; s. See Hung and Hong Jim (Chuu) P.; student St. Louis Coll., 1941; BS, Northwestern U., 1944, MD, 1947; m. Dorothea Lopez, Dec. 27, 1953. Intern Queen's Hosp., Honolulu, 1947-48; postgraduate course ophthalmology N.Y.U., Med. Sch. 1948-49; resident ophthalmology Jersey City Med. Ctr., 1949-50, Manhattan Eye, Ear, & Throat Hosp., N.Y.C., 1950-52; practice medicine specializing in ophthalmology, Honolulu, 1952-54, 56—; mem. staffs Kuakini Hosp., Children's Hosp., Castle Meml. Hosp., Queen's Hosp., St. Francis Hosp.; asst. clin. prof. ophthalmology U. Hawaii Sch. Medicine, 1966-73, now asso. clin. prof. Cons. Bur. Crippled Children, 1952-73, Kapiolani Maternity Hosp., 1952-73, Leahi Tb. Hosp., 1952-62. Capt. M.C., AUS, 1954-56. Diplomate Am. Bd. Ophthalmology. Mem. AMA, Am. Acad. Ophthalmology and Otolaryngology, Assn. for Rsch. Ophthalmology, ACS, Hawaii Med. Soc. (gov. med. practice com. 1958-62, chmn. med. speakers com. 1957-58), Hawaii Eye, Ear, Nose and Throat Soc. (pres. 1960), Pacific Coast Oto-Ophthalmological Soc., Pan Am. Assn. Ophthalmology, Mason, Shriner, Eye Study Club (pres. 1972—). Home: 346 Lewers St Honolulu HI 96815-2345

PANG, MAYBELINE MIUSZE (CHAN), software and system engineer and analyst; b. Shanghai, China, Sept. 9, 1945; came to U.S. 1964; d. Yee Sun and Margaret H. (Kong) Chan; m. Patrick Yewwah Pang, Aug. 4, 1968 (div. 1987); children: Elaine, Irene, George. BS in Physics/Math, Lincoln U., 1967; postgrad. U. Mo., 1967-68, U. Ariz., 1984-86. Application programmer Ariz. Health Sci. Ctr., Physiology Lab., Tucson, 1984-85; software engr. System and Software Engring. Dalmo Victor, Singer, Tucson, 1985-88, McDonnell Douglas Helicopter Co., Mesa, Ariz., 1988-90, Sperry Marine, Charlottesville, Va., 1990—; cons., worked with Air Force (F111), Army (Advanced Apache), Navy (Seawolf weapons, ship control, CNO-ADF) projects; comml. (Integrated Software Analysis Sys.; Sperry's docking sys.) projects; familiar with sys. analysis and design; software devel. and testing; sys. engr. and analyst for Marine Sensors. Recipient Nat. Sci. Honor Soc. award, 1967, Teaching assistantship U. Mo., 1968. Avocations: taijiquan (taichi), qigong (chikung), mind/body medicine, investments, cooking. Home: 1517 Westfield Ct Charlottesville VA 22901-1602 Office: Sperry Marine Seminole Trail Charlottesville VA 22901

PANG, PETER CHIUSING, lawyer, business consultant; b. Hong Kong, Dec. 22, 1952; came to U.S., 1964; s. Henry I. and Chun-Kwan (Siu) P.; m. Susan Feltrup, Aug. 4, 1979. AB, U. Calif., Berkeley, 1976; JD, U. Santa Clara, 1979; LLM, U. Houston, 1985. Bar: Tex. 1979, Pa. 1986. Atty. Shell Oil Co., Houston, 1979-86; asst. corp. sec., gen. corp. counsel Triton Bioscis. Inc., Alameda, Calif., 1983-86; counsel Hershey (Pa.) Foods Corp., 1986-87; gen. counsel Dole Packaged Foods Co., San Francisco, 1988—; asst. corp. sec. Castle & Cooke, Inc. Home: 252 Copper Ridge Rd San Ramon CA 94583-4581 Office: Dole Packaged Foods Co 5795 Lindero Canyon Rd Westlake Village CA 91362

PANIC, MILAN, pharmaceutical and health products company executive; b. Belgrade, Yugoslavia, Dec. 20, 1929; came to U.S., 1956, naturalized, 1963; s. Spasóje and Zorka (Krunich) P.; m. Sally Winn, Jan. 16, 1978; children—Dawn, Milan (dec.), Vivian; stepchildren—Jane, Mark, Patricia. B.S., HU Belgrade, 1955; postgrad., U. Heidelberg, Germany, 1955-56, U. So. Calif., 1957-59. Metallurgist Kaiser Steel Corp., 1956-57; chemist Cyclo-Chem. Corp., Los Angeles, 1957-58; research asst. dept. chemistry U. So. Calif., 1958-59; research chemist Biochem. Research, Los Angeles, 1959-61; pres., chmn. bd., chief exec. officer Internat. Chem. & Nuclear Corp. (name now changed to ICN Pharms., Inc.), Costa Mesa, Calif. Internat. Chem. & Nuclear Corp. (numerous affiliated companies in U.S. and fgn. countries), 1961—; prime min. Govt. of Yugoslavia, Belgrade, 1992-93; assoc. Calif. Inst. Tech. Trustee Intra-Sci. Research Found.; sponsoring com. program health scis. and tech. Harvard-Mass. Inst. Tech.; bd. dirs. Freedom's Found., Valley Forge, Pa., Grief Recovery Ctr., Santa Monica, Calif. Served with Yugoslavian Army in Partisan Resistance, WWII. Recipient Ellis Island Medal of Honor, 1986. Mem. Am. Nuclear Soc., Am., Swiss chem. socs., Internat. Soc. Chemotherapy. Mem. Serbian Orthodox Ch. Home: 1050 Arden Rd Pasadena CA 91106-4004 Office: ICN Pharms Inc 3300 Hyland Ave Costa Mesa CA 92626

PANICH, DANUTA BEMBENISTA, lawyer; b. East Chicago, Ind., Apr. 9, 1954; d. Fred and Ann Stephanie (Grabowski) B.; m. Nikola Panich, July 30, 1977; children: Jennifer Anne, Michael Alexei. A.B., Ind. U., 1975, J.D., 1978. Bar: Ill. 1978, U.S. Dist. Ct. (no. dist.) Ill. 1978, U.S. Dist. Ct. (cen. dist.) Ill. 1987, U.S. Ct. Appeals, 1987. Assoc. Mayer Brown & Platt, Chgo., 1978-86, ptnr., 1986—. Mem. ABA, Ill. State Bar Assn. Republican. Roman Catholic. Office: Mayer Brown & Platt 190 S La Salle St Chicago IL 60603-3410

PANICO, ELAINE HARTMAN, nurse; b. Phila., July 13, 1924; d. Edward Earl and Eleanor Mayo (Adams) Hartman; children: Frederick, Robert, Eleanor, Lorne, Earl, John, William, Richard, Louise. BSN, State Coll. and Med. Ctr., 1946; BS in Edn., State Tchrs. Coll., 1946; postgrad., U. Pa., 1946-49. RN Summer Boys Camp, Winaukee, N.H., 1948; instr. Glassboro (N.J.) State Coll., 1948; coll. nurse, asst. Dean State Coll., Glassboro, 1946-48; asst. dir. nurses Osteo. Hosp., Phila., 1948-49, instr. pharm. math., 1948-49; eye surg. nurse Cornell-N.Y. Hosp., N.Y.C., 1949-50; surg. supr. Balt. City Hosps., 1950-52; nurse in charge Taj Mahal Med. Office, Atlantic City, N.J., 1990; surg. office nurse Ventnor, N.J., 1960—; pub. health speaker elem. schs., Boston, 1950; RN internat. confs., Stony Brook, N.Y., 1980-85, A.C. Med. Ctr. Eye Clinic, Atlantic City, 1987-90; creator earliest postoperative surg. intensive care unit, Balt. City Hosps., 1950-52. Cert. classic ballet, 1932-42. Bd. dirs. PTA, Ventnor, 1960-83, Atlantic Performing Arts Ctr., Atlantic City, 1970-90; mem. Holy Spirit Mothers Assn., Absecon, N.J., 1966-83; sponsor South Jersey Regional Theatre, Atlantic Community Concerts, Stockton Coll. Performing Arts; fin. sec. Atlantic City Med. Ctr. Aux., 1963; chmn. spl. projects Miss. Am Pageant Scholarship Found., Very Important Hostess (V.I.H.), 1967—. Recipient Lifetime Recognition award Great Books Found., 1966-67, 15-yr. Gold award Miss Am. Pageant, 1982. Mem. AAUW, Atlantic County Med. Aux. (pres. 1984-90), U.S. Golf Assn., Internat. Platform Assn., RNs Cancer Heart Meml. Fund. (bd. dirs.), Hydrangea Club (chmn. 1964, Silver 15 Yr. award). Avocations: travel, oil painting, fishing, Chinese gourmet cooking, horseback riding, music. Home: 102 S Dudley Ave Ventnor City NJ 08406-2837 Office: 12 S Somerset Ave Ventnor City NJ 08406-2846

PANISH, MORTON B., physical chemist, consultant; b. N.Y.C., Apr. 8, 1929; s. Isidore and Fanny (Glasser) P.; m. Evelyn Wally Chaim, Aug. 20, 1951; children: Steven, Paul, Deborah. Student, Bklyn. Coll., 1946-48; BS in Chemistry, Denver U., 1950; MS in Chemistry, Mich. State U., 1951, PhD in Phys. Chemistry, 1954. Chemist Oak Ridge (Tenn.) Nat. Labs., 1954-57; mem. tech. staff RAD div. AVCO Corp., Wilmington, Mass., 1957-61, sect. chief, 1961-64; mem. tech. staff Bell Telephone Labs. (now AT&T Bell Labs.), Murray Hill, N.J., 1964-69, dept. head, 1969-86; cons. 1987—, mem. com. on micrography rsch. NRC, 1991—, mem. com. on future of space sci. priorities, 1994—. Co-author: Heterostructure Lasers, 1978, Gas Source Molecular Beam Epitaxy, 1993; contbr. numerous articles to profl. jours.; patentee in field. Mem.

dean's adv. bd. Coll. Natural Sci., Mich. State U., 1990—. Recipient Electrochem Soc. Electronics Divsn. award, 1972, Solid state medal, 1979, C&C Found. prize, Japan, 1986, Internat. Crystal Growth award Am. Assn. Crystal Growth, 1990, John Bardeen award The Minerals, Metals and Materials Soc., 1994. Fellow IEEE (Morris N. Liebmann Meml. award 1991), Am. Phys. Soc.; mem. Nat. Acad. Engring., Nat. Acad. Scis. Avocation: photography. Home and Office: 9 Persimmon Way Springfield NJ 07081-3605

PANITCH, MICHAEL B., brokerage house executive; b. 1939. Student, Mich. State U. With Sheason Lehman Hutton Inc., 1960-90, vice chmn.; with Smith Barney Harris Upham & Co., 1990-93, 94—, now vice chmn. Office: Smith Barney Harris Upham & Co 1345 Avenue Of The Americas New York NY 10105-0216

PANITZ, ESTHER LEAH, English language educator; b. N.Y.C., Mar. 9, 1922; d. Robert and Gittel (Halkin) Allentuck; widowed; children: Jonathan A., Raphael, Michael. BA, Hunter Coll., 1942; B of Hebrew Lit., Theol. Sem., 1943; MA in English and Comparative Lit., Columbia U., 1951. Tchr. Syracuse (N.Y.) Pvt. Schs., 1943-51, Washington Secondary Schs., 1950-95; lectr. Bible studies, history Temple Adas Israel, Washington, 1951-59, Temple Emanuel, Paterson, N.J., 1960-86; adj. faculty William Paterson Coll., Wayne, N.J., 1989-95; adj. faculty Seton Hall, Paramus, N.J., 1972-73; tchr. composition and rhetoric, Mercy Coll., Dobbs Ferry, N.Y., 1990—; presenter papers to coll. confs. Author: American Jewish Historical Quarterly, 1971, 72, 74, The Alien in Their Midst, 1981, Simon Wolf: Private Conscience and Public Image, 1987, Beyon Cain: A Post-Christian Vision; contbr. revs. to Pioneer Woman, 1946-61; book rev. editor Pioneer Woman Jour., 1951-61; contbr. articles to profl. jours. Vol. tutor John C. Hart Meml. Libr.; trustee Shrub Oak Park Assn., 1993. Charles Dickens fellow. Mem. MLA, Am. Jewish Hist. Soc., N.J. Coun. Tchrs. English, N.J. English Coll. Tchr.'s Assn., Jewish. Theol. Sem. Am. Alumni Assn., Soc. St. Joseph's Hosp., Lupus Found., Dickens Fellowship (N.Y./N.J. Region), Modern Language Assn. (commn. mem. on lit. and religion), Phi Beta Kappa. Avocations: walking, mystery stories, live theatre, transcontinental railroad travel. Home: 1204 Williams Dr Shrub Oak NY 10588 Office: Maher Hall English Dept Mercy Coll 955 Broadway Dobbs Ferry NY 10522

PANITZ, LAWRENCE HERBERT, lawyer; b. N.Y.C., Feb. 3, 1941; s. Abraham Alexander and Anita Rosyln (Zuckerberg) P.; m. Karin Blaschke, May 27, 1965. AB, Princeton U., 1962; JD, Columbia U., 1965. Bar: N.Y. 1965. Assoc., Wolf, Haldenstein, Adler, Freeman & Herz, N.Y.C., 1965-69; asst. chief fgn. counsel W.R. Grace & Co., N.Y.C., 1969-74; v.p., chief internat. counsel Revlon, Inc., N.Y.C., 1974-84; exec. v.p., chief adminstrv. officer ICN Pharms., Inc., Costa Mesa, Calif., 1985-87; ptnr. Myerson & Kuhn, N.Y.C., 1988-89, Frere Cholmeley, London, Brussels, Milan, Monte Carlo, Berlin, Paris, Rome, Barcelona, 1990-92; sr. v.p. corp. devel. Trefisco AG, Zürich, Switzerland, 1993; exec. v.p. corp. devel. Quantum Economic Devel., Ltd., Zürich, 1994—; arbitrator Am. Arbitration Assn., 1966—. Founder Park Ave. Malls Planting Project, 1984; patron Met. Opera, N.Y.C., 1987—. Princeton U. fellow, 1961. Mem. Assn. of Bar of City of N.Y., Presdl. Roundtable, Heritage Found. (assoc., instr. for econ. studies, adv. com.), Rep. Senatorial Inner Circle (U.S. senate bus. adv. bd.), Rep. Eagles, Knight of Malta, Order of St. John of Jerusalem. Republican. Home: Brandschenkestr 40, 8001 Zurich Switzerland Office: Quantum Economic Devel Ltd, Talstrasse 20, 8001 Zurich Switzerland

PANKEN, PETER MICHAEL, lawyer; b. N.Y.C., Dec. 30, 1936; s. Harold Ira and Sylvia Rita (Haimes) P.; m. Beverly Muriel Goldner, June 19, 1960; children: Aaron, Melinda. BA cum laude, Haverford Coll., 1957; LLB magna cum laude, Harvard U., 1962. Bar: N.Y. 1962, U.S. Dist. Ct. N.Y. 1962, U.S. Ct. Appeals (2d cir.) 1969, 3d cir. 1988, (10th cir.) 1989, U.S. Supreme Ct. 1989. Assoc. Paul Weiss Rifkind Wharton Garrison, N.Y.C., 1962-66, Poletti Freiden Prashker Feldman & Gartner, N.Y.C., 1966-67; assoc. Parker Chapin Flattau & Klimpl, N.Y.C., 1967-72, ptnr., 1972—. Editor: Harvard Law Rev., 1961-62; editor-in-chief: ALI-ABA Resource Materials on Labor and Employment Law (1st to 8th edits.), 1982—; contbr. articles on law and bus. to profl. jours. Pres., bd. dirs. Fedn. of Handicapped, N.Y.C., 1984-92; pres. Metro N.Y. chpt. Soc. for Human Resource Mgmt., 1990-92. Mem. ABA (labor and employment sect., com. on Nat. Labor Rels. Bd. law), N.Y. State Bar Assn. (labor and employment law sect., continuing legal edn. com.), ABA-Am. Law Inst. (chmn. employment law programs), Am. Law Inst., Soc. for Human Resource Mgmt. (com. on employment practices). Office: Parker Chapin Flattau & Klimpl 1211 Avenue Of The Americas New York NY 10036-8701

PANKEY, EDGAR EDWARD, rancher; b. Irvine, Calif., May 22, 1916; s. John Henry and Emma (Bercaw) P.; m. Elizabeth Searles, Feb. 4, 1939; children—Victor Searles, James Henry, Peter Searles, Roberta Pankey Hurst. B.A., Pomona Coll., 1938. Owner Pankey Ranches, Inc., Tustin, Calif., 1949-64; owner Edgar E. Pankey Ranches, Tustin, 1945-80, Pankey Consolidated, Tustin, 1980—; grower agrl. crops, cattle in So. and Central Calif., Ariz., South Australia; owner, dir. Pankey-Blower Investment Corp., Riverside, Calif., 1963-74, Tustin East Corp., 1967-82; vice chmn. Bank of Irvine, 1973-77, chmn., 1977-83; vice chmn. Valley Irrigation Co., 1963-78; pres. Lake Woodmoor Assocs., Colorado Springs, 1980-91, Sunwood, Carson City, 1992—; bd. dirs. Sunkist, Pyrotronics, Inc., Lilac; cons., fgn. agrl. visitors U.S. State Dept., 1964-69; mem. Fed. Orange Mktg. Com., 1968-74, Calif. Citrus Adv. Com., 1959-89; mem. study mission to European Common Market, 1963; v.p. Maricopa Mining Co., 1977-81. Mem. Tustin Sch. Bd., 1951-59, pres., 1957-59; pres. Orange County Sch. Bd. Assn., 1958-59, Calif. Lemon Men's Club, 1964-66; bd. dirs. Bowers Mus., NCCJ, Orange County Grand Jury Assn.; bd. dirs. Pioneer Coun., pres., 1990-93; pres. bd. dirs. Children's Hosp., Orange County; assoc. bd. dirs. Cmty. Hosp., Santa Ana; pres. World Affairs Coun., Orange, 1977-79, chmn., 1979-80; delegate Labor Policy, London, 1983, People to People Citriculture, China, 1986; bd. dirs. Chapman U., 1980-95, treas., 1987-95; fin. chmn. Children's Hosp., 1969-80, pres., 1981-82. Capt. USAAF, World War II. Mem. Assn. Farmers Orange County (pres. 1954), Calif. Farm Bur. (governing body 1957-58), Orange County Farm Bur. (pres. 1956-57), Orange County C. of C., Aircraft Owners and Pilots Assn., Naui Scuba. Presbyterian (trustee, pres. 1955-58). Lodge: Elks. Pioneered non-cultivation for citriculture; avocado variety expts. comml. users. Office: Pankey & Co 4800 Legray Rd Arvin CA 93203

PANKEY, GEORGE ATKINSON, physician, educator; b. Shreveport, La., Aug. 11, 1933; s. George Edward and Annabel (Atkinson) P.; m. Patricia Ann Carreras, Sept. 22, 1972; children: Susan Margaret, Stephen Charles, Laura Atkinson, Edward Atkinson. Student, La. Poly. Inst., 1950-51; B.S., Tulane U., 1954, M.D., 1957; M.S., U. Minn., 1961. Diplomate Am. Bd. Internal Medicine, Am. Bd. Infectious Diseases. Intern U. Minn. Hosps. 1957-58, resident in internal medicine, 1958-60; resident in internal medicine Mpls. VA Hosp., Mpls. Gen. Hosp., 1960-61; practice medicine New Orleans, 1961—; partner Ochsner Clinic, New Orleans, 1968—; asst. vis. physician Charity Hosp. La., New Orleans, 1961-62; vis. physician Charity Hosp. La., 1962-75, sr. vis. physician, 1975—; cons. infectious diseases Ochsner Clinic and Found. Hosp., 1963—; instr. dept. medicine, div. infectious diseases Tulane U. Sch. Medicine, New Orleans, 1961-63; clin. instr. Tulane U. Sch. Medicine, 1963-65, clin. asst. prof. medicine, 1965-68, clin. asso. prof., 1968-73, clin. prof., 1973—; clin. prof. medicine La. State U. Sch. Medicine, 1979—; clin. prof. oral diagnosis, medicine and radiology La. State U. Sch. Dentistry, 1983—; cons. World Health Info. Services Inc., 1974—; dir., founder Century Nat. Bank, New Orleans; mem. medicine test com. Nat. Bd. Med. Examiners, 1979-83; mem. infectious diseases adv. bd. Hoffman-LaRoche, 1982—. Author: A Manual of Antimicrobial Therapy, 1969; editor: (with Geoffrey A. Kalish) Outpatient Antimicrobial Therapy - Recent Advances, 1989, Infectious Diseases Digest, 1983-95, Soc. Med. Assn. Program for Infectious Diseases Dial-Access, 1983-92, Ochsner Clinic Reports on Serious Hosp. Infections, 1985—, Ochsner Clinic Reports on Geriatric Infectious Diseases, 1990-93, Ochsner Clinic Reports on the Management of Sepsis, 1991-93; bd. editors: Patient Care, 1969-75, Today in Medicine, 1990—; mem. editl. bd. Nat. Infectious Disease Info. Network, 1983—; mem. editl. adv. bd. Compendium Continuing Edn. in Dentistry, 1984-95, Quinolones Bull., 1985-93; contbr. numerous articles to profl. jours. Dir. Camp Fire Inc.; Pres. New Orleans Young Republican Club, 1969-71; adv. bd. Angie Nall Sch. Hosp., Beaumont, Tex.; trustee Nall Found. for Children, Beaumont. Recipient cert. merit Am. Acad. Gen. Practice, 1969,

70. Fellow ACP, Am. Coll. Preventive Medicine, Infectious Disease Soc. Am., Am. Coll. Chest Physicians, Royal Soc. Medicine; mem. Am. Am. Assn. Contamination Control (chpt. pres. 1968-70), Am. Fedn. Clin. Research, So. Med. Assn. (certificate of award 1970), Am. Soc. Internal Medicine (del. ann. meeting 1971-72), Am. Soc. Microbiology, Am. Thoracic Soc., New Orleans Acad. Internal Medicine (pres. 1977-78), AMA, Aerospace Med. Assn., Am. Soc. Tropical Medicine and Hygiene, Am. Venereal Disease Assn., Am. Soc. Parasitologists, La. Soc. Internal Medicine (pres. 1972-73), La. Med. Soc., La. Thoracic Soc. (chmn. program com. 1968, governing council 1976-80), Surg. Infection Soc.; Immunocompromised Host Soc., Musser Burch Soc., Orleans Parish Med. Soc., N.Y. Acad. Scis., Pan Am. Med. Assn. (diplomate mem. sect. internal medicine 1971, sect. pres. infectious diseases and virology 1978-85), SAR, Huguenot Soc. Founders Manakin in Colony of Va. Clubs: Masons (32 deg), Shriners. Home: 5910 Prytania St New Orleans LA 70115-4348 Office: Ochsner Clinic & Hosp 1514 Jefferson Hwy New Orleans LA 70121-2483

PANKO, JESSIE SYMINGTON, dean; b. Jan. 19, 1935. Student, Hunter Coll., N.Y., 1959-62; BA, SUNY, 1969, MS, 1969; PhD, Syracuse U., 1974. Substitute tchr. Anderson Elem. Sch., Mariana Islands, Guam, 1964-65; tchr. Herman Ave. Elem. Sch., Auburn, N.Y., 1969-71; asst. prof. edn. dept. SUNY, Cortland, N.Y., 1971-76, Utica, Rome, N.Y., 1974-76; asst. prof. applied scis. dept. Loop Coll., Chgo., 1976-77; assoc. prof. social scis. dept. Truman Coll., Chgo., 1977-81; dir. student teaching St. Xavier Coll., Chgo., 1976—, dir. undergrad. edn., 1977-79, dir. grad. edn., 1979-81, prof. edn. ctr., 1981-83, dir. grad. prog. in edn., 1983-86, dir. edn. ctr., 1986-89, dean sch. edn., 1989-92; bd. dirs. Queen of Peace, Acad. of Our Lady; mem. com. grad. programs St. Xavier Coll., 1986-89, tchr. edn. coun., 1976—, early childhood adv. bd., 1976-92. Moffett SUNY scholar, 1969. Mem. AAUP, ASCD, Am. Assn. of Colls. of Tchr. Edn. (instl. rep. 1987—), Assn. Ind. Liberal Arts Colls. of Tchr. Edn. (instl. rep. 1986-92), Ill. Assn. of Tchr. Edn. in Pvt. Colls. (instl. rep. 1985-92), Ill. Assn. Colls. Tchr. Edn. (coll. rep. 1981-92, sec. 1990-92), Assn. Tchr. Educators, Nat. Assn. Educators Young Children, Ill. Dirs. Student Tchg., Chgo. Consortium Dirs. Student Tchg. (chairperson 1976—), Ill. Assn. Tchr. Educators, Pi Lambda Theta, Kappa Delta Pi. Office: St Xavier Coll 3700 W 103rd St Chicago IL 60655

PANKOPF, ARTHUR, JR., lawyer; b. Malden, Mass., Feb. 1, 1931. B.S. in Marine Transp., Mass. Maritime Acad., 1951; B.S. in Fgn. Service and Internat. Transp, Georgetown U., 1957; J.D., 1965. Bar: Md. 1965, D.C. 1966, U.S. Supreme Ct. 1977. Ea. area mgr. Trans Ocean Van Service of Consol. Freightway, 1958-61; with U.S. Maritime Adminstrn., 1961-65; assoc. firm Preston, Thorgrimson, Ellis & Holman, Washington, 1976-77; minority chief counsel Com. on Mcht. Marine & Fisheries U.S. Ho. of Reps., Washington, 1965-69; minority chief counsel, staff dir. Com. on Commerce, U.S. Senate, 1969-76; mng. dir. Fed. Maritime Commn., 1977-81; pvt. practice Washington, 1981-84; dir. legis. affairs Corp. Pub. Broadcasting, 1984-86, v.p., gen. counsel, sec., 1986-88; pvt. practice Washington, 1988-90; dir. fed. affairs Matson Navigation Co. Inc., Washington, 1990—. Home: 7819 Hampden Ln Bethesda MD 20814-1108

PANKOVE, JACQUES ISAAC, physicist; b. Chernigov, Russia, Nov. 23, 1922; came to U.S., 1942, naturalized, 1944; s. Evsey Leib and Miriam (Simkine) Pantchechnikoff; m. Ethel Wasserman, Nov. 24, 1950; children: Martin, Simon. B.S.E.E., U. Calif., Berkeley, 1944, M.S.E.E., 1948; Ph.D. in Physics, U. Paris, 1960. Mem. tech. staff RCA Labs., Princeton, N.J., 1948-70; physicist, fellow RCA Labs., 1970-85; prof. U. Colo., Boulder, 1985-93, prof. emeritus, 1993—; Hudson Moore Jr. Univ. prof., 1989-93, program mgr. materials and devices ctr. for Optoelectronic Computing Systems, 1986-89; Disting. Rsch. fellow Nat. Renewal Energy Lab. (formerly Solar Energy Rsch. Inst.), 1985-93; v.p. for rsch. and tech. Astralux, Inc., 1993—; vis. McKay lectr. U. Calif., Berkeley, 1968-69; vis. prof. U. Campinas, Brazil, 1975; Disting. vis. prof. U. Mo. at Rolla, 1984; participant NAS sci. exch. program with: Romania, 1970, Hungary, 1972, Yugoslavia, 1976. Mem. hon. editorial bd. Solid State Electronics, 1970-94, Solar Energy Materials, 1984—, Optoelectronics, 1986—; regional editor Crystal Lattice Defects and Amorphous Materials, 1984-90; author: Optical Processes in Semiconductors, 1971, 75; editor: Electroluminescence, 1977, Display Devices, 1980, Hydrogenated Amorphous Silicon, 1984; co-editor: Hydrogen in Semiconductors, 1991, Wide Bandgap Semiconductors, 1992; author: (ednl. film) Energy Gap and Recombination Radiation, 1962; laser sculpture, Bklyn. Mus., 1968; contbr. articles to profl. jours.; organizer sci. confs.; patentee in field. Trustee Princeton Art Assn., 1970-82; mem. Experiment-in-Arts-and-Tech., Berkeley, 1968-69. Served with U.S. Army, 1944-46. Recipient RCA achievement awards, 1952, 53, 63; David Sarnoff scholar, 1956. Fellow IEEE (J. J. Ebers award 1975, assoc. editor Jour. Quantum Electronics 1968-77, mem.-at-large IEEE awards bd. 1992—), Am. Phys. Soc.; mem. AAAS, NAE (hon.), Materials Rsch. Soc., Internat. Soc. for Optical Engring., Sigma Xi. Home: 2386 Vassar Dr Boulder CO 80303-5763 Office: U Colo Dept Elec Engring Boulder CO 80309-0425

PANKRATZ, HENRY J., management consultant; b. Brookdale, Man., Can., Feb. 19, 1939; s. John and Mary (Engbrecht) P.; m. Julia Marianna, May 30, 1981; children: Kathy, Karen, Lisa. Grad., Steinbach Collegiate, 1956; chartered acct., U. Man., 1962. Cert. FCA, FCMC. Mng. ptnr. Ernst & Young, Ottawa, Ont., Can., 1974-77; nat. dir., fin. planning and control Ernst & Young, Toronto, Ont., Can., 1977-84; mng. ptnr. Ernst & Young, Vancouver, B.C., Can., 1984-88, exec. ptnr., 1986—; chmn. Ernst & Young Cons., Toronto, 1988—; vice chmn. Ernst & Young. Former chmn. Comml. and Indsl. Devel. Commn. Ottawa-Carleton; former chmn. fin., chmn. long-range planning mem. exec. com. Red Cross, Ont. Div. Fellow Inst. Chartered Accts. Ont., Inst. Cert. Mgmt. Cons. Can., (chmn. firm mem. com.). Office: Ernst & Young, PO Box 251 Toronto Dominion Ctr., Toronto, ON Canada M5K 1J7

PANKS, GARY ALLEN, golf course architect; b. Flint, Mich., July 9, 1941; s. Allen T. and Lois (Dennis) P.; m. Judith Ann Panks, Oct. 9, 1972; children: Brian, Paul. BS in Landscape Artihtecture, Mich. State U., 1964. Registered landscape architect, Ariz. Landscape architect N.Y. State Dept. Pub. Works, N.Y.C., 1964-65, Maricopa County Parks and Recreation, Phoenix, 1965-67; architect, land planner City of Phoenix, 1967-71; golf course architect Gary Panks Assocs., Scottsdale, Ariz., 1971—, Graham & Panks Internat., Scottsdale, 1988—. Designer of courses include Grayhawk Course, Scottsdale, Ariz. Recipient Best New Pub. Course in Ariz. award Golf Digest mag., 1986, Top Three New Resort Courses in U.S. award, 1989. Mem. Airz Soc. Landscape Architects (Honor award), U.S. Golf Assn., Ariz. Golf Assn. (bd. dirs., mem. exec. com.). Avocations: golf, hunting, fishing. Office: Graham & Panks Internat 8777 E Via de Ventura Ste 315 Scottsdale AZ 85258

PANLILIO, ADELISA LORNA, public health physician; b. Manila, Jan. 23, 1949; came to U.S., 1955; d. Filadelfo and Elsie Belle (Nessia) P. AB, Radcliffe Coll., 1969; MD, SUNY Downstate Med. Coll., Bklyn., 1973; MPH, Harvard Sch. Pub. Health, 1988. Intern in pediatrics Babies Hosp. Columbia-Presbyn., N.Y.C., 1973-74, resident in pediatrics, 1974-75; pediatric hematology fellow Downstate/Kings County Hosp. Med. Ctr., Bklyn., 1975-76, blood banking fellow, 1976-77; asst. med. dir. ARC Blood Services, Nashville, 1977-80, med. dir., 1980-84, acting dir., 1984-85, med. dir., 1985-87; epidemic intelligence service officer Ctr. Disease Control, USPHS, Atlanta, 1988—; asst. clin. prof. pathology Vanderbilt U. Sch. Medicine, Nashville, 1977-87. Contbr. articles to med. jours. V.p., bd. dirs. Nashville CARES, 1986-87. Mem. Am. Assn. Blood Banks, Alpha Omega Alpha. Office: Ctr Disease Control 1600 Clifton Rd NE Atlanta GA 30329-4046

PANNER, BERNARD J., pathologist, educator; b. Youngstown, Ohio, Oct. 9, 1928; s. Morris W. and Matilda (Giber) P.; m. Molly R. Seidenberg, Feb. 11, 1962; children—Morris J., Aaron M., Daniel Z. A.B., Western Res. U., 1949, M.D., 1953. Diplomate Am. Bd. Pathology. Intern in internal medicine Kings County Hosp., Bklyn., 1953-54; resident in pathology Boston City Hosp., 1954-55, Strong Meml. Hosp., Rochester, N.Y., 1958-60; asst. prof. pathology Sch. Medicine, U. Rochester, 1960-67, assoc. prof., 1967-72, prof., 1972—; pathologist Strong Meml. Hosp., Rochester, 1972—; cons. Genesee Hosp., Rochester, 1974—. Contbr. articles to profl. jours. Served with USNR, 1955-57. Recipient Mapstone Teaching prize Sch. Medicine, U. Rochester, 1981. Mem. Internat. Acad. Pathology, Am. Assn. Pathologists, Internat. Soc. Nephrology, Am. Soc. Nephrology, Sigma Xi. Democrat.

Jewish. Home: 330 Wilmot Rd Rochester NY 14618-2947 Office: U Rochester Sch Medicine Dept Pathology 601 Elmwood Ave Rochester NY 14642-9999

PANNER, OWEN M., federal judge; b. 1924. Student, U. Okla., 1941-43, LL.B., 1949. Atty. Panner, Johnson, Marceau, Karnopp, Kennedy & Nash, 1950-80; judge, now sr. judge U.S. Dist. Ct. Oreg., Portland, 1980—. Office: US Dist Ct 335 US Courthouse 620 SW Main St Portland OR 97205-3023

PANNETON, JACQUES, librarian; b. Trois-Rivières, Que., Can., May 7, 1943; s. Marcel and Bernadette (Page) P.; married; children—Anne-Marie, Luce. B.L.S., U. Montréal, 1964. Cataloguer Bibliothèque de Trois-Rivières, 1964-65; dep. librarian, then head librarian Bibliothèque Centrale de Pret de la Mauricie, Trois-Rivières, 1965-74; head librarian Bibliothèque de la Ville de Montréal, 1974—; prof. pub. libraries U. Montréal Library Sch., 1974-75; mem. Com. Cons. du Livre, Govt. Que., 1976; mem. adv. bd. Nat. Library Can., 1978—; mem. com. d'étude sur bibliothèques publiques Govt. Qué., 1987; invited guest German libraries, German Fed. Republic, summer 1976, Brit. libraries, spring 1978. Contbr. articles to profl. jours. Mem. Canadian, Am., Que. library assns., Corp. Profl. Librarians Que. (past pres.), Assn. pour l'avancement des sci. et des techniques de la documentation, Council Adminstrs. Large Urban Pub. Libraries, Internat. Fedn. Library Assns., Internat. Assn. Met. City Libraries. Office: Bibliothèque de Montreal, 5650 d'Iberville St Ste 400, Montreal, PQ Canada H2G 3E4

PANNONE, RICHARD R., treasurer; b. Providence, June 17, 1942; s. Angelo and Dora (DeOrchis) P.; m. Conatance M. Bloomfield, Sept. 27, 1975; children—Richard R. Jr., Kevin A., Shawn R. B.A., Brown U., 1964; M.B.A., U.R.I., 1970. With Fleet Nat. Bank, Providence, 1964-67, acct. officer, 1967-69; controller Westminster Properties, Providence, 1969-73; mgr. corp. fin. Fleet Fin. Group, Providence, 1973-78, asst. treas., 1978-83, treas., 1983—. Mem. fin. com. St. Philip's Parish, Greenville, R.I., 1984—. Mem. Nat. Assn. Corp. Treas. Roman Catholic. Club: University (Providence). Avocations: golf; swimming; reading. Office: Fleet Fin Group Inc 211 Perimmeter Ctr Pky Atlanta GA 30346

PANOFSKY, WOLFGANG KURT HERMANN, physicist, educator; b. Berlin, Germany, Apr. 24, 1919; came to U.S., 1934, naturalized, 1942; s. Erwin and Dorothea (Mosse) P.; m. Adele Du Mond, July 21, 1942; children: Richard, Margaret, Edward, Carol, Steven. A.B., Princeton U., 1938, DSc (hon.), 1983; Ph.D., Calif. Inst. Tech., 1942; D.Sc. (hon.), Case Inst. Tech., 1963, U. Sask., 1964, Columbia U., 1977, U. Hamburg, Fed. Republic Germany, 1984, Yale U., 1985; hon. degree, U. Beijing, Peoples Republic China, 1987; DSc (hon.), U. Rome, 1988; hon. degree, Uppsala U., Sweden, 1991. Mem. staff mem. radiation lab. U. Calif., 1945-51, asst. prof., 1946-48, asso. prof., 1948-51; prof. physics Stanford U., 1951-89, prof. emeritus, 1989—; dir. Stanford (High Energy Physics Lab., Stanford Linear Accelerator Center), 1962-84, dir. emeritus, 1984—; Am. del. Conf. Cessation Nuclear Tests, Geneva, 1959; mem. President's Sci. Adv. Com., 1960-65; cons. Office Sci. and Tech., Exec. Office Pres., 1965-73, U.S. ACDA, 1968-81; mem. gen. adv. com. to White House, 1977-81; mem. panel Office of Sci. and Tech. Policy, 1977; with nat. def. rsch. Calif. Inst. Tech. and Los Alamos, 1942-45; chmn. bd. overseers Superconducting Supercollider Univs. Rsch. Assn., 1984-93; mem. com. to provide interim oversight DOE nuc. weapons complex NAS, 1988-89, mem. DOE panel on nuc. warhead dismantlement and spl. nuc. materials control, 1991-92; active Commn. Particles and Field of Internat. Union of Pure and Applied Physics, 1985-93. Decorated officer Legion of Honor; recipient Lawrence prize AEC, 1961; Nat. Medal Sci., 1969; Franklin medal, 1970; Ann. Pub. Service award Fedn. Am. Scientists, 1981; Enrico Fermi award Dept. Energy, 1979; Shoong Found. award for sci., 1983, Hilliard Roderick prize Sci. AAAS, 1991; named Calif. Scientist Yr., 1966. Mem. NAS (chmn. com. on internat. security and arms control 1985-93, mem. on scholarly comm. with People's Republic of China 1987-92), AAAS, Am. Phys. Soc. (v.p., pres. 1974), Phi Beta Kappa, Sigma Xi. Home: 25671 Chapin Rd Los Altos CA 94022-3413 Office: Stanford Linear Accelerator Ctr PO Box 4349 Palo Alto CA 94309-4349

PANSINI, MICHAEL SAMUEL, energy company executive, consultant; b. Molfetta, Italy, July 12, 1928; came to U.S., 1935; s. Ralph and Isabel (Cirilli) P.; m. Anna D'Angelo, June 5, 1949 (div. 1970); children: Elizabeth, Valerie, Michael; m. Elizabeth Bischoff, Oct. 3, 1970 (div. Feb. 1992); 1 child, Elissa Michelle. B.S., NYU, 1950, M.B.A., 1952, LL.M., 1960; LL.D., Fordham U., 1956. Bar: N.Y. 1956, U.S Tax Ct. Tax mgr. Pfizer Corp., N.Y.C., 1951-64; asst. treas. Hooker Chem. Corp., N.Y.C., 1964-69; treas., dir. United Indsl. Corp., N.Y.C., 1969-72; sr. v.p., gen. counsel Beker Industries Corp., Greenwich, Conn., 1972-87; pres., dir. Panmer, Inc., 1987—; tax, fin. cons., 1993—; v.p. corp. counsel Champion Energy Corp. and affiliates, 1991-93, Champion Holdings Co. and affiliates, 1993—; v.p., chmn. various coms. Tax Exec. Inst., N.Y.C., 1963-72; pres., dir. Fed. Tax Forum, Inc., N.Y.C., 1961-72; dir. Intelligent Bus. Communications Corp. Mem. Rep. Town Com. 19th Dist., Stamford, Conn., 1993—; commr. Econ. Devel. Commn., Stamford, 1994—. Republican. Home and Office: 76 Lawrence Hill Rd Stamford CT 06903-2120

PANSKY, EMIL JOHN, entrepreneur; b. Manhattan, N.Y., June 1, 1921; s. Stanislaus and Anna (Jankovic) P.; m. Billie B. Byrne, May 27, 1955; 1 adopted child, Jimmy. BME, Cooper Union Coll., 1941; MBA, Harvard U., 1949; MADE, NYU, 1950. Registered prof. engr., Mich. Chief insp. flight line Republic Aviation, Farmingdale, L.I., 1941-45, salvage engr., 1946-47; product control supr. to product control mgr. Ford Motor, Detroit, 1949-51; asst. plant mgr. Anderson Brass, Birmingham, Ala., 1951-53; asst. v.p. to v.p. mfg. Cummins Engine, Columbus, Ind., 1953-54; pvt. practice Emil J. Pansky Assoc., San Leandro, Calif., 1954—; pres. Calif. Mfrs. Tech. Assn., San Francisco, 1978-80; cons. in field. Patentee die cast auto wheels, 1965. Pres. Menlo Circus Club, Menlo Park, Calif., 1974-81, Home Owners Assn., Kanuela, Hawaii, 1989-95; bd. dirs. No. Calif. Tennis Assn., San Francisco, 1984-87. Mem. ASME (life), Harvard Club San Francisco (bd. dirs. 1988-92), Harvard Bus. Sch. Club San Francisco (bd. dirs. 1970-73, cons. 1994-95). Democrat. Avocations: tennis, chess. Home: 901 Jackling Dr Hillsborough CA 94010 Office: Emil J Pansky Assoc 1666 Timothy Dr San Leandro CA 94577

PANTAGES, LOUIS JAMES, lawyer; b. Plainfield, N.J., Apr. 29, 1916; s. Dimitrios Louis and Bessie (Massas) P.; m. Dorothea Carol Adams, Dec. 16, 1950; children: James, Peter, Elaine Marie. A.B., Rutgers U., 1938, LL.B. 1940. Bar: N.J. 1941, U.S. Dist. Ct. N.J. 1941, U.S. Dist. Ct. (so. dist.) N.Y. 1955, U.S. Supreme Ct. 1960, U.S. Ct. Appeals (3d cir.) 1967. Since practiced in Newark; with firm Cox & Walburg, 1938-54; partner Mead, Gleeson, Hansen & Pantages, 1954-68, Gleeson, Hansen & Pantages, 1968-72, Hansen, Pantages, Sellar & Zavesky, 1972-77, Pantages Sellar Richardson & Stuart, 1977-82, Stein, Bliablias, McGuire, Pantages & Gigl, 1982—; trial lawyer in cts. of N.J., U.S. Dist. cts. of N.J., U.S. Dist. Ct., So. Dist. N.Y., U.S. Supreme Ct., others. Capt. M.I., AUS, 1942-46; Capt. M.I., U.S. Army, 1950-52. Fellow Am. Coll. Trial Lawyers, Internat. Acad. Law and Sci.; mem. ABA, N.J. Bar Assn., Essex County Bar Assn., Am. Judicature Soc., Trial Attys. N.J., N.J. Def. Assn., Internat. Assn. Def. Counsel, Fedn. Ins. and Corp. Counsel, Def. Rsch. Inst., Am. Arbitration Assn., Arbitration Forums, Inc., Rutgers Law Sch. Alumni Assn., Essex Fells Country Club, Hellenic Univ. Club N.Y. Republican. Greek Orthodox. Avocations: art, antiques, travel, ballet, music. Home: 36 Windemere Rd Upper Montclair NJ 07043-2544 Office: 354 Eisenhower Pky Livingston NJ 07039-1023

PANTAZELOS, PETER GEORGE, financial executive; b. Cambridge, Mass., Dec. 8, 1930; s. George P. and Marion (Nichols) P.; m. Hytho Haseotes, May 26, 1963; children: George, Marion. BSEE, Northeastern U., 1953; MSEE, MIT, 1955; Acctg. Cert., Bentley Corp., Waltham, Mass., 1975. Mgr. engring. dept. Thermo Electron Engring. Corp., Waltham, Mass., 1960-68; v.p. corp. planning Thermo Electron Corp., Waltham, Mass., 1968-72, v.p-ops. fin., 1972-80, exec. v.p., 1980—. Mem. IEEE, Am. Mgmt. Assn., Fin. Execs. Inst., Eta Kappa Nu, Tau Beta Pi, Sigma Xi. Mem. Greek Orthodox Ch. Club: Brae Burn (Newton, Mass.). Avocations: golfing; gardening. Office: Thermo Electron Corp 101 1st Ave Waltham MA 02154-1160

PANTEL, GLENN STEVEN, lawyer; b. Plainfield, N.J., Sept. 25, 1953; s. Donald and Sarah Libby (Pearlman) P.; m. Lisa Pamela Krop, June 28, 1981; 1 child, Adam Scott. AB, Johns Hopkins U., 1975; JD, U. Pa., 1978. Bar: N.J. 1978, U.S. Dist. Ct. N.J. 1978, Pa. 1978, Fla. 1980, U.S. Ct. Appeals (3d cir.) 1982. Law clk. to presiding judge U.S. Dist. Ct. (so. dist.), Miami, Fla., 1978-79; from assoc. to ptnr. Shanley & Fisher P.C., Morristown, N.J., 1979—; also bd. dirs. Trustee Friday Evening Club Cultural Presenters, Morristown, 1984—, Integrity, Inc., Drug and Alcohol Abuse Program, Newark; trustee, mem. scholarship com. 200 Club of Somerset County. Mem. ABA, Fla. Bar Assn., N.J. Bar Assn., Morris County Bar Assn., Phi Beta Kappa. Avocations: skiing, sailing. Home: 3 Cross Way Mendham NJ 07945-3120 Office: Shanley & Fisher PC 131 Madison Ave Morristown NJ 07960-6086

PANTEL, STAN ROY, newspaper publishing executive; b. Victoria, Tex., 1950. Degree, U. Tex. V.p. ops. Atlanta Jour.-Constitution. Office: Atlanta Journal-Constitution 72 Marietta St NW Atlanta GA 30303-2804*

PANTENBURG, MICHEL, hospital administrator, health educator, holistic health coordinator; b. Denver, Oct. 6, 1926; d. Arthur Robert and Alice (McKenna) P. Diploma, Providence Nursing Sch., Kansas City, Kans., 1951; B.S. in Nursing Edn., St. Mary Coll., Leavenworth, Kans., 1958; M. in Nursing, Cath. U. Am., 1960. Joined Sisters of Charity, Roman Catholic Ch., 1945; lic. amateur radio operator. Dir. nursing Providence Hosp., Kansas City, Kans., 1958-62; nursing coordinator Sisters of Charity, Leavenworth, 1962-67; hosp. adminstr. St. Mary Hosp., Grand Junction, Colo., 1967-73, St. Vincent Hosp., Billings, Mont., 1973-84; dir. focus on leadership program Gonzaga U., Spokane, Wash., 1985-92; chaplain pastoral care dept. St. Marys Hosp. and Med. Ctr., Grand Junction, Colo., 1994—; dir. Norwest Bank, Billings. Co-author: Management of Nursing (CHA award 1969), 1967. Bd. dirs. De Paul Hosp., Cheyenne, Wyo., 1980—, Ronald McDonald House, Billings, 1982—. Named Woman of Yr., Bus. and Profl. Women, Billings, 1979. Mem. Cath. Hosp. Assn. (bd. dirs., sec.), Am. Hosp. Assn. (regional del. 1975-80), Am. Coll. Hosp. Adminstrn., Mont. Hosp. Assn. (pres.), Billings C. of C. (v.p. 1977-78). Avocations: hiking; skiing. Office: Pastoral Care Dept St Marys Hosp & Med Ctr Grand Junction CO 81501

PANTOLIANO, JOE, actor; b. Hoboken, N.J., Sept. 12, 1951. Actor: (stage prodns.) Brothers, 1982, Orphans, 1983, One Flew Over the Cuckoo's Nest, Italian American Reconciliation, The Death Star, Visions of Kerouac, (feature films) The Godfather Part II, 1974, The Idol Maker, 1980, Monsignor, 1982, Risky Business, 1983, Eddie and the Cruisers, 1983, The Mean Season, 1985, Goonies, 1985, Running Scared, 1986, The In Crowd, 1987, The Squeeze, 1987, Scenes from the Goldmine, 1987, Amazon Women on the Moon, 1987, La Bamba, 1987, Empire of the Sun, 1987, Midnight Run, 1988, Downtown, 1990, The Last of the Finest, 1990, Short Time, 1990, Zandalee, 1991, Used People, 1992, Three of Hearts, 1993, The Fugitive, 1993, Baby's Day Out, 1994, Calendar Girl, 1994, Steal Big, Steal Little, 1995, Bad Boys, 1995; (TV movies) More Than Friends, 1978, Alcatraz: The Whole Shocking Story, 1980, Destination: America, 1987, El Diablo, 1990, One Special Victory, 1991, Through the Eyes of a Killer, 1992, (TV miniseries) From Here to Eternity, 1979, Robert Kennedy and His Times, 1985, (TV spl.) Mr. Roberts, 1984 (TV Series) Free Country, 1978, The Fanelli Boys, 1990-91, (guest) Tales From the Crypt, Amazing Stories, L.A. Law, The Hitchhiker. Office: UTA 9560 Wilshire Blvd 5th Floor Beverly Hills CA 90212*

PANTUSO, VINCENT JOSEPH, food service consultant; b. Charleston, W.Va., Aug. 13, 1940; s. Fortunato F. Pantuso and Josephine Malcom (Ginestra) Pantuso Messer; m. Carol Barber, Dec. 10, 1964 (div. 1976); children—Lisa, Barbara, Tina, m. Nancy Josephine Chellman, Sept. 30, 1978. Student, Drexel U.; BSBA, St. Joseph's U., 1968; postgrad., Rollins Coll., 1984-85. Asst. mgr. Marriott Hotels, Inc., Bethesda, Md., 1962-64; v.p. sales mktg. ARA Services, Inc., Phila., 1964-72; sr. v.p. Interstate United Corp., Chgo., 1972-84; pres. V.J. Pantuso Services, Inc., Orlando, Fla., 1984—, New Vista Services, Inc., 1988—. Mem. Nat. Assn. Concessionaires (bd. dirs. 1982—, pres. 1989-91, chmn. 1991-94, Master Concessionaire, Chgo. 1985), Nat. Assn. Food Equipment Mfrs. (doctorate 1989). Republican. Episcopalian. Club: Citrus (Orlando). Avocation: fishing. Home: 9325 Bay Vista Estate Blvd Orlando FL 32836-6304

PANUSKA, JOSEPH ALLAN, university president; b. Balt., July 3, 1927; s. Joseph William and Barbara Agnes (Preller) P. BS, Loyola Coll., Balt., 1948; PhD, St. Louis U., 1958; STL, Woodstock Coll., 1961; LLD (hon.), U. Scranton, 1974. Joined S.J., 1948; ordained priest Roman Cath. Ch., 1960. Instr. dept. physiology Emory U. Sch. Medicine, 1962-63; asst. prof. biology Georgetown U., 1963-66, assoc. prof., 1966-72, prof., 1973; provincial, bd. dirs. Jesuit Conf. Md. Province (S.J.), 1973-79; acad. v.p., dean faculties, prof. biology Boston Coll., 1979-82; pres. U. Scranton, Pa., 1982—; mem. Pa. Commn. Ind. Colls. and Univs., 1982—, mem. exec. com., treas., 1987-91, vice chmn., 1988-89, chmn., 1990-91; mem. President's Commn., NCAA, 1989-90. Mem. editl. bd. Crybiology, 1968-88, editor-in-chief, 1971-74; contbr. chpts. to books, articles to sci. rsch. jours. Mem. corp. Am. Found. Biol. Rsch., 1967-85, pres. bd. dirs., 1974-79, v.p., 1979-83; trustee Loyola Coll., 1979-85, St. Joseph's U., 1979-84, U. Scranton, 1970-73, St. Peter's Coll., 1971-72, Woodstock Coll., 1973-76, Fordham U., 1982-88, Cambridge Ctr. for Social Studies, 1973-79 (pres. 1973-79), Corp. Roman Cath. Clergymen, 1973-79 (pres. 1973-79); rector Jesuit Community at Georgetown U., 1970-73; bd. dirs. United Way Pa., 1985-87, Scranton Preparatory Sch., 1984-90; chmn. Pa. Commn. for Ind. Colls. and Univs., 1990-91; bd. dirs. John Carroll U., 1992—, Nat. Inst. Environ. Renewal, 1992—. NIH postdoctoral trainee, 1962-63; Danforth Found. Harbison prize for disting. teaching, 1969; vis. fellow St. Edmunds Coll., Cambridge U., 1969. Mem. Am. Physiol. Soc., Soc. for Cryobiology, Soc. Exptl. Biology and Medicine, Assn. Jesuit Colls. and Univs. (bd. dirs. 1982—, treas. 1993—), Pa. Assn. Colls. and Univs. (exec. com., adv. com. to State Bd. Edn. 1990-91), Scranton C. of C. Home and Office: U Scranton Office of Pres Scranton PA 18510 *In order to be happy in a leadership role and to succeed in it, I have to possess a sense of coherence with my life values. I also need to recognize that my own activity makes a real difference in the empowerment of others so that there is a multiplier effect which extends me beyond my own person and activity.*

PANVINI, ROBERT S., physics educator; b. Bklyn., Apr. 22, 1937; s. Charles and Sara (Panvini) P.; m. Doria Jean Bacigalupi, Aug. 16, 1959; children: Robert S. Jr., Lisa, Christopher. BS in Physics, Rensselaer Poly. Inst., 1958; postgrad., Brown U., 1958-60; PhD, Brandeis U., 1965. Research assoc. Brookhaven Nat. Lab., Upton, L.I., N.Y., 1965-67, asst. physicist, 1967-69, assoc. physicist, 1969-71; assoc. prof. physics Vanderbilt U., Nashville, 1971-80, prof., 1980—; chmn., organizer Vanderbilt High Energy Conf. Series, 1973—. Contbr. over 100 articles to profl. jours. NSF research grantee, 1971—. Mem. Am. Phys. Soc. (div. particles and fields). Avocations: classical music, opera, travel, hiking, photography. Home: 4317 Flower Valley Dr Rockville MD 20853-1884 Office: Vanderbilt U Dept Physics and Astronomy Nashville TN 37235

PANY, KURT JOSEPH, accounting educator, consultant; b. St. Louis, Mar. 31, 1946; s. Joseph Francis and Ruth Elizabeth (Westerman) P.; m. Darlene Dee Zabish, June 3, 1971; children: Jeffrey, Michael. BSBA, U. Ariz., 1968; MBA in Mgmt., U. Minn., 1971; PhD in Accountancy, U. Ill., 1977. CPA, Ariz., cert. fraud examiner. Staff auditor Arthur Andersen & Co., Mpls., 1968-69, Touche Ross & Co., Phoenix, 1971-73; teaching asst. U. Minn., Mpls., 1969-71; teaching asst. auditing and acctg. U. Ill., Urbana, 1972-76; asst. prof. acctg. Ariz. State U., Tempe, 1977-81, assoc. prof., 1981-85, Arthur Andersen/Don Dupont prof. acctg., 1985-91; mem. acctg. and auditing standards com. State of Ariz., Phoenix, 1989—; reviewer Jour. Acctg. and Pub. Policy, 1983—. Contbg. author: CPA Exam. Rev., 1983—; co-author: Principles of Auditing, 1988—, Auditing, 1993—; co-editor Auditing: A Jour. Practice and Theory, 1984-88; mem. editl. bd. Advances in Acctg., 1982—, Jour. Acctg. Edn., 1983—; reviewer Acctg. Rev., 1984—; ad hoc editor, 1989—; contbr. numerous articles to profl. jours. Active various child-related orgns. Peat, Marwick, Mitchell & Co. Found. grantee, 1985. Fellow AICPA (auditing stds. divsn. 1989-90, acctg. lit. selection com. 1989-90, acctg. lit. awards com. 1979-83, mem. auditing stds. bd. 1995—); mem. Am. Acctg. Assn. (tech. program com. 1980-81, chairperson Western region

auditing sect. 1981-83, acctg. lit. nominating com. 1982-84, 88-89, acctg. lit. selection com. 1989-90, dir. auditing stds., chmn. auditing stds. com. 1989-90), Ariz. Soc. CPA's (auditing stds. com. 1978-81, ethics com. 1981-84). Avocation: baseball. Office: Ariz State U Sch of Accountancy Tempe AZ 85287

PANZ, RICHARD, library director; b. Buffalo, Sept. 14, 1947; s. Stanley Joseph and Amelia (Kalicki) P.; m. Elizabeth Mary Gordon, Oct. 31, 1971; children: Tracy E., Bethany J. BS, Canisius Coll., 1969; MLS, Syracuse U., 1971. Cert. pub. libr., N.Y. Br. libr. Buffalo and Erie County Pub. Libr., Buffalo, 1971-73, asst. dept. head, 1973-75, yound adult dept. bus. reference libr., 1975-77; asst. dir. Willard Pub. Libr., Battle Creek, Mich., 1977-79; dir. Finger Lakes Libr. Sys., Ithaca, N.Y., 1979-89, Rochester (N.Y.) Pub. Libr./Monroe County Libr. Sys., 1989—; bd. dirs. Reynolds Libr., Inc., Rochester; mem. Regents Adv. Coun. on Librs., Albany, N.Y., 1985-89; chmn. N.Y. State LSCA Adv. Coun., Algany, 1981-86. Contbr. to book: Selecting a Bibliographic Utility, 1989; contbr. articles to profl. jours. Bd. dirs. Monroe County Bar Assn. Found., Rochester, 1994—, Rundel Found., Rochester, 1989—, WXXI Pub. Broadcasting Coun., Rochester, 1994—; mem. 2000 Citizens Adv. Coun., Rochester, 1991-93, Goals for Greater Rochester Cultural Resources Planning Coun., 1991-93; chmn. adv. com. Rochester Regional Libr. Coun., 1994—. Recipient Outstanding Alumni award Syracuse Sch. Info. Studies, 1990, Ray Murray award N.Y. State Libr. Assts. Assn., 1994. Mem. ALA, N.Y. Libr. Assn. (v.p. 1987, Outstanding Svc. to Librs. award 1988), Pub. Libr. Sys. Dirs. of N.Y. (exec. bd.), Pub. Libr. Assn. Avocations: golf, photography, running. Home: Richester Pub Libr 375 Yarmouth Rd Rochester NY 14610 Office: Rochester Pub Libr 115 South Ave Rochester NY 14604

PANZAR, JOHN C., economist, educator, consultant; b. Chgo. Heights, Ill., May 17, 1947; s. Roland and Gwendolyn Venita (Bishir) P.; m. Anne Davis Laws, June 21, 1970; children: John Roland, Luke William. BA cum laude with distinction in Econs., Carleton Coll., 1969; AM in Econs., Stanford U., 1973, PhD in Econs., 1975. Rsch. asst. Stanford U., 1970-74, teaching asst., 1972; lectr. in econs. San Francisco State U., 1972-73; mem. tech. staff Bell Labs., 1974-83, head econ. analysis rsch. dept., 1980-83; prof. econs. Northwestern U., 1983—, prof. econs. and transp., 1985—, chmn. dept. econs., 1988-92, Louis W. Menk prof. econs., 1988—; vis. adj. assoc. prof. econs. U. Calif., Berkeley, 1977; vis. prof. econs. U. Pa., 1983; mem. editorial bd. Jour. Regulatory Econs., 1988—, Jour. Econ. Lit., 1983-85, Jour. Info. Econs. and Policy, 1982—; mem. bd. dirs. Telecommunications Policy Rsch. Conf.; referee numerous jours. in field; cons. to numerous corps., industry groups, govt. agys., law firms and consulting firms. Author: (books) Regulation, Service Quality, and Market Performance: A Model of Airline Rivalry, 1979, (with W.J. Baumol and R.D. Willig) Contestable Markets and the Theory of Industry Structure, 1982, revised edit. 1987; contbr. articles to profl. jours. Recipient numerous fellowships. Mem. AEA (mem. commn. grad. edn. in econs. 1988-91), European Assn. for Rsch. in Indsl. Econs., Internat. Telecommunications Soc., Econometric Soc. Home: 2207 Washington Ave Wilmette IL 60091 Office: Econ Dept Northwestern U 2003 Sheridan Rd Evanston IL 60201

PANZER, MARY CAROLINE, museum curator; b. Flint, Mich., May 29, 1955; d. Milton and Carline Alice (Weis) P. BA, Yale U.; MA, Columbia U., 1980; PhD, Boston U., 1990. Asst. prof. U. Kans., Lawrence, 1989-91; curator photographs Spencer Mus. Art, Lawrence, 1989-91; asst. dir. SMART Mus. Art, Chgo., 1991; curator photographs Nat. Portrait Gallery Smithsonian Instn., Washington, 1992—. Mem. Am. Studies Assn., Coll. Art Assn., Oracle, Mid-Atlantic Radical Historians Orgn., Orgn. Am. Historians. Office: Nat Portrait Gallery Smithsonian Instn Mrc # 213 Washington DC 20560

PANZER, MARY E., state legislator; b. Waupun, Wis., Sept. 19, 1951; d. Frank E. and Verna L. P.; 1 adopted child, Melissa. BA, U. Wis., 1974; mem., Wis. State Ho. Reps. from 53rd dist. Mem. Ho. Reps. 53rd dist. State of Wis., Madison, mem. Senate 20th dist. Home: 635 W Tamarack Dr West Bend WI 53095-3653 Office: Wis State Senate State Capital Madison WI 53702

PANZER, MITCHELL EMANUEL, lawyer; b. Phila., Aug. 2, 1917; s. Max and Cecelia (Kassner) P.; m. Edith Budin, Apr. 13, 1943; children: Marcy C., Leslie S. Katz. AB with distinction and 1st honors, Temple U., 1937; JD magna cum laude, U. Pa., 1940; LLD honoris causa, Gratz Coll., 1972. Bar: Pa. 1942, U.S. Dist. Ct. (ea. dist.) Pa. 1948, U.S. Ct. Appeals (3d cir.) 1949, U.S. Supreme Ct. 1961. Gowen Meml. fellow U. Pa. Law Sch., 1940-41; law clk. Phila. Ct. Common Pleas, No. 7, 1941-42; assoc. Wolf, Block, Schorr and Solis-Cohen, Phila., 1946-54, ptnr., 1954-88, of counsel, 1988—; spl. adv. counsel Fed. Home Loan Mortgage Corp., Fed. Nat. Mortgage Assn., 1972-82; dir. emeritus, former counsel St. Edmond's Savs. and Loan Assn.; former dir. State Chartered Group, Pa. Bldg. and Loan Assn. Treas., Fedn. Jewish Agys. Greater Phila., 1982-86, v.p., 1982-86, trustee, 1963—, mem. exec. com., 1981-86, hon. life trustee, 1992—; trustee emeritus Pa. Land Title Inst., 1992—; bd. overseers Gratz Coll., 1958—, pres., 1962-68. Served to capt. USAF, 1942-46. Decorated Bronze Star medal; recipient Man of Year award Gratz Coll. Alumni Assn., 1964. Mem. Am. Coll. Real Estate Lawyers, ABA (chmn. spl. com. on residential real estate transactions 1972-73), Pa. Bar Assn. (mem. spl. com. on land titles), Phila. Bar Assn. (chmn. com. censors 1966, chmn. bd. govs. 1971, parliamentarian 1965-67, 71, chmn. charter and by-laws com. 1972), Jewish Publ. Soc. (trustee 1966-81, 85-88, v.p. 1972-75, sec. 1975-78), Order of Coif (pres. 1961-63, exec. com.). Jewish. Clubs: 21 Jewel Square (Phila.); Masons. Patentee in field. Home: 505 Oak Ter Merion Station PA 19066-1340 Office: Wolf Block Schorr & Solis-Cohen 12th Fl Packard Bldg 15th & Chestnut Sts Philadelphia PA 19102

PAO, YIH-HSING, engineer, educator; b. Nanking, China, Jan. 19, 1930; s. Te-Cheng and Tsin-Han (Hsiao) P.; m. Amelia K.T. Shih, Sept. 7, 1957; children: Winston, May, Sophia. B.Eng., Nat. Taiwan U., Taiwan, Republic of China, 1952; M.S. in Mechanics, Rensselaer Polytech. Inst., N.Y., 1955; Ph.D. in Applied Mechanics, Columbia U., N.Y.C., 1959. Asst. prof. Cornell U., Ithaca, N.Y., 1958-62, assoc. prof., 1962-68, prof., 1968-84; chmn. dept. theoretical and applied mechanics Cornell U., Ithaca, 1974-80; Joseph C. Ford prof. Cornell U., Ithaca, N.Y., 1984—; dir. Inst. Applied Mechanics, Nat. Taiwan U., 1984-86, 89-94, prof., 1984—. Co-author: Diffraction of Elastic Waves and Dynamic Stress Concentration, 1972; contbr. chpts. to books, articles to profl. jours.; editor in field. Fellow ASME, Am. Acad. Mechanics; mem. U.S. NAE, Academia Sinica, ROC. Office: Inst Applied Mechs, Nat Taiwan U, Taipei 107, Taiwan

PAO, YOH-HAN, engineering educator; m. Helen Chung-Ying Koo; children: John D., Robin A. BS in Gen. Engring., Henry Lester Inst., Shanghai, China; PhD in Applied Physics, Pa. State U.; postdoctoral studies, U. of Chgo., Edinburgh U. Mem. tech. staff AT&T Bell Labs., Murray Hill, N.J., 1962-67; head dept elec. engring. and applied physics Case Western Res. U., Cleve., 1969-78; dir. Ctr. for Intelligent Systems Rsch. Cleve.; also George S. Dively Disting. Prof. Engring. Case Western Res. U., Cleve.; dir. Elec. Computer & Systems Engring. NSF, 1978-80; chmn., pres. AI Ware Inc., Cleve. Office: Case Western Res U Dept Elec Engring/Comp Sci Cleveland OH 44106

PAOLETTA, MARK R. A., federal lawyer; b. 1962. BA, Duquesne U.; JD, Georgetown U. Bar: 1984, 87. Asst. couns. to the Pres. Exec. Office of the Pres., Washington, 1991—; ptnr. O'Connor & Hannan, Washington, 1993—. Office: O'Connor & Hannan 1919 Pennsylvania Ave NW Washington DC 20006-3400

PAOLINI, GILBERT, literature and science educator; b. L'Aquila, Italy; naturalized citizen, 1954; s. John and Assunta A. (Turavani) P.; m. Claire Jacqueline Landro; children: Angela Janet, John Frank. B.A., U. Buffalo, 1957, M.A., 1959; postgrad. Middlebury Coll., summer 1960, 61; Ph.D., U. Minn., 1965. Lectr. Spanish Rosary Hill Coll., Buffalo, 1957-58; instr. Italian and Latin lit. U. Mass., Amherst, 1958-60; instr. Spanish and Italian Syracuse U., 1962-65, asst. prof., 1965-67; assoc. prof. Spanish lit. Tulane U., New Orleans, 1967-76, prof., 1976—; dir. Tulane scholars and honors program Tulane U., 1981-83, chmn. colloquia dept., 1981-83; Originator Spanish Culture Week New Orleans, 1977, 79; chmn. adv. com. Jambalaya

program Nat. Endowment Humanities, New Orleans, 1975-80; Spanish essay reader Ednl. Testing Svc., Princeton, 1979-85; co-founder, gen. chmn. La. Conf. on Hispahic Langs. and Lits., 1981, 83, 85, 87, 89, 93. Author: Bartolome Soler: novelista: Procedimientos estilisticos, 1963; An Aspect of Spiritualistic Naturalism in the Novel of B.P. Galdos: Charity, 1969; mem. editorial bd.: Forum Italicum, 1967-71, Critica Hispanica, 1979—, Discurso Literario, 1985—, Letras Peninsulares, 1987—; assoc. editor: South Central MLA Bull. 1978-80; editor: La Chispa'81: Selected Procs., 1981, Papers on Romance Literary Relations, 1983, La Chispa '83: Selected Procs., 1983, La Chispa '85: Selected Procs., 1985, La Chispa '87: Selected Procs. 1987, La Chispa '89: Selected Prods., 1989, La Chispa '93: Selected Procs. 1993; cons. editor South Central Rec., 1988-92; contbr. articles to profl. jours. With AUS, 1952-54, USAFRES, 1954-57. Recipient Disting. Service award Sociedad Espanola, 1979, Knight Cross of Order of Isabel the Catholic, 1984. Mem. MLA, AAUP, Am. Assn. Tchrs. Spanish and Portuguese (chmn. pub. rels. com. 1981-86, pres. La. chpt. 1979-81, 88-89), Am. Assn. Tchrs. Italian, Am. Assn. Advancement Humanities, Asociacion Internacional de Hispanistas, Southeastern Am. Soc. 18th Century Studies (exec. v.p.), Asociacion Internacional de Galdosistas, Phi Sigma Iota, Sigma Delta Pi (v.p. for Southwest 1989-92). Office: Tulane Univ 304 Newcomb Hall New Orleans LA 70118

PAOLINO, RICHARD FRANCIS, manufacturing company executive; b. Fall River, Mass., Feb. 16, 1945; s. Emelio and Sylvia (Fasciani) P.; m. Elizabeth Jane Maloney, Sept. 9, 1973; children: Christopher Matthew, Kathryn Elizabeth. AB in Engring. Sci., Dartmouth Coll., 1967; MBA in Mktg. and Fin., U. Chgo., 1973. Plant engr. Polaroid Corp., Cambridge, Mass., 1967; from salesman to asst. br. mgr., Fed. Products Corp., Chgo., 1967-74; area mgr., nat. accounts mgr. Husky Injection Molding Systems, Chgo. and Toronto, Can., 1974-76; v.p. mktg. Quality Measurement Systems Inc., Penfield, N.Y., 1976-78; dir. mktg. Automation and Measurement div. Bendix Corp., Dayton, Ohio, 1978-82; gen. mgr. Boice div. MTI, Latham, N.Y., 1982-85; v.p., gen. mgr. coordinate Measuring Systems Group, Brown & Sharpe Mfg. Co., North Kingstown, R.I., 1985—; condr. seminars, lectr. in field. Bd. dirs. Automation Software, Inc., Providence, R.I., Leitz Messtechnik GmbH, Wetzlar, Germany, Brown & Sharpe-Precizika, Vilinus, Lithuania; pres. mng. dir. DEA S.p.A. 1st lt. USMCR, 1967-69. Mem. Soc. Mfg. Engrs. (past chmn. quality assurance tech. coun.), Am. Soc. Quality Control, Machinery and Allied Products Mktg. Coun., Mfr.'s Alliance for Productivity and Innovation (gen. mgrs. coun.), Assn. Mfg. Tech. Address: 16 Quincy Adams Rd Barrington RI 02806 Office: Brown & Sharpe Mfg Co 200 Frenchtown Rd North Kingstown RI 02852

PAOLINO, RONALD MARIO, clinical psychologist, consultant, psychopharmacologist, pharmacist; b. Providence, Mar. 15, 1938; s. Lawrence and Mary Corinne (Guglielmi) P.; m. Eileen Frances Quimby, June 18, 1960; children: Lisa Katherine, David Lawrence. Student, Providence Coll., 1955-56; BS in Pharmacy, U. R.I., 1959; MS in Pharmacology, Purdue U., 1961, PhD in Psychopharmacology, 1963, postdoctoral studies in clin. psychology, 1972-74; postdoctoral studies in existential analytic psychotherapy, Okla. Inst. Existential Analysis and Psychotherapy, 1974-75; MA (hon.), Brown U., 1977. Lic. psychologist, R.I., pharmacist, R.I.; nat. registered health svc. provider in psychology; cert. arbitrator; cert. nat. registered group psycho-therapists. Intern dept. psychiatry and behavioral scis. U. Okla. Health Scis. Ctr., 1974-75; David Ross predoctoral fellow dept. pharmacology/toxicology Purdue U., 1961-63; NIMH postdoctoral fellow in psychology dept. psychology Yale U., 1963-65; asst. prof. pharmacology U. Conn. Sch. Pharmacy, 1965-67; assoc. prof. psychopharmacology Purdue U., 1967-74; NIMH fellow in clin. psychology U. Okla. Health Scis. Ctr., 1974-75; coord. group psychotherapy tng. program Brown U. Program in Medicine, 1983-85, assoc. prof. psychiatry and human behavior, 1976-90; pvt. practice; chief drug dependency treatment program VA Med. Ctr., Providence, 1975-87, dir. biofeedback clinic, 1977-87; chief, crisis mgmt. program, primary hostage negotiator; mem. Pharmacology and Therapeutic Agts. Com., 1979-87, VA Med. Ctr., coord. VA Contracted Half-Way Project for Substance Dependent Vets., 1981-85, chmn. Pain Mgmt. Task Force, 1984-85, mem. Supervisory Level Pharmacy Profl. Standards Bd., 1990—, mem. Mgmt. Suicidal and Violent Patient Task Force, 1990-91, chmn. Com. Prevention & Mgmt. of Disturbed Behaviors, 1991—, chief crisis mgmt. program, 1993—, advisor FBI Hostage Negotiations, 1991—, chmn. Outpatient Psychiatry Svcs. Reorganization Task Force, 1991, mem. VA-Dept. Def. Desert Storm Emergency Plan Com., 1991; advisor OSHA Dept. Labor for Violence in the Work Place, 1994—; mem. substance abuse and prevention grant application rev. com. R.I. Adv. Coun. on Substance Abuse, 1982—, prevention, edn. and tng. com. on substance abuse, 1981—, chmn. 1981-82; adj. assoc. prof. psychology, U. R.I., 1982—; mem. planning com. State Conf. on Substance Abuse in the Hispanic Community, 1986; mem. alcohol awareness commn. Episc. Diocese of R.I., 1983-85; gubernatorial appointee Gov.'s Permanent Coun. on Drug Abuse Control, 1978-82; mem. rev. com. for funding of state drug abuse programs R.I. Single State Agy. on Drug Abuse, R.I. Dept. Mental Health Retardation and Hosps., 1978-82 cons. Nurses Renewal Com., 1980-81, substance abuse prevention edn. for elem. sch. children R.I. chpt. ARC, 1977, mem. suicide prevention steering com., 1977; mem.Interagy. Drug Abuse Steering Com., Lafayette, Ind. 1969-72; bd. dirs. Providence VA Med. Ctr. Credit Union; mem. bd. cert. for alcoholism counselors R.I. Assn. Alcohol Counselors, 1979-81; mem. Gov.'s Task Force on Substance Abuse at Adult Correctional Instn., 1977-78, Gov.'s Task Force on Mental Health Svcs. at Adult Correctional Instn., 1977-78, chmn. reclassification of inmates com., 1977-78; chmn. com. on edn. and cert. biofeedback practioners Conn. Biofeedback Soc., 1977-78; summer faculty fellow U. Conn., 1967; vis. scientist lectr. Assn. Am. Colls. Pharmacy, 1972-73; cons. to bus., unions, law enforcement. Author: (2 chpts.) Drug Testing: Issues and Options, 1991; contbr. 37 articles to profl. jours. Bd. dirs. R.I. chpt. Samaritans Internat. Suicide Prevention Orgn., 1978-80, v.p. Experience Jesus Inc.; mem. community adv. bd. Spina Bifida Assn. R.I., 1980-83. Recipient Citation award for svc. and contbns. to formulation of state policy for treatment and prevention of drug abuse Gov. R.I., 1983, Letter of Commendation, Gov.'s R.I. Adv. Coun. on Substance Abuse, 1986, vc. Recognition award DAV, 1990, Spl. Contb Providence VA Med Ctr., 1990. Mem. APA, Am. Group Psychotherapy Assn., Am. Soc. for Pharmacology and Exptl. Therapeutics, Internat. Brain Rsch. Orgn., Internat. Narcotic Enforcement Officers Assn., R.I. Group Psychotherapy Soc. (pres. 1991-93, continuing edn. dir. for psychologists 1990—, exec. bd. 1986—, tng. faculty 1985—, co-dir. tng. 1986-87, tng. adv. bd. 1985-86), R.I. Psychol. Assn. (chmn. substance abuse ins. subcom. 1986-87, Gov.'s Coun. on Mental Health State Plan Com. 1982-84), Hostage Negotiators of Am., Rho Chi Hon. Pharm. Soc., Sigma Xi. Office: PO Box 59 Barrington RI 02806-0159

PAOLUCCI, ANNE ATTURA, playwright, poet, English and comparative literature educator; b. Rome; d. Joseph and Lucy (Guidoni) Attura; m. Henry Paolucci. BA, Barnard Coll; MA, Columbia Ph.D, 1963. Mem. faculty English dept. Brearley Sch., N.Y.C., 1957-59; asst. prof. English and comparative lit. CCNY, 1959-69; univ. research prof. St. John's U., Jamaica, N.Y., 1969—; prof. English St. John's U., 1975—, acting head dept. English, 1973-74, chmn. dept. English, 1982-91, dir. doctor of arts degree program in English, 1982—; Fulbright lectr. in Am. drama U. Naples, Italy, 1965-67; spl. lectr. U. Urbino, summers 1966-67, U. Bari, 1967, univs. Bologna, Catania, Messina, Palermo, Milan, Pisa, 1965-67; disting. adj. vis. prof. Queens Coll. CUNY; bd. dirs. World Centre for Shakespeare Studies, 1972—; spl. guest Yugoslavia Ministry of Culture, 1972; rep. U.S. at Internat. Poetry Festival, Yugoslavia, 1981; founder, exec. dir. Council on Nat. Lits., 1974—; mem. exec. com. Conf. Editors Learned Jours.-MLA, 1975—; del. to Fgn. Lang. Jours., 1977—; mem. adv. bd. Commn. on Tech. and Cultural Transformation, UNESCO, 1978—; vis. fellow Humanities Research Centre, Australian Nat. U., 1979; rep. U.S. woman playwright Inter-Am. Women Writers Congress, Ottawa, Ont., Can., 1978; organizer, chmn. profl. symposia, meetings; TV appearances; hostess Mags. in Focus, Channel 31, N.Y.C., 1971-72; mem. N.Am. Adv. Council Shakespeare Globe Theatre Center, 1981—; mem. Nat. Grad. Fellows Program Fellowship Bd., 1985—; mem. Nat. Garibaldi Centennial Com., 1981; mem. Nat. Grad. Fellows Program, 1985—; trustee Edn. Scholarship, Grants Com. of NIAF, 1990—; guest speaker with E. Ahoe Ohio No. State U, 1990. Author: (with H. Paolucci) books, including Hegel On Tragedy, 1962, From Tension to Tonic: The Plays of Edward Albee, 1972, Pirandello's Theatre: The Recovery of the Modern Stage for Dramatic Art, 1974, Poems Written for Sbek's Mummies, Marie Menken, and Other Important Persons, Places, and Things,

1977, Eight Short Stories, 1977, Sepia Prints, 1985, 2nd edit., 1986; plays include Minions of the Race (Medieval and Renaissance Conf. of Western Mich. U. Drama award 1972), Cipango!, 1985, pub. as book, 1985, 86, videotape excerpts, 1986, 1992, Three Short Plays, 1994; performed N.Y.C. and Washington, 1988-89, Winterthur Mus., U. Del., 1990; The Actor in Search of His Mask, 1987, Italian transl. and prodn., Genoa, 1987; poems Riding the Mast Where It Swings, 1980, Gorbechev in Concert, 1991; contbr. numerous articles, revs. to profl. jours.; editor, author: introduction Dante's Influence on American Writers, 1977; gen. editor tape-cassette series China, 1977, 78; founder Coun. on Nat. Lit.; gen. editor series Rev. Nat. Lits, 1970—, CNL/Quar. World Report, 1974-76, semi-annual 1977-84, annual 1985—; full-length TV tape of play Cipango! for pub. TV and ednl. TV with original music by Henry Paolucci, 1990. Bd. dirs. Italian Heritage and Culture City-wide com., 1986—; Pres. Reagan appointee Nat. Grad. Fellows Program Fellowship Bd., 1985-86, Nat. Coun. Humanities, 1986—, Ann. award, FIERI, 1990; pres. Columbus: Countdown, 1992 Fedn.; mem. Gov. Cuomo's Heritage Legacy Project for Schs., 1989—; bd. dirs. Am. Soc. Italian Legions of Merit (chmn. cultural com. 1990—). Named one of 10 Outstanding Italian Ams. in Washington, awarded medal by Amb. Rinaldo Petrignani, 1986; named Cavaliere Italian Republic, 1986, "Commendatore" of the Italian Republic Order of Merit, 1992; recipient Notable Rating for Mags. in Focus series N.Y. Times, 1972, Woman of Yr. award Dr. Herman Henry Scholarship Found., 1973, Amita award, 1970, award Women's Press Club N.Y., 1974, Order Merit, Italian Republic, 1986, Gold medal for Quincentenary Can. trustee NIIAF, 1990, ann. awards Consortium of Italian-Am. Assns., 1991, Am.-Italian Hist. Assn., 1991, 1st Columbus award Cath. Charities, 1991, Leone di San Marco award Italian Heritage Coun. of Bronx and Westchester Counties, 1992, Children of Columbus award Order of Sons of Italy in Am., 1993, 1st Nat. Elena Cornaro award Order of Sons of Italy 1993; Columbia U. Woodbridge hon. fellow, 1961-62; Am. Council Learned Socs. grantee Internat. Pirandello Congress, Agrigento, Italy, 1978. Mem. Internat. Shakespeare Assn., Shakespeare Assn. Am., Renaissance Soc. Am., Renaissance Inst. Japan, Internat. Comparative Lit. Assn., Am. Comparative Lit. Assn., MLA, Am. PEN, Hegel Soc. Am., Dante Soc. Am. (v.p. 1976-77), Am. Found. Italian Arts and Letters (founder, pres.), Pirandello Soc. (pres. 1978—), Nat. Soc. Lit. and Arts, Nat. Book Critics Circle, Am. Soc. Italian Legions of Merit (bd. dirs. 1990—). Office: St John's U Jamaica NY 11439 *My own first practical premise has been to organize every task (even routine chores) so that there is always time and energy for whatever important projects come up. There is enough room in the day for doing a number of things—and for creating "space" every so often to do one's own special work (writing fiction or poetry or plays, in my case). Organization is all-important; but perhaps the basic premise in intellectual things is organic growth, letting "in" those things that are meaningful because they already suggest an intrinsic pattern. In my case, I discovered long after the projects and books themselves had taken shape and had been published, that I had been tending for a number of years more and more exclusively toward drama and dramatic criticism and theory. Well, that, obviously, was my own potential "law" organizing from within my various interests. One must continue to allow for new interests to revitalize those already familiar.*

PAONE, PETER, artist; b. Phila., Oct. 2, 1936; s. George and Angelina (Vitrella) P.; m. Alma Alabilikian, 1976. B.A., Phila. Mus. Coll. Art, 1958. Instr. Phila. Mus. Coll. Art, Pratt Inst., others; head graphics dept. Fleisher Art Meml., 1959-62; tchr. Pa. Acad. Fine Arts, 1978—, also chmn. graphics dept.; instr. Positano Art Sch., Italy, 1961. One man shows, Ft. Worth Mus., 1963, Grippi Gallery, 1959, 60, 61, Print Club, Phila., 1961-64, Robinson Gallery, Houston, 1978-79, Pa. Acad. Fine Arts, 1983, Phila. Print Club, 1983, Ryder Coll., Pa., 1991; exhibited in group shows, Dallas Mus., 1964, Paris (France) Biennial, 1963, Lehigh (Pa.) U., 1962, Bklyn. Mus., 1962, Contemporary Am., 1961, Phila. Mus. Art, 1960, 61, 63, Otis Art Inst., Los Angeles, 1964, Syracuse U., 1964, La Escuela Nacional, Mexico City, Vanderbilt U., N.Y. World's Fair, Exhbn. Pakistan, 1967, Clydie Jessop Gallery, London, 1968, David Gallery, Houston, Kennedy Gallery, N.Y.C., 1970-72, Hooks-Epstein Gallery, 1978, 80, 81, 82, 83, 85, 87, 88, 90, Rider Coll. of N.J., 1991; represented in permanent collections, Library of Congress, Phila. Mus. Art, Sumner Found., N.Y. Mus. Modern Art, Princeton Library, Phila. Library, Gen. Mills, Phila. Print Club, Rosenwald Collection, Carl Sandburg Meml. Library, Syracuse U., Ft. Worth Mus., Victoria and Albert Mus., Brit. Mus., Art Inst. Chgo., Yale U. Recipient award of merit Phila. Print Club, 1983; Tiffany Found. grantee, 1962, 64; John Simon Guggenheim fellow, 1965-66; grantee Penn Council for the Arts, 1985. Mem. NAD (assoc.). Home: 1027 W Westview St Philadelphia PA 19119-3718 *Somewhere between the world of realism and surrealism, there is a world that deals with the reality of relationships, favoring the substance of the imagination rather than the substance of everyday vision. Objects that seemingly have no real relationship to each other in their existence are juxtaposed in the life of the artist. They have touched each other and have become part of the vision, and in turn have become his iconography. There is no urgency in this vision. The private reality has always been there and always will be. The viewer is allowed to question his knowledge of it, and in doing so, he often is uneasy and bewildered before the assemblage. This, at first, implies fantasy; this is not true. Instead, this is a reconstruction of reality, not an escape from it.*

PAPA, VINCENT T., financial insurance company executive; b. Bklyn., Dec. 11, 1946; s. Frank R. and Carmela (Farruggia) P.; m. Karen Ann Conroy, July 4, 1969; children: Kimberly, Jennifer, Kristen. BBA, Hofstra U., 1969; AAS, Nassau Community Coll., 1967; CPA, N.Y. Staff acct. Arthur Andersen & Co., N.Y.C., 1969-72; comptroller Finserv Corp., N.Y.C., 1972-80; v.p. and treas. Orion Capital Corp., N.Y.C., 1980—. Mem. AICPA, Nat. Assn. Corp. Treas., Am. Mgmt. Assn., N.Y. State Soc. CPAs, Ins. Soc. N.Y. Office: Orion Capital Corp 600 Fifth Ave New York NY 10020

PAPACHRONIS, DARLENE R., hospital administrator; b. Hammond, Ind., Apr. 5, 1947; d. Steve J. and Agnes Susan (Spudich) Markovich; divorced; 1 child, Dawn Renee. BS in Health Arts, Coll. of St. Francis, Joliet, Ill., 1978, MS in Helath Svcs. Adminstrn., 1984. RN, Ind., Ill. Staff nurse med.-surg. St. Catherine Hosp., East Chicago, Ind., 1968-69, staff nurse emergency rm., 1969-71; asst. dir. nursing St. Catherine Hosp., East Chicago, 5, 1971-74, maternal-child coord., 1974-80, dir. nursing support svcs., 1980-88, v.p. nursing, 1988—. Mem. Ind. Orgn. Nurse Execs., Northwest Ind. Orgn. Nurse Execs., Nat. Assn. Quality Assurance Profls., Ind. Assn. Quality Assurance Profls. Avocations: reading, needlepoint, oil painting. Office: St Catherine Hosp 4321 Fir St East Chicago IN 46312-3097

PAPADAKIS, CONSTANTINE N., dean, civil engineering educator; b. Athens, Greece, Feb. 2, 1946; came to U.S., 1969; s. Nicholas and Rita (Masciotti) P.; m. Eliana Apostolidos, Aug. 28, 1971; 1 child, Maria. Diploma in Civil Engring., Nat. Tech. U. Athens, 1969; MS in Civil Engring., U. Cin., 1970; PhD in Civil Engring., U. Mich., 1973. Cert. profl. engr., Mich., Va., Ohio, Greece. Engring. specialist, geotechnical group Bechtel, Inc., Gaithersburg, Md., 1974-76; supr. and asst. chief engr. geotechnical group Bechtel, Inc., Ann Arbor, Mich., 1976-81; v.p. bd. dirs. water resources div. STS Cons. Ltd., Ann Arbor, 1981-84; v.p. water and environ. resources dept. Tetra Tech-Honeywell, Pasadena, Calif., 1984; head dept. civil engring. Colo. State U., Ft. Collins, 1984-86; dean Coll. Engring. U. Cin., 1986—; dir. Groundwater Rsch. Ctr., 1986—; dir. Ctr. Hill Solid and Hazardous Waste Rsch. Ctr. EPA, Cin., 1986-93; adj. prof. civil engring. U. Mich., 1976-83; cons. Gaines & Stern Co., Cleve., 1983-84, Honeywell Europe, Maintal, Fed. Republic of Germany, 1984-85, Arthur D. Little, Boston, 1984-85, Camargo Assocs., Ltd., Cin., 1986, King Fahd U. Rsch. Inst., Dhahran, Saudi Arabia, 1987, King Abdulaziz City for Sci. and Tech., Riyadh, Saudi Arabia, 1991, Henderson & Bodwell Cons. Engrs. Inc., 1991, Cin. Met. Sewer Dist., 1992; acting pres. Ohio Aerospace Inst., 1989-90; interim pres. Inst. Advanced Mfg. Sci. Ohio Edison Tech. Ctr., 1989-90; bd. govs. Edison Materials Tech. Ctr., 1988—; adv. bd., founding mem. Hamilton County Bus. Incubator, 1988—; bd. dirs. Fidelity Fed. Bank. Author: Problems on Strength of Materials, 1968, Sewer Systems Design, 1969; editor: Fluid Transients and Acoustics, 1978, Pump-Turbine Schemes, 1979, Small Hydro Power Fluid Machinery, 1982; Megatrends in Hydraulics, 1987; contbr. over 55 articles to profl. jours. Mem. Greater Cin. C. of C. Blue Chip Campaign for Econ. Devel. Task Force, 1988-93, bd. dirs. Bus. Assistance Ctr., 1989—; mem. Ohio Coun. on Rsch. and Econ. Devel., 1988, Ohio Sci. and Tech. Commn. Adv. Group, 1989-90, 92—; coun. mem. St.

Nicholas Ch. Parish, Ann Arbor, 1981-84; mem. City of Ft. Collins Drainage Bd., 1984-86; bd. dirs. Dan Beard coun. Boy Scouts Am., 1995—, Intelligent Vehicle Hwy. Soc. Ohio, 1994—. Recipient Horace W. King scholarship civil engring. dept. U. Mich., 1971-73, 6 Bechtel Merit awards, 1974-79, Young Engr. of Yr. award Mich. Soc. Profl. Engrs., Ann Arbor, Mich., 1982, Disting. Engr. award Engrs. and Scientists Cin. Tech. Socs. Coun., 1989. Fellow ASCE (pres. Ann Arbor br. 1980-81, pres.-elect Mich. sect. 1983-84, hydraulics divsn. publ. com. 1980-83), ASME (chmn. fluid transients com. 1978-80, mem. fluids engring. divsn. awards com. 1981-84); mem. NSPE (legis. and govt. affairs com. 1994—, chair profl. engrs. in edn. divsn. 1995—), Am. Soc. Engring. Edn., Order of the Engr., Internat. Assn. for Hydraulic Rsch., Ohio Engring. Dean's Coun. (chmn.-elect 1989-91), Rotary, Sigma Xi, Chi Epsilon, Tau Beta Pi. Greek Orthodox. Avocations: photography, classical music, travel, swimming, racquetball. Home: Indian Hill 7354 Sanderson Pl Cincinnati OH 45243-4045 Office: U Cinn Coll Engring Mail Location 18 Cincinnati OH 45221-0018

PAPADAKIS, EMMANUEL PHILIPPOS, physicist, university research director, consultant; b. N.Y.C., Dec. 25, 1934; s. Philippos E. and Helen (Eastman) P.; m. Stella Christopher, Sept. 4, 1960; children: Susan H., Philip E., Christopher E., Nicholas E. S.B. in Physics, M.I.T., 1956, Ph.D. in Physics, 1962; M.M. in Mgmt, U. Mich., 1979. Mem. tech. staff Bell Telephone Labs., Allentown, Pa., 1962-69; dept. head Panametrics, Inc., Waltham, Mass., 1969-73; prin. staff engr. Ford Motor Co., Detroit, 1973-75, supr., 1975-87; ptnr. E&S Antiques, Ames, Iowa, 1978—, pres. Quality Systems Concepts Inc., 1991—; assoc. dir. Ctr. for Nondestructive Evaluation, Iowa State U., Ames, 1988—; adj. prof. Northeastern U. extension, Waltham, 1970-73, elec. engring. and computer engring. Iowa State U., 1988—; cons. acoustics and ultrasonic testing systems, 1969-73, 88—. Contbr. numerous articles on electronics, ultrasonics, acoustics, nondestructive testing, crystallography and quality to profl. jours.; assoc. editor IEEE Transactions on Ultras, Ferroelectrics and Frequency Control, 1972-92; assoc. tech. editor Materials Evaluation, 1975-87, rsch. coord., 1980-86, quality concepts coord., 1986-88, tech. editor, 1988—; reviewer various jours. in physics, testing materials and sci. instrumentation. Fellow IEEE, Acoustical Soc. Am. (Biennial award 1968), Am. Soc. for Nondestructive Testing (Mehl honor lect. 1979, Tutorial award 1993); mem. ASTM, Am. Phys. Soc., Soc. Mfg. Engrs., Am. Soc. Quality Control, Soc. Automotive Engrs., Sigma Xi. Patentee in field; developer method and instrument for measuring ultrasonic velocity, method for bonding thin slabs to substrates, instrument for sheet metal texture determination, method using DSSS in ultrasonic flaw detection. Office: Ctr Nondestructive Evaluation Iowa State U Ames IA 50011

PAPADAKOS, NICHOLAS PETER, retired state supreme court justice; b. Hoboken, N.J., Jan. 24, 1925; s. Petros and Olga (Christopoulou) P.; m. Roula Sakellariou, 1950; children: Peter, James, Thomas. LL.B., Columbus Law Sch., Washington, 1952; B.A., Dickinson Coll., 1949. Bar: D.C. 1952, Pa. 1957, U.S. Supreme Ct. 1975. Atty. Dept. Labor, Washington, 1950-55; office mgr. Pa. Dept. Labor, McKeesport, 1955-57; pvt. practice McKeesport, Pa., 1957-75; judge Ct. of Common Pleas, Pitts., 1976-84; justice Pa. Supreme Ct., 1984-95; solicitor Versailles Sch. Dist., McKeesport, Pa., 1964-65, Port Vue Borough, Pa., 1969-75, City of McKeesport, 1974-75; instr. in bus. law Pa. State U.-McKeesport, 1960-75; mem. nat. panel arbitrators Am. Arbitration Assn., 1986. Laic chmn. Greek Orthodox Diocese of Pitts.; past mem., past chmn. U.S. Selective Service Bd., McKeesport, Pa., early 1970s; bd. dirs. Mendelssohn Choir, Pitts. Served to sgt. A.C., U.S. Army, 1943-46; PTO. Mem. Pa. State Trial Judges Conf., Greek-Am. Progressive Assn., Am. Hellenic Ednl. Progressive Assn., Tall Cedars Club, Optimists Club, Lions, Elks, Masons. Democrat.

PAPADEMETRIOU, GEORGE CONSTANTINE, priest, director, educator; b. Thasos, Greece, Apr. 11, 1932; came to U.S., 1947; s. Constantine G. and Ourania C. (Katsifas) P.; m. Athanasia Antoniou, June 26, 1960; children: Dean, Jane, Tom. BTh, Holy Cross Orthodox Sem., 1959; MTh, Tex. Christian U., 1966; PhD, Temple U., 1977; MLS, Simmons Coll., 1983. Pastor Greek Orthodox Archdiocese, 1960—; libr. dir. Hellenic Coll., 1981—; assoc. prof. theology and philosophy Holy Cross Orthodox Sem., Brookline, Mass., 1978—. Author: Introduction to Saint Gregory Palamas, 1973, Essays on Orthodox Christian-Jewish Relations, 1990, Maimonides and Palamas on God, 1994. Mem. AHEPA, Mass. Commn. on Christian Unity, Orthodox Theol. Soc. Am., Am. Acad. Religion, Am. Theol. Libr. Assn. Office: Hellenic Coll 50 Goddard Ave Brookline MA 02146-7496

PAPAGEORGE, TOD, photographer, educator; b. Portsmouth, N.H., Aug. 1, 1940; s. Theodore and Eileen Elizabeth (Flanigan) P.; m. Pauline Whitcomb, Feb. 3, 1962 (div. 1970); m. Deborah Flomenhaft, June 4, 1987; 1 child, Theo. BA in English Lit., U. N.H., 1962; MA, Yale U., 1979. Lectr. in photography MIT, Cambridge, Mass., 1974-75; lectr. in visual studies Harvard U., Cambridge, 1975-76; Walker Evans prof. of photography Yale U., New Haven, 1978-79, prof. photography, 1978—; vis. instr. in photography The Parsons Sch. Design, N.Y.C., 1969-72, The Pratt Inst. of Art, N.Y.C., 1971-74, The Cooper Union Sch. Art, N.Y.C., 1971-74; adj. lectr. in photography Queens Coll., N.Y.C., 1972-74. Guest dir. exhbn., Mus. Modern Art, N.Y.C., 1977, Yale Art Gallery, 1981; one-man shows include Light Gallery, N.Y.C., 1973, 79, Cronin Gallery, Houston, 1977, Art Inst. Chgo., 1978, Galerie Zabriskie, Paris, 1979, Stills Photography Group, Edinburgh, Scotland, 1980, Daniel Wolf Gallery, N.Y.C., 1981, 85, Akron (Ohio) Art Mus., 1981, Sheldon Meml. Art Gallery, Lincoln, Nebr., 1981, Franklin Parrasch Gallery, N.Y.C., 1991; group shows include Mus. Modern Art, N.Y.C., 1971, 73, 74, 76, 77, 78, 79, 91, Lowe Art Mus., Coral Gables, Fla., 1974, Balt. Mus. Art, 1975, Mus. Fine Arts, Boston, 1976, 91, Thomas Gibson Gallery, London, 1976, Galerie Zabriskie, Paris, 1977, 87, U. Colo., 1977, Houston Mus. Fine Arts, 1977, Art Inst. Chgo., 1979, Corcoran Gallery Art, Washington, 1980, Fraenkel Gallery, San Francisco, 1981, Daniel Wolf Gallery, N.Y.C., 1982, 83, 86, Albright-Knox Mus., Buffalo, 1983, The Whitney Mus. Art, N.Y.C., 1983, The Photographer's Gallery, London, 1983, Nat. Mus. Am. Art, Washington, 1984, The Dog Mus., N.Y.C., 1984, The Barbican Nat. Gallery, London, 1985, Light Gallery, N.Y.C., 1985, Centro Reina Sophia, Madrid, Spain, 1987, N.Y. State Mus., Albany, 1987, Worcester (Mass.) Art Mus., 1990, 94, Jewish Mus. Art, Wellesley, Mass., 1990, Musee De La Photographie, Mont-Sur-Marchienne, Belgium, 1991, Franklin Parrasch Gallery, N.Y.C., 1992, others; represented in permanent collections Mus. Modern Art, Art Inst. Chgo., Boston Mus. Fine Arts, Yale U. Art Gallery, Bibliothéque Nationale, Paris, Mus. Fine Arts, Houston, Dallas Mus. Fine Arts, Nat. Mus. Am. Art, Washington, J.B. Speed Mus., Louisville, Seattle Art Mus., Kunsthaus, Zurich, Switzerland, others; commd. by Aperture, Inc., 1975, Balt. Mus. Art, 1975, Seagrams Corp., 1975, Mus. Modern Art, N.Y., 1977, AT&T, 1978, Yale U. Art Gallery, 1981, Warner Comm., 1983; author: Walker Evans and Robert Frank: An Essay on Influence, 1981; editor: Public Relations: The Photographs of Garry Winogrand, 1977. Guggenheim fellow, 1970, 77; Nat. Endowment Arts fellow, 1973, 76. Subject of numerous articles and publs. Home: 122 Cottage St New Haven CT 06511-2406 Office: Yale U Sch Art PO Box 208270 New Haven CT 06520-8270

PAPAGEORGIOU, JOHN CONSTANTINE, management science educator; b. Kallithea, Greece, Nov. 22, 1935; came to U.S., 1969, naturalized, 1975; m. Thalia Christidou, 1969; children: Constantine, Elena, Demetrios, Antigone. B.Sc., Athens (Greece) Sch. Econs. and Bus. Scis, 1957; diploma tech. sci., U. Manchester, Eng., 1963, Ph.D. in Mgmt. Scis, 1965. Lectr. Athens Sch. Econs. and Bus. Scis.; also postgrad. Inst. Bus. Adminstrn., Athens, 1966-68; asst. prof. mgmt. Wayne State U., 1969-71; assoc. prof. mgmt. scis. St. Louis U., 1971-72; vis. prof. ops. rsch. Athens Sch. Econs. and Bus. Scis., 1972-73; assoc. prof. ops. analysis U. Toledo, 1974-76; assoc. prof. mgmt. sci. and coord. Coll. Profl. Studies, U. Mass., Boston, 1976-78; prof., coord. Coll. Profl. Studies, U. Mass., 1978-80; prof. mgmt. scis. dept. Coll. Mgmt. U. Mass., 1980—, chmn. mgmt. scis. dept., 1980-85; assoc. dean Coll. Mgmt. U. Mass., 1995—; head dept. econ. research Agrl. Bank Greece, 1966-67; ops. analyst Esso-Pappas Indsl. Co., Greece, 1967-68; spl. adv. Center Planning and Econ. Research, Greece, 1972-73; cons. in field; condr. seminars. Author: Introduction to Operations Research (in Greek), 1973, Fundamentals of Operations Research, 1973, Management Science and Environmental Problems, 1980; co-author: Data on the Greek Economy, 1966; assoc. editor technos: Ops. Mgmt. Newsletter; spl. issues editor: Interfaces; guest editor: Internat. Jour. Tech. Mgmt.; mem. editorial bd. Jour. Managerial Issues, Southwestern Bus. Rev.; editor: TIMS COLIME

Newsletter; contbr. articles to profl. jours. Served to 2d lt. Greek Army, 1958-60. Greek Govt. scholar, 1962-65; NATO postdoctoral fellow, 1965; Air Force Office Sci. Research fellow, summer 1980. Fellow AAAS; mem. Ops. Rsch. Soc. Am. (1985 nat. meeting program com.), Inst. Mgmt. Scis. (nat. meeting com., 1985, faculty-in-residence com., coll. officer, chpt. officer, activities com.), Am. Inst. Decision Scis. (nat. innovative edn. com. 1981, programs and meetings com. 1983), Hellenic Ops. Rsch. Soc., Sigma Xi. Address: 14 Putney Rd Wellesley MA 02181-5315 *Our achievements are a function of our goals. I usually set ambitious but achievable goals and I try to achieve them through hard work, persistence, and belief in God's help. I believe that there is always room for improvement in the status-quo and that a continuous search for improvements is the major factor for continuous progress.*

PAPAI, BEVERLY DAFFERN, library director; b. Amarillo, Tex., Aug. 31, 1949; d. Clarence Wilbur and Dora Mae (Henderson) Daffern; m. Joseph Andrew Papai, Apr. 3, 1976. BS in Polit. Sci., West Tex. State U., Canyon, 1972; MSLS, Wayne State U., 1973. Head extension dept. and Oakland County Subregional Libr. The Farmington Cmty. Libr., Farmington Hills, Mich., 1973-79, coord. adult svcs., br. head, 1980-83, asst. dir., 1983-85, dir., 1985—; cons. U.S. Office of Edn., 1978, Batatelle Meml. Inst., Columbus, Ohio, 1980; presenter in field. Contbr. articles to profl. jours. Bd. dirs. Mich. Consortium, 1987-91; trustee Libr. of Mich., 1989-92, vice chair, 1991, chair, 1992; del. White House Conf. on Librs. and Info. Svcs., 1991; founder, treas., fiscal agt. METRO NET Libr. Consortium, 1993—. Recipient Athena award Farmington/Farmington Hills C. of C. and Gen. Motors, 1994; Amarillo Pub. Libr. Friends Group fellow, 1972, Wayne State U. Inst. of Gerontology fellow, 1972. Mem. ALA (officer), Mich. Libr. Assn. (chair specialized libr. svcs. roundtable 1975, chair conf. program 1982, chair pub. policy com. 1988-89, chair devel. com. 1994-95, chair ann. conf. and program coms. 1995-96, Loleta D. Fyan awrd 1975), LWV of Mich., Farmington Exch. Club, Coun. on Resource Devel. Democrat. Roman Catholic. Home: 6805 Wing Lake Rd Bloomfield Hills MI 48301 Office: The Farmington Cmty Libr 32737 W Twelve Mile Rd Farmington Hills MI 48334

PAPALEO, ANTHONY See FRANCIOSA, ANTHONY

PAPALIA, DIANE ELLEN, human development educator; b. Englewood, N.J., Apr. 26, 1947; d. Edward Peter and Madeline (Borrin) P.; m. Jonathan Finlay, June 19, 1976; 1 child, Anna Victoria Finlay. A.B., Vassar Coll., 1968; M.S., W.Va. U., 1970, Ph.D. (NSF fellow), 1971. Asst. prof. child and family studies U. Wis., Madison, 1971-75; assoc. prof. U. Wis., 1975-78, prof., 1978-87, coordinator child and family studies, 1977-79; adj. prof. psychology in pediatrics U. Pa. Sch. Medicine, 1987-89. Co-author: (with Sally W. Olds) A Child's World: Infancy Through Adolescence, 1975, 6th edit., 1993, Human Development, 1978, 6th edit., 1995, Psychology, 1985, 2d edit., 1988; contbr. articles to profl. jours. Am. Council on Edn. fellow, 1979-80; U. Wis. grantee. Fellow Gerontol. Soc.; mem. Am. Psychol. Assn., Soc. Research in Child Devel., Nat. Council Family Relations, Psi Chi. Home: 402 E 64th St New York NY 10021-7826

PAPALIOLIOS, COSTAS DEMETRIOS, physics educator; b. Brooklyn, N.Y., May 15, 1931; s. Demetrios K. and Helen (Georgiou) P.; m. Alice Wochele, Sept. 7, 1963; children—Andreas, Dimitri. B.S., Rensselaer Poly. Inst., 1953; A.M., Harvard, 1960, Ph.D., 1965. Mem. tech. staff Bell Telephone Labs., 1953-55; prof. physics Harvard, 1966—; physicist Smithsonian Astrophys. Obs., 1965. Served with AUS, 1955-57. Home: 40 Long Ridge Rd Carlisle MA 01741-1837 Office: Harvard U Dept. Physics Cambridge MA 02138

PAPANEK, GUSTAV FRITZ, economist, educator; b. Vienna, Austria, July 12, 1926; s. Ernst and Helene P.; m. Hanna Kaiser, June 13, 1947; children: Thomas H., Joanne R. Papanek Orlando. BA in Agrl. Econs., Cornell U., 1947; MA in Econs, Harvard U., 1949, PhD, 1951. Economist, dep. dir. program planning for Asia, tech. coop. adminstrn. Dept. State, 1951-53; econ. adv., then dir. adv. group to planning commn. Harvard U., Pakistan, 1954-58; dep. dir., then dir. Devel. Adv. Svc. Harvard U., 1958-70; dir. adv. group to planning commn. Harvard U. Indonesia, 1971-73; prof. econs. Boston U., 1974-92, prof. emeritus, 1992—, chmn. dept., 1974-82, interim dir., 1977-80, dir. Ctr. for Asian Devel. Studies, 1983-90, dir. Asian program, 1991-92; dir., cons. team devel. studies to planning commn. Govt. of Indonesia, 1987-89; cons. Boston Inst. for Developing Econs., Ltd., 1987—; cons. in field. Author: Pakistan's Development: Social Goals and Private Incentives, 1967, The Indonesian Economy, 1980, Development Strategy, Growth Equity and the Political process in Southern Asia, 1986; co-author: Decision Making for Economic Development, 1971, The Indian Economy, 1988; several other books; contbr. articles to profls. jours. With AUS, 1944-46. Grantee Ford Found., AID, World Bank, UN Devel. Program, UN Univ., HEW, Asian Devel. Bank. Mem. Am. Econs. Assn., Am. Agrl. Econs. Assn., Soc. Internat. Devel. (past mem. exec. com.), Assn. Comparative Econ. Studies (pres. 1982), Assn. Asian Studies (pres. New Eng. conf. 1975-77), Pakistan Econ. Assn. Home: 2 Mason St Lexington MA 02173-6315

PAPANEK, VICTOR, designer, educator, writer; b. Vienna, Austria, Nov. 22, 1926; came to U.S., 1939; s. Richard Franz Josef and Helene (Von Spitz) P.; m. Winifred Nelson, 1951 (div. 1957); 1 child, Nicolette; m. Harlanne Herdman, July 29, 1966 (div. 1989); 1 child, Jennifer Satu. BArch, BFA in Design, Cooper Union, 1950; student with Frank Lloyd Wright, 1949; cert., Inst. Gen. Semantics, Chgo. 1956; M.S., MIT, 1955; D.H.L. (hon.), Marycrest Coll., 1983; Ph.D. (hon.), U. Victoria, 1984, U. Zagreb, Yugoslavia, 1986. Head Ind. Design and Product Devel. Office, 1964—; instr. Ont. Coll. Art U. Toronto, 1954-59; vis. guest prof. creative engring. R.I. Sch. Design, Providence, 1959; assoc. prof. art and design SUNY-Buffalo, 1959-62; head dept. product design and assoc. prof. design N.C. State Coll., 1962-64; vis. guest critic Penland Sch. Crafts, N.C., summers 1963-67; assoc. prof. art and design Purdue U., Lafayette, Ind., 1964-68, prof., 1968-70, chmn. environ. and indsl. design dept., 1968-70; prof. Calif. Inst. Arts, Valencia, Calif., 1970-71, dean, 1971-72; vis. guest prof. Kunstakademiets Arkitekskole, Copenhagen, Denmark, 1972-73; vis. prin. lectr. Faculty of Art and Design Manchester Poly. Inst., 1973-75; vis. guest prof. architecture and indsl. design Carleton U., Ottawa, Ont., Can., 1975-76; prof., chmn. dept. design Kansas City Art Inst., 1976-81; J.L. Constant Disting. prof. design U. Kans., Lawrence, 1981—; scholar in residence Schumacher Coll., Dartington, Eng., 1991-93; design cons. WHO, Geneva, 1969—, Planet Products Pty. Australia, 1979—, Dartington Industries, South Devon, Eng. 1980-83, Croatia Products, Zagreb, Yugoslavia, 1984—. Author: Creative Engineering: Students Workbook, 1961, Creative Engineering: Instructor's Handbook, 1961, Miljon Och Miljonerna: Design Som Tjanst Eller Fortjanst, 1970, Design for the Real World: Human Ecology and Social Change, 1971, Big Character Poster No. 1: Work Chart for Designers, 1973, (with Jim Hennessey) Nomadic Furniture: Where To Buy and How To Build Furniture that Folds, Stacks, Inflates, Is Light-Weight for Moving, or Can Be Thrown Away and Re-Cycled, 1973, Nomadic Furniture 2: More About Where To Buy and How To Build Furniture That Folds, Stacks, Inflates, Is Light-Weight For Moving, or Can Be Thrown Away and Be Re-Cycled, 1974, (with Jim Hennessey) How Things Don't Work, 1977, Viewing the World Whole, 1983, Design for Human Scale, 1984, Design for the Real World, revised edit., 1985; contbr. chpts. to books and articles to profl. jours.; exhibitions: Mus. of Modern Art, N.Y.C., 1962, Internat. Design Ctr., West Berlin, 1973, Gallery Grada Zagreb, 1974. Recipient Design award UNESCO, 1963, Gold medal Art Dirs. Club Am., 1968, Honours award Internat. Council of Socs. of Indsl. Design, 1981, Augustus St. Gaudens medal Cooper Union, 1987, IKEA Internat. award Sweden and Holland, 1989, numerous grants. Fellow Chartered Soc. Designers, Am. Scandinavian Found. (hon.), Design Student Coun. New Zealand, Soc. Designers in Ireland, Design Soc. Mex. (diplomat) Creative Edn. Found.; mem. Internat. Congress Socs. of Indsl. Design, Developing Countries Design Info. Group (co-founder), Industrielle Designere Danmark, Indsl. Design Inst. Australia, Indsl. Designers Soc. Am., Soc. Designers Ireland (hon. life), Croatian Designers Soc., Gliding Assn. Australia, Am. Soaring Soc., Grafik Design Austria. Anglican. Avocations: flying gliders and soaring planes; cookery; writing science fiction. Office: U Kans Sch Architecture Marvin Hall 417 Lawrence KS 66045

PAPARELLA, MICHAEL M., otolaryngologist; b. Detroit, Feb. 13, 1933; s. Vincent Paparella and Angela Creat; m. Treva Buzard, Oct. 2, 1992; children: Mark, Steven, Lisa. BS, U. Mich., 1953, MD, 1957. Diplomate Am. Bd. Otolaryngology (guest examiner 1967-75, bd. dirs. 1976, mem. standards and residencies com. 1976, fgn. med. grads. com. 1978, credentials com. 1984-85, examiner 1976—); lic. physician, Mich., Mass., Ohio, Minn. Rotating intern Emanuel Hosp., Portland, Oreg., 1957-58; resident in otolaryngology Henry Ford Hosp., Detroit, 1958-61, jr. mem. staff, 1960-61; mem. geographic staff, asst. Mass. Eye and Ear Infirmary, Boston, 1963-64; instr. Harvard U. Med. Sch., Boston, 1963-64; asst. prof. otolaryngology, dir. otological research lab. Ohio State U., Columbus, 1964-67; mem. staff dept. otolaryngology Ohio State U. Hosps., 1964-67; prof., chmn. dept. otolaryngology U. Minn., Mpls., 1967-84, dir. otopathology lab., 1967—, clin. prof., 1984—; mem. staff U. Minn. Hosps., 1967-84; pres. Minn. Ear, Head and Neck Clinic, Mpls., 1984—; dir. Nat. Temporal Bone Bank Program Midwestern Ctr., Mpls., 1979—; cons. VA Hosp., Dayton, Ohio, 1964-67. Mem. editorial bd. Minn. Med. Assn. Medicine, The Laryngoscope, Modern Medicine, Am. Jour. Clin. Research, Am. Jour. Otolaryngology, Jour. Otolaryngology, Annals Otology, Rhinology & Laryngology, Acta Oto-Laryngologica; editor: (films) Surgical Techniques and Auditory Research, Surgical Treatment for Intractable External Otitis, Tympanoplasty, parts 1 and 2, Endolymphatic Sac, Canalplasty; (books) Atlas of Ear Surgery, 1968, 2d ed., 1971, 3d ed., 1980, Biochemical Mechanisms in Hearing and Deafness, 1970, Clinical Otology: An International Symposium, 1971, Year Book of the Ear, Nose & Throat, 1972, 73, 74, 75, Otolaryngology: Basic Sciences and Related Disciplines, 1973, 2d. ed. vol. I, 1980, Otolaryngology: Ear, vol. II, 1973, 2d ed., 1980, Otolaryngology: Head and Neck, vol. III, 1973, 2d ed., 1980, Year Book of Otolaryngology, 1976, 77, 78, 79, 80, 81, 82, 83, 84, 85, 86, Boies's Fundamentals of Otolaryngology: A Textbook of Ear, Nose and Throat Diseases, 5th ed., 1978, Ear Clinics International, vols. I-III, 1982, Medicassette Otolaryngology, 1986; also contbr. numerous articles. Founder, sec., bd. dirs. Internat. Hearing Found., 1984—; mem. Pre-sch. Med. Survey Vision and Hearing. Grantee NIH, Am. Otological Soc., Deafness Research Found., Hartford Found., Guggenheim Found., Bodman Found.; recipient Kobrak Research award, 1960, Amicitiae Sacrum honor Collegium Oto-Rhino-Laryngologicum, 1976; named Brinkman lectr. U. Nijmegen, Holland, 1986, Guest of Honor 5th Asia-Oceanic Meeting, Korea, 1983. Fellow ACS, Am. Acad. Ophthalmology and Otolaryngology (assoc. sec. continuing edn., assoc. sec., chmn. undergrad. edn. subcom., chmn. otorhinolaryngology self-improvement com., chmn. subcom. on evaluation new info. and edn. of hearing and equilibrium com., head and neck surgery equilibrium subcom. 1984-86, Merit award 1975); mem. Acad. Medicine Columbus County, Acad. Medicine Franklin County, Am. Assn. for Lab. Animal Scis., AMA, Am. Neurotology Soc. (audiology study com. 1976), Am. Otological Soc. (trustee research fund, pres.), Assn. Acad. Depts. Otolaryngology (pres. pro tem, organizer 1971-72, sec.-treas. 1972-74, pres. elect 1974-76, pres. 1976-78), Barany Soc., Better Hearing Inst. (adv. bd.), Deafness Research Found. (trustee, Centurion Club), Collegium Oto-Rhino-Laryngologicum Amicitiae Sacrum, Columbus Ophthalmology and Otolaryngological Soc., Hennepin County Med. Soc., Mpls. Hearing Soc. (bd. dirs.), Minn. Acad. Medicine, Minn. Acad. Ophthalmology and Otolaryngology (council), Minn. Coll. Surgeons, New England Otolaryngological Soc., Ohio State Med. Soc., Pan Am. Med. Assn. Soc. Univ. Otolaryngologists (exec. council 1969-71), Triological Soc. (v.p. middle sect. 1976, council mem. 1976, asst. editor), Alpha Kappa Kappa, Sigma Xi. Lodge: Lions (dir. hearing ctr., adv. council hearing ctr.). Offic 25th Ave S # 200 Minneapolis MN 55454-1443

PAPARELLI, ANGELO A., lawyer; b. Mich., 1949. BA, U. Mich., 1971; JD, Wayne State U., 1976. Bar: Mich. 1976, U.S. Supreme Ct. 1980, U.S. Ct. Appeals (6th cir.) 1980, Calif. 1981, U.S. Ct. Appeals (9th cir.) 1982. Law clk. to Hon. Dorothy C. Riley Mich. Ct. Appeals, 1976-78; ptnr. Bryan Cave, L.A., Irvine, Calif. Mem. adv. bd. Internat. Trade Consortium, City of Irvine, Calif., 1990—. Mem. ABA (mem. immigration coordinating com. 1989-92, chmn. immigration nationality com. sect. internat. law and practice 1991—), Am. Immigration Lawyers Assn. (bd. govs. 1988-94, chair com. office mgmt. and budget/paperwork reduction act 1991-93, co-chair visa practice com. 1989-90, chair treaty investors and traders com. 1988-89, 90-91, 93-94, vice chair Dept. State visa office liaison com. 1987-88, chair task force on consular rev. and representation 1985, treas. 1985-86, vice chair 1986-87, chair 1987-88, So. Calif. chpt.), L.A. County Bar Assn. (mem. immigration sect. exec. bd. dirs. 1985—), State Bar Calif. (mem. standing com. profl. responsibility and conduct 1986-87). Office: Bryan Cave 777 S Figueroa St Ste 2700 Los Angeles CA 90071 also: 18881 Von Karman Blvd # 250 Irvine CA 92715

PAPAZIAN, DENNIS RICHARD, history educator, political commentator; b. Augusta, Ga., Dec. 15, 1931; s. Nahabed Charles and Armanouhe Marie (Pehlevanian) P.; m. Mary Arshagouni. BA, Wayne State U., 1954; MA, U. Mich., 1958; NDG, Moscow State U., 1962; PhD, U. Mich., 1966. Head dept. social and behavioral scis. U. Mich., Dearborn, 1966-69, head div. lit., sci. and the arts, 1969-73, assoc. dean acad. affairs, 1973-74; dir. Armenian Assembly Am., Washington, 1975-79; dir. grad. studies U. Mich., Dearborn, 1979-85, prof. history, dir. Armenian Rsch. Ctr., 1985—; fellow Ctr. for Russian and East-European Studies, U. Mich., Ann Arbor, 1982-92; chmn. bd. dirs. Mich. Ethnic Heritage Studies Ctr., U. Mich., 1987-92. Author: St. John's Armenian Church, 1974. Editor: The Armenian Church, 1983. Bd. dirs. Armenian Apostolic Soc., Southfield, Mich., 1968—; chmn. bd. dirs. Alex Manoogian Found., Taylor, Mich., 1969-77; mem. evaluation team Ind. Schs. Assn. Central States, Chgo., 1985; polit. commentator WXYZ-TV, ABC, Detroit, Southfield, 1984—, WWJ-Radio, Detroit, 1984—; bd. dirs. Southeastern Mich. chpt. ARC, 1988—, chmn. internat. svcs. co., 1988—, disaster and mil. family svcs. com., 1988—. Scholar/diplomat U.S. Dept. State, Washington, 1976; grantee NEH, Washington, 1977, AID, Washington, 1978, Knights of Vartan, 1984; recipient Dadian Armenian Heritage award, 1993. Mem. AAUP (chpt. pres. 1962-65), Nat. Assn. Armenian Studies and Rsch. (bd. dirs. 1961-91), Nat. Ethnic Studies Assn. (bd. dirs. 1976-85), Am. Hist. Assn., Soc. Armenian Studies (pres. exec. com. 1988-91, sec./treas. exec. com. 1991-95), Am. Assn. Advancement of Slavic Studies, Am. Acad. Polit. Sci., Armenian Students Assn. (Arthur S. Dadian Armenian Heritage award 1993), Knights of Vartan. Armenian Orthodox. Avocations: reading; travel. Home: 17550 Roxbury Ave Southfield MI 48075-4235 Office: U Mich 4901 Evergreen Rd Southfield MI 48075

PAPE, ARTHUR EDWARD, lawyer; b. Hartford, Conn., Oct. 30, 1939; s. Edward N. and Janet Pape; m. Barbara Nichols, Dec. 1962; children: Ann, Amy Pape Bloomberg. BA in English cum laude, U. Pitts., 1963; JD, Harvard U., 1965. Bar: Ohio 1965, Ill. 1976. Atty. Thompson, Hine & Flory, Cleve., 1965-73; ptnr. real estate devel. co. Bossel, Pape & Assoc., Cleve., 1973-75; sr. atty. 1st Nat. Bank Chgo., 1975-78, counsel, 1978-81; ptnr. Greenberger and Kaufmann, Chgo., 1981-86, Katten, Muchin & Zavis, Chgo., 1986—. Mem. ABA, Am. Coll. Real Estate Lawyers, Ill. Bar Assn. Chgo. Bar Assn., Lambda Alpha Internat. Home: 1002 S Wheaton Ave Wheaton IL 60187-6470 Office: Katten Muchin & Zavis 525 W Monroe St Ste 1600 Chicago IL 60661-3693

PAPE, WILLIAM JAMES, II, newspaper publisher; b. Waterbury, Conn., Aug. 14, 1931; s. William B. and Helen (Cronan) P.; m. Patricia Moran, Oct. 15, 1959; children: William B. II, Andrew J. BS, U.S. Naval Acad., 1953; MBA, Harvard U., 1959; LHD (hon.), Teikyo Post U., 1991. Commd. ensign USN, 1953, advanced through grades to lt., 1955, resigned, 1957; asst. treas. Ea. Color Printing Co., Waterbury, 1959-63; pres., treas. Ea. Color Printing Co., Avon, Conn., 1977-87; v.p., asst. treas. Am.-Republican Inc., Waterbury, 1963-64, asst. publisher, comptroller, v.p., 1964-72, pres., treas., 1972—; also bd. dirs.; pub. Waterbury Republican-Am., 1972—; v.p., asst. treas. & dir. Paper Delivery, Inc., 1972-88; editor, pub. Waterbury Rep.-Am., 1988—; bd. dirs. Paper Delivery Inc., Waterbury, Platt Bros., Waterbury, Greater Waterbury Health Network, Inc. bd. dirs. Conn. Coun. Freedom of Info., 1968-88, Conn. Citizens for Jud. Modernization, pres., 1973-75, Conn. Bus. and Industry Assn. 1980-83, Naugatuck Valley Devel. Corp., Regional Action Coun., Waterbury, 1991; bd. dirs. Waterbury YMCA, 1970-78, trustee, 1972—, chmn. trustees, 1976-85; trustee Northeast Utilities, 1974—, Conn. Pub. Expenditure Coun. Inc., 1974-77, mem. Conn. policy & econ. coun., 94—, Teikyo Post U., 1976—; grants com. Waterbury Found., 1980-87; pub. affairs com. Waterbury Hosp., 1984-90, past trustee; incorporator Conn. Found. for Open Govt. Inc.; active Conn. Legislature Commn. to Study Modernization and Unification of Cts., 1973-75, Citizens

for Better Govt. Through Reorganization, 1977. Mem. Am. Judicature Soc. (assoc. dir. 1975-76), New England Newspaper Assn. (Conn. bd. govs. 1983-87), Conn. Bar Assn. (task force conflict of interest 1979—), Conn. Daily Newspaper Assn. (pres. 1970, exec. com. 1971-91), Waterbury C. of C. (exec. com., v.p. 1975, chmn. 1977-79, dir. 1980-83, vice-chmn. transp. 1981—), Navy League U.S. (communications bd. 1982), Waterbury Club, Madison Beach Club, Highfield. Republican. Roman Catholic. Avocations: sailing, firearms, walking, carpentry. Home: Old Sherman Hill Rd Woodbury CT 06798 Office: Waterbury Rep-Am PO Box 2090 389 Meadow St Waterbury CT 06722-2090

PAPEN, FRANK O'BRIEN, banker, former state senator; b. Dec. 2, 1909; m. Julia Stevenson; 1 child, Michele Papen-Daniel. LLD (hon.), N.Mex. State U., 1988. Dir. First Nat. Bank Dona Ana County, Las Cruces, N.Mex., 1957-60, exec. v.p., 1957-60, pres., 1960-71, chmn. bd. dirs., chief exec. officer, 1971-82, 88—, pres., chmn. bd. dirs., 1982-87; mem. Ho. of reps. State of N.Mex., 1957-58, senator, 1969-84; vice-chmn. 12 regional adv. com. on banking practices and policies, 1965-66; mem. adv. com. on fed. legis., 1966; mem. N.Mex. State Investment Council, 1963-67; mem. N.Mex. Dept. Devel. Adv. Council, 1967-68; mem. steering com. Edn. Commn. States; mem. Albuquerque dist. adv. council SBA; pres. N.Mex. State U. Pres. Assocs. Mem. N.M. Ho. of Reps., 1957-58 (chmn. legis. fin. com. and legis. sch. study com.), N.M. State Senate, 1969-84. Recipient Citizen of Yr. award N.Mex. Assn. Realtors, 1966, Branding Iron award N.Mex. State U., 1977, The Pres.'s award for Service N.Mex. State U., 1983, Regent's medal N.Mex. State U., 1985, N.Mex. Sch. Banking Leadership award, 1987, Bob Haynsworth Sportsmanship award Sunland Park Race Track, 1987. Mem. Am. Bankers Assn. (savs. bond chmn. N.Mex. 1964-66), N.Mex. Bankers Assn. (pres., mem. exec. com. 1965-66), Las Cruces C. of C. (past pres.). Democrat. Lodges: Kiwanis, KC. Office: PO Box Fnb Las Cruces NM 88004-9536

PAPENFUSE, EDWARD CARL, JR., archivist, state official; b. Toledo, Oct. 15, 1943; m. Sallie Fisher; children: Eric, David. BA in Polit. Sci., Am. U., 1965; MA in History, U. Colo., 1967; PhD, Johns Hopkins U., 1973. Assoc. editor Am. Hist. Rev., Washington, 1970-73; asst. archivist Md. Hall of Records, Annapolis, 1973-75, archivist, 1975—, commr. land patents, 1975—. Author: In Pursuit of Profit: The Annapolis Merchants in the Era of the American Revolution, 1975, (with others) Directory of Maryland Legislators, 1635-1789, 1974, (with others) Maryland: A New Guide to the Old Line State, 1976, The Hammond-Harwood House Atlas of Historical Maps of Maryland, 1608-1908, 1982; also articles and revs. Mem. Johns Hopkins U. Med. Archives. NEH grantee; recipient Disting. Svc. award to State Govt. Nat. Gov.'s Assn., 1985, Marylander of Yr. award Md. Colonial Soc., 1985. Fellow Soc. Am. Archivists, Md. Hist. Soc., Am. Antiquarian Soc. Home: 206 Oakdale Rd Baltimore MD 21210-2520 Office: Md State Archives 350 Rowe Blvd Annapolis MD 21401-1685

PAPER, LEWIS J., lawyer, educator; b. Newark, Oct. 13, 1946; s. Sidney and Dorothy (Neiman) P.; m. Jan Clachko, Sept. 4, 1972; children: Lindsay, Brett. B.A., U. Mich., 1968; J.D., Harvard U., 1971; LL.M., Georgetown U., 1972. Bar: D.C. 1971, N.J. 1975, Md. 1984. Fellow, Inst. Pub. Interest Representation, Georgetown U. Law Sch., Washington, 1971-72; staff atty. Citizens Communications Ctr., Washington, 1972-73; legis. counsel to Sen. Gaylord Nelson, U.S. Senate, 1973-75; assoc. atty. Lowenstein, Sandler, Brochin, Kohl & Fisher, Newark, 1975-78; asst. gen. counsel Fed. Communications Commn., Washington, 1978-79, assoc. gen. counsel, 1979-81; ptnr. Grove, Engelberg & Gross, Washington, 1981-86, Keck, Mahin & Cate, 1986—; adj. prof. law Georgetown U. Law Sch., Washington, 1983-86. Author: John F. Kennedy: The Promise and the Performance, 1975, 79, Brandeis: An Intimate Biography, 1983, Empire: William S. Paley and the Making of CBS, 1987. Contbr. articles to newspapers, mags., and profl. jours. Office: Keck Mahin & Cate 1201 New York Ave NW Washington DC 20005

PAPERNIK, JOEL IRA, lawyer; b. N.Y.C., May 4, 1944; s. Herman and Ida (Titefsky) P.; m. Barbara Ann Barker, July 28, 1972; children: Deborah, Ilana. BA, Yale U., 1965; JD cum laude, Columbia U., 1968. Bar: N.Y. 1969. Assoc. Shea & Gould, N.Y.C., 1968-76, ptnr., 1976-91; sr. ptnr., chmn. corp. and securities dept., mem. exec. com. Squadron, Ellenoff, Plesent, Sheinfeld & Sorkin, N.Y.C., 1991—; lectr. various panels. Author: Risks of Private Foreign Investments in the U.S. Served with USAR, 1967-73. Mem. ABA (forum on sports and entertainment law, sect. on corp. law), Assn. of Bar of City of N.Y. (chmn., lectr., corp. law com., securities regulation com., chair 1933 Act subcom.), N.Y. State Bar Assn. (lectr. various panels, securities law com.), N.Y. Tri-Bar Opinion Com. (steering com., lectr.), Yale Club. Club: Yale (N.Y.C.). Office: Squadron Ellenoff Plesent Sheinfeld & Sorkin 551 Fifth Ave New York NY 10176

PAPERT, SEYMOUR AUBREY, mathematician, educator, writer; b. Pretoria, South Africa, Mar. 1, 1928; came to U.S., 1964; s. Jack and Betty P.; m. Androula Christofides, Apr. 10, 1963 (div.); 1 dau., Artemis; m. Sherry Turkle, Dec. 18, 1977. B.A., U. Witwatersrand, S. Africa, 1949, Ph.D., 1952; Ph.D., Cambridge U., Eng., 1959. Co-dir. artificial intelligence lab. MIT, Cambridge, 1967-73, dir. Logo Group, 1970-81, prof. math. and edn., 1964—, Cecil and Ida Green prof. edn., 1974-80; vis. prof. math. Rockefeller U., N.Y.C., 1980-81; sci. dir. Centre Mondial Informatique et Ressource Humaine, Paris, 1982-83. Author: (with Marvin Minsky) Perceptrons, 1969, Artificial Intelligence, 1974, (with McNaughton) Non-Counting Automata, 1971, Mindstorms: Children, Computers..., 1980. Marconi Internat. fellow, 1981; J.S. Guggenheim fellow, 1980. Office: MIT Media Lab Epistemology & Learning Grp Rm E15-313 Cambridge MA 02139

PAPET, LOUIS M., federal official, civil engineer; b. White Castle, La., June 14, 1933; s. Leonce A. and Corrine C. (Comedux) P.; m. Lee Anna Blanchard, May 30, 1959; children: Louis M. Papet Jr., Benjamin J. Papet. BSCE, La. State U., 1954-57. Registered profl. civil engr. La.; land surveyer La. Project engr. La. Dept Hwys., Baton Rouge, La., 1957-61; hwy. engr. U.S. Bur. Pub. Roads, Ala., N.C., Ga., Md., 1963-81; divsn. administr. U.S. Fed. Hwy. Administrn., Harrisburg, Pa., 1981-85, Atlanta, Ga., 1985-88; chief, pavement divsn. U.S. Fed. Hwy. Administrn., Washington, 1989—. With Army Civil Engrs., 1952-54. Home: 2785 Rudder Dr Annapolis MD 21401

PAPIANO, NEIL LEO, lawyer; b. Salt Lake City, Nov. 25, 1933; s. Leo and Ruth Ida (Cotten) P. B.A., Stanford, 1956, M.A. in Polit. Sci, 1957; J.D., Vanderbilt U., 1961. Bar: Calif. bar 1961. Partner Iverson, Yoakum, Papiano & Hatch (and predecessor firm), Los Angeles, 1961—; bd. dirs. Nederlander Orgn. and related cos., SCOA Industries, Inc., Ocean Tech., Inc., King Nutronics, Inc. V.p. Los Angeles County Welfare Planning Coun., 1966-71; chmn. L.A. Forward, 1970-71; vice chmn. Cal. Com. for Welfare Reform, 1972; mem. Calif. Jud. Selection Com. 1972-74; co-finance chmn. Rep. State Central Com., 1975; treas. L.A. Opera Co., 1964, bd. dirs. 1965; treas. So. Calif. Choral Music Assn., 1964, bd. dirs., 1964-73; bd. dirs. Citizens Adv. Coun. on Pub. Transp., Orthopedic Hosp., Stanford U. Athletic Bd., Nat. Athletic Health Inst., L.A. Music Ctr. Operating Co., L.A. Light Opera; bd. govs. USO, 1967-71, Performing Arts Coun. L.A. Music Ctr., 1981-87, Greater L.A. Homeless Partnership, 1985—, L.A. Olympic Com., 1986-88; bd. trustees The Am. U., 1980—. Mem. Am., Calif. bar assns., Los Angeles Area C. of C. (pres. 1966, dir. 1964-67, 72-75), California Club, Los Angeles Country Club, Rotary, Phi Delta Theta. Office: Iverson Yoakum Papiano & Hatch One Wilshire Bldg 27th Floor 624 S Grand Ave Ste 2700 Los Angeles CA 90017-3328

PAPIKE, JAMES JOSEPH, geology educator, science institute director; b. Virginia, Minn., Feb. 11, 1937; s. Joseph John and Sistine Marie (Tassi) P.; m. Pauline Grace Maras, Sept. 6, 1958; children: Coleen, Coreen, Jimmy, Heather. BS in Geol. Engring. with high honors, S.D. Sch. Mines and Tech., 1959; PhD, U. Minn., 1964. Rsch. geologist U.S. Geol. Survey, Washington, 1964-69; assoc. prof. dept. earth and space scis. SUNY, Stony Brook, 1969-71, prof., 1971-82, chmn. dept., 1971-74; prof. dept. geology and geol. engring. S.D. Sch. Mines and Tech., Rapid City, 1982-87, Disting. prof., 1987-90, dir. Inst. for Study Mineral Deposits, 1982-90, dir. Engring. and Mining Expt. Sta., 1984-90; Regents' prof. dept. geology, dir. Inst. Meteoritics, U. N.Mex., Albuquerque, 1990—; mem. adv. com. for earth scis. NSF, 1985-89, Continental Sci. Drilling Rev. Group, Dept. Energy, 1986-87,

Lunar and Planetary Sample Team, 1990—, Lunar Outpost Site Selection Com., 1990-91, organizing com. for FORUM for Continental Sci. Drilling, 1990—, adv. com. Inst. Geophysics and Planetary Physics, Los Alamos Nat. Lab., 1991—. Assoc. editor procs. 4th Lunar Sci. Conf., 1973, Jour. Geophys. Rsch., 1975-77, 82-84; editor procs. Internat. Conf: The Nature of Oceanic Crust, 1976, Luna 24 Conf., 1977, Conf. on Lunar Highlands Crust, 1980; guest editor spl. issue Geophys. Rsch. Letters, 1991; mem. editorial bd. Procs. Lunar and Planetary Sci. Confs., 1987; contbr. numerous articles to profl. jours. Recipient NASA medal, 1973, Centennial Alumni award S.D. Sch. Mines and Tech., 1985; grantee NSF, NASA, Dept. Energy, 1969—. Fellow Geol. Soc. Am., Mineral. Soc. Am. (life, MSA medal 1974, past mem. coun.), Soc. Econ. Geologists (mem. coun.); mem. Am. Geophys. Union (past sec.), Geochem. Soc. (v.p. 1988-89, pres. 1989-91), Meteoritical Soc., Mineral. Assn. Can. Roman Catholic. Home: 103 La Mesa Placitas NM 87043 Office: U NMex Inst Meteoritics Northrop Hall Rm 313 Albuquerque NM 87131-1126

PAPINEAU-COUTURE, JEAN, composer, educator; b. Montreal, Que., Can., Nov. 12, 1916; s. Armand and Marie-Anne (Dostaler) P.-C.; m. Isabelle Baudouin, June 15, 1944 (dec. Oct. 1987); children—Nadia, Ghilaine, François. Doctorat honorifique, U. Sask., 1967. Prof. Conservatoire de Que., 1946-64; mem. faculté de musique U. Montreal, 1951-85; sec. faculté U. Montréal, 1953-67, vice-doyen, 1968, doyen, 1968-73. Composer several commd. works for, CBC also Zagreb Bienale, 1969—. Pres. Centre de Musique Canadienne, 1973-74, Société de musique contemporaine du Québec, 1966-73, Canadian Music Council, 1968-69; mem. Conseil canadien de Recherches pour les Scis. humaines, 1973-79; bd. dirs. Ency. Canadian Music. Recipient Prix Calixa Lavallée, 1962, Ordre du Can., 1968, Companion of Order of Can. 1994, médaille Centre Canadien de la musique, 1973, Prix Denise Pelletier, 1981, Diplôme D'Honneur of Can. Conf. of Arts, 1986, Gov. Gens. Performing Arts award, 1994; decorated grand officer de l'Ordre du Quebec, 1989. Mem. SOCAN. Home: 4694 Lacombe, Montreal, PQ Canada H3W 1R3

PAPKIN, ROBERT DAVID, lawyer; b. New Bedford, Mass., Feb. 26, 1933; s. Barney and Rose (Shuster) P.; m. Rachel Friedberg, Aug. 29, 1965; children: Steven C., Daniel M. AB, Harvard U., 1954, LLB, 1957. Bar: Mass. 1957, D.C. 1964. Legal asst. NRLB, Washington, 1958-61; assoc. Cox, Langford & Brown, Washington, 1963-66, ptnr., 1966-73; ptnr. Squire, Sanders & Dempsey, Washington, 1973—. Trustee Art Svcs. Internat., 1990—, Am. Friends of the Venezuelan Indians, 1991—. Served with U.S. Army, 1957-58, 61-62. Mem. ABA, D.C. Bar Assn., Fed. Bar Assn., Internat. Bar Assn., Met. Club Washington D.C., Cosmos Club. Democrat. Jewish. Home: 8200 Lilly Stone Dr Bethesda MD 20817-4506 Office: Squire Sanders & Dempsey PO Box 407 1201 Pennsylvania Ave NW Washington DC 20004-2401

PAPOULIS, ATHANASIOS, electrical engineering educator; b. Athens, Greece, Jan. 18, 1921; s. Lazarus and Eftichia (Throumoulos) P.; m. Caryl J. Engwall, Dec. 19, 1953; children: Irene, Helen, James, Ann, Mary. ME, Poly. Inst. Athens, 1941, EE, 1942; MSEE, U. Pa., 1947, MA in Math., 1948, PhD, 1950. Instr. U. Pa., 1948-51; asst. prof. Union Coll., 1951-52; prof. elec. engring. Polytechnic U., Bklyn., 1952-90; University prof. Poly. Inst. N.Y., Bklyn., 1990, prof. emeritus, 1991—; vis. prof. U. Darmstadt, Germany, 1959-60, UCLA, 1964-65, Stanford U., 1965—, U. Calif., Irvine, 1992-94, Northeastern U., Boston, 1995. Author: The Fourier Integral, 1962, Probability and Stochastic Processes, 1965, 3d edit., 1991 (ISI selection as Citation Classic 1980), Systems in Optics, 1968, Signal Analysis, 1977, Circuits and Systems, 1980, Probability and Statistics, 1989; also numerous articles. NSF Teaching fellow, 1959-60; Recipient Disting. Alumni Gold medal Moore Sch., U. Pa., 1973, Humboldt U.S. Scientist award, 1985. Fellow IEEE (life, edn. medal 1984). Home: PO Box 238 Huntington NY 11743

PAPP, LASZLO GEORGE, architect; b. Debrecen, Hungary, Apr. 28, 1929; came to U.S., 1956: m. Judith Liptak, Apr. 12, 1952; children: Andrea, Laszlo-Mark (dec. 1978). Archtl. Engr., Poly. U. Budapest, 1955; MArch, Pratt Inst., 1960. Designer Harrison & Abramovitz, Architects, N.Y.C., 1958-63; ptnr. Whiteside & Papp, Architects, White Plains, N.Y., 1963-67; pres. Papp Architects, P.C., White Plains, N.Y., 1967—. Mem. Pres.'s Adv. Com. on Pvt. Sector Initiatives; mem. adv. com. Westchester C.C., 1971—, Iona Coll., New Rochelle, N.Y., 1982—, Norwalk State Tech. Coll., 1983—; v.p. Clearview Sch., 1985-89, pres., 1990-91; councilman Town Coun. New Canaan, Conn., 1993—. Fellow AIA (reg. dir. 1983-85); mem. Internat. Union Architects (rep. habitat com. 1986-90), N.Y. State Assn. Architects (v.p. 1977-80, pres. 1981), Am.-Hungarian Engrs. Assn. (bd. dirs. 1978-90), Am. Coun. World Fedn. Hungarians (pres. 1993—), Hungarian Univ. Assn. (pres. 1958-60), Westchester County C. of C. (bd. dirs. 1968-71, vice chmn. bd. for area devel. 1983-89, chmn. bd. dirs. 1989-90), Am.-Hungarian C. of C. (charter 1989—). Home: 1197 Valley Rd New Canaan CT 06840-2428 Office: Papp Architects PC 711 S Broadway White Plains NY 10601-3531

PAPP, LEANN ILSE KLINE, respiratory therapy educator; b. Niles, Ohio, June 18, 1944; d. Lee Andrew and Mildred Alice (Vaughan) Kline; m. Roger John Papp, July 11, 1964; 1 child, Lisa Marie. Student, John Carroll U., 1962-63; AAS in Respiratory Therapy, Sinclair C.C., Dayton, Ohio, 1975; ADN, Manatee Jr. Coll., Bradenton, Fla., 1983; B in Allied Health Edn., Ottawa U. of Kansas City, Overland Park, Kans., 1988. RN, Fla., Ark.; cert. respiratory therapy technologist, registered respiratory therapist, BCLS instr., Am. Heart Assn., cert. hypnotherapist. Staff therapist Childrens' Med. Ctr., Dayton, 1975-79; staff therapist L.W. Blake Hosp., Bradenton, Fla., 1979; chief therapist The Breath Ctr., Sarasota, Fla., 1979-83; mem. clin. faculty Sarasota Meml. Hosp., 1983-84; spl. procedures therapist, mem. clin. faculty North Little Rock (Ark.) Meml. Hosp., 1984-85; clin. edn. coord. St. Vincent Infirmary, Little Rock, 1985-86; dir. clin. edn. for respiratory therapy tech. Pulaski Vo-Tech, North Little Rock, 1986-88; staff therapist Cobb Gen. Hosp., Austell, Ga., 1988-89; program dir. respiratory therapy tech. Coosa Valley Tech. Inst., Rome, Ga., 1989—; cons. Applied Measurement Profls., Lenexa, Kans, 1991-92, 93-94; faculty Am. Heart Assn., Marietta, Ga., 1991—; advisor Ga. Coun. on Vocat. Edn., Atlanta, 1991-94; mem. ednl. comm. Author: Nosocomial Infection and Control, 1993; co-author: Georgia State Standards-Respiratory Therapy Technology, 1989-90, 93-94. Co-chairperson Cystic Fibrosis Found., Atlanta, 1990; mem. edn. com. Am. Lung Assn., 1995. Recipient Commr.'s award of Excellence Ga. Dept. Tech. and Adult Edn., 1994. Mem. Am. Assn. Respiratory Care, Ga. Soc. Respiratory Care (mem. edn. com. 1993—, mem. health care reform com. 1995), Ga. Vocat. Assn., Health Occupations Educators (Outstanding New Tchr. award 1992), Lambda Beta Soc. Office: Coosa Valley Tech Inst 785 Cedar Ave Rome GA 30161

PAPPAGEORGE, GEORGE C., architect. Student, Ecole Des Beaux Arts, Versailles, France, 1974-75; BArch, U. Ill., Chgo., 1978. Registered arch., Ill. Planner Urban Planning Cons., Chgo., 1976-78; arch./designer Rudich Pappageorge Archs., Chgo., 1978; pvt. practice Chgo., 1978-79; developer/ptnr. 1815 N. Orchard Partnership, Chgo., 1980-81; assoc. arch. Kenneth A. Schroeder Assocs., Chgo., 1979-81; prin. Pappageorge Haymes Ltd., Archs., Chgo., 1981—; adj. prof. U. Ill. Mem. AIA, Chgo. Archtl. Club. Office: Pappageorge Haymes Ltd 814 N Franklin St Ste 400 Chicago IL 60610-3109

PAPPAGIANIS, DEMOSTHENES, microbiology educator, physician; b. San Diego, Mar. 31, 1928; s. George John and Mary (Terzakis) P.; m. Alice Ertel, Jan. 28, 1956; children: Michele, Marika. A.B., U. Calif.-Berkeley, 1949, M.A., 1951, Ph.D., 1956; M.D., Stanford U., 1962. Diplomate Am. Bd. Microbiology. Rotating intern Walter Reed Gen. Hosp., Washington, 1962-63; assoc. prof. Sch. Public Health, U. Calif., Berkeley, 1963-67; prof. med. microbiology Sch. Medicine, U. Calif., Davis, 1967—; chmn. dept. med. microbiology Sch. Medicine, U. Calif., 1968-85; assoc. mem. Armed Forces Epidemiol. Bd. Contbr. to profl. jours. and books. Served from 1st lt. to capt. M.C. U.S. Army, 1962-63. Recipient Meridian award Med. Mycol. Soc. Ams. 1986, Calif. medal Am. Lung Assn. Calif. 1988, Rhoda Benham award Med. Mycol. Soc. Am., 1992, Charles E. Smith Meml. award, 1994. Fellow Infectious Disease Soc. Am.; mem. Am. Soc. Microbiology, Am. Thoracic Soc., Calif. Thoracic Soc., Internat. Soc. Human and Animal Mycology, Sigma Xi, Alpha Omega Alpha. Home: 1523 Orange Ln Davis CA 95616-0912 Office: U Calif Sch Medicine Dept Med Microbiology Davis CA 95616

PAPPANO, ROBERT DANIEL, financial company executive; b. Chgo., Apr. 8, 1942; s. John Robert and Lucille Carmelita (Metallo) P.; m. Karen Marie Muellner, July 2, 1966; children: John, Kimberly, Robert, William. BS in Commerce, DePaul U., Chgo., 1964; MBA, Roosevelt U., Chgo., 1982. CPA, Ill. Audit supr. Alexander Grant & Co., Chgo., 1964-73; with W.W. Grainger, Inc., Skokie, Ill., 1973—, asst. to contr., 1973-75, contr., corp. acct., 1975-78, contr., asst. treas., 1978-84, v.p., contr., asst. treas., 1984-85, v.p., treas., asst sec., 1985-95; v.p. financial reporting and investor rels. W W Grainger Inc., 1995—. 1st lt. U.S. Army, 1965-67, Vietnam. Mem. AICPA, Ill. CPA Soc., Fin. Execs. Inst. Roman Catholic. Office: W W Grainger Inc 5500 Howard St Skokie IL 60077-2699

PAPPAS, ALCESTE THETIS, consulting company executive, educator; b. Dix Hills, N.Y., May 5, 1945; d. Costas Ernest and Thetis (Hero) P.; m. Sylvan V. Endich, Sept. 13, 1987. AB, U. Calif.-Berkeley, 1967, PhD, 1978; EdM, Harvard U., 1969. Cert. guidance counselor, Mass., secondary sch. tchr., Mass. Dir. student-young alumni affairs Calif. Alumni Assn., Berkeley, 1969-71; dir. residential programs U. Calif., Berkeley, 1971-73, dir. housing and childcare, 1973-79; sr. cons., mgr. Peat, Marwick, Mitchell & Co., N.Y.C., 1979-80, 80-82, sr. mgr., 1982-84; ptnr. in charge edn., other instns. Peat, Marwick, Main & Co., N.Y.C., 1984-93; pres. Pappas Cons. Group, Inc. (alliance firm of KPMG Peat Marwick), N.Y.C., 1993—; speaker in field. Contbr. articles to profl. jours., author monographs. Mem. Merola Opera Bd., San Francisco, 1978-80, Calif. Alumni Council, 1976-79; bd. overseers Regents Coll., 1986-89; bd. dirs., mem. fin. com. Hellenic Coll. and Holy Cross Sch. Theology, Brookline, Mass., 1983-87, Seabury Western Theol. Sem., Evanston, Ill., 1983-89; bd. dirs. N.Y. Chiropractic Coll., 1986-88, Com. on Econ. Devel., 1986-88, Greek Orthodox Archdiocese Council, N.Y.C., 1985-89; bd. dirs., vice chmn. St. Basil Acad., 1983-87; bd. dirs., mem. exec. com. YWCA, N.Y.C., 1985-90, Catalyst, 1988-90; chairperson capital campaign com. U. Calif., Berkeley, exec. v.p. exec. coun. Coll. Letters and Sci.; trustee Clark U., U. Calif. Found., 1993; bd. dirs. Empire Coll., 1983-87. Named mem. Acad. Women Achievers, YWCA, N.Y.C., 1984. Mem. Mid. States Assn. Schs. and Colls. (bd. dirs., fin. com. 1984-89, planning com. 1988-89), Mortar Bd., Pi Lambda, Lambda Theat, Prytanean. Avocations: opera; gourmet cooking; travel. Office: Pappas Cons Group Inc Alliance Firm KPMG Peat Marwick 345 Park Ave New York NY 10154-0001

PAPPAS, CHRISTINE ANN, nursing administrator; b. Bklyn., Aug. 1; d. James Nicholas and Ann (Sidronie) Pappas; m. Hugh Hudgins Bradley, Mar. 28, 1982; 1 child, Tonia Lee. AAS, SUNY, 1964; BS, Columbia U., 1966; MA, NYU, 1973. Cert. Nursing Administr.-Advanced Am. Nurses Credentialing Ctr. Med.-surg. nursing instr. St. Peters Sch. Nursing, N.J., 1966-69; insvc. nursing instr. ICU Beth Israel Med. Ctr., Newark, 1969-73; assoc. DON acute care Muhlenberg Hosp., N.J., 1973-75; assoc. DON Long Beach (Calif.) Meml. Med. Ctr., 1975-81, DON, 1981-84, dir. patient care svcs., 1984-86, v.p. nursing, 1986-90, acting adminstr., 1989-90; v.p. nursing L.I. Jewish Med. Ctr., N.Y., 1990—; mem. Long Beach Med. Ctr. Cancer Inst., 1987-89, adv. com. program mgmt. for nurses Johnson and Johnson Wharton Fellows, Phila., 1991—. Co-author: (resource booklet) Clinical Ladders for Registered Nurses, 1984; contbr. articles to profl. jours. Chmn. LaMarisa Assistance League Newport Beach, Calif., 1987-90. Mem. Am. Orgn. Nurse Execs. (chairperson div. assocs. 1979-80, chair nursing svc. administr. survey com. 1980-83, bd. dirs. 1984-87, nominating com. 1989-91), Deans and Dirs. Greater N.Y., Calif. Orgn. Nurse Execs. (bd. dirs. 1978-81, nominating com. 1984-86), Sigma Theta Tau (Upsilon and Iota Lambda chpts.). Office: L I Jewish Med Ctr 270-05 76th Ave New Hyde Park NY 11042

PAPPAS, EDWARD HARVEY, lawyer; b. Midland, Mich., Nov. 24, 1947; s. Charles and Sydell (Sheinberg) P.; m. Laurie Weston, Aug. 6, 1972; children: Gregory Alan, Steven Michael. BBA, U. Mich., 1969, JD, 1973. Bar: Mich. 1973, U.S. Dist. Ct. (ea. dist.) Mich. 1973, U.S. Dist. Ct. (we. dist.) Mich. 1980, U.S. Ct. Appeals (6th cir.) 1983, U.S. Supreme Ct. 1983. Ptnr. firm Dickinson, Wright, Moon, Van Dusen & Freeman, Detroit and Bloomfield Hills, Mich., 1973—; mediator Oakland County Cir. Ct., Pontiac, Mich., 1983—; hearing panelist Mich. Atty. Discipline Bd., Detroit, 1983—, chmn., 1987—; mem. bus. tort subcom. Mich. Supreme Ct. Com. Standard Jury Instructions, 1992-94. Trustee Oakland Community Coll., Mich., 1982-90, Oakland-Livingston Legal Aid, 1982-90, v.p., 1982-85, pres., 1985-87; trustee, adv. bd. Mich. Regional Anti-Defamation League of B'nai B'rith, Detroit, 1983-90; mem. nat. and community rels. agy. div. Jewish Welfare Fedn.; planning commn. Village of Franklin, Mich., 1987-91, chmn. 1989-91, councilman, 1991-92, chmn. charter com., 1993-94; bd. dirs. Franklin Found., 1989-92; trustee The Settlement Ctr., 1992—. Fellow Mich. State Bar Found., Oakland Bar-Adams Pratt Found., ABA Found.; mem. ABA, Fed. Bar Assn., State Bar Mich. (co-chmn. nat. moot ct. competition com. 1974, 76, com. on legal aid, chmn. standing com. on atty. grievances 1989-92, comml. litigation com., civil procedure com. 1992-94), Oakland County Bar Assn. (vice-chmn. continuing legal edn. com., chmn. continuing legal edn. com. 1985-86, mediation com. 1989-90, chmn. mediation com. 1990-91, bd. dirs. 1990—, chmn. select com. Oakland County cir. ct. settlement week 1991, chmn. strategic planning com. 1992-93, editor Laches monthly mag. 1986-88, co-chair task force to improve justice systems in Oakland County 1993—), Am. Judicature Soc., Mich. Def. Trial Lawyers, Def. Rsch. and Trial Lawyers Assn., (com. practice and procedure), B'nai B'rith Barristers. Home: 32223 Scenic Ln Franklin MI 48025-1702 Office: Dickinson Wright Moon Van Dusen & Freeman 525 N Woodward Ave Bloomfield Hills MI 48304-2971

PAPPAS, GEORGE DEMETRIOS, anatomy and cell biology educator, scientist; b. Portland, Maine, Nov. 26, 1926; James and Anna (Dracopoulos) Pappatheodoros; m. Bernice Levine, Jan. 14, 1952; children: Zoe Alexandra, Clio Nicollette. BA, Bowdoin Coll., 1947; MS, Ohio State U., 1948, PhD, 1952; DSc (hon.), U. Athens, Greece, 1988. Vis. investigator Rockefeller Inst., N.Y.C., 1952-54; assoc. in anatomy Coll. Physicians and Surgeons, Columbia U., N.Y.C., 1956-57, asst. prof. anatomy, 1957-63, assoc. prof., 1963-66; prof. anatomy Albert Einstein Coll. Medicine, Yeshiva U., N.Y.C., 1967-77, prof. neurosci., 1974-77, vis. prof. neurosci., 1977—; prof., head dept. anatomy and cell biology U. Ill. Coll. Medicine, Chgo., 1977—; trustee Marine Biol. Lab., Woods Hole, Mass., 1975-81. Author: (with others) The Structure of the Eye, 1961, Growth and Maturation of the Brain, vol. IV, 1964, Nerve as a Tissue, 1966, The Thalmus, 1966, Pathology of the Nervous System, vol. 1, 1968, Structure and Function of Synapses, 1972, Methodological Approaches to the Study of Brain Maturation and Its Abnormalities, 1974, Advances in Neurology, vol.12, 1975, The Nervous System, vol. 1 The Basic Neurosciences, 1975, Cellular and Molecular Basis of Synaptic Transmission, 1988, also author many conf. procs.; contbr. over 200 articles to profl. jours.; former mem. editorial bd. Anatomical Record, Biol. Bull., Brain Rsch., Jour. Neurocytology, Microstructure; patentee method inducing analgesia by implantation of cells releasing neuroactive substances. Arthritis and Rheumatism Found. fellow, 1954-56; recipient career devel. award Columbia U., 1964-66; rsch. grantee NIH. Fellow AAAS, N.Y. Acad. Scis., Inst. Medicine Chgo.; mem. Am. Soc. Cell Biology (pres. 1974-75), Am. Assn. Anatomists (chmn. pub. policy com. 1981-82), Assn. Anatomy Chmn. (exec. com. 1978-80, pres. 1981-82), Electron Microscopy Soc. Am. (program chmn. 1984-85), N.Y. Soc. Electron Microscopy (pres. 1967-68), Soc. for Neurosci. (pres. Chgo. chpt. 1985-86), Harvey Soc., Internat. Brain Rsch. Orgn., Cajal Club, Sigma Xi. Home: 506 W Roscoe St Chicago IL 60657-3519 Office: U Ill Coll Medicine Dept Anatomy & Cell Biology 808 S Wood St Chicago IL 60612-4325

PAPPAS, GEORGE FRANK, lawyer; b. Washington, Oct. 5, 1950; s. Frank George and Lora Marie (Stauber) P.; m. Susan Elizabeth Bradshaw, Apr. 25, 1980; children: Christine Bradshaw, Alexandra Stauber. BA, U. Md., 1972, JD, 1975. Bar: Md. 1976, D.C. 1991, U.S. Dist. Ct. Md. 1976, U.S. Dist. Ct. (D.C. cir.) 1986, U.S. Dist. Ct. (we. dist.) Tex. 1993, U.S. Ct. Appeals (4th cir.) 1976, U.S. Ct. Appeals (D.C. cir.) 1984, U.S. Ct. Appeals (fed. cir.) 1991, U.S. Ct. Appeals (2d cir.) 1993, U.S. Ct. Appeals (6th and 7th cirs.) 1994, U.S. Supreme Ct. 1984. Assoc. H. Russell Smouse, Balt., 1976-81; assoc. Melnicove, Kaufman, Wiener & Smouse, Balt., 1981-83, prin., 1983-88; ptnr. Venable, Baetjer and Howard, Balt., 1988—; lectr. Wash. Coll. Law, Am. U., Washington, 1980-84; mem. moot ct. bd., 1974-75; Master of the Bench , Inn XIII, Am. Inns of Ct. Contbr. articles to profl. jours. Founding adviser-of-record Internat. Trade Law Jour., 1974-75. 1st lt. USAF, 1972-76. Mem. ABA, Nat. Assn. R.R. Trial Counsel, Internat. Assn. Def. Counsel, Md. Bar Assn.

(chmn. internat. coml. law sect., 1980-81), Am. Intellectual Property Law Assn., U.S. Trademark Assn., Omicron Delta Kappa, Phi Kappa Phi, Phi Beta Kappa. Republican. Greek Orthodox. Club: L'Hirondelle. Home: 9 Roland Ct Baltimore MD 21204-3550 Office: Venable Baetjer & Howard 2 Hopkins Pla 1800 Mercantile Bank & Trust Bldg Baltimore MD 21201 also: 1201 New York Ave NW Ste 1000 Washington DC 20005-3917

PAPPAS, PETER WILLIAM, zoology educator; b. Pasadena, Calif., Dec. 9, 1944; s. William and Rosalie (Ashton) P.; m. Carolyn Ann Clague, Jan. 25, 1966; children: Allyson Rosalie Pappas Horsley, Nicholas W. BA, Humboldt State U., Arcata, Calif., 1966, MA, 1968; PhD, U. Okla., 1971. NIH postdoctoral fellow Rice U., Houston, 1971-73; asst. prof. zoology Ohio State U., Columbus, 1973-77, assoc. prof., 1977-82, prof., 1982-89, chairperson, prof., 1989—. Editor: Biology of Eucestoda, 1983; contbr. articles to profl. jours. Mem. Am. Soc. Parasitologists (H.B. Ward medal 1984), Ann. Midwestern Conf. Parasitologists. Home: 1709 Andover Rd Columbus OH 43212 Office: Ohio State U Zoology Dept 1735 Neil Ave Columbus OH 43210

PAPPAS, SANDRA LEE, state senator; b. 1949; m. Neal Gosman, 1986; 3 children. BA, Met. State U., 1986; MPA, Harvard U., 1994. Former mem. Minn. Ho. of Reps.; now mem. Minn. State Senate; part-time coll. instr. Mem. Democrat Farmer Labor Party. Home: 182 Prospect Blvd Saint Paul MN 55107-2136 Office: Minn State Senate Capitol G-27 Saint Paul MN 55155

PAPPAS, TED PHILLIP, architect; b. Jacksonville, Fla., Mar. 3, 1934; s. Phillip and Fifika George (Katsivelou) P.; m. Mary Lee Bone, July 14, 1962; children—Mary Katherine, Christina Lynn, Mark Phillip. B.Arch., Clemson U., 1958, B.S., 1957. Registered architect, Fla., S.C., Ga., Md. Staff architect various firms, Jacksonville, Fla., 1960-67; pres. Pappas Assocs. Architects, Inc., Jacksonville, Fla., 1967—; pres. Nat. Am. Accrediting Bd., 1993. Chmn. March of Dimes, Duval County, Fla., 1974, Capitol Ctr. Planning Commn., 1976-86; mem. Jacksonville Downtown Devel. Council, 1975-86, Jacksonville Com. of 100, 1975-86, Visual Pollution Com., 1985; exhibit chmn. Jacksonville Arts Festival, 1977; co-chmn. Riverside Arts Festival, 1978, Heritage Days, Jacksonville, 1992; bd. dirs. N. Fla. coun. Girl Scouts U.S.A., Inc.; chmn. recreation com. Jacksonville Community Coun., Inc., 1979; mem. JaxPride, 1989; bd. dirs. YMCA, 1982; mem. The Bolles Sch. Headmaster's Adv. Bd., 1983; mem. Jacksonville Historic Preservation Commn., 1984—, Greenscape; pres. parish coun. St. John the Divine Greek Orthodox Ch., 1973-74; mem. archdiocean coun. Greek Orthodox Archdiocese of N. and S. America, 1975-79; v.p. exec. com. Greek Orthodox Nat. Shrine Com., 1981-84; mem. exec. com. St. Photios Greek Orthodox Shrine; chmn. St. Photios 21st Century Com., Archon Greek Orthodox Ch.; mem. adv. coun. dept. architecture U. Fla., 1986—; mem. Clemson U. Alumni Coun., 1986—; sustaining mem. Clemson Bd. Visitors; mem. Pres.'s Adv. Coun. Clemson U., 1990—; chmn. Jacksonville Heritage Days, 1993, Jacksonville Urban League; rep. bd. trustees St. Photios Found., 1994. Capt. U.S. Army, 1958-60. Recipient numerous awards including Fla. Trust of Historic Preservation award for restoration of Carnegie Library; Preservation award City Jacksonville and Jacksonville Historic Landmarks Commn., 1984, Anthony L. Pullara award; John W. Dyal Meml. award, 1984, Outstanding Concrete Structure award for The Beaches Br. Library Fla. Concrete and Products Assn., Inc., 1987, Excellence in Architecure award AIA Jacksonville, 1988, Disting. Svc. award Clemson U., 1991. Fellow AIA (chmn. practice commn. 1985, mem. exec. com., v.p. 1985, 1st v.p.; pres. elect 1987, nat. pres. 1988, regional dir. Fla./Caribbean Region, 1982-84), Royal Archtl. Inst. Can. (hon. fellow); mem. Am. Archtl. Found. (regent), Fla. Assn. AIA (exec. com. 1978-84, pres. 1981, pres. Jacksonville chpt. 1976, Gold Medal award 1984, 2 Excellence in Architecture awards 1988), Octagon Soc., Nat. Archtl. Accrediting Bd. (pres. elect 1992), Fla. Found. for Architecture. Clubs: River, Meninak (bd. dirs. 1985), Fla. Yacht, Seminole (bd. dirs. 1985-90), St. Johns Dinner (bd. dirs. 1984-85, pres. 1986-87), Third Thursday, Epping Forest Yacht. Home: 1807 Elizabeth Pl Jacksonville FL 32205-9125 Office: Pappas Assocs Architects Inc PO Box 41245 100 Riverside Ave Jacksonville FL 32202-4925

PAPPE, STUART H., film editor. Editor: (films) The Killers, 1964, The Loved One, 1965, The President's Analyst, 1967, Bob & Carol & Ted & Alice, 1969, Alex in Wonderland, 1970, (with Gordon Scott and Maury Winetrobe) The Gumball Rally, 1976, An Unmarried Woman, 1978, Oliver's Story, 1978, (with Ronald Roose) The Wanderers, 1979, Carny, 1980, Class, 1983, Songwriter, 1984, (with Robert Lawrence) 8 Million Ways to Die, 1986, The Big Town, 1987, Moon Over Parador, 1988, Enemies, A Love Story, 1989, Scenes from a Mall, 1991, What's Love Got to Do with It?, 1993, (with John Carter and Pembroke Herring) Sister Act 2: Back in the Habit, 1993. Office: care Motion Picture Editors 7715 Sunset Blvd #220 Los Angeles CA 90046*

PAPPER, EMANUEL MARTIN, anesthesiologist; b. N.Y.C., July 12, 1915; s. Max and Lillian (Weitzner) P.; m. Patricia Meyer, Nov. 30, 1975; children: Richard Nelson Papper, Patrick Goldstein, Amy Goldstein. AB, Columbia U., 1935; MD, NYU, 1938; MD (hon.), Univ. Uppsala, Sweden, 1964, U. Turin, Italy, 1969, U. Vienna, Austria, 1977; DSc (hon.), Columbia U., 1988; PhD, U. Miami, 1990. Diplomate Am. Bd. Anesthesiology (dir. 1956-65, pres. 1964-65). Fellow medicine NYU, 1938-39, fellow physiology, 1940, asst. prof., 1946-49, assoc. prof., 1949; intern Bellevue Hosp., 1939-40, resident in anesthesiology, 1940-42; prof. anesthesiology, chmn. dept. Columbia U.; also dir. anesthesiology service Presbyn. Hosp., 1949- 69; dir. anesthesiology, vis. anesthesiologist Francis Delafield Hosp., 1951-69; v.p. med affairs, dean, prof. anesthesiology U. Miami, 1969-81, prof. pharmacology, 1972-81; dir. Abbott Labs., No. Trust Bank of Fla., Miami; cons. div. med. scis. NRC, 1954-69, Huntington (N.Y.) Hosp., 1949-69; nat. cons. surgeon gen. USAF, 1963-70; mem. surgery study sect. NIH, 1958-62; civilian cons. First Army, USN; prin. cons. Nat. Inst. Gen. Med. Scis., 1965-66, chmn. project com. sat. med. research program, 1966-70; mem. nat. heart council NIH, 1962-66; hon. cons. Royal Prince Alfred Hosp., Sydney, Australia. Author 250 sci. papers pub. in various med. jours., 3 textbooks. Bd. dirs. PBS-Channel 2, Miami, 1984—. Served from 1st lt. to maj. M.C. U.S. Army, 1942-46; chief anesthesiology sect. Torney, Dibble and Walter Reed hosps. Recipient Silver medal City of Paris, 1972; established E.M. Papper chair in anesthesiology Columbia U. Coll. Physicians and Surgeons, 1984, E.M. Papper lectures in anesthesiology Columbia U. and UCLA, 1978. Hon. fellow Royal Coll. Anaesthetists (England), Royal Coll. Surgeons (Ireland, faculty anaesthetists), Royal Soc. Medicine (England); mem. N.Y. Acad. Medicine (1st pres. sect. anesthesiology), Am. Surg. Assn., Am. Soc. Anesthesiologists (pres. 1967-68), N.Y. State Soc. Anesthesiologists (past pres.), NRC (chmn. com. anesthesia 1962-67), Am. Coll. Anesthesiologists, World Fedn. Soc. Anesthesiologists (v.p.), Am. Soc. Pharmacology and Exptl. Therapeutics, AMA, N.Y. Acad. Scis., N.Y. Co. Med. Soc., Am., N.Y. socs. anesthesiologists, AAAS, Am. Assn. Thoracic Surgery, Harvey Soc, Am. Soc. Clin. Investigation, Am. Thoracic Soc., Assn. Univ. Anesthetists (co-founder, 1st pres.), Pan Am. Med. Assn., Assn. Anaesthetists Gt. Britain and Ireland (hon.), Swedish Soc. Anesthesiologists (hon. mem.), Finnish Soc. Anesthesiologists (hon. mem.), Israeli Soc. Anesthesiologists (hon. mem.), Australian Soc. Anaesthesiologists (hon. mem.), N.Y. State Soc. Anesthesiologists (hon. mem.), D.C. Soc. Anesthesiologists (hon. mem.), German Soc. Anesthesiologists (hon. mem.), Halsted Soc., Japan Soc. Anesthesiologists (hon.), Am. Soc. Anesthesilogists (pres. 1969), Phi Beta Kappa, Sigma Xi, Alpha Omega Alpha. Clubs: Cosmos (Washington); Century Assn. (N.Y.C.). Home: 1 Grove Isle Dr Miami FL 33133-4101 Office: PO Box 016370 Miami FL 33101-6370

PAPSIDERO, JOSEPH ANTHONY, social scientist, educator; b. Niagara Falls, N.Y., Nov. 7, 1929; s. Vincent and Mary Angela (Gallo) P.; m. Wilma Alice Toye, Aug. 26, 1950; children: Michael J., John A., Mary J., Mark V. Ed.B., U. Buffalo, 1953, Ed.M., 1956; M.P.H., U. N.C., 1961; Ed.D., Case Western Res. U., 1970. Health educator North Tonawanda (N.Y.) Dept. Pub. Health, 1953-56; health educator, asst. exec. dir. Tb and Heart Assn. of Montgomery County, Md., 1956-61; USPHS trainee, 1960-61; program dir. Tb and Respiratory Disease Assn. of Cleve., 1961-67; planning assoc. Health Planning and Devel. Commn., Health and Welfare Fedn. of Cleve., 1967-69; planning cons. Met. Health Planning Corp., Cleve., 1969-71; sr. instr. dept. community health Sch. Medicine, Case Western Res. U., Cleve., 1969-71; asst. prof. human medicine Mich. State U., East Lansing,

---

1971-73, assoc. prof., 1973-77, prof., 1977-78, prof. community health scis. Coll. Human Medicine and Coll. Osteo. Medicine, 1978-85, assoc. dir. Office Health Services, Edn. and Research, Coll. Human Medicine, 1973-78, chmn. dept. community health sci., 1983-93, dir. divsn. geriatrics and long term care dept. physical medicine and rehab., 1993—, dir. cmty. integrated med. programs and studies Coll. Osteo. Medicine, 1993—, co-dir. Ctr. for Aging Studies, Geriatric Edn. Ctr., 1988-90, dir. Ctr. for Policy Analysis in Aging and Long-Term Care, 1987—; cons. to pub. and pvt. orgns. and agys.; pres. Active Life Systems Inc.; vis. prof. U. Rome, 1992—. Editor, contbg. author: (with others) Chance for Change: Implications of the Chronic Disease Module Study, 1979; mem. editorial bd. Aging: Clin. and Exptl. Rsch.; contbr. articles to profl. jours. Mem. Am. Psychol. Assn., Am. Public Health Assn., Assn. Tchrs. Preventive Medicine, Am. Coll. Epidemiology, Gerontol. Soc., Am. Geriatric Soc. Roman Catholic. Research gerontology/geriatrics, long-term care, epidemiology, health services and policy. Office: Mich State U A310 Fee Hall East Lansing MI 48824

PAQUET, GILLES, economist, university administrator; b. Quebec City, Que., Can., July 19, 1936; s. Charles Noel and Rosette (Marois) P.; m. Muriel Moisan, Oct. 21, 1958; children: Pascale, Valerie. B.A., Laval U., Can., 1956, B.Phil., 1956, M.A., 1960; postgrad., Queen's U., Can., 1960-62. Lectr., asst. prof. econs. Carleton U., Ottawa, Ont., Can., 1963-67; asso. prof Carleton U., 1967-73, prof, 1973-81; dean Carleton U. (Faculty Grad. Studies and Research), 1973-79; dean Faculty of Adminstrn. U. Ottawa, 1981—, prof., 1981-88; research dir. Senate Com. on Sci. Policy, Ottawa, 1968-70. Author: (with J. P. Wallot) Patronage et Pouvoir dans le Bas Canada, 1973; editor: (with N. H. Lithwich) Urban Studies: A Canadian Perspective, 1968, The Multinational Firm and the Nation State, 1972; Administration: Unity and Diversity, 1986, (with M. von Zur-Muehlen) Education Canada?, 1987; La Pensée Économique au Québec Francais, 1989, (with M von Zur Muehlen) Edging Toward the Year 2000, 1989, (with O. Gelinier) Management en crise, 1991. Fellow Royal Soc. Can. (sec.-treas. 1983-86), Royal Soc. Arts (London); mem. Order of Can., Can. Econs. Assn. (sec.-treas. 1967-81), Can. Fedn. Deans Mgmt. and Adminstrv. Studies (chmn. 1984-86), French Can. Assn. Advancement of Sci. (pres. 1986-87), Soc. Sci. and Human Research Coun. Office: U Ottawa Dept Bus Admin, PO Box 415, Ottawa, ON Canada K1N 6N5

PAQUETTE, JACK KENNETH, management consultant, antiques dealer; b. Toledo, Ohio, Aug. 14, 1925; s. Hector J. and Nellie (McCormick) P.; m. Jane Russell, Sept. 13, 1947; children: Jan Eriksen, Mark Russell, Mary Beth, John Eric. Student, Baldwin-Wallace Coll., 1943-44, Marquette U., 1944; B.A., Ohio State U., 1949, M.A., 1951; postgrad., Wayne State U., 1966. Editor monthly pub. Bur. Motor Vehicles, State of Ohio, 1947-49; asst. city editor, copy editor Ohio State Jour., 1949-51; copywriter Owens-Ill., Inc., Toledo, 1951-53; copy chief mktg. dept Owens-Ill., Inc., 1953-55, asst. advt. mgr. mktg. dept., 1955-59; advt. mgr. Owens-Ill. Inc. (Libbey div.), 1959-61; mgr. advt. and sales promotion Owens-Ill., Inc. (Libbey products), 1961-64, mgr. customer mktg. services glass container div., 1964-67, dir. corporate orgn. planning, 1967-69, v.p. adminstrv. div., dir. corp. relations, 1969-70, corporate v.p., dir. corp. relations, 1970-80, corp. v.p., asst. to chmn. bd., 1980-84, cons., 1984-86; pres. Paquette Enterprises, 1984—; owner The Trumpeting Angel, antiques, 1985—; mem. adv. bd. Cresset Chem. Co., 1987—. Author: A History of Owens-Illinois Inc., (1818-1984), 1985, The Glassmakers, 1994. Bd. dirs. Toledo YMCA, 1970-74, Vis. Nurse Svc., 1970-73, Children's Services Bd., 1973-80, Toledo council Boy Scouts Am., trustee, v.p. fin., 1978-84; mem. Advt. Club Toledo, 1951-75, trustee, 1960-62; hon. bd. dirs. Greater Toledo area chpt. ARC, 1970—; mem. adv. bd. Mercy Hosp., Toledo, 1981-84, Mary's Adult Day Care Ctr., 1989-93, St. Anthony's Children's Ctr., 1993; mem. pub. rels. com. Catholic U. Am., 1979-82; chmn. U.S. Savs. Bonds, Lucas County, 1977-79; trustee Bowling Green State U. Found., 1976-83, pres., 1980-82; mem. Nat. Commn. on a Free and Responsible Press, 1980-83; v.p. trustee Toledo Repertoire Theatre, 1984-88; trustee Crosby Gardens, 1983-89, chmn. 1987-88; trustee Toledo Botanical Gardens, 1989-90, chmn. emeritus and hon. trustee, 1990—; mem. pres.'s council Toledo Mus. Art, Bowling Green State U.; trustee Riverside Hosp. Found., 1984-94, chmn. 1986-89; mem. Juvenile Justice Adv. Bd., 1986-87; advisor R.B. Hayes Presdl. Ctr., 1990-92. With USNR, 1943-46, PTO. Recipient Gold Key award Pub. Rel. News, 1970, Silver Anvil award Pub. Rel. Soc., 1971, 72; named to Toledo Clean Hall of Fame, 1983. Mem. Soc. Journalists (co-founder Columbus, Northwestern Ohio chpts.), Ohio Mfrs. Assn. (v.p., trustee 1969-84), Keep Am. Beautiful, Inc. (nat. chmn., exec. com., 1978-84, chmn. emeritus, mem. nat. adv. coun. 1984—), Bus. Com. for the Arts (corp. liason 1980-84), Pub. Affairs Council, Glass Packaging Inst. (chmn. com. govtl. relations 1973-80), NAM, U.S. C. of C., Toledo C. of C., Martin County (Fla.) Hist. Soc., Western Great Lakes Hist. Soc., Toy Soldier Collectors of Am. Soc., Am. Legion (Toledo post), Pi Sigma Alpha. Clubs: Toledo Press (founding trustee), Toledo, Torch, Rotary. Home and Office: 2355 Parliament Sq Toledo OH 43617-1256

PAQUETTE, JOSEPH F., JR., utility company executive; b. Norwood, Miss., Aug. 24, 1934; married. BS in Civil Engring., Yale U., 1956. Pres. CMS Energy Corp., until 1988; chmn., pres., chief exec. officer Phila. Electric Co., 1956-86, 88-90, chmn., chief exec. officer, dir., 1990—; chief fin. officer, exec. v.p. Consumer Power Co., 1986-87, vice chmn., chief fin. officer, since 1987; also chmn. Susquehanna Electric Co. Office: Phila Electric Co PO Box 8699 Philadelphia PA 19101-8699

PAQUETTE, LEO ARMAND, chemistry educator; b. Worcester, Mass., July 15, 1934; m. Estelle I. Baril, 1957; 5 children. BS, Coll. of the Holy Cross, 1956, DSc (hon.), 1984; PhD in Organic Chemistry, MIT, 1959. Rsch. assoc. chemist Upjohn Co., 1959-63; from asst. prof. to prof., 1963-81, Kimberley prof, 1981-84; disting. U. prof. chemistry Ohio State U., 1987—; Alfred P. Sloan Found. fellow, 1966-67, Guggenheim fellow, 1976-77; vis. prof. Mich. State U., 1968, U. Iowa, 1970, U. Colo. 1974, U. Calif., Santa Barbara, 1975, U. Groningen, 1975, Tex. A&M U., 1979, Northwestern U., 1981, U. Heidelberg, 1984, U. Paris, 1985, U. Freiburg, 1989; mem. Chem. Divsn. Adv. Com. NSF; mem. Bd. Chem. Sci. & Tech. Nat. Rsch. Coun., 1984-87; mem. Med. Chem. Study section NIH (chmn. 1985-88, editor-in-chief Organic Reactions 1988—). Author 800 rsch. papers in organic chemistry. Recipient Nat. award Creative Work in Synthetic Organic Chemistry, 1984, Sr. Humboldt award W. Germany, 1989,Arthur C. Cope Scholar award, 1987, Ernest Guenther award, 1992, Disting. Internat. Award Nat. Sci. Coun., Rep. China, 1992, 1st France/Belgium award Rsch. Excellence, 1993. Fellow Japanese Soc. Prom. Sci.; mem. NAS, Royal Soc. Chem., Am. Chem. Soc. (Morley medalist 1971). Research in synthetic organic chemistry; organosilicon reagents; unusual molecules; molecular rearrangements; transition metal catalysis. Office: Ohio State U Dept Chemistry 120 W 18th Ave Columbus OH 43210-1173*

PAQUETTE, RICHARD, airport executive; married; 2 children. V.p. airport devel. Calgary Airport, AB, Can. Mem. Calgary Conv. and Visitors Bureau, Alta. Aviation Coun. Mem. Am. Assn. Airport Execs., Calgary C. of C., Calgary Rotary Club. Avocations: golf, skiing, bike riding, photography, hockey. Office: Calgary International Airport, 2000 Airport Rd NE, Calgary, AB Canada T2E 6W5

PAQUIN, ANNA, actress; b. New Zealand, 1983; d. Mary P. Appeared in (film) The Piano, 1993 (Academy Award best supporting actress 1993, Golden Globe nomination best supporting actress 1993), Jane Eyre, 1995. Office: William Morris Agency 151 El Camino Beverly Hills CA 90212*

PAQUIN, PAUL PETER, retired mortgage finance executive; b. Marlboro, Mass., Aug. 20, 1943; s. Adolph Phileous and Hazel Ann (Duplessis) P.; m. Lorraine Theresa Belliveau, June 26, 1965; children: Renée, Michele, Kenneth, Raymond. BSBA, Clark U., 1968, MBA, 1971; PhD, ABD, Cath. U., 1982. Fin. analyst Honeywell Inc., Framingham, Mass., 1963-67, Sprague Electric Co., Worcester, Mass., 1969-72; sr. analyst Fed. Nat. Mortgage Assn., Washington, 1972-76, dir. investor rels., 1976-85, v.p. investor rels., 1985-89, sr. v.p. investor rels., 1989-94; ret., 1994. Mem. Nat. Investor Rels. Inst. (pres. capitol area chpt., 1979, officer 1978-80).

PARACCHINI, ALBERTO M., banker; b. Ponce, Puerto Rico, Apr. 25, 1932; s. Henry and Fatima (Menendez) P; m. Carmen Maria Rocafort, Aug. 18, 1956; children: Carmen Maria, Rosalind, Henry Alberto, Alberto

Jose. BS in Econs., U. Pa., 1953, MBA, 1957. With Banco de Ponce (P.R.) from 1957, v.p. loan dept., 1966-67, sr. v.p., from 1967; now chmn. bd. dirs. Banco Popular de P.R., Hato Rey. served to lt. AUS, 1953-55. Office: Banco De Ponce Plz Degetau Ponce PR 00731 also: BanPonce Corp 209 Calle Munoz Rivera S Carolina PR 00985-6249

PARADIS, ANDRE, librarian; b. Quebec City, Que., Can., June 26, 1938; s. Theodule and Marcelle (Letarte) P.; m. Helene Legare, July 1, 1968. B.A., Seminaire de Quebec, 1960; diplome bibliotheconomie, U. Laval, 1963; baccalaureat en bibliotheconomie, U. Montreal, 1966. With Bibliotheque Municipale de Quebec, Quebec City, 1962-76; head br. office Bibliotheque Municipale de Quebec, 1963-65, chief librarian, 1966-75, chief tech. services, 1975-76; with Que. Pub. Libraries Service, 1976—. Mem. Corporation des Bibliothecaires Professionnels du Quebec. Home: 8580 De Marseille St, Charlesbourg, PQ Canada G1G 3S6 Office: 225 Grande-Allee Est, Bloc B 3d Floor, Quebec, PQ Canada

PARADIS, JAMES GARDINER, historian; b. Walker, Minn., Oct. 3, 1942; s. Louis Adelard and Rosalie Jane (Gardiner) P.; m. Judith Ellen Schmuckler, July 3, 1970; children: Emily, Rosalind. BS in Natural Sci., St. John's U., 1964; AM in English, NYU, 1971; PhD in English, U. Wash., 1976. Chemistry instr. Harar Tchr. Tng. Inst., Harar, Ethiopia, 1964-66; sci. tchr. Pub. Sch. 143, N.Y.C., 1966-71; English instr. Univ. Wash., Seattle, 1974-76; asst. prof. sci. and tech. communication MIT, Cambridge, Mass., 1977-79, assoc. prof., 1983-89, chmn. writing prog., 1982-85, prof., 1990—; communications cons. Exxon Chemicals Corp., Baton Rouge, La., 1982-83, U.S. Dept. of Interior, Anchorage, Alaska, 1983, Brookhaven Nat. Lab., L.I., N.Y., 1978-90. Author: Thomas Henry Huxley, 1978; co-editor: Victorian Science and Values, 1981, Evolution and Ethics, 1989, Textual Dynamics of the Professions, 1991; editorial cons. MIT Press/Harvard U., 1980-89. Adv. com. Driscoll Elem. Sch., Brookline, Mass. 1990-91. Recipient devel. grant Internat. Bus. Machines, 1986-87, rsch. grant NEH, 1979-80, Am. Philos. Soc., 1979. Mem. Modern Lang. Assn., History of Sci. Soc., Soc. for Tech. Communications, British Soc. for History of Sci. Avocations: rock and ice climbing, cycling, winter mountaineering. Home: 26 Salisbury Rd Brookline MA 02146-2105 Office: MIT 77 Massachusetts Ave Cambridge MA 02139-3594

PARADISE, LOUIS VINCENT, psychology educator, university provost; b. Scranton, Pa., Apr. 19, 1946; s. Louis Benjamin and Lucille (Bochicchio) P.; children: Christopher, Gabrielle. BS, Pa. State U., 1968; MS, Bucknell U., 1974; PhD, U. Va., 1976. Lic. psychologist, profl. counselor; cert. sch. psychologist. Assoc. prof. Cath. U. Am., Washington, 1976-83; prof. edn., chmn. edn. leadership U. New Orleans, 1983—, dean Coll. Edn., 1990-92, univ. vice chancellor for acad. affairs, 1992—. Author: Ethics in Counseling and Psychotherapy, 1979, Questioning: Skills for the Helping Process, 1979, Counseling in Community College, 1982. 1st lt. U.S. Army, 1968-72. Du-Pont scholar U. Va., 1974. Mem. APA, ACA (ethics com. 1986-89), Am. Edn. Rsch. Assn., So. Assn. Counselor Edn. (chmn. ethics com. 1988-89), Chi Sigma Iota (founding chpt. pres. 1985-87). Roman Catholic. Avocations: running, cycling. Office: U New Orleans Office Acad Affairs New Orleans LA 70148

PARADISE, PHILIP (HERSCHEL), artist; b. Ontario, Oreg., Aug. 26, 1905; s. Joseph Richard and Bessie Ana (Green) P.; m. Virginia Dare McCormick, Oct. 21, 1934 (dec. 1953); children: Virginia Gail, Philip Lee; m. Alice Hancock Johns, Nov. 5, 1959. Grad., Chouinard Art Inst., Los Angeles, 1927. tchr. Chouinard Art Inst., 1932-40, dir. fine arts dept., 1936-40; summer guest instr. U. Calif. at Santa Barbara, Calif. Arts and Crafts, Oakland, Tex. Western Coll.; lectr. Scripps Coll. Exhibited all prin. invitational and competitive exhbns. in U.S., including, Pa. Acad. Fine Arts, Whitney Mus. Am. Art, Met. Mus. Art, Los Angeles County, Denver, San Diego mus., Nat. Gallery Art, Art. Inst. Chgo.; represented in permanent collections, Library of Congress Print Collection, Pa. Acad. Fine Arts, Cornell U., Spokane Art Assn., Los Angeles County Fair Assns., others; editorial illustrations in True; motion picture prodn. design and art dir. major studios. Recipient award Oakland Ann. Watercolor Exhbn., 1938, award Los Angeles County Fair Assn., 1938, Dana medal Pa. Acad. Fine Arts, 1939, 2d pl. oil Calif. State Fair Assn., 1949, Smithsonian Archives Am. Art award, 1990, Life Time Achievements award Laguna Beach Mus., 1991, others. Mem. Calif. Watercolor Soc. (pres. 1939), Am. Watercolor Soc. (life), NAD, Soc. Motion Picture Art Dirs. Address: 31 W Carrillo St Santa Barbara CA 93101-3212

PARAMORE, JAMES MARTIN, church executive; b. Salt Lake City, May 6, 1928; s. James Frank and Ruth Colorado (Martin) P.; m. Helen Heslington, Dec. 7, 1951; children: James Richard, Jolene, David, Christine, Lisa, Paul. Student, Monterey Peninsula Coll., 1947-48; BA in Sociology and Econs., Brigham Young U., 1961; postgrad., U. Utah, 1963. Missionary Ch. of Jesus Christ of Latter Day Saints, France and Gelgium, 1946-51; ch. seminary tchr. Ch. of Jesus Christ of Latter Day Saints, Pleasant Grove, Utah, 1962-63; mission pres. Ch. of Jesus Christ of Latter Day Saints, Brussels, 1966-69; exec. sec. coun. of 12 apostles Ch. of Jesus Christ of Latter Day Saints, Salt Lake City, 1970-77, gen. authority, 1977—, mem. Presidency of the Seventy, 1987—; elec. distbn. engr. Geneva works U.S. Steel, Provo, Utah, 1955-57, process engr., 1957-62; cons. U. Utah, Salt Lake City, 1963-66; mem. adv. bd. Bonneville Telecomm., Salt Lake City, 1983-87; regional rep. LDS Ch. in Western USA and France, 1971-77. Vice chmn. Utah Com. on Children and Youth, Salt Lake City, 1965-66; pres., bd. dirs. Nat. Com. on Children and Youth, Washington, 1965-66; pres., bd. dirs Sharon Community Edn. and Recreation Assn., Orem, Utah, 1960-66; mem. devel. com. Orem Golf Course, 1960-63; mem. Orem City Coun., 1963-66. Sgt. U.S. Army, 1946-48, USNG; 1st lt. USNG, 1946, 57-61. Republican. Avocations: home design and building. Home: PO Box 24 Draper UT 84020-0024 Office: Ch of Jesus Christ LDS 47 E South Temple Salt Lake City UT 84150

PARAN, MARK LLOYD, lawyer; b. Cleve., Feb. 1, 1953; s. Edward Walter and Margaret Gertrude (Ebert) P. AB cum laude in Sociology, Harvard U., 1977, JD, 1980. Bar: Ill. 1980, Mass. 1986, Tex. 1993. Assoc. Wilson & McIlvaine, Chgo., 1980-83, Lurie Sklar & Simon, Ltd., Chgo., 1983-85, Sullivan & Worcester, Boston, 1985-92; pvt. practice, Boston, 1992; pvt. practice, Euless, Tex., 1992—. Mem. ABA, State Bar Tex. Avocations: tornado hunting, observation of severe thunderstorms, photography. Home and Office: 1050 W Ash Ln Apt 1015 Euless TX 76039-2161

PARCELLS, BILL (DUANE CHARLES PARCELLS), professional football coach; b. Englewood, N.J., Aug. 22, 1941; m. Judith Parcells; children: Suzy, Jill, Dallas. B.A., Wichita State U., 1964. Asst. coach Hastings Coll. (Nebr.), 1964, Wichita State U. (Kans.), 1969, U.S. Mil. Acad., 1966-69, Fla. State U., Tallahassee, 1970-72, Vanderbilt U., Nashville, 1973-74, Tex. Tech U., Lubbock, 1975-77; head coach U.S. Air Force Acad., Colorado Springs, Colo., 1978; asst. coach New Eng. Patriots, NFL, 1980; asst. coach N.Y. Giants, NFL, 1981-82, head coach, 1983-91; NFL studio analyst NBC Sports, 1991-92; head coach New England Patriots, NFL, 1993—. Coach NFL championship team N.Y. Giants, 1986. Address: New England Patriots RR 1 Foxboro MA 02035*

PARCH, GRACE DOLORES, librarian; b. Cleve., May; d. Joseph Charles and Josephine Dorothy (Kumel) P. B.A., Case Western Res. U., 1946, postgrad., 1947-50; B.L.S., McGill U., 1951; M.L.S., Kent State U., 1973; postgrad., Newspaper Library Workshop, Kent State U., 1970, Cooper Sch. Art, 1971-72, API Newspaper Library Seminar, Columbia U., 1971, Coll. Librarianship, U. Wales, 1984, 85. Cert. literacy instr., Ohio. Publicity librarian Spl. Services U.S. Army, Germany, 1951; post librarian Spl. Services U.S. Army, Italy, 1952; USAF base librarian, 1953-54; br. librarian Cleveland Heights (Ohio) Pub. Library, 1954-63; asst. head reference div. Va. State Library, Richmond, 1964; dir. Twinsburg (Ohio) Pub. Library, 1965-70; dir. newspaper library Cleve. Plain Dealer, 1970-83; county librarian N.C., 1987-92; cons. Cath. Library Assn., 1961-64; mem. home econs. adv. com., Summit County, 1969, books/job com., 1968; mem. adv. com. Guide to Ohio Newspapers, 1793-1973, 1971-74. Contbr. articles to Plain Dealer, N. Summit Times, Twinsburg Bull., Sun Press; author: Where In the World But in the Plain Dealer Library, 1971; Editor: Directory of Newspaper Libraries in the U.S. and Canada, 1976. Recipient MacArthur Found. award, 1988, Libr. of Am. award, 1988. Mem. McGill U. Alumnae Assn.

(sec. 1973), Kent State U. Alumni Assn., ALA (rep. on joint com. with Cath. Library Assn. 1967-70), John Cotton Dana award 1967, Library Pub. Rels. Coun. award 1972), Cath. Library Assn. (co-chmn. 1960-63), Spl. Libraries Assn. (chmn. newspaper library directory com. 1974-76, chmn. pub. relations Cleve. chpt. 1973, chmn. edn. com. newspaper div. 1982-83, mem. edn. com. nominating com. 1984), Ohio Library Assn., Western Res. Hist. Soc., Am. Soc. Indexers, Cleve. Mus. Art Assn., Coll. and Research Librarians, Nat. Micrographic Assn., Women Space, Women's Nat. Book Com., Nat. Trust Hist. Preservation. Roman Catholic. Clubs: Cleve. Athletic, Cleve. Women's City. Home: 688 Jefferson St Bedford OH 44146-3711

PARCHER, JAMES VERNON, civil engineering educator, consultant; b. Drumright, Okla., July 21, 1920; s. James Augustus and Pearl (Sharp) P.; m. Martha Hoff Ruckman, Aug. 7, 1943; children: Carol Susan Parcher McLeod, James Robert, David Loris, Dee Ellen Parcher Casey, Kay Elaine Parcher Heiserman. BS, Okla. State U., 1941, MS, 1948; MA, Harvard U., 1967; PhD, U. Ark., 1968. Maintenance engr. Remington Arms Co., Kings Mills, Ohio, 1941-42; instr. Okla. State U., Stillwater, 1947-48; asst. prof. Okla. State U., 1948-54, asso. prof., 1954-67, prof., 1967-85, prof. emeritus, 1985—, head dept. civil engring., 1969-83. Author: A History of the Oklahoma State University College of Engineering, Architecture and Technology, 1988, (with R.E. Means) Physical Properties of Soils, 1962, Soil Mechanics and Foundations, 1968. Served with C.E. AUS, 1942-46, 50-52. Mem. ASCE, NSPE, Okla. Soc. Profl. Engrs., Res. Officers Assn., Am. Assn. Retired People, Phi Kappa Phi, Sigma Tau, Chi Epsilon. Home: 1024 W Knapp Ave Stillwater OK 74075-2709

PARDEE, ARTHUR BECK, biochemist, educator; b. Chgo., July 13, 1921; s. Charles A. and Elizabeth B. (Beck) P.; m. Ruth Sager; children by previous marriage: Michael, Richard, Thomas. B.S., U. Calif. at Berkeley, 1942; M.S., Calif. Inst. Tech., 1943, Ph.D., 1947; D (hon.), U. Paris, 1993. Merck postdoctoral fellow U. Wis., 1947-49; mem. faculty U. Calif. at Berkeley, 1949-61, assoc. prof., 1957-61; NSF fellow Pasteur Inst., 1957-58; prof. biology, chmn. dept. biochem. scis. Princeton, 1961-67; prof. biochemistry Princeton U., 1961-75; Donner prof. sci. Princeton, 1966; prof. Dana Farber Cancer Inst. and biochem. pharmacology dept. Harvard Med. Sch., Boston, 1975—; Mem. research adv. council Am. Cancer Soc., 1967-71. Co-author: Experiments in Biochemical Research Techniques, 1957; editor: Biochemica et Biophysica Acta, 1962-68. Trustee Cold Spring Harbor Lab. Quantitative Biology, 1963-69. Recipient Young Biochemists travel award NSF, 1952, Krebs Medal Fedn. European Biochem. Socs., 1973, Rosenstiel award Brandeis U., 1975, 3M award Fedn. Am. Socs., Exptl. Biology, 1980, CIIT Prize, 1993; Princess Takamatu lectr., 1990. Fellow AAAS; mem. Nat. Acad. Sci. (editorial bd. proc. 1971-73, com. on scis. and pub. policy 1973-76), Am. Chem. Soc. (Paul Lewis award 1960), Am. Soc. Biol. Chemists (treas. 1964-70, pres. 1980-81), Am. Assn. Cancer Research (pres. 1985-86), Am. Soc. Microbiologists, Japanese Biochem. Soc., Ludwig Inst. Cancer Res. (sci. com. 1988—), Chem. Industry Inst. Toxicology (Founder's award), Phi Beta Kappa, Sigma Xi. Home: 30 Codman Rd Brookline MA 02146-7555 Office: Dana-Farber Cancer Inst 375 Longwood Ave Boston MA 02215-5328

PARDEE, OTWAY O'MEARA, computer science educator; b. Seattle, June 26, 1920; s. Otway and Mary Gertrude (O'Meara) P.; m. Marilynn Lowrie, Aug. 9, 1946; children—Irene, Loraine, Suzanne. B.S. in Elec. Engring., U. Wash., 1941; Ph.D. in Elec. Engring., Stanford U., 1948. Instr. math. Syracuse U., N.Y., 1948-52, asst. to assoc. prof., 1952-69, dir. Computing Ctr., 1962-69, prof. computer sci., 1969-86; prof. emeritus Syracuse U., 1986—. Served with U.S. Navy (USNR) 1944-46. Mem. AAUP (pres. Syracuse U. chpt. 1960), Assn. Computing Machinery (chmn. Syracuse chpt. 1963), Am. Math. Soc., Math. Assn. Am., Am. Phys. Soc., IEEE, Sigma XI, Tau Beta Pi. Avocations: camping; photography. Home: 843 Maryland Ave Syracuse NY 13210-2502 Office: Syracuse U Ctr for Sci and Tech Ste 4-116 Syracuse NY 13244-4100

PARDEE, SCOTT EDWARD, securities dealer; b. New Haven, Oct. 11, 1936; s. William Durley and Catherine (Eames) P.; m. Aida Milagros Fuentes Tavarez, Jan. 29, 1966; 1 child, Alan Alexander. B.A., Dartmouth Coll., 1958; Ph.D., MIT, 1962. Research asst. Fed. Res. Bank, Boston, 1959-62; teaching asst. in econs. MIT, Cambridge, Mass., 1961-62; research economist Fed. Res. Bank N.Y., N.Y.C., 1962-66, mgr. fgn. dept., 1967-70, asst. v.p. fgn. dept., 1970-74, v.p. fgn. dept., 1974-79; tchr. banking and fin. NYU, 1965-67, Am. Inst. Banking, 1969-72; adj. prof. Grad. Sch. Bus. Columbia U., N.Y.C., 1972-75; dep. mgr. fgn. ops. Fed. Res. System Open Market Account, 1975-79, mgr. fgn. ops., 1979-81; exec. v.p., dir. Discount Corp. N.Y., N.Y.C., 1981-86; dir. Am. Internat. Group, 1982-86; vice chmn. Yamaichi Internat. Am. Inc., N.Y.C., 1986-88, chmn., 1988—, also sr. advisor. Author: A Study of Inter-City Wage Differentials, 1962. Trustee Geonomics Inst., 1994—, Woodrow Wilson Fellowship Found., 1994—; mem. coun. Rockefeller U., 1994—; chmn. coun. for econs. MIT, 1994—. Woodrow Wilson fellow MIT, 1958-59; recipient Dr. Louis M. Spadaro award Fordham U., 1980. Mem. Union League Club, Phi Beta Kappa. Home: 250 South End Ave New York NY 10280-1074 Office: Yamaichi Internat Am Inc 2 World Trade Ctr Ste 9650 New York NY 10048-0002

PARDEN, ROBERT JAMES, engineering educator, management consultant; b. Mason City, Iowa, Apr. 17, 1922; s. James Ambrose and Mary Ellen (Fahey) P.; m. Elizabeth Jane Taylor, June 15, 1955; children—Patricia Gale, James A., John R., Nancy Ann. B.S. in Mech. Engring. State U. Iowa, 1947, M.S., 1951, Ph.D., 1953. Reg. profl. engr. Iowa, Calif.; lic. gen. contractor Calif. Indsl. engr. LaCrosse Rubber Mills, 1947-50; assoc. dir. Iowa Mgmt. Course, 1951-53; assoc. prof. indsl. engring. Ill. Inst. Tech., 1953-54; prof. engring. mgmt. Santa Clara U., 1955—, dean Sch. Engring., 1955-82; prin. Saratoga Cons. Group (Calif.), 1982—; Mem. Sec. Navy's Survey Bd. Grad. Edn., 1964. Mem. Saratoga Planning Commn., 1959-61. Served to 1st lt., Q.M.C. AUS, 1943-46. Named to Silicon Valley Engring. Hall of Fame Silicon Valley Engring. Coun., 1993. Mem. ASME (chmn. Santa Clara Valley sect. 1958), Am. Soc. Engring. Edn. (chmn. Pacific N.W. sect. 1960), Am. Inst. Indsl. Engrs. (chmn. 1958-63, dir. ASEE-ECPD affairs 1963-68), Nat. Soc. Profl. Engrs., Engrs. Council Profl. Devel. (dir. 1964-65, 66-69), Soc. Advancement Mgmt., ASEM, Sigma Xi, Tau Beta Pi. Roman Catholic. Home: 18932 Bonnie Ridge Way Saratoga CA 95070-5010 Office: Santa Clara U Sch Engring Santa Clara CA 95053

PARDES, HERBERT, psychiatrist, educator; b. Bronx, N.Y., July 7, 1934; s. Louis and Frances (Bergman) P.; m. Judith Ellen Silber, June 9, 1957; children: Stephen, Lawrence, James. BS, Rutgers U., 1956, MD, SUNY, Bklyn., 1960; DSc (hon.) SUNY, 1990. Straight med. intern Kings County Hosp., 1960-61, resident in psychiatry, 1961-62, 64-66; asst. prof. psychiatry Downstate Med. Ctr., Bklyn., 1968-72, prof., chmn. dept., 1972-75; dir. psychiat. services Kings County Hosp., Bklyn., 1972-75; prof., chmn. dept. psychiatry U. Colo. Med. Sch., 1975-78; dir. psychiat. services Colo. Psychiat. Hosp., Denver, 1975-78; dir. NIMH, Rockville, Md., 1978-84; asst. surgeon gen. USPHS, 1978-84; prof. psychiatry Columbia U., N.Y.C., 1984—, chmn. dept., 1984—; dir. Psychiat. Inst., 1984-89, v.p. for health scis. and dean faculty of medicine, 1989—. Committeeman, Kings County Dem. Com., 1972-75; pres. sci. bd. Nat. Alliance for Research on Schizophrenia and Depression. Capt. M.C., AUS, 1962-64. Decorated Army Commendation medal; ann. hon. lectr. Downstate Med. Ctr. Alumni Assn., 1972, recipient Alumni Achievement medal, 1980, William Menninger award ACP, 1992, Dorothy Dix award Mental Illness Fedn., 1992, Vester Mark award, 1993. Mem. AAMC (chair-elect 1994—), Am. Psychiat. Assn. (v.p. 1986-88, pres. 1989-90, Disting. Svc. award 1993), Inst. Medicine, Am. Psychoanalytic Assn., Coun. of Deans (adminstrv. bd., chair-elect 1993-94, chair 1994-95), Phi Beta Kappa, Alpha Omega Alpha. Contbr. articles to med. jours. Home: 15 Claremont Ave Apt 93 New York NY 10027-6814 Office: Columbia U Coll Phys & Surgeons Dept Psychiatry 630 W 168th St New York NY 10032-3702 also: NY State Psychiat Inst 722 W 168th St New York NY 10032-2603

PARDO, DOMINICK GEORGE (DON PARDO), broadcasting announcer; b. Westfield, Mass., Feb. 22, 1918; s. Dominik J. and Waleria (Romaniak) P.; m. Catherine A. Lyons, Aug. 22, 1939; children: Paula Kay, Dona Marie, Michael D., David J., Katherine A. Student, Emerson Coll., 1942. Announcer Sta. WJAR, 1942-44. Actor, 20th Century Players, Sta. WJAR, Providence, 1938-40; announcer radio and TV, NBC, N.Y.C.,

1944—; announcer for radio shows Pepper Young's Family, The Doctors; announcer TV shows Ford 50th Anniversary Show, 1953 (Sylvania TV award), Fred Allen's Judge for Yourself, Martha Raye Shows, 1953-58, Arthur Murray Party, Four Star Revue, Colgate Comedy Hour, Kate Smith Hour, Show of Shows, Caesar's Hour, Jonathan Winters Show; TV game shows Winner Take All, 1950, Price is Right (original), 1956-83, Jeopardy, 1964-75, Saturday Night Live, 1975-81, 83—; numerous other shows, including, Bill Stern's Sports, Magnificent Montague; others; newscaster, 1944-54. Office: care NBC Press Dept 30 Rockefeller Plz New York NY 10112-0002*

PARDUE, DWIGHT EDWARD, venture capitalist; b. North Wilkesboro, N.C., Aug. 3, 1928; s. Gilbert F. and Nina (Glass) P.; m. Annie Eller, Mar. 24, 1951; children: Richard S., Dwight E. Cert., Clevenger Bus. Coll., 1956. Dir. warehousing Lowe's Co., Inc., North Wilkesboro, 1956-57; store mgr. Lowe's Co., Inc., Sparta, N.C., 1957-59, Richmond, Va., 1959-70; regional v.p. Lowe's Co., Inc., North Wilkesboro, 1970-75, sr. v.p. store ops., 1975-78, exec. v.p. sales and store ops., 1978-86, sr. exec. v.p., 1986-90; pres., investor D. Pardue & Assocs., Wilkesboro, N.C., 1990—; mem. steering com. Home Ctr. Leadership Coun., Nat. Home Ctr. Home Improvement Congress and Exposition, 1983-86; bd. dirs. Wilkes Nat. Bank, North Wilkesboro, N.C.; chmn. bd. Community Bancshares, Inc., Wilkesboro, 1992—. Served with U.S. Army, 1950-52. Mem. Oakwoods Country Club, Jefferson Landing Golf Club, Masons. Office: D Pardue & Assocs PO Box 791 North Wilkesboro NC 28659-0791

PARDUE, HARRY L., chemist, educator; b. Big Creek, W.Va., May 3, 1934; m. Mary Schultz; 1 child, Jonathan. BS, Marshall U., 1956, MS, 1957; PhD in Chemistry, U. Ill., 1961. From asst. to assoc. prof. Purdue U., West Lafayette, Ind., 1961-70, prof. chemistry, 1970—, head dept. chemistry, 1983-87. Mem. Am. Chem. Soc. (Chem. Instrumentation award Anal Chem. divsn. 1982, Analytical Chemistry award 1995), Am. Assn. Clin. Chemists (award 1979, Samuel Natelson award 1982, Anachem award 1990). Achievements include research in instrumentation for chemical research, chemical kinetics. Office: Purdue U Dept Chem 1393 Brown Bldg W West Lafayette IN 47907-1393*

PARDUE, LARRY G., botanical garden administrator, educator; b. Glasgow, Ky., Dec. 6, 1944; s. Samuel Robert and Etta Belle (Napier) P.; children: James, Robert, Mathew. BA, U. South Fla., 1967, MA, 1970. Plant info. officer N.Y. Botanical Garden, N.Y.C., 1969-75; v.p. Wild Flower Preservation Soc., N.Y.C., 1970-73; exec. dir. Hort. Soc. N.Y., N.Y.C., 1975-88, Marie Selby Botanical Garden, Sarasota, Fla., 1988-94, Crosby Arboretum, Picayune, Miss., 1994—. Office: Crosby Arboretum PO Box 190 1986 Ridge Rd Picayune MS 39466

PARDUE, MARY LOU, biology educator; b. Lexington, Ky., Sept. 15, 1933; d. Louis Arthur and Mary Allie (Marshall) P. B.S., William and Mary Coll., 1955; M.S., U. Tenn., 1959; Ph.D., Yale U., 1970; D.Sc. (hon.), Bard Coll., 1985. Postdoctoral fellow Inst. Animal Genetics, Edinburgh, Scotland, 1970-72; assoc. prof. biology MIT, Cambridge, 1972-80; prof. MIT, 1980—; summer course organizer Cold Spring Harbor Lab., N.Y., 1971-80; mem. rev. com. NIH, 1974-78, 80-84, nat. adv. gen. med. scis. coun., 1984-86, sci. adv. com. Wistar Inst., Phila, 1976—; mem. health and environ. rsch. adv. com. U.S. Dept. Energy, 1987-94. Mem. editorial bd. Chromsoma, Molecular and Cellular Biology, Biochemistry; contbr. articles to profl. jours. Mem. rev. com. Am. Cancer Soc., 1990-93, Howard Hughes Med. Inst. Adv. Bd., 1993—. Recipient Esther Langer award Langer Cancer Rsch. Found., 1977, Lucius Wilbur Cross medal Yale Grad. Sch., 1989; grantee NIH, NSF, Am. Cancer Soc. Fellow AAAS, NAS (chmn. genetics sect. 1991-94, coun. 1995—), Am. Acad. Arts and Sci. (coun. mem. 1982—, exec. com. 1994—); mem. NRC (bd. on biology 1989-95), Genetics Soc. Am. (pres. 1982-83), Am. Soc. Cell Biology (coun. 1977-80, pres. 1985-86), Phi Beta Kappa, Phi Kappa Phi. Office: MIT Dept Biology 68-670 77 Massachusetts Ave Cambridge MA 02139-3594

PARDUE, MICHAEL EDWARD, electronics company executive; b. West Palm Beach, Fla., Nov. 13, 1949; s. Frank Edward and Clare (McElwain) P.; m. Phyllis Maime Copeland; children: Michelle, Robert, Wendy, Dan, Jeff. BSBA, U. Fla., 1972. CPA. Acct. Arthur Andersen & Co., Miami, Fla., 1972-75; fin. mgr. Sterling Precision Corp., West Palm Beach, 1975-78; various positions Sensormatic Electronics, Deerfield, Fla., 1978-88, CFO, CEO, exec. v.p., 1988—. Bd. dirs. Jr. Achievement, Ft. Lauderdale, Fla., 1988-90, Palm Beach Econ. Coun., 1989—; mem. com. Boy Scouts Am., West Palm Beach, 1982—. Republican. Roman Catholic. Avocation: fishing.

PARDUS, DONALD GENE, utility executive; b. Stafford Springs, Conn., Aug. 1, 1940; s. William L. and Marion (Wondrasck) P.; m. Marilyn L. Riquier, June 10, 1961; children: David J., Susan L., Linda M. BS in Bus. Adminstrn, U. Hartford, Conn., 1966; grad., Harvard U. 1977. Internal auditor Conn. Light and Power Co., Berlin, 1958-67; fin. asst., then asst. treas. N.E. Utilities Svc. Co., Berlin, 1967-79; v.p., chief fin. officer, treas. Eastern Utilities, Boston, 1979-85, pres., chief fin. officer, 1985-87, pres., chief oper. officer, trustee, 1987-89, pres., chief exec. officer, trustee, 1989-90, chmn., chief exec. officer, trustee, 1990—; chmn., dir. Blackstone Valley Electric Co., Newport Electric Corp., Eastern Edison Co., Montaup Electric Co., EUA Svc. Corp., EUA Investment Corp., EUA Ocean State Corp., EUA Cogenex Corp.; bd. dirs. Conn. Yankee Atomic Power Co., Maine Yankee Atomic Power Co., Yankee Atomic Elec. Co., Vt. Yankee Nuclear Powr Co. Office: Eastern Utilities Assocs PO Box 2333 1 Liberty Sq Boston MA 02107

PARÉ, JEAN-JACQUES, civil engineer, geotechnical and dam safety consultant; b. Quebec City, Que., Can., Mar. 14, 1929; s. Charles-Auguste and Anna (Delorme) P.; m. Germaine Everell, Sept. 7, 1955; children: Pierre, Marc, Louis, Francois. BA, Coll. St. Jean-Eudes, Quebec City, 1950; BSCE, Laval U., Quebec City, 1955; diploma in concrete, Imperial Coll., London, 1956, diploma in soil mechanics, 1957. Registered profl. engr., Que. Soil engr. Que. Hwy. Dept., Quebec City, 1957-60; lectr. soil mechanics U. Sherbrooke, Que., 1960-65; head soil mechanics TECSULT, Montreal, Que., 1965-72; head geotechnique dept. James Bay Energy Corp., Montreal, 1973-87; geotech. advisor Shawinigan-Lavalin, Montreal, 1988-91, SNC-Shawinigan, Montreal, 1991-93; pvt. practice cons. Verdun, 1994—. Contbr. over 50 articles on dam engring. to profl. jours. Pres. Monseigneur Codère Found., Montreal, 1979-82. Recipient best paper medal Civil Engring. Inst. Can., 1987; Athlone fellow, London, 1955-57. Fellow Engring. Inst. Can.; mem. Can. Geotech. Soc., Internat. Congress Large Dams, Profl. Engrs. Que. Avocations: tennis, skiing. Home and Office: 100 Berlioz Apt 1707, Verdun, PQ Canada H3E 1N4

PAREDES, ALFONSO, psychiatrist; b. Mexico City, Sept. 19, 1926; came to U.S., 1951, naturalized, 1960; s. Cipriano and Dolores (Fernandez) P.; m. Lois E. Foster, Sept. 24, 1954; children—Alfonso Jr., John M., Nancy M., Susan M. M.D., U. Mex., 1951. Intern St. Joseph Hosp., Kansas City, Mo., 1951-52; fellow in psychiatry Herrick Meml. Hosp., Berkeley, Ga., 1952-53; resident in psychiatry U. Kans., Kansas City, Kans., 1953-55; sr. asst. resident in psychiatry U. Md. Psychiat. Inst., Balt., 1955-56; asst. prof. psychiatry U. Okla., Oklahoma City, 1960-64; prof. U. Okla., 1969-79; prof. psychiatry U. So. Calif. and: dep. dir. mental health Los Angeles County, 1979-81; prof. psychiatry U. Calif., Los Angeles, 1981—; asso. prof. psychiatry Jefferson Med. Coll., Phila., 1964-69. Pres. Oklahoma City Council on Alcoholism, 1970-75, Okla. Psychiatry Assn. of Ams., 1972-74. Fellow Am. Psychiat. Assn., Am. Coll. Psychiatrists; mem. AAAS, Am. Psychopathol. Assn., N.Y. Acad. Scis., Sigma Xi. Roman Catholic. Home: 524 Buena Ave San Marino CA 91108-1338 Office: West Los Angeles VA Med Ctr 11301 Wilshire Blvd Los Angeles CA 90073-1002

PAREDES, AMERICO, English language educator; b. Brownsville, Tex., Sept. 3, 1915; s. Justo and Clotilde (Manzano-Vidal) Paredes-Cisneros; m. Amelia Sidzu Nagamine, May 28, 1948; children: Julia, Americo, Alan, Vicente. B.A. U. Tex., Austin, 1951, M.A., 1953, Ph.D., 1956. Journalist, 1936-50; mem. faculty U. Tex., Austin 1951—; Ashbel Smith prof. English and anthropology U. Tex., 1981-83, Dickson, Allen and Anderson Centennial prof., 1983—; Dickson, Allen and Anderson Centennial prof. emeritus, 1985—. Author: With His Pistol in His Hand, 1958, Folktales of Mexico,

1970, A Texas-Mexican Cancionero, 1976, George Washington Gomez, 1990, Between Two Worlds, 1991, Uncle Remus Con Chile, 1993, Folklore and Culture on the Tex.-Mex. Border, 1993, The Hammon and the Beans and Other Stories, 1994; editor: Jour. Am. Folklore, 1968-1973. With AUS, 1944-46. Decorated Order of Aztec Eagle (Mex.), 1990; Order of José de Escandón (Mex.), 1991; recipient Charles Frankel prize NEH, 1989; Guggenheim fellow, 1962. Mem. Am. Folklore Soc. (award 1990), Acad. Norteamericana de la Lengua Espanola, Mex. Acad. History. Office: Univ Tex Dept English Austin TX 78712

PAREDES, JAMES ANTHONY, anthropologist, educator; b. N.Y.C., Sept. 29, 1939; s. Antonio and Mildred Olene (Brown) P.; m. Anna Hamilton, Nov. 25, 1959 (div. 1984); children: J.A. Jr., Anna Teresa P. Lesinski, Sara Caroline P. Dominguez; m. Elizabeth Dixon Purdum, Aug. 10, 1985 (div. 1994); 1 stepchild, David Joseph Plante. BA, Oglethorpe U., 1961; MA, U. N.Mex., 1964, PhD, 1969. Rsch. coord. Upper Miss. Mental Health Ctr., Bemidji, Minn., 1966-67; asst. prof., acting dir. Am. Ind. Studies Bemidji State Coll., 1967-68; community devel. specialist U. Minn. Agrl. Extension Svc., Bemidji, 1967-68; asst. prof. dept. anthropology Fla. State U., Tallahassee, 1969-74, assoc. prof., 1974-78, prof., 1979—, chmn. dept., 1974-77, 84-90; adj. prof. dept. anthropology U. Fla., Gainesville, 1979—; cons. Nat. Marine Fisheries Svc., Galveston, Tex., 1987-88, Bur. Indian Affairs, Washington, 1985, 92, Fed. Recognition Panel, Assn. on Am. Indian Affairs, N.Y.C., 1987-88. Author: Indios de los Estados Unidos Anglosajones, 1992; editor: Anishinabe: Six Studies of Modern Chippewa, 1980, Indians of the Southeastern United States in the Late 20th Century, 1992; author or co-author numerous articles, chpts. in books, revs. Mem. Sci. and Statis. Com., Gulf of Mex. Fishery Mgmt. Coun., Tampa, Fla., 1978-88. Recipient svc. award Poarch Creek Indians, 1990, Woodrow Wilson Found. fellow U. N.Mex., 1961-62; Nat. Inst. Mental Health predoctoral fellow U. N.Mex., 1968-69; Rockefeller Inst. for Study of So. Culture and Religion fellow, Fla. State U., 1978. Fellow Am. Anthrop. Assn., Soc. for Applied Anthropology (assoc. editor 1983-88, pres. 1993-95); mem. So. Anthrop. Soc. (pres. 1988-89), Fla. Acad. Scis. (sect. chair 1984-85), Sigma Xi (Fla. State U. chpt. pres. 1977-78). Democrat. Avocations: carpentry, yard work, walking. Office: Fla State U Dept Anthropology Tallahassee FL 32306

PAREIGIS, JOYCE ANN, nursing administrator; b. Nemacolin, Pa., Sept. 6, 1938; d. Andrew T. and Emma P. (Borzik) Urda; m. Lawrence H. Pareigis, Nov. 24, 1962; children: Larry, Charles, Jim. BSN, U. Pitts., 1961, MS in Nursing Edn., 1963. RN, Pa., Tenn. Asst. prof. med., surg. nursing U. Pitts Sch. Nursing; dir. nursing Bayfront Med. Ctr., St. Petersburg, Fla., Morton F. Plant Hosp., Clearwater, Fla., Meml. Med. Ctr., Savannah, Ga.; sr. v.p. St. Thomas Hosp., Nashville; adj. faculty Vanderbilt U., Aquinas Jr. Coll. Fellow J&J Wharton Program for Nurse Execs. Mem. AHA (chair ctr. for nursing adv. coun.), Tenn. Orgn. Nurse Execs. (pres.), Tenn. Health Assn. (chair task force in nursing), Am. Orgn. Exec. Nurses (candidate in recognition program), Sigma Theta Tau. Office: St Thomas Hosp 4220 Harding Rd Nashville TN 37205-2095

PARELL, MARY LITTLE, federal judge, former banking commissioner; b. Fond du Lac, Wis., Aug. 13, 1946; d. Ashley Jewell and Gertrude (McCoy) Little; m. John Francis Parell, May 28, 1972 (div. 1990); children: Christie, Morgan, Shawn, John Brady. AB in Polit. Sci. cum laude, Bryn Mawr Coll., 1968; JD, Villanova U., 1972; LLD (hon.), Georgian Ct. Coll., 1987. Bar: N.J. 1972. Assoc. McCarter & English, Newark, 1972-80, ptnr. 1980-84; commr. N.J. Dept. Banking, Trenton, 1984-90; assoc. gen. counsel Prudential Property & Casualty Ins. Co., Holmdel, N.J., 1991-92; judge U.S. Dist. Ct. N.J., 1992—; chmn. bd. Pinelands Devel. Credt Bank. Bd. trustees Exec. Commn. Ethical Standards, Trenton, 1984-90, Corp. Bus. Assistance, Trenton, 1984-91, N.J. Housing & Mortgage Fin. Agy., Trenton, 1984-90, N.J. Cemetery Bd. Assn., 1984-90, N.J. Hist. Soc., 1976-79., YMCA of Greater Newark, 1973-76, Diocesan Investment; mem. Supreme Ct. N.J. Civil Practice Com., 1982-84, Supreme Ct. N.J. Dist. Ethics Com., 1982-84; lay assessor Ecclesiastical Ct. Episc. Diocese Newark, 1980-84. Fellow Am. Bar Found.; mem. ABA, N.J. Bar Assn., Princeton Bar Assn. Office: US Courthouse 402 E State St Rm 252 Trenton NJ 08605-0515

PARENT, ANDRÉ, neurobiology educator, researcher; b. Montreal, Que., Can., Oct. 3, 1944; s. Lucien and Yvette (Gagné) P.; m. Doris Côté, July 8, 1970; children: Geneviève, Philippe, Martin. BSc, U. Montreal, 1967; PhD in Neurobiology, U. Laval, Quebec City, Que., 1970; postgrad., Max-Planck Inst., Frankfurt, Germany, 1971. Asst. prof. anatomy Laval U. Med. Sch., 1971-76, assoc. prof., 1976-81, prof., 1981—, sr. dir. Neurobiology Rsch. Ctr., 1985-92. Author: Comparative Neurobiology of the Basal Ganglia, 1986. Studentship Med. Rsch. Coun. Can., 1967-70, fellow, Frankfurt, 1970-71, scholar, 1973-78. Mem. Royal Soc. Can., Internat. Brain Rsch. Orgn. Avocations: music, reading. Office: Enfant Jesus Hosp Neurobiology Ctr, 1401 18th St, Quebec, PQ Canada G1J 1Z4

PARENT, GILBERT, mem. Can. Ho. of Commons; b. Mattawa, Ont., Can., July 25, 1935; m. Joan Davis, Aug. 23, 1958; children: Michèle Hundertmark, Monique Finley, Madeleine Thomas, Thér250se. BSc, St. Joseph's Coll.; MA, Niagara U.; MEdn, U. N.Y. M.P. Ho. of Commons, Ottawa, Ont., Can., 1974; re-elected, 1979, 88; Parliamentary Sec.to Min. Veterans Affairs Ottawa, Ont., Can., 1977-79, Parliamentary Sec. to Min. of Labour, 1979-81, Parliamentary Sec. to Min. Fitness and Amateur Sports, 1981-83; Speaker of the House Ho. of Commons, Ottawa, Ont., Can.; appted. Critic for Youth, 1989, Labour, 1992; assoc. critic CIDA, 1989, Industry, 1992. Mem. Can.-U.S. Parliamentary Assn. (vice-chair). Office: House of Commons, Rm 685 Confederation Bldg, Ottawa, ON Canada K1A 0A6*

PARENT, LOUISE MARIE, lawyer; b. San Francisco, Aug. 28, 1950; d. Jules D. and Mary Louise (Bartholomew) P.; m. John P. Casaly, Aug. 5, 1980. AB, Smith Coll., 1972; JD, Georgetown U., 1975. Bar: N.Y. 1976, U.S. Dist. Ct. (so. dist.) N.Y. 1976. Assoc. Donovan Leisure, N.Y.C., 1975-77; various positions, then gen. counsel Am. Express Info. Svcs. Corp., N.Y.C., 1977-92; dep. gen. counsel Am. Express Co., N.Y.C., 1992-93, exec. v.p., gen. counsel, 1993—; mem. legal adv. com. N.Y. Stock Exch. Bd. dirs. A Better Chance Inc., Cooke Found. Bd. Rvw. Mem. ABA (com. depts. corp. law). Home: 1170 Fifth Ave New York NY 10029-6527 Office: Am Express Co Am Express Tower World Fin Ctr New York NY 10285

PARENT, MARK, engring company executive, computer support company executive. Grad., Western New England Coll., 1970. Pres. U. E., Inc., Holyoke, Mass., 1979—. Office: U E Inc Cross Rd Industrial Park Holyoke MA 01040*

PARENT, RODOLPHE JEAN, Canadian air force official, pilot; b. Thurso, Que., Can., June 16, 1937; s. Eugène Jean and Eliane Marie (Raby) P.; m. Michelle Marie Masse, Aug. 10, 1963; children—Stéphane, Nathalie, Cynthia. Student, Coll. Militaire Royal de St-Jean, 1958-61; B.Sc., Royal Mil. Coll. Can., Kingston, Ont., 1963. Commd. Royal Can. Air Force, 1958; advanced through grades to brig.-gen., 1984; joined 425 Squadron for ops. on CF-101 aircraft Bagotville, Que., 1964-69; worked for Directorate of Recruiting and Selection at Nat. Def. Hdqrs., Ottawa, Ont., Can., 1969-71; chief of ops. 433 Tactical Fighter Squadron, Bagotville, 1972-75, Can. Forces Base Bagotville, 1975-76; comdg. officer 433 Tactical Fighter Squadron, 1976-80; asst. dir. personnel careers Nat. Def. Hdqrs., Ottawa, 1980-81; base comdr. Can. Forces Base Lahr, Federal Republic Germany, 1981-83; commandant Coll. Militaire Royal de Saint-Jean, Que., 1983-86; dir. gen. personnel careers other ranks Nat. Def. Hdqrs., Ottawa, 1986-89; def. attaché Paris, 1989-92; ret., 1992. Decorated Order of Mil. Merit, Order of St. John of Jerusalem. Roman Catholic. Avocations: hockey; tennis; windsurfing.

PARENTE, EMIL J., chemical engineering executive; b. N.Y.C., Aug. 2, 1930; m. Phyllis Sara Gordon, Mar. 15, 1970; children: Victoria Rebecca, Stephen Raphael. BSChemE, Cooper Union, 1953; MSChemE, NYU, 1957. Process engr. Vitro Corp. Am., 1953-54; from process engr. to project mgr. Fluor, Singmaster & Breyer Inc., 1954-63; from project mgr. to v.p., gen. mgr. petroleum chem. div. sales The Ralph M. Parsons Co., 1963-78; v.p., then sr. v.p. sales Fluor Corp., 1978-82; sr. v.p., gen. mgr. advanced tech. div. and telecommunications div. Fluor Corp., Irvine, Calif., 1982-84; pres. Fluor Tech. Inc., Irvine, 1984-86; pres. govt. sector Fluor Daniel, Inc.,

Irvine, 1986—; lectr. on energy and synthetic fuels. Contbr. papers to profl. jours. Mem. Am. Inst. Chem. Engrs., Am. Petroleum Inst., U.S. C. of C. (energy com. 1981-84), U.S.-Arab C. of C. (bd. dirs. 1975-78). Office: F D Svcs Inc 100 Fluor Daniel Dr Greenville SC 29607-2762 Also: Fluor Corp 3333 Michelson Dr Irvine CA 92730-0001

PARENTE, MICHAEL, electrical engineer; b. Bklyn., Mar. 3, 1941; s. Rocco and Florence (Ferrone) P.; m. Kathleen Geissler, Dec. 27, 1964; children: Kathryn, Carol. BSEE, Poly. Inst. Bklyn., 1962, MSEE, 1963. Registered electromagnetic compatibility engr. Supr. Bell Labs., Whippany, N.J., 1963-83; dir. electromagnetic compatibility Bell Comm. Rsch., Morristown, N.J., 1984-92; mem. adv. bd. Protection Engrs. Group, Bethesda, Md., 1980-92; mem. Accredited Standards Com. C62, 1984—, spl. rapporteur CCITT Study Group 5, 1988-92. Contbr. articles to profl. jours.; inventor blocking oscillator, 1970; co-inventor DC to DC converter system, 1969, arcing fault detection system, 1970. Adult leader Boy Scouts Am., Florham Park, N.J., 1967-92; trustee Florham Park Pub. Libr., 1981-92. Fellow IEEE (chmn. low voltage comm. protective devices 1983—, Standards medallion 1988, outstanding working group 1995); mem. Tau Beta Pi, Eta Kappa Nu.

PARENTE, WILLIAM JOSEPH, political science educator; b. Chgo., July 7, 1937; s. Salvatore S. and Genevieve (Rooney) P.; m. Diane Alpern, Nov. 30, 1963; children: Elizabeth, Margaret, William Joseph, Caroline, Rebecca, Catherine, Abigail, Christopher, Natalya. A.B. cum laude, Xavier U., Ohio, 1961; Ph.D. (Woodrow Wilson fellow, Woodrow Wilson dissertation fellow), Georgetown U., 1970. Woodrow Wilson intern Wilberforce (Ohio) U., 1965-66; asst. prof., chmn. polit. sci. dept. Antioch Coll., 1966-69, assoc. dean faculty, 1969-70; dean Coll. Arts and Scis., U. Scranton, Pa., 1970-85; assoc. prof. polit. sci. Coll. Arts and Scis., U. Scranton 1970-73, prof., 1973—; Fulbright scholar Chulalongkorn U., Bangkok, Thailand, 1985-86, Inst. for Policy Studies, Washington, 1986-87; mem. nat. Fulbright screening com. for East Asia, Southeast Asia; mem. adv. com. Inst. Internat. Edn.; cons. on world affairs to Peace Corps. Author articles in field. Fellow Inst. Acad. Deans, 1971, Inst. Ednl. Mgmt., Harvard Bus. Sch., 1972, Fulbright fellow, Korea, 1974, Indonesia, 1978, Germany, 1980, Thailand, 1985-86, fellow NEH Seminar, U. Va., 1976, Harvard U., 1985, Columbia U., 1988, George Mason U., Va., 1990, UCLA, 1991, U. Mich., 1992, William and Mary, 1993, U. Iowa, 1994; scholar-diplomat program State Dept., 1970, 73; vis. scholar in humanities NYU, 1989. Fellow Union Experimenting Colls. and Univs., Inst. for Policy Studies, Soc. for Religion in Higher Edn.; mem. Am. Polit. Sci. Assn., Assn. Jesuit Colls. and Univs. (chmn. conf. on internat. edn. 1981-85), Alpha Sigma Nu (nat. sec.-treas. 1979-82, nat. pres. 1983-85), Pi Sigma Alpha, Eta Sigma Phi, Alpha Sigma Lambda, Tau Kappa Alpha, Phi Alpha Theta. Roman Catholic. Office: U Scranton Scranton PA 18510

PARESKY, DAVID S., travel company executive; b. Boston, Sept. 27, 1938; s. Paul and Ada (Rudnick) P.; m. Linda Kotzen, Aug. 18, 1963; children: Pamela, Laura, Mark. BA, Williams Coll., 1960; JD, Harvard U., 1963, MBA, 1965. Bar: Mass. Pres., chmn. bd. Crimson Travel Service, Inc., Cambridge, Mass., 1965-89; pres., CEO Thomas Cook Travel, Cambridge, 1989-94, also chmn. bd. dirs. Dir., Gov.'s Mgmt. Task Force, Boston, 1979-83, Mass. Port Authority, Boston 1980-83; mem. Bd. Higher Edn., Boston 1980; trustee New Eng. Med. Ctr., 1982-83; mem. Bd. Regents of Higher Edn., Boston, 1980-86. Mem. Mass. Bar Assn., Am. Soc. Travel Agts., Travel Trust Internat., Greater Boston C. of C., Young Pres. Orgn. (chmn. New Eng. chpt. 1985), Phi Beta Kappa. Home: 231 Winter St Weston MA 02193-1034

PARET, PETER, historian; b. Berlin, Apr. 13, 1924; s. Hans and Suzanne Aimée (Cassirer) P.; m. Isabel Harris, Sept. 23, 1961; children: Suzanne Aimée, Paul Louis Michel. BA, U. Calif., Berkeley, 1949; Ph.D., U. London, 1960, DLitt, 1992; DLitt, U. S.C., 1995. Resident tutor, delegacy of extramural studies Oxford U., 1959-60; research assoc. Center of Internat. Studies, Princeton U., 1960-62, 63; vis. asst. prof. U. Calif., Davis, 1962-63; assoc. prof. U. Calif., 1963-66, prof., 1966-69; prof. history Stanford U., 1969-77, Raymond A. Spruance prof. internat. history, 1977-86; Andrew W. Mellon Prof. in humanities Inst. Advanced Study, Princeton, N.J., 1986—; mem. Inst. for Advanced Study, Princeton, 1966-67; fellow Ctr. for Advanced Study in Behavioral Scis., Stanford, Calif., 1968-69; vis. fellow London Sch. Econs., 1972-73; NEH fellow, 1979-80; sr. fellow Hoover Instn., Stanford U., 1988-93. Author: (with John Shy) Guerrillas in the 1960's, 1962, French Revolutionary Warfare from Indochina to Algeria, 1964, Yorck and the Era of Prussian Reform, 1966, Clausewitz and the State, 1976, rev. edit., 1985; The Berlin Secession, 1980, Art as History, 1988, (with Beth Irwin Lewis and Paul Paret) Persuasive Images, 1992, Understanding War, 1992; editor, translator: (with Michael Howard) On War (C. v. Clausewitz), 1976, (with Daniel Moran) Historical and Political Writings (C. v. Clausewitz), 1992; editor: Frederick the Great, 1968, Frederick the Great—A Historical Profile, 1972, Sisyphus or the Limits of Education, 1973, The Age of German Liberation, 1977, Berliner Secession, 1981, Makers of Modern Strategy, 1986, (with Ekkehard Mai) Sammler, Stifter & Museen, 1993. Served with inf. U.S. Army, 1943-46. Fellow AAAS, Royal Hist. Soc., Hist. Kom zu Berlin, Leo Baeck Inst., London Sch. Econs. (hon.); mem. Am. Philos. Soc. (Jefferson medal), Soc. for Mil. History (Samuel Eliot Morison medal). Office: Sch Hist Studies Inst Advanced Study Princeton NJ 08540

PARETSKY, DAVID, microbiology educator; b. Bklyn., Nov. 15, 1918; s. Joe and Ethel (Krupnick) P.; m. Mary Ellen Edwards, Dec. 22, 1942; children: Jeremy L., Sara N., Daniel P., Jonathan M., Nicholas G. B.S., Coll. City N.Y., 1939; Ph.D., Iowa State U., 1948. Instr. Iowa State Coll., 1947-48; asst. prof. Rensselaer Poly. Inst., 1948-51; mem. faculty U. Kans., 1951—, chmn. dept. microbiology, 1957-76, prof. microbiology, 1959—, Univ. distinguished prof., 1976-89, Univ. distinguished prof. emeritus, 1989—; vis. prof. oncology, special fellow NIH, U. Wis., 1964-65; past mem. microbiology rev. panel NIH; past mem. cancer research tng. grant com. Nat. Cancer Inst.; past mem. coop. coll.-sch. sci. program NSF; advisor U.S. Army Med. R & D Command, 1984-87; mem. Kans. Lab. Adv. Commn., 1957-75; speaker Found. for Bacteriology, 1971-72; vis. prof. dept. microbiology Hadassah Med. Sch., Jerusalem, 1976. Editorial bd.: Applied Microbiology, 1963-76. Served with AUS, 1943-46. Fellow AAAS, Am. Acad. Microbiology; mem. Am. Soc. Biol. Chemists, Soc. Am. Microbiologists (council 1960-63, pres. Mo. Valley br. 1966-67), Soc. Am. Rickettsial (pres. elect 1986-87), Phi Beta Kappa. Jewish. Research on Rickettsial biochemistry, microbial physiology, host parasite interaction. Home: 2834 Missouri Lawrence KS 66046 Office: Dept Microbiology Univ Kansas Lawrence KS 66044

PARETSKY, SARA N., writer; b. Ames, Iowa, June 8, 1947; d. David Paretsky and Mary E. Edwards; m. S. Courtenay Wright, June 19, 1976; children: Kimball Courtenay, Timothy Charles, Philip William. BA, U. Kans., 1967; MBA, PhD, U. Chgo., 1977. Mgr. Urban Rsch Ctr., Chgo., 1971-74, CNA Ins. Co., Chgo., 1977-85; writer, 1985—. Author: (novels) Indemnity Only, 1982, Deadlock, 1984 (Friends of Am. Writers award 1985), Killing Orders, 1985, Bitter Medicine, 1987, Blood Shot, 1988 (Silver Dagger award Crime Writers Assn., 1988), Burn Marks, 1990, Guardian Angel, 1992, Tunnel Vision, 1994, also numerous articles and short stories. Pres. Sisters in Crime, Chgo., 1986-88; dir. Nat. Abortion Rights Action League Ill., 1987—. Named Woman of Yr. Ms mag., N.Y.C., 1987. Mem. Crime Writers Assn. (Silver Dagger award 1988), Mystery Writers Am. (v.p. 1989), Authors Guild, Chgo. Network. Avocations: baseball, opera. *

PARFET, DONALD REID, pharmaceutical executive; b. Kalamazoo, Sept. 26, 1952; s. R. Ted and Martha (Gilmore) P.; m. Ann Peelor Van DeWater, July 21, 1973; children: Sydney, Rachel. BA in Econs., U. Ariz., 1975; MBA in Fin., U. Mich., 1977. With Acctg. & Fin. Profit. Devel. Program Upjohn Co., Kalamazoo, 1977-80; mktg. contr. domestic pharm. divsn. Upjohn Co., Kalamazoo, 1980-82, contr. domestic pharm. administrn., 1982-85, v.p. administrn., 1986-89, sr. v.p. administrn., 1989-91, exec. v.p. administrn., 1991—; exec. v.p. Upjohn Healthcare Systems, 1985. Contbr. articles to profl. jours. Chmn. adv. coun. U. Mich. Bus. Sch.; active U. Okla. State Ctr. Molecular Medicine, Leadership Edn. & Devel.; bd. dirs. First of Am. Nat. Assn. Mfrs.; chmn. bd. trustees Kalamazoo Coll.; trustee Bronson Hosp., Coun. Mich. Founds. Avocations: sailing, skiing, tennis. Home: 4841 Ridgewood Richland MI 49083-9550 Office: Upjohn Co 7000 Portage Rd Kalamazoo MI 49001

PARFET, WILLIAM UPJOHN, medical supplies manufacturing company executive; b. Ann Arbor, Mich., 1946. BA with honors, Lake Forest Coll., 1970; MBA, U. Mich., 1972; D. of Pub. Svc. (hon.), Western Mich. U., 1993. With Upjohn Co., Kalamazoo, 1972-93, asst. to treas., 1978-79, fin. corp. fin. and treasury adminstrv. svcs., 1979-81, corp. contr., 1981-82, v.p., corp. contr., 1982-84, corp. v.p., treas., 1984-88, corp. v.p. consumer products, healthcare svcs., pharm. strategic planning, 1988-89, corp. exec. v.p., 1989-90, pres., 1991-93, vice chmn. bd., 1993; resigned, 1993; pres., CEO Richard-Allan Med., 1993—; bd. dirs. Upjohn Co., Old Kent Fin. Corp., CMS Energy, Universal Foods, Stryker Corp. Bd. dirs. Coun. Econ. Devel. Mem. Fin. Execs. Inst. (bd. dirs., bd. of CEO coun. econ. devel.).

PARFIT, GAVIN J., international management executive; b. Durban, South Africa, Oct. 15, 1947; m. Isabel Barzun; children: Elizabeth, Emily. ACIS, U. Natal, South Africa, 1970; MBA, Cranfield Inst. Tech., U.K., 1974. CEO Henry Vale & Co., South Africa, 1966-72; pres., CEO Golodetz Corp., N.Y.C., 1987—; dir. Chem. Bank Internat., Ltd., N.Y.C., London, 1983-87; v.p. Chemical Bank, N.Y., London, 1975-83. Trustee Turtle Bay Music Sch., N.Y.C., 1993. With South African Air Force, 1965. Home: 150 E 77th St Apt 5A New York NY 10021-1927 Office: Golodetz Corp 142 W 57th St New York NY 10019

PARHAM, ELLEN SPEIDEN, nutrition educator; b. Mitchells, Va., July 15, 1938; d. Marion Coote and Rebecca Virginia (McNiel) Speiden; m. Arthur Robert Parham, Jr., Dec. 16, 1961; children: Katharine Alma, Cordelia Alyx. BS in Nutrition, Va. Poly. Inst., 1960; PhD in Nutrition, U. Tenn., 1967, MEd in Counseling, 1994. Registered dietitian. Asst. prof. to prof. No. Ill. U., DeKalb, Ill., 1966—; coord. programs in dietetics No. Ill. U., DeKalb, 1981-86, 90—, coord. grad. faculty in Human and Family Resources, 1985-87; cons. on nutrition various hosps., clins. and bus., Ill., 1980—; founder, dir. Horizons Weight Control Program, DeKalb, 1983-91; founder, leader "Escaping the Tyranny of the Scale" Group, 1994—; co-chair Nutrition Coalition for Ill., 1989-90; ptnr., mgr. Design on Fabric, 1986—. Bd. editors Jour. Nutrition Edn., 1985-90, Jour. Am. Dietetic Assn., 1991—; contbr. articles to profl. jours. Mem. Am. Inst. Nutrition, Soc. Nutrition Edn., Am. Dietetic Assn., Am. Home Econs. Assn., Soc. Nutrition Edn. (treas. 1991-94), N.Am. Assn. Study Obesity. Avocations: painting in watercolor, gardening, reading.

PARHAM, JAMES ROBERT, lawyer; b. East St. Louis, Ill., June 3, 1921; s. James Elbert and Edith Virginia (May) P.; m. Caroline Short, Nov. 4, 1950 (dec.); m. Elizabeth Joan Rinck, June 29, 1957; children: James R., Jr., Joseph R., J. Randolph. A.B., Princeton U., 1943; J.D. with honors, U. Ill. 1948. Bar: Ill. 1948, U.S. Dist. Ct. (so. dist.) Ill. 1948, U.S. Supreme Ct. 1968. Assoc., Pope & Driemeyer, East St. Louis, 1948-59, ptnr., Belleville, Ill., 1960-84, Thompson & Mitchell, 1985—; mem. adv. council Ill. Inst. for Continuing Legal Edn., Springfield, Ill., 1965-74. Contbr. articles to profl. jours. Sec., YMCA of S.W. Ill., Belleville, 1979-84. Served with U.S. Air Corps, 1943, 45, USAFR, 1950-53. Recipient Man of Yr. award Bicounty YMCA, Belleville, 1973; Disting. Service award Ill. Inst. Continuing Edn., 1974. Fellow Am. Bar Found., Ill. State Bar Found.; mem. Ill. State Bar Assn. (chmn. state tax sect. 1974), ABA, Met. St. Louis Bar Assn., Res. Officers Assn., Order of Coif. Republican. Methodist. Clubs: St. Clair Country (Belleville, v.p. 1955-56); Grey Oaks Country Club (Naples, Fla.). Lodge: Rotary (pres. Belleville St. Louis club 1976-77). Home: 7535 Claymont Ct # 3 Belleville IL 62223-2018 Office: Thompson & Mitchell 525 W Main St PO Box 750 Belleville IL 62222

PARINS, ROBERT JAMES, professional football team executive, judge; b. Green Bay, Wis., Aug. 23, 1918; s. Frank and Nettie (Denissen) P.; m. Elizabeth L. Carroll, Feb. 8, 1941; children: Claire, Andrea, Richard, Teresa, Lu Ann. B.A., U. Wis., 1940, LL.B., 1942. Bar: Wis. Supreme Ct. 1942. Sole practice law Green Bay, 1942-68; dist. atty. Brown County, Wis., 1949-50, cir. judge, 1968-82, res. judge, 1982—; pres. Green Bay Packers, Inc., 1982-90, chmn. bd., 1990-92; hon. chmn. bd., 1992-94. Mem. Wis. State Bar Assn. Roman Catholic. Office: Green Bay Packers PO Box 10628 Green Bay WI 54307-0628

PARIS, DEMETRIUS THEODORE, electrical engineering educator; b. Stavroupolis, Thrace, Greece, Sept. 27, 1928; came to U.S., 1947, naturalized, 1954; s. Theodore P. and Aspasia (Yannakis) Paraskevopoulos; m. Elsie Edwards, Jan. 5, 1952. B.S., Miss. State U., 1951; M.S., Ga. Inst. Tech., 1958, Ph.D., 1962. With Westinghouse Electric Corp., 1952-58, Lockheed-Ga. Co., 1958-59; asst. prof. elec. engring. Ga. Inst. Tech., 1959-63, assoc. prof., 1963-66, prof., 1966—, asst. dir. elec. engring., 1966-69, dir., 1969-89, v.p for rsch and grad. programs, 1989—; cons. Sci.-Atlanta, Inc., Lockheed-Ga. Co., U.S. Army Ltd. War Lab., Aberdeen, Md. Author: Basic Electromagnetic Theory, 1969. Recipient Sigma Xi award for best research paper by a mem. Ga. Inst. Tech. faculty, 1965. Fellow IEEE (editor trans on edn. 1976-79, Centennial medal 1984, ednl. activities bd. meritorious svc. citation 1989, IEEE rep. to Accrditation Bd. for Engring. and Tech. bd. dirs. 1990-95); mem. IEEE Edn. Soc. (Achievement award 1980, pres. 1986), Am. Soc. Engring. Edn., Sigma Xi, Kappa Mu Epsilon, Tau Beta Pi, Eta Kappa Nu, Phi Kappa Phi. Home: 2797 Alpine Rd NE Atlanta GA 30305-3401

PARIS, PAUL CROCE, mechanics educator, engineering consultant, researcher; b. Buffalo, Aug. 7, 1930; s. Russell Horace and Martha Elizabeth (Robertson) P.; m. Elizabeth Alderman, Jan. 13, 1963 (div. 1974); children: Gail Elizabeth, Anthony James; m. Christine Ellen Anders, Jan. 10, 1980. BS in Engring. Mechanics, U. Mich., 1953; MS in Applied Mechanics, Lehigh U., 1955, PhD in Applied Mechanics, 1962. Instr. mechanics Lehigh U., Bethlehem, Pa., 1955-57, asst. prof., 1962-63, assoc. prof., 1965-72, asst. prof. Inst. Rsch. 1962-64; asst. prof. civil engring. U. Wash., Seattle, 1957-62; pres., chief exec. officer Del. Rsch. Corp., Hellertown, Pa., 1968—; prof. mechanics Washington U., St. Louis, 1976—; program dir. NSF, Washington, 1964-65; vis. prof. Brown U., Providence, 1974-76; cons. Westinghouse, U.S. Steel, Boeing Co., Lawrence Radiation Lab., Rand Corp., NRC, NASA, others. Co-author: The Stress Analysis of Cracks Handbook, 1973, 2d edit., 1985; contbr. numerous articles to profl. jours. Fellow ASTM (award of merit 1972, Fracture Mechanics medal 1987), Internat. Congress on Fracture (hon.), Internat. Fatigue Series (hon. life); mem. Commanderie de Bordeaux (comdr. 1980—), Commanderie de Laugier, Sigma Xi. Avocations: piloting, wildlife conservation. Home: PO Box 13 Cherryville MO 65446-0013 Office: Washington U Dept Mech Engring Saint Louis MO 63130

PARIS, PETER JUNIOR, religion educator, minister; b. New Glasgow, N.S., Can., May 30, 1933; s. Freeman Archibald and Violet Agatha (Jewell) P.; m. Shirley Ann McMillen, May 13, 1961; children: Valerie Lynn ToKunbo, Peter Brett. BA, Acadia U. Wolfville, N.S., 1956, BD, 1958; MA, U. Chgo., 1969, PhD, 1975; DD (hon.), McGill U., 1989, Acadia U., 1990. Ordained minister African United Bapt. Assn. N.S. Gen. sec. U. Alta. chpt. Student Christian Movement Can., Edmonton, 1958-61, spl. travelling sec. Toronto, 1964-65; nat. travelling sec. Student Christian Movement Nigeria, Ibadan, 1961-64; instr. urban studies Associated Coll. of Mid-West, Chgo., 1969-70; instr. ethics and soc. Howard U. Div. Sch., Washington, 1970-72; asst. prof. ethics and soc. Vanderbilt U. Div. Sch., Nashville, 1972-77, assoc. prof., 1977-83, prof., 1983-85; Elmer G. Homrighausen prof. Christian social ethics Princeton (N.J.) Theol. Seminary, 1985—; sr. fellow Mathey Coll., Princeton U., 1988—; cons. Assn. Theol. Schs., Indpls., 1986—; W.E.B. DuBois Inst., Harvard U., 1988—; lectr. U. S.Africa, Pretoria, Aug.- 1988; fellow W.E.B. DuBois Inst., Harvard U., 1990. Author: Black Leaders in Conflict, 1978 (excerpts in Congl. Record May 1981), rev. as Black Religious Leaders: Conflict in Unity, 1991, The Social Teaching of the Black Churches, 1985; co-editor: Justice and the Holy, 1989; mem. editorial bd. Soundings: An Interdisciplinary Jour., Jour. Religion, Jour. Religious Ethics; author essays and chpts. in books. Ford Found. fellow Ctr. Urban Studies, U. Chgo., 1968-70, Woodrow Wilson fellow, 1990; rsch. grantee Lilly Endowment, Vanderbilt U., NRC, Princeton Theol. Seminary. Fellow Soc. for Values in Higher Edn.; mem. Am. Acad. Religion (assoc. dir. 1983-85, v.p. 1993, pres.-elect 1994, pres. 1995), Soc. Christian Ethics (bd. dirs. 1977-82, v.p. 1990, pres. 1991), Soc. for Study Black Religion (founding), Am. Theol. Soc. Democrat. Office: Princeton Theol Sem Dept of Theology CN 821 Princeton NJ 08542

PARIS, ZACHARY T., lawyer; b. Cleve., Aug. 30, 1948. BA, Yale U., 1970, JD, 1973. Bar: Ohio 1973. Law clk. U.S. Dist. Ct. (no. dist.) Ohio; ptnr. Jones, Day, Reavis & Pogue, Cleve. Mem. Phi Beta Kappa. Office: Jones Day Reavis & Pogue North Point 901 Lakeside Ave E Cleveland OH 44114-1190

PARISEAU, WILLIAM G., mining engineer, educator. Prof. dept. mining & engring. U. Utah, Salt Lake City. Recipient Rock Mechanics award Soc. Mining, Metallogy & Exploration, 1990. Office: U Utah Dept Mining & Engring 315 W B Browning Bldg Salt Lake City UT 84112-1118*

PARISER, RUDOLPH, chemical company executive, consultant; b. Harbin, China, Dec. 8, 1923; came to U.S., 1941, naturalized, 1944; s. Ludwig Jacob and Lia (Rubinstein) P.; m. Margaret Louise Marsh, July 31, 1972. BS in Chemistry, U. Calif., Berkeley, 1944; PhD in Phys. Chemistry, U. Minn., 1950. With E.I. du Pont de Nemours & Co., Wilmington, Del., 1950-89, with elastomer chems. dept., 1967-79, dir. pioneering rsch., 1974-79, rsch. dir. polymer products dept., 1980-81, dir. polymer sci. cen. R & D dept., 1981-86, dir. advanced materials sci. cen. R & D dept., 1986-89; cons., pres. R. Pariser & Co., Inc., Hockessin, Del., 1989—; mem. materials rsch. adv. com. Nat. Sci. Found., 1986-89. Assoc. editor Jour. Chem. Physics, 1966-69, Chem. Physics Letters, 1967-70, Du Pont Innovation, 1969-75; mem. adv. bd. Jour. Polymer Sci., 1980-89; mem. editl. bd. New Polymeric Materials, 1985-94; patentee in field; contbr. articles to sci. jours. With U.S. Army, 1944-46. Mem. AAAS, Am. Chem. Soc., Am. Phys. Soc., Internat. Union Pure and Applied Chemistry, Phila. Interlocuters (pres. 1972-76), Sigma Xi, Phi Lambda Upsilon, Du Pont Country Club, Rodney Sq. Club, Univ. and Whist Club Wilmington. Avocations: skiing, tennis, golf, sailing, gardening.

PARISH, FRED, engineering company executive, architectural firm executive; b. 1942. Pres. C P R Assoc., Inc., De Pere, Wis., 1972—. Office: C P R Assoc Inc 421 Laweence Dr De Pere WI 54115*

PARISH, J. MICHAEL, lawyer, writer; b. Decatur, Ill., Nov. 9, 1943; s. John Mitchell and Gladys Margaret (Daulton) P.; m. Susan Lee Sgarlat, July 24, 1976 (div.); m. Ellen R. Harnett, Dec. 3, 1991; children: Margaret Ruth, William Walter. AB cum laude, Princeton U., 1965; LLB, Yale U., 1968. Assoc. LeBoeuf Lamb et al, N.Y.C., 1968-73, ptnr., 1974-89; ptnr. Winthrop Stimson Putnam & Roberts, N.Y.C., 1989-95, Reid & Priest, N.Y.C., 1995—; bd. dirs. Forum Funds, Portland, Maine. Contbr. poetry to mags. Dir. PBS Am. Poetry Project, 1985-90; coord. Yale Law Sch. Clinton Election com. Mem. Princeton Club N.Y. Avocations: soccer referee, coach Little League, poetry. Home: 100 Riverside Dr New York NY 10024-4822 Office: Reid & Priest 40 W 57th St New York NY 10019

PARISH, JAMES ROBERT, author, cinema historian; b. Cambridge, Mass., Apr. 21, 1944; s. Fred Arthur and Ann Lois (Magilevy) P. BA, U. Pa., 1964, LLB, 1967. Pres. Entertainment Copyright Rsch.Co. Inc., N.Y.C., 1967-68; film reporter, reviewer, interviewer Variety, Motion Picture Daily, 1968-69; entertainment publicist Harold Rand & Co., 1969-70; freelance writer, publicist, film book cons., film reviewer, novelist, 1970—. Author: (with P. Michael) The Emmy Awards: A Pictorial History, 1970, The Fox Girls, 1971, The Great Movie Series, 1971 (with A.H. Marill) The Cinema of Edward G. Robinson, 1972, The Slapstick Queens, 1972, The Paramount Pretties, 1972, (with R. Bowers) The MGM Stock Company, 1973, Actors TV Credits, 1950-72, 73, Good Dames, 1973, (with M.R. Pitts) The Great Spy Pictures, 1973, The RKO Gals, 1973, (with S. Whitney), The George Raft File, 1973, (with M.R. Pitts) Film Directors: A Guide to Their American Pictures, 1974, Hollywood's Great Love Teams, 1974, (with S. Whitney) Vincent Price Unmasked, 1974, The Great Movie Heroes, 1975, (with D. Stanke), The Glamour Girls, 1975, The Debonairs, 1975, (with L. DeCarl) Hollywood Players: The Forties, 1975, (with J. Ano) Liza! (The Liza Minnelli Story), 1975, (with M.R. Pitts) The Great Gangster Pictures, 1975, The Elvis Presley Scrapbook, 1975, (with W. Leonard) Hollywood Players: The Thirties, 1976, (with D. Stanke) The All Americans, 1976, Film Directors: A Guide to Western Europe, 1976, Great Child Stars, 1976, The Jeanette McDonald Story, 1976, (with D. Stanke) The Leading Ladies, 1977, (with M.R. Pitts) The Great Science Fiction Pictures, 1977, Film Actors Guide: Western Europe, 1977, The Elvis Presley Scrapbook (update), 1977, (with M. Trost) Actors TV Credits: Supplement One, 1977, (with M.R. Pitts) Hollywood on Hollywood, 1978, (with R. Braff et al.) Hollywood Character Actors, 1978, (with G. Mank and D. Stanke) The Hollywood Beauties, 1978, (with W. Leonard) The Funsters, 1979, (with D. Stanke) The Forties Gals, 1980, (with G. Mank) The Hollywood Reliables, 1980, The Great American Movies Book, 1980, (with G. Mank) The Best of MGM, 1981, (with M.R. Pitts) The Great Spy Pictures II, 1986, (with M.R. Pitts) The Great Gangster Pictures II, 1987, (with M.R. Pitts) The Great Western Pictures II, 1988, Black Action Pictures from Hollywood, 1989, (with M.R. Pitts) The Great Science Fiction Pictures II, 1990, (with V. Terrace) Complete Actors TV Credits, 1990, (with M.R. Pitts) Hollywood Songsters, 1990, The Great Cop Pictures, 1990, Prison Pictures from Hollywood, 1991, (with M.R. Pitts) Hollywood's Great Musicals, 1992, (with D. Stanke) Hollywood Baby Boomers, 1992, Prostitution in Hollywood Film, 1992, The Hollywood Death Book, 1992; Let's Talk: America's Favorite Talk Show Hosts, 1993, Gays and Lesbians in Mainstream Hollywood, 1993, Hollywood's Celebrity Death Book, updated and expanded, 1993, Ghosts and Angels on the Hollywood Screen, 1994, Today's Black Hollywood, 1995, Pirates and Seafaring Swashbucklers, 1995; assoc. editor: The American Movies Reference Book, 1969, TV Movies, 1969, The Great American Movie Book, 1980. Mem. Phi Beta Kappa. Address: 4338 Gentry Ave Apt 1 Studio City CA 91604-1764 *To succeed in one's ambitions requires an unyielding avoidance of other people's skepticisms.*

PARISH, JOHN COOK, insurance executive; b. Montezuma, Iowa, Mar. 26, 1910; s. Ariel Robert and Mary Ora (Cook) P.; m. Elizabeth Myers, Sept. 2, 1936; children: John C., Michael Myers, Judith, Robert S. Student, UCLA; B.A., Graham Coll., 1936. Officer Dollar S.S. Lines, Seattle, 1930-31; with Ginn & Co. (pubs.), Manila, 1933-34; sec. to U.S. rep. Warsaw, Poland, 1934; with St. Paul Fire & Marine Ins. Co., 1936—, exec. spl. agt., 1943-44, asst. mgr. Pacific dept., 1947-48, asst. sec., 1948-50, sec., 1950-68, v.p., 1968—; also dir.; sec. St. Paul Mercury Ins. Co., 1950-68, v.p., 1968—; also dir.; v.p. St. Paul Ins. Co., 1968—. Mem. Bishop's council Minn. Espiscopal Diocese; past pres., treas. Summit Sch. for Girls, St. Paul; past pres. Indianhead council Boy Scouts Am., past regional chmn. and mem. nat. exec. bd., internat. commr., v.p., 1972-78; hon. v.p. U.S. Found. for Internat. Scouting; chmn. St. Paul United Fund, 1963, pres., 1966; trustee Endowment Fund, Seabury Western Theol. Sem., Am. Humanics Found.; v.p. U.S. Found. Internat. Scouting, Salem Found.; bd. dirs. Inst. Ecumenical and Cultural Research, St. John's Coll.; mem. World Scout Com.; bd. trustees Naples (Fla.) Community Hosp.; sr. warden Trinity By the Cove Episcopal Ch., Naples, 1981-82. Decorated Cross of St. George Colombia); Recipient Silver Tamaraw award Philippine Islands; Inter-Am. award Service to Youth, Silver Beaver, Silver Antelope, Silver Buffalo and Disting. Eagle awards Boy Scouts Am.; Bronze Wolf award for service to youth of world; Emerald Flower award Republic of China; Baden Powell fellow World Scout Found., 1982. Mem. St. Paul C. of C. (dir. 1973—), Beta Theta Pi. Clubs: Somerset Country (St. Paul), Minn. (St. Paul) (dir. 1968); Royal Poinciana (Naples, Fla.) (past pres. and dir.). Home: 122 Moorings Park Dr Apt G607 Naples FL 33942

PARISH, LAWRENCE CHARLES, physician, editor; b. Cambridge, Mass., Oct. 12, 1938; s. Fred A. and Ann Lois (Magilavy) P.; m. Sheila Gail Rovner, July 31, 1966; children: Daniel Howard, Jennifer Leigh. Student, U. Mich., 1955-56; AB, U. Pa., 1959; MD, Tufts U., 1963. Diplomate Am. Bd. Dermatology, 1969. Asst. prof. dermatology U. Pa., Phila., 1969-73, clin. assoc. prof., 1973-80, adj. assoc. prof. comparative dermatology Sch. Vet. Medicine, 1973-87, prof. comparative dermatology, 1987—; clin. assoc. prof. Jefferson Med. Coll., Phila., 1980-84, clin. prof., 1984—; clin. prof. Jefferson Ctr. for Internat. Dermatology, 1987—; vis. prof. Yonsei U., Seoul, Korea, 1983—, Zagazig U., Egypt, 1990—. Author: Louis A. Duhring, Pathfinder for Dermatology, 1967; (with John Crissey) The Dermatology and Syphilology of the 19th Century, 1981; (with others) Cutaneous Infestations of Man and Animal, 1983, Practical Management of the Dermatologic Patient, 1986; (with John Pettit) Manual of Tropical Dermatology, 1984, (with F.G. Gschnait) Manual of Sexually Transmitted Diseases, 1989, (with others) Pediatric Dermatology, 1989, (with Gary P. Lask) Aesthetic Dermatology,

1991, (with others) Color Atlas of Sexually Transmitted Diseases, 1991, (with others) Color Atlas of Difficult Diagnoses i Dermatology, 1994, Manual of Medical Mycology (with others) 1995; editor-in-chief Internat. Jour. Dermatology, 1981—, Clinics in Dermatology, 1983—; mem. editorial bd. Cutis, P&T, Clinical Therapeutics Chronical Dermatologica, Annali Italiani di Dermatologia, Jour. European Acad. Dermatology and Venereology, Drug Therapy, Medicina Cutanea Ibero-Latino-Am. and Decubitus Ulcer, Advances in Therapeutics, Gulf Jour. of Dermatology. Served to maj. U.S. Army, 1967-69; Korea. Recipient Andreus Bello award First Order of Venezuela. Fellow ACP, Coll. Physicians Phila. (chair sect. med. history 1975-78, founding chair sect. dermatology 1982-85); hon. mem. Polish Acad. Dermatology, British Assn. Dermatologists, Am. Acad. Vet. Dermatology, Venezuela Soc. Dermatology, Bulgarian Soc. Dermatology; corr. mem. French Soc. Dermatology and Venereology, Italian Soc. Dermatology and Venereology, Israeli Soc. Dermatology, Istanbul Dermatol. Soc.; mem. Am. Dermatol. Assn., Can. Dermatology Assn., Internat. Soc. Dermatology, History of Dermatology Soc. (founding mem. 1972—), Masons, B'nai Brith. Jewish. Avocations: gardening, travel, history of medicine, genealogy, collecting majollica and bargeware. Home: 941 Bryn Mawr Ave Penn Valley PA 19072-1524 Office: 1819 Jf Kennedy Blvd Philadelphia PA 19103

PARISH, LOUIS LEON, oil company executive; b. Ardmore, Okla., Sept. 17, 1925; s. Lloyd Leon and Ola Emily (Cox) P.; m. Shelley Louise Turner, Dec. 22, 1946 (div. 1972); m. Susie Alice Farris, Oct. 14, 1972; children—Patricia, Larry. B.S. in Bus., Okla. U. Dist. landman Tenneco Oil Co, Midland, Tex., 1955-57; dist. mgr. Tenneco Oil Co, 1957-63; div. exploration mgr. Tenneco Oil Co, Midland, 1963-66; chief landman Tenneco Oil Co, Houston, 1966-70; v.p., div. gen. mgr. Tenneco Oil Co, Denver, 1970-82; sr. v.p. Tenneco Oil Co, Houston, 1982—. Served with USN, 1943-45, PTO. Decorated Purple Heart medal. Mem. Am. Petroleum Inst., Cert. Profl. Landmen. Republican. Baptist. Clubs: Pet, Raveneaux Country (Houston). Avocations: hunting, fishing. Office: Tenneco Oil Co PO Box 2511 Houston TX 77252-2511

PARISH, RICHARD LEE, engineer, consultant; b. Kansas City, Mo., May 31, 1945; s. Charles Lee and Ruth (Duncan) P.; m. Patricia Ann Erickson, June 2, 1968; children: Christie Lynn White, Kerry Anne. BS in Agrl. Engring. U. Mo., 1967, MS in Agrl. Engring., 1968, PhD, 1970. Registered profl. engr., Ohio. Asst., then assoc. prof. engring. Univ. Ark., Fayetteville, 1969-74; mgr. mech. research and devel. O.M. Scott & Sons Co., Marysville, Ohio, 1974-83; assoc. prof., then prof. La. State U., Baton Rouge, 1983—; pvt. practice engring. cons. Baton Rouge, 1984—; cons. in equipment design and evaluation, expert witness testimony in agrl. and hort. equipment, 1984—. Contbr. over 100 articles to profl. jours. and trade pubs.; patentee in field (3). Bd. dirs. Agrl. Missions Found. Recipient Quality award ITT, 1979, Rsch. Dirs. award O.M. Scott Co., 1978; NSF fellow, 1967-69; rsch. grantee Cotton Inc., Raleigh, N.C., 1970-74, 91-93, 95, La. Dept. Natural Resources, 1985-87, Italian Trade Commn., 1988-90. Mem. Am. Soc. Agrl. Engrs. (chmn. agrl. chem. application com. 1982-83, power and machinery div. program com. 1986-87), La. Vegetable Growers Assn., Am. Soc. Hort. Sci. Republican. Baptist. Avocations: gardening, woodwork, bicycling. Home: 834 Forge Ave Baton Rouge LA 70808 Office: La State U Dept Biol and Agrl Engring Baton Rouge LA 70803-4505

PARISH, ROBERT LEE (CHIEF), professional basketball player; b. Shreveport, La., Aug. 30, 1953; m. Nancy Parish; 1 child, Justin. Student, Centenary Coll., 1972-76. Center Golden State Warriors, San Francisco, 1976-80, Boston Celtics, 1980-94; with Charlotte Hornets, 1994—; player NBA Championship Teams, 1981, 84. Named to Sporting News All-Am. First Team, 1976, NBA All-Star Team, 1981-87, 90-91. Office: Charlotte Hornets One Hive Dr Charlotte NC 28217*

PARISH, THOMAS SCANLAN, human development educator; b. Oak Park, Ill., Jan. 24, 1944; s. Robert S. and Florence Catherine (Fleming) P.; m. Joycelyn Pingel, Oct. 2, 1964; children: Robert V., Kimberly E., David G., Thomas P., Kathryn E. BA, No. Ill. U., 1968; MA, Ill. State U., 1969; PhD, U. Ill., 1972. Instr. psychology Parkland Coll., Champaign, Ill., 1971-72; asst. prof. Okla. State U., Stillwater, 1972-76; assoc. prof. Kans. State U., Manhattan, 1976-80, prof., 1980—, asst. to dean of edn., 1992—; assoc. dir. Arios, Kans., 1994—; rsch. coord. for Midwest Desegration Asst. Ctr., 1994—. Assoc. editor: Jour. of Social Studies Rsch., 1994—; cons. editor Jour. Genetic Psychology, 1984—, Jour. Reality Therapy, 1992—, The Genetic, Social and General Psychology Monographs, 1984—; contbr. articles to profl. jours. Bd. dirs. Friendship Tutoring Program, Manhattan, 1982-91, Stillwater Awareness Coun., 1973-74; co-founder, bd. dirs. Youth Alternatives, Inc., Champaign, 1971-72. Fellow Am. Psychol. Soc.; mem. Am. Ednl. Rsch. Assn., APA, Assn. Reality Therapists, Soc. for Rsch. in Child Devel. (bd. dirs.), Phi Delta Kappa, Phi Kappa Phi. Home: 3313 Germann Dr Manhattan KS 66502-8446 Office: Kans State U Coll of Edn Bluemont Hall Manhattan KS 66506

PARISI, JOSEPH (ANTHONY), magazine editor, writer-consultant, educator; b. Duluth, Minn., Nov. 18, 1944; s. Joseph Carl Parisi and Phyllis Susan (Quaranta) Schlecht. B.A. with honors, Coll. St. Thomas, 1966; M.A., U. Chgo., 1967, Ph.D., 1973. Asst. prof. Roosevelt U., Chgo., 1969-78; assoc. editor POETRY Mag., Chgo., 1976-83; acting editor POETRY Mag., 1983-85, editor, 1985—; vis. prof. U. Ill., Chgo., 1978-87; cons., writer ALA, Chgo., 1980—; cons. NEH, 1983—. Author: The Poetry Anthology, 1912-1977, 1978, Voices and Visions Reader's Guide, 1987, Marianne Moore: The Art of a Modernist, 1990, (listener's guide) Poets in Person, 1992; contbr. articles and reviews to profl. jours.; producer, dir. (audio series on NPR) Poets in Person, 1991. Recipient Alvin Bentley award Duns Scotus Coll., 1963; fellow U. Chgo., 1966-69. Mem. Delta Epsilon Sigma. Club: Cliff Dwellers. Avocations: piano, photography, book and record collecting. Office: Poetry Mag 60 W Walton St Chicago IL 60610-3305

PARIZA, MICHAEL WILLARD, research institute executive, microbiology and toxicology educator; b. Waukesha, Wis., Mar. 10, 1943; married; 3 children. BSc in Bacteriology, U. Wis., 1967; MSc in Microbiology, Kans. State U., 1969, PhD in Microbiology, 1971. Postdoctoral trainee McArdle Lab. for Cancer Rsch. U. Wis., Madison, 1973-76, asst. prof. Food Rsch. Inst. dept. Food Microbiology and Toxicology, 1976-81, assoc. prof., 1981-84, prof., 1984—, assoc. dept. chmn., 1981-82, dept. chmn. food microbiology and toxicology, 1982—, dir. Food Rsch. Inst., 1986—, disting prof., 1993—; with Wis. Clin. Cancer Ctr., Environ. Toxicology Ctr., Dept. Nutritional Scis., Dept. Food Sci.; mem. Inst. Medicine's Food Forum; mem. com. on comparative toxicity naturally occurring carcinogens NAS; trustee Internat. Life Scis. Inst.-N.Am., 1986—. With U.S. Army, 1969-71. Office: U Wis Food Rsch Inst 1925 Willow Dr Madison WI 53706-1187

PARIZEAU, JACQUES, Canadian government official; b. Montréal, Aug. 9, 1930; s. Gérard and Germaine (Biron) P.; m. Alicja Poznanska, Apr. 12, 1956 (dec. 1990); children: Bernard, Isabelle; m. Lisette LaPointe, Dec. 12, 1992. Degree, Inst. d'études politiques, Paris, 1952; PhD in Econs., London Sch. Econs., 1955. Prof. École des Hautes Études commerciales, Montréal, 1955-65, 67-70, 85-89; chmn. Inst. Applied Econs., Montréal, 1970-73; mem. Can. Nat. Assembly, Que., 1976-84, 89—; pres. Parti Québécois Can. Nat. Assembly, 1988—; min. fin. Québec Govt., 1976-84, min. revenue, 1976-84, pres. treasury bd., 1976-81, min. fin. instns., 1981-82, chmn. ministerial econ. devel. com., 1981-82, prime min., 1994—; econ. and fin. adviser Premiers of Québec: Lesage, Johnson, Bertrand, Que., 1961-69; pres. Que. Fin. Instns. Task Force, 1970-73; chmn. Comm. of Enquiry on Future of Municipalities, Que., 1985. Editor L'Actualité économique, Montréal, 1955-61; chmn. bd. dirs. Daily Le Jour, Montréal, 1974-75; bd. dirs. Daily Le Devoir, Montréal, 1985-87. Bd. dirs. U. Montréal, 1969-74; bd. dirs. bd. govs. Théâtre du Nouveau-Monde, Montréal, 1988-92; pres. No com. on Referendum on Charlottetown Accord, Que., 1992. Mem. Club de la Garnison (Que.), Knowlton Golf and Country Club (Lac Brome). Roman Catholic. Avocations: reading, music, gardening. Office: Parti Québécois, 7370 St-Hubert, Montreal, PQ Canada H2R 2N3

PARIZEK, ELDON JOSEPH, geologist, college dean; b. Iowa City, Apr. 30, 1920; s. William Joseph and Libbie S. P.; m. Mildred Marie Burger, Aug. 9, 1944; children—Richard, Marianne, Elizabeth, Amy. B.S., U. Iowa, 1942, M.S., 1946, Ph.D., 1949. Instr. U. Iowa, 1947-49; asst. prof. geology U. Ga.,

1949-54, asso. prof., 1954-56; asso. prof. U. Kansas City, 1956-63; prof. U. Mo., Kansas City, 1963—; chmn. dept. geoscis. U. Mo., 1968-78; dean U. Mo. (Coll. Arts and Scis.), 1979-86. Served with USN, 1942-45. Fellow Geol. Soc. Am.; mem. AAUP, Assn. Mo. Geologists, AAAS, Sigma Xi. Roman Catholic. Research, numerous publs. on mass wasting, slope failure, underground space, geology of West Mo. Home: 6913 W 100th Shawnee Mission KS 66212 Office: 5100 Rockhill Rd Kansas City MO 64110-2446

PARK, CAROLE ROPER, state legislator; b. Kansas City, Mo., Sept. 18, 1939; d. Rudolph Joseph and Rose (Mus) Roper; m. William Basil Park, Apr. 24, 1960 (div. May 1962); 1 child, Jennifer. BA in Edn., U. Mo., 1964. Cert. tchr., Mo. Asst. buyer Rothschild's & Harzfelds, Kansas City, 1959-62; tchr. Kansas City Pub. Schs., 1964-76; mem. Mo. Gen. Assembly, Jefferson City, 1977—; mem. state task force on Alzheimers Disease, own. indigent health care. Recipient Monsignor Elmer H. Behrmann award for Outstanding Contbns. to Mental Retardation and Devel. Disabilities, Disting. Svc. award Meritorial Svcs. Mental Health Assn., Legis. Leadership award Mo. State Coalition Community Mental Health Ctrs., Lawmaker award Mo. Mental Health Commn., Profl. award Ark of Life, Project Life, award Neiborhood Coun., award for Outstanding Svc. C. of C.; Carole Roper Park Day named in her honor City of Independence, Mo., Oct., 1994. Mem. NCSL (task force on disabilities), Am. Fedn. Tchrs., Nat. Order Women Legislators, Mo. Order Women Legislators, Friends of Truman Campus, U. Mo. Kansas City Alumni Assn., Sugar Creek Dem. Club. Roman Catholic. Avocations: traveling, reading. Home: 11415 Gill St Sugar Creek MO 64054 Office: Mo Ho of Reps State Capitol Rm 313C Jefferson City MO 65101

PARK, CHARLES DONALD, SR., financial executive; b. N.Y.C., Aug. 1, 1945; s. Charles and Madeline (Springer) P.; m. Pauline De Meo; children: Paula, Madeline. BA, Pace U., 1968, MBA, 1970. Coord. fin. reports Gen. Telephone & Electronics, N.Y.C., 1968-70; mgr. fin. analysis Mobil Corp., N.Y.C., 1970-73; mgr. corp. bus. planning and analysis Gen. Instrument, N.Y.C., 1973-74; controller Microelectronics Group Gen. Instrument, Hicksville, N.Y., 1974-77, chief fin. officer, 1977-81; corp. dir., fin. analysis Bendix, Southfield, Mich., 1981-82; v.p. fin. and administrn. MCI Internat., Inc., Rye Brook, N.Y., 1982-86; sr. v.p. fin. Sprague Techs., Inc., Stamford, Conn., 1987—. Office: Sprague Techs Inc 4 Stamford Forum Stamford CT 06901-3202

PARK, CHUI SUH, pharmacist; b. Sinuiju, Dem. People's Rep. Korea, Aug. 26, 1941; came to U.S., 1969; s. Seung Ryong and Jong Nam (Kim) P.; m. Youn Jin Kim, May 4, 1968; children: Clara, Sharon. BS, Seoul Nat. U., 1964, MS, 1967; MS, Purdue U., 1972; BS, U. Utah, 1976. Registered pharmacist Korea, Calif., Nev., Colo. Pharmacist Hanil Pharm. Industrial Co. Ltd., Seoul, Rep. of Korea, 1966-69, De Jay Drugs, L.A., 1976-79, Disco Drugs, Riverside, Calif., 1979-80, Clark Drugs, L.A., 1980—. Mem. Am. Pharm. Assn., Calif. Employee Pharmacist Assn., Calif. Korean Pharmacist Assn., Seoul Nat. U. Coll. of Pharmacy Alumni Assn. (pres. 1994-95). Democrat. Roman Catholic. Avocations: reading, travel, the game of go. Home: 1236 Cranbrook Pl Fullerton CA 92633 Office: Clark Drugs #7 650 E El Segundo Blvd Los Angeles CA 90059

PARK, CHUL, aerospace engineer; b. Taegn, Korea, June 8, 1934; came to U.S., 1964; s. Hyung-jin and Har-woon (Ryang) P.; m. Chyon Sue Sohn, Sept. 28, 1962; children: Sora, Pora, Marie. BS, Seoul (Korea) Nat. U., 1957, MS, 1960; PhD, Imperial Coll., London, 1964. Rsch. assoc. NASA Ames Rsch. Ctr., Moffett Field, Calif., 1964-67, aerospace engr., 1967-90, sect. head, 1990-92, staff scientist, 1993—. Author: Nonequilibrium Hypersonic Aerothermodynamics, 1990; patentee in field. Dir. Korean-Am. Music Supporters Assn., Cupertino, Calif., 1989—. 1st lt. Korean Air Force, 1958-61. Fellow AIAA (assoc., Thermophysics award 1994). Home: 21194 Bank Mill Rd Saratoga CA 95070 Office: NASA Ames Research Ctr Mail Stop 230-2 Moffett Field CA 94035*

PARK, CHULL, mathematician, educator; b. Seoul, Korea, Feb. 29, 1932; married, 1964; 2 children. BS, Seoul Nat. U., 1959; MS, So. Ill. U., 1964; PhD in Math., U. Minn., 1968. Asst. prof. math. Miami U., Oxford, Ohio, 1968-74, assoc. prof. math., 1975-81, prof. math. and statistics, 1981—; tchr. Sook Myung High Sch., 1959-62; asst. prof. math. Bemidji State Coll., 1967-68. Recipient Thermophysics award AIAA, 1994. Mem. Am. Math. Soc., Math. Assn. Am., Inst. Math. Statistics. Achievements include research in Gaussian stochastic processes including Wiener process (Brownian motion process), absorption probabilities of Wiener processes, stochastic integrals, stochastic differential equations, laws of iterated logarithms. Office: Miami U Dept Math & Statistics Oxford OH 45056-1618*

PARK, CHUNG IL, librarian; b. Chang-won, Korea, Aug. 25, 1938; s. Zung S. and Bong-y (Choo) P.; m. Jung Yoo, Aug. 30, 1969; children: Charlotte, Sue, Andrew. BA, Yonsei U., 1961; MLS, U. So. Calif., L.A., 1971; postgrad., U. Ill., 1975. Libr., mem. faculty Malcolm X Coll., Chgo., 1972—. Compiler, editor: (books) Best Sellers and Best Choices 1980-83, Best Books by Consensus 1984-88, Advertisement Digest: Library and Information Services, 1979; editor COINT, 1980-88; contbr. articles to profl. jours. Mem. ALA, Am. Fedn. Tchrs. Avocation: automobile travel. Home: 9302 Parkside Ave Morton Grove IL 60053 Office: Malcolm X Coll 1900 W Van Buren Chicago IL 60612

PARK, DAVID ALLEN, physicist, educator; b. N.Y.C., Oct. 13, 1919; s. Edwin Avery and Frances (Paine) P.; m. Clara Justine Claiborne, Aug. 18, 1945; children: Katharine, Rachel, Paul, Jessica. A.B., Harvard, 1941; Ph.D., U. Mich., 1950. Instr. Williams Coll., 1941-44; ops. research on radar countermeasures Harvard U. and Eng., 1944-45; instr. U. Mich., 1950; mem. Inst. Advanced Study, Princeton, 1950-51; mem. faculty Williams Coll., 1952-88, prof. physics, 1960-88, emeritus, 1988—; sr. vis. Cambridge (Eng.) U., 1962-63; vis. lectr. U. Ceylon, 1955-56, 72, Mass. Inst. Tech., 1966; vis. prof. U. N.C. 1964. Author: Quantum Theory, 1964, 3d edit., 1991, Contemporary Physics, 1964, Strong Interactions, 1966, Classical Dynamics and Its Quantum Analogues, 1979, 2d edit., 1990, The Image of Eternity, 1980, (with P.J. Davis) No Way, 1987, The How and the Why, 1988. Fellow Am. Phys. Soc.; mem. Internat. Soc. for Study Time (pres. 1973-76). Office: Williams Coll Dept Physics Williamstown MA 01267

PARK, JAMES THEODORE, microbiologist, educator; b. Palo Alto, Calif., Aug. 3, 1922; s. Charles V. and Frances A. (Odenheimer) P.; m. Helen Sternberg, Dec. 13, 1952; children: Jane Frances, David Franklin, Elizabeth Ann. A.B., Central Mich. U., 1943, D.Sc., 1963; M.S., U. Wis., 1944, Ph.D., 1949. Biochemist Ft. Detrick, Md., 1949-53; germ-free animal research unit Walter Reed Army Med. Center, 1953-57; asso. prof., then prof. microbiology Vanderbilt U. Sch. Medicine, 1958-62; chmn. dept. Tufts U. Sch. Medicine, 1962-70, prof., 1962-93, prof. emeritus microbiology, 1993—; mem. study sect. biochem. microbiology Nat. Inst. Allergy and Infectious Diseases, 1964-68; microbiology tng. com. Nat. Inst. Gen. Med. Scis., 1971-73; chmn. microbial physiology and genetics study sect. NIH, 1985-88; vis. scientist Karolinska Inst. Stockholm, 1995. Editorial bd.: Jour. Bacteriology 1964-69, Antimicrobial Agts. and Chemotherapy, 1983-86. NSF sr. postdoctoral research fellow Cambridge (Eng.) U., 1957-58; NIH spl. fellow U. Umea, Sweden, 1969-70. Mem. Am. Acad. Arts and Scis., Am. Soc. Biol. Chemists, Am. Soc. Microbiology, Soc. Gen. Microbiology. Home: 11 Bradford Rd Weston MA 02193-2104 Office: 136 Harrison Ave Boston MA 02111-1800

PARK, JOHN THORNTON, academic administrator; b. Phillipsburg, N.J., Jan. 2, 1935; s. Dawson J. and Margaret M. (Thornton) P.; m. Dorcas M Marshall; June 1, 1956; children: Janet Ernst, Karen Daily. BA in Physics with distinction, Nebr. Wesleyan U., 1956; PhD, U. Nebr., 1963. NSF postdoctoral fellow Univ. Coll., London, 1963-64; asst. prof. physics U. Mo. Rolla, 1964-68, assoc. prof. physics, 1968-71, prof., 1971—; chmn. dept. physics, 1977-83, vice chancellor acad. affairs, 1983-85, 86-91, interim chancellor, 1985-86, 91-92, chancellor, 1992—; vis. assoc. prof. NYU, 1970-71; pres. Talema Electronics, Inc., St. James, Mo., 1983—; prin. investigator NSF Rsch. Grants, 1966—; bd. dirs. Mo. Tech. Corp., Jefferson City, Mo., 1994—. Contbr. articles to profl. jours. Fellow Am. Phys. Soc. (mem. divsn. elec. and atomic physics); mem. Am. Assn. Physics Tchrs., Rotary. Methodist.

PARK, JOSEPH CHUL HUI, computer scientist; b. Seoul, Korea, Aug. 6, 1937; s. Don Gil and Eui Kyung (Shin) P.; m. Young Ja Yoon, Aug. 17, 1968; children: Esther Y.J., Maria Y.S., David Y.W., Jonathan Y.S. BA, Coll of Wooster, Ohio, 1959; BS, MIT, 1959; MS, U. Ill., 1961, PhD, 1967. Mem. rsch. staff Stanford Linear Accelerator Ctr Stanford U., 1969-72, 73-75; assoc. prof., then prof. computer sci. Korea Advanced Inst. of Sci., Seoul, 1975-82; head Computer Sci. Rsch. Ctr. Korea Advanced Inst. Sci., Seoul, Korea, 1980-82; mem. tech. staff Braegen Corp., Milpitas, Calif., 1982-86; Hewlett-Packard Labs., Palo Alto, Calif., 1986-92; mgr. compiler R&D Advanced Processor div. Intergraph Corp., Palo Alto, 1992-93; sr. staff engr. SPARC Labs., Sun Microsystems Compter Corp., Mountain View, Calif., 1993—; lectr. in computer engring. Santa Clara (Calif.) U., 1987—. Mem. IEEE, Assn. Computing Machinery. Baptist. Home: 14800 Masson Ct Saratoga CA 95070

PARK, KI SU, architectural firm executive. Mng. ptnr. Gruen Assocs., L.A. Recipient Whitney M. Young, Jr. Citation Architectural Inst. Am., 1994. Office: Gruen Assocs 6330 San Vicente Blvd Los Angeles CA 90048-5425*

PARK, LEE CRANDALL, psychiatrist; b. Washington, July 15, 1926; s. Lee I. and Alice (Crandall) P.; m. Barbara Anne Merrick, July 1, 1953; children: Thomas Joseph, Jeffrey Rawson; m. Mary Woodfill Banerjee, Apr. 27, 1985; stepchildren: Stephen Kumar, Scott Kumar. Grad., Putney Prep. Sch., Vt.; B.S. in Zoology, Yale, 1948; M.D., Johns Hopkins, 1952. Diplomate Nat. Bd. Med. Examiners, Am. Bd. Psychiatry and Neurology. Intern medicine Johns Hopkins Hosp., Osler Clinic, Balt., 1952-53; resident psychiatry USN Hosp., Oakland, Calif., 1954; resident psychiatry Henry Phipps Psychiat. Clinic, 1955-59, asst. psychiatrist, 1955-59, staff psychiatrist, 1959—, staff dept. medicine, 1970—, dir. psychiat. outpatient svcs. and community psychiatry program, 1972-74, asst. dir. clin. svcs. dept. psychiatry, 1973-74, mem. departmental coun., 1974-76; fellow psychiatry Johns Hopkins U., 1955-59, faculty in psychiatry, 1959—, assoc. prof. 1971—; physician charge psychiat. svcs. student health svc., 1961-73; vis. psychiatrist Balt. City Hosp., 1960-61; co-prin., prin. investigator NIMH Psychopharmacology Rsch. Br. Outpatient Study of Drug-Set Interaction, 1960-68, co-dir. (with Eugene Meyer) Time-Limited Psychotherapy Rsch. Grant, 1969-73; pvt. practice psychiatry, 1964—; cons. Met. Balt. Assn. Mental Health, 1961-63, Bur. Disability Ins., Social Security Adminstrn., 1964-81; attending staff Seton Psychiat. Inst., 1966-73, exec. bd., 1970-73; staff Sheppard and Enoch Pratt Hosp., 1974—; rsch. includes borderline and narcissistic conditions, long-term effects of childhood emotional abuse, interrelationships of psychotherapy and pharmacotherapy, time ltd. psychotherapy, ethical considerations in clin. rsch. Contbr. articles and chpts. to profl. jours. and books. Served to lt. M.C., USNR, 1953-55, div. psychiatrist 1st Marine Div., Korea, staff psychiatrist USN Hosp., Camp Pendelton, Calif., 1954-55. Fellow Am. Psychiat. Assn. (life, mem. assembly 1983-93), AAAS; mem. AMA, AAUP, Am. Psychosomatic Soc., Internat. Soc. Study of Personality Disorders, Am. Soc. Adolescent Psychiatry, Am. Coll. Neuropsychopharmacology, Am. Assn. Pvt. Practicing Psychiatrists, Md. Psychiat. Soc. (pres. 1978-79), Soc. Psychotherapy Rsch., N.Y. Acad. Scis., Group Therapy Network, Md. Interdisciplinary Coun. Children and Adolescents (treas. 1980-87), Med. and Chirurg. Faculty Md., Balt. City, Baltimore County Med. Socs., Johns Hopkins Med. and Surg. Assn., Am. and Md. Assn. Pvt. Practicing Psychiatrists, SAR, Crandall, Denison and Van Voorhees Socs., Nat. Soc. of the Sons and Daughters of the Pilgrims, Johns Hopkins Club (Balt.), Met. Club (Washington), Farmington Country Club (Charlottesville, Va.), Chevy Chase (Md.) Country Club, Phi Beta Pi. Home: 308 Tunbridge Rd Baltimore MD 21212-3803 Office: 1205 York Rd Ste 35 Lutherville Timonium MD 21093-6268

PARK, LELAND MADISON, librarian; b. Alexandria, La., Oct. 21, 1941; s. Arthur Harris and Jane Rebecca (Leland) P. Student, McCallie Sch., 1957-59; A.B., Davidson Coll., 1963; M.L.S., Emory U., 1964; postgrad., Simmons Coll., 1968; Adv.M. in L.S., Fla. State U., 1973, Ph.D., 1974. Reference librarian Pub. Library of Charlotte and Mecklenburg County, N.C., 1964-65; head reference and student personnel Davidson (N.C.) Coll. Library, 1967-70, asst. dir., 1970-75, dir., 1975—; cons. coll. cons. network So. Assn. Colls. and Schs.; vis. lectr. Emory U., summer 1972; temporary instr. Fla. State U., 1973; libr. cons.; bd. dirs. Southeastern Libr. Network, 1978-81; conf. spkr.; chmn. state adv. com. Libr. Svcs. and Constrn. Act, 1975-79; mem. N.C. State Libr. Commn., 1983-85, 87-92, chmn., 1989-92; mem. Davidson (N.C.) Town Appearance Commn., 1986-93, Hist. Conservation Commn., 1994—. Editor Southeastern Librarian, 1976-78; acad. sect. editor N.C. Libraries, 1972-77; contbr. articles to profl. jours. Mem. Wake County Citizens for Better Librs., N.C., 1965-67; sec. com. libr. affairs Piedmont U. Ctr., 1969-70, chmn., 1970-72; mem. nat. bd. cons. NEH, 1976—; clk. mission com. St. Alban's Episcopal Mission, Davidson, N.C., 1969-72, layreader, 1970-75, treas., 1975-86. Recipient H.W. Wilson library periodical award, 1979, Alumni Achievement award The McCallie Sch., 1989, Order of Long Leaf Pine presented by N.C. Gov. James G. Martin, 1993. Mem. ALA, Southeastern Libr. Assn. (chmn. coll. and univ. sect. 1976-78, exec. bd. 1976-78), N.C. Libr. Assn. (2d v.p. 1975-77, 1st v.p. 1981-83, pres. 1983-85), Metrolina Libr. Assn. (pres. 1969-71), Mecklenburg County Libr. Assn. (treas. 1969-70), Soc. of Cin. (2d v.p. Ga. Soc. 1982-83), SAR, Mil. Order World Wars, Raleigh Jaycees (chmn. libr. com. 1965-67), Res. Officer Assn., SCV, Soc. Colonial Wars, S.C. Huguenot Soc., Beta Phi Mu, Sigma Nu, Omicron Delta Kappa. Democrat. Lodge: Rotary. Home: PO Box 777 235 Ney Circle Davidson NC 28036 Office: Davidson Coll E H Little Libr PO Box 1837 Davidson NC 28036-1837

PARK, MARY WOODFILL, information consultant; b. Nevada, Mo., Nov. 20, 1944; d. John Prosser and Elizabeth (Devine) Woodfill; m. Salil Kumar Banerjee, Dec. 29, 1967 (div. 1983); children: Stephen Kumar, Scott Kumar; m. Lee Crandall Park, Apr. 27, 1985; stepchildren: Thomas Joseph, Jeffrey Rawson. BA, Marywood Coll., 1966; postgrad., Johns Hopkins U., 1983, Goucher Coll., 1986. Asst. to dir. U. Pa. Librs., Phila., 1968-69; investment libr. Del. Funds, Phila., 1969-71; investment officer Investment Counselors Md., Balt., 1980-84, 1st Nat. Bank Md., Balt., 1984-85; founder Info. Consultancy, Balt., 1985—; lectr. Villa Julie Coll., Balt., 1989, Loyola Coll., Balt., 1991-92, Cath. U., 1993. Editor, contbr. to profl. publs. Vol. Internat. Visitors' Ctr., Balt., 1979-80, 91; del. White House Conf. on Librs.; v.p. bd. dirs. Friends of Goucher Libr., 1988-90; mem. industry applications com. Info. Tech. Bd., State of Md., 1993—. Mem. Spl. Librs. Assn. (pres. Balt. chpt. 1991-92, mem. network coord. coun. Sailor project 1993—), Am. Soc. Info. Sci., Assn. Ind. Info. Profls., Md. Libr. Assn., Info. Futures Inst., Soc. Competitive Intelligence Profls., Hamilton St. Club (bd. dirs. 1989-92). Office: The Info Consultancy 308 Tunbridge Rd Baltimore MD 21212-3803

PARK, ROBERT MCILWRAITH, science and engineering educator; b. Glasgow, Scotland, July 28, 1957; came to U.S., 1988; s. Robert McIlwraith and Elsie (Black) P.; m. Katherine Jean Angers, Dec. 21, 1985. BSc with honors, U. Glasgow, 1978, PhD, 1982. Sr. rsch. scientist 3M Can., Inc., Toronto, 1982-86, rsch. specialist, 1986-88; assoc. prof. dept. materials sci. and engring. U. Fla., Gainesville, 1988-93, prof., 1993—. Contbr. chpts. to books, more than 50 articles to profl. jours. Recipient 3M Circle of Tech. Excellence award 1986, Rsch. Initiation award NSF, 1989, Rank prize for Optoelectronics, 1993. Achievements include patent for invention of a P-type doping process for the semiconductor zinc selenide. Office: U Fla Dept Materials Sci and Engring Gainesville FL 32611

PARK, RODERIC BRUCE, university chancellor; b. Cannes, France, Jan. 7, 1932; came to U.S., 1932; s. Malcolm Sewell and Dorothea (Turner) P.; m. Marijke DeJong, Aug. 29, 1953; children: Barbara, Marina, Malcolm. AB, Harvard U., 1953; PhD, Calif. Inst. Tech., 1958. Postdoctoral fellow Calif. Inst. Tech., 1958, Lawrence Radiation Lab., Berkeley, Calif., 1958-60; prof. botany U. Calif., Berkeley, 1960-89, prof. plant biology, 1989-93, prof. emeritus, 1993—; chmn. dept. instrn. in biology U. Calif., 1965-68; provost, dean U. Calif. (Coll. Letters and Sci.), 1972-80, vice chancellor, 1980-90; chancellor U. Colo., Boulder, 1994—; pres. Brickyard Cove Harbors, Inc., 1975-77; dir. William Kaufmann, Inc. 1976-86; mem. corp. Woods Hole Oceanographic Inst., 1974-80; mem. Harvard Vis. Com. on Biochemistry and Molecular Biology, 1990-93. Co-author: Cell Ultrastructure, 51967, Papers on Biological Membrane Structure, 1968; Biology editor W.H. Freeman & Co., 1966-74; Contbr. articles to profl. jours. Trustee Athenian Sch., 1980—, U. Calif.-Berkeley Found., 1986-90; pres. Jepson Endowment, 1992—, pres., 1994—; bd. dirs. Assoc. Harvard Alumni,

1976-79; bd. overseers Harvard U., 1981-87; mem. exec. com. Coun. Acad. Affairs, 1986-90, chmn., 1988-89; mem. exec. com. Nat. Assn. State Univs. and Land Grant Colls., 1988-90; mem. vis. com. Arnold Arboretum, 1981-88, chmn., 1986-88; acting dir. Univ. and Jepson Herbaria, 1991-93. Recipient New York Bot. Gardens award, 1962. Fellow AAAS; mem. Am. Soc. Plant Physiologists, Am. Bot. Soc., Am. Soc. Photobiology, Danforth Assn. (pres. San Francisco chpt. 1972), Richmond Yacht Club (commodore 1972, dir. found. 1992—), Transpacific Yacht Club, Explorers Club. Home: Office 301 256 Cactus Ct Boulder CO 80304 Office: U Calif Regent Adminstr Ctr Univ Colo Boulder CO 80309-0017

PARK, ROGER COOK, law educator; b. Atlanta, Jan. 4, 1942; s. Hugh and Alice (Cook) P.; m. Rosemarie J. Lilliker, June 14, 1967 (div. 1979); 1 child, Matthew; m. Suzanne Nicole Howard, Feb. 18, 1984; stepchildren: Sophie Currier, Nicholas Currier. BA cum laude, Harvard U., 1964, JD magna cum laude, 1969. Bar: Mass. 1969, Minn. 1973. Law clk. to Hon. Bailey Aldrich U.S. Ct. Appeals, Boston, 1969-70; with Zalkind & Silverglate, Boston, 1970-73; prof. Law Sch. U. Minn., Mpls., 1973-95, Fredrikson and Byron profl. Law Sch., 1990-95; disting. prof. law Hastings Coll. of Law U. Calif., San Francisco, 1995—; vis. prof. Stanford U. Law Sch., Palo Alto, Calif., summer 1977, Boston U. Sch. of Law, 1981-82, U. Mich. Law Sch., Ann Arbor, fall 1984; bd. dirs. Ctr. for Computer-Aided Legal Instrn., 1978—; adv. group Civil Justice Reform Act. Author: Computer Aided Exercises in Civil Procedure, 1979, 4th edit., 1995, Handbook of Trial Objections, 1991, Waltz and Park Casebook on Evidence, 8th edit., 1994; contbr. articles to profl. jours. Lt. U.S. Army, 1964-66, Vietnam. Mem. ABA (subcom. on fed. rules of evidence, rules of criminal procedure and evidence com. criminal justice sect. 1988—), Acad. Trial Lawyers Minn. (bd. dirs. 1988—), Am. Law Inst., Am. Assn. Law Schs. (chair evidence sect. 1994). Office: U Calif Hastings Coll of Law 200 McAllister St San Francisco CA 94102

PARK, ROY HAMPTON, JR., advertising executive; b. Raleigh N.C., July 23, 1938; s. Roy Hampton and Dorothy Goodwin (Dent) P.; m. Elizabeth Tetlow Parham, July 29, 1961; children: Elizabeth P. Fowler, Roy H., III. BA in Journalism, U.N.C., 1961; MBA, Cornell U., 1963. Sr. account exec., rev. bd. exec., advt. planning dir., awards chmn., pers. group head J. Walter Thompson Co., N.Y.C., and Miami, Fla., 1963-70; v.p. mktg. and account mgr. Kincaid Advt. Agy., div. First Union Nat. BanCorp, Inc., Charlotte, N.C., 1970-71; v.p. Park Outdoor Advt., Ithaca, N.Y., 1971-75; v.p. advt. and promotion Park Broadcasting, Inc., Ithaca, 1976-81; mng. editor Park Communications Newsletter, 1976-81; mng. dir. Ag Rsch. Advt. Agy., Ithaca, 1976-84; v.p. and gen. mgr. Park Outdoor Advt., 1981-84; pres., chief exec. officer, dir. Park Outdoor Advt. of N.Y., Inc., 1984—; pres. Outdoor Advt. Coun. N.Y., Inc., 1986-91, chmn., dir., 1992—; dir. Park Comm., Inc., 1993—; dir., sr. v.p. RHP, Inc., 1994—. Mem. region I plans bd. Inst. Outdoor Advt., 1984-86; founding mem. alumni exec. coun. Cornell U. Johnson Grad. Sch. Mgmt., 1984-88; bd. vis. U. N.C. Sch. Journalism & Mass. Comm., 1994—; chmn. Ithaca Assembly Cotillion, 1979-81; dir. pub. rels. Tompkins County Conf. and Tourist Coun., 1976; exec. com. Tompkins County Rep. Fin. Com. 1983-84; chmn. Fin. Com. MacNeil for Assembly, 1984-86, co-chmn., 1978-82; bd. dirs. Tompkins County Coun. Arts, 1976; chmn. pub. relations com. United Way Tompkins County, 1973-74, loaned publicity exec. 1977; bd. chmn., publicity dir. Junior Olympics 1973-74; dir. pub. rels. United Fund Raleigh, N.C., 1961; fin. com. Special Children's Ctr., 1979. Recipient Project of Yr. award, 1974. Mem. Tompkins County C. of C. (chmn. legis. action com. 1976, acting chmn. nominating com. 1976, chmn. sign ordinance com. 1975-76, pub. rels. coun. 1976, chmn. sign ordinance com. recognition award 1975), Charlotte (N.C.) C. of C. (pub. rels. com. 1970-71), Ithaca Yacht Club, Republican. Presbyterian. Office: Park Outdoor Advt PO Box 6477 Ithaca NY 14851-6477

PARK, THOMAS JOSEPH, biology researcher, educator; b. Balt., June 8, 1958; s. Lee Crandall and Barbara Ann (Merrick) P.; m. Stephanie Suzanne Reynolds, June 22, 1985. BA, Johns Hopkins U., 1987; PhD, U. Md., 1988. Vis. scientist Coll. of France, Paris, 1988-89; rsch. fellow U. Tex., Austin, 1989—. Contbr. chpt. to book, articles to Jour. of Neurosci., Jour. of Comparative Psychology, Hearing Rsch. Grantee NIMH, 1986, Nat. Ctr. Sci. Rsch., Paris, 1988, NIH. Mem. AAAS, Soc. for Neurosci., Assn. for Rsch. in Otolaryngology. Office: U Tex Dept Zoology Austin TX 78712

PARK, WILLIAM H(ERRON), financial executive; b. Monongahela, Pa. Sept. 19, 1947; s. William M. and Marjorie (Herron) P.; m. Mary Cornell, June 25, 1977; children: William H., Douglas C. BS in Indsl. Engring. with distinction Cornell U., 1969, MBA, 1970. Engr. True Temper Corp., Geneva, Ohio, 1970-72; with Price Waterhouse & Co., Boston, 1972-82; exec. v.p., CFO United Asset Mgmt. Corp., Boston, 1982—; v.p. The Regis Fund Inc., 1992—; pres. No. Light Asset Mgmt., 1992—; bd. dirs. The Chautauqua Found., Inc., 1992—; mem. fin. com. and trustee Chautauqua Inst., 1994—. Treas., trustee Tower Sch. in Marblehead, 1982-92. Mem. Am. Inst. CPA's, Mass. Soc. CPAs, Pleon Yacht Club (dir. and treas. 1987-92). Home: 3 Ft Sewall Ter Marblehead MA 01945-3505 Office: United Asset Mgmt Corp One Internat Pl Boston MA 02110

PARK, WILLIAM WYNNEWOOD, law educator; b. Philadelphia, Pa., July 2, 1947; s. Oliver William and Christine (Lindes) P. BA, Yale U., 1969; JD, Columbia U., 1972; MA, Cambridge U., 1975. Bar: Mass. 1972, D.C. 1980. Assoc. Coudert Frères, Paris, 1972-75; fellow Selwyn Coll., U. Cambridge, Eng., 1975-77; assoc. Hughes, Hubbard & Reed, Paris, 1977-79; prof. law Boston U., 1979—; counsel Ropes & Gray, Boston; v.p. London Ct. Internat. Arbitration dir. Morin Ctr. Banking Law Studies, Boston I., 1990-93; adj. prof. Fletcher Sch. Tufts U., MEdford, Mass., 1980-86; vis. prof. U. Dijon, France, 1983-84, Inst. Univ. de Hautes Etudes Internat., Geneva, 1983. Author: International Chamber of Commerce Arbitration, 1984, 2nd edit., 1990, International Forum Selection, 1995; contbr. articles and book revs. to profl. jours. Trustee Mass. Bible Soc. Fellow Chartered Inst. Arbitrators; mem. SPDR, Am. Soc. Internat. Law Assn., Union Internat. Avocats, Soc. of Cin. Republican. Unitarian. Home: 36 King St Cohasset MA 02025 Office: Boston U Law Sch 765 Commonwealth Ave Boston MA 02215 also: Ropes and Gray 1 International Pl Boston MA 02110

PARKANY, JOHN, business educator, international financial consultant; b. Budapest, Hungary, Jan. 28, 1921; came to U.S., 1947; s. Sandor and Renee (Linksz) P.; m. Betty Ruth Baird, Oct. 30, 1954; children: John Stephen, Ann Emily, Nancy. J.D., U. Budapest (Hungary), 1945; M.A., Georgetown U., 1949; Ph.D., Columbia U., 1955. Mktg. research mgr. Formica Corp., Cin., 1956-61; assoc. prof. Xavier U., Cin., 1961-62; mgr. econ. research Weyerhaeuser Co., Tacoma, Wash., 1962-73; v.p., sr. internat. economist Wells Fargo Bank N.A., San Francisco, 1973-80; Richard S. Reynolds Jr. prof. bus. adminstrn. Coll. of William and Mary, Williamsburg, Va., 1980-91; prof. emeritus Coll. of William and Mary, Williamsburg, 1991—. Mem. council econ. advisors Gov. Wash. State, Olympia, 1967-73; pres. Council Fgn. Affairs, Tacoma, Wash., 1968-69. Mem. Nat. Assn. Bus. Economists (v.p. San Francisco chpt. 1973-74), Am. Econ. Assn. Home: 151 Ridings Cove Williamsburg VA 23185-3903

PARKE, ROBERT LEON, communications executive; b. Jersey City, Aug. 28, 1940; s. Edwin Gager and Alice Elizabeth (Servis) P.; m. Geraldine R. Pavlick, Sept. 2, 1967; children: Cheryl Lynn, Tracy Ann, David Scott. Grad. high sch., Jersey City. Asst. bookkeeper Snow-Kist Frozen Foods, Jersey City, 1964-67; supr. accounts receivable Swift Line Transfer Co., Inc., North Bergen, N.J., 1967-69; contr. Imperial Cartage Co., Inc., Jersey City, 1969-79; supr. inventory mgmt. Vista United Telecommunications, Lake Buena Vista, Fla., 1980—; corp. sec. Imperial Warehouse Co., Inc., Jersey City, 1968-79, Arbe Transfer Co. Inc., 1968-79; v.p. Cole Foods, Inc., Jersey City, 1968-79;. Spl. min. of the eucharist Diocese Orlando, Fla., 1992; vol. Gave Kids The World, Kissimmee, Fla.; mem. Pemberton Twp. Zoning Bd., Browns Mills, N.J., 1977-79; trustee, bd. dirs. Browns Mills Improvement Assn., 1974-79; trustee Rebecca Worf Meml. Fund Browns Mills, N.J., Parke Soc., S.E. Milw. Bob Parke Day proclaimed by Twp. of Pemberton, 1979; scholar NAPM Ctrl. Fla. Inc. Mem. Nat. Notary Assn., Fla. Notary Assn., Am. Soc. Notaries, Purchasing Mgmt. Assn. Ctrl. Fla., Nat. Assn. Purchasing Mgmt. (scholarship for continued edn., Ctrl. Fla. Most Suportive Mem. 1994). Office: Vista United Telecommunications 3100 Bonnet Creek Rd Lake Buena Vista FL 32830

PARKER, ADRIENNE NATALIE, art educator, art historian, lecturer; b. N.Y., May 23, 1925; d. Benjamin and Bertha (Levine) Lefkowitz; m. Norman Richard Parker, July 22, 1945; children: Dennis, Jonathan W., Steven L. BA cum laude, Hunter Coll., 1945; MFA, Montclair Coll., 1975; postgrad., Instituto Des Artes, San Miguel, Mex., 1987. Instr. art, English Granby High Sch., Norfolk, Va., 1945-46; instr. art Mahwah (N.J.) Bd. Edn., 1970-75, Daus. of Miriam Home for the Aged, Clifton, N.J., Fedn. Home, Paterson, N.J.; instr. art, history Bergen C.C., Paramus, N.J., 1980—. One-woman show Bergen C.C.; exhibited in group shows N.J. Art Educators, Bergen County Art Educators, N.J. Tercentenary (1st place), Pine Libr., Sara Delano Roosevelt House, Hunter Coll., Woodstock Art Assn., 1990-95, Fair Lawn Art Assn., 1991 (award), Palisade Guild Spinners and Weavers, 1994, Bergen C.C., 1994, 95. Editor Fairlawn H.S. PTA, Thomas Jefferson Jr. H.S.; pres. The Comty. Sch., Fairlawn, 1983-86, bd. dirs.; mem. art adv. exhbn. com. Pine Libr., 1992, 93, 94, 95. Mem. N.J. Art Educators, Bergen County Art Educators, Wood Stock Art Assn., Fairlaw Art Assn., Hunter Coll. Alumni Assn. (bd. dirs. no. N.J. chpt. 1970—, pres. 1977-79, program chmn./v.p. 1993-94), Palisade Guild Spinners and Weavers (founder, editor, charter) Phi Beta Kappa. Avocations: hiking, cross country skiing, travel, archeology, study of primitive cultures. Home: 3827 Fair Lawn Ave Fair Lawn NJ 07410-4395

PARKER, ALAN JOHN, veterinary neurologist, educator, researcher; b. Portsmouth, Eng., Oct. 28, 1944; came to U.S., 1969; s. William Barton and Emily (Begley) P.; m. Heather Margaret Nicholson, Oct. 30, 1971; children: Alyxander John, Robert William. B.Sc. with honors, Bristol U., 1966, B.V.Sc. with honors, 1968; M.S., U. Ill., 1973, Ph.D., 1976. Diplomate Am. Coll. Vet. Internal Medicine-Neurology, European Coll. Vet. Neurology. Intern Vet. Coll., U. Calif.-Davis, 1969-70; instr. vet. clin. medicine U. Ill., Urbana, 1970-71, 72-76, asst. prof., 1976-77, assoc. prof., 1977-82, prof., 1982—; cons. pharm. cos., seminar presenter; cons. in neurology Berwyn Vet. Hosp., Chgo., 1973—, Lake Shore Animal Hosp., Chgo., 1978—. Contbr. numerous articles to sci. jours., chpts. to books. Active Boy Scouts Am., Champaign, Ill., 1982—; active Presbyn. Ch., Monticello, Ill., 1979—. Recipient Vigil Honor and Founder's award Order of the Arrow, Boy Scouts Am.; sci. grantee various orgns., 1972—. Mem. AVMA, Am. Animal Hosp. Assn., Brit. Vet. Assn., Ill. State Vet. Assn. Republican. Office: U Ill Coll Vet Medicine 1008 W Hazelwood Dr Urbana IL 61801-4714

PARKER, ALAN WILLIAM, film director, writer; b. London, Feb. 14, 1944; s. William Leslie and Elsie Ellen P.; m. Annie Inglis, July 30, 1966; children: Lucy Kate, Alexander James, Jake William, Nathan Charles. Student Brit. schs. Advt. copywriter, 1966-69, dir. TV commls. Author: screenplay Melody, 1968; novel Bugsy Malone, 1975, Puddles in the Lane, 1977; author, dir.: No Hard Feelings, 1972, Our Cissy, 1973, Footsteps, 1973, Bugsy Malone, 1975 (5 Brit. Acad. awards) Come See the Paradise, 1990; dir.: The Evacuees (Brit. Acad. award, Internat. Emmy award, Press Guild U.K. award), Midnight Express (6 Golden Globe awards, 3 Brit. Acad. awards, 2 Oscar awards), Fame, 1980 (Brit. Acad. award, Golden Globe award, 2 Oscar awards), Shoot the Moon, 1982, Pink Floyd-The Wall, 1982, Birdy, 1984 (Grand Prix Spl. du Jury, Cannes Film Festival), A Turnip Head's Guide to the British Cinema, 1986, Angel Heart, 1987, Mississippi Burning, 1988 (Oscar award), The Commitments, 1991, The Road to Wellville, 1994. Recipient 4 Brit. Acad. awards. Mem. Brit. Acad. Film and TV Arts, Dirs. Guild Am., Writers Guild G.B., Writers Guild Am., Dirs. Guild G.B. Office: care Robert Bookman Creative Artists Agy 9830 Wilshire Blvd Beverly Hills CA 90212-1825

PARKER, ALFRED BROWNING, architect; b. Boston, Sept. 24, 1916; s. James Arden and Jewel (Fry) P.; m. Martha Gifford, Sept. 17, 1942 (div. Mar. 1956); children—Derek Browning, Gifford, Robin Zachary, Jules Graham, Quentin Dart; m. Jane Britt, June 13, 1959 (dec. July 1971); 1 child, Lebritia Browning; m. Shirley Goldin, May 25, 1980; (div. Nov. 1984); m. Euphrosyne Pantelis Nittis, Feb. 7, 1992. B.S. in Arch. with honors, U. Fla., 1939; postgrad., Royal Acad. Stockholm, Sweden, 1939; DFA honoris causa, Internat. Fine Arts Coll., Miami, Fla., 1978. Prof. Coll. Architecture, U. Fla., 1940-46, 94—; pvt. practice as Alfred Browning Parker (architect), Miami, Fla., 1946—; chmn., founding dir. Solar Reactor Techs. 1976—. Author: You and Architecture, 1965; works include House Beautiful Pacesetter Home, 1954, 59, 64, Alliance Machine Co. bldg, 1958, Gen. Capital Corp, Miami, 1960, Woodsong, 1969, Miamarina, 1971, Musa Isle Housing for Elderly, 1974, Fread Sanctuary Beth El Synagogue, 1976, St. Louis Ch, 1980. Charter mem. Coconut Grove Citizens Com. Slum Clearance, 1947—. Served to lt. (s.g.) USNR, 1942-46. Recipient Nat. Conf. Ch. Architecture award Merit Am. Soc. Ch. Architecture, 1965; Architects award Soc. Am. Foresters, 1971; Outstanding Concrete Structure in Fla. award Fla. Concrete Assn., 1973; Silver Medal award Fla. South chpt. AIA, 1976; Disting. Architecture Alumnus award Coll. Architecture, U. Fla., 1992; Exchange scholar Am.-Scandinavian Found., 1939; Pan American travel fellow Mexico, 1940. Fellow AIA (pres. S. Fla. 1949, Regional archtl. award 1954, 55, 56, 57, 58, Nat. award of merit 1959, Honor award 1965, Honor award Fla. Assn. 1967, 70; mem. Nat. Council Archtl. Registration Bds., Guild Religious Architecture, Fla. Assn. Architects, Zool. Soc. Fla. (pres. 1959), Assn. Cuban Architects in Exile, Phi Eta Sigma, Phi Kappa Phi, Sigma Delta Psi, Beta Theta Pi, Gargoyle, Blue Key. Office: PO Box 330975 Miami FL 33233 I seek to live harmoniously in my environment and to be a conservationist of both human and material resources. Educated and experienced as an architect, I utilize whatever skill I possess to this cause. I am grateful for love, family, and freedom.

PARKER, ANGELO PAN, lawyer; b. Detroit, Feb. 10, 1945; s. Pan A. and Clementine (Kaplanis) P.; m. Dena Apostle, Mar. 9, 1975; children: Denise, Alyssa. BBA, St. Mary's U., San Antonio, Tex., 1967, JD, 1970. Bar: Tex. 1970, Nebr. 1973. Ptnr. Kutak Rock, Omaha, 1973-80, McCall, Parkhurst & Horton, Dallas, 1980-85, Strasburger & Price, L.L.P., Dallas, 1986—. 1st lt. U.S. Army, 1970-73. Office: Strasburger & Price LLP 4200 Nations Bank Plz 901 Main St Dallas TX 75202-3707

PARKER, ANN (ANN PARKER NEAL), photographer, graphic artist; b. London, Mar. 6, 1934; d. Russell Johnston and Mildred Grace (Best) P.; m. Avon Neal, Oct. 31, 1964. Student, R.I. Sch. Design, 1952-54; B.F.A., Yale U., 1956. V.p. Thistle Hill Press, North Brookfield, Mass., 1979—; artist-in-residence Altos de Chavon, Dominican Republic, 1983, 84; panel mem. Fulbright Hays Com. for Photography, Film and Video, 1983, 85, 86. Freelance photographer and graphic artist, 1956—, exhbns. include, Santa Fe Ctr. Photography, 1982, Focus Gallery, San Francisco, 1983, Altos De Chavon, Dominican Republic, 1984, 86, 87, Nat. Mus. Art, La Paz, Bolivia, 1985, Princeton U. Library, N.J., 1986, Instituto Dominicano de Cultura Hispanica, Santa Domingo, Dominican Republic, 1987, Gallery of Graphic Arts, N.Y.C., 1987, Maxwell Mus. Anthropology U. N.Mex., Albuquerque, 1988, Gallery Twerenbold, Luzern, Switzerland, 1991, San Antonio Mus. Assns., 1992, Worcester (Mass.) Art Mus., 1993, Gallery of Graphic Arts, N.Y.C., 1994, Lumina Gallery, Taos, N.Mex., 1995; work pub. in Smithsonian mag., Am. Heritage, Life, Americana, Aperture, Natural History, others; works in permanent collections, N.Y. Pub. Library, George Eastman House, Rochester, N.Y., Met. Mus. Art, N.Y.C., Mus. Modern Art, N.Y.C., Mus. Fine Arts, Boston, Ctr. Creative Photography, Tucson, MIT, Library of Congress, Smithsonian Instn., Rosenwald Collection, Mellon Collection, Whitney Mus., others.; art books Ephemeral Folk Figures, 1969, Molas, 1977, Scarecrows, 1978, Early American Stone Sculpture, 1982, Los Ambulantes, 1982. Ford Found. grantee, 1962-63, 63-64; recipient 1st place award Mass. Open Photography, 1978, Am. Inst. Graphic Arts Design awards, 1956, 77, 79, Mass. Arts Lottery Council award, 1988. Address: Thistle Hill North Brookfield MA 01535

PARKER, BARBARA Z., bank executive. Trust and investment mgr. Midlantic Corp., Edison, N.J. Office: Midlantic Corp 499 Thornall St Edison NJ 08837

PARKER, BARRY JAMES CHARLES, retail executive; b. St. Louis, Sept. 9, 1947; s. James M.C. and Ruth E. (Cummings) P.; m. Donna Nardin, June 19, 1970; children: Thomas J.J., Michael B.B. BA, Washington U., St. Louis, 1969; MBA, U. Pa., 1971. Buyer, dist. merchandise mgr. F & R Lazarus & Co., Columbus, Ohio, 1971-75; v.p. and gen. merchandise mgr. sr. v.p. The Children's Place, Pinebrook, N.J., 1975-85; pres. County Seat Stores Inc., Dallas, 1985—, chmn. bd., pres., chief exec. officer, 1989—.

Mem. Internat. Coun. Shopping Ctrs., Nat. Retail Fedn., Young Pres.'s Orgn. Roman Catholic. Avocations: tennis, skiing, golf. Office: County Seat Stores Inc 17950 Preston Rd Ste 1000 Dallas TX 75252-5638

PARKER, BETTY MORRIS, association administrator retired; b. Gordonsville, Va., Feb. 28, 1933; d. Benjamin and Evie (Hall) Morris; m. James Clayton Parker, Feb. 28, 1958; children: Patricia, Paula, James Jr. BA, U. Ctrl. Fla., 1985. Cert. profl. health educator, smoking cessation trainer; accredited pub. rels. profl. Bookkeeper State Farm Ins., Richmond, Va., 1954-56, Daytona Beach, Fla., 1956-59; program adminstr. Am. Lung Assn., Daytona Beach, Fla., 1978-85, regional dir., 1985—; pres. Fla. Congress Lung Staff Devel., 1988-89; regional dir. Spaceport region Am. Lung Assn. of Fla., 1985-95. Mem. legis. com. Daytona Beach/Halifax Area C. of C., 1990—; charter mem., sec. U. Ctrl. Fla., Volusia/Flagler Alumni Assn., Daytona Beach, 1990; chairperson Volusia County Sch. Health Adv. Coun. 1991. Recipient Sci. Fair Judge award Sch. Bd. Brevard County, 1982. Mem. Fla. Pub. Rels. Assn., Pilot Club of Halifax Area (pub. rels. area leader 1995—), Brevard County Vol. Health Assn. (pres. 1984-85), Am. Assn. Univ. Women (scholarship com. chmn. 1995—), Mus. Arts & Sci., Daytona Beach, Art League of Daytona Beach. Baptist. Avocations: tennis, bridge, painting, gardening, aerobics. Home: 2115 S Peninsula Dr Daytona Beach FL 32118-5235

PARKER, BOBBY EUGENE, SR., college president; b. Wortham, Tex., May 28, 1925; s. Thomas W. and Stacy (Beasley) P.; m. Marietta Vickrey, Sept. 1, 1946; children: Bobby Eugene Jr., Mark. AA, Westminster Jr. Coll., 1948; BS, Sam Houston State Coll., 1951; MS, Baylor U., 1954, EdD, 1964; LLD (hon.), Houston Bapt. U., 1990. Prin., counselor pub. schs. Richland and Mexia, Tex., 1948-57; dean students Howard Payne Coll., Brownwood, Tex., 1957-59; mem. faculty Baylor U., Waco, Tex., 1960-69; v.p. Mary Hardin-Baylor Coll., Belton, Tex., 1969-71; pres. U. Mary Hardin-Baylro, 1971-91, chancellor, 1991—; hon. pres. Allen Jr. Coll., Kuji Iwate Japan, 1992. Mem. King's Daus. Hosp. Assn., Heart O' Tex. coun. nat. Boy Scouts Am.; trustee Bell County Mus. History and Art; bd. dirs. Greater Waco Safety Coun., 1963-67, Waco Girl's Club, 1967-69, Tex. Safety Assn., 1963; pres. coun. Heart of Tex. Athletic Conf. With USNR, 1943-46. Recipient Spl. achievement award Tex. Safety Assn., 1965, Exemplary medal San Marcos Bapt. Acad., 1991; named Man of Yr. Belton Area C. of C., 1978, Outstanding Christian Educator Mexican Bapt. Conv.; fellow Paul Harris. Mem. Internat. Platform Assn., Tex. Baptist Sch. Adminstrs. Assn., Tex. Found. Vol. Supported Colls. and Univs. (former chmn. bd.), Assn. Am. Colls., Am. Council Edn., Ind. Colls. and Univs. of Tex. (former mem. exec. bd.), Nat. Assn. Intercollegiate Athletics (former pres. adv. com.), Belton C of C. (past bd. dirs.), East Tex. C of C., Killeen C. of C., Temple C. of C., Friends of Scott and White. Lodge: Rotary Internat. (Gov. 1984, Dist. Gov.'s Role of Fame; Gov. Dist. 587 1986-87). Home: 2506 River Oaks Dr Belton TX 76513-1654 Office: U Mary Hardin Baylor PO Box 8001 Belton TX 76513-0999

PARKER, BRENT MERSHON, retired medical educator, internist, cardiologist; b. St. Louis, July 3, 1927; s. William Bahlmann and Florence (Mershon) P.; m. Martha Shelton, Aug. 1, 1953; children: Martha Parker Burgess, Elizabeth, Margaret. MD cum laude, Wash. U., St. Louis, 1952. Diplomate Am. Bd. Internal Medicine. Intern and asst. resident N.Y. Hosp.-Cornell, N.Y.C., 1952-54; asst. resident, fellow Barnes Hosp., Wash. U., St. Louis, 1954-57; cardiology sect. chief VA Hosp., U. Oreg., Portland, 1957-59; asst. prof. to assoc. prof., co-dir. cardiovascular div., chief adult cardiac catheterization Wash. U. Sch. Medicine, St. Louis, 1959-73; prof. medicine U. Mo., Columbia, 1973-89, prof. emeritus, 1989-94, chief of staff, assoc. dean, 1976-82, chief of cardiology, 1983-89; mem. colloquium faculty Merck, Sharp and Dohme, West Point, Pa., 1980-86. Author or co-author 58 papers in referred jours., 6 book chpts., teaching papers, others. Bd. dirs. St. Louis Heart Assn., 1962-73, v.p. 1972-73; bd. dirs. Mo. Heart Assn., 1965-75, pres. 1970-71. Served with USNR, 1945-46. Recipient Arthur Strauss award St. Louis Heart Assn., 1973, 3 teaching awards U. Mo. Sch. Medicine, 1974, 75, 86, Preventive Cardiology Acad. award, Nat. Heart Lung and Blood Inst., 1982-87, Alumni Achievement award Washington Univ. Sch. Medicine, 1992; Brent Mershon Parker professorship estab. in honor U. Mo., 1989. Fellow ACP, Am. Coll. Cardiology (Mo., Kans. council rep 1973-77), Clin. Cardiology Soc. Am. Heart Assn.; mem. Am. Fedn. Clin. Research, Cen. Soc. for Clin. Research, Alpha Omega Alpha, Sigma Xi. Episcopalian. Avocations: choral singing, jogging, camping, back packing.

PARKER, CARL, state senator; b. Port Arthur, Tex., Aug. 6, 1934; B.A., U. Tex., 1955, LL.B., 1958; m. Beverly Steigler Parker; children: Valerie Lynn, Christian Ann, Carl Allen. Admitted to Tex. bar, 1958; ptnr. firm Parker, Parks & Rosenthal, L.L.P., Port Arthur; mem. Tex. Ho. of Reps., 1963-77; mem. Tex. State Senate, 1977-95, pres. pro tempore, 1982; speaker pro tempore Tex. Ho. Reps., 1973. Served with USNR. Mem. Port Arthur C. of C. Club: Lions. Home: 3838 Chandelle Ln Port Arthur TX 77642 Office: 1 Plaza Sq Port Arthur TX 77642-5513 Also: 1800 Guadalupe Austin TX 78701-1235

PARKER, CATHERINE SUSANNE, psychotherapist; b. Norwood, Mass., Nov. 4, 1934; d. George Leonard and Hazel Olga (Remmer) P. BA, Bates Coll., 1956; MSW, U. Denver, 1961. Diplomate Acad. Cert. Social Workers; cert. social worker, Colo. Social worker Taunton (Mass.) State Hosp., 1956-59; social worker Ft. Logan Mental Health Ctr., Denver, 1961-66, clin. team leader, 1966-72; dir. adult services Western Inst. Human Resources, Denver, 1973-74; pvt. practice psychotherapy Denver, 1974—; instr. U. Denver, 1977-79; workshop facilitator Arapahoe Community Coll., 1986—. Mem. Nat. Assn. Social Workers, Internat. Transactional Analysis Assn. Avocations: tennis, skiing, fishing, antiques, gardening. Home: 6453 S Downing St Littleton CO 80121-2517 Office: Denver Mental Health 165 Cook St Ste 100 Denver CO 80206-5308

PARKER, CHARLES A., insurance company executive. BS, U. Colo., 1956. With H.C. Wainwright & Co., 1979-78; exec. v.p. Continental Corp., N.Y.C., from 1978; now exec. v.p. for investments Continental Corp.; also exec. v.p. Continental Ins. Co. 1st lt. USAF, 1956-58. Office: Continental Corp 180 Maiden Ln New York NY 10038-4925

PARKER, CHARLES BRAND, JR., training company executive; b. Washington, Sept. 15, 1936; s. Charles Brand and Annie Laura (Chambers) P.; m. Grace Carolyn McGunigal, Sept. 8, 1959; children: Christopher Arlen, Shannon James. AB, George Washington U., 1960; BD, Southeastern Sem., Wake Forest, N.C., 1963, ThM, 1969; EdD, N.C. State U., 1978. Coll. minister Meredith Coll., Raleigh, 1967-71; exec. dir. Triangle Complex, Inc., Raleigh, 1971-72; project dir. N.C. Manpower Coun., Raleigh, 1972-74; dir. Office Employment & Tng., Raleigh, 1974-80; rsch. dir. Thad Green Enterprises, Inc., Raleigh, 1980-83; pres. Tng. Resources, Inc., Raleigh, 1983—; cons. N.C. Adv. Coun. on Vocat. Edn. Raleigh, 1984-91; initiator Fed. Job Corps Ctr., Kittrell, N.C.; dir. N.C. Employment & Tng. Coun., Raleigh, 1978-80. Author: Youth Labor Market Prospects for the 1980s, 1982, Establishing Employment and Training Performance Criteria for Youth: Trends and Techniques, 1982, Entrepreneurship: Implications for Training Economically Disadvantaged Youth, 1982; editor: An Analysis of the Major Elements of Transition of Youth From School to Work, 1982, Employment and Training of Minority Youth in the 1980s, 1982, Public Funding for Education in North Carolina, 1984, Biennial Rev. North Carolina's Achievement in Accomplishing the Purposes of the Vocational Education Act and the Job Training Partnership Act 1986-88, 1989, companion vol. 1988-90, 1991. With USNR, 1954-62. Southeastern Sem. fellow, Wake Forest, N.C., 1965; recipient Outstanding Adminstrn. award U.S. Dept. Labor, Raleigh, 1975, Boss of Yr. award Am. Bus. Woman's Assn., Raleigh, 1979. Mem. Raleigh C. of C., Raleigh Civitan Club. Democrat. Baptist. Avocations: gardening, entrepreneurship, historic preservation, phys. fitness, writing. Home: 4717 Stanford St Raleigh NC 27609-5333 Office: Tng Resources Inc 214 New Bern Pl Raleigh NC 27601-1416

PARKER, CHARLES WALTER, JR., consultant, retired equipment company executive; b. nr. Ahoskie, N.C., Nov. 22, 1922; s. Charles Walter and Minnie Louise (Williamson) P.; m. Sophie Nash Riddick, Nov. 26, 1949; children: Mary Parker Hutto, Caroline Parker Robertson, Charles Walter III, Thomas Williamson. B.S. in Elec. Engring. Va. Mil. Inst., 1947; Dr. Engring. (hon.), Milw. Sch. Engring., 1980. With Allis-Chalmers Corp.,

1947-87; dist. mgr. Allis-Chalmers Corp., Richmond, Va., 1955-57, Phila., 1957-58; dir. sales promotion industries group Allis-Chalmers Corp., Milw., 1958-61; gen. mktg. mgr. new products Allis-Chalmers Corp., 1961-62, mgr. mktg. services, 1962-66, v.p. mktg. and public relations services, 1966-70, v.p., dep. group exec., 1970-72, staff group exec. communications and public affairs, 1972-87, ret., 1987; prin. Charles Parker & Assocs., Ltd., Milw., 1987—; retired chmn. bd. dirs. Associated Dental Svc. Inc., Milw., 1989-93; founding mem. World Mktg. Contact Group, London; bd. dirs. Internat. Gen. Ins. Corp., Dinermite Corp. Gen. chmn. United Fund Greater Milw. Area, 1975; trustee Boy Scouts Am. Trust Fund, Milw.; bd. dirs. Jr. Achievement; pres. bd. trustees Univ. Sch. Milw., 1978-80; trustee Carroll Coll., Waukesha, Wis.; bd. dirs. Milw. Children's Hosp.; bd. regents Milw. Sch. Engring.; mem. Greater Milw. Com.; chmn. bd. dirs. Milw. Found., 1987-89. Served to capt. AUS, 1943-46, ETO. Decorated Bronze Star. Mem. NAM (dir.), IEEE (assoc.), Wis. C. of C. (pres. 1974-76), Sales and Mktg. Execs. Internat. (pres., CEO 1974, 75, Eduardo Rihan Internat. Mktg. Exec. of Yr. award 1979), Wis. Mfrs. and Commerce Assn. (exec. com.), Pi Sigma Epsilon (pres. 1976-77, trustee and chmn. nat. found. 1979-86), Kappa Alpha. Home: 4973 N Newhall St Milwaukee WI 53217-6049 Office: PO Box 92398 828 N Broadway Milwaukee WI 53202-3611

PARKER, CHRISTOPHER WILLIAM, lawyer; b. Evanston, Ill., Oct. 26, 1947; s. Robert H. and Dorothy Boynton P.; m. Mary Ann P., Dec. 28, 1984. BA, Tufts U., 1969; JD, Northeastern U., 1976. Bar: Mass. 1977, U.S. Dist. Ct. Mass. 1977, U.S. Dist. Ct. (we. dist.) Tenn. 1986, U.S. Ct. Appeals (1st cir.) 1988, U.S. Supreme Ct. 1988. Law clk. to judge U.S. Bankruptcy Ct. Mass. dist., Boston, 1976-77; assoc. Fletcher, Tilton & Whipple, Worcester, Mass., 1977-79; counsel U.S. Trustee, Boston, 1979-81; assoc. Craig and Macauley P.C., Boston, 1982-84, ptnr., 1984-87; counsel Hinckley, Allen, Snyder & Comen, Boston, 1987-88, ptnr., 1989-91; ptnr. McDermott, Will & Emery, Boston, 1991—. Mem. ABA, Mass. Bar Assn., Am. Bankruptcy Inst. Boston Bar Assn., Comml. Law League. Club: Union Boat (Boston). Home: 45 Walnut St Lynnfield MA 01940-2009 Office: McDermott Will & Emery 75 State St Boston MA 02109-1807

PARKER, CLEA EDWARD, university president; b. Talisheek, La., Apr. 2, 1927; s. William A. and Lutritia (Davis) P.; m. Peggy Ann Faciane, June 21, 1953; children—Brian, Stephen, Karen, Robin. B.A., Southeastern La. U., 1948; M.Ed., La. State U., 1952, Ed.D., 1965. Coach, tchr. Rugby Acad., New Orleans, 1948-50; tchr., prin., supr. instr., dir. curriculum and instrn. St. Tammany Parish Sch. Bd., 1950-67; prof. edn., head dept. student teaching Nicholls State Coll., Thibodaux, La., 1967-68; acting pres. Southeastern La. U., Hammond, 1968; pres. Southeastern La. U., 1968-80, pres. emeritus, 1980—; liaison La. State Dept. Edn., Higher Edn. and Bds. for Edn. in La., 1986; vis. lectr. La. State U., 1965-89; Past pres. St. Tammany Parish Tchrs. Assn., La. Assn. Supervision and Curriculum Devel.; past pres. elementary dept. La. Tchrs. Assn.; chmn. Pres.'s Council La. Bd. Edn., 1972-73; v.p. Conf. La. Colls. and Univs., 1973-74, pres., 1974-75; pres. elect Gulf South Conf., 1974-75, pres., 1975-76; mem. Steering Com. on Curriculum Devel. and Revision for Career Edn. for State La., 1973; mem. adv. council for State Plan for Career Edn., 1973. Mem. planning com. Gov.'s Conf. on Aging, 1976; v.p. chpt. 15 La. Good Samaritans, 1987-88; bd. dirs. Assn. for Retarded Citizens, pres.-elect, 1981; mem. Zemurray Park Recreation Commn., Hammond, 1992-95; chmn. bd. Lallie Kemp Meml. Hosp., 1993-94; bd. chmn. Lallie Kemp Med. Ctr., 1994-95. With USCGR, 1945, 93-94. Named Hon. State Farmer La., 1970; Distinguished Alumnus of Yr. Southeastern La. U. Alumni Assn., 1977, 91, 92. Mem. Am. Assn. State Colls. and Univs. (com. on nat. service 1972-73, task force on aging 1975-76, 78-79, mem. nominating com. 1977—, state rep. for La. 1979—, com. agr., renewable resources and rural devel. 1979-80, Service to Edn. award 1980), Hammond C. of C., La. Assn. for Sch. Execs., Phi Delta Kappa, Kappa Delta Pi. Roman Catholic. Clubs: K.C. (lectr. 1982, 85, 90-91, chancellor 1983-84, 87—), Rotary (dir. Hammond, internat. service dir. 1972), Ozone Ramblers Camping (pres. 1988). Home: 10 Golden Dr Hammond LA 70401-1010

PARKER, DAVID FORSTER, real estate development consultant; b. Sarnia, Ont., Can., July 4, 1934; s. George William and Bessie Havergal (Forster) P.; m. Marilynn Catherine McFadden, Oct. 15, 1960; children: John Christopher, Stephen, David, Daniel. Student, U. Toronto (Can.), 1954-57; BS, Mich. State U., 1964, M. Urban Planning, 1965; D. Pub. Adminstrn., SUNY, Albany, 1980. Cert. Am. Inst. Cert. Planners. Prin. Tricon Ltd. Builders, Sarnia, Ont., 1957-62; urban planner N.Y. State Dept. Transp., Albany, 1965-66; asst. to dir. N.Y. State Budget, Albany, 1967-69; pres. Audubon Devel. Corp., Buffalo, 1969-76; dep. dir. Sadat City, Cairo, Egypt, 1976-79; cons. Milton Keynes (Eng.), 1979-80; v.p. Bos Corp., Jacksonville, Fla., 1980-82; prin. Clark Parker Assocs., Jacksonville, 1982-90, Clark Parker Realty, Jacksonville, 1982—; pres. Fla. Real Estate Clinic, Inc., 1991—. Author: Marketing New Homes, 1990 (recognition 1990), Selling New Homes, 1990 (recognition 1990); contbr. articles to profl. jours. Chmn. Albany Citizens Against Poverty, 1966-67, Cen. Jacksonville Residential Task Force, 1986-88, Mayor's Housing Com., Jacksonville, 1990—. Mem. Inst. Residential Mktg., Nat. Assn. Home Builders, C of C., S.E. Resort Real Estate Coun., Urban Land Inst., Am. Inst. Cert. Planners, SPEBSQSA (greater Jacksonville chpt. pres. 1990-92, sunshine dist. dir. 1993—, v.p. 1995), Selva Marina Country Club, Phi Kappa Phi, Beta Alpha Sigma, Phi Sigma Alpha. Home: 1739 Live Oak Ln Jacksonville FL 32233-5605 Office: Parker Assocs 2251 Saint Johns Bluff Rd S Jacksonville FL 32246-2309

PARKER, DAVID RAYMOND, services industry executive; b. Corpus Christi, Tex., July 6, 1943; s. Jesse Raymond P. and Mary Jane (Valentine) Arrington; m. Judith Evans, Aug. 2, 1969. B.S. in Engring., U.Tex., 1966; M.B.A., Harvard Grad. Sch. Bus., 1972. Dist. ops. mgr. AT&T Long Lines div., Dallas, 1968-70; mgr. Boston Cons. Group, 1972-76; v.p. strategic planning Am. Can Co., Greenwich, Conn., 1976-78, v.p. metal container packaging, 1978-81, sr. v.p.and sector exec. metal container packaging, 1981-83, exec. v.p. packaging 1983-84; sr. exec. v.p., chief operating officer Bus. Services Group Ryder System, Inc., Miami, Fla., 1984-89, pres. vehicle leasing and svcs. div., 1989—; dir. Am. Can of Can., Am. Can (U.K.) Ltd., Envases Venezolanos, 1983—; bd. dirs. Can. Mfrs. Inst., 1981—, Sun Bank/ Miami N.A., Sun Banks, Inc. Active Nat. Planning Assn., Washington, 1982; Internat. Mgmt. and Devel., 1982, U.S. Coun. Internat. Bus., N.Y.C., 1982; bd. dirs. Exec. Coun. on Fgn. Diplomats, Armonk, N.Y., Inst. for Ednl. Leadership, Inc., Washington; bd. trustees Fla. Internat. U. With USAR, 1968-74. Harvard U. Fredrich Sheldon fellow, 1972; Baker scholar Harvard U., 1972. Episcopalian. Clubs: Harvard Faculty, Harvard Bus. Avocation: golf. Office: Ryder System Inc 3600 NW 82nd Ave Miami FL 33166-6623

PARKER, DAVID SCOTT, architect; b. New Harmony, Ind.; s. Donald Kenneth and Shirley Ann (Martin) P. BS in Architecture, U. Va., 1982; MArch, Harvard U. 1984. Registered architect, Conn. Pa., N.J., N.Y. Curator Historic New Harmony, Inc., 1982; project mgr. Machado-Silvetti, Boston, 1985; designer Richard Meier & Ptnrs., L.A., 1985-87; prin. Schwarz, Parker & Assocs., Southport, Conn., 1983-88, David Scott Parker, Architects, Southport, 1988—; commr., vice-chmn. Fairfield (Conn.) Historic Dist. Commn., 1989—; dir. Moravian Archives, Bethlehem, Pa., 1992—, Historic Bethlehem, Inc., 1993—. Dir. Fairfield Hist. Soc., 1991—, Southport Conservancy, 1992—, Sasquanaug Assn., Southport, 1993—, Marcella Sembrich Meml. Assn., corp. sec. Recipient award Inst. Bus. Designers, Conn., 1992, 1st prize Interiors Exposition for Historic Bldgs., 1993, Hon. Mention ASID, 1992. Mem. AIA. Home: 275 Center St Southport CT 06490 Office: David Scott Parker Architects PO Box 491 Southport CT 06490

PARKER, DONALD FRED, college dean, human resources management educator; b. Oilton, Okla., Nov. 7, 1934; s. Robert Fred Parker and Georgia Marie (Culley) Meek; m. Jo Ellen Dunfee, Apr. 6, 1963; children: Margaret Elizabeth, Emily Lyle. BA in Sociology, U. Okla., 1957; MS in Personnel Adminstrn., George Washington U., 1966; PhD in Human Resource Mgmt., Cornell U., 1975. Commd. ensign USN, 1957, advanced through grades to capt., 1977; staff officer with chief naval ops. USN, Washington, 1969-71; comdg. officer, exec. officer, Patrol Squadron Ten USN, Brunswick, Maine, 1974-76; prof. Naval War Coll. USN, Newport, R.I., 1976-78; comdg. officer Navy Personnel Research & Devel. Ctr. USN, San Diego, 1978-80; ret. USN,

1980; asst. prof. Grad. Sch. Bus., U. Mich., Ann Arbor, 1980-84; prof. human resources mgmt., dean Coll. Commerce and Industry U. Wyo., Laramie, 1984-91; Sara Hart Kimball dean bus., prof. human resources mgmt. Oreg. State U., Corvallis, 1991—; advisor U.S. West Wyo. State Bd. Advisors, Cheyenne, 1986-91; bd. dirs. Unicover Corp., Rocky Mountain FSB; ex-officio dir. Wyo. Indsl. Devel. Corp., Casper, 1987; vis. prof. Acad. Internat. Econ. Affairs, Hsinchu, Taiwan, 1986-91. Author numerous articles, book chpts., case studies. Mem. Acad. of Mgmt. (human resource mgmt. div. dir. 1983-85), Midwest Assn. Deans and Dept. Chairs in Bus. (pres.), Phi Kappa Phi. Avocations: jogging, skiing, hiking. Home: 4400 NW Honeysuckle Dr Corvallis OR 97330-3355 Office: Oreg State U Coll Bus Bexell Hall # 200 Corvallis OR 97331-2601

PARKER, DONALD HENRY, psychologist, author; b. Syracuse, N.Y., Apr. 18, 1912; s. Henry Melvin and Ethel (Madden) P.; m. Fritzi Taylor; 1 child, Dona Jean (Mrs. Roger Sell). B.A. cum laude, U. Fla., 1950, M.A. in Psychology, 1952; Ed.D. in Guidance, Columbia U., 1957. With Sears, Roebuck & Co., 1930-43; propr. Personnel Research Counselors (psychol. testing and guidance), Jacksonville, Fla., 1946-50; psychologist Childrens Home Soc. Fla., 1948-50; psychologist, reading cons. Bradford County schs., Fla., 1950-51; lectr., dir. Reading Lab., U. N.C., 1951-53; dir. Reading Center, Charlotte pub. schs., also Charlotte Coll., N.C., 1954-55; reading cons. Westchester County pub. schs., N.Y.; also instr. reading Columbia U., 1955-57; prof. edn., dir. Reading Lab., U. Bridgeport, Conn., 1957-58; multilevel cons. Sci. Research Assos., Chgo., 1957-64; dir. Inst. for Multilevel Learning Internat., 1964—; Biofeedback Counseling Center, Monterey, Calif., 1976-79; lectr. on multilevel philosophy (application of psychology of individual differences, devel. psychology and psychology of learning to theory that schooling consists of tng. and edn.), 1950—; cons. U.S. AID, Venezuela, 1965-67; participant, lectr. photopsychography, body-mind harmony and health 1st World Congress Parapsychology and Psychotronics, Prague, Czechoslovakia, 1973, 2d world congress, Monte Carlo, 1975; lectr. in Europe, 1960, 63, 71, 78, S.E. Asia, Australia, N.Z., 1969, Africa, India, Thailand, Hong Kong, Philippines, 1971; ednl. cons. to China, 1980, U.S.S.R., 1985. Author: SRA Reading Labs., 1957— (used by over 61,000, 000 students in 62 countries), Schooling for Individual Excellence, 1961, Schooling for What?, 1970, Photopsychography: New Image of Man, 1974, SRA Reading Power for Home Schooling, 1991; founder (with Sean Shanahan, Patricia Larkin), Gateway Literacy Project, 1992, Failing Schools! Why?, 1993; contbr. articles to profl. jours. Served with USN, 1943-46. Mem. Am. Psychol. Assn., Internat Reading Assn., Assn. Supervision and Curriculum Devel., Internat. Assn. Psychotronics Research, Am. Personnel and Guidance Assn., Phi Delta Kappa. Address: Heartsong House 148 San Remo Rd Carmel CA 93923 *Increasingly, during the last few years of my eighty-two on Planet Earth, I have been influenced by the ancient Oriental philosophy of Yin-Yang, the dynamism and, yes, the continuum of possibility between good-bad, black-white, day-night, man-woman, and so on. While we may decry the one and cherish the other, we cannot have the one without the other. Still further, the truth usually lies somewhere along a line between the two. When I discover that truth, I act upon it to the best of my ability.*

PARKER, DONALD HOWARD, landscape architect; b. Boston, July 27, 1922; s. Glennes Arthur Sheldon and Vida Mary (Kendrew) P.; m. Ella Mae Stinson, Sept. 8, 1945 (dec. 1983); children—Randall Tebow, Sheldon Kendrew, Susan Bowen, Elizabeth Stinson; m. Helen Jackson Anthony, June 19, 1987; 1 stepchild, Scott Douglas Paul. B.S., U. Mass., Amherst, 1946, B. in Landscape Architecture, 1947. Registered landscape architect Va., N.C., N.Y., Mass. Landscape draftsman L.E. Moore, C.E., Boston, 1947-48, Leo A. Novick, L.A., N.Y.C., 1948-49; asst. landscape architect Colonial Williamsburg (Va.) Found., 1949-60, chief landscape architect, 1960-85; pvt. practice landscape architecture Williamsburg, 1949—; adv. com. Hist. Am. Bldg. Survey, 1969-71, Smithsonian Instn., 1977-80. Contbr. chpts. to books, articles to profl. jours. Active, Boy Scouts Am., 1958-84. Served to 2d lt. U.S. Army, 1942-45. Recipient Dist. Grad. award Dept. Land Architecture, U. Mass., 1984; Paul Harris fellow Rotary Found., 1981. Fellow Am. Soc. Landscape Architects (trustee Potomac chpt. 1977, Va. chpt. 1978-83, treas. Va. chpt. 1984-86, Disting. Svc. award Va. chpt. 1994); mem. Nat. Assn. Olmsted Parks, Assn. Preservation Va. Antiquities, Williamsburg Jr. C. of C. (v.p. 1950-56), Williamsburg Inn Lawn Bowling Club (pres. 1985-90, sec.-treas. 1991-93, treas. 1994—, tournament dir. 1985-94), Rotary (pres. Williamsburg club 1979-80). Avocations: sports, gardening, canoeing, traveling, lawn bowling. Home and Office: 108 Archers Hope Rd Williamsburg VA 23185-4406

PARKER, DONALD LESTER, technology company executive; b. Mobile, Ala., Dec. 19, 1944; s. Orin Harvey and Lois B. (Burdette) P.; m. Linda Jean Busby, Dec. 18, 1970; children: Amanda Leigh, Allison Ann. BS, Spring Hill Coll., 1966; PhD, Mich. State U., 1971. Research asst. Mich. State U. 1968-71; asst. prof. Iowa State U., Ames, 1975-79, assoc. prof., 1980—; v.p. research & devel. QMS, Inc., Mobile, Ala., 1981-82; sr. v.p. QMS, Inc., Mobile, 1983-84, sr. v.p. corp. technology, 1985-86, sr. v.p. mktg. and technology, 1987, exec. v.p. products and technology, 1987—; adj. prof. computer & info. scis., U. So. Ala., 1986—. Contbr. articles to profl. jours. Mem. AAUP, Assn. Computing Machinery, IEEE, Am. Assn. for Artificial Intelligence, Ala. Acad. Sci., Am. Electronics Assn., Am. Mgmt. Assn., Am. Phys. Soc., AAAS, Fedn. Am. Scientists, Tech. Assn. Graphic Arts, Ala. State Research Resource Adv. Coun., Nat. Computer Graphics Assn., World Future Soc. Home: 6420 Tokeneak Trl Mobile AL 36695-2940 Office: QMS Inc 1 Magnum Pass Mobile AL 36618

PARKER, DONN BLANCHARD, information security consultant; b. San Jose, Calif., Oct. 9, 1929; s. Donald William and Miriam Estelle (Blanchard) P.; m. Lorna Ruth Schroeder, Aug. 16, 1952; children: Diane Parker Wisdom, David. B.A., U. Calif, Berkeley, 1952, M.A., 1954. Sr. engr. Gen. Dynamics Co., San Diego, 1954-62; staff cons. Control Data Corp., Palo Alto, Calif., 1962-69; sr. mgmt. systems cons. SRI Internat., Menlo Park, Calif., 1969—; speaker San Francisco Commonwealth Club, 1991. Author: Crime by Computer, 1976, Ethical Conflicts in Computer Technology, 1977, 89, Computer Security Management, 1982, Fighting Computer Crime, 1983. Rsch. grantee NSF, 1971-79, U.S. Dept. Justice, 1979—; recipient Individual Achievement award Info. Systems Security Assn., 1991-92. Mem. Assn. Computing Machinery (sec. 1969-75), Am. Fedn. Info. Processing Socs. (bd. dirs. 1974-76), Am. Soc. Indsl. Security. Republican. Lutheran. Office: SRI Internat Menlo Park CA 94025

PARKER, DOUGLAS MARTIN, lawyer; b. Chgo., Mar. 6, 1935; s. Lewis Wallace and Elaine (Schulz) P.; m. Angela Macintosh, June 5, 1965; children: Heather Louise, Melissa Meredith. A.B., Cornell U., 1956, LL.B., 1958. Bar: N.Y. 1961, U.S. Supreme Ct. 1966, D.C. 1969. Assoc. Mudge Rose Guthrie Alexander & Ferdon, N.Y.C., 1958-59, 62-69, ptnr., 1977-94, of counsel, 1995; ptnr, Lankler & Parker, Washington, 1969-73; with Office of Counsel to Pres., 1973; dep. gen. counsel HUD, 1974-77. Served to capt. U.S. Army, 1959-62. Mem. Am. Arbitration Assn. (cons. arbitration panel). Republican. Congregationalist. Home: 7 Highwood Rd South Orleans MA 02662 Office: Mudge Rose Guthrie Alexander & Ferdon 180 Maiden Ln New York NY 10038-4925

PARKER, EDNA G., federal judge; b. Johnston County, N.C., 1930; 1 child, Douglas Benjamin. Student, N.J. Coll. for Women (now Douglass Coll.). B.A. with honors, U. Ariz. 1953; postgrad., U. Ariz. Law Sch.; LL.B., George Washington U., 1957. Bar: D.C. Law clk. U.S. Ct. Claims, 1957-59; atty.-advisor Office of Gen. Counsel, Dept. Navy, 1959-60; trial atty. civil and tax div. Dept. Justice, 1960-69; adminstrv. judge Contract Appeals Bd., Dept. Transp., 1969-77; spl. trial judge U.S. Tax Ct., 1977-80, judge, 1980—. Mem. ABA, Fed. Bar Assn., D.C. Bar, D.C. Bar Assn., Women's Bar Assn. of D.C., Nat. Assn. Women Lawyers, Nat. Assn. Women Judges. Office: US Tax Ct 400 2nd St NW Washington DC 20217-0002

PARKER, EUGENE NEWMAN, retired physicist, educator; b. Houghton, Mich., June 10, 1927; s. Glenn H. and Helen (MacNair) P.; m. Niesje Meuter, 1954; children—Joyce, Eric. BS, Mich. State U., 1948; PhD, Calif. Inst. Tech., 1951; DSc, Mich. State U., 1975; Doctor Honoris Causa in Physics and Math., Univ. Utrecht, The Netherlands, 1986; Doctor of Philosophy Honoris Causa in Theoretical Physics, U. Oslo, 1991. Instr.

math. and astronomy U. Utah, 1951-53, asst. prof. physics, 1953-55; mem. faculty physics U. Chgo., 1955-95, prof. dept. physics, 1962-95, prof. dept. astronomy and astrophysics, 1967-95, prof. emeritus, 1995—. Author: Interplanetary Dynamical Processes, 1963, Cosmical Magnetic Fields, 1979, Spontaneous Current Sheets in Magnetic Fields, 1994. Recipient Space Sci. award AIAA, 1964, Chapman medal Royal Astron. Soc., 1979, Gold medal, 1992, Disting. Alumni award Calif. Inst. Tech., 1980, Karl Schwarzschild award Astronomische Gesselschaft, 1990; named James Arthur Prize Lectr. Harvard-Smithsonian Ctr. Astrophysics, 1986. Mem. NAS (H. K. Arctowski award 1969, U.S. Nat. Medal of Sci. award 1989), Am. Astron. Soc. (Henry Norris Russell lectr. 1969, George Ellery Hale award 1978), Am. Geophys. Union (John Adam Fleming award 1968, William Bowie medal 1990), Am. Acad. Arts and Scis., Norwegian Acad. Sci. and Letters. Achievements include development of theory of the origin of the dipole magnetic field of Earth; of prediction and theory of the solar wind and heliosphere; of theoretical basis for the X-ray emission from the Sun and stars. Home: 1323 Evergreen Rd Homewood IL 60430-3410

PARKER, EVERETT CARLTON, clergyman; b. Chgo., Jan. 17, 1913; s. Harry Everett and Lillian (Stern) P.; m. Geneva M. Jones, May 5, 1939; children: Ruth A. (Mrs. Peter Weiss), Eunice L. (Mrs. George Kolczun, Jr.), Truman E. AB, U. Chgo., 1935; BD magna cum laude, Chgo. Theol. Sem., 1943, Blatchford fellow, 1944-45, DD, 1964; DD, Catawba Coll., Salisbury, N.C., 1958; L.H.D., Fordham U., 1978, Tougaloo Coll., 1987. Pastor Waveland Ave. Congl. Christian Ch., 1943; asst. pub. service and war program mgr. NBC, 1943-45; founder-dir. Protestant Radio Commn., 1945-50; lectr. communication Yale Div. Sch., 1946-58, dir. communications research project, 1950-54; dir. Office Communication United Ch. Christ, 1954-83; sr. research assoc., adj. prof. Fordham U., 1983—; founder citizen movement to protect minority rights in media, 1963—; chmn. broadcasting and film commn. Nat. Coun. Chs., 1969-72, mem. gen. bd., 1966-72; chair Study Commn. on Theology, Edn. and Electronic Media, 1985-87; founder Found. for Minority Interests in Media, 1985—, treas., 1985—; Hispanic Telecommunications Network, 1986—; mem. adv. com. on advanced TV svcs., Consumer Adv. Group FCC, 1988-92. Producer-dir.: nat. TV programs including series Off to Adventure, 1956, Tangled World, 1965; originator: series Six American Families, PBS-TV, 1977; Author: Religious Radio, 1948, Film Use in the Church, 1953, The Television-Radio Audience and Religion, 1955, Religious Television, 1961, (with others) Television, Radio, Film for Churchmen, 1969, Fiber Optics to the Home: The Changing Future of Cable, TV and The Telephone, 1989. Recipient Human Relations award Am. Jewish Com., 1966, Faith and Freedom award Religious Heritage Found., 1966, 77, Alfred I. DuPont-Columbia U. award pub. service in broadcasting, 1969; Roman Cath. Broadcasters Gabriel award pub. service, 1970; Lincoln U. award significant contbn. human relations, 1971; Racial Justice award Com. for Racial Justice, United Ch. Christ, 1973; Ch. Leadership award Council for Christian Social Action, 1973; Public Service award Black Citizens for a Fair Media, 1979, Pioneer award World Assn. for Christian Communication, 1988; Congl. citation, 1993. Club: Yale (N.Y.C.). Home: 11 Midland Ave White Plains NY 10606-2828 Office: Fordham University Dept Communications Bronx NY 10458

PARKER, FRANK LEON, environmental engineering educator, consultant; b. Somerville, Mass., Mar. 23, 1926; s. Benjamin James and Bertha (Cohen) P.; m. Elaine Marilyn Goldman, Aug. 22, 1954; children: Nina Madeline, Aaron Bennet, Stephan Alexander, David Seth. BS, MIT, 1948; MS, Harvard U., 1950, PhD, 1955. Registered profl. engr., N.Y. Engr. U.S. Bur. Reclamation, Riverton, Wyo., 1948; field engr. Rockland Light & Power Co., Nyack, N.Y., 1949-50; cons. Howard M. Turner, Boston, 1955; sect. chief IAEA, Vienna, Austria, 1960-61; chief radioactive waste disposal research sect. Oak Ridge Nat. Lab., 1956-66; Disting. prof. environ. and water resources engring. Vanderbilt U., Nashville, 1989—, Alexander Heard Disting. prof., 1988; Westinghouse Savannah River Disting. Sci. prof. Clemson (S.C.) U., 1991—, Harvie Branscomb Disting. prof., 1994-95; cons. Adv. Com. on Reactor Safeguards, 1970-90, sci. adv. bd. Panel EPA, 1982-83, U.S. Dept. Energy, Hanford, Wash., 1970—, Office Nuclear Waste Isolation, Battelle, 1975-87, chmn. bd. radioactive waste mgmt. NAS, 1985-91; commr. Monitored Retrievable Storage Rev. Commn., 1988-89. Mem. Port Authority Nashville, 1979-90; mem. Nashville Appeals Bd., 1979-88; mem. Jewish Community Rels. Coun., Nashville, 1981-87. With U.S. Army, 1943-46. Mem. NAE, Soc. Risk Analysis, AAAS, Am. Nuclear Soc., Am. Geophys. Union, Health Physics Soc., Nat. Coun. Radiation Protection and Measurements (consociate). Co-author: Physical and Engineering Aspects of Thermal Pollution, 1970; Engineering Aspects of Thermal Pollution, 1969; Biological Aspects of Thermal Pollution, 1969. Home: 4400 Iroquois Ave Nashville TN 37205-3832 Office: PO Box 1596 Nashville TN 37202-1596

PARKER, FRANKLIN, writer, educator; b. N.Y.C., June 2, 1921; m. Betty June Parker, June 12, 1950. BA, Berea Coll., 1949; MS, U. Ill., 1950; EdD, Vanderbilt U., 1956. Librarian, speech tchr. Ferrum (Va.) Coll., 1950-52; librarian Belmont Coll., Nashville, 1952-54; circulation librarian George Peabody Coll. Tchrs. Vanderbilt U., Nashville, 1955-56; assoc. prof. edn. SUNY, New Paltz, 1956-57, U. Tex., Austin, 1957-64; prof. edn. U. Okla., Norman, 1964-68; Benedum prof. edn. emeritus W. Va. U., Morgantown, 1968-86; prof. emeritus, 1986; disting. vis. prof. Ctr. for Excellence in Edn. No. Ariz. U., 1986-89; disting. vis. prof. Coll. Edn. and Psychology Western Carolina U., 1989-94; research fellow U. Coll. Rhodesia, Africa, 1957-58, Rhodes-Livingstone Inst. Social Research, Africa, 1961-62; vis. prof. edn. U. Calgary, Alta., Can., summer 1969, U. Alta., Edmonton, summer 1970, No. Ariz. U., Flagstaff, summer 1971, U. Lethbridge, Can., (summers) 1971-73, Meml. U., Nfld., summer 1974; mem. Internat. Conf. African Adminstrn., Cambridge, (Eng.) U., 1957, European Bur. Adult Edn., Finland and Fed. Republic of Germany, 1966, nat. conf. White House Conf. on Edn., 1965, Nat. Fgn. Policy Conf. of Educators Dept. State, 1966; cons. Office Edn. HEW, 1970-75, NSF, 1980-86; cons. pubs. Macmillan, Merrill, Tchrs. Coll. Press, Wm. C. Brown, 1988—. Author: African Development and Education in Southern Rhodesia, 1960, 74, Africa South of the Sahara, 1966, George Peabody, A Biography, 1971, rev. edit., 1995, The Battle of the Books: Kanawha Country, 1975, What Can We Learn from the Schools of China?, 1977, British Schools and Ours, 1979; co-author: John Dewey: Master Educator, 2d rev. edit., 1961, Government Policy and International Education, 1965, Church and State in Education, 1966, Strategies for Curriculum Change: Cases from 13 Nations, 1968, Dimensions of Physical Education, 1969, International Education: Understandings and Misunderstandings, 1969, Understanding the American Public High School, 1969, Education in Southern Africa, 1970, Curriculum for Man in an International World, 1971, Administrative Dimensions of Health and Physical Education Programs, Including Athletics, 1971, Education and the Many Faces of the Disadvantaged, 1972, The Saber-Tooth Curriculum, meml. edit., 1972, Accelerated Development in Southern Africa, 1974, Myth and Reality: A Reader in Education, 1975, Six Questions: Controversy and Conflict in Education, 1975, Crucial Issues in Education, 6th rev. edit., 1977, Censorship and Education, 1981, Academic Profiles in Higher Education, 1993; series compiler and editor American Dissertations on Foreign Education, A Bibliography with Abstracts, vol. I Can., 1971, vol. II India, 1972, vol III Japan, 1972, vol. IV Africa, 1973, vol. V Scandinavia, 1974, vol. VI China, 1975, vol. VII Korea, 1976, vol. VIII Mex., 1976, vol. IX South Am., 1977, vol. X Cen. Am., 1978, vol. XI Pakistan, Bangladesh, 1979, vol. XII Iran and Iraq, 1980, vol. XIII Israel, 1980, vol. XIV Middle East, 1981, vol. XV Thailand, 1983, vol. XVI Asia, 1985, vol. XVII Pacific, 1986, vol. XVIII Philippines, 1986, vol. XIX Australia and New Zealand, 1988, vol. XX Great Britain, 1990; (with Betty June Parker) Education in Puerto Rico and of Puerto Ricans in the U.S.A., vol. I, 1978, vol. II, 1984; Women's Education—A World View: Annotated Bibliography of Doctoral Dissertations vol. I, 1979; U.S. Higher Education: A Guide to Information Sources, 1980; Women's Education—A World View: Annotated Bibliography of Books and Reports, vol. II, 1981, Education in the People's Republic of China, Past and Present: Annotated Bibliography, 1986, Education in England and Wales: An Annotated Bibliography, 1991; spl. cons. U.S. and internat. edn. terms The Random House Dictionary of the English Language, 2d edit., 1987; mem. editorial bd. Jour. of Thought, 1965-80, Western Carolina U. Jour. Edn., 1969-76, W. Va. U. Mag., 1969-78, Ednl. Studies, 1975-77, Rev. Edn., 1977-86, Core (Collected Orignal Resources in Edn.), 1977—, Internat. Jour African Hist. Studies, 1977-86 Edn. Digest, 1976-80, U.S.A. Today, 1981—, Collier's Yearbook, 1965-72, Compton's Yearbook, 1965-66, Dictionary of Am. Biography, supplement 5, 1951-55, 77, Dictionary of Scientific Biography, vol. 8, 1973, vol. 10, 1974, vol. 14, 1976, McGraw-Hill Ency. of

World Biography, 1973, Acad. Am. Ency., 1979, Reader's Digest Almanac and Yearbook, 1968-73, others; mem. editorial bd., regular contbr. Americana Ann., 1961-89. Served with USAAF, 1942-46. Sr. Fulbright research scholar, 1961-62. Mem. African Studies Assn., S.W. Philosophy Edn. Soc. (pres. 1960), Am. Acad. Polit. and Social Sci., Am. Ednl. Research Assn., US Comparative and Internat. Edn. Soc. (feature writer 1963-68, v.p. 1963-64, internat. sec. 1965-68), Can. Comparative and Internat. Edn. Soc., Comparative Edn. Soc. Europe, History Edn. Soc. (pres. 1963-64), Appalachian Writers Assn., Kappa Delta Pi (life mem., Harold R.W. Benjamin fellow internat. edn. 1957-58, sec. com. on internat. edn. 1968-70), Phi Delta Kappa (life, research award chmn. commn. on internat. relations in edn. 1963-67), Phi Gamma Mu, Phi Kappa Phi (life).

PARKER, FRED L, federal judge; b. 1938. BA, U. Mass., 1962; LLB, Georgetown U., 1965. With Lyne, Woodworth & Everts, Boston, 1965-66, Office Atty. Gen., Montpelier, Vt., 1969-72, Langrock and Sperry, Middlebury, Vt., 1972-75; ptnr. Langrock, Sperry, Parker & Stahl, Middlebury, 1975-82, Langrock, Sperry, Parker & Wool, Middlebury, 1982-90; fed. judge U.S. Dist. Ct. (Vt. dist.), 1990—; mem. conduct bd. Vt. Supreme Ct., 1975-79, jud. conduct bd., 1982-88. Active Vt. Lawyers Project. Mem. Vt. Bar Assn. (chair spl. com. reform of judiciary 1988-89), Chittenden County Bar Assn. Office: US Dist Ct 11 Elmwood Ave Fl 5 Burlington VT 05401-4366*

PARKER, GEORGE, retired pen manufacturing company executive; b. Janesville, Wis., Nov. 9, 1929; s. Russell C. and Eleanor (Jackson) P.; m. Nancy E. Bauhan, Aug. 11, 1951; children: George Safford III, Elizabeth, Martha, Patricia. B.A., Brown U., 1951, LL.D. (hon.), 1986; M.A., U. Mich., 1952; LL.D. (hon.), Milton Coll., 1974. With Parker Pen Co., Janesville, 1952-86; beginning as asst. to gen. mgr. Gilman Engring. Co. subs. Parker Pen Co., successively asst. domestic advt. mgr., fgn. advt. mgr., dir. fgn. sales, dir. domestic sales, v.p., gen. mgr., 1958-60, exec. v.p., 1960-66, pres., 1966-77, 81-82, chief exec. officer, 1966-80, 81-82, chmn. bd., 1976-86; chmn. bd. Manpower Inc., 1976-86; pres., chmn. Caxambas Assocs. of Fla., Inc., 1986—; chmn. bd. BANCWIS Corp., 1971-84, dir. emeritus, chmn. bd. 1971-84; bd. dirs. Bank of Wis.; chmn. bd. Moebius Printing Co., Milw., 1992-93. Chmn. Wis. Rep. Fin. Com., 1971-73, state chmn., 1974-76; mem. Nat. Rep. Fin. Com., 1971-73; mem. Rep. Nat. Com., 1974-76; chmn. bd. dirs., chief exec. officer Janesville Found.; bd. dirs., pres. Marco Island Taxpayers Assn., 1993-94; fellow Lake Forest Acad.; trustee emeritus Brown U., Beloit Coll.; chmn. emeritus bd. fellows Beloit Coll.; dir. Wis. Acad. Found., 1994—.

PARKER, GEORGE EDWARD, III, lawyer; b. Detroit, Sept. 26, 1934; s. George Edward and Lucia Helen (Muir) P.; m. Margaret G. Koehler; children—George, David, Benjamin. A.B., Princeton U., 1956; J.D., U. Mich., 1959. Bar: Mich. 1959, D.C. 1981, Fla. 1982. Assoc. Miller, Canfield, Paddock & Stone, Detroit, 1959-68; ptnr. Miller, Canfield, Paddock & Stone, 1968—. Bd. dirs. Detroit Symphony Orch., 1984; chmn. Future Planning, United Found., 1984; trustee Hannan House, 1975—; David Whitney Fund, Katherine Tuck Fund. Republican. Office: Miller Canfield Paddock et al 150 W Jefferson Ave Ste 2500 Detroit MI 48226-4432

PARKER, GERALD WILLIAM, physician, medical center administrator, retired air force officer; b. Susquehanna, Pa., Oct. 22, 1929. B.S., Union Coll., Schenectady, 1951; M.D., N.Y. Med. Coll., 1955. Diplomate Nat. Bd. Med. Examiners, Am. Bd. Internal Medicine; lic. physician, N.Y., Tex., D.C. Intern Ellis Hosp., Schenectady, 1955-56; resident internal medicine Wilford Hall, USAF Med. Ctr., San Antonio, 1958-61; resident in gastroenterology Water Reed Army Med. Ctr., Washington, 1965-66; commd. capt. U.S. Air Force, 1956, advanced through grades to brig. gen., 1980, retired, 1986; chair dept. medicine USAF Hosp., Clark AFB, Philippines, 1967-69; chief internal medicine Malcolm Grow USAF Med. Ctr., Andrews AFB, Washington, 1969-70; chair dept. medicine Malcolm Grow USAF Med. Ctr., 1970-72, Wilford Hall USAF Med. Ctr., Lackland AFB, Tex., 1972-75; dir. hosp. services Wilford Hall USAF Med. Ctr., 1975-77; comdr USAF Hosp., Torrejon Air Base, Spain, 1977-78; dep. dir. med. plans and resources Office of Surgeon Gen. USAF, Washington, 1978-80; dir. med. plans and resources Office of Surgeon Gen. USAF, 1980-81; dir. med. inspection AF Inspection and Safety Ctr., Norton AFB, Calif., 1981-83; dep. surgeon gen. for ops. AF Med. Service Ctr., Brooks AFB, Tex., 1983-85; dir. profl. affairs and quality assurance Office of Surg. Gen., USAF, Washington, 1985-86; dep. dir., chief profl. services King Health Ctr., U.S. Soldiers and Airmens Home, Washington, 1986—. Decorated Air Force D.S.M. with oak leaf cluster, Legion of Merit with oak leaf cluster, Bronze Star, Air Medal with oak leaf cluster. Fellow ACP; mem. AMA, Soc. AF Physicians, D.C. Med. Soc., Am. Geriatric Soc., ACP Execs., Alpha Omega Alpha. Office: King Health Ctr USSAH 3700 N Capitol St NW Washington DC 20317-9998

PARKER, GORDON RAE, natural resource company executive; b. Cape Town, South Africa, Dec. 2, 1935; came to U.S., 1981; s. David Rae and Gwen Elizabeth (Armstrong) P.; m. Pamela Margaret Pearce, Sept. 1, 1962; children: Gillian Rae, David Rae. BS, Mont. Coll. Mineral Sci. and Tech., 1958, MS, 1959; MBA, U. Cape Town, 1966. Mng. dir. Tsumeb Corp., Namibia, South Africa, 1975-81; mng. dir. O'okiep Copper Co., Cape, South Africa, 1975-81; v.p. Newmont Mining Corp., N.Y.C., 1981-84, pres., 1984-86, CEO, 1985-86, chmn., also bd. dirs., 1986—; bd. dirs. The Williams Cos., Inc., Newmont Gold Co., Newmont Australia Ltd., Peabody Holding Co. Inc.; past chmn. World Gold Council, 1986—; chmn. Western regional council, 1987—. Fellow Instn. Mining and Metallurgy (London), South African Inst. Mining and Metallurgy; mem. AIME, British North Am. Com. Clubs: Mining, Sky, Union League (N.Y.C.); Blind Brook (Purchase, N.Y.); Silver Spring Country (Ridgefield, Conn.), Mid Ocean, Hamilton, Bermuda. Avocation: golf. Home: 13 Sunset Dr Englewood CO 80110-4033*

PARKER, H. LAWRENCE, rancher, investor, retired investment banker; b. Portchester, N.Y., June 16, 1926; s. Raeburn H. and Alice (Lawrence) P.; m. Eleanor Sage, Mar. 3, 1951 (div. 1967); children: Katherine, Richard, Michael, Douglas (dec.); m. Regine Hawes, Nov. 15, 1994. B.A., Yale U., 1949. With Morgan Stanley & Co., N.Y.C., 1950—; ptnr. Morgan Stanley & Co., 1959-75, mng. dir., 1975-83, adv. dir., 1984—; pres. Morgan Stanley Can. Ltd., 1976-79, chmn., 1979-84; mem. adv. bd. on edn. and tng. Sec. Navy, 1985-87. Trustee Green Mountain Valley Sch., Waitsfield, Vt., 1981-91. Served with USMCR, 1944-46. Mem. Investment Bankers Assn. Am. (bd. govs. 1966-70, pres. 1969), Nat. Assn. Securities Dealers (gov. 1981-84), Sublette County Hist. Soc. (trustee 1987-91). Clubs: Nat. Golf Links Am., Links (N.Y.C.), Blind Brook, Augusta Nat. Golf (Ga.), Bedford Golf and Tennis, Jupiter Island, Seminole Golf. Home: PO Box 287 Daniel WY 83115-0287

PARKER, HAROLD TALBOT, history educator; b. Cin., Dec. 26, 1907; s. Samuel Chester and Lucile (Jones) P.; m. Louise Salley, July 9, 1980. Ph.B., U. Chgo., 1928, Ph.D., 1934; postgrad., Cornell U., 1929-30. Mem. faculty Duke U., Durham, N.C., 1935-77, prof. history, 1957-77, emeritus, 1977—; adj. prof. U. Ala., Huntsville, 1978-81; faculty U. N.C., Chapel Hill, 1984. Author: The Cult of Antiquity and the French Revolutionaries, 1937, Three Napoleonic Battles, 1944, 83, (with Marvin Brown) Major Themes in Modern European History, 3 vols., 1974, Bureau of Commerce in 1781, 1979, An Administrative Bureau During the Old Regime, 1993; editor: (with Richard Herr) Ideas in History, 1965, Problems in European History, 1979, (with Georg Iggers) International Handbook of Historical Studies, 1979, Theory and Social History, 1980, (with L.S. Parker) Proc. Consortium of Revolutionary Europe, 1981, 84, 85, 86; assoc. editor Historical Dictionary of Napoleonic Years, 1989; regional editor, contbg. author: Great Historians of the Modern Age, 1991; contbr. articles to profl. jours. Served with USAAF, 1942-45. Recipient Disting. Svc. award Consortium on Revolutionary Europe, 1993, Disting Svc. award So. Hist. Assn. European History Sect., 1993. Mem. Soc. for French Hist. Studies (pres. 1957, Disting. Svc. award 1989), AAUP (pres. Duke U. chpt. 1960), Phi Beta Kappa (pres. Duke chpt. 1961). Episcopalian. Home: 100 7th Street Ext West Columbia SC 29169-7151

PARKER, HARRY JOHN, retired psychologist, educator; b. Sioux City, Iowa, Jan. 18, 1923. A.B., Elmhurst Coll., 1947; M.A., Northwestern U., 1953, Ph.D., 1956, postgrad., 1958; postgrad., Roosevelt U., 1957-58; LittD, Elmhurst Coll., 1990. Lic. psychologist, Okla. Tex. Counselor Northwestern U. Counseling Ctr., Chgo., 1952-56; counseling psychologist Northwes-

tern U. Counseling Ctr., 1956-59, asst. dir., 1957-58, dir., 1958-59; pvt. practice counseling psychologist Chgo., 1956-59, Okla., 1959-69, Tex., 1969—; prof. edn. U. Okla., 1959-69; dir. manpower planning, regional med. program and Sch. Health Related Professions U. Okla. Med. Ctr., Oklahoma City, 1967-69; prof. preventive medicine and pub. health U. Okla. Med. Ctr., 1966-69, prof. human ecology, 1969; assoc. dean Sch. Allied Health Scis. U. Tex. Southwestern Med. Ctr., Dallas, 1969-74; prof. phys. medicine and rehab. U. Tex. Southwestern Med. Ctr., 1969-90; prof. psychiatry U. Tex. Southwestern Med. Ctr., 1969-90, prof. rehab. sci., 1970-90; adj. prof. rehab. U. N. Tex., 1990; adj. prof. psychology Ill. Inst. Tech., 1990—, Tex. Woman's U., 1991—; adj. prof. allied health edn. U. Tex. Southwestern Med. Ctr., Dallas, 1990—. Contbr. articles to profl. jours. Served with U.S. Army, 1943-46. Fellow Am. Psychol. Assn.; mem. Southwestern Psychol. Assn., Dallas Psychol. Assn., Tex. Psychol. Assn., Sigma Xi, Phi Delta Phi, Alpha Eta.

PARKER, HARRY LAMBERT, university rowing coach; b. Fitchburg, Mass., Oct. 28, 1935; s. Lambert Achilles and Ruth Margaret (Burnham) P.; m. Kathryn E. Keeler, Aug. 10, 1985; children: George Franklin, David Lambert. A.B., U. Pa., 1957. Rowing coach Harvard U., 1960—; coach U.S. Olympic team, 1964, 68, 72, 80, 84; mem. U.S. Olympic Rowing com., 1964-68, 72-84; head coach U.S. Women's Olympic rowing team, 1976. Mem. town meeting, Winchester (Mass.), 1971-73. Served with USNR, 1957-60. Mem. Rowing Hall of Fame., U.S. Rowing Assn. (dir. 1966-85). Coach U.S. eight-oared crew, silver medalist 1972 Olympics, nat. intercollegiate championship crews Harvard U., 1983, 85, 87, 88, 89, 92; coach Harvard U. crew winners Grand Challenge Cup, Henley Royal Regatta, 1985, Ladies Challenge Plate, 1973, 90, Brittania Challenge Cup, 1993. Home: 26 Hancock St Winchester MA 01890-2002 Office: Harvard Univ 60 John F Kennedy St Cambridge MA 02138-4943

PARKER, HARRY LEE, retired military officer, counselor; b. Birmingham, Ala., Feb. 20, 1944; s. Guy Milburn and Grace (Lee) P.; m. Sheri Lynn Pogue (div. Oct. 1973); children: John Lee, Suzanne Grace, Stephen Scott; m. Melanie Louise Cox, Apr. 20, 1979; 1 child, Christopher Robert. BA, Miss. State U., 1966; MS, Johns Hopkins U., 1980; postgrad., U.S. Army Command & Staff Coll. 1982. Commd. 2d lt. U.S. Army, 1966, advanced through grades to lt. col.; maintenance officer 85th Maintenance Bn., Hanau, Fed. Republic of Germany, 1967-69; commanding officer 143d Engr. Co. and A Co. 34th Engr. Bn., Long Binh, Vietnam, 1969-70; chief plans and ops. div. Dir. of Logistics, Ft. Rucker, Ala., 1971-73; supply and maintenance officer 97th Signal Bn. NATO, Mannehim, Fed. Republic of Germany, 1973-76; asst. materiel officer 8th Maintenance Battalion, Grossalheim, Fed. Republic Germany, 1977; tng. evaluator HQ 1st US Army, Ft. Meade, Md., 1978-81; logistics coord. Cuban Task Force, Ft. Indiantown Gap, Pa., 1980; project officer Dept. Def., Project Office, Mobile Electric Power, Washington, 1982-85; chief of maintenance U.S. Army South, Ft. Clayton, Panama, 1985-88; prof. mil. Sci. Army ROTC, Miss. State U., Starkville, Miss., 1988-90; ops. officer 101st area support group, Guardian City, Saudia Arabia, logistics officer, 1st Corps Support Command, XVIII Airborne Corps., Damman, Saudi Arabia (Desert Shield and Desert Storm), 1990-91; career/coop. edn. counselor Cen. Fla. C.C., Ocala, Fla., 1992—. Presbyn. elder. Decorated 2 Bronze Stars, 3 Meritorious Svc. medals, 5 Army Commendation medals. Mem. Ret. Officers Assn., Am. Legion, Miss. State U. Alumni Assn., Sigma Chi (life). Avocations: woodworking, pilot, scuba diving, boating, computers. Home: 2021 SE 10th Ct Ocala FL 34471-5457 Office: Ctrl Fla C C Placement Ocala FL 33478-1388

PARKER, HARRY S., III, art museum administrator; b. St. Petersburg, Fla., Dec. 23, 1939; s. Harry S. Parker and Catherine (Baillie) Knapp; m. Ellen McCance, May 23, 1964; children: Elizabeth Day, Thomas Baillie, Samuel Ferguson, Catherine Allan. A.B. magna cum laude, Harvard U., 1961; M.A., NYU, 1966. Exec. asst., adminstrv. asst. to dir. Met. Mus. Art, N.Y.C., 1963-66, exec. asst. to pres., 1966-67, exec. asst. to dir., 1967, chmn. dept. edn., 1971-73; vice dir. edn., 1971-73; dir. Dallas Mus. Art, 1974-87, Fine Arts Mus. San Francisco, 1987—. Mem. Am. Assn. Mus. (v.p.) Assn. Art Mus. Dirs., Century Assn., Bohemian Club. Home: 171 San Marcos Ave San Francisco CA 94116-1462 Office: Fine Arts Mus of San Francisco Golden Gate Pk San Francisco CA 94118*

PARKER, HENRY GRIFFITH, III, insurance executive; b. Plainfield, N.J., Oct. 27, 1926; s. Henry Griffith and Ruth Martin (Van Auken) P.; m. Audrey Lansing Turner, May 11, 1957; children: Henry Griffith, IV, Elizabeth Wright. AB, Princeton U., 1948; postgrad., U. Pa. Sch. Law. With Chubb & Son, Inc., 1949—; v.p., 1968-70, sr. v.p., 1971-92, mng. dir., 1986-92; v.p. Fed. Ins. Co., 1968-73, sr. v.p., 1973-91; v.p. Vigilant Ins. Co., 1966-91, mgr. internat. div., 1967-84; chmn. adv. bd. Bolivar Compania de Seguros, Ecuador, 1968-84, bd. dirs. Chubb Pacific Underwriting Mgmt. Svcs. Pte. Ltd., Singapore, Alliance Assurance Co. Am., N.Y.C., Sun Ins. Office Am. Inc., N.Y.C., The London Assurance Am. Inc., N.Y.C., The Sea Ins. Co. Am., N.Y.C.; mem. industry sector adv. com. on svcs. U.S. Dept. Commerce, Washington; bd. dirs. Nat. Fgn. Trade Coun., chmn. declarations com., 1974-81, chmn. ins. com., 1976-81; chmn. internat. policy com. U.S.C. of C., 1970-73; chmn. U.S. del. XII-XIII-XX-XXII-XXII Hemispheric Ins. Conf., Chile, 1969, Paraguay, 1987, Panama, 1985, Buenos Aires, 1989; chmn. Internat. Ins. Adv. Coun., Washington, 1970-73, 85-90, chmn. Internat. Com. Am. Ins. Assn., 1991-93; mng. advisor, Industrial Re-International Inc., 1992—; mem. N.J. Commn. on Internat. Trade, 1986—; chmn. bus. adv. com. bus. coun. UN, 1988—; mem. adv. bd. Liaison Office Peoples Ins. Co. China. Appeared on numerous TV and radio programs; contbr. articles to profl. jours. Chmn. bd. Overlook Hosp., Summit, N.J., 1973-80; trustee Drew U., Madison, 1974—; bd. dirs. Nat. Assn. to Prevent Blindness, N.J. Dist. Export Coun. Lt. (j.g.) USNR, 1944-46. Recipient Internat. Ins. award U.S.C. of C., 1981, Disting. Service award Internat. Ins. Council, 1988. Mem. Nat. Assn. Ins. Commrs. (chmn. internat. adv. com.), Am. Ins. Assn. (chmn. internat. com.), Psi Upsilon. Republican. Episcopalian. Clubs: Downtown Assn. (N.Y.C.), Princeton (N.Y.C.), River (N.Y.C.); Devon Yacht, Morris County (N.J.) Golf, Morristown Field. Home: 38 East Ln Madison NJ 07940-2652 Office: PO Box 1615 15 Mountain View Rd Warren NJ 07059

PARKER, HERBERT GERALD, state official; b. Fayetteville, Ark., May 13, 1929; s. Otis James and Anna Berthina (Fisher) P.; m. Florida Lucylle Fisher, June 27, 1959; 1 child, Christie Lynne. BS, U. Nebr., Omaha, 1962; MS, N.C. A&T State U., Greensboro, 1970; PhD, Fla. State U., Tallahassee, 1982. Commd. 2d. lt. U.S. Army, 1947, advanced through grades to col., 1969; served advisor mil. assistance advisory group Republic of China, Taiwan, 1962-65; prof. mil. sci. N.C. A&T State U., Greensboro, 1965-68; comdr. all U.S. Spl. Forces units the Delta, S. Vietnam, 1968-69; dir. nonresident instrn. U.S. Army Civil Affairs Sch., Ft. Gordon, Ga., 1969-71, commandant and dir., Ft. Bragg, N.C. 1971-73; prof. mil. sci., dept. head Fla. A&M U., Tallahassee, 1973-77; ret., 1977; chief Crimes Compensation Bur., State of Fla., 1979-87, chief internal auditor Fla. Dept. Edn., 1988-91, dir. of adminstrn. Fla. dept. edn., 1991-94. Bd. dirs. Opportunities Industrialization Centers, Leon County United Way, 1977-81, Fla. Victim/Witness Network, 1985-87; bd. dirs. Nat. Assn. Crime Victims Compensation Bds., 1981-87 (pres. 1984-86); mem. Nat. Urban League; pres. Fla. A&M U Boosters Club, 1983-85; mem. Tallahassee Urban League, 1982—, pres., 1985-87; mem. Tallahassee Cmty. Rels., 1993—, Tallahassee Sr. Citizens Found., 1994—, Tallahassee Sr. Citizens Adv. Bd.. Decorated Silver Star, Legion of Merit (2), Bronze Star (3), Purple Heart, Air Medal (3); recipient disting. service award Boy Scouts Am., 1969. Mem. Nat. Assn. Social Scientists, U.S. Army Civil Affairs Assn. (Disting. Service award, 1973), Assn. Parents and Teachers, Tallahassee C. of C., Fla. State U. Coll. Edn. Alumni Assn. (sec. 1991-93), Mil. Order of the World Wars, 555th Parachute Infantry Assn., Inc., Capital 'Chordsmen (treas. 1991-94), Capital Rotary Club (Paul Harris fellow), Sigma Phi Phi (sire archer/pres. 1992-94), Kappa Alpha Psi, Phi Kappa Phi. Democrat. Methodist. Clubs: Jack and Jill of Am., Am. Bowling Congress, Univ. Men's League (pres.), Fla. A&M Credit Union Bowling League (pres.), Champion Chevrolet Men's Classic Bowling League, Hilmas Park Men's Golf Assn., Bass Anglers Sportsman Soc., Winewood Men's Golf Assn. (v.p.), Toastmasters Internat. (assn. v.p., pres. Ft. Bragg chpt 1971-73), Nat. Geog. Soc. Home: 3510 Tullamore Ln Tallahassee FL 32308-3127 Office: Dir of Adminstrn Fla Dept Edn The Capitol Tallahassee FL 32399

PARKER, ISRAEL FRANK, national association consultant; b. Sylvania, Ga., Oct. 29, 1917; s. Cornelius Dean and Mary Eunice (Lewis) P.; m. Mary Alice, Dec. 26, 1938; 1 dau., Rebecca Gaye. Student, Ga. So. U., 1935-36, U. Ala., Birmingham, 1942-43, 49-50. Bus. mgr. United Bakery Workers Local 441, Birmingham, 1941-42; internat. rep. Retail, Wholesale and Dept. Store Union, AFL-CIO, Birmingham, 1942-52, asst. regional dir. So. area, 1957-60; regional dir. So. area Retail, Wholesale and Dept. Store Union, AFL-CIO, 1970-76; internat. sec.-treas. Retail, Wholesale and Dept. Store Union, AFL-CIO, N.Y.C., 1976-80; bd. govs. Nat. Assn. of Unemployment Ins. Appellate Bds., 1989-90; mem. bd. appeals Ala. Unemployment Compensation; trustee Retail, Wholesale and Dept. Store Internat. Union and Industry Health and Benefit Fund and Pension Fund; past chmn. Internat. Found. Employee Benefit Plans; chmn. Ala. Trade Union Coun. for Histadrut, 1970; bd. dirs. Found. for Internat. Meetings. Treas. Canterbury Meth. Men., 1993. Served with USN, 1944-46. Named Man of Yr. Birmingham Frat. Order Police, 1972. Mem. Altadena Valley Golf and Country Club. Home: 745 Bentley Dr Birmingham AL 35213-2543

PARKER, JAMES, retired curator; b. Boston, Jan. 22, 1924; s. Cortlandt and Elizabeth (Gray) P. A.B., Harvard U., 1946. Fellow in European decorative arts, 16th-19th centuries Met. Mus. Art, N.Y.C., 1951; asst. Met. Mus. Art, 1952-54, asst. curator, 1954-62, assoc. curator, 1962-68, curator, 1968-93; adj. prof. Inst. Fine Arts, NYU, 1968-69, 71-72, 80. Author: (with others) Decorative Art from the Samuel H. Kress Collection at the Metropolitan Museum of Art, 1964; Contbr. articles to museum bulls. Trustee French Inst.-Alliance Francaise, N.Y.C. Served with F.A. AUS, 1944-45, PTO. Club: Union (N.Y.C.). Home: 17 E 89th St New York NY 10128-0615 Office: Met Mus Art Fifth Ave # 82nd St New York NY 10028

PARKER, JAMES AUBREY, federal judge; b. Houston, Jan. 8, 1937; s. Lewis Almeron and Emily Helen (Stuessy) P.; m. Florence Fisher, Aug. 26, 1960; children: Roger Alan, Pamela Elizabeth. BA, Rice U., 1959; LLB, U. Tex., 1962. Bar: Tex. 1962, N.Mex. 1963. With Modrall, Sperling, Roehl, Harris & Sisk, Albuquerque, 1962-87; judge U.S. Dist. Ct. N.Mex., Albuquerque, 1987—; mem. Standing Com. on Rules of Practice and Procedures of U.S. Cts., N.Mex. Commn. on Professionalism, 1986—. Articles editor Tex. Law Rev., 1961-62. Mem. ABA, Fed. Judges Assn., Am. Judicature Soc., Am. Bd. Trial Advocates, Tex. Bar Assn., N.Mex. Bar Assn., Albuquerque Bar Assn., Order of Coif, Chancellors, Phi Delta Phi. Avocations: ranching, fly fishing, running, skiing. Office: US Dist Ct PO Box 566 Albuquerque NM 87103-0566

PARKER, JAMES FLOYD, minister, pension fund executive; b. Ann Arbor, Mich., Nov. 2, 1946; s. Ivan William and Elnor (Coles) P.; m. Sharon Kay Metty, June 14, 1969; children: Ryan Christopher, Brent Eugene, Scott Coles. B in Bus. Adminstrn., U. Mich., 1968; MDiv, Garrett-Evang. Theol. Sem., Evanston, Ill., 1971; postgrad., U. Pa., 1981; DD (hon.), Adrian Coll., 1987. Campus minister, intern Northwestern U., Evanston, 1968-69, U. Ill at Chgo., 1969-70; asst. minister Batavia (Ill.) United Meth. Ch., 1970-71; adminstrv. trainee United Meth. Ch. Gen. Bd. Pensions, Evanston, 1971-72, asst. gen. sec., 1972-75, asst. actuary, 1976-78, assoc. gen. sec., 1978-81, treas., 1982-86, gen. sec., 1987—. Sec. MABC Credit Union, Evanston, 1972-78; chair investment com. 1st United Meth. Ch., Arlington Heights, Ill., 1989—; mem. exec. com. Ch. Pensions Conf., 1987—; mem. steering com. Ch. Alliance, 1987—. Mem. U. Mich. Alumni Assn., Phi Kappa Phi, Beta Gamma Sigma. Avocations: church choir, volleyball, soccer coaching. Home: 2529 Route Long Grove IL 60047 Office: Gen Bd of Pensions United Meth Ch 1200 Davis St Evanston IL 60201-4118

PARKER, JAMES ROGER, chemist; b. L.A., July 19, 1936. BS, Pomona Coll., 1958; PhD, Iowa State U., 1964. Lab. asst. Ames (Iowa) Lab atomic Energy Commn., 1958-64; analytical supr. PPG Industries, Natrium, W.Va., 1964-73, Corpus Christi, Tex., 1973-82; agrl. chemist PPG Industries, Barberton, Ohio, 1982-89; infrared spectroscopist PPG Industries, Monroeville, Pa., 1989—. Contbr. articles to profl. jours. Mem. Am. Chem. Soc., Soc. for Applied Spectroscopy, Spectroscopy Soc. Pitts., Soc. for Analytical Chemists Pitts., Phi Lambda Upsilon. Achievements include research in analytical chemistry of metal halides, iodine compounds, alkali metal oxides, coordination chemistry of phosphine oxides, qualitative identifications with proton magnetic resonance spectroscopy, polymer analyses with photoacoustic infrared spectroscopy. Office: PPG Industries 440 College Park Dr Monroeville PA 15146-1536

PARKER, JENNIFER WARE, chemical engineer, researcher; b. Berkeley, Calif., Apr. 18, 1959; d. Raymond Paul and Maureen Christina (Trehearne) Ware; m. Henrik Davidson Parker, July 30, 1983; children: Katherine Joyce, Nathaniel Henrikson. BSChemE, Princeton U., 1980; MSChemE, UCLA, 1983, PhDChemE, 1986. Devel. engr. Am. Pharmaseal, Glendale, Calif., 1980-81; rsch. engr. Crump Inst. Med. Engring, UCLA, 1986-87; sr. engr. The BOC Group, Murray Hill, N.J., 1987-90, lead engr., 1990-92; sr. engr. CFM Techs., Inc., West Chester, Pa., 1993—. Contbr. articles to profl. jours. Mem. Am. Inst. Chem. Engrs., N.Y. Acad. Scis. Avocations: sports, music, gardening. Home: 201 W Country Club Ln Wallingford PA 19086

PARKER, JOAN, public relations executive; b. N.Y.C., Oct. 13, 1935; d. Albert and Elizabeth (Durgin) P.; m. Francis Shea (div. 1964); 1 child, Sarah Young; m. Dale Coenen; children: Stephen, Adrian. Student, Hood Coll., 1953-55, Tobé Coburn Sch., 1956. Asst. to pub. relations dir. Elizabeth Arden, N.Y.C., 1956-57; acct. exec. Rowland Co., N.Y.C., 1958-60; owner pub. relations firm N.Y.C., 1969-81; dir. consumer products pub. relations N.W. Ayer Pub. Relations Co., N.Y.C., 1981-82, dir. pub. relations, 1982—; EVP, dir. Ayer & Ptnrs., 1994—. Dir. House of Vision, Chgo., 1983-85, Wolverine Worldwide, Grand Rapids, Mich., 1983—. Recipient Director's Choice award NWEA, 1990. Mem. Pub. Relations Soc. Am. (acad. counselor), Tobé Coburn Alumni Assn. (Most Disting. Alumni 1980), Fashion Group, Women's Jewelry Assn. Avocation: tennis. Office: Ayer Pub Rels 825 8th Ave New York NY 10019-7416

PARKER, JOHN GARRETT, lawyer; b. Roanoke Rapids, N.C., Mar. 6, 1947; s. Ben Thatch and Sarah Louise (Lessiter) P.; m. Helen Shell Nethercutt, Aug. 23, 1969; 1 child, Sarah Helen. BA in Econs., U. N.C. 1969, JD, 1976. Bar: Ga. 1976, U.S. Dist. Ct. (no. dist.) Ga. 1977, U.S. Ct. Appeals (5th and 11th cirs.) 1981, U.S. Ct. Appeals (9th cir.) 1986, U.S. Dist. Ct. (mid. dist.) Ga. 1989, U.S. Ct. Appeals (8th cir.) 1993. Assoc. atty. Hensell, Post, Brandon & Dorsey, Atlanta, 1976-83; ptnr. Hansell & Post, Atlanta, 1983-87, Paul, Hastings, Janofsky & Walker, Atlanta, 1987—. Cochair Clark for Cong. com., Cobb County, Ga., 1992. Lt. U.S. Army, 1970-73. Mem. ABA, Atlanta Bar Assn., State Bar of Ga., Order of Coif. Republican. Episcopal. Avocations: hunting, golf. Home: 1001 Byrnwyck Rd NE Atlanta GA 30319-1665 Office: Paul Hastings Janofsky & Walker 600 Peachtree St Ste 2400 Atlanta GA 30308

PARKER, JOHN MALCOLM, management and financial consultant; b. Halifax, N.S., Can., June 13, 1920; s. Charles Fisher and Mabel (Hennigar) P.; came to U.S., 1936, naturalized, 1942; m. Irene Wilson Davis, Oct. 11, 1942 (dec. Nov. 1987); 1 child, Elane Parker Jones; m. Kathryn Harvey Smithey, Apr. 22, 1989. Cert. internal auditor. With Standard Oil Co. N.J., Charlotte, N.C., 1941, Duke Power Co., Charlotte, 1941-42, So. Bell Tel. & Tel. Co., Charlotte, 1946-50, Atlanta, 1950-68, with South Central Bell Telephone Co., Birmingham, Ala., 1968-83; asst. v.p., gen. internal auditor; pres. Omega Assocs., Inc., 1983—; commr. gen. assembly Presbyn. Ch. of U.S., 1968, 81. Served with AUS, 1942-46. Mem. Inst. Mgmt. Accts. (pres. local chpt. 1972-73, nat. dir.). Am. Mgmt. Assn., Inst. Internal Auditors (pres. chpt. 1978-79, dist. dir. 1979-81, regional dir. 1981-83, internat. vice chmn. 1983-84, internat. bd. dirs. 1979-87, v.p. found. 1984-85). Internat. Platform Assn. Republican. Home: 4509 Clairmont Ave Birmingham AL 35222-4438 Office: Omega Assocs Inc PO Box 530452 Birmingham AL 35253-0452

PARKER, JOHN VICTOR, federal judge; b. Baton Rouge, La., Oct. 14, 1928; s. Fred Charles and LaVerne (Sessions) P.; m. Mary Elizabeth Fridge, Sept. 3, 1949; children: John Michael, Robert Fridge, Linda Anne. B.A., La. State U., 1949, J.D., 1952. Bar: La. 1952. Atty. Parker & Parker, Baton Rouge, 1954-66; asst. parish atty. City of Baton Rouge, Parish of East Baton Rouge, 1956-66; atty. Sanders, Downing, Kean & Cazedessus, Baton Rouge, 1966-79; chief judge U.S. Dist. Ct., Middle Dist. La., Baton Rouge, 1979—;

vis. lectr. law La. State U. Law Sch. Served with Judge Adv. Gen.'s Corps U.S. Army, 1952-54. Mem. ABA, Am. Judicature Soc., Am. Arbitration Assn., La. State Bar Assn. (past mem. bd. govs.), Baton Rouge Bar Assn. (past pres.), Order of Coif, Phi Delta Phi. Democrat. Club: Baton Rouge Country. Lodges: Masons (32 deg.); Kiwanis (past pres.). Office: US Dist Ct 228 Federal Bldg 707 Florida St Baton Rouge LA 70801-1713

PARKER, JOHN WILLIAM, pathology educator, investigator; b. Clifton, Ariz., Jan. 5, 1931; s. Vilas William and Helen E. Parker; m. Barbara A. Atkinson, June 8, 1957; children: Ann Elizabeth, Joy Noelle, John David, Heidi Susan. BS, U. Ariz., 1953; MD, Harvard U., 1957. Diplomate Am. Bd. Pathology. Clin. instr. pathology U. Calif. Sch. Medicine, San Francisco, 1962-64; asst. prof. U. So. Calif. Sch. Medicine, L.A., 1964-68, assoc. prof., 1968-75, prof., 1975—; dir. clin. labs., 1974-94, vice chmn. dept. pathology, 1985—, dir. pathology reference labs., 1991-94; assoc. dean sci. affairs U. So. Calif., 1987-89, v.p. univ. faculty senate, 1991-92; co-chmn. 15th Internat. Leucocyte Culture Conf., Asilomar, Calif., 1982; chmn. 2d Internat. Lymphoma Conf., Athens, Greece, 1981; v.p. faculty senate U. So. Calif., 1991-92; bd. dirs. ann. meeting Clin. Applications of Cytometry, Charleston, S.C., 1988—. Founding editor (jour.) Hematological Oncology, 1982-93; assoc. editor Jour. Clin. Lab. Analysis, 1985—; co-editor: Intercellular Communication in Leucocyte Function, 1983; founding co-editor (jour.) Communications in Clin. Cytometry, 1994—; contbr. over 150 articles to profl. jours., chpts. to books. Named sr. oncology fellow Am. Cancer Soc., U. So. Calif. Sch. Medicine, 1964-69, Nat. Cancer Inst. vis. fellow Walter and Eliza Hall Inst. for Med. Research, Melbourne, Australia, 1972-73. Fellow Coll. Am. Pathologists, Am. Soc. Clin. Pathologists; mem. Am. Assn. Pathologists, Am. Soc. Hematology, Internat. Acad. Pathology, Clin. Cytometry Soc. (v.p., pres.-elect 1993-95, pres. 1995—), Phi Beta Kappa, Phi Kappa Phi. Avocations: gardening, reading, hiking. Office: U So Calif Sch Medicine CSC 107 2250 Alcazar St Los Angeles CA 90032

PARKER, JONATHAN EDWARD, beverage products company executive; b. Cin., 1936. Grad., Ga. Inst. Tech., 1959, Harvard U., 1963. Exec. v.p. ops. Coca-Cola Foods, Houston. Office: Coca-Cola Foods PO Box 2079 2000 Saint James Pl Houston TX 77056-4125

PARKER, JOSEPH B., JR., psychiatrist, educator; b. Knox County, Tenn., July 8, 1916; s. Joseph B. and Sue (York) P.; m. Phyllis Maxine Foster, May 25, 1946; children: Suzanna Margaret, Joseph B. III. B.S., U. Tenn., 1939, M.D., 1941. Diplomate: Am. Bd. Psychiatry and Neurology. Intern Knoxville Gen. Hosp., 1941-42; resident Duke U. Hosp., Durham, N.C., 1946-48; resident in psychiatry St. Elizabeth Hosp., Washington, 1944-45; practice medicine specializing in psychiatry Durham, 1948-49, 53-59, Memphis, 1949-53, Lexington, Ky., 1959-70; instr. psychiatry Duke U. 1948-49, assoc. prof., 1953-59; assoc. prof. psychiatry, dir. Child Guidance Clinic U. Tenn. Coll. Medicine, 1949-53; chief psychiatry VA Hosp., Durham, 1953-59; prof., chmn. dept. psychiatry U. Ky. Med. Ctr., 1959-69; prof. psychiatry Duke Med. Ctr., 1970-83, prof. emeritus, 1983—; vis. faculty U. Pitts., 1967, Harvard, 1968-69; cons. USPHS Hosp., VA Hosp., Lexington. Editor: Psychotherapeutics, 1979. Mem. prof. adv. com. Cerebral Palsy; mem. prof. adv. com. Jr. League Opportunity Workshop; mem. Gov. Ky. Adv. Council Mental Health, 1962—; Gov. Ky. Manpower Commn., 1963—; exec. com., trustee Central Ky. Mental Health Bd. Served to lt. comdr., M.C. USNR, 1942-46. Fellow Am. Psychiat. Assn. (cons. continuing edn. project 1971—), Am. Coll. Psychiatrists, So. Psychiat. Assn. (regent, pres. 1972), Ky. Psychiat. Assn. (past pres.); mem. Am. Psychopath. Assn., Soc. Biol. Psychiatry, Delta Tau Delta, Phi Chi, Delta Phi Alpha, Alpha Omega Alpha. Address: 24 Stoneridge Cir Durham NC 27705-5510

PARKER, JOSEPH MAYON, printing and publishing executive; b. Washington, N.C., Oct. 11, 1931; s. James Mayon and Mildred (Poe) P.; m. Lauretta Owen Dyer, Mar. 23, 1957; children: Katherine Suzanne, Joseph Wilbur. Student, Davidson Coll., 1949-51; BA, U. N.C., 1953, MPA, 1992; postgrad., Carnegie Inst. Tech., 1955-56. Mgr. print div. Parker Bros., Inc., Ahoskie, N.C., 1956-71, chief editorialist, 1961-77, gen. mgr., 1971-77, pres., chief exec. officer, 1977—; dir. Governor's Hwy. Safety Program, 1993—; treas. Chowan Graphic Arts Found., Murfreesboro, N.C., 1971-90, pres. 1990-92. Editor, columnist five community newspapers, N.C.; panelist: (TV talk show) North Carolina This Week, 1986-89. Mem. Ind. Devel. Commn., 1974-86; vice chmn. N.C. Goals and Policy Bd., Raleigh, 1977-84; trustee Pitt County Meml. Hosp., 1980-88; pres. Com. of 100, Winton, N.C., 1984-87; chmn. Northeastern N.C. Tomorrow, Elizabeth City, 1981-84, sec., 1984-90; del. Dem. Nat. Conv., N.Y.C., 1980, platform com., 1988; dist. chmn. N.C. Dem. Ctrl. Com., 1980-82. With U.S. Army, 1953-54, col. USAR, 1954-88. Mem. Soc. Profl. Journalists, East N.C. Press Assn. (past pres.), N.C. Press Assn., Nat. Newspaper Assn. (state chmn. 1976-83), Roanoke Island Hist. Assn. (vice-chmn. 1987-89), Ea. C. of C. (past chmn.), Rotary, Raleigh Exec. Club. Democrat. Methodist. Avocations: golf, reading. Home: 4500 Connell Dr Raleigh NC 27612-5600 Office: 215 E Lane St Raleigh NC 27601-1035

PARKER, KELLIS E., SR., legal educator, lawyer, musician; b. 1942. J.D., Howard U., 1968. Bar: Colo. 1970. Law clk to presiding judge U.S. Ct. Appeals, 1968-69; acting prof. U. Calif., Davis, 1969-72; assoc. prof. Columbia U., N.Y.C., 1972-75, prof., 1975—; prof. law wkshe and Isidor Sulzbacher, Columbia U. Law Sch., 1994—. Mem. bd. dirs. City Club (N.Y.C.); cons. Legal Def. and Edn. Funds, Inc., NAACP, 1972—; mem. exec. com. Nat. Com. Against Discrimination in Housing, 1974—. Author: Modern Judicial Remedies, 1975. Office: Columbia U Sch Law 435 W 116th St New York NY 10027-7201

PARKER, LEONARD SAM, architect, educator; b. Warsaw, Poland, Jan. 16, 1923; came to U.S. 1923; s. Rueben and Sarah (Kollica) Popuch; m. Betty Mae Buegen, Sept. 1, 1948 (dec. 1983); children—Bruce Aaron, Jonathan Arthur, Nancy Anne, Andrew David. BArch., U. Minn., 1948; MArch., MIT, 1950. Sr. designer Eero Saarinen Assocs., Bloomfield Hills, Mich., 1950-56; prin. dir. design The Leonard Parker Assocs., Mpls., 1957—, The Alliance Southwest, Phoenix, 1981-87; prof. grad. program Sch. Architecture, U. Minn., Mpls., 1959—; pres. Minn. Archtl. Found., 1991. Author: Abandoning the Catalogs, 1979, Rivers of Modernism, 1986, Collaboration-Same Bed, Different Dream?. Panel mem. Mpls. City Hall Restoration Com., Am. Arbitration Assn., USAF bd. visitors (chmn.). Served with U.S. Army, 1943-46; ETO. Firm has received 67 nat. and regional awards for design excellence. Fellow AIA; mem. Minn. Soc. Architects (pres. 1981, Gold medal 1986, pres. Mpls. chpt. 1979), Tau Sigma Delta. Home: 3936 Willmatt Hl Hopkins MN 55343-6944 Office: The Leonard Parker Assocs 430 Oak Grove St Minneapolis MN 55403-3234

PARKER, LEWIS E. S., orthopedic company executive, commercial vineyard operator; b. Washington, Aug. 19, 1941; s. Alvin McAdam and Rebecca (Harry) P.; children: Andrea L., Lara J. B.S. in Civil Engring., Lehigh U., 1963; M.B.A. in Fin., U. Pa., Phila., 1965. Dir. systems Climax Molybdenum Co., Greenwich, Conn., 1968-70; v.p., controller Amax Carbon Prodn. Co., Chgo., 1970-74; v.p. fin. Am. Instrument div. Baxter Travenol, Silver Springs, Md., 1974-76; v.p. Hazelton Labs. Corp., Vienna, Va., 1976-87; v.p. Kirschner Med. Corp., Timonium, Md., 1991-94, pres., 1994—. Mem. Fin. Execs. Inst. (pres. 1978-79), Nat. Assn. Life Sci. Industries (bd. dirs. 1979-83). Office: Kirschner Med Corp 10720 Gilroy Rd Hunt Valley MD 21031

PARKER, LYNDA MICHELE, psychiatrist; b. Phila., Sept. 28, 1947; d. Albert Francis and Dorothy Thomasinia (Herriott) P.; A.B., C. W. Post Coll., 1968; M.A. (Martin Luther King Jr. scholar 1968-70), N.Y.U., 1970; M.D., Cornell U., 1974; postgrad. N.Y. Psychoanalytic Inst., 1977-82. Intern, N.Y. Hosp., N.Y.C., 1975; resident in psychiatry Payne Whitney Clinic, N.Y.C., 1975-78; psychiatrist in charge day program Cabrini Med. Center, N.Y.C., 1978-79, attending psychiatrist, 1978—; admitting psychiatrist inpatient psychiat. treatment Payne Whitney Clinic, N.Y.C., 1978—, supr. psychiatry residents 1978—, supr. long-term psychotherapy, 1980-82; attending psychiatrist N.Y. Hosp., Cornell Med. Center, 1979—; practice medicine specializing in psychiatry, N.Y.C., 1979—; instr. psychiatry Cornell U. Med. Coll., 1979-86, asst. prof., 1986—; psychiatry, N.Y. Med. Coll., 1978—; psychiat. cons. Bldg. Service 32BJ Health Fund, 1983-89, Inwood House, N.Y.C., 1983-86, Time-Life Inc., 1986—; Ind. Med. Examiners, 1986—; Epilepsy Inst., 1986-87, asst. med. dir., 1987-88, med. dir.,

1988; ind. med. examiner Rep. Health Care Rev. Scis. Mem. adv. bd. St. Bartholomew Community Preserve, N.Y.C. Mem. Am. Psychiat. Assn., Am. Womens Med. Assn. Episcopalian. Office: 219 E 69th St Apt 1J New York NY 10021-5453

PARKER, MACEO, jazz musician, alto saxophone; b. Kinston, N.C.. Student, Agrl. and Tech. Coll. N.C. (now N.C. Agrl. and Tech. U.). Musician James Brown, 1964-84, Own Group, 1984—. Albums include: Roots Revisited, 1990, Mo' Roots, 1991, 92, Live on Planet Groove, 1992, Southern Exposure, 1994. Office: Verve Digital Records 825 8th Ave New York NY 10019-7416*

PARKER, MARY EVELYN, former state treasurer; b. Fullerton, La., Nov. 8, 1920; d. Racia E. and Addie (Graham) Dickerson; m. W. Bryant Parker, Oct. 31, 1954; children: Mary Bryant, Ann Graham. BA, Northwestern State U. La., 1941, hon. doctorate, 1987; diploma in social welfare, La. State U., 1943. Social worker Allen Parish, La., 1941-42; personnel adminstr. War Dept., Camp Claiborne, La., 1943-47; editor Oakdale, La., 1947-48; exec. dir. La. Dept. Commerce and Industry, Baton Rouge, 1948-52; with Mut. of N.Y., Baton Rouge, 1952-56; chmn. La. Bd. Pub. Welfare, Baton Rouge, 1950-51; commr. La. Dept. Pub. Welfare, Baton Rouge, 1956-63, La. Div. Adminstrn., 1964-67; treas. State of La., 1968-87. Chmn. White House Conf. on Children and Youth, 1960; pres. La. Conf. on Social Welfare, 1959-61; mem. Democratic Nat. Com., 1948-52; bd. dirs. Woman's Hosp., Baton Rouge; trustee Episcopal High Sch., Baton Rouge Gen. Hosp. Found.; mem. adv. council Coll. Bus., Tulane U., New Orleans. Named Baton Rouge Woman of Yr., 1976. Baptist. Home: 141 Duster Dr Natchez MS 39120-5263

PARKER, MARY-LOUISE, actress; b. Ft. Jackson, S.C., Aug. 2, 1964. Attended. Bard Coll. Actress: (theatre) Hay Fever, 1987, The Miser, 1988, The Art of Success, 1989, The Importance of Being Earnest, 1989, Prelude to a Kiss, Broadway, 1990-91 (Theatre World award 1990), Babylon Gardens, 1991, (films) Signs of Life, 1989, Longtime Companion, 1990, Grand Canyon, 1991, Fried Green Tomatoes, 1991, Mr. Wonderful, 1993, Naked in New York, 1994, The Client, 1994, Bullets Over Broadway, 1994, Boys on the Side, 1995, (TV movies) Too Young the Hero, 1988, A Place for Annie, 1994. Office: William Morris Agency 151 El Camino Beverly Hills CA 90212*

PARKER, MAYNARD MICHAEL, journalist, magazine executive; b. L.A., July 28, 1940; s. Clarence Newton and Virginia Esther (Boyce) P.; m. Judith Karen Seaborg, Dec. 11, 1965 (div.); 1 child, Francesca Lynn; m. Susan Fraker, Sept. 15, 1985; children: Nicholas Maynard, Hugh Fraker. B.A., Stanford U., 1962; M.A. Columbia U. 1963. Reporter Life mag., 1963-64, corr. Hong Kong Bur., 1966-67; corr. Hong Kong Bur. Newsweek, 1967-69; Saigon bur. chief Newsweek, Vietnam, 1969-70; chief Hong Kong Bur. Newsweek, 1969-73, sr. nat. affairs editor, 1975-77, asst. mng. editor, 1977-80, exec. editor, 1980-82, editor, 1982—; mng. editor Newsweek Internat. Newsweek, N.Y.C., 1973-75. Contbr. articles to Fgn. Affairs, Fgn. Policy, Reporter, Atlantic. Chmn. Stanford Alumni Bd. 1st lt. inf. U.S. Army, 1964-66. Mem. Am. Soc. Mg. Editors (bd. dirs), Coun. on Fgn. Rels., Stanford U. Alumni Bd. (chmn.), Overseas Press Club. Episcopalian. Avocations: reading, skiing, tennis, fly-fishing. Office: Newsweek Mag 444 Madison Ave New York NY 10022-6903

PARKER, MEL, editor; b. N.Y.C., Feb. 11, 1949; s. David Parker and Mollie (Kantorowicz) Lederman; m. Diane Nancy Goldberg, June 27, 1971; children: Emily, David. AB, Rutgers U., 1971; AM in English, N.Y.U., 1973. Editorial researcher Esquire Mag., N.Y.C., 1973; grad. asst. NYU, 1974-77; adj. lectr. CUNY, 1977-78; editor Leisure Books, N.Y.C., 1978-81; sr. editor Playboy Paperbacks, N.Y.C., 1981-82; sr. editor Berkley Pub. Group, N.Y.C., 1982-85, exec. editor, 1985-86, editor-in-chief, 1986-87; v.p., editor in chief Warner Paperbacks, N.Y.C., 1987-90, pub., 1990—. Office: Warner Books Inc Time-Life 1271 Avenue Of The Americas New York NY 10020-1300

PARKER, MICHAEL (MIKE PARKER), congressman; b. Laurel, Miss., Oct. 31, 1949; m. Rosemary Prather; children: Adrian, Marisa, Thomas. BA, William Carey Coll., 1970. Operator various businesses; mem. vet. affairs com., textile caucus, sunbelt caucus, arts caucus 101st-104th Congresses from 4th Miss. dist., 1989—, mem. pub. works and transp. com., economic devel. subcom., water resources subcom., aviation subcom., 1989—. Presbyterian. Office: US Ho of Reps 1410 Longworth Washington DC 20515-2404*

PARKER, NANCY WINSLOW, artist, writer; b. Maplewood, N.J., Oct. 18, 1930; d. Winslow Aurelius and Beatrice (Gaunt) P. B.A., Mills Coll., 1952; student, Sch. Visual Art, N.Y.C., Art Students League. Pub. relations exec. N.Y. Soccer Club, N.Y.C., 1961-63; with RCA, N.Y.C., 1964-67; art dir. Appleton-Century-Crofts, N.Y.C., 1968-70; staff designer Holt Reinhart & Winston, N.Y.C., 1970-73; free lance writer, illustrator, 1974—. Author, illustrator: The Man with The Take-Apart Head, 1974, The Party at the Old Farm, 1975, Mrs. Wilson Wanders Off, 1976, Love from Uncle Clyde, 1977, The Crocodile Under Louis Finneberg's Bed, 1978, The President's Cabinet, 1978, rev. edit., 1991, The Ordeal of Byron B. Blackbear, 1979, Puddums, The Cathcarts' Orange Cat, 1980, Poofy Loves Company, 1980 (ALA Notable Book 1980), The Spotted Dog, 1980, The President's Car, 1981, Cooper, The McNallys' Big Black Dog, 1981, Love from Aunt Betty, 1983, The Christmas Camel, 1983, The United Nations from A to Z, 1985; co-author: Bugs, 1987, Frogs, Toads, Lizards and Salamanders, 1990, Working Frog, 1992, Money, Money, Money, 1995; illustrator: Oh, A Hunting We Will Go!, 1974, Warm as Wool, Cool as Cotton, The Story of Natural Fibers, 1975, The Goat in the Rug, 1976, Willy Bear, 1976 (CHristopher award 1976), Sweetly Sings the Donkey, 1976, The Substitute, 1977, Hot Cross Buns and Other Old Street Cries, 1978, No Bath Tonight, 1978, My Mom Travels a Lot, 1981 (Christopher 1981), Paul Revere's Ride, 1985, General Store, 1988, Aren't You Coming Too?, 1988, Peter's Pockets, 1988, the Jacket I Wear in the Snow, 1989, At Grammy's House, 1990, Black Crow, Black Crow, 1991, When The Rooster Crowed, 1991, Barbara Frietchie, 1992, The Dress I'll Wear to the Party, 1992, Sheridan's Ride, 1993, Here Comes Henny, 1994, The Bag I'm Taking to Grandma's, 1995. Sec. East 74th St. Block Assn., 1974-83. Recipient various awards, 1974—; Jane Tinkham Broughton fellow, 1975. Mem. Author's Guild, Mills Coll. Club of N.Y., Mantoloking Yacht Club. Home: 51 E 74th St New York NY 10021-2716

PARKER, OLIVIA, photographer; b. Boston, June 10, 1941; d. Harvey Perley and Barbara Ellen (Churchill) Hood; m. John Otis Parker, Apr. 4, 1964; children: John Otis, Helen Elizabeth. B.A., Wellesley Coll., 1963. Tchr. photog. workshops, 1975—; trustee Friends of Photography, 1981-92, 95—, v.p., 1985-89. Photographer, 1969—; Author: (monographs) Signs of Life, 1978, Under the Looking Glass, 1983, Weighing the Planets, 1987; portfolios of black and white photographs Ephemera, 1977, Lost Objects, 1980; one-woman shows include. Vision Gallery, Boston, 1976, 77, 79, 82, 83, 86, 87, Friends of Photography, Carmel, Calif., 1979, 81, Marcuse Pfeifer, N.Y.C., 1980, 83, George Eastman House, Rochester, N.Y., 1981, Art Inst. Chgo., 1982, Photo Gallery Internat., Tokyo, 1983, 84, 87, Fotografie Forum Gallery, Frankfurt, Germany, 1985, Lieberman and Saul, N.Y.C., 1988, Mus. Photgraphic Arts, San Diego, 1988, Photographers' Gallery, London, 1990, Brent Sikkema, N.Y.C., 1990, 91, Parco, Tokyo, 1991, ICAC/Weston, Tokyo, 1992, Vision, San Francisco, 1993, Robert Klein, Boston, 1993; group shows include, Mus. Fine Arts, Boston, 1978, 92, 93. Chgo. Art Inst. 1978, Internat. Ctr. Photography, N.Y.C., 1985, 87, Fogg Art Mus. Harvard U., 1989; represented in permanent collections, Mus. Modern Art, N.Y.C., Art Inst. Chgo., Boston Mus. Fine Arts, Victoria and Albert Mus., London. Bd. dirs. MacDowell Colony, 1988—; trustee Art Inst. Boston, 1992—. Artists Found. fellow, 1978. Mem. Soc. for Photog. Edn. Club: Chilton. Office: care Brent Sikkema 4th Fl 252 Lafayette St Fl 4 New York NY 10012-4069

PARKER, OMAR SIGMUND, JR., lawyer; b. Jacksonville, Fla., Apr. 10, 1945; s. Omar Sigmund and Dorothea (Heath) P.; children: Omar Sigmund, Christopher Michael, Julie Anne, Melissa Suzanne, Amy Kathleen. BA, U. Wash., 1968; JD, U. Oreg., 1971. Bar: Wash. 1971, U.S. Dist. Ct. (we. dist.) Wash. 1971, U.S. Ct. Appeals, 1972. Ptnr. Perkins Coie, Seattle, 1971—.

Contbr. articles to profl. jours. Bd. dirs. YMCA Youth and Govt. Program, Seattle, 1973-75. Mem. ABA, Wash. State Bar Assn., King County Bar Assn., Am. Coll. Real Estate Lawyers, Am. Coll. Mortgage Attys., Overlake Golf and Country Club, Order of Coif. Avocation: golf. Office: Perkins Coie 1201 3d Ave 40th Fl Seattle WA 98101-3099

PARKER, ORA DEAN SIMMONS, elementary school educator; b. McComb, Miss., Mar. 8, 1939; d. Malcolm Charles and Gladys Sophronia (Carruth) Simmons; m. George Lewis Parker, May 28, 1960; children: Gladys Wandalee, Lewis Gydale. BS, U. So. Miss., 1959; AA, SW Miss. Jr. Coll., 1958. Cert. elem. tchr., Miss. Tchr. kindergarten South Pike Sch. Dist., Magnolia, Miss., 1st Bapt. Ch., Magnolia; coord. drug program Fernwood Kindergarten Sch. Active community and ch. orgns. Recipient Outstanding Tchr. award. Mem. NEA, Miss. Edn. Assn., South Pike Edn. Assn. (sch. rep.). Home: RR 1 Box 116B Perkinston MS 39573-9611

PARKER, PATRICK JOHNSTON, entrepreneur, philanthropist; b. London, Apr. 4, 1931; came to U.S. 1942; s. Russell Johnston and Mildred Grace (Best) P.; m. Evelyn Heims, Nov. 12, 1952 (div. Aug. 1985); children: Karen, Russell; m. Patricia Marie Sobchak, Sept. 3, 1985 (div. May 1992); children: Katherine, Michael; m. Sally Fulton, Aug. 1992. BA, U. Chgo., 1955, MBA, 1957. Asst. prof. U. Calif., Berkeley, 1957-61; assoc. dean, prof. U. Rochester (N.Y.) Grad. Sch. Mgmt., N.Y., 1966-69; prof. U.S. Naval Postgrad. Sch., Monterey, Calif., 1961, 74—; mem. rsch. staff Ctr. for Naval Analysis, Arlington, Va., 1962-64; dir. tactical air programs Dept. Def., Washington, 1964-66, dep. asst. sec. def. intelligence, 1972-74; pres., chief exec. officer Hickok Mfg. Co., Rochester, 1969-72; chmn. bd. dirs. Cameron Scott Cosmetics, Menlo Park, Calif., 1988-93; pres., chmn. bd. trustees Aequus Inst., Montclaire, Calif., 1985—; mem. chief of naval ops. exec. panel USN, 1971-87, chmn., 1971-73. Author: (with Brian Dailey) Soviet Strategic Deception, 1988; contbr. articles to profl. jours. Trustee Shimer Coll., Mt. Carroll, Ill., 1968-72, St. John's Coll., Annapolis, Md., 1992—; dep. dir. Def. Transition Team, Pentagon, 1980; bd. overseers Ctr. Naval Analysis, 1966-72. Mem. Rochester (N.Y.) Yacht Club, Los Altos (Calif.) Hounds Club, Genessee Valley Club (Rochester, N.Y.). Republican. Episcopalian. Avocations: breeding horses, fox hunting. Home and Office: 1993 Orchard Rd Hollister CA 95023-9420

PARKER, PATRICK STREETER, manufacturing executive; b. Cleve., 1929. BA, Williams Coll., 1951; MBA, Harvard U., 1953. With Parker-Hannifin Corp. and predecessor, Cleve., 1953—, sales mgr. fittings div., 1957-63, mgr. aerospace products div., 1963-65, pres. Parker Seal Co. div., 1965-67, corp. v.p., 1967-69, pres., 1969-71, pres. and chief exec. officer, 1971-77, chmn. and chief exec. officer, 1977-84, chmn. bd., 1984—, pres., 1982-84, also bd. dirs., 1982—. Bd. trustees Case Western Res. U.; With USN, 1954-57. Mem. Union Club, Country Club, Pepper Pike Club. Office: Parker Hannifin Corp 17325 Euclid Ave Cleveland OH 44112-1290

PARKER, PETER D.M., physicist, educator, researcher; b. N.Y.C., Dec. 14, 1936; s. Allan Ellwood and Alice Francis (Heywood) P.; m. Judith Maxfield CUrren, Dec. 27, 1958; children: Stephanie, Gregory, Gretchen. BA, Amherst Coll., 1958; PhD, Calif. Tech., 1963. Physicist Brookhaven Nat. Labs., Upton, N.Y., 1963-66; prof. Yale U., New Haven, Conn., 1966—. Office: Yale U Physics Dept Wright Nuclear Structure 272 Whitney Ave New Haven CT 06511-8124

PARKER, PIERSON, minister, religion educator; b. Shanghai, China, May 27, 1905; s. Alvin Pierson and Susie Estelle (Williams) P.; m. Mildred Ruth Sorg, June 12, 1933; 1 son, Peter Pierson. A.B., U. Calif., 1927; student, So. Meth. U., 1928-29; M.A., Pacific Sch. Religion, 1933, Th.D. magna cum laude, 1934; S.T.D., Ch. Div. Sch. of Pacific, 1964. Ordained to ministry Congregational Ch., 1936, Episcopal Ch., 1944; instr. Bibl. lang. and lit. Pacific Sch. Religion, 1934-36; pastor North Congl. Ch., Berkeley, Calif., 1936-44; St. Andrew's Episc. Ch., Oakland, Calif., 1944-47; pres. No. Calif. Congl. Conf., 1938-39; lectr. Bibl. lit. Ch. Div. Sch. Pacific, 1940-43; instr., 1943-44, asst. prof., 1944-47, assoc. prof., 1947-49; Glorvina Rossell Hoffman prof. N.T. lit. and interpretation Gen. Theol. Sem., N.Y.C., 1949-74; sub-dean Gen. Theol. Sem., 1972-74; chaplain to seminarians Diocese of Los Angeles, 1974-83; disting. prof.-in-residence Cathedral of St. John the Divine, N.Y.C., 1977; prof. N.T. Grad. Sch. Theology, U. of South, 1951-52, 54-55, 56-57, 58-60, 67-69, 71-74; priest-in-charge Trinity Cathedral, Newark, 1953-54; research scholar Oxford U., 1957; lectr. N.T., St. Augustine's Coll., Canterbury, Eng., 1955; seminar asso. Columbia U.; vis. prof. Pacific Sch. of Religion, Ch. Div. Sch. Pacific, 1965, 1966, Seminario del Caribe, 1970, NT Maryknoll Sem., Ossining, N.Y. 1971-73, U. of South, 1975, Bloy Episc. Sch. Theology, 1978-79; priest-in-charge Ch. of Holy Spirit, Nice, France, 1962, St. Helena's Ch., Istanbul, Turkey, 1969; canon Cathedral Ch. of St. Paul, Los Angeles, 1977-81, Diocese of Los Angeles, 1981—; assoc. rector St. Ambrose Ch., Claremont, Calif., 1990—. Author: Interpreters' Bible (vol. on Deuteronomy), 1951, (with H.H. Shires, G.E. WRight) The Gospel Before Mark, 1953, Inherit the Promise, 1957, Christ Our Hope, 1958, Meditations on the Life of Christ, 1959, Good News in Matthew, 1976, A China Childhood, 1993; co-author: New Synoptic Studies, 1983; mem. editorial bd. Anglican Theol. Rev., 1949, Jour. Bibl. Lit., 1960-74; contbr. religious publs., Ency. Am. Mem. Studiorum Novi Testamenti Societas, Soc. Bibl. Lit. (pres. Pacific Coast sect. 1944-48, mem. council 1944, v.p. Middle Atlantic sect. 1959-60, pres. 1960-61, archivist 1976-83, nat. hon. pres. 1978), Pacific Theol. Group, Inst. Antiquity and Christianity, Pacific Sch. Religion Alumni Assn. (pres. 1943-46), Alpha Sigma Phi. Home: 650 W Harrison Ave Claremont CA 91711-4595

PARKER, R. JOSEPH, lawyer; b. St. Louis, June 29, 1944; s. George Joseph and Ann Rosalie (VanVactor) P.; m. Theresa Gaynor, Aug. 26, 1967; children: Christa Michele, Kevin Blake. AB, Georgetown U., 1966; JD, Boston Coll., 1969. Bar: Ohio 1969. Law clk. to judge U.S. Ct. Appeals (6th Cir.), Akron, Ohio, 1969-70; assoc. Taft, Stettinius & Hollister, Cin., 1970-78; ptnr. Taft, Stettinius & Hollister, Cin., 1978—; arbitrator Am. Arbitration Assn., Cin., 1980—; mem. faculty Nat. Inst. for Trial Advocacy, 1990—; mem. faculty advanced trial advocacy program IRS, 1993—. Editor Law Rev. Ann. Survey Mass. Law, 1967-69. Bd. dirs. West End Health Ctr., Inc., Cin., 1972-76, Legal Aid Soc. Cin., 1982-85; chmn. bd. dirs. Vol. Lawyers for Poor Found., Cin., 1986-88; master Am. Inn of Court, 1984—. Mem. Ohio State Bar Assn., Cin. Bar Assn., Cin. Country Club, Order of Coif. Democrat. Roman Catholic. Avocations: golf, squash. Office: Taft Stettinius & Hollister 1800 Star Bank Bldg 425 Walnut St Cincinnati OH 45202-3957

PARKER, REE, real estate investor; b. Monroe, Ga., Apr. 9, 1929; d. Reuben Parker and Cornie McDaniel; divorced; 1 child, Patricia. Dental Hygiene cert., Ohio State U., 1953; postgrad., U. Miami. Lic. marriage and family therapist. Dental hygienist Miami, Fla., 1953-55; interior designer, decorator Miami, 1955-57; real estate investor Fla., Ga., 1957—. Design and rebuild old homes, 1975-85. Charity work Abaco Islands, Coconut Grove Battered Children, 1980—, North Dade Children's Home; active Dem. party, Miami, 1953, presdl. elections; vol. Coconut Grove Cmty. Svcs. Recipient award for charity, dentistry for children, Coral Gables Dental Clinic, 1953-83. Mem. Miami Dental Assn. (hon.), Nat. Hygienist Assn., State and Local Hygienist Assn. (officer), Coral Gables Garden Club, Coral Gables Country Club, Coral Gables Gun Club, Coral Gables Fleet Club, Ohio State Alumni Assn. (social dir. 1975-85), Greater Miami Opera Guild, 30 Year Club, Platform Club (Washington), Alpha Kappa Gamma. Home: 3591 Rockerman Rd Miami FL 33133-3232

PARKER, RICHARD DAVIES, lawyer, educator; b. 1945. A.B., Swarthmore Coll., 1967; J.D. Harvard U., 1970. Bar: Mass. 1973. Law clk. to presiding judge, U.S. Ct. Appeals, Washington, 1970-71; law clk. to assoc. justice Potter Stewart, U.S. Supreme Ct., Washington, 1971-72; atty. Children's Def. Fund, Cambridge, Mass., 1973-74; asst. prof. Harvard U., Cambridge, 1974-79, prof., 1979—. Office: Harvard U Law Sch Langdell Hall Cambridge MA 02138

PARKER, RICHARD E., building products manufacturing company executive. Formerly v.p., now exec. v.p. Morgan Products Ltd., Oshkosh, Wis. Office: Abtco Inc 1 Neenah Ctr 600 Neenah WI 54956

PARKER, ROBERT ALLAN RIDLEY, astronaut; b. N.Y.C., Dec. 14, 1936; s. Allan Elwood and Alice (Heywood) P.; m. Joan Audrey Capers, June 14, 1958 (div. 1980); children: Kimberly Ellen, Brian David Capers; m. Judith S. Woodruff, Apr. 2, 1981. A.B., Amherst Coll., 1958; Ph.D., Calif. Inst. Tech., 1962. NSF postdoctoral fellow U. Wis., 1962-63, asst. prof. then assoc. prof. astronomy, 1963-74; astronaut NASA, Johnson Space Center, 1967-91; dir. policy plan Office Space Flight, NASA Hdqs., Washington, 1991, dir. space ops. utilization program, 1992—; mem. support crew Apollo XV and XVII, mission scientist Apollo XVII, program scientist Skylab program, mission specialist for Spacelab 1, ASTRO-1, 1983, 90. Mem. Am. Astron. Soc., Phi Beta Kappa. Office: Code MO NASA-HQ Washington DC 20546

PARKER, ROBERT ANDREW, artist; b. Norfolk, Va., May 14, 1927; s. William Clay and Harriet (Cowdin) P.; m. Dorothy Lane Daniels, Nov. 20, 1948; children: Christopher, Anthony, Eric, Geoffrey, Nicholas. B.A.E., Sch. Art Inst. Chgo., 1952; student, Atelier 17, N.Y.C., 1952-53. Now tchr. Parsons Sch., N.Y.C.; lectr. Pa. State U., 1981, Bklyn. Mus., 1981, New Sch. for Social Rsch., 1982, Phila. Coll. Art, 1982, Am. U., 1984, R.I. Sch. Design, 1984, NAD, 1985, Sch. Visual Arts, 1985, Skowhegan Sch. Painting and Sculpture, 1965, Sch. of Visual Arts, 1960-70, Syracuse U., 1975, Parsons Sch. Design, N.Y.C., 1980-85, Pratt Inst. 1985. Illustrated: handcolored ltd. edits. Marianne Moore poems, 1962; one-man shows include, Roko Gallery, N.Y.C., 1954, 55, 56, 58, World House Gallery, N.Y.C., 1961, Terry Dintenfass Gallery, N.Y.C., annually 1965—, Kilkenny Arts Festival, Ireland, Bklyn. Mus. 1983, Jay Gallery, N.Y.C., Gallerit, Stockholm, 1984, Mattatuck Mus., Waterbury, Conn., 1985, Wash. U., St. Louis, 1985, Munson Gallery, Santa Fe, 1985; group exhbns. include Watercolors, Drawings and Prints, Met. Mus., 1952, Young Am. Print Makers, Mus. Modern Art, 1953, Young Am., Whitney Mus., 1957, Recent Acquisitions, Mus. Modern Art, 1957, Laon Mus., Aisne, France, 1956, New Sch. Social Research, 1965, 72, Gallery Modern Art, N.Y.C., 1965, Mus. Modern Art, 1966, Herron Mus. Art, Indpls., 1967, Bklyn. Mus., 1968, 69, Kennedy Galleries, N.Y.C., 1974, Neuberger Mus., SUNY at Purchase, 1974, AAA Galleries, N.Y.C., 1976, 84, Inst. Contemporary Art, Boston, 1976, Ind. U. Mus., 1977, NAD, N.Y.C., 1977, 79, SUNY at Potsdam, 1977, Butler Inst. Am. Art, Ohio, 1987, Green Mountain Gallery, N.Y.C., 1979, Squibb Gallery, Princeton, 1979, Pratt Inst. Graphics Ctr., Bklyn., 1979, Ark. Fine Arts Ctr., 1982, 84, Redding (Calif.) Mus., 1984, Sylvan Cole Gallery, N.Y.C., 1985; represented in permanent collections Mus. Modern Art, Whitney Mus., Met. Mus., Bklyn. Mus., Am. Acad. Arts and Letters, Morgan Library, Dublin Mus., Los Angeles County Mus.; included in pvt. collections Joseph Hirshhorn, Monroe Wheeler, William Lieberman, Roy Neuberger, Marianne Moore, Mrs. John D. Rockefeler III, Sir Basil Goulding, Bart., Winthrop Paul Rockefeller, King Gustaf XVI of Sweden, Queen Sylvia, Charles, Prince of Wales, Her Highness Elizabeth, the Queen Mother; artist in residence, Sch. Visual Arts, N.Y.C., 1968; drawings and paintings for film Lust for Life, 1955; illustrator for film The Days of Wilfred Owen, 1966; illustrator for poetry of Keith Douglas for film How to Kill, 1980; numerous sets, backdrops and costumes. Assoc. Nat. Acad. Served with USAAF, 1945-46. Recipient Richard and Hinda Rosenthal award Nat. Inst. Arts and Letters, 1962; grantee Tamarand Lithography Workshop, Los Angeles, 1967; John Simon Guggenheim Found. fellow, 1969-70. Address: Terry Dintenfass Gallery 50 W 57th St New York NY 10019

PARKER, ROBERT BROWN, novelist; b. Springfield, Mass., Sept. 17, 1932; s. Carroll Snow and Mary Pauline (Murphy) P.; m. Joan Hall, Aug. 26, 1956; children: David, Daniel. BA, Colby Coll., 1954; MA, Boston U., 1957, PhD, 1971; LittD (hon.), Northeastern U., 1987. Various bus. and advt. positions N.Y.C. and Boston, 1956-62; lectr. Boston U., 1962-64; mem. faculty Lowell (Mass.) State Coll., 1964-66, Bridgewater State Coll., 1966-68; asst. prof. English Northeastern U., Boston, 1968-73, assoc. prof., 1973-76 prof., 1976-79; lectr. Suffolk U., 1965-66; co-chmn. Parker-Farman Co., 1960-62. Author: (with others) The Personal Response to Literature, 1970, (with Peter L. Sandberg) Order and Diversity: The Craft of Prose, 1973, Godwulf Manuscript, 1974, God Save the Child, 1974, (with John R. Marsh) Sports Illustrated Weight Training, 1974, Mortal Stakes, 1975, Promised Land, 1976 (Edgar Allan Poe award for best novel Mystery Writers Am. 1976), The Judas Goat, 1978, (with Joan Parker) Three Weeks in Spring, 1978, Wilderness, 1979, Looking for Rachel Wallace, 1980, Early Autumn, 1981, A Savage Place, 1981, Surrogate: A Spenser Short Story, 1982, Ceremony, 1982, The Widening Gyre, 1983, Love and Glory, 1983, Valediction, 1984, The Private Eye in Hammett and Chandler, 1984, A Catskill Eagle, 1985, Parker on Writing, 1985, Taming a Seahorse, 1986, Pale Kings and Princes, 1987, Crimson Joy, 1988, Playmates, 1989, (with Raymond Chandler) Poodle Springs, 1989, Stardust, 1990, Perchance to Dream, 1990, A Year at the Races, 1990, Pastime, 1991, Double Deuce, 1992, Paper Doll, 1993, Walking Shadow, 1994, All Our Yesterdays, 1994, Spenser's Boston, 1994; screenwriter with Joan Parker: (TV movies) Spenser: Ceremony, 1993, Spenser: Pale Kings and Princes, 1993; contbr., cons.: (TV series) Spenser: For Hire, 1985-88, A Man Called Hawk, 1989-90. Served with U.S. Army, 1954-56. Mem. Writers Guild Am. Avocations: jogging, weightlifting. *

PARKER, ROBERT FREDERIC, university dean emeritus; b. St. Louis, Oct. 29, 1907; s. Charles T. and Lydia (Gronemeyer) P.; m. Mary L. Warner, June 20, 1934; children: David Frederic, Jane Eleanor (Mrs. Howard H. Hush, Jr.). B.S., Washington U., St. Louis, 1925, M.D., 1929. Diplomate: Am. Bd. Microbiology. Asst. radiologist Washington U. Med. Sch., 1929-30, instr. medicine, 1932-33; asst. Rockefeller Inst., 1933-36; mem. faculty Case Western Res. U., 1936—, prof. microbiology, 1954-77, prof. emeritus, 1977—, assoc. dean, 1965-73, dean, 1973-76, dean emeritus, 1976—. Mem. Cleve. Acad. Medicine (past bd. dirs.), Am. Soc. Clin. Investigation, Central Soc. Clin. Research, Am. Acad. Microbiology, Sigma Xi, Alpha Omega Alpha. Spl. research virus immunology, quantitative aspects virus infection, tissue culture, action of antibiotics. Home: Apt 436 1890 E 107th St Cleveland OH 44106-2243 Office: 2085 Adelbert Rd Cleveland OH 44106-2236

PARKER, ROBERT GEORGE, radiation oncology educator, academic administrator; b. Detroit, Mich., Jan. 29, 1925; s. Clifford Robert and Velma (Ashman) P.; m. Diana Davis, June 30, 1977; children by previous marriage: Thomas Clifford, James Richardson. BS, U. Wis., 1946, MD., 1948. Diplomate Am. Bd. Radiology (trustee 1978—, pres. 1988-90). Intern U. Nebr. Hosp., Omaha, 1948-49; resident in radiology Western Res. U., Cleve., 1949-50; resident in radiology U. Mich., Ann Arbor, 1950, 52-54, instr. in radiology, 1954-55; staff radiotherapist Swedish Hosp. Tumor Inst., Seattle, 1955-58; prof. radiology U. Wash., Seattle, 1958-77; prof. radiation oncology UCLA, 1977—. Lt. USN, 1950-52. Fellow Am. Coll. Radiology; mem. Am. Soc. Therapeutic Radiologists (pres. 1975-76), AMA (radiology residency rev. com.), Radiol. Soc. N.Am. (bd. dirs. 1984-90, pres. 1991-92). Office: UCLA Dept Radiation Oncology 200 UCLA Medicine Plz Los Angeles CA 90024

PARKER, ROBERT LEE, SR., petroleum engineer, drilling company executive; b. Tulsa, July 16, 1923; s. Gifford Clevel and Gladys Carolyn (Baker) P.; m. Catherine Mae McDaniel, Dec. 16, 1944; children: Robert Lee, Carolyn Louise, Debra Ann. B.S., U. Tex., 1944; LL.D. (hon.), John Brown U., 1967, Oral Roberts U., 1977. With Parker Drilling Co., 1947—, owner, mgr., 1953—, pres., 1954-92, chmn. bd., 1967—; bd. dirs. CWI, Inc.; dir. Bank Okla., Enterra Corp., Mapco Inc.; chmn. Nat. Energy Task Force, 1981-82. Chmn. St. Francis Hosp., Tulsa, U. Tex. Engring. Found.; trustee U. Tulsa, 1st Methodist Ch., Tulsa; bd. dirs. Tulsa YMCA, Jr. Achievement, So. Meth. U.; active Boy Scouts Am. Served with U.S. Army, 1945-47. Named Distinguished Engring. Grad. U. Tex., 1969. Mem. Am. Petroleum Inst., Internat. Assn. Drilling Contractors, Okla. Ind. Petroleum Assn., Soc. Profl. Engrs. Republican. Clubs: So. Hills Country, Tulsa, Houston, Odessa Country. Office: Parker Drilling Co 8 E 3rd St Tulsa OK 74103 *A discipline of character and work, an enthusiasm for life and an awareness of God's constant help have all had positive impacts on my life.

PARKER, ROBERT LEE, JR., drilling company executive; b. Midland, Tex., Nov. 9, 1948; s. Robert Lee and Catherine Mae (McDaniel) P.; m. Carolyn Diane Daniel, June 1971 (div. 1974); 1 dau., Christy Diane; m. 2d, Patricia Ann Dollarhite, Oct. 21, 1977 (div. 1984); children—Robert Lee III, Austin Leeann; m. Risa Elaine Blackman, Nov. 24, 1986. Student Okla. State U., 1967-68; M.B.A., U. Tex., 1972. Contract rep. Parker Drilling Co., Tulsa, 1972-73, mgr. U.S. ops., 1973-74, v.p., 1974-76, exec. v.p., 1976-77,

pres., chief operating officer, 1977-91, pres., chief exec. officer, 1991—, also dir.; bd. dirs. Alaska Air Group Inc. Bd. dirs. United Way, Tulsa, 1983-88, ARC, Tulsa chpt., 1985—. Recipient 3d place award Tex. Trophy Hunters Assn., 1983. Republican. Methodist. Office: Parker Drilling Co 8 E 3rd St Tulsa OK 74103-3616

PARKER, ROBERT M., federal judge; b. 1937. BBA, U. Tex., 1961, JD, 1964. Bar: Tex. 1964. Ptnr. Parish & Parker, Longview, Tex., 1964-65, Kenley & Boyland, Longview, Tex., 1965, Roberts, Smith & Parker, Longview, 1966-71, Rutledge & Parker, Ft. Worth, 1971-72, Nichols & Parker, Longview, 1972-79; judge U.S. Dist. Ct. (ea. dist.) Tex., 1979-94, chief judge, 1991-94; judge U.S. Ct. Appeals (5th Cir.), Tyler, Tex. Mem. ABA, Tex. Bar Assn. Office: Ste 100 221 W Ferguson St Tyler TX 75702

PARKER, SAM, financial executive; b. N.Y.C., June 30, 1935; s. John and Ida; B.B.A. in Public Acctg., Baruch Coll., City U. N.Y., 1962; m. Mary Rengifo, Oct. 5, 1970. Auditor, Eisner and Lubin, C.P.A.s, N.Y.C., 1962-65; mng. partner Parker and Mulligan, C.P.A.s, N.Y.C., 1965-67; asst. controller Korvettes Stores, N.Y.C., 1967-70; auditor Peat Marwick Main & Co., C.P.A.s, N.Y.C., 1970-74; dir. fin. and adminstrn. Nat. Bur. Econ. Research, Inc., Cambridge, Mass., 1974—; cons. in field. Served with AUS, 1958. C.P.A., N.Y., Mass. Mem. Am. Inst. C.P.A.s, Greater Boston C. of C. (Exec. Club), Pan Am. Soc. New Eng. (treas. 1981-82). Author articles in field. Office: Nat Bur of Econ Rsch 1050 Massachusetts Ave Cambridge MA 02138-5317

PARKER, SARA ANN, librarian; b. Cassville, Mo., Feb. 19, 1939; d. Howard Franklin and Vera Irene (Thomas) P. B.A., Okla. State U., 1961; M.L.S., Emporia State U. Kans., 1968. Adult svcs. librarian Springfield Pub. Libr., Mo., 1972-75, bookmobile dir., 1975-76; coord. S.W. Mo. Libr. Network, Springfield, 1976-78; libr. developer Colo. State Libr., Denver, 1978-82; state librarian Mont. State Libr., Helena, 1982-88, State Libr. Pa., Harrisburg, 1988-90; Pa. commr. librs., dep. sec. edn. State of Pa., Harrisburg, 1990—; cons. and lectr. in field. Author, editor, compiler in field; contbr. articles to profl. jours. Sec., Western Coun. State Librs., Reno, 1984-88, mem. Mont. State Data Adv. Coun., 1983-88, Mont. Telecommunications Coun., 1985-88, WLN Network Coun., 1984-87, Kellogg ICLIS Project Mgmt. Bd., 1986-88. Recipient President's award Nature Conservancy, 1989, Friends award Pa. Assn. Ednl. Communications and Techs., 1989; fellow Inst. Ednl. Leadership, 1982. Mem. ALA, Chief Officers State Libr. Agys. (chair N.E. 1991-92, v.p., pres. elect 1994—), Mont. Libr. Assn. (bd. dirs. 1982-88), Mountain Plains Libr. Assn. (sec. chmn. 1980, pres. 1987-88). Home: 226 A Erford Rd Camp Hill PA 17011 Office: State Libr Pa PO Box 1601 Harrisburg PA 17105-1601

PARKER, SARAH JESSICA, actress; b. Nelsonville, Ohio, Mar. 25, 1965. Actress: (theatre) The Innocents, 1976, The Sound of Music, 1977, Annie, 1978, The War Brides, 1981, The Death of a Miner, 1982, To Gillian on Her 37th Birthday, 1983, 84, Terry Neal's Future, 1986, The Heidi Chronicles, 1989, (films) Rich Kids, 1979, Somewhere Tomorrow, 1983, Firstborn, 1984, Footloose, 1984, Girls Just Want to Have Fun, 1985, Flight of the Navigator, 1986, L.A. Story, 1991, Honeymoon in Vegas, 1992, Hocus Pocus, 1993, Striking Distance, 1993, Ed Wood, 1994, Miami Rhapsody, 1995, (TV movies) My Body, My Child, 1982, Going for the Gold: The Bill Johnson Story, 1985, A Year in the Life, 1986, The Room Upstairs, 1987, Dadah Is Death, 1988, The Ryan White Story, 1989, Twist of Fate, 1989, In the Best Interest of the Children, 1992, (TV series) Square Pegs, 1982-83, A Year in the Life, 1987-88, Equal Justice, 1990-91, (TV pilots) The Alan King Show, 1986. Office: CAA 9830 Wilshire Blvd Beverly Hills CA 90212*

PARKER, SCOTT JACKSON, theatre director; b. Ft. Bragg, N.C., July 28, 1945; s. John William and Darice Lee (Jackson) P. MA, U. N.C., 1971; MFA, U. Va., 1978. Mng. dir. Duke U. Theatre, Durham, N.C., 1970-76; gen. mgr. East Carolina U. Theatre, Greenville, 1980-85; producer The Lost Colony Outdoor Drama, Manteo, N.C., 1986-89; dir. Inst. of Outdoor Drama U. N.C., Chapel Hill, N.C., 1990—; v.p. Paul Green Found., nationwide, 1989—. Producer, mgr., dir., scene designer. With U.S. Army, 1969-70. Mem. Nat. Theatre Conf. (sec. 1994—), Assn. for Theatre in Higher Edn. (founding mem. 1987), Southeastern Theatre Conf. (pres. 1982), Arts Advs. of N.C. (pres. 1993-94), The Players Club N.Y.C. Democrat. Baptist. Avocations: white water Kayaking, camping, hiking. Office: U NC Inst Outdoor Drama Cb # 3240 Chapel Hill NC 27599

PARKER, SCOTT LANE, management consultant; b. Phila., Feb. 23, 1946; s. Waldo G. and Nettie M. (Fulton) P.; m. Irene H. Lewis (div. Sept. 1969); m. Claudia E. Nebel, June 14, 1948; children: Adam Michael, Jay Maxwell, Zachary Scott. BA in Econs., U. Va., 1969, MBA, 1971. Mgmt. cons. The MAC Group, 1971-88, co-mng. dir., 1988-90; sr. v.p. operational support Gemini Consulting, Mc Lean, Va., 1991-92; sr. v.p. global strategic initiatives Gemini Consulting, Cambridge, Mass., 1993-94; lectr. strategic mgmt. U. Md., College Park, 1994—. William Michael Shermet scholar U. Va., 1970; U.S. Steel fellow, U. Va., 1970. Office: 1420 Beverly Rd Ste 240 Mc Lean VA 22101

PARKER, SCOTT SMITH, hospital administrator; b. Salt Lake City, Mar. 3, 1935; married. BA, U. Utah, 1960; MA, U. Minn., 1962. Adminstrv. resident Northwestern Hosp., Mpls., 1961-62, asst. administr., 1962-67; adminstr. Southside Hosp., Mesa, Ariz., 1967-71; v.p. Good Samaritan Med. Ctr., Phoenix, 1971-73; adminstr. Hoag Meml. Hosp. Presbyn., Newport Beach, Calif., 1973-75; pres. Intermountain Health Care, Salt Lake City, 1975—, Mem. Am. Hosp. Assn. (bd. dirs. 1980-83, chmn. elect, 1985-86, chair 1986-87, past chmn. 1987), Internat. Hosp. Fed. (exec. com. 1991—, pres. elect 1993), Ariz. Hosp. Assn. (pres. 1972). Home: 1014 Woodmoor Bountiful UT 84010 Office: Intermountain Health Care Inc 36 S State St 22nd Fl Salt Lake City UT 84111

PARKER, SCUDDER HOLDEN, state senator; b. Newport, N.H., Aug. 16, 1943; s. Scudder Merrill and Elizabeth (Holden) P.; m. Pamela Winslow Lovell, Oct. 14, 1943; children: Kathryn Winslow, Emily Hallett. BA magna cum laude, Williams Coll., 1965; MDiv, Union Theol. Sem., N.Y.C., 1968. Ordained to mininstry Congregational Ch. Pastor Third Congl. Ch. and Lower Waterford Congl. Ch., St. Johnsbury and Lower Waterford, Vt., 1969—; state senator from Vt., 1980—; chmn. senated fin. com. Vt. State Senate, Montpelier, Vt., 1984—, joint energy com., 1987. Contbr. articles to profl. jours. Organizer, co-chmn. town planning effort Town of St. Johnsbury,. Democrat. Club: Sphinx (St. Johnsbury). Avocations: poetry, farming, gardening. Home: PO Box 88 East Saint Johnsbury VT 05838-0088 Office: State Senate Office State Capitol Montpelier VT 05602

PARKER, STEPHEN L., architectural firm executive. BArch, U. Md., 1972. Registered architect, Md., D.C., Va., Del. Pres. Grimm and Parker, Architects, Engrs. and Planners, Calverton, Md., 1972—; chmn. Md. Archtl. Rev. Bd.; speaker in field. Prin. works include Walt Whitman High Sch., Bethesda, Md., East Columbia Libr., Columbia, Md., Anne Arundel C.C. Allied Health Bldg., Annapolis, Md., Inst. Tech. Montgomery Coll., Rockville, Md., U. Md. Soccer Stadium, Prince George's County Justice Ctr., Hyattsville, Md. Recipient over 20 archtl. design awards and competitions. Mem. AIA (pres. Md. soc., past pres. Potomac Valley chpt.), Nat. Coun. Archtl. Registration Bds. Office: Grimm & Parker 4061 Powder Mill Rd # 401 Calverton MD 20705

PARKER, SUSAN BROOKS, rehabilitation administrator; b. Newport, N.H., Nov. 7, 1945; d. Ronald Elliott and Elizabeth Louise (Wiggins) P.; married. children: Jeffrey Roberts, Mark Brooks. BS in English and French, U. Vt., 1968; MSW in Social Planning, Boston Coll., 1978. Activities dir. Avery Vt. Inns, Fairlee, 1968-71, retail buyer, 1969-75, mgr., 1972-74; aftercare worker Orange County Mental Health, Bradford, Vt., 1974-76; adminstrn. asst. Mass. Assn. for Mental Health, Boston, 1976-77; mental health planner Tri-City Area Office, Malden, Mass., 1977-78; exec. dir. Grafton County Human Services Commn., Lebanon, N.H., 1978-80, N.H. Developmental Disabilities Council, Concord, N.H., 1980-87; commr. Dept. of Mental Health, Augusta, Maine, 1987-89; assoc. commr. U.S. Social Security Adminstrn., Balt., 1989-93; sec. gen. Rehab. Internat., N.Y.C., 1994—; cons. Nat. Gov.'s Assn., Washington, 1985-86, Office of Health and Developmental Services, Washington, 1987; directorship Nat. Assn. of Devel.

Disabilities, Washington, 1983-87, Cen. N.H. Mental Health Ctr., Concord, 1985-87; cons. in field. Author: poetry collection Scheme, 1965; contbr. articles to newspapers and profl. jours. Pres. PTO, Fairlee, Vt., 1972-73; dir. Ford Sayre Ski Program, Fairlee, 1972-76; active United Way, Concord, 1983-86; bd. dirs. PTO Rundlett Jr. high Sch., Concord, 1982-85; pres. U.S. Coun. for Internat. Rehab., 1993. Recipient Assn. Retarded Citizens Children's Disability Pub. Policy award, 1992, Kathryn C. Arneson award People to People, 1992, Commr.'s citation for outstanding efforts in developing policy Social Security Adminstrn., 1992, Dep. Commn.'s citation for outstanding exec. leadership, 1993; named Outstanding Alumnus Boston Coll., 1991, Adminstrn. Devel. Disabilities prin. investigator grantee, 1986. Mem. Am. Assn. Mental Retardation, Nat. Assn. State Mental Health Program Dirs., Nat. Assn. Retarded Citizens, Concord Luncheon Club. Avocations: skiing, canoeing, mountain climbing, reading, travel. Office: Rehab Internat 25 E 21st St New York NY 10010

PARKER, THOMAS LEE, business executive; b. Ft. Worth, Aug. 23, 1921; s. J.T. Parker and Frances Gertrude (Rogers) Heer; m. Frances N. Newlon, Dec. 14, 1943 (dec. 1981); children: Richard T. (dec.), Pamela Parker Gartin. B.S. in Bus. Adminstrn., Ohio State U., 1943. Sales rep. Frozen Drumstick Sales Co., Columbus, Ohio, 1946-47; pres. Drumstick Inc., Columbus, 1958-62; pres. Big Drum, Inc., Columbus, 1962-83, chmn. bd., 1983-86; sec.-treas., gen. mgr. Cream Cone Machine Co., Columbus, 1948-57; dir. Ohio Semitronics. Mem. Nat. Adv. Coun. Boy Scouts Am., Dallas; trustee Ohio History of Flight Mus. Served to maj. U.S. Army, 1943-46, ETO. Decorated Bronze Star; recipient Service to Mankind Columbus Sertoma Club, 1975, Silver Beaver Boy Scouts Am., 1975, Silver Antelope Boy Scouts Am., 1977, Silver Buffalo Boy Scouts Am., 1986; Baden Powell fellow World Scouts, Geneva, 1982. Mem. Delta Tau Delta. Republican. Clubs: Scioto Country (pres. 1977); Athletic (Columbus) (pres. 1971). Lodges: Masons.

PARKER, WILLIAM H., III, federal official; b. Westbrook, Maine, May 4, 1937; s. William H. II and Anne Marney (Delaney) P.; m. Joan Moody Currier, June 17, 1959; children: Laurie Jean, Michael Currier, Suzan Elizabeth, Julie Ann. BS, U. Maine, 1960; MS, Northeastern U., 1966; MEM, U. Detroit, 1981, MBA, 1982; postgrad., Nova U. Diplomate Am. Acad. Environ. Engrs. Project engr. Camp Dresser & McKee, Boston, 1962-72, v.p., 1972-75; v.p. E.C. Jordan, Portland, Maine, 1975-77; sr. v.p., reg. mgr. Camp Dresser & McKee, Detroit, 1977-87, bd. dirs., 1982-87; sr. v.p. CDM Fed. Programs Corp., Washington, 1987-88, bd. dirs., 1987-88; dep. asst. sec. Dept. of Def., Washington, 1988-90; dir. environ. programs EG&G Inc., Wellesley, Mass., 1990—; bd. dirs. Parker Currier Inc., Brunswick, Maine; fin. cons. VMI, treas., pres., 1993—, White River Junction, Vt., 1987-90; presenter Congl. test, 1988-90; keynote speaker tech. and profl. socs., 1988—. Contbr. articles to profl. jours. Mem., chmn. planning bd. Town of Reading, Maine, 1968-73; mem. Town Meeting, Reading, 1969-75, Mcpl. Light Bd., Reading, 1974-75. 1st lt. U.S. Army, 1960-62. Recipient Outstanding Pub. Svc. medal Sec. of Def., 1989. Mem. ASCE, NSPE, Mass. Soc. Profl. Engrs (Young Engr. of Yr. award 1971), Am. Def. Preparedness Assoc., Engring. Socs. New Eng. (New Eng. award 1990), Soc. Am. Mil. Engrs., Water Pollution Control Fedn., Am. Water Works Assn., Mass. Jaycees (Boston top profl. jours., state v.p. 1970-72, Econ. Club Detroit, Detroit Club, Sigma Xi, Tau Beta Pi, Alpha Kappa Psi, Beta Gamma Sigma, Phi Kappa Phi, Chi Epsilon. Republican. Roman Catholic. Avocations: reading, writing, traveling. Home: 15 Montclair Rd West Newbury MA 01985-2216 Office: EG&G Inc 45 William St Wellesley MA 02181-4004

PARKER, WILLIAM NELSON, economics educator; b. Columbus, Ohio, June 14, 1919; s. Murray Nelson and Evalyn Mae (Gares) P.; m. Josephine Yvonne Forbus, Sept. 20, 1948; children: Yvonne Victoria, Jarrett Nelson. A.B. magna cum laude, Harvard, 1939, M.A., 1941, Ph.D., 1951; M.A., Yale, 1962. Economist atomic energy com. U.S. Senate, 1946, Dept. State, 1947-48; cons. President's Materials Policy Commn., 1951; asst. prof. econs. Williams Coll., 1951-56; assoc. prof., then prof. econs. U. N.C. at Chapel Hill, 1956-62; prof. econs. Yale, 1962-89, emeritus, 1989—, dir. grad. studies in econs., 1968-72, 74-78; Del. to Am. Coun. Learned Socs., 1975-78; chmn. Coun. on West European Studies, 1985-89; dir. Mellon West European Project, 1987-92. Co-author: Coal and Steel in Western Europe, 1957; Editor, contbr.: Trends in the American Economy in the Nineteenth Century, 1958, The Structure of the Cotton Economy of the Antebellum South, 1970, American Economic Growth, 1972, European Peasants and Their Markets, 1976; Economic History and the Modern Economist, 1986; co-editor: Jour. Econ. History, 1960-66; Author: Europe, America, and the Wider World, Vol. I, 1984, Vol. II, 1990. Served to maj. AUS, 1941-45. Nat. fellow Harvard U., 1935-41, Social Sci. Rsch. Coun. fellow, 1948-51, 62-63, Ford Faculty fellow, 1958-59, Resources for Future rsch. fellow, 1955-57, Guggenheim fellow, 1966-67, St. Anthony's Coll. fellow, 1972-73, Australian Nat. U. vis. fellow, 1983, 89. Mem. Am. Philos. Soc., Econ. History Assn. (pres. 1969-70), Agrl. History Assn. (pres. 1979-80), Am. Econ. Assn. (rep. adv. com. U.S. Archives 1978-81), Am. Acad. Arts and Scis. Contbr. 1st Internat. Conf. Econ. History, Stockholm, Sweden, 1960, 3d conf., Munich, Germany, 1965, 7th conf., Edinburgh, 1978; U.S./USSR Historians Conf., Moscow, 1978, Tallinn, 1987; Sapporo Am. Studies Conf., Japan, 1981; French-Am. Rsch. project on Ecole Des Hautes Etudes, Paris, 1984-85. Home: 144 Edgehill Rd Hamden CT 06517-4011

PARKES, KENNETH CARROLL, ornithologist; b. Hackensack, N.J., Aug. 8, 1922; s. Walter Carroll and Lillian Carolyn (Capelle) P.; m. Ellen Pierce Stone, Sept. 6, 1953. B.S., Cornell U., 1943, M.S., 1948, Ph.D., 1952. Curator birds Cornell U., 1947-52; mem. staff Carnegie Mus. of Natural History, Pitts., 1953—; curator birds Carnegie Mus., 1962-86, chief curator life scis., 1975-85, sr. curator birds, 1986—; research fellow epidemiology and microbiology U. Pitts., 1956, vis. lectr. Pymatuning Field Lab., 1957, adj. mem. grad. faculty, 1963—; Mem. adminstrv. bd. Lab. Ornithology, Cornell U., 1962-68, 70-75; bd. trustees Del. Mus. Natural History, 1996-90. Taxonomic editor: Avian Biology, 1971-75; co-editor, 1977-93; cons. on bird art to artists, pubs.; contbr. articles to profl. jours., encys. Served with AUS, 1943-46. Fellow Am. Ornithologists Union (2d v.p. 1975-76); mem. Audubon Soc. Western Pa. (trustee 1982-91), Wilson Ornithol. Soc. (pres. 1973-75), numerous other profl. socs. Democrat. Unitarian. Office: Carnegie Museum Natural History 4400 Forbes Ave Pittsburgh PA 15213-4080

PARKHURST, CHARLES, retired museum director, art historian; b. Columbus, Ohio, Jan. 23, 1913; s. Charles Percy and Isabella (Woodbridge) P.; m. Elizabeth Huntington Rusling, June 15, 1938 (div. 1962); children: Andrew, Christopher, Bruce; m. Rima Zevin Julyan, Sept. 1, 1962 (div. 1972); 1 child, Brooke; stepchildren: Candace, David, Mark; m. Carol Canda Clark, July 18, 1986. B.A., Williams Coll., 1935; A.M., Oberlin Coll., 1938; M.F.A., Princeton, 1941. Rd. and bridge constrn. worker Danali Park Alaska Rd. Commn.; tchr. music, coach basketball Wasilla, Alaska, 1935-37; Research asst. Nat. Gallery of Art, Washington, 1941-42, asst. curator (registrar), 1942-43; dep. chief, monuments, fine arts and archives sect. Allied Mil. Govt. in both U.S. Zones, Germany, 1945-46; asst. curator Albright Art Gallery, Buffalo, 1946-47; asst. prof. art and archaeology Princeton (N.J.) U.; asst. dir. Princeton (N.J.) Art Mus., 1947-49; head dept. fine arts, dir. Art Mus., prof. history and appreciation of art Oberlin (Ohio) Coll., 1949-62; dir. Balt. Mus. Art, 1962-70; asst. dir., chief curator Nat. Gallery Art, Washington, 1971-83, ret., 1983; co-chmn. Mus. Art Williams Coll., 1983-84, mem. vis. faculty, 1980, Clark vis. prof., 1985-86, acting dir. grad. program in art history, 1986-87, dir. M.B. Prendergrast Systematic Catalogue project, 1983-87; interim dir. Smith Coll. Mus. Art, 1991-92, emeritus dir., 1992; faculty fellow Fund for Advancement Edn., 1952-53; Fulbright rsch. scholar U. Utrecht, Netherlands, 1956-57; vis. faculty U. Minn., 1953, UCLA, 1964, Johns Hopkins U., 1971, U. Wis., 1979, Williams Coll., 1980-92; lectr. on art, color theory and museology; chmn. Md. Arts Coun., 1967-68; chmn. Md. Revolutionary War Bicentennial Commn., 1968-70, Gov.'s Coun. on Arts in Md., 1966-68; trustee, officer Williamstown Regional Art Conservation Lab., 1983-90; ind. cons. Asian Art Mus., 1993-94. Contbr. articles to profl. jours. Commr. Nat. Mus. Am. Art, 1983-93; overseer Case Western Res. U., Cleve., 1982-86; trustee Amon Carter Mus., 1987-93; dep. scys. Hillstead Mus., Farmington, Conn., 1994—. Served with USNR, 1943-62. Decorated chevalier Legion d'Honneur de la Republique Française, 1947; recipient research grants Am. Council Learned Socs. and Am. Philos. Soc., 1961. Mem. Coll. Art Assn. (pres. 1958-60, bd. dirs.), Intermus. Conservation Assn. (co-founder), Assn. Art Mus. Dirs., Am. Assn. Mus. (pres. 1966-68, founder, mem. mus. accreditation com. 1970-76). Office: 33 Dana Pl Amherst MA 01002-2212

PARKHURST, CHARLES LLOYD, electronics company executive; b. Nashville, Aug. 13, 1943; s. Charles Albert Parkhurst and Dorothy Elizabeth (Ballou) Parkhurst Crutchfield; m. Dolores Ann Oakley, June 6, 1970; children: Charles Thomas, Deborah Lynn, Jere Loy. Student, Hume-Fogg Tech. Coll., 1959-61; AA, Mesa Community Coll., 1973; student, Ariz. State U., 1973-76. Mem. design staff Tex. Instruments, Dallas, 1967-68; mgr. design Motorola, Inc., Phoenix, 1968-76; pres. LSI Cons., Inc., Tempe, Ariz., 1976-85, LSI Photomasks, Inc., Tempe, 1985-94, Charles Parkhurst Books, Inc., Prescott, Ariz., 1994—. Mem. Rep. Congl. Leadership Coun., Washington, 1988; life mem. Rep. Presdl. Task Force, 1990. Served as cpl. USMC, 1961-64. Mem. Bay Area Chrome Users Soc., Nat. Trust Hist. Preservation, Ariz. State U. Alumni Assn. (life). Baptist. Avocations: genealogy, coin collecting, scuba diving, book collecting. Office: Charles Parkhurst Books Inc PO Box 10850 Prescott AZ 86304-0850

PARKIN, GERARD FRANCIS RALPH, chemistry educator, researcher; b. Middlesbrough, Cleveland, Eng., Feb. 15, 1959; s. Ralph and Clementine (Gill) P.; m. Rita K. Upmacis. BA with honors, Oxford (Eng.) U., 1981, MA, 1984, PhD, 1985. NATO/SERC (U.K.) postdoctoral rsch. fellow Calif. Inst. Tech., 1985-88; asst. prof. Columbia U., N.Y.C., 1988-91, assoc. prof., 1991-94; prof., 1994—. Contbr. more than 70 articles to profl. jours. A.P. Sloan Rsch. fellow; recipient Presdl. Faculty fellowship NSF, 1992—, Camille and Henry Dreyfus Tchr.-Scholar award, 1991, Am. Chem. Soc. award in Pure Chemistry, 1994. Roman Catholic. Achievements include discovery that bond stretch isomerism in an artifact. Office: Columbia U 116th St And Broadway New York NY 10027

PARKIN, STUART S. P., materials scientist. Rsch. staff mem. IBM Almaden Rsch. Ctr., San Jose, Calif. Recipient Internat. prize for New Materials Am. Physical Soc., 1994. Office: IBM Almuden Rsch Cter K 32/ 801 650 Harry Rd San Jose CA 95120-6001*

PARKINS, FREDERICK MILTON, dental educator, university dean; b. Princeton, N.J., Sept. 8, 1935; s. William Milton and Phyllis Virginia (Plyler) P.; m. Carolyn V. Rude; children: Bradford, Christopher, Eric. Student, Carleton Coll., 1953-56; D.D.S., U. Pa., 1960; M.S.D. in Pedodontics, U. N.C., Chapel Hill, 1965; Ph.D. in Physiology, 1969. Instr. pedodontics U. N.C., 1965-67; asst. prof. pedodontics U. Pa., 1967-68, dir. Dental Aux. Utilization program, chmn. pedodontics, 1968-69; assoc. prof., head pedodontics U. Iowa, Iowa City, 1969-72; prof., head pedodontics U. Iowa, 1972-75; asst. dean acad. affairs U. Iowa (Coll. Dentistry) 1974-75, asso. dean acad. affairs, 1975-79, dir. continuing edn., 1975-77; prof. pedodontics, dean Sch. Dentistry, U. Louisville, 1979-85, prof. pediatric dentistry, 1985—; mem. Hillenbrand Fellowship adv. com. Am Fund Dental Health, 1980-85; cons. Div. Dental Health USPHS, 1969-72; dental cons., med. staff Children's Hosp. Phila., 1968-71; med. staff Kosair Children's Hosp. Louisville, 1983—; cons., mem. pedodontic adv. com. Council Dental Edn., 1974-80, chmn. pedodontic adv. com., 1978-80, cons. council on legislation, 1978-79; dental cons. Aux. Utilization VA, 1968-69; cons. Bur. Health Resources Devel., 1974-76, Dept. Army, 1980—, numerous others. Assoc. editor: Jour. Preventive Dentistry, 1973-79; editorial bd., 1980-83; editorial reviewer: Jour. Pediatrics, 1969—, Jour. Dental Edn, 1978—, Jour. AMA, 1979—; asso. editor: Jour. Clin. Preventive Dentistry, 1979-84; Contbr. chpts. to textbooks, articles to profl. publs. Bd. govs. Youth Performing Arts Coun., Louisville-Jefferson County Sch. Dist., 1980—, pres., 1986-88; bd. govs. Regional Cancer Ctr., U. Louisville, 1979-84, Univ. Hosp., 1979-84; mem. human studies com. U. Louisville, 1988-90. Robert Wood Johnson Congl. fellow Inst. of Medicine, 1977-78; USPHS postdoctoral fellow, 1963-67; NIH grantee, 1971-75; Recipient Earle Banks Hoyt Teaching award, 1969. Fellow AAAS, Am. Acad. Pediat. Dentistry (chmn. rsch. com. 1972-73, Am. Rsch. award 1968, chmn. advanced edn. com. 1974-75, chmn. dental care programs com. 1978-80); mem. ADA, Am. Coll. Dentistry, Am. Soc. Dentistry for Children (exec. bd. Iowa unit 1969-75, award com. 1973-76, edn. com. 1974-77, chmn. rsch. adv. com. 1973-76), Biophys. Soc., Internat. Assn. Dental Rsch., N.Y. Acad. Dentistry, Ky. Dental Assn. (exec. bd. 1979-84), Am. Assn. Dental Schs. (coun. of deans 1979-84, chmn. pedodontics sect. 1976, chmn. continuing edn. sect. 1979, legis. com. 1978-83), Louisville Dental Alumni Assn. (bd. govs. 1979-84), Am. Assn. Dental Rsch. (nat. affairs com. 1978-85), Acad. Laser Dentistry (chmn. edn. and rsch. com. 1995—), Southeastern Soc. Pediatric Dentistry, U.S. Power Squadron (bd. govs. 1987-93, sec. 1989, adminstrv. officer 1990, exec. officer 1991, comdr. 1992), Omicron Kappa Upsilon (pres. Wa. chpt. 1991-92), Louisville Boat Club, Rotary. Unitarian. Home: 6424 Marina Dr Prospect KY 40059 Office: U Louisville Sch Dentistry Dept Orthodontic Pediatric & Geriatric Denistry Rm 306 Louisville KY 40292

PARKINSON, BRADFORD W., aeronautical engineering educator. Prof. dept. aeronautics and astronautics Stanford U. Fellow AIAA, Royal Inst. Navigation; mem. NAE, IEEE. Office: Stanford U Dept Aeronautics and Astronautics Stanford CA 94305

PARKINSON, DENNIS, biology educator, soil biology researcher; b. Bolton, Eng., Sept. 1, 1927; emigrated to Can., 1964; s. Charles and Helen (Rushton) P.; m. Verna Armstrong, Jan. 17, 1953 (div. 1973); children: David, Nicholas, Louise. B.Sc. with honors, U. London; 1951; Ph.D., U. Nottingham, Eng., 1956. Lectr. botany U. Liverpool, Eng., 1956-64; prof. biology U. Waterloo, Ont., Can., 1964-67, U. Calgary, Alta., 1957—; dir. Kananaskis Ctr. Environ. Rsch., Alta., 1983-89. Editor: Ecology of Soil Fungi, 1960, Ecology of Soil Bacteria, 1966; author: Methods for Study of Soil Organisms, 1972; contbr. articles sci. jours. Served with Brit. Army, 1946-49. Fellow Royal Soc. Can. Office: U Calgary, Dept Biol Scis, Calgary, AB Canada T2N 1N4

PARKINSON, ETHELYN MINERVA, author; b. nr. Oconto, Wis., Sept. 13, 1906; d. James Nelson and Ethel Mabelle (Bigelow) P. Teaching certificate, County Normal Sch., Oconto Falls, Wis., 1923; R.N., Bellin Meml. Sch. Nursing, 1928. Author: Double Trouble for Rupert, 1958, Triple Trouble for Rupert, 1960, Good Old Archibald, 1960, The Merry Mad Bachelors, 1961, The Terrible Troubles of Rupert Piper, 1963, The Operation that Happened to Rupert Piper, 1966, Today I Am a Ham, 1968, Higgins of the Railroad Museum, 1970, Elf King Joe, 1970, Never Go Anywhere with Digby, 1971, Rupert Piper and Megan, the Valuable Girl, 1972, Rupert Piper and the Dear, Dear Birds, 1976 (Jr. Lit. Guild selection), Rupert Piper and the Boy Who Could Knit, 1979. Recipient Wis. Dramatic Soc. 1st place for playwriting, 1933; 1st place children's fiction Scholastic Book Services, 1957; Abingdon award, 1970; award of merit Wis. Hist. Soc., 1971. Republican. Presbyn. Address: 1031 Anderson Dr Green Bay WI 54304-5000 *I look at any success I may have had most humbly and most thankfully. I'm humble because I have a feeling that I haven't done things, but rather that things have happened to me. Perhaps that's because people have inspired and so helped me, all the way, children especially. I'm dedicated to giving as much happiness as I can to children, through my writing, and other ways. Childhood seems shorter now than ever, and when one of my stories makes children happy, makes them laugh, I am happy, too, and grateful.*

PARKINSON, GEORGINA, ballet mistress; b. Brighton, Eng., Aug. 20, 1938. Studied with Royal Ballet Sch. Mem. Royal Ballet, London, from 1955, soloist, from 1959, then prin.; ballet mistress Am. Ballet Theatre, N.Y.C., 1978—. Created roles in: La Belle Dame Sans Merci (Andree Howard), The Invitation (Kenneth MacMillan), Romeo and Juliet (Kenneth MacMillan), Mayerling (Kenneth MacMillan), The Concert (Jerome Robbins), Enigma Variations (Sir Frederick Ashton), Daphnis and Chloe (John Cranko), Everlast (Twyla Tharp). Office: care Am Ballet Theatre 890 Broadway New York NY 10003-1211*

PARKINSON, JOSEPH L., electronics company executive, lawyer; b. San Antonio, Aug. 6, 1945; s. Douglas R. and Jane E. (Peck) P.; child by previous marriage, Jay Curtis. BA, Columbia U., 1967; JD, Tulane U., 1971; LLM in Taxation, NYU, 1972. Bar: La. 1971, Idaho 1975. Law clk. to judge U.S. Ct. Appeals (5th cir.), New Orleans, 1972-73; asst. prof. law Tulane U., New Orleans, 1973-74; cons. Baker & McKenzie, N.Y.C., 1974-75; asst. prof. law NYU, 1974-75; assoc. Moffatt, Thomas, Barrett & Blanton, Boise, Idaho, 1975-77; ptnr. Lloyd & Parkinson, Boise, 1978-80, Parkinson, Lojek & Penland, Boise, 1980-84; pres. Micron Tech., Inc., Boise, 1980-85, chmn., chief exec. officer, 1985—; bd. dirs. Sematech, Austin, Tex., Standard Microsystems, Long Island, N.Y. Trustee Boise State U. Found.,

1985—; bd. dirs. Idaho Health Facilities Authority, Boise, 1986—. Mem. Semiconductor Industry Assn. (bd. dirs. 1988—), Arid Club, Crane Creek Country Club. Avocations: hunting, fishing, skiing, ranching. Office: Micron Tech Inc PO Box 6 Boise ID 83707-0006

PARKINSON, MARK VINCENT, state legislator, lawyer; b. Wichita, Kans., June 24, 1957; s. Henry Filson and Barbara Ann (Gilbert) Horton; m. Stacy Abbott, Mar. 7, 1983; children: Alex Atticus, Sam Filson, Kit Harlan. BA in Edn., Wichita State U., 1980; JD, Kans. U., 1984. Assoc. Payne and Jones Law Firm, Olathe, Kans., 1984-86; ptnr. Parkinson, Foth & Reynolds, Lenexa, Kans., 1986—; mem. Kans. Ho. Reps., 1990-92, Kans. Senate, 1993—. Mem. ABA, Johnson County Bar Found. (pres. 1993—), Kans. Bar Assn. Republican. Avocations: travel, running, movies. Office: Parkinson Foth & Reynolds 13628 W 95th St Lenexa KS 66215

PARKINSON, RICHARD A., consumer products company executive. With First Security Bank, 1973-81, Rick Warner Ford, 1981-84; exec. v. pres., assistant gen. manager Assoc. Food Store Inc., Salt Lake City, 1984—. Office: Assoc Food Stores Inc 1812 Empire Rd Salt Lake City UT 84104-3809

PARKINSON, ROGER P., publishing company executive; b. 1941. BA, Dartmouth Coll., 1964; MBA, Harvard U., 1966. With Newsweek Mag., 1969-75; from asst. to gen. mgr. then v.p. adminstrn. Washington Post, 1975-80; pres. pub. Courier Express, Buffalo, 1980-82; with Cowles Media Co., Mpls., 1980—, v.p., sr. v.p., dep. pub. Star Tribune, Mpls., 1982-83, exec. v.p., sr. v.p. pub. then exec. v.p. pub., from 1983, noe pres. pub. 1st lt. U.S. Army, 1966-69. Office: Star Tribune 425 Portland Ave Minneapolis MN 55488-0001

PARKINSON, THOMAS IGNATIUS, JR., lawyer; b. N.Y.C., Jan. 27, 1914; s. Thomas I. and Georgia (Weed) P.; AB, Harvard U., 1934; LLB, U. Pa., 1937; m. Geralda E. Moore, Sept. 23, 1937; children: Thomas Ignatius III, Geoffrey Moore, Cynthia Moore. Admitted to N.Y. bar, 1938, since practiced in N.Y.C.; assoc. Milbank, Tweed, Hope & Hadley, 1937-47, partner, 1947-56; pres. Mar Ltd., 1951—; pres. Breecom Corp., 1972-80, chmn. bd., 1980—; dir., exec. com. Pine St. Fund, Inc., N.Y.C., 1949-83, Trustee State Communities Aid Assn., 1949-83; dir. Pop. Policy Assn., 1949-53; bd. dirs., exec. com. Milbank Meml. Fund, 1948-84. Mem. Am. Bar Assn., Assn. Bar City N.Y., Pilgrims U.S.A., Brit. War Relief Soc. (officer), Met. Unit Found., Phi Beta Kappa. Clubs: Down Town Assn., Knickerbocker, Union. Office: Breecom Corp 780 3rd Ave Fl 25 New York NY 10017-2024

PARKINSON, WILLIAM CHARLES, physicist, educator; b. Jarvis, Ont., Can., Feb. 11, 1918; came to U.S., 1925, naturalized, 1941; s. Charles Franklin and Euphemia Alice (Johnston) P.; m. Martha Bennett Capron, Aug. 2, 1944; children: Martha Reed, William Reid. B.S.E., U. Mich., Ann Arbor, 1940, M.S., 1941, Ph.D., 1948. Physicist Applied Physics Lab., Johns Hopkins U., 1942-46, OSRD, 1943-44; mem. faculty U. Mich., 1947—, prof. physics, 1958-88, prof. emeritus physics, 1988—, dir. cyclotron lab., 1962-77; mem. subcom. nuclear structure NRC, 1959-68; mem. nuclear physics sub panel mgmt. and costs nuclear program, 1969-70; adv. panel physics NSF, 1966-69; cons. grad. sci. facilities, 1968, chmn. postdoctoral fellowship evaluation panel, 1969, cons. to govt. and industry, 1955—. Quondam mem. Trinity Coll., Cambridge, Eng. Recipient Ordnance Devel. award Navy Dept., 1946; Fulbright research scholar Cavendish Lab., Cambridge U., 1952-53. Fellow Am. Phys. Soc.; mem. N.Y. Acad. Scis., Biophys. Soc., Grad. "M" Club (awarded hon. "M" 1991), Sigma Xi, Phi Kappa Phi, Kappa Kappa Psi. Patentee in field. Home: 1600 Sheridan Dr Ann Arbor MI 48104-4052 Office: Univ Mich Dept Physics Ann Arbor MI 48109

PARKMAN, PAUL DOUGLAS, federal agency administrator; b. Auburn, N.Y., May 29, 1932; m. Elmerina Leonardi, July 2, 1955. BS, St. Lawrence U., 1957, DSc (hon.), 1990; MD, SUNY, 1957. Diplomate Am. Bd. Pediatrics. Intern Mary Imogene Bassett Hosp., Cooperstown, N.Y., 1957-58; resident in pediatrics Upstate Med. Ctr. Hosp., SUNY, Syracuse, 1958-60; commd. med. officer, NIH Walter Reed Army Inst. Rsch., Washington, 1960-63; chief sect. gen. virology Lab. Viral Immunology NIH, HEW, Washington, 1963-72; dir. div. virology Bur. Biologics FDA, Bethesda, Md., 1972-73; dep. dir. Bur. Biologics FDA, 1973-82, dep. dir. Ctr. for Drugs & Biologics, 1982-87, dir. Ctr. for Biologics Evaluation and Rsch., 1987—. Recipient Superior Svc. award HEW, 1966, Disting. svc. award HEW, 1969, Letter of Commendation Pres. L.B. Johnson, 1966, E. Mead Johnson award Am. Acad. Pediatrics, 1968, Max Weinstein award U.S. Cerebral Palsy, 1967; award for disting. svc. to children Parents' Mag., 1969, Gold Plate award Am. Acad. Achievement, 1979, Internat. award J.P. Kennedy Jr. Found., 1971, Centennial medallion Upstate Med. Ctr., 1972; named one of Ten Outstanding Young Men, U.S. Jaycees, 1967. Mem. AAAS, Assn. Immunology, Soc. Pediatric Rsch. (emeritus), Am. Epidemiol. Soc., Am. Soc. Microbiology, Am. Acad. Microbiology. Office: Evaluation & Rsch Fda Ctr Biologics Bethesda MD 20892

PARKO, EDITH MARGARET, special education educator; b. Sanford, Fla., Sept. 1, 1943; d. Clarence Robert Jones and Domarious (LeCroy) Varn; m. Joseph Edward Parko Jr., Apr. 16, 1966; 1 child, Kimberly Graham. AA, U. Fla., 1963; BA, Stetson U., 1965; MA, Atlanta U., 1970; PhD, Ga. State U., 1984. Lic. tchr., sch. counselor, instrnl. leadership, Ga. Tchr. sci. Seminole County Bd. Edn., Sanford, Fla., 1965-66; tchr. sci./math. Atlanta City Schs., 1966-68; tchr. emotionally disturbed Ga. Mental Health Inst., Atlanta, 1972-79; tchr. learning disabilities The Howard Sch., Atlanta, 1983-87; cons. Ga. Dept. Edn., Atlanta, 1987-88; tchr. emotionally disturbed Atlanta City Schs., 1988-90, researcher, 1990-91, coord. learning disabilities, 1991—. Author children's lit. Mem. Coun. Exceptional Children (president, outstanding adminstr. 1995, metro atlanta C.E.C.), Learning Disabilities Assn., Am. Fedn. Tchrs. Avocations: golf, writing, reading, trout fishing. Home: 325 Elmira Pl NE Atlanta GA 30307

PARKS, DARRELL LEE, vocational education consultant; b. Richmond, Ind., Apr. 16, 1937; s. Garland H. and Goldie J. (Kimmel) P.; m. Naomi Joan Rust, Aug. 16, 1958; children: Pamela Sue, Patricia Jo, Rebecca Ann, Brian Lee. BS in Agr., Ohio State U., 1959, MS in Agrl. Edn., 1965, PhD in Agrl. Edn., 1968; postdoctoral student, Miami U., Oxford, Ohio, 1974-75. Tchr. agr. Parkway Local Schs., Mercer County, Ohio, 1959-62, Canal Winchester Local Schs., Franklin County, Ohio, 1963-65; supr. itinerant tchrs. Ohio State U., Columbus, 1965-66; supr. agrl. edn. Ohio State Dept. Edn., Columbus, 1966-70, asst. dir. vocat. edn., profl. staff and curriculum devel., 1970-71, 75-78, asst. dir. vocat. edn., div. planning and evaluation, 1971-72, dir. vocat. and career edn., 1982-95, ret., 1995; adminstrv. specialist instrnl. program mgmt. Gt. Oaks Joint Vocat. Sch. Dist., Cin., 1972-75; dir. Nat. Acad. Vocat. Edn. Nat. Ctr. Rsch. in Vocat. Edn., Columbus, 1978-79; adj. prof., lectr. Grad. Sch. Ohio State U., 1979-95; cons. in field; presenter at profl. confs. Contbr. articles to nat. jours. and mags. Trustee Northwest Civic Assn., Columbus, 1978-79; trustee, Little League baseball coach North Columbus Sports Assn., 1990. Recipient Disting. Alumni award Ohio State U. Coll. Agr., 1991. Mem. Nat. Acad. Surps. Agrl. Edn., Nat. Vocat. Agr. Tchrs. Assn., Ohio Vocat. Agr. Tchrs. Assn., Ohio Vocat. Assn. (life), Nat. Vocat. Dirs. Assn., Am. Vocat. Edn. Pers. Devel. Assn. (pres. 1976-77), Nat. Assn. State Dirs. Vocat. Edn. (pres. 1990), Nat. Future Farmers Am. Alumni Assn. (life, hon. Am. Farmer degree 1984), Mason (Ohio) Lions (charter), Phi Delta Kappa, Gamma Sigma Delta. Republican. Methodist. Avocations: nature study, woodworking. Home: 1355 Slade Ave Columbus OH 43235-4058

PARKS, ED H., judge; b. Tulsa, July 21, 1922. BS, U. Tulsa, 1947, LLB, 1950. Bar: Okla. 1950. Asst. atty. Tulsa County, 1953-57; ptnr. Boyd & Parks, Tulsa, 1957-77; judge trial div. Ct. on Jud., Oklahoma City, 1977-84, mem. appellant div., 1985-87; judge Ct. Criminal Appeals (Jud. Dist.) Okla., Oklahoma City, 1984—; presiding judge Ct. Criminal Appeals (no. dist.) Okla., Oklahoma City, 1987-88 — Past chmn. Tulsa County Dem. Com. Capt. USMC, World War II, Korea. Fellow Okla. Bar Assn. (law sch. com. sect. 1977-79); mem. Assn. Trial Lawyers Am. (Okla. Trial Lawyers Assn. (Outstanding State Ct. Judge award 1986, 88, 90), Tulsa Trial Lawyers Assn., Tulsa County Bar Assn. (exec. com. 1975-76, 80-81), Okla. Bar

Found. (trustee 1988—). Office: Ct Criminal Appeals 231 State Capital Bldg Oklahoma City OK 73105

PARKS, GEORGE RICHARD, librarian; b. Boston, Apr. 11, 1935; m. Carol A. Richmond; children: Elizabeth, Jennifer, Geoffrey. A.B. summa cum laude, U. N.H., 1959; M.A.L.S., U. Mich., 1962; postgrad., Johns Hopkins, 1959-65; EFM cert. Sch. Theology, U. of the South, 1985. Preprofl. young adult librarian Enoch Pratt Free Library, Balt., 1960-61; ctrl., br. librarian Enoch Pratt Free Library, 1962-65, asst. to asst. dir., 1965-66; asst. dir. for adminstrn., libraries U. Rochester, 1966-68, chief adminstrv. officer, 1968-69; dean of libraries U. R.I., 1969-80; univ. librarian Colgate U., 1980-85, U. So. Maine, Portland, 1985—; lectr. in field, cons. libr. bldg.; cons. antique map collection; mem. exec. bd. Greater Portland Theol. Libr., 1986-88, Maine Community Cultural Alliance, 1992—; mem. exec. bd. So. Maine Libr. Dist., 1990—, chmn., 1993. Apptd. Maine State Libr. Commn., 1994—. Recipient Margaret Mann award U. Mich., 1962; Phillips Exeter Acad. scholar, 1952-54; U. N.H. scholar, 1955-59; Johns Hopkins U. scholar, 1959-60; Enoch Pratt Free Library scholar, 1961-62. Mem. ALA, Assn. Coll. Rsch. Librs. (pres. New Eng. chpt. 1975, chmn. nat. conf. 1978, coll. librs. sect. planning com. 1994—), Consortium R.I. Acad. Rsch. Librs. (chmn. 1972-73), Maine Libr. Assn., New Eng. Libr. Assn. (conf. planning com. 1992—), Libr. Adminstrn. and Mgmt. Assn. (exec. bd. bldgs. and equipment sect., libr. bldg. awards com. 1983-85), Phi Beta Kappa, Phi Kappa Phi, Beta Phi Mu. Home: 4 Pierce St Westbrook ME 04092-2331 Office: U So Maine Librs 314 Forest Ave Portland ME 04101-2000

PARKS, GORDON ROGER ALEXANDER BUCHANAN, film director, author, photographer, composer; b. Ft. Scott, Kans., Nov. 30, 1912; s. Jackson and Sarah (Ross) P.; m. Sally Alvis, 1933 (div. 1961); m. Elizabeth Campbell, 1962 (div. 1973); m. Genevieve Young, Aug. 26, 1973 (div. 1979); children by previous marriage: Gordon (dec.), Toni Parks Parsons, David, Leslie. Student pub. schs., Ft. Scott, St. Paul; DFA (hon.), Md. Inst., 1968, Fairfield U., 1969; D (hon.), Boston U., 1969; LittD (hon.), Kans. State U., 1970; LHD (hon.), St. Olaf Coll., 1973; DFA (hon.), Colby Coll., 1974; DLit (hon.), MacAlester Coll., 1974; D (hon.), Lincoln U., 1975; HHD (hon.), Thiel Coll., 1976; DA (hon.), Columbia Coll., 1977; DFA (hon.), Rutgers U., 1980, Pratt Inst., 1981; LHD (hon.), Suffolk U., 1982; DFA (hon.), Kansas City Art Inst., 1984; LHD (hon.), Art Ctr. Coll. Design, 1986; DA (hon.), Hamline U., 1987; DFA (hon.), Am. Internat. Coll., 1988; HHD (hon.), Savannah Coll. Art and Design, 1988; D (hon.), U. Bradford, Eng., 1989; DFA (hon.), Rochester Inst. Tech., 1989, SUNY, 1990, R.I. Coll., 1990, Parsons Sch. Design, 1991, Manhattanville Coll., 1992, Coll. New Rochelle, 1992, Skidmore Coll., 1993; LittD (hon.), Montclair State U., 1994. Freelance fashion photographer Mpls., 1937-42; photographer Farm Security Adminstrn., 1942-43, OWI, 1944, Standard Oil Co., N.J., 1945-48, Life mag., 1948-68; idl. photographer, film maker, 1954—; color and black and white cons. various motion picture prodns., U.S. and Europe, 1954—. Writer, producer, dir.: The Learning Tree, 1969; dir.: (films) Shaft, 1972, Shaft's Big Score, 1972, The Super Cops, 1974, Leadbelly, 1976, Odyssey of Solomon Northup, 1984, Moments Without Proper Names, 1986 (Silver medal Internat. Film Festival 1989); creator, composer, dir. Martin, 1990; TV documentary: Diary of a Harlem Family, 1968 (Emmy award); author: Flash Photography, 1947, Camera Portraits: The Techniques and Principals of Documentary Portraiture, 1948, The Learning Tree, 1963, A Choice of Weapons, 1966 (Notable Book award ALA 1966), A Poet and His Camera, 1968, Whispers of Intimate Things, 1971, Born Black, 1971, In Love, 1971, (poetry) Moments Without Proper Names, 1975, Flavio, 1977 (Christopher award 1978), To Smile in Autumn, 1979, (novel) Shannon, 1981, Voices in the Mirror, 1990, (photography, paint and poetry) Arias in Silence, 1994; founder, editorial dir. Essence mag., 1970-73; composer Piano Concerto, 1953, Tree Symphony, 1967, 3 piano sonatas, 1956, 58, 60, modern works for piano and wind instruments, (film scores) The Learning Tree (Libr. Congress Nat. Film Registry Classics film honor, 1989), Shaft's Big Score, The Odyssey of Solomon Northup, Moments Without Proper Names; dir., composer (film) Ballet for Martin Luther King, 1991; poetry: Gordon Parks: A Poet and His Camera, Gordon Parks: Whispers of Intimate Things, In Love, Moments Without Proper Names; traveling exhibits in U.S. and abroad, 1990. Bd. dirs. Schomburg Ctr. for Research in Black Culture, Am. Arts. Alliance, W. Eugene Smith Meml. Fund, Black Tennis and Sports Found., Rondo Ave. Inc., St. Paul; Harlem Symphony Orch., N.Y.C.; mem. adv. com. Kans. Ctr. for the Book; bd. advocates Planned Parenthood Fedn. Am. Inc.; patron N.Y. City Housing Authority Symphony; supporter Apple Corps Theatre, N.Y.C., Quindaro Project, Kans., numerous other civic activities. Decorated Comdr. de l'Ordre des Arts et des Lettres (Republique Francaise); recipient Julius Rosenwald award for photography, 1942, award NCCJ, 1964, awards Syracuse U. Sch. Journalism, 1961, Newhouse citation Syracuse U., 1963, awards Phila. Mus. Art, 1964, awards N.Y. Art Dirs. Club, 1964, 68, Frederic W. Brehm award, 1962, Carr Van Anda Journalism award Ohio U., 1970, Carr Van Anda Journalism award U. Miami, 1964, Pres.'s fellow award R.I. Sch. Design, 1984, Am. Soc. Mag. Photographers award, 1985, Nat. Medal Arts award Commonwealth Mass. Communications, 1988, Kans. Gov.'s medal, 1986, Nat. medal of Arts, 1988, World Press Photo awa, 1988, N.Y.C. Mayor's award, 1989, Artist of Merit Josef Sudek medal, 1989, award Internat. Ctr. Photography, 1990; named Kansan of Yr. Sons and Daus. Kans., 1985. Mem. Urban League N.Y., ASCAP, Writers Guild, NAACP (Spingarn award 1972, Hall of Fame 1984), Acad. Motion Pictures Arts and Scis., AFTRA, Am. Inst. Pub. Service, Nat. Urban League Guild, Internat. Mark Twain Soc. (hon.), Newspaper Guild, Assn. Composers and Dirs., Dirs. Guild (nat. dir.), Dirs. Guild N.Y., Am. Soc. Mag. Photographers (Photographer of Yr. award 1960, 85), Nat. Assn. for Am. Composers and Condrs., Stylus Soc. (hon.), U.S. Tennis Assn. Inc., Am. film Inst.Kappa Alpha Mu. Clubs: Pen; Black Tennis and Sports Found. (bd. dirs.). Home: 860 United Nations Plz New York NY 10017-1810

PARKS, HAROLD FRANCIS, anatomist, educator; b. Anna, Ill., Sept. 28, 1920; s. Guy Clay and Margaret (McCumiskey) P.; m. Margaret Bryner, Sept. 11, 1948; children—Edwin Thomas, Margaret Caroline. B.Ed., So. Ill. U., 1942; Ph.D., Cornell U., 1950. Tchr. music Martinsville (Ill.) High Sch., 1942; asst. band dir. Cornell U., 1942-43, dir. bands, 1943-46, teaching asst. comparative anatomy and histology and embryology, 1945-50, prof. zoology, 1961-64; instr., then asst. prof. anatomy U. N.C. Med. Sch., 1950-54; asst. prof., then assoc. prof. anatomy U. Rochester Sch. Medicine and Dentistry, 1954-61; prof. anatomy U. Ky. Med. Center, 1964-91, chmn. dept., 1964-79; vis. scientist Karolinska Inst., 1956; Exec. com. Ky.-Mich.-Ohio Regional Med. Library Program. Mem. AAAS, Am. Inst. Biol. Scis., Am. Assn. Anatomists (com. on status of women in anatomy 1978-80), Am. Soc. Cell Biology, Electron Microscopy Soc. Am., Am. Soc. Zoologists, So. Soc. Anatomists (council 1968-69), Assn. Anatomy Chmn. (council 1971-72), Sigma Xi, American Kappa Upsilon (hon.), Phi Kappa Phi. Home: 837 Cahaba Rd Lexington KY 40502-3318

PARKS, J. MICHAEL, telecommunications executive; b. Independence, Mo., Dec. 29, 1950; s. Emory C. and Lorene (Belt) P.; m. Maureen C. Weston; children: Christopher Michael, Daniel John. BS in Edn., U. Kans., 1973. Sales rep. Ingersoll-Rand Corp., Kansas City, Mo., 1973-75; sales rep., then sr. v.p. First Data Resources/Am. Express Info. Svcs. Co., Omaha, San Francisco, Boston, Atlanta, 1976-88; chief exec. officer Call Interactive (joint venture of Am. Express Info. Svcs. Corp. and AT&T), Omaha, 1989—; bd. dirs. Commerce Bank Omaha, Data Transmission Network Inc., Am. Express Info. Svcs. Corp., WATS Mktg. of Am. Inc. Chief YMCA Indian Guide Program, Omaha, 1988-89; Cub Scouts den leader local chpt. Boy Scouts Am., Omaha, 1989—. Methodist. Avocations: golf, tennis, camping. Office: Call Interactive 2301 N 117th Ave Omaha NE 68164-3688

PARKS, JAMES FRANKLIN, JR., librarian; b. Louisville, Miss., Oct. 14, 1942; s. James Franklin Sr. and Lorene Elizabeth (Reed) P.; m. Betty Graves, Aug. 15, 1964; children: Kathryn Leigh, William Daniel. BA, Miss. Coll., 1964; MLS, Peabody Coll., 1967. Circulation libr. Miss. Coll., Clinton, 1964-68; head circulation dept. U. Ala., Tuscaloosa, 1968-69; coll. libr. Millsaps Coll., Jackson, Miss., 1969—; faculty pres. Millsaps Coll., Jackson, 1991-93; instr. libr. sci. U. Extension Ctr., Jackson, 1970-73, lectr. libr. sci., Jackson State U., 1975. Editor Miss. Librs., 1979-80, Joint editor, 1977-78; book reviewer Coll. and Rsch. Librs. 1976-80; contbr. articles to jours. in field. Coun. on Libr. Resources fellow, 1975. Mem. AAUP, ALA (councilor 1979-83), Southeastern Libr. Assn., Miss. Libr. Assn. Avocations:

travel, bicycle riding. Home: 103 Jill Cv Clinton MS 39056-4603 Office: Millsaps Coll Libr PO Box 150148 Jackson MS 39210

PARKS, JEFFREY A., lawyer; b. Bethlehem, Pa., Nov. 30, 1948; s. Albert R. and Marilyn H. Parks; m. Susan Fulcher, feb. 2, 1973; 1 child, Jonathon C. Ba, Lehigh U., 1970; JD, U. Pa., 1973. Bar: Pa. Ptnr. Newman, Fox & Parks, bethlehhem, 1975-91, Eckert Seamans Cherin & Mellott, Allentown, Pa., 1991—; lectr. estate planning Northampton Community Coll., Bethlehem, 1979-81, 90-91. Chmn. Northampton County Dem. Com., 1980-82; mem. Bethlehem Tourism Authority, 1980—; founder, pres. Bethlehem-Schwabisch Gmund Assn., 1981—, Bethlehem Musikfest Assn., 1984—. Named Young Man of Yr., Bethlehem Area Jaycees, 1983. Mem. Rotary. Democrat. Lutheran. Office: Eckert Seamans Cherin et al 609 Hamilton Mall Allentown PA 18101-2111

PARKS, JOE BENJAMIN, state legislator; b. McAlester, Okla., Dec. 17, 1915; s. James Allen and Mary Florence (Youngblood) P.; m. Florence M. Evans, Oct. 25, 1941; children: Anne, Kathryn. BS in Pub. Adminstrn., Okla. State U., 1939. Div. dir. U.S. VA, Washington, 1946-56; spl. asst., cons. U.S. GSA, Washington, 1957-58; mgr. dist. EDP div. RCA Corp., Washington, 1959-65; mgr. Ea. region Dashew Bus. Machines, Arlington, Va., 1966-68; assoc. adminstr. social and rehab. svc. U.S. Dept. Health, Edn. & Welfare, Washington, 1969-73; dir. mktg. govt. systems div. Booz, Allen & Hamilton, Washington, 1974-75; ptnr. Forbes & Parks, Dover, N.H., 1976—; mem. N.H. State Legislature, Concord, 1985-92, chmn. joint com. on elderly affairs, 1987-92; mem. com. on health, human svcs. and elderly N.H. State Legislature, 1987-90; chmn. subcom. mileage and electronic roll call, 1989-90, vice chmn. legis. adminstrn. com., 1990-91, mem. appropriations com., 1991-92; proprietor Portsmouth (N.H.) Athenaenum, 1992—; corporator Wentworth Douglas Hosp., Dover, 1980-89; Berr Par Par, Inc., 1994—. Columnist Nat. Antiques Rev., 1975-77, Boston Globe N.H. Weekly 1987-88, Foster's Daily Democrat (Dover, N.H.), 1988-90; freelance writer, 1990—. Vice chmn. N.H. State Rep. Com., 1987-88; chmn. Strafford County Reps., 1988. Decorated Bronze Star. Congregationalist. Avocation: rhododendron hybridizing. Home and office: 195 Long Hill Rd Dover NH 03820-6108

PARKS, JOHN ROBERT, lawyer; b. Rantoul, Ga., July 31, 1952; s. Robert Eugene and Wanda Jean (Nohren) P. BS, U. Ill., 1974; JD, MBA, Columbia U., 1977. Bar: Ga. 1978, Ill. 1981. Staff atty. Atty.'s Title Guaranty Fund, Champaign, Ill., 1980-81; assoc. Powell, Goldstein, Frazer & Murphy, Atlanta, 1977-80, ptnr., 1981—. Contbr. articles to profl. jours. Active United Way, 1980-83. Mem. ABA, Ga. Bar Assn., Atlanta Bar Assn., Ga. Racquetball Assn., Ashford Club, Sportslife Club. Mem. United Ch. of Christ. Home: 2412 Littlebrooke Dr Atlanta GA 30338 Office: Powell Goldstein Frazer & Murphy 191 Peachtree St NE Fl 16 Atlanta GA 30303-1740

PARKS, JOHN SCOTT, pediatric endocrinologist; s. John Louis and Mary Dean (Scott) P.; m. Georgia Bigley, May 7, 1959; children: Stephanie Dean, Paige Wallace Parks Adams, John Thurston. AB in Am. Studies magna cum laude, Amherst Coll., 1961; MD, U. Pa., 1966, PhD in Biochemistry, 1971. Diplomate Nat. Bd. Med. Examiners, Am. Bd. Pediat. Intern in pediat. Children's Hosp. Phila., 1967-68, resident in pediat., 1968-69; clin. assoc. endocrinology br. Nat. Cancer Inst. NIH, Bethesda, Md., 1969-71; endocrinology fellow Children's Hosp. Phila., 1971-73; from instr. pediat. to assoc. prof. pediat. U. Pa., 1971-83; asst. physician, asst. endocrinologist Children's Hosp. Phila., 1972-74, assoc. physician, assoc. dir. endocrinology, 1974-80, assoc. endocrinologist, 1974-82, dir. hypothyroidism program, 1978-81, sr. physician, dir. adolescent medicine, 1980-82; from assoc. prof. pediat. to prof. pediat. Emory U., Atlanta, 1982—, assoc. prof. biochemistry, 1983—, dir. pediat. endocrinology, 1982—; pediat. endocrinologist Henrietta Egleston Hosp., 1982—, Grady Meml. Hosp., 1982—; lectr. in field. Author books; contbg. author over 40 book chpts.; contbr. over 55 articles to profl. jours. Bd. dirs. Spruce Hill Cmty. Assn., 1967-69, Hill Top Prep. Sch., 1977-81. Recipient fellowship NIH, 1963-64, 66-67, 75-80, GM Nat. scholarship, 1957-61, Ford Found. fellowship, 1960-61, Am. Cancer Soc. fellow, 1962-63, Morton McCutcheon award, 1963, Merck award, 1966, numerous rsch. awards, 1964—. Mem. Am. Pediat. Soc., Endocrine Soc. (organizing com. 1990), Soc. for Pediat. Rsch., Coll. Physicians and Surgeons of Phila., Lawson Wilkins Pediat. Endocrine Soc. (program com. chair 1983-87, bd. dirs. 1990-93), Spinx Soc., Scarab Soc., Phi Beta Kappa, Sigma Upsilon. Office: Emory Univ Sch Medicine Div Pediat Endocrinology 2040 Ridgewood Dr NE Atlanta GA 30322

PARKS, LLOYD LEE, oil company executive; b. Kiefer, Okla., Dec. 9, 1929; s. Homer Harrison and Avis Pearl (Motes) P.; m. Mary Ellen Scott, Aug. 20, 1948; children: Connie Jo, Karyn Ann, Rebecca Lee. Student, Okla. State U., 1948-50, Tulsa U., 1957-58; Harvard U. Bus. Sch., 1965. Acct. Deep Rock Oil Corp., 1951-54; chief acct. Blackwell Oil & Gas Co., Tulsa, 1954-60; sec. treas. Blackwell Oil & Gas Co., 1960-62; v.p., controller Amax Oil & Gas Inc., Houston, 1962-67, pres., CEO, 1968—92; v.p. Amax, Inc., 1975-92; pvt. practice oil and gas and real estate investment Salado, Tex., 1992—. Served with AUS, 1946-48, 50-51. Mem. Ind. Petroleum Assn. Am. (dir.), Mill Creek Country Club, Wildflower Country Club (Temple, Tex.), Lions Club. Republican. Office: PO Box 1021 Salado TX 76571-1021

PARKS, MADELYN N., nurse, retired army officer, university official; b. Jordan, Okla. Diploma, Corpus Christi (Tex.) Sch. Nursing, 1943; B.S.N., Incarnate Word Coll., San Antonio, 1961; M.H.A. in Health Care Adminstrn, Baylor U., 1965. Commd. 2d lt. Army Nurse Corps, 1943, advanced through grades to brig. gen., 1975; basic tng. Fort Meade, Md., 1944; staff nurse eye ward Valley Forge (Pa.) Gen. Hosp., 1944; served in India, Iran, Italy, 1944-45; gen. duty staff nurse Fort Polk, La., 1951; nurse eye clinic Tripler Army Med. Center, Hawaii, 1951-54; staff nurse eye, ear, nose and throat ward Brooke Army Med. Center, San Antonio, 1954-57; ednl. coordinator Fort Dix, N.J., 1957-58; instr., supr. enlisted med. tng. U.S. Army Med. Tng. Center, Fort Sam Houston, Tex., 1959-61; chief nurse surg. field hosp. 62d Med. Group, Germany, 1961-62, sr. nurse coordinator, 1962-63; adminstrn. resident Letterman Gen. Hosp., San Francisco, 1964-65; dir. clin. specialist course Letterman Gen. Hosp., 1965-67; chief nurse 85th Evacuation Hosp., Qui Nhon, Vietnam, 1967-68; asst. chief nursing sci. div., asst. prof. Med. Field Service Sch., U.S Army-Baylor U. Program in Health Care Adminstrn., 1968-72; chief nurse surgeons office Hdqrs. Continental Army Command, Fort Monroe, Va., 1972-73; chief dept. nursing Walter Reed Army Med. Center, Washington, 1973-75; chief Army Nurse Corps, Office of Surgeon Gen., Dept. Army, Washington, 1975-79; ret. Army Nurse Corps, Office of Surgeon Gen., Dept. Army, 1979; faculty assoc. adminstr. U. Md., 1974-78. Decorated D.S.M., Army Commendation medal with 2 oak leaf clusters, Legion of Merit, Meritorious Service medal; recipient Alumna of Distinction award Incarnate Word Coll., 1981. Mem. Ret. Officers Assn., AMEDD Mus. Found. Address: 5211 Metcalf Dr San Antonio TX 78239

PARKS, MICHAEL CHRISTOPHER, journalist; b. Detroit, Nov. 17, 1943; s. Robert James and Rosalind (Smith) P.; m. Linda Katherine Durocher, Dec. 26, 1964; children: Danielle Anne, Christopher, Matthew. AB, U. Windsor, Ont., Can., 1965. Reporter Detroit News, 1962-65; corr. Time-Life News Service, N.Y.C., 1965-66; asst. city editor Suffolk Sun, Long Island, N.Y., 1966-68; polit. reporter, foreign corr. The Balt. Sun, Saigon, Singapore, Moscow, Cairo, Hong Kong, Peking, 1968-80; fgn. corr. L.A. Times, L.A., Peking, Johannesburg, Moscow, Jerusalem, 1980-95, dpty. fgn. editor, 1995—. Recipient Pulitzer Prize, 1987. Mem. Royal Commonwealth Soc. London. Club: Foreign Corr. (Hong Kong). Office: L A Times Times Mirror Sq Los Angeles CA 90012

PARKS, PATRICIA JEAN, lawyer; b. Portland, Oreg., Apr. 2, 1945; d. Robert and Marion (Crosby) P.; m. David F. Jurca, Oct. 17, 1971 (div. 1976). BA in History, Stanford U., 1963-67; JD, U. Penn., Phila., 1967-70. Bar: N.Y. 1971, Wash. 1974. Assoc. Milbank, Tweed, Hadley & McCoy, N.Y.C., 1971-73; assoc. Shidler, McBroom, Gates & Lucas, Seattle, 1974-81, ptnr., 1981-90; ptnr. Preston, Thorgrimson, Shidler, Gates & Ellis, Seattle, 1990-93; pvt. practice Seattle, 1993—. Active Vashon Allied Arts, Mountaineers, N.W. Women's Law Ctr., Wash. State Women's Polit. Caucus. Mem. NOW, ABA, Wash. State Bar Assn. (past pres. tax sect., past

chair gift and estate tax com.), Washington Women in Tax, Washington Women Lawyers, Seattle-King County Bar Assn., Employee Stock Ownership Plan Assn., Western Pension Conf., Pension Roundtable, Wash. Athletic Club. Avocations: kayaking, hiking, Contra dancing, bird watching. Home: 14028 Glen Acres Rd SW Vashon WA 98070 Office: 1301 5th Ave Ste 3800 Seattle WA 98101

PARKS, PAUL, corporate executive; b. Indpls., May 7, 1923; s. Cleab Jiles and Hazel (Crenshaw) P.; m. Virginia Loftman, Sept. 18, 1971; children: Paul, Pamela, Stacey. BS in Civil Engring., Purdue U., 1949; postgrad., MIT, 1958, U. Mass.; DEng, Northeastern U., 1994. Registered profl. engr., Mass. With Ind. State Hwy. Commn., Indpls., 1949-51; designer Stone & Webster Engring., Boston, 1951, Fay, Spofford & Thorndike, Boston, 1951-52; missile designer Chance Vought Aircraft, Boston, 1952-53; nuclear engr. Pratt & Whitney Aircraft, Boston, 1953-57; pntr. architecture and engring. firm, Boston, 1957-67; adminstr. Boston Model City Adminstrn., 1968-76; sec. ednl. affairs Commonwealth of Mass., Boston, 1976—; pres. Paul Parks and Assocs. Inc., Boston, 1979—; lectr. Tufts U. Sch. Civil Engring., 1968—; mem. northeastern regional bd. Fannie Mae, 1994—. Cons. gen. acctg. office Mayor's Com. Adminstrn. Justice; mem. Atty. Gen.'s Adv. Com. Civil Rights, 1969-71; mem. health task force Boston Fed. Exec. Bd.; adviser Boston Mothers for Adequate Welfare, 1966-68; speech therapist Vets. Lang. Clinic, Mass. Gen. Hosp., 1964-66; mem. Mass. Adv. Coun. on Edn., 1968-71, Mass. Com. Children and Youth, 1962-67; chmn. Mass. adv. com. to U.S. Civil Rights Commn., 1961-73; chmn. urban affairs com. Mass. Fedn. Fair Housing and Equal Rights, 1961-67; mem. Community Ednl. Coun., 1961-73; pres. Com. for Community Ednl. Devel. Inc., 1968-74; presdl. adv. commn. Nat. Coun. Ednl. Programs for Women, 1976-81; pres. Boston Pub. Libr.; mem. zoning bd. appeals City of Boston; adult leader youth programs Roxbury YMCA, 1951-58; trustee Brigham Hosp., Women's Hosp.; bd. dirs. Mass. Planned Parenthood Assn., Mass. Mental Health Assn., Mass. Soc. Prevention Blindness, Boston Coll. Upward Bound Program; chmn. sch. com. City of Boston, 1992—; mem. regional adv. coun. Fannie Mae. Served with AUS, 1943-46, ETO, PTO. Mem. ASCE, NSPE, NAACP (co-chmn. edn. com. 1960-68, v.p. Boston br. 1965-70), Nat. Acad. Pub. Adminstrn., Ams. Dem. Action (nat. bd. 1971-74, state bd. 1970-74), Greater Boston C. of C. (edn. com.). Mem. United Ch. of Christ (mem. nat. social action bd. 1963-68). Home: 78 Woodhaven St Mattapan MA 02126-1730 Office: 100 Boylston St Ste 815 Boston MA 02116-4610

PARKS, RICHARD WILLIAM, economics educator, consultant; b. Utica, N.Y., Oct. 16, 1938; s. Robert W. and Josephine M. (Murphy) P.; m. Sally Litzer, July 2, 1960; children—Alexandra, Joshua. A.B., Harvard U., 1960; M.A. in Stats., U. Calif.-Berkeley, 1964, Ph.D. in Econs., 1966. Asst. prof. U. Chgo., 1965-70; assoc. prof. econs. U. Wash., Seattle, 1970-78, prof., 1978—, dir. Inst. for Econ. Research, 1970-76, acting chmn. dept. econs., 1972-73; vis. prof. econs. U. Hawaii, summer 1972; Fulbright lectr., Argentina, 1968; cons. in field. Contbr. articles to profl. publs. Ford Found. dissertation fellow, 1964-65; NSF grantee, 1972-74, 81-83; Hoover Instn. nat. fellow Stanford U., Calif., 1976-77. Mem. Am. Econ. Assn., Am. Finance Assn., Econometric Soc., Western Econ. Assn., Phi Beta Kappa. Home: 505 Boston St Seattle WA 98109-2132

PARKS, ROBERT EMMETT, JR., medical science educator; b. Glendale, N.Y., July 29, 1921; s. Robert Emmett and Carolyn M. (Heinemann) P.; m. Margaret Ellen Ward, June 15, 1945; children: Robert Emmett III, Walter Ward, Christopher Carr. AB, Brown U., 1944; MD, Harvard U., 1945; PhD, U. Wis., 1954. Intern Boston's Children's Hosp., 1945-46; rsch. assoc. Amherst (Mass.) Coll., 1948-51; postdoctoral fellow Enzyme Inst., Madison, Wis., 1951-54; mem. faculty U. Wis. Med. Sch., 1954-63, prof. pharmacology, 1961-63; prof. med. sci. Brown U., Providence, 1963-91, prof. emeritus, 1991—, dir. grad. program in pharmacology and exptl. pathology, 1978-81, chmn. sect. biochem. pharmacology, 1978-83, 83-91; cons. in field. Contbr. articles to profl. jours. With AUS, 1943-45, 46-48. Acad. medicine scholar John and Mary Markle Found., 1956-61. Mem. Am. Soc. Pharmacology and Exptl. Therapeutics, Am. Soc. Biol. Chemists, Am. Assn. Cancer Rsch. (bd. dirs. 1982-86), Sigma Xi. Home: 62 Alumni Ave Providence RI 02906-2310 Office: Brown U 429 Biomed Ctr Providence RI 02912

PARKS, ROBERT HENRY, consulting economist, educator; b. New Orleans, Sept. 20, 1924; s. Charles Samuel and Amelia (England) P.; m. Inta Kondrats, Sept. 20, 1958; children: Karen E., Robert R., Alison J.; m. Annette Fiechter, Dec. 10, 1982 (div.). A.B. in Econs., Swarthmore Coll., 1949; M.A., Ph.D. in Econs., U. Pa., 1958. Economist Econ. Forecasting div. Gen. Electric Co., 1958-61; dir. econ. research Life Ins. Assn. Am., 1961-68; chief economist Maj. Wall St. Investment Firms, 1968-80; pres. Robert H. Parks & Assocs., Inc., N.Y.C., 1980—; cons. to instnl. investment officers; prof. fin., dir. Inst. Internat. Fin. Pace U., Wharton Sch. (U. Pa.), Baruch (CUNY). Contbr. articles to profl. jours. Democrat. Home and Office: 31 Sherwood Rd Short Hills NJ 07078-2038

PARKS, R(OBERT) KEITH, missionary, religious organization administrator; b. Memphis, Tex., Oct. 23, 1927; s. Robert Crews and Allie Myrtle (Cowger) P.; m. Helen Jean Bond, May 24, 1952; children: Randall, Kent, Eloise, Stanley. BA, U. North Tex., 1948; BD, Southwestern Bapt. Theol. Sem., 1951, ThD, 1955; LittD (hon.), Hardin-Simmons U., 1976; D Missions (hon.), Calif. Bapt. Coll., 1980; STD (hon.), S.W. Bapt. Coll., Bolivar, Mo., 1981; DD (hon.), U. Richmond, 1987. Ordained to ministry So. Bapt. Conv., 1950. Pastor Red Springs (Tex.) Bapt. Ch., 1950-54; instr. Bible Hardin-Simmons U., Abilene, Tex., 1953-54; missionary Fgn. Mission Bd., So. Bapt. Conv., Indonesia, 1954-68; area dir. S.E. Asia Fgn. Mission Bd., So. Bapt. Conv., Richmond, Va., 1968-75; dir. div. mission support, 1975-79, pres., 1980-92; global missions coord. Coop. Bapt. Fellowship, Atlanta, 1993—; mem. past chmn. Inter-Agy. Coun., So. Bapt. Conv., 1980-92; trustee Bapt. Joint Com. on Pub. Affairs, Washington, 1980-91. Author: Crosscurrents, 1966, World in View, 1987; also numerous articles. Recipient Disting. Alumnus award Southwestern Bapt. Theol. Sem., 1980, U. North Tex., 1991, E.Y. Mullins Denomination Svc. award So. Bapt. Theol. Sem., 1989. Office: Coop Bapt Fellowship Box 450329 Atlanta GA 30345-0329

PARKS, ROBERT MYERS, appliance manufacturing company executive; b. Nevada, Mo., July 18, 1927; s. Cecil R. and Marcella (Myers) P.; m. Audrey Lenora Jones, June 18, 1955; children—John Robert, Janet M. Parks Huston. B.S., U. Mo., 1949; M.B.A., Harvard, 1952. Asst. dept. mgr. Jewett & Sherman Co., Kansas City, Mo., 1949-50; staff cons. Harbridge House, Inc., Boston, 1952; v.p. Electronic Splty. Co., Inc., Los Angeles, 1952-57; pres. Parks Products, Inc., Hollywood, Calif., 1957—, Generalist Industries, Inc., Hollywood, 1960-73; chmn. bd. Shaver Corp. Am., Los Angeles, 1965—; lectr. mktg. UCLA Extension div., 1960-61. Contbr. articles on mktg. and bus. mgmt. to profl. publs.; patentee in field. Active YMCA; bd. dirs. Hollywood Presbyn. Med. Center Found.; mem. dean's adv. council U. Mo. Bus. Sch.; mayor's task force on L.A. River Cahuenga Pass Coalition. Served with USNR, 1944-45. Mem. Sales and Marketing Execs. Assn., C. of C., Navy League, World Affairs Council, Calif. Caballeros, Rangers, Vaqueros del Desierto, Los Caballeros, Rancheros Visitadores, E Clampus Vitus, Delta Sigma Pi, Sigma Chi. Presbyn. Clubs: Mason (Shriner), Los Angeles Breakfast, Braemar Country, Saddle and Sirloin. Home: 7421 Woodrow Wilson Dr Los Angeles CA 90046-1322 Office: 3611 Cahuenga Blvd Hollywood CA 90068-1205

PARKS, SALLIE ANN, county official, public relations executive, marketing professional; b. Detroit, Sept. 5, 1936; d. Bert A. Rennie and Edna V. (Lampman) Moran; m. Donald K. Parks, Aug. 22, 1959 (div. 1983); children: Sheri Lynn, Steven Rennie. BA, Cen. Mich. U., 1959; postgrad., Mich. State U., 1962. Cert. accredited pub. relations profl. Editor Pinellas Classroom Tchrs. Assn., Clearwater, Fla., 1967-73; sub. tchr. Pinellas County Schs., Fla., 1972-74; real estate mgmt. Clearwater, 1971-74, bus. mgr., 1974-76; exec. dir. Pinellas County Arts Coun., Clearwater, 1976-81; dir. community relations Mease Health Care, Dunedin, Fla., 1981-86; pub. relations cons. tchr. Tokyo, Japan, 1986-87; dir. pub. rels. and mktg. Mease Health Care, Dunedin, 1987-92; county commr. Pinellas County, Clearwater, Fla., 1992-95, vice chmn., 1995; chair long term care subcom. Nat. Assn. Counties; bd. dirs. Fla. Assn. Counties; chair Dist. V Juvenile Justice Bd.; mem. Met. Planning Orgn. Pinellas County, Pinellas County Arts Coun., Juvenile Welfare Bd. Pinellas County, Cmty. Health Purchasing Alliance

Dist. V, Tampa Bay Regional Planning Coun. Area Agy. on Aging and Long Term Care subcom., Pinellas County Juvenile Boot Camp Task Force, Success by Six Task Force. Pres. Am. Heart Assn., Suncoast chpt., Clearwater, 1990-92; vice chairperson Clearwater Pub. Libr. Found., 1989; pres. LWV, Clearwater, 1972, PEO Sisterhood, Clearwater, 1975; trustee Pinellas Marine Inst. Recipient Athena award, Women in Communications, 1983, Leadership in the Arts award, Soroptimist Internat., 1980. Mem. Nat. Press Women, Fla. Pub. Rels. Assn. (past pres.). Republican. Presbyterian. Avocations: travel, theatre, music. Office: Office Bd Commrs 315 Court St Clearwater FL 34616

PARKS, THOMAS W., electrical engineering educator, consultant; b. Buffalo, Mar. 16, 1939; s. William K. and Mildred (Walzer) P.; m. Martha B., May 4, 1963; children: Alice J., Thomas M., Susan E. B.E.E., Cornell U., 1961, M.S., 1964, Ph.D., 1967. Co-op. engr. Cornell Aero Lab., Buffalo, 1958-61; elec. engr. Gen. Electric Advanced Electronics Center, Ithaca, N.Y., 1961-63; asst. prof. elec. engring. dept. Rice U., Houston, 1967-72, assoc. prof., 1972-77, prof. elec. engring., 1977-86; prof. elec. engring. Cornell U., Ithaca, N.Y., 1986—. Editor: IEEE Acoustics Speech and Signal Processing Soc., 1979-80. Recipient sr. scientist award A.V. Humboldt Found., Bonn, West Germany, 1972, Sr. Fulbright fellow Fulbright Found., 1973. Fellow IEEE (mem. com. 1978-80, tech. achievement award 1981); mem. IEEE Acoustics Speech and Signal Soc. (award 1988, Spira award for excellence in teaching 1992). Office: Sch of Elec Engring Cornell U Ithaca NY 14853

PARKYN, JOHN WILLIAM, editor, writer; b. London, Dec. 7, 1931; came to U.S., 1967; citizen, 1973; s. James R. and Eva M. (Dix) P.; m. Sybil (Judy) Hetherington; 1 child, Elaine. Student, Dulwich Coll., 1943-48. Staff writer Bus. Mag., London, 1954-56, Amalgamated Press, London, 1956-58; features editor Woman's Illustrated mag., London, 1958-60; staff writer Internat. Pub. Corp., London, 1960-61; editor Westward mag. Daily News Ltd., London, 1961-64; assoc. editor Daily Telegraph mag., London, 1964-66; features editor King mag. Europress, Ltd., London, 1966-67; assoc. editor Tropic mag. Miami (Fla.) Herald, 1967-69; editor Tropic mag., 1969-77; editor Calif. Today mag. San Jose (Calif.) Mercury News, 1977-83; editor Sunshine: The Mag. of South Fla. Sun-Sentinel Co. (subs. Tribune Co.), Ft. Lauderdale, Fla., 1983—; cons. Het Parool newspaper, Amsterdam, 1965. Contbr. numerous articles to Am. and Brit. mags. Chmn. Sunday Mag. Editors Conf., Louisville, 1973. With RAF, 1950-52. Recipient Outstanding Use of Editl. Color award Editor & Pub. mag., 1974, 75, 77, Nat. Headliner award, 1976, 79; named Editor Best Weekly Mag. in State Fla. Press Club, 1985-93. Mem. Sunday Mag. Editors Assn. Office: Sun-Sentinel Co 200 E Las Olas Blvd Fort Lauderdale FL 33301-2293

PARLER, WILLIAM CARLOS, lawyer; b. Cameron, S.C., Aug. 12, 1929; s. Marion Carlos and Anna (Keller) P.; m. Anne Hemenway, Aug. 13, 1955; children: William Carlos, Blair Hemenway, Bethanie Rene, Beatrice Carolyn. B.S., U.S. Naval Acad., 1951; LL.B. magna cum laude, U. S.C.-Columbia, 1958; LL.M., Harvard U., 1959. Bar: S.C. 1958, U.S. Dist. Ct. (ea. and we. dists.) S.C. 1958, U.S. Ct. Appeals (D.C. cir.) 1967, U.S. Supreme Ct. 1966. Atty., AEC, Germantown, Md., 1959-70; counsel to Congl. Joint Com. on Atomic Energy, Washington, 1971-72, 75-76; adminstrv. judge AEC, Washington, 1973-74; sr. atty. Nuclear Regulatory Commn., Bethesda, Md., 1977-81, legis. counsel, Washington, 1982, sr. atty., 1983—; group leader Spl. Inquiry Group on Three Mile Island Accident, Bethesda, 1979; gen. counsel Nuclear Regulatory Commn., 1986—; govt. mem. Adminstrv. Conf. U.S. Author, editor: Background TMI Accident, Vol. II, 1980; adviser: History of U.S. Atomic Energy. Contbr. articles to profl. jours. Active Naval Res. and def. related orgns., 1971—. With USN, capt. res. ret. Recipient Outstanding Performance award AEC, 1965, Outstanding Achievement award Nuclear Regulatory Commn., 1980, Presdl. Disting. and Meritorious Exec. Rank award, Disting. Svc. award NRC, 1992, Disting. Govt. Svc. award ABA, 1993. Mem. Naval Res. Assn. (Disting. svc. award), Wig and Robe Soc., Phi Beta Kappa. Office: Nuclear Regulatory Commn Gen Counsel 11555 Rockville Pike Rockville MD 20852

PARLIN, CHARLES C., JR., retired lawyer; b. Trenton, Feb. 12, 1928; s. Charles C. and Miriam (Boyd) P.; m. Joan Bona, June 28, 1948; children: C. Christopher, Robert B., Timothy B. B.A., U. Chgo., 1946; LL.B., U. Pa., 1949. Bar: N.Y. 1951. Assoc. firm Shearman & Sterling, N.Y.C., 1950-59, ptnr., 1959-90, of counsel, 1990-92, ret., 1992. Home: Pudding Ln Silver Bay NY 12874

PARMELEE, ARTHUR HAWLEY, JR., pediatric medical educator; b. Chgo., Oct. 29, 1917; s. Arthur Hawley and Ruth Frances (Brown) P.; m. Jean Kern Rheinfrank, Nov. 11, 1939; children—Arthur Hawley III, Ann (Mrs. John C. Minahan, Jr.), Timothy, Ruth Ellen. B.S., U. Chgo., 1940, M.D., 1943. Diplomate Am. Bd. Pediatrics (examiner 1966—). Intern U.S. Naval Hosp., Bethesda, Md., 1943-44; extern Yale Inst. Child Devel., 1947, New Haven Hosp., 1947-48, Los Angeles Children's Hosp., 1948-49; mem. faculty UCLA Med. Sch., 1951—, prof. pediatrics, 1967-88, emeritus, 1988, dir. div. child devel., 1964-88; mem. Brain Research Inst., 1966-88, Mental Retardation Research Center, 1970-88; rsch. prof. pediatrics U. Göttingen, Fed. Republic Germany, 1967-68; mem. com. child devel. rsch. and public policy NRC, 1977-81; cons. Nat. Inst. Child Health and Human Devel., 1963-70, Holy Family Adoption Service, 1949-80. Author articles, chpts. in books. Trustee Los Angeles Children's Mus., 1979. Served with USN, 1943-47. Recipient C. Anderson Aldrich award in child devel., 1975; Commonwealth fellow Centre de Recherches Biologiques Neonatales, Clinique Obstetricale Baudelocque, Paris, 1959-60; fellow Ctr. Advanced Study in the Behavioral Scis., Stanford U., 1984-85; recipient Soc. for Rsch. in Child Devel. award (Disting. Scientific Contbns. to Child Devel.), 1993. Mem. Am. Pediatric Soc., Soc. Pediatric Research, Western Soc. Pediatric Research, Am. Acad. Pediatrics (chmn. com. of sect. child devel. 1966), Assn. Ambulatory Pediatrics (council 1966-69), Soc. Research in Child Devel. (pres. 1983-85), Assn. Psychophysiol. Study Sleep, AMA, Los Angeles County Med. Soc., Phi Beta Kappa. Home: 764 Iliff St Pacific Palisades CA 90272-3927 Office: Univ Calif Dept Pediatrics Los Angeles CA 90024

PARMELEE, DAVID FREELAND, biologist, educator; b. Oshkosh, Wis., June 20, 1924; s. Gale Freeland and Helen Dale (MacNaughton) P.; m. Jean Marie Peterson, Dec. 4, 1943; 1 dau., Helen Gale. BA, Lawrence U., Appleton, Wis., 1950; MS, U. Mich., 1952; PhD, U. Okla., 1957. Grad. asst., then instr. U. Okla., 1952-58; from asst. prof. to prof. biology Kans. State U., Emporia, 1958-70; prof. ecology and behavioral biology U. Minn., Mpls., 1970-92, chmn. field biology program, 1970-84; curator birds Bell Mus. U. Minn., 1985-92; rsch. curator ornithology U. Nev., Las Vegas, 1992—; dir. field ops. bird virus and parasite rsch. studies U. Okla. Med. Ctr., 1963-65; program dir. U. Minn. Forestry and Biol. Sta., Lake Itasca, 1970-86, Cedar Creek Natural History Area, 1970-84; lectr. on cruise vessels to Arctic and Antarctic for Travel Dynamics, N.Y.C., 1988—, Space Expedition, Inc., Seattle, 1993—, Cheesemans' Ecology Safaries, 1994—. Served with USMCR, 1943-46. Recipient Native Son award Rotary Internat., 1982; grantee NSF-U.S. Antarctic Research Program, 1972-90, Canadian Arctic Research Programs-NSF-Arctic Inst. N.Am.-Nat. Museum Can., 1953-71; recipient Conservation Edn. award Kans. Wildlife Fedn., Conservation Edn. award Sears-Roebuck Found., 1965; Antarctic site named Parmelee Massif in his honor. Fellow Explorers Club; mem. Orgn. Biol. Field Stas. (pres. 1984-85), Brit. Ornithol. Union, Cooper Ornithol. Soc., Wilson Ornithol. Soc., Nature Conservancy.

PARMELEE, HAROLD J., construction company executive; b. 1937. BA, Bowdoin Coll., 1959; BSCE, MIT, 1960. With Turner Constrn. Co., 1960—, field engr., 1960-70, v.p., 1970-80, group v.p., northeast region, 1980-86, v.p. eastern div., frm 1986, then COO, exec. v.p., pres., 1990—, also CEO, bd. dirs. Office: Turner Corp 375 Hudson St New York NY 10014

PARMENTER, CHARLES STEDMAN, chemistry educator; b. Phila., Oct. 12, 1933; s. Charles Leroy and Hazeltene Lois (Stedman) P.; m. Patricia Jean Patton, Mar. 31, 1956; children: Tighe Stedman, Kyle Kirkland, Leigh Patton. BA, U. Pa., 1955; Ph.D in Phys. Chemistry, U. Rochester, 1963. Tech. rep. photo products E.I. du Pont de Nemours & Co., 1958; NSF fellow chemistry Harvard U., Boston, 1962-63, NIH rsch. fellow, 1963-64, from asst. prof. to prof., 1964-88; Disting. prof. chemistry Ind. U., Bloomington, 1988—; Simon H. Guggenheim fellow U. Cambridge, 1971-72; vis. fellow

Joint Inst. Lab. Astrophysics, Nat. Bur. Standards and U. Colo., 1977-78, 92. Lt. USAF, 1956-58. Recipient Humboldt Sr. Scientist award Tech. U. Munchen, 1986; Fulbright Sr. Scholar Griffith U., Australia, 1980. Fellow AAAS, Am. Phys. Soc.; mem. NAS, Am. Chem. Soc. (chmn. div. physical chemistry 1986-87). Research in photochemistry, laser spectroscopy, energy transfer. Office: Ind U Dept of Chemistry Bloomington IN 47405

PARMENTER, ROBERT HALEY, physics educator; b. Portland, Maine, Sept. 19, 1925; s. LeClare Fall and Esther (Haley) P.; m. Elizabeth Kinnecom, Oct. 27, 1951; children: David Alan, Douglas Ian. B.S., U. Maine, 1947; Ph.D., Mass. Inst. Tech., 1952. Mem. staff solid state and molecular theory group Mass. Inst. Tech., 1951-54; guest scientist Brookhaven Nat. Lab., 1951-52; mem. staff Lincoln Lab., 1952-54, RCA Labs., 1954-66; vis. scientists RCA Labs., Zurich, Switzerland, 1958; acting head solid state research group RCA Labs., 1962-65; prof. physics U. Ariz., 1966—, chmn. dept., 1977-83; mem. NASA rsch. adv. com. electrophysics, 1964-68, chmn., 1966-68, mem. rsch. and tech. adv. com. basic rsch., 1966-68; vis. lectr. Princeton (N.J.) U., 1960-61. Served with USNR, 1944-46. Fellow AAAS, Am. Phys. Soc. (chmn. div. condensed matter physics 1967-68); mem. Sigma Xi, Tau Beta Pi. Achievements include predicted the existence of the acoustoelectric effect, the enhancement of the transition temperature of a superconductor by means of tunneling extraction. Home: 1440 E Ina Rd Tucson AZ 85718-1175 Office: U Ariz Physics Dept Tucson AZ 85721

PARNAS, DAVID LORGE, computer scientist, engineer, educator; b. Plattsburgh, N.Y., Feb. 10, 1941; s. Jacob M. and Hildegarde Marienne (Lorge) P.; m. Lillian Lai Ngan Chik, Nov. 7, 1979; children: Jacob McNeil, Henrietta Heng Li. BS, Carnegie Inst. Tech., 1961, MS, 1964, PhD, 1965; Dr. honoris causa, Eidgenössische Technische Hochschule, Zürich, Switzerland, 1986. Mem. faculty Carnegie Mellon U., 1965-73, U. Md., 1965; vis. advisor Philips-Electrologica, Apeldoorn, Netherlands, 1969-70; prof. Technische Hochschule Darmstadt, W. Ger., 1973-76; prof. computer sci. U. N.C., Chapel Hill, 1976-82; vis. scientist IBM, Bethesda, Md., 1980-82; computer scientist Naval Rsch. Lab., Washington, 1972-86; prof. computer sci. U. Victoria, B.C., Can., 1982-86; mem. faculty McMaster U., Hamilton, Ont., Can., 1991—; cons. Bell Labs., TRW, Inc., DEC, BNR. Recipient Norbert Wiener award, 1987. Fellow Royal Soc. Can., Assn. Computing Machinery; mem. IEEE (sr.), Gesellschaft fur Informatik. Home: 551 Old Dundas Rd, Ancaster, ON Canada L9G 3J3 Office: McMaster U Comm Rsch Lab, Dept Elec/Computer Engring, 1280 Main St W, Hamilton, ON Canada L85 4K1 Only the truth allows us to be free. Science is a search for the truth.

PARNELL, FRANCIS WILLIAM, JR., physician; b. Woonsocket, R.I., May 22, 1940; s. Francis W. and Dorothy V. (Lalor) P.; m. Diana DeAngelis, Feb. 27, 1965; children: Cheryl Lynn, John Francis, Kathleen Diana, Alison Anne, Thomas William. Student, Coll. Holy Cross, 1957-58; AB, Clark U., 1961; MD, Georgetown U., 1965. Diplomate: Nat. Bd. Med. Examiners, Am. Bd. Otolaryngology. Intern Univ. Hosps., Madison, Wis., 1965-66; resident in gen. surgery Univ. Hosps., Madison, 1966-67, otolaryngology, 1967-70; pvt. practice medicine specializing in otolaryngology San Rafael, Calif., 1972-75, Greenbrae, Calif., 1972-75, 78—; chmn., CEO Parnell Pharms., Larkspur, Calif., 1982—; cons. corp. med. affairs, 1978-82; corp. med. dir. Becton, Dickinson & Co., Rutherford, N.J., 1976-78; clin. instr. U. Calif. at San Francisco, 1972-75, asst. clin. prof., 1975-76; Alt. del., U.S. Del. 27th World Health Assembly WHO, Geneva, 1974. Contbr. articles to profl. jours. Candidate Calif. State Assembly, 1988; bd. dirs. Marin Coalition, 1986—, treasurer Ross (Calif.) Sch. Dist., 1981-89. Maj. M.C., AUS, 1970-72; lt. col. M.C., USAR, 1985-94. Fellow ACS (gov. 1988-94), Am. Acad. Otolaryngology. Home: PO Box 998 Ross CA 94957-0998 Office: 1100 S Eliseo Dr Greenbrae CA 94904-9999

PARNELL, THOMAS ALFRED, physicist; b. Lumberton, N.C., Nov. 24, 1931; s. Johnathan Alfred and Lula Beale (Lashley) P.; m. Elizabeth G. Brite, June 4, 1955; children: Marc Thomas, Gina Ann. BS in Physics, U. N.C., 1954, M.S. in Physics, 1962, Ph.D. in Physics, 1965. Rsch. adj., dept. physics U. N.C., Chapel Hill, 1962-65; ops. analyst U.S. Air Force Europe, Wiesbaden, W. Ger., 1965-66; asst. prof. physics Marshall U., Huntington, W.Va., 1966-67; physicist NASA-Marshall Space Flight Center, Huntsville, Ala., 1967-69; chief astrophysics br. NASA-Marshall Space Flight Center, 1969—; mem. grad. faculty U. Ala., Huntsville. Contbr. articles to profl. jours. Served with USN, 1954-58. Recipient Exceptional Sci. Achievement medal, Outstanding Leadership medal NASA. Mem. Am. Phys. Soc., Sigma Xi. Club: Monte Sano (Huntsville). Home: 907 Corinth Cir SE Huntsville AL 35801-2064 Office: Marshall Space Flight Ctr ES 84 Huntsville AL 35812

PARODE, ANN, banker, lawyer; b. L.A., Mar. 3, 1947; d. Lowell Carr and Sabine (Phelps) P. BA, Pomona Coll., 1968; JD, UCLA, 1971. Bar: Calif. 1972, U.S. Dist. Ct. (so. dist.) Calif. 1972, U.S. Ct. Appeals (9th cir.) 1975. Assoc. Luce, Forward et al, San Diego, 1971-75; gen. counsel, exec. v.p., sec. San Diego Trust & Savings, 1975-94; judge pro tem San Diego Mcpl. Ct., 1978-84. Bd. dirs. San Diego Cmty. Found., 1989—, chmn., 1994-96; bd. dirs. La Jolla Cancer Rsch. Found., 1995—. Mem. Calif. Bar Assn. (corp. law com. 1980-83, client trust fund commn. 1986-90, chmn. 1989-90), San Diego County Bar Found. (founder, bd. dirs., pres. 1980-83), San Diego Bar Asns. (bd. dirs. 1977-81, v.p. 1977-78, 80-81, treas. 1979-80), Law Libr. Justice Found. (pres. 1994).

PARR, CAROLYN MILLER, federal court judge; b. Palatka, Fla., Apr. 17, 1937; d. Arthur Charles and Audrey Ellen (Dunklin) Miller; m. Jerry Studstill Parr, Oct. 12, 1959; children: Kimberly Parr Trapasso, Jennifer Parr Turek, Patricia Audrey. BA, Stetson U., 1959; MA, Vanderbilt U., 1960; JD, Georgetown U., 1977; LLD (hon.), Stetson U., 1986. Bar: Md. 1977, U.S. Tax Ct. 1977, D.C. 1979, U.S. Supreme Ct. 1983. Gen. trial atty. IRS, Washington, 1977-81, sr. trial atty. office of chief counsel, 1982; spl. counsel to asst. atty. gen. tax divsn. U.S. Dept. Justice, Washington, 1982-85; judge U.S. Tax Ct., Washington, 1985—. Nat. Def. fellow Vanderbilt U., 1959-60; fellow Georgetown U., 1975-76; recipient Spl. Achievement award U.S. Treasury, 1979. Mem. ABA, Md. Bar Assn., Nat. Assn. Women Judges, D.C. Bar Assn., Women Judges Fund for Justice (bd.). Office: US Tax Ct 400 2nd St NW Washington DC 20217-0002

PARR, FERDINAND VAN SICLEN, JR., lawyer; b. Bklyn., June 13, 1908; s. Ferdinand Van Siclen and Mabel Kendrick (Skidmore) P.; m. Helene Elizabeth Ham, Sept. 7, 1938; children: Elizabeth Ham, Grant Van Siclen, Sarah Leota. BA, Wesleyan U., 1929; JD, St. Lawrence U., 1933. Bar: N.Y. 1934. With Bond & Mortgage Guarantee Co., N.Y.C., 1929-33; with Title Guarantee and Trust Co., 1933-37, asst. trust officer, 1935-37; with Lewis & Kelsey, 1937-41; ptnr. Parr, Doherty, Polk & Sargent, and predecessors, 1941-70, Whitman & Ransom, 1970—; bd. dir. First Investors Life Ins. Co. Trustee emeritus Wesleyan U. Mem. Bar Assn. City N.Y., Phi Beta Kappa, Chi Psi, Phi Delta Phi. Clubs: Univ., Morris County Golf. Office: 200 Park Ave New York NY 10166

PARR, GRANT VAN SICLEN, surgeon; b. N.Y.C., Dec. 30, 1942; s. Ferdinand Van Siclen and Helene H. P.; m. Helen Mushat Frye, July 1, 1967; children: Kathleen Gage, Helen Johnston. A.B. with honors, Wesleyan U., 1965; M.D., Cornell U., 1969. Diplomate: Am. Bd. Thoracic Surgery, Am. Bd. Surgery. Intern, resident U. Hosps. of Cleve., 1969-71; resident in surgery U. Ala. Hosps., Birmingham, 1971-74; chief resident in surgery U. Ala. Hosps., 1974-75, resident in cardiovascular and thoracic surgery, 1975-77; practice medicine specializing in thoracic surgery Hershey, Pa., 1978-82; mem. staff Presbyn.-U. Pa. Med. Ctr., Phila., 1982-88, chief div. Thoracic surgery, 1984-88, acting chmn. Dept. Surgery, 1988; chief cardiovascular surgery Presbyn.-U. Pa. Med. Ctr., 1984-88; asst. prof. cardiothoracic surgery M.S. Hershey Med. Center, Hershey, Pa., 1987-88; chief cardiovascular surgery Morristown (N.J.) Meml. Hosp., 1988—; asst. prof. Pa. State U., 1978-82; clin. assoc. prof. surgery U. Pa., 1982-89; assoc. prof. clin. surgery Columbia U., 1992—; chief cardiovascular surgery Overlook Hosp., 1988—; Atlantic Health Systems, 1988—. Contbr. articles on thoracic surgery to med. jours. Fellow Am. Coll. Cardiology, ACS, Am. Coll. Chest Physicians, Phila. Coll. Physicians; mem. Internat. Cardiovascular Soc., Assn. of Acad. Surgeons, Am. Assn. Thoracic Surgery, Phila. County Med. Soc., Soc. Thoracic Surgeons, Soc. Critical Care Medicine, Pa., Thoracic Surg. Soc., John W. Kirklin Soc., AMA, Pa. Med. Assn., Morris

PARMET, HERBERT SAMUEL, historian, educator; b. N.Y.C., Sept. 28, 1929; s. Isaac and Fanny (Scharf) P.; m. Joan Kronish, Sept. 12, 1948; 1 child, Wendy. BS, SUNY, Oswego, 1951; MA, Queens Coll., 1957; postgrad., Columbia U., 1958-62. Prof. history Grad. Sch. CUNY, 1968—, disting. prof. history, 1983—; cons. ABC-TV, N.Y.C., 1983, KERA-TV, Dallas, 1986-91, WGBH-TV, Boston, 1988-91. Author: Aaron Burr: Portrait of an Ambitious Man, 1967, Never Again: President Runs for a Third Term, 1968, Eisenhower and the American Crusades, 1972, The Democrats, 1976, Jack: The Struggles of John F. Kennedy, 1980, JFK: The Presidency of John F. Kennedy, 1983, Richard Nixon and His America, 1990; editorial bd. Presdl. Studies Quar. Cpl. U.S. Army, 1952-54. Grantee, NEH, 1987. Fellow Soc. Am. Historians, Simons Rock Coll. of Bard; mem. Am. Hist. Assn., Orgn. Am. Historians, Authors Guild. Avocation: photography. Home: 36 Marsten Ln Hillsdale NY 12529-5816 Office: Queensborough CC Dept History 56th Ave at Springfield Blvd Flushing NY 11364

PARMER, DAN GERALD, veterinarian; b. Wetumpka, Ala., July 3, 1926; s. James Lonnie and Virginia Gertrude (Guy) P.; 1 child by previous marriage, Linda Leigh; m. Donna Louise Kesler, June 7, 1980; 1 child, Dan Gerald. Student L.A. City Coll., 1945-46; DVM, Auburn U., 1950. Gen. practice vet. medicine, Galveston, Tex., 1950-54, Chgo., 1959-83; vet. in charge Chgo. Commn. Animal Care and Control, 1974-88; med. dir. food protection divsn. Chgo. Dept. Health, 1988-93; ret. 1993; chmn. Ill. Impaired Vets. Com.; tchr. Highlands U., 1959; humane officer Elmore County, 1994—; dir. sales for south, southeast and lower midwest Am. Vet. Identification Devices, Norco, Calif., 1993—. Pres. Elmore County Humane Soc. Served with USNR, 1943-45, PTO; served as staff vet. and 2d and 5th Air Force vet. chief USAF, 1954-59. Decorated 9 Battle Stars; recipient Vet. Appreciation award U. Ill., 1971, Commendation, Chgo. Commn. Animal Care and Control, 1987. Mem. VFW, AVMA (nat. com. for impaired vets., coun. pub. health and regulatory medicine 1990—), Ill. Vet. Medicine Assn. (chmn. civil def. and package disaster hosps. 1968-71, Pres.' award 1988), Chgo. Vet. Medicine Assn. (bd. govs. 1969-72, 74-81, pres. 1982), South Chgo. Vet. Medicine Assn. (pres. 1965-66), Am. Animal Hosp. Assn. (dir.), Ill. Acad. Vet. Practice (pres. 1993), Nat. Assn. of Professions, Am. Assn. Zoo Vets., Am. Assn. Zool. Parks and Aquariums, Elmore County Humane Soc. (pres. 1994-95), Midlothian Country Club, Valley Internat. Country Club, Masons, Shriners, Kiwanis. Democrat. Discoverer Bartonellosis in cattle in N.Am. and Western Hemisphere, 1951; co-developer bite-size high altitude in-flight feeding program USAF, 1954-56. Address: 6720 Post Oak Ln Montgomery AL 36117 Office: Am Vet Identification Devices 3179 Hamner Ave Norco CA 91760

PARMER, HUGH Q., state senator, marketing company executive; b. Aug. 3, 1939. BA, Yale U.; MA U. Tex., Arlington. Mem. Tex. Senate; chair intergovtl. relations com., Dem. caucus com.; mem. state affairs com., adminstrn. com., health and human resources com. Office: Tex Senate PO Box 12068 Austin TX 78711-2068

PARMER, JESS NORMAN, university official, educator; b. Elkhart, Ind., Nov. 23, 1925; s. Jess Noah and Zayda Irene (Tressler) P.; m. Bessie Norma Peterson, September 12, 1948; children: Thomas Norman, Sarah Irene. B.A., Ind. U., 1949; M.A., U. Conn., 1951; Ph.D., Cornell U., 1957. Resident in Malaya, Southeast Asia program, Cornell U., 1952-55; instr., then asst. prof. history U. Md., 1956-59; mem. faculty No. Ill. U., 1959-67, prof. history, 1960-67, chmn. dept., 1959-63; assoc. dean Coll. Arts and Scis. Ohio U., also dir. Center Internat. Studies, 1967-69, asst. dean faculties for internat. studies, 1969-75; v.p. acad. affairs Trinity U., San Antonio, 1975-82, prof. history, 1975-90; prof. South East Asia Studies Ohio U., Athens, 1990—; cons. business, govt., edn.; Peace Corps rep. in Malaya, 1961-63, Tanzania, summer 1965, Malawi, summer, 1966, Korea, 1967; lectr. Fgn. Service Inst., 1958, 61, 65; vis. prof. history Nat. U. Malaysia, 1984; cons. social scis. com. Ill. Curriculum Program, 1961; cons. various corps.; vis. fellow Cornell U., 1987-88, vis. prof. 1989; luce scholar in res. Ohio U., 1990-91. Author: Governments and Politics of Southeast Asia, 2d edit, 1964, Colonial Labor Policy and Adminstration, 1960, Southeast Asia: Documents of Political Development and Change, 1974, People and Progress: A Global History, 1977. Served with inf. AUS, 1944-46, ETO. Mem. AAUP, ACLU, Assn. Asian Studies (chmn. S.E. Asia regional council 1968-72, dir. 1969-72), Midwest Conf. Asian Affairs (chmn. library com. 1960-61), Southwest Conf. Asian Studies (pres. 1982-83), Am. Hist. Assn., Sons of the Am. Revolution, Torch Internat., Cornell Club N.Y. Office: Ohio U Ctr Internat Studies 56 East Union St Athens OH 45701-2987 I find my life full of opportunity, excitement and satisfaction. Satisfaction comes from seeing ideas find institutional or behavioral expression and influencing people in positive ways. Self-fulfillment, hard work, respect for others, and honesty have been guiding principles and I have found them compatible and rewarding.

PARMITER, JAMES DARLIN, safety engineer; b. McKeesport, Pa., Apr. 5, 1934; s. James Harry and Ruth Adeline (Ulm) P.; student Pa. State U., 1952-56; m. Nancy Jane Light, Aug. 24, 1954; children: James Victor, David Baird. With Gen. Motors Co., Wilmington, Del., 1962-65; with Boeing Helicopter Co., Ridley Park, Pa., 1965-84, mgr. safety and indsl. hygiene, 1967-84; occupational safety and health mgr. Phila. Naval Shipyyard, 1984-94, dir. occupational safety, health, and environ., 1994—; mem. faculty Pa. State U., Cheyney State Coll., West Chester U., Del. County Community Coll.; also cons. Mem. Gov.'s Adv. Com. on Occupational Safety and Health for Pa., 1967-84, Adv. Com. on Occupational Safety and Health Pa. State U., 1967-83; mem. Springfield Sch. Bd., 1969-75, Delaware County Sch. Bd., 1969-75. With USN, 1953-63, comdr. res. (ret.). Recipient Ben Franklin award Greater Phila. Safety Coun., 1981; Phila. Vision award Phila. Optometric Soc., 1972. Mem. Nat. Safety Coun. (aerospace sect. gen. chmn. 1974-76), Am. Soc. Safety Engrs. (pres. Phila. 1980-82, Safety Profl. of Yr. for region XII, 1982), Phila. Safety Coun. (chmn. bd. 1974-75), Am. Helicopter Soc., Am. Indsl. Hygiene Assn., Assn. Fed. Safety and Health Profls., Nat. Assn. Supts. Shore Establishments, Fed. Mgrs. Assn., Am. Philatelic Assn., Pa. State U. Alumni Assn., Masons, Shriners. Republican. Methodist. Home: 242 Brock Rd Springfield PA 19064-3116 also: 5525 Bay Ave Ocean City NJ 08226-1241 Office: Phila Naval Shipyard Code 106 Philadelphia PA 19112-5087

PARMLEY, LOREN FRANCIS, JR., medical educator; b. El Paso, Tex., Sept. 19, 1921; s. Loren Francis and Hope (Bartholomew) P.; m. Dorothy Louise Turner, Apr. 4, 1942; children—Robert Turner, Robert James, Kathryn Louise. B.A., U. Va., 1941, M.D., 1943. Diplomate Am. Bd. Internal Medicine, Am. Bd. Internal Medicine-Cardiovascular Disease. Commd. 1st lt. U.S. Army, 1944; advanced through grades to col., 1968; intern Med. Coll. Va., 1944; resident in internal medicine Brooke Gen. Hosp., San Antonio, 1948-49, U. Wis. Gen. Hosp., Madison, 1949-51; asst. prof. mil. med. sci. Med. Coll. U. Wis., Madison, 1949-51; acute attache (med.) U.S. Embassy, New Delhi, 1953-55; fellow in cardiovascular disease Walter Reed Gen. Hosp., Washington, 1956-57; chief medicine and cardi-

ology Letterman Gen. Hosp., San Francisco, 1958-63; med. and cardiology cons. U.S. Army Europe, Heidelberg, Germany, 1963-64; chief medicine Walter Reed Gen. Hosp., Washington, 1965-68; prof. medicine, asst. dean Med. U. S.C., Spartanburg, 1968-75; dir. med. edn. Spartanburg Gen. Hosp., Spartanburg, 1968-75; prof. medicine U. South Ala., Mobile, 1975-87, chief div. cardiology, 1980-87, prof. emeritus medicine, 1988—; lectr. medicine U. Calif.-San Francisco, 1959-63; clin. assoc. prof. medicine Georgetown U., Washington, 1967-68; clin. prof. medicine Med. Coll. Ga., Augusta, 1969-75; cons. internal medicine Surgeon Gen. U.S. Army, Washington, 1966-68. Contbg. author: The Heart, 1966, 70, 74, 78 Cardiac Diagnosis and Treatment, 1976, 80, The Heart in Industry, 1960, 70. Recipient Gold award sci. exhibit Am. Soc. Clin. Pathologists and Coll. Am. Pathologists, 1959; Certificate of Achievement in cardio-vascular disease Surgeon Gen. U.S.A., Washington, 1962; Bronze Medallion Meritorious Service, Am. Heart Assn., S.C., Columbia, 1969, 73; decorated Legion of Merit. Fellow ACP, Am. Coll. Cardiology (bd. govs. U.S. Army 1967, S.C. 1969-73), Am. Coll. Chest Physicians; mem. Am. Heart Assn. (fellow coun. on clin. cardiology), Soc. Med. Cons. to Armed Forces, Kiwanis. Republican. Episcopalian. Avocations: golf, swimming. Home: 549 Fairway Dr Kerrville TX 78028-6440 also: 5862 Falls Church Rd Mobile AL 36608 Office: U South Ala Coll Medicine Dept Medicine Mastin Bldg 2451 Fillingim St Rm 414 Mobile AL 36617

County Golf Club, NYU Club, Beacon Hill Club. Office: Morristown Meml Hosp 100 Madison Ave Morristown NJ 07960-6095

PARR, HARRY EDWARD, JR., financial executive; b. Dayton, Ohio, Sept. 2, 1928; s. Harry Edward and Naomi Theresa (Oesbeck) P.; m. Suzanne Johnson, Oct. 3, 1953; children: Constance, Cynthia, Claudia, Brian, Patrick. BSBA, U. Dayton, 1951. With Chrysler Corp., Detroit, 1953-66; v.p., controller Diebold, Inc., Canton, Ohio, 1966-78, v.p., treas., 1978-82, sr. v.p. fin., treas., 1982-91, also bd. dirs., ret., 1991. Bd. dirs. Jr. Achievement Stark County, Canton United Way; trustee Walsh Coll., Canton, Canton Cultural Ctr. for Arts; trustee, mem. devel. bd. Stark County; bd. dirs. Aultman Hosp. Served to 1st lt. U.S. Army, 1951-53. Mem. Fin. Execs. Inst., Nat Assn. Accts., Planning Execs. Inst., Canton C. of C. (former trustee). Club: Brookside Country (Canton).

PARR, JAMES GORDON, writer; b. Peterborough, Eng., May 26, 1927; went to Can., 1953; s. Reuben Scotney and Edith Grace (Rollings) P.; children: Mark Anthony, Katharine Elizabeth, Daniel John; m. Carole Elizabeth Vaughan, Dec. 1975. BSc, U. Leeds, Eng., 1947; PhD, U. Liverpool, Eng., 1953; LLD (hon.), U. Windsor, 1984. Registered profl. engr., Ont. Lectr. U. Liverpool, 1948-53; research assoc., lectr. U. B.C., Vancouver, 1953-55; assoc. prof., then prof. U. Alta., Edmonton, 1955-64; dean applied sci. U. Windsor, Ont., Can., 1964-72; chmn. com. univ. affairs Govt. Ont., Toronto, 1972; dep. minister Ministry Colls. and Univs., Govt. Ont., 1973-79; chmn., chief exec. officer TVOnt., Toronto, 1979-85; dir. gen. Ont. Sci. Ctr., Don Mills, 1985-88; founding pres. Indsl. Research Inst., U. Windsor, 1967-83. Author: Man, Metals and Modern Magic, 1958, (with A. Hanson) An Introduction to Stainless Steel, 1965, (with A. Hanson) The Engineer's Guide to Steel, 1965, Any Other Business, 1977, Is There Anybody There? Collected Verse, 1979, Megafart, a novel, 1990, Essays, 1992. Recipient Centennial medal Can., 1967, Jubilee medal, 1977. Fellow Royal Soc. Can., Am. Soc. Materials Internat., Ryerson Polytech. Inst., Ont. Inst. for Studies in Edn., Arts and Letters Club (Toronto) (pres. 1982-84). Home: 10 Governor's Rd, Toronto, ON Canada M4W 2G1

PARR, LLOYD BYRON, state official; b. Arvada, Colo., Oct. 27, 1931; s. Earle Ruly and Leva Corinne (Livengood) P.; m. Franess Clyde Durham, Dec. 30, 1951; children: Russell Owen, Christopher Lee, Ryan Whitney. Diploma, Compton (Calif.) Jr. Coll., 1950; student, No. Mount State U., 1964-65, U. Ark., Little Rock, 1969-70. Lic. civil engring. technician. Enlisted USN, 1950, aviation machinist mate, 1950-54; surveyor Denver Water Bd., 1955-56; enlisted USAF, 1957, advanced through grades to master sgt., 1971; site developer USAF, Korea, Okinawa, Turkey, Vietnam, 1957-73; ret. USAF, 1973; airport engr. State of Mo., Jefferson City, 1974-80, adminstr. aviation, 1981—. Sunday sch. tchr. Ch. of Christ, Eldon, Mo., 1973—. Decorated Bronze Star. Mem. Nat. Assn. State Aviation Ofcls. (bd. dirs. 1991-92, fin. com. 1988-93, treas. 1993-94, 2d v.p. 1994—), Am. Assn. State Hwy. and Transp. Ofcls. (aviation com. 1986—). Office: Mo Hwy & Transp Dept Capital and Jefferson Sts PO Box 270 Jefferson City MO 65102-0270 *Few of we mortals have the opportunity to contribute something truly unique to our world. Most of us can either add a few bricks to the wall of life or, if we choose to, we can tear down what others have built. I can only hope that the few bricks I add during my life will lend strength and color to the wall.*

PARR, ROBERT GHORMLEY, chemistry educator; b. Chgo., Sept. 22, 1921; s. Leland Wilbur and Grace (Ghormley) P.; m. Jane Bolstad, May 28, 1944; children: Steven Robert, Jeanne Karen, Carol Jane. AB magna cum laude with high honors in Chemistry, Brown U., 1942; PhD in Phys. Chemistry, U. Minn., 1947; D (hon.), U. Leuven, 1986. Asst. prof. chemistry U. Minn., 1947-48; mem. faculty Carnegie Inst. Tech., 1948-62, prof. chemistry, 1957-62; prof. chemistry Johns Hopkins U., 1962-74, chmn. dept., 1969-72; William R. Kenan, Jr. prof. theoretical chemistry U. N.C., Chapel Hill, 1974-90, Wassily Hoeffding prof. chem. physics, 1990—; vis. prof. chemistry, mem. Center Advanced Study U. Ill., 1962; distinguished vis. prof. State U. N.Y. at Buffalo, also Pa. State U., 1967; vis. prof. Japan Soc. Promotion Sci., 1968, 79, U. Haifa, 1977, Free U. Berlin, 1977; Firth prof. U. Sheffield, 1976; Coochbehar prof. Indian Assn. Cultivation of Sci., 1990; Sandoval Vallarta prof. UAM-Iztapalapa, 1992; chmn. com. postdoctoral fellowships in chemistry Nat. Acad. Sci.-NRC, 1961-63; chmn. panel theoretical chemistry Westheimer com. survey chemistry Nat. Acad. Sci., 1964; mem. coun. Gordon Rsch. Conf., 1974-76; mem. Commn. on Human Resources, NRC, 1979-82; mem. coun. Inst. for Molecular Sci., Okazaki, Japan, 1986-88; bd. trustees Inst. for Fundamental Chemistry, Kyoto, Japan, 1988—. Author: Quantum Theory of Molecular Electronic Structure, 1963, Density-Functional Theory of Atoms and Molecules, 1989, also numerous articles.; Assoc. editor: Jour. Chem. Physics, 1956-58, Chem. Revs, 1961-63, Jour. Phys. Chemistry, 1963-67, 77-79, Am. Chem. Soc. Monographs, 1966-71, Theoretica Chimica Acta, 1966-69, 92—; bd. editors: Jour. Am. Chem. Soc, 1969-77; adv. editorial bd.: Internat. Jour. Quantum Chemistry, 1967—, Chem. Physics Letters, 1967-79. Recipient Outstanding Achievement award U. Minn., 1968, N.C. Disting. Chemist award, 1982; fellow U. Chgo., 1949; research asso., 1957; Fulbright scholar U. Cambridge, Eng., 1953-54; Guggenheim fellow, 1953; NSF sr. postdoctoral fellow U. Oxford (Eng.) and Commonwealth Sci. and Indsl. Research Orgn., Melbourne, Australia, 1967-68; Sloan fellow, 1956-60. Fellow AAAS, Am. Phys. Soc. (chmn. divsn. chem. physics 1963-64); mem. NAS, AAUP, Am. Chem. Soc. (chmn. divsn. phys. chemistry 1978, Irving Langmuir award in chem. physics 1994), Am. Acad. Arts and Sci., Indian Nat. Sci. Acad., Internat. Acad. Quantum Molecular Sci. (v.p. 1973-79, pres. 1991—), Phi Beta Kappa, Sigma Xi, Phi Lambda Upsilon, Pi Mu Epsilon. Home: 701 Kenmore Rd Chapel Hill NC 27514-2019 Office: U NC Dept Chemistry Chapel Hill NC 27599-3290

PARR, ROYSE MILTON, lawyer; b. Elk City, Okla., Sept. 11, 1935; s. Clinton Riley and Ruth Caroline (Royse) P.; m. Sheila Ann Harshaw, May 28, 1960; children: Clint Howard, Reagan Royse. B.S., Okla. State U., 1958; J.D., U. Tulsa, 1964. Bar: Okla. 1964. Research scout Jersey Prodn. Research Co., Tulsa, 1960-64; atty. Sun Oil Co., 1964-70, White Shield Corp., 1970-71; sec., atty., asst. gen. counsel MAPCO, Inc., Tulsa, 1971—; gen. counsel, dir. Seminole Pipeline Co., 1989—; lectr. Southwestern Legal Found., 1977. Vice chmn. Tulsa County Election Bd., 1973—; pres. Ret. Sr. Vol. Program, 1982-83. Served to 1st lt. U.S. Army, 1958-60; capt. Res. 1960-63. Mem. Am. Bar Assn., ASME, Soc. Petroleum Engrs., Okla. Bar Assn., Tulsa County Bar Assn., Am. Soc. Corp. Secs. (pres. Okla. chpt. 1983-84), Phi Delta Phi. Republican. Methodist. Clubs: Oaks Country, Kiwanis (Tulsa). Office: Mapco Inc 1800 S Baltimore Ave Tulsa OK 74119-5284

PARRAMORE, BARBARA MITCHELL, education educator; b. Guilford County, N.C., Aug. 29, 1932; d. Samuel Spencer and Nellie Gray (Glosson) Mitchell; m. Lyman Griffis Worthington, Dec. 23, 1956 (div. 1961); m. Thomas Custis Parramore, Jan. 22, 1966; children: Lisa Gray, Lynn Stuart. AB, U.N.C., Greensboro, 1954; MEd, N.C. State U., 1959; EdD, Duke U., 1968. Counselor, thcr. Raleigh City Schs., 1954-59, sch. prin., 1959-65; prof. dept. of curriculum and instrn. N.C. State U., 1970—; acad. specialist Office Internat. Edn., U.S. Info. Svcs., sec. sch. initiative program, The Philippines, 1987. Author: The People of North Carolina, 1972, 3rd edit. 1983. Japan Inst. Social and Econ. Affairs fellow, 1980; N.C. AAUW award for juvenile lit., 1973, Holladay medal for excellence N.C. State U., 1994. Mem. ASCD, N.C. ASCD (pres. 1994—), N.C. Coun. for Social Studies (pres. 1985-87), Assn. Tchr. Educators, Delta Kappa Gamma, Kappa Delta Pi. Home: 5012 Tanglewood Dr Raleigh NC 27612-3135

PARRETT, SHERMAN O., lawyer; b. Cin., Jan. 8, 1943; s. Earl and Ruby (Angel) P.; m. Rosalind K. Brooks, Sept. 21, 1985; children: Laura, Samantha. BSEE, U. Cin., 1965; JD with honors, George Washington U., 1969. Bar: Calif. 1970, D.C. 1971, Ariz. 1992. Assoc. Flehr, Hohbach et al., San Francisco, 1970-73; ptnr. Cushman, Darby & Cushman, Washington, 1973-86, Irell & Manella, L.A., 1986-91, Streich Lang, Phoenix, 1991-94, Snell & Wilmer, Phoenix, 1994—. Office: Snell & Wilmer One Arizona Ctr Phoenix AZ 85004-0001

PARRIGIN, ELIZABETH ELLINGTON, lawyer; b. Colon, Panama, May 23, 1932; d. Jesse Cox and Elizabeth (Roark) Ellington; m. Perry G. Parrigin, Oct. 8, 1975. BA, Agnes Scott Coll., 1954; JD, U. Va. 1959. Bar:

Tex. 1959, Mo. 1980. Atty. San Antonio, 1960-69; law libr. U. Mo., Columbia, 1969-77, rsch. assoc., 1977-82; atty. pvt. practice, Columbia, 1982—. Elder, clk. of session First Presbyn. Ch., Columbia; mem. permanent jud. commn. Presbyn. Ch. U.S., 1977-83, mem. advisory com. on constitution, 1983-90. Mem. ABA, Mo. Bar Assn. (chmn. sub-com. revision of Mo. trust law 1988-92). Democrat. Presbyterian. Avocations: music, gardening, reading. Home: 400 Conley Ave Columbia MO 65201-4219 Office: 224 N 8th St Columbia MO 65201-4844

PARRIOTT, JAMES DEFORIS, retired oil company executive, consultant; b. Moundsville, W.Va., Aug. 21, 1923; s. James D. and Bessie (Sadler) P.; m. Marynette Sonneland, Aug. 3, 1946; children—James Deforis III, Sara Graham. Student, Ohio Wesleyan U., 1941-43; LL.B., U. Colo., 1949. Bar: Colo. bar 1949, practice in Denver 1949-53. Asst. city atty. Denver, 1950-51; asst. atty. gen. Colo., 1952-53; chief counsel Bur. Land Mgmt., Dept. Interior, 1953, assoc. solicitor lands and minerals, 1954-56; atty. Ohio Oil Co., Washington, 1956-60, Findlay, Ohio, 1960-62; mgr. employee relations Marathon Oil Co., 1962-69, dir. pub. affairs, 1969-74, dir. pub. and govt. affairs, 1974-85; sr. cons. Hill and Knowton, Inc., Los Angeles. Council pres. Boy Scouts Am. Served as pilot, 2d lt. USAAF, 1943-46. Mem. ABA, Fed. Bar Assn., Pacific Corinthian Yacht Club (commodore), Phi Alpha Delta, Phi Gamma Delta. Episcopalian. Home: 2825 Harbor Blvd Oxnard CA 93035-3952

PARRIS, NINA GUMPERT, curator, writer, researcher, photographer; b. Berlin, Ger., Sept. 11, 1927; came to U.S., 1937, naturalized, 1944; d. Martin and Charlotte (Blaschko) Gumpert; m. Arthur Parris, Feb. 13, 1949 (div. 1974); children: Carl Joseph, Thomas Martin. BA, Bryn Mawr Coll., 1968; MA, U. Pa., 1969, PhD, 1979. Teaching fellow U. Mich., Ann Arbor, 1969-70; lectr. Phila. Coll. Art, 1970-71; research assist. Phila. Mus. Art, 1970-71; curator, lectr. U. Vt. Robert Hall Fleming Mus., Burlington, 1971-79; chief curator Columbia Mus., S.C., 1979-89, Bass Mus. of Art, Miami Beach, Fla., 1989—; resident faculty visual arts Vt. Coll. Norwich Univ., 1991—. Author: Prints, Paintings and Drawings in Collection of Robert Hall Fleming Mus., 1979, (collection catalogue) S.C. Collection Columbia Mus., 1985, (exhibition catalogue) Through a Master Printer, 1985, The South Carolina Collection of the Columbia Museum, 1987; columnist, State newspaper, Columbia, 1984—; exhibited in one person show at Living Learning Ctr., U. Vt., 1994, Meteor Gallery, Columbia, S.C., 1994, St. Michael's Coll. McArthur Arts Ctr. Bd. dirs. Photography Cooperative, Montpelier, Vt., 1977-79, Chittenden Arts Coun., Burlington, Vt., 1976-78. Woodrow Wilson fellow, 1968, Univ. fellow Ford Found., 1968-72; grantee NEA, NEH, S.C. Com. Humanities, Vt. Coun. Arts. Mem. Am. Assn. Museums (pres. curator's com. 1985-87, v.p. 1983-85). Office: Columbia Mus 318 20th St # 111 Miami FL 33139-1908

PARRIS, ROBERT, composer; b. Phila., May 21, 1924; s. Louis and Rae (Oettinger) P. B.S. in Music Edn, U. Pa., 1945, M.S., 1946; B.S., Juilliard Sch. Music, 1948; student, Ecole Normale de Musique, Paris, Frnace, 1952-53. Mem. faculty Wash. State Coll., 1948-49, Juilliard Summer Sch., 1948; pvt. tchr., 1949-63; prof. music George Washington U., 1963—; mem. Broadcast Music, Inc. Composer: Concerto for Five Kettledrums and Orchestra, 1961, Fantasy and Fugue for Solo Cello; Lamentations and Praises, 1966, Sonata for Solo Violin, 1967, The Messengers for Orchestra, 1974; rec. artist: (albums) Concerto for Trombone and Orchestra, Book of Imaginary Beings; (symphonic variations) commd. by Nat. Endowment for Arts, Rostropovich and Nat. Symphony Orch., 1987; solo recitals on harpsichord and piano, also in chamber music. Home: 3307 Cummings Ln Bethesda MD 20815-3239 Office: George Washington U Acad Ctr 21st And I St NW Washington DC 20052

PARRIS, STANFORD E., congressman; b. Champaign, Ill., Sept. 9, 1929; s. Verne E. and Edna (Kendall) P. BS, U. Ill., 1950; JD, George Washington U., 1958. Bar: Va. 1958, D.C. 1976. Pres. Woodbridge (Va.) Lincoln Mercury Corp., 1965-79; mem. Va. Ho. of Dels., 1969-72, 93d Congress from 8th Va. Dist., 1973-75, 97th-101st Congresses from Va. 8th dist., 1981-90; mem. fin. com., cts. of justice com., inter-state cooperation com., counties, cities and towns com., mem. banking, fin. and urban affairs com., mem. D.C. com., chmn. Joint Senate-Ho. of Reps. Caucus; sec. of state Commonwealth of Va., 1978; chmn. Rep. Task Force Econ. Policy. Mem. Fairfax County (Va.) Bd. Suprs., 1964-67; bd. dirs. Fairfax County YMCA; trustee George Mason U., Fairfax. Served with USAF, 1950-54, Korea. Decorated D.F.C., Air medal, Purple Heart; recipient Watchdog of the Treasury award, 1973-74, 1981-90. Mem. ABA, Va. Bar Assn., D.C. Bar Assn., Fairfax County C. of C., Am. Legion, Delta Theta Phi. Episcopalian. Clubs: Alexandria (Va.); Rotary. Office: Dept Transp St Lawrence Seaway Devel Corp 400 7th St SW Washington DC 20590

PARRISH, ALMA ELLIS, elementary school educator; b. Peoria, Ill., Mar. 28, 1929; d. William Edward and Marie (Allton) Ellis; m. Clyde R. Parrish, Jr., Nov. 20, 1949; children: Clyde R. III, Charles, Donald, Royce, Christopher. BS, Bradley U., Peoria. Cert. elem. tchr., S.C., Ill. Tchr. Community Consol. Sch. Dist. 59, Elk Grove Village, Ill., Sipp Sch. Dist., Peoria, Kershaw County Sch. Dist., Camden, S.C. Mem. KCRA, S.C. Edn. Assn., Tchrs. Coun. Dist. 59 (pres., com.), Kershaw County Edn. Assn. (sec., PACE com.), Ill. Ret. Tchr.'s Assn., S.I. Coun.

PARRISH, ALVIN EDWARD, former university dean, medical educator; b. Washington, Sept. 6, 1922; s. John Edward and Thyrza Carrie (Morse) P.; m. Mary Wharton Votaw, June 2, 1945; children—Karen Marie, Anne Elizabeth. M.D., George Washington U., 1945. Intern D.C. Gen. Hosp., Washington, 1945-46; instr. physiology George Washington U., 1947-48; resident medicine Gallinger Municipal Hosp. and VA Hosp., Washington, 1948-50; chief resident medicine Gallinger Municipal Hosp., 1950-51; asst. chief med. service VA Hosp., Washington, 1951-57; chief metabolic lab. VA Hosp., 1955-57; assoc. dean Sch. Medicine, George Washington U., 1957-66, prof. medicine, 1964-91, prof. medicine emeritus, 1991—; chief renal lab. George Washington div. D.C. Gen. Hosp., 1957-66, clin. coordinator, 1960-66; dir. div. renal diseases George Washington Univ. Medical Center, 1967-79; dir. office of human rsch. George Washington U. Hosp., 1979-89. Author books, articles. Served to capt., M.C. AUS, 1946-47; lt. col. Res. Mem. A.C.P., AMA, Am. Diabetes Assn., N.Y. Acad. Sci., AAAS, So. Soc. Clin. Investigation, Am. Soc. Nephrology, Am. Fedn. Clin. Research, Flying Physicians Assn., Pi Kappa Alpha. Home: 5908 Calla Dr Mc Lean VA 22101-3307 Office: George Washington Univ Hosp Washington DC 20037

PARRISH, BARRY JAY, marketing executive; b. Chgo., Sept. 3, 1946; s. Hy J. and Shirley F. (Fimoff) Perelgut; 1 child, Jeffrey Scott. BA, Columbia Coll., 1968; MBA, U. Chgo., 1971. Asst. advt. mgr. Libby McNeill & Libby, Chgo., 1965-67; advt. and promotion mgr. McGraw-Hill Pubs. Co., Chgo., 1967-69; creative dir., account exec. Holt Communication div. Bozell & Jacobs, Chgo., 1969-72; account supr. Linder Advt. div. Dailey & Assocs., San Francisco, 1972-75; v.p., account supr. internat. Arthur E. Wilk Advt., Chgo., 1975-76; exec. v.p. Shaffer/MacGill & Assocs., Chgo., 1976-81; v.p. dir. Grey II, Grey Advt., Chgo., 1981-88; exec. v.p. Gardner, Stein & Frank, Inc., Chgo., 1988-89; v.p. mktg. Reno-Sparks Conv. and Visitors Authority, 1989-90; sr. v.p. sales and mktg. N.W. Lodging, Inc., Seattle, 1991; v.p. sales & mktg. Howard Johnson/Hospitality Franchise Systems, Inc., Parsippany, N.J., 1991—. Contbr. articles to profl. jours., newspapers, mags. TV commls. judge CLIO awards, 1978, 79, U.S. Film Festival, 1980-81, 84; chmn. Reno/Tahoe Rsch. Coun., Reno/Tahoe Tourism Task Force. Served with USMC, to 1972. Recipient awards Houston Internat. Film Festival, Nat. Employment Assn., Coun. Sales Promotion Agys., Internat. Specialty Advt. Assn., others. Home: 16 Fells Manor Rd Caldwell NJ 07006-6126 Office: Howard Johnson Franchise Systems 339 Jefferson Rd Parsippany NJ 07054-3707

PARRISH, CARMELITA, secondary school educator; b. Varina, N.C., Mar. 19, 1934; d. James Robert and Nita Mae (Webb) Beal; m. John J. Parrish, Aug. July 24, 1953 (dec.); children: Deborah Joy Parrish White, Toni Lynne Parrish Altenburg. AA, Mid. Ga. Coll., 1979; BS in Edn., Ga. State U., 1981; MEd, Valdosta State U., 1988, U. Ga., 1993. Secondary tchr. English, graphic arts, Spanish Ware County Bd. Edn., Waycross, Ga., 1981-91; tchr. Spanish, English Telfair County Bd. Edn., McRae, Ga., 1991-92, Pickens County H.S., Jasper, Ga., 1992—; co-advisor Spanish Club; advisor yearbook; tchr. Spanish, journalism. Former leader Girl Scouts USA, Spain;

Sunday sch. tchr.; band chaperone tour leader student travel in Europe, 1985—. Recipient Star Tchr. award, 1987. Mem. ASCD, NEA, Nat. Coun. Tchrs. English, Ga. Assn. Educators (legislator contact team), So. Assn. Colls. and Schs. (evaluation com.), Phi Kappa Phi. Home: 119 Navaho Trl Jasper GA 30143-1207 Office: 670 W Church St Jasper GA 30143-1410

PARRISH, DAVID WALKER, JR., legal publishing company executive; b. Bristol, Tenn., Feb. 8, 1923. BA, Emory & Henry Coll., 1948, LLD, 1978; BS, U.S. Merchant Marine Acad., 1950; LLB, U. Va., 1951. Pres. The Michie Co., Charlottesville, Va., 1969-89, vice chmn., 1989—. Home: Colthurst Farm 114 Falcon Dr Charlottesville VA 22901-2013 Office: The Michie Co 701 E Water St PO Box 7587 Charlottesville VA 22906

PARRISH, EDGAR LEE, financial services executive; b. Washington, Apr. 11, 1948; s. Frank Jennings Parrish and Lorene (Lomax) Parrish; m. Katherine Ellen MacLachlan, Sept. 12, 1987; children: Robert Alexander Wilson, Stephen Edgar MacLachlan. BS in Commerce, U. Va., 1970. Sr. v.p. Wheat, First Securities, Inc., Washington, 1971-79; v.p. Merrill Lynch, Pierce, Fenner & Smith, Inc., Washington, 1979-82, Phila., 1982-85; sr. v.p., fin. cons. Shearson Lehman Bros., Inc., Phila., 1985-87; sr. v.p. fin. cons., mem. chmn.'s coun. Shearson Lehman Bros., Inc., Washington, 1987-93, mem. dirs. coun., 1986; sr. v.p. investments PaineWebber, Inc., Washington, 1993—; pres. HESCO Corp., Manassas, Va., 1989—, also bd. dirs. Capt. USAFR, 1970-76. Mem. U. Va. Club (Washington), U. Va. Alumni Assn. Democrat. Episcopalian. Home: 4502 Wetherill Rd Bethesda MD 20816-1813 Office: PaineWebber Inc Franklin Sq 1300 I St NW Washington DC 20005-3314

PARRISH, FRANK JENNINGS, food company executive; b. Manassas, Va., Dec. 29, 1922; s. Edgar Goodloe and Alverda (Jennings) P.; m. Lorene Lomax, Feb. 11, 1944 (div. Apr. 1984); children: Edgar Lee, Julia Lorene; m. Mary Jane Biser, Aug. 25, 1984. Student, Va. Poly. Inst.; 1942-43; grad., Indsl. Coll. Armed Forces, 1972. Pres. Manassas Frozen Foods, Inc., 1946—; pres., mgr. Certified Food Buyers Service, Inc., 1953—; pres. First Nat. Acceptance Co., 1966—; v.p. Manassas Ice & Fuel Co. Mem. bus. adminstrn. adv. com. No. Va. Community Coll.; chmn. bd. North Va. coun. Am. Heart Assn., 1987-88; mem. inaugural com., 1961, vice-chmn. inaugural parade com. Maj. USAAF, 1943-46, CBI; ret. brig. gen. comdr. 909th TAC Airlift Group 1969-73, USAF; moblzn. asst. DCS plans and ops. Hdqrs., 1973-79. Decorated Legion of Merit, Air medal. Mem. Nat. Inst. Locker and Freezer Provisioners Am. (past pres., Industry Leadership award 1968), Va. Frozen Foods Assn. (past pres., dir.), Hump Pilots Assn., Va. Meat Processors (pres. 1986-90), Kiwanis. Methodist (chmn. bd. trustees 1958-66). Home: 9107 Park Ave Manassas VA 22110-4350 Office: 9414 Main St Manassas VA 22110-5424 *Do unto others as you would have them do unto you.*

PARRISH, JAY See PIFER, ALAN

PARRISH, JOHN ALBERT, dermatologist, research administrator; b. Louisville, Ky., Oct. 19, 1939; Children: Lynn, Susan, Mark. BA, Duke U., 1961; MD, Yale U., 1965. Diplomate Am. Bd. Dermatology. Medicine intern U. Mich., Ann Arbor, 1965-67; dermatology resident Harvard Med. Sch., Boston, 1969-72; dermatologist Mass. Gen. Hosp., Boston, 1972-87, dir. Wellman labs., 1975—, dir. cutaneous biology rsch. lab. Harvard, 1987—; chief dermatology Harvard Med. Sch., Boston, 1987—; dermatology cons. Beth Israel Hosp., Boston, 1973—. Author: A Doctor's Year in Vietnam, 1972, Dermatology and Skin Care, 1975, Effects of Ultraviolet Radiation on the Immune System, 1983; co-author: Science of Photomedicine, 1982, Photoimmunology, 1983. Lt. Commdr. USN, 1968-89. Decorated Vietnamese Cross Gallantry with gold; recipient Outstanding Gen. Med. Officer award USN, 1969; Dohi lectr. Japanese Soc. Dermatology, 1990. Mem. Am. Soc. Dermatology (photobiology task force 1972—, Marion B. Sulzberger award 1988), Am. Soc. Lasers in Surgery and Medicine (pres. 1987-88), Am. Soc. Photobiology (coun. 1978-82), Soc. Investigative Dermatology (Wm. Montagna award 1982). Achievements include developing novel and safe effective treatment of psoriasis. Office: Mass Gen Hosp Derm Wel 2 32 Fruit St Boston MA 02114-2620

PARRISH, JOHN BRETT, manufacturing executive; b. Clinton, Ill., Sept. 9, 1934; s. John Craig and Mary Lucille (Brett) P.; m. Lori Ann Burge, Mar. 15, 1990; children from previous marriage: Michael, Douglas, Lynn, Scott. AB in Econs., U. Ill., 1960. With GE Co., 1960-81; vice pres. fin. GE do Brazil S.A., Sao Paulo, 1976-79, v.p. and gen. mgr. consumer products, 1979-81; v.p. fin. services Burlington No. Inc., Seattle, 1981-82, v.p. and treas., 1982, sr. v.p. and chief fin. officer, 1982-83; chmn. and chief exec. officer Glacier Park Co. affiliate Burlington No., Inc., Seattle, 1983-85; exec. v.p. CEM Assocs., Inc., Bellevue, Wash., 1985-86; pres. Parrish, Inc., Seattle, 1986—. Woodrow Wilson fellow, 1960. Mem. Phi Beta Kappa. Home: 4507 102nd Ln NE Kirkland WA 98033-7645

PARRISH, OVERTON BURGIN, JR., pharmaceutical corporation executive; b. Cin., May 26, 1933; s. Overton Burgin and Geneva Opal (Shinn) P. B.S., Lawrence U., 1955; M.B.A., U. Chgo., 1959. With Pfizer Inc., 1959-74; salesman Pfizer Inc., Chgo., 1959-62; asst. mktg. product mgr. Pfizer Inc., N.Y.C., 1962-63; product mgr. Pfizer Inc., 1964-66, group product mgr., 1966-67, mktg. mgr., 1967-68, v.p mktg., 1969-70; v.p., dir. ops. Pfizer Internat., 1970-71, exec. v.p. domestic pharm. div. 1971-72; exec. v.p., dir. Pfizer Internat. Divsn., 1972-74; pres., chief operating officer G.D. Searle Internat., Skokie, Ill., 1974-75, pres., chief exec. officer, 1975-77; pres. Worldwide Pharm./Consumer Products Group, 1977-86; pres., chief exec. officer Phoenix Health Care, Chgo., 1987—; chmn. Wis. Pharmacal Co., Inc., 1990—; CEO, bd. dirs. Wis. Pharmiacal Co., Inc., Chgo., 1994—; co-chmn. Inhalon Pharms., 1991-95, also bd. dirs.; chmn. CEO ViatiCare Ltd., 1993—, also bd. dirs. Author: The Future Pharmaceutical Marketing; International Drug Pricing, 1971. Trustee Mktg. Sci. Inst.; trustee Food and Drug Law Inst., 1979—, Lawrence U., 1983—. Served to 1st lt. USAF, 1955-57. Mem. Am. Mktg. Assn., Am. Mgmt. Assn., Beta Gamma Sigma, Phi Kappa Tau. Office: 505 N Lake Shore Dr Chicago IL 60611-3427 Office: Phoenix Health Care 919 N Michigan Ave Chicago IL 60611-1601

PARRISH, RICHARD B., manufacturing executive; b. Kalispell, Mont., June 4, 1938; s. Richard Wiley and Helen (Bancroft) P.; m. Susan Spring, Aug. 27, 1960; children: Julie Parrish Whalen, Mike. Grad., U. Wash., 1961; grad. exec. program, Stanford U., 1977. With Boise Cascade Corp., 1961—; acct. Boise Cascade Corp., Seattle, Portland, 1961-65; Timberlands mgr. Boise Cascade Corp., Salem, Oreg., 1965-67; asst. region mgr. Boise Cascade Corp., Medford, Oreg., 1967-70, region mgr., 1970-77; mgr. West Coast area Boise Cascade Corp., Portland, Oreg., 1977-80; v.p. ops. Boise Cascade Corp., Boise, Idaho, 1980-86; v.p., gen. mgr. Boise Cascade Corp., Boise, 1986-89, sr. v.p., gen. mgr., 1989—. Mem. Western Wood Products Assn. (chmn. 1986-88), Am. Lumber Standards (vice chmn 1986—), Nat. Forest Products Assn. (bd. govs. 1987—, Mem. of Yr. 1991), Am. Plywood Assn. (trustee 1986—). Republican. Episcopalian. Office: Boise Cascade Corp 1 Jefferson Sq Boise ID 83728-0001

PARRISH, ROBERT ALTON, retired pediatric surgeon, educator; b. Augusta, Ga., Sept. 10, 1930; s. Robert Alton and Thelma Elizabeth (Roney) P.; children: Joyce Ann, Cynthia Ann. A.B., Mercer U., 1951; M.S., U. Ga., 1953; M.D., Med. Coll. Ga., 1956. Diplomate: Am. Bd. Surgery. Intern Bapt. Meml. Hosp., Memphis, 1956-57; resident in surgery U. Tenn., Memphis, 1957-62; gen. surgeon Med. Coll. Ga., Aususta, 1962-64; asst. prof. surgery Med. Coll. Ga., Augusta, 1964-67, assoc. prof., 1967-70, prof. pediatric surgery, chief pediatric surgery, 1970-93, prof. emeritus pediatric surgery, 1993—; cons. to hosps. Named Outstanding Tchr. of Yr. Med. Found. Ga., Med. Coll. Ga., 1966. Fellow ACS; mem. Am Assn. Surgery of Trauma, So. Surg. Assn., Am. Acad. Pediatrics, Alpha Omega Alpha, Phi Sigma, Alpha Epsilon Delta. Methodist. Home: 433 Scott Way Augusta GA 30909-9591

PARRISH, THOMAS KIRKPATRICK, III, marketing consultant; b. Richmond, Va., May 18, 1930; s. Thomas Kirkpatrick and Sally Cary (Friend) P.; divorced; children: Linn Cary, Wayne Elizabeth, Susan Scott, Thomas Kirkpatrick IV. A.B., Princeton U., 1952. Product mgr. Vick Chem. Co., N.Y.C., 1955-58; v.p. Benton & Bowles Advt. Agy., N.Y.C.,

1958-65; pres. Am. Chicle Co. div. Warner-Lambert Co., Morris Plains, N.J., 1965-70, Life Savers Inc. div. Squibb Corp., N.Y.C., 1970-73, Lanvin-Charles of Ritz Inc. subs. Squibb Corp., N.Y.C., 1974-76; dir. parent co. Squibb Corp., 1974-77; group dir. new bus. devel. Gillette Co., Boston, 1977-78; exec. v.p. SSC & B, Inc., N.Y.C., 1978-81; sr. assoc. Am. Comm. Corp., 1982-86; prin. The Parrish Co., N.Y.C., 1986—. Mem. N.Y. State Republican Com., 1962-63; bd. dirs. YMCA Ctr. for Internat. Mgmt. Studies, N.Y.C., 1970-85. Served to lt., jr. grade USN, 1952-55. Home: 215 E 73d St New York NY 10021

PARRISH, WILLIAM EARL, history educator; b. Garden City, Kans., Apr. 7, 1931; s. Earl Milton and Anna Maye (Stoker) P.; m. Ellen Kaye Vickers, June 14, 1959 (div. 1971); m. Helen Sue Lewis Stoppel, June 2, 1972; children: Michael William Lewis. BS with honors, Kans. State U., 1952; MA, U. Mo., 1953, PhD, 1955. Asst. prof. to Harry S. Truman prof. in Am. history Westminster Coll., Fulton, Mo., 1955-78, dean of coll., 1973-75; prof. history Miss. State U., Mississippi State, 1978—, head dept. history, 1978-85. Author: David Rice Atchison of Missouri, 1961, Turbulent Partnership, Missouri and the Union, 1963, Missouri Under Radical Rule, 1865-1870, 1965, A History of Missouri, Vol. III, 1860-1875, 1973, (with Charles T. Jones, Jr. and Lawrence Christensen) Missouri: The Heart of the Nation, 1992; gen. editor Sesquicentennial History of Missouri, 5 vols., 1971—. Mem. Mo. Adv. Coun. on Hist. Preservation, 1967-78; chmn. Mo. Am. Revolution Bicentennial Com., 1974-77; nat. adv. bd. Soc. of Civil War Historians, 1986—; mem. State Hist. Records Adv. Bd., 1980—. Recipient proclamation for quarter century of svc. Gov. of Mo., 1978, award of merit Am. Assn. State and Local History, 1974. Mem. Orgn. Am. Historians, Western History Assn., So. Hist. Assn., Nat. Trust Hist. Preservation, Miss. Hist. Soc. (pres. 1995-96), State Hist. Soc. Mo. (life), Rotary, Phi Alpha Theta (internat. pres. 1985-87), Phi Gamma Delta (historian 1989—). Presbyterian. Avocation: deltiology. Office: Miss State U Dept History Drawer H Mississippi State MS 39762 Home: 703 Bonnie Rd Starkville MS 39759-2104

PARROTT, ROBERT HAROLD, pediatrician, educator; b. Jackson Heights, N.Y., Dec. 29, 1923; s. Harold Leslie and Ruth Mabel (Hargrove) P.; m. Paula McDonough, June 2, 1951; children: Timothy, Maureen, Daniel, Theresa, Christopher, Edward. Student, Fordham U.; M.D., Georgetown U., 1949. Intern Hosp. of St. Raphael, New Haven, Conn., 1949-50; resident Children's Hosp. of D.C., 1950-52; staff pediatrician, chief Pediatric Unit, Lab. of Clin. Investigation, Nat. Inst. Allergy and Infectious Diseases, NIH, Bethesda, Md., 1952-56; physician-in-chief, dir. Research Found., Children's Hosp. of D.C., Washington, 1956-62, dir., 1962-85, dir. emeritus, 1985—; prof. pediatrics George Washington U., Washington. Mem. AMA, Am. Acad. Pediatrics, Am. Pediatric Soc., Am. Acad. Med. Dirs., Am. Coll. Physician Execs., D.C. Med. Soc., Infectious Diseases Soc. Club: Cosmos (Washington). Home: 13064 Deanmar Dr Highland MD 20777-9519 Office: Children's Nat Med Ctr 111 Michigan Ave NW Washington DC 20010-2970

PARRY, ATWELL J., JR., state senator, retailer; b. Ogden, Utah, June 14, 1925; s. John Atwell and Nina Virginia (McEntire) P.; m. Elaine Hughes, Feb. 6, 1946; children—Bonnie, Michael, Jay, Donald, David, Delbert, Kent. Student pub. schs., Nampa, Idaho. Salesman, Kay's Packing Co., Nampa, 1947-54, credit mgr., 1954-55; plant mgr. Stone Poultry Co., Nampa, 1955-56; salesman Nestle Chocolate Co., 1956-64; owner, mgr. Melba Foods, Idaho, 1964-82; mem. Idaho Senate, 1981—; bd. dirs. Western Idaho Tng. Ctr., 1987-90; chmn. Senate Finance Com. and co-chmn. Joint Fin. and Appropriations Com., 1987—; chmn. Idaho State Bd. for Nat. Ctr. for Constl. Studies, 1988-90. Bd dirs. Alcohol Treatment Ctr., Nampa, 1978-82; mem. adv. bd. Mercy Med. Ctr., Nampa, 1976-81; mem. Melba City Council, 1971-74. Recipient Silver Beaver award Boy Scouts Am., 1959, Service award Mercy Med. Ctr., Outstanding Rep. Legislator in Idaho State award, 1993. Republican. Mormon.

PARRY, DALE D., newspaper editor. BS in Journalism cum laude, Ball State U., Muncie, Ind., 1981. Feature writer, editor and columnist Richmond (Ind.) Palladium-Item, 1981-84; feature writer Cin. Enquirer, 1984-86, asst. features editor, 1986-87; editor Today section The Dallas Morning News, 1987-90; assignment editor The Way We Live sect. Detroit Free Press, 1990-92, dep. features editor, 1992-94, features editor, 1993—. Mem. Am. Assn. Sun. and Feature Editors. Office: Detroit Free Press 321 W Lafayette Detroit MI 48231

PARRY, HUGH JONES (JAMES CROSS), social scientist, educator, author; b. London, Mar. 10, 1916; came to U.S., 1919, naturalized, 1924; s. John and Jane Myfanwy (Jones) P.; m. Helen Mason Weston, May 30, 1941 (div. 1960); 1 son, John; m. Betty Brawer, Mar. 10, 1961; 1 son, Brian. A.B., Yale, 1937, postgrad., 1938; M.S., Columbia, 1939; PhD., U. So. Calif., 1949. Asso. dir. Opinion Research Center, U. Denver, 1947-49; also prof. sociology; asst. dir. Troop Attitude Research br., U.S. Forces in Europe, 1950-52; project dir. evaluation staff U.S. High Commn. for Germany, 1952-53; research officer Am. embassy, Paris, 1956-58; chief Western European br., survey research div. USIA, 1958-61; survey dir. Office Research and Analysis, 1961-62, chief of survey research and analysis, 1961-62, chief of survey research div., 1962-63; dir. research Office Research and Analysis, Western Europe, 1963-66; asso. dir. Social Research Group; prof. sociology George Washington U., Washington, 1966-82; research cons., editor, writer, 1983—. Author: (with Leo P. Crespi) Public Opinion in Western Europe, 1953, Root of Evil, 1957, The Dark Road, 1959, The Grave of Heroes, 1961, To Hell for Half a Crown, 1967. Served to lt. USNR, 1942-46. Creative writing grantee Nat. Endowment for Lit., 1975; fellow Va. Ctr. for the Creative Arts, 1990, 92, 93; winner PEN short story contest, 1987. Mem. Am. Assn. Pub. Opinion Rsch., Am. Hist. Assn., Am. Sociol. Soc., Cosmos Club (Washington), Phi Beta Kappa, Phi Delta Theta. Home: 4814 Falstone Ave Bethesda MD 20815-5542

PARRY, LANCE AARON, newspaper executive; b. Allentown, Pa., Sept. 4, 1947; s. Harwood Clayton Bachman and Iola Mary (Johnson) P.; m. Virginia Eleanor Ford, Apr. 24, 1971; children: Halloran Lee, Christine Ford. BS in Edn., Kutztown U., 1969; postgrad., W.Va. U., 1970. With Call-Chronicle Newspapers, Allentown, 1970-81, mng. editor, 1979-81; asst. news editor The Phila. Inquirer, 1982-84; systems editor, 1982-84, night news editor, 1984-86, news editor daily edit., 1986-87, news editor Sunday edit., 1987-89, sr. editor/systems and tech., 1989-93, page design dir., 1993-94, features news editor, 1994—. Recipient 1st Place award for front page design Pa. Newspaper Pubs. Assn./Pa. Soc. Newspaper Editors, 1985, 87, 88, Disting. Alumnus award Kutztown U., 1992; Sigma Delta Chi scholar, 1969. Mem. Soc. Profl. Journalists, Pen and Pencil Club. Democrat. Presbyterian. Home: 16 Salisbury Ln Malvern PA 19355-2836 Office: The Phila Inquirer 400 N Broad St Philadelphia PA 19130-4099

PARRY, ROBERT TROUTT, bank executive, economist; b. Harrisburg, Pa., May 16, 1939; s. Anthony C. and Margaret M. (Troutt) P.; m. Brenda Louise Grumbine, Dec. 27, 1956; children: Robert Richard, Lisa Louise. BA magna cum laude, Gettysburg (Pa.) Coll., 1960; MA in Econs., U. Pa., 1961, PhD, 1967. Asst. prof. econs. Phila. Coll. Textiles and Sci., 1963-65; economist Fed. Res. Bd., Washington, 1965-70; v.p., chief economist Security Pacific Nat. Bank, Los Angeles, 1970-76, sr. v.p., chief economist, 1976-81, exec. v.p., chief economist, 1981-86; pres., chief exec. officer Fed. Res. Bank San Francisco, 1986—; bd. dirs. Nat. Bur. Econ. Rsch.; mem. adv. bd. Pacific Rim Bankers Program; mem. policy adv. bd. Ctr. for Real Estate and Urban Econs., U. Calif., Berkeley, mem. exec. com. Inst. Bus. and Econs. Rsch.; bd. dirs. San Francisco Bay Area Coun.; mem. Bay Area Econ. Forum; lectr. Pacific Coast Banking Sch., 1976-78; mem. adv. coun. SRI Internat. Mem. econ. vis. com. U. Pa.; mem. exec. bd. Boy Scouts Am., 1993—; bd. dirs. United Way, 1995. NDEA fellow, 1960-63. Mem. Nat. Assn. Bus. Economists (pres. 1979-80), Am. Econ. Assn. Home: 90 Overhill Rd Orinda CA 94563-3131 Office: Fed Res Bank San Francisco PO Box 7702 San Francisco CA 94120-7702

PARRY, ROBERT WALTER, chemistry educator; b. Ogden, Utah, Oct. 1, 1917; s. Walter and Jeanette (Petterson) P.; m. Marjorie J. Nelson, July 6, 1945; children: Robert Bryce, Mark Nelson. BS, Utah State Agr. Coll., 1940; MS, Cornell U., 1942; PhD, U. Ill., 1946; DSc (hon.), Utah State U., 1985. Research asst. NDRC Munitions Devel. Lab., U. Ill. at Urbana, 1943-45, teaching fellow 1945-46; mem. faculty U. Mich., 1946-69, prof. chemistry

1958-69; Distinguished prof. chemistry U. Utah, 1969—; indsl. cons., 1952—; chmn. bd. trustees Gordon Rsch. Conf., 1967-68. Chmn. com. teaching chemistry Internat. Union Pure and Applied Chemistry 1968-74. Recipient Mfg. Chemists award for coll. teaching, 1972, Sr. U.S. Scientist award Alexander Von Humboldt-Stiftung (W. Ger.), 1980, First Utah award medal of Sci. State Utah, 1987. Mem. Am. Chem. Soc. (Utah award Utah Sect. 1978, past chmn. inorganic div. and div. chem. edn., award for distinguished service to inorganic chemistry 1965, for chem. edn., 1977, dir. 1973-83, bd. editors jour. 1969-80, pres.-elect 1981-82, pres. 1982-83, Priestly medal 1993), Internat. Union Pure and Applied Chemistry (chmn. U.S. nat. com.), AAAS, Sigma Xi. Founding editor Inorganic Chemistry, 1960-63. Research, publs. on some structural problems of inorganic chemistry, and incorporation results into theoretical models; chemistry of phosphorus, boron and fluorine. Home: 5002 Fairbrook Ln Salt Lake City UT 84117 Office: U Utah Dept Chemistry Henry Eyring Bldg Salt Lake City UT 84112-1194

PARSEGHIAN, GENE, talent agent; b. Oneonta, N.Y., Dec. 11, 1944; s. Richard and Leona (Spickerman) P.; life ptnr. Michael D. Colberg; 1 child, Rachel Colberg-Parseghian. BA, Antioch Coll., 1967; MFA, Stanford U., 1970. Owner Parseghian Assocs., Inc., N.Y.C., 1977-78; founding ptnr., owner Kimble/Parseghian, Inc., N.Y.C., 1978-81, DHKPR, N.Y.C., 1981-84, Triad Artists, Inc., N.Y.C., 1984-92; sr. v.p. William Morris Agy., Inc., N.Y.C., 1992—; bd. dirs. Artsgenesis, N.Y.C. Active mem. Creative Coalition, N.Y.C., 1991—. Democrat. Office: William Morris Agy Inc 1325 Ave of the Americas New York NY 10019-4701

PARSEGIAN, V. ADRIAN, biophysicist; b. Boston, May 28, 1939; s. Voscan Lawrence and Varsenig (Boyajian) P.; m. Valerie Phillips, Mar. 2, 1963; children: Andrew, Homer, Adam. AB, Dartmouth Coll., Hanover, N.H., 1960; PhD, Harvard U., 1965. Rsch. physicist Phys. Scis. Lab., DCRT, NIH, Bethesda, Md., 1967—. Editor Biophys. Jour., 1977-80, Biophys. Discussions, 1978—; contbr. over 100 articles to profl. jours.; editorial bd. 10 jours. NIH Dirs. award, 1974. Mem. Biophys. Soc.

PARSHALL, GEORGE WILLIAM, research chemist; b. Hackensack, Minn., Sept. 19, 1929; s. George Clarence and Frances (Virnig) P.; m. Naomi B. Simpson, Oct. 9, 1954; children: William, Jonathan, David. B.S., U. Minn., 1951; Ph.D., U. Ill., 1954. Research chemist E.I. duPont de Nemours & Co., Wilmington, Del., 1954-65; research supr. E.I. duPont de Nemours & Co., 1965-79, dir. chem. sci., 1979-92, cons., 1992—; mem. chem. stockpile disposal com. NRC, Washington, 1992—; bd. chem. sci. NRC, Washington, 1983-86; Reilly lectr. Notre Dame U., 1980; Ipatieff lectr. Northwestern U., 1994. Author: Homogeneous Catalysis, 1980, 2d rev. edit. 1992; editor: Inorganic Syntheses, 1974, Jour. Molecular Catalysis, 1977-80. Recipient Bailar medal in inorganic chemistry U. Ill., 1976, Chem. Pioneer award Am. Inst. Chemists, 1992. Mem. Am. Chem. Soc. (award in inorganic chemistry 1983, award for leadership in chem. research mgmt. 1989), Nat. Acad. Sci., Am. Acad. Arts Scis., Catalysis Soc. (Phila Catalyst Club award 1978). Episcopalian. Home: 2504 Delaware Ave Wilmington DE 19806-1220

PARSHALL, GERALD, journalist; b. St. Paul, Apr. 24, 1941; s. William Elmer and Evelyn (Steckling) P.; m. Sandra Grant, Dec. 20, 1970. B.A., U. Minn., 1963; M.A., U. Mich., 1964; grad. fellow, U. Chgo., 1966-67. Reporter York (Pa.) Gazette and Daily, 1968, Balt. Evening Sun, 1968-71; Capitol Hill staff U.S. News & World Report, Washington, 1971-77; sr. editor U.S. News & World Report, 1977-79, asst. mng. editor, 1979-90, sr. writer, 1990—; mem. Exec. Com. of Periodical Corrs., U.S. Congress, 1974-80, chmn., 1979-80. Served to 1st lt. U.S. Army, 1964-66. Recipient Front Page award Washington-Balt. Newspaper Guild, 1971, Silver Gavel award ABA, 1983. Home: 1004 Congress Ln McLean VA 22101-2116 Office: 2400 N St NW Washington DC 20037-1153

PARSKY, GERALD LAWRENCE, lawyer; b. West Hartford, Conn., Oct. 18, 1942; s. Isadore and Nettie (Sanders) P.; m. Susan Haas, June 26, 1966; children: Laura, David; m. Robin Cleary, Jan. 27, 1980. A.B., Princeton U., 1964; J.D., U. Va., 1968. Bar: N.Y. 1969, D.C. 1974, Calif. 1983. Assoc. Mudge Rose Guthrie & Alexander, N.Y.C., 1968-71; spl. asst. to under sec. U.S. Treasury Dept., Washington, 1971-73; exec. asst. to dep. sec. Fed. Energy Office U.S. Treasury Dept., 1973-74, asst. sec. internat. affairs, 1974-77; sr. ptnr. Gibson, Dunn & Crutcher, Los Angeles, 1977-90; of counsel Gibson, Dunn & Cruther, L.A., 1990-92; chmn. Aurora Capital Ptnrs., L.A., 1990—. Bd. govs. Performing Arts Council, Los Angeles Music Ctr. Recipient Alexander Hamilton award U.S. Treasury, 1976. Mem. ABA, Coun. Fgn. Rels., N.Y. Princeton Club, Calif. Club, Racquet Club, Anandale Club, Beach Club. Office: Aurora Capital Ptnrs 1800 Century Park E Los Angeles CA 90067

PARSLEY, ROBERT HORACE, lawyer; b. Erwin, Tenn., Apr. 9, 1923; s. Millard Fillmore and Daisy Laurel (Garland) P.; m. Georganna Alice Strake, Apr. 11, 1952; children—Robert, Sharon, Brian, Sandra, Sally, David, John, Daniel, Jana. J.D.S., U. Va., 1949. Assoc. Baker & Botts, Houston, 1949-53; assoc. Butler & Binion, Houston, 1953-55, ptnr., 1955-94, of counsel, 1994—; bd. dirs. Stewart and Stevenson Svcs. Inc., Houston; trustee Southwestern Legal Found., Dallas, 1980, Southwestern Law Enforcement Inst., Dallas, 1980. Mem. Tex. State Commn. for Mental Health and Mental Retardation, Austin, 1972-78; vice chmn. Tex. State Commn. on Jud. Conduct, Austin, 1983-89; pres. bd. trustees St. Elizabeth Hosp. Found., Houston, 1984-90; bd. dirs. Strake Jesuit Coll. Prep., Houston, 1973—, San Jose Clinic, 1990—, South Tex. Sch. Law, 1994—; pres. St. Joseph's Hosp. Found., 1993-95, trustee, 1988—. Served to 1st lt. USAAF, 1942-46, Panama. Recipient Order of Benemerenti (Vatican). Fellow Tex. Bar Found.; mem. ABA, Tex. Bar Assn., Houston Bar Assn. Republican. Presbyterian. Clubs: Houston, Houston Country. Home: 12 E Broad Oaks Dr Houston TX 77056-1202 Office: Butler & Binion 1600 1st Interstate Bank Plz Houston TX 77002

PARSONAGE, ROBERT RUE, college president; b. Mpls., Aug. 20, 1937; s. Charles William and Blanche Marion (Rue) P.; m. Ruth Lull, Dec. 27, 1969; children: Noah Hale, Ethan Lull. BA, Carleton Coll., 1959; BD, Pacific Sch. Religion, Berkeley, Calif., 1963; ThM, Harvard U., 1970; PhD, Hartford Sem., 1975. Ordained min. United Ch. Christ, 1963. Chaplain, asst. prof. religion Springfield (Mass.) Coll., 1963-73; exec. edn. Nat. coun. Chs., N.Y.C., 1973-87; pres., prof. religion and philosophy Northland Coll., Ashland, Wis., 1987—; mem. exec. com. coun. higher edn. United Ch. of Christ, N.Y.C., 1990—; Wis. Found. Ind. Colls., Madison, 1991—; bd. dirs. Meml. Med. Ctr. Author: Public Service Function of American Higher Education, 1975; author, editor: Church Related Higher Education, 1978; editor: Invitation to Dialogue: Theology of Campus Ministry, 1986. Mem. Ashland Econ. Devel. Com., 1987—. Mem. Rotary. Office: Northland Coll 1411 Ellis Ave Ashland WI 54806-3925

PARSONS, A. PETER, lawyer; b. Norwood, Mass., May 29, 1945; s. Charles A.A. and Elizabeth P. (Coombs) P.; children—A. Peter, Christopher P.; m. Elizabeth A. Lee, Aug. 24, 1991; 1 child Alex W. A.A., Palm Beach Jr. Coll., 1968; B.S., Fla. Atlantic U., 1969; J.D., Duke U., 1973. Bar: Wash. 1973, U.S. Dist. Ct. (ea. and we. dists.) Wash. 1974, U.S. Ct. Appeals (9th cir.) 1974; C.P.A., Fla., Wash. Acct., Haskins & Sells, Ft. Lauderdale, 1969-70; tax cons. Arthur, Young & Co., Portland, Oreg., 1972; law clk. Wash. Supreme Ct., 1973-74; atty. Perkins, Coie, Seattle, 1974-77; mem., mng. dir. Weinrich, Gilmore & Adolph, Seattle, 1978-87; ptnr. Davis, Wright & Tremaine 1988—; adj. prof. U. Puget Sound, 1974-75; lectr. U. Wash., 1978-81. Mem. editorial bd. Duke U. Law Jour., 1971-73. Contbr. articles to legal jours. Chmn. bd. dirs. PIVOT, non-profit corp., Seattle, 1975-78; bd. dirs. council planning affiliates United Way, Seattle, 1979-82, Group Theater, Seattle, 1984-86; chmn. bd. dirs. MIT Enterprise Forum, Seattle, 1984—; founder, bd. dirs. Rainier Found., Seattle, 1983—, Wash. State Biotechnology Assn. 1991—. Served with USAF, 1963-67. Mem. ABA, Wash. Bar Assn., Am. Intellectual Property Law Assn., Computer Law Soc., Am. Inst. CPAs, Wash. Soc. CPAs, Seattle-King County Bar Assn., Am. Coll. of Mediators. Clubs: Rainier, Seattle Yacht. Home: 1223 Spring St Seattle WA 98104 Office: Davis Wright & Tremaine 2600 Century Sq 1501 Fourth Ave Seattle WA 98101

PARSONS, ANDREW JOHN, management consultant; b. Kingston, Surrey, Eng., July 22, 1943; came to U.S., 1968; s. S. John and Hylda P. (Wili) P.; m. Carol Ann Iannucci, June 6, 1970; children: Alexandra,

Katherine. BA, MA, Oxford U., 1965; MBA, Harvard U., 1970. Account exec. Leo Burnett, London, 1965-68; from strategic planning dir. to v.p. mktg. Prestige Group Ltd. div. Am. Home Products, N.Y.C. and London, 1970-76; v.p. mktg. Kurzweil Computer Products div. Xerox Corp., Cambridge, Mass., 1979-80; assoc. McKinsey & Co., Inc., N.Y.C., 1976-82, prin., 1982-88, dir. consumer industries sector, mktg. ctr., sr. ptnr., 1988—; underwriting mem. Lloyds of London, 1986—. Contbr. articles to profl. jours. Chmn. adv. bd. Salvation Army, Greater N.Y., 1983—; bd. dirs. United Way, N.Y.C., 1988—; trustee Sarah Lawrence Coll., Bronxville, N.Y., 1993—. Baker scholar Harvard Bus. Sch., 1970. Mem. Siwanoy Country Club. Home: 56 Hereford Rd Bronxville NY 10708-5408 Office: McKinsey & Co Inc 55 E 52d St New York NY 10022

PARSONS, CHARLES DACRE, philosophy educator; b. Cambridge, Mass., Apr. 13, 1933; s. Talcott and Helen B. (Walker) P.; m. Marjorie Louise Wood, Sept. 6, 1968; children: Jotham Wood, Sylvia Anne. A.B., Harvard U., 1954, A.M., 1956, Ph.D., 1961; postgrad., U. Cambridge, Eng., 1954-55. Jr. fellow Soc. Fellows, Harvard U., 1958-61, asst. prof. philosophy, 1962-65; asst. prof. philosophy Cornell U., 1961-62; assoc. prof. philosophy Columbia U., N.Y.C., 1965-69; prof. Columbia U., 1969-89, chmn. dept., 1976-79, 85-89; prof. Harvard U., Cambridge, Mass., 1989—, Edgar Pierce prof. philosophy, 1991—; George Santayana fellow in philosophy Harvard U., 1964-65; vis. fellow All Souls Coll., Oxford, Eng., 1979-80. Author: Mathematics in Philosophy, 1983; editor (with others): Kurt Goedel, Collected Works, vol. III, 1995; editor Jour. Philosophy, 1966-90, cons. editor, 1990—; contbr. articles to profl. jours. NEH fellow, 1979-80, Guggenheim fellow, 1986-87, Netherlands Inst. Advanced Study fellow, 1987, Ctr. for Advanced Study in the Behavioral Scis. fellow, 1994-95. Fellow Am. Acad. Arts and Scis.; mem. Assn. for Symbolic Logic (sec. 1971-76, v.p. 1986-89, pres. 1989-92), Am. Philos. Assn. Home: 16 Ellery Sq Cambridge MA 02138-4229 Office: Harvard U Emerson Hall Cambridge MA 02138

PARSONS, DAVID, artistic director, choreographer. Dancer Paul Taylor Dance Co., 1978-87; founder, artistic dir. Parsons Dance Co., 1987—. Choreographer The Envelope, 1984, Sleep Study, 1987, Elysian Fields, 1988, Reflections of Four, 1991, A Hairy Night on Bald Mountain, 1991, Bachiana, 1993, Destined, 1993, Ring Around the Rosie, 1993. Office: Parsons Dance Co c/o Sheldon Soffer Mgt Inc 130 W 56th St New York NY 10019-3818

PARSONS, DONALD D., bishop. Bishop of Alaska Evang. Luth. Ch. in Am., Anchorage. Office: Synod of Alaska 1847 W Northern Lights Blvd # 2 Anchorage AK 99517-3342

PARSONS, DONALD JAMES, retired bishop; b. Phila., Mar. 28, 1922; s. Earl and Helen (Drabble) P.; m. Mary Russell, Sept. 17, 1955; children—Mary, Rebecca, Bradford. B.A., Temple U., 1943; M.Div., Phila. Div. Sch., 1946, Th.D., 1951, D.D. (hon.), 1964; postgrad., U. Nottingham, Eng., 1968; D.C.L., Nashotah (Wis.) House, 1973. Ordained priest Episcopal Ch., 1946, consecrated bishop, 1973; curate Immanual Ch., Wilmington, Del., 1946-49; rector St. Peter's Ch., Smyrna, Del., 1949-50; prof. N.T., Nashotah House, 1950-73, pres., dean, 1963-73; bishop Diocese of Quincy, Ill., 1973-88. Author: A Life-time Road to God, 1966, In Time with Jesus, 1973, Holy Eucharist: Rite Two, 1976. Home: 308 W Edgevale Pl Peoria IL 61604-1607

PARSONS, EDMUND MORRIS, investment company executive; b. Houston, Oct. 19, 1936; s. Alfred Morris and Virgina (Hanna) P. AB, Harvard U., 1958; MBA, U. Pa., 1961; MS, MIT, 1970. Pres. Fredonia Enterprises, Inc., Houston, Tex., 1990—; fgn. service officer U.S. Dept. State, Washington, 1965-90; 1st sec. Am. Embassy, Mexico City, 1973-76; economist Fed. Res. Bank N.Y., N.Y.C., 1976-77; chief food aid div. U.S. Dept. State, Washington, 1977-80, dir. office devel., 1981-82, dir. office econ. policy, 1983-84; dep. chief mission U.S. Mission to FAO, Rome, 1985-86; dir. Office Ecology and Natural Resources U.S. Dept. State, Washington, 1986-88; dir. Office of Internat. Narcotics Control Programs, 1988-89; min.-counselor for econ. affairs Am. Embassy, Mexico City, 1989-90; pres. Fredonia Enterprises, Inc., Houston, 1990—; co-chmn. Tropical Forest Task Force, Washington, 1986-88; dep. U.S. rep. UN FAO, Rome 1985-86; alt. U.S. rep. to environ. program U.S. Del. Nairobi, Kenya, 1987. Capt. USAF, 1962-72. Mem. Am. Fgn. Svc. Assn., Houston Restaurant Assn. (bd. dirs. 1992—), Houston World Affairs Coun. (bd. dirs. 1995—), Consular Corps of Houston (hon.), Houston Hispanic C. of C., Coun. Fgn. Rels. (Houston com.), Univ. Club (Houston). Republican. Methodist. Avocation: geneology.

PARSONS, EDWIN SPENCER, clergyman, educator; b. Brockton, Mass., Feb. 16, 1919; s. Edwin Webber and Ethel Faunce (Marsh) P.; m. Eleanor Millard, Nov. 3, 1944; children: William Spencer, Ellen, James Millard, Bradford Delano. A.B., Denison U., 1941, D.D., 1967; B.D., Andover Newton Theol. Sch., 1945; D.D., Kalamazoo Coll., 1966; L.H.D., Chgo. Coll. Osteo. Medicine, 1978. Ordained to ministry Am. Baptist Ch., 1944; asst. minister First Bapt. Ch., Newton Centre, Mass., 1945-47; exec. dir. Bapt. Student Found., Inc., Cambridge, Mass., 1947-59; pastor Hyde Park Union Ch., Chgo., 1959-65; assoc. prof. ethics U. Chgo. Div. Sch., 1965-78, prof., 1978-81; dir. ministerial field edn., 1977-79, asst. to dean, 1981-88; dean Rockefeller Meml. Chapel, 1965-79; v.p. dir. New Eng. office Health Resources Ltd., Kansas City, Mo., 1979-89; cons. dept. ch. and soc. Am. Bapt. Chs. of Mass., 1979-86, also editor Mass. Bapt. News, 1983-85; chmn. strategy and action com., bd. dirs. Mass. Council Chs., 1983-85; adj. prof. Andover Newton Theol. Sch., 1981-85. Author: The Christian Yes or No, 1964; contbr.: Belief and Ethics, 1978. Pres. Council Hyde Park-Kenwood Chs. and Synagogues, 1963; chmn. Abortion Rights Assn. Ill., 1974-79; founder, chmn. Ill. Religious Coalition for Abortion Rights, 1975, Ill. Clergy Consultation Services on Problem Pregnancies, 1971-79; bd. dirs., chmn. clergy adv. com. Planned Parenthood Assn., Chgo., 1977-79; bd. dirs. Hyde Park YMCA, Facing History and Ourselves Nat. Found., 1983-87; bd. govs. Internat. House, Chgo., 1969-79; trustee Packard Manse (Mass.), Bapt. Theol. Union, 1960-70, 81—; pres., bd. mgrs. Ministers and Missionaries Benefit Bd., 1975-81; mem. policy council Religious Coalition for Abortion Rights of Mass., 1980-86; sec., treas. Bolton Inst. for Sustainable Future, 1983-87; mem. gen. bd., mem. exec. com., mem. commn. on Christian unity Am. Bapt. Chs., 1963-72, 74-81; bd. dirs. Planned Parenthood League of Mass., 1984-92; interim assoc. dir. Mass Coun. Chs., 1988-89. Democrat. Home: 69 Fort Point Rd Weymouth MA 02191-2146

PARSONS, ELMER EARL, retired clergyman; b. Cloverland, Wash., Oct. 4, 1919; s. Claud Solomon and Bessie Lillian (Campbell) P.; m. Marjorie Emma Carlson, Aug. 29, 1942; children—Karl Elmer, James Myron, Helen Joy, Ann Elizabeth, Lois Marie, Louise Melba. BA, Seattle Pacific U., 1942; S.T.B., N.Y. Theol. Sem., 1945; S.T.M., Asbury Theol. Sem., Wilmore, Ky., 1955; D.D. (hon.), Greenville (Ill.) Coll., 1958. Ordained to ministry Free Methodist Ch., 1944; acad. dean Wessington Springs (S.D.) Coll., 1945-47; missionary to China, 1947-49, missionary to Japan, 1949-54; supt. Japan Free Meth. Mission, 1950-54; pres. Central Coll., McPherson, Kans., 1955-64, Osaka (Japan) Christian Coll., 1964-74; Asia area sec., Free Meth. Ch., 1964-74; bishop Free Meth. Ch. N.Am., 1974-83. Author: Witness to the Resurrection, 1967. Chmn. Free Meth. Study Commn. on Doctrine. Named Alumnus of Year Seattle Pacific U., 1976. Mem. Wesleyan Theol. Soc.

PARSONS, ERVIN IVY, JR., petroleum company executive; b. Moran, Tex., June 26, 1928; s. Ervin Ivy and Eva Lena (Childers) P.; m. LaVerne Good, Nov. 3, 1951; children: Robert Sherrell, Eva Louise. BBA, U. Houston, 1957. With Continental Oil Co., 1963-64, asst. treas., 1970-72, treas., 1972-74, fin. exec. additional subsidiaries, 1963-70; sr. v.p.fin. Tex. Oil & Gas Corp., Dallas, 1974-76, also bd. dirs.; pres., Holly Corp., then vice chmn. bd. Served with USAF, 1951-53. Clubs: Dallas, 25 Yr., Petroleum of Dallas. Home: 6 Chameleon Ct Austin TX 78738-1323 Office: Holly Corp 100 Crescent Ct Dallas TX 75201-1832

PARSONS, ESTELLE, actress; b. Lynn, Mass., Nov. 20, 1927; d. Eben and Elinor (Mattson) P.; m. Richard Gehman, Dec. 19, 1953 (div. Aug. 1958); children: Martha and Abbie (twins); m. Peter L. Zimroth, Jan. 2, 1983; 1 child, Abraham. B.A. in Polit. Sci., Conn. Coll. Women, 1949; student, Boston U. Law Sch., 1949-50. Stage appearances include: Happy Hunting,

1957, Whoop Up, 1958, Beg, Borrow or Steal, 1960, Threepenny Opera, 1960, Mrs. Dally Has a Lover, 1962, Ready When You Are C.B, 1964, Malcolm, 1965, Seven Descents of Myrtle, 1968, And Miss Reardon Drinks a Little, 1971, Mert and Phil, 1974, The Norman Conquests, 1975-76, Ladies of the Alamo, 1977, Miss Margarida's Way, 1977-78, The Pirates of Penzance, 1981, The Shadow Box, 1994; adapted, dir., performer Orgasmo Adulto Escapes from the Zoo, 1983, The Unguided Missile, Baba Goya, 1989, Shimada, 1992; film appearances include: Bonnie and Clyde, 1966; Rachel, Rachel, 1967, I Never Sang for My Father, 1969, Dick Tracy, 1990, Boys On The Side, 1995; TV appearances include: Roseanne, 1990—; artistic dir. N.Y. Shakespeare Festival Players, 1986. Recipient Theatre World award, 1962-63, Obie award, 1964; recipient award Motion Picture Acad. Arts and Scis., 1967; Recipient Medal of Honor, Conn. Coll., 1969. Home: 505 West End Ave New York NY 10024-4320 *It's in attempting all, that one succeeds.*

PARSONS, GEORGE RAYMOND, JR., lawyer; b. N.Y.C., May 5, 1938; s. George Raymond and Gertrude (Blackburn) P.; m. Katharine P. Sook, Oct. 16, 1982; children—Timothy, Geoffrey, Amy, Julia, Elizabeth. BA with distinction, Wesleyan U., 1959; LLB with honors, Cornell U., 1962. Bar: N.Y. 1962, U.S. Dist. Ct. (we. and no. dists.) N.Y. 1962, Fla. 1974. Assoc. Nixon, Hargrave, Davans & Doyle, Rochester, N.Y., 1962-69, ptnr., 1970—; lectr. continuing legal edn. programs. Contbr. articles to Cornell Law Rev., 1961-62, New Republic; contbr. John Updike Newsletter; editor-in-chief: Cornell Law Rev., 1961-62. Officer, bd. dirs. Rochester Philharm. Orch., 1976-83, Rochester Children's Nursery, 1967-73; trustee Rochester Pub. Libr., 1978-81, 83—, pres. bd. trustees, 1986-87, 94—; pres. Friends Rochester Pub. Libr., 1972-75, Friends U. Rochester Librs., 1989-91; trustee Monroe County Libr. System, 1986-87, 94—, Rochester Regional Libr., 1987—, Halcyon Hill Found., 1992—, Rochester Regional Libr. Coun., 1988—, pres. 1994—; bd. dirs. Rundel Libr. Found., Inc. 1989—, Writers and Books, 1991—; del. N.Y. State Gov.'s Conf. on Librs. and Info. Svcs., 1990; trustee's vis. com. on librs. U. Rochester, 1991—. Mem. ABA, N.Y. Bar Assn., Monroe County Bar Assn., Am. Coll. of Trust and Estate Counsel, Estate Planning Council Rochester. Democrat. Office: Nixon Hargrave et al Clinton Sq PO Box 1051 Rochester NY 14603-1051

PARSONS, GEORGE WILLIAM, city planner, educator; b. West Monroe, La., Aug. 1, 1930; s. Henry Vardaman and Virgie Mae (Hosch) P.; m. Beth Nale, Aug. 2, 1991; children: Lauren, Layne, Lonn. BS, La. Tech. U.; MS, La. State U. Planning engr. USAF, Riverside, Calif., 1955-58; dir. Monroe-Ouachita Regional Planning Commn., Monroe, La., 1958-72; exec. dir. Shreveport (La.) Met. Planning Commn., 1972-76, City Planning & Devel. Programs, Monroe, 1976-79; dir. Dept. Planning & Policy Gov.'s Office State of Miss., Jackson, 1980-83; coord. Miss. Main Street program Small Town Ctr. Miss. State U., Mississippi State, 1983-86, assoc. prof., 1983—, dir. Ctr. for Small Town rsch. and design, 1986—, dir. Commn., Econ. Devel. Ctr., 1989—; interim exec. dir. Oktibbeha County Exec. Devel. Assn., Starkville, Miss., 1989-90. Pres. Riverside Swim & Tennis Club, 1975; bd. dirs. Chauvin Racquet Club, Monroe, 1978-79; disting. pres. Monroe Optimist Club. Recipient Disting. Svc. award Jaycees, Monroe, named Outstanding Man of the Yr., 1963. Mem. Am. Inst. Cert. Planners, Am. Soc. Landscape Architects, Am. Mgmt. Assn., Coun. State Planning Agys. (bd. dirs. 1981-83), Coun. State Community Action Agys. (exec. com. 1982-83), Miss. Gov.'s Policy Coun. Home: 227 Hiwassee Dr Starkville MS 39759-2117 Office: Community/Econ Devel Ctr Ctr for Small Town Rsch & Design 240 Giles Barr Ave Mississippi State MS 39762

PARSONS, GEORGE WILLIAMS, retired medical center administrator, cattle rancher; b. Natural Bridge, Va., Jan. 21, 1918; s. George Washington and Mary Elizabeth (Williams) P.; m. Miriam Rebecca Boyer, May 2, 1942; children: Mary Locke Parsons Black, Anne Boyer Parsons Talkington, George Russell. Student, Washington and Lee U., 1935-37; B.S. in Edn., U. Va., 1941; grad., USNR Tng. Sch., 1942, USNR Officer Candidate Sch., 1944, USNR Command Sch., 1944, Ind. Coll. Armed Forces, 1963, Fed. Health Care Inst., 1966. Tchr. Winchester, Va., 1941-42; asst. phys. dir. VA Hosp., Roanoke, Va., 1946-47; asst. chief spl. services VA Hosp., 1947-51; chief spl. services VA Hosp., Lyons, N.J., 1951-58; spl. asst. to hosp. mgr. VA Hosp., Pitts., 1958-62; asst. dir. VA Hosp., Clarksburg, W.Va., 1962-67, Erie, Pa., 1967-69, Marion, Ind., 1969-72, Bklyn., 1972-75; dir. VA Outpatient Clinic, Lubbock, Tex., 1975-76; dir. VA Med. Center, Bklyn., 1976-82, Alexandria, La., 1982-86; faculty, preceptor M.P.H./M.B.A. Program in Health Adminstrn., Columbia U.; faculty NYU; mem. dean's com. Tulane U. Sch. Medicine, New Orleans, 1982-86; chmn. Fed. Exec. Bd., N.Y.C., 1982; cluster leader Presdl. Mgmt. Intern Program, Nat. Inst. Public Affairs, 1980-82; mem. dist. bd. Health Systems Agy., Bklyn.; chmn. Combined Fed. Campaign for all VA Med. Facilities in N.Y.C., all fed. agys. in Rapides Parish (La.), 1984; mem. Rockbridge County (Va.) Farm Bur., Natural Bridge Ruritan Club; aide de camp Gov. David Treen, State of La., 1982, Gov. Edwin Edwards, State of La., 1985. Lt. comdr. USNR, 1942-46; PTO. Decorated 11 decorations and awards including two Presdl. Unit Commendations; recipient Outstanding Achievement award Am. Legion, 1975, Disting. Svc. award, 1975, Recognition award, 1978, Recognition award VFW, 1975, 83, United Vets. Assn. award Queens, N.Y., 1979; 9 citations and awards, 1980; 7 awards and citations, 1982; Outstanding Career award VA, 1986; also numerous other awards and commendations from VA, vets., civic orgns., 1946-86. Fellow Am. Coll. Healthcare Execs. (oral examiner), Royal Soc. Health; mem. Assn. Mil. Surgeons U.S. (pres. N.Y. chpt. 1979-80), Am. Hosp. Assn., La. Hosp. Assn. (pres. Central Dist. 1983-84), Sr. Exec. Service U.S. Govt., Fed. Hosp. Inst. Alumni Assn., N.Y. Acad. Scis. Res. Officers Assn. U.S.A. (pres. W.Va. chpt. 1967), Greater Alexandria/Pineville C. of C. (mil. affairs com. 1982-86), VFW (comdr Post 484 1949-50). Club: Rotary (pres. 1958, 71). Home: 1905 Canterbury Ln Villa E-20 Sun City Center FL 33573

PARSONS, HARRY GLENWOOD, retired surgeon; b. San Bernardino, Calif., Mar. 5, 1919; s. Harry Glenwood and Evelen May (Peris) P.; m. Rubyann Kattenhorn, Sept. 28, 1986. AB, Stanford (Calif.) U., 1942, MD, 1946. Diplomate Am. Bd. Surgery, Am. Bd. Thoracic Cardio-Vascular Surgery. Intern Stanford Hosp., San Francisco, 1941-42, Rockor fellow in surg. rsch., 1944-45, asst. resident in surgery, 1945-52, chief resident in surgery, 1952-53, Boyd fellow in thoracic cardiovasc. surgery, 1953-54; asst. clin. prof. surgery Stanford Med. Sch., 1955-65; med. dir. faculty head Weimar (Calif.) Med. Ctr., 1955-72; ret. Capt. M.C. U.S. Army, 1940-44. Fellow ACS; mem. AMA, Western Thoracic Surg. Soc., Placer Nevada County Med. Assn. (pres. 1979), Calif. Med. Assn. (del.), Alpha Omega Alpha. Avocation: flying.

PARSONS, HENRY MCILVAINE, psychologist; b. Lenox, Mass., Aug. 31, 1911; s. Herbert and Elsie Worthington (Clews) P.; m. Renee Colman, 1938 (div. 1945); 1 son, Robert; m. Marina Svetlova, 1949 (div. 1957); m. Marjorie Thorson, 1957. BA, Yale U., 1933; MA, Columbia U., 1947; PhD, U. Calif., Los Angeles, 1963. Reporter N.Y. Herald Tribune, 1935-42; organizer N.Y. Newspaper Guild, 1942; asst., then lectr. psychology Columbia U., 1947-52; research asso. N.Y. U., 1951-52; supr. Electronics Research Labs., Columbia U., 1952-58; mem. human factors staff Douglas Aircraft Co., Long Beach and Santa Monica, Calif., 1956-58; sr. human factors scientist, br. head System Devel. Corp., Santa Monica and Falls Church, Va., 1958-68; self-employed cons., 1968-69; 70-73; sr. research Riverside Research Inst., N.Y.C., 1969-70; exec. dir. Inst. Behavioral Research Inc., Silver Spring, Md., 1974-79; pres. Exptl. Coll. of Inst. Behavioral Research, Silver Spring, 1974-80; mgr. human factors projects Human Resources Research Orgn., Alexandria, Va., 1983-90; sr. staff scientist Essex Corp., Alexandria, Va., 1983-90; adj. prof. Lehigh U., 1983-84. Author: Man-Machine System Experiments, 1972; also chpts. in books, articles in jours. Served with USNR, 1942-45. Fellow AAAS, APA (pres. divsn. 21 1975-76, Franklin V. Taylor award 1992), Human Factors Soc. (pres. 1968-69, Pres.'s Disting. Svc. award 1993), Washington Acad. Scis., Am. Psychol. Soc.; mem. N.Y. Acad. Scis., Ergonomics Soc., Sigma Xi. Clubs: Century (N.Y.C.); Cosmos (Washington). Home: 1600 S Eads St Apt 1223 N Arlington VA 22202-2930 Office: Human Resources Rsch Orgn 66 Canal Center Plz Alexandria VA 22314-1591

PARSONS, IRENE, management consultant; b. North Wilkesboro, N.C.; d. Everett T. and Martha (Minton) P. B.S. in Bus. Edn. and Adminstrn, U.

N.C., 1941, LL.D. (hon.), 1967; M.S. in Pub. Adminstrn, George Washington U., 1965. Tchr. Roanoake Rapids (N.C.) High Sch., 1941-42; rep. U.S. Civil Service Commn., 1942-43; with VA, 1946-74, asst. adminstr. vets. affairs, dir. personnel, dir. equal employment opportunity, 1965-74; mgmt. cons., 1974—; Exec. com. Pres.'s Study Group Careers for Women. Served to lt. USCGR, 1943-46. Recipient Fed. Woman's Outstanding Achievement award, 1966, Silver Helmet award Amvets, 1971, Career Svc. award Nat. Civil Svc. League, 1972, Disting. Alumni Achievement award George Washington U., 1973; named to Brevard Coll. Hall of Fame, 1984. Mem. Assn. Fed. Woman's Award Recipients (chmn. 1972-76).

PARSONS, JAMES JEROME, geographer, educator; b. Cortland, N.Y., Nov. 15, 1915; s. James Jerome and Edith (Gere) P.; m. Betty Rupp, Oct. 30, 1942; children—David, John, Sally. A.B., U. Calif. at Berkeley, 1937, M.A., 1939, Ph.D., 1948. Mem. faculty U. Calif. at Berkeley, 1946—, prof. geography, 1959—, chmn. dept. geography, 1960-66, 75-80. Author: Antioqueño Colonization in Western Colombia, 1949, San Andrés and Providencia, 1955, The Green Turtle and Man, 1962, Antioquia's Corridor to the Sea, 1967, Hispanic Lands and Peoples: Selected Writings of James J. Parsons, 1988. Served to maj. USAAF, 1941-45. Recipient Pedro Justo Berrio medal Dept. Antioquia, Colombia, 1987; Guggenheim fellow in Spain, 1959-60. Mem. AAAS, Assn. Am. Geographers (pres. 1974-75), Am. Geog. Soc. (David Livingstone medal 1985), Assn. Pacific Coast Geographers (pres. 1952), Acad. Colombiana de Historia (hon.). Home: 670 Woodmont Ave Berkeley CA 94708-1234

PARSONS, JEFFREY ROBINSON, anthropologist, educator; b. Washington, Oct. 9, 1939; s. Merton Stanley and Elisabeth (Oldenburg) P.; m. Mary Thomson Hrones, Apr. 27, 1968; 1 child, Apphia Hrones. B.S., Pa. State U., 1961; Ph.D., U. Mich., 1966. Asst. prof. anthropology U. Mich., Ann Arbor, 1966-71; assoc. prof. U. Mich., 1971-76, prof., 1976—, dir. mus. anthropology, 1983-86; vis. prof. Universidad Nacional Autonoma de Mexico, 1987; vis. prof. Universidad Buenos Aires, 1994. Author: Prehistoric Settlement Patterns in the Texcoco Region, Mexico, 1971; (with William T. Sanders and Robert Santley) The Basin of Mexico: The Cultural Ecology of a Civilization, 1979; (with E. Brumfield et al) Prehispanic Settlement Patterns in the Southern Valley of Mexico, 1982; (with M. Parsons, et al) Chinampa Agriculture and Aztec Urbanization in the Valley of Mexico, 1985, (with Mary H. Parson) Maguey Utilization in Highland Central Mexico, 1990, The Production and Consumption of Salt During Postclassic Times in the Valley of Mexico, 1994. Research grantee NSF, 1967, 70, 72-73, 75-76, 81, Nat. Geog. Soc., 1984, 86, 88. Mem. Am. Anthrop. Assn., Soc. Am. Archaeology, AAAS, Inst. Andean Rsch., Inst. Andean Studies, Sociedad Mexicana de Antropologia, Sociedad Argentina de Antropologia. Office: Museum of Anthropology U Mich Ann Arbor MI 48109

PARSONS, JOHN RUSSELL, retail company executive; b. Birmingham, Mich., Jan. 12, 1931; s. John Russell and G. Lola (Dubey) R.; m. Carol Butcher; children: Joanne, Julia, Jeff, Janee. BS, Mich. State U. Nat. mgr. home fashion accessories Sears, Roebuck and Co., Chgo., 1969-72, nat. mgr. linens and domestics, 1972-76, nat. mgr. furniture, 1976-77, v.p. womens accessory group, 1977-81, v.p. home improvement group, 1981—. Episcopalian. Office: Sears Roebuck & Co Sears Tower Chicago IL 60684

PARSONS, JUDSON ASPINWALL, JR., lawyer; b. Rochester, N.Y., Dec. 15, 1929; s. Judson A. and Frances (Holsopple) P.; m. Chesley Kahmann, Aug. 8, 1959; children: Ames, Brockett. BA, Amherst Coll., 1951; LLB, Harvard U., 1954. Bar: N.Y. 1954, N.J. 1973. Asst. U.S. atty. So. Dist. N.Y., N.Y.C., 1954-55; assoc. Dewey, Ballantine, Bushby, Palmer & Wood, N.Y.C., 1958-65, ptnr., 1966-82; pres. Orbiting Clef Prodns., Inc., Summit, N.J., 1982-86; spl. counsel Laughlin, Markensohn, Lagani & Pegg, P.C., Morristown, N.J., 1986-90, Parsons & Pegg, Morristown, 1990-91; sole practice, 1991—. Served to 1st lt. U.S. Army, 1955-58. Office: 108 Woodland Ave Summit NJ 07901

PARSONS, KEITH I., lawyer; b. Davenport, Iowa, Apr. 28, 1912; s. Alfred and Cora Pearl (McDowell) P.; m. Lorraine Watson, June 28, 1939; children: Robert, Susan, James. Ph.B., U. Chgo., 1933, J.D., 1937. Bar: Ill. 1938. Asst. to sec. U. Chgo., 1934-37; since practiced in Chgo.; asst. chief, later chief legal div. Chgo. Ordnance Dist., 1942-46; ptnr. firm Milliken, Vollers & Parsons, 1946-64, Ross, Hardies, O'Keefe, Babcock & Parsons, 1965-83; of counsel firm Ross & Hardies, 1983—. Mem. Hinsdale (Ill.) Bd. Edn., 1957-63, pres., 1959-63; mem. bd. govs. Ill. State Colls. and Univs., 1970-73. Served to lt. col. AUS, 1942-46. Mem. ABA, Ill. Bar Assn., Chgo. Bar Assn. (past chmn. corp. law com., mem. bd. mgrs. 1967-69), Chgo. Law Club, Legal Club (past pres.), Phi Beta Kappa, Psi Upsilon, Hinsdale Golf Club, Chikaming Country Club. Home: 315 N La Grange Rd La Grange IL 60525-5600 Office: 150 N Michigan Ave Ste 2500 Chicago IL 60601-7525

PARSONS, KERMIT CARLYLE, urban planning educator, former university dean; b. Cleve., July 15, 1927; s. Kermit Carlyle and Emma (Siebert) P.; m. Janice Ingram Patten, June 30, 1951; children: John Everett, Stephen Carl, Katherine Ingram. B. Arch., Miami U., Oxford, Ohio, 1951; M.R.P., Cornell U. 1953. Registered architect, Ohio. Head community planning sect. Cleve. City Planning Commn., 1953-57; mem. faculty Cornell U., 1957—, chmn. dept. city and regional planning, 1964-71, prof., 1965—, dean Coll. Architecture, Art and Planning, 1971-80, dean emeritus, 1980—; dir. Cornell in Washington, 1985-88; grad. faculty real estate rep. Cornell U., 1988-93; vis. prof. U. P.R., 1969-70; assoc. cons. William Gould & Assos., 1970-72; cons. Ford Found., 1970-76, Philippine Ministry Edn. and Culture, 1979-80, IBRD (World Bank), 1980-84, AID, 1984-85; cons. coll and univ., devel. planning, also city planning cons. Author: The Cornell Campus: A History of its Planning and Development, 1968, (with others) Public Land Acquisition for New Communities and the Control of Urban Growth, 1973, (with Pierre Clavel) National Growth Policy-An Institutional Prespective, 1976; also articles, book chpts. Served with USNR, 1945-46. Recipient Seipp prize Miami U., 1949, Dunbar award, 1951; Univ. fellow Cornell U., 1951-53; fellow Woodrow Wilson Internat. Center for Scholars, 1977; grantee Ford Found., N.Y. Urban Devel. Corp., Nat. Endowment Arts. Mem. AIA, Soc. Coll. and Univ. Planning (pres. 1968-69), Am. Planning Assn. (pres. N.Y. upstate chpt. 1966-68), Am. Inst. Cert. Planners, Soc. Archtl. Historians, Urban Land Inst., Soc. City and Regional Planning History (keynote speaker biannual nat. conf. 1989). Home: RD 2 1604 Dryden Rd Freeville NY 13068-9634 Office: 117 Sibley Hall Cornell U Ithaca NY 14853

PARSONS, LEONARD JON, marketing educator, consultant; b. Pitts., Sept. 1, 1942; s. Leonard J. and Marion Jane (Williams) P.; m. Julia Grieve, Jan. 23, 1965; children: Lorelei, Leonard Jon Jr. BSChemE, MIT, 1964; MS in Indsl. Adminstrn., Purdue U., 1965, PhD in Indsl. Adminstrn., 1968. Asst. prof. Ind. U., Bloomington, 1968-70; assoc. prof. Claremont (Calif.) Grad. Sch., 1970-77; prof. marketing Ga. Inst. Tech., 1977—; vis. scholar MIT, Cambridge, fall 1973; Fulbright-Hays sr. scholar Cath. U. Leuven, Belgium, spring 1977; vis. prof. INSEAD, France, fall 1984, Norwegian Sch. Mktg., Oslo, fall 1989, UCLA, spring 1990, Advt. Edn. Found., Anheuser Busch, St. Louis, summer 1993; mem. rsch. and test devel. com. Grad. Mgmt. Admissions Coun., 1988-90. Author: Using Microcomputers in Marketing, 1986; co-author: Market Response Models, 1990, Marketing Management, 1995, others; edtl. bd. Jour. Mktg. Rsch., 1970-80, 83-85, Jour. Bus. Rsch., 1973-79, Jour. Mktg., 1978-80; assoc. editor: Decision Scis., 1976-79; mktg. dept. editor: Mgmt. Sci., 1980-82; contbr. numerous chpts. to books, articles to profl. jours. Recipient first prize rsch. design contest Am. Mktg. Assn., 1971-72. Mem. Am. Statis. Assn. (chmn. stats. in mktg. sect. 1995), European Mktg. Acad. (mem. exec. com. 1981-84), Theta Delta Chi, Beta Gamma Sigma, Phi Kappa Phi. Office: Ga Inst Tech Sch Mgmt Atlanta GA 30332-0520

PARSONS, MERRIBELL MADDUX, museum consultant; b. San Antonio. BFA, Newcomb Coll., 1964; MA, M.Phil., Inst. Fine Arts, NYU, 1968. Curator of sculpture and decorative arts Mpls. Inst. Arts, 1969-74, chief curator, 1974-79; vice-dir. for edn. Met. Mus. Art, N.Y.C., 1979-87; dir. Columbus Mus. Art, Ohio, 1987-95. Author: Sculpture: David Daniels Collection; editor, author exhbn. catalogues and articles. Mem. pub. art com. Greater Columbus Arts Coun., 1989, Downtown Planning Group, Columbus, 1989. Clawson Mills fellow Met. Mus. Art, 1967; NEA professional grantee, Washington, 1972. Mem. Am. Assn. Mus. Dirs., Am. Assn.

Museums, C. of C. (bd. dirs. 1990—). Office: 486 E Olmos Dr San Antonio TX 78212

PARSONS, RICHARD DEAN, banker, lawyer; b. N.Y.C., Apr. 4, 1948; s. Lorenzo Locklair and Isabelle (Judd) P.; m. Laura Ann Bush, Aug. 30, 1968; children: Gregory, Leslie, Rebecca. Student, U. Hawaii, 1968; JD, Union U., Albany, N.Y., 1971; LLD (hon.), Adelphi U., 1990, Medgar Evers Coll., N.Y.C. 1991. Bar: N.Y. 1972. Asst. counsel to gov. State of N.Y., Albany, 1971-73, 1st asst. counsel to gov., 1973-74; dep. counsel to v.p. Office of V.P., Washington, 1975; gen. counsel, assoc. dir. domestic coun. White House, Washington, 1975-77; ptnr. Patterson Belknap Webb & Tyler, N.Y.C., 1977-88; pres., chief oper. officer Dime Savs. Bank N.Y., N.Y.C., 1988-90, chmn., chief exec. officer, 1990-95; pres. Time Warner, N.Y.C., 1995—; bd. dirs. Fed. Nat. Mortgage Assn., Washington, 1989—, Philip Morris Cos., N.Y.C., Time Warner Inc., N.Y.C. Trustee Rockefeller Bros. Fund, N.Y.C., 1989—, Howard U., Washington 1989—, Met. Mus. Art, N.Y.C., 1990—. Office: Dime Savs Bank NY 589 Fifth Ave New York NY 10017-1923

PARSONS, ROBERT EUGENE, transportation consultant; b. Cin., Apr. 19, 1931; s. Charles Eugene and Samantha Ellen (Snider) P.; m. Beverly Greenhalgh, Dec. 30, 1949; children: Brian Scott, Barry Lawrence, Robert Stephen, Kimberly Ann. ME, U. Cinn., 1954; MSME, Drexel Inst. Tech., 1959. Registered profl. engr., Calif., Nev., Md., Ohio. Asst. project engr. The Martin Co., Balt., 1956-62; sect. mgr., 1962-64; dep. dir. Supersonic Transp. Office FAA, Washington, 1964-71; dir. rsch. and devel. plans U.S. Dept. Transp., Washington, 1971; assoc. adminstr. Fed. RR Adminstrn., Washington, 1975-80; dir. rsch. field methods Nat. Bur. Standards, Gaithersburg, Md., 1980-81; dir. RR rsch. and devel. program U. Calif., Berkeley, 1981-84; cons. Walnut Creek, Calif., 1986-90; dir. program on advanced technology for hwy. U. Calif. Berkeley, 1984—; prin. Parsons Transp. Assocs., Walnut Creek, Calif.; cons. Assn. Am. R.R.s, Washington, U. Calif., Calif. Dept. Transp., U.S. Dept. Transp., Radar Control Sys., Rand, Sys. Control Tech., Intelligent Vehicle Hwy. Soc. Techs., Inc., Lawrence Livermore Nat. Lab., French Inst. Transp. Safety, Intelligent Vehicle Hwy. Soc. Am., chmn. sys. arch. com.; cons. IMRA Am., Inc., JHK & Assocs., Sci. Atlanta and Va. Tech.; active transp. rsch. bd. groups. Contbr. articles to profl. jours. Mem. SAE, Intelligent Transp. Soc. Am., Intelligent Transp. Sys. of Va. (chmn. strategic planning com.). Methodist. Avocations: computer work, woodworking. Home: 3106 Cove Ridge Rd Midlothian VA 23112-4354

PARSONS, VINSON ADAIR, retired computer software company executive; b. Frankfort, Ky., Oct. 22, 1932; s. Richard Adair and Nina (Mefford) P.; m. Elizabeth Ann Peltier, June 2, 1956. A.S., Mitchell Coll., 1959; B.S., U. Conn., 1960; AMP, Harvard U., 1985. Auditor, Price Waterhouse & Co. (C.P.A.s), Hartford, Conn., 1960-65; controller Pervel Industries Inc., Plainfield, Conn., 1965-70; v.p., controller Akzo Am. Inc., Asheville, N.C., 1970-71, 73-83, v.p., chief fin. officer, 1983-86; v.p., chief fin. officer System Software Assocs. Inc., Chgo., 1986-89, also bd. dirs.; ret., 1990; dir. Am. Tape Co., BRIntec Co., Control Tech. Corp. Served with USN, 1953-57. Mem. Am. Mgmt. Assn., Fin. Execs. Inst., Inst. Mgmt. Accts. (pres. local chpt. 1969-70). Clubs: Asheville Country; University (N.Y.C.); Reems Creek Golf. Home and Office: 15 Preston Ct Weaverville NC 28787-8907

PARSONS, VIRGINIA MAE, psychology educator; b. Milw., Oct. 27, 1942; d. John T. and Mable (Myers) Lakso; m. Ralph F. Parsons, Oct. 5, 1968; children: Ralph F. III, Robert, Jeanne. BA, U. Wis., Milw., 1964; MA, U. Iowa, 1967, PhD, 1970. Asst. prof. U. Wis.-Parkside, Kenosha, Wis., 1970-76; prof. psychology Carroll Coll., Waukesha, Wis., 1976—. Contbr. articles to profl. jours. NSF grantee, 1962-64, 72, 77, Carroll Coll., 1978, 80, 88. Mem. AAAS, Am. Psychol. Soc., N.Y. Acad. Sci., Sigma Xi, Psi Chi. Avocations: photography, swimming, music. Office: Carroll Coll 100 N East Ave Waukesha WI 53186-5593

PARSONS-SALEM, DIANE LORA, lawyer; b. Arlington, Mass., Apr. 17, 1945; d. Hugh Crocker and Tryphena Grace (Reader) Parsons; m. William Stephen Holloway, Mar. 20, 1993; 1 child, Nicole D. Salem. BA, Boston U., 1967; JD, Suffolk U., 1970. Bar: Mass. 1970, U.S. Dist. Ct. Mass. 1972, U.S. Supreme Ct. 1979. Atty. Allstate Ins. Co., Weston, Mass., 1970-72; assoc. Haig Der Manuelian, Boston, 1972-80; sr. assoc. Widett, Slater & Goldman, P.C., Boston, 1980-84; real estate atty. Friendly Ice Cream Corp., Wilbraham, Mass., 1984-87; asst. gen. counsel Hardee's Food Systems, Inc., Rocky Mount, N.C., 1987-90, dep. gen. counsel, 1990—. Mem. ABA, Mass. Bar Assn. Home: 724 Eagles Ter Rocky Mount NC 27804-6404 Office: Hardees Food Systems Inc 1233 Hardees Blvd Rocky Mount NC 27804-2815

PARTAIN, CLARENCE LEON, radiologist, nuclear medicine physician, educator, administrator; b. Memphis, July 12, 1940; s. Archie Leon and Vergie (Young) P.; m. Judith Stafford, Jan., 1964; children: David Blane, Terri Ellyn, Amy Leigh. B.S.N.E., U. Tenn., 1963; M.S.N.E., Purdue U., 1965, Ph.D. in Nuclear Engring., 1967; M.D., Washington U., St. Louis, 1975. Diplomate: Am. Bd. Nuclear Medicine, Am. Bd. Radiology; registered profl. engr., Mo. Asst. prof. nuclear engring. U. Mo.-Columbia, 1968-71, assoc. prof., 1971-75; resident N.C. Meml. Hosp., Chapel Hill, 1975-79; assoc. prof. radiology U. N.C.-Chapel Hill, 1978-79; assoc. prof. Vanderbilt U., Nashville, 1980-85; prof. radiology and biomed. engring. Vanderbilt U., 1985—, vice chmn. radiology, 1989-92, dir. nuclear medicine, 1981-85, dir. magnetic resonance imaging, 1983-92, chmn. radiology, 1992—; cons. NIH, Bethesda, Md., 1980—. Author: Nuclear Magnetic Resonance (NMR) Imaging, 1983, NMR Imaging: Clinical Utility and Correlation, 1984, Thyroid and Parathyroid Imaging, 1986, Magnetic Resonance Imaging, 2d edit., 1988, Correlative Image: Nuclear Medicine, Magnetic Resonance, Computer Tomography, Ultrasound, 1988; editl. bd. Acad. radiology, Magnetic Resonance Imaging, Jour. Magnetic Resonance Imaging, Jour. Nuclear Medicine. AEC Spl. fellow, 1964-66; grantee Nat. Inst. Neurosci., Communicative Diseases and Stroke, 1977-78. Fellow Am. Coll. Nuclear Physicians, Am. Coll. Radiology, Soc. Magnetic Resonance Imaging (bd. dirs.); mem. AMA, IEEE, Radiol. Soc. N.Am., Assn. Univ. Radiologists (exec. coun.), Soc. Nuclear Medicine (trustee, Benedict Casson lectr. 1981), Am. Roentgen Ray Soc. (exec. coun.), Soc. Magnetic Resonance in Medicine (trustee), Sigma Phi Epsilon. Baptist. Home: 211 High Lea Rd Brentwood TN 37027-4944 Office: Vanderbilt U Med Ctr 1611 21st Ave S Nashville TN 37212-3103

PARTAIN, EUGENE GARTLY, lawyer; b. Memphis, Oct. 4, 1930; s. Eugene Gardner and Zoe (Allen) P.; m. Ute Agnes Reinsch, July 8, 1952; children—Gia Michele, Matthew Reinsch. B.A., Duke U., 1952, LL.B. 1958; M.A., Northwestern U., 1959. Bar: Ga. 1961, U.S. Supreme Ct. 1980. Sr. ptnr. King & Spalding, Atlanta. Served to capt. USAF, 1952-54. Fellow Am. Coll. Trial Lawyers, Internat. Acad. Trial Lawyers, Internat. Soc. Barristers, Am. Bd. Trial Advocates; mem. ABA, Atlanta Bar Assn. (exec. com.), Ga. Def. Lawyers Assn. (pres. 1982-83), Best Lawyers in Am., Old War Horse Lawyers Club, Lawyers Club of Atlanta. Presbyterian. Office: King & Spalding 191 Peachtree St NE Ste 4900 Atlanta GA 30303-1763

PARTAIN, LARRY DEAN, solar research engineer; b. McKinney, Tex., Apr. 27, 1942; s. Archie Leon and Vergie Ann (Young) P.; m. Deborah Patton, July 1986; children: Lauren Elizabeth, Catherine Ann. BSEE, U. Tenn., 1965; PhD, Johns Hopkins U., 1971. Assoc. prof. elec. engring. U. Del., Newark, 1971-78; engr. Engring. Research div. Lawrence Livermore Nat. Lab., Calif., 1978-80; sr. research engr. Chevron Research Co., Richmond, Calif., 1980-87; sr. scientist, mktg. mgr. Varian Ginzton Research Ctr., Palo Alto, Calif., 1987—. Co-author/editor: Solar Cells and Their Applications, 1995; contbr. articles to tech. jours.; patentee microwave sensor, solar cells, solar arrays, optical switch. Solar Energy Rsch. Inst. grantee, 1978-79, 84-86; duPont rsch. grantee, 1974-75; grantee USAF Wright Aero. Lab., 1984-85, 88-90, 91-93, Sandia Nat. Labs., 1985-86, Naval Surface Warfare Ctr., 1994, 95. Mem. IEEE, Sigma Xi. Office: Varian Rsch Ctr 3075 Hansen Way Palo Alto CA 94304-1025 *Technical advances are keyed to the pragmatic scientists' search for simple, accurate, and predictive physical models. This contrasts with the search for truth—a seductive and distracting abstraction better left to philosophers and theologians.*

PARTAN, DANIEL GORDON, lawyer, educator; b. Gardner, Mass., Aug. 2, 1933; s. Toivo Antero and Lempi Sivia (Adamson) P.; m. Doris Liepmann, June 8, 1957; children: Andrew Stewart, Matthew Alexander, Sarah Ruth, Iliana Maria, Juan Carlos. AB, Cornell U., 1955; LLB, Harvard U., 1958, LLM, 1961. Bar: Mass. 1959. Rsch. assoc. Harvard Law Sch., 1961, Rule of Law Ctr., Duke U. Law Sch., 1962-65; assoc. prof. U. N.D., 1964-65; assoc. prof. law Boston U., 1965-68, prof., 1968—; mem. NAFTA dispute settlement roster and binat. dispute panel U.S.-Can. Free Trade Agreement; cons. Dept. State, UN Devel. Program, Am. Acad. Arts and Sci.; pres., chmn. Bd. dirs. UN Assn. Greater Boston, 1969-71, 76-77; chmn. Brookline Selectmen's Com. on Harvard Energy Plant, 1976—; vis. scholar Harvard Law Sch., 1977-78; vis. fellow Cambridge (Eng.) U., 1972. Author: Population in the United Nations System, 1973, Documentary Study of the Politicization of UNESCO, 2 vols., 1975, The International Law Process, 1992; co-author: Legal Problems of International Administration, 1968, The United States and the International Labor Organization, 1980; co-editor: Corporate Disclosure of Environmental Risks: U.S. and European Law, 1990; contbr. articles to books and jours. Mem. ABA, Boston Bar Assn., Commn. to Study the Orgn. Peace, Am. Law Inst., Acad. Coun. UN System, Am. Soc. Internat. Law, Internat. Law Assn., European Communities Studies Assn., UN Assn. Office: 765 Commonwealth Ave Boston MA 02215-1401

PARTANEN, CARL RICHARD, biology educator; b. Portland, Oreg., Nov. 23, 1921; s. Emil and Ellen (Engstrom) P.; m. Jane Nelson, June 24, 1961; children: Karen, Kirsten, Richard (dec.). Student, Multnomah Jr. Coll., 1946-48; B.A., Lewis and Clark Coll., 1950; M.A., Harvard, 1951, Ph.D., 1954. Am. Cancer Soc. postdoctoral research fellow Columbia, 1954-55, Harvard, 1955-57; research asso. Childrens Cancer Research Found., Boston, 1957-61; asso. prof. biology U. Pitts., 1961-64, prof. biology, 1964-86, chmn. biology, 1964-70, prof. emeritus, 1987—; Research fellow U. Edinburgh, Scotland, 1971-72, U. Nottingham, Eng., 1978-79. Contbr. articles to profl. jours. Served with AUS, 1942-45, ETO. Recipient Distinguished Achievement award Lewis and Clark Coll., 1968. Mem. Am. Genetic Assn., Bot. Soc. Am., Soc. for Devel. Biology, Soc. for In Vitro Biology, Am. Inst. Biol. Sci. Home: 1112 Farragut St Pittsburgh PA 15206-1746 Office: U Pitts Dept Biol Scis Pittsburgh PA 15260

PARTCH, KENNETH PAUL, editor, consultant; b. Mt. Vernon, N.Y., June 22, 1925; s. Edward Augustus and Grace Jane (Crabb) P.; m. Dorothy Sophia Iversen, July 16, 1953; children—Marjorie, Stephen, Jessica. A.B. Bklyn. Coll., 1949. Mng. editor Moore Publishing Co., 1955, Chain Store Age mag., 1955-59, Sales Mgmt. mag., 1961; editor Food Topics mag., 1961-68; dir. mktg. Grocery Mfrs. Am., 1969-70; editor Chain Store Age-Supermarket Group, N.Y.C., 1970-77; cons. to supermarket industry, 1977-80; editor-in-chief Supermarket Bus. mag., 1980—. Contbr. to Wharton Mag. Served with USAAF, 1943-46. Decorated Air medal; recipient Jesse Neal award Assoc. Bus. Press, 1968, Grand award ABP Points of Light Award, 1991. Mem. Sigma Delta Chi. Home: 20 Devils Gardens Rd Norwalk CT 06854-3315

PARTEE, BARBARA HALL, linguist, educator; b. Englewood, N.J., June 23, 1940; d. David B. and Helen M. Hall; m. Morriss Henry Partee, 1966 (div. 1971); children: Morriss M., David M., Joel T.; m. Emmon Werner Bach, Nov. 2, 1973. BA with high honors in Math., Swarthmore Coll., 1961; PhD in Linguistics, MIT, 1965; DSc (hon.), Swarthmore Coll., 1989, Charles U., Prague, Czechoslovakia, 1992. Asst. prof. UCLA, 1965-69, assoc. prof., 1969-73; assoc. prof. linguistics and philosophy U. Mass., Amherst, 1972-73, prof., 1973-90. Disting. Univ. prof., 1990—, head dept. linguistics, 1987-93; fellow Ctr. for Advanced Study in Behavior Scis., 1976-77; mem. bd. mgrs. Swarthmore Coll., 1990—. Author: (with Stockwell and Schachter) The Major Syntactic Structures of English, 1972, Fundamentals of Mathematics for Linguists, 1979, (with ter Meulen and Wall) Mathematical Methods in Linguistics, 1990; editor: Montague Grammar, 1976; co-editor: (with Chierchia and Turner) Properties, Types and Meaning, Vol. I: Foundational Issues, Vol. II: Semantic Issues, 1989; mem. editoral bd: Language, 1967-73, Linguistic Inquiry, 1972-79, Theoretical Linguistics, 1974—, Linguistics and Philosophy, 1977—. Recipient Chancellor's medal U. Mass., 1977; NEH fellow, 1982-83; Internat. Rsch. and Exchanges Bd. fellow, 1989-90. Mem. NAS (chair anthropology sect. 1993—), Linguistic Soc. Am. (pres. 1986), Am. Philos. Assn., Assn. Computational Linguistics, Am. Acad. Arts and Scis., Sigma Xi. Home: 50 Hobart Ln Amherst MA 01002-1321 Office: U Mass Dept Linguistics Amherst MA 01003 *I had the good fortune to have loving and encouraging parents and stimulating teachers, and to find a field of inquiry which I love and can contribute to. My husband is my best friend and closest colleague, and my children are a source of joy.*

PARTHASARATHY, RAJAGOPAL, writer, literature educator; b. Tirupparaitturai, India, Aug. 20, 1934; came to U.S., 1982; s. Krishnaswamy and Ambujam Rajagopal; m. Shobhan Koppikar, Oct. 26, 1969; children: Gautam, Arjun. BA, Bombay U., 1957, MA, 1959; Diploma in English Studies, Leeds (Eng.) U., 1964; PhD, U. Tex., 1987. Lectr. in English Ismail Yusuf Coll., Bombay, 1959-62, Mithibai Coll., Bombay, 1962-63, 64-65; lectr. in English lang. teaching Brit. Coun., Bombay, 1965-66; asst. prof. English Presidency Coll., Madras, 1966-67; lectr. in English South Indian Edn. Soc. Coll., Bombay, 1967-71; regional editor Oxford U. Press, Madras, 1971-78; editor Oxford U. Press, Delhi, 1978-82; asst. prof. English Skidmore Coll., Saratoga Springs, N.Y., 1986-92, assoc. prof., 1992—; dir. program in Asian studies, 1994—; dir. poetry workshop Stella Maris Coll., Madras, 1972-75; part-time lectr. in book pub. Coll. Vocat. Guidance, Delhi U., New Delhi, 1979-81. Author: (verse) Rough Passage, 1977; editor (verse) Ten Twentieth-Century Indian Poets, 1976, (with J.J. Healy) Poetry from Leeds, 1968; translator: (verse and prose) The Tale of an Anklet: An Epic of South India (The Cilappatikaram of Ilanko Atikal), 1993. Recipient Ulka Poetry prize Poetry India, 1966, PEN/Book-of-the-Month Club Translation citation, 1994; Brit. Coun. scholar, 1963; U.S. Dept. State exch. visitor, 1978. Mem. MLA, Am. Lit. Translators Assn., Assn. for Asian Studies, Phi Kappa Phi. Avocations: travel, classical music, gardening. Home: 8 Salem Dr Saratoga Springs NY 12866-3726 Office: Skidmore Coll Dept English 815 N Broadway Saratoga Springs NY 12866-1632

PARTHUM, CHARLES ALBERT, civil engineer; b. Lawrence, Mass., Sept. 26, 1929; s. Albert and Elsie Ida (Eichner) P.; m. Mary Catherine Wiggin, Oct. 20, 1956; children: Stephen Charles, Julie Elizabeth. BSCE, Northeastern U., 1951. With Camp Dresser & McKee, Inc., Boston, 1951—; ptnr. Camp Dresser & McKee, Inc., 1967—, sr. v.p. dir., 1971-92; cons., 1992—; cons. EPA, 1980. Treas., deacon, moderator, clk. Tabernacle Ch., Salem, Mass.; chmn. Engr.-Joint Contacts Documents Com., 1980. With USN, 1952-55. Recipient Outstanding Civil Engring. Alumnus award Northeastern U., 1989. Mem. NSPE, ASCE (bd. dirs. 1987-90, William H. Wisely Am. Civil Engr. award 1993, pres.-elect 1994-95), Am. Acad. Environ. Engrs. (diplomate), Boston Soc. Civil Engrs. (hon., pres. 1975-76), Water Pollution Control Fedn. (chmn. constrn. and bylaws com. 1972-77), Am. Water Resources Assn., Mass. Soc. Profl. Engrs., Am. Water Works Assn., New England Water Works Assn., New England Water Pollution Control Assn., Chi Epsilon (hon.). Office: One Cambridge Ctr Cambridge MA 02142

PARTINGTON, JAMES WOOD, naval officer; b. Omaha, Jan. 16, 1939; s. Lee Edward and Carol Virginia (Wood) P.; m. Barbara Jean Arline, July 15, 1961; children: Jennifer, Kathleen, Mary Elizabeth. BA, U. R.I., 1970; grad., Naval War Coll., 1971. Commd. ensign USN, 1961, advanced through grades to rear adm., 1989; ops. officer Attack Squadron 122, Lemoore, Calif., 1974-77; comdg. officer Attack Squadron 27, Lemoore, 1977-80, Strike Fighter Squadron 125, Lemoore, 1980-82; coord. F/A 18 program Chief Naval Ops., Washington, 1982-84; comdg. officer Naval Air Sta., Lemoore, 1984-86; chief of staff Cruiser Destroyer Group 5, San Diego, 1986-87; dir. Naval Aviation Officer Assignments, Washington, 1987-88; comdr. Strike Fighter Wings Atlantic, Jacksonville, Fla., 1988-90, Naval Tng. Ctr., Great Lakes, Ill., 1990-92; v.p., dir. corp. planning Sr. Technologies Inc., 1992-94; pres. Partington and Associates, Lincoln, 1994—. Decorated Legion of Merit, DFC, Air medal (28), Meritorious Svc. medal. Mem. U.S. Naval Inst., Assn. Naval Aviation, Naval Order of U.S. Roman Catholic. Avocations: sailing, tennis, scuba diving.

PARTNOY, RONALD ALLEN, lawyer; b. Norwalk, Conn., Dec. 23, 1933; s. Maurice and Ethel Marguerite (Roselle) P.; m. Diane Catherine Keenan, Sept. 18, 1965. B.A., Yale U., 1956; LL.B., Harvard U., 1961; LL.M., Boston U., 1965. Bar: Mass. 1962, Conn. 1966. Atty. Liberty Mut. Ins. Co., Boston, 1961-65; assoc. counsel Remington Arms Co., Bridgeport, Conn., 1965-70; gen. counsel Remington Arms Co., 1970-88, sec., 1983-93; sr. counsel E.I. du Pont de Nemours & Co., Wilmington, Del., 1985—. Served with USN, 1956-58; to capt. USNR (ret.). Mem. ABA, Sporting Arms and Ammunition Mfrs. Inst. (chmn. legis. and legal affairs com. 1971-86), Am. Judicature Soc., U.S. Navy League (pres. Bridgeport coun. 1975-77, nat. dir. Comm. pres. 1977-80, v.p. Empire region 1980-85), Naval Res. Assn. (3d dist. pres., nat. exec. com. 1981-85), Chancery Club, Harvard Club of Boston, Harvard Club of Phila., Yale Club of N.Y.C. Home: 616 Bayard Rd Kennett Square PA 19348-2504 Office: 1007 Market St Wilmington DE 19898

PARTON, DOLLY REBECCA, singer, composer, actress; b. Sevier County, Tenn., Jan. 19, 1946; d. Robert Lee and Avie Lee (Owens) P.; m. Carl Dean, May 30, 1966. Country music singer, rec. artist, composer, actress, radio and TV personality; entrepreneur, owner entertainment park Dollywood, established 1985. Radio appearances include Grand Ole Opry, WSM Radio, Nashville, Cass Walker program, Knoxville; TV appearances include Porter Wagoner Show, from 1967, Cass Walker program, Bill Anderson Show, Wilburn Bros. Show, Barbara Mandrell Show; rec. artist, Mercury, Monument, RCA, CBS record cos.; star movie Nine to Five, 1980, The Best Little Whorehouse in Texas, 1982, Rhinestone, 1984, Steel Magnolias, 1989, Straight Talk, 1991; albums include Here You Come Again (Grammy award 1978), Real Love, 1985, Just the Way I Am, 1986, Portrait, 1986, Think About Love, 1986, Trio (with Emmylou Harris, Linda Ronstadt) (Grammy award 1988), 1987, Heartbreaker, Great Balls of Fire, Rainbow, 1988, White Limozeen, 1989, Home for Christmas, 1990, Eagle When She Flies, 1991, Slow Dancing with the Moon, 1993 (Grammy nomination, Best Country Vocal Collaboration for Romeo (with Tanya Tucker, Billy Ray Cyrus, Kathy Mattea, Pam Tillis, & Mary-Chapin Carpenter), (with Tammy Wynette and Loretta Lynn) Honky Tonk Angels, 1994; composer numerous songs including Nine to Five (Grammy award 1981, Acad. award nominee and Golden Globe award nominee 1981); author: Dolly, 1994. Recipient (with Porter Wagoner) Vocal Group of Yr. award, 1968; Vocal Duo of Yr. award All Country Music Assn., 1970, 71; Nashville Metronome award, 1979; Am. Music award for best duo performance (with Kenny Rogers), 1984; named Female Vocalist of Yr., 1975, 76; Country Star of Yr., Sullivan Prodns., 1977; Entertainer of Yr., Country Music Assn., 1978; People's Choice award, 1980, 88; Female Vocalist of Yr., Acad. Country Music, 1980; Dolly Parton Day proclaimed, Sevier County, Tenn., designated Oct. 7, 1967, Los Angeles, Sept. 20, 1979; recipient Grammy awards for best female country vocalist, 1978, 81, for best country song, 1981, for best country vocal performance with group, 1987; co-recipient (with Emmylou Harris and Linda Ronstadt) Acad. Country Music award for album of the yr., 1987; named to Small Town of Am. Hall of Fame, 1988, East Tenn. Hall of Fame, 1988. Address: c/o Maureen O'Connor Rogers & Cowan 10000 Santa Monica Blvd Los Angeles CA 90067-7007*

PARTON, JAMES, historian; b. Newburyport, Mass., Dec. 10, 1912; s. Hugo and Agnes (Leach) P.; m. Jane Audra Bourne, Dec. 9, 1950 (dec. 1962); children: James III, Dana (dec.), Sara. A.B., Harvard U., 1934. Asst. E.L. Bernays, N.Y.C., 1934-35; aviation editor Time Mag., 1935-36, bus. and financial editor, 1937-39, asst. gen. mgr., 1940, bus. mgr. air express edit., 1941; promotion mgr. Time-Life Internat., 1945; editorial dir. Pacific Coast news burs. Time, Inc., 1947; editor and pub. Los Angeles Ind., 1948-49; cons. U.S. Dept. State, 1949; promotion dir. N.Y. Herald Tribune, 1950; asst. to pres., chmn. Herald Tribune Forum and dir. N.Y. Herald Tribune, Inc., 1951-53; v.p., treas. Thorndike, Jensen & Parton, Inc., 1953-57; founder, pres. Am. Heritage Pub. Co., Inc., 1954-70; pres. Ency. Brit. Ednl. Corp., Chgo., 1970-72; chmn. exec. com. Ency. Brit. Ednl. Corp., 1973; pres. James Parton & Co., N.Y.C., 1973-81, Parton Enterprises, Inc., 1981-84; dir. planning study Custom House Inst., N.Y.C., 1973; chmn. Nat. Advt. Rev. Bd., 1974-76; asst. librarian for pub. edn. Library of Congress, 1976-77; chmn. exec. com. Hist. Times, Inc., 1979-81; chmn. U.S. Army com. which produced ofcl. Eighth Air Force book Target-Germany, 1943. Author: "Air Force Spoken Here", General Ira Eaker and the Command of the Air, 1986. Editor, pub. Impact, The Army Air Forces Confidential Picture History of World War II, 8 vols, 1980. Trustee Loomis Inst., 1952—, pres., 1964-66, chmn., 1967-70; trustee USAF Hist. Found., 1955—; bd. visitors Air U., 1988-91. Commd. 2d lt. in USAAF, 1942; advanced through grades to lt. col. 1944. Decorated Legion of Merit, Bronze Star, European Theater ribbon with 4 battle stars. Mem. Harvard Club (N.Y.C.), Army and Navy Club (Washington). Home: PO Box 796 Hanover NH 03755-0796

PARTRIDGE, BRUCE JAMES, lawyer, educator; b. June 4, 1926; Syracuse, N.Y.; came to Can., 1969; s. Bert James and Lida Marion (Ross) P.; m. Mary Janice Smith, June 13, 1948 (dec. 1986); children: Heather Leigh, Eric James, Brian Lloyd, Bonnie Joyce; m. May S. Archer, May 28, 1988; stepchildren: Sheila Archer, Laurel Archer. AB cum laude, Oberlin Coll., Ohio, 1946; LLB, Blackstone Coll., Chgo., 1950, JD, 1952; LLB, U. B.C., 1974. Bar: B.C. 1976, N.W.T. 1980. Rsch. physicist Am. Gas Assn., Cleve., 1946-48; bus. administr. Rochester Inst. Tech., N.Y., 1953-58, Baldwin-Wallace Coll., Berea, Ohio, 1951-53, Cazenovia (N.Y.) Coll., 1948-51; v.p. bus. and mgmt., U. Del., Newark, Del., 1958-63; v.p. adminstrn. Johns Hopkins U., Balt., 1963-69; pres. U. Victoria, B.C., Can., 1969-72; assoc. Clark, Wilson & Co., Vancouver, B.C., 1975-78; successively solicitor, mng. solicitor, gen. solicitor, v.p. law and gen. counsel, sec. Cominco Ltd., Vancouver, 1978-88; exec. dir. Baker & McKenzie, Hong Kong, 1988-90; v.p. Pacific Creations Inc., 1990-92; faculty Camosun Coll., 1992—. Co-author: College and University Business Administration, 1968. Chmn. editorial com. Purchasing for Higher Education, 1962. Contbr. numerous articles to profl. jours. Chmn. commn. on adminstrv. affairs Am. Council on Edn., Washington, 1966-69; mem. Pres.'s Com. on Employment of Handicapped, Washington, 1967-69; mem. adv. council Ctr. for Resource Studies, Queen's U.; bd. dirs. L'Arche in the Americas; mem. adv. council Westwater Research Centre, U. B.C. Mem. Law Soc. B.C., Law Soc. of N.W. Ters., Assn. Can. Gen. Counsel, Fedn. Ins. and Corp. Counsel, Def. Research Inst. (product liability com.), Am. Corp. Counsel Assn., Vancouver Club, Aberdeen Marine Club, Hong Kong Football Club. Office: Camosun Coll, 4461 Interurban Rd, Victoria, BC Canada V8X 3X1

PARTRIDGE, MARK VAN BUREN, lawyer; b. Rochester, Minn., Oct. 16, 1954; s. John V.B. and Constance (Brainerd) P.; m. Mary Roberta Moffitt, Apr. 30, 1983; children: Caitlin, Lindsay, Christopher. BA, U. Nebr., 1978; JD, Harvard U., 1981. Bar: Ill. 1981, U.S. Dist. Ct. (no. dist.) Ill. 1981, U.S. Dist. Ct. (ea. dist.) Mich. 1983, U.S. Ct. Appeals (4th cir.) 1986, U.S. Ct. Appeals (5th cir.) 1993. Assoc. Pattishall, McAuliffe, Newbury, Hilliard & Geraldson, Chgo., 1981-88, ptnr., 1988-; arbitrator Cook County Mandatory Arbitration Bd., 1989—; adj. prof. John Marshall Law Sch., Chgo., 1990—. Author: (with others) Winning With Computers, 1993. Vol. Chgo. Vol. Legal Svcs., 1983—; mem. editl. bd. Trademark Reporter, 1994—. Mem. ABA (com. chair 1989-91, 92—), Am. Intellectual Property Law Assn. (com. chair 1989-91), Intellectual Property Law Assn. Chgo. (com. chair 1993—). Avocations: genealogy, travel, computers. Office: Pattishall McAuliffe Newbury Hilliard & Geraldson 311 S Wacker Dr Chicago IL 60606-6618

PARTRIDGE, ROBERT BRUCE, astronomy educator; b. Honolulu, May 16, 1940; s. Robert B. and Laura Lea (Johnson) P.; m. Jane C. Widseth, Aug. 28, 1976; children: John D. W., Carl E. W. AB, Princeton U., 1962; PhD, U. Oxford, Eng., 1965. From instr. to asst. prof. Princeton (N.J.) U., 1965-70; assoc. prof. Haverford (Pa.) Coll., 1970-76, dean, 1982-85, prof., 1976—, Bettye and Howard Marshall prof. of natural scis., provost, 1990-95; cons. NASA, NSF, 1988—. Contbr. numerous articles to profl. jours. Rhodes scholar, U. Oxford, 1962-65; Alfred Sloan fellow, 1971-76, Fulbright fellow, Norway, 1979-80, Guggenheim fellow, 1988-89. Home: 628 Overhill Rd Ardmore PA 19003-1007 Office: Haverford Coll Astronomy Dept Haverford PA 19041*

PARTRIDGE, WILLIAM RUSSELL, federal executive; b. Torrance, Calif., Jan. 9, 1927; s. Frederick Walter and Dorothy (Keller) P.; m. Phyllis Ruth Squires, Feb. 6, 1949; children: William M., Carol C., Mark F. Student, U.

Idaho, W. Va. U., 1944-45; BA, Pomona Coll., 1949; MPA, Syracuse U., 1950; MBA, UCLA, 1963. Various mgmt. positions U.S. AEC, Oak Ridge, 1950-55; staff asst., adminstr. mgmt devel., ops. analyst Gen. Offices and Rocketdyne div./N.Am. Aviation Co., L.A., 1955-61, mgr. mgmt. systems, 1961-65; project engr. info. systems div. autonetics Gen. Offices and Rocketdyne div./N.Am. Aviation Co., Anaheim, Calif., 1965-69; ops. rsch. scientist System Devel. Corp., Santa Monica, Calif., 1961; various govt. positions to asst. inspector gen. DOE, 1975-87; staff mem. House Appropriations Com., 1987-90; dep. inspector gen., sr. exec. svc. Fed. Emergency Mgmt. Agy., Annapolis, 1990—. With AUS, 1944-46. Mem. Am. Soc. Pub. Adminstrn., Ops. Rsch. Soc. Am. Office: Federal Emergency Mgmt Agy Washington DC 20472

PARTRIDGE, WILLIAM SCHAUBEL, retired physicist, research company executive; b. Ranchester, Wyo., Jan. 20, 1922; s. William Clayton and Elsie (Schaubel) P.; m. Jeannette Noble, Mar. 21, 1942; children—Nancy, Dianne, William Noble, Carol, Murray Noble (dec.). B.A., U. Wyo., 1946, M.A., 1948; Ph.D., U. Utah, 1951. Staff scientist U. Calif., Los Alamos, 1951-52; asst. dir. explosives research group U. Utah, Salt Lake City, 1952-55; assoc. research prof., dir. high velocity research lab. U. Utah, 1955-58, v.p. for research, 1966-79; pres. U. Utah Rsch. Inst., 1972-83, Utah Bioresearch, 1983-89, ret.; chmn. bd. Tech. Rsch. Assocs., Inc., 1983-89; pres. gen. mgr. Utah R & D Co., Salt Lake City, 1958-64; staff scientist Jet Propulsion Lab., Pasadena, Calif., 1964-66; mem. exec. com. Nat. Coun. Univ. Rsch. Adminstrs., 1969-71; pres., gen. mgr. U. Utah Rsch. Inst., 1972-83; mem. nat. adv. com. on planning and instl. affairs NSF, 1971-73; nat. adv. rsch. resources coun. NIH, 1974-78, mem. adv. com. to dir. NIH, 1981-84. Contbr. articles to profl. jours. Served to capt. USAAF, World War II. Patentee in field. Home: PO Box 17407 Salt Lake City UT 84117

PARVER, JANE W., lawyer. AB summa cum laude, Tufts U.; MA, Fletcher Sch. Law and Diplomacy; JD, Columbia U., 1972. Bar: N.Y. 1973. Law clerk so. dist. N.Y. U.S. Dist. Ct., 1972-73; asst U.S. atty. so. dist. N.Y. criminal divsn. U.S. Atty's. Office, 1976-81; chief Major Crimes Unit, 1981-84; exec. asst. U.S. Atty., chief Pub. Corruption Unit, 1984-85; ptnr. Kaye, Scholer, Fierman, Hays & Handler, N.Y.C. Office: Kaye Scholer Fierman Hays & Handler 425 Park Ave New York NY 10022-3506

PARVIAINEN, ASKO, engineering company executive, consultant. Pres. Outokumpu Engring. Enterprises, Owings Mills, Md. Office: Outokumpu Engring Entps 10055 Red Run Blvd Owings Mills MD 21117*

PARVIN, PHILIP E., retired agricultural researcher, educator; b. Manatee, Fla., July 3, 1927; s. Clinton Fisk and Beatrice (Ward) P. MS, Miss. State U., Starkeville, 1950; PhD, Mich. State U., 1965. Asst. prof. U. Fla., Gainesville, 1952-55; extension specialist U. Calif., Davis, 1963-66; gen. mgr. Rod McLellan Co., San Francisco, 1966-68; horticulturist Maui Agrl. Rsch. Ctr. U. Hawaii, Kula, 1968-93. Contbr. over 100 articles to profl. jours. With U.S. Army, 1945-46. Fellow Am. Soc. for Hort. Sci.; mem. Am. Acad. Floriculture (hon.), South African Protea Prodrs. and Exporters (hon. life), Internat. Protea Assn. (hon. life, chmn. rsch. com. 1983-89), Protea Growers Assn. Hawaii (hon. life), Rotary (pres. Maui chpt. 1981-82). Republican. Methodist. Achievements include development of Hawaii protea industry. Home: 2395 Nuremberg Blvd Port Charlotte FL 33983

PARZEN, EMANUEL, statistical scientist; b. N.Y.C., Apr. 21, 1929; s. Samuel and Sarah (Getzel) P.; m. Carol Tenowitz, July 12, 1959; children: Sara Leah, Michael Isaac. AB in Math., Harvard U., 1949; MA, U. Calif., Berkeley, 1951, PhD, 1953. Research scientist Columbia, 1953-56, asst. prof. math. statistics, 1955-56; faculty Stanford, 1956-70, asso. prof. statistics, 1959-64, prof., 1964-70; prof. statistics State U. N.Y. at Buffalo, 1970-73, prof. statis. sci., 1973-78; distinguished prof. statistics Tex. A and M U., College Station, 1978—; guest prof. Imperial Coll., London, 1961-62; vis. prof. MIT, 1964-65, Harvard U., 1976, 88, Ctr. for Advanced Study in Behavioral Scis., 1983-84. Author: Stochastic Processes, 1962, Modern Probability Theory and its Applications, 1960, Time Series Analysis Papers, 1967, also articles. Fellow AAAS, Internat. Statis. Inst., Am. Statis. Assn., Royal Statis. Soc., Inst. Math. Statistics; mem. Am. Math. Soc., Soc. Indsl. and Applied Math., Bernoulli Soc., N.Y. Acad. Scis., Phi Beta Kappa, Sigma Xi. Research in time series analysis, non-parametric statistical data modeling, change analysis. Office: Tex A&M U Dept Stats College Station TX 77843-3143

PARZEN, STANLEY JULIUS, lawyer; b. N.Y.C., Feb. 6, 1952. BA, Earlham Coll., 1973; LLB cum laude, Harvard U., 1976. Bar: Ill. 1978, U.S. Dist. Ct. (no. dist.) Ill. 1978, U.S. Dist. Ct. (no. dist.) Calif. 1989, U.S. Ct. Appeals (7th cir.) 1981, U.S. Ct. Appeals (8th cir.) 1983, U.S. Ct. Appeals (5th cir.) 1992, U.S. Ct. Appeals (D.C. cir.) 1992, U.S. Ct. Appeals (2d cir.) 1990. Law clk. to judge U.S. Ct. Appeals 4th cir., 1976-77; ptnr. Mayer, Brown & Platt, Chgo. Mem. Phi Beta Kappa. Office: Mayer Brown & Platt 190 S La Salle St Chicago IL 60603-3410

PASACHOFF, JAY MYRON, astronomer, educator; b. N.Y.C., July 1, 1943; s. Samuel S. and Anne (Traub) P.; m. Naomi Schwartz, Mar. 31, 1974; children: Eloise Hilary, Deborah Donna. A.B., Harvard U., 1963, A.M. (NSF fellow), 1965, Ph.D. (NSF fellow, N.Y. State Regents fellow for advanced grad. study), 1969. Research physicist Air Force Cambridge Research Labs., Bedford, Mass., 1968-69; Menzel research fellow Harvard Coll. Obs., Cambridge, Mass., 1969-70; research fellow Hale Obs., Carnegie Instn., Washington, and Calif. Inst. Tech., Pasadena, 1970-72; dir. Hopkins Obs. Williams Coll., Williamstown, Mass., 1972—; chmn. astronomy dept. Williams Coll., 1972-77, 91-92, asst. prof. astronomy, 1972-77, assoc. prof., 1977-84, prof., 1984, Field Meml. prof. of astronomy, 1984—; adj. asst. prof. astronomy U. Mass., Amherst, 1975-77, adj. assoc. prof., 1977-83, adj. prof., 1986—; vis. colleague and vis. assoc. prof. astronomy Inst. for Astronomy, U. Hawaii, 1980-81, vis. colleague, 1984-85; vis. scientist Inst. d'Astrophysique, Paris, 1988; mem. Inst. Advanced Study, Princeton, 1989-90, Harvard-Smithsonian Ctr. for Astrophysics, 1993-94; solar eclipse expdns., Mass., 1959, Que., Can., 1963, Mex., 1970, asst. dir. Harvard-Smithsonian-Nat. Geog. Expdn., P.E.I., Can., 1972, NSF expdn., Harvard-Smithsonian-Williams Expdn., Kenya, 1973; NSF expdn., Colombia, 1973 (annular eclipse), Australia, 1974, Pacific Ocean, 1977, Man., Can., 1979, NSF expdn., India, 1980, Hawaii/Pacific, 1981, NSF expdn. Indonesia, 1983, Miss., 1983 (annular eclipse), Papua New Guinea, 1984, Sumatra, Indonesia, 1988, Finland, 1990, Hawaii, 1991, Calif., 1992 (annular eclipse), Pacific near Africa, 1992, N.H., 1994, Chile, 1994; rsch. fellow Owens Valley Radio Obs., summer 1973, U.S.-Australia Coop. Sci. Program, Australian Nat. Radio Astron. Obs., 1974; guest investigator NASA Orbiting Solar Obs.-8, 1975-79; Lockhart lectr. U. Man., 1979; mem. physical sci. bd. World Book Ency., 1989—. Author: Contemporary Astronomy, 1977, 4th edit., 1989, Astronomy Now, 1978, Astronomy: From Earth to the Universe, 1979, 4th edit. 1991, subsequent edits. 1993, 95; A Brief View of Astronomy, 1986, First Guide to Astronomy, 1988, First Guide to the Solar System, 1990, Journey Through the Universe, 1992; co-author: (with Marc L. Kutner, Naomi Pasachoff) Student Study Guide to Contemporary Astronomy, 1977, (with Kutner, Pasachoff and N.P. Kutner) Student Study Guide to Astronomy Now, 1978; (with M.L. Kutner) University Astronomy, 1978, Invitation to Physics, 1981; (with N. Pasachoff, T. Cooney) Physical Science, 1983, 2d edit., 1990, Earth Science, 1983, 2d edit., 1990; (with D.H. Menzel) A Field Guide to the Stars and Planets, 2d edit., 1983, 3d edit., 1992; (with R. Wolfson) Physics, 1987, 2nd edit., 1995, (Extended with Modern Physics, 1989, 2nd edit. 1995), (with N. Pasachoff and others) Discover Science, 7 vols., 1989; (with Michael Covington) Cambridge Eclipse Photography Guide, 1993; (with Len Holder and James DeFranza) Calculus, 1995, Single Variable Calculus, 1994, Multivariable Calculus, 1995; (with Edward Cheng, Patrick Osmer and Hyron Spinrad) The Farthest Things in the Universe, 1994; editor (with J. Percy) The Teaching of Astronomy, 1990; assoc. editor: Jour. Irreproducible Results, 1972-94, Annals of Improbable Rsch., 1994—; abstractor from Am. jours. for Solar Physics, 1968-78; cons. editor McGraw-Hill Ency. Sci. and Tech., 1983—; co-editor-in-chief (with S.P. Parker), McGraw-Hill Ency. of Astronomy, 1993; cons. Random House Dictionary, 1983-86, Nat. Geographic Atlas, 5th edit., 1981, 6th edit., 1990; phys. sci. bd. World Book Encyclopedia, 1989—; contbr. articles to profl. jours. and encys., articles and photographs to non-tech. pubs. Recipient bronze medal Nikon Photo Contest Internat., 1971, photograph aboard

NASA Voyagers, 1977, Dudley award Dudley Obs., 1985; grantee NSF, 1973-75, 79-83, 88—. Nat. Geog. oc. 1973-86, 91-92, Rsch. Corp., 1973-74, 75-78, 82-88, Getty Found., 1994-95. Fellow AAAS (chair sect. D. 1987-88), Royal Astron. Soc., Am. Phys. Soc. (mem.- at-large Am. Phys. Soc./Am. Assn. Physics Tchrs. Forum on Edn. 1995—), N.Y. Acad. Sci., Internat. Planetarium Soc.; mem. AAUP (chpt. pres. 1977-80), Internat. Astron. Union (U.S. nat. rep. Commission on Teaching Astronomy 1976—, chmn. Eclipse Working Group 1991—, rep. to Com. on Teaching Sci. to Internat. Coun. Sci. Unions 1991-93), Am. Astron. Soc. (astronomy edn. adv. com. 1990—, astronomy news com. 1991—), Astron. Soc. Pacific, Union Radio Sci., Am. Assn. Physics Tchrs. (astronomy com. 1983-87), Sigma Xi (chpt. pres. 1973-74, nat. lectr. 1993—). Home: 1305 Main St Williamstown MA 01267-2630 Office: Hopkins Obs Williams Coll Williamstown MA 01267

PASAHOW, LYNN H(AROLD), lawyer; b. Ft. Eutiss, Va., Mar. 13, 1947; s. Samuel and Cecelia (Newman) P.; m. Leslie Aileen Cobb, June 11, 1969; 1 child, Michael Alexander. AB, Stanford U., 1969; JD, U. Calif., Berkeley, 1972. Bar: Calif. 1972, U.S. Ct. Appeals (9th cir.) 1972, U.S. Dist. Ct. (no. dist.) Calif. 1973, U.S. Dist. Ct. (cen. dist.) Calif. 1974, U.S. Supreme Ct. 1976, U.S. Dist. Ct. (ea. dist.) Calif. 1977, U.S. Ct. Appeals (fed. cir.) 1990. Law clk. judge U.S. Dist. Ct. (no. dist.) Calif., San Francisco, 1972-73; assoc. McCutchen, Doyle, Brown & Enersen, San Francisco, 1973-79, ptnr., 1979—; dir. Copyright Soc. N. Calif., San Francisco. Author: Pretrial and Settlement Conferences in Federal Court, 1983; co-author: Civil Discovery and Mandatory Disclosure: A Guide to Effective Practice, 1994; contbr. articles to profl. jours. Trustee Sierra Sch., El Cerrito, Calif., 1991-93. Mem. ABA, Calif. Bar Assn., Am. Intellectual Property Law Assn. Democrat. Office: McCutchen Doyle Brown & Enersen 3 Embarcadero Ctr 28th Fl San Francisco CA 94111 Notable cases include: duPont vs. Cetus, PCR patent litigation, nicotine patch patent litigation.

PASAMANICK, BENJAMIN, psychiatrist, educator; b. N.Y.C., N.Y., Oct. 14, 1914; s. Alex and Elizabeth (Moskalik) P.; m. Hilda Knobloch, May 1, 1942 (div. July 1982); m. Lidia Laba, Aug. 27, 1982. A.B., Cornell U., 1936; M.D., U. Md., 1941. Intern State Hosp., Bklyn., 1941, Harlem Hosp., N.Y.C., 1942; resident N.Y. State Psychiat. Inst., 1943; asst. Clinic Child Devel., Yale U., New Haven, 1944-46; chief children's in-patient and out-patient services Neuropsychiat. Inst., U. Mich. Hosp., Ann Arbor, 1946-47; chief children's psychiat. services Kings County Hosp., Bklyn., 1947-50; psychiatrist Phipps Clinic, Johns Hopkins Hosp., Balt., 1952-55, Harriet Lane Home, 1951-55; asst. prof. Johns Hopkins U. Sch. Hygiene and Pub. Health, 1950-52, asso. prof. pub. health adminstrn., 1953-55; prof. psychiatry Ohio State U., 1955-65, adj. prof. sociology and anthropology, 1963-65; clin. prof. psychiatry U. Ill. Coll. Medicine, Chgo., also Chgo. Med. Sch.; asso. dir. research Ill. Dept. Mental Health, 1965-67; pres. N.Y. Sch. Psychiatry, N.Y.C., 1968-72; Sir Aubrey and Lady Hilda Lewis prof. social psychiatry N.Y. Sch. Psychiatry, 1972-84; asso. commr. N.Y. State Dept. Mental Hygiene, 1968-76; adj. prof. psychology NYU, 1968-75, rsch. prof. psychiatry and behavioral scis., 1984—; rsch. prof. Albany Med. Coll., 1978-80, prof. emeritus, 1980, research prof. med. library scis., 1978-84; clin. prof. preventive and community medicine N.Y. Med. Coll., 1976-77; Cutter lectr. preventive medicine Harvard, 1960; Purkinje lectr. U. Prague, 1963; rsch. adj. prof. epidemiology Sch. Pub. Health and Adminstrv. Medicine, Columbia U., N.Y.C., 1967-77; adj. prof. pediatrics Albany Med. Coll., 1972-77; prof. psychiatry and behavioral sci. Sch. Medicine, SUNY, Stony Brook, 1978-84; mem. com. mental retardation Coun. State Govt.; chmn. com. on standardization of diagnosis WHO; chmn. com. mental health U.S. Com. on Vital and Health Stats.; Percy Bailey lectr. U. Ill.; Lawrence Kolb Sr. lectr. 25th Anniversary NIH. Author 17 books.; contbr. numerous articles to profl. jours.; mem. numerous editorial bds. of professional jours. Recipient Sci. Distinction award World Assn. Psychiat. Rehab., 1994, Cert. of Recognition for Contbns. to Psychiat. Epidemiology and Biostatistics, Harvard Inst. Psychiat. Epidemiology and Genetics, 1995. Mem. APHA (governing coun. 1956, Rema Lapouse Gold medal 1977), APA (pres. divsn. child, youth and family svcs. 1987), Am. Psychopath. Assn. (Stratton award 1961, pres. 1967, Hamilton medal 1968), Orthopsychiat. Assn. (pres. 1971), Am. Psychiat. Assn. (Hofheimer Rsch. award 1949, 67, Agnes Purcell McGavin award 1986), World Assn. for Psychocial Rehab. (bd. dirs., Sci. Distinction award 1994), Am. Anthrop. Assn., Am. Sociol. Assn., Am. Coll. Psychiatrists, Am. Coll. Epidemiologists, Am. Coll. Neuropsychopharmacology, Psychonomic Soc., Soc. Biol. Psychiatry, Acad. Child Psychiatry, Theobald Smith Soc. (founder, pres. 1986-93, sec. 1993), History of Sci. Soc., Soc. for Study of Social Problems, others. Address: 12 N Ferry St Schenectady NY 12305

PASANELLA, GIOVANNI, architect, architectural educator; b. N.Y.C., Jan. 13, 1931; children: Marco, Nicolas. Student, Cooper Union, 1949-53, Yale U., 1953-58. Registered architect, N.Y. Designer Edward L. Barnes, N.Y.C., 1959-64; prin. Giovanni Pasanella, N.Y.C., 1964-76; co-owner Pasanella & Klein, N.Y.C., 1976—; critic architecture U. Ky., Lexington, 1963, Yale U., New Haven, 1964; adj. prof. architecture Columbia U., N.Y.C., 1965-87; vis. fellow urban studies Inst. of Architecture, 1975. Project dir. Inst. of Urban Environ. Columbia U., N.Y.C., 1965-68; cons. architecture to chmn. N.Y. Planning Commn., 1967; cons. urban design City of Lucca, Italy, 1985; bd. trustees Il Piccolo Teatro dell' Opera, Bklyn., 1986, Yale U. traveling fellow, 1958-59; Architecture award Archtl. Record, 1974, 75. Fellow AIA (Residential award N.Y. Soc. 1971); mem. Soc. of Archtl. Historians, Mcpl. Arts Soc. Office: Pasanella & Klein Architects 330 W 42nd St New York NY 10036-6902 Home: Cannizzaro, Via Fondi CAmaiore, Lucca Italy

PASANELLA, MARCO, furniture designer; s. Giovanni and Ann P. BA cum laude, Yale U., 1984. Pres., creative dir. The Pasanella Co., Inc., N.Y.C., 1986—; instr. Parsons Sch. of Design, 1993—; freelance writer, photographer for Elle, Casa Vogue, others, 1987—; co-founder Nat. Initiative for Courtesy & Etiquette, 1991-92. Contbg. editor Taxi Mag., 1987-90; rocking chair acquired by Cooper-Hewitt Mus., Smithsonian Inst. Nat. Mus. Design for permanent collection, 1991, etiquette placemat and napkin prodn. series, 1993, rocking chair acquired by Pres. Bill Clinton for pvt. quarters of White House; contbr. numerous articles to newspapers and profl. jours. Vol. project coord. Bailey House; organized renovation AIDS hospice lounge, 1987-88; mem. renewable energy com. Creative Coalition of Arts, 1990-91; mem. exec. com. Contemporary Arts Coun. of Mus. Modern Art, 1987-89. Named to Internat. Design 40: A Guide to Am.'s Leading Design Innovators, 1993, to Met. Home's Design 100: The Best Am. Has to Offer, 1994; recipient spl. recognition for excellence in design Internat. Contemporary Furniture Fair, N.Y.C., 1992; winner nat. design competition 2001: How Will We Live? Sony Corp., Metropolis Mag., Parsons Sch. Design, 1991. Mem. Furniture Soc. (charter 1991—). Office: The Pasanella Co 45 W 18th St New York NY 10011-4609

PASANO, MICHAEL S., lawyer; b. Kansas City, Mo., Mar. 10, 1951; s. Angelo S. and Rachel (Young) P. AB, Georgetown U., 1973; JD, Yale U., 1976. Bar: Fla., Mo., U.S. Ct. Appeals (5th, 11th and D.C. cirs.), U.S. Supreme Ct. Asst. U.S. atty. U.S. Atty.'s Office, Washington, 1977-81; lawy clk. to justice U.S. Dist. Ct., Washington, 1976-77; asst. U.S. atty. U.S. Atty.'s Office So. Dist. Fla., Miami, 1981-85; from assoc. to ptnr. Zuckerman, Spaeder, Taylor & Evans, Miami, 1985—. Office: Zuckerman Spaeder Taylor & Evans 201 S Biscayne Blvd Ste 900 Miami FL 33131-4326

PASCAL, C(ECIL) BENNETT, classics educator; b. Chgo., May 4, 1926; s. Jack and Goldie (Zeff) P.; m. Ilene Joy Shulman, Feb. 1, 1959; 1 child, Keith Irwin. BA, UCLA, 1949, MA, 1950; MA, Harvard U., 1953, PhD, 1956. Instr. U. Ill., Champaign, 1955-56, Cornell U., Ithaca, N.Y., 1957-60; asst. prof. U. Orege., Eugene, 1960-75, prof. classics, 1975—; head dept., various years - 1965-85. Author: Cults of Cisalpine Gaul, 1964; contbr. articles to profl. jours. Mem. Eugene Bicycle Com., 1971-83. Served with USN, 1944-46. Traveling fellow, Italy, Harvard U., 1956-57, Fulbright-Hays fellow, Rome, 1957-58. Mem. Am. Philol. Assn., Classical Assn. Pacific N.W. (pres. 1965-66), AAUP, Archeol. Inst. of Am. (past pres., sec. Eugene Soc.). Democrat. Jewish. Avocations: skiing, fishing, novel writing. Home: 330 Fulvue Dr Eugene OR 97405-2788 Office: U of Oreg Dept Classics Eugene OR 97403

PASCAL, DAVID, artist; b. N.Y.C., Aug. 16, 1918; s. Boucour and Carolina (Finor) P.; m. Theresa Auerbach, Aug. 24, 1962; 1 child, Jeffrey

B. Student, Am. Artists Sch., 1936-38; M Practioner, N.Y. Tng. Inst. Neuro-Linguistic Programming, 1992. Instr. Sch. Visual Arts, N.Y.C., 1955-58; lectr. mus., schs.; congresses N.Y., Paris, Italy, Sao Paulo, Buenos Aires, Argentina; organizer 1st Am. Internat. Congress Comics, N.Y.C., 1972; artistic counselor to bd. dirs. Lucca Internat. Comics Congresses, 1976—; participant overseas tours for Def. Dept., 1957, 58, 61; Auditor Coll. de Pataphysique, Paris. One-man show Librairie Le Kiosque, Paris, 1965, Museu de Arte, Sao Paulo, Brazil, Graham Gallery, N.Y.C., 1973, Museude Arte Moderna Rio de Janeiro, Brazil, 1973, Man and His World, Montreal, 1974, 75, World Gallery, N.Y.C., 1977, Musee d'Angouleme, France, 1983, 1st Cartoon Biennale Invitational, Davos, Switzerland, 1986, group show, Musee des Arts Decoratifs, 1967, Pinocchio/Graphis Invitational Exhbn., Venice, 1987, École Nat. Supérieure des Beaux-Arts, Paris, 1989 ; drawings appeared in Paris-Match; others; 73 1971); author, illustrator: The Art of Inferior Decorating, 1963, 15 Fables of Krylov, 1965 (in permanent exhibit at Congl. Library), The Silly Knight, 1967, Perspectives, 1985; also publ.: comics An American Expressionism (in archives Mus. of Art, Sao Paulo); editor "An American in Paris" issue Pilote Mag., Paris, 1988; co-editor spl. internat. comics issues Graphis mag, Zurich, Switzerland, Goofus, Paris, 1975; regular contbr. to The New Yorker. Served with U.S. Mcht. Marine, 1940-45. Recipient Dattero d'Oro Salone Indtelle Umorismo, Italy 1963, Illustrator's award Nat. Cartoonists Soc. 1969, 77, Phenix award, Paris 1971. Mem. Nat. Cartoonists Soc. (fgn. affairs sec. 1963—), Internat. Comics Orgn. (Am. rep. 1970—), Association des Auteurs de Comics et de Cartoons (Am. rep.). Home and Studio: 133 Wooster St New York NY 10012-3176 Work is adult play. Knowing what you really want to do and finding the best ways to do it are the keys to joy of life.

PASCAL, FRANCINE, writer; b. N.Y.C., May 13, 1937; d. William and Kate (Dunitz) Rubin; m. Jerome Offenberg, Sept. 9, 1958; children: Jamie, Laurie, Susan; m. John Robert Pascal, Aug. 18, 1964 (dec. 1981). BS, NYU, 1958. Author: Hanging Out With Cici, 1977, My First Love and Other Disasters, 1979, Hand Me Down, Kid, 1980 (Dorothy Canfield Fisher award, 1982, Meml. Childrens Book award, Bernard Versele award, Brussels), Save Johanna!, 1981, Love and Betrayal, 1985, Hold the Mayo, 1985, If Wishes Were Horses, 1994; collaborator on book of musical George M!, 1968; creator young adult book series Sweet Valley High, 1983, Sweet Valley Twins, 1986, Sweet Valley Kids, 1989, Sweet Valley University, 1993. Mem. PEN, NOW, Dramatist's Guild, Writer's League, Screen Writer's Guild.

PASCAL, ROGER, lawyer; b. Chgo., Mar. 16, 1941; s. Samuel A. and Harriet E. (Hartman) P.; m. Martha Hecht, June 16, 1963; children: Deborah, Diane, David. AB with distinction, U. Mich, 1962; JD cum laude, Harvard U., 1965. Bar: Ill. 1965, U.S. Dist. Ct. (no. dist.) Ill. 1965, U.S. Ct. Appeals (7th cir.) 1969, U.S. Supreme Ct. 1976, Wis. 1985, U.S. Ct. Appeals (2d and 9th cirs.) 1986. Assoc. Schiff Hardin & Waite, Chgo., 1965-71, ptnr., 1972—; adj. prof. law Northwestern U. Law Sch., 1994—. Bd. dirs.: mem. exec. com. Chgo. Law Enforcement Study Group, 1975-80, pres., 1978-80; pres. Harvard Law Soc. Ill., 1976-78; bd. dirs. ACLU of Ill., 1984—, gen. counsel, 1986—. Mem. ABA (antitrust and litigation sects.), Pub. Interest Law Initiative (bd. dirs. 1989—), Fund for Justice (bd. dirs. 1986—), Chgo. Council lawyers (bd. dirs. 1970-74, 80-84), Chgo. Legal Assistance Found. (bd. dirs. 1985-88), Phi Beta Kappa. Clubs: University, Metropolitan (Chgo.). Office: Schiff Hardin & Waite 7200 Sears Tower Chicago IL 60606

PASCALE, DANIEL RICHARD, judge; b. Racine, Wis., Mar. 22, 1940; s. Domenic and Fannie Colette (Julian) P.; m. Mary Sara McDonald, June 28, 1986. AB cum laude, Harvard U., 1962; JD, U. Chgo., 1965. Bar: Ill. 1966, U.S. Ct. Appeals (7th cir.) 1967, U.S. Dist. Ct. (no. dist.) Ill. 1969, U.S. Supreme Ct. 1972. Asst. corp. counsel City of Chgo., 1966-72, chief appellate atty., 1972-79, 1st dep. corp. counsel, 1979-84; ptnr. Rudnick & Wolfe, Chgo., 1984-90; judge Circuit Ct. of Cook County, Ill., 1990-94; adminstrv. dir. Adminstrv. Office of Ill. Cts., Chgo., 1995—. Bd. dirs. DeKoven Found., Racine, 1986—; adv. bd. Art Resources in Teaching, Chgo., 1987-94; v.p. Episcopal Homes Mgmt., Inc., Milw., 1988—. Mem. ABA, Ill. Bar Assn., Chgo. Bar Assn. Democrat. Episcopalian. Office: 160 N LaSalle Chicago IL 60601

PASCARELLA, PERRY JAMES, magazine editor; b. Bradford, Pa., Apr. 11, 1934; s. James and Lucille Margaret (Monti) P.; m. Carol Ruth Taylor, May 4, 1957; children: Cynthia, Elizabeth. AB, Kenyon Coll., 1956; Coll. William and Mary, William and Mary Coll., 1957; postgrad., George Washington U., 1958. Credit reporter Dun & Bradstreet, Cleve., 1956, 60; asst. editor Steel mag., Cleve., 1961-63, asso. editor, 1963-67, bus. editor, 1968-69, mng. editor, 1969; mng. editor Industry Week mag., Cleve., 1970-71, exec. editor, 1971-86, editor-in-chief, 1986-89; v.p. editorial Penton Pub. Inc., 1989—; lectr. in field. Author: Technology - Fire in a Dark World, 1979, Humanagement in the Future Corporation, 1981, The New Achievers, 1984, The Purpose-Driven Organization, 1989; contbg. author: Optimistic Outlooks, 1982, Creating a Global Agenda, 1984, Leadership in a New Era, 1994. Lt. comdr. USNR, 1957-60. Recipient Disting. Service award Kenyon Coll., 1975, 81, Am. Bus. Press Crain award, 1992; Carnegie scholar, 1952-56. Mem. World Future Soc., Am. Teilhard Assn. Future of Man, U. Akron Inst. for Future Studies (bd. advisors). Presbyterian (elder). Home: 30413 Winsor Dr Cleveland OH 44140-1143

PASCH, ALAN, philosophy educator; b. Cleve., Dec. 1, 1925; s. P. Jerome and Esther (Broverman) P.; m. Eleanor Kudlich Berna, Dec. 27, 1950; 1 child, Rachel. B.A., U. Mich., 1949; M.A., New Sch. Social Research, 1952; Ph.D., Princeton U., 1955; Bamford fellow, 1955. Instr. philosophy Ohio State U., 1956-59, asst. prof., 1959-60; assoc. prof. philosophy U. Md., College Park, 1960-67, prof., 1967—. Author: Experience and the Analytic, 1958; also articles, revs. Served with AUS, 1944-46, PTO. Mem. Am. Philos. Assn. (exec. dir. 1969-72, sec.-treas. Eastern div. 1965-68), Aristotelian Soc., Metaphys. Soc. Am., Washington Philosophy Club (pres. 1978-79), AAUP, ACLU. Office: U Md Dept Philosophy College Park MD 20742

PASCHALL, DOUGLAS DUANE, headmaster; b. Murray, Ky., Mar. 9, 1944; s. Ratliffe and Velna Gray (Douglas) P.; m. Rosemary Anne Souter, July 28, 1968; children: Rachel, Andrew. BA, U. of South, Sewanee, Tenn., 1966, U. Oxford, United Kingdom, 1968; MA, U. Oxford, United Kingdom, 1972, PhD, 1977. Asst. prof. U. Tenn., Chattanooga, 1969-71; from asst. prof. to prof. U. of South, 1971-88, assoc. dean, 1979-84; headmaster Montgomery Bell Acad., Nashville, Tenn., 1988—; pres. British Studies at Oxford, 1981, 83, 87, 91, tutor, 1976, 79, 85. Editor: Homewords, 1986, Touchstone, 1985-87. Chmn. Tenn. Arts Commn., Nashville, 1984-86; active Tenn. Humanities Coun., Nashville, 1981-87; bd. dirs. Am. Cancer Soc., Nashville, 1988-91. Rhodes scholar, 1966-69. Mem. Am. Assn. Rhodes Scholars, South Atlantic MLA, Nat. Assn. Ind. Schs. Avocations: writing, gardening, piano and music, travel. Office: Montgomery Bell Acad 4001 Harding Rd Nashville TN 37205-1998

PASCHALL, LEE MCQUERTER, retired communications consultant; b. Sterling, Colo., Jan. 21, 1922; s. Lee McQuerter and Agnes (Woldridge) P.; m. Bonnie Jean Edwards, Oct. 24, 1942; children: Patricia Ann Grillos, Stephen Lee, David Edward. B.A., U. Ala., 1957; M.A., George Washington U., 1964. Served with U.S. Army, 1940-46; communications engr. Colo. Air N.G., Denver, 1946-51; commd. maj. U.S. Air Force, 1951, advanced through grades to lt. gen., 1974, ret., 1978; ind. cons. Springfield, Va., 1978-81; pres., chief exec. officer Am. Satellite Co., Rockville, Md., 1981-84, chmn., 1984-85; dir. Radiation Systems Inc., Gen. Data Comm Industries. Contbr. numerous articles to profl. publs. Mem. com. rev. nat. communications system initiatives NRC, 1982-88. Decorated Legion of Merit with oak leaf cluster; decorated disting. service medals; recipient Eascon IEEE, 1979. Mem. Armed Forces Communications-Electronics Assn. (chpt. pres., nat. bd. dirs. Disting Service), Air Force Assn. Mem. Disciples of Christ. Home and Office: 1513 Hampton Hills Cir Mc Lean VA 22101-6018

PASCHANG, JOHN LINUS, retired bishop; b. Hemingford, Nebr., Oct. 5, 1895; s. Casper Paschang and Gertrude Huser. D. of Canon Law, Cath. U. Am., Washington, 1925, MA, 1926, PhD, 1927; JD (hon.), Creighton U., 1960. Pastor St. Rose Ch., Hooper, Nebr., 1921-23, Holy Cross Ch., Omaha, 1927-51; bishop Grand Island, Nebr., 1951-72; ret., 1972. Author: The Sacramentals, 1925, The Popes and Revival of Learning, 1927. Mem.

KC (state chaplain 1938-42). Republican. Roman Catholic. Avocation: missionary work. Home: St Josephs Home 320 E Decatur St West Point NE 68788

PASCHKE, DONALD VERNON, music educator; b. Menominee, Mich., Oct. 22, 1929; s. Leo Carl Ferdinand and Augusta O. (Fritz) P.; m. Helen Inez Burton, Feb. 17, 1951; children: David Vernon, Celeste Eileen. MusB, BS in Choral Music Edn., U. Ill., 1957, 58, 61; MusM in Voice, 1958; D Mus. Arts, U. Colo., 1972. Instr. music Berea (Ky.) Coll., 1958-62; asst. prof. music Eastern N.Mex. U., Portales, 1962-71, assoc. prof., 1971-76, prof., 1976-94; prof. emeritus, 1994. Translator, editor: A Complete Treatise on the Art of Singing, Part Two (Manuel Garcia II), 1975; Part One, 1984. Songleader Portales Men's Breakfast, 1976—, pres., 1974-76, 89-91, v.p. 1988-89, pres., 1989-91; chancel choir dir. 1st Presbyn. Ch., Clovis, N.Mex., 1976—. With U.S. Army, 1951-53. Mem. Nat. Edn. Assn., Nat. Assn. Tchrs. Singing (lt. gov. N.Mex. 1968-72, v.p. Gt. Plains chpt. 1972-74, chpt. pres. 1974-78). Pi Kappa Lambda, Phi Kappa Phi. Republican. Presbyterian. Avocations: photography, do-it-yourself projects. Home: 228 Kansas Dr Portales NM 88130-7121

PASCHKE, EDWARD F., artist, illustrator; b. Chicago, Ill., June 22, 1939. B.F.A., Art Inst. Chgo., 1961, M.F.A., 1970. Instr. painting Art Inst. Chgo., 1974-76, Columbia Coll., Chgo., 1976-78; prof. drawing Northwestern U., Evanston, Ill., 1977-78. Retrospective, Contemporary Art Ctr., Cin., 1975, exhbns., Art Inst. Chgo., 1970-72, Whitney Mus. Am. Art, N.Y.C., 1972-74, 81, XII Vienal de São Paulo, Brazil, 1973, Mus. Contemporary Art, Chgo., Mexico City and Washington, 1974, 75, 77, Art Inst. Chgo., 1974, Ottawa Royal Mus. Art. Ont., Can., 1974, Nat. Collection Fine Arts, Washington, 1975, Mayor Gallery, London, 1980, Camoen Arts Ctr., London, 1981, Ceolfrith Gallery, Sunderland Arts Ctr., Eng., 1981, Cleve. Mus. Art, 1981, Haus der Kunst, Munich, Germany, 1982, Pace Gallery, N.Y.C., 1982, Mus. Contemporary Art, Chgo., 1982, Univ. Gallery, U. Mass., 1982, Gore Fine Arts, Chgo., 1983, Phyllis Kind Gallery, N.Y.C., 1984, Hirshhorn Mus., Washington, 1984, Mus. of Modern Art, N.Y., 1984, Whitney Museum, Brooklyn Museum, Metropolitan Museum of Art, 1986, Turman Gallery, Indiana U., 1991, Caestecker Gallery, Ripon Coll., Wisc., 1992; group shows, Twelve Contemporary Masters, Art Inst. Chgo., 1992; represented permanent collections: Art Inst. Chgo., Mus. des XX Jahrhundert, Vienna, Austria, Darthea Speyer Gallery, Paris, Mus. Contemporary Art, Chgo., Mus. Modern Art, Vienna, Austria, Mus. Boymans, Rotterdam, Netherlands, Musee d'Art Moderne Nationale, Paris, Balt. Art Mus., Ill. Bell Telephone Co., N.Y.C. and Chgo., Phila. Mus. of Art, Whitney Mus., Seattle Art Mus., Corcoran Gallery, Washington. Recipient Logan medal Art Inst. Chgo., 1973; Raymond fellow, Ponte del Arte fellow Art Inst. Chgo., 1961,70; Cassandra Found. grantee, 1972. Office: care Phyllis Kind Gallery 313 W Superior St Chicago IL 60610-3515

PASCO, DUANE NOBLE, artist; b. Seattle, May 14, 1932; s. Duane Noble Doolittle and Della Artiel (Turner) Pasco; m. Katie Marie McAuliffe, Mar. 4, 1967; children: Shelley, John, Amy; m. Audrey Stenvahl, 1957 (div. 1963); children: Audrey, Brian. Grad. high sch., Seattle. Tchr. Alaska Native Brotherhood, Ketchikan, 1971, K'San Village, Hazelton, B.C., Can., 1969-71, Evergreen State Coll., Olympia, Wash., 1971, Native Cultural Ctr., Sitka, Alaska, 1977, Totem Heritage Ctr., Ketchikan, 1978, 80, Kitenmax Sch. N.W. Art, K'San Village, Hazelton, 1983, U. Wash., 1984, 85, 86, Ketchikan Community Coll., 1984, U. Alaska, 1985; cons. Nat. Park Svc., Sitka Nat. Hist. Park (Alaska), 1978, Nat. Native Indian Artists' Symposium, Vancouver, B.C., 1983. artist in residence Pacific Sci. Ctr., Seattle, 1985. Group shows include Seattle Ctr., 1980, 82, 83, State Capitol Mus., Olympia, Wash., 1981, Field Mus. Natural History, Chgo., 1982, Robert Adams Gallery, San Francisco, 1982, Pacific Sci. Ctr., Seattle, 1982, Stonington Gallery, Seattle, 1983, Oreg. Mus. for Sci. and History, Portland, 1983, Gallery Mack, Seattle, 1984, Scanlon Gallery, Ketchikan, Alaska, 1985, Quintna's Gallery, Portland, 1986, 87, 88, Partlow Gallery, Olympia, 1986, Bellevue (Wash.) Art Mus., 1987, Snow Goose Gallery, Seattle, 1988, Marianne Partlow Gallery, Olympia, Wash., 1988; represented in permanent collections Alaska State Mus., Juneau, U. B.D. Mus. Anthropology, Vancouver, U. Tokyo, Wash. State Hist. Mus., Seattle; vis. artist S.E. Alaska Indian Coun., Sitka, 1979; contbr. articles in field to profl. jours. Sgt. U.S. Army, 1957-60, Korea. Recipient 1st Place award Edmonds Art Festival, 1967; study grantee Alaska State Coun. for the Arts, Anchorage, 1984, Inst. Alaska Native Arts, Juneau, 1984, Nat. Endowment for the Arts, Washington, 1985. Home and Office: 19330 Widme Rd NE Poulsbo WA 98370-8917

PASCO, HANSELL MERRILL, retired lawyer; b. Thomasville, Ga., Oct. 7, 1915; s. John and Katherine (Merrill) P.; m. Williamine Carrington Lancaster, June 28, 1941; children: Hansell Merrill, Dabney, Robert, Elizabeth, Carrington. B.A., Va. Mil. Inst., 1937; LL.B., U. Va., 1940. Bar: Va. bar 1939. Ptnr. Hunton & Williams, Richmond, Va., 1948-81, sr. counsel, 1981—; mng. partner Hunton & Williams, 1968-76. Chmn. State Counsel Higher Edn. for Va., 1978-80; trustee Protestant Episcopal Sem., Alexandria, Va., 1980-85. Served with U.S. Army, 1940-45. Office: Hunton & Williams Riverfront Plz E Tower 951 E Byrd St Richmond VA 23219-4040

PASCOE, CHARLES THOMAS, JR., computer systems company executive; b. Blacksburg, Va., July 21, 1941; s. Charles Thomas Sr. and Annie Pearl (Grubb) P.; m. Carole Ruth Kouse, Dec. 23, 1962 (div. 1991); children: Charlotte Ruth, Cheryl Anne, Carrie Marie, Charles John. BA in Music, Wittenberg U., 1963. Comm.-electronics officer USAF, Wright-Patterson AFB, Ohio, 1964-71; line control mgr. Gulf & Western's Assocs. Computer Svcs. Co. Inc., South Bend, Ind., 1971-74; telecom. group mgr. Continental Ill. Nat. Bank & Trust Co., Chgo., 1974-75; maj. acct. exec. COMTEN, Lombard, Ill., 1977-76; computer cons. Va., 1977-79; systems applications engr. ADT Sec. Systems, Fed. Mktg. Group, Alexandria, Va., 1979-82; cons. Wang Labs. Inc., Bethesda, Md., 1982-84; mktg. rep. Prime Computer Inc., Rockville, Md., 1984-86; telemktg. mgr. legal info. svcs. div. Sterling Software, Rockville, 1986-89; telesvcs. mgr. Internat. Telesystems Corp., Herndon, Va., 1989-91; computer cons. Future Sys. Design, Fairfax, Va., 1992—. 1st lt. USAF, 1964-68. Mem. DAV, Masons, Phi Mu Alpha Sinfonia, Alpha Tau. Avocation: golf. Office: PO Box 2225 Merrifield VA 22116-2225

PASEN, ROBERT MARTIN, psychologist; b. N.Y.C., June 21, 1945; s. Sidney and Florence (Weitzman) P.; m. Launa Gayle Riedlinger, Aug. 1976; children: Adam Jeffrey, Ashley Elizabeth. BA, Rutgers U., Newark, 1967; MA, Bowling Green State U., 1970; PhD, Northwestern U., 1977. Lic. clin. psychologist, cert. addictions counselor, Ill.; health svc. provider in psychology, Ind. From instr. to asst. prof. psychology William Rainey Harper Coll., Palatine, Ill., 1970-80, assoc. prof. psychology, 1980-89; pres. Inst. for Stress Mgmt., Hoffman Estates, Ill., 1979—; chmn., CEO Inst. Mental Health Cons., Ltd., Hoffman Estates, 1988—; mem. profl. staff Forest Hosp., Des Plaines, Ill., 1979—, Charter Barclay Hosp., Chgo., 1981—, Chgo. Lakeshore Hosp., 1982—, Good Shepherd Hosp., Barrington, Ill., 1990—, Woodlands Hosp., Hoffman Estates, Ill., 1990—, Linden Oaks Hosp., Naperville, Ill., 1990—; cons. dept. psychiatry Cook County Hosp., Chgo., 1971-81; cons. Police-Community Rels. Tng. Program, Newark, 1967-68; nat. trustee Forest Inst. Profl. Psychology; lectr. and presenter in field. Contbr. articles to profl. jours. Mem. No. Ill. Critical Incident Stress Debriefing Team, 1990—; mem. Endowment for the Arts, 1990—; vol. disaster mental health svc. provider ARC, 1992—; mem. Lincoln Park Zool. Soc., 1979—, Friends of Channel 11, 1979—. Benton and Bowles Rsch. fellow, 1966-67. Mem. APA, Ill. Psychol. Assn., Ill. Assn. Chiefs of Police (police psychologist com.), Ill. Juvenile Officers Assn., Am. Assn. Suicidology, Ill. Assn. Suicidology, Am. Labor Mgmt. Adminstrs. and Cons. on Alcoholism, Assn. Advancement of Psychology. Office: Inst Mental Health Cons Ltd 2500 W Higgins Rd Ste 1065 Hoffman Estates IL 60195

PASEWARK, WILLIAM ROBERT, author, management consultant; b. Mt. Vernon, N.Y., Sept. 9, 1924; s. William and Barbara (Hermann) P.; m. M. Jean McHarg, Mar. 17, 1956; children: William Robert, Lisabeth Jean, Jan Alison, Carolyn Ann, Scott Graham, Susan Gayle. B.S., NYU, 1949, M.A., 1950, Ph.D., 1956. Instr. NYU, 1949-51; assoc. prof. Meredith Coll., Raleigh, N.C., 1951-52; asst. prof. Mich. State U., 1952-56; prof. Tex. Tech. U., Lubbock, 1956-82; author, owner Office Mgmt. Cons., 1982—; cons. bus. and ednl. agys., lectr. in field, 1955—; field reader rsch. div. U.S. Office Edn., 1966—; mem. commn. to revise curricula Tex. Edn. Agy., 1974—; mem. adv.

com. Lubbock Vocat. Office Edn.; mem. regional bd. examiners Am. Assn. Bus. Colls.; vis. prof. Calif. State U., Fresno, 1959, No. Ariz. State U., 1969, Ctrl. Conn. State Coll., 1974. Author: Individualized Instruction in Business and Office Education, 1973, Electronic and Mechanical Printing Calculator Course, 1974, Electronic Display Calculator Course, 1975, 2d edit., 1984, Clerical Office Procedures, 6th edit., 1978, Rotary Calculator Course, 1962, Ten-Key Listing Machine, 5th edit., 1981, Key-Driven Calculator Course, 1962, Full-Keyboard Adding Listing Machine Course, 3d edit., 1963, Secretarial Office Procedures, 10th edit., 1982, Duplicating Machine Processes, 1971, 2d edit., 1975, Office Machines Course, 1971, 5th edit., 1979, Curso de Máquinas de Oficina, 1977, Técnicas Secretariales y Procedimientos de Oficina, 1978, Machine Transcription Word Processing, 1979, 2d edit., 1987, Electronic Printing Calculator Course, Canadian edit., 1980, Electronic Printing Calculator, 3d edit., 1990, Electronic Calculating Machines Simulation, 4th edit., 1991, Procedures for the Modern Office, 7th edit., 1983, Electronic Display-Printing Calculator, 1983, Reprographics, 1983, Super Calc 3 Learning, Using, and Mastering, 1986, Electronic Office Machines, 6th edit., 1987, The Office: Procedures and Technology, 1987, 2nd edit., 1993 (Textbook Excellence award in bus. Text and Acad. Authors Assn. 1994, William Holmes McGuffy award for textbook excellence and longevity Text and Acad. Authors Assn. 1994), Working With SuperCalc 4, 1987 (Danish transl. 1987), Machine Transcription, Dictation, and Proofreading: An Introduction, 1987, Danish Translation of Supercalc 4, 1987, Microsoft Works: Tutorial and Applications IBM Version, 1991, Calculating Machines Simulation, A Short Course, 1991, Electronic Calculators: Display, Print, Display-Print, 2d edit., 1992, Microsoft Works: Tutorial and Applications Macintosh Version, 1992, Calculator Math for Job and Personal Use, 1992, Ten-Key Skill Builder, 1992, PFS: First Publisher: Tutorial and Applications, IBM 3.0, 4.0, 1993, Publish It!: Tutorial and Applications, IBM version 2.0, 1993, Publish It! Apple version, 1993, Microsoft Works for Windows, 1994, Microsoft Works 3.0 Macintosh, 1994 (Textbook Excellence award in computer text Text & Acad. Authors Assn. 1994), Microsoft Works for Windows 3.0 Tutorial and Applications, Express Publisher Tutorial and Applications, 1994, Microsoft Works DOS 3.0 Quick Course, 1994; assoc. editor: Am. Bus. Edn. Yearbook, 1953; contbr. articles to profl. jours. Adviser Lubbock Opportunities Industrialization Center; mem. Tex. Bus. Tchr. Edn. Council; v.p. Lubbock Econ. Council, 1983, pres., 1984; pres. Lubbock Area Presbyn. Council, 1969; chmn. Lubbock City-County Child Welfare Bd., 1973-74; active local Boy Scouts Am., United Fund. Served with USMCR, 1943-46. Recipient Founders Day award N.Y.U., 1956; Outstanding Educator of Am. award, 1970; citation Tex. Ho. of Reps., 1973; Tex. Bus. Tchr. of Year award, 1973. Mem. Nat. Bus. Edn. Assn., Nat. Assn. Bus. Tchr. Edn., Mountain-Plains Bus. Edn. Assn., Tex. Bus. Edn. Assn. (chmn. legislative com. 1973-80), Nat. Assn. Tchr. Edn. for Bus. and Office Edn., Edn. for Bus. Coordinating Council, Bus. State Suprs. and Tchr. Educators (nat. planning com.), W. Tex. Bus. Edn. Assn. (pres. 1958), Better Bus. Bur. (edn. com.), Am. Vocat. Assn. (pres. bus. and office div. 1976-77, dir. 1976-77, nat. adv. council 1976-84, award of merit 1978), Office Systems Research Assn., Text and Acad. Authors Assn., Authors Guild, Internat. Platform Assn., Lubbock Execs. Assn. (bd. dirs.), Lubbock C. of C., PTA (local pres. 1972), Delta Pi Epsilon, Phi Delta Kappa, Kappa Phi Kappa, Pi Omega Pi, Alpha Kappa Psi, Kappa Delta Pi. Clubs: Lion (past dir.), Lubbock Country. Research in office adminstrn. and ednl. systems. Home: 4403 11th St Lubbock TX 79416-4814 Office: Ste 504A 1901 University Ave Lubbock TX 79410

PASHEK, ROBERT DONALD, economics educator emeritus; b. The Dalles, Oreg., Feb. 27, 1921; s. Gregory and Mary M. (Bonomi) P.; children: William J., Nicole M. A.B., Central Wash. Coll., 1949; M.A., State U. Iowa, 1950; Ph.D., U. Ill., 1955; postgrad., Columbia U., 1947, Inst. Minerva, Zurich, 1947-48. Asst. prof. U. Wichita, 1953-55; asst. prof. Pa. State U., 1956-58, prof., 1960—, head dept. bus. logistics, 1964-73; assoc. dean Pa. State U. (Coll. Bus. Adminstrn.), 1973-87, dir. internat. programs, 1987-89, prof. emeritus, 1989; vis. prof. San Francisco State U., 1963-64; cons. Commonwealth of Pa., U.S. AID, U.S. Dept. Commerce. Served with AUS, 1944-46. Named Transp. Man of Year Delta Nu Alpha, 1964. Mem. Coun. Transp. Rsch. Ctrs. (pres. 1981-82), Am. Soc. Transp. and Logistics (past pres., dir. Joseph C. Scholeen award for excellence 1985), Am. Econ. Assn. (Disting. Mem. award Pub. Utilities Group 1985), Transp. Rsch. Forum, Beta Gamma Sigma, Alpha Kappa Psi. Research on econ. and social impact hwys., transport systems planning, logistic systems design and planning. Home: 5102 Washington Ave N Seattle WA 98103-6143 Office: Bus Adminstrn Bldg Pa State Univ University Park PA 16802

PASINETTI, PIER MARIA, author; b. Venice, Italy, June 24, 1913; came to U.S., 1946, naturalized, 1952; s. Carlo and Maria (Ciardi) P. Dottore in Lettere, U. Padua, Italy, 1935; Ph.D. in Comparative Lit., Yale U., 1949. Fellow La. State U., 1935-36, U. Calif. at Berkeley, 1936-37; lectr. U. Stockholm, 1942-44; prof. Italian and comparative lit. UCLA, 1949—. Author: L'ira di Dio, 1942, Venetian Red, 1960, The Smile on the Face of the Lion, 1965, From the Academy Bridge, 1970, Suddenly Tomorrow, 1971, Dall' Estrema America, 1975, Il Centro, 1979, Dorsoduro, 1983, Life for Art's Sake: Studies in the Literary Myth of the Romantic Artist, 1985, Melodramma, 1993; also articles, revs., film scripts. Recipient Fiction award Nat. Inst. Arts and Letters, 1965. Mem. Authors Guild. Club: Elizabethan Yale. Office: 1259 Dorsoduro, Venice Italy 30123

PASINI, ALBERT R., engineer. Recipient Centennial award Assn. of Profl. Engrs., Geologists and Geophysicists of Alberta, 1992. Home: 1001 2120 Argyle Ave, West Vancouver, BC Canada V7V 1A4*

PASK, JOSEPH ADAM, ceramic engineering educator; b. Chgo., Feb. 14, 1913; s. Adam Poskoczem and Catherine (Ramanauskas) P.; m. Margaret J. Gault, June 11, 1938; children: Thomas Joseph, Kathryn Edyth. B.S., U. Ill., 1934, Ph.D., 1941; M.S., U. Wash., 1935. Ceramic engr. Willamina Clay Products Co., Oreg., 1935-36; teaching asst. ceramic engring. U. Ill., 1938, instr., 1938-41; asst. ceramic engr. electrotech. lab. U.S. Bur. Mines, 1941; assoc. ceramic engr. N.W. Exptl. Sta., 1942-43; asst. prof. ceramic engring., head dept. Coll. of Mines, U. Wash., Seattle, 1941-43; research ceramist, lamp div. Westinghouse Electric Corp., N.J., 1943-46; research engr. ceramic sect. Westinghouse Electric Corp., 1946-48; assoc. prof. ceramic engring., head ceramic group div. materials sci. and engring. U. Calif. at Berkeley, 1948-53, founder program ceramic engring. and sci., 1948, prof., 1953-80, prof. emeritus, 1980—, vice chmn. div., 1956-57, chmn. dept., 1957-61; asso. dean grad. student affairs U. Calif. at Berkeley (Coll. Engring.), 1969-80; sr. faculty scientist Lawrence Berkeley Lab.; John Dorn Meml. lectr. Northwestern U., 1977; Mem. clay mineral com. NRC; mem. materials adv. bd., chmn. ad hoc com. ceramic processing, adv. commn. metallurgy div. U.S. Bur. Standards; chmn. NSF study objective criteria in ceramic engring. edn., U.S.-China Seminar on Basic Sci. of Ceramics, Shanghai, 1983. Recipient John F. Bergeron Meml. Svc. award Ceramic Engring. div. U. Wash., Seattle, 1969, gold medal for research and devel. French Soc. for Research and Devel., 1979, Berkeley citation U. Calif., 1980, Alumni honor award for disting. service in engring. U. Ill. Coll. Engring., 1982, Outstanding Achievement in Edn. award Com. of Confucius, 1982, Internat. Prize Japan Fine Ceramics Assn., 1988, Engring. Alumni Achievement award U. Wash. Coll. Engring., 1991. Fellow AAAS, Am. Ceramic Soc. (disting. life mem., v.p. 1953-54, pres. ednl. coun. 1954-55, trustee 1959-62, chmn. electronics div. 1959-60, John Jeppson award 1967, Ross Coffin Purdy award 1979), Mineral. Soc., Acad. Dental Materials; mem. NAE, Nat. Inst. Ceramic Engrs., N.Y. Acad. Scis., Am. Soc. Metlas, Brit. Ceramic Soc., Internat. Acad. Ceramics, Am. Soc. Engring. Edn. (brit. materials com. 1961-63, Centennial Cert. 1993), Clay Minerals Soc., Ceramics Soc. Japan (hon., Centennial medal 1991), Materials Rsch. Soc. Japan (hon.), Keramos, Sigma Xi, Tau Beta Pi, Alpha Sigma Mu. Home: 994 Euclid Ave Berkeley CA 94708-1437 Office: U Calif Dept Material Sci & Mineral Eng Berkeley CA 94720 *Whatever success I have had can be attributed to hard work generated by a desire for success and recognition by my peers. This attitude was generated by my mother who came to this country, a land of opportunities, as an immigrant from Lithuania at the age of 16 without any knowledge of English. There was no question in her mind—and consequently mine—that I would get an education and be successful.*

PASKAY, ALEXANDER L., federal judge, law educator; b. Mohacs, Hungary, Nov. 5, 1922; J.D., U. Budapest, 1944; J.D., U. Miami, 1958. Bar: Fla. 1958. Research asst. U.S. Dist. Ct. (so. dist.) Fla., Miami, 1958-61; research asst. U.S. Dist. Ct. (mid. dist.) Fla., Tampa, 1961-63; bankruptcy judge U.S.

Dist. Ct. (mid. dist.) Fla., Tampa, 1963—; adj. prof. law Stetson U. Law, St. Petersburg, Fla., 1973—, also chmn. ann. bankruptcy seminar; faculty Pacific Bankruptcy Inst., Western Mountain Bankruptcy Law Inst., Northeast Bankruptcy Law Inst., Northwest Bankruptcy Conf., Internat Insolvency Conf., Milano, Italy. Mem. adv. council Consumer Credit Counseling Service of Tampa. V.p., bd. dirs. Am. Bankruptcy Inst. Mem. bd. govs. Nat. Conf. Bankruptcy Judges, ABA, Fla. Bar Assn., Hillsborough County Bar Assn., Am. Judicature Soc. Author: Handbook for Trustees and Receivers in Bankruptcy, 2d edit. 1978; co-author: Colliers Bankruptcy Manual, Vol. II; Norton Bankruptcy Law and Practice, Vol. VI; revising editor Bankruptcy Code and Rules pamphlet. Office: US Bankruptcy Ct 4921 Memorial Hwy Ste 260 Tampa FL 33634-7506

PASLOV, EUGENE T., state education official. Supt. edn. Nevada. Office: Nev Dept Edn 400 W King St Carson City NV 89703-4215

PASMAN, JAMES S., JR., aluminum company executive; b. East Orange, N.J., 1930. Grad., Upsala Coll., 1956, NYU, 1962. Formerly pres., chief exec. officer Kaisertech Ltd., Oakland, Calif.; chmn., chief exec. officer Kaiser Aluminum subs. KaiserTech Ltd., Oakland; bd. dirs. Chem. Corp. subs. KaiserTech Ltd., Oakland; pres., chief oper. officer Nat. Intergroup Inc., Pitts., 1989-92. Office: Nat Intergroup Inc 1220 Senlac Dr Carrollton TX 75006-7019

PASMANICK, KENNETH, bassoonist; b. Rochester, N.Y., Aug. 23, 1924; s. Philip and Rose (Levitt) P.; m. Frances Virginia Cohen, Dec. 22, 1946; children: Philip, Anne. Student, Eastman Sch. Music, 1942-43, Juilliard Sch. Music, 1946-47; BA, Am. U., 1962. Am. specialist abroad for Dept. State, El Salvador and Costa Rica, 1966-67; instr. bassoon Am. U., Washington; prof. U. Md. Performed with Martha Graham Ballet tour and at Ziegfield Theater, 1946; prin. bassoonist Nat. Symphony Orch., 1947—, Washington Opera Soc.; performed: (world premiere) Serenata for Bassoon and Chamber Orch. (Gian Francesca Malipiero), 1962, (world premiere) The Windhover (Robert Evett); Concerto for Bassoon and Orch., 1971, (world premiere) Bassoon Concerto (David Amram), 1972, N.Y. premiere, Jan. 1993, rec. with Newport Classics Recs., (U.S. premiere) Concerto for Bassoon and Orch. (Gunther Schuller), 1985, Air for Bassoon and Strings (Alec Wilder), 1994; European premiere with Radio Orch. of Saarbrücken, Germany, 1992, rec. with GM Recs., 1992; founder, mem. Nat. Symphony Wind Soloists. Served in USAAF, 1943-46. Recipient Gold medal for cultural contbn. in Costa Rica. Home: 5227 Chevy Chase Pky NW Washington DC 20015-1747 *Irrational culturally induced ideas aside, I see no limits on the creative capacities of humans to forge a just and rational world for all its inhabitants.*

PASNICK, RAYMOND WALLACE, labor union official, editor; b. New Kensington, Pa., Apr. 29, 1916; s. Stanley and Mary Ann (Grzewienska) P.; m. Margaret Solberg, Mar. 3, 1937; children: Victor Keith, Raymond Gene. Ed. pub. schs. Editor Aluminum Workers Jour., New Kensington, 1936-37; publicity dir. Aluminum Workers Am., Pitts., 1937-44; asst. editor Steel Labor, Pitts., 1944-46; editor Steel Labor, 1962-78; Midwest editor, also Midwest dir. edn. United Steelworkers Am., Chgo., 1946-62; nat. editor, dir. comm. United Steelworkers Am., 1962-65; dir. pub. rels. United Steelworker Am., Pitts., 1965-78; editor OLDTIMER quar., 1978-86; vol. editor Steelworker Oldtimer, 1986—. Pub. mem. Chgo. Bd. Edn., 1955-66. Recipient of Civil Rights award Jewish Labor Com. Chgo., 1962, Man of Year award Chgo. unit Nat. Frontiersmen, 1963. Mem. Internat. Labor Press Assn. (pres. 1972-74), Am. Fedn. Tchrs., Chgo. Newspaper Guild (treas. 1948-56, v.p. 1957). Democrat. Roman Catholic. Home and Office: 2248 Country Club Dr Pittsburgh PA 15241-2335

PASQUARELLI, JOSEPH J., real estate development, engineering and construction executive; b. N.Y.C., Mar. 5, 1927; s. Joseph and Helen (Casabona) P.; B.C.E. cum laude, Manhattan Coll., 1949; m. JoAnne Brienza, June 20, 1964; children: Ronald, Richard, June, Joy. Engr. Madigan-Hyland, N.Y.C. and Burns & Roe Inc., N.Y.C., 1949-56; sr. engr., asst. to exec. dir. Office of Sch. Bldgs., N.Y.C. Bd. Edn., 1956-67; dir. design and constrn. mgmt. City U., N.Y., 1967-72; dir. constrn. mgmt. Morse/Diesel Inc., N.Y.C., 1972-76; dir. projects and proposals Burns & Roe Indsl. Svcs. Corp., Oradell, N.J., 1976-80, dir. facilities and infrastructure, 1980-86; dir. design engring, constrn., devel. mgmt. Xerox Realty Corp., Stamford, Ct., 1986-89; exec. v.p. The Galvin Group N.Y.C., 1989-90; assoc. prin. Pei/Galvin Holdings, Ltd., N.Y.C., 1990-93; sr. v.p. Pei Group Holdings, Ltd., N.Y.C., 1993—. Served with U.S. Army, 1944-46. Licensed profl. engr., N.Y., N.J. Fellow ASCE; mem. N.Y. Bldg. Congress (past gov., chmn. legis. com.), NSPE, Mcpl. Engrs., Am. Arbitration Assn., Chi Epsilon. Club: Essex Fells Country. Contbr. articles to profl. jours. Home: 38 Oak Pl North Caldwell NJ 07006-4554 Office: Pei Group Holdings Ltd 10 Rockefeller Plz 12th Fl New York NY 10020

PASQUERILLA, FRANK JAMES, real estate developer and manager; b. Johnstown, Pa., Sept. 4, 1926; s. Harry and Sabina (D'Alfonso) P.; m. Sylvia Theresa Guarino, Jan. 12, 1957; children—Mark E., Leah M. Student, Internat. Corr. Schs., 1944-50; LLD (hon.), U. Notre Dame, 1982; HHD (hon.), St. Francis Coll., Loretto, Pa., 1969, Mt. St. Mary's Coll., Emmitsburg, Md., 1990. With Phila. Q.M. Depot, 1944-46; hwy. insp. Pa. Dept. Hwys., Holidaysburg, 1946-50; with Crown Am. Realty Trust (formerly Crown Constrn. Co.), Johnstown, Pa., 1951—, pres., 1956—, also chmn. bd., 1988—; bd. dirs. Johnstown Area Regional Industries, 1974—; dir., mem. exec. com. U.S. Nat. Bank, Johnstown. Pres. Johnstown Jaycees, 1950-51, Pa. Jaycees, 1953-54; nat. v.p. U.S. Jaycees, 1954-55; del. Pa. Constl. Conv., 1967; trustee U. Notre Dame, 1984—. Decorated knight comdr. Order St. Gregory the Gt. (Vatican); Solidarity Order (Italy); Prime Minister's Silver Anniversary medal (Israel); recipient Assisi award St. Francis Coll., Loretto, Pa., 1980, Humanitarian award Nat. Italian Am. Found., 1990; named Man of Yr. Order Sons of Italy in Am., 1990. Mem. Internat. Council Shopping Ctrs. (trustee 1983), Italian Sons and Daus. Am., Sunnehanna Club, Travelers Club, Elks. Republican. Roman Catholic. Avocations: opera, travel, football. Home: 945 Menoher Blvd Johnstown PA 15905-2566 Office: Crown Am Pasquerilla Plz Johnstown PA 15907

PASQUIER, JOËL, music educator; b. Montmorency, France, Sept. 25, 1943; arrived in Can., 1967; s. Jean de Raymonde (Gourdin) P.; m. Anne Vachon, Nov. 28, 1970; 1 child, Ariane. Grad. in piano and chamber music, Conservatoire Nat. Superieur de Musique, Paris, 1962. Prof. Conservatoire de Musique de St. Germain-en-Laye, France, 1964-65; grad. asst. Sch. Music, Ind. U., Bloomington, 1965-67; tchr. piano Ecole de Musique, U. Laval, Quebec, Can., 1967—; dir. Ecole de Musique, U. Laval, Quebec, 1988-91. Appeared as solo pianist concert halls, radio, TV, with chamber and symphony orchs. in France, U.S., Can., The Netherlands. Fulbright scholar Ind. U., 1965. Mem. Mus. Que. Yacht Club. Office: U Laval Sch Music, Pavillon Casault, Sainte-Foy, PQ Canada G1K 7P4

PASS, BOBBY CLIFTON, entomology educator; b. Cleveland, Ala., Nov. 4, 1931; s. Rufus Clifton and Alma Antoinette (Payne) P.; m. Annie Ruth Rutherford, Aug. 17, 1955; 1 child, Kevin Clifton. Student, Snead Jr. Coll., 1949-50; BS in Agr. Edn., Auburn U., 1952, MS in Entomology, 1960; PhD in Entomology, Clemson U., 1962. Rsch. asst. Auburn (Ala.) U., 1958-60, Clemson (S.C.) U., 1960-62; asst. prof. U. Ky., Lexington, 1962-67, assoc. prof., 1967-68, assoc. prof., chair, 1968, prof., chmn., 1969—; cons. USAID/Indonesia, 1985—, UK/Shandong Agr. U., People's Republic China, 1986—. Contbr. articles on insect mgmt. to profl. jours. Mem. Entomological Soc. Am. (pres. 1986-87, governing bd. 1983-88), Am. Registry Profl. Entomologists (cert., pres. 1979-80), Can. Entomological Soc., Internat. Orgn. for Biol. Control, S.C. Entomological Soc., Kans. Entomological Soc., Ky. Acad. Sci., Soc. Sigma Xi, Gamma Sigma Delta, Phi Kappa Phi. Democrat. Methodist. Home: 3234 Pepperhill Rd Lexington KY 40502-3545 Office: U Ky Dept Entomology Lexington KY 40546-0091

PASSAGE, DAVID, diplomat; b. Charlotte, N.C., June 16, 1942; s. John T. and Virginia (Beam) P. BA, U. Denver, 1964; MS, Georgetown U., 1966. With U.S. State Dept., 1966—; various positions U.S. State Dept: London, Australia, Ecuador, Vietnam, El Salvador, Botswana; dep. spokesman U.S. State Dept., Washington, spl. asst. to Sec. of State Henry Kissinger; dir. for Africa Nat. Security Coun. Staff, The White House, Washington; U.S. amb. to Botswana; polit. adviser to U.S. Spl. Opers. Command MacDill AFB, Fla. Avocations: environment and conservation. Office: 7701 Tampa Point Blvd

Mac Dill A F B FL 33621-5323 Home: 2413 Bay Shore Blvd Tampa FL 33629

PASSAGE, STEPHEN SCOTT, energy company executive; b. Miami, Oct. 10, 1946; s. John Thompson and Virginia Frances (Beam) P.; m. Ellen Shapiro, Aug. 21, 1988. BS in Civil Engring., Pol. Sci., MIT, 1969; MA in Pol. Sci., New Sch. Soc. Rsch., 1972, MA in Econs., 1975. Cer. Profl. Engr. Mem. engring. dept. Port Authority N.Y. and N.J., 1969-86; pres. Montenoy Power Corp., N.Y., 1986—; chmn. IWSA. Contbr. articles to profl. jours. Chmn. 607 West End Ave Corp., 1991—. Mem. ASME, NSPE. Avocations: chess, hiking, tennis, canoeing, reading. Office: Montenay Power Corp 800 3rd Ave New York NY 10022-7601

PASSANEAU, ROBERT J., computer company executive; b. 1937. BS, U. Ill., 1959. Br. mgr. IBM Corp., 1959-80; with XL/Datacomp, Inc., 1980-81, exec. v.p., 1981-87, pres., 1987—, CEO, 1988—. Office: X L Datacomp Inc 908 N Elm StreetRd # 800 Hinsdale IL 60521*

PASSANO, E. MAGRUDER, JR., publishing executive; b. Balt., Oct. 2, 1942; s. Edward M. and Mildred P. (Nelson) P.; m. Helen C. Marikle, Sept. 4, 1971; children: Catherine, Tammy, Sarah. B.S., Johns Hopkins U., 1967, M.L.A., 1969. With Waverly, Inc., Balt., 1965—, salesman, 1970-73, v.p., 1973-75, v.p. adminstrn., sec., 1975-90. vice chmn. sec., 1990—. Pres., Passano Found., Balt., 1982—, Am. Lung Assn. Md., 1982-84; mem. exec. com. Vol. Council for Equal Opportunity, Balt., 1978— ; ; pres. (CHA) Combined Health Agys., Md., 1985-87, chmn. exec. com., 1987—; pres. 12:30 Club Balt., 1981-83; mem. exec. com. Balt. City Life Museums, 1982-93, v.p. 1987-93, trustee emeritus, 1993—; mem. adv. council Johns Hopkins U. Sch. Continuing Studies, 1984—, exec. chair cancer chpt., Johns Hopkins U. Sch. cmty. devel. iniative; mem. Md. Gov.'s Commn. on High Blood Pressure and Related Cardiovascular Risk Factors, 1986—; bd. govs. Md. New Directions, Inc., 1987-94; bd. dirs., mem. exec. com. YMCA Ctrl. Md. 1988—; bd. dirs., chair edn. com. Pride of Balt., 1990—; bd. dir. Independent Coll. Fund Md., 1994—. Served with USN, 1963-65. Recipient Prince Hall Bicentennial award Masons, 1975; citations Mayor of Balt., 1976, City of Balt., 1977, Vol. of Yr. award for outstanding service to CICHA, 1984-85, Presdl. award for outstanding service to Am. Lung Assn. Md., 1985, Disting. Service award Soc. Profl. Journalists, 1987. Mem. Purchasing Mgmt. Assn. Md. (chmn. com. 1968-70), Balt. Jaycees (v.p. 1974-76, internat. senator 1975), Greater Balt. Minority Purchasing Council (Service award 1978), Soc. Colonial Wars (chpt. gov., 1989-91), Johns Hopkins U. Alumni Assn. (pres. Balt. 1984-86, Univ. Heritage award 1987). Democrat. Episcopalian. Home: 3925 Linkwood Rd Baltimore MD 21210-3001 Office: Waverly Inc 428 E Preston St Baltimore MD 21202-3923

PASSANO, EDWARD MAGRUDER, printing company executive; b. Towson, Md., Dec. 22, 1904; s. Edward Boetler and Eleanor (Isaac) P.; m. Mary Troy Fleming, Apr. 2, 1982; 1 son, Edward Magruder. B.S. in Econs., Johns Hopkins U., 1927. With Waverly Press, Inc. (name changed to Waverly Inc. 1988), Balt., 1927-82, treas., 1946-68, pres., 1963-71, chmn. exec. com., 1971-75, also bd. dirs., 1982. Bd. dirs., treas. Passano Found., Inc., 1970—. Mem. Soc. Colonial Wars (life, gen. coun.). Republican. Episcopalian. Home: 6873 Travelers Rest Point Easton MD 21601-9805 Office: Waverly Inc 351 W Camden St Baltimore MD 21201-2436

PASSANTINO, RICHARD J., architect; b. N.Y.C., Apr. 4, 1934; s. Charles V. and Ruth M. (Defina) P.; m. Erika F. Dethlefs, Sept. 1, 1962; children: Stefan C., Fiona R. BS in Architecture, U. Cin., 1957. Registered architect, D.C., Md., Va., Fla., Ky., Mo., N.J.; cert. Nat. Coun. Archtl. Registration Bds. Rsch. assoc. McLeod, Ferrara, Ensign, Washington, 1960-70; founding prin. Richard J. Passantino, AIA Architects, Bethesda, Md., 1970-80; pres. SAIC Architects, McLean, Va., 1980-90, LEA/Passantino & Bavier, Arlington, Va., 1990-94, Passantino & Bavier, Bethesda, Md., 1994—; speaker to various ednl. instns. in U.S., 1970—; AIA rep. Union Internat. Architects, 1985-88; mem. nat. archtl. juries throughout U.S., 1975—. Co-author: Urban Schools in Europe, 1963; contbr. numerous articles to profl. jours.; designer 7 earthquake resistant schs. in So. Italy, 1985-88, psychiat. hosp., Leesburg, Va., 1979, Haile Selassie U., Addis Ababa, Ethiopia; designer modifications Am. Consulate Gen., Ecuador, Am. embassies, Papua-New Guinea, The Philippines, Liberia, Ghana, also others. Bd. dirs. Nat. Child Rsch. Ctr., Washington, 1969-74. 1st lt. USAF, 1958-60; capt. USAFR, 1960-62. Recipient award for sch. architecture exhbn. Am. Assn. Sch. Bd. Adminstrs., 1984. Mem. AIA (corp., steering com. architecture for edn. 1979#), Coun. for Ednl. Facilities Planners (co-recipient Projects of Distinction award 1993), Assn. for Childhood Edn. Internat., Assn. Sch. Bus. Ofcls. Internat. (award of excellence 1986), Nat. Hist. Trust, Soc. Am. Mil. Engrs. Avocations: tennis, photography, travel. Office: Passatino Bavier Architects 12601 Lloydminster Dr North Potomac MD 20878

PASSEY, GEORGE EDWARD, psychology educator; b. Stratford, Conn., Sept. 28, 1920; s. Henry Richard and Elizabeth (Angus) P.; m. Algie Aldridge Ashe, Nov. 18, 1950; children—Richard Ashe, Elizabeth Aldridge, Mary Louise. B.S., Springfield Coll., 1942; M.A., Clark U., 1947; Ph.D., Tulane U., 1950. Asst. prof. U. Ala., Tuscaloosa, 1952-55; assoc. prof. U. Ala., 1955-56, 57-59, prof., 1959-63; prof. psychology, chmn. div. social and behavioral scis. U. Ala., Birmingham, 1967-73; prof. engring. U. Ala., 1969-84, Disting. Service prof. psychology, 1984-85, Disting Service prof. emeritus, 1985—; chair U. Ala. (Sch. Social and Behavioral Scis.), 1973-84; research scientist Lockheed Ga. Co., Marietta, Ga., 1956-57, 63-65, cons., 1965-67; prof. Ga. Inst. Tech., 1965-67. Served with USNR, 1942-46, PTO; with USAF, 1951-52. Fellow Am. Psychol. Assn.; mem. So. Soc. for Philosophy and Psychology, Southeastern Psychol. Assn., Ala. Psychol. Assn., Pine Harbor Golf and Racquet Club, Coosa Pines Golf Club, Sigma Xi. Home: 7141 Skyline Dr Pell City AL 35125-9304 *Whatever success I have enjoyed ought to be attributed to the attempt I have made to carry out the admonitions of my parents to make choices only after having appraised the alternatives in terms of their consequences, to weigh ethical considerations above all others, never to demand of others what one is unwilling to give of himself, and to work untiringly for those causes to which one is committed.*

PASSI, BETH, school administrator. Dir. Blake Lower Sch., Hopkins, Minn., 1982—. Recipient elem. sch. recognition award U.S. Dept. Edn., 1989-90, 93-94, Bush prin. leadership fellow, 1993-94. Office: Blake Lower Sch 110 Blake Rd Hopkins MN 55343

PASSIDOMO, JOHN MICHAEL, lawyer; b. White Plains, N.Y., Jan. 11, 1952; s. John Anthony and Gloria (Massaglia) P.; m. Kathleen Cinotti, Sept. 22, 1979; children: Catarina, Francesca. BA cum laude, Boston Coll., 1974; JD, Stetson U., 1977. Bar: Fla. 1978. Ptnr. Frost & Jacobs, Naples, Fla., 1980—. Pres.-elelct Fine Arts Soc. Collier County, Naples, 1988; mem. planning adv. bd. City of Naples, 1986—, vice chmn., 1987—. Mem. Collier County Real Estate Attys. (chmn. 1988—),Collier County Bar Assn. (pres. 1987-88), Vol. Lawyers Project (pres. 1984-86). Club: Tiger Bay (Naples) (pres. 1988—). Lodge: Rotary (bd. dirs. Naples chpt. 1983-84). Home: 2200 Southwinds Dr Naples FL 33940-7656 Office: Frost & Jacobs 4001 Tamiami Trl N Naples FL 33940

PASSMORE, HOWARD CLINTON, JR., geneticist, biological sciences educator; b. Drexel Hill, Pa., Sept. 12, 1942; s. Howard Clinton and Thelma (Walter) P.; m. Irene Grace Wrigley, Aug. 22, 1964; children: Lisa, Heather. AB, Franklin and Marshall Coll., 1964; PhD, U. Mich., 1970. Asst. prof. genetics Rutgers U., New Brunswick, N.J., 1971-77, assoc. prof., 1977-88, prof., 1988—, dir. grad. program in microbiology and molecular biology, 1995—; assoc. dir. Bur. Biol. Rsch., 1982-85; mem. mammalian genetics study sect. NIH, 1988-92. Rsch. grantee NIH, 1978—. Mem. Am. Assn. Immunologists, Genetics Soc. Am., Am. Soc. Human Genetics. Home: 21 W Mill Rd Long Valley NJ 07853-3435 Office: Rutgers U Bur of Biol Rsch PO Box 1059 Piscataway NJ 08855-1059

PASSMORE, JAN WILLIAM, insurance company executive, investor; b. Winchester, Ind., Nov. 9, 1940; s. Gale Orth and Helen Louise (Hoskinson) P.; m. Pamela Boa, Feb. 14, 1964. Student Nebr. State U., 1959-61; BS, Ball State U., 1963. With Aetna Life & Casualty, 1964-75, Western region dir., San Jose, Calif., 1972-75; broker, Sanders & Sullivan, San Jose, 1975-78, partner, 1978-80, pres., 1979-81; pres., CEO Corroon & Black, San Jose, 1981-88, chmn. 1988-90; pres. First Richmond Corp., First Richmond Realtors, 1991-93; v.p. Prestwick, Inc. 1991-93; pres. exec. com. Industries, Inc.; chmn. nat. adv. council INA Marketdyne, 1980-82; chmn. bd. Econ. Devel. Corp. Wayne County, Ind., 1993; chmn. Nat. Adv. Coun. Cigna Corp., 1993-96; chmn. Aetna Life & Casualty Regional Adv. Council, 1982-84, 87-89. Chmn. bd. Goodwill Industries, 1978-80, 86-89; pres. Boy Scouts Am., 1981-83; bd. dirs. Music and Arts Found., 1980-85, Alexian Bros. Hosp. Found., 1978-85, Small Bus. Devel. Ctr. Region # 9, 1993-95, chmn., 1994; chmn. bd. Hope Rehab., 1985-87; chmn. bd. dirs. Santa Clara County United Way; mem. San Jose Trolley Commn.; past pres. bd. trustees Alum Rock United Meth. Ch.; past pres. bd. trustees 1st Meth. Ch. San Jose; nat. council rep. Boy Scouts Am., 1985-90; chmn. bd. Mayor's Blue Ribbon Commn. Fin. City of Richmond, Ind., 1993.; chmn. fin. 1st Meth. Ch., Richmond. Recipient Silver Beaver award, Benefactors award Boy Scouts Am., Mayoral Proclamation City of San Jose, Suprs. Proclamation County of Santa Clara, Proclamation from Calif. State Assembly; named Citizen of Yr., Aetna Life & Casualty Co., 1975, Disting. Citizen of Yr. Santa Clara County, 1985; INA-Marketdyne Golden Circle, 1977-82, 87; named hon. Ky. Col. Mem. Western Assn. Ins. Brokers (trustee 1987-90), Nat. Assn. Ind. Ins. Agts., Richmond-Wayne County C. of C. (chmn. 1993, bd. dirs. 1990-95). Republican. Clubs: San Jose Country Club (treas., bd. dirs.), Scotts Boys Club (pres. 1994—, trustee 1992—), Sainte Claire, Spartan Found., Pres.'s Council San Jose State U., Aetna Life and Casualty Gt. Performers, Forest Hills Country Club, Columbia Club, Masons, Shriners, Kiwanis (pres. Mechanicsburg, Pa. chpt. 1969, lt. gov. Pa. 1970-72, pres. San Jose chpt. 1986, mem. Richmond club 1990—, bd. dirs. 1991-93), Kiwanis Internat. (legion of honor 30 years). Home: 2121 Reeveston Rd Richmond IN 47374-5752 Office: PO Box 1441 Richmond IN 47375-1441

PASSMORE, MICHAEL FORREST, environmental administrator; b. Oroville, Calif., July 9, 1947; s. Audley Forrest and Betty Beryle (Elkin) P.; m. Laura Ann Travis, Sept. 7, 1968 (div. 1985); children: Travis Forrest, Robert Bryan: m. Elise Jean Bechtold, Nov. 9, 1985; 1 child, Heather Elise. BS, Oreg. State U., 1974, MS, 1977; PhD, Tex. A&M U., 1981. Research asst. Oreg. State U., Corvallis, 1974-77, research assoc., 1977; grad. fellow Rob and Bessie Welder Wildlife Found., Sinton, Tex., 1977-80; wildlife biologist Environ. Resources Br. U.S. Army Corps Engrs., Walla Walla, Wash., 1980-87; asst. chief U.S. Army Corps Engrs., Walla Walla, 1986-87, chief, 1987—; master bird bander Fish and Wildlife Service, 1981—; citizen ambassador, wildlife biology del. People-to-People Internat., China, 1987; cert. wildlife biologist, 1987—. Co-author manual: Raptors on COE Lands, 1986; contbr. articles to profl. publs. Coach youth sports, 1984—; mem. com. Walla Walla Parks Aviary Devel., 1983; vol. Boy Scouts Am., Walla Walla, 1986–. Mem. Wildlife Soc. (mem. spl. award com. 1987-88), Wilson Ornithol. Soc., Western Bird Banding Assn., Nat. Mil. Fish and Wildlife Assn., Northwest Scie. Assn. Methodist. Avocations: hunting, wildlife photography, camping, bowling, softball. Home: 1126 Chestnut Dr Walla Walla WA 99362-3824 Office: US Army Corp Engrs Bldg 602 Walla Walla WA 99362

PASSON, RICHARD HENRY, university administrator; b. Hazleton, Pa., Aug. 18, 1939; s. Henry Richard and Grace Miriam (Bernstein) P.; m. Margaret Rose Ferdinand, Aug. 14, 1965; children—Michael, Rebecca, Christopher. B.A. (Bishop Hafey scholar), King's Coll., Pa., 1961; M.A., U. Notre Dame, 1963, Ph.D. (NDEA fellow), 1965. From instr. to prof. English U. Scranton, 1964-73, chmn. English dept., 1970-73, fgn. student adviser, 1965-67; dean Coll. Arts and Scis., Creighton U., Omaha, 1973-77; acad. v.p. St. Joseph's U., Phila., 1977-84; provost U. Scranton, Pa., 1984—. Contbr. articles profl. jours. Recipient grant Nat. Assn. Fgn. Students, 1966. Mem. Modern Lang. Assn., Am. Assn. Higher Edn., Am. Assn. Acad. Deans. Democrat. Roman Catholic. Office: U Scranton Office of Provost Scranton PA 18510

PASSOW, AARON HARRY, education educator; b. Liberty, N.Y., Dec. 9, 1920; s. Morris and Ida (Wiener) P.; m. Shirley Siegel, July 2, 1944; children: Michael Joel, Deborah Miriam, Ruth Gertrude. B.A. cum laude, SUNY-Albany, 1942, M.A., 1947; Ed.D. (Romiett Stevens scholar), Columbia U., 1951. Tchr. sci., math. Stony Point High Sch., N.Y., 1942-43; sci. tchr. Eden Central Sch., N.Y. 1946-48; instr. edn., supr. math. SUNY, Albany, 1948-51; mem. faculty Columbia U. Tchrs. Coll., 1951-91, prof. emeritus edn., 1991—, prof. edn., 1952-91, Jacob H. Schiff prof. edn., 1972-91, chmn. dept. curriculum and teaching, 1968-77, chmn. com. urban edn., 1965-77, dir. div. ednl. instns. and programs, 1975-80; prof. emeritus, 1991—; research assoc. Horace Mann-Lincoln Inst. Sch. Experimentation, 1952-65; Fulbright lectr., vis. prof. edn. U. Stockholm, 1967—68; vis. prof. Bar-Ilan (Israel) U., 1973, 81, Tel Aviv U., 1981; dir. Study Washington Pub. Schs., 1966-67; ednl. cons., lectr. edn. disadvantaged, edn. gifted and curriculum devel. Co-author: Organizing for Curriculum Development, 1953, Planning for Talented Youth, 1955, Developing a Curriculum for Modern Living, 1957, Improving the Quality of Public School Programs, 1960; author: Secondary Education for All: The English Approach, 1961; also articles.; editor: Curricular Crossroads, 1962, Education in Depressed Areas, 1963, Education of Disadvantaged: A Book of Readings, 1967, Developing Programs for the Disadvantaged, 1968, Deprivation and Disadvantage: Nature and Manifestations, 1970, Reaching the Disadvantaged Learner, 1970, Urban Education in the 1970s, 1971, Opening Opportunities for Disadvantaged Learners, 1972, The National Case Study: An Empirical Study of 21 National Educational Systems, 1976, Secondary Education Reform: Retrospect and Prospect, 1976, American Secondary Education: The Conant Influence, 1977, The Gifted and the Talented: Their Education and Development, 1979, Education for Gifted Children and Youth, 1980, Reforming the Schools in the 1980s, 1984, Gifted Young in Science: Potential through Performance, 1989, International Handbook of Research and Development of Giftedness and Talent, 1993, Changing Demographics, Changing Schools, 1995. Mem. Englewood Bd. Edn., N.J., 1969-72, pres., 1971. Served to 1st lt. USAAF, 1943-46. Recipient Disting. Alumnus award SUNY-Albany, 1969, Disting. Svc. to Edn. medal Columbia U.; Kappa Delta Pi fellow, 1958-59. Mem. NEA (life), ASCD (bd. dirs. 1959-62, chmn. rsch. commn. 1961-63, co-chmn. task force edn. culturally disadvantaged 1964-66), Nat. Soc. Study Edn. (bd. dirs. 1975—), Met. Assn. Study Gifted (pres. 1957-58), World Coun. for Gifted and Talented Children (hon. bd. dirs. 1979-85, pres. 1985-90, pres. 1987-91), Am. Ednl. Rsch. Assn., Kappa Delta Pi (Laureate chpt., hon.). Jewish (pres. temple 1966-67). Home: 394 Eton St Englewood NJ 07631-4719 Office: Columbia U Tchrs Coll New York NY 10027

PASSWATER, BARBARA GAYHART, real estate broker; b. Phila., July 10, 1945; d. Clarence Leonard and Margaret Jamison; m. Richard Albert Passwater, June 2, 1964; children: Richard Alan, Michael Eric. AA, Goldey-Beacom Coll., 1963; BA, Salisbury State U., 1982. Notary pub., Md. Sec. DuPont, Wilmington, Del., 1963-65, Nuclear-Chgo., Silver Spring, Md. 1965-67; office mgr. Montgomery County Sch. System, Wheaton, Md., 1977-79; adminstrv. asst. Solgar Nutritional Rsch. Ctr., Berlin, Md., 1979—; assoc. broker Prudential-Groff Realty, Berlin, Md., 1983-87, ReMax, Inc., Berlin, Md., 1987-88; broker, mgr. River Run Sales Ctr., Berlin, Md., 1988—. Treas. Ocean Pines (Md.) Vol. Fire Dept. Aux., 1981-84; emergency med. tech. Ocean Pines (Md.) Vol. Fire Dept., 1983—; sec. Ocean Pines (Md.) Fire Dept., 1990—; mem. Foster Care Review Bd., Snow Hill, Md., 1984—. Mem. Beta Sigma Phi, Phi Kappa Phi. Avocations: photography, nature studies. Office: River Run 11605 Masters Ln Berlin MD 21811

PASSWATER, RICHARD ALBERT, biochemist, author; b. Wilmington, Del., Oct. 13, 1937; s. Stanley Leroy and Mabel Rosetta (King) P. BS, U. Del., 1959; PhD, Bernadean U., 1976. Cert. firefighter; m. Barbara Sarah Gayhart, June 2, 1964; children: Richard Alan, Michael Eric. Supr. instrumental analysis lab. Allied Chem. Corp., Marcus Hook, Pa., 1959-64; tech. svcs. rep. F&M Sci. Corp., Avondale, Pa., 1965; dir. applications lab. Am. Instrument Co., Silver Spring, Md., 1965-77; dir. Am. Gen. Enterprises, Minn.; former daily broadcaster Sta. WMCA, N.Y.C., 1980-88; former daily broadcaster Sta. WRNG, Atlanta, 1982-85; rsch. dir. Solgar Nutritional Rsch. Ctr., 1978—; corp. v.p. Solgar Co., Inc.; chmn. Worcester County Emergency Planning Com.; bd. dirs. Worcester Meml. Hosp., Atlantic Gen. Hosp., River Run Assn; pres. 1989-92, Subaqueous Exploration and Archeology Ltd. Author: Guide to Fluorescence Literature, vol. 1, 1967, vol. 2 1970, vol. 3, 1974, Supernutrition, 1975, Supernutrition For Healthy Hearts, 1977, Super Calorie, Carbohydrate Counter, 1978, Cancer and Its Nutritional Therapies, 1978, 83, 93, The Easy No-Flab Diet, 1979, Selenium As

Food and Medicine, 1980, The Slendernow Diet, 1982, (with Dr. E. Cranton) Trace Elements, Hair Analysis and Nutrition, 1983, The New Supernutrition, 1991, The Longevity Factor, 1993, Cancer Prevention and Nutritional Therapy, 1993, (with Ben Friedrich and Hans Kugler) Heart Health, 1994; contbg. author: Fire Protection Guide to Hazardous Materials, 1991; editor Fluorescence News, 1966-77, Jour. Applied Health Scis., 1982-83; mem. editorial bd. Nutritional Perspectives, 1978-96, The Body Forum, 1979-88, Jour. Holistic Medicine, 1981-88, VIM Newsletter, 1979—; contbg. editor Firehouse Mag., 1988-94; Jour Applied Nutrition; contbr. over 350 health articles to mags.; co-editor booklet series Your Good Health; sci. adv. and columnist Whole Foods mag.; patentee in field. bd. dirs. Sci. Documentation Ctr., Dunfermline, Eng.; Am. Found. Firefighter Health and Safety; chief Ocean Pines Vol. Fire Dept., 1984-93; active Emergency Med. Tech.; adviser Nat. Inst. Nutrition Edn.; past adv. bd. Stephen Decatur High Sch., Worcester County Dept. Edn. Cubmaster, 1975-79. Named Citizen of Yr. Ocean Pines, Md., 1987, 5th Ann. Achievement award, 1989, VFW Cert. of Commendation, 1988, Industry award Nat. Inst. Nutritional Edn., 1991; inducted into Delmarva Fireman's Hall of Fame, 1993. Fellow Internat. Acad. Preventive Medicine, Am. Inst. Chemists; mem. ASTM, AAAS, Am. Chem. Soc., Gerontology Soc., Am. Geriatric Soc., Am. Aging Assn., Soc. Applied Spectroscopy, Internat. Found. Preventive Medicine (v.p.), Internat. Union Pure and Applied Chemistry, Royal Soc. Chemistry (London), Internat. Acad. Holistic Health and Medicine, Capital Chem. Soc., Nutrition Today Soc., Am. Acad. Applied Health Scis. (pres., bd. dir.), Internat. Found. Preventive Medicine (v.p., dir.), Inst. Nutritional Rsch., Internat. Platform Assn., N.Y. Acad. Scis., Nat. Fire Protection Assn. (cert. firefighter level III, com. on properties of hazardous chemicals), Pi Kappa Alpha. Office: 11017 Manklin Meadows Ln Berlin MD 21811-9340

PASSY, CHARLES, arts critic; b. N.Y., Jan. 9, 1964; s. Victor and Beverly (Green) P.; m. Leslie M. Olsen, Dec. 15, 1989; 1 child, Jacob E. BA, Columbia U., 1985. Assoc. Jay K. Hoffman and Assocs., N.Y., 1983-87; sr. editor, mng. editor Ovation Mag., N.Y., 1988-89; editor Classical Mag., N.Y., 1989-91; editor-in-chief Musical Am. Pub., N.Y., 1991-92; staff writer The Palm Beach Post, West Palm Beach, 1992—; announcer, prod. WNYC FM, N.Y., 1984-85; entertainment stringer N.Y. Newsday, 1987-92. Author: (with others) New Voices: Selected University and College Prize Winning Poems, 1989, The New Grove Dictionary of Jazz, The New Grove Dictionary of Music and Musicians in the United States, 1989; editor: (with others) The Letters of Virgil Thomson, 1988; contbr. numerous articles to jours. in field. Recipient Poetry award Acad. Am. Poets Columbia U., 1985, Criticism awards Soc. Profl. Journalists, 1995, Fla. Press Club, 1993, Fla. Soc. Newspaper Editors, 1993; fellow Knight Ctr. for Specialized Journalism, 1993. Mem. Music Critics Assn., Louis August Jonas Found. Avocations: poetry, baseball, theater, collecting sports memorabilia, reading. Home: 5481 Eagle Lake Dr Palm Beach Gardens FL 33418 Office: Palm Beach Newspapers Inc 2751 S Dixie Hwy West Palm Beach FL 33405-1233

PASTAN, IRA HARRY, biomedical science researcher; b. Winthrop, Mass., June 1, 1931; s. Jacob and Miriam (Ceder) P.; m. Linda Olenik, June 14, 1953; children—Stephen, Peter, Rachel. B.S., Tufts U., 1953, M.D., 1957. Med. house officer Yale U. New Haven Hosp., 1957-59; clin. assoc. Nat. Inst. Arthritis and Metabolic Disease, NIH, Bethesda, Md., 1959-61, sr. investigator sect. on endocrine biochemistry, clin. endocrinology br., 1963-69; postdoctoral fellow Lab. of Cellular Physiology Nat Heart and Lung Inst. NIH, Bethesda, Md., 1961-62; head molecular biology sect. endocrinology br. Nat. Cancer Inst., NIH, Bethesda, Md., 1969-70, chief lab. molecular biology, 1970—. Author: An Atlas of Immunofluorescence, 1985; author, editor: Endocytosis, 1985; contbr. articles to profl. jours. Recipient Van Meter prize Am. Thyroid Assn., 1971, Superior Service award Dept. HEW and NIH, 1973, Meritorious Service medal USPHS, NIH, Nat. Cancer Inst., 1983, Disting. Service medal, 1985. Mem. Nat. Acad. Scis., Am. Soc. Biol. Chemists, Am. Soc. Clin. Investigation, Am. Soc. Cell Biology, Am. Soc. Microbiology, Peripatetic Club. Office: Nat Cancer Inst 900 Rockville Pike 37-4E16 Bethesda MD 20892

PASTAN, LINDA OLENIK, poet; b. N.Y.C., May 27, 1932; d. Jacob L. and Bess (Schwartz) Olenik; m. Ira Pastan, 1953; children: Stephen, Peter, Rachel. Ba, Radcliffe Coll., 1954; MS, Simmons Coll., 1955; MA, Brandeis U., 1957. Author: (poetry) A Perfect Circle of Sun, 1971, On the Way to the Zoo, 1975, Aspects of Eve, 1975, The Five Stages of Grief, 1978 (Alice Fay di Castagnola award Poetry Soc. Am. 1978), Setting the Table, 1980, Waiting for My Life, 1981, PM/AM: New and Selected Poems, 1983 (Am. Book award nomination 1983), A Fraction of Darkness: Poems, 1985, The Imperfect Paradise, 1988, Heroes in Disguise, 1991, An Early Afterlife, 1995. Recipient Dylan Thomas Poetry award Mademoiselle, 1958, Virginia Faulkner award Prairie Schooner, 1992; Nat. Endowments for the Arts fellow; Maryland Arts Coun. grantee. Jewish. Office: 11710 Beall Mountain Rd Potomac MD 20854*

PASTER, HOWARD G., public relations/public affairs company executive; b. N.Y.C., Dec. 23, 1944. BA with honors, Antioch U., 1966; MS in Journalism, Columbia U., 1967. Legis. dir. UAW, 1977-80; exec. v.p. Timmons & Co., 1980-92; asst. to pres. and dir. Office Legis. Affairs White House, Washington, 1993; chmn., CEO Hill and Knowlton, Inc., N.Y.C., 1994—; bd. dirs. Ctr. Nat. Policy. Bd. dirs. Christmas-in-April. Office: Hill and Knowlton Inc 466 Lexington Ave New York NY 10017

PASTERNACK, ROBERT FRANCIS, chemistry educator; b. N.Y.C., Sept. 20, 1936; 2 children. B.A., Cornell U., 1957, Ph.D. in Chemistry, 1962. Research assoc. in chemistry U. Ill., Champaign, 1962-63; from asst. to prof. chemistry Ithaca Coll., N.Y., 1963-76, Charles A. Dana Endowed prof. chemistry, 1976-82; Edmund Allen prof. chemistry Swarthmore Coll., Pa., 1984—; invited speaker seminars, colls., univs., nat. internat. meetings, confs. including Bioinorganic Chem., Italy, Portugal, Gordon Rsch. Confs., Spanish Royal Soc. Chem., many others; lectr. series Nankai U., China, U. Messina, Italy; mem. adv. com. Rsch. Corp.; mem. sci. & art com. Franklin Inst.; co-organizer, chmn. workshop on rsch. at undergrad. instn. NSF, mem. undergrad. curriculum chem.; vis. prof., vis. rschr. U Messina, U. Paris, Nakai, Rome, King's Coll., London, Fritz Haber Inst., Berlin; co-developer A Unified Lab. Program; initiator, chmn. C.P. Snow Lectr. Series. Author, co-author more than 90 sci. pubs. Mem. com. on sci. and the arts Franklin Inst., 1992—. Grantee NSF, 1965-68, 69-72, 77-78, 83-84, 86—, Petroleum Rsch. Fund, 1967-74, 86-88, NIH, 1971-89, Monsanto Corp., 1986-92, Rsch. Corp., 1974-75, 78-79, 84-85, Danforth Assocs., 1978-84, Camille and Henry Dreyfus Found., 1981, 85, NATO, 1979, 88-89; recipient Camille and Henry Dreyfus Teaching/Scholar award, 1987-89, NSF Manpower Improvement award, King's Coll., U. London, 1977-78; NSF sci. faculty fellow U. Rome, 1968-70. Mem. AAAS, Am. Chem. Soc., N.Y. Acad. Sci., Sigma Xi. Office: Swarthmore Coll Dept Chemistry Swarthmore PA 19081

PASTERNAK, KATHRYN ANN, filmmaker; b. Edmonton, Alta., Canada, Aug. 21, 1961; d. William Paul and Barbara Ellen (Wright) P. AB magna cum laude, Harvard U., 1985; cert., Sorbonne U., Paris, 1984. Post-prodn. coord. Leitmotif Films, N.Y.C., 1989, Apollo Assocs., N.Y.C., 1989; assoc. producer Visible Pictures, N.Y.C., 1989; asst. to agt. Creative Artists Agy., L.A., 1989-90; researcher, assoc. producer Nat. Geog. Soc. TV, L.A., 1990—. Worked on films including Rock on a Red Horse, 1988, Vienna is Different, 1989, For All Mankind, 1989, Terezin Diary, 1989, The Soul of Spain, 1990. Recipient Pulitzer Rsch. award Harvard U., 1984; grantee Robert Flaherty Film Seminar, 1989. Fellow Royal Soc. for Encouragement of Arts, Mfrs. and Commerce; mem. Internat. Documentary Assn., Ind. Feature Project West, Women in Film, Phi Beta Kappa. Home: 8432 Willoughby Ave West Hollywood CA 90069-4217

PASTIN, MARK JOSEPH, management executive consultant, society adminstrator; b. Ellwood City, Pa., July 6, 1949; s. Joseph and Patricia Jean (Camenite) P.; m. Joanne Marie Reagle, May 30, 1970 (div. Mar. 1982); m. Carrie Patricia Class, Dec. 22, 1984 (div. June 1990); m. Christina M. Brecto, June 15, 1991. BA summa cum laude, U. Pitts., 1970; MA, Harvard U. 1972, PhD, 1973. Asst. prof. Ind. U., Bloomington, 1973-78, assoc. prof., 1978-80; prof. mgmt., dir. Ariz. State U., Tempe, 1988-92; founder, bd. CTG, Inc., Tempe, 1983—; chmn., CEO, pres. Coun. of Ethical Orgns., Inc. Alexandria, Va., 1986—; sr. v.p. Strategic Mgmt. Sys., Alexandria, Va., 1994—; mem. adv. bd. Aberdeen Holdings, San Diego, 1988-90; dir. Sandpiper Group, Inc., N.Y.C., 1987—, S.W. Projects, Inc., San Diego,

1988-90, Learned, Nicholson, Ltd., 1990-91; chmn. bd. Japan Am. Soc. Phoenix, Found. for Ethical Orgns.; cons. GTE, Southwestern Bell, St. Louis, 1987-89, Tex. Instruments, MicroAge Computers, Med-Tronic, Blood Sys., Inc., Opus Corp., GTE, NyNex, Am. Express Bank, Kaiko Bussan Co., Japan, Arex Co., Japan, Century Audit Co., Japan, Scottsdale Meml. Hosp., Consanti Found., Lincoln Electric Co.; vis. faculty Harvard U., 1980; invited presenter Australian Inst. Mgmt., Nippon Tel. & Tel., Hong Kong Commn. Against Corruption, 1984, Young Pres.'s Orgn. Internat. U., 1990, Nat. Assn. Indsl. & Office Parks, 1990, ABA, 1991, Govt. of Brazil, 1991. Author: Hard Problems of Management, 1986 (Book of Yr. award Armed Forces Mil. Comptrs. 1986, Japanese edit., 1994, Power By Association, 1991, The State of Ethics in Arizona, 1991, Planning Forum, 1992; editor: Public-Private Sector Ethics, 1979; columnist Bus. Jour.; contbr. articles to jours. Founding bd. mem. Tempe Leadership, 1985-89; bd. mem. Ctr. for Behavioral Health, Phoenix, 1986-89, Tempe YMCA, 1986—, Valley Leadership Alumni Assn., 1989—; mem. Clean Air Com., Phoenix, 1987-90. Nat. Sci. Found. fellow, Cambridge, Mass., 1971-73; Nat. Endowment for the Humanities fellow, 1975; Exxon Edn. Found. grant, 1982-83. Mem. Strategic Mgmt. Soc. (invited presenter 1985), Am. Soc. Assn. Execs. (invited presenter 1987-95), Bus. Ethics Soc. (founding bd. mem. 1983), Found. Ethical Orgns. (chmn. 1988, pres.), Pres.'s Assn., Am. Mgmt. Assn., Ariz. Club, Golden Key Nat. Hon. Club, Harvard Club, Ariz. Club, Phi Beta Kappa. Avocations: golf, racquetball, running. Home: 7206 Park Terrace Dr Alexandria VA 22307 Office: 112 S West St Alexandria VA 22314

PASTINE, MAUREEN DIANE, university librarian; b. Hays, Kans., Nov. 21, 1944; d. Gerhard Walter and Ada Marie (Hillman) Hillman; m. Jerry Joel Pastine, Feb. 5, 1966. AB, in English, Ft. Hays State U., 1967; MLS, Emporia State U., 1970. Reference librarian U. Nebr.-Omaha, 1971-77; undergrad. libr. U. Ill., Urbana, 1977-79; reference librarian, 1979-80; univ. libr. San Jose State U.-Calif., 1980-85; dir. librs. Wash. State U., Pullman, 1985-89; ctrl. univ. libr. So. Meth. U., 1989—; mem. adv. bd. Foothill Coll. Libr. 1983-85; leader ednl. del. librs. to People's Republic of China, 1985, Australia/New Zealand, 1986, Soviet Union, 1988, East & West Germany, Czechoslovakia, Hungary, Austria, 1991, Rio de Janeiro, 1993. Co-author: Library and Library Related Publications: A Directory of Publishing Opportunities, 1973; asst. compiler: Women's Work and Women's Studies, 1973-74, 1975; compiler procs. Teaching Bibliographic Instruction in Graduate Schools of Library Science, 1981; editor: Integrating Library Use Skills into the General Education Curriculum, 1989; co-editor: In the Spirit of 1991: Access to Western European Libraries and Literature, 1992; contbr. articles to profl. publs. Recipient Disting. Alumni Grad. award Emporia State U., 1986, Dudley Bibliog. Instruction Libr. of Yr. award, 1989. Mem. ALA (chmn. World Book-ALA Goal awards jury 1984-85), Assn. Coll. and Rsch. Librs. (editorial adv. bd. BIS Think Tank 1982-85, chmn. bibliographic instrn. sect. 1983-84, editorial bd. Choice 1983-85, chmn. Miriam Dudley Bibliographic Instrn. Libr. of Yr. award 1984-85, mem. task force on librarians as instrs. 1986—, chair task force internat. rels. 1987-89, BIS Libr. of Yr. 1989, rep. to AAAS/CAIP, 1989—, chair internat. rels. com. 1990-94, rsch. libr. of yr. award's com. 1994—, ALA pay equity com. 1994—), Libr. Adminstrn. and Mgmt. Assn. (chmn. stats. sect. com. on devel., orgn., planning and programming 1982-83, sec. stats. sect. exec. com. 1982-83, mem. at large 1986—), ALA Libr. Rsch. Round Table, Wash. Libr. Assn., Assn. Libr. Collections & Tech. Svcs. Divsn., Libr. and Info. Tech. Assn., Assn. Specialized and Coop. Libr. Agencies (chair multi-lincs internat. networking discussion group 1990-92), Libr. Rsch. Roundtable, Women's Studies Sect., Eng. and Am. Lit. Studies Discussion Group, Tex. Libr. Assn., Pacific N.W. Libr. Assn., Phi Kappa Phi, Beta Phi Mu. Home: 8720 Hanford Dr Dallas TX 75243-6416 Office: So Meth U Cen Univ Librs Fondren Lib Dallas TX 75275-0135

PASTOR, ED, congressman; b. June 28, 1943. Mem. Maricopa County Bd. Suprs., Phoenix, Ariz., 1976-91; mem. 102nd-104th Congresses from Ariz. 2nd dist., 1991—. Office: House Of Representativ Washington DC 20515

PASTOREK, NORMAN JOSEPH, facial surgeon; b. Moline, Ill., Feb. 8, 1939; s. Joseph Andrew and Rose (Faurone) P.; m. Janice Marie Gloss, Apr. 27, 1986; children: Kate Harvial, Kelly Taylor. AB, Augustana Coll., 1960; MD, U. Ill. Chgo., 1964. Diplomate Am. Bd. Otolaryngology. Intern San Francisco Gen. Hosp., 1964-65; resident U. Ill. Hosps., Chgo., 1965-69; pvt. practice medicine specializing in facial plastic surgery N.Y.C; clin. asst. prof. N.Y. Hosp. Cornell Med. Coll., 1971-83, dir. div. facial plastic surgery dept. otolaryngology, 1977—, clin. assoc. prof., 1983-91, clin. prof., 1991—; examiner Am. Bd. Otolaryngology, 1971, 91-93. Author: Blepharoplasty, 1983, 3d edit., 1994; editor: Aesthetic Facial Surgery, 1990. Lt. comdr. USN, 1969-71. Fellow Am. Acad. Otolaryngology, Am. Bd. Otolaryngology (examiner 1991—), Am. Acad. Facial Plastic and Reconstructive Surgery (v.p. eastern region 1982-86, pres.-elect 1989-90, pres. 1990-91), ACS; mem. Westchester Country Club, Alpha Omega Alpha. Republican. Episcopalian.

PASTORELLE, PETER JOHN, film company executive, radiological services and waste management company executive; b. White Plains, N.Y., Jan. 23, 1933; s. Dominic John and Marguerite Delphine (Xavier) P.; m. Maria Rita Delcampo, Oct. 10, 1970; children: Clyda, Betchie, Jomar. B.S., Fordham U., 1955; M.A., NYU, 1961; B.D., SUNY-Maryknoll, 1963. Radio news writer Western Conn. Broadcasting, Stamford, 1964-65; producer, dir. United Nations TV, N.Y.C., 1965-70; pres. The NDL Orgn., Inc., Peekskill, N.Y. from 1970, now chief exec. officer; pres. Peter Pastorelle Prodns., Mount Kisco, N.Y., 1970—, NDL Transport, Inc., 1984—, NDL Radon Services, Inc., 1988—; lectr. Am. Inst. Plant Engrs., Phila., 1981, Am. Chem. Soc., Phila., 1981, Low Level Radioactive Waste Mgmt. Decision Makers Forum, Fla., 1993; Blue Ribbon panelist NATAS, N.Y.C., 1980—; mem. Maxey Flats Steering Com.; mem. exec. com. N.Y. State Low Level Waste Group. Producer, writer films; Face of Hunger, 1976 (Dept. Commerce award), Samoa: Culture in Crisis, 1982 (Gold award), Water, 1978 (Silver award), composer film scores for UN including Faces of My Brother, Face of Hunger, Messengers of Peace; contbg. writer Radwaste Mag., 1994—. Mem. del. Citizen Amb. Program Nuclear Fuels Mgmt., Russia, Ukraine; mem. chm's adv. bd. Rep. Nat. Com., 1994. Served with U.S. Army, 1956-58. Mem. Health Physics Soc., Am. Nuclear Soc., Radiation Research Soc., N.Y. Acad. Sci., Pres.'s Club Fordham U. Republican. Roman Catholic. Home: PO Box 318 Mount Kisco NY 10549-0318 Office: The NDL Orgn Inc PO Box 791 Mount Kisco NY 10549

PASTORINO, ROBERT STEPHEN, diplomat, ambassador; b. San Francisco, Mar. 16, 1940; s. Adolph Stephen Pastorino and Florence Pierangeli; m. Frances Veronica Estepa, Nov. 4, 1961; children: Shannon Francesca, Stephen Robert, Susan Teresa. BA in Internat. Rels., San Francisco State U., 1964. Internat. banker Bank of Tokyo, San Francisco, 1965-66; fgn. svc. officer Dept. State, Washington, 1967, econ. officer, 1971-74, dep. dir. Mexican Affairs 1979-82, trade negotiator, 1982-84; fgn. svc. officer U.S. Embassy, Caracas, Venezuela, 1967-69; comml. officer U.S. Consulate Gen., Hermosillo, Mexico, 1969-71; comml. attache U.S. Embassy, Lisbon, Portugal, 1974-77, Bogota, Columbia, 1977-79; econ., polit. counselor U.S. Embassy, Mexico City, 1984-86; dep. chief of mission U.S. Embassy, Tegucigalpa, Honduras, 1987, Mexico City, 1989-91; amb. U.S. Embassy, Santa Domingo, Dominican Republic, 1992—; dep. asst. sec. def. Dept. Def., Washington, 1987-89; asst. to President U.S. Nat. Security Coun., Washington, 1988-89. Recipient Superior Merit award Dept. State, 1986, Superior Honor award Dept. State, 1989. Avocations: travel, sports, reading. Office: Dominican Republic Unit 5500 APO AA 34041-0008

PASTREICH, PETER, orchestra executive director; b. Bklyn., Sept. 13, 1938; s. Ben and Hortense (Davis) P.; m. Jamie Garrard Whittington; children by previous marriages: Anna, Milena, Emanuel, Michael. A.B. magna cum laude, Yale Coll., 1959; postgrad., N.Y. U. Sch. Medicine, 1959-60; studied trumpet, with Robert Nagle at Yale U., with Raymond Sabarich, Paris. Asst. mgr. Denver Symphony, Balt. Symphony; mgr. Greenwich Village Symphony, N.Y.C., 1960-63; gen. mgr. Nashville Symphony, 1963-65, Kansas City Philharmonic, 1965-66; asst. mgr., mgr. St. Louis Symphony, 1966-78, exec. dir., 1966-78; exec. dir. San Francisco Symphony, 1978—; instr. orch. mgmt. Am. Symphony Orch. League; bd. dirs. Nat. Com. for Symphony Orch. Support; founder San Francisco Youth Orch.; rep. planning and constrn. Davies Symphony Hall, San Francisco Symphony,

1980. Author: TV comml., 1969 (CLIO award); contbr. articles to various newspapers. Mem. recommendation bd. of the Avery Fisher Artist Program, Yale U. Council com. on music; past mem. adv. panel Nat. Endowment for the Arts, co-chmn. music panel, 1985; founding mem. bd. dirs. St. Louis Conservatory, mem. policy com. Maj. Orch. Mgrs. Conf., chmn., 1980; bd. dirs. Laumeier Sculpture Park, St. Louis, Stern Grove Festival, San Francisco Conv. and Visitors Bur.; chmn. fund campaign French-Am. Internat. Sch., San Francisco. Served with U.S. Army, 1960. Recipient First Disting. Alumnus award Yale U. Band, 1977, cert. Merit Yale Sch. Music, 1984. Mem. Am. Symphony Orch. League (dir., chmn., former chmn. task force on mgmt. tng.; mem. exec. and long-range planning com., chmn. standing com. on adminstrv. policy), Assn. Calif. Symphony Orchs. (dir.), Bankers Club of San Francisco. Club: Yale (N.Y.C.). Office: San Francisco Symphony Davies Symphony Hall San Francisco CA 94102*

PASVOLSKY, RICHARD LLOYD, parks, recreation, and environment educator; b. Englewood, N.J., Feb. 16, 1924; s. Valentine and Ellen Isabel (Stoughton) P.; m. Jo Anne Evans, June 16, 1968. BEd, Panzer Coll., 1950; MA in Edn., NYU, 1955; D in Recreation, Ind. U., 1973. Asst. supt. recreation City of Rutland, Vt., 1951-53; supt. recreation City of Montpelier, Vt., 1953-55; dir. parks and recreation Twp. of Parsippany-Troy Hills, N.J., 1955-62; asst. prof. outdoor and environ. edn. N.J. State Sch. Conservation, Branchville, 1962-71; assoc. prof. edn. Ramapo Coll. N.J., Mahwah, 1972-84, coach archery, 1973-84; dir. N.J. State Coll. divsn. of the Nat. Archery Assn., 1978-84; adj. prof. Kean Coll. N.J., Union, 1985—; instr. archery, dir. dance and recreation World Archery Ctr., Pomfret, Conn., 1964—; dir. N.J. Coll. divsn. Nat. Archery Assn., 1978-84. Advisor to choreographer, cons. prodn. office closing ceremonies Statue of Liberty Centennial Celebration, 1986; rec. artist: Square Dances, 1961, 91, mag. articles, 1954-66; columnist Lines About Squares, 1983—. Instr. dance camp staff Lloyd Shaw Found., 1981—, bd. dirs., 1982-88; bd. trustees Sussex County Sr. Legal Resources Ctr., 1992—. With U.S. Army, 1943-46, ETO. Recipient Alumni award Panzer Coll. N.J., 1979, Spl. Alumni award, 1987; named to Ramapo Coll. Athletic Hall of Fame, 1993. Mem. AAHPERD (Recreator of Yr. Ea. Dist. 1977), N.J. Alliance Health, Phys. Edn., Recreation and Dance, Callers Coun., Callerlab, Phi Delta Kappa. Avocations: calling square dances, ballroom dancing, skiing, golf, tennis. Home: 31 Newton Ave Branchville NJ 07826 Office: Kean Coll NJ Phys Edn Dept Union NJ 07083

PATAI, RAPHAEL, former anthropology educator; b. Budapest, Hungary, Nov. 22, 1910; s. Joseph and Edith (Ehrenfeld) P.; children: Jennifer Patai Schneider, Daphne Patai Strauss. Ph.D., U. Budapest, 1933, Hebrew U. Jerusalem, 1936. Mem. faculty Hebrew U., 1937-47; dir., founder Palestine Inst. Folklore and Ethnology, 1944-48; prof. anthropology Dropsie Coll., Phila., 1948-57; vis. lectr. Columbia U., 1948, 54-56, 60-61, New Sch. Social Research, 1948; vis. prof. U. Pa., 1948-49, Ohio State U., 1956; lectr. N.Y. U., 1951-53; vis. lectr. Princeton U., 1952-54; dir. research Theodor Herzl Inst., N.Y.C.; editor Herzl Press, 1956-71; prof. anthropology Fairleigh Dickinson U., 1966-76; vis. prof. Judaic studies Bklyn. Coll., 1971-72. Adv. editor Judaism: Ency. Americana, 1969-; author: numerous books, including The Hebrew Goddess, 1967, 2d edit., 1978, 3rd edit., 1990, The Arab Mind, 1973, 83, (with Jennifer Patai) The Myth of the Jewish Race, 1975, 2d. edit., 89, The Jewish Mind, 1977, The Messiah Texts, 1979, Gates to the Old City, 1980, 81, The Vanished Worlds of Jewry, 1980, On Jewish Folklore, 1983, The Seed of Abraham: Jews and Arabs in Contact and Conflict, 1986, Nahum Goldmann: His Missions to the Gentiles, 1987, Ignaz Goldziher and His Oriental Diary, 1987, Apprentice in Budapest: Memories of a World That Is No More, 1988, Robert Graves and the Hebrew Myths, 1992, Between Budapest and Jerusalem, 1992, Journeyman in Jerusalem, 1992 , The Jewish Alchemists: A History and Source Book, 1994, The Jews of Hungary: History, Culture, Psychology, 1995; editor: Herzl Yr. Book, 1958-71, Ency. of Zionism and Israel, 1971, Erich Brauer's The Jews of Kurdistan, 1993, (with Emanuel S. Goldsmith) Thinkers and Teachers of Modern Judaism, 1994, (with Goldsmith) Events and Movements in Modern Judaism, 1995. Pres. Am. Friends of Tel Aviv U., 1956-60. Mem. Syria-Lebanon-Jordan research project Human Relations Area Files, Inc., New Haven, 1955-56. Home: 39 Bow St Flushing NY 11375-5262

PATAKI, ANDREW, bishop; b. Palmerton, Pa., Aug. 30, 1927. Student, St. Vincent Coll., St. Procopious Coll., Lisle, Ill., Sts. Cyril and Methodius, Byzantine Cath. Sem., Grigorian U., Rome. Ordained priest Roman Cath. Ch., 1952. App. aux. bishop of Passaic, N.J. Byzantine Cath. diocese, 1983; bishop of Parma Ohio, 1984—. Home: 8924 Stover Ln Cleveland OH 44141-2033 Office: 1900 Carlton Rd Cleveland OH 44134-3129*

PATAKI, GEORGE E., governor; b. Peekskill, N.Y., June 24, 1945; m. Elizabeth (Libby) Rowland; children: Emily, Teddy, Allison, George Owen. BA, Yale U., 1967; JD, Columbia U. Sch. Law, 1970. Mayor City of Peekskill, Westchester, N.Y., 1982-84; elected mem. State Assembly, N.Y., 1985-92, State Senate, N.Y., 1993—; assoc. Law Firm of Dewey, Ballantine, Bushby, Palmer & Wood, 1970-74; ptnr. Law Firm Plunckett & Jaffe, P.C., N.Y.C., White Plains,, Albany and Peekskill, 1974-89; co-proprietor Pataki Farm, Peekskill, N.Y. Advanceman Friends of Rockefeller Team, 1970; upstate campaign coord. Com. to Elect Gov. Wilson, 1974; mem. Peekskill Rep. City Com., 1974—, chmn. 1977-83; mem. N.Y. State Rep. Com., 1980-85. Address: Office of the Gov State Capitol Albany NY 12224*

PATCH, LAUREN NELSON, insurance company, chief executive officer; b. Lexington, Ky., Apr. 14, 1951; s. Nathaniel M. and Gertrude (Lasseter) P.; m. Helen Sloneker, June 30, 1973; children: Henry L., John Stewart. BS, U. Ky., 1973; attended case. program, U. Mich., 1990. With Ohio Casualty Ins. Co., Hamilton, 1973—, pres., 1991, also bd. dirs., 1987—; pres. Ohio Casualty Corp.; bd. dirs. Ins. Svcs. Office; dir. First Fin. Bancorp. Bd. dirs. Hamilton-Fairfield Arts Coun., 1990—, Dan Beard Coun. Boy Scouts. Mem. Young Pres. Assn. (Cin. chpt.), Wyoming Golf Club (bd. dirs. 1989—). Republican. Episcopalian. Avocations: golf, reading. Office: Ohio Casualty Ins Co 136 N 3d St Hamilton OH 45025-0001

PATCHAN, JOSEPH, lawyer; b. Bklyn., June 29, 1922; m. Nancy Joy Letaw, Jan. 7, 1952; children: Reed, Judith, David. B.S., Miami U., Oxford, Ohio, 1943; J.D., Cleve. State U., 1952. Bar: Ohio 1952, D.C. 1977. Pvt. practice law, 1955-69; judge U.S. Bankruptcy Ct., No. Dist. Ohio, 1969-75; ptnr. Baker & Hostetler, Cleve., 1975-91; dep. gen. counsel Resolution Trust Corp., Washington, 1991-94; dir. exec. Office for U.S. Trustees, U.S. Dept. Justice, Washington, 1994—; mem. adj. faculty Cleve. State U. Law Sch., 1959-74; mem. faculty Nat. Bankruptcy Seminar, Fed. Jud. Ctr., Washington, 1971-77; mem. adv. com. bankruptcy rules U.S. Jud. Conf., 1978-91; lectr. bankruptcy law seminars. Author: Practice Comments to Rules of Bankruptcy Procedure, 1973-91; contbr. articles on bankruptcy law to profl. publs. Served with USN, 1943-46. Fellow Am. Coll. Bankruptcy; mem. ABA (rep. nat. conf. lawyers and collection agys., chmn. 1985-88), Ohio Bar Assn., Cleve. Bar Assn. (chmn. bankruptcy and comml. law sect. 1984-86), D.C. Bar Assn., Nat. Conf. Bankruptcy Judges (assoc.), Am. Judicature Soc. Am. Bankruptcy Inst., Army and Navy Club (Washington). Jewish. Office: 901 E St NW #700 Washington DC 20530

PATE, FINDLAY MOYE, agriculture educator, university center director; b. Davisboro, Ga., Jan. 24, 1941; s. William Wayne and Valeria Moye P.; m. Vicky Lee Scruggs, Jan. 15, 1961; children: Julie, Celia, Joel, Craig. Student, Abraham Baldwin Agr., Tifton, Ga., 1961-63; BS, U. Ga., 1965, PhD, 1970; MS, Oreg. State U., 1967. From asst. to assoc. prof. Everglades rsch. ctr. U. Fla., Belle Glade, 1970-83; prof., dir. Ona rsch. ctr. U. Fla., Ona, 1983—. Methodist. Achievements include development of a feeding system of adding natural protein to a liquid molasses feed for cattle. Office: U Fla Ona Rsch Ctr RR 1 Box 62 Ona FL 33865-9706

PATE, JAMES LEONARD, oil company executive; b. Mt. Sterling, Ill., Sept. 6, 1935; s. Virgil Leonard and Mammie Elizabeth (Taylor) P.; m. Donna Charlene Pate, Oct. 23, 1955; children: David Charles, Gary Leonard, Jennifer Elizabeth. Prof. econs. Monmouth (Ill.) Coll., 1965-68; sr. economist Fed. Res. Bank Cleve., 1968-72; chief economist B.F. Goodrich Co., Akron, Ohio, 1972-74; asst. sec. Dept. Commerce, Washington, Ohio, 1974-76, spl. adviser to White House, 1976, sr. v.p. fin., 1976; v.p. fin. Pennzoil Co., Houston, Ohio, 1976-89, exec. v.p., 1989, exec. v.p., chief oper. officer, 1990, pres., chief exec. officer, 1990-94, also chmn. bd., 1994—. Contbr. articles to profl. jours. and text books. Bd. govs. Rice U.; mem.

Senate Monmouth Coll.; bd. dirs. Am. Petroleum Inst., Nat. Petroleum Coun. Fellow Royal Econ. Soc.; mem. Pi Gamma Mu. Republican. Office: Pennzoil Co PO Box 2967 Houston TX 77252-2967

PATE, JAMES WYNFORD, surgeon; b. Wedowee, Ala., Aug. 28, 1928; s. Wynford N. and Annie (Blount) P.; m. Anne Stephenson, Aug. 1, 1948; children: James W., Susan Anne, Patricia Lee. Student, Emory U., 1944-46; M.D., Med. Coll. Ga., 1950. Diplomate: Am. Bd. Surgery, Am. Bd. Thoracic Surgery. Intern Nat. Naval Med. Center, Bethesda, Md., 1950-51; resident U. Ala.-Birmingham Hosp., 1953-55, VA Teaching Group Hosp., Memphis, 1957—; asso. dept. surgery U. Ala., 1953-55; asst. chief thoracic surgery VA Hosp., Memphis, 1957-59; mem. faculty dept. thoracic surgery Med. Units U. Tenn., Memphis, 1958—; asso. prof. Med. Units U. Tenn., 1959-65, prof. surgery, 1965—, Univ. Disting. prof., 1989—, chmn. dept., 1974-89; chief cardiothoracic surgery Regional Med. Ctr. ; mem. staff Baptist Meml. Hosp., Memphis; chmn. planning com. Memphis Regional Med. Program, 1965-74; chmn. surg. drugs and devices U.S. Pharmacopeial Conv., 1980-90. Author: (with others) Surgery of Surgery, 1965; contbr. profl. jours. Served to capt. USNR, 1950-53, 83-91. Fellow ACS (gov. 1989—), Am. Coll. Cardiology, Am. Coll. Chest Physicians, Royal Soc. Health (Gt. Britain); mem. So. Thoracic Surg. Assn. (past pres.), Soc. Thoracic Surgeons (founder), Soc. Vascular Surgery, Am. Thoracic Surgery, Am. Thoracic Soc., Société Internationale de Chirurgie, Southeastern Surg. Congress, Accreditation Coun. for Grad. Med. Edn. Office: 956 Court Ave Memphis TN 38103-2814

PATE, JOHN GILLIS, JR., financial consultant, accounting educator; b. Chattanooga, Jan. 27, 1928; s. John Gillis Pate and Iona Estelle (Bowman) Pate Ketchman; m. Daphne Mae Davis, Feb. 8, 1946; children: John Gillis III, Daphne Iona, Donna Gay. Student U. Tampa, 1947-48; AA with highest honors, U. Fla., 1950; BS cum laude, Fla. State U., 1953, MS, 1958; PhD, Columbia U., 1968. Cert. Cost Analyst, cert. Office Automation Profl. Mgr. Grocery Concession, Albany, Ga., 1944-45, Variety Store, Panama City, Fla., 1946-47; asst. to CPA Standard Brands, Inc., Birmingham, Ala., 1951-53, acctg. supervisory trainee, Birmingham, Ala., 1953-54; grad. asst. Fla. State U., Tallahassee, 1957-58; asst. to CPA, Pensacola, Fla., 1956-58; pub. acct., Pensacola, 1958; asst. prof. U. Ga., Athens, 1958-60; lectr. Columbia U., N.Y.C., 1961-64; asst. prof. Bernard M. Baruch Coll. of CUNY, 1963-69; prof. acctg. U. Tex.-El Paso, 1969-85, U. S.C., Spartanburg, 1988-93; cons. resource person Personnel Dept. City of El Paso, 1981-88; cons. resource person finance and human resources Charles Lea Ctr., Spartanburg, 1988—. Co-author: Accounting Trends and Techniques, 1967-88; Author: Index C.P.A. Exams and Unofficial Answers, 1974-81, Index to Accounting and Auditing Services, 1971; contbr. articles to ann. profl. publs. Tither, Coronado Bapt. Ch., El Paso, 1969-86, Buck Creek Bapt. Ch., Spartanburg, 1987—; cons. Alderman of El Paso, 1982, County Councilman of Spartanburg, 1991—. Served as lt. j.g. USN, 1955-56. Columbia U. fellow, 1960; Earhart Found. fellow, 1960; Am. Acctg. Assn. fellow, 1960; recipient Haskins and Sells award, 1960; Ford Found. fellow, 1961-62. Mem. AICPAs (cons.), Am. Acctg. Assn., Nat. Assn. Accts., Inst. Cost Analysis, Office Automation Soc. Internat., Beta Alpha Psi, Beta Alpha Chi. Republican. Clubs: Lancer's; Sertoma. Lodges: Moose, Masons, Shriners. Home and Office: 106 Lori Cir Spartanburg SC 29303-5527

PATE, MICHAEL LYNN, lawyer; b. Ft. Worth, Tex., July 9, 1951; s. J.B. and Mary Anna (Hable) P.; m. Barbara Ann Linch, May 28, 1977. AA, Schreiner Coll., 1971; BS, Tex. Wesleyan Coll., 1973; JD, U. Tex., 1975. Bar: Tex. 1976, D.C. 1983, U.S. Tax Ct. 1986, U.S. Supreme Ct. 1987. Adminstrv. asst. to Senator Sherman, counsel natural resources com. Tex. Senate, 1976-77; adminstrv. asst. to Lt. Gov. Bill Hobby, Austin, Tex., 1977-79; legis. asst. Senator Bentsen, Washington, 1979-81, legis. dir., 1981-86; ptnr. Bracewell & Patterson, Washington, 1986—. Mem. ABA, Tex. Bar Assn., D.C. Bar Assn. Democrat. Methodist. Avocations: basketball, tennis, golf. Office: Bracewell & Patterson 2000 K St NW Ste 500 Washington DC 20006-1840

PATE, ROBERT HEWITT, JR., counselor educator; b. Abingdon, Va., Apr. 5, 1938; s. Robert Hewitt and Esther Frances (Kirk) P.; m. Ellen O'Neal Pope, Dec. 11, 1960; children: Robert Hewitt III, Mary Ellen Pate Barton. AB, Davidson Coll., 1960; MEd, U. Va., 1965; PhD, U. N.C., 1968. Lic. prof. counselor, Va. Marketer Sinclair Refining Co., Abingdon, Va., 1960-61, 63-64; counselor St. Andrews Presbyterian Coll., Laurinburg, N.C., 1965-66; prof. counselor edn. U. Va., Charlottesville, 1968—, interim dean, 1994-95; adj. faculty Fed. Exec. Inst., Charlottesville, 1978—. Author: Being A Counselor, 1983. Elder local Presbyn. ch. 1st lt. U.S. Army 1961-63. Mem. Am. Counseling Assn., Va. Counselors Assn. (pres. 1983-84). Avocation: reading. Home: 836 Flordon Dr Charlottesville VA 22901-7810 Office: U Va Ruffner Hall 405 Emmet St S Charlottesville VA 22903-2495

PATE, SAMUEL RALPH, engineering corporation executive; b. Thorsby, Ala., Oct. 27, 1937; s. Ralph Elvin and Frances Roberta (Marcus) P.; children: Lisa, Sherri, Frances. BS in Aero. Engring., Auburn U., 1960; MS in Mech. Engring., U. Tenn., 1965, PhD, 1977. Registered profl. engr., Tenn. With Sverdrup Tech., Inc., 1960-69, project and rsch. engr. AEDC, 1969-74, mgr. rsch., engring., and testing projects br., 1975-78, dep. dir., Propulsion Wind Tunnel Facility, 1978-83; v.p. and gen. mgr. Tech. Group, Tullahoma, Tenn., 1983, sr. v.p. Tech. and Operational Groups, 1983—, 1984-87; v.p., gen. mgr. AEDC Engring. and Ops. Group, 1987-90, Sverdrup Corp A & E Group, 1990—; pres. Sverdrup Tech., Inc.; adviser U.S.-German Aero. Data Exchange; guest lectr., U. Tenn. Contbr. articles, reports to profl. jours. Served with NG, 1955-59. Recipient Arch T. Colwell Merit award Soc. Automotive Engrs., 1983. Fellow AIAA (assoc., chmn. nat. ground testing com., Gen. H.H. Arnold award Tenn. sect. 1969). Office: Sverdrup Tech Inc PO Box 884 600 William Northern Blvd Tullahoma TN 37388-4729*

PATE, ZACK TAYLOR, JR., nuclear power company executive; b. Albany, Ga., July 27, 1936; s. Zack Taylor Sr. and Maxine (Kearse) P.; m. Bettye Eoline Bryan, Apr. 26, 1959. BS, U.S. Naval Acad., 1958; PhD in Nuclear Engring., MIT, 1970. Commd. ensign USN, 1958, advanced through grades to capt.; chief engr. nuclear submarines USN, Charleston, S.C., 1965-66; exec. officer nuclear submarines USN, New London, Conn., 1970-76; commanding officer nuclear submarines USN, Charleston, 1976-77; spl. asst. to adm. Naval Reactors Hdqrs. USN, Washington, 1977-80; resigned USN, 1980; asst. to pres., then div. dir. Inst. Nuclear Power Ops., Atlanta, 1980-83, exec. v.p., chief operating officer, 1983-84, pres., chief exec. officer, 1984—. Recipient Legion of Merit, 1976. Mem. Am. Nuclear Soc. Home: 806 Kinloch St NW Atlanta GA 30327-3628 Office: Inst of Nuclear Power Ops 1100 Circle 75 Pky Ste 1500 Atlanta GA 30339-5957

PATÉ-CORNELL, MARIE-ELISABETH LUCIENNE, industrial engineering educator; b. Dakar, Sénégal, Aug. 17, 1948; came to U.S., 1971; d. Edouard Pierre Lucien and Madeleine (Tournissa) Paté; m. C. Allin Cornell, Jan. 3, 1981; children: Philip, Ariane. Eng. Degree, Grenoble (France) U., 1971; MS in Ops. Rsch., Stanford U., 1972, PhD in Engring.-Econ. Systems, 1978. Asst. prof. in civil engring. MIT, 1978-81; asst. prof. indsl. engring. Stanford (Calif.) U., 1981-84, assoc. prof. indsl. engring., 1984-91, prof. indsl. engring., 1991—; cons. U.S. Water Resource Coun., 1979, EPA, 1980, Electric Power Rsch. Inst., 1985. WHO, 1988, Shell Oil, 1990, Texaco, 1991. Contbr. numerous articles to profl. jours. Numerous rsch. grants. Mem. NAE, Soc. for Risk Analysis (councilor 1985-86, pres. 1995), Ops. Rsch. Soc. Am., Inst. for Mgmt. Scis. Avocations: tennis, swimming, chess, music. Home: 110 Coquito Way Menlo Park CA 94028-7404 Office: Stanford U Dept Indsl Engring Stanford CA 94305

PATEL, CHANDRA KUMAR NARANBHAI, communications company executive, educator, researcher; b. Baramati, India, July 2, 1938; came to U.S., 1958, naturalized, 1970; s. Naranbhai Chaturbhai and Maniben P.; m. Shela Dixit, Aug. 20, 1961; children: Neela, Meena. B.Engring., Poona U., 1958; M.S., Stanford U., 1959, Ph.D., 1961. Mem. tech. staff Bell Telephone Labs., Murray Hill, N.J., 1961-93, head infrared physics and electronics rsch. dept., 1967-70, dir. electronics rsch. dept., 1970-76, dir. phys. rsch. lab., 1976-81, exec. dir. rsch. physics and acad. affairs div., 1981-87, exec. dir. rsch., materials sci., engring. and acad. affairs div., 1987-93; trustee Aerospace Corp., L.A., 1979-88; vice chancellor rsch. UCLA, 1993—; mem. governing bd. NRC, 1990-91; bd. dirs. Newport Corp., Fountain Valley,

Calif., Cal Micro Devices Corp., Milpitas, Calif., Accuware Corp., Santa Monica, Calif. Contbr. articles to tech. jours. Chmn. Calif. Biomed. Found., 1994—; mem. exec. bd. Calif. Healthcare Inst., 1995—. Recipient Ballantine medal Franklin Inst., 1968, Coblentz award Am. Chem. Soc., 1974, Honor award Assn. Indians in Am., 1975, Founders prize Tex. Instruments Found., 1978, award N.Y. sect. Soc. Applied Spectroscopy, 1982, Schawlow medal Laser Inst. Am., 1984, Thomas Alva Edison Sci. award N.J. Gov., 1987. Fellow AAAS, IEEE (Lamme medal 1976, medal of honor 1989), Am. Acad. Arts and Scis., Am. Phys. Soc. (coun. 1987-91, exec. com. 1987-90, George E. Pake prize 1988, pres. 1995—), Optical Soc. Am. (Adolph Lomb medal 1966, Townes medal 1982, Ives medal 1989), Indian Nat. Sci. Acad. (fgn.); mem. NAS (coun. 1988-91, exec. com. 1989-91), NAE (Zworykin award 1976), Gynecol. Laser Surgery Soc. (hon.), Am. Soc. for Laser Medicine and Surgery (hon.), Third World Acad. Scis. (assoc.), Sigma Xi (pres. 1994—). Home: 1171 Roberto Ln Los Angeles CA 90077-2302 Office: UCLA Vice Chancellor Research 405 Hilgard Ave Los Angeles CA 90095-1405

PATEL, HOMI BURJOR, apparel company executive; b. Bombay, June 28, 1949; s. Burjor Ratan and Roshen Burjor (Marfatia) P.; married; children: Neville H., Cyrus H., Natasha E. BS in Stats., U. Bombay, 1973; MBA in Fin. and Mktg., Columbia U., 1975. Exec. asst. to pres. Corbin Ltd., N.Y.C., 1976, dir. mktg., 1978; with subs. Hartmarx Corp., Chgo., 1979—; v.p., gen. mgr. Fashionaire Apparel Inc., Chgo., 1979-81; exec. v.p. Austin Reed of Regent St., Chgo., 1981-82, M. Wile and Co., Buffalo, 1982-84; pres., chief exec. officer M. Wile & Co., Johnny Carson Apparel, Intercontinental Apparel, Buffalo, 1984—; group exec. v.p. Hartmarx Mens Apparel Group Corp., Buffalo, 1987-91; chmn., ceo Hartmarx Mens Apparel Group Corp., Chgo., 1991-92; pres., COO Hartmarx Corp., Chgo., 1992—; bd. dirs., 1994—. Mem. Clothing Mfrs. Assn. Am. (bd. dirs. 1984—, chmn. mills rels. com. 1986—, exec. v.p. 1989—, pres. 1991, chief labor negotiator for U.S. tailored clothing industry), Univ. Club N.Y., Chgo. Club. Office: Hartmarx Corp 101 N Wacker Dr Fl 23 Chicago IL 60606

PATEL, MARILYN HALL, federal judge; b. Amsterdam, N.Y., Sept. 2, 1938; d. Lloyd Manning and Nina J. (Thorpe) Hall; m. Magan C. Patel, Sept. 2, 1966; children: Brian, Gian. B.A., Wheaton Coll., 1959; J.D., Fordham U., 1963. Bar: N.Y. 1963, Calif. 1970. Mng. atty. Benson & Morris, Esq., N.Y.C., 1962-64; sole practice N.Y.C., 1964-67; atty. U.S. Immigration and Naturalization Svc., San Francisco, 1967-71; sole practice San Francisco, 1971-76; judge Alameda County Mcpl. Ct., Oakland, Calif., 1976-80, U.S. Dist. Ct. (no. dist.) Calif., San Francisco, 1980—; adj. prof. law Hastings Coll. of Law, San Francisco, 1974-76. Author: Immigration and Nationality Law, 1974; also numerous articles. Mem. bd. of visitors Fordham U. Sch. of Law. Mem. ABA (litigation sect., jud. adminstrn. sect.), ACLU (former bd. dirs.), NOW (former bd. dirs.), Am. Law Inst., Am. Judicature Soc. (bd. dirs.), Calif. Conf. Judges, Nat. Assn. Women Judges (founding mem.), Internat. Inst. (bd. dirs.), Advs. for Women (co-founder). Democrat. Avocations: piano playing; travel. Office: US Dist Ct PO Box 36060 450 Golden Gate Ave San Francisco CA 94102

PATEL, MUKUND RANCHHODLAL, electrical engineer, researcher; b. Bavla, India, Apr. 21, 1942; came to U.S., 1966; s. Ranchhodlal N. and Shakariben M. Patel; m. Sarla Shantilal, Nov. 4, 1967; children: Ketan, Bina, Vijal. BEng, Sardar U., Vidyanagar, India; MEng with honors, Gujarat U., Ahmedabad, India; PhD in Engring., Rensselaer Poly. Inst., 1972. Registered profl. engr., Pa.; chartered mech. engr., U.K. lectr. elec. engring. Sardar U., Vidyanagar, India, 1965-66; sr. devel. engr. GE, Pittsfield, Mass., 1967-76; mgr. R & D, Bharat Bijlee (Siemens) Ltd., Bombay, 1976-80; fellow engr. Westinghouse R & D Ctr., Churchill, Pa., 1980-84, mem. senate, 1982-84; pres. Induction Gen., Inc., Pitts. 1984-86; prin. engr. rsch. and devel. Space Divsn. GE, Princeton, Pa., 1986—; cons. Nat. Productivity Coun., New Delhi, 1976-80. Assoc. editor IEEE Insulation Mag.; contbr. articles to nat. and internat. profl. jours. Fellow Inst. Mech. Engrs.; mem. IEEE (sr.), Am. Soc. Sci. Rsch. (hon., nat. com. on electric power engring. edn.), Elfun Soc. Vols., Tau Beta Pi, Eta Kappa Nu, Omega Rho. Achievements include patents and invention awards on electromechanical design of superconducting generators; NASA award for research on space power systems; international authority in the area of electromechanical design of large power transformers. Home: 1199 Cobblestone Ct Yardley PA 19067-4751 Office: GE Astro Space PO Box 800 Princeton NJ 08543-0800

PATEL, RAMANLAL L., engineering executive; b. Gujarat, India, Nov. 12, 1945; came to U.S., 1966; s. L.V. and J.L. Patel; m. Manju Patel; children: Prakash, Amit. BS, Gujarat U., 1966; BSME, U. Toledo, 1969, MBA, 1976. With Bendix Corp., 1969-81; exec. v.p. ops. Bendix-Toledo Stamping (Allied-Signal Corp.), 1982-85; pres. Andrews Corp. (The Henley Group), 1985-88, Johnson Filtration Sys. Inc. divsn. Wheelabrator, 1988-91; group pres. Wheelabrator Clean Water Group, 1990-91; pres., CEO Wheelabrator Engineered Sys. Inc., St. Paul, 1991—. Author: Automation, 1982; patentee for intake-exhaust rocker arm design-function, others. Mem. steering com. Soc. Automotive Engrs., 1976-78. Office: Wheelabrator Engineered Sys 55 Shuman Blvd Naperville IL 60563

PATEL, RONALD ANTHONY, newspaper editor; b. Detroit, Oct. 7, 1947; s. Chhotalal Ukabhai and Joan (Kaczynski) P.; m. Jane Elizabeth Douglas-Willan, Sept. 5, 1974; 1 child, Wendy Elizabeth; m. Susan Florence Winters, Nov. 16, 1982. Student, Wayne State U., 1965-69. Asst. city editor Royal Oak (Mich.) Daily Tribune, 1967-69; rewriteman, copyeditor Detroit News, 1969-70; asst. news editor Newsday, Garden City, N.Y., 1970-73; news editor Phila. Inquirer, 1973-80, asst. mng. editor, 1980-86, assoc. mng. editor for features, 1986—. Contbr. to Elements of Newspaper Design (Steven Ames), 1989. Mem. Am. Assn. Sunday and Feature Editors (sec. 1979, pres. 1982), Newspaper Features Coun. (bd. dirs. 1990, meeting chmn. 1991, sec.-treas. 1992, pres. 1993), Pen and Pencil Club (pres. 1990—), Sigma Delta Chi. Office: Phila Inquirer 400 N Broad St Philadelphia PA 19130-4099

PATEL, VIRENDRA CHATURBHAI, mechanical engineering educator; b. Mombasa, Kenya, Nov. 9, 1938; came to U.S., 1969, naturalized, 1975; s. Chaturbhai S. and Kantaben N. (Rai) P.; m. Manjula Patel, May 29, 1966; children: Sanjay, Bindiya. BSc with honors, Imperial Coll., London, 1962; PhD, Cambridge (Eng.) U., 1965; PhD (hon.), Tech. U. Civil Engring., Bucharest, Romania, 1994. Sr. asst. in research Cambridge U., 1965-69; vis. prof. Indian Inst. Tech., Kharagpur, 1966; cons. Lockheed Ga. Co., Marietta, 1969-70; mem. faculty U. Iowa, Iowa City, 1971—; prof. mech. engring. U. Iowa, 1975—, chmn. div., 1976-82, chmn. mech. engring., 1978-82, U. Iowa Found. Disting. prof., 1990—; research engr. Iowa Inst. Hydraulic Research, 1971—, dir., 1994—; mem. Iowa Gov. Sci. Advisory Council, 1977-83; mem. resistance com. Internat. Towing Tank Conf., 1978-87; vis. prof. U. Karlsruhe, W. Ger., 1980-81, Ecole Nationale Superieure de Mechanique, Nantes, France, 1984; jubilee prof. Chalmers Inst. Tech., Goteborg, Sweden, 1988; cons. in field. Author: Three Dimensional Turbulent Boundary Layers, 1972, also articles; assoc. editor AIAA Jour., 1987-90. Recipient Sr. Scientist award Alexander von Humboldt Found., 1980, 93. Fellow ASME, AIAA (assoc.); mem. Am. Soc. Engring. Edn., Soc. Naval Archtl. Marine Engrs., Sigma Xi, Pi Tau Sigma. Home: 1212 Teg Dr Iowa City IA 52246-4622 Office: Inst Hydraulic Research U Iowa 404 Hydraulics Lab Iowa City IA 52242-1585

PATELLA, LAWRENCE M., city official; b. Danbury, Conn., Aug. 10, 1929; s. Frank Peter and Benevanuti (Negri) P.; m. Nancy Blackford, Dec. 13, 1953 (dec.); children: Richard, Terri Patella McHenry, DEbra Patella Holton, Susan Patella Planz, Michael; m. Nancy Lee Blakey, Apr. 22, 1978. AA, Mesa Coll., San Diego, 1976. Enlisted USN, 1947, commd. ensign, 1958, advanced through grades to lt. comdr.; asst. force ops. officer Amphibious Force Pacific Fleet, 1967-70; comdr. USS Wood County, 1970-74; dir. ship to shore dept. US Naval Amphibious Sch., Little Creek, Va., 1974-76; exec. officer USS Duluth, 1974-76; commanding officer USS Mount Vernon, 1976-78; mgr. navigation divsn. Port of Portland, Oreg., 1978—; exec. dir. Western Dredging Assn., Vancouver, Wash., 1992—. Decorated Bronze Star with Comba V, Navy Commendation medals (4). Mem. Ret. Officers Assn. (Columbia River chpt. pres. 1990-93), Navy League (1st v.p. 1994-95). Republican. Episcopalian. Avocations: golf, gardening, volunteer work. Home: 2714 NE 42d Cir Vancouver WA 98663 Office: Western Dredging Assn PO Box 5797 Vancouver WA 98668

PATENT, DOROTHY HINSHAW, author, photographer; b. Rochester, Minn., Apr. 30, 1940; d. Horton Corwin and Dorothy Kate (Youmans) Hinshaw; m. Gregory Joseph Patent, Mar. 21, 1964; children: David Gregory, Jason Daniel. BS, Stanford U., 1962; MA, U. Calif., Berkeley, 1965, PhD, 1968; postgrad, U. Wash., 1965-67. Postdoctoral fellow Sinai Hosp., Detroit, 1968-69, Stazione Zoologica, Naples, Italy, 1969-70; acting asst. prof. U. Mont., Missoula, 1977. Author: The Way of the Grizzly, 1987, Buffalo: The American Bison Today, 1986, The Whooping Crane: A Comeback Story, 1988, Babies!, 1988, Christmas Trees, 1987 (Jr. Lit. Guild selection 1987), Wheat, The Golden Harvest, 1987, A Horse of a Different Color, 1988, Looking at Dolphins and Porpoises, 1989, Where the Wild Horses Roam, 1989, How Smart Are Animals?, Places of Refuge, 1992, Feathers, 1992, Dogs: The Wolf Within, 1993, Nutrition: What's in The Food We Eat?, 1992, Horses: Understanding Animal Behavior, 1994, What Good is a Tail?, 1994, Deer and Elk, 1994, Alligators, 1994, others. Recipient Eva L. Gordon award Am. Nature Study Soc., 1986. Mem. Am. Inst. Biol. Scis., Soc. Children's Book Writers and Illustrators, Authors Guild. Avocations: gardening, racquetball, travel.

PATERNO, JOSEPH VINCENT, college football coach; b. Bklyn., Dec. 21, 1926; s. Angelo Lafayette and Florence (de LaSalle) P.; m. Suzanne Pohland, May 12, 1962; children: Diana Lynne, Mary Kathryn, David, Joseph Vincent, George Scott. B.A., Brown U., 1950, LL.D., 1975. Asst. football coach Pa. State U., 1950-66, head football coach, 1966—. Author (with Bernard Asbell): The Paterno Principle, 1989; Paterno: By the Book, 1989. Served with AUS, 1945-46. Named Coach of Yr. Walter Camp Football Found., 1972, Coach of Yr. Washington Touchdown Club, 1973, 86, Coach of Yr. Football Writers Assn. Am., 1978, 82, 86; coached Nat. Collegiate Champions, 1982, 86, Named Sports Illustrated's 1986 Sportsman of the Yr. Mem. Am. Football Coaches Assn. (dir., Coach of Yr. awards 1968, 78, 82, 86). Ranked 4th in All-Time Divsn. IA Coaching Victories, 1st among active coaches. Office: Pa State U Dept Athletics University Park PA 16802*

PATERNOTTE, WILLIAM LESLIE, brokerage house executive; b. Phila., Apr. 26, 1945; s. Alexander Leslie Paternotte and Mary (Harris) Waterbury; m. Nancy Brewster, June 15, 1968; children: Nancy Moffett, William Brooks, Christopher Brewster. AB, Princeton U., 1967; MBA, U. Pa., 1969. Fin. analyst Alex Brown & Sons, Balt., 1969-79, dir. research, 1979-92, dir. mktg. and client svcs., 1992—; bd. dirs. JB's Restaurants, Inc., Salt Lake City. Trustee Gilman Sch., Balt., 1986—, Adirondack Mountain Res., St. Huberts, N.Y., 1987-90; pres. bd. dirs. Bryn Mawr Sch., Balt., 1981-84. Mem. Balt. Security Analyst Soc. (pres. 1978-79), Fin. Analyst Fedn., Inst. Chartered Fin. Analysts, Md. Club, Green Spring Valley Hunt Club, Ausable Club, Caves Valley Golf Club. Republican. Episcopalian. Avocations: skiing, golf, fishing, biking. Home: 2 Chetwick Ct Owings Mills MD 21117 Office: Alex Brown & Sons Inc 135 E Baltimore St Baltimore MD 21202-1646

PATERSON, ALAN LEONARD TUKE, mathematics educator; b. Dunfermline, Scotland, Mar. 8, 1944; s. William and Isabella (MacMaster) P.; m. Christina Mackie Anderson, Sept. 20, 1969; children: Mark, Lydia, Stephen. BS, U. Edinburgh, Scotland, 1966, MS, 1967, PhD, 1969. Prof. U. Aberdeen, Scotland, 1969-88, U. Western Ont., Can., 1984, U. B.C., Can., 1985, U. Miss., 1988—. Author: Amenability, 1988. Mem. Edinburgh Math. Soc., London Math Soc., Am. Math Soc. Avocation: philosophy. Home: 1001 Harland Dr Oxford MS 38655-5303 Office: U Miss Dept Math University MS 38655

PATERSON, BASIL ALEXANDER, lawyer; b. N.Y.C., Apr. 27, 1926; s. Leonard J. and Evangeline (Rondon) P.; m. Portia Hairston, 1953; children: Daniel, David. B.S., St. John's Coll., 1948; J.D., St. John's U., 1951. Bar: N.Y. 1952. Ptnr. Paterson, Michael, Jones and Cherot, N.Y.C., 1956-77, Meyer, Suozzi, English & Klein, P.C., Mineola, N.Y., 1983—; mem. N.Y. State Senate, 1965-70; dep. mayor for labor relations City of N.Y., 1978; sec. of state State of N.Y., 1979-82; pres. Inst. Mediation and Conflict Resolution, 1971-77; chmn. 2d Jud. Screening Com.; assoc. chmn. N.Y. State Sentencing Guidelines Com.; commr. Port Authority N.Y. and N.J. vice chmn. Dem. Nat. Com., 1972-78, mem., 1972-78. Recipient Eagleton Inst. Politics award; Disting. Service award Guardians Assn. N.Y. Police Dept.; City Club of N.Y. award; Black Expo award; Excellence medal St. John's U.; Kibbe award CUNY. Roman Catholic. Office: Meyer Suozzi English & Klein PC 1505 Kellum Pl Mineola NY 11501-4811

PATERSON, EILEEN, radiation oncologist, educator; b. Bklyn., Oct. 16, 1939; d. John Alexander and Frances (Rabito) P.; m. Bruce Joseph Benedict, Jan. 2, 1981. BA, Wilson Coll., Chambersburg, Pa., 1961; MD, Woman's Med. Coll. Pa., 1965. Diplomate Am. Bd. Radiation Oncology, Am. Bd. Nuclear Medicine. Intern Highland Park, Rochester, N.Y., 1965-66; resident radiology (radiation therapy) U. Rochester, 1966-69; asst. prof. radiation oncology U. Rochester, N.Y., 1970-83, assoc. prof., 1983—; chief dept. radiation oncology Rochester Gen Hosp., 1983—; cons. Arnot Ogden Hosp., Elmira, N.Y., 1970-74, Genesee Hosp., Rochester, 1983—. Contbr. articles to med. jours. Mem. Am. Coll. Radiology, Am. Soc. Therapeutic Radiology and Oncology. Avocations: raising and showing German shepherds and Missouri fox trotting horses. Office: Rochester Gen Hosp 1425 Portland Ave Rochester NY 14621-3001

PATERSON, KATHERINE WOMELDORF, writer; b. Qing Jiang, China, Oct. 31, 1932; came to U.S., 1940; d. George Raymond and Mary Elizabeth (Goetchius) Womeldorf; m. John Barstow Paterson, July 14, 1962; children: Elizabeth Polin, John Barstow, David Lord, Mary Katherine Nah-he-sah-pe-che-a. A.B., King Coll., Bristol, Tenn., 1954, Litt.D. (hon.), 1978; M.A., Presbyn. Sch. Christian Edn., 1957; postgrad, Kobe Sch. of Japanese Lang., 1957-60, Union Theol. Sem., 1961-62; M.R.E., Union Theol. Sem., 1962. Tchr. Lovettsville (Va.) Elementary Sch., 1954-55; missionary Presbyn. Ch., Japan, 1957-61; master sacred studies and English Pennington (N.J.) Sch. for Boys, 1963-65. Author: Who Am I?, 1966, rev. 1992, To Make Men Free, 1973, Justice for All People, 1973, The Sign of the Chrysanthemum, 1973, Of Nightingales That Weep, 1974 (Phoenix award Children's Literary Assn. 1994), The Master Puppeteer, 1976 (Nat. Book award for Children's Lit.), Bridge to Terabithia, 1977 (Newbery medal), The Great Gilly Hopkins (Nat. Book award for Children's Lit., Newbery honor book, Christopher award 1978), Angels and Other Strangers, 1979, Jacob Have I Loved, 1980 (Newbery medal), Gates of Excellence, 1981, Rebels of the Heavenly Kingdom, 1983, Come Sing, Jimmy Jo, 1985, Park's Quest, 1988, The Spying Heart, 1989, The Tale of the Mandarin Ducks, 1990 (Boston Globe/Hornbook award), Lyddie, 1991 (IBBY honors list Internat. Bd. Books Young People), The Smallest Cow in the World, 1991, The King's Equal (Irma Simonton Black award Bank Street Coll. of Edn.), 1992, Flip-Flop Girl, 1994; co-author (with John Paterson) Consider the Lilies, 1986; translator: The Crane Wife, 1981, The Tongue Cut Sparrow, 1987. U.S. nominee for Hans Christian Andersen award, 1979, 89; recipient New Eng. Book award New Eng. Booksellers Assn., 1982, Union medal Union Theol. Sem., 1992. Mem. Authors Guild, PEN, Children's Book Guild Washington. Democrat. Office: Lodestar/Dutton 375 Hudson St New York NY 10014

PATERSON, RICHARD DENIS, financial executive; b. Ottawa, Ont., Can., Oct. 13, 1942; m. Antoinette Paterson; children: Christopher, Russell, Kathlyn, Victoria, Connor. B in Commerce, Concordia U., Montreal, Que., Can., 1964. Auditor Coopers & Lybrand, Montreal, 1964-67; acct. Genstar Corp., Montreal, 1967-69; dir. fin. and adminstrn. Indussa Corp. (subs. Genstar Corp.), N.Y.C., 1969-73; v.p., comptroller Genstar Corp., Montreal and San Francisco, 1973-83; sr. v.p., CFO Genstar Corp., San Francisco, 1983-87; exec. v.p. Genstar Investment Corp., San Francisco, 1987—; bd. dirs. Wolverine Tube, Inc., Gentek Bldg. Products, Inc.; chmn. bd. dirs. Prestolite Electric Inc.; chmn., bd. dirs. Seaspan Internat. Ltd. Mem. Order Chartered Accts. Que. Office: Genstar Investment Corp Metro Tower Ste 1170 950 Tower Ln Foster City CA 94404-2121

PATERSON, ROBERT E., trading stamp company executive; b. Kearny, N.J., Nov. 30, 1926; s. Robert McKinley and Ethel (Brookes) P.; m. Eileen Josephine Connolly; children: Carol, Joan, Robert, Richard, Donald, Jeffrey. MBA, Columbia U., 1971. Cert. fin. planner. Sr. v.p. fin., treas. The Sperry & Hutchinson Co., Inc., N.Y.C., 1952-87, also bd. dirs.; mem. Nat. Assn. Accts., 1954-89, nat. treas., 1985-88; bd. dirs. Govt. Obligations Fund,

1986-87. Elected mem. Borough Coun., 1991-95. Served with U.S. Army, 1944-45, PTO.

PATHAK, SUNIT RAWLY, business owner, consultant, journalist; b. Calcutta, India, Feb. 14, 1953; came to U.S., 1973; s. Santosh K. and Bira (Laharry) P.; m. Koruna Dutt; 1 child, Adrit. BA, Calcutta U., 1972; BBA, U. Ga., 1975; MBA, U. Ark., 1978. Sr. analyst Norton-Christensen, Oklahoma City, 1981-84; bus. cons. Cactus Feeders, Inc., Dumas, Tex., 1984-85; analyst, controller Grindwell-Norton, Calcutta, 1985-87; prin. Tech. Venture Cons., Inc., Amarillo, Tex., 1985—, Venture Mktg. Cons., Inc., Santa Barbara, Calif., 1985—; journalist Morris Communications, Amarillo, 1987-92; ptnr. internat. Mktg. Inc./Venture Mktg. Cons., Inc., Amarillo, 1989—; assoc. N.W. Environ. Tng. Inst., Amarillo, 1992—; mng. editor Claude (Tex.) News, 1992-93; assoc. Dameron Petroleum, Midland, Tex., Cease Fire, Inc., Southfield, Mich., Tech. Spray, Amarillo, Tex., McKee & Assocs., Washington, Willcorp Industries, Oxnard, Calif. Fundraiser United Way, Oklahoma City, 1983; patron Nitish Laharry Children's Libr., Calcutta, 1984—. Fundraiser United Way, Oklahoma City, 1983; patron Nitish Laharry Children's Libr., Calcutta, 1984—. Recipient English Lit. prize Brit. Coun., 1969; Rotary Dist. 690 scholar, 1973. Mem. Inst. Mgmt. Accts. (v.p. membership Amarillo chpt. 1989-90), Meeting Planners Internat., Tex. Press Assn., Santa Barbara C. of C., Petroleum Club (Bakersfield, Calif.), Calcutta Cricket Club, Indian Polo Assn., Dalhart Country Club, Calcutta Club, Santa Barbara Polo & Racquet Club. Hindu. Avocations: polo, tennis, international air travel. Office: Tech Venture Cons Inc PO Box 744 Port Hueneme CA 93044-0744

PATIL, POPAT NARAYAN, pharmacology-pharmacy educator; b. Chinchkhede, Maharashtra, India, Oct. 26, 1934; s. Narayan Varuji and Rukhamini (Motiram) Bedse-Patil; m. Betty Baldwin, Dec. 20, 1964; children: Anand, Anita, Vikas. B.Pharm., Gujarat U., India, 1956; MS, Ohio State U., 1960, PhD, 1963. Asst. prof. pharmacology Ohio State U., Columbus, 1965, assoc. prof., prof., 1972—. Contbr. articles to profl. jours. Recipient Humboldt award, 1980-81. Mem. AAAS, Am. Soc. Pharmacology and Exptl. Therapeutics, Ohio Acad. Sci. Achievements include research on steric requirements for the activation of adrenoreceptors, activities of imidazolines, relevance of drug melanin interactions, ocular pharmacology and toxicology, autonomic nervous system pharmacology. Office: Ohio State Univ Coll Pharmacy Parks Hall 500 W 12th Ave Columbus OH 43210-1214

PATIN, ROBERT WHITE, insurance company executive; b. Pitts., Oct. 24, 1942; s. Robert White and Mary (Bilque) P.; m. Lorraine Cedik, Aug. 14, 1965; children—Alyson, Jennifer. B.A. in Langs. and Psychology, Muskingum Coll., 1964. C.L.U. Vice pres. CG Equity Sales, Hartford, Conn., 1972-75; dir. mktg. services Conn. Gen. Life, Hartford, 1975-78, v.p.-reins. div., 1978-80; pres. Puritan Life Ins. Co., Providence, 1980-82; pres. Puritan Ins. Cos., Providence, 1982—. Exec. v.p., bd. dirs. Big Bros., Hartford, 1975-80; exec. v.p. Jr. Achievement, Providence, 1983-84; bd. dirs. Providence Found., 1980-84. Methodist. Home: 337 Sheridan Rd Winnetka IL 60093-4227 Office: Puritan Ins Cos 1301 Atwood Ave Johnston RI 02919-4908 also: Washington Nat Corp 300 Tower Pky Lincolnshire IL 60069-3665

PATINKIN, MANDY, actor; b. Chgo., Nov. 30, 1952; s. Lester and Doris (Sinton) P.; m. Kathryn Grody, June 15, 1980. Student, U. Kans., 1970-72, Juilliard Sch. Drama, 1972-74. Actor N.Y. Shakespeare Festival, 1975-81; plays include Hotspur in Henry IV, Part 1, Hudson Guild, N.Y.C., Rebel Women, Hamlet, Leave it to Beaver is Dead, Savages; (Broadway) Evita (Tony award 1980), Shadow Box, Sunday in the Park with George, 1984, The Knife, 1987, The Winter's Tale, 1989, Mandy Patinkin in Concert: Dress Casual, 1989, The Secret Garden, 1991; films include The Big Fix, 1979, Ragtime, 1981, Yentl, 1983, Daniel, 1983, French Postcards, 1979, The Last Embrace, 1979, Night of the Juggler, Maxie, 1985, The Princess Bride, 1987, The House on Carroll Street, 1988, Alien Nation, 1988, Dick Tracy, 1990, The Doctor, 1991, True Colors, 1991, The Music of Chance, 1993, Life with Mikey, 1993, Indian Warrior, 1994; TV appearances include That Thing on ABC, That Second Thing on ABC, Taxi, Midnight Special, (series) Chicago Hope, 1994—; albums: Mandy Patinkin, 1989, Mr. Arthur's Place, Experiment, 1994. Recipient Music Achievement award Drama League, 1989. Mem. AFTRA, Screen Actors Guild, Actors Equity Assn.

PATINKIN, MARK ALAN, newspaper columnist; b. Chgo., Jan. 12, 1953; s. Harold Samson and June (Marks) P.; m. Heidi James, May 10, 1986; children: Ariel Janes, Alex Janes. BA, Middlebury Coll., 1974; PhD in Journalism (hon.), Johnson and Wales Coll., 1985, R.I. Coll., 1989. Reporter Utica (N.Y.) Daily Press, 1974-76, Providence Jour.-Bulletin, 1976-79; syndicated columnist Providence Jour. and Scripps Howard News, 1979—. Author: An African Journey, 1985, The Silent War, 1989. Finalist Pulitzer prize, 1987; recipient Presdl. End Hunger award, 1991. Jewish. Office: Providence Jour Bull 75 Fountain St Providence RI 02902-0050

PATINO, DOUGLAS XAVIER, foundation and university administrator; b. Calexico, Calif., Apr. 11, 1939; s. Jose Luis and Maria Teresa (Seymour) P.; m. Barbel Wilna Hoyer, Aug. 13, 1970; 1 child, Viktor Xavier. AA, Imperial Valley Coll., 1960; BA, Calif. State U., San Diego, 1962, MA, 1966; PhD, U.S. Internat. U., 1972. Deputy dir. Sacramento (Calif.) Concilio, Inc., 1968-69; v.p. student affairs U. So. Colo., Pueblo, 1973-75; dep. dir. for planning and svc. br. to dir. Calif. Employment Devel. Dept., dir.; sec. Calif. Health & Welfare Agy., 1975-83; dir. Ariz. Dept. of Econ. Security, Phoenix, 1983-87; pres., chief exec. officer Marin Community Found., Larkspur, Calif., 1987-91; pres. New Partnership Found. and Patino Group, San Rafael, Calif., 1991-93; vice chancellor Calif. State U., Long Beach, 1993—; commr. Wm. T. Grand Found., 1986-88. Mem. Sec. of U.S. Dept. of Labor Task Force, Ariz., 1985-86, Staff Adv. Com. of the Human Resource Com., Nat. Gov. Assn., Washington, 1983-86; bd. dirs. Calif. Leadership, Santa Cruz, Calif., 1985-95, No. Calif. Grantmakers, 1990-91, Ariz. Assn. Bus., 1984; chair U.S. Savs. Bond Dr. for State of Calif., 1982; trustee Nat. Hispanic U., Oakland, Calif., 1987-90, Hispanic Community Fund, San Francisco, 1989-95, C.S. Mott Found., 1995—; bd. dirs. Calif. Sch. Profl. Psychology, 1989-94, Coun. on Found., Washington, 1990—, Found. Ctr., N.Y., 1993. Recipient Azteca award Human Devel. Corp., 1991, Leadership award Nat. Concilors of Am. and United Way of Bay Area, 1990, Disting. Performance award, Nat. Alliance of Bus., Washington, 1985, Superior Svc. Mgmt. award, Am. Soc. Pub. Adminstrn., 1985, Humanitarian award, Los Padrinos, Inc., 1981, Small and Minority Bus. award for the State of Calif., 1982, Disting. Alumni award, Calif. Jr. Community Coll. Assn., Sacramento, 1982, Silver Spur award, Nat. Fedn. of Charros in Guadalajaro, Jalisco, Mex., 1974, Calif. Community Svc. award, Former Gov. Ronald Reagan, Sacramento, 1973. Mem. chair, Hispanics in Philanthropy, Am. Pub. Welfare Assn. (bd. dirs., Leadership award 1987), Rotary, 1987-93. Office: Calif State U 400 Golden Shore #122 Long Beach CA 90802-4275 Office: Calif State U 400 Golden Shore #116 Long Beach CA 90802-4275

PATINO, ISIDRO FRANK, law enforcement educator; b. San Antonio, Mar. 10, 1943; s. Isidro F. and Maria (Narro) P.; children: Michael, Rebecca, Karleen. BS, Calif. State U., L.A., 1973; MBA, U. Redlands, 1995. Records comdr. Placentia (Calif.) Police Dept., 1980-85; asst. dean Criminal Justice Tng. Ctr. Golden West Coll., Huntington Beach, Calif., 1986-89, assoc. dean instrm., 1989-92; divsn. dean dept. pub. svc. Rio Hondo Coll., Whittier, Calif., 1992—; pres., mem. State Chancellors Adv. Com. Pub. Safety Edn., 1991—; chmn. So. Calif. Pub. Safety Tng. Consortium, 1994—, active, 1993—. Mem. Calif. Law Enforcement Assn. of Records Suprs. (pres. so. chpt. 1985-87, state pres. 1986-87), Calif. Acad. Dirs. Assn. (vice-chmn. 1987-88, chmn. 1988-89), Acad. Criminal Justice Scis., Western and Pacific Assn. Criminal Justice Educators, Calif. Assn. Adminstrn. of Justice Educators, Calif. Peace Officers Standards and Tng. Basic Course Consortium (chmn. instrn. com. 1987-88), World Future Soc. (pres. Orange County/Long Beach chpt. 1988-92), Nat. Assn. Field Tng. Officers (nat. pres. 1992-93), Nat. Assn. Chiefs of Police, Am. Soc. Law Enforcement Trainers. Roman Catholic.

PATKAU, JOHN, architect; b. Winnipeg, Man., Can., Aug. 18, 1947; s. Abe John and Bertha (Klassen) P.; m. Patricia Frances Gargett, Aug. 10, 1974. BA, U. Manitoba, 1969, BA in Environ. Studies, 1969, MArch, 1972. Registered architect, B.C., Ont. Designer Erickson/Massey Architects, Can., 1971; pvt. practice Winnipeg, Can., 1972-73; design architect Zeidler Partnership Architects, Toronto, Can., 1974-75; project architect Bittorf

Holland Christianson Architects, Toronto, Can., 1975-77; prin. John Patkau Architect Ltd., Edmonton, Can., 1977-83; ptnr. Patkau Archs. Inc., Vancouver, B.C., Can., 1984—; chmn. edn. com. Alta. Assn. Architects, 1981; vis. critic U. Calgary, 1981, 92, U. Waterloo, 1987, 89, U. Pa., 1987, Tech. U. N.S., 1987, U. B.C., 1988, 89, UCLA, 1989; design critic U. B.C., 1985-86; urban design panel Vancouver, 1990-92; vis. prof. William Lyon Somerville Lectureship U. Calgary, 1994; Eliot Noyes vis. design critic Harvard U., 1995. U. Man. Alumni scholar, Alsip, Black Tile and Lumber Co. scholar, Isbister scholar U. Man.; Ctrl. Mortgage and Housing fellow; recipient Man. Assn. Architects prize, Progressive Architecture citation, 1981, Progressive Architecture award, 1993, 95, Can. Architects award, 1983, 86, 87, 89, 90, 92, 94, Wood Coun. First award, 1984, Gov. Gen. medal, 1986, 90, 92, 94, Gov. Gen. award, 1990, Lt. Gov. Archtl. medal, 1992, Honor award, 1992. Fellow Royal Archtl. Inst. Can. (chmn. design com. 1987); mem. Archtl. Inst. B.C., Royal Can. Coll. Art, Ont. Assn. Architects. Office: Patkau Archs, 560 Beatty St Ste L110, Vancouver, BC Canada V6B 2L3

PATKAU, PATRICIA, architect, architecture educator; b. Winnipeg, Manitoba, Can., Feb. 25, 1950; d. John Frederick and Aileen Constance (Emmett) Gargett; m. John Robert Patkau, Aug. 10, 1974. BA in Interior Design, U. Manitoba, 1973; MA in Architecture, Yale, New Haven, Conn., 1978. Arch. John Patkau Archs., Edmonton, Ont., Can., 1979-83; ptnr. Patkau Archs., Vancouver, B.C., Can., 1983—; asst. prof. Sch. Architecture UCLA, U.S.A., 1988-90; assoc. prof. Sch. Architecture U. B.C., Can., 1992—; vis. critic U. Calgary, 1981, 87, U. Waterloo, 1987, U. Pa., U.S.A., 1987, U. Toronto, 1988, Southern Calif. Inst. Architecture, U.S.A., 1990, UCLA, 1991, U. Oreg., U.S.A., 1992, MIT, U.S.A., 1993, Yale U., 1993; design critic U. B.C., 1984-87; vis. prof. Harvard U., U.S.A., 1993, U. Calgary, 1994. Recipient Nat. Soc. Interior Designers award, 1972, Mary Levy prize, 1973, IDIM Silver medal, 1973, U. Manitoba Gold medal, 1973, Central Mortgage and Housing fellow, 1977, 78, Progressive Architecture citation, 1981, 93, Can. Architect Excellence award, 1983, 86, 87, 89, 90, 92, 94, Can. Wood Coun. First award, 1984, Honor award, 1992, Gov. Gen. Architecture medal 1986, 90, 92, 94, Gov. Gen. Architecture award, 1990, Lt. Gov. Architecture medal, 1992, Can. Wood Coun. award, 1991,. Fellow Royal Archtl. Inst. Can.; mem. Archtl. Inst. B.C. (Honor award 1988). Office: Patkau Archs, 560 Beatty St Ste L110, Vancouver, BC Canada V6B 2L3

PATKIN, JUDITH KENT, human rights agency executive; b. Englewood, N.J., Dec. 16, 1935; d. George and Helen (Hurwitch) Kent; m. Stewart Sidney Patkin, July 19, 1959; children: Ruth Margot, Karen Beth. BS, Bates Coll., 1957; PhD, Tufts U., 1962. Rsch. asst. Harvard U. Med. Sch., Boston, 1965-67; cons. Home Base Sch., Watertown, Mass., 1972-74; exec. dir. Action for Post-Soviet Jewry, Inc., Waltham, Mass., 1980—. Office: Action for Post-Soviet Jewry Inc 24 Crescent St Ste 306 Waltham MA 02154

PATMOS, ADRIAN EDWARD, university dean emeritus; b. Paterson, N.J., June 29, 1914; s. Adrian and Myra (Van Splinter) P.; m. Pearl Van Den Heuvel, Apr. 25, 1942; children: Adrian Edward III, Bruce Douglas. A.B. magna cum laude, N.Y.U., 1935, A.M., 1936; Penfield scholar, 1937-38; grad. study, Am. U., 1936-37. Asst. prof. econs. Wittenberg U, 1938-47, assoc. prof., head dept., 1947-50, prof. econs., 1950—, head dept., 1950-64, dir. mgmt. devel. program, 1952-79, eve. sessions, 1952-78; dean Wittenberg U. (Sch. Community Edn.), 1955-79, dean emeritus, 1979—; jr. accountant Def. Plant Corp., Curtiss-Wright Corp., summer 1943; vis. instr. Ohio Wesleyan U., summer 1944; spl. field rep. NLRB, 1946; vis. lectr. econs. N.Y.U., 1946-47, summer 1948; vis. prof. econs. USAF Inst. Tech., 1949, 50; cons. Clark C.C., 1982-84, Urbana U., 1983-94. Chmn. Clark County Health Facilities Planning Com., 1965-66, City commr., Springfield, Ohio, 1958-62, mayor, 1960-62; Trustee United Way, Springfield and Clark County, 1960-74; trustee Clark Tech. Coll., 1965-78, chmn., 1969-71; trustee Springfield Community Hosp., 1975-84, Elderly United, 1979-92. Recipient Wittenberg award for meritorious service to univ., 1964; Silver Knight award Nat. Mgmt. Assn.; Kiwanis award for disting. service to community; Sta. WIZE award for outstanding community service; Community Service award C. of C., 1979; award of distinction Bd. Realtors; Outstanding Service in Community Labor-Mgmt. Relationships award Fed. Mediation Service; citation as one of Ohio's foremost educators Ohio Senate; Medal of Honor for leadership in liberal arts edn., 1987. Mem. Ohio Coll. Assn. (pres. adult edn. sect. 1959-60), Am. Econ. Assn., Phi Beta Kappa, Phi Gamma Delta, Blue Key. Baptist. Lodge: Kiwanis.

PATNAUDE, WILLIAM E., architect; b. Sanger, Calif., Sept. 24, 1937; s. Eugene Joseph Patnaude and Vera Mae (Giles) Patnaude Fagan; m. Mary Esther Simerly, Aug. 22, 1971 (div. 1987); children—Nathaniel, Matthew. B.Arch., U. Calif., Berkeley, 1961; postgrad., Calif. State U.-Fresno, 1968-72. Registered architect, Calif., Oreg., Wash., Idaho, Nev., N.Mex., Colo., Utah. Draftsman, architect Robert Stevens Assoc., Santa Cruz, Calif., 1963-66; architect Llewelyn Davies, Weeks & Ptnrs., London, 1966; architect Allen Y. Lew, Fresno, Calif., 1967-69, assoc., 1969-74; v.p.; architect Lew & Patnaude, Inc., Fresno, Calif., 1978-84; pres. Lew & Patnaude, Inc., 1985—; instr. Calif. State U., Fresno, 1968-81. Constn. arbitrator Am. Arbitration Assn., 1976—; chair central area plan citizen's adv. com. City of Fresno, 1991-93, chair gen. plan update com., 1994-95; bd. dirs. Fresno Arts Ctr., 1971-74, Fresno County Alliance for the Arts, 1986-88, 91-94. With USNR, 1961-63. Recipient Award of Merit, Calif. Hist. Preservation Conf., Orange County, 1983; Award of Excellence Woodwork Inst. Calif., 1982. Fellow AIA (nat. dir. 1983-85, pres. Calif. coun. 1982, San Joaquin chpt. 1978, Awards of Excellence, 1972-83); mem. Constrn. Specifications Inst. (pres. Fresno chpt. 1977), Owls Club, Rotary. Democrat. Avocations: photography; fine wines. Home: 4190 N Van Ness Blvd Fresno CA 93704-4213 Office: Lew & Patnaude Inc 1050 S St Fresno CA 93721-1407

PATON, LELAND B., investment banker; b. Worcester, Mass., Nov. 30, 1943; s. Andrew John and Anne Louise (Kehoe) P.; m. Nancy Carlon Nation, May 13, 1978; children: Scott Bartlett, Mark Grosvenor, Elisabeth Anne. Asst. sec. New England Mcht. Nat. Bank, Boston, 1965-69; with Prudential Bache Securities Inc., 1969—; mgr. N.Y. instl. sales, N.Y.C., 1976-77; dir.mktg., from 1977, sr. v.p., from 1977, also dir., mem. exec. com.; now capital mkts. group pres. Prudential Securities Inc.; exchange ofcl. Am. Stock Exchange; bd. dirs. Chgo. Bd. of Options Exchange. Mem. N.Y. Stock Exchange, Securities Industry Assn. (chmn. mktg. com. 1981, bd. dirs.), Securities Inst. Inst. (bd. dirs.), Am.Mktg. Assn., Bond Club, N.Y., Apawamis Club, Harvard Club, Mid-Ocean Club, Long Cove Club. Office: Prudential Securities Inc One Seaport Plz New York NY 10292

PATON WALSH, JILL, author; b. London, England, Apr. 29, 1937; d. John Llewelyn and Patricia (Dubern) Buss; m. Antony Edmund Paton Walsh, Aug. 5, 1961; Children: Edmund, Margaret, Clare. Author: Hengest's Tale, 1966, The Dolphin Crossing, 1967, Fireweed, 1969, (with Kevin Crossley-Holland, World Book Festival award 1970) Wordhoard, 1969, Goldengrove 1972, Farewell Great King, 1972, Toolmaker, 1973, The Dawnstone, 1973, The Emperor's Winding Sheet, 1974 (Whitbread prize 1974), The Huffler, 1975, The Island Sunrise: Prehistoric Culture in the British Isles, 1975, Unleaving, 1976 (Boston Globe, Horn Book award 1976), Children of the Fox: Crossing to Salamis, 1977, The Walls of Athens, 1978, Persian Gold, 1978, A Chance Child, 1978, The Green Book, 1981, Babylon, 1982, Parcell of Patterns, 1983 (Universe prize 1984), Lost and Found, 1984, Gaffer Samson's Luck, 1984 (Smarties Grand prix 1984), Lapsing, 1985, A School for Lovers, 1989, Birdy and the Ghosties, 1990, "Grace", 1991, Matthew and the Sea Singers, 1992, When Grandma Came, 1992, The Wydham Case, 1993, Knowledge of Angels, 1994, A Piece of Justice, 1995. Addres: c/o David Higham Assocs, 5-8 Lower John St, Gown 80 London W1R 3PE, England

PATRICELLI, ROBERT E., health care company executive; b. Hartford, Conn., Dec. 9, 1939; s. Leonard J. and Lydia E. Patricelli; m. Margaret Patricelli; children—Thomas, Alison. A.B. with high honors, Wesleyan U., Middletown, Conn., 1961; LL.B. cum laude, Harvard U., 1965. Bar: N.Y. 1967. White House fellow U.S. Dept. State, Washington, 1965-66; minority counsel U.S. Senate Subcom. Employment, Manpower and Poverty, Washington, 1966-69; dep. asst. sec., dep. undersec. HEW, Washington, 1969-71; v.p. Greater Hartford Process, Devco, Conn., 1971-75; adminstr. Urban

Mass Transp. Adminstrn., U.S. Dept. Transp., Washington, 1975-77; v.p. govt. relations CIGNA Corp., Hartford, Conn., 1977-79, v.p., sr. v.p., exec. v.p. corp. services, 1979-83, pres. affiliated bus. group, 1983-86; chmn., chief exec. officer Value Health Inc., Avon, Conn., 1987—. Bd. dirs. Hartford Hosp., 1994—, Health Spring, Inc., 1994-95; bd. dirs. U.S. C. of C., 1990—, chmn. health and employee benefits com., 1990-94; trustee N.E. Utilities Corp., 1993—, Wesleyan U., 1993—. Recipient Disting. Alumnus award Wesleyan U., 1986; Fulbright scholar U. Paris, 1962. Mem. Inst. of Medicine. Office: Value Health Inc 22 Waterville Rd Avon CT 06001-2066

PATRICK, ALLAN, drug store and variety store executive; b. 1946. Student, U. Md. Installer Western Elec. Co., 1964-66; control clk. RCA Corp., 1966-67; collection mgr. William Iselin & Co., 1967-71; asst. mgr. Genovese Drug Store Inc., Melville, N.Y., 1971-80, v.p. div. ops., 1980-86, v.p., dir. merchandising, 1986-87, sr. v.p., dir. merchandising and distbn. ops., 1987-90, exec. v.p., 1990—, also bd. dirs. Office: Genovese Drug Stores Inc 80 Marcus Dr Melville NY 11747-4230

PATRICK, CARL LLOYD, theatre executive; b. Honaker, Va., Dec. 6, 1918; s. Deward and Virginia Mae (McGraw) P.; m. Frances Estelle Wynn, Feb. 14, 1943; children: Carl Lloyd Jr., Michael Wynn. Ed. high sch., Dublin, Md. Gen. mgr. Martin Theatres, Columbus, Ga., 1945-69, pres., 1969-70; pres. Fuqua Industries, Inc., Atlanta, 1970-78, vice chmn., 1978-82; chmn. Carmike Cinemas, Inc., Columbus, 1982—; bd. dirs. Columbus Bank & Trust Co. Trustee Columbus Mus., 1983—, Ga. Southwestern Coll., Americus, 1984—, Columbus Coll., 1985—; bd. dirs. Columbus Tech. Inst., 1988—. Maj. U.S. Army, 1941-45. Mem. Nat. Assn. Theatre Owners (Sherrill Corwin award 1984, Hassanein Humanitarian award 1986, Exhibitor of the Decade award 1990). Methodist. Avocation: golf. Home: 2701 Lynda Ln Columbus GA 31906-1248 Office: Carmike Cinemas 1301 First Ave Columbus GA 31901

PATRICK, CRAIG, professional hockey team executive; b. Detroit, May 20, 1946; s. Lynn P.; m. Sue Patrick; children—Erin, Cory, Ryan. M.B.A., U. Denver. Hockey player Calif. Golden Seals, 1971-74; hockey player St. Louis Blues, 1974-75, Kansas City, 1975-76, World Hockey Assn., Minn., 1976-77, Washington Capitals, 1977-79; v.p., gen. mgr. N.Y. Rangers, N.Y.C., 1981-86; dir. athletics and recreation Univ. Denver, 1987-89; gen. mgr., exec. v.p. Pitts. Penguins, 1989—. Capt., U.S. Nat. Team, World Championships, Moscow, 1979; asst. mgr. and asst. coach U.S. Olympic Hockey Team, 1980. Office: Pitts Penguins Civic Arena Gate # 9 Pittsburgh PA 15219*

PATRICK, DENNIS, actor, director; b. Phila., Mar. 14, 1918; s. William John and Mary Katherine (Tydings) Harrison; m. Barbara Cason, Nov. 7, 1970 (dec. June 1990); children: Christine Tydings, Michaela De Paoli. Appeared in: numerous plays including Marat/Sade, The Wayward Saint, The Sea Gull, N.Y.C., 1983; actor, dir. over 2000 television shows; film appearances include Story of Nicola Tesla; TV film appearances include Code Name: Diamond Head, 1977, The Georgia Peaches, 1980, The Sophisticated Gents, 1981, Advice to Lovelorn, War and Remembrance 1981, Coach, Eight is Enough, Dallas, It's the Gary Shandling Show, Time Travelers, Daddy's Gone Hunting, Deadly Honeymoon; movies Chances Are, 1989, The Air Up There, also Desperately Seeking Susan, Heated Vengence, Joe, Major Dundee, Guilty Bystander. Mem. Screen Actors Guild, AFTRA, Dirs. Guild Am. Club: Lambs.

PATRICK, DEVAL LAURDINE, lawyer; b. Chgo., July 31, 1956; s. Laurdine Kenneth and Emily Mae (Wintersmith) P.; m. Diane Louise Bemus, May 5, 1984; children: Sarah Baker, Katherine Wintersmith. AB cum laude, Harvard Coll., 1978, JD, 1982; JD (hon.), Dist. Columbia Law Sch., 1994. Bar: Calif. 1983, D.C. 1985, Mass. 1987, U.S. Dist. Ct. Mass. 1987, U.S. Dist. Ct. (cen. dist.) Calif. 1983, U.S. Ct. Appeals (1st and 5th cirs.) 1984, U.S. Ct. Appeals (9th and 11th cirs.) 1984, U.S. Supreme Ct. 1988. Law clk. to Hon. Stephen Reinhardt U.S. Ct. Appeals (9th cir.), L.A., 1982-83; asst. counsel NAACP Legal Def. Fund, N.Y.C., 1983-86; ptnr. Hill & Barlow, Boston, 1986-94; asst. atty. gen. civil rights divsn. U.S. Dept. Justice, Washington, 1994—. Dir., mem. exec. com., chmn. New Eng. steering com. NAACP Legal Def. and Edn. Fund, Inc., 1991-94, vice chmn. Mass. Jud. Nominating Coun., 1991-93; trustee, mem. exec. com. Milton Acad., 1985—; overseer WGBH, 1993-94; corporator Milton Hosp., 1991-94. Recipient George Leisure award Harvard Law Sch., 1981; Rockefeller Traveling fellow, 1978. Mem. ABA (numerous bds. and coms.), Mass. Bar Assn., Mass. Black Lawyers Assn., Boston Bar Assn. (coun. mem. 1993), Harvard Club of Boston, Harvard Alumni Assn. (dir. 1993—). Avocations: squash, cooking, gardening.

PATRICK, GEORGE W., lawyer; b. Pitts. 1942. AB cum laude, Georgetown U., 1964; LLB, U. Pa., 1968. Bar: Pa. 1968. Ptnr. Dechert, Price & Rhoads, Phila. Office: Dechert Price & Rhoads 4000 Bell Atlantic 1717 Arch St Philadelphia PA 19103-2713

PATRICK, H. HUNTER, lawyer, judge; b. Gasville, Ark., Aug. 19, 1939; s. H. Hunter Sr. and Nelle Frances (Robinson) P.; m. Charlotte Anne Wilson, July 9, 1966; children: Michael Hunter, Colleen Annette. BA, U. Wyo., 1961, JD, 1966. Bar: Wyo. 1966, U.S. Dist. Ct. Wyo. 1966, Colo. 1967, U.S. Supreme Ct. 1975. Mcpl. judge City of Powell (Wyo.), 1967-68; sole practice law Powell, 1966-88; atty. City of Powell, 1969-88; justice of the peace County of Park, Wyo., 1971-88; bus. law instr. Northwest Community Coll., Powell, 1968—; dist. judge State of Wyo. 5th Jud. Dist., 1988—. Editor: Bench Book for Judges of Courts of Limited Jurisdiction in the State of Wyoming, 1980-90. Dir. cts. Wyo. Girls State, Powell, 1982-85, 89-93. Mem. ABA (state del. to ho. of dels. 1994—, Wyo del judician adminstrn. divsn., Pub. Svc. award for ct.-sponsored Law Day programs 1990, 92), Wyo. Bar Assn., Colo. Bar Assn., Park County Bar Assn. (sec. 1969-70, pres. 1970-71), Wyo. Assn. Cts. Ltd. Jurisdiction (pres. 1973-80), Am. Judicature Soc., Wyo. Dist. Judges Conf. (vice chair 1994-95, chair 1995—). Presbyterian (elder). Avocations: photography, travel, fishing, camping, bicycling. Home: PO Box 941 Powell WY 82435-0941 Office: PO Box 1868 Cody WY 82414-1868

PATRICK, HUGH TALBOT, economist, educator; b. Goldsboro, N.C., Feb. 22, 1930; s. Talbot and Paula (Miller) P.; B.A., Yale U., 1951; M.A. in Far Eastern Studies, U. Mich., 1955, M.A. in Econs., 1957; Ph.D. in Econs., 1960; M.A. (hon.), Yale U., 1968; children—Stephen, Matthew, Catherine. Econ. analyst U.S. Govt., 1951-52; lectr. econs. U. Mich., 1958-60; asst. prof. econs. Yale U., New Haven, 1960-64, assoc. prof., 1964-68, prof. Far Eastern econs., 1968-84, dir. Yale Econ. Growth Center 1976-79, 80-83; R.D. Calkins prof. internat. bus. Columbia U., 1984—; vis. prof. U. Bombay, 1961-62; mem. Japan-U.S. Econ. Relations Group, 1978-81, Nat. Com. for Pacific Econ. Coop.; dir. Ctr. on Japanese Econ. and Bus., Columbia U., 1986—. Ford Found. fellow, 1957-58; Am. Council Learned Socs. grantee, 1962; Guggenheim fellow, 1964-65; Fulbright research grant, 1964-65; Fulbright-Hays NDEA fellow, 1968-69; Assn. Asian Studies Disting. lectr., 1977. Mem. Japan Soc. (dir. 1973-79, 81—), Social Sci. Research Council (dir., chmn. 1985—), Pacific Basin Inst., Pacific Trade and Devel. Confs. (chmn.). Democrat. Editor: Japanese Industrialization and Its Social Consequences, 1976, Japanese High Technology Industries-Lessons and Limitations of Industrial Policy, 1986; co-author, co-editor: Asia's New Giant-How the Japanese Economy Works, 1976; chapter author: (co-editor with Masahiko Aoki) The Japanese Finance Main Bank System: Its Relevance for Developing and Transforming Economies, 1994, (co-editor with Larry Meissner) Pacific Basin Industries in Distress: Structural Adjustment and Trade Policy in Nine Industrialized Economies, 1991 (Masayoshi Ohira Meml. prize, 1992); co-editor: (with Yung Chul Park) The Financial Development of Japan, Korea, and Taiwan: Growth, Repression and Liberalization, 1994. Office: Columbia U 522 Uris Hall New York NY 10027

PATRICK, JOHN JOSEPH, social sciences educator; b. East Chicago, Ind., Apr. 14, 1935; s. John W. and Elizabeth (Lazar) P.; m. Patricia Grant, Aug. 17, 1963; children—Rebecca, Barbara. A.B., Dartmouth Coll., 1957; Ed.D., Ind. U., 1969. Social studies tchr. Roosevelt High Sch., East Chicago, 1957-62; social studies tchr. Lab. High Sch., U. Chgo., 1962-65; research assoc. Sch. Edn., Ind. U., Bloomington, 1965-69, asst. prof., 1969-74, assoc. prof., 1974-77, prof. edn., 1977—; dir. social studies devel. ctr., 1986—, dir. ERIC clearinghouse for social studies, social sci. edn., 1986—;

bd. dirs. Biol. Scis. Curriculum Study, 1980-83; ednl. cons. Author: Progress of the Afro-American, 1968, The Young Voter, 1974; (with L. Ehman, Howard Mehlinger) Toward Effective Instruction in Secondary Social Studies, 1974, Lessons on the Northwest Ordinance, 1987; (with R. Remy) Civics for Americans, 1980, rev. edit. 1986; (with Mehlinger) American Political Behavior, 1972, rev. edit. 1980, (with C. Keller) Lessons on the Federalist Papers, 1987; America Past and Present, 1983; (with Carol Berkin) History of the American Nation, 1984, rev. edit., 1987; Lessons on the Constitution, 1985, James Madison and the Federalist Papers, 1990, How to Teach the Bill of Rights, 1991, Ideas of the Founders on Constitutional Government: Resources for Teachers of History and Government, 1991, Young Oxford Companion to the Supreme Court of the United States, 1994, Founding the Republic: A Documentary History, 1995. Bd. dirs. Law in Am. Soc. Found., 1984-88, Social Sci. Edn. consortium, 1984—; mem. Gov.'s Task Force on Citizenship Edn., Ind., 1982-87; active Ind. Commn. on Bicentennial of U.S. Constn., 1986-92; bd. dirs. Coun. for the Advancement of Citizenship, Nat. History Edn. Network, 1994—; mem. Natr. Coun. for History Standards, 1991-94. Mem. ASCD, Nat. Coun. Social Studies, Social Sci. Edn. Consortium (v.p. 1985-87), Coun. for Basic Edn., Am. Polit. Sci. Assn., Am. Hist. Assn., Orgn. Am. Historians, Phi Delta Kappa. Home: 1209 E University St Bloomington IN 47401-5045 Office: Ind U 2805 E 10th St Bloomington IN 47408-2601

PATRICK, LYNN ALLEN, construction and land development company executive, lawyer; b. Stettler, Alta., Can., Dec. 7, 1935; s. Allen Russell and Florence Lorene (Lynn) P.; m. Roberta Colleen Hughes, May 9, 1959; children: Diane Elizabeth, Ross Gordon. B.Sc., U. Alta., Edmonton, Can., 1957, LL.B., 1960. Bar: Alta. 1961. Ptnr. Cormie Kennedy, Edmonton, Alta., 1961-83; sr. v.p., gen. counsel Mutual Fund Group, Edmonton, 1983-88; pres. Stuart Olson Constrn., Inc., Edmonton, 1989-92; v.p., corp. counsel, sec. The Churchill Corp., 1992—. Past pres., trustee Minerva Found., Edmonton; adv. council mem. Minster of Edn., Alta.; gov. Banff Ctr. Mem. Can. Bar Assn., Edmonton Bar Assn., Law Soc. Alta., Royal Glenora Club (Edmonton). Progressive. Home: 64 Quesnell Rd, Edmonton, AB Canada T5R 5N2 Office: The Churchill Corp, 10180 101st St Ste 2280, Edmonton, AB Canada T5J 3S4

PATRICK, MICHAEL WYNN, theatre executive; b. Columbus, Ga., May 17, 1950; s. Carl L. and Frances E. (Wynn) P.; m. Jayne Johnston, Mar. 26, 19761 child, Michael W. II. BS, Columbus Coll., 1972. Successively dist. mgr., v.p. film, v.p. spl. projects Martin Theatres, Columbus, 1972-81; pres., chief exec. officer Carmike Cinemas, Columbus, 1981—; bd. dirs. Columbus Bank and Trust Co. Mem. Nat. Assn. Theatre Owners (v.p.), Will Rogers Inst. (dir.), Variety Internat. (dir.), Motion Picture Pioneers (dir.), Green Island Country Club, Country Club of Columbus. Methodist. Avocations: golf, fishing. Office: Carmike Cinemas Inc 1301 1st Ave Columbus GA 31901-2109

PATRICK, RICHARD M., professional hockey team executive; b. Victoria, B.C., Can., Oct. 20, 1946; married; 3 children. Ed. Dartmouth Coll., Am. U. Washington. Ptnr. Lewis, Mitchell & Moore; exec. v.p. Washington Capitals Hockey Team, Landover, Md.; now pres & alternate gov. Washington Capitals, 1992—. Office: Washington Capitals Usair Arena Landover MD 20785

PATRICK, ROBERT WINTON, JR., lawyer; b. Tifton, Ga., Jan. 11, 1940; s. Robert Winton and Marguerite (Ryner) P.; m. Celia; children—Celia Dean, Marguerite Elizabeth, Sallie Louise. B.A. with honors, Fla. State U. 1961; J.D. with distinction, Yale U. 1964. Bar: Ga. 1964. Ptnr. Powell, Goldstein, Frazer & Murphy, Atlanta, 1964—; spl. counsel Atlanta Crime Commn., 1967-69; adj. prof. law Emory U., 1968-74. Author: Georgia Appellate Practice Handbook, 1977, The Georgia Lawyers Basic Practice Handbook, 1980; editor-in-chief The Atlanta Lawyer, 1971-73; contbg. editor Litigation, ABA, 1976-80. Chmn. Ga. Dem. Presdl. Campaign, 1972. Woodrow Wilson hon. fellow. Fellow Am. Coll. Trial Lawyers, Internat. Soc. Barristers; mem. Assn. Trial Lawyers Am. (sustaining mem.), N.Y. State Trial Lawyers Assn., Pa. Trial Lawyers Assn., Tex. Trial Lawyers Assn., Lawyers Club of Atlanta, The Real Lawyers Club (mem. chmn. 1986-87, pres. 1987-88), Commerce Club, Yale Club of Atlanta, The Gov.'s Club, Aston-Martin Owner's Club, Sigma Alpha Epsilon. Office: Powell Goldstein Frazer & Murphy 11th Fl C&S Nat Bank Bldg 35 Broad St NW Atlanta GA 30335-5601

PATRICK, RUTH (MRS. CHARLES HODGE), limnologist, diatom taxonomist, educator; b. Topeka, Kans.; d. Frank and Myrtle (Jetmore) P.; m. Charles Hodge, IV, July 10, 1931; 1 son, Charles, V. BS, Coker Coll., 1929, LLD, 1971; MA, U. Va., 1931, PhD, 1934; DSc, Beaver Coll., 1970, PMC Colls., 1971, Phila. Coll. Pharmacy and Sci., 1973, Wilkes Coll., 1974, Cedar Crest Coll., 1974, U. New Haven, 1975, Hood Coll., 1975, Med. Coll. Pa., 1975, Drexel U., 1975, Swarthmore Coll., 1975, Bucknell U., 1976, Rensselaer Poly. Inst., 1976, St. Lawrence U. 1978; LHD, Chestnut Hill Coll., 1974; DSc, U. Mass., 1980, Princeton U., 1980, Lehigh U., 1983, U. Pa., 1984, Temple U., 1985, Emory U., 1986, Wake Forst U., 1986, U. S.C., 1989, Clemson, 1989, Glassboro State Coll., 1992. Asso. curator microscopy dept. Acad. Natural Scis., Phila., 1939-47; curator Leidy Micros. Soc., 1937-47, curator limnology dept., 1947—, chmn. limnology dept., 1947-73; occupant Francis Boyer Research Chair, 1973—, chmn. bd. trustees, 1973-76, hon. chmn. bd. trustees, 1976—; lectr. botany U. Pa., 1950-70, adj. prof., 1970—; guest Fellow of Saybrook Yale, 1975; participant Am. Philos. Soc. limnology expdn. to, Mexico, 1947; leader Catherwood Found. expdn. to, Peru and Brazil, 1955; del. Gen. Assembly, Internat. Union Biol. Scis., Bergen, Norway, 1973; Dir. E.I. duPont, Pa. Power and Light Co.; Chmn. algae com. Smithsonian Oceanographic Sorting Center, 1963-68; mem. panel on water blooms Pres.'s Sci. Adv. Com., 1966; mem. panel on water resources and water pollution Gov.'s Sci. Adv. Com., 1966; mem. nat. tech. adv. com. on water quality requirements for fish and other aquatic life and wildlife Dept. Interior, 1967-68; mem. citizen's adv. council Pa. Dept. Environ. Resources, 1971-73; mem. hazardous materials adv. com. EPA, 1971-74, exec. adv. com., 1974-79, chmn. com.'s panel on ecology, 1974-76; mem. Pa. Gov.'s Sci. Adv. Coun., 1972-78; mem. exec. adv. com. nat. power survey FPC., 1972-75; mem. coun. Smithsonian Instn., 1973—; mem. Phila. Adv. Council, 1973-76; mem. energy R & D adv. coun. Pres.'s, Energy Policy Office, 1973-74; mem. adv. coun. Renewable Natural Resources Found., 1973-76, Electric Power Rsch. Found., 1973-77; mem. adv. com. for rsrch. NSF., 1973-74; mem. gen. adv. com. ERDA, 1975-77; adv. bd. sec. energy, 1975-89; mem. com. on human resources NRC, 1975-76; mem. adv. council dept. biology Princeton, 1975-80; mem. com. on sci. and arts Franklin Inst., 1978—; mem. univ. council com. Yale Sch. Forestry and Environ. Studies, 1978-80; mem. sci. adv. council World Wildlife Fund-U.S., 1978—; trustee Aquarium Soc. Phila., 1951-58, Henry Found.; bd. mgrs. Wistar Inst. Anatomy and Biology. Author: Rivers of the United States, Vol. 1, 1994, Rivers of the United States, Vol. 2—Chemical and Physical Characteristics, 1995, (with C.W. Reimer) Diatoms of the United States, Vol. 1, 1966, Vol. II, Part 1, 1975; author: (with others) Ground Water Contamination in the United States, 1983, 2d edit., 1987, Surface Water Quality: Have the Laws Been Successful?, 1992; mem. editorial bd. (with C.W. Reimer) Science, 1974-76, American Naturalist; trustee Biological Abstracts, 1974-76; contbr. over 150 articles to profl. jours. Recipient Disting. Dau. of Pa. award, 1952, Richard Hopper Day Meml. medal Acad. Natural Scis., 1969, Gimbel Phila. award, 1969; Gold medal YWCA, 1970, Lewis L. Dollinger Pure Environment award Franklin Inst., 1970, Pa. award for excellence in sci. and tech., 1970, Eminent Ecologist award Ecol. Soc. Am., 1972, Phila. award, 1973, Gold medal Pa. State Fish and Game Protective Assn., 1974, Internat. John and Alice Tyler Ecology award, 1975, Gold medal Phila. Soc. for Promoting Agr., 1975, Pub. Service award Dept. Interior, 1975, Iben award Am. Water Resources Assn., 1976, Outstanding Alumni award Coker Coll., 1977, Francis K. Hutchinson medal Garden Club of Am., 1977, Golden medal Royal Zool. Soc. Antwerp, 1978, Green World award N.Y. Bot. Garden, 1979, Hugo Black award U. Ala., 1979, Sci. award Gov. Pa., 1988, Founders award Soc. Environ. Toxicology and Chemistry, 1982, Environ. Regeneration award Rene Du Bois Ctr., 1985, Disting. Citizen award Pa., 1989, Pa. Gov.'s award, 1988, Excellence award N.Am. Benthological Soc., 1993; Sci. Edn. Ctr. named in her honor U. S.C., 1989. Fellow AAAS (com. environ. alterations 1973-74); mem. Nat. Acad. Scis. (chmn. panel com. on pollution 1966, mem. com. sci. and pub. policy 1973-77, mem. environ. measurements panel of com. on remote sensing

programs for earth resource surveys 1973-74, mem. nominating com. 1973-75), Nat. Acad. Engring. (com. environ. engring.'s ad hoc study on explicit criteria for decisions in power plant siting 1973), Am. Philos. Soc. (Benjamin Franklin Outstanding Sci. Achievement award 1993), Am. Acad. Arts and Scis., Bot. Soc. Am. (mem. Darbarker prize com. 1956, merit award 1971), Phycol. Soc. Am. (pres. 1954), Internat. Limnological Soc., Internat. Soc. Plant Taxonomists, Am. Soc. Plant Taxonomy, Am. Soc. Limnology and Oceanography, Water Pollution Control Fedn. (hon.), Soc. Study Evolution, Am. Soc. Naturalists (pres. 1975-76), Ecol. Soc. Am., Am. Inst. Biol. Scis., Internat. Phycol. Soc., Soc. Sigma Xi. Presbyterian. Office: Acad Natural Scis 19th at Benjamin Franklin Pkwy Philadelphia PA 19103

PATRICK, SUE FORD, diplomat; b. Union Springs, Ala., Nov. 9, 1946; d. Oscar Ford and Mildred (Hunter) Ford Carter; m. Henderson M. Patrick, Dec. 24, 1973; 1 child, Lauren. BA, Coll. Notre Dame of Md., 1967; postgrad., U. Va., 1967-69, 70-72; MA, Boston U., 1982; postgrad., Nat. War Coll., Washington, 1991-92. Joined Fgn. Svc., Dept. State, 1972; vice-consul Am. Consulate, Udorn, Thailand, 1973-74; desk officer Dept. State, Washington, 1976-78, 2d sec., 1982-84, spl. asst. refugee programs, 1984-85; 2d sec. U.S. Embassy, Nairobi, Kenya, 1978-81; 1st sec. polit. affairs U.S. Embassy, Abidjan, Ivory Coast, 1985-88; dep. chief of mission U.S. Embassy, Kigali, Rwanda, 1988-91, Nat. War Coll., Washington, 1991-92; adv. on NATO policy Office of Sec. of Def., The Pentagon, Washington, 1992-93, dir. office of fgn. civil. mil. affairs, 1993-94; congl. affairs advisor Office Regional Security Policy Dept. State, Washington, 1994—. Mem. Am. Fgn. Svc. Assn. Roman Catholic. Avocations: jogging, climbing. Home: 2715 Colt Run Rd Oakton VA 22124-1101 Office: Office Regional Security Policy EAP/RSP Rm 5313 Dept State Washington DC 20520

PATRICK, THOMAS H., brokerage house executive; b. 1944. BA, Rutgers U., 1965; MBA, U. Pitts., 1966. Equity rsch. analyst Mellon Nat. Bank, 1966-68; prin. Sears, Chgo., 1970-72; with White Weld & Co., 1972-79; chief fin. officer, exec. v.p. Life Investors Inc., Cedar Rapids, Iowa, 1979-81; mng. dir. Merrill Lynch Capital Mkts., 1982-89; formerly chief fin. officer, exec. v.p. Merrill Lynch & Co. Inc., now exec. v.p. equity mkts. group. Office: Merrill Lynch & Co Inc World Financial Ctr 250 Vesey St New York NY 10281-1012

PATRICK, UEAL EUGENE, oil company executive; b. Ky., Mar. 10, 1929; s. Clevel and Maxine (Hackworth) P.; m. Nancy Sparrow, Mar. 7, 1953; children: Steve, Rick, Sherry, Mark. BA, Mich. State U., 1955. Acct. Bond and Co., Jackson, Mich., 1955-57; contr., then exec. v.p., mgr. Midway Supply Co., Jackson, 1957-62; pres., chief exec. officer, bd. dirs. Patrick Petroleum Co., Mich., Jackson, 1969—, Patrick Petroleum Corp., Jackson, 1962—, Patrick Racing Team, Inc., 1971-92; pres., chief exec. officer, sec., bd. dirs. Fayette Corp., 1968-76; pres., chief exec. officer, trustee, Patrick Oil and Gas Corp., 1968-90; chmn. bd. Mark Aviation, Inc., 1971-81; chmn. bd., chief exec. officer Jet Way, Inc., 1971-81; chief exec. officer, bd. dirs. K & C Corp., 1974-81, Western Stamping Corp., 1972-79; pres., chief exec. officer Patrick Energy Co., 1980-90, Patrick Properties, Inc., 1980—; pres., bd. dirs. Patrick Petroleum Internat., Inc., 1972-90, Patrick Petroleum Internat. Australia, Inc., 1972-80, Patrick Petroleum Internat. Indonesia, Inc., 1972-80, Patrick Petroleum U.K. Ltd., 1974-80, Patrick Petroleum Italiana, Inc. (S.P.A.), 1974-80; chmn. bd. Championship Auto Racing Teams, Inc., 1978-82; chmn. bd., chief exec. officer, bd. dirs. Belibe Coal Corp., 1978-84, Black Nugget Coal Co., Inc., 1978-84, Patrick Coal Corp., 1978-84; sec.-treas. Jackson Towing Co., 1972-84; bd. dirs. Vermillion Bay Land Co., Jackson Found. With USAF, 1948-52. Mem. Am. Petroleum Inst., Ind. Petroleum Assn. Am. (bd. dirs. 1968-80), Oil Investment Inst. (gov. 1970-81), Mich. Oil and Gas Assocs., Detroit Athletic Club, Detroit Renaissance Club, Jackson Country Club. Republican. Clubs: Jackson Country. Office: 301 W Michigan Ave Jackson MI 49201-2120

PATRICK, WILLIAM HARDY, JR., wetland biogeochemist, educator, laboratory director; b. Johns, Miss., Nov. 9, 1925; s. William Hardy and Alma (Webb) P.; m. Ruth Martin, Dec. 21, 1951; children: Terry Lynn, William Hardy, Carol Ann, Henry Carr. B.S., La. State U. 1950, M.S., 1951; Ph.D., La State U., 1954; D.Honoris Causa, U. Ghent (Belgium), 1979. Asst. prof. agronomy dept. La. State U., Baton Rouge, 1953-56, assoc. prof., 1956-61, prof., 1961-76, prof. marine scis., 1977-78, Boyd prof. marine scis., 1978—; dir. Wetland Biogeochemistry Inst., Baton Rouge; Moore lectr. in ecology U. Va., 1985, York lectr. U. Fla., 1989; cons. numerous govt., indsl. orgns. Contbr. articles to sci. jours. Organizer, dir. La. Methodist World Hunger Scholarship Program, Baton Rouge, 1979—. Served with AUS, 1944-46. grantee numerous research orgns., 1963—. Fellow AAAS, Am. Soc. Agronomy, Soil Sci. Soc. Am. (internat. award 1992, Rsch. award 1993); mem. Sigma Xi, Phi Kappa Phi. Republican. Methodist. Home: 888 Dubois Dr Baton Rouge LA 70808-5008 Office: Louisiana St Univ Wetland Biogeochemistr Baton Rouge LA 70803

PATRIKIS, ERNEST T., lawyer, banker; b. Lynn, Mass., Dec. 1, 1943; s. Theodore A. and Ethel (Stasinopolous) P.; m. Emily Herrick Trueblood, Mar. 18, 1972. BA, U. Mass., 1965; JD, Cornell U., 1968. Bar: N.Y. 1969. Exec. v.p., gen. counsel Fed. Res. Bank N.Y., 1968-95 1st v.p., 1995—; dep. gen. counsel Fed. Open Market Com., 1988-95. Contbr. articles to legal jours. Mem. Assn. of Bar of City of N.Y. (banking law com. 1982-84, 90—, futures regulation com. 1986-89); N.Y. State Bar Assn. (chmn. com. internat. banking, securities and fin. transaction 1987-91, banking law com. 1986—, vice chmn. internat. practice sect. 1991—), ABA (subcom. on gen. banking matters 1986). Home: 20 E 9th St New York NY 10003-5944 Office: Fed Res Bank NY 33 Liberty St New York NY 10005-1011

PATRON, JUNE EILEEN, former government official; b. N.Y.C., May 15; d. Irving B. and Mollie Patron; A.B. in Govt. with honors, Clark U., Worcester, Mass., 1965; M.A., Am. U., 1967. With U.S. Dept. of Labor, 1966-95, dir. Black Lung benefits program, 1976-79, asst. adminstr. pension and welfare benefit programs, 1979-84, assoc. dir. pension and welfare benefit programs, 1984-88, dir. program svcs., 1988-95, ret., 1995; mem. Sr. Exec. Svc. Recipient various awards Dept. Labor. Home: 3001 Veazey Ter NW Washington DC 20008-5405

PATRON, SUSAN HALL, librarian, writer; b. San Gabriel, Calif., Mar. 18, 1948; d. George Thomas and Rubye Denver (Brewer) H.; m. René Albert Patron, July 27, 1969. BA, Pitzer Coll., 1969; MLS, Immaculate Heart Coll., 1972. Children's libr. LA Pub. Libr., 1972-79, sr. children's libr., 1980—; reviewer Sch. Libr. Jour., 1980—, Pubs. Weekly, 1986-91, The Five Owls, 1987—; mem. award com. Friends of Children and Lit. Award, 1984. Author: Burgoo Stew, 1991, Five Bad Boys, Billy Que, and the Dustdobbin, 1992, Maybe Yes, Maybe No, Maybe Maybe, 1993 (ALA Notable Book 1994), Bobbin Dustdobbin, 1993, Dark Cloud Strong Breeze, 1994, (with Christopher Weiman) Marbled Papers, 1979. Mem. ALA (Caldecott award com. 1988), Calif. Libr. Assn. (Patricia Beatty award com. 1987-89, 91-92), Internat. Bd. on Books for Young Children, Soc. of Children's Book Writers and Illustrators, So. Calif. Coun. on Lit. for Children and Young People (awards com. 1985), Authors Guild. Office: LA Pub Libr Childrens Svcs 630 W 5th St Los Angeles CA 90071 Home: 2004 Vine St Los Angeles CA 90068

PATRONELLI, RAYMOND, church administrator. Asst. gen. overseer Christian Ch. of N. Am. Office: Christian Church of North Am 6203 Kelly Rd Plant City FL 33565-3567

PATTEN, BEBE HARRISON, minister; b. Waverly, Tenn., Sept. 3, 1913; d. Newton Felix and Mattie Priscilla (Whitson) Harrison; m. Carl Thomas Patten, Oct. 23, 1935; children: Priscilla Carla and Bebe Rebecca (twins), Carl Thomas. D.D., McKinley-Roosevelt Coll., 1941; D.Litt., Temple Hall Coll. and Sem., 1943. Ordained to ministry Ministerial Assn. of Evangelism, 1935; evangelist in various cities of U.S., 1933-50; founder, pres. Christian Evang. Chs. Am., Inc., Oakland, Calif., 1944—; Patten Acad. Christian Edn., Oakland, 1944—; Patten Bible Coll., Oakland, 1944-83; chancellor Patten Coll., Oakland, 1983—; founder, pastor Christian Cathedral of Oakland, 1950—; held pvt. interviews with David Ben-Gurion, 1972, Menachim Begin, 1977, Yitzhak Shamir, 1991; condr. Sta. KUSW world-wide radio ministry, 70 countries around the world. 1989-90, Stas. WHRI and WWCR world coverage short wave, 1990—. Founder, condr.: radio program The Shepherd Hour, 1934—; daily TV, 1976—, nationwide telecast, 1979—;

Author: Give Me Back My Soul, 1973; Editor: Trumpet Call, 1953—; composer 20 gospel and religious songs, 1945—. Mem. exec. bd. Bar-Ilan U. Assn., Israel, 1983; mem. global bd. trustees Bar-Ilan U., 1991. Recipient numerous awards including medallion Ministry of Religious Affairs Israel, 1969; medal Govt. Press Office, Jerusalem, 1971; Christian honoree of yr. Jewish Nat. Fund of No. Calif., 1975; Hidden Heroine award San Francisco Bay coun. Girl Scouts U.S.A., 1976, Golden State award Who's Who Hist. Soc., 1988; Ben-Gurion medallion Ben-Gurion Rsch. Inst., 1977; Resolutions of Commendation, Calif. Senate Rules Com., 1978, 94; hon. fellow Bar-Ilan U., Israel, 1981; Dr. Bebe Patten Social Action chair established Bar-Ilan U., 1982. Mem. Am. Assn. for Higher Edn., Religious Edn. Assn., Am. Acad. Religion and Soc. Bibl. Lit., Zionist Orgn. Am., Am. Assn. Pres. of Ind. Colls. and Univs., Am. Jewish Hist. Soc., Am.-Isreal Pub. Affairs Com. Address: 2433 Coolidge Ave Oakland CA 94601-2630 *He that labors in any great or laudable undertaking has his fatigues first supported by hope, and afterwards rewarded by joy. To strive with difficulties, and to conquer them, is the highest human felicity. I am not afraid of tomorrow for I have seen yesterday and I love today.*

PATTEN, BERNARD MICHAEL, neurologist, educator; b. N.Y.C., Mar. 23, 1941; s. Bernard M. and Olga (Vaccaro) P.; m. Ethel Doudine, June 18, 1964; children: Allegra, Craig. AB summa cum laude, Columbia Coll., 1962; MD, Columbia U., 1966. Med. intern N.Y. Hosp. Cornell Med. Ctr., N.Y.C., 1966-67; resident neurologist Columbia Presbyn. Med. Ctr., N.Y.C., 1967-69, chief resident neurologist, 1969-70; assoc. prof. neurology Baylor Coll. Medicine, Houston, 1973—; asst. chief med. neurology NIH, Bethesda, Md., 1970-73; mem. med. bd. Nat. Myasthenia Gravis Found., 1973—, Nat. AmyoTrophic Lateral Sclerosis Found., 1982—, Nat. Myositis Assn., 1995—. Contbr. over 100 articles to profl. jours. With USPHS, 1970-73. Rsch. grantee NIH, pvt. founds., nat. health orgns. Fellow ACP, Royal Coll. Physicians. Roman Catholic. Achievements include discoverer (with others) L-Dopa for Parkinson's disease; pioneered use of immune suppression for myasthenia gravis, diagnosis and treatment of medical and neurological complications of breast implants. Home: 1019 Baronridge Dr Seabrook TX 77586-4001 Office: Baylor Coll Medicine 1 Baylor Plz Houston TX 77030-3498

PATTEN, CHARLES ANTHONY, management consultant, arbitrator, retired manufacturing company executive, author; b. Allentown, Pa., May 12, 1920; s. Charles Henerie and Mae (Doyle) P.; m. Kathleen Marie Breene, Jan. 6, 1951; children: Charles Anthony Jr., Amy Elizabeth Goddard, Nancy Kathleen Hansen. B.S.M.E., Lehigh U., 1942. With Roy Mfg. Co., 1947-63, works mgr., 1956-63; v.p. mfg. White Motor Corp., 1963-68, Colt Industries, 1968-69; With Dravo Corp., Pitts., 1942-47, 69-85; gen. mgr. engring. works div. Dravo Corp., 1970-71, corp. v.p., gen. mgr. engring. works div., 1971-75, corp. group v.p., chief exec. officer Dravo Mfg. Group, 1975-81, corp. sr. v.p., mem. corp. policy com., chief exec. officer Dravo Mfg. Group, 1981-83, corp. sr. v.p., asst. to pres. and chief exec. officer, mem. exec. com., 1984-85; pres. C.A. Patten Enterprises, 1985—; bd. dirs., v.p. Dravo (Can.) Ltd., 1975-85; dir., pres. Dravo-Okura Co. Ltd., 1974-79; dir. Dravo Mfg. (Can.) Ltd., 1975-83, Tru Weld Grating Inc., 1983-85; v.p. Dravo Internat., Inc., 1974-85. Trustee Ohio Valley Gen. Hosp., McKees Rocks, Pa., 1975-82, Marietta (Ohio) Coll., 1979-89, emeritus trustee, 1989—; bd. dirs. Vocat. Rehab. Center of Allegheny County, 1972-79, Jr. Achievement of S.W. Pa., 1975-80. Mem. ASME, Neville Island Mfrs. Assn. (pres. 1975-85), Am. Arbitration Assn. (panel of arbitrators, 1989—), Duquesne Club. Republican. Roman Catholic. Home and Office: 3204 Clearvue Rd Pittsburgh PA 15237-1632 *The successful manager is a time-oriented goal setter. Without waiting for others to ask him, he envisions things that should happen and thinks through possible paths to reach the goals. When the goals are reached, he is quick to laud and praise his people for their accomplishment.*

PATTEN, DUNCAN THEUNISSEN, ecologist educator; b. Detroit, Oct. 13, 1934; s. Marc T. and Doris (Miller) P.; m. Eva Chittenden, July 27, 1957; children: Michael, Marc, Robin, Scott. BA, Amherst Coll., 1956; MS, U. Mass., Amherst, 1959; PhD, Duke U., 1962. Asst. prof. ecology Va. Poly. Inst., Blacksburg, 1962-65; asst. prof. ecology Ariz. State U., Tempe, 1965-67, assoc. prof., 1967-73, prof., 1973—, dir. ctr. environ. studies, 1980—. Contbr. articles to profl. jours. Fellow AAAS, Ariz.-Nev. Acad. Sci.; mem. Ecol. Soc. Am. (bus. mgr. 1979-95), Brit. Ecol. Soc., Soc. Range Mgmt., Am. Inst. Biol. Scis., Soc. Wetland Scientists, Am. Water Resource Assn., Soc. Conservation Biology, Sigma Xi. Office: Arizona State Univ Ctr for Environ Studies Box 873211 Tempe AZ 85287-3211

PATTEN, GERLAND PAUL, lawyer; b. Lewisville, Ark., Jan. 5, 1907; s. George Washington and Cleopatra (Sims) P.; m. Ira E. Barrett, June 10, 1927; children—Gerald William, Yvonne Claire. LL.B., Ark. Law Sch., 1938, J.D., 1980. Bar: Ark. 1933. Telegraph operator C., R.I.&P. Ry., 1923-31; since practiced in Little Rock; instr. Ark. Law Sch., 1935-44, prof. 1944-67, asst. dean, 1949-67; asst. U.S. atty. Little Rock, 1948-54; v.p., gen. counsel Nat. Investors Security Co., 1957-67; sec., treas., dir. Jess Odom Enterprises, Inc., Little Rock, Marifran Investments, Inc., Little Rock, Maryco Investments, Inc., Little Rock, State Investment Corp., Little Rock, Perryco Investments, Inc., Oklahoma City, Investors Equity Corp., Oklahoma City, Royal Investments Okla., Inc., Oklahoma City, to 1967; pres. Gerland P. Patten & Co., Little Rock, 1960—. Chmn. budget com. of Greater Little Rock Community Chest and Council, 1938; chmn. Pulaski County Welfare Bd., 1940-46; pres. Council Social Agys., Little Rock, 1943-44. Served as 2d lt. U.S. Army, 1944 46. Mem. Ark. Bar Assn. (sec. 1947-50), Pulaski County Bar Assn., Ark. Trial Lawyers (pres. 1973). Methodist. Home: 8 Sunset Cir Little Rock AR 72207-1718 Office: 1095 Union Nat Bank Bldg Little Rock AR 72201

PATTEN, JOHN W., magazine publisher; b. Summit, N.J., 1930. Grad., Dartmouth Coll., 1953. Pres. Bus. Week mag. Office: Bus Week 40th Fl 1221 Ave Of The Americas New York NY 10020-1001*

PATTEN, LANNY RAY, industrial gas industry executive; b. St. Joseph, Mo., July 31, 1934; s. E.L. and Sarah Catherine (Langner) P.; m. Ann Rogers Hall, Oct. 26, 1957; children: David, John, Jeffrey, Mark. BS in Engring., Iowa State U., 1956; AMP, Harvard U., 1976. Field engr. Carrier Corp., Kansas City, Mo., 1957; sales engr. Air Products and Chems., Inc., Allentown, Pitts., Chgo., 1960-63; dist. mgr. Air Products and Chems. Inc. Cleve., 1964-66; region mgr. Air Products and Chems., Inc., Pitts., 1966-68; div. gen. sales mgr. Air Products and Chems., Inc., Allentown, Pa., 1969-75; v.p., div. gen. mgr. Air Products and Chems., Inc., Allentown, 1975-88, sr. v.p., gases and equipment, 1988-90; pres., COO Airgas Inc., Radnor, Pa., 1990-91; pres., chief exec. officer CylServ, Inc., West Choshohocken, Pa., 1992—. Chmn. Lehigh U. Parents Assn., Bethlehem, Pa., 1977-90; campaign com. chmn. Good Shepherd Home, Allentown, 1989-90; mem. Boy Scouts Am., Allentown, 1978-90; pres., coach Youth Baseball Assn., Allentown, 1970-83. USAF Officer, 1957-60. Recipient PACE award for Engring. Achievement Iowa State U., 1990, Friend of Lehigh award, 1991. Mem. Compressed Gas Assn. (exec. bd. dirs. 1977-91), Internat. Oxygen Mfg. Assn. Allentown A.C. of C. (exec. bd. dirs. 1978-82), Kappa Sigma. Republican. Episcopalian. Avocations: baseball, golf, reading. Home: 1306 Club House Rd Gladwyne PA 19035-1006

PATTEN, ROBERT LOWRY, English language educator; b. Oklahoma City, Apr. 26, 1939; s. Charles H. and Helen (Lowry) P.; m. Faith L. Harris, June 12, 1960 (div. 1974); children: Jocelyn S., Christina S. BA, Swarthmore Coll., 1960; MA, Princeton U., 1963, PhD, 1965. Lectr. Bryn Mawr (Pa.) Coll., 1964-66, asst. prof. Rice U., Houston, 1966-69; assoc. prof. 1969-71, assoc. prof., 1971-76, prof. English, 1976—, chair, dept. of English, 1991-92, master Grad. House, 1992-95; pres. PEN S.W., Houston, 1989-92. Author: Charles Dickens and His Publishers, 1978, George Cruikshank's Life, Times, and Art, vol. 1, 1992, vol. 2, 1995; editor: (book by Charles Dickens) Pickwick Papers, 1972, 10th rev. edit., 1981; George Cruikshank: A Revaluation, 1974, 2d edit., 1992, (with John O. Jordan) Literature in the Marketplace, 1995; editor SEL: Studies in English Lit., 1978-84, 90—. Bd. dirs. Cultural Arts Coun., Houston, 1979-80, Tex.Com. for the Humanities, 1979-80; pres., bd. dirs. Houston Ctr. for the Humanities, 1976-84. NEH fellow, 1968-69, 77-78, 87-88; Guggenheim fellow, 1980-81; Nat. Humanities Ctr. fellow, 1987-88; Nat. Gallery of Art Assoc., 1988-89. Mem. AAUP, MLA, PEN Am. Ctr., Dickens Fellowship, Dickens Soc., Grolier Club, Phi Beta Kappa (pres. Beta chpt. Tex. 1991-94). Episcopalian. Avocations:

travel, opera. Office: Rice U Dept English MS 30 6100 Main St Houston TX 77005-1892

PATTEN, RONALD JAMES, university dean; b. Iron Mountain, Mich., July 17, 1935; s. Rudolph Joseph and Cecelia (Fuse) Pataconi; m. Shirley Ann Bierman, Sept. 5, 1959; children: Christine Marie, Cheryl Ann, Charlene Denise. B.A., Mich. State U., 1957, M.A., 1959; Ph.D., U. Ala., 1963. Acct. Price Waterhouse & Co., Detroit, 1958; instr. No. Ill. U., 1959-60; asst. prof. U. Colo., 1963-65; assoc. prof. Va. Poly. Inst. and State U., 1965-67, prof., 1967-73, head dept. accounting, 1968-73; dir. research Financial Accounting Standards Bd., Conn., 1973-74; dean Sch. Bus. Adminstrn., U. Conn., Storrs, 1974-88; chief of party-Eastern Caribbean Arthur D. Little Internat., 1988-89; dean Coll. Commerce and Kellstadt Grad. Sch. Bus. De Paul U., Chgo., 1989—; cons. to industry; bd. dirs. Transco Inc.; mem. individual investors adv. com. N.Y. Stock Exch., 1993—. Contbr. articles to profl. jours., chpts. to books. Served to 2d lt. F.A. AUS, 1958. Recipient Nat. Quartermaster award Nat. Quartermaster, Assn., 1956. Mem. AICPAs, Am. Acctg. Assn., Inst. Mgmt. Accts., Acad. Internat. Bus. (Dean of Yr. award 1987), Internat. Assn. for Acctg. Edn. and Rsch., Chgo. Coun. on Fgn. Rels., Ill. Joint Coun. Econ. Edn. (trustee 1989—), Execs. Club Chgo., Econ. Club Chgo., Pacioli Soc., Scabbard and Blade, Golden Key, Beta Gamma Sigma (bd. govs. 1975-90, nat. sec.-treas. 1980-82, nat. v.p. 1982-84, nat. pres. 1984-86), Beta Alpha Psi (bd. dirs. 1992-94), Delta Simga Pi, Phi Kappa Phi, Delta Mu Delta. Avocations: hiking, skiing, walking, golf, travel. Home: 334 N Montclair Ave Glen Ellyn IL 60137-5253

PATTEN, THOMAS HENRY, JR., management, human resources educator; b. Cambridge, Mass., Mar. 24, 1929; s. Thomas Henry and Lydia Mildred (Lindgren) P.; m. Jule Ann Miller, Aug. 27, 1972; children—Laurie Kathryn, Rhonda Josephine, Jenny Lydia. A.B., Brown U., 1953; M.S., Cornell U., 1955, Ph.D., 1959. Dir. program planning Ford Motor Co., Dearborn, Mich., 1957-65; prof. mgmt. and sociology U. Detroit, 1965-67; prof. orgnl. behavior and personnel mgmt. Sch. Labor and Indsl. Relations, Mich. State U., E. Lansing, 1967-84; prof. mgmt. and human resources Calif. State Poly. U., Pomona, 1984—; cons. in field. Author: The Foreman: The Forgotten Man of Management, 1968, Manpower Planning and the Development of Human Resources, 1971, OD-Emerging Dimensions and Concepts, 1973, A Bibliography of Compensation Planning and Administration, 1960-1974, 2d rev. edit., 1981, 3d rev. edit., 1987, Pay: Employee Compensation and Incentive Plans, 1977, Classics of Personnel Management, 1979, Organizational Development Through Teambuilding, 1981, A Manager's Guide to Performance Appraisal, 1982, Fair Pay: The Managerial Challenge of Comparable Job Worth and Job Evaluation, 1988. Served with USMC, 1946-51. Mem. ASTD (chmn. orgn. devel. div. 1972), Indsl. Rels. Rsch. Assn. (chpt. pres. 1970-71), Am. Sociol. Assn., Internat. Pers. Mgmt. Assn., Internat. Indsl. Rels. Assn., Orgnl. Behavior Teaching Soc., Inst. Applied Behavioral Sic., Acad. Mgmt., Am. Compensation Assn. Home: 353 Independence Dr Claremont CA 91711 Office: Calif State Poly U Dept Mgmt & Human Resources 3801 W Temple Ave Pomona CA 91768-4083 *Human values come first.*

PATTEN, THOMAS LOUIS, lawyer; b. Mo., Oct. 3, 1945; m. Sherry V. Patten; children: Elizabeth, Caroline, Brooke. BS, U. Mo., 1967, JD, 1969. Bar: Mo. 1969, D.C. 1972, U.S. Dist. Ct. D.C. 1972, U.S. Claims Ct. 1972, U.S. Ct. Appeals (fed. cir.) 1972, U.S. Supreme Ct. 1972, U.S. Ct. Appeals (9th cir.) 1974, U.S. Ct. Appeals (4th cir.) 1981, Va. 1983, U.S. Dist. Ct. (ea. and we. dists.) Va. 1983. Ptnr Latham & Watkins, Washington. Fellow Am. Coll. Trial Lawyers. Office: Latham & Watkins Ste 1300 1001 Pennsylvania Ave NW Washington DC 20004-2585

PATTERSON, ALAN BRUCE, obstetrician, gynecologist; b. Indpls., Apr. 23, 1953; s. Samuel S. and Eunice Selma (Brenner) P. BS, Tulane U., 1975; MD, Ind. U., 1979. Diplomate Am. Bd. Ob-Gyn. Resident in ob-gyn St. Vincent Hosp., Indpls., 1979-83; mem. staff Metro Health, Indpls., 1983-91; pvt. practice Pompano Beach, Boca Raton, Fla., 1991—; mem. staff, cons., instr. Meth. Hosp., Indpls, 1983-91; instr. Nurse Pitocin Cert. Course, 1985; cons. Indpls. Planned Parenthood, 1982-83, United Parcel Service, Indpls., 1982-83. Recipient Outstanding Citizens award DAR, 1971. Fellow Am. Coll. Ob-Gyn; mem. Palm Beach County Med. Soc., Fla. Med. Assn., Am. Cancer Soc., Boca Raton C. of C., Phi Beta Kappa, Phi Eta Sigma, Beta Beta Beta. Jewish. Avocations: jogging, swimming, wine collecting, photography, racing. Home: 19090 Fox Landing Dr Boca Raton FL 33434-5154 Office: MDPA 550 SW 3rd St Ste 105 Pompano Beach FL 33060-6944 also: 1000 NW 9th Ct Ste 103 Boca Raton FL 33486-2268 also: 9441 W Sample Rd #205 Coral Springs FL 33065

PATTERSON, ANITA MATTIE, union administrator; b. Birmingham, Ala., Feb. 19, 1940; d. John Evans Patterson and Flora Ella (Paul) Patterson/Mitchell; m. LeRoy Harold Walden, Mar. 19, 1958 (dec. Apr. 1966); children: Christopher Ann, DeRoy, Chanita. Student, Wayne State U., 1968-72, 72-78, Wayne State U., 1976-79. Sr. counselor City of Detroit, 1965-79; area dir. AFSCME, Washington, 1979—; exec. bd. Coalition Labor Union Women, Washington, exec. dir., 1975-77; chair nat. women's com. Coalition Black Trade Unionists, Washington, 1985—; tchg. fellow AFL-CIO Organizing Inst., Washington, 1992—; ofcl. election observer South Africa Election, 1994. Active So. Regional Coun., Atlanta, 1992—; mem. social svcs. com. Salem Bapt. Ch., Atlanta, 1990—. Recipient Cmty. Svcs. award A. Philip Randolph Inst., 1990, Cmty. Svcs. award So. Christian Leadership Coun., 1991, Leadership award Ga. State Legislature Black Caucus, 1992, Disting. Recognition award City of Detroit, 1989, Sojourner Truth award Coalition of Black Trade Unionists, 1994, Labor award Operation PUSH, 1994; named Addie L. Wyatt Women of Yr., Coalition of Black Trade Unionists, 1990. Mem. Nat. Coun. Negro Women (ad hoc labor com. 1986—), Recognition award 1989, Svc. award 1988), Marracci Ct. # 32. Democrat. Avocations: reading, crossword puzzles, word games, golf, traveling. Office: AFSCME Internat Area Office 1720 Peachtree St Ste 150B Atlanta GA 30309

PATTERSON, AUBREY BURNS, JR., banker; b. Grenada, Miss., Sept. 25, 1942; s. Aubrey Burns and Elizabeth (Patten) P.; m. Ruby Kathryn Clegg, Dec. 12, 1964; children: Aubrey B. III, Clayton H., Jennifer L. BBA, U. Miss., 1964; MBA, Mich. State U., 1969. Sr. v.p. Bank of Miss., Tupelo, 1972-83, pres., 1983—, chmn., chief exec. officer, 1990—, also bd. dirs.; bd. dirs. BancorpSouth, Inc., Vol. Bank, Jackson, Tenn. Former chmn. bd. dirs. Salvation Army, Tupelo, 1978—; bd. dirs. Cmty. Devel. Found., chmn. bd., 1994-95; bd. dirs. Columbia Theol. Sm., Decatur, Ga., U. Miss. Found., Miss. Univ. For Women Found., Miss. Econ. Coun., Jackson, 1986—, chmn., 1994; bd. dirs. North Miss. Health Svcs. Inc., 1987—, exec. com.; moderator St. Andrews Presbytery Presbyn. Ch. USA. Capt. USAF, 1965-72. Mem. Am. Bankers Assn. (govt. rels. coun.), Miss. Bankers Assn. (pres. 1995—), Robert Morris Assocs., Soc. Internat. Bus. Fellows, Tupelo Country Club, Union City Club, Kiwanis (pres. Tupelo 1987), Beta Gamma Sigma, Beta Alpha Psi. Presbyterian. Home: 1 Overdale Dr Tupelo MS 38801-1237 Office: Bancorp Miss Ins 1 Mississippi Plz Tupelo MS 38801

PATTERSON, CHARLES DAROLD, librarian, educator; b. Wahpeton, N.D., Aug. 8, 1928; s. Charles Irwin and Inez Fern (Slagg) P. B.Sc., Bemidji State U., 1950; M.A., U. Minn., 1956; M.Music, W.Va. U., 1964; advanced cert., U. Pitts., 1968, Ph.D., 1971. Tchr. music Fargo (N.D.) public schs., 1950; jr. reference librarian U. Minn. Libraries, 1954-55; head librarian Bemidji (Minn.) State U., 1955-58; dir. libraries, asst. prof. Glenville (W.Va.) State Coll., 1958-62; asst. prof. W.Va. U., 1962-66; instr. Grad. Sch. Library and Info. Scis. U. Pitts., 1966-71, asst. prof., 1971-72; assoc. prof. Sch. Library and Info. Sci. La. State U., Baton Rouge, 1972-78; prof. Sch. Library and Info. Sci. La. State U., 1978-93; prof. emeritus, 1993; Del. La. Gov.'s Conf. on Library and Info. Services, 1978. Author: Analysis of Library of Congress Music Subject Headings, 1971, JEL Cumulative Index, 1979, supplement, 1982, (with D.G. Davis) ARBA Guide to Library Science Literature, 1987; editor: W.Va. Libraries, 1963-66; mem. editorial bd.; Jour. of Edn. for Librarianship, 1975-79, editor, 1980-84; editor: Jour. Edn. for Library and Info. Sci., 1984-88; asst. editor Reference Services Review, 1986-93; contbr. articles to profl. jours. Served with U.S. Army, 1950-52. Recipient La. State U. Faculty Excellence award, 1984, ALA/Beta Phi Mu award, 1989. Mem. ALA (chmn. scholarship jury 1972-73), W.Va. Library Assn. (chmn. coll. and univ. library sect. 1960-61, exec. bd. 1960-61, 64-66), Assn. Coll. and Research Libraries (pres. Tri-state chpt. 1972), Assn. Am.

Library Schs. (exec. bd. 1980-88), La. Library Assn., Southeastern Library Assn., AAUP (pres. chpt. 1985-86), Am. Guild Organists (dean chpt. 1985-86), Pitts. Bibliophiles, Univ. Chamber Music Soc. (pres., dir. 1979-80), Beta Phi Mu. (dir.-at-large 1982-85). Methodist. Home: 1480 Kenmore Ave Baton Rouge LA 70808-1130 also: Birchmont Beach Bemidji MN 56601 Office: La State U Sch Libr and Info Sci Baton Rouge LA 70803 *When one is confident in his own mind that he has, with given abilities, done his very best, then perhaps he has paid for his niche in eternity.*

PATTERSON, CHARLES ERNEST, lawyer; b. Rockford, Ill., Jan. 4, 1941; s. Alvin Maurice and Helen Mae (Mitchell) P. A.B. cum laude, U. Kans., 1963; J.D. with distinction U. Mich., 1966. Bar: Mo. 1966, U.S. Dist. Ct. (we. dist.) Mo. 1966, U.S. Ct. Mil. Appeals 1968, U.S. Supreme Ct. 1969, U.S. Ct. Appeals (8th cir.) 1971, Calif. 1985, U.S. Dist. Ct. (cen., no. dists.) Calif. 1985. Assoc. Watson, Ess, Marshall & Enggas, Kansas City, Mo., 1966-74, ptnr., 1974-85; ptnr. Lillick, McHose & Charles, Los Angeles; chmn. exec. com. 1987—; now ptnr. Pillsbury Madison & Sutro, L.A.; chmn. various coms. Def. Research Inst. 1978—; bd. govs. Legal Aid of Western Mo., 1978-80; mem. bench/bar com. Western div. Mo. Ct. Appeals, 1983—, 16th Jud. Cir. Ct. Mo., 1983—; mem. fed. practice com. U.S. Dist. Ct. (we. dist.) Mo. 1983—. Contbr. articles to profl. jours. Bd. dirs. Boys Clubs Greater Kansas City, Inc., 1974-78, Dismas House Kansas City, 1978-84, Mo. Assn. for Ex-Offenders, 1976-79, YMCA, 1976-79; v.p. Heart of Am. Rugby Football Union, Kansas City, 1976-78; pres. Pre Trial Diversion Services, Inc., Kansas City, 1976-78, Kansas City Vietnam Vets. Meml. Fund, 1984—; mem. bd. Kansas City Arts Council, 1984, Mo. Boys Town, 1983-84. Served to capt. USMC, 1966-69; Vietnam. Decorated Bronze Star medal with Combat V, Vietnamese Cross of Gallantry with Palm, Vietnamese Medal of Honor. Mem. ABA (ho. of dels. 1984—), Mo. Bar (bd. govs. 1978-84, pres. 1983-84, Award of Merit 1984, Jud. Conf. award 1984), Kansas City Bar Assn., Lawyers Assn. Kansas City, Western Mo. Def. Lawyers Assn. (pres. 1981-82), Mo. Orgn. Def. Lawyers (bd. dirs. 1984-85), Internat. Assn. Ins. Counsel. Clubs: Kansas City, Carriage (Kansas City, Mo.). Office: Pillsbury Madison & Sutro 725 S Figueroa St Ste 1200 Los Angeles CA 90017-5413

PATTERSON, CLAIR CAMERON, nuclear chemist, biogeochemist, educator; b. Des Moines, June 2, 1922; s. Claire C. and Vivian (Henney) P.; m. Lorna J. McCleary, Mar. 3, 1944; children: Cameron C., Claire Keister, Charles Warner, Susan Patterson- Hill. BS, Grinnel Coll., 1943; MS, U. Iowa, 1944; PhD, U. Chgo., 1951, postgrad., 1952; hon. degree, Grinnell Coll., 1972, U. Paris, 1977. Geochemist Calif. Inst. Tech., Pasadena, 1952—. Patentee in field; contbr. articles to profl. jours. Fellow AAAS; mem. NAS (Lawrence medal) Geochem.Cosmica Arts, Sigma Xi. Office: Calif Inst Tech Dept Geochemistry Pasadena CA 91125

PATTERSON, DAVID ANDREW, computer scientist, educator, consultant; b. Evergreen Park, Ill., Nov. 16, 1947; s. David Dwight and Lucie Jeanette (Ekstrom) P.; m. Linda Ann Crandall, Sept. 4, 1967; children: David Adam, Michael Andrew. BS in Math., UCLA, 1969, MS in Computer Sci., 1970, PhD, 1976. Mem. tech. staff Hughes Aircraft Co. L.A., 1972-76, Thinking Machines Corp., Cambridge, Mass., 1979; prof. computer sci. div. U. Calif., Berkeley, 1977—, chmn., 1990-93, Pardee chair, 1992—; cons. Sun Microsystems, Inc., Mountain View, Calif., 1984—; com. to study scope and role of computer sci. NAS, Washington, 1990-92; chmn. program com. 4th Symposium on Archtl. Support for Operation Systems and Computer Architecture, Santa Clara, Calif., 1991; mem. Mgmt. Ops. Working Group NASA, 1992—; co-chair program com. Hot Chips Symposium IV, Stanford, Calif., 1992. Author: A Taste of Smalltalk, 1986, Computing Unbound, 1989, Computer Architecture: A Quantative Approach, 1990, Computer Organization & Design: The Hardware/Software Interface, 1993. Recipient Disting. Teaching award U. Calif., Berkeley, 1982. Fellow IEEE, ACM (Karl V. Karlstrom Outstanding Educator award 1991); mem. NAE, Computing Rsch. Assn. (bd. dirs. Washington 1991—, chair 1993—), Spl. Interest Group on Computer Architecture of ACM (bd. dirs. 1987-90, chair 1993—). Avocations: biking, football, soccer. Office: U Calif Computer Sci 635 Sodahali Berkeley CA 94720

PATTERSON, DAWN MARIE, dean, consultant, writer; b. Gloversville, N.Y., July 30; d. Robert Morris and Dora Margaret (Perham) P.; m. Robert Henry Hollenbeck, Aug. 3, 1958 (div. 1976); children: Adrienne Lyn, Nathaniel Conrad. BS in Edn., SUNY, Geneseo, 1962; MA, Mich. State U., 1973, PhD, 1977; postgrad., U. So. Calif. and Inst. Ednl. Leadership. Librarian Brighton (N.Y.) Cen. Schs., 1962-67; asst. to regional dir. Mich. State U. Ctr., Bloomfield Hills, 1973-74; grad. asst. Mich. State U., East Lansing, 1975-77; cons. Mich. Efficiency Task Force, 1977; asst. dean Coll. Continuing Edn., U. So. Calif., Los Angeles, 1978-84; dean, assoc. prof. continuing edn. Calif. State U., Los Angeles, 1985—; CEO Acclaims Enterprises Internat.; pres. Co-Pro Assocs. Mem. Air Univ. Bd. Visitors, 1986-90, Commn. on Extended Edn. Calif. State U. Calif., 1988-91; Hist. Soc., Los Angeles Town Hall, Los Angeles World Affairs Council. Dora Louden scholar, 1958-61; Langworthy fellow, 1961-62; Edn. Professions Devel. fellow, 1974-75; Ednl. Leadership Policy fellow, 1982-83; Leadership Calif., 1992, Leadership Am., 1994. Mem. AAUW (pres. Pasadena br. 1985-86), Am. Assn. Adult and Continuing Edn. (charter), Nat. Univ. Continuing Edn. Assn., Internat. Assn. Continuing Edn. and Tng. (bd. dirs. 1990—), Calif. Coll. and Mil. Educators Assn. (pres.), Los Angeles Airport Area Edn. Industry Assn. (pres. 1984), Rotary Club of Alhambra (bd. dirs.), Fine Arts (Pasadena), Zonta (pres. 1994—), Kappa Delta Pi, Phi Delta Kappa, Phi Beta Delta, Phi Kappa Phi. Republican. Unitarian. Office: 5151 State University Dr Los Angeles CA 90032-4221

PATTERSON, DENNIS GLEN, Canadian government official, lawyer; b. Vancouver, B.C., Can., Dec. 30, 1948; common law wife: Marie Uviluq; children: Bruce, George, Jessica, Alexander. BA with distinction, U. Alta., Edmonton, 1969; LLB, Dalhousie U., Halifax, N.S., 1972. Bar: N.S. 1972, B.C., 1974. Exec. dir. Maliiganik Tukisinniavik, Iqaluit, N.W.T., Can., 1975-81; mem. legis. assembly, Iqaluit Govt. of N.W.T., Yellowknife, 1979-93, minister edn., 1981-88, minister aboriginal rights and constl. devel., 1981-87, minister responsible for women, 1985; govt. leader, 1987-91, mem. cabinet, 1991-92, now mem. legis. assembly. Avocations: seal hunting, piano. Office: Legis Assembly of NWT, PO Box 1320, Yellowknife, NT Canada X1A 2L9

PATTERSON, DENNIS JOSEPH, management consultant; b. Honolulu, Apr. 13, 1948; s. Joseph John and Dorothy Elizabeth (Snajkowski) P.; m. Susan Tyra Pedlow, Dec. 31, 1981; children: Valerie Jean, Christina Elizabeth. BA, Elmhurst (Ill.) Coll., 1970; MA, George Washington U., 1973. Asst. dir. Vancouver (B.C.) Gen. Hosp., 1973-76, dir., 1975-76; v.p. Shaugnessy Hosp., Vancouver, 1976-79; pres. Westcare, Vancouver, 1979-84; mgr. Ernst & Whinney, Chgo., 1984-86, sr. mgr., 1986-88, ptnr., 1988-93; pres. FHP Internat. Cons. Group, Inc., Fountain Valley, Calif., 1993—. Contbr. articles to profl. jours. fin. mgr. Electoral Action Movement, Vancouver, 1978; trustee George Washington U., Calif. Sch. Profl. Psychology. Fellow Am. Coll. Healthcare Execs.; mem. Royal Vancouver Yacht Club, Va. Country Club, Manhattan Beach C.C., Phi Gamma Mu. Republican. Anglican. Avocations: sailboat racing, golf. Office: FHP Internat Cons Group Inc 3515 Harbor Blvd Costa Mesa CA 92626

PATTERSON, DONALD FLOYD, human, medical and veterinary genetics educator; b. Maracaibo, Venezuela, Feb. 2, 1931; came to U.S., 1932; s. Carl Earl and Dayne (Murphy) P.; m. Nancy Hankins, Dec. 19, 1953 (dec. Feb. 1990); children: Russell H., Wade D. DVM, Okla. State U., 1954; DSc, U. Pa., 1967. Diplomate Am. Coll. Veterinary Medicine, Am. Bd. Internal Medicine, Am. Bd. Cardiology. Intern Angell Meml. Hosp., Boston, 1954-56; instr. Okla. State U., Stillwater, 1956; instr., asst. prof. Vet. Sch. U. Pa., Phila., 1958-64, from assoc. prof. to prof. Vet. Sch., 1966-73, chief sect. med. genetics, 1970, Sheppard prof. med. genetics Vet. Sch., 1973—, prof. human genetics Med. Sch., 1974—; NIH spl. fellow divsn. med. genetics Johns Hopkins U., Balt., 1964-66. Author computer program for canine genetic diseases; contbr. over 300 papers to sci. and med. jours. Capt. USAF, 1956-58. Recipient Merit award Am. Animal Hosp. Assn., 1982, NIH, 1988, 93, Med. Rsch. award World Congress Vet. Medicine, 1992. Fellow Am. Coll. Cardiology, Phila. Coll. Physicians; mem. AVMA (Gaines Rsch. award 1972, Achievement award 1995), Am. Soc. Human Genetics. Democrat. Avocations: canoeing, poetry, literature. Office: U Pa Sch Vet Medicine 3900 Delaney St Philadelphia PA 19104-6010

PATTERSON, DONALD LEE, music educator; b. Colorado Springs, Colo., Aug. 14, 1947; s. Thurman Alvin and Bernice Eileen (May) P.; m. Janet Louise Andrews, Feb. 19, 1971. MusB, U. Denver, 1969; MusM, Manhattan Sch. Music, 1972; MusD, U. North Tex., 1977. Staff accompanist Harlem Sch. Arts, N.Y.C., 1970-72, Manhattan Sch. Music, N.Y.C., 1970-72; music instr. Angelo State U., San Angelo, Tex., 1972-74; teaching fellow U. North Tex., Denton, 1974-76; music prof. U. Wis., Eau Claire, 1976—. Co-author: Vincent Persichetti: A Bio-bibliography, 1989; author (sound rec.) EDUCO, Inc., Contemporary Recording Soc. Mem. Am. Liszt Soc., Sonneck Soc., Music Tchrs. Nat. Assn. (cert.), Recs. for Contemporary Rec. Soc., Educo, Inc., Kappa Kappa Psi, Phi Mu Alpha Sinfonia, Pi Kappa Lambda. Home: 2130 15th St Eau Claire WI 54703-2655 Office: U Wis Music Dept Eau Claire WI 54702

PATTERSON, DONIS DEAN, bishop; b. Holmesville, Ohio, Apr. 27, 1930; s. Raymond J. and Louella Faye (Glasgo) P.; m. JoAnne Nida, Dec. 22, 1951; children: Christoper Nida, Andrew Joseph. BS, Ohio State U., 1952; STB, Episcopal Theol. Sch., 1957; M Div, Episcopal Divinity Sch., 1972; DD (hon.), Nashotah House Sem., 1984, U. of South, 1986. Rector St. Andrews Ch., Washington Court House, Ohio, 1957-63, St. Marks Ch., Venice, Fla., 1963-70, All Sts. Ch., Winter Park, Fla., 1970-83; bishop Episcopal Diocese Dallas, 1983-92; asst. bishop Episcopal Diocese of Ctrl. Gulf Coast, 1994; trustee Seabury Western Theol. Sem., Evanston, Ill., 1981-82, U. of South, 1983-92, Episcopal Theol. Sem. S.W., 1983-92. Chmn. Episcopal Ch. House of Bishops Armed Forces Com., 1989-93. Col., chaplain U.S. Army, 1952-54, Korea.

PATTERSON, ELIZABETH JOHNSTON, former congresswoman; b. Columbia, SC, Nov. 18, 1939; d. Olin DeWitt and Gladys (Atkinson) Johnston; m. Dwight Fleming Patterson, Jr., Apr. 15, 1967; children: Dwight Fleming, Olin DeWitt, Catherine Leigh. BA, Columbia Coll., 1961; postgrad. in polit. sci., U. S.C., 1961, 62, 64; LLD (hon.), Columbia Coll., 1987; D Pub. Svc. (hon.), Converse Coll., 1989. Pub. affairs officer Peace Corps, Washington, 1962-64; postgrad. VISTA, OEO, Washington, 1965-66; D Pub. Svc. Head Start and VISTA, OEO, Columbia, 1966-67; tri-county dir. Head Start, Piedmont Community Actions, Spartanburg, S.C., 1967-68; mem. Spartanburg County Coun., 1975-76, S.C. State Senate, 1979-86, 100th-102nd Congresses from 4th S.C. dist., 1987-93. Trustee Wofford Coll., 1975-81; bd. dirs. Charles Lea Ctr., 1978-90, Spartanburg Coun. on aging; pres. Spartanburg Dem. Women, 1968; v.p. Spartanburg County Dem. party, 1968-70, sec., 1970-75; trustee Columbia Coll., 1991—. Mem. Bus. and Profl. Women's Club, Alpha Kappa Gamma. Methodist. Office: PO Box 5564 Spartanburg SC 29304-5564

PATTERSON, ELLMORE CLARK, banker; b. Western Springs, Ill., Nov. 29, 1913; s. Ellmore Clark and Harriet Emma (Wales) P.; m. Anne Hyde Choate, Sept. 28, 1940; children: Michael Ellmore, Arthur Choate, Robert Ellmore, David Choate, Thomas Hyde Choate. Grad., Lake Forest Acad., 1931; B.S., U. Chgo., 1935. With J. P. Morgan & Co., Inc., N.Y.C., 1935-39, 39-41, 46-59; v.p. J. P. Morgan & Co., Inc., 1951-59; exec. v.p. Morgan Guaranty Trust Co. N.Y. (merger J.P. Morgan and Guaranty Trust Co.), 1959-65, dir., chmn. exec. com., 1967-68, pres., 1969-71, chmn., 1971-77, chmn. exec. com., 1978; with Morgan Stanley & Co., 1939; dir. comml. Union Corp., Engelhard Hanovia, Inc.; chmn. dirs. adv. coun. Morgan Guaranty Trust Co.; mem. Presdl. Com. on Fin. Structure and Regulation, 1970-72. Bd. mgrs. Meml. Hosp. Cancer and Allied Diseases, N.Y.C.; Sloan-Kettering Inst. Cancer Center, N.Y.C., U. Chgo., Mass. Inst. Tech. Served from ensign to lt. comdr. USNR, 1941-46. Mem. Psi Upsilon. Episcopalian. Clubs: Links (N.Y.C.); Bedford (N.Y.); Golf and Tennis; Jupiter Island (Hobe Sound, Fla.); Fishers Island Country; Seminole Golf (Palm Beach, Pla.). Office: 23 Wall St New York NY 10260-0023

PATTERSON, EUGENE CORBETT, retired editor, publisher; b. Valdosta, Ga., Oct. 15, 1923; s. William C. and Annabel (Corbett) P.; m. Mary Sue Carter, Aug. 19, 1950; 1 child, Mary Patterson Fausch. Student, North Ga. Coll., Dahlonega, 1940-42; AB in Journalism, U. Ga., 1943; LL.D. Tusculum Coll., 1965, Harvard U., 1969, Duke U., 1978, Stetson U., 1984, Ind. U., 1990; Litt.D., Emory U., 1966, Oglethorpe Coll., 1966, Tuskegee U., 1966, Roanoke Coll., 1968, Mercer U., 1968, Eckerd Coll., 1977, U. South Fla., 1986, Dillard U., 1992; Colby Coll., 1994. Reporter Temple (Tex.) Daily Telegram and Macon (Ga.) Telegraph, 1947-48; mgr. for S.C. United Press, 1948-49; night bur. mgr. United Press, 1949-53; mgr. London bur. United Press, also chief corr. U.K., 1953-56; v.p., exec. editor Atlanta Journal-Constitution, 1956-60; editor Atlanta Constitution, 1960-68; mng. editor Washington Post, 1968-71; prof. polit. sci. Duke U., 1971-72; editor, pres. St. Petersburg (Fla.) Times, 1972-84, chmn., chief exec. officer, 1978-88, editor emeritus, 1988—; editor, pres. Congl. Quar., Washington, 1972-86; chmn., chief exec. officer Congl. Quar., 1978-88; chmn. bd., chief exec. officer Fla. Trend mag., 1980-88, Ga. Trend mag., 1984-88, Ariz. Trend mag., 1986-88, Governing mag., 1987-88, Modern Graphic Arts, Inc., 1978-88, Poynter Inst. Media Studies, 1978-88, Poynter Fund, 1978-88. Vice chmn. U.S. Civil Rights Commn., 1964-68; mem. Pulitzer Prize Bd., 1973-84; trustee ASNE Found., 1981-84, U. Ga. Found., 1988-89, North Ga. Coll. Found., 1991-93, Am. Press Inst., Reston, Va., 1983-88, Duke U., 1988-94, Fla. Bar Found., 1992-93, LeRoy Collins Ctr. for Pub. Policy, 1990-93. Decorated Silver Star, Bronze Star with oak leaf cluster in 10th Armored Divsn., Gen. Patton's 3rd Army; recipient Pulitzer prize for editl. writing Columbia U., 1966, William Allen White Nat. Citation award U. Kans., 1980, Elijah Parish Lovejoy award Colby Coll., 1994. Fellow Soc. Profl. Journalists; mem. Am. Soc. Newspaper Editors (pres. 1977-78), St. Petersburg Yacht Club, Vinoy Club. Home: Snell Isle 1967 Brightwaters Blvd NE Saint Petersburg FL 33704 Office: 535 Central Ave Saint Petersburg FL 33701

PATTERSON, FLORENCE GHORAM, real estate broker; b. Savannah, Ga., Mar. 20, 1936; d. Ernest and Ida (Robinson) Ghoram; m. Carl Patterson (div. 1986); children: Chrysetta Patricia, Carl Jr. Student, CCNY. Lic. real estate broker, N.Y. Mgr. Am. Express Credit Card, N.Y.C., 1958-59; asst. v.p. Citicorp, N.Y.C., 1967-84; exec. dir., founder Pamoja Internat. Cultural Exch., Inc., Helena, N.Y., 1982—; editor International Cookbook, 1992—; v.p. Parent Tchr. Support Group, Ft. Covington, N.Y., 1989-91, pres., 1991—. Committeewoman Dem. Ctrl. Com., Suffolk County, N.Y., 1984; founder Deer Park (N.Y.) NAACP, 1968; v.p. United Civic Assn. Deer Park, 1982, pres., 1983-84; v.p. parent tchr. support group Ft. Covington, N.Y., 1989-91, pres., 1991-92; pres. PTA/PTSA Salmon River Ctrl. Sch., 1992-93, v.p. 1994, rep. bldg. level team, 1994-95; facilitator secondary bldg. level team Compact for Learning, 1994—; organizer Festival of Drums Multicultural Celebration. Recipient Cert. of Merit Universal Sons and Daus. of Ethiopia, Inc., 1985, County Legislator, Babylon, N.Y., 1985, Proclamation County Exec., Suffolk County, 1985, Town of Islip, N.Y., 1986, Personalities of Am. Cultural award, 1992. Mem. NAFE, AMA, Nat. Trust for Hist. Presertion, Am. Mus. Natural History (hon advisor), Nat. Arbor Day Found. Mem. Spiritual Tch. Avocations: ice skating, reading, dancing. Home and Office: RR 2 Box 162 Brasher Falls NY 13613-9621

PATTERSON, GLENN WAYNE, botany educator; b. China Grove, N.C., Mar. 9, 1938; s. Simpson Wayne and Alice (Fisher) P.; m. Nancy Ann deLesdernier, Sept. 2, 1961; children: Steven, Eric, Alan. B.S., N.C. State U., 1960; M.S., U. Md., 1963, Ph.D., 1964. Asst. prof. dept. botany U. Md., College Park, 1964-69, assoc. prof., 1969-73, prof. botany, 1973—, chmn. dept., 1977-87, acting assoc. dean Colls. Agriculture and Life Scis., 1986-89. Recipient Biol. Scis. award Washington Acad. Scis., 1971. Mem. Am. Soc. Plant Physiologists, Am. Oil Chemists Soc. Office: Dept Botany Univ Md College Park MD 20742

PATTERSON, GRACE LIMERICK, library director; b. N.Y.C., Nov. 21, 1938; d. Robert and Frieda (Zeiontz) Limerick; m. Joseph Nathaniel Patterson (dec.); children: Lorrayne Carole, Joseph Nathaniel Jr. BA in Sociology, Edn., CUNY, 1971; MLS, Columbia U., 1975; MS in Comm., Coll. New Rochelle, 1989. Cert. libr. N.J. Exec. dir. Manhattanville Community Outreach, N.Y.C., 1971-74; br. and outreach svcs. Paterson (N.J.) Pub. Libr., 1975-79; media specialist II Passaic County C.C., Paterson, 1979-81; coord. outreach svcs. Irvington (N.J.) Pub. Libr., 1981-84; assoc. prof. libr. Rockland C.C., Suffern, N.Y., 1984-89; libr. dir. Hudson County C.C., Jersey City, 1989—. Editor jours. in field. Exec. bd. dirs Essex-Hudson Region II, Orange, N.J., 1991; vol Ridgewood (N.J.) Schs., 1981-83; Ridgewood Centennial Com. First Night, 1993. U.S. Dept. Edn. fellow,

1974-75. Mem. ALA (com., chairperson Black Caucus pub. rels. 1990-92), N.J. Libr. Assn. Avocations: photography, oral history, travel, geneology, public speaking. Office: Hudson County CC 900 Bergen Ave Jersey City NJ 07306

PATTERSON, GRADY LESLIE, JR., state treasurer; b. Abbeville, S.C., Jan. 13, 1924; s. Grady Leslie and Claudia (McClain) P.; m. Marjorie Harrison Faucett, Dec. 22, 1951; children—Grady Leslie III, Steven G., M. Lynne, Laura A., Amy S., M. Beth. LLB, U. S.C., 1950, BS, 1975, LLD (hon.), 1980; LLD (hon.), The Citadel, 1985; HHD (hon.), Lander Coll., 1990; LLD (hon.), U. Charleston, S.C., 1992, Clemson U., 1992. Bar: S.C. 1950. County service officer Abbeville County, S.C., 1950; ops. officer S.C. Air N.G., Columbia, 1952-59; asst. atty. gen. State of S.C., Columbia, 1959-66, treas., 1967-94. Served with USAAF, 1943-46; maj. USAF, 1950-52, 61-61, ret. Maj. Gen. Decorated D.S.M. USAF. Mem. S.C. Bar Assn. Democrat. Presbyterian. Avocations: golf; jogging. Home: 3016 Petigru St Columbia SC 29204-3618 Office: 914 Richland St Ste C Columbia SC 29202

PATTERSON, HARLAN RAY, finance educator; b. Camden, Ohio, June 27, 1931; s. Ernest Newton and Beulah Irene (Hedrick) P.; children by previous marriage: Kristan Lee, Elizabeth Jane, Nolan Gene. BS cum laude, Miami U., Oxford, Ohio, 1953, MBA, 1959; PhD, Mich. State U., 1963. Asst. prof. fin. U. Ill., Champaign-Urbana, 1962-66; mem. faculty Ohio U., Athens, 1966—; prof. fin. Ohio U., 1977—; vis. prof., fellow Chgo. Merc. Exc., 1971; fin. cons., researcher projects for industry. Contbr. articles to acad. and profl. jours. Chmn. City of Athens Rainbow Adv. Bd., 1972-77; state chmn. scholarship com. for Ohio Rainbow Girls, 1975-87. Commd. officer USN, 1953-56. Recipient Fred Astaire Bronze I Achievement level; named Congressional Alternate to West Point, 1949; won competitive appointment U.S. Naval Acad., 1950; NROTC scholar, 1950; Stonier fellow, 1961, Mortgage Banking fellow, 1974, Found. Econ. Edn. fellow, 1965, 67, 69, 71. Mem. Masons, Shriners, Order Eastern Star (worthy patron 1989, 92), Phi Beta Kappa (pres. faculty chpt. 1975), Beta Gamma Sigma (faculty adviser), Phi Eta Sigma, Alpha Kappa Psi, Delta Sigma Pi, Sigma Tau Alpha (adviser), Omicron Delta Epsilon, Pi Kappa Alpha. Republican. Avocation: dance classes. Home: 9B Station St Athens OH 45701-2758

PATTERSON, HAROLD DEAN, superintendent of schools; b. Alexander City, Ala., May 29, 1932; s. Obed Howard and Sara Bell (Joiner) P.; m. Shirley Bryant, May 31, 1958; children: Lisa Jane, Anne Leslie, Harold Dean Jr. BS, Auburn U., 1954; MA, Vanderbilt U., 1957, EdD, 1964. Cert. sch. adminstr., Ala., S.C., Ill. Tchr. Bessemer (Ala.) High Sch., 1957-63, asst. prin., 1959-62; prin. North Hall, Evanston (Ill.) Twp. High Sch., 1964-66; prin. Mountain Brook (Ala.) High Sch., 1966-71; assoc. supt. Greenville County Schs., Greenville, S.C., 1971-74; supt. Sumter County Sch. Dist. 17, Sumter, S.C., 1974-82, Spartanburg County Sch. Dist. 7, Spartanburg, S.C., 1982-88, Guntersville (Ala.) City Schs., 1988—. Mem. S.C. Gov.'s Com. on Financing Edn., Columbia, 1983, S.C. Pvt. Industry Coun., Columbia, 1984-88, S.C. Legis. Oversight Com., Columbia, 1984; pres. Peabody alumni bd. Vanderbilt U., Nashville, 1989-90. 2d lt. U.S. Army, 1954-56. Recipient Outstanding Educator award Florence chpt. Phi Delta Kappa, 1981, The Exec. Educator 100 award The Exec. Educator mag., 1987. Mem. Am. Assn. Sch. Adminstrs. (chmn. legis. corp. 1985—, mem. exec. com. 1988-91, James R. Kirkpatrick award 1987), Ala. Assn. Sch. Adminstrs., Nat. Assn. Secondary Sch. Prins. (Rotary dist. 6860 gov. 1995—). Methodist. Avocation: golf. Home: 5020 Neely Ave Guntersville AL 35976-8102 Office: Guntersville City Schs PO Box 129 Newman St Guntersville AL 35976

PATTERSON, HARRY See HIGGINS, JACK

PATTERSON, JAMES, mayor; b. San Mateo, Calif., Feb. 18, 1948; m. Sharon LeTourneau, 1968; children: B.J., Jason, Lindsay. BA in Polit. Sci. summa cum laude, Calif. State U., Fresno, 1992. Radio broadcasting exec. Sta. KIRV-AM, Fresno, Calif., 1968—; mayor City of Fresno, 1993—. Chmn. NO on Measure H Com., 1989, Criminal Justice and Law Enforcement Commn., 1990-91; vice chmn. YES on Measure E Com., 1988; mem. Human Rels. Commn., City of Fresno, 1987-91; bd. dirs. Leadership Fresno Alumni Assn., 1989-91, Fresno County YFC/Campus Life, 1984-88. Mem. Fresno City and County C. of C. (chmn. local govt. affairs com. 1990-91, bd. dirs. FRESPAC 1990-91, city budget rev. com. 1989-91, privatization task force 1988-89, charter sect. 809 rev. task force 1987-88). Office: Office of the Mayor/City Coun City Hall 2600 Fresno St Fresno CA 93721-3650

PATTERSON, JAMES BRENDAN, JR., advertising agency executive; b. Newburgh, N.Y., Mar. 22, 1947; s. Charles H. and Isabelle (Morris) P. B.A., Manhattan Coll., 1969; M.A., Vanderbilt U., 1970. With J. Walter Thompson Co., N.Y.C., 1971—; chmn. J. Walter Thompson U.S., 1987—. Author: novels including The Thomas Berryman Number, 1976 (Edgar Allen Poe award Mystery Writers Am.), The Jericho Commandment, 1979, Virgin, 1980, Legends, 1983, Black Market, 1986. Recipient 6 Clio awards, 1983; recipient Effie awards, 1983. Mem. Phi Beta Kappa. Home: 25 Central Park W Apt 7-q New York NY 10023-7210 Office: J Walter Thompson USA Inc 466 Lexington Ave # 6 New York NY 10017-3140

PATTERSON, JAMES MILTON, marketing specialist, educator; b. De-Queen, Ark., Oct. 15, 1927; s. Charles Edward and Phoebe Allene (Steel) P.; m. Della Jeanne Hays, July 3, 1964; children—J. Marshall, Julia M.; children by previous marriage—Robert T., Donald A. B.S., U.S. Mcht. Marine Acad., 1948; M.B.A. (Teagle Found. fellow), Cornell U., 1954, Ph.D. (Ford Found. dissertation fellow), 1961. Third mate Esso Shipping Co., 1948-52; instr. in bus. adminstrn. Northwestern U., 1957-60; lectr. Center for Programs in Govt. Adminstrn., U. Chgo., 1959; asst. prof. mktg. Ind. U., 1960-63, assoc. prof., 1963-69, prof., 1969—, chmn. dept. mktg., 1972-78, asso. dir. Poynter Ctr., 1980, acting dir., 1981, co-sec. U. Faculty Coun. pres. Bloomington Faculty Coun.; dir. Ind. U. Inst. for Advanced Study, 1994—; bd. dirs. Inst. Advanced Study; cons. petroleum mktg.; expert witness on antitrust and mktg. Author: Marketing: The Firm's Viewpoint, 1964, Highway Robbery: An Analysis of the Gasoline Crisis, 1974, Competition Ltd.: The Marketing of Gasoline, 1972. Served with USMM, 1945-48. Mem. Assn. for Practical & Profl. Ethics. Democrat. Home: 2431 N Dunn St Bloomington IN 47408-1117 Office: Ind U Inst Advanced Study Bloomington IN 47405

PATTERSON, JAMES RANDOLPH, physician; b. Lancaster, Pa., Jan. 30, 1942; m. Linda Lewis Patterson, Nov. 22, 1969. AB, U. Pa., 1964; MD, Columbia U., 1968. Diplomate Nat. Bd. Med. Examiners, Am. Bd. Internal Medicine, Subspecialty of Pulmonary Disease. Pulmonary and critical care specialist The Oregon Clinic, Portland, 1975—; clin. prof. medicine Oreg. health Scis. U., Portland, 1978—; mem. Am. Bd. Internal Medicine, Phila., 1995—; trustee Collins Med. Trust, Portland, Oreg., 1992—. Contbr. numerous articles to profl. jours. Recipient Class of 1964 award U. Pa., Van Loan award Am. Lung Assn. Oreg., 1990, Meritorious Achievement award Oreg. Health Scis. U., 1991; named Class Pres. Coll. Physicians and Surgeons of Columbia U., 1968, Tchr. of Yr. Providence Med. Ctr., Portland, Oreg., 1976, Internist of Yr., 1983, Best Doctors in Am., 1992-95. Mem. AMA, Am. Thoracic Soc., Am. Coll. Chest Physicians, Oreg. Lung Assn., North Pacific Soc. of Internal Medicine, Pacific Interurban Clin. Club, Multnomah County Med. Soc., Oreg. Med. Assn., Oreg. Soc. Ctirical Care Medicine. Office: The Oregon Clinic 507 NE 47th Ave Portland OR 97213

PATTERSON, JAMES WILLIS, pathology and dermatology educator; b. Takoma Park, Md., Dec. 29, 1946; s. James Clark and Helen (Hendricks) P.; m. Julie Wyatt, Dec. 30, 1989; 1 child, James Wyatt. BA, Johns Hopkins U., 1968; MD, Med. Coll. Va., 1972. Diplomate Am. Bd. Dermatology, Am. Bd. Dermatopathology, Nat. Bd. Med. Examiners. Fellow dermatopathology Armed Forces Inst. Pathology, Washington, 1979-80; rotating intern in medicine Med. Coll. Va., Richmond, 1972-73, resident in dermatology, 1973-76, assoc. prof. pathology and dermatology, 1982-89, prof., 1989-92, dir. dermatopathology, 1982-92; clin. prof. dermatology and pathology Med. Coll. of Va., 1992—; with Dermatology Assocs. of Va., 1992—, Va. Dermatopathology Svcs., Richmond, 1992—; clin. instr. dermatology U. Colo. Med. Ctr., Denver, 1980-82; cons. in pathology McGuire VA Hosp., Richmond, 1982—; cons. in pathology and dermatology Kenner Army Hosp., Ft. Lee, Va., 1982—. Author: Dermatology: A Concise Textbook, 1987; contbr. more than 100 articles on dermatology and pathology to med. jours.; asst. editor Jour. Cutaneous Pathology, 1989-94.

Mem. nat. alumni schs. com. Johns Hopkins U., 1986—. With M.C., U.S. Army, 1976-82, col. Res. Recipient Stuart McEwen award Assn. Mil. Dermatologists, 1980, 82. Fellow ACP, Am. Acad. Dermatology, Am. Soc. Dermatopathology; mem. Va. Dermatol. Soc. (sec.-treas. 1984-88, v.p. 1988-89, pres. 1989-90), Johns Hopkins U. Alumni Assn. (pres. cen. Va. chpt. 1989), Tau Epsilon Phi (life). Republican. Presbyterian. Avocations: American history, baseball, golf. Office: 5600 Grove Ave Richmond VA 23226-2102

PATTERSON, JERRY EUGENE, author; b. Fort Worth, May 2, 1931; s. Charles Edward and Lois (Pruitt) P. B.A., U. Tex., 1952, M.A., 1955; postgrad., Yale U., 1955-57, Columbia U., 1968. Asst. editor Hispanic Am. Hist. Rev., 1954; manuscript. div. librarian Yale U. Library, 1955-57; cataloguer Edward Eberstadt & Sons, N.Y.C., 1958-61; with Parke-Bernet Galleries, N.Y.C., 1962-68; asst. v.p. Parke-Bernet Galleries, 1964-65, v.p., 1965-68; U.S. rep. Christie, Manson & Woods, N.Y.C., 1968-71; sr. v.p. Sotheby Parke Bernet Inc., 1980-83; Cons. Library of Congress, 1964-67. Author: Autographs, a Collectors Guide, 1973, A Collector's Guide to Relics and Memorabilia, 1974, Antiques of Sport, 1975, The City of New York, 1978, Porcelain, 1979, Living It Up: A Guide to the Named Apartment Houses of New York, 1984, The Vanderbilts, 1989; mng. editor: Artnewsletter, 1975-78; Contbr. to: Auction Antiques Ann, 1971, also articles on rare books, manuscripts and art market to Am. and fgn. periodicals. Republican. Episcopalian. Home: 176 E 77th St New York NY 10021-1909

PATTERSON, JOAN MARIE, maternal/child health educator, psychologist; b. Austin, Minn., Aug. 24, 1943; d. W. Donald and Dorothy (Hazel Kulzer) Engel; children: Susan, James. BA, U. Minn., 1974, MA, 1980, PhD, 1983. Lic. psychologist, Minn. Rsch. assoc. U. Minn., St. Paul, 1983-84; rsch. assoc. U. Minn., Mpls., 1988-89, asst. prof., 1989-93, assoc. prof., 1993—, 1993—; dir. rsch. Ctr. for Children with Chronic Illness and Disability, Mpls., 1989, chair maternal & child health program, 1994—. Editor 5 books; contbr. articles to profl. jours. Mem. APHA, APA, Assn. for Care of Children's Health, Am. Assn. Marriage and Family Therapy, Nat. Coun. on Family Rels., Family Resource Coalition, Am. Family Therapy Assn., Groves Conf. on Marriage and Family, Phi Kappa Phi, Gamma Sigma Delta, Delta Omega. Office: U Minn Sch Pub Health 420 Delaware St SE Minneapolis MN 55455-0374

PATTERSON, JOHN DE LA ROCHE, JR., lawyer; b. Schenectady, N.Y., July 8, 1941; s. John de la Roche Sr. and Jane C. (Clay) P.; m. Michele F. Demarest, Nov. 28, 1987; children: Daniel C., Sara R., Amy C. BA, Johns Hopkins U., 1963; LLB, Harvard U., 1966. Bar: Mass. 1968. Vol. Peace Corps, Chad, 1966-67; assoc. Foley, Hoag & Eliot, Boston, 1967-73, ptnr., 1974—, exec. com., 1989—. Chmn. Kodaly Ctr. Am. Inc., Newton, Mass., 1977-87. Mem. ABA, Boston Bar Assn. Democrat. Avocations: sailing, tennis, travel, reading. Office: Foley Hoag & Eliot 1 Post Office Sq Boston MA 02109-2103

PATTERSON, JOHN MALCOLM, judge; b. Goldville, Ala., Sept. 27, 1921; s. Albert Love and Agnes Louise (Benson) P.; m. Florentine M. Sawyers, Oct. 17, 1975; children—Albert L., Barbara Louise. BA, Ala. 1949. Bar: Ala. bar 1949. Practiced in Phenix City, 1949-51, 53-55; atty. gen., securities commr. State of Ala., 1955-59; gov. of Ala., 1959-63; practice law Montgomery, Ala., 1963-84; judge Ala. Ct. Criminal Appeals, 1984—; chief judge Ct. of the Judiciary; cattle farmer. Bd. editors: Ala. Law Review, 1948-49. Chmn. bd. Lyman WArd Mil. Acad. Served to maj., F.A. AUS, 1940-45; maj. 1951-53. Nominated one of 10 outstanding young men of U.S., 1956, one of four outstanding young men of Ala. Jr. C. of C. Mem. ABA, Ala. Bar Assn., VFW, Am. Legion. Farrar Order of Jurisprudence, Ala. Acad. Honor, Alpha Tau Omega, Phi Alpha Delta, Sigma Delta Kappa, Phi Eta Sigma, Omicron Delta Kappa. Office: PO Box 301555 Montgomery AL 36130-1555

PATTERSON, JOSEPH H., chemical company executive; b. 1939. PhD, Univ. N.C. With Celanese Corp., 1967-87; pres. fibers & film and advanced tech. groups Hoechst Celanese Corp., Charlotte, N.C. Office: Hoechst Celanese Fibers & Film PO Box 32414 Charlotte NC 28232-2414

PATTERSON, JOSEPH REDWINE, lawyer; b. Corsicana, Tex., Apr. 16, 1927; s. Joseph Isham and Caroline Anderson (White) P.; m. Ann Louise Cumber, Mar. 9, 1976; children—Joseph Redwine, Amy Cumber. B.A. in Philosophy, So. Methodist U., 1948, M.A. in Govt, 1951, J.D., 1954. Bar: Tex. 1954. Asst. dist. atty. Dallas County, 1955-56; assoc. gen. counsel Traders and Gen. Ins. Co., Dallas, 1957; ptnr. firm Patterson, Lamberty, Stanford & Walls, Dallas, 1957—; ptnr. PLS Properties (real estate), Dallas, 1971—. Contbr. legal jours. Founding dir. Dallas chpt. Action on Smoking and Health; mem. cancer choir University Park United Meth. Ch., Dallas. Served with USN, 1945-46. Fellow Tex. Bar Found., Dallas Bar Found.; mem. ABA, Tex. Bar Assn., Cross Country Club Dallas. Democrat. Home: 6131 Meadow Rd Dallas TX 75230-5058 Office: 2011 Cedar Springs Rd Dallas TX 75201-1808

PATTERSON, KENT E., environmental services consultant, hydrogeologist; b. 1947. BS in Civil Engring., MS in Bio-Environ. Engring., Okla. State U., 1968. With Corps of Engrs., Tulsa, 1968-70, Roy F. Weston Inc., Richmond, Va., 1970-77; with Environ Resource Mgmt., 1977—, now pres., CEO. Office: Environ Resources Mgmt 855 Springdale Dr Exton PA 19341*

PATTERSON, LYDIA ROSS, industrial relations specialist, consulting company executive; b. Carrabelle, Fla., Sept. 3, 1936; d. Richard D. Ross and Johnnie Mae (Thomas) Kelley; m. Edgar A. Corley, Aug. 1, 1964 (div.); 1 child, Derek Kelley; m. Berman W. Patterson, Dec. 18, 1981. BA, Hunter Coll., 1958. Indsl. rels. specialist U.S. Dept. Energy, N.Y.C., 1966-68; regional dir./mgr. Div. Human Rights State of N.Y., N.Y.C., 1962-66, 68-76; v.p. Bankers Trust Co., N.Y.C., 1976-87; pres., chief exec. officer Extend Cons. Svcs., N.Y.C., 1985—; v.p., mgr. Merrill Lynch and Co. Inc., N.Y.C., 1987-90; seminar speaker Columbia U., Wharton Sch. Bus., Harvard U., Duke U., Cornell U., 1976-85; mem. conf. bd. Cornell U., Bus. Policy Rev. Coun., Exec. Leadership Coun. Bd. dirs. Project Discovery Columbia U., 1988, CUNY, Vocat. Edn. Adv. Coun., 1990. Mem. Am. Soc. Pers. Adminstrn., N.Y. and Nat. Urban League, Employment Mgrs. Assn., Fin. Women's Assn. (govt. and community affairs com. 1986-87), Women's Forum, Employment Dissemination of Info., Wellington Community Edn. Found. (bd. dirs. 1992—). Office: 12689 Coral Breeze Dr West Palm Beach FL 33414-8070

PATTERSON, MARIA JEVITZ, microbiology-pediatric infectious disease educator; b. Berwyn, Ill., Oct. 23, 1944; d. Frank Jacob and Edna Frances (Costabile) Jevitz; m. Ronald James Patterson, Aug. 22, 1970; children: Kristin Lara, Kier Nicole. BS in Med. Tech. summa cum laude, Coll. St. Francis, Joliet, Ill., 1966; PhD in Microbiology, Northwestern U., Chgo., 1970; MD, Mich. State U., 1984. Diplomate Am. Bd. Med. Examiners, Am. Bd. Pediatrics Gen. Pediatrics, Am. Bd. Pediatrics Infectious Diseases. Lab. asst., instr. med. microbiology for student nurses Med. Sch. Northwestern U., Chgo. 1966-70; postdoctoral fellow in clin. microbiology affiliated hosps. U. Wash., Seattle, 1971-72; asst. prof. microbiology and pub. health Mich. State U., East Lansing, 1972-77, assoc. prof., 1977-82, assoc. prof. pathology, 1979-82, lectr. dept. microbiology and pub. health, 1982-87, resident in pediatrics affiliated hosps., 1984-85, 86-87, clin. instr. dept. pediatrics and human devel., 1984-87, assoc. prof. microbiology-pub. health-pediatrics-human devel., 1987-90, prof., 1990—; staff microbiologist dept. pathology Lansing Gen. Hosp., 1972-75; dir. clin. microbiology grad. program. Mich. State U., 1974-81, staff microbiologist, 1978-81; postdoctoral fellow in infectious diseases U. Mass. Med. Ctr., Worcester, 1985-86; asst. dir. pediatrics residency Grad. Med. Edn. Inc., Lansing, 1987-90; med. dir. Pediatrics Health Ctr. St. Lawrence Hosp., Lansing, Mich., 1987-90, Ingham Med. Ctr., 1990-94; cons. clin. microbiology Lansing Gen. Hosp., 1972-75, Mich. State U., 1976-82, Ingham County Health Dept., 1988—, Am. Health Cons., 1993; cons. to editorial bd. Infection and Immunity, 1977; presenter seminars. Contbg. author: Microbiology: Principles and Concepts, 1982, 3d edit., 1991, Pediatric Emergency Medicine, 1992; contbr. articles to profl. jours. and publs. Mem. hon. com. Lansing AIDS Meml. Quilt, 1993. Recipient award for teaching excellence Mich. State U. Coll. Osteo. Medicine, 1977, 78, 79, 80, 83, Disting. Faculty award Mich. State U., 1980,

Woman Achiever award, 1985, excellence in pediatric residency teaching award, 1988, Alumni Profl. Achievement award Coll. of St. Francis, 1991; grantee renal disease divsn. Nat. Dept. Pub. Health 1976-82. Fellow Pediatric Infectious Diseases Soc., Am. Acad. Pediatrics; mem. Am. Coll. Physician Execs., Am. Soc. Microbiology, Am. Soc. Clin. Pathologists (affiliate, bd. registrant), South Ctrl. Assn. Clin. Microbiology, Infectious Diseases Soc. Am., Mich. Soc. Infectious Diseases, N.Y. Acad. Scis., Kappa Gamma Pi, Lambda Iota Tau. Roman Catholic. Home: 1520 River Ter East Lansing MI 48823-5314 Office: Mich State Univ Microbiology/Pub Health East Lansing MI 48824-1101

PATTERSON, MARY-MARGARET SHARP, writer, editor, media strategist; b. Fairmont, W.Va. July 12, 1944; d. H. Sutton Sharp and Columbia Strock; m. David Sands, June 15, 1968; 1 child, Scott Sutton. BA cum laude, Ohio State U., 1966, MA, 1967. Media coordinator Am. Hosp. Assn., Chgo., 1969; feature and mag. writer Chgo. Today newspaper, 1969-70; reporter Houston Chronicle, 1971-73; instr. journalism U. Houston, 1974-76; asst. prof. Utica (N.Y.) Coll. U. Syracuse, 1976-78; dir. undergrad. studies coll. journalism U. Md., College Park, 1978-82, editor, 1982; dir. information and devel. Audubon Naturalist Soc. Cen. Atlantic States, Inc., Chevy Chase, Md., 1982-89; dir. media rels. Defenders of Wildlife, Washington, 1989-90; resident Johns Hopkins-Nanjing U. Ctr. for Chinese and Am. Studies, Nanjing, China, 1990-91; sr. writer, editor Am. Assn. Ret. Persons, Washington, 1993—; cons. project Africa Carnegie Mellon U. Pitts., 1969; newspaper div. head summer journalism inst. Trinity U., San Antonio, 1979-81; columnist San Antonio Mag., 1976-79; cons. Callahan & Assoc., Washington, 1992—. Contbr. numerous articles and book revs. to newspapers and mags. Mem. Chevy Chase Presbyn. Ch. Choir, Washington, 1980—, ruling elder, 1993—. Recipient Reporting Excellence award The Newspaper Fund, Cleve., 1966; Univ. Grad. fellow Ohio State U., 1966, Nat. Grad. fellow Women in Communications, 1967. Mem. Soc. Profl. Journalists, Mortar Bd., Washington Ind. Writers, Inc., Kappa Tau Alpha. Democrat. Avocations: music, swimming, walking, French, Chinese.

PATTERSON, NEIL, science publisher; b. Toronto, Ont., Can., Oct. 15, 1933; came to U.S., 1960; s. John and Anne (Atherley) P.; m. Noel Elizabeth Coe, June 10, 1959 (div. 1978); children: Tove Elizabeth, Julia Lee; m. Ippy Tarleton Gizzi, Jan. 29, 1979; 1 child, George Tarleton. BA, U. Toronto, 1954; postgrad., U. Paris, 1954-55. Mng. editor McGraw-Hill, Can., Toronto, 1955-60; v.p., editorial dir., co-founder Benjamin-Cummings formerly W.A. Benjamin, Inc., N.Y.C., 1960-66, Worth Pubs., Inc., N.Y.C., 1966-76; dir. coll. dept. W.W. Norton & Co., N.Y.C., 1976-80; pres. W.H. Freeman, San Francisco, N.Y.C., 1980-84; co-founder Sci. Am. Books, San Francisco, N.Y.C.; pres., co-founder Neil Patterson Pubs.-A Viacom/ Paramount Co., Chapel Hill, N.C., 1984-95; founder, pres., CEO Harper Science-A Harper Collins Imprint, Chapel Hill, 1995—; bd. dirs. U. N.C. Pub. Inst. Bd. dirs. N.C. Bot. Garden, Chapel Hill. Mem. Biochem. Soc. (bd. dirs. 1991-94). Home: 3010 Arthur Minnis Hillsborough NC 27278 Office: Harper Science 101 B St Carrboro NC 27510

PATTERSON, ORLANDO, sociologist; b. Jamaica, June 5, 1940; came to U.S., 1970.; Charles A. Patterson and Almina (Morris); m. Nerys Wyn Thomas, Sept. 5, 1965; children: Rhiannon, Barbara. BS, U. of the West Indies, 1962; PhD, London Sch. of Econs., 1965; MA, Harvard U., Harvard, 1971; LHD (hon.), Trinity Coll., Conn., 1992. Asst. lectr. U. of London, London Sch. Econs. and Polit. Sci., 1965-67; lectr. U. of W. Indies, 1967-70; vis. lectr. Harvard U., Harvard, 1970-71, Allston Burr sr. tutor, 1971-73, prof. sociology, 1971—; vis. mem. Inst. Advanced Study, Princeton, N.J., 1975-76; vis. fellow, Wolfson Coll., Cambridge U., 1978-79; Phi Beta Kappa vis. scholar, 1988-89; mem. tech. advisory com. to prime min. and govt. of Jamaica, 1972-74, sp. advisor to prime min. of Jamaica, 1973-80. Author: (novels) The Children of Sisyphus, 1964 (1st prize Dakar Festival Negro Arts 1966), An Absence of Ruins, 1967, Die the Long Day, 1972, (nonfiction) The Sociology of Slavery, 1967, Ethnic Chauvinism, 1977, Slavery and Social Death, 1982 (co-winner Ralph Bunche award Am. Polit. Sci. Assn. 1983), Freedom; vol. 1, Freedom in the Making of Western Cluture, 1991 (Nat. Book award Nat Book Found. 1991); contbr. Stories from the Caribbean, 1965. Recipient UCLA medal, 1992; Guggenheim fellow, 1978-79. Mem. Am. Acad. Arts and Scis., Am. Sociol. Assn. (citation for disting. contbn. to scholarship 1983). Office: Harvard Univ Dept of Sociology William James Cambridge MA 02138

PATTERSON, PAUL H., biology educator, neuroscientist; b. Chgo., Oct. 22, 1943; s. Paul H. and Marjorie (Hall) P. BA, Grinnell Coll., 1965; PhD, Johns Hopkins U., 1970. Postdoctoral fellow, dept. neurobiology Harvard Med. Sch., Boston, 1970-73, asst. prof. neurobiology, 1973-78, assoc. prof., 1978-83; prof., biology div. Calif. Inst. Tech., Pasadena, 1983—; cons. AMGEN, Thousand Oaks, Calif., 1990—. Author: Readings in Developmental Neurobiology, 1982; assoc. editor: Ann. Rev. Physiology, 1982-83, Jour. Neurosci., 1980-85, 88—, Neuron, 1987—. Recipient Research Career Devel. award NIH, Bethesda, Md., 1974, W. Alden Spencer award Columbia Coll. Physicians and Surgeons, N.Y.C., 1984, McKnight Found. Neurosci. award, Mpls., 1982, 85, 88; Rita Allen Found. scholar, 1979; Jacob Javits Neurosci. Investigator award NIH, 1988; Burton L. Baker lectr. U. Mich., 1989. Fellow AAAS, mem. Soc. for Neurosci., Soc. Developmental Biology, Am. Soc. Cell Biology. Office: Calif Inst of Tech Biology Div Pasadena CA 91125

PATTERSON, RICHARD NORTH, writer, lawyer; b. Berkeley, Calif., Feb. 22, 1947; s. Richard Wallace and Marjorie Frances (North) P.; m. Laurie Anderson, Apr. 13, 1993; children: Shannon Heath, Brooke North, Adam Chandler, Chase Kenyon, Katherine Jeanne Blunt, Stephen Thomas Blunt. BA History, Ohio Wesleyan U., 1968; JD, Case Western Reserve, 1971. Bar: Ohio, 1971, D.C., 1973, Ala., 1975, Calif., 1984. Asst. atty. gen. State of Ohio, 1971-73; with divsn. enforcement SEC, Washington, 1973-75, San Francisco, Calif., 1878-81; assoc. atty. Berkowitz, Lefkovits & Patrick, Birmingham, Ala., 1975-77, ptnr., 1978; assoc. McCutchen, Doyle, Brown & Enerson, San Francisco, Calif., 1985-87, ptnr., 1987-93, of counsel, 1993-94. Author: The Lasko Tangent, 1979, The Outside Man, 1981, Escape the Night, 1983, Private Screening, 1985, Degree of Guilt, 1993, Eyes of a Child, 1995, The Final Judgement, 1995. Recipient Edgar Allen Poe award Best 1st Novel 1979 Mystery Writers Am.

PATTERSON, ROBERT EDWARD, lawyer; b. Los Angeles, Sept. 14, 1942; s. Ellis Elwood and Helen (Hjelte) P.; m. Christina Balboni, Oct. 2, 1971; 1 child, Victor Ellis. BA, UCLA, 1964; JD, Stanford U., 1972, grad. bus. exec. program, 1986. Bar: Calif. 1972. Ptnr. Graham & James, Palo Alto, Calif., 1972—. Served to lt. comdr. USN, 1964-69. Mem. Rotary, Palo Alto Club, Menlo Circus Club, Bohemian Club. Democrat. Office: Graham & James 5 Palo Alto Sq Ste 1000 Palo Alto CA 94306

PATTERSON, ROBERT HOBSON, JR., lawyer; b. Richmond, Va., Jan. 30, 1927; s. Robert Hobson and Margaret S. (Sargent) P.; m. Luise Franklin Wyatt, June 15, 1952; children—India, Robert Hobson, Margaret. B.A., Va. Mil. Inst., 1949; LL.B., U. Va., 1952. Bar: Va. 1952, U.S. Ct. Appeals (4th cir.) 1953, U.S. Supreme Ct. 1955. Assoc. McGuire, Woods, Battle & Boothe, Richmond, 1952-56, ptnr., 1956—, sr. ptnr., chmn. exec. com., 1978-89, chmn., 1984-89. Pres. bd. visitors Va. Mil. Inst., 1975; pres. Va. Home for Boys, 1975. Served with USNR, 1945-46. Fellow Am. Coll. Trial Lawyers, Am. Bar Found.; mem. ABA (various offices), Am. Bar Assn. (pres. 1963-65). Republican. Episcopalian. Clubs: Commonwealth, Country of Va. Office: McGuire Woods Battle & Boothe LLP 1 James Ctr 901 E Cary St Richmond VA 23219

PATTERSON, ROBERT HUDSON, library director; b. Alexandria, La., Dec. 11, 1936; s. Hubert Hudson and Beth (Jones) P.; 1 child, Jennifer Bookhart. B.A., Millsaps Coll., Jackson, Miss., 1958; M.A., Tulane U., 1963; M.L.S., U. Calif., Berkeley, 1965. Mem. profl. staff Tulane U. Libr., New Orleans, 1965-69, 73-76, asst. dir. collection devel., 1973-76; head spl. collections cataloging U. Tex., Austin, 1970-73; dir. librs. U. Wyo., Laramie, 1976-81, U. Tulsa, 1981—; chmn. exec. bd. Wyo. State Libr. Adv. Com., 1976-81; mem. bd. Okla. State Libr. Adv. Com., 1981-84; mem. adv. coun. Bibliog. Ctr. for Rsch., Denver, 1978-81; past mem. exec. bd. S.E. La. Libr. Network; bd. dirs. Amigos Bibliog. Coun., 1983-86; cons. NEH, Harry Ransom Humanities Rsch. Ctr., U. Tex., Austin. Editor Conservation Adminstrn. News, 1979-93; contbr. articles to profl. jours. Pres. Western

Conservation Congress, 1981-82. Sr. fellow CLR/UCLA, 1989. Fellow Internat. Boswell Inst.; mem ALA (various offices), Okla. Libr. Assn. (various offices).

PATTERSON, ROBERT LOGAN, librarian, country and western dance promoter; b. Pitts., Mar. 12, 1940; s. Walter Glenn and June (Logan) P. BA, U. Vt., 1962; MA, San Jose State Coll., 1965; MEd, Boston State Coll., 1979; cert. advanced grad. study Northeastern U., 1982; PhD, Saybrook Inst., 1983. With IBM, London, 1966-68, Info. Dynamics Corp., 1968-70; systems libr. Boston Theol. Inst., 1971-73, Dr. Solomon Carter Fuller Mental Health Clinic, Boston, 1978-79, Boston Evening Med. Center Mental Health Clinic, 1979-81, Mystic Valley Mental Health Center, Arlington, Mass., 1981-82, Cambridgeport Problem Ctr., Cambridge, Mass., 1982-84, U. Mass., Boston, 1973—; owner Tex. Dance Workshops, Houston, Country & Western Dancing U.S.A., Nashville; dir. video prodns.; psychology extern Boston Inst. Psychotherapies, 1981-82, Cambridge Hosp. Psychotherapy Center, 1982-84; prin. psychologist Mass. State Svc. Mem. SAR, Mass. Tchrs. Assn., Strictly Country Dancers, Tex. Country Western Dance Assn., New Eng. Country Two Steppers Club, United Country Western Dance Coun., Psi Chi, Kappa Delta Pi. Home: 8 Winthrop Ave Bedford MA 01730-2223 Office: U Mass Harbor Campus Boston MA 02125

PATTERSON, ROBERT PORTER, JR., federal judge; b. N.Y.C., July 11, 1923; s. Robert Porter and Margaret (Winchester) P.; m. Bevin C. Daly, Sept. 15, 1956; children: Anne, Robert, Margaret, Paul, Katherine. AB, Harvard U., 1947; LLB, Columbia U., 1950. Bar: N.Y. 1951, D.C. 1966. Law clk. Donovan, Leisure, Newton & Lumbard, N.Y.C., 1950-51; asst. counsel N.Y. State Crime Commn. Waterfront Investigation, 1952-53; asst. U.S. atty. Chief of Narcotics Prosecutions and Investigations, 1953-56; asst. counsel Senate Banking and Currency Com., 1954; assoc. Patterson, Belknap, Webb & Tyler, N.Y.C., 1956-60, ptnr., 1960-88; judge U.S. Dist. Ct. (so. dist.) N.Y., 1988—; counsel to minority select com. pursuant to house resolution no. 1, Washington, 1967; mem. Senator's Jud. Screening Panel, 1974-88, Gov.'s Jud. Screening Panel, 1975-82, Gov.'s Sentencing Com., 1978-79. Contbr. articles to profl. jours. Chmn. Wm. T. Grant Found., 1974-94, Prisoners' Legal Services N.Y., 1976-88; dir. Legal Aid Soc., 1961-88, pres., 1967-71; chmn. Nat. Citizens for Eisenhower, 1959-60, Scranton for Pres., N.Y. State, 1964; trustee Havens Relief Fun Soc., Millbrook Sch., 1966-78, Vera Inst. Justice, 1981—, New Sch. for Social Rsch., 1986-94, George C. Marshall Found., 1987-93; mem. exec. com. Lawyers Com. for Civil Rights Under Law, 1968-88; mem. Goldman Panel for Attica Disturbance, 1972, Temporary Commn. on State Ct. System, 1971-73, Rockefeller U. Council, 1986-88, exec. com. N.Y. Vietnam Vets. Meml. Commn., 1982-85, Mayor's Police Adv. Com., 1985-87. Served to capt. USAAF, 1942-46. Decorated D.F.C. with cluster, Air medal with clusters. Mem. ABA (ho. of dels. 1976-80), N.Y. State Bar Assn. (pres. 1978-79), Assn. Bar City N.Y. (v.p. 1974-75), N.Y. County Lawyers Assn. Am. Law Inst., Am. Judicature Soc. (bd. dirs. 1979). Republican. Episcopalian. Home: Fair Oaks Farm Cold Spring NY 10516 Office: US Court House 500 Pearl St New York NY 10007

PATTERSON, ROBERT YOUNGMAN, JR., retired lawyer, utility executive; b. West Palm Beach, Fla., Feb. 1, 1921; s. Robert Youngman and Christine Helene (Johnson) P.; m. Lorraine Hillyer, June 14, 1952; children: Robert Youngman III, Patricia Hillyer. B.A., U. Fla., 1942, LL.B., J.D., 1950. Bar: Fla. 1950. Sole practice Jacksonville, 1950-52; from asst. counsel to asst. gen. counsel Fla. Pub. Service Commn., Tallahassee, 1952-58; gen. atty., asst. sec.-treas. Fla. Gas Co. (and subs.), Winter Park, 1959-62, v.p., gen. atty., 1959-79; dir. state and community affairs Continental Resources Co., 1979-88, Fla. Gas. Transmission Co., Maitland, 1979-88; cons., 1988-91, ret., 1991; mem. Fla. Nuclear Devel. Commn., 1957-60; chmn. Assoc. Industries Fla., 1976. Served to capt. AUS, World War II, ETO. Decorated Purple Heart. Mem. ABA, Fed. Power Bar Assn. (past chmn. rate com.), Fed. Energy Bar Assn., Fla. Bar Assn. (past chmn. adminstrv. law com., chmn. adminstrv. law sect. 1978, chmn. energy com. 1981), Orange County Bar Assn., ICC Practitioners Assn., Am. Judicature Soc., Interstate Southern natural gas assns., Fla. Natural Gas Assn. (W.J. Smith Disting. Svc. award 1989), Fla. C. of C., Tallahassee C. of C., Orlando C. of C. (past chmn. state legislation com.), Winter Park C. of C. (dir., past chmn. congl. action com.), U. Fla. Alumni Assn., Kappa Sigma, Delta Theta Phi. Democrat. Episcopalian. Clubs: Univ. (Orlando and Winter Park); Orlando Country, Citrus, Governors, Capital City, Killearn Country. Home: 1940 Via Contessa Winter Park FL 32789-1568 Office: PO Box 1305 Winter Park FL 32790-1305 *Always have the highest respect for God, your family and your fellow man; honesty and perserverance will overcome all obstacles with such respect.*

PATTERSON, RONALD PAUL, publishing company executive, clergyman; b. Ashland, Ohio, Dec. 4, 1941; s. Donald Edward and Mildred (Niswender) P.; m. Marlene Pfahler, Sept. 1, 1962; children: Paul Edward, Mark Loren. BA, Malone Coll., 1963; MDiv, United Theol. Sem., Dayton, Ohio, 1967; MA, Syracuse U., 1970; DD, Cen. Meth. Coll. 1988. Ordained to ministry United Methodist Ch., 1967. Editor youth pubs. Otterbein Press, Dayton, 1964-68; assoc. editor The Upper Room, Nashville, 1970-74; editor Word Books, Waco, Tex., 1974-77; editorial dir. Abingdon Press, Nashville, 1977-88; book editor United Meth. Ch. Pub. House, 1977-88, v.p., 1984-88, sr. editor Ch. Resources, 1988-92; pub., CEO United Meth. Reporter, Dallas, 1992—; v.p. Religious Pub. Rels. Coun. Nashville, 1970-74; jr. coll. instr. creative writing, Waco; leader writers' workshops. Author: (with others) The Kyle Rote Story, 1975; editor: Come On, Let's Pray, 1972; compiler: The Coming of Easter, 1973; founding editor Alive Now! devotional publ.; editorial dir. Quar. Rev., 1980-87; contbr. articles to mags. Tchr. Tenn. State Prison, Nashville, 1984-88; vice chmn. pastor-parish com., Hermitage, Tenn., 1984-86. Recipient George Washington Honor medal Nat. Freedom Found., Valley Forge, Pa., 1960, Paul M. Hinkhouse award Religious Pub. Relations Council, N.Y.C., 1973; named one of Outstanding Young Men Am., 1972. Mem. Am. Acad. Religion, Religion Pub. Group, Christian Publs. Assn., Southeastern Pubs. Assn. (exec. com. 1985-88), Pubs. Assn. of South (treas.), Evang. Christian Pubs. Assn. (bd. dirs. 1987-88), Protestant Ch.-owned Pubs. Assn. (bd. dirs.), Internat. Pubs. Assn. World Meth. Coun., Downtown Rotary Club (Dallas). Democrat. United Methodist. Avocations: boating, refinishing furniture, golf. Home: 1563 Waterside Ct Dallas TX 75218 Office: 2520 W Commerce Dallas TX 75212

PATTERSON, RONALD R(OY), health care systems executive; b. Baton Rouge, Mar. 4, 1942. BS, U. Houston, 1965; MS, Trinity U., San Antonio, 1973. Asst. adminstr. Med. Br. Tex. U., Galveston, 1972-75; asst. v.p. Hosp. Affiliates Internat., Nashville, 1975-81; chief oper. officer Affiliated Hosp. Systems, Houston, 1981-82; sr. v.p. Republic Health Corp., Dallas, 1982-88; pres. Miller Patterson Inc., Plano, Tex., 1988-89; ind. healthcare mgmt. cons. Plano, 1989-90; sr. v.p. Harris Meth. Health System, Ft. Worth, Tex., 1990-91; exec. v.p., COO Champion Healthcare Corp., Houston, Tex., 1991—. Fellow Am. Coll. Healthcare Execs.; mem. Tex. Hosp. Assn. (vice chmn. multi-hosp. constituency 1987). Avocation: photography. Office: Champion Healthcare Corp Ste 320 14340 Torrey Chase Blvd Houston TX 77014-1021

PATTERSON, RUSSEL HUGO, JR., neurosurgeon, educator; b. Apr. 1, 1929; s. Russel Hugo and Virginia (Fox) P.; m. Juliet Boyd, Nov. 25, 1955; children: Juliet Richie, Russel Hugo III, Alexander Canning. BA, Stanford U., 1948; MD, Cornell U., N.Y.C., 1952. Diplomate Am. Bd. Neurol. Surgery (vice chmn. 1981-82). Intern in surgery N.Y. Hosp., N.Y.C., 1952-53, asst. resident surgeon, 1955-57, asst. resident neurosurgeon, 1957-59, resident neurosurgeon, 1959-60, successively provisional asst. asst. attending, assoc. attending neurosurgeon, 1960-71, attending surgeon-in-charge, 1971—; rotating resident in neurosurgery Meml. Hosp., N.Y.C., 1957-60, cons. assoc. neurosurgeon 1966—; assoc. attending surgeon, 1971—; asst. in surgery Cornell U. Med. Coll., N.Y.C., 1955-59, from instr. to clin. instr., 1959-63, asst. prof. surgery, 1963-68, assoc. prof., 1968-71, prof., 1971—; pvt. practice N.Y.C., 1962—. Contbr. numerous articles to profl jours. With M.C. U.S. Army, 1953-55. Mem. AMA, ACS, AAAS, Med. Soc. State N.Y., N.Y. County Med. Assn., N.Y. Soc. Neurosurgery (pres. 1976-78), Am. Assn. Neurol. Surgeons (pres. 1985-86), N.Y. Neurol. Soc., N.Y. State Neurosurg. Soc. (pres. 1972-73), Pan Am Med. Assn., N.Y. Acad. Medicine, N.Y. Med. and Surg. Soc. (sec. 1973-75, pres. 1981), Internat. Soc. Surgery, Am. Surg. Assn., Soc. Neurol. Surgeons (pres. 1989-90), Am. Acad. Neurol. Surgeons (sec. 1972-76, pres.-elect 1982, pres. 1984), Soc. Stereotaxic and Functional

Surgery, Internat. Soc. Pediatric Neurosurgery, Soc. Brit. Neurol. Surgeons (corr.), Nat. Med. Vets. Soc., German Neurosurgical Soc. Office: 525 E 68th St New York NY 10021-4873

PATTERSON, RUSSELL, conductor, opera executive; b. Greenville, Miss., Aug. 31, 1930; s. Dudley Russell and Elizabeth (Taylor) P.; m. Teresa Gutierrez de Celis, Aug. 28, 1979; children: Richard Russell, Christopher Leonard. B.A., B.Mus., S.E. La. U., 1950; M.Mus., Kansas City Conservatory of Music, 1952; D.M.A., U. Mo. at Kansas City. Prof. music Kansas City Conservatory of Music, 1960-68; mem. profl. com. Met. Opera, 1962—; condr. Kansas City Symphony, 1982-83, artistic dir., 1982-86, condr. emeritus, 1986—; cons. Ford Found. Musician with Baton Rouge Symphony, 1948-50, Brevard Music Festival, 1947-49, Kansas City Philharmonic Orch., 1951-59, Bayrische Staatsoper, Munich, Germany, 1952-53; condr. Kansas City Philharmonic Orch., 1965-66, Point Lookout (Mo.) Festival, 1967—, Kansas City Ballet, 1965-66, Am. Ballet Co., European tour, 1958; gen. dir., Lyric Opera of Kansas City, 1958—, artistic dir., Missouri River Festival, 1976—; dir. Sunflower Music Festival, 1978—. Mem. opera com. Mo. Council Arts, 1965-69; mem. music panel Nat. Endowment Arts, 1970-72; mem. Univ. Assocs. U. Mo. at Kansas City, 1970—. Recipient Alice M. Ditson condrs. award Columbia U., 1982, W.F. Yates medalion William Jewell Coll.; named Disting. Alumni Southeast La. U. Mem. Friends of Art, Opera America (v.p. 1971-73), Phi Mu Alpha Sinfonia, Pi Kappa Lambda, Mensa. Home: 4618 Warwick Blvd Apt 1A Kansas City MO 64112-1751 Office: Lyric Opera Lyric Theater 1029 Central St Kansas City MO 64105-1619*

PATTERSON, SAMUEL CHARLES, political science educator; b. Omaha, Nov. 29, 1931; s. Robert Foster and Garnet Marie (Jorgensen) P.; m. Suzanne Louise Dean, June 21, 1956; children—Polly Ann, Dean Foster, Grier Edmund. B.A., U. S.D., 1953; M.S., U. Wis., 1956, Ph.D., 1959. Asst. prof. polit. sci. Okla. State U., Stillwater, 1959-61; asst. prof. U. Iowa, Iowa City, 1961-64, assoc. prof., 1964-67, prof., 1967-85, Roy J. Carver prof., 1985-86; prof. Ohio State U., Columbus, 1986—; vis. prof. U. Wis., 1962, U. Okla., 1968-78, U. Essex, Colchester, Eng., 1969-70. Author: (with others) Representatives and Represented, 1975, A More Perfect Union, 4th edit., 1989; co-author: The Legislative Process in the United States, 4th edit., 1986, Comparing Legislatures, 1979; editor: American Legislative Behavior, 1968; co-editor: Comparative Legislative Behavior: Frontiers of Research, 1972, Parliaments in the Modern World, 1994; editor: (with others) Handbook of Legislative Research, 1985, Political Leadership in Democratic Societies, 1991; editor Am. Jour. Polit. Sci., 1973-73; co-editor Legis. Studies Quar., 1981-85; mng. editor Am. Polit. Sci. Rev., 1985-91. Served with U.S. Army, 1953-55. Recipient Disting. Scholar award Ohio State U., 1990; fellow Social Sci. Rsch. Coun., 1961, 67, Guggenheim, 1984-85; vis. fellow Brookings Instn., 1984-85, Ctr. Advanced Study in Behavioral Scis., 1993-94; Fulbright Bologna chair, 1995—. Mem. Internat. Polit. Sci. Assn., So. Polit. Sci. Assn., Can. Polit. Sci. Assn., Am. Polit. Sci. Assn., Midwest Polit. Sci. Assn. (pres. 1980-81), Com. for Party Renewal, Phi Beta Kappa, Phi Kappa Phi, Pi Sigma Alpha. Office: Ohio State U Dept Polit Sci 2140 Derby Hall 154 N Oval Mall Columbus OH 43210

PATTERSON, SOLON P., investment counselor; b. Atlanta, Nov. 11, 1935; s. Pete George and Frances (Marinos) P.; m. Marianna Reynolds, Oct. 29, 1960; children: John Solon, Joseph Peter. BBA, Emory U., 1957, MBA, 1958. Chartered fin. analyst, chartered investment counselor. Security analyst, portfolio mgr. Piedmont Adv. Corp., N.Y.C., 1958-62; investment counselor Montag & Caldwell, Atlanta, 1962-73, pres., chief exec. officer, 1973-84, also chmn., 1977—; trustee, chmn. fin. com. Gammon Theol. Sem., Atlanta. Mem. Regional Bd. Nat. Conf. of Christians and Jews; bd. visitors Wake Forest (N.C.) Babcock Grad. Sch. Mgmt. Named Atlanta's Outstanding Young Man of Yr in Bus., Atlanta Jr. C. of C., 1968. Mem. Ga. C. of C., Nat. Assn. Bus. Economists, Atlanta Econs. Club (pres. 1974-75), Atlanta Soc. Fin. Analysts (pres. 1968-69), Fin. Analysts Fedn. (chmn. 1977-78), Soc. Internat. Bus. Fellows. Republican. Greek Orthodox. Clubs: Commerce, Piedmont Driving (Atlanta). Lodge: Rotary. Home: 1360 Barron Ct NW Atlanta GA 30327-1804 Office: Montag & Caldwell Inc 3343 Peachtree Rd NE Ste 1100 Atlanta GA 30326-1015

PATTERSON, STEVE, professional hockey team executive; b. Beaver Dam, Wis., Sept. 21, 1957. BBA with honors, U. Tex., 1980, JD, 1984. Bar: Tex. 1984. Gen. mgr., profl. basketball team counsel Houston Rockets, 1984-89, profl. basketball mktg. exec. group ticket sales, mgr., bus. ops. exec., gen. mgr., 1989-94; pres. profl. hockey team Houston Aeros, 1994—. Office: Houston Aeros 24 Greenway Plz Ste 800 Houston TX 77046

PATTERSON, W. MORGAN, college president; b. New Orleans, Oct. 1, 1925; s. E. Palmer and Jess Margaret (Wood) P.; m. Ernestine North, June 10, 1948; children—W. Morgan, II, Jay North. B.A., Stetson U., 1950, D.D. (hon.), 1979; M.Div., New Orleans Baptist Theol. Sem., 1953, Th.D., 1956; postdoctoral, Oxford U., 1965-66, 72-73. Prof. ch. history New Orleans Bapt. Theol. Sem., 1956-59; prof. ch. history, David T. Porter prof. ch. history, dir. grad. studies So. Baptist Theol. Sem., Louisville, Ky., 1959-76; dean acad. affairs Golden Gate Bapt. Theol. Sem., Mill Valley, Calif., 1976-84; pres. Georgetown Coll., Ky., 1984-91; vis. prof. Midwestern Bapt. Theol. Sem., Kansas City, Mo., La. Coll., Pineville, 1991-92, Golden Gate Bapt. Theol. Sem., Mill Valley, Calif., 1992-94, New Orleans Bapt. Theol. Sem., 1995; chmn. hist. commn. So. Bapt. Conv., Nashville, 1969-72; honored guest 2d Vatican Coun., Rome, 1965. Author: Baptist Successionism: A Critical View, 1969; co-editor: Professor in the Pulpit, 1963; contbr., editor: Ency. Southern Baptists; book rev. editor Review and Expositor, 1965-70. Served as flight officer USAAF, 1943-46. Recipient Disting. Alumnus award Stetson U., 1992, Disting. Svc. award for outstanding contbn. to Bapt. history Hist. Commn., So. Bapt. Conv., 1993; Am. Assn. Theol. Schs. fellow, 1965-69. Mem. Am. Soc. Ch. History, So. Bapt. Hist. Soc. (pres. 1979-80), William H. Whitsitt Bapt. Heritage Soc., Conf. on Faith and History Commn. on Bapt. Heritage of Bapt. World Alliance. Avocations: travel; philately; collecting books. Home: 7 Pierce Dr Novato CA 94947-4450

PATTERSON, WILLIAM BRADFORD, surgical oncologist; b. New Rochelle, N.Y., June 25, 1921; s. Arthur Henry and Gertrude Claire (Hough) P.; m. Helen Russell Ross, May 17, 1943; children: William Bradford, Rebecca H. Bruns, Linda Stevens, Stuart Ross. A.B., Harvard U., 1943, M.D., 1950. Diplomate: Am. Bd. Surgery. Chemist E.I. DuPont Co., 1942-44; intern Peter Bent Brigham Hosp., Boston, 1950-51; resident in surgery, 1951-56; surgeon Boston City Hosp., 1956-59; practice medicine specializing in surgery Boston, 1963-70; chief Pondville Hosp., 1959-63; prof. surgery U. Rochester, N.Y., 1970-78; assoc. dir. for cancer control Dana Farber Cancer Inst., Boston, 1978-91; vis. prof. surgery Harvard Med. Sch., 1978-89; cons. Nat. Cancer Inst. Contbr. chpts. to books, articles to med. jours. Served with USNR, 1944-46. Fellow ACS; mem. Mass. Med. Soc., Boston Surg. Soc., New Eng. Surg. Soc., New Eng. Cancer Soc. Democrat. Congregationalist. Home: RR 1 Box 59 Middlebury VT 05753-9505

PATTERSON, WILLIAM ROBERT, lawyer; b. Wathena, Kans., Feb. 25, 1924; s. George Richard and Jessie (Broadbent) P.; m. Lee Rhyne, Aug. 16, 1947; children: Martha, Robert, Elizabeth. Student, U. Rochester, 1943-44; A.B., Lenoir-Rhyne Coll., 1947; LL.B. with distinction, Duke U., 1950. Bar: Ga. 1951, D.C. 1962. Asso. firm Sutherland, Asbill & Brennan, Atlanta, 1950-58; partner Sutherland, Asbill & Brennan, 1958—; trustee Ga. Tax Conf., 1980-83, pres., 1980-82; lectr. in field. Mem. bd. visitors Duke U. Law Sch., 1973-87, chmn. 1977-87, life mem., 1987—; trustee Pace Acad., Atlanta, 1958-89, trustee emeritus, 1989—; mem. devel. bd. Lenoir-Rhyne Coll., 1976-79, trustee, 1980-89; elder Trinity Presbyterian Ch., Atlanta. With USN, 1942-46. Fellow Am. Coll. Mortgage Attys. (bd. regents 1993—); mem. ABA, Ga. State Bar, Atlanta Bar Assn., D.C. Bar Assn., Am. Coll. Real Estate Lawyers (bd. govs. 1987-90), Atlanta Lawyers Club, Am. Law Inst., So. Fed. Tax Inst. (trustee 1957-90, adv. trustee 1990—, pres. 1974-75, chmn. 1975-76), Atlanta Tax Forum (trustee 1977-83, pres. 1981-82), Order of Coif, Cherokee Town and Country Club, Commerce Club, Peachtree Club. Home: 2939 Rivermeade Dr NW Atlanta GA 30327-2039 Office: Sutherland Asbill & Brennan First Union Pla 23d Fl 999 Peachtree St NE Atlanta GA 30309-3964

PATTERSON, WILLIAM S., lawyer; b. Kings Mountain, N.C., July 16, 1947. BA, Wake Forest U., 1969; JD with honors, U. N.C., 1973. Bar: N.C. 1973. Staff atty. interpretive divsn. Office Chief Counsel U.S. Dept. Treasury, 1973-75, staff atty. tax ct. litigation divsn., 1975-77; ptnr. Hunton & Williams, Raleigh, N.C. Office: Hunton & Williams PO Box 109 1 Hanover Sq 14th Fl Raleigh NC 27602

PATTERSON, WILLIAM WAYNE, business executive; b. Overton, Tex., Mar. 23, 1943; s. Samuel Ashley and Marguerite (Robinson) P.; B.B.A., U. Tex., 1965, LL.B., 1967; postgrad. cert. comparative law Universidad Nacional de Mexico, 1967; m. Janie Chiles, Dec. 27, 1969; children: Perrin Ashli, Shawn Adair, Andrew Clay. Acct., Peat, Marwick, Mitchell & Co., Houston, 1968-74; controller Keystone Internat., Inc. Houston, 1974-76, sec.-treas., 1976-78, v.p. fin., 1978-86, exec. v.p., 1986-89; group pres. systems and controls group, 1985-86, also bd. dirs., 1978—; chmn., CEO Tex. Microsystems Inc., Houston, 1989—. Trustee Shriners Hosp. Crippled Children; mem. adv .bd. Child Abuse Prevention Council; bd. dirs. Ronald McDonald House. C.P.A., Tex. Mem. Am. Inst. C.P.A.s, ABA. Episcopalian. Clubs: Houstonian, Masons, Houston Country Club. Office: Tex Microsystems Inc PO Box 42963 Houston TX 77242-2963

PATTESON, ROY KINNEER, JR., clergyman, administrator; b. Richmond, Va., Oct. 27, 1928; s. Roy Kinneer and Mary (Anderson) P.; m. Edna Pauline Cox, Apr. 15, 1950; children: Stephen, David. B.A., U. Richmond, 1957; B.D., Union Theol. Sem., 1961; Th.M., Duke U., 1964, Ph.D., 1967. Ordained to ministry Presbyterian Ch. in U.S.A., 1961. Fellow Duke U. Inst. Medieval and Renaissance Studies, 1968; pres. So. Sem. Jr. Coll., 1970-72; v.p. Mary Baldwin Coll., 1972-77; pres. King Coll., Bristol, Tenn., 1977-79; asst. to pres. Va. Wesleyan Coll., 1979-81, v.p., 1981-85; v.p. Westminster-Canterbury of Hampton Rds., Inc., Virginia Beach, Va., 1985-88; asst. sec. bd. trustees Westminster-Canterbury of Hampton Rds., Inc., 1986-88; dir. Norfolk (Va.) Sr. Ctr., 1987-88; cons. Marts & Lundy Inc., Rockbridge Baths, Va., 1988-92; pastor Pittsboro and Mt. Vernon Springs Presbyn. chs., Pittsboro, N.C., 1962-65; mem. mission council and chmn. budget com. Shenandoah Presbytery, 1973-77; chmn. com. on higher edn. Norfolk Presbytery, 1980-82; mem. community adv. bd. Madison Coll., 1975-77; bd. dirs. Tenn. Ind. Coll. Fund; v.p. Mid-Appalachian Ind. Council, 1978-79. Vice pres. Rockbridge Hist. Soc., Lexington, Va., 1970-77; chmn. edn. com. Staunton-Augusta C. of C. Served with U.S. Army, 1948-49; with U.S. N.G., 1949-52. Recipient Grad. Scholar award Duke U., 1966. Rotary. Office: PO Box 130 Rockbridge Baths VA 24473

PATTI, ANDREW S., consumer products company executive; b. 1940. With Standard Brands, 1961-63, 65-67; pres. Armour Handcrafts Inc., Phoenix, 1982-86; now pres., chief exec. officer Armour Internat. Corp., Phoenix; with Dial Corp., Phoenix, 1986—, now pres., chief oper. officer. With U.S. Army, 1963-65. Office: Dial Corp Consumer Products Group 1850 N Central Ave Phoenix AZ 85077

PATTI, SISTER JOSEPHINE MARIE, health science facility administrator; b. Buffalo, July 5, 1934; d. Joseph John and Caroline Mary (Mayer) P. BS, D'Youville Coll., Buffalo, 1964; MHA, Xavier U., Cin., 1974. Joined Grey Nuns of Sacred Heart, Roman Cath. Ch., 1954. Med. technologist Griffin Meml. Hosp., Kodiak, Alaska, 1964-70; asst. supr., sr. med. tech. A.B. Hepburn Hosp., Ogdensburg, NY, 1970-72; adminstrv. res. St. Joseph's Infirmary, Atlanta, 1973-74; adminstr. Kodiak (Alaska) Island Hosp., 1974-78; adminstrv. asst. St. Joseph's Hosp. Inc., Atlanta, 1978-79; asst. adminstr. St. Joseph's Hosp., 1979-80; dir., mission effective St. Joseph's Hosp., Atlanta, 1986-88, asst. v.p., 1988-90; v.p. mise effect St. Joseph's Hosp., 1990—; adminstr. Motherhouse, Grey Nuns of the Sacred Heart, Yardley, Pa., 1980-85; dir. St. Joseph's Mercy Care Corp., Atlanta, 1988—; chairperson bd. dirs. Atlanta Cmty. Health Program for the Homeless, 1988-91; vice chairperson bd. dirs. Mercy Mobile Health Program, 1991-94; dir. South Ctrl. Health Planning and Devel., Inc., Anchorage, 1976-77. Mem. adv. bd. Lifelink Ga., 1988-91; mem. instnl. rev. bd. AIDS Rsch. Consortium, Atlanta, 1988—; dir. North Atlanta Sr. Svcs., 1988-93; bd. dirs. Mercy Sr. Care, 1991—; sec. 1991-93; mem. Hispanic Svcs. Adv. Bd., 1991-94; bd. dirs. Cath. Social Svcs., Inc., 1992—. Fellow Am. Coll. Health Care Execs. Office: Saint Joseph's Hosp Atlanta 5665 Peachtree Dunwoody Rd NE Atlanta GA 30342-1701

PATTILLO, MANNING MASON, JR., academic administrator; b. Charlottesville, Va., Oct. 11, 1919; s. Manning Mason and Margaret (Camblos) P.; m. Martha A. Crawford, June 8, 1946; children: Manning Mason III, Martha Crawford, John Landrum. Student, Johns Hopkins U., 1937-38; BA with highest honors, U. of South, 1941, DCL, 1993; student, U. Calif. at Berkeley, 1941-42; AM, U. Chgo., 1947, PhD, 1949; LLD, LeMoyne Coll., 1967, St. John's U., 1968, Oglethorpe U., 1994; LHD, U. Detroit, 1968, Coll. New Rochelle, 1967, Park Coll., 1973; LittD, St. Norbert Coll., 1967. From instr. to assoc. prof. higher edn. U. Chgo., 1949-56; assoc. dir. Lilly Endowment, Inc., Indpls., 1956-60; exec. dir. for edn. Lilly Endowment, Inc., 1961-62; dir. Danforth commn. on ch. colls. and univs., 1962-66; assoc. dir. The Danforth Found., 1964-66, v.p., 1966-67; pres. The Found. Center, N.Y.C., 1967-71; adj. prof. N.Y. U., 1968-71; dir. spl. projects U. Rochester, 1972-75; pres. Oglethorpe U., Atlanta, 1975-88, chancellor, 1988—; cons. in field; tech. asst., then assoc. sec. commn. on colls. and units. North Cen. Assn. Colls. and Secondary Schs., 1948-56; cons. USAF Acad., 1952, Phillips Exeter Acad., 1974; chmn. IBM Incentive awards com., 1970-75; adv. com. Brookings Instn., 1970-71; vis. prof. Inst. Higher Edn., U. Ga., 1988—; bd. dirs., chmn. Fidelity Nat. Bank. Author: (with D.M. Mackenzie) Church Sponsored Higher Education in the United States, 1966, (with D.M. Mackenzie) Eight Hundred Colleges Face the Future, 1965, Private Higher Education in the United States, 1990, The Episcopal Church: Diagnosis and Reform, 1989; contbr. articles to profl. jours. Mem. pres.'s adv. coun. Wellesley Coll., 1969-72; trustee Seabury Press, Japan Internat. Christian U., 1970-72, Le Moyne Coll., 1970-83, Sacred Heart U., 1968-75, U. of South, 1984-88, St. Martin's Episc. Sch.; bd. dirs., chmn. Atlanta Coll. Art, 1984—, Howard Sch.; trustee Greater Rochester Community Found., 1973-75, pres., 1975; trustee, chmn. Nat. Coun. on Philanthropy, 1968-80; trustee, chmn. bd. trustees Park Coll., 1967-74; provost St. Mary's Coll. of Md., 1975; bd. visitors Kanuga Confs., Inc.; pres., life trustee Ga. Found. for Ind. Colls. 1977-79; chmn. Univ. Center in Ga., 1978-79; pres. Assn. Pvt. Colls. and Univs. of Ga., 1980-81; trustee, chmn. Ga. Spl. Olympics; trustee, mem. exec. com. Nat. Assn. Ind. Colls. and Univs., Ind. Coll. Funds of Am., 1982-86; co-dir. Coll. Cons. Network, So. Assn. Colls. and Schs., 1988—; mem. De Kalb County Community Relations Commn.; chmn. De Kalb Community Coun. on the Aging; mem. commn. on colls. and steering com. on revision accrediting procedures So. Assn. Colls. and Schs.; vice-chmn bd. dirs. Woodruff Arts Ctr.; mem. adv. coun. ARC. With AUS, 1942-46. Mem. Nat. Assn. Scholars, Assn. for Higher Edn., Nat. Assn. Ind. Schs. (bd. dirs.), Guild of Scholars, English Speaking Union (dir., pres. br., nat. bd. dirs.), Country Day Sch. Headmasters Assn. U.S. (hon.), Atlanta Hist. Soc., Dekalb C. of C. (dir., chmn.), Phi Beta Kappa, Omicron Delta Kappa, Kappa Sigma. Episcopalian (vestryman, sr. warden, mem. cathedral chpt., diocesan council, standing com.). Clubs: Century (N.Y.C.); Commerce, Capital City. Lodge: Rotary. Office: Office of Chancellor Oglethorpe Univ 4484 Peachtree Rd NE Atlanta GA 30319-2737

PATTIS, S. WILLIAM, publisher; b. Chgo., July 3, 1925; s. William Robert and Rose (Quint) P.; m. Bette Z. Levin, July 16, 1950; children: Mark Robert, Robin Quint Himovitz. BS, U. Ill., 1949; postgrad., Northwestern U., 1949-50. Exec. v.p., pub. United Bus. Pubs., 1949-59; chmn., CEO 3M/Pattis, 1959-88; pres. NTC Pub. Group, Lincolnwood, Ill., 1961—; dir. P-B Comm., Winnetka, Ill., 1978—; bd. dirs. 1st Colonial/Highwood; mem. book and libr. com. USIA, Washington, 1988-89, chmn., 1989-93; mem. exec. com. Pub. Hall of Fame, 1987—; chmn. US-USSR Bilateral Info. Talks, Moscow, 1990. d. dirs. 1st Colonial/Highwood; mem. book and libr. com. USIA, Washington 1986-89, chmn., 1989-93; mem. exec. com. Pub. Hall of Fame, 1987—. Mem. Pres.'s Coun. Youth Opportunity, 1968-70; bd. dirs. Photography Youth Found., 1973-77, Expt. in Internat. Living, 1970, Inst. Human Creativity, 1983—, Annenberg Ctr. for Health Scis., 1991—; trustee Eisenhower Med. Ctr., Rancho Mirage, Calif., 1989—; trustee Am. Coun. Tchrs. Russian, 1992—; bd. dirs. Nat. Security Edn. Act, Washington, 1993-94; lord of manor, Kirkbride, Eng., 1989—. Recipient Human Rels. award Am. Jewish Com., 1971, Paul Simon award Cen. States Conf. on Tchg. Fgn. Langs., 1992. Mem. Standard Club (Chgo.), Northmoor Country Club

(Highland Park, Ill.), Tamarisk Country Club (Rancho Mirage). Home: 195 Elder Ln Highland Park IL 60035-5368 Office: NTC Pub Group 4255 W Touhy Ave Lincolnwood IL 60646

PATTISHALL, BEVERLY WYCKLIFFE, lawyer; b. Atlanta, May 23, 1916; s. Leon Jackson and Margaret Simkins (Woodfin) P.; children by previous marriage: Margaret Ann Arthur, Leslie Hansen, Beverly Wyckliffe, Paige Terhune Pattishall Watt, Woodfin Underwood; m. Dorothy Daniels Mashek, June 24, 1977. BS, Northwestern U., 1938; JD, U. Va., 1941. Bar: Ill. 1941, D.C. 1971. Pvt. practice law Chgo., 1946—; ptnr. Pattishall, McAuliffe, Newbury, Hilliard & Geraldson and predecessor firms, Chgo.; dir. Juvenile Protective Assn. Chgo., 1946-79, pres., 1961-63, hon. dir., 1979—; dir. Vol. Interagy. Assn., 1975-78, sec., 1977-78; U.S. del. Diplomatic Confs. on Internat. Trademark Registration Treaty, Geneva, Vienna, 1970-73, Diplomatic Conf. on Revision of Paris Conv., Nairobi, 1981; mem. U.S. del. Geneva Conf. on Indsl. Property and Consumer Protection, 1978; adj. prof. trademark, trade identity and unfair trade practices law Northwestern U. Sch. Law, Chgo. Author: (with David C. Hilliard) Trademarks, Trade Identity and Unfair Trade Practices, 1974, Unfair Competition and Unfair Trade Practices, 1985, Trademarks, 1987, Trademarks and Unfair Competition, 1994; contbr. articles to profl. jours. Lt. comdr. USNR, WWII, ETO, PTO, ATO, ret. comdr. Fellow Am. Coll. Trial Lawyers (bd. regents 1979-83); mem. ABA (chmn. sect. patent, trademark copyright law 1963-64), Internat. Patent and Trademark Assn. (pres. 1955-57, exec. com. 1955—), assn. Internat. Pour La Protection Propriete Indsl. (mem. of honor), Ill. Bar Assn., Chgo. Bar Assn., D.C. Bar Assn., Chgo. Bar Found. (dir. 1977-83), U.S. Trademark Assn. (dir. 1963-65), Legal Club, Law Club (pres. 1982-83), Econ. Club, Chikaming Country Club, Univ. Club, Mid-Am. Club, U. Va. Lile Law Soc. (sr. counselor), Selden Soc. (London, Ill. rep.). Office: Pattishall McAuliffe Newbury Hilliard & Geraldson 311 S Wacker Dr Ste 5000 Chicago IL 60606-6618

PATTISON, ABBOTT LAWRENCE, sculptor; b. Chgo., May 15, 1916; s. William L. and Bonnie (Abbott) P.; m. Mary Grant, June 2, 1945; children: William G., Grant A., Harry, Jean. BA, Yale, 1937, BFA, 1939. Tchr. Chgo. Art Inst., 1946-51; instr. Skowhegan Art Sch., 1955-56. Sculptor in residence U. Ga., 1953-54; affiliated Feingarten Gallery, Los Angeles, Fairweather Hardin Gallery, Chgo., Alwin Gallery, London; major commns. include Mayo Clinic, Rochester, Minn., Cen. Nat. Bank, Cleve., U. Chgo., Chgo. State U., Ill. Capitol Bldg., Lincoln Library, Springfield, Ill., Northbrook (Ill.) Library, New Trier West High Sch., Northfield Ill., Culligan Internat. & Commerce Plaza, Oak Brook, Ill.; 1st Logan prize and purchase Art Inst. Chgo. 1942, Eisendrath prize 1946, 1st Pauline Palmer prize for sculpture 1950, prize 1953, 3d prize contemporary sculpture show Met. Mus. Art 1951, 1st prize Chgo. Sculptor Show, Art Cen. 1955, 1st prize McCormick Pl. Art Show 1962, prize Bundy Mus., Waitsfield, Vt. 1963; work in China and Japan, 1940, Europe, 1950-51, 55-56, 58, 60-61, Italy, 1955-56, 58, 60-61; represented in collections Art Inst. Chgo., Corcoran Gallery, Washington, Phoenix Museum, Calif. Palace Legion of Honor, others; represented permanent collections at Whitney Mus., N.Y.C., Israel State Mus. Jerusalem, San Francisco Mus., Buckingham Palace, London, Eng., Yorkshire (England) Sculpture Park, U.S. State Dept., St. Louis Mus., Palm Springs Desert Mus., Portland (Maine) Mus., Addison Gallery Am. Art., Davenport Mus., Evansville Mus. Capt. USN, 1942-45. Recipient of Yale U.'s 1st traveling fellowship, 1939, 1st Logan prize Art Inst. Chgo. 1942. Address: PO Box 583 Winnetka IL 60093-0583 also: Caldbeck Gallery 12 Ekm St Rockland ME 04841

PATTISON, ROBERT MAYNICKE, architect; b. Colonia, N.J., Feb. 22, 1923; s. Maynicke Munn Pattison and Lillian Cornelia (Garretson) Pattison Fox; divorced; children: Jeannine (Mrs. D. Harper), Darrel Keith, Michael Shaun. Lic. architect, Ohio. Project coord. Walker & Weeks, Cleve., 1948-60; project architect Shaefer, Flynn & Williams, Cleve., 1960-62; v.p. Williams-Pattison Assoc., Inc., Cleve., 1962-74; prin. Robert M. Pattison, Architect, Berea, Ohio, 1974-85, 90—; architect, plan examiner City of Cleve. Bldg Dept., 1985-90; project architect Dalton-Dalton-Newport A/E, Shaker Heights, Ohio, 1977-78; asst. supr. Turner Constrn., Inc., Cleve., 1980; architect Lawson Co., Cuyahoga Falls, Ohio, 1980-81. Co-author: IEEE White Book, 1979. With USN, 1943-45. Mem. Kiwanis (pres. Middleburg Heights club 1991-92). Republican. Home and Office: 444 Woodlawn Cir Berea OH 44017-1231

PATTON, ALTON DEWITT, electrical engineering educator, consultant, research administrator; b. Corpus Christi, Tex., Feb. 1, 1931; s. Alton G. and Civilia Louise (Taylor) P.; m. Nancy Jo Elder, Mar. 1, 1959; children: Elizabeth, Carolyn. BEE, U. Tex., Austin, 1957; MEE, U. Pitts., 1961; PhD in Elec. Engring., Tex. A&M U., 1972. Registered profl. engr., Tex. Engr. Westinghouse Electric Corp., Pitts., 1957-65; prof. elec. engring. dept. Tex. A&M U., College Station, 1965-79, 82—, head elec. engring. dept., 1992—, Brockett prof., 1986, Dresser prof., 1987, dir. Electric Power Inst., 1976-79, 85-92; rsch. fellow Tex. Engring. Expt. Sta., College Station, 1985; dir. Ctr. for Space Power Tex. Engring. Expt. Sta., 1987-92; pres. Associated Power Analysts Inc., College Station, Tex., 1973—. Contbr. articles to elec. engring. jours., 1960—. Fellow IEEE (prize paper award 1975, 94); mem. NSPE, Internat. Conf. on Large High Voltage Electric Systems, Internat. Astronautical Fedn. Republican. Presbyterian. Avocations: fishing, hunting, photography, stamp and coin collecting. Home: 1217 Merry Oaks Dr College Station TX 77840-2608 Office: Tex A&M U Elec Engring Dept College Station TX 77843

PATTON, CARL ELLIOTT, physics educator; b. San Antonio, Sept. 14, 1941; s. Carl Elliott and Geraldine Barnett (Perry) P. BS, MIT, 1963; MS, Calif. Inst. Tech., 1964, PhD, 1967. Sr. scientist Raytheon Co., Waltham, Mass., 1967-71; assoc. prof. physics Colo. State U., Ft. Collins, 1971-75, prof., 1975—; IEEE Magnetics Soc. Disting. lectr., 1993. editor-in-chief IEEE Transactions on Magnetics, 1987-91. Fellow IEEE, Am. Phys. Soc. Office: Colo State Univ Dept Physics Fort Collins CO 80523

PATTON, CARL VERNON, academic administrator, educator; b. Coral Gables, Fla., Oct. 22, 1944; s. Carl V. and Helen Eleanor (Benkert) P.; m. Gretchen West, July 29, 1967. B.S. in Community Planning, U. Cin., 1967; M.S. in Urban Planning U. Ill.-Urbana, 1969, M.S. in Pub. Administrn. 1970; M.S. in Pub. Policy, U. Calif.-Berkeley, 1975, Ph.D. in Pub. Policy, 1976. Instr. to prof. U. Ill., 1968-83, dir. Bureau of Urban and Regional Planning Research, 1977-79, prof., chmn. dept., 1979-83; prof., dean Sch. Architecture and Urban Planning, U. Wis., Milw., 1983-89; v.p. acad. affairs, prof. polit. sci., geography and urban planning U. Toledo, 1989-92; pres. Ga. State U., Atlanta, 1992—. Author: Academia in Transition, 1979 (with others) The Metropolitan Midwest, 1985; (with David Sawicki) Basic Methods of Policy Analysis and Planning, 1986, rev. 2d edit., 1993; (with Kathleen Reed) Guide to Graduate Education in Urban and Regional Planning, 1986, 88; editor: Spontaneous Shelter: International Perspectives and Prospects, 1988, (with G. William Page) Quick Answers to Quantitative Problems: A Pocket Primer, 1991; assoc. editor Jour. of Planning Edn. and Research, 1983-87, mem. editorial bd. 1987-89; mem. editorial bd. Habitat International, 1991—, Atlanta International Magazine, 1993—; contbr. articles to profl. jours. Chmn. Community Devel. Commn., Urbana, 1978-82; mem. Civic Design Ctr., Milw., 1983-87; mem. City of Milw. Art Commn., 1988-89, ToledoVision, 1989-92, Toledo Art Ctr. Bd., 1989-92, City of Toledo Bd. Community Rels., 1990-92; bd. dirs. Atlanta YMCA, The Downtown Atlanta Partnership, Ctrl. Atlanta Progress, Ga. Rsch. Alliance, Ctrl. Atlanta Hospitality Childcare, Inc., Atlanta Convention and Vis. Bur.; mem. exec. com. The Fairlie-Poplar Task Force, The Univ. Ctr. in Ga.; mem. Ga. Coun. on Econ. Edn. Atlanta Neighborhood Devel. Ptnrship. Fellow NIMH, 1973-75, U. Ill. Center for Advanced Studies, 1973-74. Mem. Am. Planning Assn., Am. Int. Cert. Planners, Assn. Collegiate Schs of Planning (v.p. 1985-87, pres. 1989-91), Atlanta C. of C. Avocations: racquetball, jogging, photography, travel. Home: 3807 Tuxedo Rd NW Atlanta GA 30305 Office: Ga State U Office of President University Plz Atlanta GA 30303-3083

PATTON, DAVID WAYNE, health care executive; b. Utica, N.Y., June 15, 1942; s. Dale Willard and Eleanor (Miller) P.; BS, Ariz. State U., 1964; MHA, U. Minn., 1966; MA, Claremont U., 1989, MBA, 1991; m. Barbara Jean; children: Jodi Lynn, Steven Wayne. Asst. adminstr. Maricopa County Gen. Hosp., Phoenix, 1969-71; adminstr. Holy Rosary Hosp., Miles City,

Mont., 1971-74; exec. dir. St. Luke's Hosp., Aberdeen, S.D., 1974-79; pres., CEO Parkview Episcopal Med. Ctr., Pueblo, Colo., 1979-84; founder Leadership Pueblo, 1982; pres. Community Health Corp. and Riverside (Calif.) Community Hosp., 1984-92; pres. DevelopMed Inc., Fullerton, Calif., 1993-95; adminstr., chief exec. officer Kona Cmty. Hosp., Kealakekua, Hawaii, 1995—; Bd. dirs. San Louis Valley Health Maintenance Orgn., 1982-84, World Pres. Orgn., Riverside C. of C., 1986-91, pres. 1988-89; campaign chmn. United Way of the Inland Valleys, 1989-90; founder, chmn. Leadership Riverside, 1987-89. Served to capt. USAF, 1966-69. Fellow Am. Coll. Healthcare Execs. (regent 1976-79). Republican. Home: 662 Colonial Cir Fullerton CA 92635-2773

PATTON, DIANA LEE WILKOC, artist; b. New Rochelle, N.Y., June 28, 1940; d. August E. and Meta Diane (Neuburg) Wilkoc; m. Gardner C. Patton, Aug. 10, 1963; children: Michael, Talryn, Shawn. AB cum laude Brown U., 1962; postgrad. Pan-Am. Art Inst., 1962-63. Svc. mgr. Lord and Taylor, N.Y.C., 1962-63; tchr. adult edn., Mountain Lakes, N.J., 1972-74, Somerville, N.J., 1978-82, Bound Brook Adult Sch., 1982—; artist in watercolors, pen and ink, acrylics, jewelry created; one-woman and group shows N.E. U.S., Perth, Australia, 1977, spl. bicentennial exhibit, Trenton, 1976, Rutgers U., 1980, Brookdale Coll., 1982, Camden County Coll., 1986, Morris County Coll., 1988, Bergen Mus. Arts and Scis., 1987, 88, 90, 91, North Gallery, Far Hills, 1982, 86, Clarence Dillon Gallery, 1989, 91, Princeton Med. Ctr. 1993, 94; work represented pvt. and public collections in U.S., Australia, N.Z., Germany, Luxembourg, Japan, Eng.; designer ofcl. poster N.J. Festival of Ballooning, 1990, Arc Challenge Races, 1993, 94; instr. in field; developer art appreciation courses for children and adults; toymaker, 1973-76. Winner bronze medal in watercolor Nat. Mystic (Conn.) Outdoor Art Festival, 1977; Mayor's Purchase prize Franklin Twp., 1976; Tri-State Watercolor award Somerset County Coll., 1978; Best in Show Raritan Valley Art Assn., 1978, 94; award Garden State Watercolor Soc., 1979, 1994, 95; 1st and 2d and Best in Show awards Somerset and Westfield Art Assns. shows; 1st place for profl. watercolor Plainfield Tri-State Arts Festival, 1983, 85, 87, N.E. Art Festival, 1993, 95; Tewksbury award, 1990, 2d place in watercolor Internat. Miniature Art Show, Washington, 1983; best in show and Grumbacher award Caldwell State show, 1984; 1st place Carrier Clinic Tri-State 1984; Grumbacher Bronze award, 1984, Grumbacher Silver award, 1985, 88, 94, Watercolor award Artists League Cen. N.J. show Cornelious Lowe Mus., 1986, Winsor-Newton award Am. Artists Proleague, 1987, Robert Simmons award, 1989, Basking Ridge Environmental Ctr. award, 1994; Best in Show N.J. State Juried, Piscataway, 1988; 2d place N.J. Miniature Art Soc., 1989; 1st prize Raritan Valley, 1992, 93, 1st mixed media B.R. Environ. Ctr., 1991; artist-in-residence grant Middlesex Librs., 1983-92, watercolor demonstrator, 1983—; TV appearances, State of the Arts-N.J., 1986, Midday (spl. art shows), 1986, TKR, 1995. Elisha Benjamin scholar Brown U., 1960. Mem. Garden State Watercolor Soc., Miniature Art Socs., Fla., N.J., Washington, AAUW (life, various offices 1963-73), art assns. Raritan Valley (pres. 1980-82), Somerset, Westfield, North Haven (Maine), Essex Watercolor Club, Am. Artists Profl. League. Presbyterian. Clubs: Hanover Squares (co-pres. 1972-73), Morris County Folk Dancers (co-pres. 1963). Home and Studio: 497 Stony Brook Dr Bridgewater NJ 08807-1945

PATTON, GEORGE SMITH, military officer; b. Boston, Dec. 24, 1923; s. George Smith, Jr. and Beatrice Banning (Ayer) P.; m. Joanne Holbrook, June 14, 1952; children: Margaret, George, Robert, Helen, Benjamin. BS, U.S. Mil. Acad., 1946; MPS, George Washington U., 1965. Commd. 2d lt. U.S. Army, 1946, advanced through grades to maj. gen.; 1973; parachutist Germany, 1947-51; assigned Armor Br., 1949; instr. tank offense sect. Armored Sch. Fort Knox, Ky., 1952-53; comdr. Co. A, 140th Tank Bn. Korea, 1953, exec. officer I, Corps Reconnaissance Bn., 1953-54; co. tactical officer dept. tactics U.S. Mil. Acad., 1954-56; officer exec. dept. U.S. Naval Acad., 1956-57; assigned Command and Gen. Staff Coll., Fort Leavenworth, Kans., 1957-58; a.d.c. comdg. gen. 7th Army and comdr. in chief U.S. Army, Europe, 1958-60; exec. officer 1st squadron 11th Armored Cav. Regt. Straubing, Germany, 1960-61; assigned Armed Forces Staff Coll. Norfolk, Va., 1961-62; assigned U.S. Army War Coll. Carlisle Barracks, Pa., 1964-65; spl. forces ops. officer Mil. Assistance Command Vietnam, 1962-63; comdr. 2/81 Armor, 1st Armored Div. Fort Hood, Tex., 1963-64; chief Mainland S.E. Asia br. Far East-Pacific div. Office Dep. Chief Staff for Mil. Ops., Dept. Army, 1965-67; chief force devel. div. U.S. Army, Vietnam, 1967-68; comdg. officer 11th Armored Cav. Regt. Vietnam, 1968-69; assigned U.S. Army Primary Helicopter Ctr., Ft. Wolters, Tex., 1969-70, Ft. Rucker, Ala., 1969-70; asst. div. comdr. for support 4th Armored div. Hdqrs. U.S. Army, Europe, 1970-71; comdt. U.S. Army Armor Sch. Fort Knox, 1971-73; dir. security assistance Hdqrs. U.S. European Command, 1973-74, comdr. Army Readiness Region, 1974-75; comdr. 2d Armored Div. Fort Hood, 1975-77; dep. comdg. gen. U.S. VII Corps, 1977-79; dir. readiness Hdqrs. Dept. Army Materiel Devel. and Readiness Command Alexandria, Va.; 1979-80; ret., 1980; instr. history U. Md., 1960-61. Mem. West Point Fund, Alexandria, Va.; trustee Essex Agrl. and Tech. Inst., Hathorne, Mass. Decorated D.S.C. with oak leaf cluster, Silver Star with oak leaf cluster, Legion of Merit with two oak leaf clusters, D.F.C., Bronze Star with oak leaf cluster, Purple Heart; Cross of Gallantry with gold, silver and bronze stars Vietnam; Army Forces Honor medal 1st class. Mem. Assn. U.S. Army, Armor Assn., Blackhorse Assn., Ducks Unltd., N.E. Farm Bur., Legion of Valor, Am. Legion, VFW, Coun. Nat. Policy. Home: 650 Asbury St South Hamilton MA 01982-1321

PATTON, GEORGE THOMAS, JR., credit agency executive; b. Birmingham, Ala., Sept. 22, 1929; s. George Thomas and Jewell Inez (Garner) P.; m. Hope Kirby, Dec. 20, 1953; children—Thomas Kirby, Neal Garner. B.A., Birmingham-So. Coll., 1949. With Gen. Motors Acceptance Corp., Detroit, 1949—, treas., 1970-72, v.p., 1972-78, exec. v.p., 1978—, dir., 1974—. Chmn. Municipal Planning Bd., Norwood, N.J., 1966-72; Trustee Pascack Valley Hosp., Westwood, N.J., 1975-81; chmn. planning commn. Village of Bingham Farms, Mich., 1989—. Mem. Sigma Alpha Epsilon, Omicron Delta Kappa. Presbyn. (elder). Office: GMAC 3044 W Grand Blvd Detroit MI 48202-3091

PATTON, JAMES RICHARD, JR., lawyer; b. Durham, N.C., Oct. 27, 1928; s. James Ralph and Bertha (Moye) P.; m. Mary Margot Maughan, Dec. 29, 1950; children: James Macon, Lindsay Fairfield. AB cum laude, U. N.C., 1948; postgrad., Yale U., 1948; JD, Harvard U., 1951. Bar: D.C. bar 1951, U.S. Supreme Ct. 1963. Attache of Embassy; spl. asst. to Am. ambassador to Indochina, 1952-54; with Office Nat. Estimates, Washington, 1954-55; atty. Covington & Burling, Washington, 1956-61; founding ptnr., chmn. exec. com. Patton, Boggs & Blow, Washington, 1962—; Lectr. internat. law Cornell Law Sch., 1963-64, U.S. Army Command and Gen. Staff Coll., 1967-68; Mem. Nat. Security Forum, U.S. Air War Coll., 1965, Nat. Strategy Seminar, U.S. Army War Coll., 1967-70, Global Strategy Discussions, U.S. Naval War Coll., 1968, Def. Orientation Conf., 1972; mem. Com. of 100 on Fed. City, Washington; mem. adv. council on nat. security and internat. affairs Nat. Republican Com., 1977-81; bd. dirs. Madeira Sch., Greenway, Va., 1975-81, Lawyers Com. for Civil Rights Under Law, Washington, Legal Aid Soc. Washington; mem. Industry Policy Adv. Com. for Trade Policy Matters, 1984-87; councillor of Atlantic Council of U.S., 1987-90; mem. visiting com. Ackland Art Mus. U. N.C., 1987—, Nat. Coun. Anderson Ranch Arts Ctr., 1987—. Adv. coun. mem. Johns Hopkins U. Sch. Advanced Internat. Studies, 1992; nat. bd. dirs. Aspen Inst., 1987-90; nat. coun. mem. Whitney Mus., 1992—; bd. dirs., exec. com. Nat. Mus. Natural History, Smithsonian, 1992—; trustee Aspen Music Assocs., 1993—. Mem. ABA (past com. chmn.), Inter-Am. Bar Assn. (past del.). Internat. Law Assn. (past com. chmn.), Am. Soc. Internat. Law (treas., exec. coun.), Washington Inst. Fgn. Affairs, Nat. Gallery (collectors com. 1993-95), Gerrard Soc., Met. Club (Washington), Phi Beta Kappa, Alpha Epsilon Delta.

PATTON, JOANNA, advertising agency owner; b. Quincy, Ill., Dec. 20, 1946; d. John H. and Jane Vandike P. Student Stetson U., 1964-66, Fla. State U., 1966-67. Para legal, Miami, Fla., 1968-74; exec. asst. Louis Nizer, Atty., N.Y.C., 1974-77; adminstrv. asst. to pres. Constant, N.Y.C., 1977-78, mgr. pub. rels., 1978, dir. pub. rels., 1978-79, mktg. dir., 1980-81; owner Joanna Patton Advt., N.Y.C., 1982-83; ptnr. Levinger & Patton, N.Y.C., 1983-86, Lotas Minard Patton McIver, Inc. 1986—. Hon. co-chair Cannes Advt. Film Festival Gala. Mem. Fashion Group, Advt. Women N.Y. Office: Lotas Minard Patton McIver 152 W 57th St New York NY 10019

PATTON, JOËLLE DELBOURGO, publishing executive; b. Alexandria, Egypt, Sept. 10, 1953; came to U.S., 1960; d. Edward Daniel and J. Andrée (Domergue) Delbourgo; m. Lewis Foster Patton, May 16, 1976; children: Caroline Emily, Andrew David. Student, Vassar Coll., 1970-72; BA, Williams Coll., 1974; MA, Columbia U., 1975. Editorial asst. Bantam Books, N.Y.C., 1975-76; assoc. editor, 1976-78, assoc. editor, 1978-80; sr. editor Ballantine Del Rey Fawcett Ivy Books div. Random House Inc., N.Y.C., 1980-81, exec. editor, 1981-83, editor-in-chief, 1983-86, v.p., editor-in-chief trade books, 1986-89, editor-in-chief hard cover books and trade paperback, 1990—. Columbia faculty fellowship, 1974-75. Mem. Phi Beta Kappa. Office: Ballantine Del Rey Fawcett Ivy Books Div of Random House Inc 201 E 50th St New York NY 10022-7703

PATTON, JOSEPH DONALD, JR., management consultant; b. Washington, Pa., Jan. 4, 1938; s. Joseph Donald and Priscilla Ann (Johnson) P.; BS in Phys. Scis. and Math. Edn., Pa. State U., 1959; MBA in Mktg., U. Rochester (N.Y.), 1970; m. Susan Oertel, June 3, 1967; children: Jennifer Ann, Joseph Donald, III. Tchr., Aschaffenburg (W.Ger.) Am. Sch., 1963-64; with Xerox Corp., Rochester, 1964-75, mgr. field engring., 1973-75; pres. Patton Cons., Inc., Rochester, 1975-93, Hilton Head, S.C., 1993—; mem. adj. faculty Rochester Inst. Tech., SUNY, Geneseo. Served as capt. U.S. Army, 1959-63. Registered profl. quality engr., Calif.; cert. profl. logistician; cert. quality engr.; cert. reliability engr.; cert. service exec. Fellow Am. Soc. Quality Control (reliability and maintainability tech. award 1982), Soc. Logistics Engrs. (Sole Armitage medal 1980, 82); sr. mem. Instrument Soc. Am.; mem. Assn. Field Service Mgrs. (publs. award 1981), Nat. Assn. Service Mgrs. (life cert. svc. exec.), Am. Prodn. and Inventory Control Soc. Republican. Presbyterian. Author 5 texts in field; contbr. over 100 articles to profl. jours. Office: Patton Consultants Inc 4 Covington Pl Hilton Head Island SC 29928-7665

PATTON, MATTHEW HENRY, lawyer; b. Carrollton, Ga., July 20, 1936; s. Matthew H. and Mary Frances (Alexander) P.; m. Dianne Campbell, Nov. 24, 1983; children: Melanie Louise, Amanda Elizabeth, John Campbell, Stephen Patton. AB in History, Duke U., 1958; postgrad., So. Bapt. Theol. Sem., 1960; JD, Emory U., 1963. Bar: Ga. 1963, U.S. Supreme Ct. 1981. Assoc. Kilpatrick & Cody, Atlanta, 1963-69, ptnr., 1969—. Mem. Fulton County Bd. Elections, 1967-70, Ga. State Election Bd., 1970-75; chmn. 5th Congl. Dist. Reps., Atlanta, 1975-77, Ga. Reps., Atlanta, 1979-81, mem. Rep. Nat. Com., 1979-81. Mem. State Bar Ga. (bd. govs. 1974—, pres. younger lawyers sect. 1970-71), Atlanta Bar Assn. (chmn. litigation sect. 1981-82), Am. Bd. Trial Advs. (adv., pres. Ga. chpt. 1988-90). Home: 1255 Birmingham Rd Alpharetta GA 30201-2691 Office: Kilpatrick & Cody 1100 Peachtree St Ste 2800 Atlanta GA 30309

PATTON, NANCY MATTHEWS, elementary education educator; b. Pitts., Apr. 7, 1942; d. Thomas Joseph and Sara Theresa (Jocunskas) Matthews; m. Jack E. Patton, July 20, 1974; children: Susan, Steven. BS in Edn., Ind. U. of Pa., 1963; grad. student, U. Pitts. 4th grade tchr. Elroy Sch., Pitts., 1980-91; 6th grade tchr. Brentwood Middle Sch., Pitts., 1991—; sponsor Brentwood Middle Sch. newspaper; coach Brentwood Varsity Cheerleaders, 1981-93. Councilperson Brentwood Borough Coun., 1988—, v.p., 1994—; sec. Brentwood Dem. Com., 1989—. Mem. NEA, Nat. Sci. Tchrs. Assn., Pa. State Edn. Assn., Brentwood Century Club. Democrat. Roman Catholic. Avocations: reading, community service. Home: 105 Hillson Ave Pittsburgh PA 15227-2941

PATTON, NORMAN S., church adminstrator. Pres. Ch. of God Fgn. Missionary Bd., Anderson, Ind. Office: Ch of God PO Box 2498 Anderson IN 46018-2498

PATTON, PAUL E., state official; b. Fallsburg, KY. Grad. in mech. engring., U. Ky., 1959. With coal bus., until 1979, dep. sec. transp.; judge-exec. Pike County, 1981; lt. gov., sec. econ. devel., pres. senate State of KY, Frankfort, KY, 1991—; served on Ky. Crime Commn., Ky. Tourism Commn., Task Force for Workplace Literacy; former mem. Prichard Com. for Acad. Excellence. Mem. bd. overseers Bellarmine Coll., bd. trustees Pikeville Coll.; chmn. Ky. Dems., 1981-83; del. Dem. Nat. Conv.; served numerous terms Pike County Dem. Exec. Com. Office: Office of Lt Gov The Capitol Frankfort KY 40601

PATTON, RICHARD BOLLING, food company executive; b. Pitts., Jan. 8, 1929; s. Melvin Gerald and Anne (King) P.; m. Mary Ann Bickford, June 8, 1963; children—Pamela Watson, Edward Bickford, Richard Randolph, Jennifer Bolling. B.A., Yale U., 1952; M.B.A., Harvard U., 1954. Product mgr. Heinz U.S.A., Pitts., 1958-62; gen. mgr. mktg. Heinz-Australia, 1964-66; asst. v.p. Ogden Corp., N.Y.C., 1966-68; v.p. passenger sales and services TWA, N.Y.C., 1968-70; pres. N. Am. Cunard Line, Ltd., N.Y.C.; also dir. Cunard Line, Ltd., Cunard Steamship Co., Ltd., Cunard Trafalgar Hotels, Ltd., 1970-73; v.p. mktg. and sales, then v.p. tomato products and condiments div. Heinz U.S.A., 1973-76, pres., 1976-80; area dir. H.J. Heinz Co., Pitts., 1980-82, sr. v.p., dir., 1982—; bd. dirs. Weight-Watchers Internat. Bd. dirs. Pa. Economy League, African-Am. Inst. 1st lt. USMCR, 1954-57. Clubs: Pitts. Golf, Duquesne (Pitts.); Fox Chapel Golf; Yale, The Brook (N.Y.C.); John's Island (Fla.). Lodge: Knights of Malta. Home: 340 Shores Dr Vero Beach FL 32963-3904 Office: H J Heinz Co 600 Grant St Pittsburgh PA 15219-2857

PATTON, RICHARD WESTON, mortgage company executive; b. Evanston, Ill., Sept. 26, 1931; s. Robert Ferry and Sue Buckley P.; m. Lynda A. Kruse, Feb. 2, 1971; 1 child, Robert Weston. B.A., Amherst Coll., 1954. Sales engr. Thermo Fax Sales Corp., Chgo., 1958-60; account exec. Nat. Mortgage Investors, Inc., Chgo., 1960-61; sales mgr. Nat. Mortgage Investors, Inc., Pasadena, Calif., 1962-66; asst. v.p. Nat. Mortgage Investors, Inc., 1966-67, v.p., 1967-69, exec. v.p., 1969-73, pres., chief exec. officer, dir., 1973-84, vice-chmn. bd., 1984-90; pres. Richard W. Patton Enterprises, Pasadena, 1990—; pres., chmn. exec. com., dir. Ocean Park Restaurant Corp., Santa Monica, Calif., 1977-88; dir. Cenfed Bank, Cenfed Corp. Bd. dirs. Pasadena Boys' Club, 1963-66; mem. steering com. Amherst Coll. Capital Fund Drive, 1963-66; bd. dirs. Opera Assocs., 1984—. Served with USMCR, 1955-58. Mem. Amherst Coll. Alumni Assn. (bd. dirs. 1963—, pres. 1977-79, 86-89), Overland Club (sec., bd. dirs.), Kroenstadt Ski Club (past pres.). Office: Rich W Patton Enterprises 3644 San Pasqual St Pasadena CA 91107-5419

PATTON, ROBERT FREDERICK, lawyer, banker; b. New Castle, Pa., Dec. 9, 1927; s. Wylie E. and Lena Francis (Gardner) P.; m. Virginia Lee Reehl, Aug. 15, 1952; children: Thomas E., Barbara L., Susan G., Laura L. A.B., Westminster Coll., New Wilmington, Pa., 1950; J.D., Harvard U., 1953. Bar: Pa. 1954. Assoc. Buchanan, Ingersoll, Rodewald, Kyle & Burger, Pitts., 1953-60, ptnr., 1960-83; chmn. Union Nat. Corp., 1983-89; vice chmn. Integra Fin. Corp., Pitts., 1989, now bd. dirs.; chmn. Bank Cons. Assocs., Pitts., 1990—; bd. dirs. Armstrong World Industries, Inc.; adj. prof. U. Pitts. Law Sch., 1978. Trustee Westminster Coll., 1976-91, sec., 1978-93, chmn., 1988-91; vice moderator Pitts. Presbytery, 1987; chmn. Allegheny County Mental Health/Mental Retardation Bd., 1977-80; trustee Montefiore Hosp., 1985-90, Jewish Healthcare Found., 1990-94. Mem. Am. Law Inst., Am. Bar Found., Allegheny Bar Assn., Duquesne Club, Chartiers Country Club, Nauset Beach Club. Republican. Home: 293 Dixon Ave Pittsburgh PA 15216-1207 Office: Bank Cons Assocs 5800 Usx Tower Pittsburgh PA 15219

PATTON, ROGER WILLIAM, lawyer, educator; b. Spokane, Apr. 18, 1945; s. Kenneth Randall and Dorothy (Mostoller) P.; m. Susan L. Budd, June 15, 1968; 1 child, Michael Andrew. BS, Oreg. State U., 1968; JD, U. Calif., San Francisco, 1971. Bar: Wash. 1971, Calif. 1972. Asst. pub. defender Alameda County Pub. Defender, Oakland, Calif., 1972-78; counsel Kaiser Engrs. Internat., Oakland, 1978-79; ptnr. Patton, Wolan & Boxer, Oakland, 1979—; assoc. prof. law Armstrong Law Sch., Berkeley, Calif., 1976-84; adj. prof. Calif. State U., Hayward, 1984-87; assoc. prof. law Oakland Law Sch., 1990—. Capt. U.S. Army Res., 1968-72. Mem. Calif. State Bar (adminstrn. of justice com. 1989—), Fed. Bar No. Calif., Asian Law Caucus, Dem. Lawyers Club, Alameda Divers (pres. 1990-91). Democrat. Avocations: scuba diving, bicycling, astronomy, adventure travel, watching baseball and basketball. Office: Patton Wolan & Boxer 80 Grand Ave # 600 Oakland CA 94612

PATTON, STEPHEN RAY, lawyer; b. Crawfordsville, Ind., Aug. 29, 1953; s. Don C. and Marlene (Miller) P.; m. Linda L. Wilson, Sept. 3, 1977; children: Andrew Caleb, Sean Patrick. BA, Ind. U., 1976; JD magna cum laude, Georgetown U., 1978. Bar: Ill. 1978, U.S. Dist. Ct. (no. dist.) Ill. 1978. Assoc. Kirkland & Ellis, Chgo., 1978-84, ptnr., 1984—; chmn. Lakeview Clinic, Chgo. Vol. Legal Svcs. Found. Mem. ABA (litigation sect.). Office: Kirkland & Ellis 200 E Randolph Dr Chicago IL 60601-6401

PATTON, STUART, biochemist, educator; b. Ebenezer, N.Y., Nov. 2, 1920; s. George and Ina (Neher) P.; m. Colleen Cecelia Lavelle, May 17, 1945; children—John, Richard, Gail, Thomas, Mary Catherine, Patricia, Joseph. B.S., Pa. State U., 1943; M.S., Ohio State U., 1947, Ph.D., 1948. Chemist Borden Co., 1943-44; research fellow Ohio State U., Columbus, 1946-48; mem. faculty Pa. State U., University Park, 1949-80, prof., 1959-80; Evan Pugh rsch. prof. agr. Pa. State U., 1980-82; adj. prof. neuroscis. Sch. Medicine U. Calif., San Diego, 1981—; vis. scientist Scripps Instn. Oceanography; cons. in field, 1950—. Author: (with Robert Jenness) Principles of Dairy Chemistry, 1959, (with Robert G. Jensen) Biomedical Aspects of Lactation, 1975. Served to lt. (j.g.) USNR, 1944-46. Recipient Borden award chemistry milk Am. Chem. Soc., 1957, Agrl. and Food Chemistry award, 1975; Alexander von Humboldt sr. scientist award, 1981. Mem. Am. Dairy Sci. Assn. (bd. dirs 1963-66), Am. Soc. Biochemistry and Molecular Biology, Am. Soc. Cell Biology. Home: 6208 Avenida Cresta La Jolla CA 92037-6510 Office: U Calif San Diego Ctr Molecular Genetics 0634-J La Jolla CA 92093

PATTON, THOMAS EARL, lawyer; b. Nov. 25, 1940; s. Thomas E. and Alice F. (Rodarmel) P.; m. Patricia Mann, Aug. 12, 1965 (dec.); m. Barbara Wood, Sept. 21, 1974; 1 child, David Earl. A.B., Cath. U. Am., 1962, J.D. summa cum laude, 1965. Bar: N.Y. 1966, D.C. 1966, Va. 1982. Assoc. Sullivan & Cromwell, N.Y.C., 1965-69; mem. Williams Connolly & Califano, Washington, 1970-75; asst. gen. counsel U.S. Dept. Energy, Washington, 1977-78; ptnr. Schnader, Harrison, Segal & Lewis, Washington, 1979-94; disting. lectr. Cath. U. Am., 1970-90; nat. arbitrator Am. Arbitration Assn.; bd. dirs. Voice Computer Techs. Corp., Linus Techs., Inc., Elcotel, Inc. Author: Securities Litigation, 1989, Federal Procedure Casebook, 1990; contbr. articles to profl. jours.; editor in chief Cath. U. Am. Law Rev. Mem. Washington World Affairs Coun., 1980—. Mem. ABA, D.C. Bar (founder and chair litigation sect.). Cosmos Club, Internat. Club (Washington), Washington Golf and Country Club (Arlington, Va.). Roman Catholic. Office: Tighe Patton Tabackman & Babbin 1750 Pennsylvania Ave NW Washington DC 20006

PATTON, THOMAS F., college administrator, pharmaceutical chemist; b. McKeesport, Pa., Aug. 14, 1948; s. Floyd E. and Alberta I (Trager) P. m. Denise Pretzer, Mar. 1, 1986; 1 child, Patrick. BS, U. Wis., 1971, MS, 1973, PhD, 1975. Prof. U. Kansas, Lawrence, 1975-86, assoc. vice chancellor, 1981-85; assoc. dir. The Upjohn Co., Kalamazoo, Mich., 1986-88; v.p. ops. Oread Labs., Lawrence, Kans., 1988-90; sr. dir. pharm. R&D Merck, Rahway, N.J., 1990-93; v.p. pharm. R&D Dupont-Merck, Wilmington, Del., 1993-94; pres. St. Louis Coll. Pharm., 1994—. Fellow AAAS, Acad. Pharm. Scis., Am. Assn. Pharm. Scis., Rho Chi, Sigma X. Office: St Louis Coll Pharmacy 4588 Parkview Pl Saint Louis MO 63110

PATTON, WENDELL MELTON, JR., retired management educator, consulting psychologist, college president; b. Spartanburg, S.C., July 10, 1922; s. Wendell Melton and Emily Jane (Harris) P.; m. Martha Jane Matthews, July 5, 1944; children: Wendell III, Leland, Melissa, Brooks B. Student, Wofford Coll.; B.S., U. Ga., 1946, M.S., 1948; Ph.D., Purdue U., 1950; grad., Advanced Mgmt. Course, Colgate U.; LL.D., Wake Forest U., 1961. Lic. psychologist, N.C., Ga. Asst. registrar U. Ga., 1946-48, asst. prof., 1946-48; prof. edn. and psychology Lander Coll., 1948, treas., dept. head, 1948-52; sr. asso. Bruce Payne & Assos., Inc., mgmt. cons., 1952-55; asst. gen. mgr. Shuford Mills, Inc., Hickory, N.C., 1955-59; pres. High Point U., N.C., 1959-81; prof. mgmt. U. S.C., Conway, Coastal Carolina Coll., 1982-87; past dir. Furniture Library, N.C. Assn. Ind. Colls. and Univs., Piedmont U. Ctr., Guilford Tech. Coll., Wachovia Bank and Trust, Jefferson Pilot Mutual Funds. Contbr. articles to trade and profl. publs. Served as capt. Air Transport Command AUS, 1942-45. Mem. Am. Mgmt. Assn., Am. Psychol. Assn., SAR, Sigma Xi, Phi Kappa Phi, Delta Kappa Pi, Psi Chi. Methodist. Club: Rotarian. Home: 414 E Covenant Towers 5001 Little River Rd Myrtle Beach SC 29577-2478

PATTULLO, ANDREW, former foundation executive; b. Omaha, Feb. 12, 1917; s. Andrew and Dorothy Anna (Askwith) P.; m. Jean Harriet Fralick, May 1, 1941; children: Andrew, Douglas Ernest. BS in Bus. Adminstrn, U. Nebr., 1941, D.Sc. (hon.), 1979; M.B.A. in Hosp. Adminstrn, U. Chgo., 1943; D.Adm. (hon.), Can. Sch. Mgmt., 1981; D.Sc. (hon.), U. Alta., 1982, Georgetown U., 1983. Fellow W.K. Kellogg Found., Battle Creek, Mich., 1943-44; assoc. dir. div. hosps. W.K. Kellogg Found., 1944-51, dir. div. hosps., 1951-67, program dir., 1967-71, v.p. programs, 1971-75, v.p., 1978-82; ret., 1982; trustee W.K. Kellogg Found., 1972-82; non-resident lectr. U. Mich. Sch. Public Health, 1960-88; mem. Fed. Hosp. Council, 1963-75; mem. Nat. Adv. Com. on Nursing Home Adminstrn., 1968-69; mem. com. on health careers Nat. Health Council, 1964-70; cons. USPHS, 1962-64, Bur. Health Services Research, Dept. HEW, 1968-78; mem. vis. com. for sponsored research M.I.T., 1976-79; mem. nat. adv. council Health Services Research Center, U. Mo.-Columbia, 1977-82; mem. adv. council Mich. Health Facilities, 1965-72, Mich. Mental Health Facilities (Gov.'s Action Com. on Health Care), 1963-66; chmn. community betterment award com. (Mich. Welfare League), 1962, 63; mem. (Mich. Adv. Hosp. Council), 1960-72, (Gov.'s Commn. on Govtl. Relations), 1954-56, (Adv. Commn. Prepaid Hosp. and Med. Care), 1962; hon. prof. Cayetana Hereida U. (Lima), Peru, 1982, U. Sao Paulo Sch. Pub. Health (Brazil), 1982. Mem. editorial bd.: Inquiry, 1980-81. Pres. Battle Creek Area United Fund, 1963, chmn. fund drive, 1960; pres. Battle Creek YMCA, 1959-60, Nottawa Trails council Boy Scouts Am., 1957-60; Trustee Calhoun County chpt. ARC, 1962-65; bd. dirs. Great Lakes Health and Edn. Found., 1973-74; bd. dirs. Calhoun County unit Am. Cancer Soc., 1976-78, chmn. com. on founds. Mich. div., 1978-79; trustee Mich. Health Council, 1951-74, pres., 1967; mem. Calhoun County Bd. Social Services, 1982-90; trustee Southwestern Mich. Rehab. Hosp., 1982—, First Congl. Ch., Battle Creek, 1982-89. Recipient Distinguished Service award U. Chgo. Hosp. Adminstrn. Alumni Assn., 1955; Tri-State Hosp. Assembly award, 1963; award of merit Am. Assn. Hosp. Planning, 1966; award for advancement edn. in hosp. adminstrn. Assn. U. Programs in Hosp. Adminstrn., 1968; Key award for meritorious service Mich. Hosp. Assn., 1970; Trustees award Am. Hosp. Assn., 1972; Disting. Service award Mich. Health Council, 1973; Disting. Achievement award Ohio State U. Hosp. Adminstrn. Alumni, 1982; George Findlay Stephens award Can. Hosp. Assn., 1982; named to Mich. Health Hall of Fame, 1978; Disting. Service award Hosp. Mgmt. Systems Soc. of Am. Hosp. Assn., 1974; Silver Beaver award Boy Scouts Am. Fellow Am. Pub. Health Assn., Am. Coll. Hosp. Adminstrs. (hon.); mem. Am. Hosp. Assn. (adv. coun. hosp. rsch. and ednl. trust 1960-67, mem. coun. rsch. and edn. 1959-62, life mem., chmn. adv. com. Ctr. for History of Hosps. and Healthcare Admnistrns., 1985—), Mich. Hosp. Assn. (trustee 1949-55, pres. 1954-55, life mem.), Internat. Hosp. Fedn., Mich. Pub. Health Assn., Can. Coll. Health Service Execs. (hon.), Latin Am. Hosp. Fedn. (hon.), Duke U. Hosp. Adminstrn. Alumni Assn. (hon.), Sao Paulo Hosp. Assn. (hon.). Home: 162 Feld Ave Battle Creek MI 49017-1312

PATTY, ANNA CHRISTINE, middle school educator; b. Atlanta, Aug. 25, 1937; d. Henry Richard and Gertrude (Smith) Johnson; children: Robert E., C. Wayne Jr., Christine E. BS in Math., U. Ga., 1959; MA in Edn., Va. Poly. Inst. and State U., 1991. Cert. tchr., Va. Mgr. Steak and Ale Restaurants, Inc., Dallas, 1982-84; bus. mgr. Nova Plaza Corp, Charlotte, N.C., 1984-86; asst. mgr. WoodLo, Inc, Charlotte, 1986-87; food activity mgr. Army and Air Force Exch. Svc., Schweinfurt, Fed. Republic Germany, 1987-89; substitute tchr. Montgomery County Schs. Christiansburg, Va., 1989-91; rsch. asst. Va. Poly. Inst. and State U., Blacksburg, 1990-91; math. and sci. middle sch. tchr. Hampton (Va.) City Schs., 1991—; mem. NSTA/APST Summer Inst., U. Md., 1992; EXCEL coach C.N.U., 1993-95. With Operation Path Finders, Sandy Hook, N.J., 1993. Mem. NEA, Va. Educators Assn., Nat. Sci. Tchrs. Assn. (summer inst. participant 1992), Va. Middle Sch. Assn., Va. Sci. Tchrs., Nat. Coun. Tchrs. Math. Republican.

Unitarian. Avocations: hiking, camping, herbs, wine tasting, cooking. Home: 121 Signature Way Apt 315 Hampton VA 23666-5939

PATTY, CLAIBOURNE WATKINS, JR., lawyer; b. Cleve., Feb. 19, 1934; s. Claibourne Watkins and Eleanor (Todd) P.; m. Barbara Benton, May 4, 1968; children—Claibourne Watkins III, William Jordan. B.A., U. of South, 1955; J.D., U. Ark. 1961. Bar: Ark. 1961. Law clk. U.S. dist. judge, Ft. Smith, 1961-63; pvt. practice Little Rock, 1963-68; asst. ins. commr. State of Ark., 1968-69; trust officer Union Nat. Bank of Little Rock, 1969-77; asst. dean U. Ark. Sch. Law, Little Rock; also exec. dir. Ark. Inst. for Continuing Legal Edn., 1977-86; law clk. 2d Div. Chancery Ct., Pulaski County, 1986-89; of counsel Gruber Law Firm, Little Rock, 1989—; lectr. law Ark. Sch. Law, 1965; bd. dirs., chmn. Pulaski County Legal Aid Bur., 1966-69. Bd. dirs., pres. Family Svc. Agy. of Ctrl. Ark., 1976-81, 86-93; bd. dirs., pres. Good Shepherd Ecumenical Retirement Ctr., 1975—; mem. Ark. adv. com. U.S. Commn. on Civil Rights, 1985-89. With AUS, 1955-57. Mem. Beta Theta Pi, Phi Alpha Delta. Office: Gruber Law Firm 315 N Broadway St North Little Rock AR 72114-5379

PATTY, R. BRUCE, architect; b. Kansas City, Mo., Jan. 25, 1935; s. Charles Everett and Sarah Louise (Pendleton) P.; m. Donna Jean Watts, June 1, 1958; children—Kristin, Jennifer, Scott. B.S. in Architecture, U. Kans., 1958. Cert. Nat. Council Archtl. Registration Bds. V.p. Kivett & Myers (architects), Kansas City, Mo., 1959-70; prin. Patty Berkebile Nelson Immenschuh Architects Inc., Kansas City, Mo., 1970-90; pres. Patty/Archer/Architects/Engrs., Kansas City, 1991-94; v.p. dir. arch. design Burns & McDonnell, Kansas City, MO, 1994—; Mem. chancellors assos. U. Kans., 1980—; bd. dirs. Downtown, Inc., 1972—, v.p., 1978-79, U. Kans. Alumni Assn., 1990—. Prin. works include Kansas City Internat. Airport, 1968 (Design award Kans. chpt. AIA 1974), Truman Office Bldg, Jefferson City, Mo., 1975 (Design award State of Mo. 1976), Kansas City Police Sta, 1976 (Design award Central States AIA 1980). Recipient Disting. Alumni award U. Kans., 1983. Fellow AIA (pres. Kansas City chpt. 1974, nat. dir. 1980-82, nat. v.p. 1983, nat. pres. 1985), Royal Archtl. Inst. Can. (hon.); mem. Greater Kansas City C. of C. (bd. dirs.), Fedn. Collegicos Architects, Mex. (hon.), University Club (bd. dirs., pres. 1990), Indian Hills Country Club (bd. dirs.), Rotary (bd. dirs.). Presbyterian. Home: 3840 W 56th St Shawnee Mission KS 66205-2784 Office: Burns and McDonnell PO Box 419173 Kansas City MO 64141

PATTYN, REMI CEASAR, management consultant; b. Chatham, Ont., Can., Jan. 12, 1922; came to U.S., 1927, naturalized, 1932; s. Achille J. and Marie (Simoens) P.; m. Mary Devine, Nov. 10, 1945; children: John Martin, Drew Remi, Lynn Mary, Diane Marie, Carol Anne, Neal Remi. B.S. in Indsl. Engring. Ill. Inst. Tech., 1950; M.B.A., U. Chgo., 1954; postgrad., Ind. U. Law Sch., 1961. Methods engr. Internat. Register Co., Chgo., 1939-44; acting dir. adminstrn. Chgo. Housing Authority, 1950-52; mgmt. cons. Booz, Allen & Hamilton, Chgo., 1952-56; asst. sec., personnel dir. Chgo. Aerial Industries, Inc., Barrington, Ill., 1956-58; v.p. personnel relations Public Service Co. Ind., Inc., 1958-74; v.p. adminstrv. services Public Service Co. Ind., Inc., Plainfield, 1974-77; sr. v.p. ops. Public Service Co. Ind., Inc., 1977-79, sr. v.p. and asst. to pres., 1979-81; pres. Pattyn & Assocs., Inc. (mgmt. cons.), Indpls., 1981—; mem. asso. faculty Ind. U., Purdue U., 1965-77; lectr. Ind. U. Med. Sch., 1967-80, Bus. Roundtable, 1970-84; chmn. coordinating com. Ind. Constrn.-Anti-Inflation Roundtable, 70-76, co-chmn., 1980-84; dir. State Corp.; mem. nat. labor relations council State Chambers Commerce, 1971-83; chmn. Ind. Council Econ. Edn., 1973-75; trustee Joint Council on Econ. Edn., 1980-82. Chmn. fund campaign Ind. Mental Health Assn., 1977-79; past bd. dirs. Ind. div. Am. Cancer Soc.; nominee for sec. of labor, Pres. of U.S., 1980; commr. Marion County Met. Devel. Commn., 1982-85; adv. com. bd. trustees Indpls. Mus. Art, 1983-89. Served with USNAF, 1944-47. Recipient Outstanding Indsl. Engr. Alumnus award Ill. Inst. Tech., 1974, Alumni award of merit, 1976; Jefferson award for community svc. State of Ind., 1979, Paul Samuelson Enterprise award for community leaders, 1992. Mem. Am. Soc. Personnel Adminstrn. (past pres. Indpls. chpt., chmn. pres.'s nat. council 1977-79), Ill. Inst. Tech. Alumni Assn. (pres. Indpls. 1963-85), Edison Electric Inst. (past chmn. personnel relations com.), Ind. C. of C. (chmn. personnel and labor relations com. 1984-86), Delta Lambda Xi. Republican. Roman Catholic. Clubs: Ulen Country, Arcadian Shores, Sloane Gardens Ltd. (London). Home and Office: 728 Round Hill Rd Indianapolis IN 46260-2918

PATY, DONALD WINSTON, neurologist; b. Peking, China, Sept. 25, 1936; s. Robert Morris and Katherine (Behenna) P.; m. Jo Anne Haymore, Dec. 28, 1958; children: Morris Britten, Beverly Behenna, Breay Winston, Donald Blake. B.A., Emory U., 1958, M.D., 1962. Intern Duke U., 1962-63; resident in medicine and neurology Emory U., 1965-70; fellow in immunology MRC Demyelinating Diseases Unit, U. Newcastle-upon-Tyne, Eng., 1970-72; asst. prof., then prof. neurology U. Western Ont. (Can.) Med. Sch., 1972-80; prof. neurology, head div. U. B.C. Med. Sch., Vancouver, 1980—; sec.-gen. XV World Congress of Neurology, Vancouver, B.C., 1993; advisor London (Ont.) chpt. Multiple Sclerosis Soc. Can., 1972-80; sec. exec. com., med. adv. bd. Internat. Fedn. Multiple Sclerosis Socs. Author articles in field.; Mem. editorial bds. profl. jours. Bd. dirs. London Symphony, 1978-80; chmn. grants rev. com. Multiple Sclerosis Soc. of Can.; mem. exec. com. med. adv. bd. Internat. Fed. Multiple Sclerosis Socs. Served with USPHS, 1963-65. Fellow Can. Life Ins. Assn., 1972-77; grantee Multiple Sclerosis Soc. Can.; grantee Med. Research Council Can.; recipient John Dystel Rsch. award Multiple Sclerosis Soc./ Am. Acad. Neurology, 1995, Sir Richard Cave award Multiple Sclerosis Soc. Gt. Britain and Northern Ireland, 1995, Charcot awardInternat. Fedn. of Multiple Sclerosis Socs., 1995. Fellow ACP, Royal Coll. Physicians and Surgeons Can. (chmn. com. in neurology 1982-86); mem. Am. Acad. Neurology, Can. Neurol. Soc. (pres. 1989-90), Am. Neurol. Assn., Brit. Assn. Neurologists (hon.), World Fedn. Neurology (chmn. pub. rels. com., chmn. multiple sclerosis rsch. group), Alpha Omega Alpha. Unitarian. Home: 3657 W 24th Ave, Vancouver, BC Canada V6S 1L7

PATZ, ARNALL, physician; b. Elberton, Ga., June 14, 1920; s. Samuel and Sarah (Berman) P.; m. Ellen B. Levy, Mar. 12, 1950; children: William, Susan, David, Jonathan. BS, Emory U., 1942, MD, 1945. Pvt. practice ophthalmology Balt., 1951-70; faculty ophthalmology Johns Hopkins Sch. Medicine, 1955—, prof., 1973—; William Holland Wilmer prof., chmn. dept. ophthalmology, dir. Wilmer Ophthal. Inst., 1979-89; mem. Nat. Diabetes Adv. Bd., 1977-80. First recipient Edward Lorenzo Holmes award Inst. Medicine Chgo., 1954, Helen Keller Prize for Vision Rsch. Helen Keller Rsch. Found., 1994; Sight-Saving award D.C. Soc. Prevention Blindness, 1954; E. Mead Johnson award Am. Acad. Pediatrics, 1956; Albert Lasker award Am. Pub. Health Assn., 1956; 1st Seeing Eye Research Prof. Ophthalmology award, 1970; Derrick Vail medal Ill. Soc. Prevention of Blindness, 1981; Jules Stein award for Disting. Ophthalmic Achievement Research to Prevent Blindness, 1981; David Rumbough Sci. award Juvenile Diabetes Found. Internat., 1983; 1st Isaac C. Michaelson award Israel Acad. Scis. and Humanities, 1986; 1st Paul Henkind lectureship The Macula Soc., 1989. Mem. AMA (Billings silver medal 1973), Am. Acad. Ophthalmology (honor award 1973, sr. honor award 1981, pres.-elect 1986, pres. 1987), Assn. for Rsch. in Vision and Ophthalmology (Friedenwald Meml. award 1980, Weisenfeld award 1993), Nat. Soc. Prevention of Blindness (v.p. 1981—, 1st Disting. Scientist award), Am. Ophthal. Soc. (Howe medal 1991), Balt. City Med. Soc., Md. Soc. Prevention Blindness (past pres.), Pan-Am. Assn. Ophthalmology, Md. Soc. Eye Physicians and Surgeons. Home: 2A Slade Ave Baltimore MD 21208-5214 Office: Johns Hopkins Med Insts 600 N Wolfe St Baltimore MD 21287-0001

PATZ, EDWARD FRANK, lawyer; b. Balt., Aug. 25, 1932; s. Maurice A. and Violet (Furman) P.; m. Betty Seldner Levi, Nov. 18, 1956; children—Evelyn Anne, Edward Frank, Thomas L. B.S., U. Md., 1954, LL.B., 1959. Bar: Md. 1959. Partner firm Weinberg and Green and predecessor firms, Balt., 1959—. Bd. dirs. Jewish Family and Children's Service, 1965-71; mem. regional bd. dirs. NCCJ. Mem. ABA, Md. Bar Assn., Balt. Bar Assn., Comml. Law League Am., Am. Bankruptcy Inst., Ctr. Club, Suburban of Balt. Country Club (bd. govs., pres.), Caves Valley Golf Club, Hammock Dunes Club. Home: 15 Evan Way Baltimore MD 21208-1700 Office: Weinberg & Green 100 S Charles St Baltimore MD 21201-2725

PAUGH, THOMAS FRANCIS, magazine editor, writer, photographer; b. Newark, Mar. 15, 1929; s. George Ruel and Gladys (Organ) P.; m. Martha Anne Freeze, Apr. 10, 1954; children—Jennifer Paugh Kopp, Lawrence David. B.A., Colgate U., 1952. Photographer, reporter Ridgewood News, N.J., 1954-55; reporter Bergen Record, Hackensack, N.J., 1955-56; assoc. editor Sports Afield, N.Y.C., 1957-62; managing editor, 1962-67; field editor Sports Afield, Miami, Fla., 1967-76; regional editor Outdoor Life, Miami, 1977-78; editor-in-chief Sports Afield, N.Y.C., 1978-94, editor emeritus, 1994—. Columnist, Sports Afield, 1967-76, editor, The Sports Afield Treasury of Fly Fishing, 1989; contbr. articles to profl. jours. Served to 1st lt., USAF, 1952-54. Recipient Nat. Mag. award, 1987, 92. Mem. Outdoor Writers of Am. Avocations: fishing, hunting, photography, painting. Office: Sports Afield 250 W 55th St New York NY 10019-5201

PAUL, ANDREW MITCHELL, venture capitalist; b. N.Y.C., Feb. 10, 1956; s. John William and Bobba Lorraine (Ice) P.; m. Margaret Rae Batchelor, Sept. 19, 1987. BA, Cornell U., 1978; MBA, Harvard U., 1983. Mktg. rep. IBM Corp., N.Y.C., 1978-81; assoc. Hambrecht & Quist Venture Capital Co., San Francisco, 1983-84; gen. ptnr. Welsh, Carson, Anderson & Stowe, N.Y.C., 1984—; bd. dirs. Wuorum Health Group, Nashville, Lincare Inc., St. Petersburg, Fla., Nat. Surgery Ctrs., Inc., Chgo., Ross System, Inc., Palo Alto, Calif., Medcath, Inc., Charlotte, N.C. Mem. Info. Industry Assn. (chmn. new bus. com. 1987—), Nat. Venture Capital Assn., N.Y. Venture Capital Assn., Lupus Found (chmn. fin. com.), Bronxville Field Club, Siwanoy Country Club. Avocations: tennis, golf, skiing, biking, traveling. Home: 313 Central Pky Mount Vernon NY 10552-1118 Office: Welsh Carson Anderson & Stowe One World Fin Ctr Ste 3601 New York NY 10281

PAUL, ARA GARO, university dean; b. New Castle, Pa., Mar. 1, 1929; s. John Hagop and Mary (Injejikian) P.; m. Shirley Elaine Waterman, Dec. 21, 1962; children: John Bartlett, Richard Goyan. B.S. in Pharmacy, Idaho State U., 1950; M.S., U. Conn., 1953, PhD. in Pharmacognosy, 1956. Cons. plant physiology Argonne (Ill.) Nat. Lab., 1955; asst. prof. pharmacognosy Butler U., Indpls., 1956-57; mem. faculty U. Mich., Ann Arbor, 1957—; prof. pharmacognosy U. Mich., 1969—; dean U. Mich. (Coll. Pharmacy), 1975—; vis. prof. microbiology Tokyo U., 1965-66; mem. vis. chemistry faculty U. Calif., Berkeley, 1972-73; del. U.S. Pharmacopeial Conv., 1980, 90. Contbr. articles to profl. jours. Recipient Outstanding Tchr. award Coll. Pharmacy, U. Mich., 1969, Outstanding Alumnus award Idaho State U., 1976, Profl. Achievement award Coll. Pharmacy, Idaho State U., 1990; G. Pfeiffer Meml. fellow Am. Found. Pharm. Edn., 1965-66, Disting. Svc. Profile award Am. Found Pharm. Edn., 1992; fellow Eli Lily Found., 1951-53, Am. Found. Pharm. Edn., 1954-56, NIH, 1972-73. Fellow AAAS; mem. Am. Pharm. Assn., Mich. Pharm. Assn., Am. Soc. Pharmacognosy, Acad. Pharm. Scis., Am. Assn. Colls. Pharmacy, Washtenaw County Pharm. Assn., Am. Soc. Hosp. Pharmacists, Am. Assn. Pharm. Scientists, Phi Lambda Upsilon, Sigma Xi, Phi Delta Chi, Phi Sigma Kappa, Rho Chi. Home: 1415 Brooklyn Ave Ann Arbor MI 48104-4496 Office: U Mich Coll Pharmacy Ann Arbor MI 48109-1065

PAUL, ARTHUR, artist, graphic designer, illustrator, art and design consultant; b. Chgo., Jan. 18, 1925; s. William and Becky (Goldenberg) P.; m. Beatrice Miller, Dec. 24, 1949 (div. 1973); children: William Warren, Fredric; m. Suzanne Seed, Mar. 8, 1975; 1 dau., Nina. Student, Inst. Design, 1947-51. Vice-pres., art dir. HMH Pub. Co., Playboy, Chgo., 1962-82; also sr. art dir., corp. art dir. Playboy mag.; pres. Art Paul Design; freelance artist Chgo., 1984—; lectr. in field. Free lance illustrator, designer, 1951-53; designer 1st issue: Playboy mag, 1953, Playboy Rabbit symbol, 1953; exhibited in one man shows at, Etc. Gallery, 1949, 500D Gallery, 1965, U. Ill., 1965; organizer, exhibitor: travelling exhbn. Beyond Illustration-The Art of Playboy; museums, Europe, Asia, U.S., 1971-73, Can., 1976-77; author: Vision-Art Paul, 1983, Art of Playboy, 1986; designer PBS-TV title for humorous feature film presentations on American Playhouse; prodn. design cons. (PBS-TV movie) Who Am I This Time?. Trustee Chgo. Mus. Contemporary Art, 1970-86; apptd. trustee by Gov. of Ill. to Ill. Summer Sch. of Arts, 1987—. Served with USAAF, 1943-46. Recipient numerous art awards, 1951 including Polycule award Art Dirs. Club Phila., 1975, Art Direction Mag. award, 1975, Gold medal for Chgo. Film Festival poster Art Dirs. Club N.Y., 1980, Top Midwest Mktg. award Playboy TV Subscription Ad, 1979, 82, Gold medal for exhbn. Beyond Illustration City of Milan, 1971, Profl. Achievement award IIT Inst. Design Alumni Assn., 1983; Art Inst. scholar, 1943; named to Art Dirs. Hall of Fame, 1986. Mem. 27 Designers Chgo. (hon.), Alliance Graphique Internationale. Home: 175 E Delaware Pl Chicago IL 60611-1756 *Design is more than a sense of order for me. It is beauty and common sense. To draw, to paint and to look at art is in the fabric of my life. I enjoy working with ideas and seeing them develop into a reality, after which I am fortunate enough to learn whether they have performed as intended.*

PAUL, BENJAMIN DAVID, anthropologist, educator; b. N.Y.C., Jan. 25, 1911; s. Phillip and Esther (Kranz) P.; m. Lois Fleischman, Jan. 4, 1936; children: Robert Allen, Janice Carol. Student, U. Wis., 1928-29; AB, U. Chgo., 1938, PhD in Anthropology, 1942. Lectr., rsch. dir. Yale U., 1942-44; community orgn. expert Inter-Am. Ednl. Found., 1946; from lectr. to assoc. prof. anthropology Harvard U., 1946-62, dir. social sci. program Sch. Pub. Health, 1951-62; prof. anthropology Stanford (Calif.) U., 1963—, chmn. dept., 1967-71, dir. program in medicine and behavioral sci., 1963-70; cons. NIH, 1957—. Editor: Health, Culture and Community: Case Studies of Public Reactions to Health Programs, 1955, Changing Marriage Patterns in a Highland Guatemalan Community, 1963, The Maya Midwife as Sacred Professional, 1975, Mayan Migrants in Guatemala City, 1981, The Operation of a Death Squad in San Pedro la Laguna, 1988. 2d lt. AUS, 1944-46. Travelling fellow Social Sci. Rsch. Coun., 1940-41, Ctr. Advanced Study Behavioral Scis. fellow, 1962-63. Fellow Am. Anthrop. Assn.; me. Phi Beta Kappa, Sigma Xi. Ethnographic field rsch. in Guatemala, 1941, 62, 64-65, 68-69, 73-79, 83-84, 91-93. Home: 622 Salvatierra St Palo Alto CA 94305-8538 Office: Stanford U Dept Anthropology Stanford CA 94305

PAUL, CHARLES S., motion picture and television company executive; b. 1949. BA, Stanford U., 1971; JD, U. Santa Clara, 1975. Law clk. U.S. Supreme Ct., 1975-76; with Cooley Castro Huddleson & Tatum, 1976-79; with Atari Inc., 1979-85, sr. v.p.; gen. counsel, pres. coin-operated games div., 1983-85; with MCA, Inc., Universal City, Calif., 1985—, v.p., pres. MCA Enterprises div., 1986-89, exec. v.p., 1989, also bd. dirs. Office: MCA 100 Universal City Plz Universal City CA 91608

PAUL, CHARLOTTE F., nursing educator; b. Clarendon, Tex., Jan. 13, 1941; d. William Clyde Peggram and Sibyl (Rattan) Jones; m. Robert M. Paul, Apr. 4, 1964; children: Peter, Lauraine. Diploma, St. Anthony's Hosp. Sch. Nursing, Amarillo, Tex., 1961; student, Amarillo Coll., 1958-65; BS, Syracuse U., 1972, MS, 1973, PhD in Edn. Adminstrn., 1979; postgrad., Wright State U., 1977-79, U. Tex., El Paso, 1983-86. Nurse St. Anthony's Hosp., Amarillo, Tex., 1961-65; evening charge nurse Upstate Med. Ctr. SUNY, Syracuse, 1966-68, VA Hosp. Gen. Hosp., Syracuse, 1965-66; asst. to head nurse Meml. Hosp., Syracuse, 1966-68; nurse IV therapy Community-Gen. Hosp., Syracuse, 1968-72; instr. Syracuse Gen. Sch. System, 1972; asst. dir. insvc. edn. House of Good Samaritan Hosp., Watertown, N.Y., 1973-74; instr. SUNY Sch. Nursing, Syracuse, 1974-75, Syracuse U. Sch. Nursing, 1975-76; asst. dean Wright State U., Dayton, Ohio, 1977-79; assoc. prof. Edinboro U. Pa., 1979-86, prof., 1986—, chairperson dept. grad. studies, 1980-82, chairperson dept. nursing, 1987-89; coord. quality assurance William Beaumont Army Med. Ctr., Ft. Bliss, Tex., 1982-85; adj. assoc. prof. U. Tex., El Paso 1982-85; cons. in field. Contbr. articles to profl. jours., papers in field. Bd. dirs. ARC, Syracuse, 1970-77, Erie County Emergency Mgmt. Agy.; chairperson Lake Erie Higher Edn. Coun., 1972-74, cons., 1987—; mem. Coun. on Aging Com. on Long Term Care, Dayton, 1977-78. Lt. col. USAR. Recipient Unit Citation award CAP, 1968, Excellence in Nursing Edn. award, 1992, Leadership and Svc. award Lake Area Health Edn. Ctr., 1994; Gladys Post scholar, 1958-61, Rodney Horle scholar, 1971-72, Nellie Hurly scholar, 1971-72; grantee HEW, 1977, Wright State U., 1977-78, William Beaumont Army Med. Ctr., 1986, Edinboro (Pa.) U., 1979-80, 91; Nightingale Soc. fellow, 1988; named to Internat. Profl. and Bus. Women's Hall of Fame. Mem. APHA, Gerontol. Soc. Am., St. Anthony's Hosp. Sch. Nursing Alumni Assn., Syracuse U. Alumni Assn., N.Y. Acad. Sci., Assn. Mil. Surgeons, U.S. Nightengale Soc., Nat. Ski Patrol (life), Kiwwanis (bd.

dirs. Edinboro club 1987-95, pres. 1988-89, v.p. 1987-88), Sigma Theta Tau (advisor), Pi Lambda Theta (pres. local chpt. 1973-75). Republican. Office: Edinboro U Pa 139 Centennial Hall Edinboro PA 16412

PAUL, CHRISTIAN THOMAS, retired insurance company executive; b. Southington, Conn., Feb. 11, 1926; s. Scott E. and Magdeline E. (Zwick) P.; m. Shirley Welch, Dec. 27, 1952; children: Colleen Paul Quinn, Cynthia Paul Newman, David, Christine. BS, Yale U., 1948. With The Travelers Ins. Co., Hartford, Conn., Kansas City, Mo., and Cin., 1948—; 2d v.p. The Travelers Ins. Co., Hartford, 1968-71, v.p., 1971-85, sr. v.p., 1985-88; chmn. bd. dirs. Ctr. for Corp. Health Promotion, Reston, Va., Travelers Plan Adminstrs., Inc., Hartford, Travelers Health Network, Inc.; bd. dirs. Resource Info. Mgmt. Systems, Inc., Oakbrook, Ill.. Constitution State Service Co., Hartford. Served as naval aviation cadet USN, 1943-45. Mem. Life Ins. Mktg. Research Assn., Health Ins. Assn. Am. Avocation: golf. Home: 50 Metacomet Rd Farmington CT 06032-1801 also: 59 Great Oak Rd East Orleans MA 02643

PAUL, COURTLAND PRICE, landscape architect, planner; b. Pasadena, Calif., Mar. 11, 1927; s. Charles Price and Ethyle Louisa (Stanyer) P.; m. Kathryn Nadine Knauss, July 5, 1947; children: Pamela Kathryn, Courtland Scott, Kimberly Carol, Robyn Annette, Sanford Elliott. AA, John Muir Coll., 1948; student, Calif. Poly. U., 1948-49. Lic. landscape architect Ariz., Nebr., Nev., Calif. Founder, sr. prin., landscape architect Peridian Group, P.C., Pasadena, 1951—; examiner oral test Calif. Bd. Landscape Archs., 1987—, pres., 1964; lectr. Calif. Poly. U., Pomona, Tex. A&M U., UCLA, Orange Coast Coll. Bd. dirs. Landscape Architecture Found., 1981-85 (pres. 1983). Served with USN, 1944-46. Recipient Achievement award Calif. Landscape Contractors Assn., 1963, citation award Pasadena Beautiful Found., 1969, Landscape Architecture award of merit Calif. Garden Clubs, 1970, commendation resolution Calif. State Senate Rules Com., 1 986, Profl. of Yr. Life Mem. award, 1986, 1st outstanding svc. to industry and environ. award Long Beach/O.C., Meridian award Landscape Contractors Assn., Max Tipton Meml. award, 1993; named Man of Yr. Landscape and Irrigation mag., 1987. Fellow Am. Soc. Landscape Archs. (at-large coun. fellows); mem. Calif. Coun. Landscape Archs. (pres. 1958, Outstanding Svc. citation 1984). Office: Peridian Internat 17848 Sky Park Blvd Irvine CA 92714-6401

PAUL, DONALD ROSS, chemical engineer, educator; b. Yeatesville, N.C., Mar. 20, 1939; s. Edgar R. and Mary E. (Cox) P.; m. Sally Annette Cochran, Mar. 28, 1964 (dec. Jan. 1995); children: Mark Allen, Ann Elizabeth. B.S., N.C. State Coll., 1961; M.S., U. Wis., 1963, Ph.D., 1965. Research chem. engr. E.I. DuPont de Nemours & Co., Richmond, Va., 1960-61; instr. chem. engring. dept. U. Wis., Madison, 1963-65; research chem. engr. Chemstrand Research Center, Durham, N.C., 1965-67; asst. prof. chem. engring. U. Tex., Austin, 1967-70; assoc. prof. U. Tex., 1970-73, prof., 1973—, T. Brockett Hudson prof., 1978-85, Melvin H. Gertz Regents chmn. chem. engring., 1985—, chmn. dept. chem. engring., 1977-85; dir. Center for Polymer Research, 1981—; Turner Alfrey vis. prof. Mich. Molecular Inst., 1990-91; cons. in field. Author: (with F.W. Harris) Controlled Release Polymeric Formulations, 1976, (with S. Newman) Polymer Blends, 2 vols., 1978, (with Y.P. Yampolskii) Polymeric Gas Separation Membranes. Recipient award Engring. News Record, 1975, Ednl. Svc. award Plastics Inst. Am., 1975, awards U. Tex. Student Engring. Coun., 1972, 75, 76, award for engring. teaching Gen. Dynamics Corp., 1977, Joe J. King Profl. Engring. Achievement award, 1981, Holcott Engring. Rsch. award, 1994, Disting. Engring. Alumnus award N.C. State U., 1994, Outstanding Grad. Teaching award U. Tex., 1994. Mem. Am. Chem. Soc. (Doolittle award 1973, Phillips award in applied polymer sci. 1984), Am. Inst. Chem. Engrs. (South Tex. best fundamental paper award 1984, Materials Engring. and Scis. Div. award 1985), Soc. Plastics Engrs. (Outstanding Achievement in Rsch. award 1982, Internat. Edn. award 1989, Internat. award 1993), Fiber Soc., Nat. Acad. Engring., Nat. Materials Adv. Bd., Phi Eta Sigma, Tau Beta Pi, Phi Kappa Phi, Sigma Xi. Home: 7001 Valburn Dr Austin TX 78731-1818 Office: U Tex Dept Chem Engring Ctr Polymer Rsch EPS 206 Austin TX 78712

PAUL, DOUGLAS ALLAN, insurance executive; b. Chgo., Feb. 9, 1949; s. Eugene Frank and Flo Sinclair (Broomhead) P.; m. Pamela DeGroot, Oct. 20, 1984. BS, Rensselaer Polytechnic Inst., Troy, N.Y., 1971; MBA, U. Pa., 1976. Asst. dir. admissions and alumni affairs Rensselaer Polytechnic Inst., 1971-74; sr. mgr. McKinsey and Co. Inc., N.Y.C., 1977-82; v.p. strategic planning Am. Internat. Group, N.Y.C., 1983—; bd. dirs. Fischbach Corp., Russian Am. Investment Bank. Mem. Wall St. Planning Group (exec. dir. 1984—). Home: 284 W 11th St New York NY 10014-2413 Office: Am Internat Group Inc 70 Pine St New York NY 10270-0001

PAUL, ELDOR ALVIN, agriculture, ecology educator; b. Lamont, Alta., Can., Nov. 23, 1931; s. Reinhold and Ida (Mohr) P.; m. Phyllis Ellen Furhop, Aug. 3, 1955; children: Lynette, Linda. BS, U. Alta., 1954, MS, 1956; PhD, U. Minn., 1958. Asst. prof. U. Saskatchewan, Saskatoon, Can., 1959-64, assoc. prof., 1964-70, prof., 1970-80; mem. faculty, chmn. dept. plant and soil biology U. Calif., Berkeley, 1980-85; mem. faculty, chairperson dept. of crop and soil sciences Mich. State U., East Lansing, 1985-94; prof. crop and soil sci., 1994—; vis. prof. U. Ga., Athens, 1972-73, USDA, Ft. Collins, 1992-93. Author: Soil Microbiology and Biochemistry, 1988; editor: Soil Biochemistry, vols. 3-5, 1973-81, Isotopic Techniques in Plant Soil and Aquatic Biology, 1991-94; contr. 190 articles on microbial ecology and soil microbiology. Fellow AAAS, Soil Sci. Soc. Am., Can. Soc. Soil Sci., Am. Soc. Agronomy; mem. Internat. Soc. Soil Sci. Soil Biology (chmn. 1978-82), Am Soc. Microbiology, Am. Ecol. Soc. Home: 4232 Sugar Maple Ln Okemos MI 48864-3225 Office: Mich State U Dept Crop & Soil Scis East Lansing MI 48824

PAUL, ELIAS, food company consultant; b. Michigan City, Ind., Nov. 16, 1919; s. Phillip P. and Esther (Kranz) P.; m. Gloria Payne, Aug. 24, 1942; children—Nancy E., Janet L. B.S., U. Ill. 1947. Exec., div. mgr. Swift & Co., Chgo., 1947-64; exec. operating com. Hygrade Food Products, Detroit, 1965; v.p., gen. mgr. meat div. Cudahy Co., Phoenix, 1966; pres. Cudahy Co., 1966-71; also chief exec. officer, dir.; chmn. bd. Am. Salt Co., Kansas City, Mo., 1966-71, Milk Specialties Co., Dundee, Ill.; ret. pres., chief exec. officer, dir. John Morrell & Co., Chgo.; chmn. bd. Golden Sun Feed Co, John Morrell & Co. Ltd.; dir. United Brands, Foster Grant, Baskin Robbins; cons. United Brands, Boston.; Vice chmn., dir. Am. Meat Inst., ret. Mem. Ariz. Retirement System Bd.; chmn. Investment Adv. Council. Served to maj. Chem. Corps, AUS, 1941-46. Mem. Chgo. Bd. Trade, Chgo. Merc. Exchange, Internat. Monetary Market, Phoenix Country Club, Forest Highlands Country Club, Gamma Sigma Delta, Phi Kappa Phi. Home: 140 E San Miguel Phoenix AZ 85012

PAUL, EVE W., lawyer; b. N.Y.C., June 16, 1930; d. Leo I. and Tamara (Sogolow) Weinschenker; m. Robert D. Paul, Apr. 9, 1952; children: Jeremy Ralph, Sarah Elizabeth. BA, Cornell U., 1950; JD, Columbia U., 1952. Bar: N.Y. 1952, Conn. 1960, U.S. Ct. Appeals (2nd cir.) 1975, U.S. Supreme Ct. 1977. Assoc. Botein, Hays, Sklar & Herzberg, N.Y.C., 1952-54; pvt. practice Stamford, Conn., 1960-70; staff atty. Legal Aid Soc., N.Y.C., 1970-71; assoc. Greenbaum, Wolff & Ernst, N.Y.C., 1972-78; v.p. legal affairs Planned Parenthood Fedn. Am., N.Y.C., 1979—, v.p. gen. counsel, 1991—. Contbr. articles to legal and health publs. Trustee Cornell U., Ithaca, N.Y., 1979-84; mem. Stamford Planning Bd., Conn., 1967-70; bd. mem. Stamford League Women Voters, 1960-62. Harlan Fiske Stone scholar Columbia Law Sch., 1952. Mem. ABA, Conn. Bar Assn., Assn. of Bar of City of N.Y., Stamford Bar Assn., U.S. Trademark Assn. (chairperson dictionary listings com. 1988-90), Phi Beta Kappa, Phi Kappa Phi. Office: Planned Parenthood Fedn 810 7th Ave New York NY 10019-5818 *The ability to plan the number and timing of my children has made it possible for me to enjoy career, marriage and family.*

PAUL, FRANK, retired consulting company executive; b. Germany, Apr. 13, 1924; came to U.S., 1947, naturalized, 1953; s. Georg and Hedwig (Muenz) P.; m. Trudy Maier, Apr. 9, 1947; 1 son, Robert. B.B.A. summa cum laude, Baruch Coll., CCNY, 1960. Acctg. supr. S. Augstein Co., College Point, N.Y.C., 1953-58; controller Werner Mgmt. Cons., N.Y.C., 1958-61; v.p. fin. adminstrn. Werner Mgmt. Cons., 1961-67; exec. v.p. Werner Assocs., N.Y.C., 1968-84; also dir.; pres. ORU Group Inc., N.Y.C., 1973-84; bd. dirs. Treasurer Reliance Cons. Group Inc; cons., 1983-84.

PAUL, FRANK WATERS, mechanical engineer, educator, consultant; b. Jersey Shore, Pa., Aug. 28, 1938. BSME, Pa. State U., 1960, MSME, 1964; PhD in Mechanical Engring., Lehigh U., 1968. Registered profl. control engr.. Calif. Control engr. Hamilton Standard div. United Techs. Corp., 1961-64; instr. mechanical engring. Lehigh U., Bethlehem, Pa., 1964-68; asst. prof. mechanical engring. Carnegie-Mellon U., Pitts., 1968-73, asst. prof., 1973-77; assoc. prof. Clemson (S.C.) U., 1977-79, prof., 1979-83, McQueen Quattlebaum prof., 1983—; cons. numerous cos. including Westinghouse Electric, 1969, 82-83, Alcoa Rsch. Labs., 1976-80, State of N.J., Dept. Higher Edn., 1986, Dunlop Sports, Inc., 1988, BPM Tech., 1992—; hon. prof. engring. Hull U., Eng., 1990—, Dora Jones vis. prof. elec. engring. 1993; bd. dirs. Ctr. for Advanced Mfg.; lectr. to colls. and univs., U.S. and abroad. Author: (book, with others) Progress in Heat and Mass Transfer, Vol. 6, 1972, Metals: Processing and Fabrication, Encyclopedia of Materials Science and Engineering, 1986; contbr. articles to IEEE Control Systems mag., Jour. of Engring. for Industry (ASME), Jour. of Dynamic Systems Measurement and Control (ASME), and other scholarly publs. Sabbatical United Techs. Rsch. Ctr., 1985-86, Hull U., 1993. Mem. ASME (participant and paper reviewer Dynamic Systems and Control divsn. 1968—, chmn. panel on robotics 1985-87), Am. Soc. Engring. Educators, Soc. Mech. Engrs. (charter mem. Robotics Internat.), Pi Tau Sigma, Tau Beta Pi, Sigma Tau, Sigma Xi. Achievements include-patents related to manufacturing automation. Office: Clemson U Coll Engring Fluor Daniel Bldg Clemson SC 29634

PAUL, GORDON LEE, behavioral scientist, psychologist; b. Marshalltown, Iowa, Sept. 2, 1935; s. Leon Dale and Ione Hickman (Perry) P.; m. Joan Marie Wyatt, Dec. 24, 1954; children: Dennis Leon, Dana Sue, Joni Lynn. Student, Marshalltown Community Coll., 1953-54, San Diego City Coll., 1955-57; B.A., U. Iowa, 1960; M.A., U. Ill., 1962, Ph.D., 1964. Social sci. analyst VA Hosp., Danville, Ill., 1962; counseling psychologist U. Ill., Urbana, 1963; clin. psychologist VA Hosp., Palo Alto, Calif., 1964-65; pvt. practice clin. psychology, 1964-65; asst. prof. psychology U. Ill., Champaign-Urbana, 1965-67; assoc. prof. U. Ill., 1967-70, prof., 1970-80; Cullen disting. prof. psychology U. Houston, 1980—; pvt. practice psychology Champaign, 1965-80, Houston, 1980—; psychotherapy rsch. cons., Palo Alto, 1964-65; cons. Ill. Dept. Mental Health, 1965-73, 78-82, NIMH, 1968-78; adviser Ont. (Can.) Mental Health Found., 1968-69, NSF, 1968-69, Can. Coun., 1969-75, VA, 1972, 80—, APA, 1970—, UCLA/VA Med. Ctr./Camarillo Schizophrenia Rsch. Ctr., 1978-93, Alliance for Mentally Ill, 1980—. Author: Insight vs. Desensitization in Psychotherapy, An Experiment in Anxiety Reduction, 1966, Anxiety and Clinical Problems, 1973, Psychosocial Treatment of Chronic Mental Patients, 1977, Assessment in Residential Treatment Settings, Part 1, 1986, Observational Assessment Instrumentation for Service and Research, Part 2, 1987, Part 3, 1988; mem. editl. bd. Behavior Therapy, 1969-75, Behavior Therapy and Exptl. Psychiatry, 1969—, Schizophrenia Bull., 1971—, Jour. Abnormal Psychology, 1972-76, Jour. Residential Treatment, 1983—, Jour. Psychopathology and Behavioral Assessment, 1985—; cons. editor Jour. Applied Behavior Analysis, 1966-77, 81—, Psychol. Bull., 1967—, Jour. Abnormal Psychology, 1970-72, 76—, Psychosomatic Medicine, 1971-77, Psychophysiology, 1972—, Archives Gen. Psychiatry, 1973-74, Behavior Therapy, 1976-87, Profl. Psychologist, 1977-87, Hosp. Community Psychiatry, 1980-94, Biobehavioral Revs., 1980-84, Jour. Cmty. Psychology, 1983, Am. Psychologist, 1983—, Brit. Jour. Clin. Psychology, 1985-87, Nervous and Mental Disease, 1992, Current Directions in Psychol. Sci., 1992—; contbr. articles to profl. jours. Served with USN, 1954-58. Recipient Creative Talent award Am. Inst. Rsch., 1964, Teaching award U. Ill., 1968, 75; rsch. award Mental Health Assn., 1985; listed among 353 best mental health experts in nation Good Housekeeping, 1994; NIMH fellow, 1963-64. Fellow Am. Psychol. Assn. (corr. com. 1965-70, pres. sect. III, div. 12 1972-73, exec. com. div. 12 1974-77, Disting. Scientist award sect. III, div. 12 1977), Am. Psychol. Soc., Am. Clin. Psychosocial Rsch., Am. Assn. Applied and Preventive Psychology; mem. Midwestern Psychol. Assn., Tex. Psychol. Assn., Houston Psychol. Assn., Assn. for Advancement Psychology, Phi Beta Kappa, Chi Gamma Iota. Subject of NIMH sci. report monograph, 1981: Treating and Assessing the Chronically Mentally Ill: The Pioneering Research of Gordon L. Paul. Home: 6239 S Braeswood Blvd Houston TX 77096-3715 Office: Psychology Dept U Houston Houston TX 77004

PAUL, GORDON WILBUR, marketing educator; b. Muskegon, Mich., Aug. 12, 1933; s. Wilbur M. and Ruth Hansen P.; m. Gloria W (Borns), Apr. 29, 1961; children: Christopher G., Bradley A. BS, Tulsa U., 1955; MBA, U. Tex., 1962; PhD, Mich. State U., 1966. Material controller Brunswick Corp., Muskegon, Mich., 1959-61; assoc. prof. La. State U., Baton Rouge, 1965-69; prof., chmn. U. Mass., Amherst, 1969-77; prof. U. Cen. Fla., Orlando, 1977—; lectr. in field; Fulbright lectr., Portugal, 1985, 90, Athens, Greece, 1974. Author: (with others): Consumer Behavior: An Integrated Approach, 1975, Marketing Management, 1991, Marketing Management Strategy and Programs, 1994. Served to capt. USAF, 1955-58. Mem. Am. Mktg. Assn., Am. Inst. Decision Scis., Sales and Mktg. Execs., SW Mktg. Assn., So. Mktg. Assn. (v.p. 1987). Methodist. Avocation: boating.

PAUL, HERBERT MORTON, lawyer, accountant, taxation educator; b. N.Y.C.; s. Julius and Gussie Paul; married; children: Leslie Beth, Andrea Lynn. BBA, Baruch Coll.; MBA, NYU, LLM; JD, Harvard U. Ptnr. Touche Ross & Co., N.Y.C.; assoc. dir.-tax Touche Ross & Co., dir. fin counseling; mng. ptnr. Herbert Paul, P.C., N.Y.C., 1983—; prof. taxation, trustee NYU. Author: Ordinary and Necessary Expenses; editor: Taxation of Banks; adv. tax editor The Practical Accountant; mem. adv. bd. Financial and Estate Planning, Tax Shelter Insider, Financial Planning Strategist, Tax Shelter Litigation Report; bd. dirs. Partnership Strategist, The Business Strategist; cons. Professional Practice Management Mag.; mem. panel The Hot Line; advisor The Partnership Letter, The Wealth Formula; cons. The Insider's Report for Physicians; mem. tax bd. Business Profit Digest; cons. editor physician's Tax Advisor; bd. fin. cons. Tax Strategies for Physicians; tax and bus. advisor Prentice Hall; contbg. editor Jour. of Accountancy. Trustee NYU, mem. bd. overseers Grad. Sch. Bus.; mem. com. on trusts and estates Rockefeller U.; trustee Alvin Ailey Am. Dance Theatre, Associated Y's of N.Y.; bd. dirs. Alumni Fedn. of NYU; co-chmn. accts. divsn. Fedn. Philanthropies. Mem. Inst. Fed. Taxation (adv. com. chmn.), Internat. Inst. on Tax and Bus. Planning (adv. bd.), Assn. of Bar of City of N.Y., NYU Tax Soc. (pres.), Bur. Nat. Affairs-Tax Mgmt. (adv. com. on exec. compensation), Am. Inst. CPAs (com. on corp. taxation), Tax Study Group, ABA (tax sect.), N.Y. County Lawyers Assn., N.Y. State Soc. CPAs Dir. (chmn. tax div. com. on fed. taxation, gen. tax com., furtherance com., com. on relations with IRS, bd. dirs.), Nat. Assn. Accts., Assn. of Bar of City of N.Y., Accts. Club of Am., Pension Club, Nat. Assn. Estate Planners (bd. dirs.), N.Y. Estate Planning Coun. (bd. dirs.), N.Y. C. of C. (tax com.), Grad. Sch. Bus. of NYU Alumni Assn. (pres.), Pres. Council (NYU). Clubs: Wall St., City Athletic (N.Y.C.), Inwood Country.

PAUL, JAMES CAVERLY NEWLIN, law educator, former university dean; b. Chestnut Hill, Pa., Apr. 30, 1926; s. William Allen Butler and Adelaide Sims (Newlin) P.; m. Margaret Morris Clausen, June 25, 1948; children: Nicholas Newlin, Martha Morris, Adelaide Sims. B.A., Princeton U., 1948; J.D., U. Pa., 1951. Bar: Pa. bar 1952. Legal sec. to Chief Justice U.S., 1951-53; asst. prof. U. N.C., 1953-55; asst. dir. Inst. Govt., U. N.C., 1953-55; prof. law, dir. Inst. Legal Research, U. Pa., 1955-63; prof. law, dean and founder of faculty of law Haile Selassie U., Ethiopia, 1963-67; v.p. acad. affairs Haile Selassie U., 1967-69; exec. v.p. Ednl. and World Affairs, N.Y.C., 1969-70; dean Sch. Law, Rutgers U., Newark, 1970-74, prof. law, 1970—; Newhouse scholar in law, 1984—; William J. Brennan prof., 1988—; exec. sec., trustee Internat. Ctr. for Law in Devel., N.Y.C., 1974—; founding mem., sec.-treas. Internat. Third World Legal Studies Assn., N.Y.C., 1980—; adj. prof. Columbia U., 1973—; cons. Constl. Commn. of Transitional Govt. of Ethiopia, 1992-93. Author: Rift in the Democracy, 1951, (with others) Federal Censorship, 1961, Ethiopian Constitutional Development, 1969, Lawyers in the Third World, 1981, The International Context of Rural Poverty in the Third World, 1986. Candidate for U.S. Congress from 9th Dist. Pa. 1958; del. Dem. Nat. Conv., 1960. Served with USNR, 1943-46, PTO. Recipient spl. medal for distinguished service to univ. edn. in Ethiopia, 1969. Mem. Am. N.J., Pa. bar assns., Internat. Third World Legal Studies Assn. (sec.-treas. 1980—), Order of Coif. Club: Distinctive (N.Y.C.). Home: 417 Clark St South Orange NJ 07079-2943 Office: 15 Washington St Newark NJ 07102-3105 *My life in law and teaching about law gives satisfaction because it enables me to direct my energies towards thinking about* social justice, individual dignity, and the possibilities of attaining more of the conditions enabling these ideals. But that satisfaction is tempered by constant realization of my own frailities and the failure everywhere of people, particularly those most fortunately endowed, to be guided by principled thinking.

PAUL, JAMES ROBERT, energy company executive; b. Wichita, Kans., Sept. 10, 1934; s. Harold Robert and Zona Belle (Marlatt) P.; BS, Wichita State U., 1956; m. Julia Ann Haigh, Aug. 14, 1955; children: John Robert, Jeffrey James, Julie Renee. With Boeing Co., Wichita, 1956-67; mgmt. cons. Peat, Marwick, Mitchell & Co., Houston, 1967-70; v.p. fin. and adminstrn. Robertson Distbn. Systems, Inc., Houston, 1970-73; treas. Coslo. Interstate Gas Co., Colorado Springs, 1973-74; treas. The Coastal Corp., Houston, 1974-75, v.p. fin., 1975-78, sr. v.p. fin., 1978-81, chief fin. officer, from 1981, sr. exec. v.p., from 1981, pres., chief oper. officer from 1978, now pres., chief exec. officer, dir.; chmn., chief exec. officer Cosbel Petroleum Corp., 1978—; chmn. bd. Am. Natural Resources Co. Mem. Am. Petroleum Inst., Fin. Execs. Inst. Republican. Methodist. Office: Coastal Corp Coastal Tower 9 Greenway Plz Houston TX 77046

PAUL, JAMES WILLIAM, lawyer; b. Davenport, Iowa, May 3, 1945; s. Walter Henry and Margaret Helene (Hillers) P.; m. Sandra Kay Schmid, June 15, 1968; children: James William, Joseph Hillers. BA, Valparaiso U., 1967; JD, U. Chgo., 1970. Bar: N.Y. 1971, U.S. Ct. Appeals (2d cir.) 1971, U.S. Dist. Ct. (so. and ea. dists.) N.Y. 1972, U.S. Supreme Ct. 1977, U.S. Ct. Appeals (6th cir.) 1981, Ind. 1982, U.S. Dist. Ct. (no. dist.) Ind. 1982, U.S. Claims Ct. 1989, U.S. Dist. Ct. (ea. dist.) Mich. 1989, U.S. Ct. Appeals (fed. cir.) 1991. Assoc. Rogers & Wells, N.Y.C., 1970-78, ptnr., 1978—; dir. officer Musica Sacra, Inc., 1972-81. Bd. dirs. Turtle Bay Music Sch., Am. Lutheran Publicity Bur. Recipient Disting. Alumnus award Valparaiso U., 1994. Mem. ABA (antitrust sect. ins. com.), Assn. Bar City N.Y. (civil ct. com.), Fed. Bar Council (young lawyers com.). Democrat. Clubs: Yale (N.Y.C.), Sky (N.Y.C.), Quaker Hill Country (Pauling, N.Y.). Home: 500 E 85th St Apt 12H New York NY 10028-7406 also: 5 Curtis Dr Sherman CT 06784-1220 Office: Rogers & Wells 200 Park Ave Ste 5200 New York NY 10166-0153

PAUL, JOHN, health care executive; b. 1950. Grad., Indiana U. Pa., 1972; MBA, U. Pitts., 1984. Field auditor dept. auditor, Bur. State Aided Instns. Commonwealth of Pa., Pitts., 1972-74; with Western Psychiat. Inst. and Clinic U. Pitts., 1974—, with med. and health care divsn., 1986—; with Presbyn.-Univ. Hosp., Pitts., 1987—. Office: Presbyn-Univ Health Sys Desoto at Ohara St Pittsburgh PA 15213

PAUL, JOHN JOSEPH, bishop; b. La Crosse, Wis., Aug. 17, 1918; s. Roland Philip and Louise (Gilles) P. B.A., Loras Coll., Dubuque, Iowa, 1939; S.T.B., St. Mary's Sem., Balt., 1943; M.Ed., Marquette U., 1956. Ordained priest Roman Catholic Ch., 1943; prin. Regis High Sch., Eau Claire, Wis., 1948-55; rector Holy Cross Sem., La Crosse, 1955-66, St. Joseph's Cathedral, La Crosse, 1966-77; aux. bishop Diocese of La Crosse, 1977-83, bishop, 1983—. Office: PO Box 4004 La Crosse WI 54602-4004

PAUL, JUSTUS FREDRICK, historian, educator; b. Boonville, Mo., May 27, 1938; s. Firdel W. and Emma L. (Frankenfeld) P.; m. Barbara Jane Dotts, Sept. 10, 1960; children: Justus, Rebecca, Ellen. A.B., Doane Coll., Crete, Nebr., 1959; M.A., U. Wis., 1960; Ph.D., U. Nebr., 1966. Tchr. Wausau High Sch., Wis., 1960-62; instr. history U. Nebr., 1963-66; mem. faculty U. Wis., Stevens Point, 1966—; prof. history U. Wis., 1973—, chmn. dept., 1969-86, chmn. faculty senate, 1977-79, 83-85, dean Coll. Letters and Scis., 1986—. Author: Senator Hugh Butler and Nebraska Republicanism, 1976, The World Is Ours: The History of the University of Wisconsin-Stevens Point, 1894-1994, 1994; editor: Selected Writings of Rhys W. Hays, 1977; co-editor: The Badger State: A Documentary History of Wisconsin, 1979; contbr. articles to profl. jours. Chmn. Portage County (Wis.) Bd. Adjustment, 1976-90; moderator 1st Congl. United Ch. of Christ, 1988-90; bd. dirs. Monteverdi Master Chorale, 1988-90, sec., 1988-89, pres., 1989-90; bd. govs., 1994—; bd. dirs. United Ch. Family Svcs., 1992—, sec., 1994, treas., 1995. Grantee State of Wis., 1974-80; Grantee Am. Assn. State and Local History, 1968-69. Mem. Am. Hist. Assn., Orgn. Am. Historians, Hist. Soc. Wis., Nebr. Hist. Soc. Mem. United Ch. Christ. Home: 2001 Country Club Dr Stevens Point WI 54481-7009 Office: Coll Letters and Scis U Wis 130 CCC Stevens Point WI 54481

PAUL, LEE GILMOUR, lawyer; b. Denver, July 27, 1907; s. Russell Barnett and Mary Ellen (Gilmour) P.; m. Gordon Dodge Leupp, Apr. 14, 1934; children: Jenifer Paul Bode, Mary Paul Collins, Deborah Paul Clemo. A.B., Bowdoin Coll., 1929, LL.D. (hon.), 1978; LL.B., Harvard, 1932. Bar: Calif. bar 1933. Pvt. practice Los Angeles, 1934-42; industry mem. Shipbldg. Commn., NWLB, 1942-46; partner Paul, Hastings, Janofsky & Walker, Los Angeles, 1946-80, of counsel, 1980—. Pres., Pasadena (Calif.) Child Guidance Clinic, 1964-65; Pres. Los Angeles Boys Club Found., 1980—; chmn. Pasadena Council Alcoholism, 1966-68; trustee Boys and Girls Aid Soc. Los Angeles County, 1968-72; bd. dirs. Pasadena's Charity Bank; trustee Pasadena Pub. Libr.; chmn. Criminal Justice Legal Found., 1989; trustee Pasadena Humane Soc. Mem. Am., Los Angeles County bar assns., Sigma Nu. Clubs: California (Los Angeles); Valley Hunt (Pasadena). Home: 230 S Arroyo Blvd Pasadena CA 91105-1507 also: 517 Emerald Bay Laguna Beach CA 92651 Office: Paul Hastings Janofsky & Walker 555 S Flower St Los Angeles CA 90071-2300 Address: 695 Town Center Dr Costa Mesa CA 92626-1924

PAUL, LES, entertainer, inventor; b. Waukesha, Wis., June 9, 1915; s. George and Evelyn (Stutz) Polfuss; m. Mary Ford (dec. 1977); children: Lester, Gene, Colleen, Robert, Mary. Student pub. schs., Waukesha. Appeared on numerous radio programs throughout Midwest, in 1920's and 1930's; formed Les Paul Trio, 1936-37, and appeared with Fred Waring, N.Y.C.; appeared on first television broadcast with an orch. from NBC, N.Y.C., 1939; mus. dir., WJJD and WIND, Chgo., 1941; appeared with Mary Ford on own television show, Mahwah, N.J., 1953-57; host: Edison 100th Anniversary of invention of phonograph at Edison Home, West Orange, N.J., 1977; numerous TV, club appearances, especially Fat Tuesday's, N.Y.C.; recs. include: Lover and Brazil, 1948, Nola, 1949, Goofus, 1950, Tennessee Waltz, 1950, Little Rock Getaway, 1950, Mockin' Bird Hill, 1951, Just One More Chance, 1951, Walkin' and Whistlin' Blues, 1951, How High The Moon, 1951 (Hall of Fame award 1979), Smoke Rings, 1952, The World's Waiting For The Sunrise, 1952, Tiger Rag, 1953, Meet Mr. Callaghan, 1953, Jazz Me Blues, 1952, Vaya Con Dios, 1954, Chester and Lester, 1976 (Grammy award), Guitar Monsters, 1977 (Grammy nominee), The Legend and the Legacy, 1991, The Best of the Capitol Masters with Mary Ford, 1992. Served with Armed Forces Radio Service, World War II. Les Paul and Mary Ford named to Grammy Hall of Fame, 1977; Grammy Achievement award for contbns. to rec., musical instruments industry; named to Rock 'N' Roll Hall of Fame, 1988; named to Wis. Performing Artists Hall of Fame, 1990. Mem. AFTRA, ASCAP, SAG, Audio Engring. Soc., Am. Fedn. Musicians. Pioneer multi-track tape recorder; inventor 1st 8-track tape recorder; inventor sound-on-sound recording; creator Les Paul electric solid body guitars; consultant, Gibson Guitar Corp., Nashville. *To be successful requires hard work, determination, a positive attitude, believing in one's self, a God given talent and luck.* •

PAUL, M(ALCOLM) LEE, psychology educator; b. Shreveport, La., July 13, 1951; s. Francis Malcolm and Ava Aileen (Boyles) P.; m. Stephanie Maxfield, July 23, 1994. BS, Abilene Christian U., 1974, MS, 1977; EdD, Nova U., 1986. Lic. profl. counselor, Tex. Entertainer Six Flags Over Tex., Arlington, 1965-78; dir. univ. svcs. and rsch. Abilene Christian U., Dallas, 1977-82; v.p. for psychol. svcs. Security Rsch. Cons., Dallas, 1980-82; prof. of psychology Amber U., Garland, Tex., 1980—; assoc. prof. psychology Southwestern Christian Coll., Terrell, Tex., 1991—; pvt. practice psychotherapy, Dallas, 1982—; mem. ethics com. Baylor Hosp., Garland. Co-author: The Parable of Man, 1980. Named one of Outstanding Young Men of Am., 1979. Mem. APA, ACA. Mem. Ch. of Christ. Avocations: scuba diving, hunting, music. Office: Dr M Lee Paul 9535 Forest Ln Ste 200 Dallas TX 75243-5959

PAUL, MARTIN AMBROSE, physical chemist; b. N.Y.C., June 29, 1910; s. Martin and Rosena (Sing) P.; m. Genevieve Wells, June 28, 1935; children:

Harriet (Mrs. J. Henry Jonquiere), Dorothy (Mrs. Duvall A. Jones). B.A., CCNY, 1930; M.A., Columbia U., 1931, Ph.D., 1936. Instr. CCNY, 1930-42; research supr. Explosives Research Lab., NDRC, Bruceton, Pa., 1942-45; asst. prof. chemistry Triple Cities Coll., Syracuse U., 1946-48, asso. prof., 1948-50; prof. chemistry Harpur Coll., State U. N.Y. at Binghamton, 1950-65, chmn. dept., 1950-60; exec. sec. div. chemistry and chem. tech. Nat. Acad. Scis.-NRC, Washington, 1965-74; cons., 1974—; Vis. prof. Cornell U., several summers, U. Calif. at Los Angeles, 1957-58, Columbia, 1960-61; Exec. sec. XXIII Internat. Congress Pure and Applied Chemistry, 1971, sec. commn. on symbols, terminology and units, 1967-71, chmn., 1971-73, sec. com. on nomenclature and symbols, 1975-79. Author: Principles of Chemical Thermodynamics, 1951, Physical Chemistry, 1962, (with King, Farinholt) General Chemistry, 1967; also articles. Recipient Naval Ordnance Devel. award, 1946; John Simon Guggenheim fellow, 1957. Fellow A.A.A.S. (v.p., chmn. chemistry sect. 1972); Benjamin Franklin fellow Royal Soc. Arts; mem. Am. Chem. Soc., AAUP, Phi Beta Kappa, Sigma Xi, Phi Lambda Upsilon. Club: Cosmos (Washington). Research on measurement of acidity in highly acid media, nature of indicators, catalysis by acids, thermodynamic properties of solutions, sci. policy. Home: 1772 Horatio Ave Merrick NY 11566-2949

PAUL, MAURICE M., federal judge; b. 1932. BSBA, U. Fla., 1954, LLB, 1960. Bar: Fla. 1960. Assoc. Sanders, McEwan, Mims & MacDonald, Orlando, Fla., 1960-64; ptnr. Akerman, Senterfitt, Eidson, Mesmer & Robinson, Orlando, 1965-66, Pitts, Eubanks, Ross & Paul, Orlando, 1968-69; judge U.S. Cir. Ct. (9th cir.) Fla., 1973-82; judge, now chief judge U.S. Dist. Ct. (no. dist.) Fla., 1982—. Office: US Dist Ct 110 E Park Ave Tallahassee FL 32301-7726

PAUL, OGLESBY, physician; b. Villanova, Pa., May 3, 1916; s. Oglesby and Laura Little (Wilson) P.; m. Marguerite Black, May 29, 1943 (dec. Sept. 1979); children: Marguerite, Rodman; m. Jean Lithgow, Jan. 17, 1981. A.B. cum laude, Harvard U., 1938, M.D. cum laude, 1942. Diplomate: in cardiovascular disease Am. Bd. Internal Medicine. Intern. Mass. Gen. Hosp., Boston, 1942-43; asst. medicine Harvard Med. Sch., 1946-49; clin. asso. prof. medicine U. Ill., 1952-62, clin. prof. medicine, 1962; asst. attending physician Presbyn.-St. Luke's Hosp., 1951-54, asso. attending physician, 1954-59, attending physician, 1959-62; chief div. medicine Passavant Meml. Hosp., Chgo., 1963-72; prof. medicine Northwestern U., 1963-77; med. dir. Univ. Med. Assos., 1973-75, v.p. health scis., 1973-75; prof. medicine Harvard U. Sch. Medicine, Boston, 1977-82; prof. medicine emeritus, 1982—; dir. admissions Harvard U. Sch. Medicine, 1977-82; sr. physician Brigham and Women's Hosp., Boston, 1977-82, sr. physician emeritus, 1982—; cons. U.S. Naval Hosp., Great Lakes, Ill., 1959-74; Mem. joint U.S.-U.K. Com. for Study Coronary and Pulmonary Disease, 1959—. Chmn. gov.'s adv. com. Ill. Regional Med. Program on Heart Disease, Cancer and Stroke, 1967-70; dirs. Internat. Soc. Cardiology Found. Served from lt. (j.g.) to lt. M.C. USNR, 1943-46. Fellow ACP, Am. Coll. Cardiology, Royal Soc. Medicine (Eng.); mem. Assn. U. Cardiologists, Am. Heart Assn. (pres. 1960-61), Chgo. Heart Assn. (pres. 1966-67), Am. Epidemiol. Soc., Am. Clin. and Climatol. Assn. Home: 40 Woods End Rd Dedham MA 02026-5823 Office: Harvard U Med Sch Countway Library 10 Shattuck St Boston MA 02115-6011

PAUL, PHILIP FRANKLIN, JR., management consultant; b. Chgo., Feb. 1, 1941; s. Philip Franklin and Dorothy (Hite) P.; m. Anne Catherine Rush, June 12, 1960; children: James Franklin, Philip Franklin III, Patricia Joy. BS in Indsl. Mgmt., U. So. Calif., 1963; grad. exec. program, Dartmouth Coll., 1976. Pres., Communications Equipment Co., Beverly Hills, Calif., 1960-63; supr. communications engring. Autonetics div. N.Am. Rockwell, 1963-66; mgr. field mktg. Honeywell Info. Systems, 1966-70, dir. product and strategic planning, 1970-74, dir. systems mgmt. and engring., 1974-78; mgmt. cons. to electronics industry, Sudbury, Mass., 1979-86; sr. v.p. ops. Adelie Corp., 1986-88; v.p. bus. devel. Computer Task Group, Buffalo, 1988-91, v.p. communications systems, 1992-94; cons. to chmn. Ameridata Techs., Inc. (formerly Sage Techs., Inc.), Stamford, Conn., 1994—, pres., Ameridata Tng. Co., Blue Bell, Pa., 1995—. mem. faculty Northeastern U., 1974-79, Boston U. Sch. of Pub. Health, 1981-93. Author: Management Systems for Planning, 1975, Executive Decision Systems, 1982. Mem. IEEE (past chmn. communications group, sr. mem.). Home: 86 Brandywine Dr Buffalo NY 14221-1804

PAUL, RICHARD WRIGHT, lawyer; b. Washington, May 23, 1953; s. Robert Henry Jr. and Betty (Carey) P.; m. Paula Ann Coolsaet, July 25, 1981; children: Richard Haven, Timothy Carey, Brian Davis. AB magna cum laude, Dartmouth Coll., 1975; JD, Boston Coll., 1978. Bar: Mich. 1978, U.S. Dist. Ct. (ea. dist.) Mich. 1978, U.S. Ct. Appeals (6th cir.) 1982, U.S. Supreme Ct. 1989, U.S. Dist. Ct. (we. dist.) Mich. 1991. Assoc. Dickinson, Wright, Moon, Van Dusen & Freeman, Detroit, 1978-85, ptnr., 1985—; mediator Wayne County Cir. Ct. Mem. ABA, Def. Rsch. Inst., Detroit Bar Assn., Mich. Def. Trial Counsel, Dartmouth Lawyers Assn. Oakland County Bar Assn., Assn. Def. Trial Counsel, Alumni Coun. Dartmouth Coll., Dartmouth Detroit Club (pres. 1980—). Avocations: tennis, cycling. Office: Dickinson Wright Moon Van Dusen & Freeman 1 Detroit Ctr 500 Woodward Ave Ste 4000 Detroit MI 48226

PAUL, ROBERT, lawyer; b. N.Y.C., Nov. 22, 1931; s. Gregory and Sonia (Rijock) P.; m. Christa Holz, Apr. 6, 1975; 1 child, Gina. BA, NYU, 1953; JD, Columbia U., 1958. Bar: Fla. 1958, N.Y. 1959. From assoc. to ptnr. Paul, Landy, Beiley & Harper, P.A., Miami, 1964—; counsel Republic Nat. Bank Miami, 1967—. Past pres. Fla. Philharm., Inc., 1978-79; trustee U. Miami. Mem. ABA, N.Y. Bar Assn., Fla. Bar Assn., Inter-Am. Bar Assn., Fla. Zool. Soc., French-Am. C. of C. of Miami (pres. 1986-87). Home: 700 Alhambra Cir Miami FL 33134-4808

PAUL, ROBERT ARTHUR, steel company executive; b. N.Y.C., Oct. 28, 1937; s. Isadore and Ruth (Goldstein) P.; m. Donna Rae Berkman, July 29, 1962; children: Laurence Edward, Stephen Eric, Karen Rachel. AB, Cornell U., 1959; JD, Harvard U., 1962, MBA, 1964. With Ampco-Pitts. Corp. (formerly Screw & Bolt Corp. Am.), 1964—, v.p. 1969-71, exec. v.p., 1972-79, pres., COO, 1979-94, pres., CEO, 1994—, treas., 1973-79, dir., 1969—; v.p. asst. sec., asst. treas., bd. dirs. Louis Berkman Co.; bd. dirs. Integra Fin. Corp., Ribozyme Pharms., Inc.; gen. ptnr. Romar Trading Co.; instr. Grad. Sch. Indsl. Adminstrn. Carnegie Mellon U., 1966-69; trustee Cornell U. Trustee H.L. and Louis Berkman Found., Presbyn. Univ. Hosp.; trustee, pres. Ampco-Pitts. Found.; vice chmn. Jewish Healthcare Found. Pitts. Mem. ABA, Mass. Bar Assn., Harvard Club (N.Y.), Concordia Club, Pitts. Athletic Club, Duquesne Club. Republican. Jewish. Office: Ampco-Pitts Corp 600 Grant St Pittsburgh PA 15219-2702

PAUL, ROBERT CAREY, lawyer; b. Washington, May 7, 1950; s. Robert Henry and Betty Jane (Carey) P. AB, Dartmouth Coll., 1972; JD, Georgetown U., 1978. Assoc. Milbank Tweed Hadley and McCloy, N.Y.C., 1978-85; ptnr. Dechert Price and Rhoads, N.Y.C., 1986-89; counsel Rockefeller & Co., Inc., N.Y.C., 1995—, atty., 1995—. Home: 310 E 46th St #9B New York NY 10017 Office: Rockefeller & Co Inc 30 Rockefeller Plz New York NY 10112

PAUL, ROBERT DAVID, management consultant; b. N.Y.C., Nov. 1, 1928; s. Joseph Wolf and Freda (Sturm) P.; m. Eve Weinschenker, Apr. 9, 1952; children: Jeremy Ralph, Sarah Elizabeth. BS in Engring., U. Mich., 1950. Administv. asst. Martin E. Segal Co., N.Y.C., 1950; naval architect Gibbs & Cox, N.Y.C., 1951; with The Segal Co., N.Y.C., 1953—, pres., 1967-76, vice chmn., 1977-91, chmn., 1991-94; dir., cons. Segal Co., N.Y.C., 1994—; trustee Employee Benefit Rsch. Inst., Washington, 1978-94, chair fellow com., 1994; bd. dirs. Wiss, Janey, Elstner Assocs., Northbrook, Ill., Empire Blue Cross Blue Shield, Theater for a New Audience. Contbr. articles to profl. jours. Cpl. U.S. Army, 1951-53. Mem. Soc. Human Resources Mgmt., Am. Compensation Assn., Am. Benefits Conf., Internat. Found. Employee Benefit Plans (past chmn. corp. com.), Univ. Club. Avocations: naval and mil. history, jazz piano. Office: The Segal Co 1 Park Ave New York NY 10016-5802

PAUL, ROBERT DENNIS, lawyer; b. Worcester, Mass., June 29, 1941; s. Alexander and Margaret M. (Connelly) P. BA summa cum laude, Boston Coll., 1963; LLB, Harvard Law Sch., 1966; LLM, NYU Grad. Sch. Law,

1967. Bar: D.C. 1968, Mass. 1970, U.S. Dist. Ct. Mass. 1970, U.S. Ct. Appeals (1st cir.) 1971, U.S. Supreme Ct. 1975, U.S. Ct. Appeals (5th cir.) 1978, U.S. Ct. Appeals (9th cir.) 1985, U.S. Ct. Appeals (D.C. cir.) 1988, U.S. Dist. Ct. Md. 1989, U.S. Ct. Appeals (4th cir.) 1990. Trial atty. U.S. Dept. Justice, Washington, 1967-70; assoc. Goodwin, Procter & Hoar, Boston, 1970-76, ptnr., 1976-86; gen. counsel FTC, Washington, 1986-88; ptnr. Shaw, Pittman, Potts & Trowbridge, Washington, 1988—; bd. dirs. Tel America Media, Inc., Phila. Mem. Acton Conservation Com., Mass., 1976. Mem. ABA (vice chmn. 1989-90, coun. 1986-89, program com. chmn. 1984-86, publ. chmn. 1983-84, antitrust sect.), D.C. Bar Assn., Bar Assn. of D.C., Fed. Bar Assn., New Eng. Antitrust Conf. (chmn., spkr. 1974-93), Longwood Cricket Club (Chestnut Hill, Mass.), City Club (Washington), Tower Club (Vienna, Va.). Republican. Roman Catholic. Avocations: tennis, scuba diving, skiing. Office: Shaw Pittman Potts & Trowbridge 2300 N St NW Washington DC 20037-1122

PAUL, ROBERT GREGORY, electronic company executive; b. Rockford, Ill., Mar. 5, 1942; s. George A. and Leona (Mueller) P.; m. Margaret Kennedy, June 22, 1984; children: Katherine, Robert, Andrew. B.S.M.E., U. Wis., 1964; M.B.A., Stanford U., 1966. Asst. treas. The Allen Group Inc., Melville, N.Y., 1971-73, treas., 1973-74, v.p.-treas., 1974-76; v.p. fin. Antenna Specialists Co., Cleve., 1976-77, v.p. ops., 1977-78, pres., 1978—. Home: 1965 Mornington Ln Apt 14 Cleveland OH 44106-2871 Office: Antenna Specialists Co 30500 Bruce Industrial Pky Cleveland OH 44139-3996 Other: Allen Group Inc 25101 Chagrin Blvd # 350 Beachwood OH 44122-5619

PAUL, ROLAND ARTHUR, lawyer; b. Memphis, Jan. 19, 1937; s. Rol and Hattye (Mincer) P.; m. Barbara Schlesinger, June 10, 1962; children: Deborah Lynn, Arthur Eliot. B.A. summa cum laude, Yale U., 1958; LL.B. magna cum laude, Harvard U., 1961. Bar: N.Y. 1962, Mich. 1978, Conn. 1989. Law clk. to judge U.S. Ct. Appeals, 1961-62; fgn. affairs officer, spl. asst. to gen. counsel Dept. Def., 1962-64; assoc. firm Cravath, Swaine & Moore, N.Y.C., 1964-69; counsel fgn. relations subcom. security commitments U.S. Senate, 1969-71; assoc. firm Simpson Thacher Bartlett, N.Y.C., 1971-73; v.p., gen. counsel Howmet Corp., Greenwich, Conn., 1976—; v.p., gen. counsel, dir. Pechiney Corp., Greenwich, Conn., 1984—. Author: American Military Commitments Abroad. Mem. Council Fgn. Relations, Am. Bar Assn., Mich. Bar Assn. Home: 8 Ellery Ln Westport CT 06880-5202 Office: Pechiney Corp 475 Steamboat Rd Greenwich CT 06830-7144

PAUL, RONALD NEALE, management consultant; b. Chgo., July 22, 1934; s. David Edward and Frances (Kusel) P.; m. Nona Maria Moore, Dec. 27, 1964 (div. Oct. 1981); children: Lisa, Karen, Brenda; m. Georgeann Elizabeth Lapkoff, Apr. 10, 1982. BS in Indsl. Engring., Northwestern U., 1957, MBA, 1958. Asst. to pres. Victor Comptometer Co., Chgo., 1958-64; cons. Corplan, Chgo., 1964-66; pres. Technomic Inc., Chgo., 1966—; mng. ptnr. L/P Ptnrs., Chgo., 1978—; bd. dirs. Summit Restaurants, Salt Lake City. Co-author: The 101 Best Performing Companies in America, 1986, Winning the Chain Restaurant Game, 1994. Mem. Am. Mktg. Assn., Am. Mgmt. Assn., Planners Forum, Pres.'s Assn., Beta Gamma Sigma. Avocations: reading, racquetball. Office: Technomic Inc 300 S Riverside Plz Ste 1940 Chicago IL 60606-6613

PAUL, RONALD STANLEY, research institute executive; b. Olympia, Wash., Jan. 19, 1923; s. Adolph and Olga (Klapstein) P.; m. Margery Jean Pengra, June 5, 1944; children: Kathleen Paul Crosby, Robert S., James N. Student, Linfield Coll., 1940-41, Reed Coll., 1943-44, Harvard U., 1945; BS, U. Oreg., 1947, MS, 1949, PhD, 1951. Physicist, research mgr. Gen. Electric Co., Richland, Wash., 1951-64; asso. dir. Battelle N.W. Labs., Richland, 1965-68; dir. Battelle N.W. Labs., 1971-72, Battelle Seattle Research Ctr., 1969-70; v.p. ops. Battelle Meml. Inst., Columbus, Ohio, 1973-76, sr. v.p., 1976-78, exec. v.p., 1978-81, pres. 1981-87, chief exec. officer, 1984-87, assoc. trustee, 1986-92; lectr. modern physics Center for Grad. Studies, Richland, 1951-62; IAEA cons. to Japan, 1962. Contbr. articles to profl. jours. Trustee Linfield Coll., 1970-73, Denison U., 1982-88, Oreg. Mus. Sci. and Industry, 1971-72, Columbus Ctr. Sci. and Industry, 1973-87, Columbus Cancer Clinic, 1974-87, Columbus Children's Hosp. Research Found., 1975-87, Franklin U., 1987; trustee Pacific Sci. Ctr., 1969-74, Found. assoc., 1989—; v.p. exec. bd. Cen. Ohio council Boy Scouts Am., 1976-87; mem. exec. bd. of fellows Seattle-Pacific Coll., 1970-73; bd. overseers Acad. for Contemporary Problems, 1971-75; mem. nat. adv. bd. Am. U., 1982-86, Ohio State U. Found., 1985-87; bd. dirs. Edward Lowe Found., 1985—. Served with USAAF, 1943-46. Recipient Silver Beaver award Boy Scouts Am., 1986. Mem. Am. Phys. Soc., Am. Nuclear Soc., Sigma Xi, Sigma Pi Sigma, Pi Mu Epsilon. Republican. Presbyterian. Home: 7706 173rd St SW Edmonds WA 98026-5018

PAUL, SHERMAN, retired English language educator; b. Cleve., Aug. 26, 1920; s. Jacob and Gertrude (Leavitt) P.; m. Grace McDowell, May 1, 1943; children—Jared, Meredith, Erica, Jeremy. B.A., U. Iowa, 1941; M.A., Harvard, 1948, Ph.D., 1950. Instr. English U. Iowa, 1946; teaching fellow Harvard U., 1948-50, instr., tutor, 1950-52; asst. prof. U. Ill., Urbana, 1952-55; assoc. prof. U. Ill., 1955-57, prof., 1957-67; past mem. Center for Advanced Study, U. Ill.; M.F. Carpenter prof. U. Iowa, Iowa City, 1967-74; Carver disting. prof. U. Iowa, 1974-88; vis. prof. U. Vienna, Austria, 1957-58; Fulbright lectr., 1957-58. Author: Emerson's Angle of Vision, 1952, The Shores of America, 1958, Louis Sullivan, 1962, Edmund Wilson, 1965, Randolph Bourne, 1966, The Music of Survival, 1968, Hart's Bridge, 1972, Repossessing and Renewing, 1976, Olson's Push, 1978, The Lost America of Love, 1981, In Search of the Primitive, 1986, In Love with the Gratuitous, 1987, Hewing to Experience, 1989; For Love of the World, 1992; mem. editorial bd. Am. Lit., 1975—; mem. adv. com. PMLA, 1973-77. Served to capt. USAAF, 1942-46, PTO. Recipient Bowdoin prize Harvard, 1950; Ford Found. fellow, 1952; Guggenheim fellow, 1963-64. Mem. Modern Lang. Assn. Am., Phi Beta Kappa. Home: 3834 Morningside Ln SE Bemidji MN 56601-7323

PAUL, STEPHEN HOWARD, lawyer; b. Indpls., June 28, 1947; s. Alfred and Sophia (Nahmias) P.; m. Deborah Lynn Dorman, Jan. 22, 1969; children: Gabriel, Jonathan. AB, Ind. U., 1969, JD, 1972. Bar: Ind. 1972, U.S. Dist. Ct. (so. dist.) Ind. 1972. Assoc. Baker & Daniels, Indpls., 1972-78, ptnr., 1979—. Editor in chief Ind. U. Law Jour., 1971. Pres. Belle Meade Neighborhood Assn., Indpls., 1974-78; v.p. counsel Brentwood Neighborhood Assn., Carmel, Ind., 1985-88, pres., 1988-91. Mem. ABA (state and local tax com. 1985—), sports and entertainment law com.), Am. Property Tax Counsel (founding mem.), Ind. State Bar Assn., Order of Coif. Republican. Jewish. Office: Baker & Daniels 300 N Meridian St Indianapolis IN 46204-1749

PAUL, THOMAS A., book publisher. Pres. Gale Rsch. Co., Detroit, Mich., 1987-90; pres., CEO Internat. Thomson Pub., Stamford, Conn., 1990—. Office: Internat Thomson Pub 1 Station Pl Stamford CT 06902

PAUL, THOMAS FRANK, lawyer; b. Aberdeen, Wash., Sept. 23, 1925; s. Thomas and Loretta (Ounstead) P.; m. Dolores Marion Zaugg, Apr. 1, 1950; children: Pamela, Peggy, Thomas Frank. BS in Psychology, Wash. State U., 1951; JD, U. Wash., 1957. Bar: Wash. 1958, U.S. Dist. Ct. (no. and so. dists.) Wash. 1958, U.S. Ct. Appeals (9th cir.) 1958, U.S. Supreme Ct. 1970. Ptnr., shareholder, dir. LeGros, Buchanan & Paul, Seattle, 1958—; lectr. on admiralty and maritime law. Mem. ABA (chmn. com. on admiralty and maritime litigation 1982-86), Wash. State Bar Assn., Maritime Law Assn. U.S.A. (com. on nav. and C.G. matters 1981-82, com. on U.S. Mcht. Marine program 1981-82, com. on practice and procedure 1982-86, com. on limitation of liability 1982-86, com. on maritime legislation 1982—), Asia Pacific Lawyers Assn., Rainier Club, Columbia Tower Club. Republican. Home: 1323 Willard Ave W Seattle WA 98119 Office: LeGros Buchanan & Paul 701 5th Ave Seattle WA 98104

PAUL, WILLIAM, physicist, educator; b. Deskford, Scotland, Mar. 31, 1926; came to U.S., 1952; s. William and Jean (Watson) P.; m. Barbara Anderson Forbes, Mar. 28, 1952; children—David, Fiona. M.A., Aberdeen U., Scotland, 1946; Ph.D., Aberdeen U., 1951; A.M. (hon.), Harvard U., 1960; D Honoris Causa, Paris, 1994. Asst. lectr., then lectr. Aberdeen U., 1946-52; mem. faculty Harvard U., 1953—, Gordon McKay prof. applied physics 1963-91, Mallinckrodt prof. applied physics, 1991—, prof. physics,

1980—; professeur associé U. Paris, 1966-67; cons. solid state physics, 1954—; Ripon prof., Calcutta, 1984. Author: Handbook on Semiconductors: Band Theory and Transport Properties, 1982; co-editor: Solids Under Pressure, 1963, Amorphous and Liquid Semiconductors, 1980. Carnegie fellow, 1952-53; Guggenheim fellow, 1959-60; Humboldt awardee, 1990; fellow Clare Hall Cambridge U., 1974-75. Fellow Am. Phys. Soc., Brit. Inst. Physics, N.Y. Acad. Scis., Royal Soc. Edinburgh; mem. AAAS, Sigma Xi. Home: 2 Eustis St Lexington MA 02173-5612 Office: Harvard U Pierce Hall Cambridge MA 02138

PAUL, WILLIAM DEWITT, JR., artist, educator, photographer, museum director; b. Wadley, Ga., Sept. 26, 1934; s. William DeWitt and Sonoma Elizabeth (Tinley) P.; m. Dorothy Hefling, Sept. 2, 1962; children: Sarah Elizabeth, Barbara Susan, Dorothy Ann. Student, Emory U., summer 1952, U. Rome, summer 1953, Ga. State Coll. Bus. Adminstrn., Atlanta, 1953—; summer 1956; B.F.A., Atlanta Art Inst., 1955; A.B., U. Ga., 1958, M.F.A., 1959. Instr. art and art history Park Coll., Parkville, Mo., 1960-61; dir. exhbns., instr. art history Kansas City (Mo.) Art Inst., 1959-64, curator study collections, asst. prof. art, 1964-65; coordinator basic courses dept. art, asst. prof. art U. Ga., Athens, 1965-67; curator Ga. Mus. Art, asso. prof. art, 1967-69, dir., asso. prof., 1969-80; chmn. visual arts rev. panel Ga. Council for Arts and Humanities, 1976-77; v.p. Arts Festival Atlanta, 1982, 84, 85, trustee, 1982-93; guest artist Arts Festival Atlanta, 1987; mem. parents council Randolph-Macon Woman's Coll., Lynchburg, Va., 1986-87. Exhibited in one man shows at Ga. Mus. Art, 1959, Atlanta Art Assn., 1959, Unitarian Gallery, Kansas City, 1960, Palmer Gallery, Kansas City, 1965, Heath Gallery, Atlanta, 1976, Hunter Mus. Art, Chattanooga, 1976, Forum Gallery, N.Y.C., 1977, Madison (Ga.) Morgan Cultural Ctr., 1980, Columbus (Ga.) Mus. Arts and Scis., 1980, Macon (Ga.) Mus. Arts and Sci., 1980, Banks Haley Gallery, Albany, Ga., 1980, Augusta Richmond County Mus., 1980, Heath Gallery, Atlanta, 1982, Moon Gallery, Berry Coll., Rome, Ga., 1983, Bathhouse Gallery, Atlanta, 1987, MIA Gallery, Seattle, 1988, Valencia C.C., Orlando, Fla., 1991, numerous site-specific installations, 1986-87; exhibited group shows, New Arts Gallery, Atlanta, 1961, Kansas City Art Inst., 1960-64, Park Coll., 1960, Mulvane Art Ctr., Topeka, 1965, Palazzo Venezia, Rome, 1984, Elaine Benson Gallery, Bridgehampton, L.I. N.Y., 1986, Dulin Gallery Art, Knoxville, Tenn., 1986, 1987 Atlanta Biennale, Nexus Contemporary Art Ctr., Atlanta, Valencia C.C., Orlando, 1988, Greg Kucera Gallery, Seattle, 1989, Sandler-Hudson Gallery, Atlanta, 1992, Gasperi Gallery, New Orleans, 1993, Contemporary Arts Ctr., New Orleans, 1994, others; represented in permanent collections Gen. Mills, Inc., Mpls., Hallmark Cards, Kansas City, Little Rock Arts Ctr., Ga. Mus. Art, U. Ga., Art in Embassies Program USIA; (recipient numerous awards for paintings). Ford Found. faculty enrichment grantee, 1978. Mem. Am. Fedn. Arts (trustee 1969-81), Coll. Art Assn., Am. Assn. Museums (council 1981), Lovis Corinth Meml. Found., Ga. Alliance Arts Edn. (dir. 1975-77), Phi Kappa Phi. Home: 150 Bar H Ct Athens GA 30605-4702

PAUL, WILLIAM ERWIN, immunologist, researcher; b. Bklyn., June 12, 1936; s. Jack and Sylvia (Gleicher) P.; m. Marilyn Heller, Dec. 25, 1958; children—Jonathan M., Matthew E. A.B. summa cum laude, Bklyn. Coll., 1956; M.D. cum laude, SUNY-Downstate Med. Ctr., 1960, DSc (hon.), 1991. Intern, asst. resident Mass. Meml. Hosp., Boston, 1960-62; clin. assoc. Nat. Cancer Inst. NIH, Bethesda, Md., 1962-64; postdoctoral fellow, instr. NYU Sch. Medicine, N.Y.C., 1964-68; sr. investigator Lab. Immunology Nat. Inst. Allergy and Infectious Diseases, NIH, Bethesda, Md., 1968-70, chief Lab. Immunology, 1970—; dir. Office of AIDS Rsch. NIH, Bethesda, Md., assoc. dir. AIDS rsch., 1994—; mem. bd. sci. advisors Jane Coffin Childs Meml. Fund for Med. Research, 1982-90; G. Burroughs Mider lectr. NIH, 1982; mem. sci. rev. bd. Howard Hughes Med. Inst., 1979-85, 87-91, mem. med. adv. bd., 1992—; mem. bd. sci. coms. Meml. Sloan-Kettering Cancer Ctr., N.Y.C., 1984-92; chmn. adv. com. Harold C. Simmons Arthritis Rsch. Ctr., 1984-90; bd. dirs. Fed. Am. Soc. Experimental Biology, 1985-88; mem. bd. basic biology Nat. Res. Council, 1986-89; mem. select com. Alfred P. Sloan Jr. Prize, Gen. Motors Cancer Res. Fedn., 1986-87; sci. adv. coun. Cancer Rsch. Inst., 1985-94; mem. com. to visit div. med. sci., bd. overseers Harvard Coll., 1987-93; Carl Moore lectr. St. Medicine, Washington U., St. Louis, 1986; mem. adv. com. Pew Scholars Program in Biomed. Scis., 1988-91; Richard Gershon lectr. Yale U. Sch. Medicine, 1986; Nelson Med. lectr., U. Calif., Davis, 1988; Disting. Alumnus lectr., Univ. Hosp., Boston, 1989; Anderson med. lectr. U. Va., 1990, La Jolla sci. lectr., 1991, Wellcome vis. prof. Wayne State U., 1991, mem. Adv. Com. dept. of Molecular Bio., Princeton U., 1993-94, annual lectr., Dutch Soc. for Immunology, 1992, Yamamuro Meml. lectr. Osaka U., 1992, Kunkel lectr., Johns Hopkins U Sch. of Medicine, 1993; Welcome vis. prof. SUNY Stony Brook, 1993; Benacerraf lectr. Harvard Med. Sch., 1993. Editor: Fundamental Immunology, 1984, 2d edit., 1989, 3d edit., 1993, Annual Rev. of Immunology, Vols. 1-12, 1983—; adv. editor Jour. Exptl. Medicine, 1974—; assoc. editor Cell, 1985—; transmitting editor Internat. Immunology, 1989—; corr. editor Procs. of Royal Soc. Series B, 1989-93; mem. editorial bd. Molecular Biology of the Cell, 1990-92; contbg. editor Proceedings of the Nat. Acad. Scis. U.S.A., 1992-94; contbr. numerous articles to profl. jours. Served with USPHS, 1962-64, 75—. Alumni Founders' prize Tex. Instruments Found., Dallas, 1979, Alumni medallion SUNY-Downstate Med. Ctr., 1981, Disting. Svc. medal USPHS, 1985, 3M Life Scis. award, 1988, Tovi Comet-Wallerstein prize CAIR Inst., Bar-Ilan U., 1992, 6th Ann. award for excellence in immunologic rsch. Duke U., 1993, Alumni honors Bklyn. Coll., 1994. Fellow Am. Acad. Arts and Scis.; mem. NAS, Inst. Medicine NAS, Am. Soc. Clin. Investigation (pres. 1980-81), Am. Assn. Immunologists (pres. 1986-87), Assn. Am. Physicians, Scandinavian Soc. Immunology (hon.). Office: NIH Bldg 31 Rm 4C02 31 Center Dr MSC 2340 Bethesda MD 20892-2340

PAUL, WILLIAM F., manufacturing company executive. Previously pres., chief exec. officer Sikorsky Aircraft, Stratford, Conn.; now sr. v.p. defense and space systems United Techs. Corp., Hartford, Conn. Office: United Techs Co United Techs Bldg Hartford CT 06101

PAUL, WILLIAM GEORGE, lawyer; b. Pauls Valley, Okla., Nov. 25, 1930; s. Homer and Helen (Lafferty) P.; m. Barbara Elaine Brite, Sept. 27, 1963; children—George Lynn, Alison Elise, Laura Elaine, William Stephen. B.A., U. Okla., 1952, LL.B., 1956. Bar: Okla. bar 1956. Pvt. practice law Norman, 1956; ptnr. Oklahoma City, 1957-84; partner Crowe & Dunlevy, 1962-84; sr. v.p., gen. counsel Phillips Petroleum Co., Bartlesville, Okla., 1984—; assoc. prof. law Oklahoma City U., 1964-68; adv. bd. Martindale Hubbell, 1990—. Author: (with Earl Sneed) Vernon's Oklahoma Practice, 1965. Bd. dirs. Nat. Ctr. for State Cts., 1993—, Am. Bar Endowment, 1986—. 1st lt. USMCR, 1952-54. Named Outstanding Young Man Oklahoma City, 1965, Outstanding Young Oklahoman, 1966. Fellow Am. Bar Found. (chmn. 1991), Am. Coll. Trial Lawyers; mem. ABA, Okla. Bar Assn. (pres. 1976), Oklahoma County Bar Assn. (past pres.), Nat. Conf. Bar Pres. (pres. 1986), U. Okla. Alumni Assn. (pres. 1973), Order of Coif, Phi Beta Kappa, Phi Delta Phi, Delta Sigma Rho. Democrat. Presbyterian. Home: 1800 Country Club Rd Bartlesville OK 74006-6205 Office: Phillips Petroleum Co 1219 Adams Bldg Bartlesville OK 74004

PAUL, WILLIAM MCCANN, lawyer; b. Cambridge, Mass., Feb. 9, 1951; s. Kenneth William and Mary Jean (Lamson) P.; m. Janet Anne Forest, Feb. 25, 1984; children: Emily L'Engle, Andrew Angwin, Elizabeth Seton. Student, U. Freiburg, Fed. Republic of Germany, 1971-72; BA, Johns Hopkins U., 1973; JD, U. Mich., 1977. Bar: D.C. 1978, U.S. Dist. Ct. D.C. 1978, U.S. Ct. Claims 1984, U.S. Ct. Appeals (4th cir.) 1980, U.S. Ct. Appeals (fed. cir.) 1983. Law clk. to judge U.S. Ct. Appeals (5th cir.), Austin, Tex., 1977-78; assoc. Covington & Burling, Washington, 1978-87, ptnr., 1987-88, 89—; dep. tax legis. counsel U.S. Treasury Dept., 1988-89. Mem. ABA, D.C. Bar Assn., Order of Coif. Presbyterian. Home: 5604 Chevy Chase Pky NW Washington DC 20015-2520 Office: Covington & Burling PO Box 7566 1201 Pennsylvania Ave NW Washington DC 20004-2401

PAULAUSKAS, EDMUND WALTER, real estate broker; b. Lowell, Mass., Nov. 16, 1937; s. Vladas and Barbara (Antonavicius) P.; m. Joyce Wagenhauser, Feb. 5, 1977. BS in Bus., Boston U., 1959; M Div., Oblate Coll. of SW, 1976; PhD in Psychology, Sussex U., Brighton, Eng., 1979. Lic. real estate broker, lic. mortgage broker, Fla.; ordained priest Roman Cath. Ch., 1970. Priest Diocese of Beaumont, Tex., 1970-77; psychotherapist

Houston Dept. Pub. Health, 1979-84; pres., broker Vets. Realty, Ft. Lauderdale, Fla., 1984—. Producer TV program Catholic Church Today, 1975. Mem. Ft. Lauderdale Bd. Realtors. Home: Unit 1 N 4250 Galt Ocean Dr Unit 1N Fort Lauderdale FL 33308

PAULES, PALMER L., engineering director; b. Yorkanna, Pa., Aug. 5, 1936; s. Lester B. and Velma V. (Heffner) P.; m. Sandra J. Mellinger; children: Christina, Stephanie. BS in Physics, Dickinson Coll., 1959; MA in Adminstrn., George Washington U., 1973; MS in Engring., U. Mich., 1975. Elec. engr. Bendix Corp., York, Pa., 1959-63, Olmsted Air Force Base, Middletown, Pa., 1963-65; supr. elec. engr. Material Testing Directorate, Aberdeen Proving Ground, Md., 1965-70, sr. elec. engr., 1970-86; divsn. chief, instr. devel. divsn. Combat Systems Test Activity, Aberdeen Proving Ground, Md., 1981-86, dir. devel. & analysis directorate, 1986-92, dir. engring. directorate, 1992—. Office: US Army Material Commmand US Army COmbat Systems Test Act Engring Directorate Aberdeen Proving Ground MD 21005-5059*

PAULEY, BRUCE FREDERICK, history educator; b. Lincoln, Nebr., Nov. 4, 1937; s. Carroll Righter and Blanche Marie (Hulsebus) P.; m. Marianne Barbara Utz, Dec. 21, 1963; children: Mark Allan, Glenn Hamilton. BA, Grinnell Coll., 1959; MA, U. Nebr., 1961; PhD, U. Rochester, 1966. Instr. history Coll. of Wooster (Ohio), 1964-65, U. Nebr., Lincoln, 1965-66; asst. prof. history U. Wyo., Laramie, 1966-71; from assoc. prof. to prof. history U. Ctrl. Fla., Orlando, 1971—; chmn. faculty senate U. Ctrl. Fla., 1978-79. Author: The Habsburg Legacy, 1867-1939, 1972, Hahnenschwanz und Hakenkreuz: Steirischer Heimatschutz und österreichischer Nationalsozialismus, 1918-1934, 1972, Hitler and the Forgotten Nazis: A History of Austrian National Socialism, 1981, Der Weg in den Nationalsozialismus: Ursprünge und Entwicklung in Österreich, 1988, From Prejudice to Persecution: A History of Austrian Anti-Semitism, 1992 (Charles Smith prize So. Hist. Assn. best book European history 1991-92, best book Austrian studies Austrian Cultural Inst. 1992-93), Eine Geschichte des österreichischen Antisemitismus: Von der Ausgrenzung zur Auslöschung, 1993. Chmn. parents' adv. com. Oviedo (Fla.) High Sch., 1981-82. Fulbright fellow, 1963-64, rsch. fellow NEH, 1972, 87. Mem. Am. Hist. Assn., German Studies Assn. (exec. com. 1986-89), Conf. Group for Ctrl. European History, Soc. Austrian and Habsburg Historians. Avocations: traveling to historical sites, photography, golf. Office: U Cen Fla Orlando FL 32816

PAULEY, JANE, television journalist; b. Indpls., Oct. 31, 1950; m. Garry Trudeau; 3 children. BA in Polit. Sci, Ind. U., 1971; D. Journalism (hon.), DePauw U., 1978. Reporter Sta. WISH-TV, Indpls., 1972-75; co-anchor WMAQ-TV News, Chgo., 1975-76, The Today Show, NBC, N.Y.C., 1976-90; corr. NBC News, N.Y.C., 1976—; prin. writer, reporter NBC Nightly News, 1980-82, substitute anchor, 1990—; co-anchor Early Today, NBC, 1982-83; prin. corr. Real Life With Jane Pauley, NBC, 1990; co-anchor Dateline NBC, 1992—. Office: NBC News 30 Rockefeller Plz New York NY 10112*

PAULEY, ROBERT REINHOLD, broadcasting executive, financial executive; b. New Canaan, Conn., Oct. 17, 1923; s. Edward Matthew and Grace Amanda (Smith) P.; m. Barbara Anne Cotton, June 22, 1946; children: Lucinda Teed, Nicholas Andrew, Robert Reinhold Jr., John Adams. Student, Harvard U., 1946, MBA, 1951; DSc (hon.), Curry Coll., 1966. With radio sta. WOR, 1951-52, NBC, 1953-56, CBS, 1956-57; account exec. ABC, 1957-59, sales mgr., 1959-60, v.p. in charge, 1960-61, pres., 1961-67; pres. Mutual Broadcasting System, N.Y.C., 1967-69; v.p. corp. fin. E.F. Hutton & Co., Inc., 1971-81; founder, chmn. TV News Inc., N.Y.C.; founder Nat. Black Network, N.Y.C.; founder, pres. Cablenet Internat. Corp. and Cablenet News, N.Y.C.; disting. lectr. U. S.C., Spartanburg. Trustee Curry Coll.; bd. dirs. Found. To Improve TV; mem. steering com. Citizens Democracy Corps U.S. Dept. State. Mem. Radio-TV Execs. Soc., SAR, St. Nicholas Soc. Clubs: Harvard (Boston, N.Y.C.), Myopia Hunt, Tryon Hounds. Home: PO Box 217 Landrum SC 29356-0217

PAULEY, STANLEY FRANK, manufacturing company executive; b. Winnipeg, Man., Can., Sept. 19, 1927; came to U.S., 1954, naturalized, 1961; s. Daniel and Anna (Tache) P.; m. Dorothy Ann Ruppel, Aug. 21, 1949; children: Katharine Ann, Lorna Jane. B.E.E., U. Man., 1949. With Canadian Industries Ltd., Kingston, Ont., 1949-53; sr. engring. asst. Canadian Industries Ltd., 1952-53; controls designer Standard Machine and Tool Co. Ltd., Windsor, Ont., 1953-54; prodn. supt. E.R. Carpenter Co., Richmond, Va., 1954-57, pres., 1957-83, chmn., CEO, 1983-94; chmn., CEO, Carpenter Co. (formerly E.R. Carpenter Co.), Richmond, 1994—, also bd. dirs.; bd. dirs. Carpenter Co. of Can., Carpenter de mexico, Carpenter Plc., Carpenter S.A., Am. Filtrona Corp., Carpenter GMBA, Mentor Portfolio Fund. Trustee U. Richmond, Hampden-Sydney Coll., Va. Mus. Found., Va. Mus. Fine Arts. Mem. Commonwealth Club, Forum Club, Country Club of Va. Republican. Presbyterian. Home: 314 St Davids Ln Richmond VA 23221-3708 Office: Carpenter Co 5016 Monument Ave Richmond VA 23230-3620

PAULIKAS, GEORGE ALGIS, physicist; b. Pagegiai, Lithuania, May 14, 1936; came to U.S., 1949, naturalized, 1955; s. George and Olga (Pacas) P.; m. Joan Marie Gross, Sept. 7, 1957; 1 child, Nancy Marie. B.S. in Engring. Physics, U. Ill., Chgo. and Urbana, 1957, M.S. (univ. fellow 1957-58), 1958; Ph.D. in Physics (NSF fellow 1958-61), U. Calif., Berkeley, 1961. With Aerospace Corp., El Segundo, Calif., 1961—, head space particles and fields dept., 1968, dir. space scis. lab., 1968-81, v.p. labs., 1981-85, group v.p. devel., 1985-89, group v.p. programs, 1989-94, exec. v.p., 1992—; mem. various ad hoc coms. NAS, 1970, 73, 79, 80, ann. 1984-87, 91-92, mem. com. solar and space physics, 1977-80; adv. coun. geophysics U. Calif., 1973-75, exec. com. space scis. lab., Berkeley, 1978-81; sci. adv. bd. USAF, 1975-82, 91—; cons. Lawrence Berkeley Lab., 1961-66, Office Space Scis., NASA, 1975-82, Los Alamos phys. div. adv. com., 1983—, Naval Rsch. Adv. Com., 1984-86, Naval Studies Bd., 1989—; mem. def. space tech. com. NRC, 1987-92. Author papers in field; asso. editor: Jour. Geophys. Research, 1972-75. Trustee Calif. Mus. of Sci. and Industry, 1994—. Recipient Aerospace Corp. Trustees Disting. Achievement award, 1980; Meritorious Civilian Service award U.S. Air Force, 1981, U. Ill. Alumni Dist. Eng. award, 1992. Fellow AIAA (chmn. tech. com. space sci. and astronomy 1976-77), Am. Phys. Soc.; mem. Am. Geophys. Union, Sigma Xi. Home: 1537 Addison Rd Palos Verdes Estate CA 90274 Office: Aerospace Corporation 2350 E El Segundo Blvd El Segundo CA 90245-4691

PAULIN, HENRY SYLVESTER, antiques dealer, emeritus educator; b. Cleve., Nov. 8, 1927; s. Sylvester and Mary (Zimmerman) P.; m. Florence Caroline Schwegman, Aug. 30, 1952. BS in Edn. Kent (Ohio) State U., 1955; M.A., Ohio State U., 1958, Ph.D., 1964. Tchr. indsl. arts Brimfield Jr.-Sr. High Sch., Kent, 1954-55, Zanesville High Sch., 1955-57; instr. ceramics Art Inst., Zanesville, 1956-57; asst. prof., then asso. prof. indsl. arts State U. Coll., Oswego, N.Y., 1956-63; instr. Ohio State U., 1961-63; assoc. prof., coordinator Indsl. Arts Div., Kent State U., 1963-67; prof. and chmn. dept. design and industry San Francisco State U., 1967-80, prof. emeritus, 1980—; propr. Paulin Place (Fine Antiques and Paintings), Oxford, Ohio, 1980—; vis. prof. No. Ill. U., summer 1965. Served with AUS, 1946-48. Mem. Calif. Tchrs. Assn., Oxford C. of C., Oxford Retail Mchts. Assn., Epsilon Pi Tau, Phi Delta Kappa. Home: 6294 Fairfield Rd Oxford OH 45056-1555

PAULIN, SVEN JOSEF KARL, radiologist, educator; b. Oct. 18, 1926. Miriam H. Stoneman prof. radiology Harvard U., Cambridge, Mass.; with dept. radiology Beth Israel Hosp., Boston. Mem. Radiol. Soc. N.Am. Home: 260 Charles River St Needham MA 02192 Office: Harvard U 25 Shattuck St Boston MA 02115

PAULINO, SISTER MARY MCAULEY, principal; b. Inarajan, Guam, Aug. 24, 1934; d. Mariano Torres Paulino. BA in Edn., U. Guam, 1974; M in Pvt. Sch. Adminstrn., U. S.F., 1992; postgrad., U. Guam. tchr. religious edn., Guam. V.p. Archdiocese of Agana, Guam; prin. Santa Barbara Sch., Dededo, Guam, 1978-81, Cathedral Grade Sch., 1986-90, 92—; coach math Olympiad and spelling bee. Recipient Appreciation award for support of Guam historic preservation, faithful and valuable svc. to edn., commendation and congratulatory resolution 20th Guam Legis., Gov.'s Art award 1989.

Mem. Nat. Cath. Educators Assn., ASCD, Internat. Reading Assn., Civic Ctr. Guam Found., Phi Delta Kappa.

PAULL, LAWRENCE G., production designer; b. Chgo., Apr. 13, 1946; s. Albert and Sally (Miller) P.; m. Marcy Bolotin, Oct. 23, 1983; 1 child, Michael. BA, Univ. of Ariz., 1968. Prodn. designer: (films) Little Fauss and Big Halsey, 1970, Chandler, 1971, The Hired Hand, 1971, A Tattered Web, 1971, Star Spangled Girl, 1971, They Only Kill Their Masters, 1972, Murder Once Removed, 1972, She Waits, 1972, Second Chance, 1972, Heat of Anger, 1972, The Naked Ape, 1973, The Last American Hero, 1973, The Nickel Ride, 1974, Terror on the Fortieth Floor, 1974, The Stranger Who Looks Like Me, 1974, W. W. and the Dixie Dance Kings, 1975, The Bingo Long Traveling All-Stars and Motor Kings, 1976, Sherlock Holmes in New York, 1976, Which Way Is Up?, 1977, Tail Gunner Joe, 1977, The Storyteller, 1977, A Circle of Children, 1977, Blue Collar, 1978, FM, 1978, Friendly Fire, 1979, How to Beat the High Cost of Living, 1980, In God We Trust, 1980, Doctor Detroit, 1982, Rehearsal for Murder, 1982, Blade Runner, 1982 (Academy award nomination best art direction 1982, British Academy award best art direction 1983), (with Augustin Huarte) Romancing the Stone, 1984, American Flyers, 1985, (with Todd Hallowell) Back to the Future, 1985, (with Bill Elliot) Cross My Heart, 1987, Project X, 1987, License to Drive, 1988, Cocoon: The Return, 1988, Harlem Nights, 1989, (with Geoff Hubbard) The Last of the Finest, 1990, (with Hubbard) Predator 2, 1990, City Slickers, 1991, Unlawful Entry, 1992, Memoirs of an Invisible Man, 1992, Born Yesterday, 1993, (with Richard Hudolin) Another Stakeout, 1993, The Naked Gun 33 1/3: The Final Insult, 1994. Office: care Craig Jacobsen Hansen Jacobson & Teller 450 N Roxbury Dr 8th Fl Beverly Hills CA 90210*

PAULL, RICHARD ALLEN, geologist, educator; b. Madison, Wis., May 20, 1930; s. Ethra Harold and Martha (Schaller) P.; m. Rachel Kay Krebs, Mar. 6, 1954; children: Kay Marie, Lynn Ellen, Judith Anne. B.S., U. Wis., 1952, M.S., 1953, Ph.D., 1957. Party chief Pan Am. Petroleum Co., 1955-57; research group leader Jersey Prodn. Research Co., 1957-62; mem. faculty U. Wis.-Milw., 1962—, chmn. dept. geol. scis., 1962-66, prof., 1966—; cons. in field, 1966—. Author books, papers in field. Served with USAF, 1953-55. Hon. curator Milw. Museum; recipient Amoco Distinguished Teaching award, 1975. Fellow Geol. Soc. Am. (chmn. ann. meeting 1970, tech. program com. 1970, 77, membership com. 1977-80, chmn. 1980); mem. AAAS, Am. Assn. Petroleum Geologists (chmn. sci. fair award com. 1980, membership com. 1981-87, vis. petroleum geologists com. 1982-87, pub. affairs com. 1982-85), Soc. Econ. Paleontologists and Mineralogists, Nat. Assn. Geology Tchrs. (v.p. 1976-77, pres. 1977-78), Am. Geol. Inst. (governing bd. 1977-79, sec. and exec. com. 1986-88), Nature Conservancy, Sigma Xi. Home: 722 E Carlisle Ave Milwaukee WI 53217-4834 Office: U Wis Dept Geoscis Milwaukee WI 53201

PAULLING, JOHN RANDOLPH, JR., naval architecture educator, consultant; b. Doniphan, Mo., Jan. 8, 1930; s. John Randolph and Ruth Elizabeth (Braschler) P.; m. Charlotte Lansing Peabody, Dec. 19, 1952; children: John Randolph III, Ruth Frances, Thomas Dudley. BS, MIT, 1952, MS, 1953, Naval Architect profl. degree, 1954; DEngring., U. Calif., Berkeley, 1958. From instr. to prof. U. Calif., Berkeley, 1954-91, prof. emeritus., 1991—; rsch. engr. Det Norske Veritas, Oslo, 1962-63; vis. prof. U. N.S.W., Sydney, Australia, 1975, U. Tokyo, 1979; vis. rsch. engr. Nat. Maritime Inst., London, 1980; mem. adv. com. USCG, 1988—. Contbr. articles to profl. jours. Named Eminent Ocean Engr. Japan Soc. for Promotion of Sci., 1979. Fellow Soc. Naval Architects and Marine Engrs. (v.p. 1985-88, David Taylor medal 1985), Royal Instn. Naval Architects; mem. NAE, Japan Soc. Naval Architects, Richmond Yacht Club, Faculty Club. Congregational. Avocations: sailing, woodworking. Office: U Calif Dept Naval Architecture Rm 202 NA Bldg Berkeley CA 94720

PAULSEN, DIANA, religious organization administrator. Exec. dir. Reformed Church in Am., N.Y.C. Office: Reformed Church in Am 475 Riverside Dr Rm 1811 New York NY 10115

PAULSEN, FRANK ROBERT, college dean emeritus; b. Logan, Utah, July 5, 1922; s. Frank and Ella (Ownby) P.; m. Marye Lucile Harris, July 31, 1942; 1 son, Robert Keith; m. Lydia Ransier Lowry, Nov. 1, 1969. B.S. Utah State U., 1947; M.S., U. Utah, 1948, Ed.D., 1956; Kellogg Found. postdoctoral fellow, U. Oreg., 1958; Carnegie Found. postdoctoral fellow, U. Mich., 1959-60. High sch. prin. Mt. Emmons, Utah, 1948-51; supt. schs. Cokeville, Wyo., 1951-55; from asst. prof. to assoc. prof. U. Utah, 1955-61; prof. edn., dean Sch. Edn. U. Conn., 1961-64; dean Coll. Edn. U. Ariz., Tucson, 1964-84, dean emeritus, prof. emeritus higher edn., 1984—; scholar-in-residence Fed. Exec. Inst., Charlottesville, Va., 1970; Disting. prof. edn. U. Bridgeport, summer 1972; dir. Am. Jour. Nursing Pub. Co., N.Y.C., Am. Capital Growth Fund, Am. Series Portfolio Stock Co., Houston, Am. Gen. Equity Fund, Am. Capital Bond Fund, Am. Capital Convertible Securities Fund, Am. Capital Exchange Fund, Am. Series Portfolio Co., Am. Capital Income Trust; exec. com. New Eng. Council Advancement Sch. Adminstrn., 1962-64; trustee Common Sense Trust Co., Houston. Author: The Administration of Public Education in Utah, 1958, Contemporary Issues in American Education, 1966, American Education: Challenges and Images, 1967, Changing Dimensions in International Education, 1968, Higher Education: Dimensions and Directions, 1969, also numerous articles. Trustee Joint Council Econ. Edn., 1962-70; v.p., dir. Southwestern Coop. Ednl. Lab., 1965-67; bd. dirs. Nat. League for Nursing, 1965-69, mem. com perspectives, 1966-72; dir., chmn. exec. com. ERIC Clearinghouse on Tchr. Edn., 1968-70; bd. dirs. Tucson Mental Health Center, 1968-70. Served with AUS, 1942-46, PTO. Mem. Aerospace Med. Assn., NEA, Assn. Higher Edn., Am. Assn. Sch. Adminstrs., Am. Acad. Polit. and Social Sci., John Dewey Soc., Utah Acad. Letters, Arts and Scis., Ariz. Acad., Am. Assn. Colls. Tchrs. Edn. (Conn. liaison officer 1962-64, mem. studies com. 1962-68, dir.), Ariz. Assn. Colls. Tchr. Edn. (pres. 1972-80), AAES, Am. Ednl. Research Assn., Kappa Delta Pi, Pi Sigma Alpha, Pi Gamma Mu, Phi Delta Kappa. Lodge: Rotary.

PAULSEN, JOANNA, publishing executive. Pres., sales manager Amereon House, Mattituck, N.Y. Office: Amereon House PO Box 1200 Mattituck NY 11952-0921

PAULSEN, SERENUS GLEN, architect, educator; b. Spooner, Wis., July 27, 1917; s. Serenus Justin and Edna Anne (Dalton) P.; m. Virginia C. Habel, Jan. 26, 1944; children: Thomas J., Nancy Lee (Mrs. John Marshall). Student, U. Ill., 1938-42; B.Arch. cum laude, U. Pa., 1947; Diploma in Architecture and City Planning, Royal Acad. Art, Stockholm, 1948. With Carroll, Grisdale & Van Alan (Architects), Phila., 1946-47, Eero Saarinen & Assos., Bloomfield Hills, Mich., 1949-51, 53-57; chief designer Reisner & Urbahn (Architects), N.Y.C., 1951-52; prin. Glen Paulsen Assos., Birmingham, Mich., 1958-69; prin., v.p. Tarapata-MacMahon-Paulsen Assos., Inc. (Architects), Bloomfield Hills, 1969-77; pres. Cranbrook Acad. Art, head dept. architecture, 1966-70; prof., chmn. Masters Program in Architecture U. Mich., 1976-78, Emil Lorch prof. architecture, 1982-85, prof. emeritus, 1985—; Mem. Nat. Com. on Urban Planning and Design, 1971-72; archtl. commn. U. Wash., Seattle, 1968-76. (Recipient 3d prize Bi-Nat. Competition for Design Rainbow Center Plaza, Niagara Falls, N.Y. 1972). Govt. services Cranbrook Acad. Art. Served with C.E. USAAF, 1942-46. Fellow AIA (honor awards Detroit chpt. for Shapero Hall of Pharmacy 1965, Our Shepherd Lutheran Ch. 1966, Ford Life Sci. Bldg. 1967, Birney Elementary Sch. Detroit 1971, Fed. Bldg., Ann Arbor, Mich. 1978, gold medal for 1980 Detroit chpt.); mem. Mich. Soc. Architects, (Robert F. Hastings award 1985). Home: #3 Southwick Ct Ann Arbor MI 48105 Office: U Mich Coll Architecture and Urban Planning Ann Arbor MI 48109

PAULSEN, THOMAS DEAN, naval officer; b. Watford City, N.D., Apr. 14, 1936; s. H. Arthur and Agnes Lillian (Quale) P.; m. Marbeth Hirsch, Dec. 18, 1960; children—Kari Anne, Kendel Ames, Katherine, Avery F. B.S. in Elec. Engring., U.S. Naval Acad., 1960; M.S. in Computer Sci., U.S. Naval Postgrad. Sch., Monterey, Calif., 1970. Commd. ensign U.S. Navy, 1960, advanced through grades to capt.; 1980; weapons and communications officer USS Corporal, Charleston, S.C., 1960-63; navigation and ops. officer USS Theodore Roosevelt, Groton, Conn., 1963-68; exec. officer USS Sailfish, Pearl Harbor, Hawaii, 1970-72, USS Reeves, Pearl Harbor, 1973-75; comdg.

officer USS Whipple, Pearl Harbor, 1975-77; fleet ASW readiness officer staff, comdr. 7th Fleet, Yokosuka, Japan, 1977-80; dir. profl. devel. div. U.S. Naval Acad., Annapolis, Md., 1980-83; comdg. officer USS Blue Ridge, Yokosuka, 1984—. Co-author: Naval Officer's Guide, 1983. Recipient Meritorious Service medal Sec. Dept. Navy, 1980, Navy Commendation medal, 1977, Navy Achievement medal, 1972. Mem. Naval Inst., U.S. Naval Acad. Alumni Assn. Office: Navy Department Washington DC 20350-2000

PAULSEN, VIVIAN, magazine editor; b. Salt Lake City, May 10, 1942; d. Paul Herman and Martha Oline (Blattman) P. B.A.A., Brigham Young U., 1964, postgrad., 1965; postgrad., U. Grenoble, France, 1966. Cert. tchr., Utah. Tchr. French Granite Sch. Dist., Salt Lake City, 1966-67; assoc. editor New Era mag., Salt Lake City, 1970-82; mng. editor Friend mag., Salt Lake City, 1982—. Am. Field Service scholar, 1959; grad. fellow Brigham Young U., 1964-66. Mem. Soc. Children's Book Writers. Republican. Mem. Ch. of Jesus Christ of Latter-day Saints. Office: The Friend 50 E North Temple Salt Lake City UT 84150-0001

PAULSON, BELDEN HENRY, political scientist; b. Oak Park, Ill., June 29, 1927; s. Henry Thomas and Evelina (Belden) P.; m. Louise D. Hill, Jan. 9, 1954; children: Eric, Steven. A.B., Oberlin (Ohio) Coll., 1950; M.A., U. Chgo., 1955, Ph.D., 1962. With Italian service mission Naples 1950-53; organizer Homeless European Land Program, Sardinia, 1957-59; with UN High Commn. Refugees, Rome, 1960-61; mem. faculty U. Wis., Milw., also; U. Wis. extension, 1962—, prof. polit. sci., 1969—; chmn. Center Urban Community Devel., 1967-90; co-founder High Wind Assn. for Renewable Energy Experimentation and Modeling an Alternative Community, 1980; co-founder, pres. Plymouth Inst. for Sustainable Devel.; hon. rsch. prof. Internat. Tech. and Economy Inst, Inst. for Sci. of Scis., Shanghai, China, 1990—. Author: The Searchers, 1966; also articles. Served with USNR, 1945-46. Findhorn Found. fellow; grantee Social Sci. Rsch. Coun., 1967-68. Mem. Am. Polit. Sci. Assn., World Futurist Soc., Internat. Ctr. Integrative Studies, Soc. Sustainable Futures. Home: W7122 County Rd U Plymouth WI 53073-4538 Office: U Wis Dept Urban Community Devel 929 N 6th St Milwaukee WI 53203-1404

PAULSON, BERNARD ARTHUR, oil company executive, consultant; b. Lakeview, Mich., July 12, 1928; s. Arthur Bernard and Genevieve Talbard (Bushley) P.; m. Joan Lee Curtiss, Dec. 4, 1954; children: James, Joseph (dec.), Ann, Thomas (dec.), Bernadette, Patricia, Steven. B.S. in Chem. Engring., Mich. State U.-East Lansing, 1949. Registered profl. engr., Tex. Process engr. Mid-West Refineries Inc., Alma, Mich., 1949-57; plant mgr. Kerr-McGee Corp., Cleve. and Wynnewood, Okla., 1957-66; v.p. Coastal States Petrochemical, Corpus Christi, Tex., 1966-71, Koch Industries Inc., St. Paul and Wichita, 1974-88; cons. Koch Industries Inc., Corpus Christi, Tex., 1988—; pres. Koch Refining Co., Wichita, 1981-88; bd. dirs. Hitox Corp. Am. Chmn., pres. Cleve. Area Hosp. Corp., 1962; dir. Ada Wilson Hosp. Found.; pres. Corpus Christ Bd. Trade. 1st lt. USAF, 1955-57. Recipient Claud R. Erickson Disting. Alumnus award Mich. State U., 1994. Mem. Am. Inst. Chem. Engrs. (fuels and petrochem. award 1989), Nat. Petroleum Refiners Assn., Refining Am. Petroleum Inst., Wichita Area C. of C. (bd. dirs.), Bd. Trade, Corpus Christi Country Club, Corpus Christi Town Club (dir.), Elks. Home and Office: 5310 Greenbriar Dr Corpus Christi TX 78413-2827

PAULSON, BOYD COLTON, JR., civil engineering educator; b. Providence, Mar. 1, 1946; s. Boyd Colton and Barbara (McKinstry) P.; m. Jane Margaret Kingdon, Feb. 12, 1970; children: Jeffrey Boyd, Laura Jane. BS, Stanford U., 1967, MS, 1969, PhD, 1971. Asst. prof. U. Ill., Urbana, 1972-73; asst. prof., assoc. prof. civil engring. Stanford (Calif.) U., 1974, prof., 1984-89, Obhayashi prof. engring., 1989-91, Charles Leavell prof. civil engring., 1991—; mem. civil engring. adv. com. NSF, 1983-84; mem. U.S. Nat. Com. on Tunneling, 1986-89; mem. com. on constrn. superconducting supercollider in Tex., NAS, 1988-89; presenter in field. Author: Computer Applications in Construction, 1995; co-author: Professional Construction Management, 1978, 2d edit., 1984, 3d edit., 1992; also articles. Coach Am. Youth Soccer Orgn., Menlo Park, Calif., 1978-84; advisor Boy Scouts Am., Menlo Park, 1980-90. Fellow Humboldt Found., Munich, 1983, Brit. Coun., Glasgow, Scotland, 1990-91, Fulbright fellow, 1990-91. Mem. ASCE (chmn. constrn. div. 1986-87, Huber rsch. prize 1980, Constrn. Mgmt. award 1984, Peurifoy Rsch. award 1993), Am. Soc. for Engring. Edn., Assn. for Computing Machinery. Achievements include research on human-computer systems for project management, in analytical modeling and simulation of construction operations, in conceptual and theoretical work to develop software for construction robots, in tunneling in urban environments, in low-cost housing. Office: Stanford U 4020 Civil Engring Stanford CA 94305-4020

PAULSON, DAVID L., newspaper publishing executive. Treas. Los Angeles Times. Office: Los Angeles Times Times Mirror Sq Los Angeles CA 90053*

PAULSON, DONALD ROBERT, chemistry educator; b. Oak Park, Ill., Sept. 6, 1943; s. Robert Smith and Florence Teresa (Beese) P.; m. Elizabeth Anne Goodwin, Aug. 20, 1966; children: Matthew, Andrew. Ba, Monmouth Coll., 1965; PhD, Ind. U., 1968. Asst. prof. chemistry Calif. State U., Los Angeles, 1970-74, assoc. prof., 1974-78, prof., 1979—, chmn. dept., 1982-90; vis. prof. U. B.C., Vancouver, Can., 1977-78, U. Sussex, Brighton, Eng., 1984-85. Author: Alicyclic Chemistry, 1976; contbr. articles to profl. jours. Named Outstanding Prof., Calif. State U., Los Angeles, 1978. Mem. Am. Chem. Soc., Chem. Soc. (London), InterAm. Photochem. Soc., Nat. Assn. Sci. Tchrs., Sigma Xi. Democrat. Episcopalian. Avocations: photography, hiking, soccer. Home: 1627 Laurel St South Pasadena CA 91030-4710 Office: Calif State U Dept Chemistry 5151 State University Dr Los Angeles CA 90032-4221

PAULSON, GLENN, environmental scientist; b. Sycamore, Ill., Sept. 14, 1941; s. Orville Magnuson and Clarice Hope (Lewis) P.; m. Linda Joyce Cooper, May 17, 1985. BA with honors, Northwestern U., 1963; PhD, Rockefeller U., 1971; ScD (hon.), L.I. U., 1972. Dir. sci. for citizen program New Sch. for Social Rsch., N.Y.C., 1967-69; exec. dir. Scientists' Com. for Pub. Info., N.Y.C., 1971-72; staff scientist, adminstr. sci. support prog. Natural Resources Def. Coun., N.Y.C., 1971-74; asst. commr. N.J. Dept. Environ. Protection, Trenton, 1974-79; v.p. Nat. Audubon Soc., N.Y.C., 1979-82, sr. v.p., 1982-84; v.p. Clean Sites, Inc., Alexandria, Va., 1984-88; dir. Ctr. for Hazardous Waste Mgmt. Ill. Inst. Tech., Chgo., 1988-90, rsch. prof. dept. environ. engring., 1988-95; pres. Paulson and Cooper, Inc., 1992—; chmn. environ. mgmt. adv. bd. Dept. Energy, 1992-94. Editor, author: Environment, USA, 1974; contbr. articles to profl. jours. Bd. dirs. Citizens for Clean Air, N.Y.C., 1965-74, Rene Dubos Ctr., N.Y.C., 1981-90. NSF grantee, 1976, A.W. Mellon Found. grantee, 1979-84, Coalition on Superfund grantee, 1988-89; Rockefeller Univ. fellow, 1963-71. Fellow AAAS, Am. Inst. Chemists; mem. Am. Chem. Soc., Soc. for Environ. Toxicology and Chemistry, Coun. for Advancement Sci. Writing (bd. dirs. 1968—), Soc. Risk Assessment, Sec. Energy Adv. Bd. (charter member. 1990-93), Phi Beta Kappa. Avocation: outdoor activities. Office: Paulson and Cooper Inc PO Box 1541 Jackson Hole WY 83001

PAULSON, JAMES MARVIN, engineering educator; b. Wausau, Wis., Jan. 1, 1923; s. Gustav Victor and Susanna (Dracy) P.; m. Marjorie Beulah Burton, May 11, 1946; children—Vicki Rae, Michael James. B.S. in Civil Engring, The Citadel, 1947; M.S. in Civil Engring, Ill. Inst. Tech., 1949; Ph.D., U. Mich., 1958. Registered profl. engr., Mich. Chemical Wausau Iron Works, 1946; engr. Charles Whitney Cons. Engr., Milw., 1948-49; faculty Wayne State U., Detroit, 1949—, prof., 1961-85, chmn. dept. civil engring., 1967-72, assoc. dean Coll. Engring., 1973-83, prof. emeritus, 1985—; v.p. Civil Engrs., Inc., 1954—; cons. in field. Served with AUS, 1943; Served with USMCR, 1943-46. Mem. ASCE (life). Nat. Soc. Profl. Engrs. (life), Am. Soc. for Engring. Edn., Sigma Xi, Tau Beta Pi, Chi Epsilon. Presbyterian. Home: PO Box 23 Greenbush MI 48738-0023

PAULSON, JOHN DORAN, newspaper editor, retired; b. Grand Forks, N.D., Oct. 1, 1915; s. Holger D. and Irene E. (Finkle) P.; m. Zoe Y. Bean Hensley, July 6, 1946 (dec. Aug. 1993); children: James L., Michael D., Christine R., David E., Patrick R. Student, U.N.D., 1932-34; B.S., U. Minn., 1936. Copy editor Mpls. Star, 1936; reporter The Forum, Fargo, N.D.-Moorhead, Minn., 1937-39; polit. writer The Forum, 1939-51, mng.

editor, 1951-56, editor, 1957-80; v.p. Dakota Photographics Inc., Fargo, 1963-93. Del. N.D. Constl. Conv., 1971-72. Served with AUS, 1942-46. Mem. Am. Soc. Newspaper Editors. Home: 1362 2nd St N Fargo ND 58102-2725

PAULSON, KENNETH MICHAEL, quality control executive; b. Mauston, Wis., Mar. 27, 1945; s. Norman and Margret (Brown) P.; m. Kathryn Ann Stachowski, Aug. 27, 1966; children: Kurt, Kevin, Kraig. BBA in Sales and Mktg., Spencerian Coll., 1967. V.p. Delta Advt., Md., 1975-85; v.p. sales and mktg. Marthens, Davenport, Iowa, 1985-86; with sales dept. No. Am. Paper, Chgo., 1986; dir. sales and mktg. cream cone div. Drumstick Alco Std., Columbus, Ohio, 1987; dir. process improvement Nestle Dairy Systems, Columbus, 1987—. Bd. dirs Iowa Guild for Infant Survival, Davenport, 1980-87, Sudden Infant Death Syndrome Alliance, Columbus, 1986-92; del. Rep. party convs., Iowa, 1988; coun. mem. Holy Family Parish, Davenport, 1985-88. Mem. Am. Soc. for Quality Control, Assn. for Quality and Participation, Ohio Quality and Productivity Forum. Roman Catholic. Home: 565 S Spring Rd Westerville OH 43216 Office: Nestle Dairy Systems 1700 17th Ave Westerville OH 43081

PAULSON, PAUL JOSEPH, advertising executive; b. White Plains, N.Y., Sept. 25, 1932; s. Paul and Ann (Loughlin) P.; m. Kathryn P. Keeler, June 30, 1962; children: Thomas, Mark, Kathryn, John, Clifford. BSBA, Ohio State U., 1954; MBA, U. Pa., 1959. With Compton Advt. Inc., N.Y.C., 1959-78; mgmt. supr. Compton Advt. Inc., 1965-78, sr. v.p., 1968-78, also exec.; dir. pres., dir. Doyle Dane Bernbach Inc., N.Y.C., 1978-83; pres., chief exec. officer Isidore & Paulson, Inc., N.Y.C., 1983-93; chmn., pres., CEO Paulson & Co. Mktg. Svcs., Greenwich, 1993—; mem. Ohio State U. Alumni Adv. Coun., 1982—; pres. coun. mem. Ohio State U., 1993—. Author: Fundamentals of Consumer Goods Marketing, 1966. Chmn. Christmas for Underprivileged Children, N.Y.C., 1963—. Served to lt. (j.g.) USNR, 1955-58, MTO, ETO. Mem. Wharton Grad. Bus. Sch. Alumni Assn. (pres. N.Y.C. club 1963-65, dir. 1972—), Ohio State U. Alumni Assn., Wharton Grad. Bus. Sch. Roman Catholic. Clubs: N.Y. (dir.), Milbrook, Sigma Chi. Home: 45 W Brother Dr Greenwich CT 06830-6726

PAULSON, PETER JOHN, librarian, publishing company executive; b. N.Y.C., Jan. 30, 1928; s. Peter John and Lillian Agnes Elaine (Neuman) P.; m. Josephine C. Bowen, Dec. 5, 1953; children: David, Debora. B.Social Scis. cum laude, CCNY, 1949; M.A. in History, Columbia, 1950; M.A. in LS, SUNY, Albany, 1955. Library asst. N.Y. State Library, Albany, 1952-55; head, gift and exchange sect. N.Y. State Library, 1955-65, head catalog sect., 1965-66, prin. librarian tech. services, 1966-71, dir., 1972-85; exec. dir. OCLC Forest Press, 1985—; adj. asst. prof. library sci. State U. N.Y. at Albany, 1960-71; Adv. com. Ohio Coll. Library Center, 1970-71; adv. council to pub. printer depository libraries, 1972-77, chmn., 1975-77; com. fed. depository library service N.Y. State, 1960-70, chairperson, 1960-70; bd. dirs. Capital Dist. Libr. Coun., Nat. Info. Standards Orgn., N.E. Document Conservation Ctr. Mem. ALA (chmn. com. on legislation 1980-82, pres. state library agy. sect. 1982-83), N.Y. Library Assn. (pres. 1975), Hudson-Mohawk Library Assn. (v.p. 1964), SUNY-OCLC Network (governing bd. 1980-82), Phi Beta Kappa. Home: 24 Tillinghast Ave Albany NY 12204-2312 Office: OCLC Forest Press 85 Watervliet Ave Albany NY 12206-2023

PAULSON, RONALD HOWARD, English and humanities educator; b. Bottineau, N.D., May 27, 1930; s. Howard Clarence and Ethel (Tvete) P.; m. Barbara Lee Appleton, May 25, 1957 (div. 1982); children: Andrew Meredith, Melissa Katherine. BA, Yale U., 1952, PhD, 1958. Instr. U. Ill., 1958-59, from asst. to assoc. prof., 1959-63; prof. English Rice U., Houston, 1963-67; prof. English Johns Hopkins U., Balt., 1967-75, chmn. dept., 1968-75, Andrew W. Mellon prof. humanities, 1973-75, Mayer prof. humanities, 1984—, chmn. dept., 1985-91; prof. English Yale U., New Haven, Conn., 1975-84, Thomas E. Donnelly prof., 1980-84, Ward Phillips lectr., 1978, Alexander lectr., 1979, Brown and Haley lectr., 1979, Hodges lectr., 1980. Author: Theme and Structure in Swift's Tale of a Tub, 1960, Fielding, 1962, Hogarth's Graphic Works, 1965, rev. edits., 1970, 89, Fictions of Satire, 1967, Satire and the Novel, 1967, (with Thomas F. Lockwood) Fielding: The Critical Heritage, 1969, Satire: Modern Essays in Criticism, 1971, Hogarth: His Life, Art and Times, 1971, Rowlandson: A New Interpretation, 1972, Emblem and Expression: Meaning in Eighteenth Century English Art, 1975, The Art of Hogarth, 1975, Popular and Polite Art in the Age of Hogarth and Fielding, 1979, Literary Landscape: Turner and Constable, 1982, Book and Painting: Shakespeare, Milton and the Bible, 1983, Representations of Revolution, 1983, Breaking and Remaking, 1989, Figure and Abstraction in Contemporary Painting, 1990, Hogarth Vol. 1: The Modern Moral Subject, 1991, Hogarth Vol. 2: High Art and Low, Hogarth Vol. 3: Art and Politics, 1993, The Beautiful, Novel, and Strange: Aesthetics and Heterodoxy, 1995; also numerous essays. 1st lt. AUS, 1952-54. Sterling fellow 1957-85, Guggenheim fellow 1965-66, 1986-87, NEH fellow 1977-78. Fellow Am. Acad. Arts and Scis.; mem. Am. Soc. for 18th Century Studies (pres. 1986-87). Home: 2722 St Paul St Baltimore MD 21218-4332 Office: Johns Hopkins U Dept English Baltimore MD 21218

PAULSON, STANLEY FAY, association executive; b. Atwater, Minn., Mar. 5, 1920; s. Adolph and Ida May (Fay) P.; m. Margaret Nan Appelquist, Sept. 8, 1944; children—Richard Stanley, Lynn Edith. B.A. in Philosophy, U. Minn., 1942, M.A., 1949, Ph.D., 1952; B.D., Bethel Theol. Sem., 1944. Instr. U. Minn., 1948-53; research asso. studies in lang. and behavior Bur. Naval Research, 1952-53; overseas instr. U. Md. Program in Germany and Eng., 1953-54; asst. prof. U. Minn., 1954-56; mem. faculty San Francisco State U., 1956-66, prof. speech, chmn. dept., 1959-62, v.p. acad. affairs, 1963-65, acting pres., 1965-66; prof. chmn. dept. speech Pa. State U., 1966-69, dean Coll. Liberal Arts, 1969-84; bd. dirs. Assn. Am. Colls., 1978-85, chmn. bd., 1983-84, v.p., 1985-87; presdl. search cons. Assn. Governing Bd. Univs. and Colls., Washington, 1987-88; sr. cons. Acad. Cons. Service, Washington, 1988—. Author: (with Bystrom, Ramsland) Communicating Through Speech, 1951; also articles. Served to lt. (j.g.) USNR, 1945-46. Fulbright lectr. Kanazawa (Japan) U., 1962-63. Mem. Speech Communication Assn. (vice chmn. group methods sect. 1961-62), Western Speech Assn. (counselor pub. address 1961—), AAUP, Internat. Communication Assn., Council Colls. Arts and Scis. (dir. 1971-75, v.p. 1972, pres. 1973). Home: 5500 Friendship Blvd Apt 2403N Bethesda MD 20815-7218 Office: Acad Search Consultation Svc 1818 R St NW Washington DC 20009-1692

PAULSON, WILLIAM LEE, state justice; b. Valley City, N.D., Sept. 3, 1913; s. Alfred Parker and Inga Gertina (Wold) P.; m. Jane E. Graves, Sept. 8, 1938; children: John T., Mary (Mrs. Mikal Simonson). B.A., Valley City State Univ. Coll., 1935; J.D., U. N.D., 1937. Bar: N.D. 1937. Practiced in Valley City, 1937-66; state's atty. Barnes County, 1941-50, 59-66; assoc. justice N.D. Supreme Ct., 1967—; Pres. N.D. States Attys. Assn., 1964; dir. for N.D. Nat. Dist. Attys. Assn., 1963-65. Pres. Valley City Jaycees, 1943; dist. v.p. U.S. Jaycees, 1945-46; bd. dirs. Valley City State U. C., 1960-61; judge Am. Legion Oratorical Contest, 1970-72; mem. nat. awards jury Freedoms Found. at Valley Forge, 1969-71, 77; chancellor Episcopal Ch. N.D., from 1965; Mem. alumni adv. bd. U.N.D. from 1971. Mem. Am. Bar Assn., State Bar N.D., U. N.D. Alumni Assn. (pres. Valley City Area 1963-65, Sioux award 1973). Clubs: Elk, K.P, Eagle, Mason (Shriner). Home: 1009 E Highland Acres Rd Bismarck ND 58501-2417 Office: Supreme Ct Chambers State Capitol Bismarck ND 58505

PAULSON, WILLIAM ROSS, foreign language educator, researcher; b. Rockford, Ill., Aug. 31, 1955; s. William Arvid and Janet Christine (Westerman) P. BA in French and Maths., Rockford Coll., 1976; MA in French, Princeton (N.J.) U., 1978, PhD in French, 1981. Asst. prof. Mt. Holyoke Coll., South Hadley, Mass., 1981-87; assoc. prof. French lit. U. Mich., Ann Arbor, 1989-95, prof. French, 1995—, chair dept. Romance Langs. & Lits., 1992—; mem. exec. com. U. Mich. Press, Ann Arbor, 1991-94. Author: Enlightenment, Romanticism, and the Blind in France, 1987, The Noise of Culture: Literary Texts in a World of Information, 1988, Sentimental Education: The Complexity of Disenchantment, 1992; co-translator: The Natural Contract (Michael Serres) 1995. French Govt. grantee, 1979; Am. Coun. Learned Socs. fellow, 1984. Mem. Modern Lang. Assn. Am., Soc. for Lit. and Sci., Societe des Etudes Romantiques et dix-neuviemistes, Phi Beta Kappa. Office: U Mich Dept of Romance Langs Ann Arbor MI 48109-1275

PAULSTON, CHRISTINA BRATT, linguistics educator; b. Stockholm, Sweden, Dec. 30, 1932; came to U.S., 1951; d. Lennart and Elsa (Facht) Bratt; m. Rolland G. Paulston, July 26, 1961; children: Christopher-Rolland, Ian Rollandsson. B.A., Carleton Coll., 1953; M.A. in English and Comparative Lit., U. Minn., 1955; Ed.D., Columbia U., 1966. Cert. tchr., Minn. Tchr. Clara City and Pine Island High Schs., Minn., 1955-60, Am. Sch. of Tangier, Morocco, 1960-62, Katrineholm Allmanna Laroverk, Katrineholm, Sweden, 1962-63, East Asian Library, Columbia U., N.Y.C., 1963-64; asst. instr. Tchrs. Coll., Columbia U., 1964-66; instr. U. Punjab, Chandigarh, India, summer 1966, Pontificia Universidad Catolica Del Peru, Lima, 1966-67; cons. Instituto Linguistico de Verano, Lima, 1967-68; asst. prof. linguistics U. Pitts., 1969-75, prof., 1975—, asst. dir. English Lang. Inst., 1969-70, dir. English Lang. Inst., 1970—, acting dir. Lang. Acquisition Inst., fall 1971, acting chmn. dept. gen. linguistics, 1974-75, chmn., 1975-89. Author books and numerous articles on linguistics. Recipient research award Am. Ednl. Research Assn., 1980; Fulbright-Hays grantee, Uruguay, 1985. Mem. Assn. Tchrs. of English to Speakers of Other Langs. (2d v.p., conv., chmn. 1972, exec. com. 1972-75, rsch. com. 1973-75, 78-80, chmn. 1973-75, 1st v.p. 1975, pres. 1976), Linguistics Soc. Am. (com. linguistics and pub. interest 1973-77), Internat. Assn. of Tchrs. of English as a Fgn. Lang., Am. Council on Teaching of Fgn. Langs., MLA (exec. com. lang. and soc. 1975-76), Ctr. Applied Linguistics (trustee 1976-81, exec. com. 1980, publs. com. 1981, research com. 1981), Eastern Competitive Trailriding Assn. Democrat. Episcopalian. Office: U Pitts Linguistics Pittsburgh PA 15260

PAULUS, JOHN DAVID, economist; b. Petoskey, Mich., July 26, 1943; s. George Emil and Daisy Helen (Hulbert) P.; m. Carol Ann Jones, Sept. 1, 1962; children—Susan, John, Andrew, Sharon. A.B., U. Mich.-Dearborn, 1965; Ph.D., U. Chgo., 1972. Programmer analyst Ford Motor Co., Dearborn, Mich., 1965-67; systems analyst Gen. Electric Co., Detroit, 1967-68; sr. economist Fed. Res. Bd., Washington, 1972-78; sr. v.p. Fed. Res. Bank Mpls., 1978-79; v.p. Goldman Sachs and Co., N.Y.C., 1979-82; mng. dir., chief economist Morgan Stanley and Co., N.Y.C., 1982—. Contbr. numerous articles to profl. jours., newspapers and mags. Mem. Am. Econ. Assn., Nat. Assn. Bus. Economists. Office: Morgan Stanley and Co 1251 Ave Of The Americas New York NY 10020-1104

PAULUS, NORMA JEAN PETERSEN, lawyer, state school system administrator; b. Belgrade, Nebr., Mar. 13, 1933; d. Paul Emil and Ella Marie (Hellbusch) Petersen; LL.B., Willamette Law Sch., 1962; LL.D., Linfield Coll., 1985; m. William G. Paulus, Aug. 16, 1958; children: Elizabeth, William Frederick. Sec. to Harney County Dist. Atty., 1950-53; legal sec., Salem, Oreg., 1953-55; sec. to chief justice Oreg. Supreme Ct., 1955-61; admitted to Oreg. bar, 1962; of counsel Paulus and Callaghan, Salem, mem. Oreg. Ho. of Reps., 1971-77; sec. state State of Oreg., Salem, 1977-85; of counsel firm Paulus, Rhoten & Lien, 1985-86; supt. pub. instrn. State of Oreg., 1990—; Oreg. exec. bd. US West, 1985—; adj. prof. Willamette U. Grad. Sch, 1985; mem. N.W. Power Planning Com., 1986-89. Fellow Eagleton Inst. Politics, 1971; mem. Pacific NW Power Planning Council, 1987-89; adv. com. Defense Adv. Com. for Women in the Service, 1986, Nat. Trust for Hist. Preservation, 1988—; trustee Willamette U., 1978—; bd. dirs. Benedictine Found. of Oreg., 1980—, Oreg. Grade. Instn. Sci. and Tech., 1985—, Mid Willamette Valley council Camp Fire Girls, 1985-87; overseer Whitman Coll., 1985—; bd. cons. Goodwill Industries of Oreg.; mem. Salem Human Relations Commn., 1967-70, Marion-Polk Boundary Commn., 1970-71; mem. Presdl. Commn. to Monitor Philippines Election, 1986. Recipient Distinguished Service award City of Salem, 1971; Path Breaker award Oreg. Women's Polit. Caucus, 1976; named One of 10 Women of Future, Ladies Home Jour., 1979. Woman of Yr., Oreg. Inst Managerial and Profl. Women, 1982, Oreg. Women Lawyers, 1982, Woman Who Made a Difference award Nat. Women's Forum, 1985. Mem. Oreg. State Bar, Nat. Order Women Legislators, Women Execs. in State Govt., Women's Polit. Caucus Bus. and Profl. Women's Club (Golden Torch award 1971), Zonta Internat., Delta Kappa Gamma.

PAULUS, STEPHEN HARRISON, composer; b. Summit, N.J., Aug. 24, 1949; s. Harrison Child and Patricia Jean (Clark) P.; m. Patricia Ann, July 18, 1975; children: Gregory Stephen, Andrew Christopher. Student, Macalester Coll., 1967-69; B.A. U. Minn., 1969-71, M.A., 1972-74, Ph.D., 1974-78. Co-founder, fundraiser Minn. Composers Forum, St. Paul, 1973-84; Exxon/Rockefeller composer in residence Minn. Orch., Mpls., 1983-87; composer in residence Santa Fe Chamber Music Festival, summer 1986; Regent's lectr. U. Calif., Santa Barbara, Nov. 1986; composer in residence Atlanta Symphony Orch., 1988-92, Dale Warland Singers, 1991-92; composer in residence Aspen Festival, summer, 1992. Performances with Tanglewood Festival, 1980, Edinburgh Festival, 1983, Aldeburgh Festival, 1985; composer (orchestral works) Sinfonietta, Concertante, Ordway Overture, Concerto for Orchestra, Seven Short Pieces for Orchestra, Translucent Landscapes, Spectra, Reflections: Four Movements on a Theme of Wallace Stevens, Divertimento for Harp and Chamber Orchestra, Trumpet Concerto, Suite from Harmoonia, Suite from The Postman Always Rings Twice, Ground Breaker--An Overture for Constrn. Instruments and Orch., Symphony in Three Movements, Street Music, Manhattan Sinfonietta, Violin Concerto, Symphony for Strings, Concerto for Violin, Cello & Orch., Organ Concerto, Violin Concerto No. 2, (recordings) Violin Concerto, Concertante and Symphony for Strings, Songs: Bittersuite, All My Pretty Ones, Artsongs, (for orch.) Violin Concerto (Kennedy Ctr. Friedheim award for 3d pl. Am. Works for Orch., 1988), Symphony for Strings, Street Music, Echoes Between the Silent Peaks, (operas) The Woodlanders, The Postman Always Rings Twice, The Woman At Otowi Crossing, The Village Singer, Harmoonia, The Woman at Otowi Crossing; (for chorus and orch.), So Hallow'd Is the Time, (5 carols for chorus and strings) Christmas Tidings, Letters for the Times, North Shore, Canticles: Songs and Rituals for the Easter and the May, Voices, (chamber work) Seven for the Flowers Near the River, Seven Miniatures, Fantasy in Three Parts, Quartessence, others, also numerous works for chamber groups including Partita for Violin and Piano, Music for Contrasts (string Quartet), String Quartet No.2, Quartessence, (for soprano voice, piano, percussion and string quartet) Letters From Colette, American Vignettes (for cello and piano); (for solo voice) All My Pretty Ones, Artsongs, Mad Book, Shadow Book: Michael Morley's Songs, Elizabethan Songs, Bittersuite for baritone and piano, (solo voice/bass-baritone and vn, vc. pf.) The Long Shadow of Lincoln; (for solo instruments) Two Moments for Guitar, (piano) Translucent Landscapes; (for chorus) Madrigali di Michelangelo, Four Preludes on Playthings of The Wind, Peace, Personals, Marginalia, Echoes Between the Silent Peaks, Jesu Carols, Meditations of Li Po, Love's Philosophy, Three Songs for Mixed Chorus, The Earth Sines, The Elixir, (narrative and chamber orch.) Voices from the Gallery, (chamber) Music of the Night (for violin, voice and percussion), (choral) Visions from Hildegard, Part I (for flute, oboe, timpany, percussion, organ and chorus), Part Two (for brass quintet, percussion and chorus), (for narrator and chamber orch.) Voices from the Gallery, (vocal) Songs of Love and Longing, (chamber/instrumental) Air on Seurat, (chorus) Three Songs for Mixed Chorus, Christ Our Passover, (piano) Preludes, (organ duet) The Triumph of the Saint, (chorus and chamber ensemble) Whitman's Dream. Recipient Outstanding Achievement award U. Minn., 1991, Disting. Alumni award, 1991, Lancaster Symphony Orch. Composer's award, 1994; Guggenheim fellow, 1982-83, NEA fellow, 1978; NEA Consortium grantee, 1987. Mem. ASCAP (bd. dirs. 1990), Am. Music Ctr., Minn. Composers Forum (v.p. 1984-87, bd. dirs.). Avocations: tennis, reading. Home and Office: 1719 Summit Ave Saint Paul MN 55105-1833

PAULY, BRUCE HENRY, engineering consultant; b. Washington, Nov. 11, 1920; s. Elmer George and Charlotte May (Weck) P.; m. Dorothy Buhrman Rollins, June 20, 1945; 1 child, Margaret MacKenzie Pauly Price. B.S. in Mech. Engring., Va. Poly. Inst., 1941; M.S. in Engring. Adminstrn., Case Inst. Tech., 1965. Registered profl. engr., Pa. lic. pvt. pilot. Sect. mgr. Aviation Gas Turbine div., Westinghouse Electric Corp., Lester, Pa., 1945-52; sales mgr. aircraft (Pesco) Borg-Warner Corp., Bedford, Ohio, 1952-55; v.p. research and engring. Weatherhead Co., Cleve., 1955-69; v.p. engring. Eaton Corp., Cleve., 1969-82; co-owner, dir. Crystaloid Electronics Co., Hudson, Ohio, 1983-85; mem. vis. com. Fenn Coll. Engring., Cleve. State U., 1973-85; mem. engring. adv. com. Cuyahoga Community Coll., Cleve., 1979—; exec. com. Coll. Engring. Va. Poly Inst. and State U., Blacksburg, 1980—; mem. Transp. Research Bd. NRC, Washington, 1982-84. Patentee turbojet control, hydraulic pump, gas regulator, hose crimper. Mem. task force Pres.' Pvt. Sector Survey, Washington, 1982; mem. Cleve. Sr. Council, 1983—. Served to lt. col. USAAF, 1941-45, ETO; USAF Ret.

Res., 1986—. Decorated Legion of Merit; decorated Bronze Star, Croix de Guerre (France). Mem. AIAA (co-chmn. nat. aerospace propulsion conf. Cleve 1982), Soc. Automotive Engrs. (chmn. motor vehicle council 1981-82), Nat. Conf. on Fluid Power (gen. chmn. 1977), Cleve. Engring. Soc. (bd. govs. 1979-81), Chagrin Valley C. of C., Mil. Order World Wars (comdr. Cleve. 1984-85). Res. Officers Assn., Cheshire Cheese Club (Cleve), Pi Tau Sigma, Pi Delta Epsilon. Republican. Episcopalian. Home: 143 Kenton Rd Chagrin Falls OH 44022-2503

PAULY, JOHN EDWARD, anatomist; b. Elgin, Ill., Sept. 17, 1927; s. Edward John and Gladys (Myhre) P.; m. Margaret Mary Oberle, Sept. 3, 1949; children: Stephen John, Susan Elizabeth, Kathleen Ann, Mark Edward. B.S., Northwestern U., 1950; M.S., Loyola U., Chgo., 1952, Ph.D., 1955. Grad. asst. gross anatomy Stritch Sch. Medicine, Loyola U., Chgo., 1953-54; rsch. asst. anatomy Chgo. Med. Sch., 1952-54, research instr., 1954-55, instr. in gross anatomy, 1955-57, assoc. in gross anatomy, 1957-59, asst. prof. anatomy, 1959-63, asst. to pres., 1960-62; asso. prof. anatomy Tulane U. Sch. Medicine, 1963-67; prof., head dept. anatomy U. Ark. for Med. Scis., Little Rock, 1967-83; prof., head dept. physiology and biophysics U. Ark. for Med. Scis., 1978-80, vice chancellor for acad. affairs and sponsored rsch., 1983-92, associate dean Grad. Sch., 1983-92, prof. anatomy, 1992-95, prof. emeritus, 1995—; tech. adviser Ency. Brit. Films, 1956; mem. safety and occupational health study sect. Nat. Inst. Occupational Safety and Health, Ctr. for Disease Control, 1975-79; vis. prof. faculty medicine Kuwait U., 1993, 94. Author: (with Hans Elias) Human Microanatomy, 1960, 3d edit. 1966, (with Elias and E. Robert Burns) Histology and Human Microanatomy, 1978; editor: (with Lawrence E. Scheving and Franz Halberg) Chronobiology, 1974, (with Heinz von Mayersbach and Lawrence E. Scheving) Biological Rhythms in Structure and Function, 1981, The American Association of Anatomists, 1888-1987. Essays on the History of Anatomy in America and a Report on the Membership-Past and Present, 1987, (with Lawrence E. Scheving) Advances in Chronobiology, 1987, (with Dora K. Hayes and Russel J. Reiter) Chronobiology: Its Role in Clinical Medicine, General Biology and Agriculture, 1990; editor Am. Jour. Anatomy, 1980-92; co-mng. editor Advances in Anatomy, Embryology and Cell Biology, 1980—; mem. adv. editorial bd. Internat. Jour. Chronobiology, 1973-83; contbr. articles to profl. jours. Served with USNR, 1945-47. Recipient merit certificates AMA, 1953, 59; Bronze award Ill. Med. Soc., 1959; Lederle Med. Faculty award, 1966. Fellow AAAS; mem. Am. Assn. Anatomists (sec.-treas. 1972-80, pres. 1982-83, Centennial award 1987, Henry Gray award 1995), So. Soc. Anatomists (pres. 1971-72), Assn. Anatomy Chmn. (sec.-treas. 1969-71), Am. Physiol. Soc., Internat. Soc. Chronobiology, Pan-Am. Assn. Anatomy, Internat. Soc. Electrophysiol. Kinesiology, Internat. Soc. Steriology, Consejo Nacional de Profesores de Ciencias Morfologicas (hon.), Sigma Xi, Sigma Alpha Epsilon. Roman Catholic.

PAUMGARTEN, NICHOLAS BIDDLE, investment banker; b. Phila., Apr. 30, 1945; s. Harald Paumgarten and Elise Biddle (Robinson) Tyson; m. Carol Marshall, June 24, 1966; children—Nicholas Biddle, Alexander. B.A. U. Pa., 1967; M.B.A., Columbia U., 1971. Mng. dir. 1st Boston Corp., N.Y.C., 1971—. Office: First Boston Corp Park Ave Pla 55 E 52nd St New York NY 10055-0002

PAUP, MICHAEL LEE, lawyer; b. Wichita, Kans., Oct. 27, 1941; s. Harold Harry and Dorothy (Herrman) P.; m. Bernis Lewis, March 18, 1967; children: Jennifer, Julie. BA, Columbia Coll., 1963; LLB, U. Va., 1969. Bar: Va. 1969, U.S. Ct. Appeals (2d, 3d, 4th, 5th, 6th, 7th, 8th, 9th, 10th, 11th, D.C., Fed. cirs.), U.S. Supreme Ct. Mgmt. intern U.S. Dept. Navy, Washington, 1964-65; budget analyst, 1965-66; atty. tax divsn. U.S. Dept. Justice, Washington, 1969-80, chief appellate sec. tax divsn., 1980-87, dep. asst. atty. gen. tax divsn., 1987—. Mem. ABA, Fed. Bar Assn. (officer, tax sec. 1986—). Home: 3350 Rose Ln Falls Church VA 22042-4031 Office: Dept Justice Tax Divsn 10th & Constitution Ave NW Washington DC 20530-0001

PAUSA, CLEMENTS EDWARD, electronics company executive; b. South Gate, Calif., Oct. 18, 1930; s. Oscar Clements and Kathleen Patricia (O'Toole) P.; m. Janice Mary Hanson, Jan. 22, 1955; children: Geoffrey Clements, Ronald Edward. Student, UCLA, 1948-50; BS, U. Calif., Berkeley, 1953, MS, 1954, cert. in bus., 1960. Product mgr. Fairchild Semiconductor Corp., 1959-62, mgr. plant, 1962-64; gen. mgr. Fairchild Hong Kong Ltd., 1964-67, dir. plant group, 1967-68; dir. internat. mfg. Nat. Semiconductor Corp., Santa Clara, Calif., 1968-70, gen. mgr. Far East ops., 1970-73, v.p. internat. mfg., 1973-86, corp. v.p. internat. mfg., 1986-90, corp. v.p. internat. mfg. emeritus, 1991—; dir. Coopers & Librand Cons.; bd. dirs. 8 subs. cos., 2 J.V. cos. Mem. internat. adv. bd. U. Santa Clara, 1984—. Served to capt. USNR, 1952-81. Mem. Naval Res. Assn., Res. Officer's Assn., Calif. Alumni Assn., Delta Chi Alumni Assn. (v.p., pres. 1978-86). Republican. Roman Catholic. Office: Coopers & Lybrand 10 Almaden Blvd San Jose CA 95113

PAVALON, EUGENE IRVING, lawyer; b. Chgo., Jan. 5, 1933; m. Lois M. Frenzel, Jan. 15, 1961; children: Betsy, Bruce, Lynn. BSL, Northwestern U., 1954, JD, 1956. Bar: Ill. 1956. Sr. ptnr. Pavalon & Gifford, Chgo., 1970—; mem. com. on discovery rules Ill. Supreme Ct., 1981—; lectr., mem. faculty various law schs.; bd. dirs. ATLA Mut. Ins. Co. Former mem. state bd. dirs. Ind. Voters Ill; bd. overseers Inst. Civil Justice, Rand Corp., 1993—; mem. vis. com. Northwestern U. Law Sch., 1990—. Capt., USAF, 1956-59. Fellow Am. Coll. Trial Lawyers, Internat. Soc. Barristers, Internat. Acad. Trial Lawyers, Roscoe Pound Found. (life fellow, pres. 1988-90); mem. ABA, Chgo. Bar Assn. (bd. mgrs. 1978-79), Ill. Bar Assn., Ill. Trial Lawyers Assn. (pres. 1980-81), Trial Lawyers for Pub. Justice (founding mem., v.p. 1991-92, pres.-elect 1992-93, pres. 1993-94), Assn. Trial Lawyers Am. (parlimentarian 1983-84, sec. 1984-85, v.p. 1985-86, pres. elect 1986-87, pres. 1987-88), Am. Bd. of Profl. Liability Attys. (diplomate), Chgo. Athletic Assn., Standard Club. Author: Human Rights and Health Care Law, 1980, Your Medical Rights, 1990; contbr. articles to profl. jours., chpts. in books. Home: 1540 N Lake Shore Dr Chicago IL 60610-1623 Office: Pavalon & Gifford 2 N La Salle St Chicago IL 60602-3702

PAVÃO, LEONEL MAIA (LEE PAVÃO), advertising executive; b. Fall River, Mass., Jan. 30, 1934; s. Leonel M. and Maria (Raposo) P.; m. Joan Frances Hersey, Oct. 4, 1957; children: Mark, Christopher, Leah, Sarah. BS in Advt. Design, U Mass., Dartmouth, 1956. Art dir. to creative dir. J. Walter Thompson, N.Y., Holland, Miami, Spain, 1956-70; ptnr. Powers & Pavão, N.Y.C., 1970-73; v.p., nat. creative dir. JWT Brazil, 1974-76; mng. dir. J. Walter Thompson, Lima, Peru, 1976-80; pres., chief exec. officer J. Walter Thompson, São Paulo, Brazil, 1980-88; dir. J. Walter Thompson, worldwide, 1982-88; pres. Latin Am. region J. Walter Thompson, 1985-88; pres. Lee M. Pavão, Chapel Hill, N.C., 1988—. Designer U.S. stamp design Nat. Grange, 1967. Chair Parks & Recreation Commn., Chapel Hill, 1991-93; exec. bd. Friends of Sr. Ctr., Chapel Hill, 1991-93; chair Space Location & Design Requirements Commn., 1991—; vice chair exec. bd. The Childhood Trust serving dept. psychiatry U. N.C., Chapel Hill, 1990-93, chair, 1993—, chair long range planning com., 1991-92; mem. Commodores Club, permanent sec., JWT archives endowment Duke U., 1989—; mem. Task Force on Aging, Orange County, 1990-91, Chapel Hill Town Coun., 1993—, Chapel Hill/Orange County Visitor's Bur. Bd., 1993, vice chair, 1994, Chapel Hill Mus. Study Com., 1994. With U.S. Army, 1957-59. Named Personality of Yr., Rio de Janeiro Stock Exch. Mag., 1983, Bursinessman of Yr., São Paulo Chamber, 1984; recipient Tendecia award Bloch Editors, Rio de Janeiro, 1984, Advt. Man of Yr. columnist's award Brazil, 1986, Outstanding Achievement in Bus. award McGraw Hill and Madia Assocs., 1987. Mem. Am. Chamber São Paulo, Am. Chamber Lima Peru (dir. 1977-79, distinction award 1979), Carolina Club, U.N.C., Chapel Hill, N.Y. Athletic Club (N.Y.C.), Lima Golf Club, San Francisco Golf Club São Paulo. Avocations: golf; photography; antique and classic car collecting. Office: 1507 E Franklin St Ste 35 Chapel Hill NC 27514-2887

PAVAROTTI, LUCIANO, lyric tenor; b. Modena, Italy, Oct. 12, 1935; s. Fernando and Adele (Venturi) P.; m. Adua Veroni, Sept. 30, 1961; children—Lorenza, Cristina, Giuliana. Diploma magistrale, Istituto Magistrale Carlo Sigonio, 1955; studies with, Arrigo Pola, Ettore Campogalliani. Formerly tchr. elem. schs.; salesman ins. Debut as Rodolfo in La Bohème, Reggio Emilia, Italy, 1961; roles include Edgardo in debut Lucia di Lam-

mermoor, Amsterdam, 1963, the Duke in debut Rigoletto,Carpi, 1961, Rodolfo in La Bohème, Covent Garden, 1963, Tonio in debut The Daughter of the Regiment, Covent Garden, 1966, appeared in Lucia di Lammermoor, Australia, 1965, Am. debut, Miami, Fla., 1965; numerous European performances including Italy, Vienna Staatsoper, Paris; performed with San Francisco Opera, 1967, debut, Met. Opera, N.Y.C., 1968; appeared in The Daughter of the Regiment, Met. Opera, 1971, Elisir d'Amore, Met. Opera, 1973, La Bohème, Chgo. Opera, 1973, La Favorita, San Francisco Opera, 1973, Il Trovatore, San Francisco Opera, 1975, Bellini I Puritani, Met. Opera, 1976, Ponchielli La Gioconda, San Francisco Opera, 1979, Aida, San Francisco Opera, 1981, Mozart, Idomeneo, Met. Opera, 1982, Verdi, Ernani, Met. Opera, 1983, Tosca, Met. Opera, 1995; numerous internat. performances including La Scala, Milan, Hamburg, Teatro Colon, Buenos Aires, Australian Opera, Sydney; concert series of Am. and internat. cities, including Carnegie Hall, 1973, Buenos Aires, Moscow, Beijing, Hong Kong, Tokyo, including arena concerts, Madison Square Garden, 1984, and major cities in America, Europe, South America; appeared in film Yes, Giorgio, 1983; established Opera Co. of Philadelphia/Luciano Pavarotti Vocal Competition, 1980; rec. artist on Winner Concorso Internationale, Reggio Emilia, 1961; appeared in PBS TV spl. (with Placido Domingo & Jose Carreras) The Three Tenors, 1994. Named Artist of Yr. Gramophone, 1992; recipient Grammy award, 1981, 1988. Office: care Herbert Breslin 119 W 57th St New York NY 10019-2303*

PAVEN, NATHAN SAMUEL, lawyer; b. Malden, Mass., Aug. 17, 1925; s. Morris and Leah Paven; m. Ruth Marshall, June 22, 1952; children: Nathalie, Melissa Paven-Paquette, Andrew. AB, Harvard Coll., 1948, LLB, 1951. Bar: Mass. 1951, U.S. Dist. Ct. Mass., 1954, U.S. Ct. Appeals (1st cir.), 1955. Atty., advisor Office of Price Stabilization, Washington, 1951-53; assoc. Schlesinger & Manuelian, Boston, 1953-55; ptnr. Mason & Paven, Boston, 1955-71, Flamm, Paven & Feinberg, Boston, 1971-83, Paven & Norton, Braintree, Mass., 1983—; asst. atty. gen. Mass. Office of Atty. Gen., Boston, 1958-60, spl. asst. atty. gen., 1964-66. Mem. Mass. Consumer Coun., 1963-67. With U.S. Army, 1943-45, ETO. Democrat. Office: Paven & Norton 10 Forbes Rd Braintree MA 02184-2605

PAVIK, MALVIN A., department stores executive; b. 1932. With Montgomery Ward & Co. Inc., 1953—; v.p. territorial mgr. east territory Montgomery Ward & Co. Inc, 1985-86; sr. v.p. stores Montgomery Ward & Co. Inc., 1986-87, exec. v.p. territorial mgr. east territory, 1987—. Office: Montgomery Ward & Co Inc Montgomery Ward Plz Chicago IL 60671

PAVILANIS, VYTAUTAS, microbiology educator, physician; b. Kaunas, Lithuania, June 7, 1920; s. Kazys and Antonina (Eimontas) P.; m. Irene Stencelis, Mar. 8, 1947; children: Alain, Christine Gaputis, Marina Pavilanis Branigan, Ingrid. MD, U. Kaunas, 1942; diploma in microbiology, Institut Pasteur, Paris, 1947, diploma in serology and hematology, 1948; hon. doctorate, U. Que., 1988, 89. Asst. prof. pathology U. Kaunas, 1942-44; resident physician Siegburg, Germany, 1944-45; asst. Institut Pasteur, Paris, 1945-48; asst. prof. U. Montreal, Can., 1948; head virus dept. Institut Armand-Frappier, Ville de Laval, Que., Can., 1948-75; sci. dir. Institut Armand-Frappier, 1970-75, research coordinator, 1975-78, dir. quality control, 1976-79, asst. dir. teaching and research, 1978-82; assoc. prof. U. Montreal, 1956-85, prof. emeritus, 1985—; prof. U. Que., 1974-85, prof. emeritus, 1985—; cons. in field. Contbr. articles to profl. jours. Recipient Queen's Jubilee medal Can., 1977, Prix d'excellence Province of Que., 1993. Fellow Royal Soc. Can., Royal Coll. Physicians (Can.); mem. Can. Soc. Microbiology (2d v.p. 1966, award 1984), Can. Public Health Assn. (chmn. lab. sect. 1969), Virology Club Montreal (pres. 1969), Coll. Physicians and Surgeons P.Q., Can. Med. Assn., Can. Assn. Med. Microbiologists, Soc. Microbiology P.Q., N.Y. Acad. Sci. Home: 4742 The Boulevard, Westmount, PQ Canada H3Y 1V3 Office: PO Box 100, Ville de Laval, PQ Canada H7N 4Z3

PAVIN, COREY, professional golfer. mem. Ryder Cup Team, 1993. PGA Tour top U.S. golfer, leading money winner, 1991, 6th on PGA Tour 1992; Tour Wins include: Honda Classic, 1992, L.A. Open, 1994, Nissan Open, 1995, U.S. Open, 1995. Address: care PGA Tour 112 TPC Blvd Ponte Vedra Beach FL 32082*

PAVLICK, HARVEY NAYLOR, financial executive; b. San Francisco, May 29, 1942; s. Leopold Ferdinand and Anna Cathrine (Naylor) P. BA, San Francisco State U., 1965; MA, U. Chgo., 1968; D in Philosophy, Claremont Grad. Sch., 1974. Dir. ann. fund Union Coll., Schenectady, N.Y., 1968-70; dir. corp. and found. funding U. Calif., Berkeley, 1975-78; prin. Hyde Park Properties, Ltd., San Francisco, 1979-83; pres. Am. Equity Coun., Inc., Irvine, Calif., 1984—; chmn. bd. dirs. Investment Grade Real Estate Coun., Inc., Irvine; chmn. exec. com. Ahwahnee-Pacific Coun., Napa, Calif., 1990—. Sponsor Friends Huntington Libr., San Marino, Calif., 1986—, Children, Inc., Alexandria, Va., 1984—; mem. World Affairs Coun. of Orange County, Santa Ana, Calif., 1986, L.A. County Mus. Art, 1988—; donor Friends of San Francisco Symphony, 1990—. Mem. World Affairs Coun. L.A., Pi Sigma Alpha.

PAVLICK, WALTER EUGENE, lawyer, manufacturing company executive; b. Youngstown, Ohio, Mar. 3, 1934; s. George and Jennie (Perko) P.; m. Barbara Ann Slatsky, Sept. 8, 1956; children: Gary, Randy, Ronald. B.S. in Engring, Case Inst. Tech., 1956; J.D., George Washington U., 1959; M.B.A., Toledo U., 1967. Bar: Va. 1959, Ohio 1960, Ind. 1973, Wis. 1980. Patent examiner U.S. Patent Office, Washington, 1956; patent agt. Robertshaw-Fulton Controls Co., Washington, 1957-59; counsel Dana Corp., Toledo, 1959-72; chief counsel, sec. Nat. Homes Corp., Lafayette, Ind., 1972-79, Nat. Homes Acceptance Corp., 1972-79; sr. v.p., gen. counsel Modine Mfg. Co., Racine, Wis., 1979—; dir. Racine Comml. Airport, St. Marys Hosp. Mem. Va., Ind., Ohio, Wis. bar assns. Presbyterian. Clubs: Racine Country, Indoor Tennis Am. Home: 103 Old Pine Cir Racine WI 53402-2303 Office: Modine Mfg Co 1500 De Koven Ave Racine WI 53403-2540

PAVLIK, JAMES WILLIAM, chemistry educator; b. Chgo., Sept. 22, 1937; s. Victor William and Rose (Jaros) P.; m. children—Claire, David, Anne. A.B., Carthage Coll., 1959; M.S., Va. Poly. Inst. and State U., 1961; Ph.D., George Washington U., 1970. Asst. prof. chemistry Haile Sellasie I U., Addis Ababa, Ethiopia, 1967-69; research scientist George Washington U., Washington, 1969-70; from asst. prof. to assoc. prof. chemistry U. Wis., River Falls, 1970-74; prof. chemistry Worcester Poly. Inst., Mass., 1974—; cons. in field. Contbr. articles to profl. jours. Recipient Award for Outstanding Teaching, Worcester Poly. Inst., 1981. Mem. Am. Chem. Soc., Inter-Am. Photochem. Soc., Sigma Xi. Home: 11 Sawyer Rd Northborough MA 01532-1353 Office: Dept Chemistry Worcester Poly Inst Institute Rd Worcester MA 01609-2706

PAVLIK, NANCY, convention services executive; b. Hamtramck, Mich., July 18, 1935; d. Frank and Helen (Vorobojoff) Phillips; m. G. Edward Pavlik, June 30, 1956; children: Kathleen, Christine, Laureen, Michael, Bonnie Jean. Student, U. Ariz., 1956-80. Exec. sec. Mich. Bell, Detroit, 1951-56, RCA, Camden, N.J., 1956-58; owner, pres. Southwest Events Etc., Scottsdale, Ariz., 1969—. Chmn. hospitality industry com. Scottsdale City Coun., 1989—; bd. dirs. Scottsdale Curatorial Bd., 1987-89. Mem. Soc. Incentive Travel Execs., Meeting Planners Internat., Am. Soc. Assn. Execs., Indian Arts and Crafts Assn., Scottsdale C. of C. (bd. dirs., tourism steering com. 1984-88), Contemporary Watercolorists Club. Democrat. Roman Catholic. Avocations: watercoloring, Indian arts, crafts. Home: 7500 E Mccormick Pky # 33 Scottsdale AZ 85258-3454 Office: SW Events Etc 8233 E Paseo Del Norte A-600 Scottsdale AZ 85258

PAVLIK, WILLIAM BRUCE, psychologist, educator; b. Cleve., Feb. 29, 1932; s. William Frank and Mary (Meco) P.; m. Mary Katherine Findley, May 22, 1979; children by previous marriage: William James, Heather Ann, Russell Matthew, James Clark; 1 child, Amelia Katherine. B.S., Western Res. U., 1953; M.A., Ohio State U., 1955, Ph.D., 1956. Asst. prof. psychology Western Mich. U., 1956-60; asst. prof., then asso. prof. Rutgers U., 1960-68; prof. psychology Va. Poly. Inst. and State U., 1968-77, chmn. dept., 1968-72; prof. psychology U. Ga., Athens, 1977-94; ret., head dept., 1977-84. Author articles in field. Mem. Eastern Psychol. Assn., Southwestern Psychol. Assn. (pres. 1985-86), Psychonomic Soc. Home: 555 Forest Rd Athens GA 30605-3823

PAVONY, WILLIAM H., retail executive; b. Bklyn., Mar. 1, 1940; s. Harry and Mollie (Leibell) P.; m. Geraldine Rice, June 10, 1961; 1 child, Sheryl. BBA cum laude, Hofstra U., 1960. CPA, N.Y., Tex. Mgr. Arthur Andersen & Co. Inc., N.Y.C., 1960-73; group sr. v.p. Purolator Svcs. Inc., New Hyde Park, N.Y., 1973-75; v.p. contr. Purolator Inc., Piscataway, N.J., 1975-78; sr. v.p. Zale Corp., Dallas, 1978-85; sr. v.p. fin., chief fin. officer Alexander's Inc., N.Y.C., 1985-88, exec. v.p., chief fin officer, 1988-89; exec. v.p. adminstrn. The Kobacker Co., Columbus, Ohio, 1989-93; also bd. dirs.; exec. v.p. Arthur Rutenberg Homes, Clearwater, Fla., 1993-94; CFO Color Tile, Inc., Ft. Worth. Treas., bd. dirs. Tex. Vis. Nurses Assn., Dallas, 1984-85. Mem AICPA, Fin. Execs. Inst. (past bd. dirs. North Tex. chpt., sec. Columbus chpts.), N.Y. Soc. CPAs, Inst. Mgmt. Accts. Home: 7308 Monticello Pkwy Colleyville TX 76034 Office: Color Tile Inc 515 Houston St Fort Worth TX 76102

PAVSEK, DANIEL ALLAN, banker, educator; b. Cleve., Jan. 18, 1945; s. Daniel L. and Helen A. (Femec) P.; m. M. Ellen Canfield, Apr. 11, 1980 and July 26, 1985 (div. Sept. 1981 and Aug. 1989). A.B., Maryknoll Coll., Glen Ellyn, Ill., 1966; M.A., Maryknoll Sch. Theology, Ossining, N.Y., 1971, Cleve. State U., 1972; Ph.D., Case Western Res. U., 1981. Pres. Council Richmond Heights, Ohio, 1972-75; lectr. econs. Cleve. State U., 1972-75; asst. prof. Baldwin-Wallace Coll., Berea, Ohio, 1975-81; v.p., economist Ameritrust Co., Cleve., 1981-91; dean, prof. econs. Harry F. Byrd Jr. Sch. Bus. Shenandoah U., Winchester, Va., 1992—; adj. prof. bus. adminstrn. Baldwin-Wallace Coll., Berea, Ohio, 1981-91. Mem. Am. Econ. Assn., Nat. Tax Assn., Pub. Choice Soc., Nat. Assn. Bus. Econs. Democrat. Home: 231 Woodberry Ln Apt 119 Winchester VA 22601-3592

PAWLEY, RAY LYNN, zoological park herpetology curator; b. Midland, Mich., Nov. 7, 1935; s. Lynn Richard and Alice Marie (Skelton) P.; m. Ethel Marie Condon, Feb. 19, 1955 (div. 1974); children: Ray Allyn, Shanna Sue, Cynthia Ann, Dawn Marie, Brandon Earl, Dareen Joy. Student in zoo adminstrn., Mich. State U., 1954-57. Asst. curator/lectr. Black Hills Reptile Gardens, Rapid City, S.D., summers 1952-53; owner, adminstr. Reptile Exhibit, St. Ignace, Mich., 1957-59; animal coord. Marlin Perkin's Wild Kingdom Marlin Perkins' Wild Kingdom (Don Meier Prodns.), Chgo., 1961-62; zoologist Lincoln Park Zool. Gardens, Chgo., 1961-64; curator Brookfield (Ill.) Zoo, 1964—; assoc. dept. zoology Field Mus. Natural History, Chgo.; internat. zoo and conservation cons., Russia, Latvia, Mex., Kenya, China, Ecuador, Czechoslovakia; past instr. herpetology Field Mus., Colll. of DuPage, Triton Coll.; lectr., cons. in field. Contbr. more than 60 articles to profl. jours. and popular mags. Immediate past v.p. Ill. Endangered Species Protection Bd., Springfield; liaison Endangered Species Tech. Adv. Com., Springfield. Mem. Am. Zoo Assn. (3 Outstanding Svc. awards), Chgo. Acad. Scis. (life), Chgo. Herpetol. Soc. (life, cons.), others. Avocations: hiking, archaeology, art, mechanics, paleontology. Home: PO Box 218 Hinsdale IL 60522-0218 Office: Chicago Zool Park Brookfield IL 60513

PAWLSON, LEONARD GREGORY, physician; b. Victoria, Tex., 1943. MD, U. Pitts., 1969; MPH, U. Wash., 1976. Diplomate Am. Bd. Internal Medicine. Intern, affiliate hosps. Stanford U., 1969-70, resident in medicine, 1970-71; fellow in endocrinology U. Wash., 1973-75, Robert Wood Johnson clin. scholar, 1975-76; asst. prof. medicine and health care scis. George Washington U., Washington, 1976-80, assoc. prof. med. and health care scis., 1980-85, prof. health care scis., medicine, and health svcs. mgmt. and policy, 1985—, assoc. chmn. dept. health care scis., 1978-90, acting chmn., 1987-90, chmn., 1990—; attending physician George Washington Hosp., 1976—. Robert Wood Johnson health policy fellow, 1986-87; bd. dirs. Bon Secours Hosp. System, 1993—, U.S. Soliders and Airmans Home, 1992—. Robert Wood Johnson health policy fellow, 1986-87. Mem. ACP, Am. Geriatrics Soc. (past pres. and chmn. bd., editor law and pub. policy sect. Jour. of Am. Geriatrics Soc.); mem. Soc. Gen. Internal Medicine (past bd. dirs.). Office: George Washington U Med Ctr Dept Health Care Scis 2150 Pennsylvania Ave NW Washington DC 20037-2377

PAWSON, ANTHONY J., molecular biologist. Sr. scientist Samuel Lunenfeld Rsch. Inst., Toronto, Ont., Can. Recipient Gairdner Found. Internat. award Gairdner Found., 1994. Office: Samuel Lunenfeld Rsch Inst, 600 University Ave, Toronto, ON Canada H5G 1X5*

PAWULA, KENNETH JOHN, artist, educator; b. Chgo., Feb. 4, 1935; s. John and Clara (Brzezinski) P.; student Northwestern U., 1956, Art Inst. Chgo., 1956; B.F.A., U. Ill., 1959; M.A. in Painting, U. Calif., Berkeley, 1962. Graphic designer Motorola, Inc., Chgo., 1959-60; grad. asst. printmaking U. Calif., Berkeley, 1961-62, asso. in art, 1962-63; archaeol. delineator for Islamic excavation Am. Research Center, Egypt, 1964-65; instr. Sch. of Art, U. Wash., Seattle, 1965-67, asst. prof., 1967-73, asso. prof., 1974—; participant artist-in-residence program of Ecole Superieure Des Beaux-Arts D'Athenes at Rhodos Art Center, Greece, 1978; cons. to Wydawnictwo Interpress, Warsaw, Poland, 1978; mem. art jury ann. painting, drawing and sculpture show Art Mus. of Greater Victoria, Can., 1971, Unitarian Art Gallery, Seattle, 1968, Cellar Gallery, Kirkland, Wash., 1968, Lakewood Artist's Outdoor Exhibit, Tacoma, Wash., 1968; participant Painting Symposium, Janow Podlaski, Poland, 1977. One-man shows of paintings include: Univ. Unitarian Fine Arts Gallery, Seattle, 1970, Polly Friedlander Gallery, Seattle, 1970, Lynn Kottler Galleries, N.Y.C., 1971, U. Minn. Art Gallery, Mpls., 1971, Art Mus. of Greater Victoria, Can., 1972, Second Story Gallery, Seattle, 1972, Yuuhigaoka Gallery Osaka, Japan, Universidade Federal Fluminense Niteroi, Rio de Janiero, Brazil, 1990, Pyramid Gallery, N.Y.C., 1991; group shows include: Worth Ryder Gallery, U. Calif., Berkeley, 1962, Seattle Art Mus., 1964, 70, 65, 66, Frye Art Mus., Seattle, 1966, San Francisco Art Ins., 1966, Henry Gallery, U. Wash., Seattle, 1966, 67, 70, State Capitol Mus., Olympia, Wash., 1967, Attica Gallery, Seattle, 1967, 69, Sec. of State's Office, Olympia, 1968, Eastern Mich. U., Ypsilanti, 1968, Rogue Gallery, Medford, Oreg., 1968, Marylhurst Coll., Oreg., 1968, Spokane Art Mus., 1968, Cheney Cowles Mus., Spokane, 1969, Jade Gallery, Richland, Wash., 1969, Alaska U., 1970, Polly Friedlander Gallery, Mpls., 1971, Anchorage Art Mus., 1972, U. Nev. Art Gallery, 1972, Juneau (Alaska) Art Mus., 1972, Springfield (Mo.) Art Mus., 1973, U. N.D. Grand Forks, 1974, Washington and Jefferson Coll., Washington, Pa., 1975, MacMurray Coll., Jacksonville, Ill., 1976, Gallery of Fine Arts, Eastern Mont. Coll., 1976, Inst. of Culture, Janow Podlaski, Poland, 1977, Seattle Arts Commn., 1978, Polish Cultural Center, Buffalo, 1979, Cabo Frio Internat. Print Biennial, Brazil, 1983, Sunderland (Eng.) Poly. U. Faculty Exchange Exhbn., 1984, Internat Art Biennial Mus. Hosio Capranica-Viterbo, Italy, 1985; represented in permanent collections: San Francisco Art Mus., Seattle Art Mus., Henry Gallery, U. Wash., Seattle, Highline Coll., Midway, Wash., Marylhurst Coll., Art Mus., Janow Podlaski, Poland, Tacoma Nat. Bank, Fine Arts Gallery of San Diego. Mem. Coll. Art Assn., AAUP. Home: 2242 NE 177th St Seattle WA 98155-5241 Office: U Wash Coll Arts & Scis Sch Art Dm # 10 Seattle WA 98195

PAXON, L. WILLIAM, congressman; b. Buffalo, Apr. 29, 1954; s. Leon W. and Mary P. (Sellers) P. BA, Canisius Coll., 1977. Mem. Erie County Legis., N.Y., 1978-82, N.Y. State Assembly, 1983-89, 101st-104th Congresses from 31st (now 27th) N.Y. dist., 1989—; chair Nat. Rep. Congrl. Com.; mem. com. on commerce. Mem. Buffalo C. of C., Lions. Roman Catholic. Youngest mem. in history of Erie County Legislature. Office: US Ho of Reps 2436 Rayburn HOB Washington DC 20515-3227 also: 5500 Main St Williamsville NY 14221*

PAXSON, LOWELL WHITE, television station executive; b. Rochester, N.Y., Apr. 17, 1935; s. Donald Earl and Maybelle L. (White) P.; m. Jean Louise Blauvelt, May 2, 1961 (div. Apr. 1977); children: Todd L., Devon W., Julie; m. Barbara Ann Chapman, Nov. 19, 1977 (div. Nov. 1988); children: Thomas, Jennifer; m. Marla J. Bright, Jan. 6, 1990; 1 child, Nicole. BA, Syracuse U., 1956. Pres., owner Sta. WACK-AM, Newark, N.Y., 1957-61, Sta. WKSN-AM/FM, Jamestown, N.Y., 1961-68, Sta. WNYP-TV, Jamestown, 1966-68, Sta. WTBY-AM, Waterbury, Conn., 1968-70, Sta. WYND-AM, Sarasota, Fla., 1968-74, Sta. WAVS-AM, Ft. Lauderdale, Fla., 1973-77, Sta. WWQT-AM, Clearwater, Fla., 1977-83, Sta. WHBS-FM, Holiday, Fla., 1977-83; pres. Full Circle Mktg., Fla., 1968-77; founder, pres emeritus Home Shopping Network, St. Petersburg, Fla., 1982-91; founder, pres. Paxson Broadcasting, St. Petersburg and Clearwater, 1991—; owner WHPT-FM/WHNX-AM, St. Petersburg 1991—, WWNX-AM/FM, Orlando, WROO-FM, Jacksonville, Fla., WTZA-FM, Miami, Fla., WLVE-FM, Miami; operator WMGF-FM, Orlando, WVRI-FM, Orlando, WAIA-FM, Jacksonville, WZNZ-AM, Jacksonville, WNZS-AM, Jacksonville. Trustee Milligan Coll., Tenn., 1987—; bd. dirs. Broadcap, Washington, 1986—; mem. Coun. of 100 of Pinellas County, St. Petersburg, 1985—; chmn. City of Sarasota Planning and Zoning Commn., 1970-74. Capt. U.S. Army, 1956-57. Mem. Nat. Assn. Broadcasters, Nat. Cable TV Assn., Direct Mktg. Assn. Am., Roebling Soc. Republican. Avocations: yachting, deep sea fishing. Home: 700 Spottis Woode Ln Clearwater FL 34616-5266 Office: Paxson Broadcasting 18401 US Highway 19 N Clearwater FL 34624-1739 also: Sta WMGF-FM Ste 220 2500 Maitland Center Pky Maitland FL 32751-4179

PAXSON, RICHARD, newspaper editor. Editor Va. news desk, Va. weeklies The Washington Post. Office: The Washington Post 1150 15th St NW Washington DC 20071*

PAXTON, BILL, actor, writer, director; b. Ft. Worth, May 17, 1955; s. John Lane and Mary Lou (Gray) P; m. Louise Newbury. Student, NYU; studies with Stella Adler, Vincent Chase. Actor: (feature films) Mortuary, 1981, Stripes, 1981, The Lords of Discipline, 1982, Streets of Fire, 1983, Impulse, 1983, Weird Science, 1984, Terminator, 1984, Commando, 1985, Aliens, 1985 (Saturn award Acad. of Sci. Fiction, Fantasy, and Horror Films 1986), Near Dark, 1986, Pass the Ammo, 1987, Next of Kin, 1989, The Last of the Finest, 1990, Navy Seals, 1990, Predator 2, 1990, One False Move, 1992, Hurricane, 1992, The Vagrant, 1992, Indian Summer, 1993, Boxing Helena, 1993, Tombstone, 1993, True Lies, 1994, Frank and Jesse, 1994, Apollo 13, 1995, (TV movies) Deadly Lessons, 1983, The Atlanta Child Murders, 1985, An Early Frost, 1985, (TV mini-series) Fresno, 1986, (TV series) The Hitch-Hiker, 1986; dir. (theatrical short) Fish Heads, 1982 (Spl. Award Melbourne Film Festival 1982); producer, co-author (theatrical short) Scoop, 1983. Mem. Screen Actors Guild. Office: care Hildy Gottlieb Internat Creative Mgmt 836 Greenway Dr Beverly Hills CA 90210-3006 also: care Carla Schalman Rogers and Cowan 10000 Santa Monica Blvd Los Angeles CA 90067-7007*

PAXTON, DAN RICHARDS, human resources executive; b. Salt Lake City, Nov. 27, 1947; s. Lester Cline and Helen (Richards) P.; m. Diana Paxton, Jan. 3, 1973; children: Marc, Jonathan, Danielle. BS in Edn., U. Utah, 1970; MS in Edn., Utah State U., 1971; D. in Edn., Brigham Young U., 1976. Advisor mgmt. tng. devel. Atlantic Richfield Co., Los Angeles, 1976-78; asst. dean, dir. undergrad. programs Georgetown U., Washington, 1978-83; mgr. mgmt. tng. Frito-Lay, Dallas, 1983, mgr. orgn., human resources devel., 1983-84, group mgr. mgmt. devel., 1984-85; sr. dir. human resources devel. Pizza Hut, Wichita, Kans., 1985-86; v.p. human resources PepsiCo Inc., Purchase, N.Y., 1986-89; v.p. personnel Pepsi Cola, Somers, N.Y., 1989—; asst. prof. mgmt. orgn. behavior Georgetown U., Washington, 1981-83; vis. prof. Brigham Young U., Provo, Utah, 1979. Served to lt. U.S. Army, 1981-83. Mem. Acad. of Mgmt., Am. Soc. Tng. & Devel., Metro. N.Y. Assn. for Applied Psychology, N.Y. Human Resource Planners Soc., Am. Soc. for Personnel Administrn. Office: Pepsi Cola Company 700 Anderson Rd Somers NY 10589

PAXTON, J. WILLENE, retired university administrator; b. Birmingham, Ala., Oct. 30, 1930; d. Will and Elizabeth (Davis) P. AB, Birmingham So. Coll., 1950; MA, Mich. State U., 1951; EdD, Ind. U., 1971. Nat. cert. counselor, lic. profl. counselor, Tenn. Dormitory dir. Tex. Tech U., Lubbock, 1951-53; counselor Mich. State U., East Lansing, summer 1951, 52; dir. univ. ctr. and housing SUNY, Fredonia, 1953-56, assoc. dean of students, 1956-57; asst. dean of women U. N.Mex., Albuquerque, 1957-63; dean of women East Tenn. State U., Johnson City, 1963-68, 70-78, dir. counseling ctr., 1978-92; ret., 1992. Sec. administrv. bd. Meth. Ch., 1983-86, chmn., 1994—, chmn. fin. campaign, 1995, social concerns com., 1991-93, program chmn. Good Timers fellowship, 1995, pres. Sunday Sch. class, 1994; tng. dir. Contact Teleministries, Inc., 1983-87, chmn., 1988, 95, vice chmn., 1993-94; bd. dirs. Asbury Ctrs., 1990—, chmn. policy com., 1995. Mem. AAUW (br. pres.), APA, ACA, Tenn. Psychol. Assn., Assn. Univ. and Coll. Counseling Ctr. Dirs. (conv. planning com. 1991), Am. Coll. Pers. Assn. (media bd., newsletter editor), Nat. Assn. Women Deans, Adminstrs. and Counselors, Tenn. Assn. Women Deans and Counselors (state pres., v.p., program chmn.), Delta Kappa Gamma (chpt. pres. 1974-76, state rec. sec. 1977-79, v.p. 1979-81, chmn. nominating com. 1981-83, chmn. leadership devel. com. 1983-85. internat. rsch. com. 1982-84, chmn. self-study com. 1985-87, chmn. com. to study exec. sec. 1987-89, state pres. 1989-91, parliamentarian 1991-93, internat. com. 1992-94, mem. awards com. 1993-95, chmn. internat. conv. meal functions com. 1994, State Achievement award 1987), East Tenn. Edn. Assn. (chmn. guidance divsn.), Gen. Federated Woman's Club (pres. 1980-81, 88-89, 95—, 2nd v.p. 1991-95), Univ. Women's Club (v.p. 1993-94, pres. 1994—), ETSU Retirees Assn. (bd. dirs. 1995, program com.). Home: 1203 Lester Harris Rd Johnson City TN 37601-3335

PAXTON, ROBERT OWEN, historian, educator; b. Lexington, Va., June 15, 1932; s. Matthew W. and Nell B. (Owen) P.; m. Sarah Plimpton, Dec. 9, 1983. B.A., Washington and Lee U., 1954, LittD (hon.), 1974; B.A., Oxford (Eng.) U., 1956, M.A., 1961; Ph.D., Harvard U., 1963; DHL (hon.), SUNY, Stony Brook, 1994; DL (hon.), U. Caen, France, 1994. Instr. history U. Calif., Berkeley, 1961-63, asst. prof., 1963-67; asso. prof. SUNY, Stony Brook, 1967-69; prof. history Columbia U., 1969—, chmn. dept., 1980-82, dir. Inst. on West Europe, 1991-95. Author: Parades and Politics at Vichy, 1966, Vichy France: Old Guard and New Order, 1940-44, 1972, Europe in the Twentieth Century, 1975, 2d edit., 1985; co-author: Vichy France and the Jews, 1981; co-editor: De Gaulle and the U.S., 1994. Served with USNR, 1956-58. Decorated chevalier Ordre National des Arts et des Lettres (France), officer Ordre National du Mérite (France); Rhodes scholar, 1954-56; Am. Coun. Learned Socs. fellow, 1974-75; Rockefeller Found. fellow, 1978-79; German Marshall Fund fellow, 1986. Fellow Am. Acad. Arts and Letters; mem. Am. Hist. Assn., Soc. d'histoire moderne, Linnaean Soc. N.Y. (pres. 1978-80). Home: 460 Riverside Dr Apt 72 New York NY 10027-6820 Office: Columbia U Dept History New York NY 10027

PAXTON, TOM, songwriter, entertainer, author; b. Chgo., Oct. 31, 1937; s. George Burton and Esther Hildegard (Peterson) P.; m. Margaret Ann Cummings, Aug. 5, 1963; children: Jennifer Ann, Katherine Claire. BFA, U. Okla., 1959. Rec. artist with Elektra, Flying Fish, Hogeye, Reprise, Vanguard, Mountain Railroad, Pax Records, 1962—; owner Pax Records. Folk artist, U.S., Can., Gt. Brit., Scandanavia, France, Germany, Australia, N.Z., 1960—; albums include Ramblin' Boy, 1964, Ain't That News, 1965, Outward Bound, 1966, Morning Again, 1968, The Things I Notice Now, 1969, Number 6, 1970, The Compleat Tom Paxton, 1971, How Come the Sun, 1971, Peace Will Come, 1972, New Songs for Old Friends, 1973, Something in My Life, 1975, New Songs from the Briar Patch, 1977, Heroes, 1978, Up and Up, 1980, The Paxton Report, 1980, One Million Lawyers...and Other Disasters, 1986, The Marvelous Toy and Other Gallimaufry, 1987, Even a Gray Day, And Loving You, 1987, Politics, 1989, The Authentic Guitar of Tom Paxton, 1989, It Ain't Easy, 1991; author: (children's books) Jennifer's Rabbit, 1988, Belling The Cat, 1990, Englebert the Elephant, 1990, Aesop's Fables Retold in Verse, 1988, Androcles and The Lion, 1991. Bd. dirs. Kerrville Polk Festival, 1990. Mem. ASCAP, AFTRA, Am. Fedn. Musicians, Screen Actors Guild, World Folk Music Assn. (hon. chmn. bd.). Office: Pax Records PO Box 2256 East Hampton NY 11937-0296*

PAYCHECK, JOHNNY, country western musician; b. Greenfield, Ohio, May 31, 1941. Played with Faron Young, George Jones, Ray Price; songs include A-11, 1965, Heartbreak Tennessee, 1966, The Lovin' Machine, 1966, Apartment No. 9, Touch My Heart, She's All I Got, Someone to Give My Love to, 1972, Love is a Good Thing, 1972, Something About You I Love, 1973, Mr. Lovemaker, 1973, Song and Dance Man, 1973, Slide Off Your Satin Sheets, 1974, I'm the Only Hell Mama Ever Raised, 1974, Take This Job and Shove It, 1974, Maybellene, 1978, You Can Have Her, 1979, You Better Move On, 1980, I Can't Hold Myself in Line, 1981, I Never Got Over You, 1983; albums include Double Trouble (with George Jones), Greatest Hits, Take This Job and Shove It, Armed and Crazy, Everybody's Got a Family, Back On The Job, Mr. Lovemaker. *

PAYDOS, CHARLES J., insurance company executive; b. Ware, Mass., Sept. 24, 1940; s. Benjamin John and Helen Victoria (Jesyk) P.; m. Carol Jean Roby, Nov. 30, 1963; children—Jennifer Ann, Timothy Bryce. B.S., U. Mass., 1962. Vice pres. Phoenix Mut. Life Ins. Co., Hartford, Conn., 1978-82, sr. v.p. group and pensions, 1982-87, exec. v.p., 1987—; dir. Phoenix Am. Life Ins. Co., Wilmington, Del., Phoenix Holdings, Hartford. Fellow Soc. Actuaries; mem. Am. Acad. Actuaries. Republican. Avocations: photography; cycling; marathons; collecting 1930 jazz recordings. Home: 20 Wyndcliffe Park Bloomfield CT 06002-2142 Office: Phoenix Mut Life Ins Co 1 American Row Hartford CT 06115

PAYN, CLYDE FRANCIS, technology company executive, consultant; b. Auckland, New Zealand, Jan. 17, 1952; came to U.S., 1973; s. Phillip Francis and Ngaire Eunice P.; m. Betsy Ann Dannels, June 17, 1978; children: Tamara, Brittany, Erik. Cert., Auckland Inst. Tech., 1971; MBA, Vanderbilt U., 1981. Tech. mgr. Carborundum (N.Z.) Ltd., Auckland, 1968-73; mem. product application tech. staff Carborundum Co., Niagara Falls, N.Y., 1973-78; mgr. product mktg. Universal Abrasives, Phila., 1978-80; bus. mgr., catalyst advocate Johnson Matthey, Inc., Phila., 1980-84; pres. Catalyst Cons., Inc., Phila., 1984—; CEO Catalyst Group, Phila., 1988—. Pres. Hideaway Hill Civic Assn., Maple Glen, Pa., 1988, 89. Mem. AIChE, Am. Chem. Soc., Catalysis Soc., Comml. Devel. Assn., Chem. Mktg. Rsch. Assn., Polymer Mfg. Engrs. Assn. Achievements include development of new process technology, catalyst and product development for petroleum, petrochemical, chemical and environmental industries. Office: The Catalyst Group Inc PO Box 637 Spring House PA 19477-0637

PAYNE, ANCIL HORACE, retired broadcasting executive; b. Mitchell, Oreg., Sept. 5, 1921; s. Leslie E. and Pearl A. (Brown) P.; m. Valerie Dorrance Davies, Apr. 6, 1959; children: Anne Sparrow, Alison Louise, Lucinda Catherine. Student, Willamette U., 1939-41, U. Oreg., 1941, U. Notre Dame, Ohio State U., 1943; B.A. U. Wash., 1947; postgrad., Am. U., 1950-51; hon. PhD, Willamette Univ., 1991. Adminstrv. asst. to congressman, Washington, 1949-52; gen. mgr. Martin Van Lines, Anchorage, 1952-56; mgr. Frontiers-Oreg. Ltd., Portland, Oreg., 1956-59; asst. v.p. bus. div. King Broadcasting Co., Seattle, 1959-63, v.p., 1963-70, exec. v.p., 1970-71, pres., 1971-87; chmn. bd. affiliates NBC, 1975-79; bd. dirs. Airborne Freight Co., 1977-94. Mem. Oreg. Bd. Higher Edn., 1966-70; bd. dirs. Centrum Found., Cobalt Inc., U. Wash. Press. Lt. (j.g.) USNR, 1942-45, PTO. Mem. Monday Club, Rainier Club, Phi Beta Kappa Assoc., Alpha Delta Sigma. Episcopalian. Home: 1107 First Ave # 2001 Seattle WA 98101 Office: Ancil H Payne & Assocs 1107 1st Ave Apt 606 Seattle WA 98101

PAYNE, ANITA HART, reproductive endocrinologist, researcher; b. Karlsruhe, Baden, Germany, Nov. 24, 1926; came to U.S. 1938; d. Frederick Michael and Erna Rose (Hirsch) Hart; widowed; children: Gregory Steven, Teresa Payne-Lyons. BA, U. Calif., Berkeley, 1949, PhD, 1952. Rsch. assoc. U. Mich., Ann Arbor, 1961-71, asst. prof., 1971-76, assoc. prof., 1976-81, prof., 1981—; assoc. dir. Ctr. for Study Reprodn., 1989-94; vis. scholar Stanford U., 1987-88; mem. reproductive biology study sect. NIH, Bethesda, Md., 1978-79, biochem. endocrinology study sect., 1979-83, population rsch. com. Nat. Inst. Child Health and Human Devel., 1989-93. Assoc. editor Steroids, 1987-93; contbr. book chpts., articles to profl. jours. Recipient award for cancer rsch. Calif. Inst. for Cancer Rsch., 1953, Acad. Women's Caucus award U. Mich., 1986. Mem. Endocrine Soc. (chmn. awards com. 1983-84, mem. nominating com. 1985-87, coun. 1988-91), Am. Soc. Andrology (exec. coun. 1980-83), Soc. for Study of Reprodn. (bd. dirs. 1982-85, sec. 1986-89, pres. 1990-91). Office: Stanford U Med Ctr Dept Gynecology/Obstetrics Div Reproductive Biology Stanford CA 94305-5317

PAYNE, BILLY (WILLIAM A. PAYNE), real estate lawyer, sports association executive; m. Martha Payne. JD, U Ga Law School. Head Atlanta Com. for the Olympic Games 1996, 1992—. Office: US Olympic Com 1750 E Boulder St Colorado Springs CO 80909-5746

PAYNE, CHRISTINE BABCOCK, career psychologist; b. Junction City, Kans., Jan. 14, 1943; d. David Edward and Dorothy (Viner) Babcock; m. James R. Payne, Oct. 16, 1982; children: Terrence Thomas, Melanie Payne Tate. AA, Stephens Coll., 1963; BA, Parsons Coll., 1966; MS, Calif. Coast U., 1993, postgrad., 1993—. Tchr. Page-Park Sch., St. Louis, 1966-68; assoc. buyer Famous-Barr Dept. Store, St. Louis, 1968-70; pers. asst. Gimbel's Dept. Store, N.Y.C., 1970-71; tng. dir. Gimbel's East, N.Y.C., 1971-72; employment mgr. Hosp. for Spl. Surgery, N.Y.C., 1972-73; pers. dir. J.B. Ivey & Co., Orlando, Fla., 1973-75; dir. employer rels. Okla. Employment Security Commn., Tulsa, 1980-84; pers. dir. Sanger-Harris Dept. Store, Tulsa, 1982; dir. career devel. Women's Ctr. U. Tulsa, 1988-93; pres., owner Transitions Counseling Ctr., Tulsa, 1992—; counseling dir. career and ednl. svcs. Resonance Ctr. for Women, Tulsa, 1993; coord. dislocated worker program Ctrl. Okla. Vo-Tech Sch., Drumright, 1984-86. Author: Tearing Down the Walls: An Adult Woman's Guide to Education and Financial Aid, 1993. Speech writer State Senator Ted V. Fisher, Okla., 1986; pres. Vol. Svc. Coun., St. Louis, 1975-79. Recipient Mayor's Pinnacle award for Outstanding Contbn. in Area of Edn., Mayor's Commn. on Status of Women, Tulsa, 1993. Mem. ACA, NAFE, Nat. Career Devel. Assn., Nat. Assn. Fin. Aid Adminstrs., Adult Career Devel. Network, Assn. for Measurement Evaluation in Counseling Devel. Avocations: writing, genealogy. Office: Transitions Counseling Ctr 4853 S Sheridan Ste 606 Tulsa OK 74145

PAYNE, DONALD M., congressman; b. Newark, July 16, 1934. BA, Seton Hall U. Freeholder Essex County, 1973-78; ins. co. exec., prior to 1989, former v.p. computer forms mfr.; mem. Newark Mcpl. Coun., 1982-89, 101st-104th Congresses from 10th N.J. dist., 1989—; mem. econ. and ednl. opportunity com., mem. internat. rels. com. Chmn. World YMCA Refugee and Rehab. Com., 1973-81; pres YMCA's of USA. Democrat. Office: US Ho of Reps 2244 Rayburn HOB Washington DC 20515-3010 also: 970 Broad St Rm 1435-B Newark NJ 07102*

PAYNE, EDWARD CARLTON, archbishop; b. Hartford, Conn., Aug. 4, 1928; s. Robert Carlton and Margaret Ilon (Bohnar-Donovan) P. Lic.Th., Santa Maria del Gracia, 1947; Lic.Sac.Th., St. Francis Sem., 1966; B.S. Peoples U., 1973, M.Div., 1976, D.S.M., 1971, D.A.E.H., 1973; D.D., St. Ephrem's Inst., 1974. Ordained deacon, 1947, archdeacon, 1951, presbyter, 1953, priest, 1966, archpriest, 1967; rector's asst. Grace Episcopal Ch., Hartford, Conn., 1947-51; asst. chaplain St. Mary and All Saints Episcopal Ch., Higganum, Conn., 1947-50; chaplain's asst. St. Elizabeth's Episcopal Chapel, Hartford, Conn., 1947-55; dir., prior Order of the Cross, Hartford, Conn., 1951—; rector's asst. Ch. of the Good Shepherd, Hartford, 1951-55, St. James Episcopal Ch., Hartford, 1956-57; rector Holy Cross Old Roman Cath. Ch., Hartford, 1966—; canon Old Cath. Cathedral Ch. of Christ-on-the-Mount, Mariavite-Russian Orthodox Ch., Woodstock, N.Y., 1967-68; sr. pastor Old Roman Cath. Cathedral Ch. of the Holy Saviour, Niagra Falls, N.Y., 1971-81; dean of Conn.-R.I. Old Roman Cath. Ch., 1968-69, bishop of Conn.-R.I., 1969-72, archbishop of New Eng., 1972—; metropolitan, exarch of Ugro-Finnic Peoples,, 1975—; patriarch Old Roman Cath. Hungarian Orthodox Ch. Patriarchate of N. Am., 1975—; Slavonic World Patriarchate of Am. World Patriarchates, 1994—; patriarch West Community Ch., East Granby, Conn., 1976—; pres. Council of Bishops, Am. World Patriarchates of Byelorussian-Ukrainian Orthodox Cath. Ch., 1975-78, 94—; staff mem. Open Hearth Mission, Hartford, 1985-91; Patriarchate Hungarian-Slovonic Orthodox, 1994; moderator United Cath. Conf., Boston, 1967-69; interim pastor Christ Cath. Ch. of the Transfiguration, Boston, 1970-72; instr. Independent Cath. Seminarium, 1970—; mem. Synod of No.Am. Old Roman Ch., 1966-85; mem. Commn. on Liturgy and Music, 1968-70; hon. chaplain N.S.K.K. Motorcycle Club, Hartford, Conn., 1974-75; interim organist Our Saviour's Polish Nat. Cath. Ch., Hartford, Conn., 1957, Warburton Community Congregational Ch. (United Ch. of Christ), Hartford, Conn., 1959-60, Hartford Elks Lodge, 1962-64, organist, 1964—; chaplain, organist, counselor Culbro Tobacco Co., Windsor and Simsbury, Conn., 1967, 77-78. Editor: The Silver Cross, 1951—; The Independent Catholic, 1970—; The Associated Traditionalist, 1974-75; Asst. editor: The Augustinian, 1966-70. Chmn. Hartford area Peter A. Reilly Def. Com., 1974-76; chmn. Bradley J. Ankuda Def. Com., 1977-78. Recipient God and Country award First Hartford Council Area, 1949; recipient cert. of appreciation Quirk Middle Sch., Hartford, Conn., 1978; prelate Order of St. Nicholas, Kent, Eng. 1971; nominee Cmdr. Orthodox Order of St. Gregory the Illuminator, Holy Russian Orthodox Ch. in Exile. Mem. Traditionalist Clergy Assn. (sec. 1974-75), Red Men Club, Elks. Republican. Performer, instr., composer, ar-

ranger tenor banjo, mandolin, bugle, piano, organ, and carillon. Office: PO Box 290261 Wethersfield CT 06129-0261 Be "Furchtlos und Treu" ("Fearless and Faithful"). Never consider yourself to be a failure or you'll be one. Keep on keeping on, no matter what the odds. Go onward and upward, using all stumbling blocks as stepping stones, even though you have to burn bridges so that you don't retreat. And, above all, offer many prayers of thanks to God every day, for that's what the Eucharist means: THANK-SGIVING.

PAYNE, ELIZABETH ELEANORE, surgeon, otolaryngologist; b. Detroit, Mar. 17, 1945; d. Richard Franklin and Eleanore Grace (Dieterich) P.; 1 child from previous marriage, Julia Elizabeth Komanecky. Student, St. Olaf Coll., 1962-64; MD, U. Iowa, 1968. Cert. Am. Bd. Otolaryngology, Am. Acad. Otolaryngic Allergy; lic. in medicine, Minn., Iowa. Intern Phila. Gen. Hosp., 1968-69; resident gen. surgery U. Minn., Mpls., 1969-70; resident otolaryngology U. Minn., 1970-74, clin. asst. prof. dept. otolaryngology, asst. clin. prof. dept. family practice and community health; pvt. practice, Mpls., 1974—; mem. med. staff North Meml. Med. Ctr., Mpls., Children's Med. Ctr., Abbott Northwestern Hosp. Contbr. articles to profl. jours. Mem. AMA, Am. Acad. Otolaryngology Head and Neck Surgery, Am. Acad. Otolaryngic Allergy, Minn. State Med. Assn., Minn. Acad. Otolaryngology Head and Neck Surgery (coun. mem.), Minn. Acad. Medicine, Hennepin County Med. Assn. Office: Affiliated Otolaryngologists 3366 Oakdale Ave N Ste 307 Minneapolis MN 55422-2985

PAYNE, EUGENE EDGAR, insurance company executive; b. San Antonio, Aug. 9, 1942; s. Eugene Edgar and Louise (Speer) P.; m. Karen S. James, June 10, 1978; children: Kelly Lynn, Katherine Louise, Mary Patricia, Kerry Erin, Kimberley Ann, Thomas Julius. B.S., Tex. A&M U., 1964, M.S., 1965; Ph.D. (research fellow 1968-70), U. Okla., 1970. Mgmt. cons. E.I. DuPont de Nemours Co., Del., 1965-68; dir. mgmt. info. systems, spl. cons. Electronic Data Systems Corp., Dallas, 1970-71; dir. planning and mgmt. systems U. Tex., Dallas, 1971-74; v.p. fin. and mgmt. S.W. Tex. State U., San Marcos, 1974-81; v.p. fin. and adminstrn. Tex. Tech U., 1981-88, Tex. Tech Health Ctr., Lubbock, 1981-88; treas. Tex. Tech U. Found., 1981-88; exec. v.p. Investors Life Ins. of N.Am., Austin, Tex., 1988—, Investors Life of Calif., 1988—, Standard Life Ins. of Miss., 1988—, InterContinental Life of N.J., 1988—; exec. v.p. Family Life Ins. Co., 1991—, Fin. Industries Corp., Austin, Tex., 1991—; cons. in field. Contbr. articles to profl. jours. Vestry, fin. com. St. Christopher's Episc. Ch., 1983-86; chmn. bd. trustees All Saints Episc. Sch., Lubbock, 1985-89, Episc. Sem. of Southwest, Austin, Tex., 1985-89. NDEA fellow, 1969. Mem. Am. Inst. Indsl. Engrs. (Sr.), Inst. Mgmt. Scis., Ops. Research Soc., Assn. Computing Machinery, Assn. Instl. Research, Soc. Coll. and Univ. Planning, Nat. Assn. Coll. and Univ. Bus. Officers, Rotary. Home: 1300 Circle Ridge Dr Westlake Hills TX 78746-3402 Office: FIC Ins Group Ste 1400 701 Brazos St Austin TX 78701-3232

PAYNE, FRANCES ANNE, literature educator, researcher; b. Harrisonburg, Va., Aug. 28, 1932; d. Charles Franklin and Willie (Tarvin) P. B.A., Shorter Coll., 1953, B.Mus., 1953; M.A., Yale U., 1954, Ph.D., 1960. Instr. Conn. Coll., New London, 1955-56; instr. U. Buffalo, 1958-60, lectr., 1960, asst. prof., 1960-67; assoc. prof. SUNY, Buffalo, 1967-75; prof. English and medieval lit. SUNY, 1975—; adj. fellow St. Anne's Coll., Oxford, Eng., 1966-67, 68-69. Author: King Alfred and Boethius, 1968; Chaucer and Menippean Satire, 1981. Contbr. articles to scholarly publs. AAUW fellow, Oxford, 1966-67; Research Found. grantee SUNY Central, Oxford, 1967, 68, 71, 72; recipient Julian Park award SUNY-Buffalo, 1979. Mem. Medieval Acad. Am., Internat. Arthurian Soc., New Chaucer Soc., Internat. Soc. Anglo-Saxonists, Pi Kappa Lambda. Office: SUNY-Buffalo 306 Clemens Hall Buffalo NY 14260

PAYNE, FRED R(AY), aerospace engineering educator, researcher; b. Mayfield, Ky., Jan. 26, 1931; s. Joe L. and Bonnie (Vincent) P.; m. Marilyn Maassen, Oct. 12, 1957; children: John F., Kevin R., Joel F. BS in Physics, U. Ky., 1952; MS Aero. Engring., Pa. State U., State College, 1964, PhD, 1966. Registered profl. engr., Tex. Commd. 2d lt. USAF, 1952, advanced through grades to maj., 1966, resigned, 1966; prof. Pa. State U., State Coll., 1966-68; design specialist Gen. Dynamics, Ft. Worth, 1968-69; prof. U. Tex., Arlington, 1969—, aero. engring. grad. advisor, 1973-82, 92—; bd. dirs. TRL-Aero. Engring., U. Tex., 1972—; organizer profl. confs. Editor Integral Methods in Sci. Engring., 1986-91; editor newsletter Ft. Worth Chess Club, 1973-78, Tex. Chess Assn., 1977-78; contbr. articles to profl. jours. Chess instr. Dan Danciger Community Ctr., Ft. Worth, 1973-77; youth dir. Ft. Worth Chess Club, 1973-78. Rsch. grantee USN, NSF, NASA, 1963-67, 75-91, Orgn. Rsch. Fund, 1975-89; faculty fellow NASA Ames Rsch. Ctr., 1988, 89. Mem. Am. Math. Soc., Am. Phys. Soc., Am. Acad. Mechanics, Soc. for Indsl. and Applied Math., Ky. Chess Club, Tex. Chess Club (pres. 1950-52, 73-75), Sigma Xi (pres. U. Tex.-Arlington chpt. 1990-92). Avocations: chess master (postal), classical music, gardening. Office: U Tex Aerospace Engring Arlington TX 76019

PAYNE, GARELD GENE, vocal music educator, medical transcriptionist; b. Colony, Okla., Aug. 27, 1931; s. Eugene A. and Agnes D. (Chastain) P.; children: Gareld, S. Raymond, Lynn Dita, Jana Lee. MusB, Oklahoma City U., 1965; MusM in Edn., North Tex. State U. (name change to U. North Tex.), 1969; ednl. specialist, Pitts. State U., 1989; postgrad., Okla. State U. Ind. organist, pianist numerous nightclubs, nationwide, 1956-64; instr. vocal, instrumental music Muenster (Tex.) Ind. Sch. Dist., 1965-69; tchr. vocal music Dallas Ind. Sch. Dist., 1966-74, Carrizo Springs (Tex.) Ind. Sch. Dist., 1976-79, Coffeyville (Kans.) Unified Sch. Dist., 1979-91. Rec. artist (album) Evening With Gareld, 1984; composer publ. anthems. With USAF, 1950-53. Scholar Oklahoma City U., 1949. Mem. Am. Fedn. Musicians, NEA, Am. Orff-Schulwerk Assn., Am. Recorder Soc., Am. Theater Organ Soc., Am. Guild Organist Orgns. of Am. Kodaly Educators, Phi Mu Alpha Sinfonia Frat., Phi Delta Kappa. Republican. Methodist. Avocations: astrology, oil and water color painting, cooking, reading, computers. Home: 3627 NW 15th St Oklahoma City OK 73107-4423

PAYNE, G(EORGE) FREDERICK, educational administrator; b. Summerville, S.C., Jan. 29, 1941; s. Fred N. and Lota (Griffith) P.; m. Kay Martin, June 23, 1963; children: John F., Mark C., Janet E. Student Ga. Inst. Tech., 1959-60, U.S. Naval Acad., 1960-62; BS, U. S.C., 1963, MA, 1966; MRE, Luth. Theol. Sem., 1968; postgrad. U. Ga., 1969-71; LLD (hon.) Lincoln Meml. U., 1988. From instr. to asst. prof. Ga. So. Coll., Statesboro, 1966-78; dir. admission Brewton-Parker Coll., Mt. Vernon, Ga., 1978-80; v.p. for devel. North Greenville Coll., Tigerville, S.C., 1980-86; pres. Limestone Coll., Gaffney, S.C., 1986-91, dir. various grants 1976-91; spl. agt., registered rep. Prudential Fin. Svcs., 1991-92; dir. ITT Tech. Inst., Greenville, S.C., 1992—. Author: An Introduction to the Principles of Geography: Facts, Skills, Concepts, and Models, 1973; also articles. Active Leadership Greer, S.C., 1980-81, regent, 1982-84; active AACTion Consortium, 1980-82, Leadership Greenville, S.C., 1982-83; bd. dirs. Greenville County unit Am. Cancer Soc., 1985-86; advisor Cherokee County Arts Council, 1986-91. Served with USN, 1960-62. Recipient Disting. Service award Brewton-Parker Coll., 1980, Disting. Service award North Greenville Coll., 1986. Mem. Council for Advancement and Support Edn., Greater Greer C. of C. (bd. dirs. 1981-84). Baptist. Lodge: Rotary. Avocation: reading. Office: ITT Tech Inst 1 Marcus Dr Bldg 4 Patewood Bus Ctr Greenville SC 29615

PAYNE, GERALD OLIVER, elementary education educator; b. East St. Louis, Ill., July 17, 1930; s. Amos Oliver and Suzanne Louise (Goussery) P.; m. Nancy Louise Ecklund, Aug. 8, 1959; children: Paul Clifton, Christopher Amos, Scott Eric, Miriam Louise, Susan Jeannette. BA, Yale U., 1953; MusB, U. Dubuque, Iowa, 1957; PhD, U. Wis., 1969. Tchr. pub. schs. Aspen, Colo., 1959-61; tchr. pub. schs. Madison, 1961-65; coord. fgn. langs., 1964-69, asst. dir. curriculum, 1967-69; assoc. prof. edn. SUNY, Buffalo, 1969-71, prof. edn., 1971-86, chmn. dept. curriculum and supervision, 1975-78, coord. cert. advanced studies in adminstrn. and supervision, 1969-75, 78-86, assoc. chmn. dept. elem. edn. and reading, 1985-86; chmn. dept. edn. and psychology Warren Wilson Coll., N.C., 1986-90, chmn. div. social sci. and humanities, 1987-90; tchr. Hendersonville County Schs., Hendersonville, N.C., 1990—. Mem. working com. Fgn. Lang. Educators Wis., 1968-69; mem. North Central Evaluation Teams, 1967, 68, 69; cons. Ednl. Prof. Devel. Assistance project Lackawanna (N.Y.) Pub. Schs., 1969-74; coll. rep. Coll. Assn. for Devel. Ednl. Administrn., N.Y. State, 1969-84; cons. middle sch. Cheektowaga (N.Y.) Central Schs., 1974; cons. Orchard Park (N.Y.) Middle Sch., 1974-76, Alden (N.Y.) Middle Sch., 1975, Geneva (N.Y.) Middle Sch., 1979. Contbr. articles to profl. jours. Chmn. troop com. Greater Niagara Frontier coun. Boy Scouts Am., Lewiston, N.Y., 1974-76, scoutmaster, 1976-79; advisor Explorer Post, 1979-83, Order of Arrow, 1978-83; elder 1st Presbyn. Ch., Lewiston, 1978-83, 1st Presbyn. Ch., Hendersonville, N.C., 1991-94. Mem. NEA (life), Western N.Y. Yale Alumni Assn. (mem. schs. com. 1972-83, dir. 1977-83), Nat. Middle Sch. Assn., Assn. for Supervision and Curriculum Devel., Phi Delta Kappa (exec. com. 1978-81, sec. 1985-86, pres.-elect 1986). Republican. Lodge: Masons. Home: RR 4 Box 287 Hendersonville NC 28739-9442 Office: Hendersonville County Schs 414 4th Ave W Hendersonville NC 28739

PAYNE, GLORIA MARQUETTE, business educator; b. Elkins, W.Va., Dec. 21, 1923; d. Anthony and Roselyn Marquette; m. Carl Wesley Payne, Mar. 6, 1950; 1 child, Mary Debra Payne Moore. BA, Davis and Elkins Coll., MHL (hon.), MA, W.Va. U.; PhD, U. Pitts., 1975; postgrad., NYU Fashion Inst. Tech. Cert. designed appearance cons. Sec. Equitable Ins. Co., Elkins, 1943-44; tchr., dept. head Spencer (W.Va.) High Sch., 1944-45; prof. bus. Davis & Elkins Coll., Elkins, 1945-93; image cons. Elkins, 1988-93, bus. cons., 1970-93; mgr. Elkins Wallpaper Shop, 1945-65; owner Merle Norman Cosmetic Studio, Elkins, 1950-56; dir. tchr. workshops W.Va. U., Marshall U., State Dept. Edn., Charleston, W.Va., summers; dir. designer appearance World Modeling Assn., N.Y.C., 1989—; instr. modeling Davis & Elkins Coll., 1990-93. Author: A Methods Class is Interesting and Challenging, 1970, The Oak or the Pumpkin; mem. editl. bd. Nat. Assn. of Business Teachers Edn. Pub., 1993, 94; contbr. articles to profl. jours. Chair Bi-Centennial, City of Elkins; dir. Elkins Fair, City of Elkins; pres. St. Brendans Parish; judge National Main State Forest Festival Parades, 1988-94; rep. Region I at Dallas Nat. Conv., 1994 (one of five nat. finalists); div. chair bus., econs., and tourism. Recipient Outstanding Prof. award Sears-Roebuck Co., Lois Latham award for Excelence in Teaching, Community Svc. award Elkins C. of C., 1992, award for Outstanding Educator W.Va. Vocat. Assn., 1994, Region I award for Outstanding Vocational Educator; 1st recipient James S. McDonnell Found. Fully Endowed Acad. Chair in Bus. and Econs.; named Educator of Yr., W.Va. Women's Club, Outstanding Educator AAUW. Mem. Am. Bus. Writers Assn., W.Va. Bus. Edn. Assn. (past pres., Outstanding Prof., Outstanding Svc. award, Outstanding Bus. Educator award), Tri-State Bus. Edn. Assn. (historian, outstanding svc. award, Tchr.-Educator of the South award 1991), World Modeling Assn. (v.p. 1988-90, modeling award 1989), Designed Appearance U.S. (dir. 1990-93), W.V.C. of C., Beta Sigma Phi (advisor), Beta Alpha Beta (advisor), Pi Beta Phi, Phi Beta Lambda (advisor), The Fashion Club (advisor). Democrat. Roman Catholic. Avocations: flower arranging, modeling. Home: 301 Davis St Elkins WV 26241-4030 Office: Davis & Elkins Coll 100 Sycamore St Elkins WV 26241-3996

PAYNE, HARRY CHARLES, historian, educator; b. Worcester, Mass., Mar. 25, 1947. BA, Yale U., 1969, MA, 1969, MPhil, 1970; hon. degree, Hamilton Coll., 1988, Colgate U., 1989, Williams Coll., 1993, Amherst Coll., 1994. Mem. faculty Colgate U., Hamilton, N.Y., 1973-85, prof. history, 1982-85, provost, 1985; provost, acting pres. Haverford (Pa.) Coll., 1985-88; pres. Hamilton Coll., Clinton, N.Y., 1988-93, Williams Coll., Williamstown, Mass., 1994—. Contbr. numerous articles and revs. to scholarly publs. Bd. dirs. Clark Art Inst., Williamstown Theatre Festival, Barnard Coll., NAICY. Overseas fellow Churchill Coll., Cambridge U., Eng., 1977. Mem. Am. Soc. Eighteenth-Century Studies (Article prize 1977). Office: Williams Coll Office of Pres Williamstown MA 01267

PAYNE, HARRY MORSE, JR., architect; b. Norwood, Mass., Nov. 3, 1922; s. Harry Morse and Edna May (Beardsley) P.; m. Helen Marion Beasley, Aug. 29, 1946; children: Harry Morse, Thomas Beasley, Amelia Morse. Student, Boston Archtl. Center, 1946-49, MIT, 1949-50. Draftsman William G. Upham, Norwood, 1946-47; designer William Riseman Assos., Boston, 1947-49, Harry J. Korslund, Norwood, 1949-51, William Hoskins Brown, Boston, 1951-52; designer, prin. dir. The Architects Collaborative, Cambridge, Mass., 1952-86; pres. The Architects Collaborative, 1975-77, emeritus, 1986—; emeritus Boston Archtl. Center, 1963-65, 71-73; asst. prof. Harvard U. Grad. Sch. Design, 1954-63. Prin. works include U.S. Embassy, Athens, Greece, U. Bagdad (Iraq), Temple Israel, Boston, Quincy Sch, Boston. Served with USN, 1943-46. Fellow AIA; mem. Boston Soc. Architects, Mass. State Assn. Architects, New Eng. Hist. and Geneal. Soc., The Colonial Soc. Mass., Mass. Soc. Genealogists (pres. 1986-88), Lincoln Hist. Soc. (pres. 1990-92). Home: 245 Aspen Cir Lincoln MA 01773-4922 Office: Architects Collaborative 46 Brattle St Cambridge MA 02138-3700

PAYNE, HOWARD JAMES, insurance company executive; b. Des Moines, Iowa, Oct. 22, 1940; s. James W. and Wilma F. (Kever) P.; m. Mary J. Kellam, June 8, 1963; children: Scott D., Steven M. MBA, U. Iowa, 1986. CPCU; assoc. in underwriting, assoc. in mgmt. Underwriter Allied Ins. Co., Des Moines, 1963-70; br. underwriting mgr. Allied Ins. Co., Phoenix, 1973-75; asst. br. mgr. Allied Ins. Co., Santa Rosa, Calif., 1975-77; casualty underwriting mgr. Am. States Ins. Co., Indpls., 1970-73; asst. v.p. underwriting Lumberman's Mut. Ins. Co., Mansfield, Ohio, 1977-80; asst. v.p., underwriting mgr. Hastings (Mich.) Mutual Ins. Co., 1980-82; v.p. underwriting John Deere Ins. Co., Moline, Ill., 1982-86, v.p. program mgr. 1986-90; v.p. credit ins. mgr. John Deere Ins. Co, Des Moines, 1990-93; v.p., spl. program mgr. John Deere Transp., Brookfield, Wis., 1993—; ins. instr. Am. States Ins. Co., Indpls., 1971-73, CPCU chpt., Phoenix, 1973-75; ins. instr. and advisor C.C. Mansfield, Ohio, 1978-80; pres. Am. States Credit Union, Indpls., 1973. Mem. CPCU Soc., West Des Moines C. of C. Republican. Avocations: tennis, physical fitness, reading. Home: 1579 S Moorland Rd # D202 New Berlin WI 53151 Office: John Deere Transp 350 N Sunny Slope Rd Brookfield WI 53005

PAYNE, JOHN ROSS, rare books and archives appraisal-consulting company executive, library science educator; b. Clarksville, Tex., Dec. 4, 1941. BA, Tex. Christian U., 1963; MLS, North Tex. State U., 1967. Successively acting dir., asst. to dir., assoc. libr. for acquisitions, assoc. libr. for ops., rsch. assoc. Harry Ransom Humanities Rsch. Ctr. U. Tex., Austin, 1969-85, prof. Grad. Sch. Libr. and Info. Sci., 1988-89, 91—, prof. grad. course in rare books and lit. manuscripts, 1989—; dir. Payne Assocs., 1978—. Author: A Bibliography of W. H. Hudson, 1977, Modern British Fiction: An Exhibit, 1972; co-author: (with Elizabeth Johnson) Katherine Mansfield: An Exhibit, 1973, (with Adrian Goldstone) A Bibliographical Catalogue of John Steinbeck, 1975; contbr. articles to profl. jours. Lilly fellow Ind. U., 1967-68. Mem. ALA, Am. Soc. Appraisers (state dep. dir.), Appraisers Assn. Am., Soc. Am. Archivists (hon., speaker at Atlanta meeting 1988), Manuscripts Soc., Tex. Libr. Assn., Tex. State Hist. Assn., Book Club of Tex., Grolier Club, Book Collectors of L.A. Home: 2309 Camino Alto Austin TX 78746-2404

PAYNE, KENNETH EUGENE, lawyer; b. Kansas City, Kans., Jan. 12, 1936; s. Felton T. and Irene Elizabeth (Snyder) P.; m. Deidre Lee Hood, Aug. 11, 1957; children: Steven Scott, Kendra Ann. BS, U. Kans., 1959; JD, Am. U., 1965. Bar: Mo. 1965, D.C. 1967. Assoc., Irons, Birch, Swindler & McKie, Washington, 1966-69, Irons, Stockman, Sears & Santorelli, 1969-71; asst. gen. counsel U.S. Dept. Commerce, Washington, 1971-73; ptnr. Finnegan, Henderson, Farabow, Garrett & Dunner, Washington, 1973—; del. Inter-Am. Commn. on Sci. and Tech. Transfer, U.S. Dept. State; cons. UN Indsl. Devel. Orgn.; lectr. Practicing Law Inst., Licensing Law and Bus. Inst. Capt. U.S. Army, 1960-68. Mem. Licensing Execs. Soc. Internat. (treas. 1986-87, pres.-elect 1988, pres. 1989), Licensing Execs. Soc. U.S. and Can. (pres.-elect 1982-83, pres. 1983-84), ABA, Am. Patent Law Assn., Assn. Trial Lawyers Am. Republican. Methodist. Contbr. articles to profl. jours. Home: 4415 N 33d St Arlington VA 22207 Office: Finnegan Henderson Farabow et al Ste 700 1300 I St NW Washington DC 20005-3315

PAYNE, LADELL, college president; b. Birmingham, Ala., Dec. 6, 1933; s. Clyde Ladell and Martha Gerusia (McBrayer) P.; m. Mary Jean Taylor, Aug. 23, 1954; children—Lisa, Jennifer. B.A. with honors, Samford U., 1955; M.A. in English, La. State U., 1956; Ph.D. in English, Stanford U., 1966. From instr. to prof. English, chmn. dept. lit. and presdl. asst. Claremont McKenna Coll., Calif., 1960-79; pres. Randolph-Macon Coll., Ashland, Va., 1979—; Fulbright lectr. U. Vienna, Austria, 1971-72; nat. cons. Ctr. for Study So. Culture, U. Miss., Oxford, 1980—; adminstrv. assoc.

Am. Coun. on Edn., Washington, 1979, mem. nat. panel, commn. on women in higher edn., 1981—; founding mem. pres.'s commn. Nat. Collegiate Athletic Assn., 1984—. Author: Thomas Wolfe, 1969, Black Novelists and the Southern Literary Tradition, 1981; contbr. articles on William Faulkner, Robert Penn Warren, Thomas Wolfe, and Ellen Glasgow to profl. jours. Mem. Va. bd. dirs. NCCJ, 1980-92, chmn. Va. region, Richmond, 1982-85; trustee, mem. exec. com. The Collegiate Schs., Richmond, 1986-89. NEH fellow, 1973. Mem. Nat. Assn. Ind. Colls. and Univs. (bd. dirs. 1990-93), Coun. on Postsecondary Accreditation (bd. dirs. 1991-93), Phi Kappa Phi. Methodist. Avocation: classical music. Office: Randolph-Macon Coll Office of the President Ashland VA 23005

PAYNE, LAWRENCE EDWARD, mathematics educator; b. Enfield, Ill., Oct. 2, 1923; s. Robert Ulysses and Harriet (Lasher) P.; m. Ruth Marian Winterstein, Dec. 27, 1948; children: Steven L., John E., Marcia G., Christopher J., Michele T. Student, Miami U., Oxford, Ohio, 1943-44; B.S. in Mech. Engring, Iowa State U., 1946, M.S. in Applied Math, 1948, Ph.D., 1950; DSc (hon.), Nat. U. Ireland, 1990. Jr. engr. Linde Air Products, North Tonawanda, N.Y., 1946-47; asst. prof. math. U. Ariz., 1950-51; research assoc. U. Md., 1951-52, asst. prof., 1952-55, asso. prof., 1955-60, prof., 1960-65; prof. Cornell U., Ithaca, N.Y., 1965-94; prof. emeritus Cornell U., Ithaca, N.y., 1994—; dir. Center for Applied Math. Cornell U., 1967-71, 76-77, 80-81; Lectr. in field; cons. Nat. Bur. Standards, 1958-65. Mem. editorial bd. Jour. of Elasticity, Applicable Analysis, Math. Methods in the Applied Sciences, Stability and Applied Analysis of Continuous Media; contbr. articles to profl. jours. Served with USNR, 1943-46. Recipient Sci. Achievement Math. award Washington Acad. Scis., 1962, Citation of Merit Iowa State U., 1992; NSF sr. postdoctoral fellow, 1958-59. Mem. Am. Math. Soc. (Steele prize in math. 1972), Soc. Indsl. Applied Math., Am. Acad. Mechanics, Soc. Engring. Sci., Soc. Natural Philosophy, Internat. Soc. for the Interaction Mechanics and Math., Royal Soc. of Edinburgh (elected hon. mem. 1991), Sigma Xi. Office: Cornell U Dept Math Ithaca NY 14853

PAYNE, LESLIE, newspaper editor, columnist, journalist, author; b. Tuscaloosa, Ala., July 12, 1941; m. Violet S. Cameron; children—Tamara Olympia, Jamal Kenyatta, Haile K. B.A., U. Conn., 1964. Reporter Newsday, L.I., N.Y., 1969-73, copy editor, mng. editor, 1973, minority affairs specialist, 1974-77, nat. corr., 1977-81, syndicated columnist, 1980—, nat. editor, 1981-85, asst. mng. editor, 1985—; judge Pulitzer Prize Selection Com., 1983, 84, Emmy Blue-Ribbon Panel, Acad. TV Arts and Scis., 1981, 83. Author: Life and Death of the Symbionese Liberation Army, 1976; co-author: Heroin Trail, 1974. Served to capt. U.S. Army, 1963-69. Decorated Bronze Star; recipient Pulitzer prize, 1974, Tobenkin award Columbia U., 1978, World Hunger Media award UN, 1983, Unity award Lincoln U., Journalism prize Howard U., AP and UPI awards (commentary), 1984, numerous other awards. Mem. Nat. Assn. Black Journalists (pres. 1981-83), Com. to Protect Journalists, Internat. Press Inst. Avocations: painting; softball; mountain climbing. Office: Newsday Inc 235 Pinelawn Rd Melville NY 11747-4226*

PAYNE, LEWIS FRANKLIN, JR. (L.F. PAYNE), congressman; b. Amherst Va., July 9, 1945; m. Susan King; children: Graham, Hunter, Sara, Anna. BA, Va. Mil. Inst., 1967; MBA, U. Va. Mem. 100th-104th Congresses from 5th Va. dist., Washington, 1988—. Democrat. Presbyterian. Office: US Ho of Reps 1119 Longworth Washington DC 20515*

PAYNE, MAXWELL CARR, JR., retired psychology educator; b. Nashville, Feb. 9, 1927; s. Carr and Mary Evans (Tarpley) P.; m. Juanita Campbell, Oct. 17, 1958; children: Maxwell Carr III, Elizabeth Campbell, Mary Allison. AB, Vanderbilt U., 1949; AM, Princeton U., 1950, PhD, 1951. Rsch. assoc. U. Ill., Urbana, 1951-54; asst. prof. psychology Ga. Inst. Tech., Atlanta, 1954-60, assoc. prof., 1961-65, 1965-90, ret., 1991; cons. Lockheed-Ga. Co., Marietta, 1963; testing dir. Aircrew Ctr., Am. Insts. Rsch., Atlanta, 1960-75; faculty Atlanta Sch. Art, 1970; mem. Ga. State Bd. Examiners of Psychologists, 1970-74. Contbr. articles to profl. jours. Sunday Sch. tchr. Northside United Meth. Ch., Atlanta, 1989—. With USNR, 1944-46. Recipient Disting. Tchr. award Ga. Inst. Tech., 1970. Fellow AAAS; mem. Am. Psychol. Assn., Ga. Psychol. Assn. (Cert. of Merit), Southeastern Psychol. Assn., So. Soc. Philosophy and Psychology (treas. 1971-74, pres. 1985-86), Ga. Inst. Tech. Faculty Club (pres. 1970), Phi Beta Kappa, Sigma Xi, Phi Kappa Phi, Omicron Delta Kappa, Beta Theta Pi. Avocation: gardening. Home: 3035 Farmington Dr NW Atlanta GA 30339-4704

PAYNE, MEREDITH JORSTAD, physician; b. St. Louis, Feb. 7, 1927; d. Louis Helmar and Cleone Gladys (Brandal) Jorstad; m. Spencer Payne, 1948 (div. 1959); m. James McGarity, 1965 (div. 1977); children: Maureen Meredith, James Louis. AB, Washington U., St. Louis, 1947, MD, 1950. Diplomate Am. Bd. Surgery, Am. Bd. Plastic Surgery. Intern gen. surgery St. Louis City Hosp., 1950-51, asst. resident surgery, 1951-54; chief surg. resident Roswell Park Meml. Hosp., Buffalo, 1954-55; chief plastic surgery resident Allentown (Pa.) Gen. Hosp., 1955-57; clin. instr. surgery Washington U. Med. Sch., 1957-70; vis. surgeon Homer G. Phillips Hosp., St. Louis, 1957-70; staff St. Luke's; St. Mary's Hosp., Vets. Hosp., St. Louis and Bethesda, 1990—; assoc. prof. plastic surgery (clin.) St. Louis U. Sch. Medicine, St. Louis, 1986—; bd. dirs. Blue Cross and Blue Shield, St. Louis, 1985-89; med. dir. St. Luke's Cleft Palate Clinic. Contbr. articles to profl. jours. Fellow ACS; mem. Am. Soc. Plastic and Reconstructive Surgery, AMA, Mo. Med. Assn. (coun. 1988—), St. Louis Met. Med. Soc. (councillor 1986-89), Am. Cleft Palate Assn., Roswell Park Surgery Assn., So. Med. Assn., Washington U. Med. Alumni Assn., Am. Geriatrics Soc., Midwestern Assn. Plastic Surgeons, Mo. Assn. Plastic & Reconstructive Surgery (sec. 1994, treas. 1995), St. Louis Area Plastic Surgeons (pres. 1989-94), Pan Am. Med. Assn., City Hosp. Alumni Assn. (v.p. 1995), Soc. Head and Neck Surgeons, Coll. Club (bd. dirs. St. Louis 1983-85), University Club, Order of Ea. Star, Zonta (St. Louis pres 1968-69). Avocations: skiing, tennis, sewing, knitting, gardening. Home: 7314 Westmoreland Dr Saint Louis MO 63130-4240 Office: 224 S Wood Mill Rd Ste 320 Chesterfield MO 63017

PAYNE, MICHAEL DAVID, English language educator; b. Dallas, Jan. 17, 1941; s. Fred G. Payne and Jocie Marie (Kirkham) Lundberg; m. Laura Asherman, Dec. 26, 1973; children: Jeffrey, Jennifer, Albert, Edward. Student, U. Calif.-Berkeley, 1958-59, 61; B.A., So. Oreg. Coll., 1962; Ph.D., U. Oreg., 1969. Tchr. English, Medford (Oreg.) Sr. High Sch., 1962-63; instr. English, U. Oreg., Eugene, 1963-69; asst. prof. to prof. English, Bucknell U., Lewisburg, Pa., 1969—, chmn. dept. history, 1980-82, chmn. dept. English, 1982-88, 92-94, Presdl. prof., 1982-86, John P. Crozer prof. English lit., 1986—; dir. Bucknell Univ. Press, 1972-76; assoc. editor Bucknell Rev., 1970-85, editor, 1985-88. Author: Irony in Shakespeare's Roman Plays, 1974, Reading Theory, 1993; editor: Contemporary Essays on Style, 1969, Shakespeare: Contemporary Critical Approaches, 1979; Text, Interpretation, Theory, 1985, Perspective, 1986, Criticism, History, and Intertextuality, 1987, The Senses of Stanley Cavell, 1988, Blackwell Dictionary of Cultural and Critical Theory, 1995; general editor Bucknell Lectures in Lit. Theory, 1990—; contbr. articles to profl. jours. Recipient Lindback award for disting. teaching, 1976; Folger Shakespeare Library fellow, 1973; NEH fellow, 1974; Bucknell Alumni fellow, 1978-79. Mem. Johnson Soc. London, Inst. for Romance Studies (U. London), MLA, Coll. English Assn., Phi Beta Kappa (hon.). Home: 1704 Jefferson Ave Lewisburg PA 17837-1632

PAYNE, MICHAEL LEE, association management executive; b. Monroe, N.C., Aug. 6, 1948; s. Robert H. and Martha (Brooks) P. BA in History, U. S.C., 1970, BA in Journalism, 1971; BA in Polit. Sci., 1972. Program dir. Coastal Plains Reg. Commn., Washington, 1972-75; dir. fed. rels. Office Coastal Zone Mgmt. NOAA, Washington, 1975-80; investment specialist Econ. Dirs. Adminstrn. U.S. Dept. Commerce, Washington, 1980-82; dep. to asst. sec. for congl. affairs Office of Sec. U.S. Dept. Commerce, Washington, 1982-84; v.p. Smith-Bucklin Assoc., Washington, 1984—, sr. v.p.; presenter to hospitality industry. Author: Complete Guide to Non-Profit Management, 1993; contbr. numerous articles to profl. publs. Mem. Am. Soc. Assn. Execs., Profl. Convention Mgrs. Assn., Meeting Profls. Internat. Avocations: travel, tennis, fishing, handball, biking. Office: Smith-Bucklin Assoc 1200 19th St Washington DC 20036

PAYNE, PAUL D., finance company executive. Exec. v.p., coo Mercedes-Benz Credit Corp., Norwalk, Conn. Office: Mercedes-Benz Credit Corp 201 Merritt 7 700 Norwalk CT 06851

PAYNE, ROBERT E., federal judge; b. 1941. BA in Polit. Sci., Washington and Lee U., 1963; LLB magna cum laude, Washington & Lee U., 1967. Assoc., ptnr. McGuire, Woods, Battle & Boothe, Richmond, Va., 1971-92; fed. judge U.S. Dist. Ct. (ea. dist.) Va., 1992—; mem. Jud. Conf. 4th Cir. Capt. U.S. Army, 1967-71. Mem. ABA, Va. Bar Assn., Va. State Bar Assn., Va. Assn. Def. Attys. (chmn. comml. litigation sect. 1989-91), Richmond Bar Assn., Order of Coif. Episcopalian. Office: Lewis F Powell Jr US Courthouse 10th and Main Sts Richmond VA 23219

PAYNE, ROBERT WALTER, psychologist, educator; b. Calgary, Alta., Can., Nov. 5, 1925; s. Reginald William and Nora (Cowdery) P.; m. Helen June Mayer, Dec. 1948 (div. 1972); children: Raymond William, Barbara Joan, Margaret June; m. Josephine Mary Riley Adams, Mar. 1977 (div. 1982); children: George Reginald Alexander, Robin Charles; m. Jean Isobel Dawson, Aug., 1983. B.A., U. Alta., 1949; Ph.D., U. London, Eng., 1954. Lectr. psychology Inst. Psychiatry U. London, 1952-59; prof. psychology Queens U., Kingston, Ont., 1959-65; prof. psychology, chmn. dept. behavioral sci. Temple U. Med. Sch., Phila., 1965-73; prof. dept. psychiatry Temple U. Med. Sch., 1973-78; med. research scientist III Eastern Pa. Psychiat. Inst., Phila., 1965-78; prof. psychology U. Victoria, B.C., Can., 1978-91, prof. emeritus, 1991—, dean Faculty Human and Social Devel., 1978-83. Contbr. articles to profl. jours. Recipient Stratton Research award, 1964. Fellow Am. Psychol. Assn., Brit. Psychol. Soc., Canadian Psychol. Assn., Am. Psychopath. Assn. Home: 2513 Sinclair Rd, Victoria, BC Canada V8N 1B5

PAYNE, ROGER LEE, geographer; b. Winston-Salem, N.C., Oct. 26, 1946; s. Irvin Lee and Gladys Odel (Binkley) P.; m. Sara Lucinda Parker, Aug. 16, 1970 (div. Feb. 1992); 1 child, Jennifer Nicole. BA, East Carolina U., 1969, MA, 1972. Geographer, chief geog. names U.S. Geol. Survey, Reston, Va., 1974—; instr. geography and history Pan Am. Inst./U.S. Geog. Survey, 1989—; exec. sec. U.S. Bd. Names, U.S. Geol. Survey, Washington, 1990—; part-time instr. East Carolina U., Greenville, N.C., 1969-71, George Washington U., Washington, 1977—, George Mason U., Fairfax, Va., 1979-83, Benjamin Franklin U., Washington, 1985-87; del. UN, N.Y.C., 1987—; mem. scientist exch. Geol. Survey, Beijing, 1989; instr. Nat. Black Colls., Howard U., 1985. Author: Urban Development in South Africa, 1972, Place Names of Outer Banks, 1985, Manuals on Auto Names, 1987, 89; coord., editor: (book series) National Gazetter U.S., 1982—; contbr. articles, revs. to profl. jours. Chmn. E. Carolina Blood Dr., Greenville, 1969. Lt. USAF, 1970-72. Recipient Guy Buzzard award Gamma Theta Upsilon, 1970; Superior Svc. award Geol. Survey, 1988. Fellow Explorers Club; mem. Assn. Am. Geographers (various coms. 1969—, pres. mid-Atlantic divsn. 1981-82, treas., sec.), Am. Name Soc. (pres. 1989), Am. Nat. Std. Inst. (rep. 1986), Cosmos Club. Avocations: hiking, volleyball. Home: PO Box 3356 Reston VA 22090-1356 Office: US Geol Survey 523 National Ctr 12201 Sunrise Valley Dr Reston VA 22092

PAYNE, ROY STEVEN, judge; b. New Orleans, Aug. 30, 1952; s. Fred J. and Dorothy Julia (Peck) P.; m. Laureen Fuller, Sept. 8, 1973; children: Julie Elizabeth, Kelly Kathryn, Alex Steven, Michael Lawrence. BA with distinction, U. Va., 1974; JD, La. State U., 1977; LLM, Harvard U., 1980. Bar: La. 1977, U.S. Dist. Ct. (we. dist.) La. 1980, U.S. Ct. Appeals (5th cir.) 1980, U.S. Supreme Ct. 1983. Law clk. to judge U.S. Dist. Ct., Shreveport, La., 1977-79; assoc. Blanchard, Walker, O'Quin & Roberts, Shreveport, 1980-83, ptnr., 1984-87; U.S. Magistrate judge, we. Dist. La., Shreveport, 1987—; instr. New Eng. Sch. Law, Boston, 1979-80. Contbr. articles to profl. jours. Chmn. Northwest La. Legal Svcs. Assn., Shreveport, 1984-85. Mem. 5th Cir. Bar Assn., La. State Bar Assn. (editorial bd. Forum jour., 1983-87, legal aid com.), Fed. Magistrate Judges Assn., Shreveport Bar Assn., La. Assn. Def. Counsel (bd. dirs. 1987), Harry V. Booth Am. Inn of Ct. (pres. elect 1994-95), Order of Coif, Rotary, Phi Kappa Phi, Phi Delta Phi. Methodist. Home: 12494 Harts Island Rd Shreveport LA 71115-8505 Office: US Courthouse 300 Fannin St Ste 4300 Shreveport LA 71101-3141

PAYNE, SIDNEY STEWART, archbishop; b. Fogo, Nfld., Can., June 6, 1932; s. Albert and Hilda May (Oake) P.; m. Selma Carlson Penney, Oct. 11, 1962; children—Carla, Christopher, Robert, Angela. B.A., Meml. U. Nfld., 1958; L.Th., Queen's Coll., Nfld., 1958; B.D., Gen. Synod, 1966; D.D. (hon.), Univ. of King's Coll., Halifax, 1981. Ordained deacon Anglican Ch., 1957, priest, 1958. Ordained to ministry Anglican Ch., 1957; parish pastor Happy Valley Labrador, 1957-65, Bay Roberts, Nfld., 1965-70, St. Anthony, Nfld., 1970-78; bishop Anglican Diocese of Western Nfld., 1978-90; met. Ecclesiastical Province of Can., archbishop Western Nfld., 1990—. Home: 13 Cobb Ln, Corner Brook, NF Canada A2H 2V3 Office: Anglican Diocesan Ctr, 25 Main St, Corner Brook, NF Canada A2H 1C2

PAYNE, THOMAS CHARLES, architect; b. Chatham, Ont., Dec. 9, 1949; s. Lloyd George and Dorothy Elizabeth (Webster) P.; m. Irma Osadsa, Sept. 21, 1974; children: Natalia Sophia, Nicholas Alexander. AB, Princeton U., 1971; attended, Ecole des Beaux Arts, 1971-72; MArch, Yale Sch. Architecture, 1974. With Barton Myers Assocs., 1979-87; ptnr. Kuwabara Payne McKenna Blumberg Architects, 1987—; adj. asst. prof. arch. U. Toronto, 1986-89; guest critic sch. arch. U. Toronto, Harvard Grad. Sch. Design, U. Waterloo. recent projects include Art Gallery Ont. Stage III, Woodsworth Coll. U. of Toronto, Trinity Coll. Master Plan, Stratford Festival Master Plan, Stauffer Library, Queen's U., The Fields Inst. U. Toronto; projects incl. Portland Centre for Performing Arts, Open Air Theatre Earl Bales Park N. York, Ont. Recipient Gov. Gen's award for Architecture Royal Architecture Inst. of Can., 1992; fellow Woodsworth Coll. U. Toronto. Mem. Am. Inst. Architecture, Royal Archtl. Inst. Can., Ont. Archtl. Assn. Home: 200 Glen Rd, Toronto, ON Canada M4W 2X1 Office: Kuwabara Payne McKenna Blumberg Architects, 322 King St W 3rd Fl, Toronto, ON Canada M5V 1J2

PAYNE, TYSON ELLIOTT, JR., retired insurance executive; b. Dallas, May 25, 1927; s. Tyson Elliott and Winnie Claris (Denman) P.; m. Billie Jane Spears, Aug. 28, 1948; children: David Tyson, Sally Jane. B.J., U. Tex., 1949. CLU, ChFC. Sports editor Lufkin (Tex.) News, 1949-51, Tyler (Tex.) Courier Times, 1951-53; with Am. Nat. Ins. Co., Galveston, Tex., 1953-88; v.p. health ins. ops. Am. Nat. Ins. Co., St. Louis, 1965-1970; v.p. mktg. Am. Nat. Ins. Co., Galveston, 1970-86; pvt. practice ins. agt. Austin, Tex., 1987-88; exec. v. p., dir. Sch. of Ins. & Fin. Svcs. at U. Houston, 1988-92; ret., 1992. Elder Presbyn. Ch. With USNR, 1945-46. Home: 8110 Cardin Dr Austin TX 78759-8704

PAYNE, WILLIAM BRUCE, lawyer; b. Tulsa, Apr. 18, 1943; s. Marvin Ream and Audrey Arlene (Jones) P.; m. Suzanne Cooper, June 4, 1966; children: Allison, Stephanie. BS, U. Okla., 1965, JD, 1968. Bar: Minn. 1968, U.S. Dist. Ct. Minn. 1968, U.S. Ct. Appeals (8th cir.) 1968. Fin. ptnr. Dorsey & Whitney, Mpls., 1968—; sec., bd. dirs. Deltak Corp., Mpls. 1st lt. USAR, 1968-74. Mem. ABA, Minn. Bar Assn., Minikahda Club. Office: Dorsey & Whitney 220 S 6th St Minneapolis MN 55402

PAYNE, WILLIAM HAYDON, broadcasting executive; b. Washington, July 3, 1939; s. William Howard and LoRena Elizabeth (Haydon) P.; m. Gail Ann Curtis, July 3, 1960; children—Anne Marguerite, Kelly Gail, Haydon Michelle, William Haydon, II. B of Indsl. Arts in Electronic Engring., Oklahoma City U., 1961. Announcer Sta. KOMA, Oklahoma City, 1959-61; electronic technician FAA, Oklahoma City, 1961-62; owner, gen. mgr. Sta. KWHP, Edmond, Okla., 1962-79; owner, pub. Graphic Newspaper, Oklahoma City, 1973-77; owner, pres. also morning drive air personality for country music radio Sta. KTFX, Tulsa, 1977—; pres. Central Broadcast Co., 1977—; pres. Internat. Idea Bank, 1987—. Pub. Edmond Map, 1964-81. Deacon 1st Presbyn. Ch., Edmond, 1962-65. Recipient numerous service and appreciation awards. Mem. Nat. Broadcasters Assn., Radio Advt. Bur., Okla. Broadcasters Assn., Okla. Press Assn., Oklahoma City Advt. Club, Edmond C. of C. (medal of merit 1979), Better Bus. Bur., Sigma Tau Gamma. (past pres.). Democrat. Club: Edmond Kiwanis (past pres.). Pioneer Time of Day machine. Office: KTFX (FM) 8107 E Admiral Pl Tulsa OK 74115-8116

PAYNE, WILLIAM HOWARD, lawyer; b. Norfork, Ark., Oct. 8, 1909; s. William Joseph and Maude Isabel (Harris) P.; m. LoRena Elizabeth, Nov. 9, 1934 (dec. June 1963); children: William Haydon, Jo Anne Payne Brown. Student, George Washington U., 1937-41, Georgetown U., 1937-41; JD, Southeastern U., 1941. Newspaperman El Reno (Okla.) Daily Tribune and El Reno Am., 1929-33; chief staff com. on Indian affairs U.S. Ho. of Reps., Washington, 1934-41; sole practice law Washington, 1942—; founder, chmn. bd. dirs. Found. for Am. Indian Tribal History, Washington, 1979; claims atty. Cheyenne-Arapaho Indian Tribes of Okla., 1948-72, gen. counsel, 1948-62; claims atty. Fort Peck Sioux Tribe of Mont., 1957-82; gen. counsel Cheyenne River Sioux Tribe of S.D., 1957-72; claims atty. Cheyenne River Sioux Tribe, 1957-82. Co-author: Folks Say of Will Rogers, 1936; author: (movie script) Marque and Reprisal, 1957. Pres. League Young Dems., Canadian County, Okla., 1932-33, floor leader Little Congress, Washington, 1934. Served as lt. USN, 1944-46. Recipient citation U.S. Sec. Navy, 1946. Mem. Methodist Episcopal Ch. Clubs: Nat. Lawyers, Nat. Press. Lodges: Masons (32d degree), Elks. Avocations: swimming, hunting, fishing, tennis. Office: Law Offices 700 S Kelly Edmond OK 73003

PAYNE, WILLIAM JACKSON, microbiologist, educator; b. Chattanooga, Aug. 30, 1925; s. Henry Frederick and Maude (Fonda) P.; m. Jane Lindsey Marshall, June 16, 1949; children: William Jackson, Marshall, Lindsey. BS, Coll. William and Mary, 1950; MS, U. Tenn., 1952, PhD, 1955. Instr. bacteriology U. Tenn., 1953-54; mem. faculty U. Ga., 1955-95, prof. microbiology, head dept., 1962-77, Alumni Found. Disting. prof., 1982-95, acting dean Franklin Coll. Arts and Scis., 1977-78, dean Franklin Coll. Arts and Scis., 1978-88; vis. professorial fellow U. Wales, Cardiff, 1975, hon. professorial fellow, 1977-87; cons. U. Ala., 1959, 68, 70, 85, Philip Morris Co., 1981, Iowa State U., 1988, Howard U., 1989, U. Ctrl. Fla., 1992, U. Tenn., 1994—; summer research participant Oak Ridge Nat. Lab., 1960; chmn. Com. Nat. Registry Microbiologists, 1966-72; cons. U.S. EPA, 1971; mem. biol. oceanography panel NSF, 1976-77; mem. nitrogen-fixation panel CRGO U.S. Dept. Agr., 1982; mem. vis. com. So. Assn. Colls., Miss. State U., 1983; vis. lectr. Ctr. for Environ. Biotech., Danish univs.-Copenhagen, Aarhus, Aalborg, 1989. Author: (with D.R. Brown) Microbiology: A Programmed Presentation, 1968, 2d edit., 1972, (transl. to Spanish, 1975), Denitrification, 1981, also articles; mem. editl. bd. Applied and Environ. Microbiology, 1974-79, Environ. Ethics, 1982-85; U. Ga. Press, 1975-78, 88-91. Trustee Athens Acad., 1967-72. Served with USNR, 1943-46. Recipient M.G. Michael award 1960, creative rsch. award U. Ga., 1982, Alumni Achievement award McCallie Sch., 1993. Fellow Am. Acad. Microbiology; mem. Am. Soc. Microbiology (pres. southeastern br. 1963, found. lectr. 1972-73, dir. found. 1973-76, chmn. found. com. 1977-82, com. undergrad. and grad. edn. 1974-77, steering com. undergrad. faculty-mentor enhancement program 1988-90, P.R. Edwards award southeastern br. 1972), Ga. Acad. Sci., Athens City Club, Sigma Xi (pres. U. Ga. chpt. 1963, rsch. award U. Ga. chpt. 1973), Phi Kappa Phi (pres. U. Ga. chpt. 1983), Sigma Alpha Epsilon. Episcopalian. Home: 111 Alpine Way Athens GA 30606-4002

PAYNE, W(ILLIAM) SPENCER, retired surgeon; b. St. Louis, Mar. 22, 1926; s. Richard Johnson and Mary (Matthews) P.; m. Maureen J.S. Divertie, Oct. 3, 1959; children: Susan Mary, William Spencer, Sarah Elspeth. Student, DePauw U., Greencastle, Ind., 1944-45, Haverford (Pa.) Coll., 1945-46; MD, Washington U., St. Louis, 1950; MS, U. Minn., 1960. Intern, then resident in internal medicine St. Louis City Hosp., 1950-52, resident in gen. surgery, 1954-55; resident in gen. surgery, then resident in thoracic surgery Mayo Grad. Sch., Rochester, Minn., 1955-61; practice medicine specializing in surgery Rochester, 1962-90, ret., 1990; cons. thoracic and cardiovascular surgery Mayo Clinic and Mayo Found., 1962—; prof. surgery Mayo Med. Sch., 1974—, James C. Masson prof. surgery, 1982-87; head sect. gen. thoracic surgery Mayo Clinic, 1987-90; mem. staff Rochester Meth., St. Mary's, Rochester State hosps.; bd. dirs. Am. Bd. Thoracic Surgery, 1985-89. Author: The Esophagus, 1974, Manual of Upper Gastrointestinal Surgery, 1985; contbr. 273 articles to prof. jours.; mem. editorial bd. Annals of Thoracic Surgery, 1987-89. Lt. M.C., USNR, 1952-54, Korea. Recipient Howard K. Gray award Mayo Assn., 1959. Mem. ACS, Am. Surg. Assn., Am. Assn. Thoracic Surgery, Soc. Thoracic Surgeons, Am. Coll. Chest Physicians, Central Surg. Assn., Minn. Surg. Soc., Internat. Assn. Study Lung Cancer, Mayo Alumni Soc. Thoracic Surgery, Priestly Soc., Internat. Soc. Diseases of the Esophagus (hon.), Esophageal Surg. Club (hon.), Soc. of Thoracic and Cardiovascular Surgeons of Great Britain and Ireland (hon.), U. Club (Rochester), Madeline Island Yacht Club (LaPointe, Wis.). Presbyterian. Office: Mayo Clinics 200 1st St SW Rochester MN 55905-0001

PAYNTER, HARRY ALVIN, retired trade association executive; b. Miami, Ariz., July 22, 1923; s. Harry and Mabel Vera (Moore) P.; m. Betty Clarice Wilkins, Dec. 3, 1944; children: Harry Alvin, Steven Wilkins, Barbara Elizabeth, Susan Moore. BS, Okla. State U., 1948; M.B.A., Harvard U., 1954; postgrad., Air Command and Staff Coll., 1957, Armed Forces Staff Coll., 1961, Nat. War Coll., 1969. Commd. 2d lt. AC U.S. Army, 1943; advanced through grades to col. USAF, 1968; service as flight comdr. 8th Air Force, World War II and Berlin airlift; asst. air attache (Am. embassy), Karachi, Pakistan, 1958-60; air attache (Am. embassy), Quito, Ecuador, 1965-67, Vietnam, 1969; prof. aerospace studies Dartmouth, 1967-68; ret. 1970; mng. dir. Gas Appliance Mfrs. Assn., Inc., N.Y.C., 1970-73; pres. Gas Appliance Mfrs. Assn., Inc., Arlington, Va., 1973-88. Decorated D.F.C., Air medal with 3 oak leaf clusters, Purple Heart, Joint Services Commendation medal with oak leaf cluster U.S.; Abdon Calderon Ecuador; recipient Am. Bankers award, 1947; named Ecuador Hon. Command Pilot. Mem. Can. Gas Assn. (life), Guild Ancient Supplers (hon.), Am. Soc. Gas Engrs. (hon.), Air Force Assn., Ret. Officers Assn., Am. Soc. Assn. Execs., Nat. Press Club. Phi Kappa Phi. Presbyterian. Home: 1416 N Inglewood St Arlington VA 22205-2735

PAYNTER, JOHN PHILIP, conductor; b. Dodgeville, Wis., May 29, 1928; s. Wilfred William and Minnie Elizabeth (Clark) P.; m. Marietta Margaret Morgan, Sept. 10, 1949; children—Bruce David, Megan Elizabeth. B.M., Northwestern U., 1950, M.Mus. in Composition, 1951; LHD, DePaul U., 1992. Mem. faculty Sch. of Music, Northwestern U., 1951—; prof. conducting, 1974—; pres. Mid-West Internat. Band and Orch. Clinic. Dir. bands, 1953—; condr., musical dir., Northshore Concert Band, 1958—; composer and arranger numerous works. Mem. ASCAP (small awards panel 1988), Am. Bandmasters Assn. (past pres.), Nat. Band Assn. (co-founder, past pres.), World Assn. Symphonic Bands and Ensemble (past pres.), Phi Mu Alpha Sinfonia (life), Phi Eta Sigma, Pi Kappa Lambda. Mem. United Ch. of Christ. Home: 1437 Hollywood Ave Glenview IL 60025-2225 Office: Sch Music Northwestern U Evanston IL 60208

PAYSON, HENRY EDWARDS, forensic psychiatrist, educator; b. N.Y.C., May 12, 1925; s. Aurin Eliot and Lois Elizabeth (Chickering) P.; m. Barbara Louise Jarvis, Mar. 29, 1958; children: Ann Elizabeth, John Eliot, Sally Lynn, Susan Gail. B.S., Harvard Coll., 1948; M.D., Columbia U., 1952; M.S.L., Yale U. Law Sch., 1978; A.M. (hon.), Dartmouth Coll., 1981. Diplomate: Am. Bd. Med. Examiners, Am. Bd. Psychiatry and Neurology, Am. Bd. Forensic Psychiatry. Research fellow in medicine Columbia U. unit Goldwater Meml. Hosp., 1952-53; intern Osler Clinic, Johns Hopkins Hosp., 1953-54; resident in psychiatry Phipps Clinic, 1955-58; resident in internal medicine Duke U. Hosp., 1954-55; asst. prof. psychiatry and medicine Yale U. Sch. Medicine; also attending physician Yale-New Haven Med. Center, 1958-63; asst. prof. psychiatry Dartmouth Med. Sch., 1963-68, assoc. prof., 1968-78, prof., 1978-90, prof. emeritus, 1990—; chief forensic psychiatry, dept. psychiatry; attending psychiatrist Hitchcock Clinic, Dartmouth-Hitchcock Med. Center, 1972-90; chief in-patient service Dartmouth-Hitchcock Mental Health Center, 1969-71; cons. VA Hosp., White River Junction, Vt., 1972-91, N.H. Hosp., 1980-87, VA Hosp., Manchester, N.H. 1981-91, N.H. Prison, 1984-88, Cottage Hosp., Woodsville, N.H., 1990—; dir. Disturbed Offender Project of N.H., 1972-73. Contbr. articles to profl. publs. Mem. N.H. Guardian Adv. Council, 1979-83. Served with AUS 1943-46. NIMH career tchr., 1961-63. Fellow Am. Psychiat. Assn. (life); mem. AAAS, Am. Acad. Psychiatry and Law, N.H. Psychiat. Soc. (pres. 1977-78). Office: The Aldrich House PO Box 845 Norwich VT 05055

PAYSON, MARTIN DAVID, entertainment company executive, lawyer; b. N.Y.C., Jan. 4, 1936; s. Joseph J. and Stella (Riemer) P.; m. Doris Leah

Greenberg; children: Michele, Leslie, Eric. A.B., Cornell U., 1957; LL.B. cum laude, NYU, 1961. Bar: N.Y. 1961. Assoc. Paul Weiss Rifkind Wharton & Garrison, N.Y.C., 1961-67; instr. Law Sch., U. Mich., Ann Arbor, 1963-64; ptnr. Polier Tulin & Payson, N.Y.C., 1967-70; gen. counsel Warner Communications, Inc., N.Y.C., 1970—; also dir. Warner Communications, Inc.; now vice chmn. Time Warner Inc., N.Y.C. Chmn. entertainment div. United Jewish Appeal-Fedn. Joint Campaign, N.Y.C., 1982-84; mem. pres.'s council Tulane U., New Orleans, 1984—; trustee Fedn. Jewish Philanthropies N.Y., N.Y.C., 1983—. Mem. ABA, Assn. Bar City N.Y. Democrat. Office: Time Warner Inc 1271 Ave Of The Americas New York NY 10020-1300

PAYSON, RONALD SEARS, biology educator; b. Springfield, Mass., Oct. 17, 1938; s. Peter Martin and Beatrice Thelma (Sears) Farrell; m. Cynthia Myrtle Henderson Smith, July 17, 1965 (div. Jan. 1977); children: Melinda Martha Payson-English, Ronald Sears Payson Jr.; m. Karen L. Payson; children: Angelique Payson-Bernstein, Marcus A. Payson. AASN, U. of the State of N.Y.; BS, U. Mass., MAT in Biology/Ecology. R.N. Prof. biol. scis. Columbia-Greene C.C., 1970-94, prof. emeritus; cons. Spinrut Hill Assocs., Craryville, N.Y., 1994—. Sec. bd. dirs. N.E. Marine Environ. Inst.; bd. dirs. Hudson River Sloop Clearwater; treas. Vol. Fire Co. Home: PO Box 262 Craryville NY 12521-0262

PAYTON, BENJAMIN FRANKLIN, college president; b. Orangeburg, S.C., Dec. 27, 1932; s. Leroy Ralph and Sarah (Mack) P.; m. Thelma Louise Plane, Nov. 28, 1959; children: Mark Steven, Deborah Elizabeth. BA, S.C. State Coll., 1955; BD (Danforth grad. fellow 1955-63), Harvard U., 1958; MA, Columbia U., 1960; PhD, Yale U., 1963; LLD (hon.), Eastern Mich. U., 1972; LHD (hon.), Benedict Coll., 1972; LittD (hon.), Morgan State U., 1974, U. Md., 1987; LLD, Morris Brown Coll., Lehigh U., 1990. Asst. prof. sociology of religion and social ethics Howard U., Washington; also dir. Howard U. (Community Rsch.-Svc. Project, 1963-65); exec. dir. dept. social justice and Commn. on Religion and Race Nat. Coun. Chs. of Christ in U.S.A., 1966-67; pres. Benedict Coll., Columbia, S.C., 1967-72; program officer higher edn. and rsch. Ford Found., 1972-81; pres. Tuskegee (Ala.) U., 1981—; mem. nat. rev. bd. (Ctr. for Cultural and Tech. Exchange between U.S. and Asia); mem. Commn. on Pre-Coll. Edn. in Math., Sci. and Tech. NSF; ednl. advisor to V.P. George Bush during Seven-Nation Tour of Africa, 1982; team leader U.S. Presdl. Task Force on Agrl. and Econ. Devel. to Zaire; bd. dirs. AmSouth Bancorp., AmSouth Bank, ITT Corp., Libr. Corp., Sheraton Corp., Sonat, Inc.; mem. vis. com. Dept. Humanities MIT, 1988—; vis. com. bd. overseers Harvard U., 1989—. Author: (with Dr. Seymour Melman) A Strategy for the Next Stage in Civil Rights: Metropolitan-Rural Development for Equal Opportunity, 1966. Mem. vis. com. bd. overseers Harvard; mem. nat. commn. on higher edn. issues Am. Coun. Edn.; bd. dirs. Ala. Shakespeare Festival, Challenger Space Sci. Edn. Ctr. Recipient Billings 1st Pl. Prize Harvard U., 1957, Gold medal award Napoleon Hill Found., 1987, Benjamin E. Mays award, 1988, Centennial Alumnus award S.C. State Coll., 1988; named South Carolinian of Year by statewide TV-Radio, 1972. Mem. NAACP, Am. Soc. Scholars, Am. Sociol. Assn., Soc. for Religion in Higher Edn. (dir.), Assn. Governing Bds. (pres.'s adv. coun.), Phi Beta Kappa, Alpha Phi Alpha, Alpha Kappa Mu, Sigma Pi Phi. Home: 399 Montgomery Rd Grey Columns Tuskegee AL 36083 Office: Office of the Pres Tuskegee Univ Tuskegee AL 36088

PAYTON, SALLYANNE, law educator; b. 1943. BA, Stanford U., 1964, LLB, 1968. Bar: Calif. 1969, D.C. 1969. Staff asst. to Pres. of U.S. White House Domestic Coun., Washington, 1971-73; chief counsel urban mass transp. adminstrn. U.S. Dept. Transp., Washington, 1973-76; assoc. prof. Mich. U., Ann Arbor, 1976-85, prof., 1985—. Trustee Stanford U., 1972-82; mem. Adminstrn. Conf. U.S., 1980—; bd. dirs. Roosevelt Ctr. Am. Policy Studies, 1982—. Office: U Mich Law Sch 625 S State St Ann Arbor MI 48109-1215

PAYTON, THOMAS WILLIAM, corporate finance consultant executive; b. Toronto, Ont., Can., Sept. 7, 1946. With Can. Imperial Bank of Commerce, Toronto; dir. Bramalea Ltd., Toronto, 1981-82, v.p., 1982-88, sr. v.p., 1988-90, sr. v.p., treas., 1991-93; pres. DelLyn Advisors Inc., 1993—; dir. Cadillac Fairview, Inc., 1994—. Office: DelLyn Advisors Inc, 8 King St E Ste 810, Toronto, ON Canada M5C 1B5

PAYTON, WALTER (SWEETNESS), professional race car driver, former professional football player; b. Columbia, Miss., July 25, 1954; s. Peter Edward and Alyne Payton; m. Connie Payton; children: Jarrett, Brittney. BA in Communications, Jackson State U. Running back Chgo. Bears, 1975-88; played Pro Bowl, 1976-86; mem. NFL Championship team, 1985; professional race car driver, 1993—. Representative for Food for Thought Program, Bryan Foods, 1993—. Named NFC Player of Yr., The Sporting News, 1976-77, to NFC All-Star Team, 1976-78, NFC Player of Yr., UPI, 1977, NFL Most Valuable Player, Profl. Football Writers Am., 1978, played in nine Pro Bowls, inducted into Pro Football Hall of Fame, 1993; Black Athlete of the Year, Gordon's Gin, 1985. NFL all-time rushing leader. Office: Walter Payton Inc 1700 E Golf Rd Schaumburg IL 60173*

PAYZANT, THOMAS, school superintendent; b. San Diego; recipient Howard J. McGraw, Jr. Prize in Education, McGraw-Hill, 1992. Office: Elem & Secondary Edn 400 Maryland Ave SW Washington DC 20202-0001

PAZ, OCTAVIO, poet, Mexican diplomat; b. Mex., Mar. 31, 1914; s. Octavio Paz and Josephina Lozano; m. Elena Garro, 1937 (div.); m. Marie José Tramini, 1964. Student, U. Mex. Sec. Mex. Embassy, Paris, 1945; chargé d'affaires Mex. Embassy, Tokyo, 1951, secretariat external affairs, 1953-58; extraordinary and plenipotentiary minister Mex. Embassy, Paris, 1959-62; Mex. amb. to India, 1962-68; vis. prof. U. Tex., Austin, U. Pitts. 1968-70; Simón Bolívar prof. Latin Am. studies, 1970; fellow Churchill Coll., Cambridge U., 1970-71; Charles Eliot Norton prof. poetry Harvard U., 1971-72; Regent's fellow U. Calif., San Diego; now dir. Revista Vuelta, Mexico City; founder literary rev. Barandal, 1931; mem. editorial bd., columnist El Popular; co-founder Taller, 1938; co-founder, editor El Hijo Prodigo, 1943-46; editor Plural, 1971-75; founder, editor Vuelta, 1976—. Author: (poetry) Luna Silvestre, 1933, No pasarán!, 1936, Raíz del hombre, 1937, Bajo tu clara sombra y otros poemas sobre España, 1937, Entre la piedra y la flor, 1941, A la orilla del mundo y primer día, 1942, Libertad bajo palabra, 1949, Aguila o sol?, 1951 (pub. as Eagle or Sun?, 1970), Semillas para un himno, 1954, Piedra de sol, 1957 (pub. as Sun Stone, 1963), La estación violenta, 1958, Agua y viento, 1959, Libertad bajo palabra: obra poética 1935-1958, 1960, Salamandra 1958-1961, 1962, Selected Poems, 1935-1957, 1963, Viento entero, 1965, Vrindaban, Madurai, 1965, Blanco, 1967, Disco visuales, 1968, Ladera este (1962-1968), 1969, La centana: poemas 1935-1968, 1969, Configurations, 1958-1969, 1971, Renga, 1971, Topoemas, 1971, Early Poems 1935-1955, 1973, Pasado en claro, 1975, Vuelta, 1976, A Draft of Shadows and Other Poems, 1979, Selected Poems, 1979, Airborn/Hijos del aire, 1981, Poemas 1935-1975, 1981, Poemas recientes, 1981, Instante y revelación, 1982, Selected Poems, 1984, Cuatro chopos/The Four Poplars, 1985, Arbol adentro, 1987 (pub. as A Tree Within, 1988), Nineteen Ways of Looking at Wang Wei, 1987, The Collected Poems of Octavio Paz 1957-1987, 1988, Lo mejor de Octavio Paz: el fuego de cada día; (prose) El laberinto de la soledad, 1950 (pub. as The Labyrinth of Solitude: Life and Thought in Mexico, 1961), Aguila o Sole, 1951, El arco y la lira: el poema, la revelación poética, poesía e historia, 1956 (pub. as The Bow and the Lyre: The Poem, the Poetic Revelation, Poetry and History, 1973), Las peras del olmo, 1957, Tamayo en la pintura mexicana, 1959, Cuadrivio, 1965, Los signos en rotación, 1965, Puertas al campo, 1966, Claude Lévi-Strauss; o El nuevo festín de Esopo, 1967 (pub. as Claude Lévi-

Strauss: An Introduction, 1970), Corriente alterna, 1967 (pub. as Alternating Current, 1973), Marcel Duchamp; o, El castillo de la pureza, 1968 (pub. as Marcel Duchamp; or, The Castle of Purity, 1970), México: la última década, 1969, Conjunciones y disyunciones, 1969 (pub. as Conjunctions and Disjunctions, 1974), Posdata, 1970 (pub. as The Other Mexico: Critique of the Pyramid, 1972), Las cosas en su sitio: sobre la literatura española del siglo XX, 1971, Los signos en rotación y otros ensayos, 1971, Traducción: literatura y literalidad, 1971, Apariencia desnuda: la obra de Marcel Duchamp, 1973 (pub. as Marcel Duchamp: Appearance Stripped Bare, 1979), El signo y el garabato, 1973, Solo a dos voces, 1973, Teatro de signos/transparencias, 1974, Versiones y diversiones, 1974, Los hijos del limo: del romanticismo a la vanguardia, 1974 (pub. as Children of the Mire: Modern Poetry from Romanticism to the Avant-Garde, 1974), El mono gramético, 1974 (pub. as The Monkey Grammarian, 1981), La búsqueda del comienzo: escritos sobre el surrealismo, 1974, The Siren and the Seashells and Other Essays on Poets and Poetry, 1976, Xavier Villaurrutia en persona y en obra, 1978, El ogro filantrópico: historia y política 1971-1978, 1979, Rufino Tamayo: Myth and Magic, 1979, México en la obra de Octavio Paz, 1979, Rufino Tamayo, 1982, Sor Juana Inés de la Cruz, o, Las trampas de la fe, 1982 (pub. as Sor Juana, or, The Traps of Faith), Tiempo nublado, 1983 (pub. as One Earth, Four or Five Worlds: Reflections on Contemporary History, 1985), Sombras de obras: arte y literatura, 1983, Günter Gerzo, 1983, Hombres en su siglo y otros ensayos, 1984 (pub. as On Poets and Others, 1986), Pasión crítica: conversaciones con Octavio Paz, 1985, Convergences: Essays on Art and Literature, 1987, Generaciones y semblanzas: escritores y letras de México, 1987, El pelegrino en su patria: historia y política de México, 1987, Los privilegios de la vista: arte de México, 1987, Primeras letras, 1931-1943, 1988, One World or the Other, 1989, Poesía, mito, revolución, 1989, La otra voz: poesía y fin de siglo, 1990 (pub. as The Other Voice, 1992), Essays on Mexican Art, 1993, My Life With the Wave, 1994, The Double Flame, 1995; adapter: (plays) La hija de Rappaccini, 1956; editor: Voces de España, 1938, Laurel: antología de la poésia moderna en lengua española, 1941, Anthologie de la poésie mexicaine, 1952, Anthología poética, 1956, Anthology of Mexican Poetry, 1958, Tamayo el la pintura mexicana, 1959, Magia de la risa, 1962, Antología by Fernando Pessoa, 1962, Cuatro poetas contemporáneos de Suecia: Martinson, Lundkvist, Ekelöf, y Lindegren, 1963, Poesía en movimiento: Mexico 1915-1966, 1966, Remedios varo, 1966, Antología by Xavier Villaurrutia, 1980; translator: Sendas de Oku by Basho, 1957, Veinte poemas by William Carlos Williams, 1973, 15 poemas by Guillaume Appollinaire, 1979. Guggenheim fellow, U.S., 1944; recipient Grand Prix Internat. de Poesie (Belgium), 1963, Jerusalem prize, 1977, Critics prize (Spain), 1977, Nat. prize for letters (Mex.), 1977, Grand Golden Eagle Internat. Festival (Paris) 1979, Grand Aigle d'Or (Nice), 1979, Premio Ollin Yoliztli (Mex.), 1980, Miguel de Cervantes prize (Spain), 1982, Neustadt Internat. prize for literature, 1982, Wilhelm Heinse medal (Germany), 1984, Fedn. German Book Trade Peace prize, 1984, Gran Cruz de Alfonso X el Sabrio, 1986, T.S. Eliot award for creative writing Ingersoll Found., 1987, Alexis de Toqueville prize Inst. France, 1988, Nobel Prize in literature, 1990. Mem. AAAL (hon.). Office: Revista Vuelta Amigos del Arte AC, Avenida Contreras 516 Piso 3, 10200 Mexico City Mexico also: care Churchill Coll, Cambridge England*

PAZANDAK, CAROL HENDRICKSON, liberal arts educator; b. Mpls.; d. Norman Everard and Ruth (Buckley) Hendrickson; m. Bruce B. Pazandak (dec. 1986); children: David, Bradford, Christopher, Eric, Paul, Ann; m. Joseph P. O'Shaughnessy, May 1991. PhD, U. Minn., 1970. Asst. dir. admissions U. Minn., Mpls., 1970-72, asst. dean liberal arts, 1972-79, asst. to pres., 1979-85, office of internat. edn., acting dir., 1985-87, asst. prof. to assoc. to prof. liberal arts, 1970—; vis. prof. U. Iceland, Reykjavik, 1984, periods in 1983, 86, 87, 88, 89, 90-92, 93, 94; vis. rsch. prof. U. Oulu, Finland, 1993; exec. sec. Minn.-Iceland Adv. Com., U. Minn., 1984—; cons. U. Iceland, 1983—; co-chair Reunion of Sisters-Minn. and Finland Confs., 1986—. Editor: Improving Undergraduate Education in Large Universities, 1989. Past pres. Minn. Mrs. Jaycees, Mpls. Mrs. Jaycees; formerly bd. govs. St. John's Preparatory Sch., Collegeville, Minn.; former bd. trustees Coll. of St. Teresa, Winona, Minn. Recipient Partnership award for contbn. to advancing shared interests of Iceland and Am., 1994; named to Order of the Falcon, Govt. of Iceland, 1990, Coll. Liberal Arts Alumna Notable Achievement, 1995. Mem. Internat. Coun. Psychologists, Am. Psychol. Assn., Am. Coun. Edn. (former steering com. Nat. Identification Program for Women in Higher Edn. Administrn. 1983-86), Soc. Advancement of Scandinavian Studies. Home: 1361 Prior Ave S Saint Paul MN 55116-2656 Office: U Minn N 247 Elliott Hall 75 E River Rd Minneapolis MN 55455-0432

PAZIRANDEH, MAHMOOD, rheumatologist, consultant; b. Hamadan, Iran, Jan. 1, 1932; came to U.S., 1966; naturalized U.S. Citizen, 1977; s. Rahim and Zahra (Shoushtar) P.; m. Parvin Danesh, Apr. 19, 1961; children: Bruce, Justin, Navid. MD, U. Tehran, 1958; postgrad., Eng., 1959-64, Pitts. U., 1967-68. Diplomate Am. Bd. Internal Medicine and Rheumatology. Asst. prof. Tehran U., Iran, 1964-67; clin. assoc. Cleve. Clinic Found., 1969-70; clin. instr. Case Western Res. U., Cleve., 1970-72, sr. clin. instr., 1972-78, clin. asst. prof., 1978-93, clin. assoc. prof., 1993—; bd. dirs. med. edn. Lake Hosp., Cleve., 1984-95, pres. med. staff, 1990-93; dir. med. edn. Euclid Hosp., Cleve., 1971-73; dir. quality assurance, 1989-93. Contbr. articles to profl. jours. Speaker pub. edn. radio, TV and seminars, Cleve., 1984—; chmn. pub. forums Arthritis Found., Cleve., 1985—, trustee, 1986-95, chmn. pub. edn. com., 1987—. Recipient recognition svc. award Arthritis Found., 1976, Robert Stecher Vol. award, 1988, Nat. Vols. Svc. citation, 1989; Eng. and Iranian Govt. scholar, 1959-63. Fellow ACP Am. Coll. Rheumatology; mem. Am. Soc. Internal Medicine, Ohio State Med. Assn. (del. 1989-95), Lake County Med. Soc. (pres. 1988—), Cleve. Rheumatism Soc. (pres. 1974), N.Y. Acad. Scis. Republican. Avocations: arts, antiques. Home: 124 Pheasant Ln Chagrin Falls OH 44022-4043 Office: Case Western Res U 36100 Euclid Ave Willoughby OH 44094-4456

PAZUR, JOHN HOWARD, biochemist, educator; b. Zubne, Czechoslovakia, Jan. 17, 1922; came to U.S., 1946, naturalized, 1961; s. John and Mary (Bonko) P.; m. Jean Josephine Glabais, Nov. 22, 1950; children—Robert Leslie, Barbara Jean, Beverly Ann, Carolyn Jo. B.S., U. Guelph, 1944; M.S., McGill U., 1946; Ph.D., Iowa State U., 1950. Instr. chemistry Iowa State U., 1950-51; asst. prof. biol. chemistry U. Ill., 1951-52; mem. faculty U. Nebr., 1952-66; prof. biochemistry, 1959-66, chmn. dept. 1960-66; prof. biochemistry Pa. State U., 1966—, chmn. dept., 1966-74. Mem. Am. Chem. Soc., Am. Soc. Biol. Chemists. Home: Unit 306 403 S Allen St State College PA 16801 Office: Penn State U 108 Althouse Lab University Park PA 16802

PEABODY, ROBERT LEE, political science educator, researcher; b. Seattle, Dec. 23, 1931; s. Keith R. and Pearl B. (Starr) P.; divorced; children: Susan, Llyn, Jennifer. BBA, U. Wash., 1954, MA in Polit. Sci., 1956; PhD in Polit. Sci., Stanford U., 1960. Post-doctoral fellow Brookings Instn., Washington, 1960-61; from asst. to assoc. prof. polit. sci. Johns Hopkins U., Balt., 1961-68, prof., 1969—; Congl. intern Office of Ho. Majority Whip Hale Boggs, 1965; assoc. dir. Am. Polit. Sci. Assn. Study Congress, 1965-75; staff asst., speech writer for Speaker Carl Albert U.S. Ho. of Reps., 1975-76; cons. PBS, 1979-80, 82, Everett McKinley Dirksen Congl. Leadership Rsch. Ctr., 1980-82, Covington & Burling, 1982-83; dir. Former Mems. Congress Oral History Project, 1980-81; mem. nat. adv. bd. The Carl Albert Ctr., 1979—. Author: Organizational Authority, 1964, (with Ralph K. Huitt) Congress: Two Decades of Analysis, 1969, (with Berry, Frasure and Goldman) To Enact a Law: Congress and Campaign Finance, 1972, Leadership in Congress: Stability, Succession and Change, 1976,; editor: (with Nelson W. Polsby) New Perspectives on the House of Representatives, 1963, 4th rev. edit., 1992, Education of a Congressman (Rep. Morris K. Udall), 1972, Cases in American Politics, 1976; adv. editor Politics and Public Policy Series, Congl. Quarterly Press, 1976-84; contbr. articles and book revs. to profl. jours. Grantee Lyndon Baines Johnson Found., 1982-83; Ford Found. fellow Stanford U., 1959-60, Social Sci. Rsch. Coun. fellow Mich. Survey Rsch. Ctr., 1964-65, Faculty fellow Ford Found., 1969-70; Evans scholar Western Golf Assn., 1950-54, Resident scholar Nuffield Coll. Oxford U., 1974-75. Mem. Phi Beta Kappa. Home: 705 D St NE Washington DC 20002 Office: Johns Hopkins U Dept Polit Sci 34th & Charles Baltimore MD 21218

PEABODY, WILLIAM TYLER, JR., retired paper manufacturing company executive; b. Melrose, Mass., Mar. 17, 1921; s. William Tyler and

Dorothy (Atkinson) P.; m. Florence Marshall, July 27, 1946; children: Carol Peabody Moomey, William Tyler III, Janet Peabody Barrow, Marshall R. A.B. cum laude, Harvard U., 1942, postgrad. Grad. Sch. Arts and Scis., 1946-47, LL.B., 1949. Bar: N.Y. 1950. Asso. firm Root, Ballantine, Harlan, Bushby & Palmer, N.Y.C., 1949-54; with law div. Scott Paper Co., Phila., 1954-62, 67-85; asst. to gen. mgr. Scott Paper Co., Everett, Wash., 1962-67; asst. sec. Scott Paper Co., 1965-71, corp. sec., 1971-83, asst. sec., 1983-84, ret. Pres. Knollwood Terrace Civic Assn., Carle Place, N.Y., 1952-53; pres. Carle Place Taxpayers Assn., 1953-54; bd. dirs. Nether Providence Cmty. Assocs., Inc., Wallingford, Pa., 1969-75, pres., 1973-75; bd. dirs. Ethel Mason Day Care Ctr., Wallingford, 1976-81, pres., 1979-80; vestryman St. Mary's Episc. Ch., Carle Place, N.Y., 1953-54; vestryman, jr. warden Trinity Episc. Ch., Everett, Wash., 1965-67; chmn. Rose Valley Folk, 1977-78; bd. dirs. Helen Kate Furness Free Libr., Wallingford, 1984-87, v.p., 1986-87; Chester-Wallingford chpt. ARC, 1991—, exec. com., 1992—, 1st vice chmn., 1994-95, chmn., 1995—; bd. dirs. Everett, Wash. Area C. of C., 1965-67; Snohomish County Family Counseling Svc., Everett, 1962-67, pres., 1965; pres. Wallingford, Pa. Swim Club, 1960-61. Lt. USNR, 1942-46. Mem. ABA, Am. Soc. Corp. Secs. (dir. 1977-81, pres. Middle Atlantic group 1976-77), Harvard Club (Phila., sch. com. 1959-62, 76-90). Home: 15 Rose Valley Rd Media PA 19063-4217

PEACE, BARBARA LOU JEAN, education educator; b. Valdosta, Ga., Jan. 11, 1939; d. Billington Philip and Hattie Lougene (Dollar) Peace. Student, Valdosta State Coll., 1956-58; BA in English, Tenn. Temple U., 1961; postgrad., Fla. State U., 1962-63; MS in Indsl. and Orgnl. Psychology, Valdosta State U., 1994. Receptionist ITT, Thompson Industries, Valdosta, Ga., 1961; child welfare worker Lowndes County Welfare Dept., Valdosta, 1961-62; supr. child welfare divsn. Muscogee County Dept. Family & Children Services, Columbus, Ga., 1963-66; dir. social work Valdosta-Lowndes County Headstart Program, 1966-73; tchr. English & Remedial Reading Valdosta City Sch. System, 1966-73; tchr. advisor English & Psychology Valdosta Technical Inst., 1973—; chair South Ga. Consortium Psychology Tchrs., 1994-95; advisor Vocat. Indsl. Clubs Am., 1981-88, 90—, adv. coun., 1982-86, planning com. regional leadership conf., 1984, coord. state leadership contests, state advisor officer tng., presenter leadership confs., 1986; advisor Valdosta Tech. Inst., 1981-88, 90—, quality coun. mem., 1994, chair blood drive, 1994-95; past vica craft adv. Valdosta H.S., Lowndes H.S. Sponsor ARC Blood Drive, Valdosta, 1984-88, Ga. Sheriffs' Boys' Ranch, Arts, Inc.; vol. Am. Heart Assn., Am. Lung Assn., 1994—; contbr. Am. Cancer Soc., United Way; active personnel, finance, nominating and kindergarten and kitchen coms. Azalea City Bapt. Ch., adult choir, dir. children's choir, tchr. Sunday Sch., nursery worker; bd. dirs., pianist, advisor/counsellor, tutor Valdosta Korean Bapt. Ch., 1985-92. Mem. Am. Vocational Assn., Ga. Vocational Assn., Vocat. Ga. Assn., Vocational Edn. Spl. Needs Personnel, Action Travelers (bd. dirs. 1970—), Adventuretour Exchange Club (sponsor 1981-85). Republican. Baptist. Avocations: traveling, music, stamp collecting, gourmet cooking. Office: Valdosta Tech Inst RR 1 Box 65 Valdosta GA 31602-9801

PEACE, H. W., II, oil company executive; b. Clinton, Okla., May 21, 1935; s. Herman Wilbern and Bernice (Mitchell) P.; m. Norma June Williams; children: Hugh William, Susannah Lee. BS in Geology, U. Okla., 1959, MS in Geology, 1964; postgrad., U. S.W. La., 1968. Jr. geologist Union Oil Co. Calif., Houston, 1964-65; area geologist Union Oil Co. Calif., Lafayette, La., 1965-70; geologist dist. exploration Union Oil Co. Calif., Oklahoma City, 1970-77; mgr. Rocky Mountain exploration Union Oil Co. Calif., Casper, Wyo., 1977-80; mgr. div. exploration Cotton Petroleum Corp., Tulsa, 1980-83; v.p. exploration Hadson Petroleum Corp., Oklahoma City, 1983-85, exec. v.p., chief operating officer, 1985-88, also bd. dirs.; exec. v.p., chief ops. officer Mosswood Oil and Gas Co., Oklahoma City, 1985-88; exec. v.p., chief ops. officer Anadarko Supply Co., Oklahoma City, 1986-88, also bd. dirs.; mng. ptnr. EXAD, Oklahoma City, 1988-91; pres., chief exec. officer, dir. Panhandle Royalty Co., Oklahoma City, 1991—. Dir. sch. geology adv. com. U. Okla., Norman, 1984—, vice chmn. 1988-89, chmn. 1989-90, exec. com. 1990—. Lt. USN 1959-63, capt. USNR, 1963-82, retired list 1995. Mem. Am. Assn. Petroleum Geology (rep. del. or alt. 1984—), Soc. Exploration Geophysicists, Soc. Econ. Paleontologists and Mineralogists, Petroleum Assn. Wyo. (v.p. 1979-80), Tulsa Geol. Soc., Oklahoma City Geol. Soc. (chmn. profl. affairs 1976-77), Naval Res. Assn., Cherokee Hills Homeowners Assn. (pres. 1971-73), Fieldstone Homeowners Assn. (pres. 1983), Navy League. Republican. Lodge: Civitan. Avocations: golf, swimming, hiking. Office: Panhandle Royalty Co 5400 N Grand Blvd Ste 210 Oklahoma City OK 73112-5654

PEACHEY, LEE DEBORDE, biology educator; b. Rochester, N.Y., Apr. 14, 1932; s. Clarence Henry and Eunice (DeBorde) P.; m. Helen Pauline Fuchs, June 7, 1958; children: Michael Stephen, Sarah Elizabeth Keating, Anne Palmer Lorenz. BS, Lehigh U., 1953; postgrad., U. Rochester, 1953-56; Ph.D. (Leitz fellow), Rockefeller U., 1959; MA (hon.), U. Pa., 1971. Research asso. Rockefeller U., 1959-60; asst. prof. zoology Columbia U., 1960-63, asso. prof., 1963-65; asso. prof. biochemistry and biophysics U. Pa., Phila., 1965-70; prof. biology U. Pa., 1970—; adj. prof. molecular, cellular and developmental biology U. Colo., 1990-94; mem. molecular biology study sect. NIH, 1969-73; mem. Biomed. Rsch. Tech. Rev. Com., NIH, 1994—; mem. Mayor's Sci. and Tech. Adv. Coun., Phila., 1972—; chmn. Gordon Rsch. Conf. on Muscle, 1983. Editor: Third and Fourth Conferences on Cellular Dynamics, N.Y. Acad. Scis., 1967, First and Second Confs. on Cellular Dynamics, 1968, Am. Physiol. Soc. Handbook on Skeletal Muscle, 1983; mem. editorial bd. Tissue and Cell, 1969—, Jour. Cell Biology, 1970-73, Pitman Series in Cellular and Development Biology, 1977—, Microscopy Rsch. and Technique, 1982-93, Advances in Optical and Electron Microscopy, 1983—, Neuroimage, 1991—, Jour. Microscopy, 1992—, Bioimages, 1993—; contbr. articles to sci. jours. Trustee Keith R. Porter Endowment for Cell Biology, Narberth, Pa., 1981—. Guggenheim and Fulbright-Hays fellow, 1967-68, Overseas fellow Churchill Coll., Cambridge, Eng., 1967-68, Fogarty Sr. Internat. fellow, 1979-80, hon. rsch. fellow U. Coll., London, 1979-80; Royal Soc. (London) guest rsch. fellow, Cambridge, 1986; grantee NSF, 1960-72, NIH, 1973—, Muscular Dystrophy Assn., Am. 1973-91. Fellow AAAS; Mem. Electron Microscopy Soc. Am. (council 1975-78, pres. 1982), Am. Soc. Cell Biology (program chmn. 1965, council 1966-69), Biophys. Soc. (program chmn. 1976, council 1976-80, exec. com. 1976-82, pres. 1981-82), Internat. Union Pure and Applied Biophysics (council 1978-84, v.p. 1984-87, pres. 1987-90, chmn. commnn. on cell and membrane biophysics 1981-84, hon. v.p. 1990-93), Physiol. Soc. (Eng.); mem. Internat. Soc. Stereology (internat. stereology software com. 1982—), Soc. Gen. Physiologists. Achievements include research in mechanisms of muscle cell contraction; development of methods in light and electron microscopy; development of computer graphic methods for three-dimensional image analysis and reconstruction. Home: 606 Old Gulph Rd Narberth PA 19072-1622 Office: U Pa Dept Biology Philadelphia PA 19104-6018

PEACOCK, A(LVIN) WARD, textile company executive; b. Durham, N.C., June 17, 1929; s. Erle Ewart and Vera Louise (Ward) P.; m. Barbara Sheppard White, July 2, 1955; children: Alvin Ward, Stephen White, Nancy Lay. B.S. in Commerce, U. N.C., 1950; M.B.A., Harvard U., 1952. Asst. to v.p. Erwin Mills, Inc., Durham, 1953-55, sec., 1957-62, sec.-treas., 1962-64; v.p. Dixie Yarns, Inc., Chattanooga, 1964-76, sr. v.p., 1976-81; sr. v.p. Springs Industries, Fort Mill, S.C., 1981-86; exec. v.p. Springs Industries, Fort Mill, 1986-92; bd. dirs. Am. Mfg. Co., Chattanooga, Metrolina Food Bank; regional dir. First Wachovia Corp., Charlotte, N.C., 1988-92. Trustee Holston Conf. Colls., Tenn., 1968-79, Sci. Mus. Charlotte, 1990-94; bd. dirs. Chattanooga Meml. Hosp., 1979-81, Charlotte Symphony, 1990-94, Greater Carolinas chpt. ARC, 1988-94; dir. Allied Arts Fund, 1978-81, Metrolina Food Bank, 1994—; mem. Chattanooga Wastewater Regulation Bd., 1978-81. 1st lt. USAF, 1955-57. Mem. Tenn. Mfrs. Assn. (chmn. bd. dirs. 1980-81), Chattanooga Mfrs. Assn. (pres. 1968-69), Am. Textile Mfrs. Inst., Univ. Club, River Hills Club, Phi Beta Kappa, Alpha Kappa Psi, Sigma Nu. Republican. Methodist. Home: 22 Wood Hollow Rd Lake Wylie SC 29710-8920

PEACOCK, DOUGLAS W., manufacturing executive; b. 1938. B.S., Wash. State U., 1962; Ph.D., U. of Ill., 1966. With Westinghouse Elec. Co., 1972-87, with IMO Industries Inc., 1987—, former exec. v.p. power systems, now exec. v.p. instruments and aerocomponents. Office: IMO Industries Inc 3450 Princeton Pike Trenton NJ 08648-1206

PEACOCK, ERLE EWART, JR., surgeon, lawyer, educator; b. Durham, N.C., Sept. 10, 1926; s. Erle Ewart and Vera Louise (Ward) P.; m. Mary Louise Lowrey, Apr. 17, 1954; children: James Lowrey, Susan Louise, Virginia Gayle. Cert. in medicine, U. N.C., 1947, BS, 1990; MD, Harvard U., 1949; JD, U.N.C., 1993. Bar: N.C. 1993. Intern, asst. resident surgery Roosevelt Hosp., N.Y.C., 1949-51; intern asst. resident gen. surgery U. N.C. Hosps., Chapel Hill, 1953-54, chief resident gen. surgery, 1954-55; resident in plastic surgery Barnes Hosp., St. Louis, 1955-56; mem. faculty dept. surgery U. N.C., Chapel Hill, 1956-69; prof. surgery, head div. plastic surgery U. N.C., 1965-69; prof., chmn. dept. surgery U. Ariz., Tucson, 1969-77; prof. surgery Tulane U., New Orleans, 1977-82; pvt. practice surgery Chapel Hill, N.C., 1982—; vis. prof. surgery U. Va., Charlottesville, 1983—; chief hand surgery Valley Forge Army Hosp., Phoenixville, Pa., 1951-53; pres. Am. Bd. Plastic Surgery, 1975. Author: Wound Repair, 1977, 3d edit., 1982; assoc. editor: Am. Jour. Surgery, 1967—, Surgery Yearbook, 1970-89, Plastic and Reconstructive Surgery, 1972-78; asst. editor: Jour. Surg. Rsch., 1970-76. With USN, 1945-46; capt. M.C., U.S. Army, 1951-53. Served with U.S. Navy, 1945-46; served to capt. M.C. U.S. Army, 1951-53. Recipient Yandell medal Louisville Surg. Soc., 1972, McGraw medal Detroit Surg. Soc., 1973, Disting. Svc. award U. N.C., 1979, Jacob Markowitz award Acad. Surg. Rsch., 1993, Lifetime Achievement award Wound Healing Soc., 1994. Mem. AAAS, ACS, ABA, Womack Surg. Soc. (pres. 1979-80), Soc. U. Surgeons (treas. 1965-68), Plastic Surgery Rsch. Coun. (pres. 1966), Am. Surg. Assn., Am. Bd. Plastic Surgery (pres. 1976), Am. Assn. Plastic Surgeons (Clinican of Yr. 1985), Am. Soc. Surgery Hand, Interant. Soc. Surgeons, So. Surg. Assn., Rotary, Alpha Omega Alpha. Republican. Methodist. Home: 645 Rock Creek Rd Chapel Hill NC 27514-6714 Office: Patterson Dilthey Clay & Bryson Attys at Law 4020 Westchase Blvd Ste 550 Raleigh NC 27607-3942

PEACOCK, GEORGE ROWATT, retired life insurance company executive; b. Lakeland, Fla., Aug. 27, 1923; s. Robert and Annie Keane (Rowatt) P.; m. Virginia Jenkins, June 7, 1952; 1 child, Robert George. B.A., U. Fla., 1948, postgrad., 1948-49; postgrad., U. N.C., 1949-50, 51, Ind. U., summers 1966, 67. With Equitable Life Assurance Soc. U.S., 1952-88; v.p., head real estate dept. Equitable Life Assurance Soc. U.S., N.Y.C., 1974-77; sr. v.p., head equities sector Equitable Life Assurance Soc. U.S., 1977-80, sr. v.p., head real estate sector, 1980-84; chmn., chief exec. Equitable Real Estate Investment Mgmt., Inc., 1984-88; pres., chief exec. officer Carluke Inc., 1988—; past pres. Planters Redevel. Corp., St. Louis, 1984-87; trustee Equitable Life Mortgage & Realty Investors, 1981-83; bd. dirs. E.Q.K. Realty Investors, Arbor Properties Trust (formerly E.Q.K. Green Acres); emeritus mem. adv. bd. govs. Wharton Real Estate Ctr., U. Pa., 1985—. Author papers in field. Trustee Urban Land Inst., 1982-88; bd. govs. Central Atlanta Progress, 1984-86. Served with USAAF, 1942-45; with USAF, 1950-51. Decorated Purple Heart. Mem. Am. Soc. Real Estate Counselors, Urban Land Inst., Brit. Am. Property Investment Council, Am. Inst. Real Estate Appraisers, Real Estate Bd. N.Y. (past gov.), Phi Beta Kappa, Phi Kappa Phi, Phi Gamma Delta. Democrat. Office: 3414 Peachtree Rd NE Atlanta GA 30326-1113

PEACOCK, HUGH ANTHONY, agricultural research director, educator; b. Cairo, Ga., May 30, 1928; s. Leslie Hugh and Annie John (Aldrege) P.; m. Mary Helen Willis, Oct. 8, 1949; children: Ramon Anthony, Elizabeth Ann, Mary Evelyn. BS in Agronomy, U. Fla., 1952, MS in Agronomy, 1953; PhD, Iowa State U., 1956. Rsch. assoc. Iowa State U., Ames, 1955-56; asst. agronomist U. Fla., Leesburg, 1957-58; rsch. agronomist Ga. Exptl. Sta. USDA, Experiment, 1959-73; dir. Agrl. Rsch. & Edn. Ctr. U. Fla., Jay, 1973—. Contbr. articles to Agronomy Jour., Crop Sci., Plant Disease, Jour. Nematology. Director Hist. Soc. Santa Rosa County, Milton, Fla., 1979-80, Kiwanis Club of Milton, 1988-89, chmn. agrl. com., 1987-89. Cpl. U.S. ARmy, 1946-47, CBI. John D. Rockefeller Inst. scholar, 1953. Mem. Environ. Enhancement Assn. West Fla. (bd. dirs. Pensacola chpt. 1976—), Am. Soc. Agronomy (assoc. editor 1980-83), Am. Genetic Assn., Crop Sci. Soc. Am. (assoc. editor 1976-80), Alpha Zeta, Phi Kappa Phi, Sigma Xi, Gamma Sigma Delta. Methodist. Achievements include research in number of genes controlling defoliation vs. non-defoliation in cotton; effect of heterosis and combining ability on yield of cotton, effect of nitrogen fertilization on yield; effect of skip-row culture on fiber characteristics of cotton; yield response of cotton to spacing, effect of seed source on seedling vigor, yield and lint of upland cotton; a cone-type planter for experimental plots; subsurface sweep for applying herbicides; yield responses of soybean cultivars to Meloidogyne incognita. Office: U Fla Agr Rsch Ctr RR 3 Box 575 Jay FL 32565-8926

PEACOCK, JAMES DANIEL, lawyer; b. Moorestown, N.J., Dec. 19, 1930; s. L. Lawrence and Esther H. Peacock; m. Joan Peacock, June 14, 1953; children: Elizabeth Levine, Martha McLaughlin, Margaret Mae Daly, Mary Anne Friedman. AB, Duke U., 1952; LLB, U. Md., 1957. Bar: M. 1957, U.S. Ct. Appeals (4th cir.) 1959, U.S. Dist. Ct. Md. 1957, U.S. Supreme Ct. 1976. Of counsel Semmes Bowen & Semmes, Balt., 1957—. Trustee Sheppard & Enoch Pratt Hosp., Towson, Md., 1964— (chair 1993—). Fellow Am. Coll. Trial Lawyers (state chair 1985-86, adj. state chair 1992-93), ABA, Md. State Bar Assn., Am. Bar Found., Md. Bar Found.; mem. Balt. City Bar Assn., Balt. County Bar Assn., Wednesday Law Club (pres. 1987-88). Home: 105 Bonnie Hill Rd Baltimore MD 21204-4209 Office: Semmes Bowen & Semmes 401 Washington Ave Towson MD 21204-4883

PEACOCK, JUDITH ANN See ERWIN, JUDITH ANN

PEACOCK, LAMAR BATTS, retired physician; b. Albany, Ga., Sept. 21, 1920; s. Herbert A. and Helen Marian (LeVan) P.; m. Jane Bonner, June 7, 1947; children: Helen Lee (Mrs. Richard Paul Wade), Linda Jane (Mrs. Mathew Gossage), Lamar Bonner. BA, Emory U., 1941; MD, Med. Coll. Ga., 1946. Diplomate: Am. Bd. Internal Medicine. Intern Univ. Hosp., Augusta, 1946-47; resident Univ. Hosp., 1947-48; fellow internal medicine U. Va. Hosp., Charlottesville, 1948-49; resident Univ. Hosp., Augusta, 1949-50; practice medicine specializing in internal medicine and allergy Atlanta, 1950-91; mem. staff St. Joseph's Infirmary, Crawford Long Hosp., Piedmont Hosp., Grady Meml. Hosp., Hughes Spalding Pavilion, Northside Hosp., West Paces Ferry Hosp., all Atlanta, Cobb Gen. Hosp., Austell, Ga., Douglasville (Ga.) Hosp.; instr. internal medicine Ga. Bapt. Hosp., Atlanta, 1950-58, chief medicine, 1958-72; mem. faculty Emory U. Sch. Medicine, Atlanta, 1950—, asst. clin. prof. medicine, 1962—; instr. internal medicine Sch. Dentistry, 1958—. Chief med. br., health services Atlanta Met. Area Civil Def., 1960-63; mem. Ga. Pub. Health Assn., 1967-69, Ga. Bd. Health, 1966-72, Ga. Vocational Rehab. Council, 1973—; Pres. trustees Med. Coll. Ga. Found., 1963. Fellow ACP, Am. Coll. Allergy and Immunology (nat. pres. 1972-73), Am. Acad. Allergy and Immunology; mem. AMA, Am. Heart Assn., Ga. Heart Assn., Am. Soc. Internal Medicine, Ga. Soc. Internal Medicine, 5th Dist. Med. Soc., Ga. Thoracic Soc., Med. Assn. Atlanta (prs. 1965), Med. Assn. Ga. (1st v.p. 1966-67), Southeastern Allergy Assn. (pres. 1963-64), So. Med. Assn., Cherokee Town and Country Club. Episcopalian. Home: 3120 Verdun Dr NW Atlanta GA 30305-1940

PEACOCK, LELON JAMES, psychologist, educator; b. Brevard, N.C., May 25, 1928; s. L.J. and Dorothy (Barrett) P.; m. Marian Davis, June 8, 1945; children: Lynn Barrett, Janice Davis, Timothy Lee. Student, Emory U., 1945-47; A.B., Berea Coll., 1950; M.S., U. Ky., 1952, Ph.D., 1956. Psychophysiologist U.S. Army Med. Research Lab., Ft. Knox, Ky., 1954-56; rsch. assoc., acting dir. Yerkes Labs. of Primate Biology, Inc., Orange Park, Fla., 1956-59; assoc. prof. psychology U. Ga., Athens, 1959-65; prof. U. Ga. 1966-90, prof. emeritus, 1990—. Author: (with R.V. Heckel) Textbook of General Psychology, 1966; Contbr. articles profl. jours. Recipient U. Ga. M.G. Michael Research award, 1964. Fellow AAAS; mem. APA, So. Soc. Philosophy and Psychology (pres. 1973-74), Soc. Neurosci., Sigma Xi, Phi Kappa Phi. Home: 145 Woodland Way Athens GA 30606-4349

PEACOCK, MARKHAM LOVICK, JR., English educator; b. Shaw, Miss., Sept. 19, 1903; s. Markham Lovick and Mary (Patton) P.; m. Dora Greenlaw, Dec. 29, 1928. Grad., Webb Sch., 1921; B.A., Washington and Lee U., 1924, M.A., 1926; Ph.D. Johns Hopkins, 1936. Mem. faculty Va. Polytech. Inst. 1926—, prof. English, 1945—, chmn. dept., 1960-66. Author: The Critical Opinions of William Wordsworth, 1949, also critical, ednl. and lit. articles. Mem. Am. Assn. U. Profs., Nat. Council of Tchrs. English, Modern Lang. Assn., Internat. Fedn. of Modern Langs. and Lits.,

Modern Humanities Research Assn., Acad. Polit. Sci., N.E.A., Guild of Scholars. Omicron Delta Kappa, Lambda Chi Alpha, Sigma Upsilon, Phi Kappa Phi, Gold Triangle. Episcopalian. Clubs: Shenandoah; Tudor and Stuart (Balt.), Johns Hopkins (Balt.); Princeton. Home: 801 Draper Rd SW Blacksburg VA 24060-5117

PEACOCK, MARY WILLA, magazine editor; b. Evanston, Ill., Oct. 23, 1942; d. William Gilbert and Mary Willa (Young) P. B.A., Vassar Coll. 1964. Assoc. lit. editor Harper's Bazaar mag., N.Y.C., 1964-69; staff editor Innovation mag., N.Y.C., 1969-70; editor in chief, co-founder, sec.-treas., pres. Rags mag., N.Y.C., San Francisco, 1970-71; co-founder, features editor Ms. mag., N.Y.C., 1971-77; pub., pres. Rags mag., N.Y., 1977-80; sr. editor Village Voice, N.Y.C., 1980-85, style editor, 1985-89; editor-in-chief Model mag., N.Y.C., 1989—, editorial cons., 1991—; fashion dir. Lear's Mag., N.Y.C., 1992-94; dep. editor In Style Mag., 1994, Mirabella mag., 1994—.

PEACOCK, MOLLY, poet; b. Buffalo, June 30, 1947; d. Edward Frank and Pauline Ruth (Wright) P. BA magna cum laude, Harpur Coll., Binghamton, N.Y., 1969; MA with honors, Johns Hopkins U., 1977. Adminstr., lectr. in English, SUNY-Binghamton, 1970-76; lectr. Johns Hopkins U., Balt., 1977-78, Barnard Coll., 1989-93; instr. English, Friends Sem., N.Y.C., 1981-92; poet-in-residence Del. Arts Coun., Wilmington, 1978-81, Bucknell U., NYU, Sarah Lawrence Coll.; poetry instr., 1990—. Author: And Live Apart, 1980; Raw Heaven, 1984, Take Heart, 1989, Original Love, 1995; contbr. poems to The New Yorker, The New Republic, The Nation. Danforth Found. fellow, 1976; Yaddo fellow, 1980, 82, 89, Ingram Merrill Found., 1981, 86, New Va. Rev., 1983; grantee Creative Artists Pub. Svc. Program, 1977, N.Y. Found. for Arts, 1985, NEA, 1991; Lila Wallace/Woodrow Wilson fellow, 1994. Mem. PEN, Poetry Soc. Am. (governing bd. 1988—, pres. emeritus). Home: 505 E 14th St Apt 3G New York NY 10009 also: 229 Emery St E, London, ON Canada N6C 2E3

PEACOCK, PATRICIA ANNE, academic program director; b. Crestline, Ohio, Aug. 5, 1944; children: Carolyn Frances, Kristin Maude. BA, U. So. Colo., 1976; MEd, Colo. State U., 1978; EdD, Rutgers U., 1986. Apprentice coord., cert. pub. mgr. Adminstrv. asst. Antioch (Ill.) Humanistic Soc., 1968-73; exec. sec. Ozite Corp., Libertyville, Ill., 1973-74; coordinator Dist. 11 Community Edn., Colorado Springs, Colo., 1974-76, Community Edn. Poudre R-1, Ft. Collins, Colo., 1976-83; program mgr. vocat. edn. N.J. Dept. Edn., Trenton, 1979-83, asst. dir. adult edn., 1983-86; dir. Rutgers U. Regional Small Bus. Devel. Ctr., Camden, N.J., 1986—. Author weekly column Small Bus. for Courier Post. Bd. dirs. Family Counseling Svc., Camden, 1986-90, Palmyra (N.J.) Harbour Condominium Assn., 1985-88; sec., bd. dirs. Community Accts. Phila., 1988-90; mem. Camden County Pvt. Industry Coun., 1991—; mem. Camden County coun. Girl Scouts U.S., 1993—. Named Woman who made a Difference in edn. Camden County Commn. on Women, 1989. Mem. N.J. Assn. Women Bus. Owners (Rose and Scroll award 1988—). Avocations: writing, reading, seminars. Office: Rutgers U Sch Bus Third at Penn Sts Camden NJ 08102

PEAGLER, OWEN F., colege administrator; b. New Milford, Conn., Nov. 28, 1936; s. Robert James and Myrtle (Gary) P.; m. Joyce Hancock (div. 1983); children: Catherine, Robert; m. Teresa Boone, Mar. 20, 1985; 1 child, Kirin. BS, Western Conn. State U., 1956; MA, NYU, 1959, profl. diploma, 1964. Tchr. New Milford Pub. Schs., 1955-56; dir. guidance White Plains (N.Y.) Pub. Schs., 1957-69; dean sch. continuing edn. Pace U., N.Y.C., 1969-78, Ea. Conn. State U., Willimantic, 1978—; chmn. bd. WAVE, Inc., Washington, 1976—; cons., V.I., 1970-73. Svc. dept. community affairs State of Del., Wilmington, 1982-83; asst. to N.Y. Rep. State Chmn. N.Y. Rep. State Com., Albany, 1970-78; chmn. Pres'. Adv. Coun. on Edn. Disadvantaged Children, Washington, 1973-78. Named N.Y. State Young Man of Yr. N.Y. Jr. C. of C., 1964; recipient Outstanding Coll. Programs award Conn. Nat. Guard, 1988. Home: 57 Boughton Rd Old Lyme CT 06371-1321 Office: Ea Conn State U Office of the Dean Edn 83 Windham St Willimantic CT 06226-2295

PEAK, DAVID, physicist, educator, researcher; b. Bklyn., Nov. 28, 1941; s. William Henry and Blanche Ethel (Seckendorff) P.; m. Terry L. Handwerger, June 3, 1983. BS, SUNY, New Paltz, 1965; PhD, SUNY, Albany, 1969. Physics instr. SUNY, Albany, 1971-75; asst. prof. physics Union Coll., Schenectady, N.Y., 1975-78; assoc. prof. physics Union Coll., Schenectady, 1978-85, prof. physics, 1985-87, Frank & Marie Bailey prof. physics, 1987—; E. Claiborne Robins Disting. Prof. Sci. U. Richmond, 1993—; vis. fellow Princeton (N.J.) U., 1978-79; vis. scientist Argonne (Ill.) Nat. Lab., 1983-84; mem. Union Coll. Bd. Trustees, Schenectady, 1985-88, Nat. Confs. on Undergrad. Rsch. Governing Bd., 1988—, chair 1992—; trustee Dudley Observatory, 1992—. Author: Order and Chaos: Art and Magic, 1991; contbr. 40 articles to profl. jours. Recipient Profl. Devel. award NSF, Washington, 1978, Meritorious Svc. award, Alumni Coun. Union Coll., Schenectady, 1990, New Liberal Arts Spl. Leave award, Sloan Found., 1990-91. Mem. Coun. on Undergrad. Rsch. (founding mem., sec. 1985-87), Am. Physical Soc. (mem. exec. com. N.Y. state), Am. Astron. Soc., Am. Assn. Physics Tchrs., Sigma Xi (com. on sci. edn.). Achievements include research on nature of reactions in condensed media, ion beam processing of thin films, mechanical properties of soft condensed matter. Office: Union Coll Physics Dept Schenectady NY 12308

PEAK, WILLIAM ROY, newspaper editor; b. Canton, Ill., Mar. 19, 1943; s. James Roy and Helen Marie (Lesko) P. BS, U. Ill., 1965. Copy editor Peoria (Ill.) Jour. Star, 1966-70, reporter, 1970-71, asst. city editor, 1971-91, night city editor, 1991—. Mem. Ducks Unltd. Roman Catholic. Avocations: hunting, fishing, trap and skeet shooting, decoy collecting. Home: 270 N 2d Ave Canton IL 61520 Office: Peoria Jour Star 1 News Plaza Peoria IL 61643

PEAKE, FRANK, middle school educator; b. Elgin, S.C., Oct. 25, 1939; s. Barney and Elrie (Branham) P. AA, Anderson Coll., 1966; BS, U. S.C., 1968; MA in Teaching, The Citadel, 1976. Cert. tchr. S.C. Classroom tchr. Berkeley Jr. High, Moncks Corner, S.C., 1968-70, Berkeley Middle Sch., Moncks Corner, 1970-85, 90—, Macedonia Middle Sch., Moncks Corner, 1986-88, North Ctrl. High, Kershaw, S.C., 1988-89. With S.C. Air Nat. Guard, 1959-65. Mem. Nat. Coun. Tchrs. Math, Mensa. Republican. Baptist. Avocations: reading. Home: 195 Peake Rd Elgin SC 29045 Office: Berkeley Middle Sch 320 N Highway 17 A Moncks Corner SC 29461

PEAL, JAMES ALBERT, psychiatrist; b. Chgo., Jan. 11, 1922; s. Allen Saunders and Helen (Goines) P.; m. Edithie Ventura Figueroa, Oct. 19, 1951; children: James A. II, Arturo A. BS, Mich. State Coll., 1943; MD, Howard U., 1948. Diplomate Nat. Bd. Med. Examiners, Am. Bd. Psychiatry and Neurology; clic. physician, Md., Conn., Calif., Va. Intern Harlem Hosp., N.Y.C., 1948-49; resident Norwich (Conn.) State Hosp., 1949-51, USN Hosp., Oakland, Calif., 1954-56; staff psychiatrist Napa State Hosp., Imola, Calif., 1955-57, Agnew (Calif.) State Hosp., 1957-58; chief of clin. svcs. Calif. Med. Facility Dept. Corrections, Vacaville, 1958-59; asst. supt. psychiat. svcs. Stockton (Calif.) State Hosp., 1959-63, assoc. supt. clin. svcs., 1963-64; asst. dir. divsn. svcs. to mentally ill Mich. Dept. Mental Health, Lansing, 1964-67; dir. Fresno County (Calif.) Dept. Mental Health, 1967-70; sr. psychiatrist San Joaquin County (Calif.) Mental Health Svcs., 1970-72; pvt. practice Stockton and Sacramento, Calif., 1973-92; staff psychiatrist Tex. Dept. of Mental Health and Mental Retardation, Vernon, 1992-93, Southwestern Va. Mental Health Inst., Marion, 1993—; civilian cons. psychiatry USAF Hosp., Travis AFB, 1958-64, spl. cons. Calif. Dept. Corrections, 1959-64, cons. Office of Pub. Defender, Sonoma County, Calif., 1973-93; chief psychiat. cons. for prosecution in second Juan Corona trial, 1982; founder, dir. John Hale Mental Health Ctr., San Francisco, 1973-78; med. advisor Social Security Adminstrn., Adminstrv. Law Judges, 1973-93; mem. staff Harbor Gen. Hosp., Torrance, Calif., chief gen. practice, 1951-53; assoc. prof. U. So. Calif., 1968-72; asst. prof. U. Calif., Davis, 1973-78. Cons. Adult Authority, Calif., Dist. Atty.'s Office and Sheriff's Office, San Joaquin County, appt. dep. sheriff; bd. dirs. Family Svc., Stockton, Calif. (pres. 1964). Capt. U.S. Army, 1953; Maj. USAFR. Fellow Am. Psychiat. Assn. (life); mem. AMA, Am. Assn. Group Psychotherapy, Psychiat. Soc. Va., Inc., Mich. State Med. Soc., Mich. Soc. Neurology and Psychiatry, Calif. Med. Assn., Ctrl. Calif. Psychiat. Assn., Ingham County Med. Soc.,

San Joaquin County Med. Soc., Rotary Internat. Office: Southwestern Va Mental Health Inst 502 E Main St Marion VA 24354-3320

PEALE, RUTH STAFFORD (MRS. NORMAN VINCENT PEALE), religious leader; b. Fonda, Iowa, Sept. 10, 1906; d. Frank Burton and Anna Loretta (Crosby) Stafford; m. Norman Vincent Peale, June 20, 1930; children: Margaret Ann (Mrs. Paul F. Everett), John Stafford, Elizabeth Ruth (Mrs. John M. Allen). AB, Syracuse U., 1928, LLD, 1953; LittD, Hope Coll., 1962; LHD (hon.), Milw. Sch. Engring., 1985, Judson Coll., 1988; LHD, Milw. Sch. Engring., 1985. Tchr. math. Cen. High Sch., Syracuse, N.Y., 1928-31; nat. pres. women's bd. domestic missions Ref. Ch. Am., 1936-46; sec. Protestant Film Commn., 1946-51; chmn. Am. Mother's Com., 1948-49; pres., editor-in-chief, gen. sec., CEO, chmn. bd. dirs. Peale Ctr. for Christian Living, 1940—; nat. pres. bd. domestic missions Ref. Ch. in Am., 1955-56; mem. bd. N. Am. Missions, 1963-69, pres., 1967-69; mem. gen. program council Ref. Ch. in Am., 1968—; mem. com. of 24 for merger Ref. Ch. in Am. and Presbyn. Ch. U.S., 1966-69; v.p. Protestant Council N.Y.C., 1964-66; hon. chancellor Webber Coll., 1972—; co-founder, pub. Guideposts, N.Y.C., 1945—, pres., 1985-92, chmn. bd., 1992—; pres. Fleming H. Revell, Tarrytown, N.Y., 1985-92; founder Ruth Stafford Peale Ctr., Syracuse, 1989—. Appeared on: nat. TV program What's Your Trouble, 1952-68; Author: I Married a Minister, 1942, The Adventure of Being a Wife, 1971, Secrets of Staying in Love, 1984; founder, pub. (with Dr. Peale) Guidepost mag., 1957—; co-subject with husband: film One Man's Way, 1963. Trustee Hope Coll., Holland, Mich., Champlain Coll., Burlington, Vt., Stratford Coll., Danville, Va., Lenox Sch., N.Y.C., Interchurch Center Syracuse U., 1955-61; bd. dirs. Cook Christian Tng. Sch., Lord's Day Alliance U.S.; mem. bd. and exec. com. N.Y. Theol. Sem., N.Y.C.; sponsor Spafford Children's Convalescent Hosp., 1966—; bd. govs. Help Line Telephone Center, 1970—, Norman Vincent Peale Telephone Center, 1977; mem. nat. women's bd. Northwood Inst., 1981. Named New York State Mother of Yr., 1963, Disting. Woman of Yr. Nat. Art Assn., Religious Heritage Am. Ch. Woman of Yr., 1969; recipient Cum Laude award Syracuse U. Alumni Assn. N.Y., 1965, Honor Iowans' award Buena Vista Coll., 1966, Am. Mother's Com. award religion, 1970, Disting. Svc. award Coun. Chs., N.Y.C., 1973, Disting. Citizen award Champlain Coll., 1976, Disting. Svc. to Community and Nation award Gen. Fedn. Women's Clubs, 1977, Horatio Alger award, 1977, Religious Heritage award, 1979, joint medallion with husband Soc. for Family of Man, 1981, Soc. Family of Man award, 1981, Alderson-Broaddus award, 1982, Marriage Achievement award Bride's Mag., 1984, Gold Angel award Religion in Media, 1987, Adela Rogers St. John Roundtable award, 1987, Disting. Achievement award Am. Aging, 1987, Paul Harris award N.Y. Rotary, 1989, Leader's award Arthritis Found. Dutchess County, 1992, Norman Vincent Peale award Internat. Platform Assn., 1994, The Dave Thomas Well Done! award, 1994, Norman Vincent Peale award for positive thinking, 1994. Mem. Insts. Religion and Health (bd. exec. com.), Am. Bible Soc. (bd. trustees 1948-93, hon. trustee 1993—), United Bible Soc. (v.p.), The Interchurch Ctr. (bd. dirs. 1957-92, chair 1982-90), Nat. Coun. Chs. (v.p 1952-54, gen. bd.; treas. gen. dept. United Ch. Women, vice chmn. broadcasting and film commn. 1951-55, program chmn. gen. assembly 1966), N.Y. Fedn. Women's Clubs (chmn. religion 1951-53, 57-58), Home Missions Coun. N.A. (nat. pres. 1942-44, nat. chmn. migrant com. 1948-51), Nat. League Am. Pen Women (hon. life), PEO, Alpha Phi (Frances W. Willard award 1976). Republican. Office: Peale Ctr Christian Living 66 E Main St Pawling NY 12564-1409

PEALE, STANTON JERROLD, physics educator; b. Indpls., Jan. 23, 1937; s. Robert Frederick and Edith May (Murphy) P.; m. Priscilla Laing Cobb; June 25, 1960; children: Robert Edwin, Douglas Andrew. BSE, Purdue U., 1959; MS in Engring. Physics, Cornell U., 1962, PhD in Engring. Physics, 1965. Research asst. Cornell U., Ithaca, N.Y., 1962-64, research assoc., 1964-65; asst. research geophysicist, asst. prof. astronomy UCLA, 1965-68; asst. prof. physics U. Calif., Santa Barbara, 1968-70, assoc. prof. 1970-76, prof., 1976-94, prof. emeritus, rsch., 1994—; mem. com. lunar and planetary exploration NAS-NRC, Washington, 1980-84, lunar and planetary geosci. rev. panel, 1979-80, 86-89, 94—, Planetary Sys. Sci. Working Group, 1988-93, Lunar and Planetary Sci. Coun., 1984-87; lunar sci. adv. group NASA-JPL, Pasadena, Calif., 1970-72. Assoc. editor: Jour. Geophys. Research, 1987; contbr. articles to profl. jours. Recipient Exceptional Scientific Achievement medal NASA, 1980, James Craig Watson award Nat. Acad. Scis., 1982; vis. fellowships U. Colo., Boulder, 1972-73, 1979-80. Fellow AAAS (Newcomb Cleveland prize 1979), Am. Geophys. Union; mem. Am. Astron. Soc. (divsns. planet sci. and dynamic astronomy, Dirk Brouwer award 1992), Internat. Astron. Union. Avocation: gardening. Office: U Calif Dept Physics Santa Barbara CA 93106

PEANASKY, ROBERT JOSEPH, biochemist, medical educator; b. Menominee, Mich., Oct. 18, 1927; s. Joseph John and Sophia E. (Simeth) P.; m. Elizabeth R. Bender, Sept. 12, 1953; children: Joseph F., Michael J., Paul J., Robert A., John S. B.S. cum laude, Marquette U., 1951, M.S., 1953; Ph.D., U. Wis.-Madison, 1957. NSF trainee Marquette U., Milw., 1957, 58, 60, Dartmouth U., Hanover, N.H., 1959; asst. prof. Marquette U. Med. Sch., Milw., 1960-65, assoc. prof., 1965-67; assoc. prof. U. S.D. Med. Sch., Vermillion, 1967-70, prof., 1970-91, prof. emeritus, 1991—, dept. chmn. 1986-89; vis. scientist U. Ky. Med. Ctr., Lexington, 1965, U. Marseille-aix-en-Provence, 1966-67; vis. prof. Purdue U., West Lafayette, Ind., 1977; participant confs. in field; mem. Great Plains Regional Review and Research Adv. Com., 1969-72. Served to cpl. U.S. Army, 1946-47. USPHS fellow, 1960-62; recipient Career Devel. award USPHS, 1962-67; NIH grantee, 1961-90. Mem. Am. Chem. Soc. (chmn. sect. 1972), Am. Soc. Biochemistry and Molecular Biology, Soc. Exptl. Biology and Medicine (referee editor proceedings 1969-78, mem. council 1976-79), S.D. Acad. Scis. (exec. com. 1983-85), Sigma Xi (pres. local chpt. 1979-80). Democrat. Roman Catholic. Home: 931 7th St Plover WI 54467-2242

PEAPPLES, GEORGE ALAN, automotive executive; b. Benton Harbor, Mich., Nov. 6, 1940; s. Arthur L. and Kathleen C. (Peters) P.; m. Rebecca Dean Sowers, June 27, 1962; children: Lucia Christine, Sarah Bouton. BA in Econs., U. Mich., 1962, MBA in Fin., 1963. Fin. analyst Gen. Motors Corp., Detroit, 1964-68; dir. capital analysis and investment N.Y.C., 1968-73; asst. div. comptroller Delco Moraine div. Dayton, Ohio, 1973-75; asst. treas. bank relations Detroit, 1975-77, asst. comptroller, 1980-82; group dir. strategic bus. planning Chevrolet-Pontiac-Canada group Warren, Mich., 1984-86; v.p. Detroit, 1986—; v.p. Gen. Motors of Can., Ltd., Oshawa, Ont., 1982-84, pres., gen. mgr., 1986-94; asst. sec. of Navy U.S. Dept. Def., 1977-80; v.p. industry-govt. rels. GM, Washington, 1994—; bd. dirs. Nat. Assn. Mfrs., Am. Coalition for Traffic Safety and Fed. City Coun.; mem. vis. com. U. Mich. Mem. Coalition for Vehicle Choice. Recipient Disting. Pub. Svc. award Washington, 1980. Mem. Phi Kappa Phi. Office: 1660 L St Nw Ste 401 Washington DC 20037 also: GM Bldg 3044 W Grand Blvd Detroit MI 48202

PEARCE, COLMAN CORMAC, conductor, pianist, composer; b. Dublin, Leinster, Ireland, Sept. 22, 1938; came to U.S., 1987; s. Charles Edward and Elizabeth Mary (Byrne) P.; m. Eithne McGrath, Jan. 25, 1964 (div. 1991); 1 child, Deborah. BMus, Nat. U. Ireland, Dublin, 1960; studied with Franco Ferrara, 1965, pvt. pupil of Hans Swarowsky, 1969. From staff condr. to prin. condr. Radio TV Ireland (RTE), Dublin, 1965-83; prin. condr., music dir. Miss. Symphony Orch., Jackson, 1987—; dir. orch. studies, Royal Irish Acad. Music, Dublin, 1970-78; music examiner, Dept. Edn., Dublin, 1955-87; choral arranger, Castle Tours, Limerick, Ireland, 1974—. Avocations: art collecting, reading, theatre, travel. Home: 5045 Meadow Oaks Park Dr Jackson MS 39211-4816 Office: Miss Symphony Orch PO Box 2052 201 E Pascagoula St Jackson MS 39201-4114

PEARCE, DAVID HARRY, biomedical engineer; b. Newport News, Va., July 20, 1943. BSEE, Va. Poly. Tech. and State U., 1966; PhD, U. Va., 1972. Registered profl. engr., Miss. Asst. prof. med. physiology U. Miss. Med. Sch., Jackson, Miss., 1972-74, E. Tenn. State U. Sch. Medicine, JohnsonCity, Tenn., 1974-75; biomed. engr. Miss. Meth. Rehab. Ctr., Jackson, Miss., 1975-82, dir. biomedical engring., 1987—; v.p. Bobby J. Hall & Assocs., McComb, Miss., 1982-87; grant administr. HUD Block Grant, Magnolia, Miss., 1985-87. Contbr. articles to profl. jours. Young Investigator Pulmonary award NIH, 1973. Mem. IEEE, Am. Soc. Hosp. Engrs., Assn. Advancement of Med. Instrumentation, Jackson Photo Soc. (pres. 1980), Miss. Writers Assn. (treas. 1992). Avocations: photography, wood-

working, writing. Home: 230 Greenfield Pl Brandon MS 39042-9008 Office: Miss Meth Rehab Ctr 1350 E Woodrow Wilson Ave Jackson MS 39216-5198

PEARCE, DONALD JOSLIN, retired librarian; b. Southampton, Eng., May 31, 1924; came to U.S., 1949, naturalized, 1952; s. Alfred Ernest and Constance May (Jeffrey) P.; m. June Inez Bond, Dec. 7, 1946; children—Kristin, Kim. Student, Sch. Oriental and African Studies, U. London, 1942-43; A.B., George Washington U., 1953; M.S. in LS, Cath. U. Am., 1954. Part-time library asst. U.S. Dept. Agr., 1949-54; student asst. George Washington U. Library, 1950-53; circulation librarian Denison U., 1954-56; staff Ohio State U. Library, 1956-59, asst. acquisition librarian, 1958-59; head librarian, asst. prof. U. N.D., 1959-69, chief bibliographer, 1969-73, asst. dir. libraries, 1973-75, asst. prof. Oriental philosophy, 1969-75; library dir., asst. prof. philosophy U. Minn., Duluth, 1975-88, ret., 1988; Chmn. staff orgn. round table Ohio Library Assn., 1958-59. Served with Brit. Army, 1943-47. Mem. ALA, N.D. Library Assn. (pres. 1965-67), Minn. Library Assn. (sec. 1978-80, v.p. 1985, pres. 1986), Assn. Coll. Reference Librarians, Mountain Plains Library Assn. (v.p. 1968-69), Buddhist Assn., Phi Beta Kappa, Beta Phi Mu. Home: 1804 Vermilion Rd Duluth MN 55803-2509

PEARCE, DRUE, state legislator; b. Fairfield, Ill., Apr. 2, 1951; d. H. Phil and Julia Detroy (Bannister) P. AB, Ind. U., 1973; MPA, Harvard U., 1984. Sch. tchr. Clark County, Ind., 1973-74; curator Louisville Zoo, 1974-77; dir. Summerscene, Louisville, 1974-77; asst. v.p. Alaska Nat. Bank of the North, 1977-82; legis. aide to Alaska State Rep. John Ringstad, 1983; mem. Alaska Ho. of Reps., 1984-88; state senator Alaska Senate, 1988—, pres. senate, 1995—. Mem. Alaska Resource Devel. Coun., Alaska Women's Polit. Caucus. Mem. DAR, Alaska C. of C. Republican. Home: 6035 Tanaina Dr Anchorage AK 99502-1832 Office: Office of the State Senate State Capitol Juneau AK 99811

PEARCE, GEORGE HAMILTON, archbishop; b. Boston, Jan. 9, 1921; s. George Hamilton and Marie Louise (Duval) P. BA, Marist Coll. and Sem., Framingham, Mass., 1943. Tchr. Marist Coll. & Sem., Bedford, Mass., 1947-48, St. Mary's High Sch., Van Buren, Maine, 1948-49; missionary Roman Catholic Vicariate of Samoa, 1949-67, vicar apostolic of Samoa, 1956-66; bishop Diocese of Samoa, 1966-67; archbishop Archdiocese of Suva, Suva, Fiji, 1967-76; apostolic adminstr. Diocese of Agana, Guam, 1969; pres. Episcopal Conf. of the Pacific, 1969-71; staff mem. Bethany House of Intercession, Hastings-on-Hudson, N.Y., 1977-83; asst. to bishop Diocese of Providence, 1983—. Home: 30 Fenner St Providence RI 02903-3603

PEARCE, HARRY JONATHAN, lawyer; b. Bismarck, N.D., Aug. 20, 1942; s. William R. and Jean Katherine (Murray) P.; m. Katherine B. Bruk, June 19, 1967; children: Shannon P., Susan J., Harry M. BS, USAF Acad., Colorado Springs, Colo., 1964; JD, Northwestern U., 1967. Bar: N.D. 1967, Mich. 1986. Mcpl. judge City of Bismarck, 1970-76, U.S. magistrate, 1970-76, police commr., 1976-80; sr. ptnr. Pearce & Durick, Bismarck, 1970-85; assoc. gen. counsel GM, Detroit, 1985-87, v.p., gen. counsel, 1987—. Mem. vis. com. Sch. Law., Northwestern U.; mem. bd. visitors U.S. Air Force Acad.; chmn. 6th cir. corp. com. for fair compensation of Fed. Judiciary; trustee Howard U.; nat. bd. dirs. MADD; chmn. Product Liability Adv. Coun. Found.; founding mem. minority counsel demonstration program Commn. on Opportunities for Minorities in the Profession, ABA. Capt. USAF, 1964-70. Hardy scholar Northwestern U., Chgo., 1964-67; recipient Alumni Merit award, 1991. Fellow Am. Coll. Trial Lawyers, Internat. Soc. Barristers; mem. Am. Law Inst., Mich. Gen. Counsel Assn., Assn. Gen. Counsel. Avocations: amateur radio, woodworking, sailing. Office: GM Corp PO Box 33122 3031 W Grand Blvd Detroit MI 48202-3008*

PEARCE, PAUL FRANCIS, retired aerospace electronics company executive; b. Boston, Sept. 17, 1928; s. George Hamilton and Marie Louise (Duval) P.; m. Gilda Troisi Apr. 11, 1953; children: Janet, Theresa, Diane. BSEE (Edwards scholar), MIT, 1950; M.S., Mass. Inst. Tech., L.A., 1952; postgrad. (Hughes fellow), U. Calif., Los Angeles, 1957-58, U. So. Calif., 1958-59, Inst. Mgmt. Northwestern U., 1966. Project engr. Trans-Sonics, Inc., Burlington, Mass. 1952-55; sect. head application engring., strategic systems Hughes Aircraft Co., Culver City, Calif., 1955-59; with Lockheed Electronics Co., Plainfield, N.J., 1959-67; gen. mgr. div. mil. systems Lockheed Electronics Co., 1964-65, v.p., gen. mgr., 1965-67; v.p., div. mgr. Tele-Dynamics div. AMBAC Industries, Inc., Ft. Washington, Pa, 1967-74; group v.p. comml. and aerospace electronics group AMBAC Industries, Inc., Carle Place, N.Y., 1973-80; pres. James G. Biddle Co., Blue Bell, Pa., 1980-93, ret.; bd. dirs. AVO Internat. Ltd., 1987-91. Mem. Armed Forces Communications and Electronics Assn. (pres. 1969-71), Inst. Nav., Delaware Valley Mfrs. Assn. (sr. vice chmn. 1987-89, chmn. 1990-92—), Greater Phila. C. of C., Ft. Washington Indsl. Park Mgmt. Assn. (gov. 1973-74), Sigma Xi. Clubs: Mfrs'. Golf and Country (Oreland, Pa.) (handicap chmn. 1987-90), St. David's Golf Club (Wayne, Pa.).

PEARCE, RONALD, retired cosmetic company executive; b. Whitstable, County of Kent, Eng., Apr. 29, 1920; came to U.S., 1949; s. Fernley Charles and Medora Kate (Lissenden) P.; m. Olive Stacey, Apr. 4, 1942; children: David Fernley, Jane Ryding Robertson. Cambridge matriculation, Lindisfarne Coll., Ruabon, North Wales, U.K., 1937. Chief cashier Westminster Bank, Croydon, Eng., 1947-48; comml. officer Brit. Consulate, Dallas, 1949-52; v.p. World Gift Co., Dallas, 1953-63, Nelson Electronics, Dallas, 1963-68; stockbroker Walston & Co., Dallas, 1968-73; dir. purchasing Mary Kay Cosmetics, Inc., Dallas, 1973-85; pres. Global Water Techs., Inc., 1992—. Chmn. bd. Dallas Lighthouse for the Blind, 1987. Served to flight lt. RAF, 1940-46. Republican. Episcopalian. Home: 6918 Lloyd Valley Ln Dallas TX 75230-3129

PEARCE, WILLIAM JOSEPH, public broadcasting executive; b. Ponca City, Okla., Jan. 15, 1925; s. William Thomas and Mary Madeline (Fitzgerald) P.; m. Michaele Evelyn Mitchell, Aug. 1, 1958 (div. June 1962); m. Mary Simmen, June 1, 1964 (div. Mar. 31, 1982); children: Margaret Wickens, Daniel Ethan.; m. Noel Knille, Sept. 1, 1983 (div. Dec. 1988); children: Ryder Fitzgerald and Tyler Lightsinger (twins); stepchildren: Laura Rutherford Stone, Alexandra Garret Stone. B.A., U. Miami, 1950; postgrad., U. Conn., 1952-53; M.S., Syracuse U., 1959; grad. Advanced Mgmt. Program, Harvard U., 1976, Wharton Sch., U. Pa. Tchr. public schs. East Lyme, Conn., 1953-56; tchr. Dept. Air Force, Japan, 1956-58; exec. producer TV N.Y. State Edn. Dept., Albany, 1959-60; dir. radio-TV Brown U., 1960-65; cons. ETV, Rochester (N.Y.) City Sch. Dist., 1966-68; gen. mgr. Sta. WLIW-TV, Plainview, N.Y., 1968-69; pres., gen. mgr. Sta. WXXI-TV-AM-FM, Rochester, 1969—; bd. dirs. Native Am. Pub. Broadcasting Consortium, N.Y. State Gov.'s TV-Film Advisor. Bd., Am. Program Svc., Rochester Sch. Arts; chmn. N.Y. State Pub. Broadcasting Stas., Brookings Inst. Ctr. Advanced Study, Rochester. Mem. bd. mgmt. Rochester YMCA Camps; v.p. fin. Urbanarium, Rochester Devel. Community. With Signal Corps, USN, 1943-46, PTO. Recipient George Foster Peabody award, numerous other spl. radio and TV programming and prodn. awards for public affairs and performance programs, Civic medal for edn. City of Rochester. Mem. Nat. Assn. Pub. TV Stas., Nat. Pub. Radio, Nat. Assn. Broadcasters, N.Y. State Broadcasters Assn. (bd. dirs.), Rochester Radio Reading Svc., Eastern Ednl. TV Network, Rochester C. of C., VFW, Univ. Club of Rochester (bd. dirs.), Tennis Club of Rochester, Rotary. Roman Catholic. Office: 280 State St Rochester NY 14614-1033

PEARCE, WILLIAM MARTIN, history educator; b. Plainview, Tex., Mar. 11, 1913; s. Will Martin and Annie Eugenia (Bates) P.; m. Frances Elizabeth Campbell, Sept. 6, 1939; children—William Martin III, Richard Campbell. A.A., Kemper Mil. Sch., 1932; A.B., Tex. Tech. U., 1935; M.A., Tex. Tech U., 1937; Ph.D., U. Tex., 1952; LL.D., Tex. Wesleyan Coll., 1978. Instr. history Tex. Tech Coll., 1938-42, 46-47, asst. prof. history, 1949-53, asso. prof. history, 1953-55, prof., head dept. history, 1955-60, v.p. coll., 1960-68; dir. Tex. Tech Coll. (Archeol. Field Sch.), Glorieta, N.Mex., 1948, Tex. Tech Coll. (Valley of Mexico), 1949; pres. Tex. Wesleyan Coll., 1968-78; author: The Matador Land and Cattle Company, 1964. Served as lt. AUS, 1942-45. Decorated Bronze Star, Purple Heart; recipient Distinguished Alumnus award Tex. Tech U., 1975. Mem. Panhandle-Plains Hist. Soc. (dir.), Phi Alpha Theta, Pi Kappa Alpha, Phi Kappa Phi. Methodist. Home: 101D N Troy Ave Lubbock TX 79416-3029

PEARCY, ROBERT WOODWELL, botany educator; b. Boston, Aug. 28, 1941; s. Charles Miles and Elizabeth (Woodwell) P.; m. Carol Beth Hilliard; children: Shannon, Dean. BS, U. Mont., 1963, MS, 1965; PhD, Colo. State U., 1969. Postdoctoral fellow Dept. Plant Biology Carnegie Inst., Washington, Stanford,, Calif., 1969-71; asst. prof. biology SUNY, Albany, 1971-74; asst. prof. to assoc. prof. U. Calif., Davis, 1974-83, prof., 1983-90, chmn. dept. botany, 1990-94; mem. adv. com. NSF, 1979-83, U.S. Dept. Agriculture, 1987; program mgr. USDA/CRGO, 1989-90. Author numerous sci. pubs. Mem. AAAS, Am. Soc. Plant Physiologists, Ecol. Soc. Am., Australia Soc. Plant Physiologists. Avocation: fly fishing. Home: 227 Diablo Ave Davis CA 95616-0431 Office: Univ of Calif Davis Sect Plant Biology Davis CA 95616

PEARL, GEORGE CLAYTON, architect; b. London, Tex., Nov. 4, 1923; s. George William and Virgie Adlaid (Ford) P. BArch, U. Tex., 1950. Dir. design Stevens, Mallory, Pearl & Campbell, Albuquerque, 1953-89, dir. emeritus, 1989—. One man shows include St. Johns Coll., Santa Fe, 1987. Chmn. Albuquerque Landmarkers and Urban Conservation Commn., 1980-85; bd. advisors Nat. Trust for Hist. Preservation, Washington, 1976-86; bd. dirs. N.Mex. Archtl. Found., Santa Fe, 1988—, Hispanic Cultural Found., Albuquerque, 1985-90; active Commn. for Preservation Hist. N.Mex. Chs.; mem. Capitol Arts Found., 1990—, Guadaupe Hist. Found., 1991—; pres. N.Mex. Archtl. Found., 1991—. Recipient Bunting award Albuquerque Conservation Assn., 1988, Life Achievement award Historic Preservation State N.M.. 1993, Lifetime Achievement award Design and Historic Preservation Albuquerque Community Found. Fellow AIA (Silver medal western mountain region 1987). Democrat. Roman Catholic. Home: 215 12th St NW Albuquerque NM 87102-1815

PEARL, HELEN ZALKAN, lawyer; b. Washington, Sept. 12, 1938; d. George and Harriet (Libman) Zalkan; m. Jason E. Pearl, June 27, 1959; children: Gary M., Esther H., Lawrence J. BA with hons., Vassar Coll. 1959; JD, U. Conn., 1978. Bar: Conn. 1978, U.S. Dist. Ct. Conn. 1978. Mkt. rsch. analyst Landers, Frary & Clark, New Britain, Conn., 1960-61; managerial statistician Landers, Frary & Clark, 1961-62; real estate salesperson Denuzze Co., New Britain, 1966-70; property mgr. self-employed New Britain, 1970-75; legal asst. Atty. Gen. Office, State of Conn., Hartford, 1978; assoc. Weber & Marshall, New Britain, 1978-83; ptnr. Weber & Marshall, 1983—; hearing officer Commn. on Human Rights & Opportunities, State of Conn., 1980—; spl. master State of Conn. Judicial Dept., 1986—. New Britain rep. to Cen. Conn. Regional Planning Agy., 1973-75, 84—, chmn., 1990-92; mem. New Britain Bd. Fin. and Taxation, 1973-77; founder, mem. Conn. Permanent Commn. on Status of Women, 1975-82; also others. Recipient Women in Leadership award, YWCA of New Britain, 1988, Book award for torts, Am. Jurisprudence, 1976, Econs. prize, Vassar Coll., 1959. Mem. AAUW (pres. 1970-72), Conn. Bar Assn. (family law sect., women and the law sect.), New Britain Bar Assn., League Women Voters (Conn. specialist 1987—), Hartford Vassar Club, Phi Beta Kappa. Democrat. Jewish. Avocations: travel, theater, reading, cooking. Home: 206 Hickory Hill Rd New Britain CT 06052-1010 Office: Weber & Marshall PO Box 1568 New Britain CT 06050-1568

PEARL, MARY CORLISS, wildlife conservationist; b. N.Y.C., July 5, 1950; d. George Carleton and Margaret Lyon (Scheuer) Pearl; m. Charles Alfred Pillsbury, Oct. 21, 1972 (div. 1979); m. Don Jay Melnick, Oct. 3, 1981; children: Meredith, Seth. BA, Yale U., 1972, MPhil, 1976, PhD, 1982. Dir. corp. devel. World Wildlife Fund, N.Y.C., 1983-85; head N.Y. office World Wildlife Fund, 1984-85; adminstr. conservation progs. Wildlife Conservation Internat., N.Y.C., 1985-87; asst. dir. Wildlife Conservation Internat., 1988—; vis. scholar Dept. Biol. Sci., Stanford U., 1987-88; adj. prof. CUNY; cons. UNDP. Editorial advisor Wildlife Conservation mag., 1988—; editor: Conservation for the 21st Century, 1989; contbr. articles to profl. jours. Founding mem. Cons. in Higher Edn. Group of the Rainforest Alliance, N.Y.C., 1988—; founder Calvin Hill Daycare Ctr., New Haven, 1970; trustee Gomez Found., N.Y.C., 1985—; bd. govs. Soc. for Conservation Biology, 1991—. Recipient David Lapham award, Yale U., 1971; AAUW fellow, 1980. Fellow Explorers Club; mem. AAAS, Am. Soc. Primatologists, Internat. Primatology Soc., Internat. Union for Conservation of Nature (primate specialist group species survival commn.), Soc. for Conservation Biology (bd. govs.). Avocations: squash, birding, reading, history. Home: 605 W 115th St New York NY 10025-7722 Office: Wildlife Conservation Inter NY Zool Soc Bronx NY 10460

PEARL, MELVIN E., lawyer, film producer; b. Chgo., Feb. 25, 1936; s. Morris M. and Helen;m. Lynn B.; children: Steven, Robert, Julie. BBA, U. Wis., 1957; LLB, Northwestern U., 1960. Spl. trial atty. IRS, Washington, 1960-65; assoc. Gottlieb & Selwin, Chgo., 1965-74; ptnr. Katten, Muchin & Zavis, Chgo.; 1974—; bd. dirs. Cole Taylor Fin. Group, 1984-89, Guarantee Reserve Life Ins. Co., 1984-89, DeLaurentis Entertainment Group, 1986-89. Office: Katten Muchin & Zavis 525 W Monroe St Ste 1600 Chicago IL 60661-3693

PEARL, MINNIE (SARAH OPHELIA COLLEY CANNON), entertainer; b. Centerville, Tenn., Oct. 25, 1912; d. Thomas Kelly and Fannie Tate (House) Colley; m. Henry R. Cannon. Ed., Ward-Belmont Coll. Dir. amateur plays, Atlanta and surrounding areas, 1934-40; performer, WSM Grand Ole Opry, Nashville, 1940—; TV appearances include The World's Largest Indoor Country Music Show, 1978, A Country Christmas, Hee Haw, Johnny Cash and the Country Girls; rec. artist, Everest, RCA, Starday rec. cos.; Records include Story of Country Music, Minnie Pearl, Minnie Pearl at the Party, Answer to Giddyup and Go; Author: Minnie Pearl: Am. Autobiography, 1980. Recipient Woman of the Year award, Billboard; All Time Great award, Billboard; 1987 Roy Acuff Community Service Award, Country Music Found.; named to Country Music Hall of Fame, 1972; Pioneer Award, Acad. of Country Music, 1987. Address: Judy Seale Refugee International 209 Tenth Ave S Ste 347 Nashville TN 37203

PEARL, WILLIAM RICHARD EMDEN, pediatric cardiologist; b. N.Y.C., Nov. 1, 1944; s. William Emden and Sara (Gilston) P.; m. Karlyn Katsumoto, July 9, 1978; children: Jeffrey, Kristine. BA, Queens Coll., 1966; MD, SUNY, Bklyn., 1970. Diplomate Am. Bd. Pediatrics, Am. Bd. Pediatric Cardiology. Intern Roosevelt Hosp., N.Y.C., 1970-71; resident N.Y. Hosp.-Cornell Med. Ctr., N.Y.C., 1971-72; fellow Albert Einstein Coll. Medicine, N.Y.C., 1972-74; asst. prof. U. Hawaii, Honolulu, 1974-76; asst. prof. Tex. Tech. Med. Sch., El Paso, 1976-82, assoc. prof., 1982-92; chief pediatric cardiology William Beaumont Army Med. Ctr., El Paso, 1976-94; assoc. prof. med. branch U. Tex. Med. Br., Galveston, 1994—; cons. Miami (Fla.) Children's Hosp., 1988, Driscoll Children's Hosp., Corpus Christi, Tex., 1992, Thomason Hosp., El Paso, 1976-92. Contbr. articles to profl. jours. Col. USAR, 1974-92. N.Y. State Bd. Regents scholar, 1962-66, Fed. Health Careers scholar, 1967-70; NIH fellow, 1972-73; recipient Dept. of Army Commendation for outstanding sci. achievement, 1984. Fellow Am. Acad. Pediatrics, Am. Coll. Cardiology; mem. Am. Heart Assn. (coun. on cardiovascular disease in the young 1982). Office: U Tex Med Br C240 Children's Hosp 301 University Blvd Galveston TX 77555

PEARLMAN, DAVID SAMUEL, allergist; b. Syracuse, N.Y., Jan. 20, 1934; s. Benjamin Norman and Sylvia Rene (Karp) P.; m. Doris Ann Greenberg, Apr. 16, 1966; children—Michael, Melanie. Student, Cornell U., 1951-54; M.D., SUNY, Syracuse, 1958. Diplomate Am. Bd. Allergy and Immunology (dir. 1973-78). Intern, then asst. resident in pediatrics Univ. Hosps., Cleve., 1958-60; chief resident in pediatrics U. Colo. Med. Center, Denver, 1960-61; mem. faculty U. Colo. Med. Center, 1962—; clin. prof. pediatrics, 1978—; dir. pediatric allergy tng. program, 1964-66, co-dir., 1966-73; practice medicine specializing in allergy Denver, 1972—; assoc. Colo. Allergy and Asthma Clinic, 1972—; acting chief dept. pediatric allergy Nat. Jewish Hosp. and Rsch. Ctr., 1972-73, sr. staff physician pediatrics allergy, 1973-92; mem. allergy and infectious disease tng. grant com. NIH, 1970-72. Contbr. articles to med. jours. Served to maj. M.C. AUS, 1967-69. Fellow U. Colo. Med. Center, 1961-62; Fellow NIH, 1963-66, 69-72. Fellow Am. Acad. Pediatrics (chmn. sect. on allergy and Clin. Immunology, 1992-94), Am. Acad. Allergy (exec. com. 1978-81), Am. Coll. Allergists; mem. Soc. Pediatric Rsch., Western Soc. Pediatric Rsch., AAAS, Am. Soc. Cert. Allergists, Am. Thoracic Soc., Am. Coll. Chest Physicians, Rocky Mountain Pediatric Soc., Colo. Allergy Soc., Joint Council Allergy and Immunology (bd. dirs. 1985-92, pres. 1988-90), Colo. Med. Soc., Denver Med. Soc.,

Adams-Aurora County Med. Soc., Friends of Chamber Music (dir. 1965-81). Jewish. Address: 6029 E Prentice Pl Englewood CO 80111

PEARLMAN, JERRY KENT, electronics company executive; b. Des Moines, Mar. 27, 1939; s. Leo R. Pearlman; married; children: Gregory, Neal. BA cum laude, Princeton U., 1960; M.B.A., Harvard U., 1962. With Ford Motor Co., 1962-70; v.p. fin. dir. Behring Corp., 1970-71; controller Zenith Electronics Corp., Glenview, Ill., 1971-74, v.p., 1972-74, v.p. fin., 1974-78, sr. v.p. fin., 1978-81, sr. v.p. fin., group exec., 1981-83, chief exec. officer, 1983-95, chmn., 1984-95, also dir.; dir. Stone Container Corp., First Chgo. Corp. Dir. Evanston (Ill.) Hosp.; trustee Mus. Sci. and Industry, Northwestern U. Office: Zenith Electronics Corp 1000 Milwaukee Ave Glenview IL 60025-2423*

PEARLMAN, LOUIS JAY, aviation and promotion company executive; b. Flushing, N.Y., June 19, 1954; s. Herman and Reenie (Nevler) P. BA, Queens Coll., 1976; MBA, Century U., 1980; Degree in Sales Mgmt., SUNY, Buffalo, 1980; PhD in Bus. Adminstrn., Century U., 1983. Pres. Commuter Helicopter Corp., N.Y.C., 1974-75; pres., chief operating officer Trans Continental Airlines, Inc., N.Y.C., 1975—; gen. mgr. U.S. Westdeutsche Luftwerbung GmbH, N.Y.C., 1976-85; chmn., pres., CEO Airship Internat. Ltd., N.Y.C., 1982—; bd. dirs., 1985—; pres., CEO Trans Continental Records, Inc., 1992—; pres. Backstreet Boys, Inc., 1993—; cons. Queens Coll., CUNY, 1977—; bd. dirs. Fed. Airlines Corp., N.Y.C. Author: Survey and Analysis of the Airline Industry, 1983; song writer. Active Mitchell-Linden Civic Assn., Flushing, 1980-82, Kissimmee (Fla.) Mcpl. Airport, 1985—. Mem. U.S. Power Squadron, Wings Club (disting., recipient Lighter-than-Air award 1987), Lighter-than-Air Soc. (hon.), Young Entrepreneurs Am., Young Millionaires Club, Internat. Air Transport Assn., Blimp Port U.S.A. (pres. 1987—), Friar's Club (N.Y.C.). Avocations: flying airplanes, helicopters and blimps, swimming, bowling, music, boating. Home: 9235 Ridge Pine Trl Orlando FL 32819-4884 Office: Airship Internat Ltd Trans Continental Airlines 7380 Sand Lake Rd Ste 350 Orlando FL 32819-5256

PEARLMAN, RONALD ALAN, lawyer; b. Hamilton, Ohio, July 10, 1940. A.B. with honors, Northwestern U., 1962, J.D. cum laude, 1965; LL.M. in Taxation, Georgetown U., 1967. Bar: D.C. 1991, U.S. Tax Ct. 1969, U.S. Supreme Ct. 1968. Atty. office chief counsel IRS, Washington, 1965-69; assoc. Thompson & Mitchell, St. Louis, 1969-70, ptnr., 1970-83; dep. asst. sec. for tax policy Dept. Treasury, Washington, 1983-84, asst. sec. tax policy, 1984-85; ptnr. Bryan, Cave, McPheeters & McRoberts, St. Louis, 1986-88; chief of staff joint com. on taxation U.S. Congress, Washington, 1988-90; ptnr. Covington & Burling, Washington, 1991—; adj. prof. Sch. Law Washington U., St. Louis, 1972-83; mem. Tax Found. Adv. Coun., 1986-88, BNA Tax Mgmt. Adv. Bd., 1986-88, 93—; participant ednl. seminars. Mem. bd. editors Northwestern U. Law Rev.; contbr. articles to various publs. Bd. dirs. Jewish Fedn. St. Louis, 1975-83, sec., 1981-82, mem. leadership devel. coun., 1973-75; mem. taxes and spending com. St. Louis Regional Commerce and Growth Assn., 1974-80; mem. adv. com. to dir. revenue State of Mo., 1969-79, chmn., 1978-79; bd. dirs. Jewish Ctr. for Aged, St. Louis, 1978-83, pres., 1987-88; children. children's svcs. budget panel United Way of Greater St. Louis, 1979-82; bd. dirs. Mo. Colls. Fund, 1988, Mo. Bot. Garden, 1987-88. Fellow Am. Coll. Tax Counsel; mem. ABA (vice chair govt. rels. com., exec. coun., tax sect. 1986-88, chmn. subcom. on incorp. of com. on corp. stockholder relationships 1974-76), Am. Law Inst. (tax adv. group, cons. tax integration project) N.Y. State Bar Assn. (mem.-at-large exec. com., tax sect. 1991-93), Mo. Bar (chmn. taxation com. 1976-78), Met. St. Louis Bar Assn. (taxation sect. 1969-83, chmn. sect. 1974-75, exec. com. 1974-75), D.C. Bar (tax section), Fed. Bar Assn. (tax sect.), Mid-Am. Tax Conf. (chmn. planning com. 1979), Order of Coif. Office: Covington & Burling PO Box 7566 1201 Pennsylvania Ave NW Washington DC 20004-2401

PEARLSTEIN, LEONARD, advertising agency executive. Pres., chief exec. officer Keye/Donna/Pearlstein, L.A., until 1991; pres., chief operating officer Lord, Dentsu & Ptnrs., N.Y.C., 1991—. Office: Lord Dentsu & Ptnrs 4751 Wilshire Blvd Los Angeles CA 90010-3827

PEARLSTEIN, PHILIP, artist; b. Pitts., May 24, 1924; s. David and Libbie (Kalser) P.; m. Dorothy Cantor, Aug. 20, 1950; children: William, Julia, Ellen. BFA, Carnegie Inst. Tech., 1949; MA, NYU, 1955. Instr. Pratt Inst., 1959-63; vis. critic Yale U., 1962-63; from asst. prof. to prof. art dept. Bklyn. Coll., 1963-84, now Disting. prof. emeritus. Shows include Tanager Gallery, N.Y.C., 1955, 59, Peridot Gallery, N.Y.C., 1956, 57, 59, Allan Frumkin Gallery, N.Y.C., 1962, 63, 65, 69, 72, 74, 76, 78, 80, 83, Frumkin Gallery, Chgo., 1960, 65, 69, 73, 75, 80, 81, Hirschl & Adler Mod., N.Y.C., 1985, 88, 91, 92, 93, Robert Miller Gallery, N.Y.C., 1995, Kansas City Art Inst., 1962, Ceeje Gallery, 1965, 66, Reed Coll., 1965, 79, Galerie Thelen, Cologne, Germany, 1972, Galleri Ostergren, Malmo, Sweden, 1972, Galerie Kornfeld, Zurich, Switzerland, 1972, Staatliche Museen-Kupferstichkabinett, Berlin, 1972, Kunstverein, Hamburg, Germany, 1972, Editions La Tortue, Paris, 1973, Donald Morris Gallery, Detroit, 1973, 76, 80, 94, Gimpel Fils Ltd., London, 1975, 79, Marianne Friedland Gallery, Toronto, Ont., Can., 1975, 81, Springfield (Mo.) Art Mus., 1978, 95, Harkus Krakow Gallery, Boston, 1978-79, Myers Fine Arts Gallery, SUNY, Plattsburg, 1979, Galerie Jöllenbach, Cologne, Germany, 1979, 89, Carnegie-Mellon U., Pitts., 1979, Assoc. Am. Artists, 1980, FIAC, Paris, 1980, Brooke Alexander Gallery, 1980, 81, Ringling Mus. Art, Sarasota, Fla., 1981, San Antonio Mus. Art, 1981, (Retrospective) Milw. Art Mus., The Bklyn. Mus., The Pa. Acad. Fine Arts, Phila., The Toledo Mus. Art, 1983-84, Carnegie Inst. Mus. Art, Pitts., 1982, Brody's Gallery, Washington, 1983, Images Gallery, Toledo, 1984, Hirschl and Adler Modern, N.Y.C., 1985, 88, 92, 93, Galerie Rudolph Zwirner, Cologne, Germany, 1989, 91, Compass Rose Gallery, Chgo, 1991, Printworks Gallery, Chgo., 1990, Condeso Lawler Gallery, N.Y.C., 1991, P.S. 1, N.Y., 1992, Butler Art Inst, Youngstown, Ohio, 1992, Tokashima Art Mus., Japan, 1992; group shows at Carnegie Internat., 1955, 64, 67, Whitney Mus. Am. Art, 1955, 56, 58, 62, 65, 67, 70, 72, 73, 74, 79, 91, U. Ill., 1965, 67, 68, Providence Art Club, 1965, U. Mich. Mus., 1965, Corcoran Gallery, 1967, Vassar Coll., 1968, Milw. Art, 1969, Pa. Acad. Fine Arts, 1971-72, Indpls. Mus. Art, 1972, Galerie Lowenadler, Stockholm, Sweden, 1973, Nat. Acad. Arts and Letters, N.Y.C., 1973 (award), Yale U., 1973, 74, Hofstra U., 1973, Helsinki (Finland) Mus. Art, 1974, Art Inst. Chgo., 1974, Cleve. Mus. Art, 1974, America 1976 Bicentennial Exhbn., U.S. Dept. Interior, 1976, Wildenstein Gallery, N.Y.C., 1976, many others, retrospective exhbns., Finch Coll., 1974, U. Tex., Austin, 1974, Cranbrook Acad. Art, Mich., 1974, Notre Dame U., 1975, Grand Rapids (Mich.) Art Mus., 1975, Kalamazoo Inst. Arts, Tampa Bay Art, 1975, Miami Art, 1975, Philbrook Art, 1980, Chryler Mus., 1980, Akron Art Mus., 1981, San Antonio Mus., 1981, Honolulu Acad. of Art, 1994; represented in permanent collections, Phila. Mus. Art, San Antonio Mus. Assn., Pa. State U., Whitney Mus., Mus. Modern Art, N.Y. U., Met. Mus. of Art, Bklyn Mus. Carnegie Mus., Syracuse U., James A. Michener Found., Hirshhorn Mus., Corcoran Gallery, Art Inst. Chgo., Milw. Art Ctr., Ludwig Collection, Aachen, Germany, Sydney and Frances Lewis Found., Richmond, Va., Bklyn. Mus., Cleve. Mus. Art, Milw. Mus., others. Fulbright fellow to Italy, 1958-59; Guggenheim fellow, 1971-72; Nat. Endowment for Arts grantee, 1968; NAD assoc., 1983.

PEARLSTEIN, ROBERT M., physics educator; b. N.Y.C., Oct. 16, 1937; s. Joseph and Sylvia (Leibow) P.; m. Linda Ellen Schecter, June 19, 1960; children: Daniel A., Deborah N. AB in Physics, Harvard U., 1960; PhD in Physics, U. Md., 1966. Physicist Inst. Muscle Rsch. Marine Biol. Lab., Woods Hole, Mass., 1962-63; rsch. asst., pub. health svc. fellow U. Md., College Park, 1963-66; NSF postdoctoral fellow biology divsn. Oak Ridge (Tenn.) Nat. Lab., 1966-67, mem. rsch. staff biology divsn., 1967-76, leader photosynthesis group biology divsn., 1972-75, coord. solar energy rsch., 1975-77, mem. rsch. staff chemistry divsn., 1975-78; lectr. Oak Ridge Grad. Sch. Biomed. Scis. U. Tenn., 1969-78; sr. rsch. scientist Battelle Columbus (Ohio) Labs., 1978-82; prof., chmn. physics Ind. U.-Purdue U., Indpls., 1983-90, prof. physics, 1983—; Argonne fellow Argonne (Ill.) Nat. Lab., 1994—; scholar Harvard Club Washington, 1955-56; jr. engr. Baird-Atomic, Inc., Cambridge, Mass., 1958-60; physicist Nat. Bureau Standards, Washington, 1960-61; teaching asst. U. Md., Colleg Park, 1962; predoctoral fellow Pub. Health Svc., 1965-66; postdoctoral fellow NSF, 1966-67; chmn. organizing com. Internat. Conf. on Photosynthetic Unit, Gatlinburg, Tenn.,

1969-70; sec., treas. photochemistry and photobiology group Biophys. Soc., 1970-71; vis. scientist Swiss Fed. Inst. Tech., Zurich, summers, 1984, 85; lectr. Bat-Sheva summer sch. on photosynthesis Weizmann Inst., Rehovot, Israel, 1988; faculty rsch. participant Argonne Nat. Labs., summers, 1992, 93. Author: (with others) Excited States of Biological Molecules, 1976, Excitons, 1982, Photosynthesis: Energy Conversion by Plants and Bacteria, 1982, Advances in Photosynthesis Research, 1984, Antennas and Reaction Centers of Photosynthetic Bacteria—Structure, Interactions, and Dynamics, 1985, Photosynthesis, 1987, Photosynthetic Light-Harvesting Systems, 1988, The Photsynthetic Bacterial Reaction Center, 1988, Chlorophylls, 1991; assoc. editor Biophys. Jour., 1981-84; guest editor Photochemistry and Photobiology, 1971; mem. hon. editorial bd. Photochemistry and Photobiology, 1971-73; contbr. articles to profl. jours. Fellow AAAS, Am. Phys. Soc. (chem. divsn., biol. physics divsn., biophys. lectr. Ohio State sect. Fall meeting 1969, publs. com. divsn. biol. physics 1975-78, program com. divsn. biol. physics 1975-76, exec. com. divsn. biol. physics 1982-85, fellowship com. divsn. biol. physics 1990—, Biol. Physics prize 1994); mem. Biophys. Soc., Am. Soc. Photobiology, Sigma Xi. Office: Ind U-Purdue U Dept Physics 402 N Blackford St Indianapolis IN 46202*

PEARLSTEIN, SEYMOUR, artist; b. Bklyn., Oct. 14, 1923; s. Morris Lazarus and Anna (Bassiur) P.; m. Toby Tessie Rubinstein, Mar. 21, 1943; children: Judith Helene, Lawrence Jonathan. Cert., Pratt Inst., Bklyn., 1950, Art Students League N.Y., 1954; student of Jack Potter. Owner, illustrator, designer Sy Pearlstein Advt. Art Studio, N.Y.C., 1946-71; artist-painter rep. by Far Gallery, N.Y.C., 1969-81; prof. N.Y.C. Tech. Coll., CUNY, Bklyn., 1971-94, prof. emeritus, 1994—, chmn. art and advt. design dept., 1985-88. One-man shows Silvermine Guild of Artists, New Canaan, Conn., 1973, Far Gallery, 1973, 75, 78, Klitgord Center, N.Y.C. Community Coll., 1974, De Mers Gallery, Hilton Head, S.C., 1975, Adelphi U., Garden City, N.Y., 1979, Grace Gallery, N.Y.C. Tech. Coll., 1992, group shows, A.M. Sachs Gallery, N.Y.C., 1971, Springfield (Mo.) Art Mus., 1971, Am. Acad. Arts and Letters, N.Y.C., 1975, 76, 77, NAD, N.Y.C., 1986, 87, 89, 91, 92, Butler Inst. Art, Ohio, 1975, Ball State U., Queens Mus., N.Y.C., 1978, 81, U.S. Dept. State Art In Embassies Program, N.Y. Hist. Soc., 1981, Colo. Heritage Mus., Denver, 1981, 82, 86, Am. Watercolor Soc., N.Y.C., Ingber Gallery, N.Y.C., 1985, Audubon Artists, N.Y.C., 1990, 91, 92, Allied Artists Am., N.Y.C., 1988, 89, 90, 91, Phila. Mus. Sales and Loan Gallery, Nat. Arts Club, N.Y.C., 1989, others; represented in permanent collections, Mus. N.Mex., Santa Fe, Mint Mus. Art, Charlotte, N.C., NAD, N.Y.C., Fine Arts Gallery, San Diego, Adelphi U., Queens Mus., N.Y.C., Munson-Williams-Proctor Inst., Utica, N.Y., N.Y.C. Tech. Coll., Bklyn. Served with AUS, 1942-46. Recipient Gold medal Nat. Acad. Design, 1969, Hassam Fund Purchase award Am. Acad. Arts and Letters, 1969, 77, Gold medal of honor Nat. Arts Club, 1970, Ranger Fund Purchase award NAD, 1971, 82, Gold medal Soc. Illustrators, 1972, Nat. Inst.-Am. Acad. Arts and Letters grant, 1975. Mem. NAD (sec. coun.) 1980-84, W.H. Leavin prize 1985), Am. Watercolor Soc. (bd. dirs. 1979-80, Watercolor U.S.A. award 1971), Art Students League of N.Y. (life), Allied Artists Am. (bd. dirs. 1976-79, E. Lowe award 1969, gold medal 1980, George Tweed Meml. award 1989, 92), Audubon Artists (bd. dirs. 1986-89, 91-93, Grumbacher award 1971, Fabri medal 1980), Alliance Figurative Artists (chmn. 1976-77), Profl. Staff Congress. Home: 52 Dartmouth St Forest Hills NY 11375-5142 Office: NYC Tech Coll CUNY 300 Jay St Brooklyn NY 11201-2902

PEARLSTINE, NORMAN, editor; b. Phila., Oct. 4, 1942; s. Raymond and Gladys (Cohen) P.; m. Nancy Colbert Friday, 1988. A.B., Haverford Coll., 1964; LL.B., U. Pa., 1967. Staff reporter Wall Street Jour., Dallas, Detroit, L.A., 1968-73; Tokyo bur. chief Wall Street Jour., 1973-76; mng. editor Asian Wall Street Jour., Hong Kong, 1976-78; exec. editor Forbes Mag.; Los Angeles, 1978-80; nat. news editor Wall Street Jour., N.Y.C., 1980-82; editor, pub. Wall Street Jour./Europe, Brussels, 1982-83; mng. editor, v.p. Wall Street Jour., N.Y.C., 1983-91, exec. editor, 1991-92; pres., chief exec. officer Friday Holdings, L.P., N.Y.C., 1993-94; editor-in-chief Time Warner, Inc., N.Y.C., 1994—. Pres. Atsuko Chiba Found.; bd. dirs. Am. Woman's Econ. Devel. Recipient Editor of Yr. award Nat. Press Found., 1989. Mem. ABA, D.C. Bar Assn. (trustee), N.Y. Hist. Soc. (former chmn.), Coun. Fgn. Rels. Office: Time Warner Inc 1271 Avenue of the Americas New York NY 10020

PEARMAN, REGINALD JAMES, educational administrator; b. N.Y.C., May 23, 1923; s. William H. Astoria Arabell (Webb) P.; children: Jeanita, Lydia, Reginald. B.S., NYU, 1950; Ed.D., U. Mass., 1974. Cert. tchr., N.Y. Tchr., N.Y.C. Pub. Schs., 1951-55, supr., 1955-62; with Fgn. Service, State Dept., Caracas, Venezuela, 1962-65, Peace Corps, Washington, 1965-67 AID, Washington, 1967-69; dir. job devel. N.Y.C. Human Resources Adminstrn., 1969-71; ednl. program specialist U.S. Dept. Edn., Washington, 1971-74; mem. adv. com. women's equity U.S. Office of Edn., 1974, task force arts and humanities, 1975-76, task force edn. of gifted, 1976-77, basic edn., 1977, urban edn., 1978, pub. sch. adminstrn., 1979; mem. adv. bd. internship program Am. Pub. Transit Assn., 1977-79; mem. White House Initiative for Historically Black Colls. and Univs., 1982-83; tchr. Calif. State Coll.-Los Angeles, 1966, Cornell U./N.Y. State Sch. Labor and Indsl. Relations, 1968, 70, U. Md., College Park, 1974-76; with Md. Dept. Employment and Tng., Wheaton, 1985-86; counseling coord. Montgomery Coll., 1987—; mem. scholarship selection com. Creative Edn. Found., 1991-92; discussion leader Creative Problem Solving Inst., SUNY, Buffalo, 1991-92; grad. adviser U. Mass./D.C. Publ. Sch. project; also cons. Served with U.S. Army, 1944-47; PTO. Bd. dirs. D.C. Striders youth sports club, Inst. Scholar Athletes, 1992; mem. Pres.'s Coun. Youth Opportunity, 1968; mem. D.C. ofcls. com. Nat. Youth Games, 1983; ofcl. Potomac Valey Track and Field Assn.; mem. platform com. N.Y. State Liberal Ind. party, 1968. Mem. NCAA All Am. Track Team, 1949, U.S. Olympic Team, Helsinki, 1952. NCCJ fellow, 1953; U. Havana scholar, 1955; U. Pitts. fellow, 1967; named to NYU Hall of Fame, 1974, Pa. Relay Carnival Hall of Fame, 1994; recipient Disting. Alumni award, 1977, Brotherhood in Sports award B'nai B'rith, 1954. Mem. Nat. Alliance Black Sch. Educators (higher edn. commn.), Inst. Scholar Athletes (bd. dirs.), Phi Delta Kappa. Lutheran. Established 4 Am. records and 3 world records in running events in middle distances. Home: 9118 September Ln Silver Spring MD 20901-3705

PEARSALL, GEORGE WILLIAM, materials scientist, mechanical engineer, educator, consultant; b. Brentwood, N.Y., July 13, 1933; s. Milo Dickerson and Margaret Elizabeth (White) P.; m. Patricia Louise Stevens, Oct. 11, 1962. B. Metall. Engring., Rensselaer Poly. Inst., 1955; Sc.D. (Am. Soc. Metals fellow), MIT, 1961. Registered profl. engr., N.C. Research engr. Dow Chem. Co., Midland, Mich., 1955-57; research asst. MIT, 1959-60, asst. prof. metallurgy, 1960-64; assoc. prof. mech. engring. Duke U., 1964-66, prof., 1966-81, prof. mech. engring. and materials sci., 1981—, prof. pub. policy studies, 1981—; acting dean Sch. Engring., 1969-71, dean, 1971-74, 82-83; trustee Triangle Univs. Ctr. for Advanced Studies, 1976-92, chmn. exec. com., 1983-88; dir. Duke-IBM Product Safety Inst., 1979-90. Author: (with W.G. Moffatt and J. Wulff) The Structure and Properties of Materials, 1964; edtl. bd. Jour. Products Liability, Proceedings of the IEEE; contbr. articles to profl. jours. Served with AUS, 1957. Mem. AAAS, ASME, ASTM, Soc. Risk Analysis, Am. Soc. Metals, Soc. Plastics Engrs., Sigma Xi, Phi Lambda Upsilon, Tau Beta Pi, Pi Tau Sigma. Home: 2941 Welcome Dr Durham NC 27705-5555

PEARSALL, OTIS PRATT, lawyer; b. Bklyn., Apr. 25, 1932; s. Willard Hall and Marilla Houghton (Pratt) P.; m. Nancy Jeanne Boden, July 7, 1956; 1 child, Melissa Mather. B.A., Yale U., 1953, LL.B., 1956. Bar: N.Y. 1957, U.S. Dist. Ct. (so. and ea. dist.) N.Y. 1958, U.S. Dist. Ct. (no. dist.) N.Y. 1966, U.S. Tax Ct. 1966, U.S. Ct. Appeals (2d cir.) 1960, U.S. Ct. Appeals (10th cir.) 1972, U.S. Ct. Appeals (9th cir.) 1976, U.S. Supreme Ct. 1963. Assoc. Hughes, Hubbard, Blair & Reed, N.Y.C., 1956-59, 60-63; asst. U.S. atty. U.S. Atty.'s Office So. Dist. N.Y., N.Y.C., 1959-60; ptnr. Hughes Hubbard & Reed, N.Y.C., 1964-91, mem. firm com., 1984-85, mem. exec. com., 1985-87; ptnr. Arnold & Porter, N.Y.C., 1991—. Bd. dirs. Mcpl. Art Soc. N.Y., N.Y.C. 1967-74, v.p., 1973-74; trustee Soc. for Preservation of L.I. Antiquities, Setauket, N.Y., 1969-77, Bklyn. Mus., 1986-92, 93—, mem. adv. bd., 1992-93; bd. dirs. L.I. Hist. Soc., Bklyn., 1971-82; mem. N.Y.C. Historic City Com., 1987-88; trustee The Green-Wood Cemetery, Bklyn., 1992—. Recipient Green Star award Environ. Action Coalition, Inc., 1989, Landmark Lion award N.Y. Hist. Dists. Coun., 1993. Fellow Am. Coll. Trial Lawyers; mem. ABA, Bridgehampton (N.Y.) Club (pres. 1989-91), India House Club, Calif. Club, Phi Beta Kappa. Republican. Congregationalist. Avocation: restoration of historic structures. Home: 157 Willow St

Brooklyn NY 11201-2201 Office: Arnold & Porter 399 Park Ave New York NY 10022-4614

PEARSE, ROBERT FRANCIS, psychologist, educator; b. Detroit, Nov. 15, 1916; s. Forrest F. and Sarah (Roberts) P.; m. Shirley Daniels, Dec. 22, 1947; children: Donald, Richard, Mary Jean. AM, U. Chgo., 1947, PhD, 1950. Diplomate Am. Bd. Profl. Psychology; cert. psychologist, N.Y. Dir. human resources Stop & Shop, Inc., Boston, 1959-64; prof. organizational behavior Boston U., 1964-81; disting. lectr., chmn. mgmt. and mktg., Coll. Bus. Rochester (N.Y.) Inst. Tech., 1981-93, disting. lectr. emeritus, 1993—; cons., Weldon-Harwood Corp., N.Y.C., 1964-72; sr. cons. on exec. effectiveness, improving leadership, Am. Mgmt. Assn., 1961-86. Author: Self Directed Change for the Mid Career Manager, 1976, The High Performance Nonprofit Organization, 1992. 1st lt. USAFR, 1948-53. Fellow APA. Avocations: tennis, sailing. Home: 564 Surrey Hill Way Rochester NY 14623-3016 Office: Rochester Inst Tech Coll Bus 1 Lomb Memorial Dr Rochester NY 14623-5603

PEARSE, WARREN HARLAND, association executive, obstetrician and gynecologist; b. Detroit, Sept. 28, 1927; s. Harry Albridge and Frances (Wressell) P.; m. Jacqueline Anne Langan, June 15, 1950; children: Kathryn, Susan, Laurie, Martha. B.S., Mich. State U., 1948; M.B., M.D., Northwestern U., 1950. Intern. Univ. Hosp., Ann Arbor, Mich., 1950-51; resident obstetrics and gynecology, 1951-53, 55-56; practice medicine specializing obstetrics and gynecology Detroit, 1956-58; mem. faculty U. Nebr. Med. Center Omaha, 1959-71, Found. prof., chmn. dept. obstetrics and gynecology, 1962-71; asst. dean U. Nebr. Med. Center Omaha (Med. Coll.), 1963-71, mem. residency rev. com. obstetrics and gynecology, 1968-71; dean Med. Coll. Va., Richmond, 1971-75; exec. dir. Am. Coll. Obstetrics and Gynecology, 1975-93; cons., 1993—; Chmn. research adv. group Maternal Child Health Service, Health Scis. Mental Health Adminstrn., HEW, 1967—; cons. family planning Office Econ. Opportunity, 1970—. Author: (with R.W. Stander) Obstetrics and Gynecology at the University of Michigan, 1969; Contbr. chpts., articles tech. lit. Served from 1st lt. to capt. AUS, 1953-55. Mem. Am. Coll. Obstetrics and Gynecology (dist. sec., treas. 1964-68, vice chmn. 1968-71), Am. Gynecology Soc., Soc. Gynecology Investigation, Assn. Profs. Gynecology and Obstetrics (sec., treas. 1969—), Alpha Omega Alpha. Home: 350 S River Landing Rd Edgewater MD 21037-1549 Office: American College of Obs & Gyns 700 14th St NW # 600 Washington DC 20005-2010

PEARSON, ALBERT MARCHANT, food science and nutrition educator; b. Oakley, Utah, Sept. 3, 1916; s. Levi and Mary (Marchant) P.; m. Harriet Eilenberger, Nov. 16, 1946; children—Richard A., Carol Jane, Marian Beth, Donna Gay, David C. B.S., Utah State U., 1940; M.S., Iowa State U., 1941; Ph.D., Cornell U., 1949. Grad. asst. Iowa State U., 1940-41, Cornell U., 1946-49; asst. prof., then assoc. prof. U. Fla., 1949-54; mem. faculty Mich. State U., 1954-89, prof. food sci. and human nutrition, 1961-89; adj. prof. animal sci. Brigham Young U., 1989-90; courtesy prof. anima sci. Oreg. State U., 1991—. Served with USMCR, 1942-45, PTO. Mem. Am. Soc. Animal Sci. (sec.-treas. 1965-68, pres. 1969-70), Reciprocal Meat Conf. (chmn. 1956), Sigma Xi, Phi Kappa Phi. Spl. research body composition, muscle proteins, flavor components in meat. Home: 7765 Bates Rd S Salem OR 97306-9419 Office: Oreg State U Dept Animal Sci Corvallis OR 97331

PEARSON, BELINDA KEMP, economist, consultant; b. Kansas City, Mo., Apr. 14, 1931; d. William Ewing and Margaret Norton (Johnson) Kemp; m. Carl Erik Pearson, Sept. 15, 1953; children: Erik, Frederick, Margaret. BA, Wellesley Coll., 1952; MA, Tufts U., 1954, PhD, 1958. Rsch. asst. Harvard U., Cambridge, Mass., 1954-55; instr. econs. Suffolk U., Boston, 1956-59; lectr. econs., Wellesley Coll., Mass., 1964-65; econ. analyst, asst. econs. Seafirst Bank, Seattle, 1966-79, v.p., 1974-85; chief economist, 1979-85; dir. Lektor, Inc., Issaquah, Wash., 1984—, pres., 1987—; mem. Wash. Gov's. Coun. Econ. Advisors, Olympia, 1979—; dir. Pacific N.W. Regional Econ. Conf., 1979—, chair, Seattle Conf., 1987; mem. Western Blue Chip Econ. Forecast Panel, 1988—; mem. King County, Wash., Land Capacity Task Force, 1995; mem. bd. regents Wash. State U., Pullman, 1985-90, v.p., 1988-90, Regents Found. Investment Com. of Wash. State U., 1987-91; mem. Wash. State Libr. Commn., Olympia, 1976-84. Fulbright scholar London Sch. Econs., 1952-53. Mem. Am. Econ. Assn., Nat. Assn. Bus. Economists (chmn. arrangements 1982 ann. meeting), Seattle Economists Club (pres. 1973-74), Mcpl. League, City Club (Seattle) (chmn. reports com. 1986-88), pres. LWV, Lake Wash. East, 1993-95. Office: Lektor Inc 4227 Providence Point Fr SE Issaquah WA 98027

PEARSON, CHARLES THOMAS, JR., lawyer; b. Fayetteville, Ark., Oct. 14, 1929; s. Charles Thomas and Doris (Pinkerton) P.; m. Wyma Lee Hampton, Sept. 9, 1988; children: Linda Sue, John Paddock. B.S., U. Ark., 1953, J.D., 1954; postgrad., U.S. Naval Postgrad. Sch., 1959; A.M., Boston U., 1963. Bar: Ark. bar 1954. Practice in Fayetteville, 1963—; dir. officer N.W. Comms., Inc., Dixieland Devel., Inc., Jonlin Investments, Inc., World Wide Travel Svc., Inc., Okliania Farms, Inc., N.W. Arl. Land & Devel., Inc., Garden Plaza Inns, Inc. Word Data, Inc., M.P.C. Farms, Inc., Fayetteville Enterprises, Inc., NWA Devel.Co., Delta Comm., Inc.; past. dir., organizer N.W. Nat. Bank. Adviser Explorer Scouts, 1968—; past pres. Washington County Draft Bd.; past pres. bd. Salvation Army. Served to comdr. Judge Adv. Gen. Corps USNR, 1955-63. Mem. ABA, Ark. Bar Assn., Washington County Bar Assn., Judge Advs. Assn., N.W. Ark. Ret. Officers Assn. (past pres.), Methodist Men (past pres.), U. Ark. Alumni Assn. (past dir.), Sigma Chi (past pres. N.W. Ark. alumni, past chmn. house corp.), Alpha Kappa Psi, Phi Eta Sigma, Delta Theta Phi. Republican. Methodist. Clubs: Mason (32 deg., K.T., Shriner), Moose, Elk, Lion, Metropolitan. Office: 36 E Center St Fayetteville AR 72701-5301

PEARSON, CLARENCE EDWARD, management consultant; b. Chgo., Apr. 22, 1925; s. Edward and Irene (Silander) P.; m. June Waldhe, Apr. 21, 1951 (dec. 1967); 1 child, Scott. BS, No. Ill. U., 1950; MPH, U. N.C., 1952. Instr. Mt. Prospect (Ill.) Pub. Schs., 1950-51; dir. health edn. DuPage County Health Dept., Wheaton, Ill., 1952-55; chief health edn. St. Louis Health Dept., 1955-57; dir. health and hosps. Health and Welfare Council, St. Louis, 1957-61; dir. health and safety Met. Life Ins. Co., N.Y.C., 1961-87; prof. edn. Columbia Tchrs. Coll., 1975—; prof. pub. health U. N.C., 1987—; pres. Universal Health Concepts, N.Y.C., 1984-87; bd. dirs. Health Info. Co.; bd. dirs. Nat. Coun. Internat. Health, Washington, 1981-84; pres. Profl. Exam. Svc., N.Y.C., 1984—; v.p. Peter Drucker Found. for Nonprofit Mgmt., 1990—; adv. bd. C. Everett Koop Inst.; bd. overseers Dartmouth Med. Sch., 1992—. Co-author: Managing Health Promotion, 1982; contbr. chpts. to books in field. Co-chmn. Scandinavian-Ams. for Rockefeller presdl. campaign, N.Y., 1968. Served as staff sgt. U.S. Army, 1943-46. Recipient Disting. Career award Am. Pub. Health Assn., Washington, 1981, Gold Medal for Achievement, Columbia U., N.Y.C., 1984, Internat. Health award Asia Pacific Consortium, Honolulu, 1984, Porter Prize, Pitts. Health Ctr., 1986. Fellow Am. Pub. Health Assn. (governing council 1970-78), The Univ. Club (N.Y.C.). Home: 530 E 23rd St New York NY 10010-5022 Office: Peter Drucker Foundation for Nonprofit Mgmt 320 Park Ave 3d Fl New York NY 10022-6839

PEARSON, DANIEL S., lawyer; b. N.Y.C., Oct. 9, 1930; children: Elizabeth Oster, William M., Charles M.; m. Fredricka G. Smith, June 19, 1982; 1 child, Deardre Smith. BA, Amherst Coll., 1952; JD, Yale U., 1958. Bar: Fla. 1959, U.S. Supreme Ct. 1967, N.Y. 1982, U.S. Ct. Appeals (1st, 5th, 9th and 11th, DC cirs.). Asst. U.S. atty. U.S. Atty.'s Office, Miami, 1961-63; pvt. practice Miami, 1963-67; ptnr. Pearson, Josefsberg & Tarre, P.A., Miami, 1967-80; judge Dist. Ct. Appeal (3rd dist.), Miami, 1980-89; ptnr. Holland & Knight, Miami, 1989—; adj. prof. U Miami Sch. Law; lectr. Practicing Law Inst., Fla. Bar. Served with USCG, 1951-54. Mem. ABA, Am. Law Inst., Am. Coll. Trial Lawyers, Am. Acad. Appellate Lawyers, Am. Bd. Trial Advocates, Order of Barristers, Dade County Bar Assn. Home: 7580 Erwin Rd Miami FL 33143-6273 Office: Holland & Knight 701 Brickell Ave Miami FL 33131-3209

PEARSON, DAVID PETRI, chemist; b. Portland, Oreg., Oct. 24, 1926; s. Brewer Petri and Laura Alvine (Johnson) P.; m. Patricia Margaret Cowan, June 4, 1949; children—Kathryn A. James P.; Rebecca L., Kristine R., Judith G. B.A. in Chemistry, Reed Coll., 1949; M.S. in Phys. Chemistry, Oreg. State U., 1953; Ph.D. in Phys. Chemistry, U. So. Calif., 1960. Research chemist Phillips Petroleum Co. (AEC), Idaho Falls, Idaho, 1957-62, Bartlesville, Okla., 1962-69; lectr. in chemistry, Portland State U., 1969-71; asst. prof. chemistry So. Oreg. State Coll., Ashland, 1971-72; research assoc. Oreg. Grad. Ctr., Beaverton, 1972-74; sr. chemist Portland Gen. Electric Co., 1975-87; ret., 1987. Patentee in field. Served to cpl. USAAF, 1946-47. Mem. Am. Chem. Soc. (treas. Portland sect. 1979-82, chmn. 1983), Electrochem. Soc. Clubs: Am. Alpine, Idaho Alpine (sec. Idaho Falls 1961, pres. 1962). Republican. Presbyterian. Home: 6324 SW Radcliffe St Portland OR 97219-5749

PEARSON, DAVIS, architect; b. Bryn Mawr, Pa., June 10, 1925; s. Rodney S. and Bertha (Bott) P.; m. Priscilla Ball (dec. 1990); children: Davis Jr., Leslie B Jessell, Donald S.; m. Anne Grim, 1991. BArch, Pa., 1950. Registered arch., Pa., N.J., Del., Fla.; cert. Nat. Coun. Archtl. Registration Bd. Assoc. Mirick Pearson Batcheler, Phila., 1954-60, ptnr., 1960-93; cons. HLM/MPB Archs., Phila., 1995—; chmn. Lower Merion Planning Commn., 1986-89, active, 1970-92; bd. dirs. Devon Manor Corp., also sec., Main Line Health, Inc. Prin. works include The Episc. Acad., various bldgs., Medford Leas, Cathedral Village, Dunwoody Village, Devon Manor Retirement Communities, others. Bd. mgrs., treas. Saunders House; trustee The Chapin Home; life trustee The Episc. Acad., trustee emeritus, 1991; past pres. The Merion Civic Assn.; bd. dirs. Merion Cmty. Assn., pres., 1976-92, Cmty. Health Affiliates; active The Carpenters Co., Phila. Mem. AIA, Tau Sigma Delta. Office: HLM/MPB Archs 262 S 23rd St Philadelphia PA 19103-5580

PEARSON, DONALD EMANUAL, chemist, educator; b. Madison, Wis., June 21, 1914; s. Gustav E. and Clara (Bjelde) P.; m. Gwen Smiseth, June 5, 1950; children: Donald T., Jeanah C., Sam S. Grad., U. Wis., 1936, U. Ill., 1940. Chemist Pitts. Plate Glass Co., Milw., 1940-42; tech. aide OSRD, 1942-45; chemist MIT, 1945-46; faculty Vanderbilt U., Nashville, 1946-79; prof. chemistry Vanderbilt U., 1954-79, prof. emeritus, 1979—; pvt. practice as cons., chem. rschr. Nashville; cons. in chem. and environ. problems, arson cases; rsch. dir Reclamation Svcs., Madisonville, Ky.; mem. Com. for Reorgn. of Tenn. Dept. Health; NSF resident to Tenn. Toxics Program. Author: (with R.C. Elderfield) Phenazines, 1956, (with C.A. Buehler) Survey of Organic Syntheses, 1970, Vol. II, 1977; also numerous articles. Mem. Am. Chem. Soc. Discoverer new method of substitution in aromatic compounds, new rearrangement hydrazone; research on mechanisms of Beckmann rearrangement, reactions in polyphosphoric acid; structure of diuretic mercuhydrin; synthesis of barbiturates, anti-malarials, plant regulatory substances and spin labels.

PEARSON, DOUGLAS N., battery manufacturing company executive. Formerly v.p. Monroe (Mich.) Auto Equipment Co.; now exec. v.p. Exide Corp., Reading, Pa. Office: Exide Corp PO Box 14205 Reading PA 19612-4205

PEARSON, GERALD LEON, food company executive; b. Mpls., June 24, 1925; s. Perry and Lillian (Peterson) P.; m. Beverly Mary Schultz, Nov. 10, 1946; children: Steven, Perry, Liecia. Grad., Trimont (Minn.) High Sch., 1943. Treas. Trimont Packing Co., 1946-52; v.p. Beef Specialists of Iowa, 1952-68, pres., chief exec. officer, 1969-80, chmn. bd., chief exec. officer, 1972-80; chmn. Beef Specialists of Iowa Inc., 1983-94; bd. dirs. Graffaloy, Inc., El Cajon, Calif., dir. applied mem. tech., Minnetonka, Minn.; chmn., CEO World Champions of Golf Inc.; owner Brooks Golf Club, Okoboji, Iowa. Pres. Pearson Art Found.; bd. dirs. Bethany Coll., Lindsborg; commr. Nat. Mus. Am. Art-Smithsonian Instn., 1995. With USN, 1943-46. Mem. Swedish Royal Roundtable, Swedish Council Am. (bd. dirs.). Home: 7224 E Stagecoach Pass Carefree AZ 85262-5003 Office: Beef Wolrd Cahamions of Golf PO Box 5148 Spencer IA 51301 also: PO Box 5148 Spencer IA 51301

PEARSON, GERALD P., hospital administrator; b. 1944. With St. Joseph Hospital, Elgin, Ill., 1963-83; exec. v.p. Franciscan Sisters Health Care Corp., Frankfort, Ill., 1983-89, pres., 1989—. Office: Franciscan Sisters Health Care Corp 9223 W Francis Rd Frankfort IL 60423

PEARSON, GERTRUDE BOOTH, state legislator; b. Quincy, Mass., Apr. 16, 1918; d. Gilbert Alexander and Grace Ripley (Dunn) Booth; m. Gray Waite Pearson, Apr. 10, 1947 (dec. Dec. 1970); children: Grace Pearson Lilly, Gray Waite Pearson Jr. Student, Simmons Coll., Boston, 1935-37; BEd, Keene (N.H.) State Coll., 1960, MEd, 1970. Tchr. Thayer High Sch., Winchester, N.H., 1960-63, Keene (N.H.) High Sch., 1963-82; mem. N.H. Legis., Concord, 1989—. Chmn. Cheshire County Delegation, Keene, 1992—; treas. N.H. Fedn. Rep. Women, Concord, 1990—. Named Keene State Coll. President's Outstanding Woman of N.H., 1992. Mem. N.H. Ret. Tchrs. Assn. (pres. 1990-92), Friends of the Keene Pub. Libr. (pres. 1988-89). Avocations: golf, travel, bridge. Home: 445 Park Ave Apt 5 Keene NH 03431 Office: N H General Ct Concord NH 03301

PEARSON, HENRY CHARLES, artist; b. Kinston, N.C., Oct. 8, 1914; s. A. Louis and Estelle P. BA, U. N.C., 1935; MFA, Yale U., 1938; postgrad., Art Students League, 1953-56. Stage scene designer, 1937-42; instr. art New Sch. Social Research, N.Y.C., 1965—, Pa. Acad. Fine Arts, Phila., 1973-88. Exhbns. include, Workshop Gallery, N.Y.C., 1958, Stephen Radich Gallery, N.Y.C., 1960-70, The Responsive Eye, Mus. Modern Art, 1965, 29th Biennial Exhibition, Corcoran Gallery Art, Washington, 1965, Retrospective N.C. Mus. Art, Raleigh, N.C., 1968, Drawings USA, Minn. Mus. Art, St. Paul, 1971-73, Betty Parsons Gallery, N.Y.C., 1971-76, Art Students League Centennial, 1975, Truman Gallery, N.Y.C., 1976-79, Marilyn Pearl Gallery, N.Y.C., 1980—; retrospective Columbia, S.C. Mus. Art, 1988, Henry Pearson and Friends Arts Ctr., Kinston, N.C., 1993; represented in permanent collections, Mus. Modern Art, N.Y.C., Met. Mus. Art, N.Y.C., Whitney Mus. Am. Art, N.Y.C., Albright-Knox Gallery, Buffalo, N.C. Mus. Art, Raleigh; represented in commd. works include: List Art Posters, 1965, N.Y. Film Festival poster, 1968; Illustrator: Rime of the Ancient Mariner, 1964, Five Psalms, 1969, Seamus Heaney's Poems and a Memoir, 1982, Seamus Heaney's Three Short Poems, 1993-94. With AUS, 1942-48, USAF, 1948-53. Ford Found. fellow, 1964; Recipient gold medal for achievement in the fine arts N.C. Gov., 1970. Mem. Am. Abstract Artists, Century Assn. Studio: 58 W 58th St New York NY 10019

PEARSON, HENRY CLYDE, federal judge; b. Ocoonita, Va., Mar. 12, 1925; s. Henry James and Nancy Elizabeth (Seals) P.; m. Jean Calton, July 26, 1956; children—Elizabeth, Frances, Timothy Clyde. Student Union Coll. 1947-49; LL.B., U. Richmond, 1952. Bar: Va. 1952, U.S. Ct. Appeals (4th cir.) 1957, U.S. Supreme Ct. 1958. Sole practice, Jonesville, Va., 1952-56; asst. U.S. atty. Western Dist. Va., Roanoke, 1956-61; ptnr. Hopkins, Pearson & Engleby, Roanoke, 1961-70; judge U.S. Bankruptcy Ct. Western Dist. Va., Roanoke, 1970—; participant Va. Continuing Edn. Seminars; mem. adv. com. fed. rules bankruptcy procedure. Mem. Va. Ho. of Reps., 1954-56, Va. Senate, 1968-70; Republican nominee Gov. of Va., 1961. Served with USN, 1943-46; PTO. Mem. Va. State Bar, ABA, Va. Trial Lawyers Assn., Assn. Trial Lawyers Am., Am. Judicature Soc., Am. Judges Assn., Fed. Bar Assn., Delta Theta Phi, Tribune Jefferson Senate, Am. Legion, VFW. Methodist. Clubs: Masons, Shriners. Editorial bd. Am. Survey Bankruptcy Law, 1979. Office: US Courthouse PO Box 2389 Roanoke VA 24010-2389

PEARSON, JAMES BOYD, JR., electrical engineering educator; b. McGehee, Ark., June 3, 1930; s. James Boyd and Lydia Frances (Lacey) P.; m. Marian Scarborough, Feb. 16, 1957; children: Sarah, Jane, Carol, Catherine, Susan, Joanne. BSEE, U. Ark., 1958, MSEE, 1959; PhD, Purdue U., 1962. Asst. prof. electrical engring. Purdue U., Lafayette, Ind., 1962-65; assoc. prof. Rice U., Houston, 1965-70, prof., 1970-79, J.S. Abercrombie prof., 1979—. Served to capt. USAF, 1952-55. Fellow IEEE. Office: Rice Univ Dept Elec and Computer Engring Houston TX 77251

PEARSON, JEREMIAH W., III, military career officer, federal agency official; b. Indpls., Jan. 25, 1938; m. Patricia Van Gysel. B in Aeronautical Engring., Ga. Inst. Tech., 1960; MS in Systems Mgmt., U. So. Calif., 1973; grad., U.S. Naval Test Pilot Sch., 1966, Armed Forces Staff Coll., 1973, Air War Coll., 1982. Commd. 2d lt. USMC, 1960, advanced through grades to maj. gen., 1989; naval aviator 2d Marine Aircraft Wing USMC, Beaufort, S.C., 1961-64; flight instr. Naval Air Station USMC, Meridian, Miss., 1964-65; flight test divsn. U.S. Naval Test Pilot Sch. USMC, Patuxent River, Md., 1966-67; 1st Marine Aircraft Wing USMC, DaNang, Vietnam, 1968-69;

project officer AWG-14 Radar, AIM-7F missile, Naval Missile Test Ctr., Flight Test USMC. Pt. Mugu, Calif., 1969-73; maintenance officer VMFA-232 USMC, Western Pacific, 1973-74; aviation plans officer Office Dep. Chief of Staff Aviation, HQ USMC, Washington, 1974-77; commd. HQ and Maintenance Squadron 24, 1st Marine Amphibious Brigade USMC, Marine Corps Air Station, Kaneohe Bay, Hawaii, 1977-78, comd. VMFA-235, 1978-81; asst. chief staff logistics, chief staff 5th Marine Amphibious Brigade, 3d Marine Aircraft Wing USMC, El Toro, Calif., 1982-84, comd. Marine Aircraft Group 11, 1984-86; asst. wing comdr. 3d Marine Aircraft Wing, FMF. Pacific, Marine Corps. Air Station USMC, El Toro and Santa Ana, Calif., 1986; comdr. forward HQ Element/Inspector Gen. U.S Ctrl. Command USMC, MacDill AFB, Fla., 1986-88; asst. dep. chief staff aviation HQ USMC, 1988-89; commdg. gen. 4th Marine Aircraft Wing USMC, New Orleans, 1989-90; commdg. gen. Marine Corps. Rsch., Devel., Acquistion Command USMC, Washington, 1990; dep. comdr. Marine Ctrl. Command Riyadh, Saudi Arabia; assoc. adminstr. Office of Space Flight NASA, Washington, 1992. Decorated Defense Disting. Svc. medal, D.S.M., D.F.C., Bronze Star with Combat "V", Air medals (26) with gold star, Combat Action ribbon, Navy Unit Commendation, Nat. Def. Svc. medal, Vietnam Svc. medal, Southwest Asia Svc. medal, Rep. Vietnam Meritorious Unit Citation, Rep. Vietnam Campaign medal, Kuwait Liberation medal, others. Office: Nasa Space Flight Office Assoc Administr Washington DC 20546

PEARSON, JOHN, mechanical engineer; b. Leyburn, Yorkshire, U.K., Apr. 24, 1923; came to U.S., 1930, naturalized, 1944; s. William and Nellie Pearson; m. Ruth Ann Billhardt, July 10, 1944 (wid. Nov. 1984); children: John, Armin, Roger; m. Sharoll L. Chisolm, Sept. 8, 1993. B.S.M.E., Northwestern U., 1949, M.S., 1951. Registered profl. engr., Calif. Rsch. engr. Naval Ordnance Test Sta., China Lake, Calif., 1951-55, head warhead rsch. br., 1955-58, head solid dynamics br., 1958-59, head detonation physics group, 1959-67; head detonation physics div. Naval Weapons Ctr., China Lake, Calif., 1967-83, sr. rsch. scientist, 1983—; cons., lectr. in field; founding mem. adv. bd. Ctr. for High Energy Forming, U. Denver; mem. bd. examiners Sambalpur U., India, 1982-83. Author: Explosive Working of Metals, 1963; Behavior of Metals Under Impulsive Loads, 1954; contbr. articles to profl. publs; patentee impulsive loading, explosives applications. Charter mem. Sr. Svc. U.S., 1979. With C.E., U.S Army, 1943-46, ETO. Recipient L.T.E. Thompson medal, 1965, William B. McLean medal, 1979, Superior Civilian Svc. medal USN, 1984, Haskell G. Wilson award, 1985, cert. of recognition Sec. Navy, 1975, merit award Dept. Navy, 1979, cert. of commendation Sec. Navy, 1981, Career Svcs. award Sec. Navy, 1988, John A. Ulrich award Am. Def. Preparedness Assn., 1991; 1st disting. fellow award Naval Weapons Ctr., 1989. Fellow ASME; mem. Am. Soc. Metals, Am. Phys. Soc., AIME, Fed. Exec. League, Sigma Xi, Tau Beta Pi, Pi Tau Sigma, Triangle. Home and Office: PO Box 1390 858 N Primavera St Ridgecrest CA 93555-7907

PEARSON, JOHN DAVIS, naval officer; b. Pinetops, N.C., June 22, 1939; s. Hugh Oliver Sr. and Lillian Marie (Williams) P.; m. Georgeanne Spalding, Dec. 29, 1962; children: Brian Davis, Elizabeth Ann. BS in Naval Sci., U.S. Naval Acad., Annapolis, Md., 1961; MS in Underwater Acoustics, U.S. Naval Postgrad. Sch., Monterey, Calif., 1970. Commd. USN, advanced through ranks to rear adm., 1989; engr. officer USS California, Norfolk, Va., 1971-76; exec. officer USS Richmond K. Turner, Norfolk, 1976-77; instr. Prospective Engr. Officer Course, Idaho Falls, Idaho, 1977-79; commdg. officer USS Thomas C. Hart, Norfolk, 1979-81, USS Truxtun, San Diego, 1981-84; officer in charge Sr. Officer Ship Material Readiness Course, Idaho Falls, 1984-86; div. dir. Office Chief of Naval Ops., Washington, 1987-89; dep. comdr. Joint Task Force Four, Key West, Fla., 1989—. Decorated Legion of Merit. Avocations: golf, fishing, skiing.

PEARSON, JOHN EDWARD, lawyer; b. Jamaica, N.Y., Aug. 20, 1946; s. Stanley Charles and Rose Margaret (Manning) P.; m. Laura Marie Johannes, Dec. 28, 1968; children: Laura Rose, Jack. BA, Manhattan Coll., 1968; JD, St. John's U., 1972. Bar: N.Y. 1973, Fla. 1981, U.S. Dist. Ct. (so. dist.) N.Y. 1977, U.S. Dist. Ct. (so. dist.) Fla. 1982, U.S. Ct. Appeals (11th cir.) 1982, U.S. Ct. Appeals (5th cir.) 1982. Assoc. Sage, Gray, Todd & Sims, N.Y.C., 1972-78, ptnr., 1979; ptnr. Sage, Gray, Todd & Sims, Miami, Fla., 1980-87; ptnr. Hughes, Hubbard & Reed, Miami, 1987-91, 94—, N.Y.C., 1992-93. Author jour. article (Best Article award 1971). With USMCR, 1968-69. Mem. ABA, Fla. Bar Assn., N.Y. State Bar Assn., Assn. Bar City N.Y., Dade County Bar Assn., N.Y. County Lawyers Assn., Greater Miami C. of C. (trustee). Republican. Roman Catholic. Avocations: sailing, running. Home: 276 Seaview Dr Key Biscayne FL 33149 Office: Hughes Hubbard & Reed 801 Brickell Ave Miami FL 33131

PEARSON, LARRY LESTER, journalism educator, communication consultant; b. Sioux Falls, S.D., Sept. 27, 1942; s. Lester Loren and Lois Ursula (Cochran) P.; m. Alice Marie Simons, Sept. 15, 1979; children: Gregory Eric, Hillary Yvette, Andrew Todd. Ba cum laude, U. Minn., 1964, PhD, 1990; MA, U. Wis., 1969. Newsman UPI, Mpls., 1962-63; newsman Daily American, Rome, Italy, 1964-65; instr. Journalism St., U. Wis., 1965-67; with Mpls. Tribune, 1967-85, wire editor, 1970-72, news editor, 1972-82; news editor Mpls. Star & Tribune, 1982; asst. prof. U. Alaska, Anchorage, 1985-92, assoc. prof., 1992—, dir. Ctr. for Info. Tech., 1990-92; spl. cons. to Alaska Ho. Com. on Telecomm., 1985-90. Mem. Internat. Communication Assn., Am. Soc. Newspaper Design, Assn. Edn. in Journalism and Mass Communication. Lutheran. Home: 2410 E 16th Ave Anchorage AK 99508-2906 Office: U Alaska Anchorage AK 99508

PEARSON, MARGIT LINNEA, real estate company executive; b. Weymouth, Mass., Nov. 6, 1950; d. Eric Gustav and Evelyn (Forest) P. BA, Simmons Coll., 1972; MBA, Harvard U., 1975. Sr. mgr. McKinsey & Co., Inc., N.Y.C., 1975-83; pres. Berkey, Inc., Greenwich, Conn., 1987-89, APC Corp., Hawthorne, N.J., 1990-91; mng. dir. Renaissance, N.Y.C., 1992-93; pres. Sunset Point Devel., Charleston, S.C., 1987—. bd. dirs. NORMAL Found., N.Y.C., 1985—, C.C.A., Desert Chorale, Santa Fe, 1994—. Avocations: art, skiing, travel. Home: 9 E 96th St New York NY 10128 Office: 1590 Canyon Rd Santa Fe NM 87501

PEARSON, NATHAN WILLIAMS, investment management executive; b. N.Y.C., Nov. 26, 1911; s. James A. and Elizabeth (Williams) P.; m. Kathleen P. McMurtry, Apr. 9, 1947; children: James S. (dec.), Nathan Williams. A.B., Dartmouth Coll., 1932; M.B.A., Harvard, 1934; LLD (hon.), Thiel Coll., 1972. With U.S. Steel Corp., 1939-42; mgr. research Matson Navigation Co., 1946-47; controller Carborundum Co., 1947-48; with T. Mellon and Sons, Pitts., 1948-70; v.p., gov. T. Mellon and Sons, 1957-70; chmn., chief exec. officer, chmn. emeritus Mellon Bank N.A. & Mellon Bank Corp., Pitts., 1987—; fin. exec. for Paul Mellon, 1948—. Chmn. Pitts. Theol. Sem., 1987. Served from lt. (j.g.) to comdr. USNR, 1942-46. Mem. Allegheny Country Club, Harvard-Yale Princeton Club, Duquesne Club, Laurel Valley Golf Club, Edgeworth Club, Rolling Rock Club (Ligonier, Pa.), Racquet and Tennis Club. Republican. Presbyterian. Home: 10 Woodland Rd Sewickley PA 15143-1123 Office: Mellon Bank Corp Three Mellon Bank Ctr Ste 3903 525 William Penn Pl Pittsburgh PA 15219-1711

PEARSON, NORMAN, urban and regional planner, administrator, academic and planning consultant, writer; b. Stanley, County Durham, Eng., Oct. 24, 1928; arrived in Can., 1964; s. Joseph and Mary (Pearson) P.; m. Gerda Maria Josefine Riedl, July 25, 1972. BA in Fine Arts with honors in Town and Country Planning, U. Durham (Eng.), 1951; PhD in Land Economy and Ecol. Planning, Internat. Inst. Advanced Studies, 1979; MBA, Pacific Western U., Colo., 1980, DBA, 1982; PhD In Mgmt., Calif. U. for Advanced Studies, 1986. Cons. Stanley Urban Dist. Council, U.K., 1946-47; planning asst. Accrington Town Plan and Bedford County Planning Survey, U. Durham Planning Team, U.K., 1947-49, Allen and Mattocks, cons. planners and landscape designers, Newcastle upon Tyne, U.K., 1949-51; adminstrv. asst. Scottish Div., Nat. Coal Bd., Edinburgh, Scotland, 1951-52; planning asst. London County Coun., Westminster, U.K., 1953-54; planner Central Mortgage and Housing Corp., Ottawa, Ont., Can., 1954-55; planning analyst City of Toronto (Ont., Can.) Planning Bd., 1955-56; dir. planning Hamilton Wentworth Planning Area Bd., Hamilton, Ont., 1956-59, Burlington (Ont.) and Suburban Area Planning Bd., Can., 1959-62; commr. planning City of Burlington, Ont., 1959-62; pres. Tanfield Enterprises Ltd., London, Ont., Can., 1962—, Norman Pearson & Assocs. Ltd., London, Ont., Can., 1962—, Internat. Planning Mgmt. Cons., London, Ont., Can.,

1962—, Leahy, Pearson, Toll & Assocs. Ltd., London, Ont., Can., 1993-95; cons. in urban, rural and regional planning, 1962—; life mem. U.S. Com. for Monetary Research and Edn., 1976—; spl. lectr. in planning McMaster U., Hamilton, 1956-64, Waterloo (Ont.) Luth. U., 1961-63; asst. prof. geography and planning U. Waterloo (Ont.), 1963-67; assoc. prof. geography U. Guelph (Ont.), 1967-72, chmn., dir. Ctr. for Resource Devel.; prof. polit. sci. U. Western Ont., London, 1972-78; chmn. bd. dirs. Alma Coll., St. Thomas, Ont., 1990—; adj. prof. of ecological planning and land econs. Internat. Inst. for Advanced Studies, Clayton, Mo., 1980-89; core faculty Doctoral Program in Adminstrn/Mgmt. Walden U., Mpls., 1986—, chair adminstrn.-mgmt., 1989—; mem. acad. coun. Walden U., 1992—; mem. bd. regents Calif. U. for Advanced Studies, Petaluma, 1987-94; mem. Social Scis., Econ. and Legal Aspects Com. of Rsch. Adv. Bd. Internat. Joint Commn., 1972-76; cons. to City of Waterloo, 1973-76, Province of Ont., 1969-70; advisor to Georgian Bay Regional Devel. Coun., 1968-72; real estate appraiser, province of Ont., 1976—; pres., chmn. bd. govs. Pacific Western U., Canada, 1983-84. Author: Franchise & Partnership: A New Concept of Urban Development, Pipilines & Farming; (with others) An Inventory of Joint Programmes and Agreements Affecting Canada's Renewable Resources, 1964, An Emerald Light, 1994, Light Beyond the Craft in Canada, 1994; editor, co-author (with others) Regional and Resource Planning in Canada, 1963, rev. edit., 1970; editor (with others) The Pollution Reader, 1968; contbr. numerous articles on town planning to profl. jours. and chpts. to books. Pres. Unitarian Ch. of Hamilton, 1960-61. With RAFVR, 1951-53, res., 1953-60. Decorated knight of grace Sovereign Order St. John of Jerusalem, 1979, knight Order St. Lazarus of Jerusalem, 1991, Internat. Order of Merit, 1991, Order Internat. Fellowship, 1995. Fellow Royal Town Planning Inst. (Bronze medal award 1957), Lambda Alpha Internat., Royal Econ. Soc.; mem. Internat. Soc. City and Regional Planners, Am., Canadian insts. planners, Canadian Polit. Sci. Assn. L'Association Internationale des Ingenieurs et des Docteurs ès Sciences Appliquées à l'Industrie. Clubs: Empire; Ontario; University (London), Baconian. Office: PO Box 5362, Station A, London, ON Canada N6A 4L6

PEARSON, NORMAN RALSTON, librarian; b. Johnsonburg, Pa., Dec. 9, 1939; s. Axel Enoch and Ella Odessa (Bowers) P.; m. Ann Rose Davis, June 22, 1963; 1 child, Sean Ralston. BS, Waynesburg (Pa.) Coll., 1962; MLS, U. Pitts., 1969; EdS, Bowling Green State U., 1976. Tchr. Bradford (Pa.) Area Schs., 1962-69; libr. asst. U. Pitts., Bradford, 1967-69; assoc. libr. tech. svcs. Findlay (Ohio) Coll., 1969-75; editor N.W. Ohio Consortium, Bowling Green, 1975-76; intern Bowling Green State U., 1975-76; assoc. dir. librs. Indiana U. Pa., 1976-77; asst. libr. tech. svcs Wright State U., Dayton, Ohio, 1977-81; head serials dept. U. Del., Newark, 1981-85; head tech. svcs. Wittenberg U., Springfield, Ohio, 1985—. Editor, mng. editor Dayton Miami Valley Consortium, 1978-81. Corning Glass Works grantee, 1968. Mem. ALA, Am. Soc. Info. Sci., Assn. Coll. and Rsch. Librs., Assn. Libr. Collections and Tech. Libr. Svcs., Lutheran Historic Conf. Roman Catholic. Avocations: antiques, collectibles, book collecting, genealogy. Home: 31 W Hebble Ave Fairborn OH 45324-4901 Office: Wittenberg U Thomas Libr PO Box 720 Springfield OH 45501-0720

PEARSON, OSCAR HARRIS, plant breeder, geneticist; b. Stratham, N.H., Jan. 17, 1902; s. Frank Harris and Grace Eunice (Gowen) P.; m. Helen Ruth Monosmith, Dec. 15, 1929; children: Robert, David, Ann, Charles, George, Sandra. BS, U. N.H., 1923, MS, 1925; PhD, U. Calif., Berkeley, 1928. Jr. olericulturist U. Calif., Davis, 1928-33; head seed R & D Ea. States Farmers Exch., West Springfield, Mass., 1934-59; dir. seed R & D Seed Rsch. Specialists, Hollister, Calif., 1959-63, Niagara Seed, San Juan Bautista, Calif., 1963-67; sr. rsch. assoc. plant breeding dept. Cornell U., Ithaca, N.Y., 1967-70; cons. Bud Senegal, Dakar, 1970-75. Contbr. articles to profl. jours. Fellow AAAS, Am. Soc. Hort. Sci. (Asgrow award 1969). Achievements include basic program of hybrid cabbage seed prodn., devel. of Pearson tomato cultivar, the Butter and Sugar high quality hybrid sweet corn, other cultivars; isolation of a "n" male sterile cabbage for use in hybrid seed prodn. Office: 62 Reise Terr Portsmouth RI 02871

PEARSON, PAUL BROWN, nutritionist, educator; b. Oakley, Utah, Nov. 28, 1905; s. Levi and Ada (Brown) P.; m. Emma Snow, June 20, 1933 (dec.); children—Paula (Mrs. Raymond Soller), Marilyn (Mrs. Walter Johnson). B.S., Brigham Young U., 1928; M.S. (Walsh fellow), Mont. State U., 1930; Ph.D. (fellow), U. Wis., 1937. Asst. prof. Mont. State U. 1930-31; research assoc. U. Calif., 1932-35; prof. A&M Coll. Tex., 1937, disting. prof., 1941, dean grad. sch., head dept. biochemistry and nutrition, 1947; chief biology AEC, 1949-58, cons., 1958-70; prof. Johns Hopkins U., 1951-58; with program in sci. and engring. Ford Found., 1958-63; pres., sci. dir. Nutrition Found., 1963-72; chmn. dept. nutrition Drexel U., 1972-73; prof. dept. family and community medicine and dept. nutrition and food sci. U. Ariz., Tucson, 1974—; chief dept. nutrition U. Autónoma de Guadalajara, Mexico, 1974-84; prof. U. Autónoma de Guadalajara, Mexico, 1984—; Collaborator Bur. Animal Industry.; cons. Pres.'s Sci. Adv. Com., Nat. Agr. Rsch. Adv. Com., 1952-58; del. 6th Internat. Zootechnic Congress, Copenhagen, 1952, 2d Internat. Biochem. Congress, Paris, 1952, U.S.-Japan Conf. on Radiobiology, Tokyo, 1954, World Conf. Peaceful Uses Atomic Energy, Geneva, 1955, Internat. Symposium on Biochemistry of Sulphur, Roscoff, France, 1956; mem. exec. com. div. biol. and agrl. NRC, 1950-52; liaison Food and Nutrition Bd.; program com. Internat. Congress on Nutrition, 1960; chmn. adv. com. P.R. Nuclear Ctr., 1962-73; del. White Ho. Conf. Internat. Cooperation, 1965, White Ho. Conf. on Food, Nutrition and Health, 1969; adv. com. McCollum-Pratt Inst.; trustee Food Drug Law Inst., 1967-85, Nutrition Found., 1972-74; mem. com. Internat. Union of Nutrition, 1970-76. Author bulls. NRC, numerous sci. publs. on nutrition and biochemistry. Fellow AAAS, Soc. for Animal Sci., Am. Inst. Nutrition; mem. Biochem. Soc. London, Am. Chem. Soc., Brit. Nutrition Soc., Soc. Biol. Chemists, El Coligeo de Medicos Cirujanos de Jalisco. Clubs: Lochinvar, Cosmos. Home: 3025 E 6th St Tucson AZ 85716-4837 Office: U Ariz Dept Family & Community Med Tucson AZ 85721 also: U Autonoma Guadalajara, Faculty Medicine, Apdo Postal 1-440, 44100 Guadalajara Jalisco, Mexico

PEARSON, PAUL DAVID, lawyer, mediator; b. Boston, Jan. 22, 1940; s. Bernard J. and Ruth (Bayla) Munschauer; children—David Todd, Lisa Kari. AB, Bucknell U., 1961; LLB, U. Pa., 1964. Bar: Mass. 1966, N.Y. 1987. Staff atty., tech. assoc. lab. of community psychiatry, dept. psychiatry Harvard Med. Sch., Boston, 1966-68; assoc. Snyder Tepper & Berlin, Boston, 1968-71, ptnr., 1971-77; with Hill & Barlow, Boston, 1977-87, ptnr., chmn. family law dept.; with Hodgson, Russ, Andrews, Woods and Goodyear, Buffalo, 1987—, chmn. family law dept., lectr. Mass. Continuing Legal Edn., New Eng. Law Inst.; instr. law and mental health Boston Psychoanalytic Soc. and Inst., 1975-87; lectr. in field. Trustee, v.p., legal counsel Boston Ballet Soc.; trustee, chmn., legal counsel Wayland (Mass.) Townhouse; trustee Family Counseling Service (region West); mem., chmn., clk. Wayland Zoning Bd. Appeals; v.p., counsel, Arts Wayland Found., 1982-87; vis. fellow Woodrow Wilson Found., 1985-87, Mass. Gov.'s Spl. Commn. on Divorce, 1985-87; lectr. dept. psychiatry SUNY-Buffalo Med. Sch., 1989—; bd. dirs. Jewish Community Ctr. Greater Buffalo and Buffalo chpt., Am. Jewish Com., 1991—, Arts Coun. Buffalo and Erie County, 1992—. Served to capt. Mil. Police Corps, USAR. Fellow Am. Acad. Matrimonial Lawyers (pres., bd. mgrs. Mass.); mem. ABA (family law com.), Mass. Bar Assn. (chmn. family law sect.), Boston Bar Assn. (family law com., legis. chmn.), N.Y. Bar Assn. (family law com.), Erie County Bar Assn. (chmn. alternative dispute resolution com., family law com.). Contbr. articles to profl. jours. Home: 605 Lebrun Rd Buffalo NY 14226-4232 Office: Hodgson Russ Andrews Woods & Goodyear 1 M & T Plz Ste 1800 Buffalo NY 14203

PEARSON, PAUL GUY, university president emeritus; b. Lake Worth, Fla., Dec. 5, 1926; s. Eric Conrad and Dora Wilma (Capen) P.; m. Winifred Clowe, June 30, 1951; children: Thomas, Jean, Andrew. Student, Palm Beach Jr. Coll., 1946-47; B.S. with honors, U. Fla., 1949, M.S., 1951, Ph.D., 1954; Litt.D. (hon.), Rutgers U., 1982; LL.D. (hon.), Juniata Coll., 1983; commd. de L'ordre de merite, Grand Duchy of Luxembourg, 1988. Asst. prof. U. Tulsa 1954-55; asst. prof. Rutgers U., New Brunswick, N.J., 1955-60; assoc. prof. Rutgers U., 1960-64, prof., 1964-81, assoc. provost, 1972-77, exec. v.p., 1977-81, acting pres., 1978; pres. prof. Miami U., Oxford, Ohio, 1981-92; bd. dirs. Union Ctrl. Life Ins., Cin., S.W. Ohio Sr. Svcs., Cin., Nat. Conservancy, Ohio; trustee Ohio No. U., Ada. Mem. U.S. Army Sci. Bd., 1984-86. Served with USNR, 1944-46. Fellow AAAS; mem.

Am. Inst. Biol. Scis. (governing bd. 1968-79, v.p. 1977, pres. 1978), Rotary Internat. (Paul Harris fellow), Phi Beta Kappa (assoc.). Home: 5110 Bonham Rd Oxford OH 45056

PEARSON, PAUL HAMMOND, physician; b. Bolenge, Belgian Congo; s. Ernest B. and Evelyn (Utter) P. B.S., Northwestern, 1944, B.Medicine, 1946, M.D., 1947; M.P.H., UCLA, 1963. Diplomate: Am. Bd. Pediatrics. Intern Los Angeles County Gen. Hosp., 1946-47; resident Cin. Children's Hosp., 1949-51; fellow convulsive disorders and electroencephalography Johns Hopkins Hosp., Balt., 1951-53; resident in child psychiatry U. B.C., Can., Vancouver, 1976-77; practice medicine specializing in pediatrics L.A., 1953-62; chief mental retardation br. USPHS div. chronic disease, 1963-65; asst. dir. mental retardation program Nat. Inst. Child Health and Human Devel., NIH, 1965-66; spl. asst. to surgeon gen. USPHS, 1966-67; C.L. Meyer prof. child health, prof. pub. health and preventive medicine, dir. Meyer Children's Rehab. Inst., 1967-81, McGaw prof. adolescent medicine, dir. adolescent medicine, 1982-89, prof. emeritus dept. pediatrics, 1989—; mem. grad. faculty U. Nebr. Coll. Medicine, Omaha, 1967—; med. dir. Univ. Hosp. Eating Disorder Program U. Nebr. Coll. Medicine, 1983-89, sr. cons. Univ. Hosp. Eating Disorder Program, 1989—; from instr. to asst. clin. prof. U. So. Calif. Med. Sch., 1953-62; from assoc. clin. prof. pediatrics to clin. prof. pediatrics Georgetown U. Sch. Medicine, Washington, 1963-67; Cons., mem. profl. services program com. United Cerebral Palsy Assn., 1969-72, mem. nat. awards com., 1971; Am. Acad. Pediatrics liaison rep. to Am. Acad. Orthopedic Surgery, 1969-73; apptd. to Nat. Adv. Council Services and Facilities for Developmentally Disabled Dept. Health. Edn. and Welfare, 1971-75; councilor Accreditation Council Facilities for Mentally Retarded, Joint Commn. on Accreditation Hosps., 1973-74; fellow adolescent medicine Boston Children's Hosp. Med. Center, 1981. Cons. editor: Am. Jour. Mental Deficiency, 1970-72; Contbr. articles to profl. jours. Mem. com. on accessible environments Nat. Acad. Scis., 1974-77. Served to capt. MC AUS, 1947-49. Mem. Am. Acad. Pediatrcs (com. on children with handicaps 1969-75, com. sect. on child devel. 1974—), Am. Assn. Mental Deficiency, Nat. Assn. for Retarded Children, Greater Omaha Assn. for Retarded Children (dir.), Am. Pub. Health Assn., Am. Acad. Cerebral Palsy and Developmental Medicine (exec. com. 1971-76, chmn. sci. program com. 1972-74, sec. 1974-77, mem. research and awards com. 1977-78, pres. 1981-82, bd. dirs. 1982-84), Assn. Univ.-Affiliated Facilities (exec. com. 1973—, v.p. 1974-75, pres. 1975-76, dir. 1971-78), Soc. Adolescent MedicineAlpha Omega Alpha. Home: 1123 N 122d St Omaha NE 68154 Office: U Nebr Med Ctr Dept Pediatrics Omaha NE 68198

PEARSON, PAUL HOLDING, insurance company executive; b. Worcester, Mass., Feb. 14, 1940; s. Malcolm D. and Myra L. (Holding) P.; m. Judith N. Howe, July 13, 1958 (div. June 1974); children: Scott D., Todd E.; m. Anne Beck, July 26, 1974. BA in Bus. and Econs., U. Maine, 1961. C.L.U., 1971. Jr. life underwriter State Mut. Am., Worcester, 1961-63, life underwriter, 1963-67, sr. life underwriter, 1967-69; dir. life underwriting Security Mut. Life Ins. Co., Binghamton, N.Y., 1969, 2d v.p. underwriting, 1970, v.p., 1971-75, sr. v.p. ins. services div., 1975-79, exec. v.p., 1979-81, pres., 1981—; chief exec. officer, 1987—; chmn., CEO, bd. dirs. SML Properties corp., Binghamton, Security Equity Life Ins. Co., Binghamton, 1987-93. Trustee, treas. Lourdes Meml. Hosp., Binghamton, 1978-92; mem. SUNY Found., Binghamton, 1982-89; trustee, chmn. fin. com. Elmira Coll., 1983-87; bd. dirs. Broome C.C. Found., 1982-91, pres. 1985-86; pres. New Industries for Broome, Binghamton, 1985—, N.Y. State Bus. Devel. Coun., 1987—; bd. dirs. Valley Devel. Found., 1987-91, Bus. Coun. of N.Y., 1988—, Am. Coun. Life Ins., 1990-93. Mem. Assn. for Advanced Life Underwriting, Nat. Assn. Life Underwriters, Broome County C. of C. (bd. dirs. 1980-88, chmn. 1986), Binghamton C/C Live Wire Club. Office: Security Mut Life Ins Co NY Court House Sq PO Box 1625 Binghamton NY 13902-1625

PEARSON, PHILLIP THEODORE, veterinary clinical sciences and biomedical engineering educator; b. Ames, Iowa, Nov. 21, 1932; s. Theodore B. and Hazel C. (Christianson) P.; m. Mary Jane Barlow, Aug. 28, 1954; children: Jane Catherine, Bryan Theodore, Todd Wallace, Julie Ann. DVM, Iowa State U., 1956, PhD, 1962. Intern Angell Meml. Animal Hosp., Boston, 1956-57; instr. Coll. Vet. Medicine Iowa State U., 1957-59, asst. prof., 1959-63, assoc. prof., 1963-64, prof. vet. clin. scis. and biomed. engr.-ing., 1965-72, 89—, dean, 1972-89; dir. Vet. Med. Rsch. Inst., 1972-89; prof. Sch. Vet. Medicine. U. Mo., 1964-65. Bd. dirs. Iowa Sate Meml. Union, 1970-84; v.p. Iowa State Meml. Union, 1975; chmn. coun. of deans Assn. Am. Vet. Medicine Colls., 1978-79. Recipient Riser award, 1956; distinguished Tchr. award Norden Labs., 1962; Gaines award Gen. Foods Corp., 1966; Outstanding Tchr. award Iowa State U., 1968; Faculty citation, 1974; named Iowa Vet. of the Yr., 1988. Mem. AVMA, Iowa Vet. Medicine Assn., Am. Animal Hosp. Assn., Am. Assn. Vet. Clinicians, Am. Coll. Vet. Surgeons (bd. regents 1972, pres. 1977), Nat. Acad. Practice, Kiwanis (bd. dirs., pres. Ames 1966—), Sigma Xi, Phi Kappa Phi, Phi Zeta, Alpha Zeta, Gamma Sigma Delta (Alumni award of merit 1991). Home: 1610 Maxwell Ave Ames IA 50010-5536

PEARSON, RALPH GOTTFRID, chemistry educator; b. Chgo., Jan. 12, 1919; s. Gottfrid and Kerstin (Larson) P.; m. Lenore Olivia Johnson, June 15, 1941 (dec. June 1982); children—John Ralph, Barry Lee, Christie Ann. B.S., Lewis Inst., 1940; Ph.D., Northwestern U., 1943. Faculty Northwestern U., 1946-76, prof. chemistry, 1957-76; prof. chemistry U. Calif., Santa Barbara, 1976-89, prof. emeritus, 1989—; Cons. to industry and govt., 1951—. Co-author 5 books. Served to 1st It. USAAF, 1944-46. Guggenheim fellow, 1951. Mem. Am. Chem. Soc. (Midwest award 1966, Inorganic Chemistry award 1969), Nat. Acad. Sci., Phi Beta Kappa, Sigma Xi, Phi Lambda Upsilon (hon.). Lutheran. Achievements include being originator prin. of hard and soft acids and bases.

PEARSON, RICHARD JOSEPH, archaeologist, educator; b. Kitchener, Ont., Can., May 2, 1938; s. John Cecil and Henrietta Anne (Wallwin) P.; m. Kazue Miyazaki, Dec. 12, 1964; 1 child, Sarina Riye. B.A. in Anthropology with honours, U. Toronto, 1960; Ph.D., Yale U., 1966. Asst. prof., then assoc. prof. archaeology U. Hawaii, 1966-71; mem. faculty U. B.C., Vancouver, 1971—; now prof. archaeology U. B.C. Author: The Archaeology of the Ryukyu Islands, 1969, Higashi Ajia no Kodai Shakai to Kokogaku, 1984, Windows on the Japanese Past, Studies in Archaeology and Prehistory, 1986, Ancient Japan, 1992; contbr. articles to profl. jours. Guggenheim fellow. Mem. Am. Anthrop. Assn., Soc. Am. Archaeology, Indo-Pacific Prehistory Assn., Assn. Asian Studies. Office: Dept Anthropology/Sociology, U BC, Vancouver, BC Canada V6T 1Z1

PEARSON, ROBERT GREENLEES, writing services company executive; b. Kansas City, Mo., Feb. 19, 1917; s. Ridley Stillson and Agnes (Greenlees) P.; m. Laura Gray Betsy Dodge, Jan. 3, 1945; children—Bradbury, Wendy, Robert Ridley. A.B. with honors, U. Kans., 1938. Mgr. corporate public relations Shell Oil Co. (N.Y. Head Office), 1938-71; v.p. public relations Council Better Bus. Bur. (N.Y. Hdqrs.), 1971-73; writer public affairs dept. Mobil Oil Corp., N.Y.C., 1973-74; sr. advisor Alcoholics Anonymous World Services, Inc., N.Y.C., 1974-85; pres. Robert Pearson Assocs., Writing Svcs., Riverside, Conn., 1985—; Bd. dirs. Nat. Safety Council; pres. Fairfield County (Conn.) Council on Alcoholism, 1962. Author: Oil for Victory, 1946, The J.C. Nichols Chronicle, 1994; contbr. articles to profl. jours. Served to lt. comdr. USNR, 1941-45. Congregationalist. Clubs: Riverside (Conn.); Yacht, Dutch Treat. Home: 17 Jones Park Dr Riverside CT 06878-2205 Office: PO Box 671 Riverside CT 06878-0671

PEARSON, ROGER, organization executive; b. London, Aug. 21, 1927; s. Edwin and Beatrice May (Woodbine) P.; m. Marion Primrose Simms, June 3, 1959; children: Edwin, Sigrid, Emma, Rupert. BS with honors, U. London, 1951, MS, 1964, PhD, 1969. Chmn. Pakistan Tea Assn., 1954; mng. dir. Octavius Steel & Co. of Pakistan Ltd., Chittagong, East Pakistan, 1959-65; chmn. Plummer Bros., Ltd., Chittagong, East Pakistan, 1959-65, Chittagong Warehouses, Ltd., Chittagong, East Pakistan, 1960-65; chmn. dept. sociology and anthropology Queens Coll., Charlotte, N.C., 1970-71; chmn. dept. anthropology U. So. Miss., Hattiesburg, 1971-74; dean acad. affairs, dir. research Mont. Coll. Mineral Sci. Tech., Butte, 1974-75; exec. dir. Council for Econ. and Social Studies, Washington, 1975—. Author: Eastern Interlude, 1954, Introduction to Anthropology, 1978, Anthropological Glossary, 1985, Race, Intelligence and Bias in Academe, 1991, Shockley on Eugenics and Race, 1992; editor: Ecology and Evolution, 1982; editor, pub.

Jour. Indo-European Studies, 1973—, Jour. Social Polit. and Econ. Studies 1976—. Trustee, Benjamin Franklin U., Washington, 1984-87. Served to lt. Brit. Indian Army, 1945-48. Fellow Inst. Chartered Secs. Adminstrs. (London), Inst. Dirs. (London), Galton Inst. (London), RD. Clubs: Oriental, Reform (London); Army and Navy (Washington). Office: Coun Econ and Social Studies 1133 13th St NW Apt C-2 Washington DC 20005

PEARSON, ROGER LEE, library administrator; b. Galesburg, Ill., Dec. 7, 1940; s. Clifford Emmanuel and Lillian Louise (Fisher) P. B.A., Knox Coll., 1963; M.A. in Sociology, U. Nebr.-Omaha, 1968; M.A. in Library Sci., Rosary Coll., 1974. Vol. U.S. Peace Corps, Brazil, 1964-66; extension service supr. Brown County Libr., Green Bay, Wis., 1974-75; system adminstr. Nicolet Libr. System, Green Bay, 1976-77; exec. dir. South Central Libr. System, Madison, Wis., 1977-81; dir. Corpus Christi Pub. Librs., Tex., 1981-84, Naperville (Ill.) Pub. Librs., 1984—; lectr. Grad. Sch. Libr. and Info. Sci., Rosary Coll., River Forest, Ill., 1991—. Mem. ALA, Ill. Libr. Assn., Rotary Internat. Democrat. Avocations: walking, travel research, Brazilian and Mex. studies. Home: 200 E 5th Ave Apt 313 Naperville IL 60563-3174 Office: Naperville Pub Libr 200 W Jefferson Ave Naperville IL 60540-5351

PEARSON, RONALD DALE, retail food stores corporation executive; b. Des Moines, 1940; married. B.S. in Bus. Adminstrn., Drake U., 1962. With Hy-Vee Food Stores Inc., Chariton, Iowa, 1962—, former exec. v.p., now pres., chief operating officer, CEO, chmn.; dir. Beverage Mfrs., Inc., Civic Ctr. Cts., Inc. Office: Hy-Vee Food Stores Inc 1801 Oceola Ave Chariton IA 50049*

PEARSON, ROY LAING, business administration educator; b. Victoria, Hong Kong, Oct. 18, 1939; s. Roy Ross and Martha Ann L.; m. Louise Elliott Johns, June 11, 1960; 1 child, Cynthia Laing. BS in Commerce, U. Va., 1961, PhD in Econs., 1968. Asst. prof. Sch. Bus. Adminstrn. U. Ark., Fayetteville, 1964-68; assoc. prof. Centenary Coll. La., Shreveport, 1968-71; assoc. prof. bus. adminstrn. Coll. William and Mary, Williamsburg, Va., 1971-76; prof. bus. adminstrn. Coll. William and Mary, 1976-87, dir. Bur. Bus. Rsch., 1985—, Chancellor prof. bus. adminstrn., 1987—; v.p. Mid-Atlantic Rsch., Inc., Williamsburg, Va., 1979—; sec.-treas. McKinley Land Co., Inc., Williamsburg, 1969—. Editor, author newsletter: Virginia Business Report, 1984—. Bd. dirs. Williamsburg Community Hosp., 1985-90; gov.'s adv. bd. economists Commonwealth of Va., Richmond, 1984—; mem. trust fund adv. com. Va. Employment Commn., 1984—. NSF fellow, 1963. Mem. Va. Assn. Economists (pres. 1990-91, bd. dirs. 1985-91), Assn. for Univ. Bus. and Econ. Rsch. (bd. dirs. 1991-92, v.p. 1992-94, pres. 1994—), Nat. Assn. Bus. Economists, Internat. Inst. Forecasters, Richmond Assn. Bus. Economists, Nat. Economists Club. Avocations: scuba diving, underwater photography, science fiction. Home: 718 Jamestown Rd Williamsburg VA 23185-3914 Office: Coll William & Mary Sch Bus Adminstrn Williamsburg VA 23185

PEARSON, ROY MESSER, JR., clergyman; b. Somerville, Mass., Mar. 10, 1914; s. Roy Messer and Bessie M. (Ricker) P.; m. Ruth Simmons, July 12, 1936; children: Beverly, Bradford; m. Barbara K. Cerello, Sept. 1, 1990. AB magna cum laude, Harvard U., 1935; BD cum laude, Andover Newton Theol. Sch., 1938; DD, Amherst Coll., 1957, Brown U., 1971; LLD, Emerson Coll., 1966, Colby Coll., 1967; LHD, Norwich U., 1968; DSO, Curry Coll., 1969. Minister Southville (Mass.) Federated Ch., 1936-38; ordained to ministry Congl. Ch., 1938; minister First Congl. Ch. Swanzey, N.H., 1938-40, Amherst, Mass., 1940-47; minister Hancock Congl. Ch., Lexington, Mass., 1947-54; lectr. Andover Newton Theol. Sch., 1951-54, dean, 1954-65, pres., 1965-79, also trustee; pres. Andover Theol. Sem., 1954-65, Bartlett prof. sacred rhetoric, 1954-79 ; preacher Nat. Council Chs. in Brit. Isles, 1951; regular radio preacher Mass. Council Chs., 1952-57; preacher Internat. Congl. Council Brit. Isles, 1957; interim minister, Peterborough, Newport, New London, Hanover, Hopkinton, and Warner, N.H., 1979-87. Author: Here's Faith for You, 1953, This Do-And Live, 1954, The Hard Commands of Jesus, 1957, Seeking and Finding God, 1958, The Ministry of Preaching, 1959; Contbg. author: (ed. G. Paul Butler) Best Sermons of 1955, 1955, Hear Our Prayer, 1961, The Preacher: His Purpose and Practice, 1963, The Believer's Unbelief, 1963, Best Sermons of 1964, 1964, Best Sermons of 1968, 1968, Prayers for All Occasions, 1990; also articles religious periodicals. Served as 1st lt. Chaplains Corps AUS, 1944. Recipient Churchman award for best sermon of the year, 1948; Am. Assn. Theol. fellow, 1960-61. Mem. Phi Beta Kappa. Club: University (Boston). Home: 31 Stony Brook Rd PO Box 870 New London NH 03257 *With the advance of my age and the growth of my faith I find myself a Christian agnostic. It is not that I believe less. Rather, that I believe more. God is too great for me to comprehend his immensities.*

PEARSON, THOMAS ARTHUR, epidemiologist, educator; b. Berlin, Wis., Oct. 21, 1950; married; 2 children. BA, Johns Hopkins U., 1973, MD, 1976, MPH, 1976, PhD in Epidemiology, 1983. Fellow cardiology Johns Hopkins Sch. Medicine, 1981-83, from asst. prof. to assoc. prof. medicine, epidemiology, 1983-88; prof. epidemiology Columbia U., 1988—; dir. Mary Imogene Bassett Rsch. Inst., 1988—; chmn. monitoring bd. CARDIA Project, Nat. Heart, Lung & Blood Inst., 1987—; rsch. com. Md. Heart Assn., 1986-88, nat. rsch. com. Am. Heart Assn., 1987-92; mem. coun. Epidemiology, 1987—, vice chair 1994-95; commr. Md. Coun. Phys. Fitness, 1985-88; mem. clin. applications & prevention commn. NIH, 1987-91, chair, 1990-91. Mem. ACP, Am. Fedn. Chem. Rsch., Am. Coll. Epidemiology, am. Coll. Preventive Medicine, Am. Coll. Physicians, Am. Coll. Cardiology, Assn. Tchrs. Preventive Medicine, Soc. Epidemiol. Rsch. (Rsch. prize 1978). Achievements include research in the etiology and pathogenesis of atherosclerosis. Office: Mary Imogene Bassett Med Rsch Inst 1 Atwell Rd Cooperstown NY 13326

PEARSON, WALTER DONALD, editor, columnist; b. Pittsfield, Mass., Feb. 5, 1916; s. Edgar C. and Edna (Scott) P.; divorced; children: Florence, Donald, Sharon; m. Elsa Swanson; 1 child, Richard. Student, Dartmouth Coll., 1941-43. Advt. salesman, 1935-41; securities broker Charles A. Day Co., Boston, 1947-55; founder, owner, mgr. First New Eng. Securities Co., Inc., Southbridge, Mass., 1955-71; now owner, editor Pearson Investment Letter, Dover, Fla.; fin. columnist World Intelligence Rev.; free-lance columnist various publications; fin. advisor, investment mgr. Author: Investing for the Millions, 1990. With inf. U.S. Army, 1943-45, ETO. Decorated Bronze star, Croix de Guerre (France), Combat Infantry badge. Home: 1628 White Arrow Dr Dover FL 33527-5741

PEARSON, WILLARD, former army officer; b. West Elizabeth, Pa., July 4, 1915; s. John Alfred and Mary Catherine (Mehrmann) P.; m. Reba E. Barton, Sept. 12, 1947; children: Richard Barton, Joan Louise, Patricia Jean. Student, Duquesne Bus. Coll., 1933-35; M.S., Columbia U., 1953; postgrad., Army War Coll., 1956-57; postgrad. in mgmt., U. Pitts., 1962; M.A., George Washington U., 1963. Commd. 2d It. U.S. Army Res., 1936; advanced through grades to It. gen. U.S. Army, 1971; comdg. gen. 1st Brigade, 101st Airborne Div. Vietnam, 1966-67; J3, USMACV Saigon, 1967-68; dir. individual tng. ODCSPER, Hdqrs. Dept. Army Washington, 1968-69; comdg. gen. Ft. Lewis, Wash., 1969-71, V Corps U.S. Army Europe, 1971-73; supt. Valley Forge Mil. Acad. and Jr. Coll., Wayne, Pa., 1973-85. Mem. Franklin Inst., Phila. Orchestra Assn., Friends Independence Nat. Hist. Park; bd. advisors Vietnam Veterans Meml. Inst.; trustee Chapel of 4 Chaplains, exec. v.p. 1985—; dir. Citizens Crime Commn. Phila. Decorated D.S.M. with 2 oak leaf clusters, Silver Star medal with two oak leaf clusters, Legion of Merit with two oak leaf clusters, Bronze Star medal with two oak leaf clusters, Combat Inf. badge with star, Air medal with six oak leaf clusters; Republic of Korea Presdl. Commendation; Mil. Order of Merit Korea; Vietnamese Order 4th and 5th Classes; Vietnamese Gallantry Cross with palm; Grand Cross Merit with star Fed. Repub. Germany; Pa. D.S.M. Mem. Accuracy in Media, Am. Legion, Am. Security Coun., Assn. U.S. Army, Coun. for Inter-Am. Security, Mil. Order World Wars, Nat. Assn. Uniformed Svcs., 101st Airborne Div. Assn. Olympia Assn., Navy League, VFW, Res. Officers Assn., Nat. Sojourners Inc., Beta Gamma Sigma. Presbyterian. Club: Penn. Lodge: Masons (33 degree), Shriners (knight comdr. ct. honor). Master parachutist. Address: 375 Red Coat Ln Wayne PA 19087

PEARSON, WILLIAM JAMES, finance company executive; b. Ogdensburg, N.Y., Jan. 31, 1938; s. John A. and Mary (McDonald) P.; m. Deborah A. DeOrsey, Dec. 30, 1983. BA in History and English, Hamilton

---

Coll., 1960. Various positions N.Y. Telephone, Kingston, 1960-66, comml. mgr., 1966-70; mgr. personnel adminstrn. Paul Revere Ins. Group, Worcester, Mass., 1970-72; mgr. personnel Paul Revere Ins. Group, Worcester, 1972-74, 2nd v.p., dir. personnel, 1974-79, v.p. human resources, 1979-87; sr. v.p. human resources Avco Fin. Services, Irvine, Calif., 1987-95; exec. v.p. human resources Avco Fin. Svcs., Costa Mesa, Calif., 1995—; chmn., founding mem. Exec. Human Resource Forum So. Calif., 1993-94. Mem. Am. Soc. Personnel Adminstrn. (nat. govt. affairs com. nat. chmn. 1987), Personnel Mgmt. Assn. (exec. com. 1987). Home: 21 Terraza Del Mar Dana Point CA 92629-1157 Office: Avco Fin Svcs Inc 600 Anton Blvd Costa Mesa CA 92628-5011

PEART, SHERRY HARTMAN, lawyer; b. Houston, Jan. 13, 1951; d. Earl Creston and Alice Marie (Johnson) Hartman; m. John Edward Peart, Mar. 29, 1987; 1 child, Christopher Johnson. BA, U. Tex., 1973, JD, 1975; cert. Modern English Law, London Sch. Econ., 1974. Bar: Tex. 1976. Assoc. Jordan, Ramsey & Hill, Dallas, 1976-77; atty. Sun Oil Co. (Del.), Dallas, 1977-84; sr. atty. Sun Exploration and Prodn. Co., Dallas, 1984-90; chief counsel Oryx Energy Co., Dallas, 1990—; dir., v.p. Oryx Credit Union, Dallas, 1988-91. Mem. Dallas Bar Assn. Avocations: skiing, tennis, travel. Office: Oryx Energy Co 13155 Noel Rd Dallas TX 75240-5067

PEASBACK, DAVID R., recruiting company executive; 1 child, Jennifer. B.A., Colgate U., 1955; LL.B., U. Va., 1961. Mgmt. trainee Proctor & Gamble, N.Y.C., 1955-56; assoc. Covington & Burling, Washington, 1961-64; litigation counsel Litton Industries, Inc., Beverly Hills, Calif., 1965-67; v.p. Bangor Punta Ops., Greenwich, Conn., 1968-71; assoc. Heidrick and Struggles, N.Y.C., 1972-76, ptnr., 1976-88, pres., chief exec. officer, 1983-87; vice-chmn., chief exec. officer Canny, Bowen, Inc., N.Y.C., 1988—. Served as sgt. USMC, 1956-58. Office: Canny Bowen Inc 200 Park Ave New York NY 10166*

PEASE, DAVID GORDON, artist, educator; b. Bloomington, Ill., June 2, 1932; s. Gordon A. and June (Stephens) P.; m. Julie Jensen, Mar. 29, 1956; children: Lisa Kay, Kerry Susan. B.S. U. Wis., 1954, M.S., 1955, M.F.A. 1958. Instr. art Mich. State U., 1958-60; mem. faculty Tyler Sch. Art, Temple U., Phila., 1960-83; prof. Tyler Sch. Art, Temple U., 1970-83, chmn. painting dept., 1968-77, dean, 1977-83; prof., dean Yale U. Sch. Art, New Haven, 1983—; vis. faculty mem. Yale U. Summer Sch. Music and Art, 1970-72. One-man shows include Baylor U., 1972, U. Wis., 1972, Pa. Acad. Fine Arts, 1977, Terry Dintenfass Inc., N.Y.C., 1969, 71, 76, Phila. Art Alliance, 1961, 70; group exhbns. include Carnegie Internat., Pitts., 1961, Corcoran Biennial, Washington, 1961, 63, Whitney Annual, N.Y.C., 1963; represented in permanent collections Whitney Mus. Am. Art, Phila. Mus. Art, Pa. Acad. Fine Arts, Des Moines Art Center, Pa. State U., U. Wis., Temple U., Hallmark Cards Inc., Columbia Pictures, others. Trustee Louis Comfort Tiffany Found., 1988—. With U.S. Army, 1955-57. Recipient William A. Clark award Corcoran Biennial, 1963, Lindbeck Found. Disting. Teaching award, 1968, Disting. Alumni award U. Wis., 1991; Guggenheim Found. fellow, 1965-66; Tiffany Found. grantee, 1975-76. Mem. Coll. Art Assn. Am., Nat. Assn. Schs. Art, Nat. Coun. Art Adminstrs. (bd. dirs. 1984-87), Alliance Ind. Colls. of Art (bd. dirs. 1988-91), Assn. Ind. Colls. Art and Design (trustee 1992—). Home: 95 Thankful Stow Rd Guilford CT 06437-2529 Office: Yale U Sch Art 180 York St New Haven CT 06511-4804

PEASE, DENISE LOUISE, state bank regulator; b. Bronx, N.Y., Mar. 15, 1953; d. William Henry Jr. and Louise Marion (Caswell) P. BA, Columbia U., 1978, postgrad., 1981-82; postgrad., Baruch Grad. Sch Pub Adminstrn., 1982-83, Institut Européen d'Administration des Affaires INSEAD, 1990. Exec. spl. asst. to county exec. N.J. Office of the County Exec., County of Essex (N.J.), 1982-83; urban analyst III State of N.Y. Dept. Banking, 1983-86, exec. asst. to the supt. of banks, 1986-87; dep. supt. of banks State of N.Y. Dept. Banking, N.Y.C., 1987—; mem. N.Y. State Gov.'s Econ. Devel. Sub-cabinet. Adv. bd. Cornell U. Coop. Extension; mgmt. program adv. bd. Sch. Bus. SUNY, 1990; mem. Alfred U. Devel. Com., mentoring program N.Y. State Women in Govt.; U.S. del. Europe Am. Emerging Leaders Conf., 1993. Named to Salute to Outstanding African Am. Bus. and Profl. Women, Dollar & Sense Mag., 1990, one of Outstanding Young Women in Am., 1979-81; recipient N.Y. State Assembly Citation of Merit, 1988, Profl. Achievement award Nat. Assn. Negro Bus. and Women's Club, 1981, Cmty. Svc. award N.Y. State Black and Puerto Rican Legislators Assn., 1993; Nat. Urban fellow, 1982-83, Charles H. Revson fellow Columbia U., 1981-82. Mem. NAACP (life mem.), Nat. Coun. of Negro Women (life mem.), Coalition of 100 Black Women, Fin. Women's Assn. N.Y. (bd. dirs.). Office: NY State Banking Dept 2 Rector St Fl 18 New York NY 10006-1819

PEASE, DONALD E., dairy farmer, food products company executive; b. 1936. Dairy farmer Susquehanna, Pa.; with Curtice Burns Foods Inc. (formerly Curtice-Burns Inc.), chmn. bd., 1989—; bd. dirs. Agway Inc. Office: Curtice-Burns Foods Inc PO Box 681 90 Linden Park Rochester NY 14625-2711

PEASE, EDWARD ALLAN, lawyer, former state senator, university official; b. Terre Haute, Ind., May 22, 1951; s. Robert Richard and Joanna Rose (Pilant) P.; A.B. with distinction (Wendell Willkie scholar), Ind. U., Bloomington, 1973, J.D. cum laude, Indpls., 1977; postgrad. Memphis State U., 1977-76, Ind. State U., 1978-85. Gen. law clk. appellate and contracts div. Office Ind. Atty. Gen., Indpls., 1974-75; nat. dir. alumni affairs Pi Kappa Alpha Frat., Memphis, 1975-76; admitted to Ind. bar, 1977; partner firm Thomas, Thomas & Pease, Brazil, Ind., 1977-84; of counsel firm Thomas & Thomas, Brazil, 1984—; v.p. Ind. State U., 1993; mem. Ind. Senate, 1980-92, chmn. Judiciary Com.; chmn. Ind. Commn. Trial Cts., 1987-89; mem. adv. bd. 1st Bank & Trust Co. Clay County; mem. exec. bd. Wabash Valley council Boy Scouts Am., 1972—, exec. bd. east cen. region, 1986-88, v.p., 1977-84, pres., 1984-88, mem. nat. Order of Arrow com., 1984—, nat. vice chmn., 1990-93, nat. chmn., 1993—. Recipient Silver Beaver award Boy Scouts Am., 1975, Silver Antelope, 1992. Mem. Ind. Bar Assn., Phi Beta Kappa, Pi Kappa Alpha (nat. pres. 1988-90). Republican. Club: Columbia (Indpls). Office: Ind State U 340 Gillum Hall ISU Terre Haute IN 47809

PEASE, ELLA LOUISE, elementary education educator; b. Kokomo, Ind., May 31, 1928; d. James E. and Carrie Alice (Ringer) Earnest; m. Harold Edwin Pease, Aug. 10, 1985; children: Charles Miller, James Miller, Ricky Ensley, Wanda Cisna. BS, Ball State U., 1956, MA, 1959; postgrad., Ind. U., Ft. Wayne. Tchr. 1st grade Union Twp. (Ind.) Pub. Schs., 1953-56, Wells City (Ind.) Pub. Schs., Forest Park Schs., Ft. Wayne, Ind., 1956-93. Docent Ft. Wayne Art Mus.; libr. Simpson United Meth. Ch., Ft. Wayne bd. dirs., mem. child care bd. Mem. Internat. Reading Assn., Ret. Ind. Tchrs. Assn., Ft. Wayne Ret. Tchrs. Assn. Home: 5108 E State Blvd Fort Wayne IN 46815-7467

PEASE, ROGER FABIAN WEDGWOOD, electrical engineering educator; b. Cambridge, Eng., Oct. 24, 1936; came to U.S., 1964; s. Michael Stewart and Helen Bowen (Wedgwood) P.; m. Caroline Ann Bowring, Sept. 17, 1960; children: Emma Ruth, Joseph Henry Bowring, James Edward. BA, Cambridge U., Eng., 1960, MA, 1964, PhD, 1964. Rsch. fellow Trinity Coll., Cambridge, 1963-64; asst. prof. U. Calif., Berkeley, 1964-67; mem. tech. staff AT&T Bell Labs., Murray Hill, N.J., 1967-78; prof. elec. engring. Stanford (Calif.) U., 1978—; cons. IBM, San Jose, Calif., 1964-67, Xerox Corp., Palo Alto, Calif., 1978-84, Perkin Elmer Co., Hayward, Calif., 1979-90, Lawrence Livermore (Calif.) Labs., 1984-92, Affymax Rsch. Inst., 1989-93, Affymetrix, 1993—; mem. tech. adv. bd. Ultratech Stepper, 1990—. Contbr. over 100 articles to profl. jours. Patentee (8) in field. Scoutmaster Boy Scouts Am., Holmdel, N.J., 1977-78. Pilot officer RAF, 1955-57. Fellow IEEE (Rappaport award 1982), San Jose Sailing Club. Avocations: sailboat racing, windsurfing. Home: 838 Esplanada Way Stanford CA 94305-1015 Office: Stanford U Dept Elec Engring Stanford CA 94305

PEASLAND, BRUCE RANDALL, financial executive; b. Buffalo, N.Y., Mar. 24, 1945; s. Kenneth Arthur and Edith Grace (Bristow) P.; m. Debra Myers Peasland, June 13, 1981; children: Michael John, Timothy Scott, Amanda Jean. BS, U. So. Calif., 1971, MBA in Fin., 1978; JD, Western St. U., 1983. Price and cost analyst McDonnell Douglas Corp., Long Beach, Calif., 1966-70; cost mgr. The Gillette Co., Santa Monica, Calif., 1971-78; controller Lear Siegler Inc., Santa Ana, Calif., 1978-85, British Petroleum,

Hitco, Newport Beach, Calif., 1986-87; v.p. fin., dir. Control Components Inc., Rancho Santa Margarita, Calif., 1987-90; chief fin. officer MacGillivray Freeman Films, Laguna Beach, Calif., 1990-91; exec. v.p., chief fin. officer Intervest Industries Inc, Carlsbad, Calif., 1992—. Youth advisor YMCA, Dana Point, Calif., 1985—. With USMC, 1963-69. Recipient of Mgr. of Yr. award Nat. Mgmt. Assn., 1984. Fellow U. So. Calif. MBA Assn.; mem. Nat. Assn. of Accts., Nat. Mgmt. Assn. (dir. 1978-85), U. So. Calif. Trojan Club, U. So. Calif. Alumni Club. Republican. Episcopalian. Avocations: sailing, snow skiing. Home: 25211 Yacht Dr Dana Point CA 92629-1439 Office: Intervest Industries Inc 7720B El Camino Real Ste 201 Carlsbad CA 92009

PEASLEE, JAMES M., lawyer; b. Scranton, Pa., Sept. 1, 1952; s. Robert Victor and Jean (Mark) P. BA, Yale U., 1973, MA, 1973; JD, Harvard U., 1976; LLM in Taxation, NYU, 1979. Bar: N.Y. 1977. Assoc. Cleary Gottlieb, Steen & Hamilton, N.Y.C., 1976-84, ptnr., 1984—. Office: Cleary Gottlieb Steen & Hamilton 1 Liberty Pla New York NY 10006

PEASLEE, MARGARET MAE HERMANEK, zoology educator; b. Chgo., June 15, 1935; d. Emil Frank and Magdalena Bessie (Cechota) Hermanek; m. David Raymond Peaslee, Dec. 6, 1957; 1 dau., Martha Magdalena Peaslee-Levine. A.A., Palm Beach Jr. Coll., 1956; B.S., Fla. So. Coll., 1959; med. technologist, Northwestern U., 1958, M.S., 1964, Ph.D., 1966. Med. technologist Passavant Hosp., Chgo., 1958-59; med. technologist St. James Hosp., Chicago Heights, Ill., 1960-63; asst. prof. biology Fla. So. Coll., Lakeland, 1966-68, U.S.D., Vermillion, 1968-71; assoc. prof. U.S.D., 1971-76, prof., 1976, acad. opportunity liaison, 1974-76; prof., head dept. zoology La. Tech. U., Ruston, 1976-90, assoc. dean, dir. grad. studies and rsch., prof. biol. scis. Coll. Life Scis., 1990-93; v.p. for acad. affairs U. Pitts. at Titusville, Pa., 1993—. Contbr. articles to profl. jours. Fellow AAAS; mem. AAUP, Am. Inst. Biol. Scis., Am. Soc. Zoologists, S.D. Acad. Sci. (sec.-treas. 1972-76), N.Y. Acad. Scis., Pa. Acad. Sci., La. Acad. Sci. (pres. 1979-81, pres. 1983), Sigma Xi, Phi Theta Kappa, Phi Rho Pi, Phi Sigma, Alpha Epsilon Delta. Office: U Pitts at Titusville Titusville PA 16354-0287

PEAT, RANDALL DEAN, defense analysis company executive, retired air force officer; b. Chicago, July 6, 1935; s. Thomas R. and Lulu M. (Ray) P.; m. Joyce Enid Hunter, Sept. 15, 1956; children—Brian James, Sondra Lee Peat Gadell. B.S. in Journalism, Medill Sch. Journalism Northwestern U., Evanston, Ill., 1956, M.S. in Journalism Mgmt., 1957. Commd. officer U.S. Air Force, 1957, advanced through ranks to maj. gen.; pilot, instr. Strategic Air Command, Westover AFB and Clinton-Sherman, Okla., 1958-66; asst. air attache Am. Embassy, Djakarta, Indonesia, 1967; pilot Pacific Command Airborne Command Post, Hickam AFB, Hawaii, 1968-70; staff officer 7th Air Force, Saigon, Vietnam, 1971, Hdqrs. U.S. Air Force, Pentagon, D.C., 1972-75, SHAPE, Belgium, 1976-79, Hdqrs. U.S. Air Force, Pentagon, D.C., 1980-81; dep. dir. plans Office Joint Chief of Staff, Pentagon, D.C., 1982-84; asst. chief of staff ops. Supreme Hdqrs. Allied Powers Europe, Belgium, 1984-87; chief of staff Strategic Air Command, Offutt AFB, Nebr., 1987-89; v.p. R&D Assocs., Europe, 1989—. Decorated Air medal, Bronze Star, Meritorious Service medal, Def. Superior Service medal, Def. Disting. Service medal; Republic of Vietnam Cross of Gallantry with Palm, Republic of Vietnam Campaign medal. Mem. Daedalians (vice flight capt. 1976), Air Force Assn., Pi Alpha Mu. Avocations: cooking; hiking; painting; British mystery writers. Home: Rue des Allies 43, B-7870 Lens Belgium also: LOGICON RDA 6053 W Century Blvd Los Angeles CA 90045-6430

PEATTIE, LISA REDFIELD, urban anthropology educator; b. Chgo., Mar. 1, 1924; d. Robert and Margaret (Park) Redfield; m. Roderick Peattie, June 26, 1943 (dec. 1962); children—Christopher, Sara, Miranda, Julia; m. William A. Doebele, 1973 (div.). M.A., U. Chgo., 1950, Ph.D., 1968. Faculty mem. dept. urban studies MIT, Cambridge, 1965—, prof. urban anthropology, 1968-85; now prof. emeritus, sr. lectr. MIT; cons. World Bank, 1975, 76, 81, UN, 1980. Author: The View from the Barrio, 1968, Thinking About Development, 1982, (with W. Ronco) Making Work, 1983, (with Martin Rein) Women's Claims, 1983, Planning: Rethinking Ciudad Guayana, 1987. Recipient Paul Davidoff award Am. Soc. Collegiate Schs. of Planning, 1989. Mem. Am. Anthrop. Assn., Soc. Applied Anthropology. Office: Dept Urban Studies MIT Cambridge MA 02139

PEAVEY, HARTLEY DAVIS, electronics company executive; b. Meridian, Miss., Dec. 30, 1941; s. Joseph B. and Sarah (Davis) P.; m. Melia McRae, Nov. 18, 1977; children: Joseph Thomas, Marcus Clinton. BS, Miss. State U., 1965. Founder, owner, pres. Peavey Electronics, Miss., 1965—, Corby, Eng., 1986—; mem. industry sector adv. com. on consumer goods for trade policy matters Commerce Dept., Washington, 1987—; mem. adv. bd. Musicfest U.S.A.; industry spokesman music and audio field, mktg. and internat. trade. matters. Mem. Lauderdale County Econ. Devel. Authority, 1984-90; mem. adv. bd. Meridian Mcpl. Airport, 1986-90; mem. corp. sponsor Miss. World's Fair Council, 1984. Served with Miss. NG, 1965-71. Recipient Pres.'s "E" award for exports U.S. Commerce Dept., 1978, Indsl. Glove award Gov. of Miss., 1980, Nat. Heritage award Queen City Sertoma Club, 1982, Presdl. "E Star" award for excellence in exporting, 1985, Miss. Export Excellence award 1983, 86; honored as one of 84 most notable people in State of Miss., Miss. Mag., 1983; named Patron of Excellence Miss. State U., 1982, Mississippian of Yr. Miss. Broadcasting Assn., 1984, Man of Yr. Meridian Star, 1984, Outstanding Alumnus of Yr. Miss. Assn. Vocat. Edu-cators, 1985, Capts. of Industry tribute State of Miss. Jackson Bus. Jour., 1988; Ann. Hartley Peavey Day named in his honor, Apr. 20, 1982, Mer-idian; inducted Rock Walk of Fame, Hollywood, Calif., 1990, Jr. Achieve-ment Miss. Bus. Hall of Fame, 1990; Hartley Peavey Entrepreneurial award established in hisname bus. com. Meridian/Lauderdale C of C., 1989, Har-tley D. Peavey Auditorium named in his honor Ross Collin's Vocat. Sch., 1989. Mem. Nat. Assn. Musical Mchts. (bar code com. 1989, inducted Hall of Fame 1988), Nat. Assn. Mfrs. (state dir. 1989-90), Meridian Mfrs. Assn., Am. Music Conf. (bd. dirs. 1986-87), Audio Engring. Soc., Creative Audio & Music Electronics Orgn. (bd. dirs.), Nat. Assn. Young Music Merchants (hon.), City of Morton C. of C. (bd. dirs.), Nat. Assn. Young Music Merchants (hon.), City of Morton C. of C., City of Decatur C. of C., Meridian C. of C. Office: Peavey Electronics Co PO Box 2898 711 A St Meridian MS 39301-5422

PEAVEY, MELIA MCRAE, electronics company executive; b. Meridian, Miss., Aug. 18, 1954; d. John L. McRae, Jr. and Doris (Hagwood) Good-man; m. Hartley D. Peavey, Nov. 18, 1977; children—Joseph Thomas, Marcus Clinton. Vice pres. Peavey Electronics Corp., Meridian, 1980—; pres. Audio Media Research, Meridian, 1980—, PV Fin., Meridian, 1984—, D & D Trucking; bd. dirs. First United Bank, Meridian, 1982—. Bd. dirs. Jr. Achievement, Meridian, 1983, Blood Services, Meridian, 1984—. Republican. Baptist. Office: Peavey Electronics Corp 711 A St PO Box 2898 Meridian MS 39302

PEAVLER, NANCY JEAN, editor; b. Kansas City, Mo., Dec. 19, 1951; d. Elmer Alfred and Ruth Lenoris (Peterson) Zimmerli; m. Craig Eugene Peavler, Dec. 6, 1975; 1 child, Matthew Dean. Assoc., Kansas City (Kans.) Community Coll., 1976. Staff writer The Kansas City Kansan, 1972-73; assoc. editor Capper's Stauffer Communications, Topeka, 1976-87, editor, 1987—. Precinct com.-woman Shawnee County Rep. Party, Topeka, 1985-87. Mem. Women in Communications (chair chpt. publicity, chair freedom of info. com. 1991-92, v.p membership/recruitment 1992-93), Beta SIgma Phi (sec. 1978-79, chpt. v.p. 1979-80). United Methodist. Office: Capper's 1503 SW 42nd St Topeka KS 66609

PEAVY, ROBERT A., lawyer; b. Apr. 7, 1938. BA, U. Colo., 1961; JD, U. Tex., 1966. Bar: D.C. 1967, U.S. Supreme Ct. 1971, U.S. Claims Ct. 1988. Ptnr. Morgan, Lewis & Bockius, Washington. Mem. European Maritime Law Orgn. (dir. 1991—). Office: Morgan Lewis & Bockius 1800 M St NW Washington DC 20036-5869

PECANO, DONALD CARL, truck, trailer and railcar manufacturing ex-ecutive; b. Los Angeles, Dec. 2, 1948; s. Domenick Lawrence and Carlotta Noble (Martello) P.; m. Sandra Ann Tuminello, Apr. 26, 1969; children: Julie Ann, Melissa Ann, Donald Carl. B.S. in Acctg, Pa. State U., 1970; M.B.A. in Mktg. Youngstown State U., 1981; postgrad., Case Western Res. U., 1995. C.P.A., Pa. Contr. Atlas Guard Service subs. SERVISCO, East Orange, N.J., 1974-76; asst. to pres. SERVISCO, Hillside, N.J., 1976-77; v.p fin. Columbus Svcs., Inc. subs. SERVISCO, New Castle, Pa., 1977-82; dir.

fin. East Mfg. Corp. and subs. cos., 1982-88, v.p.fin. and adminstrn., 1988—, also mem. exec. com.; v.p fin. Intermodal Techs. Inc., 1991—; v.p. East Railcar Corporation, 1993—; Weatherhead profl. fellow Case Western Res. U., 1995. Weatherhead profl. fellow Soc. Case Western Res. U., 1995. Republican. Roman Catholic. Office: 1871 State Route 44 Randolph OH 44265 *Placing the best interests of the company ahead of your own is ultimately in your own best interest.*

PECCARELLI, ANTHONY MARANDO, judge; b. Newark, Apr. 12, 1928; s. Adolph and Mary (Marano) P.; m. Mary Dearborn Hutchinson, Dec. 23, 1953; children: Andrew Louis, David Anthony, Laura Elizabeth. BS, Beloit Coll., 1953; JD, John Marshall Law Sch., 1959; M in Jud. Studies, U. Nev., 1990. Bar: Ill. 1961, U.S. Dist. Ct. (no. dist.) Ill., U.S. Supreme Ct. Supr. real estate and claims Gulf Oil Corp., Chgo., 1956-61; asst. state's atty. DuPage County, Wheaton, Ill., 1961-65; first asst. state's atty. DuPage County State's Atty., Wheaton, Ill., 1965-69; mem.-del. Ill. Constnl. Conv., Springfield, 1969-70; exec. dir. Ill. State's Atty. Assn. Elgin, 1970-71; ptnr. Barclay, Damisch & Sinson, Chgo., 1971-79; assoc. cir. judge 18th Jud. Cir. Ct., Wheaton, 1979-82; cir. judge, 1982-93; chief judge 18th Jud. Cir. Ct., Wheaton, 1989-93; cir. judge State of Ill., Wheaton, 1982-93; presiding judge domestic rels. divsn., 1982-83, presiding judge law divsn., 1987-89; chief judge 18th Judicial Cir., 1989-93; justice 2nd dist. Ill. Appellate Ct., Wheaton, 1993—; chair Ill. Jud. Conf. Ill. Supreme Ct., Springfield, 1987-89. Contbr. articles to profl. jours. Bd. dirs., treas. DuPage Coun. for Child Devel.; bd. dirs. Ctrl. DuPage Pastoral Counseling Ctr.; chair Wheaton Com. for Jud. Reform, 1962; trustee Midwestern U., 1993—. Cpl. USMC, 1946-48. Mem. DuPage County Bar Assn. (pres. 1972-73), DuPage County Legal Assistance Fedn. (pres. 1973-74), DuPage County Lawyer Referral Svc. (pres. 1972),. Congregationalist. Office: Ill Appellate Ct 211 S Wheaton Ave Wheaton IL 60187-5251

PECHILIS, WILLIAM JOHN, lawyer; b. Brockton, Mass., May 13, 1924; s. John and Kaleroe (Karmeris) P.; m. Kay Dillon, June 7, 1958; children: Julie W., Karen P., John D. Ba, Harvard U., 1946, LLB, 1951. Bar: Mass. 1951. Law clk. to assoc. justice Supreme Judicial Ct., Boston, 1951-52; assoc. Goodwin, Procter and Hoar, Boston, 1952-61, ptnr., 1961-94, of counsel, 1995—. Trustee Concord (Mass.) Acad., 1978-80, Wang Inst. Grad. Studies, Tyngsboro, Mass., 1979-87, Wang Ctr. for Performing Arts, 1983—, Anatolia Coll., Boston, 1984-91; mem. fin. com. Weston, Mass., 1972-74. With USNR, 1943-46, PTO. Fellow Am. Coll. Trust and Estate Counsel; mem. ABA, Mass. Bar Assn., Boston Bar Assn., Harvard Club, Weston Golf Club, Woods Hole Golf Club, Phi Beta Kappa. Avocation: golf. Home: 101 Ash St Weston MA 02193-1940 Office: Goodwin Procter and Hoar Exchange Pl Boston MA 02109-2808

PECHUKAS, PHILIP, chemistry educator; b. Akron, Ohio, Oct. 30, 1942; s. Alphonse and Evelyn (Grebenak) P.; children: Rolf Birkhoff, Maria Ber-enson, Sarah Landau, Fiona Veronese, Amy Hayes. BS, Yale U., 1963; PhD, U. Chgo., 1966. Asst. prof. chemistry Columbia U., N.Y.C., 1967-72, assoc. prof., 1972-78, prof., 1978—, chmn. dept. chemistry, 1984-87. Contbr. articles to profl. jours. Fellow Nat. Bur. Standards, 1966-67, Alfred P. Sloan Found., 1970-74, J.S. Guggenheim Found., 1975, Haverford Coll. 1985. Fellow Am. Phys. Soc.; mem. Am. Chem. Soc. (chmn. theoretical chemistry subdivision 1985-86), Humboldt Sen. Scientist, 1993-94. Office: Columbia U Dept Chemistry 116th St and Broadway New York NY 10027

PECK, ABRAHAM, editor, writer, educator, magazine consultant; b. N.Y.C., Jan. 18, 1945; s. Jacob and Lottie (Bell) Peckolick; m. Suzanne Wexler, Mar. 19, 1977; children: Douglas Benjamin, Robert Wexler. B.A., N.Y. U., 1965; postgrad., CUNY, 1965-67. Engaged in community or-ganizing and tutoring, 1962-64; with N.Y.C. Welfare Dept., 1965-67; free-lance writer, 1967—; writer, organizer Chgo. Action Youth Internat. Party, 1968; editor Chgo. Seed, 1968-70; treas. Seed Pub., Inc., 1968-70; mem. coordinating com. Underground Press Syndicate, 1969; assoc. editor Rolling Stone mag., San Francisco, 1975, contbg. editor, from 1976; cons. various mags., 1984—; ednl. cons. Asian Sources Media Group, Hong Kong, Manila, 1989—; feature writer Chgo. Daily News, 1977-78; with features dept. Chgo. Sun-Times, 1978-81; from asst. prof. to assoc. prof. Medill Sch. Journalism, Northwestern U., 1981-92, prof., 1992—, dir. M.S.J. mag. pub. program, 1982—, chmn. mag. program, 1988—, mem. sch. ops. com., 1990—, dir. Nat. Arts Journalism Program, 1993—; critic at large Sta. WBBM, 1979-82; editor, co-founder Sidetracks, alt. newspaper supplement, Chgo. Daily News, 1977-78; mem. exec. com. Assn. for Edn. in Journalism and Mass Communication, Mag. div., 1987-89, 1992—, pres., 1994—; mem. adv. bd. Academe Mag., Am. Assn. Univ. Profs., 1990—, Heartland Jour., 1990—, Technos, 1992. Editor: Dancing Madness, 1976; author: Uncovering the Sixties: The Life and Times of the Underground Press, 1985, 91; cons. editor, contbr.: The Sixties, 1977; contbr.: The Eighties: A Look Back, 1979, Voices From the Underground, 1993. Served with AUS, 1967. Office: Northwestern U Medill Sch Journalism 1845 Sheridan Rd Evanston IL 60201-5004

PECK, ABRAHAM JOSEPH, historian; b. Landsberg, Fed. Republic of Germany, May 4, 1946; came to U.S., 1949.; s. Shalom W. and Anna (Koltun) P.; m. Jean Marcus, June 21, 1969; children: Abby, Joel. BA, Am. U., 1968, MA, 1970; PhD, U. East Anglia, Eng., 1977; postgrad., U. Hamburg, Fed. Republic Germany, 1973-74. Adminstrv. dir. Am. Jewish Archives, Cin., 1976—; lectr. in Judaic studies U. Cin., 1980—; mem. in-ternat. adv. bd. Internat. Ctr. for Holocaust Studies, 1986—; mem. adv. bd. Nat. Cath. Inst. for Holocaust Studies, 1988—; founding mem. Greater Cin. Interfaith Holocaust Found., 1986—. Author: Radicals and Reactionaries, 1978; editor Jews and Christians After the Holocaust, 1982; co-editor Am. Rabbinate: A Century of Continuity and Change 1883-1983, 1985, Studies in the American Jewish Experience II, 1984, Queen City Refuge: An Oral History of Cincinnati's Jewish Refugees from Nazism, 1989, Sephardim in the Americas: Studies in Culture and History, 1993; editor The German-Jewish Legacy in America: From Bildung to the Bill of Rights, 1989, Selected Documents of World Jewish Congress, 1939-50, 2 vols., 1991; contbr. articles to profl. jours. Spl. advisor U.S. Holocaust Meml. Coun., Washington, 1982-86; bd. dirs. Am. Jewish Com., Cin., 1978-84, Anti-Defamation League of Ohio, Ind. and Ken., Columbus, 1982-86, Jewish Community Rels. Coun., Cin., 1980-86; mem. Am. Hist. Found., Orgn. Am. Historians. Fullbright Found. fellow, 1973-74; Ohio Program in the Humanities grantee, 1980, 83, 85. Mem. Assn. Jewish Studies, Soc. for Scholarly Pub., Soc. of Am. Archivists. Avocations: travel, raising dogs. Office: Am Jewish Archives 3101 Clifton Ave Cincinnati OH 45220-2404

PECK, ALEXANDER NORMAN, physical education educator, day camp administrator; b. Akron, Ohio, Sept. 6, 1934; s. Kenneth Owen and Elizabeth (Leckie) P.; m. Joan katherine Lombardi, Oct. 19, 1958; children: Alexander Norman II, Gregory C., Glenn P., Douglas A. BS, SUNY, Cortland, 1957, MA, NYU, 1988. Tchr. phys. edn. Hewlet-Woodmere (N.Y.) Schs., 1959-60, Syosset (N.Y.) Pub. Schs., 1960-62, North St. Elem. Sch., White Plains, N.Y., 1962-68; tchr., chair dept., coord. athletics, coach football and wrestling Highlands Jr. High Sch., White Plains, 1968-79; tchr. phys. edn., team leader White Plains Middle Sch., 1979—; group leader Mohawk Day Camps, White Plains, 1960-69, dir. boys program, 1970-87, asst. dir. camp., 1988—. Cub Master Boy Scouts Am., Mamaroneck, N.Y., asst. dist. commr., White Plains; chair site utilization com. Rye Neck Schs., Mamaroneck; active White Plains PTA (Svc. award 1963). Mem. Am. Assn. Health, Phys. Edn., Recreation and Dance, N.Y. State Assn. Health, Phys. Edn., Recreation and Dance (zone pres., chair state legislature), N.Y. State Tchrs. Assn. (zone v.p.), N.Y. State United Tchrs., N.Y. State High Sch. Athletic Assn. (zone chair modified sports, svc. award), White Plains Tchrs. Assn. (treas. 1966-68), Am. Camping Assn. (presenter tri state camping conv. 1986, 89, 93, 94). Avocations: antiques, photography, military history. Home: 1 Overdale Rd Rye NY 10580-1022 Office: White Plains Middle Sch 128 Grandview Ave White Plains NY 10605-3225

PECK, ARTHUR JOHN, JR., diversified manufacturing executive; b. Trenton, N.J., Mar. 2, 1940; s. Arthur John and Mary Ellen (Kelly) P.; m. Susan Williams Lodge, July 18, 1970; children: David A., Margaret E. BA in Hist., Yale U., 1962; LLB, Washington & Lee U., 1968. Lawrenceville Sch., N.J., 1962-65; Atty. Shearman & Sterling, N.Y.C., 1968-72; asst., assoc. counsel Corning (N.Y.), Inc., 1972-81, asst. sec., 1981-88, sec., 1988—; sec. Teddington Co. Ltd., Corning Inc. Found., Corning Europe, Inc., Corning

Inc., Corning Internat. Corp.; dir., sec. Corning Fgn. Sales Corp., Watkins Glen Internat., Inc., Corning Classic Charities, Inc.; asst. sec. Corning Enterprises, Inc., Corning Mus. Glass, Market St. Restoration Corp.; trustee, sec. The Rockwell Mus.; dir. Wislan, S.A. Office: Corning Inc Riverfront Plaza Corning NY 14831

PECK, AUSTIN H., JR., lawyer; b. Pomona, Calif., Dec. 25, 1913; s. Austin H. and Helen (Templeton) P.; m. Jean Albertson, Nov. 9, 1939; children: Julie, Francesca, Lisa, P. Lindelef. A.B. with distinction, Stanford, 1935, J.D., 1938. Bar: Calif. 1938. Since practiced in Los Angeles; mem. firm Latham & Watkins, 1946-76, of counsel, 1976-92. Trustee emeritus Orthopaedic Hosp. L.A.; nat. coun. House Ear Inst.; trustee Cancer Found. Santa Barbara, Calif. Mem. Am., Calif., Los Angeles bar assns., Zeta Psi, Phi Delta Phi. Clubs: California (Los Angeles), Los Angeles Country (Los Angeles); Birnam Wood (Montecito, (Calif.), Valley (Montecito, (Calif.); Sunset, Chancery, Cypress Point. Home: 770 San Ysidro Ln Santa Barbara CA 93108-1323 Office: 633 W 5th St Los Angeles CA 90071-2005

PECK, BERNARD SIDNEY, lawyer; b. Bridgeport, Conn., July 26, 1915; s. James and Sadie P.; m. Marjorie Eloise Dean, Apr. 10, 1943; children: Daniel Dean, Constance Lynn. B.A., Yale U., 1936, LL.B., 1939. Bar: Conn. 1939, Fla. 1979, N.Y. 1982. Pvt. practice Bridgeport 1939-84; ptnr. Goldstein and Peck, 1946-84; judge Mcpl. Ct., Westport, Conn., 1951-55; ptnr. Peck & Peck, Naples, Fla., 1983-87, Porter, Wright, Morris & Arthur, Naples, 1987-90, Peck, Peck & Volpe, Naples, 1990-92, Peck, Volpe & Sul-livan, Naples, 1992-94; Peck & Skrivan, Naples, 1994—. Moderator town meeting, Westport, 1950-51; mem. Westport Republican Town Com., 1951-79; pres. Westport YMCA, 1957, trustee, 1964-84; pres. endowment bd. YMCA Naples, 1987-88. Capt. AUS, 1942-46. Fellow Am. Coll. Trial Lawyers, Internat. Acad. Trial Lawyers; mem. ABA, Collier County Bar Assn., Phi Beta Kappa. Clubs: Linville (N.C.) Ridge Country; Royal Poin-ciana Golf (dir. 1983-90, pres. 1987-93), Yale (trustee 1985—) (Naples, Fla.). Home: 4951 Gulf Shore Blvd N Apt 202 Naples FL 33940-2685 Office: Peck & Skrivan Ste 103 5801 Pelican Bay Blvd Naples FL 33963 also: 21 Crest Trl Linville Ridge NC

PECK, CAROL FAULKNER, poet, writer, publisher, educator; b. Detroit, June 20, 1934; d. Edward Carroll and Barbara Ann (Fite) Faulkner; m. Lawrence David Peck, Dec. 18, 1954; children: David Edward Peck, Wendy Carol Peck Webster. BA in English, U. Mich., 1958; MA in English, U. Md., 1964; postgrad. in Teaching Creative Writing, U. Denver, 1977. Artist-in-edn. Md. State Arts Coun., Balt., 1971—; lectr. in English U. Md. Univ. Coll., Coll. Park, Md., 1971—; writer in residence Sidwell Friends Sch., Washington, D.C., 1978-91; poetry workshop leader Montgomery County Pub. Schs. Alternative Programs, Rockville, Md., 1978—; leader numerous poetry and writing workshops for ednl. and other audiences, 1971—; editl. bd. Md. Engring. Jour., 1968-84; edited novels and dissertations for writers of same; owner carolpeck prodns., pacem Press. Author: From Deep Within, 1989; contbr. numerous articles to ednl. jours., poems to poetry and literary mags. Vol. poetry workshop leader Bethesda Retirement and Nursing Ctr., Chevy Chase, Md., 1978-91; judge numerous sch. and lit. groups poetry and writing contests; vol. Hospice Caring, Inc., 1994—. Assembly scholar U. Mich., 1953; recipient Hopwood award, 1953, first prize sonnet div. Alex-andria Br., Nat. League of Am. PEN Women, 1984, Disting. Achievement award Ednl. Press Assn. Am., 1989, Excellence in Teaching award U. Md./ U. Coll., 1993. Mem. Writers Ctr., Md. Coun. Tchrs. of English Lang. Arts, Internat. Women's Writing Guild, Alpha Lambda Delta, Phi Beta Kappa, Phi Kappa Phi. Home and Office: 14910 Brownstone Dr Burtonsville MD 20866-1849

PECK, CHARLES EDWARD, retired construction and mortgage executive; b. Newark, Dec. 1, 1925; s. Hubert Raymond and Helen (White) P.; m. Delphine Murphy, Oct. 15, 1949; children: Margaret Peck Iovino, Charles Edward, Katherine Peck Koustmer, Perry Anne Peck Flanagan. Grad., Phillips Acad., 1943; student, MIT, 1944; BS, U. Pa., 1949. With Owens-Corning Fiberglas Corp., various locations, 1949-61; sales mgr. home bldg. products Owens-Corning Fiberglas Corp., Toledo, 1961-66; v.p. home bldg. products mktg. div. Owens-Corning Fiberglas Corp., 1966-68, v.p. construction group, 1968-75, v.p. bldg. materials group, 1976-78, exec. v.p., 1978-81, bd. dir.; co-chmn. The Ryland Group, Columbia, Md., 1981-82; chmn., chief exec. officer The Ryland Group, Columbia, Md., 1982-90; dir. The Delaware Group of Funds, 1991—; sec. Enterprise Homes, Inc., 1992—; mem. statutory vis. com. U.S. Nat. Bur. Standards, 1972-77; mem. adv. com. Fed. Nat. Mortgage Assn., 1977-78, 85-86; mem. vis. com. MIT-Harvard Joint Ctr. for Urban Studies; chmn. Prodrs. Adv. Forum, 1977-81. Mem. vis. com. Harvard U. Grad. Sch. Design, 1981-86; chmn. Howard County United Way Campaign, Md., 1987, chmn. community partnerships, 1991-94; bd. dirs. Nat. Inst. for Urban Wildlife, 1986-90, United Way Cen. Md., 1987-91, Howard County Gen. Hosp., 1988-94, Columbia Festival, Inc., 1988-91, NAHB Rsch. Found., 1989-92, Alliance to End Childhood Lead Poisoning, 1990-93; mem. adv. bd. U. Md. Engring. Sch., 1990—; mem. adv. bd. continuing edn. Johns Hopkins U., 1988-91; mem. policy adv. bd. Harvard Joint Ctr. Housing Studies, 1984-94; chmn. chancellor's adv. coun. U. Md. System, 1988—; chmn. Univ. Md. Found., 1990-94, bd. dirs., 1990—; exec. fellow Kennedy Sch., Harvard U., 1990-92; chmn. Affordable Housing Ini-tiative, Columbia, Md., 1990-92; bd. overseers U. Md., College Park, 1994—; mem. Victory '94 com. Md. State Rep. Party, chmn. election inquiry funding com., 1994-95. 2d lt. USAAF, 1944-46. Mem. U.S.C. of C. (bd. dirs. 1975-81), Ohio C. of C. (bd. dirs. 1975-81), Depressiona and Related Affective Disorders Assn. (pres. 1986-89, bd. dirs. 1986—, pres. 1993-94), Rotary of Columbia, Talbot Country Club, City Club, Ctr. Club, Caves Valley Gold Club, Phi Gamma Delta. Home: 7649 Woodstream Way Laurel MD 20723-1163 Office: PO Box 1108 Columbia MD 21044-0102

PECK, DALLAS LYNN, retired geologist; b. Cheney, Wash., Mar. 28, 1929; s. Lynn Averill and Mary Hazel (Carlyle) P.; m. Tevis Sue Lewis, Mar. 28, 1951 (dec.); children: Ann, Stephen, Gerritt. B.S., Calif. Inst. Tech., 1951, M.S., 1953; Ph.D., Harvard U., 1960. With U.S. Geol. Survey, 1954-95; asst. chief geologist, office of geochemistry and geophysics U.S. Geol. Survey, Washington, 1967-72, geologist, geologic div., 1972-77, chief geolo-gist, 1977-81, dir. 1981-93, geologist, 1993-95, emeritus scientist, 1995—; mem. Lunar Sample Rev. Bd., 1970-71; chmn. earth scis. adv. com. NSF, 1970-72; vis. com. dept. geol. scis. Harvard U., 1972-78; mem. Earthscis. Adv. Bd., Stanford U., 1982-93; chmn. com. earth scis. Fed. Coord. Coun. Sci., Enring. and Tech., 1987-92; mem. sci., tech. com. UN Decade for Nat. Disaster Reduction, 1992-94. Recipient Meritorious Svc. award Dept. Interior, 1971, Disting. Svc. award, 1979; Presdl. Meritorious Exec. award, 1980, Disting. Alumni award Calif. Inst. Tech., 1985, Ian Campbell medal Am. Geol. Inst., 1994. Fellow AAAS, Geol. Soc. Am., Am. Geophys. Union (pres. sect. volcanology, geochemistry and petrology 1976-78). Home: 2524 Heathcliff Ln Reston VA 22091-4225

PECK, DANIEL FARNUM, chemical company executive; b. Port Jervis, N.Y., Aug. 6, 1927; s. John Flint and Frances Ann (Farnum) P.; m. Ardyce Chase Hoover, July 14, 1951 (dec. July 1979); children: Cheryl H. Gerber, Daniel Farnum Jr., Laurie A. Peck Perry; m. Barbara Ann Gunning Gil-linder, Sept. 5, 1980. BSchemE, Clarkson U., 1950. Field engr. Rsch. Corp., Bound Brook, N.J., 1950-51; process devel. engring. supr. Nat. Starch and Chem. Corp., Plainfield, N.J., 1951-55, prodn. dept. head, 1955-60; div. supr. Nat. Starch and Chem. Corp., Indpls., 1960-67; plant and mfg. mgr. Nat. Starch and Chem. Corp., Meredosia, Ill., 1967-72, dir. mfg., 1972-76, div. v.p., 1976-80, corp. v.p., 1980-84, group v.p., 1984-89, ret., 1989; also bd. dirs. Nat. Starch and Chem. Corp., Bridgewater, N.J. Mem. Envelope Mfrs. Assn., Soc. Chem. Industry, Adhesive Mfrs. Assn., Adhesive Sealant Coun. (pres. edn. found., bd. dirs.). Avocations: boating, golf, bridge, hunting, fishing.

PECK, DEANA S., lawyer; b. Wichita, Kans., Nov. 6, 1947; d. Richard Rector Williams and Elva Alene (Davis) Williams; m. Frederick Page Peck, June 16, 1967 (div. Nov. 1981); 1 child, Paige. BA, Wichita State U., 1970; JD, U. Kans., 1975. Bar: Ariz. 1975, U.S. Dist. Ct. Ariz. 1975, U.S. Ct. Appeals (9th cir.) 1981, U.S. Ct. Appeals (10th cir.) 1990, U.S. Ct. Appeals (fed. cir.) 1991. Assoc. Streich Lang, Phoenix, 1975-80, ptnr., 1980—; vis. lectr. U. Kans. Sch. of Law, Lawrence, 1985. Mem. ABA, Maricopa County Bar Assn., State Bar Ariz. (antitrust coun.), Kans. U. Law Soc. (bd. govs. 1980-82). Office: Renaissance One 2 N Central Ave Phoenix AZ 85004-2391

PECK, DIANNE KAWECKI, architect; b. Jersey City, June 13, 1945; d. Thaddeus Walter and Harriet Ann (Zlotkowski) Kawecki; m. Gerald Paul Peck, Sept. 1, 1968; children: Samantha Gillian, Alexis Hilary. BArch, Carnegie-Mellon U., 1968. Architect, P.O.D. Research & Devel., 1968, Kohler-Daniels & Assocs., Vienna, Va., 1969-71, Beery-Rio & Assocs., Annandale, Va., 1971-73; ptnr. Peck & Peck Architects, Occoquan, Va., 1973-74, Peck, Peck & Williams, Occoquan, 1974-81; corp. officer Peck Peck & Assocs., Inc., Woodbridge, Va., 1981—; chief exec. officer, interior design group Peck Peck & Assoc., 1988—. Work pub. in Am. Architecture, 1985. Vice pres. Vocat. Edn. Found., 1976; chairwoman architects and engrs. United Way; mem. Health Systems Agy. of No. Va., commendations, 1977; mem. Washington Profl. Women's Coop.; chairwoman Indsl. Devel. Authority of Prince William, 1976, vice chair, 1977, mem., 1975-79; developer research project Architecture for Adolescents, 1987-88; mem. inaugural class Leadership Am., 1988, Leadership Greater Washington; mem. D.C. Coun. Metrication, 1992—, D.C. Hist. Preservation League, Rep. Nat. Com. Recipient commendation Prince William Bd. Suprs., 1976, State of Art award for Contel Hdqrs. design, 1985, Best Middle Sch. award Coun. of Ednl. Facilities Planners Internat., 1989, Creativity award Masonry Inst. Md., 1990, First award, 1990, Detailing award, 1990, Govt. Workplace award for renovations of Dept. of Labor Bldg., 1990, Creative Use of Materials award Inst. of Bus. Designers, 1991, 1st award Brick Inst. Md., 1993, award Brick Inst. Va., 1994; named Best Instl. Project Nat. Comml. Builders Coun.; subject of PBS spl.: A Success in Howard Co. Mem. Soc. Am. Mil. Engrs., Prince William C. of C. (bd. dir.). Republican. Roman Catholic. Club: Soroptimist. Research on inner-city rehab., adolescents and the ednl. environ. Office: 2050 Old Bridge Rd Woodbridge VA 22192

PECK, DONALD VINCENT, musician; b. Yakima, Wash., Jan. 26, 1930; s. Clarence Leon and Bertha A. (Compin) P. Diploma in Music, Curtis Inst. Music, 1951; student, Seattle U., 1948-49. With Seattle Symphony Orch., 1947-49, Nat. Symphony Orch., Washington, 1951-52; prin. flutist Kansas City Philharmonic Orch., 1955-57, Chgo. Symphony Orch., 1957—; instr. flute and woodwind ensemble DePaul U., Chgo.; guest soloist with various orchs. Served with USMCR, 1952-55. Office: care Chgo Symphony Orch 220 S Michigan Ave Chicago IL 60604-2508 also: Parsons Artists Mgmt PO Box 160 Highland Park IL 60035-0160*

PECK, EDWARD LIONEL, retired foreign service officer, corporate executive; b. Los Angeles, Mar. 6, 1929; s. Alexander George and Rae (Lee) P.; m. Heather Dianne Hicks-Beach, Jan. 20, 1957 (div. July 1971); m. Ann Day Slevin, May 5, 1974; children—Heather Anne, Brian Michael, Thomas William, Julia Katherine. B.S., UCLA, 1956; M.B.A., George Washington U., 1973. Joined Fgn. Service Dept. State, Washington, 1957, intelligence specialist, 1968-71, spl. asst., 1971-74; econ. counselor U.S. Embassy, Cairo, 1974-77; chief of mission U.S. Interests Sect., Baghdad, Iraq, 1977-80; dir. Office of Egyptian affairs Washington, 1980-82; ambassador U.S. Embassy, Nouakchott, Mauritania, 1983-85; dep. dir. Vice Pres.' Task Force on Combatting Terrorism, 1985-86; dir. Office of Career Transition, 1986-88; ret., 1989; pres. Fgn. Svcs. Internat., 1989—; exec. sec. Am. Acad. Diplomacy, 1989-92; trainer, lectr., cons. on fgn. affairs, internat. bus., 1990—; dir. polit. tradecraft program Nat. Fgn. Affairs Tng. Ctr., Arlington, Va., 1991—; sr. assoc. Global Bus. Access Ltd., Washington, 1991—; Woodrow Wilson vis. fellow, 1993—. Served to capt. U.S. Army, 1946-49, 50-52. Recipient Meritorious Honor award Dept. State, 1967, 73, 77, 79, Superior Honor award Dept. State, 1974, 88, Wilbur J. Carr award, 1989; Rivkin award Am. Fgn. Svc. Assn., 1973. Home and Office: 106 Grafton St Bethesda MD 20815-3426

PECK, EDWIN RUSSELL, real estate management executive; b. Akron, Ohio, Aug. 19, 1931; s. Roy Zola and Mary Susan (Snyder) P.; m. Lou Ellen Smith, Oct. 28, 1949; children—Edwin Russell, Lori Rae. B.S. in Gen. Bus., San Diego State U., 1957. Mortgage trainee South Pacific Corp., San Diego, 1957-58; asst. sec., loan officer Southland Savs., Lamesa, Calif., 1958-60; supr. Phoenix Mut. Life Ins. Co., Hartford, Conn., 1960-63; v.p. comml. loan T.J. Bettes Co., Houston, 1963-68; sr. v.p. comml. loan Am. Mortgage Co., Houston, 1968-72; sr. v.p. real estate S.C.I., Houston, 1972-87, cons., 1987—. Served with USN, 1949-52; Japan/Korea. Republican. Presbyterian. Home: 11738 Oak Valley Dr Houston TX 77065-2937 Office: Service Corp Internat 1929 Allen Pky Houston TX 77019-2506

PECK, ELLIE ENRIQUEZ, retired state administrator; b. Sacramento, Oct. 21, 1934; d. Rafael Enriquez and Eloisa Garcia Rivera; m. Raymond Charles Peck, Sept. 5, 1957; children: Reginaldo, Enrico, Francisca Guerrero, Teresa, Linda, Margaret, Raymond Charles, Christina. Student polit. sci. Sacramento State U., 1974. Tng. services coord. Calif. Div. Hwys., Sacramento, 1963-67; tech. and mgmt. cons., Sacramento, 1968-78; expert examiner Calif. Pers. Bd., 1976-78; tng. cons. Calif. Pers. Devel. Ctr., Sacramento, 1978; spl. cons. Calif. Commn. on Fair Employment and Housing, 1978; community svcs. rep. U.S. Bur. of Census, No. Calif. counties, 1978-80; spl. cons. Calif. Dept. Consumer Affairs, Sacramento, 1980-83, project dir. Golden State Sr. Program, 1980-83; dir. spl. programs for Calif. Lt. Gov., 1983-90, ret., 1990; pvt. cons., 1990—; cons., project dir. nat. sr. health issues summit Congress Calif. Srs. Edn. and Rsch. Fund, 1995; project dir. SSI/QMB Outreach Project, 1993-94. Author Calif. Dept. Consumer Affairs publ., 1981, U.S. Office Consumer Edn. publ., 1982. Bd. dirs Sacramento/Sierra Am. Diabetes Assn., 1989-90. Author: Diabetes and Ethnic Minorities: A Community at Risk. Trustee, Stanford Settlement, Inc., Sacramento, 1975-79; bd. dirs. Sacramento Emergency Housing Ctr., 1974-77, Sacramento Community Svcs. Planning Coun., 1987-90; v.p. Calif. Advs. for Nursing Home Reform, 1990—; v.p. bd. dirs. Calif. Advocates; campaign workshop dir. Chicano/Latino Leadership Conf., 1982-95; v.p. Comision Femenil Nacional, Inc., 1987-90; del. Dem. Nat. Conv., 1976; mem. exec. bd. Calif. Dem. Cen. Com., 1977-89; chairperson ethnic minority task force Am. Diabetes Assn., 1988-90; steering com. Calif. Self-Esteem Minority Task Force, 1990-93. Recipient numerous awards including Outstanding Community Svc. award Comuicaciones Unidos de Norte Atzlan, 1975, 77, Outstanding Svc. award, Chicano/Hispanic Dem. Caucus, 1979, Vol. Svc. award Calif. Human Devel. Corp., 1981, Dem. of Yr. award Sacramento County Dem. Com., 1987, Outstanding Advocate award Calif. Sr. Legis., 1988, 89, Calif. Assn. of Homes for Aging, Advocacy award, 1989, Resolution of Advocacy award, League Latin-Ams. Citizens, 1989, Meritorious Svc. to Hispanic Community award Comite Patriotico, 1989, Meritorious Svc. Resolution award Lt. Gov. of Calif., 1989, Cert. Recognition award Sacramento County Human Rights Commn., 1991, Tish Sommers award Older Women's League/Joint Resolution Calif. Legislature, 1993, Latino Eagle award in govt. Tomas Lopez Meml. Found., 1994. Mem. Hispanic C. of C., CongressCalif. Srs.; Sacramento Gray Panthers, Latino Dem. Club Sacramento County (v.p. 1982-83). Home and Office: 2667 Coleman Way Sacramento CA 95818-4459

PECK, ERNEST JAMES, JR., academic administrator; b. Port Arthur, Tex., July 26, 1941; s. Ernest James and Karlton Maudean (Luttrell) P.; children from previous marriage: David Karl, John Walter; m. Frances R. Taylor; 1 stepchild, Michael R. Taylor. BA in Biology with honors, Rice U., 1963, PhD in Biochemistry, 1966. Rsch. assoc. Purdue U., West Lafayette, Ind., 1966-68, asst. prof., 1968-73; asst. prof. Baylor Coll. Medicine, Houston, 1973-74, assoc. prof., 1974-80, prof., 1980-82; prof., chmn. biochemistry Sch. Med. Sci., U. Ark., Little Rock, 1982-89; dean sci. and math. U. Nev., Las Vegas, 1989-95; vice chancellor acad. affairs U. Nebr., Omaha, 1995—; adj. prof. U. Ark., Pine Bluff, 1988-89; program dir. NSF, Washington, 1988-89; mem. editl. bd. Jour. Neurosci. Rsch., N.Y.C., 1982-92. Co-author: Female Sex Steroids, 1979, Brain Peptides, 1979. Recipient Rsch. Career award NIH, Nat. Inst. of Child Health and Human Devel., 1975-80; NIH fellow, 1964-66. Fellow AAAS; mem. Am. Chem. Soc., Am. Soc. Biochemistry and Molecular Biology, Am. Soc. Neurochemistry, Endocrine Soc., Sigma Xi. Avocations: fishing, hunting. Office: U Nebr-Omaha Vice Chancellor Acad Affair 60th and Dodge Sts Omaha NE 68182-0001

PECK, FRED NEIL, economist, educator; b. Bklyn., Oct. 17, 1945; s. Abraham Lincoln and Beatrice (Pikholtz) P.; m. Jean Claire Ginsberg, Aug. 14, 1971; children: Ron Evan, Jordan Shefer, Ethan David. BA, SUNY, Binghamton, 1966; MA, SUNY, Albany, 1969; PhM, NYU, 1984; PhD, Pacific Western U., 1984; MS in Edn., Coll. New Rochelle, 1993. Lectr. SUNY, Albany, 1969-70; research asst. N.Y. State Legislature, Albany,

1970; sales and research staff Pan Am. Trade Devel. Corp., N.Y.C., 1971; v.p., economist The First Boston Corp., N.Y.C., 1971-88; mng. dir. Sharpe's Capital Mkt. Assocs. Inc., N.Y.C., 1988-89; pres., chief economist Hillcrest Econs. Group, N.Y.C., 1989-93; dir. edn. The Ednl. Advantage, Inc., New City, N.Y., 1990—; adj. prof. Hofstra U., Hempstead, N.Y., 1975; lectr. NYU, 1982; mem. faculty New Sch. for Social Rsch., N.Y.C., 1974—; coord. computer aided instrn. N.Y.C. Bd. of Edn., 1990—. Author, editor: (biennial publ.) Handbook of Securities of U.S. Government, 1972-86. Mem. ASCD, Am. Econ. Assn., La. Econ. Assn., Econometric Soc., Nat. Assn. Bus. Economists, Am. Statis. Assn., Doctorate Assn. of N.Y. Educators, Beta Gamma Sigma (hon. soc.), Phi Delta Kappa. Democrat. Jewish. Lodges: Knights Pythias, Knights Khorassan. Office: PS 169 & JHS 60 420 E 12th St New York NY 10009 *March in one place long enough and eventually you will wind up leading the parade of progress...No one grows old. When you tire of learning, of experiencing new things your are old.*

PECK, GARNET EDWARD, pharmacist, educator; b. Windsor, Ont., Can., Feb. 4, 1930; s. William Crozier and Dorothy (Marenette) P.; m. Mary Ellen Hoffman, Aug. 24, 1957; children: Monique Elizabeth, Denise Anne, Philip Warren, John Edward. B.S. in Pharmacy with Distinction, Ohio No. U., 1957; M.S. in Indsl. Pharmacy, Purdue U., 1959, Ph.D., 1962. Sr. scientist Mead Johnson Research Center, 1962-65, group leader, 1965-67; assoc. prof. indsl. and phys. pharmacy Purdue U., West Lafayette, 1967-73; prof. Purdue U., 1973—, dir. indsl. pharmacy lab., 1975—, assoc. dept. head, 1989—; cons. in field. Contbr. articles to profl. jours. Mem. West Lafayette Mayor's Advisory Com. on Community Devel., 1973—; mem. West Lafayette Citizen's Safety Com., 1974-81; mem. West Lafayette Park Bd., 1981—, pres., 1983—. Served with U.S. Army, 1951-53. Recipient Lederle Faculty award Purdue U., 1976. Recipient Lederle Faculty award Purdue U., 1976; knight Holy Sepulchre. Roman Catholic. Office: Purdue U Sch Pharmacy & Pharm Scis Dept Industrial & Physical Pharm West Lafayette IN 47907

PECK, GARY LAWRENCE, dermatologist, researcher; b. Detroit, Oct. 15, 1938; s. Marvin Max Peck and Renee Louise (Lerman) Peck Dopulos; m. Harriet Lee Ceasar, June 19, 1960; children: Julie Marsha, Tobi Elizabeth, Rachel Catherine. MD, U. Mich., 1962. Diplomate Am. Bd. Dermatology. Intern St. Luke's Hosp., San Francisco, 1962-63; resident in dermatology U. Chgo. Hosps. and Clinics, 1963-66; sr. investigator dermatology br. Nat. Cancer Inst., NIH, Bethesda, Md., 1969-90; prof. dept. dermatology U. Md. Sch. Medicine, Balt., 1991-93; lectr. Am. Acad. Dermatology, 1977-87, U. Md., and numerous others; cons. in field. Author chpts. in books; patentee in field for rsch. on vitamin A derivative as acne treatment; contbr. over 60 articles to profl. jours. Capt. USAF, 1966-68, med. dir. USPHS, 1976-90. Recipient fellowship USPHS, 1965-66, 68-69. Mem. Am. Acad. Dermatology, Soc. Investigative Dermatology, Washington, D.C. Dermatol. Soc., French Soc. Dermatology (foreign corr.). Avocations: international folk dancing, photography, travel. Office: Washington Cancer Inst Washington Hosp Ctr 110 Irving St NW Washington DC 20010

PECK, GREGORY, actor; b. La Jolla, Calif., Apr. 5, 1916; m. Greta Rice, 1942 (div. 1949); m. Veronique Passani; 5 children. Ed., U. Calif.; Neighborhood Playhouse Sch. Dramatics. Mem. Nat. Council on Arts, 1965—. Actor: (plays) including Sons and Soldiers, (films) including: Keys of the Kingdom, 1945, Valley of Decision, 1945, Spellbound, 1945, The Yearling, 1946, Duel in the Sun, 1947, The Macomber Affair, 1947, Gentlemen's Agreement, 1947, The Paradine Case, Yellow Sky, The Great Sinner, 1948, Twelve O'Clock High, 1949, The Gunfighter, 1950, Captain Horatio Hornblower, 1951, Only the Valiant, 1951, David and Bathsheba, 1951, Snows of Kilamanjaro, 1952, Roman Holiday, 1953, Night People, Man With a Million, Purple Plains, Moby Dick, 1954, Man in the Grey Flannel Suit, 1956, The Designing Woman, 1956, The Bravados, 1958, Pork Chop Hill, 1959, Beloved Infidel, 1959, On The Beach, 1959, Guns of Navarone, 1961, To Kill a Mockingbird (Acad. award as best actor 1962), Cape Fear, 1962, How the West Was Won, 1963, Captain Newman, M.D, 1963, Behold a Pale Horse, 1964, Mirage, 1965, Arabesque, 1966, Mackenna's Gold, 1967, The Chairman, 1968, The Stalking Moon, 1968, Marooned, 1969, I Walk the Line, 1970, Shootout, 1971, Billy Two-Hats, 1972, Amazing Grace and Chuck, 1987, Old Gringo, 1989, Cape Fear, 1991, Other People's Money, 1991; co-producer, star: (films) The Big Country, 1958; producer, star: (films) The Omen, 1976, MacArthur, 1977, The Boys from Brazil, 1978, The Sea Wolves, 1981, The Scarlet and Black, 1983, (TV miniseries) The Blue and the Gray, 1982, The Portrait, 1993; rec.: (audio cassette) The New Testament, 1985-86. Nat. chmn. Am. Cancer Soc., 1966; founder, prof. La Jolla Playhouse, 1947-52. Recipient Presdl. Medal of Freedom, Jean Hersholt Humanitarian award, 1968, Life Achievement award Am. Film Inst., 1989, Career award Cannes Film Festival, 1989, Kennedy Ctr. Honors, 1991, Lifetime Achievements award Lincoln Ctr., N.Y.C., 1992, Legion d'Honneur, France, 1993. Mem. Acad. Motion Picture Arts and Scis. (gov.; pres. 1967-70), Am. Film Inst. (founding chmn. bd. trustees 1967-69).

PECK, HARRY, public relations executive. Exec. v.p. Charles Ryan Assoc. Inc. Office: Charles Ryan Assocs Inc PO Box 2464 1012 Kanawha Blvd E Charleston WV 25239*

PECK, JAMES STEVENSON, banker; b. Wilmington, N.C., Mar. 14, 1923; s. Oscar and Christine (Stevenson) P.; m. Frances Grainger Marburg, June 19, 1948; children: Frances Grainger, James Stevenson, Christine Stevenson. B.S., U. N.C., 1943; postgrad., Rutgers U., 1955. With Union Trust Co. of Md., Balt., 1947—; pres. Union Trust Co. of Md., 1969-72, chmn., 1972—; chmn. Union Trust Bancorp, Balt., 1972—; chmn. exec. com. Signet Banking Corp., Richmond, 1985—; dir. SAFECO Title Ins. Co. Md., U.S. Fidelity & Guaranty Co., Crown Central Petroleum Corp. Bd. dirs Keswick Home for Incurables, United Fund, Greater Balt. Com.; trustee Johns Hopkins Hosp.; chmn. Balt. Corp. for Housing; bd. visitors U. N.C. Served to lt. (j.g.) USNR, 1943-46. Clubs: Elkridge, Maryland, Merchants (Balt.). Office: Signet Bank Md PO Box 1077 Baltimore MD 21203-1077

PECK, JOHN THOMAS, newspaper editor; b. Tucson, June 6, 1950; s. George Thomas and Treva Lorraine (Myers) P. Student in philosophy, Colo. Coll., 1968-71; student, U. Ariz., 1973—. Theater/dance writer, critic Ariz. Daily Star, Tucson, 1974-80, news desk utility editor, 1980-83, arts editor, 1984-85, features editor, 1985-86, mng. editor, 1987—; program coord. Nat. Critics Inst./Nat. Playwrights Conf., Waterford, Conn., 1975, 76, 77; adj. prof. in journalism U. Ariz., Tucson, 1981, 89; cons. in field. Contbr. articles, columns to profl. publs. Mem. grante com. Tucson Community Found., 1986—; bd. dirs. Friends of Tucson Libr., 1988—, Sportsman's Fund, Tucson, 1985-88; mem. Primavera Found., Tucson, 1989—. Critic fellow Nat. Cortex Inst., 1974, Am. Dance Festival, 1975; fellow NEH, 1978, Western States Arts Found. Mem. Parke County Hist. Co., Monzú Soc., Anzona Press Club, Old Pueblo Club. Democrat. Avocations: collecting American poetry and British humor books, dogs, historical restoration. Home: 239 W Franklin St Tucson AZ 85701-1021 Office: Ariz Daily Star 4850 S Park Ave PO Box 26807 Tucson AZ 85714

PECK, MARYLY VANLEER, college president, chemical engineer; b. Washington, June 29, 1930; d. Blake Ragsdale and Ella Lillian (Wall) VanLeer; m. Jordan B. Peck, Jr., June 15, 1951; children: Jordan B. III, Blake VanLeer, James Tarleton VanLeer, Virginia Ellaine.; m. 2d, Walter G. Ebert, Sept. 3, 1983 (dec. June 1990); m. 3d Edwin L. Carey, Apr. 13, 1991. Student, Ga. Inst. Tech., 1948, 55-58, Duke U., 1947-48; B.Ch.E. Vanderbilt U., 1951; M.S.E., U. Fla., 1955, Ph.D., 1963. Chem. engr. Naval Research Lab., Washington, 1951-52; chem. engr. Med. Field Research Lab., Camp LeJeune, N.C., 1952; asso. research and instr. U. Fla., Gainesville, 1953-55; chem. engr., research asso. Ga. Tech. Engr. Sta., Atlanta, 1956-58; lectr. Ga. State Coll., Atlanta, 1957-58; lectr. math. East Carolina Extension, Camp Lejeune, 1959; sr. research engr. Rocketdyne div. N.Am. Aviation Co., 1961-63; self-employed as lectr., cons., 1963; assoc. prof. Campbell Coll., Buie's Creek, N.C., 1963-66; prof. Campbell Coll., 1966; acad. dir. St. John's Episcopal Sch., Upper Tumon, Guam, 1966-68; chmn., prof. phys. scis. U. Guam, Agana, 1968-73; dean Coll. Bus. and Applied Tech. U. Guam, 1973-74, dean Community Career Coll., 1974-77; pres. Cochise Coll., Douglas, Ariz., 1977-78; systems planning analyst Urban Pathfinders, Inc., Balt., 1978-79; dean undergrad. studies U. Md. Univ. Coll., College Park, 1979-82; pres. Polk Community Coll., Winter Haven, Fla., 1982—. Founder, pres. Guam Acad. Found. 1972-77; bd. dirs. Cochise Coll. Found., 1977-78;

charter bd. dirs. Turnaround Inc., 1987-91, chmn. 1990—; bd. dirs. United Way Cen. Fla., 1986—, bd. dirs. All Saints Acad., 1994—, vice chmn., 1992, chair-elect, 1993, chmn. 1994; founding mem. Prince George's Ednl. TV Cable Coalition; mem. Prince George's Cable TV Ednl. Adv. Group, 1980-82, Polk County Coun. Econ. Edn., 1982; sec. Polk Community Coll. Found., 1982—; mem. Polk County Coordinating Coun. Vocat. Edn., 1982-91, PRIDE Adv. Coun.; vice chmn. Fla. Job Tng. Coordinating Coun., 1983-87, Fla. Edn. Fund Bd., 1988-93. Named Disting. Alumnus, U. Fla., 1992, Woman of Distinction Girl Scouts U.S.A., 1994; fellow NSF, 1961-63. Fellow Soc. Women Engrs. (nat. v.p. 1962-63); mem. AAUW, Am. Inst. Chem. Engrs., Am. Chem. Soc., NSPE, Am. Assn. for Higher Edn., Am. Assn. Community and Jr. Colls., Am. Assn. Univ. Adminstrs., Rotary, Sigma Xi, Tau Beta Pi, Chi Omicron Gamma, Phi Kappa Phi, Delta Kappa Gamma. Episcopalian. Home: 1290 Howard Ter NW Winter Haven FL 33881-3158 Office: Polk Community Coll 999 Avenue H NE Winter Haven FL 33881-4256

PECK, MERTON JOSEPH, educator, economist; b. Cleve., Dec. 17, 1925; s. Kenneth Richard and Charlotte (Hart) P.; m. Mary McClure Bosworth, June 13, 1949; children—Richard, Katherine, Sarah, David. AB, Oberlin Coll., 1949; AM, Harvard U., 1951, PhD, 1954; AM (hon.), Yale U., 1963. Teaching fellow, instr. econs. Harvard U., Boston, 1951-55, asst., then assoc. prof. bus. adminstrn., 1956-61; asst. prof. econs. U. Mich., Ann Arbor, 1955-56; dir. systems analysis Office Sec. Def., Washington, 1961-63; prof. econs. Yale U., New Haven, Conn., 1963—; chmn. dept. Yale U., New Haven, 1967-74, 77-84, acting dean sch. of orgn. and mgmt., 1987-88; Mem. Council Econ. Advisers, Exec. Office of Pres., 1968-69; cons. in field, 1954—. Author: (with others) The Economics of Competition in the Transportation Industries, 1959, Competition in the Aluminum Industry, 1945-58, 1961, (with F. Scherer) The Weapons Aquisition Process, An Economic Analysis, 1962, (with others) Technological Change, Economic Growth and Public Policy, 1967, Federal Regulation of Television, 1973; Contbr. (with others) articles to profl. jours. With AUS, 1944-46. Mem. Am. Econ. Assn., Am. Assn. U. Profs., Lawn Club, Yale Club. Home: 27 Temple Ct New Haven CT 06511

PECK, M(ORGAN) SCOTT, psychiatrist, writer; b. N.Y.C., May 22, 1936; s. David W. and Elizabeth (Saville) P.; m. Lily Ho, Dec. 27, 1959; children: Belinda, Julia, Christopher. AB in Social Relations, Harvard U., 1958; grad. in medicine, Case Western Res. U., 1963. Intern Tripler Med. Ctr., Honolulu; resident Letterman Gen. Hosp., San Francisco; chief, dept. of pyschology AUS Med. Ctr., Okinawa, Japan, 1967-70; asst. chief of psychiatry and neurology Office of the Surgeon Gen., Washington, 1970-72; pvt. practice psychiatry New Preston, Conn., 1972-84; co-founder Found. for Community Encouragement, 1984. Author: The Road Less Traveled, 1978, People of the Lie, The Hope for Healing Human Evil, 1983, (with others) What Return Can I Make?, 1985, The Different Drum, 1987, (novel) A Bed By the Window, 1990, A World Waiting to Be Born, 1993, Further Along the Road Less Traveled: The Unending Journey Toward Spiritual Growth, 1993, In Search of Stones: A Pilgrimage of Faith, Reason & Discovery, 1995, The House of Charon, 1990, (forwards to) Break-Point & Beyond: Mastering the Future Today, 1992, The Path of the Everday Hero: Drawing on the Power of Myth to Meet Life's Most Important Challenges, 1991, A Question of Values: Six Ways We Make the Personal Choices that Shape Our Lives, 1991, Exploring The Road Less Traveled, 1985, The Friendly Snowflake: A Fable of Faith, Love & Family. Lt. col. AUS; res. 1972. Office: Simon & Schuster Trade 1230 Avenue of the Americas New York NY 10020-1513 Home: New Preston Marble RR 1 Washington Depot CT 06793-9804*

PECK, NEIL, lawyer; b. Bronx, N.Y., June 1, 1939; s. Louis and Mollie (Zwick) P.; m. Carol O. Joplin, May 3, 1969 (div. June 1980); children: Mary Minns, Grace Leisure; m. Margaret McCulloch Coakley, Apr. 14, 1990. BA, Tufts U., 1959; JD, Yale U., 1962. Bar: N.Y. 1962, U.S. Dist. Ct. (so. dist.) N.Y. 1963, U.S. Ct. Appeals (2d cir.) 1963, U.S. Ct. Appeals (10th cir.) 1975, U.S. Supreme Ct. 1966. Assoc. U.S. atty. U.S. Dist. Ct. (so. dist.) N.Y., 1963-69; assoc. Hughes, Hubbard & Reed, N.Y.C., 1966-69; v.p. Gt. Western United, Denver, 1969-72; chmn. exec. com. Davis, Graham & Stubbs, Denver, 1991—; mem. exec. com. Ctr. Pub. Resources, N.Y.C., 1988—. Chmn. Colo. Lottery Commn., 1982-84; mem. search com. Yale Law Sch. Assn., devel. bd.; mem. Bd. Overseers of Social Scis. Tufts U., 1989—. Recipient Yale medal Yale Alumni Assn., 1983. Mem. ABA (com. chair, div. dir. sect. litigation 1975—). Avocation: squash. Office: Davis Graham & Stubbs 370 17th St Ste 4700 Denver CO 80202-5682

PECK, RALPH BRAZELTON, civil engineering educator, consultant; b. Winnipeg, Man., Can., June 23, 1912; (parents Am. citizens); s. Orwin K. and Ethel Indie (Huyck) P.; m. Marjorie Elizabeth Truby, June 14, 1937; children: Nancy Jeanne Peck Young, James Leroy. D in Civil Engring., Rensselaer Poly. Inst., 1937; postgrad., Harvard U., 1938; D Eng. (hon.), Rensselaer Poly. Inst., 1974; DSc (hon.), Laval U., 1987. Registered profl. engr., structural engr. Ill.; civil engr., Calif. Structural detailer Am. Bridge Co., Ambridge, Pa., 1937; asst. subway engr. City of Chgo., 1939-43; chief engr. testing Holabird & Root, Sciotto Ordnance Plant, Marion, Ohio, 1943; research asst. prof. soil mechanics U. Ill., Champaign-Urbana, 1943-48, research prof. found. engring., 1948-57, prof. found. engring., 1957-74, prof. emeritus, 1974—; cons. founds., tunnels, earth dams, landslides, throughout U.S. and various fgn. countries, 1943—. Author: (with K. Terzaghi) Soil Mechanics in Engring. Practice, 1948, 2 edit., 1967, (with T.H. Thornburn and W.E. Hanson) Foundation Engineering, 1953, 2 edit., 1973, Judgment in Geotechnical Engineering: The Professional Legacy of Ralph B. Peck, 1984; contbr. over 200 tech. papers. Recipient Disting. Civilian Svc. award Dept. of Army, 1973, Moles Non-mem. award, 1973, Nat. Medal Sci. Pres. Gerald Ford, 1974, Golden Beaver award 1983, Disting. Svc. award Deep Founds Inst., 1984, award of merit Am. Cons. Engrs. Coun., 1988. Fellow Geol. Soc. Am.; mem. NAE, ASCE (hon.; nat. dir. 1962-65; Norman medal 1944, Wellington prize 1965, Terzaghi award 1969, Washington award 1976, Pres.'s award 1986, John Fritz medal 1987, Rickey medal 1988), Am. Acad. Arts and Scis., Internat. Soc. Soil Mechanics and Found. Engring. (pres. 1969-73), Southeast Asian, Japanese, Mexican Socs. Soil Mechanics (hon.), NSPE (award 1972), Sigma Xi, Chi Epsilon, Tau Beta Pi, Phi Kappa Phi. Home: 1101 Warm Sands Dr SE Albuquerque NM 87123-4328

PECK, RICHARD CLEON, magistrate judge; b. Falls City, Nebr., Sept. 16, 1917; s. N. Cleon and Ella M. (Way) P.; m. Dorothy E. Perrin, June 20, 1942; 1 son, Richard D. A.B., U. Nebr., 1941, LL.B., 1943. Bar: Nebr. 1943, U.S. Dist. Ct. Nebr. 1943, U.S. Ct. Appeals (8th cir.) 1947. Law clk. U.S. Ct. Appeals (8th cir.), 1943; practice, Plattsmouth, Nebr., 1946-56; mem. Begley & Peck; judge Cass County (Nebr.) Ct., 1948-50; atty. Cass County, 1950-56; asst. U.S. atty. Dept. Justice, Omaha, 1956-59; clk. U.S. Dist. Ct. Nebr. 1959-75; magistrate U.S. Dist. Nebr., Omaha, 1970—; mem. seminar faculty Fed. Jud. Ctr., 1969-77. Served as spl. agt. CIC, U.S. Army, 1943-46; ETO. Mem. Nebr. Bar Assn., ABA, Nat. Council U.S. Magistrates, Order of Coif, Phi Delta Phi. Republican. Presbyterian. Clubs: Kiwanis (Omaha); Masons. Office: 9000 US Courthouse PO Box 129 Omaha NE 68101-0457

PECK, RICHARD EARL, academic administrator, playwright, novelist; b. Milw., Aug. 3, 1936; s. Earl Mason and Mary Amanda (Fry) P.; m. Donna Joy Krippner, Aug. 13, 1960; children: Mason, Laura. AB magna cum laude, Carroll Coll., Waukesha, Wis., 1961; MS, U. Wis., 1962, PhD, 1964. Asst. prof. U. Va., Charlottesville, 1964-67; assoc. dean, prof. Temple U. Phila., 1967-84; dean arts and scis. U. Ala., 1984-88; provost, v.p. academic affairs Ariz. State U., Tempe, 1988-89, interim pres., 1989-90; pres. U. N.Mex., Albuquerque, 1990—. Editor: Poems/Nathaniel Hawthorne, 1967, Poems/Floyd Stovall, 1967; author: (books) Final Solution, 1973 (nominated for John W. Campbell award as Best Sci. Fiction Novel of 1973 by Sci. Fiction Rsch. Assn.), Something for Joey, 1978, Passing Through, 1982, (plays) Sarah Bernhardt and the Bank, 1972, Don't Trip over the Money Pail, 1976, The Cubs Are in fourth Place and Fading 1977, Phonecall, 1978, Bathnight, 1978, Prodigal Father, 1978, Lovers, Wives and Tennis Players, 1979, Curtains, 1980, A Party for Wally Pruett, 1982, Allergy Tests, 1982, Your Place or Mine, 1987, (films) Starting over Again, 1982, What Tangled Webs, 1974, Tutte le Strade Portanno a Roma, 1974, Il Dottino, 1974; contbr. numerous scholarly articles to lit. jours., book revs., travel articles and humor columns to newspapers and mags., papers to univ. orgns. and writers' confs. Bd. dirs. East Valley Partnership (Econ. Devel. Orgn.), Sci. and Tech., Samaritan Health Svcs.; gubernatorial appointee, bd. dirs. Ala.

Humanities Found.; mem. Nat. Found. for Post-Secondary Edn.; bd. dirs. Phila. Alliance for Teaching Humanities in the Schs., Dela. Valley Faculty Exch.; adv. bd. Ea. Pa. Theater Coun.; chmn. Temple U. Bicentennial Festival of Am. Arts, 1976; mem. Univ. Negotiating Team in re: Temple-AAUP faculty contract. Capt. USMC, 1954-59. Recipient Whitman Pub. scholarship, 1959-63, Woodrow Wilson fellowship, 1961-62, Knapp Found. fellowship, 1962-63, C. Brooks Fry award Theater Americana, Altadena, Calif., 1979. Mem. MLA, Northeast MLA. Conf. Univs. and Colls. Arts, Letters and Scis., Coun. Colls. Arts and Scis., Nat. Assn. State Univs. and Land-Grant Colls. Home: 1901 Roma Ave NE Albuquerque NM 87106-3824 Office: U NMex Office of Pres Albuquerque NM 87131

PECK, RICHARD HYDE, hospital administrator; b. Ft. McClelland, Ala., Aug. 30, 1941; s. Robert H. and Elizabeth M. P.; m. Barbara Mansfield Dec. 27, 1964; children—Catherine, Nancy, Joanne. A.B. in Econs, U. N.C., 1963; M.S. in Health Adminstrn, Duke U., 1966. Adminstrv. asst. U. Hosps., Cleve., 1966-67, asst. adminstr., 1967-69; asst. dir. Duke U. Hosp., 1969-71, asso. dir., 1971-73, adminstrv. dir., 1973-81; asso. prof. health adminstrn. program Duke U.; chief exec. officer Eliza Coffee Meml. Hosp., Florence, Ala., 1981—; bd. dirs. Ala. Blue Cross and Blue Shield, 1986—; mem. med. ctr. adv. council U. Ala., Birmingham, 1983—. Campaign dir., pres.-elect The Shoals United Way, 1986. Mem. Am. Coll. Hosp. Adminstrs, Am. Hosp. Assn., Ala. Hosp. Assn. (bd. dirs. Trust 1983), Florence area C of C. (bd. dirs.). Democrat. Presbyterian. Office: Pub Hosp Bd 205 S Marengo St Florence AL 35630

PECK, RICHARD WAYNE, novelist; b. Decatur, Ill., Apr. 5, 1934; s. Wayne Morris and Virginia (Gray) P. Student, Exeter (Eng.) U., 1954-55; B.A., DePauw U., 1956; M.A., So. Ill. U., 1959. Mem. faculty Sch. Edn., Hunter Coll., 1965-71; lectr. in field. Author: books for adolescents, including Are You in the House Alone?, 1977 (Edgar Allen Poe award 1977), Father Figure, 1978, Secrets of the Shopping Mall, 1979; (poetry anthology) Sounds and Silences, 1970; (novels for adults) New York Time; Contbr. articles on architecture and local history to N.Y. Times. Asst. dir. Council Basic Edn., Washington, 1969-70. Served with U.S. Army, 1956-58. English-Speaking Union fellow Jesus Coll., Oxford (Eng.) U., 1973; winner Nat. Prize for Young People's Lit. ALA, 1990. Mem. Authors Guild, Authors League, Delta Chi. Republican. Methodist. Home: 155 E 72nd St New York NY 10021-4371

PECK, ROBERT A., newspaper publisher; b. Riverton, Wyo., Oct. 7, 1924; s. LeRoy E. and Elvira Eugenia (Sostrom) P.; m. Cordelia S. Peck, Oct. 5, 1949; children: Christopher, George, Steven. BA, U. Wyo., 1949. Pub. The Riverton Ranger, 1949—; mem. Wyoming State Senate, 1991—; bd. dirs. Pacific Power, Portland, Oreg., Am. Nuclear Corp., Casper, Wyo. Pres. Central Wyo. Coll. Bd., Riverton, 1966-81; sec. CWC Found., Riverton, 1968—. Staff sgt. U.S. Army, 1943-45, ETO. Mem. Soc. Profl. Journalists, Masons, Phi Beta Kappa. Republican. United Methodist. Office: The Riverton Ranger 421 E Main PO Box 993 Riverton WY 82501-0993

PECK, ROBERT DAVID, educational foundation administrator; b. Devil's Lake, N.D., June 1, 1929; s. Lester David and Bernice Marie (Peterson) P.; m. Lylia June Smith, Sept. 6, 1953; children: David Allan, Kathleen Marie. BA, Whitworth Coll., 1951; MDiv, Berkeley (Calif.) Bapt. Div. Sch., 1958; ThD, Pacific Sch. Religion, 1964; postgrad., U. Calif., Berkeley, 1959-60, 62-63, Wadham Coll., Oxford U., Eng., 1963. Music tchr. pub. schs. Bridgeport, Wash., 1954-55; prof., registrar Linfield Coll., McMinnville, Oreg., 1963-69; asst. dir. Ednl. Coordinating Coun., Salem, Oreg., 1969-75; assoc. prof. Pacific Luth. U., Tacoma, 1976-79, U. Puget Sound, Tacoma, 1977; v.p. John Minter Assocs., Boulder, Colo., 1979-81, Coun. Ind. Colls., Washington, 1981-84; adminstrv. v.p. Alaska Pacific U., Anchorage, 1984-88; pres. Phillips U., Enid, Okla., 1988-94, chancellor, 1994-95; chmn. The Pres. Found. for Support of Higher Edn., Washington, 1995—; pres. Phillips U. Ednl. Enterprises Inc., 1994-95; cons. Higher Edn. Exec. Assocs., Denver, 1984—; owner Tyee Marina, Tacoma, 1975-77; yacht broker Seattle, 1977-79. Author: Focusing: An Alternative to Strategic Planning, 1983, also articles. Dem. county chmn., McMinnville, 1968, Dem. candidate for state Ho. of Reps., McMinnville, 1969; pres. McMinnville Kiwanis, 1965-69. Cpl. Signal Corps, U.S. Army, 1952-54. Carnegie Corp. grantee, 1982, 84. Mem. Okla. Ind. Coll. Assn. (sec. 1989—). Mem. Christian Ch. Avocations: sailing, sculpting. Office: Pres Found for Support Higher Edn 1919 Pennsylvania Ave Washington DC 20006

PECK, ROBERT MCCRACKEN, naturalist, science historian, writer; b. Phila., Dec. 15, 1952; s. Frederick William Gunster and Matilda (McCracken) P. BA in Art History, Princeton U., 1974; MA, U. Del., 1976. Dir. Pocono Lake (Pa.) Preserve Nature Ctr., 1971, 72; asst. to dir. Natural History Mus. Acad. Natural Scis., Phila., 1976-77; tech. dir. Bartram Heritage Study U.S. Dept. Interior and Bartram Trail Conf., Atlanta and Montgomery, Ala., 1977-78; spl. asst. to pres. Acad. Natural Scis., Phila., 1977-82, acting v.p. Nat. History Mus., 1982-83, fellow, 1983—; cons. BBC, Eng., 1987-92; bd. dirs. Phila. Conservationists, Natural Lands Trust, Phila., Libr. Co. of Phila., Phila. City Inst.; mng. editor Frontiers, 1979-82; lectr. in field. Author: A Celebration of Birds: The Life and Art of Louis Agassiz Fuertes, 1982, Headhunters and Hummingbirds: An Expedition Into Ecuador, 1987, Wild Birds of America: The Art of Basil Ede, 1991, Land of the Eagle: A Natural History of North America, 1991, German edit., 1992; author: (with others) William Bartram's Travels, 1988, John Cassin's Illustrations of the Birds of California, Texas, Oregon, British and Russian America, 1991; author: (foward) The Birds of America by John James Audubon, 1985; editor: Bartram Heritage Report, 1978; author (with others), editor: Philadelphia Wildfowl Exposition Catalog, 1979; contbr. chpts. to books, articles to mags. and newspapers including The New York Times. Trustee Chestnut Hill Acad., Phila.; bd. dirs. RARE Ctr. Tropical Bird Conservation, Mus. Coun. of Phila. Recipient Richard Hopper Day Meml. award Acad. Natural Scis. of Phila., 1991; Eleanor Garvey fellow in printing and graphic arts Houghton Libr., Harvard U., 1995. Fellow Royal Geographic Soc., Explorers Club (various coms. 1983—, Explorers award 1988); mem. Soc. History of Natural History, Sigma Xi. Achievements include discovering of a new species of frog, Eleutherodactylus pecki; research on orthogptera indigenous to the Caribbean, status of invasive African Desert Locusts in the West Indies, study of the endangered Cuban Parrot, the Orinoco River and its tributaries, botanical, entomological, ichthyological, herpetological, and malacological specimens for the Smithsonian Instn. and the Acad. of Natural Sciencs; organization and participation in expeditions which discovered several new species of fish in Guayana Shield, Venezuela, discovered several new species of amphibians and insects as well as two new races of birds in Ecuador, investigated the ecological, economic and political impact of instream-flow legislation on the Yellowstone River Basin. Office: Academy of Natural Sciences 1900 Benjamin Franklin Pkwy Philadelphia PA 19103

PECK, ROBERT STEPHEN, lawyer, educator; b. Bklyn., Dec. 11, 1953; s. Irwin and Edith Rose (Welt) P. BA in Polit. Sci., George Washington U., 1975; JD, Cleve.-Marshall Law Sch., 1978; postgrad., NYU, 1978; LLM, Yale U., 1990. Bar: N.Y. 1979, U.S. Dist. Ct. (so. and ea. dists.) N.Y. 1979, D.C. 1989. Congl. aide U.S. Ho. of Reps., Washington, 1972-74; div. dir. Automated Correspondence, Washington, 1974-75; law clk. to presiding justice Cleve. Mcpl. Ct., 1976; editor Matthew Bender & Co., N.Y.C., 1977-78; legal dir. Pub. Edn. Assn., N.Y.C., 1978-82; staff dir. ABA, Chgo., 1982-87, Washington, 1987-89; jud. fellow U.S. Supreme Ct., 1990-91; legis. counsel ACLU, 1991—; adj. prof. American U., Washington, 1991—; legal advisor Freedom to Read Found., Chgo., 1986—; exec. com. bd. trustees, 1987-90, pres., 1988-90, trustee, 1993—; bd. dirs. Nat. Constl. Ctr., 1990-93; lectr. on constl. law, legal ethics. Author: We the People, 1987, The Bill of Rights and the Politics of Interpretation, 1991; co-author: Speaking and Writing Truth, 1985; editor: Understanding the Law, 1983, Blessings of Liberty, 1986, To Govern A Changing Society, 1990; contbr. numerous articles on constl. law to law revs. Mem. N.Y. State Edn. Adv. Bd., Albany, N.Y., 1979-81; bd. dirs. Nat. Com. on Pub. Edn. and Religious Liberty, 1995—, Ams. for Religious Liberty, 1995—. NEH grantee 1983, 85. Mem. ABA (chmn. pub. election law com. 1983-85, 87-90). Democrat. Jewish. Avocations: tennis, music, travel. Office: ACLU 122 Maryland Ave NE Washington DC 20002-5610

PECK, WILLIAM ARNO, physician; b. New Britain, Conn., Sept. 28, 1933; s. Bernard Carl and Molla (Nair) P.; m. Patricia Hearn, July 10, 1982; children by previous marriage: Catherine, Edward Pershall, David Nathaniel; stepchildren: Andrea, Elizabeth, Katherine. A.B., Harvard U., 1955; M.D., U. Rochester, N.Y., 1960. Intern, then resident in internal medicine Barnes Hosp., St. Louis, 1960-62; fellow in metabolism Washington U. Sch. Medicine, St. Louis, 1963; mem. faculty U. Rochester Med. Sch., 1965-76, prof. medicine and biochemistry, 1973-76, head div. endocrinology and metabolism, 1969-76; John E. and Adaline Simon prof. medicine, co-chmn. dept. medicine Washington U. Sch. Medicine, St. Louis, 1976-89; physician in chief Jewish Hosp., St. Louis, 1976-89; prof. medicine and exec. vice chancellor med. affairs, dean sch. medicine, pres. univ. med. ctr. Washington U., St. Louis, 1989—; chmn. endocrinology and metabolism adv. com. FDA, 1976-78; chmn. gen. medicine study sect. NIH, 1979-81; chmn. Gordon Conf. Chemistry, Physiology and Structure of Bones and Teeth, 1977; chmn. Consensus Devel. Conf. on Osteoporosis, NIH, 1984; co-chmn. Workshop on Future Directions in Osteoporosis, NIH, 1987; chmn. Spl. Topic Conf. on Osteoporosis, U.S. FDA, 1987. Editor Bone and Min. Research Annuals, 1982-88; contbr. med. jours. Pres. Nat. Osteoporosis Found., 1985-90. Served as med. officer USPHS, 1963-65. Recipient Mosby Book award Alpha Omega Alpha, 1960, Doran J. Stephens award U. Rochester Sch. Medicine, 1960, Lederle Med. Faculty award, 1967, NIH Career Program award, 1970-75, Commr.'s Spl. citation FDA, 1988. Fellow ACP, AAAS; mem. Am. Soc. Biol. Chemists, Am. Physiol. Soc., Am. Soc. Clin. Investigation, Am. Fedn. Clin. Rsch., Am. Diabetes Assn., Am. Soc. Bone and Mineral Rsch. (pres. 1983-84), Assn. Am. Physicians, Endocrine Soc., Orthopedic Rsch. Soc., Nat Inst. Arthritis, Musculoskeletal and Skin Diseases (adv. coun. 1986-89), Assn. Am. Med. Colls. (adminstrv. bd. Coun. of Deans 1993—), Sigma Xi, Alpha Omega Alpha (bd. dirs. 1992—). Home: 2 Apple Tree Ln Saint Louis MO 63124-1601 Office: Washington U Sch Medicine 600 S Euclid Ave Saint Louis MO 63110-1010

PECK, WILLIAM HENRY, museum curator, art historian, archaeologist, author, lecturer; b. Savannah, Ga., Oct. 2, 1932; s. William Henry Peck and Mildred (Bass) Peck Tuten; m. Ann Amelia Keller, Feb. 2, 1957 (dec. 1965); children: Alice Ann, Sarah Louise; m. Elsie Holmes, July 8, 1967; 1 child, William Henry IV. Student Ohio State U., 1950-53; BFA, Wayne State U., 1960, MA, 1961. Jr. curator Detroit Inst. Arts, 1960-62, asst. curator, 1962-64, assoc. curator, 1964-68, curator ancient art, 1968—, acting chief curator, 1984-88, sr. curator, 1988—; lectr. art history Cranbrook Acad. Art, Bloomfield Hills, Mich., 1963-65; vis. lectr. U. Mich., Ann Arbor, 1970; adj. prof. art history Wayne State U., Detroit, 1966—; excavations in Egypt, Mendes, 1964-66, Precinct of Mut, Karnak, 1978—. Author: Drawings from Ancient Egypt, 1978, The Detroit Institute of Arts: A Brief History, 1991; co-author: Ancient Egypt: Discovering its Splendors, 1978, Mummies, Diseases and Ancient Cultures, 1980; also articles. With U.S. Army, 1953-55. Ford Motor Co. travel grantee, 1962; Am. Research Ctr. Egypt fellow, 1971; Smithsonian Instn. travel grantee, 1975; recipient Award in the Arts Wayne State U., 1985. Mem. Archaeol. Inst. Am., Am. Research Ctr. Egypt, Internat. Assn. Egyptologists, Soc. Study Egyptian Antiquities, Am. Assn. Mus. Democrat. Episcopalian. Avocations: origami; performance of early music. Office: Inst Arts 5200 Woodward Ave Detroit MI 48202-4008

PECKER, DAVID J., magazine publishing company executive, financial executive; b. N.Y.C., Sept. 24, 1951; m. Karen Balan, Oct. 31, 1987. BBA, Pace U., postgrad. CPA, N.Y. Sr. auditor Price Waterhouse & Co.; mgr. fin. reporting Diamandis Communications, Inc., N.Y.C., 1979; dir. fin. reporting Diamandis Communications, Inc., dir. acctg., asst. contr., 1983; COO, CFO, exec. v.p. pub. Hachette Mags., Inc., N.Y.C., 1990-91, pres., COO, 1991-92, pres., CEO, COO, 1992—; mem. Fashion Group's Internat. Adv. Bd., The N.Y. City Partnership Com.; mem. bd. dirs. The Madison Square Boys & Girls Club, Friends Indeed. Bd. dirs. Pace U., N.Y.C. Mem. Am. Mgmt. Assn., Mag. Pubs. Am. (exec. com.). Office: Hachette Mags Inc 1633 Broadway New York NY 10019-6708

PECKHAM, BARRY, newspaper publishing executive. V.p. circulation The Dallas Morning News, Tex. Office: The Dallas Morning News Communication Ctr Young & Houston Sts Dallas TX 75202*

PECKHAM, DONALD EUGENE, retired utilities company executive; b. Willis, Kans., Nov. 28, 1922; s. Rolland Claude and Winona Maude (Lewis) P.; m. Evelynn Darlene Dodson, Dec. 20, 1949 (dec.). B.A. cum laude in Acctg, Eastern N.Mex. U., 1953; M.B.A., U. Ariz., 1954. Acct. Ill. Power Co., Decatur, Ill., 1954-57; with Public Service Co. of N.Mex., Albuquerque, from 1957, sec., 1968-70; sec., asst. treas. Public Service Co. of N.Mex. 1970-74, sec., treas., 1974-79, sec., asst. treas. from 1979; sec. Paragon Resources, Inc., 1972-75, sec., asst. treas., from 1975; sec. Sunbelt Mining Co., Inc., 1980-81, sec., asst. treas., from 1981; sec. Meadows Resources, Inc., from 1981; now ret. Served with USMC, 1943-46. Republican. Lodge: Elks.

PECKHAM, HOWARD HENRY, librarian, educator; b. Lowell, Mich., July 13, 1910; s. Herman Algernon and Harriet May (Wilson) P.; m. Dorothy Koth, July 28, 1936; children: Stephen Wilson, Angela Zidana (Mrs. Thomas Hewett). A.B., U. Mich., 1931, A.M., 1933; Litt.D., Olivet Coll., 1975. Chief editorial writer Grand Rapids (Mich.) Press, 1935; curator manuscripts Clements Library of Am. History, U. Mich., 1936-44, lectr. library sci., 1942-46, univ. war historian, 1943-44; dir. Ind. Hist. Bur., Indpls., 1945-53, Clements Library, 1953-77; prof. history U. Mich., 1953-77; cons. Office Naval History, USN Dept., 1966-78. Bassoonist, Hendersonville Symphony, 1977-86; Author: (with R.G. Adams) Lexington to Fallen Timbers, 1942, (with C. Storm) Invitation to Book Collecting, 1946, Pontiac and the Indian Uprising, 1947, Captured by Indians, 1954, The War for Independence, 1958, The Colonial Wars, 1964, The Making of the University of Michigan, 1967, The Toll of Independence, 1974, History of the W.L. Clements Library 1923-73, 1973, Indiana, a Bicentennial History, 1978, Historical Americana, 1980, (juvenile non-fiction) William Henry Harrison, 1951, Nathanael Greene, 1956, Pontiac Young Ottawa Leader, 1963; editor: George Croghan's Journal of 1767, 1939, (with L.A. Brown) Revolutionary War Journals of Henry Dearborn, 1939, Guide to the Manuscript Collections in the Clements Library, 1942, (with S.A. Snyder) Letters From Fighting Hoosiers, 1948, (with C.A. Byrd) Bibliography of Indiana Imprints, 1955, Narratives of Colonial America, 1971, Sources of American Independence, 1978, Ind. Hist. Bull, 1945-53, Liberty's Legacy, 1987; assoc. editor: Am. Heritage quar, 1949-54. Fellow Soc. Am. Archivists (founding mem., mem. council), Am. Assn. State and Local History (pres. 1954-56, mem. council), Am., Miss. Valley hist. assns., Mass. Hist. Soc., Bibliog. Soc. Am., Am. Antiquarian Soc., Adelphic Alpha Pi, Hendersonville Country Club. Congregationalist. Home: 600 Carolina Village Rd Box 361 Hendersonville NC 28792-2827

PECKHAM, JOHN MUNROE, III, investment executive, author; b. Abington, Mass., July 25, 1933; s. John Munroe and Mildred (Davis) P.; children: Lisa, Holly, John M. IV. AB, Tufts U., 1955; postgrad., Columbia U., 1955-56. Pres. Peckham Boston Adv. Co., 1964—; pres., chmn. Boston Hall Corp., Boston, 1987—; pres. Boston Hall Pub. Co., 1988—; Founder Realtors Concerned for Realtors, Chgo., 1986—; mem. bd. advisors Kids Stop, Boston, 1988-89; bd. dirs. Am. Fedn. for Children and Youth, L.A., 1988-89. Lt. comdr. USN, 1956-62. Mem. Nat. Assn. Realtors (v.p.), Realtors Nat. Mktg. Inst. (v.p. 1988), Internat. Fedn. Realtors, Inst. Real Estate Mgmt., Ten Club (pres. Boston chpt. 1974-79), Friends of Bill W. Republican. Baptist. Avocations: bicycling, swimming, cribbage, speaking, reading. Office: Boston Hall Corp 4 Longfellow Pl Apt 2003 Boston MA 02114-2830

PECKHAM, P. HUNTER, biomedical engineer, educator; b. Elmira, N.Y., June 23, 1944; married; 2 children. BS, Clarkson Coll. Tech., 1966; MS, Case Western Res. U., 1968, PhD in Biomed. Engring., 1972. Rsch. assoc. Case Western Res. U., 1972-74, instr. divsn. orthapedic surgery, 1974-78; rsch. biomed. engr. Med. Ctr. Cleve. VA, 1976—; prof. orthopedics Case Western Res. U., 1978—; prof. biomed. engring., 1979—; dir. FES Ctr., 1990—; mem. staff Cuyohoga Coun. Hosp., 1981—. Recipient Rsch. Career Devel. award NIH, 1978. Mem. IEEE, Am. Spinal Injury Assn., Am. Inst. Med. and Biol. Engring., Rehab. Engring. Soc. N.Am., Internat. Med. Soc. Paraplegia. Achievements include research in technology for rehabilitation of the severely disabled, restoration of movement of the arm and hand using

functional neuromuscular stimulation. Office: Case Western Reserve U Rehab Engring Ctr/Cleveland Metro Hosp/3395 Scranton Rd/Room H 611 Cleveland OH 44109-1900*

PECKOLICK, ALAN, graphic designer; b. N.Y.C., Oct. 3, 1940; s. Charles and Belle (Binenbaum) P.; m. Jessica Margot Weber, June 3, 1984. AAS, Pratt Inst., Bklyn., 1968. Art dir. McCann-Erickson, 1964-68; graphic designer Herb Lubalin, 1968-72; v.p., creative dir. Lubalin, Smith, Carnase, Inc., N.Y.C., 1972-74, LCS & P Design Group, Inc., N.Y.C., 1974-76; pres. Lubalin Peckolick Assoc., N.Y.C., 1976-81, Pushpin, Lubalin, Peckolick, N.Y.C., 1981-86, Peckolick and Ptnrs., N.Y.C., 1986-89; design dir. Addison Design Cons., N.Y.C., 1989-91; chmn. Peckolick Inc., N.Y.C., 1991—; bd. advisors Designworld mag., Victoria, Australia, 1983—, Herb Lubalin Study Ctr., N.Y.C.; lectr. Pratt Inst., Parsons Sch. Design, Sch. Visual Arts, also various orgns. Co-author, designer: Herb Lubalin Graphic Designer, 1986; exhibited at Sony Gallery, Tokyo, 1989. Bd. dirs. Glaucoma Found., 1993, Whale Conservation Inst., 1994. Recipient awards AIGA, Art Directors Club awards. Mem. N.Y. Art Dirs. Club (6 gold medals, over 50 awards), N.Y. Type Dirs. Club (bd. dirs.), Alliance Graphique Internationale, Art Dirs.Club Bergen (Norway) (hon.). Avocations: automobile racing, painting, collecting art and prints, cooking, travel. Home: 30 E 10th St New York NY 10003-6202 Office: Peckolick Inc 41 E 11th St New York NY 10003-4602

PECORA, ROBERT, chemistry educator; b. Bklyn., Aug. 6, 1938; s. Alfonso Edward and Helen (Buscavage) P. A.B., Columbia U., 1959, A.M., 1960, Ph.D., 1962. Asst. prof. chemistry Stanford U., 1964-71, assoc. prof., 1971-78, prof., 1978—; chmn. chemistry, 1992—; vis. prof. U. Manchester, (Eng.), 1970-71, U. Nice, (France), 1978; cons. chemistry to maj. corps. Co-author: Dynamic Light Scattering, 1976; contbr. articles to profl. jours. Recipient Sr. Scientist award Alexander von Humboldt Found., 1985; NSF fellow, 1960-62, Am. Acad. Scis. postdoctoral fellow U. libre de Bruxelles, Belgium, 1963. Fellow AAAS, Am. Phys. Soc.; mem. Am. Chem. Soc. Home: 707 Continental Cir Mountain View CA 94040-3366 Office: Stanford U Dept Chemistry Stanford CA 94305

PECSOK, ROBERT LOUIS, chemist, educator; b. Cleve., Dec. 18, 1918; s. Michael C. and Katherine (Richter) P.; m. Mary Bodell, Oct. 12, 1940; children: Helen Pecsok Wong, Katherine, Jean Pecsok Nagle, Michael, Ruth Pecsok Hughes, Alice, Sara Pecsok Lima. S.B. summa cum laude, Harvard, 1940, Ph.D., 1948. Prodn. foreman Procter & Gamble Co., Balt., 1940-43; instr. chemistry Harvard, 1948; asst. prof. chemistry U. Calif. at Los Angeles, 1948-55, asso. prof., 1955-61, prof., 1961-71, vice chmn. dept., 1965-70; prof., chmn. dept. U. Hawaii, Honolulu, 1971-80; dean natural scis. U. Hawaii, 1981-89; sci. adviser FDA, 1966-69. Author: Principles and Practice of Gas Chromatography, 1959, Analytical Methods of Organic and Biochemistry, 1966, Modern Methods of Chemical Analysis, 1968, 2d edit., 1976, Modern Chemical Technology, 1970, rev. edit. 1989, Physicochemical Applications of Gas Chromatography, 1978. Served as lt. USNR, 1943-46. Recipient Tolman medal, 1971; Guggenheim fellow, 1956-57; Petroleum Research Fund Internat. fellow, 1963-64. Mem. Am. Chem. Soc., Am. Inst. Chemists, Phi Beta Kappa, Alpha Chi Sigma, Phi Lambda Upsilon. Home: 13855 Riverhead Ct San Diego CA 92129-3222

PEDDICORD, KENNETH LEE, academic administrator; b. Ottawa, Ill., Apr. 5, 1943; s. Kenneth Charles and Elizabeth May (Hughes) P.; m. Patricia Ann Cullen, Aug. 2, 1969; children: Joseph, Clare. BSME, U. Notre Dame, 1965; MSNE, U. Ill., 1967, PhD, 1972. Registered profl. engr., Tex. Rsch. nuclear engr. Swiss Fed. Inst. for Reactor Rsch., Würenlingen, Switzerland, 1972-75; asst. prof. nuclear engring. Oreg. State U., Eugene, 1975-79, assoc. prof. nuclear engring., 1979-82; prof. nuclear engring. Tex. A&M U., College Station, 1983—, head dept. nuclear engring., 1985-88, asst. dir. rsch. Tex. Engring. Experiment Sta., 1988-91, dir. Tex. Experiment Sta., 1991-93, assoc. dean coll. engring., 1990-91, interim dean coll. engring., 1991-93, interim dep. chancellor engring., 1993-94, assoc. vice chancellor for strategic programs, 1994—; vis. scientist Joint Rsch. Centre-Ispra Establishment, EURATOM, Ispra, Italy, 1981-82; cons. EG&G Idaho, Inc., Idaho Falls, Idaho, 1979, Portland (Oreg.) Gen. Electric Co., 1980, Battelle Human Affairs Rsch. Ctr., Bellevue, Va., 1984, Los Alamos (N.Mex.) Nat. Lab., 1984-89, Pa. Power & Light, Allentown, Pa., 1986, Argonne Nat. Lab., Idaho Falls, 1989, Univs. Space Rsch. Assn., Houston, 1989—, Ark. Dept. Higher Edn., Little Rock, 1990; speaker in field; mem. Nat. Rsch. Coun. Com. on Advanced Space Based High Power Techs., 1987-88, NASA OAET Aerospace Rsch. and Tech. subcom., 1987—, SP-100 Materials Sci. Rev Com., DARPA/NASA/DOE, 1984-86, Nuclear Engring. Edn. for Disadvantaged, 1978—, sec., 1978-80, vice chair, 1985-88, chair, 1988-91; John and Muriel Landis Scholarship Com., 1979—, chair, 1985—; mem. adv. bd. for nuclear sci. and engring., 1984-86; mem. tech. program com. Internat. Conf. on Reliable Fuels for Liquid Metal Reactors, 1985-86; mem. Tex. Transp. Inst. Rsch. Coun., 1987—; Tex. A&M Rsch. Found. Users' Coun., 1989—. Contbr. articles to profl. jours. Recipient Best Paper award AIAA 9th Ann. Tech. Symposium Johnson Space Ctr., 1984. Mem. ASME, NSPE, Am. Nuclear Soc. (cert. governance 1983, 84, 85, Materials Sci. and Tech. Divsn. Chmn's. award 1989, mem. materials sci. and tech. disvsn. exec. com 1983-86, sec.-treas. 1985-86, vice-chmn./chair-elect 1986-87, chair 1987-88, bd. dirs. 1988-91, mem. edn. divsn. exec. com 1979-82, sec.-treas. 1982-83, vice-chmn./chair-elect 1983-84, chair 1984-85, mem. student activities com. 1976—, chair 1978-81, Oreg. sect. Edn. com. 1976, 79, 80, Oreg. sect. bd. dirs. 1977), Am. Soc. Engring. Edn., Tex. Soc. Profl. Engrs., Univ. Space Rsch. Assn. (mem. sci. coun. engring.), Pi Tau Sigma, Alpha Nu Sigma. Office: Office of Chancellor John B Connally Bldg 301 Tarrow 7th Fl College Station TX 77843-1122

PEDDICORD, ROLAND DALE, lawyer; b. Van Meter, Iowa, Mar. 29, 1936; s. Clifford Elwood and Juanitas Irene (Brittain) P.; m. Teri Linn O'Dell; children: Erin Sue, Robert Sean. BSBA with honors, Drake U., 1961, JD with honors, 1962. Bar: Iowa 1962; cert. civil trial specialist Nat. Bd. Trial Advs. Asst. atty. gen. State of Iowa, 1962-63; assoc. Steward, Crouch & Hopkins, Des Moines, 1962-65; ptnr. Peddicord, Wharton, Thune & Spencer, Des Moines, 1968—; lectr. in law Drake U., 1962-68; lectr. law Coll. Osteo. Medicine, Des Moines, 1965-72. Editor and chief Drake Law Rev., 1961-62. Past mem. nat. bd. dirs., nat. coun. YMCA of U.S.A., past vice chmn. nat. bd.; bd. dirs. past chmn. Greater Des Moines YMCA, 1968-89. With USMC, 1954-57. Mem. ABA, ATLA, Iowa Bar Assn., Polk County Bar Assn., Iowa Trial Lawyers Assn., Iowa Acad. Trial Lawyers, Am. Bd. Trial Advs. (sec.), C. Edwin Moore Inn, Am. Inns of Ct. (pres.), Iowa Workers' Compensation Attys., Iowa Def. Counsel Assn., Def. Rsch. Inst., Lawyer and Pilots Bar Assn., Aircraft Owners and Pilots Assn., Confrerie de Chaine des Rotisseurs (pres.), Des Moines Club, Wakonda Club, Met. Club, Pioneer Gun Club, Order of Coif, Delta Sigma Chi, Omicron Delta Kappa, Beta Gamma Sigma. Republican. Methodist. Office: 405 6th Ave Ste 700 Des Moines IA 50309-2433 Office: Peddicord Wharton Thune Spencer PO Box 9130 Des Moines IA 50306-9130

PEDEN, IRENE CARSWELL, electrical engineer, educator; b. Topeka, Sept. 25, 1925; d. Jay Horton and Lena (Anderson) Carswell; m. Leo J. Peden, Aug. 28, 1962; stepchildren: Jefri Lyn, Jennifer. B.S., U. Colo., 1947; M.S., Stanford U., 1958, Ph.D., 1962. Jr. engr. Del. Power & Light Co. Wilmington, 1947-49; jr. engr. Stanford Research Inst., 1949-50, research engr. in antenna research group, 1950-52, 54-57; research engr. Midwest Research Inst., Kansas City, Mo., 1952-54; research asst. Hansen Microwave Lab. Stanford U., 1958-61; acting instr. in elec. engring. Stanford U., 1959-61; asst. prof. elec. engring. U. Wash., 1961-64, assoc. prof., 1964-71, prof., 1971—; assoc. dean Coll. Engring., 1973-76, assoc. chair dept. elec. engring., 1983-86; mem. nat. adv. drug com. FDA 1971-74; mem. adv. council Sch. Engring., Stanford U., 1972-78; mem. space physics bd. Nat. Acad. Scis., 1974-76; adv. bd. Alaska Geophys. Inst., 1977-80 mem. adv. com. for applied sci. and research applications NSF 1977-81, 84—, now adv. com. for engring.; mem. Army Sci. Bd. 1978-87, vice chmn., 1983-86, chmn., 1986-87, chmn. ad hoc subgroup intelligent robotices, 1981-82, chmn. functional subgroup research, 1982-83, chmn. summer study, tng. and tng. tech., 1985, tactical I&W, Korea, 1985, tactical I&W, Alutians, 1986; adv. bd. U.S. Mcht. Marine Acad., 1978-84. Regional judging panel White House Fellows Program, 1976, 77; bd. visitors U. Calif.-Davis, 1984—; mem. engring. devel. Council U. Colo., 1984—; mem. disciplinary screening com. on engring. Council Internat. Exchange of Scholars, 1985-86; mem. preliminary screening com. Kellogg Found., 1986—, mem. interview team, 1986; mem. adv. com. Group VIII Fellows, 1987—. Recipient Golden Lyre award Iota Iota alumnae chpt. Alpha Chi Omega, 1968, Nat. Achievement award, 1972; named Woman of Achievement, Seattle Theta Sigma Phi, 1966, Woman of Year, Seattle sect. Quota Internat., 1971, Disting. Contbr. to Edn., Seattle Fedn. Women's Clubs, 1971; Disting. Alumnus award U. Colo., 1974. Fellow IEEE (chmn. Seattle sect. 1965-66, editorial bd. procs. 1965-70, 78-83, mem. coms. 1966-69, 71—, v.p. ednl. activities 1976, 77, dir., exec. com., fellows com. 1978—, awards bd. 1981, Centennial medal 1984), Explorer's Club, AAAS; mem. IEEE Antenna and Propagation Soc. (administrv. com. 1981-84), Soc. Women Engrs. (sr., chmn. Pacific N.W. sect. 1967-68, Nat. Achievement award 1973), Accreditation Bd. for Engring. and Tech. (engr-ing. edn. and accreditation com. 1975—, chmn. region VII 1976-77, chmn. engring. accreditation commn. 1981-82, dir. 1982—, exec. com. 1984-86), Internat. Union Radio Sci. (commn. on fields and waves 1976—), U.S. Nat. Com. (mem.-at-large project bd. 1988—) Am. Soc. Engring. Edn., Am. Geophys. Union, N.Y. Acad. Scis., Morter Bd. (hon. mem. Tolo chpt.), NAE, Sigma Xi, Tau Beta Pi. Home: 8752 Sand Point Way NE Seattle WA 98115 Office: U Wash Dept Elec Engring Seattle WA 98195

PEDEN, KATHERINE GRAHAM, industrial consultant; b. Hopkinsville, Ky., Jan. 2, 1926; d. William E. and Mary (Gorin) P. Student pub. schs. Vice pres. radio sta. WHOP-CBS, Hopkinsville, 1944-68; owner sta. WNVL, Nicholsville, Ky., 1961-71; commr. commerce Ky., 1963-67; mem. Gov. Ky. Cabinet, Frankfort, 1963-67; pres., cons. Katherine G. Peden & Assos. Inc., Louisville; indsl. and community developers Katherine G. Peden & Assos. Inc.; bd. dirs. Westvaco Corp., Bank of Louisville; mem. adv. bd. Norfolk So. Corp.; mem. Ky. Environ. Commn. Chmn. Louisville and Jefferson County Riverport Authority, 1975-80; civilian aide to Sec. of Army., 1978-82; mem. com. Pres's. Commn. on Status of Women, 1961-62; mem. Pres's. Commn. on Civil Disorders, 1967; pres. Ky. Derby Festival, 1979-80; Democratic nominee U.S. Senate, 1968; mem. adv. council U. Ky. Coll. Bus.; trustee Spalding U., 1980-86; bd. dirs. Louisville-Jefferson County Air Bd. Named Woman of Year Hopkinsville, 1952. Mem. Fedn. Bus., Profl. Women's Clubs (pres. state 1955-56, 1st nat. v.p. 1960-61, nat. pres. 1961-62). Mem. Christian Ch. (deaconess 1956-59, 60-63). Home: 2118 S Virginia St Hopkinsville KY 42240-3614 Office: PO Box 6268, Louisville KY402060, 268

PEDERSEN, DWITE A., state senator, alcohol/drug abuse counselor; b. Chamberlain, S.D., Oct. 20, 1941; s. Lauritz Elmer and Helen Marie (Lind-skov) P.; m. Priscilla Frances Dougherty, Apr. 3, 1970; children: Andrew, Michaela, Megan. Student, So. State U., 1960-61, So. State Tchrs. Coll., 1963-64, Doane Coll., 1989—. Cert. Alcohol/Drug Abuse Counselor, Nebr. Apprentice mortician Hobart Funeral Home, Rapid City, S.D., 1962; elem. tchr. Walcott Sch. Dist. 55, Reliance, S.D., 1962-64; from cottage counselor to dean of men Father Flanagan's, Boys Town, Nebr., 1964-75; owner, operator Denker Bar and Ballroom, Elkhorn, Nebr., 1976-77; from acct. to bus. adminstr. Internat. Trucks, Omaha, 1978-82; from counselor trainee to head counselor Eppley Treatment Ctr., Omaha, 1983; dir. adolescent Dual Diagnosis Luth. Med. Ctr., Omaha, 1985-89; substance abuse counselor Elkhorn, 1990—; state senator State of Nebr., Lincoln, 1993—. Pres. Men's Club St. Pat's Cath. Ch., 1977—, Elkhorn Concerned Citizens, founder. Recipient Svc. to Youth award Elkhorn Schs., 1990. Mem. Nat. Assn. Substance Abuse Counselors, N.E. Assn. Substance Abuse Counselors, Eagles. Republican. Avocations: family, church, politics, travel. Home: 21440 Shamrock Rd Elkhorn NE 68022-2024 Office: Nebr Legislature 1103 State Capital Lincoln NE 68509

PEDERSEN, GEORGE J., engineering company executive, computer support company executive; b. 1935. Student, Rutgers U., 1952-53. Contracts mgr. VitroLabs, West Orange, N.J., 1953-68; with Mantech Internat. Corp., Fairfax, Va., 1968—; now chmn. bd., sec. Mantech Internat. Corp. Office: Mantech Internat Corp 12015 Lee Jackson Hwy Fairfax VA 22033-3300*

PEDERSEN, KEN, recording industry executive. CFO Virgin Records Am. Inc., Beverly Hills, Calif. Office: Virgin Records Am Inc 338 N Foothill Rd Beverly Hills CA 90210*

PEDERSEN, KNUD GEORGE, economics educator, former university president; b. Three Creeks, Alta., Can., June 13, 1931; s. Hjalmar Neilsen and Anna Marie (Jensen) P.; m. Joan Elaine Vanderwarker, Aug. 15, 1953 (dec. 1988); children: Greg, Lisa; m. Penny Ann Jones, Dec. 31, 1988. Diploma in Edn., Provincial Normal U., 1952; BA, U. B.C., 1959; MA, U. Wash., 1964; PhD, U. Chgo., 1969. Asst. prof. econs. of edn. U. Toronto; asst. prof. econs. of edn., assoc. dir. U. Chgo., 1970-72; dean, assoc. prof., then prof. U. Victoria, B.C., 1972-75; acad. v.p., prof. U. Victoria, 1975-79; pres., prof. Simon Fraser U., Vancouver, B.C., 1979-83, U. B.C., Vancouver, 1983-85; pres., vice-chancellor U. Western Ont., London, Can., 1985-94, prof. econs. of edn., 1985—; bd. dirs. Assn. Univs. and Colls., Can., 1979-84, chmn., 1989-91; bd. dirs. Vancouver Bd. Trade, 1983-85; pres. Can. Club Vancouver, 1983-84; mem. coun. trustees Inst. for Rsch. on Pub. Policy, Ottawa, Ont., Can., 1983-89; chmn. Coun. Ont. Univs., 1989-91. Author: The Itinerant Schoolmaster, 1972; contbr. chpts. to books. Decorated officer Order of Can., Order of Ont.; recipient 125th Anniversary of Confedn. of Can. medal; fellow Ford Found., 1965-68, Can. Coll. Tchrs., 1977, Royal Soc. for Encouragement of Arts, 1984; also 11 major scholarships. Mem. Semiahmoo Golf and Country Club. Avocations: golf, fishing, skiing.

PEDERSEN, NORMAN A., lawyer; b. Modesto, Calif., Dec. 29, 1946; s. Melvin R. and Hilda R. (Akenhead) P. BA, U. Calif., Berkeley, 1970, MA, 1972; JD, UCLA, 1975. Bar: Calif., D.C. Trial atty. Fed. Power Commn., Washington, 1975-77; asst. to commr. Fed. Regulatory Commn., Washington, 1977-79; ptnr. Kadison, Pfaelzer, Woodard, Quinn & Rossi, Washington, 1979-87, Graham & James, Washington, 1987-88, Jones, Day, Reavis & Pogue, Washington, 1989—. Home: 5063 Loughboro Rd NW Washington DC 20016-2615 Office: Jones Day Reavis & Pogue 1450 G St NW Ste 600 Washington DC 20005-2088

PEDERSEN, PAUL RICHARD, composer, educator; b. Camrose, Alta., Can., Aug. 28, 1935; s. Richard and Anna (Rasmussen) P.; m. Jean Frances Stollery, Aug. 6, 1956; children: Rebecca, David (dec.), Katherine, Andrew. B.A., U. Sask., 1957; Mus.M., U. Toronto, 1961, Ph.D., 1970. Music dir. Camrose Lutheran Coll., 1962-64; prof. McGill U., Montreal, Que., 1966-90, chmn. dept. theory, 1970-74, dir. Electronic Music Studio, 1971-74, assoc. dean faculty of music, 1974-76, dean faculty of music, 1976-86, dir. McGill records, 1976-90; dean Faculty Music, U. Toronto, Ont., Can., 1990-95. Contbr. articles to music jours.; Composer: chamber music Woodwind Trio No. 1, 1956, Woodwind Trio No. 2, 1957, Chorale Prelude No. 2, 1958, Lament, 1958, Ricercare, 1958, Woodwind Quintet (commd. Saskatoon Summer Festival), 1959, Come Away, 1959, Fugue, 1959, Sonata for Violin and Piano (commd. Andrew Dawes), 1960, Serial Composition, 1965, An Old Song of the Sun and the Moon and the Fear of Loneliness, 1973, Wind Quintet No. 2, 1975; choral works Ecclesiastes XII, 1958, Psalm 117, 1959, All praise to Thee, 1960, Built on a Rock, 1961, Passion Oratorio, 1961, rev., 1990, God Himself is Present, 1961, O Darkest Woe, 1961, Psalm 134, 1961, On the Nativity of Christ, 1963; 12 Chorales, SAB Choir, 1974, chorale mass, SAB Choir, 1983, De Profundis Choir and Orch., 1987; electronic music The Lone Tree, 1964, Themes from the Old Testament, 1966, Fantasie, 1967, Origins, 1967, For Margaret, Motherhood and Mendelssohn, 1971; orchestral music Concerto for Orchestra, 1961, Lament, 1962. Recipient Can. Council awards, 1958, 59, 73; Queen Elizabeth II Ont. scholar, 1965; Province of Ont. grad. fellow, 1964-65. Mem. Candian League Composers. Home: 70 Indian Grove, Toronto, ON Canada M6R 2Y4 Office: U Toronto Faculty Music, Toronto, ON Canada M5S 1A1

PEDERSEN, RICHARD FOOTE, academic administrator; b. Miami, Ariz., Feb. 21, 1925; s. Ralph Martin and Gertrude May (Foote) P.; m. Nelda Newell Napier, May 9, 1953; children: Paige Elizabeth, Jonathan Foote, Kendra Gayle. BA summa cum laude, Coll. of Pacific, 1946; MA, Stanford U., 1947; PhD, Harvard U., 1950; LLD (hon.), George Williams Coll., 1964, U. of Pacific, 1966. Teaching fellow, tutor Harvard U., Cambridge, Mass., 1949-50; with UN econ. and social affairs Dept. State, Washington, 1950-53; adviser econs. and social affairs U.S. Mission to UN, N.Y.C., 1953-55; adviser polit. and security affairs, 1956-59, sr. advisor polit. and security

affairs, 1959-64, minister, counselor, 1964-66, ambassador, sr. adviser to U.S. rep., 1966-67; ambassador, dep. U.S. rep. in UN security council UN, N.Y.C., 1967-69; counselor Dept. State, 1969-73; ambassador to Hungary, 1973-75; sr. v.p. internat. U.S. Trust Co., 1975-78; pres. Am. U., Cairo, 1978-90; dir. internat. programs Calif. Poly Pomona U., 1990—; mem. adv. bd. Nat. Coun. U.S.-Arab Rels., 1985—; trustee Consortium for Internat. Devel., 1990—. Mem. Nat. Coun. of YMCA's, 1961-73; trustee Ctr. for Civic Edn., 1995—; Physicians for Peace, 1988-90. With AUS, 1943-45, ETO. Recipient Sumner Peace prize Harvard U., 1950, Outstanding Alumnus award U. Pacific, 1962; named to Order of Sacred Treasure, Gold and Silver Star, Govt. of Japan, 1987; named One of 10 Outstanding Young Men, U.S. Jr. C. of C., 1956; awarded Order of Scis. and Arts, first class Govt. of Egypt, 1990. Mem. Royal Inst. Internat. Affairs, Coun. Fgn. Rels., Am. Soc. Internat. Law, L.A. Com. on Fgn. Rels., L.A. Coun. World Affairs, Am. Fgn. Svc. Assn., Middle East Inst., UN Assn. Am., Internat. Assn. Univ. Pres., Assn. Internat. Edn. Adminstrs. Democrat. Congregationalist. Clubs: Harvard (N.Y.); Cosmos (Washington). Avocations: swimming, tennis, Egyptology, local history. Home: Twilight Park Haines Falls NY 12436 also: 2503 N Mountain Ave Claremont CA 91711-1545

PEDERSEN, WESLEY NIELS, public relations and public affairs executive; b. South Sioux City, Nebr., July 10, 1922; s. Peder Westergaard and Marie Gertrude (Sorensen) P.; m. Angela Kathryn Vavra, Oct. 17, 1948; 1 son, Eric Wesley. Student, Tri-State Coll., Sioux City, Iowa, 1940-41; BA summa cum laude, Upper Iowa U.; postgrad., George Washington U., 1958-59. Editor, writer Sioux City Jour., 1941-50; corr. N.Y. Times, Life, Time, Fortune, 1948-50; editor Dept. State, 1950-53; fgn. svc. officer Dept. State, Hong Kong, 1960-63; fgn. affairs columnist, roving corr., counselor summit meetings and fgn. ministers confs. USIA, 1953-60, chief, worldwide spl. publs. and graphics programs, 1963-69; chief Office Spl. Projects, Washington, 1969-78, Office Spl. Projects, Internat. Communication Agy., 1978-79; v.p. Fraser Assocs., pub. rels., Washington, 1979-80; dir. communications and pub. rels. Pub. Affairs Coun., Washington, 1980—; lectr. creative communications Upper Iowa U., 1975; chmn., Europe, Ambassadorial Internat. Affairs Seminar, Fgn. Svc. Inst., 1975; lectr. internat. pub. rels. Pub. Rels. Inst., Am. U., 1976; lectr. bus. and mgmt. div. NYU, 1976, 77, 78; cons. pub. rels., editorial and design; del. founding sessions 1st Amendment Congress, Phila. and Williamsburg, Va., 1980, exec. com., 1980. Columnist: Pub. Rels. Jour., 1980-85; author: Legacy of a President, 1964, American Heroes of Asian Wars, 1969; co-author: Effective Government Public Affairs, 1981; editor: Escape At Midnight and Other Stories (Pearl S. Buck), 1962, Exodus From China (Harry Redl), 1962, China's Men of Letters (K. E. Priestley), 1963, Children of China (Pearl S. Buck and Margaret Wylie), 1963, Destination the Moon (William Howard), 1964, Man on the Moon, 1964, Bounty From the Land, 1965, The Americans and the Arts (Howard Taubman), 1969, The Dance in America (Agnes de Mille), 1969, Getting the Most from Grassroots Public Affairs Programs, 1980, Cost-Effective Management for Today's Public Affairs, 1987, Making Community Relations Pay Off: Tools and Strategies, 1988, Winning at the Grassroots: How to Succeed in the Legislative Arena by Mobilizing Employees and Other Allies, 1989, Leveraging State Government Relations, 1990, Managing the Business-Employee PAC, 1992, Adding Value to the Public Affairs Function, 1994, Pub. Affairs Rev. mag., 1980-86, Impact newsletter on nat. and internat. pub. affairs, 1980—; contbr. to The Commissar, 1972, Informing the People: A Public Affairs Handbook, 1981, The Practice of Public Relations, 1984; mem. editorial bd. Pub. Rels. Quar., 1975—, Fgn. Svc. Jour., 1975-81; mem. adv. bd. Pub. Rels. News, 1991—; contbr. articles to profl. jours. Founding chmn. bd. dirs. Nat. Inst. for Govt. Pub. Info. Rsch., Am. U., 1977-80. Served with USAAF, 1943-46. Recipient 2 awards A.P. Mng. Editors Assn., Iowa, 1949, Meritorious Svc. award USIA, 1963, Presdl. commendation, 1964, 1st prizes Fed. Editors Assn., 1970, 74-75, 1st prizes Soc. Tech. Communication, 1974, 75-76, Gold award Internat. Newsletter Conf., 1982, Silver award, 1985, Eddi award for design excellence Editor's Workshop, 1983, Gold Circle award for outstanding communications Am. Soc. Assn. Execs., 1988-89, Editors' Forum award, 1988-90, 94, 95, Assn. Trends award, 1989-95, Grand prize Nat. Ann. Report Conf., 1989, Communications Concepts awards, 1989-95, Grand Prize, 1992, MerComm awards, 1990-95, Nat. Media Conf. award, 1989, 90, Internat. Acad. Commn. Arts and Scis. award 1994, Grand Prize, 1995; named Most Outstanding Info. Officer in Exec. Br., Govt. Info. Orgn., 1975, Ky. Col. and Adm. Nebr. Navy, 1984. Mem. Am. Fgn. Svc. Assn., Internat. Assn. Bus. Communicators (Communicator of Yr. Washington chpt. 1978, various awards 1973, 76-78, 84, 90, 94), Nat. Assn. Govt. Communicators (pres. 1978-79, Communicator of Yr. 1977, Disting. Svc. award 1978), Pub. Rels. Soc. Am. (mem. Counselor's Acad. 1980—, chmn. 1st Amendment task force 1980-81, co-recipient Thoth award 1980, 81, 94, 95), Fgn. Svc., Nat. Press Club, Overseas Press Club. Episcopalian. Home: 5214 Sangamore Rd Bethesda MD 20816-2322 Office: Pub Affairs Coun 1019 19th St NW Ste 200 Washington DC 20036-5105 *Keenness of mind and an abundance of luck, it is said, are the key ingredients of personal success. The truth be told, however, I've performed only one act of brilliance in my lifetime: the selection of my parents. But I've had an enormous amount of good fortune, a fact manifestly clear to anyone who has ever met my wife and son. They, thank goodness, chose me.*

PEDERSEN, WILLIAM FRANCIS, JR., lawyer; b. N.Y.C., Apr. 4, 1943; s. William F. and Priscilla S. (Auchincloss) P.; m. Ellen L. Frost, Feb. 2, 1974; children: Mark Francis, Claire Ellen. BA, Harvard U., 1965, LLB, 1968. Bar: Mass. 1969, D.C. 1978. Assoc. Ropes & Gray, Boston, 1969-72; staff atty. EPA, Washington, 1972-75; dep. gen. counsel, then assoc. gen. counsel EPA, 1976-85; staff counsel Senate Com. on Govt. Ops., Washington, 1975-76; lectr. Harvard Law Sch., 1985-86; of counsel Perkins Coie, Washington, 1987—, ptnr., 1989-94; ptnr. Shaw, Pittman, Potts & Trow-bridge, Washington, 1994—. Contbr. articles to profl. jours. Mem. ABA (standing com. on environ. law 1987-89). Democrat. Episcopalian. Office: Shaw Pittman Potts & Trowbridge 2300 N St NW Washington DC 20037-1122

PEDERSON, ARNOLD S., chemical company executive. Pres. Pam Oil Inc., Sioux Falls, S.D. Office: Pam Oil Inc 200 S Petro Ave Sioux Falls SD 57107-0571

PEDERSON, CON, animator. Grad., UCLA. Former writer, animator Walt Disney; animator Graphic Films Corp.; co-founder Abel & Assocs.; sr. animator MetroLight Studios, L.A., 1987—; animator for Redstone rocket project, also Explorer Satellite program. Spl. effects supr., animated models designer (film) 2001: A Space Odyssey. Office: MetroLight Studios 5724 W 3rd St Ste 400 Los Angeles CA 90036-3078

PEDERSON, GEORGE LUDVIG, mayor, retired law enforcer; b. Ft. Dauphin, Madagascar, Dec. 4, 1924; s. Peter Christian and Petra Ingara (Berge) P.; m. Verlene Ann Partlow, Feb. 4, 1950; 1 child, Teresa Lynn Breitinger. Master's degree, Golden State U., 1986. Capt. L.A Sheriff's Dept., 1954-84; city councilman City of Santa Clarita, Calif., 1992, mayor pro-tem, 1993, mayor, 1994—. With USN, 1943-46. Avocation: golf. Office: City of Santa Clarita 23920 Valencia Blvd Santa Clarita CA 91355

PEDERSON, GORDON ROY, state legislator, retired military officer; b. Gayville, S.D, Aug. 8, 1927; s. Roy E. and Gladys F. (Masker) P.; m. Betty L. Ballard, Mar. 8, 1955; children: James D., Carol A. Pederson Niemann, Nancy G. Pederson Holub, Gary W. Student, Yankton Coll., 1948-50, Fla. State U., 1963; advanced course, Infantry Sch., 1958-59. Drafted U.S. Army, 1945-47, commd. 2d lt., 1952, advanced through grades to lt. col., 1967, served Korean War, 1950-54; served CONUS World War II, platoon leader 17th infantry regiment, 7th infantry divsn. U.S. Army, Korea, 1953-54; rifle co. commdr. 10th mountain divsn. U.S. Army, Germany, 1955-58; instr., dir. instrn. U.S. Army Jungle Warfare Tng. Ctr. U.S. Army, Ft. Sherman, Canal Zone, 1961-63, comdr. post, 1963-64; 1st bri., 1st infantry divsn. U.S. Army, Vietnam, 1965-66; dir. tng. hdqs. U.S. Army, Ft. Leonard Wood, 1966-68; advisor Ministry of Nat. Def., Rep. China on Taiwan, Rep. China on Taiwan, 1969-70; retired U.S. Army, 1970; rep. S.D. Ho. Reps., Pierre, 1977—; operator Dairy Queen, Wall, S.D.; chmn. transp. com. S.D. Ho. Reps., 1979-93; bd. dirs. Wall Med. Svcs. 1984-93; mem. state of affairs com., commerce com., 1993. Del. S.D. Rep. Conv. 1974-78, 80-82, 84, 86, 88, 90, 92, Nat. Rep. Conv., 1976, 80, 84, 88, 92; bd. dirs. Legis. Rsch. Coun., 1988, 90, 92. Decorated Bronze Star, Medal of Merit, U.S. Presdl.

Unit Citation, Rep. Korea Presdl. Unit Citation, Rep. Vietnam Presdl. Unit Citation, Combat Infantry Badge with Star, Legion of Merit, Air Medal with 2 Oak Leaf Clusters, Army Accomodation medal with 2 oak leaf clusters, Cross of Gallantry with Palm, Republic Vietnam. Mem. VFW, DAV, Am. Legion, Retired Officers Assn., Wall C. of C., Internat. Lions Club. Lutheran. Home: PO Box 312 116 W 7th St Wall SD 57790 Office: SD Ho of Reps State Capital Bldg Pierre SD 57501

PEDERSON, RENA, newspaper editor. Editorial page editor Dallas Morning News. Office: The Dallas Morning News 508 Young St Dallas TX 75265*

PEDERSON, THORU JUDD, biologist, research institute director; b. Syracuse, N.Y., Oct. 10, 1941; s. Thorvald and Ruth (Judd) P.; m. Judith Bennett, Mar. 26, 1966; children: David, Christopher. BS, Syracuse U., 1963, PhD in Zoology, 1968. Rsch. assoc. cell biology Albert Einstein Coll. Med., N.Y.C., 1968-71; staff scientist Worcester Found. for Exptl. Biology, Shrewsbury, Mass., 1971-73, sr. scientist, 1973-83, prin. scientist and dir. Cancer Ctr., 1983—, pres., sci. dir., 1985—; trustee Mass. Biotech. Rsch. Inst.; dir. Hybridon, Inc.; mem. Med. Rsch. Com. Mass. div. Am. Cancer Soc., 1980-90; chmn. fellowships com. Marine Biol. Lab., Woods Hole, Mass.; sci. advisor Matritech, Inc. Mem. editorial bd. Jour. Cell Biology; contbr. numerous articles, papers to publs. in field. Trustee James Mountain Meml. Fund. Recipient Hudson Hoagland award Worcester Found., 1982; named Scholar Leukemia Soc. Am., 1972-77, Nat. lectr. Sigma Xi, 1984-86; grantee NIH, 1971—. Fellow AAAS; mem. Am. Soc. Cell Biology, Am. Soc. Biochemistry and Molecular Biology. Office: Worcester Found Exptl Biology 222 Maple Ave Shrewsbury MA 01545-2795*

PEDERSON, TONY WELDON, newspaper editor; b. Waco, Tex., Oct. 27, 1950; s. Lloyd Moody and Ida Frances (Walker) P.; m. Julianne Kennedy, Mar. 21, 1974. B.A., Baylor U., 1973; M.A., Ohio State U., 1976. Sports writer Waco (Tex.) Tribune, Tex., 1970-73; sports writer Houston Chronicle, 1974-75, copy editor, 1976-80, sports editor, 1980-83, mng. editor, 1983—; adj. faculty U. Houston, 1977-79. Mem. Houston Coun. Fgn. Rels. Mem. Nat. AP Mng. Editors Assn., Tex. AP Mng. Editors Assn. Methodist. Avocations: golf; reading. Office: Houston Chronicle Pub Co 801 Texas St Houston TX 77002-2906

PEDERSON, VERNON R., judge; b. N.D., Sept. 11, 1919; s. John and Tilda (Torgerson) P.; m. Evelyn I. Kraby, Oct. 11, 1952; children: Kathryn, Mark (dec.), Mary. Student, Minot State Coll., 1937-40; B.S., U. N.D., 1947, LL.B., 1949, J.D., 1969. Bar: N.D. 1949. Individual practice law Minot, N.D., 1949-51; spl. agent atty. Office Price Stabilization, Fargo, N.D., 1951-53; asst. atty. gen. State of N.D., Bismarck, 1953-74; assoc. justice N.D. Supreme Ct., Bismarck, 1975-85, surrogate judge, 1985—; gen. counsel N.D. State Hwy. Dept., 1953-74. Bd. dirs. N.D. Community Found., 1976-83. Served with U.S. Army, 1941-45. Mem. Am., N.D., Burleigh County bar assns., Am. Judicature Soc., Inst. Jud. Adminstrn. Lutheran. Home: 2029 N 2nd St Bismarck ND 58501-1737 Office: Supreme Ct Capitol Bldg Bismarck ND 58505

PEDERSON, WILLIAM DAVID, political scientist, educator; b. Eugene, Oreg., Mar. 17, 1946; s. Jon Moritz and Rose Marie (Ryan) P. BS in Polit. Sci., U. Oreg., 1967, MA in Polit. Sci., 1972, PhD in Polit. Sci., 1979. Teaching asst. polit. sci. dept. U. Oreg., Eugene, 1975-77; instr. govt. dept. Lamar U., Beaumont, Tex., 1977-79; asst. prof. polit. sci. dept. Westminster Coll., Fulton, Mo., 1979-80; asst. prof., head polit. sci. and pre-law Yankton Coll. U. S.D., 1980-81; prof. polit. sci. dept. La. State U., Shreveport, 1981—; program analyst NIH, Bethesda, Md., summer 1973; assoc. prof. jr. state program Am. U., Washington, summer 1984; rsch. assoc. Russian and East European Ctr. U. Ill., Urbana, summers 1982-94; founding dir. Washington semester La. State U., Shreveport, 1982-91, Presdl. Conf. Series, 1992—; editorial staff writer The Times, Shreveport, 1990. Author: The Rating Game in American Politics, 1987; editor: The Barberian Presidency, 1989; Congressional-Presidential Relations: Governmental Gridlock, 1991; co-editor: Grassroots Constitutionalism, 1988; Morality and Conviction in American Politics, 1990, Great Justices of the U.S. Supreme Court: Ratings and Case Studies, 1993, 2d edit., 1994, Lincoln and Leadership: A Model for a Summer Teachers Institute, 1993; Abraham Lincoln: Sources and Style of Leadership, 1994, Abraham Lincoln: Contemporary, 1995; guest editor Quarterly Jour. Ideology, 1994; contbr. articles to profl. jours. Mem. Mayor's Comm. on the Bicentennial U.S. Constn., 1987; active Barnwell Ctr., Shreveport, 1984, Am. Rose Soc., Shreveport, 1982. Served with U.S. Army, 1968-70. Recipient tng. award NIH 1973; Outstanding Prof. award Westminster Coll. 1980, La. State U., 1984; grantee La. State U., 1982, La. Endowment for Humanities, 1987, 93; fellow NEH, 1981-85. Fellow Am. Polit. Sci. Assn., Am. Judicature Soc.; mem. Abraham Lincoln Assn. (mem. bd. dirs. 1994, dir. conf. in the south, 1992, dir. 1st summer Inst. on Abraham Lincoln, 1993, grantee 1992, 93, Achievement award 1994), Ctr. Study Presidency, Internat. Soc. Polit. Psychology, Am. Studies Assn, Internat. Lincoln Assn. (bd. dirs. 1994—, pres. 1990-93). Office: La State U Dept Polit Sci One University Pl Shreveport LA 71115-2301

PEDICINI, LOUIS JAMES, manufacturing company executive; b. Detroit, June 29, 1926; s. Louis I. and Myra Ann (Bergan) P.; m. Ellen Sylvia Mulden, June 5, 1948; 1 child, Eric Louis. B.S.E.E., Wayne U., 1955. Dept. head Gen. Motors Corp., 1948-58; exec. v.p. Lester B. Knight & Assos., Inc., Chgo., 1959-76; pres. v.p. ops. Pullman Trailmobile, Chgo., 1976-81; mng. dir. Ingersoll Engrs. Inc., Rockford, Ill., 1981-82; pres. George Fischer Foundry Systems Inc., Holly, Mich., 1982-93; also bd. dirs.; chmn. George Fischer Corp., Bloomingdale, Ill., 1994—. Served with U.S. Army, 1944-46. Fellow Inst. Brit. Foundrymen; mem. Am. Foundrymen's Soc. (past bd. dirs., William H. McFadden gold medal 1994), Skokie Country Club, Plaza Club. Republican. Office: 230 Covington Dr Bloomingdale IL 60108-3106

PEDINI, KENNETH, physician; b. Hartford, Conn., Mar. 19, 1940; s. Daniel Victor and Elizabeth Catherine Pedini; m. Egle Damijonaitis; children: David D., Julian A. AB in Philosophy, Trinity Coll., 1962; MD, Boston U., 1966. Diplomate Nat. Bd. Med. Examiners, Am. Bd. Radiology. Resident radiology Boston City Hosp., 1967-70, chief resident radiology, 1969-70, jr. staff radiologist, 1970-71; jr. staff radiologist U. Hosp., Boston, 1970-71; ptnr. Shawsheen Radiology, Andover, Mass., 1971—; sr. radiologist Lawrence (Mass.) Gen. Hosp., 1971-75; dir. radiology, 1976-87; sr. radiologist Melrose (Mass.)-Wakefield Hosp., 1971-93, chief radiologist, 1993—; pres. L & M Radiology Inc., Andover, Mass., 1994—; bd. trustees Lawrence Gen. Hosp., 1984-89; pres. L&M Radiology Inc., Andover, Mass., 1994—. Bd. trustees Lawrence Gen. Hosp. Health Enterprises Inc., 1990-93; co-founder Andover Sch. of Montessori, 1975—. Fellow Am. Coll. Radiology (councilor 1979-81); mem. Mass. Radiol. Soc. (pres. 1985-86, pres.-elect 1984-85, v.p. 1983-84, exec. com. 1977-87), Mass. Med. Soc., Stonehorse Yatch Club.

PEDLEY, JOHN GRIFFITHS, archaeologist, educator; b. Burnley, Eng., July 19, 1931; came to U.S., 1959; s. George and Anne (Whitaker) P.; m. Mary Grace Sponberg, Aug. 30, 1969. BA, Cambridge (Eng.) U., 1953, MA, 1959; postgrad. (Norton fellow), Am. Sch. Classical Studies, Athens, Greece, 1963-64; PhD, Harvard U., 1965. Loeb research fellow in classical archaeology Harvard U., 1969-70; asst. prof. classical archaeology and Greek U. Mich., Ann Arbor, 1965-68; assoc. prof. U. Mich., 1968-74, acting chmn. dept. classical studies, 1971-72, 75-76; dir. Kelsey Mus. Archaeology, 1973-86, prof., 1974—; guest scholar J. Paul Getty Mus., vis. scholar UCLA, 1989; resident in archaeology Am. Acad. in Rome, 1990; mem. staff excavations, Sardis, Turkey, 1962-64, Pylos, Greece, 1964, co-dir. excavations, Apollonia, Libya, 1966-68; field dir. Corpus Ancient Mosaics, Tunisia, Thysdrus, 1972-73; co-prin. investigator excavations, Carthage, N.Africa, 1975-79, dir. excavations, Paestum, Italy, 1982-85. Author: Sardis in the Age of Croesus, 1968, Ancient Literary Sources on Sardis, 1972, Greek Sculpture of the Archaic Period: The Island Workshops, 1976, Paestum: Greeks and Romans in Southern Italy, 1990, Greek Art and Archaeology, 1992, The Sanctuary of Santa Venera at Paestum, Vol. 1, 1993; editor: New Light on Ancient Carthage, 1980; co-editor: Studies Presented to GMA Hanfmann, 1971. Am. Coun. Learned Socs. fellow, 1972-73; grantee Am. Philol. Soc., 1979, Nat. Endowment Arts Mus., 1974, 77, 79, 80, NEH, 1967, 75, 77, 83, 84; NEH fellow, 1986. Home: 1233 Baldwin Ave Ann Arbor MI 48104-3623 Office: Kelsey Mus U Mich Ann Arbor MI 48109

PEDOE, DANIEL, mathematician, writer, artist; b. London, Eng., Oct. 29, 1910; came to U.S., 1962, naturalized, 1972; B.Sc., U. London, 1930; B.A., Magdalene Coll., Cambridge, Eng., 1933, Ph.D., 1937; postgrad., Princeton U., 1935-36. Instr. Southampton U., Birmingham U., Eng., 1936-47; Leverhulme rsch. fellow Cambridge (Eng.) U., 1947-48; reader U. London, 1948-52; prof. U. Khartoum, 1952-59, U. Singapore, 1959-62, Purdue U., 1962-64; prof. math. U. Minn., Mpls., 1964-81. Author: Circles, 1957, Gentle Art of Mathematics, 1958, Projective Geometry, 1963, A Course in Geometry, 1970, Geometry and the Liberal Arts, 1976; co-author: Methods of Algebraic Geometry, 3 vols., 1947-53, Japanese Temple Geometry Problems, 1990. Recipient Lester R. Ford award for expository writing Math. Assn. Am., 1968. Mem. Am. Math. Assn. Home: 704 14th Ave SE Minneapolis MN 55414-1595

PEDRAM, MARILYN BETH, reference librarian; b. Brewster, Kans., Apr. 3, 1937; d. Edgar Roy and Elizabeth Catherine (Doubt) Crist; m. Manouchehr Pedram, Jan. 27, 1962 (Oct. 28, 1984); children: Jaleh Denise, Cyrus Andre. BS in Edn., Kans. State U., 1958; MLS, U. Denver, 1961. Cert secondary educator, Mo. 7th grade tchr. Clay Ctr. (Kans.) Pub. Schs. 1958-59, Colby (Kans.) Pub. Sch. System, 1959-60; reference libr. Topeka (Kans.) Pub. Libr., 1961-62, extension dept. head, 1963-64, reference libr., 1964-65; br. libr. asst. Denver Pub. Libr., 1965-67; reference libr. Kansas City (Mo.) Pub. Libr., Plaza Br., 1974-79, Kansas City (Mo.) Main Libr., 1979—. Mem. AARP, ALA, Mo. Libr. Assn., Pub. Libr. Assn., Kansas City Assn. Law Librs., Gluten Intolerance Group of N.Am., Celiac Sprue Assn., Kans. State U. Alumni Assn., Kansas City Online Users Group, Nat. Parks and Conservation Assn. Avocations: flower gardening, gourmet cooking, travel, reading, walking. Office: Kansas City Pub Libr 311 E 12th St Kansas City MO 64106-2412

PEDRAZA, PEDRO, academic director; b. N.Y.C., Sept. 30, 1946; s. Pedro Pedraza Algarin and Catherine (Martinez) Pedraza; m. Irza Ortiz, Sept. 3, 1964 (div. 1980); children: Pedro III, Andre; m. Enercida Guerrero, June 14, 1985; children: Lucas, Xiomara. BA, Occidental Coll., 1968; MS, Columbia U., 1973. Rsch. dir. Ctr. for Puerto Rican Studies CUNY, N.Y.C., 1973—, acting dir. Ctr. for Puerto Rican Studies, 1994. Bd. dirs. Educators for Social Responsibility, N.Y.C., 1990-94, Advocates for Children, N.Y.C. 1987-94. Home and Office: Hunter Coll Ctr Puerto Rican Studies 160 E 107th St # 1 New York NY 10029

PEDROTTI, LENO STEPHANO, physics educator; b. Zeigler, Ill., May 21, 1927; s. Celeste Louis and Dolores (Galeaz) P.; m. Wilma Jean Sullivan, June 23, 1951; children—Daro Stephano, Michael Louis, Sandra Maria, Laura Jean, Catherine Ann, Leno Matthew, Mary Ann, John Owen. B.S. in Edn, Ill. State U., 1949; M.S. in Physics, U. Ill., 1951; Ph.D. U. Cin., 1961. Teaching asst. U. Ill., Urbana, 1949-51; prof. physics, chmn. dept. Air Force Inst. Tech., Wright-Patterson AFB, Ohio, 1951-82, prof. emeritus, 1982—; cons., editor Ctr. Occupational Rsch. & Devel., Waco, Tex., 1975-82; sr. v.p., 1982—; presenter in field, 1982—; author, editor, lectr. laser and electro-optics Engring. Tech., Inc., Waco, 1978—; mem. indsl. adv. com. laser electro-optics program Cin. Tech. Coll., 1981-82; tech. cons. Univ. Eye Surgeons, Inc., Ohio State U., 1979-82; mem. exec. com. joint svcs. optical program Optical Scis. Ctr., U. Ariz., 1975-82. Author: Principles of Technology, 1986, Introduction to Optics, 1987, rev. edit., 1993, Applied Mathematics, 1988; contbg. author: Technical Prep Associate Degree: A Win/Win Experience, 1991, The Science Technology, Society Movement, 1993; contbr. articles to profl. jours. Faculty fellow NSF, 1959. Mem. Am. Nuclear Soc., Am. Phys. Soc. (vice chmn. then chmn. So. Ohio sect. 1974-76), Laser Inst. Am. (bd. dirs. 1974-84), Am. Assn. Physics Tchrs., Am. Soc. Engring. Edn., Optical Soc. Am., Am. Vocat. Assn. (Outstanding Mem. award 1988 vocat. instrnl. materials affiliate), Nat. Council Tchrs. Math., Sigma Xi, Tau Beta Pi (Outstanding Tchr. award 1961, 62, 63, 68), Sigma Pi Sigma. Home: 11006 Trailwood Dr Waco TX 76712-3131 Office: Cord 601 Lake Air Dr Waco TX 76710-5878

PEEBLER, CHARLES DAVID, JR., advertising executive; b. Waterloo, June 8, 1936; s. Charles David and Mary E. (Barnett) P.; student Drake U., 1954-56; m. Susie Jacobs, June 5, 1958 (div. 1977); children: David Jacobs, Mark Walter; m. Tonita Worley, Nov. 12, 1979; 1 son, Todd Whitney. Asst. to exec. v.p. J.L. Brandeis & Sons, Omaha, 1956-58; with Bozell, Jacobs, Kenyon & Eckhardt (formerly Bozell & Jacobs), 1958—, v.p., mem. plans. bd. 1960-65, pres. mid-continent ops., Omaha, 1965-67, pres., CEO, 1967-86, CEO, 1986—. Hon. chmn. bd. dirs. Am. Craft Mus.; bd. dirs. Nat. Jr. Achievement of Am. Mem. Drake U., Southampton Hosp., Gtr. N.Y. Coun. Boy Scouts Am., Madison Square Boys and Girls Club, Nat. Ctr. Learning Disabilities; partnership corp. com. Central Park Conservancy; campaign steering com. Morehouse Sch. Medicine. Mem. Nat. Golf Links Am., CEO Orgn., Blind Brook Club (Purchase), Eldorado Country Club (Indian Wells), Old Baldy Club, Mill Reef Club, Meadow Club (Southampton). Home: 166 E 64th St New York NY 10021-7478 Office: Bozell Worldwide 40 W 23rd St New York NY 10010-5200

PEEBLES, CARTER DAVID, lawyer; b. Chgo., July 9, 1934; s. Carter Davis and Vera Virginia (Howd) P.; m. Donna Ruth Hostetter, Aug. 3, 1957; children: John Carter, Mary Elizabeth, Sarah Anne. A.B., DePauw U., 1956; M.A., U. Stockholm, Sweden, 1955; J.D., U. Chgo., 1959. Bar: Ind. 1959, Ill. 1960. Ptnr. Peebles, Thompson, Rogers & Skelloff and predecessor firms, Ft. Wayne, Ind., 1976-91; pvt. practice law Ft. Wayne, 1991—; faculty labor relations Purdue U. Regional Campus; U.S. commr., 1961-71, U.S. magistrate, 1971-84. Author: (with others) Model Business Corporation Act, 3 vols, 1960, Indiana Bankruptcy Handbook, 2d edit, 1976, Business Practice Under the UCC, 1970, (with Daniel E. Johnson) Indiana Legal Business Forms, 2 vols, 1967, Forms and Comment, 2 vols, 1970, (with James A. Knauer) Indiana Collection Law, 1981, (with Jerald I. Ancel) Farm Foreclosure Prevention, 1983, (with Thomas L. Ryan) The Farmer in Financial Distress, 1985, (with David H. Kleiman) Farmers and Lenders - The Financial Dilemma, 1986, (with Daniel J. Skekoff) Basic Bankruptcy in Indiana, 1987, (with J.T. Massey) Farm Foreclosure Defense, 1990; contbr. articles to profl. jours. Bd. dirs. Antioch Found., Religious Instrn. Assn., Religious Heritage of Am. Mem. ABA, Ill., Ind., Allen County Bar Assns., Am. Bankruptcy Inst., Am. Agrl. Law Assn., Phi Delta Phi. Lodges: Masons, Shriners, Jesters. Home: 6737 Blue Mist Rd Fort Wayne IN 46819-1503 Office: 1325 Spy Run Ave Fort Wayne IN 46805 *As a young man, I was passionate, and later compassionate. Now, cynicism has me. Men used to do business on a handshake; now, a lengthy contract seems made only to be broken. People seem to seek the unfair advantage, forgetting that the only "good deal" is the deal fair to both sides. Fortunately, most people don't want something for nothing, will recognize a moral obligation and, many times, possess deep moral courage. If there is revolution in this country, it will not be black against white or have against have-not, but care against care-not. It appears that compassion wins after all.*

PEEBLES, DAVID L., light manufacturing executive. Chmn. bd. Ferguson Enterprises Inc., Newport News, Va., 1989—. Office: Ferguson Enterprises Inc 618 Bland Blvd Newport News VA 23602

PEEBLES, JAMES W., publishing executive. BTheology, Am. Baptist Theol. Seminary; BA Romance Langs., Music Edn., Tenn. State U., MA Romance Langs.; MA Linguistics, Bi-Cultural Studies, U. Maine; PhD, U. Madrid. Tchr. various pub., pvt. schs.; pres., founder Winston-Derek Pub. Group (Winston-Derek record co. subs. 1986), Nashville. Contbr. The Original African Heritage Study Bible, author over 750 books, papers in field. Office: Winston-Derek Publishing Co 1722 W End Ave Nashville TN 37203-2602

PEEBLES, PEYTON ZIMMERMAN, JR., electrical engineer, educator; b. Columbus, Ga., Sept. 10, 1934; s. Peyton Zimmerman Peebles Sr. and Maida Erlene (Denton) Dials; m. Barbara Ann Suydam, Sept. 6, 1969; children: Peyton Zimmerman III, Edward Arlen. BSEE, Evansville Coll., 1957; MSEE, Drexel Inst., 1963; PhD, U. Pa., 1967. Design engr. RCA, Moorestown, N.J., 1958-64, systems engr., 1966-69; prof. U. Tenn., Knoxville, 1969-75, 76-81; vis. prof. U. Hawaii, Honolulu, 1975-76; prof. U. Fla., Gainesville, 1981-84, 1990—, assoc. chmn., 1984-90; cons. in field. Author: Communication System Principles, 1976, Probability, Random Variables and Random Signal Principles, 1980, 3d edit., 1993, Digital Communication Systems, 1987; prin. author: Principles of Electrical

Engineering, 1991; contbr. articles to profl. jours.; patentee in field. Capt. USAFR, 1957-61. David Sarnoff fellow, 1964-66. Fellow IEEE; mem. Sigma Xi, Eta Kappa Nu, Tau Beta Pi, Sigma Pi Sigma, Phi Beta Chi. Methodist. Avocations: fishing, painting, woodworking. Office: U Fla Elec Engring Dept Gainesville FL 32611

PEEBLES, PHILLIP JAMES E., physicist, educator; b. Winnipeg, Man., Can., May 25, 1935; married Alison Peebles; children: Lesley, Ellen, Marion. BS, U. Man., 1958; PhD, Princeton U., 1962; DSc (hon.), U. Toronto, 1986, U. Chgo., 1986, McMaster U., 1989, U. Man., 1989. Instr. Princeton U., N.J., 1961-62, rsch. assoc., 1962-64, rsch. staff mem., 1964-65, from asst. prof. to prof., 1965-84, Albert Einstein prof. sci., 1984—. Recipient A.C. Morrison award Natural Sci. N.Y. Acad. Sci., 1977, Eddington medal Royal Astronomy Soc., 1981, Heineman Prize, Am. Astronomy Soc., 1982. Fellow Am. Acad. Arts and Scis., Am. Phys. Soc., Royal Soc., Royal Soc. Can.; mem. NAS (fgn. assn.), AAAS, Am. Astronomy Soc., Internat. Astron. Union. Office: Princeton U Dept Physics Jodwin Hall PO Box 708 Washington Rd Princeton NJ 08544-0708*

PEEBLES, ROBERT ALVIN, horse breed registry executive; b. Petersburg, Va., June 29, 1947; s. William Benjamin and Winifred (Morris) P.; m. Mary Jane Heyel, Mar. 24, 1986. Staff accountant Haskins & Sells, Miami, Fla., 1970-74; bus. mgr. Mackle Co., Miami, 1978-79; parks mgr. Dade County Parks and Recreation, Miami, 1975-77; bus. mgr. Shutts & Bowen, Miami, 1979-82; pres. Nat. Show Horse Registry, Louisville, 1982—, Chenoweth Run, Inc., Louisville, 1983—. Mem. Am. Horse Coun. (horse show adv. com. 1987), Am. Horse Shows Assn. (mem. lic. ofcls. com., clinics com., nat. show horse com.), Midwest Nat. Show Horse Assn., United Profl. Horsemen's Assn., Arabian Horse Assn. (pres., bd. dirs. 1974-77, treas. S.E. region 1976-78), Rock Creek Riding Club (bd. dirs.). Republican. Methodist. Avocations: swimming, horseback riding, golf. Home: 3305 Mount Shasta Way Louisville KY 40241 Office: Nat Show Horse Registry 11700 Commonwealth Dr Louisville KY 40299-2344

PEECHATKA, WALTER NORMAN, government official; b. East Stroudsburg, Pa., Sept. 3, 1939; s. Walter Clinton and Lillian Mae (Post) P.; m. Bonita Louise Umholtz, Apr. 20, 1968; children—Troy, Trent. B.S. in Forestry, Pa. State U., University Park, 1961. Asst. supt. coop. for mgmt. Dept. Forests and Waters, Harrisburg, Pa., 1967-69; program specialist State Soil and Water Conservation Commn., Harrisburg, 1969-71; dir. Bur. Soil and Water Conservation, Harrisburg, 1971-82; exec. vice. pres. Soil Conservation Soc. Am., Ankeny, Iowa, 1982-87; dir. Bur. Plant Industry Pa. Dept. Agr., Harrisburg, 1987-91, dep. sec. for regulatory programs, 1991-95, exec. dep. sec., 1995—. Served to capt. USAR, 1962-64. Recipient Pres.'s Citation, Soil Conservation Soc. Am., 1983, Disting. Svc. award Nat. Assn. Conservation Distrs., 1986. Mem. Am. Assn. Soil Conservation Adminstrv. Officers (pres. 1978), Pa. Forestry Assn. (pres. 1973-74). Lutheran. Office: Pa Dept Agr Exec Dep Sec Exec Office 2301 N Cameron St Harrisburg PA 17110-9408

PEELE, ROGER, hospital administrator; b. Elizabeth City, N.C., Dec. 24, 1930; s. Joseph Emmett and Catherine (Groves) P.; m. Diana Egan, June 15, 1963 (dec.); children: Amy, Rodney, Holly; m. Gail Nelson Oct. 15, 1992. A.B., U. N.C., 1955; M.D., U. Tenn., 1960. Cert. adminstrv. psychiatry, 1970 cert. forensic psychiatry, 1982. Intern St. Elizabeths Hosp., Washington, 1960-61; resident in psychiatry St. Elizabeths Hosp., 1961-64, tng. officer, 1964-67, chief of service William A. White div., 1967-69; dir. Area D Community Mental Health Center, 1969-73, asst. supt., 1974-75, 77-79, acting supt., 1975-77, chmn. dept. psychiatry, 1979—; clin. instr. psychiatry George Washington U., 1965-67, asst. clin. prof., 1967-71, assoc. clin. prof., 1971-79, clin. prof., 1979—; asst. dir. NIMH, 1978-79; chief clin. officer D.C. Commn. on Mental Health, 1987-91. Contbr. articles on clin., forensic and adminstrv. issues in Am. psychiatry to profl. jours. Served with USAF, 1950-53. Superior Service award HEW, 1967. Fellow Am. Coll. Psychiatry, Am. Psychiat. Assn. (speaker 1986-87, Adminstr. of Yr. 1989); mem. AMA, D.C. Med. Soc., Am. Assn. Psychiat. Adminstrs. (past pres.), Group for Advancement Psychiatry, Med. Soc. St. Elizabeth's Hosp. (past pres.), Fed. Physicians Assn. (past pres.). Episcopalian. Home: 5302 41st St NW Washington DC 20015-1904 Office: St Elizabeths Campus Washington DC 20032 *A key to effective treatment is not to allow the seductiveness of logic to narrow one's observations.*

PEELER, BOB, state official; b. Gaffney, S.C., 1952; s. Smith and Sally (Bratton) P.; m. Bett Carter; children: Caroline, Robert, Er. V.p. Peeler's Milk; former chmn. Cherokee County Sch. Bd., S.C. State Bd. Edn.; now lt. gov. State of S.C.; founding mem. advancement bd. Coll. Commerce, Clemson U. Mem. S.C. Dairy Assn. (past pres.), Cherokee County C. of C. (past pres.), Sertoma Internat. (life), Rotary (Gaffney), Masons, York Rite. Republican. Methodist. Office: Office Lt Gov PO Box 142 Columbia SC 29202

PEELER, SCOTT LOOMIS, JR., foreign language educator; b. Rome, Ga., Aug. 25, 1947; s. Scott Loomis Sr. and Emily Willis P. BA in Spanish and French, U. South Fla., 1969, MA in Spanish and Edn., 1974; EdD candidate, Ariz. State U., 1982-91. Cert. tchr., Fla. Tchr. Spanish Polk County Schs., Lakeland, Fla., 1969—; tchr. Brandon (Fla.) Adult and Community Sch., 1978-79, Hillsborough Community Coll., Fla., 1986; grad. research asst. Ctr. Indian Edn., Ariz. State U., Tempe, 1983-84; bi-lingual census worker U.S. Dept. Census, Tampa, 1980; part-time tchr. tribal mgmt. prog. Scottsdale (Ariz.) Community Coll., 1988; lectr. in field. Author: Historical Markers and Monuments in Tampa and Hillsborough County, Florida, 1994; contbr. articles to profl. jours. Donor Peeler Am. Indian Scholarship U. South Fla., 1986; active Ptnrs. of Ams., Sister Cities Internat., Tampa, 1972—, chair edn. com., bd. dirs., 1990—; mem. Tampa Hist. Soc., 1972—, bd. dirs. 1994—, Mus. Cherokee Indian (life), Ybor City Mus. (charter); started ptnr. city relationship between Lakeland, Fla. and Valledupar, Cesar, Colombia, 1977; co-chair Ariz. Indian Edn./Native Am. Legal Issues Conf., 1984; mem. pres.'s coun. U. South Fla.; mem. Sister Cities Com., Lakeland Fla. (del. on official visit to Japan, 1993). Recipient Teaching Incentive award Carnation Milk Corp., Phoenix, 1984, named one of Outstanding Young Men of Am., Montgomery, Ala., 1984; Am. Indian Leadership prog. grantee Ariz. State U., 1982-84; Newberry Library fellow Am. Indian Ctr. History, Chgo., 1981. Mem. Nat. Indian Edn. Assn. (Ariz. steering com. 1984), Huguenot Soc. S.C. (life), Fla. Geneal. Soc., U. South Fla. Alumni Assn., Christian Hope Indian Eskimo Fellowship, Cajun Connection, Alliance Francaise, Nat. Congress Am. Indians, Tampa Trolley Soc., Krewe of the Knights of Sant 'Yago, Tampa Bay Area Camellia Soc., Nat. Mus. Am. Indians (charter), Nat. Indian Adult Edn. Assn. (planning conf. in Tampa 1995). Home: 433 Summit Chase Dr Valrico FL 33594-3841 Office: George Jenkins High Sch 6000 Lakeland Highlands Rd Lakeland FL 33813

PEELER, STUART THORNE, petroleum industry executive and independent oil operator; b. Los Angeles, Oct. 28, 1929; s. Joseph David and Elizabeth Fiske (Boggess) P.; m. Sylvia Frances Townley, Nov. 5, 1985. B.A., Stanford U., 1950, J.D., 1953. Bar: Calif. 1953. Ptnr. Musick, Peeler & Garrett, Los Angeles, 1958-73; with Santa Fe Internat. Corp., Orange, Calif., 1973-81; v.p., sec., assoc. gen. counsel Santa Fe Internat. Corp., 1973-74, sr. v.p., gen. counsel, dir., 1975-81; vice-chmn. bd., chmn. exec. com. Supron Energy Corp., 1978-82; chmn. bd., chief exec. officer Statex Petroleum, Inc., 1982-89; chmn., pres. and chief exec. officer Putumayo Prodn. Co., 1989—; bd. dirs. Cal Mat Co., Homestake Mining Co., Homestake Gold of Australia Ltd., Chieftain Internat. Inc. Trustee J. Paul Getty Trust; mem. U.S. Tuna Team, 1957-67, capt., 1966. Served with U.S. Army, 1953-55. Decorated Army Commendation medal. Mem. State Bar Calif., Am. Judicature Soc., AIME, Theta Chi, Phi Delta Phi, Tucson Country Club. Republican. Congregationalist. Office: PO Box 35852 Tucson AZ 85740-5852

PEENO, LARRY NOYLE, state agency administrator, consultant; b. Evansville, Ind., Dec. 24, 1941; s. Paul Albert and Marcella (Imogene) Franz; m. Margaret Marie Graf, June 8, 1973. AB, Western Ky. U., 1968, MA, 1969; EdD, U. Mo., 1977. Cert. tchr. Mo. Art tchr. Normandy Sr. High Sch., St. Louis, 1974-90, chmn. art dept., 1979-88; dist. art coord. Normandy Sch. Dist., St. Louis, 1983-88; fine arts supr. Dept. Elem. and Secondary Edn., Jefferson City, Mo., 1990—; mem. adv. bd. St. Louis Art Mus., 1988—. Contbg. author: Supervision and Administration: Programs,

Positions, Perspectives, 1991, Nat. Standards For Arts Edn.: What Every Young American SHould Know and Be Able To Do in The Arts, 1994, Nat. Visual Arts Standards, 1994; editor Show-Me-Art newsletter, 1983-84. With USAF, 1959-62. Mem. ASCD, Nat. Art Edn. Assn. (nat. program coord. 1993, bd. dirs. 1995—, Nat. Newsletter award 1983-84, Award of Excellence 1983-84), Nat. Assn. State Dirs. Art Edn., Mo. Art Edn. Assn. (Secondary Art Tchr. of Yr. 1987-88, Outstanding Art Educator award 1983-84), Music Educators Nat. Conf., Mo. Music Educators Assn. Office: Dept Elem and Secondary Edn 205 Jefferson State Ofc Jefferson City MO 65102

PEEPLES, RUFUS RODERICK, JR. (RODDY PEEPLES), farm and ranch news radio broadcaster; b. Tehuacana, Tex., July 3, 1932; s. Rufus Roderick and Josephine (Gray) P.; m. Bettimae Scrivener, Aug. 8, 1953; children: James Roderick, Deidre Lynn. BA, Tex. A&M Coll., 1953. Farm dir. KADA Radio, Ada, Okla., 1953-56, KGNO Radio, Dodge City, Kans., 1956-59, KLIK Radio, Jefferson City, Mo., 1959; assoc. farm dir. KWFT Radio, Wichita Falls, Tex., 1959-64; farm and ranch dir. and owner Voice of S.W. Agr. Radio Network, San Angelo, Tex., 1964—; mem. adv. bd. Tex. Agrl. Lifetime Leadership Program, College Station, 1987—, West Tex. Boys Ranch, San Angelo, 1966—; mem. devel. coun. Tex. A&M U. Coll. Agr. and Life Scis., 1992—. Named Man of Yr. in Tex. Agr., Tex. Assn. County Agrl. Agts., 1984; recipient Ann. Comms. award Tex. Profl. Agrl. Workers, 1982. Mem. Nat. Assn. Farm Broadcasters (pres. 1982, Farm Broadcaster of Yr. 1992), San Angelo C. of C. Republican. Methodist. Avocations: flying, music, photography.

PEEPLES, WILLIAM DEWEY, JR., mathematics educator; b. Bessemer, Ala., Apr. 19, 1928; s. William Dewey and Thelma Jeannette (Chastain) P.; m. Katie Ray Blackerby, Aug. 30, 1956; children: Mary Jeannette, William Dewey III, Gerald Lewis, Stephen Ray. B.S., Samford U., 1948; M.S., U. Wis., 1949; Ph.D., U. Ga., 1951. Rsch. mathematician Ballistics Rsch. Lab., Aberdeen, Md., summer 1951; mem. faculty Samford U., Birmingham, Ala., 1951-56, prof. math., 1959—, head dept., 1967—; mem. faculty Auburn U., 1956-59; cons. Hayes Internat. Corp. Co-author: Modern Mathematics for Business Students, 1969, Finite Mathematics, 1974, Modern Mathematics with Applications to Business and the Social Sciences, 4th edit, 1986, Finite Mathematics with Applications to Business and the Social Sciences, 1981, 2d edit., 1987; Contbr. articles to profl. publs. Served to 1st lt. AUS, 1954-56. Mem. Am. Math. Soc., Math. Assn. Am., Asst. Council Tchrs. Math., Ala. Coll. Tchrs. Math. (pres. 1969), Sigma Xi, Pi Mu Epsilon, Phi Kappa Phi (pres. 1977), Lambda Chi Alpha. Baptist (deacon, chmn. 1986). Club: Mason (Shriner). Home: 419 Poinciana Dr Birmingham AL 35209-4129

PEER, GEORGE JOSEPH, metals company executive; b. St. Louis, Aug. 26, 1925; s. George J. and Melba (Rahning) P.; m. Mary Jane Hazlewood, Feb. 14, 1948; children—Linda, Gary, Steven, Scott. B.S., Purdue U., 1945, M.S., 1948; postgrad., Advanced Mgmt. Program, Harvard, 1967. Operating supr. Republic Steel Corp., Canton, Ohio, 1948-54; various sales positions to v.p. sales Basic, Inc., Chgo., Cleve., 1954-63; v.p. marketing Handy & Harman, N.Y.C., 1963-71; dir. Handy & Harman, 1971-75, group v.p. precious metals, 1972-75; chmn., pres., chief exec. officer Multi-Metal Wire Cloth, Inc., 1975-88; pres. Holyoke Wire Cloth Co., 1975-88, Multi-Wedge Corp., 1976-88, United-Holyoke Corp., 1980-86; pres., chief exec. officer Liquid-Solids Separation Corp., 1988-93, dir., 1988—; bd. dirs. Lewis Corp., chmn. Phillips Steel Fabricators, Inc., 1989-93. Chmn. bd. Lucas Milhaupt, Inc., Cudahy, Wis., 1967-75. Served with USNR, 1943-46, 51-53. Mem. Am. Mgmt. Assn., Nat. Indsl. Conf. Bd., Am. Inst. Mining and Metall. Engrs., Tau Beta Pi, Kappa Delta Rho. Republican. Conglist. Clubs: Mount Kisco Country, Cornell of N.Y. Home: 21-31 Croton Lake Rd Katonah NY 10536 Office: PO Box 9 Northvale NJ 07647

PEER, LARRY HOWARD, literature educator; b. Ogden, Utah, Jan. 2, 1942; s. Howard Harvey and Edna Celina (Baron) P. BA, Brigham Young U., 1963, MA, 1965; PhD, U. Md., 1969. From asst. to assoc. prof. U. Ga., Athens, 1968-75; assoc. prof. Brigham Young U., Provo, Utah, 1975-78, prof., 1978—; acting head dept. comparative lit. U. Ga., Athens, 1973-74, Brigham Young U., Provo, 1978-81; pres. Western Regional Honors Coun., 1978-79; exec. dir. Am. Conf. on Romanticism, 1992—. Author: Beyond Haworth, 1984, The Reasonable Romantic, 1986, The Romantic Manifesto, 1988. Mem. MLA, Am. Comparative Lit. Assn. (exec. officer 1988-94), Am. Soc. for Aesthetics, Rocky Mountain Soc. for Aesthetics (pres. 1986-87), Internat. Byron Soc., Internat. Brontë Soc. Mem. LDS Ch. Avocation: travel. Office: Brigham Young U Comparative Lit Dept Provo UT 84602

PEERCE, LARRY, film director; b. Bronx, N.Y.; s. Jan Peerce. Dir.: One Potato, Two Potato, 1964, The Incident, 1967, Goodbye Columbus, 1969, The Sporting Club, 1971, A Separate Peace, 1972, Ash Wednesday, 1973, The Other Side of the Mountain, 1975, Two Minute Warning, 1976, The Other Side of the Mountain-Part II, 1978, The Bell Jar, 1979, Why Would I Lie?, 1980, Love Child, 1982, Hard to Hold, 1984, Wired, 1989; TV films include A Stranger Who Looks Like Me, 1974, I Take These Men, 1983, Love Lives On, 1985, The Fifth Missile, 1986, Prison for Children, 1987, Elvis and Me, 1988, The Court-Martial of Jackie Robinson, 1990, Murder at the PTA Luncheon, 1990, A Woman Named Jackie, 1991, Child of Rage, 1992, Poisoned by Love: The Kern County Murders, 1993; miniseries include Queenie, 1987, The Neon Empire, 1989. Office: 12700 Ventura Blvd Studio City CA 91604-2429 also: 225 W 34th St Ste 1012 New York NY 10125*

PEERCE, STUART BERNARD, lawyer; b. N.Y.C., Oct. 18, 1931; s. Jacob Perlmutter and Celia (Alpern) P.; m. Lois Peerce; children: Steven L., Marjorie J. Peerce Fuerst, Carol L. A.B., Columbia U., 1952, J.D., 1954. Bar: N.Y. 1954. Assoc. Donovan, Leisure, Newton & Irvine, N.Y.C., 1954-62, ptnr., 1963—. Harlan Fiske Stone scholar, 1952, 53. Mem. ABA, Assn. of Bar of City of N.Y. Home: 245 E 58th St New York NY 10022-1201 Office: Donovan Leisure Newton & Irvine 30 Rockefeller Plz New York NY 10112-0001

PEERMAN, DEAN GORDON, magazine editor; b. Mattoon, Ill., Apr. 25, 1931; s. Staley Jacob and Irene (Monen) P. B.S. with highest distinction, Northwestern U., 1953; postgrad., Cornell U., 1953-54; B.D., Yale, 1959; D.D., Kalamazoo Coll., 1987. With Christian Century Found., 1959—; copy editor Christian Century mag., 1959-61, assoc. editor, 1961-64, mng. editor, 1964-81, exec. editor, 1981-85, sr. editor, 1985—. Author: (with M.E. Marty) Pen-ultimates, 1963, (with Marty, L.M. Delloff, J.M. Wall) A Century of The Century, 1987; editor: Frontline Theology, 1967; co-editor: (with Marty) New Theology 1-10, 1964-73, A Handbook of Christian Theologians, 1965, enlarged edit., 1984, (with Alan Geyer) Theological Crossings, 1971. Contbr.: Chile: Under Military Rule, 1974. Active Chgo. community theater groups. Mem. ACLU, Fellowship of Reconciliation, Amnesty Internat., Clergy and Laity Concerned, Phi Beta Kappa. Democrat. Baptist. Office: 407 S Dearborn St Chicago IL 60605-1111

PEERS, MICHAEL GEOFFREY, archbishop; b. Vancouver, B.C., Can., July 31, 1934; s. Geoffrey Hugh and Dorothy Enid (Mantle) P.; m. Dorothy Elizabeth Bradley, June 29, 1963; children: Valerie Anne Leslie, Richard Christopher Andre, Geoffrey Stephen Arthur. Zert.edlnn., U. Heidelberg, Fed. Republic Germany, 1955; BA, U. B.C., Vancouver, 1956; Licentiate in Theology, Trinity Coll., Toronto, Ont., 1959, DD (hon.), 1977; DD (hon.), St. John's Coll., Winnipeg, Man., 1981, Wycliffe Coll. Toronto, 1987, Kent U., Canterbury, Eng., 1988, Montreal Diocesan Coll., Que., Can., 1989, Coll. of Emmanual and St. Chad, Sask., Can., 1990, Thorneloe U., 1991; DCL (hon.), Bishop's U., Lennoxville, Que., 1993. Ordained to ministry Anglican Ch. as deacon, 1959, as priest, 1960, consecrated bishop, 1977. Asst. curate St. Thomas Ch., Ottawa, 1959-61; chaplain U. Ottawa, 1961-66; rector St. Bede's Ch., Winnipeg, 1966-72, St. Martin's Ch., Winnipeg, 1972-74; dean of Qu'Appelle, Regina, Sask., 1974-77; bishop Qu'Appelle, 1977-82, archbishop, 1982-86; instr. Ottawa Tchrs. Coll., 1962-66, St. Paul's High Sch., Winnipeg, 1967-69.

PEERY, TROY ALFRED, JR., home furnishing company executive; b. Fredericksburg, Va., May 3, 1946; s. Troy Alfred and Lola E. (Jenkins) P.; m. Lynn Margaret Howard, July 19, 1969; children: Troy III, Casey Lynn. AA, Bluefield Coll., 1966; BS in Acctg., Va. Poly. Inst. and State U., 1968. CPA, Va. Staff acct. Arthur Young & Co., Richmond, Va., 1968-72; controller Heilig Meyers Co., Richmond, 1972-74, treas., 1974-80, sec.-treas., 1980-82, sr. v.p. fin., 1982-84, exec. v.p., 1984-86, pres., 1986—, also bd.

dirs. Mem. adv. bd. acctg. dept. Va. Poly. Inst. and State U., Blacksburg, 1986—; bd. dirs. Med. Coll. Va. Found., Richmond, 1987—; bd. dirs. Arts Council Richmond Inc., 1986—, v.p., 1987—. Fellow Fin. Execs. Inst. (pres. Va. chpt. 1984-85, bd. dirs. 1982-86). Baptist. Clubs: Hermitage Country (bd. dirs. 1984—, pres. 1987—), Westwood Racquet (Richmond); Farmington Country (Charlottesville, Va.). Office: Heilig Meyers Co 2235 Staples Mill Rd Richmond VA 23230-2946

PEET, CHARLES D., JR., lawyer; b. N.Y.C., Sept. 3, 1935; s. Charles D. and Margaret Louise (Sherman) P.; m. Penny Levy, July 29, 1967; children—Alisa, Amanda. B.A., Yale U., 1957; J.D., Harvard U. 1960. Bar: N.Y. 1962. Assoc. Milbank, Tweed, Hadley & McCloy, N.Y.C., 1960-68, ptnr., 1969—. Mem. ABA, N.Y. State Bar Assn., Assn. Bar N.Y.C. Internat. Bar Assn. Office: Milbank Tweed Hadley & McCloy 1 Chase Manhattan Plz New York NY 10005-1401

PEET, CREIGHTON HOUCK, brokerage firm executive; b. N.Y.C., Oct. 30, 1938; s. Creighton Byrd and Bertha Anne (Houck) P.; m. Dana Appel Weiss, Mar. 10, 1984; 1 child, Miles Creighton; children by previous marriage: Creighton Christopher, Ross Creighton. B.S. in Chem. Engring., Tufts U., Medford, Mass., 1961; M.B.A., U. Pa., Phila., 1963. Analyst Irving Trust Co., N.Y.C., 1963-66; investment analyst Eastman Dillon, N.Y.C., 1966-70; various mgmt. positions Cowen & Co., N.Y.C., 1970—, now ptnr. Home: 101 Central Park W New York NY 10023-4204 Office: Cowen & Co Financial Sq New York NY 10005

PEETE, CALVIN, professional golfer; b. Detroit, July 18, 1943; s. Dennis and Irenia (Bridgeford) P.; m. Christine Sears, Oct. 24, 1974; children: Charlotte, Calvin, Rickie, Dennis, Kalvanetta. Grad. in adult edn., Highland Park Schs., Detroit, 1982; cert. degree hon., Wayne State U., 1983. Profl. golfer Sawgrass, Fla., 1975-84; winner Greater Milw. Open, 1979, 82, Anheuser-Busch Classic, 1982, Atlanta Classic, 1983, Phoenix Open, 1985, Tournament Players Championship, 1985-86, U.S. F & G, 1986; exhibitionist Ptnrs. for Youth, Miami, Fla., 1982—; Desert Mahie Jr. Golf, Phoenix, 1983—, City of Atlanta Jr. Golf, 1983—, Calvin Peete-Augustus J. Calloway Golf Tournament, Detroit, 1983—; mem. U.S.A. Team vs. Japan, 1982-83, Ryder Cup Team, 1983, 85. Active supporter Sickle Cell Anemia Found., Palm Beach and Lee Counties (Fla.). Recipient Ben Hogan award, 1983, Good Guy award Gordin Gin, 1983, Jackie Robinson award for athletics Ebony Mag., 1983, Vardon trophy, 1984. Mem. Profl. Golfers Assn. Democrat. Baptist. Winner 12 PGA Tournaments, $2.3 million in prize money; led PGA tour in driving accuracy 10 consecutive years, 1981-90. Office: Calvin Peete Enterprises Inc 2050 Collier Ave Fort Myers FL 33901-8123*

PEETE, RUSSELL FITCH, JR., aircraft appraiser; b. Memphis, June 15, 1920; s. Russell Fitch and Louise Gift (Edmondson) P.; m. Esther Eletha Mosley, Feb. 7, 1942 (dec. Jan. 1987); children: Miriam, Russell III, William; m. Margery May George, Sept. 2, 1988. BS in Aerospace Engring., Miss. State U., 1942. Dredge hand U.S. Corp. Engrs., West Memphis, Ark., 1937; rodman U.S. Corp. Engrs., Mobile, Ala., 1939; rsch. engr. Chicago & Southern Airlines, Memphis, 1941-51; tech. sales rep. Lockheed Corp., Burbank, Calif., 1951-82; ops. analyst Flying Tiger Line, L.A., 1982; dir. sales engring. Cammacorp, El Segundo, Calif., 1982-85, Anacorp, Marina Del Rey, Calif., 1987-89; aviation cons. Avcons, Sedona, Ariz., 1985—; aircraft appraiser Nat. Aircraft Appraiser Assn., Tucson, 1993—; cons. Avcons, Camarillo, Calif., 1985-86. Sec. Conejo Y's Mens Clubs, Thousand Oaks, Calif., 1960-63. With U.S. Army, 1944-46. Mem. Soc. Automotive Engrs., Exptl. Aircraft Assn., Aircraft Owners and Pilots Assn., Confederate Air Force, Internat. Aerobatic Club, Nat. Aircraft Appraisers Assn. Republican. Lutheran. Avocations: flying, photography, golf, travel. Office: 63652 E Squash Blossom Ln Tucson AZ 85737-1263

PEETE, WILLIAM PETTWAY JONES, surgeon; b. Warrenton, N.C., Mar. 29, 1921; s. Charles Henry and Lucy Pettway (Jones) P.; m. Mary Frances Hart, Feb. 7, 1960; 1 child, Marianna Jones. AB, U. N.C., 1942; MD, Harvard U., 1947. Fellow in pathology Peter Bent Brigham Hosp., Boston, 1943-44; house officer Mass. Gen. Hosp., Boston, 1947-54; instr. Harvard U. Med. Sch., 1953-55; asst. to dean Duke U. Med. Sch., Durham, N.C., 1955-63; asst. prof., assoc. prof. Duke U. Med. Sch., 1955-64, prof. surgery, 1964-92, prof. emeritus surgery, 1992—; bd. dirs. Nations Bank, Durham; cons. Physicians for Peace, Am. Family Life, Inc.; Rsch. Triangle Park, Batelle Corp., Patient Problems. Moseley fellow, 1954-55. Mem. N.C., Surg. Assn., So. Surg. Assn., So. Surg. Club, Soc. for Surgery of Alimentary Tract.

PEETZ-LARSEN, HANS, trading company executive; b. Odense, Denmark, May 15, 1940; came to U.S., 1974; s. Mads Soren and Gudrun (Pedersen) L.; m. Inga Peetz, Feb. 7, 1976; children: Anne-Marie, Inge-Lise, Niels Christian. Diploma, Copenhagen Merchant Sch, 1960, East Asiatic Co. Comml. Sch., 1960. Mgmt. trainee East Asiatic Co. Ltd., Copenhagen, 1957-60; mgr. East Asiatic Co. Ltd., Bangkok, Thailand, 1962-64; br. mgr. East Asiatic Co. Ltd., Haadyai, South Thailand, 1964-67; dir. mktg. Thailand Machinery activities, Bangkok, 1967-69; gen. mgr. Thailand Machinery Activities East Asiatic Co. Ltd., Bangkok, 1969-74; pres. East Asiatic Co. Ltd., N.Y.C., 1983—; Heidelberg Eastern, Inc., N.Y.C., 1974—, EAC USA Inc., N.Y.C., 1983—, EAC Can. Inc., 1984—, EAC Graphics USA Inc., 1985—, EAC Nevada Inc., 1986—; dir. East Asiatic Co., Ltd., Copenhagen, East Asiatic Co. Inc., EAC Nev. Inc., Heidelberg Eastern, Inc., N.Y.C., Transam. S.S. Corp., Stamford, Conn., Plumrose, Inc., Can., East Asiatic Co. de Mexico, West Indian Co., Ltd., St. Thomas, V.I., EAC Nevada Inc., EAC Can Inc., EACOM Timber, Vancouver, DAK Foods Inc. Trustee Am. Scandanavian Found. 1987—. Mem. Graphic Arts Tech. Found. (bd. dirs. 1977-80, 84—), Nat. Printing Equipment and Supply Assn. (bd. dirs. 1975-77, 80-83), Soderstrom Soc. of Nat. Assn. Printers and Lithographers, Danish Am. C. of C., German Am. C. of C. Clubs: North Hempstead Country (Port Washington, N.Y.); Royal Danish Yacht (Copenhagen); Dansk Samvirke (bd. dirs. 1986—). Avocations: gardening, fishing, bridge, golf, reading. Office: The E Asiatic Co Inc 73-45 Woodhaven Blvd Glendale NY 11385

PEGELS, C. CARL, management science and systems educator; b. Barendrecht, South Holland, Netherlands, Feb. 26, 1933; came to U.S., 1962, naturalized, 1968; s. Bertus and Adriana Maria (Denotter) P.; children—Janice Joy, Kevin Carl. BS in Mech. Engring., Detroit Inst. of Tech., 1961, MS, PhD; Mgmt., Purdue U., 1963, 66. Prodn. engr. Ford Motor, Windsor, Can., 1955-62; instr. Purdue U., W. Lafayette, Ind., 1962-66; prof. SUNY-Buffalo, 1966—; v.p. Ctr. for Mgmt. Systems, Buffalo, 1978-91. Author: Basic for Business, 1973, Health Care & Elderly, 1980, Japan vs The West, 1984, Q.C. in Health Care, 1985, Decision Support Systems for Production and Operations Management, 1986, Management and Industry in China, 1987, Strategic Management for Hospitals and Health Care Corporations, 1987, Health Care and the Older Citizen, 1988, Decision Support Systems for Management Science/Operations Research, 1989, Strategic Information Systems, 1993. Krannert fellow, 1966; Krannert scholar Purdue U., 1963. Mem. Ops. Research Soc. Am., Inst. Mgmt. Sci., Am. Inst. Decision Scis. Avocations: long distance runner. Home: 63 Ruskin Rd Buffalo NY 14226-4255 Office: SUNY at Buffalo Sch of Mgmt Buffalo NY 14260

PEGIS, ANTON GEORGE, English educator; b. Milw., Feb. 21, 1920; s. George Anton and Eugenia (Stathas) P.; m. Harriet Louise Stevens, June 1, 1949; children: Stefani Elizabeth, Penelope Eugenia. A.B., Western State Coll. Colo., 1949; M.A., Denver U., 1951, Ph.D., 1956. Jr. engr. N. Shore Gas Co., Waukegan, Ill., 1946-47; instr. Ft. Lewis Coll., 1952-53; process control technician Gates Rubber Co., Denver, 1953-54; prof. English Colo. Sch. Mines, Golden, 1954—; asst. to pres. Colo. Sch. Mines, 1964-68, v.p. for devel., 1968-73, v.p. for external affairs, 1973-74, prof. English, 1975-82, prof. emeritus, 1982—; cons. U.S. Bur. Mines, Office of Mineral Reports, Washington, Regional Tng. Center, Office of Personnel Mgmt., Denver, 1983, CSC, San Francisco, 1974-94. Author: Social Theory in the Novels of Ford Madox Ford, 1956, An Intensive Course in English for Foreign Engineering Students, 1957, Humanism and the Practical Order, 1964, Excellence and the Odyssean Philosophy, 1965, Platonism in the Renaissance Lyric, 1965, Education for Leadership, 1966, Totality in Engineering Education, 1968, Course Recommendations for the Resource Engineer, 1968, Encroachment of Competing Land Uses on Mineral Development, 1976. Chmn. United Way Fund; sec. Colo. Sch. Mines Found.; pres. Roland Valley

---

Civic Assn., 1974-75. Served with AUS, 1940-46; maj. AUS, ret. Appointed hon. disting. sgt. 121st Field Arty. Regiment, 1988. Named Outstanding Prof., Tau Beta Pi, 1963, Hon. Colonel 115th Engring. Rgt., 1988; recipient Outstanding Prof. award Colo. Sch. Mines, 1976; Amoco Found. awards. Mem. Golden C. of C. (pres. 1968), Am. Soc. Engring. Edn. (chmn. Rocky Mountain sect.), Am. Alumni Council (chmn. dist. VII 1971-72), Modern Lang. Assn., Blue Key, Theta Chi, Alpha Psi Omega. Home: 415 Scenic Ct Golden CO 80401-2533

PEGRAM, JOHN BRAXTON, lawyer; b. Yeadon, Pa., June 29, 1938; s. William Bement and Marjorie (Rainey) P.; m. Patricia Jane Narbeth; Aug. 21, 1965; children: Catherine, Stephen. AB in Physics, Columbia U., 1960; LLB, NYU, 1965. Bar: N.Y. 1965, U.S. Supreme Ct. 1971. Engr. Fairchild Camera and Instrument Corp., Clifton, N.J., 1960-66; assoc. Davis Hoxie Faithfull and Hapgood, LLP, N.Y.C., 1966-71; ptnr. Davis Hoxie Faithfull and Hapgood, N.Y.C., 1972—. Editor The Trademark Reporter jour., 1984-86, mem. editorial adv. bd., 1986—; contbr. articles to profl. jours. Fellow Am. Bar Found. (life); mem. IEEE, ABA (chmn. Antitrust Law sect. com. on patents, trademarks and knowhow 1986-89, mem. Legal Econs. sect., Bus. Law sect., Intellectual Property Law sect., mem. spl. com. on U.S. Appeals for Fed. Cir. 1984-88, chmn. sect. com. on small bus. 1987-89, chmn. ad hoc com. on security interests 1989-92, chmn. spl. com. on atty. opinions 1992-94, chmn. com. fed. practice and procedure 1994—, mem. nominating com. 1989-90), Fed. Bar Coun., Fed. Cir. Bar Assn., N.Y. State Bar Assn., Assn. of Bar of City of N.Y., Am. Intellectual Property Law Assn. (chmn. fed. practice and procedure com. 1974-76, chmn. unauthorized practice com. 1977-79, chmn. trade secrets com. 1992-94, mem. Japan study com. 1992—, mem. editl. bd. Quarterly Jour. 1994—), Fed. Cir. Bar Assn., N.Y. Intellectual Property Law Assn. (sec. 1981-84, dir. 1984-86, pres. 1989-90), U.S. Bar/Japan Patent Office Liason Coun. (del. 1990—), Am. Phys. Soc., Chartered Inst. Patent Agts. (fgn. mem.), Inst. Trade Mark Agts. (overseas mem.), Am. Judicature Soc., Internat. Patent Club, Internat. Patent & Trademark Assn., Internat. Trademark Assn. (bd. dirs. 1985-87, mem. fin. com. 1987—, U.S. Dist. Ct. for Dist. of Del. intellectual property litigation adv. com. 1994—, U.S. Dist. Ct. for Eastern Dist. of N.Y. neutral evaluation and mediation panels 1994—, U.S. Dist. Ct. for So. Dist. of N.Y. mediation panel 1994—, mem. publ. bd. 1995—). Office: Davis Hoxie Faithfull & Hapgood 45 Rockefeller Plz New York NY 10111-0002

PEHL, GLEN EUGENE, risk and insurance consultant; b. Woodford, Wis., Aug. 10, 1932; s. Henry Earnest and Ella Viola Pehl; m. Mazie Lee McCrackin, July 9, 1960; children—Keith, Tracey. B.S. in Bus. Adminstrn., Ala. Poly. Inst., 1958. Indsl. account rep. Am. Mut. Liability Ins. Co., Charlotte, N.C., 1958-60, br. sales mgr., 1960-64, dist. sales mgr., 1964-66; chmn., pres., treas. Indsl. Ins. Mgmt. Corp. and Corp. Life Cons., Inc., Charlotte, 1966—; dir. N.C. Self-Insurers Assn., 1976-80; lectr. Trustee Alexander Children's Home, Charlotte, 1982—. Served with USAF, 1951-55. Decorated Nat. Def. medal. Mem. N.C. Citizens Assn. Republican. Presbyterian. Clubs: Charlotte City, Cedarwood Country. Lodge: Masons. Office: Indsl Ins Mgmt Corp PO Box 220926 Charlotte NC 28222

PEHLKE, ROBERT DONALD, materials and metallurgical engineering educator; b. Ferndale, Mich., Feb. 11, 1933; s Robert William and Florence Jenny (McLaren) P.; m. Julie Anne Kehoe, June 2, 1956; children: Robert Donald, Elizabeth Anne, David Richard. B.S. in Engring. U. Mich., 1955; S.M., Mass. Inst. Tech., 1958, Sc.D. 1960; postgrad., Tech. Inst., Aachen, Ger., 1956-57. Registered profl. engr., Mich. Mem. faculty U. Mich., 1960—, prof. materials sci. and engring., 1968—, chmn. dept., 1973-84; cons. to metall. industry; vis. prof. Tohoku U., Sendai, Japan, 1994. Author: Unit Processes of Extractive Metallurgy, 1973; Editor, contbr. numerous articles to profl. jours. Pres. Ann Arbor Amateur Hockey Assn., 1977-79. NSF fellow, 1955-56; Fulbright fellow, 1956-57. Fellow Am. Soc. Metals (mem. tech. divs. bd. 1982-84, sec. metals acad. com. 1977), Minerals, Metals and Materials Soc. of AIME (Gold Medal award extractive metallurgy div. 1976); mem. NSPE, Iron and Steel Soc. of AIME (Disting. life mem., chmn. process tech. div. 1976-77, dir. 1976-79, Howe meml. lectr. 1980), Germany, London, Japan Socs. Iron and Steel, Am. Foundrymen's Soc., Am. Soc. Engring. Edn., N.Y. Acad. Sci., Sigma Xi, Tau Beta Pi, Alpha Sigma Mu (pres. 1977-78). Home: 9 Regent Dr Ann Arbor MI 48104-1738 Office: U Mich Materials Sci & Engring Dow Bldg 2300 Hayward St Rm 2146B Ann Arbor MI 48109-2136

PEHRSON, GORDON OSCAR, JR., lawyer; b. San Antonio, Feb. 18, 1943; s. Gordon Oscar and Frances (Burns) P.; m. Janice Sue Hagedorn, May 17, 1969; children: Christopher Wells, Ashley Stewart; m. Sharon Ann McNellage, Jan. 1, 1983. AB, Coll. William and Mary, 1964; JD, U. Mich., 1967; postgrad., U. London, 1967-68. Bar: Ill. 1968, D.C. 1969, U.S. Ct. Claims 1968, U.S. Ct. Mil. Appeals 1968, U.S. Ct. Appeals (D.C. cir.) 1976, U.S. Supreme Ct. 1976, U.S. Ct. Appeals (3d and 5th cirs.) 1979, U.S. Ct. Appeals (Fed. cir.) 1982, U.S. Tax Ct. 1990. Assoc. Sutherland, Asbill & Brennan, Washington, 1970-75, ptnr., 1975—; adj. prof. law Georgetown U., Washington, 1977-81; bd. advisors The Ins. Tax Rev., 1986—. Contbr. articles on tax law to profl. jours.; editor The Ins. Tax Rev., 1986-94. Bd. dirs. U.S. Supreme Ct. Hist. Soc., 1993—, Food for All Seasons Found., 1992-94; bd. advisors Hartford Inst. Ins. Taxation, 1993—. Fellow in internat. law U. Mich., 1967. Mem. ABA (co-chair fin. and taxation com. sect. torts and ins. practice, chair tax procedure com. 1994—, sect. adminstrv. law and regulatory practice 1994—), Fed. Cir. Bar Assn. (chair tax appeals com. 1994—), D.C. Bar Assn., Am. Law Inst., Econs. Club of Washington, Met. Club (Washington), Nat. Press Club (Washington), Order of Coif. Episcopalian. Home: 4517 Foxhall Cres NW Washington DC 20007-1056 Office: Sutherland Asbill & Brennan 1275 Pennsylvania Ave NW Ste 1000 Washington DC 20004-2404

PEI, IEOH MING, architect; b. Canton, China, Apr. 26, 1917; came to U.S., 1935, naturalized, 1954; s. Tsu Yee Pei and Lien Kwun Chwong; m. Eileen Loo, June 20, 1942; children: T'ing Chung, Chien Chung, Li Chung, Liane. BArch, MIT, 1940; MArch, Harvard U., 1946; DFA (hon.), U. Pa., 1970, Rensselaer Poly. Inst., 1978, Carnegie Mellon U., 1980, U. Mass., 1980, Brown U., 1982, NYU, 1983, Dartmouth Coll., 1991, Northeastern U.; LLD, Chinese U., Hong Kong, 1970, Pace U.; LHD, Columbia U., 1980, U. Colo., 1982, U. Rochester, 1982, U. Hong Kong 1990, Am. U. Paris, 1990. Practice architecture N.Y.C., 1939-42; asst. prof. Harvard Grad. Sch. Design, 1945-48; dir. archtl. div. Webb & Knapp, Inc., 1948-55; with Pei Cobb Freed & Partners (formerly I.M. Pei & Ptnrs., I.M. Pei & Assos.), N.Y.C., 1955—. Prin. projects include Mile High Ctr., Denver, Nat. Ctr. Atmospheric Rsch., Boulder, Colo., Dallas City Hall, John Fitzgerald Kennedy Libr., Boston, Can. Imperial Bank Commerce Complex, Toronto, Overseas Chinese Banking Corp. Ctr., Singapore, Dreyfus Chemistry Bldg. MIT, East-West Ctr. U. Hawaii, Honolulu, Mellon Art Ctr. and Choate Rosemary Hall Sci. Ctr., Wallingford, Conn., Univ. Plz. NYU, Johnson Mus. Art Cornell U., Ithaca, N.Y., Washington Sq. East, Phila, Everson Mus. Art, Syracuse, N.Y., Nat. Gallery Art, East Bldg., Washington, Wilmington Tower, Raffles City, Singapore, West Wing Mus. Fine Arts, Boston, expansion and modernization of Louvre Mus., Paris, Morton H. Meyerson Symphony Ctr., Dallas, MIT Arts and Media Ctr., Jacob K. Javits Conv. Ctr., N.Y.C., Fragrant Hill Hotel, Beijing, Tex. Commerce Tower, Houston, Bank of China, Hong Kong, Creative Artists Agy., Beverly Hills, Calif., Guggenheim Pavilion, Mount Sinai Med. Ctr., N.Y.C., Rock n' Roll Hall of Fame and Mus., Cleve., Mus. Modern Art, Athens, Greece, Miho Mus. of Art, Shiga, Japan, Bilbao (Spain) Estuary Project, Four Seasons Hotel, N.Y.C., others; planning projects include S.W. Washington Redevelopment Plan, Govt. Ctr. Redevelopment Plan, Boston, Oklahoma City Downtown Redevelopment Plan, Bedford Stuyvesant Super Block, Bklyn., master plan Columbia U. Mem. Nat. Def. Rsch. Com., Princeton, N.J., 1943-45, Nat. Coun. Humanities, 1966-70, Nat. Coun. on Arts, 1981-84. MIT traveling fellow, 1940, Wheelwright fellow Harvard, 1951; Thomas Jefferson Meml. medal for Architecture, 1976, gold medal for architecture Am. Acad. Arts and Letters, 1979, Nat. Arts Club Gold medal of honor, 1981, Mayor's award of Honor for Art and Culture, N.Y.C., 1981, La Grande Medaille D'or L'Académie d'Architecture, 1981, Pritzker Architecture prize, 1983, Medal of Liberty, 1986, Medal of French Legion of Honor, 1988, Nat. Medal of Art, 1988, Praemium Imperiale Japan Art Assn., 1989, UCLA Gold medal, 1990, Colbert Found. first award for Excellence, 1991, Excellence 2000 award, 1991, Freedom medal, 1993. Fellow AIA (Medal of Honor N.Y. chpt. 1963, Gold Medal 1979); hon. fellow ASID; mem. Nat. Inst. Arts and Letters (Arnold Brunner award 1961), Am. Acad. Arts and Scis., Am. Acad. and

---

Inst. Arts and Letters (chancellor 1978-80), Royal Inst. Brit. Architects, NAD, Urban Design Council. Office: Pei Cobb Freed & Ptnrs 600 Madison Ave New York NY 10022-1615

PEI, MING L., civil engineering educator; b. Peking, China, Apr. 17, 1923; came to U.S.; 1944; s. I. Hsiang and Chao H. (Wu) P.; m. Yen Fen Kiang, Sept. 2, 1951; children: Victor C., Daniel C. BS., Oreg. State U., 1945; M.S., Cornell U., 1946, Ph.D. 1948. Asst. prof. civil engring. Nat. Central U., Nanking, China, 1948-49; mem. faculty City Coll. CUNY, 1950—, prof. civil engring., 1963-86, prof. emeritus, 1986—, chmn. dept., 1965-68, chief Computation Ctr., 1963-71, chmn. dept. computer sci. Computation Ctr., 1968-71; cons. to govt. and industry, 1951—. Home: 104 River Edge Rd Bergenfield NJ 07621-1132

PEIMBERT, MANUEL, astronomer; b. Mexico City, June 9, 1941; s. Gonzalo Peimbert and Catalina Sierra; m. Silvia Torres, Aug. 25, 1962; children: Antonio, Mariana. BS, U. Nacional Autónoma de Mex., 1962; PhD in Astronomy, U. Calif., Berkeley, 1967. Postdoctoral fellow U. Calif., Berkeley, 1967-68; prof. astronomy U. Nacional Autónoma de Mex., Mexico City, 1968—. Author over 100 research articles, 1960—; editor Revista Mexicana de Fisica, 1981-85. Recipient Guillaume Budé medal Coll. de France, Paris, 1974, Nat. Prize of Scis. Govt. of Mex., 1981. Fellow Third World Acad. Scis.; mem. NAS (fgn. assoc.), Am. Astron. Soc. (councilor 1975-78), Internat. Astron. Union (v.p. 1982-88), Royal Astron. Soc. U.K. (fgn. assoc.), Acad. de la Investigacion Cientifica (Scis. prize 1971), Soc. Mexicana de Fisica. Office: Inst de Astronomia, APDO Postal 70-264, 04510 Mexico City Mexico

PEIPERL, ADAM, kinetic and video sculptor; b. Sosnowiec, Poland, June 4, 1935; came to U.S., 1953, naturalized, 1958; s. Jacob and Fanny (Alster) P.; m. Martha Rose Dorf, June 15, 1958; children: Maury, Laurence, Linda. Grad., Cours Complémentaire Général, Paris, 1952; B.S. in Chemistry, George Washington U., 1957; postgrad., Pa. State U., 1959. Cons. in Russian sci. lit. Libr. Congress, Washington, 1959-61, 66-67; chemist Nat. Bur. Standards, Washington, 1961-63; sci. translator Am. Inst. Physics, N.Y.C., 1973—. One-man shows include Smithsonian Mus. Am. History, 1968-88, Balt. Mus. Art, 1969, Pa. Acad. Fine Arts, 1969, Marlborough Gerson Gallery, N.Y.C., 1969, Smithsonian Mus. History and Tech., 1972, Electric Gallery, Toronto, Ont., Can., 1975, Phila. Art Alliance, 1978; group shows include Washington Gallery Modern Art, 1968, Corcoran Gallery Art, 1968, Kent State U., McKay Art Inst., San Antonio, 1969, NASA Manned Spacecraft, Houston, 1970-71, Nat. Mus. Am. Art, 1972-82, Meml. Art Gallery, U. Rochester, 1978, Foster Harmon Galleries Am. Art, Sarasota, Fla., 1982-83, Artworks Gallery, Santa Barbara, Calif., 1989; represented in permanent collections at Pa. Acad. Fine Arts, Smithsonian Instn., Mus. Boymans-van Beuningen, Rotterdam, The Netherlands, John F. Kennedy Ctr. for Performing Arts, U. Md.; made first kinetic polarized-light sculpture in water, 1968; designer polarized-light kaleidoscope interiors, 1989; kaleidoscope photographs published on book covers for Prentice-Hall, Inc., 1991, 92, Mayfield Pub. Co., 1992, 94, Modern Curriculum Press, 1993; made poster for elektra Entertainment, 1990; art for Anderson Consulting brochure, 1995, Time-Life Book-of-the-Month, 1995; creator video projection of kinetic sculpture in stage collaboration with choreographer Maida Withers and singer Marilia, Yokohama, Japan, 1995. Home: 1135 Loxford Ter Silver Spring MD 20901-1130

PEIPERT, JAMES RAYMOND, journalist; b. Alton, Ill., Nov. 15, 1942; s. Lawrence George and Virginia Pauline (Sieve) P.; m. Mary Ellen Finney, Aug. 1, 1970; children: Benjamin, Matthew, Thomas. BA, So. Ill. U., 1965. Reporter, editor AP, Chgo., 1965-68, N.Y.C., 1968-70; corr. AP, Moscow, 1970-74, London, 1974-80; news editor AP, Johannesburg, South Africa, 1980-81; East Africa bur. chief AP, Nairobi, Kenya, 1981-86; nat./fgn. editor Fort Worth Star-Telegram, 1986—. With U.S. Army, 1965-67. Roman Catholic. Avocations: bicycling, maintaining 1967 Mustang, reading. Office: Fort Worth Star Telegram PO Box 1870 Fort Worth TX 76101-1870

PEIRANO, LAWRENCE EDWARD, civil engineer; b. Stockton, Calif., May 13, 1929; s. Frank Lloyd and Esther Marie (Carigiet) P.; m. Mary Ellen Alabaster, July 26, 1952; children: Thomas Lawrence, Ellen Marie. BSCE, U. Calif., Berkeley, 1951, MSCE, 1952. Registered profl. engr., Calif.; diplomate Am. Acad. Environ. Engrs. Assoc. civil engr. Calif. Div. Water Resources, 1952-53; with Kennedy Engrs., Inc., San Francisco, 1953-55, project mgr., 1960-79, v.p., chief environ. engr., 1974-79; dir. ops. Kennedy/ Jenks Engrs., Inc., San Francisco, 1979-86; sr. v.p., regional mgr. Kennedy/ Jenks/Chilton, Inc., San Francisco, 1986-90; exec. v.p., chief tech. officer Kennedy/Jenks Cons., Inc. (formerly Kennedy Engrs., Inc.), San Francisco, 1990-94, also bd. dirs., chmn. bd., 1972-94, ret., 1994; spl. lectr. san. engring. U. Calif., Berkeley, 1976. Served with U.S. Army, 1953-55, Korea. James Monroe McDonald scholar, 1950-51. Fellow ASCE (life); mem. Water Environ. Fedn., Am. Water Works Assn., Internat. Assn. on Water Quality, Sierra Club, U.S. Ski Assn., U. Calif. Alumni Assn., Tau Beta Pi, Chi Epsilon. Republican. Roman Catholic. Home: 3435 Black Hawk Rd Lafayette CA 94549-2326

PEIRCE, BROOKE, English language educator; b. Washington, Jan. 2, 1922; s. Charles Brooke, Jr. and Nancy Ley (Bass) P.; m. Carol Emily Marshall, July 12, 1952. B.A., U.Va., 1943; M.A., Harvard U., 1947, Ph.D. 1954. Teaching fellow Harvard U., 1948-51; instr. English U. Va., 1951-54; mem. faculty Goucher Coll., 1954-85, prof. English, 1966-85, prof. humanities, 1985—, chmn. dept. English and dramatic arts, 1964-69, 72-75, chmn. faculty humanities, 1964-66, 72-73, 79; vis. prof. English, SUNY Coll.-Oswego, 1985-87; lectr. Villa Julie Coll., 1989—. Author: (with Carol Peirce) Introduction to English Literature 2 vols., 1954. Treas. Edgar Allan Poe Soc., Balt., 1959-66, mem. bd., 1959—. Served with U.S. Army, 1943-45. Nat. Endowment for Humanities fellow, 1977-78; recipient Disting. Tchr. award, 1979. Mem. Modern Lang. Assn., Raven Soc. of U. Va., Classical Assn., Phi Beta Kappa. Democrat. Home: 705 Warren Rd Cockeysville Hunt Valley MD 21030-2824

PEIRCE, CAROL MARSHALL, English educator; b. Columbia, Mo., Feb. 1, 1922; d. Charles Hamilton and Helen Emily (Davault) Williams; m. Brooke Peirce, July 12, 1952. AB, Fla. State U., 1942; MA, U. Va., 1943; PhD, Harvard U., 1951. Head English dept. Fairfax Hall, Waynesboro, Va., 1943-44; instr. English Cedar Crest Coll., Allentown, Pa., 1944-46, Harvard U., 1952-53; asst. dean instrn. Radcliffe Coll., Cambridge, 1950-53; head English extension home study U. Va., Charlottesville, 1953-54; asst. dir. admissions Goucher Coll., Towson, Md., 1956-62; prof. English and comm. design U. Balt., 1968—, chmn. dept., 1968-94, gen. edn. core coord., 1985-87, Disting. teaching prof. Coll. Liberal Arts, 1981-82, chmn. humanities div., 1972-79; chmn. bd. New Poets Series, 1975-85; vis. scholar Lucy Cavendish Coll., U. Cambridge, Eng., 1977-78; co-coord. On Miracle Ground: The Internat. Lawrence Durrell Conf., 1980, 82, 90; co-coord. conf. Evermore! Celebrating the 150th Anniversary of Edgar Allan Poe's "Raven," 1995. Author: (with Brooke Peirce) A Study of Literary Types and an Introduction to English Literature from Chaucer to the Eighteenth Century, 1954, A Study of Literary Types and an Introduction to English Literature from the Eighteenth Century to the Present, 1954; editor: (with Lawrence Markert) On Miracle Ground: Second Lawrence Durrell Conference Proceedings, 1984; guest editor: (with Ian S. MacNiven) Lawrence Durrell Issue, Parts I and II, Twentieth Century Literature, Fall, Winter, 1987; contbr. essays to: Poe and Our Times, 1986, Critical Essays on Lawrence Durrell, 1987, Into the Labyrinth: Essays on the Art of Lawrence Durrell, 1989, On Miracle Ground: Essays on the Fiction of Lawrence Durrell, 1990, Dictionary of Literary Biography Yearbook, 1990, St. James Reference Guide to English Literature, 1991, Poe's Pym: Critical Explorations, 1992, Selected Essays on the Humor of Lawrence Durrell, 1993, Lawrence Durrell: Comprehending The Whole, 1994; assoc editor: Deus Loci: The Lawrence Durrell Jour., 1990-92, co-editor, 1993—. McGregor fellow, DuPont fellow U. Va., 1943; Harvard tutor, Anne Radcliffe traveling fellow Harvard U., 1951. Mem. MLA, Edgar Allan Poe Soc. (bd. dirs. 1973-89, pres. 1989—), Lawrence Durrell Soc. (mng. ed. newsletter 1980-85, internat. pres. 1994—), Md. Assn. Depts. English, Phi Beta Kappa, Chi Delta Phi, Phi Alpha Theta, Phi Kappa Phi. Home: 705 Warren Rd Cockeysville Hunt Valley MD 21030-2824 Office: Univ Balt Dept Lang Lit and Comm Dsgn Baltimore MD 21201

PEIRCE, DONALD OLUF, elementary education educator; b. Boulder, Colo., Mar. 5, 1939; s. James Girdwood and Ruth Julia (Wagner) P.; m. Joyce Arleen Kovatch. BS, Temple U., 1971, MEd, 1978. Cert. elem. tchr., reading specialist, Pa. Remedial reading tchr. Bartram High Sch., Phila., 1975-80; reading, English, Lang. arts tchr. Locke Elem. Sch., Phila., 1981—. With USMCR, 1963-68. Mem. Del. Valley Reading Assn. Republican. Episcopalian. Avocations: music composition, piano, swimming, cinema, travel. Office: Locke Elementary School 46th & Haverford Ave Philadelphia PA 19139

PEIRCE, GEORGE LEIGHTON, airport administrator; b. Worcester, Mass., Mar. 9, 1933; s. George Leighton and Grace Hislop (McDougall) P.; m. Carolyn Janasy, Oct. 7, 1968; children: Jennifer Lindsey, Amanda Leighton. B.B.A., U. Mass., 1961. Supr. mgmt. engrng. services Port Authority of, N.Y. and N.J., 1961-69; airport mgr. Stewart Airport, Newburgh, N.Y., 1970; asst. mgr. LaGuardia Airport, Flushing, N.Y., 1970-75; gen. mgr. LaGuardia Airport, 1975-94; bd. dirs. Lighthouse, Inc., N.Y.C. 1989-94, Americas' Sail, Huntington, N.Y. Mem. Queens adv. bd. Salvation Army, 1980-94; chmn. adv. bd. Queens Lighthouse for Blind, 1980-94; bd. dirs., treas., vice chmn. OPSAIL; bd. dirs. Couri Found. Ridgefield, Conn. With USAF, 1954-58, Mass. Air N.G., 1959-61. Recipient Outstanding Community Svc. award Greater N.Y. Coun. Boy Scouts Am., 1978, Outstanding Pub. Svc. award Dept. Transp., 1986, Meritorious Pub. Svc. award USCG, 1986, Pub. Svc. award N.Y. Urban League, 1991, Disting. Svc. award Port Authority N.Y., N.J., 1992. Mem. Queens C. of C., Coll. Aeronautics, Acad. Aero. (adv. bd.), 1976-94, LaGuardia Kiwanis (bd. dirs., past pres.), North Beach Club (past pres., bd. dirs.). Home: 392 Brett Rd Fairfield CT 06430-1720

PEIRCE, JOHN WENTWORTH, architect; b. Boston, Feb. 9, 1912; s. Thomas W. and Gabrielle (Dexter) P.; m. Grace Minot, June 27, 1934; children—Thomas W., Lucy (Mrs. David Scanlon III), John W. A.B. cum laude, Harvard, 1933; postgrad. Archtl. Sch., 1933-35; M.Arch., MIT, 1947. Individual practice architecture Boston, 1938-42; assoc. Shepley, Bulfinch, Richardson & Abbott, Boston, 1948-60; ptnr. Peirce & Pierce, Boston, 1960-71, Peirce Pierce & Kramer, 1971-75; Mem. Mass. Bd. Registration for Architects, 1954-59, chmn., 1957; mem. Mass. Insp.-Gen. Council, 1981-85. Prin. archtl. works include Shields Warren Radiation Lab, N.E. Deaconess Hosp., Boston, Trinity Episcopal Ch, Topsfield, Mass., Loeb Marine Lab, Woods Hole, Mass., Art/Music Bldg., St. Mark's Sch., Southboro, Mass. Chmn. Topsfield Conservation Commn., 1965-71; commr. Ipswich River Watershed Dist., 1968—, chmn., 1976-80; bd. dirs. Ipswich River Watershed Assn., 1976-87; trustee Essex County Greenbelt Assn., 1961-71, pres., 1966-77, dir., 1977—; trustee Trustees Pub. Reservations, 1966-83; bd. dirs. Plymouth County Wildlands Trust, 1973-79, 81-84, 87—, trustee; 1984-87. Served to lt. comdr. USNR, 1942-46. Recipient Ann. Conservation award Mass. Trustees of Reservations, 1975, Open Space award Mass. Conservation Council, 1977, Conservation award Ipswich River Watershed Assn., 1984, Conservation award New Eng. Wildflower Soc., 1988. Fellow AIA; mem. Mass. Assn. Architects (pres. 1968), Boston Soc. Architects (v.p. 1968, pres. 1969). Clubs: Bournes Cove Yacht (Wareham, Mass.) (commodore 1966-68); St. Botolph (Boston). Home and Office: Witch Hill 9 Garden St Topsfield MA 01983

PEIRCE, NEAL R., journalist; b. Phila., Jan. 5, 1932; s. J. Trevor and Miriam deS. (Litchfield) P.; m. Barbara von dem Bach-Zelewski, Apr. 18, 1959; children: Celia, Andrea, Trevor. B.A., Princeton U., 1954; postgrad., Harvard U., 1957-58. Legis. asst. Office of U.S. Rep. Silvio Conte of Mass., 1959; polit. editor Congl. Quar., 1960-69; co-founder, contbg. editor Nat. Jour., Washington, 1969—; cons. and commentator elections CBS News, 1962, 67-76, NBC News, 1964-66; lectr. in field; syndicated newspaper columnist Washington Post Writers Group; dir. Peirce-Phelps, Inc., Phila.; mem. faculty Salzburg (Austria) Seminar, 1980, 84; first Weinberg prof. Princeton U.'s Woodrow Wilson Sch. Pub. and Internat. Affairs, 1992. Author: The People's President, 1968, 2 edit., 1981, The Megastates of America, 1972, The Pacific States of America, 1972, The Mountain States of America, 1972, The Great Plains States America, 1973, The Deep South States of America, 1974, The Border South States, 1975, The New England States, 1976, The Mid-Atlantic States of America, 1977, The Great Lakes States of America, 1980, The Book of America: Inside Fifty States Today, 1983, Citistates: How Urban America Can Prosper in A Competitive World, 1993, Breakthroughs: Recreating The American City, 1993; co-editor: Investing in America, 1982, Corrective Capitalism, 1987; editor spl. series Phoenix Republic and Gazette, 1987, Seattle Times, 1989, Balt. Sun, 1991, Owensboro Messenger-Inquirer, 1991, Dallas Morning News, 1991, St. Paul Pioneer-Press, 1991, Raleigh News & Observer, 1993, Spokane Spokesman-Rev., 1994, Phila. Inquirer, 1995. Founder, chmn. S.W. Neighborhood Assembly and Cmty. Coun., Washington, 1963-65; mem. exec. com. Nat. Civic League, 1990—; trustee German Marshall Fund of U.S., 1987—; adv. com. Trust for Pub. Land, 1984—, Nat. Acad. Pub. Adminstrn., 1992—, Alliance for Redesign of Govt., 1993—; bd. dirs. Inst. for Ednl. Leadership, 1987—; mem. Nat. Commn. State and Local Pub. Svc., 1991—. With CIC, AUS, 1954-57. Fellow Woodrow Wilson Internat. Center Scholars, 1971-74. Mem. Newfound Lake Regional Assn. (v.p. 1989-92), Phi Beta Kappa. Episcopalian. Club: Federal City (Washington). Home and Office: 610 G St SW Washington DC 20024

PEIRSON, WALTER RUSSELL, oil company executive; b. Rock Island, Ill., 1926; married. Graduate, U. Ill. With Standard Oil Co. (Ind.), 1955-61, Gen. Gas Corp., 1961-64, Tuloma Gas Products Co., Inc., 1964-68; v.p. mktg. Am. Oil Co., Chgo., 1968-71, exec. v.p. mktg., refining, transp. and supply, 1971-74; pres. Amoco Oil Co. formerly Standard Oil Co. (Ind.), Chgo., 1974-78, exec. v.p., 1978—, also dir.; bd. dirs. Am. Nat. Bank, Chgo., Fed. Signal Corp. Served with USAAF, 1943-46. Office: Amoco Corp 225 W Wacker Dr Ste 2900 Chicago IL 60606-1229

PEISER, ROBERT ALAN, financial executive; b. N.Y.C., Apr. 17, 1948; s. Donald Edward and Natalie Audrey (Phillips) P.; m. Kathleen Lorraine Reilly, Jan. 11, 1970; children: Karyn, Brian, Craig, Scott. BA, U. Pa., 1969; MBA, Harvard U., 1972. Dir. corp. fin. TWA, N.Y.C., 1972-77, sr. v.p. fin., CFO, 1983-86, exec. v.p. fin, CFO, 1994—; treas. Hertz Corp., N.Y.C., 1977-80; staff v.p., treas. ops. RCA Corp., N.Y.C., 1980-81; v.p., treas., Trans World Corp., N.Y.C., 1982-83; sr. v.p., CFO ALC Comm. Corp., Birmingham, Mich., 1986-88; sr. v.p. fin., CFO Borman's Inc., Detroit, 1988-89; pres., CEO Orange-Co. Inc., Bartow, Fla., 1989-92; with Bahadur, Balen & Kazerski, Ltd., Southfield, Mich., 1992-94. Trustee Mich. chpt. Leukemia Soc. Am. Mem. Fin. Execs. Inst., Birmingham Athletic Club. Home: 326 Lakewood Dr Bloomfield Hills MI 48304-3533 Office: TWA 1 City Ctr 515 N 6th St 19th fl Saint Louis MO 63101

PEISS, CLARENCE NORMAN, physiology educator, college dean; b. Ansonia, Conn., Jan. 3, 1922; s. Alexander and Rose P.; m. Evelyn Schwartz, July 17, 1949; children: Kathy Lee, Robert Laurence. A.B., Stanford U., 1946, A.M., 1948, Ph.D., 1949. Postdoctoral fellow Johns Hopkins U., 1949-50; sr. instr. St. Louis U. Sch. Medicine, 1950-52, asst. prof., 1952-54; mem. faculty Loyola U. of Chgo. Stritch Sch. Medicine, 1954—, prof. physiology, 1958-85, assoc. dean Grad. Sch., 1972-78, assoc. dean for acad. affairs, 1975-78; dean Loyola U. Chgo. Stritch Sch. Medicine, 1978-82, prof. and dean emeritus, 1985—; v.p. acad. affairs, dean Scholl Coll. Podiatric Medicine, Chgo., 1985-87; liaison scientist Office of Naval Research, London, 1965-66; mem. physiology study sect. NIH, 1966-70; cons. Nat. Heart Inst. Contbr. chpts. to books; articles to profl. jours. in field of tissue metabolism, temperature regulation and central Nervous system control of cardiovascular and respiratory systems. Served with M.C. U.S. Army, 1943-46. Decorated Purple Heart, Bronze Star; Royall Victor scholar, 1939-43; Markle Scholar in Acad. Medicine, 1953-58. Mem. AAAS, Am. Physiol. Soc., AMA, Council Med. Deans.

PEKARIK, ANDREW JOSEPH, museum administrator; b. Lebanon, Pa., Nov. 8, 1946; s. Andrew Joseph and Anna Theresa (Kaczyk) P.; m. Julia Baldwin Meech, Aug. 4, 1972. B.A., Fordham U., 1968; M.A., Columbia U., 1977, M.Phil., 1979, Ph.D., 1983. Tchr. math. Camden Central High Sch., N.Y., 1968-69; curator Burke Collection, N.Y.C., 1973-84; dir. Asia Soc. Galleries, N.Y.C., 1984—. Author: Japanese Ceramics, 1978, Japanese Lacquer 1600-1900, 1980; editor: Ukifune, 1982. Served to lt. USN, 1969-72.

Mem. Am. Assn. Mus. Dirs. Home: 12 E 97th St New York NY 10029-6918 Office: Asia Soc Galleries 725 Park Ave New York NY 10021-5088

PEKARSKY, MELVIN HIRSCH, artist; b. Chgo., Sept. 18, 1934; s. Abe and Inda (Levin) P. Student, Sch. of Art Inst., Chgo., 1951-52; B.A., Northwestern U., 1955, M.A., 1956. Faculty Northwestern U., 1955-56; faculty Kendall Coll., 1960-67, chmn. art dept., 1965-67; asst. dean Sch. Visual Arts, N.Y.C., 1967-68; assoc. dean Sch. Visual Arts, 1968-69; grad. faculty NYU, 1970-71; assoc. prof. art SUNY, Stony Brook, 1975-84, prof. art, 1984—; chmn. dept. SUNY, 1977-78, 84-89. One-man shows include Gimpel and Weitzenhoffer, N.Y.C., 1974, Lehigh U., 1975, Ball State U. Gallery, Muncie, Ind., 1975, G.W. Einstein Co., Inc., N.Y.C., 1975, 77, 78, 80, 81, 82, 84, 86, 88, 91, 95, Hull Gallery, Washington, 1978, Centro Colombo-Americano, Bogotá, Colombia, 1980, 112 Greene St. Gallery, N.Y.C., 1980, 82, Marianne Deson Gallery, Chgo., 1987, Butler Inst. Am. Art, Youngstown, Ohio, 1990, The Mus. at Stony Brook, 1993; group shows include Chgo. Art Inst., 1966, Whitney Mus., N.Y.C., 1971, Bklyn. Mus., 1974, Cleve. Mus., 1978, Cooper-Hewitt Mus., 1971, Mus. Modern Art Corp.,Lending and Adv. Svc. Exhbns., Kuznetsky-Most Galleries, Moscow, 1989, NAD, N.Y.C., 1990, public murals commns., Houston and Crosby Sts., N.Y.C., 1972, Lafayette and Bleecker Sts., N.Y.C., 1969; represented in permanent collections, Cleve. Mus., Fogg Mus. Art, Harvard U., Indpls. Mus., Westinghouse Corp., Corcoran Gallery Art, Yale U., Notre Dame U., AT&T, Chase Manhattan Bank, other pub. and corp. collections, also pvt. collections. Founding mem., v.p., bd. dirs. City Walls, 1969-77. Served with Combat Engrs. AUS, 1957-59. Recipient grants in public art through City Walls Kaplan Fund, 1969, City Walls Bernhard Found., 1971, City Walls N.Y. State Council on Arts, 1970, City Walls Nat. Endowment for the Arts, 1971. Mem. Coll. Art Assn. Am. Home: Box 1575 Stony Brook NY 11790 Office: SUNY Art Dept Stony Brook NY 11794-5400

PEKRUHN, JOHN EDWARD, retired architect, educator; b. Steubenville, Ohio, May 19, 1915; s. William Frederick and Grace (Phillipson) P.; m. Nancy Ingram McMahon, Aug. 1, 1942; children—Susan (Mrs. Earl Glotfelty), John Phillipson. B.Arch., Carnegie Mellon U., 1938; postgrad., Harvard Grad. Sch. Design, 1940. Designer-draftsman Shreve, Anderson & Walker, Charlestown, Ind., 1941-42, Giffels & Vallet, Texarkana, Tex., 1942-43; rsch. group jet turbine Westinghouse Electric Corp., South Philadelphia, 1944-45; designer William Lescaze, N.Y.C., 1946; designer, head architecture Norman Bel Geddes & Co., N.Y.C., 1947; architect John Pekruhn, Pitts., 1947-67, John Pekruhn & Assos., Pitts., 1967-81; ret., 1981; prof. Carnegie Mellon U., Pitts., 1947-79; prof. emeritus Carnegie Mellon U., 1979—. Mem. Pitts. City Planning Commn., 1965-70. Fellow AIA. Episcopalian. Home: 209 Farmington Rd Pittsburgh PA 15215-1632

PÉLADEAU, MARIUS BEAUDOIN, art consultant, retired museum director; b. Boston, Jan. 27, 1935; s. Marius and Lucienne (Beaudoin) P.; m. Mildred L. Cole, Feb. 26, 1972. B.A. cum laude, St. Michael's Coll., 1956; M.S., Boston U., 1957; M.A., Georgetown U., 1962. Assoc. editor Public Utilities Fortnightly, Washington, 1962-66; adminstrv. asst., press sec. to U.S. Congressman J. P. Vigorito, Washington, 1967-72; dir. Maine League Hist. Socs. and Mus.'s, Monmouth, 1972-76, William A. Farnsworth Library and Art Mus., Rockland, Maine, 1976-87; gen. mgr. The Theater at Monmouth, Maine, 1989; cons. in field, 1990—. Author: The Verse of Royall Tyler, 1968, The Prose of Royall Tyler, 1972, Chansonetta: The Life and Photographs of Chansonetta Stanely Emmons, 1858-1937, 1977. Trustee Jones Mus. Glass and Ceramics; guest curator L.C. Bates Mus., Hinckley, Maine. Fellow Co. Mil. Historians; mem. Vt. Hist. Soc. Democrat. Roman Catholic.

PELADEAU, PIERRE, publishing company executive; b. Montreal, Apr. 11, 1925; s. Henri and Elmire (Fortier) P.; m. Raymonde Chopin, May 26, 1954; children: Eric, Isabelle, Pierre-Karl, Anne-Marie; m. Line Parisien, May 24, 1979; children: Esther, Pierre Jr., Jean. L.Ph., U. Montreal, 1945, M.A., 1947; B.C.L., McGill U., Montreal, 1950; Dr honoris cause, U. Que., U. Sherbrooke. With Quebecor Inc.; pub., printing and forest products holding co. exec. Quebecor Inc., Montreal, 1965—; editor, pres., chief exec. officer Quebecor Inc., 1965—; bd. dirs. Donohue Inc., Sodarcan Inc. 1st chancelor Ste.-Anne U., Novia Scotia, 1988. Mem. Order of Can., Nat. Order Que. Club: Saint-Denis. Office: Quebecor inc, 612 Rue Saint-Jacques ouest, Montreal, PQ Canada H3C 4M8

PELAEZ, EMMANUEL N., ambassador; b. Nov. 30, 1915. LLB, U. Manila, Philippines, 1938. Spl. prosecutor People's Ct., Philippines, 1946; congressman Misamis Oriental, 1949-53, 65-67; senator Philippines, 1953-59, 63-67, v.p., sec. fgn. affairs, 1961-65; mem. Interim Batasang Pambansa, 1978-84; mem. exec. com., 1982-83; amb. E. and P. to U.S., 1986—; chief gov. negotiator Mindanao and Cordillera Peace Talks, 1987—; Philippine permanent rep. to UN, 1987-88; spokesman Philippine panel Rep. of the Philippine U.S. Military Bases Negotiations, 1956, mem. panel, 1976; del. to various ASEAN Confs., Interparliamentary Union and other internat. confs. Office: Embassy of the Philippines 1617 Massachusetts Ave NW Washington DC 20036-2274

PELAEZ, MARC Y.E., federal official, career naval officer; b. Hollywood, Fla., Apr. 1, 1946; s. Genaro Julio Jr. and Odette (Delorme) P.; m. Sheila Prom, June 8, 1968; children: Jeannine Lynn, John Marc. Grad., U.S. Naval Acad., 1968. Commd. ensign USN, 1968, advanced through grades to rear adm., 1993; various assignments USS Bolivar, 1969-72; assignment officer submarine/nuclear power divsn. Naval Mil. Pers. Command, 1972-75; engr. officer USS Tunny, 1976-79; exec. officer USS James Monroe, 1979-80; asst. rsch. and devel. submarines Naval Sea Systems Command, Washington, 1981-83; mgr. advanced submarine combat system Naval Sea Systems Command; comdr. USS Sunfish, 1984-88; program mgr. advanced submarine tech. program, exec. asst. to asst. sec. of Navy for rsch., devel. and acquisition Def. Advanced Rsch. Projects Agy.; chief naval rsch. Dept. of Navy, Arlington, Va. Decorated Def. Superior Svc. Medal, Legion of Merit with gold star. Avocation: sailing. Office: Chief Of Naval Research 800 N Quincy St Arlington VA 22217

PELAEZ, ROLANDO FEDERICO, economics educator, consultant,; b. Washington, May 5, 1940; s. Rolando Juan and Maria Gertrudis (Bringuier) P. BS, La. State U., 1962, MA, 1964; PhD in Econs., U. Houston, 1973; postgrad., Rice U., 1978-79. Teaching fellow U. Houston-Univ. Park, 1970-71, instr., 1971-73; asst. prof. N.Mex. State U., 1973-74; assoc. prof. U. St. Thomas, 1980-87; asst. prof. Southeastern La. U., 1976; asst. prof. U. Houston-Downtown, 1977-80, assoc. prof. fin. Coll. Bus., 1987—; expert witness forensic economist; vis. asst. prof. U. Houston-Univ. Park, 1974-75; spkr., presenter confs. in field. Contbr. articles to profl. jours. OAS doctoral fellow, 1970. Mem. Am. Econ. Assn., Am. Statis. Assn., So. Finance Assn., Southwestern Econ. Assn., Southwestern Finance Assn., Western Econ. Assn., Nat. Assn. Forensic Economists. Home: 8318 Daycoach Ln Houston TX 77064-8201

PELAVIN, DIANE CHRISTINE, small business owner, research analyst; b. Pensacola, Fla., Nov. 13, 1943; d. Raymond Thomas and LaVerne Norma (Rousch) Blakemore; m. Sol H. Pelavin, Aug. 14, 1966; children: Shayna, Adam. BA, So. Ill. U., 1965; MS, San Jose (Calif.) State U., 1979. Tchr., 1965-68; planning analyst EPRI, Palo Alto, Calif., 1977-78; rsch. analyst

NTS Rsch. Corp., Durham, N.C., 1978-82; v.p., co-founder Pelavin Assocs., Inc., Washington, 1982-94; pres., co-founder Chesapeake Inst., Washington, 1991-94. Contbr. numerous articles to profl. jours. Mem. Sch. and Cmty. Vol. and fundraiser, 1971-95. U. Chgo. fellow, 1966, NSF fellow, 1968. Mem. Am. Edn. Rsch. Assn. Avocations: scuba diving, hiking, travel, reading. Office: 1000 Thomas Jefferson NW Washington DC 20007

PELAVIN, MICHAEL ALLEN, lawyer; b. Flint, Mich., Sept. 5, 1936; s. B. Morris and Betty (Weiss) P.; m. Natalie Katz, June 18, 1960; children: Mark, Gordon. Student U. Mich., 1954-55, Wayne State U., 1955-57; JD, Detroit Coll. Law, 1960. Bar: Mich. 1960, U.S. Tax Ct. 1966, U.S. Ct. Appeals (6th cir.) 1969, N.Y. 1989. Assoc. Pelavin & Powers, P.C., Flint, Mich., 1960-63, ptnr., 1963-71, pres., 1980—; trustee Mut. of Am. Life Ins. Co., 1981—; chair Nat. Jewish Community Rels. Adv. Coun., 1986-89. Chmn. young leadership cabinet United Jewish Appeal, 1973; pres. Flint Jewish Fedn., 1974-77; chmn. Bishop Internat. Airport Authority, 1990—. Mem. ABA, N.Y. State Bar Assn., Assn. Trial Lawyers Am., Mich. Bar Assn. Democrat. Home: 6168 Sierra Pass Flint MI 48532-2134 Office: Pelavin & Powers PC 801 S Saginaw St Flint MI 48502-1509

PELC, KAROL I., engineering management educator, researcher; b. Czestochowa, Poland, July 29, 1935; came to U.S., 1985; s. Stanislaw Pelc and Kamilla (Hecko) Pelc-Kosna; m. Ryszarda Lidia Ryglewicz, Sept. 24, 1959; 1 child, Dariusz. MScEE, Tech. U. Wroclaw, Poland, 1958, PhD in Econs., 1976; PhD in Electronics, U. Uppsala, Sweden, 1968. Electronic design engr. Rsch. Inst. Tech. U. Wroclaw, Poland, 1957-60; prodn. & engrng. mgr. Energopomiar Co., Wroclaw, 1960-65; rsch. asst. dept. electronics U. Uppsala, 1961-62; assoc. dir. div. Inst. Electric Power Industry, Wroclaw, 1966-68; rsch. dir. Tech. U. Wroclaw, 1968-70; founder, dir. Forecasting Rsch. Ctr., Wroclaw, 1971-81; lectr., dir. Jelenia Gora Coll. br. Tech. U. Wroclaw, 1982-85; prof. Mich. Technol. U., Houghton, 1985—; vis. prof. Indian Inst. Tech., Bombay, 1981, Stevens Inst. Tech., Hoboken, N.J., 1993; vis. scholar Japan Ctr. for Mich. Univs., Hikone, 1992; mem. innovation task force Internat. Inst. for Applied Systems Analysis, Laxenburg, Austria, 1983-84; chmn. forecasting seminar Polish Acad. Scis., Warsaw, 1974-81; v.p. div. Soc. Mgmt. and group, Wroclaw, 1979-80. Author: Planning of Research and Development, 1981; mem. editl. bd. Technol. Forecasting and Social Change, R&D Mgmt., Eng., Transformations, Poland; contbr. over 80 articles to scholarly jours.; patentee in field. Mem. Internat. Assn. Mgmt. Tech., Internat. Assn. for Rsch. and Devel. Mgmt., Am. Soc. Engring. Mgmt., Engring. Mgmt. Soc. of IEEE, Acad. Mgmt. Roman Catholic. Avocations: classical music, tourism, cross-country skiing, bicycling. Office: Mich Technol Univ Sch Bus & Engring Administrn Houghton MI 49931

PELCZAR, MICHAEL JOSEPH, JR., microbiologist, educator; b. Balt., Jan. 28, 1916; s. Michael Joseph and Josephine (Polek) P.; m. Merna M. Foss, Aug. 28, 1941; children: Ann Foss, Patricia Mary, Michael Rafferty, Rita Margaret, Josephine Merna, Julia Foss. BS, U. Md., 1936, MS, 1938; PhD, U. Iowa, 1941; DSc (hon.), Utah State U., 1986. Diplomate: Am. Bd. Microbiology. Instr. bacteriology U. Iowa, 1940-41; asst. prof., assoc. prof. bacteriology U. Md., College Park, 1946-50; prof. microbiology U. Md., 1950-78; prof. emeritus, 1978—, v.p. grad. studies and research, 1966-78, v.p. emeritus, 1978—; pres. Council Grad. Schs. in U.S., Washington, 1978-84; pres. emeritus Council Grad. Schs. in U.S., 1984—; mem. microbiology adv. panel Office Naval Rsch., 1965-70; spl. cons. Random House Dictionary of English Lang., 1965; councilor Oak Ridge Asso. Univs., Inc., 1959-66; also bd. dirs.; mem. So. Regional Edn. Bd., Coun. Grad. Edn. in Agrl. Scis., 1967; mem. departmental com. on biol. scis. U.S. Dept. Agr. Grad. Sch., 1967-76; chmn. Spl. Meeting on Neisseria WHO, Geneva, Switzerland, 1964, mem. expert adv. panel on bacterial diseases, 1967-77; mem. Gov.'s Sci. Adv. Bd., 1967—, chmn., 1967-72; mem. organizing com. for XVII Gen. Assembly NRC, div. biology and agr. Internat. Union Biol. Scis., 1968; chmn. bd. on human resource data and analysis Commn. on Human Resources, NRC, 1975-79; mem. exec. com. Coun. Grad. Schs., 1976-78; mem. Nat. Sea Grant Rev. Panel, 1979-89; mem. adv. com. Nat. Rsch. Coun., 1987—. Co-author: Microbiology, 5th edit, 1986, Elements of Microbiology, 1981, Microbiology: Concepts and Applications, 1993; editorial bd.: Jour. of Bacteriology, 1965-69; Contbr. sect. to: Ency. Brit, 1969, 94; articles to profl. jours. Ency. Ednl. Research. Recipient Nat. Sea Grant Assn. award, 1991. Fellow AAUP (past br. pres.), Nat. Adminstrn. Acad. Univ. Rsch. (founding mem. 1985); mem. AAAS, Am. Acad. Microbiology, Am. Inst. Biol. Scis. (bd. govs., past vis. lectr.), Am. Soc. Microbiology (bd. govs., past com. chmn., councilor, br. pres., hon. mem. 1986—), Internat. Assn. Microbiology, Washington Acad. Scis., Nat. Assn. State Univs. and Land-Grant Colls. (chmn. coun. for rsch. policy and adminstrn., cons. higher edn. rsch. administrn.), Cosmos Club, Phi Beta Kappa (assoc. 1989), Sigma Xi (ann. award sci. achievement 1968), Phi Kappa Phi, Sigma Alpha Omicron. Research microbial physiology. Home: PO Box 133 300 Avalon Farm Ln Chester MD 21619

PELÉ (EDSON ARANTES DO NASCIMENTO), professional soccer player; b. Três Corações, Minas Gerais, Brazil, Oct. 23, 1940; came to U.S., 1975; s. João Ramos do Nascimento and Celeste Arantes; m. Rosemeri Cholbi, Feb. 21, 1966 (div.); children: Kely Cristina, Edson, Jennifer; m. Assíria Lemos, April 30, 1994. Grad. in phys. edn., Santos U., 1972. Soccer player with Santos Football Club, Sao Paulo, 1956-74, N.Y. Cosmos, N.Y.C., 1975-77; chmn. Pepsi Internat. Youth Soccer Program, 1972—; pres. Empresas Pelé, Santos; chmn. Pelé Soccer Camps, 1978—; dir. soccer clinics. Author: Eu Sou Pelé, 1962, Jogando com Pelé, 1974, My Life and the Beautiful Game, 1977, Pelé Soccer Training Program, 1982; appeared in: films Eu sou Pelé, 1964, A Marcha, 1973, Istoé Pelé, 1974, Pelé, The Master and His Method, 1973, Pelé's New World, 1975, Pelé, 1977, Os Trombadinhas, 1979, Victory, 1981, A Minor Miracle, 1983, Hot Shot, 1985; composer: numerous songs in Samba style including Saudação Criança, 1969, Vexamão, 1970; soundtrack for film Pelé, 1977. Active Spl. Olympics, 1978—. Served with Brazilian Army, 1958. Recipient Internat. Peace award, 1978, WHO medal, 1989; named Athlete of Century, 1980. Player 4 World Cups, 1958, 62, 66, 70, won 3 times, Brazilian Nat. Team, 1957-71; scored 1, 282 goals (1,364 games) total; 1088 goals (1114 games) for Santos Football Club, 97 goals (111 games) for Brazilian Nat. Team, 65 goals (108 games) for Cosmos. Address: 75 Rockefeller Plz New York NY 10019-6907*

PELED, ABRAHAM, computer company executive; b. Suceava, Romania, Sept. 21, 1945; came to U.S., 1971; s. Leon and Laura (Pachter) B.; m. Judith Oberndorf, Aug. 22, 1967; 1 child, Daphna. BSEE, Technion U., Israel, 1967, MSEE, 1970; MAEE, Princeton U., 1973, PhDEE, 1974. Postdoctoral fellow IBM, Yorktown Heights, N.Y., 1974-76; mem. rsch. staff Haifa (Israel) Sci. Ctr. IBM, 1976-78; mgr. signal process T.J. Watson Rsch. Ctr. IBM, Yorktown Heights, 1978-80; function mgr. CS dept. San Jose (Calif.) Rsch. Lab. IBM, 1980-83; dir. tech. planning rsch. dir. IBM, Yorktown Heights, 1983-85, v.p. rsch. systems and software rsch. div., 1985-93; sr. v.p. bus. devel. Elron Electronic Industries, Haifa, Israel, 1993—. Author: Digital Signal Processing, 1976. Tech. officer Israeli Army Signal Corps, 1967-71. Fellow IEEE; mem. Univs. Space Rsch. Assn. (trustee 1987-92), Nat. Rsch. Coun. (elected mem. computer sci. and tech. bd. 1989-93). Office: Elron Electronic Industries, Matam Indsl Park, Haifa Israel

PELEG, BEZALEL, mathematician; b. Afula, Israel, Feb. 25, 1936; s. Moshe and Malka Peleg; m. Zmira Madorski, July 1, 1965; children: Gad, Avner, Orith. MSc, Hebrew U., Jerusalem, 1961, PhD, 1964. Hebrew U., Jerusalem, 1962-63, instr., 1963-64, lectr., 1964-65, 66-69, sr. lectr., 1969-71, assoc. prof., 1971-76, prof.?; asst. prof. U. Mich., Ann Arbor, 1965-66; rsch. fellow Ctr. Econ. Rsch. Tilburg U., The Netherlands, 1993-94; vis. prof. dept. econs. Va. Poly. Inst. and State U., 1986. Author: Game Theoretic Analysis of Voting in Committees, 1984. Fellow Econometric Soc.; mem. Am. Math. Soc., N.Y. Acad. Scis. Office: Hebrew U, Inst Maths, 91904 Jerusalem Israel

PELFREY, LLOYD MARVIN, college president; b. Hamilton, Ohio, June 13, 1931; s. Addie Herbert and Vina Marie (Miller) P.; m. Mary Irene Rohrer, May 9, 1957; children: Rhonda, Theda, Brenda. BA, Cin. Bible Coll., 1953; MA, Cin. Christian Sem., 1955, BD, 1959. Ordained to ministry Ch. of Christ/Christian Chs., 1953. Min. Ch. of Christ, Eaton, Ohio, 1951-56; min. Christian Ch., Englewood, Tenn., 1957, Prairie Hill, Mo., 1958-62; acad. dean Cen. Christian Coll., Moberly, Mo., 1957-73, pres., 1973—; mem. N.Am. Christian Conv., 1971-73, 84-86; mem. adv. com. Chaplaincy Endorsement Commn., 1973—; chmn. Christian Educators Conf., 1973; mem. convening com. Open Forum, 1989—. Contbr. articles to religious jours. Chmn. Citizens' Involvement and Human Devel. Com., Moberly, 1974, 75. Mem. Evan. Theol. Soc., Presdl. Assn. Christian Colls. (pres. 1981-82, sec. 1984-85, 94-95), Midwest Conf. Christian Colls. (sec. 1967-70, 72-73, pres. 1970-72), Kiwanis (pres. 1973-74). Home: 418 Woodland Ave Moberly MO 65270-2234 Office: Cen Christian Coll 911 E Urbandale Dr Moberly MO 65270-1997

PELHAM, JUDITH, hospital administrator; b. Bristol, Conn., July 23, 1945; d. Marvin Curtis and Muriel (Chodos) P.; m. Jon N. Coffee, Dec. 30, 1992; children: Rachel, Molly, Edward. BA, Smith Coll., 1967; MPA, Harvard U., 1975. Various govt. postions, 1968-72; prin. analyst Urban Systems, Cambridge, Mass., 1972-73; dir. devel. and planning Roxbury Dental and Med. Group, Boston, 1975-76; asst. to dir. for gen. medicine and ambulatory care Peter B. Brigham Hosp., Boston, 1976-77, asst. dir. ambulatory care, 1977-79; asst. v.p. Brigham and Women's Hosp., Boston, 1980-81; dir. planning and mktg. Seton Med. Ctr., Austin, Tex., 1980-82, pres., 1982-92, chief exec. officer, 1987-92; pres., chief exec. officer Daughters of Charity Health Services, Austin, 1987-92; pres. Mercy Health Svcs., Farmington Hills, Mich., 1993—; cons. Robert W. Johnson Found., 1979-80; bd. dirs. Mercy Health Svcs., Am. Healthcare Sys., Healthcare Rsch. and Devel. Inst., Inc., Amgen Bd.; bd. trustees Mercy Health Found., 1993-94, Mercy Internat. Health Svcs., 1993-94; mem. audit and fin. com. AMHS, 1994—, membership com., 1994. Author: Financial Management of Ambulatory Care, 1985; contbr. articles to profl. jours. Trustee A. Shivers Radiation Therapy Ctr., Austin, 1982-92, Marywood Maternity and Adoption Agy., 1982-86; bd. dirs. Quality of Life Found., Austin, 1985, Austin Rape Crisis Ctr., adv. bd., 1986-88; bd. dirs., trustee League House, 1982-93, Seton Fund, 1982-93; mem. Gov's Job Tng. Coordinating Council, 1983-85; adv. council U. Tex. Social Work Found., 1983-85; charter mem. Leadership Tex., Austin, 1983-93. Recipient Leadership award YWCA, Austin, 1986. Mem. Am. Coll. Healthcare Execs., Am. Hosp. Assn., Tex. Hosp. Assn. (mem. various couns. 1982-87), Austin Area Rsch. Orgn., Cath. Health Assn. (bd. dirs. 1987-95, com. on govt. rels. 1984-91), Tex. Conf. Cath. Health Facilities (bd. dirs. 1985-89, pres. 1988), Cath. Health Assn. (sec., treas. 1982-95, chair fin. com. 1992-95). Office: Mercy Health Svcs 34605 Twelve Mile Rd Farmington Hills MI 48331

PELHAM, THOMAS GERALD, lawyer; b. Hartford, Ala., Nov. 23, 1943; s. Roy W. and Annie Louise (Blackburn) P.; m. Vivian Holden, Feb. 1, 1969; children: Christopher Holden, Evan Blackburn. BA, Fla. State U., 1965; MA, Duke U., 1967; JD, Fla. State U., 1971; LLM, Harvard U., 1977. Bar: Fla. 1971. Ptnr. Brown, Smith, Young & Pelham, Tallahassee, 1971-76; profl. law So. Meth. U., Dallas, 1977-80; ptnr. Carlton Fields Law Firm, Tallahassee, 1980-82, Akerman, Senterfitt & Edison, Tallahassee, 1982-84, Culpepper, Pelham, Turner & Mannheimer, Tallahassee, 1985-87; sec. Fla. Dept. Community Affairs, Tallahassee, 1987-91; ptnr. Holland & Knight, Tallahassee, 1991-93, Apgar, Pelham, Pfeiffer & Theriaque, Tallahassee, 1993—; adj. prof. law Fla. State U., Tallahassee, 1992—; chmn. bd. dirs. Legal Environ. Assistance Found., Tallahassee; mem. Gov's Environ. Land Mgmt. Study Com., Tallahassee, 1992. Author: State Land Use Planning and Regulation, 1979. Mem. Tallahassee-Leon County Planning Com., 1985-87, Capitol Ctr. Planning Commn., Tallahassee, 1982-85. Recipient Govtl. Conservationist of Yr. award Fla. Audubon Soc., 1990, Spl. Friend of Fla. award 1000 Friends of Fla., 1988, 90, Person of Yr. award Fla. Environ. Mag., 1990. Mem. ABA (urban, state and local law sect.), Urban Land Inst., Fla. Bar (chmn. environ. and land use law sect. 1990-91), Am. Planning Assn. (Fla. chpt. v.p. chpt. affairs 1992-94, pres.-elect 1994—), Econ. Club Fla. Avocations: reading, travel, jazz, movies, jogging. Office: Apgar Pelham Pfeiffer & Theriaque 909 E Park Ave Tallahassee FL 32301-2646

PELIKAN, JAROSLAV JAN, history educator; b. Akron, Ohio, Dec. 17, 1923; s. Jaroslav Jan and Anna (Buzek) P.; m. Sylvia Burica, June 9, 1946; children: Martin, Michael, Miriam. Grad. summa cum laude, Concordia Jr. Coll., Ft. Wayne, Ind., 1942; BD, Concordia Theol. Sem., St. Louis, 1946; PhD, U. Chgo., 1946; MA (hon.), Yale U., 1961; DD (hon.), Concordia Coll., Moorehead, Minn., 1960, Concordia Sem., 1967, Trinity Coll., Hartford, Conn., 1987, St. Vladimir's Orthodox Theol. Sem., 1988, Victoria U., Toronto, 1989, U. Aberdeen, Scotland, 1995; LittD (hon.), Wittenberg U., 1960, Wheeling Coll., 1966, Gettysburg Coll., 1967, Pacific Luth. U., 1967, Wabash Coll., 1988, Jewish Theol. Sem., 1991; HHD (hon.), Providence Coll., 1966, Moravian Coll., 1986, Jewish Theol. Sem., 1991; LLD (hon.), Keuka Coll., 1967, U. Notre Dame, 1979; LHD (hon.), Valparaiso U., 1966, Rockhurst Coll., 1967, Albertus Magnus Coll., 1973, Coe Coll., 1976, Cath. U. Am., 1977, St. Mary's Coll., 1978, St. Anselm Coll., 1983, U. Nebr.-Omaha, 1984, Tulane U., 1986, Assumption Coll., 1986, LaSalle U., 1987, Carthage Coll., 1991, U. Chgo., 1991, So. Meth. U., 1992, SUNY, Albany, 1993; ThD (hon.), U. Hamburg, 1971, St. Olaf Coll., 1972; STD, Dickinson Coll., 1986; DSc in Hist., Comenius U., Bratislava, 1992; ScD (hon.), Loyola U., Chgo., 1995. Faculty Valparaiso (Ind.) U., 1946-49, Concordia Sem., St. Louis, 1949-53, U. Chgo., 1953-62; Titus Street prof. eccles. history Yale U., 1962-72, Sterling prof. history, 1972—; William Clyde DeVane lectr., 1984-86, dir. div. humanities, 1974-75, chmn. Medieval studies, 1974-75, 78-80, dean Grad. Sch., 1973-78; Gray lectr. Duke U., 1960, Ingersoll lectr. Harvard U., 1963, Gauss lectr. Princeton U., 1980, Jefferson lectr. NEH, 1983, Richard lectr. U. Va., 1984, Rauschenbusch lectre. Colgate-Rochester Divinity Sch., 1984, Gilson lectr. U. Toronto, 1985, Hale lectr. Seabury-Western Sem., 1986, Mead-Swing lectr. Oberlin Coll., 1986, Gross lectr. Rutgers U., 1989; bd. dirs. Nat. Humanities Ctr., 1984-90, Univ. Support Svcs. Inc., 1992—; adv. bd. Ctr. Theol. Inquiry, 1984-90; mem. coun. The Smithsonian Instn., 1984-90; U.S. chmn. U.S. Czechoslovak Commn. on Humanities and Social Scis., 1987—. Author: From Luther to Kierkegaard, 1950, Fools for Christ, 1955, The Riddle of Roman Catholicism, 1959 (Abingdon award 1959), Luther the Expositor, 1959, The Shape of Death, 1961, The Light of the World, 1962, Obedient Rebels, 1964, The Finality of Jesus Christ in an Age of Universal History, 1965, The Christian Intellectual, 1966, Spirit Versus Structure, 1968, Development of Doctrine, 1969, Historical Theology, 1971, The Christian Tradition, 5 vols., 1971-89, Scholarship and Its Survival, 1983, The Vindication of Tradition, 1984, Jesus through the Centuries, 1985, The Mystery of Continuity, 1986, Bach Among the Theologians, 1986, The Excellent Empire, 1987, The Melody of Theology, 1988, Confessor Between East and West, 1990, Imago Dei, 1990, Eternal Feminines, 1990, The Idea of the University: A Reexamination, 1992, Christianity and Classical Culture, 1993, Faust the Theologian, 1995, also introductions to works of others; editor, translator: Luther's Works, 22 vols., 1955-71, The Book of Concord, 1959; editor: Makers of Modern Theology, 5 vols., 1966-68, The Preaching of Chrysostom, 1967, Interpreters of Luther, 1968, Twentieth-Century Theology in the Making, 3 vols., 1969-70, The Preaching of Augustine, 1973, The World Treasury of Modern Religious Thought, 1991, Sacred Writings, 7 vols., 1992; mem. editorial bd. Collected Works of Erasmus, Classics of Western Spirituality, Evangelisches Kirchenlexikon, Emerson's Nature, 1986, The World Treasury of Modern Religious Thought, 1990; departmental editor Ency. Britannica, 1958-69; adminstrv. bd. Papers of Benjamin Franklin; chmn. publs. com. Yale Univ. Press, 1979-90, 92—; v.p. bd. govs., 1988—; contbr. to many symposia, jours., encys. Pres. 4th Internat. Congress for Luther Research, 1971, New Eng. Congress on Edn., 1976-77. Recipient Abingdon award, 1959; Pax Christi award St. John's U., Collegeville, Minn., 1966, Colman J. Barry award, 1995, John Gilmary Shea prize Am. Cath. Hist. Assn., 1971, nat. award Slovak World Congress, 1973, religious book award Cath. Press Assn., 1974, Christian Unity award Atonement Friars, 1975, Bicentennial award Czechoslovak Soc. Arts and Scis., 1976, Wilbur Cross medal Yale U. Grad. Sch. Assn., 1979, Profl. Achievement award U. Chgo. Alumni Assn., 1980, Shaw medal Boston Coll., 1984, Comenius medal Moravian Coll., 1986, Alumnus of Yr. award U. Chgo. Div. Sch., 1986, Bicentennial medal Georgetown U., 1989, award for excellence Am. Acad. Religion 1989, Umanità award Newberry Libr., 1990; recipient Festschrift: Schools of Thought in the Christian Tradition, 1984; sr. fellow Carnegie Found. for Advancement Tchg., 1982-83. Fellow Medieval Acad. Am. (councillor, Haskins medal 1985); mem. Am. Hist. Assn., Am. Soc. Ch. History (pres 1965), Internat. Congress Luther Rsch. (pres. 1971), Am. Acad. Arts and Scis. (v.p. 1976-94, pres. 1994), Am. Philos. Soc. (councillor 1984-87), Coun. Scholars of Libr. of Congress (founding chmn. 1980-83), Elizabethan Club, Mory's, Phi Beta Kappa (senator United chpts. 1985-90). Home: 156 Chestnut Ln Hamden CT 06518-1604 Office: Yale U Dept History 1504A Yale Sta New Haven CT 06520-7425

PELISEK, FRANK JOHN, lawyer; b. Wauwatosa, Wis., June 8, 1930; s. Frank Pelisek and Virginia Pancost; m. Jane Olga Bauman (div.), Susan M., David P.; m. Jill Ann Grootemaat, Apr. 4, 1975. BS in Econs., U. Wis., 1954, LLB, 1958; D in Comml. Sci. (hon.), U. Wis., Milw., 1990. Atty. Michael, Best & Friedrich, Milw., 1958—. 1st lt. U.S. Army, 1954-56. Office: Michael Best & Friedrich 100 E Wisconsin Ave Milwaukee WI 53202-4107

PELL, ARTHUR ROBERT, human resources development consultant, author; b. N.Y.C., Jan. 22, 1920; s. Harry and Rae (Meyers) P.; m. Erica Frost, May 19, 1946; children—Douglas, Hilary. AB, NYU, 1939, MA, 1944; PhD, Calif. Coast U., 1977; profl. diploma, Cornell U., 1943. Personnel dir. Eagle-Electric Mfg. Co., Long Island City, N.Y., 1946-50, North Atlantic Constructors, N.Y.C., 1950-53; v.p. Harper Assos., Inc. (personnel consultants), N.Y.C., 1953-75; cons. Human Resources Mgmt., 1975—; adj. asso. prof. mgmt. Sch. Continuing Edn., N.Y.C., 1962-84; lectr. Baruch Sch. Bus. and Pub. Adminstrn. Coll. City N.Y., 1948-67; adj. asso. prof. mgmt. Coll. Bus. Adminstrn., St. John's U., 1971-76. Author: (with W.B. Patterson) Fire Officer's Guide to Leadership, edit., 1963, Placing Salesmen, 1963, Placing Executives, 1964, Police Leadership, 1967, How to Get the Job You Want After 40, 1967, Recruiting and Selecting Personnel, 1969, (with M. Harper) Starting and Managing an Employment Agency, 1970, Recruiting, Training and Motivating Volunteer Workers, 1972, Be a Better Employment Interviewer, 1972, rev. edits., 1978, 86, 94, The College Graduate Guide to Job Finding, 1973, (with Wilma Rogalin) Women's Guide to Executive Positions, 1975, (with Albert Furbay) College Student's Guide to Career Planning, 1975, (with Dale Carnegie Assocs.) Managing Through People, 1975, rev. edits., 1978, 1987, Choosing a College Major: Business, 1978, Enrich Your Life: The Dale Carnegie Way, 1979, The Part Time Job Book, 1984, Making the Most of Medicare, 1987, rev. edit., 1990, (with George Sadek) Resumes for Engineers, 1982, Resumes for Computer Professionals, 1984, How to Sell Yourself on an Interview, 1982, The Job Finder's Kit, 1989, Getting the Most from Your People, 1990, Diagnosing Your Doctor, 1991, The Supervisor's Infobank, 1994; editorial cons. for revision Dale Carnegie's How to Win Friends and Influence People, 1981; author syndicated feature The Human Side; also articles. Served with AUS, 1942-46. Office: 111 Dietz St Hempstead NY 11550-7625

PELL, CLAIBORNE, senator; b. N.Y.C., Nov. 22, 1918; s. Herbert Claiborne and Matilda (Bigelow) P.; m. Nuala O'Donnell, Dec. 1944; children: Herbert Claiborne III, Christopher T. Hartford, Nuala Dallas Yates, Julia L.W. Student, St. George's Sch., Newport, R.I.; A.B. cum laude, Princeton U., 1940; A.M., Columbia U., 1946; 46 hon. degrees. Enlisted USCGR, 1941; served as seaman, ensign North Atlantic sea duty, Africa, Italy; hospitalized to U.S., 1944; instr. Navy Sch. Mil. Govt., Princeton, 1944-45; capt. USCGR; ret.; on loan to State Dept. at San Francisco Conf., 1945, State Dept., 1945-46, U.S. embassy, Czechoslovakia, 1946-47; established consulate gen. Bratislava, Czechoslovakia, 1947-48; vice consul Genoa, Italy, 1949; assigned State Dept., 1950-52; v.p., dir. Internat. Rescue Com.; senator from R.I., 1961—; ranking minority mem. Fgn. Rels. Com., Labor and Human Resources Subcom. on Edn., Arts, and Humanities; mem. Rules and Adminstrn. Com., Joint Com. on Libr. and Congl. Intern Program, Senate Dem. Policy Com.; U.S. del. Internat. Maritime Consultative Orgn., London, 1959, 25th Gen. Assembly, 1970. Author: Megalopolis Unbound, 1966, (with Harold L. Goodwin) Challenge of the Seven Seas, 1966, Power and Policy, 1972. Hon. bd. dirs. World Affairs Council R.I.; trustee St. George's Sch.; trustee emeritus Brown U.; Cons. Democratic Nat. Com., 1953-60; exec. asst. to chmn. R.I. State Dem. Com., 1952-54; chmn. R.I. Dem. Fund drive, 1952, Dem. nat. registration, chmn., 1956, co-chmn., 1962; chief delegation tally clk. Dem. Nat. Conv., 1956, 60, 64, 68. Decorated knight Crown of Italy, Grand Cross Order of Merit Italy, Red Cross of Merit Portugal, Legion of Honor France, comdr. Order of Phoenix Greece, Grand Cross Order of Merit Liechtenstein, Grand Cross Order of Christ Portugal, Order of Henry the Navigator, Portugal, Grand Cross Order of N. Star Sweden, Grand Cross of Merit Knights of Malta, Grand Officer of Merit Luxembourg, Grand Comdr. Lebanon; recipient Caritas Elizabeth medal Cardinal Franz Koenig, Grand decoration of honor in silver with sash Austria, Gold medal of St. Barnabas (Cyprus), recipient Pres.'s Fellow award R.I. Sch. Design, medal Nat. Order of Cedar, Hugo Grotius Commemorative medal The Netherlands, recipient Harold W. McGraw, Jr. Prize in Education, McGraw-Hill, 1988. Mem. Soc. Cin. Episcopalian. Clubs: Hope (Providence); Knickerbocker (N.Y.C.), Racquet and Tennis (N.Y.C.), Brook (N.Y.C.); Metropolitan (Washington); Travellers (Paris); Reading Room (Newport); White's (London). Office: US Senate 335 Russell Senate Bldg Washington DC 20510 *I have a seven word definition of my job and of my life: "Translate ideas into events, and help people.".*

PELL, ERNEST EUGENE, broadcasting executive; b. Paducah, Ky., Mar. 15, 1937; s. Ernest Joseph and Edna Marie (Stewart) P.; m. Linda Winthrop, July 17, 1959 (div. May 1985); children: Anne Frances, Jennifer Susan; m. Linda Ann Holwick, June 15, 1985. BA in English, Harvard U., 1959; MS in Journalism, Boston U., 1962. Anchorman WBZ-TV, Boston, 1963-67, WBZ-TV, WCVB-TV, Boston, 1975-77; polit. corr. Westinghouse Broadcasting Co., Washington, 1967-69; dir. fgn. news Westinghouse Broadcasting Co., London, Eng., 1969-74; fgn. corr. NBC News, Moscow, 1977-80; Washington corr. NBC News, 1980-82; dep. dir. Voice of Am., Washington, 1983-84, dir., 1984-85; pres. Radio Free Europe/Radio Liberty, Munich, Fed. Republic Germany, 1985—. Served to lt. (j.g.) USNR, 1959-62. Nieman fellow Harvard U., 1974-75, vis. fellow, 1977; recipient Best Fgn. Reporting award Overseas Press Club, 1974, Outstanding Alumnus award Boston U., 1981; named to Ky. Journalism Hall of Fame; decorated Grand Cross Order of merit Ger. Govt., 1992. Mem. Metropolitan Club (Washington). Republican. Club: Metropolitan. Avocations: golf, tennis, classical music, model railroading. Home: Dehmel Str 8, 8000 Munich 81, Federal Republic of Germany Office: Radio Free Europe/Radio Liberty Ste 804 1201 Connecticut Ave NW Washington DC 20036-2605 also: Radio Free Europa/Radio Liberty Inc, Oettingenstr 67, 8000 Munich 22, Federal Republic of Germany

PELL, JONATHAN LAURENCE, artistic administrator; b. Memphis, Oct. 20, 1949; s. Burton Marshall and Eleanor (Leopold) P. BA, U. So. Calif., 1971. Interior designer Gene Morse Assocs., Wichita, Kans., 1971-77; mgr. Internat. Artists Mgmt., N.Y.C., 1977-79, Robert Lombardo Assocs., N.Y.C., 1979-80; TV producer Sta. WNET, N.Y.C., 1980-83; dir. artistic administration The Dallas Opera, 1984—; dir. publicity John Curry Skating Co., N.Y.C., 1983; prodr. Jerome Kern Centennary Gala Town Hall, N.Y.C., 1984; vocal competition judge Pavarotti Competition, Ctr. for Contemporary Opera, Marguerite McCammon Competition, San Antonio Opera Guild, Richard Tucker award, others. Scenic and Costume designer for plays, musicals and ballets for various cos., 1970-76; host The Dallas Opera Radio Hour, WRR, 1994—. Mem. Richard Tucker award selection com. Mem. Opera Am. Office: Dallas Opera 3102 Oak Lawn Ave Ste 450 Dallas TX 75219-4259

PELL, WILBUR FRANK, JR., federal judge; b. Shelbyville, Ind., Dec. 6, 1915; s. Wilbur Frank and Nelle (Dickerson) P.; m. Mary Lane Chase, Sept. 14, 1940; children: Wilbur Frank III, Charles Chase. A.B., Ind. U., 1937, LL.D. (hon.), 1981; LL.B. cum laude, Harvard U., 1940; LL.D., Yonsei U., Seoul, Korea, 1972, John Marshall Sch. Law, 1973. Bar: Ind. 1940. Pvt. practice Shelbyville, 1940-42, 45-70; spl. agt. FBI, 1942-45; sr. ptnr. Pell & Good, 1949-56, Pell & Matchett, 1956-70; judge U.S. Ct. Appeals (7th cir.), 1970—, now sr. judge; mem. 3 judge spl. divsn. U.S. Ct. Appeals (D.C. cir.), appointing ind. counsel, 1987-92; dep. atty. gen., 1953-55; dir., chmn. Shelby Nat. Bank, 1947-70. Bd. dirs. Shelbyville Community Chest, 1947-49, Shelby County Fair Assn., 1951-53; dir. Shelby County Tb Assn., 1948-70, pres., 1965-66; dist. chmn. Boy Scouts Am., 1956-57; mem. pres.'s council Nat. Coll. Edn., 1972-87; dir. Westminster Found., Ind. U.; hon. dir. Korean Legal Center. Fellow Am. Coll. Probate Counsel, Am. Bar Found.; mem. ABA (judge Edward R. Finch Law Day USA Speech award 1973), Ind. Bar Assn. (pres. 1962-63, chmn. ho. of dels. 1968-69), Fed. Bar Assn., Ill. Bar Assn., Shelby County Bar Assn. (pres. 1957-58), 7th Fed. Cir. Bar Assn., Am. Judicature Soc., Am. Coun. Assn., Shelby County C. of C., Nat. Conf. Bar Pres.'s, Riley Meml. Assn., Ind. Soc. Chgo. (pres. 1978-79), Harvard Law Soc. Ill. (pres. 1980-81), Rotary (dist. gov. 1952-53, internat. dir 1959-61), Union League, Legal Club (pres. Chgo. 1976-77), Law Club (pres. Chgo. 1984-85), Kappa Sigma, Alpha Phi Omega, Theta Alpha Phi, Tau Kappa Alpha, Phi Alpha Delta (hon.). Republican. Presbyterian (elder,

deacon). Office: US Ct Appeals 7th Cir 219 S Dearborn St Apt 2760 Chicago IL 60604-1803

PELLA, MILTON ORVILLE, retired science educator; b. Wilmot, Wis., Feb. 13, 1914; s. Charles August and Ida Marie (Pagel) P.; m. Germaine Marie Reich, Dec. 9, 1944. B.E., Milw. State Tchrs. Coll., 1936; M.S., U. Wis., 1940, Ph.D., 1948. Tchr. sci. and math. Wyler Mil. Acad., 1937-38; tchr. elementary sch. Delavan Pub. Schs., 1938-39; tchr. sci. U. Wis. High Sch., 1939-42; prof. sci. edn. U. Wis., Madison, 1946-80, prof. emeritus, 1980—; With Fgn. Ednl. Service, Turkey, 1959, Iran, Turkey, Jordan, Syria, Lebanon, 1961, 62, Jordan, Lebanon, 1963, 64, 65, 66, 68, Costa Rica, 1967, Saudi Arabia, 1969, Nigeria, 1968, 69, Lebanon and Egypt, 1971-81. Author: Physical Science for Progress, 3d edit, 1970, Science Horizons—The Biological World, (with Branley and Urban), 1965-70. Served with AUS, 1942-46. Fellow A.A.A.S.; mem. Central Assn. Sci. and Math. (pres. 1955), Nat. Assn. for Research in Sci. Teaching (pres. 1966), Nat. Sci. Tchrs. Assn. (dir. 1950, 60). Club: Masons. Home: 5518 Varsity Hl Madison WI 53705-4652

PELLEGRENE, THOMAS JAMES, JR., editor, researcher; b. Wilmington, Del., Dec. 26, 1959; s. Thomas J. and MaryBelle (McGowan) P.; m. Pamela Heinecke, Apr. 5, 1986. BS in Journalism, Northwestern U., 1981, MS in Journalism, 1982. Staff writer Ft. Wayne (Ind.) Journal-Gazette, 1982-87, bus. editor, 1987—. Mem. Soc. Profl. Journalists. Office: Fort Wayne Journal-Gazette 600 W Main St Fort Wayne IN 46802-1408

PELLEGRINI, ANNA MARIA, soprano; b. Pretoro, Chieti, Italy, July 15, 1944; arrived in Can., 1959, naturalized, 1964; d. Vincenzo and Giuseppina (Pietrantonio) P.; m. Steven Murray Thomas, Aug. 13, 1974; 1 son, Vincent Thomas. Student, U. Toronto, Ont., Can., Faculty of Music, 1962-65. Tchr. voice Italian repertoire. Debut as Gilda in Rigoletto, Can. Opera Co., 1965; leading roles in: Cosi Fan Tutte, La Boheme, Turandot, I Pagliacci, Elektra; title roles in: Madama Butterfly, Manon Lescaut, Can. Broadcasting Corp. TV prodn. Madama Butterfly, 1977; appeared in maj. opera houses throughout the world. Recipient prize Met. Opera Nat. Auditions, 1966, Caravello d'Oro Ufficio Di Turismo, Genova, 1970, medallion honoring her and Puccini Sindico di Teatro Comunale di Treviso, 1974. Mem. Can. Actors Equity, Brit. Equity, Que. (Can.) Union des Artistes, Am. Guild Mus. Artists, Assn. Can. TV and Radio Artists. Office: Sardos Artist Mngmt Corp 180 West End Ave New York NY 10023*

PELLEGRINI, ROBERT J., psychology educator; b. Worcester, Mass., Oct. 21, 1941; s. Felix and Teresa (Di Muro) P.; 1 child, Robert Jerome. BA in Psychology, Clark U., 1963; MA in Psychology, U. Denver, 1966, PhD in Social Psychology, 1968. Prof. San Jose (Calif.) State U., 1967—; rsch. assoc. U. Calif., Santa Cruz, 1989-90; pres. Western Inst. for Human Devel., San Jose, 1985—. Author: Psychology for Correctional Education; contbr. articles to profl. jours. Mem. Phi Beta Kappa. Office: San Jose State U Dept Psychology San Jose CA 95192

PELLEGRINO, EDMUND DANIEL, physician, educator, former university president; b. Newark, June 22, 1920; s. Michael J. and Marie (Catone) P.; m. Clementine Coakley, Nov. 17, 1944; children: Thomas, Virginia, Michael, Andrea, Alice, Leah. BS, St. John's U., 1941, DSc (hon.), 1971; MD, NYU, 1944; 39 hon. degrees. Diplomate Am. Bd. Internal Medicine. Intern Bellevue Hosp., N.Y.C., 1944-45; asst. resident medicine Bellevue Hosp., 1948-49; resident medicine Goldwater Meml. Hosp., N.Y.C., 1945-46; fellow medicine NYU, 1949-50; supervising Tb physician Homer Folks Hosp., Oneonta, N.Y., 1950-53; dir. internal medicine Hunterdon Med. Center, Flemington, N.J., 1953-59; med. dir. Hunterdon Med. Center, 1955-59; prof., chmn. dept. medicine U. Ky. Med. Center, 1959-66; prof. medicine SUNY, Stony Brook, 1966-72; v.p. for health scis., dir. Health Scis. Center SUNY, 1968-73, dean Sch. Medicine, 1968-72; v.p. health affairs U. Tenn. System; chancellor U. Tenn. Med. Units, Memphis, 1973-75; prof. med. Yale U., New Haven, 1975-78; pres. Yale-New Haven Med. Center, 1975-78, Cath. U. Am., Washington, 1978-82; prof. philosophy and biology Cath. U. Am., 1978-82; John Carroll prof. medicine and med. ethics Georgetown U., Washington, 1982—; dir. Kennedy Inst. Ethics, Washington, 1983-88; dir. Ctr. for Advanced Study Ethics Georgetown U., Washington, 1988-94; dir. Ctr. for Clin. Bioethics, 1991—, acting chief Divsn. Gen. Internal Medicine, 1993-94. Founding editor Jour. Medicine and Philosophy, 1983— . Served with USAAF, 1946-48. Master ACP; fellow N.Y. Acad. Medicine; mem. Inst. Medicine of NAS, AMA, Assn. Am. Physicians, Medieval Acad. Am., Metaphys. Soc. Am., N.Y. Acad. Sci., Am. Clin. and Climatol. Assn. Office: Georgetown U Ctr for Clin Bioethics Washington DC 20007

PELLEGRINO, JAMES MARTIN, dentist; b. Massena, N.Y., Apr. 26, 1939; s. Frank A. and Mary E. (Martin) P.; m. Patricia Ann Viskovich, June 27, 1964; children: James, Lynn, Joanne, Andrea, Micheal. BS, Coll. of Holy Cross, 1961; DDS, SUNY, Buffalo, 1965. Pvt. practice Massena, 1965—. Bd. dirs. Massena Meml. Hosp., 1990, St. Law County Red Cross, Potsdam, N.Y., 1990. Mem. Am. Dental Assn., Dental Soc. (5th dist. pres.-elect 1994, pres. 1995), St. Law County Dental Soc. (pres. 1976), Massena Rotary (pres. 1975, Paul Harris fellow 1992), Monday Luncheon Club (pres. 1993), Elks, Knights of Columbus. Republican. Roman Catholic. Avocation: boating. Home: 24 Windsor Rd Massena NY 13662 Office: 55 E Orvis St Massena NY 13662

PELLEGRINO, JAMES WILLIAM, college dean, psychology educator; b. N.Y.C., Dec. 20, 1947; s. Vincent and Emily (Nicosia) P.; m. Barbara Jo Sposato, June 6, 1970 (div. 1975); 1 child, Christopher Michael; m. Susan Rosen Goldman, Dec. 23, 1978; children: Joshua Goldman, Seth Goldman. BS in Psychology, Colgate U., 1969; MS in Experimental, Quantitative Psychology, U. Colo., 1970, PhD in Experimental, Quantitative Psychology, 1973. Asst. prof. U. Pitts., 1973-78, assoc. prof., 1978-79; assoc. prof. U. Calif., Santa Barbara, 1979-83, prof., 1983-89; Frank Mayborn prof. Vanderbilt U., Nashville, Tenn., 1989—, dean Peabody Coll. Edn. and Human Devel., 1991—; co-dir. Learning Tech. Ctr. Vanderbilt U., 1989-91; proposal reviewer NSF, Can. Rsch. Coun., Australian Rsch. Coun.; presenter in field. Author: (with others) Cognitive Psychology and Instruction, 1978, Handbook of Semantic Word Norms, 1978, Memory Organization and Structure, 1979, Aptitude, Learning and Instruction: Cognitive Process Analyses, How Much and How Can Intelligence Be Increased, 1982, Advances in Instructional Psychology, vol. II, 1982, Handbook of Research Methods in Human Memory and Cognition, 1982, Advances in the Psychology of Human Intelligence, 1982, Individual Differences in Cognition, 1983, Human Abilities: An Information Processing Approach, 1984, Test Design: Developments in Psychology and Psychometrics, 1985, International Encyclopedia of Education, 1985, What is Intelligence?, 1986, Arthur Jensen: Consensus and Controversy, 1987, Intelligence and Cognition: Contemporary Frames of Reference, 1987, Metacognition, Motivation and Understanding, 1987, Test Validity, 1988, Learning and Individual Differences: Abilities, Motivation and Methodology, 1989, The Psychology of Learning and Motivation, 1989, The Proceedings of the 22nd Annual Hawaii International Conference on System Sciences, 1989, Vision and Action: The Control of Grasping, 1990, Learning Disabilities: Theoretical and Research Issues, 1990, Intelligence: Reconceptualization and Measurement, 1991, Philosophy of Science, Cognitive Psychology, and Educational Theory and Practice, 1992, New Approaches to Testing: Rethinking Aptitude, Achievement and Assessment, 1992, Cognitive Approaches to Automated Instruction, 1992; co-author: Human Intelligence: Perspectives and Prospects, 1985, Testing: Theoretical and Applied Perspectives, 1989, Instruction: Theoretical and Applied Perspectives, 1991; contbr. numerous articles to profl. jours. NIMH fellow; Colgate U. scholar, N.Y. State Regents scholar, Westchester County GOP scholar. Caddie scholar; recipient Austen Colgate award, Phil R. Miller award, Outstanding Young Men in Am. award. Mem. AAAS, Am. Ednl. Rsch. Assn. (various coms.), Midwestern Psychol. Assn., Rocky Mountain Psychol. Assn., N.Y. Acad. Sci., European Assn. Rsch. on Learning and Instrn., Cognitive Sci. Soc., Soc. Multivariate Experimental Psychology, Computers in Psychology, Soc. Mathematical Psychology, Soc. Rsch. and Child Devel., Psychonomic Soc., Sigma Xi, Phi Beta Kappa, Psi Chi. Avocations: sports, gardening, music. Home: 44 Park Crescent Circle Nashville TN 37215 Office: Vanderbilt U Box 329 Peabody Coll Nashville TN 37203

PELLEGROM, DANIEL EARL, international health and development executive; b. Three Rivers, Mich., May 29, 1944; s. Francis Robert and Regina Elizabeth (Valentine) P.; m. Sally Margaret Stukenbroeker, Nov. 30, 1944; children: Daniel, Jr., Benjamin, Sara. BA, Western Mich. U., 1966; MDiv, Union Theol. Seminary, 1969. Ordained to ministry, Presbyn. Ch., 1970. Dir. coll. programs Planned Parenthood Fedn., N.Y.C., 1969-71; exec. dir. Memphis Planned Parenthood, 1971-75, Md. Planned Parenthood, Balt., 1975-85; pres. Pathfinder Internat., Watertown, Mass., 1985—; bd. dirs. Alan Guttmacher Inst., N.Y.C.; bd. dirs., treas. Advocates for Youth, Washington, 1991—; mem. exec. com., bd. dirs. Inter Action, Washington, 1988-92; bd. dirs. Brush Found., Cleve., 1991—. Mem. Gov.'s conf. on children and youth State of Md., Balt., 1978-80; assoc. sch. hygiene and pub. health Johns Hopkins U., Balt., 1984-85. Recipient Leadership award Greater Balt. Com., 1983-84. Mem. APHA. Democrat. Avocations: baseball, travel, hiking. Home: 48 Bound Brook Rd Newton MA 02161-2036 Office: Pathfinder Internat 9 Galen St Ste 217 Watertown MA 02172-4521

PELLERZI, LEO MAURICE, lawyer; b. Cumberland, Md., June 14, 1924; s. John and Ida Lezzer (Regis) P.; m. Betty Lou Mearkle, Jan. 17, 1946; children: Jon Lou, Cheryl M., John C., Michele S. Julie A., Laura M., Jeffrey C. LL.B., George Washington U., 1949, LL.M., 1950. Bar: D.C. bar 1949, also U.S. Supreme Ct 1949. Atty. ICC, 1949-51, ECA, 1951-52; atty. Subversive Activities Control Bd., 1952-56, asst. gen. counsel, 1956-59; adminstv. law judge ICC, 1959-65; gen. counsel U.S. Civil Svc. Commn., 1965-68; asst. atty. gen. for adminstrn. Dept. Justice, 1968-73; chmn. bd. Govt. Svcs., Inc., 1971-73; gen. counsel Am. Fedn. Govt. Employees, AFL-CIO, 1973-78; chmn. bd. Flag Filter Corp., 1978-85; pvt. practice law Washington, 1978-90. Gen. counsel Lafayette Fed. Credit Union, 1956-59; pres. Fed. Adminstrv. Law Judges Conf., 1963-65. Served with USAAF, 1943-45; lt. col. Res. Decorated Air medal with 4 oak leaf clusters; recipient Commrs.'s award U.S. Civil Svc. Commn., 1968, Justice Tom C. Clark award Fed. Bar Assn., 1967. Mem. ABA, Fed. Bar Assn. (pres. D.C. chpt. 1962-63, chmn. com. gen. counsel 1966-67), George Washington U. Alumni Assn. Roman Catholic. Home: 106 Indian Spring Dr Silver Spring MD 20901-3017

PELLETIER, ARTHUR JOSEPH, state legislator, industrial arts and computer programming educator; b. Exeter, N.H., Dec. 13, 1946; s. Joseph Telesphor and Elsie Jane (Dillon) P.; m. Marsha Lynn Mingle, May 19, 1973; 1 child, John. Diploma N.H. Vocat. Tech. Inst., 1966; B.A., Kans. State U., 1970, M.S., 1972. Cert. in secondary edn., guidance. Asst. to dir. Kans. State U. Div. Continuing Edn., Manhattan, 1971-74; tchr. drafting Portsmouth High Sch., N.H., 1974-86; tchr. computer programming McIntosh Coll., Dover, N.H., 1982-84; assoc. prof. N.H. Vocat.-Tech. Coll., Stratham, N.H., 1986-87; kitchen designer Area Kitchen Ctr., Portsmouth, 1987; mem. N.H. Ho. Reps., 1993—; mem. legis. sci. tech. and energy com., 1991—; co-founder N.H. Coalition for Edn. Bd. dirs. N.H. Citizen Action, 1991—. Mem. World Future Soc., Seacoast I.B.M. Users Group. Avocations: radio-controlled model aircraft; tennis; photography. Home: 94 Back River Rd Dover NH 03820-4411

PELLETIER, CHARLOTTE M., nurse administrator; b. Manchester, N.H., Sept. 8, 1940; d. Bertrand and Edythe (Crossley) P. Diploma, Mary Hitchcock Meml. Hosp., Hanover, N.H., 1961; BSN, Boston U., 1964; MS, U. No. Colo., 1984. Cert. advanced nursing adminstrn. Asst. dir. nursing St. Joseph Hosp., Denver, 1964-76; adminstr., chief exec. officer Brighton (Colo.) Community Hosp., 1976-78; asst. administr. Swedish Med. Ctr., Englewood, Colo., 1978-86; sr. v.p. Erlanger Med. Ctr., Chattanooga, Tenn., 1986—. Mem. Am. Orgn. Nurse Execs., Tenn. Orgn. Nurse Execs. Office: Erlanger Med Ctr 975 E 3d St Chattanooga TN 37403

PELLETIER, LOUIS CONRAD, surgeon, educator; b. Montreal, Que., Can., Mar. 15, 1940; s. Conrad L. and Lucienne (Rochette) P.; m. Louise Montpetit, June 26, 1965; children: Conrad R., Marie-Helene. B.A., Brefeul Coll., Montreal, 1959; M.D., U. Montreal, 1964. Resident in cardiovascular and thoracic surgery U. Montreal, 1964-70, chmn. dept. surgery, 1986-94; rsch. asst. Mayo Clin. Found., Rochester, Minn., 1970-72; mem. dept. surgery Maisonneuve-Rosemont Hosp., Montreal, 1972-76, Sacré-Coeur Hosp., Montreal, 1972-80; mem. dept surgery Montreal Heart Inst., 1979—, head dept. surgery, 1979-87. Contbr. articles to profl. jours. Mem. adminstrv. bd. College Stanislas, Montreal, 1979-86, Que. Heart Found., 1980-84. Recipient Young Investigator's award Am. Coll. Cardiology, 1972; Med. Rsch. Coun. Can. scholar U. Montreal, 1973-78. Fellow Royal Coll. Physicians and Surgeons Can.; mem. ACS, Association des Medecins de Langue Francaise du Canada, Can. Med. Assn., Royal Coll. Can., Assn. Cardiovascular and Thoracic Surgery Que., Can. Cardiovascular Soc., Montreal Cardiac Soc., Clin. Rsch. Club Que. Soc. Thoracic Surgeons, Can. Assn. Clin. Surgeons, Sociedad de Cardiocirujanos, Coun. on Cardiovasular Surgery, Am. Heart Assn., Internat. Soc. for Heart Transplantation, Can. Soc. Cardiovascular and Thoracic Surgeons, Am. Assn. Thoracic Surgery. Roman Catholic. Avocations: skiing, sailing. Office: Montreal Heart Inst, 5000 E Belanger, Montreal, PQ Canada H1T 1C8

PELLETIER, MARSHA LYNN, state legislator, secondary school educator; b. Mt. Pleasant, Mich., July 29, 1950; d. Eugene Russell and Mary Ellen (Edde) Mingle; m. Arthur Joseph Pelletier, May 19, 1973; 1 child, John Frederick. BS in Home Econs. and Edn., Kans. State U., 1971, MS in Edn. Guidance and Counseling, 1972. Lic. rela estate broker, N.H. Conf. coord., guidance counselor Kans. State U., Manhattan, 1971-73; home econs. tchr. Franklin (Mass.) High Sch., 1974, Exeter (N.H.) High Sch., 1974-75, Barrington (N.H.) Mid. Sch., 1975-81, Pentucket Regional Jr. High Sch., West Newbury, Mass., 1981-82; realtor assoc. Century 21 Ocean and Norword Realty, Portsmouth, N.H., 1983-86; interior design tchr., cons. U. N.H., Durham, 1986-87; home econs. tchr. Dover Jr. High Sch., 1983—; rep. Dist. 12 Dover N.H. Ho. of Reps., Concord, 1992-94; ind. real estate broker Dover, 1986—. mem. Health Task Force, Dover and Concord, 1993-94; mem. bd. trustees St. John's Meth. Ch., 1995—. Mem. NEA (local pres. negotiator, membership chair, leadership exec. com., rep. 1979—), Nat. Coalition for Consumer Edn., Alpha Delta Kappa. (v.p. historian altruistic chmn. 1984-89). Democrat. Avocations: gardening, aerobics, designing, sewing, cooking. Home: 94 Back River Rd Dover NH 03820

PELLETIER, S. WILLIAM, chemistry educator; b. Kankakee, Ill., July 3, 1924; s. Anthony Amos and Estella Edith (Hays) P.; m. Leona Jane Bledsoe, June 18, 1949; children: William Timothy, Jonathan Daniel, Rebecca Jane, Lucy Ruth, David Mark, Sarah Lynn. B.S. with highest honors in Chem. Engring., U. Ill., 1947; Ph.D. in Organic Chemistry, Cornell U., 1950. Instr. chemistry U. Ill., 1950-51; mem. staff Rockefeller Inst., 1951-62, assoc. prof. organic chemistry, 1961-62; prof. chemistry, head dept. U. Ga., 1962-69, Alumni Found. disting. prof., 1969—, provost, 1969-76, Univ. prof., 1976—; dir. Inst. for Natural Products Research, 1976—; Gordon lectr., New Hampton, N.H., 1955, 59, 69; lectr. German Acad. Agrl. Scis., 1959; Am. Swiss Found. lectr.; Zurich, Basel, Bern and Geneva, Switzerland, 1960; Commemorative dedication lectr. Shionogi Research Lab., Osaka, Japan, 1961; Victor Coulter lectr. U. Miss., 1965; Nason-Piston lectr. Bost Pub. Library, 1982; Plenary lectr. 32d Internat. Congress on Medicinal Plant Rsch., Antwerp, Belgium, 1984; lectr. for internat. symposia in Berlin, Melbourne, Hong Kong, Kyoto, Prague, Stockholm, London, Riga, Latvia, Varna, Bulgaria, also other lectures in, Eng., Italy, India, Israel, Taiwan, Japan; mem. health medicinal chemistry study panel NIH, 1968-72. Author: Chemistry of the Alkaloids, 1970, Alkaloids: Chemical and Biological Perspectives, vols. 1-9, 1983-95, 7 monographs on Am. etcher John Taylor Arms, 1975-93, catalogue of etchings of Charles Meryon and Jean-Francois Millet, 1994; Adriaen van Ostade Etchings of Peasant Life in Holland's Golden Age, 1994; bd. editors Jour. Organic Chemistry, 1966-70, Heterocycles, 1979—, Jour. Natural Products, 1980—, Phytochem. Analysis, 1989—, Trends in Heterocyclic Chemistry, 1990—, also numerous articles. Pres. bd. Flushing Christian Day Sch., 1956-60; bd. advisers Ga. Mus. Art, 1968—; bd. dirs. Center for Research Libraries, Chgo., 1975-81. Served with USNR, 1944-46. Fellow AAAS, Royal Soc. Arts (London), Royal Soc. Chemistry (London); mem. Am. Chem. Soc. (chmn. N.E. Ga. sect. 1968, Charles Herty medal 1971, So. Chemists award 1972), Am. Soc. Pharmacognosy (Rsch. Achievement award 1991), Worldwide Discipleship Assn. (bd. dirs. 1980-88), Sigma Xi, Phi Eta Sigma, Tau Beta Pi, Sigma Tau. Presbyn. (elder). Spl. research structure and stereochemistry diterpenoid alkaloids, applications of carbon-13 nuclear magnetic resonance to structure determination, synthesis of terpenes, X-ray crystallographic structures of natural products. Office: U Ga Dept Chemistry Athens GA 30602-2556

PELLETREAU, ROBERT HALSEY, diplomat; b. Patchogue, N.Y., July 9, 1935; s. Robert H. and Mary (Pigeon) P.; m. Pamela Day, Dec. 17, 1966; children: Katherine Day, Erica Pigeon, Elizabeth Anne. B.A., Yale U., 1957; LL.B., Harvard U., 1961. Bar: N.Y. 1961. Assoc. firm Chadbourne, Parke, Whiteside & Wolfe, N.Y.C., 1961-62; joined U.S. Fgn. Service, 1962; service in Morocco, Mauritania, Lebanon, Algeria, Jordan and Syria; ambassador to Bahrain, 1979-80, dep. asst. sec. def., 1980-81, 85-87, dep. asst. sec. state, 1983-85, ambassador to Tunisia, 1987-91, ambassador to Egypt, 1991-93; asst. sec. state U.S. Dept. State, Washington, 1994—. Served with USNR, 1957-58. Mem. Am. Fgn. Service Assn., Middle East Inst., Coun. Fgn. Rels. Office: US Dept State Rm 6242 (NEA) Washington DC 20520

PELLETT, THOMAS ROWAND, retired food company executive; b. Franklin, N.J., Dec. 2, 1925; s. Thomas Lawrence and Elizabeth (Rowand) P.; m. Anne G. Iffert, July 1, 1950; children: Nancy Anne, Deborah Rowand, Thomas Lawrence II. B.S. in Mech. Engring, Princeton, 1947; M.B.A., U. Pa., 1949. Financial analyst Johns-Manville Co., N.Y.C., 1949-51; asso. Lehman Bros., N.Y.C., 1951-56; asst. treas. Red Owl Stores, Inc., Mpls., 1956-59; treas. Red Owl Stores, Inc., 1959-68; sr. v.p., CFO Pet Inc., St. Louis, 1968-87, sr. v.p. adminstrn., corp. officers, 1987-90; bd. dirs. Fortis Capital Fund, Fortis Growth Fund, Fortis Govt. Securities Fund, Fortis Money Fund, Fortis Securities, Inc., Fortis Fiduciary Fund, Spl. Portfolios Inc., Fortis Govt. Money Fund, Fortis Tax Exempt Fund, Fortis Advantage Portfolios, Fortis Series Fund, Fortis Global Fund. Served with USNR, 1944-45. Mem. Fin. Execs. Inst. Home: 731 Havenwood Circle Dr Saint Louis MO 63122-1424

PELLEY, MARVIN HUGH, mining executive; b. St. Anthony, Nfld., Can., Nov. 24, 1947; s. Hugh Albert Pelley and Alma Josie (Harnett) Roberts; m. Velma Delilah Gillard, Nov. 5, 1965; 1 child, Rhonda Mary-Jane. Diploma in engring., Meml. U. Nfld., St. John's, 1969, BSc, 1969; B in Engring. with distinction, Tech. U. N.S., Halifax, 1973. Registered profl. engr. Contract miner Whissel Mining Ltd., Nfld., 1969-71; planning engr. Kaiser, N.S., 1972; gen. foreman opers. Iron Ore Co. Can, Nfld., 1973-74, chief engr., 1975-78; exec. v.p./ptnr. Baumgartl & Assoc., Nfld., 1978-81; mgr. tech. svcs. Denison Mines Ltd. Quintette, B.C., 1981-86; v.p. engring./transp. Curragh Resources Inc., Y.T., 1986-87; exec. v.p. mining Curragh Resources Inc., Ont., 1987-91, pres. projects and coal, 1991-92, pres. corp. devel. and projects, 1992-93; pvt. cons., 1993—; bd. dirs. Stronsay Corp., Ont., Pelly River Mines Ltd., Vancouver, B.C., S-R Internat. Inc., Colo.; presenter in field. Mem. Am. Inst. Mining Engring., Canadian Inst. Mining and Metallurgy, Assn. Profl. Engrs Nfld., Assn. Profl. Engrs. B.C., Assn. Profl. Engrs. Yukon, B.C. Mining Assn. (bd. dirs. 1989). Avocations: reading, outdoor activities, canoeing, fishing, golf. Office: Curragh Inc, 95 Wellington St W Ste 1900, Toronto, ON Canada M5J 2N7

PELLI, CESAR, architect; b. Tucuman, Argentina, Oct. 12, 1926; came to U.S., 1952, naturalized, 1964; s. Victor V. and Teresa S. (Suppa) P.; m. Diana Balmori, Dec. 15, 1950; children: Denis G., Rafael A. BArch cum laude, U. Tucuman, 1949; MS in Architecture, U. Ill., 1954. Assoc. firm Eero Saarinen & Assocs. (Architects), 1954-64, Daniel, Mann, Johnson & Mendenhall, 1964-68, Gruen Assocs. Inc., L.A., 1968-77, Cesar Pelli & Assocs., New Haven, Conn., 1977—; dean Sch. Architecture, Yale U., New Haven, 1977-84. Works include Pacific Design Center and Expansion, Los Angeles (Honor award So. Calif. chpt. AIA 1976, Design award for Progressive Architecture 1987), Mus. Modern Art Expansion, N.Y.C., U.S. Embassy, Tokyo, Japan, World Fin. Ctr. and Winter Garden, N.Y.C. (Bard award), Cleve. Clinic (Honor award AIA 1986), Herring Hall, Rice U., Houston (Honor award AIA 1986), Carnegie Hall Tower, N.Y.C. (Honor award AIA 1994, Design award AIA/Conn. Soc. Architects. 1991, Plaza Tower, Costa Mesa (Honor award Orange County chpt. AIA 1991), Boyer Ctr. Molecular Medicine Yale U. (Design award AIA/Conn.), St. Luke's Med. Tower, Houston (Honor award Modern Healthcare/AIA 1991), NationsBank Corp. Ctr., Charlotte, NTT Corp. Hdqrs., Tokyo, New North Terminal, Washington Nat. Airport, Ohio Ctr. for the Arts, Cin., Kuala Lumpur City Centre, Malaysia, Francis Lehman Loeb Art Ctr. Vassar Coll., Poughkeepsie, N.Y.; bd. govs. Perspecta mag.; editor Yale Seminars on Architecture, 1981, 82. Fellow AIA (Firm award 1989, named to top ten list of living Am. archs. 1991, Gold medal 1995); mem. NAD (Arnold M. Brunner Meml. prize 1978), Am. Acad. Arts and Letters (academician), Internat. Acad. Architecture (academician). Office: Cesar Pelli & Assocs care Janet Kagan 1056 Chapel St New Haven CT 06510

PELLINO, CHARLES EDWARD, JR., lawyer; b. Chgo., May 2, 1943; s. Charles Edward Sr. and Ella (Diacomedico) P.; m. Melinda Poorman, Aug. 20, 1966; children: Charles, Tracy, William. BA, Drake U., 1965; JD, U. Wis., 1968. Bar: Wis. 1968, U.S. Dist. Ct. (we. dist.) Wis. 1972, U.S. Tax Ct 1984, U.S. Dist. Ct. (ea. dist.) Wis. 1985, U.S. Ct. Appeals (7th cir.) 1985, U.S. Supreme Ct. 1985. Assoc. McAndrews, Fritschler & Huggett, Madison, Wis., 1968-70; ptnr. Fritschler, Ross, Pellino & Protzman, Madison, 1970-73, Fritschler, Pellino & Assocs., Madison, 1973-76, Fritschler, Pellino, Schrank & Rosen, Madison, 1976-88, Fritschler, Pellino, Rosen and Mowris, Madison, 1988—; bd. dirs. Frontier Econ. Devel. Corp., N.Y.C. Contbr. articles to profl. jours. Mem. ABA, Wis. Bar Assn., Nat. Assn. Criminal Def. Lawyers, Wis. Acad. Trial Lawyers, Wis. Assn. Criminal Def. Lawyers (sec.-elect 1991—). Avocations: flying, golf. Office: Pellino Rosen Mowris & Kirkhuff PC 131 W Wilson St Ste 1201 Madison WI 53703-3262

PELLOUX, REGIS MARC NOEL, materials engineering educator; b. Passy, France, Dec. 24, 1931; came to U.S., 1955; s. Francois and Fernande (Trappier) P.; m. Isabel H. Pelloux, Dec. 26, 1956; children: Marc, Elizabeth A. BA, Lycee, Genoble, France, 1950; diplome ingenuer, Ecole Centrale, Paris, 1955; MS, MIT, 1956, ScD, 1958. Registered profl. engr. Mass. Rsch. asst. MIT, Cambridge, 1955-58; rsch. scientist The Boeing Co., Seattle, 1960-68; prof. MIT, Cambridge, 1968—; tech. cons. in field. Contbr. numerous articles to profl. jours. 1st lt. French Army, 1958-61. Fellow ASM; mem. AIME, ASTM. Home: 39 Prospect St Winchester MA 01890-3161 Office: MIT Cambridge MA 02139

PELLOW, DAVID MATTHEW, lawyer, law educator; b. Batavia, N.Y., Oct. 5, 1950; s. Louis Matthew and M. Beverly (Sizing) P.; m. Barbara Terry Walzer, Aug. 24, 1975; children:—Matthew Aaron, Jonathan Adam. B.S. in Bus. Adminstrn., Boston Coll., 1972; J.D., U. Mich., 1975. Bar: N.Y. 1976, U.S. Dist. Ct. (no. dist.) N.Y. 1976, U.S. Ct. Appeals (3d cir.) 1980, U.S. Supreme Ct. 1981, U.S. Dist. Ct. (we. dist.) N.Y. 1985. Ptnr. Bond, Schoeneck & King, Syracuse, N.Y.; adj. asst. prof. labor law LeMoyne Coll., Syracuse, N.Y., 1981—; bd. dirs. Legal Services Central N.Y. Inc., Syracuse 1978-81. Active N.Y. State Human Rights Arbitration Adv. Com., 1990—. Contbr. articles to profl. jours. Mem. ABA (labor and employment law sect.), N.Y. State Bar Assn., Indsl. Relations Research Assn. (v.p. central N.Y. chpt. 1981-82). Office: Bond Schoeneck & King 1 Lincoln Ctr 18th Fl Syracuse NY 13202-1324

PELOFSKY, JOEL, lawyer; b. Kansas City, Mo., June 23, 1937; s. Louis J. and Naomi (Hecht) P.; m. Brenda L. Greenblatt, June 19, 1960; children: Mark, Lisa, Carl. AB, Harvard U., 1959; LLB, 1962. Bar: Mo. 1962, U.S. Dist. Ct. (we. dist.) Mo. 1962, U.S. Ct. Appeals (8th cir.) 1968, U.S. Ct. Appeals (10th cir.) 1970. Law clk. to judge U.S. Dist. Ct. (we. dist.) Mo., 1962-63; mem. Miniace & Pelofsky, Kansas City, Mo., 1965-80; asst. pros. atty. Jackson County (Mo.), 1967-71; mem. Kansas City (Mo.) City Council, 1971-79; judge U.S. Bankruptcy Ct., Western Dist. Mo., Kansas City, 1980-85; ptnr. Shughart, Thomson & Kilroy P.C., Kansas City, 1986-95; apptd. trustee Ark., Mo., Nebr., 1994—; intermittant lectr. in law U. Mo.; mem. Region I, Law Enforcement Assistance Adminstrn. Bd. dirs. Greater Kansas City Mental Health Found.; mem. adv. bd. Urban League, Kansas City, Mo., chmn. human resource devel. com. Mo. Mcpl. League; bd. dirs., mem. exec. com. Truman Med. Ctr., Kansas City, Mo., pres. bd. 1988-90, chmn. bd., 1990-92; trustee Menorah Med. Ctr., Kansas City, Mo. Served to lt. U.S. Army, 1963-65. Mem. ABA, Mo. Bar, Kansas City Bar Assn., Comml. Law League. Office: US Trustee 806 Fed Office Bldg 911 Walnut Kansas City MO 64105-1917

PELOQUIN, GARRY WAYNE, retired hospital executive; b. Feb. 7, 1937; s. Lud and Dorlene P.; m. Dorthe Rauholt, Aug. 1989; children: Garry Lud and Jerry Wayne (twins). BS in Biology, U. Ala., Tuscaloosa, 1964; MS Health Planning and Adminstrn., U. Cin., 1986. Lic. nursing home adminstr., qualified exec., Ala. Chief radiol. technologist. dir. sch. radiologic tech. Bapt. Hosp., Memphis, 1965-66; adminstr. Magnolia Haven Nursing Home, Tuskegee, Ala., 1966-69, Macon County Hosp., Russellville, Ala., 1969-72, N. Ala. Hosp., Russellville, 1972-74; pres. Humana Hosp., Augusta, Ga., 1974-94; ret., 1994; mem. lectr. Ala. State Radiol. Soc. Conv., Birmingham (2d pl. sci. award 1965). Recipient Civil Def. Spl. Commendation and Svc. award, Gov. Ala. Home: 3528 Carnoustie Dr Augusta GA 30907-9504

PELOSI, MARCO ANTONIO, obstetrician/gynecologist; b. Lima, Peru, Oct. 5, 1942; came to the U.S., 1968; m. Luisa Garcia-Pacheco, 1962; children: Marco, Carlo, Monica. BS, U. Peruana Mayor de San Marcos, Lima, 1962; MD, U. Peruana Cayetano Heredia, Lima, 1968. Cert. Am. Bd. Ob-Gyn. Intern Navy Med. Ctr., Lima, 1967-68; intern dept. ob-gyn. U. Medicine and Dentistry of N.J., Martland Hosp., Newark, 1968-69; resident dept. ob-gyn. CMDNJ-NJMC/Martland Hosp., Newark, 1969-72, fellow oncology dept. ob-gyn., 1972-74; pvt. practice, 1975—; instr. dept. ob-gyn. UMDNJ-N.J. Med. Sch., Newark, 1972-75, clin. asst. prof., 1975-80, 80—; clin. asst. prof. dept. ob-gyn. Hahnemann Med. Coll. Phila., Pa., 1980—; attending physician dept. ob-gyn. UMDNJ-N.J. Med. Sch., Newark, 1972—; Bayonne (N.J.) Hosp., 1974—, St. Joseph Hosp., Paterson, N.J., 1974—; St. Elizabeth Hosp., Elizabeth, N.J., 1979-87, Meadowlands Hosp., Secaucus, N.J., 1979—, Greenville Hosp., Jeresey City, N.J., 1980—; dir. dept. ob-gyn. Bayonne (N.J.) Hosp., 1987—; presenter. Contbr. chpts. to books and articles, abstracts to profl. jours. Recipient 1st prize The Female Patient's 1st Annual Photo Contest, The Female Patient Mag., 1988, Physician's Recognition award AMA, 1979, 81, 84, 87, 90, 93, Sci. Exhibit Recognition award, Sci. Exhibit Achievement award 83rd Annual Sci. Assembly, So. Med. Assn., Washington, 1989, Physician's Recognition award Med. Soc. N.J., 1993. Fellow ACS, AGOG (Philip F. Williams award 1972, Continuing Edn. award 1972, 79, 82, 84, 87, 90, 93), Internat. Coll. Surgeons, Am. Fertility Soc., N.J. Ob-Gyn. Soc., Am. Inst. Ultrasound in Medicine; mem. Am. Soc. Profs. Ob.-Gyn., Soc. for Minimally Invasive Surgery, Soc. Laparoendoscopic Surgeons, N.J. Med. Soc., Passaic County Med. Soc., Am. Soc. Cytology, Pan Am. Cancer Cytology Soc., Gynecol. Urology Soc., Med. Collectors Assn., Am. Assn. for the History Medicine, Internat. Soc. Physicians Historians, Am. Assn. Gynecol. Laparoscopists, Royal Soc. Medicine, Med. History Soc. N.J. Office: Pelosi Womens Med Ctr 350 Kennedy Blvd Bayonne NJ 07002

PELOSI, NANCY, congresswoman; b. Balt., Mar. 26, 1941; d. Thomas J. D'Alesandro Jr.; m. Paul Pelosi; children: Nancy Corinne, Christine, Jacqueline, Paul, Alexandra. Grad., Trinity Coll. Former chmn. Calif. State Dem. Com., 1981; committeewoman Dem. Nat. Com., 1976, 80, 84; fin. chmn. Dem. Senatorial Campaign Com., 1987; mem. 99th-102d Congresses from 5th Calif. dist., 1987-1992, 103rd Congress from 8th Calif. dist., 1993—; mem. appropriations com., subcoms. labor, HHD & edn., fgn. ops., D.C.; intelligence (vice chairperson) com., standard official conduct com. Office: US House of Rep 2457 Rayburn Washington DC 20515-0508*

PELOSO, JOHN FRANCIS XAVIER, lawyer; b. N.Y., Oct. 7, 1934; s. Rocco C. and Victoria (Musco) P.; m. Elizabeth Byrne Peloso, Oct. 7, 1961; children: Alycia, John, Matthew. BA, Fordham U., 1956, LLB, 1960. Bar: N.Y. 1960, U.S. Dist. Ct. (so. dist.) N.Y. 1962, U.S. Ct. Appeals (2nd cir.) 1967, U.S. Supreme Ct. 1968. Law clk. to judge U.S. Dist. Ct. (so. dist.) N.Y., 1960-61; asst. to U.S. Atty. U.S. Atty.'s Office N.Y., 1961-65; assoc. Carter Ledyard & Milburn, N.Y., 1965-70; chief trial counsel NYRO-SEC, N.Y., 1970-75; ptnr. Sage Gray Todd & Sims, N.Y., 1975-87, Morgan, Lewis & Bockius, N.Y., 1987—; speaker in field. Contbr. articles to profl. jours. Capt. inf. USAR, 1956-64. Mem. ABA (sect. corp., banking and bus. law, mem. com. fed. regulation securities 1975—, litigation co-chmn. com. securities litigation 1983-87, com. on liaison with jud. 1987-88, mem. coun. 1989-91), Assn. of Bar of City of N.Y. (arbitration com. 1970-73, fed. legis. com. 1975-78, fed. cts. com. 1982-86), Nat. Assn. Securities Dealers (nat. panel arbitrators 1975—, nat. arbitration com. 1982-85). Office: Morgan Lewis & Bockius 101 Park Ave New York NY 10178-0060

PELOTTE, DONALD EDMOND, bishop; b. Waterville, Maine, Apr. 13, 1945; s. Norris Albert and Margaret Yvonne (LaBrie) P. AA, Eymard Sem. and Jr. Coll., Hyde Park, N.Y., 1965; BA, John Carroll U., 1969; MA, Fordham U., 1971, PhD, 1975. Ordained priest Roman Cath. Ch., 1972. Provincial superior Blessed Sacrament, Cleve., from 1978; ordained coadjutor bishop Diocese of Gallup, N.Mex., 1986-90, bishop, 1990—; nat. bd. dirs. Maj. Superiors of Men, Silver Spring, Md., 1981-86, Tekakwitha Conf., Great Falls, Mont., 1981—. Author: John Courtney Murray: Theologian in Conflict, 1976. 1st native Am. bishop. Mem. Cath. Theol. Soc. Am., Am. Cath. Hist. Soc. *

PELSTER, WILLIAM C., lawyer; b. St. Louis, May 11, 1942; s. William R. and Marie C. (Graefe) P.; m. Terry C. Cuthbertson, Aug. 9, 1969. BA, Oberlin Coll., 1964; JD, U. Mich., 1967. Bar: Mo. 1967, N.Y. 1968, U.S. Dist. Ct. (so. dist.) N.Y. 1968, U.S. Ct. Appeals (2d cir.) 1968, U.S. Supreme Ct. 1972. Law clk. to presiding justice U.S. Ct. Appeals (2d cir.), N.Y.C., 1967-68; assoc. Donovan, Leisure, Newton & Irvine, N.Y.C., 1968-75; ptnr. Skadden, Arps, Slate, Meagher & Flom, N.Y.C., 1976—. Trustee Cancer Care Inc., N.Y.C., 1975—. Mem. ABA, Assn. of Bar of City of N.Y. Office: Skadden Arps Slate Meagher & Flom 919 3rd Ave New York NY 10022-3903

PELTASON, JACK WALTER, university president; b. St. Louis, Aug. 29, 1923; s. Walter B. and Emma (Hartman) P.; m. Suzanne Toll, Dec. 21,1946; children: Nancy Hartman, Timothy Walter H., Jill K. BA, U. Mo., 1943, MA, 1944, LLD (hon.), 1978; AM, Princeton U., 1946, PhD, 1947; LLD (hon.), U. Md., 1979, Ill. Coll. 1979, Gannon U., 1980, U. Maine, 1980, Union Coll., 1981, Moorehead (N.D.) State U., 1980; LHD (hon.), 1980, Ohio State U., 1980, Mont. Coll. Mineral Scis. and Tech., 1982, Buena Vista Coll., 1982, Assumption Coll., 1983, Chapman Coll., 1986, U. Ill., 1989. Asst. prof. Smith Coll., Mass., 1947-51; asst. prof. polit. sci. U. Ill., Urbana, 1951-52, assoc. prof., 1953-59, dean Coll. Liberal Arts and Scis., 1960-64, chancellor, 1967-77; vice chancellor acad. affairs U. Calif., Irvine, 1964-67, chancellor, 1984-92; pres. U. Calif. System, Oakland, 1992—. Am. Coun. Edn., Washington, 1977-84; Cons. Mass. Little Hoover Commn., 1950. Author: The Missouri Plan for the Selection of Judges, 1947, Federal Courts and the Political Process, 1957, Fifty-eight Lonely Men, 1961, Understanding the Constitution, 13th edit., 1994, orig. edition, 1949, (with James M. Burns) Government By the People, 16th edit., 1995, orig. edit., 1952; contbr. articles and revs. to profl. jours. Recipient James Madison medal Princeton U., 1982. Fellow Am. Acad. Arts and Scis.; mem. Am. Polit. Sci. Assn. (council 1952-54), Phi Beta Kappa, Phi Kappa Phi, Omicron Delta Kappa, Alpha Phi Omega, Beta Gamma Sigma. Home: 18 Whistler Ct Irvine CA 92715 also: 70 Rincon Rd Kensington CA 94707-1047 Office: U Calif Office of Pres 300 Lakeside Dr Oakland CA 94612-3550

PELTIER, EUGENE JOSEPH, civil engineer, former naval officer, business executive; b. Concordia, Kans., Mar. 28, 1910; s. Frederick and Emma Helen (Brasseau) P.; m. Lena Evelyn Gennette, June 28, 1932 (dec.); children: Marion Joyce, Eugene Joseph (dec.), Carole Josephine, Kenneth Noel, Judith Ann. B.S. in Civil Engring., Kans. State U., 1933, LL.D., 1961. Registered profl. engr., Mo., N.Y., Kans., Fla., Va., Calif. Commd. lt. (j.g.) U.S. Navy, 1936, advanced through grades to rear adm., 1957; asst. public works officer Great Lakes, Ill., 1940-42; sr. asst. supt. civil engr. Boston, 1942-44; officer in charge 137th Constrn. Bn. Okinawa, 1945, officer in charge 54th Constrn. Regt., 1945; officer various public works assignments Pensacola, Fla., 1945-46, Memphis, 1946-49, Jacksonville, Fla., 1949-51; dist. public works officer (14th Naval Dist.), 1951-53; asst. chief maintenance and materials Bur. Docks Washington, 1953-56; comdg. officer Pt. Hueneme, 1956-57; chief Bur. Yards and Docks, Navy Dept. Washington, 1957-62; chief of civil engrs., 1957-62, ret., 1962; instrumentman, resident engr. Kans. Hwy. Comm., Norton, Topeka, Chanute, 1934-40; v.p. Sverdrup & Parcel & Assocs., Inc., St. Louis 1962-64; sr. v.p. Sverdrup & Parcel & Assos., Inc., 1964-66, exec. v.p., 1966-67, pres., dir. 1967-75, chief exec. officer, 1972-75, ptnr., 1966-75, cons., 1975-82; pres. dir. Sverdrup & Parcel & Assos., N.Y.,

Inc., 1967-75; dir. Sverdrup & Parcel Internat., Inc., 1967-75; v.p., dir. ARO, Inc., Tullahoma, Tenn., 1966-75; cons. EPA, 1976-80; dir. Merc. Trust Co., St. Louis, 1971-81. Mem. emeritus Civic Progress, Inc.; bd. dirs. YMCA, St. Louis, 1972-76. Decorated Legion of Merit; recipient citation Am. Inst. Steel Constrn., 1973. Mem. ASCE (hon.), Am. Public Works Assn. (1 of Top Ten Public Works Men of Year 1960), Soc. Mil. Engrs. (pres. 1960-61), Am. Concrete Inst., Am. Road and Transp. Builders Assn. (pres. 1972-73), Nat. Soc. Profl. Engrs., Mo. Soc. Profl. Engrs., Public Works Hist. Soc. (pres. 1977-78, trustee 1975-79), Nat. Acad. Engring., Cons. Engrs. Council (award of Merit 1962), Sigma Tau, Phi Kappa Phi. Clubs: Army-Navy Country (Washington); Old Warson Country (St. Louis).

PELTON, JAMES RODGER, librarian; b. St. Louis, Mar. 21, 1945; s. Norman C. and Leona V. (Schulte) P.; m. Sandra Lee Birdsell, Mar. 29, 1969; 2 daus., Joni Lee, Vicki Sue. B.A., U. Mo., 1967, M.L.S., 1969. Br. librarian Scenic Regional Library, Union, Mo., 1968-71; administr. Daniel Boone Regional Library - Columbia Center, Columbia, Mo., 1971-78; cons. La. State Library, Baton Rouge, 1978-80; dir. Shreve Meml. Library, Shreveport, La., 1980—. Mem. ALA, La. Library Assn. Home: 3201 Old Mooringsport Rd Shreveport LA 71107-3926 Office: 424 Texas St Shreveport LA 71101-3522

PELTON, JOAN ELISABETH MASON, music company executive; b. Bristol, Pa., Feb. 15, 1932; d. William and Mary-Scott (Ryder) Mason; m. Clifford L. Pelton, Feb. 29, 1952 (div. 1977); children: William, Seth, Jesse, Aaron. BA, Pomona Coll., Claremont, Calif., 1953. Owner, chief exec. officer Silo Inc./Alcazar Inc., Waterbury, Vt., 1977—. Musician recording The Hammered Dulcimer, 1972; producer records Kitchen Junket, 1977, several new releases, particularly children's, 1988-92. Bd. dirs. Champlain Valley Folk Festival. Mem. Nat. Assn. Ind. Record Distbrs. (bd. dirs. 1984-91, ½—), Women Bus. Owners Network. Office: Silo Inc/Alcazar Prodns Inc PO Box 429 Waterbury VT 05676-0429

PELTON, JOHN STAFFORD, finance company executive; b. Windsor, Ont., Can., May 10, 1946; s. Stafford Baker and Gertrude Pelton; m. Ethelwyn Lillian Darlene Pelton, May 24, 1969; children: Sarah, Rebecca, Charles, Elizabeth. B in Comm., U. Toronto, Ont., 1969. C.A., 1972. CFO Canavest House, Ltd., Toronto, 1973-74; CFO Fed. Industries Ltd., Winnipeg, Manitoba, Can., 1974-86; v.p. corp. devel., 1986-87; sr. v.p., dir., head mergers and acquisitions Merrill Lynch Can. Inc., Toronto, 1987-88; pres., COO, dir. FT Capital Ltd. (formerly Fin. Trustco Capital Ltd.), Toronto, 1988-90, Morgan Fin. Corp., Toronto, 1988-91; pres., COO, mng. ptnr. Greystone Ptnrs. Inc., Toronto, 1989-91; pres., COO, dir. Fed. Industries Ltd., Winnipeg, 1991-92, pres., CEO, dir., 1992—. Office: Federal Industries Ltd, 180 Attwell Dr Ste 400, Etobicoke, ON Canada M9W 6A9

PELTON, RALPH A., insurance company executive; b. Milw., Jan. 26, 1932; s. Roman Henry and Anastasia Katherine (Kolasinski) Pelczynski; m. Barbara Ann Schooltz, May 11, 1957; children: Ann, Mark, David, Susan, Tim. BSBA in Fin., Marquette U., 1954. From trainee to v.p. Northwestern Mut. Life Ins. Co., Milw., 1956—. Pres. council Boy Scouts of Am., Milw., 1986-87. With U.S. Army, 1954-56. Roman Catholic. Office: Northwestern Mut Life Ins Co 720 E Wisconsin Ave Milwaukee WI 53202-4703

PELTON, RUSSELL GILBERT, lawyer; b. Monticello, N.Y., July 23, 1914; s. William and May (Morgan) P.; m. Marion Gosart, Dec. 14, 1940; children: William, Marjorie, Marilyn Pelton Barringer. BS, Syracuse U., 1935; JD, George Washington U., 1944. Bar: D.C. 1944, N.Y. 1947, U.S. Supreme Ct. 1948, U.S. Dist. Ct. N.Y. 1947, U.S. Dist. Ct. (fed. dist.) 1963. Ptnr., Darby & Darby, N.Y.C., 1945-56; sr. v.p. N.Am. Philips Corp., N.Y.C., 1956-75; exec. v.p. US Philips Corp., N.Y.C., 1968-75; of counsel Rogers, Hoge & Hills, N.Y.C., 1976-78; ptnr. Spellman, Joel & Pelton, White Plains, N.Y., 1979-81, Eslinger & Pelton, N.Y.C., 1983-85; officer, dir. Tech. Container Corp., N.Y.C., 1977—; former dir. Ferroscube Corp., Savgerties, N.Y., Polyseal Corp., N.Y.C.; lectr. Practising Law Inst., 1953-69; arbitrator, mediator Am. Arbitration Assn., 1985—. Vice-pres. Siwanoy council Boy Scouts Am., 1948-53; v.p. Rye Neck Bd. Edn., Mamaroneck, N.Y., 1952-62; mem. Zoning Bd. Appeals, 1966-70; town justice, 1970-85; trustee Syracuse U., 1967-73. Served with Signal Corps, U.S. Army, 1941-45. Mem. ABA, Am. Patent Law Assn. (past chmn. com. antitrust), N.Y. State Bar Assn. (ethics com., Iolta com.), N.Y. Patent Law Assn. (past bd. govs.), State Magistrates Assn., County Magistrates Assn. (treas., v.p., pres.), Westchester County Bar Assn. (dir., chmn. ethics com.), Assn. Bar City N.Y. (patent com.), IEEE, Am. Radio Relay League, Aircraft Owners and Pilots Assn. Clubs: Wings, Cloud (N.Y.C.), Winged Foot Golf (Mamaroneck, N.Y.), Waccabuc Country (South Salem, N.Y.), Masons, Elks. Patentee in field. Home: 3 Oxford Rd Larchmont NY 10538-1428

PELTON, RUSSELL MEREDITH, JR., lawyer; b. Chgo., May 14, 1938; s. Russell Meredith and Mildred Helen (Baumrucker) P.; m. Patty Jane Rader, Aug. 12, 1961; children: James, Thomas, Michael, Margaret. BA, DePauw U., 1960; JD, U. Chgo., 1963. Bar: Ill. 1963, U.S. Supreme Ct. 1979. Assoc. Peterson, Ross, Schloerb & Seidel, Chgo., 1966-72, ptnr., 1972-90; ptnr. Oppenheimer, Wolff & Donnelly, 1990—, Chgo. mng. ptnr., 1992-95; co-founder, gen. counsel Chgo. Opportunities Industrialization Ctr., 1969-83; gen. counsel Delta Dental Plan Ill., 1979—; bd. dirs. First United Life Ins. Co., 1979-82. Pres. Wilmette Jaycees, 1970; chmn. Wilmette Sch. Bd. Caucus, 1970-71; Wilmette Dist. 39 Bd. Edn., 1972-80; bd. dirs. Wilmette United Way, 1980-86, campaign chmn., 1983-85, pres., 1985-86; Wilmette Zoning Bd. Appeals, 1989—, chmn. 1990—. Served to capt. USAF, 1963-66. Mem. Chgo. Bar Assn., Ill. Bar Assn., ABA, Ill. Trial Lawyers Assn., Soc. Trial Lawyers. Office: Oppenheimer Wolff & Donnelly Two Prudential Plz 45th Fl 180 N Stetson Ave Chicago IL 60601-6710

PELTZ, ALAN HOWARD, manufacturing company executive; b. N.Y.C., July 16, 1944; s. Harry and Rachel (Hammer) P.; BBA in Acctg., CCNY, 1966; MBA in Fin., Pace U., 1971; grad. advanced mgmt. program, Harvard U., 1988; m. Frieda Wichter, Nov. 16, 1968; children: Jason, Elissa. Corp. auditor RCA, N.Y.C., 1966-69; sr. fin. analyst Celanese Chem. Co., N.Y.C., 1969-70; asst. treas. Baker Industries, Inc., Parsippany, N.J., 1970-74; v.p. fin., adminstrn., human resources, mgmt. info. systems Burndy Corp., Norwalk, Conn., 1974-93, v.p., CFO, 1993—; v.p. fin. Framatome Connectors Internat., Paris, 1993—; mem. faculty Fairfield (Conn.) U., 1979-80; bd. dirs. Elderhouse, 1985, Friends of Norwalk Coll., 1986, Hasbrook Hosp. Served as sgt. USMC, 1967-68. Fellow Internat. House Columbia, 1965. Mem. Fin. Execs. Inst., Internat. Treasury Orgn., Norwalk C. of C. (bd. dirs. 1984—), Nat. Assn. Corp. Treas., Mfrs. Alliance Productivity and Innovation Inc. (fin. coun. II), Nat. Elec. Mfrs. Assn. (human resources). Republican. Jewish. Avocations: racquetball, skiing, tennis. Office: Burndy Corp Richards Ave Norwalk CT 06854-2318

PELTZ, NELSON, manufacturing company executive; b. N.Y.C., June 24, 1942; s. Maurice Herbert and Claire (Wechsler) P.; m. Claudia Peltz; children by previous marriage: Andrew, Brooke. MBA, U. Pa., 1962. With A. Peltz & Sons, Inc., N.Y.C., 1963-70; pres., chief exec. officer APS Food Systems, Inc., N.Y.C., 1970-72, Flagstaff Corp., N.Y.C., 1972-78, Coffee-Mat Corp. (merged with Flagstaff Corp. 1976), Kenilworth, N.J., 1975-76; formerly chmn. bd., chief exec. officer Trafalgar Industries, Inc., N.Y.C.; chmn. bd., chief exec. officer Triangle Industries, Inc. (now Trian Group Ltd. Partnership), N.Y.C., 1984—; also bd. dirs.; chmn. bd., chief exec. officer Avery Inc. (now Trian Group Ltd. Partnership); chmn. bd. NPM Group, Inc.; gen. ptnr. Brook Fund. Trustee U.S. Olympic Ski Team, 1975—. Mem. Young Pres.'s Orgn., Madison Sq. Garden Club, Old Oaks Country Club, City Athletic Club. Office: SE Public Svc Co 2001 NW 107th Ave Fl 2 Miami FL 33172*

PELTZIE, KENNETH GERALD, hospital administrator, educator; b. Kansas City, Nov. 17, 1933; s. Sam and Leah (Unell) P.; m. Suzan Francis Orringer, July 19, 1964; 1 child, Sharon Lynn. BA, Washington U., 1955; MS, Columbia U., 1958. Adminstrv. officer USAF Hosp., Dyess AFB, Tex., 1958-61; budget examiner Officer Mgmt. & Budget, 1961-66; assoc. administr. Sinai Hosp. Detroit, 1966-72; v.p. Chi Systems, Ann Arbor, Mich., 1972-80; sr. v.p. Robert Douglas Assocs., Houston, 1980-82; exec. v.p. Community Hosp. of Indpls., 1982-86; pres. Affiliated Hosps. Ind., Indpls., 1982-86; v.p.

corp. strategy Bethesda Healthcare Corp., Boynton Beach, Fla., 1987—; adj. asst. prof. Fla. Atlantic U., Boca Raton, 1991—; mem. adv. bd. Stewart James Rsch. Ctr., Boca Raton, Fla., 1991—. Co-author: Continued Care & Cost Containment, 1974; contbr. articles to profl. jours. Mem. com. United Way of Palm Beach County, West Palm Beach, Fla., 1992-93; active Leadership Palm Beach. Fellow ACHE; mem. Am. Hosp. Assn., Internat. Hosp. Fedn., Soc. Healthcare Plannig & Mktg., Rotary Club Delray Beach. Office: Bethesda Meml Hosp 2815 S Seacrest Blvd Boynton Beach FL 33435-7995

PELTZMAN, SAM, economics educator; b. Bklyn., Jan. 24, 1940; s. Benjamin Raphael and Ceil (Heller) P.; m. Nancy Virginia Bradney, Sept. 7, 1952; children: Shira Malka, Talya Rose. BBA, CCNY, 1960; PhD, U. Chgo., 1965. Prof. econs. UCLA, 1964-73; sr. staff economist Council of Econ. Advisers, Washington, 1970-71; prof. econs. grad. sch. bus. U. Chgo., 1973-87, Sears, Roebuck prof., 1987—; dir. Ctr. for Study The Economy and The State U. Chgo., U. Chgo., 1992—; vis. fellow Inst. for Advanced Study Hebrew U., Jerusalem, 1978. Co-author: Public Policy Toward Mergers, 1967; editor Jour. Law and Econs.; contbr. articles to profl. jours. Mem. Am. Econ. Assn. Jewish. Office: U Chgo Grad Sch Bus 1101 E 58th St Chicago IL 60637

PELUSO, DAVID ANTHONY, clinical pharmacist, consultant; b. Hartford, Conn., Dec. 21, 1957; s. Dominic Anthony and Mary (Carbone) P.; m. Annette Pope; 1 child, Anthony James. BS in Biology, BS in Pharmacy, U. Conn., 1981; advanced mgmt. tng. program, Jackson Meml. Med. Ctr., 1985; PharmD, Southeastern U. Health Scis., 1992. Lic. pharmacist Fla., S.C. Hosp. pharmacy technician U. Conn. Health Ctr., Farmington, Conn., 1979-81; ambulatory pharmacy technician Burgdorf Health Clinic, Hartford, 1980-81; clin. pharmacist I med. svcs. U. Miami/ Jackson Meml. Hosp., Miami, Fla., 1981-83, supr. pharmacy ops., 1983-89, clin. staff pharmacist med. svcs., 1989—, medication surveillance pharmacist, 1993—; pharmacist Home Maintenance Solutions & Svcs., Inc., Ft. Lauderdale, Fla., 1993—; presenter in field. Mem. Am. Soc. Hosp. Pharmacists, Kappa Psi (pres. Nu chpt. 1980). Achievements include research in comparative evaluation of ranitidine oral syrup to an antacid suspension in decreasing intragastric acidity; comparison of serum aminoglycoside concentrations achieved in elderly and younger patients using a simple TDM computer program; prospective review of appropriateness of use of oral and parenteral H-2 antagonists; prospective review of appropriateness of use of oral theophylline and parenteral aminophylline products; utilization evaluation of granulocyte colony stimulating factor. Avocations: semi-professional baseball, surfing, volleyball, beachcombing, traveling, private pilot. Home: 6832 NW 26th Terrace Fort Lauderdale FL 33309

PELZ, ROBERT LEON, lawyer; b. N.Y.C., Nov. 18, 1918; s. Leon S. and Fanny M. (Berk) P.; m. Mary Jane Gips, Feb. 11, 1949; children: Kathryn Louise, Robert Leon. A.B., Columbia U., 1939, J.D., 1942. Bar: N.Y. 1942. Since practiced in N.Y.C.; ptnr. Hess Segall Guterman Pelz Steiner & Barovick, 1953-86, Loeb and Loeb, N.Y.C., 1986—; chmn. bd. dirs. Commentary mag. Life trustee, former v.p. Fedn. Jewish Philanthropies; chmn. legal com., former chmn. bd. dirs., now dir. Fedn. Jewish Philanthropies Service Corp.; former trustee Coll. Pharm. Scis. of Columbia; former chmn. bd. trustees Am. Jewish Com. Served to capt. AUS, World War II. Office: Loeb and Loeb 345 Park Ave New York NY 10154-0001

PEMBERTON, DONALD T., church administrator. Dir. of pub. CH. of God. Office: Church of God PO Box 2430 Cleveland TN 37320

PEMBERTON, HARRISON JOSEPH, educator, philosopher; b. Orlando, Fla., Mar. 3, 1925; s. Harrison Joseph and Frances (Chappell) P. A.B., Rollins Coll., 1949; M.A., Yale U., 1951, Ph.D., 1953. Instr. Yale U., 1951-54; asst. prof. U. Va., 1954-62; mem. faculty Washington and Lee U., 1962—, prof. philosophy, chmn. dept., 1967-90; vis. prof. U. Tex., summers 1962, 66, 69, Chung Chi Coll., Chinese U. Hong Kong, 1971. Author: The Parmenides of Plato: The Critical Moment for Socrates. Served with U.S. Army, 1943-46. Fellow Pierson Coll., Yale, 1952-54, NEH fellow U. Tex. 1986. Mem. Phi Beta Kappa. Home: 602 S Main St Lexington VA 24450-2246

PEMBERTON, JEFFERY KENNETH, publisher; b. Detroit, Sept. 28, 1931; s. Kenneth Percy and Mildred Ann (Shoemaker) P.; m. Jenne-Lee Chase, Apr. 8, 1961; children: Holly, Adam, Heather, Andrew, Christopher. B.A. in Journalism, U. Mich., 1956. Reporter Wall Street Jour., Pitts., 1956-60; dir. advt. H.K. Porter Co., Inc., Pitts., 1960-65; contract sales mgr. Herbick & Held Printing, Pitts., 1965-68; mktg. mgr. Aspen Systems Corp., Pitts., 1968-70, N.Y. Times Info. Bank, N.Y.C., 1970-75; pres., publisher Online, Inc., Conn., 1976—. Episcopalian. Home: 11 Tannery Ln Wilton CT 06883 Office: Online Inc 462 Danbury Rd Wilton CT 06897-2125

PEMBERTON, JOHN DE JARNETTE, JR., lawyer, educator; b. Rochester, Minn., Apr. 21, 1919; s. John de Jarnette and Anna Trego (Hogeland) P.; m. Frances E. Werner, July 23, 1973; children by previous marriage: Ann O., Sarah F., Caro G., Nancy S., James de Jarnette. B.A., Swarthmore (Pa.) Coll., 1940; LL.B., Harvard U., 1947. Bar: N.C. 1949, Minn. 1950, N.Y. 1969, Calif. 1976. Acting asst. prof., then assoc. prof. Duke U. Law Sch., Durham, N.C. 1947-50; ptnr. Pemberton, Michaels, Bishop & Seeger, Rochester, 1950-62; nat. exec. dir. ACLU, 1962-70; prof. U. San Francisco Law Sch., 1973-86; dep. gen. counsel, then acting gen. counsel EEOC, 1971-73; regional atty. dir. office EEOC, San Francisco, 1986-94; adj. lectr. NYU Law Sch., 1968-70, U. San Francisco Law Sch., 1986—; mem. legal com. No. Calif. chpt. ACLU, 1973-86. Assoc. editor and/or editor sects. in law jours. Chmn. Olmsted County (Minn.) Republican Party, 1958-61; commnr. Minn. Fair Employment Practices Com., 1961-62; exec. com Leadership Conf. Civil Rights, 1967-68. Served with Am. Field Service, 1941-45. Mem. ABA, Calif. Bar Assn. Quaker. Home: 11739 Laurel Dell Ave Monte Rio CA 95462-9740

PEMPEL, T. J., political science educator; b. Dec. 15, 1942. BS cum laude, Columbia U., 1966, MA, 1969, PhD, 1972. Dept. rsch. asst. East Asian Inst. Columbia U., N.Y.C., 1971-72; asst. prof. dept. govt. Cornell U., Ithaca, N.Y., 1972-77, assoc. prof. dept. govt., 1977-81, dir. China-Japan Program, 1980-85, prof. dept. govt., 1981-91; prof. dept. polit. sci. U. Colo., Boulder, 1991-93, dir. Ctr. for Comparative Politics, 1991-93; Glen B. and Cleone Orr Hawkins Prof. of Polit. Sci. U. Wis. Madison, 1993—, chair East Asian Studies program, 1993—; vis. rschr. Tokyo U., 1975-76; vis. prof., rschr. Kyoto (Japan) U., 1986; vis. prof. U. Hawaii, 1989; adj. prof. Johnson Sch. Mgmt. Cornell U., Ithaca, N.Y., 1984-91; chair polit. sci. com. Ctr. for Internat. Exch. of Scholars, 1988-90, active, 1987-90, mem. com. on trade policy, 1983; cons. The Conf. Bd., 1980, Multinational Strategies, 1981. Author: (with Douglas Ashford and Peter Katzenstein) Bibliography of Comparative Public Policy in Britain, West Germany, Japan and France, 1976, (with Douglas Ashford and Peter Katzenstein) Comparative Public Policy--A Cross National Bibliography, 1978, Patterns of Japanese Policymaking, 1978, Policy and Politics in Japan: Creative Conservatism, 1981, (with Thomas Ilgen) Trading Technology: Europe and Japan in the Middle East, 1986, Japan: Dilemmas of Success, 1986; author chpts. to books; editor, author chpts.: Policymaking in Contemporary Japan, 1977, Uncommon Democracies: The Politics of One Party Dominance, 1990, also Spanish translation, 1991; contbg. editor The Japan Interpreter, 1975-79; series co-editor: Policy and Politics in Industrial States; English translation editor: Bibliography of Higher Education and the Student Problem in Japan, 1972, Educational Standards in Japan, 1973, Research Documents on Comparative Higher Education, 1976; mem. editl. bd. China-Japan Rsch. Papers, 1973-83, Jour. Pub. Policy, Asia Pacific Rev.; contbr. articles to profl. jours. Served USMC, 1960-64. N.Y. State Tchg. fellow, 1966-67, Herbert H. Lehman fellow, 1967-70, Fulbright-Hayes fellow, 1970-71; grantee NSF, 1974-77, Office of Edn., 1975-77, Fulbright Hayes Faculty Rsch., 1975-76, NEH, 1975-78, Social Sci. Rsch. Coun., 1978-79, Ford Found., 1979-81, 84, 85, Henry Luce Found., 1979-81, Dept. Edn.-Nat. Rsch. Ctr., 1981-83, 83-85, Japan Found., 1985-86, World Bank, 1992, Assn. Asian Studies, 1992. Mem. Am. Polit. Sci. Assn. (chair com. for internat. rsch.), Social Sci. Rsch. Coun. (mem. com. on rsch. grants to Japan 1973-76, mem. joint com. for Japanese studies 1978-83), Assn. Am. Univ. Presses (mem. Hiromi Arisawa Prize com. 1990). Office: U Wis Dept Polit Sci 409 North Hall 1050 Bascom Mall Madison WI 53706

PEÑA, FEDERICO FABIAN, federal official; b. Laredo, Tex., Mar. 15, 1947; s. Gustavo J. and Lucille P.; m. Ellen Hart, May 1988. BA, U. Tex., Austin, 1969, JD, 1972. Bar: Colo. 1973. Ptnr. Pena & Pena, Denver, 1973-83; mayor City and County of Denver, 1983-91; pres. Peña Investment Advisors, Inc., Denver, 1991-93; sec. U.S. Dept. of Transp., Washington, 1993—; assoc. Harvard U. Ctr. for Law and Edn., Cambridge, Mass.; mem. Colo. Bd. Law Examiners. Mem. Colo. Ho. of Reps., 1979-83, Dem. leader, 1981. Named Outstanding House Dem. Legislator, Colo. Gen. Assembly, 1981. Roman Catholic. Home: 3517 Sterling Ave Alexandria VA 22304-1834 Office: Dept of Transportation Office Sec 400 7th St SW Washington DC 20590*

PENA, MANUEL, JR., state senator; b. Cashion, Ariz., Nov. 17, 1924; s. Manuel and Elvira (Gomez) P.; student public schs.; m. Aurora Cruz, June 13, 1945; children: Yolanda, Mary, Henry, Steve, Patricia, Geraldine, Manuel III. Owner Pena Realty & Ins. Agy., Phoenix, 1951-90; ret.; pres. emeritus Pena Ins. Agy., 1990; pres. Penasco, Inc.; mem. Ariz. state adv. com. U.S. Commn. Civil Rights, 1974, Ariz. Ho. of Reps., Phoenix, 1967-72, Ariz. Senate, Phoenix, 1973—. Exec. sec. Ariz. Athletic Commn., 1964-66, 67-71; bd. dirs. Ariz. Consumers Coun., 1960—; commr. human rels. City of Phoenix, 1967-71. With U.S. Army, 1945-46. Mem. VFW, Am. Legion (comdr.). Democrat. Roman Catholic. Office: State Capitol Office of State Senate PO Box 6482 Phoenix AZ 85007

PENA, RAYMUNDO JOSEPH, bishop; b. Corpus Christi, Tex., Feb. 19, 1934; s. Cosme A. and Elisa (Ramon) P. D.D., Assumption Sem., San Antonio, 1957. Ordained priest Roman Catholic Ch., 1957; asst. pastor St. Peter's Ch., Laredo, Tex., 1957-60, St. Joseph's-Our Lady of Fatima, Alamo, Tex., 1960-63, Sacred Heart, Mathis, Tex., 1963-67, Christ the King and Our Lady of Pillar Parishes, Corpus Christi, 1967-69; pastor Our Lady of Guadalupe Parish, Corpus Christi, 1969-76; v.p. Corpus Christi Diocesan Senate of Priests, 1970-76; aux. bishop of San Antonio, 1976-80; bishop of El Paso, 1980—; v.p. San Antonio Ecumenical Coun., 1978-80. Mem. Nat. Conf. Cath. Bishops, U.S. Cath. Conf. (chmn. bishops' com. for hispanic affairs 1987-90, bishops' com. for ch. in L.Am. 1994—). Home: 481 St Matthews St El Paso TX 79907-4214 Office: 499 St Matthews St El Paso TX 79907-4200

PENCE, IRA WILSON, JR., material handling research executive, engineer; b. Pontiac, Mich., June 18, 1939; s. Ira Wilson and Fern Elizabeth (Fraser) P.; m. JoAnna Springer, Sept. 25, 1959; children: Ira W. III, Teresa Ann, Deidre Lynn. BS, U. Mich., 1962, MSEE, 1964, PhD, 1970. Rsch. engr. Willow Run Labs., Ypsilanti, Mich., 1960-67, Dow Lab., Ann Arbor, Mich., 1967-70, GE, Schenectady, N.Y., 1970-80; engring. mgr. GE, Charlottesville, Va., 1980-83; v.p. engring. Unimation, Inc., Danbury, Conn., 1983-87; dir. MHRC Ga. Inst. Tech., Atlanta, 1987-94; cons. Superior Motor, Hartford, 1987-89; bd. dirs. Wesley Foundation; adv. council Westinghouse, Pittsburgh, 1983-87. Editor: Progress in Material Handling and Logistics, 1988; Material Handling for 90's, 1990. Trustee United Meth. Ch., 1988—. Recipient New Product of Yr. award Innovation Today, 1985. Mem. IEEE (sr., sect. chmn. 1978), ASME (MHE div. chair 1994). Republican. Methodist. Avocations: cabinet making, golf. Office: Ga Inst Tech 765 Ferst Dr Atlanta GA 30332-0205

PENCE, MARTIN, federal judge; b. Sterling, Kans., Nov. 18, 1904; m. Eleanor Fisher, Apr. 12, 1975. Bar: Calif. 1928, Hawaii 1933. Practice law Hilo, Hawaii, 1936-45, 50-61; judge 3d Circuit Ct., Hawaii, 1945-50; chief judge U.S. Dist. Ct., Hawaii, 1961-74; sr. judge U.S. Dist. Ct., 1974—. Office: US Dist Ct 1036 Maunawili Loop Kailua HI 96734-4621

PENCE, ROBERT DUDLEY, biomedical research administrator, hospital administrator; b. Hillsboro, Ohio, June 16, 1928; s. Glenn Roush and Mildred (Wright) P. BA cum laude, Miami U., Oxford, Ohio, 1950; postgrad., U. Montpellier, France, 1950-51. Mktg. rep. Tex. Petroleum Co., West Africa, 1956-58; mgr. lab. and office svcs. Sloan-Kettering Inst. for Cancer Rsch., N.Y.C., 1958-68; bus. mgr., cancer rsch. inst. New Eng. Deaconess Hosp., Boston, 1968-72, adminstr. Shields Warren Radiation Lab., 1970-78, asst. dir., 1972-86, adminstrv. dir., cancer rsch. inst., 1974-88, adminstrv. dir. Shields Warren Radiation Lab., 1978-88, dir. div. of rsch., 1986-88, cons., 1988—; field liaison fellow ACS, Chgo., 1981-88. Pres. Am. Cancer Soc., Brookline, Mass. Served to lt. (j.g.) USN, 1951-55. Fulbright scholar, Montpellier, 1950. Mem. Assn. Community Cancer Ctrs. (del.), Internat. Union Against Cancer (U.S. standing com.), Assn. Am. Cancer Insts., Soc. Rsch. Adminstrs. (charter), Nat. Coun. Univ. Rsch. Adminstrs., Nat. Tumor Registrars Assn. (advisor 1980—), Tumor Registrars Assn. New Eng. (bd. dirs. 1975—), Phi Beta Kappa. Home: 30 Driftwood Cir Norwood MA 02062-5505

PENDER, NOLA J., community health nursing educator, researcher; b. Lansing, Mich., Aug. 16, 1941; d. Frank and Eileen (Schoenhals) Blunk; m. Albert R. Pender, Aug. 28, 1965; children: Andrea, Brent. BS, Mich. State U., 1964, MS, 1965; PhD, Northwestern U., Evanston, Ill., 1969. Prof. nursing No. Ill. U., DeKalb, dir. health promotion rsch. program; dir. Ctr. Nursing Rsch., Ann Arbor, Mich.; vis. prof. U. Mich. Sch. Nursing, researcher in field. Contbr. articles to med. jours. Fellow Am. Acad. Nursing; mem. ANA (chmn. rsch. cabinet 1982-84), Midwest Nursing Rsch. Soc. (pres. 1985-87), Am. Acad. Nursing (pres.-elect 1989—), NIH (nat. adv. coun. nursing rsch. Nat. Ctr. for Nursing Rsch. 1987-90, rsch. program grantee 1985-87). Office: U Mich Ctr Nursing Rsch 400 N Ingalls St Rm 4236 Ann Arbor MI 48109-0482

PENDERECKI, KRZYSZTOF, composer, conductor; b. Debica, Poland, Nov. 23, 1933; s. Tadeusz and Zofia P.; m. Elzbieta Solecka; children: Lukasz, Dominique. Grad. State Acad. Music, Krakow, 1958; student, Arthur Malawski and Stanislaw Wiechowicz; Dr. honoris causa, U. Rochester, St. Olaf Coll., Northfield, Minn., Cath U., Leuven, Belgium, U. Bordeaux, France, Georgetown U., Belgrade U., Madrid U., Spain, Adam Mickiewicz U., Warsaw U., Poland, 1993, U. Catolica Argentina, Buenos Aires, 1994, Acad. Music, Cracow, 1994, Acad. Music, Warsaw, 1994. Prof. composition Krakow State Sch. Music, 1959-65, Folkwang Hochschule für Musik, Essen, Fed. Republic Germany, 1966-68; composer-in-residence Sch. Music, Yale U., alternate years; guest condr. London Symphony Orch., Polish Radio Orch., Berlin Philharm. Orch. Composer: Psalms of David for chorus and percussion, 1958, Emanations for 2 string orchs., 1959, Strophes for soprano, narrator and 10 instruments, 1959, Dimensions of time and silence, 1959-61, Anaklasis, 1959-60, Threnody for the Victims of Hiroshima, 1960, Psalmus for tape, 1961, Polymorphia, 1961; Fluorescences, 1961, Stabat Mater, 1962, Canon, 1962, Sonata for cello and orch., 1964, St. Luke Passion, 1965, De Natura Sonoris I, 1966, Dies Irae, 1967, Capriccio for violin and orch., 1967, Capriccio for cello Solo, 1968; opera The Devils of Loudun, 1968-69; Utrenja for double chorus, soloists and orch., 1969-71, Cosmogony, 1970, Utrenja II-Resurrection, 1971, Actions for jazz ensemble, 1971, Partita for harpsichord, 4 solo instruments and orch., 1971-72, Cello Concerto, 1967-72; for double chorus, soloists and orchestra Ecloga VIII for 6 male voices, 1972; Symphony 1, 1972-73, Canticum Canticorum Salomonis for 16 voices and chamber orch., 1972-73, Magnificat, 1973-74, When Jacob Awoke for orch., 1974, Violin Concerto, 1976-77, Paradise Lost (rappresentazione), 1976-78, (Christmas) Symphony No. 2, 1980, Te Deum, 1979-80, Lacrimosa, 1980, Agnus Dei for a cappella chorus, 1981, Cello Concerto No. 2, 1982, Requiem, 1983, Concerto per Viola, 1983, Polish Requiem, 1983-84, The Black Mask, 1986, Der Unterbrochene Gedanke, 1987, Adagio, 1989, Ubu Rex, 1991, Sinfonietta for orchestra, 1990-91, Symphony No. 5 for orchestra, 1991-92, Partita for orchestra, rev. edit., 1991, Flute concerto, 1992-93, Quartet for Clarinet and String Trio, 1993, Divertimento per Cello solo, 1994, Violin Concerto No. 2, 1992-95, also other works; guest condr. NDR Symphony Orch., Hamburg, Federal Republic of Germany. Recipient 1st prize for Strophes Polish Composers Assn., 1959, UNESCO award, Fitelberg prize and Polish Ministry Culture award all for Threnody, 1960, Krakow composition prize for Canon, 1961, grand prize State N. Rhine-Westphalia all for St. Luke Passion, 1966, Pax prize Poland, 1966, Jurzykowski prize Polish Inst. Arts and Scis., 1966, Sibelius award, 1967, Prix d'Italia, 1967-68, Polish 1st Class State award, 1968, Gottfried von Herder prize, 1977, prix Arthur Honegger, 1978, Sibelius prize Wihouri Found., 1983, Wolf Found. prize, 1987, 3 Grammy awards, Gamma prize Acad. Rec. Arts and Scis., 1988, Manuel de Falla Gold medal Accademia de Bellas Artes, Granada, 1989, Das Grosse Verdienstkreuz des

Verdienstordens der Bundesrepublik Deutschland, 1990, 2 Grammy nominations, 1992, Grawermeyer Music award, 1992, Österreichische Ehrenzeichen für Wissenschaft und Kunst, 1994; grantee several founds., govts., insts. Mem. Royal Acad. Mus. London (hon.), Accademia Nazionale di Santa Cecilia (Roma) (hon.), Royal Swedish Acad. Music, Akademie der Kuenste West Berlin (extraordinary mem.), Akademie der Kuenste E. Ger. (corr.), Academia Nacional de Bellas Artes (Buenos Aires) (corr.), Académie Internationale de Philosophie et l'Art(Berne), L'Académie Nationale des Sciences, Belles-lettres et Arts (Bordeaux), Academia Scientiarium et Artium Europaea (Salzburg), L'Ordre de Saint Georges de Bourgogne (officier, Brussels). Creator original notational system allowing aleatory freedom for performer within sects. of precise duration. Home: ul Cisowa 22, 30229 Cracow Poland Office: ICM Artists Ltd 8942 Wilshire Blvd Beverly Hills CA 90211 also: Panstwowa Wyzsza Szkola Muzyczna, ul Starowislna, 31-038 Cracow Poland

PENDERGAST, JOHN JOSEPH, III, lawyer; b. Lewiston, Maine, Jan. 29, 1936; s. John Joseph and Grace (McCarty) P.; m. Joan Shaw Cole, June 14, 1958; children: John Joseph IV, Timothy S., Terrence B., Mary R., Michael C., Joan M. B.A., Yale U., 1957, LL.B., 1960. Bar: R.I. 1961, U.S. dist. Ct. R.I. 1961, U.S. Ct. Appeals (1st cir.) 1963. Assoc. Hinckley, Allen, & Snyder, Providence, 1966—, ptnr., co-chmn. labor dept., 1966—; instr. U. R.I., Kingston, 1984-88, adj. prof. Providence Coll., 1984-86. Author: (with others) The Developing Labor Law, 2d edit., 1983, Labor and Employment Arbitration, 1988, NLRA Law & Practice, 1992. Mem. Cath. Charities panel Diocese of Providence, 1976—; bd. dirs. Smith Hill Center, Providence, 1978-93; v. Providence Boys Clubs, 1970-72, bd. dirs., 1990—. Mem. ABA (labor law sect.), The Best Lawyers in Am., Am. Coll. Hosp. Attys., Indsl. Rels. Rsch. Assn., Hosp. Assn. Labor Execs., R.I. Bar Assn., Sakonnet Yacht Club, University Club, Yale Club of R.I. (Providence). Avocations: antiques, fly fishing. Home: 21 Violet St Providence RI 02908-4825 Office: Hinckley Allen & Snyder 1500 Fleet Ctr Providence RI 02903

PENDERGAST, WILLIAM ROSS, lawyer; b. Kansas City, Mo., Oct. 1, 1931; s. Francis Gregory and Florence (Ross) P.; m. Dorothy Victoria Dusic, Aug. 5, 1961; children—William Ross, Patrick Fitzwilliam. B.S., Rockhurst Coll., 1952; J.D., U. Mo.-Columbia, 1957. Bar: Mo., D.C., U.S. Supreme Ct. Assoc. Meyer & Smith, Kansas City, Mo., 1957-61; trial atty. FDA, Washington, 1961-65; ptnr. McLean, Morton & Boustead, Washington, 1965-68, McMurray and Pendergast, Washington, 1968-79, 83, Arent, Fox, Kintner, Plotkin & Kahn, Washington, 1983—; chmn. ABA Food and Drug Com., Washington, 1970-79; dir. Nat. Source Vitamin E Assn., Washington, 1984—. Contbr. articles to profl. jours. Served with U.S. Army, 1950-52. Mem. ABA, Fed. Bar Assn. Democrat. Roman Catholic. Clubs: Metropolitan, Chevy Chase. Office: Arent Fox Kintner Plotkin & Kahn 1050 Connecticut Ave NW Washington DC 20036-5339

PENDERGRAFT, NORMAN ELVEIS, art history educator, art museum director; b. Durham, N.C., Mar. 4, 1934; s. Harvey W. and Essie (Wilson) P. AB, U. N.C., 1962, MA in Coll. Teaching, 1967; postgrad., Conservatory Music G. Rossini, Pesaro, Italy, 1963-65, Ohio U., 1969-71, U. Calif., Berkeley, 1979 (summer). Tchr. N.W. High Sch., Greensboro, N.C., 1961-62; tchr. English, The English Ctr., Ancona, Italy, 1964-65; prof. art dept. N.C. Ctrl. U., Durham, 1966—, dir. Art Mus., 1976—; guest curator Artistic Legacy: Collection of Art from CIAA Schs., Diggs Gallery at WSSU. Exhibit organizer, author catalog: Gullah Life Reflections: Painting by Jonathan Green, 1988, Where Myth Stirs: Paintings by Jim Moon, 1991, Joy of Living: Romance Bearden's Late Work, 1993, Charles Alston: New Negro Artist, 1994, Yohannes Gedamu: Painter, 1995. Bd. dirs. Stagville Hist. Preservation Soc., Durham County, 1989—; program chmn. Durham Hist. Preservation Soc., 1991-93. With USN, 1954-58. Recipient Friends of Arts award N.C. Art Edn. Assn., 1984; selected to attend NEH Roman Painting 1480-1550: New Approaches seminar, Rome, 1992. Mem. AAUP, Am. Assn. Mus., Southeastern Mus. Conf., Coll. Art Assn., N.C. Mus. Coun. (past pres. art sect.). Democrat. Avocations: travel, walking. Home: 208 Watts St Durham NC 27701-2037 Office: NC Ctrl U NCCU Art Mus PO Box 19555 Durham NC 27707-0099

PENDERGRASS, HENRY PANCOAST, physician, radiology educator; b. Bryn Mawr, Pa., Jan. 29, 1925; s. Eugene Percival and Rebecca (Barker) P.; m. Carol Lowe Dodson, Aug. 27, 1960 (dec. Aug. 1993); children: Sharon (dec.), Lisa (dec.), Deborah, Margaret; m. Carol Minster Roberts, Oct. 2, 1994. Student, U.S. Naval Acad., 1944-46; A.B., Princeton U., 1948; M.D., U. Pa., 1952; M.P.H., Harvard U., 1969. Diplomate: Am. Bd. Radiology, Am. Bd. Nuclear Medicine. Intern Pa. Hosp., 1953-54; mem. staff and faculty U. Pa. Med. Sch. and Univ. Hosp., Phila., 1953-58, 60-61; clin. asst. in neuroradiology Inst. Neurology Queen Sq., London, 1959-60; mem. staff and faculty Harvard U. Med. Sch. and Mass. Gen. Hosp., Boston, 1958-59, 61-76; prof. radiology Vanderbilt U. Sch. Medicine, Nashville, 1976—, vice chmn., 1976-89. Mem. editorial bd. Am. Family Physician, 1980-94, Jour. Digital Imaging, 1987—; contbr. chpts. to books, articles to med. jours. Mem. cancer control rev. com. Nat. Cancer Inst., 1975-79; Bd. dirs. state and local div. Am. Cancer Soc., 1976-85; mem. Project Hope Med. Mission, Peru, 1962; trustee Harpeth Hall Sch., Nashville, 1983-88. With U.S. Army, USN, 1943-46. Am. Cancer Soc. grantee, 1956-57; Nat. Cancer Inst. grantee, 1957-58; Nat. Inst. Neurol. Disease and Blindness grantee, 1959-60; Nat. Inst. Gen. Med. Scis. grantee, 1968-69. Fellow Am. Coll. Radiology (life mem., benefactor, counselor, steering com. 1968-73, bd. chancellors 1977-81), AMA (mem. Ho. of Dels. 1986—, sect. coun. on radiology 1978—, sec. 1987—, sect. on med. schs. 1979—, Disting. Svc. Gold medal 1994, grad. med. edn. adv. com. 1994—), Coun. Med. Splty. Socs., Am. Roentgen Ray Soc., Brit. Inst. Radiology, Ea. Radiol. Soc. (pres., trustee 1968-72 sci. program chmn. 1964, 72, 79), Assn. Univ. Radiologists, Mass. Radiol. Soc. (v.p. 1967-68, 75-76), Mass. Med. Soc. (counselor 1968-76), Nashville Acad. Medicine (chmn. com. on ethics 1981-82, Nat. Bd. Med. Examiners 1995—), Radiol. Soc. N.Am. (bd. dirs. 1972-77, chmn. 1975-76, pres.-elect and pres. 1977-78, Gold medal 1984, trustee RSNA Rsch. and Edn. Fund 1984-90, fund sec.-treas 1988-90), Am. Soc. Emergency Radiology, Tenn. Med. Assn., Tenn. Radiol. Soc. (pres.-elect, then pres. 1985-86, exec. com. 1984-88), Mid. Tenn. Radiol. Soc. (pres. 1984-85, sec., treas. 1985-94), Soc. Thoracic Imaging, Soc. Magnetic Resonance in Medicine, Sigma Xi, Delta Psi. Presbyterian. Clubs: Belle Meade Country, Amateur Ski (N.Y.); Cap and Gown (Princeton, N.J.). Office: Vanderbilt U Sch Medicine 1621 21st Ave S Nashville TN 37232-0001

PENDERGRASS, TEDDY (THEODORE D. PENDERGRASS), musician; b. Phila., Mar. 26, 1950; m. Karin Michelle Still, June 20, 1987; children: Tisha, Ladonna, Teddy. Student public schs. Drummer for various groups, 1966-69; Singer, lead singer Harold Melvin & Blue Notes, 1969-75; solo artist, 1975—; pres. Teddy Bear Enterprises, Phila. Squire, Memphis. albums include: Life Is a Song Worth Singing, 1978, Teddy, 1979, T.P., 1980, Live Coast to Coast, 1980, It's Time for Teddy, 1981, Teddy Pendergrass, 1982, This One's For You, 1982, Heaven Only Knows, 1983, Greatest Hits, 1984, Love Language, 1984, Workin' It Back, 1985, Joy, 1988, Truly Blessed, 1991, A Little More Magic, 1993. Recipient civic and pub. service awards., Image award NAACP, 1973, 80, Black Achievement award Ebony Mag., 1979, award outstanding mus. contbn. Afro-Am. Hist. Mus., 1983, award of merit City of Detroit, 12 gold and 7 platinum albums; recipity Keys to Cities, Lakeland (Fla.), Detroit, Savannah (Ga.), Memphis; named New Artist of 1977 for Top Pop Album Billboard Mag. *

PENDERY, EDWARD STUART, deputy county judge; b. Dayton, Ky., June 1, 1931; s. Edward Stuart and Marguerite Garnet (Owens) P.; m. Nancy Jean Burck, Aug. 22, 1958; children: Michael Edward, Darren Frederick, Eric Christopher. Student, U.S. Tech. Sch., 1952. R.R. dep. chief clk. N.Y. Ctrl. R.R., Cin., 1950-51; R.R. comml. agt. C & WC Rlwy., Cin., 1955-58; salesman Pittsburg Paint & Glass, Cin., 1958-63; ops. mgr. Am. Laundry/ Econo Sales, Cin., 1963-67; pvt. practice I.P.C.S. Pub., Ft. Thomas, Ky., 1967-68, 74-86; mag. sales and display wds staff Cin. (Ohio) Mag., 1969-74; dep. county judge Campbell County Ky., Newport, Ky., 1986—. Editor, originator: (tabloids) North Ky. Sports Scene, 1976—, Bellevue News, 1980—, Shopping Guides, 1980—. Chmn. site group North Ky. U., Highland Heights, 1968; chmn. study group Ft. Thomas (Ky.) Sch. Sys., 1970; dir. North Ky. U. Norse Club, Highland Heights, 1971-89, Famous Stars H.S. Program, Bellevue, Ky., 1978-94; mem. Bellevue Civic Assn., 1980—; North Ky. Adminstrs. Group, Newport, 1986-94, Libr. Site Com., Cold

Spring, Ky., 1993-94, Nat. Alliance Bus., 1993. Staff sgt. USAF, 1951-55. Named Ky. Col., Ky. Gov., 1967; recipient Meritorious Svc. award Cub Scouts, 1968. Mem. Am. Assn. Ret. Persons, Elks, Am. Legion, North Ky. U. Norse Club. Democrat. Avocation: golf. Home: 38 Homestead Pl Fort Thomas KY 41075

PENDLETON, ALAN R., conservation agency executive; b. Riverside, Calif., May 26, 1940; s. Roy Clayton and Carolyn (Parker) P.; m. Joyce Ellen Edwards, Aug. 22, 1964; 1 child, David. AB, U. Calif., Berkeley, 1961; JD, U. Calif., San Francisco, 1969. Bar: Calif. Tchr. Anderson Valley Sch. Dist., Boonville, Calif., 1970; atty. San Francisco Bay Conservation and Devel. Commn., 1971-76, chief regulatory functions, 1976-81, dep. dir., 1981-83, exec. dir., 1983—; bd. dirs. East Brothers Light Station, Richmond, Calif., Flowerlane, Inc., Oakland, Calif.; mem. environ. com. 9th Dist. Ct. Calif., 1985—. Contbr. articles to profl. jours. Mem. Save San Francisco Bay Assn., Berkeley. Lt. USAF, 1962-67. Mem. Bay Area Planning Dirs. Assn. (bd. dirs. 1987—), Calif. Bar Assn., Sierra Club. Avocations: backpacking, cross-country skiing, wine collecting. Office: San Francisco Bay Conservation & Devel Commn 30 Van Ness Ave Ste 2011 San Francisco CA 94102-6026

PENDLETON, BARBARA JEAN, retired banker; b. Independence, Mo., Aug. 14, 1924; d. Elmer Dean and Martha Lucille (Friess) P. Student, Cen. Mo. State Coll., 1942; D of Bus. Adminstrn. (hon.), Avila Coll., 1986. V.p. Grand Ave. Bank, Kansas City, Mo., 1962-76, exec. v.p., 1976-79; vice chmn. City Bank & Trust Co., Kansas City, 1979-82, chmn., 1982-83; exec. v.p. United Mo. Bank of Kansas City, 1983-93, United Mo. Bancshares, Inc., 1990-93; bd. dirs. Shepherd Ctrs. of Am., Inc., 1992—. Vice chmn., mem. Dept. Def. adv. com. Women in Svc., Washington, 1967069; chmn. 1992—; chmn. City of Kansas City Employee Retirement Fund, 1985—. Recipient Matrix award Press Women, 1963, Wohelo award Campfire, Inc., 1979. Mem. Fin. Women Internat. (nat. pres. 1972-73), Am. Humanics, Inc. (chmn. 1987-88). Club: Cen. Exchange (Kansas City) (pres. 1983-84). Office: United Mo Bank NA PO Box 419226 1010 Grand Blvd Kansas City MO 64106-2220

PENDLETON, ELMER DEAN, JR., retired military officer, international consultant; b. Kansas City, Mo., June 26, 1927; s. Elmer Dean and Martha Lucille (Friess) P.; m. Anne Bittner, Sept. 10, 1971; children: V. Allison Connor, John K. Lange, Christian D. Pendleton. BS, U.S. Mil. Acad., West Point, 1951; MS, George Washington U., 1969. Commd. 2d lt. U.S. Army, 1951, advanced through grades to maj. gen., 1977, ret., 1986; platoon leader 11th airborne div., Fort Campbell, Ky., 1951-52; co. commdr. 7th infantry div., Korea, 1952-53, 82d airborne div., Fort Bragg, N.C., 1954-56; instr. Ranger Sch., Eglin AFB, Fla., 1957-58; aide to comdg. gen. Teheran, Iran, 1958; staff officer 3d inf. (Old Guard), Washington, 1958-59, Dept. of Army, Washington, 1960-63; bn. commdr. 24th inf. div., Berlin, Fed. Republic Germany, 1964-65; sector advisor Can Tho, Vietnam, 1965-66; bn. commdr. 1st inf. div., Vietnam, 1966-68; brigade commdr. 1st inf. div. and II field force, G-3, Vietnam, 1969-70; corps G-3 XVIII airborne corps, Fort Bragg, N.C., 1971-74; dep. chief of staff and chief of staff XVIII airborne corps, 1974-75; commdr. 1st corps Support Command, Fort Bragg, N.C., 1975-78, 1th Support Command, Taegu, Korea, 1978-80; logistics officer U.S. Readiness Command, MacDill AFB, Fla., 1980-81; ops. officer U.S. Readiness Command, 1981-82; chief Joint U.S. Mil. Mission for Aid to Turkey, Ankara, 1982-86; cons. Internat. Activities, Washington, 1986—. Decorated D.S.M., Def. D.S.M., Silver Star with 3 oak leaf clusters, Legion of Merit with 2 oak leaf clusters, D.F.C. with 2 oak leaf clusters, Bronze Star with 8 oak leaf clusters and V device, Combat Infantry Badge 2d award, 44 Air medals, Purple Heart, others. Mem. Am. Turkish Coun. (bd. dirs., chmn. def. and fgn. affairs com.), ITEC, Inc. (pres.), Army-Navy Club (Washington). Home and Office: 3028 Knoll Dr Falls Church VA 22042-3111

PENDLETON, EUGENE BARBOUR, JR., business executive; b. nr. Louisa, Va., Apr. 2, 1913; s. Eugene Barbour and Virginia (Goodman) P.; m. Mildred McLean, June 18, 1938; children: Barbara Jane Pendleton Wootton, Sally Anne Pendleton Campbell, Nancy McLean Pendleton Wheeler, Susan Virginia Pendleton Hayden, Martha Christina Pendleton Perry. Student, Va. Mil. Inst., 1930-31, Hampden-Sydney Coll., 1931-34. Organizer, mgr. Gen. Ins. Agy., 1937-42; treas. Louisa County, Va., 1946-58; field rep. Va. Dept. Taxation, 1958-60; treas. State of Va., 1960-64; treas. So. States Coop., 1964-80, v.p. fin., 1977-78; v.p. fin. Truxmore Industries Inc., Richmond, Va., 1978-86, retired, 1986; mem. adv. bd. Jefferson Nat. Bank. Bd. dirs., past pres. Richmond Businessmen's Assn.; v.p., mem. exec. com. Atlantic Rural Expn.; past mem. exec. com. Richmond Home for Boys, Va. Edn. Fund; past bd. dirs. Richmond Symphony.; Mem. bd. suprs., Louisa County, 1937-42; mem. Ho. of Dels., Va. Gen. Assembly, 1966-70; Past pres. Va. Thanksgiving Festival. Served from ensign to lt. USNR, 1942-46, ETO. Mem. Va., Richmond chambers commerce, Bond Club Va., County and City Treas. Assn. Va. (past pres.), Nat. Assn. State Treas., Mil. Order World Wars (past comdr.), Navy League U.S. (pres.), 1st Families Va. (pres., coun.), Soc. of Va. (v.p.), Am. Legion, VFW (past comdr.), Downtown Club (Richmond, past pres.), Commonwealth Club, Country Club of Va., Shriners, Masons. Mem. Christian Ch. (past elder, mem. bd.). Home: 8007 Dunsmore Rd Richmond VA 23229-7411

PENDLETON, GARY H(ERMAN), life insurance agent; b. Stuart, Va., Mar. 8, 1947; s. Herman P.; m. Laura Jeanes, Feb. 14, 1976; children: Blair J., Gray E. BS, SUNY, Albany. CLU, ChFC. Dir. intergovt. relations N.C. Dept. Transp., Raleigh, 1973-76; pres. Preferred Planning and Ins., Inc., Raleigh, 1976—; mem., chmn. N.C. State Banking Commn., 1985-89. Chmn., county commr. Wake County, N.C., 1992—; active N.C. Bd. Community Colls., 1989-91, N.C. Econ. Devel. Bd., 1991-93. Brig. gen. (ret.) N.C. State Def. Forces. Presbyterian. Avocations: snow skiing, boating, fishing, hunting. Home: 2908 Lake Boone Pl Raleigh NC 27608-1151 Office: 2601 Oberlin Rd Ste 201 Raleigh NC 27608-1319

PENDLETON, MARY CATHERINE, foreign service officer; b. Louisville, Ky., June 15, 1940; d. Joseph S. and Katherine R. (Toebbe) P. BA, Spalding Coll., 1962; MA, Ind. U., 1969; cert., Nat. Def. U., 1990; D (hon.), U. N. Testemitanu, Moldova, 1994. Cert. secondary tchr., Ky. Tchr. Presentation Acad., Louisville, 1962-66; vol. Peace Corps, Tunis, Tunisia, 1966-68; employment counselor Ky. Dept. for Human Resources, Louisville, 1969-75; gen. svcs. Am. Embassy, Khartoum, Sudan, 1975-77; consular officer Am. Embassy, Manila, Philippines, 1977-79; adminstrv. officer Am. Embassy, Bangui, Cen. African Republic, 1979-82, Lusaka, Zambia, 1982-84; post mgmt. officer Dept. of State Bur. European and Can. Affairs, Washington, 1984-87; adminstrv. counselor Am. Embassy, Bucharest, Romania, 1987-89; dir. adminstrv. tng. divsn. Fgn. Svc. Inst., Arlington, Va., 1990-92; ambassador Am. Embassy, Chisinau, Moldova, 1992—. Bd. dirs. Am. Sch. of Bucharest, 1987-89. Named to Honorable Order of Ky. Cols., 1988. Democrat. Roman Catholic. Avocations: family history research, outdoor activities. Home and Office: Am Embassy Chisinau Dept of State Washington DC 20521-7080

PENDLETON, MOSES ROBERT ANDREW, dancer, choreographer; b. St. Johnsbury, Vt., Mar. 28, 1949; s. Nelson Augustus and Mary Elizabeth (Patchel) P. B.A., Dartmouth Coll., 1971. Co-founder, dir., choreographer, dancer Pilobolus Dance Theater, Washington, Conn., 1971—; founder, artistic dir. Momix Dance Theater, Washington, 1980—. Choreographer numerous works including Pilobolus, 1971, Anendrom, 1972, Walklyndon, 1972, Ocellus, 1972, Ciona, 1973, Monkshood's Farewell, 1974, Untitled, 1975, Eve of Samhain, 1977, Alraune, 1975, Lost in Fauna, 1976, Shizen, 1977, Bonsai, 1978, Day Two, 1981, Elva, 1987, Debut C, 1988, Accordion, 1989, Fantasy on a Variation on a Theme, 1989; choreographer Am. premiere of Jean Coeteau's Les Marie de la tour Eiffel, 1988; actor, dancer: (film) Pilobolus and Joan, 1974; choreographer: Erik Satie Festival, Paris Opera, 1978; co-choreographer: Molly's Not Dead, 1978; choreographer: (for Pilobolus Dance Theater) Day Two 1981, Stabat Mater, 1985, Carmina Burana Side II, 1985; Joffrey Ballet Relache, 1980, Closing Ceremonies 1980 Winter Olympics, Berlin Opera Tutuguri, 1981, Moses Pendleton Presents Moses Pendleton, 1982, Ballet de Nancy, France, Pulcinella, 1985, (for Momix Dance Theater) Kiss Off Spiderwoman, 1986, Spawning, 1986, Venus Envy, 1986, Medusa, 1986, Preface to Preview, 1986, excerpts from Gifts from the Sea, 1986, (opera for Spoleto Festival) Platee, 1987,

Passion, 1991; tchr. artist-in-residence at univs. throughout U.S., 1977; tchr., condr. workshops. Recipient Edinborough Fringe Festival Scotman's award, 1973, Berlin Critic's prize, 1975; Nat. Endowment for Arts grantee, 1975-76; Guggenheim fellow in choreography, 1977. Democrat. Office: Momix PO Box 35 Washington Depot CT 06794-0035*

PENDLETON, SUMNER ALDEN, financial consultant; b. Boston, May 2, 1918; s. Sumner Maynard and Ethel Parker (Phinney) P.; m. Nancy Curtiss Welles, June 8, 1941; children: Nancy Alden Pendleton Dyer, John Welles. SB cum laude, Harvard U., 1939, MBA, 1941. With Gen. Electric Co., 1945-50, Ford Motor Co., 1950-53; asst. to corp. contr. to contr. electronics div. Curtiss-Wright Corp., 1953-60; asst. contr. fin. analysis, audit and data processing methods ITT Corp., 1960-63; contr., asst. sec. Joy Mfg. Co., Pitts., 1963-67; v.p. fin. treas. Ryan Homes, Inc., Pitts., 1967-71; v.p. corp. devel. Ryan Homes, Inc., 1971-74; v.p., sec., treas. Ryan Homes Fin. Co., 1970-74; chmn., treas. Unidyne Corp., Pitts., also, 1975-80, Bergoo Coal Co., Pitts., 1975-78; assoc. exec. dir. budget and fin. United Presbyn. Ch. U.S.A., 1976-78; fin. cons., 1978-81; dir., v.p. fin., treas. Hytronics Corp., 1979-81; lic. sales assoc. VR Bus. Brokers, Clearwater, 1990-92, 95—; lic. sales assoc. bus. brokers Metro Bay Assocs., Clearwater, Fla., 1992-94; mgmt. fin. cons. 1974—; chmn., treas., bd. dirs. Consource Plastic Recycling Corp., Tampa, 1992—; mem. Svc. Corps Ret. Execs., 1981—, v.p., sec., treas. Pinellas chpt., 1983-85, pres., 1985-86, chmn., 1986-87. Gen. campaign chmn. Community Chest Ridgewood, Hohokus and Midland Park, N.J., 1959-60, pres., 1960-62; treas. Southminster Presbyn. Ch., Mt. Lebanon, Pa., 1966-76, trustee, 1965-68, elder 1968-71, past deacon, head usher, Sunday sch. tchr. Lt. comdr. USNR, 1941-45; capt. Res. ret. Decorated Silver Star; recipient Acctg. Profession Exec. of Yr. award Robert Morris Coll., 1973; Baker scholar Harvard Bus. Sch., 1941. Mem. Fin. Execs. Inst. (dir. Newark 1961-62), Nat. Assn. Accts. (Lybrand cert. 1955, pres. Paterson chpt. 1955-56, nat. dir. 1957-59, v.p. 1965-66, mem. com. 1966-69), Stuart Cameron McLeod Soc. (pres. 1975-76), Harvard Bus. Sch. Assn. Pitts. (v.p. 1968-69, pres. 1969-70, chmn. bd. govs. 1970-71), Harvard Club of Fla. West Coast (v.p. 1982-84, pres. 1984-86, bd. dirs. 1986-94), Harvard Bus. Sch. Club Fla. West Coast (bd. dirs. 1986—). Home: 2163 Waterside Dr Clearwater FL 34624-6658 Office: Ste 305 4625 E Bay Dr Clearwater FL 34624

PENDLETON, TERRY LEE, baseball player; b. L.A., July 16, 1960; m. Catherine Grindulo Marquey, Oct. 27, 1984. Student, Oxnard Coll., Calif., Fresno State U., Calif. Baseball player St. Louis Cardinals, 1982-90, Atlanta Braves, 1990—; with Fla. Marlins, 1994—. Winner Most Valuable Player award Baseball Writers' Assn., Am., 1991, Gold Glove award 1987, 89, 92; mem Nat. League All-Star Team, 1992; Nat. League Batting Champion, 1991; named N.L. Comeback Player of the Yr. The Sporting News, 1991, Third Baseman on the Sporting News N.L. All-Star Team, 1991. Office: Fla Marlins 2269 NW 199th St Opa Locka FL 33056*

PENDLEY, WILLIAM PAUL, naval officer, international relations educator; b. Paris, Ky., June 21, 1936; s. Louis Tyler and Virginia Lorene (Poplin) P.; m. Anne Carrol Cooke, Dec. 13, 1958; children: Stephen Tyler, Robert Randolph, Lisa Carrol, Leslie Brooks. BS in Engring., U.S. Naval Acad., 1958; MA, Am. U., Washington, 1965. Commd. ens. USN, 1958, advanced through grades to rear adm., 1983; comdg. officer Patrol Squadron 45, Jacksonville, Fla., 1975-76; ops. officer Patrol Wing 11, U.S. Atlantic Fleet, Jacksonville, 1976-78, commdr., 1979-81; exec. sec. for joint chief of staff matters Chief Naval Ops., Washington, 1978-79, planner for joint chief of staff matters, 1981-82, dir. plans policy and strategy div., 1985-86; exec. asst. to comdr. in chief U.S. Pacific Fleet, Pearl Harbor, Hawaii, 1982-83; commdr. patrol wings U.S. Atlantic Fleet, Brunswick, Maine, 1983-85; commdr. Naval Forces Korea, Seoul, 1986-89; sr. mem. UN Mil. Armistice Commn., 1986-89; dir. strategic plans and policy USCINCPAC, Camp H. M. Smith, Hawaii, 1990-91; dep. asst. sec. def. for East Asia and Pacific affairs Dept. Defense, Washington, 1992-93; prof. internat. rels. Air War Coll., Maxwell AFB, Ala., 1993—; fellow Georgetown U. Leadership Seminar, Washington, 1985. Co-author: Nuclear Coexistence, 1994; contbr. articles to profl. jours. Decorated Def. D.S.M. with oak leaf cluster, Legion of Merit with 4 gold stars; named hon. Ky. Col., 1975; recipient Def. medal for disting. pub. svc., 1995. Mem. U.S. Naval Inst., Phi Kappa Phi, Pi Gamma Mu. Methodist. Club: Army Navy (Arlington, Va.). Avocations: flying, golf, tennis, skiing. Home: 6445 Eastwood Glen Dr Montgomery AL 36117 Office: Air War Coll 325 Chennault Cir Maxwell AFB AL 36112

PENEGAR, KENNETH LAWING, law educator; b. Charlotte, N.C., May 12, 1932; s. Oscar General and Ethel Meredith (Lawing) P.; m. Sarah Willard, Sept. 7, 1963; children: David, Sarah Elizabeth. B.A. in History, U. N.C., 1954, J.D. with honors, 1961; postgrad., London Sch. Econs., 1958; LL.M., Yale U., 1962. Bar: N.C. 1961, D.C. 1963. Clk. to Hon. Charles Fahy U.S. Ct. Appeals (D.C. cir.), 1962-63; asst. prof. law U. N.C., 1963-66, assoc. prof. 1966-69; assoc. firm Shea & Gardner, Washington, 1969-71; prof. law, dean U. Tenn., 1971-86; prof. law, dean So. Meth. U., Dallas, 1986-88, spl. asst. to pres., 1988-89; Ford Found. vis. prof. Delhi U., India, 1967-68; vis. scholar Harvard U. Sch. Law, 1980-81, Ford U. Ceará, Brazil, summer 1985; vis. prof. law Boston U., 1980-81; mem. contract appeals bd. TVA, 1975—; mem. panel arbitrators Am. Arbitration Assn.; pres. Dallas Mediation Svc., 1989-90; cons. in field. Contbr. articles to profl. jours. Trustee Lawyers Com. for Civil Rights Under Law, 1976—; delegation leader for legal edn. to China for Citizens' Ambassador program, spring 1989. Served with USN, 1954-57. London House fellow U.K. Fellow Am. Bar Found., Tex. Bar Found.; mem. ABA, Tenn. Bar Assn., Dallas Bar Found. (trustee 1986-88), 6th Cir. Jud. Conf. U.S. (life mem.), Am. Law Inst., Acad. Polit. and Social Sci., Internat. Assn. Legal and Social Philosophy, Assn. Am. Law Schs. (exec. com.), Order of Coif, Order of Golden Fleece, Phi Kappa Phi, Omicron Delta Kappa, Phi Alpha Delta. Episcopalian. Democrat. Office: So Meth U Sch of Law Dallas TX 75275

PENFIELD, CAROLE H. (KATE PENFIELD), minister, church official. Grad., Andover Newton Theol. Sch. Co-pastor Ctrl. Bapt. Ch., Providence, 1st Bapt. Ch. Am.; Providence; dir. Ministers Coun. of ABC USA; mem. regional and nat. mins. coun. and senate Am. Bapt. Chs., v.p., 1994—; mem. state Senate ethics com. R.I. Legislature; pres. R.I. State Coun. Chs., 1987-89. Editor Ministry, Am. Bapt. Chs. Office: ABC in the USA PO Box 851 Valley Forge PA 19482

PENFIELD, PAUL LIVINGSTONE, JR., electrical engineering educator; b. Detroit, May 28, 1933; s. Paul Livingstone and Charlotte Wentworth (Gilman) P.; m. Martha Elise Dieterle, Aug. 24, 1956 (dec. Apr. 1988); children: David Wesley, Patricia Jane, Michael Baldwin. BA, Amherst Coll., 1955; ScD, MIT, 1960. Asst. prof. elec. engring. MIT, Cambridge, 1960-64, assoc. prof., 1964-69, prof., 1969—, head dept. elec. engring. and computer sci., 1989—. Author: Frequency-Power Formulas, 1960, MARTHA User's Manual, 1971; co-author: Varactor Applications, 1962, Electrodynamics of Moving Media, 1967, Tellegen's Theorem and Electrical Networks, 1970. Sr. postdoctoral fellow NSF, 1966-67. Fellow IEEE (chmn. Boston sect. 1971-72, Darlington award 1983, Centennial medal 1984); mem. Nat. Assn. Engring., Am. Phys. Soc., Assn. for Computing Machinery, Audio Engring. Soc., Sigma Xi. Avocation: field identification of ferns and fern hybrids. Office: MIT Dept Elec Engring Cambridge MA 02139

PENHOET, EDWARD, biochemicals company executive; b. Oakland, Calif., Dec. 11, 1940. AB, Stanford U., 1963; PhD, U. Wash., 1968. Office: Chiron Corp 4560 Horton St Emeryville CA 94608-2916

PENHUNE, JOHN PAUL, science company executive, electrical engineer; b. Flushing, N.Y., Feb. 13, 1936; s. Paul and Helene Marguerite (Beux) P.; m. Nancy Leigh Peabody, Sept. 6, 1958 (div. Apr. 1982); children: Virginia Burdet, James Peabody, Sarah Slipp; m. Marceline Helen Porath, Feb. 15, 1986; 1 child, Marcelline Helen Broadhurst. BSEE, MIT, 1957, PhDEE, 1961; postgrad., U. Grenoble, France, 1959; postgrad. in bus., Harvard U., 1973. Asst. prof. elec. engring. MIT, Cambridge, 1962-64; mem. tech. staff Lincoln Lab MIT, Lexington, 1964-66; supr. radar group Bell Tel. Labs., Whippany, N.J., 1966-68; asst. dir. Advanced Ballistic Missile Def. Agy., Washington, 1968-69; pres. Concord Rsch. Corp., Burlington, Mass., 1969-73; indl. sci. cons. Carlisle, Mass., 1973-79; bd. dirs. Phys. Dynamics, Inc., La Jolla, Calif., 1979-81; sr. v.p. for rsch. Sci. Applications Internat. Corp., San Diego, 1981—; chair indsl. adv. bd. Inst. Biomed. Engring., U. Calif., San Diego, 1992—, mem. CONNECT steering com., 1993—; mem. bd. visitors

Coll. Engring. U. Calif., Davis, 1993—. Author: Case Studies in Electromagnetism, 1960; patentee in field. Bd. dirs. La Jolla (Calif.) Chamber Music Soc., 1985-87. 1st lt. U.S. Army, 1961-62. Recipient Meritorious Civilian Svc. award Dept. Army, 1968. Mem. Cosmos Club (Washington), San Diego Yacht Club., Eta Kappa Nu, Tau Beta Pi, Sigma Xi, Phi Kappa Sigma. Avocations: boating, classical music. Home: 6730 Muirlands Dr La Jolla CA 92037-6315 Office: Sci Applications Internat Corp 1241 Cave St La Jolla CA 92037-3602

PENICK, GEORGE DIAL, JR., foundation executive; b. San Juan, P.R., Apr. 17, 1948; s. George Dial and Marguerite Murchison (Worth) P.; m. Carol Davis Bonham, Jan. 30, 1971; children: Holladay Bonham, Robert Anderson. BA, Davidson Coll., 1970; EdM, Harvard U., 1976, M in Pub. Adminstrn., 1977, EdD, 1982. Asst. to dir. Learning Inst. N.C. Durham, 1970-71; child devel. adminstr. N.C. Office for Children, Raleigh, 1973-75; sr. research asst. Harvard U.-MIT Joint Ctr. for Urban Studies, Cambridge, 1978-79; assoc. dir. Mary Reynolds Babcock Found., Winston-Salem, N.C., 1979-85; exec. dir. Jessie Ball duPont Fund, Jacksonville, Fla., 1986-90; pres. Found. for the MidSouth, Jackson, Miss., 1990—; bd. dirs. Miss. Chem. Corp.; bd. dirs. Nat. Charities Info. Bus., vice chair, 1990—; bd. dirs. Nat. Cathedral Assn., 1993—, Coun. on Founds., 1994—; bd. dirs. Episcopal Presiding Bishops Fund for World Relief, 1994—; bd. dirs. Southeastern Coun. Founds., 1983-89. Sr. warden St. Philip's Episcopal Ch., Germanton, N.C., 1981-83; gen. chmn. diocesan conv. Episcopal Diocese N.C., Raleigh, 1981; mem. Leadership Jacksonville, 1987-88, Leadership La., 1994; bd. dirs. Practical and Cultural Edn. Ctr. for Girls, Jacksonville, 1987-90, pres., 1989-90; bd. dirs. Jacksonville Community Coun., Inc., 1987-90. 1st lt. U.S. Army, 1971-73. Recipient Columbia Book award Columbia Tchrs. Coll., 1970. Mem. Harvard Club of N.Y.C. Democrat. Club: Harvard of N.Y.C. Avocations: jogging, stamp collecting, children. Home: 138 Highland Hills Ln Flora MS 39071-9536 Office: Found for the Mid South 308 E Pearl St 4th Fl Jackson MS 39201

PENICK, JOE EDWARD, petroleum consultant; b. Frederick, Okla., Nov. 8, 1920; s. Jesse Olin and Grace Ann (Lane) P.; m. Norma Gene Scott, Oct. 18, 1942; children: Joe Edward, David Scott. B.S., U. Okla., 1942; grad., Exec. Devel. Program, Cornell U., 1963. Research engr. Magnolia Petroleum Co., Dallas, 1942-46; with Mobil Oil Corp., 1942-85; refinery mgr. Mobil Oil Corp., Torrance, Calif., 1961-67; v.p. mfg. Mobil Oil Corp., N.Y.C., 1967-76; sr. v.p. for research and engring. Mobil Oil Corp., 1977-85; pres. Mobil Research and Devel. Corp., 1977-85. Mem. Dirs. Indsl. Rsch., Springdale Golf Club, Bedens Brook Club, Nassau Club. Patentee petroleum refining. Office: 181 Library Pl Princeton NJ 08540-3072

PENICNAK, A. JOHN, manufacturing company executive; b. Chgo., Sept. 14, 1938; s. Clyde A. and Helen J. P.; Fern E. Penicnak; children: Deke, Christine, Helen, Adrianna. AB, Ripon Coll., 1960; MA, U. S.D., 1961; PhD, U. Mass., 1965. With Pfizer, Inc., N.Y.C., 1965-76; sr. v.p. Cosmair, Inc., N.Y.C., 1976—. Contbr. articles to profl. jours.; patentee in field. Fellow Am. Inst. Chemists, Soc. Cosmetic Chemists; mem. Am. Acad. Dermatology, N.Y. Acad. Sci., Rockaway River Country Club. Home: 151 Lookout Rd Mountain Lakes NJ 07046-1214 Office: Cosmair Inc 575 5th Ave New York NY 10017-2422

PENIKETT, ANTONY DAVID JOHN, Canadian government official; b. Nov. 14, 1945; s. Erik John Keith and Sarah Ann (Colwell) P.; m. Lula Mary Johns, 1974; children—John Tahmoh, Sarah Lahlil, Stephanie Yahsan. Exec. asst. to nat. leader New Dem. Party, Ottawa, Ont., Canada, 1975-76, nat. pres., 1981-85, fed. councillor, 1973—; leader New Dem. Party, Whitehorse, Y.T., Canada, 1980—; campaign mgr. New Dem. Party, N.W.T., Canada, 1972; city councillor City of Whitehorse, Y.T., Canada, 1977-79; elected mem. Yukon Legis. Assembly, 1978—; opposition leader Yukon Legis. Assembly, Y.T., Canada, 1982-85; elected govt. leader Yukon Terr. Yukon Legis. Assembly, 1985-92. Author (film): The Mad Trapper, 1972; La Patrouille Perdue, 1974. Mem. Christian Socialist Ch. Home: PO Box 4584, Whitehorse, YK Canada Y1A 2R8 Office: Yukon Territorial Govt, PO Box 2703, Whitehorse, YK Canada Y1A 2C6

PENISTEN, GARY DEAN, entrepreneur; b. Lincoln, Nebr., May 14, 1931; s. Martin C. and Jayne (O'Dell) P.; m. Nancy Margaret Golding, June 3, 1951; children: Kris D., Janet L., Carol E., Noel M. B.S. in Bus. Adminstrn., U. Nebr., Omaha, 1953; LLD (hon.), Concordia Coll., 1993. With Gen. Electric Co., 1953-74; mgr. group fin. ops. power generation group Gen. Electric Co., N.Y.C., 1973-74; asst. sec. navy fin. mgmt., 1974-77; sr. v.p. fin., chief fin. officer, dir. Sterling Drug Inc., N.Y.C., 1977-89; sr. v.p. fin., health group Eastman Kodak Co., N.Y.C., 1989-90; prin. Penco Inc., Bronxville, N.Y., 1990—; chmn. bd. Reprotech Document Svcs. Inc.; bd. dirs. Foster Ptnrs. Inc., Food Ct. Entertainment Network Inc., Acme United Corp. Inc. Bd. dirs. Goodwill Industries Greater N.Y.; chmn. bd. Goodwill Industries Internat. Found., 1989—; mem. corp. adv. bd. Concordia Coll., Bronxville, N.Y., 1991—. U. Nebr. Coll. Bus., Omaha, 1990—. Recipient Disting. Public Service award Navy Dept., 1977; Alumni Achievement citation U. Nebr., Omaha, 1975. Mem. Fin. Execs. Inst., Navy League U.S., Rotary, Union League, Econs. Club (N.Y.C.), Siwanoy Country Club. Republican. Unitarian. Home and Office: 10 Fordal Rd Bronxville NY 10708-2416

PENKAVA, ROBERT RAY, radiologist, educator; b. Virginia, Nebr., Jan. 30, 1942; s. Joseph Everet and Velta Mae (Oviatt) P.; m. Kathry Bennett Secrest, Apr. 6, 1973; children: Ashley Secrest, J. Carson Bennett. AB BS, Peru State Coll., Nebr., 1963; MD, U. Nebr., Omaha, 1967. Intern Lincoln Gen. Hosp., Nebr., 1967-68; resident Menorah Med. Cen., Kansas City, 1968-71; chief resident Menorah Med. Ctr., Kansas City, 1970-71; adj. faculty U. Mo., Kansas City, 1970-71; staff radiologist Ireland Army Hosp., Ft. Knox, Ky., 1971-72, chief, dept. radiology & nuclear med., 1972-73; staff radiologist Deaconess Hosp., Evansville, Ind., 1973—, dir. dept. radiology, 1992—; mem. faculty U. So. Ind., Evansville, 1973—; assoc. faculty Ind. U. Coll. Med., Bloomington, 1973—; med.-dir. Sch. Radiol. Tech. U. So. Ind., Evansville, 1978—; dep coroner Vanderburgh County, 1991—; chmn. So. Ind. Health Systems, 1980-83; pres. Vanderburgh County Med. Soc. Service Bur., 1979—, mem. roentgen soc. liaison com. Ind. Bd. Health, 1968; dep. coroner Vanderburgh County, 1992—. Author numerous articles on med. ultrasound, nuclear med., angiography, and computed tomography. Chmn. profl. div. United Way of So. Ind., 1983; bd. dirs. S.W. Ind. Pub. Broadcasting, 1978-84, S.W. Ind. PSRO, 1982; v.p. Mesker Zoo Found., bd. dirs., 1991—. Maj. U.S. Army, 1971-73. Named Sci. Tchr. of Year, Lewis & Clark Jr. High Sch., 1963. Mem. AMA, Evansville Med. Radiol. Assn. (treas. 1987—), Tri-State Radiology Assn. (pres.), Vanderburgh County Med. Soc. (pres.), Physicians Svc. Bur. (treas.), Magnetic Resonance Imaging, Inc. (treas.), Am. Coll. Radiology, Radiol. Soc. N.Am., Am. Roentgen Ray Soc., Am. Inst. Ultrasound in Medicine, Soc. Cardiovascular and Interventional Radiology. Avocations: golf, boating, flying. Office: 611 Harriet St Evansville IN 47710-1781

PENLAND, ARNOLD CLIFFORD, JR., college dean, educator; b. Asheville, N.C., Oct. 8, 1933; s. Arnold Clifford and Pearl (Bailey) P.; m. Jean Wall (div. 1967); 1 child, Marcia Jean; m. Joan Eudy; 1 child, Elizabeth Bailey. BS, Western Carolina U., 1956; MA, Vanderbilt U., 1959; MEd, Duke U., 1966; PhD, Fla. State U., 1983. Tchr. of music Reidsville (N.C.) Pub. Schs., 1956-60; supr. of music Raleigh (N.C.) Pub. Schs., 1960-67; supr. of music and rsch. Smoky Mt. Cultural Arts Devel. Assn., Sylva, N.C., 1967, 1968-69; state supr. of music State Dept. of Edn., Columbia, S.C., 1969-70; assoc. prof. of music U. of Fla., Gainesville, 1970-80, prof. of music, 1980—, assoc. dean and prof. Coll. of Fine Arts, 1981—; prog. dir. Raleigh Cultural Ctr., Inc., 1962-67; music dir. various ch. choirs, N.C. and Fla., 1956-80; ednl. cons. Nat. Grass Roots Opera, Co., Raleigh, 1962-67, bd. dirs. Fla. League of the Arts. Contbr. articles to profl. jours. Mem. Gainesville Cultural Commn., 1975-76, v.p. Alachua County Arts Coun., Inc., 1976-77; bd. dirs. Arts Coun. of Raleigh, Inc., 1963-65. Recipient Disting. Service Citation, Federated Music Clubs of N.C., 1966; grantee Office of Edn., 1967-69. Mem. Nat. Assn. Acad. Affairs Adminstrn. (pres. 1990-92), Regional Assn. Acad. Affairs Adminstrn. (pres. 1985-86), Music Educators Nat. Conf., Coll. Music Soc. (life), Lions (v.p. Raleigh chpt. 1963-66), Kiwanis (Kiwanian of Yr. award 1989-90, bd. dirs. 1992-96), Order of Omega, Phi Delta Kappa (pres. North Ctrl. Fla. chpt. 1985-86), Sigma Phi Epsilon. Democrat. Presbyterian. Avocations: gardening, cooking. Office: U Fla Coll

Fine Arts 115800 Gainesville FL 32611-5800 *In life one can do anything one chooses to do if one is genuinely committed.*

PENLAND, JOHN THOMAS, import/export and development companies executive; b. Guntersville, Ala., Mar. 31, 1930; s. James B. and Kathleen (Bolding) P.; m. Carolyn Joyce White, May 30, 1961; children—Jeffrey K., Mark A., Michael J. B.A., George Washington U., 1957. Vice pres., dir. Rouse, Brewer, Becker & Bryant, Inc., Washington, 1957-63; staff mem. SEC, Washington, 1963-67; pres., dir. INA Trading Corp, Phila., 1968-69; v.p. INA Security Corp., Phila., 1967-69; v.p. Shareholders Mgmt. Co., Los Angeles, 1969, sr. v.p., 1970, exec. v.p., 1970-73, pres., 1973-75, also bd. dirs.; v.p. Shareholders Capital Corp., Los Angeles, 1972-73; v.p., dir. several mut. funds managed by Shareholders Mgmt. Co., 1970-75; pres., chmn., chief exec. officer HMO Internat. and its subs., Los Angeles, 1975; founder, pres., chmn. Pendlar Corp. Atlanta, 1977—; chmn., pres. Bella Vista Developers, Inc., Albuqueque, 1977—; chmn. CompuComp Corp., Atlanta, 1977-81; chmn., pres. Fran Stef Corp., N.Y.C., 1982-89; pres., chmn. Engineered Products Corp. Dandridge, Tenn., 1983-90; founder, chmn. CEO Am. Accessories Inc., Covington, Ga., 1983—; founder, pres., chmn. United Am. Products Corp., Dandridge, 1983-89; founder, chmn. Chamisa Properties, Inc., Albuqueque, 1988-94, Glorieux Ltd., Atlanta, 1988—, Ga. Ptnrs. Ltd., Covington, 1988-94; founder, chmn., dir. Premier Trading Internat., Inc., Atlanta, 1989—; founder, dir. Chamisa Enterprises, Inc., Covington, 1990—; founder, mng. ptnr. Ft. Hill Ptnrs., Knoxville, Tenn., 1990-93; chmn. Einson Freeman & Detroy Corp., Fair Lawn, N.J., 1978-83; founder, dir., pres. West Point Contract Packaging, Inc., Winston-Salem, N.C., 1991—; founder, mng. ptnr. Harbor View, Ltd., Fernandina Beach, Fla., 1992-94; founder, chmn. West Point TEch. Assembly, Inc., Winston-Salem, N.C., 1993—; dir. BKP Industries, Inc., Monroe, Ga., 1995—. Served with AUS, 1948-55. Republican. Episcopalian. Home: PO Box 549 Social Circle GA 30279-0549 Office: 3261 Highway 278 NE Covington GA 30209

PENMAN, BRIAN EDWARD, radio personality; b. Wilkensburg, Pa., Aug. 1, 1959; s. Edward John and Dorothy May (Smead) P.; m. Melisa Joan Felty, Sept. 27, 1980; children: Kurtiss William, Damian Brian. Student, Los Medanos Community Coll., Pittsburg, Calif., 1978; student, Ohlone Community Coll., Fremont, Calif., 1982-83. Maintenance engr. Clear Pane Window Cleaning, Concord, Calif., 1975-83; welder C.M. Farr Constrn. Co., San Ramon, Calif., 1979-82; air personality Sta. KLOQ, Merced, Calif., 1982-83, Sta. KSTN, Stockton, Calif., 1983-84, Sta. KWUN, Concord, 1984-85, Sta. KITS-FM, San Francisco, 1985-86, Sta. KIOI-FM, San Francisco, 1986-89, Sta. KKIS, San Francisco, 1989-90, KXXX-FM, San Francisco, 1989-91, KFRC-FM, San Francisco, 1991—. Bd. regents communications dept. Ohlone Community Coll., 1986—; media liaison Walk Am., San Francisco area March of Dimes, 1986; vol. Jerry Lewis Telethon, Oakland, Calif., 1988. Mem. M.H. DeYoung-Steinhart Aquarium. Republican. Avocations: sightseeing, kite flying, photography, recording, boating. Office: Sta KFRC-FM 500 Washington St San Francisco CA 94111-2906

PENMAN, PAUL DUANE, nuclear power laboratory executive; b. Williston, N.D., Sept. 25, 1937; s. Robert Roy and Kathryn Erica (Hagstrom) P.; m. Cornelia Dennis, Jan. 9, 1960 (div. June 1986); children: Anne, Robert, Jill; m. Carrie B. Silverblatt, July 14, 1986. BS in Engring. Physics, U. Colo., 1959; MS in Physics, U. Louisville, 1965. Asst. prof. U. Louisville, 1962-65; engr. Bettis Atomic Power Lab., West Mifflin, Pa., 1965-71, mgr., 1971-77, in charge lab. ops., 1977-82, in charge nuclear core mfg., 1982-92; mgr. performance and quality Westinghouse Electro-Mech. Divsn., Cheswick, Pa., 1992-93, mgr. performance quality improvement, 1994—. Leader Boy Scouts Am., Pitts., 1977-80. Lt. USN, 1959-64. Mem. U.S. Naval Inst., Gyro Internat. (bd. dirs., pres. 1988-90), U. Colo. Alumni Assn. (pres. Pitts. 1971-80). Republican. Home: 105 Urick Ct Monroeville PA 15146-4919

PENMAN, SHELDON, biology educator; b. N.Y.C., July 24, 1930; s. Samuel and Rae P. BA, Pa. State U., 1954; PhD, Columbia U., 1958. Instr. physics Columbia U., N.Y.C., 1958-59; asst. prof. physics U. Chgo., 1959-61; assoc. in physics Columbia U. and Bell Telephone Labs., N.Y.C., 1961-62; asst. prof. biochemistry Albert Einstein Coll. Medicine, N.Y.C., 1964-65; research assoc. in biology MIT, Cambridge, 1964-64, asst. prof. then assoc. prof. biophysics and microbiology, 1965-70, prof. biology, 1970—. Author over 200 sci. articles; patentee in field. Guggenheim fellow, 1983. Fellow AAAS; mem. Nat. Acad. Scis., Sigma Pi Sigma. Jewish. Avocations: music, literature, computer programming. Home: 5325 Metro St San Diego CA 92110-2608 Office: Mass Inst Tech 77 Massachusetts Ave Bldg 56535 Cambridge MA 02139-4307

PENN, ARTHUR HILLER, film and theatre producer; b. Phila., Sept. 27, 1922; s. Harvy and Sonia (Greenberg) P.; m. Peggy Maurer, Jan. 27, 1955; children: Matthew, Molly. Student, Joshua Logan's Stage Co., Black Mountain Coll., Asheville, N.C., U. Perugia, Florence, Italy, Actors Studio, Los Angeles; studied with Michael Chekhov. Joined Army Theatre Co. during World War II; worked in TV, 1951-53; producer plays for Broadway theatre including The Miracle Worker (Tony award 1960), All The Way Home, Toys in the Attic, Two for the Seesaw, In the Council House, Wait Until Dark, Sly Fox, Monday After the Miracle; films include The Left-Handed Gun, 1957, The Miracle Worker, 1962, Mickey One, 1964, The Chase, 1965, Bonnie and Clyde, 1967, Alice's Restaurant, 1969, Little Big Man, 1971, Night Moves, 1975, The Missouri Breaks, 1976, Four Friends, 1981, Target, 1985, Dead of Winter, 1987; co-dir. film Visions of Eight, 1973; dir. theatre: Golden Boy, Hunting Cockroaches. Office: care Sam Cohn Internat Creative Mgmt 40 W 57th St New York NY 10019-4001 also: William Morris Agy 151 El Camino Beverly Hills CA 90212

PENN, GERALD MELVILLE, pathologist; b. Toledo, Mar. 24, 1937; s. Melville Delroy and Hildegarde Agnes (Wammus) P.; m. Joyce Earl, June 5, 1965; children: Gerald Bradley, David Joshua. MD, Ohio State U., 1964, PhD, 1975. Cert. Am. Bd. Pathology. Head hematology sect. Bethesda (Md.) Naval Hosp., 1970-72; chief clin. pathology Children's Hosp., Columbus, Ohio, 1972-81; dir. lab. medicine Grant Med. Ctr., Columbus, 1981—; assoc. prof. Consolidated Bio-Med. Labs., Dublin, Ohio, 1972-78; chmn. Am. Bd. Med. Lab. Immunology, Washington, 1982-85. Author: Interpretation of Immunoelectrophoretic Patterns, 1978, The Clinical Use and Interpretation of Agarose Gel Electrophoresis Patterns, 1982; editor: Manual of Clinical Laboratory Immunology, 1992. Chmn. med. coun. Health Coalition of Ctrl. Ohio, Columbus, 1991-92. Lt. comdr. USN, 1970-72. Recipient Commendation for Meritorious Svc., USN Nat. Naval Med. Ctr., Bethesda, 1972. Fellow Am. Soc. Clin. Pathology (dep. sec. 1973-78, CCE Meritorious Svc.), Coll. Am. Pathologists; mem. Acad. Medicine Columbus (sec.-treas. 1992—). Republican. Roman Catholic. Office: Grant Med Ctr 111 S Grant Ave Columbus OH 43215

PENN, IRVING, photographer; b. Plainfield, N.J., June 16, 1917; s. Harry and Sonia P.; m. Lisa Fonssagrives, 1950; 1 son. Tom. Painter, 1941; first photographs pub. in Vogue, 1943; exhbns. include Mus. Modern Art, N.Y.C., 1984; rep. photographs in permanent collections Met. Mus. Art, Mus. Modern Art, N.Y.C.; author: Moments Preserved, collection of 300 photographs, 1960, Worlds in a Small Room, 1974, Inventive Paris Clothes 1909-1939, 1977, Flowers, 1980, Passage, 1991.

PENN, JOHN GARRETT, federal judge; b. Pittsfield, Mass., Mar. 19, 1932; s. John and Eugenie Gwendolyn (Heyliger) P.; m. Ann Elizabeth Rollison, May 7, 1966; children: John Garett II, Karen Renee, David Brandon. BA, U. Mass., 1954; LLB, Boston U., 1957; postgrad. pub. and internat. affairs, Princeton U., 1967-68. Bar: Mass 1957, D.C. 1970. Trial atty. Dept. Justice, Washington, 1961-65, atty. tax div., 1961-70; then reviewer, asst. chief gen. litigation sect., assoc. judge Superior Ct. of D.C., Washington, 1970-79; judge U.S. Dist. Ct. D.C., Washington, 1979-92, chief judge, 1992—. Ex-officio dir. day care program D.C. Dept. Recreation, 1978—. Served with JAGC U.S. Army, 1958-61. Nat. Inst. Pub. Affairs fellow, 1967. Mem. Nat. Bar Assn., Mass. Bar Assn., Washington Bar Assn., Bar Assn. D.C. (hon.), Am. Judicature Soc., Boston U. Law Sch. Alumni Assn. Episcopalian. Office: US Dist Ct DC US Courthouse 333 Constitution Ave NW Washington DC 20001

PENN, LYNN SHARON, materials scientist; b. Iowa City, June 18, 1945; d. Robert Joseph and Dorothy Evelyn (Etsinger) Johnson; m. Arthur Leon Penn, June 24, 1968; 1 child, Ethan. AB, U. Pa., 1966; MA, Bryn Mawr

Coll., 1970, PhD, 1974. Chemist Lawrence Livermore Nat. Lab., Livermore, Calif., 1974-78; sr. scientist Textile Rsch. Inst., Princeton, N.J., 1978-80, Ciba-Geigy Corp., Ardsley, N.Y., 1980-83; prin. scientist Midwest Rsch. Inst., Kansas City, Mo., 1983-86; rsch. prof. Polytechnic U., Bklyn., 1987-91; prof. U. Ky., Lexington, 1991—; chair Gordon Rsch. Conf. on Sci. of Adhesion, 1992. N.Am. editor Internat. Jour. Adhesion and Adhesives; contbr. articles to profl. jours. Mem. Am. Soc. Testing Materials, Soc. Adv. Materials and Process Engring., Fiber Soc., Adhesion Soc. (sec. 1982-90), Kappa Kappa Gamma. Jewish. Home: 31 Division Ave Nyack NY 10960-4405

PENN, SEAN, actor; b. Burbank, Calif., Aug. 17, 1960; s. Leo and Eileen (Ryan) P.; m. Madonna Louise Ciccone, Aug. 16, 1985 (div.); 2 children: Dylan Frances, Hopper Jack. Appearances include (Broadway debut) Heartland, others include Slab Boys, Hurlyburly, 1988; (films) Taps, 1981, Fast Times at Ridgemont High, 1982, Bad Boys, 1983, Crackers, 1984, Racing with the Moon, 1984, The Falcon and the Snowman, 1985, At Close Range, 1986, Shanghai Surprise, 1986, Colors, 1988, Judgment in Berlin, 1988, Casualties of War, 1989, We're No Angels, 1989, State of Grace, 1990, Carlito's Way, 1993; dir., writer: The Indian Runner, 1991, The Crossing Guard, 1995; (TV movie) The Killing of Randy Webster, 1981. Office: William Morris Agy 151 El Camino Beverly Hills CA 90211*

PENN, STANLEY WILLIAM, journalist; b. N.Y.C., Jan. 12, 1928; s. Murray and Lillian (Richman) P.; m. Esther Aronson, July 12, 1952; children—Michael, Laurel. Student, Bklyn. Coll., 1945-47; B. Journalism, U. Mo., 1949. With Wall St. Jour., 1952-90; investigative reporter N.Y. bur., 1957-90. (Co-recipient Pulitzer prize for nat. reporting 1967). Home: 380 Riverside Dr New York NY 10025-1822

PENNACCHIO, JOSEPH, apparel executive. Pres., coo Jordan Marsh Stores Corp., Cin. Office: Jordan Marsh Stores Corp 7 W 7th St Cincinnati OH 45202-2424

PENNANT-REA, RUPERT LASCELLES, banker, economist; b. Harare, Zimbabwe, Jan. 23, 1948; came to Britain, 1966; s. Peter Athelwold and Pauline Elizabeth (Cresey) Pennant-Rea; m. Louise Greer, Oct. 3, 1970 (div. 1976); m. Jane Trevelyan Hamilton, Aug. 18, 1979 (div. 1986); children—Emily Trevelyan, Rory Marcus; m. Helen Jay, June 24, 1986; 1 child, Edward Peter. B.A. with honors, Trinity Coll., Dublin, 1970; M.A., U. Manchester, 1972. Economist, Confedn. Irish Industry, Dublin, 1970-71, Gen. and Mcpl. Workers Union, Eng., 1972-73, Bank of Eng., 1973-77; journalist The Economist, London, 1977-93, editor, 1986-93; dep. chmn. Bank England 1993—. Author: Gold Foil, 1979; The Pocket Economist, 1983; The Economist Economics, 1986. Recipient Wincott prize for fin. journalism Wincott Found., London, 1984. Mem. Ch. of Eng. Clubs: Marylebone Cricket, Reform (London), Hanare (Zimbabwe). Avocations: music; tennis. Office: Bank of England, London EO2 1HG, England

PENNARIO, LEONARD, concert pianist, composer; b. Buffalo, July 9, 1924; s. John D. and Mary (Chiarello) P. Student music, U. So. Calif., 1942; student piano with, Guy Maier, Isabelle Vengerova. Profl. debut Dallas Symphony, 1936; performed with Los Angeles Philharm., 1939, N.Y. Philharm. 1943; composer: Midnight on the Cliffs, (piano) Variations on the Kerry Dance, also piano concerto and other works for piano; soloist orchs. in Phila., Chgo., Boston, N.Y.C., Los Angeles, St. Louis, others; performed concerts in Eng., Italy, Fed. Republic of Germany, Holland, France, Scandinavian countries, Austria; toured in South Africa, 1959, Europe, 1960; featured pianist chamber music concerts with Heifetz & Piatigorsky; recorded albums for RCA, Angel, CBS Masterworks. Mem. Calif. Scholarship Fedn. Served with USAAF, World War II. Mem. Ephebian Soc., ASCAP. Roman Catholic.

PENNEL, MARIE LUCILLE HUNZIGER, elementary education educator; b. Oregon, Mo., Jan. 16, 1934; d. William Henry and Milree (Huff) Hunziger; m. Berres H. Pennel, Mar. 6, 1955; children: Patricia Lu Pennel Wolfe, Pamela Cille Pennel Ginther. BS, Northwest Mo. State U., 1954; MS, Kans. U., 1959; postgrad., Kans. State U. Cert. elem. tchr., Kans. 1st grade tchr. Lawrence, Kans.; kindergarten tchr. Atchison, Kans., Unified Sch. Dist. 415, Hiawatha, Kans., 1972-94. Recipient Outstanding Svc. award, Lawrence Jaycees, 1958, 59. Mem. NEA, Kans. Edn. Assn., ASCD, Assn. for Childhood Edn. Internat., Kappa Delta Pi, Delta Kappa Gamma. Home: 403 Woodbury Ln Hiawatha KS 66434-1525

PENNELL, WILLIAM BROOKE, lawyer; b. Mineral Ridge, Ohio, Oct. 28, 1935; s. George Albert and Katherine Nancy (McMeen) P. AB, Harvard U., 1957; LLB cum laude, U. Pa., 1961; m. Peggy Polsky, June 17, 1958; children: Katherine, Thomas Brooke. Bar: N.Y. 1963, U.S. Dist. Ct. (so. dist.) N.Y. 1964, U.S. Dist. Ct. (ea. dist.) N.Y. 1964, U.S. Ct. Appeals (2d cir.) 1966, U.S. Ct. Claims 1966, U.S. Tax Ct. 1967, U.S. Supreme Ct. 1967. Clk. U.S. Dist. Ct., (so. dist.) N.Y., N.Y.C., 1961-62; assoc. Shearman & Sterling, N.Y.C., 1962-71, ptnr., 1971-91. Recent case editor U. Pa. Law Rev., 1960-61. Bd. govs. Bklyn. Heights Assn., 1964-74, pres., 1969-71; chmn. bd. Willoughby House Settlement, 1972—. Served with U.S. Army, 1957. Fellow Salzburg Seminar Am. Studies, 1965. Mem. Rembrandt Club. Office: PO Box 249 Canaan NY 12029

PENNEMAN, ROBERT ALLEN, retired chemist; b. Springfield, Ill., Feb. 5, 1919; s. Allen Frederick and Beryl (McNeeley) P.; m. Mary Ellen Emerick, July 25, 1942; children: Jacqueline, Cindy, Dean. A.B. summa cum laude, Millikin U. Decatur, Ill., 1941, Sc.D. (hon.), 1961; M.S., U. Ill., 1942, Ph.D. in Inorganic Chemistry, 1947. Chemist Ill. Hwy. Lab., Springfield, 1941; chemist metall. lab. U. Chgo., 1942-45; research assoc. Clinton Labs., Oak Ridge, 1945-46; chemist, staff mem., group and assoc. div. leader Los Alamos Nat. Lab., 1947-84, ret., 1984; adj. prof. U. N.Mex., 1950—; cons., lectr. in field. Editl. bd. Inorganic Chesitry, 1962-66 (founding mem.), Inorganic and Nuclear Chemistry Letters, 1968—; contbr. articles to profl. jours. Recipient Disting. Performance award Los Alamos Nat. Lab. 1981, Award of Excellence Los Alamos Nat. Lab. 1986. Mem. Am. Chem. Soc. (chmn. N.Mex. chpt. 1956), Nat. Acad. Scis. (participant workshop 1983), Sigma Xi, Phi Kappa Phi, Alpha Chi Sigma. Home: 12201 LaVista Grande Dr Albuquerque NM 87111-6710 Office: Los Alamos Nat Lab PO Box 1663 Los Alamos NM 87545-0001

PENNER, HANS HENRY, historian; b. Sacramento, Jan. 29, 1934; s. Hans Henry and Frieda Marie (Haehnel) P.; m. Anna M. Tardiff, Sept. 27, 1958. D.B., U. Chgo., 1958, M.A., 1962, Ph.D., 1965. Instr. U. Vt., 1962-65; asst. prof. Dartmouth Coll., 1965-71, Preston Kelsey prof. religion, 1991—, dean faculty, 1980-85; Pres. Am. Acad. Religion New Eng., 1980-81. Editorial bd. Am. Acad. Religion; contbr. articles to profl. jours.; Danforth fellow, 1968-69; Dartmouth Faculty fellow, 1967; Fulbright research grantee, 1966; Am. Council Learned Socs. grantee, 1979. Mem. Assn. Asian Studie, Am. Soc. St. Religion, Internat. Assn. History of Religion. Home: PO Box 642 Hanover NH 03755-0642 Office: Dartmouth Coll 6306 Thornton Hanover NH 03755

PENNER, HARRY HAROLD HAMILTON, JR., pharmaceutical company executive, lawyer; b. Norfolk, Va., July 29, 1945; s. Harry H.H. and Leona F. (Vossler) P.; m. Irene Anne Uanino, June 22, 1968; children: Harry III, Emilie A., Stephanie M., Christopher D., Scott T., Rebecca S., Andrew E. BA, U. Va., 1967; JD, Fordham U., 1970; LLM in internat. law, NYU, 1975. Bar: N.Y. 1971. Assoc. Choate Regan Davis & Hollister, N.Y.C., 1971-75; counsel Pinkertons Inc., N.Y.C., 1975-78; atty. Boehringer Ingelheim Ltd., Ridgefield, Conn., 1978-81; v.p., gen. counsel Novo Labs. Inc., Wilton, Conn., 1981-85; exec. v.p., gen. counsel Novo Industri A/S, Bagsvaerd, Denmark, 1985-88; pres. Novo Nordisk of N.Am. Inc., N.Y.C., 1988-93; exec. v.p. Novo Nordisk A/S, Bagsvaerd, Denmark, 1985-93; pres., CEO Neurögen Corp., Branford, Conn., 1993—; bd. dirs. Zymogenetics Inc., Seattle, chmn., 1988-89; bd. dirs. Anergen, Inc., Redwood City, Calif., Novo Nordisk Pharms., Inc., Princeton, N.J., Entotech, Inc., Davis, Calif., Novo Nordisk Bioindustrials, Inc., Danbury, Conn., Novo Nordisk BioChem, Inc., Franklinton, N.C., Novo Nordisk Pharm. Industries, Inc., Novo Nordisk Biotech. Inc., Davis, Tech. Unlimited, Inc., Wooster, Ohio. Bd. dirs Am. Club in Copenhagen, 1986-88, Copenhagen Internat. Jr. Sch., 1985-88; co-founder Danish Corp. Lawyers Assn., 1987-88. Mem. Internat. Bar Assn.,

Assn. Bar City of N.Y., N.Y. Bar Assn., Biotech. Industry Orgn. (bd. dirs.), Danish Am. C. of C. (bd. dirs., pres.), Am. Scandinavian Found. (trustee), European Am. C. of C. (bd. dirs., treas.). Republican. Roman Catholic. Avocations: running, tennis. Office: Neurogen Corp 35 Northeast Industrial Rd Branford CT 06405

PENNER, STANFORD SOLOMON, engineering educator; b. Unna, Germany, July 5, 1921; came to U.S., 1936, naturalized, 1943; s. Heinrich and Regina (Saal) P.; m. Beverly Preston, Dec. 28, 1942; children: Merilynn Jean, Robert Clark. BS, Union Coll., 1942; MS, U. Wis., 1943, PhD, 1946; Dr. rer. nat. (hon.), Technische Hochschule Aachen, Germany, 1981. Research asso. Allegany Ballistics Lab., Cumberland, Md., 1944-45; research scientist Standard Oil Devel. Co., Esso Labs., Linden, N.J., 1946; sr. research engr. Jet Propulsion Lab., Pasadena, Calif., 1947-50; mem. faculty Calif. Inst. Tech., 1950-63, prof. div. engring., jet propulsion, 1957-63; dir. research engring. div. Inst. Def. Analyses, Washington, 1962-64; prof. engr-ing. physics, chmn. dept. aerospace and mech. engring. U. Calif. at San Diego, 1964-68, vice chancellor for acad. affairs, 1968-69, dir. Inst. for Pure and Applied Phys. Scis., 1968-71, dir. Energy Ctr., 1973-91; bd. dirs. Ogden Corp., Optodyne Corp.; U.S. mem. adv. group aero. rsch. and devel. NATO, 1952-68, chmn. combustion and propulsion panel, 1958-60; mem. adv. com. engring. scis. USAF-Office Sci. Rsch., 1961-65; mem. subcom. combustion NACA, 1954-58; rsch. adv. com. air-breathing engines NASA, 1962-64; mem. coms. on gas dynamics and com. Internat. Acad. Astronautics, 1969-80; ; nat. lectr. Sigma Xi, 1977-79; chmn. DOE fossil energy rsch. working group, 1978-82, assembly engring., NAE, 1978-82; chmn. NAS/NRC U.S. Nat. Com. ITASA, 1978-82; mem. commn. engring. tech. system, NRC, 1982-84; spl. guest Internat. Coal Sci. Confs., 1983, 85, 87, 89, 91; mentor Defense Sci. Studies Group, 1985-93; chmn. Studies Municipal Waste Incineration NSF, 1988-89, Calif. Coun. Sci. Tech., 1992; chmn. DOE advanced fuel cell commercialization working group, 1993-95. Author: Chemical Reactions in Flow Systems, 1955, Chemistry Problems in Jet Propulsion, 1957, Quantitative Molecular Spectroscopy and Gas Emissivities, 1959, Chemical Rocket Propulsion and Combustion Research, 1962, Thermodynamics, 1968, Radiation and Reentry, 1968; sr. author: Energy, Vol. I (Demands, Resources, Impact, Technology and Policy), 1974, 81, Energy, Vol. II (Non-nuclear Energy Technologies), 1975, 77, 84, Energy, Vol. III (Nuclear Energy and Energy Policies), 1976; editor: Chemistry of Propellants, 1960, Advanced Propulsion Techniques, 1961, Detonations and Two-Phase Flow, 1962, Combustion and Propulsion, 1963, Advances in Tactical Rocket Propulsion, 1968, In Situ Shale Oil Recovery, 1975, New Sources of Oil and Gas, 1982, Coal Combustion and Applications, 1984, Advanced Fuel Cells, 1986, Coal Gasification: Direct Applications and Syntheses of Chemicals and Fuels, 1987, CO2 Emissions and Climate Change, 1991, Commercialization of Fuel Cells, 1995; assoc. editor Jour. Chem. Physics, 1953-56; founder Jour. Quantitative Spectroscopy and Radia-tive Transfer, 1960-92, Jour. Def. Rsch., 1963-67, Energy-The Internat. Jour., 1975—. Recipient spl. award People-to-People program, NATO, pub. svc. award U. Calif., San Diego, N. Manson medal Internat. Colloquia on Gas-dynamics of Explosions and Reactive Systems, 1979, internat. Columbus award Internat. Inst. Comm., Genoa, Italy, 1981, disting. assoc. award U.S. Dept. Energy, 1990; Guggenheim fellow, 1971-72. Fellow Am. Phys. Soc., Optical Soc. Am., AAAS, N.Y. Acad. Scis., AIAA (dir. 1964-66, past chmn. com., G. Edward Pendray award 1975, Thermophysics award 1983, Energy Systems award 1983), Am. Acad. Arts and Scis.; mem. Nat. Acad. Engring., Internat. Acad. Astronautics, Am. Chem. Soc., Sigma Xi. Home: 5912 Avenida Chamnez La Jolla CA 92037-7402 Office: U Calif San Diego 9500 Gilman Dr La Jolla CA 92093-0411

PENNEY, ALEXANDRA, magazine editor-in-chief, writer; married; 1 child. Grad., Smith Coll.; MA, Hunter Coll., 1977. Editor health and beauty Glamour mag.; editor at large Bantam Doubleday; editor-in-chief Self mag., 1989—. Author: How to Make Love to a Man, 1981, Great Sex, 1985, How to Keep Your Man Monogamous, 1989; contbr. articles to N.Y. Times Mag., Vogue, others. Office: Self Magazine Conde Nast Publs Inc 350 Madison Ave New York NY 10017-3704*

PENNEY, ALPHONSUS LIGUORI, archbishop; b. St. John's, Nfld., Can., Sept. 17, 1924; s. Alphonsus Liguori and Catherine (Mullaly) P. L.Ph., U. Ottawa, 1945, L.Th., 1949; LL.D. Meml. U. Nfld., 1980. Ordained priest Roman Cath. Ch., 1949. Named vicar forane Roman Cath. Ch., 1960, vicar gen., 1971, prelate of honour, 1971, asst. priest, then parish priest, 1949-72; bishop Roman Cath. Ch., Grand Falls, Nfld., 1973-79; archbishop Roman Cath. Ch., St. John's, Nfld., 1979-91, archbishop emeritus, 1991—; chmn. Cath. Edn. Com., 1979-91. Served with RCAF, 1952-57. Address: Box 1029, Almonte, ON Canada K0A 1AO

PENNEY, CHARLES RAND, lawyer, civic worker; b. Buffalo, July 26, 1923; s. Charles Patterson and Gretchen (R) P. BA, Yale U., 1945; JD, U. Va., 1951; DFA (hon.), SUNY, 1995. Bar: Md. 1952, N.Y. 1958, U.S. Supreme Ct. 1958. Law sec. to U.S. Dist. Ct. Judge W.C. Coleman, Balt., 1951-52; dir. devel. office Children's Hosp., Buffalo, 1952-54; sales mgr. Amherst Mfg. Corp., Williamsville, N.Y., 1954-56, also; Delevan Electronics Corp., East Aurora, N.Y.; mem. firm Penney & Penney, Buffalo, 1958-61; pvt. practice, Niagara County, N.Y., 1961—. Numerous contemporary art collection exhbns. include Mus. Modern Art, N.Y.C., 1962, Whitney Mus. Am. Art, N.Y.C., 1963, 79, 80, Burchfield-Penney Art Ctr., 1973, 92, Meml. Art Gallery, Rochester, 1976, 78, 83, 88, U. Iowa, 1978, Columbus (Ohio) Gallery Fine Arts, 1979, Whitte Meml. Mus., San Antonio, 1979, U. N.C., 1979, Ga. Mus. Art, 1979, Hunter Mus. Art, Chattanoga, Tenn., 1980, Brooks Meml. Art Gallery, Memphis, 1980, Portland (Maine Mus. Art), 1980, Arts Ctr., South Bend, Ind., 1980, The Bowers Mus., Santa Ana, Calif., 1980, Beaumont (Tex.) Art Mus., 1981, 88, Meadows Mus. Art, Shreveport, La., 1981, 88, Cedar Rapids (Iowa) Mus. Art, 1983, Roland Gibson Art Gallery, Potsdam, N.Y., 1983, 84, Met. Mus. Art, 1984, San Jose Mus. Art, 1985, Tampa Mus., 1986, Boston Athenaeum, Mass., 1986, The New Britain (Conn.) Mus. Art, 1986, Currier Gallery Art, Manchester, N.H., 1987, Miss. Mus. Art, Jackson, 1987, others; selected works from art collections exhibited at Met. Mus. Art, N.Y. Hist. Soc., 1987, San Francisco Mus. Art, 1963, Walker Art Ctr., Mpls., 1963, Pa. Acad. Fine Arts, 1964, and 25 U.S. Embassies, 1965-72, U. Ariz., Tucson, 1965, 66, Albright-Knox Art Gallery, Buffalo, 1967, 87, Cleve. Mus. Art, 1972, Indpls. Mus. Art, 1973, Whitney Mus. Am. Art, N.Y., 1979, 80, Milw. Mus. Art, 1984, Wad-sworth Atheneum, Hartford, 1986, Corcoran Gallery Art, Washington, 1987, U. Mich., 1993, Terra Mus. Am. Art, 1993. Bd. dirs. Buffalo State Coll. Found.; hon. life trustee Burchfield-Penney Art Ctr.; mem. Friends of Mt. Hope Cemetery, Rochester. 2d lt. U.S. Army, 1943-46. Recipient Disting. Svc. to Culture award Coll. Arts and Scis., SUNY, Potsdam, 1983, Pres.' Disting. Svc. award Buffalo State Coll., 1991; named Disting. fellow Cultural Studies of the Burchfield-Penney Art Ctr. Fellow The Explorers Club; mem. AARP, Everson Mus. Art, Textile Mus., Albright-Knox Art Gallery Buffalo (life), Buffalo Mus. Sci. (life), Buffalo and Erie County Hist. Soc. (life), Niagara County Hist. Soc. (life), Old Ft. Niagara (life), Buffalo Soc. Artists (hon. trustee), Hist. Lockport (life), Landmark Soc. of Western N.Y. (life), Nat. Trust Hist. Preservation, Am. Ceramic Circle, Rochester Mus. and Sci. Center, Historic Lewiston (life), Friends of U. Rochester Libraries (life), Meml. Art Gallery U. Rochester (hon. bd. mgrs., hon. life), Winslow Homer Soc. of the Dir's. Circle, Smithsonian Instn., Rochester Hist. Soc. (life); U.S. Holocaust Meml. Mus. (charter), Mus. Am. Folk Art, Am. Hist. Print Collectors Soc. (bd. dirs.), Burchfield Homestead Soc. (hon. life), Libr. Con-gress, Whitney Mus. Am. Art, Am. Craft Coun., Archives Am. Art, Mar-garet Woodbury Strong Mus. (charter), Met. Mus. Art, Mus. Modern Art, Mark Twain Soc. (hon.), U. Rochester's Pres.'s Soc. (hon. life), Cleve. Mus. Art, Cleve. Artists' Found., U. Iowa's Pres.'s Club (hon. life), Va. Law Found., Roland Gibson Art Gallery, SUNY Coll. of Arts and Sci., Ctr. African Studies, Castellani Art Mus. Niagara U., Nat. Geog. Soc. (life), Internat. Sculpture Ctr., Nat. Acad. of Design, Hist. Soc. of the Tonawandas (life), Pres.'s Circle Buffalo State Coll. (hon. life), Craftsman Homeowners Club, Nat. Mus. Am. Indian (charter), Drawing Ctr. N.Y.C., Niagara Coun. Arts, U.S. Holocaust Meml. Mus. (charter), Heisey Collectors of The Rochester Area, Peanut Pals, Am. Legion, Library of Congress, Guggenheim Mus., Friends of the Mount Hope Cemetary, Rochester, N.Y., Burchfield Homestead Soc., Salm, Ohio, Grolier Club, Chi Psi, Phi Alpha Delta. Clubs: Automobile (Lockport); Zwicker Aquatic, Niagara County Antiques (hon.); Rochester Art (hon. life). Office: 538 Bewley Building Bldg Lockport NY 14094-2934 I have tried to strive for excellence in whatever I undertake, be it small or large. What success I may have achieved has required initiative,

imagination, and dedication to the task at hand. Satisfaction comes from the hard work that leads to an objective. In all that I do I adhere to the Golden Rule and to fairness, honesty, and understanding in human relationships. I try to maintain a sense of humor at all times. And I enjoy living in a small community because it is from such areas that the strength of America comes.

PENNEY, PEARCE JOHN, retired librarian; b. St. Anthony, Nfld., Can., Mar. 10, 1928; s. Edgar and Elsie Belle (Bussey) P.; m. Amy Parrill, Aug. 30, 1950; children—Wayne, David, Donald, Reneé. B.A., Mt. Allison U., 1957; M.Div., Pinehill Div. Sch., 1959; M.S. in Library Scis, Syracuse U., 1968. Tchr., 1946-50; ordained to ministry United Ch. of Can., 1959; pastor various chs., 1959-67; librarian, head of acquisitions Meml. U., St. John's, Nfld., 1968-71, U. Guelph, Ont., 1971-72; chief provincial librarian Nfld. Pub. Library Services, St. John's, 1972-93. Mem. Can. Libr. Assn., Atlantic Provinces Libr. Assn., Nfld. Libr. Assn. Home: 24 Parsons Rd, Saint John's, NF Canada A1A 2J1

PENNEY, SHERRY HOOD, university chancellor, educator; b. Marlette, Mich., Sept. 4, 1937; d. B. Jean (Stoutenburg) Hood; m. Carl Murray Penney, July 8, 1961 (div. 1978); children: Michael Murray, Jeffrey Hood; m. James Duane Livingston, Mar. 30, 1985. BA, Albion Coll., 1959, LLD (hon.), 1989; MA, U. Mich., 1961; PhD, SUNY, Albany, 1972. Vis. asst. prof. Union Coll., Schenectady, N.Y., 1972-73; assoc. higher edn. N.Y. State Edn. Dept., Albany, 1973-76; assoc. provost Yale U., New Haven, Conn., 1976-82; vice chancellor acad. programs, policy and planning SUNY System, Albany, 1982-88; acting pres. SUNY, Plattsburgh, 1986-87; chancellor U. Mass., Boston, 1988—; chmn. bd. dirs. Nat. Higher Edn. Mgmt. Sys., Boulder, Colo., 1985-87; mem. commn. on higher edn. New Eng. Assn. Schs. and Colls., Boston, 1979-82, Mid. States Assn. Schs. and Colls., Phila., 1986-88; mem. commn. on women Am. Coun. Edn., Wash-ington, 1979-81, commn. on govt. rels., 1990—; bd. dirs. Boston Edison Co., Am. Coun. on Edn., Carnegie Found. for Advancement of Teaching, 1994—. Author: Patrician in Politics, 1974; editor: Women in Management in Higher Education, 1975; cons. editor Change mag. and Jour. Higher Edn. Mgmt.; contbr. articles to profl. jours. Trustee Berkeley Div. Sch., Yale U., 1978-82, John F. Kennedy Libr. Found.; bd. dirs. Albany Symphony Orch., 1982-88, U. Mass. Found., 1988—, Mcpl. Rsch. Bur., Boston, 1990—, New England Coun., New England Aquarium, Boston Plan for Excellence, Boston Pvt. Industry Coun., 1994—, Greater Boston One to One Leadership Coun., The Environ. Bus. Coun., Greater Boston C. of C. (pres. execs. club 1993-94), John F Kennedy Library Found.; chair Boston Higher Edn. Partnership; mem. exec. com. Challenge to Leadership; corp. mem. United Way, 1990—, Hers Mid Adlantic Adv. Bd., NASULGC Commn. Urban Affairs, The Ednl. Resource Inst., 1994. Recipient Disting. Alumna award Albion Coll., 1978. Mem. Am. Coun. Edn. (bd. dirs.), Am. Assn. Higher Edn., Orgn. Am. Historians, Internat. Assn. Univ. Pres., Nat. Assn. State Univs. and Land Grant Colls., Greater Boston C. of C. (bd. dirs.), Yale Club (N.Y.C.) St. Botolph Club, Boston (Boston). Unitarian. Office: U of Mass 18 Tremont St Ste 800 Boston MA 02108

PENNIMAN, CLARA, political scientist, educator; b. Steger, Ill., Apr. 5, 1914; d. Rae Ernest and Alethea (Bates) P. B.A., U. Wis., 1950, M.A., 1951; Ph.D., U. Minn., 1954. Legal sec., 1934-37; administrv. asst. Wis. Employment Service, 1937-47; mem. faculty U. Wis., 1953—, prof. polit. sci., 1961-84, prof. emeritus, 1984—, chmn. dept., 1963-66; dir. Center for Pub. Policy and Administrn., 1968-74, Oscar Rennebohm prof. pub. administrn., 1974-84; Assoc. Brookings Instn., 1972-76; examiner-cons., mem. higher edn. commn. N. Central Assn. Colls.; vis. lectr. Johns Hopkins, summer 1958. Author: State Income Taxation, 1980; co-author: The Minnesota Department of Taxation, 1955, State Income Tax Administration, 1959, Government in the Fifty States, 1960; Contbr. to: Politics in the American States, 1965, 71, 76. Pres. League Women Voters, Madison, 1956-58; mem. Gov. Wis. Tax Impact Study Commn., 1959, Gov.'s Higher Edn. Merger Com., 1971-73; Mayor Madison Met. Com., 1957-58, Madison Redistricting Com., 1960-63; mem. adv. com. govts. div. Bur. Census, 1962-65, mem. state compensation study com., 1983. Recipient Outstanding Achievement award U. Minn., Disting. Service award U. Wis.-Madison. Mem. Am. Polit. Sci. Assn. (v.p. 1971-72, past mem. nat. coun.), Midwest Polit. Sci. Assn. (pres. 1965), ASPA, AAUP (pres. state conf. 1972-73), Nat. Assn. Schs. Pub. Administrn. (coun. 1973-75), Am. Acad. Pub. Administrn., Altrusa (pres. Madison chpt. 1968-69), Phi Beta Kappa, Phi Kappa Phi. Home: 6209 Mineral Pt Rd Apt 1404 Madison WI 53705

PENNIMAN, NICHOLAS GRIFFITH, IV, newspaper publisher; b. Balt., Mar. 7, 1938; s. Nicholas Griffith Penniman III and Esther Cox Lony (Wight) Keeney; m. Linda Jane Simmons, Feb. 4, 1967; children: Rebecca Helmle, Nicholas G. V. AB, Princeton U., 1960. Asst. bus. mgr. Ill. State Jour. Register, Springfield, 1964-69, bus. mgr., 1969-75; asst. gen. mgr. St. Louis Post-Dispatch, 1975-84, gen. mgr., 1984-86, pub., 1986—. Chmn. Downtown St. Louis, Inc., 1988-90, Mo. Health and Ednl. Facilities Adminstrn., 1982-85, Ill. State Fair Bd., Springfield, 1973-75, St. Louis Sports Com., 1992-93; trustee St. Louis Country Day Sch., 1983-86; bd. dirs. St. Louis Arts and Edn. Coun., 1987—, St. Louis area Boy Scouts Am., 1987—, Regional Commerce Assn., 1995—; v.p. Fair Found., Gateway Arch Park Extension; pres. Forest Park Forever, 1991-93; chmn. Caring Found. for Children, 1988-91. With U.S. Army, 1962-67. Clubs: St. Louis Country, Noonday (pres. 1994). Avocation: tennis. Home: 1240 Lay Rd Saint Louis MO 63124-1872 Office: Pulitzer Pub Co 900 N Tucker Blvd Saint Louis MO 63101-1069

PENNIMAN, RICHARD WAYNE See LITTLE RICHARD

PENNIMAN, W. DAVID, information scientist, management consultant; b. St. Louis, Dec. 19, 1937; s. William Leon and Laura Mae (Van Winkle) P.; m. Charlotte Ann Meder, Mar. 17, 1973; children: Kara, Rachel, John; 1 child by previous marriage, Jessica. BS in ME, U. Ill., 1960, MS in Journalism, Communications, 1962; PhD in Communication Theory, Ohio State U., 1975. Registered profl. engr., Ohio. Assoc. dir. engring. publs. U. Ill. Coll. Engring., Urbana, 1965-66; research scientist info. systems Battelle Columbus Labs., Columbus, Ohio, 1966-69, assoc. mgr. info. systems, 1969-77; research scholar Internat. Inst. Applied Systems Analysis, Laxenburg, Austria, 1977; mgr. research Online Computer Library Ctr., Dublin, Ohio, 1978-79, dir. software devel., 1979-82, v.p. planning and research, 1982-84; dir. libraries and info. systems AT&T Bell Labs., Murray Hill, N.J., 1984-90, dir. info. svcs. group, 1990-91; pres. Coun. on Libr. Resources, Inc., Wash-ington, 1991-95; bd. dirs., chmn. Engring. Info. Inc., N.Y.C., 1983-91; governing com. Forest Press Inc., Albany, N.Y., 1985-88; adv. com. info. sci. Rutgers U., 1982-91. Author numerous book chpts. and articles in profl. jours. Advisor United Way, Columbus, 1981-83. Served with U.S. Army, 1963-65. Named Tech. Person of the Yr. Columbus Tech. Council, 1982, U.S. Del. to Internat. Inst. for Applied Systems Analysis, 1977. Fellow AAAS; mem. IEEE (sr.), ALA, Am. Soc. Info. Sci. (pres. 1988-89), Assn. for Computing Machinery. Avocations: antique automobiles, hiking. Home and Office: 13840 Dufief Mill Rd Gaithersburg MD 20878-3845

PENNINGER, FRIEDA ELAINE, retired English language educator; b. Marion, N.C., Apr. 11, 1927; d. Fred Hoyle and Lena Frances (Young) P. AB, U. N.C., Greensboro, 1948; MA, Duke U., 1950, PhD, 1961. Copywriter Sta. WSJS, Winston-Salem, N.C., 1948-49; asst. prof. English Flora Macdonald Coll., Red Springs, N.C., 1950-51; tchr. English Barnwell, S.C., 1951-52, Brunswick, Ga., 1952-53; instr. English U. Tenn., Knoxville, 1953-56; instr., asst. prof. Woman's Coll. U. N.C. Greensboro, 1956-58, 60-63; asst. prof., assoc. prof. U. Richmond (Va.), 1963-71; chair., dept. English Westhampton Coll., Richmond, 1971-78; prof. English U. Richmond, 1971-91, Bostwick prof. English, 1987-91; ret., 1991. Author: William Caxton, 1979, Chaucer's "Troilus and Criseyde" and "The Knight's Tale": Fictions Used, 1993, (novel) Look at Them, 1990; compiler, editor: English Drama to 1660, 1976; editor: Festschrift for Prof. Marguerite Roberts, 1976. Fellow Southeastern Inst. of Mediaeval and Renaissance Studies, 1965, 67, 69. Democrat. Presbyterian. Home: 2701 Camden Rd Greensboro NC 27403-1438

PENNINGTON, BEVERLY MELCHER, financial services company exe-cutive; b. Vermillion, SD, Feb. 8, 1931; d. Cecil Lloyd and Phyllis Cecelia (Walz) M.; m. Glen D., Sept. 1, 1965 (dec. Aug. 1986); 1 child, Terri Lynn. BS, U. S.D., Vermillion, 1952. Enrolled agt. cert. IRS 1989. Sec.

budget dept. Bur. of Indian Affairs, Aberdeen, S.D., 1952-53, pvt. sec., 1953-54; pvt. sec. U.S. P.H.S. Indian Health, Aberdeen, 1954-55; administr. asst. U.S. Pub. Health Svc., Anchorage, 1955-58, U.S. Pub. Health, Dental Pub. Health, Washington, 1958-61; grant adminstr. Dental Pub. Health, Wash-ington, 1961-65; co-owner Penn Mel Marina, Platte, S.D. 1965-74; co-owner Pennington Tax Service, Platte, 1974-86, owner, 1986-93; pres., CEO, White Tiger Fin. Svc., Inc., Platte, 1994—. Contbr. articles to profl. jours. Mem. Platte Women's Club, sec., 1965-68, pres., 1968-70, 89-91; mem. Libr. Bd., sec., 1982-85. Fellow Am. Soc. Tax Profls. (sec. 1989-91, 2d v.p. 1995); mem. NAFE, Platte C. of C. (v.p. 1989, pres. 1990), Lyric Theatre Mus. Soc. (pres. 1988-92), U.S. C. of C., Washington Dakota Cen. Com. Republican. Presbyterian. Avocations: collecting jewelry, reading, dress designing, gourmet cooking. Office: White Tiger Fin Svc Inc 420 Main Platte SD 57369

PENNINGTON, CATHERINE ANN, legal technology consultant; b. Washington, Jan. 4, 1950; d. William Carter and Marcia Moss (Lewis) P. BS, U. Md., 1975; MS, Am. U., 1977; MLS, Brigham Young U., 1980, JD, 1980. Bar: Tex. 1981. Acquisitions asst. Am. U., Washington, 1976-77; libr. asst. Brigham Young U., Provo, Utah, 1977-80; sr. reference libr. So. Meth. U., Dallas, 1980-81; law libr. Johnson & Swanson, Dallas, 1981-85; cons., sr. libr. N.Y. Pub. Libr., N.Y.C., 1985-86; assoc. law libr. St. John's U., Jamaica, N.Y., 1986-89, asst. prof. div. libr. and info. sci., 1987-89, adj. prof. law, 1988-89; dir. libr. svcs. Chadbourne & Parke, N.Y.C., 1989-94; prin. Pennington Consulting, 1994—. Author: Microcomputer Software Selection for Law Libraries, 1987-93, (with others) videotape Organizing a Small Law Firm Library, 1985, Planning the Small Law Office Library, 1994, Microsoft Word for Windows in One Hour for Lawyers, 1995. Dem. precinct chair Dallas County, Tex., 1983-85; sec. St. George Civic Club, S.I., N.Y., 1988-90, v.p., 1990-92. Fellow ABA (chair libr. com. 1987-90, chair rsch. skills 1990-92, law practice mgmt. sect. 1992, editor-in-chief network 21 1992-94, coun. 1994—); mem. Am. Assn. Law Librs. (chair pvt. law libr. sect. 1985-86, Bender grantee 1981). Mormon. Avocations: quilting, swimming, skiing. Office: 17 Carroll Pl Staten Island NY 10301-1503

PENNINGTON, DONALD HARRIS, physician; b. Clarksville, Ark., Sept. 13, 1945; s. John Powers and Verna Olive (Harris) P.; m. Susan Myree Snyder, Aug. 27, 1966 (div. Aug. 1982); children: Thomas Walter, Aimee Myree, John Herrick. BA, U. of the Ozarks, 1968; MD, U. Ark., 1972; wine diploma, Calif. Dept. Agr., 1973. Intern St. Vincent Infirmary, Little Rock, 1973; physician, founding ptnr. Clarksville Med. Group, P.A., 1972-93; physician Mercy Med. Svcs., Inc., Ft. Smith, Ark., 1993—; cons. family planning svcs. Ark. State Bd. of Health, 1973-93. Founding mem., musician Ft. Douglas (Ark.) Backporch Bluegrass Symphony, 1976-91; acoustic double bassist River Valley Jazz Union, Russellville, Ark., 1991—. Bd. dirs. Johnson County Regional Hosp., Clarksville, 1973-82; asst. ch. organist 1st United Meth. Ch., Clarksville, 1968—; full-time ch. organist 1st Presbyn. Ch., Clarksville, 1994—; active ACLU, Planned Parenthood Fedn., The League to Make a Difference, Nat. Abortion Rights League. With Ark. NG, 1963-69. Mem. AMA, Assn. Am. Physicians for Human Rights, Nat. Trust for Historic Preservation, Ark. Med. Soc. (county del. 1972—), Ark. Acad. Family Practice, Am. Guild Organists. Democrat. Avocations: restoration of historic homes, antiques, family history, music, historical preservation. Home: 317 N Johnson St Clarksville AR 72830-2931

PENNINGTON, MARY ANNE, art museum director, museum manage-ment consultant, art educator; b. Franklin, Va., Apr. 12, 1943; d. James Clifton and Martha Julia (Futrell) P.; m. Walter Joseph Shackelford, Nov. 26, 1981. Student East Carolina U., 1962; BFA, Va. Commonwealth U., 1965, MFA, 1966; postgrad. Cameron U., 1970, East Carolina U., 1972, U. N.C., Chapel Hill, 1980. Instr. art Presbyn. Coll., Clinton, S.C., 1966-69; tchr. art in Pitt County, 1970-71, Greenville City (N.C.) Sch. Systems, 1971-73; instr. art Pitt Community Coll., 1972-73; coordinator visual arts and humanities program, Ludwigsberg, Fed. Republic Germany, 1974-76; vis. artist-in-residence Salt Pond Art Ctr., Blacksburg, Va., summer, 1978; asst. prof. art Pembroke State U., N.C., 1976-80; exec. dir. Greenville Mus. Art, 1980-87, The Lauren Rogers Mus. of Art, Laurel, 1987-93, Huntington (W.Va.) Mus. Art, 1994—; guest curator Slidell (La.) Arts Ctr., 1993, Artemis. Roanoke, Va., 1993; judge art competition, 1980—; speaker N.C. Dept. Corrections, 1980-87; guest lectr. art Converse Coll., Spartanburg, S.C., 1966, U. So. Miss., 1993; coord. cultural arts program Jones County Leadership Inst., 1989-90, participant, 1990-91, chair curriculum com., 1991-92, chair bd. dirs.; field reviewer Inst. Mus. Svcs., 1986-92; mem. project support grants panel Miss. Arts Commn., 1990-93; mem. Jones County Competitive Community Program Team, chair adv. task force, 1991-92; adj. prof. visual art U. So. Miss. and Jones County Jr. Coll., 1993-94. Author: Application of Industrial Sand Casting to Sculpture, 1966, Handbook to the Collection of the Lauren Rogers Mus. Art, 1989, Museum in The Schools Education Program, 1989, moderator Long Range Plan Panel, 1992, Ms. Conf. on the Arts; art columnist Laurel Leader Call, 1990-93, The Herald Dispatch, 1994; also articles. Bd. dirs. Pitt-Greenville Arts Council; program coordinator Pitt-Greenville Leadership Inst., 1982-87; bd. dirs., v.p. Parents As Resource Tchrs., 1990-91; advisory bd. chmn. Marshall Artists Series Edn. Com., 1994—; bd. dirs. Huntington C. of C., 1994—. Recipient Vol. award N.C. Gov., 1981; 2 N.C. Arts Council scholarship awards, 1980, 87, N.C. Disting. Women award, 1986. Mem. Am. Assn. Mus. (accreditation surveyor 1990—, mus. assessment program reviewer 1990—, mus. assessment program surveyor 1991—), Southeastern Mus. Conf., Inc. (steering com. 1990-91), N.C. Mus. Council (bd. dirs. 1986-87), Miss. Mus. Assn. (bd. dirs. 1990-94, v.p. 1992-94), Miss. Inst. Arts and Letters (bd. govs. 1990-94, v.p. 1992-93, pres. 1993-94, chair Visual Arts Award, 1991, 92), Jones County C. of C. (adv. bd. dirs. 1990-93).

PENNINGTON, RICHARD MAIER, management consultant, retired in-surance company executive, lawyer; b. Phila., Aug. 2, 1926; s. Richard and Mildred (Locke) P.; m. Apr. 20, 1963; children—Elizabeth Ann, Catherine Carter. BA, Haverford Coll., 1950; LL.B., Temple U., 1961. Bar: Pa. 1963. Claims work with INA, Phila., 1953-57, 1957-76, East v.p., 1976-77; v.p. Atlantic Mut. Ins. Co., N.Y.C., 1977-78; sr. v.p., 1979-92; mem. exec. com. Ins. Com. for Arson Control, Chgo., 1982-91. Served with U.S. Army, 1945-46. Mem. ABA.

PENNINGTON, WILLIAM MARK, sportswriter; b. Hartford, Conn. Dec. 12, 1956; s. Albert William and Lillian Anne (Lewis) P.; m. Joyce Hand, July 14, 1990; children: Anne D'Amour, Elise Holly. BS, Boston U., 1978. Re-porter The Bristol Press, Bristol, Conn., 1976-77, The Associated Press, Boston, 1977, The Providence Jour.-Bull., Providence, 1977-79, The Stamford Advocate, Stamford, Conn., 1979-84; reporter The Record, Hack-ensack, N.J., 1984-89, columnist, sr. writer, 1989—. Author: The Winning Spirit, 1991; contbg. author: (book) Best Sports Stories, 1983, 85, 87, 94. Recipient Best Story award Associated Press Sports Editors, 1985, 89, 91, 93, Best Columnist award, 1983, 89. Mem. Baseball Writers Assn. of Am., Boston U. Football Alumni Assn., New England Hist. Genealogical Soc. Roman Catholic. Office: The Record 150 River St Hackensack NJ 07601-7110

PENNISTEN, JOHN WILLIAM, computer scientist, linguist, actuary; b. Buffalo, Jan. 25, 1939; s. George William and Lucy Josephine (Gates) P. AB in Math. and Chemistry with honors, Hamilton Coll., 1960; postgrad., Harvard U., 1960-61, U.S Army Lang. Sch., 1962-63; MS in Computer Sci. with honors, N.Y. Inst. Tech., 1987; cert. in taxation, NYU, 1982; cert. in profl. banking, Am. Inst. of Banking of Am. Bankers Assn., 1982; cert. Asian Langs., NYU, 1992. Actuarial asst. New Eng. Mut. Life Ins. Co., Boston, 1965-66; asst. actuary Mass. Gen. Life Ins. Co., Boston, 1966-68; actuarial assoc. John Hancock Mut. Life Ins. Co., Boston, 1968-71; asst. actuary George B. Buck Cons. Actuaries, Inc., N.Y.C., 1971-75, Martin E. Segal Co., N.Y.C., 1975-80; actuary Laiken Siegel & Co., N.Y.C., 1980; cons. Bklyn., 1981—; timesharing and database analyst banklink corp. cash mgmt. div. Chem. Bank N.Y.C., 1983-85; programmer analyst Empire Blue Cross and Blue Shield, N.Y.C., 1986-88, Mt. Sinai Med. Ctr., N.Y.C., 1988-89, French Am. Banking Corp. (subs. Banque National de Paris), N.Y.C., 1989; sr. programmer analyst Dean Witter Reynolds, Inc., N.Y.C., 1989-92; com-puter specialist for software N.Y.C. Dept. Fin., 1992—; enrolled actuary U.S. Fed. Pension Legis. Bklyn., 1976—. Contbr. articles to profl. jours. With U.S. Army, 1961-64. Mem. AAAS, MLA, Soc. Actuaries (fellow), Prac-tising Law Inst., Assn. Computing Machinery, IEEE Computer Soc., Am. Assn. Artificial Intelligence, Linguistic Soc. Am., Assn. Computational

Linguistics, Am. Math. Soc., Math. Assn. Am., Nat. Model R.R. Assn. (life), Nat. Ry. Hist. Soc., Ry. and Locomotive Hist. Soc. (life), Bklyn. Heights Assn., Met. Opera Guild, Am. Friends of Covent Garden, Harvard Gra. Soc., Am. Legion, Phi Beta Kappa, others. Home: 135 Willow St Brooklyn NY 11201-2255

PENNOCK, DONALD WILLIAM, mechanical engineer; b. Ludlow, Ky., Aug. 8, 1915; s. Donald and Melvin (Evans) P.; B.S. in M.E. U., Ky., 1940, M.E., 1948; m. Vivian C. Kern, Aug. 11, 1951; 1 son, Douglas. Stationary engring., constrn. and maintenance Schenley Corp., 1935-39; mech. equipment design engr. mech. lab. U. of Ky., 1939; exptl. test engr. Wright Aero. Corp., Paterson, N.J., 1940, 1941, investigative and adv. engr. to personnel div., 1941-43; indsl. engr. Eastern Aircraft, div. Gen. Motors, Linden, N.J., 1943-45; factory engr. Carrier Corp., Syracuse, N.Y., 1945-58, sr. facilities engr., 1958-60, corporate material handling engr., 1960-63, mgr. facilities engring. dept., 1963-66, mgr. archtl. engring., 1966-68, mgr. facilities engring. dept., 1968-78. Staff, Indsl. Mgmt. Center, 1962, midwest work course U. Kan., 1959-67. Mem. munitions bd. SHIAC, 1950-52; trustee Primitive Hall Found., 1985—. Elected to Exec. and Profl. Hall of Fame, 1966. Registered profl. engr., Ky., N.J. Fellow Soc. Advancement Mgmt. (life mem., nat. v.p. material handling div. 1953-54); mem. ASME, NSPE, Am. Material Handling Soc. (dir. 1950-57, chmn. bd., pres. 1950-52), Am. Soc. Mil. Engrs., Am. Mgmt. Assn. (men. packaging council 1950-55, life mem. planning council), Nat. Material Handling Conf. (exec. com. 1951), Found. N.Am. Wild Sheep (life), Internat. Platform Assn., Tau Beta Pi. Protestant. Mng. editor Materials Handling Engring. (mag. sect.), 1949-50; mem. editorial adv. bd. Modern Materials Handling (mag.), 1949-52. Contbr. articles to tech. jours. Contbg., cons. editor: Materials Handling Handbook, 1958. Home: 24 Pebble Hill Rd Syracuse NY 13214

PENNOYER, PAUL GEDDES, JR., lawyer; b. N.Y.C., Feb. 11, 1920; s. Paul G. and Frances (Morgan) P.; m. Cecily Henderson, Feb. 5, 1949; children—Jennifer, Deidre, Paul T., Sheldon K., William M. B.S., Harvard U., 1942, LL.B., 1948. Bar: N.Y. 1949, U.S. Dist. Ct. (so. and ea. dists.) N.Y. 1952, U.S. Supreme Ct. 1972, U.S. Ct. Appeals (2d cir.) 1964, U.S. Ct. Appeals (4th cir.) 1986, U.S. Ct. Appeals (11th cir.) 1987. Assoc. Bingham Englar Jones & Houston, N.Y.C., 1949-55, ptnr., 1955-63; ptnr. Chadbourne & Parke, N.Y.C., 1963-89; of counsel, 1989—. Vice pres., trustee Frick Collection, 1975—; trustee L.I. U., 1975-85. Served to lt. USN, 1942-45. Decorated Navy Cross, Air Medal (2). Mem. ABA, N.Y. State Bar Assn., Assn. Bar City N.Y., N.Y. Bar found., Am. Coll. Trial Lawyers, N.Y. Yacht Club. Republican. Episcopalian. Office: Chadbourne & Parke 30 Rockefeller Plz New York NY 10112-0001

PENNOYER, ROBERT M., lawyer; b. N.Y.C., Apr. 9, 1925. B.A., Harvard U., 1946; LL.B., Columbia U., 1950. Bar: N.Y. 1951, U.S. Supreme Ct. 1971. Partner firm Patterson, Belknap, Webb & Tyler, N.Y.C., 1962—; asst. U.S. atty. criminal div. So. Dist., N.Y., 1953-55; asst. to gen. counsel Office of Sec. of Def., Dept. Def., Washington, 1955-57; spl. asst. to asst. sec. of def. for internat. security affairs Office of Sec. of Def., Dept. Def., 1957-58. Trustee Carnegie Instn. Washington, 1968-89, John Merck Fund, 1982—; Mrs. Giles Whiting Found., 1970—, Met. Mus. Art, 1966, Pierpont Morgan Libr., 1969—, Columbia U., 1982-88, Boyce Thompson Inst. for Plant Rsch., Cornell U., 1974—. Lt. (j.g.) USNR, 1944-46. Mem. ABA, N.Y. State Bar Assn., Assn. Bar City N.Y., Century Assn. Office: Patterson Belknap et al 1133 Ave of the Americas New York NY 10036

PENNY, CHARLES RICHARD, retired advertising executive; b. Abilene, Tex., Dec. 22, 1934; s. Alvis Burnett and Cleo (Ward) P.; m. Linda Louise Felton, Aug. 25, 1956; children: Diane Marie, Roxanne Lynne, Marianne Felton. BBA in Mktg.-Advt., Baylor U., 1956; grad. mktg. mgmt. and advt. seminar, Harvard, 1970; fundamentals of fin., Wharton Sch., U. Pa., 1976. Prodn. mgr. McCann-Erickson Advt. Agy., Dallas, 1956-58; account exec. McCann-Erickson Advt. Agy., Houston, 1959-60; account exec., v.p., stockholder Ritchie Advt. Agy., Houston, 1961-66; account exec., v.p. Weekley & Valenti Advt. Agy., Houston, 1967-70; exec. v.p., dir., stockholder Weekley, Elliott & Penny Advt. Agy., Houston, 1971-72; pres., dir., stockholder Weekley & Penny Advt. Agy., Houston, 1973-84; chmn., chief exec. officer Penny & Speier Inc., Houston, 1984-93, retired, 1993. Mem. Houston Advt. Club (dir. 1965), Deerwood Club, Greenspoint Club., Bay Oaks Club. Home: 12503 Mossycup Dr Houston TX 77024-4936

PENNY, LAURA JEAN, librarian; b. Union City, Tenn., June 25, 1956; d. Glen Jones and Harriet Smith (Gould) P. BS in Econs., Lambuth Coll., 1978; MLS, U. Ariz., 1980. Asst. librarian local history and genealogy Pikes Peak Library Dist., Colorado Springs, 1981-84; info. officer Inmos Corp., Colorado Springs, 1984-86; dir. library Colo. State Hosp., Pueblo, 1987—. Author: A Tempstuous Voyage, 1987, Abstracts of Crawford County, 1987, Abstracts of Washington County, 1988. Pres. El Paso County Democratic Women's Club, Colorado Springs, 1986-87; chmn. El Paso County Democratic Com., 1987—. Mem. Colo. Council Library Devel., Pikes Peak Genealogical Soc. (editor 1985-87). Methodist. Avocations: politics, genealogy, writing, skiing. Home: 7340 Woody Creek Dr #101 Colorado Springs CO 80911 Office: Colo State Hosp 1600 W 24th St Pueblo CO 81003-1499

PENNY, ROGER PRATT, management executive; b. Buffalo, July 13, 1936; s. George Albert and Louise (Mings) P.; m. Judith Stevens, Aug. 25, 1957; children: David, Sarah, Julia. BA in Adminstrv. Engring., Union Coll., 1958. Registered profl. engr., N.Y., Ind., Pa. From supt. to sr. mgr. Bethlehem Steel Corp., Lackawanna, N.Y., 1958-83; gen. mgr. Bethlehem Steel Corp., Burns Harbor, Ind., 1983-87; sr. v.p. Bethlehem (Pa.) Steel Corp., 1987-92, bd. dirs., bd. dirs., pres., chief oper. officer, 1992—. Mem. United Way, Buffalo, 1960-82; chmn. campaign United Way Porter County, Valparaiso, Ind., 1986; mem. Orchard Park Town Coun., 1970-82; mem. adv. bd. Purdue U. Lafayette, Ind., 1985-86; mem. adv. bd. Bus. Sch. Valparaiso U., 1986; bd. dirs. Minsi Trails coun., v.p. exploring Boy Scouts Am., Lehigh Valley, Pa., 1988—; trustee St. Luke's Hosp. Mem. Am. Iron and Steel Inst., Assn. Iron and Steel Engrs., Valparaiso C. of C. (dir. 1985-86), Orchard Park C. of C., Buffalo C. of C., Sand Creek Club (pres. 1983-86) Buffalo Soccer Club (pres. 1960-75, sec.), Saucon Valley Country Club. Republican. Episcopalian. Office: Bethlehem Steel Corp Martin Tower 1170 Eighth Ave Bethlehem PA 18016-7699

PENNY, TIMOTHY JOSEPH, congressman; b. Albert Lea, Minn., Nov. 19, 1951; s. Jay C. and Donna (Haukoos) P.; m. Barbara J. Christianson, Oct. 18, 1975; children: Jamison, Joseph, Molly, Marcus. B.A., Winona State U., 1974; postgrad., U. Minn., 1975. Mem. Minn. Senate from Dist. 30, 1977-82, 98th-103d Congresses from 1st Minn. Dist., 1983-94; mem. agr. com., vets affairs com., chmn. fgn. agr. and hunger subcom. Mem. Minn. State Univ. Bd., 1974-77; co-chmn. Dem. budget study group Whip-At-Large. With USNR. Recipient Disting. Service award U. Minn., 1982, Spark Plug award Communicating for Agr., 1980, Nat. Comdr.'s award DAV, 1989. Mem. New Richland (Minn.) Jaycees, Waseca Pals, Inc., Waseca and Freeborn County Assn. for Retarded Citizens. Democrat. Lutheran. Office: US House of Reps 436 Cannon House Bldg Washington DC 20515

PENROD, JAMES WILFORD, choreographer, dancer; b. Provo, Utah, July 22, 1934; s. Joseph Keller and Virginia Rose (Zobell) P. BA in English, U. So. Calif., 1964; MFA in Dance, U. Calif., Irvine, 1974; CMA, Inst. Movement Studies, 1990. Mem. faculty Am. Sch. Dance, Hollywood, Calif., 1958-68, U. So. Calif., Idyllwild, 1957-59; prof. dance U. Calif., Irvine, 1966—, chmn. dept., 1981-89, 91-94; co-artistic dir. Dancer's Dance Co., Los Angeles, 1969-84, Penrod Plastino Movement Theatre, Irvine, 1968-84, choreographer, 1958—. Profl. dancer on TV, in movies and on stage; choreographer original works.; Author: Movement for the Performing Artist, 1974; co-author: Dancer Prepares, 1970. Grantee U. Calif., 1967—. Mem. SAG, AFTRA, AGVA, Nat Dance Assn., Congress Rsch. in Dance (dir. 1983-85), Orange County Performing Arts Dance Alliance (bd. dirs. 1986-89), Dance Notation Bur. (adv. bd. dirs. 1988-90), Screen Extras Guild, Actors Equity, Am. Guild Mus. Artists. Home: 4645 Green Tree Ln Irvine CA 92715-2250

PENROD, KENNETH EARL, medical education consultant; b. Blanchester, Ohio, Mar. 30, 1916; s. William F. and Josie Alma (Carman) P.;

m. Virginia Hogue, June 29, 1942; children: Caroline (dec.), Bruce Hogue. B.S., Miami (Ohio) U., 1938; Ph.D., Iowa State Coll., 1942. Asst. prof. physiology Boston U. Sch. Medicine, 1946-50; asso. prof. physiology Duke U. Sch. Medicine, 1950-57, prof., 1957-59, asst. dean, 1952-59; founding v.p. for med. affairs, prof. physiology W.Va. U., 1959-65; provost for med. ctr., prof. physiology Ind. U., Indpls., 1965-69; vice chancellor for med. and health scis. State U. System Fla., Tallahassee, 1969-74; exec. dir. community hosp. grad. med. edn. program Fla. Bd. Regents, Tallahassee, 1974-85; ex-dir. MGT of Am., Inc.; spl. cons. AID, Latin Am. Mem. editorial bd. Jour. Med. Edn, 1957-65; contbr. to sci. jours. in physiol. and health edn. Served from 2d lt. to capt. USAAF, 1942-46. Mem. Am. Physiol. Soc., Assn. for Acad. Health Centers (incorporator), Assn. Am. Med. Colls., AAAS, Rotary, Phi Beta Kappa, Sigma Xi, Phi Kappa Phi, Phi Kappa Tau, Alpha Omega Alpha. Presbyterian. Home: 913 Lasswade Dr Tallahassee FL 32312-2831

PENROD-HILL, BARBARA M., nursing administrator; d. Robert F. and Marion L. (Sutter) Penrod. BSN, Mercy Coll. of Detroit, 1970; MSN, Wayne State U., Detroit, 1977. Camp nurse Children's Hosp. of Mich., Detroit, summer 1970; staff nurse pediatrics unit Camp Sea Gull, Charlevoix, Mich., 1971-72; staff nurse children's unit Psychiat. Ctr. of Mich., St. Clair Shores, 1972-73; affiliate nurse instr., part-time nursing supr. Harper Hosp., 1973-74; head nurse children's unit, 1974-77, clin. nurse specialist children's svc., 1977-78, adminstrv. asst. to hosp. med. dir., 1978-80; dir. psychiat. nursing U. Mich. Med. Ctr., Ann Arbor, 1980-83; pres., chief exec. officer Amicare Home Health Svcs., Ann Arbor, 1988—; adminstr. nursing svcs. Catherine McAuley Health Ctr., 1987-90; v.p. patient care svcs. St. Joseph Mercy Hosp., 1990-95; v.p. clin. integration Mission Health Sys., 1995—; pvt. practice nurse therapist Botsford Gen. Hosp., 1977-79; adj. instr. U. Mich. Sch. Nursing, 1981—, non-resident lectr., Sch. of Pub. Health, 1988—; adj. lectr. Sch. of Nursing, 1989—; adminstr. nursing and clin. svcs. Catherine McAuley Health Ctr., 1985-87. Contbr. articles to profl. jours. Mem. ANA, Mich. Nurse's Assn., Mich. Assn. for Emotionally Disturbed Children, Mental Health Assn. in Mich., Am. Orgn. Nurse Execs., Mich. Orgn. Nurse Execs., Greater Detroit Area Orgn. Nurse Execs. (bd. dirs., chair issues com.), Sigma Theta Tau.

PENROSE, CHARLES, JR., association executive; b. Phila., Oct. 9, 1921; s. Charles and Beatrice (d,Este) P.; m. Ann Lucille Cantwell, Apr. 17, 1943; children: James, Thomas, John. Grad., Episcopal Acad., Overbrook, Pa., 1940. Exec. sec. Newcomen Soc. N.Am (N.A.), Phila., 1946-48; dist. sales mgr. Phila., for; Fitchburg Paper Co., Mass., 1948-50, 52-53; sales mgr. A.M. Collins Mfg. Co., Phila., 1953-54; v.p. sales A.M. Collins Mfg. Co., 1954-55; sales mgr. A.M. Collins div. Internat. Paper Co., N.Y.C., 1955; asst. to sales mgr. fine paper and bleached bd. div., 1956-57; sr. v.p., chief exec. officer Newcomen Soc. in N.Am., Downingtown, Pa., 1957-61; also dir. Newcomen Soc. in N.Am.; pres., CEO Newcomen Soc. U.S., 1961-87, chmn., 1987-89, chmn. emeritus, 1989—; sr. v.p. N. Am. Newcomen Soc., London, 1957-89, hon. v.p., 1989—; pres., CEO Newcomen publs. in N. Am., Inc., 1958-61, trustee, 1948-61; pres., dir. Rocaton, Inc., Darien, Conn., 1960-61. Author: They Live on a Rock in the Sea The Isles of Shoals in Colonial Days, 1957. Sec., asst. treas. Chester County Investment Fund Assn., Phila., 1959-64; v.p. Brit. Am. Ednl. Found., Inc., N.Y.C., 1968-70, pres., 1970-75, trustee, 1968-81. Served to capt. USAAF, 1940-46, S.W. Pacific; served to capt. AUS, 1950-52, Germany. Mem. Most Venerable Order Hospice of St. John of Jerusalem (London). Mem. Newcomen Soc. U.S., Newcomen Soc. London, Royal Soc. Arts (Benjamin Franklin fellow 1980), Pilgrims of U.S., First Troop Phila. City Calvary (hon.), Nat. Inst. Social Scis., Soc. Am. Historians, Marine Hist. Assn., N.H. Hist. Soc., Mt. Washington Obs., Sandwich (N.H.) Hist. Soc. (trustee 1992-94, v.p. 1994—), Chi Psi Omicron. Republican. Episcopalian. Clubs: Tokeneke (Darien.) Tamworth Outing (N.H.); Wonalancet Outdoors (N.H.). Home: Briar Farm North Sandwich NH 03259 Office: 412 Newcomen Rd Exton PA 19341-1999

PENRY, JAMES KIFFIN, physician, neurology educator; b. Denton, N.C., Aug. 21, 1929; s. Robert Lee and Addie Cordelia (Leonard) P.; m. Sarah Doub, Mar. 20, 1955; children: Martin D., Denny K., Edith C. BS magna cum laude, Wake Forest U., 1951, MD, 1955. Diplomate Am. Bd. Psychiatry and Neurology. Commd. 2d lt. USAF, 1955, advanced through grades to maj., 1964; rotating intern Pa. Hosp., Phila., 1955-56; asst. resident in internal medicine and neurology N.C. Bapt. Hosp., Winston-Salem, 1956-58; asst. in neurology Bowman Gray Sch. Medicine, Wake Forest U., 1957-58; asst. resident, then resident in neurology Boston City Hosp., 1958-60; fellow in neurology Harvard Med. Sch., Cambridge, Mass., 1959-60; neurologist, chief neurology svc. USAF Hosp., Maxwell AFB, Ala., 1960-62; chief neurology svc. USAF Hosp., Tachikawa, Japan, 1962-65, Andrews AFB, Md., 1965-66; resigned, 1966; dir. USPHS, Bethesda, Md., 1966-79; dir. Neurol. Disorders Program, chief epilepsy br. Nat. Inst. Neurol. and Communicative Disorders and Stroke, NIH, 1975-79; prof. neurology, assoc. dean for rsch. devel. Bowman Gray Sch. Medicine, Wake Forest U., 1979-89, prof. neurology, sr. assoc. dean for rsch. devel., 1989-93; pres., prof. neurology Epilepsy Inst. N.C., 1993—; hon. prof. U. Santo Domingo, Dominican Republic, 1987; dir. Comprehensive Epilepsy Ctr., N.C. Bapt. Hosp., Winston-Salem, 1989-93; cons. FDA, 1975-80, Nat. Inst. Neurol. and Communicative Disorders and Stroke, 1979-90, Burroughs Wellcome Co., 1979-90; lectr. in field. Author 30 books and monographs; co-author: (with J.R. Lacy) Infantile Spasms, 1976; (with M.E. Newmark) Photosensitivity and Epilepsy: A Review, 1979, Genetics of Epilepsy: A Review, 1980; editor: Epilepsy: The Eighth International Symposium, 1977; co-editor: (with others) Antiepileptic Drugs, 1972, 3d edit., 1989, Experimental Models of Epilepsy, 1972, Antiepileptic Drugs: Quantitative Analysis and Interpretation, 1978, Advances in Epileptology: (Xth-XIIth) Epilepsy International Symposium, 1980-82, Genetic Basis of the Epilepsies, 1982, Antiepileptic Drug Therapy in Pediatrics, 1983, Idiosyncratic Reactions to Valproate: Clinical Risk Patterns and Mechanism of Toxicity, 1992; editor Merritt-Putnam epilepsy clin. series, 1982-83; mem. editorial bd. Forefronts of Neurology, 1979—, Metabolic Brain Disease, 1986-90; mem. internat. adv. bd. Advances in Neurology; contbr. numerous articles to profl. jours., book chpts. Decorated Meritorious Svc. medal; recipient Disting. Alumnus award Bowman Gray Sch. Medicine, 1975, 80, 90. Fellow Am. Acad. Neurology; mem. AMA, Am. Neurol. Assn., Am. Epilepsy Soc. (membership com. 1970-71, chmn. constn. com. 1971-72, coun. 1971-73, program com. 1973, nat. pres. 1974, mem. long range planning com. 1978-79, William G. Lennox award 1980, Category I Clin. Rsch. award 1993), Am. Neurol. Assn., Assn. for Rsch. in Nervous and Mental Disease, Am. Electroencephalographic Soc., Ea. Assn. Electroencephalographers, Epilepsy Found. Am. (hon. life, Disting. Svc. award 1975, 25 Yrs. Svc. award 1993, Pearce Bailey award 1979, bd. dirs. 1989—), Phi Beta Kappa, Alpha Omega Alpha. Office: Epilepsy Institute of NC Box 24458 Winston Salem NC 27114

PENSE, ALAN WIGGINS, metallurgical engineer, academic administrator; b. Sharon, Conn., Feb. 3, 1934; s. Arthur Wilton and May Beatrice (Wiggins) P.; m. Muriel Drews Taylor, June 28, 1958; children—Daniel Alan, Steven Taylor, Christine Muriel. B.Metall. Engring., Cornell U., 1957; M.S., Lehigh U., 1959, Ph.D., 1962. Research asst. Lehigh U., Bethlehem, Pa., 1957-59, instr., 1960-62, asst. prof., 1962-65, asso. prof., 1965-71, prof., 1971—, chmn. dept. metallurgy and materials engring., 1977-83, assoc. dean Coll. Engring. and Applied Scis., 1983-84, 1988-90, v.p., provost, 1990—; assoc. dir. Ctr. Advanced Tech. for Large Structural Systems NSF, 1986-89; cons. adv. com. on reactor safeguards NRC, 1965-86. Author: (with R.M. Brick and R.B. Gordon) Structure and Properties of Engineering Materials, 4th edit, 1978; also articles. Recipient Robinson award Lehigh U., 1965, Stabler award, 1972; Danforth fellow, 1974-86. Fellow Am. Soc. Metals, Am. Welding Soc. (William Spraragan award 1963, Adams membership award 1966, Jennings award 1970, Adams lectr. 1980, William Hobart medal 1982, hon. mem. 1986, fellow 1992, Plummer lectr. 1995); mem. ASTM, Am. Soc. Engring. Edn. (Western Elec. award 1968), Internat. Inst. Welding, Nat. Acad. Engring. Republican. Evang. Congregationalist (pres. bd. trustees Evang. Sch. Theology). Home: 2227 West Blvd Bethlehem PA 18017-5025 Office: 27 Memorial Dr W Bethlehem PA 18015-3005 Achievement of significant goals in our life must be balanced by the quality of that life itself, for what we are is as important as what we do.

PENSKAR, MARK HOWARD, lawyer; b. Detroit, Mar. 4, 1953; s. Sol Leonard and Frances (Rosenthal) P.; m. Carol Ann Steuart, Aug. 7, 1977; children: David, Rebecca. BA, U. Mich., 1974, MPP, 1975, JD, 1977. Bar: Calif. 1977, U.S. Dist. Ct. (no. dist.) Calif. 1977, (ea. and cen. dists.) Calif.

1983, (so. dist.) 1988, U.S. Ct. Appeals (9th cir.) 1987, U.S. Tax Ct. 1993. Assoc. Pillsbury, Madison and Sutro, San Francisco, 1977-84, ptnr., 1985—; panelist Superior Court early settlement program, San Francisco. Mem. Com. for Inst. Pub. Policy Studies. Mem. ABA, San Francisco Bar Assn., Commonwealth Club, Phi Gamma Delta (past pres. Bay Area grad. chpt.), Phi Alpha Delta. Avocations: camping, golf, wine collecting. Home: 29 E Altarinda Dr Orinda CA 94563-2415 Office: Pillsbury Madison & Sutro 235 Montgomery St San Francisco CA 94104-2902

PENSKE, ROGER S., manufacturing and transportation executive; b. 1937; married. Grad., Lehigh U., 1958. With Alcoa Aluminum, Pitts., 1958-63, George McKean Chevrolet, Phila., 1963-65; prin. Penske Corp., Red Bank, N.J., pres., chmn. bd.; chmn. bd., pres. Penske Transp. Inc., Detroit, Pa. Internat. Raceway, Nazareth, 1986—; CEO Detroit Diesel Corp., chmn. bd. dirs.; pres. Competition Tire West, inc., Brooklyn, Mich.; chmn. bd. dirs. Penske Truck Leasing Corp., Penske Speedway, Inc., Detroit, Penske Automotive Group, Detroit, Outer Drive Holidays, Inc., Detroit, D Longo, Inc., El Monte, Calif.; sec. Ilmore Engring., Inc., Redford, Mich. Office: Detroit Diesel Corp 13400 W Outer Dr Detroit MI 48239 also: Penske Truck Leasing Corp RR 10 Reading PA 19606

PENSON, EDWARD MARTIN, management consulting company executive; b. N.Y.C., Aug. 30, 1927; s. Michael and Cecile (Cohan) P.; m. Georgann Ellen McCune, June 25, 1975; children: Jeffery, Albert, Cynthia. B.A. cum laude, U. Fla., 1950, Ph.D., 1955; M.A., Ohio U., 1951. Prof. communication Ohio U., Athens, 1955-75, dean, 1965-75, v.p., 1969-75; pres., prof. Salem State Coll., Mass., 1975-78; prof., chancellor U. Wis.-Oshkosh, 1978-89, chancellor emeritus, 1989—; pres. Penson-Strawbridge, Inc., mgmt. cons., 1989—; cons. Royal McBee, Litton Industries, Ohio Credit Union, Battelle Meml. Inst., 1963-66, U. Nev., 1980-81, Paine Art Ctr., 1985, Acad. Ednl. Devel., King Fiesal U., 1986, OshKosh B'Gosh, Inc., 1987, Akron U., 1988, Baker Paper Co., 1990; bd. dirs. Valley Bank, Wis. Contbr. numerous articles to profl. jours., chpts. to books. Bd. dirs. Retarded Citizens, Salem, Mass., 1975-78; bd. dirs. Econ. Devel. Council, North Shore, Mass., 1976-78, Ohio student loan commr., Columbus, 1971-75. Mem. Communication Assn. Am., Internat. Communication Assn., Am. Assn. State Colls. and Univs., Nat. Assn. Student Personnel Adminstrs., Sigma Alpha Eta, Phi Kappa Phi, Alpha Lambda Delta, Psi Chi, Rotary (Salem, Mass. and Oshkosh, Wis.). Home and Office: Lake Yvette Estates Rte 1 Box 3152 Becky Ct Havana FL 32333

PENTKOWSKI, RAYMOND J., superintendent. Supt. Addison-Rutland Supervisory Union, Fair Haven, Vt. Named state finalist Nat. Supt. of Yr. award, 1989. Office: Addison-Rutland Supr Union North Park Pl Fair Haven VT 05743

PENTZ, PAUL, hardware company executive; b. 1940. BS, Cornell U., 1969. With AmyNG, 1962-68, Gen. Foods Corp., 1962-69; v.p. Jewel Cos., 1969-78; group mdse. mgr. Servistar Corp., East Butler, Pa., 1978-79, v.p. mdse. advt., 1979-83, sr. v.p. advt. mdse., 1983-86, sr. v.p. mdse. advt. inventory control, 1986-93, CEO, 1993—. Office: Servistar Corp 1 Servicestar Way East Butler PA 16029

PENZ, ANTON JACOB, retired accounting educator; b. Cleve., Feb. 22, 1906; s. Stephen F. and Elizabeth (Prokosch) P.; (married); children—Alton Jeffry, David Alan. B.S. in Elec. Engring, Cleve. State U., 1933; M.A. in Edn, Western Res. U., 1936; M.B.A., Northwestern U., 1942; Ph.D., Ohio State U., 1947. Prof. Davis and Elkins Coll., 1937-40; lectr. Rennselaer Poly. Inst., 1944; asst. prof. La. State U., 1944-47; prof. accounting, head dept. U. Ala., 1947-71, prof. emeritus, 1971—; Distinguished vis. prof. U. Nev., Reno, spring 1972, U. Colo., Boulder, spring 1973, Va. Commonwealth U., Richmond, spring 1975, U. Md., College Park, spring 1979; cons., lectr. AID, Lima, Peru, 1965-66, Guyana, 1967. Author: Manual De Contabilidad Y Costos, 1966; Editor: Accounting Teachers Guide, 1953, Professional Developments: Accounting Teachers Guide, 1953, Accountancy, A Vocation and Profession, 1958, Guide to Accounting Instruction: Concepts and Practices, 1968, Introducing the Profession: A Guide to Accounting Instruction, 1968. Del. various congresses. Mem. Nat. Assn. Accountants (Lybrand award 1951), Fin. Execs. Inst., Am. Accounting Assn. (v.p. 1962-63), Beta Alpha Psi (pres. 1955-56, editor newsletter 1953-55). Home: Pine Valley # F-31 800 Rice Valley Rd N Tuscaloosa AL 35406-1671 Office: Box AC Tuscaloosa AL 35486

PENZER, MARK, lawyer, editor, corporate trainer, former publisher; b. Bklyn., Nov. 22, 1932; s. Ed and Fay (Weinberg) P.; m. Eileen Malen, Aug. 12, 1962; children: Matthew, Nicole; m. Nydia A. Rey, Nov. 25, 1984. B.B.A., CCNY; J.D., Fordham U. Bar: N.Y. 1968, D.C. 1973, Fla. 1982, U.S. Dist. Ct. (ea. dist.) N.Y. 1976, U.S. Dist. Ct. (so. dist.) Fla. 1991; cert. instr. DMA, 1986. Free-lance writer, 1950-83; editorial asst. Hearst mags., N.Y.C., 1955; asst. editor Hearst mags., 1956, assoc. editor, 1957-66; columnist N.Y. Jour.-Am., 1960-62; editor in chief Rudder mag., 1967-69, editorial dir., 1970-74; editor in chief True, 1970-73, editor at large, 1973-75; pub., editor in chief Jour. Energy Medicine, 1978-81; Medicare hearing officer Miami, Fla., 1981-82; pres. Success Internat., Inc., Coral Gables, Fla., 1984-85; adj. prof. bus. and tech. writing Fla. Internat. U., small bus. mgmt., U. Miami, 1986-89; pres. Heroica, Inc., Miami Lakes, Fla., 1989-90; pvt. practice Law Offices of Mark Penzer, Hialeah and Miami Lakes, Fla., 1991—; tchr. creative writing Dade County Off Campus Edn. Author: The Motorboatman's Bible, 1965, The Powerboatman's Bible, 1977; asst. editor: The Path of Least Resistance, 1989, Do It!, 1991. Served with AUS, 1953-55. Mem. Hialeah-Miami Lakes Bar Assn. (pres. 1990-92).

PENZIAS, ARNO ALLAN, astrophysicist, research scientist, information systems specialist; b. Munich, Germany, Apr. 26, 1933; came to U.S., 1940, naturalized, 1946; s. Karl and Justine (Eisenreich) P.; m. Anne Pearl Barras, Nov. 25, 1954; children: David Simon, Mindy Gail, Laurie Ruth. BS in Physics, CCNY, 1954; MA in Physics, Columbia U., 1958, PhD in Physics, 1962; Dr. honoris causa, Observatoire de Paris, 1976; ScD (hon.), Rutgers U., 1979, Wilkes Coll., 1979, CCNY, 1979, Yeshiva U., 1979, Bar Ilan U., 1983, Monmouth Coll., 1984, Technion-Israel Inst. Tech., 1986, U. Pitts., 1986, Ball State U., 1986, Kean Coll., 1986, U. Pa., 1992, Ohio State U., 1988, Iona Coll., 1988; Drew U., 1989; ScD (hon.), Lafayette Coll., 1990, Columbia U., 1990, George Washington U., 1992, Rensselaer Univ., 1992, U. Pa., 1992; Bloomfield Coll., 1994. Mem. tech. staff Bell Labs., Holmdel, N.J., 1961-72, head radiophysics rsch. dept., 1972-76; dir. radio research lab. Bell Labs., 1976-79, exec. dir. rsch., communications scis. divs., 1979-81, v.p. rsch., 1981—; now exec. dir. rsch. physics divsn.; Bloomfield Coll., 1994; bd. dirs. A.D. Little; adj. prof. earth and scis. SUNY, Stony Brook, 1974-84, Univ. Disting. lectr., 1990; lectr. dept. astrophys. scis. Princeton U., 1967-72, vis. prof., 1972-85; rsch. assoc. Harvard Coll. Obs., 1968-80; Edison lectr. U.S. Naval Rsch. Lab., 1979; Kompfner lectr. Stanford U., 1979; Gamow lectr. U. Colo., 1980; Jansky lectr. Nat. Radio Astronomy Obs., 1983; Michelson Meml. lectr., 1985; Grace Adams Tanner lectr., 1987; Klopsteg lectr. Northwestern U., 1987; grad. faculties alumni Columbia U., 1987-89; Regents' lectr. U. Calif., Berkeley, 1990; Lee Kuan Yew Disting. visitor Nat. U. Singapore, 1991; mem. astronomy adv. panel NSF, 1978-79, mem. indsl. panel on sci. and tech., 1982—, disting. lectr., 1987, affiliate Max-Planck Inst. für Radioastronomie, 1978-85, chmn. Fachbeirat, 1981-83; researcher in astrophysics, info. tech., its applications and impacts. Author: Ideas and Information Managing in a High-Tech World, 1989 (pub. in 10 langs.); mem. editorial bd. Ann. Rev. Astronomy and Astrophysics, 1974-78; mem. editorial bd. AT&T Bell Labs. Tech. Jour., 1978-84, chmn. 1981-84; assoc. editor Astrophys. Jour., 1978-82; contbr. over 100 articles to tech. jours.; several patents in field. Trustee Trenton (N.J.) State Coll., 1977-79; mem. bd. overseers U. Pa. Sch. Engring. and Applied Sci., 1983-86; mem. vis. com. Calif. Inst. Tech., 1977-79; mem. Com. Concerned Scientists, 1975—, vice chmn., 1976—; mem. adv. bd. Union of Couns. for Soviet Jews, 1983—; bd. dirs. IMNET, 1986-91, Coun. on Competitiveness, 1989-92. With U.S. Army, 1954-56. Named to NJ Lit. Hall of Fame, 1991; recipient Herschel medal Royal Astron. Soc, 1977, Nobel prize in Physics, 1978, Townsend Harris medal CCNY, 1979, Newman award, 1983, Joseph Handleman prize in the scis., 1983, Grad. Faculties Alumni award Columbia U., 1984, Achievement in Science award Big Brothers Inc., N.Y.C., 1985, Priestly award Dickinson Coll., 1989, Pender award U. Pa., 1992. Mem. NAE, NAS (Henry Draper medal 1977), AAAS, IEEE (hon.), Am. Astron. Soc., Am.

Phys. Soc. (Pake prize 1990), Internat. Astron. Union, World Acad. Arts and Sci.

PENZIEN, JOSEPH, structural engineering educator; b. Philip, S.D., Nov. 27, 1924; s. John Chris and Ella (Stebbins) P.; m. Jeanne Ellen Hunson, Apr. 29, 1950 (dec. 1985); children—Donna Marie, Karen Estelle, Robert Wayne, Charlene May; m. Mi-jung Park, June 16, 1988. Student, Coll. Idaho, 1942-43; B.S., U. Wash., 1945; S.c.D., Mass. Inst. Tech., 1950. Mem. staff Sandia Corp., 1950-51; sr. structures engr. Consol. Vultee Aircraft Corp., Fort Worth, 1951-53; asst. prof. U. Calif. at Berkeley, 1953-57, asso. prof., 1957-62, prof. structural engring., 1962-88, prof. emeritus, 1988—; dir. Earthquake Engring. Research Center, 1968-73, 77-80; cons. engring. firms; chief tech. adv. Internat. Inst. of Seismology and Earthquake Engring., Tokyo, Japan, 1964-65; chmn. bd. Ea. Internat. Engrs., Inc., 1980-90, Internat. Civil Engring. Cons., Inc., 1990—. NATO Sr. Sci. fellow., 1969. Fellow Am. Acad. Mechanics; hon. mem. ASCE (Walter Huber Research award, Alfred M. Freudenthal medal, Nathan M. Newmark medal), Earthquake Engring. Rsch. Inst. (hon., Hausner medal), IAEE (hon.); mem. Am. Concrete Inst., Structural Engrs. Assn. Calif., Seismol. Soc. Am., Nat. Acad. Engring. Home: 800 Solana Dr Lafayette CA 94549-5004 Office: Davis Hall Univ Calif Berkeley CA 94720

PENZL, HERBERT, German language and linguistics educator; b. Neufelden, Austria, Sept. 2, 1910; came to U.S., 1936, naturalized, 1944; s. Johann and Hedwig (Schmidt) P.; m. Vera Rothmüller, Aug. 21, 1950. Grad., Gymnasium Vienna, Austria, 1929; hon. fellow, Brown U., 1932-34; Ph.D., U. Vienna, 1935. Editorial asst. Linguistic Atlas of U.S., Providence, 1932-34; asst. prof. Rockford (Ill.) Coll., 1936-38, U. Ill., Urbana, 1938-50; assoc. prof. U. Mich., Ann Arbor, 1950-53; prof. German U. Mich., 1953-63; prof. Germanic philology U. Calif., Berkeley, 1963-84; Smith-Mundt prof. gen. linguistics U. Kabul, Afghanistan, 1958-59; vis. prof. Georgetown U., 1951-53, Northwestern U., 1960, 65, U. Calif., Irvine, 1966, U. Colo., Boulder, 1969, Australian Nat. U., Canberra, 1970, SUNY-Buffalo, 1971, U. Vienna, Austria, 1980-81, U. Regensburg, 1981, U. Munich, 1982-83, U. Klagenfurt, Austria, 1986, Ariz. State U., Tempe, 1988. Author: A Grammar of Pashto, 1955, A Reader of Pashto, 1962, Geschichtliche deutsche Lautlehre, 1969, Lautsystem und Lautwandel in den althochdeutschen Dialekten, 1971, Methoden der germanischen Linguistik, 1972, Vom Urgermanischen zum Neuhochdeutschen, 1975, J. Ch. Gottsched's Deutsche Sprachkunst; edition and commentary, 1978; Frühneuhochdeutsch, 1984, Althochdeutsch, 1986, Mittelhochdeutsch, 1989, Englisch: eine Sprachgeschichte nach Texten (350 bis 1992), 1994; assoc. editor American Journal of Germanic Linguistics and Literatures, 1989—; contbr. over 150 articles to profl. jours. Served with AUS, 1943-45. Guggenheim fellow, 1967; Fulbright award to Germany, 1982-83; recipient Berkeley Citation, U. Calif., 1980, Österreichisches Ehrenkreuz für Wissenschaft und Kunst I. Klasse, Govt. Austria, 1981. Mem. MLA, Linguistic Soc. Am. (exec. com. 1981-83), Am. Dialect Soc., Am. Name Soc., Internat. Vereinigung Für Germanistik, Am. Assn. Tchrs. German (hon.), Societas Linguistica Europaea, Soc. for Germanic Philology, Aus. Acad. Scis. (hon.). Address: U Calif care Dept German Berkeley CA 94720

PEOPLES, DAVID WEBB, screenwriter; b. Middletown, CT; s. Joe Webb Peoples. B.A. English, UC Berkeley, 1962. Scripts include Blade Runner, 1982, Leviathan, 1989, Dead Fall, 1990, Unforgiven, 1992 (Academy award nomination best original screenplay 1992), Hero, 1992; dir., writer: The Blood of Heroes, 1990. Office: Shapiro/Lichtman Agy 8827 Beverly Blvd Los Angeles CA 90048*

PEOPLES, JOHN, JR., physicist, researcher; b. S.I., N.Y., Jan. 22, 1933; s. John and Annie Alice (Wall) P.; m. Brooke Detweiler, Dec. 16, 1955; children—Jennet, Vanessa. B.S. in Elec. Engring., Carnegie Inst. Tech., 1955; M.A. in Physics, Columbia U., 1961, Ph.D. in Physics, 1966. Engr. Martin Marietta Co., Middle River, Md., 1955-60; asst. prof. physics Columbia U., N.Y.C., 1966-69; asst. prof. Cornell U., Ithaca, N.Y., 1969-71, assoc. prof., 1972; scientist Fermilab, Batavia, Ill., 1972—; dir. Fermilab, Batavia, 1989—; mem. high energy physics adv. panel Dept. Energy, Washington, 1976-80, 84-85. Contbr. articles to profl. jours. Alfred Sloan Found. fellow, 1970. Fellow Am. Phys. Soc. (chmn. div. particles and fields 1984). Home: 201 Ford St Geneva IL 60134-1449 Office: Fermi Nat Accelerator Lab MS 105 PO Box 500 Batavia IL 60510-5000 Office: Fermilab Directors Office PO Box 500 Batavia IL 60510

PEOPLES, JOHN ARTHUR, JR., former university president, consultant; b. Starkville, Miss., Aug. 26, 1926; s. John Arthur and Maggie Rose (Peoples) P.; m. Mary E. Galloway, July 13, 1951; children: Kathleen, Mark Adam. B.S., Jackson State U., 1950; M.A., U. Chgo., 1951, Ph.D., 1961. Tchr. math. Froebel Sch., Gary, Ind., 1951-58; asst. prin. Lincoln Sch., Gary, 1958-62; prin. Banneker Sch., Gary, 1962-64; asst. to pres. Jackson (Miss.) State U., 1964-66, v.p., 1966-67, pres., 1967-84; Trustees disting. prof. Univs. Ctr. of Jackson, 1984-85; asst. to pres. SUNY, Binghamton, 1965-66; cons. in higher edn., 1985—; lectr. summers numerous univs. and colls. Contbr. articles to profl. jours. Active Boy Scouts Am.; bd. govs. So. Regional Edn. Bd.; bd. visitors Air U.; adv. com. U.S. Army Command and Gen. Staff Coll.; mem. Commn. Excellence Am. Assn. State Colls. and Univs.; bd. commrs. Jackson Airport Authority. Served with USMCR, 1944-47. Recipient Disting. Am. award Nat. Football Found., Presdl. citation, Lifetime Achievement award Nat. Black Coll. Alumni Found., 1993—; named to Southwestern Athletic Hall of Fame. Mem. Am. Council Edn. (chmn. dir. 1975), Am. Assn. Higher Edn. (dir. 1971-74), NEA, Miss. Tchrs. Assn., Jackson C. of C. (econ. council), Alpha Kappa Mu, Phi Kappa Phi, Phi Delta Kappa, Omega Psi Phi (Man of Year, Sigma Omega chpt. 1966), Sigma Pi Phi. Lodge: Masons (33 deg.).

PEOPLES, THOMAS EDWARD, publisher, executive, writer; b. Cleve., Oct. 26, 1915; s. Robert Stephen and Mary Frances (Box) P.; m. Helen Catherine Mullaney, Jan. 9, 1943; children—Michael Thomas, Mary Dennis, Thomas Edward, James Robert. Student, John Carroll U., 1933-37. Staff photographer Central Press Assn. div. Hearst Corp., 1938-41; staff photographer Internat. News Photos, Cleve., 1946, bur. mgr., 1947-52; picture editor Newspaper Enterprise Assn., Cleve., 1953-58; comics prodn. editor Newspaper Enterprise Assn., 1958-68, dir. comic art, 1968-76, v.p., 1972-76. Author: syndicated comic page Our Boarding House with Maj. Hoople, 1959-69, Major Hoople Football Forecast, 1959-91. Served to 1st lt. U.S. Army, 1941-46, PTO. Mem. Cleve. Newspaper and Newsreel Cameramens Assn. (pres. 1950-51), Newspaper Comics Council (exec. bd. 1968-76, promotion dir. 1972-73), Nat. Cartoonists Soc., Sigma Delta Chi. Democrat. Roman Catholic. Home: 1095 Circle Ter W # B Delray Beach FL 33445-2905 *Every day we should attempt to do some deed for the betterment of society and one's fellowmen. The performance of these deeds may or may not be anonymous but they must never be done with the aim of financial reward or personal or social gain. Our efforts to help our fellowmen may not be crowned with success every time, but it is in the trying we receive our reward.*

PEPE, FRANK A., cell and developmental biology educator; b. Schenectady, May 22, 1931; s. Rocco and Margherita (Ruggiero) P. B.S., Union Coll., 1953; Ph.D., Yale U., 1957. Instr. anatomy U. Pa., Phila., 1957-60, assoc. in anatomy, 1960-63, asst. prof., 1963-65, assoc. prof., 1965-70, prof., 1970-92, chmn. dept. anatomy, 1977-90, prof. cell. and devel. biology, 1992—. Editor: Motility in Cell Function, 1979. Recipient Rsch. Career Devel. award USPHS, 1968-73, Raymond C. Truex Disting. Lecture award Hahneman U., 1988. Fellow AAAS; mem. Am. Assn. Anatomists, Am. Chem. Soc., Am. Inst. Biol. Scis., Am. Soc. Cell Biology, N.Y. Acad. Scis., Biophys. Soc., Microscopy Soc. Am., Sigma Xi. Home: 4614 Pine St Philadelphia PA 19143-1808 Office: U Pa Sch Medicine Philadelphia PA 19104-6508

PEPE, STEPHEN PHILLIP, lawyer; b. Paterson, N.J., Oct. 30, 1943; s. Vincent Attilio and Emma (Opletal) P.; m. Catherine B. Hagen, Dec. 8, 1990. BA, Montclair (N.J.) State Coll., 1965; JD, Duke U., 1968. Bar: Calif. 1969, J.S. Dist. Ct. (no., so., ea. and cen. dists.) Calif. 1975, U.S. Ct. Appeals (9th cir.) 1975, U.S. Sup. Ct. 1978. Assoc. O'Melveny & Myers, L.A., 1968-75, prtnr, 1976—, chmn. labor and employment law dept., 1989-92. Co-author: Avoiding and Defending Wrongful Discharge Claims, 1987; co-editor: Guide to Acquiring and Managing a U.S. Business, 1992, Calif. Employment Law Letter, 1990—. Bd. visitors Duke Law Sch., 1992—; bd. trustees Montclair State Coll. Found., 1991; pres. Inst. Indsl. Rels. Assn. With USAR, 1969-75. Mem. Am. Hosp. Assn. (labor adv. com. 1975-90), Mchts. and Mfrs. Assn. (bd. dirs., chmn. legal com. 1989—), Calif. Club (chmn. employee rels. com., chmn. legal com. 1980—). Democrat. Roman Catholic. Club: Calif. (chmn. employee relations com., chmn. legal com. 1989—). Avocations: wine collecting, wine making, wine judging. Office: O'Melveny & Myers 400 S Hope St Los Angeles CA 90071

PEPE, STEVEN DOUGLAS, federal judge; b. Indpls., Jan. 29, 1943; s. Wilfrid Julius and Roselda (Gehring) P. BA cum laude, U. Notre Dame, 1965; JD magna cum laude, U. Mich., 1968; postgrad., London Sch. Econs. and Polit. Sci., 1970-72; LLM, Harvard U., 1974. Bar: Ind. 1968, D.C. 1969, U.S. Dist. Ct. Ind. 1968, U.S. Dist. Ct. D.C. 1969, Mass. 1973, Mich. 1974, U.S. Dist. Ct. (ea. dist.) Mich. 1979. Law clk. Hon. Harold Leventhal U.S. Cir. Ct. Appeals, Washington, 1968-69; staff atty. Neighborhood Legal Svcs. Program, 1969-70; cons. Office of Svcs. to Aging, Lansing, Mich., 1976-77, Administr. Aging, Dept. Health and Human Svcs., 1976-78; U.S. magistrate judge Eastern Dist., Ann Arbor, Mich., 1983—; mem. Biregional Older Am. Advocacy Assistance Resource and Support Ctr., 1979-81; cons., bd. dirs. Ctr. Social Gerontology; clin. prof. law, dir. Mich. Clin. Law Program, U. Mich. Law Sch., 1974-83; adj. prof. law U. Detroit Mercy Sch. Law, 1985; lectr. U. Mich. Law Sch., 1985-95. Editor Mich. Law Rev.; contbr. articles to profl. jours. Recipient Reginald Heber Smith Cmty. Lawyer fellowship, 1969-70; Mich.-Ford Internat. Studies fellow, 1970-72, Harvard Law Sch. Clin. Teaching fellow, 1972-73. Mem. ABA, State Bar Mich., State Bar Ind., D.C. Bar, Fed. Bar Assn., Washtenaw County Bar Assn., Am. Inn Court XI, U. Detroit Mercy, Pi Sigma Alpha, Order of Coif. Office: US District Court PO Box 7150 Ann Arbor MI 48107-7150

PEPER, CHRISTIAN BAIRD, lawyer; b. St. Louis, Dec. 5, 1910; s. Clarence E. and Christine (Baird) P.; m. Ethel C. Kingsland, June 5, 1935; children: Catherine K. Peper Larson, Anne Peper Sale, Christian B. A.B. cum laude, Harvard, 1932; LL.B., Washington U., 1935; LL.M. (Sterling fellow), Yale, 1937. Bar: Mo. 1934. Since practiced in St. Louis; of counsel Peper, Martin, Jensen, Maichel & Hetlage.; lectr. various subjects Washington U. Law Sch., St. Louis, 1943-61; ptnr. A.G. Edwards & Sons, 1945-67; pres. St. Charles Gas Corp., 1953-72; bd. dirs. St. Louis Steel Casting Inc., Hydraulic Press Brick Co., El Dorado Paper Bag Mfg. Co., Inc. Editor: An Historian's Conscience: The Correspondence of Arnold J. Toynbee and Columba Cary-Elwes, 1986. Contbr. articles to profl. jours. Mem. vis. com. Harvard Div. Sch., 1964-70; counsel St. Louis Art Mus. Mem. ABA, Mo. Bar Assn., St. Louis Bar Assn., Order of Coif, Phi Delta Phi, Noonday Club, Harvard Club (St. Louis), East India Club (London). Roman Catholic. Home: 1454 Mason Rd Saint Louis MO 63131-1211 Office: 720 Olive St Saint Louis MO 63101-2338

PEPER, GEORGE FREDERICK, editor; b. Nyack, N.Y., Jan. 25, 1950; s. Gerhard Wilhelm and Doris Elene (Bargfrede) P.; m. Elizabeth Marshall White, May 20, 1978; children: Timothy William, Christopher Scott. BA in English and Comparative Lit., Princeton U., 1972; postgrad., Yale U., 1973. Assoc. editor Winchester Press, N.Y.C., 1973-75; communications dir. Met. Golf Assn., N.Y.C., 1976; assoc. editor, exec. editor Golf mag., N.Y.C., 1976-78; editor Golf mag., 1979-90; editor-in-chief Golf Mag., 1990—; editl. dir. Golf Mag. Properties, N.Y.C., 1992—; sr. v.p., editl. dir., 1994. Author: Scrambling Golf, 1977, Golf's Supershots, 1982, Masters Tournament anns., 1983—, The PGA Championship, 1916-84, 1985, Golf Courses of the PGA Tour, 1986, 94, Grand Slam Golf, 1991, Golfwatching: A Viewer's Guide to World Golf, 1995; (with Greg Norman) Shark Attack: Greg Norman's Guide to Aggressive Golf, 1988, Greg Norman's Instant Lessions, 1993; scriptwriter: Jack Nicklaus-the Year in Golf, 1994, Official U.S. Open Video, 1994, Official PGA Championship Video, 1994; editor: Golf in America: The First 100 Years, 1988, Shinnecock Hills GC, 1891-91, scriptwriter: Jack Nicklaus-The Year in Golf, 1994, Official U.S. Open Video, 1994, Official PGA Championship Video, 1994. Mem. Golf Writers Assn., Am. Met. Golf Writers Assn., Am. Soc. Mag. Editors, Sleepy Hollow Country Club (Scarborough, N.Y.), Loch Lomond Golf Club (Scotland), Royal and Ancient Golf Club of St Andrews (Scotland). Office: Golf Magazine 2 Park Ave New York NY 10016-5603

PEPIN, JEAN-LUC, retired Canadian government official, political science lecturer; b. Drummondville, Que., Can., Nov. 1, 1924; s. Victor and Antoinette (Morel) P.; m. Sheila Mary Brock-Smith, Apr. 12, 1952; children—Aude, Nicolas. B.A., U. Ottawa, 1945, L.Ph., 1946, LLL., 1956, diploma higher law studies, 1964; student, Inst. d'Etudes Politiques, Paris, France, 1950; hon. degrees, U. Sherbrooke, U. Laval, U. Ottawa, Bishop's U., Carleton U. Prof. polit. sci. U. Ottawa, 1951-56, 58-63, head dept., 1961-63; rep. Nat. Film Bd. Can. in Europe, 1956-58; M.P. for Drummond, 1963-72; parliamentary sec. to minister trade and commerce, 1963-65, minister mines and tech. surveys, 1965, energy, mines and resources, 1966-68, industry, trade and commerce, 1968-72; pres. cons. and trading firm Interimco, Ltd., Ottawa, 1972-75; chmn. Anti Inflation Bd., Ottawa, 1975-77; cochmn. Task Force on Canadian Unity, 1977-79; polit. commentator CBC, 1958-63; Ottawa correspondent Le Magazine Maclean, 1961; M.P. for Ottawa-Carleton, 1979-84, minister of transport, 1980-83, minister of external relations, 1983-84; lectr. in field. Decorated companion Order of Can., 1978. Home: 16 Rothwell Dr, Ottawa, ON Canada K1J 7G4

PÉPIN, MARCEL, broadcast executive; b. Ste-Cécile-de-Lévrard, Que., Can., 1941. BA, U. Ottawa, Can., 1961. Etudes supérieures en Lettres françaises, 1962-64; B in Pedagogy, U. Montreal, Can., 1962. Lectr. U. Ottawa, 1962-64; corr. Parliament Le Droit, Ottawa, 1964-68; gen. mgr. Conseil économique de l'Outaouais, 1968-69; asst. to mng. editor info. La presse, 1970-73, columnist labor sect., 1973-74; chief parliamentary bur. La presse, Ottawa, 1974-77; chief editor Le Soleil, Que., 1977-82; pres. Commn. d'accès à l'information, 1982-88; chief editor French Radio News CBC, 1988-90, gen. mgr. programs French Radio Info., 1990-91; v.p. French Radio SRC CBC, 1991—; pres. Communauté Radios Publiques Langue Française Radio France, 1993—; former treas. Conseil de presse du Que.; former pres. Campagne Centraide 1994, Ministères et agences du govt. fed., Montreal et region met. Mem. conseil d'adm. Musée des religions de Nicolet. Recipient Prix Olivar-Asselin, 1982. Mem. La tribune des journalists (former bd. dirs.), Syndicat des journalistes de La Presse (former pres.), Fédn. professionnelle des journalistes du Que. (former v.p.). Office: PO Box 6000, 1400 René-Lévesque Blvd E, Montreal, PQ Canada H3C 3A8

PEPINE, CARL JOHN, physician, educator; b. Pitts., June 8, 1941; s. Charles John and Elizabeth (Hovan) P.; m. Lynn Divers, Aug. 3, 1963; children: Mary Lynn, Anne, Elizabeth. B.S., U. Pitts., 1962; M.D., N.J. Coll. Medicine, 1966. Intern Allegheny Gen. Hosp., U. Pitts., 1966-67; resident in internal medicine Jefferson Med. Coll. Hosp., Phila., 1967-68, naval med. ctr., 1968-69, fellow in physiology and cardiovascular disease, 1969-71; asst. prof. medicine Jefferson Med. Coll., Phila., 1971-74; asst. prof. medicine U. Fla., Gainesville, 1974-75, assoc. prof., 1975-79, prof., 1979—, co-dir. div. cardiovascular medicine, 1982—; dir. cardiology catheterization lab. Shands Hosp., U. Fla., Gainesville, 1974-86; chief cardiology VA Regional Med. Ctr., Gainesville, 1979-94. Mem. editl. bd. Revs. in Contemporary Pharmacotherapy, Aspirin Rsch. Update, Jour. Cardiovascular Mgmt., Am. Jour. Geriatric Cardiology, Cardiac Chronicle, Internat. Jour. Cardiology; editor in chief Jour. Myocardial Ischemia; contbr. articles to profl. jours.; developer catheters to measure blood flow and heart circulation. Served to comdr. USN, 1968-74. Recipient Faculty Rsch. prize in clin. sci., U. Fla., 1989-90, Pioneer Investigator award Internat. Soc. Holter Monitoring, 1990, Rsch. Achievement award Internat. Soc., 1990, 91, 92, Paul Dudley White award Assn. Mil. Surgs., 1991; grantee Dept. of Def., 1971-74, VA, 1975-90, NHLBI, 1985—. Fellow Am. Coll. Cardiology (gov. for Fla. 1986-87, chmn. bd. govs. 1986-87, bd. trustees 1985-87, 90—, pres. Fla. chpt. 1986-87, chmn. ann. sci. sessions 1990), Am. Heart Assn. (coun. on clin. cardiology and on circulation, bronze award 1983), Am. Fedn. Clin. Rsch., Soc. Cardiac Angiography, Am. Soc. Clin. Investigation; mem. Assn. U. Cardiologists, Pi Kappa Alpha, Alpha Omega Alpha. Research on dynamics of coronary circulation, effects of coronary artery spasm and stenosis, silent myocardial ischemia, effects of lasers on blood vessels, calcium antagonists, ambulatory monitoring. Office: U Fla 1600 SW Archer Rd PO Box 100277 Gainesville FL 32610

PEPITONE, BYRON VINCENT, former government official; b. New Brunswick, N.J., June 9, 1918; s. Joseph James and Sarah Frances (Byron) P.; m. Marolynn Mary Mills, June 9, 1940; children: Byron II, James S. Student, U.S. Army Command and Gen. Staff Coll., 1944, Air. U. Air Command and Staff Coll., 1950, NATO Def. Coll., 1955. Commd. 2d lt. USAAF, 1942; advanced through grades to col. USAF, 1953; ret., 1970; dep. dir. SSS, Washington, 1970-72; acting dir. SSS, 1972-73, dir., 1973-77; ret., 1977. Decorated D.S.M., Legion of Merit with 2 oak leaf clusters, USAF Commendation medal, U.S. Army Commendation medal with oak leaf cluster; recipient Distinguished Service medal SSS, 1972. Mem. USAF Assn. Home: 2265 SW Creekside Dr Palm City FL 34990-2528

PEPLAU, HILDEGARD ELIZABETH, nursing educator; b. Reading, Pa., Sept. 1, 1909; d. Gustav and Ottylie (Elgert) P. Diploma, Pottstown Hosp. Sch. Nursing, 1931; BA, Bennington Coll., 1943; MA, Columbia U. N.Y.C. 1947, EdD, 1953; cert., William Alanson White Inst., 1953; DSc (hon.), Alfred U., 1970, Duke U., 1974, Columbia U., 1983, Rutgers U., New Brunswick, N.J., 1985; Doctor of Nursing Sci. (hon.), Boston Coll., 1972; Doctor of Humane Letters (hon.), U. Indpls., 1987; LHD (hon.), Ohio State U., 1990; DSc (hon.), Ind. U., 1994, U. Ulster, No. Ireland, 1994. RN, N.J., Calif. Exec. officer Coll. Health Svc., Bennington (Vt.) Coll., 1938-43; dir. grad. program psychiatric nursing Tchrs. Coll., Columbia U., N.Y.C., 1948-53; exec. dir. ANA, Washington, 1969-70; dir. grad. program psychiatric nursing Rutgers U., New Brunswick, N.J., 1955-74; prof. emerita Rutgers U., New Brunswick, 1974—. Author: Interpersonal Relations in Nursing, 1952; contbr. numerous articles to profl. publs. and jours., 1942—. 1st lt. Nurse Corps, U.S. Army, 1943-45. Mem. ANA, Am. Acad. Nursing (designated Living Legend 1994), Internat. Coun. Nurses (3d v.p. 1977-81, bd. dirs. 1973-77), Nat. League Nursing. Democrat. Lutheran. Home: 14024 Otsego St Sherman Oaks CA 91423-1225

PEPPAS, NIKOLAOS ATHANASSIOU, chemical engineering educator, consultant; b. Athens, Greece, Aug. 25, 1948; s. Athanassios Nikolaou Peppas and Alice Petrou Rousopoulou; m. Lisa Brannon, Aug. 10, 1988. Diploma in Engring., Nat. Tech. U., Athens, 1971; ScD, MIT, 1973. Rsch. assoc. MIT, Cambridge, Mass., 1975-76; asst. prof. chem. engring. Purdue U., West Lafayette, Ind., 1976-78, assoc. prof., 1978-81, prof., 1981—, Showalter Disting. prof., 1993—; vis. prof. U. Geneva, 1982-83, Calif. Inst. Tech., Pasadena, 1983, U. Paris, 1986, Hoshi U., Japan, 1994, Hebrew U., Jerusalem, 1994; adj. prof. U. Parma, Italy, 1987; cons. in field; mem. adv. bd. several cos. Author: Biomaterials, 1982, Hydrogels in Medicine and Pharmacy, 1987, One Hundred Years of Chemical Engineering, 1989, Pulsatile Drug Delivery, 1993, Biopolymers, 1993, Superabsorbent Polymers, 1994, Hydrogels, 1995; contbr. articles and abstracts to jours. in field. Active Indpls. Symphony Orch., Indpls. Mus. Arts, Holy Trinity Orthodox Ch. Indpls. Fellow Am. Inst. Med. Biol. Engrs., Am. Assn. Pharm. Scientists, Soc. Biomaterials; mem. AIChE (chmn. materials divsn. 1988-90, Materials Engring. Sci. award 1984, Bioengring. award 1994), Am. Chem. Soc., Am. Phys. Soc., N.Y. Acad. Sci. Controlled Release Soc. (pres. 1987-88, Founders award 1991), Soc. Biomaterials (Clemson award 1992), Am. Soc. Engring. Edn. (AT&T award 1982, Curtis McGraw award 1988, G. Westinghouse award 1992), Polymer Pioneers, numerous others. Avocations: opera, rare maps, record collecting, wine collecting, archaeology. Office: Sch Chem Engring Purdue U West Lafayette IN 47907

PEPPER, ALLAN MICHAEL, lawyer; b. Bklyn., July 5, 1943; s. Julius and Jeanette (Lasovsky) P.; m. Barbara Benjamin, Aug. 30, 1964; children—Leslie Anne, Joshua Benjamin, Adam Richard, Robert Benjamin. B.A. summa cum laude, Brandeis U., 1964; LL.B. magna cum laude, Harvard U., 1967. Bar: N.Y. 1968, U.S. Dist. Ct. (so. and ea. dists.) N.Y. 1968, U.S. Ct. Appeals (2d cir.) 1968, U.S. Supreme Ct. 1988. Law clk. U.S. Ct. Appeals for 2d Circuit, N.Y.C., 1967-68; assoc. Kaye, Scholer, Fierman, Hays & Handler, N.Y.C., 1968-74, ptnr., 1975—; lectr. in field. Mem. exec. com., assoc. nat. chmn. Brandeis U. Alumni Fund, 1979-82, nat. chmn., 1982-85, chmn. 25th Reunion gift com., 1989, mem. devel. com., trustee, 1982-85, pres., councillor, 1980—; trustee Brandeis U., 1985—, sec., 1992-93, budget and fin. com., 1988—, chmn. com. strategic plan, 1990-91, mem. acad. affairs com., 1985-92, mem. student life and phys. facilities com., 1985-89, vice chmn. ad hoc by-laws com., 1988-89, long range planning com., 1989-91, chmn. audit com. 1991—, exec. com., 1990-91; bd. dirs. Styles Brook Homeowners Assn., 1990—, exec. com., 1994—; mem. nominating com. Edgemont Sch. Bd., 1992-93; trustee Edgemont Sch. Found., 1994—. Recipient Henry Jones-Golda Meier Bnai Brith Youth Services award, 1986, L.I. Press Valedictory medal, 1960; Felix Frankfurter scholar Harvard U. Law Sch., 1964-65; Louis D. Brandeis hon. scholar Brandeis U., 1964. Mem. ABA, Assn. of Bar of City of N.Y. (mem. law firm mgmt. com. 1987-91), N.Y. State Bar Assn. (comml. and fed. lit. sect., vice chmn. com. on discovery 1993—), Brandeis U. Alumni Assn. (exec. com. 1982-85, alumni giving strategic planning com., 1992, Alumni Svc. award 1988), Phi Beta Kappa (L.I. Alumni award 1960). Democrat. Jewish. Lodge: B'nai B'rith (pres. Henry Jones Lodge 1982-84, mem. Westchester-Putnam council 1982-85, bd. govs. dist. 1, 1985-86). Office: Kaye Scholer Fierman Hays & Handler 425 Park Ave New York NY 10022-3506

PEPPER, BEVERLY, artist, sculptor; b. Bklyn., Dec. 20, 1924; d. Irwin Edward and Beatrice Evadne (Horenstein) Stoll; m. Curtis G. Pepper, Oct. 11, 1949; children: Jorie Graham, John Randolph. Studied with, Fernand Leger, Andre L'Hote; student, Pratt Inst., 1939-41, D.F.A. (hon.), 1982; student, Art Students League, N.Y.C., 1944; D.F.A. (hon.), Md. Inst., 1983. Prof. meritus U. Perugia, Italy, 1987. One-woman shows include Marlborough Gallery, N.Y.C., 1969, Galerie Hella Nebelung, Dusseldorf, Ger., 1971, Piazza Margana, Rome, 1971, Parker St. Gallery, Boston, 1971, Qui Arte Contemporanea, Rome, 1972, Marlborough Galleria d'Arte, Rome, 1972, Tyler Sch. of Art, Temple U. Abroad, Rome, 1973, Hammarskjold Plaza Sculpture Garden, N.Y.C., 1975, Met. Mus. Art, Miami, Fla., 1976, San Francisco Mus. Art, 1976, 86, Seattle Mus. Art, 1977, Princeton U., 1978, Indpls. Mus. Art, 1978, Todi Piazza and Sala delle Pietra, 1979, Gimpel-Hanover Gallery, Zurich, 1980, Ronald Greenberg Gallery, St. Louis, 1980, Davenport Art Gallery, 1981, Hansen Fuller Goldeen Gallery, San Francisco, 1981, Laumeier Internat. Sculpture Park, St. Louis, 1982 Galleria Il Ponte, Rome, 1982, John Berggrun Gallery, San Francisco, 1983, 1985, Adams-Middleton Gallery, Dallas, 1985, Andre Emmerich Gallery, N.Y.C., 1975, 77, 79, 80, 82, 84, 86, 87, 89, 90, 91, 93, Columbus (Ohio) Mus. Art, 1986, Charles Cowles Gallery, N.Y.C., 1987, 90, 94, Albright-Knox Art Gallery 20 yr. traveling survey exhbn., 1986, Visual Arts Ctr. MIT, Cambridge, Mass., 1989, James Corcoran Gallery, Santa Monica, Calif., 1989, 90, Contemporary Sculpture Ctr. Tokyo, 1991, Met. Mus. Art, N.Y.C., 1991, Narni all Rocca, Narna, Italy, 1991; group shows include XXIII Biennale di Venezia, Venice, Italy, 1972, Mus. Phila. Civic Center, 1974, Finch Coll. Mus. Art, N.Y.C., 1974, Marlborough Gallery, N.Y.C., 1974, Janie C. Lee Gallery, Houston, 1975, New Orleans Mus. Art, 1976, Documenta 6, Kassel, Ger., 1977, Quadriennale di Roma, Rome, 1977, Seattle Mus., 1979, Bklyn. Mus. Art, 1986, 87, Bienale de Sculpture, Monte Carlo, 1991, Galleria Comunale d'Arte Moderna, Spoletto, Italy, 1992, Chelsea Harbour Sculpture '93, London, 1993, Queens Mus. Art, Corona Park, N.Y., 1994; represented in numerous permanent collections including Met. Mus. Art, N.Y.C., Fogg Mus., Cambridge, Mass., Albright-Knox Art Gallery, Buffalo, Jacksonville (Fla.) Mus. Modern Art, Galleria d'Arte Moderna, Florence, Italy, Walker Art Center, Mpls., Instituto Italiano di Cultura, Stockholm, Sweden, Power Inst. Fine Arts, Sydney, Australia, Galleria Civica d'Arte Moderna, Turin, Italy, Albertina Mus., Vienna, Hirshhorn Mus. and Sculpture Garden, Washington, Worcester (Mass.) Art Mus., Parkersburg (W.Va.) Art Mus., Smithsonian Inst., Washington, Dartmouth Coll., Hanover, N.H., Atlantic Richfield Co., L.A., Rutgers U., Wright, Runstad & Co., Seattle, Niagara Frontier Transp. Authority, Buffalo, Johns Hopkins Hosp., John Deere Foundry, East Moline, Ill.; commns. include Amphisculpture, AT&T, Bedminster, N.J., 1974-76, Dartmouth Coll., 1976-77, Sol i Onbra, 1986-91, City Barcelona, 1986—, Teatre Celle, Villa Celle, Postoia, Italy, 1989-91, Terana Altar II, Smithsonian Inst., Nat. Mus. Am. Art, Washington, 1990-91, Gotanno Community Park, Adachi-ku Machizukuri Corp., Neo-Hodos, Tokyo, 1992, Split Ritual, U.S. Nat. Arboretum, Washington, 1992, Palingenesis, Credit-Suisse, Zurich, 1992-94, The Garden at 26 Fed/ Plz., Gen. Svcs. Adminstrn., N.Y.C., 1992—, Jerusalem Ritual, Jerusalem Found., Israel, 1994. Recipient award Nat. Endowment of Arts, 1976, 79, award GSA, 1975. Honor award Nat. Women's Caucus for Art, 1994. Home: Torre Gentile di Todi (PG) Italy

06059 Office: Andre Emmerich Gallery 41 E 57th St New York NY 10022-1908

PEPPER, DAVID M., physicist, educator, author, inventor; b. L.A., Mar. 9, 1949; s. Harold and Edith (Kleinplatz) P.; m. Denise Danyelle Koster, Mar. 19, 1992. BS in Physics summa cum laude, UCLA, 1971; MS in Applied Physics, Calif. Inst. Tech., 1974, PhD in Applied Physics, 1980. Mem. tech. staff Hughes Rsch. Labs., Malibu, Calif., 1973-87, sr. staff physicist, 1987-91, head nonlinear and electro-optic devices sect., 1989-91, sr. scientist, 1991—; adj. prof. math. and physics Pepperdine U., Malibu, 1981—. co-author: Optical Phase Conjugation, 1983, Laser Handbook, Vol. 4, 1985, Optical Phase Conjugation, 1995, Spatial Light Modulator Technology, 1995, CRC Handbook of Laser Science and Technology, 1995; tech. referee profl. jours.; contbr. articles to tech. jours. including Sci. Am.; holder 15 patents. Mem. Sons and Daughters of 1939 Club, 2d Generation of Martyrs Meml., Mus. Holocaust. Recipient Rudolf Kingslake award Soc. Photo-Optical Instrumentation Engrs., 1982, Publ. of Yr. award Hughes Rsch. Lab., 1986; NSF trainee Calif. Inst. Tech., 1971; Howard Hughes fellow Hughes Aircraft Co., 1973-80. Fellow Optical Soc. Am.; mem. AAAS, IEEE (guest editor, assoc. editor), SPIE (guest editor), N.Y. Acad. Scis., Am. Phys. Soc., Internat. Coun. Sci. Unions (com. on sci. and tech. in developing countries), Sigma Xi (v.p. 1986-87, chpt. pres. 1987-88, 90-91, 91-92), Sigma Pi Sigma. Avocations: classical music, travel, sports, astronomy, nature. Office: Hughes Rsch Labs RL 65 3011 Malibu Canyon Rd Malibu CA 90265-4797 *Personal philosophy: We all have a profound, meaningful purpose and mission in life—the challenge is to identify, appreciate, realize and embrace our dreams and goals.*

PEPPER, DOROTHY MAE, nurse; b. Merill, Maine, Oct. 16, 1932; d. Walter Edwin and Alva Lois (Leavitt) Stanley; m. Thomas Edward Pepper, July 1, 1960; children: Walter Frank, James Thomas. RN, Maine Med. Ctr. Sch. Nursing, Portland, 1954. RN, Calif. Pvt. duty nurse Lafayette, Calif.; staff nurse Maine Med. Ctr., Portland, 1954-56, Oakland (Calif.) VA Hosp., 1956-58; pvt. duty nurse, dir. RN's Alameda County, Oakland. Mem. Profl. Nurses Bur. Registry, Maine Writers and Pubs. Alliance, Standardbred Pleasure Horse Orgn. Avocation: writing.

PEPPER, H. L. PERRY, hospital administrator; b. Phila., Dec. 4, 1942; s. Dickinson Sergeant and Hester (Laning) P.; m. March Wier, Dec. 7, 1968; children: Meredith Franklin, Page Camp. BA in Sociology, U. Pa., 1967, MBA in Health Econs., 1973. Mktg. analyst Smith Kline & French, Phila., 1968-70; asst. dir. Presbyn. U. Pa. Med. Ctr., Phila., 1973-77; pres. The Chester County Hosp., Phila., 1977—. Chmn. Del. Valley Health Edn. and Rsch. Found. Forum, 1983; bd. dirs. Christ Ch. Hosp./Kearsley Home, Phila., 1972—, chmn., 1974-82; mem. Corp. Hosp. Rating Project, adv. com. Leonard Davis Inst. Health Econs., 1989—; mem. exec. com. Phila. Buy-Right Project, 1989—; mem. Terris Soc., The Phila. Health Policy Forum; chmn. Mid. Atlantic Health Congress Bd. Govs., 1987. Mem. Am. Hosp. Assn. (policy com. 1989—, del. Chgo. 1991-93, Edna Fagan Disting. Svc. award 1990), Hosp. Assn. Pa. (trustee 1982-84, 86, 89, chair 1988), Del. Valley Hosp. Coun. bd. dirs. 1979-85, 86, chair 1990-91, sec.-treas. 1990-91, HAP rep. 1986), Am. Coun. Healthcare Execs. (regents adv. coun. 1987, 88, 90, 91), Vol. Hosps. Am. (dir. East partnership 1991), Phila. Coll. of Physicians (hon.), Pa. League for Nurses Inc. (bd. dirs. 1986, 87, 88), Phila. Club, Sunday Breakfast Club, Mayflower Soc., Soc. of 1812, Adminstrs. Club Greater Phila., Merion Cricket Club, Pi Gamma Mu, Beta Gamma Sigma. Office: The Chester County Hosp 701 E Marshall St West Chester PA 19380-4412

PEPPER, IAN L., environmental microbiologist, research scientist, educator; b. Tonypandy, Wales, U.K., Oct. 5, 1946. BSc in Chemistry, U. Birmingham, U.K., 1970; MS in Soil Biochemistry, Ohio State U., 1972, PhD in Soil Microbiology, 1975. Post-doctoral rsch. assoc. Wash. State U. 1975-76; asst. prof., asst. rsch. sci. dept. soils, water and engring. U. Ariz., 1971-81, assoc. prof., assoc. rsch. sci., 1971-88, prof., rsch. sci. dept. soil and water sci. and microbiology, 1988—, chair undergrad. program in environ. sci., 1993—. Contbr. articles to profl. jours. Recipient Ciba-Geigy award, 1983. Fellow Am. Acad. Microbiology, Am. Soc. Agronomy, Soil Sci. Soc. Am. Office: Univ of Arizona 429 Shantz Bldg Tucson AZ 85721

PEPPER, JANE G., bank executive. Dep. chmn. Fed. Reserve Bank of Phila., Pa. Office: Fed Reserve Bank of Phila 100 N 6th St Philadelphia PA 19106

PEPPER, JEFFREY MACKENZIE, publishing executive; b. Dallas, June 11, 1957; s. Doris Jane (Mackenzie) P.; m. Martha Helen Stearns, July 27, 1985; children: Katherine McRaven, Anne Mackenzie. BA, Coll. Wooster, 1979. Sales rep. Acad. Press, N.Y.C., 1979-82; program editor Addison-Wesley Pub. Co., Reading, Mass., 1982-83, acquisitions editor, 1983-86; sr. editor Osborne McGraw-Hill, Berkeley, Calif., 1986-90, editor-in-chief, 1990-95; v.p., editl. dir. Acad. Press Profl., Chestnut Hill, Mass., 1995—. Contbr. articles to profl. jours. Avocations: storytelling, computers, gardening.

PEPPER, JOHN ENNIS, JR., consumer products company executive; b. Pottsville, Pa., Aug. 2, 1938; s. John Ennis Sr. and Irma Elizabeth (O'Connor) P.; m. Frances Graham Garber, Sept. 9, 1967; children: John, David, Douglas, Susan. BA, Yale U., 1960; PhD (hon.), Mt. St. Joseph Coll., St. Petersburg (Russia) U. With Procter & Gamble Co., Cin., 1963—, gen. mgr. Italian subs., 1974-77; v.p., gen. mgr. div. packaged soap and detergent Proctor & Gamble Co., Cin., 1977-80, group v.p., 1980-84, exec. v.p., 1984-86, pres. U.S. bus., 1986—, pres. internat. bus., 1990—, also bd. dirs.; bd. dirs. Xerox Corp., Motorola, Inc. Trustee Cin. Symphony Orch., Cin. Med. Inst.; group chmn. Cin. United Appeal Campaign, 1980; trustee Xavier U., 1985-89, mem. exec. com., 1989; trustee Cin. Coun. World Affairs, Cin. Art Mus., Ctr. Strategic & Internat. Studies, Christ Ch. Endowment Fund; gen. chmn. United Way Campaign, 1994; co-chair Gov.'s Edn. Coun., State of Ohio; mem. adv. coun. Yale Sch. Mgmt.; mem. schs. com. Cin. Bus. Com.; co-chmn. Cin. Youth Collaborative. Served to lt. USN, 1960-63. Mem. Am. Soc. Corp. Execs., Nat. Alliance Businessmen (chmn. communication com.), Soap and Detergent Assn. (bd. dirs.), Yale Club, Queen City Club, Commonwealth Club, Comml. Club. Office: Procter & Gamble Co 1 Procter Gamble Plz Cincinnati OH 45202

PEPPER, JONATHON LESTER, newspaper columnist; b. Dearborn, Mich., Aug. 23, 1955; s. Joseph Daniel and Norma (McIntyre) P.; m. Diane Sharon Garelis, May 12, 1984; children: Jonathon Jay, Lauren Claire, Scott Joseph. BA, Mich. State U., 1977. Copywriter Detroit Free Press, 1977-84, reporter, 1984-87; nat. corr. Detroit News, 1987-91, bus. columnist, 1991—. Mem. Writers Guild Am., The Newspaper Guild. Office: The Detroit News 615 W Lafayette Blvd Detroit MI 48226-3124

PEPPERCORN, JOHN EDWARD, chemical company executive; b. Hutchinson, Kans., Sept. 3, 1937; s. John Edward and Lorena Fay (Hirt) P.; m. Mary Claire Purcell, July 25, 1961; children: Michael Edward, Mark Purcell. BSBA, U. Kans., 1960; grad. Tuck Exec. Program, Dartmouth Coll., 1978. Mgr. plastic sales Gulf Oil Chems., Houston, 1966-69, mktg. mgr., 1973-77, v.p. U.S. plastics, 1977-83, v.p. aromatics and derivatives, 1981-83; gen. mgr. Gulf Plastic Products Co., Morristown, N.J., 1969-72; v.p. domestic mktg. Gulf Oil Products, Houston, 1983-85; v.p., gen. mgr. aromatics Chevron Chem. Co., Houston, 1985; sr. v.p. indsl. chems. Chevron Chem. Co., San Francisco 1985-86, sr. v.p., 1986-89, pres., chief exec. officer, 1989—. Served to capt. U.S. Army, 1960-61. Mem. Soc. Plastic Industry (bd. dirs. 1978-81), Flexible Packaging Assn. (bd. dirs. 1980-82). Office: Chevron Chem Co 575 Market St San Francisco CA 94105-2823

PEPPERCORN, MARK ALLEN, gastroenterologist, educator; b. Cleve., Sept. 28, 1942; s. David and Adelle Peppercorn; m. Margaret Tova Bessin; children: Jeffrey, Daniel. AB cum laude, Harvard U., 1964, MD cum laude, 1968. Diplomate Am. Bd. Internal Medicine with subspecialty in gastroenterology. Intern in internal medicine Beth Israel Hosp., Boston, 1968-69, asst. resident in internal medicine, 1969-70, chief resident in internal medicine, 1973-74, fellow in gastroenterology dept. medicine, 1972-73, asst. physician in internal medicine, 1974-85, assoc. physician dept. medicine, 1985-88, physician dept. medicine divsn. gastroenterology, 1988—; clin. fellow in internal medicine Harvard Med. Sch., Boston, 1968-70, rsch. fellow

in internal medicine, 1972-73; clin. assoc. arthritis and rheumatism br. Nat. Inst. Arthritis and Metabolic Diseases, NIH, Boston, 1970-72; asst. prof. medicine Harvard U. Med. Sch., Boston, 1974-84, assoc. prof. medicine, 1984—; mem. human studies com. Harvard Med. Sch., 1979-80, bd. advisors standing com., 1983-88, com. on grading, 1988, Peabody Soc. rev. com. for infectious disease and musco-skeletal block, 1991, chmn. Peabody Soc. rev. com. for introduction to clinic, 1992, continent ostomy adv. group, 1992, subcom. on skills and procedures for second year students, 1993, 25th reunion orgn. com., 1993, Peabody Soc. curriculum com., 1993; mem. gastroenterology rev. com. for Harvard U., MIT, 1990; faculty advisor Francis Weld Peabody Soc., 1990; dir. core clerkship in medicine Beth Israel Hosp., Boston, 1974—, ward attending in medicine, 1974—, attending in gastroenterology, 1974—, lectr., 1974—, coord. inter-hosp. GI rounds, 1975—, instr., 1980—, dir. gastroenterology clinic, 1974-86, mem. med. internship selection com., 1974—, pharmacy com., 1974—, nutrition com., 1980—, ambulatory care com., 1990—; mem. utilization rev. com. Recuperative Ctr., Boston, 1980—; vis. prof. Univ. Hosp., Cleve., 1990, Bridgeport (Conn.) hosp., 1990, U. Chgo. Med. Ctr., 1988, Mid-Maine Med. Ctr., Augusta, 1991, McGill Med. Sch., Montreal, Que., Can., 1991, U. Colo., 1993, Brooke Army Hosp. and Wilfred Hall Air Force Hosp., San Antonio, 1993, Jersey Shore Med. Ctr. Nepture, N.J., 1993, Columbia Presbyn. Hosp. for Physicians and Surgeons, N.Y.C., 1993, Portsmouth (Va.) Naval Hosp., 1993, U. Pitts. Med. Ctr., 1993; cons. in field. Mem. editorial bd. Jour. Clin. Gastroenterology, 1993—; contbr. articles to profl. publs. Francis Weld Peabody fellow, 1990; named Best Gastroenterologist in Boston, Boston Mag. Physicians Poll, 1992, 95. Fellow Am. Coll. Gastroenterology (ednl. affairs com. 1991—, gov. for Mass. 1990-92); mem. AMA (cons. for drug evaluations 1990—), Am. Gastroenterol. Assn. (mem. patient care com. 1985-87, mem. rsch. initiatives com. 1989—, abstract rev. com. 1989—, chmn. abstracts rev. com. 1993—, editor Gastroenterology 1989—), Nat. Found. for Ileitis and Colitis, Inflammatory Bowel Disease Forum (pres. 1987-89), Am. Coll. Physicians, CCFA (med. adv. com. Boston chpt. 1990—, patient care com. 1990—). Home and office: 330 Brookline Ave Boston MA 02215

PEPPERDENE, MARGARET WILLIAMS, English educator; b. Vicksburg, Miss., Dec. 25, 1919; d. O.L. and Jane (Stocks) Williams. B.S., La. State U., 1941; M.A., Vanderbilt U., 1948, Ph.D., 1953. Div. Instr. English U. Oreg., 1946-47; teaching fellow Vanderbilt U., 1948-50; instr., then asst. prof. Miami U., Oxford, Ohio, 1952-56; mem. faculty Agnes Scott Coll., 1956—, prof. English, chmn. dept., 1967—. Author articles. Editor: That Subtile Wreath: Lectures Presented at the Quatercentenary Celebration of the Birth of John Donne, 1973. Served to lt. USNR, 1943-46. Fulbright fellow, 1950-51; Ford Found. grad. fellow, 1951-52; AAUW fellow, 1954-55; research fellow Dublin Inst. Advanced Studies, 1954-55; Guggenheim fellow, 1956-57; recipient Gov.'s Award in Humanities, Ga., 1987. Home: 418 Glendale Ave Decatur GA 30030-1922

PEPPERS, JERRY P., lawyer; b. Cleve., Mar. 8, 1946; s. Jerry P. and Katherine M. Peppers; m. Sue E. Schafer, June 14, 1969; children: Amy E., Erica K., Christina A., Michele S. BBA, Ohio U., 1968; JD, Duke U., 1971. Bar: N.Y. 1972. Assoc. Winthrop, Stimson, Putnam & Roberts, N.Y.C., 1971-81, ptnr., 1982—; mgmt. com., 1995—; bd. dirs. Firth Rixson, Inc., Rochester, N.Y., Monroe Forgings, Inc., Rochester, Progenitor, Inc., Columbus, Ohio, Viking Metall. Corp., Reno. Editor: (booklet) Outline of Mergers and Acquisitions in the United States, 14th edit., 1995. Trustee Ohio Univ. Found., Athens, 1991—, Fox Meadow Athletic Assn., Scarsdale, Scarsdale Youth Soccer Club, Inc., Scarsdale Maroon and White Club. Mem. ABA, Internat. Bar Assn., India House, Fox Meadow Tennis Club (Scarsdale, N.Y.). Avocation: coaching soccer (lic. FIFA). Office: Winthrop Stimson Putnam & Roberts 1 Battery Park Plz New York NY 10004

PEPPET, RUSSELL FREDERICK, accountant; b. Chgo., Oct. 3, 1939; s. George Russell and Elizabeth (Foster) P.; m. Rosemary Meyer, June 18, 1960; children—Cynthia, Jeffrey, Scott. B.S. in Math, Mich. State U., 1960; M.B.A., Northwestern U., 1964. C.P.A., Ill., Minn. Cons. Peat, Marwick, Mitchell & Co., Chgo., 1961-68; head mgmt. cons. dept. Peat, Marwick, Mitchell & Co., Mpls., 1968-72; partner Peat, Marwick, Mitchell & Co., 1969-88; sr. cons. partner for Continental Europe, Paris, 1972-78, partner-in-charge mgmt. cons. dept., N.Y.C. office, 1978-81, vice chmn. mgmt. cons., 1981-86; mng. ptnr. San Jose Bus. Unit, 1986-88; v.p. internat. devel. Towers Perrin, N.Y.C., 1989-90; vice-chmn. Quirk Carson Peppet Inc., N.Y.C., 1990—; bd. dirs. AFS-USA, treas., 1991-92, chmn., 1992—. With U.S. Army, 1962-64. Mem. Am. Inst. C.P.A.'s. Club: Sky (N.Y.C.). Home: 150 E 69th St # 18G New York NY 10021-5704 Office: Quirk Carson Peppet Inc 99 Park Ave New York NY 10016-1503

PEPPLER, WILLIAM NORMAN, aviation association executive; b. Hanover, Ont., Can., June 29, 1925. Student public shcs., Hanover. Charter pilot Leavens Bros., Toronto, Ont., 1945-48; chief flying instr. Sky Harbour Air Service, Goderich, Ont., 1949-51; survey pilot Spartan Air Services, Ottawa, Ont., 1951-57; mgr. Can. Owners and Pilots Assn., Ottawa, 1957—; editor Can. Flight Mag., 1957—; Can. Bur. Aviation News, 1957—. Office: 77 Metcalfe, Ottawa, ON Canada K1P 5S4

PEPYNE, EDWARD WALTER, lawyer, former educator; b. Springfield, Mass., Dec. 27, 1925; s. Walter Henry and Frances A. (Carroll) P.; m. Carol Jean Dutcher, Aug. 2, 1958; children—Deborah, Edward, Jr., Susan, Byron, Shari, Randy, David, Allison, Jennifer. B.A., Am. Internat. Coll., 1948; M.S., U. Mass., 1951, Ed.D., 1968; postgrad., NYU, 1952-55; prof. diploma, U. Conn., 1964; J.D., Western New Eng. Coll., 1978. Bar: Mass. 1978, U.S. Supreme Ct. 1981. Prin., tchr. Gilbertville Grammar Sch., Hardwick, Mass., 1948-49; sch. counselor West Springfield High Sch., Mass., 1949-53; instr. NYU, 1953-54; supt. schs. New Shoreham, R.I., 1954-56; asst. prof. edn. Mich. State U., 1956-58; sch. psychologist, guidance dir. Pub. Sch. System, East Long, Mass., 1958-62; lectr. Westfield State Coll., 1961-65; dir. pupil services Chicopee Pub. Sch., 1965-68; assoc. prof. counselor edn. U. Hartford, West Hartford, Mass., 1968-71, prof., 1971-85, dir. Inst. Coll. Counselors Minority and Low Income Students, 1971-72, dir. Div. Human Services, 1972-77; cons. Aetna Life & Casualty Co., Hartford, 1962-75; hearing officer Conn. State Bd. Edn., 1980—; exec. dir. Sinapi Assocs., 1959-78; pvt. practice, Ashfield, Mass., 1978—. Co-author: Better Driving, 1958; assoc. editor: Highway Safety and Driver Education, 1954; chmn. editorial com.: Man and the Motor Car, 5th edit., 1954; contbr. numerous articles to profl. jours. Chief Welfare Svcs. Civil Def., Levittown, N.Y., 1953-54; chmn. Ashfield Planning Bd., Mass., 1979-83; moderator Town of Ashfield, 1980-81, town counsel, Charlemont, Mass., 1983-84; mem. jud. nominating coun. Western Regional Com., 1993—. Mem. ABA, APA, Mass. Bar Assn., Mass. Acad. Trial Attys., Am. Pers. and Guidance Assn., New Eng. Pers. and Guidance Assn. (bd. dirs.), New Eng. Ednl. Rsch. Orgn. (pres. 1971), Am. Assn. Sch. Adminstrs., Am. Ednl. Rsch. Assn., Mt. Tom Amateur Radio Assn., Franklin County Amateur Radio Club, Elks, Kiwanis (pres. 1988-89, lt. gov. div. 12, 1991-92), Masons (master 1994—), Shriners, Phi Delta Kappa. Home: PO Box 31 134 Ashfield Mountain Rd Ashfield MA 01330-9622 Office: PO Box 345 134 Ashfield Mountain Rd Ashfield MA 01330-9622

PERADOTTO, JOHN JOSEPH, classics educator, editor; b. Ottawa, Ill., May 11, 1933; s. John Joseph and Mary Louise (Giacometti) P.; m. Noreen Doran, Aug. 29, 1959 (div. 1982); m. Marlene Rosen, Aug. 29, 1992; children: Erin, Monica, Noreen, Nicole. B.A., St. Louis U., 1957, M.A., 1958; Ph.D., Northwestern U., 1963. Instr. classics and English Western Wash. U., Bellingham, 1960-61; instr. Georgetown U., 1961-63, asst. prof. classics, 1963-66; asst. prof. classics SUNY, Buffalo, 1966-69, assoc. prof., 1969-73; prof., chmn. classics U. Tex., Austin, 1973-74; prof. classics SUNY-Buffalo, 1974—, Andrew V.V. Raymond prof. classics, 1984—, Disting. teaching prof., 1990—, chmn. dept., 1974-77, dean div. undergrad. edn., 1978-82; Martin lectr. Oberlin Coll., 1987; dir. summer seminar for coll. tchrs. NEH, 1976, for secondary sch. tchrs., 1984. Author: Classical Mythology: An Annotated Bibliographical Survey, 1973, Man in the Middle Voice: Name and Narration in the Odyssey, 1990; also articles and revs.; founding assoc. editor: Arethusa, editor-in-chief, 1974—; mem. bd. editors SUNY Press, 1978-81; editor: SUNY Press Classical Series, 1981—, Classical Literature and Myth Analysis, 1977, Women in the Ancient World, 1978, 983; co-editor: Population Policy in Plato and Aristotle, 1975, The New Archilochus, 1976, Augustan Poetry Books, 1980, Indo-European

Roots of Classical Culture, 1980, Vergil: 2000 Years, 1981, Texts and Contexts: American Classical Studies in Honor of J.P. Vernant, 1982, Semiotics and Classical Studies, 1983, Audience-oriented Criticism and the Classics, 1986, Herodotus and the Invention of History, 1987, The Challenge of Black Athena, 1989, Pastoral Revisions, 1990, Reconsidering Ovid's Fasti, 1992, Bakhtin and Classical Studies, 1993, Rethinking the Classical Canon, 1994, Horace: 2000 Years, 1995. Fellow Center for Hellenic Studies, 1972-73; Recipient Chancellor's award for teaching excellence State U. N. Y., 1975. Mem. Am. Philol. Assn. (dir. 1974-77, pres. 1990), Classical Assn. Atlantic States (exec. com. 1976-78). Office: Dept Classics State U NY Buffalo NY 14260

PERAHIA, MURRAY, pianist; b. N.Y.C., Apr. 19, 1947; s. David and Flora P.; m. Naomi Shohet Ninette, 1980; 2 children. MS, Mannes Coll. Music; student, Jeannette Haien, Arthur Balsam, Mieczyslaw Horszowski. Appeared with Berlin Philharm., Chgo. Symphony Orch., English Chamber Orch., Boston Symphony Orch., N.Y. Philharm., Cleve. Orch., Los Angeles Philharm., Phila. Orch., others; performed with Budapest, Guarneri and Galimir string quartets; frequent performer, artistic dir.: Aldeburgh Festival, 1983-89; past participant: Marlboro Music Festival; recital tours in U.S., Can., Europe and Japan; recs. for SONY Classical; 1st Am. to record the Complete Mozart Concertos as condr. with English Chamber Orch., recorded complete Beethoven concertos with Haitink concertgebouw Orch. Recipient Kosciusko Chopin prize, 1965, Avery Fisher prize, 1975, over 10 maj. rec. awards. Office: care Edna Landau IMG 22 E 71st St New York NY 10021-4911

PERAINO, ROY T., banker; b. 1928; married. Grad. Wharton Sch. Fin., U. Pa., 1955, Rutgers U. Sch. Banking, 1963. With Continental Bancorp. Inc., 1958—, formerly chmn., chief exec. officer, now chmn. Continental Bank, Norristown, Pa.; pres. Midatlantic Corp., Edison, N.J. Office: Midlantic Corp Metro Park Pla PO Box 600 Edison NJ 08818-0600

PERCAS DE PONSETI, HELENA, foreign language and literature educator; b. Valencia, Spain, Jan. 17, 1921; came to U.S., 1940, naturalized, 1950; m. Ignacio V. Ponseti, 1961. Baccalaureat, Paris, France, 1939; B.A., Barnard Coll., 1942; M.A., Columbia, 1943, Ph.D., 1951. Tchr. lang. and lit. Barnard Coll., 1942-43, Russell Sage Coll., 1943-45, Columbia U., 1945-47, Queens Coll., 1946-48; mem. faculty Grinnell Coll., 1948—, prof. lang. and lit., 1957—, Roberts Honor prof. modern fgn. langs., 1961-62, Richards prof. modern fgn. langs., 1963-82, prof. emerita, 1982—. Author: La Poesia Femenina Argentina, 1810-1950, 1958, Cervantes y su concepto del arte, 1975, Cervantes the Writer and Painter of Don Quijote, 1988. Mem. Cervantes Soc. Am. (founding mem., com. 1979—, assoc. editor jour. Cervantes 1981), Asociacion de Cervantistas Alcala de Henares Spain, 1987 (charter). Home: 110 Oakridge Ave Iowa City IA 52246-2935

PERCOCO, THELMA ANN, nurse, educator; b. Newton, Kans., Sept. 11, 1935; d. Menno J. and Lydia A. (Miller) Hirschler; m. Richard A. Percoco, June 5, 1960. Diploma in nursing, Bethel Deaconess Hosp., Newton, 1957; BS in Nursing, Fla. State U., 1960; MS in Nursing, Tex. Women's U., 1977. RN, Tex. Staff nurse, team leader VA Hosp., Albuquerque, 1957-58, 60; staff nurse State Tuberculosis Hosp., Tallahassee, 1960, West Haven (Conn.) VA Hosp., 1960, 61; staff nurse, team leader, than head nurse and surg. supr. Houston VA Hosp., 1961-79; instr. Lee Coll., Baytown, Tex., 1979—, Lead Inst., 1987-93; acting divsn. chair allied health Lee Coll., Baytown, Tex., 1993-94; com. mem. Am. Cancer Soc. Contbr. articles to various publs. Chair Pine Bluff Civic Assn., La Porte, Tex., 1984—. Named Tchr. of Yr., Lee Coll., 1987. Mem. ANA, Nat. League for Nursing, Tex. League for Nursing (pub. rels. com. 1990), Tex. Nurses Assn. (chair allied health divsn. 1992-93).d. Avocation: sailboat racing. Home: 1 Pine Bluff St La Porte TX 77571-6677 Office: Lee Coll 511 S Whiting St Baytown TX 77520-4796

PERCUS, JEROME KENNETH, physicist, educator; b. N.Y.C., June 21, 1926; s. Philip M. and Gertrude B. (Schweiger) P.; m. Ora Engelberg, May 20, 1965; children: Orin, Allon. B.S.E.E., Columbia U., 1947, M.A., 1948, Ph.D., 1954. Instr. elec. engring. Columbia U., N.Y.C., 1952-54; asst. prof. Stevens Inst. Tech., Hoboken, N.J., 1955-58; assoc. prof. NYU, N.Y.C., 1958-65; prof. physics NYU, 1965—; dir. Nat. Biomed. Research Found. Author: Many-Body Problem, 1963, Kinetic Theory and Statistical Mechanics, 1969, Combinatorial Methods, 1971, Combinatorial Methods in Developmental Biology, 1977, Mathematical Methods in Developmental Biology, 1978, Mathematical Methods in Enzymology, 1984, Lectures on the Mathematics of Immunology, 1986; editor: Pattern Recognition, Jour. Statis. Physics, Jour. Comp. Molecular Biology. With USN, 1944-46. Recipient Pregel Chemistry Physics award N.Y. Acad. Scis., 1975, Joel Henry Hildebrand award in the Theoretical and Exptl. Chemistry of Liquids, Am. Chem. Soc., 1993, Pattern Rec. Soc. award, 1992. Fellow AAAS, Am. Phys. Soc.; mem. Am. Math. Soc., Sigma Xi. Office: NYU 251 Mercer St New York NY 10012-1185

PERCY, ANN BUCHANAN, museum curator; b. Lynchburg, Va., Nov. 13, 1940; d. John Tucker and Margaret Buchanan (Peck) Percy; m. W.B. Dixon Stroud, Aug. 4, 1989. BA, Sweet Briar Coll., 1962; MA, Pa. State U., 1965; PhD, Courtauld Inst. Art, U. London, 1974. Art history editor Pa. State U. Press, University Park, 1969-72; asst., assoc., acting curator of drawings Phila. Mus. Art, 1972-84, curator of drawings, 1984—. Author: (exbn. catalogues) Giovanni Benedetto Castiglione: Master Draughtsman of the Italian Baroque, 1971; co-author: Bernardo Cavallino of Naples, 1616-1656, 1984; Francesco Clemente: Three Worlds, 1990; contbr. articles to The Burlington Mag., Master Drawings, 1967-68. Fulbright fellow, Naples, Rome, 1964-65; Samuel H. Kress fellow, Nat. Gallery Art, Washington, 1967-68; Chester Dale fellow, Nat. Gallery Art, Rome, 1968-69; vis. scholar J. Paul Getty Mus., 1987. Mem. Print Coun. Am. Democrat. Office: Phila Mus Art PO Box 7646 Philadelphia PA 19101-7646

PERCY, LEE EDWARD, motion picture film editor; b. Kalamazoo, Feb. 10, 1953; s. Richard Noyes and Helen Louise (Sheffield) P. Student, Goodman Sch., Chgo., 1971, Juilliard Sch., 1972; AB, U. Calif., Santa Cruz, 1977. Radio news reporter McGovern Campaign, Chgo., 1972; cons. Kjos Pub. Co., Chgo., 1973-74; dir. VisArt, Ltd., San Francisco, 1977; ind. film editor L.A., 1978—. Editor: motion pictures: Re-Animator, 1984, Kiss of the Spiderwoman, 1985, Slam Dance, 1987, Checking Out, 1988, Blue Steel, 1989, Reversal of Fortune, 1990, Year of the Gun, 1991, Single White Female, 1992, Against the Wall, 1993 (Eddie award 1995, nominated for Cable ACE award), Corrina, Corrina, 1994, Kiss of Death, 1995, Before and After, 1995. Mem. Am. Cinema Editors, Editors Guild Hollywood, Motion Picture Editors N.Y.

PERCY, S. W., oil industry executive; b. 1946. BA in Mech. Engring. Rensselaer Polytechnic Inst.; MBA, U. Mich.; JD, Cleve. State U. With Standard Oil Co., 1976—; exec. v.p. BP Am., Inc., BP Exploration & Oil Inc.; pres., CEO BP Oil Co. Divsn. Office: BP America Inc 200 Public Sq Cleveland OH 44114

PERDEW, JOHN PAUL, physics educator, condensed matter and density functional theorist; b. Cumberland, Md., Aug. 30, 1943. BS, Gettysburg Coll., 1965; PhD, Cornell U., 1971. Postdoctoral fellow U. Toronto (Ont., Can.), 1971-74, Rutgers U., New Brunswick, N.J., 1974-77; prof. physics Tulane U., New Orleans, 1977—, chair physics dept., 1991-94; vis. scientist Nordita, Copenhagen, Argonne Nat. Lab., ETH Zurich, ITP Santa Barbara, Naval Rsch. Lab., Washington; invited lectr. more than 30 internat. confs. Contbr. more than 110 sci. articles to profl. jours. NSF Rsch. grantee, 1978—; recipient Tulane LAS award for excellence in rsch., 1990. Fellow Am. Phys. Soc.; mem. Am. Assn. Physics Tchrs., Phi Beta Kappa, Sigma Xi. Office: Tulane U Dept Physics New Orleans LA 70118

PERDUE, BEVERLY MOORE, state legislator, geriatric consultant; b. Grundy, Va., Jan. 14, 1948; d. Alfred P. and Irene E. (Morefield) Moore; children: Garrett, Emmett. BA, U. Ky., 1969; MEd, U. Fla., 1974, PhD, 1976. Pvt. lectr., writer, cons. 1980-86; pres. The Perdue Co., New Bern, N.C., 1989—; rep. N.C. State Gen. Assembly, Raleigh, 1986-90; senator N.C. Gen. Assembly, Raleigh, 1990—. Bd. dirs. Nations Bank, New Bern, 1985—, N.C. United Way, Greensboro, 1990-92; exec. mem. N.C. Dem.

PERDUE

3248

WHO'S WHO IN AMERICA

Party, Raleigh, 1989—; bd. mem. N.C. Equity, Raleigh, 1992; mem. N.C. travel bd. Nat. Conf. of State Legislators. Named Outstanding Legislator, N.C. Aging Network, 1989, 92, Toll fellow Nat. Conf. State Legislators, Lexington, Ky., 1992. Mem. Nat. Coun. on Aging, Bus. and Profl. Women, Rotary. Episcopalian. Home: 211 Wilson Point Rd New Bern NC 28562-7519 Office: Perdue & Co PO Box 991 507 Pollack St New Bern NC 28562 also: NC Senate Raleigh NC 27601

PERDUE, CHARLES L., JR., anthropology educator; b. Panthersville, Ga., Dec. 1, 1930; s. Charles L. Sr. and Eva Mae (Samples) P.; m. Nancy J. Martin; children: Martin Clay, Marc Charles, Kelly Scott, Kevin Barry (dec.). Student, North Ga. Coll., 1948-49, Santa Rosa (Calif.) Jr. Coll., 1953; AB in Geology, U. Calif., Berkeley, 1958, postgrad., 1958-59; MA in Folklore, U. Pa., 1968, PhD in Folklore, 1971. Engring. writer Convair Astronautics, Vandenberg AFB, Calif., 1959-60; geologist, mineral classification branch U.S. Geological Survey, Washington, 1960-67; asst. prof. English dept. U. Va., Charlottesville, 1971-72, asst. prof. English and sociology, anthropology depts., 1972-73, asst. prof. English and anthropology depts., 1973-76, assoc. prof., 1976-92, prof., 1992—; cons. in field. Author: Outwitting the Devil: Jack Tales from Wise County, Virginia, 1987, Pig's Foot Jelly, Persimmon Beer: Foodways from the Virginia Writers' Project, 1992, (with others) Weevils in the Wheat: Interviews with Virginia Ex-Slaves, 1976; contbr. articles to profl. jours. With U.S. Army, 1951-54. Univ. Predoctoral fellow U. Pa., 1967-71; Wilson Gee Inst. Rsch. grant U. Va., 1974, 75; Rsch. grant NEH, 1980-81, 84; Sesquicentennial Assoc. award Ctr. for Advanced Studies U. Va. 1978-79, 87-88. Mem. Am. Folklore Soc. (exec. bd. 1980-83, book rev. editor jour. 1986-87), Mid. Atlantic Folklore Assn. (founding mem., bd. dirs.), Nat. Coun. for Traditional Arts (bd. dirs. 1971-87, pres. 1973-79), Va. Folklore Soc. (archivist/editor 1974-89, archivist 1990—). Office: U Va Dept Anthropology Cabell Hall Charlottesville VA 22903

PERDUE, CHRISTINE H., lawyer; b. Huntington, W. Va., Mar. 18, 1949. BA, Oberlin Coll., 1971; JD, Duke U., 1974. Bar: Va. 1974, D.C. 1989. Ptnr. Hunton & Williams, Fairfax, Va.; adj. prof. U. Richmond, 1981-83. Mem. ABA, Va. Bar Assn. (chair labor law sect. 1992—), Fairfax Bar Assn., Phi Beta Kappa. Office: Hunton & Williams 3050 Chain Bridge Rd PO Box 1147 Fairfax VA 22030

PERDUE, FRANKLIN P., poultry products company executive; m. Mitzi Henderson Ayala, July 1988. Chmn. exec. com. Perdue Farms Inc., Salisbury, Md., Perdue Inc. subs. Perdue Farms Inc., Salisbury; chrm., dir. Perdue Farms, Inc. Office: Perdue Farms Inc PO Box 1537 Salisbury MD 21802-1537*

PERDUE, GARLAND DAY, surgeon, educator, hospital director; b. Clermont, Ga., Mar. 19, 1926; s. Garland Day and Nina (Keith) P. B.A., Emory U., 1948, M.D., 1952. Ptnr., Emory Clinic, Atlanta, 1957, clinic dir., 1984-93; mem. faculty Emory U. Sch. Medicine, Atlanta, 1955—, prof. surgery, 1971—, dean clin. affairs, 1983-93; med. dir. Emory U. Hosp., Atlanta, 1983-93; exec. dir. Emory U. System Health Care, 1993—. Mem. Specialty Surg. Socs., Am. Surg. Assn., So. Surg. Assn., Soc. Vascular Surgery, Internat. Soc. Cardiovascular Surgery, Internat. Soc. Surgery. Contbr. articles to profl. jours. Home: 1980 Carrington Ct Stone Mountain GA 30087-1446 Office: Emory U Hosp 1364 Clifton Rd NE Atlanta GA 30322-1102

PERDUE, JAMES, food products executive; b. 1949. BS, Wake Forest U., 1973; MA in Marine Biology, Southeastern Mass. U., 1976; PhD in Fisheries, U. Wash., 1983. With U. Md., Cambridge, 1976-78; CEO Perdue Transp., Inc., Salisbury, Md., 1991—, chmn. bd. Office: Perdue Farms Inc Old Ocean City Rd Salisbury MD 21802*

PERDUE, JAMES EVERETT, university vice chancellor emeritus; b. Auburn, Nebr., June 24, 1916; s. James O. and Hazel D. Perdue; m. Raedeen Tibbetts, Apr. 9, 1939; children: Pamela Jane, Darcy Clare; m. 2d, June Harrison Ward, Aug. 14, 1988. Student, Nebr. Wesleyan U., 1933-34; A.B., Nebr. State Tchrs. Coll., 1937; A.M., No. Colo. State U., Greely, 1940; Ph.D., Stanford U., 1952; LL.D., U. Denver, 1965. Coach, tchr. social studies DeWitt High Sch., Nebr., 1937-38; head social sci. dept. Ft. Morgan High Sch., Colo., 1938-41; ednl. rep. Row, Peterson and Co., 1941-43; acting dean Coll. Arts and Scis., U. Denver, 1946-48, assoc. dean, 1948-51; univ. budget officer U. Denver, 1951-52, asst. to chancellor, 1952-53; prof. social sci., dean Coll. Arts and Scis., U. Denver, 1953-65; pres., prof. social sci. SUNY-Oswego, 1965-77; assoc. chancellor SUNY System, 1977-78, vice chancellor for acad. programs, policy and planning, 1978-81; acting v.p. acad. affairs SUNY-Oswego, 1981; founding dean Coll. Arts and Sci. Ark. State U., 1981-82; provost, chief operating officer U. Ark., 1983; cons. to colls. and univs., 1981—; cons. N.J. State System Higher Edn., 1988; interim v.p. Met. State Coll., Denver; trustee Oswego City Savs. Bank; bd. dirs. Acad. Collective Bargaining Service, 1973—, chmn., 1974—; chmn. Oswego County Heart Fund, 1973; vestry mem. St. Charles Episcopal Ch., 1988; bd. dirs. Heritage Found., 1990—; trustee Morgan C.C. Found., 1990-95, pres. 1992-95. Served as ops. and communications officer USNR, 1943-46. Recipient Disting. Ednl. Service award Peru State, 1966; Outstanding Male Educator award U. N.C. 1975; Meritorious Service award Am. Assn. State Colls. and Univs., 1972; Adminstrv. Leave award Danforth Found., 1972. Mem. Am. Conf. Acad. Deans (vice chmn. 1963-64, exec. bd. 1959-64, nat. chmn. 1965-66), Am. Assn. State Colls. and Univs. (dir. 1967-72, pres.-elect 1976), Ft. Morgan Country Club (trustee 1990-93), Phi Beta Kappa, Pi Gamma Mu, Phi Delta Kappa. Home: 504 E 6th Ave Fort Morgan CO 80701-3217

PERDUE, JUDY CLARK, academic administrator; b. N.Y.C.; d. Christopher Thompson and Iris Ramona (Turner) C.; m. Tito Perdue, July 27, 1957; 1 child, Melanie. BA, Ind. U., 1967; MA, U. Iowa, 1970; MS, Iowa State U., 1980; PhD, U. Ga., 1987. Cataloger Iowa State U. Libr., Ames, 1970-74, head gifts and exchange, 1974-78; head librarian and asst. prof. biology E. Ga. Coll., Swainsboro, 1988-92; head libr., assoc. prof. biology Floyd Coll., Rome, Ga., 1992-94, chair sci. math. and phys. edn., 1994—. Contbr. articles to profl. jours. Fellow Royal Entomol. Soc. London; mem. Assn. So. Biologists, Ga. Libr. Assn., ALA, Entomol. Soc. Am., Acarological Soc. Am., Delta Kappa Gamma, Delta Phi Alpha. Office: Floyd Coll Libr Hwy 27 Rome GA 30162

PERDUE, THEDA, history educator, author; b. McRae, Ga., Apr. 2, 1949; d. James Howard and Ouida (Davis) P. AB, Mercer U., 1972; MA, U. Ga., 1974, PhD, 1976. From asst. prof. to assoc. prof. history Western Carolina U., Cullowhee, N.C., 1975-83; prof. history Clemson (S.C.) U., 1983-88, U. Ky., Lexington, 1988—; editor Indians of S.E., U. Nebr. Press, Lincoln, 1985—; cons. Smithsonian Instn., Washington, 1989; Fulbright lectr. N.Z., 1988. Author: Slavery and the Evolution of Cherokee Society, 1979, Native Carolinians, 1985, The Cherokee, 1988; editor: Nations Remembered, 1980, Cherokee Editor, 1983; co-editor: Southern Women, 1993; mem. editorial bd. Jour. Women's History, 1992—, Ethnohistory, 1992—. Newberry Libr. fellow, 1978, Rockefeller Found. fellow, 1980-81. Mem. Am. Hist. Assn., Orgn. Am. Historians, Am. Soc. for Ethnohistory, So. Hist. Assn., So. Assn. for Women Historians (pres. 1985-86). Democrat. Office: U Ky Dept History Pot # 1715 Lexington KY 40506

PERDUNN, RICHARD FRANCIS, management consultant; b. Trenton, N.J., Dec. 12, 1915; s. Francis R. and Edith (Nogle) P.; m. Eugenia E. Morel, June 7, 1941; 1 child, Justine Reneau; m. Doris D. Andrus, Jan. 30, 1993. B.S., Lehigh U., 1939; postgrad. student, U. Pitts., 1939-40, Johns Hopkins, 1941-42. With U.S. Steel Co., also Glenn L. Martin, 1939-43, supt. machine and assembly, 1941-43; partner Nelson & Perdunn (engrs. and cons., also); v.p. Penco Corp., 1947-49; with Merck & Co., 1949-54, mgr. adminstrn., 1951-54; with Stevenson, Jordan & Harrison (mgmt. engrs.), N.Y.C., 1954-68; exec. v.p. Stevenson, Jordan & Harrison (mgmt. engrs.), 1962-64, pres. 1964-68; pres., chief exec. officer Bachman-Jacks, Inc., Reading, Pa., 1968-71; sr. v.p. Golightly Internat., N.Y.C., 1971—; also dir Golightly Internat.; chmn. Perdunn Assocs., Inc., 1979—; dir. West Point & Annapolis Text Book Pub. Co., 1948—, Indsl. Edn. Films Inc., 1966—,

Eldun Corp., 1964—, Security Nat. Bank, Newark, 1964—; Surburban Life Ins. Co., 1966—, Mainstem Inc., 1965—, Greenhouse Decor Inc., 1961—, Neuwirth Mut. Fund Inc., 1975—; Lectr. on finance and mfg. in, U.S., Can., Eng., Sweden. Assoc. editor: Systems and Procedures Quar, 1948-51; Contbr. articles to profl. publs. Bd. dirs. Inst. Better Confs., Internat. Inst. Bus. Devel., Inst. Urban Affairs, People Care, Inc.; dir. finance Assn. Help for Retarded Children. Served with USAAF, 1942-47. Mem. N.Y.C.C. of C., Council Econ. Devel., Am. Mgmt. Assn., AIM (pres.'s council), Newcomen Soc. N.Am., Systems and Procedures Assn. Am., Soc. Advanced Mgmt. Home: 28 Bay Point Harbour Point Pleasant NJ 08742 also: 600 Square Brielle NJ 08730

PEREIRA, CELINA ANTONIETA, physician; b. Bombay, India, Dec. 21, 1941; came to U.S., 1967; d. João Costa and Adelina (DeSousa) P.; m. Donald Andrew McGowan; children: Malini, Meena. MD, Grant Med. Coll., Bombay, 1965. Resident in pediats. Boston City Hosp., 1967-69, R.I. Hosp., Providence, 1969-70; instr. in pediats. Brown U., Providence, 1973-75; staff physician U. R.I., Kingston, 1975—. Contbr. articles to profl. jours. Vol. hospice VNA, Wakefield, R.I., 1994; active World Spiritual U. Fellow Am. Acad. Pediats. (diplomate), R.I. Med. Soc., Washington County Med. Soc. Roman Catholic. Avocations: travel, music, reading. Office: U RI Health Svcs Kingston RI 02881

PERELL, EDWARD ANDREW, lawyer; b. Stamford, Conn., Mar. 30, 1940; s. Sydney C. and Dorothy (Barger) P.; m. Nan Lifflander, Oct. 10, 1959; children: Stephanie Perell Krause, Timothy R. BA, Yale Coll., 1962, LLB, 1965. Bar: N.Y. 1966. Assoc. Debevoise & Plimpton, N.Y.C., 1965-72, ptnr., 1973-88, 93—; ptnr. Debevoise & Plimpton, N.Y.C. and London, 1989-93. Contbr. numerous articles on securities laws, mergers and acquisitions to profl. publs. Chmn. bd. dirs. Fedn. Protestant Welfare Agys., N.Y.C., 1983-87; chmn. bd. dirs. Graham-Windham Family Svcs., N.Y.C., 1970-77. Mem. ABA, Assn. of Bar of City of N.Y., Internat. Bar Assn., Yale Clubs of N.Y. and London, Law Soc. of England and Wales. Home: Cricket Ln Dobbs Ferry NY 10522 also: 14 Sutton Pl S New York NY 10022-3071 Office: Debevoise & Plimpton 875 3rd Ave New York NY 10022-6225

PERELLA, SUSANNE BRENNAN, librarian; b. Providence, Mar. 19, 1936; d. Laurence J. and Harriet E. (Delaplane) Brennan. B.A., U. Conn., 1960; M.L.S., U. Mich., 1967. Head M.B.A. Library, Univ. Conn., Hartford, 1964-66; asst. librarian Cornell Univ. Grad. Sch. Bus., Ithaca, N.Y., 1967-72; head reader's services FTC Library, Washington, 1972-79; library dir. FTC Library, 1979-92; libr. dir. Libr. and Info. Svcs. U.S. Treasury, Washington, 1992—. Mem. Law Librarians Soc., Spl. Libraries Assn., Am. Assn. Law Libraries, Fed. Library and Info. Ctr. Com. Office: US Dept Treasury Libr 1500 Pennsylvania Ave NW Washington DC 20220-0002

PERELLE, IRA B., psychologist; b. Mt. Vernon, N.Y., Sept. 16, 1925; s. Joseph Yale and Lillian (Schaffer) P.; student U. Tex.; grad. in elec. engring. R.C.A. Inst., 1951; student Iona Coll.; B.S., M.S., Ph.D., Fordham U.; m. Diane A. Granville, 1982; 1 child, Jessica Eve. Prodn. mgr. Arden Jewelry Case Co., 1946-49; became chief engr. Westlab Electronic Service Engrs., 1949; ptnr. Westlab, 1954; pres. Westlab, Inc., 1955-64, chmn. bd., 1956; pres. Westchester Research and Devel. Labs., 1953-65; exec. dir. Interlink, Ltd., 1966—; dir. Atlantic Research Inst., 1975—; cons. higher edn. divsn. U.S. Dept. of Edn., 1994—; cons. ednl. research Fordham U., Catholic U. of P.R., Bayamon (P.R.) Central U., World U., San Juan, P.R., John Jay Coll., N.Y.C., Rockland C.C., N.Y.; rsch. cons. So. Westchester County Bd. Coop. Ednl. Services; stats. cons. City of Mt. Vernon (N.Y.), Reader's Digest, Pleasantville, N.Y., GT&E Inc., CUNY; served as expert witness for N.Y. State Tax Ct.; assoc. Columbia U. Seminars; prof. dept. psychology NYU; prof. dept. bus. and econs.; dept. psychology Mercy Coll., Dobbs Ferry N.Y.; prof. Grad. Sch. Bus., L.I. U.; adj. prof. SUNY-Purchase, Fordham U., N.Y.C.; vis. prof. Fairleigh Dickenson U.; faculty adv. com. Mercer County Coll., 1969-73; conf. leader Nat. Conf. Ednl. Tech., 1971-73. Mem. staff Civil Def., 1954-74; bd. dirs. Mid-Hudson Inst., Dobbs Ferry, N.Y. Served as radio instr. USAAF, 1943-46. Mem. IEEE, N.Y. Zool. Soc., Assn. Ednl. Communication and Tech., N.Y. State Ednl. Communication Assn., Audio Engring. Soc., Acoustical Soc. Am., Am. Inst. Physics, Am. Psychol. Assn., Am. Ednl. Research Assn., AAAS, Animal Behavior Soc., Am. Genetic Assoc. N.Y. Acad. Scis. Author: A Practical Guide to Educational Media for the Classroom Teacher, 1974; also articles; research on laterality for evolutionary biology. Discoverer Perelle Phenomenon, psychology-attention. Office: Mercy Coll Dobbs Ferry NY 10522

PERELMAN, LEON JOSEPH, paper manufacturing executive, university president; b. Phila., Aug. 28, 1911; s. Morris and Jennie (Davis) P.; m. Beverly Waxman, Jan. 27, 1945 (div. Apr. 1960); children: Cynthia, David. B.A., LaSalle Coll., 1933, LL.D., 1978; postgrad., U. Pa. Law Sch., 1933-35; L.H.D. (hon.), Dropsie U., 1976. Ptnr. Am. Paper Products Co. (later Am. Paper Products Inc.), Phila., 1935-42, pres. 1943—; pres. Am. Cone & Tube Co. Inc., Phila., 1953—, United Ammunition Container Inc., Phila. 1961—; Ajax Paper Tube Co., Phila., 1962—; vice chmn. bd. Belmont Industries, Phila. 1963—; pres. Dropsie U., Phila. 1978—. Author: Perelman Antique Toy Mus., 1972. Fin. chmn. Valley Forge council Boy Scouts Am., 1968; founder, bd. dirs. Perelman Antique Toy Mus., Phila., 1969; pres. West Park Hosp., 1975-78, 81—; trustee La Salle U., Balch Inst. Ethnic Studies. Served to 1st lt. USAAF, 1942-45. Recipient citation Jewish Theol. Sem., 1965; Beth Jacob award, 1966; award Pop Warner Little Scholars Inc., 1972; Cyrus Adler award Jewish Theol. Sem., 1976. Mem. AAUP, Jewish Publ. Soc. Am. (treas. 1983, v.p. 1991), Franklin Inst., Am. Assn. Mus. Republican. Jewish. Clubs: Union League (Phila.); Masons, Shriners. One of the highlights of my life was the establishment of an antique toy museum to keep intact in a permanent place, in order to provide inspiration and pleasure for the general public and stimulate interest in old toys and to give students, antiquarians and collectors an opportunity for study and research in the history and development of one of the world's largest collections of children's toys during the past hundred years.

PERELMAN, MELVIN, pharmaceutical company executive; b. Omaha, Oct. 12, 1930; s. Benjamin and Sarah (Fox) P.; m. Jill Louise Stott, Aug. 1, 1953; children: Steven Eric, Wendy Lynn, Kent Bryan. BS, Northwestern U., 1952; PhD, Rice U., 1956; postdoctoral research, Fed. Inst. Tech., Zurich, 1956-57. Organic chemist Eli Lilly and Co., Indpls., 1957-58, sr. organic chemist, 1958-62, corp. trainee, 1962-64, staff asst. to exec. dir. control, 1964, mng. dir. rsch. activities in Eng., 1964-70, elected v.p. Eli Lilly Internat., 1969, exec. dir. facilities planning, 1970-72, v.p. devel. rsch., 1972-74, v.p. facilities planning, 1974-76, pres. Eli Lilly Internat. Corp, 1976-86, exec. v.p. and pres. Lilly Rsch. Labs., 1986—, also bd. dirs.; exec. v.p., pres. Lilly Rsch. Labs., 1986—. Contbr. articles to profl. jours., 1954-64; patentee in field. Chmn. founding bd. Indpls. Zool. Soc., 1986—; bd. dirs. PSI Resources, Inc., PSI Energy, Inc., Plainfield, 1980—. Home: 3030 W 116th St Carmel IN 46032-9563 Office: Eli Lilly & Co Lilly Corporate Ctr Indianapolis IN 46285

PERELMAN, RONALD OWEN, diversified holding company executive; b. Greensboro, N.C., 1943; s. Raymond and Ruth (Caplan) P.; m. Claudia Cohen; 4 children. BA, U. Pa., 1964; MBA, Wharton Sch. Fin., 1966. With Belmont Industries Inc., 1966-78; chmn., chief exec. officer, dir. MacAndrews & Forbes Holdings Inc., Wilmington, Del., 1983—; chmn., chief exec. officer MacAndrews & Forbes Group Inc. (subs.), N.Y.C., 1978—; chmn., chief exec. officer, dir. Revlon Group Inc. (subs. MacAndrews & Forbes Group Inc.), N.Y.C., 1985—; chmn. Revlon Inc. (subs.), N.Y.C., 1985—; also chmn. Nat. Health Labs. Inc., La Jolla, Calif., 1985—, Andrews Group Inc., N.Y.C., 1985—. Jewish. Office: Revlon Group Inc 21 E 63rd St New York NY 10021 also: MacAndrews & Forbes Group Inc 36 E 63rd St New York NY 10021 Office: National Health Labs Inc 7590 Fay Ave La Jolla CA 92037*

PERENCHIO, ANDREW JERROLD, film and television executive; b. Fresno, Calif., Dec. 20, 1930; s. Andrew Joseph and Dorothea (Harvey) P.; m. Robin Green, July 16, 1954 (div.); children: Candace L., Catherine M., John Gardner; m. Jacquelyn Lume. BS, UCLA, 1954. V.p. Music Corp. Am., 1958-62, Gen. Artists Corp., 1962-64; pres., owner theatrical agy. Chartwell Artists, Ltd., L.A., from 1964; chmn. bd. Tandem

Prodns., Inc. and TAT Communications Co., L.A., 1973-83; pres., chief exec. officer Embassy Pictures, L.A., from 1983; now pres. Chartwell Partnerships Group, L.A. Promoter Muhammad Ali-Joe Frazier heavyweight fight, 1971, Bobby Riggs-Billie Jean King tennis match, 1973. Served to 1st lt. USAF, 1954-57. Clubs: Bel-Air Country (Los Angeles); Westchester (N.Y.) Country; Friars (N.Y.C.). Office: Chartwell Partnerships Group 1901 Avenue of Stars Ste 680 Los Angeles CA 90067

PERERA, GEORGE A., physician; b. N.Y.C., Dec. 29, 1911; s. Lionello and Carolyn (Allen) P.; m. Anna Paxson Rhoads, Dec. 22, 1934; children: Marcia (Mrs. Nicholas B. Van Dyck), David Rhoads. A.B., Princeton U., 1933; M.D., Columbia U., 1937, Sc.D. in Medicine, 1942. Diplomate: Am. Bd. Internal Medicine (dir. 1957-64, vice chmn. 1963-64). Intern Presbyn. Hosp., N.Y.C., 1937-39; resident medicine Presbyn. Hosp., 1941-43; asst. resident Peter Bent Brigham Hosp., Boston, 1939-40; asst. physiology N.Y. U., 1940-41; mem. staff Presbyn. Hosp., 1943-71, attending physician, 1960-71; faculty Columbia U. Coll. Physicians and Surgeons, 1946-71, prof. medicine, 1958-71, asso. dean, 1962-70. Trustee Riverdale Country Sch., N.Y.C., 1949-80, pres., 1977-80; trustee Mary Imogene Bassett Hosp., Cooperstown, N.Y., 1961-80, Columbia U. Press, 1961-64, 66-69, Bridges of Understanding Found., 1973-77; trustee Concern for Dying, 1975-81, v.p., 1978-79, 80-81; alumni trustee Columbia U., 1974-80; mem. corp. Haverford Coll., 1979-87; bd. dirs. Kendal-Crosslands Comty., 1983-94. Fellow ACP, AAAS; mem. N.Y. Acad. Medicine (v.p. 1968-70, trustee 1973-78), Assn. Am. Physicians (emeritus), Alpha Omega Alpha. Home: Kendal At Longwood # 159 Kennett Square PA 19348

PERERA, LAWRENCE THACHER, lawyer; b. Boston, June 23, 1935; s. Guido R. and Faith (Phillips) P.; m. Elizabeth A. Wentworth, July 5, 1961; children: Alice V. Perera Lucey, Caroline F. Perera Barry, Lucy E., Lawrence Thacher. B.A., Harvard U., 1957, LL.B., 1961. Bar: Mass. 1961, U.S. Supreme Ct. 1973. Clk. Judge R. Ammi Cutter, Mass. Supreme Jud. Ct., Boston, 1961-62; assoc. firm Palmer & Dodge, Boston, 1962-69; ptnr. Palmer & Dodge, 1969-74; judge Middlesex County Probate Ct., East Cambridge, Mass., 1974-79; partner firm Hemenway & Barnes, Boston, 1979—; mem. faculty and nat. coun. Hon. Nat. Jud. Coll., Reno, prof./pres. Mass. Continuing Legal Edn., Inc., 1988-90. Chmn. Boston Fin. Commn., 1969-71; overseer Brigham & Women's Hosp., Boston; chmn. bd. overseers Boston Opera Assn.; dir. Boston Lyric Opera; chmn. Back Bay Archtl. Commn., 1966-72; trustee Sta. WGBH Ednl. Found., Boston Athenaeum; trustee emeritus Wang Ctr. Performing Arts; vice-chmn. The Boston Found. Fellow Am. Acad. Matrimonial Lawyers, Am. Coll. Trust and Estate Counsel; mem. ABA, Am. Bar Found., Am. Law Inst., Mass. Bar Assn., Mass. Bar Found., Boston Bar Assn.. Home: 18 Marlborough St Boston MA 02116-2101 Office: 60 State St Boston MA 02109-1801

PERES, JUDITH MAY, journalist; b. Chgo., June 30, 1946; d. Leonard H. and Eleanor (Seltzer) Zurakov; m. Michael Peres, June 27, 1972; children: Dana, Avital. BA, U. Ill., 1967. Acct. exec. Daniel J. Edelman Inc., Chgo., 1967-68; copy editor Jerusalem (Israel) Post, 1968-71, news editor, 1971-75, chief night editor, 1975-80, editor, style book, 1978-80; copy editor Chgo. Tribune, 1980-82, rewriter, 1982-84, assoc. fgn. editor, 1984-90, nat. editor, 1990-95, nat./fgn. editor, 1995—. Office: Chicago Tribune 435 N Michigan Ave Chicago IL 60611

PERESS, GILLES, photographer; b. Nevilly-S-Seine, France, Dec. 29, 1946; came to U.S., 1975; s. Albert and Thelma (Dirats) P. Student, Institut b'Etudes Politiques, Paris, 1966-68, Universite De Vincennes, Paris, 1968-71. Mem. Magnum Photos Inc., N.Y.C., Paris, London, 1975-84, v.p., 1984-85, pres., 1986-87, 89-90; represented by Howard Greenberg Galley, N.Y.C. Author: Telex: Iran, 1984 (Prix du Premier Livre award 1984), Power in the Blood: The North of Ireland, Farewell to Bosnia, 1994; exhibited in one-man and group shows at Mass. Inst. Tech., Cambridge, 1977, Arts Coun. Gt. Brit., London Adakyu, Grand Gallery, Tokyo, 1979, Inst. Art and Urban Resources, N.Y., 1984, Palais de Luxembourg, Paris Internat. Ctr. for Photography, N.Y., 1981, Side Gallery, Newcastle-upon-Tyne Centre Kodak, Paris, 1982, Blue Sky Gallery, Portland, 1983, Corcoran Gallery, Washington, 1985, Musee de la Villette, Paris, 1986, Carpenter Ctr. for Visual Arts, Harvard U. 1986, The Mus. Contemporary Photography, Chgo., 1987, Hippolyte Gallery, Helsinki, Finland, 1988, Ranta Gallery, Oulu, Finland, 1986, Burden Gallery, N.Y., 1986, Alternative Mus., N.Y., 1989. Palais de Tokyo, Paris, 1989, Internat. Mus. Photography, Rochester U. South Fla., Tampa, 1989, Canon Image Ctr., Amsterdam, 1989, Centre Nationale de la Photographie, Paris, 1989, Mus. Photographic Arts, San Diego, 1989, Arbetets Mus, Norrkoping Sweden, 1989, Art Inst. Chgo., 1990, Sala de Exposiciones del Canal de Isabel II, Madrid, 1990, Musee d'Elysée, Lausanne, 1990, Alternative Mus., N.Y., 1990, Internat. Ctr. Photography N.Y., 1990, David Winton Bell Gallery Brown U., Providence, R.I., 1992, Lillehammer (Norway) Art Mus., 1993, Corcoran Gallery, Washington, 1994, La Primavera Barcelona, 1994, P.S. 1, N.Y.C., 1994, Photomus. Winterthur, Switzerland, 1994; represented in permanent collections Mus. Modern Art, N.Y.C., Metropolitan Mus. Art, Minn. Art Inst., Mus. Fine Arts, Houston, The Art Inst. Chgo., Arts Coun. Gt. Brit., London, Bibliothèque Nationale, Paris, Centre Nationale de la Photograhie, Paris, First Bank Minn., Mpls., Found. Leitz, Rueil-Malmaison, Found. Nationale pour la Photographie, Paris, Internat. Mus. Photography at George Eastman House, The Minn. Inst. Art, Musée d'Art Moderne, The Mus. of the Moving Image, The Mus. Modern Art, The N.Y. Hist. Soc., The Phila. Mus. Art, Side Gallery, U. Soth Fla. Art Mus; contbr. photos to profl. jours. Recipient W. Eugene Smith award in Humanistic Photography, Ernst Haas award Harvard U.; Daad grantee Harvard U., grantee NEA; Gahan fellow Harvard U., Guggenheim fellow, La Found. de France fellow, Nat. Endowment for Arts fellow. Mem. Am. Soc. Mag. Photographers. Office: Howard Greenberg Gallery 120 Wooster St New York NY 10012

PERESS, MAURICE, symphony conductor, musicologist; b. N.Y.C., Mar. 18, 1930; s. Haskell Ben Ezra and Elka (Tygier) P. B.A., N.Y.U., 1951; postgrad., Mannes Coll. Music, NYU Grad. Sch. Musicology. Asst. condr. Mannes Coll. Music, 1957-60; music dir. NYU, 1958-61; asst. condr. New York Philharmonic, 1961-62; music dir. Corpus Christi (Tex.) Symphony, 1961-74, Austin Symphony, 1970-72, Kansas City Philharm., 1974-80; dir. Bur. Indian Affairs pilot project Communication through Music, 1968; faculty Queens Coll., 1969-70, 83—; mus. dir. world premiere Bernstein Mass, J.F. Kennedy Center, Washington, 1971. Pub.: musical adaptation and devel. Ellington Opera, Queenie Pie; orchestrations: Ellington, New World 'a Comin', Black Brown and Beige, Bernstein West Side Story Overture; reconstrn. Gershwin's "Strike Up the Band", 1929, Paul Whiteman's Historic Aeolian Hall concert of 1924 (recorded Musical Heritage Soc.); Duke Ellington's First Carnegie Hall concert, 1944; George Antheil's 1927 Carnegie Hall "Ballets Mécanique" concert (recorded Musical Heritage Soc.); James Reese Europes Clef Club concert, 1912, First "All Negro" concert composed and performed by African Ams. in Carnegie Hall; author: Some Music Lessons for American Indian Youngsters, 1968; contbr. articles profl. jours. Served with AUS, 1953-55. Named Millicent James fellow NYU, 1955; Mannes Coll. scholar, 1955-57. Mem. ASCAP, Conductor's Guild, The Friends of Earl Robinson (pres.), Dvorak Am. Soc. (bd. dirs.), Am. Soc. for Jewish Music (bd. dirs.). Jewish. Home: 310 W 72nd St New York NY 10023-2675

PERETZ, EILEEN, interior designer; b. N.Y.C., Oct. 29, 1934; d. Leo and Mary Miller; m. David Peretz, Aug. 28, 1955; children: Deborah, Adam. BA in Fine Art, CCNY, 1956; Cert. in Interior Design, N.Y. Sch. Interior Design, N.Y.C., 1964. Interior design asst. Narden & Radoszy, N.Y.C., 1956; assoc. interior designer Renee Ross Interiors, N.Y.C., 1964-70; chief interior designer Peretz & Marks Interiors, N.Y.C., 1972-82; sole propr. Eileen Peretz Interiors Inc., N.Y.C., 1970-72, pres. 1982—; cons., mentor, lectr. Marymount Coll., N.Y.C., 1980; lectr. Fashion Inst. Tech.; cons., Paris. Columnist for weekly newspaper Our Town, N.Y.C., 1976-79. Mem. ASID (assoc.), Allied Bd. Trade. Home and Office: 300 Central Park W New York NY 10024 also: 32 Rue de Varenne, Paris 75007, France

PEREY, RON, lawyer; b. Cleve., Feb. 2, 1943; s. John Perecinsky and Anne (Nagy) Disman; 1 child, Page Suzanne. BA in Polit. Sci., Miami U., Oxford, Ohio, 1965; JD cum laude, Ohio State U., 1968. Bar: Wash. 1968, U.S. Dist. Ct. (we. dist.) Wash. 1968, U.S. Ct. Appeals (9th cir.) 1973, U.S. Supreme Ct. 1985. Assoc. Reed McClure, Seattle, 1968-71, ptnr., 1971-82; ptnr. Perey

& Smith, Seattle, 1982-86, Perey Langley, Seattle, 1986-92; owner Law Offices of Ron Perey, Seattle, 1992—; speaker in field. Contbr. articles to profl. jours. Mem. ABA (litigation sect.), Seattle-King County Bar Assn., Assn. Trial Lawyers Am., Wash. State Trial Lawyers Assn. (mem. bd. govs. 1983-85), Am. Bd. Trial Advs., Wash. State Bar Assn. (mem. bd. govs. 1994-97), Damage Attys. Round Table. Avocations: traveling, reading, hiking, jogging. Office: Market Place Tower 2025 1st Ave Ste 350 Seattle WA 98120-2100

PEREYRA-SUAREZ, CHARLES ALBERT, lawyer; b. Paysandu, Uruguay, Sept. 7, 1947; came to U.S., 1954, naturalized, 1962; s. Hector and Esther (Enriquez-Sarano) P.-S.; m. Susan H. Cross, Dec. 30, 1983. BA in History magna cum laude, Pacific Union Coll., 1970; postgrad., UCLA, 1970-71; JD, U. Calif., Berkeley, 1975. Bar: Calif. 1975, D.C. 1980. Staff atty. Western Ctr. Law and Poverty, Inc., Los Angeles, 1976; trial atty. civil rights div. U.S. Dept. Justice, Washington, 1976-79; asst. U.S. atty., criminal div. U.S. Dept. Justice, Los Angeles, 1979-82; sr. litigation assoc. Gibson, Dunn & Crutcher, Los Angeles, 1982-84; sole practice Los Angeles, 1984-86; ptnr. McKenna & Cuneo, Los Angeles, 1986—. Democrat. Avocations: tennis, jogging, travel. Office: McKenna & Cuneo 444 S Flower St Los Angeles CA 90071-2901

PEREZ, ANDREW, III, architect. Student, Georgetown U., 1958; BArch, U. Tex., 1961; postgrad., U. Calif., Berkeley, 1965-66. Registered architect, Tex., Calif.; cert. Nat. Coun. Archtl. Registration Bd. Founder, mng. ptnr. O'Neill & Perez, Architects, 1969-84, Andrew Perez Assocs., Architects, 1984—; dir. coord. architecture and interior design programs U. Tex., San Antonio, 1988—; prin.-in-charge master planning and urban design svcs. City of San Antonio, Pan Am. U., Ft. Hood, Tex., various Tex. communities; vis. lectr. Universidad Nacional Autonoma de Mex., Instituto Tecnologico de Nuevo Laredo y la Academia de Arquitectura, Tex. A&M u., U. Houston, 1987; vis. critic U. Tex., San Antonio, San Antonio Coll., Trinity U.; juror various archtl. design competitions. Prin. works include Bank of San Antonio, 1974 (Design Excellence award Bldg./Owners Mgmt. Assn., Precast Concrete Inst. 1976), Gill Cos. Office Bldg., 1975 (Design Excellence award Bldg./Owners Mgmt. Assn. 1977), Mullins Ranch Ho., Muldoon, Tex., (Design Excellence award San Antonio chpt. AIA 1978, Honor award Tex. Soc. Architects 1979), Baird Residence, Marble Falls, Tex. (Honor award Tex. Soc. Architects 1978), Mexican Am. Unity Coun. Ctr., 1978 (Design Excellence award San Antonio chpt. AIA 1978, Adaptive Reuse award San Antonio Conservation Soc. 1979), Bandera br. Gill Savs. (Honor award Tex. Soc. Architects 1981, Design Excellllence award San Antonio chpt. AIA 1984), Victoria Cts. Phases I & II renovation, 1979-86 (Design Excellence award San Antonio chpt. AIA 1982), Child Care Ctr., Brooks AFB, Tex., 1981 (1st Honor award USAF Design Awards 1980, 1st Pl. Design award USAF Design Competition, 1980), St. Paul Sq. Block Improvements, 1982 (Honor award, Design Excellence award San Antonio chpt. AIA 1982), Diagnostic Unit Tex. Dept. Corrections, Huntsville, Tex., 1983, Straus Ranch Ho., Bexar County, Tex. (2 Design Excellence awards San Antonio chpt. AIA 1984, Honor award Tex. Soc. Architects 1984, one of 8 Outstanding Examples of Architecture in Tex. during Past 150 Yrs. Tex. Architect Mag. 1986), Logistical Systems Ops. Ctr., Kelly AFB, 1984, adminstrv. offices Alamo C.C. Dist., 1984, U.S. Border Patrol Sta., Eagle Pass, Tex., 1984 (Design Excellence award San Antonio chpt. AIA 1984), City Pub. Libr. & Lagoon/Pk. Devel., Farmers Branch, Tex., 1985 (Design Excellence, Honor award San Antonio chpt. AIA 1987), McAllister Ranch Ho., Magic Springs, Tex. (Design Excellence award San Antonio chpt. AIA 1985), U.S. Post Office, San Antonio, 1985, Consolidated Support Ctr., Brooks AFB, Tex., 1985, Univ. Ctr. U. Tex., San Antonio, 1986, Health & Phys. Edn. Facility Pan Am. U., 1986, Minten Residence, 1986 (Design Excellence award San Antonio chpt. AIA 1987), The Edn. Ctr., 1986 (John & Joyce Karr award Tex. Hist. Commn. 1987, Design Excellence award San Antonio chpt. AIA 1987), Manske Meml. Libr., Farmers Branch (1st Pl. Design award City of Farmers Branch Design Competition 1981, Design Excellence award San Antonio chpt. AIA 1987), County Line Rad Fire Sta., New Braunfels, Tex., 1987, Tex. Air N.G. Hdqs., 1990, Cahill Residence, San Antonio, 1991, Longoria Residence, Helotes, Tex., 1993-94, others. Pres. parents-tchrs. coun. St. Anthony Sch., 1979, founding treas., bd. dirs. 1985-88, mem. devel. com.; mem. parish bd. Our Lady Grace Ch., 1980-82; chmn. Mayor & City Coun.'s Hist. Sites and Structures Task Force, 1982-87, Task Force Redrafting San Antonio Hist. Preservation Ordinance, 1985-87, Master Plan Task Force for City of San Antonio, 1992, City of San Antonio Hist. Rev. Bd., 1991-92, City of San Antonio Hist. and Design Rev. Commn., 1992—; mem. Task Force Developing hist. Preservation Incentives Program, 1986; founder/v.p. San Antonio Hist. Found., 1988; bd. dirs. Sites. KSTX and KPAC, 1984—, San Antonio Mus. Assn., 1986—, chmn. facilities com., 1987—, sec. bd. dirs., 1991—. With USN, 1963-65, capt. Res. ret. Fellow AIA (past pres., v.p., sec. San Antonio chpt., mem. urban desi 1984-86, mem. and past chmn. San Antonio chpt. found., co-chmn. graphic and publs. com. nat. conv. 1986); mem. Nat. Trust Hist. Preservation, Tex. Soc. Architects (bd. dirs. 1982-85), Urban Design Inst. Office: Andrew Perez Assocs Architects 3737 Broadway Ste 270 San Antonio TX 78209-6547

PEREZ, CARLOS A., radiation oncologist, educator; b. Colombia, Nov. 10, 1934; came to U.S., 1960, naturalized, 1969; children: Carlos S., Bernardo, Edward P. B.S., U. de Antioquia, Medellin, 1952, M.D., 1960. Diplomate: Am. Bd. Radiology (trustee 1985—). Rotating intern Hosp. U. St. Vincente de Paul, Medellin and Caldas, 1958-59; resident Mallinckrodt Inst. Radiology, Washington U. Sch. Medicine, St. Louis, 1960-63; mem. faculty Mallinckrodt Inst. Radiology, Washington U. Sch. Medicine, 1964—, prof. radiology, 1972—, dir. radiation oncology ctr., 1976—; fellow radiotherapy M.D. Anderson Hosp. and Tumor Inst., U. Tex., Houston, 1963-64. Coeditor: Basis and Clinical Practice of Radiation Oncology, Principle and Practice of Gynecologic Oncology; editl. bd. Internat. Jour. Radiation and Physics, 1975—; contbr. articles to med. jours. Fellow Am. Coll. Radiology; mem. AAAS, AMA, Internat. Assn. Study Lung Cancer, Am. Soc. Clin. Oncology, Am. Soc. Therapeutic Radiologists (pres. 1981-82, Gold medal 1992), Am. Radium Soc., Am. Assn. Cancer Rsch., Am. Assn. Cancer Edn., Radiol. Soc. N.Am., Brit. Inst. Radiology, Mo. Radiol. Soc., Mo. Accad. Sci., Mo. Med. Soc., St. Louis Med. Soc., Greater St. Louis Soc. Radiologists, Radiation Rsch. Soc. Home: 78 Lake Forest Saint Louis MO 63117 Office: Washington U Radiation Oncology Ctr 4511 Forest Pk Ave Saint Louis MO 63108-2138

PEREZ, FRANCISCO IGNACIO, clinical psychologist, educator; b. Havana, Cuba, May 21, 1947; came to U.S., 1960; s. Francisco J. and Maria F. (Villa) P.; m. Georgina Montero, Aug. 27, 1971; children: Francisco A., Teresa M. BA, U. Fla., 1969, MA, 1971, PhD, 1972. Lic. psychologist, Tex. Asst. prof. edn. U. Houston, 1972-74; asst. prof. neurology & psychiatry Baylor U. Coll. Medicine, Dallas, 1974-80; pvt. practice clin. psychology, Houston, 1980—; clin. asst. prof. neurology and phys. medicine Baylor Coll. Medicine, Houston, 1980—; asst. prof. occupational psychology Health Sci. Ctr. Sch. Pub. Health U. Tex., 1993—. Bd. dirs. Houston Community Youth Ctr., Stroke Club, Houston. NIMH research grantee, 1976-77; mem. med. adv. bd. Multiple Sclerosis Soc., Crons & Ilietis Found. Mem. Am. Psychol. Assn., Internat. Neuropsychology Soc., Assn. Advancement Behavior Analysis, Biofeedback Soc. Am. Roman Catholic. Contbr. articles to profl. jours. Home: 5603 Palisade Falls Trl Humble TX 77345-1907 Office: 6560 Fannin Suite 1224 Houston TX 77030

PEREZ, GERALD S. A., retail executive educator; b. Agana, Guam, Mar. 3, 1943; s. Jose B. and Veronica S. (San Agustin) P.; m. Kathleen M. Conrow, June 14, 1966; children: Sherry, Steven, Mike. B.S. in Forestry, U. Idaho, 1965, M.S. in Wildlife Mgmt. (John Hay Whitney fellow, Wildlife Mgmt. Inst. fellow), 1969. Wildlife biologist to dep. dir. Guam Dept. Agr., Agana, 1966-71; dir. Dept. Land Mgmt., 1971-74; dir. budget and mgmt. Office of Gov., 1974-75; pres. Guam C. of C., Agana, 1976-83; v.p. retail ops. Duty Free Shoppers Ltd., Tamuning, Guam, 1983—; adj. instr. ornithology U. Guam, 1967—; acting dean Land Grant Coll., 1973; instr. job devel. program Guam Economic Opportunity Commn., 1968; pres. Duty Free Shoppers Ltd. Partnership, Guam, DFS Guam, 1989—; regents U. Guam, 1987—; exec. sec. Guam Territorial Planning Commn., Guam Hist. Site and Place Name Commn.; mem. Gov.'s Adv. Council and Legis. Rev. Com., Mental Health Advisory Bd., 1976—; Internat. Council Protection of Endangered Bats, 1972—; contract officer land and water conservation funds. Contbr. articles to profl. jours. Chmn. Guam Ednl. Telecommunications Corp.; pres. Micronesian Regional Tourism Council,

1980—; vice chmn. Guam Growth Council, 1976—; co-chmn. Anderson AFB Community Council, 1976—; mem. civilian adv. bd. Naval Forces Marianas, 1978—; chmn. budget and fin. com. U. Guam Bd. Regents, 1988—; bd. dirs. Guam Visitors Bur. Govt. scholar, 1963-65; Young Men's League scholar, 1968; John Hay Whitney fellow, 1968; fellow Wildlife Mgmt. Inst., 1968. Mem. Air Force Assn. (v.p. arc light chpt. 1987—), Guam C. of C. (bd. dirs.). Phi Sigma, Xi Sigma Pi. Home and Office: PO Box 7746 Agana GU 96931-7746 *Service to mankind has been my guide to professional fulfillment. It has enabled me to better understand the diversity of man, the conditions which have formed his very being, and the journeys which are open to his choosing.*

PEREZ, GERARD VINCENT, art publishing company executive; b. LeMans, France, Oct. 5, 1946; came to U.S., 1971; s. Georges and Marie-Laurence (Anziani) P.; m. Nancy J. Rudin, Apr. 23, 1976; children: Samantha, Amanda. BA, B. Franklin Coll., Orleans, France, 1966; MBA, ESCAE Marseille, France, 1970; postgrad., Am. Grad. Sch. Internat. Mgmt., Glendale, Ariz., 1973. Owner, mgr. Mariettes Unltd., St. Tropez, France, 1967-69; sales engr. Paper Converting Machine Co., Inc., Green Bay, Wis., 1973-75; mgr. sales J.D. Marshall Internat., Skokie, Ill., 1975-77; pres. Fine Art Resources, Inc., Chgo., 1977-86, London Contemporary Art, Prospect Heights, Ill., 1986-91, Art Emotion Corp., Prospect Heights, 1991—. Served with French Armed Forces, 1970-71. Home: 1758 S Edgar St Palatine IL 60067-7435

PEREZ, JEAN-YVES, engineering company executive; b. 1945. Ingenieur Civil Engring., Ecole Centrale des Arts et Manufactures, Paris, 1970; MS, U. Ill., 1971. With Soletanche Enterprise, 1972—; pres. Woodward-Clyde Cons., Denver. With French Air Force, 1971-72. Office: Woodward-Clyde Cons 4582 S Ulster St Ste 600 Denver CO 80237-2637*

PEREZ, JOHN CARLOS, biology educator; b. Park City, Utah, Apr. 29, 1941; s. John Cano and Elma May (Ivie) P.; m. Patsy May, Oct. 26, 1963; 9 children. B.S. in Molecular and Genetic Biology, U. Utah, 1967, M.A. in Zoology, Mankato State Coll., Minn., 1972; Ph.D. in Bacteriology, Utah State U., 1972. Research assoc. in bacteriology Utah State U., Logan, 1970-72; asst. prof. biology Tex. A&I U., Kingsville, 1972-75, a prof., dir. MBRS-NIH program, 1975-85, prof., 1981—. Contbr. articles to profl. jours. Served with U.S. Army, 1960-63. Named Outstanding Citizen of Kingsville, 1976; recipient Disting. Research award Tex. A&I U., 1979; recipient numerous grants for research and teaching, 1976—. Mem. Am. Soc. Microbiology, Am. Soc. Toxinology, Tex. Assn. Coll. Tchrs., Sigma Xi. Mormon (stake pres.). Office: Tex A&I U Biology Dept Campus Box 158 A&I Kingsville TX 78363

PEREZ, JOSEPH DOMINIQUE, physics educator; b. New Orleans, Oct. 17, 1942; s. Joseph D. Jr. and Elvira (Herkender) P.; m. Judith Rey Kemper, Sept. 4, 1964 (div. Sept. 1970); children: Stephen, Carla; m. Karni R. Glanz, Sept. 5, 1972; children: Michael, Joshua. BS in Physics, Loyola U. of S., New Orleans, 1964; PhD, U. Md., 1968. Postdoctoral fellow Inst. for Pure and Applied Physics, U. Calif., San Diego, 1969-71; assoc. prof. U. So. Calif., L.A., 1971-74; scientist, mgr. rsch. and devel. div. Lockheed, Palo Alto, Calif., 1974-88; prof., head physics dept. Auburn (Ala.) U., 1988—. Contbr. tech. articles to profl. jours. Mem. adv. com. Ctr. for Comml. Devel. of Space, Auburn, 1989—. Fellow AIAA (assoc.); mem. Am. Phys. Soc., AAAS, Am. Geophys. Union, Nat. Laser User's Facility (steering com. 1989-91). Avocations: tennis, bicycling. Home: 535 Cary Dr Auburn AL 36830-2501 Office: Auburn U Physics Dept 206 Allison Auburn AL 36849

PEREZ, JOSEPHINE, psychiatrist, educator; b. Tijuana, Mex., Feb. 10, 1941; came to U.S., 1960, naturalized, 1968. BS in Biology, U. Santiago de Compostela, Spain, 1971; MD, 1975. Clerkships in internal medicine, gen. surgery, otorhinolaryngology, dermatology and venereology Gen. Hosp. of Galicia (Spain), 1972-75; resident in gen. psychiatry U. Miami (Fla.), Jackson Meml. Hosp. and VA Hosp., Miami, 1976-78; practice medicine specializing in psychiatry, marital and family therapy, individual psychotherapy, Miami, Fla., 1979—; nuclear medicine technician, EEG technician, supr. Electrographic Labs., Encino, Calif., 1963-71; emergency room physician Miami Dade Hosp., 1975; attending psychiatrist Jackson Meml. Hosp., 1979—; asst. dir. adolescent psychiat. unit, 1979-83; mem. clin. faculty U. Miami Sch. Medicine, 1979—; clin. instr. psychiatry, 1979—. Mem. AMA (Physicians' Recognition award 1980, 83, 86, 89), Assn. for Marital and Family Therapy (cert. clin. mem., treas. 1982-84, pres.-elect 1985-87, pres. 1987-89), Am. Psychiat. Assn., Am. Med. Women's Assn., Assn. Women Psychiatrists, South Fla. Psychiat. Soc. Office: 420 S Dixie Hwy Ste 4A Coral Gables FL 33146

PEREZ, LILLIAN, non-profit association executive; b. N.Y.C., Mar. 3, 1957; d. Gilberto and Aida Luz (Velazquez) P. BA Polit. Sci., Spanish, Rutgers U., 1979; MPA in Pub. Fin. Mgmt., Am. U., 1985, MBA in Mgmt. and Industrial Rels., 1988. Cert. budget analyst. Community devel. intern Met. Washington Coun. Govts., Washington, 1983-84; fin. mgmt. intern IRS, Washington, 1984-85; program evaluator U.S. GAO, Washington, 1985-88; legis. and grants officer D.C. Commn. on the Arts and Humanities, Washington, 1988—; chmn. D.C. Congl. Art Competition Panel, 1989; mem. ann. conf. planning com. Nat. Assembly State Arts Agys., Washington, 1989-90, Inter-DC. Grants-making Task Force, Washington, 1989; mem. benefit com. Capitol Women's Network; keynote speaker IMF Visitors' Ctr.; guest lectr. George Washington U. Author: Directory of Special Transportation Services, 1984, Information of EPA's Proposal to Delete Chemicals from Groundwater Monitoring USGAO, 1987; former co-editor, contbr. Guernica (Rutgers U. fgn. lang. publ.); contbr. to Art Lines, NPRC Reports, El Foro. Mem. Nat. Conf. Puerto Rican Women, Washington, 1992, Humane Soc. of U.S., Nat. Coun. of Hispanic Women, D.C. Hispanic Employees Assn.; mgr. Flute Ensemble; panel mem. Loy Krathong Festival Competition; John R. Rischer Jr. pub. affairs speaker, 1991; D.C. Mayor's com. on Persons with Disabilities Journalism Scholastic Competition, 1992; bd. dirs. XXIII Hispanic Festival of Washington, The Washington Area Coun. Alcoholism and Drug Abuse, Inc., 1993-94, La Luna Theatre, 1992; mem. Latino adv. com. Nat. Mus. Women in Arts, 1994; mem. steering com. OAS Mus. Art Auction, 1994; mem. planning com. Washington Salsa & Jazz Festival, 1993; mem. Latino Bus. Leaders Fighting AIDS, mem. latino adv. com. Whitman-Walker Clinic, 1994, mem. OAS mus. art auction host com., 1994; mem. adv. com. Dare to Dream Career Prospects Nat. Mus. Women in the Arts. Recipient cert. of merit Office of D.C. Mayor, Cert. Appreciation, Nat. Coun. Hispanic Women, Am. U. scholar, 1984-86. Mem. NAFE, Am. Soc. for Pub. Adminstrs., Nat. Network Grantsmakers, Coun. Govtl. Ethics Laws, Cultural Alliance Greater Washington. Avocations: writing poetry, painting ceramics. Office: Nat Puerto Rican Coalition Inc 1700 K St NW Ste 500 Washington DC 20006

PEREZ, LOUIS MICHAEL, newspaper editor; b. Tampa, Fla., May 30, 1946; s. Louis M. and Mary Elizabeth (Mansell) P.; m. Betty Louise Yates, Mar. 22, 1969 (div. May 1980); 1 child, Christian Marcos; m. Donna Marie Pence, Oct. 8, 1982; children: Louis Michael Jr., Ty Pence, Shea Marie. Student, Loyola U., New Orleans, 1964-66; BS in Journalism, U. Fla., 1969. Reporter/corr. Tampa Tribune, Gainesville, Fla., 1966-69; asst. to dean Coll. Edn. U. Fla., Gainesville, 1969-70, adj. prof. Coll. Journalism, 1975-76; reporter Gainesville Sun, 1970-76, editorial writer, 1974-76; editorial page editor The Ledger, Lakeland, Fla., 1981-83, exec. editor, 1981—; vis. prof. Coll. Journalism U. Fla., 1982; judge journalism awards Scripps-Howard Found., 1988; juror Pulitzer Prizes com., 1994, 95. Recipient Best Editorial award Fla. Bar Assn., 1977. Mem. Am. Soc. Newspaper Editors, Fla. Soc. Newspaper Editors (pres. 1981-82, bd. dirs. 1980-83, 88-90, 1st pl. Best Feature Article award 1972). Roman Catholic. Home: 5220 Waterwood Run Bartow FL 33830 Office: The Ledger PO Box 408 Lakeland FL 33802-0408

PEREZ, PETER MANUEL, woodworking products company executive; b. Elkhart, Ind., Mar. 16, 1940; s. Manuel J. and Ida (Osborn) P.; m. Carroll Greenleaf, Jan. 8, 1963; children: Carter M., Leland T. Student, Phillips Acad., 1955-58; B.A., Yale U., 1962; M.B.A. with honors, Ind. U., 1967. With C.G. Conn, Elkhart, 1967-77, pres., 1974-77; exec. v.p. CBS Mus. Instruments, Deerfield, Ill., 1977-78; pres. Steinway & Sons, Long Island City, N.Y., 1978-82; pres., chmn. bd., chief exec. officer Aeolian Pianos Inc., Memphis, 1983-85; pres., chief exec. officer Eagle Vision, Inc. (med.

products), Memphis, 1985-90, also bd. dirs.; pres. Carter Products Co., Inc., Grand Rapids, Mich., 1990—, also bd. dirs.; bd. dirs. WMMA. With USN, 1962-65. Mem. Hinsdale Golf Club, Summit, N.Y., Athletic Club, Crescent Club, Les Ambassadeurs, Peninsular Club, Beta Gamma Sigma. Office: Carter Products Co Inc 437 Spring Ave NE Grand Rapids MI 49503-1952

PEREZ, ROSIE, actress, choreographer; b. Bklyn.; d. Ismael Serrano and Lydia Perez. dramatic appearances include: (T.V.) 21 Jump Street, WIOU, (film) Do the Right Thing, 1989, White Men Can't Jump, 1992, Night on Earth, 1992, Untamed Heart, 1993, Fearless, 1993 (Acad. award nom. Best Supporting Actress 1994), It Could Happen To You, 1994, Somebody to Love, 1995. Office: CAA 9830 Wilshire Blvd Beverly Hills CA 90212*

PEREZ-GIMENEZ, JUAN MANUEL, federal judge; b. San Juan, P.R., Mar. 28, 1941; s. Francisco and Elisa (Gimenez) P.; m. Carmen R. Ramirez, July 16, 1964; children: Carmen E., Juan C., Jorge E., Jose A., Magdalena. BBA, U. P.R., 1963, JD, 1968; MBA, George Washington U., 1965. Bar: P.R. 1968. Ptnr. Goldman, Antonetti & Davila, San Juan, 1968-71; asst. U.S. atty. San Juan, 1971-75, U.S. magistrate, 1975-79; judge U.S. Dist. Ct. P.R., San Juan, 1979—. Mem. ABA, Fed. Bar Assn., Colegio de Abogados. Roman Catholic. Office: US Courthouse CH-125 Fed Bldg 150 Carlos Chardon Ave San Juan PR 00918-1765

PEREZ-MENDEZ, VICTOR, physics educator; b. Guatemala, Aug. 8, 1923; came to U.S., 1946; m. 1949; 2 children. MS, Hebrew U., Israel, 1947; PhD, Columbia U., 1951. Rsch. assoc. Columbia U., N.Y.C., 1951-53, staff physicist, 1953-61; sr. scientist Lawrence Berkeley Lab., U. Calif., Berkeley, 1960—, vis. lectr. Hebrew U., 1959—; prof. physics dept. radiology U. Calif., San Francisco, 1968—. Fellow IEEE, AAAS, Am. Phys. Soc., N.Y. Acad. Sci.; mem. Soc. Photo Instrumentation Engrs. Office: U Calif Lawrence Berkeley Lab Berkeley CA 94720

PERFETTI, ROBERT NICKOLAS, career education coordinator, educator; b. Staples, Minn., Jan. 8, 1937; s. Nickolas Albert and Lila Bertha (Beurge) P. BS, St. Cloud State U., 1960; postgrad., Bemidji State U., 1961-62, Calif. State U., L.A., 1964-68, Pepperdine U., 1967-68; MA, La Verne U., 1970; postgrad., U. So. Calif., 1972-73, Point Loma U., Pasadena, Calif., 1974-75; EdD, Pacific States U., 1975. Cert. admistr., counselor, secondary, community coll., jr. high sch., adult, and elem. edn. Calif. Prin. Richmond (Minn.) Pub. Schs., 1960-62; elem. tchr. Sebeka (Minn.) Sch. Dist., 1962-63; team leader lang. arts, social sci. and summer sch. Rowland Unified Sch. Dist., Rowland Heights, Calif., 1965-76, coord. math. lab., 1976-79, secondary counselor, 1979-81, coord. work experience edn., career edn. and career ctr., 1991—, home ind. study coord., 1992—; coord. Gender Equity, 1980—, Job Tng. Partnership Act, 1980—; advisor Nat. Vocat. Tech. Honor Soc., 1991—. Editor: (profl. newspaper) Reaction. Officer parish coun. Our Lady of the Assumption Ch., Claremont, Calif., chmn. edn. com.; chmn. PTA, Rowland Heights; rep. fed. project, Rowland Heights; scoutmaster, chmn. troop com. Boy Scouts Am. Recipient Svc. Commendation Rowland Unified Sch. Dist., 1978; named. L.A. County Tchr. of Yr. Calif. State Dept. Edn., 1975, Outstanding Secondary Educator of Am., 1974, Giano Tchr. of Yr. Giano Intermediate Sch., 1973, Tchr. of Yr. Rowland Unified Sch. Dist., 1974. Mem. NEA (life), Calif. Tchrs. Assn., Assn. Rowland Educators (v.p.), Calif. Assn. Work Experience Educators (v.p.), Alpha chpt. v.p.), Alpha Phi Omega (pres.), Pi Delta Epsilon (pres.), KC (3d degree). Roman CAtholic. Avocations: water sports, traveling, research, writing. Home: 3137 Robin Way Pomona CA 91767-1070 Office: Rowland High Sch 2000 Otterbein Ave Rowland Heights CA 91748

PERFIDO, RUTH S., lawyer; b. Pitts., Oct. 10, 1941. BA, Newcomb Coll., 1963; JD, U. Pitts., 1977. Bar: Pa. 1977. Ptnr. Reed Smith Shaw & McClay, Pitts. Office: Reed Smith Shaw & McClay Mellon Sq 435 6th Ave Pittsburgh PA 15219-1886

PERHACH, JAMES LAWRENCE, pharmaceutical company executive; b. Pitts., Oct. 26, 1943; s. James Lawrence and Elizabeth Louise (Hoffman) P.; m. Judith Irene Selter, Apr. 15, 1967; children: Laura Anne, Amy Elizabeth. BS, U. Dayton, 1966; MS, U. Pitts., 1969, PhD, 1971. Sr. scientist dept. pharmacology Mead Johnson Rsch. Ctr., 1971-74, sr. investigator dept. biol. rsch., 1974-76, sr. rsch. assoc. dept. biol. rsch., 1976-77, sr. rsch. assoc. dept. pathology and toxicology, 1977-78, prin. rsch. assoc. dept. pathology and toxicology, 1978-80; dir. pharmacology Wallace Biol. Rsch., Wallace Labs. div. Carter-Wallace Inc., Cranbury, N.J., 1980, exec. dir. biol. rsch., 1980-84, assoc. dir. clin. rsch., 1984-85, dir. clin. investigation, 1985-87, v.p. clin. pharmacology and pharmacokinetics, 1987—; adj. prof. toxicology Phila. Coll. Pharmacy and Sci., 1981—; assoc. faculty Evansville Ctr. Med. Edn., Ind. U., 1973-80; lectr. grad. physiology U. Evansville, 1973-79; grad. teaching asst. U. Pitts., 1967-69, instr. pharmacology and exptl. therapeutics, 1968-69; mem. substance abuse com. Tri-State Area Health Planning Council, Evansville, 1972-75; mem. addictions med. edn. program Evansville Ctr. for Med. Edn-Ind. Sch. Med., 1972-78, Drug Utilization Rev. Council of State of N.J., 1983—; apptd. med. pharmacologist, 1983, sec., 1984, chmn., 1985-86; vis. asst. prof. dept. pharmacy practice and adminstrn., Coll. Pharmacy Rutgers U., 1993—. Fellow Am. Coll. Clin. Pharmacology; mem. AAAS, Am. Soc. Clin. Pharmacology and Therapeutics, Am. Soc. Pharmacology and Exptl. Therapeutics, Am. Coll. Toxicology, European Soc. Toxicology, Soc. Exptl. Biology and Medicine, Soc. Neurosci., N.Y. Acad. Sci., Physiol. Soc. Phila., Drug Info. Assn., Sigma Xi. Research in drug discovery, elucidation of mechanism of action and safety evaluation of new therapeutic agents. Home: 6 Highfield Ct Lawrenceville NJ 08648-1077 Office: Wallace Labs 301B College Rd E Princeton NJ 08540-6604

PERHAM, ROY GATES, III, industrial psychologist; b. Hackensack, N.J., Apr. 22, 1958; s. Roy Gates Jr. and Titania Joan (Robbitts) P. BA with honors, Bates Coll., 1980; MS, Stevens Inst. Tech., 1982, PhD, 1989. Intern Sen. Edmund S. Muskie, Washington, 1978; psychometrician Lab. Psychol. Studies Stevens Inst. Tech., Hoboken, N.J., 1981-83, instr., 1985, adj. asst. prof., 1990—; adj. asst. prof. Fairleigh Dickinson U., Rutherford, N.J., 1986; sr. assoc. AAI Orgnl. Performance Cons., Florham Park, N.J., 1990—; WordStar coord. N.Y. Computer Soc., N.Y.C., 1985-88. Chmn. Juvenile Conf. Com., Hasbrouck Heights and Wood-Ridge, N.J., 1985—; mem. N.J. State Juvenile Delinquency Commn., Trenton, N.J., 1988-91; county exec.'s rep. Bergen County Youth Svcs. Commn., 1990—, chair, 1994—; chair Bergen County Task Force on Youth Violence, 1993—. Named Citizen of Yr., Lions Club of Hasbrouck Heights, N.J., 1988. Mem. APA, Am. Psychol. Soc., Met. N.Y. Assn. for Applied Psychology, Soc. for Indsl./ Orgnl. Psychology, N.Y., Phi Beta Kappa, Psi Chi. Home: 269 Raymond St Hasbrouck Heights NJ 07604-1723 Office: AAI Orgnl Performance Cons 23 Vreeland Rd Florham Park NJ 07932-1510

PERILLO, GIULIO, controller; b. Udine, Italy, May 16, 1946; came to U.S., 1947; m. Mary Kathleen Gore, June 29, 1968; children: Christopher, Tara. BA in Econs., Rutgers U., 1968; MBA in Mktg., Seton Hall U., 1977. Mgr. mfg. acctg. Ortho Pharm. Co., Sommerville, N.J., 1977-78, div. controller, 1978-80; group controller Ortho Pharm. Co., Raritan, N.J., 1980-83; v.p. fin., finance Pitman-Moore, Inc., Washington Crossing, N.J., 1983-84; v.p. surg. products Rorer Group Inc., Ft. Washington, Pa., 1984-85, corp. controller, 1985-86, v.p., controller, 1986—. Served to 1st lt. U.S. Army, 1969-72. Home: 2085 Grantham Ave Berwyn PA 19312-2119 Office: Rhone Plenc Rrer Pharm 500 Arcola Rd Collegeville PA 19426-0107

PERIN, DONALD WISE, JR., former association executive; b. Newton, Mass., Feb. 28, 1915; s. Donald Wise and Beatrice Franklin (Cobb) P.; m. Jean Newcomb Mulcahy, Dec. 5, 1942; children: William Kirk, Betsy Cobb, Donald Wise. Student, Norwich U., 1932-34; B.A., Columbia U., 1936. With Gt. Am. Indemnity Co., N.Y.C., 1936-50; asst. sec. Gt. Am. Indemnity Co., 1946-50; asst. sec.-treas. Nat. Assn. Ins. Agts., N.Y.C., 1950-54; v.p. Alexander & Co., Chgo., 1954-63, Great Am. Ins. Co., N.Y.C., 1964-69; dir. research Ind. Ins. Agts. of Am., N.Y.C., 1970-79; exec. v.p. Ind. Ins. Agts. of Am., 1979-81, exec. v.p. emeritus, 1981. Served with U.S. Army, 1940-46, PTO. Mem. Am. Soc. Assn. Execs., Soc. C.P.C.U.'s, Sigma Alpha Epsilon. Republican. Methodist. Home and Office: Monument Ave Bennington VT 05201

PERINI, DAVID B., construction company executive; b. Framingham, Mass., May 19, 1937; s. Louis R. and Florence R. P.; m. Eileen Callahan, July 14, 1962; children: Jennifer, David, Kristin, Timothy, Andrea. BS, Coll. of Holy Cross, 1959; JD, Boston Coll., 1962. Asst. to gen. counsel Perini Corp., Framingham, 1962-65; div. counsel Midwest and S.W. divs. Perini Corp., Evansville, Ind., 1965-67; div. counsel Western div., 1968; asst. gen. counsel Framingham, Evansville, Ind., 1968-69, v.p., gen. counsel, 1969-71, vice chmn. bd., 1971-72, pres., chmn., 1972—; bd. dirs. Framingham; chmn. Perini Investment Properties, Inc., State St. Boston Corp., New England Telephone Co., Dennison Mfg. Co. Mem. exec. bd. Boston council Boy Scouts Am., 1976; mem. Pres.' Council Holy Cross Coll., trustee, 1977—. Decorated knight Order of Malta, 1979; recipient Merit citation NCCJ, 1980; named 1 of 10 Outstanding Young Leaders, Boston Jr. C. of C., 1973; medalist Italian Am. Charitable Soc., 1979. Mem. ABA, Mass. Bar Assn., World Assn. Lawyers, Moles (pres. 1980), Soc. Am. Mil. Engrs., Associated Gen. Contractors Am. (chmn. internat. constrn. com. 1980—), Associated Gen. Contractors Mass. (dir. 1973-75). Office: Perini Corp PO Box 9160 Framingham MA 01701-9160

PERINI, JOSEPH R., corporate executive; b. Framingham, Mass., Sept. 7, 1930; m. Rosemarie P.; 5 children. B.S. in Engring., Va. Polytech. Inst., 1952; postgrad. U. Hawaii, 1954-55, Boston U., 1957; LL.D., St. Anselem's Coll., 1980. Sr. v.p., chmn. exec. com., bd. dirs., vice chmn., pres. Perini Internat. Corp., Framingham. Bd. dirs., chmn. Family Counseling and Guidance Ctrs. Inc., 1970-73; active Algonquin council Boy Scouts Am., Named Disting. Citizen of Yr.; Algonquin council Boy Scouts Am., 1979. Mem. Am. Road and transp. Builders Assn. (bd. dirs., nat. chmn. 1983-84), Constrn. Industries Mass. (1st pres., past bd. dirs.), ASCE, Am. Soc. Mil. Engrs., Assn. Profl. Engrs. (Can.), Moles. Lodges: Knights of Don Orione (gen. chmn., named Don Orione Home Man of Yr. 1976); Knights of Malta. Office: Perini Corp PO Box 9160 Framingham MA 01701-9160

PERITZ, ABRAHAM DANIEL, business executive; b. Ellenville, N.Y., Aug. 12, 1940; s. Harry and Ida (Koblin) P.; m. Marleen Minkoff, Dec. 12, 1964; children—Alaine, Marc. B.A., Hartwick Coll., Oneonta, N.Y., 1962; postgrad., Baruch Coll., 1967. Asst. restaurant mgr. Concord Hotel, Kiamesha Lake, N.Y., 1962-64; with Ruder Finn, Inc., N.Y.C., 1965—, v.p., controller, 1972-75, chief fin. officer, 1976-82, treas., 1983—. Treas. Kingsley Sq. Townhouse Assn., Freehold, N.J., 1974-75. Served with USAR, 1964. Democrat. Jewish. Home: 127 Kingsley Way Freehold NJ 07728-1667 Office: Ruder Finn Inc 301 East 57th Street New York NY 10022

PERKIEL, MITCHEL H., lawyer; b. N.Y.C., Oct. 26, 1949; s. Frank and Ella Perkiel; m. Lois E. Perkiel, June 24, 1984; children: Joshua L., Alexa Kim, Griffin. BA, SUNY, Stony Brook, 1971; JD, New York Law Sch., 1974. Bar: N.Y. 1975, U.S. Dist. Ct. (so. and ea. dists.) N.Y. 1975, U.S. Ct. Appeals (2d cir.) 1975, Conn. 1988. Law clk. to presiding justice N.Y. County Civil Ct., 1975; assoc. Levin & Weintraub & Crames, N.Y.C., 1975-80, ptnr., 1980-90; with Kaye, Scholer, Fierman, Hayes & Handler, N.Y.C. Notes and comments editor New York Law Rev., 1973-74. Served with USAR, 1969-73. Mem. ABA, Assn. of Bar of City of N.Y., N.Y. County Lawyers Assn. Office: Kaye Scholer Fierman Hayes & Handler 425 Park Ave New York NY 10022-3506

PERKIN, GORDON WESLEY, international health agency executive; b. Toronto, Ont., Can., Apr. 25, 1935; came to U.S., 1964; s. Irvine Boyer and Jean (Laing) P.; m. Elizabeth Scott, Dec. 21, 1957; children: Scott, Stuart. MD, U. Toronto, 1959. Asst. dir. clin. research Ortho Research Found., Raritan, N.J., 1962-64; assoc. med. dir. Planned Parenthood Fedn. Am., N.Y.C., 1964-66; program advisor Ford Found., N.Y.C., 1966-67; regional program advisor Ford Found., Bangkok, 1967-69, Rio de Janeiro, 1973-76; program officer Ford Found., N.Y.C., Mexico City, 1976-80; project specialist Ministry Fin. and Econ. Planning, Accra, Ghana, 1969-70; cons. World Health Orgn., Geneva, 1971-73; pres. Program for Appropriate Tech. in Health, Seattle, 1980—; affiliate prof. pub. health, U. Wash., Seattle. Contbr. numerous articles to profl. jours. Am. Pub. Health Assn. fellow, 1970. Mem. Planned Parenthood Fedn. Am. (bd. dirs. 1983-89), Planned Parenthood Seattle-King County (bd. dirs. 1982—, mem. exec. com. 1983-86), Nat. Coun. for Internat. Health (bd. govs. 1984-95), Nat. Acad. Scis. (com. mem. 1987-90), Alan Guttmacher Inst. (bd. dirs. 1985-90), Assn. Reproductive Health Profls., Alpha Omega Alpha. Office: PATH 4 Nickerson St Seattle WA 98109-1651

PERKIN, HAROLD JAMES, social historian; b. Stoke-on-Trent, Eng., Nov. 11, 1926; s. Robert James and Hilda May (Dillon) P.; B.A. 1st class with distinction (major scholar coll., Bell exhibitioner univ.), Cambridge U., 1948, M.A., 1952; m. Joan Griffiths, July 3, 1948; children—Deborah Jane, Julian Robert. Asst. lectr., then lectr. social history Manchester U., 1951-65; sr. lectr. Lancaster U., 1965—; prof. social history, 1967-84, dir. centre social history, 1975-84; Andrew W. Mellon disting. prof. humanities Rice U., Houston, 1984; prof. history Northwestern U., Evanston, Ill., 1985—, prof. higher edn., 1987—; vis. fellow Princeton U., 1979-80; fellow Nat. Humanities Center, N.C., 1983-84. Served with RAF, 1948-50. Recipient Gold medal Nat. Inst. Ednl. Research, Tokyo, 1982. Fellow Royal Hist. Soc., 1969—, John Simon Guggenheim fellow, 1989-90; v.p. Social History Soc. U.K. (founding chmn. 1976), Econ. History Soc., Soc. Study Labour History, History of Edn. Soc., Assn. U. Tchrs. (pres. 1970-71). Author: The Origins of Modern English Society, 1780-1880, 1969; Key Profession: The History of the Association of University Teachers, 1969; New Universities in the U.K., 1969; The Age of the Railway, 1970; The Age of the Automobile, 1976; The Structured Crowd, 1980; Professionalism, Property and English Society since 1880, 1981; The Rise of Professional Society: England since 1880, 1989, Higher Education and English Society, Japanese translation, 1993; editor: Studies in Social History, 1957—. Home: 106 St Mary's Mansions, London W2 1SZ, England Office: Hist Dept Northwestern U 633 Clark St Evanston IL 60208

PERKIN, REGINALD LEWIS, physician, educator; b. Toronto, Ont., Can., Oct. 16, 1930; s. Lewis Lorne and Betty Alma (Parks) P.; m. Alison Beverly Smith, June 5, 1954; children: Tom, Anne, Scott, Sandra. M.D., U. Toronto, 1954. Intern Toronto Gen. Hosp., 1954-55; resident in gen. practice Wellesley Hosp. and Hosp. Sick Children, Toronto, 1955-56; chief dept. family pratice Mississauga Hosp. (Ont.), Toronto, 1967-75; chmn. dept. family and community medicine U. Toronto, 1969-70, prof., 1969-85; sr. ptnr. Dixie Rd. Med. Assocs., Mississauga, 1962-85; exec. dir. Coll. Family Physicians of Can., 1985—; vis. prof. Royal Australian Coll. Gen. Practitioners, 1982; staff Toronto Western Hosp., U. Toronto, 1966—. Contbr.: The Nature of General Family Practice, 1983; articles to profl. jours. Gen. chmn. Applewood United Ch., Mississauga, 1974-75, 91-92; bd. govs. Mississauga Symphony Orch., 1973-78; chorister Whiteoaks and Mississauga Choral Soc., 1977-88. Fellow Coll. Family Physicians Can. (cert., pres. 1981-82), Royal Coll. Physicians and Surgeons Can. (hon.), Royal Coll. Gen. Practitioners, Royal Australian Coll. Gen. Practitioners; mem. Can. Med. Assn., Ont. Med. Assn., Victorian Acad. Gen. Practice, Mississauga Golf and Country Club, Caledon Ski Club, Alpha Omega Alpha. Home: 1409 Dixie Rd, Mississauga, ON Canada L5E 2P5 Office: Coll Family Physicians Can, 2630 Skymark Ave, Mississauga, ON Canada L4W 5A4

PERKINS, A. WILLIAM, printing executive; b. Tampa, Fla., Nov. 17, 1925; s. Alfred William and Grace Aurora (Lay) P.; children: Leslie, A. William III. Student, George Washington U., 1943-49. Pres. Perkins Warehouse Co., Alexandria, Va., 1965—; pres. emeritus Old Dominion Printing Co., Alexandria, 1988—; bd. dirs. Essex Corp., Alexandria. Founding chmn. Didlake Inc.; chmn. Carpenters Shelter, Alexandria, 1988-91; pres. Alexandria Vol. Bur., 1984-86, others. With USN, 1944-46, 49-50. Recipient Volunteer Excellence, Gov. of Va., 1988; named Washingtonian of Yr., 1982. Mem. Army Navy Country Club. Office: Warehouse Co 520 N Fayette St Alexandria VA 22314

PERKINS, ALAN J., lawyer; b. Brockton, Mass., Nov. 10, 1953; s. Jean Zelman and Elinor Frances (Cohen) P.; m. Katherine Anne Wilson, Nov. 1, 1980. Student, Clark U., 1971-73; BA, Northwestern U., 1976; JD, Emory U., 1978. Bar: Tex. 1978. Assoc. Gardere & Wynne, Dallas, 1978-84, ptnr., 1984—. Bd. dirs. Jingle Bell Run 1985—. Mem. ABA, Tex. Bar Assn., Dallas Bar Assn., Dallas Area Indsl. Devel. Assn., East Dallas C. of C. (bd.

dirs., chmn. devel. com. 1985-86). Avocations: sports, reading. Office: Gardere & Wynne 1500 Diamond Shamrock Tower Dallas TX 75201

PERKINS, BOB(BY) F(RANK), geologist, dean; b. Greenville, Tex., Dec. 9, 1929; s. William Frank and Vela Beatrice (Richey) P.; m. Patricia Katharine Woodhull, May 25, 1954; children: Katharine Harriet, Marianna Lea, Orrin Woodhull. B.S., So. Methodist U., 1949, M.S., 1950; Ph.D., U. Mich., 1956. Instr. geology and biology So. Meth. U., 1950-51, 53-56; asst. prof. geology U. Houston, 1956-57; rsch. paleontologist Shell Devel. Corp., Houston, 1957-66; prof. geology La. State U., Baton Rouge, 1966-75; chmn., dir. Sch. Geosci. La. State U., 1973-75; prof. geology, dean Grad. Sch., U. Tex., Arlington, 1975—, also assoc. v.p. research, 1975-93; exec. dir. Gulf Coast sect. Soc. Econ. Paleontologists and Mineralogists Found., 1983—. Editor: 15 vol. series Geoscience and Man, 1970-75; contbr. articles to profl. jours. Fellow Geol. Soc. Am., AAAS, Tex. Acad. Sci.; mem. Paleontol. Soc., Am. Assn. Petroleum Geologists, Paleontol. Soc. Gt. Britain, Soc. Econ. Paleontologists and Mineralogists, Malacological Soc. London. Home: 1416 Creekford Dr Arlington TX 76012-2108

PERKINS, BRADFORD, history educator; b. Rochester, N.Y., Mar. 6, 1925; s. Dexter and Wilma (Lord) P.; m. Nancy Nash Tucker, June 18, 1949 (dec.); children: Dexter III, Matthew Edward, Martha Nash. A.B., Harvard U., 1946, Ph.D., 1952. From instr. to assoc. prof. history U. Calif. at, Los Angeles, 1952-62; prof. history U. Mich., 1962—, chmn. dept., 1971-72, 80-81; Commonwealth Fund lectr. Univ. Coll., London, Eng., 1964; vis. prof. history Brandeis U., 1970, Ecole des Hautes Etudes en Sciences Sociales, Paris, 1983; Albert Shaw lectr. Johns Hopkins U., 1979; mem. council Inst. Early Am. History and Culture, 1968-71; program dir. Nat. Endowment for Humanities Fellowships in Residence for Coll. Tchrs., 1974-75. Author: The First Rapprochement: England and the United States, 1795-1805, 1955, Youthful America, 1960, Prologue to War: England and the United States, 1805-1812, 1961, Causes of the War of 1812, 1962, Castlereagh and Adams: England and the United States, 1812- 1823, 1964, The Great Rapprochement: England and the United States, 1895-1914, 1968, The Creation of a Republican Empire, 1993. Served with AUS, 1943-45, ETO. Decorated Bronze Star.; Recipient Bancroft prize, 1965, Disting. Faculty award U. Mich., 1986; Warren fellow, 1969-70; Social Sci. Research Council faculty research fellow, 1957-60; Guggenheim fellow, 1962-63. Mem. Am. Hist. Assn., Soc. Am. Historians, Orgn. Am. Historians (coun. 1969-72), Soc. Historians Am. Fgn. Rels. (coun. 1967-72, pres. 1974, Graebner award 1992), Mass. Hist. Soc., Am. Antiquarian Soc. Home: 3401 Berry Rd Ypsilanti MI 48198-9423

PERKINS, BRITTEN LEE, architectural firm executive; b. June 17, 1959. BArch, U. Houston. Mng. prin. EDI Architecture, Houston, 1979—. Contbr. articles to profl. jours. Mem. AIA (chmn. nat. housing com. 1993, mem. mentor program, judge local and regional design award programs), Greater Houston Builders Assn., Nat. Assn. Home Builders, Tex. Soc. Archs. Office: EDI Architecture 3731 Briarpark 300 Houston TX 77042

PERKINS, CHARLES, III, newspaper editor; b. Brockton, Mass., July 25, 1952; s. Charles II and Barbara Perkins; m. Linda C. Burroughs, Jan. 4, 1985. BA, Dartmouth Coll., 1975. Editor Journal-Opinion, Bradford, Vt., 1977-78; reporter, editor The Union Leader and N.H. Sunday News, Manchester, N.H., 1978-81; Sunday editor N.H. Sunday News, Manchester, 1981-84; mng. editor The Union Leader and N.H. Sunday News, Manchester, 1984-92, exec. editor, 1992—. Office: The Union Leader Box 9555 Manchester NH 03108

PERKINS, DALE WARREN, library director; b. Wichita, Kans., Feb. 27, 1933; s. Lawrence Waldo and Georgia (Powell) P.; m. Linda Ann Perkins, Aug. 14, 1960 (div. Feb. 1974); 1 child, Kerry; m. Barbara Lee Miller, Apr. 12, 1976. BA, Ball State U., 1958; MLS, Kansas State U., 1960. Libr. Mid-Columbia Regional Libr., Kennewick, Wash., 1960-62; dir. Baker (Oreg.) City Libr., 1962-65; field libr. Idaho State Libr., Boise, 1965-66; coord. Mountain Valley Libr. System, Sacramento, Calif., 1967-70; dir. San Luis Obispo (Calif.) City-County Libr., 1970—. Contbr. articles to profl. jours. With USAF, 1954-55. Mem. ALA, Calif. Library Assn., Calif. Inst. Libraries (past pres.). Democrat. Home: 741 Stratford St Pismo Beach CA 93449-2444 Office: San Luis Obispo Libr 3220 S Higuera St San Luis Obispo CA 93401-6925

PERKINS, DAVID, English language educator; b. Philadelphia, Pa., Oct. 25, 1928; s. Dwight Goss and Esther M. (Williams) P. A.B., Harvard U., 1951, M.A., 1952, Ph.D., 1955. Mem. faculty Harvard U., 1957—, prof. English, 1964-94, chmn. dept. English, 1976-81, chmn. dept. lit., 1987-89, prof. emeritus, 1994—; vis. prof. Goettingen U., 1968-69. Author: The Quest for Permanence: the Symbolism of Wordsworth, Shelley and Keats, 1959, Wordsworth and the Poetry of Sincerity, 1964, English Romantic Writers, 1967, A History of Modern Poetry: From the 1890's to the High Modernist Mode, 1976, A History of Modern Poetry, Vol. 2, Modernism and After, 1987; (with W. Jackson Bate) British and American Poets: Chaucer to the Present, 1986, Is Literary History Possible, 1991; editor: The Teaching of Literature: What is Needed Now, 1988, Theoretical Issues in Literary History, 1991; mem. editorial adv. bd. Keats-Shelley Jour., 1962-89, The Wordsworth Circle. Served with AUS, 1955-57. Guggenheim fellow, 1962, 73; Fulbright fellow, 1968-69; Am. Council Learned Socs. fellow, 1977. Mem. Am. Acad. Arts and Scis., Cambridge Sci. Club. Home: 984 Memorial Dr # 304 Cambridge MA 02138-4701

PERKINS, DAVID LAYNE, SR., architect; b. Picayune, Miss., Mar. 3, 1925; s. Robert E. and Henrietta (Browne) P.; m. Edna Blanche Rice, Jan. 23, 1954; children—David Layne Jr., Richard Scott. B.Arch., Tulane U., 1954. Registered architect, La. Designer, draftsman Curtis & Davis Architects, New Orleans, 1954; asst. prof. U. Southwestern La., Lafayette, 1954-57, 86-87, 88; prin. David L. Perkins, Architect, Lafayette, 1955-75; pres., sr. ptnr. Perkins-Guidry-Young, Architects, Inc., Lafayette, 1975-85; pres., sr. ptnr., chmn. Perkins-Guidry-Beazley-Ostteen, Architects, Inc., Lafayette, 1985-90; pvt. practice cons. architect Lafayette, 1990—; bd. dirs. St. Joseph's Home; past pres., 1st v.p., treas., bd. dirs. Nat. Archtl. Accrediting Bd.; past dir. gulf states region AIA Nat Bd. Dirs.; past pres., v.p., bd. dirs. La Architects Assn.; mem. dean's council Tulane U. Sch. Arch. Prin. works include office bldgs., Lafayette Pub. Library, neuropsychiat. clinic. Mem. adv. bd. Lafayette Cath. Service Ctr. Inc. Served to capt. USAF, 1943-45, 51-52. Fellow AIA (pres. So. La. chpt. 1963-64, honor award So. La. chpt. 1982, 83, 85, bd. dirs. 1975-78, award of excellence 1982); mem. La. Architects Assn. (honor award 1963, 64, 70, 74, 82, 83). Republican. Presbyterian. Avocation: boating, woodworking. Home: 503 Marjorie Blvd Lafayette LA 70503-3147 Office: PO Box 51762 Lafayette LA 70505-1762

PERKINS, DONALD S., department store chain executive; b. 1927. With Jewel Cos., 1953-83; with KMart Corp., Troy, Mich., 1986—, chmn. bd., 1995—. Office: KMart Corp 3100 W Big Beaver Rd Troy MI 48084*

PERKINS, DOROTHY A., marketing professional; b. Weiser, Idaho, Aug. 13, 1926; d. Ross William and Josephine Stanford (Gwilliam) Anderson; m. Leonard Taylor Perkins, Nov. 16, 1948; children: Larry Taylor, Michael A., Drew A., Nancy. Grad. high sch., Boise, Idaho. Sec. Meadow Gold Dairies, Boise, 1944-46; sec. to supt. Idaho State Police, Boise, 1946-48, Idaho State Dept. Edn., Boise, 1952-56; sec. to maintenance engr. Idaho State Dept. Hwys., Boise, 1956-58; adminstrv. sec. asst. mgr. Casper (Wyo.) C. of C., 1962-72, exec. v.p., 1972-91; mktg. rep. World Wide Travel, Casper, 1991—. Mem. Wyo. Ho. of Reps., 1982—, chmn. house labor, health and social svcs. com., 1990—; found. bd. dirs., pres. Nat. Hist. Ctr., 1995. Mem. Wyo. C. of C. Execs. (sec.-treas. 1978-91, past pres.), Mountain States Assn. (bd. dirs. 1979-91, past pres.), Wyo. Hwy. Users Fedn. (bd. dirs. 1978—, pres. 1993—). Republican. Avocations: reading, walking, sewing, music. Home: 1014 Surrey Ct Casper WY 82609-3270 Office: World Wide Travel PO Box 9370 Casper WY 82609-0370

PERKINS, DWIGHT HEALD, economics educator; b. Chgo., Oct. 20, 1934; s. Lawrence Bradford and Margery (Blair) P.; m. Julie Rate, June 15, 1957; children: Lucy Fitch, Dwight Edward, Caleb Blair. B.A., Cornell U., 1956; A.M., Harvard U., 1961, Ph.D., 1964. From instr. to assoc. prof. Harvard U., Cambridge, Mass., 1963-69, prof. econs., 1969-81, assoc. dir. East Asian Research Ctr., 1973-77, chmn. dept. econs., 1977-80, H.H. Burbank prof. polit. economy, 1981—; dir. Harvard Inst. Internat. Devel., Cambridge, 1980—; dir. Nat. Com. on U.S.-China Rels., 1991—; cons. permanent subcom. on investigations U.S. Senate, 1974-80; H.M. Jackson vis. prof. Chinese studies U. Wash., 1985, Phi Beta Kappa lectr., 1992-93; mem. Internat. Adv. Group to Prime Min. of Papua, New Guinea, 1991-92; cons. Korea Devel. Inst., 1972-80. Author: Agricultural Development in China, 1368-1968, 1969, Market Control and Planning in Communist China, 1966, China: Asia's Next Economic Giant?, 1986, (with E.S. Mason and others) The Economic Modernization of Korea, 1980, (with S. Yusuf) Rural Development in China, 1984, (with M. Gillis and others) Economics of Development, 1983, 3d edit., 1992; editor: China's Modern Economy in Historical Perspective, 1975, (with M. Roemer) Reforming Economic Systems in Developing Countries, 1991. Mem. Vis. Com. Far Ea. Studies, U. Chgo., 1973-77; mem. bd. govs. East-West Ctr., Honolulu, 1979-82; co-moderator Aspen Inst. Seminar on Korea, Colo., 1980-83. Lt. (j.g.) USNR, 1956-58. Fgn. Area Tng. fellow Ford Found., N.Y., 1958-62; NSF Sci. Faculty fellow Tokyo, 1968-69. Mem. Assn. Asian Studies, Assn. Comparative Econ. Systems (past pres.), Am. Econ. Assn., Phi Beta Kappa. Home: 64 Pinehurst Rd Belmont MA 02178-1504 Office: Harvard Inst Internat Devel One Eliot St Cambridge MA 02138-5781

PERKINS, EDWARD J., diplomat; b. Sterlington, La., June 8, 1928; m. Lucy Liu; children: Katherine, Sarah. Student, U. Calif., Lewis and Clark Coll.; BA, U. Md., 1967; MPA, U. So. Calif., 1972, DPA, 1978; studied French, Fgn. Service Inst., 1983; LLD (hon.), U. Md., 1990, St. John's U., 1990, Lewis and Clark Coll., 1988; LHD (hon.), Winston-Salem State U., 1990; LHD (hon.), Bowie State Coll., 1993; HHD (hon.), St. Augustine Coll., 1991, Beloit Coll., 1990, U. So. Calif., 1995. Chief of pers. Army and Air Force Exch. Svc., Taipei, Taiwan, 1958-62; dep. chief Army and Air Force Exch. Svc., Okinawa, Japan, 1962-64; chief pers. and adminstrn. Army and Air Force Exchange Service, Okinawa, Japan, 1964-66; asst. gen. svcs. officer Far East bur. AID, 1967-69, mgmt. analyst, 1969-70; asst. dir. for mgmt. U.S. Ops. Mission to Thailand, 1970-72; staff asst. Office of Dir. Gen. Fgn. Svc., 1972, personnel officer, 1972-74; adminstrv. officer Bur. Near Eastern and South Asian Affairs, 1974-75; mgmt. analysis officer Office Mgmt. Ops., Dept. State, 1975-78; counselor for polit. affairs Accra, Ghana, 1978-81; dep. chief of mission Monrovia, Liberia, 1981-83; dir. Office of West African Affairs, Bur. African Affairs, Dept. State, 1983-85; U.S. amb. to Liberia, 1985-86, U.S. amb. to South Africa, 1986-89; dir. gen., dir. pers. Fgn. Svc., Dept. of State, Washington, 1989-92; U.S. rep. to UN N.Y.C., 1992-93; U.S. amb. to Australia Canberra, 1993—. Contbr. articles to profl. publs. Bd. dirs. Lewis and Clark Coll., 1994—. Recipient Presdl. Meritorious Svc. award, 1987, Presdl. Disting. Svc. award, 1989, Meritorious Honor award AID, 1967, Disting. Alumni award U. So. Calif., 1991, Achievement award So. U., 1991, award for outstanding svc. as fgn. svc. officer Una Chapman Cox Found., 1989, Living Legend award The Links, Inc., 1989. Fellow Nat. Acad. Pub. Adminstrn.; mem. VFW, ASPA, Conf. Minority Pub. Adminstrs., Navy League, Sigma Pi Phi, Kappa Alpha Psi, Inc. (Laurel Wreath award 1993, C. Rodger Wilson Leadership Conf. award 1990, Disting. Svc. award 1989, Outstanding Achievement award for Fgn. Svc. 1986), Phi Kappa Phi. Office: Am Embassy Canberra Dept State Washington DC 20521-7800

PERKINS, ELIZABETH ANN, actress; b. Queens, N.Y., Nov. 18, 1960; d. James Perkins and Jo Milton. Grad., Goodman Theatre, Chgo., 1981. Films include: About Last Night, 1986, From the Hip, 1987, Sweet Hearts Dance, 1988, Big, 1988, Love at Large, 1990, Enid is Sleeping, 1990, Avalon, 1990, He Said/She Said, 1991, The Doctor, 1991, Indian Summer, 1993, The Flinstones, 1994, Miracle on 34th Street, 1994, Moonlight and Valentino, 1995; TV film: For Their Own Good, 1992. Office: c/o Susan Culley & Assocs 150 S Rodeo Dr Ste 220 Beverly Hills CA 90212-1825

PERKINS, FLOYD JERRY, theology educator; b. Bertha, Minn., May 9, 1924; s. Ray Lester and Nancy Emily (Kelley) P.; m. Mary Elizabeth Owen, Sept. 21, 1947 (dec. June 1982); children: Douglas Jerry, David Floyd, Sheryl Pauline; m. Phyllis Genevra Hartley, July 14, 1984. AB, BTh, N.W. Nazarene Coll., 1949; MA, U. Mo., 1952; MDiv, Nazarene Theol. Sem., 1952; ThM, Burton Sem., 1964; PhD, U. Witwatersrand, Johannesburg, South Africa, 1974; ThD, Internat. Sem., 1994. Ordained to Christian ministry, 1951. Pres. South African Nazarene Theol. Sem., Florida Transvaal, Africa, 1955-67; pres. Nazarene Bible Sem., Lourenzo Marques, Mozambique, 1967-73, Campinas, Brazil, 1974-76; prof. missions N.W. Nazarene Coll., Nampa, Idaho, 1976; prof. theology Nazarene Bible Coll., Colorado Springs, Colo., 1976—; chmn., founder com. higher theol. edn. Ch. of Nazarene in Africa, 1967-74; sec. All African Nazarene Mission Exec., 1967-74; ofcl. Christian Council Mozambique, 1952-74. Author: A History of the Christian Church in Swaziland, 1974. Served with USN, 1944-46. Mem. Soc. Christian Philosophers, Evang. Theol. Soc., Am. Schs. Orientan Rsch., Am. Soc. Missiology, Assn. Evang. Missions Profs. Republican. Avocation: golf. Home: 1529 Lyle Dr Colorado Springs CO 80915-2009 Office: Nazarene Bible Coll 1111 Chapman Dr Colorado Springs CO 80916 *Personal philosophy:* Be cheerful, hopeful, courageous, honest, candid, faithful, committed, loyal, and the whole world will be yours!.

PERKINS, FRANK OVERTON, marine scientist, educator; b. Fork Union, Va., Feb. 14, 1938; s. Frank Otie and Mary Ella (Hughes) P.; m. Beverly Anne Weeks. BA, U. Va., 1960; MS, Fla. State U., Tallahassee, 1962, PhD, 1966. Marine scientist Va. Inst. Marine Sci., Coll. William and Mary, Gloucester Point, Va., 1966-69; sr. marine scientist Va. Inst. Marine Sci., Coll. William and Mary, Gloucester Point, 1969-77, asst. dir. 1977-81, dir., dean Sch. Marine Sci., 1981-91, prof. marine sci., 1991—. Baptist. Home: 101 Loblolly Ct Yorktown VA 23692-4252 Office: Va Inst of Marine Sci College of William and Mary Gloucester Point VA 23062

PERKINS, FREDERICK MYERS, retired oil company executive; b. Tallahassee, Fla., Oct. 7, 1928; s. Frederick Myers and Nancy Evelyn (Turner) P.; m. Rosemary Ross, Dec. 21, 1950; children: Lucille Lambert Reed, Nancy Evelyn Cavanagh, Matthew Myers. B.Ch.E., U. Fla., 1951, M.S., 1952. Prodn. research engr. Humble Oil & Refining Co., Houston, 1952-62; prodn. staff coordinator, 1963-65; reservoir engr. Humble Oil & Refining Co., New Orleans, 1965-66; prodn. mgr. Humble Oil & Refining Co., Corpus Chrisiti, Tex., 1966-70; petroleum economist Standard Oil Co. N.J., N.Y.C., 1962-63; dep. mgr. Esso Australia Ltd., Sydney, 1970-72; gen. mgr. natural gas Exxon Co. U.S.A., Houston, 1972-76, v.p. prodn., 1976-79, dep. mgr. producing Exxon Corp., 1979-80, v.p. gas, 1980-85, v.p. producing, 1985-86; pres. Exxon Prodn. Research Co., Houston, 1986-93; ret., 1993. Patentee in field. Served with U.S. Army, 1946-47, PTO. Mem. Soc. Petroleum Engrs., Galveston Country Club, Petroleum Club.

PERKINS, GEORGE HOLMES, architectural educator, architect; b. Cambridge, Mass., Oct. 10, 1904; s. George Howard and Josephine (Schock) P.; m. Georgia Hencken, June 3, 1933; children—Gray H., Jennifer H. Student, Phillips-Exeter Acad., 1922-22; A.B., Harvard U., 1926, M.Arch., 1929; LL.D., U. Pa., 1972. Instr. architecture U. Mich., 1929-30; instr. architecture Harvard, 1930-36, asst. prof., 1936-39, asso. prof., 1939-42, Norton prof. regional planning, chmn. dept., 1945-51; dean, chmn. dept. architecture Grad. Sch. Fine Arts, U. Pa., 1951-71, prof. architecture and urbanism, 1971—; practicing architect and city planner, 1933—; asst. regional rep., acting dir. urban devel. div. Nat. Housing Agy., 1942-45; cons. Brit. Ministry of Town and Country Planning, 1946, UN, 1946, 55-56; cons. to Govt. Turkey, 1958-60, Balt. Redevel. Authority, Cambridge Redevel. Authority, Worcester Redevel. Authority.; Mem. Cambridge Planning Bd., 1950-51; dir. Phila. Housing Assn., 1951-56, pres., 1953-56; dir. Citizens Council City Planning, 1951-54; chmn. Phila. Zoning Commn., 1955-58, Phila. City Planning Commn., 1958-68; dir. Phila. Port Corp., Old Phila. Devel. Corp., Phila. Indsl. Devel. Corp. Author: Comparative Outline of Architectural History, 1937; editor: Jour. Am. Inst. Planners, 1950-52; contbr. articles to profl. jours. Mem. Phila. Commn. Higher Edn.; Trustee Fairmount Park Art Assn., 1965—. Fellow A.I.A. (chancellor coll. fellows 1964-66); mem. Am. Inst. Planners, Am. Soc. Planning Ofcls., Nat. Assn. Housing Ofcls., World Soc. Ekistics; hon. corr. mem. Royal Inst. Architects Can. Clubs: The Country (Brookline); Franklin Inn (Phila.), Rittenhouse (Phila.). Philadelphia Cricket (Phila.), Art Alliance (Phila.); Century (N.Y.C.). Home: 82 Bethlehem Pike Philadelphia PA 19118-2821

PERKINS, HERBERT ASA, physician; b. Boston, Oct. 5, 1918; s. Louis and Anna (Robinson) P.; m. Frances Snyder, Sept. 2, 1942; children: Susan, Deborah, Dale, Karen, Erin. A.B. cum laude, Harvard U., 1940; M.D. summa cum laude, Tufts U., 1943. Intern Boston City Hosp., 1944, resident, 1947-48; practice medicine specializing in transfusion medicine, 1953—; clin. instr. Stanford Med. Sch., 1953-57, asst. clin. prof., 1957-58; hematologist Open Heart Surgery Team, Stanford Hosp., San Francisco, 1955-58, Jewish Hosp., St. Louis, 1958-59; dir. rsch. Irwin Meml. Blood Ctrs., San Francisco, 1959-78, med. and sci. dir., 1978-90, exec. dir.: 1987-91, pres., 1991-93, sr. med. scientist, 1993—; asst. prof. medicine Washington U., St. Louis, 1958-59, U. Calif., San Francisco, 1959-66, assoc. prof., 1966-71, clin. prof. 1971—. Co-editor: Hepatitis and Blood Transfusion, 1972; assoc. editor: Transfusion. Served to maj. M.C., U.S. Army, 1944-47. Mem. AAAS, Am. Assn. Blood Banks (chmn. sci. adv. com. 1972-73, chmn. standards com. 1968-71, chmn. com. on organ transplantation and tissue typing 1970-80, bd. dirs. 1982-86), Am. Soc. Hematology, Internat. Transfusion Soc., Transplantation Soc., Am. Fedn. Clin. Rsch., Am. Soc. Histocompatibility and Immunogenetics (pres. 1985-86), Nat. Marrow Donor Program (chair bd. dirs., chmn. com. on stds. 1987-94, chmn. fin. com. 1987-94). Home: 520 Berkeley Ave Menlo Park CA 94025-2323 Office: Irwin Meml Blood Ctrs 270 Masonic Ave San Francisco CA 94118-4496

PERKINS, HOMER GUY, manufacturing company executive; b. New Haven, Oct. 23, 1916; s. Frank W. and Emily (Oesting) P.; m. Dorothy C. Stock, Jan. 24, 1942; children: Maribeth Perkins Grant, Homer Guy Jr., Hazel Mary Perkins Adolphson, Dorothy Catherine, Caroline Ann, Faith Elizabeth Perkins Crotteau, Ruth Emily Perkins Sico. BA in Internat. Rels., Yale U., 1938; LLD (hon.), Westfield (Mass.) State Coll., 1977. With Stanhome, Inc. (formerly Stanley Home Products, Inc.), Westfield, 1939—, v.p.: 1965-66, exec. v.p., 1966-70, pres. chief exec. officer, 1970-78, chmn., 1978-81, also bd. dirs. Treas Stanley Park of Westfield, 1949—; pres. Citizens Scholarship Found., Easthampton, Mass., 1966-67, Easthampton Community Chest, 1960-61; chmn. fin. com., bd. dirs. western Mass. coun. Girl Scouts U.S., 1966-69; mem. devel. com. Clarke Sch. Deaf, Northampton, 1965-68; mem. fin. com. Town of Easthampton, 1962-70, chmn. 1967-68; dir. Frank Stanley Beveridge Found., Westfield, 1956—, pres. 1966-87; trustee Cooley Dickinson Hosp., Northampton, 1963-70, 84-92, chmn. bd., 1989-91; pres. bd. trustees Northampton Sch. Girls, 1964-73; bd. dirs. Porter Phelps Huntington Found., Hadley, Mass., 1960-92, Guild of Holy Child, Westfield, 1969-76; bd. overseers Williston Acad., Easthampton, 1961-64, Old Sturbridge (Mass.) Village, 1970-76; v.p. bd. trustees Williston-Northampton Sch., 1970-75, pres. 1975-78. With USAAF, 1942-46. Mem. Direct Selling Assn. (chmn. 1975, dir., mem. Hall of Fame), , Paperweight Collectors Assn. (pres. 1991—), Lions (past pres. Easthampton club). Home: 8 Carol Ave Easthampton MA 01027-1904

PERKINS, JACK EDWIN, lawyer; b. Portola, Calif., May 25, 1943; s. Charles James and Vira Almena (Wing) P.; m. Barbara Kay Nielson, Jan. 18, 1969; children: Jill Christy, Kelli Anne. BA, San Jose State Coll., 1966; JD, Hastings Coll. Law, 1972. Bar: Calif. 1972, D.C. 1989. Asst. U.S Atty., Dept. Justice, San Francisco, 1973-74; staff atty. Dept. Justice, Washington, 1972, 74-80, legis. counsel, 1980-86, dep. asst. atty. gen., 1986-90; chief adminstrv. hearing officer Exec. Office for Immigration Rev., Falls Church, Va., 1990—. Served to capt. USMC, 1966-69, Vietnam. Recipient John Marshall award Dept. Justice, 1986. Avocations: tennis, jogging, racquetball. Home: 3310 Fallen Tree Ct Alexandria VA 22310-2262 Office: Exec Office Immigration Rev 5107 Leesburg Pike Washington DC 20530-0864

PERKINS, JAMES FRANCIS, physicist; b. Hillsdale, Tenn., Jan. 3, 1924; s. Jim D. and Laura Pervis (Goad) P.; A.B., Vanderbilt U., 1948, M.A., 1949; Ph.D., 1953; m. Ida Virginia Phillips, Nov. 23, 1949; 1 son, James F. Sr. engr. Convair, Fort Worth, Tex., 1953-54; scientist Lockheed Aircraft, Marietta, Ga., 1954-61; physicist Army Missile Command Redstone Arsenal, Huntsville, Ala., 1961-77; cons. physicist, 1977—. Served with USAAF, 1943-46. AEC fellow, 1951-52. Mem. Am. Phys. Soc., Sigma Xi. Contbr. articles to profl. jours. Home and Office: 102 Mountain Wood Dr SE Huntsville AL 35801-1809

PERKINS, JAMES L., lawyer; b. Des Moines, Iowa, Oct. 8, 1931. AB, Drake U., 1953, JD, 1954; grad., Northwestern Coll. Law. Bar: Iowa 1954, Ill. 1955. Ptnr. Winston & Strawn, Chgo. Mem. ABA, State Ill. Bar Assn., Chgo. Bar Assn., Order of Coif, Delta Theta Phi. Office: Winston & Strawn 35 W Wacker Dr Chicago IL 60601-1614

PERKINS, JAMES PATRICK, advertising executive; b. Chgo., Dec. 6, 1939; s. John Alfred and Mary Grace (Quinlan) P.; student U. Ill., 1959-60, Western Ill. U., 1961; m. Sarah Reed Simkins, Sept. 13, 1975; children: Brian Patrick, Kevin Matthew, Quinn Cecile. Sales and mktg. exec. Glidden-Durkee, 1964-65; advt. mgr. Amvar Chem. Co., 1965-69; indsl. coatings rep. Benjamin Moore Co., 1969-71; account exec. JTC Advt., 1971-74; creative dir., pres. Laven, Fuller & Perkins Advt.-Mktg., Chgo., 1974—. Bd. dirs., mem. adv. bd. Booth Meml. Hosp., Salvation Army, Chgo., 1978-81. Sgt. U.S. Army, 1961-62. Mem. Chgo. Advt. Club, Orlando Ad Club, Employment Mgrs. Assn., Fla. Hosp. Adminstrs., Barclay Club (Chgo.), Club Internat. (Chgo.), Submarine Club. Roman Catholic. Avocations: watercolor painting, railroading, reading, golf. Home: 1314 Scott Ave Winnetka IL 60093-1463 Office: 280 W Canton Ave Ste 104 Winter Park FL 32789

PERKINS, JAMES WOOD, lawyer; b. New Bedford, Mass., Oct. 14, 1924; s. Ralph Chamberlain and Louise Bartlett (Allen) P.; m. Margaret Neale Heard, Feb. 3, 1951; children: Charles H., James A., George H. AB, Harvard U., 1945, JD, 1948; postgrad. Harvard Div. Sch., 1993—. Bar: Mass. 1948, U.S. Dist. Ct. Mass. 1948. Engr. Sylvania Electric Products, Inc., Salem, Mass., 1944-45; assoc. Palmer & Dodge, Boston, 1948-54, ptnr., 1955-91, mng. ptnr., 1986-89, of counsel, 1992—; mediator Mass. Appeals Ct., 1993—. Mem. ABA (chmn. sect. local govt. law 1970-71, sect. del. 1974-78), Nat. Assn. Bond Lawyers (pres. 1985-86). Office: Palmer & Dodge 1 Beacon St Boston MA 02108-3106

PERKINS, JOHN ALLEN, lawyer; b. New Bedford, Mass., Sept. 13, 1919; s. Ralph Chamberlain and Louise Bartlett (Allen) P.; m. Lydia Bullard Cobb, Sept. 9, 1944; children: John A., Susan W., Robert C., William B. A.B., Harvard U., 1940, LL.B., 1943. Bar: Mass. Of counsel Palmer & Dodge, Boston; clk. Social Law Library, 1961-83; grad. researcher Univ. Coll., Oxford U., 1978; bd. dirs. Greater Boston Legal Services, Inc., 1972-91. Author: The Prudent Peace—Law as Foreign Policy, 1981; contbr. articles to profl. jours. Mem. Dedham (Mass.) Sch. Com., 1959-65, chmn., 1963-65, town counsel, Dedham, 1971-72. Mem. Am. Law Inst., Am. Coll. Trust and Estate Counsel, Mass. Bar Assn. (dir. 1973-75), Internat. Acad. Estate and Trust Law (exec. coun. 1990-94), Boston Bar Assn. (council 1972-75, v.p. 1981-82, pres. 1982-84). Home: 203 Highland St Dedham MA 02026-5835 Office: Palmer & Dodge 1 Beacon St Boston MA 02108-3106

PERKINS, KENT, television and movie producer; b. Alexandria, La., Feb. 11, 1948; s. Dee M. Jr. and M. Elaine (Posey) P.; m. Ruth Buzzi, Dec. 10, 1978. BA in English and Psychology, North Tex. State U., 1970; MA, Tex. Wesleyan Coll., 1972. Pres. Tex. Talent, Inc., Los Angeles, 1978—; producer NBC, Burbank, Calif., 1987—; assoc. dir. Northwest Bankshares, Ft. Worth, 1972-83. Performed as actor in various Film and TV prodns. including "Nashville Palace," 1980, "Any Which Way You Can", 1980, "Buckaroo Banzai", 1986; author: (book) Once Upon a Crime, 1987, (screenplay) To Protect and Serve. Dir. Rep. Presdl. Task Force, Los Angeles, 1984; bd. dirs. Ft. Worth Rehab. Ctr., 1972-83. Mem. SAG, Writer's Guild of Am., Nat. Police Chief's Assn., Los Angeles C. of C., Rolls Royce Owners of Am. Lodge: Kiwanis Internat. Clubs: Am. Equestrian, Los Angeles Yacht. Avocations: horse breeder and trainer, flying, antique restoration, automobile restoration. Office: NBC Burbank 3000 W Alameda Ave Ste 237C Burbank CA 91523-0001 also: Bois d'arc Ranch PO Box 222 Caddo OK 74729-0222

PERKINS, LAWRENCE BRADFORD, JR., architect; b. Chgo., Jan. 13, 1943; s. Lawrence Bradford and Margery Isabella (Blair) P.; m. Phyllis Barbara Friedman, Sept. 11, 1966; children: Rachael Naomi, Judith Eve, Rebecca Abigail. BA, Cornell U., 1967; MBA, Stanford U., 1969; BArch, CCNY, 1976. Registered architect, N.Y., Ohio, Ill., Conn., Pa., N.J., Ga.,

Fla., Mo., Ariz., Tex. Pres. Perkins Eastman Archs., N.Y.C., 1983—, Omnidata Svcs., N.Y.C., 1971-73; mng. ptnr. Llewelyn-Davies Assocs., N.Y.C., 1973-77, Perkins & Will, N.Y.C., 1977-81; ptnr. Attia & Perkins, N.Y.C., 1981-83. Author chpts. to books; contbr. articles to profl. jours. Bd. dirs. Castle Gallery Coll. New Rochelle, N.Y., 1985—, Settlement Housing Fund, N.Y.C., 1991—, Helen Keller Internat., N.Y.C., 1993—, various other village bds. and coms. Fellow AIA (mem. various coms.), Am. Inst. Cert. Planners, Cornell U. Coun., Epsilon Assn. (pres. 1993—). Home: 4 Rectory Ln Scarsdale NY 10583 Office: Perkins Eastman Archs 437 Fifth Ave New York NY 10016

PERKINS, LEEMAN LLOYD, music educator, musicologist; b. Salina, Utah, Mar. 27, 1932; s. Milton Lloyd and Ida Margaret (Johnson) P.; m. Marianne Suzanne Contesse, Nov. 14, 1956; children: Eric Raymond, Bruce Philippe, Marc Christian, Patrick Thierry. BFA, U. Utah, 1954; PhD, Yale U., 1965. Instr. Boston U., 1964; instr. Yale U., 1964-67, asst. prof., 1967-71, dir. undergraduate studies in music history, 1969-70; assoc. prof. music history, coord. for musicology U. Tex., Austin, 1971-75, assoc. prof. music history, grad. adv. for musicology, 1976; prof. music Columbia U., N.Y.C., 1976—, chmn. dept music, 1985-90; instr. advanced seminar in Medieval History, Smith Coll., 1968; vis. assoc. prof. music Columbia U., 1975; vis. prof. Boston U., 1978; dir. NEH Summer Seminar, 1977. Contbr. with others Johannes Lheritier Opera Omnia, 1969, The Mellon Chansonnier, 1979; contbr. to profl. jours. Chmn. grad. musicology com., Columbia U., 1980-84. Sgt. U.S. Army, 1957-59. Recipient James Morris Whiton Fund award Yale U., 1965, The Otto Kinkeldey award Am. Musicological Soc., 1980; Trumbull Coll. fellow Yale U., 1966-71, Lewis-Farmington fellow Yale U., 1962-63, Morse fellow Yale U., 1967-68, Am. Coun. Learned Soc. fellow, 1973-74, NEH fellow, 1979, 1984-85, French Archival Scis. fellow Newberry Libr. Center for Renaissance Studies, 1991; Martha Baird Rockefeller grantee, 1963-64, Paul Mellon Found. grantee, 1972, Am. Coun. Learned Soc., 1972, 82, U. Tex. grantee, 1975.. Mem. Am Musicological Soc. (chmn. program com. 1979, bd. dirs. 1980-81, adv. bd.; 1985-86, chmn. ad hoc sub com., 1985-86, exec. com. delegate, 1989-92), Internat. Musicological Soc., The Renaissance Soc. of Am., Amici Thomae Mori, Phi Beta Kappa, Phi Kappa Phi. Mormon. Office: Columbia U Dept of Music Dodge Hall 703 New York NY 10027

PERKINS, LUCIAN, photographer. Grad., U. Texas. Intern The Washington Post, 1979, now staff photographer. Named Newspaper Photographer of Yr. Pictures of Yr. competition, 1993; recipient Pulitzer Prize for explanatory journalism, 1995. Office: The Washington Post 1150 15th St NW Washington DC 20071*

PERKINS, MALCOLM DONALD, lawyer; b. Milton, Mass., Aug. 29, 1914; s. John Forbes and Mary (Coolidge) P.; m. Sheila Delano Redmond, Feb. 1, 1944; children: Malcolm Donald, Sara D., Samuel, William H. AB magna cum laude, Harvard U., 1936, LLB, 1939. Bar: N.Y. 1940, Mass. 1946. Assoc. firm Parker & Duryee, N.Y.C., 1939-41, Herrick & Smith, Boston, 1946-52; partner Herrick & Smith, 1952-85, of counsel, 1985-86; of counsel Condit & Assocs., 1986—. Pres. bd. trustees Isabella Stewart Gardner Mus., Boston, 1976-91, Milton Acad., 1968-76, Greater Boston Legal Svcs., 1971-74. With USAAF, 1942-46. Mem. Am. Bar Assn., Am. Law Inst., Boston Bar Assn. Club: Tavern (Boston). Home: 64 Bradlee Rd Milton MA 02186-1232 Office: 260 Franklin St Boston MA 02110-3112

PERKINS, MARVIN EARL, psychiatrist, educator; b. Moberly, Mo., June 1, 1920; s. Marvin Earl and Nannie Mae (Walden) P.; A.B., Albion Coll., 1942; M.D. Harvard U., 1946; M.P.H. (USPHS fellow), Johns Hopkins U., 1956; L.H.D., Albion Coll., 1968; grad. U.S. Army Command and Gen. Staff Coll., 1966, U.S. Army War Coll., 1972; m. Mary MacDonald, May 24, 1943 (div.); children: Keith, Sandra, Cynthia, Marvin, Mary, Irene; m. 2d, Sharon Johnstone, May 20, 1978; 1 dau., Sharon. Intern, Henry Ford Hosp., Detroit, 1946-47; post surgeon, hosp. comdg. officer Fort Eustis, Va., 1948; resident physician psychiatry Walter Reed Army Hosp., Washington, 1949-52; chief psychiatry br., psychiatry and neurology cons. div. Office U.S. Army Surgeon Gen., Washington, 1952-53, chief records rev. br., 1953-55; chief psychiat. svcs. div. D.C. Dept. Pub. Health, 1955-58, chief bur. mental health, 1959-60; lectr. Johns Hopkins U., Balt., 1960-65; adj. prof. Columbia U., 1961-67; prof. psychiatry Coll. Physicians and Surgeons, Columbia U., 1972-77; prof. psychiatry N.Y. Coll. Medicine, 1977-78; prof. behavioral medicine and psychiatry U. Va. Sch. Medicine, 1978—; dir. N.Y.C. Community Mental Health Bd., 1960-68, commr. mental health svcs., 1961-68; dir. psychiatry Beth Israel Medical Center, N.Y.C., 1967-72, dir. Morris J. Bernstein Inst., 1968-72; dir. Community Mental Health Svcs. Westchester County, 1972-77; dir. psychiatry Westchester County Med. Center, 1977-78; med. dir. Mental Health Svcs. of Roanoke Valley, 1978-82; med. dir. Roanoke Valley Psychiat. Ctr., 1980-82, pres. med. staff, 1985-86; med. dir., pres. med staff Catawba Hosp., 1988-91. With AUS, 1943-46; col. M.C. Res. ret. Diplomate in psychiatry Am. Bd. Psychiatry and Neurology; certified mental hosp. adminstr. Am. Psychiat. Assn. Fellow Am. Psychiat. Assn. (life), N.Y. Acad. Medicine (life); mem. AMA, Group Advancement Psychiatry, Roanoke Acad. Medicine, Nat. Geneal. Soc., New Eng. Hist. Geneal. Soc., N.Y. Psychiat. Soc., Neuropsychiat. Soc. Va., Med. Soc. Va., State Hist. Soc. Mo. (life), N.Y. Hist. Soc., Res. Officers Assn. (life) Mil. Order of World Wars (perpetual). Home: 9940 Grove Hill Rd Fincastle VA 24090-3514 Office: U Va Dept Psychiatry Charlottesville VA 22903 also: VA Med Ctr Salem VA 24153

PERKINS, MERLE LESTER, French language educator; b. West Lebanon, N.H., Apr. 16, 1919; s. Charles Elisha and Ethel (Armstrong) P.; m. Barbara Marion Cunningham, June 16, 1951; children: Elizabeth Cunningham, Janet Blair. AB, Dartmouth Coll., 1941; AM, Brown U., 1942, PhD in French, 1950. Instr. French Brown U., 1944-50, U. Chgo., 1950-53; mem. faculty U. Calif., Davis, 1953-67; prof. French U. Calif., 1963-67, chmn. dept. fgn. langs., 1962-65, chmn. dept. Italian and French, 1965-67; prof. French U. Wis., 1967—, chmn. grad. studies French, 1967-74, 77-89, Pickard Bascom prof. French, 1983—; dir. univs. Mich. and Wis. Year in France, Aix-en-Provence, 1976-77, chmn. admissions, 1979-89. Author: The Moral and Political Philosophy of the Abbé de Saint-Pierre, 1959, Voltaire's Concept of International Order, 1965, J.J. Rousseau on History, Liberty, and National Survival, 1968, Jean-Jacques Rousseau on the Individual and Society, 1974, Diderot on the Time-Space Continuum, 1982, Montesquieu on National Power and International Rivalry, 1986, Six French Philosophes on International Rivalry and War, 1989, Marquis De Sade, His Ethics and Rhetoric: Suspense in Sade, 1989, Diderot: A Study Guide, 1990, Enlightenment Writers, Their Contributions to Two Revolutions, 1993, Ordeal of Arms, Air Combat, Europe and the Balkans, 1993; also anthology, articles, revs. Served with USAAF, 1942-45. Decorated Air medal with 3 oak leaf clusters.; Parker fellow Dartmouth Coll., 1941-42; Edwards fellow Brown U., 1948-49; Penrose Fund grantee Am. Philos. Soc., 1956-57, 72-73, 74-75; Fulbright research grantee France, 1960-61, 67-68. Mem. Am. Assn. Tchrs. French, Philol. Assn. Pacific Coast, Modern Lang. Assn. (grantee 1956-57), Internat. Assn. for 18th Century Studies, Modern Humanities Research Assn., Phi Beta Kappa. Episcopalian. Office: U Wis Dept French 1220 Linden Dr Madison WI 53706-1557

PERKINS, RALPH LINWOOD, business executive, public health administration specialist; b. Orono, Maine, July 17, 1914; s. Ralph L. and Zilla (Sawyer) P.; m. Hilda Beatrice Morrison, Sept. 1, 1938; children: Sylvia Lucille Perkins Nespoli, Jacquelyn Sue Perkins Lowe-Vosburgh. BSME, U. Maine, 1935; MS in Hosp. Adminstrn., Columbia, 1950. With U.S. Engrs. Dept., Quoddy, Me., 1935-37, NYA in, Me., Ohio and W.Va., 1937-44; with USPHS W.Va., Miss., La., D.C. and N.Y., 1944-48; asst. adminstrv. officer USPHS Hosp., S.I., 1949-50, adminstrv. officer, 1950-63; asso. dir. Hosp. U. Pa., 1963-64, exec. dir., 1964-74; sr. adviser Chi Systems, Inc., Ann Arbor, Mich., 1974-78; Lectr. Columbia Sch. Pub. Health and Adminstrv. Medicine, 1961-74. Past chmn. Delaware Valley Hosp. Council Forum.; Former bd. dirs. West Phila. Community Mental Health Consortium. Recipient Commendation Medal USPHS, 1963. Fellow Am. Coll. Health Care Execs. (life); mem. Am. Hosp. Assn. (life), Maine Hosp. Assn., Delaware Valley Hosp. Coun. (past dir. past pres. forum, sec.-treas.), Assn. Mil. and Med. Colls., Hosp. Assn. Pa. (past trustee), Commd. Officers Assn. USPHS (life). Methodist. Home and Office: 517 Fairfax Rd Drexel Hill PA 19026-1210

PERKINS, ROBERT LOUIS, physician, educator; b. Bradford, Pa., Feb. 20, 1931; s. Robert Marcell and Lola Ruth (Freeman) P.; m. Ruth Caloccia, Sept. 7, 1952 (dec. 1978); children: Cathy Lynn, Robert Louis; m. Penelope Joel Brodgen, Dec. 24, 1983. AB, W.Va. U., 1953, BS, 1954; MD, Johns Hopkins U., 1956; MS in Medicine, Ohio State U., 1962. Diplomate Am. Bd. Internal Medicine. Instr. medicine Ohio State U., Columbus, 1961-65, asst. prof., 1965-69, assoc. prof., 1969-73, prof. medicine, 1973—, prof. med. microbiology, 1974—, Pomerene prof., 1977-82, Saslaw prof., 1982-90, dir. infectious diseases div., 1971-87; dir. med. edn. Grant Med. Ctr., Columbus 1990—. Contbr. chpts. to books, numerous articles to profl. jours. Served to capt. USAF, 1958-60. NIH fellow, 1960-62. Fellow ACP, Infectious Disease Soc. Am.; mem. Ctrl. Soc. for Clin. Rsch., Am. Fedn. Clin. Rsch. Republican. Methodist. Avocations: model aviation; golf. Home: 2285 Pinebrook Rd Columbus OH 43220-4327 Office: Grant Med Ctr Med Edn 111 S Grant Ave Columbus OH 43215-1898

PERKINS, RONALD DEE, geologist, educator; b. Covington, Ky., May 18, 1935; s. Stanley E. and Pauline L. (Green) P.; m. Beverly L. Hughes, June 8, 1957; children—Lisa, Debra. B.S., U. Cin., 1957; M.S., U. N.Mex., 1959; Ph.D. in Geology, Ind. U., 1962. Research geologist Shell Devel. Co., Houston, 1962-63; project leader Shell Devel. Co., Coral Gables, Fla., 1963-68; mem. faculty Duke U., Durham, N.C., 1968—; prof. geology Duke U., 1975—, chmn. dept., 1978-90; cons. to industry. Author numerous papers in field. NSF grantee, 1969-80. Mem. Internat. Assn. Sedimentologists, Soc. Econ. Paleontologists and Mineralogists (sec.-treas. 1978-82), Geol. Soc. Am., Am. Assn. Petroleum Geologists, Sigma Xi. Office: Duke U Dept Geology West Campus Old Chemistry Bldg Durham NC 27708

PERKINS, ROSWELL BURCHARD, lawyer; b. Boston, May 21, 1926. A.B. cum laude, Harvard U., 1945, LL.B. cum laude, 1949, LLD (hon.), Bates Coll., 1988. Bar: Mass. 1949, N.Y. 1949. Assoc. Debevoise, Plimpton & McLean, N.Y.C., 1949-53; ptnr. Debevoise & Plimpton, and predecessor firms, N.Y.C., 1957—; asst. sec. U.S. Dept. Health, Edn. amd Welfare, 1954-56; counsel to Gov. Nelson A. Rockefeller, State of N.Y., 1959; asst. counsel spl. subcom. Senate Commerce Com. to investigate organized crime in interstate commerce, 1950; chmn. N.Y.C. Mayor's Task Force on Transp. Reorgn., 1966; mem. Pres.'s Adv. Panel on Personnel Interchange, 1968; chmn. adv. com. Medicare Adminstrn. Contracting Subcontracting HEW, 1973-74; dir. Fiduciary Trust Co. N.Y., 1993—; trustee Bowery Savs. Bank, 1975-82. Mem. N.Y. Lawyers Com. Civil Rights, 1970-73; mem. nat. exec. com., 1973-75, co-chmn., 1973-75; adv. coun. Woodrow Wilson Sch. Pub. and Internat. Affairs, Princeton U., 1967-69; bd. dirs. The Commonwealth Fund, 1974—; bd. dirs. Sch. Am. Ballet, 1974-85, chmn. bd., 1976-80; dir., sec. N.Y. Urban Coalition, 1967-74; trustee Pomfret Sch., 1961-80; The Brearley Sch., 1969-75; dir. Salzburg Seminar Am. Studies, 1970-80; mem. overseers vis. com. Kennedy Sch. Govt., Harvard U., 1971-77, Harvard and Radcliffe Colls., 1958-64, 1971-77. Recipient Spl. Merit Citation of Am. Judicature Soc., 1989, Harvard Law Sch. Assn. award, 1994. Mem. ABA (comm. on law and economy 1975-79; mem. house of dels. 1980-93), N.Y. State Bar Assn., Assn. Bar City of N.Y. (chmn. spl. com. on fed. conflict of interest laws 1958-60), Assn. Harvard Alumni (pres. 1970-71), Am. Law Inst. (mem. coun. 1969, pres. 1980-93, chmn. coun. 1993—), Am. Arbitration Assn. (bd. dirs. 1966-71). Author: The New Federal Conflict of Interest Law; editor Harvard Law Rev. Home: 1120 Fifth Ave New York NY 10128-0144 Office: Debevoise & Plimpton 875 3rd Ave New York NY 10022

PERKINS, SAMUEL, lawyer; b. Boston, Dec. 16, 1948; s. Malcolm and Sheila D. (Redmond) P.; m. Nancy Joy Reed, June 22, 1975; children: Molly, Sara, Benjamin, Emily. AB cum laude, Harvard U., 1970; JD, Boston U., 1976. Bar: Vt. 1977, U.S. Dist. Ct. 1977, Mass. 1984, U.S. Dist. Ct. Mass. 1984, U.S. Ct. Appeals (1st cir.) 1992. Asst. atty. gen. Atty. Gen.'s Office, Montpelier, Vt., 1977-78; assoc. Welch & Graham, White River Junction, Vt., 1978-81; ptnr. Welch, Graham, Perkins & Manby, White River Junction, 1981-83; assoc. Morrison, Mahoney & Miller, Boston, 1983-87, ptnr., 1987—. Mem. Mass. Bar Assn., Boston Bar Assn., Def. Rsch. Inst., Mass. Def. Lawyers Assn. Office: Morrison Mahoney & Miller 250 Summer St Boston MA 02210

PERKINS, SAMUEL THOMAS, lawyer; b. Ft. Leavenworth, Kans., Sept. 26, 1946; s. David Mural and Helene Mathilde (Berg) P.; m. Ruth Ann Nelson, July 29, 1967 (div. 1975); m. M. Carolyn Cox, Sept. 23, 1978; children: William Frank Cox Perkins, Leni Camille Mermod Perkins. AB summa cum laude, Brown U., 1967; JD, Yale U., 1974. Bar: D.C. 1975, U.S. Dist. Ct. D.C. 1975, U.S.C. Appeals (fed. cir.) 1993. Ptnr. Steptoe & Johnson, Washington1, 1974—. Editor Yale Law Jour., 1973-74. With US Army, 1968-70, Vietnam. Woodrow Wilson Found. scholar, 1967-68. Republican. Avocations: travel, historical studies, coaching youth sports teams. Office: 1330 Connecticut Ave NW Washington DC 20036-1704

PERKINS, THOMAS HAYES, III, furniture company executive; b. Brookhaven, Miss., Nov. 18, 1922; s. Thomas H. Jr. and Clara Louretta (Whittington) P. BS, La. State U. Owner T.H. Perkins Furniture, Inc. Chmn. Miss. Regional Housing Authority, McComb. With U.S. Army, 1943-44. Decorated Purple Heart, Bronze Star. Mem. Internat. Camellia Soc. (pres. 1988-94). Independent. Home: 415 Natchez Ave Brookhaven MS 39601 Office: T H Perkins Furniture 520 Brookway Blvd Brookhaven MS 39601

PERKINS, THOMAS JAMES, venture capital company executive; b. Oak Park, Ill., Jan. 7, 1932; s. Harry H. and Elizabeth P.; m. Gerd Thune-Ellefsen, Dec. 9, 1961; children: Tor Kristian, Elizabeth Siri. B.S.E.E., M.I.T., 1953; M.B.A., Harvard U., 1957. Gen. mgr. computer div. Hewlett Packard Co., Cupertino, Calif., 1965-70, dir. corp. devel., 1970-72; gen. partner Kleiner & Perkins, San Francisco, 1972-80; sr. ptnr. Kleiner Perkins Caufield & Byers, San Francisco, from 1980; chmn. bd. Tandem Computers, Inc., Cupertino, Calif.; chmn. bd. Tandem Computers, Genentech; dir. Spectra Physics., Corning Glass Works, Collagen Corp., LSI Logic Corp., Hybritech Inc., Econics Corp., Vitalink Communications Corp. Author: Classic Supercharged Sports Cars, 1984. Trustee San Francisco Ballet, 1980—. Mem. Nat. Venture Capital Assn. (chmn. 1981-82, pres. 1980-81). Clubs: N.Y. Yacht, Links, Am. Bugatti (pres. 1983—). Office: Tandem Computers Inc 10435 Tantau Ave Cupertino CA 95014-3548 also: Genentech Inc 460 Point San Bruno San Francisco CA 94080*

PERKINS, THOMAS KEEBLE, oil company researcher; b. Dallas, Jan. 31, 1932; s. James Thomas and Willie Fae (Keeble) P.; m. Anita Aliene Smith, July 20, 1963; children—Julia, Stephen. B.S., Tex. A&M U., 1952, M.S., 1953; Ph.D., U. Tex., 1957. Engr. Dow Chem. Co., Freeport, Tex., 1952; instr., asst. prof. U. Tex., Austin, 1955-57; from research engr. to disting. research adviser ARCO Exploration and Prodn. Tech., Plano, Tex., 1957-94, ret., 1994; trustee S.W. Research Inst., San Antonio, 1984—. Contbr. numerous articles to profl. jours.; patentee in field. Recipient Atlantic Richfield Tech. Achievement award, 1980, 90, 91. Mem. Soc. Petroleum Engrs. (C.K. Ferguson award com. 1973-75, Disting. lectr. 1977-78, Lester C. Uren award 1978, J. F. Carll award com. 1984-86, tech. editor jour. 1981-84, J.F. Carll award 1993), Nat. Acad. Engring. Republican. Methodist.

PERKINS, VAN L., university administrator, educator, conservationist; b. Standardville, Utah, May 22, 1930; s. Howard Edward and Maude (Larsen) P.; m. Colleen Campbell, Feb. 14, 1951 (div. Aug. 1986); children: Mark E., Cheryl, Scott C., Brett C., Regan; m. Katherine Marie Bennett, Jan. 17, 1986. BA, U. Utah, 1956; MA, Harvard U., 1958, PhD, 1966. Purchasing agt. Bechtel Corp., San Francisco, 1951-55; instr. to asst. prof. Brigham Young U., Provo, Utah, 1960-64; asst. prof. U. Calif., Riverside, 1964-68; assoc. prof. U. Calif., 1968-73, prof., 1973-91, prof. emeritus, 1991—; assoc. dean Grad. Sch. U. Calif., Riverside, 1971-73; vice chancellor U. Calif., Riverside, 1973-78, exec. vice chancellor, 1987-88; cons. in higher edn. mgmt., 1977—; mus. orgn. and mgmt., 1982. Author: Crisis in Agriculture, 1969; contbr. articles to profl. jours. Mgr. U.S. Senatorial and Ho. Reps. Campaigns, Utah and Calif., 1962, 64, 80; mem. adv. com. U.S. Commn. on Civil Rights, 1978-84; conservation chair Santa Fe group Sierra Club, 1992—. Served with U.S. Army, 1950-52. Recipient George Emory Fellows prize U. Utah, 1956, Edwards Meml. prize Agrl. History Soc., 1965; Danforth fellow, 1956, co, 1962-64. Mem. ACLU, Sierra Club, Southern Utah Wilderness Alliance, Audubon Soc., Wilderness Soc., Phi Beta Kappa,

Phi Kappa Phi. Democrat. Home: RR 7 Box 128H Santa Fe NM 87505-9286 Office: U Calif-Riverside Dept History Riverside CA 92521

PERKINS, SISTER VICTORIA MARIE, school system administrator; b. Dodge City, Kans., June 27, 1942; d. Ward and Mamie (Lavery) P. BA, St. Mary Coll., Leavenworth, Kans.; MA, Ohio State U.; postgrad., U. Mo., Kansas City. Tchr. St. Daniel the Prophet Sch., Chgo., 1962-63; tchr. math Bishop Ward High Sch., Kansas City, Kans., 1965-76; tchr. Bishop Hogan High Sch., Kansas City, Mo., 1976-77, prin., 1977-87; assoc. supt. sch.s Diocese Kansas City-St. Joseph (Mo.), 1987-88, supt. schs., 1988—; del. Nat. Congress for Cath. Schs. for 21st Century, 1991. Named Career Woman of Yr. Career Club Kansas City and The Jones Store Co., 1985; recipient UMOJA award Black Cath. Caucus, 1987. Mem. Nat. Cath. Ednl. Assn., Nat. Coun. Tchrs. Math., Chief Adminstrs. Cath. Edn., Mo. Coun. Am. Pvt. Edn., Mo. Cath. Conf., Greater Kansas City Literacy Task Force, Harmony in a World of Difference. Democrat. Avocations: running, crocheting, needlepoint. Home: 3215 Windsor Ave Kansas City MO 64123-1134 Office: Schs Supt PO Box 419037 Kansas City MO 64141-6037

PERKINS, WHITNEY TROW, political science educator emeritus; b. Boston, Feb. 28, 1921; s. Wesley Trow and Hazel Alice (Mason) P; m. Kathryn A. Sylvester, June 28, 1947; children—Rebecca, Mason, Wesley, Rachel. A.B., Tufts U., 1942; Ph.D., Fletcher Sch. Law and Diplomacy, 1948. Asst. prof. internat. relations U. Denver, 1948-53; from assoc. prof. to prof. polit. sci. Brown U., Providence, 1953-84; chmn. Internat. Relations Concentration, Brown U., 1955-84; cons. U.S.-P.R. Commn. on Status of Puerto Rico, 1965. Author: Denial of Empire: The United States and its Dependencies, 1962; Constraint of Empire: The United States and Caribbean Interventions, 1981. Served to capt. USAF, 1942-45, PTO. Recipient Fulbright Research award, 1951-52. Mem. Am. Polit. Sci. Assn., Internat. Studies Assn., Phi Beta Kappa. Democrat. Avocations: tennis; squash; hiking. Home: 11 Catalpa Rd Providence RI 02906-2614

PERKINS, WILLIAM ALLAN, JR., retired lawyer; b. Charlottesville, Va., Dec. 19, 1925; s. William Allan and Hazlehurst (Bolton) P.; m. Ann Patterson, Jan. 30, 1950 (div. 1980); children—William Allan III, Ann B., Howell W., Channing P.; m. Elizabeth Ragland, May 10, 1980. Student, Duke U.; LL.B., U. Va., 1949. Bar: Va., 1949. Ptnr. McGuire, Woods, Battle & Boothe and predecessor firms, Charlottesville, Va., 1949-93; ret. McGuire, Woods, Battle & Boothe and predecessor firms, Charlottesville, 1993. Former chmn. Miller Fund, 1982—; mem. Perry Found., 1955—. Mem. Charlottesville-Albemarle Bar Assn. (pres. 1972-73), Va. Trial Lawyers Assn. (pres. 1965-66), Va. Bar Assn. (council 1977-84), SAR, Indian Creek Yacht and Country Club. Episcopalian. Clubs: Fishing Bay Yacht (past commodore) (Deltaville, Va.); Redland (pres. 1965-66), Farmington, Colonnade (Charlottesville). Avocations: sailing; fishing. Home: PO Box 534 Deltaville VA 23043-0534 Office: McGuire Woods Battle & Boothe PO Box 1288 Charlottesville VA 22902-1288

PERKINS, WILLIAM CLINTON, company executive; b. Decatur, Ill., Mar. 7, 1920; s. Glen Rupert and Frances Lola (Clinton) P.; m. Eunice Cagle, Sept. 7, 1939 (div. 1954); stepchildren: William Rea Cagle, Howard Christy Cagle; 1 child, Clinton Colcord; m. Lillian Wuollet, Sept. 7, 1955 (div. 1965); m. Shirley Thomas, Oct. 24, 1969. BS Mil. Sci. and Meteorology, U. Md., 1954; MS in Bus. and Pub. Adminstrn., Sussex Coll., Eng. 1975. Commd. USAF, 1943-73, advanced through grades to col.; with Ship Systems div. Litton Ind., Culver City, Calif., 1973-75; dir. materiel Hughes Aircraft Co., Tehran, Iran, 1974-78; mgr. internat. s/c Northrop Corp., Dahran, Saudi Arabia, 1978-81; dir. materiel CRS, Riyadh, Saudi Arabia, 1981-83; head major subcontracts Lear Ziegler Corp., Santa Monica, Calif., 1984-88; pres., CEO Ice Village Ctrs., Inc., L.A., 1988—; bd. dirs. Ice Village Ctrs., Inc. L.A., Forefront Industries, Maywood, Calif. Bd. dirs. World Children's Transplant Fund, L.A., 1987—; mem. Mayor's Space Adv. Com., L.A., 1970-74; mem. aerospace hist. com. Mus. Sci. and Industry, L.A., 1988—. Mem. AIAA (sect. chmn. 1970), Ret. Officers Assn. (pres. 1992—), Soc. for Non-destructive Testing (program chmn. 1973), Am. Soc. Quality Control, Am. Meteorol. Soc., Sigma Alpha Epsilon (alumni chpt. pres. 1974-76). Avocations: golf, scuba diving, sailing, flying, gardening. Home: 8027 Hollywood Blvd Los Angeles CA 90046-2510

PERKINS, WILLIAM H., JR., finance company executive; b. Rushville, Ill., Aug. 4, 1921; s. William H. and Sarah Elizabeth (Logsdon) P.; m. Eileen Nelson, Jan. 14, 1949; 1 child, Gary Douglas. Ed., Ill. Coll. Pres. Howlett-Perkins Assos., Chgo.; mem. Ill. AEC, 1963-84, sec., 1970-84; mem. adv. bd. Nat. Armed Forces Mus., Smithsonian Instn., 1964-82. Sgt.-at-arms Democratic Nat. Conv., 1952, 56, del.-at-large, 1964, 68, 72; spl. asst. to chmn. Dem. Nat. Com., 1960; mem. Presdl. Inaugural Com., 1961, 65, 69, 73. Served with U.S. Army, 1944-46. Mem. Ill. Ins. Fedn. (pres. 1965-84), Ill. C. of C. (chmn. legis. com. 1971), Chgo. Assn. Commerce and Industry (legis. com., Raoul Wallenberg Humanitarian award 1993), Internat. Platform Assn., Sangamo Club, Masons, Shriners. Methodist. Home: 52 N Cowley Rd Riverside IL 60546-2042 Office: Ste 6 19 Riverside Rd Riverside IL 60546-2263

PERKINS, WILLIAM HUGHES, speech pathologist, educator; b. Kansas City, Mo., Feb. 21, 1923; s. William C. and Edna (Hughes) P.; m. Jill Thompson, June 16, 1952; children: Christopher, Scott, Alizon, Kyle. BS, Southwest Mo. State U., 1943; MA, U. Mo.-Columbia, 1949, PhD, 1952. Lic. speech pathologist, Calif. Asst. prof. communications arts and scis. dept. speech sci. and tech. U. So. Calif., L.A., 1952-56, assoc. prof., 1956-60, prof., 1960-88, dir. Stuttering Ctr., 1957-88, disting. prof. emeritus, 1988—. Author: Speech Pathology, 1967, Human Perspectives in Speech and Language Disorders, 1977; adv. editor Coll.-Hill Press, San Diego, 1980-87; editor Jour. Speech and Hearing Disorders, 1977-81; Current Therapy of Communications Disorders, 1983-84, Functional Anatomy of Speech, Language and Hearing, 1986; editor in chief Seminars in Speech and Lang., 1983-90, Recent Advances in Communication Disorders, 1984, Stuttering Prevented: A Guide for Parents, 1991. Served to lt. comdr. USN, 1943-46. Fellow Am. Speech and Hearing Assn. (Honors of Assn. award 1983). Home: 5425 Weatherford Dr Los Angeles CA 90008-1048

PERKINS, WILLIAM RANDOLPH, electrical engineer, educator; b. Council Bluffs, Iowa, Sept. 1, 1934. AB cum laude, Harvard U., 1956; MS, Stanford U., 1957, PhD, 1961. Instr. Stanford (Calif.) U., 1959-60; asst. prof. U. Ill., Urbana, 1961-65, assoc. prof., 1965-69, prof., 1969—, assoc. Ctr. for Advanced Study, 1971-72. Contbr. over 150 articles to profl. jours. Recipient Halliburton Edn. Leadership award U. Ill., 1986-87. Fellow IEEE (Centennial medal 1984, editor-in-chief IEEE Press 1992-94); mem. IEEE Control Sys. Soc. (pres. 1985, Disting. Mem. award 1986). Office: U Ill Coord Sci Lab 1308 W Main St Urbana IL 61801

PERKINSON, DIANA AGNES ZOUZELKA, import company executive; b. Prostejov, Czechoslovakia, June 27, 1943; came to U.S., 1962; d. John Charles and Agnes Diana (Sincl) Zouzelka; m. David Francis Perkinson, Mar. 6, 1965; children: Dana Leissa, David. BA, U. Lausanne (Switzerland), 1960; MA, U. Madrid, 1961; MBA, Case Western Res. U., 1963. Cert. internat. mktg. Oxford (Eng.) U., 1962. Assoc. Allen Hartman & Schreiber, Cleve., 1963-64; interpreter Tower Internat. Inc., Cleve., 1965-76; pres. Oriental Rug Importers Ltd., Cleve., 1979—; pres. Oriental Rug Designers, Inc., Cleve., 1980—; pres. Oriental Rug Cons., Inc., Cleve., 1980—; chmn. Foxworthy's Inc., Ft. Myers, Naples, Sanibel, Fla.; bd. dir. Beckwith & Assocs., Inc., Cleve., Secura Inc., Dallas, Dix-Bur Investments, Ltd., Real Estate By Design. Trustee, Cleve. Ballet, 1979, exec. com., 1981; mem. chmn. grantsmanship Jr. League of Cleve., 1982; mem. mem. Cleve. Found.; Women in Philanthropy, 1982; trustee Ft. Myers Symphony, 1990. Mem. Women Bus. Owners Assn., Oriental Rug Retailers Am. (bd. dir. 1983), Cleve. Racquet Club, Recreation League, The League Club (Naples, Fla.), Hillbrook Club, Univ. Club (Ft. Myers, Fla.), Lancaster Yacht Club. Republican. Roman Catholic. Home: Ravencrest PO Box 477 Sanibel FL 33957-0477 Office: Oriental Rug Importers Ltd Inc 2430 Periwinkle Way Sanibel FL 33957-3207 also: 17001 Captiva Rd Captiva Island FL 33924

PERKOFF, GERALD THOMAS, physician, educator; b. St. Louis, Sept. 22, 1926; s. Nat and Ann (Schwartz) P.; m. Marion Helen Maizner, June 7,

1947; children: David Alan, Judith Ilene, Susan Gail. M.D. cum laude, Washington U., 1948. Intern Salt Lake City Gen. Hosp., 1948-49, resident, 1950-52; from instr. to asso. prof. medicine U. Utah, 1954-63; chief med. service Salt Lake VA Hosp., 1961-63; asso. prof., then prof. medicine Washington U. Sch. Medicine, St. Louis, 1963-79; chief Med. Service, St. Louis City Hosp., 1963-68, prof. preventive medicine and pub. health, dir. div. health care research, 1968-79; Curators prof. and assoc. chmn. dept. family and community medicine and prof. medicine U. Mo., Columbia, 1979-91, Curators prof. emeritus, 1991—; co-dir. program health care and human values U. Mo., 1984-85; chmn. nat. adv. com. Robert Wood Johnson Clin. Scholars Program, 1989—; dep. dir. Robert Wood Johnson Found. Generalist Physician Initiative, 1991—; career rsch. prof. neuromuscular diseases Nat. Found. Neuromuscular Diseases, 1961; founder, dir. Med. Care Group of Washington U., 1968-78. Contbr. articles profl jours. Served as jr. asst. surgeon USPHS, 1953-54. John and Mary F. Markle scholar med. sci., 1955-60; Henry J. Kaiser Sr. fellow Ctr. Advanced Studies in Behavioral Sci., Stanford, 1976-77, 85-86. Mem. Am. Soc. Clin. Investigation, Soc. Tchrs. Family Medicine, Assn. Am. Physicians, Inst. Medicine (Nat. Acad. Scis.). Home: 1300 Torrey Pines Dr Columbia MO 65203-4826 Office: U Mo Sch Medicine Dept Family & Community Medicine M228 Med Scis Columbia MO 65212

PERKOVIC, ROBERT BRANKO, international management consultant; b. Belgrade, Yugoslavia, Aug. 27, 1925; came to U.S., 1958, naturalized, 1961; s. Slavoljub and Ruza (Pantelic) P.; m. Jacquelyn Lee Lipscomb, Dec. 14, 1957; children: Bonnie Kathryn, Jennifer Lee. M.S. in Econs, U. Belgrade, 1954; B.F.T., Am. Grad. Sch. Internat. Mgmt., 1960; grad. Stanford exec. program, Stanford U., 1970. Auditor Gen. Foods Corp., White Plains, N.Y., 1960-62; controller Gen. Foods Corp., Mexico City, 1962-64; dir. planning Monsanto Co., Barcelona, Spain, 1964-67; dir. fin. Monsanto Co., Europe, Brussels, 1967-70; dir. fin. planning-internat. Monsanto Co., St. Louis, 1970-71; asst. treas. Monsanto Co., 1971-72, Brussels, 1972-74; corp. treas. Fiat-Allis Inc. & BV, Deerfield, Ill., 1974-78; v.p. treas. TRW Inc., Cleve., 1978-88; pres. RBP Internat. Cons., Cleve., 1988—; dir. U.S. Bus. Coun. for Southeastern Europe, Inc. Active Cleve. Commn. on Fgn. Relations. Inc. Served with Yugoslavian Army, 1944-47. Mem. Fin. Execs. Inst., Cleve. Treas. Club (bd. dirs., pres.), Mayfield Village (Ohio) Racquet Club. Office: RBP Internat Cons 26 Pepper Creek Dr Cleveland OH 44124-5248

PERKOWITZ, SIDNEY, physicist, educator, author; b. Bklyn., May 1, 1939; s. Morris and Sylvia (Gray) P.; m. Sandra Price; 1 child, Michael Abram. BS, N.Y. Poly., N.Y.C., 1960; MS, U. Pa., 1962, PhD, 1967. Rsch. physicist Gen. Telephone & Electronics Labs., Bayside, N.Y., 1966-69; asst. prof. physics Emory U., Atlanta, 1969-74, assoc. prof., 1974-79, prof., 1979-87, Charles Howard Candler prof., 1987—, chmn. dept., 1980-83; vis. prof. U. Calif.-Santa Barbara, 1983-84; cons. Santa Barbara Rsch. Ctr., Sunnyvale, Calif., 1975-78, Nat. Rsch. Coun. Can., Ottawa, 1988-91, Nat. Inst. Standards and Tech., Gaithersburg, Md., 1990—; vis. scientist Southeastern Univs. Rsch. Assn., Washington, 1990-91; adj. prof. humanities Atlanta Coll. Arts, 1989—; mem. adv. panel Exptl. Gallery, Smithsonian Instn., Washington. Author: Optical Characterization of Semiconductors, 1993, Empire of Light, 1995; editor, contbr. numerous articles and essays to sci. publs. Grantee Sloan Found. Rsch. Corp., AEC, NIH, NSF, Office Naval Rsch., U.S. Dept. Energy, U.S. Dept. Def., TRW Corp., Korea Inst. Sci. and Tech., Lockheed Corp., Oak Ridge Nat. Lab. Mem. AAAS, Am. Phys. Soc., Soc. for Lit. and Sci. (v.p.), Phi Beta Kappa. Avocations: movies, crossword puzzles, music, hiking. Office: Emory U Rollins Rsch Ctr Physics Dept Atlanta GA 30322-2430

PERKOWSKI, JAN LOUIS, language and literature educator; b. Perth Amboy, N.J., Dec. 29, 1936; m. Liliana Asenova Daskalova, May 24, 1989. AB, Harvard U., 1959, AM, 1960, PhD, 1965. Asst. prof. U. Calif. Santa Barbara, 1964-65; assoc. prof. U. Tex., Austin, 1965-74; prof. U. Va., Charlottesville, 1974—. Author: A Kashubian Idiolect in U.S., 1969, Vampires, Dwarves & Witches Among the Ontario Kashubs, 1972, Vampires of the Slavs, 1976, Gusle & Ganga Among the Hercegovinians of Toronto, 1978, The Darkling-A Treatise on Slavic Vampirism, 1989. Grantee, fellow Ford Found., Harvard U., Kościuszko Found., U. Tex., Am. Philos. Soc., Nat. Mus. Man, U. Va., NEH, Kennan Inst., numerous others. Mem. Am. Assn. for the Advancement of Slavic Studies, Am. Assn. Tchrs. of Slavic and East European Langs. Office: U Va Dept Slavic Langs & Lits 109 Cabell Hall Charlottesville VA 22903

PERKS, BENJAMIN WINWOOD, accountant; b. Springfield, Ohio, Feb. 24, 1942; s. Ben Wheldon and Nancy (Turner) P.; m. Sally West Morris, July 16, 1966; children: James Winwood, David Addison. BA, Denison U., 1964; JD, U. Cin., 1967, MBA, 1968; profl. acctg. program degree, Noethwestern U., 1970. CPA, Ill., Ariz., Calif., Iowa, N.C. Staff acct., ptnr. Price Waterhouse, Chgo., 1968-83; mng. ptnr. Price Waterhouse, Tucson, 1983-87, Newport Beach, Calif., 1987—. Bd. dirs., mem. exec. com. Boy Scouts Am., Newport Beach, 1987, United Way, Newport Beach, 1988, campaign chmn., Tucson, 1986. Mem. AICPA, ABA. Avocations: golf, tennis, racquetball. Office: Price Waterhouse 660 Newport Center Dr Ste 600 Newport Beach CA 92660-6407

PERLBERG, JULES MARTIN, lawyer; b. Chgo., Jan. 28, 1931; s. Maurice and Louise Mae (Schonberger) P.; m. Dora Ann Morris, Dec. 22, 1968; children: Julia, Michael. BBA with high distinction, U. Mich., 1952, JD with high distinction, 1957. Bar: Ill. 1958, D.C. 1964; C.P.A., Ill. Acct. Arthur Andersen & Co., Chgo., 1954-55; faculty U. Mich. Law Sch., Ann Arbor, 1957-58; assoc. Sidley & Austin and predecessor firm, Chgo., 1958-65, ptnr., 1966—. Mem. Glencoe (Ill.) Bd. Edn., 1980-87, pres., 1985-86; bd. dirs. Juvenile Diabetes Found., Chgo., 1981—, v.p. 1983-85, treas., 1988-90; exec. bd. Am. Jewish Com., Chgo., 1978-88, v.p., 1981-83; trustee New Trier Twp. Schs., 1987-91, pres., 1989-91; class co-chairperson parents com. Duke U., 1992-94. 1st lt. U.S. Army, 1952-54. Recipient Gold medal Ill. Soc. C.P.A.s 1955. Mem. ABA, Chgo. Bar Assn. Clubs: Legal, Law; Mid-Day (Chgo.); Standard. Home: 568 Westly Rd Glencoe IL 60022-1071 Office: Sidley & Austin 1 First Nat Plz Chicago IL 60603

PERLE, EUGENE GABRIEL, lawyer; b. N.Y.C., Dec. 21, 1922; s. Philip and Simme (Meschenberg) P.; m. Ellen Carlotta Kraus, Nov. 26, 1953 (dec. 1964); 1 child, Elizabeth Anne; m. Ruth Friedberg Lerner, May 23, 1972 (div. 1977); m. Patricia Fitzpatrick Sinnott, Jan. 24, 1981. BA, Queens Coll., 1943; JD, Yale U., 1949. Bar: N.Y. 1950. Assoc. Cravath, Swaine & Moore, N.Y.C., 1949-53; asst. counsel N.Y. State Moreland Commn. Investigation Harness Racing, N.Y.C., 1953-54; assoc. Gordon, Brady, Caffrey & Keller, N.Y.C., 1954-56; assoc. gen. atty. Time Inc., N.Y.C., 1956-66; pub. counsel Time Inc., 1966-73, v.p. law, 1973-80, corp. v.p. law, 1980-85; counsel Proskauer Rose Goetz & Mendelsohn, N.Y.C., 1985-92, Chapman & Fennell, 1992-94; mem. Ohlandt, Greeley, Ruggiero & Perle, Stamford, Conn., 1995—. Co-author: The Publishing Law Handbook, 1984-94; mem. editorial bd.: Yale Law Jour., 1948-49; mem. adv. bd.: Bur. Nat. Affairs Patent, Trademark and Copyright Jour., 1972-86; contbr. to Bull Copyright Soc. U.S.A. Trustee Baron deHirsch Fund, 1959-87, hon. trustee, 1988—; commr. Nat. Commn. New Technol. Uses Copyrighted Works, 1975-78; bd. dirs. N.Y. Sch. for Circus Arts, Inc., 1979-87, Am. Arbitration Assn., 1979-84; justice of peace City of Norwalk, Conn., 1960-63. Lt. USNR, 1943-46. Mem. ABA (chmn. copyright divsn. 1970-71, 86-87, chmn. com. copyright and new tech. 1971-73, chmn. com. economics profession 1976, coun. patent, trademark and copyright sect. 1979-83, governing bd. forum com. comms. law 1979-85, chmn. related fields and future devels. divsn. forum com. entertainment and sports industries 1979), Copyright Soc. U.S.A. (trustee 1962-64, 69-70, 71-74, pres. 1976-78, hon. trustee 1978—), U.S. Trademark Assn. (bd. dirs. 1969-72, 74-77, v.p 1972-73), Assn. of Bar of City of N.Y., Sunningdale Country Club, Century Assn. Club, Adms. Cove Club. Democrat. Office: Ohlandt Greeley et al One Landmark Sq Stamford CT 06901

PERLE, GEORGE, composer; b. Bayonne, N.J., May 6, 1915; s. Joseph and Mary (Sanders) Perlman; m. Laura Slobe, 1940; m. Barbara Philips, Aug. 11, 1958 (dec.); children: Kathy, Annette; 1 stepchild, Max Massey; m. Shirley Gabis Rhoads, June 6, 1982; 1 stepchild: Paul Rhoads, Daisy Rhoads. MusB, DePaul U., 1938; MusM, Am. Conservatory of Music, 1942; Ph.D., NYU, 1956. Mem. faculty U. Louisville, 1949-57, U. Calif., 1957-61, Juilliard Sch. Music, 1963, Yale U., 1965-66, U. So. Calif., summer

1965, Tanglewood, summers 1967, 80, 87; from asst. prof. to assoc. prof. to prof. CUNY, 1961-85, prof. emeritus, 1985—; composer-in-residence San Francisco Symphony, 1989-91; vis. Birge-Cary prof. music SUNY, Buffalo, 1971-72; vis. prof. U. Pa., 1976, 80, Columbia U., 1979, 83; vis. Ernest Bloch prof. music U. Calif., Berkeley, 1989; vis. disting. prof. music NYU, N.Y.C. 1994. Author: Serial Composition and Atonality 1962, 6th edit., 1991, Twelve-Tone Tonality, 1977, 2d edit., 1995, The Operas of Alban Berg, vol. 1, 1980, vol. 2, 1985, The Listening Composer, 1990, The Right Notes, 1995, Style and Idea in the Lyric Suite of Alban Berg, 1995; contbr. articles in Am., fgn. mus. jours.; composer: Pantomime, Interlude and Fugue, 1937, Little Suite for Piano, 1939, Two Rilke Songs, 1941, Sonata for Solo Viola, 1942, Three Sonatas for Clarinet, 1943, Piano Piece, 1945, Hebrew Melodies for Cello, 1945, Lyric Piece for Cello and Piano, 1946, Six Preludes for Piano, 1946, Sonata for Solo Cello, 1947, Solemn Procession for Band, 1947, Sonata for Piano, 1950, Three Inventions for Piano, 1957, Quintet for Strings, 1958, Wind Quintet I, 1959, Sonata I for Solo Violin, 1959, Wind Quintet II, 1960, Fifth String Quartet, 1960-67, Three Movements for Orchestra, 1960, Monody I for flute, 1960, Music for The Birds of Aristophanes, 1961, Monody II for double bass 1962, Serenade I for Viola and Chamber Ensemble, 1962, Three Inventions for Bassoon, 1962, Sonata II for Solo Violin, 1963, Short Sonata for Piano, 1964, Solo Partita for Violin and Viola, 1965, Six Bagatelles for Orch., 1965, Concerto for Cello and Orch., 1966, Wind Quintet III, 1967, Serenade II for Chamber Ensemble, 1968, Toccata for Piano, 1969, Suite in C for Piano, 1970, Fantasy-Variations for Piano, 1971, Sonata Quasi una Fantasia for Clarinet and Piano, 1972, Seventh String Quartet, 1973, Songs of Praise and Lamentation for chorus and orch. 1974, Six Etudes for Piano, 1976, 13 Dickinson Songs, 1978, Concertino for Piano, Winds, and Timpani, 1979, A Short Symphony, 1980; Ballade for Piano, 1981, Sonata a quattro, 1982, Serenade III for Piano and Chamber Ensemble, 1983, Six New Etudes for Piano, 1984, Wind Quintet IV, 1984, Sonata for Cello and Piano, 1985, Sonatina for Piano, 1986, Sonata a cinque, 1986, Dance Fantasy for Orch., 1986, Lyric Intermezzo for chamber orch., 1987, Lyric Intermezzo for fifteen players, 1987, Lyric Intermezzo for piano, 1987, New Fanfares for brass ensemble, 1987, Sinfonietta, 1987, Windows of Order for string quartet, 1988, Sextet for winds and piano, 1988, Concerto for Piano and Orchestra, 1990, Sinfonietta II, 1990, Concerto No. 2 for Piano and Orch., 1992, Adagio for Orch., 1992, Transcendental Modulations (commd. for 150 anniversary N.Y. Philharmonic), 1993, Phantasyplay for Piano, 1994. Served with AUS, 1943-46, ETO, PTO. Recipient Nat. Inst. Arts and Letters award, 1977, Pulitzer prize, 1986; Guggenheim fellow, 1966-67, 74-75, MacArthur fellow, 1986; grantee Am. Council Learned Socs., 1968-69, Nat. Endowment for the Arts, 1978-79, 85. Fellow Am. Acad. Arts and Scis.; mem. Am. Musicol. Soc., ASCAP (Deems Taylor award 1973, 78, 81), Am. Acad. Arts and Letters.

PERLE, RICHARD NORMAN, government official; b. N.Y.C., Sept. 16, 1941; s. Jack Harold and Martha Gloria (Needell) P.; m. Leslie Joan Barr, July 31, 1977; 1 child, Jonathan Barr. BA, U. So. Calif., 1964; postgrad. in econs., U. London, 1962-63; MA, Princeton U., 1967. Asst. sec. internat. security policy Dept. Def., Washington, 1981-87; prof. staff mem. subcom. nat. security Senate Com. on Govt. Ops., Washington, 1970-72; profl. staff mem. committee on armed services U.S. Senate, Washington, 1969-80; resident fellow Am. Enterprise Inst. for Pub. Policy Rsch., Washington, 1987—. Office: Am Enterprise Inst Pub Policy Rsch 1150 17th St NW Washington DC 20036-4603

PERLESS, ELLEN, advertising executive; b. N.Y.C., Sept. 9, 1941; d. Joseph B. and Bertha (Messinger) Kaplan; m. Robert L. Perless, July 2, 1965. Student, Smith Coll., 1958-59, Bard Coll., 1959-62. Copywriter Doyle, Dane Bernbach, N.Y.C., 1964-70, Young & Rubicam, N.Y.C., 1970-74; creative supr. Young & Rubicam, 1974-76, v.p., creative supr., 1977, v.p., assoc. creative dir., 1978, sr. v.p., assoc. creative dir., 1979-84; v.p., assoc. creative dir. Leber Katz Ptnrs., 1984-85, sr. v.p., creative dir., 1986-87; sr. v.p., sr. creative dir. FCB/Leber Katz Ptnrs., N.Y.C., 1987-93, sr. v.p., group creative dir., 1994—. Recipient Clio awards, Andy awards, awards Art Dirs. Club N.Y., N.Y. Festivals, One Club. Home: 37 Langhorne Ln Greenwich CT 06831-2611 Office: FCB/Leber Katz Ptnrs 150 E 42 St New York NY 10017

PERLESS, ROBERT L., sculptor; b. N.Y.C., Apr. 23, 1938; s. Meyer and Ethel (Glassman) P.; m. Ellen R. Kaplan, July 2, 1965. Student, U. Miami, Fla., 1955-59. One-man exhbns. include Bodley Gallery, N.Y.C., 1968, 70, Galerie Simonne Stern, New Orleans, 1969, Bernard Danenberg Gallery, N.Y.C., 1970-72, Bonino Gallery, N.Y.C., 1976; group exhbns. include Bodley Gallery, 1970, Whitney Mus., 1970, Forum Gallery, N.Y.C., 1975, Bonino Gallery, 1975, Houston Gallery, 1976, Aldrich Mus., Ridgefield, Conn., 1978, Taft Mus., Cin., 1980, Aldrich Mus., 1987, 94, Stamford (Conn.) Mus., 1989, Bruce Mus., Greenwich, Conn., 1989, Andre Emmerich's Top Gallant Farm, 1991, 92, 93, 94, 95; represented in permanent collections: Whitney Mus., Aldrich Mus., Chrysler Mus., Norfolk, Va., Everson Mus., Syracuse, N.Y., Okla. Art Center, Oklahoma City, Phoenix Art Mus., Stamford (Conn.) Mus. Address: 37 Langhorne Ln Greenwich CT 06831-2611

PERLEY, MARY JO, health facility administrator; b. Columbus, Ohio, Sept. 23, 1949; d. Ward B. and Phyllis (Edwards) P.; m. Gary Ross Calvert, June 13, 1970 (div. Jan. 1979); children: Christiana Lynn, Geoffrey Ross; m. Donald John Lehman, Mar. 19, 1988; stepchildren: Sarah, Christopher. BSN, Tex. Christian U., 1972; MSN, Ohio State U., 1981, PhD, 1986. Staff nurse U.S. Darnall Army Hosp., Ft. Hood, Tex., 1972-74; instr. maternal/child Mercy Hosp. Sch. Nursing, Scranton, Pa., 1974-76; head nurse L&D St. Ann's Hosp., Columbus, Ohio, 1978-80, dir. perinatal nursing, 1980-84; adminstr. emergency med. svcs. Ohio Bd. Regents, Columbus, Ohio, 1984-86; v.p. nursing U. Hosps. of Cleve., 1986-88, sr. v.p. nursing, 1988-90; v.p. patient care svcs. Presbyn. Hosp. Dallas, 1990—; cons. Ohio Bd. Regents, Columbus, 1984; project dir. U. Hosp. Cleve., 1989-90. Author: (book chpt.) Violence Against Women, 1990, NAACOG Educational Series, 1991; contbr. articles to profl. jours. Mem. choir First United Meth. Ch., Richardson, Tex. Recipient Disting. Alumna award Ohio State U., 1986, Women of Profl. Excellence award YWCA, 1988. Mem. ANA, Tex. Nurses Assn., Tex. Orgn. Nurse Execs., DFW Nurse Exec. Forum (pres. elect 1990—), So. Nursing Rsch. Soc., Nat. Assn. Women's Health Profls. (bd. dirs. 1988-92), Am. Orgn. Nurse Execs., Sigma Theta Tau. Avocations: golf, gardening. Office: Presbyn Hosp 8200 Walnut Hill Ln Dallas TX 75231

PERLIK, WILLIAM R., lawyer; b. Pitts., May 20, 1925; s. Charles A. and Teresa Anna (Kraft) P.; m. Annabel Virginia Shanklin, June 16, 1949; children—Ronald A., Lynn C. BA, Oberlin Coll., 1948; J.D., Yale U., 1951. Bar: D.C. 1952, Va. 1955, U.S. Supreme Ct. 1974. Law clk. to judge U.S. Ct. Appeals, Washington, 1951-52; assoc., then ptnr. Cox Langford Stoddard & Cutler, Washington, 1952-62; ptnr., of counsel Wilmer Cutler & Pickering, Washington, 1962—; adj. prof. politics Oberlin Coll., Ohio, 1973—. Trustee, chmn., mem. exec. com. Oberlin Coll., 1980—; pres. Va. Sch Bd. Assn., 1971-72; mem. and chmn. Fairfax County Sch. Bd., Va., 1964-72; pres. Fairfax County Fedn. Citizens Assns., 1958. Served with U.S. Army, 1943-46; ETO. Recipient Edn. award Fairfax Edn. Assn., 1960; Citizen of Yr. award Washington Evening Star, 1961. Mem. ABA. Avocations: music; hiking; gardening. Home: 1249 Daleview Dr Mc Lean VA 22102-1538 Office: Wilmer Cutler & Pickering 2445 M St NW Washington DC 20037-1435

PERLIN, ARTHUR SAUL, chemistry educator; b. Sydney, N.S., Can., July 7, 1923; s. Benjamin and Eva (Gaum) P.; m. Ruth Laurel Freedman, Nov. 18, 1950; children—Anna, Louise, Deborah, Myra, David. B.Sc., McGill U., Can., 1944, M.Sc., 1946, Ph.D., 1948. Research officer Nat. Research Council Can., Ottawa, Ont., Can., 1948-67; E.B. Eddy prof. chemistry McGill U., Montreal, Que., Can., 1967-91, prof. chemistry emeritus, 1991—; research scientist Pulp and Paper Research Inst. Can., Montreal, Que., 1967—. Contbr. articles to profl. jours., chpts. to books; patentee in field. Fellow Royal Soc. Can., Chem. Inst. Can.; mem. Am. Chem. Soc. (C.S. Hudson award 1979). Home: 3445 Drummond St, Montreal, PQ Canada H3G 1X9 Office: McGill U, Dept Chemistry, Montreal, PQ Canada H3C 3G1

PERLIN, SEYMOUR, psychiatrist, educator; b. Passaic, N.J., Sept. 27, 1925; s. Samuel and Fanny (Horowitz) P.; m. Ruth Joan Rudolph, Aug. 21, 1958; children: Jonathan Brian, Steven Michael, Jeremy Francis. Student, Johns Hopkins U., 1943-44; B.A. summa cum laude, Princeton U., 1946; M.D., Columbia U., 1950; grad., Washington U. Psychoanalytic Inst. Diplomate Am. Bd. Psychiatry and Neurology. Intern Univ. Hosp., Ann Arbor, Mich., 1951-52; resident N.Y. State Psychiat. Inst., 1950-51, 53-54, Manhattan State Hosp., 1952; practice medicine specializing in psychiatry and psychoanalysis Bethesda, Md., 1954-59, Stanford, Calif., 1959-60, N.Y.C., 1960-63, Balt., 1964-72, Bethesda, 1974—; chief div. psychiatry Montefiore Hosp., 1960-63; dir. clin. care and tng. Henry Phipps Psychiat. Clinic, Johns Hopkins Hosp., 1964-72; sr. research scholar Ctr. for Bioethics, Kennedy Inst., Georgetown U., Washington, 1974-78; clin. prof. psychiatry UCLA Sch. Medicine, 1973-74; clin. prof. psychiatry George Washington U. Sch. Medicine, 1974-76, prof., 1977—, also dir. residency tng., 1977-93; lectr. psychiatry Columbia U., 1963-64; assoc. prof. psychiatry Johns Hopkins Sch. Medicine, 1964-65, prof., 1966-72, dep. chmn. dept. psychiatry and behavioral scis., 1969-72; program dir. Fellowship Program in Suicidology, 1967-72; adv. council Univ. health services Princeton, 1970-82; vis. fellow Princeton U., 1973, Oxford U., 1974; Joseph P. Kennedy fellow medicine, law and ethics, 1974-75; chief sect. psychiatry Lab. Clin. Sci., NIMH, 1955-59, mem. clin. program-project com., 1967-70; fellow Ctr. Advanced Study in Behavioral Scis., 1959-60; chmn. mental health study sect. B, div. research grants NIH, 1964-66; cons. Community Mental Health Services, Md. Dept. Mental Hygiene, 1964-72; chmn. bd. dirs. Youth Suicide Nat. Ctr., 1985-87. Cons. editor: Jour. Suicide and Life Threatening Behavior, 1970-89; editorial bd.: Johns Hopkins Med. Jour, 1970-72; editor: Handbook for the Study of Suicide; co-editor: Ethical Issues in Death and Dying; contbr. numerous articles to med. jours. Served with USNR, 1944-46, with USPHS, 1954-58. Recipient Meirhoff award in pathology, 1950, Bicentennial Silver medal for achievement in psychiatry, 1967, both Coll. Phys. and Surg. Columbia. Fellow Am. Psychiat. Assn.; mem. Washington Psychoanalytic Soc., Med. Soc. D.C., Washington Psychiat. Soc., Am. Assn. Suicidology (pres. 1969-70, Dublin award 1978, ann. lectureship in suicidology in his name George Washington U. 1995). Home: 5125 Westbard Ave Bethesda MD 20816-1413 Office: Dept Psychiatry George Washington U Sch Medicine 2150 Pennsylvania Ave NW Washington DC 20037

PERLIS, DONALD M., artist; b. N.Y.C., July 29, 1941; s. Herman and Sylvia M. (Marks) P.; m. Theresa Brown, June 9, 1968. Student, Art Students League, 1961, Sch. Visual Arts, N.Y.C., 1965, Skowhegan Sch., 1965. Exhibited paintings at Whitney Mus., N.Y.C., Graham Gallery, 1971, 75, Sindin Galleries, N.Y.C., 1993, Charas/Elbohio, 1993; documentary film on artist produced by Time Capsule Films, 1993. Mem. NAD. Home: 105 E 9th St New York NY 10003-5401

PERLIS, MICHAEL STEVEN, magazine publisher; b. Feb. 12, 1953; s. Sanford and Vivian (Lee) P.; m. Marilyn Dunlap, May 5, 1979; children: Morgan, Steve. BA in Psychology, Syracuse U., 1976. Mktg. dir. Bretton Woods (N.H.) Resort, 1976-78; exec. dir. Mt. Washington Valley C. of C., North Conway, N.H., 1978-80; pub. N.H. Profiles mag., N.Eng. Guide Rumford Nat. Graphics, Concord, N.H., 1980-81; v.p., pub. New Eng. Pubs., Camden, Maine, 1981-82, pres., 1982-84; pub. spls. Rodale Press, Inc., Emmaus, Pa., 1984-85, pub. Runners World mag., 1985-86, group pub., 1986-87; pres. Internat. Data Group, Peterborough, N.H., 1987-89; sr. v.p., pub. Playboy Enterprises, Chicago, 1989-90, sr. v.p., pres. - publishing group, 1990-92, exec. v.p., pres. - publishing group, 1992-94; pub. Details mag., 1994—. Mem. Mag. Pubs. Am. (exec. com. 1989—), Young Pres. Org., 1990—. •

PERLIS, SHARON A., lawyer; b. New Orleans, Oct. 2, 1945; d. Rogers I. and Dorothy (Koehl) P. BA in French, Principia Coll., 1967; JD, Tulane U., 1970. Officer, dir. Perlis Inc., New Orleans, 1973—; pres. SILREP Internat. Co., Metairie, 1984-95; officer, dir. Internat. Adv. Svcs., Inc., New Orleans, 1985-89; prin. Perlis & Hogg, Metairie, 1985—; legal counsel La. Ins. Rating Commn., 1980-84; adminstrv. law judge State of La., 1980-84; mem. Econ. Devel. Adv. Coun. for State of La., 1982-84; dir. The Chamber/ New Orleans and The River Region, 1990-95, Bd. of Trade, 1990-94; exec. com. small bus. coun., 1987-89, chmn. small bus. coun., 1988, exec. com. East Jefferson coun., 1989—; dir. World Trade Ctr., 1985—, vice-chmn. internat. bus. com.; dir. New Orleans br. Fed. Res. Bank of Atlanta, 1982-88, chmn., 1984, 86, 88; bd. of commr. Port of New Orleans, 1992-95, vice chmn., 1995. Mem. human rels. commn. City of New Orleans, 1992-93; mem. exec. bd. La. Coun. Econ. Edn., 1986-89, Pvt. Enterprise Edn. Found., 1986-89; state del. White House Conf. on Small Bus., La. rep. internat. trade issues, 1986; dir. Metro YMCA, 1990-95; exec. com. agy. rels. United Way, 1987-90; mem. exec. com. Jr. Achievement Project Bus., 1987; vice chmn. La. Dist. Export Coun. Recipient Achiever's award Woman Bus. Owners Assn., 1994, Advocacy of Yr. award Small Bus. Adminstrn., 1988. Mem. Phi Alpha Eta. Avocations: reading, sailing, tennis. Office: Perlis & Hogg Ste 404 3421 N Causeway Blvd Metairie LA 70002-3751

PERLMAN, BARRY STUART, electrical engineer, researcher; b. Bklyn., Dec. 5, 1939; s. Harold Wallace and Jane (Cohen) P.; m. Carolyn Amelia Francis; 1 child, David Matthew. BEE, CCNY, 1961; MSEE, Poly. Inst. N.Y., 1964, PhD in Electrophysics, 1973. Mem. tech. staff, comms. lab. RCA Corp., N.Y.C., 1961-68; mem. tech. staff RCA Labs., Princeton, N.J., 1968-81, mgr. computer aided design and testing, 1981-86, head design automation rsch., 1986-88; chief microwave photonic devices Electronics and Power Svcs. Directorate, Army Rsch. Lab., Ft. Monmouth, N.J., 1988-95; dir. electronics div. Phys. Scis. Directorate, Army Rsch. Lab., Ft. Monmouth, 1995—; pres. INTEREX, Los Altos, Calif., 1981-83, also bd. dirs.; rep. adv. group on electron devices Group A Office of Undersec. of Def.; mem. tech. adv. bd. U. R.I.; mem. tech. adv. bd. Ctr. High Frequency Microelectronics, U. Mich.; mem. Computer Applications to Electromagnetics Edn./ind. adv. bd. NSF and U. Utah, 1990—; mem. ind. adv. bd. for MiniCAD Ctr., U. Colo., 1989—; Ctr. prof. microwave/lightwave engring. Drexel U., Phila., 1992—. Editor: Advances in Microwaves, 1974; mem. editorial bd. MW.MMW CAD, 1992—; contbr. articles to profl. jours.; patentee in field. Bd. dirs. YMCA, Princeton, 1975-78; pres. Home Owners Assn., E. Windsor, N.J., 1976-78; instr. Am. Heart Assn., N.J., 1978-82; chief rescue squad, E. Windsor, 1978-82. Fellow IEEE (awards and advancement com. 1987—); mem. Microwave Theory and Tech. Soc. of IEEE (editl. bd., chmn. CAD com. MTT-1 1985-92, MTT adcom. 1990-94, tech. coord. com. 1994—, edn. com. 1990-93, chmn. 1991-93, fin. com. 1990-92, IMS tech. program com. 1978—, others), Circuits and Sys., Automated RF Techniques Group (treas. 1984-88, v.p. 1990-91). Avocations: scouting, woodworking, photography, camping, gardening, tennis. Office: Army Rsch Lab EPSD PSD Fort Monmouth NJ 07703-5000

PERLMAN, BURTON, judge; b. New Haven, Dec. 17, 1924; s. Phillip and Minnie Perlman; m. Alice Weihl, May 20, 1956; children: Elizabeth, Sarah, Nancy, Daniel. B.E., Yale U., 1945, M.E., 1947; LL.B., U. Mich., 1952. Bar: Ohio, 1959, N.Y. 1953, Conn. 1952, U.S. Dist. Ct. (so. and ea. dists.) N.Y. 1954, U.S. Ct. Appeals (2d cir.) 1953, U.S. Ct. Appeals (6th cir.) 1959, U.S. Dist. Ct. (so. dist.) Ohio 1959. Assoc. Armand Lackenbach, N.Y.C., 1952-58; pvt. practice, Cin., 1958-61; assoc. Paxton and Seasongood, 1961-67; ptnr. Schmidt, Effton, Josselson and Weber, 1968-71; U.S. magistrate U.S. Dist. Ct. (so. dist.) Ohio, 1971-76; U.S. bankruptcy judge, 1976—; chief bankruptcy judge so. dist. Ohio, 1986-93; adj. prof. U. Cin. Law Sch., 1976—. Served with U.S. Army, 1944-46. Mem. ABA, Fed. Bar Assn., Am. Judicature Soc., Cin. Bar Assn. Office: US Bankruptcy Ct 719 US Courthouse 5th & Walnut Sts Cincinnati OH 45202

PERLMAN, D(AVID), biochemist, educator; b. Madison, Wis., Feb. 6, 1920; s. Selig and Eva (Shaber) P.; m. Katõ Lenárd, Aug. 18, 1968. B.A., U. Wis., 1941, M.S., 1943, Ph.D., 1945. Biochemist Hoffmann-LaRoche, Inc., 1945; microbiologist Merck & Co., 1945-47; biochemist Squibb Inst. for Med. Research, 1947-67; prof. Sch. Pharmacy, U. Wis. Madison, 1967—, dean, 1968-75; Chmn. 3d Internat. Congress Genetics of Indsl. Microorganisms, 1968-75, Kremers prof. pharm. biochemistry, 1979—; chmn. Conf. on Antimicrobial Agts. and Chemotherapy, 1966, 67, Gordon Research Conf. on Coenzymes and Metabolic Pathways, 1966. Editor: Advances Applied Microbiology, 1968—, Ann. Reports Fermentation Processes, 1977—; Contbr. articles to profl. jours. Guggenheim fellow, 1966. Fellow Am. Acad. Microbiology, N.Y. Acad. Scis., Acad. Pharm. Scis.; mem. Am. Chem.

PERLMAN, DAVID, science editor, journalist; b. Balt., Dec. 30, 1918; s. Jess and Sara P.; m. Anne Salz, Oct. 15, 1941; children: Katherine, Eric, Thomas. A.B., Columbia U., 1939, M.S., 1940. Reporter Bismarck (N.D.) Capital, 1940; reporter San Francisco Chronicle, 1940-41, reporter, sci. editor, 1952-77, city editor, 1977-79, assoc. editor, sci. editor, 1979—; reporter New York Herald Tribune, Paris, N.Y.C., 1945-49; European corr. Colliers mag. and New York Post, 1949-51; Regents prof. human biology U. Calif., San Francisco 1974; vis. lectr. China Assn. Sci. and Tech., Beijing, Chengdu and Shanghai, 1983; sci. writer-in-residence U. Wis., 1989. Contbr. articles to major mags. Founding dir. Squaw Valley (Calif.) Community of Writers; dir. Alan Guttmacher Inst., 1985—; trustee Scientists Inst. for Pub. Info., 1986-94. Served with inf. USAAF, 1941-45. Recipient Atomic Indsl. Forum award, 1975, Westinghouse Sci. Writing award, 1976, Ralph Coates Roe medal ASME, 1978, Margaret Sanger Community Svc. award, 1981, Fellows' medal Calif. Acad. Scis., 1984, Career Achievement award Soc. Profl. Journalists, 1989, Glenn T. Seaborg award Internat. Platform Assn., 1993; Poynter fellow Yale U., 1984, Carnegie fellow Stanford U., 1987. Fellow Calif. Acad. Scis.; mem. AAAS (adv. bd. Science-81-86 mag., com. Pub. Understanding of Sci. 1985-90), Coun. for Advancement Sci. Writing (pres. 1976-80), Nat. Assn. Sci. Writers (pres. 1970-71, Disting. Sci. Journalism award 1994), Astron. Soc. Pacific (dir. 1976-78), Sigma Xi. Office: Chronicle Pub Co 901 Mission St San Francisco CA 94103-2988

PERLMAN, ITZHAK, violinist; b. Tel Aviv, Aug. 31, 1945; s. Chaim and Shoshana P.; m. Toby Lynn Friedlander, 1967; 5 children. Student, Tel Aviv Acad. Music, Juilliard Sch.; Meadowmount Sch. Music.; hon. degree in music, Tufts U., 1986. Appeared with N.Y. Philharm., Cleve. Orch., Phila. Orch., Nat. Symphony Orch., most orchs. in U.S., with Berlin Philharm., English Chamber Orch., London Symphony, London Philharm., Royal Philharm., BBC Orch., Vienna Philharm, Concertgebouw; participant numerous music festivals, including Ravinia Festival, Berkshire Music Festival, Aspen Music Festival, Israel Festival, Wolf Trap Summer Festival, recital tours, U.S., Can., S.Am., Europe, Israel, Australia, Far East; recorded for Angel, London, RCA Victor, DG, CBS records. Recipient Leventritt prize 1964; The Art of Perlman, (with Janet Goodman Guggenheim), Itzak Perlman's Greatest Hits, (with Kathleen Battle) The Bach Album, (with Andre Previn) A Different Kind of Blues, (with Andre Previn) It's A Breeze, (with Pinchas Zucherman) Duets for Violins. Recipient Leventritt prize, 1964, Grammy awards, 1977, 78, 80-82, 87, Award - Medal of Liberty, 1986; hon. doctorates from Harvard U., Yale U, Brandeis U., Hebrew U.- Jerusalem. also: EMI Classics/Angel Records c/o CEMA Distrs 21700 Oxnard St #700 Woodland Hills CA 91367*

PERLMAN, JUDY PLATT, lawyer; b. Oak Park, Ill., Sept. 11, 1949. BA, U. Mich., 1971; JD, Case Western Res. U., 1974. Bar: Ill. 1975, U.S. Dist. Ct. (no. dist.) Ill. 1975. Ptnr. Lord, Bissell & Brook, Chgo. Mem. Chgo. Bar Assn. Office: Lord Bissell & Brook Harris Bank Bldg 115 S La Salle St Stes 2600-3600 Chicago IL 60603-3801

PERLMAN, LAWRENCE, technology company executive; b. St. Paul, Apr. 8, 1938; s. Irving and Ruth (Mirsky) P.; children: David, Sara. BA, Carleton Coll., 1960; JD, Harvard U., 1963. Bar: Minn. 1963. Law clk. for fed. judge, 1963; assoc., ptnr. Fredrikson & Byron, Mpls., 1964-75; gen. counsel, exec. v.p. U.S. pacing ops. Medtronic, Inc., Mpls., 1975-78; sr. ptnr. Oppenheimer, Wolff & Donnelly, Mpls., 1978-80; sec., gen. counsel, v.p. corp. svcs. Control Data Corp., Mpls., 1980-82; pres. Comml. Credit Co., 1983-85, Imprimis Technology, 1985-88; pres., chief oper. officer Control Data Corp., Mpls., 1989; pres., chief exec. officer Control Data Corp. (now Ceridian Corp.), 1990-92; chmn., pres., CEO Ceridian Corp., Mpls., 1992—; bd. dirs. Ceridian Corp., Kmart Corp.,Inter-Regional Fin. Group, Inc., Seagate Tech., Inc., The Valspar Corp., Computer Network Tech.; mem. nat. adv. bd. Chem. Banking Corp. Chmn., Bd. Dirs. Walker Art Ctr.; regent University of Minnesota, 1992-95. Mem. Bus. Roundtable (mem. policy com.). Office: Ceridian Corp 8100 34th Ave S Minneapolis MN 55425-1640

PERLMAN, MATTHEW SAUL, lawyer; b. Washington, Aug. 30, 1936; s. Jacob and Helen (Aronson) P.; m. Julia Gertrude Hawks, June 22, 1966; children—Penelope Leah, Deborah Jane, Sarah Louise, Jacob Henry. A.B., Brown U., 1957; LL.B., Harvard U., 1960. Bar: D.C. 1960, Md. 1960, U.S. Supreme Ct. 1965. Atty. Air Force Gen. Counsel's Office, Washington, 1960-65; mem. Armed Services Bd. of Contract Appeals, Washington, 1965-67; gen. counsel Pres.' Commn. on Postal Orgn., Washington, 1967; asst. gen. counsel Dept. Transp., Washington, 1967-69; ptnr. Arent, Fox, Kintner, Plotkin & Kahn, Washington, 1969—; mem. Pres. Reagan's Transition Team for GSA, Washington, 1980-81; mem. adv. bd. Fed. Contracts Report, Washington, 1969—; overseas corr. Internat. Constn. Law Rev., London, 1983—. Contbr. articles to profl. jours. Pres. Civic Assn. River Falls, Potomac, Md., 1975-77; mem. Montgomery County Md. Citizens Adv. Commn. for Rock Run AWT Plant, 1979-85. Served to capt. USAF, 1960-63. Mem. ABA (pub. contracts sect.), Fed. Bar Assn., Cosmos Club. Republican. Jewish. Home: 10517 Stable Ln Potomac MD 20854-3867 Office: Arent Fox Kintner Plotkin & Kahn 1050 Connecticut Ave NW Washington DC 20036-5303

PERLMAN, RHEA, actress; b. Bklyn., Mar. 31; m. Danny DeVito, Jan. 8, 1982; children: Lucy Chet, Gracie Fae, Jake. Grad., Hunter Coll. Has appeared in numerous Broadway plays; founder Colonades Theatre Lab., N.Y.C.; various roles in TV movies include I Want to Keep My Baby!, 1976, Stalk the Wild Child, 1976 Intimate Strangers, 1977, Having Babies II, 1977, Mary Jane Harper Cried Last Night, 1977, Like Normal People, 1979, Drop Out Father, 1982, The Ratings Game (cable), 1984, Dangerous Affection, 1987, A Family Again, 1987, To Grandmothers House We Go, 1992, A Place To Be Loved, 1993; TV series include Taxi, Cheers, 1982-1993; motion pictures include Love Child, 1982, My Little Pony (voice only) 1986, Enid is Sleeping, 1990, Ted and Venus, 1991, Class Act, 1992, There Goes The Neighborhood, 1992, Canadian Bacon, 1995. Recipient Emmy award for Outstanding Supporting Actress in a Comedy Series, 1984, 85, 86, 89, Am. Comedy award for funniest supporting female-TV. Office: CAA 9830 Wilshire Blvd Beverly Hills CA 90212*

PERLMAN, RICHARD WILFRED, economist, educator; b. Mt. Vernon, N.Y., Dec. 15, 1923; s. Uriel and Annie (Feitelberg) P.; m. Irma Lowenthal, Sept. 18, 1949; children: Abel, David, Laura, Jennifer. AB, Cornell U., 1947; PhD, Columbia U., 1953. Asst. prof. econs. Adelphi U., Garden City, N.Y., 1953-57; assoc. prof. Adelphi U., 1957-64; prof. econs. U. Wis., Milw., 1964—, chmn. dept., 1965-68, 74-77; NRC prof. Brookings Instn., 1958-59; Fulbright lectr. Inst. Politecnico Nacional, Mexico City, 1964, Autonomous U. Madrid, 1972. Author: Economics of Education, 1973, Labor Theory, 1969, Economics of Poverty, 1976, (with others) An Anthology of Labor Economics, 1972, Economics of Unemployment, 1984, Issues in Labor Economics, 1989, Sex Discrimination in the Labor Market, 1994. Mem. President's Com. on EEO, 1963. Rsch. fellow U. Melbourne, Australia, 1985; hon. rsch. fellow U. Birmingham, 1990-93, sr. fellow, 1993-96; Fulbright rsch. scholar, Australia, 1987. Mem. Am. Econ. Assn., Indsl. Relations Research Assn., Phi Beta Kappa. Home: 3341 N Summit Ave Milwaukee WI 53211-2930

PERLMAN, ROBERT L., pediatrics, pharmacology and physiology educator; b. Chgo., Aug. 15, 1938; s. Henry B. and Dorothy (Zimmerman) P.; m. Caryle Geier. BA, U. Chgo., 1957, BS, 1958, MD, 1961, PhD, 1963. Diplomate Am. Bd. Pediatrics. Intern Bellevue Hosp., N.Y.C., 1963-64; resident in pediatrics 1964-65; staff assoc. Nat. Inst. of Arthritis, Bethesda, Md., 1965-68; sr. investigator Nat. Inst. of Arthritis, Bethesda, 1968-71; assoc. prof. Harvard Med. Sch., Boston, 1971-81; tutor Harvard U., Boston, 1975-81; prof. U. Ill. Chgo., 1981-86; prof. depts. pediatrics, pharmacology, and psychol. sci. U. Chgo., Chgo., 1986—; mem. bd. sci. counselors Nat. Cancer Inst., Bethesda, 1983-87. Jewish. Office: U Chgo 5841 S Maryland Ave Chicago IL 60637-1470

PERLMAN, WILLA M., publishing executive; b. Bklyn., Nov. 18, 1959; d. Amir Eytan Cohen, Mar. 24, 1991; 1 child, Jonathan. BA in Arts and Scis., Barnard Coll., 1981. Dir. children's books Harcourt Brace, San Diego, 1987-91; editorial dir. Willa Perlman book Harper Collins, N.Y.C., 1991-93; pres. pub. children's divsn. Simon & Schuster, N.Y.C., 1993—. Jewish. Office: Simon & Schuster 1230 6th Ave New York NY 10021

PERLMUTH, WILLIAM ALAN, lawyer; b. N.Y.C., Nov. 21, 1929; s. Charles and Roe (Schneider) P.; m. Loretta Kaufman, Mar. 14, 1951; children: Carolyn, Diane. AB, Wilkes Coll., 1951; LLB, Columbia U., 1953. Bar: N.Y. 1954. Assoc. Cravath, Swaine & Moore, N.Y.C., 1955-61; ptnr. Stroock & Stroock & Lavan, N.Y.C., 1962—; bd. dirs. Knogo North Am. Inc., Hauppauge, N.Y. Editor Columbia U. Law Rev., 1952-53. Trustee Aeroflex Found., N.Y.C., 1965—, Harkness Founds. for Dance, N.Y.C., 1976—, Wilkes U., Wilkes-Barre, Pa., 1980—, Weininger Found., 1985—, NYU Med. Ctr., 1995—; trustee Hosp. for Joint Diseases Orthopaedic Inst., N.Y.C., 1980—; chmn. bd. trustees, 1994—. Mem. N.Y. State Bar Assn., Assn. of Bar of City of N.Y., Harmonie Club. Jewish. Home: 880 Fifth Ave New York NY 10021-4951 Office: Stroock & Stroock & Lavan 7 Hanover Sq New York NY 10004-2696

PERLMUTTER, ALVIN HOWARD, television and film producer; b. Poughkeepsie, N.Y., Mar. 24, 1928; s. Fred and Jennie (Albert) P.; children: James F., Stephen H., Tom W. Student, Colgate U., 1945-47; B.A., Syracuse U., 1949. Dir. pub. affairs Sta. WNBC, also Sta. WNBC-TV, N.Y.C., 1957-59; program mgr. Sta. WNBC-TV, 1959-61; exec. producer Nat. Ednl. TV, 1961—; v.p. news documentaries NBC, from 1975; pres. Alvin H. Perlmutter Inc., N.Y.C.; instr. TV news and pub. affairs NYU, 1957, Fairleigh Dickinson U., 1962; cons. John and Mary Markle Found., Pub. Agenda Found.; chmn. Dore Schary Awards for film and TV, Anti-Defamation League. Producer: series Assignment America; Great American Machine, Consumer Reports Presents, Money Matters, Cover Story, Black Journal; various spl. programs including: Native Land, The Primal Mind, Adam Smith's Money World series, Family Computing series, Priceless Treasures of Dresden, The Perpetual People Puzzle; exec. producer: Report From Philadelphia, The Secret Government, The Power of Myth. Chair Dore Schary awards, Anti-Defamation League; bd. dirs. N.Y. Open Ctr. 1st lt. AUS, 1950-53. Recipient various citations and awards including 5 Emmy awards, Peabody award, Robert Kennedy award. Mem. Acad. TV Arts and Scis. (gov. N.Y. chpt., nat. trustee, chmn. awards com. 1968), Assn. Pub. TV Producers (chmn. 1969). Clubs: Overseas Press (N.Y.C.), University; Coffee House. Home: 27 W 86th St New York NY 10024-3615 Office: 45 W 45th St New York NY 10036-4602

PERLMUTTER, DIANE F., communications executive; b. N.Y.C., Aug. 31, 1945; d. Bert H. and Frances (Smith) P. Student, NYU Grad. Sch. of Bus., 1969-70; AB in English, Miami U., Oxford, Ohio, 1967. Writer sales promotion Equitable Life Assurance, N.Y.C., 1967-68; adminstrv. asst. de Garmo, Inc., N.Y.C., 1968-69, asst. account exec., 1969-70, account exec., 1970-74, v.p., account supr., 1974-76; mgr. corp. advt. Avon Products, Inc., N.Y.C., 1976-79, dir. communications Latin Am., Spain, Can., 1979-80, dir. brochures, 1980-81, dir. category merchandising, 1981-82, group dir. motivational communications, 1982-83, group dir. sales promotion, 1983-84, v.p. sales promotion, 1984, v.p. internat. bus. devel., 1984-85, area v.p. Latin Am., 1985, v.p. advtg. and campaign mktg., 1985-87, v.p. U.S. operational planning, 1987; cons. N.Y.C., 1987-88; sr. v.p. Burson-Marsteller, N.Y.C., 1988-90, exec. v.p., mng. dir. consumer products, 1991-93, bd. dirs., 1992—, co-chief operating officer, 1993-94, chief operating officer, 1994—; chairperson ann. meeting Direct Selling Assn., Washington, 1982; v.p. Nat. Home Fashions League, N.Y.C., 1976-78; adj. instr. SUNY/Fashion Inst. Tech., 1992—; bd. dirs. Double L.P. Industries, Inc. Founding bd. mem. Am. Red Magen David for Israel, N.Y.C., 1970-75; mem. adv. coun. Miami Sch. Bus., 1986—, Miami Sch. Applied Scis., 1978-81. Mem. Pub. Rels. Soc. Am., Advt. Women of N.Y., Women in Communications, Miami U. Alumni Assn. (pres., chair 1986), Publicity Club N.Y. (bd. dirs. 1994—), Beta Gamma Sigma. Avocation: interior design. Office: Burson-Marsteller 230 Park Ave S New York NY 10003-1513

PERLMUTTER, DONNA, music and dance critic; b. Phila.; d. Myer and Bessie (Krasno) Stein; m. Jona Perlmutter, Mar. 21, 1964; children: Aaron, Matthew. BA, Pa. State U., 1958; MS, Yeshiva U., 1959. Music and dance critic L.A. Herald Examiner, 1975-84, L.A. Times, 1984-94, N.Y. Times Contbr., 1994—; dance critic Dance Mag., N.Y.C., 1980—; music critic Opera News, N.Y.C., 1981—; Ovation Mag., N.Y.C., 1983-89; panelist, speaker various music and dance orgns. Author Shadowplay: The Life of Antony Tudor, 1991. Recipient Deems Taylor award for excellence in writing on music ASCAP, 1991. Mem. Music Critics Assn. Home: 10507 Le Conte Ave Los Angeles CA 90024-3305

PERLMUTTER, JACK, artist, lithographer; b. N.Y.C., Jan. 23, 1920; s. Morris and Rebecca (Schiffman) P.; m. Norma Mazo, Dec. 24, 1942; children: Judith Faye, Ellen. Staff Dickey Gallery, D.C. Tchrs. Coll., 1951-68, dir., 1962-68, prof. art; prof. art, chmn. printmaking dept. Corcoran Gallery Art, Washington, 1960-82; resident artist St. Olaf Coll., Minn., Gibbs Art Gallery, Charleston, S.C., Mus. Sch. Art, Greenville, S.C.; vis. prof. art U. Costa Rica, San Jose, 1983; Fulbright research prof. painting and printmaking Tokyo U. Arts, 1959-60; art cons. Pres.'s Com to Hire Handicapped; now curator exhibits Cosmos Club, Washington. NASA artist for: 1st Saturn V moon rocket, Apollo 6, Apollo 16, Orbiter Columbia (space shuttle), Voyager II; contbg. editor: Art Voices South, 1979-80, Art Voices, 1980-82; numerous one-man shows, U.S. and Tokyo, including: Balt. Mus. Art, Brandeis U., Corcoran Gallery Art, Dintenfass Gallery, N.Y.C., Makler Gallery, Phila., Smithsonian Inst., Yoseido Gallery, Tokyo, C. Troup Gallery, Dallas, Nat. Acad. Scis., 1981, Arts Club Washington, 1981, Annapolis, Md., 1982, and gllleries in Amsterdam, Rotterdam, The Hague and Costa Rica; exhibited nat. shows, U.S., Switzerland, Yugoslavia, traveling exhibits, Europe, S.Am., Can.;permanent collections include Bklyn. Mus., Cin. Mus. Art, Carnegie Inst. Art, Corcoran Gallery Art, Library Congress, Met. Mus. Art, N.Y.C., Nat. Gallery Art, Washington, Phila. Mus. Art, Walker Gallery, Mpls., Nat. Mus. Modern Art, Tokyo, U.S. Embassies in Bucharest, Budapest, Bonn, Dublin, London, Prague, Tokyo, others. Recipient awards for paintings and prints from Balt. Mus. Art, Libr. Congress, Corcoran Gallery Art, Butler Inst. Arts, Smithsonian Inst., Soc. Am. Graphic Artists, First Internat. Exhbn. Fine Arts in Saigon, Mus. Fine Arts in Saigon, Mus. Fine Art, Boston, others. Fellow Internat. Inst. Arts and Letters; mem. Soc. Am. Graphic Artists. Club: Cosmos (Washington). Prints, drawings and biog. data in Art Archives Am. Studio: 2511 Cliffborne Pl NW Washington DC 20009-1511

PERLMUTTER, JEROME HERBERT, communications specialist; b. N.Y.C., Oct. 17, 1924; s. Morris and Rebecca (Shiffman) P.; m. Evelyn Lea Friedman, Sept. 19, 1948; children: Diane Muriel, Sandra Pauline, Bruce Steven. AB cum laude, George Washington U., 1949; MA, Am. U., 1957. Chief editor svc., prodn. editor NEA, Washington, 1949-50; editor in chief Jour. AAHPER, Washington, 1950-51; editor Rural Elec. News, REA, USDA, Washington, 1951-53; publ. writer Agrl. Rsch. Svc., 1953-56; chief, editor br. Office Info. 1956-60; sec. Outlook and Situation Bd., 1960-62; chief econ. reports Econ. Rsch. Svc., 1960-62; chief div. pub. and reprodn. svcs. U.S. Dept. State, Washington, 1962-79; pres. Perlmutter Assocs., 1979—; writing cons. CSC, 1956, World Bank, 1967—; communication cons. European Investment Bank, Can. Internat. Devel. Agy., Inter-Am. Devel. Bank, Internat. Monetary Fund; faculty agr. grad. sch. U. Md., also Fgn. Svc. Inst.; pub. cons. White House Conf. on Children and Youth, 1971. Author: A Practical Guide to Effective Writing, 1965; Contbr. articles profl. jours. Coord. fed. graphics Nat. Endowment for Arts, 1972-79, graphic designer, conv. of maj. nat. conf., com., 1980. With USNR, 1943-46. Recipient award U.S. Jr. C. of C., 1963. Mem. Am. Assn. Agr. Coll. Editors, Assn. Editl. Bus. (bd. dirs.), Fed. Editors Assn., Am. Farm Econ. Assn., Soc. Tech. Comm. (bd. dirs.), Md. Literacy Coun., Soc. Profl. Journalists, Phi Beta Kappa, Phi Eta Sigma, Artus. Home: 1511 Glade Dr Silver Spring MD 20906

PERLMUTTER, LOUIS, investment banker, lawyer; b. Cambridge, Mass., Oct. 3, 1934; s. Kermit H. and Rachel (Ehrlich) P.; m. Barbara Patricia Sondik, Dec. 11, 1966; children: Kermit, Eric. B.A., Brandeis U., 1956; J.D., U. Mich., 1959. Bar: Mass. 1959, N.Y. 1961. Law practice N.Y.C.,

1960-65; asst. to pres. New Eng. Industries, N.Y.C., 1965-67; pres. Octagon Assocs., N.Y.C., 1967-75; sr. v.p. White Weld, N.Y.C., 1975-78; mgn. dir. Merrill Lynch, White, Weld, N.Y.C., 1978; mng. dir. Lazard Freres, N.Y.C., 1978—. Contbr. articles to profl. and gen. interest publs. Chmn. bd. trustees Brandeis U., Waltham, Mass.; chmn., coun. econ. advisors, coun. fgn. rels., US/Middle East Project; Am. Jewish Congress, N.Y.C., 1988-94; mem. Overseas Devel. Coun., Washington; mem. com. visitors U. Mich. Law Sch.; mem., adv. bd. N.Y.-Israel Econ. Devel. Partnership, UN Assn. USA (chmn. exec. com. South). Mem. Econ. Club of N.Y. Home: 39 E 79th St New York NY 10021-0230 Office: Lazard Freres & Co LLC 1 Rockefeller Plz New York NY 10020-2001

PERLOE, SIDNEY IRWIN, primatologist, educator; b. Bklyn., June 21, 1932; s. Herman and Helen (Cutler) P.; m. Judith Gregory, June 9, 1957 (dec. Feb. 1971); children: Deborah, Jonathan; m. Paulette Jellinek, May 20, 1977; children: Alexandra, Gabriel. AB, NYU, 1953; PhD, U. Mich., 1959. Asst. prof. Yale U., New Haven, Conn., 1958-61; asst. prof. Haverford (Pa.) Coll., 1961-64, assoc. prof., 1964-68, prof., 1968—. Contbr. articles to profl. jours. Mem. Am. Psychol. Soc., Am. Soc. Primatologists, Internat. Primatological Soc., Internat. Soc. Human Ethology. Office: Haverford Coll 370 Lancaster Ave Haverford PA 19041-1392

PERLOFF, JOSEPH KAYLE, cardiologist; b. New Orleans, Dec. 21, 1924; s. Richard and Rose (Cohen) P.; m. Marjorie G. Mintz; children: Nancy L., Carey E. BA, Tulane U., 1945; pre-med. student, U. Chgo., 1946-47; MD, La. State U. at New Orleans, 1951; MA (hon.), U. Pa., 1973. Diplomate Am. Bd. Internal Medicine, Am. Bd. Cardiovascular Disease. Intern Mt. Sinai Hosp., N.Y.C., 1951-52, resident in pathology, 1952-53, resident in medicine, 1953-54; Fulbright fellow Inst. Cardiology, London, 1954-55; resident in medicine Georgetown U. Hosp., Washington, 1955-56, fellow in cardiology, 1956-57; clin. instr. medicine Georgetown U. Sch. Medicine, Washington, 1957-59, instr. medicine, 1959-61, asst. prof. medicine, 1961-66, assoc. prof., 1966-70, prof., 1970-72, dir. cardiac diagnostic lab., 1959-68, asst. dir. div. cardiology, 1968-72; prof. medicine and pediatrics U. Pa. Sch. Medicine, Phila., 1972-77, chief cardiovascular sect., 1972-77; prof. medicine and pediatrics UCLA Sch. Medicine, 1977—, Streisand/AMA chair in cardiology, 1983; cons. Nat. Heart, Blood and Lung Inst. Author: Physical Exam Heart and Circulation, 1990, Clinical Recognition of Congenital Heart Disease, 1987, The Cardiomyopathies, 1988, Congenital Heart Disease in Adults, 1991; co-author: Congenital Heart Disease After Surgery, 1983. Ensign USN, 1943-46, PTO. Recipient The Best of UCLA award Chancellor's Selection, 1987; Residency Career Devel. award NIH, 1959-69. Fellow ACP, Am. Coll. Cardiology; mem. Am. Fedn. Clin. Rsch., Assn. Univ. Cardiologists, Alpha Omega Alpha. Office: UCLA Sch Medicine Cardiology 47 123 Chs Los Angeles CA 90024

PERLOFF, MARJORIE GABRIELLE, English and comparative literature educator; b. Vienna, Austria, Sept. 28, 1931; d. Maximilian and Ilse (Schueller) Mintz; m. Joseph K. Perloff, July 31, 1953; children—Nancy Lynn, Carey Elizabeth. A.B., Barnard Coll., 1953; M.A., Cath. U., 1956, Ph.D., 1965. Asst. prof. English and comparative lit. Cath. U., Washington, 1966-68; asso. prof. Cath. U., 1969-71; asso. prof. U. Md., 1971-73, prof., 1973-76; Florence R. Scott prof. English U. So. Calif., Los Angeles, 1976—; prof. English and comparative lit. Stanford U., Calif., 1986—, Sadie Dernham prof. humanities, 1990—. Author: Rhyme and Meaning in the Poetry of Yeats, 1970, The Poetic Art of Robert Lowell, 1973, Frank O'Hara, Poet Among Painters, 1977, The Poetics of Indeterminacy; Rimbaud to Cage, 1981, The Dance of the Intellect: Studies in the Poetry of the Pound Tradition, 1985, The Futurist Moment: Avant-Garde, Avant-Guerre and the Language of Rupture, 1986, Poetic License: Essays in Modern and Postmodern Lyric, 1990, Radical Artifice: Writing Poetry in the Age of Media, 1991; editor: Postmodern Genres, 1990; co-editor: John Cage: Composed in America, 1994; contbg. editor: Columbia Literary History of the U.S., 1987; contbr. preface to Contemporary Poets, 1980; A John Cage Reader, 1983. Guggenheim fellow, 1981-82, NEA fellow, 1985; Phi Beta Kappa scholar, 1994-95. Mem. MLA (exec. coun. 1977-81, Am. lit. sect. 1993—), Comparative Lit. Assn. (pres. 1993-94), Lit. Studies Acad. Home: 1467 Amalfi Dr Pacific Palisades CA 90272-2752 Office: Stanford U Dept English Stanford CA 94305

PERLOFF, ROBERT, psychologist, educator; b. Phila., Feb. 3, 1921; s. Myer and Elizabeth (Sherman) P.; m. Evelyn Potechin, Sept. 22, 1946; children: Richard Mark, Linda Sue, Judith Kay. A.B., Temple U., 1949; M.A., Ohio State U., 1949, Ph.D., 1951; D.Sc. (hon.), Oreg. Grad. Sch. Profl. Psychology, 1984; D.Litt. (hon.), Calif. Sch. Profl. Psychology, 1985. Diplomate: Am. Bd. Profl. Psychology. Instr. em Antioch Coll., 1950-51; with personnel research br. Dept. Army, 1951-55, chief statis. research and cons. unit., 1953-55; dir. research and devel. Sci. Research Assos., Inc., Chgo., 1955-59; vis. lectr. Chgo. Tchrs. Coll., 1955-56; mem. faculty Purdue U., 1959-69, prof. psychology, 1964-69; field assessment officer univ. Peace Corps Chile III project, 1962; Disting. Svc. prof. bus. adminstrn. and psychology U. Pitts. Joseph M. Katz Grad. Sch. Bus., 1969-90, Disting. Svc. prof. emeritus, 1991—; dir. rsch. programs U. Pitts. Grad. Sch. Bus., 1969-77; dir. Consumer Panel, 1980-83; bd. dirs. Book Center.; cons. in field, 1959—; adv. com. assessment exptl. manpower research and devel. labs. Nat. Acad. Scis., 1972-74; mem. research rev. com. NIMH, 1976-80, Stress and Families research project, 1976-79. Contbr. articles to profl. jours.; editor Indsl. Psychology, 1963-65, Evaluator Intervention: Pros and Cons; book rev. editor Personnel Psychology, 1952-55; co-editor: Values, Ethics and Standards Sourcebook, 1979, Improving Evaluations; bd. cons. editors Jour. Applied Psychology; bd. advs. Archives History Am. Psychology, Psychol. Svc. Pitts., Recorded Psychol. Jours.; guest editor Am. Psychologist, 1972, Edn. and Urban Soc., 1977, Profl. Psychology, 1977; adv. editor Contemporary Psychology, 1994—. Bd. dirs., v.p. Sr. Citizens Svc. Corp., Calif. Sch. Profl. Psychology, Greater Pitts. chpt. ACLU; chmn. Nat. adv. com. Inst. Govt. and Pub. Affairs, U. Ill., 1986-89. Decorated Bronze Star; Robert Perloff Grad. Rsch. Assistantship in Inst. Govt. and Pub. Affairs, U. Ill., named in his honor, 1990; Robert Perloff Career Achievement award Knowledge Utilization Soc., named in his honor, 1991. Fellow AAAS, Am. Psychol. Assn. (mem. at-large exec. com. div. consumer psychology 1964-67, 70-71, pres. div. 1967-68, mem. coun. reps. 1965-68, 72-74, chmn. sci. affairs com., div. consumer psychology 1968-69, edn. and tng. bd. 1969-72, chmn. finance com., treas., dir. 1974-82, chmn. investment com. 1977-82, pres., 1985, mem. adv. bd., mem. bd. sci. affairs 1994—, mem task forces intellegence and Intelligence Tests, author column Standard Deviations in jour.), Ea. Psychol. Assn. (pres. 1980-81, dir. 1977-80); mem. Am. Psychol. Soc., Internat. Soc. Psychology, Internat. Assn. Applied Psychology, Pa. Psychol. Assn. (Disting. Svc. award 1985), Assn. for Consumer Rsch. (chmn. 1970-71), Am. Psychol. Found. (v.p. 1988-89, pres. 1990-92), Am. Evaluation Assn. (pres. 1977-78), Soc. Psychologists in Mgmt. (Disting. Contbn. to Psychology Mgmt. award 1989, pres. 1993-94), Knowledge Utilization Soc. (pres. 1993-95), Sigma Xi (pres. U. Pitts. chpt. 1989-91), Beta Gamma Sigma, Psi Chi. Home: 815 St James St Pittsburgh PA 15232-2112 *Experiment. Innovate responsibly. Take risks judiciously. Do not shrink from new ventures for fear of failure. No one is immune from adversity. The hallmark of a successful achieving person is his or her ability to snap back after misfortune, and to benefit from and not be immobilized by failure.*

PERLONGO, DANIEL JAMES, composer; b. Gaastra, Mich., Sept. 23, 1942; s. James and Camille (Fittante) P. Mus.B. in Composition, U. Mich., 1964, Mus.M., 1966; Corso di Perfezionamento, Accademia di S. Cecilia, Rome, 1968. Assoc. prof. music Indiana (Pa.) U., 1968—. Composer (for orchestra) Myriad, 1968, Ephemeron, 1972, Concertino, 1980, Lake Breezes, 1990, Concerto for Piano and Orchestra, 1992, Shortcut from Bratislava for Piano and Orch., 1994, (chamber orch.) Variations, 1973, Voyage, 1975, (chamber music) Improvision for Four, 1965, Improvisation 2, 1966, Eufonia, poetica e sonora, 1966, (string trio) Intervals, 1967, (ensemble pieces) Movement for 8 Players, 1967, Semblance for string quartet, 1969-70, String Quartet II, 1983, (percussion quartet) For Bichi, 1968, Movement in Brass, 1969, (various works) Process 7, 5, 3 for 6 in 12, for flute, oboe, clarinet, 3 percussions, 1969, Tre Tempi for flute, oboe, clarinet, violin, cello, 1971, Fragments for flute and cello, 1972, Structure, Semblance and Tune for tuba and percussion, 1973, (wind ensemble) Changes, 1970, (violin) Violin Solo, 1971, (double bass) Episodes, 1966, (for oboe, clarinet and bassoon) Ricercar, 1976, (solo piano) Piano Sonata, 1965, Suite for Piano, 1988, Serenade, 1977, First Set, 1990, (saxophone quartet) Aureole, 1978, (brass quintet) Summer Music, 1979, (solo bass clarinet) Soliloquy, 1980, (soprano voice and piano) Six Songs, 1980, (solo organ) Tapestry, 1981, (winds, percussion and piano) Montalvo Overture, 1984, (piano and woodwind quintet) A Day At Xochimilco, 1987, (trombone and organ) Novella, 1988, (mezzo soprano, violin, clarinet and piano) By Verse Distills, 1989, (wind ensemble) Preludes and Variations, 1991, (horn and harp) Arcadian Suite, 1993. Fulbright fellow Italy, 1966; Italian Govt. grantee, 1967; recipient Joseph Bearns prize Columbia U., 1966; Rome prize, 1971, 72; award Nat. Inst. Arts and Letters, 1975, Internat. Double Reed Soc. prize, 1979, New Music for Young Ensembles prize, 1979, Nebr. Sinfonia prize, 1981; Nat. Endowment Arts grantee, 1981, 95; Guggenheim fellow, 1982. Office: Indiana U of Pa Cogswell Hall Indiana PA 15701

PERLOV, DADIE, management consultant, association executive; b. N.Y.C., June 8, 1929; d. Aaron and Anna (Leight) Heitman; m. Norman B. Perlov, May 29, 1950; children—Nancy Perlov Rosenbach, Jane, Amy Perlov Schenkein. BA, NYU, 1950; postgrad., Adelphi U., 1963, Vanderbilt U., 1973. Cert. assn. exec., N.Y. Exec. dir. ops. Open City, N.Y.C., 1962-64; field svcs. dir. Nat. Coun. Jewish Women, N.Y.C., 1968-74; exec. dir. N.Y. Libr. Assn., N.Y.C., 1974-81, Nat. Coun. Jewish Women, N.Y.C., 1981-90; founder, pres. Consensus Mgmt. Group, N.Y.C. and Washington, 1989—; cons. HEW, 1975-76; pres.-elect Internat. Coun. Libr. Assn. Execs., 1979-80; exec. mem. Conf. of Pres., 1981-90, strategic planner, lectr., facilitator, trainer in field. Contbr. articles to profl. jours. Dem. committeewoman, 1966; mem. N.Y. Zool. Soc., 1959—, adv. bd. Nat. Inst. Against Prejudice and Violence, 1985-89, profl. adv. com. for Hornstein program in Jewish communal svc. Brandeis U., 1989-90; bd. visitors Pratt Inst., Bklyn., 1980-84; bd. dirs. Pres. Coun. on Handicapped, 1981—; facilitator Nursing Summit, 1994. Recipient Recognition award N.Y. Libr. Assn., 1978, BUDDY award NOW Legal Def. and Edn. Found., 1989, cert. N.Y. State Legislature, 1978; named N.Y. State Exec. of Yr., 1980, One of Am.'s 100 Most Important Women, Ladies' Home Jour., 1988. Fellow Am. Soc. Assn. Execs. (cert. 1978, evaluator 1980—, bd. dirs. 1987-90, bd. Found. 1990-92, Excellence award 1983); mem. LWV (chpt. pres. 1960-62), N.Y. Soc. Assn. Execs. (pres. 1985, Outstanding Assn. Exec. 1989, Outstanding Svc. award 1991), Global Perspectives in Edn. (bd. dirs.), Nat. Orgn. Continuing Edn. (coun.), Audubon Soc., N.Y. Citizens Coun. on Libns. (bd. dirs. 1981-84), Am. Arbitration Assn. (mem. panel). Avocations: writing, mycology, history, music, art.

PERLOW, GILBERT J(EROME), physicist, editor; b. N.Y.C., Feb. 10, 1916; s. David and Esther (German) P.; m. Mina Rea Jones. AB, Cornell U., 1936, MA, 1937; PhD, U. Chgo., 1940. Instr. physics U. Minn., Mpls., 1940-41; physicist Naval Ordnance Lab., Washington, 1941-42, Naval Rsch. Lab., Washington, 1942-52; rsch. assoc. physics dept. U. Minn., Mpls., 1952-53; assoc. physicist Argonne (Ill.) Nat. Lab., 1953-57, sr. physicist, 1957—; editor Jour. Applied Physics Am. Inst. Physics/Argonne Nat. Lab., 1970-73, editor Applied Physics Letters, 1970-90, consulting editor Applied Physics Letters, 1990—; vis. assoc. prof. physics U. Wash., Seattle, 1957; vis. prof. German univs., Munich, Berlin; exch. physicist AERE Harwell, Berkshire, Eng., 1961. Contbr. over 70 articles to profl. jours., also chpts. to books; author numerous U.S. patents. Recipient Alexander von Humboldt award Alexander von Humboldt Found., Tech. U. Munich, 1972. Fellow Am. Phys. Soc.; mem. Chgo. Corinthian Yacht Club (life mem., commodore 1974). Avocations: sailing, woodworking, painting. Home: 4919 Northcott Ave Downers Grove IL 60515 Office: Argonne Nat Lab Physics Divsn 9700 S Cass Ave Argonne IL 60439

PERLSTADT, SIDNEY MORRIS, lawyer; b. Warsaw, Poland, May 9, 1907; came to U.S. 1916, naturalized, 1920; s. Isaac H. and Sarah (Carmel) P.; m. Mildred Penn, Mar. 5, 1935 (dec.); children—Harry, Susan Perlstadt Serota; m. Bessie Lendrum, Jan. 25, 1961 (dec.). Ph.B., U. Chgo., 1928; J.D., DePaul U., 1942. C.P.A., Ill. Bar: Ill. 1943, U.S. Dist. Ct. (no. dist.) Ill. 1944, U.S. Tax Ct. 1944. Revenue agt. IRS, San Francisco and Chgo., 1935-43; ptnr. Sonnenschein, Nath & Rosenthal, Chgo., 1944—. Mem. Ill. Pub. Employees Pension Laws Commn., 1973-84; trustee Indsl. Areas Found. Mem. Chgo. Bar Assn., Ill. Bar Assn., ABA. Club: Cliff Dwellers (Chgo.). Home: 175 E Delaware Pl Chicago IL 60611-1730 Office: Sonnenschein Nath Rosenthal Suite 8000 233 S Wacker Dr Chicago IL 60606

PERLSTEIN, ABRAHAM PHILLIP, psychiatrist; b. N.Y.C., Apr. 15, 1926; s. Benjamin William and Pauline (Gittler) P.; m. Shirley Ann Rubenstein, July 10, 1949; children: Judith Paula, Susan Carol, Bernard William. BS, U. Oreg., 1949; MD, NYU, 1953. Diplomate Am. Bd. Psychiatry and Neurology. Cons. alcoholism dir. SUNY, Bklyn., 1958—; clin. asst. prof. psychiatry, 1957—; med. dir. Peninsula Counseling Ctr., Woodmere, N.Y., 1973-78; psychiat. cons. geriatrics, 1978-90; pvt. practice Elmont, N.Y., 1957-90; assoc. psychiat. dir. Frankling Gen. Hosp., Valley Stream, N.Y., 1980-82; attending psychiatrist Kings County Hosp. Ctr., Bklyn., 1957-90, SUNY, U. Hosp. Bklyn., 1963-90, Franklin Gen. Hosp., Valley Stream, 1990-90; adj. clin. asst. prof. psychiatry Cornell U. Med. Coll., N.Y.C., 1978-90; assoc. attending psychiatrist North Shore U. Hosp., Manhasset, N.Y., 1978-90. Sgt. U.S. Army, 1944-46. Fellow Am. Psychiat. Assn. (life). Avocations: music, art, sports. Office: Columbia River Mental Health Svcs PO Box 1337 Vancouver WA 98666

PERMAN, NORMAN WILFORD, graphic designer; b. Chgo., Feb. 17, 1928; s. Jacob and Ida (Ladenson) P.; m. Lorraine Shaffer, July 22, 1956; children: Jonathan Dean, Margot Bess. Student, Corcoran Sch. Art, Washington, 1946-47, Northwestern U., 1948-50; BFA, Art Inst. Chgo., 1951. Asst. to designer Everett McNear, Chgo., 1951-52; ind. graphic designer specializing booklets, annual reports, exhibits, packaging and books Chgo. 1953—; guest lectr. U. Ill., Chgo.; curator 75th Anniversary Exhbn. Arts Club of Chgo., 1992; lectr. in field; juror various nat. and regional exhbns. Designer: (records and ednl. materials) Invitations to Personal Reading, 165 vols., 1965, Sounds I Can Hear, Talkstarters, 1966, Health and Growth, 1970, Mathematics Around Us, 1974, Good for Life Exhibit, 1978, Invitation to Mathematics, 1984, Health for Life, 1986; editor: Form and Meaning, 1962; exhbns. include Art Inst. Chgo., 1954-62, 68, U. Ill., 1960, 62, 64, U. Wis., 1957, Am. Inst. Graphic Arts, 1958, 60-61, 63-64, 66, 68, 70, 72, 74, 76, 79-81, 83, State Dept. USSR, 1964, Art Dirs. Club, N.Y.C., 1961, 63, 65, 69, HUD Art in Architecture Exhibit, Smithsonian Instn., 1973, 50 Yrs. Graphic Design in Chgo. Exhibit, 1977; represented in numerous design jours., annuals and graphics books. With USN, 1946-48. Recipient award Art Dirs. Club, Chgo., 1960, 62, 65, 68, award Art Dirs. Club, N.Y.C., 1961-82, Gold medal Direct Mail Assn., 1961, 64. Fellow Am. Ctr. for Design (bd. dirs., chmn. Allerton Park Conf. 1962, nat. pres. 1965-66, exhibits 1952-89, award 1952-86); mem. Assn. Am. Curators (v.p. 1982), Am. Inst. Graphic Arts (award 1960-85), 27 Chgo. Designers, Art Inst. Chgo. (chmn. alumni fund), Oriental Inst., Coun. Fgn. Rels., Arts Club of Chgo. (bd. dirs.). Democrat. Avocations: photography, mountain trekking, travel, music.

PERMUTT, SOLBERT, physiologist, physician; b. Birmingham, Ala., Mar. 6, 1925; s. Harry and Rachel (Damsky) P.; m. Loretta Paul, Jan. 17, 1952; children—Nina Rachel, Thomas Joshua, Lisa Ellen. M.D., U. So. Calif., 1949. Intern U. Chgo. Clinics, 1949-50, resident medicine, 1952, research assoc. dept. anatomy, 1950-52; resident medicine Montefiore Hosp., N.Y.C., 1954-56; fellow medicine and environmental medicine Johns Hopkins Med. Sch., 1956-58; chief div. cardiopulmonary physiology Nat. Jewish Hosp., Denver, 1958-61; asst. prof. physiology Sch. Medicine, U. Colo., 1960-61; mem. faculty Sch. Hygiene and Pub. Health, Johns Hopkins, 1961, prof. environ. health sci., 1965—; prof. medicine Johns Hopkins U. Sch. Med., 1972—, dir. respiratory div. dept. medicine, 1972-81, prof. anesthesiology, 1978—; head physiology div., environ. health sci. John Hopkins Sch. Hygiene and Pub. Health, 1976-79; dir. pulmonary div. Francis Scott Key Med. Ctr. (John Hopkins Med. Instn.), 1981-87, dir. pulmonary rsch., div. pulmonary medicine, 1986-87, dir. rsch. div. pulmonary and critical care medicine, 1988—; assoc. dir. Johns Hopkins Asthma and Allergy Ctr., 1990—; Cons. space sci. bd. Nat. Acad. Sci., 1966-67, mem. com. effects atmospheric contaminants human health, 1968-70; mem. project com. Heart and Lung Program, NIH, 1970-74; mem. sci. adv. council Children's Asthma Research Inst. and Hosp., Denver, 1973-75; mem. expert panel Nat. Inst. Allergy and Infectious Diseases, 1972-74; mem. nat. adv. com. for Cal. Primate Research Center, 1972-75; vice chmn. council on cardiopulmonary diseases Am. Heart Assn., 1974-75, chmn., 1976—, mem. research com., 1979-85; nat. adviser Aspen Lung Confs., 1974—; mem. pulmonary disease

adv. com. HHS and NIH, 1979-83. Mem. editorial bd. publs. Am. Physiol. Soc. Circulation Research, 1965—, La Revue Française des Maladies Respiratories, 1975—; contbr. articles to profl. jours. Served with U.S. Army, 1943-46, 53-54. Recipient Gold medal Am. Coll. Chest Physicians, 1977, Louis and Artur Lucian award McGill U., 1980; fellow Nat. Found. Infantile Paralysis, 1956-58. Mem. Am. Lung Assn. (George Wills Comstock award 1988, Edward Livingston Trudeau medal 1992), Cardiovascular System Dynamics Soc., Am. Med. Assn. (reference panel for diagnostic and therapeutic tech. assessment-DATTA), Assn. Am. Physicians, Johns Hopkins Med. and Surg. Assn., Md. Soc. Med. Rsch., Am. Thoracic Soc., Am. Physiol. Soc., AAAS, Am. Heart Assn. (Citation for Disting. Svc. to Rsch. 1979-84, Disting. Achievement award Cardiopulmonary Coun. 1986). Home: 2303 Sulgrave Ave Baltimore MD 21209-4405

PERNA, FRANK, JR., manufacturing company executive; b. Detroit, Jan. 15, 1938; s. Frank and Mary (Cataldo) P.; m. Monika Doering, May 10, 1960; children: Laura, Reneé, Christopher. BSME, Gen. Motors Inst., 1960; MSEE, Wayne State U., 1966; MBA in Mgmt. (Sloan fellow), MIT, 1970. Asst. to dir. reliability Gen. Motors Corp., Detroit, 1955-70; v.p., dir. engring. Sun Electric Corp., Crystal Lake, Ill., 1971-77, exec. v.p. ops., 1977-78, pres., chief exec. officer, 1978-81; v.p. group exec. Whittaker Corp., Los Angeles, 1983-85; pres. MagneTek, Inc., Los Angeles, 1985—; bd. dirs. 1st State Bank and Trust, Hanover Park, Ill., 1st Nat. Bank of Hoffman Estates, Ill. Named one of Outstanding Young Man of Am., 1968. Mem. Bd. Profl. Engrs. Avocations: skiing, golf, tennis, wind surfing. Office: MagneTek Inc 11150 Santa Monica Blvd Los Angeles CA 90025-3333 Office: Magnetek Electric Inc 400 S Prairie Ave Waukesha WI 53186

PERO, JOSEPH JOHN, retired insurance company executive; b. N.Y.C., Nov. 5, 1939; s. Joseph John and Grace Margaret (Picchione) P.; m. Margaret Ann Carey, July 11, 1964; children: Ann Marie, Christopher. B.S., Manhattan Coll., 1961; M.B.A., NYU, 1967. With GM, 1963-94; dir. profit and investment analysis Gen. Motors Corp., N.Y.C., 1973-76; asst. treas., sec. to exec. com. Gen. Motors Corp., Detroit, 1976-79, N.Y.C., 1980-81; exec. v.p.-fin. Motors Ins. Corp. (subs. Gen. Motors Corp.), Detroit, 1981-87, pres., 1987-94; ret., 1994. Bd. dirs. Inner City Bus. Improvement Forum, Detroit, 1978-79; trustee Mt. Elliot Cemetery Assn., 1978-79; bd. dirs., treas. Ryan Sr. Residences of Archdiocese of Detroit. With Army N.G., 1963-69. Mem. Nat. Assn. Ind. Insurers (bd. govs.), Forest Lake Country Club. Home: 4097 Waterwheel Ln Bloomfield Hills MI 48302-1871

PEROCCHI, PAUL PATRICK, lawyer; b. Lowell, Mass., Jan. 16, 1948; s. Paul Joseph and Eleanor (Darragh) P.; m. Joyce Theresa Guglielmino, Aug. 18, 1984; children: Anna Kate, Eliza Tess. BA, Harvard U., 1970; JD, Suffolk U., 1975. Bar: Mass. 1975, U.S. Dist. Ct. Mass. 1976, U.S. Ct. Appeals (1st cir.) 1976. Assoc. White, Inker, Aronson, Connelly & Norton, P.C., Boston, 1975-80, ptnr., 1980-84; assoc. Brown, Rudnick, Freed & Gesmer, Boston, 1984-86, ptnr., 1987—. Contbr. chpts. to books and articles to profl. jours. Fellow Am. Acad. Matrimonial Lawyers; mem. Mass. Acad. Trial Attys. (chmn. family law com. 1980-86, Mass. Bar Assn. (family law sect.). Democrat. Roman Catholic. Home: 394 Boston St North Andover MA 01845-6308 Office: Brown Rudnick Freed & Germer One Financial Ctr Boston MA 02111

PERONI, GERALDINE, film editor. Editor: (films) (with Francoise Coispeau) Vincent & Theo, 1990, The Player, 1992, Short Cuts, 1993. Office: care Motion Picture Editors 7715 Sunset Blvd #220 Los Angeles CA 90046*

PERONI, PETER A., II, psychologist, educator; b. Trenton, N.J., Nov. 14, 1942; s. Peter A. and Mary D. (DiLeo) P. BA, LaSalle U., 1964; MA, Trenton State Coll., 1967, MAT, 1969; EdD, Rutgers U., 1977. Cert. secondary sch. social studies, student pers. svcs.; lic. psychologist, Pa. Tchr. St. Anthony High Sch., Trenton, 1964-67, Lawrence Twp. (N.J.) Pub. Schs., 1967-68; counselor Bucks County C.C., Newtown, Pa., 1968-72, prof., 1972—; consulting psychologist N.J. Dept. Health, Trenton, 1977-84; dir. clin. svcs. New Horizon Treatment Svcs., Trenton, 1984-88. Author: The Burg: An Italian-American Community at Bay in Trenton, 1979; writer, coproducer (TV): The Burg: A State of Mind, 1980; author: Academic Success Through Self-Conditioning, 1982. N.J. Commn. for Humanities grantee, 1980. Avocation: motorcycle touring. Home: 52 Hollynoll Dr Trenton NJ 08619 Office: Bucks County Community Coll Swamp Rd Newtown PA 18941

PEROT, H. ROSS, investments and real estate group executive, data processing services company executive; b. June 27, 1930; married; 4 children. Ed., U.S. Naval Acad. Data processing salesman IBM Corp., 1957-62; founder Electronic Data Systems Corp., Dallas, 1962-84, chmn., CEO, also dir., to 1986; now with The Perot Group, Dallas; chmn. Hillwood Devel. Corp., Dallas 1984—; founder Perot Systems Corp., Washington, 1988—; independent cand. for Pres. of U.S., 1992. Author: Not For Sale at Any Price, 1993. Served with USN, 1953-57. Recipient Internat. Disting. Entrepreneur award, U. Man., 1988, The Winston Churchill award, 1986, The Raoul Wallenberg award, The Jefferson award, The patrick Henry award, The Nat. Bus, Hall of Fame award, The Sarnoff award, The Eisenhower award, The Smithsonian Computerworld award, The Horatio Alger award. Office: The Perot Group 12377 Merit Dr Ste 1700 Dallas TX 75251-2239

PERRAULT, RAYMOND, Canadian legislator, senator; b. Vancouver, B.C., Can., Feb. 6, 1926; s. Ernest Alphone and Florence (Riebel) P.; m. Barbara Joan Walker, Aug. 10, 1963; children: Yvonne Marie, Mark Raymond, Robert Ernest Albert. B.A., U. B.C., 1947. Mem. B.C. Legislature, 1960-68; mem. Can. Ho. of Commons, 1968; parliamentary sec. Minister of Labor, 1970, Manpower and Immigration, 1971; summoned to Senate, 1973; leader of Govt. in Senate, 1974-79, leader of opposition, 1979-80; govt. leader in senate, 1980-82; Can. minister of sports, 1982; Can. sessional del. and spokesman of Spl. com., UN, N.Y.C., 1969; mem. 1st Can. govt. delegation to Peoples Republic China, 1971; Can. rep. and govt. spokesman Internat. Labour Orgn., Geneva, Switzerland, 1972; mem. Can. Parliamentary delegation to USSR, 1975; leader Can. delegation UN Water Conf., 1977; Leader Liberal Party, B.C., 1959; mem. standing senate com. on banking, trade and commerce, standing senate com. on transp. and comm., mem. spl. joint com. reviewing Can. fgn. policy, mem. spl. senate com. on euthanasia and assisted suicide; bd. dirs. Citizens Trust. Bd. dirs. N.W. Sports; hon. chmn. Vancouver Baseball Canadians. Mem. Vancouver Club. Roman Catholic. Office: The Senate, Ho of Commons, Ottawa, ON Canada K1A 0A4

PERREAULT, SISTER JEANNE, college president; b. Providence, Dec. 13, 1929; d. Alphonse and Malvina I. (Chevalier) P. BSEd, Cath. Tchrs. Coll., Providence, 1959; MS, Cath. U., Washington, 1968; EdD (hon.), Salve Regina U., 1990. Tchr. elem. sch. St. Ann Sch., West Warwick, R.I.; tchr. jr. high sch. St. John Jr. High Sch., West Warwick; tchr. high sch. Notre Dame High Sch., Berlin, N.H.; assoc. prof. Rivier Coll., Nashua, N.H., pres., 1980—; mem. Gov.'s Task Force for Edn. Mem. State of N.H. Post-Secondary Edn. Commn., Concord; bd. dirs. Ctr. for Econ. Devel. for Nashua Area, Bishop Guertin High Sch., Nashua. Mem. AAUP, Am. Coun. Colls., Assn. Cath. Colls. and Univs., N.H. Coll. and Univ. Coun.

PERREAULT, WILLIAM DANIEL, JR., business administration educator; b. N.Y.C., Apr. 7, 1948; s. William Daniel Sr. and Barbara Louise (Peckham) P.; m. Pamela Pittard, May 27, 1972; children: Suzanne Elizabeth, William Daniel III. BS, U. N.C., 1970, PhD, 1973. Asst. prof. U. Ga., Athens, 1973-76; asst. prof. U. N.C., Chapel Hill, 1976-79, assoc. prof., 1979-81, prof., 1981-83, Hanes prof., 1983-88; vis. prof. Stanford (Calif.) U., 1986-87, assoc. dean, 1988-92. Kenan prof., 1988—. Co-author: The Marketing Game, 1994, Essentials Marketing, 1994, Basic Marketing, 1993; editor: Jour. Mktg. Rsch., 1982-85; contbr. articles to profl. jours. Chmn. adv. com. Bur. Census, Washington, 1982-86. Mem. Am. Mktg. Assn. 9.v.p. 1986, 95, bd. dirs. 1986-89, 94-95), Decision Scis. Inst. (coun. 1977), Assn. Dir. Consumer Rsch. Conf. (chmn. 1976—), Mktg. Sci. Inst. (trustee 1989-94), Phi Beta Kappa. Republican. Presbyterian. Office: U NC Cb 3490 Carroll Hall # 012A Chapel Hill NC 27599

PERREGO, VIRGINIA, mathematics educator; b. Wilkes-Barre, Pa., May 19, 1945; d. Harold Paul adn Frances (Austin) Trethaway; m. William Charles Perrego, Aug. 3, 1968; children: David, Melissa, Mark. BS, Marywood Coll., 1967, MLS, 1968. Cert. tchr., N.Y. Tchr., sch. libr. Taft Elem. Sch., Washingtonville, N.Y. 1968-73; tchr., math. I instr. Round Hill Elem. Sch., Washingtonville, 1983—; math instr. Washingtonville Middle Sch., 1992-93; fam. math. trainer 4th grade Round Hill, 1993-94; mem. Philosophy Com., Washingtonville, 1989-91; math. tchr. rep. Congruency Com.-Dist., Washingtonville, 1989—. Tchr. bd. rep. PTA, Washingtonville; bldg. camp group leader St. Mary's Ch., Washingtonville, 1990—. Grantee for grad. study Nat. Dept. Def. Mem. Assn. Math. Tchrs. of N.Y., Nat. Coun. Tchrs. of Math. Republican. Roman Catholic. Home: RR 1 Box 603B Campbell Hall NY 10916-9801 Office: Round Hill Elem Sch Rt 208 S Washingtonville NY 10992

PERRELLA, JAMES ELBERT, manufacturing company executive; b. Gloversville, N.Y., May 30, 1935; s. James E. and A. Irene (Ferguson) P.; m. Diane F. Campesi; 1 child, Joy. B.S.M.E., Purdue U., 1960, M.S.I.M., 1961. Gen. mgr. Centac div. Ingersoll-Rand Co., Mayfield, Ky., 1972-75; gen. mgr. Air Compressor Group Ingersoll-Rand Co., Woodcliff Lake, N.J., 1975-77, corp. v.p., pres. Air Compressor Group, 1977-82, exec. v.p., 1982-92, pres., 1992—, chmn., CEO, 1993—, also dir. Named Disting. Alumnus Sch. Mech. Engring., Purdue U., 1982; named Disting. Alumnus Krammert Mgmt. Sch., Purdue U., 1982. Office: Ingersoll-Rand Co 200 Chestnut Ridge Rd Westwood NJ 07675 also: 3501 St Charles Blvd, Kirkland, PQ Canada H9H 4S3

PERRET, JOSEPH ALOYSIUS, banker, consultant; b. Phila., Feb. 26, 1929; s. Joseph Henry and Mary Rose (Martin) P.; m. Nancy S. Bott, June 24, 1950; children—Kathlyne, Robert, Susan, Michael. Student, U. Pa., 1953-57, Temple U., 1957-58, Stonier Grad. Sch. Banking, 1966. Head analyst Phila. Nat. Bank, 1953-57; spl. banking rep. Burroughs Corp., Phila., 1957-59; v.p. First Pa. Banking & Trust Co., Phila., 1959-66, Md. Nat. Bank, Balt., 1966-70; sr. v.p. Md. Nat. Bank, 1970-75, Comml. Credit Co., Balt., 1975-78, Sanwa Bank Calif., Los Angeles, 1978-91; cons., 1991—; chmn. bd. Star System, Inc., San Diego. Mem. Am. Bankers Assn., Data Processing Mgmt. Assn., Balt.-Washington Regional Clearing House (chmn. 1970), Calif. Bankers Cleanring House Assn. (chmn. 1990). Clubs: Country of Md; Merchants (Balt.); Friendly Hills Country (Whittier, Calif.). Home and Office: 3023 S Rio Claro Dr La Puente CA 91745-5954

PERRET, PETER JAMES, symphony conductor; b. Rochester, Minn., Mar. 25, 1941; s. George E. and Margaret (Minge) P.; m. Chao Mei-Wah, Mar. 23, 1966 (div. Apr. 1978); 1 child, Ondine; m. Debra Skeen, May 24, 1986; 1 child, Zachary. Student, Royal Conservatory, Brussels, 1964, Diplome Superieru, 1966. Chief producer Swiss Broadcasting Corp., Geneva, 1967-72; prin. condr. Capetown (Peoples Republic of Africa) Symphony, 1972-74; Exxon arts endowment condr. Buffalo Philharmonic, 1975-78; music dir. Winston-Salem (N.C.) Symphony, 1978—; vis. prof. U. Capetown, 1973-74; scholar-in-residence Canisius Coll., Buffalo, 1976, 77; prof. conducting N.C. Sch. of the Arts, Winston-Salem, 1980-88. Composer: (classical music) Symphonie Élégiaque, 1989; recordings on Koch Internat., Albany Records, Vienna Modern Masters. Avocations: cooking, tennis, sailing, mycology, reading. Home: 644 N Spring St Winston Salem NC 27101-1327 Office: Winston-Salem Symphony Roger L. Stevens Ctr 610 Coliseum Dr Winston Salem NC 27106-5390

PERRICH, JERRY ROBERT, environmental consulting company executive; b. San Bernadino, Calif., Nov. 21, 1947; s. Robert Joseph and Donaldeen Joan (Arthurs) P.; m. M. Jane Palmer, Sept. 23, 1972; children: William Joseph, Robert James, Michael Jonathan. BS in Engring., Case Inst. Tech., 1969; MS in Engring., U. Louisville, 1974, PhD in ChemE, 1976. Registered profl. engr., Ohio. Application engr. Am. Air Filter, Louisville, 1972-73; project engr. Olin Corp., Brandenburg, Ky., 1975-77; prodn. supr. E.I. DuPont, Louisville, 1977-80; dir. engring. N.Am. Carbon, Columbus, Ohio, 1980-88; plant supt. OPG Industries, Lewisburg, Ohio, 1988-89; v.p. Qsource Environ. Svcs., Miamisburg, Ohio, 1989-91; dir. indsl. bus. devel., assoc. v.p. Environ. Sci. & Engring., Inc., Peoria, Ill., 1991—; cons. Louisville, 1976-80. Author: The ESE National Precipitation Databook, 1992; editor Activated Carbon, 1981; patentee in field; contbr. articles to profl. jours. 1st lt. U.S. Army, 1969-72. Mem. Am. Inst. Chem. Engrs., Sigma Xi, Phi Kappa Phi, Tau Beta Pi. Home: 10065 Mallet Dr Spring Valley OH 45370-9648 Office: Environ Sci & Engring 245 Elmwood Dr Centerville OH 45459

PERRIER, BARBARA SUE, artist; b. Akron, Ohio, Oct. 7, 1937; d. Willis Austin and Mary Gladys (Campbell) Bibler; m. David John Perrier, July 14, 1956 (div. Nov. 1972); children: David John Jr., Kenneth James, Mark Richard. AA in Comml. Art, AA in Liberal Arts, Ventura Coll., 1991. Artist Anointed Brush Studio, Oxnard, Calif., 1987—. One-woman shows at Columbia Arts Ctr., Vancouver, Wash., 1988, Gallery Los Olivos, 1993; exhibited in group shows at Santa Paula Soc. of Arts 3d Annual Fall Show, 1992, Gloria Dei Art Show, Camarillo, Calif., 1991, 92, 13th Annual Nat. Bald Eagle Conf. Art Show, 1992, 53d Annual City of Santa Paula Art Show, 1989, 5th Annual Buenaventura Art Assn. Art Show, Ventura, 1988, Westlake Village 15th Annual Art Show, 1988, Oct. West Wildlife Art Show, Burbank, Calif., 1993, Decoy & Wildfowl Carvers Wildlife Art Show, 1994, Spectacular Monuments Art Show, 1994, Fallbrook Nature Conservancy Art Show, 1995, October West Wildlife Art Show, 1995. Mem. Calif. Gold Coast Watercolor Soc. (charter, pres. 1992), So. Calif. Wildlife Artist Assn. (pres. 1995). Baptist. Avocations: camping, travel, photography. Home and Office: Anointed Brush Studio 1231 Masthead Dr Oxnard CA 93035

PERRILL, FREDERICK EUGENE, information systems executive; b. Charlotte, N.C., Sept. 13, 1939; s. Frederick Eugene and Dorothy (Miller) P.; m. Kathryne Sims, June 1, 1963. BS in Engring., U.S. Naval Acad., 1962; MS in Bus., Naval Postgrad. Sch., 1969; postgrad., NAval War Coll., 1972-73. USCG Masters lic. Commd. ensign USN, 1962, advanced through grades to capt., 1982; supply officer USS Biddle DDG-5, 1962-63, USS Hermitage LSD-34, 1963-64; comptr. Amphibious Staff, 1964-68; dir. MIS systems, acctg., transp. Naval Supply Depot, Yokouka, Japan, 1969-72; project mgr. fin. systems design Asst. Sec. of Navy, 1973-76; dir. logistics USS Concord, 1976-78; project mgr. Fin. Systems, Washington, 1978-81; commanding officer Fin. and Acctg. Ctr., San Diego, 1981-83; dir. ops. Naval Supply Ctr., Oakland, 1984-85; asst. chief of staff MIS, COMMS. Naval Airforce Pacific, Coronado, Calif., 1985-86; ret. Naval Airforce Pacific, Coronado, 1986; sr. group mgr. Planning Rsch. Corp., San Diego, 1986-87; v.p. OPS/COO R.D. Ram Corp., San Diego, 1987-88; dir. Fourth Generation Tech., LaJolla, Calif., 1988-90; pres. Perrill Info. Systems, San Diego, 1990—; cons. Titan Corp. LaJolla, 1991—, Monger Industries, San Diego, 1988—, Delfin Corp., San Jose, 1990-91, Dobbs Ho., Memphis, 1986; farmer owner Pine Tree (property mgmt. co.), 1965—; owner, pres. Ancient Mariner Boat Svcs., 1990—. Contbr. articles to profl. jours. Asst. scout master Boy Scouts Am., Yokosuka, Japan, 1969-72; Protestant lay leader USS Concord AFS-5, Norfolk, Va., 1976-78. Mem. VFW, Naval Sailing Assn., Am. Legion, Humane Soc. of U.S., Disabled Am. Vets. Presbyterian. Avocations: sailing, skiing, camping. Home: 4785 Seda Dr San Diego CA 92124

PERRIN, CHARLES R., light manufacturing executive; b. 1945. BA in History, Trinity Coll., 1967; MBA, Columbia U., 1969. With Gen. Foods Corp., 1969-73; various mgmt. positions with Chesebrough-Pond's, Inc., 1973-85; with Duracell Inc., Bethel, Conn., 1985—; v.p., pres. Duracell N.Am. Duracell Internat. Inc., 1988—, pres., COO internat. devel. markets, 1992—. Office: Duracell Internat Inc Berkshire Indsl Park Bethel CT 06801

PERRIN, EDWARD BURTON, health services researcher, biostatistician, public health educator; b. Greensboro, Vt., Sept. 19, 1931; s. J. Newton and Dorothy E. (Willey) P.; m. Carol Anne Hendricks, Aug. 18, 1956; children: Jenifer, Scott. BA, Middlebury Coll., 1953; postgrad. (Fulbright scholar) in stats, Edinburgh (Scotland) U., 1953-54; MA in Math. Stats., Columbia U., 1956; PhD, Stanford U., 1960. Asst. prof. preventive medicine U. Wash., Seattle, 1962-65; assoc. prof. U. Wash., 1965-69, prof., 1969-70, prof., chmn. dept. biostats., 1970-72, prof. dept. health services, 1975—, chmn. dept., 1983-94; prof. (hon.) West China U. of Med. Scis., Szechwan, Peoples Republic of China, 1988—; overseas fellow Churchill Coll., Cambridge U., 1991-92; clin. prof. dept. cmty. medicine and internat. health Sch. Medicine, Georgetown U., Washington, 1972-75; dep. dir. Nat. Ctr. for Health Stats., HEW, 1972-73, dir., 1973-75; rsch. scientist Health Care Study Ctr., Battelle Human Affairs Rsch. Ctrs., Seattle, 1975-76, dir., 1976-78; dir. Health and Population Study Ctr. Battelle Human Affairs Rsch. Ctrs., Seattle, 1978-83; sr. cons. biostats. Wash./Alaska regional med. programs, 1967-72; biometrician VA Co-op Study on Treatment of Esophageal Varices, 1961-73; mem. Epidemiology and Disease Control Study Sect., NIH, 1969-73; chmn. health svcs. rsch. study sect., HEW, 1976-79; chmn. health svcs R&D field program rev. panel, VA, 1988-91; chmn. health svcs. info. steering com. State of Washington, 1993-94; mem. nat. adv. coun. AHCPR, 1994—; mem. com. on nat. stats. NRC, NAS, 1994—; chmn. scientific adv. com. Med. Outcomes Trust, 1994—. Contbr. articles on biostats., health services and population studies to profl. publs.; mem. editorial bd.: Jour. Family Practice, 1978-90, Public Health Nursing, 1992—. Mem. tech. bd. Milbank Meml. Fund, 1974-76. Recipient Outstanding Service citation HEW, 1975. Fellow AAAS, Am. Pub. Health Assn. (Spiegelman Health Stats. award 1970, program devel. bd. 1971, chmn. stats. sect. 1978-80, governing coun. 1983-85, stats. sect. recognition award 1989), Am. Statis. Assn. (mem. adv. com. to divsn. statis. policy 1975-77); mem. Assn. Health Svcs. Rsch. (pres. 1994-95), Inst. Medicine of Nat. Acad. Sci. (chmn. membership com. 1984-86, mem. bd. on health care svcs. 1987—, forum health stats. 1994-95, chmn. com. on clin. evaluation 1990-93), Biometrics Soc. (pres. Western N.Am. Region 1971), Inst. Math. Stats., Internat. Epidemiologic Assn., Sigma Xi, Phi Beta Kappa. Home: 4900 NE 39th St Seattle WA 98105-5209 Office: U Wash Dept Health Svcs Box 357660 Seattle WA 98195

PERRIN, GAIL, editor; b. Boston, Oct. 14, 1938; d. Hugh and Helen (Baxter) P. B.A., Wellesley Coll., 1960. Copy girl Washington Daily News, summers, 1954-57, reporter, 1958, 60-61, acting women's editor, food editor, 1961-62, rewrite reporter, 1963-65; reporter Honolulu Star Bull., 1959; women's editor Boston Globe, 1965-71, asst. met. editor, 1971-74, food editor, 1974-92; food cons., free-lance writer, 1992—. Mem. Assn. Food Journalists, Women's Culinary Guild.

PERRIN, JOHN PAUL, medical school president; b. Bay City, Mich., Feb. 23, 1943; s. Eugene Elmer and Helen Christine (Macey) P.; m. Michele Webb-Greenfelder; 1 child, Marie Helen. BA cum laude, Alma Coll., Mich., 1965; JD, William and Mary Coll., 1967; grad. with honors, USAF Officers Tng. Sch., Lackland AFB, Tex., 1968. Bar: Va. 1967, D.C. 1970. Career trainee CIA, McLean, Va., 1967-68; sole practice law Fairfax, Va., 1970-72; ptnr. Elson, Kilcarr, Perrin & Waters, Fairfax, Va., 1972-75; dir. Washington office Am. Osteo. Assn., Washington, 1975-82; exec. dir. Am. Osteo. Assn., Chgo., 1982-91; pres. The Univ. of Health Scis. Coll. of Osteopathic Medicine, 1991—. Mem. Fairfax City Council, Va., 1978-82. Served to 1st lt. USAF, 1968-70. Mem. Va. State Bar Assn., D.C. Bar Assn., Kansas City C. of C. (metro affairs com.), N.E. Kans. City C. of C. (sec. 1992), Hallbrook Golf and Country Club, The Plaza Club, Kiwanis (pres. Annandale, Va. chpt. 1970-71), Masons. Republican. Presbyterian. Avocations: golf, sailing, skiing, writing. Home: 3223 Gladstone Blvd Kansas City MO 64123 Office: Coll of Osteopathic Medicine Univ of Health Scis 2105 Independence Blvd Kansas City MO 64124

PERRIN, KENNETH LYNN, university chancellor; b. L.A., July 29, 1937; s. Freeman Whitaker and Lois Eileen (Bowen) P.; m. Shirley Anne Cupp, Apr. 2, 1960; children: Steven, Lynne. BA, Occidental Coll., 1959; MA, Calif. State U., Long Beach, 1964; PhD, Stanford U., 1969. Lic. in speech pathology, Calif. Chmn. dept. communicative disorders U. Pacific, Stockton, Calif., 1969-77; dir. edn. and sci. programs Am. Speech-Lang.-Hearing Assn., Rockville, Md., 1977-80; dean Faculty Profl. Studies West Chester U. Pa., 1980-82; acting acad. v.p. West Chester U., 1982, pres., 1983-91; pres. Coun. on Postsecondary Edn., Washington, 1991-93; chancellor, system sr. v.p. U. Hawaii, Hilo and West Oahu, 1993—; cons. in field, 1969-76; pres. north region Calif. Speech Hearing Assn., 1975-76. Co-author: monograph Prevalence of Communicative Disorders, 1981; contbr. articles to profl. jours.; editor: Guide to Graduate Education Speech Pathology and Audiology, 1980. Chmn. Southeastern chpt. Greater Brandywine Br. ARC; trainee Vocat. Rehab. Adminstrn., 1965-69. Named Disting. Alumnus Sch. Humanities Calif. State U., Long Beach, 1988. Fellow Am. Speech-Lang.-Hearing Assn. (vice chmn. edn. tng. bd. 1975-77 cert. clin. competence in speech pathology); mem. West Chester C. of C. (pres. 1988). Home: 543 Kaanini St Hilo HI 96720 Office: Univ of Hawaii at Hilo 200 W Kawili St Hilo HI 96720-4091

PERRIN, NOEL, environmental studies educator; b. N.Y.C., Sept. 18, 1927; s. Edwin Oscar and Blanche Browning (Chenery) P.; m. Nancy Hunnicutt, Nov. 26, 1960 (div. 1971); children: Elisabeth, Amy; m. 2d Annemarie Price, June 20, 1975 (div. 1980); m. Anne Spencer Lindbergh, Dec. 26, 1988 (dec. 1993). B.A., Williams Coll., 1949; M.A., Duke U., 1950; M.Litt., Cambridge U., 1958. Copy boy Daily News, N.Y.C., 1950-51; assoc. editor Med. Econs., Oradell, N.J., 1953-56; instr. U. N.C. Woman's Coll., Greensboro, 1956-59; from instr. to prof. English Dartmouth Coll., Hanover, N.H., 1959-90, prof. environ. studies, 1991—. Author: A Passport Secretly Green, 1961, Dr. Bowdler's Legacy, 1969, Giving Up the Gun, 1979, Second Person Rural, 1980, Third Person Rural, 1983, A Reader's Delight, 1988, A Noel Perrin Sampler, 1991, Last Person Rural, 1991, Solo: Life with an Electric Car, 1992; columnist, Washington Post Book World, 1980-86, 89-91. Served to 1st lt. arty. AUS, 1951-52. Decorated Bronze Star; Guggenheim Found. fellow, 1970, 85. Episcopalian. Home: RR 1 Box 8 Thetford Center VT 05075-9701 Office: Dartmouth College Environ Studies Program Hanover NH 03755

PERRIN, ROBERT, writer, consultant; b. Ann Arbor, Mich., Aug. 21, 1925; s. John Stephenson and Narcissa Elizabeth (Merkel) P.; m. Barbara J. Groom, June 25, 1949; children: Stephen, Jennifer Perrin Hummel. BS, U. Minn., 1945. Reporter United Press Assn., Detroit, 1948-49, Detroit Free Press, 1949-55; adminstrv. asst. U.S. Senate, Washington, 1955-66; asst. dir. U.S. Office Econ. Opportunity, Washington, 1966-68, dep. dir., 1968-70; v.p. Mich. State U., East Lansing, 1970-79; vice chancellor SUNY System, Albany, 1979-85; exec. v.p. Tchrs. Ins. and Annuity Assn.—Coll. Retirement Equities Fund, N.Y.C., 1987-92; cons. Dept. State, 1993-94. Contbr. articles to mags., newspapers. Lt. USNR, 1943-46, PTO. Fellow Reid Found., 1954.

PERRIN, ROBERT MAITLAND, solicitor, oil company executive; b. Calgary, Alta., Can., Aug. 19, 1950; s. Albert Maitland and Elizabeth Winifred (Chalmers) P.; m. Denise Richardson, Aug. 23, 1975. BA, U. Calgary, 1972, MBA, 1988; LLB, U. Alta., Edmonton, 1973. Bar, Law Soc. Alberta, 1974. Solicitor McLaws & Co., Calgary, 1975; solicitor, then sr. solicitor, dir. internat. taxes Hudson's Bay Oil & Gas, Calgary, 1975-82; corp. sec. Interprovincial Pipe Line and Interhome Energy Ltd., Calgary, 1987-91; sr. solicitor, counsel Home Oil Co. Ltd., Calgary, 1982-87, v.p., gen. counsel, 1991-95, v.p., gen. counsel, corp. sec., 1995—. Mem. Can. Bar Assn., Can. Petroleum Law Found., Can. Coun. Sr. Legal Execs. (mem. conf. bd.), Assn. Gen. Counsel Alta., Alta. Law Soc., Alpine Club Can. Avocations: squash, hiking, cycling. Office: Home Oil Co Ltd, 324 8th Ave SW Ste 3200, Calgary, AB Canada T2P 2Z5

PERRIN, STEPHANIE B., headmistress; b. Quincy, Mass., Oct. 12, 1940; d. Richard Lee and Sylvia (Swenson) Bonnell; m. Peter Blake (divorced); 1 child, Jonathan; m. Stephen Gale; 1 child, Jesse. AB, Boston U., 1967; MA of Teaching, Harvard U., 1968, CAS, 1976. Tchr. Abbor Acad., Andover, Mass., 1968-72, Phillips Acad., Andover, 1972-77; acad. dean Walnut Hill Sch., Natick, Mass., 1978-84, headmistress, 1984—. Democrat. Episcopalian. Home: 24 Highland St Natick MA 01760-2108 Office: Walnut Hill Sch for the Arts 12 Highland St Natick MA 01760-2199

PERRINE, RICHARD LEROY, environmental engineering educator; b. Mountain View, Calif., May 15, 1924; s. George Alexander and Marie (Axelson) P.; m. Barbara Jean Gale, Apr. 12, 1945; children: Cynthia Gale, Jeffrey Richard. A.B., San Jose State Coll., 1949; M.S., Stanford U., 1950, Ph.D. in Chemistry, 1953. Cert. environ. profl., 1987. Research chemist Calif. Research Corp., La Habra, 1953-59; assoc. prof. UCLA, 1959-63, prof. engring. and applied sci., 1963-92, prof. emeritus, 1992—, chmn. environ. sci. and engring., 1971-82; prin. Aspen Environ. Group, 1990-93; v.p. Sage Resources, 1988-91; cons. environ. sci. and engring., energy resources, flow in porous media; mem. Los Angeles County Energy Commn., 1973-81; mem. adv. council South Coast Air Quality Mgmt. Dist., 1977-82; mem. air conservation com. Los Angeles County Lung Assn., 1970-84; mem. adv. com. energy div. Oak Ridge Nat. Lab., 1987-90; mem. policy bd. Inst. Environ. and Natural Resource Rsch. and Policy U. Wyo., 1994—. Editor in chief The Environ. Profl., 1985-90. Served with AUS, 1943-46. Recipient Outstanding Engr. Merit award in environ. engring. Inst. Advancement Engring., 1975; ACT-SO award in field of chemistry West Coast region NAACP, 1984. Mem. AAAS, Am. Chem. Soc., Soc. Petroleum Engrs., Am. Inst. Chem. Engrs., Can. Inst. Mining and Metallurgy, N.Am. Assn. Environ. Edn., Nat. Assn. Environ. Profls. (cert.), Air and Waste Mgmt. Assn., Assn. Environ. Engring. Profs., Sierra Club, Wilderness Soc., Audubon Soc., Sigma Xi, Tau Beta Pi, Phi Lambda Upsilon. Home: 22611 Kittridge St West Hills CA 91307-3609 Office: U Calif Boelter Hall Rm 6266H Los Angeles CA 90024-1593

PERRINE, VALERIE, actress; b. Galveston, Tex., Sept. 3, 1943; d. Kenneth and Renee (McGinley) P. Student, U. Ariz., 1961. Screen debut Slaughterhouse Five, 1972; other films include The Last American Hero, 1973, Lenny, 1974 (Best actress award Cannes Film Festival, 1975, Best Supporting Actress, N.Y. Film Circle, 1975, Actress of Yr. award United Motion Pictures Assn., 1975, award most promising newcomer to leading film roles Brit. Acad., 1975), W.C. Fields and Me, 1976, Mr. Billion, 1977, Superman, 1978, The Electric Horseman, 1979, Magician of Lublin, 1979, Can't Stop the Music, 1980, Superman II, 1980, Agency, 1981, The Border, 1982, The Mask, 1985, Water, 1986, Maid to Order, 1987, Bright Angel, 1991, Boiling Point, 1994; TV movies include The Couple Takes A Wife, 1972, Steambath, 1972, Whenn the Girls Come Out To Play, 1974, Ziegfield 1978, Marian Rose White, 1982, Malibu, 1983, When Your Lover Leaves, 1983, Una Casa a Roma, 1987, Una Donna d'Affare, 1987, Sweet Bird of Youth, 1989, The Mountain of Diamonds, 1990; (TV series) Leo and Liz in Beverly Hills, 1986; (TV miniseries) The Secrets of Lake Success, 1993. Mem. SAG, AFTRA. Address: Borinstein Orich & Bogart 8271 Melrose #110 Los Angeles CA 90046*

PERRIS, ELIZABETH L., federal judge; b. 1951. AB, U. Calif., 1972; JD, U. Calif., Davis, 1975. Admitted to bar, 1976. Bankruptcy judge U.S. Dist. Ct. Oreg., 1984—. Office: US Dist Ct 900 Security Pacific Plz 1001 SW 5th Ave Portland OR 97204-1118

PERRIS, TERRENCE GEORGE, lawyer; b. Los Angeles, Oct. 18, 1947; s. Theodore John Grivas and Penny (Sfakianos) Perris. BA magna cum laude, U. Toledo, 1969; JD summa cum laude, U. Mich., 1972. Bar: Ohio 1972, U.S. Tax Ct. 1982, U.S. Ct. Claims 1983, U.S. Supreme Ct. 1983. Law clk. to judge U.S. Ct. Appeals (2d cir.), N.Y.C., 1972-73; law clk. to Justice Potter Stewart U.S. Supreme Ct., Washington, 1973-74; assoc. Squire, Sanders & Dempsey, Cleve., 1974-80, ptnr., 1980—; v.p., trustee SS&D Found., Cleve., 1984—; lectr. in field; nat. coord. Taxation Practice Area, 1987—; chmn. Cleve. Tax Inst., 1993. Mem. vis. com. U. Mich. Law Sch., 1986—. Capt. U.S. Army, 1974. Mem. ABA, Ohio Bar Assn., Cleve. Bar Assn. (subchpt. C of internal revenue code task force), Supreme Ct. Hist. Soc., Tax Club Cleve., Order of Coif, Union Club of Cleve., U. Mich. Club of Cleve., The Club of Cleve., Pres.'s Club (Ann Arbor, Mich.), Phi Kappa Phi. Republican. Eastern Orthodox. Avocation: landscape gardening. Office: Squire Sanders & Dempsey 4900 Society Ctr 127 Public Sq Cleveland OH 44114-1304

PERRISH, ALBERT, steel company executive; b. Vancouver, B.C., Can., Nov. 18, 1914; came to U.S., 1920; s. Sam and Nettie (Prezant) P.; m. Leora Claire Quiat, Jan. 12, 1962 (dec. 1984); m. Helen Ann Frazin, June 11, 1985; children: Peggy, Kathleen. BSBA, UCLA, 1938. Commr. City of L.A. Harbor Dept., 1961-64, pres., 1964; exec. Ferro Union Inc., Torrance, Calif., 1964—; mem. adv. bd. U.S. Dept. Commerce, Washington, 1946-50, Small Bus. Adminstrn., Washington, 1955-56. Capt. USAAF, 1942-46. Recipient Star of Solidarity, Pres. of Italy, 1954, Order of Leopold, King of Belgium, 1962, Order of Merit, Govt. of France, 1962. Mem. Am. Inst. Internat. Steel (founder, pres. West Coast chpt. 1959—). Office: Ferro Union Inc 1000 W Francisco St Torrance CA 90502

PERRITT, HENRY HARDY, JR., law educator; b. Little Rock, Ark., Dec. 30, 1944; s. Henry Hardy and Margaret Frances (Floyd) P. SB in Engring., MIT, 1966, SM in Mgmt., 1970; JD, Georgetown U., 1975. Bar: Va. 1976, Pa. 1977, D.C. 1981, U.S. Supreme Ct. 1981, U.S. Ct. Appeals (3d cir.) 1979, U.S. Ct. Appeals (2d cir.) 1979, U.S. Ct. Appeals (6th cir.) 1983. Sr. sales planner Lockheed Corp., Marietta, Ga., 1968-71; exec. sec. Cost of Living Coun., Washington, 1972-75; legis. analyst U.S. Dept. Commerce, 1971-72; mem. staff White House, Washington, 1975; dep. undersec. U.S. Dept. Labor, Washington, 1975-76; gen. counsel labor Conrail, Phila., 1976-81; prof. law Villanova U., 1981—; cons. atty. Morgan, Lewis & Bockius, Washington, 1981-90, Conrail, 1981-90. Author: Employee Dismissal Law and Practice, 1984, 2d edition, 1987, Labor Injunctions, 1986, How to Practice Law With Computers, 1988, Employee Benefits Claims Law and Practice, 1989, Workplace Torts Rights and Liabilities, 1990, Americans With Disabilities Act Handbook, 1990; contbr. articles to profl. jours. Apptd. vice chmn. Coal Commn. U.S. Sec. of Labor, 1990. Mem. ABA (chmn. com. on r.r. and airline labor law 1983-86, chmn. com. on regulatory initiatives and info. tech., adminstrv. law sect., co-vice chmn. dispute resolution com., adminstrv. law sect. 1987-90), Assn. Am. Law Schs. (chmn. sect. on law and computers 1991), Racquet Club. Republican. Unitarian. Home: 26 Rosedale Rd Wynnewood PA 19096-3524 Office: Villanova Law Sch Villanova PA 19085

PERRON, PIERRE O., science administrator; b. Louiseville, Que., Can., Aug. 19, 1939; m. Rachel DesRosiers. BA in Scis. with honors, Laval (Can.) U., 1959, BASc in Metall. Engring., 1963; PhD in Metallurgy, U. Strathclyde, Glasgow, Scotland, 1966. Rsch. officer Chalk River Nuclear Labs. Atomic Energy of Can. Ltd., 1966-68; mgr. radiation protection dept. Hydro Que., 1968-71; dir. material scis. Que. Indsl. Rsch. Ctr., 1971-75, dir. R&D, 1975-82; assoc. dep. minister Dept. Energy and Resources Govt. of Que., Quebec City, 1982-85, Dept. Energy, Mines and Resources Can., Ottawa, 1985-89; pres. Nat. Rsch. Coun. Can., Ottawa, Ont., 1989-94. Office: Nat Rsch Coun Canada, Montreal Rd Bldg M 58, Ottawa, ON Canada K1A 0R6

PERRONE, NICHOLAS, mechanical engineer, business executive; b. Apr. 30, 1930. B. Aero. Engring., Poly. Inst. Bklyn., 1951, M.S., 1953, Ph.D., 1958. Research asst., then assoc. applied mechanics Bklyn. Poly. Inst., 1951-58; asst. prof., then assoc. prof. Pratt Inst. 1958-62; sr. scientist Structural Mechanics br. Office Naval Research, Washington, 1962-67; acting head dept. Structural Mechanics br. Office Naval Research, 1967-68 dir. program, 1968-69, 71-82; pres. CASA Gifts Inc., 1983-85; dep. to pres. Advanced Tech. and Research Inc., 1986-87; pres. Perrone Forensic Cons. Inc., 1987—; lectr. civil engring. Cath U. Am., 1962-64, adj. prof., 1965—; spl. research fellow NIH, Georgetown U., 1969-70; participant numerous workshops, confs., symposia; lectr. in field. Contbg. author: Biodynamics, 1980; editor or co-editor numerous monographs; editorial adv. bd.: Advances in Engring. Software, Computers and Structures, Engineering Fracture, Pressure Vessels and Piping; contbr. numerous articles to profl. jours. Fellow AAAS, ASME, Am. Acad. Mechanics; mem. ASCE, AIAA, N.Y. Acad. Sci., Am. Soc. Engring. Edn., Soc. Automotive Engrs., Soc. Mfg. Engrs., Am. Acad. Forensic Sci., Inst. Injury Recuction. Address: 12207 Valerie Ln Laurel MD 20708

PERROS, THEODORE PETER, chemist, educator; b. Cumberland, Md., Aug. 16, 1921; s. Peter G. and Christina (Sioris) P.; m. Electra Paula Zolotas, July 21, 1973 (div.). BS, George Washington U., 1946, MS, 1947, Ph.D., 1952; postgrad. Technische Hochschule, Munich, Germany. Analyst research div. U.S. Naval Ordnance Lab., 1943-46; faculty George Washington U., Washington, 1946—; prof. chemistry and forensic scis., 1946—; chmn. dept. forensic sci., 1971-73, chmn. dept. chemistry, 1980-88; v.p. Meridian-West Assos., 1978—; rsch. chemist Bur. Ordnance, 1949; rsch. dir. Air Force Office Sci. R&D, 1958-59; cons. U.S. Naval Ordnance Lab., 1953-56; fed. commr., chmn. bd. dirs. Interstate Commn. Potomac River Basin, 1980; sec. Ahepa Ednl. Found., 1969-78; mem. Chesapeake Bay Sci. and Tech. Adv. Com., 1993. Author: (with William F. Sager) Chemical Principles,

1961, (with C.R. Naeser, W. Harkness) Experiments in General Chemistry, 1961, College Chemistry, 1966; Contbr. (with C.R. Naeser, W. Harkness) articles to profl. jours. Pres. So. Intercollegiate Athletic Conf., 1968, Hellenic Rep. Club of Washington, 1968-70, D.C. Heritage Groups Coun., 1980; campaign chmn. Nat. Rep. Heritage Groups Coun., 1977-78, recipient Kurt Voldemars Meml. award for disting. svc., 1985; mem. D.C. Rep. State Com., 1980—; exec. com. Rep. Nat. Com., 1994-95; chmn. Nat. Rep. Heritage Groups Coun., 1994-95. Named Disting. Prof. in Edn. George Washington U., 1990, Award of Distinction, CHS Alumni Assn., 1992; NSF fellow, 1959; AEC grantee, 1951-53, Rsch. Corp. grantee, 1953-54. Fellow Am. Inst. Chemists, Am. Acad. Forensic Scis., Washington Acad. Scis.; mem. Am. Chem. Soc., Soc. Applied Spectroscopy, German Lang. Soc., Chem. Soc. London, Gesellschaft Deutscher Chemiker, Philos. Soc. Washington, Am. Hellenic Edni. Progressive Assn. (pres. Inst. Arts and Scis., pres. Washington chpt. 1976-78, dist. gov. 1982-83, supreme gov. 1985-86, AHEPA Acad. Achievement award 1984), Sigma Xi, Omicron Delta Kappa, Alpha Chi Sigma (pres. 1964, bd. gov.'s 1986-88, Profl. Merit award 1985, Profl. Chemistry award 1985). Research on stabilities of inorganic coordination polymers, preparation and characterization fluorine containing compounds transition metals. Home: 5825 3rd Pl NW Washington DC 20011-2106

PERROT, PAUL NORMAN, museum director; b. Paris, France, July 28, 1926; came to U.S., 1946, naturalized, 1954; s. Paul and K. Norman (Derr) P.; m. Joanne Stovall, Oct. 23, 1954; children—Paul Latham, Chantal Marie Claire, Jeannine, Robert. Student, Ecole du Louvre, 1945-46, N.Y. U. Inst. Fine Arts, 1946-52. Asst. The Cloisters, Met. Mus. Art, 1948-52; asst. to dir. Corning (N.Y.) Mus. Glass, 1952-54, asst. dir. mus., 1954-60, dir., 1960-72; editor Jour. Glass Studies, 1959-72; asst. sec. for mus. programs Smithsonian Instn., Washington, 1972-84; dir. Va. Mus. Fine Arts, 1984-91; dir. Santa Barbara Mus. Art, 1991-94, cons., 1994—; lectr. glass history, aesthetics, museology; past v.p. Internat. Coun. Mus. Found.; past pres. N.E. Conf. Mus.; past pres. Internat. Centre for Study of Preservation and Restoration of Cultural Property, Rome, mem. coun., 1974-88. Author: Three Great Centuries of Venetian Glass, 1958, also numerous articles on various hist. and archael. subjects. Former trustee Winterthur Mus.; former trustee, treas. Mus. Computer NEtwork; mem. internat. Cons. Com. for the Preservation of Moenjodaro; chmn. adv. com. World Monuments Fund; mem. vis. com. Getty Conservation Inst. Mem. Am. Assn. Mus. (past v.p., coun. 1967-78), N.Y. State Assn. Mus. (past pres.), Internat. Assn. History Glass (past v.p.) Corning Friends of Library (past pres.), So. Tier Library System (past pres.).

PERROTTA, FIORAVANTE GERALD, lawyer; b. Lynbrook, N.Y., July 26, 1931; s. Ercole John and Frances (Raimondi) P. B.A., St. John's Coll., 1952, J.D., 1955. Bar: N.Y. 1955, U.S. Supreme Ct. 1971. Asst. U.S. atty. So. Dist. N.Y., 1955-57; assoc. Jackson Nash Brophy Barringer & Brooks, 1957-58; asst. counsel Gov. Rockefeller, N.Y. State, 1959-60, spl. asst., 1961-62; assoc. Simpson Thacher & Bartlett, 1960-61; dep. supt., gen. counsel N.Y. State Ins. Dept., 1963, 1st dep. supt., 1964-66; v.p. USLIFE Holding Corp., 1966-67; exec. asst. to Mayor Lindsay N.Y.C., 1968, fin. administr., 1969-70; ptnr. Rogers & Wells, N.Y.C., 1970—; bd. dirs. Sun Life Ins. & Annuity Co. N.Y., Northstar Life Ins. Co., Bankers Security Life Ins. Soc. Commr. State Ins. Fund, 1971-77; mem. N.Y. State Fin. Control Bd.; pres. bd. trustees N.Y. Foundling Hosp. Named Young Ins. Man of Yr. N.Y. Ins. Fedn., 1966. Mem. ABA, N.Y. State Bar Assn., Assn. Bar City N.Y., Am. Arbitration Assn. (panel arbitrators), Phi Delta Phi. Republican. Roman Catholic. Home: 20 Sutton Pl S New York NY 10022-4165 also: Clark Ln Essex CT 06426 Office: Rogers & Wells 200 Park Ave New York NY 10166-0153 also: 4041 Gulf Shore Blvd N Naples FL 33940

PERRUCCI, ROBERT, sociologist, educator; b. N.Y.C., Nov. 11, 1931; s. Dan and Inez (Mucci) P.; m. Carolyn Land Cummings, Aug. 4, 1965; children: Mark Robert, Celeste Ann, Christopher Robert, Alissa Cummings, Martin Cummings. B.S., SUNY, Cortland, 1958; M.S. (Social Sci. Research Council fellow), Purdue U., Ph.D., 1962. Asst. prof. sociology Purdue U., West Lafayette, Ind., 1962-65; asso. prof. Purdue U., 1965-67, prof., 1967—, head dept., 1978-87; vis. Simon prof. U. Manchester (Eng.), 1968-69; Bd. dirs. Ind. Center on Law and Poverty, 1973-76. Author: Sociology, 1983, Circle of Madness, 1974, Divided Loyalties, 1980, The Triple Revolution, 1971, Profession Without Community, 1968, The Engineers and the Social System, 1998, Mental Patients and Social Networks, 1982, Plant Closings: International Context and Local Consequences, 1988, Networks of Power, 1989, Japanese Auto Transplants in the Heartland: Corporatism and Community, 1994; editor: The American Sociologist, 1982—, Social Problems, 1993—; contbr. articles to profl. jours. Served with USMC, 1951-53. Recipient grants NSF, 1966-68, 76-78, grants NIMH, 1969-72. Mem. Am. Sociol. Assn., Soc. Study Social Problems (dir. 1980—), N. Central Sociol. Assn. (pres. 1973-74). Home: 305 Leslie Ave West Lafayette IN 47906-2411 Office: Dept Sociology Purdue U West Lafayette IN 47907

PERRY, A. MICHAEL, banker; b. Huntington, W.Va., May 31, 1936; s. Austin Lee and Virginia (Cole) P.; m. Henriella Mylar, 1958; children—Michele, Melanie, Audy. B.A., Marshall U., 1958; LL.B., W.Va. U., 1961. Ptnr. Huddleston, Bolen, Beatty, Porter, Copen, Huntington, 1961-81; chmn. bd., chief exec. officer 1st Huntington Nat. Bank, 1981-88, chmn. bd., 1981—; pres., chief exec. officer Key Bancshares W.Va., Inc., Huntington, 1983-85, Key Centurion Bancshares, Inc.,, 1985—. Trustee Alderson Broaddus Coll., 1984-89, Greater Ashland Found. Inc.; bd. dirs. Tri-State Cultural Devel. Plan; mem. adv. bd. Marshall Artists Series, Huntington, 1987-89; mem. bd. trustees U. W.Va. system, vice chairperson. Recipient Advocate of Yr. award SBA, 1985, Citizen of Yr. award Huntington newspaper, 1987. Mem. W.Va. Research League (bd. dirs., v.p.), W.Va. Bankers Assn. (bd. dirs., chmn. govt. and legis. com., chmn. interstate banking task force), W.Va. C. of C. (mem. exec. com., chmn.-elect 1989), Order of Coif, Omicron Delta Kappa. Baptist. Club: Rotary (past pres.). Avocations: farming, collecting farm and kitchen implements. Home: 3350 Harvey Rd Huntington WV 25704-9112 Office: Banc One Ctr Charleston WV 25301 also: PO Box 1113 Charleston WV 25324

PERRY, ANTHONY JOHN, retired hospital executive; b. Dighton, Mass., Oct. 19, 1919; s. Antone and Jessie P.; m. Harriet M. McGirr, Nov. 26, 1949; children: Joan Perry, Martha. B.S. in Bus. Coll. Mass. at Bridgewater, 1942; MHA, Northwestern U., 1952. Flight supt. Trans World Airlines, Lisbon, Portugal, 1946-47; sta. mgr. Peruvian Internat. Airlines, N.Y.C., 1947-49; with adminstrn. Decatur and Macon County Hosp. (now Decatur Meml. Hosp.), Decatur, Ill., 1952-94, administr., 1961-94, exec. v.p., 1969-74, pres., CEO, 1974-86; ret., 1994; cons. in field, 1986—; mem. bd. MMI Cos., 1985-95; pres. Mental Health Assn. Macon County, 1957; mem. Tech. Coun. Means and Methods of Financing Health Care for Ill. Bd. dirs. Macon County chpt. ARC, 1960-66, South Cen. Ill. Health Planning Council, 1969—, United Way Decatur and Macon County, 1960-66, Voluntary Hosps. Am., 1977-86; mem. adv. bd. Grad. Studies Ctr., Millikin U. Served with USAAF, 1942-46. Fellow Am. Coll. Hosp. Adminstrs.; mem. Am. Hosp. Assn. (trustee, mem. regional adv. bd., chmn. coun. on fin. 1975-79), Ill. Hosp. Assn. (pres. 1972, chmn. rate rev. steering com. 1979—), Decatur Country Club, La Quinta (Calif.) Hotel Golf Club. Home: 421 Hackberry Dr Decatur IL 62521-5501 Office: Millikin Ct Suite 518 Decatur IL 62523

PERRY, B(ILLY) DWIGHT, lawyer; b. Oklahoma City, Jan. 28, 1933; s. William C. and Julia Walton (Bray) P.; m. Shirley Andersen, June 16, 1959 (div. 1973); m. Suzanne Meyer , Sept. 15, 1973; children: Scott R., Ryan W., Samantha G., Devin D. BA, U. Okla., 1955; JD, Georgetown U., 1963. Bar: D.C. 1964, U.S. Supreme Ct. 1968. Law clk. to Judge E. Barrett Prettyman U.S. Ct. Appeals (D.C. cir.), 1963-64; assoc. McCarty & Wheatley, Washington, 1964-67; assoc., then ptnr. Dow, Lohnes & Albertson, Washington, 1967-91, mng. ptnr., 1991—. Lt. arty. U.S Army, 1956-60. Mem. ABA, Fed. Communications Bar Assn., DC Bar Assn. (Young Lawyer of Yr. 1967-68), Washington Golf and Country Club. Episcopalian. Avocations: fishing, hunting. Office: Dow Lohnes & Albertson 1255 23rd St NW Washington DC 20037-1125

PERRY, BRADFORD KENT, academic administrator; b. Boston, Oct. 26, 1942; s. Robert Woodward and Louise (Kent) P.; m. Marilyn Ann Scott, June 13, 1964; children: Katherine, Susan. BA, Harvard U., 1964; MBA, Stanford U., 1970. Commd. ensign USN, 1964, advanced through grades to

lt., 1967, served in various locations, 1964-71, resigned, 1971; with Stanford (Calif.) U., 1971-88, assoc. contr., 1981-88; vice chancellor Univ. System N.H., Durham, 1988—; exec. dir. Bus. Mgmt. Inst. Stanford, 1981-86; adv. bd., New Eng. Ctr., Durham, 1988—; bd. govs. N.H. Pub. TV, Durham, 1988—. Office: Univ System NH Meyers Ctr Durham NH 03824

PERRY, CATHERINE D., judge; b. 1952. BA, Univ. of Okla., 1977; JS, Wash. Univ. Sch. of Law, 1980. Sec., law clk. Gillespie, Perry & Gentry, Sentinel, Okla., 1970, 77-78; with Armstrong, Teasdale, Kramer & Vaughn, St. Louis, 1980-90; magistrate judge U.S. Dist. Ct. (Mo. ea. dist.), 8th circuit, St. Louis, 1990-94, district judge, 1994—. Mem. Fed. Magistrate Judges Assn., Nat. Assn. of Women Judges, Am. Bar Assn., Mo. Bar Assn., Bar Assn. of Metropolitan St. Louis, Women Lawyers Assn. of Greater St. Louis. Office: US Courthouse 1114 Market St Rm 840 Saint Louis MO 63101-2043

PERRY, CHARLES EDWARD, university administrator; b. Holden, W.Va., July 25, 1937; m. Betty Laird, Sept. 17, 1960; children: Thomas Edward, Lynnette Eleanor. BA with honors in Polit. Sci., Bowling Green State U., 1958, BS in English and History, 1959, MA, 1964, LHD (hon.), 1970; cert. in philosophy, U. Mich., 1972; LL.D. (hon.), Bethune-Cookman Coll., 1969. Tchr. East Detroit pub. schs., 1959; admissions counselor Bowling Green State U., 1959-61, dir. admissions, 1961-64, dir. devel., 1964-67, asst. to pres., 1965-67; spl. asst. to gov. Fla., 1967-68; vice chancellor State Univ. System Fla., 1968-69; pres. Fla. Internat. U., Miami, 1969-75; pres., pub. Family Weekly mag., N.Y.C., 1975-76; corp. officer communications, pub. group Charter Co., Jacksonville, Fla., 1975-76; pres., chief exec. officer Golden Bear Internat./ Jack Nicklaus Cos., North Palm Beach, Fla., 1976-85; chmn., chief exec. officer Worldvest, Inc., Columbus, Ohio, 1985-87; pres., CEO The Friedkin Cos., Houston, 1987-90; chmn., CEO Western Trading & Mgmt., Houston, 1990-93; dean grad. sch. mgmt. U. Dallas, 1993—; bd. dirs. B.C. Golf, Ltd, Guardian Savs. Inc., Perry Investments Inc., Worldvest Asia Ltd., Biomed. Waste Systems Inc. Heartland Group, Applied Conversation Techs. Inc. Former bd. dirs. Orange Bowl, Palm Beach-Martin County Med. Ctr., Community TV Found. South Fla., Am. Revolution Bicentennial Commn., Fla. Internat. U. Found., Mus. Sci. Greater Miami, United Cerebral Palsy Miami, Third Century U.S.A., Houston Ballet Found., Houston Symphony; bd. visitors Longwood Coll., Fla. Commn. Quality Edn., Fla., Fla. Edn. Council, Edn. Commn. of the States, So. Region Edn. Bd. Recipient Silver Anvil award Pub. Relations Soc. Am., 1964; Spl. Appreciation award for outstanding contbns. to Fla., 1968; Certificate of Merit award Edinboro State Coll., 1972; Diamond Jubilee Celebration award City of Miami, 1971; Outstand Young Man of Am., U.S. Jaycees, 1971; Man of Year award Phi Delta Kappa, 1972; Medal of Honor Acción Pro Darien Soc., Colombia, 1973; Disting. Service award Marshall U., 1973; Distinguished Alumnus award Bowling Green State U., 1975; Centennial Alumnus award Nat. Assn. State Univs. and Land Grant Colls. Mem. Am. Assn. State Colls. and Univs., Am. Assn. Higher Edn., World Bus. Coun., Young Pres.' Orgn., Fla. C. of C. (dir.), Nat. Golf Found., U.S. Golf Assn., Fla. Hist. Soc., Pi Sigma Alpha, Alpha Kappa Delta, Phi Delta Kappa,, Sigma Nu. Clubs: Old Port Cove Yacht; Lost Tree (North Palm Beach); Muirfield Village Golf (Dublin, Ohio); The Golf, Columbus (Columbus, Ohio); Buffalo Creek Golf Club (Rockwall, Tex.); Loxahatchee Golf (Jupiter, Fla.); La Cima Club (Las Colinas, Tex.); Chandler's Landing Yacht Club (Rockwall). Office: U Dallas Grad Sch Mgmt Office of Dean 1845 E Northgate Dr Irving TX 75062-4799

PERRY, CHARLES OWEN, sculptor; b. Helena, Mont., Oct. 18, 1929; s. Owen Hindmarch and Margaret Carroll (Bache) P.; m. Sheila Alicia Henry, June 22, 1962; children—Paul, Carlo, Daniela, Patrick, Marco. Student, Columbia U., 1953; M.Arch., Yale U., 1958. Architect Skidmore Owings & Merrill, San Francisco, 1958-64, Prix de Rome Architecture, 1964-66; sculptor-in-residence Dartmouth Coll., 1973. One-man shows include Hansen Gallery, San Francisco, 1964, Waddell Gallery, N.Y.C., 1967, 70, Dartmouth Coll., 1973, Arts Club, Chgo., 1973; group shows include, Whitney Mus., 1964, 66, Spoleto Festival, 1967, Venice Biennale, 1970, Quadrienalle di Arte de Roma, 1977, Katonah Gallery, N.Y.; represented in permanent collections, Modern Art, N.Y.C., Whitney Art Inst. Chgo., San Francisco Mus. Art, Dartmouth Coll., U. Mich., Nat. Air and Space Mus., IBM, Charlotte, N.C., Hyatt Regency, San Francisco, Fed. Res. Bank, Mpls., Barnett Plaza, Tampa, Fla., Lincoln Ctr., Dallas, Shell Oil Bldg., Melbourne, Australia, Gen. Electric Hdqrs., Fairfield, Ct., Bushnell Park, Hartford, Ct., Crystal City, Arlington, Va.; patentee in furniture design field. Served with U.S. Army, 1951-53. Decorated Bronze star. Fellow Am. Acad. Rome, Nat. Acad. Design; mem. Sculptors Guild, Nat. Acad. Design Silvermine Guild. Roman Catholic. Club: Century Assn. (N.Y.C.). Home: 20 Shorehaven Rd Norwalk CT 06855-2807 Studio: 3 Raymond St Norwalk CT 06854

PERRY, CHARLES S., lawyer; b. Hibbing, Minn., June 3, 1936; s. Charles J. and Harriet (Sherman) P.; m. Julie B. Perry, Nov. 28, 1958; children: Army, Katherine, Robin. BS, George Washington U., 1961; LLB, Cath. U. Am., 1964. Bar: Va. 1965, U.S. Dist. Ct. (ea. dist.) Va. 1965, U.S. Ct. Appeals (4th cir.) 1965, U.S. Supreme Ct. 1980. Law clk. to Hon. Albert V. Bryan Sr. U.S. Ct. Appeals (4th cir.), Alexandria, Va., 1964-65; ptnr. McGuire, Woods, Battle & Boothe, Mc Lean, Va., 1970—; chmn. Alexandria Seaport Found., 1983—; bd. dirs. Bank of Alexandria. Avocations: sailing, marine pilot. Office: McGuire Woods Battle Boothe 8280 Greensboro Dr Ste 900 Mc Lean VA 22102-3892

PERRY, CHRIS NICHOLAS, advertising executive; b. Pitts., Dec. 25, 1945; s. Nicholas and Georgia (Demas) P.; m. Kathleen Clarke, June 19, 1971; children: Damien, Adam, Dana. BA, U. Pitts., 1968. Creative supr. Ketchum Communications, 1970-74; pres., creative dir. Heddinger, Perry, Davis, 1974-76; v.p., creative dir. Fahlgren & Swink, 1976-79; v.p., creative dir. Meldrum and Fewsmith Communications, Inc., Cleve., 1979-82, sr. v.p. creative services, 1982-85, exec. v.p. creative services, 1985-86, pres., chief operating officer, 1986-87, chmn., chief exec. officer, creative dir., 1987—; also bd. dirs. Mem. bd. disting. judges and advisors The N.Y. Festivals, 1988—. Recipient numerous awards for creative excellence. Mem. Am. Assn. Advt. Agys. (sec.-treas. cen. region 1990-91, chmn. 1992-93), Cleve. Advt. Club, Cleve. Soc. Communicating Arts (pres. 1985-87, Disting. Communicator award 1991), The Hermit Club, Columbia Hills Country Club, The Union Club, Firestone Country Club. Office: Meldrum & Fewsmith Comm Inc 1350 Euclid Ave Cleveland OH 44115-1815

PERRY, CYNTHIA NORTON SHEPARD, diplomat; b. Terre Haute, Ind., Nov. 11, 1928; d. George William and Flossie (Phillips) N.; m. James O. Shepard, Nov. 2, 1946 (div. June 1970); children: Donna Ross, James O. Jr., Milo Kent, Mark; m. James O. Perry, Mar. 20, 1971; children: Paula Lucille, James O. Jr. BS in Polit. Sci., Ind. State U., 1967, DCL (hon.), 1987; EdD, U. Mass., 1972; LLD (hon.), U. Md., 1984, Coppin State Coll., 1991; LHD (hon.), Chatham Coll., 1988; D of Pub. Svc., U. Mass., 1989. Sec. Nichols Investment Corp., Terre Haute, 1956-61; ednl. rep. Ohio region IBM Corp., Terre Haute, 1962-68; dir. tchrs. corps U. Mass., Amherst, 1968-71; assoc. prof. edn. Tex. So. U., Houston, 1971-74, dean internat. student affairs, 1978-82; cons., lectr., U. Nairobi U.S. Peace Corps, Kenya, 1974-76; staff devel. officer UN Econ. Com. for Africa, Addis Ababa, Ethiopia, 1976-78; chief edn. and human resources dir. AID, Washington, 1982-86; amb. to Sierra Leone, Am. Embassy, Freetown, 1986-89; amb. to Burundi, Am. Embassy, Bujumbura, 1989-93. Contbr. articles to profl. jours. Bd. dirs. Inst. for Internat. Edn. Bd. Bols., 1984, World Affairs Coun., 1984, Houston Internat. Festival, 1994, Houston Model UN, 1994, Nat. Coun. for Internat. Vis., 1994; mem. Houston Commn. on Fgn. Rels., 1984, Houston Consular Corps, 1984, Greater Houston Partnership, 1993-94; diplomat in residence Furr H.S., 1993-94. Recipient Disting. Alumni award U. Mass., 1981, Ind. State U., 1987, Exceptional Diplomacy award U. Burundi, Ctrl. Africa, 1993, Superior Honor award U.S. Dept. State, 1993, Hon. Consul Republic of Senegal, 1994. Mem. Praeclarus, Nat. Bus. and Profl. Women, Internat. Coun. for Ednl. Devel. (bd. dirs. 1984-86), Altrusan Soc. (bd. dirs. 1981-82), Delta Sigma Theta (pres. Houston chpt. 1982-83). Republican. Avocations: oil painting, creative writing, landscaping, gardening. Home and Office: 3602 S Macgregor Way Houston TX 77021-1504

PERRY, DALE LYNN, chemist; b. Greenville, Tex., May 12, 1947; s. Francis Leon and Violet (Inabinette) P. BS, Midwestern U., 1969; MS, Lamar U., 1972; PhD, U. Houston, 1974. NSF fellow dept. chemistry Rice

U., Houston, 1976-77; Miller Research fellow dept. chemistry U. Calif.-Berkeley, 1977-79; prin. investigator solid state chemistry and spectroscopy Lawrence Berkeley Lab. U. Calif., 1979—, sr. scientist, 1987—; lectr. Ana G. Mendez Ednl. Found., 1988. Author, editor: Instrumental Surface Analysis of Geologic Materials, 1990, Applications of Analytical Techniques to the Characterization of Materials, 1992, Applications of Synchrotron Radiation Techniques to Materials Science, 1993, Applications of Synchrotron Radiation Techniques to Materials Science II, 1995; contbr. articles to profl. jours. Recipient Sigma Xi Nat. Research award U. Houston, 1974. Fellow Royal Soc. Chemistry (London); mem. Am. Chem. Soc. (chmn. materials chemistry and engring. subdiv., indsl. and engring. chemistry div. 1992—), Soc. Applied Spectroscopy, Coblentz Soc., Materials Rsch. Soc. (corp. participation com. 1991—), Sigma Xi. Office: U Calif Lawrence Berkeley Lab Mail Stop 70A-1150 Berkeley CA 94720

PERRY, DAVID, priest. Ecumenical officer Nat. Episcopal Ch., N.Y.C. Office: Episcopal Ch Ctr 815 2nd Ave New York NY 10017-4503

PERRY, DAVID BRIAN, architect; b. Greensboro, N.C., Nov. 1, 1948; s. John Watson and Henrietta Molene (Thompson) P.; m. Kathleen Joffrion, May 20, 1972 (div. 1975); m. Barbara Ann Johnson, Aug. 26, 1984; children: Meaghan Kristin, Jonathan Walwyn. B in Environ. Design, La. State U., 1972. Registered architect, Tex.; NCARB cert. Project architect Perez Assocs., Architecture, New Orleans, 1975-79; v.p. architecture Interior Environs., Inc., New Orleans, 1979-83; sr. project mgr. Interior Cons., Inc., Austin, Tex., 1984-86; ptnr. Rogers Wilson Perry, Austin, 1986-89, Rogers & Perry, Austin, 1989—. Recipient Novikoff Design award Novikoff Furniture Co., 1986. Mem. AIA (Honor award for design 1989), Young Men's Bus. League (bd. dirs., asst. v.p. in charge facilities 1990-91). Roman Catholic. Avocation: golf. Office: Rogers Perry Architects 7600 Burnet Rd Ste 280 Austin TX 78757-1267

PERRY, DONALD A., cable television consultant; b. Newport News, Va., July 18, 1938. With James Broadcasting, 1961; v.p., gen. mgr. Hampton Rds. Music Corp., Hampton Rds. Cablevision Corp., Danville Cablevision Corp., 1971-70; pres., treas. Donald A. Perry & Assocs., Inc., Gloucester, Va., 1970—; prin. Am. Cablevision Corp., 1970—; sec., treas. Communications East Corp.; sec., treas. 1st Commonwealth Communications, Inc., also chmn. bd. dirs.; pres., chief oper. officer 1st Commonwealth Cablevision, Ltd.; sec. Atlantic Metrovision Corp.; owner Gourmet Mkt. Ltd. With USCG, 1956-60. Recipient J.L. Johnson award, 1984; Paul Harris fellow. Mem. Nat. Cable TV Assn., Community Antenna TV Assn. (bd. dirs.), Va. Cable TV Assn. (past pres.), So. Cable TV Assn. (past officer, past dir.), Rotary (Newport News chpt., past pres.), Tower Club. Home: 201 Country Club Rd Newport News VA 23606-3705 Office: Donald A Perry & Assocs Inc PO Box 1275 Newport News VA 23601-0275 also: Summerville Plantation Gloucester VA 23061

PERRY, DOUGLAS, opera singer. B.M., Wittenberg U.; M.A., Ball State U. Made debut as Don Basilio in Marriage of Figaro, with N.Y.C. Opera; appeared as King Kaspar in: Amahl and the Night Visitors; appeared as Timothy in: Help! Help! The Globolinks; appeared as Guillot in: Manon; Dancing Master and Brighella in: Ariadne auf Naxos; Met. Opera debut as scientist/first mate in: The Voyage (Philip Glass); European debut as Mahatma Gandhi in Satyagraha (Philip Glass); appeared as analyst in A Quiet Place (Bernstein), La Scala and Vienna Stadtsoper; featured soloist on tours and recs. with Gregg Smith Singers and Camerata Singers; performed with Sante Fe Opera, also performed with Ft. Worth Opera, Chatauqua Opera, N.Y.C. Opera, Opera Co. of Boston, Houston Grand Opera, Balt. Opera., Miami Opera, Chgo. Lyric Opera, Seattle Opera, San Francisco Opera, Opera Co. Phila.; recs. include Satyagraha, Songs from Liquid Days, A Quiet Place, Mother of Us All. Address: 170 West End Ave New York NY 10023 Office: care of Anthony George Artist Mgmt 250 West 77th St New York NY 10024 Office: Trawick Artists Mgmt Inc 1926 Broadway New York NY 10023-6915*

PERRY, ESTON LEE, real estate and equipment leasing company executive; b. Wartburg, Tenn., June 16, 1936; s. Eston Lee and Willimae (Heidle) P.; m. Alice Anne Schmidt, Oct. 21, 1961; children: Julie Anne, Jeffrey John, Jennifer Lee. B.S., Ind. State U., 1961. With Oakley Corp., 1961—, dir., 1965—, v.p., 1981-86, pres., 1986—; corp. officer Ind. State Bank, Terre Haute, 1975-80; pres. One Twenty Four Madison Corp., Terre Haute, 1979—, also bd. dirs., chmn. bd., 1981—. Bd. dirs. Aviation Commn., Terre Haute, pres., 1970; bd. dirs. Salvation Army, Terre Haute, 1975-91, mem. exec. adv. bd., 1979-87; bd. dirs. Vigo County Dept. Pub. Welfare, 1979-82, Jr. Achievement Wabash Valley, 1980-86; bd. dirs. United Way of Wabash Valley, 1984-89, chmn. fund campaign, 1984, bd. dirs. United Way of Ind., 1984-90, v.p., 1986, pres. 1988-89; trustee Oakley Found., 1970—; bd. dirs. Terre Haute Symphony Orch., 1984-87, Ind. State U. Found., 1988—; Goodwill Industries of Terre Haute, 1984—, Leadership Terre Haute, 1984-88, Cen. Eastside Assocs., 1984-88, pres., 1984-85; mem. exec. com. Ind. State U. Found., 1990-94; bd. dirs. City of Terre Haute Hulman Links Commn., pres., 1986-91; mem. President's Assocs., Ind. State U., adv. bd. Ctr. Econ. Devel., 1984—; bd. overseers Sheldon Swope Art Gallery of Terre Haute, 1984-87; nat. mem. Council on Founds.; mem. adv. com. comml. air service study Ind. Dept. Commerce; bd. assocs. Rose Hulman Inst. Tech., 1986—. Served with U.S. Army, 1955-57. Mem. Jaycees Terre Haute (v.p. 1967-69), of C. Terre Haute (bd. dir. 1984-93, vice chmn. 1986-88, chmn. 1990), Wabash Valley Pilots Assn., Aircraft Owners and Pilots Assn., Air Safety Found., Aviation Trades Assn., Lambda Chi Alpha. Clubs: Country of Terre Haute (bd. dirs.), Aero of Terre Haute; Sycamore Varsity (Ind. State U.). Lodges: Lions (pres. Terre Haute 1983-84), Elks. Home: 25 Bogart Dr Terre Haute IN 47803-2401 Office: 8 S 16th St Terre Haute IN 47807-4102

PERRY, FLOYDE E., JR., bishop. Bishop of So. Ohio Ch. of God in Christ, Shaker Heights. Office: Ch of God in Christ PO Box 320 Memphis TN 38101

PERRY, FRANK, motion picture executive, director, producer, writer; b. N.Y.C., 1930; m. Eleanor Perry (div. 1970); m. Barbara Goldsmith, 1976. Apprentice Westport (Conn.) Country Playhouse; theatre stage mgr., prodn. mgr.; mng. dir.; dir.-observer Theatre Guild, 1955, also producer; now pres., chief exec. officer Corsair Pictures; lectr. on film Harvard U., Yale U.; adj. prof. film studies NYU Grad. Film Sch.; adj. prof. film Columbia U. Dir., producer: (films) David and Lisa, 1963, Ladybug, Ladybug, 1964, The Swimmer, 1968, Last Summer, 1969, Diary of a Mad Housewife, 1970, Doc, 1971, Play It as It Lays, 1972, Rancho Deluxe, 1975, Compromising Positions, 1985, Hello Again, 1986; dir.: (films) Man on a Swing, 1972, Mommie Dearest, 1981, Monsignor, 1983; producer film Miss Firecracker, 1989; producer/dir.: (TV spls.) The Capote Trilogy, including A Christmas Memory, starring Geraldine Page, ABC Premiere Episode TV series Skag, CBS drama Dummy, (screenplays) Mommie Dearest, A Shock to the System; dir. Broadway prodn. Ladies At The Alamo, 1978; dir. J.F.K.: A One-Man Show, 1983; co-author (with Truman Capote) Trilogy, An Experiment in Multimedia. Mem., bd. dirs. Lincoln Ctr. Theatre; trustee, mem. exec. com. Actors Studio, Guild Hall; founding chmn. Guild Hall Acad. Arts; v.p., sec. Goldsmith-Perry Philanthropies, Inc. With U.S. Army, 1952-54. Recipient 3 Peabody awards, and numerous internat. film and directorial awards. Mem. Acad. Motion Picture Arts and Scis. Office: Corsair Pictures 1740 Broadway 23rd Fl New York NY 10019

PERRY, FREDERICK SAYWARD, JR., corporate executive; b. Kittery Point, Maine, Aug. 14, 1940; s. Frederick Sayward Sr. and Rita Alice (Contant) P.; m. Judith Ann Golden, June 21, 1963 (div. 1973); 1 child, Elizabeth; m. Sarah Winthrop Smith, Aug. 26, 1979; children: Mariah, Justus. BA in Maths., Harvard U., 1963. Applications engr. Block Engring. Inc., Cambridge, Mass., 1963-67, 69-71; sci. officer ACDA, Washington, 1967-69; sales mgr. Infrared Industries Inc., Waltham, Mass., 1971-75; mktg. rep. Honeywell Radiation Ctr., Lexington, Mass., 1975-77; pres. Boston Electronics Corp., Brookline, Mass., 1977—. Contbr. article to Laser Focus mag. Mem. Alexandria (Va.) Dem. Com., 1969-70, Brookline Town Meeting, 1988, mem. fin. com., 1993—; bd. dirs. Brookline Green Space Alliance, 1987—. Mem. Optical Soc. Am., Laser Inst. Am., Internat. Soc. Optical Engring. Home: 32 Bowker St Brookline MA 02146-6955 Office: Boston Electronics Corp 72 Kent St Brookline MA 02146-7360

PERRY, GAYLORD JACKSON, former professional baseball player; b. Williamston, N.C., Sept. 15, 1938. Student, Campbell Coll. Began profl. career with St. Cloud team, No. League; pitcher San Francisco Giants, 1962-71, Cleve. Indians, 1972-75, Tex. Rangers, 1975-77, 80, San Diego Padres, 1978-79, N.Y. Yankees, 1980, Atlanta Braves, 1981, Seattle Mariners, 1982-83, Kansas City Royals, 1983. Co-author: Me and the Spitter: An Autobiographical Confession, 1974. Recipient Cy Young Mem. award Am. League, 1972, Cy Young award Nat. League, 1978; mem. Nat. League All-Star team, 1966, 70, 79, Am. League All-Star team, 1972, 74; inducted into Baseball Hall of Fame, Cooperstown, N.Y., 1991. Address: PO Box 1180 Gaffney SC 29342-1180*

PERRY, GEORGE, neuroscience researcher; b. Lompoc, Calif., Apr. 12, 1953; s. George Richard and Mary Arlene (George) P.; m. Paloma Aguilar, May 21, 1983; children: Anne A., Elizabeth A. BA, U. Calif., Santa Barbara, 1974; PhD, U. Calif., Scripps Inst. of Oceanography, San Diego, 1979. Postdoctoral fellow Baylor Coll. Medicine, Houston, 1979-82; from asst. prof. to prof. pathology, neuroscis. Case Western Res. U., Cleve., 1982—, chmn. med. sch. faculty coun.; chmn. study sect. NIH, Bethesda, Md., 1988-93. Editor: Alterations in the Neuronal Cytoskeleton in Alzheimer Disease, Clin. Neuroscis., Biomedical Journal; assoc. editor American Journal Pathology, 1994—, (mem. 1992—); mem. editorial bd. Am. Jour. Pathology, 1992—, African Jour. Neuroscis., Alzheimer Assoc. Disorder; contbr. papers to profl. publs. Fellow Muscular Dystrophy Assn., 1980; recipient Career Devel. award NIH, 1988; grantee NIH, 1988—. Mem. AAAS, Electron Microscopy Soc. N.E. Ohio (treas. 1986-88, trustee 1988-90, pres. 1990-91), Am. Soc. Cell Biology, Soc. Neurosci., Am. Assn. Investigative Pathologists, Am. Assn. Neuropathologists. Democrat. Roman Catholic. Home: 2500 Eaton Rd University Heights OH 44118-4339 Office: Case Western Res U 2085 Adelbert Rd Cleveland OH 44106-4901

PERRY, GEORGE LEWIS, research economist, consultant; b. N.Y.C., Jan. 23, 1934; s. Lewis G. and Helen L. (Couloumbis) P.; m. Jean Marion West, 1956; children: Elizabeth, Lewis G., George A.; m. 2d, Dina Needleman, 1987. BS, MIT, 1954, PhD, 1961. Editor Brookings Papers on Econ. Activity, 1970—; columnist L.A. Times, 1981-93; bd. dirs. State Farm Mut. Automobile Ins. Co., Bloomington, Ill., Dreyfus Mut. Funds, N.Y.C., Fed. Realty, Bethesda, Md.; co-dir. Brookings Panel Econ. Activity. Author: Unemployment, Money Wage Rates and Inflation, 1966; editor: Curing Chronic Inflation, 1978; contbr. articles to profl. jours. Mem. Am. Econs. Assn. Office: Brookings Instn 1775 Massachusetts Ave NW Washington DC 20036-2188

PERRY, GEORGE WILLIAMSON, lawyer; b. Cleve., Dec. 4, 1926; s. George William and Melda Patricia (Arther-Holt) P. B.A. in Econs., Yale U., 1949; J.D., U. Va., 1953. Bar: Ohio 1953, D.C. 1958, U.S. Supreme Ct. 1958, U.S. Ct. Appeals (D.C. cir.) 1959. Atty. U.S. Dept. Justice, Washington, 1954-56; assoc. Roberts and McInnis, Washington, 1957-59; atty. assoc. counsel Com. on Interstate Fgn. Commerce, U.S. Ho. of Reps., Washington, 1960-65; atty., advisor ICC, Washington, 1965-68; assoc. dir. devel. Yale U., New Haven, 1968-70; dir. tax research Pan Am. World Airways, N.Y.C., 1973-75; hearing officer Indsl. Commn. Ohio, Cleve., 1978-81; sole practice, Cleve., 1981—. Served with U.S. Army, 1945-46. Mem. Soc. of Cincinnati in State of Conn., Yale Alumni Assn. (Cleve.), Concord Coalition, Phi Delta Phi. Episcopalian. Office: 1801 E 12th St Cleveland OH 44114-3500

PERRY, GEORGE WILSON, oil and gas company executive; b. Pampa, Tex., July 18, 1929; s. Frank M. and Ruth (Ingersoll) P.; m. Patricia Carberry Bowen; children: Sally, Jett Perry Pemrick, Susan Jeanne Perry Bynder, Virginia Anne Perry Haynie, Tobe Jackson Perry. BS in Petroleum Engring., U. Tulsa, 1952. Registered profl. engr., Tex. Engr. Stanolind Oil & Gas Co., Oklahoma City, 1952-53, Parker Drilling Co., Tulsa, 1953-54; drilling engr. Holm Drilling Co., Tulsa, 1954-55; drilling mgr. Mobil Oil, Victoria, Tex., Lake Charles, La., Paris, France, Anaco, Venezuela, N.Y.C., Tehran, Iran, Stavanger, Norway, New Orleans, La., 1955-79; exec. v.p. Loffland Bros. Co., Tulsa, 1979-89; pres., CEO Gas Well Properties, Inc., Dallas, 1989—; pres. George Perry Farms, Tunica, Miss., 1989—. Mem. Delta Tau Delta. Office: Gas Well Properties 5995 Summerside Dr PO Box 795302 Dallas TX 75379

PERRY, HAROLD OTTO, dermatologist; b. Rochester, Minn., Nov. 18, 1921; s. Oliver and Hedwig Clara (Tornow) P.; m. Loraine Thelma Moehnke, Aug. 27, 1944; children—Preston, Oliver, Ann, John. AA, Rochester Jr. Coll., 1942; BS, U. Minn., 1944, MB, 1946, MD, 1947; MS, Mayo Grad. Sch. Medicine, 1953. Diplomate Am. Bd. Dermatology with spl. competence in dermatopathology (mem. bd. 1979-90, v.p. 1989, pres. 1990). Intern Naval Hosp., Oakland, Calif., 1946-47; resident in dermatology Mayo Grad. Sch. Medicine, 1949-52; practice medicine specializing in dermatology Rochester, 1953-86; mem. staff Mayo Clinic, 1953-86, mem. emeritus staff, 1987—; instr., asst. prof., assoc. prof. Mayo Med. Sch., 1953-86, prof., 1978-83, Robert H. Kieckhefer prof. dermatology, 1978-83, head dept. dermatology, 1975-83, emeritus prof. dermatology, 1987—; civilian cons. dermatology to surgeon gen. USAF, 1979—. Contbr. articles to med. jours. and, chpts. to books. With USNR, 1943-45, 46-49. Mem. AMA, Am. Acad. Dermatology (pres. 1981, Sulzberger internat. lectr. 1986), Am. Dermatol. Assn. (bd. dirs. 1985-89, pres. 1989-90), Noah Worcester Dermatol. Soc. (pres. 1969), Minn. Dermatol. Soc. (pres. 1967), Chgo. Dermatol. Soc., Internat. Soc. Tropical Dermatology, Minn. Med. Assn.; hon. mem. French Dermatol. Soc., Spanish Acad. Dermatology, Brazilian Dermatol. Soc., Ga. Dermatol. Soc., Iowa Dermatol. Soc., Korean Dermatol. Soc., Bolivar Soc. Dermatology, Jacksonville Dermatol. Soc., N.Am. Clin. Dermatol. Soc. Home: 3625 SW Bamber Valley Rd Rochester MN 55902 Office: Mayo Clinic Rochester MN 55905

PERRY, I. CHET, petroleum company executive; b. Phila., Jan. 18, 1943; s. Irving Chester Sr. and Erma Jackson (McNeil) P.; 1 child, London Schade. BA in Psychology, Bus., Lake Forest Coll., 1965. Lic. real estate broker, Ill. Sr. mgmt. trainee British Overseas Airways Corp., London, Eng., 1968-69; owner Itec Internat. Ltd., Barrington, Ill., 1970—; owner Itec Refining & Mktg. Co., Ill., Barrington, 1970—, CEO, mng. dir., 1986—. Lt. U.S. Army, 1965-68, Vietnam. Decorated Bronze Star, Purple Heart. Mem. Am. Petroleum Inst., Barrington Bd. Realtors (bd. dirs. 1974-78) Forest Grove Club, Barrington Tennis Club. Republican. Quaker. Avocations: tennis, photography. Home: 444 W Russell St Barrington IL 60010-4123

PERRY, J. WARREN, health sciences educator, administrator; b. Richmond, Ind., Oct. 25, 1921; s. Charles Thomas and Zona M. (Ohler) P. BA, DePauw U., 1944; postgrad., Harvard U., 1948-49; MA, Northwestern U., 1952, PhD, 1955; DSc (hon.), D'Youville Coll., 1990. Instr. St. John's Mil. Acad., Delafield, Wis., 1944-47; counselor, asst. prof. psychology U. Ill.-Chgo., 1953-56; dir. prosthetic-orthotic edn., asst. prof. orthopaedic surgery Northwestern U. Med. Sch., 1957-61; lectr. psychology U. Chgo., 1957-61; asst. chief div. tng. Vocat. Rehab. Adminstrn., HEW, 1961-64, dep. asst. commr. research and tng., 1964-66; prof. health scis. adminstrn. SUNY-Buffalo, 1966-85, founding dean, 1966-77, dean and prof. emeritus, 1985—; Mary E. Switzer Meml. lectr. Dallas, 1977, Lexington, 1991; mem. Task Force for Legis. for Allied Health Professions; mem. com. edn. allied health professions and services, council med. edn. AMA, 1968-73; mem. nat. adv. com. Am. Dietetic Assn., 1970-75, chmn., 1972-75; mem. nat. rev. com., regional med. programs HEW, 1969-72; mem. Inst. Medicine, Nat. Acad. Scis., 1973—, mem. steering com. on manpower policy for primary care, mem. Bd. Health Promotion and Disease Prevention, 1981-83, sr. advisor, com. to study the role of allied health, com. to study med. manpower in VA, 1988-91; mem. spl. med. adv. com. VA, 1974-77; mem. task force on manpower for prevention Fogarty Internat. Inst., NIH, 1975-76; mem. acad. planning com. Mass. Gen. Hosp., 1978-80. Founding editor: Jour. Allied Health, 1972-78, editor emeritus, 1985—; contbr. articles to profl. jours. Bd. dirs. Lyric Opera Guild, Chgo., 1957-61, dir. com. opera edn., 1957-61; chmn. acad. divsn. dir., coun. trustees Buffalo Philharm. Orch., 1987-93; bd. dirs. Goodwill Industries Buffalo, 1966-76; trustee Comty. Music Sch. Buffalo, 1977-80; mem. adv. bd., v.p. Sisters of Charity Hosp., Buffalo, 1969-87, pres., 1986-88; bd. visitors U. Pitts., 1977-80; mem. coun. trustees D'Youville Coll., Buffalo, 1978-88, trustee emeritus, 1989—; bd. dirs. Am. Lung Assn. of Western N.Y., 1975-92, pres., 1983; bd. dirs. Am. Lung Assn. of N.Y.

State, 1981-85, exec. com., 1989-92; bd. dirs. ARC of Greater Buffalo, Artpark State Performing Arts Ctr., Lewiston, N.Y., 1986—; chmn. N.Y. State Coalition of Smoking or Health, Albany, N.Y., 1987-91; trustee Theodore Roosevelt Inaugural Site Found., 1987, pres., 1991-94; bd. advisors Buffalo Coun. on World Affairs, 1987-88; trustee Buffalo Opera Co., 1989-94, chmn. opera adv. coun., 1995—. Recipient Sustained Superior Svc. award HEW, 1965, Disting. Svc. award Am. Orthotics-Prosthetics Assn., 1966, Chancellor's award for adminstrv. svc. SUNY, 1977, Disting Author award Jour. Allied Health, 1978, Cert. of Merit AMA, 1979, 1st Allied Health Leadership award SUNY Stony Brook, 1988, Outstanding Individual Philantropist Nat. Soc. of Fund Raising Execs. of Western, N.Y., 1992, Pres. Circle PIN, Buffalo State Coll., 1993, 50th Anniversary Alumni Citation De Pauw Univ., 1994, Brotherhood/Sisterhood award in health NCCJ of Western N.Y., 1995; named Ky. Col., 1969, Nebr. adm., 1964; J. Warren Perry Disting. Author award given in his honor, Jour. Allied Health, 1984—; J. Warren Perry Meml. lecture given in his honor, SUNY-Buffalo, 1990—; Perry Scholarships presented in his honor, U. Buffalo Found., 1991—; J. Warren Perry Outstanding Vol. Leadership award named in his honor, western N.Y. chpt. ALA, 1994—. Fellow Assn. Schs. of Allied Health Professions (pres. 1969-70, cert. of merit 1977, Pres.'s award 1978, Honors of Society 1984); mem. APA, Am. Dietetics Assn. (hon.), Am. Personnel and Guidance Assn., Nat. Rehab. Assn., Phi Beta Kappa, Phi Delta Kappa (pres. 1955), Delta Tau Delta.

PERRY, JACQUELIN, orthopedic surgeon; b. Denver, May 31, 1918; d. John F. and Tirzah (Kuruptkat) P. B.E., U. Calif., Los Angeles, 1940; M.D., U. Calif., San Francisco, 1950. Intern Children's Hosp., San Francisco, 1950-57; resident in orthopedic surgery U. Calif., San Francisco, 1951-55; orthopedic surgeon Rancho Los Amigos Hosp., Downey, Calif., 1955—; chief pathokinesiology Rancho Los Amigos Med. Ctr., 1961—; chief stroke service Rancho Los Amigos Hosp., 1972-75; mem. faculty U. Calif. Med. Sch., San Francisco, 1966—; clin. prof. U. Calif. Med. Sch., 1973—; mem. faculty U. So. Calif. Med. Sch., 1969—, prof. orthopedic surgery, 1972—, dir. polio and gait clinic, 1972—; Disting. lectr. for hosp. for spl. surgery and Cornell U. Med. Coll., N.Y.C., 1977-78; Packard Meml. lectr. U. Colo. Med. Sch., 1970; Osgood lectr. Harvard Med. Sch., 1978; Summer lectr., Portland, 1977; Shands lectr.; cons. USAF; guest speaker symposia; cons. Biomechanics Lab. Centinela Hosp., 1979—. Served as phys. therapist U.S. Army, 1941-46. Recipient Disting. Svc. award Calif. Rehab. Facilities,1981, Pres.'s award, 1984, Milton Cohen award Nat. Assn. Rehab., 1993, Isabelle and Lenard Goldensen award for tech. United Cerebral Palsy Assn., 1981, Jow Dowling award, 1985, Profl. Achievement award UCLA, 1988, Armistad award Rancho Los Amigos Med. Ctr., Calif., 1990; named Woman of Yr. for Medicine in So. Calif., L.A. Times, 1959, Alumnus of Yr., U. Calif. Med. Sch., 1980, Physician of Yr. Calif. Employment Devel. Dept. 1994. Mem. AMA, Am. Acad. Orthop. Surgeons (Kappa Delta award for rsch. 1977), Am. Orthop. Assn. (Shands lectr. 1988), Western Orthop. Assn., Calif. Med. Soc., L.A. County Med. Soc., Am. Phys. Therapy Assn. (hon. Golden Pen award 1965), Am. Acad. Orthotists and Prosthetists (hon.), Scoliosis Rsch. Soc., LeRoy Abbott Soc., Am. Acad. Cerebral Palsy. Home: 12319 Brock Ave Downey CA 90242-3503 Office: Rancho Los Amigos Med Ctr 7601 Imperial Hwy Downey CA 90242-3456

PERRY, JAMES ALFRED, natural resources and policy management educator, researcher, consultant; b. Dallas, Sept. 27, 1945. BA in Fisheries, Colo. State U., 1968; MA, Western State Coll., 1973; PhD, Idaho State U., 1981. Sr. water quality specialist Idaho Div. Environ., Pocatello, 1974-82; area mgr. Centrac Assocs., Salt Lake City, 1982; prof. forest water quality U. Minn., St. Paul, 1982—, dir. natural resources policy and mgmt., 1985—, dir. grad. studies and water resources, 1988-92; dep. dir. AID-funded Environ. Tng. Project for Ctrl. and Ea. Europe, 1992—; vis. scholar Oxford U., Green College, Eng., 1990-91; internat. cons. in water quality. Charter mem. Leadership Devel. Acad., Lakewood, Minn., 1988. ACOP/ESCOP nat. leadership fellow, 1985-86. Mem. Minn. Acad. Scis. (bd. dirs. 1987-90), N.Am. Benthol Soc. (exec. bd. Albuquerque 1990-91), Soc. Am. Foresters, Sigma Xi, Xi Sigma Pi, Gamma Sigma Delta. Office: U Minn Dept Forest Resource 110 Green Hall 1530 Cleveland Ave N Saint Paul MN 55108-1027

PERRY, JAMES FREDERIC, philosophy educator, author; b. Washington, Jan. 21, 1936; s. Albert Walter and Helene Anna Maria (Neumeyer) P.; m. Sandra Jean Huizing, Feb. 18, 1957 (div. May 1972); children: Sandra Elaine, James Frederic Jr., Bartholomew; m. Roberta Schofield, June 6, 1984. Student, Princeton U., 1953-56, Marietta (Ohio) Coll., 1958-60; BA with honors in Philosophy, Ind. U., 1962, PhD in Philosophy of Edn., 1972. NDEA fellow in philosophy U. N.C., 1962-65; instr. N.C. State U., Raleigh, 1965-66; Univ. fellow Ind. U., 1971; adj. lectr. Ind. U., Bloomington, 1972-75; prof. philosophy Hillsborough Community Coll., Tampa, Fla., 1975—. Author: Random, Routine, Reflective, 1989; contbr. articles to profl. jours. Precinct committeeman Dem. Party, Tampa, 1988—. Nat. Def. Edn. Act fellow U. N.C., 1962-65, Univ. fellow Ind. U., 1970-71. Mem. AAUP (pres. Fla. conf. 1986-89, chair com. "A" on acad. freedom 1989—), C.C. Humanities Assn. (sec. divsn. exec. bd. 1981-89), Internat. Soc. Philos. Enquiry, Internat. Congress for Critical Thinking and Moral Critique (founding mem. S.E. coun. 1991), Soc. for Values in Higher Edn., Princeton Alumni Assn. of Fla. Suncoast (sec. 1983-86, pres. 1986—), Mensa, Authors Guild, Textbook Authors Assn. Avocations: travel, foreign travel, genealogy, commercial piloting, flight instruction. Office: Hillsborough C C PO Box 10561 Tampa FL 33679-0561

PERRY, JAMES R., construction company executive; b. 1936. With Great Lakes Dredge & Dock & Co., Ohio, 1958-67; various positions to exec. v.p. Hawaiian Dredging Constrn. Co., Honolulu, 1967-89; pres. Dillingham Constrn. Pacific Ltd., Honolulu, 1989-93; pres., CEO Dillingham Constrn. Pacific Ltd., Pleasanton, Calif., 1993—. Office: Dillingham Constrn Corp 5960 Inglewood Dr Pleasanton CA 94588

PERRY, JEAN LOUISE, dean; b. Richland, Wash., May 13, 1950; d. Russell S. and Sue W. Perry. BS, Miami U., Oxford, Ohio, 1972; MS, U. Ill., Urbana, 1973, PhD, 1976. Cons. ednl. placement office U. Ill., 1973-75; adminstrv. intern Coll. Applied Life Studies, 1975-76, asst. dean, 1976-77, assoc. dean, 1978-81, asst. prof. dept. phys. edn., 1976-81; assoc. prof. phys. edn. San Francisco State U., 1981-84, prof., 1984-90, chair, 1981-90; dean Coll. of Human and Community Scis. U. Nev., Reno, 1990—. Named to excellent tchr. list U. Ill., 1973-79. Mem. AAHPERD (fellow research consortium, pres. 1988-89), Am. Assn. Higher Edn., Am. Ednl. Research Assn., Nat. Assn. Phys. Edn. in Higher Edn., Nat. Assn. Girls and Women in Sports (guide coordinator, pres.), Delta Psi Kappa, Phi Delta Kappa. Home: 3713 Ranchview Ct Reno NV 89509-7437 Office: U Nev Coll Human and Cmty Scis/136 Reno NV 89557

PERRY, JESSE LAURENCE, JR., investment manager, financier; b. Nashville, Oct. 15, 1919; s. Jesse Laurence and Mamie Lucretia (White) P.; m. Susan Taylor White, Nov. 5, 1949 (dec. Mar. 1972); children: Robert Laurance, Judith Foulds; m. 2d Sarah Kinkead Stockell, Apr. 6, 1974. BA magna cum laude, Vanderbilt U., 1941; MBA, Harvard U., 1943; postgrad. in edn. retarded children George Peabody Coll., summer 1953. Treas., J.L. Perry Co., Nashville, 1947-48; v.p., 1949-54, pres., 1954-73, also dir.; pres., chmn. bd. Perry Enterprises, Nashville, 1973-80, pres., Naples, Fla., 1980—; 1st So. Savs. & Loan, Inc., 1973-80; pres. PortersField, Inc., Nashville, 1973-80, The Jelpee Co., Naples, Fla., 1980—; pres., Police Assistance League, 1973-74; hon. col., Staff Gov. Tenn., 1962-74; 1st v.p. Tenn. Assn. for Retarded Children, 1954-62; mem. Tenn. Mental Retardation Adv. Coun., 1966-72; bd. advisers Salvation Army, 1958-72 (founder, sec. Tenn. Bot. Garden and Fine Arts Ctr., 1958—; chmn. 5th dist. Republican Exec. Com. 1950-54; vice chmn. Tenn. Rep. Exec. Com., 1950-54; Middle Tenn. Campaign mgr., 1956, 60, 66; state mgr. Pub. Service Com. Campaign, 1964; mem. spl. com. on urban devel. Rep. Nat. Exec. Com., 1962; del. Rep. Nat. Exec. Com., 1960, vice chmn. Tenn. del., 1960, alt. del., 1968; dist. mem. Rep. State Exec. Com., 1954-75; state chmn. Rep. Capitol Club, 1971-73; state Rep. commitment, 1956-74; bd. govs. U. South, Sewanee Acad., 1968-74; trustee Task Force for the Homeless, Naples, St. Matthew's House for Homeless, Naples; bd. dirs. Substance Abuse Ministry, Naples. Served to capt. AUS, 1943-46. Decorated knight Hospitaller Order St. John Jerusalem, chevalier Ordo Constantini Magni knight (comdr.) Order Temple of Jerusalem. Mem. Episc. Churchmen Tenn. (v.p. 1956), Am. Ch. Union (v.p. 1958), SAR (chpt. pres. 1977-79), U.S. C. of C., Nat. Office Mgmt. Assn.

(pres. Nashville chpt. 1958-59), Am. Legion, English Speaking Union, Magna Charta Barons, Baronial Order Magna Charta, Gen. Soc. Colonial Wars, Ams. of Royal Descent, Plantagenet Soc., Order Crown Charlemagne, Order of Three Crusades, Phi Beta Kappa, Omicron Delta Gamma, Pi Kappa Alpha. Clubs: Nashville Exchange, Nashville Sewanee, Nashville City, Capitol Hill (Washington), Naples Harvard, Royal Poinciana Golf (Naples), Naples Yacht. Office: Perry Enterprises PO Box 915 Naples FL 33939-0915

PERRY, JOE, guitarist; b. Boston, Sept. 10, 1950. With Aerosmith, 1970-80, 84—, The Joe Perry Project, 1980-84. Albums: (with Aerosmith) Aerosmith, 1973, Get Your Wings, 1974, Toys in the Attic, 1975, Rocks, 1976, Pure Gold, 1976, Draw the Line, 1977, Live Bootleg, 1978, A Night in the Ruts, 1979, Greatest Hits, 1980, Rock in a Hard Place, 1982, Done with Mirrors, 1986, Classics Live, 1986, Permanent Vacation, 1987, Gems, 1989, Pump, 1989, Pandora's Box, 1991, Get a Grip, 1993, Big Ones, 1994, Box of Fire, 1994; (with Joe Perry Project) I've Got the Rock n' Rolls Again, Let the Music Do the Talking. Recipient (with Aerosmith) Grammy award Best Rock Group, 1994. Office: c/o Aerosmith Geffen/DGC Records 9130 Sunset Blvd Los Angeles CA 90069*

PERRY, JOHN RICHARD, philosophy educator; b. Lincoln, Nebr., Jan. 16, 1943; s. Ralph Robert and Ann (Roscow) P.; m. Louise Elizabeth French, Mar. 31, 1962; children: James Merton, Sarah Louise, Joseph Glenn. BA, Doane Coll., Crete, Nebr., 1964; PhD, Cornell U., Ithaca, N.Y., 1968; DLitt (hon.), Doane Coll., 1982. Asst. prof. philosophy UCLA, 1968-72; vis. asst. prof. U. Mich., Ann Arbor, 1971-72; assoc. prof. UCLA, 1972-74, Stanford (Calif.) U., 1974-77; prof. Stanford U., 1977-85, Henry Waldgrave Stuart prof., 1985—, chmn. dept. philosophy, 1976-82, dir. ctr. study lang. and info., 1985-86, 93—, resident fellow Soto House, 1985-91. Author: Dialogue on Identity and Immortality, 1978, (with Jon Barwise) Situations and Attitudes, 1983, The Problem of the Essential Indexical, 1993. Pres. Santa Monica Dem. Club, Calif., 1972-74. Woodrow Wilson fellow, 1964-65, Danforth fellow, 1964-68, Guggenheim fellow, 1975-76, NEH fellow, 1980-81. Mem. Am. Philos. Assn. (v.p. Pacific divsn. 1992-93, pres. 1993-94). Office: Stanford U Ctr Study Language & Information Stanford CA 94305

PERRY, KENNETH WALTER, integrated oil company executive; b. Shamrock, Tex., Feb. 24, 1932; s. Charles Bowman and Sunshine Virginia (Grady) P.; m. Mary Dean Sudderth, Aug. 28, 1953; children: Mary Martha Perry Mitchell, Kathryn Virginia. BSME, U. Okla., 1954. Sales engr. Mid-Continent Oil Well Supply Co., 1954-55; with Cosden Oil & Chem. Co., Big Spring, Tex., from 1957, jr. engr., 1957-59, project engr., 1959-60, chem. salesman, 1960-64, chem. products mgr., 1964-65, mktg. mgr., then v.p. mktg., 1965-69, v.p. chems., 1969-72, sr. v.p., 1972-76, pres., from 1976; group v.p. Am. Petrofina, Inc., Dallas, 1976-85, sr. v.p., 1985-86, pres., CEO, 1986-88, vice chmn., bd. dirs., 1989-92; CEO Nimir Petroleum Co. Ltd., Dallas, 1992—; chmn. bd. dirs. United Commerce Bank, Highland Village, Tex., 1989-92, CEO, 1990-91. Mem. bd. govs. Dallas Symphony Orch., 1987-93; bd. dirs. Dallas Coun. World Affairs, 1980; mem. engring. com. U. Okla. Aerospace, Nuclear, 1982; bd. dirs. Colo. Mcpl. Water Dist., 1972; bd. visitors Coll. Engring., U. Okla., 1990—. 1st lt. USASC, 1955-57. Mem. Am. Petroleum Inst. (bd. dirs. 1986-90), Nat. Petroleum Coun., Nat. Petroleum Refiners Assn. (chmn. petrochem. com. 1984-87), Ctr. Strategic and Internat. Studies, 25-Yr. Clubs, Petroleum Industry Club, Petrochem. Industry Club, Northwood Club, Dallas Petroleum Club. Office: Nimir Petroleum Co Ltd 5956 Sherry Ln Ste 801 Dallas TX 75225-8019

PERRY, KENNETH WILBUR, accounting educator; b. Lawrenceburg, Ky., May 21, 1919; s. Ollie Townsend and Minnie (Monroe) P.; m. Shirley Jane Kimball, Sept. 5, 1942; 1 dau., Constance June (Mrs. Linden Warfel). B.S., Eastern Ky. U., 1942; M.S., Ohio U., 1949; Ph.D., U. Ill., 1953; LL.D., Eastern Ky. U., 1983. C.P.A., Ill. Instr. Berea Coll., 1949-50, U. Ky., summer 1950; teaching asst. U. Ill. at Champaign, 1950-53, asst. prof. accounting, 1953-55, assoc. prof., 1955-58, prof., 1958—, Alexander Grant prof., 1975—; vis. prof. Northeastern U., summer 1966, Parsons Coll., 1966-67, Fla. A. and M. U., fall 1971; Carman G. Blough prof. U. Va., fall 1975; dir. Illini Pub. Co. Author: Accounting: An Introduction, 1971, Passing the C.P.A. Examination, 1964, (with N. Bedford and A. Wyatt) Advanced Accounting, 1960; contbg. author: Complete Guide to a Profitable Accounting Practice, 1965, C.P.A. Review Manual, 1971; Editor: The Ill. C.P.A. 1968-70; contbg. editor: Accountants' Cost Handbook, 1960. Served to maj. AUS, 1942-46; col. Res. ret. Named outstanding alumnus Eastern Ky. U., 1969. Mem. Am. Accounting Assn. (v.p. 1963, Outstanding Educator award 1974), Am. Inst. C.P.A.'s, Am. Statis. Assn., Nat. Assn. Accountants (dir. 1969-71), Ill. Soc. C.P.A.s (chair in accountancy), Beta Alpha Psi, Beta Gamma Sigma (Outstanding scholar 1977-78), Omicron Delta Kappa. Methodist. Home: 2314 Fields South Dr Champaign IL 61821-9302 Office: Commerce W U Ill Champaign IL 61820

PERRY, L. TOM, church official, merchant. Mem. Quorum of the Twelve, The Ch. of Jesus Christ of LDS, Salt Lake City; chmn. ZCMI, Salt Lake City. Office: LDS Ch 50 E North Temple Salt Lake City UT 84150

PERRY, LEWIS CHARLES, emergency medicine physician, osteopath; b. La Plata, Mo., Apr. 22, 1931; s. Lewis C. and Emily B. Perry; m. M. Sheryl Gupton, Oct. 30, 1953; children: David, Susan, Stephen, John. BS, U. Mo. 1958; postgrad., Louisville Presbyn. Sem., 1958-60; DO, Kirksville Coll. Osteo. Medicine, 1967. Intern Midcities Meml. Hosp., Arlington, Tex.; parish min. Presbyn. Bd. Nat. Missions, Canada, Ky., 1960-62; intern Mid Cities Meml. Hosp., Arlington; pvt. practice, Ingleside, Tex., 1968-72, Tucson, 1972-81; emergency physician Tucson Gen. Hosp., 1981-88, pres. med. staff, 1978-79, clin. instr., 1981-88; emergency physician Meml. Med. Ctr. East Tex., Lufkin, 1988—; clin. instr. Osteo. Coll. Pacific, Pomona, Calif., 1985-88. Pres. Helping Hands, Ingleside, 1969-72; bd. dirs., pres. Salvation Army, Tucson, 1978-81; commr. Cub Scouts Am., Tucson, 1975-76; bd. dirs. Unity of Tucson, Inc., 1986-88; pres. bd. dirs. Unity of Nacogdoches 1993-94. 1st lt. USAF, 1952-56. Named Physician of Yr., Tucson Gen. Hosp., 1978. Mem. Am. Legion, Rotary, Masons, Scottish Rite Shrine. Avocations: cooking, gardening. Home: 1 Columbia Ct Lufkin TX 75901-7212

PERRY, LEWIS CURTIS, historian, educator; b. Somerville, Mass., Nov. 21, 1938; s. Albert Quillen and Irene (Lewis) P.; m. Ruth Opler, June 5, 1962 (div. 1970); 1 child, Curtis Allen; m. Elisabeth Israels, Nov. 26, 1970; children: Susanna Irene, David Mordecai. A.B., Oberlin Coll., 1960; M.S., Cornell U., Ithaca, N.Y., 1964; Ph.D., Cornell U., 1967. Asst. prof. history SUNY, Buffalo, 1966-72; assoc. prof., 1972-78; prof. Ind. U. Bloomington, 1978-84; Andrew Jackson prof. history, dir. Am. studies Vanderbilt U., 1984—, dir. Am. Studies, 1992-95; Ampart lectr. U.S. Info. Service, India and Nepal, 1986, France, 1989; vis. prof. U. Leeds, 1988-89; vis. Raoul Wallenberg fellow Rutgers U., 1991-92. Author: Radical Abolitionism 1973, reissue, 1995, Childhood, Marriage, and Reform, 1980, Intellectual Life in America, 1984, Boats Against the Current, 1993; co-author: Patterns of Anarchy, 1966, Antislavery Reconsidered, 1979; editor: Jour. Am. History, 1978-84. Pres. Unitarian-Universalist Ch., Bloomington, 1983-84. N.Y. State Regents fellow, 1965-66, Am. Council Learned Socs. fellow, 1972-73, Nat. Humanities Inst. fellow, 1975-76, John Simon Guggenheim Found. fellow, 1981, NEH fellow, 1987-88. Mem. Orgn. Am. Historians (editor 1978-84), Am. Hist. Assn., Am. Studies Assn., Soc. Historians Early Am. Republic. Home: 3000 Hillsboro Pike No 73 Nashville TN 37215-1323 Office: Vanderbilt U PO Box 95B Nashville TN 37202-0095

PERRY, LOUIS BARNES, retired insurance company executive; b. Los Angeles, Mar. 4, 1918; s. Louis Henry and Julia (Stoddard) P.; m. Genevieve Patterson, Feb. 8, 1942; children: Robert Barnes, Barbara Ann, Donna Lou. B.A., UCLA, 1938, M.A. 1940, Ph.D., 1950; fellow in econs., Yale U., 1941; LL.D., Pacific U., 1964; L.H.D., Whitman Coll., 1967, Linfield Coll., 1981; D.C.S., Willamette U., 1977. Teaching asst. UCLA, 1940-41, research teaching asst., 1944-46; faculty Pomona Coll., 1947-55, asst. to pres., 1955-57, prof. econs., 1957-59; pres. Whitman Coll., Walla Walla, Wash., 1959-67; v.p., treas. Standard Ins. Co., Portland, Oreg., 1967-68; exec. v.p. Standard Ins. Co., 1968-71, pres., 1972-83, chmn., 1983-85, also bd. dirs.; investment counselor, broker Wagenseller & Durst, L.A., 1951-59; rsch. coord. So. Calif. Rsch. Coun., 1952-54; cons. Carnegie Survey Bus.

Edn., 1957-58. Author: (with others) Our Needy Aged, 1954, A History of the Los Angeles Labor Movement, 1963; Contbr. (with others) articles to profl. jours. Mem. Oreg. Bd. Higher Edn., 1975-87, pres., 1975-80. Served to maj. AUS, World War II; lt. col. Res. Mem. Am. Coll. Life Underwriters (trustee 1972-81), Rotary, Phi Beta Kappa, Beta Gamma Sigma, Phi Delta Kappa, Pi Gamma Mu, Alpha Gamma Omega, Artus. Methodist. Home: 1585 Gray Lynn Dr Walla Walla WA 99362-9282 *In looking back over the years, an unspoken and oftentime subliminal guiding principle has been to reach beyond one's realistic grasp. This concept coupled with an interest in treating others as one would like to be treated has made it possible to react to new challenges. Successfully meeting the latter has provided a varied career in a number of different fields of activity.*

PERRY, LUKE (COY LUTHER PERRY, III), actor; b. Fredericktown, Ohio, Oct. 11, 1966; s. Coy Sr. and Ann Perry; m. Minnie Sharp, Nov. 18, 1993. Appeared in TV series Loving, 1987, Another World, 1989, Beverly Hills, 90210, 1990—; appeared in films Terminal Bliss, 1992, Buffy the Vampire Slayer, 1992, The Webbers, 1993, 8 Seconds, 1994. Office: CAA 9830 Wilshire Blvd Beverly Hills CA 90212*

PERRY, MALCOLM BLYTHE, biologist; b. Birkenhead, Cheshire, Eng., Apr. 26, 1930; s. Cyril A. and Hilda (Blythe) P.; m. Eileen M. Perry, Aug. 10, 1956 (dec. 1981); children: Sara Jane, Judith Anne. B.Sc., U. Bristol, Eng., 1953; Ph.D., U. Bristol, 1956, D.Sc., 1969. Banting research fellow Queen's U., Kingston, Ont., Can., 1955; asst. prof. Queen's U., 1956-60, R.S. McLaughlin research prof., 1960-62; sr. research officer Nat. Research Council, Ottawa, Ont., 1962-81; prin. research officer Nat. Research Council, 1981—; scientist U. Cambridge, Eng., 1969, U. Paris, 1979; prof. U. Ottawa, 1982. Contbr. articles to profl. jours. Fellow Royal Soc. Can., Royal Inst. Chemistry; mem. Can. Soc. Microbiology (award 1991), Am. Soc. Microbiology. Home: 769 Hemlock Rd, Ottawa, ON Canada K1K 0K6 Office: NRC, 100 Sussex Dr, Ottawa, ON Canada K1A 0R6

PERRY, MALCOLM OLIVER, vascular surgeon; b. Allen, Tex., Sept. 3, 1929. BA, U. Tex., 1951; MD, U. Tex., Dallas, 1955. Diplomate Am. Bd. Surgery, Am. Bd. Gen. Vascular Surgery. Intern Letterman Army Hosp., San Francisco, 1955-56; resident in surgery Parkland Meml. Hosp., Dallas, 1958-62; fellow in vascular surgery U. Calif., San Francisco, 1962-63; asst. prof. surgery U. Tex., Dallas, 1962-67, assoc. prof. surgery, chief vascular surgery, 1967-71, prof. surgery, chief vascular surgery, 1971-74; prof. surgery U. Wash., Seattle, 1974-77; prof. surgery, chief vascular surgery Cornell U. Med. Coll., 1977-87, Vanderbilt U. Sch. Medicine, Nashville, 1987-91; chief vascular surgery Tex. Tech U. Health Scis. Ctr., Lubbock, 1991—. Capt. USAF, 1955-58; major Tex. Air N.G., 1960-66. Office: Tex Tech U Health Scis Ctr Dept Surgery 3601 4th St Lubbock TX 79430-0002

PERRY, MARGARET, librarian, writer; b. Cin., Nov. 15, 1933; d. Rufus Patterson and Elizabeth Munford (Anthony) P. AB, Western Mich. U., 1954; Cert. d'etudes Francaises, U. Paris, 1956; MSLS, Cath. U. Am., 1959. Young adult and reference librarian N.Y. Pub. Library, N.Y.C., 1954-55, 57-58; librarian U.S. Army, France and Germany, 1959-63, 64-67; chief circulation U.S. Mil. Acad. Library, West Point, N.Y., 1967-70; head info. library U. Rochester, N.Y., 1970-75, asst. prof., 1973-75, assoc. prof., 1975-82, asst. dir. libraries for reader services, 1975-82, acting dir. libraries, 1976-77, 80; univ. libr. Valparaiso U., Ind., 1982-93; ret., 1993; mem. Task Force on Coop. Edn., Rochester, 1972. Author: A Bio-bibliography of Countee P. Cullen, 1903-1946, 1971, Silence to the Drums: A Survey of the Literature of the Harlem Renaissance, 1976, The Harlem Renaissance, 1982, The Short Fiction of Rudolph Fisher, 1987; also numerous short stories; contbr. articles to profl. jours. Bd. dirs. Urban League, 1978-80. Recipient 1st prize short story contest Armed Forces Writers League, 1966; 2nd prize Frances Steloff Fiction Prize, 1968, 1st prize short story Arts Alive, 1990, 2nd prize short story Willow Rev., 1990; seminar scholar Schloss Leopoldskron, Salzburg, Austria, 1956. Mem. ALA, NOW. Democrat. Roman Catholic. Avocations: violin, collecting book marks, gardening, reading, travel. Home: 15050 Roaring Brook Rd Thompsonville MI 49683

PERRY, MARILYN See WIDNEY, MARILYN EDITH

PERRY, MARSHA GRATZ, legislator, professional skating coach; b. Niagara Falls, N.Y., Dec. 9, 1936; d. William Henry and Margarett Edna (Barr) Gratz; m. Robert X. Perry, Jr., Jan. 28, 1961; children: Robert, Margarett, David. Student, Elmira Coll., 1954-57; BILR, Cornell U., 1959. Coll. recruiter Imont, N.Y.C., 1959-61; skating dir. City of Bowie (Md.), 1971-86; skating coach Benfield Pines Ice Rink, Millerville, Md., 1974—; mem. Md. Ho. of Dels.; mem. Md. Ho. of Dels.; summer hockey & skating coach Washington Capitals, Landover, Md., 1986—; co-dir. Prostart Hockey Programs. Dist. dir., v.p., planning zoning dir. Crofton (Md.) Civic Assn., 1974-86; pres. West County Fedn. Cmty. Assn.; mem. AACO Drug & Alcohol adv. coun.; bd. dirs. Am. Cancer Soc., Am. Heart Assn., YMCA, Md. Hall Creative Arts. Named Citizen of Yr. Crofton Civic Assn., 1986. Mem. Assn. Women Legislators (exec. bd.). Avocations: ice hockey, figure skating, sailing. Home: 1605 Edgerton Pl Crofton MD 21114-1504 Office: MD Ho of Dels State Capital Annapolis MD 21401

PERRY, MATTHEW J., JR., federal judge; b. 1921. BS, S.C. State U., 1948, LLB, 1951. Bar: S.C. Atty. Spartanburg, S.C., 1951-61, Columbia, S.C., 1961-76; judge U.S. Ct. Mil. Appeals, Washington, 1976-79, U.S. Dist. Ct., Columbia, 1979—; instr. law U. S.C., 1973-75. Office: US Dist Ct PO Box 7307 1845 Assembly St Columbia SC 29201-2431

PERRY, MAXINE LEWIS, state official; b. Sterling, Colo., Sept. 13, 1933; d. William Merrill Lewis and Florence Elizabeth Boudreaux; m. Lowell Wesley Perry, Jan. 30, 1956; children: Lowell Wesley Jr., Scott Tyler, Merrideth Lynne. BA in English, Wayne State U., 1960; JD, Detroit Coll. Law, 1980. English and journalism tchr. Detroit Pub. Schs., 1960-74, cons.; 1989; dep. dir. civil host com. Rep. Nat. Conv., Mich., 1980; adminstrv. commr. Mich. Liquor Control Commn., Lansing, 1980-89, chairwoman, 1991—; corporate and found. programs Oakland U., Rochester, Mich., 1989-90; mem. nat. adv. com. SBA, also mem. bus. and econ. devel. com. for Great Lakes Region. Del. to Rep. Nat. Conv., 1980; bd. dirs. Boysville, Boys and Girls Clubs of Am.; mem. coun. Internat. Yr. of the Family, Lansing, 1994. Recipient citation Booker T. Washington Businessmen's Assn., 1980, Comty. award Mich. Grocers Assn., 1980, Market Watch Leaders award, 1994, Mich. State Safety Commn. award, 1994, Recognition award The Century Coun., 1995, Recognition award Mich. Liquor Vendors, 1995. Mem. NAACP (life), Mich. Alcohol Beverage Control Assn. (bd. dirs., pres.-elect 1993-94, pres. 1994—, Recognition award 1995), U. Mich. Pres. Club. Roman Catholic. Home: 29336 E Chanticleer Dr Southfield MI 48034 Office: Mich Liquor Control Commn PO Box 30005 7150 Harris Dr Lansing MI 48909

PERRY, MICHAEL CLINTON, physician, medical educator, academic administrator; b. Wyandotte, Mich., Jan. 27, 1945; s. Clarence Clinton and Hilda Grace (Wigginton) P.; m. Nancy Ann Kaluzny, June 22, 1968; children: Rebecca Carolyn, Katherine Grace. BA, Wayne State U., 1966, MD, 1970; MS in Medicine, U. Minn., 1975. Diplomate Am. Bd. Internal Medicine, Am. Bd. Hematology, Am. Bd. Oncology. Intern in internal medicine Mayo Grad. Sch. Medicine, Rochester, Minn., 1970-71, resident, 1971-72, fellow, 1972-75; instr. Mayo Med. Sch., Rochester, 1974-75; asst. prof. U. Mo., Columbia, 1975-80, assoc. prof., 1980-85, prof., 1985—, chmn. dept. medicine, 1983-91, sr. assoc. dean, 1991-94, Nellie A Smith chair oncology, dir. div. hematology/oncology, 1994—; prin. investigator Cancer and Leukemia Group B, Nat. Cancer Inst., Hanover, N.H., 1982—, exec. com., 1982-84, 1987-90. Author, co-author 30 book chpts.; editor: Toxicity of Chemotherapy, 1984, The Chemotherapy Source Book, 1991, Comprehensive Textbook of Thoracic Oncology, 1995; contbr. articles to profl. jours. Bd. dirs. Am. Cancer Soc., Mo., 1986-90. Recipient Faculty Alumni award U. Mo., Columbia, 1985, Disting. Alumnus award Wayne State U., 1995. Fellow ACP; mem. Am. Soc. Hematology, Am. Soc. Clin. Oncology, Cen. Soc. Clin. Research, Am. Soc. Internal Medicine (Young Internist of Yr. 1981), Sigma Xi, Alpha Omega Alpha. Home: 1112 Pheasant Run Columbia MO 65201-6254 Office: U Mo-Columbia 516 Ellis Fischel Cancer Ctr 115 Business Loop 70 W Columbia MO 65203

PERRY, MICHAEL DEAN, professional football player; b. Aiken, S.C., Aug. 27, 1965. Student, Clemson. Defensive tackle Cleveland Browns, 1988-94, Denver Broncos, 1994—. Voted to Pro Bowl, 1989-91, 93; named defensive tackle The Sporting News All-Pro team, 1989-93. Office: Denver Broncos 13655 Broncos Pkwy Englewood CO 80112*

PERRY, MICHAEL JOHN, law educator; b. 1945. AB, Georgetown U., 1968; JD, Columbia U., 1973. Law clk. to presiding justice U.S. Dist. Ct. N.Y., N.Y.C., 1973-74, U.S. Ct. Appeals (9th cir.), N.Y., 1974-75; asst. prof. Ohio State U., Columbus, 1975-78, assoc. prof., 1978-79, prof., 1979-83; prof. Northwestern U., Evanston, Ill., 1983—. Office: Northwestern Univ Sch Law 357 E Chicago Ave Chicago IL 60611-3008

PERRY, NORMAN ROBERT, priest, magazine editor; b. Cin., Dec. 17, 1929; s. Joseph Sylvester and May Ann (Hafertepe) P. B.A. cum laude, Duns Scotus Coll., 1954. Joined Franciscan Order, Roman Cath. Ch., 1950, ordained priest, 1958. Assoc. pastor St. Clement Ch., St. Bernard, Ohio, 1959-61, St. Therese Ch., Fort Wayne, Ind., 1961-62; tchr. Bishop Luers High Sch., Fort Wayne, Ind., 1961-62; preaching band Franciscan Friars, 1962-66; definitor St. John the Baptist Province, Cin., 1972-75; vicar provincial St. John the Baptist Province, 1975-81; editor St. Anthony Messenger, 1981—; visitator gen. Order of Friars Minor, Commissariat of the Holy Land, Washington, 1980, Acad. Am. Franciscan History, Washington, 1981; mem. office of due process Archdiocesan Adminstrv. Review Bd.; trustee Franciscan Terrace; pro-syndol judge Cin. Archdiocesan Tribunal. Author: Best of the Wiseman, 1981; assoc. editor St. Anthony Messenger, 1966-81. Recipient numerous awards for reporting, editorials, opinion and review writing. Home: St Francis Friary 1615 Vine St Cincinnati OH 45210-1200 Office: St Anthony Messenger 1615 Republic St Cincinnati OH 45210-1298

PERRY, PAUL ALVERSON, utility executive; b. Farwell, Mich., Apr. 19, 1929; s. LaVerne Seneca and Ruth Valeria (McNeal) P.; m. Mildred Mayhew Small, Apr. 13, 1957; children: Patricia Perry Larson, Ruth Perry Watkins, Robert Paul, Donna Jean. B.S.B.A., Central Mich. U., 1952. With Consumers Power Co., Jackson, Mich., 1954-84; asst. sec. Consumers Power Co., 1960-68, sec., 1968-84; sec., dir. Mich. Gas Storage Co., Jackson, 1969-84; dir. No. Mich. Exploration Co.; sec. Plateau Resources Ltd.; sec., dir. Mich. Utility Collection Service Co., Inc. Served with U.S. Army, 1952-54. Mem. Am. Soc. Corp. Secs. Home: 9110 42nd St Pinellas Park FL 34666

PERRY, RALPH BARTON, III, lawyer; b. N.Y.C. Mar. 17, 1936; s. Ralph Barton and Harriet Armington (Seelye) P.; m. Mary Elizabeth Colburn, Sept. 2, 1961; children: Katherine Suzanne, Daniel Berenson. A.B., Harvard U., 1958; LL.B., Stanford U., 1963. Bar: Calif. 1964. Assoc. and mem. Keatinge & Sterling, Los Angeles, 1963-68; mem. firm Graven Perry Block Brody & Qualls, Los Angeles, 1968—. Bd. dirs. Planning and Conservation League, 1968—; v.p. Coalition for Clean Air, pres. 1972-80, 85-88. Served with U.S. Army, 1956-58. Mem. State Bar Calif., ABA (ho. of dels. 1975—), Los Angeles County Bar Assn., Lawyers Club Los Angeles County (gov. 1968-82), Keep Tahoe Blue, Nat. Wildlife Fedn., Internat. Wildlife Fedn., Sierra Club. Home: 296 Redwood Dr Pasadena CA 91105-1339 Office: Graven Perry Block Brody & Qualls 523 W 6th St Ste 1130 Los Angeles CA 90014-1106

PERRY, ROBERT MICHAEL, consulting engineering company executive; b. N.Y.C., Dec. 5, 1931; s. Jerome and Rose P.; m. Frances Diane Gross, Feb. 2, 1957; children:—Karen, David, Janice. B.S.E., U. Mich., 1953; postgrad., Columbia U., 1955-57. Engr. Dames & Moore (Cons. Engrs.), Los Angeles, 1955-60; asso. Dames & Moore (Cons. Engrs.), 1960-65, partner, 1965-75, mng. partner, 1975—, chief fin. officer, 1980—, dir., 1981—; pres., dir. RMP Inc., 1972—. Served with C.E. U.S. Army, 1953-55. Mem. ASCE (dir., chmn. N.Y. sect. 1964-68), Profl. Services Mgmt. Assn. Club: University (Los Angeles). Home: 2736 Via Victoria Palos Verdes Peninsula CA 90274-4478 Office: Dames & Moore Inc 911 Wilshire Blvd Ste 700 Los Angeles CA 90017-3409

PERRY, ROBERT PALESE, molecular biologist, educator; b. Chgo., Jan. 10, 1931; s. Robert John and Gertruda Katherine (Hyman) Palese-Perry; m. Zoila Figueroa, Apr. 28, 1957; children—Rocco, Adele, Monique. B.S., Northwestern U., 1951; Ph.D., U. Chgo., 1956; Docteur Honoris Causa, U. Paris, 1983. Research assoc. Inst. for Cancer Research, Fox Chase Cancer Ctr., Phila., 1960-62, asst. mem., 1962-65, assoc. mem., 1965-69, sr. mem., 1969—; Stanley Reimann chair in rsch. Fox Chase Cancer Ctr., Phila., 1994—; assoc. dir. Inst. for Cancer Research, Fox Chase Cancer Ctr., 1971-74; prof. biophysics U. Pa., Phila., 1973—. Contbr. numerous research articles to profl. jours., 1957—. Guggenheim fellow, 1974; Nat. Acad. scholar USA/USSR Exch. Program, 1987. Mem. Nat. Acad. Scis. (com. on human rights 1979-86), Internat. Cell Rsch. Orgn. (pres. 1983-86), European Molecular Biology Organization. Home: 1088 Bustleton Pike Southampton PA 18966-4608 Office: Inst Cancer Research 7701 Burholme Ave Philadelphia PA 19111-2497

PERRY, ROGER LAWRENCE, printing executive; b. Ironwood, Mich., Apr. 3, 1923; s. Lawrence E. and Bessie (Thompson) P.; m. Ellen Schwandt, June 28, 1947; children: Pamela, Allison. BBA, U. Wis., 1948. V.p. Hamilton Mfg. Co., Two Rivers, Wis., 1949-56; pres., chief exec. officer Perry Printing Co., Waterloo, Wis., 1956-90, ret. Ensign USN, 1942-45. Named to Printing Hall of Fame, 1990; named Printing Industry Exec. of Yr., 1991. Republican. Methodist. Avocations: golf, fishing, guns. Mailing Address: 2081 W Picamaderos Green Valley AZ 85614

PERRY, SEYMOUR MONROE, physician; b. N.Y.C., May 26, 1921; s. Max and Manya (Rosenthal) P.; m. Judith Kaplan, Mar. 18, 1951; children: Grant Matthew, Anne Lisa, David Bennett. BA with honors, UCLA, 1943; MD with honors, U. So. Calif., 1947. Diplomate: Am. Bd. Internal Medicine. Intern LA. County Hosp., 1946-48, resident, 1948-51, mem. staff outpatient dept., 1951; examining physician L.A. Pub. Schs., 1951-52; sr. asst. surgeon Phoenix Indian Gen. Hosp., USPHS, 1952; charge internal medicine USPHS Outpatient Clinic, Washington, 1952-54; fellow hematology UCLA, 1954-55, asst. rsch. physician atomic energy project, 1955-57; asst. prof. medicine, head Hematology Tng. Program, Med. Ctr., 1957-60; instr. medicine Coll. Med. Evangelists, 1951-57; attending specialist internal medicine Wadsworth VA Hosp., Los Angeles, 1958-61; sr. investigator, medicine br. Nat. Cancer Inst., 1961-65, chief medicine br., 1965-68, mem. clin. cancer tng. com., 1966-69, chief human tumor cell biology br., 1968-71, assoc. sci. director clin. trials, 1966-71, assoc. sci. dir. for program planning, div. cancer treatment, 1971-73, dep. dir., 1973-74, acting dir., 1974; spl. asst. to dir. NIH, 1974-78, assoc. dir., 1978-80, acting dep. asst. sec. health (tech.), 1978-79; acting dir. Nat. Ctr. Health Care Tech., OASH, 1978-80, dir., 1980-82; dep. dir. Inst. for Health Policy Analysis Georgetown U. Med. Ctr., Washington, 1983-89, prof. medicine, prof. community and family medicine, 1983—, interim chmn. dept., 1989-90, chmn., 1990-93, dir. Inst. for Health Care Rsch. and Policy; sr. scholar Med. Tech. and Practice Patterns Inst., Washington, 1993—; Med. Tech. Inst., Washington; mem. adv. com. on rsch. and on the therapy of cancer Am. Cancer Soc., 1966-70, adv. com. chemotherapy and hematology, 1975-77, chmn. epidemiology, diagnosis and therapy com., 1971, grantee, 1959-60; mem. adv. com. USPHS, 1961-80; asst. surg. gen., 1980-82; mem. radiation com. NIH, 1963-70, co-chmn., 1971-73; pres. Nat. Blood Club, 1971; chmn. Interagy. Com. on New Therapies for Pain and Discomfort, 1978-80; mem. adv. panel on med. tech. and costs of medicare program Congress of U.S., 1982-84; mem. criteria working group (adjunct) NASA, 1984; cons. Nat. Ctr. Health Svcs. Rsch. and Health Care Tech., DHHS, 1985-90, Nat. Libr. of Medicine, 1985-89, Agy. for Health Care Policy and Rsch, DHHS, 1990—, Hosp. Assn. N.Y. State, 1990-91; mem. procedures rev. com. and profl. adv. panel Blue Cross/Blue Shield Nat. Capitol Area, 1987-93; advisor WHO Programme on Tech. Devel., Assessment and Transfer; mem. sci. com. Catalan office of Tech. Assessment Barcelona, Spain, 1994—. Assoc. editor Internat. Jour. Tech. Assessment in Health Care, 1984—; mem. editl. bd. Jour. Health Care Tech., 1984-87, Health Tech.: Critical Issues for Decision Makers, 1987-90, Courts, Health and the Law, 1990-91. Bd. dirs. NIH Alumni Assn. Decorated comendador Order of Merit, Peru; comendador Order Hipólito Unanue, Peru; Pub. Health Service commendation, 1967; Meritorious Service medal USPHS, 1980. Fellow ACP (adv. com. to gov. Md. on coll. affairs 1969-76, gov. for USPHS and HHS 1980-82, subcom. on clin. efficacy assessment 1982-85, chmn. health and pub. policy com. D.C. met. area 1987—); mem.

APHA, Inst. Medicine of NAS (mem. evaluation panel coun. health care tech. 1987-90, com. on evaluation med. techs. in clin. use 1981-84, chmn. rev. com. on Inst. Medicine Report on Hip Fracture 1990, mem. rev. com. on renal disease 1990, rev. com. on artificial heart 1991), Assn. Health Svcs. Rsch. (health svcs. rsch. adv. com. 1990-93), Assn. Acad. Health Ctrs., Internat. Soc. Tech. Assessment in Health Care (pres. 1985-87, bd. dirs. 1989-95), NIH Alumni Assn. (bd. dirs. 1993—), Cosmos Club. Achievements include elucidation of leukocyte physiology; initiation of the consensus development process and the technology assessment forum method to resolve controversial issues in medical care. Office: Med Tech and Practice Patterns Inst 2121 Wisco Ave Ste 220 Washington DC 20007

PERRY, SPENCE WILLIAM, lawyer; b. Jacksonville, Fla., Mar. 1, 1942; s. Florence McCarthy and Inez (Holtsford) P.; m. Cinda Brandenburg, Aug. 22, 1964 (div.); m. Cinda Brandenburg, Sept. 22, 1990. BA, Harvard U., 1963; JD, Duke U., 1966. Bar: N.H., Mass., D.C. Assoc. Sullivan & Worcester, Boston, 1969-71; planning officer Office of Emergency Preparedness, Washington, 1971-73; gen. counsel SIGMA, Washington, 1973-74; asst. gen. counsel GSA, Washington, 1975-80; dep. dir. regulatory litigation Dept. Energy, Washington, 1980-81; assoc. gen. counsel Fed. Energy Mgmt. Agy., Washington, 1981-85, gen. counsel, 1985-88; sr. policy advisor Fed. Energy Mgmt. Agy., Washington, DC, 1988-93, dep. gen. counsel, 1993—; adj. faculty Indsl. Coll. of Armed Forces, 1985-88. contbr. articles to numerous jours. Comdr. USNR, 1966-90. Office: Fed Emergency Mgmt Agy Office of the Dir 500 C St SW Washington DC 20472-0001

PERRY, TROY D., clergyman, church administrator; divorced; 2 children. Student Midwest Bible Sch.; D in Ministry (hon.), Samaritan Coll.; L.A.; D in Human Svcs., Sierra U., Santa Monica, Calif. Former pastor Ch. of God of Prophecy, Santa Ana, Calif.; founder, moderator Universal Fellowship Met. Community Chs., L.A.; rep. Met. Community Chs. and gay and lesbian rights movement numerous TV shows including 60 Minutes, Phil Donahue, The Mike Douglas Show. Author: The Lord is My Shepherd and Knows I'm Gay, Don't Be Afraid Anymore, 1991, (video) God, Gays & The Gospel: This is Our Story; contbg. editor Is Gay Good? Mem. Los Angeles County Commn. Human Rels. Recipient Humanitarian award ACLU Lesbian and Gay Rights chpt., 1978, Humanitarian award Gay Press Assn. Office: Universal Fellowship Met Comm Chs 5300 Santa Monica Blvd # 304 Los Angeles CA 90029-1196

PERRY, VINCENT ALOYSIUS, corporate executive; b. Weehawken, N.J.; s. Edwin Robert and Florence Loretta (Gutberlet) P.; m. Doris Lucille Wanckel, Dec. 3, 1944 (dec. July 1988); children: Cynthia Jeanne, Bradford Kimball. A.B., NYU, 1948, M.A., 1949. Asst. prof. fin. Lehigh U., Bethlehem, Pa., 1949-51; mgr. econs. and fin. analysis div. Gen. Foods Corp., White Plains, N.Y., 1951-59; v.p., treas. Universal Match Corp., St. Louis, 1959-61; asst. treas. Internat. Paper Co., N.Y.C., 1961-71; v.p., treas. Bangor Punta Corp., Greenwich, Conn., 1971-75; fin. v.p., treas. Ziff-Davis Pub. Co., N.Y.C., 1975-77; sr. v.p. fin. The Viguerie Co., Inc., Falls Church, Va., 1977-79. Treas. Workshop for Bus. Opportunities, N.Y.C., 1969-88. Served to capt. AUS, 1942-46, ETO. Mem. Lambda Chi Alpha. Home: 1301 Mill Hill Rd Southport CT 06490-1041

PERRY, WILLIAM JAMES, mathematical scientist, government official; b. Vandergrift, Pa., Oct. 11, 1927; s. Edward Martin and Mabelle Estelle (Dunlap) P.; m. Leonilla Mary Green, Dec. 29, 1947; children: David Carter, William Wick, Rebecca Lynn, Robin Lee, Mark Lloyd. B.S in Math, Stanford U., 1949, M.S., 1950; Ph.D., Pa. State U., 1957. Instr. math. Pa. State U., 1951-54; sr. mathematician HRB-Singer Co., State College, Pa., 1952-54; dir. electronic def. labs. GTE Sylvania Co., Mountain View, Calif., 1954-64; pres. ESL, Inc., Sunnyvale, Calif., 1964-77; tech. cons. Dept. Def., Washington, 1967-77, under sec. def. for research and engring., 1977-81; mng. dir. Hambrecht & Quist (investment bankers), San Francisco, 1981-85; chmn. Tech. Strategies & Alliances, Menlo Park, Calif., 1985-93; prof., co-dir. Ctr. for Internat. Security and Arms Control Stanford U., 1989-93; appointed Sec. Def. Pentagon, Washington, 1994—. Served with U.S. Army, 1946-47. Recipient Outstanding Civilian Service medal U.S. Army, 1962; Outstanding Civilian Service medal Def. Intelligence Agency, 1977; Disting. Public Service medal Dept. Def., 1980, 81; Medal of Achievement Am. Electronic Assn., 1980; Disting. Service medal NASA, 1981; decorated Knight Comdr.'s Cross of Fed. Republic of Germany, grand officier de l'Ordre National du Merite (France). Fellow Am. Acad. Arts and Scis.; mem. Am. Math. Soc., NAE, Sigma Xi. Home: 14 Wolfe St Alexandria VA 22314 Office: Dept Defense Office of the Secretary Pentagon Washington DC 20301-1000

PERRY, WILLIAM JOSEPH, food processing company executive; b. Sacramento, Calif., Nov. 4, 1930; s. Joseph Nasciemeto and Jennie (Nunez) P.; m. Beverly Ann Styles, Dec. 9, 1956 (div. May 1981); children: Katherine, Bill Jr., Kathleen, Barbara; m. Leslie Z. Blumberg, June 30, 1986. BS, U. Calif., Berkeley, 1953; MBA, U. So. Calif., 1995. Quality control supr. Stokely Van Camp, Oakland, Calif., 1953-54; plant mgr. Safeway Stores, Brookside div., Grandview, Wash., 1954-61, Gallo Winery, Modesto, Calif., 1961-62; gen. mgr. Bocca Bella Olive Assoc., Wallace, Calif., 1962-65; v.p. Early Calif. Ind., L.A., 1965-74, Fairmont Foods, Santa Ana, Calif., 1974-75; pres. Cal Agra Ind., Stockton, Calif., 1975-76; exec. v.p. Food Brokers Internat., L.A., 1976—; pres., co-owner G.F.F., Inc., L.A., 1981—; dir. G.F.F., Inc., L.A., 1981—, Food Brokers, Inc., L.A., 1976—, Cozad & Assoc. Ad Agy., Encino, Calif., 1985-87. Wrestling com., dir. protocol, L.A. Olympic Com., 1981-84. Mem. Nat. Food Brokers Assn., Assn. of Dressings and Sauces, Nat. Juice Processing Assn., Nat. Single Service Assn., Am. Chem. Soc., Westlake Tennis & Swim Club. Republican. Roman Catholic. Avocations: tennis, photography, bicycling, amateur sports associations. Home: 3700 Brigantine Cir Westlake Village CA 91361 Office: GFF Inc 5443 E Washington Blvd Los Angeles CA 90040-2105

PERRYMAN, MARGARET E., hospital executive; b. Sheridan, Wyo., Mar. 15, 1947; d. Ray Eugene and Eileen Juliann Perryman. BA, Carroll Coll., 1969; MBA, U. St. Thomas, 1978. Staff med. technician Children's Hosp. L.A., 1969-70, Porter Hosp., Denver, 1970-71, Denver Children's Hosp. 1971-72; lab. mgr. Mpls. Children's Med. Ctr., 1972-79, dir. support svcs., 1979-85, v.p. adminstrn., 1985-87; pres.; CEO Gillette Children's Hosp., St. Paul, 1987—, also bd. dirs.; bd. dirs. Pathfinder Resources, St. Paul; bd. dirs., pres. Children's Miracle Network, St. Paul, 1987—; adv. com. Met. HealthCare Coun., St. Paul, 1994—. Author: (book chpt.) Clinic Laboratory Management. Bd. dirs. Audubon Ctr., Sandstone, Minn. Mem. Am. Coll. Healthcare Execs., Minn. Club. Avocations: travel, gardening, reading, bicycling. Office: Gillette Children Hosp 200 University Ave E Saint Paul MN 55101-2507

PERSAUD, TRIVEDI VIDHYA NANDAN, anatomy educator, researcher, consultant; b. Port Mourant, Berbice, Guyana, Feb. 19, 1940; arrived in Canada, 1972; s. Ram Nandan and Dew (Raggy) P.; m. Gisela Gerda Zehden, Jan. 29, 1965; children: Indrani Uta and Sunita Heidi (twins), Rainer Narendra. MD, Rostock U., Germany, 1965, DSc, 1974; PhD in Anatomy, U. West Indies, Kingston, Jamaica, 1970. Intern Potsdam, Germany, 1965-66; govtl. med. officer Guyana, 1966-67; lectr., sr. lectr. anatomy dept. U. West Indies, 1967-72; assoc. prof. anatomy dept. U. Man., Winnipeg, 1972-75, prof., 1975—; assoc. prof. ob-gyn., reproductive scis., 1979—, prof. pediatrics and child health, 1989—, prof., chmn./head dept. anatomy, 1977-93, dir. Teratology Rsch. Lab., 1972—; cons. in teratology, Children's Centre, Winnipeg, 1973—; mem. sci. staff Health Scis. Centre, Winnipeg, 1973—. Author: editor 22 med. textbooks, including: Early History of Human Anatomy: From Antiquity to the Beginning of the Modern Era, 1984, (with others) Basic Concepts in Teratology, 1985, Environmental Causes of Human Birth Defects, 1991, (with K.L. Moore) The Developing Human, 5th edit., 1993, Before We Are Born, 4th edit., 1993; contbr. numerous chpts. to books, over 150 articles to profl. jours. Recipient Carveth Jr. Scientist award Can. Assn. Pathologists, 1974, Albert Einstein Centennial medal German Acad. Scis., 1975, Dr. & Mrs. H.H. Saunderson award U. Manitoba, 1985, 12th Raymond Truex Disting. Lectureship award Hahnemann U., 1990. Fellow Royal Coll. Pathologists of London, Royal Coll. Physicians of Ireland; mem. Can. Assn. Anatomists (pres. 1981-83, J.C.B. Grant award 1991), Am. Assn. Anatomists, Teratology Soc., European Teratology Soc. Office: U Man, Dept Anatomy, 730 William Ave, Winnipeg, MB Canada R3E 0W3

PERSAVICH, WARREN DALE, diversified manufacturing company executive; b. Cleve., Dec. 15, 1952; s. Nick and Sophie (Makris) P.; m. Anita Geraldine Zeleznik, Oct. 12, 1974; children: Nicholas, Katherine. BBA, Kent State U., 1975. CPA, Ohio. Staff acct. Price Water House, Cleve., 1975-76; asst. contr. Banner Industries Inc., Cleve., 1976-79, contr., 1979-86, treas., 1986-88, v.p., treas., 1988-90; sr. v.p., chief fin. officer Banner Aerospace Inc., 1990—. Mem. AICPA, Ohio Soc. CPAs. Republican. Office: Banner Aerospace Inc Washington Dulles Airport PO Box 20260 / 300 W Service Rd Washington DC 20041

PERSCHBACHER, REX ROBERT, law educator; b. Chgo., Aug. 31, 1946; s. Robert Ray and Nancy Ellen (Beach) P.; m. Debbie Bassett Hamilton; children: Julie Ann, Nancy Beatrice. AB, Stanford U., 1968; JD, U. Calif., Berkeley, 1972. Bar: Calif. 1972, U.S. Dist. Ct. (no. dist.) Calif. 1973, U.S. Dist. Ct. (so. dist.) Calif. 1979, U.S. Ct. Appeals (9th cir.) 1980, U.S. Dist. ct. (ea. dist.) Calif. 1985. Law clk. to judge U.S. Dist. Ct. (no. dist.) Calif., San Francisco 1973-74; asst. prof. law U. Tex., Austin, 1974-75; assoc. Heller, Ehrman, White & McAuliffe, San Francisco, 1975-78; asst. prof. law U. San Diego, 1978-79, assoc. prof. law, 1980-81; mem. faculty Inst. on Internat. and Comparative Law, London, 1984—; acting prof. law U. Calif., Davis, 1981-85, prof., 1988—, assoc. dean, 1993—; dir. clin. edn. Univ. Calif., Davis, 1981-93, acad. senate, law sch. rep., 1989-91; vis. prof. law Univ. Santa Clara (Calif.), summer 1986. Co-author: Civil Procedure, 1987, California Legal Ethics, 1992; contbr. articles to legal jours. Bd. dirs. Legal Svcs. of No. Calif., 1990—. Mem. ABA, Calif. Bar Assn., Am. Assn. Law Schs., Inn of Ct. Democrat. Avocations: hiking, travel. Office: U Calif Sch Law King Hall Davis CA 95616

PERSCHETZ, MARTIN L., lawyer; b. Bklyn., Sept. 15, 1952; s. Louis and Edith (Sandhaus) P.; m. Babs D. Hanfling, Mar. 23, 1980; children: Monica, Keith, Evan. BA, U. Mich., 1974; JD, SUNY, Buffalo, 1977. Bar: N.Y. 1978, U.S. Dist. Ct. (so. dist.) N.Y. 1978, U.S. Dist. Ct. (ea. dist.) N.Y. 1979, U.S. Ct. Appeals (2d cir.) 1984, U.S. Dist. Ct. (no. dist.) N.Y. 1989. Assoc. Obermaier, Morvillo & Abramowitz, N.Y.C., 1977-80; assoc. U.S. atty. So. Dist. N.Y., N.Y.C., 1980-86, chief major crimes unit, 1985-86; chief counsel N.Y.C. Spl. Commn. to Investigate City Contracts, N.Y.C., 1986; dep. commr. N.Y.C. Dept. Investigation, N.Y.C., 1986; spl. counsel Schulte, Roth & Zabel, N.Y.C., 1986-87; ptnr. Schulte, Roth & Zabel, 1988—. Contbr. article to profl. jour. Recipient Joseph Halpern award Buffalo Law Rev., 1977. Mem. ABA, N.Y.C. Bar Assn., N.Y. Coun. Def. Lawyers. Home: 271 Clayton Rd Scarsdale NY 10583-1517 Office: Schulte Roth & Zabel 900 3rd Ave New York NY 10022

PERSCHINO, ARTHUR J., secondary school principal. Prin. Columbus Magnet Sch. Recipient Elem. Sch. Recognition award U.S. Dept. Edn., 1989-90. Office: Columbus Magnet Sch 46 Concord St Norwalk CT 06854

PERSELL, CAROLINE HODGES, sociologist, educator, author, researcher, consultant; b. Fort Wayne, Ind., Jan. 16, 1941; d. Albert Randolph and Katherine (Rogers) Hodges; m. Charles Bowen Persell, III, June 17, 1967; children: Patricia Emily, Stephen David. BA, Swarthmore Coll., 1962; MA, Columbia U., 1967, PhD, 1971. Sr. assoc., then nat. coordinator Nat. Scholarship Service and Fund for Negro Students, N.Y.C., 1962-66; project dir. Bur. Applied Social Research, N.Y.C., 1968-71; asst. prof. NYU, 1971-76, assoc. prof., 1976-86, prof. 1986—, dir. grad. studies dept. sociology, 1984-87, chair, 1987-93, Robin Williams Disting. Lectr., 1993-94. Author: Education and Inequality, 1977, Understanding Society, 1984, 2d edit., 1987, 3d edit., 1990; co-author: (with Cookson) Preparing for Power, 1985, Making Sense of Society, 1992; assoc. editor: Teaching Sociology, 1983-85, Sociology of Edn., 1992—, Gender & Soc., 1992—; contbr. articles to profl. jours. Recipient Faculty Devel. award NSF, 1978-79, Women Educators' Research award, 1978; grantee Fund for Improvement of Postsecondary Edn., 1989-92, NSF Equipment Fund, 1993—. Mem. Am. Sociol. Assn. (chair sec. 1983-84, 88-89, chmn. pubs. com. 1987-89), Am. Edn. Rsch. Assn., Author's Guild, Eastern Sociol. Assn. (pres. 1995—), Internat. Sociol. Assn., Sociologists for Women in Soc. Avocations: Violin, opera, sports. Office: NYU Dept Sociology 269 Mercer St New York NY 10003-6633

PERSELLIN, ROBERT HAROLD, physician; b. Fargo, N.D., July 3, 1930; s. James Harry and Bessie (Hoffman) P.; m. Bonnie Feibleman, June 27, 1957 (dec. 1983); children: Kathleen, Jamie; m. Diane Cummings, June 14, 1986. B.S., Northwestern U., 1952, M.D., 1956, M.S., 1960. Diplomate: Am. Bd. Internal Medicine, Am. Bd. Rheumatology. Intern Charity Hosp., New Orleans, 1956-57; resident in internal medicine Northwestern U. Med. Center, 1957-60; fellow in rheumatology Southwestern Med. Sch., 1962-64; asst. medicine U. Oreg. Med. Sch., 1964-68; prof. medicine, head div. rheumatology U. Tex. Health Sci. Center, San Antonio, 1968-81; prof. family practice U. Tex. Health Sci. Ctr., San Antonio, 1993—; cons. rheumatology VA Hosps., U.S. Army, Coastal Bend Health Plan; vis. prof. rheumatology Kingstown Med. Coll.; vis. scholar Corpus Christi Coll., Cambridge U., 1979-80; vis. scientist Strangeways Rsch. Lab., Cambridge. Contbr. chpts. to books, articles to profl. jours. Bd. dirs. San Antonio Chamber Music Soc., 1970-75, 80—, pres., 1983-85; bd. dirs. Friends of Strings, 1972-75, San Antonio Bot. Soc., 1985-87; Democratic precinct committeeman Washington County, Oreg., 1966-68. Served to capt. M.C. U.S. Army, 1960-62. Fellow ACP, Am. Coll. Rheumatology (exec. com. mem.); mem. Arthritis Found. (chmn. med. and sci. com. South Ctrl. Tex. chpt.), Heberden Soc., Am. Fedn. Clin. Rsch., So. Soc. Clin. Investigation, Tex. Rheumatism Assn. (pres.), Nat. Soc. Clin. Rheumatology, Mex. Rheumatology Soc. (hon.). Office: 635 E Olmos Dr San Antonio TX 78212-2504

PERSHAN, PETER SILAS, physicist, educator; b. Bklyn., Nov. 9, 1934; s. Max J. and Rosa (Bernekow) P.; m. Patricia S. Birke, Aug. 31, 1957; children: Marc, Jill. BS, Poly. Inst. Bklyn., 1956; AM, Harvard U., 1957, PhD, 1960. Rsch. fellow Harvard U., Cambridge, Mass., 1960, asst. prof., 1961-64, assoc. prof., 1964-68, prof., 1968—; mem. lab. tech. staff Bell Telephone, Murray Hill, N.J., 1963-64; dir. Materials Rsch. Lab., Cambridge, 1974-78; vis. prof. MIT, Cambridge, 1978-79; vis. scientist Brookhaven Nat. Lab., Upton, N.Y., 1985-86, guest scientist, 1986—; cons Sperry Gyroscope Co. Great Neck, N.Y., 1961-63, RCA Corp., Princeton, N.J., 1966-73, Battelle Meml. Inst. Naval Ordnance Lab., Silver Springs, Md., 1969-71; mem. proposal rev. panel Stanford Synchrotron Radiation Lab., 1989—; mem. adv. bd. Advanced Liquid Crystalline Optical Materials Consortium, 1991—; guest scientist RISØ Nat. Lab., Denmark, 1993. Author: Structure of Liquid Crystal Phases, 1988; co-editor: Resonances, 1990; contbr. articles to profl. jours. Fellow Am. Phys. Soc. (com. internat. freedom scientists 1984-86). Home: 218 Follen Rd Lexington MA 02173 Office: Harvard U Div Applied Scis 29 Oxford St Cambridge MA 02138-2901

PERSHAN, RICHARD HENRY, lawyer; b. N.Y.C., Jan. 4, 1930; s. Benjamin and Sadie (Aronowsky) P.; m. Kathryn Schaefler, June 11, 1952; children: Lee S., Richard H., Pamela, Julia B. BA, Yale U., 1951, LLB, 1956. Bar: N.Y. 1956, U.S. Supreme Ct.1969. Assoc. Davis, Polk & Wardwell, N.Y.C., 1956-60; ptnr. Finch & Schaefler, N.Y.C. 1960-85, LeBoeuf, Lamb, Greene & MacRae, N.Y.C., 1986—. Counsel Mcpl. Art Soc., N.Y.C., 1965-70, Fine Arts Fedn., N.Y.C., 1975-80. Served to 1st lt. USAF. Fellow Am. Coll. Trust and Estate Counsel (author, editor articles and studies 1960—); mem. Assn. of Bar of City of N.Y., Yale Club. Democrat. Avocation: rowing. Home: 1435 Lexington Ave New York NY 10128-1628 Office: LeBoeuf Lamb Greene & MacRae 125 W 55 St New York NY 10019-5389

PERSHING, DAVID WALTER, chemical engineering educator, researcher; b. Anderson, Ind., Oct. 2, 1948; s. Walter L. and Treva B. (Crane) P.; m. Lynn Marie Kennard, Apr. 9, 1977; 1 child, Nicole. BSChemE, Purdue U., 1970; PhDChemE, U. Ariz., 1976. Rsch. asst. Exxon Prodn. Rsch., Houston, 1969; project engr. EPA, 1970-73; asst. prof. chem. engring. U. Utah, Salt Lake City, 1977-82, assoc. prof., 1982-85, prof., 1985—, assoc. dean Grad. Sch., 1983-87, dean Coll. Engring., 1987—; asst. to pres. Reaction Engring. Inc., Salt Lake City, 1990—; vis. scientist Internat. Flame Rsch. Found., Ijmuiden, The Netherlands, 1972-73; vis. assoc. prof. chem. engring. U. Ariz., Tuscon, 1976-77; cons. Energy and Environ. Rsch. Ctr., Irvine, Calif., 1974-90, Acurex Corp., Mountain View, Calif., 1974-79, Kennecott Corp., Salt Lake City, 1979-81, Nat. Bur. Standards, Washington, 1976-78, Geneva Steel, 1989—; assoc. dir. Engring. Rsch. Ctr., NSF, 1986—

Contbr. articles to profl. publs.; patentee in field. Maj. USPHS, 1970-73. Recipient Disting. Teaching award U. Utah, 1982, Disting. Rsch. award U. Utah, 1990; grantee NSF, PYI, 1984-90. Mem. Am. Inst. Chem. Engrs., Combustion Inst. Methodist. Office: U Utah Coll Engring 2202 Merrill Engring Bldg Salt Lake City UT 84112

PERSHING, RICHARD WILSON, communications company executive, consultant; b. L.A., June 14, 1927; s. Howard Louis and Myrtle Edith (Wilson) P.; m. Norma Louise Davis, Aug. 19, 1950; children: Tina Ann Baine, Timothy Alan. BA, Pepperdine U., 1950. Various positions Security Pacific Bank, L.A., 1950-62; sr. v.p. Home Savs. & Loan Assn., L.A., 1962-65; exec. v.p. Hale Bros. Assocs., Inc., San Francisco, 1964-68, Internat. Controls Corp., Fairfield, N.J., 1968-70; pres., CEO Hale Tech. Corp., San Francisco, 1970-84; chmn. bd. Datron Sys. Inc., Escondido, Calif., 1984—. Serves with USNR, 1945-46, PTO. Home: Datron Systems Inc 75-572 Debby Ln Indian Wells CA Office: Datron Sys Inc 304 Enterprise St Escondido CA 92029

PERSHING, ROBERT GEORGE, telecommunications company executive; b. Battle Creek, Mich., Aug. 10, 1941; s. James Arthur and Beulah Francis P.; BS in Elec. Engring., Tri-State Coll., Angola, Ind., 1961; m. Diana Kay Prill, Sept. 16, 1961, (div. Jan. 1989); children: Carolyn, Robert; m. Charlene Jean Reed Wallis, Mar. 18, 1989; stepchildren: Patrick, Julie. Communications engr. Am. Elec. Power, Ind., N.Y. and Ohio, 1961-69; design supr. Wescom, Inc., Ill., 1969-74; dir. engring. Tellabs, Inc., Lisle, Ill., 1974-78; pres., chief exec. officer, bd. dirs Teltrend, Inc., St. Charles, Ill., 1979-89, chmn. bd., 1979-88; chief exec. officer DKP Prodns. Inc., St. Charles, Ill., 1986-89; exec. cons. Teltrend, 1979-93, bd. dirs., 1988-93; asst. treas. Magnekopy Inc., Villa Park, Ill., chmn. bd.; bd. dirs. TI Investors, Inc.; advisor entrepreneurial studies U. Ill.; engring. cons. Recipient Chgo. Area Small Bus. award, 1986, INC 500 awards, 1987, 88. Mem. IEEE. Office: 1519 Kirkwood Dr Geneva IL 60134-1659

PERSICO, JOSEPH EDWARD, author; b. Gloversville, N.Y., July 19, 1930; s. Thomas Louis and Blanche (Perrone) P.; m. Sylvia La Vista, May 23, 1959; children: Vanya, Andrea. B.A., SUNY-Albany, 1952; postgrad., Columbia U., 1955. Writer on staff of gov. N.Y. State, Albany, 1955-59; commd. fgn. service officer USIA, 1959; served in USIA, Buenos Aires, Argentina, Rio de Janeiro, Brazil, 1959-62; exec. asst. to commr. N.Y. State Health Dept., Albany, 1963-66; chief speechwriter for gov. N.Y. State, Albany, 1966-74; speechwriter for v.p. U.S., Washington, 1975-77. Author: My Enemy My Brother: Men and Days of Gettysburg, 1977; (novel) The Spiderweb, 1979, Piercing the Reich: The Penetration of Nazi Germany by American Secret Agents during World War II, 1979 (Nat. Intelligence Study Ctr. prize for best book on intelligence 1979), The Imperial Rockefeller: A Biography of Nelson A. Rockefeller, 1982, Murrow: An American Original, 1988, Casey: William J. Casey, From the OSS to the CIA, 1990, Nuremberg: Infamy on Trial, 1994; collaborator: Colin Powell: My American Journey, 1995. Served to lt. (j.g.) USN, 1952-55. Recipient Disting. Alumnus award SUNY-Albany, 1982. Mem. Authors Guild, Inc. Home and Office: 222 Heritage Rd Guilderland NY 12084-9672

PERSKY, LESTER, film producer; b. N.Y.C., July 6, 1927; s. Louis and Dora P. B.A., Bklyn. Coll., 1945. Co-founder Persky-Bright Film Prod. Fin. Ptnrship., N.Y.C., 1973—; pres. Lester Persky Prodns., Inc., N.Y.C., 1979—. Credits include Shampoo, Taxi Driver, The Man Who Would Be King, The Front, Hard Times, Missouri Breaks, Funny Lady, The Wind and the Lion, The Golden Voyage of Sinbad, The Last Detail, California Split; prodr. films Boom, 1968, Fortune and Men's Eyes, 1973, Equus, 1978, Hair, 1979, Yanks, 1979, TV miniseries Poor Little Rich Girl, NBC-TV, 1987 (Best Mini-Series Golden Globe award 1988), NBC TV miniseries A Woman Named Jackie, 1991 (Best Miniseries Emmy award 1992). Mem. Democratic Nat. Fin. Com., 1977-82; Pentathlon del. U.S. Olympic Ho. of Dels., Los Angeles, 1984; mem. N.Y.C. Mayor's Council on Motion Pictures, Radio and TV, 1978-83. Served with USMS. Mem. Acad. Motion Picture Arts and Scis., Acad. TV Arts and Scis. I once received this advice from playwright Tennessee Williams: "Don't start out trying to make it commercial, just try to make it good. It may turn out to be both, but at least it will be good and that is what lasts." (And so did the advice which I attempt to follow).

PERSON, CURTIS S., JR., state senator, lawyer; b. Shelby County, Tenn., Nov. 27, 1934; married; 6 children. BS, Memphis State U., 1956; LLB, U. Miss., 1959. Practice law, Memphis; former mem. Tenn. Ho. of Reps.; mem. Tenn. Senate, 1968—; Rep. whip, 1973-74, minority caucus chmn., 1976-82; chmn. Senate Judiciary com. 95th-99th Gen. Assemblies; chief referee Juvenile Ct. of Memphis and Shelby County. Pres., Memphis-Shelby County Mental Health Assn., 1969-73, Handicapped Inc.; chmn. Memphis Commn. on Drug Abuse, 1970; charter pres. Memphis State Tiger Rebounders; past trustee Memphis State U. Found.; exec. committeeman Danny Thomas Memphis Open Golf Classic; co-chmn. Shelby County Legis. Del., 1973-74, sec., 1969, vice chmn., 1970; chmn. Shelby Rep. Del., 1977. Named Memphis and Tenn. Outstanding Young Man of Yr., Jaycees, 1969, Outstanding Legislator of Yr., Government Leader Against Drunk Driving, Tenn. MADD, 1988, Legislator of Yr., Tenn. Alcohol and Drug Assn., 1988; recipient Liberty Bell Freedom award Memphis/Shelby County Bar Assn., 1969, Tenn. Adv. of Year for Handicapped children, 1978, Outstanding Svc to Children award Tenn. Coun. Juvenile Ct. Judges, 1981, Pres'. Svc. award Tenn. Juvenile Ct. Svcs. Assn., 1981, Americanism award Memphis Civitan Club, 1986, Disting. Svc. award County Officials Assn. Tenn., 1989, Community Svc. award Tenn. Med. Assn., 1989. Mem. Tenn. Bar Assn., Miss. Bar Assn., Memphis/Shelby County Bar Assn., Memphis State U. Nat. Alumni Assn. (pres. 1970), So. Golf Assn. (past dir.), Nat. Rifle Assn. (life), Phi Alpha Delta, Phi Alpha Theta, Kappa Sigma, Omicron Delta. Presbyterian. Clubs: Masons, Shriners. Office: War Meml Bldg Rm 308 Nashville TN 37243

PERSON, DONALD AMES, SR., pediatrician, rheumatologist; b. Fargo, N.D., July 17, 1938; s. Ingwald Haldor and Elma Wilhelmenia (Karlstrom) P.; m. Blanche Durand, Apr. 28, 1962; children: Donald Ames Jr., David Wesley. Student, Gustavus Adolphus Coll., 1956-58, U. Minn., 1958-59; BS, U. N.D., 1961; MD, U. Minn., 1963. Intern Mpls.-Hennepin County Gen. Hosp., 1963-64; resident neurol. surgery Mayo Clinic and Mayo Grad. Sch. Medicine, Rochester, Minn., 1967, fellow in microbiology, 1968-70; rsch. assoc. Baylor Coll. Medicine, Houston, 1971, Arthritis Found. fellow, 1972-74, mem. faculty, asst. prof. internal medicine, 1971-78, asst. prof. pediatrics, 1980-87, resident in pediatrics, 1978-80; asst. attending pediatrics Harris County Hosp. Dist., 1980-88; rheumatologist Tex. Children's Hosp., 1980-88, attending pediatrician, 1982-88; cons. Kelsey Seybold Clinic, 1980-88, Houston Shriner's Crippled Children's Hosp., 1983-88 , Houston Meth. Hosp., 1983-88, St. Luke's Episcopal Hosp., 1983-88, Honolulu Shriner's Crippled Children's Hosp., 1988—; prof. clin. pediatrics U. Hawaii Sch. Medicine, Honolulu, 1991—; prof. clin. pediatrics Uniformed Svcs. U. Health Scis., Bethesda, Md., 1993—; chief gen. pediatric svc., 1991-94; chief ambulatory pediatrics, Tripler Army Med. Ctr., Tripler AMC, Hawaii, 1988-94, asst. chief dept. pediatrics, 1988-94, chief dept. pediatrics, 1994—; "A" proficiency designator in pediatrics from Surgeon Gen. of the Army, 1990. Contbr. articles to profl. jours. With AUS, 1964-66, col., 1987—; Arthritis Found. sr. investigator, 1975-77. Fellow Am. Acad. Pediatrics (v.p. chpt. west uniformed svcs. sect. 1994-95, mem. exec. com. uniformed svcs. sect., 1995—, adv. mem. com. Hawaii chpt. 1994—); mem. AAAS, Am. Fedn. Clin. Rsch., AMA, Am. Coll. Rheumatology, Am. Soc. Microbiology, Soc. Pediatric Rsch., Am. Soc. Tropical Medicine and Hygiene, Arthritis Found. (dir., med. adv. bd.), Assn. Mil. Surgeons U.S. (Philip Hench award 1990), Harris County Med. Soc., Houston Acad. Medicine, Houston Pediatric Soc., Internat. Orgn. Mycoplasmologists, N.Y. Acad. Sci., N.D. Acad. Sci., Soc. Exptl. Biology and Medicine, So. Soc. Pediatric Rsch., S.W. Sci. Forum, Tex. Med. Assn., Tex. Pediatric Soc., Tex. Rheumatism Assn., Tissue Culture Assn., Honolulu Pediatric Soc., U.S. Fedn. Culture Collections. Mem. Evang. Luth. Ch. in Am., deacon, 1991-94. Home: 1321 Parks Rd Honolulu HI 96819-2131 Office: Tripler Army Med Ctr Honolulu HI 96859

PERSON, EVERT BERTIL, newspaper and radio executive; b. Berkeley, Calif., Apr. 6, 1914; s. Emil P. and Elida (Swanson) P.; m. Ruth Finley, Jan. 26, 1944 (dec. May 1985); m. 2d, Norma Joan Betz, Mar. 12, 1986. Student, U. Calif., Berkeley, 1937; LHD, Calif. State Univs., 1983, Sonoma State U.,

---

1993. Co-publisher, sec.-treas. Press Democrat Pub. Co., Santa Rosa, Calif., 1945-72, editor, 1972-73, pres., pub., editor-in-chief, 1973-85; sec.-treas. Finley Broadcasting Co., Santa Rosa, 1945-72; pres. Finley Broadcasting Co., 1972-89, Kawana Pubs., 1975-85; pub. Healdsburg Tribune, 1975-85; prin. Evert B. Person Investments, Santa Rosa, 1985—; pres. Person Properties Co. Santa Rosa, 1945-70; v.p. Finley Ranch & Land Co., Santa Rosa, 1947-72, pres., 1972-79; pres. Baker Pub. Co., Oreg., 1957-67, Sebastopol (Calif.) Times, 1978-81, Russian River News, Guerneville, Calif., 1978-81; pres. publ. Kawana Pubs., 1978-85; mem. nominating com. AP, 1982-84, mem. auditing com., 1984-85. Bd. dirs. Empire Coll., Santa Rosa, 1972—, Sonoma County Taxpayers Assn., 1966-69, San Francisco Spring Opera Assn., 1974-79; bd. dirs. San Francisco Opera, 1986-95, v.p., 1988-95; pres. Calif. Newspaperboy Found., 1957-58; chmn. Santa Rosa Civic Arts Commn., 1961-62; pres. Santa Rosa Sonoma County Symphony Assn., 1966-68, Luther Burbank Meml. Found., 1979, Santa Rosa Symphony Found., 1967-77; adv. bd. Santa Rosa Salvation Army, 1959-67; commodore 12th Coast Guard Dist. Aux., 1969-70; trustee Desert Mus., Palm Springs, 1987-92, v.p. Nat. Bd. Canine Companions, Inc., 1989-92. Mem. Calif. Newspaper Pubs. Assn. (pres. 1981-82), Internat. Newspaper Fin. Execs. (pres. 1961-62), Navy League U.S., Bohemian Club, Sonoma County Press Club, Santa Rosa Golf and Country Club, The Springs Club, Santa Rosa Rotary, Masons (32 degrees KCCH), Shriners. Roman Catholic. Home: 1020 Mcdonald Ave Santa Rosa CA 95404-3525 Office: The Oaks 1400 N Dutton Ave Ste 12 Santa Rosa CA 95401-4644

PERSON, ROBERT JOHN, financial management consultant; b. Mpls., Mar. 7, 1927; s. Otto Carl and Alice Kathryn (Kasper) P.; m. Jeanette Haines, Mar. 11, 1948; 1 dau., Julie Ann. BBA, U. Minn., 1947; MS, Columbia u., 1953. Financial analyst Equitable Life Assurance Soc. U.S., N.Y.C., 1947-53; asst. v.p. bus. devel. met. banking dept. Bankers Trust Co., N.Y.C., 1953-64; v.p. bus. devel. div. Union Bank, Los Angeles, 1964-67; v.p., dir. mktg. Bank of Calif., San Francisco, 1967-70; sr. v.p. Central Nat. Bank of Chgo., 1970-72, 1st v.p., 1973-76; 1st v.p. Central Nat. Bkg. Corp., 1973-76; v.p., regional mgr. Lester B. Knight & Assos., Inc., San Francisco, 1976-77; dir. bank cons. Coopers & Lybrand, San Francisco, 1977-80; partner-in-charge, nat. dir. bank cons. Coopers & Lybrand, Chgo., 1980-89; exec. v.p. RJP Assocs., Inc., Stockton, Calif., 1989-92; instr. salesmanship sch. pub. relations N.Y. Bankers Assn., 1960-63; instr. mktg. research Stonier Grad. Sch. Banking, Rutgers U., 1964-65, 73, 75-77, Brown U., 1964; instr. Agrl. Lending Sch., Ill. Bankers Assn., 1973-74, Nat. Comml. Lending Sch., Am. Bankers Assn., 1973-76, Sch. Bank Adminstrn., U. Wis., 1982-85, Nat. Grad. Trust Sch., Northwestern U., 1982-84, Southwestern Grad. Sch. Banking, 1983-84; Vice chmn. mgmt. effectiveness com. Community Fund Chgo. Treas. Sch. Bd., Huntington, N.Y., 1957-59; Bd. dirs. Am. Cancer Soc., Chgo.; chief crusader Crusade of Mercy. Served to lt. comdr. USNR, 1944-46, ret. Recipient Florence McNeil Stanley award Columbia, 1953. Mem. Am. Bankers Assn., Bank Mktg. Assn., Am. Mgmt. Assn. (mktg. planning council), Mgmt. Centre-Europe (fin. mgmt. adv. com. 1971—), Sales and Mktg. Execs. Internat., Stockton Symphony Assn. (bd. dirs. 1989-92), Beta Gamma Sigma. Republican. Presbyn. Clubs: Eastward Ho (Cape Cod); Stockton Golf and Country (Calif.). Lodge: Elks. Home: 14406 W Trading Post Dr Sun City West AZ 85375-5791

PERSON, WILLIS BAGLEY, chemistry educator; b. Salem, Oreg., Apr. 23, 1928; s. Carl Waldo and Grace Cassity (Bagley) P.; m. Krystyna Szczepaniak, 1985. BS, Willamette U., 1947; MS, Oreg. State Coll., Corvallis, 1949; PhD, U. Calif., Berkeley, 1953. Rsch. fellow U. Minn., 1952-54; instr. Harvard U., 1954-55; asst. prof. U. Iowa, 1955-61, assoc. prof., 1961-66; NSF sr. postdoctoral fellow, vis. assoc. prof. U. Chgo., 1965-66; prof. chemistry U. Fla., Gainesville, 1966—; vis. staff Los Alamos (N.Mex.) Nat. Lab., 1975-88; UNESCO cons. state U. Campinas, Brazil, 1980; vis. prof. Royal Holloway Coll. U. London, 1978, Inst. Molecular Sci., Okazaki, Japan, 1984, U. Pierre et Marie Curie, Paris, 1985; assoc. mem. commn. molecular spectroscopy IUPAC, 1982-89; mem. spectroscopy com. IUPAC Commn., 1989—; vis. scientist Lab. chem. Phys. NIDDK/NIH, Bethesda, Md., 1993. Author: (with R.S. Mulliken) Molecular Complexes, 1969; editor: (with G. Zerbi) Vibrational Intensities in Infrared and Raman Spectroscopy, 1982; contbr. numerous articles to profl. jours. Guggenheim fellow U. Chgo., 1960-61, Chem. Soc. Sr. Postdoctoral fellow, 1978. Mem. AAAS, Am. Chem. Soc., Optical Soc. Am., Royal Soc. Chemists (London), Coblentz Soc., Soc. Applied Spectroscopy. Office: U Fla Dept Chemistry Gainesville FL 32611

PERSONICK, STEWART DAVID, electrical engineer; b. Bklyn., Feb. 22, 1947; s. Louis and Mamie (Katz) P.; m. Carol Ann Cooke, Apr. 12, 1986. B.E.E., CCNY, 1967; S.M., MIT, 1968, Sc.D., 1970. Engr. Bell Labs., Holmdel, N.J., 1967-75, engring. supr., 1975-78, dept. head, 1983-84; engring. mgr. Vidar div. TRW, Mountain View, Calif., 1978-81; research mgr. Tech. Research Ctr. TRW, El Segundo, Calif., 1981-83; cons. Pacific Palisades, Calif., 1983-84; com. mem. NRC, Washington, 1983—; div. mgr. Bell Communications Research, Red Bank, N.J., 1984-85, asst. v.p., 1985-95, gen. mgr., 1995—. Author: Optical Fiber Transmission Systems, 1981, Fiber Optics Technology and Applications, 1985; editor spl. issue on fiber optic systems, IEEE Trans., 1978, 83; IEEE misc. jours., 1975—; patentee fiber optics; contbr. chpts. in books. Fellow IEEE, Optical Soc. Am.; mem. NAE, IEEE Communications Soc. Office: Bell Communications Rsch 445 South St Rm 2A-213 Morristown NJ 07960-6438

PERSONS, J. ROBERT, lawyer; b. New Orleans, Dec. 30, 1946; s. Jo R. and Ellen (Martin) P.; m. Ann Coogler, Aug. 10, 1974; children: Rob, Ellen, Margaret. BA with distinction, U. Va., 1969; JD, U. Ga., 1972. Bar: Ga. 1972, U.S. Ct. Appeals (11th cir.) 1972. Assoc. Hurt, Richardson, Garner & Todd, Atlanta, 1972-78; ptnr. Hurt, Richardson, Garner, Todd & Cadenhead, Atlanta, 1978-85; of counsel Lord, Bissell & Brook, Atlanta, 1985-86, ptnr., 1987—. 1st. Lt. USAR, 1972-75. Mem. ABA, Atlanta Bar Assn. (bd. dirs. 1988-90, 92-93), State Bar Ga. (mem. exec. coun. young lawyers sect. 1978-79, Henry Shinn Meml. award 1972), Ga. Defense Lawyers Assn., Alumni Assn. Westminster Schs., Defense Rsch. Inst., Lawyers Club Atlanta. Democrat. Episcopalian. Avocations: golf, boating, fishing. Office: Lord Bissell & Brook One Atlantic Ctr 1201 W Peachtree St # 3700 Atlanta GA 30309

PERSONS, OSCAR N., lawyer; b. McCormick, S.C., Jan. 7, 1939; s. Abner Thaddeus and Esther (Dumas) P.; m. Virginia Van Landingham, July 16, 1988; children: Thaddeus William, Anne Laura Lacour. B in Indsl. Engring., Ga. Inst. Tech., 1960; JD, Emory U., 1967. Bar: Ga. Ptnr. Alston & Bird, Atlanta, 1967—. Mem. Ga. Election Bd., 1976—; gen. counsel Ga. Rep. Com., 1971-93; Ga. chmn. Dole for Pres. Campaign, 1987, 95; Ga. vice chmn. Bush for Pres. Campaign, 1988; Ga. co-chmn. Bush-Quayle Campaign, 1992; chmn. Coverdell for U.S. Senate, 1992, Senator Coverdell's Citizen Senate Del., 1993—; pres. Harmony Atlanta's Internat. Youth Chorus, 1995. Presbyterian. Office: Alston & Bird One Atlantic Ctr 1201 W Peachtree St NW Atlanta GA 30309-3400

PERSONS, STOW SPAULDING, historian, educator; b. Mt. Carmel, Conn., June 15, 1913; s. Frederick Torrell and Florence Isabel (Cummings) P.; m. Dorothy Mae Reuss, Sept. 4, 1943; 1 dau., Catherine. BA, Yale U., 1936, PhD, 1940. Instr. history Princeton U., 1940-45, asst. prof., 1945-50; prof. history U. Iowa, 1950—, rsch. prof., 1956-57, Carver Disting. prof., 1978-81, prof. emeritus, 1981—; acting dean Grad. Coll., 1960-61; sr. rsch. fellow NEH, 1967-68; vis. prof. Salzburg (Austria) Seminar, 1955, 61, Stetson U., 1957, San Francisco Coll., 1959, U. Wyo., 1960, U. Colo., 1964. Author: Free Religion, 1947, American Minds, 1958, The Decline of American Gentility, 1973, Ethnic Studies at Chicago, 1987, The University of Iowa in the 20th Century, 1990; editor: Evolutionary Thought in America, 1950, (with D. Egbert and T.D.S. Bassett) Socialism and American Life, 1952, Social Darwinism: Selected Essays of William Graham Sumner, 1963, The Cooperative Commonwealth (Laurence Gronlund); mem. editorial bd. Am. Quar., 1958-61, Mississippi Valley Hist. Rev., 1954-57. Fellow Fund Advancement Edn., 1954-55. Mem. Am. Hist. Assn., Orgn. Am. Historians (exec. com. 1960-63). Home: 1433 Oaklawn Ave Iowa City IA 52245-5648

PERSSON, ERLAND KARL, electrical engineer, electrical company executive; b. Soderala, Sweden, Oct. 9, 1923; came to U.S., 1949, naturalized, 1953; m. Elaine Darm; children—Ann Monn, Eric. B.S.E.E., U. Minn., 1955. Registered profl. engr., Minn. Prin. engr. Gen. Mills, Mpls., 1956-61; v.p.

engring. Electro-Craft Corp., Hopkins, Minn., 1961-72, v.p. research and devel., 1972-83, sr. v.p., chief tech. officer, 1983-86; pres. Erland Persson Co., Mpls., 1987—. Contbr. articles to profl. jours. Contbr. chpts. to books. Patentee in field. Mem. Mech. Engring. Adv. Com. U. Minn.; bd. dirs. Minn. High Tech. Council, 1984-86, mem., 1987. Fellow IEEE (mem. subcom. electric machines com., indsl. drives com.), Audio Engring. Soc. (founder Midwest chpt. 1974); mem. Eta Kappa Nu. Office: Erland Persson Co Interchange Tower 600 S Hwy 169 Ste 1275 Minneapolis MN 55426

PERSYN, MARY GERALDINE, law librarian, law educator; b. Elizabeth, N.J., Feb. 25, 1945; d. Henry Anthony and Geraldine (Sumption) P. AB, Creighton U., 1967; MLS, U. Oreg., 1969; JD, Notre Dame U., 1982. Bar: Ind. 1982, U.S. Dist. Ct. (no. and so. dists.) Ind. 1982. Social scis. librarian Miami U., Oxford, Ohio, 1969-78; staff law librarian Notre Dame (Ind.) Law Sch., 1982-84; dir. law library Valparaiso (Ind.) U., 1984-87, law librarian, assoc. prof. law, 1987—. Editor Journal of Legislation, 1981-82; mng. editor Third World Legal Studies, 1986—. Mem. ABA, Ind. State Bar Assn., Am. Assn. Law Libraries, Ohio Regional Assn. Law Libraries (pres. 1990-91). Roman Catholic. Home: 1308 Tuckahoe Park Dr Valparaiso IN 46383-4032 Office: Valparaiso U Law Libr Sch Law Valparaiso IN 46383

PERVIN, WILLIAM JOSEPH, computer science educator; b. Pitts., Oct. 31, 1930; s. Abraham and Stella (Greenberger) P.; m. Susan P. Chizeck, 1981; 1 child, Hannah; children by previous marriage: Edward, James, Rachel. B.S., U. Mich., 1952, M.S., 1952; Ph.D., U. Pitts., 1957. Prof. Pa. State U., 1957-63; vis. prof. Heidelberg (Germany) U., 1963-64; prof., chmn. U. Wis.-Milw., 1964-67; dir. Computer Center, prof. math. Drexel U., Phila., 1967-73; dir. Regional Computer Center U. Tex., Dallas, 1973-78, prof. computer scis., 1973—, chmn. computer scis., 1983-85, master sch. engring. and computer scis., 1987-94. Author: Foundations of General Topology, 1964. Mem. Assn. Computing Machinery, Am. Math. Soc., IEEE Computer Soc., Soc. Indsl. and Applied Math., Math. Assn. Am. Office: U Tex Dallas PO Box 830688 M/S EC 32 Richardson TX 75083-0688

PESCE, GAETANO, architectural, interior, industrial and graphic designer; b. La Spezia, Italy, Nov. 8, 1939; m. Francesca Lucco, 1969; children: Tata, Tato. Studied architecture, U. Venice, 1959-65, Inst. Indsl. Design, Venice, 1961-65. Ind. artist, filmaker, also co-founder Gruppo N, Padua, Italy, 1959-67; freelance designer Padua, 1962-67, Venice, 1968—; prof. archtl. planning Inst. d'Architecture et d'Etudes Urbaines, Strasbourg, France, 1975—; vis. prof., lectr. Ohio State U., Columbus, 1974, Cooper Union, N.Y., 1975, 79, 80, 83, 85, 86, Pratt Inst., N.Y., 1979, 80, 84, Ecole des Beaux-Arts, Nancy, France, 1981, U. Tech., Compiegne, 1981, Yale U., New Haven, 1983, U. Que., 1984, U. Montreal, 1984, Poly. of Hong Kong, 1985, Domus Acad., Milan, 1986, 87, U. Sao Paulo, 1987, others. Exhbns. include Galleria Bevilacqua La Masa, Venice, 1961, Hochschule für Gestaltung, Ulm, Fed. Republic Germany, 1964, Finnish Design Ctr., Helsinki, 1964, Keski Suomen Mu., Jyvsakyla, 1965, Galleria Il Canale, Venice, 1966, Galleria La Carabaga, Genoa, 1966, Galleria La Chioccciola, Padua, 1966, Linea Sud Gallery, Naples, 1967, Atelier d'Urbanisme at Architecture, Paris, 1969, Galleria Luca Palazzoli, Milan, 1974, Musee des Arts Decoratifs, Paris, 1975, Archtl. Assn., London, 1978, JDC Gallery, Tokyo, 1978, Mus. Modern Art, N.Y.C., 1979, Carnegie-Mellon U., Pitts., 1980, Centro de Arte y Comunicacion, Buenos Aires, 1981, Yale U., 1983, Mus. Decorative Arts, Montreal, 1984, Harvard U., Cambridge, Mass., 1985, U. Architecture, Hong Kong, 1985, Musee d'Art Moderne, Strabourg, 1986, Galerie Leptien 3, Frankfurt, 1988, Deutsches Architekturmuseum, Frankfurt, 1988, Max Protetch Gallery, N.Y.C., 1989, Sapporo Brewery, Tokyo, 1989, U. Que., Montreal, 1989, others; represented in collections Mus. Modern Art, N.Y.C., Met. Mus., N.Y.C., Centre Georges Pompidou, Paris, Musee des Arts Decoratifs, Paris, Keski Suomen Mus., Helsinki, Museo d'Arte Moderna, Turin, Centre Canadien d'Architecture, Montreal, Muse des Arts Decoratifs, Montreal, others; contbr. articles to profl. jours. Recipient Locarno Film Festival award, 1968, Tokyo Lighting Design Competition award, 1973, Parc de la Villette award, Paris, 1983, Office Furniture Competition award, Paris, 1983. Address: San Toma 2775, Venice Italy also: 67 Boulevard Brune, 75014 Paris France also: Pesce Ltd 543 Broadway New York NY 10012

PESCI, JOE, actor; b. Newark, N.J., Feb. 9, 1943. Film appearances include Death Collector, 1976, Raging Bull, 1980, I'm Dancing as Fast as I Can, 1982, Easy Money, 1983, Dear Mr. Wonderful, 1983, Eureka, 1983, Once Upon a Time in America, 1984, Tutti Dentro, 1984, Man On Fire, 1987, Moonwalker, 1988, Backtrack, 1988, Lethal Weapon II, 1989, Goodfellas (Acad. award Best Supporting Actor, 1991, D.W. Griffith Award, 1990), Home Alone, 1990, The Super, 1991, JFK, 1991, Lethal Weapon III, 1992, Home Alone II, 1992, The Public Eye, 1992, My Cousin Vinny, 1992, A Bronx Tale, 1993, With Honors, 1994, Jimmy Hollywood, 1994, Casino, 1995; appeared in TV series Half Nelson, 1985. Office: care CAA 9830 Wilshire Blvd Beverly Hills CA 90212-1825*

PESCUCCI, GABRIELLA, costume designer. Costume designer: (films) City of Wome, 1981, Passione d'Amore, 1982, Three Mothers, 1982, Le Nuit de Varennes, 1983, Once Upon a Time in America, 1984, The Name of the Rose, 1986, Haunted Summer, 1988, The Adventures of Baron Munchausen, 1989 (Academy award nomination best costume design 1989), Indochine, 1992, The Age of Innocence, 1993 (Academy award best costume design 1993). Office: Sandra Marsh Mgt 9150 Wilshire Blvd Ste 220 Beverly Hills CA 90210*

PESHKIN, MURRAY, physicist; b. Bklyn., May 17, 1925; s. Jacob and Bella Ruth (Zuckerman) P.; m. Frances Julie Ehrlich, June 12, 1955; children—Michael, Sharon, Joel. B.A., Cornell U., 1947, Ph.D., 1951. Instr., then asst. prof. physics Northwestern U., 1951-59; physicist, then sr. scientist Argonne (Ill.) Nat. Lab., 1959—, assoc. dir. physics div., 1972-83; fellow Weizmann Inst. Sci., Rehovoth, Israel, 1959-60, 68-69; sr. scientist SciTech Mus., Aurora, Ill., 1991—. Served with AUS, 1944-46. Home: 838 Parkside Ave Elmhurst IL 60126-4813 Office: Argonne Nat Lab Argonne IL 60439

PESHKIN, SAMUEL DAVID, lawyer; b. Des Moines, Oct. 6, 1925; s. Louis and Mary (Grund) P.; m. Shirley R. Isenberg, Aug. 17, 1947; children—Lawrence Allen, Linda Ann. B.A., State U. Iowa, 1948, J.D., 1951. Bar: Iowa 1951. Ptnr. Brigdes & Peshkin, Des Moines, 1953-66, Peshkin & Robinson, Des Moines, 1966-82; Mem. Iowa Bd. Law Examiners, 1970—. Bd. dirs. State U. Iowa Found., 1957—, Old Gold Devel. Fund, 1956—, Sch. Religion U. Iowa, 1966—. Fellow Am. Bar Found., Internat. Soc. Barristers; mem. ABA (chmn. standing com. membership 1959—, ho. of dels. 1968—, bd. govs. 1973—), Iowa Bar Assn. (bd. govs. 1958—, pres. jr. bar sect. 1958-59, award of merit 1974), Inter-Am. Bar Assn., Internat. Bar Assn., Am. Judicature Soc., State U. Iowa Alumni Assn. (dir., pres. 1957). Home: 3598 Yacht Club Dr Apt 1203 Aventura FL 33180

PESKIN, KENNETH, retail executive. Postgrad., Harvard U. Pres., chief oper. officer Pathmark div. Supermarkets Gen., N.J., 1984-86, pres., chief exec. officer, 1986-87; chmn., chief exec. officer Supermarkets Gen. Holdings Corp., N.J., 1987—. Office: Supermarkets Gen Corp 301 Blair Rd Woodbridge NJ 07095

PESKIN, MATT ALAN, professional society administrator; b. Phila., May 29, 1954; s. Bernard and Rosalie (Carson) P.; m. Janie Gross, Nov. 11, 1981; children: Lindy Allison, Michael Jay. BA in Communications, Pa. State U., 1976. Exec. dir. Nat. Town Watch Assn., Wynnewood, Pa., 1981-90; dir. Nat. Town Watch Assn., 1984-94; creator Nat. Night Out. Mem. Nat. Crime Prevention Coalition (Nat. Crime Prevention award 1986), Internat. Soc. Crime Prevention Practitioners. Office: Nat Assn Town Watch PO Box 303 7 E Wynnewood Rd Ste 215 Wynnewood PA 19096-1994

PESMEN, SANDRA (MRS. HAROLD WILLIAM PESMEN), editor; b. Chgo., Mar. 26, 1931; s. Benjamin S. and Emma (Lipschultz) P.; m. Harold W. Pesmen, Aug. 16, 1952; children: Bethann, Curtis. B.S., U. Ill., 1952. Reporter Radio and Community News Service, Chgo., 1952-53; wire editor Champaign-Urbana (Ill.) Courier, 1953; reporter, feature writer Lerner Chgo. N. Side Newspapers, 1953-55; stringer corr. Wayne (Mich.) Eagle, 1958-61; reporter, feature writer Chgo. Daily News, 1968-78; features editor Crain's Chgo. Business mag., 1978-89; corp. features editor Crain Communications,

---

Inc., 1989-95; tchr. feature writing Northwestern U. Evening Sch., 1972-81. Author: Writing for the Media, 1983; editor: Career News Service; author syndicated column Dr. Job, 1985—. Recipient Golden Key award Ill. Mental Health Dept., 1966, 71, award Inst. Psychoanalysis, 1971, Penny Mo. award, 1978, Stick o'Type award Chgo. Newspaper Guild, 1978, award AP, 1975, Peter Lisagor award Soc. Profl. Journalists, 1991. Home: 2811 Fern Ave Northbrook IL 60062-5809

PESNER, CAROLE MANISHIN, art gallery owner; b. Boston, Aug. 5, 1937; m. Robert Pesner (dec. 1983); children: Ben, Jonah. BA, Smith Coll., 1959. Asst. dir. Kraushaar Galleries, Inc., N.Y.C., 1959-86, dir., 1986-90, pres., 1991—. Author, editor publs., catalogues in field. Mem. Art Dealers Assn. Am., Internat. Fine Print Dealers Assn. Office: Kraushaar Galleries Inc 724 5th Ave New York NY 10019-4106

PESNER, SUSAN M., lawyer; b. Suffern, N.Y., July 17, 1951; d. Leon and Doris (Elias) P.; m. Steven M. Elliott, Sept. 22, 1978. BA, Am. U., Washington, 1973, JD, 1976. Bar: Va. 1980, U.S. Ct. Appeals (4th cir.) 1980, U.S. Dist. Ct. (ea. dist.) Va. 1981. Paralegal Walstad, Wickwire, Peterson, Gavin & Asselin, Vienna, Va., 1978-80; assoc. Walstad, Wickwire, Peterson, Gavin & Asselin, Vienna, 1980, Peterson & Assocs., Vienna, 1980-83; ptnr. Peterson & Pesner, P.C., Vienna, 1983-90, Peterson, Pesner, Cochran & Basha, P.C., Vienna, 1991—. Mem. Fairfax County Dem. Bus. Forum, Tysons Corner, Va., 1987—. Mem. ABA, Va. Bar Assn., Va. State Bar (area rep. 1988-91, gov. 1991—, bd. govs. real estate sect.), No. Va. Bldg. Industry Assn. (chmn. regional real estate fin. conf. 1985-87), No. Va. Young Lawyers (v.p. 1983-85), Fairfax Bar Assn. Jewish. Avocations: gardening, photography, hiking. Home: 2008 Wolftrap Oaks Ct Vienna VA 22182-5070 Office: Peterson Pesner Cochran & Basha PC 8214C Old Courthouse Rd Vienna VA 22182-3808

PESQUERA MORALES, CARLOS I., government official; b. Santurce, P.R., Aug. 7, 1956; s. Rafael Pesquera and Rainelda Barbara Morales; m. Irasema Rivera, Aug. 19, 1978; children: Carlitos, Frances. BS in Civil Engring., U. P.R., 1978; MS in Structural Engring., Cornell U., 1982, PhD in Structural Engring., 1984. Engr. 3D/Eye, Inc., Ithaca, N.Y., 1983-85; assoc. prof. civil engring. U. P.R. Mayaguez, 1986-91, prof. civil engring., 1991-92, dir. Infrastructure Rsch. Ctr., 1992-93; sec. transp. and pub. works P.R., 1993—; cons. in field. Contbr. articles to profl. jours.; devel. software systems. Mem. Am. Concrete Inst., P.R. Engrs. Profl. Assn., Tau Beta Pi. Avocations: computers, basketball. Home: Colden Ct II Arterial Hostos Ave PO Box 275 San Juan PR 00918-2995 Office: Commonwealth of PR Dept Transp & Pub Works PO Box 41269 Minillas St San Juan PR 00940-1269

PESTANA, CARLOS, physician, educator; b. Tacoronte, Tenerife, Canary Islands, Spain, June 10, 1936; came to U.S., 1968, naturalized, 1973; s. Francisco and Blanca (Suarez) P.; m. Myrna Lorena Serrato, Aug. 25, 1966; children—Becky Elizabeth, George Byron. B.S., Nat. U. Mex., 1952, M.D., 1959; Ph.D. in Surgery, U. Minn., 1965. Intern St. Mary of Nazareth Hosp., Chgo., 1959-60; resident Mayo Clinic, Rochester, Minn., 1961-65; surgeon Hosp. 20 de Noviembre Mexico City; asst. prof. surgery Nat. U. Mex., 1966-67; asst. prof. surgery U. Tex. Med. Sch. at San Antonio, 1968-70, asso. prof., 1970-74, prof., 1974—, asso. dean for acad. devel., 1971-73, asso. dean for student affairs, 1973-86, assoc. dean acad. affairs, 1986—. Recipient Edward John Noble Found. award, 1965, Piper Prof. award Minnie Stevens Piper Founds., 1972. Mem. ACS, AMA, Assn. Acad. Surgery, Nat. Bd. Med. Examiners, Tex. Med. Assn., Bexar County Med. Soc., San Antonio Surg. Soc., Soc. for Surgery Alimentary Tract, Assn. Am. Med. Colls., Physiology Soc., Sigma Xi, Alpha Omega Alpha. Home: 10123 N Manton Ln San Antonio TX 78213-1932 Office: 7703 Floyd Curl Dr San Antonio TX 78284-7700

PESTER, JACK CLOYD, oil company executive; b. Seymour, Iowa, Mar. 12, 1935; s. Cloyd Russell Pester and Esther O. (Long) Marston; m. Patricia Joanne Shay, July 21, 1956 (div. 1979); m. Barbara Dee Brazil, Aug. 13, 1979. BS in Bus. Adminstrn., Drake U. Dealer Pester Corp., Grinnell, Iowa, pres., Corydon, Iowa, CEO, Des Moines; sr. v.p. Coastal Corp., Houston; chief exec. Coastal Mart, Inc., Houston, bd. dirs., Am. Mutual Life Ins. Co., Des Moines. Bd. dirs. KFx Inc., Denver. Bd. govs. Drake U. Served with U.S. Army, 1957. Reciepient Disting. Alumni award Drake U., 1979, One in a Hundred Alumni award Drake U., 1981. Republican. Roman Catholic. Clubs: Houston City. Home: 11 Auburn Pl Houston TX 77005-2162

PESTILLO, PETER JOHN, lawyer, automotive executive; b. Bristol, Conn., Mar. 22, 1938; s. Peter and Ruth (Hayes) P.; m. BettyAnn Barraclough, Aug. 29, 1959; children: Kathleen, Karen, Kerry. BSS, Fairfield (Conn.) U., 1960; LLB, Georgetown U., 1963. Bar: D.C. 1964. Mgr. union relations planning Gen. Electric Co., N.Y.C., 1968-74; v.p. employee relations B.F. Goodrich Co., Akron, Ohio, 1974-80; v.p. labor relations Ford Motor Co., Dearborn, Mich., 1980-85; v.p. employee relations Ford Motor Co., 1985-86, v.p. employee and external affairs, 1986—. Mem. adv. bd. United Found., Detroit. Mem. Am. Arbitration Assn. (dir.), U.S.C. of C. (labor relation com.), D.C. Bar, Bus. Roundtable, Labor Policy Assn., Nat. Assn. Mfgs., UBA. Home: 338 Provencal Rd Grosse Pointe MI 48236-2959 Office: Ford Motor Co The American Rd Dearborn MI 48126

PESTKA, STANLEY, secondary school principal. Prin. Granby Meml. Mid. Sch. Recipient Blue Ribbon award U.S. Dept. Edn., 1990-91. Office: Granby Meml Mid Sch 309 Salmon Brook St Granby CT 06035-1804

PESTLE, JOHN WILLIAM, lawyer; b. Brattleboro, Vt., Feb. 28, 1948; s. Ray Irving and Annette Adelia (Lilley) P.; m. Penelope Mendenhall, Oct. 11, 1969; children: William Joseph, Sarah Lilley. BA magna cum laude, Harvard U., 1970; MA magna cum laude, Yale U., 1972; JD magna cum laude, U. Mich., 1975. Bar: Mich. 1975, U.S. Dist. Ct. (we. dist.) Mich. 1975, U.S. Dist. Ct. (ea. dist.) Mich. 1978, U.S. Ct. Appeals (6th and D.C. cirs.) 1979, U.S. Supreme Ct. 1980. Assoc. Varnum, Riddering, Wierengo & Christenson, Grand Rapids, Mich., 1975-80; ptnr. Varnum, Riddering, Schmidt & Howlett, Grand Rapids, 1980—, co-chmn. energy and telecommunications practice group, 1986—. Contbr. articles to profl. jours. Pres. Blodgett Neighborhood Assn., Grand Rapids, 1982-88; bd. dirs. Blodgett Meml. Med. Ctr. Community Rels., 1983-88, Mich. Trails coun. Girl Scouts U.S., 1982-87; trustee Harvard Glee Club Found., 1987—; sec. Nuclear Non-Oper. Owners Group, 1988-93. Mem. ABA, Fed. Energy Bar Assn. (cogeneration and small power prodn. commn.), Mich. State Bar Assn. (chmn. mcpl. utilities commn., chmn. pub. corp. law sect.), State Bar Mich. Found., Grand Rapids Bar Assn., Am. Pub. Power Assn. (vice chmn. legal sect. 1985-86, chmn. 1986-87), Harvard Club Western Mich. (sec. 1976-82). Avocations: skiing, skating, photography, gardening. Home: 515 Plymouth Ave SE Grand Rapids MI 49506-2841

PESTUREAU, PIERRE GILBERT, literature educator, literary critic, editor; b. Civray, Vienne, France, Feb. 8, 1933; came to U.S., 1991; s. Pierre and Madeleine (Bernard) P.; divorced; children: Veronique, Christophe, Charlotte; m. Ann Shepstone Wakefield, July 12, 1980. MA in Lit., U. Poitiers, France, 1955; profl. degree, Paris, 1956; PhD, Sorbonne U., Paris, 1975, SD in Lit., 1981. Prof. Nat. Edn., France, 1956-65, Tahiti, 1966-70; prof. Madagascar, 1971-78, U. Natal, Durban, South Africa, 1974-80, U. Ocean Indien, La Reunion, France, 1981-83, U. Nantes, France, 1986-91, Loyola U., Chgo., 1991—; lectr. Alliance Francaise, South Africa, U.S., 1976-95; vis. prof. San Diego State U., spring 1988, Loyola U., Chgo., spring 1990. Author: Boris Vian, 1978, Dictionnaire Vian, 1985; editor: Boris Vian Oeuvres Choisies, 1991, Romans, 1992, 93, 94, André Brink, 1992, Raymond Queneau, 1993, 94. Rep. Prof.'s Union, France, 1956-70. Sgt. Svc. Corps French Mil., 1960-62. Decorated chevalier Palmes Académiques. Office: Loyola U 6525 N Sheridan Rd Chicago IL 60626-5311

PESZKE, MICHAEL ALFRED, psychiatrist, educator; b. Deblin, Poland, Dec. 19, 1932; s. Alfred Bartlomiej and Eugenia Halina (Grebocka) P.; m. Alice Margaret Sherman, Sept. 20, 1958; children: Michele Halina Olender, Michael Alexander. BA, Trinity Coll., Dublin, Ireland, 1956; MB, BCh, BAO, Dublin U., 1956. Bd. cert. psychiatrist. Staff psychiatrist Yale Student Health Svc., New Haven, 1961-64; asst. prof. sch. medicine U. Chgo., 1964-68; cons. psychiatrist Wesleyan U., Middletown, Conn., 1968-

---

70; asst. prof. Sch. Medicine U. Conn., Farmington, 1970-73, assoc. prof., 1973-80, prof. psychiatry, 1980-90; clin. prof. U. Md. Sch. Medicine, Balt., 1991—; chief psychiatry Perry Point (Md.) VA Med. Ctr., 1991—; dir. psychiat. clin. svcs. U. Conn. Health Ctr., Farmington, 1983-87; chief VA Med. Ctr., Newington, Conn., 1987-90. Author: Involuntary Treatment of the Mentally Ill: The Problem of Autonomy, 1975; co-author: (edited by L.A. Pervin, L.R. Reik, W. Dalrymple) The College Drop-out and the Utilization of Talent, 1966, (edited by J. Zusman, E. Bertsch) The Future of Psychiatric State Hospitals, 1975; contbr. articles to profl. jours.; book reviewer Univ. Chgo. Law Rev., 1968, Conn. Law Rev., 1976, Am. Jour. Psychiatry, 1976-93. Mem. Conn.'s Jud. Law Revision Com., 1982-86, Whiting Forensic Adv. Bd., 1975-87; co-chair Commr. Mental Health's Com. to Re-write Conn. Civil Commitment Statutes, 1976-77. WHO travel fellow, United Kingdom, Denmark, Poland, 1977; U. Conn. Research grantee, 1972-87. Fellow APA (life); mem. Am. Coll. Psychiatrists, Soc. for Mil. History. Avocations: World War II military and diplomatic history, sailing. Home: PO Box 165 Perry Point MD 21902-0165

PETACQUE, ARTHUR M., journalist; b. Chgo., July 20, 1924; s. Ralph David and Fay Nora (Brauner) P.; m. Regina Battinus, Dec. 10, 1944; children: Susan Wendy Petacque Leshin, William Scott. Student, U. Ill., 1940-42; PhD (hon.), So. Ill. U., 1987. With Chgo. Sun, 1942-47; with Chgo. Sun-Times, 1947—, investigative reporter, 1957—, columnist, 1974—; crime editor World Book Ency., 1970-75; lectr. various univs. and civic orgns. Recipient Page One awards for outstanding journalism Chgo. Newspaper Guild, 1949, 57, 59, 62, 63, 65, 68; Joseph M. Fay Meml. award Chgo. Newspaper Reporters Assn., 1960; Prof. Jacob Scher-Theta Sigma Phi Daily Newswriting award Chgo. chpt. Theta Sigma Phi, 1964; John Baptist Scalabrini award for leadership Am. Community Italian Ancestry, 1966; awards for investigative reporting and spot news AP, 1963, 66, 68, (2) 74, 76; Marshall Field award for outstanding editorial contbn. in behalf of Chgo. Sun-Times, 1968; Pulitzer Prize for gen. reporting, 1974; State of Israel Prime Minister's medal, 1976; Dante award Civic Com. Italian Americans, 1980; UPI award for best spot news coverage Ill., 1980; Emmy award for ABC-TV local news spot reporting, 1984; Award for Long and Dedicated Newspaper Reporting on Crime and the Criminal Justice System, Ill. Acad. Criminology, 1985; named to Chgo. Journalism Hall of Fame Chgo Headline Club, 1990. Mem. Chgo. Newspaper Guild, Jewish War Vets. (hon.), Sigma Delta Chi, Sigma Alpha Mu. Jewish. Club: B'nai B'rith. Office: 401 N Wabash Ave Chicago IL 60611-3532 *Have tried to be fair, careful and objective in my profession, realizing that what we say about the person we write about has not only an effect on the subject but his family and friends.*

PETAK, WILLIAM JOHN, systems management educator; b. Johnstown, Pa., June 23, 1932; s. Val Andrew and Lola Agatha (Boroski) P.; m. Ramona Janet Cayuela, Dec. 28, 1957; children: Elizabeth Ann Petak-Aaron, William Matthew, Michael David. BS in Mech. Engring., U. Pitts., 1956; MBA, U. So. Calif., 1963, DPA, 1969. Engr. Northrop Corp., Hawthorne, Calif., 1956-59; test engr. Wyle Labs., El Segundo, Calif., 1959-63; we. regional mgr. Instrument div. Budd Co., Phoenixville, Pa., 1963-69; v.p. dir. J.H. Wiggins Co., Redondo Beach, Calif., 1969-81; prof. systems mgmt. U. So. Calif., L.A., 1982—, exec. dir. Inst. Safety, 1987—; chmn. earthquake mitigation com. Nat. Com. on Property Ins., Boston, 1990-92; mem. com. on natural disasters NRC, Washington, 1985-91, mem. U.S. nat. com. for the decade for natural disaster reduction, 1989-92. Co-author: Natural Hazard Risk Assessment and Public Policy, 1982, Politics and Economics of Earthquake Hazard Reduction, 1986; editor Pub. Adminstrn. Rev., 1985. Commr. County of Los Angeles, 1994—; mem. policy bd. So. Calif. Earthquake Prep. Project, L.A., 1986-92; trustee Marymount Coll., Palos Verdes, Calif., 1974—. Sgt. U.S. Army, 1950-52. Mem. Soc. for Risk Analysis, Earthquake Engring. Rsch. Inst., Am. Soc. for Pub. Adminstrn., Sigma Xi. Republican. Roman Catholic. Avocations: skiing, fishing, hiking. Office: U So Calif MC 0021 Inst Safety and Systems Mgmt Los Angeles CA 90089

PETCHESKY, ROSALIND POLLACK, political science and women's studies educator; b. Bay City, Tex., Aug. 16, 1942. BA, Smith Coll., 1964; MA, Columbia U., 1966, PhD, 1974. Prof. Hunter Coll. CUNY. Author: (books) The Individual's Rights and International Organization, 1966, Abortion and Women's Choice: The State, Sexuality and Reproductive Freedom, 1984, 2d edit. 1990 (Joan Kelly Meml. prize Am. Hist. Assn. 1984). Founder Internat. Reproductive Rights Rsch. Action Group. MacArthur fellow, 1995. Office: CUNY Hunter Coll Dept Polit Sci 695 Park Ave New York NY 10021*

PETER See L'HUILLIER, PETER

PETER, FRANCES MARCHBANK, author, editor, publisher, research agency administrator; b. Paterson, N.J.; d. Frederick James Marchbank, Jr. and Frances Grace (Witbeck) Marchbank Filter. BA with honors, Syracuse (N.Y.) U., 1959; postgrad. NYU, U. Md., The Wharton Sch. Tech. writer GE Corp., 1959-60; assoc. producer Met. Opera Broadcasts, 1960-62; treas. Souvaine Assocs., Inc., 1960-62; asst. to music critic Edward Downes, 1962-63; staff program mgmt. Gen. Electric Co., Wiesbaden, W.Ger., 1963-65, Fed. Electric Co., Frankfurt, W.Ger., 1965, Page Communications Engrs., Inc., Saigon, Vietnam and Tripoli, Libya, 1966-70; head publs. dept., mng. editor BioSci., jour. Am. Inst. Biol. Scis., Washington, 1972-75; editor Commn. on Life Scis., NRC-NAS, Washington, 1975-88, dep. dir. food and nutrition bd., 1987-90, dir. long-range planning for adminstrn., 1990-92; v.p. Peter, Marchbank and Palmer, Inc., 1980-92; cons. in field, 1992—. Recipient cert. merit Am. Inst. Biol. Scis., 1975. Mem. Soc. Scholarly Pub. (charter, editor SSP Letter 1982-84, asst. sec.-treas. 1982-84), Washington Ind. Writers, Coun. Biology Editors (publs. com.), Washington Book Pubs., Delta Delta Delta. Editorial bd. Am. Biology Tchr., 1975-76. Home and Office: 2101 Connecticut Ave NW Washington DC 20008

PETER, HELMUT W., gas company executive; b. Coburg, Bavaria, Fed. Republic Germany, July 26, 1932; came to U.S., 1959; s. Paul and Elly (Schulze) P.; m. Rosemarie Dost, May 17, 1958; children: Brigitte, Thomas, Doris. BSME, State Engring. Coll., Frankfurt, Fed. Republic Germany, 1956; postgrad., Columbia U., 1981; postgrad. in advanced mgmt. program, Harvard U., 1984. Group leader, testing custormer service engr. Adolf Messer Gmbh., Frankfurt, 1952-59; from mgr. to project mgr., then gen. mgr. Am. Messer Corp., N.Y.C., 1959-72; dir. project engring. Bklyn. Union Gas Co., 1972-74, mgr. engring. dept., 1974-77, asst. v.p., 1977-80, v.p., 1980-85, sr. v.p., chief engineer, 1985—; chmn. U.S./Japanese Gas Heat Pump Consortium, GRI-Indsl. Tech. Adv. Com., Chgo. Mem. exec. bd. dirs. Boyscouts Am., N.Y.C, Kayak and Canoe Club. Mem. ASME, Am. Gas Assn., Harvard Bus. Sch. Assn., Belleayre Mountain Ski Club. Avocations: canoeing, skiing, photography, camping, golf. Office: Bklyn Union Gas Co 1 Metrotech Ctr Brooklyn NY 11201-3850

PETER, PHILLIPS SMITH, lawyer; b. Washington, Jan. 24, 1932; s. Edward Compston and Anita Phillips (Smith) P.; m. Jania Jayce Hutchins, Apr. 8, 1961; children: Phillips Smith Peter Jr., Jania Jayce Hutchins Stone. BA, U. Va., 1954, JD, 1959. Bar: Calif. 1959. Assoc. McCutchen, Doyle, Brown, Enerson, San Francisco, 1959-63; with GE (and subs.), various locations, 1963-94; v.p. corp. bus. devel. GE (and subs.), 1973-76; v.p. GE (and subs.), Washington, 1976-79, v.p. corp. govtl. rels., 1980-94; counsel, head govt. rels. dept. Reed Smith Shaw & McClay, Washington, 1994—; bd. dirs. Inst. for Rsch. on Econs. of Taxation, 1986-89; chmn. bd. govs. Bryce Harlow Found., 1990-92. Mem. editorial bd. Va. Law Rev., 1957-59. Trustee Howard U., 1981-89; v.p. Fed. City Coun., Washington, 1979-85; bd. dirs. Carlton, 1987-90. With reserve corps U.S. Army, 1954-56. Mem. Calif. Bar Assn., Order of Coif, Wee Burn Club, Ea. Yacht Club, Farmington Country Club, Ponte Vedra Club, Lago Mar Club, Landmark Club, Congl. Country Club, Georgetown Club, Chevy Chase Club, Pisces Club, F Street Club, Coral Beach and Tennis Club, Johns Island Club, Omicron Delta Kappa. Episcopalian. Home: 10805 Tara Rd Potomac MD 20854-1341 also: Johns Island 1000 Beach Rd Vero Beach FL 32963-3429 also: Johns Island 690 Ocean Rd Vero Beach FL 32963-3516

PETER, RICHARD ECTOR, zoology educator; b. Medicine Hat, Alta., Can., Mar. 7, 1943; s. Arthur E. and Josephine (Wroblski) P.; m. Leona L. Booth, Dec. 27, 1965; children: Jason E., Matthew T.B. BSc with honors, U. Atla., 1965, PhD, U. Wash., 1969. Postdoctoral fellow U. Bristol, Eng., 1969-70; asst. prof. U. Alta., Edmonton, 1971-74, assoc. prof., 1974-79, prof., 1979—, chmn. dept. zoology, 1983-89, 90-92, dean of sci., 1992—. Contbr. more than 250 sci. papers. Recipient Pickford medal Internat. Com. on Comparative Endocrinology, 1985. Fellow AAAS, Royal Soc. Can.; mem. Can. Soc. Zoology (pres. 1991-92), Endocrine Soc., Soc. for Study of Reproduction, Internat. Soc. Neuroendocrinology, Can. Coun. of Univ. Biology Chmn. (pres. 1986-87), Internat. Fedn. Comparative Endocrinol. Socs. (pres. 1989-93).

PETER, VAL JOSEPH, social service administrator, educator, priest; b. Omaha, Nov. 20, 1934. PhB, Gregorian U., Rome, 1956, Licentiate in Sacred Theology, 1960; STD, U. St. Thomas, Rome, 1965; JCD, Lateran U., Rome, 1967; PhD (hon.), Creighton U., 1992, Coll. St. Mary, 1993. Ordained priest Roman Cath. Ch., 1960. Defender of bond Archdiocese of Omaha, 1966—; chmn. dept. theology Coll. of St. Mary, Omaha, 1966-70; prof. theology Creighton U., Omaha, 1970-84; exec. dir. Father Flanagan's Boys Home, Boys Town, Nebr., 1984—. Bd. dirs. St. Joseph Ctr. for Mental Health, 1985—, Boy Scouts Am., 1985—, NCCJ, 1985-93. Recipient Disting. Faculty award Creighton U., 1983, Presdl. citation, 1984, Archbishop Gerald T. Bergan award, 1986, Svc. to Mankind award Sertoma Internat., 1987, Creighton Prep Alumnus of Yr. award, 1988, Douglas County Bd. Commrs. award, 1990, Person of Yr. award U. Notre Dame, 1991, River City Roundup Heritage award, 1992, Toastmasters Internat. Comm. and Leadership award, 1992, Pope John XXIII award Roncalli H.S., 1993, AK-SAR-BEN Excellence in Edn. award, 1993, Nat. Direct Mktg. award Direct Mktg. Assn., 1993, Golden Apple award Met. C.C. Found., 1994; named Outstanding Humanitarian, Order Sons of Italy, 1987, Raoul Wallenberg Humanitarian of Yr., 1991. Mem. Nat. Assn. Homes and Svcs. for Children (bd. dirs.), League Civil Rights (bd. dirs. 1986-92), Am. Our Sunday Vistior Inst. (bd dirs. 1986—), Greater Omaha C. of c. (exec. com. 1991—), Omaha Cmty. Partnership, Canon Law Soc. Am., Cath. Theol. Soc. Am., Omaha 2000, Equestrian Order of Holy Sepulchre, 1989. Roman Catholic. Home and office: Father Flanagan's Boy's Home 14100 Crawford St Boys Town NE 68010-7520

PETERKIN, ALBERT GORDON, retired education educator; b. Phila., May 25, 1915; s. Albert Gordon and Eleanor Frances (Fricke) P.; m. Helen Webster, June 14, 1947; children: Eleanor Fricke, Scott Boddington, Mark Webster. BA, U. Pa., 1936; MAT, Harvard U., 1946; EdD, Columbia U., 1954. Cert. sch. adminstr., N.J., Conn., Ill. Tchr. Arms Acad., Shelburne Falls, Mass., 1938-39, Park Sch. of Buffalo, Snyder, N.Y., 1939-41; asst. prof. Lehigh U., Bethlehem, Pa., 1948-55; supt. Watchung Hills Regional High Sch., Warren, N.J., 1955-60, Westport (Conn.) Pub. Schs., 1960-70, Winnetka (Ill.) Sch. Dist. 36, 1971-77; prof. edn. Vanderbilt U., Nashville, 1977-81; ret., 1981; cons. Nat. Assn. Sch. Bus. Officers, Washington, 1968-70, Tenn. State U., Nashville, 1980-81; advisor Coun. Basic Edn., Washington, 1975; trustee Country Sch., Madison, Conn., 1985-91; chmn. master's program Iranian Sch. Devel., 1978-80, assessment instrument student devel., 1974; initiator Cooperative Individualized Reading Project, U.S. Office Edn., 1970-73. Initiator Urban Coalition Sch. Integ, Bridgeport, Conn., 1969-70; pres. Friends of Libr., Madison, 1984-85p prodr. Cmty. TV, Madison, 1984-90; mem. Madison Inland Wetlands Commn., 1985—, chmn., 1990-92. Lt. comdr. USNR, 1941-45, PTO. John Hay fellow Greenwood Found., 1965; Kettering Found. fellow, 1966, 65; Whitehead fellow Harvard Sch. Edn., 1970-71; named to Supt.'s Hall of Fame Sch. Mgmt. Study Group, 1973. Mem. Am. Assn. Sch. Adminstrs., Suburban Sch. Supts., Madison Country Club, Madison Beach Club, Phi Delta Kappa. Mem. Religious Soc. of Friends. Avocations: garden design, travel, home video, golf, music. Home: 210 Neck Rd Madison CT 06443-2720

PETERKIN, GEORGE ALEXANDER, JR., marine transportation company executive; b. Baton Rouge, Apr. 12, 1927; s. George Alexander and Genevieve (Favrot) P.; m. Nancy Girling, Jan. 27, 1965; children—George Alexander III, Julie, John Thomas, Susan, Lynn. B.B.A., U. Tex., 1948. With Dixie Carriers, Inc., Galveston, Tex.; soliciting freight agt. Dixie Carriers, Inc., New Orleans, Houston, 1949-50; asst. to pres. Dixie Carriers, Inc., Houston, 1953, pres., 1953-73, chmn. bd., 1973—; pres. Kirby Industries, Inc., Houston, 1973-76; pres. Kirby Corp., 1976-95, chmn. bd., 1995—. Bd. dirs. Tex. Med. Center, 1965—, Living Bank, 1968-86; trustee Tex. Children's Hosp., 1964—. Served with USN, 1945-46. Mem. World Pres. Orgn., Chief Execs. Orgn., Am. Bur. Shipping, Ramada Club, Houston Country Club, Bayou Club, Univ. Club N.Y. Avocations: swimming, running, golf, shooting. Home: 5787 Indian Cir Houston TX 77057-1302 Office: Kirby Corp 1775 Saint James Pl Ste 300 Houston TX 77056-3403

PETERLE, TONY JOHN, zoologist, educator; b. Cleve., July 7, 1925; s. Anton and Anna (Katic) P.; m. Thelma Josephine Coleman, July 30, 1949; children—Ann Faulkner, Tony Scott. BS, Utah State U., 1949; MS, U. Mich., 1950, PhD (univ. scholar), 1954; Fulbright scholar, U. Aberdeen, Scotland, 1954-55; postgrad., Oak Ridge Inst. Nuclear Studies, 1961. With Niederhauser Lumber Co., 1947-49, Macfarland Tree Svc., 1949-51; rsch. biologist Mich. Dept. Conservation, 1951-54; asst. dir. Rose Lake Expt. Sta., 1955-59; leader Ohio Coop. Wildlife Rsch. unit U.S. Fish and Wildlife Svc., Dept. Interior, 1959-63; asso. prof., then prof. zoology Ohio State U., Columbus, 1959-89, prof. emeritus, 1989; chmn. faculty population and environmental biology Ohio State U., 1968-69, chmn. dept. zoology, 1969-81, dir. program in environ. biology, 1970-71; liaison officer Internat. Union Game Biologists, 1965-93; co-organizer, chmn. internat. affairs com., mem. com. ecotoxicology XIII Internat. Congress Game Biology, 1979-80; pvt. cons., 1989—; mem. com. rev. EPA pesticide decision making Nat. Acad. Scis.-NRC; mem. vis. scientists program Am. Inst. Biol. Scis.-ERDA, 1971-77; mem. com. pesticides Nat. Acad. Scis., com. on emerging trends in agr. and effects on fish and wildlife; mem. ecology com. of sci. adv. council EPA, 1979-87; mem. research units coordinating com. Ohio Coop. Wildlife and Fisheries, 1963-89; vis. scientist EPA, Corvallis, 1987. Author: Wildlife Toxicology, 1991; editor: Jour. of Wildlife Mgmt., 1969-70, 84-85, 2020 Vision Meeting the Fish and Wildlife Conservation Challenges of the 21st Century, 1992. Served with AUS, 1943-46. Fellow AAAS, Am. Inst. Biol. Scis., Ohio Acad. Sci.; mem. Wildlife Disease Assn., Wildlife Soc. (regional rep. 1962-67, v.p. 1968, pres. 1972, Leopold award 1990, hon. mem. 1990, Profl. award of merit North Ctrl. sect. 1993), Nat. Audubon Soc. (bd. dirs. 1985-87), Ecol. Soc., INTECOL-NSF panel U.S.-Japan Program, Xi Sigma Pi, Phi Kappa Phi. Home: 4072 Klondike Rd Delaware OH 43015-9513 Office: Ohio State U Dept Zoology 1735 Neil Ave Columbus OH 43210-1293

PETERMAN, BRUCE EDGAR, aircraft company executive; b. Merrill, Wis., Jan. 27, 1931; s. Neton Elmer and Grace Elisabeth (Schroeder) P.; m. Constance Lenore Callsen, Feb. 9, 1952; children: Michael Lee, Jeffrey Dean, Elizabeth Ann. AA in Aero. Engring., Spartan Coll., 1951; BS in Aero. Engring., Wichita State Univ., 1955, MS in Aero. Engring., 1961. With detail design and drafting dept. Beech Aircraft Corp., Wichita, Kans., 1951-53; with design, flight test and tech. engring. depts. Cessna Aircraft Co., Wichita, 1953-72, chief engr. Wallace div., 1972-81, v.p. product engring., 1981-87, v.p. ops., 1987-89, sr. v.p., 1989—; trustee U. Kans. Ctr. for Rsch., Lawrence, 1985-88, Cessna Found., 1987—; mem. industry adv. com. Nat. Inst. Aviation Rsch., Wichita State U., 1985—; mem. aerospace engring. adv. com. U. Kans., Lawrence, 1975-89, engring. dept. adv. com., 1987-91; mem. Kans. Tech. Enterprise Corp. Ctrs. Com., 1992-94; bd. dirs., 1994—. Bd. dirs. Endowment Assn. Wichita State U., 1993—; co-chair Kans. Math. and Sci. Coalition, 1992—. Assoc. fellow AIAA; mem. Soc. Automotive Engrs. (aerospace coun. 1976-91, tech. bd. 1987-91). Avocations: instrument rated multi-engine pilot. Home: 15606 Moscelyn Ln Goddard KS 67052-9331 Office: Cessna Aircraft Co PO Box 7706 Wichita KS 67277-7706

PETERMAN, DONALD, cinematographer. Cinematographer: (films) When a Stranger Calls, 1979, Rich and Famous, 1981, King of the Mountain, 1981, Young Doctors in Love, 1982, Kiss Me Goodbye, 1982, Flashdance, 1983 (Academy award nomination best cinematography 1983), Splash, 1984, Best Defense, 1984, Mass Appeal, 1984, American Flyer, 1985, Cocoon, 1985, Star Trek IV: The Voyage Home, 1986 (Academy award nomination best cinematography 1986), Gung Ho, 1986, Planes, Trains and Automobiles, 1987, She's Having a Baby, 1988, She's Out of Control, 1989, Point Break, 1991, Mr. Saturday Night, 1992, Addams Family Values, 1993. Office: The Gersh Agency 232 N Canon Dr Beverly Hills CA 90210*

PETERMAN, JOHN L., economist; b. Elizabeth, N.J., Jan. 8, 1937; s. Otto L. and Grace E. (Caskie) P.; m. Marlowe H. Seltzer, Aug. 17, 1956; children: Lynn, Jeffrey, Karen, Colleen. BA, Drew U., 1959; PhD, U. Va., 1964. Univ. asst. prof. econs. U. Va., Charlottesville, 1964-66; from asst. to assoc. prof. U. Chgo., 1966-73; chief economist Securities Investors Protection Corp., Washington, 1973-75; economist, dep. dir., bur. dir. FTC, Washington, 1976-94; prin. Law and Econs. Cons. Group, Inc., Washington, 1994—. Contbr. articles to profl. jours. Mem. Raven Soc., Phi Beta Kappa. Office: Law and Econs Cons Group Inc 1775 Pennsylvania Ave NW Washington DC 20006

PETERNELL, BEN CLAYTON, hospitality company executive; b. Ft. Wayne, Ind., Nov. 5, 1945; s. Frank and Marabelle (Kigar) P.; m. Pamela S. Lorman, Dec. 28, 1968; children: Andrew, Mark. BA in Psychology, Hanover Coll., 1968; MBA in Mgmt. and Orgn. Behavior, Ind. U., 1970. Various mgmt. positions Firestone Tire & Rubber Co., Akron, Ohio, 1970-73; group v.p., personnel Am. Hosp. Supply Co., Evanston, Ill., 1973-85; sr. v.p human resources and corp. rels. The Promus Cos., Memphis, 1985—. Active Germantown (Tenn.) Youth Soccer Club, 1986—; mem. commn. on 21st century Rhodes Coll.; bd. dirs. Sta. WKNO pub. Radio-TV, 1987—, chmn. bd. dirs., 1991—. Mem. Conf. Personnel Officers. Presbyterian. Home: 2313 Dogwood Meadows Cv Memphis TN 38139-6709 Office: The Promus Cos 1023 Cherry Rd Memphis TN 38117-5423

PETERS, A. WINNIETT, leaf tobacco merchant, exporter; b. Tarboro, N.C., Mar. 18, 1927; s. A. Winniett and Ethel (Battle) P.; m. Sarah Walston, June 9, 1951; children: Winniett Jr. (dec.), Paxton, Walston, Tom. BS in Commerce, U. N.C., 1950. Chmn. Jas. I. Miller Tobacco Co., Wilson, N.C., also bd. dirs.; v.p. Standard Comml. Tobacco Co., Wilson, also bd. dirs.; bd. dirs. Branch Corp., Wilson, Branch Banking & Trust Co., Wilson. Mem. Wilson (N.C.) City Council, 1960. Served with USN, 1945-47, PTO. Mem. Orderof Gimghoul, Phi Beta Kappa, Phi Eta Sigma. Presbyterian. Avocations: hunting, fishing, golf. Home: 1009 Woodland Dr NW Wilson NC 27893-2172

PETERS, ALAN, anatomy educator; b. Nottingham, Eng., Dec. 6, 1929; came to U.S., 1966; s. Robert and Mabel (Woplington) P.; m. Verona Muriel Shipman, Sept. 30, 1955; children: Ann Verona, Sally Elizabeth, Susan Clare. BSc, Bristol (Eng.) U., 1951, PhD, 1954. Lectr. anatomy Edinburgh (Scotland) U., 1958-66; vis. lectr. Harvard, 1963-64; prof., chmn. dept. anatomy and neurobiology Boston U., 1966—; anatomy com. Nat. Bd. Med. Examiners, 1971-75; mem. neurology B Study sect. NIH, 1975-79, chmn., 1978-79; affiliate scientist Yerkes Regional Primate Rsch. Ctr., 1984—. Author: (with S.L. Palay and H. deF Webster) The Fine Structure of the Nervous System, 1970, 3rd edit., 1991, Myelination, 1970; contbr. (with A.N. Davison) articles profl. jours.; mem. editorial bd. Anat. Record, 1972-81, Jour. Comparative Neurology, Neurocytology, 1972-89, 93—, Cerebral Cortex, 1990—, Studies of Brain Function, Anat. and Embryology, 1989-92; editor book series: (with E.G. Jones) Cerebral Cortex, 1984—. Served to 2d lt. Royal Army Med. Corps, 1955-57. Recipient Javits neurosci. investigator award NIH, 1986. Mem. Anat. Soc. Gt. Britain and Ireland (Symington prize anatomy 1962, overseas mem. coun. 1969), Assn. Anatomy Chmn. (pres. 1976-77), Am. Anat. Assn. (exec. com. 1986-90, pres. 1992-93), Am. Soc. Cell Biology, Soc. Neuroscis., Internat. Primatological Soc., Cajal Club (Harman lectr. 1990, Cortical Discoverer award 1991). Home: 16 High Rock Cir Waltham MA 02154-2207 Office: Boston U Sch Medicine Dept Anatomy and Neurobiology 80 E Concord St Roxbury MA 02118-2394

PETERS, ALTON EMIL, lawyer; b. Albany, N.Y., Mar. 21, 1935; s. Emil and Winifred (Rosch) P.; m. Elizabeth Irving Berlin, Feb. 27, 1970; children: Rachel Canfield, Emily Anstice Fletcher. A.B. cum laude, Harvard U., 1955, LL.B., 1958. Bar: N.Y. 1958, U.S. Dist. Ct. (so. dist.) N.Y. 1963. Assoc. Bleakley, Platt, Schmidt & Fritz, 1959-65, mem., 1956-81; ptnr. Miller, Montgomery, Sogi & Brady, 1981-83, Kelley Drye & Warren, N.Y.C., 1983—. Bd. dirs. Am. Friends of Covent Garden and the Royal Ballet, N.Y.C., 1971— v.p., 1971—; mem. coun. Am. Mus. in Britain, Bath, Eng., 1970—, chmn. U.S.A., 1975-92; bd. dirs. Brit. Am. Arts Assn., N.Y.C., 1983—, chmn., 1984—; English-Speaking Union U.S., bd. dirs. N.Y. br., 1963—, chmn. 1972-88; bd. dirs. Goodwill Industries of Greater N.Y., 1965—, pres., 1968-70, chmn., 1982—; mng. dir. Met. Opera Assn., N.Y.C., 1966—, sec. 1974-86, v.p., 1986-93, chm. Executive Com., 1993—; bd. dirs. Met. Opera Guild, Inc., N.Y.C., 1965—, chmn. exec. com. 1968-70, 74-79, 1st v.p., 1979-86, pres., 1986—; bd. dirs. Lincoln Ctr. for Performing Arts, N.Y.C., 1986—; trustee Signet Assocs., Cambridge, Mass., 1957-73, treas. 1957-73, hon. trustee, 1973—; fellow Pierpont Morgan Library, Frick Collection; trustee Acad. Am. Poets, N.Y.C., 1988—, treas., 1993—, Cathedral of St. John the Divine, 1991—. Decorated Knight Order of St. John of Jerusalem, Officer Order of Brit. Empire. Mem. ABA, N.Y. State Bar Assn., Assn. Var City N.Y., Am. Judicature Soc., Am. Coll. Probate Counsel, Century Assn., Church Club, Grolier Club (coun. 1994—), Harvard Club N.Y.C., Knickerbocker Club (bd. govs. 1986-92, 94—), Pilgrims, Club of Odd Volumes. Home: 211 Central Park W New York NY 10024-6020 Office: Kelley Drye and Warren 101 Park Ave New York NY 10178-0001

PETERS, ARTHUR KING, international trade executive, author, consultant; b. Charleston, W.Va., Oct. 17, 1919; s. Arthur Cushing and Jessie (King) P.; m. Sarah Jebb Whitaker, Oct. 21, 1943; children: Robert Bruce, Margaret Adam, Michael Whitaker. AB, Cornell U., 1940; student, U.S. Army Command and Gen. Staff Coll., 1945; MA, Columbia U., 1954, PhD, 1969. With W.R. Grace and Co., 1940-50; pres., owner A.K. Peters Co., N.Y.C., 1950—; asst. prof. French lit. Hunter Coll., CUNY, 1971-74; pres., chmn. French-Am. Found., N.Y.C., 1977-83; del. U.S. Trade Mission to Peru, Argentina, 1957. Author: Cocteau and Gide, 1973, Jean Cocteau and the French Scene, 1983, Jean Cocteau and His World, 1987 (Prix Littéraire Etats-Unis-France 1989), Seven Trails West, 1995; translator, critic French lit.; contbr. articles to profl jours. Maj. M.I., U.S. Army, 1941-46. Decorated Chevalier de L'ordre des Arts et des Lettres, Govt. France, 1978, Chevalier de la Legion d'Honneur, Govt. France, 1984. Mem. MLA, Council Fgn. Relations, Assn. Am. Tchrs. French, Am. Importers Assn. (pres. 1965), Phi Delta Theta. Mem. Reformed Ch. (deacon). Clubs: Alpine; Alpine (London); University (N.Y.C.); Bronxville Field; Cercle de L'Union Interalliee (Paris). Avocations: squash, skiing, mountaineering, tennis. Home: 14 Village Ln Bronxville NY 10708-4806 Office: AK Peters Co 230 Park Ave Ste 1518 New York NY 10169-1518

PETERS, AULANA LOUISE, government agency commissioner, lawyer; b. Shreveport, La., Nov. 30, 1941; d. Clyde A. and Eula Mae (Faulkner) Pharis; m. Bruce F. Peters, Oct. 6, 1967. BA in Philosophy, Coll. New Rochelle, 1963; JD, U. So. Calif., 1973. Bar: Calif., 1974. Sec., English corr. Publimondial, Spa, Milan, Italy, 1963-64, Fibramianto, Spa, Milan, 1964-65, Turkish del. to Office for Econ. Cooperation & Devel., Paris, 1965-66; adminstrv. asst. Office for Econ. Cooperation & Devel., Paris, 1966-67; assoc. Gibson, Dunn & Crutcher, L.A., 1973-80, ptnr., 1980-84, 88—; commr. SEC, Washington, 1984-88. Recipient Disting. Alumnus award Econs. Club So. Calif., 1984, Washington Achiever award Nat. Assn. Bank Women, 1986. Mem. ABA, State Bar of Calif. (civil litigation cons. group 1983-84), Los Angeles County Bar Assn., Black Women Lawyers Assn. L.A., Assn. Bus. Trial Lawyers (panelist L.A. 1982), Women's Forum, Washington. Office: Gibson Dunn & Crutcher 333 S Grand Ave Los Angeles CA 90071-1504

PETERS, BERNADETTE (BERNADETTE LAZZARA), actress; b. Queens, N.Y., Feb. 28, 1948; d. Peter and Marguerite (Maltese) Lazzara. Student, Quintano Sch. for Young Profls., N.Y.C. Ind. actress, entertainer, 1959—. Appeared on TV series All's Fair, 1976-77; frequent guest appearances on TV; films include The Longest Yard, 1974, Vigilant Force, 1975, W.C. Fields and Me, 1975, Silent Movie, 1976, The Jerk, 1979, Heart Beeps, 1981, Tulips, 1981, Pennies from Heaven, 1982 (Golden Globe Best Actress award), Annie, 1982, Slaves of NewYork, 1989, Pink Cadillac, 1989, Impromptu, 1990, Alice, 1990; stage appearances include The Most Happy Fella, 1959, Gypsy, 1961, This is Google, 1962, Riverwind, 1966, The Penny Friend, 1966, Curly McDimple, 1967, Johnny No-Trump, 1967, George M!, 1968, Dames at Sea, 1968, La Strada, 1969, W.C., 1971, On the Town, 1971, Tartuffe, 1972, Mack and Mabel, 1974, Sally and Marsha, 1982, Sunday in the Park with George, 1983 (Tony nomination 1983), Song and Dance, 1985, Into the Woods, 1987, The Goodbye Girl, 1992-93; TV films

David, 1989, Fall From Grace, 1990, The Last Best Year, 1990; rec. artist: (MCA Records) Bernadette Peters, 1980, Now Playing, 1981. Recipient Drama Desk award for Dames and Sea, 1968; Drama Desk award nomination, 1987, 88, Tony award nominee, 1971, 74, 83, 85, Tony award for Best Actress in Song and Dance, 1986, Theatre World citation for George M!, 1968, Drama Desk award, 1986, Hasty Pudding Theatrical award, 1987 woman of the Yr., Sara Siddons Actress of Yr. award, 1993-94. Office: Judy Katz PR 1790 Broadway Ste 1600 New York NY 10019

PETERS, CHARLES GIVEN, JR., editor; b. Charleston, W.Va., Dec. 22, 1926; s. Charles Given and Esther (Teague) P.; m. Elizabeth Bostwick Hubbell, Aug. 3, 1957; 1 child, Christian Avery. BA in Humanities, Columbia U., 1949, MA in English, 1951; LLB, U. Va., 1957; LLD (hon.), U. Charleston, 1979. Bar: W.Va. 1957, D.C. 1981. Atty. Peters, Merrick, Leslie & Mohler, Charleston, 1957-61; mem. W.Va State Legislature, Charleston, 1960-62; dir. evaluation Peace Corps, Washington, 1962-68; founder, editor in chief The Washington Monthly, 1968—; Author: How Washington Really Works, 4th edit., 1994, Tilting at Windmills, 1988; editor: (with Taylor Branch) Blowing the Whistle, 1972, (with James Fallows) The System, 1975, (with Michael Nelson) The Culture of Bureaucracy, 1977, (with Jonathan Alter) Inside the System, 5th edit., 1985. Author: How Washington Really Works, 1980, Tilting at Windmills, 1988; editor: (with Taylor Branch) Blowing the Whistle, 1972, (with James Fallows) The System, 1975, (with Michael Nelson) The Culture of Bureaucracy, 1977, (with Jonathan Alter) Inside the System, 5th edit., 1985. Mgr. John F. Kennedy campaign, Kanawha County, W.Va., 1960. Served with inf. U.S. Army, 1944-46. Recipient Columbia Journalism award, 1978; named West Virginian of Yr., Charleston Gazette-Mail, 1980; Poynter fellow Yale U., 1980. Democrat. Presbyterian. Office: The Washington Monthly Co 1611 Connecticut Ave NW Washington DC 20009-1033

PETERS, CHARLES WILLIAM, research and development company manager; b. Pierceton, Ind., Dec. 9, 1927; s. Mark Frederick and Zelda May (Line) P.; m. Katharine Louise Schuman, May 29, 1953; 1 child, Susan Kay; m. 2d, Patricia Ann Miles, Jan. 2, 1981; children: Bruce Miles Merkle, Leslie Ann Merkle Sanaie, Philip Frank Merkle, William Macneil Merkle. AB, Ind. U., 1950; postgrad. U. Md., 1952-58. Supervisory rsch. physicist Naval Rsch. Lab., Washington, 1950-71; physicist EPA, Washington, 1971-76; mgr. advanced systems EATON-Consol. Controls Corp., Springfield, Va., 1976-89, v.p. Nuclear Diagnostic Systems, Inc., Springfield, Va., 1989-92, cons. Am. Tech. Inst., 1993—. With U.S. Army, 1945-47. Mem. IEEE, AAAS, Am. Phys. Soc. Home and Office: 5235 N Whispering Hills Ln Tucson AZ 85704-2510

PETERS, DAVID ALLEN, mechanical engineering educator, consultant; b. East St. Louis, Ill., Jan. 31, 1947; s. Bernell Louis and Marian Louise (Blum) P.; m. Linda J. Conley, Jan. 25, 1969; children: Michael H., Laura A., Nathan C. BS in Applied Mechanics, Washington U., St. Louis, 1969, MS in Applied Mechanics, 1970; PhD in Aeros. and Astronautics, Stanford U., 1974. Assoc. engr. McDonnell Astronautics, 1969-70; rsch. scientist Army Aeronautics Lab., 1970-74; asst. prof. Washington U., 1975-77, assoc. prof., 1977-80, prof. mech. engring., 1980-85, chmn. dept., 1982-85; prof. aerospace engring. Ga. Inst Tech., Atlanta, 1985-91; dir. NASA Space Grant Consortium Ga. Inst. Tech., Atlanta, 1989-91; dir. Ctr. for Computational Mechanics Washington U., 1992—; prof. dept. mech. engring. Washington U., St. Louis, 1991—. Contbr. 50 articles to profl. jours. Recipient sci. contbn. award NASA, 1975, 76. Fellow AIAA, ASME; mem. Am. Helicopter Soc. (jour. editor 1987-90), Am. Soc. for Engring. Edn., Internat. Assn. for Computational Mechanics (charter), Am. Acad. Mechs., Pi Tau Sigma (gold medal 1978). Baptist. Home: 7629 Balson Ave Saint Louis MO 63130-2150 Office: Washington U Dept Mech Engring Campus Box 1185 Saint Louis MO 63130

PETERS, DAVID FRANKMAN, lawyer; b. Hagerstown, Md., Aug. 15, 1941; s. Harold E. and Lois (Frankman) P.; m. Jane Catherine Witherspoon, Aug. 21, 1965; children: Catherine, Elizabeth. BA, Washington and Lee U., 1963; LLB, Duke U., 1966. Bar: Va. 1966, U.S. Dist. Ct. (ea. and we. dists.) Va., U.S. Ct. Appeals (2d, 4th, 6th, 7th and D.C. cirs.). Assoc. Hunton & Williams, Richmond, Va., 1966-73, ptnr., 1973—. Pres. Children's Home Soc. Va., Richmond, 1977-78, bd. dirs., 1970-91; trustee Westminster-Canterbury Corp., 1995—; elder, trustee 1st Presbyn. Ch., Richmond. Mem. ABA, Va. Bar Assn. (chmn. adminstrn. law com. 1985-88), Richmond Bar Assn. Lodge: Kiwanis. Avocations: photography, travel. Home: 3 Windsor Way Richmond VA 23221-3232 Office: Hunton & Williams 951 E Byrd St Richmond VA 23219-4040

PETERS, DENNIS GAIL, chemist; b. L.A., Apr. 17, 1937; s. Samuel and Phyllis Dorothy (Pope) P. BS cum laude, Calif. Inst. Tech., 1958; PhD, Harvard U., 1962. Mem. faculty Ind. U., 1962—, prof. chemistry, 1974—, Herman T. Briscoe prof., 1975—. Co-author textbooks, contbr. articles profl. jours. Woodrow Wilson fellow, 1958-59; NIH predoctoral fellow, 1959-62; vis. fellow Japan Soc. for Promotion Sci., 1980; recipient Ulysses G. Weatherly award disting. teaching Ind. U., 1969, Disting. Teaching award Coll. Arts and Scis. Grad. Alumni Assn. Ind. U., 1984, Nat. Catalyst award for Disting. Teaching Chem. Mfrs. Assn., 1988; grantee NSF. Fellow Ind. Acad. Sci., Am. Inst. Chemists; mem. Am. Chem. Soc. (grantee, Div. of Analytical Chemistry award for excellence in teaching 1990), N.Y. Acad. Scis. Home: 1401 S Nancy St Bloomington IN 47401-6051 Office: Dept Chemistry Ind U Bloomington IN 47405

PETERS, DONALD CAMERON, construction company executive; b. Milw., Mar. 25, 1915; s. Simon C. and May (Gnewuch) P.; m. Twila Bingel, Dec. 7, 1940; children: Susan (Mrs. Douglas Ingram), David C., Bruce C., Douglas C. B.S. in Civil Engring. Marquette U., 1938. Registered profl. engr., Wis., Pa. Engr. Siesel Constrn. Co., Milw., 1938-44; v.p., dir. Crump, Inc., Pitts., 1944-51; pres. Mellon-Stuart Co., Pitts., 1951-73, also bd. dirs., chmn., 1973-81; mem. 5 man gen. com rewriting Pitts. Bldg. Code. 1947; mem., chmn. Pa. Registration Bd. Profl. Engrs., 1962-82; chmn. bd. standards and appeals Pitts. Bur. Bldg. Inspection, 1960-72; past pres. Pitts. Builders Exch.; adv. bd. Liberty Mut. Ins., 1968—. Chmn. bd. suprs. Pine Twp., Allegheny County, 1953-80; chmn. Constrn. Industry Advancement Program We. Pa., 1975-93; trustee La Roche Coll., Pitts., 1967—, chmn., 1983-84; bd. dirs. North Hills Passavant Hosp., 1963-90, chmn., 1983-84. Fellow ASCE; mem. NSPE (nat. dir. 1954-57, chmn. bd. ethical rev. 1978-79), Pa. Soc. Profl. Engrs. (pres. 1953-54), Assn. Gen. Contractors Am. (nat. dir.), Pitts. C. of C. (chmn., dir. 1973-81), Master Builders Assn. Western Pa. (past pres.), SBA, Triangle, Tau Beta Pi, Alpha Sigma Nu. Club: Duquesne (Pitts.). Home: 2803 SE 18th Ct Cape Coral FL 33904-4077

PETERS, DOUGLAS DENNISON, Canadian government official, member of Parliament; b. Brandon, Man., Can., Mar. 3, 1930; s. Wilfred Seymour and Mary Gladys (Dennison) P.; m. Audrey Catherine Clark, June 26, 1954; children: David Wilfrid, Catherine Elaine Peters Gilchrist. B Commerce, Queen's U., Kingston, Ont., Can., 1963; PhD in Fin. and Commerce, U. Pa., 1969. With Bank of Montreal, Winnipeg, Man., 1950-60; chief economist Toronto (Ont., Can.)-Dominion Bank, 1966—, v.p., chief economist, 1971—, sr. v.p., chief econimist, 1980-93; M.P. for Scarborough East House of Commons, Ottawa, Ont., 1993—, sec. of state for fin., 1993—. Author: The Monetarist Counterrevolution - A Critique of Canada's Monetary Policy, 1975-1980, 1980; contbr. articles to profl. publs. Scholar Can. Coun., 1963, 64, Ford Found., 1965. Liberal. Avocation: tennis. Home: 151 Bay St # 102, Ottawa, ON Canada K1R 7T2 Office: House of Commons, Parliament Bldg Rm 442N, Wellington St, Ottawa, ON Canada K1A 0A6

PETERS, DOUGLAS SCOTT, health care executive; b. Columbus, Ohio, Nov. 2, 1943; s. Edward Alvin and Jane (Appleman) P.; m. Karen Ann Jones, June 19, 1965; children: Brian Edward, Laura Kathleen. BS, Ohio State U., 1965; MHA with distinction, U. Mich., 1967. Assoc. dir. U. Mich. Hosp., Ann Arbor, 1968-69-74; dir. U. Nebr. Hosps. and Clinics, Omaha, 1974-77; exec. dir. Henry Ford Hosp., Detroit, 1977-83, pres., 1984—; cons. PanAm. Health Orgn., Washington, 1971-73; asst. prof. dept. med. and ednl. adminstrn. U. Nebr., 1974-77. Bd. dirs. New Detroit, Inc., 1985—; cochmn. Multiple Sclerosis Testimonial Dinner, Detroit, 1985; big bro. Big Bros./Big Sisters, Omaha, 1975. Served to lt. USNR, 1967-69. Fellow Am. Coll. Healthcare Execs. (regent 1984); mem. Young Pres. Orgn., Mich Hosp. Assn. (bd. dirs.), Frontiers in Health Services Mgmt. (mem. editorial bd.

1983). Republican. Home: 1440 N State St #38 Chicago IL 60602-1610 Office: Main Line Health 259 Radnor Chester Rd Radnor PA 19087

PETERS, EDWARD MURRAY, history educator; b. New Haven, Conn., May 21, 1936; s. Edward Murray and Marjorie (Corcoran) P.; m. Patricia Ann Knapp, July 8, 1961; children—Nicole, Moira, Edward. B.A., Yale U., 1963, M.A., 1965, Ph.D., 1967. Instr. in English and history Quinnipiac Coll., Hamden, Conn., 1964-67; asst. prof. history U. Calif., San Diego, 1967-68; asst. prof. medieval history U. Pa., Phila., 1968-70; assoc. prof., 1970-81, Henry Charles Lea prof. history, 1981—, curator Henry Charles Lea Library, 1968—; gasthoogleraar KU Leuven, Belgium, 1992. Author: The Shadow King, 1970, (with A.C. Kors) Witchcraft in Europe, 1100-1750, 1972, Europe: The World of the Middle Ages, 1977, The Magician, The Witch and The Law, 1978, Europe and the Middle Ages, 1983, Torture, 1985, Inquisition, 1988, (TV series) The World of the Middle Ages, 1974, The World Around the Revolution, 1977, also articles, revs. and introductions; editor, translator: (with Jeanne Krochalis) The World of Piers Plowman, 1975; editor: Heresy and Authority in Medieval Europe, 1980. Served with AUS, 1956-59. Woodrow Wilson fellow, 1963-64, dissertation fellow, 1966-67, hon. Sterling fellow, 1966-67, ACLS fellow, 1981-82, Guggenheim fellow, 1988-89. Fellow Medieval Acad. Am., Royal Hist. Soc.; mem. Am. Hist. Assn., Medieval Acad. Am., Am. Soc. Legal History, Maiestas, Iuris Canonici Medii Aevi Consociatio, Soc. Jean Bodin, Dante Soc. Am. Home: 4225 Regent Sq Philadelphia PA 19104-4438 Office: U Pa Dept History Philadelphia PA 19104

PETERS, ELLEN ASH, state supreme court chief justice; b. Berlin, Mar. 21, 1930; came to U.S., 1939, naturalized, 1947; d. Ernest Edward and Hildegard (Simon) Ash; m. Phillip I. Blumberg; children: David Bryan Peters, James Douglas Peters, Julie Peters Haden. BA with honors, Swarthmore Coll., 1951, LLD (hon.), 1983; LLB cum laude, Yale U., 1954, MA (hon.), 1964, LLD (hon.), 1985; LLD (hon.), U. Hartford, 1983; Georgetown U., 1984; LLD (hon.), Yale U., 1985, Conn. Coll., 1985, N.Y. Law Sch., 1985; HLD (hon.), St. Joseph Coll., 1986; LLD (hon.), Colgate U., 1986, Trinity Coll., 1987, Bates Coll., 1987, Wesleyan U., 1987, DePaul U., 1988; HLD (hon.), Albertus Magnus Coll., 1990; LLD (hon.), U. Conn., 1992; LLD, U. Rochester, 1993. Bar: Conn. 1957. Law clk. to judge U.S. Circuit Ct., 1954-55; assoc. in law U. Calif., Berkeley, 1955-56; prof. law Yale U., New Haven, 1956-78; adj. prof. law; assoc. justice Conn. Supreme Ct., Hartford, 1978-84; chief justice Conn. Supreme Ct., 1984—. Author: Commercial Transactions: Cases, Texts, and Problems, 1971, Negotiable Instruments Primer, 1974; contbr. articles to profl. jours. Bd. mgrs. Swarthmore Coll., 1970-81; trustee Yale-New Haven Hosp., 1981-85, Yale Corp., 1986-92; mem. conf. Chief Justices, 1984—, pres. 1994; hon. chmn. U.S. Constl. Bicentennial Commn., 1986-91; mem. Conn. Permanent Commn. on Status of Women, 1973-74, Conn. Bd. Parsons, 1978-80, Conn. Law Revision Commn., 1978-84; bd. dirs. Nat. Ctr. State Cts., 1992—, chmn., 1994. Recipient Ella Grasso award, 1982, Jud. award Conn. Trial Lawyers Assn., 1982, citation of merit Yale Law Sch., 1983, Pioneer Woman award Hartford Coll. for Women, 1988, Disting. Svc. award U. Conn. Law Sch. Alumni Assn., 1993. Mem. ABA, Conn. Bar Assn. (Jud. award 1992), Am. Law Inst. (coun.), Am. Acad. Arts and Scis., Am. Philos. Soc. Office: Conn Supreme Ct Drawer N Sta A 231 Capitol Ave Hartford CT 06106

PETERS, ERNEST, metallurgy educator, consultant; b. Steinbach, Man., Can., Jan. 27, 1926; s. Franz Isaac Peters and Margaretha (Klassen) MacLachlan; m. Gwynneth Salome Walker, Sept. 21, 1949; children: Charlotte Ann Peters Garcia, Gwynneth Elizabeth Peters Becker. BASc, U. B.C., Can., 1949, MASc, 1951, PhD, 1956. Registered profl. engr., B.C. Metallurgist Geneva Steel Co., Provo, Utah, 1949-50; rsch. engr. Cominco Ltd., Trail, B.C., Can., 1951-53, Union Carbide Metals Co., Niagara Falls, N.Y., 1956-58; instr. U. B.C., Vancouver, 1955-56, asst. prof., 1958-65, assoc. prof., 1966-68, prof., 1968-91, prof. emeritis, 1991—; cons. Cominco Ltd., Trail, 1958-92, Kennecott Copper Corp., Salt Lake City, 1969-71, E Z Australasia, Melbourne, Australia, 1977-78, Bacon, Donaldson & Assocs., Vancouver, 1981-90, Westmin Resources Ltd., 1991—; mem. selection com. NRC Can., Ottawa, 1967-68; extractive metallurgy lectr. The Metals Soc. of AIME, Las Vegas, Nev., 1976; keynote lectr. Benelux Metallurgie, Brussels, 1977. Contbr. articles to profl. jours.; patentee in Hydromet. Mem. selection com. Killam fellowships Can. Coun., Ottawa, 1988-91. Sgt. RCAF, 1943-45. Recipient C.I.M. Alcan award, 1983, James Douglas Gold medal AIME, 1986, Mineral Scis. Edn. award AIME, 1992, Can. Materials Sci. Conf. Metal Chemistry award, 1993; named Indsl. Rsch. chair, 11 Can. cos., 1987-92; Killam fellow Can. Coun., 1983-85. Fellow Royal Soc. Can., The Metall. Soc. of AIME, Can. Inst. Mining & Metallurgy; mem. B.C. Assn. Profl. Engrs. Baptist. Avocations: skiing, windsurfing, auto control model planes. Home: 2708 W 33d Ave, Vancouver, BC Canada V6N 2G1 Office: U BC Dept Metals and Materials Engring, 309-6350 Stores Rd, Vancouver, BC Canada V6T 1Z4

PETERS, FARNSLEY LEWELLYN, retired association executive; b. Louisville, Aug. 11, 1929; s. Floyd P. and Freda E. (Meyer) P.; m. Jean Davies, June 28, 1952; children: Susan, David. B.S., U. Wis., 1952. Vice pres. F.P. Peters Moving & Storage Co., Joliet, Ill., 1954-62; dept. mgr. Madison (Wis.) C. of C., 1962-65; mgr. Greater Aurora (Ill.) C. of C., 1965-70; exec. v.p. Rockford (Ill.) Area C. of C., 1970-78, Cin. C. of C., 1978-80; pres. Iowa Assn. Bus. and Industry, Des Moines, 1981-90, ret., 1990; cons., 1991—. Served as 1st lt. U.S. Army, 1952-54. Recipient Outstanding Citizen award DuKane Valley Council, 1971. Mem. Am. Assn. C. of C. Execs. (dir.), Ill. Assn. C. of C. Execs. (pres.), Insts. for Orgn. Mgmt. (bd. regents), Ill. Jr. C. of C. (life), Alpha Chi Rho, Nat. W. Club (U. Wis.), Rotary (pres. Venice-Nokomis club 1993-94). Home: 910 Bayshore Rd Nokomis FL 34275-1920

PETERS, FRANK ALBERT, retired chemical engineer; b. Washington, June 3, 1931; s. Charles Albert and Dorothy Lynette (Paine) P.; m. Carol Beattie Taylor, Feb. 25, 1955; children: Thomas, June, Erick, Victor. B-SChemE, U. Md., 1955. Devel. engr. Celanese Corp. Am., Cumberland, Md., 1955-58; chem. Engr. U.S. Bur. Mines, College Park, Md., 1958-66; project leader U.S. Bur. Mines, College Park, Md., 1966-70; rsch. supr., 1977; chief process evaluation U.S. Bur. Mines, Washington, 1977-94, ret., 1994. Contbr. over 20 articles to profl. jours. Mem. AICE, Am. Assn. Cost Engrs. Avocations: photography, model railroading. Home: 12311 Glen Mill Rd Potomac MD 20854-1928

PETERS, FRANK LEWIS, JR., retired arts editor; b. Springfield, Mo., Oct. 19, 1930; s. Frank Lewis and Mary (Frissell) P.; m. Alba Manciani, Jan. 20, 1963; children—Carl Nathaniel, Adrian Frissell. A.B., Drury Coll., 1951; postgrad., State U. Iowa, 1953-55. Copy editor Ark. Gazette, Little Rock, 1958-59, Springfield (Mo.) Leader & Press, 1960-61; mng. editor Rome (Italy) Daily Am., 1962-64; music editor St. Louis Post-Dispatch, 1967-84, arts editor 1984-88. Co-author: (with George McCue) A Guide to the Architecture of St. Louis, 1989. Served with AUS, 1951-52. Recipient Pulitzer prize distinguished criticism, 1972. Mem. SAR, Lambda Chi Alpha. Episcopalian. Home: 11959 Lombardy Ln Saint Louis MO 63128-1516

PETERS, GARRY LOWELL, wholesale grocery executive; b. Gary, Ind., Oct. 1, 1952; s. Lowell Arwin and Geraldine Rose (Garner) P.; m. Patricia Louise Thursby, Dec. 28, 1974; children: Eric Matthew, Blake Jordan, Joel Ryan. BA, Taylor U., 1975. Route salesman Pepsi-Cola Bottling Co., Indpls., 1975-76, merchandiser, 1977, dist. mgr., 1978; merchandising mgr. Pepsi-Cola Bottling Group, Indpls., 1979-80, sales mgr., 1981-83; area v.p. Pepsi-Cola Bottling Group, Austin, Tex., 1984-86; pres. McMahan-Leib Frozen World, Inc. div. Allied Co., Indpls., 1987-88; exec. v.p. Allied Grocers Ind. div. Allied Co., Indpls., 1987-89; exec. v.p. human resources Safeway Foods, Inc., 1990—. Home: 105 Cherokee Ln Noblesville IN 46060-9073 Office: Safeway Foods Inc 3311 Shelby St Indianapolis IN 46227-3257

PETERS, GORDON BENES, musician; b. Oak Park, Ill., Jan. 4, 1931; s. Arthur George and Julia Anne (Benes) P. Student, Northwestern U., 1949-50; Mus.B., Eastman Sch. Music, 1956, Mus.M., 1962. Percussionist Rochester (N.Y.) Philharmonic Orch., 1955-59; prin. percussionist Grant Park Symphony Orch., Chgo., 1955-58; mem. faculty Rochester Bd. Edn., 1956-57, Geneseo State Tchrs. Coll., 1957-58; acting prin. percussionist Rochester, N.Y., 1958-59; prin. percussionist Chgo. Symphony Orch.,

1959—; condr., adminstr. Civic Orch. Chgo., 1966-87; condr. Elmhurst Symphony Orch., 1968-73; instr. percussion instruments Northwestern U., 1963-68, lectr., 1991; guest conductor Bangor (Maine) Symphony, 1993. Author-pub.: The Drummer: Man; arranger-pub. Marimba Ensemble arrangements; composer-pub.: Swords of Moda-Ling; editor: percussion column Instrumentalist mag, 1963-69; contbr. articles to profl. jours. Bd. dirs. Pierre Monteux Sch., Hancock, Maine, 1965—. With U.S. Mil. Acad. Band, 1950-53. Recipient Pierre Monteux disciple award conducting, 1962. Mem. Percussion Arts Soc. (pres. 1962-66), Am. Symphony Orch. League, Condrs. Guild (treas., exec. com. 1979-82, 86-90). Home: 824 Hinman Ave # 2N Evanston IL 60202-2302 Office: Chgo Symphony Orch 220 S Michigan Ave Chicago IL 60604-2508

PETERS, HENRY AUGUSTUS, neuropsychiatrist; b. Oconomowoc, Wis., Dec. 21, 1920; s. Henry Augustus and Emma N. P.; m. Jean McWilliams, 1950; children—Henry, Kurt, Eric, Mark. B.A., M.D., U. Wis. Prof. dept. neurology and rehab. medicine U. Wis. Med. Sch., Madison; mem. med. adv. bd. Muscular Dystrophy Assn. Served to lt. M.C. U.S. Navy. Fellow A.C.P.; mem. Wis. Med. Assn., Am. Acad. Neurology, Am. Psychiatric Assn. Club: Rotary. Office: 600 Highland Ave Madison WI 53792-0001

PETERS, HENRY BUCKLAND, optometrist, educator; b. Oakland, Calif., Nov. 2, 1916; s. Thomas Henry and Eleanor Bernice (Hough) P.; m. Anne Zara Ledin, Feb. 3, 1968; children—Lynn, Thomas Henry, James Clifton, Christopher Patrick, Elizabeth Anne. A.B., U. Calif. at, Berkeley, 1938; M.A., U. Nebr., 1939; D.O.S., So. Coll. Optometry, 1971, New England Coll. Optometry, 1985; D.O.S. (hon.), SUNY, 1990. Pvt. practice optometry Chico, Calif., 1939-40, Oakland, 1946-59; instr., asst. prof. U. Calif., Berkeley, 1947-62; assoc. prof., asst. dean U. Calif. (Sch. Optometry), 1962-69; prof., dean (Sch. Optometry), 1969-86; prof. public health Med. Center, U. Ala., Birmingham, 1969-87; dean and prof. emeritus U. Ala., Birmingham, 1988—; exec. dir. Research Found. U. Ala., Birmingham, 1986-89; dir. Nat. Bd. Examiners in Optometry, 1984-91; pres. Nat. Health Council, 1978-79; cons. So. Regional Edn. Bd., S.C. Commn. Higher Edn., Calif. Dept. Public Health, Lawrence Radiation Lab., Aerojet Gen., Nat. Acad. Sci. Inst. Medicine; v.p. Children's Vision Center, Oakland, 1963-69; dir. Calif. Vision Service, 1953-59; mem. optometric rev. com. Bur. Health, Manpower and Edn., HEW, 1970-73, Rev. and Program Council, Medicaid, Calif., 1966-69; dir. Community Service Council, Birmingham, 1969-76; mem. deans com. VA Hosp., Birmingham; bd. dirs. Birmingham Health Services Agy., 1976-79, chmn. manpower com., 1976-79; chmn. optometry services adv. com. VA., 1977-88, chmn. spl. adv. com. on legally blind, 1977; mem. Nat. Rev. Bd. Health Promotion with Elderly, 1980-82; mem. adv. bd. Health Policy Council N.Y., 1980-88; mem. Adv. Council on Phys. Therapy Edn., 1986-89. Author: (with Blum and Bettman) Vision Screening for Elementary Schools, 1959; History of School of Optometry, University of Alabama at Birmingham, 1994; also articles. Served to lt. USNR, 1942-46. Named Optometrist of Year, Calif. Optometric Assn., 1959; Optometrist of South, So. Council Optometrists, 1982; Thomas P. Carpenter award for disting. service Nat. Health Council, 1983. Fellow Am. Public Health Assn. (Vision Care Disting. Achievement award 1982), Am. Acad. Optometry (life, pres. 1973-74, Carel C. Koch medal 1974, diplomate pub. health sect. 1989); mem. Am. Optometric Assn. (Disting. Service award 1981), Ala. Optometric Assn. (Optometrist of Year 1973), Assn. Schs. and Colls. Optometry (pres. 1967-68, dir.), Phi Beta Kappa, Sigma Xi, Phi Delta Kappa, Beta Sigma Kappa. Home: 712 Vestavia Lake Dr Birmingham AL 35216-2030

PETERS, HOWARD NEVIN, foreign language educator; b. Hazleton, Pa., June 29, 1938; s. Howard Eugene and Verna Catherine (Miller) P.; m. Judith Anne Griessel, Aug. 24, 1963; children—Elisabeth Anne, Nevin Edward. B.A., Gettysburg Coll., 1960; Ph.D., U. Colo., 1965. Asst. prof. fgn. langs. Valparaiso (Ind.) U., 1965-69, asso. prof., 1969-75, dir. grad. div., 1967-70; acting dean Valparaiso (Ind.) U. (Coll. Arts and Scis.), 1970-71, asso. dean, 1971-74, dean, 1974-81, prof. fgn. langs., 1975—, chair dept. Fgn. Langs. and Lits., 1994—. NDEA fellow, 1960-63. Mem. Midwest MLA, Phi Beta Kappa, Sigma Delta Pi, Phi Sigma Iota. Lutheran. Home: 860 N Cr 500 E Valparaiso IN 46383 Office: Meier Hall Rm 113 Valparaiso U Valparaiso IN 46383

PETERS, JAMES RAY, accountant; b. Whittier, Calif., June 29, 1946; s. Alvin Claus and Marie (Darrow) P.; m. Maryanne Gale, June 28, 1969; children: Judd, Adam, Holly. BA, Calif. State U., Fullerton, 1971; cert. exec. program, Northwestern U., 1987. CPA, Calif.; cert. mgmt. acct. Mem. audit staff Ernst & Whinney, Orange County, Calif., 1971-83, audit ptnr., 1983-84; human resources ptnr. Ernst & Whinney, L.A., 1984-86; with recruiting dept. Ernst & Whinney, Cleve., 1986—. Author, editor, producer: (video and booklet) The Campus Interview, 1987; contbr. articles to pubs. Trustee Cleanland Ohio, Cleve., 1986—; bd. dirs. Children's Home Soc. Santa Ana, Calif., 1982-84. Named Outstanding Alumnus Sch. Bus. Calif. State U. Fullerton, 1982. Mem. AICPA, Am. Assn. Acctg., Am. Assembly Collegiate Schs. Bus. (com. 1987—), Fedn. Schs. Accountancy (com. lyceum 1986—), Mayfield Country Club (Cleve.), 13th St. Athletic Club (Cleve.), Beta Alpha Psi (chmn. adv. forum). Republican. Methodist. Avocations: running, cross country skiing. Home: 5515 Bromely Dr Agoura CA 91301-4751 Office: Ernst & Young 2000 National City Ctr Cleveland OH 44114

PETERS, JON, film producer, film company executive; b. Van Nuys, Calif., 1947; m. 2d Lesley Ann Warren; 1 child; m. 3d Christine Peters. Founder hairstyling bus.; founder Jon Peters Orgn., 1980; formed The Boardwalk Co. (with Peter Guber and Neil Bogart), Guber-Peters-Barris Co., 1988; co-chmn. Columbia Pictures Entertainment Inc., 1989-91, head Jon Peters Group, 1991—. Producer films A Star Is Born, 1976, The Eyes of Laura Mars, 1978, The Main Event, 1979, Die Laughing, 1980, Caddyshack, 1980, Six Weeks, 1982, D.C. Cab., 1983, Flashdance, 1983, Visionquest, 1984, The Color Purple, 1985, The Legend of Billie Jean, 1985, The Clan of the Cave Bear, 1986, Youngblood, 1986, The Witches ofEastwick, 1987, Innerspace, 1987, Who's That Girl, 1987, Batman, 1989 Tango andCash, 1989; exec. producer Gorillas in the Mist, 1988, Missing Link, 1989, The Bonfire of the Vanities, 1990, Batman Returns, 1992, This Boy's Life, 1993. Office: Peters Entertainment Inc 433 N Camden Dr Beverly Hills CA 90210-4425 also: Columbia Pictures Industries 10202 Washington Blvd Culver City CA 90232

PETERS, LAURALEE MILBERG, diplomat; b. Monroe, N.C., Jan. 28, 1943; d. Arthur W. and Opal I. (Mueller) Milberg; m. Lee M. Peters, May 30, 1964; children: David, Evelyn, Edward, Matthew. BA with highest honors, U. Kans., 1964, postgrad., 1965-67; student, Nat. War Coll., 1975. Asst. pub. info. officer NAS, Washington, 1967-69; joined Fgn. Svc., Dept. State, 1972, commd. sr. fgn. svc. officer, 1985; chief visa sect. Am. Embassy, Saigon, Vietnam, 1972-74; internat. fin. officer Dept. State, Washington, 1975-79; U.S. rep. to Econ. and Social Commn. for Asia and Pacific, UN, Bangkok, Thailand, 1979-81; devel. fin. officer Dept. State, Washington, 1981-82; econ. officer Israel, West Bank, Gaza, 1982-84; dir. Office Monetary Affairs Dept. State, Washington, 1984-86; econ. counselor Am. Embassy, Islamabad, Pakistan, 1986-88; career devel. officer Dept. State, Washington, 1988-89, dep. asst. sec. for personnel, 1989-91; mem. Sr. Seminar, 1991-92; U.S. Ambassador to Sierra Leone, 1992—. Various leadership positions Boy Scouts Am., 1977-88. Recipient Disting. award of merit Nat. Capitol Area Coun. Boy Scouts Am., 1986. Mem. Am. Fgn. Svc. Protective Assn. (v.p. 1981-84), Consular Officer's Assn. (sec. 1974-75), Phi Beta Kappa. Home: 6205 Mori St Mc Lean VA 22101-3150 Office: Am Embassy, Walpole & Siaka Stevens Sts, Freetown Sierra Leone

PETERS, LAWRENCE H., management educator, consultant; b. St. Louis, Oct. 19, 1945; s. Albert and Anna S. (Schmidt) P.; m. Jennifer R. Ruhl, Jan. 28, 1945; 1 child, Andrea J. AB, Washington U., St. Louis, 1968; MS, So. Ill. U., 1969; PhD, Purdue U., 1975. Asst. prof. mgmt. U. Tex., Dallas, 1975-81; assoc. prof. mgmt. So. Ill. U., Carbondale, 1981-85; prof. mgmt. Tex. Christian U., Ft. Worth, 1985—; presenter at nat. and regional profl. confs. Co-author 2 books; co-assoc. editor: Ency. of Mgmt.; co-editor: Dictionary of Human Resource Mgmt; contbr. more than 40 articles to mgmt. and indsl. psychology jours., chpts. to books. With U.S. Army, 1969-72. Grantee USAF, 1981-84, NSF, 1989-94. Fellow Am. Psychol. Soc., Soc. Indsl./Orgnl. Psychology; mem. Acad. Mgmt., S.W. Acad. Mgmt. Profls. Office: Tex Christian U MJ Neeley Sch Bus Fort Worth TX 76129

PETERS, LEO FRANCIS, environmental engineer; b. Melrose, Mass., Aug. 14, 1937; s. Joseph Leander and Mary Gertrude (Phalen) P.; m. Joan Catherine Anderson, May 20, 1961; children: Elizabeth M., Susan J., Carolyn A., Jennifer L. BS in Civil Engring., Northeastern U., Boston, 1960, MS in Civil Engring., 1966; postgrad., Harvard U., 1989. Registered profl. engr., Mass., N.H.; diplomate Am. Acad. Environ. Engrs. Jr. engr. N.Y. Dept. Transp., Albany, 1960-61; chief engr. John M. Cashman, Weymouth, Mass., 1961-62; project engr. Metcalf & Eddy, Inc., Boston, 1962-65; project engr. Weston & Sampson, Boston, 1965-67, assoc., 1967-70, ptnr., 1970-76; exec. v.p. Weston & Sampson Engrs., Inc., Boston, 1976-82; pres. Weston & Sampson Engrs., Inc., Wakefield and Peabody, Mass., 1982—; mem. Northeastern U. Corp., 1992. Clk. mem. Melrose (Mass.) Planning Bd., 1969-91. Named Young Engr. of Yr. Mass. Soc. Profl. Engrs. Fellow Am. Cons. Engrs. Coun.; mem. Am. Water Works Assn., Am. Pub. Works Assn., Water Environ. Fedn., Am. Cons. Engrs. Coun. New Eng. (pres. 1990-91), New Eng. Water Works Assn. (pres. 1989-90). Roman Catholic. Home: 187 E Emerson St Melrose MA 02176 Office: Weston & Sampson Engrs Inc 5 Centennial Dr Peabody MA 01960*

PETERS, LEON, JR., electrical engineering educator, research administ; b. Columbus, Ohio, May 28, 1923; s. Leon P. and Ethel (Howland) Pierce; m. Mabel Marie Johnson, June 6, 1953; children: Amy T. Peters Thomas, Melinda A. Peters Todaro, Maria C., Patricia D., Lee A., Roberta J. Peters Cameruca, Karen E. Peters Ellingson. B.S.E.E., Ohio State U., 1950, M.S., 1954, Ph.D., 1959. Asst. prof. elec. engring. Ohio State U., Columbus, 1959-63; assoc. prof. Ohio State U., 1963-67, prof., 1967-93, prof. emeritus, 1993—; assoc. dept. chmn. for rsch. Ohio State U., Columbus, 1990-92, dir. electro sci. lab., 1983-94. Contbr. articles to profl. jours. Served to 2d lt. U.S. Army, 1942-46, ETO. Fellow IEEE. Home: 1410 Lincoln Rd Columbus OH 43212-3276 Office: Ohio State U Electrosci Lab 1320 Kinnear Rd Columbus OH 43212-1156

PETERS, LESLIE ANN, television and radio producer; b. Baytown, Tex., Mar. 17, 1961; d. Jack Lee and Barbara Marie (Jannopoulo) P.; m. Bradford Thomas Thornburgh, June 30, 1985. Student, U. Calif., San Diego, 1984. Gen. mgr. Sta. KSDT-FM, San Diego, 1982-84; sales rep. On Air mag., San Diego, 1984-85; news announcer Sta. KPBS-FM, San Diego, 1985-88; producer, dir. ITV-TV, San Diego, 1986-88; sr. assoc. producer St. KPBS-TV, San Diego, 1987-89, producer, 1990—; ind. producer and reporter CBS News and Nat. Pub. Radio, 1988—. Mem. NCCJ, 1989. Recipient Golden Mike award Radio, TV and Newscasters Assn., 1988, 89, Spl. Event award Broadcast Industry Cong., 1988, Emmy, 1988, Cine Golden Eagle award, Am. Film and Video Festival, 1990; 1st place Huston Film Festival, 1989. Mem. Am. Women in Radio and TV (bd. dirs. San Diego chpt. 1985-86, sec. 1986-87). Democrat. Presbyterian. Avocations: racquetball, reading, travel. Home: 3131 Via De Caballo Encinitas CA 92024-9733

PETERS, MARY HELEN, library media specialist; b. Cape Girardeau, Mo., July 6, 1934; d. Wilmer Joseph and Ruby Madyliene (Knight) Lichtenegger; m. George Thomas Peters, May 25, 1952 (dec. Oct. 1992); children: Jennifer Susan Peters Dunlap, Gregory Thomas, Douglas Steward. BS in Edn., Ark. State U., 1974, MS in Edn., 1976. Cert. K-12 libr., bus. edn., secondary tchr., Ark. Tchr. bus. Westside H.S., Jonesboro, Ark., 1974-77; libr. media specialist, 1977-89; libr. media specialist Jonesboro H.S., 1989—; condr. workshops in field, including Ark. Ednl. TV Network, 1988; mem. selection and guidance com. for audio-visual Ark. Dept. Edn., 1986-89. Com. chmn. for election cir. judge Ark. 2d Jud. Dist., 1994. Mem. ASCD, NEA, Assn. Ednl. Comm. and Tech. (mem. divsn. sch. media specialists), Ark. Edn. Assn., Ark. Libr. Assn., Ark. Assn. Sch. Libr. Media Educators, Ark. Assn. for Instrnl. Media, N.E. Ark. Libr. Assn., Jonesboro Pub. Educators Assn., Ark. State U. Faculty Women's Club, (pres. 1973-74), Phi Kappa Phi, Phi Delta Kappa, Kappa Delta Pi, Pi Omega Pi, Delta Kappa Gamma (pres. Pi chpt. 1984-86, exec. com. and exec. bd. Kappa State Ark. 1984-95, 1st v.p. 1989-91, pres. 1991-93, past pres. 1993-95, condr. workshops 1987—, mem. internat. golden gift com. 1994—, Internat. Golden Gift award 1988). Avocations: gourmet cooking, music, ballroom dancing, travel. Home: 2804 Turtle Creek Jonesboro AR 72401 Office: Jonesboro HS 301 Hurricane Dr Jonesboro AR 72401

PETERS, RALPH EDGAR, business executive; b. Harrisburg, Pa., Feb. 20, 1923; s. George Edward and Rebecca Flavia (Michener) P.; m. Roberta Jane Shaffer, June 12, 1948; children: Sheila Jane, Gail Marie, Ralph Jr., Bret Edward. Student, U. Pa., 1942; BA in Bus. Adminstrn., Pa. State U., 1948. From payroll supr. to asst. budget supr. Pa. State U., 1948-52; chief acct., pers. officer Haller, Raymond & Brown, State College, Pa., 1952-54; from contr. to CEO and chmn. bd. Benatec Assocs., Inc. (formerly Berger Assocs., Inc.), Camp Hill, Pa., 1954—; bd. dirs. CCNB Bank, New Cumberland, Pa., 1972-93. Chmn. bd. advisors Pa. State U., Harrisburg, 1979—; chmn. bd. dirs. Holy Spirit Hosp., Camp Hill, 1982—; past pres. Tri-County United Way, Harrisburg, from 1978; chmn. Pvt. Industry Coun., Harrisburg, 1982-87. With U.S. Army, 1943-45, ETO, 1952-53, Korea. Recipient Community Svc. award Salvation Army, 1980, Disting. Alumnus award Pa. State U., 1980, Disting. Pennsylvanian award Greater Phila. C. of C., 1981, Catalyst award Capital Region Economic Devel., 1992. Mem. Pa. C. of C. (bd. dir.-transp. com. chmn. 1972-90), Harrisburg Area C. of C. (pres., chmn. 1979-83), Ams. for Competitive Enterprise System (pres. 1981-83), Cumberland County Transp. Authority, Susquehanna Valley Regional Airport Authority, Lions, Masons, Pa. Jaycees (pres. 1955-56, nat. v.p. 1956-57), Delta Sigma Pi. Lutheran. Office: Benatec Assocs Inc 101 Erford Rd Camp Hill PA 17011-1808

PETERS, RALPH FREW, investment banker; b. Mineola, N.Y., Mar. 21, 1929; s. Ralph and Helen Louise (Frew) P.; m. Diana Joyce Clayton, Dec. 19, 1969; children: Louise Frew, Jean Reid, Ralph Frew, Melvyn T., Richard Clayton. B.A., Princeton U., 1951; postgrad., Stonier Grad. Sch. Banking, Rutgers U., 1962. With Corn Exchange Bank & Trust Co., 1947-52; chmn. bd., dir. Discount Corp. N.Y., N.Y.C., 1955-93; dir. Investors Inc., Sun Life Ins. & Annuity of N.Y., U.S. Life Ins. Fund. Served with USNR, 1948-55. Mem. Pub. Securities Assn. (gov.). Anglers Club, Leash Club, Links Club, North Woods Club. Episcopalian.

PETERS, RALPH MARTIN, education educator; b. Knoxville, Tenn., May 9, 1926; s. Tim C. and Alma (Shannon) P.; m. Lorraine Daniel, 1949; children—Teresa, Marta. B.S., Lincoln Meml. U., 1949; M.S., U. Tenn., 1953, Ed.D., 1960. Tchr. pub. schs. Lincoln Meml. U., 1956-63, prof., dept. chmn., v.p., 1956-63, 92-95; prof. edn., dean students, dean Grad. Sch. Tenn. Tech. U., Cookeville, 1963-89; dean emeritus, 1989. Editor publs. Served with Armed Forces, World War II. Mem. Phi Kappa Phi, Phi Delta Kappa, Omicron Delta Kappa. Baptist. Club: Rotary. Home: 927 Mt Vernon Rd Cookeville TN 38501-1576

PETERS, RAYMOND EUGENE, computer systems company executive; b. New Haven, Aug. 24, 1933; s. Raymond and Doris Winthrop (Smith) P.; m. Millie Mather, July 14, 1978 (div. Nov. 1983). Student, San Diego City Coll., 1956-61; cert. Lumbleau Real Estate Sch., 1973, Southwestern Coll., Chula Vista, Calif., 1980. Cert. quality assurance engr. Founder, pub. Silhouette Pub. Co., San Diego, 1960-75; co-founder, news dir. Sta. XEGM, San Diego, 1964-68; news dir. Sta. XERB, Tijuana, Mex., 1973-74; founder, chief exec. officer New World Airways, Inc., San Diego, 1974-75; co-founder, exec. vice chmn. bd. San Cal Rail, Inc.-San Diego Trolley, San Diego, 1974-77; founder, pres. Ansonia Sta., micro systems, San Diego, 1986—; co-founder, dir. S.E. Community Theatre, San Diego, 1960-68; commr. New World Aviation Acad., Otay Mesa, Calif., 1971-77; co-founder New World Internat. Trade & Commerce Commn., Inc., 1991—. Author: Black Americans in Aviation, 1971, Profiles in Black American History, 1974, Eagles Don't Cry, 1988; founder, pub., editor Oceanside Lighthouse, 1958-60, San Diego Herald Dispatch, 1959-60. Co-founder, bd. dirs. San Diego County Econ. Opportunity Commn. 1964-67; co-founder, bd. dirs. S.E. Anti-Poverty Planning Coun., San Diego, 1966-75; co-founder, exec. dir. S.E. Anti-Poverty Program Coun., 1964-67; mem. U.S. Rep. Senatorial Inner Circle Com., Washington, 1990; mem. United Ch. Crist. With U.S. Army, 1950-53, Korea. Mem. Am. Soc. Quality Control, Nat. City C. of C., Internat. Biog. Soc., Afro-Am. Micro Systems Soc. (exec. dir. 1987—), Negro Airmen Internat. (Calif. pres. 1970-75, nat. v.p. 1975-77), Internat. Masonic Supreme Coun. (Belgium), Internat. Platform Assn., U.S.C. of C., Greater San Diego Minority C. of C. (bd. dirs. 1974—, past chmn. bd.), Masons (Most Worshipful Grand Master), Shriners (Disting. Community Svc. award 1975), Imperial Grand Potentate, Nubian Order. Republican. Avocations: creative writing, golf, world history. Home: Meadowbrook Estates # 245 8301 Mission Gorge Rd Santee CA 92071

PETERS, RICHARD T., lawyer; b. La Mesa, Calif., Sept. 24, 1946. BA, Santa Clara U., 1968; JD, UCLA, 1971. Bar: Calif. 1972. Ptnr. Sidley & Austin, L.A. Mem. State Bar Calif. (mem. debtor-creditor rels. and bankruptcy subcom. bus. law sect. 1979-81, chmn. 1981-82, mem. exec. com. bus. law sect. 1982—, chmn. 1981-82, vice chmn. 1984-85), Calif. Continuing Edn. Bar (cons. 1984—, vice chmn. 1984-85). Office: Sidley & Austin 555 W 5th St 40th Fl Los Angeles CA 90013-1010

PETERS, ROBERT WAYNE, organization executive, lawyer; b. LaSalle, Ill., Jan. 13, 1949; s. Earl Edward and Lucille Anne (Hinrichsen) P.; m. Josie M. Browne, Mar. 28, 1992. BA, Dartmouth Coll., 1971; JD, NYU, 1975. Bar: N.Y. 1976. Staff atty. Morality in Media, Inc., N.Y.C., 1985-87, asst. dir. Nat. Obscenity Law Ctr., 1987-92, pres., 1992—; guest lectr. cmty. and profl. groups. Recipient Effective Citizenship award Archdiocese of N.Y., 1987. Republican. Evangelical. Achievements include frequently quoted by national and local press and frequently a guest on electronic media on subjects of pornography and TV indecency and violence. Avocations: walking and hiking with my wife. Office: Morality in Media Inc 475 Riverside Dr New York NY 10115

PETERS, ROBERT WOOLSEY, architect; b. Mpls., Mar. 24, 1935; s. John Eugene and Adelaide Elizabeth (Woolsey) P. BArch., U. Minn., 1958; MArch., Yale U., 1961. Registered architect, N.Mex., Ariz. Dir. design Schaefer & Assocs., Wichita, Kans., 1975-76; participating assoc. Skidmore Owings & Merrill, Chgo., 1961-74; ptnr. Addy & Peters, Albuquerque, 1979-82; owner Robert W. Peters AIA Architect, Albuquerque, 1982—. Exhibited work Centre Georges Pompidou, Paris, 1980; Univ. Art Mus., Albuquerque, 1982, 92, Albuquerque Mus., 1988. Bd. dirs. Contemporary Art Soc. N.Mex. Contbr. articles to Century Mag., Progressive Architecture, House & Garden, House Beautiful, also others. Recipient honor awards N.Mex. Soc. Architects, 1980-83, 86, 87, 92; honor award HUD, 1980, 5th Nat. Passive Solar Conf., Amherst, Mass., 1981. Fellow AIA. Democrat. Roman Catholic. Club: Yale of N.Mex.

PETERS, ROBERTA, soprano; b. N.Y.C., May 4, 1930; d. Sol and Ruth (Hirsch) P.; m. Bertram Fields, Apr. 10, 1955; children: Paul, Bruce. Ed. privately; Litt.D., Elmira Coll., 1967; Mus. D., Ithaca Coll., 1968, Colby Coll., 1980; L.H.D., Westminster Coll., 1974, Lehigh U., 1977; D.F.A., St. John's U., 1982; LittD, Coll. New Rochelle, 1989. Author: Debut at the Met; Met. Opera debut as Zerlina in Don Giovanni, 1950; recorded numerous operas; appeared motion pictures; frequent appearances radio and TV; sang at Royal Opera House, Covent Garden, London, Vienna State Opera, Munich Opera, West Berlin Opera, Salzburg Festival, debuts at festivals in Vienna and Munich; concert tours in U.S., Soviet Union, Scandinavian countries, Israel, China, Japan, Taiwan, South Korea, debut, Kirov Opera, Leningrad, USSR, sang at Bolshoi Opera, Moscow (1st Am. to receive Bolshoi medal). Trustee Carnegie Hall; dir. Met. Opera Guild; chmn. Nat. Inst. Music Theater, 1991—; apptd. by Pres. Bush to Nat. Coun. Arts, 1992. Named Woman of Yr. Fedn. Women's Clubs, 1964; honored spl. ceremony on 35th anniversary with the Met. Opera Co., 1985; was 1st Am. to receive Bolshoi medal. Office: ICM Artists Ltd 40 W 57th St New York NY 10019-4070 *I believe that life is a series of just one darn thing after another. If we can learn that, we can expect, meet, and solve our problems.*

PETERS, RONALD GEORGE, investment banker; b. N.Y.C., May 28, 1944; s. William J. and Evelyn M. (Nahlikova) P.; m. Susan S. Leigh, Aug. 19, 1972; children: Gregory, William, Timothy. BSE, Princeton U., 1966; MBA, Columbia U., 1971. Dept. mgr. Procter & Gamble Co., Balt., 1966-67; v.p. Citibank, N.A., N.Y.C., 1971-80; mng. dir. Oppenheimer & Co., Inc., N.Y.C., 1980—; bd. dirs. Koret, Inc., San Francisco. 1st lt. U.S. Army, 1967-69. Mem. Twilight Cottagers (bd. dirs. 1989—, treas. 1989—). Home: 25 North Dr Carmel NY 10512-1113 Office: Oppenheimer & Co Inc 200 Liberty St New York NY 10281-1003

PETERS, SARAH WHITAKER, art historian, writer, lecturer; b. Kenosha, Wis., Aug. 17, 1924; d. Robert Burbank and Margaret Jebb (Allen) Whitaker; m. Arthur King Peters, Oct. 21, 1943; children: Robert Bruce, Margaret Allen, Michael Whitaker. BA, Sarah Lawrence Coll. 1954; MA, Columbia U., 1966; student, L'Ecole du Louvre, Paris, 1967-68; diplome, Ecole des Trois Gourmandes, Paris, 1968; PhD, CUNY, 1987. Freelance critic Art in Am., N.Y.C.; lectr. Bronxville (N.Y.) Adult Sch., Internat. Mus. Photography, 1979, Tufts U., 1979, Madison (Wis.) Art Ctr., 1984, Meml. Art Gallery, Rochester, N.Y., 1988, 91, Caramoor Mus., Katonah, N.Y., 1988, Yale U. Art Gallery, New Haven, Conn., 1989, The Cosmopolitan Club, N.Y.C., 1977, 91, Sarah Lawrence Coll., Bronxville, N.Y., 1992, The Phillips Collection, Washington, 1993, Mpls. Inst. Arts, 1993, Whitney Mus. Am. Art, Champion, Conn, 1994, U. Wis., Parkside, 1994, Nat. Wildlife Art Mus., Jackson Hole, Wyo., 1995; lectr-in-residence Garrison Forest Sch., Owings Mills, Md.; adj. asst. prof. art history C.W. Post, U. L.I. Author: Becoming O'Keeffe: The Early Years, 1991; contbr. articles to profl. jours. Mem. Coll. Art Assn., Bronxville Field Club, The Cosmopolitan Club. Avocations: horsemanship, mountaineering, tennis, cooking. Home: 14 Village Ln Bronxville NY 10708

PETERS, STANLEY THOMAS, materials engineer, consultant, educator; b. San Jose, Calif., May 16, 1934; s. Henry Stanley and Estelle Katherine (Evans) P.; m. Helen Lynn Fritz, Dec. 17, 1970. BS in Chemistry, U. Santa Clara, 1957. Registered profl. engr., Calif. Chemist W.P. Fuller & Co., South San Francisco, Calif., 1957-59; devel. engr. Lockheed Missile & Space Co., Palo Alto, Calif., 1959-61; sr. engr. Rocketdyne div. NAA, Canoga Park, Calif., 1961-65; section head Dalmo Victor div. Textron, Belmont, Calif., 1965-76; sr. design engr. Chem. Systems div. UTC, Sunnyvale, Calif., 1976-81; fellow engr. Marine div. Westinghouse Electric Corp., Sunnyvale, 1981-94; gen. mgr. process rsch., 1994—; adj. prof. Stanford U., Palo Alto, 1974-75; asst. prof. San Jose (Calif.) State U., 1988—. Author: Filament Winding Composite Structural Fabrication, 1991; editor: Tomorrows Materials: Today, 1989; contbr. articles to profl. jours. 1st lt. U.S. Army, 1959-60. Fellow Soc. for Advancement of Materials and Process Engring. (editor jour. 1972-79, nat. sec.); mem. ASM, Soc. Mfg. Engrs. Achievements include patents for Filament Wound Composite Joints to Metal End Rings, Methods of Producing a Tapered Scarf Joint. Home: 925 Sladky Ave Mountain View CA 94040-3625

PETERS, STEPHEN PAUL, pastor; b. Warsaw, Ind., May 25, 1953; s. Jack Klyne and Stellina Maxine (Mustard) P.; m. Susan Christine Jamison Peters, June 28, 1975; children: Suzanne, Stephen Jr., Scott, Stewart, Sarah, Seth. Student, Bob Jones U., 1972-73; BS, Liberty U., 1978; MA, Grace Grad. Sch., 1979. Ordained to ministry Maranatha Brethren Ch. Youth pastor Maranatha Brethren Ch., Hagerstown, Md., 1979-84; sr. pastor Cmty. Grace Brethren Ch., West Milton, Ohio, 1984—; bd. dirs. C.E. Nat., Winona Lake, Ind., v.p. 1991-93, pres., 1993—; moderator Fellowship of Grace Brethren Ch., Winona Lake, Ind., 1995—; music dir. Nat. Conf., 1987, 89, Focus I Com., 1991-93, rep. Charis I & II, 1994, 96. Editor: The Bishop, 1991. Republican. Brethren Ch. Office: Cmty Grace Brethren Ch 2261 S Miami St West Milton OH 45383

PETERS, THOMAS ROBERT, English educator, writer; b. Detroit, Nov. 14, 1929; s. Norman Addison and Eleanor H. (Schneider) P.; m. Lillian J. Tremonti, Aug. 21, 1954; children: Jennifer Leigh Hartman, Thomas R. Jr., Sarah Jeanne. BA, Hillsdale Coll., 1954; MA, Wayne State U., 1963. Screen writer Jam Handy Film Prodns., Detroit, 1956-59; secondary tchr. English, Detroit Pub. Schs., 1960-69; edn. coord. Detroit Free Press, 1969-72; mgr. pub. rels. Blue Cross, Blue Shield Mich., Detroit, 1972-86; prof. English Macomb Community Coll., Warren, Mich., 1986—; guest speaker Mich. Schs. and Colls., 1970—. Author: (novels) Education of Tom Webber, 1977, Two Weeks in the Forties, 1988, Selected Works, 1995, (play) Mensa Meeting, 1987; contbr. numerous stories, articles and poems to nat. mags., anthologies; writer several published speeches. Bd. dirs. Friends of Grosse Pointe Librs. 1978-84. With U.S. Army, 1948-49; U.S. Army Res. 1950-55. Recipient Alumni Achievement award in Literature Hillsdale Coll., 1993; grantee: Grosse Pointe Found., 1978, Utica Community Schs., 1989. Mem.

Fine Arts Soc. Detroit (pres. 1978-79). Roman Catholic. Avocations: pianist, actor, tennis player. Home: 350 Moselle Pl Grosse Pointe MI 48236-3307

PETERS, VIRGINIA, actress; b. Los Angeles, July 15, 1924; d. Peter and Tessie (Skiller) Stetzenko. Grad., Pasadena (Calif.) Playhouse, 1944; student, Los Angeles City Coll. Tchr. Burbank (Calif.) Little Theatre, 1978-80, Burbank Acad. Performing Arts, 1979—. TV appearances in Night Strangler, 1972, Love American Style, 1973, Rita Moreno Show, 1977, Laverne and Shirley, 1977, 78, Happy Days, 1977, Dallas, 1980, The Waltons, 1981, House Detective, 1985, Knight Rider, 1985, Murder She Wrote, 1986, Hunter, 1986, Hardcastle and McCormick, 1986, Cavanaughs, 1986, Paper Chase, 1986, also Days of Our Lives, Divorce Court, Grace Under Fire, 1993; film appearances include The Arrangement, 1968, The Cat People, 1981, Fast Times at Ridgemont High, 1982, Rat Boy, 1985, The Deacon Street Deer, 1985, My Demon Lover, Mr. President, The Judge, Stripped to Kill II, 1988, Hero, My Girl II; appeared in: TV movie The 11th Victim, 1979; TV pilot We Got It Made; also numerous commls. Mem. Masquers Club (past dir.), Pasadena Playhouse Alumni Assos. (past dir.). Democrat. Roman Catholic.

PETERS, WILLIAM, author, producer, director; b. San Francisco, July 30, 1921; s. William Ernest and Dorothy Louise (Wright) P.; m. Mercy Ann Miller, Oct. 12, 1942 (div. 1968); children: Suzanne Peters Payne, Geoffrey Wright, Jennifer Peters Johnson, Gretchen Peters Daniel; m. Helene Louise Yager White, May 31, 1987. BS, Northwestern U., 1947. Account exec. pub. relations J. Walter Thompson Co., Chgo., 1947-51; mem. fiction staff Ladies' Home Jour., 1951-52; article editor Woman's Home Companion, N.Y.C., 1952-53; freelance writer, Pelham, N.Y., 1953-62; producer CBS Reports, CBS News, N.Y.C., 1962-66; freelance writer, film dir. and TV producer/exec. producer N.Y.C., 1966-82; dir. Yale U. Films, New Haven, 1982-89; freelance writer, film dir., TV producer/exec. producer Guilford, Conn., 1990—; cons. race relations, 1959—, hist. TV documentaries, 1976—. Author: American Memorial Hospital--Reims, France: A History, 1955, Passport to Friendship--The Story of the Experiment in International Living, 1957, The Southern Temper, 1959, (with Mrs. Medgar Evers) For Us, The Living, 1967, A Class Divided, 1971; A More Perfect Union, 1987, A Class Divided: Then and Now, 1987; producer, writer, dir. documentaries Storm Over the Supreme Court, Parts II and III, 1963 (George F. Peabody award, Golden Gavel award ABA), (co-producer) After Ten Years: The Court and the Schools, 1964 (Nat. Sch. Bell award NEA), The Eye of the Storm, 1970 (George Foster Peabody award, Christopher award, Cine Golden Eagle award), Suddenly an Eagle, 1976 (George Foster Peabody award, Cine Golden Eagle award), Death of a Family, 1979 (Writers Guild Am. award), A Bond of Iron, 1982, A Class Divided, 1985 (Emmy award, Sidney Hillman award, Cine Golden Eagle award); others; exec. producer dramas Boswell's London Journal, 1986, others. Co-founder North Shore Citizens Com., 1946, bd. dirs., 1946-51; co-founder Pelham Com. Human Relations, 1963, vice chmn., 1963-65, chmn., 1965-66. Served to capt. USAAF, 1942-45, ETO. Decorated Air medal with 2 oak leaf clusters, D.F.C.; recipient Benjamin Franklin mag. award, 1954; Peabody TV award, 1963, 70, 76, Golden Gavel award ABA, 1963, Sch. Bell award NEA, 1964, Emmy award, Sidney Hillman award, 1985. Mem. Dirs. Guild Am., Writers Guild Am. Democrat. Home: 3108 Long Hill Rd Guilford CT 06437-3619

PETERS, WILLIAM P., oncologist, science administrator, educator; b. Buffalo, Aug. 26, 1950; m. Elizabeth Zentai; children: Emily, Abigail, James. BS, BS, BA, Pa. State U., 1972; MPhil, PhD, Columbia U., 1976, MD, 1978; postgrad., Harvard U., 1984; MBA, Duke U., 1990. Diplomate Am. Bd. Internal Medicine, Am. Bd. Med. Oncology. Prof. medicine Duke U. Med. Ctr.; assoc. dir. for clin. ops. Duke Comprehensive Cancer Ctr.; dir. bone marrow transplant program Duke U. Med. Ctr., Durham, N.C., 1984-95; pres., CEO Mich. Cancer Found., Detroit, 1995—; assoc. dean Wayne State U., Detroit, 1995—. Office: Presidents Office Michigan Cancer Found 110 E Warren Detroit MI 48201

PETERSDORF, ROBERT GEORGE, medical educator, retired association executive; b. Berlin, Feb. 14, 1926; s. Hans H. and Sonja P.; m. Patricia Horton Qua, June 2, 1951; children: Stephen Hans, John Eric. BA, Brown U., 1948, DMS (hon.), 1983; MD cum laude, Yale U., 1952; ScD (hon.), Albany Med. Coll., 1979; MA (hon.), Harvard U., 1980; DMS (hon.), Med. Coll. Pa., 1982, Brown U., 1983; DMS, Bowman-Gray Sch. Medicine, 1986; LHD (hon.), N.Y. Med. Coll., 1986; DSc (hon.), SUNY, Bklyn., 1987, Med. Coll. Ohio, 1987, Univ. Health Scis., The Chgo. Med. Sch., 1987, St. Louis U., 1988; LHD (hon.), Ea. Va. Med. Sch., 1988; DSc (hon.), Sch. Medicine, Georgetown U., 1991, Emory U., 1992, Tufts U., 1993, Mt. Sinai Sch. Medicine, 1993, George Washington U., 1994. Diplomate Am. Bd. Internal Medicine. Intern, asst. resident Yale U., New Haven, 1952-54; sr. asst. resident Peter Bent Brigham Hosp., Boston, 1954-55; fellow Johns Hopkins Hosp., Balt., 1955-59; chief resident, instr. medicine Yale U., 1957-58; asst. prof. medicine Johns Hopkins U., 1957-60, physician, 1958-60; assoc. prof. medicine U. Wash., Seattle, 1960-62, prof., 1962-79, chmn. dept. medicine, 1964-79; physician-in-chief U. Wash. Hosp., 1964-79; pres. Brigham and Women's Hosp., Boston, 1979-81; prof. medicine Harvard U. Med. Sch., Boston, 1979-81; dean, vice chancellor health scis. U. Calif.-San Diego Sch. Medicine, 1981-86; clin. prof. infectious diseases Sch. Medicine Georgetown U., 1986-94; pres. Assn. Am. Med. Colls., Washington, 1986-94, pres. emeritus, 1994—; prof. medicine U. Wash., 1994—, disting prof., 1995; disting. sr. physician VA Med. Ctr., Seattle, 1994—; cons. to surgeon gen. USPHS, 1960-79; cons. USPHS Hosp., Seattle, 1962-79; mem. spl. med. adv. group VA, 1987-94. Editor: Harrison's Priciples of Internal Medicine, 1968-90; contbr. numerous articles to profl. jours. Served with USAAF, 1944-46. Recipient Lilly medal Royal Coll. Physicians, London, 1978, Wiggers award Albany Med. Coll., 1979, Robert H. Williams award Assn. Profs. Medicine, 1983, Keen award Brown U., 1980, Disting. Svc. award Baylor Coll. Medicine, 1989, Scroll of Merit Nat. Med. Assn., 1990, 2d Ann. Founder's award Assn. Program Dirs. in Internal Medicine, 1991, Flexner award Assn. Amer. Med. Coll., 1994; named Disting. Internist of Yr. Am. Soc. Internal Medicine; Disting. Teacher award 1993, Amer. Coll. of Physicians. Fellow AAAS, ACP (pres. 1975-76, Stengel award 1980, Disting. Tchr. award 1993), Am. Coll. Phys. Execs. (hon.); mem. Inst. Medicine of NAS (councillor 1977-80), Assn. Am. Physicians (pres. 1976-77), Cosmos Club. Home and Office: 1219 Parkside Dr E Seattle WA 98112-3717 Office: VA Med Ctr 1660 Columbia Way Seattle WA 98108

PETERSEN, BENT EDVARD, mathematician, educator; b. Copenhagen, July 31, 1942; came to U.S., 1964; s. Edvard Valdemar and Grethe Julie (Larsen) P.; m. Marguerite Kathleen Anne McCrindle, Aug. 21, 1965; children: Erik, Poul, Kirsten. BS, U. B.C., Vancouver, Can., 1964; PhD, MIT, 1968. Asst. prof. math. Oreg. State U., Corvallis, 1968-74, assoc. prof. math., 1974-80, prof. math., 1980—; vis. mem. Inst. Advanced Study, Princeton, N.J., 1973-74; guest scientist Internat. Atomic Energy Agy., Trieste, Italy, 1975. Author: Introduction to the Fourier Transform and Pseudo-differential Equations, 1983. Mem. Am. Math. Soc., Math. Assn. Am., Oreg. Acad. Sci., Sigma Xi. Office: Oreg State U Dept Math Corvallis OR 97331-4605

PETERSEN, CATHERINE HOLLAND, lawyer; b. Norman, Okla., Apr. 24, 1951; d. John Hays and Helen Ann (Turner) Holland; m. James Frederick Petersen, June 26, 1973 (div.); children: T. Kyle, Lindsay Diane. B.A., Hastings Coll., 1973; J.D., Okla. U., 1976. Bar: Okla. 1976, U.S. Dist. Ct. (we. dist.) Okla. 1978. Legal intern, police legal advisor City of Norman, 1974-76; sole practice, Norman, 1976-81; intern. continuing legal edn. U. Okla. Law Ctr., Norman, 1977, 79, 81, 83, 84, 86, 89-95. Bd. dirs. United Way, Norman, 1978-84, pres., 1981; bd. dirs. Women's Resource Ctr., Norman, 1975-77, 82-84; mem. Jr. League, Norman, 1980-83, Norman Hosp. Aux., Norman, 1982-84; trustee 1st Presbyn. Ch., 1986-87. Named to Outstanding Okla. Women of 1980's, Women's Polit. Caucus, 1980, Outstanding Women Am., 1981, 83. Fellow Am. Acad. Matrimonial Lawyers (pres. Okla. chpt. 1990-91, bd. govs. 1991-95); mem. Cleve. County Bar Assn., Okla. Bar Assn. (chmn. family law sect. 1987-88, seminar instr. 1986-93, 95), Phi Delta Phi. Republican. Home: 4716 Sundance Ct Norman OK 73072-3900 Office: PO Box 1243 314 E Comanche St Norman OK 73069-6009

PETERSEN, DAVID L., lawyer. AA, Concordia Jr. Coll., Milw., 1963; BA, Concordia Sr. Coll., Ft.Wayne, Ind., 1965; JD, Valparaiso U., Ind., 1968. Bar: Wis. 1968, U.S. Dist. Ct. (ea. dist.) Wis. 1969, U.S. Ct. Appeals (7th cir.) 1972, U.S. Supreme Ct. 1988, Fla. 1989. Ptnr. Quarles & Brady, Milw. and W. Palm Beach, Fla., 1968—. Author: Wisconsin Condominium Law, 1988, 94; editor Valparaiso U. Law Rev. 1967-68; contbr. articles to profl. jours. Mem. Greater Milw. Com. Community Devel., 1983; bd. dirs. Goals for Greater Milw. 2000, 1982, Broward Com. of 100. Lt. col., instr. pilot USAF/Wis. Air N.G., 1970-90. Mem. ABA, Wis. Bar Assn., Milw. Bar Assn., Fla. Bar Assn., Broward County Bar Assn., Palm Beach County Bar, Wis. Mortgage Bankers Assn., Am. Coll. Real Estate Lawyers, Milw. Yacht Club, Palm Beach Yacht Club. Office: Quarles & Brady 222 Lakeview Ave West Palm Beach FL 33401-6145 also: Quarles & Brady 411 E Wisconsin Ave Milwaukee WI 53202-4409

PETERSEN, DONALD SONDERGAARD, lawyer; b. Pontiac, Ill., May 14, 1929; s. Clarence Marius and Esther (Sondergaard) P.; m. Alice Thorup, June 5, 1954; children: Stephen, Susan Petersen Schuh, Sally Petersen Riordan. Student, Grand View Coll., 1946-48; B.A., Augustana Coll., Rock Island, Ill., 1951; J.D., Northwestern U., 1956. Bar: Ill. 1957. Assoc. Norman & Billick and predecessors, Chgo., 1956-64, ptnr., 1965-78; counsel Sidley & Austin, Chgo., 1978-80, ptnr., 1980-93, ret., 1993; pres. Chgo. Exhibitors Corp., Chgo., 1978-85. Bd. dirs. Mount Olive Cemetery Co. Inc., Chgo., 1972-90; bd. dirs. Augustana Hosp., 1983-87, Danish Old People's Home, 1976—; bd. dirs. Luth. Gen. Hosp., Park Ridge, Ill., 1968—, chmn., 1979-81, 89-91; bd. dirs. Luth. Gen. Health System and predecessors, Park Ridge, 1980-95, chmn., 1980-81, 83-85; bd. dirs. Parkside Health Mgmt. Corp., Parkside Home Health Svcs., 1985-88. With U.S. Army, 1951-53. Mem. Chgo. Bar Assn., Ill. State Bar Assn. Club: Union League (Chgo.). Home: 241 N Aldine Ave Park Ridge IL 60068-3009 Office: 1 First Nat Plz Ste 2550 Chicago IL 60603

PETERSEN, JAMES L., lawyer; b. Bloomington, Ill., Feb. 3, 1947; s. Eugene and Cathryn Teresa (Hemmele) P.; m. Helen Louise Moser, Nov. 20, 1971; children: Christine Louise, Margaret Teresa. BA, Ill. State U., 1970; MA, Sangamon State U., 1973; JD magna cum laude, Ind. U., 1976. Bar: Ind. 1976, Fla. 1980, U.S. Dist. Cts. (no. and so. Ind.), U.S. Ct. Appeals (7th cir.), U.S. Supreme Ct. Admissions officer Sangamon State U., Springfield, Ill., 1970-71, asst. to v.p., 1971-72, registrar, 1972-73; assoc. Ice Miller Donadio & Ryan, Indpls., 1976-83, ptnr., 1983—. Pres. United Cerebral Palsy of Ctrl. Ind., 1981-83, pres. Found., 1988-90. Mem. ABA, Fla. Bar Assn., Ind. Bar Assn., Internat. Assn. Def. Counsel, Ill. State U. Alumni Assn. (pres. 1990-92), Ind. U. Law Alumni Assn. (bd. dirs. 1992—). Home: 11827 Sea Star Dr Indianapolis IN 46256-9400 Office: Ice Miller Donadio & Ryan PO Box 82001 One American Sq Indianapolis IN 46282

PETERSEN, KENNETH CLARENCE, chemical company executive; b. Chgo., Mar. 17, 1936; s. Clarence and Theresa (Tomazin) P.; m. Gladys Marie Boyte, Jan. 21, 1956; children: Robert, Michael, Karen, William, Eric, John. Student, Crane Jr. Coll., 1956-57, Wright Jr. Coll., 1957-58; BS in Chemistry, Northwestern U., 1960, MS in Organic Chemistry, 1963. Chem. lab. tech. Glidden Paint Co., Chgo., 1956-58; chemist, group leader Acme Resin Co., Forest Pk., Ill., 1958-64; group leader, research coordinator, research mgr. resin div., mgr. chemistry & tech., mgr. chem. div. mfg., v.p. mfg. then exec. v.p. Schenectady (N.Y.) Chems., Inc., 1964-81, pres., 1981-93; pres. Schenectady Internat. Inc. (formerly Schenectady Chems., Inc.), 1993—; bd. dirs. TRUSTCO, Schenectady; mem. The Fifty Group, tri-city area, 1981—. Contbr. articles to profl. jours.; holder 12 patents. bd. dirs. Schenectady Boys and Girls Club, 1980—, Sunnyview Hosp., Schenectady, 1982—, Schenectady Econ. Devel. Council, 1984—, Fund Raising Rev. Bd. Schenectady, 1985—. Mem. Am. Chem. Soc. (chmn. eastern N.Y. sect. 1979). Clubs: Mohawk, Mohawk Golf (Schenectady). Avocations: fishing, golf, bridge, poker. Office: Schenectady Internat Inc Congress And # 10th Sts Schenectady NY 12303

PETERSEN, MARTIN EUGENE, museum curator; b. Grafton, Iowa, Apr. 21, 1931; s. Martin S. and Martha Dorothea (Paulsen) P. B.A., State U. Iowa, 1951, M.A., 1957; postgrad., The Hague (Netherlands), 1964. Curator San Diego Mus. Art, 1957—; extension instr. U. Calif., 1958, lectr., 1960. Author art catalogues, articles in field. Served with AUS, 1952-54. Mem. So. Calif. Art Historians. Home: 4571 Narragansett Ave San Diego CA 92107-2915 Office: San Diego Mus Art PO Box 2107 San Diego CA 92112-2107

PETERSEN, MICHAEL JON, utility company executive; b. Longview, Wash., Feb. 26, 1945; s. Norman Clair and Ferne Opel (Christenson) P.; m. Priscilla Louise Johnson, July 24, 1971; children: Jon Matthew, Timothy Scott, Kristen Marie. BA, U. Puget Sound, 1969. CPA, Wash. Cost acct. Weyerhaeuser Co., Longview, Wash., 1970-74; controller, treas. Cowlitz Pub. Utility Dist. No.1, Longview, 1974—. V.p., treas. Cowlitz Valley chpt. Assn. for Retarded Citizens, Longview, 1971-74; area rep. Cowlitz Little League, Kelso, Wash., 1985—. Served to sgt. U.S. Army, 1967-69, Vietnam. Avocations: golf, swimming, home carpentry. Home: 2465 Archwood Dr Longview WA 98632-5782 Office: Cowlitz Pub Utility Dist #1 960 Commerce Ave Longview WA 98632-2512

PETERSEN, NORMAN RICHARD, JR., religious studies educator; b. Chgo., Aug. 25, 1933; s. Norman Richard and Mildred May (Wilson) P.; m. Antoinette DeRosa, Jan. 28, 1956; children: Kristen, Mark, Joanna. B.F.A., Pratt Inst., 1957; S.T.B., Harvard U., 1961, Ph.D., 1967. Instr., asst. prof. Wellesley Coll., Mass., 1963-69; asst. prof., then assoc. prof. religion Williams Coll., Williamstown, Mass., 1969-77; prof. Williams Coll., 1978-79, Washington Gladden prof. religion, 1980—. Author: Literary Criticism for New Testament Critics, 1978, Rediscovering Paul, The Sociology of Paul's Narrative World, 1985 (Bibl. Archeology Soc. book award 1986, Am. Acad. Religion book award 1987), The Gospel According to John and the Sociology of Light, Language and Characterization in the Fourth Gospel, 1993. Mem. Mt. Greylock Regional High Sch. Com., Williamstown, 1980-85. Served with AUS, 1952-54. Mem. Soc. Bibl. Lit., Studiorum Novi Testamenti Societas. Office: Williams Coll Dept Religion Williamstown MA 01267

PETERSEN, RAYMOND JOSEPH, publishing company executive; b. West Orange, N.J., May 9, 1919; s. Raymond Otto and Ellen (Bond) P.; Rosalie Iovin, July 22, 1949 (dec. Nov. 1970); children—R. Jeffrey, Gregory, Mary Petersen Frost, John, Teresa Petersen Bracchita, Cathy Petersen Keller, Jeanna Peterson Shephard, Matthew; m. Gayle Malles, Feb. 22, 1991. Dr. Journalism (hon.), St. Joseph's Coll., 1966. Former advt. salesman to pub. and v.p. Good Housekeeping Mag., N.Y.C., 1948-67, now publs. dir.; sr. v.p. Hearst Mags., N.Y.C., 1967-69, exec. v.p., 1969—, also bd. dirs.; testamentary trustee Hearst Founds., N.Y.C., 1969-87; past mem. bd. dirs. Supermarkets Gen. Corp., Woodbridge, N.J., Internat. Capital & Tech. Corp., N.Y.C.; past mem. bd. dirs. Brand Names Found., Mag. Advt. Bur., Acad. Food Market of St. Joseph's U., Phila., Council Better Bus. burs., Inc., and Consumer Research Inst. for Grocery Mfrs. Am., Inc.; bd. dirs. Covenant House, N.Y.C., 1987; apptd. to U.S. Nat. Commn. on Libraries and Info. Sci., Washington, 1987; nat. chmn. Religion in Am. Life, 1986, 87, 88, 89; mem. pub. service adv. com. Communications Industries Council, 1968; hon. bd. dirs. N.Y. Advt. Club, 1979; bd. dirs. Coty Awards Com., 1980-85; chmn. Nat. Advt. Rev. Council, 1980, 84. Bd. dirs. USO of Met. N.Y., N.Y.C., 1967—, v.p., 1980—; mem. chmn.'s com. United Cerebral Palsy Campaign, N.Y.C., 1980—; honoree adviser to bd. dirs. Children of Alcoholics Found., N.Y.C., 1984—; mem. adv. bd. St. Vincent's Hosp., Harrison, N.Y., 1981-86; bd. dirs. Am. Friends of Jerusalem Mental Health Ctr., N.Y.C., 1982-86, Madison Sq. Boys and Girls Clubs, N.Y.C., 1983—, Nat. Crime Prevention Council, Washington, 1985—. Named Father of Yr., 1966; recipient Good Scout award Boy Scouts Am., 1973; Silver Beaver award Boy Scouts Am., 1979; Charles E. Wilson award Religion in Am. Life, 1985; inducted Advt. Hall of Fame, 1987. Mem. Am. Hotel Found., 1971—. Republican. Roman Catholic. Office: The Hearst Corp 959 8th Ave New York NY 10019-3737

PETERSEN, ROBERT E., publisher; b. Los Angeles, Sept. 10, 1926; s. Einar and Bertha (Putera) P.; m. Margie McNally, Jan. 26, 1963. Founder, chmn. bd. Petersen Pub. Co. (pubs. Hot Rod, Motor Trend, Car Craft, Motorcyclist, Photog., Skin Diver, Teen, Hunting, Guns & Ammo, Circle

Track, Dirt Rider, Los Angeles, 1948—; founder, chmn. bd. (pubs. 4 Wheel and Off Road mags.), Los Angeles, %; owner Robert E. Petersen Prodns. (producers TV series, commls., auto shows, trade shows), Petersen Galleries, Beverly Hills, Calif., Scandia Restaurant. Mem. Los Angeles Library Commn., 1963-64; Bd. dirs. Boys Club Am., past pres. Hollywood br.; bd. dirs. Thalians. Served with USAF. Clubs: So. Calif Safari, Balboa Bay, Catalina Island Yacht, Confrerie de la Chaine des Rotisseurs. Office: Petersen Publishing Co 6420 Wilshire Blvd Los Angeles CA 90048

PETERSEN, ROLAND, artist, printmaker; b. Endelave, Horsens, Denmark, 1926; came to U.S., 1928; m. Sharane Havlina, Aug. 12, 1950; children—Dana Mark, Maura Brooke, Julien Conrad, Karena Caia. B.A., U. Calif.-Berkeley, 1949, M.A., 1950; postgrad., Han Hofmann's Sch. Fine Arts, summers 1950-51, S.W. Hayter's Atelier 17, Paris, 1950, 63, 70, Islington Studio, London, 1976, The Print Workshop, London, 1980. Tchr. State Coll. Wash., Pullman, 1952-56; mem. faculty U. Calif., Davis, 1956-91, prof. art, 1991; ret., 1991. Exhibited one-man shows: Gump's Gallery, San Francisco, 1962, Staempfli Gallery, N.Y.C., 1963, 65, 67, Adele Bednarz Gallery, Los Angeles, 1966, 69, 70, 72, 73, 75, 76, Crocker Art Gallery, Sacramento, 1965, de Young Mus., San Francisco, 1968, La Jolla Mus., 1971, Phoenix Mus., 1972, Santa Barbara Mus., 1973, USIS sponsored touring one-man exhbn., Turkey, U. Reading, Eng., 1977, 80, U. Calif., Davis, 1978, 92, Brubaker Gallery, Sarasota, Fla., 1979, Rorick Gallery, San Francisco, 1981, 82, 83, 84, 85, Himovitz-Salomon Gallery, Sacramento, 1987-88, 91, Vanderwoude Tananbaum Gallery, N.Y.C., 1987-89, Harcourts Gallery, San Francisco, 1989, 91, 93, U. Calif., Davis, 1992; group shows include Calif. Palace Legion of Honor, San Francisco Art Inst., 1962, Mus. Art, Carnegie Inst., Pitts., 1964, Obelisk Gallery, Washington, John Herron Art Inst., Indpls., 1964, Pa. Acad. Fine Arts, Phila., Crocker Art Gallery, Sacramento, 1965, 81, Art Inst. Chgo., 1965, Va. Mus. Fine Arts, Richmond, 1966, U. Ariz. Art Gallery, Tucson, 1967, Am. Cultural Center, Paris, 1971, Nat. Gallery, Washington, 1972, Otis Art Inst. Gallery, Los Angeles, 1974, Auerbach Fine Art Gallery, London, 1977, U. Wis., Madison, 1977, Bklyn. Mus., 1978, U. Ill., 1978, U. Nev., Las Vegas, 1980, Brubaker Gallery, Sarasota, Fla., 1983, U.S.A. World Print Council, San Francisco, Nat. Mus., Singapore, Nat. Gallery, Bangkok, Thailand, Amerika Haus, Berlin, Malmo Konsthall, Sweden, Museo Carrillo Gil, Mexico City, all 1984-86, Crocker Art Mus., 1991, Fresno Met. Mus., 1992, Hall of Pictures, Uman, Russia, 1992, Calif. State U., L.A., 1992, San Bernardino, 1993 Pence Gallery, Davis, Calif., 1993, Artists Contemporary Gallery, Sacramento, 1994, Andre Milan Gallery, Sao Paulo, Brazil, 1995; represented in permanent collections: de Young Mus., San Francisco, San Francisco Mus. Modern Art, Va. Mus. Fine Arts, Richmond, Mus. Modern Art, N.Y.C., Phila. Mus. Art, Whitney Mus. Am. Art, Phoenix Mus., Santa Barbara Mus., Musée Municipal, Brest, France, Smithsonian Instn. Nat. Collection Fine Arts & Archives of Am. Art, others. Served with USN, 1944-46, PTO. Recipient numerous prizes and awards, 1950—; Guggenheim fellow, 1963; U. Calif. creative arts fellow, 1967, 70, 77; Fulbright grantee, 1970. Mem. AAUP, San Francisco Art Assn., Calif. Soc. Printmakers. Home: 6 Lanai Way PO Box 1 Dillon Beach CA 94929-0001

PETERSEN, SUSAN JANE, publishing company executive; b. Akron, Ohio, Oct. 9, 1944; d. Christian Henry and Sue Elizabeth (Wigand) P.; m. Bruce S. Harris, Aug. 5, 1973; 1 child, Petersen Nathanial. B.A., Vassar Coll., 1966; M.F.A., N.Y.U., 1969. Vice pres. advt. and promotions Pocket Books, N.Y.C., 1978-80; v.p., mktg. dir. Ballantine, N.Y.C., 1980-82; exec. v.p. Ballantine Delrey Fawcett Books, N.Y.C., 1981-82, pres., 1982—; exec. v.p. Random House, Inc., N.Y.C., 1987—. Mem. Assn. Am. Pubs. (bd. dirs. 1985—), Com. Vis. Harvard U. Press. Lutheran.

PETERSEN, ULRICH, geology educator; b. Negritos, Peru, Dec. 1, 1927; s. Georg and Harriet (Bluhme) P.; m. Edith Martensen, Apr. 27, 1952 (dec. Aug. 1978); children: Erich, Armin (dec.), Heidi.; m. Eileen Borque, June 19, 1982. Mining Engr., Escuela Nacional de Ingenieros, Lima, Peru, 1954; M.A., Harvard U., 1955, Ph.D., 1963. Geologist Instituto Geológico del Peru and Instituto Nacional de Investigación y Fomento Mineros, 1946-51; geologist Cerro de Pasco Corp., Peru, 1951-54; asst. chief geologist Cerro de Pasco Corp., 1956-57, chief geologist, 1958-63; lectr. Harvard, 1963-66; assoc. prof. Harvard U., 1966-69, prof. mining geology, 1969-81, Harry C. Dudley prof. econ. geology, 1981—; cons. geologist, 1963—. Named comendador de la orden al Merito por Servicios Distinguidos Peru, 1968; recipient A. von Humboldt rsch. award, 1992-93. Mem. AAAS, Soc. Econ. Geologists (pres. 1988-89), Geol. Soc. Am., Soc. Geologica del Peru, Am. Inst. Mining and Metall. Engrs. Home: 414 Marsh St Belmont MA 02178-1109 Office: 20 Oxford St Cambridge MA 02138-2902

PETERSEN, WILLIAM OTTO, lawyer; b. Chgo., Nov. 28, 1926; s. William Ferdinand and Alma Schmidt P.; m. Jane Browne, Nov. 25, 1978. AB cum laude, Harvard U., 1949, LLB, 1952. Bar: Ill., 1952. Atty. No. Trust. Co., Chgo., 1952-55; ptnr. Vedder, Price, Kaufman & Kamholz, Chgo., 1955—. Mem. exec. bd. Ct. Theatre, 1992—; mem. vis. to U. Chgo. Libr., 1992—; bd. dirs. Chgo. Youth Ctrs., 1958—, pres., 1971, 72; bd. dirs. Taylor Inst., Chgo., 1979—, chmn., 1988—; bd. dirs. Chgo. Commons Corp., 1988—; bd. dirs., v.p. Luther I. Replogle Found., Chgo. and Washington, 1986—. With USN, 1944-46. Mem. ABA, Ill. State Bar Assn., Chgo. Bar Assn. (chmn. corp. law com 1976), Racquet Club of Chgo. (pres. 1981, 82), Univ. Club, Lake Geneva (Wis.) Country Club, Lake Geneva Yacht Club, Caxton Club. Republican. Lutheran. Home: 1120 N Lake Shore Dr Chicago IL 60611-1042 Office: Vedder Price Kaufman & Kammholz 222 N La Salle St Chicago IL 60601-1003

PETERSEN, WOLFGANG, film director; b. Emden, Fed. Republic Germany, Mar. 14, 1941. Asst. state dir. Ernst Deutsch Theatre, Hamburg, Fed. Republic Germany. Dir.: (films) The Consequence, 1977, Black and White Like Day and Night, 1978, Enemy Mine, 1985, In the Line of Fire, 1993, Outbreak, 1995; (TV) Smog (Prix Futura award 1975), For Your Love Only, Scenes of the Crime; dir., screenwriter: Das Boot, 1981 (Acad. award nomination Best Adapted Screenplay 1981), The Neverending Story, 1984, Shattered, 1991. Office: care The Chasin Agy 190 N Canon Dr # 210 Beverly Hills CA 90210-5327 Office: CAA 9830 Wilshire Blvd Beverly Hills CA 90212*

PETERSMEYER, C(HARLES) WREDE, retired broadcasting executive, venture capitalist; b. L.A., Jan. 28, 1919; s. Harry Frederick and Florence (Quayle) P.; m. Frances Carolyn Gregg, Apr. 12, 1944; children: Susan Calhoun Petersmeyer Henneke, Charles Gregg, Nancy Quayle Petersmeyer Damm. A.B. with honors, U. Calif., 1941; M.B.A. with high distinction, Harvard, 1943. Assoc. McKinsey & Co., 1946-47; pres. & founder, chmn. until 1977 of Corinthian Broadcasting Corp., N.Y.; owner sta. KOTV, Tulsa, sta. KHOU-TV, Houston, sta. KXTV, Sacramento, stas.WANE-TV, WANE-AM, Fort Wayne, stas. WISH-TV, WISH-AM, Indpls., TVS Television Network, Funk and Wagnalls, Inc.; past trustee Greenwich Savs. Bank; past dir. Dun & Bradstreet, Carte Blanche, Reuben H. Donnelly Corp. Past trustee Sarah Lawrence Coll., Pine Manor Coll., chmn. bd., 1975-78; chmn. bd. dirs. and overseers Sweet Briar Coll.; bd. dirs. Mid Atlantic Legal Found.; advisor Sprout Found; chmn. Harvard Bus. Sch. Fund, 1976-78; adv. dir. Met. Opera Assn. Served from pvt. to capt. AUS, 1943-46. Mem. Nat. Assn. Broadcasters (past dir.), Assn. Maximum Service Telecasters (past dir.), Com. Econ. Devel. (hon. trustee), Phi Beta Kappa Assos. (past dir.), Phi Beta Kappa, Delta Kappa Epsilon. Clubs: University, Harvard Bus. Sch. (N.Y.C.); John's Island (Fla.); Augusta (Ga.), Nat. Golf. Home and Office: 201 Turtle Way Vero Beach FL 32963

PETERSON, ALLEN KENNETH, healthcare administrator; b. Mpls., June 10, 1931; s. Chris Arthur and Elsie (Torgerson) P.; m. Barbara Joan Verchey, June 28, 1952. MHA, U. Minn., 1953, MHA, 1958. Hosp. CEO, v.p. Mt. Sinai Hosp., Mpls., 1958-73; CEO, v.p. Evang. Health Sys., Oak Brook, Ill., 1973-92; field rep. Joint Commn. on Accreditation of Healthcare Orgns., Oak Brook Terrace, Ill., 1993—. Served with U.S. Army, 1953-55. Home: 184 Dickinson Wheaton IL 60187 Office: Joint Commn Accreditation One Renaissance Blvd Oak Brook Mall IL 60521

PETERSON, AMY, Olympic athlete; b. Maplewood, Minn., 1971. Bronze medalist, women's 500m short-track speedskating Olympic Games, Lillehammer, Norway, 1994; Bronze medalist, women's 3000m short-track speedskating Olympic Games, 1994. Office: US Olympic Committee 1750 E Boulder St Colorado Springs CO 80909

PETERSON, ANN SULLIVAN, physician, health care consultant; b. Rhinebeck, N.Y., Oct. 11, 1928; A.B., Cornell U., 1950, M.D., 1954; M.S. (Alfred P. Sloan fellow 1979-80), M.I.T., 1980. Diplomate Am. Bd. Internal Medicine. Intern, Cornell Med. Div.-Bellevue Hosp., N.Y.C., 1954-55, resident, 1955-57; fellow in medicine and physiology Meml.-Sloan Kettering Cancer Ctr., Cornell Med. Coll. N.Y.C., 1957-60; instr. medicine Georgetown U. Sch. Medicine, Washington, 1962-65, asst. prof., 1965-69, asst. dir. clin. research unit, 1962-69; assoc. prof. medicine U. Ill., Chgo., 1969-72, asst. dean, 1969-71, assoc. dean, 1971-72; assoc. prof. medicine, assoc. dean Coll. Physicians and Surgeons, Columbia U., N.Y.C., 1972-80; assoc. prof. medicine, assoc. dean Cornell U. Med. Coll., N.Y.C., 1980-83; assoc. dir. div. med. edn. AMA, Chgo., 1983-86, dir. div. grad. med. edn., 1986-89; v.p. Mgmt. Cons. Corp. 1989-93; ind. cons., Chgo., 1993—; mem. bd. regents Uniformed Svcs. U. of Health Scis., 1984-90. John and Mary R. Markle scholar, 1965-70. Fellow ACP; mem. Mortar Board, Alpha Omega Alpha, Alpha Epsilon Delta. Contbr. articles to med. jours.

PETERSON, ARTHUR JACK, finance company executive; b. San Francisco, Aug. 31, 1941; s. Arthur Wallace and Lyyli (Tuomala) P.; m. Joanne Maria Sacco, June 28, 1946 (div. July 1987); 1 child, Michelle Marie. BS in Math., Mich. Technol. U., 1963; MBA, UCLA, 1971. Ops. rsch. analyst McDonnell Aircraft, St. Louis, 1963-66, N.Am. Rockwell, El Segundo, Calif., 1966-67, Lockheed Missile and Space, Sunnyvale, Calif., 1967-69; sales rep. Burroughs Corp., Oakland, Calif., 1971-72; various positions Fireman's Fund Ins., San Francisco, 1972-81; v.p. fin. and adminstrn. Agy. Automation, San Francisco, 1981-83; sr. v.p. corp. devel. Avco Fin. Svcs., Irvine, Calif., 1983—. Mem. Assn. Corp. Growth, Newport Beach (Calif.) Country Club. Republican. Lutheran. Avocations: golf, spectator sports, travel. Home: 24252 Tahoe Ct Laguna Beach CA 92656-4534 Office: Avco Fin Svcs Inc 3349 Michelson Dr Irvine CA 92715-1606

PETERSON, ARTHUR LAVERNE, former college president; b. Glyndon, Minn., June 27, 1926; s. John M. and Hilda C. (Moline) P.; m. Connie Lucille Harr, June 14, 1952; children: Jon Martin, Rebecca Ruth, Donna Harr, Ingrid Bliss. AB, Yale U., 1947; MSPA, U. So. Calif., 1949; postgrad., U. Chgo., 1949-50; PhD, U. Minn., 1962; LLD, Lebanon Valley Coll., 1988. Mem. Wis. State Legislature, 1951-55; from instr. to asst. prof. polit. sci. U. Wis., Eau Claire, 1954-60; assoc. prof. to prof. polit. sci. Ohio Wesleyan U., Delaware, 1961-65, 70-80; pres. Am. Grad. Sch. Internat. Mgmt., Phoenix, 1966-70; dean spl. programs Eckerd Coll., St. Petersburg, Fla., 1980-84, dir. Acad. Sr. Profls., 1987-94; pres. Lebanon Valley Coll., Annville, Pa., 1984-87; bd. dirs. Arnold Industries; asst. to chmn. Rep. Nat. Com., Washington, 1960-61; founding dir. Ctr. Internat. Bus., L.A., 1969-70; cons. Novin Inst. Polit. Affairs, Tehran, Iran, 1973; exec. dir. Fla. Assn. Colls. and Univs., 1988—. Author: McCarthyism: Ideology and Foundations, 1962; co-author: Electing the President, 1968; contbr. articles to scholarly jours. Chmn. Ohio Civil Rights Commn., 1963-65; dep. chmn. Republican Nat. Com., 1965-66; mem. Ohio Ethics Commn., 1976-80. Served to capt. USMC, 1951-52; Korea. Citizenship Clearing House Nat. Faculty fellow, 1960; recipient citation for excellence Sigma Phi Epsilon, 1977; Marshall award Ohio Wesleyan Students, 1979. Mem. Am. Polit. Sci. Assn., Am. Judicature Soc. (dir. 1975—), Soc. Polit. Enquiries (pres. 1985—), Acad. Polit. Sci., Pi Sigma Alpha (dir. 1972—), Phi Mu Alpha Sinfonia, Omicron Delta Kappa. Republican. Mem. United Ch. of Christ. Lodges: Rotary, Masons. Avocations: sailing; flying; music. Home: 552 Johns Pass Ave Saint Petersburg FL 33708-2366

PETERSON, BARBARA ANN BENNETT, history educator; b. Portland, Oreg., Sept. 6, 1942; d. George Wright and Hope (Chatfield) Bennett; m. Frank Lynn Peterson, July 1, 1967. BA, BS, Oreg. State U., 1964; MA, Stanford U., 1965; PhD, U. Hawaii, 1978; PhD (hon.), London Inst. Applied Rsch., 1991. Prof. history U. Hawaii, Honolulu, 1967—, chmn. social scis. dept., 1971-73, 75-76, asst. dean, 1973-74; prof. Asian history and European colonial history and world problems Chapman Coll. World Campus Afloat, 1974; prof. European overseas exploration, expansion, and colonialism U. Colo., Boulder, 1978; assoc. prof. U. Hawaii-Manoa Coll. Continuing Edn., 1981; Fulbright prof. history Wuhan (China) U., 1988-89; Fulbright rsch. prof. Sophia U., Japan, 1967; lectr. Capital Speakers, Washington, 1987—; tchr. Hawaii State Ednl. Channel, 1993—. Co-author: Women's Place is in the History Books, Her Story, 1962-1980: A Curriculum Guide for American History Teachers, 1980; author: America in British Eyes, 1988; editor: Notable Women of Hawaii, 1984, (with W. Solheim) The Pacific Region, 1990, 91, American History: 17th, 18th, and 19th Centuries, 1993, America: 19th and 20th Centuries, 1993; assoc. editor Am. Nat. Biography; contbr. articles to profl. publs. Participant People-to-People Program, Eng., 1964, Expt. in Internat. Living Program, Nigeria, 1966; chmn. 1st Nat. Women's History Week, Hawaii, 1982; pres. Bishop Mus. Coun., 1993-94; active Hawaii Commn. on Status of Women. Recipient state proclamations Gov. of Hawaii, 1982, City of Honolulu, 1982, Outstanding Tchr. of yr. award Wuhan (China) U., 1988, Medallion of Excellence award Am. Biog. Assn., 1989, Woman of Yr. award, 1991; Fulbright scholar, Japan, 1967, China, 1988-89; NEH-Woodrow Wilson fellow Princeton U., 1980. Fellow World Literacy Acad. (Eng.), Internat. Biog. Assn. (Cambridge, Eng. chpt.); mem. AAUW, Am. Hist. Assn., Am. Studies Assn., Am. Studies Assn. (pres. 1984-85), Fulbright Alumni Assn. (founding pres. Hawaii chpt. 1984-88, mem. nat. steering com. chairwomen Fulbright Assn. ann. conf. 1990), Am. Hist. Assn. (mem. numerous coms.), Am. Coun. on Edn., Maison Internat. des Intellectuals, France, Hawaii Found. History and Humanities (mem. editl. bd. 1972-73), Hawaii Found. Women's History, Hawaii Hist. Assn., Nat. League Am. Pen Women (contest chapprerson 1986), Women in Acad. Adminstrn., Pi Beta Phi, Phi Kappa Phi. Avocation: tennis. Home: 1341 Laukahi St Honolulu HI 96821-1407 Office: Univ Hawaii 874 Dillingham Blvd Honolulu HI 96817

PETERSON, BOB, environmental company executive, consultant; b. Buffalo, Jan. 29, 1943; s. John W. and Ruth (Janes) A.; m. Nancy C. Boda, Aug. 22, 1964; children: Kirsten Lynn, Jennifer Gail, David Robert. BSChemE, Ill. Inst. Tech., 1964; MSChemE, U. Del., 1967, DSChemE, 1968; postgrad., Harvard U., 1981. Rsch. engr. Union Carbide R&D, Bound Brook, N.J., 1968-71, rsch. mgr., 1971-78, rsch. dir., 1978-81; dir. mktg. silicones divsn. Union Carbide, Danbury, Ct., 1981-83, v.p., gen. mgr. specialty chem. divsn., 1983-88; pres. NUKEM Treatment Svcs., Mahwah, N.J., 1988-91, ENSR Cons. & Engring., Acton, Mass., 1991—; mem. adv. coun. Clarkson U. Sch. Engring., Potsdam, N.Y., 1978-88, U. Del. Dept. Chem. Engring., 1989—; RPI Dept. Chem. Engring., Troy, N.Y., 1986—. Lay leadership positions Rockaway Reformed Ch., Whitehouse Station, N.J., 1968-78, 1st Congl. Ch., Ridgefield, Conn., 1983-90. Democrat. Mem. United Ch. of Christ. Avocations: golf, travel, opera, engineering education. Office: ENSR Consulting & Engring 35 Nagog Park Acton MA 01720*

PETERSON, CARL, professional football team executive; b. Long Beach, Calif.; 1 child, Dawn. BS in Kinesiology, UCLA, 1966, M in Kinesiology, 1967, D in Adminstrn. in Higher Edn., 1970. Asst. coach Wilson High Sch., Calif., 1966, Loyola High Sch., 1967-68, Calif. State U., Sonoma, 1969-70; head coach Calif. State U., 1970-72; receivers coach UCLA, 1972-74, receivers coach, adminstrv. asst., 1974-76; coach recievers and tight ends Phila. Eagles, 1976, dir. player personnel, 1977-82; pres., gen. mgr. Phila. Stars, 1982-88; pres., gen. mgr. COO Kansas City Chiefs, Mo., 1988—; pres., CEO PhillySport Mag., Phila.; mem. nat. bd. Maxwell Football Club and Pop Warner Little Scholar Orgn. Recipient USFL Exec. of Yr. award Sporting News, 1983, 84. Mem. Young Pres. Orgn. (Kansas City chpt.). Office: Kansas City Chiefs 1 Arrowhead Dr Kansas City MO 64129*

PETERSON, CARL ADRIAN, English language educator; b. Warren, Pa., Dec. 21, 1930; s. Ludwig A. and Ida Dorothea (Jacobson) P.; m. Thalia Gouma, June 16, 1956; children: Gregory, Christopher. BA, Pa. State U., 1952, MA, 1953; PhD, U. Wis., 1961. Instr., asst. prof., assoc. prof., prof. English Oberlin (Ohio) Coll., 1958—; chair dept., 1981-85, 90-92, 94-95. Contbr. articles on English lit. and visual arts to profl. jours. Power grantee Oberlin Coll., 1968, 75, Curricular Devel. grantee, 1976, Mellon grantee, 1987, 94. Home: 394 Edgemeer Pl Oberlin OH 44074 Office: Oberlin Coll Dept English Oberlin OH 44074

PETERSON, CARL ERIC, banker, metals company executive; b. Wareham, Mass., Apr. 8, 1944; s. E. Gunnar and Ruth (Kramer) P.; m. Frances Harkness, Sept. 7, 1966; children—Robin, Alec Harkness. BA, Brown U., 1966; MA, U. Pa., 1971; grad., Sch. for Internat. Banking, 1974, Stonier Grad. Sch. Banking, 1978. With R.I. Hosp. Trust Nat. Bank, Providence, 1971-82; with Engelhard Corp., Iselin, N.J., 1982-85, Dryvit System, Inc., West Warwick, R.I., 1986, Gerald Metals, Inc., Stamford, Conn., 1987—; lectr. World Gold Markets Conf., London, 1981, Am. Mining Congress, Phoenix, 1984, 12th Internat. Precious Metals Inst. Conf., Boston, 1988. Bd. dirs., mem. adv. council Internat. House of R.I., 1974-79; mem. of corp. Woods Hole Oceanographic Instn. 1981—, audit com., 1988—; mem. R.I. Pub. Expenditure Council, 1974-82, Internat. Ctr. New Eng., 1980-81. Served to lt. USNR, 1967-70. Episcopalian. Clubs: Hope (Providence); Willow Dell Beach (Matunuck, R.I.). Office: Gerald Metals Inc High Ridge Park Stamford CT 06905-1328

PETERSON, CARL RICHARD, mechanical engineering educator, consultant; b. Detroit, Mar. 6, 1934; s. Signor and Frances Elizabeth (McClure) P.; m. Susan J. Truby, Sept. 2, 1958; children: Laura Lyne, Mark Allan. BS in Mech. Engring., U. Mich., 1956; MS in Mech. Engring., MIT, 1958, DSc in Mech. Engring., 1963. Asst. prof. dept. aeronautics and astronautics MIT, Cambridge, Mass., 1961-63, assoc. prof. dept. mech. engring. 1976-95, prof., 1995—; asst. chief spl. projects Ingersoll-Rand Rsch., Inc., Princeton, N.J., 1963-70; mgr. spl. projects Foster-Miller Assocs., Waltham, Mass., 1970-72; pres., founder RAPIDEX, Inc., Gloucester, Mass., 1972-76; chmn., co-author report Nat. Rsch. Coun., 1994. Co-author: Mechanics and Thermodynamics of Propulsion, 1964; patentee in field. Fellow ASME (founder Mining and Excavation Rsch. Inst., Washington), Tau Beta Pi. Avocations: hunting, fishing. Office: Massachusetts Inst of Technology Dept of Mech Engring 77 Massachusetts Ave Cambridge MA 02139-4307

PETERSON, CHARLES EMIL, architect; b. Madison, Minn., Aug. 23, 1906; s. Charles Emil and Mae (Nisbit) P. BA, U. Minn., 1928. With U.S. Nat. Pk. Svc., 1929-62, architect, landscape architect, San Francisco, 1929-30, resident landscape architect, Yorktown, Va., 1930-33, dep. chief architect, Washington, 1933-35, sr. landscape architect riverfront project, St. Louis, 1936-48, regional architect, Richmond, Va., 1948-49, resident architect Independence, Nat. Hist. Project, Phila., 1950-54, supervising architect historic structures, Ea. U.S., 1954-62; cons. archtl. historian, restorationist, planner, 1962—; adj. prof. architecture Columbia U., 1964-78; pioneered Hist. Am. Bldgs. Survey, 1933; conducted devel. studies, Easter Island for UNESCO, 1966-68; AIA del. II Internat. Congress Architects and Technicians Hist. Monuments, Venice, 1964, 1st-2d assemblies Internat. Coun. Monuments and Sites, Warsaw-Cracow, Poland, 1965, Oxford, Eng., 1969, Budapest, 1972; contbr. to Conf. on Edn. Restorationists, Pistoia, Italy, 1968; organized forums on restoration historic bldgs. Bldg. Research Inst., 1964, Nat. Trust, 1966, A.I.A., 1969; founder St. Louis Hist. Documents Found.; corr. mem. com. Tng. Architects for Conservation, Gt. Britain; founding mem. standing coms. Internat. Centre, Rome and originator, leader travelling summer sch. for restorationists, Europe, 1972; mem. City Phila. Hist. Commn., 1956-64; bd. dirs. Soc. Hill. neighborhood assns., 1957-68; organizer Robert Smith Celebration at Newbattle, Edinburgh and Dalkeith, Scotland, 1982. Pioneered numerous projects including Skyline Drive, Va., Great Smoky Mountains Nat. Park, Colonial Nat. Hist. Park, Williamsburg to Yorktown; restorations include Moore House, Yorktown, Va., Pierce Mill, Washington, Tempe Wicke House, Morristown, N.J., Andrew Johnson Home, Greenville, Tenn., Hampton Mansion, Balt., Independence Hall, Phila., Liberty Hall, Frankfort, Ky.; author: Colonial St. Louis, 1948, 93, The Moore House, 1981; Contbg. author: Historic Philadelphia, 1953, Philadelphia Architecture in the 19th Century, 1953, The French in the Mississippi Valley, 1965, Historic America, 1983; editor: The 1786 Carpenters' Company Rule Book, 1971, Building Early America, 1976; contbr. numerous articles to profl. jours. Served to comdr. C.E. Corps, USNR, 1941-46. Recipient Disting. Svc. award Dept. Interior, 1961, Alumni award Columbia U., 1972, Conservation Svc. award, 1976, Citation City of Phila., 1986, 94, Commendation, Gov. Hawaii, 1992; Benjamin Franklin fellow Royal Soc. of Arts, Joseph Jackson award Atwater Kent Mus., 1992; named Disting. Assoc. Ea. Nat. Pk. and Conservation Assn., 1981. Fellow AIA (medal 1979, Presdl. citation 1990, former mem. nat. com. on historic bldgs.), Athenaeum of Phila., Assn. Preservation Tech. (founder 1968, past pres., Harley J. McKee award 1988), HABS Found.; mem. Soc. Archtl. Historians (dir. 1950-64, past pres., v.p. editor Am. notes 1950-67), Nat. Trust Historic Preservation (charter, Louise du Pont Crowninshield award for superior achievement 1966), Nat. Pk. and Conservation Assn. (hon. mem. nat. adv. com.), McAneny Hist. Preservation medal 1984), Mo. Hist. Soc. (dir.), Assn. Studies in Conservation Historic Bldgs. (Gt. Britain), William Clark Soc. (founder), Independence Hall Assn. (hon. life 1987), Carpenters' Co. of City and County Phila. (co. historian emeritus), Friends of Nicholas More (convenor), Friends of HABS (sec. pro-tem), St. Andrew's Soc. Phila., Newcomen Soc. (G.B.), Phi Kappa Sigma. Address: 332 Spruce St Society Hill Philadelphia PA 19106-4201

PETERSON, CHARLES GORDON, retired lawyer; b. Lansing, Mich., May 21, 1926; s. Russell V. and Edna E. (Jones) P.; m. Clara Elizabeth Parmelee, Mar. 8, 1947; children—Wendy, Pamela, Christopher. B.S., Columbia U. Sch. Gen. Studies, 1954; LL.B., Columbia U. Sch. Law, 1956. Bar: N.Y., 1957. Legal assoc. Beekman & Bogue, N.Y.C., 1956-67; mem. Gaston & Snow, N.Y.C., 1967-91; of counsel Reid & Priest, N.Y.C., 1991-93; ret., 1993. Trustee The Riverside Ch., N.Y.C., 1968-80, 82-89, mem. bd. deacons, 1966-68; pres., bd. dirs. Lincoln Guild Housing Corp., N.Y.C., 1961-62, 84-89; pres. Lincoln Guild Housing Corp., N.Y.C., 1961-62, 84-87, v.p., 1987-89, 94—, bd. dirs., 1961-62, 84-89, 94—. Mem. Phi Beta Kappa. Republican. Baptist. Avocations: flying; swimming; piano; reading. Home: 303 W 66th St Apt 20EE New York NY 10023-6305

PETERSON, CHARLES HAYES, trading company executive; b. St. Louis, May 8, 1938; s. Edmund Herbert and Dorothy Marie (Brennan) P.; m. Auli Irene Ahonen, Nov. 28, 1981; children: Mika, Charles, Michael, Katja. BS, U.S. Naval Acad., 1960; MBA, Stanford U., 1971, JD, 1974. Commd. ensign USN, 1956, advanced through grades to capt., resigned, 1969; with USNR, 1969-89; counsel Gen. Electric, San Jose, Calif., 1973-79; div. counsel Syracuse, N.Y., 1980-83; v.p. COGEMA, Inc., Washington, 1983-87; pres. NUEXCO Trading Co., Washington, 1987-95; spl. counsel Morgan, Lewis & Bockius, 1995—. Recipient Meritorious Service medal State of Calif., 1986. Mem. Calif. Bar Assn. Lutheran. Home: 8407 River Rock Ter Bethesda MD 20817-4300 Office: NUEXCO Trading Co 1001 G St NW Ste 400 Washington DC 20001-4545

PETERSON, CHARLES LOREN, agricultural engineer, educator; b. Emmett, Idaho, Dec. 27, 1938; s. Clarence James and Jane (Shelton) P.; m. Julianne Rekow, Sept. 7, 1962; children—Val, Karl, Marianne, Cheryl Ann, Charles Lauritz, Brent. B.S., U. Idaho, 1961, M.S., 1965; Ph.D. in Engring. Sci, Wash. State U., Pullman, 1973. Registered profl. engr., Idaho, Wash. Exptl. engr. Oliver Corp., Charles City, Iowa, 1961; farmer Emmett, 1962-65; instr. math. Emmett High Sch., 1962-63; instr. freshman engring., then extension agrl. engr. U. Idaho, Moscow, 1963-67; prof. agrl. engring. U. Idaho, 1973—; asst. prof. Wash. State U., 1967-73; cons. in field. Contbr. numerous articles profl. jours. Rep. precinct committeeman, 1972-75; sec. 5th legis. dist. Idaho, 1976-79; mem. Latah County Planning and Zoning Commn., 1980-90, 1st counselor Pullman Wash. Stake Presidency, 1989—. Grantee Wash. Potato, 1971-73, U & I, Inc., 1974, Amalgamated Sugar Co., 1974, 92-93, Beet Sugar Devel. Found., 1975-85, Phillips Chem. Co., 1976-80, USDA, 1976-91, Idaho Dept. Water Resources, Energy divsn., 1992-93, Pacific N.W. and Alaska Regional Bioenergy Program, 1993-95, Star Found., 1978; recipient Excellence in Rsch. award U. Idaho, 1992-93, Best in Category award Transp. Tech. U.S. Dept. Energy, 1994. Fellow Am. Soc. Agrl. Engrs. (chmn. Inland Empire chpt. 1978-79, chmn. nat. environ. stored products com. 1978-80, chmn. biomass energy com. 1985-86, chmn. Pacific N.W. region 1984-85, chmn. T-11 Energy com. 1989-90, dir. dist. 5, 1989-91, Engr. of Year award Inland Empire chpt., 1978 nat. Blue Ribbon award 1975, Engr. of Yr. award Pacific N.W. sect. 1990, Outstanding Paper award 1990); mem. Nat. Soc. Profl. Engrs., Am. Soc. Engring. Edn., Potato Assn. Am., Am. Soc. Sugarbeet Technologists, Idaho Soc. Profl. Engrs., Nat. Assn. Colls. and Tchrs. of Agriculture (Tchr. award 1990), Soc. Automotive Engrs., Phi Kappa Phi, Sigma Xi, Gamma Sigma Delta (Outstanding Rsch. in Agriculture award 1989). Mem. LDS Ch. Office: U Idaho Agrl Engring JML # 81-b Moscow ID 83844-2040

PETERSON, CHASE N., university president; b. Logan, Utah, Dec. 27, 1929; s. E.G. and Phebe (Nebeker) P.; m. Grethe Ballif, 1956; children: Erika Elizabeth, Stuart Ballif, Edward Chase. A.B., Harvard U., 1952, M.D., 1956. Diplomate: Am. Bd. Internal Medicine. Asst. prof. medicine U. Utah Med. Sch., 1965-67; assoc. Salt Lake Clinic; dean admissions and fin. aids to students Harvard U., 1967-72, v.p. univ., 1972-78; v.p. health scis. U. Utah, Salt Lake City, 1978-83, prof. medicine, 1983—, pres., 1983-91, clin. prof. medicine, 1991—; pres. emeritus U. Utah, Salt Lake City, 1992—; bd. dirs. First Security Corp., Utah Power & Light Co., D.C. Tanner Co., OEC Med. Systems. Mem. Nat. Assn. State Univs. and Land-Grant Colls. (chmn. 1988-89, chair U.S. Ofc. Tech. Assessment adv. bd. 1990-92). Home: 66 Thaynes Canyon Dr Park City UT 84060-6711 Office: U Utah 1C26 Sch Medicine Salt Lake City UT 84112

PETERSON, COLIN HAMPTON, electronics company executive; b. Clinton, Tenn., Aug. 15, 1923. BSME, U. Miami, 1946. Dir. mfg. Ala. Metals, 1955-60; plant mgr. UDI Electronics, Fla., 1960-67, Westinghouse Corp., Ft. Lauderdale, Fla., 1967-74; prodn. mgr. paging divsn. Motorola Inc., Ft. Lauderdale, 1974-75, mgr. quality assurance portable paging divsn., 1975-77, mgr. mfg. ops. radio products group, 1977-82, dir. quality assurance & reliability, 1982-89, dir. environ. compliance & facilities, 1989-94, dir. strategies, 1994—. Creator 6-Sigma math. concept. With USMC, 1942-43. Office: Motorola Inc 8000 W Sunrise Blvd Fort Lauderdale FL 33322

PETERSON, COLLIN C., congressman; b. Fargo, N.D., June 29, 1944; children: Sean, Jason, Elliott. BA in Bus. Adminstrn. and Acctg., Moorhead State U., 1966. CPA, Minn. Senator State of Minn., 1976-86; mem. 102nd-104th Congresses from 7th Minn. dist., 1991—; mem. agrl. com., subcoms. gen. farm commodities, specialty crops and natural resources, livestock, environ. credit and rural devel., mem. govt. ops. com., chmn. subcom. employment housing and aviation, chmn. subcom. employment, housing and aviation, mem. 104th Cong. resource conservation com., rsch. and forestry subcom., livestock, dairy and poultry subcom., govt. reform and oversight com., nat. econ. growth com., nat. resources and regulatory affairs com.; ranking minority mem. With U.S. Army N.G., 1963-69. Mem. Am. Legion, Ducks Unltd., Elks, Sportsmen's Club, Rural Caucus, Mainstream Forum, Cormorant Lakes Sportsmen Club, Congl. Sportsmen's Caucus, Mainstream Forum, Congl. Rural Caucus. Democrat. Office: US Ho of Reps 1133 Longworth Washington DC 20515-2307

PETERSON, COURTLAND HARRY, law educator; b. Denver, June 28, 1930; s. Harry James and Courtney (Caple) P.; m. Susan Schwab, Gisvold, Jan. 28, 1966; children: Brooke, Linda, Patrick. B.A., U. Colo., 1951, LL.B., 1953; M.C.L., U. Chgo., 1959; J.D., U. Freiburg, Ger., 1964. Bar: Colo. 1953. Mem. faculty U. Colo. Law Sch., 1959—, prof., 1963—, dean, 1974-79, Nicholas Rosenbaum prof., 1991-94, Nicholas Doman prof., 1995—; vis. prof. U. Calif. Law Sch., Los Angeles, 1965, Max Planck Inst., Hamburg, Ger., 1969-70, U. Tex. Law Sch., Austin, 1973-74, Summer Program Tulane U., Rodos, Greece, 1993; bd. dirs. Continuing Legal Edn. in Colo., 1974-77. Author: Die Anerkennung Auslaendischer Urteile, 1964; Translator: (Bauer) An Introduction to German Law, 1965. Served to 1st lt. USAF, 1954-56. Fgn. Law fellow U. Chgo., 1957-59; Ford Found. Law Faculty fellow, 1964; Alexander von Humboldt Stiftun fellow, 1969-70. Mem. ABA, Colo. Bar Assn. (bd. govs. 1974-79), Boulder County Bar Assn., Am. Soc. Comparative Law (dir., bd. editors, trans. 1978-89), Internat. Acad. Comparative Law, Am. Law Inst. Home: 205 Camden Pl Boulder CO 80302-8032 Office: U Colo Law Sch Boulder CO 80309

PETERSON, CURTIS GERALD, broadcast executive; b. Council Bluffs, Iowa, Nov. 24, 1952; s. Scott William and Margaret Helen (Hansen) P.; m. Vicky Lynn McGee, Aug. 18, 1973; 1 child, Cory Scott. BA, U. Nebr., Omaha, 1976. Acct. exec. KMGC/KNUS, Dallas, 1977-80; gen. sales mgr. KESY Radio, Omaha, 1981-82; v.p., gen. mgr. KFRX Radio, Lincoln, Nebr., 1982-86, KAYI Radio, Tulsa, 1987-88. Republican. Roman Catholic. Avocations: basketball, softball, bicycling. Office: Sta KIDO AM 1109 Main St Ste 570 Boise ID 83702-5641

PETERSON, D. BRUCE, data processing computer services company executive. Pres., CEO Sungard Fin. Sys., Inc., Hopkins, Minn. Office: Sungard Fin Systems Inc 601 2nd Ave S Hopkins MN 55343*

PETERSON, DAVID CHARLES, photojournalist; b. Kansas City, Mo., Oct. 22, 1949; s. John Edward and Florence Athene (Hobbs) P.; m. Adele Mae Johnson, Dec. 31, 1952; children: Brian David, Scott Ryun. BS in Edn., Kansas State U., 1971; BS in Journalism, U. Kans., 1973, U. Kans., 1974. Staff photographer Topeka Capital-Jour., 1975-77, Des Moines Register, 1977—. Photographer (photo essay) Shattered Dreams-Iowa's Rural Crisis, 1986 (Pulitzer prize 1987); exhibited at Creative Ctr. Photography, Tucson, 1989. Mem. Nat. Press Photographers Assn. (Nikon sabbatical 1986). Democrat. Home: 2024 35th St Des Moines IA 50310-4438 Office: Des Moines Register News Dept 715 Locust St Des Moines IA 50309

PETERSON, DAVID FREDERICK, government agency executive; b. Washington, Apr. 4, 1937; s. Victor Henry and Alice Augusta (Vogle) P.; m. Laurie A. Cadigan, June 11, 1988. A.B., Harvard U., 1959; LL.B., Cornell U., 1962. Bar: D.C. 1963. With Metromedia Inc., N.Y.C. and Los Angeles, 1963-70; exec. dir. consumer info. ctr. GSA, Washington, 1970-76, dir. consumer affairs, 1976-82, assoc. archivist for mgmt. Nat. Archives and Records Service, 1982-83; asst. archivist for Fed. Records Ctrs. Nat. Archives and Records Adminstrn., Washington, 1983—. Served with U.S. Army, 1963. Home: 2315 N Glebe Rd Arlington VA 22207-3410 Office: Nat Archives & Records Admn 8601 Adelphi Rd College Park MD 20740-6001

PETERSON, DAVID MAURICE, plant physiologist, researcher; b. Woodward, Okla., July 3, 1940; s. Maurice Llewellyn and Katharine Anne (Jones) P.; m. Margaret Ingegerd Sundberg, June 18, 1965; children: Mark David, Elise Marie. BS, U. Calif., Davis, 1962; MS, U. Ill., 1966; PhD, Harvard U., 1968. Rsch. biologist Allied Chem. Corp., Morristown, N.J., 1970-71; plant physiologist U.S. Dept. Agr.-Agrl. Rsch. Svc., Madison, Wis., 1971—; from asst. to full prof. U. Wis., Madison, 1971—. Capt. U.S. Army, 1968-70. Fellow AAAS; mem. Am. Soc. Plant Physiologists (editorial bd. 1984-86), Am. Assn. Cereal Chemists (assoc. editor 1988-91), Crop Sci. Soc. Am. (assoc. editor 1975-78). Office: USDA Cereal Crops Rsch Unit 501 Walnut St Madison WI 53705-2334

PETERSON, DAVID ROBERT, lawyer, former Canadian government official; b. Toronto, Dec. 28, 1943; s. Clarence and Laura Marie (Scott) P.; m. Shelley Peterson, Jan. 16, 1974; children—Benjamin David, Chloe Matthews, Adam Drake Scott. BA, U. Western Ont., 1964; LLB, U. Toronto, 1967; LLD (hon.), U. Ottawa, Am. U. of Caribbean, U. Tel Aviv, U. Toronto. Bar: Ont. 1969, Queens counsel 1981. Pres. C.M. Peterson Co. Ltd., 1969-75, Cambridge Acceptance Corp., 1969-75; M.P. Ontario Parliament, Can., 1975—; leader Ont. Liberal Party, 1982; premier Province of Ont., 1985-90; sr. counsel Cassels Brock & Blackwell, Toronto; chmn. Toronto Raptors Basketball Club, Inc., SmithBooks, Inc.; bd. dirs. Rogers Comms., Ltd., Nat. Life Assurance Co., Industrielle-Alliance Life Assurance Co., Nat. Trust, Banque Nationale de Paris (Can.), Cascades Paperboard Internat. Inc., SHL Systemhouse, Inc., Speedy Muffler King Inc. Leader of the official opposition party, Liberal Party, Ont., 1982-85; dir. Legal Services, Yorkville; mem. Kidney Found. Can., Ont., Cystic Fibrosis Found. Fellow McLaughlin Coll., 1985. Mem. Law Soc. U.C., Young Pres. Orgn., London C. of C. Mem. United Ch. Christ. Clubs: London Hunt Country, London Racquets; Canadian. Avocations: theatre, riding, jogging, skiing, tennis, reading. Office: Cassels Brock & Blackwell, 40 King St W Ste 2100, Toronto, ON Canada M5H 3C2

PETERSON, DONALD CURTIS, life care executive, consultant; b. Seattle, Feb. 27, 1931; s. Arthur O. and Agnes V. (Erickson) P.; m. Marilyn Jane, June 21, 1952; children: Bruce D., Mark A., Daryl R., Debra L., Joseph J. AA, North Park Coll., 1950; cert. in mgmt., mm. Mgmt. Assn., 1965. With fgn. ops. staff Internat. Harvester Co., Chgo., 1950-54; mktg. exec. UARCO, Inc., Barrington, Ill., 1954-67; group v.p. Victor Comptometer, Lincoln, Nebr., 1967-68; pres. Nationwide Data, Wheeling, Ill., 1968-71, Nationwide Bus. Forms, Wheeling, 1968-71, Ins. Producers Bulletin, Wheeling, 1968-71, Alpha Internat., Sawyer, Mich., 1971-83; exec. dir.

Freedom Sq. U.S.A., Seminole, Fla., 1983-92; adminstr., CEO Mount Miguel Covenant Village, Spring Valley, Calif., 1992—; mktg. cons. Balt. Bus. Forms., Hunt Valley, Md., 1974-76. Supr., chmn. water bd., sanitary bd. Chikaming Twp., Lakeside, Mich., 1972-76. Served with U.S. Army, 1952-57. Republican. Baptist. Home: 10405 Pine Grove St Spring Valley CA 91978-1505

PETERSON, DONALD MATTHEW, insurance company executive; b. Mt. Vernon, N.Y., Dec. 22, 1936; s. Cornelius J. and Catherine M. (Carney) P.; m. Patricia A. Frusciante, Sept. 10, 1960; children: Daniel, Linda, David, Debra, James. BA in Econs., LaSalle U., 1958. CLU; ChFC; FSA, MAAA, EA, RHU. Actuarial analyst Met. Life, N.Y.C., 1958-63; actuarial assoc. N.Am. Co. for Life and Health, Chgo., 1963-66; pres., CEO Trustmark Ins. Co., Lake Forest, Ill., 1966—; bd. dirs. Trustmark Ins. Co., Trustmark Life Ins. Co., Star Mktg. and Adminstrs. Bd. dirs. Glenview (Ill.) Pub. Schs., 1973-76, Lake County (Ill.) United Way, 1989—, Glenview Dist. 34 Found., 1990-93, Lake Forest Hosp., 1992—, Ill. Life Ins. Coun., 1990-94, Barat Coll., 1994—, Lake Forest Grad. Sch. Mgmt., 1995—. Mem. Nat. Assn. Life Underwriters, Nat. Assn. Health Underwriters, Am. Acad. Actuaries, Health Inst. Assn. Am. (bd. dirs. 1992—), Am. Coun. Life Ins. Forum 500 (bd. dirs. 1992—), Econ. Club Chgo., North Shore Country Club, Conway Farms Golf Club. Republican. Roman Catholic. Avocations: golf, curling, swimming, running. Office: Trustmark Ins Co 400 N Field Dr Lake Forest IL 60045-2586

PETERSON, DONALD ROBERT, psychologist, educator, university administrator; b. Pillager, Minn., Sept. 10, 1923; s. Frank Gordon and Ruth (Friedland) P.; m. Jean Hole, Feb. 10, 1952 (div.); children: Wendy, Jeffrey, Roger, Lisa; m. Jane Snyder Salmon, Dec. 21, 1974. BA, U. Minn., 1948, MA, 1950, PhD, 1952. Mem. faculty U. Ill., Urbana, 1952-75, prof. clin. psychology, 1963-75, head div. clin. psychology, 1963-70, dir. Psychol. Clinic, 1961-70, dir. D. Psychology program, 1970-75; dean Grad. Sch. Applied and Profl. Psychology Rutgers U., New Brunswick, 1975-89; pres. Nat. Coun. Schs. of Profl. Psychology, 1981-83. Author: The Clinical Study of Social Behavior, 1968; co-author: Close Relationships, 1983; also articles; editor Jour. Abnormal Psychology, 1970-72. With AUS, 1943-46. Mem. N.J. Psychol. Assn., Am. Psychol. Assn. (awards for disting. contbns. to practice of psychology 1983, disting. contbns. to edn. and tng. 1989). Office: Rutgers U Grad Sch Applied & Profl Psychology New Brunswick NJ 08903

PETERSON, DONALD ROBERT, magazine editor, vintage automobile consultant; b. Sandstone, Minn., Apr. 1, 1929; s. Martin Theodore and Margaret Mildred (Dezell) P.; m. Lois Taylor, Dec. 31, 1951 (div. 1975); children: Wyatt A., Winston B., Whitney C. (dec.), Westley D., Webster E.; m. Edie Tannenbaum, Aug. 31, 1975; 1 child, Ryan Kerry. Student, U. Minn., 1947-50; B.S., Gustavus Adolphus Coll., 1952. asst. underwriter Prudential Ins. Co. Am., Mpls., 1953-64; chief health underwriter North Central Life, St. Paul, 1964-66; pres. 1st State Bank Murdock, Minn., 1967-73, EDON, Inc., Roswell, Ga., 1974—; editor Car Collector mag., Roswell, 1977-91, editor emeritus, 1992—; v.p., dir. Classic Pub. Inc., Atlanta, 1979—. Councilman, City of Murdock, 1968-72, mayor, 1972-74; del. State Republican Conv., 1970-72; treas. Swift County Rep. Com., 1970-73. Served with U.S. Navy, 1946-47. Recipient citation for disting. service Classic Car Club Am., 1965. Mem. Internat. Soc. Philos. Enquiry, Swift County Bankers Assn. (pres. 1970-73), Soc. Automotive Historians, Am. Legion, Mensa (pres. Ga. chpt. 1976-78), Milestone Car Soc., Atlanta Press Club, Classic Car Club Am. (chpt. pres. 1959, 60, 63), Rolls-Royce Owners Club, Antique Automobile Club, Vet. Motor Car Club Am., Packard Club, Horseless Carriage Club Am. Republican. Avocations: automobile collecting, internat. traveling. Home: 1400 Lake Ridge Ct Roswell GA 30076-2869 Office: 1241 Canton St Roswell GA 30075

PETERSON, DONN NEAL, forensic engineer; b. Northwood, N.D., Jan. 1, 1942; s. Emil H. and Dorothy (Neal) P.; m. Lorna Jean Kappedal, July 8, 1962 (div. July 1966); m. Donna Sue Butts Daiker, Aug. 26, 1967; children Barbara Daiker, Elizabeth Plamondon, Phoebe, Phaedra, Rosalind Peterson. BSME, U. N.D., 1963; MSME, U. Minn., 1972. Registered profl. engr. Advanced engring. courses student GE, Evendale, Ohio, 1963-66; systems engr. GE Aircraft Engine Group, Evendale, Ohio, 1963-70; prin. Donn N. Peterson & Assocs., Mpls., 1971-74; pres. Donn N. Peterson & Assocs., Inc., Mpls., 1974-85, Peterson Engring. Inc., Mpls., 1985—; instr. GE Edn. Program, 1968-69; seminar presenter State Bd. of Registration, Mpls., 1980; seminar leader Minn. Fedn. Engring. Socs., Mpls., 1990-91; speaker in field; expert witness 100 ct. trials and 100 depositions. Del. Minn. 6th Dist. Rep. Conv., Brooklyn Park, Minn., 1982. Fellow Am. Acad. Forensic Scis. (sect. chmn. 1989-90, Founders award 1991), Nat. Acad. Forensic Engrs. (bd. dirs. 1995—); mem. ASME (state chmn. 1979-80, Young Engr. of Yr. award 1976), NSPE, ASTM (chmn. subcom. 1989-95), Profl. Engrs. in Pvt. Practice (state pres. 1987-88, svc. award 1988), Soc. Automotive Engrs., Brooklyn Park C. of C. (city hwy. 610 corridor com. 1992-94), Rotary (sec. Brooklyn Park 199-93, v.p. 1993-94, pres.-elect 1994-95, pres. 1995-96, svc. award 1992). Lutheran. Achievements include devel. of successful math. models to simulate jet engine transient performance and wave dynamics in gas flow, computer simulations for vehicle and occupant dynamics during collisions. Home: 15720 15th Pl N Plymouth MN 55447-2405 Office: Peterson Engring Inc 7601 Kentucky Ave N Brooklyn Park MN 55428-1200

PETERSON, DOUGLAS PETE (PETE PETERSON), congressman; b. Omaha, Mont., June 26, 1935; m. Carlotta Ann Neal; children: Michael, Paula, Douglas. Grad. Nat. War Coll., 1975; M.A., U. Tampa, 1976; postgrad., U. Ctrl. Mich., 1977. Commd. USAF, 1954, advanced through grades to col., ret., 1980; exec. CRT Computers, 1984-90; adminstr. Dozier Sch. for Boys, 1985-90; mem. 101st-104th Congresses from 2nd Fla. Dist., 1991—; mem. appropriation com.-energy and water, agrl. Prisoner of war, Vietnam. Mem. DAV, Am. Legion, Elks. Roman Catholic. Office: 306 Cannon House Ofc Bldg Washington DC 20515*

PETERSON, DOUGLAS SHURTLEFF, state legislator, packaging company official; b. Ogden, Utah, Dec. 9, 1966; s. Lowell Skeen and Kathleen (Shurtleff) P. BS in Polit. Sci. and English, Weber State U., 1994. With UPS, Ogden, 1989—; rep. Utah Ho. of Reps., Salt Lake City, 1993—; cons. Rep. Gov.'s Assn. Pres. Assn. Students Weber State U., Ogden, 1990-91; trustee Weber State U., 1990-91; regent Utah Bd. Regents of Higher Edn., Salt Lake City, 1991-92. Republican. Mem. LDS Ch. Home: 4538 S 1725 W Roy UT 84067-3026

PETERSON, EDWARD ADRIAN, lawyer; b. St. Louis, May 19, 1941; s. Adrian J. and Virginia (Hamlin) P.; m. Catherine Frances Younghouse, Dec. 17, 1960; children: Kristin, Kendra. B.S.B.A., Washington U., St. Louis, 1963; LL.B., So. Methodist U., 1966. Bar: Tex. 1966, U.S. Dist. Ct. (no. and so. dists.) Tex. Instr. bus. law and acctg. Midwestern U., Wichita Falls, Tex., 1966-67; assoc. Schenk & Wesbrooks, Wichita Falls, 1966-67, Newman & Pickering, Dallas, 1967-72; ptnr. Moore & Peterson, Dallas, 1972-89, Winstead Sechrest & Minick P.C., Dallas, 1989—; speaker in field. Contbr. articles to legal jours. Bd. dirs. Leukemia Soc., 1970-71, North Tex. Commn., South Dallas/Fair Park Trust Fund, 1992; active No. Tex. Commn. Fellow Tex. Bar Found. (life); mem. ABA, Am. Coll. Real Estate Lawyers (chmn. professionalism and practice com.), State Bar Tex., Coll. State Bar Tex., Tex. Coll. Real Estate Attys., Dallas Bar Assn., Phi Alpha Delta, Sigma Alpha Epsilon. Lutheran. Avocation: snow skiing. Home: 9442 Spring Hollow Dr Dallas TX 75243-7533 Office: Winstad Sechrest & Minick PC 5400 Renaissance Tower Dallas TX 75270

PETERSON, EDWIN J., retired supreme court justice, law educator; b. Gilmanton, Wis., Mar. 30, 1930; s. Edwin A. and Leora Grace (Kitelinger) P.; m. Anna Chadwick, Feb. 7, 1971; children: Patricia, Andrew, Sherry. B.S., U. Oreg., 1951, LL.B., 1957. Bar: Oreg. 1957. Assoc. firm Tooze, Kerr, Peterson, Marshall & Shenker, Portland, 1957-61; mem. firm Tooze, Kerr, Peterson, Marshall & Shenker, 1961-79; assoc. justice Supreme Ct. Oreg., Salem, 1979-83, chief justice, 1983-91; ret., 1993; adj. instr. Willamette Coll. of Law, Salem, Oreg., 1994—; chmn. Supreme Ct. Task Force on Racial Issues, 1992-94; mem. standing com. on fed. rules of practice and procedure, 1987-93; bd. visitors U. Oreg. Law Sch., 1978-83, 87-93, chmn. bd. visitors. Conf. Chief Justices, 1985-87, 88-91. Chmn. Portland Citizens Sch. Com., 1968-70; vice chmn. Young Republican Fedn. Orgn., 1971; bd. visitors U. Oreg. Law Sch., 1978-83, 87-93, chmn. bd.

visitors, 1981-83. Served to 1st lt. USAF, 1952-54. Mem. ABA, Am. Judicature Soc., Oreg. State Bar (bd. examiners 1963-66, gov. 1973-76, vice chmn. profl. liability fund 1977-78), Multnomah County Bar Assn. (pres. 1972-73), Phi Alpha Delta, Lambda Chi Alpha. Episcopalian. Home: 3365 Sunridge Dr S Salem OR 97302-5950 Office: Willamette Univ Coll Law 250 Winter St SE Salem OR 97301-3900

PETERSON, ELMOR LEE, mathematical scientist, educator; b. McKeesport, Pa., Dec. 6, 1938; s. William James and Emma Elizabeth (Scott) P.; m. Sharon Louise Walker, Aug., 1957 (div. Jan. 1961); 1 child, Lisa Ann Peterson Loop; m. Miriam Drake Mears, Dec. 23, 1966; 1 child, David Scott. BS in Physics, Carnegie Mellon U., 1960, MS in Math., 1961, PhD in Math., 1964. Technician U.S. Steel Rsch. Ctr., Monroeville, Pa., summer 1959; engr. Westinghouse Atomic Power, Forest Hills, Pa., summer 1960; rsch. engr. Atomics Internat., Canoga Park, Calif., summer 1961; physicist Lawrence Radiation Labs., Livermore, Calif., summer 1963; sr. math. Westinghouse R & D, Churchill Boro, Pa., 1963-66; asst. prof. math. U. Mich., Ann Arbor, 1967-69; assoc. prof. math. and mgmt. sci. Northwestern U., Evanston, Ill., 1969-73, prof. math. and mgmt. sci., 1973-77, prof. applied math. and mgmt. sci., 1977-79; prof. math. and ops. rsch. N.C. State U., Raleigh, 1979—; vis. asst. prof. W.Va. U., dept. Math., Morgantown, 1966; vis. assoc. prof. U. Wis. Math. Rsch. Ctr., Madison, 1968-69; vis. prof. Stanford U. Ops. Rsch. Dept., 1976-77. Author: (with others) Geometric Programming, 1967, Russian trans., 1971; contbr. articles to profl. jours. Mobil Found. Rsch. grantee, 1967-69, Air Force Office Sci. Rsch. grantee, 1973-75, 76-78, NSF grantee, 1985-86. Mem. Soc. for Indsl. and Applied Math., Ops. Rsch. Soc. Am., Am. Math. Soc., Math. Assn. Am. Avocations: aerobic exercise, antique furniture. Home: 3717 Williamsborough Ct Raleigh NC 27609-6357 Office: NC State U Hillsborough St Raleigh NC 27695

PETERSON, ERLE VIDAILLET, retired metallurgical engineer; b. Idaho Falls, Idaho, Apr. 29, 1915; s. Vier P. and Marie (Vidaillet) P.; m. Rosemary Sherwood, June 3, 1955; children: Kent Sherwood, Pamela Jo. BS in Mining Engring., U. Idaho, 1940; MS in Mining Engring., U. Utah, 1941. Tech. advisor Remington Arms Co., Salt Lake City, 1941-43; constrn. engr. plutonium plant duPont, Hanford, Wash., 1943-44; R & D engr. exptl. sta. duPont, Wilmington, Del., 1944-51; plant metallurgist heavy water plant duPont, Newport, Ind., 1951-57; rsch. metallurgist metals program duPont, Balt., 1957-62, prin. project engr. USAF contracts, 1962-68; devel. engr. duPont, Wilmington, 1969-80; ret., 1980. Patentee in field; contbr. articles to profl. jours. Candidate for State Senate-Am. Party, Wilmington, 1974; com. chmn. Boy Scouts Am., Wilmington, 1975-78; treas. Local Civic Assn., Wilmington, 1977-79. Rsch. fellow U. Utah, 1940. Mem. Am. Soc. Metallurgists Internat., Del. Assn. Profl. Engrs. Republican. Avocations: lapidary, jewelry making, photography, prospecting, gardening. Home: PO Box 74 Rigby ID 83442-0074

PETERSON, ESTHER, consumer advocate; b. Provo, Utah, Dec. 9, 1906; d. Lars and Annie (Nielsen) Eggertsen; m. Oliver A. Peterson, May 28, 1932; children: Karen Kristine, Eric N., Iver E., Lars E. A.B., Brigham Young U., 1927; M.A., Columbia Tchrs. Coll., 1930; M.A. hon. degrees, Smith Coll., Bryant Coll., Carnegie Inst. Tech., Montclair Coll., Hood Coll., Maryhurst Coll., Simmons Coll., Northeastern U., U South Utah, Western Coll. Women, Oxford, Ohio, Mich. State U., U. Mich., U. Utah, Williams Coll., Georgetown U., Temple U., Goucher Coll., Tufts U. Tchr. Branch Agr. Coll., Cedar City, Utah, 1927-29, Utah State U., Winsor Sch., Boston, 1930-36, Bryn Mawr Summer Sch. for Women Workers in Industry, 1932-39; asst. dir. edn. Amal. Clothing Workers Am., 1939-44, Washington legis. rep., 1945-48; legis. rep. indsl. union dept. AFL-CIO, 1958-61; dir. Women's Bur., U.S. Dept. Labor, 1961-64, asst. sec. labor for labor standards, 1961-69; exec. vice chmn. Pres.'s Commn. on Status of Women, 1961-63, Interdeptl. Com. Status Women, 1963-65; chmn. Pres.'s Com. Consumer Interests, 1964-67, spl. asst. to President for consumer affairs, 1964-67; legis. rep. Amal. Clothing Workers Am., Washington, 1969-70; consumer adviser Giant Food Corp., 1970-77; spl. asst. to Pres. for consumer affairs, 1977-80; chmn. Consumer Affairs Council, 1979-80. Active Internat. Med. Svcs. for Health, 1987, United Srs. Health Coop., 1987, Ctr. Sci. in Pub. Interest, 1964; mem. Women's Nat. Dem. Club; NGO rep. Internat. Orgn. Consumers Union at Econ. and Social Coun. UN, 1985, appointed pub. mem. U.S. Del. to Gen. Assembly, 1993. Decorated Presdl. medal of Freedom 1981; recipient Food Industry Consumer award, 1986, Mgmt. award Brigham Young U., 1989. Mem. AAUW, Am. Home Econs. Assn. (hon.), Nat. Consumers League (pres. 1974-76, hon. pres. 1981), Cosmos Club, Phi Chi Theta (hon.), Delta Sigma Theta (hon.). Home: 3032 Stephenson Pl Washington DC 20015

PETERSON, ESTHER, secondary school principal. Prin. Orchard Lake Mid. Sch. Recipient Blue Ribbon award U.S. Dept. Edn., 1990-91. Office: Orchard Lake Mid Sch 600 Orchard Lake Rd West Bloomfield MI 48322

PETERSON, FRED MCCRAE, librarian; b. Mpls., Dec. 29, 1936. B.A., U. Minn., 1958, M.S., 1960; PhD in L.S., Ind. U., 1974. Asst. to dir. Iowa State U. Library, 1961-64, head catalog dept., 1964-67, asst. dir. library, 1967-69, assoc. dir. library, 1969-70; with Catholic U. Am., Washington, 1970-82, asst. prof., assoc. chairperson, 1973-77, acting dir. libraries, 1977-78, dir., 1978-82; univ. librarian Ill. State U., Normal, 1982—. Mem. ALA (past pres.), Ill. Library Assn. (Librian of Year 1994). Home: RR 2 Box 160 Bloomington IL 61704-9628 Office: Milner Libr 311 Ill. State U. Normal IL 61761

PETERSON, GALE EUGENE, historian; b. Sioux Rapids, Iowa, May 23, 1944; s. George Edmund and Vergene Elizabeth (Wilson) P. B.S., Iowa State U., 1965; M.A., U. Md., 1968, Ph.D., 1973. Instr. dept. history U. Md., College Park, 1971-72, Cath. U. Am., Washington, 1972-73; prin. investigator Gregory Directory project Orgn. Am. Historians, Bloomington, Ind., 1973-75; instr. dept. history Purdue U., West Lafayette, Ind., 1975-76; dir. U.S. Newspaper Project, Orgn. Am. Historians, Bloomington, Ind., 1976-78; exec. dir. Cin. Hist. Soc., 1978—. Author: (with John T. Schlebecker) Living Historical Farms Handbook, 1970, Harry S Truman and the Independent Regulatory Commissions 1945-52, 1985. Mem. Cin. Bicentennial Commn., 1983-88. Mem. Orgn. Am. Historians (treas. 1993—), Am. Assn. State and Local History, Am. Hist. Assn., Am. Assn. Mus., Midwestern Mus. Conf. (v.p.-at-large 1993—), Cincinnatus Assn., Nat. Coun. on Pub. History (bd. dirs. 1992-95). Home: 6655 Drake Rd Cincinnati OH 45243-2720 Office: Cin Hist Soc Cin Mus Ctr Cin Union Terminal Cincinnati OH 45203

PETERSON, GARY ANDREW, agronomics researcher; b. Holdrege, Nebr., Apr. 30, 1940; s. Walter Andrew and Evelyn Christine (Johnson) P.; m. Jacquelyn Charlene Flick, June 18, 1965; children: Kerstin, Ingrid. BS, U. Nebr., 1963, MS, 1965; PhD, Iowa State U., 1967. Research assoc. agronomy Iowa State U., Ames, 1964-67; prof. U. Nebr., Lincoln, 1967-84; prof. agronomy Colo. State U., Ft. Collins, 1984—. Assoc. editor AGronomy Jour., 1979-81, tech. editor, 1981-83, editor, 1984-89, editor-in-chief, 1991-96; contbr. articles to profl. jours. Fellow Am. Soc. Agronomy (Ciba-Geigy Agr. Achievement award 1974, Agronomic Achievement award-Soils 1990), Soil Sci. Soc. Am. (Applied Rsch. award 1987); mem. Soil Conservation Soc. Am. Republican. Avocations: reading, hiking, skiing. Office: Colo State U Dept Soil Crop Scis Fort Collins CO 80523

PETERSON, GEORGE EMANUEL, JR., lawyer, business executive; b. Mt. Vernon, N.Y., Mar. 8, 1931; s. George E. and Lydia Evelyn (Peterson) P.; m. Barbara Ritter, Aug. 30, 1957; children—Lisa Manvel, George Emanuel III. B.A., Yale, 1953; LL.B., U. Va., 1958. Bar: N.Y. State 1959, Conn. 1974. Assoc. firm Reid & Priest, N.Y.C., 1958-68, ptnr., 1968-70; v.p., gen. counsel Insilco Corp., Meriden, Conn., 1970-72, v.p. fin., 1972-76, v.p., sec., 1976-79, v.p., gen. counsel, 1976-89; pvt. practice New Haven, Conn., 1989—. Served to lt. USNR, 1953-55. Mem. ABA, N.Y. State Bar Assn. Home and Office: 225 Blue Trl Hamden CT 06518-1601

PETERSON, GERALD ALVIN, physicist; b. Chesterton, Ind., Apr. 12, 1931; s. Gustaf Albert and Esther Josephine (Carlson) P.; m. Doris Lee DeJonge, Dec. 22, 1953; children—Curtis Mark, Thomas Andrew, Anna Beth. BS, Purdue U., 1953, MS, 1955; PhD, Stanford U., 1962. Lectr. Yale U., New Haven, 1962-64; asst. prof., 1964-67; research scientist Inst. voor Kernphysisch Onderzoek, Amsterdam, 1967-68; assoc. prof. physics U. Mass.,

Amherst, 1968-73; prof. U. Mass., 1973—; vis. prof. U. Mainz, Fed. Republic Germany, 1975, Japan Soc. Promotion Sci., 1972, 89; U.S.-Israel Binat. Sci. Found. vis. prof. Tel Aviv U., 1983; cons. in field. Contbr. articles to profl. jours. Served with U.S. Army, 1955-57. NATO fellow, 1969, U.K. sr. rsch. fellow, 1970. Fellow Am. Phys. Soc.; mem. Sigma Xi. Congregationalist. Research in electron scattering and nuclear structure. Home: 10 Old Briggs Rd Leverett MA 01054-9759 Office: U Mass Nuclear Physics Grad Rsch Ctr Amherst MA 01003

PETERSON, GERALD C., lawyer; b. Chgo., Dec. 7, 1948. BA, Loyola U., 1969, JD, 1977. Bar: Ill. 1977. Ptnr. Winston & Strawn, Chgo. With U.S. Army, 1970-71. Decorated Bronze Star. Mem. ABA, Chgo. Bar Assn., Cook County Bar Assn. Office: Winston & Strawn 35 W Wacker Dr Chicago IL 60601-1614

PETERSON, GREGG LEE, radio station executive; b. Los Angeles, Feb. 28, 1943; s. Harry Roland and Hazel Irene (Gregg) P.; m. Beverly Elizabeth Wolfe; children: Gregg, Andrew, David. A.A., El Camino Coll., Torrance, Calif., 1962; BA, U. So. Calif., 1967. Sports editor Torrance Herald, 1960-63; reporter UPI, Los Angeles, 1965-67; assignment editor Sta. KABC, Los Angeles, 1967-68; asst. news dir., then news dir. Sta. KNX, Los Angeles, 1968-82; v.p., gen. mgr. Sta. WBBM, Chgo., 1982-89; pres. Nova Broadcasting, Santa Barbara, Calif., 1989—; bd. dirs. Chgo. Assn. Commerce and Industry, 1986-89, Ill. Broadcasters Assn., 1983-89, Radio and TV News Assn. So. Calif., 1978-82. Bd. dirs. Calif. Freedom of Info. Com., 1980-82. Recipient Grand award for editorializing Internat. Radio Festival N.Y., 1983, 84. Methodist. Avocations: swimming; tennis. Office: Nova Broadcasting 2314 N Patterson Ave Santa Barbara CA 93111

PETERSON, H. WILLIAM, chemical executive, consultant; b. Yokohama, Honshu Island, Japan, Mar. 9, 1922; came to U.S., 1924; s. Harry William and Alice (Mateer) P.; m. Doris Jane Howe, Apr. 27, 1946; children: Robert, Christine Fitzpatrick, Janet McMillan. BA in Chemistry and Botany, Colgate U., 1946; postgrad., Princeton U., 1949-50, U. Del., 1982-83. Lic. capt. U.S. inland waters U.S. Coast Guard. Researcher, developer ESSO Standard Oil Co., Bayway, N.J., 1946-51; various positions Enjay Chem. Co., N.Y.C., 1951-65; coord. world-wide chem. Gulf Oil Corp., Pitts., 1965-67; gen. mktg. mgr. Gulf Oil-Eastern Hemisphere, London, 1967-71; corp. v.p. chem. mktg., corp. v.p. mktg. Gulf Oil Can. Ltd., Montreal, Que., Can., 1971-77; CEO chems. divsn., corp. v.p. Golfoil Can., Montreal, Quebec, Can., 1971-77; chief operating officer Corpus Christi Chem. Co., Wilmington, Del., 1977-78; mng. dir. Food Machinery & Chem. Corp. Internat. Chems., Phila., 1979-80; internat. cons. Bozman, Md., 1980—. Patentee in field. Leader Young Christians Assn., 1st Bapt. Ch., Somerville, N.J., 1948-53; lay speaker, mem. adminstrn. bd. Riverview Charge, United Meth. Ch.; chaplain Mil. Order Purple Heart. With USMC, 1942-46, PTO. Decorated Purple Heart, two battle stars. Fellow Am. Inst. Chemists; mem. Am. Chem. Soc. (emeritus). Avocations: writing, philosophy, religion. Home and Office: Quakerneck Rd Mulberry Pt Bozman MD 21612

PETERSON, HAROLD ALBERT, electrical engineer, educator; b. Essex, Iowa, Dec. 28, 1908; s. John Albert and Augusta Matilda (Hultman) P.; m. Marion Frances Pray, Apr. 7, 1934; children: Joye Frances (dec.), David West, Gilbert Moseley. B.S.E.E., U. Iowa, 1932, M.S.E.E. 1933. Registered profl. engr. Elec. engr. Gen Electric Co., 1934-46; prof. elec. engring. U. Wis., 1946-75, Wis. Utilities prof. elec. power engring., 1967-75, Edward and Bennett prof. emeritus, 1975—, chmn. dept. elec. engring., 1947-67; cons. on elec. power systems analysis and edn. to industry, colls.; sr. Fulbright lectr., W. Ger., 1961; chmn. industry adv. com. on underground power transmission FPC, 1965-66. Author: Transients in Power Systems, 1951; contbr. numerous articles to profl. jours.; patentee in field. Recipient Benjamin Smith Reynolds award for outstanding teaching, 1957, ACE Centennial medal and Disting. Svc. citation U. Wis., Madison, 1991. Fellow IEEE (life, Edn. gold medal 1978, Centennial medal 1984); mem. NAE, ASME (life), NSPE (life), Am. Soc. for Engring. Edn., Rotary, Sigma Xi, Tau Beta Pi, Eta Kappa Nu. Presbyterian. Office: 501 S La Posada Cir Apt 117 Green Valley AZ 85614

PETERSON, HARRIES-CLICHY, financial consultant; b. Boston, Sept. 7, 1924; s. Edwin William and Annekathe (Lieske) P. AB, Harvard U., 1946, MBA, 1950; MA in Edn., San Francisco State U., 1993. Sci. officer Ronne Antarctic Expdn., 1947-48; staff asst. Kidder Peabody & Co., N.Y.C., 1952-53, Devel. and Resources Corp., N.Y.C., 1959-61; dir. indsl. devel. W.R. Grace & Co., Lima, Peru, 1953-57; staff asst. Devel. & Resources Corp., N.Y.C., 1959-61; bus. cons. Lima, 1961-65; v.p. internat. div. Foremost Dairies, Inc. (now McKesson Corp.), San Francisco, 1965-67; v.p. H.K. Porter Co., Inc., Pitts., 1967-68; also chmn. and dir. overseas affiliates H.K. Porter Co., Inc., 1967-68; independent fin. adviser San Francisco and Los Angeles, 1968—; cons. investment banking projects for 3d world countries, Brazil, 1981, 82, 84, Nepal, 1987, Ecuador, 1988, Kenya, 1989, Indonesia, 1989, Peru, 1989, 90, 92, 93, Hungary, 1992, Argentina, 1993, Bolivia, 1993; ind. cons. in field. Author: Development of Titanium Metals Industry, 1950, Che Guevara on Guerrilla Warfare, 1961, Petróleo: Hora Céro, 1964, Islamic Banking, 1979; contbr. articles gen. interest, bus., mil. pubis. Served to col. USMCR, 1943-45, 51-52, 57-59. Decorated Silver Star. Mem. Colegio de Economistas del Peru (co-founder, past dir.), Am. Mgmt. Assn. (conf. chmn.). Address: PO Box 100002 San Francisco CA 94119-0002 also: Donatello 131, San Borja, Lima 41, Peru *I am grateful to classical education for having shown me truth and beauty. But the challenge to apply ideals and innovation into tradition and hierarchy requires endless self-appraisal and adjustment, sometimes exhilarating, sometimes disheartening, sometimes edifying, sometimes extracting great sacrifices from self and others I might have better served. Yet, the pursuit of uncynical truth and harmonious beauty remains an unshakeable mistress needed to satisfy soul and spirit.*

PETERSON, HOWARD GEORGE FINNEMORE, sports executive; b. Presque Isle, Maine, Mar. 23, 1951; s. George Conrad and Valeda (Finnemore) P. Student New Eng. Conservatory of Music, 1967-68, Andrews U., 1968-71, Orson Welles Film Sch., 1971-72, Loma Linda U., 1972-75. Pres. Nat. Ski Touring Operators Assn., 1977-79; exec. v.p. mktg. U.S. Skiing, 1979-81, exec. dir. 1981-85, sec. gen., 1985—; chief exec. officer U.S. Ski Team, 1988—, U.S. Ski Ednl. Found., 1988-92; dir. Mountain Rescue Svc., Inc. Mem. U.S. Ski Coaches Assn. (dir.), Nat. Ski Touring Operators Assn. (dir.), Internat. Ski Fedn. (eligibility com., TV and sponsorship freestyle com., chmn. expert's group for pool questions 1988—), U.S. Olympic Properties Com., Winter Olympic Sports Coun.; sec. 1988—, Olympic Tng. Ctrs. Com. 1988—), U.S. Skiing Found. (exec. dir., trustee), Pan Am Sports Orgn. (winter games adv. com. 1988—). Author: Cross Country Citizen Racing, 1980; I Hope I Get a Purple Ribbon, 1980; Cross Country Ski Trails, 1979; Cannon: A Climber's Guide, 1972. Office: US Skiing PO Box 100 Park City UT 84060-0100

PETERSON, JAMES ALGERT, geologist, educator; b. Baroda, Mich., Apr. 17, 1915; s. Djalma Hardaman and Mary Ava (McAnally) P.; m. Gladys Marie Pearson, Aug. 18, 1944; children—James D., Wendy A., Brian H. Student, Northwestern U., 1941-43, U. Wis., 1943; B.S. magna cum laude, St. Louis U., 1948; M.S. (Shell fellow), U. Minn., 1950, Ph.D., 1951. Mem. staff U.S. Geol. Survey, Spokane, Wash., 1949-51; instr. geology Wash. State U., Pullman, 1951; geologist Shell Oil Co. 1952-65; geologist div. stratigrapher, 1958-63, sr. geologist, 1963-65; instr. geology N. Mex. State U., San Juan, (P.R.), br., 1959-65; prof. geology U. Mont. Missoula, 1965—; cons. U.S. Geol. Survey, 1976-82, rsch. geologist, 1982—. Editor: Geology of East Central Utah, 1956, Geometry of Sandstone Bodies, 1960, Rocky Mountain Sedimentary Basins, 1965, (with others) Pacific Geology, Paleotectonics and Sedimentation, 1986; Contbr. (with others) articles to profl. jours. Served to 1st lt. USAAF, 1943-46. Recipient Alumni Merit award St. Louis U., 1960, Outstanding Achievement award U. Minn., 1995. Fellow AAAS, Geol. Soc. Am.; mem. Am. Assn. Petroleum Geologists (pres. Rocky Mountain sect. 1964, Pres.'s award 1988, Disting. Svc. award 1992), Rocky Mountain Assn. Geologists (Outstanding Scientist award 1987), Four Corners Geol. Soc. (hon., pres. 1962), Am. Inst. Profl. Geologists (pres. Mont. sect. 1971), Soc. Econ. Paleontologists and Mineralogists (hon. 1985, sec.-treas. 1969-71, editor 1976-78, Disting. Pioneer Geologist award 1988), Mont. Geol. Soc. (hon. 1987), Utah Geol. Soc. Club: Explorers. Home: 301 Pattee Canyon Dr Missoula MT 59803-1624

PETERSON, JAMES KENNETH, manufacturing company executive; b. Sioux City, Iowa, Oct. 17, 1934; s. David Winfield and Beulah Lillian (Johnson) P.; m. Nanette Kay Olin, Feb. 2, 1957; children: Kimberly, Kristin, David. B.A. in Econs, Mich. State U., 1956. Research/devel. engr. Reynolds Metals Co., Richmond, Va., 1957-59, sales rep., 1959-61, dist. sales mgr., 1961-65, regional sales mgr., 1965-67, asst. to exec. v.p., 1968, mktg. dir., 1969-71; dir. nat. account sales The Continental Group, Stamford, Conn., 1971, gen. mgr. sales, 1972-73, div. gen. mgr., 1974-78, v.p., corp. officer, 1974-80, v.p., gen. mgr. global bus. devel., 1979; pres., chief oper. officer Ludlow Corp., Needham, Mass., 1980-82, also bd. dirs.; pres., CEO, dir. Graphic Packaging Corp., Paoli, Pa., 1982-89; pres., CEO Peterson Group, Easton, Md., 1989—; chmn., CEO The Petters Co., Lititz, Pa.; chmn. bd. dirs. Comml. Printers of Conn.; bd. dirs. Graphic Packaging Corp., South Chester Tube Co.; mem. Precision Strip Inc. Served to 1st lt. U.S. Army, 1957. Mem. Merion Golf Club, Merion Cricket Club, Talbot Country Club. Home: 27779 Waverly Rd Easton MD 21601-8121 Office: Peterson Group PO Box 738 Easton MD 21601-0738 also: The Petters Co 2077 Main St Lititz PA 17543-3029

PETERSON, JAMES LINCOLN, museum executive; b. Kewanee, Ill., Nov. 12, 1942; s. Reinold Gustav and Florence Josephine (Kjellgren) P.; m. M. Susan Pepin, Aug. 15, 1964; children: Hans C., Erika C. BA, Gustavus Adolphus Coll., 1964; PhD, U. Nebr., 1972. Sci. tchr. pub. schs. Ill. and Minn., 1964-68; research asst. U. Nebr., Lincoln, 1968-72; research assoc. U. Wis., Madison, 1972-74; staff ecologist Nat. Commn. Water Quality, Washington, 1974-75; v.p. research Acad. Nat. Scis., Phila., 1976-84, v.p. devel., 1982-84; pres. Sci. Mus. Minn., St. Paul, 1984—. Bd. dirs. Ea. Pa. chpt. Nature Conservancy, Phila., 1982-84, Downtown Coun., St. Paul, 1986-93; commr. St. Paul Riverfront Commn., 1987-91; mem. adv. com. Coll. Biol. Scis., U. Minn., 1989—. Mem. Assn. Sci. Mus. Dirs., Assn. Sci. and Tech. Ctrs. (pres.), Sci. Mus. Exhibit Collaborative (pres. 1986-89), Am. Assn. Mus., St. Paul C. of C. (bd. dirs. 1985-89), Informal Club (St. Paul). Office: Sci Mus Minn 30 10th St E Saint Paul MN 55101-2205

PETERSON, JAMES ROBERT, retired writing instrument manufacturing executive; b. Momence, Ill., Oct. 28, 1927; s. Clyde and Pearl (Deliere) P.; m. Betty Windham, May 12, 1949; children: Richard James, Lynn Peterson Anderson, Susan Peterson Hanske, John Windham. Student, St. Thomas Coll., 1945, Iowa State U., 1945-46, U. Colo., 1946, Northwestern U., 1946; BS in Mktg. cum laude, U. Ill., 1952; grad. exec. MBA program, Stanford U., 1967. With Pillsbury Co., Mpls., 1952-76; brand mgr. grocery products Pillsbury Co., 1953-57, brand supr. flour, 1957-61, dir. mktg., 1961-66, v.p mktg., 1966-68; v.p., gen. mgr. Grocery Products Co., 1968-71, group v.p. consumer cos., 1971-73, pres., dir., 1973-76; exec. v.p., dir. R.J. Reynolds Industries, Inc., Winston-Salem, N.C., 1976-82; pres., chief exec. officer, dir. Parker Pen Co., Janesville, Wis., 1982-85; dir. Dun & Bradstreet Corp., N.Y.C., 1977, Waste Mgmt., Inc., Oak Brook, Ill., 1980. Former mem. bd. dirs. Boy Scouts Am., past pres. Viking coun.; mem. bd. regents St. Olaf Coll., 1974-91. Lt. USN, 1945-50. Recipient Bronze Tablet award U. Ill. Mem. Pilgrims of U.S., Tequesta Country Club, Janesville Country Club, Bodega Harbour Golf, Links Club, Jupiter Hills Club. Methodist. Address: 19750 Beach Rd 505 Tequesta FL 33469

PETERSON, JANE WHITE, nursing educator, anthropologist; b. San Juan, P.R., Feb. 15, 1941; d. Jerome Sidney and Vera (Joseph) Peterson; 1 child, Claire Marie. BS, Boston U., 1968; M in Nursing, U. Wash., 1969, PhD, 1981. Staff nurse Visiting Nurse Assn., Boston, 1964-66; prof. Seattle U., 1969—; dir. nursing home project, 1990-92, chair pers. com., 1988-90; chair dept. Community Health and Psychiat. Mental Health Nursing, 1987-89; sec. Coun. on Nursing and Anthropology, 1984-86; pres. Wash. League Nursing, Seattle, 1988-90; pres. bd. Wis. Nurse Svcs., Seattle, 1988-90; contbg. cons. CSI Prodn., Okla., 1987; cons. in nursing WHO/U. Indonesia, Jakarta, fall 1989, Burma, 1995. Contbr. articles to profl. jours., chptrs. to books. Mem. Seattle Art Mus., 1986—. Fellow: Soc. for Applied Anthropology; mem. Am. Anthropological Assn., Soc. for Med. Anthropology, Nat. League for Nursing, Am. Ethological Soc. Office: Seattle U Sch Nursing Broadway and Madison Seattle WA 98122

PETERSON, JIM LEE, food service executive; b. Kansas City, Mo., Oct. 1, 1935; s. Lee C. and Lucille (Wiss) P.; m. Sue Ann Peterson, Dec. 7, 1956 (div. Jan. 1989); children: Ronald, Gaye, Craig. Student, Ottawa U., 1953-55; BA, U. Mo., Kansas City, 1957. Mgr. floor ops. Montgomery Ward & Co., Chgo., 1955-59; mgr. dist. sales Sinclair Oil Co., N.Y.C., 1959-64; pres. Food Host USA, Lincoln, Nebr., 1964-74, Whataburger, Inc., Corpus Christi, Tex., 1974-94; Bojangles' Restaurants Inc., Charlotte, N.C., 1994—; bd. dirs. 1st City Bank and Mercantile Bank Tex./Corpus Christi, Cen. Power & Light Co, Corpus Christi; mem. adv. bd. U. Nebr. Sch. Bus. and Franchising, Lincoln. Pres., bd. dirs. United Way Coastal Bend, Corpus Christi; chmn. Drug Edn., Law Enforcement and Community Unity Commn., Corpus Christi, Found. for Scis. and Arts, Corpus Christi; founder Corpus Christi Crimestoppers, Inc. Recipient Golden Chain and Operator of Yr. award Nation's Restaurant News, 1980, Silver Plate award Internat. Food Svc. Mfr. Assoc., 1983, Leadership award in food svc. mgmt. Restaurant Bus. mag., 1986, Disting. Citizen award Coastal Bend coun. Boy Scouts Am., 1989, Humanitarian of Yr. award NCCJ, Corpus Christi, 1990. Mem. Internat. Franchise Assn. (chmn. ethical standards com. 1986), Nat. Restaurant Assn. (nat. pres. 1988-89, chmn., bd. dirs. Edn. Found. 1992-93), World Bus. Coun., Corpus Christi C. of C. (pres.), Road Runners Club (Corpus Christi and N.Y.C.). Republican. Episcopalian. Avocations: running marathons, tennis, ranching, poetry, music. Home: PO Box 1338 Goliad TX 77963 Office: Bojangles' Restaurants Inc 9600 H Southern Pine Blvd Charlotte NC 28273

PETERSON, JOHN DOUGLAS, museum administrator; b. Peshtigo, Wis., July 9, 1939; s. Rubin and Ruth (Erickson) P.; m. Beth L. Lynch, July 22, 1965; children: Marie Storm, Beth Storm. BFA, Layton Sch. Art, 1962, cert. in indsl. design, 1962; MFA, Cranbrook Acad. Art, Bloomfield Hills, Mich., 1966. Asst. dir. Cranbrook Acad. Art Mus., Bloomfield Hills, Mich., 1969-70, assoc. dir., 1970-71, dir., 1971-77; exec. dir. Lakeview Mus. Arts and Scis., Peoria, Ill., 1977-82, The Morris Mus., Inc., Morristown, N.J., 1982-94; v.p. The Morris Mus. Found., Morristown 1990-94; exec. dir. Scienceport, Rye, N.Y., 1994—; bd. dirs. Morristown Info. Ctr., Gill St. Bernard Sch., 1988-94; mem. adv. panel Ill. Arts Coun., Chgo., 1980-82, N.J. State Coun. Arts, Trenton, 1984-85; reviewer Inst. Mus. Svcs., Washington, 1985-87. Bd. dirs. Peoria City Beautiful, 1982-87, Met. Detroit Arts Coun., 1972-77, New Philharmonic Orch., N.J.; chmn. Arts Coun., Triangle, 1972-73; co-chmn. Pub. Arts Com., Peoria, 1977-78. Mem. Am. Assn. Mus., Am. Assn. State and Local History, Advocates for the Arts, Mid-Atlantic Mus. Assn., New England Mus. Assn., N.J. Assn. Mus. (bd. dirs. 1990-94), Somerset Art Assn. (bd. dirs. 1990-94), N.J. Art Pride (bd. dirs. 1990-94), Morris Area Mus. Assn., Park Ave Club, Morristown Club. Home: 165 Lakeshore Dr Oakland NJ 07436-2102

PETERSON, JOHN DWIGHT, investment company executive; b. Indpls., July 20, 1933; s. J. Dwight and Mary Irene (Frisinger) P.; m. Nancy Jane Browning, July 16, 1955; children: Debbra Lee, John Dwight III, Penny Anne. B.S., Ind. U., 1955. With City Securities Corp., Indpls., 1955—; dir. City Securities Corp., 1966—, v.p., 1968-70, pres., 1970—, chmn., chief exec. officer, 1979—; dir. Lilly Indsl. Coatings, Inc., Farm Fans, Inc., Forum Group, Inc., Capital Industries, Duke Realty Investments. Mem. James Whitcomb Riley Meml. Assn., 1965—, Ind. Bd. Vocat. and Tech. Edn. 1973-81; mem. career edn. action com. Indpls. Pub. Schs., 1974-80; mem. Ind. U. Athletic Bd., 1971-74; pres. bd. dirs. Ir. Achievement Central Ind., 1979. Served as capt. U.S. Army, 1956. Mem. Young Pres. Orgn., Nat. Assn. Securities Dealers (dist. com. 8 1975-78), Indpls. Bond Club (pres. 1969), Sigma Chi. Presbyterian (elder). Clubs: Marion County Varsity (chmn. 1961-71); Columbia, University (Indpls.); Highland Golf and Country. Lodges: Masons, Rotary. Office: City Securities Corp 135 N Pennsylvania St Indianapolis IN 46204-2400

PETERSON, JOHN ERIC, physician, educator; b. Norwalk, Ohio, Oct. 26, 1914; s. Charles Augustus and Fannie Helen (Stanford) P.; m. Lodene C. Pruett, Aug. 18, 1938; children—Carol Peterson Haviland, John Eric. Student, Columbia Ir. Coll., 1932-34; M.D., Coll. Med. Evangelists, 1938. Diplomate: Nat. Bd. Med. Examiners, Am. Bd. Internal Medicine. Intern Henry Ford Hosp., Detroit, 1938-39; resident Henry Ford Hosp.,

1939-42; practice medicine specializing in internal medicine Los Angeles, 1942-56, Loma Linda, Calif., 1956—; mem. staff Los Angeles County Hosp., Riverside (Calif.) County Gen. Hosp.; mem. faculty Sch. Medicine, Loma Linda U., 1942—, prof. medicine, 1967-88, prof. medicine emeritus, 1988—, chmn. dept., 1969-80; asso. dean Sch. Medicine, Loma Linda U. (Sch. Medicine), 1965-75; mem. staff Loma Linda U. Hosp., 1967—, chief medicine service, 1969-80; rsch. assoc. Harvard Med. Sch., 1960-61; cons. to univs. and fgn. govts. Contbr. articles to various pubis. Fellow ACP; mem. AMA, Calif. Med. Assn., San Bernardino County Med. Assn., Calif. Soc. Internal Medicine, Inland Soc. Internal. Medicine, Am. Diabetes Assn., Western Soc. Clin. Investigation, Assn. Profs. of Medicine, L.A. Acad. Medicine, Diabetes Assn. So. Calif., Sigma Xi, Alpha Omega Alpha. Office: Loma Linda U Med Ctr Dept Medicine Rm 1576 Loma Linda CA 92350

PETERSON, JOHN LEONARD, lawyer, judge; b. Butte, Mont., Sept. 11, 1933; s. Roy Victor and Lena Pauline (Umhang) P.; m. Jean Marie Hollingsworth, June 10, 1957; children: Michael R., John Robert, Carol Jean. BA in Bus., U. Mont., 1957, JD, 1957. Bar: Mont. 1957, U.S. Supreme Ct. 1964, U.S. Ct. Appeals (9th cir.) 1974, U.S. Tax Ct. 1978. Assoc., McCaffery, Roe, Kiely & Joyce, 1957-63; ptnr. McCaffery & Peterson, 1963-79; sole practice, Butte, Mont., 1979-85; part-time U.S. bankruptcy judge, 1963-85; U.S. bankruptcy judge, Mont., 1985—. Bd. govs. Nat. Conf. Bankruptcy Judges, 1989-92; mem. Mont. Bd. Regents Higher Edn., 1975-82; del. Democratic Nat. Conv., 1968. Mem. Nat. Conf. Bankruptcy Judges, Assn. Trial Lawyers Am., Mont. Bar Assn., Silver Bow County Bar Assn., Butte Country Club, Butte Town Club, Butte Exch. Club, VASA Order Am., Scandinavia Fraternity of Am. Democrat. Lutheran. Office: US Dist Ct 215 Fed Bldg Butte MT 59701

PETERSON, KAREN IDA, marketing research company executive; b. Rahway, N.J., Dec. 30, 1939; d. Sigurd Thage and Harriet Erma (Pearson) P.; m. Thomas Lea Davidson, Oct. 7, 1978 (dec.). BA, Wellesley Coll. 1961; postgrad., CCNY, 1963-66. Rsch. asst. Opinion Rsch. Corp., Princeton, N.J., 1961-63; rsch. sec. Interpub. Group of Cos., N.Y.C., 1963-65; project dir., account supr., group head, v.p. Oxtoby Smith, Inc., N.Y.C., 1965-74; founder, prin., pres. Davidson-Peterson Assoc., N.Y.C. and York, Maine, 1974—; treas. Coun. of Am. Survey Rsch. Orgn., Pt. jefferson, N.Y., 1978-83; bd. dirs. Maine Publicity Bur., Hallowell. Co-author: Rural Tourism Marketing, 1994; mem. editl. rev. bd. Jour. Travel Rsch. Dir. Seashore Trolley Mus., Kennebunk, Maine, 1994—. Recipient Noah award Acad. of Travel, 1986. Mem. S.E. Tourism Soc., Women Execs. Internat. Tourism Assn. (bd. dirs., pres. 1984-89), Travel & Tourism Rsch. Assn. Internat. (bd. dirs. 1990-92). Avocations: photography, travel, antiques. Office: Davidson-Peterson Assoc Inc PO Box 350 York ME 03909-0350

PETERSON, KENT WRIGHT, physician; b. Portsmouth, Va., Apr. 16, 1943; s. Gerald Milton and Julia Elizabeth (Hoover) P.; m. Virginia Mae Sonne, Dec. 26, 1979; children: Liesl Lynn, Owen Sonne. B.A., U. N.C., Chapel Hill, 1964; M.D., U. Pa., 1968. Diplomate Am. Bd. Gen. Preventive Medicine, Am. Bd. Occupational Medicine. Intern U. Wis., 1968-69, resident, 1970-71; Robert Wood Johnson clin. scholar George Washington U., 1975-77; family physician E. Madison Clinic, Madison, Wis., 1969; chief med. officer policy devel. U.S. Cost of Living Council, Washington, 1973-74; assoc. dir. Assn. Univ. Programs in Health Adminstrn., Washington, 1974-77; exec. v.p. Am. Coll. Preventive Medicine, Washington, 1977-81; corp. mgr. preventive and environ. medicine IBM Corp., White Plains, N.Y., 1981-84; corp. med. dir. Am. Standard, N.Y.C., 1984-86; pres. Occupational Health Strategies, Charlottesville, Va., 1984—; clin. asst. prof. Georgetown U. Sch. Medicine, 1979-85; clin. assoc. prof. NYU. dept. environ. medicine, 1985—; rep. to Council Med. Specialty Socs., 1980-86 ; mem. Accreditation Council for Continuing Med. Edn., 1981-86; treas. Med. Rev. Officer Cert. Coun., 1992—. Pres. Children of the Americas Found., 1979-84. Served to maj. M.C. U.S. Army, 1971-73. Fellow Am. Coll. Preventive Medicine, Am. Coll. Occupational and Environ. Medicine (officer, bd. dirs., chmn. computers in occupational medicine com. 1986-90); mem. AMA, APHA, Assn. Tchrs. Preventive Medicine, Am. Coll. Epidemiology, N.Y. Acad. Medicine, Ramazzini Soc., Soc. Prospective Medicine (officer), World Future Soc., Coun. for Liveable World, Va. Occupational Medicine Assn. (pres. 1988-90). Home: RR 1 Box 62 Faber VA 22938-9715 Office: Occupational Health Strategies Inc 901 Preston Ave Ste 400 Charlottesville VA 22903-4421

PETERSON, KEVIN BRUCE, newspaper editor, publishing executive; b. Kitchener, Ont., Can., Feb. 11, 1948; s. Bruce Russell and Marguerite Elizabeth (Hammond) P.; m. Constance Maureen Bailey, Feb. 11, 1975 (dec. May 1975); m. Sheila Helen O'Brien, Jan. 9, 1981. B.A., U. Calgary, Alta., Can., 1968. Chief bur. Calgary Herald, 1972-75, city editor, 1976-77, news editor, 1977-78, bus. editor, 1978, mng. editor, 1978-86, editor, asst. pub., 1986-87, gen. mgr., 1987-88, pub., 1989—; pres. Canadian Univ. Press, Ottawa, Ont., Can., 1968-69; dir. New Directions for News. Harry Brittain Meml. fellow Commonwealth Press Union, London, 1979. Mem. Can. Mng. Editors (bd. dirs. 1983-87), Am. Soc. Newspaper Editors, Horsemen's Benevolent and Protective Assn., Alta. Legis. Press Gallery Assn. (v.p. 1971-76), Can. Daily Newspaper Assn. (bd. dirs. 1990—, vice chmn. treas. 1992, chmn. 1993), Calgary Petroleum Club, Ranchmen's Club, 100-to-1 Club (Arcadia, Calif.). Clubs: Calgary Petroleum, Ranchmen's, 100-to-1 (Arcadia, Calif.). Avocations: thoroughbred horse racing; art collecting. Office: Calgary Herald, 215 16th St Se, Calgary, AB Canada T2P 0W8

PETERSON, KIRK CHARLES, ballet dancer; b. New Orleans, Dec. 10, 1949; s. John Lawrence and Dorothy Ann (Wagner) P. Student pub. schs.; scholar, Harkness House for Ballet Arts. Charter mem. Harkness Youth Dancers, 1968-69; prin. dancer Harkness Ballet, 1970, Nat. Ballet, Washington, 1971-74, London Festival Ballet, 1973; mem. Am. Ballet Theatre, 1974-80, soloist, 1975-78, prin. dancer, 1978-80; prin. dancer, choreographer, ballet master Ballet Nat. de Venezuela, 1980; prin. dancer, resident choreographer, tchr. San Francisco Ballet, 1981-85; resident tchr. Met. Opera Ballet, Steps Studio; tchr. master classes, condr. lecture demonstrtions; artistic dir. Hartford Ballet, 1993—. Choreographer: The Nutcracker, Floating Weeds, Cloudless Sulphur, Othello, Overlay, Valse Triste; asst. choreographer Anything Goes, Lincoln Ctr., 1987, Anything Goes, Australia and London, 1989, Ballet Metropolitan, Columbus, Ohio, 1989; co-choreographer Shogun, Broadway, 1990; prin. roles include Albrecht in Giselle, James in La Sylphide; co-founder, dir. Omo Dancers, 1985. Recipient Bronze medal Internat. Ballet Competition, Varna, Bulgaria, 1972, Cultural award Dept. State, 1972, key to City of New Orleans, 1965, 66, 67. Mem. Am. Guild Musical Artists, Screen Actors Guild, AFTRA. Office: care Peter S Diggins Assocs 133 W 71st St New York NY 10023-3834

PETERSON, KRISTINA, publishing company executive. Pres., pub. Fodor's Travel Pubs. Inc. subs. Random House Inc. Office: Fodor's Travel Pubs Inc 201 E 50th St New York NY 10022-7703

PETERSON, LELAND WILMER, health facility administrator; b. Redwing, Minn., June 6, 1948; s. Wilmer Harry and Bertha Florence P.; m. Kristine Nelson, June 18, 1972; 1 child, Lara. BS, Wis. State U., River Falls, 1970; MPH, U. Calif., Berkeley, 1972. Adminstrv. intern Brookside Hosp., San Pablo, Calif., 1970; adminstrv. resident Alta Bates Hosp., Berkeley, Calif., 1971; adminstrv. asst. Walter O. Boswell Meml. Hosp., Sun City, Ariz., 1972-79, v.p., 1979-82, exec. v.p., 1982-86; sr. v.p. Sun Health Corp., Sun City, 1986-90, pres., chief exec. officer, 1990—; sec., treas. Phoenix Regional Hosp. Coun., 1987-88. Bd. dirs. Heard Mus. Men's Coun., Phoenix, 1986-88. Mem. Am. Coll. Healthcare Execs., Ariz. Hosp. Assn. (bd. dirs. 1991—, sec. 1990, chmn. 1991), Health Adminstrs. Forum (pres. 1981), Ariz. Assn. Asst. Hosps. (v.p. 1979), Rotary Internat. (membership chmn. 1988-89). Republican. Avocations: swimming, fishing. Office: Sun Health Corp 13180 N 103rd Dr Sun City AZ 85351-3038

PETERSON, LESLIE ERNEST, bishop; b. Noranda, Que., Can., Nov. 4, 1928; s. Ernest Victor and Blanch (Marsh) P.; m. Yvonne Hazel Lawson, July 16, 1953; children—Shauna Peterson Clay, Jennifer Peterson Glage, Kathryn Peterson Scott, Jonathan. B.A.. U. Western Ont., London, Ont., Can.; 1952; L.T.H., Huron Coll., London, Ont., Can., 1954, D.D. (hon.), 1984; tchr.'s cert., North Bay Tchrs. Coll., Ont. 1970. Ordained to ministry Anglican Ch., 1954. Priest Diocese of Algoma, Coniston, Ont., 1954-58; priest Diocese of Algoma, Elliot Lake, Ont., 1959-63, rural dean, 1961-63; priest Diocese of Algoma, North Bay, 1963-78; priest Diocese of

Algoma, Parry Sound, Ont., 1978-83, archdeacon, 1980-83; bishop Diocese of Algoma, Sault Ste. Marie, Ont., 1983-94; tchr. North Bay Elem. Sch. 1970-78; ret., 1994. Avocations: canoeing, woodworking, gardening. Address: 615 Santa Monica Rd, London, ON Canada N6H 3W2

PETERSON, LESLIE RAYMOND, barrister; b. Viking, Alta., Can., Oct. 6, 1923; s. Herman S. and Margaret (Karen) P.; m. Agnes Rose Hine, June 24, 1950; children: Raymond Erik, Karen Isabelle. Student, Camrose Luth. Coll., Alta., McGill. U., Can., London U., Eng.; LLB, U. B.C., Can., 1949; LLD, Simon Fraser U., Can., 1965, U. B.C., 1993; EdD, Notre Dame U., Nelson, Can., 1966; hon. diploma tech., B.C. Inst. Tech., 1994. Bar: B.C. 1949; called to Queens Counsel, 1960. Pvt. practice barrister Vancouver, B.C., 1949-52; with Peterson & Anderson, 1952; then with Boughton & Co. (now Boughton Peterson Yang Anderson); mem. B.C. Legislature for Vancouver Centre, 1956-63, Vancouver-Little Mountain, 1966; min. of edn., 1956-68, min. of labour, 1960-71, atty. gen., 1968-72; bd. govs. U. B.C., 1979-83, chancellor, 1987-93; bd. dirs. Can. Found. Econ. Edn., Inst. Corp. Dirs. Can., Tordiam Inc., West Vancouver Found., Karay Holdings Ltd., Amaric Prodns. Inc., Rick Hansen Enterprises Inc.; trustee Peter Wall Inst. for Advanced Studies. Bd. dirs. Portland unit Shriners Hosp. for Crippled Children; past bd. dirs. Western Soc. of Rehab., YMCA, Victoria B.C.; past pres. Twenty Club; hon. mem. Vancouver Jr. C. of C.; former v.p. Normanna Old People's Home; founding mem. Convocation, Simon Fraser U. and U. Victoria, pres., 1964-65; hon. dep. French Nat. Assembly, Paris; hon. commr. labor State of Okla.; gov. Downtown Vancouver Assn.; chmn. U. B.C. Found. With Can. Army, 1942-46, ETO. Recipient Disting. Alumnus award Camrose Luth. Coll., 1980. Fellow Royal Soc. Arts; mem. Internat. Bar Assn., Vancouver Bar Assn., Law Soc. B.C., Internat. Assn. of Govt. Labour Ofcls. (chmn. standing com., Can. mins. of edn. 1965-66), Terminal City Club (pres. 1991—), Scandinavian Bus. Men's Club (past pres.), Hazelmere Golf and Tennis Club (bd. dirs.), Union Club (Victoria), Wesbrook Soc. of U. B.C. (chmn. 1987), Order of St. Lazarus (knight comdr.), Freemason (potentate Gizeh Temple Shrine 1988). Avocations: skiing, golf, fishing, hunting. Home: 814 Highland, West Vancouver, BC Canada V7S 2G5 Office: Boughton Peterson Yang Anderson, 1055 Dunsmuir St PO Box 49290, Vancouver, BC Canada V7X 1S8

PETERSON, LINDA H., English language and literature educator; b. Saginaw, Mich., Oct. 11, 1948. BA in Lit. summa cum laude, Wheaton Coll., 1969; MA in English, U. R.I., 1973; PhD in English, Brown U., 1978. From lectr. to assoc. prof. Yale U., New Haven, 1977-92, prof., 1992—, dir. undergrad. studies English, 1990-94, chair, 1994—; dir. Bass writing program Yale Coll., 1979-89, 90—; mem. various departmental and univ. coms. Yale U., 1977—; presenter in field. Author: Victorian Autobiography: The Tradition of Self-Interpretation, 1986; co-author: Writing Prose, 1989, A Struggle for Fame: Victorian Women Artists and Authors, 1994; co-editor: Wuthering Heights: A Case Study in Contemporary Criticism, 1992, The Norton Reader, 9th edit., 1996, Instructor's Guide to the Norton Reader, 1996; mem. editorial bd. Writing Program Adminstrn., 1983-85, Coll. Composition and Comm., 1986-88, Auto/Biography Studies, 1990-93; contbr. articles to profl. jours. Resident fellow Branford Coll., 1979-87, Mellon fellow Whitney Humanities Ctr., 1984-85, fellow NEH, 1989-90. Mem. MLA (del. assembly 1984-86, mem. program com. 1986-89, mem. non-fiction divsn. com. 1988-92, mem. nominating com. 1993-94, mem. teaching of writing divsn. 1993—), Nat. Coun. Writing Program Adminstrs. (mem. cons.-evaluator program 1982—, mem. exec. bd. 1982-84, 89-90, v.p. 1985-86, pres. 1987-88), Nat. Coun. Tchrs. English (mem. CCCC nominating com. 1985, mem. coll. sect. com. 1987-90). Home: 53 Edgehill Rd New Haven CT 06511 Office: Yale U Dept English New Haven CT 06520

PETERSON, LINDA S., lawyer; b. Grand Forks, N.D., Mar. 15, 1952. BA summa cum laude, U. N.D., 1973; JD, Yale U., 1977. Bar: N.D. 1977, D.C. 1978, U.S. Dist. Ct. D.C. 1979, U.S. Ct. Appeals (D.C. cir.) 1979, U.S. Ct. Appeals (3d cir.) 1982, Calif. 1986, U.S. Ct. Appeals (fed. cir.) 1986. Law clk. Ct. of Appeals for D.C., Washington, 1977-78; ptnr. Sidley & Austin, L.A. Dep. counsel Webster Commn., 1992; mem. bd. trustees Southwestern U. Sch. Law, 1995. Mem. State Bar Calif. (rules of ct. com. 1988-91), L.A. County Bar Assn. (conf. dels. 1987-90), Women Lawyers Assn. L.A. (bd. dirs. 1989-95), Phi Beta Kappa. Office: Sidley & Austin 555 W Fifth St Ste 4000 Los Angeles CA 90013-1010

PETERSON, LOUIS ROBERT, retired consumer products company executive; b. Racine, Wis., Nov. 11, 1923; s. Edward J. and Effie (Buenning) P.; m. Marian Francis Barber, Nov. 22, 1947; children: Karen Jean, Kathleen Alice, Jill Ann. Student, Utah State Agrl. Coll., U. Wis.-Racine. With Johnson Wax Co., Racine, Wis., 1947—; sales rep. Johnson Wax Co., 1970-72, v.p. household sales, 1972-76, exec. v.p. U.S. consumer products, ptnr. in office of the chmn., 1976-86, exec. v.p. internat. consumer products, 1980—; bd. dirs. Biltmore Investors Bank, Phoenix. Past pres., bd. dirs. Racine Area United Way; bd. dirs. St. Mary's Med. Ctr. With U.S. Army, 1943-46. Mem. Northwestern U. Assocs., Conf. Bd. (internat. council), Internat. C. of C. (U.S. Council internat. bus.). Republican. Roman Catholic. Clubs: Somerset (Racine, Wis.): Pinnacle Peak Country (Scottsdale, Ariz.) (bd. dirs.). Home: RR 1 Box 1168 Hayward WI 54843-9801 also: 8723 E Clubhouse Way Scottsdale AZ 85255-4231

PETERSON, LOWELL N., light manufacturing executive; b. 1911. Supr. purchasing Enterprise Aluminum Co., 1933-1945; in charge of prodn. Kewaskum (Wis.) Mfg. Co., Inc., 1945-55, gen. mgr., 1955, exec. v.p., chmn. bd., 1976—. Office: Kewaskum Mfg Co Inc 1675 Reigle Dr Kewaskum WI 53040*

PETERSON, M. ROGER, banker, former manufacturing executive, retired air force officer; b. Chgo., June 7, 1929; s. Milton Albert and LaVergne Geraldine (Andelin) P.; m. Sally Ann Alder, Apr. 25, 1952; children: Bruce Roger, Dale Alder, Drew Alan. B.S. in Acctg., UCLA, 1955; M.S. in Mgmt., U. Colo., 1964; grad., Air Command and Staff Coll. Air U., Ala., 1965; grad. Exec. Program for Internat. and Nat. Security, J.F. Kennedy Sch. Govt., Harvard U., 1983. Joined USAF, 1955, advanced through grades to maj. gen., 1981, pilot, 1956-61, mgr. tactical missile site constrn., 1961; air officer comdg. 11th Cadet Squadron, Air Force Cadet Wing USAF Acad., 1961-64; asst. sec. Joint Chiefs of Staff and NSC matters for Hdqrs. Pentagon, 1965-68; transport pilot USAF, Vietnam, 1968; asst. officer U.S.-Japan Joint Com., Adminstrn. of Status of Forces Agreement USAF, 1968-73, chief program cost, dir. budget, 1973-76, chief plans, comptroller of Air Force, 1976-78, dir. mgmt. analysis, 1978-79, dir. programs, asst. chief of staff for research and devel., 1979-81; asst. dir. plans, policies and programs Def. Logistics Agy., Alexandria, Va., 1981-82, dep. dir., 1982-83; asst. dep. chief staff for logistics and engring. Hdqrs. USAF, Washington, 1983-84; pres., chief exec. officer advanced tech. factory, 1984-85; strategic planner United Techs. Corp., 1985-88; v.p., chief oper. officer Sikorsky Support Svcs. Inc., 1988-90; exec. asst. to mng. prtnr. O'Connor & Assocs., 1990-92; mng. dir. global ops. and svcs. Swiss Bank Corp., 1992—. Decorated Disting. Service medal; decorated Legion of Merit, Air medal with oak leaf cluster, Joint Service Commendation medal, Air Force Commendation medal with two oak leaf clusters. Mem. Air Force Assn., Beta Gamma Sigma, Sigma Iota Epsilon. Presbyterian. Designed and negotiated consolidation of U.S. Air Force bases in Tokyo, 1970-73; negotiated mil. and civil aviation agreement for return of Okinawa to Japan; created global bus. mgmt. system for Swiss Bank Corp. Home: Hubrainstrasse 8a, CH-8124 Maur Switzerland Office: Swiss Bank Corp, Opfikon, CH-8010 Zurich Switzerland also: Swiss Bank Corp c/o Jan Galayda 141 W Jackson Blvd Chicago IL 60604 *Always with honor.*

PETERSON, MARYBETH A., church administrator. Bd. chmn. Division for Ministry of the Evangelical Lutheran Church in America, Chicago, Ill. Office: Evangelical Lutheran Church Am 8765 W Higgins Rd Chicago IL 60631-4101

PETERSON, MERRILL DANIEL, history educator; b. Manhattan, Kans., Mar. 31, 1921; s. William Oscar and Alice Dwinell (Merrill) P.; m. Jean Humphrey, May 24, 1941; children: Jeffrey Ward, Kent Merrill. Student, Kans. State U., 1939-41; AB, U. Kans., 1943; PhD in History of Am. Civilization, Harvard U., 1950. Teaching fellow Harvard U., Cambridge, Mass., 1948-49; instr., then asst. prof. history Brandeis U., Waltham, Mass., 1949-55; asst. prof., bicentennial preceptor Princeton U., N.J., 1955-58; mem. faculty Brandeis U., Waltham, Mass., 1958-62, dean students, 1960-62; Thomas Jefferson Found. prof. U. Va., Charlottesville, 1962-87, Thomas Jefferson Found. prof. emeritus, 1987—, chmn. dept. history, 1966-72, dean of faculty Arts and Scis., 1981-85; Mary Ball Washington prof. Am. History University Coll., Dublin, Ireland, 1988-89; scholar in residence Bellagio Study Ctr., 1974; faculty Salzburg Seminar in Am. Studies, 1975; Lamar lectr. Mercer U., 1975; Fleming lectr. La. State U., 1980; lectr. at 15 European univs., 40 Am. colls. and univs. Author: The Jefferson Image in the American Mind, 1960 (Bancroft prize, Gold medal Thomas Jefferson Meml. Found.), Major Crises in American History, 2 vols., 1962, Democracy, Liberty and Property: The State Constitutional Convention Debates of the 1820s, 1966, Thomas Jefferson and the New Nation: A Biography, 1970, James Madison: A Biography in His Own Word, 1974, Adams and Jefferson: A Revolutionary Dialogue, 1976, Olive Branch and Sword: The Compromise of 1833, 1982, The Great Triumvirate: Webster, Clay and Calhoun, 1987; editor: Thomas Jefferson: A Historical Profile, 1966, The Portable Thomas Jefferson, 1975, Thomas Jefferson Writings, 1984, Thomas Jefferson: A Reference Biography, 1986, The Virginia Statute for Religious Freedom: Its Evolution and Consequences in American History, 1988, Visitors to Monticello, 1989, Lincoln in American Memory, 1994 (History finalist, Pulitzer prize, PBK Book award U. Va.). Bd. dirs. Thomas Meml. Found.; chmn. Thomas Jefferson Commemoration Comm., 1993-94. Guggenheim fellow, 1962-63, Ctr. for Advanced Study in Behavioral Scis. fellow, 1968-69, NEH and Nat. Humanities Ctr. fellow, 1980-81; recipient 20th Anniversary award Va. Found. for Humanities, 1994. Fellow Am. Acad. Arts and Scis.; mem. Am. Hist. Assn., So. Hist. Assn., Orgn. Am. Historians, Soc. Am. Historians, Am. Antiquarian Soc., Mass. Hist. Soc., Phi Beta Kappa. Home: 250 Pantops Mountain Rd #6 Charlottesville VA 22901

PETERSON, MILDRED OTHMER (MRS. HOWARD R. PETERSON), lecturer, writer, librarian, civic leader; b. Omaha, Oct. 19, 1902; d. Frederick George and Freda Darling (Snyder) Othmer; m. Howard R. Peterson, Aug. 25, 1923 (dec. Feb. 9, 1970). Student, U. Iowa, 1919, U. Nebr., 1921-23, Northwestern U., 1935, U. Chgo., 1943, Am. U. Switzerland, 1985. Asst. purchasing agt. Met. Utilities Dist., 1920-21; asst. U. Nebr. Library, 1921-23; tchr. piano, dir. choir Harlan, Iowa, 1924-26; dir. pub. relations and gen. asst. Des Moines Pub. Library, 1928-35; broadcaster weekly book programs Sta. WHO, Des Moines, and other Iowa radio stas.; columnist, writer Mid-West News Syndicate, Des Moines Register and Tribune; editor Book Marks, 1929-35; writer for Drug Topics, Drug Trade News, others, No. Ill., 1935; writer, spl. asst. ALA, Chgo., 1935-59, Chgo. Tribune, 1941-59; travel writer Hyde Park Herald, 1974-94; lectr. SS. Rotterdam of Holland Am. Line, 1971; lectr. tours U.S., Can., Mexico, 1977—; internat. lectr. on travel, fgn. jewelry and internat. relations, 1940—; guest lectr. on Golden Odyssey Ship Royal Cruise Line to Orient, world trip with Purdue U. Alumni, Feb.-Mar., 1988; del. 1st Assembly Librarians Ams., Washington, 1947. Contbr. articles to newspapers, periodicals, encys. and yearbooks. Chmn. India Famine Relief, 1943; a founder Pan Am. Coun., 1939, v.p., 1982-86, numerous other coms.; founder, past pres. Pan Am. Bd. Edn., 1955-58, Internat. Visitors Center, 1952-56, a founder, 1st pres. and hon. life dir. 1986; sec. Chgo. at State Dept. Conf. on Cmty. Svcs. to Fgn. Visitors; a founder COSERV (Nat. Council for Cmty. Svcs. to Internat. Visitors), Washington, 1957; mem. exec. bd., awards com. Mayor's Com. on Chgo. Beautiful; mem. Ill. Gov.'s Com. on Ptnrs. of the Americas, São Paulo, Brazil and Ill. sister states; mem. U.S. Dept. State conf. for Internat. Pan-Am. Domenican Republic, 1985, Little Rock, 1986, Jamaica, 1987 (Superior Service award 1987), Miami Beach, Fla., 1988; mem. chancellor's com. U. Nebr., conf. com. U. Chgo., 1990; former bd. dirs. council, troop leader Girl Scouts U.S., Council Bluffs, Iowa, 1926-28; mem. council, stewardship and mission bds. Hyde Park Union Ch., also 75th, 100th and 110th anniversary coms.; bd. dirs. YWCA, Chgo. Lung Assn.; women's bd. Camp Brueckner-Farr, Grad. Bapt. Student Center; mem. exec. council Friends of Sta. WTTW-TV; chairwoman Hyde Park Christmas Seals Campaign, 1985-86, 87-88 (Outstanding Service award 1987); bd. dirs. Maridian Hospice. Decorated Uruguayan medal, 1952; Internat. Eloy Alfaro medal, 1952; Order of Carlos Manuel de Cespedes Cuba; Order of Vasco Nuñez de Balboa Panama; cited by Chgo. Sun, Ill. Adult Edn. Council, 1953; recipient scholarship in Latin-Am. field U. Chgo. and Coordinator Inter-Am. Affairs, U.S. Govt., 1943, world understanding merit award Chgo. Council on Fgn. Relations, 1955, Disting. Service award Hospitality Center, 1958, Disting. Service medal U. Nebr., Disting. Service medal U. Nebr. Alumni Assn., 1963, Disting. Achievement award, 1975, Ambassador of Friendship award Am. Friendship Club, 1963, merit award YWCA for 10 yrs. as mem. bd., 1964 and Disting. Service award, 1975; Civic salute WMAQ radio, Chgo., 1965; Disting. Service award Pan-Am. Bd. Edn., 1966; also founders award, 1968; Laura Hughes Lunde Meml. award Citizens Greater Chgo., 1968; Friendship award Philippine Girl Scouts, 1971; Disting. Service award OAS, 1971; named Woman of Yr. Friends of Chgo. Sch. and Workshop for Retarded, 1975; Disting. Service trophy Fedn. Latin Am. Orgns., 1976; Merit Award WTTW-TV, Chgo., 1983; named to Sr. Citizens Hall of Fame, 1992, Chgo. Hall of Fame, 1992. Fellow Am. Internat. Acad. (life mem.); mem. Nat. Council Women U.S., Chgo. Council for USA-USSR Friendship (mem. Leaders Tour of China 1990), English Speaking Union, Japan-Am. Com., U.S.-China Friendship Assn. (bd. dirs. 1987—, Vol. award 1990), Internat. House Assn. (v.p.), Pan-Am. Bd. Edn. (founder, pres., Merit award), U.S. Capitol Hist. Soc., Ill. Hist. Soc., Nebr. Hist. Soc., Chgo. Hist. Soc., Hyde Park Hist. Soc. (charter mem. award 1978), Field Mus. Natural History, Mus. Sci. and Industry, Lincoln Park Zool. Soc., Citizenship Council Met. Chgo., Oriental Inst., Am. Heritage Coun., ALA, Ill. Libr. Assn. (local arrangements com. of nat. conf. 1976, 78, 85, 95), Internat. Fedn. Libr. Assns. (local arrangements com. 1985 Chgo.), Soc. Woman Geographers (pres. Chgo. chpt., v.p. internat. coun. 1987—), Coun. Fgn. Rels. (speakers bur.), Nat. Assn. Travel Ofcls. (Chgo. Tribune rep.), Library Internat. Rels. (ball com. 1969—), U. Nebr. Alumni Assn. (past pres. Des Moines, Rockford and Chgo. chpts.), U. Nebr. Found., U. Chgo. Internat. House Assn. (v.p. 1976—), Art Inst. Chgo., U. Chgo. Svc. League (past bd. mem., now bd. dirs. Camp Brueckner-Farr Aux.), Am. Legion Aux. (mem. state bds. Iowa and Ill.), AAUW, LWV, Children's Benefit League, Woman's Bd. United Negro Coll. Fund, Renaissance Soc., Peruvian Arts Soc., Hispanic Soc. Chgo., Chgo. Acad. Scis. (woman's bd.), Chgo. Chamber Orch. Assn., John G. Shedd Soc., Japan Am. Soc., Friends Chgo. Pub. Library, Chgo. Symphony Soc., Citizens Greater Chgo., Found. for Ill. Archaeology, Cook County Hosp. Aux., Lyric Opera Guild, Crossroads Student Center, Internat. Platform Assn., Exec. Service Corps Chgo., Friends of Grant Park Concerts, Chgo. Council for USA-USSR, Friendship U. Ill., Chgo. Internat. Programs, Friends of Parks, Friends of Downtown, Friends of Chgo. River, Met. Planning Coun., Chgo. Architecture Found., Landmarks Presrvation Coun., Open Lands Project, Women in Arts (charter mem. Washington chpt.), Geographic Soc. Chgo., Alpha Delta Pi (past pres. Omaha, Des Moines and Chgo. alumnae chpts., editor Adepheian 1938-39, woman of year award U.S. and Can. 1955), Xi Delta. Clubs: Mem. Order Eastern Star, South Shore Country, College, Quadrangle, Ill. Athletic, University of Chicago Dames, Iowa University, Lakeside Lawn Bowling, Hyde Park Neighborhood, Travellers Century (World's Most Travelled Person plaque 1993). Travelled to and lectr. on over 250 countries, including China and Albania; extensive fgn. Christmas card collection exhibited at Mus. Sci. and Industry, Chgo. Pub. Libr., Chgo. Sun Times, Des Moines Pub. Library, others, given to Chgo Pub. Libr.; donor sheet music, musical records, thousands of colored slides taken during her extensive travels to Chgo. Pub. Libr.; Egyptian jewelry to U. Chgo. Oriental Inst., E. Indian rose cut diamonds and other jewels to Smart Gallery, U. Chgo. Address: 5834 S Stony Island Ave Chicago IL 60637-2004

PETERSON, MILLIE M., state legislator; b. Merced, Calif., June 11, 1944. BS, U. Utah, 1979, MSW, 1984. Mem. Utah State Senate from 12th dist., 1991—. Mem. Assn. Am. Med. Colls. Democrat. Address: 7131 W 3800 S West Valley City UT 84120-3416 Office: Senate House State Capitol Salt Lake City UT 84114

PETERSON, MONICA (DOROTHY PETERSON), actress, singer, model, writer. Drama cert., Neighborhood Playhouse, N.Y.C., 1963, Jeff Corey Sch. Acting, 1967; student Sch. Music and Dance, Covent Garden, London, 1972; AA, Santa Monica Coll., 1983; BA, U. So. Calif., 1986. Editorial sec., writer Look mag., N.Y.C., 1964-66; asst. mgr. Venture Mag. Advt., N.Y.C., 1965-66; actress, singer, performer William Morris Agy., Hollywood, Calif., 1967-70, also London, Spain, Italy; contract player 20th Century Fox, 1967-70; contract singer, dancer, actress L.A. City Hall Theatre of Arts, 1975-80; staff writer SMC, L.A., 1981-83, newspaper editor, 1983-84; exec. asst., 1986—; script writer Crystal Awards (WIF), 1992, chair, writer, 1993; with Dem. Leadership for 21st Century L.A. Chpt., 1993, asst. p.r. media Mayoral Roundtable Whittle Communications, 1993; jazz singer-actress, 1987—; active in telecom., 1987—; exec. asst. 1987—; comml. agt. Tisherman Agy., L.A.; theatrical agt. Bonnie Allen Talent Agy., Beverly Hills, Calif., Atkins & Assocs. Agy., L.A.; Paris fashion runway model, 1993; scriptwriter, 1993; assoc. pub. rels./media Dem. Leadership 21st Century Mayoral Roundtable for Whittle Comm. Raleigh Studios, 1993, working with L.A. chpt., 1993. Editorial and entertainment editor, prodr., writer, reporter Sta. KCRW Radio Programs; extensive travel as a performer (including 2-month concert in Japan), theatre, stage, TV, radio; one-woman shows include Toys for Tots Shows, L.A., Biltmore Jazz Club, other jazz, supper clubs; contbr. articles to mags. Script analyst, editor, asst. casting dir. Inner City Cultural City, L.A., 1974-76; vol. Easter Seals, also vol. work for diabetics, homeless, needy, elderly and sick; v.p. Internat. Coun.; active Bill Clinton for Pres. Campaign, 1992, Voters Revolt Campaign, 1992; mem. Dem. Com., Washington; elected Community Bd. Dirs. Recipient Hollywood Star of Tomorrow award ABC, 1968, Overseas award USO, 1969, poetry award. Mem. SAG (v.p. minority com. 1969-71, rep. Image award 1969-72), AFTRA, Women in Film (scriptwriter, prodr. Cannes Film Festival, scriptwriter Crystal awards 1992, chair and writer Crystal awards 1993), Equity, Internat. Platform Assn., Women In Comm. (del. Cannes Film Festival 1993), U. So. Calif. Alumni Assn. Democrat. Roman Catholic. Avocations: jogging, reading, softball, music.

PETERSON, N. CURTIS, JR., landscape architect, former state senator; b. Lakeland, Fla., Aug. 23, 1922; s. N. Curtis and Caroline Ellen (Smith) P.; m. Ethel Schultz, Apr. 8, 1944; children: N. Curtis III, Peter Karl. Student, George Washington U., 1941-42, Fla. So. Coll., 1950-53. Registered landscape architect, Fla. Mem. Fla. Senate from Dist. 12, 1972-90; senate pres. pro-tem, 1980-82, senate pres., 1982-84, chmn. appropriations edn. com., 1976-82, 86-90, chmn. edn. com., 1976-78, 84-86, 1988-90, chmn. agr. com., 1974-76, vice chmn. agr. com., 1986-88. Bd. dirs. Awareness in Fla. Govt.; mem. Fla. Gov.'s Commn. on Secondary Schs., 1981-82; del. Democratic Charter Conf., 1974; commr. Edn. Commn. of States, 1973-90, chmn. edn. task force Nat. Conf. State Legislatures, 1987; sponsor achievement in secondary edn. RAISE; mem. platform com. Fla. Dem. Com., 1978-79; bd. dirs. Polk County Assn. Retarded Citizens; commr. So. Regional Edn. Bd. Named Most Effective Senator Fla. Senate, 1977, 80, 81. Mem. Fla. Nurserymen and Growers Assn. (pres. 1961-62, named Nurseryman of Yr.), Agribus Inst. Fla. (pres. 1975-76), Agrl. Tax Coun. (pres. 1967-70), Agrl. Adv. Coun. Fla. (pres. 1961-62, chmn.), Pilot Club, U. Wis., Kiwanis. Democrat. Baptist. Home: 1504 S Warren Ave Lakeland FL 33803-2063

PETERSON, NAD A., lawyer, corporate executive; b. Mt. Pleasant, Utah, 1926; m. Martha Peterson, 1948; children: Anne Carroll (Mrs. Stanford P. Darger, Jr.), Christian, Elizabeth (Mrs. Henry G. Ingersoll), Robert and Lane (twins). A.B., George Washington U., 1950, J.D., 1953. Bar: D.C. 1953, Calif. 1960, U.S. Supreme Ct. 1958. Law practice Washington, 1953-60; sec., asst. gen. counsel Dart Industries, Los Angeles, 1960-67; chief counsel Fluor Corp., Irvine, Calif., 1967-73; gen. counsel Fluor Corp., 1973-79, v.p. law, 1979-82, sr. v.p. law, 1983-84, sr. v.p., sec., 1984-93; sr. v.p., gen. counsel San Diego Gas & Electric Co., 1993—. Mem. ABA, State Bar Assn., Phi Delta Phi. Office: San Diego Gas & Electric 101 Ash St San Diego CA 92101-3096

PETERSON, NADEEN, advertising agency executive; b. McKeesport, Pa., Dec. 3, 1934; d. Michael James and LaVerna Peal (Long) Powell; m. Robert Glenn Kilzer, Dec. 24, 1966; 1 son, Douglas Robert. Student, U. Fla., 1952-53. Copywriter Ellington & Co., N.Y.C., 1961-64; v.p., assoc. creative dir. Tatham-Laird, N.Y.C., 1964-65, Foote, Cone & Belding, Inc., N.Y.C., 1966-69; v.p., sr. assoc. creative dir. Norman, Craig & Kummell, N.Y.C., 1969-70, sr. v.p., creative dir., 1975-77; sr. v.p., creative dir. Doyle, Dane, Bernbach, Inc., N.Y.C., from 1978; sr. v.p. Saatchi & Saatchi DFS Compton, N.Y.C., exec. v.p., creative dir., exec. v.p., exec. creative dir., 1987-89; vice-chmn., exec. creative dir. Saatchi & Saatchi DFS Compton (now Saatchi & Saatchi Advt.), N.Y.C., 1989—. Recipient Matrix award, 1977; named 100 Best Brightest Women in Advt. Advt. Age, 1988, vice chmn. World Wide Creative dir. advt. Woman of Yr., 1992. Office: Saatchi & Saatchi Advt 375 Hudson St New York NY 10014-3658

PETERSON, OSCAR EMMANUEL, pianist; b. Montreal, Que., Can. Aug. 15, 1925; s. Daniel and Olivia (John) P. Studied with Paul deMarky; LL.D. (hon.), Carleton U., 1973, Queen's U., 1976, Concordia U., 1979, McMaster U., 1981, U. of Victoria, 1981, U. Toronto, 1985; D.Mus. (hon.), Sackville U., 1980, U. Laval, 1985; Litt.D. (hon.), York U., 1982; D.F.A. (hon.), Northwestern U., Evanston, Ill., 1983; LLD (hon.), U. Toronto, 1985; MusD (hon.), U. Laval, 1985. Founder Advanced Sch. Contemporary Music, Toronto; former chancellor York U., 1991-94; chancellor York U., 1991. Began music career on weekly radio show, then with Johny Holmes Orchestra, Can., 1944-49; recorded with RCA Victor Records; appeared with Jazz at the Philharmonic, Carnegie Hall, 1949; toured the U.S. and Europe, 1950—; leader trio with Ray Brown, Irving Ashby, later Barney Kessel, Herb Ellis, Ed Thigpen, Sam Jones, Louie Hayes, concert appearances with Ella Fitzgerald, Eng., Scotland, 1955; appeared Stratford (Ont.) Shakespeare Festival, Newport Jazz Festival; recorded and performed solo piano works, 1972—; toured USSR, 1974, recordings with Billie Holiday, Fred Astaire, Benny Carter, Count Basie, Roy Eldridge, Lester Young, Ella Fitzgerald, Niels-Henning, Joe Pass, Orsted Pederson, Dizzy Gillespie, Harry Edison, Clark Terry; composer: Canadiana Suite, Hymn to Freedom, Fields of Endless Day, City Lights, Begone Dull Care, (with Norman McLaren) salute to Johann Sebastian Bach, music for films Big North and Silent Partner; author: Jazz Exercises and Pieces: Oscar Peterson New Piano Solos; numerous TV specials. Decorated officer Order of Canada, 1972, companion, 1984; recipient award for piano Down Beat mag. 13 times, Metronome mag. award, 1953-54, Edison award, 1962, Award of merit City of Toronto, (1st mention) 1973 (2d mention 1983), Diplome d'honneur Can. Conf. of the Arts, 1975, Grammy award 7 times, Olympic Key to Montreal, The Queen's medal, 1977, Genie Film award for film score The Silent Partner, 1978, Grand-Prix du Disques for Night Child album, 1981, Canadian Band Festival Award, 1982, Juno Hall of Fame award, 1982, George Peabody medal Peabody Conservatory of Music, Balt., 1987, Volunteer award Roy Thompson Hall, Toronto, 1987, Can. Club Arts and Letters award, N.Y.C., 1987, Officer in Order of Arts and Letters, France, 1989, Chevalier Order of Que., 1991, Lifetime Achievement Toronto Arts Award, 1991, appointed Order of Ontario, 1992, Lifetime Achievement Gov. Gens. award, 1992, Glenn Gould prize, 1993, Carnegie Hall Anniversary medal, Charlie Parker bronze medal, Ville de Salon de Provence medal, Award of Thanks, Mexico City; 12-time jazz poll winner Playboy mag.; named number one (piano) Jazz and Pop, Readers Poll 1968, 85; named to U. Calif. at Berkeley Hall of Fame, 1983, Contemporary Keyboard Hall of Fame, 1983; Oscar Peterson Day proclaimed by Baltimore, Oreg., 1981, 83; Oscar Peterson Scholarship founded in his honor Berklee Sch. of Music, Boston, 1982. Avocations: fly fishing, photography, astronomy. Office: Regal Recordings Ltd, 2421 Hammond Rd, Mississauga, ON Canada L5K 1T3

PETERSON, PATTI MCGILL, college president; b. Johnstown, Pa., May 20, 1943; d. Earl Frampton and Helen G. McGill; m. Luther D. Peterson, Aug. 31, 1968; 1 son, Lars-Anders. B.A. in Polit. Sci., Pa. State U., 1965; M.A. in Polit. Sci., U. Wis., 1968, Ph.D. in Polit. Sci., 1974; cert. advance study, Harvard U., 1977; D.Litt (hon.), Le Moyne Coll., 1983. Asst. prof. polit. sci., dean of freshman women Schiller Coll., Ger., 1968-69; asst. prof. polit. sci. SUNY-Oswego, 1971-72, asst. to pres., adj. prof., 1972-77, v.p. acad. services and planning, assoc. prof., 1978-80; pres. Wells Coll., Aurora, N.Y., 1980-87, St. Lawrence U, Canton, N.Y., 1987—; bd. dirs. Nia. Mo. Power Corp., Security Mut. Life Ins. Co., John Hancock Mut. Funds. Author numerous articles in field. Trustee Northwood Sch. Sta.; bd. overseers The Nelson A. Rockefeller Inst. Govt., 1988; trustee Assn. Am. Colls., 1987; chmn. Pub. Leadership Edn. Network, 1983-85; mem. Gov.'s Com. on Vol. Enterprise, 1983-85; pres. Assn. Colls. and Univs., N.Y., 1984-86; chair Women's Coll. Coalition, 1983-85, U.S.-Can. Fulbright Com., 1990—; mem. Com. on Nat. Challenges in Higher Edn., 1986-88. Carnegie fellow Harvard U. 1977. Mem. Am. Coun. Edn. (chmn. com. on leadership devel. and acad. adminstrn. 1982-84), Mid. States Assn. Colls. and Schs.

(cons., chmn.). Home: 54 E Main St Canton NY 13617-1419 Office: St Lawrence U Office of the President Canton NY 13617

PETERSON, PAUL QUAYLE, retired university dean, physician; b. Marissa, Ill., June 30, 1912; s. Charles Logan and Phoebe (Lewis) P.; m. Kathryn Lentz, Aug. 1936; children—Philip Lewis, Frances Anne; m. Mildred Cook Allison, Dec. 7, 1957; foster children—Patricia Elaine Allison, Susan Claire Allison. B.S., U. Ill., 1933, M.D., 1937; M.P.H., U. Mich., 1946. Diplomate Am. Bd. Preventive Medicine (service mem., vice chmn. 1976—). Intern Bethesda Hosp., Cin., 1936-37; gen. resident Meml. Hosp., Lima, Ohio, 1937-38; gen. practice medicine McLeansboro, Ill., 1939-40; practice medicine specializing in preventive medicine, 1940-46; health officer Breckenridge, Meade and Hancock counties, Ky., 1940-41, Warren, Simpson and Allen counties, 1942-45; regional cons., div. local health Ky. Health Dept., 1946-47; chief bur. direct services, asst. to dir. Ohio Dept. Health, 1948-51; asst. prof. preventive medicine Ohio State U., 1948-51; chief health div. Mut. Security Mission to China, Taipei, Taiwan, 1952-53; chief health and sanitation div. USOM (asso. states Cambodia, Laos and Vietnam), 1954; chief program services, div. internat. health USPHS, Washington, 1955; chronic disease program USPHS, 1957; asst. dir. Nat. Inst. Allergy and Infectious Diseases, NIH, 1958-61; dep. chief div. pub. health methods Office Surgeon Gen., 1961-62, chief div., 1962-64; asst. surgeon gen. USPHS, 1964, asso. chief bur. state services (community health), 1964-67; dep. dir. Bur. Health Services, 1967-68; asso. adminstr. Health Services and Mental Health Adminstrn., 1968-70; dep. surgeon gen., 1970; dean Grad. Sch. Pub. Health, U. Ill., Chgo., 1971-82, dean emeritus, 1982—; dir. office rsch. Ctr. Study Patient Care, U. Ill. Med. Ctr., 1979-86; dir. Ill. Dept. Pub. Health, 1977-79, Am. Bur. Med. Aid to China; mem. residency rev. com. Liaison Com. Grad. Med. Edn., 1976—; cons. Ctr. for Health Services Research, 1982— mem. editorial bd. Pub. Health Service World, Mil. Medicine. Recipient Disting. Service award U. Ill. Alumni Assn., 1984. Fellow Am. Pub. Health Assn. (chmn. program area com. pub. health adminstrn.); mem. Am. Assn. Pub. Health Physicians (pres. 1975-76), AMA (intersplty. adv. bd. 1975-77), Assn. Schs. Pub. Health (exec. com. 1975—), Pub. Health Service Commd. Officers Assn. (sec. D.C. 1959), AAAS, Assn. Mil Surgeons, Am. Coll. Preventive Medicine (regent 1975—), Ill. Hosp. Assn. (exec. bd. 1974-77, cert. correctional health com. of profl. cert. bd. 1990), Nat. Inst. of Health Alumni Assn. bd. dirs., 1993—, Phi Beta Pi (pres. 1935), Delta Omega. Methodist. Home: 1600 N Oak St Arlington VA 22209-2750

PETERSON, PENELOPE LORAINE, education educator; b. Moline, Ill., Nov. 25, 1949; d. Leroy P.; m. W. Patrick Dickson; children: Andrew, Joshua, Elissa. BS, Iowa State U., 1971; MS, Stanford U., 1976, PhD, 1976. Asst. prof. dept. ednl. psychology U. Wis., Madison, 1976-80, assoc. prof., 1980-81, prof. ednl. psychology, 1982-85, Sears-Bascom Prof., 1985-87; prof. ednl. psychology and tchr. edn. Mich. State U., East Lansing, 1987—, co-dir. Inst. Rsch. on Teaching, 1987—, co- dir. Elem. Subjects Ctr., 1987-92, co-dir. Ednl. Policy Practice Study, 1992— Author chpts. to books; editor: Rev. Ednl. Rsch, 1984-90; contbr. articles to profl. jours. Recipient Palmer O. Johnson award Am. Edn. Rsch. Assn., 1980, Raymond B. Cattell Early Career award Am. Ednl. Rsch. Assn., 1986, Disting. Rsch. award Assn. Tchr. Edn., 1992. Fellow Am. Psychol. Soc. Office: Mich State U Coll Edn 349 Erickson Hall East Lansing MI 48824-1034

PETERSON, PETER G., investment banker; b. Kearney Nebr., June 5, 1926; s. George and Venetia P.; m. Sally H., May 1953 (div. 1979); children: John, Jim, David, Holly, Michael; m. Joan Ganz Cooney, Apr. 26, 1980. BS, Northwestern U., 1947; MBA, U. Chgo. 1951; PhD (hon.) Colgate U., George Washington U., Northwestern U., Georgetown U. Exec. v.p. Market Facts, Chgo., 1948-52; v.p. McCann Erickson, Chgo. 1952-58; pres. Bell and Howell, Chgo., 1958-71, exec. v.p. 1958-61, CEO, 1963-71; asst. to Pres. of U.S. for Internat. Econ. Affairs, Washington, 1961-63; sec. of commerce U.S. Govt., 1972-73; CEO, chmn. bd. Lehman Bros. and Lehman Bros., Kuhn, Loeb, Inc., N.Y.C., 1973-84; chmn. The Blackstone Group, 1985—; bd. dirs. Rockefeller Ctr. Properties, Inc., Sony Corp., Transtar Inc. Author: Facing Up: How to Rescue the Economy from Crushing Debt and Restore the American Dream; editor: Readings in Market Organization and Price Policies; co-author: On Borrowed Time: How The Growth In Entitlement Spending Threatens America's Future. founding mem. Bi-Partisan Budget Appeal; pres. The Concord Coalition; trustee Commn. for Econ. Devel., Mus. Modern Art, N.Y.C. Recipient Outstanding Service award, Phoenix House, N.Y.C., 1976, Stephen Wise award, Am. Jewish Congress, 1981, U. Chgo. Alumni medal, 1983, Man of Vision award, 1994, Nebraskalander award, 1994; named to Pres. Clinton's Bi-Partisan Comm. on Entitlement Refirm, 1994. Mem. Council Fgn. Relations (chmn. bd. 1985—), Inst. Internat. Econs. (chmn. bd.), Nat. Bur. Econ. Research (trustee), Japan Soc. Republican. Clubs: Maidstone (Easthampton, N.Y.); Chgo., River, Links (Chgo.); Augusta Nat.; Burning Tree (Washington), Atlantic. Home: 435 E 52nd St Apt 17G New York NY 10022-6445 Office: The Blackstone Group 345 Park Ave New York NY 10154-0004

PETERSON, PHILIP EVERETT, legal educator; b. Galena, Ill., July 10, 1922; s. Everett Marvin and Marie Isabelle (Gleason) P.; m. Jeanne Rosanna Payette, Nov. 17, 1947; children—Christine Marie, Barbara Ellen, Claudia Ann, Patricia Eileen, Eric Karl, Kurt Kevin. Student, Loras Coll., 1948; B.S., U. Ill., 1950, J.D., 1952; LL.M., Harvard, 1958. Bar: Ill. bar 1951, Idaho bar 1955, U.S. Supreme Ct. bar 1958. Practice in Urbana, Ill., 1951-52; mem. faculty U. Idaho Law Sch., 1952-88, prof. law, 1961—, dean, 1962-67; legal cons., 1955—. Served with AUS, 1942-48; lt. col. USAF Res. Decorated Purple Heart, D.F.C. with cluster, Air medal with 3 clusters. Mem. ABA, Ill. Bar Assn., Idaho Bar Assn., AAUP. Home: 318 5th St Lewiston ID 83501-2408

PETERSON, RALPH, financial executive; b. N.Y.C., Jan. 24, 1924; s. James and Mildred (Lebowitz) P.; m. Patricia Bloom, Mar. 18, 1951; children: Jeffrey, Stacey Peterson Evans, Beth Lisa. B.B.A., CCNY, 1948. CPA, N.Y. Sr. acct. S.D. Leidesdorf Co., N.Y.C., 1948-51; mgr. Peat, Marwick, Mitchell, N.Y.C., 1951-70; sr. v.p., treas. Warner Bros., Inc., N.Y.C., 1970—; v.p., treas. Warner Bros. Inc., Burbank, Calif., 1970—, exec. v.p., treas., 1987—; sr. v.p., treas., 1987-89, exec. v.p., 1989—, also bd. dirs., mem. exec. com. Bd. dirs. Arthritis Found., Los Angeles, 1981—. Served with USAF, 1943-46. Mem. Am. Inst. CPA's, N.Y. Soc. CPA's. Office: Warner Bros Inc 4000 Warner Blvd Burbank CA 91522-0001

PETERSON, RAYMOND A., paper company executive. With Kimberly-Clark Corp., 1958-71, Nationwide Paper, 1971-75, Alco Standard Corp., 1975; pres. Carpenter Offutt Paper Co., 1981-85, Paper Corp. Am., 1985-91; pres. Unisource Worldwide Inc., Wayne, Pa.; v.p. Can. divsn. Office: Unisource Worldwide Inc 825 Duportail Rd Wayne PA 19087*

PETERSON, RICHARD ELTON, publisher; b. Spokane, Wash., Apr. 26, 1941; s. Darrel Emil and Katherine (Millar) P.; m. Ruthanne Hawkins, Aug. 12, 1977; children—Scott Edward, Andrew Richard; stepchildren—Troy Donald Slocum, Sean James Slocum. B.S. in Edn., U. Mo., 1963; M.B.A., U. Chgo., 1975; postgrad., Stanford U. Tchr. high sch. math Brunswick, Mo.; tchr. Park Ridge, Ill., 1963-65; profl. baseball player N.Y. Mets., 1963-65; with Scott, Foresman & Co., 1965-93, sales rep., 1965-70, market rsch. profl., 1970-73; mktg. coord. Scott, Foresman & Co., Calif., 1973-77; regional v.p., mgr. ea. region Scott, Foresman & Co., Oakland, N.J., 1977-78; sr. v.p./mktg. Scott, Foresman & Co., Glenview, Ill., 1978-84, sr. v.p., gen. mgr. sch. div., 1984-88, pres., CEO, 1988-93, also bd. dirs.; group v.p. Harper/Collins Pub., 1992-93; bd. dirs. Can. Pub. Corp., 1988-92. Bd. dirs. Evanston Hosp. Corp., 1991—; bd. govs. Northwestern U. Libr., 1993—. Mem. Assn. Am. Pubs. (chmn. Calif. com. 1980-86, exec. com. sch. divsn. 1985-88, 90-93, chmn. exec. com. 1986-88), Western Golf Assn. (bd. dirs. 1987—). Home: 707 Edgemont Ln Park Ridge IL 60068-2652

PETERSON, RICHARD HAMLIN, utility executive, lawyer; b. Berkeley, Calif., May 6, 1914; s. Otto Wallace and Gladys (Grinstead) P.; m. Marianne Hammond, May 17, 1957; children: John, Stephen, Richard Hamlin. A.B., U. Calif.-Berkeley, 1935, J.D., 1940. Bar: Calif. 1941. Assoc. McCutchen, Olney, Mannon & Greene, Los Angeles, 1940-43, McCutchen, Thomas, Matthews, Griffiths & Greene, San Francisco, 1946-47; atty. law dept. Pacific Gas & Electric Co., San Francisco, 1947-54, asst. gen. counsel, 1954-55, gen. counsel, 1955-69, sr. v.p., gen. counsel, 1965-69, exec. v.p., 1969-72, vice chmn. bd., 1972-76, chmn. bd., 1976-79, past bd. dirs.; chmn. bd. Pacific

Gas Transmission Co., 1974-79; dir. ANGUS Chem. Co., ANGUS Petroleum Corp. Trustee San Francisco U. High Sch., Mus. Soc. of San Francisco; chmn. Yosemite Found. Served with USNR, 1943-46; lt. comdr. Res. Mem. ABA, Calif. Bar Assn., Bar Assn. San Francisco, U. Calif. Alumni Assn. (council), Phi Beta Kappa, Order of Coif, Delta Tau Delta, Phi Delta Phi. Clubs: Pacific Union, Bohemian, Commonwealth of California (bd. govs.). Office: Pacific Gas & Electric Co PO Box 770000 1 California St F31 San Francisco CA 94177

PETERSON, RICHARD WILLIAM, lawyer, magistrate judge; b. Council Bluffs, Iowa, Sept. 29, 1925; s. Henry K. and Laura May (Robinson) P.; m. Patricia Mae Fox, Aug. 14, 1949; children: Katherine Ilene Peterson Sherbondy, Jon Eric, Timothy Richard. BA, U. Iowa, 1949, JD with distinction, 1951; postgrad., U. Nebr.-Omaha, 1972-80, 86. Bar: Iowa 1951, U.S. Dist. Ct. (so. dist.) Iowa 1951, U.S. Supreme Ct. 1991. Pvt. practice law Council Bluffs 1951—; U.S. commr. U.S. Dist. Ct. (so. dist.) Iowa, 1958-70; part-time U.S. magistrate judge U.S. Dist. Ct. (so. dist.) Iowa, 1970—; mem. nat. faculty Fed. Jud. Ctr., Washington, 1972-82; emeritus trustee Children's Square, U.S.A.; verifying ofcl. Internat. Prisoner Transfer Treaties, Mexico City, 1977, La Paz, Bolivia, 1980, 81, Lima, Peru, 1981. Contbr. articles to legal publs. Bd. dirs. Pottawattamie County (Iowa) chpt. ARC, state fund chmn., 1957-58; state chmn. Radio Free Europe, 1960-61; dist. chmn. Trailblazer dist. Boy Scouts Am., 1952-55; mem. exec. coun. Mid-Am. Coun., 1976—. With inf. U.S. Army 1943-46. Decorated Purple Heart, Bronze Star; named Outstanding Young Man Council Bluffs C. of C., 1959. Fellow Am. Bar Found.; mem. ABA, Am. Judicature Soc., Iowa Bar Assn. (chmn. com. fed. practice 1978-80), Pottawattamie County Bar Assn. (pres. 1979-80), Fed. Bar Assn., Inter-Am. Bar Assn., Supreme Ct. Hist. Soc., Fed. Magistrate Judges Assn. (pres. 1978-79), Iowa Conf. Bar Assn. Pres. (pres. 1985-87), Hist. Soc. of U.S. Cts. Eighth Jud. Cir. (pres. 1989—), Kiwanis (pres. Council Bluffs club 1957), Masons, Phi Delta Phi, Delta Sigma Rho, Omicron Delta Kappa. Republican. Lutheran. Home: 1007 Arbor Ridge Cir Council Bluffs IA 51503-5000 Office: 406 Met Bank Bldg PO Box 1661 Council Bluffs IA 51503

PETERSON, ROBERT ALLEN, marketing educator; b. N.Y.C., Mar. 25, 1944; s. Robert A. and Carrol A. (Collins) P.; m. Diane S. Femrite, June 18, 1966; children: Jeffrey, Jennifer, Matthew. B.S., U. Minn., 1966, M.S., 1968, Ph.D., 1970. Asst. prof. mktg. U. Tex., Austin, 1970-73, assoc. prof., 1973-77, prof., 1977—, John T. Stuart chair, 1985—, chmn. dept. mktg. adminstrn., 1983-85; prin. Group Seven Assocs., Austin. Author: Marketing Research, 1982, 2d edit., 1986; co-author: Modern American Capitalism, 1990, Strategic Marketing, 7th edit., 1995; editor: Jour. Mktg. Rsch., 1985-88, Jour. Acad. Mktg. Sci., 1991-94; mem. editorial bd. Jour. Mktg., Bus. Rev., Internat. Mktg. Rev. Recipient rsch. award AMA, 1988, Charles Hurwitz fellow, 1983—. Fellow Southwestern Mktg. Assn. (pres. 1977-78), Am. Mktg. Assn. (v.p. 1980-81), Acad. Mktg. Sci. (bd. govs. 1982-86, chmn. 1994—, Am. Inst. Decision Scis. (dir. 1974-75). Lutheran. Office: Univ Texas Austin TX 78712

PETERSON, ROBERT AUSTIN, manufacturing company executive retired; b. Sioux City, Iowa, July 5, 1925; s. Austen W. and Marie (Mueller) P.; m. Carol May Hudy, May 17, 1952; children: Roberta, Richard., Bruce. B.S., U. Minn., 1946, B.B.A., 1947. Credit mgr. New Holland Machine div. Sperry Rand Corp., Mpls., 1952-61, Toro Co., Mpls., 1961-68; treas. Toro Co., 1968-70, v.p. and treas. of internat. fin., 1970-83; v.p. fin., pres. Toro Credit Co., 1983-93; bd. dirs. Tesco, South Miami, Fla., Wesco Turf, Sarasota, Fla., Toro Credit Co. Chmn. Prior Lake Spring Lake Watershed Dist., 1970-80; chmn., bd. dirs. Prior Lake Bd. Edn., 1965-71; chmn. Scott County Republican Party, 1969-70; bd. dirs. Scott Carver Mental Health Center, 1969-73, Minn. Watershed Assn., 1972-76. Served to ensign USNR, 1943-46. Mem. St. Joseph's Bay Country Club, Prior Lake Yacht Club (bd. dirs.). Office: 870 Como Ave Saint Paul MN 55103

PETERSON, ROBERT BYRON, petroleum company executive; b. Regina, Sask., Can. BSc in Chem. Engring., Queen's U., Kingston, Ont., Can., 1959, MSc in Chem. Engring., 1961. Various prodn. positions Imperial Oil Ltd. and affiliates, Can. and U.S., 1960-82; pres., chief exec. officer Esso Resources Can. Ltd., Calgary, Alta., Can., 1982-85; dir. Imperial Oil Ltd., Toronto, Ont., Can., 1984—; exec. v.p., chief operating officer Imperial Oil Ltd., Toronto, 1985-88, pres., COO, 1988-92, chmn., pres., CEO, 1992—; bd. dirs. Royal Bank Can., C.D. Howe Inst., Bus. Coun. Nat. Issues. Gov. Jr. Achievement Can.; chmn. The Conf. Bd. Can. Mem. Assn. Profl. Engrs. Geologists and Geophysicists of Alta. Office: Imperial Oil Ltd, 111 St Clair Ave W, Toronto, ON Canada M5W 1K3

PETERSON, ROBERT L., meat processing executive; b. Nebr., July 14, 1932; married; children: Mark R., Susan P. Student, U. Nebr., 1950. With Wilson & Co., Jim Boyle Order Buying Co.; cattle buyer R&C Packing Co., 1956-61; cattle buyer, plant mgr., v.p. carcass prodn. Iowa Beef Processors, 1961-69; exec. v.p. ops. Spencer Foods, 1969-71; founder, pres., chmn., chief exec. officer Madison (Nebr.) Foods, 1971-76; group v.p. carcass div. Iowa Beef Processors, Inc. (name now IBP, Inc.) div. Occidental Petroleum Corp., Dakota City, Nebr., 1976-77, pres., chief operating officer, 1977-80, chief exec. officer, 1980-81, co-chmn. bd. dirs., 1981-82, chmn., chief exec. officer, pres., 1981—, also dir.; exec. v.p., dir. Occidental Petroleum Corp., Los Angeles, 1982-87. Served with Q.M.C. U.S. Army, 1952-54. Mem. Sioux City Country Club. Office: IBP Inc PO Box 515 Dakota City NE 68731-0515*

PETERSON, ROBERT MARCELLUS, hospital and nursing home administrator; b. Mpls., Jan. 26, 1944; s. Robert and Mary Ann (Van Donsel) P.; m. Marlys Alberta Carlson (div. Dec. 1984); children: Mark, Annette, Robert, Christopher, Andrew, Philip, Matt; m. Teresa Sue Rabbers, Aug. 15, 1985; 1 child, William. BS, U. Minn., 1976; MS, U. Cin., 1978. Asst. adminstr. Community Mercy Hosp., Onamia, Minn., 1970-73; adminstr. Aitkin (Minn.) Community Hosp. and Nursing Ctr., 1973-81, Mesabi Med. Ctr., Hibbing, Minn., 1981-86; chief oper. officer St. Joseph Healthcare Systems, Albuquerque, 1986-90; adminstr. Bingham Meml. Hosp., Blackfoot, Idaho, 1990—. Bd. dirs. Econ. Devel. Corp., Onamia, 1971-72, Hibbing, 1982-84. With USN, 1961-68. Fellow Am. Coll. Healthcare Execs. (bd. regents com.); mem. Idaho Hosp. Assn. (chair devel. com. 1991—), Rotary Internat. (community involvement chair). Democrat. Roman Catholic. Avocations: horseback riding, camping, fishing. Home: 1041 Berrett Dr Blackfoot ID 83221-3602 Office: Bingham Meml Hosp 98 Poplar St Blackfoot ID 83221-1799

PETERSON, ROBIN TUCKER, marketing educator; b. Casper, Wyo., July 31, 1937; s. Walfred Arthur and Mary Lurene Peterson; m. Marjorie K. Greenwald, June 25, 1963; children: Timothy, Kimberly. BS, U. Wyo., 1959, MS in Bus., 1961; Ph.D., U. Wash., Seattle, 1967. Mem. faculty Idaho State U., Pocatello, 1963-73; prof. mktg., head mktg. dept. St. Cloud (Minn.) State U., 1973-76, N.Mex. State U., Las Cruces, 1976—; Fulbright lectr., Yugoslavia, 1973; vis. scholar Ea. Mont. State Coll., 1985; Sunwest Fin. Svcs. Disting. Centennial prof. N.Mex. State U., 1991, 92. Author: Marketing-A Contemporary Introduction, 1976, Forecasting, 1976, edit., 1983, Personal Selling, 1977, Marketing in Action, 1977, Lernbook Marketing, 1984, Marketing: Concepts and Decision Making, 1987, Principles of Marketing, 1989, Argentina, 1990, Managing the Distributor Sales Network, 1990, Business Forecasting, 1992, Getting New Products to Market Rapidly, 1994; exec. editor Bus. Forecaster, 1993-94; editor: Journal of Business and Entrepreneurship, 1994; also contbr. articles to profl. publs. Served with USAR, 1962-63. Mem. Am. Mktg. Assn., Sales and Mktg. Execs. Internat., Acad. Mktg. Sci. (pres. 1977-78, 80-82), Am. Arbitration Assn. (Outstanding Educators Am. award), S.W. Small Bus. Assn. (pres. 1983-84, Outstanding Mktg. Educators award), S.W. Mktg. Assn., Western Mktg. Educators, Las Cruces C. of C., Las Cruces Sales and Mktg. Club, Beta Gamma Sigma, Phi Kappa Psi, Alpha Kappa Psi, Alpha Mu Alpha. Republican. Presbyterian. Home: 4227 Winchester Rd Las Cruces NM 88001-7544 Office: Box 5280 New Mexico State U Las Cruces NM 88001

PETERSON, RODERICK WILLIAM, television writer, producer; b. Phoenix, July 7, 1921; s. Paul Culver and Elizabeth (Butler) P.; m. Jewell Nichols, Feb. 28, 1943 (div. 1972); children: Lisa Peterson Winslow, Sally Peterson Hinson; m. Claire Whitaker, Nov. 18, 1972. Student, Phoenix Community Coll., 1939-41; B.A., U. Ariz., 1949. Program dir., writer Sta.

KTAR, Phoenix, 1949-56; program dir. Sta. KGUN-TV, Tucson, 1956-57. Freelance network radio writer, NBC, CBS, Mut. Broadcasting System, freelance writer: (TV) Bonanza, Emergency, Black Saddle, Kilpatricks, Combat, The Deputy, Wonderful World of Disney, Laramie, (film) The Chartroose Caboose, 1959, (TV series) Laramie, 1960-64; writer, assoc. producer Walt Disney Prodns., 1965-75; writer, producer: The Waltons, 1977-79, exec. producer, 1980-81; writer, producer, MTM Studios, 1981-83, exec. supervising producer, writer Falcon Crest, Lorimar Prodns.-CBS, 1984-86; writer (with Claire Whitaker) Walton Thanksgiving Reunion, 1993. Served with USAAF, 1943-46, PTO. Mem. Writers Guild Am., Hollywood TV Acad., Am. Film Inst., ASCAP. Democrat.

PETERSON, RODNEY DELOS, mediator, forensic economist; b. Sioux Falls, S.D., Nov. 10, 1932; s. Severin Ingvald and Vera (Blow) P.; m. Evelyn Koubsky, Dec. 26, 1965; children: Douglas, Russell, Stuart. B.A., Huron (S.D.) Coll., 1958; M.S. in Econs, S.D. State U., 1959; Ph.D. in Econs. and Bus. Orgn, U. Nebr., 1964; J.D., U. Denver, 1982. Instr. U. Nebr., Lincoln, 1959-64; vis. asst. prof. agrl. econs. U. Nebr., summers 1964-66; instr. adult edn. U. Omaha, part-time 1963-64; asst. prof. econs. Cen. Wash. State U., Ellensburg, 1964-65; asst. prof., then assoc. prof. U. Idaho, Moscow, 1965-68; mem. faculty Colo. State U., Ft. Collins, 1968-91; prof. econs. Colo. State U., 1971-91; mediation officer, 1985-91; prof. emeritus Colo. State U., 1991; economist Fla. Dept. Commerce, 1991—; dir. Ctr. Econ. Edn. Colo. State U., 1976-77; vis. prof. Simon Fraser U., Vancouver, B.C., Can., 1974-75, univ. mediation officer, 1985-91. Author: Student Guide to Accompany Our Changing Economy, 1976, Economic Organization in Medical Equipment and Supply, 1973, Political Economy & American Capitalism, 1991; contbr. numerous articles to profl. jours. NSF fellow, summers 1971, 73, expert witness personal injury and antitrust cases. Mem. Am. Econ. Assn., Midwest Econs. Assn., Sigma Xi, Delta Sigma Pi, Beta Gamma Sigma, Omicron Delta Epsilon (regional dir. 1975-76). Home: 5433 Pinderton Way Tallahassee FL 32311-1412 Office: Fla Dept Commerce/BEA W Gaines St Tallahassee FL 32399

PETERSON, ROGER ERIC, hardware wholesale company executive; b. Chgo., Dec. 14, 1937; s. Erick Herman and Greta (Moren) P.; m. Joyce Marlene Holtz, Aug. 22, 1959; children: Stephen, Cindy, Linda, Kristin, Kathrin, Scott. BBA, U. Miami, 1960. Indsl. engring. supr. Montgomery Ward, Chgo., 1960-63; area mgr. J.C. Penney, Wauwatosa, Wis., 1963-67; dist. devel. mgr. Ben Franklin div. City Products, Des Plaines, Ill., 1967-72; exec. v.p. C.P. Products Corp., Elkhart, Ind., 1972-76; nat. distbn. mgr. Ace Hardware Corp., Oak Brook, Ill., 1976-82, v.p. ops., 1982-85, exec. v.p., 1985-86, pres., 1986—; pres., chief executive officer, 1990—; mem. Midwest adv. bd. Allendale Ins. Co., Providence, 1986-90; bd. dirs. Home Ctr. Inst. Bd. dirs. Center Inst., 1989. Mem. Nat. Wholesale Assn. (bd. dirs. 1990—), Nat. Assn. Wholesale Distributors (bd. dirs. 1990—), Am. Scandinavian Coun. (bd. dirs. 1989—), Elgin (Ill.) Country Club. Office: Ace Hardware Corp 2200 Kensington Ct Oak Brook IL 60521*

PETERSON, ROGER LYMAN, insurance company executive; b. Cumberland, Wis., Apr. 14, 1938; s. Oscar Adolph and Myrtle (Nelson) P.; children: Jeffrey, Scott, Robert Michael. BS in Econs., Ill. Inst. Tech., 1960. CPCU, CLU; cert. assoc. in risk mgmt.; cert. ins. counselor. Field rep. Sun Atlas, Chgo., 1961-64, Western Casualty & Surety, Champaign, 1964-67, Am. States Ins. Co., Champaign, 1967-73; field rep., v.p. Tyler, Fletcher, Fink, Peterson, Champaign, 1973-83; v.p. Ins. Risk Mgrs., Champaign, 1983-94, sr. v.p., 1994—; chmn. Artran Internat., Austin, Tex., 1980-95. Bd. dirs. YMCA, Champaign, 1979—. With USCG, 1960-68. Mem. CPCU Soc., CLU Soc., Champaign County Ind. Ins. Agts. Assn. (past pres.), Lincolnshire Fields Country Club (past pres.), Cert. Ins. Counselors Soc., Chgo. Dist. Golf Assn. (committeeman). Republican. Lutheran. Avocations: golf, basketball, bridge, reading. Home: 1702 Gentry Square Ln Champaign IL 61821-5957 Office: Ins Risk Mgrs Ltd 2507 S Neil St Champaign IL 61820-7713

PETERSON, ROGER TORY, ornithologist, artist; b. Jamestown, N.Y., Aug. 28, 1908; s. Charles Gustav and Henrietta (Bader) P.; m. Mildred Warner Washington, Dec. 19, 1936; m. Barbara Coulter, July 29, 1943; children: Tory, Lee; m. Virginia Westervelt, 1976. Student, Art Students League, 1927-28, NAD, 1929-31; DSc (hon.), Franklin and Marshall Coll., 1952, Ohio State U., 1962, Fairfield U., 1967, Allegheny Coll., 1967, Wesleyan U., 1970, Colby Coll., 1974, Gustavus Adolphus Coll., 1978, Conn. Coll., 1985; HHD (hon.), Hamilton Coll., 1976; LHD (hon.), Amherst Coll., 1977, Skidmore Coll., 1981, Yale U., 1986, So. Conn. State Coll., 1991; DFA (hon.), U. Hartford, 1981, SUNY, 1986, Middlebury Coll., 1986, Long Island U., 1987; DSc (hon.), U. Conn., 1987, Meml. U. Nfld., 1987, Bates Coll., 1991; DFA (hon.), MacMurray Coll., 1989. Decorative artist, 1926; instr. sci. and art River Sch., Brookline, Mass., 1931-34; mem. adminstrv. staff Nat. Audubon Soc.; charge ednl. activities; art editor Audubon mag., 1934-43; Audubon screen tour lectr., from 1946; art dir. Nat Wildlife Fedn.; founder Roger Tory Peterson Inst. Study Natural History, 1986—; distinguished scholar-in-residence Fallingwater-Western Pa. Conservancy, 1968; del. 11th Internat. Ornithol. Congress, Basel, Switzerland, 1954, 12th, Helsinki, 1958, 13th, Ithaca, N.Y., 1962, 14th, Oxford, Eng., 1966, 15th, The Hague, Netherlands, 1970, Internat. Bird Protection Conv., Tokyo, 1960, Cambridge, Eng., 1966; mem. Internat. Galapagos Sci. Project, 1964, USARP-Operation Deepfreeze, Antarctica, 1965; chmn. Am. sect. Internat. Bird Protection Com.; Hon. trustee Uganda (Africa) Nat. Parks; sec. Nat. Audubon Soc., 1960-64; mem. council Cornell Lab. Ornithology; bd. dirs. World Wildlife Fund, 1962-76; 1st v.p. Am. Ornithologists Union, 1962-63. Engaged in bird painting and illustration bird books, 1934—; Author: Field Guide to the Birds, 1934, Junior Book of Birds, 1939, A Field Guide to Western Birds, 1941, Birds Over America, 1948, How to Know the Birds, 1949, Wildlife in Color, 1951, A Bird-Watchers Anthology, 1957, A Field Guide to the Birds of Texas, 1959, Penguins, 1979; illustrator: Birds of South Carolina, 1949, Birds of Newfoundland, 1951, Arizona and Its Bird Life, 1952, Birds of Nova Scotia, 1961, Birds of Colorado, 1965, ltd. edit. prints of birds, Mill Pond Press, 1974; author: The Field Guide Art of Roger Tory Peterson, 1990; co-author: The Audubon Guide to Attracting Birds, 1941, Field Guide to Birds of Europe, 1953, Wild America, 1955, The World of Birds, 1964, The Birds, 1963, Field Guide to Wildflowers, 1968, Field Guide to Birds of Mexico, 1973, Peterson First Guide to Birds, 1986, Peterson First Guide to Wildflowers, 1986, Save the Birds, 1989; editor: American Naturalist series, 1965—, Field Guide to Pacific Coast Fishes, 1983, Field Guide to Beetles, 1983, Field Guide to Moths of Eastern North America, 1984, Field Guide to Southwestern and Texas Wildflowers, 1984, Field Guide to Atlantic Coast Fishes, 1986, Field Guide to Western Butterflies, 1986, Filde Guide to Mushrooms, 1987, Field Guide to Hawks, 1987, Field Guide to Seashores, 1988, Field Guide to Eastern Forests, 1988, Field Guide to Birding by Ear, 1989, Field Guide to Advanced Birding, 1990, Field Guide to Medicinal Plants, 1990 (also illustrator), Field Guide to Birding by Ear: Western, 1990, Field Guide to Freshwater Fishes, 1991; contbr. articles to natural history and popular publs.; lectr. in field. Del. 19th Internat. Ornithological Congress, Quebec, 1986. Served with C.E. U.S. Army, 1943-45. Recipient Brewster Meml. medal Am. Ornithologists Union, 1944; John Burroughs medal exemplary nature writing, 1950; Geoffrey St. Hilaire gold medal French Natural History Soc., 1958; gold medal N.Y. Zool. Soc., 1961; Arthur A. Allen medal Lab. Ornithology, 1967; White Meml. Found. Conservation award, 1968; Gold medal Safari Club Phila., 1968; Paul Bartsch award Audubon Naturalist Soc., 1969; Frances Hutchinson award Garden Club Am., 1970; Gold medal N.J. Garden Club, 1970; Gold medal World Wildlife Fund, 1972; Joseph Wood Krutch medal, 1973; Explorers Club medal, 1974; Tchr. of Year award, 1974; Distinguished Pub. Service award Conn. Bar Assn., 1974; Cosmos Club award, 1976; Linné Gold medal Royal Swedish Acad. Scis., 1976; Green World award N.Y. Bot. Garden, 1976; Sarah Joseph Hale award Richards Library, 1977; Master Bird Artist medal Leigh Yankee Mus., 1978; Presdl. Medal of Freedom, 1980, Gold medal Phila. Acad. Natural Scis., 1980, Ludlow Griscom award Am. Birding Assn., 1980, Smithsonian medal, 1984, Roger Tory Peterson award Thames Sci. Ctr., 1985—, Eisenmann medal Linnaean Soc., 1986, award of Merit Chgo. Field Mus. Natural History, 1986, Disting. Community Citizen award U. Conn. ALumni Assn., 1986, N.Y. State Legis. award, 1987; named Swedish-Am. of 1977, Vasa Order of Am.; officer Order of Golden Ark Holland, 1978; Conn. Citizen of Yr., 1986, hon. pres. Internat. Council Bird Preservation, 1986; Silver Buffalo award Boy Scouts Am., 1986; Linné Davenport Coll., Yale, 1966—; recipient award of merit and naming pf owl, Otis petersonii, Field Mus. Nat. History, Chgo., 1986. Fellow AAAS, N.Y. Zool.

Soc., Am. Ornithologists Union, Linnaean Soc. N.Y. (hon.), London Zool. Soc. (hon.); mem. Nat. Audubon Soc. (life; dir. 1958-60, 65-67, Audubon medal 1971, spl. cons. 1972—), Soc. Wildlife Artists (Eng.) (v.p.), Wilson Ornithol. Soc. (life pres. 1964-65), Brit. Ornithologists Union (hon.), Cooper Ornithol. Soc., Nat. Assn. Biology Tchrs. (hon.). Clubs: Nuttall (Cambridge, Mass.); Cosmos, Biologists Field (Washington); Century Assn., Explorers (N.Y.C.); Intrepids (pres.). Office: care Houghton-Mifflin Co 2 Park St Boston MA 02108-4894*

PETERSON, ROLAND OSCAR, retired electronics company executive; b. Bklyn., Jan. 18, 1932; s. Oscar Gustaf and Klara Ingegerd (Lindau) P.; m. Agnes Frances Walsh, Sept. 12, 1953; children: Joan, Lauren, Paul, Michael. BEE, Poly. Inst. N.Y., 1953, MEE, 1954. Registered profl. engr., N.Y. Research fellow Microwave Research Inst., Bklyn., 1953-54; sr. engr. Sperry Gyroscope Co., Great Neck, N.Y., 1956-60; with Litton Industries, Inc., Woodland Hills, Calif., 1961—; v.p. advanced systems engring. Guidance and Control Systems div., Litton Industries, Inc., Woodland Hills, Calif., 1973-76; v.p. bus. devel. Guidance and Control Systems div., Litton Industries Inc., Woodland Hills, Calif., 1976-77, pres., 1977-83; v.p. Litton Industries, Inc., 1979-83; sr. v.p., group exec. Litton Industries, Inc., Beverly Hills, Calif., 1983-88, pres., chief operating officer, 1988-90, sr. v.p., group exec., chief scientist, 1990-92; retired, 1992. Regional chmn. Los Angeles United Way campaign, 1985-86. Served to 1st lt. U.S. Army, 1954-56. Recipient Disting. Alumni award Poly. Inst. N.Y., 1986. Mem. Am. Electronics Assn., Inst. Navigation (western regional v.p. 1975-76, Hays award 1982). Roman Catholic. Avocations: skiing, tennis.

PETERSON, RUDOLPH A., banker; b. Svenljunga, Sweden, Dec. 6, 1904; s. Aaron and Anna (Johannson) P.; m. Barbara Welser Lindsay, Dec. 25, 1962; children: Linnea Peterson Bennett, R. Price; stepchildren: Robert I. Lindsay, Lorna Lindsay, Anne Lindsay, Margaret Lindsay. B.S. in Commerce, U. Calif., 1925, LL.D., 1968; L.H.D., U. Redlands, 1967. With Comml. Credit Co., 1925-36; successively asst. mgr. Comml. Credit Co., San Francisco; v.p., gen. mgr. Comml. Credit Co., Mexico City; div. operations mgr. Comml. Credit Co., Chgo.; dist. mgr. Bank Am. Nat Trust & Savs. Assn., Fresno, Calif., 1936-41; v.p. Bank Am. Nat. Trust & Savs. Assn., San Francisco, 1941-46; vice chmn. bd Bank Am. Nat. Trust & Savs. Assn. 1961-63, pres., CEO, 1963-70, chmn. exec. com., 1970-75, also dir., 1961—; pres., chief exec. officer Allied Bldg. Credits, 1946-52; v.p. Transam. Corp., San Francisco, 1952-55; pres., chief exec. officer Bank of Hawaii, Honolulu, 1956-61; pres., chief exec. officer BankAm. Corp., San Francisco, 1968-70, chmn. exec. com., 1970-76, also dir., 1968—; administr. UN Devel. Programme, 1972-76; bd. dirs. Alza Corp., Mcpl. Fund for Calif. Investors, Inc., Asia Found.; chmn. Euro Can. Bank, 1982-94; administr. UN Devel. Programme, 1972-76. Mem. adv. coun. Calif. Acad. Scis. Decorated Grand Cross of Civil Merit Spain; Order of Merit Italy; named Swedish-Am. of Year Vasa Order, 1965; U. Calif. Alumnus of Year, 1968; recipient Capt. Robert Dollar Meml. award for contbn. to advancement Am. fgn. trade, 1970, Chancellor's award U. Calif., 1992. Clubs: Bohemian (San Francisco), Pacific-Union (San Francisco), Villa Taverna (San Francisco). Home: 86 Sea View Ave Piedmont CA 94611-3519 Office: Bank Am Ctr 555 California St Ste 500 San Francisco CA 94104

PETERSON, RUSSELL WILBUR, former association executive, former state governor; b. Portage, Wis., Oct. 3, 1916; s. John Anton and Emma (Anthony) P.; m. E. Lillian Turner, June 30, 1937(dec. Apr. 28, 1994); children: Russell Glen, Peter Jon, Kristin, Elin. B.S., U. Wis., 1938, Ph.D., 1942, LL.D. (hon.), 1984; D.Sc. (hon.), Williams Coll., 1975, Butler U., Springfield Coll., Stevens Inst. Tech., 1979, Gettysburg Coll., 1980, Alma Coll., 1981, Ohio State U., SUNY-Syracuse, Northland Coll., Fairleigh Dickinson U., 1981; LL.D. (hon.), Monmouth Coll., 1982, Salisbury State U., 1988; D of Humane Letters, Meadville-Lombard Theol. Sch., 1992. With E. I. DuPont de Nemours & Co., Inc., 1942-69, research dir. textile fibers dept., 1954-55, 56-59, merchandising mgr. textile fibers, 1955-56, dir. new products div. textile fibers, 1959-62, dir. research and devel. div. devel. dept., 1963-69; bd. dirs. Textile Research Inst., Princeton, N.J., 1956-63, chmn. exec. com., 1959-61, chmn. bd. dirs., 1961-63, fellow, 1969; gov. of Del., 1969-73; chmn. exec. com. Nat. Commn. Critical Choices for Am., 1973; chmn. U.S. Council on Environ. Quality, 1973-76; pres. New Directions, 1976-77, Nat. Audubon Soc., 1979-85; mem. Nat. Commn. Critical Choices for Am., 1973-74; dir. Office Tech. Assessment, U.S. Congress, 1978-79; regional v.p. Nat. Mcpl. League, 1968-78; chmn. Edn. Commn. States, 1970; chmn. com. nuclear energy and space tech. So. Govs. Conf., 1970-71; chmn. Nat. Adv. Commn. on Criminal Justice Standards and Goals, 1971-73; chmn. com. law enforcement, justice and pub. safety Nat. Govs. Conf., 1970-73; v.p. Council State Govts., 1970-71; chmn. adv. bd. Solar Energy Research Inst., 1979-83; vis prof. Dartmouth Coll., 1985, Carleton Coll., 1986, U. Wis.-Madison, 1987; chmn. Centennial Internat. Symposium, Nat. Geog. Soc., 1986-88. Chmn. Del. River Basin Commn., 1971-72; founding chmn. Bio-Energy Coun., 1976-78; bd. dirs. World Wildlife Fund, 1976-82; bd. dirs. Population Action Internat., 1973—; Alliance to Save Energy, 1979-93; bd. dirs. Global Tomorrow Coalition, 1981-91, chmn. 1981-87; regional councillor Internat. Union Conservation Nature and Natural Resources, 1981-88, v.p., 1984-88; mem. Pres.'s Commn. on Accident at Three Mile Island, 1979; pres. Internat. Coun. Bird Preservation, 1982-90; chmn. Ctr. on Consequences of Nuclear War, 1983-87; vice chmn. Better World Soc., 1985-90, pres., 1985-87; vis. com. John F. Kennedy Sch. Govt., 1979-85; Goodwill amb. UN Environ. Program, 1984—, mem. world environ. prize com., 1989—; mem. Gov. Cuomo's Environ. Adv. Bd., 1985-94; mem. adv. bd. Pace U. Sch. Law, 1988—, Earth Island Inst., 1988—; chmn. bd. Earth Lobby, 1992—; co-chmn. gov.'stask force on rejuvenating Wilmington waterfront, 1992—. Decorated Order of Golden Ark (The Netherlands); recipient Ann. award NCCJ, 1966, Gold medal World Wildlife Fund, 1971, Ann. award Comml. Devel. Assn., 1971, Gold Plate award Nat. Acad. Achievement, 1971, Parsons award Am. Chem. Soc., 1974, Audubon award Nat. Audubon Soc., 1977, Proctor prize Sigma Xi, 1978, Frances K. Hutchinson medal Garden Club Am., 1980, Robert Marshall award Wilderness Soc., 1984, Nat. Conservation medal DAR, 1989, Human and Civil Rights award Del. Human Rights Commn., 1989, Environ. Law Inst. award, 1990, Ann. award Am. Civil Liberties Found. Del., 1992, Lawrence Solid Waste award Assn. N.Am., 1993, Kiwanis Community Svc. award, 1993, Lifetime Achievement award Global Tomorrow Coalition, 1994; named Conservationist of Yr., Nat. Wildlife Fedn., 1972, Swedish-Am. of Yr., 1982. Hon. fellow Am. Inst. Chemists, AAAS (past bd. dirs.); mem. Am. Ornithologists' Union, Linnaean Soc., Fedn. Am. Scientists, Am. Chem. Soc., Del. Acad. Sci., U.S. Assn. for Club of Rome, Cosmos Club, Phi Beta Kappa, Sigma Xi (Proctor prize 1978), Phi Lambda Upsilon, Phi Kappa Phi. Unitarian. Address: 1613 N Broom St Wilmington DE 19806-3009

PETERSON, SHIRLEY D., federal agency administrator; b. Holly, Colo., Sept. 3, 1941; married; 2 children. AB, Bryn Mawr Coll., 1963; LLB, NYU, 1967. Assoc. Steptoe and Johnson, from 1969, ptnr., from 1978; asst. atty. gen. tax div. Dept. Justice, Washington; mem. asst. atty. gen.'s adv. com. on tax litigation, 1982-87; commr. IRS, Washington, 1992—. Fellow Am. Coll. Probate Counsel; mem. ABA. Home: Bethesda MD Office: IRS 1111 Constitution Ave NW Washington DC 20224

PETERSON, SKIP (ORLEY R. PETERSON, III), newspaper photographer; b. Dayton, Ohio, July 6, 1951; s. Orley Ray and Helen Louise (Stafford) P.; m. Jennifer Susan Hinders, Sept. 22, 1990; children from previous marriage: Meredith, Sam, Elizabeth; 1 stepchild, Erin. BS in Journalism, Ohio U., 1973. Staff photographer Dayton Daily News, 1973-82, chief photographer, 1982—; part-time faculty mem. U. Dayton. Contbr. photographs to mags. including Life, Time, Newsweek, Sports Illustrated, also book Photojournalism. Judge ann. contests for White House News Photographers, Ind. News Photographers Assn., Mich. Press Photographers Assn., Ky. News Photographers Assn., Soc. Profl. Journalists. Recipient awards Soc. Profl. Journalists, 1st Place Sports Feature award Pictures of Yr. Competition, 1985, Robert Carson award for outstanding contbn. to photojournalism in Ohio, Ohio Understanding award for documentary. Mem. Ohio News Photographers Assn. (chmn. bd. dirs., past pres., awards), Nat. Press Photographers Assn. (past regional dir., exec. com. bd. rep., awards). Methodist. Avocations: restoring British sports cars, golf, auto racing. Home: 440 Wing View Ln Kettering OH 45429 Office: Dayton Daily News 45 S Ludlow St Dayton OH 45402

PETERSON, SOPHIA, international studies educator; b. Astoria, N.Y., Nov. 24, 1929; d. George Loizos and Caroline (Hofstetter) Yimoyines; m. Virgil Allison Peterson, Dec. 28, 1951; children: Mark Jeffrey, Lynn Marie. BA, Wellesley (Mass.) Coll., 1951; MA, UCLA, 1956, PhD, 1969. Instr. Miami U., Oxford, Ohio, 1961-63; with W.va. U., Morgantown, 1966—, assoc. prof., 1972-79, prof., 1979—, dir. internat. studies maj., 1980-92; dir. W.Va. Consortium for Faculty & Course Devel. in Internat. Studies, Morgantown, 1980—. Author: monograph Monograph Series in World Affairs, 1979. Recipient gold medal semi-finalist CASE Prof. of Yr. award Coun. for Advancement and Support of Edn., 1987, Outstanding Tchr. award W.Va. U., W.Va. U. Coll. Arts and Scis., 1988, finalist Prof. of Yr. award W.Va. Faculty Merit Found., 1991. Mem. Internat. Studies Assn. (v.p. Mid-Atlantic chpt. 1978-86), W.Va. Polit. Sci. Assn. (pres. 1984-85), AAAUP (pres. W.Va. U. chpt. 1976-78). Democrat. Avocation: sailing. Home: 849 Vandalia Dr Morgantown WV 26505-6247 Office: WVa U Dept Polit Sci Morgantown WV 26506

PETERSON, STEVEN H., school system administrator. Supt. Washington County Sch. Dist., St. George, Utah. State finalist Nat. Supt. Yr., 1993. Office: Washington County Sch Dist 189 W Tabernacle St Saint George UT 84770-3338

PETERSON, T. ROGER, engineering company executive. MS, U. Ill., 1956. Advanced through grades to col. U.S. Army, 1953-79; pres., CEO Booker Assoc. Inc., Saint Louis, 1979—. office: Booker Associates Inc 1139 Olive St Saint Louis MO 63101-1946*

PETERSON, THEODORE BERNARD, retired journalism educator; b. Albert Lea, Minn., June 8, 1918; s. Theodore B. and Emilie (Jensen) P.; m. Helen M. Clegg, Sept. 13, 1946; children: Thane Eric, Kristin, Megan, Daniel Alan. B.A., U. Minn., 1941; M.S., Kans. State Coll., 1948; Ph.D., U. Ill., 1955. Instr., then asst. prof. journalism Kans. State Coll., 1945-48, head coll. news bur., 1945-47; instr. journalism U. Ill., 1948-55, assoc. prof., 1955-57, prof., 1957-87; dean U. Ill. (Coll. Communications), 1957-79; judge Nat. Mag. Awards, 1967-88. Author: Writing Nonfiction for Magazines, 1949, Magazines in the Twentieth Century, 1956, rev., 1964, (with F.S. Siebert, Wilbur Schramm) Four Theories of the Press, 1956, (with J.W. Jensen, Wm. L. Rivers) The Mass Media in Modern Society, 1965, rev., 1971. Recipient award for distinguished research journalism Sigma Delta Chi, Kappa Tau Alpha, 1956, Outstanding Achievement award U. Minn., 1973, Outstanding Undergraduate Teaching award U. Ill., 1987. Mem. Assn. Edn. Journalism (1st v.p. 1962, pres. 1963), Am. Council on Edn. Journalism (accrediting com. 1961-70, 72-81), Am. Assn. Schs. and Depts. Journalism (pres. 1965), Kappa Tau Alpha, Phi Kappa Phi. Home: 103 E George Huff Dr Urbana IL 61801-5807

PETERSON, TRUDY HUSKAMP, national archivist; b. Estherville, Iowa, Jan. 25, 1945. BS, Iowa State U., 1967; MA, U. Iowa, 1972, PhD, 1975. Various positions Nat. Archives, Washington, 1968-87, asst. archivist, 1987-93, dep. archivist of U.S., 1993—, acting archivist, 1993-95; Fulbright lectr. in Am. studies, 1983-84; commr. U.S.-Russia Joint Commn. on MIA/POWs, 1992—; sec. Internat. Conf. on Round Table on Archives, 1992-93, pres., 1993—. Author: Agricultural Exports, Farm Income and the Eisenhower Administration, 1979, Basic Archival Workshop Exercises, 1982, Archives and Manuscripts: Law, 1985; editor: Farmers, Bureaucrats and Middlemen: Historical Perspectives on American Agriculture, 1980; mem. editl. bd. The Am. Archivist, 1978-81; contbr. articles to profl. jours. Pres. Capitol Hill Restoration Soc., 1987-88. Fellow Soc. Am. Archivists (mem. coun. 1984-87, pres. 1990-91, held various offices, Gondos Meml. award 1973, Fellows Posner prize 1987); mem. Agrl. History Soc. (mem. exec. com. 1982-85, pres 1988-89), Soc. History in Fed. Govt. (mem. exec. com. 1987-89). Office: Nat Archives & Records Adminstrn 8th & Pennsylvania Ave NW Washington DC 20408

PETERSON, VICTOR LOWELL, aerospace engineer, management consultant; b. Saskatoon, Sask., Can., June 11, 1934; came to U.S., 1937; s. Edwin Galladet and Ruth Mildred (McKeeby) P.; m. Jacqueline Dianne Hubbard, Dec. 21, 1955; children: Linda Kay Peterson Landrith, Janet Gale, Victor Craig. BS in Aero. Engring., Oreg. State U., 1956; MS in Aerospace Engring., Stanford U., 1964; MS in Mgmt., MIT, 1973. Rsch. scientist NASA-Ames Rsch. Ctr., Moffett Field, Calif., 1956-68, asst. chief hypersonic aerodyns., 1968-71, chief aerodyn. br., 1971-74, chief thermo and gas dynamics div., 1974-84, dir. aerophysics, 1984-90, dep. dir., 1990-94; pvt. mgmt. cons., 1994—; mem. nat. adv. bd. U. Tenn. Space Inst., Tullahoma, 1984-94. Contbr. numerous articles to profl. jours. Treas. Woodland Acres Homeowners Assn., Los Altos, Calif., 1978—. Capt. USAF, 1957-60. Recipient medal for outstanding leadership NASA, 1982; Alfred P. Sloan fellow MIT, 1972-73. Fellow AIAA. Republican. Methodist. Achievements include development of numerical aerodynamic simulation system for aerospace, of method for reconstructing planetary atmosphere structure from accelerations of body entering atmosphere, of theory for motions of tumbling bodies entering planetary atmospheres. Home: 484 Aspen Way Los Altos CA 94024-7126

PETERSON, WALLACE CARROLL, SR., economics educator; b. Omaha, Mar. 28, 1921; s. Fred Nels and Grace (Brown) P.; m. Eunice V. Peterson, Aug. 16, 1944 (dec. Nov. 24, 1985); children: Wallace Carroll Jr., Shelley Lorraine; m. Bonnie B. Watson, Nov. 11, 1988. Student, U. Omaha, 1939-40, U. Mo., 1940-42; BA in Econs. and European History, U. Nebr., 1947, MA in Econs. and European History, 1948, PhD in Econs. and European History, 1953; postgrad., Handelshochschule, St. Gallen, Switzerland, 1948-49, U. Minn., 1951, London Sch. Econs. and Polit. Sci., 1952. Reporter Lincoln (Nebr.) Jour., 1946; instr. econs. U. Nebr., Lincoln, 1951-54, asst. prof., 1954-57, assoc. prof., 1957-61, prof., 1962—, chmn. dept. econs., 1965-75, George Holmes prof. econs., 1966-92; George Holmes prof. econs. emeritus, 1992—; v.p. faculty senate U. Nebr., Lincoln, 1972-73, pres. faculty senate, 1973-74; S.J. Hall disting. vis. prof. U. Nev., Las Vegas, 1983-84. Author: The Welfare State in France, 1960, Elements of Economics, 1973, Our Overloaded Economy: Inflation, Unemployment and the Crisi in American Capitalism, 1982, Market Power and the Economy, 1988, Transfer Spending, Taxes and the American Welfare State, 1991, Income, Employment and Economic Growth, 7th edit., 1992, Silent Depression: The Fate of the American Dream, 1994; contbr. articles to profl. jours. and columns to newspapers. Mem. Nebr. Dem. Cen. Com., 1968-74, vice-chmn., chmn. Nebr. Polit. Accountability and Disclosure Commn., 1977-80; chmn. Nebr. Coun. Econ. Edn., 1976-77. Capt. USAAF, 1942-46. Recipient Chmapion Media award for Econ. Understanding, 1981; Fulbright fellow, 1957-58, 64-65; Mid-Am. State Univs. honor scholar, 1982-83. Mem. ACLU, AAUP (pres. Nebr. 1963-64, nat. coun.), Assn. for Evolutionary Econs. (pres. 1976, Veblen-Commons award 1991), Am. Econs. Assn., Midwest Econs. Assn. (pres. 1968-69), Mo. Valley Econ. Assn. (pres. 1989), Assn. Social Econs. (pres. 1992, Thomas F. Devine award 1995), Fedn. Am. Scientists. Home: 4549 South St Lincoln NE 68506-1253 Office: U Nebr Dept Econs CBA Lincoln NE 68588-0489

PETERSON, WALTER FRITIOF, academic administrator; b. Idaho Falls, Idaho, July 15, 1920; s. Walter Fritiof and Florence (Danielson) P.; m. Barbara Mae Kempe, Jan. 13, 1946; children: Walter Fritiof III, Daniel John. BA, State U. Iowa, 1942, MA, 1948, PhD, 1951; HHD (hon.), Loras Coll., 1983; LHD (hon.), Clarke Coll., 1991. Instr. State U. Iowa, 1949-51, Buena Vista Coll., 1951-52; asst. prof. history, chmn. dept. history Milw. Downer Coll., 1952-57, assoc. prof. history, chmn. social sci. div., 1957-64; assoc. prof. history Lawrence U., 1964-67; prof. history, Alice G. Chapman libr. Lawrence U., 1967-70; pres. U. Dubuque, 1970-90, chancellor, 1990—; regional tng. officer Peace Corps, 1965-68; cons. history Allis-Chalmers Mfg. Co., 1959—, Home Mut. Ins. Co., 1968—, Wm. C. Brown Pub. Co., 1981—; bd. dirs. Editor: Transactions of Wis. Acad. Scis., Arts and Letters, 1965-72, The Allis-Chalmers Corporation: An Industrial History, 1977, A History of the Wm. C. Brown Companies, 1994. Advisor Templeton Prize for Progress in Religion, 1986-91; bd. dirs. Finley Hosp., pres., 1983-84; chmn. Finley Health Found., 1986—; bd. dirs. Dubuque Symphony Orch., Dubuque Art Assn., Jr. Achievement, Nat. Rivers Hall of Fame, 1984; chmn. Iowa Assn. Coll. and Univ. Pres., 1975-76; chmn. Iowa Coll. Found., 1982-83. With USAAF, 1942-45, PTO. Recipient Dubuque Citizen award, 1990, Disting. Civic Svc. award, 1991; named to Dubuque Bus. Hall of Fame, 1990. Mem. Iowa Assn. Ind. Colls. and Univs. (chmn.

1988-89), Dubuque County Hist. Soc. (bd. dirs.), Phi Alpha Theta, Kappa Delta Pi, Phi Delta Kappa. Office: U Dubuque Office of Chancellor 2000 University Ave Dubuque IA 52001-5050

PETERSON, WAYNE TURNER, composer, pianist; b. Albert Sea, Minn., Sept. 3, 1927; s. Leslie Jules and Irma Thelma (Turner) P.; m. Harriet Christiansen, 1948 (div. 1978); children: Alan, Craig, Drew, Grant. BA, U. Minn., 1951, MA, 1953; postgrad., Royal Acad. Music, London, 1953-54. Instr. music U. Minn., 1955-59; asst. prof. music Chico (Calif.) State U., 1959-60; prof. music San Francisco State U., 1960—; vis. prof. composition U. Ind., Bloomington, 1992; artist in residence Briarcombe Found., Bolinas, Calif., 1983; vis. artist Am. Acad. in Rome, 1990. Composer: Allegro for String Quartet, 1952, Introduction and Allegro, 1953, Free Variations for Orch., 1954-58, Can Death Be Sleep, 1955, Earth, Sweet Earth, 1956, (cappella chorus) Cape Ann, 1957, Three Songs for Soprano and Piano, 1957, (cappella chorus) Psalm 56, 1959, Exaltation, Dithyramb and Caprice, 1959-60, (cappella chorus) An e e Cummings Triptych, 1962, Tangents for flute, clarinet, horn and violin, 1963, An e e Cummings Cantata, 1964, Fantasy Concertante for violin and piano, 1965, Reflections, 1965, Metamorphosis for Wind Quintet, 1967, Phantasmagoria for flute, clarinet, double bass, 1968, Cataclysms, 1968, Clusters and Fragments for string orch., 1969, Ceremony After a Fire Raid, 1969, Sinfonia and Canticle for baritone voice and organ, 1969, Capriccio for Flute and Piano, 1973, Transformations for String Quartet, 1974, Trialogue for violin, cello and piano, 1975, Diatribe for violin and piano, 1975, Encounters, 1976, Rhapsody for Cello and Piano, 1976, An Interrupted Serenade for flute, harp and cello, 1978, Dark Reflections (cycle of four songs for high voice, violin and piano), 1980, Mallets Aforethought (symphony for percussion ensemble), 1981, Sextet for flute, clarinet, percussion, harp, violin and cello, 1982, Doubles for 2 flutes and 2 clarinets, 1982, Debussy Song Cycle, 1983, String Quartet, 1983-84, Ariadne's Thread for harp, flute, clarinet, horn, percussion and violin, 1985, Transformations for chamber orch., 1986, Duo for viola and cello, 1986-87, Trilogy for Orch., 1987, Labyrinth for flute, clarinet, violin and piano, 1987, The Widening Gyre for full orch., 1991, The Face of the Night, the Heart of the Dark for full orch., 1991 (Pulitzer prize for music 1992), Mallets Aforethought, 1991, String Quartet # 2, 1992, Diptych, 1992, Janus, 1993, Duo for Violin and Piano, 1993, And the Winds Shall Blow, a fantasy for saxophone quartet, symphony winds, brass and percussion, 1994; recs. with Mercury Records, Desto Records, Arch Records, Grenadilla Records, Koch Internat.; Recordings commd. Am. Music Ctr., 1959, Virtuosi of San Francisco, 1968, Unitarian Ch., 1969, Paul Mason, Inc., 1974, 87, NEA Consortium Commn., 1982, Charles Wuorinen and San Francisco Symphony, 1985, Am. Composers Symphony, Inc., 1987, San Francisco Symphony, 1991, Gerbode Found., 1990, Koussevitzky Found., 1990, Fromm Music Found., 1992, Philharmonic Orch. of Freiburg in Breisgau, Germany, 1993. Recipient 11th Ann. Norman Fromm Composer's award, 1982, Meritorious Svc. award Calif. State U. System, 1984, Top award Am. Harp Soc., 1985, Composer's award Am. Acad. and Inst. Arts and Letters, 1986, Pulitzer Prize for music, 1992; Fulbright scholar, Royal Acad. Music, 1953-54; NEA grantee, 1976, Guggenheim fellow, 1989-90, Djerassi Found. fellow, 1989-91. Home: 140 S Lake Merced Hills San Francisco CA 94132-2935*

PETERSON, WILLARD JAMES, Chinese history educator; b. Oak Park, Aug. 1, 1938; s. Otto Stewart and Catherine (Esin) P.; m. Toby Black, Aug 27, 1960. BA, U. Rochester, 1960; MA, U. London, 1964; PhD; Harvard U., 1970. Asst. prof. Dartmouth Coll., Hanover, N.H., 1970-71; prof. East Asian Studies and History Princeton (N.J.) U., 1971—. Author: Bitter Gourd, 1979, Power of Culture, 1994. Office: Dept of East Asian Studies & Hist Princeton U. Princeton NJ 08544

PETERSON, WILLIAM E., fire chief, consultant; b. Evergreen Park, Ill., July 28, 1946; s. William M. and Louise V. (Schneider) P.; m. Mary Elizabeth Petrak, June 1, 1968 (div. Mar. 1977); 1 child, Kristin Lynn; m. Diane Lynn Veit, Oct. 15, 1982. AA in Fire Sci., Moraine Valley Community Coll., 1972; BA in Fire Adminstrn., Lewis U., 1978; MA in Pub. Adminstrn. and Human Relations, Webster U., 1982. Firefighter Village of Evergreen Park, 1965-74; engr. Freeman United Coal Cos., Chgo., 1970-74; fire marshal Village of Bolingbrook, Ill., 1974-79; fire chief City of Waukegan, Ill., 1979-82, City of Plano, Tex., 1982—; adj. faculty mem. Moraine Valley Community Coll., Palos Hills, Ill., 1973-82; cons. Resource Mgmt. Assocs., Frankfort, Ill., 1979—. Served with USN, 1967-68. Harvard U. fellow, Fed. Emergency Mgmt. Agy., 1985. Mem. Internat. Assn. Fire Chiefs, Nat. Fire Protection Assn. (dir. fire services sect. 1983-86, adv. council 1982—), Ill. Fire Inspectors Assn. (pres. 1979-80), Am. Soc. Pub. Adminstrs., Soc. Fire Protection Engrs. (tech.). Roman Catholic. Lodge: Kiwanis (v.p. Waukegan club 1981-82, 2d v.p., bd. dirs. Plano club 1983-86). Home: 2617 Pickwick Ln Plano TX 75093-3530 Office: Plano Fire Dept 1409 Ave K Plano TX 75074

PETERSON, WILLIAM HERBERT, economist; b. N.Y.C., Feb. 26, 1921; s. George C. and Ann (Erickson) P.; m. Mary Jean Bennett, Feb. 17, 1949; children: Mark, Laura. BS, NYU, 1943, PhD, 1952; MS, Columbia U., 1948; hon. degree, Francisco Marroquin U., Guatemala, 1991. Asst. prof. economics Poly. Inst. Bklyn., 1948-53; prof. econs. NYU, 1953-64; economist U.S. Steel Corp., 1964-71; sr. econ. adviser U.S. Dept. Commerce, Washington, 1972-74; John David Campbell prof. Am. bus. Am. Grad. Sch. Internat. Mgmt., Glendale, Ariz., 1974-76; Burrows T. Lundy prof. philosophy of bus. Campbell U., Buies Creek, N.C., 1976-78, 88-93; Scott L. Probasco Jr. chair free enterprise, dir. Ctr. Econ. Edn. U. Tenn., Chattanooga, 1979-87; mem. Conf. Bd. Econ. Forum, 1964-71. Author: The Great Farm Problem, 1959; also monographs and articles. Mem. nat. campaign staff Nixon for Pres., 1960. Lt. (j.g.) USNR, World War II. Disting. scholar Assn. for Pvt. Enterprise Edn., 1989; recipient George Washington Medal of Honor Freedoms Found. at Valley Forge, 1990. Mem. Am. So. econ. assns., Nat. Assn. Bus. Econs., Am. Statis. Assn., Mont Pelerin Soc. Cosmos Club. Home: 700 New Hampshire Ave NW Washington DC 20037-2406

PETERSON, WILLIS LESTER, economics educator; b. Mpls., Mar. 3, 1932; s. Lester Wilfred and Valeria Leone (Slatoski) P.; m. Dorothy Feiertag, July 5, 1969. BS, U. Minn., 1960, MS, 1962; PhD, U. Chgo., 1966. Rsch. fellow U. Chgo., 1962-65; mem. faculty U. Minn., St. Paul, 1965—, prof. econs., 1972—. Author: Principles of Economics: Macro, 1971, 9th edit., 1994, Principles of Economics: Micro, 1971, 9th edit., 1994, Introduction to Economics, 1977. With U.S. Army, 1952-54. Home: 500 Constance Blvd Anoka MN 55304 Office: U Minn 337 Cla Ofc Bldg Saint Paul MN 55108

PETHICK, CHRISTOPHER JOHN, physicist; b. Horsham, Sussex, Eng., Feb. 22, 1942; s. Richard Hope and Norah Betty (Hill) P. BA, Magdalen Coll., Oxford (Eng.) U., 1962, PhD, 1965. Fellow Magdalen Coll., Oxford U., 1965-70; research assoc. U. Ill., Urbana, 1966-68, research asst. prof., 1968-69, assoc. prof. physics, 1970-73, prof. physics, 1973—; prof. physics Nordita, Copenhagen, 1975—. A.P. Sloan research fellow, 1970-72. Fellow Am. Phys. Soc.; mem. Am. Astron. Soc., European Phys. Soc. Office: U Ill Dept Physics 1110 W Green St Urbana IL 61801-3003 also: Nordita, Blegdamsvej 17, DK-2100 Copenhagen Denmark

PETICOLAS, WARNER LELAND, physical chemistry educator; b. Lubbock, Tex., July 29, 1929; s. Warner Marion and Beulah Francis (Lowe) P.; m. Virginia Marie Wolf, June 30, 1969; children—Laura M., Alicia B.; children by previous marriage—Cynthia M., Nina P., Phillip W. B.S., Tex. Technol. Coll., 1950; Ph.D., Northwestern U., 1954. Research asso. DuPont Co., Wilmington, Del., 1954-60; research div. IBM, San Jose, Calif., 1960-67; cons. IBM, 1967-69, mgr. chem. physics group, 1965-67; prof. phys. chemistry U. Oreg., 1967—; vis. prof. U. Paris-Pierre and Marie Curie, 1980-81; cons. in field. Committeeman Democratic party, Eugene, Oreg., 1967-70. Served with USPHS, 1955-57. Recipient Alexander von Humboldt award, W. Ger., 1984-85. Guggenheim fellow Max von Laue-Paul Langevin Inst., Grenoble, France, 1973-74. Fellow Am. Phys. Soc.; mem. Am. Chem. Soc., Am. Phys. Soc., Sigma Xi, Alpha Chi Sigma, Tau Beta Pi. Episcopalian. Home: 2829 Arline Way Eugene OR 97403-2527 Office: U Oregon Dept Of Chemistry Eugene OR 97403

PETIKA, DAVID M., municipal government official, editor; b. Canonsburg, Pa., Sept. 8, 1945; s. John P. and Mary (Konechny) P.; children: David Christopher, Melony Lynn; m. Deborah Jo Schmidt, Dec. 31,

1991. Student, Pinellas Tech. Coll., 1973, St. Petersburg Jr. Coll., 1974, Mid. Tenn. U., 1977, Air Force U., 1981. Dir. parks City Pinellas Park, Fla., 1973-75; animal health technician U.S. Dept. Agr., Nashville, 1976-79; dairy farmer Bell Buckle, Tenn., 1976-79; dir. parks and recreation City of Burleson, Tex., 1980-84, City of North Richland Hills, Tex., 1984-88; tech. editor Planning Rsch. Corp, Eulles, Tex., 1988-90; chief park ranger City of Boca Raton, Fla., 1990—. Adminstrv. officer U.S. Naval Sea Cadets, Naval Air Sta., Dallas. Served with USN, 1963-66, 68-70. Mem. Nat. Recreation and Park Assn. (cert. profl.), Am. Park and Recreation Soc., Nat. Inst. Park and Ground Maintenance (past v.p.), Profl. Grounds Mgmt. Soc., Nat. Youth Sports Coaches Assn. (cert. clinician), CAP (named Squadron Comdr. of Yr. 1981). Republican. Roman Catholic. Avocations: photography, woodwork.

PETILLO, JAMES THOMAS, diversified utility company executive; b. Magnolia, Ark., Aug. 13, 1944; s. Thomas Evans and Reba (Polk) P.; m. Nancy Elizabeth Moody, Apr. 15, 1967; children: Deanna Elizabeth, Thomas Evans. BS, U.S. Naval Acad., 1966; MBA, Fla. State U., 1972; PMD 44, Harvard U., 1982. Commd. ensign USN, 1966, advanced through grades to lt., resigned, 1971; adminstrv. asst. Fla. Power & Light Co., Miami, 1973-74, sr. planning analyst, 1974-75, pub. affairs coordinator, 1976; dist. mgr. Fla. Power & Light Co., Delray Beach, 1976-80; dir. mktg. and energy conservation Fla. Power & Light Co., Miami, 1980-84; v.p. Fla. Power & Light Co., Sarasota, 1984-86, Miami, 1986-87; v.p. FPL Group, North Palm Beach, 1987-88; group v.p. Fla. Power & Light Co., North Palm Beach, 1988-91; sr. v.p. Fla. Power & Light Group, Inc., North Palm Beach, 1991—; pres. Qualtec Quality Svcs., Inc., 1992—; also bd. dirs. Fla. Power & Light Co., Juno Beach; pres. Qualtec Quality Svcs., Inc., 1992—; bd. dirs. Fla. C. of C., Fla. Tax Watch. Republican. Methodist. Avocations: flying, skiing, reading. Office: Fla Power & Light Co PO Box 14000 Juno Beach FL 33408-0420

PETILLON, LEE RITCHEY, lawyer; b. Gary, Ind., May 6, 1929; s. Charles Ernest and Blanche Lurene (Mackay) P.; m. Mary Anne Keeton, Feb. 20, 1960; children: Andrew G., Joseph R. BBA, U. Minn., 1952; LLB, U. Calif., Berkeley, 1959. Bar: Calif. 1960, U.S. Dist. Ct. (so. dist.) Calif. 1960. V.p. Creative Investment Capital, Inc., L.A., 1969-70; corp. counsel Harvest Industries, L.A., 1970-71; v.p., gen. counsel, dir. Tech. Svcs. Corp., Santa Monica, Calif., 1971-78; ptnr. Petillon & Davidoff, L.A., 1978-92, Gipson Hoffman & Pancione, 1992-93; pvt. practice, Torrance, Calif., 1993-94; ptnr. Petillon & Hansen, Torrance, Calif., 1994—; dir. Pub. Counsel, Westside Legal Svcs., 1981-84; chmn. Dispute Resolution Adv. Coun., 1988-89, South Bay Sci. Park, Inc.; adj. prof. law Pepperdine Univ., 1991—. Co-author; R&D Partnerships, 2d edit., 1985, Representing Start-Up Companies, 1992, 3d edit., 1995. Chmn. Neighborhood Justice Ctr. Com., 1983-85, Middle Income Com., 1983-85; active Calif. Senate Commn. on Corp. Governance, State Bar Calif. Task Force on Alternative Dispute Resolution, 1984-85. 1st lt. USAF, 1952-54. Recipient Cert. of Appreciation L.A. City Demonstration Agy., 1975, United Indian Devel. Assn., 1981, City of L.A. for Outstanding Vol. Svcs., 1984. Mem. ABA, Calif. State Bar Assn. (pres. Pro Bono Svcs. award 1983), L.A. County Bar Found. (bd. dirs. 1986-89), L.A. County Bar Assn. (chmn. law tech. sect., alt. dispute resolution sect. 1992-94, trustee 1984-85, Griffin Bell Vol. Svc. award 1993). Avocations: backpacking, reading, music. Home: 1636 Via Machado Palos Verdes Estates CA 90274-1930 Office: Petillon & Hansen PC 21515 Hawthorne Blvd # 1260 Torrance CA 90503

PETIT, PARKER HOLMES, health care corporation executive; b. Decatur, Ga., Aug. 4, 1939; s. James Percival and Ethel (Holmes) P.; children: William Wright, Patricia Monique, Meredith Katherine. BS in Mech. Engring., Ga. Inst. Tech., 1962, MS in Engring. Mechanics, 1964; MBA, Ga. State U., 1973. Engr. Gen. Dynamics Corp., Fort Worth, Tex., 1966-67; pres., founder, chief exec. officer Healthdyne, Inc., Marietta, 1971—; bd. dirs. Atlantic S.E. Airlines, Atlanta, Healthdyne Technologies, Inc., Atlanta. Author: Primer on Composite Materials, 1968; patentee in field. Chmn. bd. dirs. Sudden Infant Death Syndrome Alliance, Washington, 1986; active nat. adv. coun. Emory U. Med. Sch., Coun. fellows for the Emory, Ga. Tech. Biomed. Tech. Rsch. Ctr. Served to 1st lt. U.S. Army, 1964-67. Recipient Humanitarian award La SocieteFrancaise de Bienfaisance, 1981; mem. Tech. Hall of Fame of Ga.; mem. Ga. Tech. Acad. Disting. Alumni, 1994; Internat. Bus. fellow, 1986. Mem. Health Industry Mfrs. Assn., Cobb County C. of C. (bd. dirs. 1980-82), Pi Kappa Phi. Republican. Methodist. Avocations: flying; oil painting; golf; tennis. Office: Healthdyne Inc 1850 Parkway Pl Marietta GA 30067-8237

PETOK, SAMUEL, retired manufacturing company executive; b. Detroit, Aug. 12, 1922; s. Harry and Jennie (Weingarten) P.; m. Fayne Joyce Myers, June 26, 1952; children—Carol, Seth, Michael. B.A. in History, Wayne State U., Detroit, 1945; postgrad., Medill Sch. Journalism, Northwestern U., 1946. Reporter Detroit Free Press, 1946-50; account exec. McCann Erickson, 1950-52; pub. relations exec. Chrysler Corp., 1952-70; Vice pres. public relations and advt. White Motor Corp., Cleve., 1971-76; dir. communications automotive ops. Rockwell Internat. Co., Troy, Mich., 1976-77; corp. staff v.p. public relations Rockwell Internat. Co., Pitts., 1977-78; v.p. communications Rockwell Internat. Co., 1978-82, sr. v.p. communications, mem. mgmt. com., 1982-88; retired. Former trustee Arthur W. Page Soc. Recipient Page One award Newspaper Guild Detroit, 1948. Mem. Pub. Rels. Soc. Am. (Silver Anvil award 1964, award Cleve. chpt. 1975), Internat. Pub. Rels. Assn., Overseas Press Club Am., The Old Guard of Princeton, Green Acres Country Club.

PETOSA, JASON JOSEPH, publisher; b. Des Moines, Iowa, Apr. 26, 1939; s. Joseph John and Mildred Margaret (Cardamon) P.; m. Theodora Anne Doleski, Aug. 12, 1972; 1 son, Justin James. Student, Marquette U., 1957-59, St. Paul Sem., 1959-63, 65-67, Colegio Paolino Internationale, Rome, 1963-65. Assoc. editor Cath. Home Mag., Canfield, Ohio, 1965-67; editor Cath. Home Mag., 1968; dir. Alba House Communications, Canfield, 1968-71; with Office of Radio and TV, Diocese of Youngstown, Ohio, 1969-71; dir. pub. relations, instr. Alice Lloyd Coll., Pippa Passes, Ky., 1971-76; writer, cons. Bethesda, Ohio, 1976-79; pres., pub. Nat. Cath. Reporter, Kansas City, Mo., 1979-85; v.p., gen. mgr. Towsend-Kraft Pub. Co., Liberty, Mo., 1985-86; pres., pub. Steadfast Pub. Co., Kansas City, 1986—; owner CF&E Ptnrs. Bd. dirs. David (Ky.) Sch., 1973-79; mem. Mayor's UN Day Com., Kansas City. Mem. Kansas City Direct Mktg. Assn., UN Assn. (bd. dirs. Met. Kansas City chpt.), Sigma Delta Chi. Roman Catholic. Office: 19 W Linwood Blvd PO Box 410265 Kansas City MO 64141

PETRAKIS, HARRY MARK, author; b. St. Louis, June 5, 1923; s. Mark E. and Stella (Christoulakis) P.; m. Diane Perparos, Sept. 30, 1945; children: Mark, John, Dean. Student, U. Ill., 1940-41, L.H.D., 1971; L.H.D., Governor's State U., 1980, Hellenic Coll., 1984, Roosevelt U., 1987. Freelance writer, tchr., lectr.; tchr. workshop classes in novel, short story; McGuffey vis. lectr. Ohio U., Athens, 1971; writer-in-residence Chgo. Pub. Library, 1976-77, Chgo. Bd. Edn., 1978-79; Kazantzakis Prof. San Francisco State U., 1992. Author: Lion at My Heart, 1959, The Odyssey of Kostas Volakis, 1963, Pericles on 31st Street, 1965 (nominated for Nat. Book award), The Founder's Touch, 1965, A Dream of Kings, 1966 (Nat. Book award nomination), The Waves of Night, 1969, Stelmark: A Family Recollection, 1970, In the Land of Morning, 1973, The Hour of the Bell, 1976, A Petrakis Reader, 28 Stories, 1978, Nick the Greek, 1979, Days of Vengeance, 1983, Reflections on a Writer's Life and Work, 1983, Collected Stories, 1986, Ghost of the Sun, 1990; contbr. short stores to mags. including, Atlantic Monthly, Sat. Eve. Post, Harper's Bazaar, Country Beautiful. (Story included in Prize Stories, also O. Henry Award 1966). Recipient awards Friends of Am. Writers, Friends of Lit., Soc. Midland Authors, Carl Sandburg award, Ellis Island medal of honor, 1995. Mem. Authors Guild, PEN, Writers Guild Am.-West. Address: 80 East Rd Dune Acres Chesterton IN 46304 *"...The older I become, the more clearly I see that there is a stunning purity in the writing of a book that I cannot achieve in my own life with its frailty and desperation. The work takes over with a life of its own. In those moments, I wouldn't trade writing with all its loneliness and sometimes with its pain, for any other profession in the world.*

PETRAKIS, LEONIDAS, research scientist, educator, administrator; b. Sparta, Greece, July 23, 1935; came to U.S., 1951, naturalized, 1956; s. Lina

Contos P.; m. Ismene Lempesis, June 21, 1959; children: Ismene L., Alexis L. BS, Northeastern U., 1958; PhD, U. Calif., Berkeley, 1961. Faculty research grantee Nat. Research Council, Can., 1961-62; prof. chemistry U. Md., College Park, 1962-63; researcher DuPont Co., Wilmington, Del., 1963-65; sr. scientist Gulf-Chevron Research Co., Richmond, Calif., 1965-89; sr. scientist Brookhaven Nat. Lab., Upton, N.Y., 1989—, chmn. dept. applied scis., 1989-94; sr. vis. lectr. Carnegie-Mellon U., Pitts., 1972-73; vis. prof. U. Paris, 1985, 91, 95; adj. prof. U. Pitts., 1981-85; mem. Coun. for Chem. Rsch. Author: Free Radicals in Syn Fuels, 1983, NMR for Liquid Fuels, 1986; editor and author four books on chemistry for fossil energy, 1978, 80, 84, 94; contbr. articles to profl. jours. Mem. environ. com. L.I. Assn.; bd. advisors Barnett Inst., Northeastern U.; mem. Organizing Group and Sci. and Bus. Adv. Bd. for L.I. Rsch. Inst. Advanced Study Inst. rsch. grantee Dept. Energy, Nat. Sci. Found, NATO, Washington, 1979-83. Mem. Am. Chem. Soc. (adv. bd. 1979-83, officer 1974-78, Pitts. award 1984), Am. Phys. Soc.(symposium organizer), AAAS, NSF (grantee, Washington 1981-85, also symposium organizer), Sigma Xi. Office: Brookhaven Nat Lab Dept Of Applied Sci Upton NY 11973 *Technological progress has its downside: complexity, obfuscation, lack of depth, alienation; homo sapiens become homo economicus and now auto-sapiens; quantity become quality, although it is clear enough that more, as in cancer, is not always better; and the wrappings are the package. It is time to take time with the poets and listen to the raindrops, time to read again the myth of the Tower of Babel, and to rediscover the lessons of entropy in everyday life.*

PETRAKIS, NICHOLAS LOUIS, physician, medical researcher, educator; b. San Francisco, Feb. 6, 1922; s. Louis Nicholas and Stamatina (Boosalis) P.; m. Patricia Elizabeth Kelly, June 24, 1947; children: Steven John, Susan Lynn, Sandra Kay. BA, Augustana Coll., 1943; BS in Medicine, U. S.D., 1944; MD, Washington U., St. Louis, 1946. Intern Mpls. Gen. Hosp., 1946-47; physician-researcher U.S. Naval Radiol. Def. Lab., San Francisco, 1947-49; resident physician Mpls. Gen. Hosp., 1949-50; sr. asst. surgeon Nat. Cancer Inst., USPHS, San Francisco 1950-54; asst. research physician Cancer Research Inst., U. Calif., San Francisco, 1954-56; asst. prof. preventive medicine U. Calif. Sch. Medicine, San Francisco, 1956-60, assoc. prof., 1960-66, prof., 1966-91, chmn. dept. epidemiology and internat. health, 1978-88, prof. emeritus, 1991—; prof. epidemiology U. Calif. Sch. Pub. Health, Berkeley, 1981-91; assoc. dir. G.W. Hooper Edn., U. Calif., San Francisco, 1970-74, acting dir., 1974-77, chmn. dept. epidemiology and internat. health, 1979-89; co-dir. Breast Screening Ctr. of No. Calif., Oakland, 1976-81; cons. Breast Cancer Task Force, Nat. Cancer Inst., Bethesda, Md., 1972-76; chmn. Biometry & Epidemiology Contract Rev. Com., Bethesda, 1977-81; mem. bd. sci. counselors, div. cancer etiology Nat. Cancer Inst., Bethesda, 1982-86; mem. scientific adv. com. Calif. State Tobacco-Related Disease Rsch. Program, 1991-93; cons. U. Crete Sch. Medicine, Heraklion, Greece, 1984; bd. dirs. No. Calif. Cancer Ctr., 1991. Contbr. over 200 research papers on breast cancer, med. oncology and hematology. Eleanor Roosevelt Internat. Cancer fellow Am. Cancer Soc., Comitato Reserche Nucleari, Cassacia, Italy, 1962; U.S. Pub. Health Service Spl. fellow Galton Lab., U. London, 1969-70; recipient Alumni Achievement award Augustana Coll., Sioux Falls, S.D., 1979, Axion award Hellenic-Am. Profl. Soc. of Calif., San Francisco, 1984, Lewis C. Robbins award Soc. for Prospective Medicine, Indpls., 1985. Mem. Am. Soc. Preventive Oncology (founding, pres. 1984-85, Disting. Achievement award 1992), Soc. for Prospective Medicine (founding), Am. Assn. Cancer Rsch., Am. Epidemiol. Soc., Am. Soc. Clin. Investigation, Am. Bd. Preventive Medicine (cert.). Home: 335 Juanita Way San Francisco CA 94127-1657 Office: U Calif Sch Medicine Dept Epidemiology and Biostats 1699 HSW San Francisco CA 94143-0560

PETRAKIS, PETER, lawyer; b. Chgo., Sept. 23, 1951. BA with honors, Loyola U., 1973, JD cum laude, 1976. Bar: Ill. 1976. Law clk. to Hon. Howard C. Ryan Ill. Supreme Ct., Chgo., 1976-77; ptnr. Katten Muchin & Zavis, Chgo.; legal writing instr. Loyola U., 1976-78. Office: Katten Muchin & Zavis 525 W Monroe St Ste 1600 Chicago IL 60661-3693

PETRALIA, RONALD SEBASTIAN, entomologist, neurobiologist; b. Lawrence, Mass., Nov. 7, 1954; s. Samuel and Rosalie (Zanfagna) P.; B.S. summa cum laude in Entomology, U. Mass., 1975; Ph.D. in Entomology and Biology, Tex. A&M U., 1979. Rsch. asst., 1975-79, rsch. assoc. Tex. A&M U., College Station, 1979-80; asst. prof. biology St. Ambrose Coll., Davenport, Iowa, 1980-85; rsch. fellow dept. anatomy George Washington U., Washington, 1985-90; sr. staff fellow Nat. Inst. for Deafness and Other Comm. Disorders., NIH, Bethesda, Md., 1991—; presenter in field. Coauthor: (book chpts. with others) Excitatory Amino Acids, 1992, The Mammalian Cochlear Nuclei: Organization and Function, 1993, Excitatory Amino Acids: Their Role in Neuroendocrine Function, 1995; contbr. articles to profl. jours. Mem. Soc. for Neurosci., Entomol. Soc. Am., Microscopy Soc. Am., Assn. Rsch. in Otolaryngology, Internat. Union for Study of Social Insects, Cambridge Entomol. Club, Sigma Xi. Roman Catholic. Home: 78 Boston St Methuen MA 01844-5359 Office: NIDCD NIH Bldg 36 Rm 5D08 900 Rockville Pike Bethesda MD 20892

PETRASH, JEFFREY MICHAEL, lawyer; b. Cleve., Dec. 14, 1948; s. Robert Anthony and Naomi Marjorie (Close) P.; m. Patricia Ann Early, May 29, 1971 (div. Mar. 1986); 1 child, Michael Stewart. AB, U. Mich., 1969, JD, 1973. Bar: Mich. 1974, D.C. 1975. Assoc. Dickinson, Wright, McKean, Cudlip & Moon, Detroit, 1973-75, Hamel, Park, McCabe & Saunders, Washington, 1975-78; from assoc. to ptnr. Dickinson, Wright, Moon, Van Dusen & Freeman, Washington, 1978—. Served to capt. U.S. Army, 1971-74. Mem. Soc. Barristers. Episcopalian. Avocation: sailing. Home: 6606 Hillandale Rd Bethesda MD 20815-6406 Office: Dickinson Wright Moon Van Dusen & Freeman 1901 L St NW Washington DC 20036-3506

PETRE, DONNA MARIE, county judge; b. Joliet, Ill., Apr. 21, 1947; d. James Jacob and Catherine (Hedrick) P.; m. Dennis Michael Styne, Sept. 4, 1971; children: Rachel Catherine, Jonathan James, Juliana Claire, Aaron Coopersmith. BA, Clarke Coll., 1969; MA, Northwestern U., 1971; JD, U. Calif., San Francisco, 1976. Bar: Calif. 1976. Jud. clk. Calif. Ct. Appeals, San Francisco, 1976-77; instr. legal rsch. and writing Hastings Coll. Law, U. Calif., San Francisco, 1976; dep. atty. gen. criminal appeals dept. State of Calif., San Francisco, 1977-80, dep. atty. gen. consumer fraud dept., 1980-83; dep. atty. gen. med. fraud dept. State of Calif., Sacramento, 1983-86; judge Yolo County Mcpl. Ct., Woodland, Calif., 1986-89, Yolo County Superior Ct., 1990—; adj. prof. trial practice U. Calif., Davis; mem. criminal justice commn. Marin County Bd. Suprs., 1982; mem. adv. com. Jud. Coun. on Adminstrv. Justice in Rural Communities, 1988—; Mng. editor Hastings Constl. Law Quar., 1975-76. Bd. dirs. Woodland Literacy Coun., 1986—; active LWV. Mem. AAUW, Calif. Judges Assn. (mem. commn. on studying problems with driving under influence of alcohol and other drugs), Yolo County Bar Assn., Women Lawyers Calif., Sacramento Women Lawyers, Bus. and Profl. Women (co-chairperson legis. 1986—), Davis C. of C., Yolo C. of C., Woodland C. of C. Republican. Office: Yolo County Superior Ct 725 Court St Woodland CA 95695-3436

PETREE, WILLIAM HORTON, lawyer; b. Winston-Salem, N.C., Nov. 4, 1920; s. Elbert Heaton and Ethel (Tucker) P.; m. Lena Morris, Dec. 23, 1943; children: William Horton Jr., Mary Jo. BS, U. N.C., 1944, LLB, 1948. Bar: N.C. 1948. Ptnr. Petree Stockton and predecessors, 1956—; past chmn. local bd. dirs. First Union Nat. Bank, Winston-Salem. Past bd. dirs., mem. exec. com. Old Salem, Inc.; past mem. campaign coordinating com. Forsyth County, N.C.; past chmn. found. com. Winston-Salem Found.; past pres. Forsyth County Tb and Health Assn.; past bd. dirs. Moravian Home; past chmn. fin. bd. Moravian Ch.; past trustee, elder; past trustee, exec. com. Salem Coll. 1st lt. USMCR, 1944-46. Mem. Forsyth County Bar Assn. (past pres.), Forsyth County Club (past dir.), Piedmont Club, Kiwanis (past dir. Winston-Salem club, pres. 1976-77), Alpha Tau Omega, Phi Delta Phi. Democrat. Mem. Moravian Ch. Home: 144 Muirfield Dr Winston Salem NC 27104-3949 Office: Petree Stockton 1001 W 4th St Winston Salem NC 27101-2400 *Enthusiasm, coupled with proper motivation, contributes most to a successful, happy and fulfilling life.*

PETREK, WILLIAM JOSEPH, college president emeritus; b. Arcadia, Wis., Feb. 26, 1928; s. Roman Casper and Agnes (Jankowski) P.; m. Sandra Lucille Nash, Nov. 24, 1961; children: Michele, Søren. B.A. cum laude, St. John's U., Minn., 1948; S.T.L. magna cum laude Gregorian U., Rome, 1952;

Ph.D. with great distinction, Higher Inst. Philosophy, U. Louvain, Belgium, 1956; DHumLitt, Richmond Coll., London. Asst. prof. philosophy, chmn. dept. philosophy Holy Cross Coll., La Crosse, Wis., 1956-60; from asst. prof. to prof. philosophy and religion DePauw U., Greencastle, Ind., 1961-71; dir. internat. edn., asst. dean internat. edn. and off-campus programs DePauw U., 1966-71; v.p. Gt. Lakes Colls. Assn., Ann Arbor, Mich., 1971-72; dean Coll. Liberal Arts, Hofstra U., Hempstead, N.Y., 1972-74; provost, dean faculties Coll. Liberal Arts, Hofstra U., 1974-76; acad. v.p. Southeast Mo. State U., Cape Girardeau, 1976-80; pres. Richmond Coll., London, 1980-92. Translator, author: introduction (Jean Nabert) Elements for an Ethic, 1969. Trustee Nassau Higher Edn. Consortium, 1973-76; exec. com. bd. Council Intercultural Studies and Programs, 1974-88; bd. nat. cons. Nat. Endowment Humanities, 1974—; bd. dirs. World Univ. Service, 1976-80; mem. Ct. Govs. Mill Hill Sch., London, 1989-94. Danforth asso., 1964; recipient Best Prof. award DePauw U., 1965; Ford Found. humanities grantee, 1970; Gt. Lakes Colls. Assn. Non-Western research grantee, 1965; hon. fellow Inst. Am. Univs., Aix-en-Provence, France, 1973. Mem. Soc. Phenomenology and Existential Philosophy, Assn. Internat. Colls. and Univs. (pres. 1984-89). Office: Richmond Coll, Queens Rd Richmond, Surrey TW10 6JP, England

PETREQUIN, HARRY JOSEPH, JR., foreign service officer; b. Ste. Genevieve, Mo., July 1, 1929; s. Harry Joseph and Crescentia Ellen (Bechter) P.; m. Katharine McDonnell Drouin, Oct. 7, 1980; children: John Andrew, Marc Christopher, Paul Nicholas. AB, Westminster Coll., 1950; B of Fgn. Trade, Am. Grad. Sch. Internat. Mgmt., 1954; postgrad., Johns Hopkins U., 1960; MA, Tufts U., 1970. Joined U.S. Fgn. Svc., 1955; assigned AID and predecessor agys., 1955—; dep. dir. S.E. Asia Regional Econ. Devel. Office, Thailand, 1970-74; U.S. coord. Senegal River Basin Authority, Dakar, 1975-76; dir. ASEAN and South Pacific Affairs, 1977-80; dir. program devel. and evaluation staff Bur. Internat. Orgn. Affairs State Dept., 1980-81; dep. dir. AID Mission, Morocco, 1981-85; coord. AID Sr. Mgmt. Course, 1985-86; Indsl. Coll. of the Armed Forces, 1986-87; faculty dept. nat. security policy Nat. War Coll., Washington, 1987-89; internat. devel. cons. Black Mountain, N.C., 1989—; adj. prof. polit. sci. Warren Wilson Coll., Swannanoa, N.C., 1993—. Lt. (j.g.) USCGR, 1951-53, comdr. Res. Recipient Superior Honor award AID, 1979, State Dept. Superior Honor award, 1981, Comdrs. award for Civilian Svc., Dept. of the Army, 1989. Mem. Soc. Internt. Devel., World Federalist Assn. (nat. bd. dirs.), Am. Fgn. Svc. Assn., UN Assn. U.S., Acad. Polit. Sci., Cousteau Soc., Common Cause, Inst. Noetic Scis., World Future Soc., Amnesty Internat., Coast Guard Combat Vets Assn., Greenpeace, Vets. for Peace, The Land Inst., Phi Alpha Theta.

PETRI, PETER ALEXANDER, economist, educator, director; b. Budapest, Hungary, Oct. 17, 1946; came to U.S., 1959; s. George and Margaret (Fejer) P.; m. Jean H. Lawrence, June 19, 1976; children: Philip, Nicholas. BA, Harvard U., 1968, PhD, 1976. Prof. of Econ. Brandeis U., Waltham, Mass., 1974—; dean Grad. Sch. Internat. Econs. and Fin., Waltham, Mass., 1994—; dir. Lemberg Prog. in Internat. Econ. & Fin., Brandeis U., Waltham 1986-94; Carl Shapiro prof. of internat. fin. Brandeis U., Waltham, 1989—; Fulbright rsch. scholar Keio U., Tokyo, 1991; cons. World Bank, Washington. Author: The Future of the World Economy, 1977, Modeling Japanese-American Trade, 1984; editor: Wassily Leontief, 1982, The Economics of the Dollar Cycle, 1990, East Asia's Trade and Investment, 1994; editor Jour. of Asian Econs., Singapore Econ. Rev. Grantee Study of Japanese Trade, U.S. State Dept., 1980, Study of U.S. Social Security, Social Security Adminstrn., 1982-83, Internat. Bus. Edn., U.S. Dept. Edn., 1989, 92, 94; Econ. Policy fellow Brookings Inst., 1979. Mem. Am. Econ. Assn., Acad. Internat. Bus. Office: Grad Sch Internat Econs & Fin Brandeis U Waltham MA 02254

PETRI, THOMAS EVERT, congressman; b. Marinette, Wis., May 28, 1940; s. Robert and Marian (Humleker) P.; m. Anne Neal, Mar. 26, 1983; 1 child, Alexandra. BA in Govt., Harvard U., 1962, JD, 1965. Bar: Wis. 1965. Law clk. to presiding justice U.S. Dist. (we. dist.) Wis., Madison, 1965-66; vol. Peace Corps, Somalia, 1966-67; aide White House, Washington, 1969-70; dir. crime and drug studies Pres.'s Nat. Adv. Coun. on Exec. Orgn., 1969; pvt. practice Fond du Lac, Wis., 1970-79; mem. Wis. State Senate, Madison, 1973-79, 96th-103rd Congress from 6th Wis. dist., Washington, D.C., 1979—. Editor: National Industrial Policy: Solution or Illusion, 1984. Republican. Lutheran. Avocations: reading, swimming, hiking, biking, skiing. Office: US Ho of Reps 2262 Rayburn Bldg Washington DC 20515

PETRICK, ALFRED, JR., mineral economics educator, consultant; b. Mt. Vernon, N.Y., Mar. 30, 1926; s. Alfred and Ruth (Updike) P.; m. Ruth Goodridge, Jan. 2, 1956; children: Elizabeth, Andrew Wayne. B.S., B.A., Columbia U., 1952, M.S., 1962; M.B.A., Denver U., 1966; Ph.D., U. Colo., 1969. Registered profl. engr., Colo. Sales engr. Ingersoll Rand Co., N.Y.C., 1953-54; project engr. U.S. AEC, Grand Junction, Colo., 1954-57; mining engr. Reynolds Metals Co., Bauxite, Ark., 1957-61, Guyana, 1957-61; mineral economist U.S. Bur. Mines, Denver, 1963-70; Coulter prof. Colo. Sch. Mines, Golden, 1984, emeritus prof., 1984—; dir. Petrick Assocs., Evergreen, Colo. Author: Economics International Development, 1977, Economics of Minerals, 1980, Preparacion y Evaluacion, 1982. Mem. com. tech. aspects strategic materials Nat. Acad. Sci., Washington, 1973-76, mem. com. surface mining and reclamation, 1979. Served with USAF, 1945-47, PTO. Fulbright research scholar U. Otago, Dunedin, New Zealand, 1986; recipient Edn. award Instituto Para Funcionarios De Las Industrias Minera y Siderurgica, Mexico City, 1981; recipient Service award Office Tech. Assessment, U.S. Congress, 1981. Mem. AIME (chmn. council econs. 1977-78, Henry Krumb lectr. 1986, service award), Profl. Engrs. Colo. Presbyterian. Home: 5544 S Hatch Dr Evergreen CO 80439-7234 Office: Colo Sch Mines Golden CO 80401

PETRICK, ERNEST NICHOLAS, mechanical engineer; b. Pa., Apr. 9, 1922; s. Aurelius and Anna (Kashak) P.; m. Magdalene Simcoe, June 13, 1946; children: Deborah Petrick Healey, Katherine Petrick Niver, Denise Petrick, Victoria Ann Petrick Kropp. B.S. in Mech. Engring. Carnegie Inst. Tech., 1943; M.S., Purdue U., 1948, Ph.D., 1955. Registered profl. engr., Mich. Faculty Purdue U., 1946-53; dir. heat transfer research Curtiss-Wright Corp., Woodridge, N.J., 1953-56; chief advanced propulsion systems Curtiss-Wright Research divsn., Quehanna, Pa., 1957-60; chief research engr. Kelsey-Hayes Co., Detroit, 1960-65; chief scientist, tech. dir. U.S. Army Tank-Automotive Command, Warren, Mich., 1965-82; chief scientist, dir. engring. labs. Gen. Dynamics, 1982-87; engring. cons., 1987—; adj. prof. engring. Wayne State U., U. Mich.; guest lectr. Oakland U.; panel mem. combat vehicles NATO, 1973-82; mem. adv. bd. on basic combustion research NSF, 1973; chmn. advanced transp. systems com. White House Energy Project, 1973; mem. vis. adv. com. NSF-RANN research program Drexel U. Coll. Engring., 1976-78; mem. Army Sci. Bd., 1983-89; cons. Air Force Studies Bd. NRC, 1991-93, cons. Def. Sci. Bd., 1994—. Contbr. articles on transp., ground vehicles, flight propulsion and project mgmt. to profl. jours. Mem. adv. bd. Wayne State U. Engring., Detroit. Served to lt. USN, 1942-46; to lt. comdr. USNR, 1946-54. Recipient certificate of achievement U.S. Army, 1967, Outstanding Performance awards, 1970, 71, 76, 82, Outstanding Mech. Engring. award Purdue U., 1991; named Disting. Engring. Alumnus Purdue U., 1966. Mem. Soc. Automotive Engrs. (nat. dir. 1980-83), Am. Def. Preparedness Assn. (chmn. land warfare survivability divsn. 1990-95, Silver medal 1992), Sigma Xi, Pi Tau Sigma. Home: 1540 Stonehaven Rd Ann Arbor MI 48104-4150

PETRICOFF, M. HOWARD, lawyer, educator; b. Cin., Dec. 22, 1949; s. Herman and Neoma P.; m. Hanna Sue, Aug. 11, 1974; children: Nicholas, Eve. BS, Am. U., 1967-71; JD, U. Cin., 1971-74; M in Pub. Adminstrn., Harvard U., 1980-81. Bar: Ohio, U.S. Ct. Appeals (D.C. cir.) 1977, U.S. Ct. Appeals (10th cir.) 1985, U.S. Ct. Appeals (6th cir.) 1989, U.S. Supreme Ct. 1989. Asst. city law dir. City of Toledo (Ohio), 1975-77; asst. atty. gen. Ohio Atty. Gen. Office, Columbus, 1977-82; ptnr. Vorys, Sater, Seymour & Pease, Columbus, 1982—; adj. prof. law Capital U. Law Sch., Columbus, 1991—. Contbr. articles to profl. jours. Reginald Heber Smith Found. fellow Washington, 1974-75. Mem. Ohio Bar Assn., Columbus Bar Assn., Ohio Oil and Gas Assn. Office: Vorys Sater Seymour & Pease PO Box 1008 52 E Gay St Columbus OH 43215-3161

PETRIE, DANIEL MANNIX, film, theatre and television director; b. Glace Bay, N.S., Can., Nov. 26, 1920; came to U.S., 1945; s. William Mark and Mary (Campbell) P.; m. Dorothea Grundy, Oct. 27, 1946; children: Daniel Mannix, Donald Mark, Mary Susan and June Anne (twins). BA, St. Francis

Xavier U., Antigonish, N.S., 1942, LittD (hon.), 1974; MA, Columbia U., 1945; postgrad., Northwestern U., 1947-48. chmn. Ctr. for Advanced Film and TV Studies Am. Film Inst. Broadway actor, 1945-46, TV dir., 1950—; TV shows include Eleanor and Franklin, ABC, 1976 (Outstanding Drama award 1976, Emmy award 1976, Critics Circle award 1976, Peabody award 1976), Harry Truman Plain Speaking, Pub. Broadcasting Sta., 1976 (Emmy nomination), Sybil, NBC, 1976 (Emmy award for Outstanding Spl. 1977, Peabody award 1976), Eleanor and Franklin: The White House Years, ABC, 1977 (Emmy award, Dirs. Guild award), Silent Night, Lonely Night, 1969, The Quinns, 1977, The Dollmaker, 1984 (Emmy nomination), The Execution of Raymond Graham, 1985 (Emmy nomination), Half a Lifetime, 1986 (Cable award), film My Name is Bill W. (Emmy and Golden Globe nominations), 1989, (also prodr.) Mark Twain and Me, 1991, A Town Torn Apart, 1992, ; dir. films including A Raisin In The Sun, 1961 (Cannes Film Festival Humanitarian award), Stolen Hours, 1963, The Idol, 1966, Buster And Billie, 1973 (London Film Festival Outstanding Film award 1974), Lifeguard, 1975, The Betsy, 1977, Resurrection, 1979, Fort Apache, The Bronx, 1980, Six Pack, 1982, The Bay Boy, 1984, Square Dance, 1986, Rocket Gibraltar, 1987, Cocoon: The Return, 1988, Lassie, 1994; theatre dir. plays including Volpone, 1971, The Cherry Orchard, 1960, Who'll Save The Plowboy, 1961, Monopoly, 1966, Mornin' Sun, 1965, A Shadow of My Enemy, 1958, A Lesson from Aloes, 1981. Served as lt. Canadian Army, 1942. Mem. Acad. Motion Picture Arts Scis., Dir's. Guild Am. (award 1977), Acad. TV Arts. Office: care Creative Artists Agy 9830 Wilshire Blvd Beverly Hills CA 90212-1825

PETRIE, DONALD ARCHIBALD, lawyer, investment banker, publisher; b. Charleston, W.Va., Apr. 27, 1921; s. James MacFarlin and Emma (Leunig) P.; m. Ruth Elfrieda Hauser, June 28, 1942 (div. 1971); children: Ann Elizabeth Sauter, James MacFarlin; m. Elizabeth M. Greenfield, Sept. 12, 1973. B.A., U. Chgo., 1942, J.D., 1947. Bar: Ill. 1947, N.Y. 1961, D.C. 1970. Partner D'Ancona, Pflaum, Wyatt & Riskind, Chgo., 1947-55; v.p. Hertz Corp., 1955-59, exec. v.p., dir., 1959-60; pres. Hertz Am. Express Internat., Ltd., 1960-61; chmn. exec. com. Avis Rent A Car, 1962-66; ptnr. Lazard Freres & Co., N.Y.C., 1967-71, 78—; of counsel Courdert Bros., Washington, 1973-74; pub. Washington Monitor, 1975-77; chmn., CEO Harper's Mag., 1982-83; chmn. Leadership Directories, Inc. Treas. Democratic Nat. Com., 1972. Mem. Century Assn., Univ. Club. Unitarian.

PETRIE, DONALD JOSEPH, banker; b. N.Y.C., Sept. 2, 1921; s. John and Elizabeth (Thomson) P.; m. Jane Adams, Aug. 27, 1949; children: R. Scott, Anne, Elizabeth, Douglas, Susan. B.B.A. Manhattan Coll., 1950. Personnel mgr. Otis Elevator Co., N.Y.C., 1951-59; personnel dir. Brown Bros. Harriman & Co., N.Y.C., 1959-68; exec. v.p. U.S. Trust Co., N.Y.C., 1968-79; sr. v.p. Marine Midland Bank, N.Y.C., 1979-86, Drake Beam Morin Inc., N.Y.C., 1986-90; chmn., chief exec. officer Webster Corp., N.Y.C., 1990—; lectr. Baruch Sch. Bus., Coll. City N.Y., 1955-58; pres., chmn. exec. and fin. coms., dir. Webster Apts., N.Y.C.; adj. prof. mgmt. Hofstra U., Hempstead, N.Y., 1986—. Author: Explaining Pay Policy, 1969, Handling Employee Questions About Pay, 1976. Capt. USAAF, 1942-46. Mem. N.Y. Chamber Commerce and Industry (chmn. mgmt. edn. and adv. com. 1964—). Home: 11 Fairview Ave Great Neck NY 11023-1462 Office: 419 W 34th St New York NY 10001-1501

PETRIE, FERDINAND RALPH, illustrator, artist; b. Hackensack, N.J., Sept. 17, 1925; s. Archibald John and Bessie (Rutherford) P.; m. Phyllis C. Haddow, Oct. 19, 1951; children: Beth, David. Advt. cert., Parson's Sch. Design, N.Y.C., 1949; student, Art Students League, 1947-48, Famous Artists Course in Illustration, 1958-59. Illustrator J. Gans Assos., N.Y.C., 1950-69. Free lance illustrator, artist, 1969—, owner, Petrie Gallery, Rockport, Mass., 1971—; represented in permanent collections, U.S. Supreme Ct., Smithsonian Instn., Washington, Indpls. Mus. Art; designer U.S. commemorative stamp design, 2 Zaire commemorative stamps, 1980; Author: Drawing Landscapes in Pencil, 1979; illustrator: The Drawing Book, 1980, The Color Book, 1981, The Alkyd Book, 1982, The Watercolorists Guide to Painting Trees, 1983, The Watercolorists Guide to Painting Skies, 1984; The Watercolorists Guide to Painting Water, 1985, Painting Nature in Watercolor, 1990. Served with U.S. Maritime Service, 1943-46. Mem. Am. Watercolor Soc., Artists Fellowship, Rockport Art Assn., Am. Artists Profl. League, N.J. Watercolor Soc. Presbyterian. Address: 51 Vreeland Ave Rutherford NJ 07070

PETRIE, GREGORY STEVEN, lawyer; b. Seattle, Feb. 25, 1951; s. George C. and Pauline (Majers) P.; m. Margaret Fuhrman, Oct. 6, 1979; children: Kathryn Jean, Thomas George. AB in Polit. Sci and Econs., UCLA, 1973; JD, Boston U., 1976. Bar: Wash. 1976, U.S. Dist. Ct. (we. dist.) Wash. 1976. Adminstr. Action/Peace Corps, Washington, 1973, Fed. Power Commn., Washington, 1974; assoc. Oles Morrison et al, Seattle, 1976-80; ptnr. Schwabe Williamson Ferguson & Burdell, Seattle, 1981-94; of counsel Krutch, Lindell, Housh, Bingham, Keller & Jones, Seattle, 1994—. Mem. ABA, Seattle-King County Bar Assn., Profl. Liability Architects and Engrs. Club: Washington Athletic (Seattle). Avocations: woodworking, skiing. Office: Krutch Lindell Housh Bingham Keller & Jones 1201 3rd Ave # 3100 Seattle WA 98101

PETRIE, JOHN RICHARD, advertising agency executive, writer; b. Astoria, Oreg., Apr. 5, 1945; s. John Richard and Margot Maxwell (Brown) P.; m. Jo Curie Joffe, Feb. 5, 1987. Student, HB Studio, 1964-65, Bowling Green U., 1966-69. Mgr. Discount Records div. CBS, Ann Arbor, Mich., 1971-73; owner King Pleasure, Ann Arbor, 1973-74; program dir. Sta. WABX-FM, Detroit, 1974-75; mgr. Midwest promotion Motown Records, Inc., Detroit, 1975, Mercury Records, Chgo., 1976; advt. mgr. Sidetracks Chgo. Daily News, 1976-77; mgr. Midwest promotion Arista Records, Inc., Chgo., 1978-79; assoc. creative dir. Leo Burnett U.S.A., Chgo., 1980-85; sr. writer HBM/Creamer-Albert J. Rosenthal, Chgo., 1986-88; copywriter Rynne-House Comm., Evanston, Ill., 1988-89; mgr. mags., jours. & periodicals Guild Books & Guild Complex, Chgo., 1990-93; interpretive svcs. John G. Shedd Aquarium, Chgo., 1994—; freelance advt. writer, prodr., instr. Columbia Coll., Nat.-Louis U., Chgo.; interpreter John G. Shedd Aquarium, Chgo., 1994; sales promotion cons. Contbr. articles to Playboy mag., Circus mag., Kitchen Sink Pub., other newspapers, mags. Democrat. Avocations: music, art, poetry, camping, writing.

PETRIE, ROY H., obstetrician, gynecologist, educator; b. Bardwell, Ky., Nov. 9, 1940; s. Randolph Hazel and Glodine (Brown) P. BS, Western Ky. U., 1961; MD, Vanderbilt U., 1965; SCD, Columbia U., 1984. Diplomate Am. Bd. Ob-gyn and div. Maternal/Fetal Medicine. Intern U. Rochester, 1965-66; resident Columbia-Presbyn. Med. Ctr., N.Y.C., 1966-70; fellow in perinatal biology U. S.C. Med. Ctr., Los Angeles, 1972-73; research assoc. Columbia U., N.Y.C., 1972-73; asst. prof. ob-gyn Coll. Physicians and Surgeons Columbia U., N.Y.C., 1973-79, assoc. ob-gyn, dept. dir. med. edn., 1979-84; prof. ob-gyn, dir. maternal/fetal medicine Washington U., St. Louis, 1984-92; prof., chmn. dept. ob-gyn. St. Louis U., 1992—. Author 7 books in field; contbr. over 100 articles on pharmacology and ob-gyn to profl. jours. Served to lt. comdr., USNR, 1970-72. Recipient Purdue-Frederick award Am. Coll. of ob-gyn, 1974; named Outstanding Educator Sloane Hosp. for Women, 1979. Mem. Soc. for Gynecol. Investigation, Soc. Perinatal Obstetricians (pres. 1984-85, v.p. 1985, sec.-treas. 1981-83), N.Y. Obstetrical Soc., N.Y. Acad. Medicine (pres. ob. sect. 1980), N.Y. Perinatal Soc., St. Louis Ob-gyn Soc. Episcopalian. Office: St Louis U Obstetrics and Gynecology 1031 Bellevue Ave Ste 410 Saint Louis MO 63117-1858

PETRIE, WILLIAM, physicist; b. Victoria, B.C. Can., Dec. 30, 1912; s. James and Amelia (Robertson) P.; m. Isabelle Ruth Chodat, May 8, 1944; children: Heather Louise (dec.), Douglas Bruce. B.A., U. B.C., Vancouver, Can., 1938; A.M., Harvard U., 1941, Ph.D., 1944. Assoc. prof. U. Sask., Saskatoon, Can., 1945-51; chief ops. research Def. Research Bd., Ottawa, Ont., Can., 1954-60, dep. chmn., 1966-68; chief Can. def. research staff Def. Research Bd., London, 1968-71; sci. advisor Apollo Energy, Victoria, 1981-83; mem. numerous sci. bds. and coms. Author: The Story of the Aurora Borealis, 1963, Guide to Orchids of North America, 1981; also numerous articles. Recipient Centennial medal Govt. of Can., 1967, numerous research grants and contracts. Fellow Royal Soc. Can. Avocations: gardening; fishing. Home: 52-1255 Wain Rd, Rural Rt 4, Sidney, BC Canada V8L 4R4

PETRILLO, CARL EDWARD, construction company executive; b. Mount Vernon, N.Y., 1940; s. Edward Joseph and Mary Helene (Pagliaro) P.; m. Kathryn Mary Smith, Aug. 28, 1965 (div. Dec. 1977); children—Carl Edward, Christina Elizabeth, Gregory Joseph; m. Dian A. Tomassetti, Nov. 24, 1979; 1 child Mathew Nino. Degree in Bus. Adminstrn., Lehigh U., 1962. Project engr. Yonkers Contracting Co., N.Y., 1964-68, supt., 1968-70, asst. to v.p., 1970-72, v.p., 1972-78, pres., 1978—; pres. Petmar Builders Co., Yonkers, 1973—; chmn., trustee Internat. Brotherhood Teamsters and Chauffers Union; mem. Pres.' Forum Constrn. Industry, 1987—. Mem. Anti-Defamation League, chmn. disting. communtiy svc. award dinner of Westchester, Putnam and Rockland Counties, N.Y., 1992, Nat. Conf. Christians and Jews, vice chmn., 1991, Am. Jewish Com., co-chmn. community svc. dinner Westchester chpt., 1992, Pvt. Industry Council, Yonkers, 1983—, Indsl. Devel. Agy., Yonkers, 1983—; bd. dirs. St. Joseph's Med. Ctr., Yonkers, Westchester County Assn., White Plains, N.Y., Am. Diabetes Assn., White Plains, Westchester-Putnam Affirmative Action Program; mem. pres.' adv. coun. Westchester Med. Ctr., 1988—; mem. Cardinal's com. laity for Most Rev. John J. O'Connor, Archbishop of N.Y. Recipient Westchester Leadership award Am. Diabetes Assn., 1984, Man of Yr. award Dominican Coll. of Blauvelt, Orangeburg, N.Y., 1985; honored by Yonkers C. of C., 1984, Westchester chpt. NCCJ for disting. svcs. in advancement of human rels., 1989; award Pvt. Sector, Westchester Minority Contractors Assn., 1984, Outstanding Svc. award St. Joseph's Med. Ctr., Yonkers, 1987, Good Scout award Boy Scouts of Am., 1990, Humanitarian award Boys Town of Italy, 1991. Mem. Moles, Gen. Contractors Assn., Yonkers C. of C. (bd. dirs. 1986). Roman Catholic. Avocations: tennis; boating; reading; photography. Office: Yonkers Contracting Co Inc PO Box 39 969 Midland Ave Yonkers NY 10704

PETRILLO, LEONARD PHILIP, corporate securities executive, lawyer; b. Toronto, June 20, 1941; s. Philip Ralph and Bernice (Kowalski) P.; children: Larissa, Matthew. BSc, U. Toronto, 1964; LLB, Osgoode Hall Law Sch., Toronto, 1967. Bar: Ont. 1969. Ptnr. Robinson & Petrillo, 1969-79; corp. counsel Seel Enterprises Ltd., 1979-81, gen. counsel Toronto Stock Exch., 1981, corp. sec., sec. to bd. govs., 1984, v.p., 1985, v.p., corp. affairs, gen. counsel, sec., 1988—. Office: Toronto Stock Exch, 2 First Canadian Pl, Toronto, ON Canada M5X 1J2

PETRIN, HELEN FITE, lawyer, consultant; b. Bklyn., June 22, 1940; d. Clyde David and Connie Marie Keaton; m. Michael Richard Petrin, June 29, 1963; children: Jennifer Lee, Michael James, Daniel John. BS, Rider Coll. (now Rider U.), 1962, MA, 1980; postgrad., Glassboro (N.J.) Coll. (now Rowan Coll.), 1981; JD, Widener U., 1987. Bar: Pa. 1989, N.J. 1990, U.S. Dist. N.J. 1990. Tchr. bus. edn. Pennsville (N.J.) Meml. High Sch., 1962-66; asst. prof. Salem Community Coll., Carney's Point, N.J., 1977-81; asst. prof. Brandywine Coll. Widener U., Wilmington, Del., 1981-87, asst. prof., adminstr., dir. paralegal program, 1987-88; dir. continuing legal edn. Widener U. Sch. Law, Brandywine, 1987-88; pvt. practice computer cons. Phila., N.J. and Del., Del., Pa., N.J., 1988—; pvt. practice law Salem, N.J., 1989—; prosecutor Pilesgrove Township, N.J., 1990-91; dep. surrogate Salem County, N.J., 1991—; word processing cons. New Castle County (Del.) Pers. Dept., 1983; mem. dist. 1 ethics com. N.J. Supreme Ct., 1993—. Pres. bd. Salem County YMCA, 1983, bd. dirs., 1980—; col. atty. Phila. Vols. for Indigent Program, 1990—, Camden Legal Svcs., Inc. for Salem County, 1990—; bd. dirs. United Way Salem County, 1991—, treas., 1994-95; mem. III com. Home Ownership and Opportunity for People Everywhere (HOPE), Salem, N.J., 1992—. Mem. ABA (chmn. young lawyers econs. com. 1990-93, vice chmn. mktg. legal svcs. com. gen. practice sect. 1993—), ATLA, N.J. Bar Assn. (exec. com. 1990-93), Pa. Bar Assn., Phila. Bar Assn. (probate adv. panel 1992—), Salem County Bar Assn. (treas. 1991-92, sec. 1992-93, v.p., pres.-elect 1993-94, pres. 1994-95), Delta Pi Epsilon (sec. bd. dirs. 1980-82). Avocations: swimming, music, walking, reading. Home: 99 Marlton Rd Pilesgrove NJ 08098 Office: 51 Market St Salem NJ 08079-1909

PETRINA, ANTHONY J., mining executive, retired. Formerly sr. v.p., chief oper. officer Placer Devel. Ltd., Vancouver, B.C., Can., exec. v.p., chief oper. officer, until 1988, pres., chief exec. officer, 1988-93; ret., 1993; bd. dirs. Miramar Mining Corp., Vancouver, Arequipa Resources Ltd., Vancouver, Metall. Mining Corp., Toronto, Pegasus Gold Corp., Vancouver. Mem. Mining Assn. B.C. (bd. dirs.), Mining Assn. Can. (past chmn.). Office: 8 Sunset Beach, West Vancouver, BC Canada V7W 1R8

PETRINOVICH, LEWIS F., psychology educator; b. Wallace, Idaho, June 12, 1930; s. John F. and Ollie (Steward) P. BS, U. Idaho, 1952; PhD, U. Calif., Berkeley, 1962. Asst. prof. San Francisco State Coll., 1957-63; from assoc. to prof. SUNY, Stony Brook, 1963-68; prof. U. Calif., Riverside, 1968-91, chmn. psychology, 1968-71, 86-89, prof. emeritus, 1991—. Author: Understanding Research in Social Sciences, 1975, Intro. to Statistics, 1976, Human Evolution, Reproduction, and Morality, 1995; editor: Behavioral Devel., 1981, Habituation, Sensitization and Behavior, 1984; cons. editor Behavioral and Neural Biology, 1972-90, Jour. Physiol. and Comparative Psychology, 1980-82, Jour. Comparative Psychology, 1983-90. Fellow Am. Psychol. Assn., Am. Psychol. Soc., Calif. Acad. Scis., Human Behavior and Evolution Soc., Western Psychol. Assn.; mem. Am. Ornithological Union (elected), Animal Behavior Soc., Sigma Xi. Home: 129 Franklin St # 146 Cambridge MA 02139 Office: U Calif Riverside Dept of Psychology Riverside CA 92521

PETRO, JAMES MICHAEL, lawyer, politician; b. Cleve., Oct. 25, 1948; s. William John and Lila Helen (Janca) P.; m. Nancy Ellen Bero, Dec. 16, 1972; children: John Bero, Corbin Marie. BA, Denison U., 1970; JD, Case Western Res., 1973. Bar: Ohio 1973, U.S. Dist. Ct. (no. dist.) Ohio 1974, U.S. Ct. Appeals (6th cir.) 1981. Spl. asst. U.S. senator W.B. Saxbe, Cleve., 1972-73; asst. pros. atty. Franklin County, Ohio, 1973-74; asst. dir. law City of Cleve., 1974; ptnr. Petro & Troia, Cleve., 1974-84; dir. govt. affairs Standard Oil Co., Cleve., 1984-86; ptnr. Petro, Rademaker, Matty & McClelland, Cleve., 1986-93, Buckingham, Doolittle & Burroughs, Cleve., 1993-95. Mem. city coun. Rocky River, Ohio, 1977-79, dir. law, 1980; mem. Ohio Ho. of Reps., Columbus, 1981-84, 86-90; commr. Cuyahoga County, Ohio, 1991-95, Ohio Auditor of State, 1995—. Mem. ABA, Ohio State Bar Assn., Cleve. Bar Assn. Republican. Methodist. Home: 315 Falmouth Dr Cleveland OH 44116-1326 Office: 88 E Broad St Columbus OH 43216

PETROCCO, WILLIAM PATRICK, retail executive; b. Jersey City, Apr. 21, 1946; s. Michael and Sarah (LoDico) P.; m. Linda Lamb, May 9, 1970; children: Billy, Alison, Christopher. BSBA, Fairleigh Dickinson U., 1968; postgrad., N.Y. Inst. Tech., 1971-72. Asst. buyer housewares J.C. Penney Co., N.Y.C., 1968-71; mdse. mgr. Shop Rite Supermarkets, Wakefern Food Corp., Elizabeth, N.J., 1971-84; sr. v.p. gen. mdse., corp. officer Peter J. Schmitt Co., Inc., West Seneca, N.Y., 1984—. Mem. Nat. Assn. Food Wholesalers, Food Mktg. Inst., Gen. Mdse. Distrbs. Council, Buffalo C. of C. Republican. Roman Catholic. Avocations: tennis, jogging. Office: Peter J Schmitt Co Inc 355 Harlem Rd Buffalo NY 14224-1892

PETROCELLI, AMERICO WILLIAM, higher education commissioner; b. Providence, Feb. 17, 1931; m. Doris Petrocelli; 4 children. BS in Chemistry, Providence Coll., 1954, MS in Chemistry, 1958; PhD in Chemistry, U. R.I., 1960; EdD (hon.), Constatinian U., 1990. Rsch. scientist Gen. Dynamics/Electric Boat, Groton, Conn., 1960-62, chief materials and engring., 1966-68, devel. engring. mgr., 1968-70; v.p. engring. Yardney Electric Div., Westerly, R.I., 1970-71, gen. mgr., 1971-75, exec. v.p., 1975-77; v.p. for bus. and fin. U. R.I., Kingston, 1977-89; commr. higher edn. State of R.I., Providence, 1989—; mem. Workforce 2000, Providence, 1988—; trustee R.I. Sch. Design, Providence, 1989—; pres. R.I. Children's Crusade for Higher Edn., Providence, 1990—; bd. dirs. Inst. for Internat. Sport, Kingston. Author: Act Creating Rhode Island Office of Higher Education, 1981; author, editor to sci. articles; patentee in field. Mem. Westerly Sch. Com., 1964-70, Westerly Civil Def. Coun., 1960-62; incorporator Westerly Hosp.; bd. dirs. United Way, Providence, 1976. 1st lt. U.S. Army. Recipient United Italian-Am. award, 1981, Goodrich award, 1986, chester H. Kirk Disting. Engr. award, 1990, Claibone Pell award, 1990, John Hope Settlement House award, 1990. Mem. Aerospace Med. Assn., Am. Inst. Chemists, Phi Kappa Phi, Sigma Xi. Roman Catholic. Home: 71 Westminster St Westerly RI 02891-2731 Office: RI Office Higher Edn 301 Promenade St Providence RI 02908-5748

PETROCELLI, ANTHONY JOSEPH, management executive, consultant; b. Bklyn., Sept. 25, 1937; s. Lucio and Carmela (Carrione) P.; m. Antoinette Cassata, May 25, 1963; 1 child, Serena Ann. BS in Mgmt., Fairleigh Dickinson, Madison, N.J., 1969, MBA, 1972. Pres. Met. Consolidated Inc. N.Y.C., 1978-84; pvt. practice mgmt. cons., 1984-88; ptnr., mng. dir. D. George Harris & Assocs., N.Y.C., 1984—, vice chmn., 1989—; vice chmn. Salt Union Ltd., U.K., 1992—, Societa Chimica Larderello SpA, Italy, 1993—, Harris Chem. Group, 1993—, Harris Specialty Chemicals, Inc., 1994—, Matthes & Weber GmbH, Germany, 1994—. Trustee Italian Am. Club, North Brunswick, N.J. State Adv. Army, 1956-58, Germany. Office: D George Harris & Assocs 399 Park Ave New York NY 10022-4614

PETRONI, DONALD VICTOR, lawyer; b. Reno, Nev., Apr. 22, 1931; s. Victor and Mary (Ceresola) P.; m. Abby Williams Richmond, June 16, 1956 (div. 1973); children: Victor, Lisa; m. Ann Gelston King, Sept. 7, 1973; stepchildren: Chisholm, Pamela, Samuel, Michael Halle. B.A., U. Nev., 1952; postgrad., Stanford U., 1953, J.D., 1958. Bar: Calif. 1959. Assoc. firm O'Melveny & Myers, Los Angeles, 1958-65; ptnr. O'Melveny & Myers, 1965—. Served with U.S. Army, 1953-55. Mem. ABA, Calif. Bar Assn., Los Angeles County Bar Assn. Democrat. Club: Regency. Home: 10770 Chalon Rd Los Angeles CA 90077-3315 Office: O'Melveny & Myers 1999 Ave of the Stars Los Angeles CA 90067-6035 also: O'Melveny & Myers 400 S Hope St Los Angeles CA 90071-2899

PETROS, RAYMOND LOUIS, JR., lawyer; b. Pueblo, Colo., Sept. 19, 1950. BS, Colo. Coll., 1972; JD, U. Colo., 1975. Bar: Colo. 1975. Jud. clk. to Justice Paul V. Hodges Colo. Supreme Ct., Denver, 1975-77; assoc. Bermingham, White, Burke & Ipsen, Denver, 1977-78; from assoc. to ptnr. Hall & Evans, Denver, 1978-81; ptnr. Kirkland & Ellis, Denver, 1981-86, Holme, Roberts & Owen, Denver, 1986—. Contbr. articles to profl. jours. Bd. dirs. Rocky Mountain Poison Control Found., Denver, 1988-94. Office: Holme Roberts & Owen Ste 4100 1700 Lincoln St Denver CO 80203-4541

PETROSIAN, VAHÉ, astrophysicist, educator; b. Arak, Iran, Sept. 13, 1938; came to U.S., 1958; s. Armenak and Chnarik (Beglarian) P.; m. Maude Denney Voegeli, Aug. 21, 1965; children: Gabrielle Elane, Meline Chnar. B.E.E., Cornell U., 1962, M.S., 1963, Ph.D., 1967. Research fellow Calif. Inst. Tech., Pasadena, Calif., 1967-69; vis. scientist Inst. Theoretical Astronomy, Cambridge, Eng., summer 1969; asst.prof. Stanford U., (Calif.), 1969-71; assoc. prof. Stanford U., 1972-79, prof., 1980—, chmn. astronomy program; vis. cons. Kitt Peak Nat. Obs., Tucson. Alfred P. Sloan fellow, 1972-74; NASA grantee, 1983; NSF grantee, 1983. Fellow Royal Astron. Soc.; mem. Internat. Astron. Union, Am. Astron. Soc., U.S. Volleyball Assn. Home: 4114 Willman Dr Palo Alto CA 94306 Office: Stanford U Ctr for Space Sci and Astrophysics ERL 304 Stanford CA 94305

PETROSKY, DANIEL J., army officer; b. Columbus, Ohio, Nov. 10, 1944; m. Barbara Tatman; 1 child, Amanda. Degree in Bus., U. Nebr., Omaha, 1972; Grad. Degree in Systems Mgmt., U. So. Calif., 1980; grad., Field Artillery Officer Candidate Sch., 1967, Command and Gen. Staff Coll., 1988, Army War Coll. Commd. 2d lt. U.S. Army, 1967, advanced through grades to brig. gen., 1993; leader arty. battery platoon, exec. officer 2/42d field arty. 197th Inf., 1967-68; platoon leader, ops. officer 4/77th aerial rocket arty. 101st Airborne Divsn., Vietnam, 1969-70; S-3 4/77th aerial field arty. 101st Airborne Div., Ft. Campbell, Ky., 1973-75; platoon leader, ops. officer 4/77th aerial field arty. 101st Airborne Divsn., Ft. Campbell, Ky., 1975-77; S-3 17th Combat Aviation Group, Korea, 1977-79; comdr. 55th Aviation Co., Korea, 1979-80; tchr. ROTC U. So. Calif., 1984-86; comdr. 4th squadron 2d Armored Cav. Regiment, Germany, 1984-87, regimental exec. officer, 1988-91; battle staff comdr. for comdr.-in-chief U.S. Atlantic Command; leader 4th brigade 1st Armored Divsn., 1991-93; chief of staff 3d Inf. Divsn., 1992-93; asst. divsn. comdr. 101st Airborne Divsn., Ft. Campbell, 1993-94; dep. commdg. gen./asst. commandant U.S. Army Aviation Ctr., Ft. Rucker, Ala., 1994—. Decorated Legion of Merit with two oak leaf clusters, Disting. Flying Cross with one oak leaf cluster, Bronze Star with one oak leaf cluster, 29 Air medals, Army Commendation medal, Army Achievement medal. Office: US Army Aviation Ctr Office Dep Comdg Gen Fort Rucker AL 36362

PETROV, NICOLAS, dance educator, choreographer; b. Novia Sad, Serbia, Yugoslavia, Dec. 13, 1933; came to U.S., 1967; s. Sergie Nicolas and Iren Rehorovic (Roboz) P.; m. Marion Freyda Brookes, Apr. 11, 1956. Ed., Govt. Theatrical Acad., Novi Sad, 1945-51; apsolvent, Drzavne Pozorisne Skole Baletski, Otsek, 1951; ed. State Ballet Acad. of Belgrade, Yugoslavia, 1951-54, Belgrade Govt. U. Fgn. Langs., 1951-55, U. de Paris à Sorbonne, 1956-58. Dancer Nat. Popular Theatre Serbi, Belgrade, 1951-54, Ballet de France de Janine Charrat, Paris, 1954-56; prin. dancer Balletto Europeo di Nervi, Genova, Italy, 1960-62; dancer, choreographer Radio TV France, Paris, 1960-67; from asst. prof. to prof. dance Point Park Coll., Pitts., 1968-78, prof., 1978—; dir. fine, applied and performing arts dept. and dance div., 1975—; founder, artistic dir. Ballet Russe de Nicolas Petrov, Paris, 1962—, Pitts. Ballet Theatre, Inc., 1967-77, Am. Dance Ensemble, Pitts., 1977-87; choreographer Pitts. Opera, 1967-73, 77—; guest dancer Leonide Massine Festival, Goteberg, Sweden, 1956-57; guest dancer and actor Theatre de Vervie Belgium, 1956-57; guest star dancer Opera Mcpl. de Marseille, Paris, 1960-62. Appeared in ballets, including Scheherazade, Swan Lake, Romeo and Juliet, Le Carnaval, Nutcracker, many others; choreographer (operas) Aida, Pitts., 1967-68, Carmen, Pitts., 1967-68, 80-81, La Traviata, Pitts., 1977-78; (ballets) Romeo and Juliet, Pitts., 1971-72, Cinderella, Pitts., 1973-74, Fantasia, Pitts., 1976-77, numerous others; director dance films including Alice in Wonderland, 1972, Carmina Catulli, 1973-74, Romeo and Juliet, 1975; author: The Dance Method, 1967. Asst. mayoral elections, Pitts., 1968, 77; vol. Pitts. Ballet Theatre. Recipient choreography award Nat. Steel Corp., 1976. Mem. AAUP, Am. Guild Music Artists, Rotary, French Masons (N.Y.C.). Avocations: building renovations, skiing, golf, boating. Home: 39 Dilworth St Pittsburgh PA 15211-1913 Office: Point Park Coll 201 Wood St Pittsburgh PA 15222-1984

PETRUCCI, VINCENT EMILIO, retired viticulture educator, consultant; b. Crockett, Calif., July 13, 1925; s. Vincent C. and Assunta (Spero) P.; m. Josephine San Julian, July 12, 1948; children: Julianne, Kristene, Stephanie, Vincent P., Teresa. BS in Biology, U. Calif., Davis, 1948, MS in Pomology, 1951; DSc (hon.), U. Calif., Fresno, 1994. Tchr. agr., asst. football and basketball coach Esparto (Calif.) H.S., 1947-48; prof. viticulture Calif. State U., Fresno, 1948-93, prof. emeritus, 1993—; dir. Viticulture Rsch. Ctr., 1977-85, dir. Viticulture and Enology Rsch. Ctr., 1985-93; mem., cons. Calif. Raisin Adv. Bd.; advisor Am. Vineyard Found.; mem. wine grape quality com. Wine Inst.; co-chmn. Calif. Grape Growers Coalition; presenter in field; cons. to numerous vineyards, univs., colls., profl. orgns. including Almaden Vineyards, Brazil, Chateau Lafite, Pouliat, France, Viticulture and Enology Expt. Sta., Montpellier, France, 1986, U. Llerido, Spain, Orgn. Internat. Orgn. Viticulturists, Rome, 1987; U.S. rep. USA Exhibit, Moldavia; participant numerous seminars, confs., meetings in field. Contbr. numerous articles to sci. jours. Mem. bd. rev. com. Boy Scouts Am.; past pres. St. Anthony's Men's Club, Young Men's Inst.; wine and juice judge Fla. State Fair, Tampa, 1990. With AC Svc., USN, 1944-45. Recipient Disting. Svc. award Calif. Assn. Future Farms, 1966, Cath. Man of Yr. award, 1968; Outstanding Tchr. award Calif. State U., 1971, Salgo-Noren Excellence in Tchg. in Agr., 1974, Man of Yr. award Wines and Vines, 1981, Disting. Svc. award Fresno County Farm Bur., 1983, award of appreciation U.S. Bur. Alcohol, Tobacco and Firearms, 1984, Lifetime Achievement award Calif. Restaurant Assn., 1990, award of appreciation Am. Soc. Farm Mgrs. and Rural Appraisers, 1990, Davis Disting. Alumni Achievement award U. Calif., Davis, 1995; also others. Mem. Am. Soc. Hort. Sci., Am. Soc. Enologists (bd. dirs. 1976), Calif. Fertilization Assn. (former mem. soil improvement com.), Ft. Washington Golf and Country Club, Phi Kappa Phi. Avocations: golf, fishing. Home: 5604 N Flora Fresno CA 93710

PETRUCELLI, FRANK, school system administrator. Supt. schs. Diocese of Paterson, Clifton, N.J. Office: Schs Div Supt 777 Valley Rd Clifton NJ 07013-2205

PETRUCELLI, R(OCCO) JOSEPH, II, nephrologist; b. Meriden, Conn., Sept. 20, 1943; s. Rocco Joseph and Marguerite Robena (Colwell) P. BA, Yale U., 1965; MD, Harvard U., 1969. Diplomate Am. Bd. Internal Medicine, Am. Bd. Nephrology. Intern, then resident Mt. Sinai Hosp.,

N.Y.C., 1969-72; fellow in nephrology U. Calif. San Francisco Med. Ctr., San Francisco, 1972-74; asst. prof. Mt. Sinai Sch. Medicine, 1978-92; assoc. prof. N.Y. Med. Coll., 1992—; vis. rschr. Karolinska Inst., Stockholm, 1970-71; exec. com. End Stage Renal Disease, N.Y.C., 1980-90, pres. 1985. Author: Medicine: An Illustrated History, 1978, trans. in 12 langs., 1978—. Pres. Bklyn. Opera Soc.; mem. med. adv. bd. Nat. Kidney Found., 1987-94, v.p., 1994; treas. Friends of Rare Book Rm. of N.Y. Acad. Medicine, 1993, sec., 1994. Recipient Richard Cabot prize Harvard Med. Sch., 1969, Boylston prize Boylston Med. Soc., 1969, John P. McGovern prize Baylor Coll. Medicine, Houston, 1993. Fellow N.Y. Acad. Medicine (libr. com. 1975—), Am. Soc. Nephrology, Internat. Soc. Nephrology. Democrat. Episcopalian. Home: 19 Fulton Ave Rye NY 10580-2515 Office: Chief Nephrology New Rochelle Med Ctr 16 Guion Pl New Rochelle NY 10801-5503

PETRY, PAUL E., insurance company executive. Exec. v.p., cfo Conn. Mut. Life Ins. Co., Hartford. Office: Conn Mut Life Ins Co 140 Garden St Hartford CT 06154-0001

PETRY, THOMAS EDWIN, manufacturing company executive; b. Cin., Nov. 20, 1939; s. Edwin Nicholas and Leonora Amelia (Zimpelman) P.; m. Mary Helen Gardner, Aug. 25, 1962; children: Thomas Richard, Stephen Nicholas, Daniel Gardner, Michael David. B.S., U. Cin., 1962; M.B.A., Harvard, 1964. Group v.p., treas. Eagle-Picher Industries, Inc., Cin., 1968-81; pres. Eagle-Picher Industries, Inc., 1981-89, COO, 1981—, CEO, 1982—, chmn. bd., 1989—. Republican. Clubs: Queen City, Terrace Park (Ohio) Country, Cin. Country. Office: Eagle-Picher Industries Inc 580 Walnut St Cincinnati OH 45202-3108*

PETSCHEK, ALBERT GEORGE, physics educator; b. Prague, Czechoslovakia, Jan. 31, 1928; came to U.S., 1938; s. Hans and Eva (Epler) P.; m. Marilyn Adiene Poth, June 25, 1949; children: Evelyn A., Rolfe G., Elaine L., Mark A. BS, MIT, 1948; MS, U. Mich., 1949; PhD, U. Rochester, 1953. Jr. research physicist Carter Oil Co., Tulsa, 1948-49; staff mem. Los Alamos (N.Mex.) Nat. Lab., 1953-68, 1980-81; sr. research scientist Systems, Sci. and Software, San Diego, 1968-71; prof. physics N.Mex. Inst. Tech., Socorro, 1966-68, 71-94; prof. emeritus, 1994—; fellow Los Alamos (N.Mex.) Nat. Lab., 1981—; cons. in field. Contbr. articles to profl. jours. Fellow AAAS; mem. AAUP, Am. Phys. Soc., Am. Astron. Soc. Republican. Mem. Unitarian Ch. Home: 122 Piedra Loop Los Alamos NM 38280 Office: NMex Inst Tech Dept Physics Socorro NM 87801

PETSKO, GREGORY ANTHONY, chemistry and biochemistry educator; b. Washington, Aug. 7, 1948; s. John and Mary (Santoro) P.; m. Carol Bannister Chamberlain, July 3, 1971 (div. 1982). BA, Princeton U., 1970; DPhil, Oxford U., 1973. Instr. Wayne State U. Med. Sch., Detroit, 1973-75, asst. prof., 1975-78; assoc. prof. MIT, 1979-85, prof. chemistry, 1985-90; Lucille P. Markey prof. biochemistry and chemistry Brandeis U., Waltham, Mass., 1990—, dir. Rosenstiel Basic Med. Scis. Rsch. Ctr., 1994—; cons. Arqule, Inc., Medford, 1993—. Editor. Jour. Protein Engring., 1988—. Recipient Max Planck prize Max Planck Gesellschaft, 1992; Rhodes scholar Oxford U., 1970, Danforth fellow, 1980; Alfred P. Sloan fellow MIT, 1978. Mem. NAS, Am. Crystallographic Assn. (Siddhu award 1981), Am. Chem. Soc. (Pfizer award 1992), Biophys. Soc., Am. Soc. Biochemistry and Molecular Biology. Avocations: writing poetry and fiction, hiking, basketball, old movies, sports cars. Home: 8 Jason Rd Belmont MA 02178 Office: Rosenstiel Ctr Brandeis U Waltham MA 02254-9110

PETT, JOHN LYMAN, banker; b. Erie, Pa., Dec. 7, 1948; s. Peter Paul and Dorothy (Rhoades) P.; m. Cynthia Gail Szwejbka, Oct. 21, 1972. BS, Gannon U., 1971; MBA, DePaul U., 1977; postgrad., Harvard Bus. Sch., 1989. Asst dir. acctg. and adminstrn. Constrn. Engring. div. Continental Can Co., Chgo., 1977-94; comml. v.p. and lending officer Mfrs. & Traders Trust Co., Buffalo, 1977-79, unit mgr. Mid. Market Lending, 1979-84, sr. v.p., chief credit officer, 1984—. Mem., cons. Erie County Fiscal Res. Com., Buffalo, 1984-86. Capt. USMC, 1971-74. Mem. Robert Morris Assocs., Am. Bankers Assocs., Wanakah Country Club (Hamburg, N.Y.). Republican. Roman Catholic. Avocations: golf, running, reading. Office: Mfrs & Traders Trust Co 1 M & T Plz Buffalo NY 14203-2301

PETTEE, DANIEL STARR, neurologist; b. N.Y.C., Feb. 15, 1925; s. Allen Danforth and Helen Marien (Starr) P.; m. Dimetra Marie Peters, June 24, 1961; children: William, Margaret, Allen. BA, Yale U., 1951; MD, Columbia U., N.Y.C., 1955. Cert. Am. Psychiatry and Neurology, 1965, Am. Bd. Clin. Neurophysiology, 1984. Rotating internship Strong Meml. Hosp. U. Rochester, N.Y., 1955-57, residency neurology, 1957-62; neurologist pvt. practice, Rochester, N.Y., 1962—; clinic dir. Rochester (N.Y.) Area Multiple Sclerosis Chpt., Rochester, N.Y., 1962-76; assoc. prof. neurology U. Rochester (N.Y.) Sch. Medicine, 1978—; clin. assoc. Dept Neurology Strong Meml. Hosp., Rochester, N.Y., 1978—; head neurology Div. Dept. Medicine The Genesee Hosp., Rochester, N.Y., 1972—; pres. Genesee Neurological Assocs., Rochester, 1974—; mem. bd. dirs. Rochester (N.Y.) Area Multiple Sclerosis Chpt., 1970-76. Contbr. articles to profl. jours. Mem. bd. dirs., singer Rochester (N.Y.) Oratorio Soc., 1960-61, 1955-78. Recipient Purple Heart, Bronze Star U.S. Army, 1944, Bronze Hope Chest for Svc. award Rochester (N.Y.) Area Multiple Sclerosis Chpt., 1976. Mem. N.Y. Acad. Sci., Rochester Acad. Sci. (astronomy sect. 1989—, bd. dirs. astronomy sect. 1993-94). Home: 150 Summit Dr Rochester NY 14620 Office: Genesee Neurol Assocs 222 Alexander St Rochester NY 14607

PETTENGILL, GORDON H(EMENWAY), physicist, educator; b. Providence, Feb. 10, 1926; s. Rodney Gordon and Frances (Hemenway) P.; m. Pamela Anne Wolfenden, Oct. 28, 1967; children—Mark Robert, Rebecca Jane. B.S., MIT, 1948; Ph.D., U. Calif., Berkeley, 1955. Staff mem. Lincoln Lab. MIT, Lexington, 1954-63, 65-68; prof. planetary physics, dept. earth, atmospheric and planetary scis. MIT, Cambridge, 1971—, dir. Ctr. Space Rsch., 1984-90; assoc. dir. Arecibo (P.R.) Obs., 1963-65, dir., 1968-71. Served with inf.; Signal Corps AUS, 1944-46. Decorated Combat Inf. badge; recipient Magellanic Premium, Am. Philos. soc., 1994. Mem. Am. Phys. Soc., Am. Astron. Soc., AAAS, Internat. Astron. Union, Internat. Radio Sci. Union, Nat. Acad. Sci., Am. Acad. Arts and Sci. Pioneer several techniques in radar astronomy for describing properties of planets and satellites; discovered 59-day rotational period of planet Mercury. Office: MIT 77 Massachusetts Ave Rm 37-641 Cambridge MA 02139-3594

PETTENGILL, HARRY JUNIOR, federal agency administrator; b. Lock Haven, Pa., Apr. 16, 1946; s. Harry Blair and Bertha Irene (Quigg) P.; m. Sandra Kaye Conway, Sept. 3, 1970; children: Keri-Beth Irene, Justin Matthew, Rebekah Ann Louise. BA, Lock Haven U., 1968; MS, Temple U., 1971; PhD, U. Mich., 1974. Dep. mgr. waste environ. studies project U.S. EPA, Washington, 1975-80; chief uranium mills licensing NRC, Washington, 1980-83; chief uranium recovery licensing NRC, Denver, 1983-88; dir. nuclear safety tech. div. Dept. Energy, Washington, 1988-90, dep. asst. sec. for health, 1990—. U.S. AEC fellow Temple U., 1968, USPHS fellow U. Mich., 1971. Mem. OECD-NEA (com. radiology protection and pub. health), Health Physics Soc. Lt. comdr. USPHS, 1977-79. Office: US Dept Energy 1000 Independence Ave SW Washington DC 20585

PETTENGILL, KROGER, investment counselor; b. Cin., Nov. 4, 1922; s. Irving Wilbert and Gertrude (Kroger) P.; m. Kathryn W. Mitchell, Oct. 6, 1945; children: Adele Pettengill Bunker, Thomas Kroger, Charles Abbott. B.A., Princeton U., 1943. With Provident Bank, Cin., 1946-49; with 1st Nat. Bank, Cin., 1949-68, v.p., 1958-64, pres., 1964-68; pres. C/B Fin. Counsel, Inc., Cin., 1973-76, Kroger Pettengill Fin. Counsel, Inc., 1976—; dir. Cin. br. Fed. Res. Bank Cleve., 1965-67. Gen. budget com. Community Chest and Council Cin. Area, 1960-66; chmn. bd. Children's Hosp. Med. Ctr., Cin., 1979-87, also trustee, chmn. investment com.; chmn. adv. com. to dean U. Cin. Coll. Medicine; chmn. bd. Berea (Ky.) Coll., 1977-87, also trustee. Republican. Episcopalian. Clubs: Commercial, Commonwealth, Queen City, Camargo (Cin.), Hole-in-the-Wall (Naples, Fla.), Naples Yacht Club. Home: 4750 Willow Hills Ln Cincinnati OH 45243-4226 Office: Kroger Pettengill Fin Counsel 3914 Miami Rd Cincinnati OH 45227-3742

PETTERCHAK, JANICE A., library director; b. Springfield, Ill., Sept. 15, 1942; d. Emil H. and Vera C. (Einhoff) Stukenberg; m. John J. Petterchak, Oct. 5, 1963; children: John A., Julie Gilmour, James. AA, Springfield

Coll., 1962; BS, Sangamon State U., 1972, MA, 1982. Supr. hist. markers Ill. State Hist. Soc., Springfield, 1973-74, asst. exec. dir., 1985-87; curator photographs Ill. State Hist. Libr., Springfield, 1974-79, assoc. editor, 1979-83, rep. local history svcs., 1983-85, libr. dir., 1987—; project dir. NEH/Ill. newspaper cataloging project. Author: Mapping a Life's Journey: The Legacy of Andrew McNally III, (booklets) Researching and Writing Local History in Illinois: A Guide to the Sources, 1987; editor: Illinois History: An Annotated Bibliography, 1995; assoc. editor Illinois Historical Jour.; contbr. articles to profl. jours. Grantee NEH, 1987-95. Mem. Ill. State Hist. Soc. (pubs. com.), Ill. Labor History Soc., Abraham Lincoln Assn. (co-editor Papers Abraham Lincoln Assn. 1981-82), Stephen A. Douglas Assn., Sangamon County Hist. Soc. (bd. dirs. 1991-94, v.p. 1994-95, pres. 1995—). Home: 19 Mallard Dr Rochester IL 62563-9753 Office: Ill State Hist Libr 1 Old State Capitol Plz Springfield IL 62701-1512

PETTERSEN, KJELL WILL, stockbroker, consultant; b. Oslo, Norway, June 19, 1927; came to U.S., 1946, naturalized, 1957; s. Jens Will and Ragna O. (Wickstrom) P.; m. Marilyn Ann Stevens, Aug. 16, 1952; children: Thomas W., Maureen, Kevin W., Maryann, Kathleen. Student, Zion Theol. Sch., 1945-49, N.Y. Inst. Finance, 1955-56. Mgr. A.M. Kidder & Co., N.Y.C., 1954-64; sr. v.p., sec., dir. Halle & Stieglitz, Fillor Bullard Co., Inc., 1964-73; sr. v.p., dir. mktg. Parrish Securities, Inc., N.Y.C., 1973-74; cons. Loeb, Rhoades & Co., N.Y.C., 1974-79; mng. dir. Prudential Securities, N.Y.C., 1979-89; pres. Arbitration Recovery Cons., Marco, Fla., 1992-93; vice chmn. Noddings Investment Group, Inc., Oakbrook Terrace, Ill., 1993—; dir. Ski for Light Inc., Mpls., Creative Arts Rehab. Ctr. Inc., N.Y.C. Dem. candidate N.Y. State Assembly, Nassau County, 1962; dir. Guadalupe Ctr., Marco YMCA; pres. Quest for Peace Internat. Mem. Security Industry Assn., Nat. Assn. Security Dealers (bd. arbitrators), N.Y. C. of C., Norwegian-Am. C. of C. (dir. Guadalupe Ctr.), Scandinavian Found., Bankers Club of Am., Norwegian Club (N.Y.C.), Marco Bay Yacht Club, Rotary. Home: 350 Rockhill Ct Marco Island FL 33937-3860

PETTERSON, DONALD K., foreign service officer, ambassador; b. Huntington Park, Calif., Nov. 17, 1930; s. Walter H. and Muriel Frances (McIntyre) P.; m. Julieta Rovirosa Argudin, Aug. 26, 1961; children: Susan, Julie, John, Brian. Student, San Luis Obispo Jr. Coll., 1952-53; BA., U. Calif., Santa Barbara, 1956, M.A., 1960; postgrad., UCLA, 1959-60, Stanford U., 1967-68. Pers. analyst State of Calif., 1958-59; teaching asst. UCLA, 1959-60; commd. fgn. service officer Dept. State, 1960; vice consul Am. embassy, Mexico City, 1961-62; vice consul Am. consulate, Zanzibar, 1963-64, prin. officer, 1965; polit. officer Lagos, 1966-67; served in pers. office Dept. State, Washington, 1968-70; dep. chief of mission Freetown, Sierra Leone, 1970-72; polit. counselor Pretoria, 1972-75; mem. policy planning staff Dept. State, Washington, 1975-77; dir. Office So. African Affairs Dept. State, 1977-78, dep. asst. sec. of state, 1978; U.S. amb. to Somalia, 1978-82; vis. disting. scholar UCLA, 1983-84; dep. dir. office Mgmt. Ops. Dept. State, Washington, 1984-86; U.S. amb. to Tanzania, 1986-89, acting dep. asst Sec. State, 1990; dir. Liberia Task Force, 1990; charge d'affaires Am. Embassy, Harare, Zimbabwe, 1990-91; U.S. amb. to Sudan, 1992—. Served with USN, 1948-52. Recipient Superior Honor award Dept. State, 1964, 71, Order of the Somali Star award; named Alumnus of Yr. U. Calif., Santa Barbara, 1965. Office: Am Emb Khartoum Unit 63900 APO AE 09829-3900

PETTEWAY, SAMUEL BRUCE, college president; b. Fayetteville, N.C., July 18, 1924; s. Walter Bernard and Margaret Maysie (Cole) P.; m. Eleanor Glenn Sugg, Nov. 27, 1948; children—Margaret Petteway Small, Samuel Bruce. B.S., N.C. State U., 1949, M.Ed., 1966, Ed.D., 1968. Gen. mgr. Homeowners Ins. and Realty Co., 1960-63; engring. tech. dept. chmn., dean occupational and transfer programs, dir. evening programs Lenoir County Community Coll., 1963-68; pres. Coll. of the Albemarle, Elizabeth City, N.C., 1968-75, N.C. Wesleyan Coll., Rocky Mount, 1975-86; prof. Va. Poly. Inst. and State U., 1973-75, East Carolina U., 1994—; pres. Philanthropic Cons., Inc., Kinston, N.C., 1986—; sec. Coll. Mgmt. Svcs., Inc., Raleigh, N.C., 1989; lic. amateur radio operator, 1992—. Pres. chpt. Am. Cancer Soc., 1960-61, Boys' Club Lenoir County, 1987-91; bd. dirs. Rocky Mount Acad., 1979-80, Triangle East, Inc., 1985-86, Meth. Home for Children, 1994—; chmn. deferred giving com. N.C. Methodist Found., 1979-86; chmn. council on ministries 1st United Meth. Ch., Rocky Mount, 1980-81; chmn. bd. trustees Art Edn. Found., 1980; mem. Nash County Bd. Health, 1985-86; local bd. dirs. Cypress Glen Retirement Home, 1993—; chmn. coun. on ministries Westminster United Meth. Ch., 1989-90. Served with USNR, 1941-46. Named Tar Heel of Week News and Observer, 1975, Today's Outstanding N.C. Citizen WNCT-TV, 1975; NSF fellow U. Ill., 1963. Mem. Nat. Assn. for Hosp. Devel., N.C. Assn. Colls. and Univs., N.C. Conf. United Meth. Ch. (chmn. bd. trustees 1973-79), Nat. Soc. Fund Raising Execs. (cert.), Rocky Mount C. of C. (bd. dirs. 1980-84), Phi Kappa Phi, Theta Alpha Phi. Democrat. Clubs: Benvenue Country, Galaxy Social; Kinston Country. Lodge: Rotary (pres. 1980-81, bd. dirs. Kinston chpt. 1988-92). Office: 708 Westminster Ln Kinston NC 28501-2770

PETTEY, WALTER GRAVES, III, lawyer; b. Bessemer, Ala., Aug. 24, 1949; s. Walter Graves Jr. and Mildred Louise (Nebrig) P.; m. Virginia McWherter Lott, Feb. 28, 1976; 1 child, Stephen Blacksher. BA, Washington & Lee U., 1971; JD, U. Ala., 1976. Bar: Ala. 1976, Tex. 1977. Law clk. to Hon. Walter P. Gewin U.S. Ct. Appeals (5th cir.), Tuscaloosa, Ala., 1976-77; assoc. Hughes & Hill, Dallas, 1977-82; assoc. Pettit & Martin, Dallas, 1983-84, ptnr., 1985-92; ptnr. Hughes & Luce, L.L.P., Dallas, 1992—. 1st lt. U.S. Army, 1971-73. Office: Hughes & Luce L L P 1717 Main St Ste 2800 Dallas TX 75201

PETTIBONE, PETER JOHN, lawyer; b. Schenectady, N.Y., Dec. 11, 1939; s. George Howard and Caryl Grey (Ketchum) P.; m. Jean Kellogg, Apr. 23, 1966; children: Stephen, Victoria. AB summa cum laude, Princeton U., 1961; JD, Harvard U., 1964; LLM, NYU, 1971. Bar: Pa. 1965, D.C. 1965, N.Y. 1968, U.S. Supreme Ct. 1974. Lectr. Heidelberg (Fed. Republic Germany) U., 1965-67; assoc. Cravath, Swaine & Moore, N.Y.C., 1967-74, Lord Day & Lord, Barrett Smith, N.Y.C., 1974-76; ptnr. Lord Day & Lord, Barrett Smith, N.Y.C. and Washington, 1976-94, Patterson, Belknap, Webb & Tyler, LLP, N.Y.C. and Washington, 1994—; pres. 1158 Fifth Ave. Corp., N.Y.C., 1991-94; pres. North Ferry Co., Shelter Island, N.Y., 1987-90; bd. dirs., vice-chmn. N.Y. State Facilities Devel. Corp., N.Y.C., 1983-89. Editor USSR Legal Materials, 1990-92. Trustee, treas. Hosp. Chaplaincy Inc., N.Y.C., 1980-86, Civitas, N.Y.C., 1984-92; mem. N.Y. State Gov.'s World Trade Coun., 1989—; mem. Coun. Fgn. Rels., 1993—; trustee Union Chapel, Shelter Island, N.Y., 1990—; bd. dirs., vice chmn. Geonomics Inst., Middlebury, Vt., 1991—; mem. vestry Ch. of Heavenly Rest, N.Y.C., 1987-93. Capt. U.S. Army, 1965-67, Heidelberg, Germany. Mem. ABA, Assn. Bar City N.Y. (chmn. com. on CIS affairs 1991-94), U.S.-USSR Trade and Econ. Coun. Inc. (U.S. co-chmn. legal com. 1980-92), U.S.-Russia Bus. Coun. (bd. dirs.), Soc. of Cin., Anglers Club N.Y.C., Shelter Island Yacht Club, Amateur Ski Club N.Y. (pres. 1980-82), Canterbury Choral Soc. (pres. 1983-84), Phi Beta Kappa. Episcopalian. Home: 1158 5th Ave New York NY 10029-6917 also: 10 Wesley Ave Shelter Island Heights NY 11965 Office: Patterson Belknap Webb & Tyler LLP 1133 Ave of the Americas New York NY 10036

PETTIGREW, L. EUDORA, university president; b. Hopkinsville, Ky., Mar. 1, 1928; d. Warren Cicero and Corrye Lee (Newell) Williams; children: Peter W. Woodard, Jonathan R. (dec.). MusB, W.Va. State Coll., 1950; MA, So. Ill. U., 1964, PhD, 1966. Music/English instr. Swift Meml. Jr. Coll., Rogersville, Tenn., 1950-51; music instr., librarian Western Ky. Vocat. Sch., Paducah, 1951-52; music/English instr. Voorhees Coll., Denmark, S.C., 1954-55; dir. music and recreation therapy W.Ky. State Psychiatric Hosp., Hopkinsville, 1956-61; research fellow Rehab. Inst., So. Ill. U., Carbondale, 1961-63, instr., resident counselor, 1963-66, coordinator undergrad. ednl. psychology, 1963-66, acting chmn. dept. ednl. psychology, tchr. corps instr., 1966; asst. prof. to assoc. prof. dept. psychology U. Bridgeport, Conn., 1966-70; chmn. dept. urban and met. studies Coll. Urban Devel. Mich. State U., East Lansing, 1974-80; assoc. provost, U. Del., Newark, 1981-86; pres. SUNY Coll. at Old Westbury, 1986—. Cons. for research and evaluation Hall Neighborhood House Day Care Tng. Project, Bridgeport, 1966-68, coordinator for edn. devel., 1968-69; cons. Bridgeport Public Schs. lang. devel. project, 1967-68, 70; cons. research/evaluation U.S. Eastern Regional Lab., Edn. Devel. Center, Newton, Mass., 1967-69; assoc. prof. U. Bridgeport,

1970, Center for Urban Affairs and Coll. of Edn., Mich. State U., East Lansing, 1970-73; cons. Lansing Model Cities Agy., Day Care Program, Lansing, Mich., 1971; trustee L.I. Community Found.; program devel. specialist Lansing Public Schs. Tchr. Corps program, 1971-73; cons. U. Pitts., 1973, 74, Leadership Program, U. Mich. and Wayne State U., 1975, Wayne County Public Health Nurses Assn., 1976, Ill. State Bd. Edn., 1976-77; chair commn. Africa SUNY, 1994—; lectr. in field; condr. workshops in field; cons. in field. Tv/radio appearances on: Black Women in Edn, Channel 23, WKAR, East Lansing, 1973, Black Women and Equality, Channel 2, Detroit, 1974, Women and Careers, Channel 7, Detroit, 1974, Black Women and Work: Integration in Schools, WITL Radio, Lansing, 1974, others.; Contbr. articles to profl. jours. Recipient Diana award Lansing YWCA, 1977, Outstanding Profl. Achievement award, 1987, award L.I. Ctr. for Bus. and Profl. Women, 1988, Educator of Yr. 100 Black Men of L.I., 1988, Black Women's Agenda award, 1988, Woman of Yr. Nassau/Suffolk Coun. of Adminstrv. Women in Edn., 1989, Disting. Ednl. Leadership award L.I. Women's Coun. for Equal Edn. Tng. and Employment, 1989, L.I. Disting. Leadership award L.I. Bus. News, 1990, Disting. Black Women in Edn. award Nat. Coun. Negro Women, 1991; named Outstanding Black Educator, NAACP, 1968, Oustanding Woman Educator, Mich. Women's Lawyers Assn. and Mich. Trial Lawyers Assn., 1975, Disting. Alumna, Nat. Assn. for Equal Opportunity in Higher Edn., 1990, Woman of Yr., Nassau County League of Women Voters, 1991. Mem. AAAS, Nat. Assn. Acad. Affairs Adminstrs., Internat. Assn. Univ. Pres. (exec. com.), Phi Delta Kappa. Office: SUNY-Old Westbury PO Box 210 Old Westbury NY 11568-0210

PETTIGREW, THOMAS FRASER, social psychologist, educator; b. Richmond, Va., Mar. 14, 1931; s. Joseph Crane and Janet (Gibb) P.; m. Ann Hallman, Feb. 25, 1956; 1 son, Mark Fraser. A.B. in Psychology, Va., 1952; M.A. in Social Psychology, Harvard U., 1955, Ph.D., 1956; D.H.L. (hon.), Governor's State U., 1979. Rsch. assoc. Inst. Social Rsch., U. Natal, Republic South Africa, 1956; asst. prof. psychology U. N.C., 1956-57; asst. prof. social psychology Harvard U., Cambridge, Mass., 1957-62, lectr., 1962-64, assoc. prof., 1964-68, prof., 1968-74, prof. social psychology and sociology, 1974-80; prof. social psychology U. Calif., Santa Cruz, 1980-94, rsch. prof. social psychology, 1994—; prof. social psychology U. Amsterdam, 1986-91; mem. com. status black Ams. NRC, 1985-88; adj. fellow Joint Ctr. Polit. and Econ. Studies, Washington, 1982—; mem. adv. bd. women's studies program Princeton (N.J.) U., 1985—. Author: (with E.Q. Campbell) Christians in Racial Crisis: A Study of the Little Rock Ministry, 1959, A Profile of the Negro American, 1964, Racially Separate or Together?, 1971, (with Frederickson, Knobol, Glazer and Veda) Prejudice, 1982, (with Alston) Tom Bradley's Campaigns for Governor: The Dilemma of Race and Political Strategies, 1988, How to Think Like a Social Scientist, 1995; editor: Racial Discrimination in the United States, 1975, The Sociology of Race Relations: Reflection and Reform, 1980, (with C. Stephan & W. Stephan) The Future of Social Psychology: Defining the Relationship Between Sociology and Psychology, 1991; mem. editorial bd. Jour. Social Issues, 1959-64, Social Psychology Quarterly, 1977-80; assoc. editor Am. Sociol. Rev, 1963-65; mem. adv. bd. Integrated Edn, 1963-84, Phylon, 1965-93, Edn. and Urban Society, 1968-90, Race, 1972-74, Ethnic and Racial Studies, 1978-95, Rev. of Personality and Social Psychology, 1980-85, Community and Applied Social Psychology, 1989—, Individual and Politics, 1989-93, New Cmty., 1994—; contbr. articles to profl. publs. Chmn. Episcopal presiding Bishop's Adv. Com. on Race Relations, 1961-63; v.p. Episcopal Soc. Cultural and Racial Unity, 1962-63; mem. Mass. Gov.'s Adv. Com. on Civil Rights, 1962-64; social sci. cons. U.S. Commn. Civil Rights, 1966-71; mem. White House Task Force on Edn., 1967; mem. nat. task force on desegregation policies Edn. Commn. of States, 1977-79; trustee Ella Lyman Cabot Trust, Boston, 1977-79; mem. Emerson Book Award com. United Chpts. Phi Beta Kappa, 1971-73. Guggenheim fellow, 1967-68; NATO sr. scientist fellow, 1974; fellow Center Advanced Study in Behavioral Scis., 1975-76; Sydney Spivack fellow in intergroup relations Am. Sociol. Assn., 1978; Netherlands Inst. Advanced Study fellow, 1984-85; recipient Kurt Lewin Meml. award Soc. for Psychological Study of Social Issues, 1987, (with Martin) Gordon Allport Intergroup Rels. Rsch. prize, 1988, Faculty Rsch. award U. Calif., Santa Cruz, 1988; Bellagio (Italy) Study Ctr. resident fellow, Rockefeller Found., 1991. Fellow Am. Psychol. Assn., Am. Sociol. Assn. (council 1979-82); mem. Soc. Psychol. Study Social Issues (council 1962-66, pres. 1967-68), NRC (com. status black Ams. 1985-88), European Assn. Social Psychology. Home: 524 Van Ness Ave Santa Cruz CA 95060-3556

PETTIJOHN, FRANCIS JOHN, geology educator; b. Waterford, Wis., June 20, 1904; m. Dorothy Bracken; 1930 (dec.); children: Norma Pettijohn Friedemann, Clare Pettijohn Maher, Loren; m. Virginia Romberger, 1990 (dec.). A.B., U. Minn., 1924, A.M., 1925, Ph.D., 1930; D.H.L. (hon.), Johns Hopkins U., 1978; Sc.D. (hon.), U. Minn. 1986. Instr. Macalester Coll., 1924-25, Oberlin Coll., 1925-29, U. Minn., 1928-29; instr. U. Chgo., 1929-31, asst. prof., 1931-39, asso. prof., 1939-46, prof., 1946-52; prof. Johns Hopkins U., Balt., 1952-73; prof. emeritus Johns Hopkins U., 1973—, chmn. dept. geology, 1963-68, acting chmn. dept. earth and planetary scis., 1970; geologist U.S. Geol. Survey, 1943-53; cons. Shell Oil Co., 1953-63; mem. adv. panel for earth scis. NSF, 1959-62; mem. adv. bd. Petroleum Research Fund., 1963-65. Author: numerous books in field including Sedimentary Rocks, 1949, 3d edit., 1973, (with P.E. Potter) Paleocurrents and Basin Analysis, 1963, 2d edit., 1977, (with P.E. Potter, R. Siever) Sand and Sandstone, 1987, 2d edit.; contbr. articles to profl. jours.; editor: Jour. Geology, 1947-52. Recipient Sorby medal Internat. Assn. Sedimentologists, 1982. Fellow AAAS, Geol. Soc. London (Wollaston medal 1974), Geol. Soc. Am. (Penrose medal 1975); mem. Soc. Econ. Paleontologists and Mineralogists (hon., pres. 1955-56, Twenhofel medal 1974), Geol. Soc. India (hon.), Geol. Soc. Finland (corr.), Soc. for Sedimentary Geology (established Francis J. Pettijohn medal 1992), Am. Assn. Petroleum Geologists, Am. Acad. Arts and Scis., Nat. Acad. Scis., Explorers Club (life), Phi Beta Kappa, Sigma Xi. Home: U51 11630 Glen Arm Rd Glen Arm MD 21057-9403 Office: Johns Hopkins U Dept Earth And Scis Baltimore MD 21218

PETTIJOHN, FRED PHILLIPS, retired newspaper executive, consultant; b. Balt., May 11, 1917; s. Fred and Adelaide Josephine (Phillips) P.; m. Elaine Wilson, Dec. 7, 1946; children: Fred Phillips, Mark Clay. B.A.E., U. Fla., 1941. Sports editor Tallahassee Democrat, 1946-53; with Fort Lauderdale (Fla.) News, 1953-82, exec. editor, 1960-68, gen. mgr., 1968-77, editorial dir., from 1977; 1st v.p. Gore Newspapers Co., from 1960; now cons. Bd. dirs. Salvation Army, 1975-79, v.p., 1979; bd. dirs. Fla. Council 100, 1976-78. Served with AUS, 1943-45. Recipient Disting. Service award Fla. Press Assn., 1976, Disting. Alumnus award U. Fla., 1977; inducted into Fla. Newspaper Hall of Fame, 1990. Mem. Fla. Press Assn. (pres. 1963-64, 69-70), AP Mng. Editors (bd. dirs. 1966-74), So. Newspaper Pubs. Assn., Lauderdale Yacht Club, Tower Club, Sigma Delta Chi, Theta Chi. Democrat. Presbyterian. Home: 911 N Rio Vista Blvd Fort Lauderdale FL 33301-3037

PETTINELLA, NICHOLAS ANTHONY, financial executive; b. Little Falls, N.Y., Sept. 9, 1942; s. Nicholas and Rose (Zuccaro) P.; m. Nancy C. Whitehouse, Oct. 28, 1978; children: Albert J., Michael A. BS, Bentley Coll., 1968; MBA, Babson Coll., 1975; postgrad. Harvard U., 1979, Stanford U., 1983. CPA, Mass. Auditor, Coopers & Lybrand, Boston, 1970-76; treas. Courier Corp., Lowell, Mass., 1976-80; controller corp. ops. Digital Equipment Corp., Maynard, Mass., 1980-81; dir. fin. Intermetrics, Inc., Cambridge, Mass., 1981-83; v.p. fin., chief fin. officer, treas., 1983—; bd. dirs. The Computer Muss., Boston, 1986—, treas. 1988—. Chmn. fin. com. Town of Ashland, Mass., 1980-82. Served with U.S. Army, 1964-66. Mem. Fin. Execs. Inst., AICPA, Inst. Mgmt. Accts., Mass. Soc. CPAs, Treas. Club Boston, Pacioli Soc. Roman Catholic. Home: 141 South St Ashland MA 01721-2263 Office: Intermetrics Inc 733 Concord Ave Cambridge MA 02138-1099

PETTINGA, CORNELIUS WESLEY, pharmaceutical company executive; b. Mille Lacs, Minn., Nov. 10, 1921; s. R.C. and Adrianna (Landaal) P.; m. Yvonne Imogene Svoboda, Dec. 22, 1943; children—Julie, Steven, Mark, Tom, Jennifer. A.B. Hope Coll., 1942; postgrad., Syracuse U., 1943; Ph.D. in Chemistry, Iowa State Coll., 1949; DSc with honors, Hope Coll., 1985; DSc (hon.), Ind. U., 1988. With Eli Lilly & Co., Indpls., 1949-86, v.p. research, devel. and control, 1966-70, v.p., asst. to pres., 1970-72, exec. v.p. 1972-86, bd. dirs. 1966-86, cons. bus. & tech., 1987—; pres. Elizabeth Arden, Inc., 1971-72, now bd. dirs.; bd. dirs. Eli Lilly Internat. Corp.,

IVAC, Cardiac Pacemakers Inc., Physio-Control, Ind. Corp. for Sci. and Tech., Indpls., Collagen Corp., Palo Alto, Calif., Atrix Labs Inc., Ft. Collins, Colo., Wyckoff Chem. Co., South Haven, Mich., Celtrix Corp., Palo Alto, Integrated Biotech. Corp., Indpls. Contbr. articles to profl. jours. Bd. overseers Sweet Briar Coll.; trustee, bd. govs., fin. com., exec. com. Indpls. Mus. Art; bd. dirs. Hanover Coll.; trustee Park-Tudor Sch., Coe Coll.; mem. corp. vis. com. dept. nutrition and food sci. M.I.T.; mem. Purdue Rsch. Found. Will with USNR, 1943-45. Fellow Nat. Cancer Inst., 1949; recipient Charles H. Best award ADA, 1986. Mem. Am. Chem. Soc., AAAS, Ind. Acad. Sci., Bus. Com. for Arts, Indpls., C of C (new bus. devel. com.), Sigma Xi. Clubs: Lambs (Indpls.), University (Indpls.), Woodstock (Indpls.), Meridian Hills Country (Indpls.); Piedmont (Lynchburg, Va.), John's Island (Vero Beach, Fla.). Home: 445 Somerset Dr W Indianapolis IN 46260-2919 Office: 44 Winterton 1010 E 86th St Indianapolis IN 46240-1810

PETTIS, RONALD EUGENE, lawyer; b. Williston, N.D., Sept. 5, 1939; s. Elmer Roy and Hildur Ann (Olson) P.; m. T. Mary Whitehead, June 12, 1961; children: Anna T. Scott, Phillip A. BA, U. Idaho, 1961; JD, U. Calif, Berkeley, 1969. Bar: Calif. 1970, U.S. Dist. Ct. (cen. dist.) Calif. 1974, U.S. Supreme Ct. 1978. Assoc. Hennigan, Butterwick & Clepper, Riverside, Calif., 1971-74, ptnr., shareholder, 1974-79; ptnr., shareholder Butterwick, Bright, Pettis & Cunnison, Inc., Riverside, 1979-82; ptnr. Gray Cary Ware & Freidenrich, San Diego, 1982—; bd. dirs. Western Maquiladora Trade Assn. Mem. bd. dirs., chmn., environ com. Border Trade Alliance. Served to capt. USMC, 1961-66. Mem. ABA, Internat. Bar Assn., Border Trade Alliance, U.S.-Mex. C. of C. (bd. dirs., pres. Pacific chpt.), Masons. Office: Gray Cary Ware & Friedenrich 1700 1st Interstate Plz 401 B St San Diego CA 92101-4223

PETTIS-ROBERSON, SHIRLEY MCCUMBER, former congresswoman; b. Mountain View, Calif.; d. Harold Oliver and Dorothy Susan (O'Neil) McCumber; m. John J. McNulty (dec.); m. Jerry L. Pettis (dec. Feb. 1975); m. Ben Roberson, Feb. 6, 1988; children: Peter Dwight Pettis, Deborah Neil Pettis Moyer. Student, Andrews U., U. Calif., Berkeley. Mgr. Audio-Digest Found., L.A., Glendale; sec.-treas. Pettis, Inc., Hollywood, 1958-68; mem. 94th-95th Congresses from 37th Calif. Dist., mem. coms. on interior, internat. rels., edn. and labor; pres. Women's Rsch. and Edn. Inst., 1979-80; bd. dirs. Kemper Nat. Ins. Cos., 1979—. Mem. Pres.'s Commn. on Arms Control and Disarmament, 1980-83, Commn. on Presdl. Scholars, 1990-92; trustee U. Redlands, Calif., 1980-83, Loma Linda (Calif.) U. and Med. Ctr., 1990—; chair Loma Linda U. Children's Hosp. Found.; bd. dirs. Former Mems. Congress, Capitol Hill Club, Washington. Mem. Morningside Country Club (Rancho Mirage, Calif.).

PETTIT, FREDERICK SIDNEY, metallurgical engineering educator, researcher; b. Wilkes Barre, Pa., Mar. 10, 1930; s. Edwin Humes and Edith Mae (Barnecut) P.; m. Lou-Jean Mary Corso, Aug. 30, 1958; children: Frederick N., Theodore E., John C., Charles A. B in Engring., Yale U., 1952, M in Engring., 1960, D in Engring., 1962. Jr. engr. Westinghouse Electric Corp., Pitts., 1952-54; engr. Avco-Lycoming, Stratford, Conn., 1957-58; postdoctoral student Max Planck Inst. Phys. Chemistry, Gottingen, Fed. Republic Germany, 1962-63; sr. staff scientist Pratt & Whitney Aircraft Co., East Hartford, Conn., 1963-79; prof. metall.-material engring. dept., chmn. U. Pitts., Pa., 1979-88; prof. U. Pitts., 1988—, Harry S. Tack prof. materials engring., 1992—; mem. adv. bd. Jour. Oxidation of Metals, Plenum Press, N.Y., 1975—. 1st lt USMC, 1954-57. NSF fellow, 1962-63. Mem. Metall. Soc. (program dir. 1982-83), Electrochem. Soc. (sec.-treas. high temperature materials div. 1979-83), Am. Soc. Metals, Materials Rsch. Soc. Roman Catholic. Home: 201 Ennerdale Dr Pittsburgh PA 15237-4026 Office: U Pitts 848 Benedum Hall Pittsburgh PA 15261-2208

PETTIT, GEORGE ROBERT, chemistry educator, cancer researcher; b. Long Branch, N.J., June 8, 1929; s. George Robert and Florence Elizabeth (Seymour) P.; m. Margaret Jean Benger, June 20, 1953; children: William Edward, Margaret Sharon, Robin Kathleen, Lynn Benger, George Robert III. B.S., Wash. State U., 1952; M.S. Wayne State U., 1954, Ph.D., 1956. Teaching asst. Wash. State U., 1950-52, lecture demonstrator, 1952; rsch. chemist E.I. duPont de Nemours and Co., 1953; grad. teaching asst. Wayne State U., 1952-53, rsch. fellow, 1954-56; sr. rsch. chemist Norwich Eaton Pharms., Inc., 1956-57; asst. prof. chemistry U. Maine, 1957-61, assoc. prof. chemistry, 1961-65, prof. chemistry, 1965; vis. prof. chemistry Stanford U., 1965; chmn. organic div. Ariz. State U., 1966-68, prof. chemistry, 1965—; vis. prof. So. African, Univs., 1978; dir. Cancer Rsch. Lab., 1974-75, Cancer Rsch. Inst., 1975—; lectr. various colls. and univs.; cons. in field. Contbr. articles to profl. jours. Mem. adv. bd. Wash. State U. Found., 1981-85. Served with USAFR, 1951-54. Recipient Disting. Rsch. Professorship award Ariz. State U., 1978-79, Alumni Achievement award Wash. State U., 1984; named Dalton Prof. Medicinal Chemistry and Cancer Rsch., 1986—, Regents Prof. Chemistry, 1990—. Fellow Am. Inst. Chemists (Pioneer award 1989, Ariz. Gov.'s Excellence award 1993); mem. Am. Chem. Soc. (awards com. 1968-71, 78-81), Chem. Soc. (London), Pharmacognosy Soc., Am. Assn. Cancer Rsch., Sigma Xi, Phi Lambda Upsilon. Office: Ariz State U Cancer Rsch Inst Tempe AZ 85287

PETTIT, GHERY DEWITT, retired veterinary medicine educator; b. Oakland, Calif., Sept. 6, 1926; s. Hermon DeWitt Pettit and Marion Esther (St. John) Menzies; m. Frances Marie Seitz, July 5, 1948; children: Ghery St. John, Paul Michael. BS in Animal Sci., U. Calif., Davis, 1948, BS in Vet. Sci., 1951, DVM, 1953. Diplomate Am. Coll. Vet. Surgeons (recorder 1970-77, pres., chmn. bd. dirs. 1978-80). Asst. prof. vet. surgery U. Calif., Davis, 1953-61; prof. vet. surgery Wash. State U., Pullman, 1961-91, prof. emeritus, 1991—; mem. Wash. State Vet. Bd. Govs., 1981-88, chmn., 1987; vis. fellow Sydney (Australia) U., 1977. Author/editor: Intervertebral Disc Protrusion in the Dog, 1966; cons. editoral bd. Jour. Small Animal Practice, Eng., 1970-88; mem. editoral bd. Compendium on C.E., Lawrenceville, N.J., 1983-86, editoral rev. bd. Jour. Vet. Surgery, Phila., 1984-86, editor 1987-92; contbr. articles to profl. jours., chpts. to books. Elder Presbyn. Ch., Pullman, 1967—. Served with USN, 1944-46. Recipient Norden Disting. Tchr. award Wash. State U. Class 1971, Faculty of Yr. award Wash. State U. Student Com., 1985. Mem. Am. Vet. Med. Assn., Sigma Xi, Phi Zeta, Phi Kappa Sigma (chpt. advisor 1981-93, 2d v.p. 1993-95). Republican. Avocations: camping, small boat sailing.

PETTIT, GHERY ST. JOHN, electronics engineer; b. Woodland, Calif., Apr. 6, 1952; s. Ghery DeWitt and Frances Marie (Seitz) P.; m. Marilyn Jo Van Hoose, July 28, 1973; children: Ghery Christopher, Heather Kathleen. BS in Electrical Engring., Wash. State U., 1975. Nuclear engr. Mare Island Naval Shipyard, Vallejo, Calif., 1975-76; electronics engr. Naval Electronic Systems Engring. Ctr., Vallejo, 1976-79; sr. engr. Martin Marietta Denver Aerospace, 1979-83; staff engr. Tandem Computers Inc., Santa Clara, Calif., 1983-90; mgr. electromagnetic capability Tandem Computers Inc., Cupertino, Calif., 1990-91, electromagnetic compatibility lead engr., 1991-95; EMC engr. Intel Corp., Hillsboro, Oreg., 1995—. Asst. cubmaster Boy Scouts Am., San Jose, Calif., 1985-86, cubmaster, 1986-88, asst. scoutmaster, 1988-90, scoutmaster, 1990-93. Mem. IEEE (sr.), Electromagnetic Capability Soc. (sec.-treas. Littleton, Colo. chpt. 1985-86, sec. Santa Clara Valley chpt. 1985-87, vice chmn. 1987-89, chmn. 1989-91, sec. Santa Clara Valley sect. 1991-92, treas. 1992-93, vice chmn. 1993-94, chmn. 1994—). Republican. Presbyterian. Avocations: target shooting, hiking, camping, amateur radio. Office: Intel Corp 5200 NE Elam Young Pky Hillsboro OR 97124

PETTIT, HORACE, allergist, consultant; b. Jan. 28, 1903; s. Horace and Katherine (Howell) P.; B.S., Harvard Coll., 1927; M.D., 1931; m. Millicent Lewis, Nov. 22, 1924 (dec.); children: Emily Connery, Horace (dec.), Deborah Myers, Norman; m. Jane Mann Hiatt, May 13, 1950 (dec.); 1 adopted child, Barbara Mann Ralph. Intern. Bryn Mawr Hosp., 1933-34; asst. instr., instr., assoc. bacteriology U. Pa. Sch. Medicine, 1932-39, instr. medicine, 1939-53; pvt. practice allergy, 1940-42, 1947-75; cons. in allergy Bryn Mawr Hosp., 1973-75, emeritus staff mem., 1979—; cons. allergist Bryn Mawr Coll., 1963-75. Served from maj. to lt. col. AUS, 1942-46. Fellow Coll. Physicians of Phila.; mem. AMA, Am. Acad. Allergy, Am. Soc. Microbiology, Phila. County, Med. Soc., Pa. Med. Soc., Phila. Allergy Soc. (pres. 1958-59), United World Federalists (mem. nat. exec. coun. 10 years), St. Andrew's Soc. Phila. Unitarian. Clubs: Harvard-Radcliffe (Phila.); Merion

Cricket (Haverford, Pa.); Camden (Maine) Yacht. Home and Office: 1400 Waverly Rd Apt 315 Gladwyne PA 19035-1254

PETTIT, JOHN W., hospital administrator; b. Detroit, Mar. 6, 1942; s. John W. and Clara (Schatz) P.; m. Kathleen Endres, Aug. 8, 1970; children: Julie, Andrew, Michael. BBA, U. Notre Dame, 1964; MBA, Mich. State U., 1974. CPA, Mich. Acct. Ernst & Ernst, Detroit, 1964-67; chief acct. Detroit Inst. Tech., Detroit, 1967-69; controller, dir. adminstrn. & fin. Mich. Cancer Found., Detroit, 1969-80; chief adminstrv. officer Dana-Farber Cancer Inst., Boston, 1980-94; exec. v.p., chief oper. officer John Wayne Cancer Inst., Santa Monica, Calif., 1995—; grant reviewer Nat. Cancer Inst., Bethesda, Md., 1979—. Pres. advanced mgmt. program Mich. State U., 1978-79. Mem. Am. Inst. CPA's. Avocations: sailing, woodworking, photography, music. Office: John Wayne Cancer Inst 2200 Santa Monica Blvd Santa Monica CA 90404

PETTIT, JOHN WHITNEY, lawyer; b. Washington, Mar. 20, 1935; s. Manson Bowers and Dagny Bernice (Rudback) P.; m. Anne McCullough, Jan. 20, 1939; children: John Whitney, Jennifer Read. BA, Duke U., 1957; JD, Georgetown U., 1960. Bar: D.C. 1960, U.S. Supreme Ct. 1965. Gen. counsel FCC, 1972-74; assoc. Hamel & Park, Washington, 1963-67, ptnr., 1967-72; gen. counsel FCC, Washington, 1972-74; ptnr. Hamel & Park, Washington, 1974-88, mng. ptnr., 1978-80, 86-88; mng. ptnr. Hopkins & Sutter, Washington, 1988-94; ptnr. Drinker Biddle & Reath, Washington, 1994—; bd. dirs. Medlantic Healthcare Group, Medlantic Enterprises, Inc. Fellow Am. Bar Found.; mem. ABA, Fed. Commns. Bar Assn., Vis. Nurse Assn Washington (chair, bd. dirs. 1990—), Met. Club, Chevy Chase (Md.) Club. Office: Drinker Biddle & Reath 901 15th St NW Washington DC 20005-2503

PETTIT, LAWRENCE KAY, university president; b. Lewistown, Mont., May 2, 1937; s. George Edwin and Dorothy Bertha (Brown) P.; m. Sharon Lee Anderson, June 21, 1961 (div. Oct. 1976); children: Jennifer Anna, Matthew Anderson, Allison Carol, Edward McLean; m. Elizabeth DuBois Medley, July 11, 1980; 3 stepchildren. BA cum laude, U. Mont., 1959; AM, Washington U., St. Louis, 1962; PhD, U. Wis., 1965. Legis. asst. U.S. Senate, 1959-60, 62; asst. & assoc. prof. dept. polit. sci. Pa. State U., 1964-67; assoc. dir. fed. rels. Am. Council Edn., Washington, 1967-69; prof., chmn. dept. polit. sci. Mont. State U., 1969-72; adminstrv. asst. to gov. State of Mont., 1973; chancellor Mont. Univ. System, Helena, 1973-79; pvt. practice ednl. cons. Mont., 1979-81; dep. commr. for acad. affairs Tex. Coordinating Bd. for Higher Edn., 1981-83; chancellor Univ. System of South Tex., 1983-86; chancellor So. Ill. U., Carbondale and Edwardsville, 1986-91, Disting. svc. prof., 1991-92; pres. Indiana U. Pa., 1992—; mem. various nat. and regional bds. and coms. on higher edn. Author: (with H. Albinski) European Political Processes, 2d edit., 1974, (with E. Keynes) Legislative Process in the U.S. Senate, 1969, (with S. Kirkpatrick) Social Psychology of Political Life, 1972, (with J. Goetz and S. Thomas) Legislative Process in Montana, 1975; mem. editorial bd. Ednl. Record, 1985—. Mem. adv. bd. Leadership Ctr. Ams., 1988-90, Ill. Coalition, 1989-92; candidate for 2d dist. U.S. Ho. of Reps., Mont., 1980; mem. Ill. Gov.'s Com. on Sci. and Tech., 1986-90; bd. dirs. Tex. Guaranteed Student Loan Corp., 1985-86; chmn. Ill.-Niigata Commn. on Edn. and Econ. Devel., 1990-92; chair bd. dirs. Nat. Environ. Edn. and Tng. Ctr., 1994—. U. Wis. fellow 1962-63, Vilas fellow U. Wis., 1963-64. Mem. AAUP (pres. Mont. conf. 1971-72), Nat. Assn. Sys. Heads (pres. 1989), Am. Coun. on Edn. (chmn. leadership commn. 1989-90, sr. fellow 1991-92), Am. Assn. Higher Edn., Am. Assn. State Colls. and Univs. (Disting. Svc. award 1991), Newcomen Soc., Duquesne Club Pitts., Allegheny Club Pitts., Pa. Soc. Ind. Country Club, Rotary, Sigma Chi (Significant Sig award 1988), Phi Kappa Phi. Episcopalian. Office: Indiana U President's Office 201 John Sutton Hall Indiana PA 15705

PETTIT, THOMAS HENRY, ophthalmologist; b. Salt Lake City, Jan. 20, 1929; s. William A. and Laura M. (Tanner) P.; m. Betty Ann Dain, June 12, 1953; children: Thomas H., Heather, Daina Lee, Drucilla, Elizabeth, Kristen. AB, UCLA, 1949; MD, U. Pa., 1955. Diplomate Am. Bd. Ophthalmology (bd. dirs. 1983-90, chmn. 1990). Intern Los Angeles County Gen. Hosp., 1955-56; resident ophthalmology Washington U., Barnes Hosp., St. Louis, 1959-61; trainee Nat. Insts. Neurol. Diseases and Blindness, St. Louis, 1959-61, spl. fellow, 1961-62; spl. fellow U. Calif. Sch. Medicine, San Francisco, 1962-63; rsch. fellow ophthalmology Sch. Medicine, UCLA, 1962-63, asst. prof. in residence, 1963-65, asst. prof. surgery-ophthalmology, 1965-67, assoc. prof., 1967-69, prof. ophthalmology, 1969-91, prof. emeritus, 1991—; mem. staff Jules Stein Eye Inst., L.A., 1965—, assoc. dir. 1971-91; cons. ophthalmology VA Hosp., Long Beach, Calif., 1963-70, Sepulveda (Calif.) VA Hosp., 1990-91; mem. staff UCLA Hosp.; attending physician Wadsworth VA Hosp., L.A., 1963-70; vis. prof. ophthalmology Washington U., St. Louis, 1969, 78, 83, U. W.Va., 1985; Zanvyl Krieger lectr. Mt. Sinai Hosp., Johns Hopkins U., 1989; guest of honor Am. Proctor Fellows meeting U. Calif. Med. Ctr., San Francisco, 1978, Ralph Heintz lectr., 1988; mem. vision rsch. com. Nat. Eye Inst., USPHS, 1977-75. Contbr. articles to profl. jours.; mem. editorial bd.: Investigative Ophthalmology, 1969-73, Am. Jour. Ophthalmology, 1985-87. Trustee Estelle Doheny Eye Found., L.A., 1968—, v.p. 1971-75. Lt. M.C., USN, 1956-63. Fellow Am. Acad. Ophthalmology and Otolaryngology (assoc. sec. continuing edn. in ophthalmology 1978-82, Honor award 1969, Sr. Honor award 1984); mem. AMA, Assn. for Rsch. in Vision and Ophthalmology, Pan-Am. Assn. Ophthalmology, L.A. Soc. Ophthalmology, Ocular Microbiology and Immunology Group, Contact Lens Assn. Ophthalmologists, Calif. Cornea Club, Am. Intraocular Implant Soc., Rsch. Study Club in Ophthalmology, Calif. Med. Soc., Los Angeles County Med. Soc., Phi Beta Kappa, Alpha Omega Alpha. Mem. LDS Ch. (bishop 1980-86). Office: UCLA Med Ctr Jules Stein Eye Instit Los Angeles CA 90024*

PETTIT, VINCENT KING, bishop; b. New Brunswick, N.J., Aug. 31, 1924; s. John Mervin and Marion (King) P.; m. Virginia Sorensen, June 17, 1950; children—Joan Anders, Ann, Vincent, Jr. B.S., Rutgers U., 1950; M.Div., Phila. Div. Sch., 1958; M.S.T., Temple U., 1963, N.Y. Theol. Sch., 1981; D.D. (hon.) Gen. Sem., N.Y.C., 1984. Ordained bishop Episcopal Ch., 1984. Rector St. George's Ch., Pennsville, N.J., 1961-67, St. Mary's Ch., Keyport, N.J., 1967-72, Trinity Ch., Cranford, N.J., 1972-81, Christ Ch., Toms River, N.J., 1981-83; bishop Diocese of N.J., Trenton, 1983—; mem. exec. coun. Episcopal Ch., N.Y.C., 1983-88; chmn. standing liturgical com., 1983—. With U.S. Army, 1942-46. Home: 104 Pilger Ct Lakehurst NJ 08733-3548 Office: Diocese of NJ 808 W State St Trenton NJ 08618-5398

PETTIT, WILLIAM THOMAS, broadcasting journalist; b. Cin., Apr. 23, 1931; s. William Porter and Kathryn (Neely) P.; m. Patricia M. Barry, Sept. 10, 1989; children by previous marriage: Debra Lynn, Anne Eileen, William James, Robert Thomas. B.A., Iowa State Tchrs. Coll., 1953; M.A., U. Minn., 1958. Reporter WOI-TV, Ames, Iowa, 1953-55, KCRG-TV, Cedar Rapids, Iowa, 1955-56, WCCO-TV, Mpls., 1956-59; reporter NBC News, Phila., 1959-61, N.Y.C., 1961-62, Los Angeles, 1962-67; reporter Pub. Broadcast Lab., 1967-68; reporter NBC News, Los Angeles, 1968-75; reporter NBC News, Washington, 1975-82, exec. v.p., 1982-85; chief nat. affairs, corr. NBC News, 1985-89, corr., London, 1989—, corr. Washington, 1992—. Recipient Emmy award, 1969, Peabody award, 1970, DuPont-Columbia award, 1970, Robert F. Kennedy Journalism award, 1970, 76, Med. Journalism award AMA, 1971, Journalism award Ohio State U., 1990. Mem. AFTRA. Office: NBC News 4001 Nebraska Ave NW Washington DC 20016

PETTITT, JAY S., architect, consultant; b. Redford, Mich., Jan. 6, 1926; s. Jay S. and Florence Marian (Newman) P.; m. Ruth Elizabeth Voigt, June 21, 1947; children—J. Stuart, Laura Ellen, Patricia Lynn, Carol Ann. B.Arch., U. Mich., 1951. Registered architect, Mich. Draftsman Frank J. Stepnoski and Son, Fond du Lac, Wis., 1951; project architect Albert Kahn Assocs., Inc., Detroit, 1951-62; chief archtl. devel. Albert Kahn Assocs., Inc., 1962-67, v.p., 1967-88, dir. architecture, 1975-88, past dir.; archtl. cons. Beulah, Mich., 1988—. Active Jr. Athletic Assn., Redford, Mich., 1959-63; com. chmn. Boy Scouts Am. 1960-65; supr. Benzonia Twp. Served with U.S. Army 1943-46, ETO. Fellow AIA; mem. Mich. Soc. Architects (pres. 1967), Am. Arbitration Assn., Am. Assn. Hosp. Planning, Engring. Soc. Detroit, U. Mich. Pres.' Club. Avocations: sailing; skiing.

PETTUS, BARBARA WYPER, bank executive; b. Hartford, Conn., Nov. 9, 1947; d. John Stuurman Wyper and Mary Blair (Goodell) Crolius; m. Charlton Messick Pettus, Apr. 19, 1975 (div., 1985). BA, Smith Coll., 1969; MLS, Simmons Coll., 1972, MBA, 1980. Adminstrv. asst. Perkins & Will Architects, Washington, 1969-71; head reference libr. Memorial Hall Libr., Andover, Mass., 1972-77; asst. dir. Memorial Hall Libr., Andover, 1977-79; asst. treas. Chase Manhattan Bank, N.Y.C., 1981-83, 2nd v.p., 1983-88, v.p. U.S. pvt. banking div., 1988-90; team leader, pvt. banking Mfrs. Hanover Trust Co., 1990-91; team leader, pvt. banking Chem. Bank, N.Y.C., 1991-94, unit mgr. pvt. banking, 1994—. Editor: (mag.) Bay State Librarian, 1977-79. Bd. dirs. Simmons Coll. Alumni Assn., Boston, 1982-84; mem. N.Y. Jr. League, 1987-90. Congregationalist. Office: Chem Bank 270 Park Ave New York NY 10017

PETTUS, MARY CATHERINE, public relations executive; b. Bellingham, Wash., Apr. 18, 1947; d. Edgar Raymond and Catherine Amanda (Selander) May; m. Drew Douglas Pettus, Dec. 22, 1970. BA in History, Western Wash. U., 1970. Store mgr. Portland Art Mus., 1970-74; store cons. Corcoran Gallery of Art, Washington, 1974-75, devel. cons., 1977; store cons. Phillips Collection, Washington, 1976; owner Mary Pettus & Assocs., Washington, 1978—. Mem. Am. Inst. Wine and Food (chair regional chpt. 1986—). Democrat. Lutheran. Home: 720 A St NE Washington DC 20002-6032 Office: Mary Pettus and Assocs Inc 720 A St NE Washington DC 20002-6032

PETTY, CHARLES SUTHERLAND, pathologist; b. Lewistown, Mont., Apr. 16, 1920; s. Charles Frederic and Mae (Reichert) P.; m. Lois Muriel Swenson, Dec. 14, 1957; children—Heather Ann, Charles Sutherland II; children by previous marriage—Daniel S., Carol L. B.S., U. Wash., 1941, M.S., 1946; M.D., Harvard U., 1950. Intern Mary Imogene Bassett Hosp., Coopertown, N.Y., 1950-52; resident in pathology Peter Bent Brigham Hosp., Children's Med. Center, New Eng. Deaconness Hosp., Boston, 1952-55; instr. pathology La. State U. Sch. Medicine, 1955-56, asst. prof., 1956-58; asst. med. examiner State of Md., 1958-67; asst. prof. forensic pathology U. Md. Sch. Medicine, 1958-64, asso. prof., 1964-67; lectr., then asso. Johns Hopkins U. Sch. Hygiene and Public Health, 1959-67, adj. prof. police adminstrn. U. Louisville, 1978—; dir. Balt. Regional ARC Blood Program, 1959-67; prof. forensic pathology Ind. U. Sch. Medicine, Indpls., 1967-69; dir. lab. Ind. Commn. on Forensic Scis., 1967-69; chief med. examiner Dallas County, 1969-91; prof. forensic scis., pathology U. Tex. Southwestern Med. Sch., Dallas, 1969—; dir. Southwestern Inst. Forensic Scis., 1969-91. Served from ensign to lt. comdr. USNR, 1941-45. Fellow Coll. Am. Pathologists, Am. Soc. Clin. Pathologists, A.C.P., Am. Acad. Forensic Scis. (pres. 1967-68); mem. Sigma Xi. Episcopalian. Home: 3964 Goodfellow Dr Dallas TX 75229-2722 Office: 5323 Harry Hines Blvd Dallas TX 75235-7200

PETTY, GEORGE OLIVER, lawyer; b. L.A., Mar. 31, 1939; s. Hugh Morton and May (Johnson) P.; m. Sandra Diane Kilpatrick, July 14, 1962; children: Ross Morton, Alison Lee, Christopher Henry. AB, U. Calif., Berkeley, 1961; LLB, U. Calif., 1964. Bar: Calif. 1965, Eng. and Wales 1986, U.S. Supreme Ct. 1976. Atty. Huovinen & White, Oakland, Calif., 1967-69; counsel Bechtel Power Corp., San Francisco, 1969-83; prin. counsel Bechtel Ltd., London, 1983-86; gen. counsel Sun-Diamond Growers of Calif., Pleasanton, Calif., 1987-95; pvt. practice, 1995—. Capt. U.S. Army, 1965-67. Mem. Calif. State Bar Assn., Alameda County Bar Assn., Eng. and Wales Bar Assn., Bar Assn. for Commerce, Fin. & Industry (Eng.), Middle Temple Inn. Office: Sun-Diamond Growers Calif 5568 Gibraltar Dr Pleasanton CA 94588-8544

PETTY, JOHN ROBERT, banker; b. Chgo., Apr. 16, 1930; s. Dewitt Talmage and Beatrice (Worthington) P.; children: L. Talmage, Robert D., George M., Victoria Lee. AB, Brown U., 1951; postgrad., NYU, 1953-54. With Chase Manhattan Bank, N.Y.C. and Paris, 1953-66; v.p. Chase Manhattan Bank, 1964-66; dep. asst. sec. Dept. Treasury, Washington, 1966-68, asst. sec. for internat. affairs, 1968-72; partner Lehman Bros., N.Y.C., 1972-76; pres., dir., chmn. exec. com. Marine Midland Banks, Inc., from 1976, chmn., chief exec. officer, 1976-88; mng. gen. ptnr. Petty-FBW Assocs., Washington, 1989-91; chmn. Fed. Nat. Payables Inc. Washington, 1992—, Fed. Nat. Svcs. Inc., 1992—; chmn. Nippon Credit Trust Co., N.Y.C.; chmn. Czech & Slovak Am. Enterprise Fund, 1991, Adv. Bd. Bank Julius Baer & Co., N.Y.C.; bd. dirs. Antec Corp., Julius Baer Securities, Inc., Magnetic Analysis Corp., Itel, Inc. With USNR, 1951-53. Mem. Council Fgn. Relations, Fgn. Bondholders Protective Council (pres.). Office: Ste 703 1620 I St NW Washington DC 20006

PETTY, KYLE, professional stock car driver; s. Richard and Lynda P. 5th in NASCAR money leaders, 1992. Winner Champion Spark Plug 500, 1993. Office: c/o NASCAR PO Box 2875 Daytona Beach FL 32115*

PETTY, MARGE, state senator; b. Ft. Wayne, Ind., Feb. 26, 1946; m. Tyrus C. Petty, 1968; children: Brandon, Megan. Senator, ranking minority, judiciary com., mem. ways & means Kans. State Senate; minority leader Ways & Means Com.; mem. Commerce Com., Fin. Institutions & Ins., Pensions and Investments; Dem. caucus policy chair KPERS Investigating Com. Episcopalian. Home: 106 NW Woodlawn Ave Topeka KS 66606-1241 Address: State Senate State Capitol Topeka KS 66612

PETTY, OLIVE SCOTT, geophysical engineer; b. Olive, Tex., Apr. 15, 1895; s. Van Alvin and Mary Cordelia (Dabney) P.; m. Mary Edwina Harris, July 19, 1921; 1 son, Scott. Student Ga. Inst. Tech., 1913-14; BS in Civil Engring., U. Tex., 1917, CE, 1920. Registered profl. engr., Tex. Adj. prof. civil engring. U. Tex., 1920-23; structural engr. R.O. Jameson, Dallas, 1923-25; pres. Petty Geophys. Engring. Co., Dallas, Inc., San Antonio, 1925-52, chmn. bd., 1952-73; chmn. bd. Petty Geophys. Engring. Co. de Mex. S.A. de C.V., 1950-73; ptnr. Petty Ranch Co., 1968—; ranching, oil, timber and investment interests 1937—. Author: Seismic Reflections, Recollections of the Formative Years of the Geophysical Exploration Industry, 1976; A Journey to Pleasant Hill, The Civil War Letters of Capt. E. P. Petty, C.S.A., 1982; patentee geophys. methods, instruments, equipment, including electro-static seismograph detector in op. on the moon and on Mars and now NASA's standard for space exploration. Benefactor, San Antonio Symphony Soc., McNay Art Mus.; mem. exec. com., founding mem. chancellor's council U. Tex. System, Austin, also founding mem., hon. life mem. Geology Found.; mem. Inst. Texan Cultures, mem. devel and adv. bds; adv. council U. Tex., Austin. Served as lt. Engrs., U.S. Army, 1917-18; AEF in France. Hon. adm. Tex. Navy; recipient Disting. Grad. award U. Tex. Coll. Engring., Austin, 1962; Tex. Acad. Sci. (hon. life) N.Y. Acad. Sci.; mem. ASCE (hon. life), AIME (Legion of Honor), Am. Assn. Petroleum Geologists, AAAS (50-yr. mem.), Am. Petroleum Inst., Nat. Soc. Profl. Engrs. (life), Am. Geophys. Union, Houston Geophys. Soc., San Antonio Geophys. Soc., South Tex. Geol. Soc., Soc. Petroleum Engrs. (Legion of Honor), Am. Assn. Petroleum Geologists (life), Soc. Am. Mil. Engrs. (life), Soc. Exptl. Geophysicists (founding mem.; hon. life), Soc. 1st Inf. Div. (founding), Tex. Soc. Profl. Engrs., Explorers Club (life), Mil. Profl. Engrs. in Pvt. Practice, Wisdom Soc., Am. Geol. Inst. (Centurian Club), Am. Assn. Petroleum Geologists Trustee Assn. (life), Chi Epsilon (hon. life), Theta Xi, Tau Beta Pi. Baptist. Clubs: San Antonio Country, Argyle, St. Anthony, Giraud. Died Mar. 2, 1994. Home: 101 E Kings Hwy San Antonio TX 78212-2961 Office: 711 Navarro St San Antonio TX 78205-1707

PETTY, RICHARD, retired professional race car driver; s. Lee and Elizabeth T. P.; m. Lynda Owens; children: Kyle, Sharon, Lisa, Rebecca. NASCAR racer, 35 years, ret., 1992; owner Car # 43. Mem. Pres.'s Council Fitness and Sport. Recipient Myers Bros. award Nat. Motorsports Press Assn., 1961, 67, 71, Excellence award NASCAR, 1987; named Grand Nat. Rookie of Year, 1959; Most Popular Driver in Grand Nat., 1962, 64, 68, 70, 74, 75, 76, 77, 78; Martini & Rossi Am. Driver of Year, 1971; Driver of Year Nat. Motorsport Press Assn., 1974-75; Driver of Quarter Century, 1991; inducted into N.C. Athletic Hall of Fame, 1973. Mem. Nat. Assn. Stock Car Auto Racing (7 time champion); Winston Cup grand nat. champion 1964, 67, 71, 72, 74, 75, 79). Entered 1015 Grand Nat. Races, winner 200, 1958-86, with 55 Superspeedway wins; winner Daytona 500, 1964, 66, 71, 73, 74, 79, 81; 1000th career Winston Cup start June 15, 1986 at Mich. Internat. Speedway; 500th consecutive start on Aug. 21, 1988 in Champion Spark Plug 500. Address: 311 Branson Mill Rd Randleman NC 27317

PETTY, RICHARD EDWARD, psychologist, educator, researcher; b. Garden City, N.Y., May 22, 1951; s. Edmund and Josephine (Serzo) P.; m. Virginia Lynn Oliver, Aug. 29, 1978. BA, U. Va., 1973; PhD, Ohio State U., 1977. Asst. prof. psychology U. Mo., Columbia, 1977-80, assoc. prof. psychology, 1981-83, Middlebush prof. psychology, 1984-85; vis. fellow Yale U., New Haven, Conn., 1986; prof. psychology Ohio State U., Columbus, 1987—; vis. prof. Princeton U., 1995; advisor com. on dietary guidelines implementation NAS, 1989-91. Author: Attitudes and Persuasion, 1986, Attitude Strength, 1995; editor Personality and Social Psychology Bull., 1988-92; contbr. articles to Jour. Personality and Social Psychology, Jour. Exptl. Social Psychology; mem. editl. bd. of 6 jours. Grantee NIMH, 1978-79, NSF, 1984-88, 90-94. Fellow AAAS, APA, Am. Psychol. Soc. Achievements include origination of the elaboration likelihood model of persuasion. Home: 2955 Scioto Pl Columbus OH 43221-4753 Office: Ohio State U 1885 Neil Ave Columbus OH 43210-1222

PETTY, THOMAS LEE, physician, educator; b. Boulder, Colo., Dec. 24, 1932; s. Roy Stone and and Eleanor Marie (Kudrna) P.; m. Carol Lee Piepho, Aug. 7, 1954; children: Caryn, Thomas, John. B.A., U. Colo., 1955, M.D., 1958. Intern Phila. Gen. Hosp., 1958-59; resident U. Mich., 1959-60, U. Colo., Denver, 1960-62; pulmonary fellow U. Colo., 1962-63, chief resident medicine, 1963-64, instr. medicine, 1962-64, asst. prof., 1964-68, assoc. prof., 1968-74, prof. medicine, 1974—; pres. Presbyn./St. Luke's Ctr. for Health Scis. Edn., 1989—; practice medicine, specializing in internal medicine, pulmonary medicine Denver, 1962—; prof. medicine Rush Univ. (Denver campus), 1992—; Cons. Fitzsimmons Army Hosp., 1970—. Author: For Those Who Live and Breathe, 1967, 2d edit., 1972, Intensive and Rehabilitative Respiratory Care, 1971, 3d edit., 1982, Chronic Obstructive Pulmonary Disease, 1978, 2d edit., 1985, Principles and Practice of Pulmonary Rehabilitation, 1993, Enjoying Life With COPD, 1995, 3d edit., others; contbr. articles to profl. jours. NIH and Found. grantee, 1966-88. Mem. Am. Lung Assn. (Colo. chpt. pres. 1975), Am. Coll. Chest Physicians (pres. 1982), Assn. Am. Physicians, Assn. of Pulmonary Program Dirs. (founding pres. 1983-84), Am. Bd. Internal Medicine (bd. govs. 1986-92), Phi Beta Kappa, Phi Delta Theta, Alpha Omega Alpha, Phi Rho Sigma (pres. 1976-78). Home: 1940 Grape St Denver CO 80220-1353 Office: Presbyn Hosp Denver CO 80218

PETTY, TOM, rock guitarist, band leader, composer; b. Gainesville, Fla., Oct. 20, 1950; s. Earl Petty. Rock guitarist, 1969—; leader Tom Petty and the Heartbreakers, 1975—. Played in local bands The Epics, Mudcrutch while in Gainesville; songwriter, musician for Leon Russell, 1974; rec. and touring artist with the Heartbreakers, albums include Tom Petty and the Heartbreakers, 1976, You're Gonna Get It, 1978, Damn the Torpedoes, 1979, Hard Promises, 1981, Long After Dark, 1982, Southern Accents, 1985, Pack Up the Plantation, 1986, Let Me Up (I've Had Enough), 1987, Full Moon Fever, 1989, Into the Great Wide Open, 1991, Tom Petty and the Heartbreakers' Greatest Hits, 1993, Wildflowers, 1994; (with The Traveling Wilburys) Traveling Wilburys Vol. 1, 1989, Traveling Wilburys Vol. 3, 1990; hit singles include Breakdown, 1978, Here Comes My Girl, 1979, Refugee, 1979, The Waiting, 1981, You Got Lucky, 1982, Don't Come Around Here No More, 1985, Jammin' Me, 1987, Free Fallin', 1989 (solo album) Wildflowers, 1995; toured the world with Bob Dylan, 1986, toured America with Georgia Satellites and Del Fuegos (Rock 'n' Roll Caravan tour), 1987. Grammy nomination (Best Rock Duo or Group Performance, 1994) for My Back Pages (with Bob Dylan, Roger McGuinn, Neil Young, Eric Clapton, and George Harrison); MTV Best Male Video (with the Heartbreakers) for Mary Jane's Last Dance; recipient MTV Video Vanguard award. Office: care Levine Schneider 6th Fl 8730 Sunset Los Angeles CA 90069

PETTYJOHN, SHIRLEY ELLIS, lawyer, real estate executive; b. Liberty, Ky., Aug. 16, 1935; d. Wesley Barker and Ada Lou (Bryant) Ellis; m. Flem D. Pettyjohn, Sept. 24, 1955; children: Deena Renee, Ellisa Denise. BS in Commerce, U. Louisville, 1974, JD, 1977. Bar: Ky. 1978, Ind. 1988; lic. real estate broker, Ky., Ind.; cert. mediator. Pres. Universal Devel. Corp., Ky. and Fla., 1984—, Pettyjohn Inc., Ky. and Ind., 1967—, Ind. Mediation Svcs., Inc., 1990—, Ky. Mediation Svcs., Inc., 1991—; v.p. Continental Investments Corp., 1986—; sr. ptnr. Pettyjohn & Assocs., Attys., 1987—. Editor Law-Hers Jour. Vice-chmn. Louisville and Jefferson County Planning Commn., 1971-75; mem. Gov.'s Conf. on Edn., 1977, jud. nominee, 1981, Met. Louisville Women's Polit. Caucus, Bluegrass State Skills Corp., 1992—, Ky. Opera Assn. Guild; elected mem. Ky. State Dem. Exec. Com., 1988-92; del. Nat. Dem. Conv. and Dem. Nat. Platform Com., 1988; bd. dirs. Ky. Dem. Hdqs., Inc., 1988-92, Pegasus Rising Inc.; chmn. Okolona Libr. Task Force. Recipient Mayor's Cert. Recognition, 1974, Mayor's Fleur de lis award, 1969-73, Excellence in Writing award Arts Club Louisville, 1986, 87, 93. Mem. ABA, NAFE, Nat. Assn. Adminstry. Law Judges, Ky. Bar Assn., Louisville Bar Assn., Women Lawyers Assn. of Jefferson County, Am. Judicature Soc., Clark County Bar Assn., Ind. Bar Assn., Ind. Assn. Mediators, Am. Inst. Planners, Women's C. of C. of Ky. (past bd. dirs., chmn. legis. com.), Am. Legion (aux.), Fraternal Order Police Assn. (award 1982), Louisville Legal Secs. (past pres., editor Law-Hers Jour.), Coun. of Women Pres. (past pres., Woman of Achievement award 1974), Louisville Visual Arts Assn. (former bd. dirs.), Louisville Ballet Guild (chair audience devel. 1989-91), Dem. Leadership Coun., Jefferson County Dem. Women's Club (past v.p.), Nat. Fedn. Dem. Women's Clubs, Spirit of 46th Club, Mose Green Club, North End Club, 12th Ward Club, S. End Club, 3rd Ward Club, Highland Pk. Club, Grass Roots Club, Harry S. Truman Club, Beargrass Club, Arts Club of Louisville (past pres.), Sigma Delta Kappa, Chi Thi Theta. Home: 6924 Norlynn Dr Louisville KY 40228-1471 Office: PO Box 787 600 E Court Ave Ste 102 Jeffersonville IN 47131-0787

PETYKIEWICZ, SANDRA DICKEY, editor; b. Detroit, Sept. 23, 1953; d. James Fulton and Alice Diane (Nowak) Dickey; m. Edward W. Petykiewicz, Oct. 17, 1981; 1 child, Kendall Lee. BA, Cen. Mich. U., Mt. Pleasant, 1975. Reporter Big Rapids (Mich.) Pioneer, 1975, Midland (Mich.) Daily News, 1975-77; reporter Saginaw (Mich.) News, 1977-79, feature editor, 1979-80; asst. metro editor, 1980-81; copy editor Washington Post, 1981-82; asst. city editor Balt. News Am., 1982-83; metro editor Jackson (Mich.) Citizen Patriot, 1983-87, editor, 1987—; bd. dirs. Mich. AP, 1987-93, pres., 1990, 91-92; bd. dirs. Mid Am. Press Inst., 1992—; mem. alumni bd. Ctrl. Mich. U., 1992—, mem. journalism adv. bd., 1992—. Pulitzer Prize juror, 1990-92. Mem. Jackson Area Quality Initiative, 1990—. Mem. Am. Soc. Newspaper Editors, AP Mng. Editors, Soc. Profl. Journalists, Bus. and Profl. Women's Club (editor newsletter 1985-86, Young Career Woman of Yr. award 1984), Rotary Club, Jackson Econ. Club (chairwoman 1992), Sigma Delta Chi. Avocations: golf, writing, reading, travel.

PETZ, EDWIN V., real estate executive, lawyer; b. Beatrice, Nebr., May 14, 1935; s. Virgil Leonard and Ruth Elenor (Thomsen) P.; m. Daphne Cross, May 17, 1958 (div. June 1964); 1 dau., Katherine J.; m Anne Higgins, Dec. 3, 1964 (div. Sept. 1993); 1 son, W. Christopher. B.A., Principia Coll., Elsah, Ill., 1955; J.D., Harvard U., 1958. Bar: N.Y. 1959, Mass. 1976. Assoc. Chadbourne, Parke, Whiteside & Wolff, N.Y.C., 1958-62; asst. gen. counsel Martin Marietta Corp., Bethesda, Md., 1963-64, 1965-75; gen. atty. sec. Bunker-Ramo Corp., Oakbrook, Ill., 1964-65; asst. gen. counsel United Brands Co., N.Y.C., 1975-82, v.p., gen. counsel, sec., 1982-84; sr. v.p., gen. counsel Milstein Properties Corp., 1985—; sr. v.p., gen counsel The Milstein Group Inc., 1992—. Mem. ABA, Assn. of Bar of City N.Y. Republican. Episcopalian. Club: University (N.Y.C.). Office: Milstein Properties Corp 1271 Ave Of The Americas New York NY 10020-1300

PETZAL, DAVID ELIAS, editor, writer; b. N.Y.C., Oct. 21, 1941; s. Henry and Aline Born (Bixer) P.; m. Arlene Anne Taylor, May 29, 1974. B.A., Colgate U., 1963. Editor Maco Publs., N.Y.C., 1964-69; mng. editor Davis Publs., N.Y.C., 1969-70; features editor Hearst Publs., N.Y.C., 1970-72; mng. editor CBS Publs., N.Y.C., 1972-79, editor, 1979-83, exec. editor, 1983-87; exec. editor Times-Mirror Mags., N.Y.C., 1987—. Author: The .22 Rifle, 1972; editor: The Experts Book of the Shooting Sports, 1972, The Experts Book of Upland Game and Waterfowl Hunting, 1975, The Experts Book of Big-Game Hunting in North America, 1976, The Ency. of Sporting Firearms, 1991. Home: PO Box 219 Bedford NY 10506-0219 Office: Times Mirror Mags 2 Park Ave New York NY 10016-5603

PETZOLD, CAROL STOKER, state legislator; b. St. Louis, July 28; d. Harold William and Mabel Lucille (Wilson) Stoker; m. Walter John Petzold,

---

June 27, 1959; children: Ann, Ruth, David. BS, Valparaiso U., 1959. Tchr. John Muir Elem. Sch., Alameda, Calif., 1959-60, Parkwood Elem. Sch., Kensington, Md., 1960-62; legis. aide Md. Gen. Assembly, Annapolis, 1975-79; legis. asst. Montgomery County Bd. Edn., Rockville, Md., 1980; community sch. coordinator Parkland Jr. High Sch., Rockville, 1981-87; mem. Md. Ho. of Dels., Annapolis, 1987—; mem. transp. budget planning Nat. Capitol Region, 1989—; vice chair energy and transp. com. Nat. Conf. State Legislatures; exec. com. Montgomery United Way Coun., 1981—. Editor Child Care Sampler, 1984, Stoker Family Cookbook, 1976. Pres. Montgomery Child Care Assn., 1976-78; mem. Md. State Scholarship Bd., 1978-87, chmn. 1985-87; chmn. Legis. Com. Montgomery County Commn. for Children and Youth, 1979-84; mem., v.p. Luth. Social Services Nat. Capitol Area, Washington, 1980-86. Recipient Statewide award Gov.'s Adv. Bd. on Homelessness; recognized for outstanding commitment to children U.S. Dept. HEW, 1980. Mem. AAUW (honoree Kensington br. 1971, honoree Md. div. 1981), Women's Polit. Caucus (chmn. Montgomery County 1981-83), Women's Caucus Md. Legislature. Democrat. Lutheran. Home: 14113 Chadwick Ln Rockville MD 20853-2103

PEUGEOT, PATRICK, insurance executive; b. Paris, Aug. 3, 1937; s. Jacques Louis and Edith (Genoyer) P.; m. Catherine Dupont, 1963; children: Hubert, Thomas, Camille. Degree, Ecole Poly., Paris, 1959, Ecol Nat. D'Adminstrn., Paris, 1965. Ins. auditor Ministry of Fin., Paris, 1962-65; auditor Cour des Comptes, Paris, 1965-83; spl. asst. Bur. Planning, Paris, 1966-70; sr. v.p. EMC, Toulouse, France, 1970-72, Hachette Inc., Paris, 1972-74; exec. v.p. ops. AGF Life, Paris, 1974-78; exec. v.p. AGF Reins., Paris, 1979-82; pres. Caisse Cen. de Reassurance, Paris, 1983-85; chmn. Scor S.A., Paris, 1984—. Home: 82 rue Notre Dame Champs, 75006 Paris France Office: Scor US Corp 110 William St New York NY 10038

PEVEC, ANTHONY EDWARD, bishop; b. Cleve., Apr. 16, 1925; s. Anton and Frances (Darovec) P. MA, John Carroll U., Cleve., 1956; PhD, Western Res. U., Cleve., 1964. Ordained priest Roman Catholic Ch., 1950. Assoc. pastor St. Mary Church, Elyria, Ohio, 1950-52, St. Lawrence Ch., Cleve., 1952-53; rector-prin. Borromeo Sem. High Sch., Wickliffe, Ohio, 1953-75; adminstrv. bd. Nat. Cath. Edn. Assn., 1972-75; pastor St. Vitus Ch., Cleve., 1975-79; rector-pres. Borromeo Coll., Wickliffe, 1979-82; aux. bishop Diocese of Cleve., 1982—; cons. Nat. Conf. Cath. Bishops Com. on Pro-Life Activities, 1990-92; mem. U.S. Cath. Conf., 1982—, Ohio Cath. Conf., 1982—, Papal Visitation Team, 1982-87, Bishops' Com. on Vocations, 1984-86, Bishops' Com. on Sci. and Human Values, 1993—, Bishops' Com. on Priestly Formation, 1993—. Mem. v.p. Slovenian-Am. Heritage Found., Cleve., 1975—. Honoree, Heritage Found., Cleve., 1982; named Man of Yr., Fedn. Slovenian Nat. Homes, Cleve., 1985; inducted into Hall of Fame, St. Vitus Alumni Assn., 1989. Democrat. Roman Catholic. Avocations: reading; music. Home and Office: Diocese of Cleve 28700 Euclid Ave Wickliffe OH 44092-2527 *Ultimately I must always remember that the Lord is totally in control of my life, no matter how complicated it may seem to be. I am here to do the Lord's will,, and wherever I go I come to do His will.*

PEVSNER, AIHUD, physicist, educator; b. Israel, Dec. 18, 1925; came to U.S., 1928, naturalized, 1934; s. Yoshua and Esther (Ben Yeshaia) P.; m. Lucille Wolf, June 19, 1949; children—Mark David, Laura Ruth, Jonathan Abram. A.B., Columbia U., 1947, A.M. in Math, 1948, Ph.D. in Physics, 1954. Mem. faculty M.I.T., Cambridge, Mass., 1953-56; mem. faculty Johns Hopkins U., Balt., 1956—; prof. physics Johns Hopkins U., 1963—; Jacob L. Hain prof. physics, 1977—, chmn. dept. physics, 1972-78. Contbr. articles on physics to sci. jours. Guggenheim fellow, 1963, 70; Fulbright fellow, 1963. Fellow Am. Phys. Soc. Home: 5806 Stuart Ave Baltimore MD 21215-4142 Office: Johns Hopkins Univ Dept Physics And Astro Baltimore MD 21218

PEW, JOHN GLENN, JR., lawyer; b. Dallas, Apr. 18, 1932; s. John Glenn Sr. and Roberta (Haughton) P. BA, U. Tex., 1954. LLB, 1955. Bar: Tex. 1955, U.S. Dist. Ct. (no. dist.) Tex. 1959, U.S. Supreme Ct. 1959, U.S. Ct. Appeals (5th cir.) 1961, U.S. Ct. Appeals (10th cir.) 1982. Ptnr., Jackson & Walker, Dallas, L.L.P., 1964—. With USNR, 1955-58. Mem. Order of Coif, Phi Beta Kappa. Republican. Presbyterian. Office: Jackson & Walker L.L.P. Ste 6000 901 Main St Dallas TX 75202-3797

PEW, ROBERT ANDERSON, real estate corporation officer; b. Phila. Aug. 22, 1936; s. Arthur Edmund and Mary Elizabeth (Elliott) P.; children from previous marriage: Robert Anderson (dec.), James Cunningham, Glenn Edgar, Joan Elliott; m. Daria S. Decerio, June 19, 1993. Student, Princeton U., 1954-56; B.S., Temple U. 1959; M.S. in Mgmt. (Alfred P. Sloan fellow), MIT, 1970; LL.D. (hon.), Widener U., 1982; D.P.S. (hon.), Temple U., 1983; L.H.D. (hon.), Gettysburg Coll., 1984. Ops. asst. prodn. div. Sun Oil Co., Premont, Tex., 1959-60; ops. asst. prodn. div. Sun Oil Co., Morgan City, La.; auditor internal audit dept. Sun Oil Co., Phila., 1960-65, staff asst. treasury dept., 1965-69, asst. to exec. v.p. corp. projects group, 1970-71, sec.-treas., mgr. financial control of products group, 1971-74, corp. sec., 1974-77; bd. dirs., pres. Helios Capital Corp. and affiliates, Wilmington, Del., 1977—; bd. dirs., CEO Radnor Corp., Phila., 1995—; bd. dirs. Sun Co., Inc., Phila., Glemede Corp., Phila., Pew Charitable Trusts, Phila., Glenmede Trust Co., Phila., Brown & Glenmede Holdings, Inc., Balt., Brown Adv. Trust Co., Balt. Trustee Children's Hosp. Phila., vice chmn. 1991—, Bryn Mawr (Pa.) Coll., vice chmn., 1991—, Curtis Inst. Music, 1993—. Served Pa. Air N.G., 1956-59. Recipient R. Kelso Carter award Widener U., 1971. Mem. Aircraft Owners and Pilots Assn. (trustee, chmn. 1974-77, 85—, vice-chmn. 1979-85), Am. Hosp. Assn. (hon.). Republican. Presbyterian. Clubs: Union League, Seal Harbor (pres. 1992—), Phila. Aviation Country, Merion Cricket, Northeast Harbor Fleet. Home: 916 Muirfield Rd Bryn Mawr PA 19010-1921 Office: Radnor Corp Ten Penn Ctr 1801 Market St Philadelphia PA 19103-1699

PEW, ROBERT CUNNINGHAM, II, office equipment manufacturing company executive; b. Syracuse, N.Y., June 4, 1923; s. Robert Carroll and Bernice (Evans) P.; m. Mary Bonnell Idema, Aug. 23, 1947; children: Robert Cunningham, John Evans, Kate Bonnell. B.A., Wesleyan U., Middletown Conn.; HHD (hon.), Aquinas Coll., LLD (hon.). Labor relations exec. Doehler-Jarvis Corp., Grand Rapids, Mich., 1948-51; with Steelcase Inc., Grand Rapids, 1952—; exec. v.p. Steelcase Inc., 1964-66, pres., 1966-75, chmn. bd., pres., from 1975, formerly chmn., chief exec. officer, now chmn. bd.; dir. Old Kent Financial Corp., Foremost Corp. Am. Bd. control Grand Valley State Coll.; bd. dirs. Econ. Devel. Corp. Grand Rapids, Mich. Strategic Fund, Nat. Orgn. on Disability; mem. Gov.'s Commn. on Jobs and Econ. Devel. Served to 1st lt. USAAF, 1942-45; to capt. USAF, 1951-52. Decorated Purple Heart, Air medal with 2 oak leaf clusters. Served Grand Rapids C. of C. (dir.), Grand Rapids Employers Assn. (dir.), Chi Psi. Episcopalian. Clubs: Lost Tree (North Palm Beach Fla.); Peninsular; University, Kent Country (Grand Rapids). Home: 11307 Old Harbour Rd No Palm Beach FL 33408-3406 Office: PO Box 1967 Grand Rapids MI 49501-1967 Office: 901 44th St SE Grand Rapids MI 49508-7575°

PEW, THOMAS W., JR., advertising executive; b. Houston, Sept. 14, 1938; s. Thomas William and Floranz (Leebow) P.; m. Laura Rice Neuhaus, June 10, 1964; children—Katherine, William, David. B.A., Cornell U., 1961. Editor, assoc. pub. Troy Daily News, Ohio, 1965-72; freelance writer, 1972-80; editor, pres. Am. West mag. Am. West Pub. Co., Tucson, 1981-89; pres. Hawkeye West, Tucson, 1986—; advt. dir. Sturm Ruger & Co., 1986—; pres. Merlin Inc., Advt. Agy., Inc., 1991—. Contbr. articles to Smithsonian Mag., Am. Heritage Mag., numerous others. Served with inf. U.S. Army, 1961-63. Avocations: skiing; guitar; backpacking.

PÉWÉ, TROY LEWIS, geologist, educator; b. Rock Island, Ill., June 28, 1918; s. Richard E. and Olga (Pomrank) P.; m. Mary Jean Hill, Dec. 21, 1944; children—David Lee, Richard Hill, Elizabeth Anne. AB in Geology, Augustana Coll., 1940; MS, State U. Iowa, 1942; PhD, Stanford U., 1952; DSc (hon.), U. Alaska, 1991. Head dept. geology Augustana Coll., 1942-46; civilian instr. USAAC, 1943-44; instr. geomorphology Stanford, 1946; geologist Alaskan br. U.S. Geol. Survey, 1946-93; chief glacial geologist U.S. Nat. Com. Internat. Geophys. Year, Antarctica, 1958; prof. geology, head dept. U. Alaska, 1958-65; prof. geology Ariz. State U., 1965-88, prof. emeritus, 1988—, chmn. dept., 1965-76; dir. Mus. Geology, 1976—; lectr. in field, 1942—; mem. organizing com. 1st Internat. Permafrost Conf. Nat. Acad. Sci., 1962-63, chmn. U.S. planning com. 2d Internat. Permafrost Conf., 1972-

---

74, chmn. U.S. del. 3d Internat. Permafrost Conf., 1978, chmn. U.S. organizing com. 4th Internat. Permafrost Conf., 1979-83; com. to study Good Friday Alaska Earthquake Nat. Acad. Scis., 1964-70, mem. glaciological com. polar research bd. 1971-73, founding chmn. permafrost com. mem. polar research bd., 1975-81; organizing chmn. Internat. Assn. Quarternary Research Symposium and Internat. Field Trip Alaska, 1965; mem. Internat. Commn. Periglacial Morophology, 1964-71, 80-88 ; mem. polar research bd. NRC, 1975-78, late Cenozoic study group, sci. com. Antarctic research, 1977-80. Contbr. numerous papers to profl. lit. Recipient U.S. Antarctic Svc. medal, 1966, Outstanding Achievement award Augustana Coll., 1969, Internat. Geophysics medal USSR Nat. Acad. Sci., 1985, Disting. Alumni award U. Iowa, 1994; named 2d hon. internat. fellow Chinese Soc. Glaciology and Geocryology, 1985. Fellow AAAS (pres. Alaska div. 1956, com. on arid lands 1972-79), Geol. Soc. Am. (editorial bd. 1975-82, chmn. cordilleran sect. 1979-80, chmn. geomorphology div. 1981-82), Arctic Inst. N.Am. (bd. govs. 1969-74, exec. bd. 1972-73), Iowa Acad. Sci., Ariz. Acad. Sci. (pres. 1982-83); mem. Assn. Geology Tchrs., Glaciological Soc., N.Z. Antarctic Soc., Am. Soc. Engring. Geologists, Internat. Permafrost Assn. (founding v.p. 1983, pres. 1988-93), Am. Quaternary Assn. (pres. 1984-86), Internat. Geog. Union. Club: Cosmos. Home: 538 E Fairmont Dr Tempe AZ 85282-3723

PEWITT, JAMES DUDLEY, academic administrator; b. Franklin, Tenn., July 28, 1930; s. James Isaac and Eleanor (Dudley) P.; m. Betty Louise Hightower, Oct. 31, 1952; children: Ransom D., James P., Thomas E. Student, Vanderbilt U., 1948-51; MBA, MS, U. So. Calif., 1964, D in Bus. Adminstrn., 1967. Commd. lt. USAF, 1952, advanced through grades to col., 1969; spl. asst. for econ. analysis Office of Sec. of Air Force, 1967; exec. to asst. sec. Air Force for Fin. Mgmt. Nat. War Coll., 1971; asst. Da Nang Air Base, Vietnam, 1972; dep. comdr. for ops. Vietnam, 1972, vice comdr. Gunfighters, 1972; chief linebacker ops. Staff of Dir. of Ops., Vietnam, 1972; dir. mgmt. analysis USAF, 1973, ret., 1973; dir. grad. sch. bus. U. Ala., Birmingham, 1973-74, asst. v.p. ops. and planning, 1974-77, v.p. adminstrn., 1977-84, sr. v.p. adminstrn., 1984-90, Disting. prof., 1990—; bd. dirs. Birmingham Cable Communications, Allied Products Co. Mem. Birmingham Airport Authority, 1986-93; chmn. bd. So. Mus. of Flight, 1993—; faculty rep. Sun Belt Conf., 1983-90, pres., 1989-90; mem. NCAA Coun., 1990-94. Decorated D.F.C. with 3 oak leaf clusters, Bronze Star, Legion of Merit with 2 oak leaf clusters, Air medal with 11 v-devices, 10 other awards and fgn. decorations. Mem. Birmingham C. of C. (bd. dirs. 1977-84, pres. 1983, chmn. 1984), Summit Club, Birmingham Country Club, Shoal Creek Country Club, Willow Point Golf and Country Club (Alex City), Army-Navy Country Club (Washington), Phi Kappa Phi, Beta Gamma Sigma, Sigma Xi, Omicron Delta Kappa, Kappa Alpha, Order of Daedalians. Avocations: flying, golf. Office: U Ala at Birmingham University Sta Birmingham AL 35205

PEYGHAMBARIAN, NASSER, optical science educator; b. Mar. 26, 1954. MS in Physics, Ind. U., 1979, PhD in Physics, 1982. Rsch. asst. prof. Optical Sci. Ctr. U. Ariz., Tucson, 1983-85, asst. prof. Optical Sci. Ctr., 1985-88, assoc. prof. Optical Sci. Ctr., 1988-91, prof. Optical Sci. Ctr., 1991—, chair lasers and photonic, 1994—. Author: Introduction to Semiconductor Optics, 1993; editor: Nonlinear Optical Materials and Devices for Photonic Switching IV, 1988, Nonlinear Photonics, 1990, Optical Bistability, 1988, (jour.) Optics Letters, 1992—; contbr. articles to profl. jours. Recipient TRW Young Faculty award, 1989-90, 3M Co.'s Young Faculty award, 1987-89. Fellow Optical Soc. Am., Am. Phys. Soc. Office: U Ariz Optical Scis Ctr Tucson AZ 85721

PEYRONNIN, JOSEPH FELIX, III, network news executive; b. Chgo., Aug. 3, 1947; s. Joseph Felix and Dorothy Ethel (Hargreaves) P. B.A., Columbia Coll., Chgo., 1970; MBA, Roosevelt U., 1979. Assignment editor WBBM-TV, Chgo., 1970-71, producer weekend and newsmakers programs, 1971-73, producer 6:00 PM News, 1973-76; assoc. producer CBS News, Chgo., 1976-79, CBS Evening News, Washington, 1979-82; sr. Washington producer CBS Evening News, 1982-86; dep. bur. chief, sr. producer CBS News, Washington, 1986-87, v.p., bur. chief, 1987-89; v.p., asst. to pres. CBS News, N.Y.C., 1989—. Bd. dirs. Gracie Sq. Hosp., N.Y.C., 1987-92. Recipient Emmy award Nat. Acad. Arts and Scis., 1975. Mem. Emil Verban Soc., Coun. on Fgn. Rels. Roman Catholic. Office: CBS News 524 W 57th St New York NY 10019-2902

PEYROUX, ROBERT ALBERT, accounting company executive; b. New Orleans, Dec. 10, 1930; s. John Alexander and Alma Marie (Guidry) P.; m. Terry Lynn DeJaive, July 27, 1951 (div. 1968); children: Dale, Gina, Donna, Neil; m. Salle Markely, May 2, 1969; 1 child, Jill. BBA, Tulane U., 1951. Staff acct. J.K. Byrne & Co., New Orleans, 1953-65, ptnr., 1965-75, mng. ptnr., 1975-85; mng. ptnr. Touche Ross, New Orleans, 1985—; bd. dirs. Inroads, Inc., New Orleans. Past pres. Vis. Nurses Assn., New Orleans, City Park, New Orleans Mus. Art.; pres. Metairie Endowment Fund, New Orleans, 1985—. Mem. Am. Inst. CPA's (council 1980, 85), La. Soc. CPA's (pres. 1975-76, Disting. Service award 1985, pres. New Orleans chpt. 1967-68, Outstanding service award 1976), Metairie C. of C. (pres. 1985-86), Rotary. Office: Touche Ross & Co 4100 Pl St Charles 201 St Charles Ave New Orleans LA 70170-4100

PEYSER, JOSEPH LEONARD, historical researcher, translator, author; b. N.Y.C., Oct. 19, 1925; s. Samuel and Sadye (Quinto) P.; m. Julia Boxer, May 30, 1948; children: Jay Randall, Jan Ellen. B.A., Duke U., 1947, M.A., 1949; profl. diploma, Columbia U., 1955; postgrad., U. Nancy, France, 1949-50; Ed.D., NYU, 1965. Prof., chmn. fgn. langs. Nancy (France) Pub. Schs., 1949-50; Tchr., chmn. fgn. langs. Monroe (N.Y.) Pub. Schs. 1951-54, Uniondale (N.Y.) Pub. Schs., 1954-61; asst. high sch. prin. Plainview, N.Y., 1961-63; mem. faculty Hofstra U., Hempstead, N.Y., 1963-68; assoc. prof. edn. Hofstra U., 1966-68; asst. dean, then asso. dean Hofstra U. (Sch. Edn.), 1964-66; interim dean Sch. Edn. Hofstra U., 1966-68; dean acad. affairs, prof. French and edn. Dowling Coll., Oakdale, N.Y., 1968-70; v.p. acad. affairs, dean faculty Dowling Coll., 1970-73; prof. French and edn. Ind. U., South Bend, 1973-94, prof. emeritus, 1994—; dean faculties Ind. U., 1973-75, chmn. fgn. lang. dept., 1987-89; vis. assoc. prof. NYU, 1964-66; adj. assoc. prof. L.I. U., 1961-63; prin. researcher, translator French Michilimackinac Rsch. Project, Mich., 1991—. Author: Letters from New France, 1981, rev. edit. Letters from New France: The Upper Country, 1686-1783, 1992; co-author: The Fox Wars: The Mesquakie Challenge to New France, 1993; translator Fort St. Joseph Manuscripts, 1978; contbr. profl. publs. Bd. dirs. South Bend Symphony, 1979-86. Served with USNR, 1943-46. Recipient Founders Day award NYU, 1966, State Hist. Soc. of Wis. Hesseltine award, 1991, French Colonial Hist. Soc. Heggoy Book prize, 1994; tchg. fellow French Ministry Edn., 1949-50, Lilly Endowment faculty fellow, 1985-86, NEH fellow, 1988, 94-95, Lundquist faculty fellow, 1989-90; Newberry Libr. rsch. assoc., 1985-86. Mem. AAUP, NEA, Ind. Hist. Soc., Ind. Assn. Historians, Hist. Soc. Mich., French Colonial Hist. Soc. (v.p. 1988-91).

PEYSER, ROXANE D., lawyer; b. Queens, N.Y., June 17, 1959; m. Ted Ross Peyser; children: Rachel Renee, Natasha Tovah, Samuel Aaron. BA in Middle Eastern Studies, George Washington U., 1981; JD, U. Houston, 1987. Bar: Tex., Ala., U.S. Dist. Ct. (so., no. dists.) Tex., U.S. Ct. Appeals (5th cir.). Intern Harris County Dist. Atty's. Office, Houston, 1987; atty. Saccomanno & Clegg, Houston, 1988-90, Graham, Bright & Smith, Dallas, 1990-92; sr. legal counsel Compass Bancshares, Inc., Birmingham, 1992-94; atty. Sirote & Permutt, P.C., Birmingham, Ala., 1994—; participant, grad. Project Corp. Leadership, Birmingham, 1993-94; section mem. meditation com. Ala. Bar Assn., 1993—. Contbr. numerous articles to profl. jours. Mem. bd. dirs. Am. Jewish Congress, Dallas, 1990-91; tchr. Temple Emanu El, Birmingham, 1993—; mem., contbr. Israel Bonds Bd., 1994—, Nat. Coun. Jewish Women, 1993—; mem. steering com. bus. & profl. women section Jewish Fedn., 1994—. Mem. ABA, Am. Corp. Counsel Assn., Tex. Bar Assn., Ala. Bar Assn., Tex. Assn. Bank Counsel. Avocations: music, writing, reading, theatre, movies. Office: Sirote & Permutt PC 2222 Arlington Ave S Birmingham AL 35205

PEYTON, DONALD LEON, retired standards association executive; b. Portland, Oreg., May 5, 1925; s. Bernard Thomas and Nelle (Moses) P.; m. Jane Frances Kirkman, Aug. 26, 1950; children: Patrick Philip, James Allen. Student, Mont. State U. 1946-47; BA, No. Colo. U., 1950. Civilian edn. specialist USAF, 1951-56; engaged in real estate Cheyenne, Wyo., 1956-

57; adminstrv. asst. to congressman, 1957-60; with U.S. C. of C., 1960-66, gen. mgr. govt. relations, 1965-66; pres. Am. Nat. Standards Inst., Inc., 1966-89, ret., 1989, Peyton Assocs., Standards Cons., White Plains, N.Y., 1989—; Lectr. govt. bus. relations Am. U., 1965-66, Amos Tuck Sch., Dartmouth, 1965—. Author: Standards and Trade in the 1990's; author monographs. Pres., Cheyenne Jr. C. of C., 1955-56. Mem. Am. Soc. Assn. Execs., Old Guard of White Plains, Univ. Club (Washington). Home and Office: 2 Beverly Rd White Plains NY 10605-3306 *My personal philosophy of life parallels that of my philosophy regarding voluntary organizations. In personal and professional life there is no hope for the self-satisfied individual or the self-satisfied organization.*

PEYTON, WILLIAM MAUPIN, treasurer, management educator; b. Richmond, Ky., Jan. 5, 1932; s. Russell Page and Amanda Thomas (Bogie) P.; m. Margaret Christine Dahl, Sept. 8, 1956; children: Michael William, Stephen Todd, John Patrick. B.S. in Bus. Adminstrn., UCLA, 1957; M.B.A. in Fin., U. So. Calif., 1967; postgrad., Harvard U., 1980. Office mgr. cost acct. Ralphs Grocery Co., Los Angeles, 1957-62; cost acctg. supr. Lockheed Air Terminal, Burbank, Calif., 1962-69; chief acctg. supr. Lockheed Air Terminal, Burbank, Calif., 1969-72, treas., 1972-80, exec. v.p., 1980-86, also dir.; treas. Lockheed Air Terminal, Panama City, 1976—; pres. Peyco, Inc., Burbank, 1986—; asst. prof. Glendale (Calif.) Coll., 1969—. Served with USAF, 1951-55. Mem. Inst. Mgmt. Accts. (dir. 1963). Republican. Episcopalian. Home: 12525 E Lupine Ave Scottsdale AZ 85259-3447

PEZ, GUIDO PETER, research chemist; b. Fiume, Italy, Feb. 10, 1941; married, 1966; 3 children. B.Sc. U. NSW, 1962; PhD in Chemistry, Monash U., Australia, 1967. Fellow McMaster U., 1967-69; rsch. chemist Allied Chem. Corp., 1969-74, sr. rsch. chemist, 1974-78, rsch. assoc., 1978-81; sr. rsch. assoc. Air Products & Chems., Inc., 1981-93, chief scientist, 1993—. Mem. Am. Chem. Soc. (Award in Inorganic Chemistry 1995). Achievements include research in synthetic inorganic and organometallic chemistry applied to catalysis, selective gas absorption materials, gas separation membranes, organofluorine chemistry, fluorinating reagents for synthesizing bio-active compounds. Office: Air Products & Chemicals Inc 7201 Hamilton Blvd Allentown PA 18195-1501*

PEZZELLA, JERRY JAMES, JR., investment and real estate corporation executive; b. Chesapeake, Va., Sept. 30, 1937; s. Jerry James Sr. and Mabel (Aydlett) P.; m. Carolyn Blades; children: James M., Stanley J., Julie Pezzella Scanlon. B.S. U. Richmond, 1963; MBA, U. Pa., 1964. Asst. v.p. Va. Nat. Bank div. Sovran Bank, Norfolk, 1964-68; chmn. bd., pres. First Am. Investment Corp., First Ga. Investment Corp., Atlanta, 1968-74; v.p. Great Am. Investment Corp., Atlanta, 1974-78; exec. v.p. Equity Fin. & Mgmt. Co., Chgo., 1978—; pres., chmn. bd. First Capital Fin. Corp., Chgo., 1983-85; pres. GAFGI Holdings Inc., Chgo., 1983—; chmn. bd. 1st Property Mgmt. Corp., 1990-92; bd. dirs. Great Am. Mgmt. and Investment, Inc., Chgo., Nat. Multi Housing coun., 1992-94, mem. exec. com. Bd. dirs., exec. com. Nat. Multi-Housing Coun., 1991-93. Mem. River Club (Chgo.). Office: Equity Fin and Mgmt Co Chicago IL 60606

PFAELZER, MARIANA R., federal judge; b. L.A., Feb. 4, 1926. AB, U. Calif., 1947; LLB, UCLA, 1957. Bar: Calif. 1958. Assoc. Wyman, Bautzer, Rothman & Kuchel, 1957-69, ptnr., 1969-78; judge U.S. Dist. Ct. (ctrl. dist.) Calif., 1978—. pres., v.p., dir. Bd. Police Commrs. City of L.A., 1974-78; bd. vis. Loyola Law Sch. Named Alumna of Yr. by UCLA Law Sch., 1980. Mem. ABA, Calif. Bar Assn. (local adminstrv. com., spl. com. study rules procedure 1972, joint subcom. profl. ethics and computers and the law coms. 1972, profl. ethics com. 1972-74, spl. com. juvenile justice, women's rights subcom. human rights sect.), L.A. County Bar Assn. (spl. com. study rules procedure state bar 1974). Office: US Dist Ct 312 N Spring St Los Angeles CA 90012-4701

PFAFF, WILLIAM WALLACE, physician, educator; b. Rochester, N.Y., Aug. 14, 1930; s. Norman Joseph and Eleanor Blakesley (Wells) P.; m. Patricia Ann Clark, June 25, 1960; children—Nancy, Karen, Margaret, Mary Catherine. A.B., Harvard U., 1952; M.D., U. Buffalo, 1956. Intern U. Chgo., 1956-57, resident, 1957-58; resident in surgery Stanford U. Med. Center, 1960-65, instr. surgery, 1965; faculty U. Fla., Gainesville, 1965—; prof. surgery U. Fla., 1971—. Contbr. numerous articles to profl. jours. Served with USPHS, 1958-60. Mem. ACS, Am. Surg. Assn., Transplantation Soc., Am. Soc. Transplant Surgery, Southeastern Surg. Congress, So. Surg. Assn., Fla. Kidney Found., Alachua County Med. Soc. (pres. 1977-78), Alpha Omega Alpha. Home: 2445 NW 15th Pl Gainesville FL 32605 Office: U Fla Dept Surgery PO Box 100286 Gainesville FL 32610-0286

PFAFFMAN, WILLIAM SCOTT, sculptor; b. Albany, Ga., July 10, 1954; s. Roy Alton and Corabel (Scales) P. BFA, Auburn U., 1976; postgrad., U. Ala., Huntsville, 1976; MA, CUNY, 1978. Curator Bklyn. Waterfront Artists Coalition, 1989-92; dir. Kentler Internat. Drawing Space, Bklyn., 1989-92, artist-in-residence, 1983; vis. artist Reed Deer (Alta., Can.) Coll., 1985, N.Y. State Coll. Ceramics, Alfred, 1985, Wayne State U., Detroit, 1985, Edinborough (Pa.) Coll., 1987, Erie (Pa.) Art Mus., 1987, John F. Kennedy H.S., Bronx, N.Y., 1987. One-man show CUNY Grad. Ctr. Mall, 1982; exhibited in group shows, 1976—, including Birmingham (Ala.) Mus. Art, 1976, The Clocktower, N.Y.C., 1984, SUNY, Purchase, 1984, Am. Acad. and Nat. Inst. Arts and Letters, N.Y.C., 1985, Queens Mus., 1985, Sculpture Space, Utica, N.Y., 1986, Erie (Pa.) Art Mus., 1987, Willis Gallery, Detroit, 1988, Sander Gallery, N.Y.C., 1988, München Gladbach, Fed. Republic Germany, 1991, Picnic Mass, Bklyn., 1993, The Drawing Room, Amsterdam, Holland, 1994, Galerie Seghaier, Vienna, Austria, 1994; commns. include Artpark Sculpture Commn., 1984, N.Y.C. Dept. Gen. Svcs., 1988; one-person installation Roermond, Holland, 1992. Project developer N.Y.C. Artist Housing Program, Bklyn., 1986-92—. Recipient award Nat. Studio Program, 1983, ann. award in art AAAL, 1985; resident Sculpture Space, 1986; fellow Pollack Krasner Found., 1987; grantee N.Y. State Coun. on Arts, 1987. Home: 190 Coffey St Brooklyn NY 11231 Studio: 353 Van Brunt St Brooklyn NY 11231

PFALTZGRAFF, ROBERT LOUIS, JR., political scientist, educator; b. Phila., June 1, 1934; s. Robert L. and Mary (Warriner) P.; m. Diane A. Kressler, May 20, 1967; children: Suzanne Diane, Robert Louis III. B.A. with honors, Swarthmore Coll., 1956; M.B.A., U. Pa., 1958, Ph.D. in Polit. Sci. (Penfield fellow), 1964; M.A. in Internat. Relations, 1959. Research assoc. Fgn. Policy Research Inst., 1964-71; asst. prof. polit. sci. U. Pa., Phila., 1964-70; dep. dir. Fgn. Policy Research Inst., 1971-73; assoc. prof. internat. politics Fletcher Sch. Law and Diplomacy, Tufts U., Medford, Mass., 1971-78, prof. internat. politics, 1978-83, Shelby Cullom Davis prof. internat. security studies, 1983—; vis. lectr. Fgn. Service Inst. Dept. State, 1970-71; George C. Marshall prof. Coll. of Europe, Bruges, Belgium, 1970-71; pres. Inst. for Fgn. Policy Analysis, Cambridge, Mass., 1976—; short term acad. guest prof. Nat. Defense Coll. Tokyo, Japan, 1981; pres. U.S. Strategic Inst., Washington, 1977-79. Author: Britain Faces Europe, 1957-1967, 1969, Politics and the International System, 1969, The Atlantic Community: A Complex Balance, 1969, The Study of International Relations, 1977, The Cruise Missile: Bargaining Chip or Defense Bargain, 1977, Power Projection and the Long Range Combat Aircraft: Missions, Capabilities and Alternative Designs, 1981, Contending Theories of International Relations: A Comprehensive Survey, 1981; co-editor: Contrasting Approaches to Strategic Arms Control, 1974, SALT: Implications for Arms Control in the 1970s, 1973, The Other Arms Race: New Technologies and Non Nuclear Conflict, 1975, Arms Transfers to the Third World: The Military Build-up in Less Industrial Countries, 1978, Intelligence Policy and National Security, 1981, Projection of Power: Perspectives, Perceptions and Problems, 1982, (with Ra'anan) The U.S. Defense Mobilization Infrastructure: Problems and Priorities, 1983, International Dimensions of Space, 1984, National Security Policy: The Decision-Making Process, 1984, The Peace Movements in Europe and the United States, 1985, co-author: American Foreign Policy: FDR to Reagan, 1996, co-editor: Selling the Rope to Hang Capitalism? The Debate on West-East Trade and Technology Transfer, 1987, Emerging Doctrines and Technologies: Implications for Global and Regional Political-Military Balance, 1987, Protracted Warfare--The Third World Arena: A Dimension of U.S.-Soviet Conflict, 1988, Guerrilla Warfare and Counter-Insurgency: U.S.-Soviet Policy in the third World, 1988, U.S. Defense Policy in an Era of Constrained Resources, 1989; co-author: Contending Theories of International Relations: A Comprehensive Study, 1990; co-editor: National

Security Decisions: The Participants Speak, 1990, The United States Army: Challenges and Missions for the 1990s, 1991, The Future of Air Power in the Aftermath of the Gulf War, 1992, Naval Forward Presence and the National Military Strategy, 1993, others; contbr. articles to scholarly jours. Guggenheim fellow, 1968-69; Relm Found. grantee, 1969. Mem. Internat. Studies Assn., Coun. Fgn. Rels., Internat. Inst. Strategic Studies, Capitol Hill Club, Army and Navy Club (Washington). Home: 663 Wallace Dr Wayne PA 19087-1911 Office: Inst Fgn Policy Analysis 675 Massachusetts Ave Cambridge MA 02139-3309

PFAU, CHARLES JULIUS, biology educator, researcher; b. Troy, N.Y., Sept. 29, 1935; m. Mary Gail Prediger (div. 1979); children: Dianne, David, Lise. BS, Rensselaer Poly. Inst., 1956; MA, Ind. U., 1958, PhD in Bacteriology, 1960. USPHS postdoctoral fellow Biophysics Yale U., New Haven, 1960-62; postdoctoral fellow Rickettsia & Virus Dept. Statens Seruminstitut, Copenhagen, 1962-64; asst. prof. microbiology U. Mass., Amherst, 1964-71; assoc. prof. biology Rensselaer Poly. Inst., Troy, N.Y., 1971-76, prof., 1976—, chair dept. biology, 1982-85; chmn. Arenavirus Study Group, Internat. Com. on Taxonomy of Viruses, 1974-81; vis. scientist Inst. Pasteur, Paris, 1983, Inst. Pathologie, U. Zurich, Switzerland, 1984, Inst. Medicinsk Mikrobiologi, Copenhagen, 1985-86, U.S. Army Med. Rsch. Inst. Infectious Diseases, Ft. Detrick, Frederick, Md., 1990, Inst. Internat. de Pathologie Cellulaire et Moleculaire, Brussels, 1991. Contbr. articles, revs. to profl. jours., chpts. to books. Recipient Career Devel. award NIH, 1965-70, I.P.A. fellow, 1979-80; Fogarty Sr. Internat. fellow, 1985-86. Mem. AAAS, Am. Assn. Immunologists, Am. Soc. Microbiology (northeastern br.). Avocations: hiking, bicycling, art and architecture, travel. Home: RD 3 27 Langmore Ln Troy NY 12180-9612 Office: Rensselaer Poly Inst Sci Ctr 1W04 Dept Biology 110 8th St Troy NY 12180-3522*

PFAU, GEORGE HAROLD, JR., stockbroker; b. Milw., May 7, 1924; s. George Harold and Elisabeth C. (Hunter) P.; m. Anne Elizabeth Mayhew; 1 child, George Harold III; children by previous marriage: Mary D., Peter W., Elizabeth C. B.S., Yale U., 1948. Tchr., 1948-49; with Fleishhacker Paper Box Co., San Francisco, 1952-54; salesman A.G. Becker & Co., San Francisco, 1954-55; v.p., sec., dir. Carl W. Stern & Co., San Francisco, 1955-57; with White Weld & Co. Inc., San Francisco, 1957-78; 1st v.p. corp. fin. dept. Blyth Eastman Dillon, San Francisco, 1978-79; sr. v.p. Paine Webber, San Francisco, 1979—; bd. dirs. Securities Investor Protection Corp. Bd. dirs. The Guardsmen, 1966-67, Pathfinder Fund, 1974-82, San Francisco Zool. Soc., 1979-80; trustee Thacher Sch., Ojai, Calif., 1967-76, Town Sch., San Francisco, 1966-70; pres. Planned Parenthood San Francisco-Alameda County, 1968-69, bd. dirs., 1965—; chmn. Lincoln Club of No. Calif., 1993—, mem. 1982—; chmn. Citizens for Better San Francisco. With C.E. AUS, 1942-44; with Am. Field Svc. 1944-45. Mem. Kappa Beta Phi, San Francisco (Calif.) Bond Club, Bohemian Club (San Francisco), Calif. Tennis Club. Office: Paine Webber 100 California St Fl 3 San Francisco CA 94111-4505

PFAU, RICHARD ANTHONY, college president; b. N.Y.C., Feb. 19, 1942; s. Hugo and Irene Beatrice P.; m. Nancy Ann DiPace, Sept. 12, 1964; children: Bradley Madison, Aleksandra Nicole. AB, Hamilton Coll., 1964; MA, U. Va., 1973, PhD, 1975. Systems analyst Equitable Life Ins. Co., N.Y.C., 1964-66; asst. prof. history Dickinson Coll., Carlisle, Pa., 1975-80; assoc. prof., assoc. dean U. Miami, Coral Gables, Fla., 1980-85; dean of faculty, provost Emory (Va.) and Henry Coll., 1985-93; pres. Ill. Coll., Jacksonville, Ill., 1993—. Author: No Sacrifice Too Great: The Life of Lewis L. Strauss, 1985. Contbr. articles, book revs. to profl. publs. Vestryman St. Thomas Episc. Ch., Abingdon, Va.; chmn., sec.-treas., exec. com., bd. dirs. Va. Found. for Humanities and Pub. Policy, Exec. Com. Fedn. Ind. Ill. Colls. and Univs. Capt. USAF, 1966-71. DuPont fellow, 1974-75; Hoover fellow, 1982. Mem. Omicron Delta Kappa, Alpha Psi Omega, Pi Delta Epsilon. Home: Barnes House 310 Lockwood Pl Jacksonville IL 62650-2225 Office: Ill Coll Jacksonville IL 62650

PFAUTCH, ROY, minister, public affairs consultant; b. St. Louis, June 24, 1936; s. Floyd and Bertha Edna (Berghoefer) P. AB, Washington U., St. Louis, 1957; BD, Princeton Theol. Sem., 1961. Ordained to ministry Presbyn. Ch., 1961. Asst. to pres. Princeton Theol. Sem., 1961-63; pres. Civic Service, Inc., St. Louis and Washington, 1963—; mem. adv. com. on voluntary fgn. aid, U.S. Dept. State, 1981-83, Nat. Service Council, 1982-83. Del. Rep. Nat. Conv., Dallas, 1984, Houston, 1992; co-chmn. Nat. Day Prayer, 1985, 89, hon. co-chmn. Presdl. Inaugural, Washington, 1985, 89; chmn. Salute to Pres. Dinner, Washington, 1986; bd. overseers Reagan scholars program Eureka (Ill.) Coll., 1982-89; mem. presbytery Elijah Prish Lovejoy, United Presbyn. Ch., 1961—; bd. dirs. St. Louis Pub. Library System, 1980-86; del. XXIV Olympics, Seoul, 1988; mem. adv. bd. Internat. Ctr. Tropical Ecology, 1991—; bd. dirs. Nat. Found. Improvement of Edn., 1992—. Mem. Internat. Assn. Polit. Cons., Am. Assn. Polit. Cons. (v.p., sec., pres. 1980-84) Am. Assn. Pub. Opinion Research, Mktg. Research Assn., Council Pub. Polls. Clubs: St. Louis, Racquet (St. Louis), St. Louis Country, 1929 'F' St. (Washington). Avocations: horse riding, gardening, reading. Home: 52 Portland Pl Saint Louis MO 63108-1242 Office: Civic Srvc Inc 1 Mercantile Ctr Ste 3101 Saint Louis MO 63101-1615 also: Civic Srvc Inc 1050 Connecticut Ave NW Ste 870 Washington DC 20036

PFEFFER, DAVID H., lawyer; b. N.Y.C., Mar. 15, 1935. B. Chem. Engring., CCNY, 1956; J.D., NYU, 1961, LL.M. in Trade Regulation, 1967. Bar: N.Y. 1961. With patent dept. U.S. Rubber Co., Wayne, N.J., 1957-61; assoc. Watson, Leavenworth, Kelton & Taggart, N.Y.C., 1961-63; assoc. Morgan & Finnegan, N.Y.C., 1963-70, ptnr., 1971—; village prosecutor Roslyn Harbor, N.Y., 1976-78, village justice, 1979—; panel of arbitrators Am. Arbitration Assn. Mem. ABA (litigation sect.), N.Y. State Bar Assn., Assn. Bar City N.Y., Nassau County Bar Assn. (coms. on patent and trademarks, fed. practice), Am. Intellectual Property Law Assn. (com. alt. dispute resolution), N.Y. Patent Trademark and Copyright Law Assn., N.Y. State Magistrates Assn., Nassau County Magistrates Assn., Order of Coif. Office: Morgan & Finnegan 345 Park Ave New York NY 10154-0001

PFEFFER, EDWARD ISRAEL, educational administrator; b. Newark, July 1, 1914; s. Jacob and Fannie Bessie (Fisher) P.; m. Anna Chinich, July 14, 1940; children—Cynthia Roberta, Bruce Paul. B.S., N.Y. U., 1937; M.A., N.J. State Tchrs. Coll., Montclair, 1942; Ed.D., Rutgers U., 1954. Tchr. Abington Ave. Sch., Newark, 1937-46; vice prin. Warren St. Sch., 1946-53; prin. Monmouth St. and Coes Pl. schs., 1953-57, Robert Treat Jr. High and Elem. Sch., 1957-64; asst. supt. spl. services Newark Dist. Pub. Schs., 1964-67, dep. supt., 1967-72, 73—, acting supt., 1972-73. Contbr. articles profl. publs. Commr. Newark Sr. Citizens Commn., 1967—; mem. Newark Juvenile Problems Commn., 1958-62; chmn. Children's Resources Commn., Council Social Agys., 1955-60; mem. exec. bd. Family and Children's Div., 1955-62; mem. Newark Commn. for UN Week, 1962—, Newark Disaster Com., 1967—, Bd. Edn., Temple B'nai Abraham, Essex County, N.J., 1964-65; Mem. exec. bd. Newark Central Community Council; mem. adv. bd. Essex County Tech. Sch. Recipient citations Newark Assn. Dirs. and Suprs., 1973, citations Newark Title I Central Parents Council, 1973. Mem. Newark Pub. Sch. Prins. Assn. (pres. 1963-64), N.J. Elementary Sch. Press Assn. (pres.), Congress Parents and Tchrs. (life), NEA (life), Am., N.J. assns. sch. adminstrs., Newark Schoolmens Assn. (bd. govs., named Outstanding Schoolman of Year 1972-73), Columbia Scholastic Press Assn. (v.p., Gold Key 1948), Urban League, NAACP, Phi Delta Kappa. Home: 507 Clinton Pl Newark NJ 07112-1703 Office: 2 Cedar St Newark NJ 07102-3015

PFEFFER, JEFFREY, business educator; b. St. Louis, July 23, 1946; s. Newton Stuart and Shirlee (Krisman) P.; m. Kathleen Frances Fowler, July 23, 1986. BS, MS, Carnegie Mellon U., 1968; PhD, Stanford U., 1972. Mem. tech. staff Research Analysis Corp., McLean, Va., 1968-69; asst. prof. U. Ill., Champaign, 1971-73; from asst. prof. to assoc. prof. U. Calif., Berkeley, 1973-79; prof. Grad. Sch. Bus., Stanford U., Calif., 1979—; vis. prof. Harvard U. Bus. Sch., Boston, 1981-82. Author: The External Control of Organizations, 1978, Organizational Design, 1978, Power in Organizations, 1981, Organizations and Organization Theory, 1982 (Terry Book award 1984), Managing with Power, 1992, Competitive Advantage Through People, 1994. Fellow Acad. Mgmt. (bd. govs. 1984-86, New Concept award 1979, Richard D. Irwin award for scholarly contbns. to mgmt. 1989); mem. Am. Sociol. Assn., Indsl. Rels. Rsch. Assn. Jewish. Avocations: cooking,

music. Home: 5 Burnett Ave San Francisco CA 94131-3317 Office: Stanford U Grad Sch of Bus Stanford CA 94305

PFEFFER, PHILIP MAURICE, distribution company executive; b. St. Louis, Jan. 20, 1945; s. Philip McRae and Jeanne (Kaufman) P.; m. Pamela Jean Korte, Aug. 28, 1965; children: John-Lindell Philip, James Howard, David Maurice. B.A. in Math. and Chemistry, So. Ill. U., 1965, M.A. in Econs., 1966; postgrad., Vanderbilt U., 1966-68. Economist Genesco, Inc., Nashville, 1968, mgr. internat. fin., 1969, asst. treas.; pres. Genesco Export Co., Nashville, 1970-75; dir. fin. planning Ingram Distribution Group, Inc., Nashville, 1976-77, v.p. fin. and adminstrn., 1977-78, exec. v.p., 1978, pres. and chief exec. officer, 1978-81, chmn. bd. and chief exec. officer, 1981—, dir., 1978—; exec. v.p. Ingram Industries, Inc., Nashville, 1981—, dir., 1981—; bd. dirs. Ingram Barge Co., Ingram Micro Inc., Ingram Coal Co., Tenn. Ins. Co.; instr. fin. and econs. U. Tenn., Nashville, 1968-77; lectr. corp. fin. Vanderbilt U., 1972-77. Bd. dirs. So. Ill. U. Found., 1982—, Nashville Area YMCA, 1982—. Recipient Long Rifle and Silver Beaver award Boy Scouts Am., Nashville, 1981, also Disting. Eagle from Nat. Coun.; Benjamin Gomez award for Disting. Contbns. to the Art of Book Pub. Mem. Fin. Execs. Inst. (pres. 1978-79), Nat. Eagle Scout Assn. (bd. dirs., Silver Wreath award), Nashville Area C. of C. (vice chmn.), Am. Wholesale Booksellers Assn. (past v.p., trustee), So. Ill. U. Alumni Assn. (past bd. dirs.), Young Pres.'s Orgn., Tenn. Assn. Bus., Rotary, Percy Priest Yacht Club (Nashville). Avocations: scouting, sailing, water sports, landscaping. Home: 836 Treemont Ct Nashville TN 37220-2114 Office: Ingram Distbn Group Inc 1 Ingram Blvd La Vergne TN 37086

PFEFFER, RICHARD LAWRENCE, geophysics educator; b. Bklyn., Nov. 26, 1930; s. Lester Robert and Anna (Newman) P.; m. Roslyn Ziegler, Aug. 30, 1953; children—Bruce, Lloyd, Scott, Glenn. B.S. cum laude, CCNY, 1952; M.S., Mass. Inst. Tech., 1954, Ph.D., 1957. Research asst. MIT, 1952-55, guest lectr., 1956; atmospheric physicist Air Force Cambridge Research Center, Boston, 1955-59; sr. scientist Columbia U., 1959-61, lectr., 1961-62, asst. prof. geophysics, 1962-64; assoc. prof. meteorology Fla. State U., Tallahassee, 1964-67; dir. Geophys. Fluid Dynamics Inst., 1967-93; prof. meteorology Fla. State U., 1967—; cons. NASA, 1961-64, N.W. Ayer & Son, Inc., 1962, Ednl. Testing Service, Princeton, N.J., 1963, Voice of Am., 1963, Grolier, Inc., 1963, Naval Research Labs., 1971-76; Mem. Internat. Commn. for Dynamical Meteorology, 1972-76. Editor: Dynamics of Climate, 1960; Contbr. articles to profl. jours. Bd. dirs. B'nai B'rith Anti-Defamation League; chmn. religious concern and social action com. Temple Israel, Tallahassee, 1971-72. Fellow Am. Meterol. Soc. (program chmn. ann. meeting 1963); mem. Am. Geophys. Union, N.Y. Acad. Scis. (chmn. planetary scis. sect. 1961-63), Sigma Xi, Chi Epsilon Pi, Sigma Alpha. Home: 926 Waverly Rd Tallahassee FL 32312-2813

PFEFFER, ROBERT, chemical engineer, academic administrator, educator; b. Vienna, Austria, Nov. 26, 1935; came to U.S., 1938, naturalized, 1944; s. Joseph and Gisela (Aberbach) P.; m. Marcia Borenstein, Dec. 24, 1960; children—Michael, Jacqueline. B.Ch.E., N.Y. U., 1956, M.Ch.E., 1958, D.Eng.Sc., 1962. Mem. faculty CCNY, 1957-92, asst. prof. chem. engring., 1962-66, assoc. prof., 1966-71, prof., 1971-92, chmn. dept. chem. engring., 1973-87, Herbert Kayser prof., 1980-92, dean grad. studies and research, dep. provost, 1987-88, provost, v.p. acad. affairs, 1988-92; v.p. rsch. and grad. studies, prof. chem. engring. N.J. Int. Tech., Newark, 1992—; vis. prof. Imperial Coll., London, 1969; Fulbright scholar Technion-Israel Inst. Tech., 1976-77; cons. in field. Contbr. articles to tech. publs. Fulbright Hays awardee, 1976-77; DuPont faculty fellow, 1962; NASA faculty fellow, 1964-65. Mem. Am. Inst. Chem. Engrs., Am. Soc. Engring. Edn., Sigma Xi, Tau Beta Pi, Phi Lambda Upsilon. Jewish. Office: NJ Inst Tech University Hts Newark NJ 07102

PFEFFER, RUBIN HARRY, publishing executive; b. Bklyn., Oct. 9, 1951; s. Martie and Idell (Treiber) P.; m. Lurie Horns; children: Stephanie, Ian, Rebecca, Vaughn. BFA in Graphic Design, Carnegie-Mellon U., 1973. Dir. art Harcourt Brace Jovanovich, San Diego, 1979-84; corp. art dir. Harcourt Brace Jovanovich, Orlando, Fla., 1984—; dir. children's books Harcourt Brace Jovanovich, San Diego, 1984-85; pres. Harcourt Brace & Co. Trade Books, San Diego, 1985—. Bd. dirs. Calif. Ballet Co., San Diego, 1986-87, Easter Seal Soc., San Diego, 1988—. Avocation: painting. Office: HB Trade Divsn 525 B St San Diego CA 92101

PFEFFERKORN, MICHAEL GENE, SR., secondary education educator, writer; b. Delano, Calif., July 19, 1939; s. E. Michael and N. Ruth (Ervin) P.; m. Sandra J. Carter, June 15, 1963; children: Michael Jr., Patricia. AB, S.E. Mo. State, 1961, BS in Secondary Edn., 1961; MEd, U. Mo. 1963. Cert. Eng., life Social Studies tchr., Mo. Tchr. De Soto (Mo.) Pub. Schs., 1961-62, Cleveland High Sch., St. Louis, 1963-84; tchr. S.W. High Sch., St. Louis, 1984-86, tchr., history dept. head, 1987-92; tchr. Gateway Inst. of Tech. High Sch., St. Louis, 1992—; cons. Internat. Edn. Consortium, St. Louis, 1989-92. Co-author: Chits, Chiselers, and Funny Money, 1976; editor Mo. Jour. Numismatics; contbr. articles to numis. jours. Pres. Carondelet Hist. Soc., 1977-78, mem., 1970—; mem. Landmarks and Urban Design Com., St. Louis, 1976-80. Mem. ASCD, Am. Fedn. Tchrs., Nat. Coun. Social Studies Tchrs., State Hist. Soc. Mo., Am. Numis. Assn., Mo. Numis Soc., Numis. Lit. Guild, World Coin Club Mo. Roman Catholic. Avocations: numismatics, writing, genealogy. Home: 6803 Leona St Saint Louis MO 63116-2833 Office: Gateway Inst of Tech 5101 Mcree Ave Saint Louis MO 63110-2019

PFEFFERKORN, SANDRA J., secondary education educator; b. St. Louis, Jan. 14, 1940; d. Albert A. and Alice C. (Lowell) Carter; m. Michael G. Pfefferkorn, June 15, 1963; children: Michael G. Jr., Patricia A. BS in Secondary Edn., SE Mo. State Coll., 1961; MEd, U. Mo., 1966. Cert. life English, Spanish, French, and reading tchr., Mo. Tchr. English, head English and fgn. lang. dept. St. Louis Bd. Edn.; English tchr. Cleveland Naval Jr. Res. Officer Tng. Corps High Sch., St. Louis. Asst. editor Mo. Jour. Numismatics. Regents scholar, 1957; fellow Mo. Writing Project, 1981. Mem. Am. Assn. Tchrs. Spanish and Portuguese (San Luis Rey chpt.), Nat. Coun. Tchrs. English, Internat. Reading Assn., Mo. Assn. Tchrs. English, AAUW. Home: 6803 Leona St Saint Louis MO 63116-2833 Office: Naval Jr Res Officer Tng Corps 4352 Louisiana Ave Saint Louis MO 63111-1097

PFEIFER, LARRY ALAN, public health service coordinator; b. Rock Springs, Wyo., July 20, 1958; s. Jack Albert and Betty Lee (Ethington) P.; m. Sandra Lynn, June 20, 1986. BS cum laude, So. Oreg. State Coll., 1983, MS in Health Edn., 1989; paramedic diploma, Rogue Community Coll., 1984; postgrad., Columbia Pacific U. Cert. paramedic, Oreg. Lt., paramedic Tualatin Valley Fire and Rescue, Portland, Oreg., 1991—; lectr. in field. Author (text) Non-Verbal Pre-Hospital Assessment of the Trauma Patient. Mem. Oreg. Paramedic Assn., Phi Kappa Phi, Kappa Delta Pi. Home: 5156 NW 173d Pl Portland OR 97229

PFEIFER, MICHAEL DAVID, bishop; b. Alamo, Tex., May 18, 1937; s. Frank and Alice (Savage) P. Student, Oblate Sch. Theology. Ordained priest Roman Cath. Ch., 1965, consecrated bishop, 1985; mem. Missionary Oblates of Mary Immaculate. Priest Roman Cath. Ch., Mexico City, 1964-1981; provincial-superior of Oblate So. U.S. Province Roman Cath. Ch., San Antonio, 1981-85; bishop Roman Cath. Ch., San Angelo, Tex., 1985—. Address: PO Box 1829 804 Ford St San Angelo TX 76902*

PFEIFER, PAUL E., state supreme court justice; b. Bucyrus, Ohio, Oct. 15, 1942; m. Julia Pfeifer; children: Lisa, Beth, Kurt. BA, Ohio State U., 1963, JD, 1966. Asst. atty. gen. State of Ohio, 1967-70; mem. Ohio Ho. of Reps., 1971-72; asst. prosecuting atty. Crawford County, 1973-76; mem. Ohio Senate, 1976-92, minority floor leader, 1983-84, asst. pres. pro-tempore, 1985-86; ptnr. Cory, Brown & Pfeifer, 1973-92; justice Ohio Supreme Ct., 1992—; chmn. jud. com. Ohio Senate, 10 yrs. Mem. Grace United Meth. Ch., Bucyrus. Mem. Bucyrus Rotary Club. Office: 30 E Broad St Fl 3 Columbus OH 43215-3414

PFEIFER, ALICE RANDEL, business manager; b. New York, N.Y., Jan. 4, 1954; d. Wilmer Henry Jr. and Lucy (Scognamilo) P.; m. Peter F. Pfeifer, June 24, 1989; 1 child, Kevin William Pfeifer. BA in Psychology, Ithaca Coll., 1975; MS in Counseling and Guidance, Syracuse U., 1977, MBA in

Accounting, 1986. Counselor Syracuse (N.Y.) Boy's Club, 1978-79; psychiat. aide SUNY Upstate Med. Ctr., Syracuse, 1980-85; computer operator, test supr. Syracuse U. Test Svcs., Syracuse, 1985-86; acct. Syracuse U. Press, Syracuse, 1987-90, bus. mgr., 1990—; acct. TJ's Big Boy, Syracuse, N.Y., 1987. Avocations: dancing, reading, art, theater, music. Office: Syracuse U Press 1600 Jamesville Ave Syracuse NY 13244

PFEIFFER, CARL E., manufacturing company executive; b. 1930. BSME, Mich. State U. With Quanex Corp., Houston, 1953-58, v.p., 1958-68, exec. v.p., 1968-71, pres., 1971-73, chmn. bd., 1973—; plant mgr. Gulf States Tube Corp. subs., v.p., 1958-68, exec. v.p., 1968-71, pres., 1971-72, treas. mem. com., now pres., chief exec. officer, also bd. dirs. Office: Quanex Corp 1900 W Loop S Ste 1500 Houston TX 77027*

PFEIFFER, ECKHARD, computer company executive. BA, Nuremberg Business, 1963; MBA, SMU, 1983. Pres. & CEO Compaq Computer, 1991—. Office: Compaq Computer Corp PO Box 692000 Houston TX 77269

PFEIFFER, ERIC ARMIN, psychiatrist, gerontologist; b. Rauental, Germany, Sept. 15, 1935; came to U.S., 1952; naturalized, 1957; s. Fritz and Emma (Saborowski) P.; m. Natasha Maria Emerson, Mar. 21, 1964; children: Eric Alexander, Michael David, Mark Armin. AB, Washington U., 1956, MD, 1960. Intern Albert Einstein Coll. Medicine, Bronx, N.Y., 1960-61; resident in psychiatry U. Rochester, N.Y., 1961-64; practice medicine specializing in psychiatry Durham, N.C., 1966-76, Denver, 1976-78; asst. prof. Duke U., Durham, 1966-69, assoc. prof., 1969-72, prof., 1973-76, project dir., 1971-76, assoc. dir., 1974-76; dir. Davis Inst. Care and Study Aging, Denver, 1976-77; prof. psychiatry U. Colo. Denver, 1976-78; prof. psychiatry, chief div. geriatric psychiatry U. South Fla. Coll. Medicine, Tampa, 1978—; dir. Suncoast Gerontology Ctr. U. South Fla. Coll. Medicine, 1980—; chief psychiatry svc. Tampa VA Med. Ctr., 1979-80; cons. in field; chmn. bd. Social Systems, Inc., 1975-76; chmn. com. on mental health and mental illness of elderly HEW, 1976-77. Author: Disordered Behavior, 1968, (with E.W. Busse) Behavior and Adaptation in Late Life, 1970, 3d edit., 1977, Successful Aging, 1974, Multidimensional Functional Assessment, 1977, Alzheimer's Disease, 1989. With USPHS, 1964-66. Markle Found. scholar acad. medicine, 1968-73; Eric Pfeiffer Chair in Alzheimer's Disease Rsch. named in his honor, U.S. Fla., 1985. Fellow Gerontol. Soc. (chmn. clin. medicine sect. 1975-76), Am. Psychiat. Assn.; mem. Am. Geriatrics Soc. (Allen Gold medal 1977), So. Psychiat. Soc., Phi Beta Kappa. Home: 5140 W Longfellow Ave Tampa FL 33629-7534 Office: 12901 Bruce B Downs Blvd Tampa FL 33612-4799

PFEIFFER, JANE CAHILL, former broadcasting company executive, consultant; b. Washington, Sept. 29, 1932; d. John Joseph and Helen (Reilly) Cahill; B.A., U. Md., 1954; postgrad., Cath. U. Am., 1956-57; LHD (hon.), Pace Coll., 1978, U. Md., 1979, Manhattanville Coll., 1979, Amherst U., 1980, Babson Coll., 1981, U. Notre Dame, 1991; m. Ralph A. Pfeiffer, Jr., June 3, 1975. With IBM Corp., Armonk, N.Y., 1955-76, sec. mgmt. rev. com., 1970, dir. communications, 1971, v.p. communications and govt. relations, 1972-76, bus. cons., 1976-78; chmn. NBC, Inc., N.Y.C., 1978-80; bus. cons., 1980—; dir. Ashland Oil Co., Mony Fin. Svcs., Internat. Paper Co., J.C. Penney Co.; trustee The Conf. Bd., 1991. Mem. pres.'s adv. com. White House Fellows, 1966, Pres.'s Gen. Adv. Commn. on Arms Control and Disarmament, 1977-80, Pres.'s Commn. Mil. Compensation, trustee Rockefeller Found., U. Md., Carnegie Hall, U. Notre Dame. White House fellow, Washington, 1966; recipient Achievement award Kapppa Kappa Gamma, 1974-80, Eleanor Roosevelt Humanitarian award N.Y. League for Hard of Hearing, 1980, Disting. Alumna award U. Md., 1975, Humanitarian award NOW, 1980, Centennial Alumna Medallion U. Md., 1988. Mem. Council on Fgn. Relations, Overseas Devel. Council. Club: Econ. of N.Y. Office: 90 Field Point Cir Greenwich CT 06830-7011

PFEIFFER, J(OHN) DAVID, mechanical engineering educator, consultant; b. Balt., Oct. 30, 1931; emigrated to Can., 1971; s. John David and Charlotte (Riggin) P.; m. Sherley Dale Bouck, June 12, 1954; children: Kristina Ann, Lisa Ellen, Amy Diane, Laura Susan. B.E.E., Cornell U., Ithaca, N.Y., 1953. Registered profl. engr., N.Y. Asst. dir. research Gen. Lab. Assocs., Norwich, N.Y., 1957-60; pres. Norwich Design Corp., 1960-63; research engr. Beloit Corp., Downingtown, Pa., 1963-69, chief research engr., 1969-71; mgr. new product devel. Dynascis. Corp., Blue Bell, Pa., 1969; assoc. prof. mech. engring. McGill U., Montreal, Que., Can., 1971-95, dir. McGill Winding Rsch. Lab., 1988-95; cons. in field. Contbr. papers on paper winding and finishing to profl. publs., 1966—; patentee rho-meter hardness tester, bi-wind paper winder; inventor speech synthesizer, alkaline manganese battery charger. Mem. Am. Soc. Engring. Edn. (TAPPI (Paper Finishing and Converting Div. medal 1978), Ordre des ingenieurs du Quebec. Office: McGill U Dept Mech Engring, 817 Sherbrooke St W, Montreal, PQ Canada H3A 2K6

PFEIFFER, JOHN EDWARD, author; b. N.Y.C., Sept. 27, 1914; s. Edward Heyman and Jeannette (Gross) P.; m. Naomi Ranson, Sept. 9, 1939; 1 son, Anthony John. B.A., Yale U., 1936. Sci. editor Newsweek mag., N.Y.C., 1936-42; sci. dir. CBS, N.Y.C., 1946-48; mem. editorial bd. Sci. Am., N.Y.C., 1948-50; free-lance writer, editor, 1950—; prof. anthropology Livingston Coll., Rutgers U., 1968—; cons. NSF, U. Chgo., Princeton U. Adv. Council for Anthropology, Tulane U., Ednl. Testing Svc. Princeton, N.J., Harvard U. Negotiation Project, Pacific Gas and Electric Co., Berkeley Study of High Risk Orgns., Harper's mag., others; mem. adv. council on anthropology Princeton U. Author: Science in Your Life, 1939, The Human Brain, 1955, The Changing Universe, 1956, From Galaxies to Man, 1959, The Thinking Machine, 1962, The Search For Early Man, 1963, The Cell, 1964, New Look at Education, 1968, The Emergence of Man, 1969, 4th edit., 1985, The Emergence of Society...A Prehistory of the Establishment, 1977, The Creative Explosion...An Inquiry into the Origins of Art and Religion, 1982; reviewer, cons. N.Y. Times Book Rev., 1982—; cons., contbg. editor Smithsonian mag. Trustee Solebury Sch., New Hope, Pa. Recipient CBS TV Writing award, 1959, Wenner-Gren Found. grant, 1961, Carnegie Corp. of N.Y. grants, 1965, 69; John Simon Guggenheim fellow, 1952, 54; Fulbright fellow, 1958; Harry Frank Guggenheim fellow, 1979-80, 80-81. Mem. AAAS, Am. Anthrop. Assn., Acad. Mgmt., Prehistoric Soc. of Eng., Soc. Am. Archeologists, Soc. Am. Anthropology, Antarctic Archaeol. Inst., Nat. Assn. Sci. Writers (past pres.), Prehistoric Soc. London. Home: 331 Lower Dolington Rd Newtown PA 18940-1696

PFEIFFER, JOHN WILLIAM, publisher, management consultant; b. Wallace, Idaho, July 10, 1937; s. John William and Mary Loretta (Schmidt) P.; children: Heidi Erika, Charles Wilson. B.A., U. Md., 1962; PhD (fellow), U. Iowa, 1968; JD, Western State U., 1982; DABS (hon.), Calif. Am. U., Escondido, 1980. Instr. U. Md., 1965-67; dir. adult edn. Kirkwood (Iowa) Community Coll., 1967-69; dir. ednl. resources Ind. Higher Edn. Telecommunications Systems, Indpls., 1969-72; pres. Univ. Assocs., San Diego, 1972-90, Pfeiffer & Co., San Diego, 1991—; adj. tchr. Ind. U., 1969-72, Purdue U., 1971-72. Author: Instrumentation in Human Relations Training, 1973, 2d edit. 1976, Reference Guide to Handbooks and Annuals, 1975, 2d edit. 1977, 3d. edit. 1981, (With Goodstein and Nolan) Applied Strategic Planning, 1986, 2d edit. 1988, (with Judith A. Pfeiffer) LBP, 1990; editor: A Handbook of Structured Experiences for Human Relations Training, 10 vols., 1969-85, The Annual Handbook for Facilitators, 10 vols. 1972-81, Group and Orgns. Studies Internat. Jour. for Group Facilitators, 1976-79, The Annual for Facilitators, Trainers and Consultants, 1982-91, Strategic Planning: Selected Readings, 1986, The Instrumentation Kit, 1988, Shaping Strategic Planning, 1988, Training Technology, 7 vols., 1988, Theories and Models, 4 vols., 1992, Plan or Die, 1993, Pfeiffer Library, 28 vols., 1993. Served with U.S. Army, 1958-62. Office: Pfeiffer & Co 8517 Production Ave San Diego CA 92121-2204

PFEIFFER, LEONARD, IV, executive recruiter, consultant; s. Leonard Jr. and Felicia Pfeiffer; m. Anna Gunnarsson. BA, Harvard U., MBA. Mktg. mgr. Am. Express, N.Y.C., 1970-72; project dir. S.T.I., N.Y.C. and San Francisco, 1972-74; v.p. R. Olivier & Assocs., N.Y.C., 1974-76, A. Kane & Assoc., N.Y.C., 1976-78; v.p., ptnr. Korn/Ferry Internat., Washington and N.Y.C., 1978—. Bd. dirs. Cmty. Found., Washington, 1982-84, Nat. Ctr. for Missing Children, 1989—; Am. Blood Bank Found., 1995—; founding mem. jr. bd. dirs. Washington Opera, 1983-93; mem. men's com. Project

Hope; devel. com. Nat. Head Injury Found. Lt. U.S. Army, 1968-70. Schepp Found. scholar, 1968-70. Mem. Am. Soc. Assn. Execs., Greater Washington Soc. Assn. Execs., Nat. Club Assn., Harvard Club (activities com., admissions com. N.Y.C. chpt. 1975-81, 1st v.p. bd. dirs. Washington chpt. 1985-87), City Club. Avocations: water and snow skiing, power and sail boating, tennis. Office: Korn Ferry Internat 900 19th St NW Washington DC 20006-2100

PFEIFFER, MARGARET KOLODNY, lawyer; b. Elkin, N.C., Oct. 7, 1944; d. Isadore Harold and Mary Elizabeth (Brody) K.; m. Carl Frederick Pfeiffer II, Sept. 2, 1968. BA, Duke U., 1967; JD, Rutgers U., 1974. Bar: N.J. 1974, N.Y. 1976, D.C. 1981, U.S. Supreme Ct. 1979. Law clk. to Hon. F.L. Van Dusen U.S. Ct. Appeals 3d cir., Phila., 1974-75; assoc. Sullivan & Cromwell, N.Y.C. and Washington, 1975-82, ptnr., 1982—. Contbr. articles to profl. jours. Mem. ABA, Internat. Bar Assn., D.C. Bar Assn., N.Y. State Bar Assn., Assn. of Bar of City of N.Y. Avocations: hiking, reading, music. Office: Sullivan & Cromwell 1701 Pennsylvania Ave NW Washington DC 20006-5805

PFEIFFER, MICHELLE, actress; b. Santa Ana, Calif., Apr. 29, 1957; d. Dick and Donna P.; m. Peter Horton (div.); 1 adopted child, Claudia Rose; m. David Kelley, Nov. 13, 1993. Student, Golden West Coll., Whitley Coll. Actress: (feature films) Falling in Love Again, 1980, Hollywood Knights, 1980, Charlie Chan and the Curse of the Dragon Queen, 1981, Grease II, 1982, Scarface, 1983, Ladyhawke, 1985, Into the Night, 1985, Sweet Liberty, 1986, Amazon Women on the Moon, 1987, Witches of Eastwick, 1987, Married to the Mob, 1988, Tequila Sunrise, 1988, Dangerous Liaisons, 1988 (Acad. award nominee 1989), The Fabulous Baker Boys, 1989 (Achievement award L.A. Film Critics Assn. 1989, D.W. Griffith award Nat. Bd. Rev. 1989, N.Y. Film Critics award 1989, Nat. Soc. Film Critics award 1990, Golden Globe award 1990, Acad. award nominee 1990), The Russia House, 1990,Frankie & Johnny, 1991, Love Field, 1992 (Acad. award nominee 1993), Batman Returns, 1992, The Age of Innocence, 1993, Wolf, 1994, Dangerous Minds, 1995; (TV movies) The Solitary Man,1979, Callie and Son, 1981, The Children Nobody Wanted, 1981, Splendor in the Grass, 1981, (TV series) Delta House, 1979, B.A.D. Cats, 1980. Named Woman of the Yr., Harvard's Hasty Pudding Theater Club, 1995. Office: care ICM 8942 Wilshire Blvd Beverly Hills CA 90211-1908*

PFEIFFER, PHYLLIS KRAMER, publisher; b. N.Y.C., Feb. 11, 1949; d. Jacob N. and Estelle G. Rosenbaum-Pfeiffer. B.S., Cornell U., 1970; postgrad. U. San Diego, 1976-78; m. Stephen M. Pfeiffer, Dec. 21, 1969; children: Andrew Kramer, Elise Kramer. Instr., Miss Porter's Sch., Farmington, Conn., 1970; tchr. N.Y.C. Bd. Edn., Dewey Jr. High Sch., 1970-73; research Hunter Coll., N.Y., 1971-72; account exec. La Jolla (Calif.) Light, 1973-75, advt. dir., 1975-77, gen. mgr., 1977-78, pub., 1978-87 ; exec. v.p. Harte Hanks So. Calif. Newspapers, 1985-87; gen. mgr. San Diego edit. L.A. Times, 1987-93; pres., pub. Marin Ind. Jour., Novato, Calif., 1993—; dir. communications center San Diego State U., 1980-93. Bd. dirs. La Jolla Cancer Research Found., 1979-82; bd. dirs. Alvarado Hosp., 1981-88, chmn. com., 1986, sec. bd., 1986; co-chmn. Operation USS La Jolla, U.S. Navy, 1980—; mem. mktg. com. United Way, 1979-81, chmn., 1983; bd. dirs. YMCA, San Diego Ballet, 1980; trustee La Jollan's Inc., 1975-78; mem. Conv. and Visitors Bur. Blue Ribbon Com. on Future, 1983, resource panel Child Abuse Prevention Found., 1983—; bd. overseers U. Calif., San Diego; mem. violent crimes task force San Diego Police Dept.; bd. dirs. Dominican Coll., San Rafael, Calif., 1994—. N.Y. Bd. Edn. grantee, 1971-72. Mem. Newspaper Assn. of Am. Avocations Pubs. Assn. (bd. dirs., exec. com.), Chancellor's Assn. U. Calif.-San Diego., Tiburon Peninsula Club. Home: 198 Stewart Dr Belvedere Tiburon CA 94920 Office: Marin Ind Jour 150 Alameda del Prado Novato CA 94949

PFEIFFER, ROBERT JOHN, transportation executive; b. Suva, Fiji Islands, Mar. 7, 1920; came to U.S., 1921, naturalized, 1927; s. William Albert and Nina (MacDonald) P.; m. Mary Elizabeth Worts, Nov. 29, 1945; children—Elizabeth Pfeiffer Tumbas, Margaret Pfeiffer Hughes, George, Kathleen. Grad. high sch., Honolulu, 1937; DSc (hon.), Maine Maritime Acad.; HHD (hon.), U. Hawaii; DHL (hon.), Hawaii Loa Coll. With Inter-Island Steam Navigation Co., Ltd., Honolulu, (re-organized to Overseas Terminal Ltd. 1950); with (merged into Oahu Ry. & Land Co. 1954), 1937-55, v.p., gen. mgr., 1950-54, mgr. ship agy. dept., 1954-55; v.p., gen. mgr. Pacific Cut Stone & Granite Co., Inc., Alhambra, Calif., 1955-56, Matcinal Corp., Alameda, Calif., 1956-58; mgr. div. Pacific Far East Line, Inc., San Francisco, 1958-60; with Matson Nav. Co., San Francisco, 1960—, v.p., 1966-70, sr. v.p., 1970-71, exec. v.p., 1971-73, pres., 1973-79, 84-85, 89-90, CEO, 1979-92, chmn. bd., bd.dirs., 1979-95, chmn. emeritus, 1995—; v.p. The Matson Co., San Francisco, 1968-70; pres. The Matson Co., 1970-82; v.p., gen. mgr. Matson Terminals, Inc., San Francisco, 1960-62; pres. Matson Terminals, Inc., 1962-70, chmn. bd., 1970-79; chmn. bd. Matson Svcs. Co., 1973-79, Matson Agys., Inc., 1973-78; sr. v.p. Alexander & Baldwin, Inc., Honolulu, 1973-77; exec. v.p. Alexander & Baldwin, Inc., 1977-79, chmn. bd., 1980-95; chmn. emeritus Alexander & Baldwin, Inc., Honolulu, 1995—; chmn. emeritus Alexander & Baldwin, Inc., 1995—, CEO, 1980-92, pres., 1979-84, 89-91; chmn. bd., pres., dir. A&B-Hawaii, Inc., 1988-89, chmn. bd., 1989-95; chmn. emeritus A&B Hawaii, Honolulu, 1995—; former mem. Gov.'s commn. on exec. salaries State of Hawaii, com. on jud. salaries. Past chmn. maritime transp. rsch. bd. Nat. Acad. Sci.; former mem. select com. for Am. Mcht. Marine Seamanship Trophy Award, commn. sociotech. systems NRC.; mem. adv. com. Joint Maritime Congress; trustee Pacific Tropical Bot. Garden, Pacific Aerospace Mus., also bd. dirs.; mem. Japan-Hawaii Econ. Coun., Army Civilian Adv. Group; vice-chmn. Hawaii Maritime Ctr.; former chmn. A Commitee on Excellence (ACE), Hawaii; mem. adv. coun. Girl Scouts U.S.A. coun. of the Pacific; mem. exec. com. Rsch. Round Table Alameda County chpt. Am. Heart Assn.; bd. govs. Japanese Cultural Ctr. Hawaii; mem. bd. nominators Am. Inst. for Pub. Svc.; life mem. Vets. Fgn. Wars U.S.; hon. co-chmn. McKinley High Sch. Found.; mem. adv. bd. Hawaii Bldg. and Constrn. Trades Coun., AFL-CIO Ednl. and Charitable Found. Lt. USNR, World War II; comdr. Res. ret. Mem. Nat. Assn. Stevedores (past pres.), Internat. Cargo Handling Coordination Assn. (past pres. U.S. com.), Propeller Club U.S. (past pres. Honolulu), Nat. Def. Transp. Assn., Conf. Bd., Containerization & Intermodal Inst. (hon. bd. advisors), 200 Club, Maui C. of C., Aircraft Owners and Pilots Assn., Standard Steamship Owners' Protection and Indemnity Assn. Ltd. (bd. dirs.) (Bermuda), Pacific Club, Outrigger Club, Oahu Country Club, Maui Country Club, Pacific Union Club, Bohemian Club, World Trade Club (San Francisco), Masons, Shriners. Republican. Home: 535 Miner Rd Orinda CA 94563-1429 Office: Alexander & Baldwin Inc 822 Bishop St Honolulu HI 96813-3925

PFEIFFER, SOPHIA DOUGLASS, state legislator, lawyer; b. N.Y.C., Aug. 10, 1918; d. Franklin Chamberlain and Sophie Douglass (White) Wells; m. Timothy Adams Pfeiffer, June 7, 1941; children: Timothy Franklin, Penelope Mersereau Keenan, Sophie Douglass. A.B., Vassar Coll., 1939; J.D., Northeastern U., 1975. Bar: R.I. 1975, U.S. Ct. Apls. (1st cir.) 1980, U.S. Supreme Ct. 1979. Editorial researcher Time, Inc., N.Y.C., 1940-41; writer Office War Info., Washington, 1941-43, N.Y.C., 1943-45; editorial staff Nat. Geog. Mag., Washington, 1958-59, 68-70; editor Turkish Jour. Pediatrics, Ankara, 1961-63; staff atty. R.I. Supreme Ct., Providence, 1975-76, chief staff atty., 1977-86; mem. Maine Ho. Reps., 1990-94; lectr. U. So. Maine, 1995—. Contbr. in field. Pres., Karachi Am. Sch. (Pakistan), 1955-56; chair, Brunswick Village Review Bd., 1986-89. Home: 15 Franklin St Brunswick ME 04011-2101

PFEIFFER, STEVEN BERNARD, lawyer; b. Orange, N.J., Jan. 19, 1947; s. Bernard Victor and Elizabeth Sophia (Bissell) P.; m. Kristin Reagan, June 27, 1970; children: Victoria Elizabeth, Rachel Catherine, Emily Dorothea, Stephanie Kristin Bissell, Andrew Steven Bernard. BA in Govt., Wesleyan U., 1969; BA in Jurisprudence, Oxford U., 1971, MA, 1983; MA in African Studies, U. London, 1973; JD, Yale U., 1976. Bar: N.J. 1976, D.C. 1978. Assoc. Fulbright & Jaworski, Houston, London, 1976-83; ptnr. Fulbright & Jaworski, London, Washington, 1983—; ptnr.-in-charge Fulbright & Jaworski, London, 1983-86; head internat. dept. Fulbright & Jaworski, Washington, 1989—; bd. dirs. Riggs Nat. Corp., Washington, Riggs Nat. Bank, Washington, Riggs AP Bank, London, Halston Borghese, Inc., N.Y.C., U. Cape Town Fund, N.Y.C. Contbr. articles to profl. jours. Alumni-elected trustee Wesleyan U., Middletown, Conn., 1976-79, charter

trustee, 1980-92, vice chmn. bd. trustees, 1986-87, chmn. bd. trustees, 1987-92, chmn. emeritus, 1992—. With USN, 1969, 72-74; asst. cinceur plans officer, Office of CNO, Washington, 1972-73; spl. asst. to Sec. of Navy, Washington, 1973-74. Rhodes scholar, 1969-72; Thomas Watson Travel fellow, The Watson Found., 1969. Mem. ABA, N.J. State Bar Assn., Am. Soc. Internat. Law, Internat. Bar Assn. (chmn. sect. energy and natural resources law), Naval Res. Assn., Internat. Inst. Strategic Studies, Coun. Fgn. Rels. Avocations: tennis, history, fishing, books. Home: 301 N View Ter Alexandria VA 22301-2609 Office: Fulbright & Jaworski LLP 801 Pennsylvania Ave NW Washington DC 20004-2615

PFEIFFER, WERNER BERNHARD, artist, educator; b. Stuttgart, Germany, Oct. 1, 1937; came to U.S., 1961; s. Jakob and Emilie (Nufer) P.; m. Maletta Sundstrom-Ziegler, Jan. 18, 1969; children: Jan-Stephen, Michaela-Veronica. Diploma, Grafische Fachschule, Stuttgart, Akademie Fine Arts, Stuttgart. Instr. Pratt Inst., Bklyn., 1961-64, prof., 1968-75, adj. prof., 1975—; asst. prof. N.Y. Inst. Tech., Westbury, 1965-67; dir. Pratt Adlib Press, Bklyn., 1968-75. Exhibited in over 50 one-man shows. Mem. Soc. Am. Graphic Artists. Avocations: skiing, travel, music. Address: Flat Rock Rd Cornwall Bridge CT 06754

PFEIL, RICHARD JOHN, electric company executive; b. Niles, Mich., Oct. 6, 1932; s. John and Marie J. (Metzger) P.; m. Donna Lindberg; children: Mary Ellen, Laura Ann, John Glenn, Eric Einar, Holly Marie. BSEE, Mich. State U., 1954; MBA, Ind. U., 1956. Elec. engr. RCA Rsch., Camden, N.J., 1955; pers. mgr. Koontz-Wagner Electric Co., South Bend, Ind., 1956-58, treas., 1958-63, pres., chief exec. officer, 1963—, chmn. bd., 1982; bd. dirs. First Source Bank, South Bend. Candidate for 3d Dist. Congressman Ind., 1980; bd. dirs., chmn. bd., mem. exec. com. Meml. Hosp., 1988—; chmn. Meml. Health System; bd. dirs. Montessori Acad. Sch. Bd. Mem. Ind. Mfrs. Assn. (bd. dirs., exec. com.). Republican. Roman Catholic. Avocations: sailing, skiing, tennis, golf, scuba diving. Home: 51707 Oakbrook Ct Granger IN 46530-8731 Office: Koontz-Wagner Elec Co 3801 Voorde Dr South Bend IN 46628-1643

PFENDER, EMIL, mechanical engineering educator; b. Stuttgart, Germany, May 25, 1925; came to U.S., 1964, naturalized, 1969; s. Vinzenz and Anna Maria (Dreher) P.; m. Maria Katharina Staiger, Oct. 22, 1954; children—Roland, Norbert, Corinne. Student U. Tuebingen, Germany, 1947-49; Diploma in Physics, U. Stuttgart, 1953, D. Ing. in Elec. Engring., 1959. Assoc. prof. mech. engring. U. Minn., Mpls., 1964-67, prof., 1967—. Contbr. articles to profl. jours. Patentee in field. Fellow ASME, ASM; mem. IEEE (assoc.), NAE, ASM Internat., Am. Phys. Soc. Home: 1947 Bidwell St Saint Paul MN 55118-4417 Office: U Minn Dept of Mech Engrg 111 Church St SE Minneapolis MN 55455-0150

PFENDT, HENRY GEORGE, retired information systems executive, management consultant; b. Frankfurt, Germany, Sept. 19, 1934; s. Georg and Elisabeth K. (Schuch) P.; m. Jane Ann Gossard, July 15, 1961; children: Katherine Ann, Henry G. Jr., Karen Jane. BS, U. Rochester, N.Y., 1972, postgrad.; 1972; postgrad., U. Mich., 1986. Dir. No. info. ctr. Eastman Kodak Internat., Göteborg, Sweden, 1972-73; sr. project mgr. Eastman Kodak Internat., Stuttgart, Fed. Republic of Germany, 1973-75; dir. adminstrv. svcs. Kodak Australasia Party Ltd., Coburg, Australia, 1975-77; dir. customer svcs. div. Kodak Australasia Party Ltd., Coburg, 1977-81; dir. mktg. Kodak Australasia Party Ltd., Australia, 1981-84; dir. architecture devel. Eastman Kodak Info. Systems, Rochester, 1984-86, dir. corp. info. systems, 1986-93; ret., 1993, bus. and info. mgmt. cons., 1993—; bd. dirs. client adv. coun. Compu Ware, Detroit. Creator concepts and mgmt. processes in field. Charter mem. adv. bd. Rochester Inst. Tech. Sch. Computer Sci. and Tech., 1987; bd. dirs. YMCA of Maplewood, Rochester, 1989—; mem. Rep. Nat. Com. With USAF, 1955-59. Recipient Industry Visionary award of 25 Most Influential Communications Execs., 1991. Mem. Soc. for Info. Mgmt., Coun. of Logistics Mgmt., Ctr. for Info. Systems Rsch., Strategic Mgmt. Soc., Internat. Platform Assn., Interact Network (assoc.), C. of C. Republican. Lutheran. Avocations: reading, golf, gardening, jogging, travel. Home: 968 East Lake Rd Dundee NY 14837

PFENING, FREDERIC DENVER, III, manufacturing company executive; b. Columbus, Ohio, July 28, 1949; s. Frederic Denver Jr. and Lelia (Bucher) P.; m. Cynthia Gordon, July 1, 1978; children: Lesley, Frederic Denver IV. BA, Ohio Wesleyan U., 1971; MA, Ohio State U., Columbus, 1976. Various positions Fred. D. Pfening Co., Columbus, 1976-88, pres., 1988—. Bd. dirs. Friends of Ohio State U. Librs., 1988—, Columbus State C. C. Devel. Found., 1991—, Hist. Sites Found., Baraboo, Wis., 1984—, pres., 1987-91. Mem. Am. Soc. Bakery Engrs., Orgn. Am. Historians, Bakery Equipment Mfrs. Assn. (bd. dirs. 1985-91), Young Pres.'s Orgn., Circus Hist. Soc. (pres. 1986-89, mng. editor Bandwagon Jour.), Rotary. Office: 1075 W 5th Ave Columbus OH 43212-2691

PFENNINGER, KARL H., cell biology and neuroscience educator; b. Stafa, Switzerland, Dec. 17, 1944; came to U.S., 1971, naturalized, 1993; s. Hans Rudolf and Delie Maria (Zahn) P.; m. Marie-France Maylié, July 12, 1974; children—Jan Patrick, Alexandra Christina. M.D., U. Zurich, 1971. Research instr. dept. anatomy Washington U., St. Louis, 1971-73; research assoc. sect. cell biology Yale U., New Haven, 1973-76; assoc. prof. dept. anatomy and cell biology Columbia U., N.Y.C., 1976-81, prof., 1981-86, prof., chmn. dept. cellular and structural biology U. Colo. Sch. Medicine, Denver, 1986—; dir. interdeptmental program in cell and molecular biology Columbia U. Coll. Physicians and Surgeons, N.Y.C., 1980-85; chmn. Given Biomed. Inst., Aspen, Colo., 1992-93. Author: Essential Cell Biology, 1990; contbr. articles to profl. jours. Recipient J.J. Herrick award Am. Assn. Anatomists, 1977; I.T. Hirschl Career Scientist award, 1977; Javits neurosci. investigator awards NIH, 1984, 91. Mem. Am. Soc. for Cell Biology, AAAS, Harvey Soc., Soc. for Neurosci., Internat. Brain Research Orgn., Internat. Soc. for Neurochemistry. Office: U Colo Health Scis Ctr Dept Cellular and Structural Biology B-111 4200 E 9th Ave Denver CO 80262

PFEUFER, ROBERT JOHN, musician; b. Cleve., Dec. 25, 1925; s. Henry Vincent and Elmo Alice (Burger) P.; m. Betty June Weller, Sept. 21, 1946; children—Barbara (Mrs. Steven Mosley), Jeanne, Susan, Catherine. B.Mus. in Edn, U. Mich., 1950, M.Mus. in Edn, 1951. Contrabassoonist, bassoonist Detroit Symphony Orch., 1951-61, Phila. Orch., 1962-91; instr. bassoon Wayne State U., 1957-61, New Sch. Music, Phila., 1969—; prin. bassoon Lynchburg Symphony, 1994—. Served with AUS, 1942-44. Mem. U.S. Power Squadron, Kappa Kappa Psi, Pi Mu Alpha. Roman Catholic. Home: RR 1 Box 481F Moneta VA 24121-9214

PFISTER, CLOYD HARRY, consultant, former career officer; b. State College, Pa., Dec. 20, 1936; s. Rudolf John Pfister and June Ruth (Braun) Pfister Gray; m. Rita Askerc Kracht, Aug. 17, 1962 (div. Mar. 1982); m. Gail Williams, Apr. 24, 1982; children, Gabriele, Catherine, Michael, Romi, Eric Williams, Lori Williams. BA in Philosophy, Oberlin Coll., 1957; MA in Internat. Rels., Am. U., 1964, postgrad., 1964-67. Enlisted U.S. Army, 1957, advanced through grades to maj. gen., 1989; staff officer Nat. Security Agy., Fort Meade, Md., 1965-68; S3 (Ops.) 303d Radio Rsch. Bn., Plantation, Vietnam, 1968-69; instr. JFK Ctr. and Sch., Fort Bragg, N.C., 1969-72; politico-mil. officer, Office Dep. Chief of Staff for Ops. Hdqrs. Dept. Army, Washington, 1972-75; comdr. 307th U.S. Army Security Agy. Bn., VII U.S. Corps, Ludwigsburg, Fed. Republic Germany, 1975-77; asst. chief of staff intelligence 8th Mech. Inf. Div., Bad Kreuznach, Fed. Republic Germany, 1977-79; Mid. East staff officer Office Sec. Def., The Pentagon, 1979-82; comdr. U.S. Army Field Sta., Berlin, 1982-84; chief of staff U.S. Army Intelligence Ctr. and Sch., Fort Huachuca, Ariz., 1984-85, dep. comdt., 1985-86; dir. intelligence (J2), Hdqrs., U.S. Cen. Command, MacDill AFB, Fla., 1986-88; dep. chief of staff intelligence Hdqrs., U.S. Army Europe and 7th Army, Heidelberg, Fed. Republic Germany, 1988-91; asst. dep. chief of staff Intelligence Hdqrs., Dept. Army, Pentagon, 1991—; cons. Def. Sci. Bd. Chmn. Combined Fed. Campaign, Fort Huachuca and Sierra Vista, Ariz. 1985. Decorated Def. D.S.M., D.S.M. Def. Superior Svc. medal, Legion of Merit with two oak leaf clusters, Nat. Intelligence D.S.M.; Ehrenkreutz der Bundeswehr (gold) (Fed. Republic Germany); other awards. Mem. Internat. Inst. for Strategic Studies, Middle East Inst., Security Affairs Support Assn., Assn. U.S. Army. Avocations: tennis, photography, gardening, computers. Office: Tech Strategies & Alliances 5242 Lyngate Ct Burke VA 22015

PFISTER, DONALD HENRY, biology educator; b. Kenton, Ohio, Feb. 17, 1945; s. William A. and Dorothy C. (Kutzr) P.; m. Cathleen C. Kennedy, July 1, 1971; children: Meghan, Brigid, Edith. AB, Miami U., Oxford, Ohio, 1967; PhD, Cornell U., 1971; AM (hon.), Harvard U., 1980. Asst. prof. biology U. P.R., Mayaguez, 1971-74; asst. prof. biology, asst. curator Farlow Herbarium Harvard U., Cambridge, Mass., 1974-77, assoc. prof. biology, assoc. curator Farlow Herbarium, 1977-80, prof. biology, curator Farlow Herbarium, 1980—, dir. univ. herbaria, 1983-95; vis. mycologist U. Copenhagen, 1978; vis. prof. field station U. Minn., Itasca, 1979; master Kirkland House Harvard U., 1982—. Contbr. over 80 articles to profl. jours. Grantee NSF, 1973-75, 81-85, 85—, Am. Philos. Soc., 1975-76, Whiting Found., 1986. Fellow Linnean Soc. London; mem. Mycol. Soc. Am. (sec. 1988-91, v.p. 1993-94, pres.-elect 1994-95), Am. Phytopath. Soc., Am. Microbiol. Soc., New Eng. Bot. Club, Sigma Xi. Office: Harvard U Herbarium 22 Divinity Ave Cambridge MA 02138

PFISTER, JAMES JOSEPH, publishing company executive; b. N.Y.C., Oct. 29, 1946; s. Stanley George and Rosemary Ann (Cullen) P.; m. Kendra Elaine Nelson, Mar. 23, 1974; 1 child, Charles Joseph. BS, Northwestern U., 1970. Mktg. supr. Nat. Register Pub. Co., Wilmette, Ill., 1970-73, dist. sales mgr., 1973-76, nat. sales mgr., 1976-80, pub., 1980-85, pres., 1985-89; pres. Marquis Who's Who, Wilmette, Ill., 1985-89, Macmillan Directory Div., Wilmette, Ill., 1985-89, Creative Black Book, N.Y.C., 1987-89, Standard Rate & Date Svc., Wilmette, 1989; v.p. Maxwell Macmillan Info. Svcs. Group, Wilmette, 1989-91; chief oper. officer (U.K.) Maxwell Communications, London, 1991-92; pres., CEO Med. Econ's. Pub., Montvale, N.J., 1992—; bd. dirs. Am. Bus. Press, BPA Internat. Sec. Libertyville (Ill.) Homeowners Assn., 1981-83, pres., 1983-85; mem. Com. toRe-elect Ronald Reagan, 1984. Served with U.S. Army, 1967-69, Vietnam. Decorated Bronze Star with V device, Bronze Star with oak leaf cluster, Air medal, Purple Heart. Mem. Chgo. Advt. Club, Am. Assn. Mus. (cons. 1978—), Pharm. Mfrs. Assn., Pharm. Advt. Coun. Republican. Avocations: model building, running, water skiing, restoring classic vehicles, photography. Office: Med Econs Pub 5 Paragon Dr Montvale NJ 07645-1725

PFISTER, KARL ANTON, industrial company executive; b. Ernetschwil St. Gallen, Switzerland, Oct. 17, 1941; came to U.S., 1966; s. Josef Anton and Paula (Hobi) P.; m. Karen Antonie Sievers; children: Kirsten, Marc, Theodore, Alexandra. Student trade sch., Rapperswil, Switzerland, 1957-61; student bus. sch., Zuerich, Switzerland, 1964-65. Tool and die maker H. Schmid, Rapperswil, Switzerland, 1957-61, Neher AG, Ebnat-Kappel, Switzerland, 1962-63; process engr. NCR, Buelach, Switzerland, 1964-66, Gretag, Regensdorf, Switzerland, 1966; tool and die maker Stoffel Fineflow Corp., White Plains, N.Y., 1966-67; mgr. mfg. Finetool Corp., Detroit, 1968; pres. Mich. Precision Ind., Inc., Detroit, 1969—; dir. Kloeckner Capital Corp., Gordonsville, Va., Mich. Precision Ind., Detroit. Consul, consulate Switzerland, Detroit, 1984—. Mem. Plum Hollow Club, Fairlane Club. Republican. Roman Catholic. Office: MPI Internat Inc 2129 Austin Ave Rochester Hills MI 48309-3668

PFISTER, PETER J., lawyer; b. Mar. 29, 1948. BA, U. Calif., Santa Barbara, 1970; JD, Yale U., 1973. Bar: Calif. 1975. Law clk. to Hon. Samuel Conti U.S. Dist. Ct. (no. dist.) Calif., 1973-74; mem. Morrison & Foerster, San Francisco. Office: Morrison & Foerster 345 California St San Francisco CA 94104-2675*

PFISTER, RICHARD CHARLES, physician, radiology educator; b. Ypsilanti, Mich., Nov. 27, 1933; s. Emil Robert and Francis Josephine (LeForge) P.; m. Sally DeAnn Haight, Dec. 31, 1956 (div. 1980); children: Kirk Alan, Gary Raymond, Karen Dawn, James Kevin, William Charles. BS, Ctrl. Mich. U., 1958; MD, Wayne State U., 1962. Assoc. prof. radiology Harvard Med. Sch. and Mass. Gen. Hosp., Boston, 1986-89; med. officer FDA, Washington, 1989-90; prof. radiology U. South Ala., Mobile, 1990-92, La. State U., New Orleans, 1993—. Editor, author: Interventional Radiology, 1982. With U.S. Army Med. Corps, 1953-55. Recipient Investigator award NIH, Washington, 1972. Fellow Am. Coll. Radiology; mem. AMA, Soc. Uroradiology (pres. 1984-85), Radiologic Soc. N.Am., Am. Roentgen Ray Soc., Soc. Cardiovascular Interventional. Avocation: sailing (Trans-Atlantic passages). Office: LSU Med Ctr 1542 Tulane Ave New Orleans LA 70112-2825

PFISTER, ROSWELL ROBERT, ophthalmologist; b. Buffalo, Jan. 19, 1938; s. Milton Albert and Florence P. Student, U. Buffalo, 1955-58; M.D., U. Mich., 1962, M.S., 1969. Diplomate Am. Bd. Ophthalmology. Intern Los Angeles County Hosp., 1962-63; resident in ophthalmology U. Mich., Ann Arbor, 1965-69; research fellow dept. cornea research Retina Found., Boston, 1969-71; clin. fellow cornea service Mass. Eye and Ear Infirmary, 1969-71; assoc. prof. U. Colo. Med. Center, Denver, 1971-75; prof., chmn. dept. ophthalmology Combined Program in Ophthalmology, U. Ala. in Birmingham-The Eye Found. Hosp., 1976-81; head research dept. ophthalmology Ellen Gregg Ingalls Eye Research Inst., 1976-81; dir. eye research labs. Brookwood Med. Ctr. (Birmingham), 1982—. Served with USAF, 1963-65. Mem. Med. Assn. Ala., Jefferson County Med. Soc., Assn. Univ. Profs. in Ophthalmology, Research to Prevent Blindness, Am. Acad. Ophthalmology, Assn. Research in Vision and Opthalmology, Ala. Acad. Ophthalmology, AMA, Colo. Ophthalmology Soc., Mich. State Med. Soc., Mass. Eye and Ear Infirmary Alumnus Soc., Corneal Soc., Colo. Soc. Prevention of Blindness (mem. med. adv. bd. 1974-76), Colo. Eye Bank (med. dir. 1974-76), Kerato-Refractave Soc. Office: 2008 Brookwood Center Dr Birmingham AL 35209-4526

PFLANZE, OTTO PAUL, history educator; b. Maryville, Tenn., Apr. 2, 1918; s. Otto Paul and Katrine (Mills) P.; m. Hertha Maria Haberlander, Feb. 20, 1951; children: Stephen, Charles, Katrine. B.A., Maryville Coll., 1940; M.A., Yale U., 1942, Ph.D., 1950. Historian Dept. State, 1948-49; instr. N.Y. U., 1950-51; asst. prof. U. Mass., 1952-58, U. Ill., 1958-61; prof. history U. Minn., 1961-76; prof. history Ind. U., 1977-86, emeritus, 1986; Stevenson Prof. of History Bard Coll., Annandale On Hudson, N.Y., 1987-92, emeritus, 1992; chmn. Conf. Group Central European History, 1978; mem. exam. bd., grad. record exam Ednl. Testing Service, 1972-76; mem. Inst. Advanced Study, 1970-71, mem. Historisches Kolleg, Munich, 1980-81. Author: Bismarck and the Development of Germany: Vol. 1.-The Period of Unification, 1815-1871, 1963 (Biennal Book award Phi Alpha Theta), rev. edit., 1990, Vol. 2-The Period of Consolidation, 1871-1880, 1990, Vol. 3-The Period of Fortification, 1880-1898, 1990 (3 vols. collectively named Most Outstanding Book in History, Govt. & Polit. Sci. by assn. Am. Pubs., 1991); co-author: A History of the Western World: Modern Times, 3d edit, 1975; editor: Innenpolitische Probleme des Bismarck-Reiches, 1983; co-editor: Documents on German Foreign Policy, 1918-1945, Vols. I-III, 1949-50; editor Am. Hist. Rev., 1976-85; mem. editorial bd. Jour. Modern History, 1971-73, Central European History, 1972-74. Served to 1st lt. U.S. Army, 1942-46. Fulbright research fellow, 1955-57; fellow Am. Council Learned Socs., 1951-52; fellow Guggenheim Found., 1966-67; fellow Nat. Endowment Humanities, 1975-76; fellow Internat. Research and Exchanges Bd., 1976; fellow Thyssen Stiftung, Essen, 1986; recipient Humanities award McKnight Found., 1962. Mem. Am. Hist. Assn., German Studies Assn.

PFLAUM, SUSANNA WHITNEY, college dean; b. Boston, Dec. 7, 1937; d. William T. and Ann. (Van Bibber) Whitney; m. Peter E. Pflaum, Apr. 10, 1963 (div. Mar. 1973); children: Melanie Ann, William E.; m. Joseph C. Grannis, Jan. 30, 1987; stepchildren: Eric Grannis, Alexander Grannis. AB cum laude, Radcliffe Coll., 1959; MEd, Harvard U., 1960; PhD, Fla. State U., 1971. Tchr. Newton (Mass.) Pub. Schs., 1960-63, Inter-Am. U., San German and Hato Rey, P.R., 1963-66; instr. Mankato (Minn.) State Coll., 1970-71; from asst. prof. to prof. U. Ill., Chgo., 1971-85; dean Honors Coll., 1982-85; dean Sch. Edn. CUNY Queens Coll., Flushing, N.Y., 1985-90; dean Bank St. Coll. N.Y.C., N.Y.C., 1990—. Author: Development of Language and Literacy in Young Children, 3d edit., 1986; editor: Aspects of Reading Education, 1978; co-editor: Celebrating Diverse Voices: Progressive Education and Equity, 1993, Experiencing Diversity: Toward Educational Equity, 1994; contbr. articles to profl. jours., 1973-92. Mem. Am. Edn. Rsch Assn., Nat. Reading Conf., Internat. Reading Assn. (Harris Rsch. award 1981). Democrat. Episcopalian. Office: Bank Street Coll New York NY 10025

PFLEIDER, JAMES KENNETH, motivation company executive; b. Chippewa Falls, Wis., Apr. 25, 1940; s. Kenneth William and Norma Elaine

(Sylvester) P.; m. Susan Marie Gregerson, Sept. 14, 1963; children: Laura Lynn, Anne Marie, Gregory James. BS, U. Minn., 1962. Salesman Pillsbury Co., Sacramento, Calif., 1962-63; region sales mgr. San Francisco, 1963-66; area sales mgr. Los Angeles, 1966-67; asst. sales mgr. Thermo Serv Products, Anoka, Minn., 1969-70, premium sales mgr. 1969-70, gen. sales mgr., 1970-71, v.p. sales, 1971-72, pres., 1972-75; pres. Coppercraft Guild, Taunton, Mass., 1975-77, Carlson Mktg. Group, Mpls., 1977—. Republican. Lutheran. Avocations: golf, racquetball, reading, touring. Home: 511 Ferndale Rd N Wayzata MN 55391-1008 Office: Gage Marketing Group 10000 Highway 55 Minneapolis MN 55441-6365

PFLUEGER, JOHN MILTON, architect; b. San Francisco, Aug. 23, 1937; s. Milton Theodore and Genevive (Wendgard) P.; BS, Stanford, 1959, BArch, 1960; m. Lynne Williams, Jan. 23, 1963; children: Peter, John Thomas, Christopher Timothy. Pres., chief exec. officer Pflueger Architects, Inc., San Francisco, 1976; lectr. Urban Life Inst., U. San Francisco, 1981; campus architect U. San Francisco, Coll. of Holy Names, City Coll. San Francisco. Mem. planning com. San Francisco Downtown Assn., 1971-83. Lic. architect, Calif., Nev., Hawaii. Mem. AIA (pub. edn. com. No. Calif. chpt. 1970-79), NCARB, Constrn. Specifications Inst., Soc. Coll. and Univ. Planning, San Francisco Planning and Urban Renewal, Sierra Club, U.S.C. of C., Calif. Acad. Scis., Soc. Am. Mil. Engrs., Delta Tau Delta. Clubs: Olympic (bldg. com. 1973-78, properties commn. 1979-81), Family (San Francisco). Major works include: Cowell Hall, Calif. Acad. Scis. (Prestress Concrete Inst. award 1969), Creative Arts Extension, City Coll. San Francisco (AIA design excellence award 1974), Fish Roundabout, Calif. Acad. Scis., 1976, Natural Energy Office Bldg., 1977 (Honor award State of Calif.), Batmale Hall, City Coll. San Francisco, 1978, Calif. Farm Bur. Fedn., Sacramento, 1980 (Owens Corning, Dept. Energy and ASHRAE awards), San Jose State U. Library, 1982, Nev. Nat. Bank Hdqrs., Reno, 1982 (ASHRAE award), Performing Arts Ctr. and Fine Arts Mus., Sierra Arts Found., Reno; 8 major bldgs. at Stanford U., including Environ. Safety Facility, 1986; Co-Generation facility and Health and Recreation Ctr., U. San Francisco, 1987; rehabilitation Santa Rosa Ferry Boat, James Licks Bathhouse, 1981, Warfield Office Bldg. and Theater, 1985; major hosps. include Shriners Hosp. for Crippled Children, Walter Reed Army Med. Ctr. (Pre-Stressed Concrete Inst., Dept. Def. design awards 1980). Office: John M Pflueger Architect 165 Lark Ln Mill Valley CA 94941-3570

PFLUEGER, M(ELBA) LEE, academic administrator; b. St. Louis, Sept. 2, 1942; d. Pless and Edna Mae (Russell) Counts; m. Raymond Allen Pflueger, Sept. 14, 1963 (div. June 1972); children: Salem Allen, Russell Counts. BS in Home Econs., Univ. Mo., 1969; MEd in Guidance and Counseling, Washington Univ., St. Louis, 1973. Ednl. psychologist Ozark Regional Mental Health Ctr., Harrison, Ark., 1974-75; from account mgr. to mgr. pers. Enterprise Leasing Co., St. Louis, 1977-79; mgr. employee rels. Eaton Corp., Houston, 1979-80; owner Nature's Nuggets Fresh Granola, St. Louis, 1980-83; dir. corp. ednl. svcs. Maryville Coll., St. Louis, 1983-84; administr. mgmt. skills devel. McDonnell Douglas, St. Louis, 1984-85, mgr. employee involvement, 1985-86, prin. specialist human resources mgmt., 1988-89; mgr. human resources McDonnell Douglas, Houston, 1986-88; dir. devel. sch. engring. U. Mo., Rolla, 1989-93, dir. devel., corp. and found. rels., 1992-93; regional dir. devel., assoc. dir. maj. gifts and capital projects Washington U., St. Louis, 1994—; part-time leader trainer Maritz Motivation, St. Louis, 1984-89. Chair United Fund Campaign for U. Mo., Rolla, 1991. Mem. PEO. Avocations: reading, theatre, classical and jazz music, yoga. Office: Washington U Office Maj Gifts and Capital Projects Campus Box 1228 One Brookings Dr Saint Louis MO 63130-4899

PFNAUSCH, EDWARD, religious association administrator. Exec. coord. Canon Law Soc. Am. Office: Canon Law Soc of Am Caldwell Hall Rm 431 Cath Univ Washington DC 20064

PFNISTER, ALLAN OREL, humanities educator; b. Mason, Ill., July 23, 1925; s. Ardon Orel and Rose Margaret (Sandtner) P.; m. Helen Edith Klobes, Dec. 18, 1948; children: Alicia Ann, Jonathan Karl, Susan Elaine. AB summa cum laude, Augustana Coll., 1945; MDiv summa cum laude, Augustana Theol. Sem., 1949; AM with honors, U. Chgo., 1951, PhD, 1955; LLD (hon.), U. Denver, 1978. Instr. in religion Augustana Coll., 1946-47; instr. in philosophy and German Luther Coll., Wahoo, Nebr., 1949-52; dean Luther Coll., 1953-54; research asst. univ. fellow U. Chgo., 1952-53, instr., 1954-57, asst. prof., 1957-58; dir. research joint bds. parish edn. Lutheran Ch. Am., 1958-59; vis. assoc. prof. U. Mich., 1959-62, assoc. prof., 1962-63; dean Coll. Liberal Arts, prof. philosophy Wittenberg (Ohio) U., 1963-67, provost, prof., 1967-69, acting pres., 1968-69; prof. higher edn. U. Denver, 1969-77, 78-90, exec. vice chancellor and acting chancellor, 1977-78, vice chancellor acad. affairs, 1984-87, assoc. provost, 1988-89, prof. emeritus, 1990—; dir. study fgn. study programs Fedn. Regional Accrediting Commns. Higher Edn., 1970-72; cons. in field; bd. dirs. Nat. Ctr. for Higher Edn. Mgmt. Systems Mgmt. Svcs.; trustee Capital U., Columbus, Ohio, 1983, vice chmn. bd., 1987-89, 91-94. Author: Teaching Adults, 1967, Trends in Higher Education, 1975, Planning for Higher Education, 1976; contbr. numerous articles on higher edn. to profl. jours. Bd. visitors Air Force Inst. Tech., 1978-83, chmn. bd. visitors, 1981-83. Recipient Outstanding Achievement Alumni award Augustana Coll., 1963. Mem. Am. Am. Assn. Higher Edn., Assn. for Study Higher Edn., Comparative and Internat. Edn. Soc., Blue Key, Phi Beta Kappa (alumnus mem.). Democrat. Home: 7231 W Linvale Pl Denver CO 80227-3556

PFORDRESHER, JOHN CHARLES, English educator; b. Chgo., Oct. 15, 1943; s. Albert George and Virginia Marie (Rausch) P.; children: Peter, Rebecca. BA, Georgetown U., 1965; PhD, U. Minn., 1970. Asst. prof. U. N.H., Durham, 1970-73; prof. English, Georgetown U., Washington, 1973—; sr. fellow Coun. for Basic Edn., Washington, 1990—. Author, editor: Variorum Edition of Tennyson's Idylls of the King, 1973; author: (with W.C. Dawson) Matthew Arnold: Prose Writings, Critical Heritage, 1979; England in Literature, 1989, Classics in World Literature, 1989. Lectr. Smithsonian Residents Assn. Program, Washington, 1987—. Mem. Nat. Coun. Tchrs. of English (dir. commn. on lit. 1989-91), Victorian Inst. (assoc. editor jour. 1985-93), S.E. 19th Century Studies Assn. (bd. dirs. 1987-92). Roman Catholic. Office: Georgetown U English Dept Washington DC 20057

PFOUTS, RALPH WILLIAM, economist, consultant; b. Atchison, Kans., Sept. 9, 1920; s. Ralph Ulysses and Alice (Oldham) P.; m. Jane Hoyer, Jan. 31, 1945 (dec. Nov. 1982); children: James William, Susan Jane Pfouts Portman, Thomas Robert (dec.), Elizabeth Ann Pfouts Klenowski; m. Lois Bateson, Dec. 21, 1984 (div.); m. Felicia Sprincenatu, 1993. B.A., U. Kans., 1942, M.A., 1947; Ph.D., U. N.C. 1952. Rsch. asst., instr. econs. U. Kans., Lawrence, 1946-47; instr. U. N.C., Chapel Hill, 1947-50, lectr. econs., 1950-52, assoc. prof. econs., 1952-58, prof. econs., 1958-87, chmn. grad. studies dept. econs. Sch. Bus. Adminstrn., 1957-62, chmn. dept. econs. Sch. Bus. Adminstrn., 1962-68; cons. econs. Chapel Hill, 1987—; vis. prof. U. Leeds, 1983; vis. rsch. scholar Internat. Inst. for Applied Systems Analysis, Laxenberg, Austria, 1983; prof. Cen. European U., Prague, 1991. Author: Elementary Economics-A Mathematical Approach, 1972; editor: So. Econ. Jour, 1955-75; editor, contbr.: Techniques of Urban Economic Analysis, 1960, Essays in Economics and Econometrics, 1960; editorial bd.: Metroeconomica, 1961-80, Atlantic Econ. Jour, 1971-; contbr. articles to profl. jours. Served as deck officer USNR, 1943-46. Social Sci. Research Council fellow U. Cambridge, 1953-54; Ford Found. Faculty Research fellow, 1962-63. Mem. AAAS, Am. Statis. Assn., N.C. Statis. Assn. (past pres.), Am. Econ. Assn., So. Econ. Assn. (past pres.), Atlantic Econ. Soc. (v.p. 1973-76, pres. 1977-78), Population Assn. Am., Econometric Soc., Math. Assn. Am., Phi Beta Kappa, Pi Sigma Alpha, Alpha Kappa Psi, Omicron Delta Epsilon. Home and Office: 127 Summerlin Dr Chapel Hill NC 27514-1925

PFRANG, EDWARD OSCAR, association executive; b. New Haven, Aug. 9, 1929; s. Luitpold and Anna P.; m. Jacquelyn Marcia Montefalco, June 7, 1958; children: Lori Ann, Leslie Jean, Philip Edward. B.S., U. Conn., 1951; M.E., Yale U., 1952; Ph.D., U. Ill., 1961. Registered profl. engr., M.D., N.Y., Calif. Sect. chief structures sect., bldg. research div. Nat. Bur. Standards, Washington, 1966-83; mgr. housing tech. program Nat. Bur. Standards, 1970-73, chief structures materials safety div., 1973-83; exec. dir. ASCE, N.Y.C., 1983—. Contbr. articles to profl. jours. Served with USNR, 1953-56. Fellow ASCE, Am. Concrete Inst.; mem. Earthquake Engring.

Inst., Sigma Xi, Tau Beta Phi, Chi Epsilon, Sigma Tau. Office: ASCE 345 East 47th St New York NY 10017

PFRIEM, BERNARD ALDINE, artist; b. Cleve., Sept. 7, 1914; s. Charles and Amanda (Ketterer) P. Student, John Huntington Poly., 1934-36; diploma, Cleve. Inst. Art, 1940. Tchr. Mus. Modern Art, N.Y.C., 1946-51; chief design U.S. Govt. Program Trade Fairs and World Fairs in Europe, 1953-56; tchr. Cooper Union Sch. Art and Architecture, N.Y.C., 1963-69, Sarah Lawrence Coll., 1969-75; founder, dir. Lacoste Sch. of the Arts, France, 1971-91, dir. emeritus, 1991—. Represented in permanent collections: Mus. of Modern Art, N.Y.C., Met. Mus., N.Y.C., Ark. Art Ctr., Little Rock, Bklyn. Mus., Utah Mus., Salt Lake City, Finch Mus., N.Y.C., Worcester (Mass.) Mus., Corcoran Gallery, Washington, Chase Manhattan Bank, N.Y.C., Columbia Banking, Savs. and Loan Assn., Rochester, N.Y., Atlantic Richfield Corp., Los Angeles, Chgo. Art Inst. Served with USAF, 1942-46. William Copley grantee, 1959; Agnes Gund travelling scholar, 1940; Mary Sugget Ranney travelling scholar. Club: Century. Office: 84710 Lacoste, Vaucluse France

PHAIR, JOSEPH BASCHON, lawyer; b. N.Y.C., Apr. 29, 1947; s. James Francis and Mary Elizabeth (Baschon) P.; m. Bonnie Jean Hobbs, Sept. 04, 1971; children: Kelly I., Joseph B., Sean P. BA, U. San Francisco, 1970, JD, 1973. Bar: Calif., U.S. Dist. Ct. (no. dist.) Calif., U.S. Ct. Appeals (9th cir.). Assoc. Berry, Davis & McInerney, Oakland, Calif., 1974-76, Bronson, Bronson & McKinnon, San Francisco, 1976-79; staff atty. Varian Assocs., Inc., Palo Alto, Calif., 1979-83, corp. counsel, 1983-86, sr. corp. counsel, 1986-87, assoc. gen. counsel, 1987-90, v.p., gen. counsel, 1990-91, v.p., gen. counsel, sec., 1991—. Bd. dirs. St. Vincent de Paul Devel. Coun., San Francisco, 1992—. Mem. Bay Area Gen. Counsel, Peninsula Assn. Gen. Counsel, The Olympic Club. Roman Catholic. Office: Varian Assoc Inc M/S V-250 3050 Hansen Way Palo Alto CA 94304-1000

PHALEN, ROBERT F., community and environmental medicine educator, occupational health educator, research scientist; b. Fairview, Okla., Oct. 18, 1940; s. Samuel Robert and Nancy Violet (Sanders) P.; m. Katherine Sue Kucala, Aug. 2, 1966; children: Robert Norman, Steven Briar. BS in Physics, San Diego State U., 1964, MS in Physics, 1966; PhD in Biophysics, U. Rochester, 1971. Engring. aide advanced systems dept. Gen. Dynamics/Astronautics, San Diego, 1962-63; asst. to radiation safety officer, lab. teaching asst. dept. physics San Diego State U., 1964-66, instr. radiological physics, basic physics, 1966; summer faculty dept. biology Rochester (N.Y.) Inst. Tech., 1970-72; postdoctoral rsch. assoc. adjct. aerosol physics Lovelace Found. Med. Edn. and Rsch., Albuquerque, 1972-74; dir. Air Pollution Health Effects Lab. U. Calif., Irvine, 1974—, from adj. asst. prof. to assoc. prof. in residence dept. community and environ. medicine, 1974-84, prof. in residence dept. community and environ. medicine, 1984, prof. dept. community and environ. medicine, 1985—, prof. occupational medicine, 1985—; cons. U.S. EPA, Washington, 1983—, mem. various panels, coms.; mem. safety and occupational health study sect., NIH, 1988-90, site visits, 1980-84, 88, chmn. spl. study sects., 1982-84, 88, 92; mem. adv. panel asbestos Am. Pub. Health Assn., 1978; chmn. confs., symposia in field; presenter in field. Author: Inhalation Studies, 1984; editorial bd. Jour. Aerosol Medicine, 1988—; recipient numerous articles to profl. jours.; contbr. chpts. books. Science adv. Prentice Day Sch., Newport Beach, Calif., 1988—, Discovery Science Ctr., Santa Ana, Calif., 1993—. AEC fellow U. Rochester, 1966-71, Def. Edn. fellow U.S. Govt., 1982—; Nat. Heart Lung & Blood Inst. Rsch. grantee—, 1988, State of Calif. Rsch. grantee, 1985—, Elec. Power Rsch. Inst. Rsch. grantee, 1980-90, Am. Legion scholar, 1959-64. Mem. AAAS, Am. Assn. Aerosol Rsch. (charter mem.), Am. Conf. Govtl. Indsl. Hygienists (chmn. com. 1982-87), Am. Indsl. Hygiene Assn., Fine Particle Soc., Soc. Aerosol Rsch., Health Physics Soc., Soc. Toxicology, Brit. Occupational Hygiene Soc. Avocations: judo, comic books, reading science fiction. Office: U Calif Irvine Air Pollution Health Effects Lab Dept Comm & Environ Medicine Irvine CA 92717-1825

PHALEN, THOMAS FRANCIS, JR., lawyer; b. Waterbury, Conn., June 27, 1938; s. Thomas Francis and Helen Theresa (Farrell) P.; m. MaryAnne Imwalle, Aug. 31, 1963; children—Thomas Francis III, Timothy J., Helene M., Brian C., Christina V. B.S., Coll. Holy Cross, 1960; J.D., Cath. U. Am., 1967. Bar: Ohio 1967, U.S. Supreme Ct. 1973, U.S. Ct. Appeals (6th cir.) 1972, U.S. Ct. Appeals (D.C. cir.) 1973, U.S. Ct. Appeals (5th cir.) 1980, U.S. Dist. Ct. (so. dist.) Ohio 1969, U.S. Dist. Ct. (no. dist.) Ohio 1972. Law clk. trial exam. div. NLRB, 1966, field atty. region 9, cin., 1967-69; ptnr. Knee, Snyder & Parks, Dayton, Ohio, 1969-73, Latimer & Swing Co., L.P.A., 1973-78; sole practice, Cin., 1978-79; ptnr. Kircher and Phalen, Cin., 1979—; lectr. U. Cin., 1979-83, Xavier U., 1980, Ohio Legal Ctr. Inst., Ohio Labor Seminar, 1983, Ohio Jud. Conf., 1984. Mem: adv. bd. AFL-CIO Lawyers Coordinating Com., 1983-87; trustee U. Cin., 1987—; mem. Dem. Cen. Com., chmn. 14th ward Cin. Served to capt. USAF, 1961-64. Mem. Ohio Bar Assn. (chmn. labor law sect 1980-83, bd. govs. 1976—). Assoc. editor: The Developing Labor Law, 2d edit., 1983—. Office: 125 E Court St Ste 1000 Cincinnati OH 45202

PHALON, PHILIP ANTHONY, marketing executive; b. Paterson, N.J., Apr. 18, 1929; s. John J. and Agnes (Maher) P.; m. Anna M. Moran. B.S., Boston Coll., 1950. Vice-pres. internat. Whittaker Corp., Los Angeles, 1972-73; v.p. internat. affairs Raytheon Co., Lexington, Mass., 1973-83; sr. v.p. corp. mktg. Raytheon Co., 1983—; dir. New Japan Radio Co., Tokyo. Bd. dirs. World Affairs Council Boston, Emerson Hosp., Concord, Mass., 1981—. Served with U.S. Army, 1950-53. Roman Catholic. Office: Raytheon Co 141 Spring St Lexington MA 02173-7899

PHAM, SI MAI, cadiothoracic surgeon, medical educator; b. Ninh Hoa, Khanh Hoa, Vietnam, Oct. 6, 1955; came to U.S. 1975; s. Tro Pham and Nhung Thi Mai; m. Marie Christine Pham, Sept. 9, 1987; 1 child, Benjamin Bartley Pham. Student, U. Saigon, Sch. Pharmacy, Vietnam, 1973-75; BS in Chem. magna cum laude, Lebanon Valley Coll., Annville, Pa., 1979; MD, U. Pitts., 1983. Diplomate Am. Bd. Surgery, Am. Bd. Thoracic Surgery. Intern, resident gen. surgery U. Pitts., Pitts., Pa., 1983-86, rsch. fellow, cardiothoracic surgery, 1986-87, sr. and chief resident, gen. surgery, 1987-89, resident cardiothoracic surgery, 1989-92, asst. prof. surgery, Sch. of Medicine, 1992—, dir. adult cardiac transplant program, Sch. of Medicine, 1993—; dir. extracorporeal membrane oxygenation svc. Presbyterian U. Hosp., Pitts., Pa., 1993—. Author: (book chpts. with others) Cardiac and Cardiopulmonary Transplantation, Rigid Bronchoesophagoscopy; contbr. to profl. jour. Recipient Am. Chemical award 1979, Radiology award U. Pitts., 1983; Am. Coll. Surgeons Faculty fellow, 1994—; grantee Children's Hosp. of Pitts., 1987, Am. Heart Assn., 1987-88, 94—, Presbyterian U. Hosp., 1987-89. Fellow Am. Coll. Surgeons (assoc.); mem. AMA, Am. Soc. Artificial Internal Organs, Internat. Soc. Heart and Lung Transplantation, Soc. Critical Care Medicine, Am. Assn. Advancement of Sci., Am. Soc. Transplant Surgeons, Soc. Thoracic Surgeons, Extracorporeal Life Support Organization, Phi Alpha Epsilon. Home: 305 Marberry Dr Pittsburgh PA 15215 Office: U Pitts Med Ctr Divsn CTS 200 Lothrop St Rm C-700 Pittsburgh PA 15213

PHAN, CHUONG VAN, biotechnologist; b. Trungthanh, Vinhlong, Vietnam, July 6, 1942; came to U.S. 1988; s. Nhac Van and Lua Thi (Nguyen) P.; m. Bang Tam Tran; 1 child, Trongvan; m. Hitomi Shimono; children: Maichi, Milan, Mica. BSc in Agr., Nat. Ctr. Agr., Saigon, Vietnam, 1969; MSc in Agr., Kyushu U., Japan, 1976, PhD in Agr., 1980. Instr. U. Cantho, Vietnam, 1969-73; rsch. scientist U. Guelph, Can., 1982-87, Hoechst Can., Inc., Regina, 1987-88; sr. rsch. scientist Agrigenetics Co., Madison, Wis., 1988-89, Sungene Tech., San Jose, Calif., 1989-90, Petoseed Co., Inc., Woodland, Calif., 1990—. Contbr. articles to profl. jours. Mem. Internat. Assn. Plant Tissue Culture, In Vitro, Japanese Jour. Breeding. Buddhist. Achievements include patents pending for combination of cytoplasmic traits, atrazine resistance and cytoplasmic male sterility, production of rapeseed exhibiting an improved fatty acid profile; combination of cytoplasmically inherited traits by haploid protoplast fusion in oil rape; high production of haploids by means of microspore/anther/ovule culture in Brassica species, vegetables and ornamentals for application in plant breeding; increase of oleic acid content mutagenesis in Rapeseed. Home: 413 Grande Ave Davis CA 95616-0213 Office: Petoseed Co 37437 State Hwy 16 Woodland CA 95695-9353

PHARES, ALAIN JOSEPH, physicist, educator; b. Beirut, Apr. 20, 1942; came to U.S., 1975, naturalized, 1982; s. Joseph Michel and Renee Cecile (Doummar) P.; m. Claude Tawa, July 27, 1968; children—Caroline, Denis, Pascal. B.S. in Engring., St. Joseph U., 1964; Docteur-es-Sciences, U. Paris, 1971; Ph.D., Harvard U., 1973. Research fellow Nat. Council Sci. Research, Lebanon, 1973-75; assoc. prof. Lebanese U., 1973-75; research fellow Internat. Centre Theoretical Physics, Trieste, Italy, 1974, Harvard U., 1975-76; vis. asst. prof. U. Mont., 1976-77; asst. prof. physics Villanova U., Pa., 1977-79, assoc. prof., 1979-82, prof., 1982—, chmn. dept., 1981-91; dir. secondary sch. sci., 1981-94. Contbr. articles to profl. jours. Recipient outstanding faculty rsch. award Villanova U., 1986; French Govt. fellow, 1964-66, IAEA fellow, 1974; grantee Villanova Rsch., 1978, NSF, 1991-94. Mem. Am. Phys. Soc., Internat. Assn. Math. and Computers in Simulation, Sigma Xi. Office: Villanova U Dept Physics Villanova PA 19085

PHARES, E. JERRY, psychology educator; b. Glendale, Ohio, July 21, 1928; s. Bruce and Gladys (West) P.; m. Betty L. Knost, Aug. 6, 1955; 1 dau., Lisa M. B.A., U. Cin., 1951; M.A., Ohio State U., 1953, Ph.D., 1955. Faculty Kans. State U., Manhattan, 1955—, prof. psychology, 1964-91, prof. emeritus, 1991—, head dept., 1967-89; Vis. asso. prof. Ohio State U., Columbus, Ohio Wesleyan U., 1961-62. Author, co-author books.; Contbr. articles to profl. jours. Research grantee NIMH, 1960, 80; Research grantee NSF, 1964-76; Research grantee Population Council, 1971. Fellow Am. Psychol. Assn., Am. Psychol. Soc. Office: Psychology Dept Kan State U Manhattan KS 66506

PHARES, LYNN LEVISAY, public relations communications executive; b. Brownwood, Tex., Aug. 6, 1947; m. C. Kirk Phares, Aug. 22, 1971; children: Laura, Margaret, Adele, Jessica. BA, La. State U., 1970; MA, U. Nebr., 1987. Asst. to advt. mgr. La. Nat. Bank, 1970-71; writer, producer, asst. v.p., account exec. Smith, Kaplan, Allen & Reynolds, Inc., Omaha, 1971-80; assoc. dir. pub. affairs U. Nebr. Med. Ctr., 1980-83; dir. pub. rels. ConAgra, Inc., Omaha, 1985-87, v.p. pub. rels., 1987-90, v.p. pub. rels. and cmty. affairs, 1987—; pres. ConAgra Found. Office: ConAgra Inc 1 Conagra Dr Omaha NE 68102-5001

PHARIS, RUTH MCCALISTER, banker; b. San Diego, Feb. 13, 1934; d. William L. and Mary E. (Beuk) McC.; grad. Del Mar Coll., Corpus Christi, Tex., 1975-79; m. E. Edwin Pharis, Mar. 14, 1953; children—Beth, Tracey, Todd. Asst. cashier Parkdale State Bank, Corpus Christi, 1970-72, asst. v.p., 1972-76, v.p., 1976-79; v.p. Cullen Center Bank & Trust, Houston, 1979-81, sr. v.p., 1982—; instr. Am. Inst. Banking, 1977-79. Mem. adv. council Houston Community Colls. Mem. Human Resource Mgmt. Assn., Bank Adminstrn. Inst. (v.p. Coastal Bend chpt. 1979), Nat. Assn. Bank Women (ednl. chmn. Coastal Bend group), Am. Inst. Banking (rep.), Tex. Bankers Assn. (council 1983-84, instr.), Coastal Bend Personnel Soc. (v.p.), Houston Personnel Assn., Corpus Christi C. of C. (mem. women's com. 1976-79). Republican. Baptist. Club: Order Eastern Star. Home: 2750 Laurel Cliff Dr New Braunfels TX 78132 Office: 600 Jefferson Houston TX 77001

PHARR, GEORGE MATHEWS, materials science and engineering educator; b. Atlanta, May 20, 1953; s. George Mathews and Patricia (Steele) P.; m. Marilyn Walker, July 14, 1979; children: George Mathews, Adam Walker. BSME, Rice U., 1975; MS in Materials Sci., Stanford U., 1977, PhD in Materials Sci., 1979. Registered profl. engr., Tex. Postdoctoral fellow Cambridge (Eng.) U., 1979-80; asst. prof. materials sci. and engring. Rice U., Houston, 1980-85, assoc. prof., 1985-91, prof., 1991—; cons. Kalium Chems., Inc., Chgo., 1987—. Editor: Thin Films: Stresses and Mechanical Properties, 1990; also over 50 articles. Recipient faculty devel. award Exxon, 1982, IBM, 1984, Young Alumni Achievement award Rice U., 1985; fellow Hertz Found., 1977. Mem. Metall. Soc. of AIME, Am. Ceramic Soc. (assoc. editor Jour. 1989–), Materials Rsch. Soc., Am. Soc. for Metals (Bradley Stoughton award 1984),. Home: PO Box 2011 Houston TX 77252-2011 Office: Rice U Dept Mech Engring PO Box 1892 Houston TX 77251-1892

PHELAN, ARTHUR JOSEPH, financial executive; b. N.Y.C., Oct. 26, 1915; s. Arthur Joseph and Josephine Adelaide (Barrett) P.; m. Mary Frances Ryan, Feb. 11, 1939; children—Jane Carolee, Leslie Diane, Sandra Christine. Student, Am. Inst. Banking, 1934-35, U. N.Y., 1935-36. With Guaranty Trust Co. of N.Y., 1933-37; accountant N.Y. Post, 1937-38; accountant Webb & Knapp, Inc., N.Y.C., 1938-41, asst. sec., 1941, comptroller, 1942-44, treas., 1944-53, v.p., treas., 1953-55, sr. v.p., 1955-65; also trustee employees profit sharing plan, exec. v.p. David Greenewald Assocs., Inc., 1965-66; sr. v.p. Lefrak Orgn., Inc., Forest Hills, N.Y., 1966-92; exec. v.p., dir. LOGO Inc., Tulsa, 1976-92. Roman Catholic. Club: North Hempstead Country. Home: 88 Summit Rd Port Washington NY 11050-3341 Office: 97-77 Queens Blvd Forest Hills NY 11374

PHELAN, CHARLOTTE ROBERTSON, journalist, book critic; b. Vernon, Tex., May 12, 1917; d. Macum and Bonita (Robertson) P. BA, Tex. Wesleyan U. 1940. City editor Daily News, Lufkin, Tex., 1941-43; an editor Tex. bur. AP, Dallas, 1943-45; publicity dir., program editor, annotator San Antonio Symphony and Grand Opera, 1945-55; staff writer Houston Post, 1955-70, film and drama critic, 1970-73, book editor, 1973-82; leader workshops, panelist in field. Dir. Guadalupe Valley Telephone Cooperative, Inc.; bd. dirs. St. Judes Home for Children; mem. Bishop's com. St. Francis by the Lake Episcopal Ch. Recipient 1st pl. feature writing Headliners Club, Austin, Tex., 1964, 1st pl. women's page series, 1968. Mem. Nat. Book Critics Circle., Pilot Internat. Democrat. Episcopalian. Club: Woodlands Country. Home: 679 Irene Dr Canyon Lake TX 78133-5293

PHELAN, ELLEN, artist; b. Detroit, Nov. 3, 1943; d. Thomas Edward and Katherine Louise (Gojlewicz) P; m. Joel Elias Shapiro, Nov. 22, 1978. BFA, Wayne State U., 1969, MFA, 1971. Instr. Wayne State U., Detroit, 1969-72, Fairleigh Dickinson U., 1974, Mich. State U., East Lansing, 1974-75, Calif. Inst. Arts, 1978-79, Bard Coll., 1980, NYU, 1981, Sch. of Visual Arts, 1981-83, Calif. Inst. Arts, 1983; prof. of practice of studio art Harvard U., Cambridge, Mass., 1995—; Milton Avery vis. lectr. Bard Coll., 1994. One-woman exhbns. include Willis Gallery, Detroit, 1972, 74, Artist's Space, N.Y.C., 1975, Susanne Hilberry Gallery, Birmingham, Mich., 1977, 79, 81, 82, 84, 86, 88, 90, 92, 94, Wadsworth Athenaeum, Hartford, Conn., 1979, Ruth Schaffner Gallery, L.A., 1979, The Clocktower, N.Y.C., 1980, Hansen-Fuller-Goldeen Gallery, San Francisco, 1980, 82, Dart Gallery, Chgo., 1981, Barbara Toll Fine Arts, N.Y.C., 1982, 85, 86, 87-88, 89, 90, 92, 93, Asher/Faure, L.A., 1989, 92, 94, Balt. Mus. Art, 1989, Albright-Knox Art Gallery, Buffalo, 1991, U. Mass. Amherst Fine Arts Ctr., 1992, Saidye Bronfman Ctr., Montreal, Que., 1993, Contemporary Mus., Honolulu, 1993, John Stoller, Inc., Mpls., 1993, Cin. Art Mus., 1994; exhibited in group shows at Detroit Inst. Arts, 1970, 80, Willis Gallery, Detroit, 1971, 79, I.L. Hudson Gallery, Detroit, 1972, Cranbrook Acad. Art, Bloomfield Hills, Mich., 1972, 79, 84, Grand Rapids (Mich.) Art Mus., 1974, Paula Cooper Gallery, N.Y.C., 1975, 76, 77, 78, 79, 90, Fine Arts Bldg., N.Y.C., 1976, Acad. der Kunste, Berlin, 1976, Susanne Hilberry Gallery, Birmingham, 1976-77, 83, 85, 91, Willard Gallery, N.Y.C., 1977, Kansas City (Mo.) Art Inst., 1977, N.A.M.E. Gallery, Chgo., 1977, Hallwalls, Buffalo, 1977, Mus. Modern Art, N.Y.C., 1978, 89, 92, Weatherspoon Art Gallery U. N.C., Greensboro, 1979, 92, Albright-Knox Gallery, Buffalo, 1979, Brown U., Providence, 1980, XIII Olympic Winter Games, Lake Placid, N.Y., 1980, Jeffrey Fuller Fine Art, Phila., 1980, Portland (Oreg.) Ctr. for Visual Arts, 1980, The Drawing Ctr., N.Y.C., 1980, 82, Brooke Alexander Gallery, N.Y.C., 1980, Mus. Contemporary Art, Chgo., 1980, 81, P.S. 1 Mus., N.Y.C., 1981, 92, Art Latitude Gallery, N.Y.C., 1981, Leo Castelli Gallery, N.Y.C., 1981, Sutton Place, Guildford, Eng., 1982, Gallerie d'Arte Moderna di Ca'Pesaro, Venice, Italy, 1982, Inst. Contemporary Art of Virgini Mus., Richmond, Va., 1982, Galerie Biedermann, Munich, 1982, Thomas Segal Gallery, Boston, 1983, Fuller-Goldeen Gallery, San Francisco 1983, 86, William Paterson Coll., Wayne, N.J., 1983, 89, Artist's Space, N.Y.C., 1983, 84, Harborside Indsl. Ctr., Bklyn., 1983, Orgn. Ind. Artists, N.Y.C., 1984, Bernice Steinbaum Gallery, N.Y.C., 1984, Brentwood Gallery, St. Louis, 1984, U. Calif., Irvine, 1984, U. No. Iowa Gallery Art, Cedar Falls, 1984, Hudson River Mus., N.Y.C., 1984, Barbara Toll Fine Arts, N.Y.C., 1984, 85, 86, 87, Detroit Focus Gallery, 1984, Cable Gallery, N.Y.C., 1984, Wayne State U., Detroit, 1984, Matthews Hamilton Gallery, Phila., 1984, Barbara Krakow Gallery, Boston, 1984, BlumHelman Warehouse, N.Y.C., 1984, Pam Adler Gallery, N.Y.C., 1985,

Daniel Weinberg Gallery, L.A., 1985, 89, Knight Gallery, Charlotte, N.C., 1985, Bank of Boston, 1986, Whitney Mus. Am. Art, Stamford, Conn., 1987, 89, Scott Hansen Gallery, N.Y.C., 1987, Saxon-Lee Gallery, L.A., 1987, Parrish Art Mus., East Hampton, N.Y., 1987, Curt Marcus Gallery, N.Y., 1988, Loughelton Gallery, N.Y.C., 1988, 90, Whitney Mus. Am. Art, N.Y.C., 1988, 91, Hillwood Art Gallery C.W. Post Campus, Brookville, N.Y., 1989, USIA traveling exbhn., 1989, Edward Thorp Gallery, N.Y.C., 1989, Pine Street Lobby Gallery, San Francisco, 1989, Fuller Gross Gallery, San Francisco 1989, Solo Press/Soho Gallery, N.Y.C., 1989, Maxwell Davidson Gallery, N.Y.C., 1989, Blum Helman Gallery, N.Y.C., 1989, R.I.S.D., Providence, 1989, Graham Modern, N.Y.C., 1990, Hood Mus. Art Dartmouth Coll., Hanover, N.H., 1990, 92, New Britain Mus. Am. Art, Hartfor, Conn., 1991, Asher-Faure, L.A., 1991, Annina Nosei Gallery, N.Y.C., 1991, Lintas Worldwide, N.Y.C., 1991, Nina Fredenheim Gallery, Buffalo, 1991, Molica Guidarte Gallery, N.Y.C., 1991, Squibb Gallery, Princeton, N.J., 1991, Cleve. State U. Gallery, 1992, Ind. Curators Inc., N.Y.C., 1992, Wexner Ctr. for the Arts, Columbus, Ohio, 1992, Transamerica Corp., San Francisco, 1992, The Gallery Three Zero, N.Y.C., 1992, Haggerty Mus. Art, Milw., Barbara Methes Gallery, N.Y.C., Asher Fauve Gallery, L.A., Hillwood Art Mus., Brookville, N.Y., Pamela Auchincloss Gallery, N.Y.C., Leo Castelli Gallery, N.Y.C.; represented in permanent collections Mus. Modern Art, N.Y.C., Whitney Mus. Am. Art, N.Y.C., Bklyn. Mus., Walker Art Ctr., Mpls., Balt. Mus., Toledo Mus. Art, Hood Mus. Dartmouth Coll., High Mus. Art, Albright-Knox Art Gallery, Moderna Museet, Stockholm, Mus. Contemporary Art, Mexico City, Detroit Inst. Arts, MIT, Whitehead Inst., Philip Morris, Inc., Volvo Corp., Chase Manhattan Bank, Chem. Bank, BankAm., Bank of Am., Prudential Ins. Co., U.S. Trust & Co., Inter Metro Industries, Lannan Found., numerous pvt. collections. Nat. Endowment for Arts grantee, 1978-79; recipient Am. Acad. Arts and Letters award, 1995, Arts Achievement award Wayne State U., 1989.

PHELAN, JOHN DENSMORE, insurance executive, consultant; b. Kalamazoo, Aug. 31, 1914; s. John and Ida (Densmore) P.; m. Isabel McLaughlin, July 31, 1937; children: John Walter, William Paul, Daniel Joseph. BA magna cum laude, Carleton Coll., 1935. Reporter New Bedford (Mass.) Standard-Times, 1935-36; with Hardware Mut. Ins. Co. (name now Sentry Ins. Co.), Stevens Point, Wis., 1936-45; with Am. States Ins. Co., Indpls., 1945-90, pres., 1963-76, chmn., 1976-79, also dir. numerous subs.; chmn. Hawes-Phelan Ins. Inc., Columbus, Ind.; bd. govs. Internat. Ins. Soc. Author: Business Interruption Primer, 1949, also later edits.; contbr. articles to profl. jours. Past pres. Marion County Assn. Mental Health; chmn. emeritus. CPCU-Harry J. Loman Found.; adv. bd. ins. dept. Ball State U. Sch. Bus. Named to Honorable Order of Ky. Colonels, Sagamore of the Wabash. Mem. CPCU Soc. (past nat pres.), CLU Soc., Woodland Country Club (Indpls.), El Conquistador Country Club (Bradenton, Fla.), Phi Beta Kappa. Presbyterian. Home: 6460 Mourning Dove Dr Apt 205 Bradenton FL 34210-4313 also: 307 Woodland Ln Carmel IN 46032-3570

PHELAN, JOHN J., JR., former stock exchange executive, corporate director; b. N.Y.C., May 7, 1931. BBA magna cum laude, Adelphi U., 1970, LLD (hon.), 1987; LLD (hon.), Hamilton Coll., 1980, Niagara U., 1985; hon. doctorate, U. Notre Dame, 1986, Tulane U., Brooklyn Polytech. Joined Nash & Co., N.Y.C., 1955, ptnr., 1957-62; sr. ptnr. Phelan & Co., N.Y.C., 1962-72, Phelan, Silver, N.Y.C., 1972-77, Phelan, Vesce, Barry & Co., N.Y.C., 1977-80; mem. N.Y. Stock Exchange, N.Y.C., 1957-80, bd. govs., 1971-72, bd. dirs., 1974-80, vice chmn., 1975-80, pres., chief oper. officer, 1980-84, chmn., chief exec. officer, 1984-91; sr. advisor Boston Cons. Group, 1992—; chmn. N.Y. Futures Exchange, 1979-85; chmn. Presdl. Bd. Advisors on Pvt. Sector Initiatives, 1986—; bd. dirs. Met. Life Ins. Co., Eastman Kodak Co., Merrill Lynch, Sonat, Cold Spring Harbor Labs.; bd. dirs. Bus. Coun. N.Y. State, vice chair bd., chmn. fin. com., 1989-90; trustee Com. for Econ. Devel., 1985-90; mem. N.Y. State Temporary Com. on Banking, Ins., and Fin. Services, 1983-84; leader del. to symposium N.Y. Stock Exchange/Peoples Bank China, Beijing, 1986; head symposium on Russian economy. Mem. cardinal's com. of laity Archdiocese N.Y., 1968—, mem. fin. coun., 1986-92; chmn. Wall St. div. NCCJ, 1973, 76; bd. dirs. Mercy Hosp., Rockville Centre, N.Y., 1976-81, N.Y. Heart Assn., 1979-84; chmn. campaigns N.Y.C. Heart Fund, 1982-83; trustee Adelphi Coll., 1980-86, chmn. bd. trustees, 1981-85; mem. Rockefeller U. Coun.; trustee Tulane U., 1983-87; mem. bd. advisors Boston U. Ctr. for Banking Law Studies, 1981-90; trustee N.Y. Med. Coll., 1984-91, Cath. Charities, 1985—, Asia Soc., 1987-93; chmn. fin. svcs. div. United Way N.Y., 1985-86, bd. govt. United Way Am., 1988-91; mem. bd. councillors Holy Sepulcher, 1985—; mem. adv. bd. Bus. Higher Edn. Forum, 1985-91; bd. dirs. Aspen Inst., past chmn. With USMC, 1951-54. Decorated knight Sovereign Mil. Order of Malta; knight Holy Sepulchre of Jerusalem; Medal of Arts and Letters (France); recipient Brotherhood award NCCJ, 1974, Ellis Island Medal of Honor, 1988, Alumni award Adelphi U., 1979, Nat. Youth Services award B'nai B'rith Found., Wall St. Man of Yr. award B'nai B'rith, 1980, Stephen S. Wise award Am. Jewish Congress, 1981, Good Scout award Greater N.Y. coun. Boy Scouts Am., 1983, Man of Yr. award Nat. Found. for Ileitis and Colitis, 1985, Chancellor's Medal award Molloy Coll., 1987, Disting. Service award Investment Edn. Inst., 1987, award of merit for disting. entrepreneurship The Wharton Sch., U. Pa., 1987, Silver Ambrosiana award Commune of Milan, 1987, Lion of Venice award City of Venice, 1987, Medal of Veneto region Govt. of Italy, 1987, Albert Schweitzer Leadership award Hugh O'Brien Youth Found., 1987, Torch of Learning award NYU Ctr. for Ednl. Rsch., 1987, C. Walter Nichols award Stern Sch. Bus. NYU, Vetty award Vietnam Vets. Ensemble Theatre Co., Gold medal 100 Yr. Assn. N.Y., Founders' award N.Y. chpt. Arthitis Found., others. Mem. Internat. Fedn. Bourses, Fedn. Internat. Bourses de Valeurs (v.p.), Nat. Audubon Soc. (bd. dirs. 1989-92), Econ. Club N.Y. (trustee 1989—).

PHELAN, KATHLEEN MCGRATH, public relations executive; b. Bethesda, Md., Oct. 18, 1956. BSBA, Am. U., 1979. Account exec. E.F. Hutton, 1983-85, Drexel Burnham, 1985-87; account exec. FRB, 1987-88, sr. assoc., 1988-89; v.p. Fin. Rels. Bd., N.Y.C., 1989-90, ptnr., dir. east coast ops., 1990—. Mem. Pub. Rels. Soc. Am. Office: Fin Rels Bd 675 3rd Ave New York NY 10017-5704*

PHELAN, MARTIN DUPONT, retired film company executive; b. Chgo., Dec. 25, 1913; s. Martin Anthony and Margaret Crespo (DuPont) P.; m. Mary Katharine Harris, Aug. 14, 1937; children—Richard H., Jeremy D. A.B., DePauw U., 1934. Mdse. exec. Montgomery Ward, Chgo., 1934-42, Butler Bros., Chgo., 1946-47; corporate officer Eastin-Phelan Corp., Davenport, Iowa, 1947-77. Served to col. U.S. Army, 1942-46. Mem. Iowa Libr. Trustee Assn. (pres. 1980), Ponte Vedra Club, Rotary. Republican. Episcopalian. Home: Guildford 207 Vicar's Landing Ponte Vedra Beach FL 32082

PHELAN, RICHARD JOHN, county administrator, lawyer; b. Chgo., Mar. 29, 1937. Ph.B., Univ. Notre Dame, 1958; J.D., Georgetown Univ., 1961. Bar: Ill. 1961. Adj. prof. Ill. Inst. Tech./Chgo.-Kent Coll. Law, 1963-74, 79-83; spl. asst. corp. counsel City of Chgo., 1974-76; former ptnr. Phelan Pope John Ltd., Chgo.; pres. Cook County (Ill.) Bd., Chgo., 1991—; chmn. Practising Law Inst., N.Y. Law Jour. Programs, 1972—; bd. dirs. Public Interest Law Internship, 1983—; Constitutional Rights Found., 1984—; spl. outside counsel Com. on Standards of Ofcl. Conduct U.S. House of Reps., 1989. Contbr. to profl. jours. Mem. exec. adv. bd. St. Joseph Hosp., 1985-88. Fellow Am. Bar Found., Am. Coll. Trial Lawyers (chmn. Ill. state com. 1988-89), Internat. Acad. Trial Lawyers (dean, bd. dirs. 1982-88, chmn. admissions com. 1986-89); mem. Ill. Bar Assn. (legal aid appts. com.), Chgo. Bar Assn. (pres. 1985-86, chmn. permanent home com. 1988-90). Office: Office Bd Pres Cook County Bldg 118 N Clark St Ste 537 Chicago IL 60602-1311

PHELAN, RICHARD MAGRUDER, mechanical engineer; b. Moberly, Mo., Sept. 20, 1921; s. Frederick William and Ethel Ray (Magruder) P.; m. Olive Bernice McIntosh, May 25, 1951; children—William James, Susan Ray. Student, Moberly Jr. Coll., 1939-41; B.S. in Mech. Engring. U. Mo., Columbia, 1943; M.M.E., Cornell U., 1950; postgrad., U. Mich., 1956-57. Instr. Cornell U., 1947-50, asst. prof. mech. engring., 1950-56, assoc. prof. 1956-62, prof., 1962-87, prof. emeritus 1988—. Author: Fundamentals of Mechanical Engineering, 1957, 3d rev. edit., 1970, Dynamics of Machinery, 1967, Automatic Control Systems, 1977. Served with USNR, 1943-46. Mem.

ASME, Am. Soc. Engring. Edn., Soc. Exptl. Stress Analysis, Am. Gear Mfrs. Assn., AAUP, AAAS, N.Y. Acad. Scis., Soc. Exptl. Mechanics, Sigma Xi, Phi Kappa Phi, Pi Tau Sigma, Tau Beta Pi. Home: 4 Cornell Walk Ithaca NY 14850-6145 Office: Cornell U Upson Hall Ithaca NY 14853

PHELAN, RICHARD PAUL, trust company executive; b. N.Y.C., Oct. 26, 1939; s. Peter James and Florence (Leary) P.; m. Bridget Burke, Sept. 17, 1966; children: Richard Matthew, Peter Michael, Robert William. Student, CCNY, 1957-58; Diploma, Am. Inst. Banking, N.Y.C., 1962; BS, NYU, 1967, MBA, 1969; MA, Columbia U., 1974. Sr. v.p. Chem. Bank (formerly Mfrs. Hanover Trust Co.), N.Y.C., 1957—. Mem. Union League Club. Republican. Roman Catholic. Home: 564 Dutch Neck Rd East Windsor NJ 08520-1124

PHELAN, ROBIN ERIC, lawyer; b. Steubenville, Ohio, Dec. 28, 1945; s. Edward John and Dorothy (Borkowski) P.; children: Travis McCoy, Tiffany Marie, Trevor Monroe. BSBA, Ohio State U., 1967, JD, 1970. Bar: Tex. 1971, U.S. Ct. Appeals (5th cir.) 1981, U.S. Ct. Appeals (11th cir.) 1981, U.S. Ct. Appeals (6th cir.) 1986, U.S. Ct. Appeals (10th cir.) 1988, U.S. Supreme Ct. Ptnr. Haynes and Boone, Dallas, 1970—; bd. dirs. Am. Bankruptcy Inst., Washington, pres., 1994. Co-author: Bankruptcy Practice and Strategy, 1987, Cowans Bankruptcy Law and Practice, 1987, Annual Survey of Bankruptcy Law, 1988, Bankruptcy Litigation Manual; contbr. articles to profl. jours. Mem. ABA (chmn. bankruptcy litigation subcom. 1990—), State Bar Tex. (chmn. bankruptcy law com. sect. bus. law 1989-91), Dallas Bar Assn. Roman Catholic. Avocation: athletics. Home: 4214 Woodfin St Dallas TX 75220-6416 Office: Haynes & Boone 3100 NationsBank Plz 901 Main St Dallas TX 75202-3789

PHELAN, THOMAS, clergyman, academic administrator, educator; b. Albany, N.Y., Apr. 11, 1925; s. Thomas William and Helen (Rausch) P. A.B. (N.Y. State Regents scholar 1942, President's medal 1945), Coll. Holy Cross, Worcester, Mass., 1945; S.T.L., Catholic U. Am., 1951; postgrad., Oxford (Eng.) U., 1958-59, 69-70. Ordained priest Roman Cath. Ch., 1951; pastor, tchr., adminstr. Diocese of Albany, 1951-58; resident Cath. chaplain Rensselaer Poly. Inst., Troy, N.Y., 1959-72; prof. history, dean Sch. Humanities and Social Scis. Rensselaer Poly. Inst., 1972-95, inst. historian, inst. dean, sr. advisor to pres., 1995—; inst. historian, inst. dean, sr. adviser to pres. Rensselaer Poly. Inst., Troy, 1995—; chmn. architecture and bldg. commn. Diocese Albany, 1968—; cons. in field. Author: Achieving the Impossible, Hudson Mohawk Gateway, 1985; author monographs, articles, revs. in field. Treas. The Rensselaer Newman Found., 1962—; pres. Hudson-Mohawk Indsl. Gateway, 1971-84, bd. dirs., exec. com., 1984—; mem. WMHT Ednl. Telecommunications, 1966-77, 84-90, chmn., 1973-77; chmn. Troy Hist. Dist. and Landmarks Rev. Commn., 1975-86, chmn. hist. adv. com., 1987—; v.p. Preservation League N.Y. State, 1979-82, mem. trustees council, 1982-87; pres. Preservation League N.Y. State, 1987-89; sec. and bd. dirs. Partners for Sacred Places, 1989—; bd. dirs. Hall of History Found., 1983-87; trustee Troy Pub. Libr., 1992—, bd. dirs.; mem. Pres.'s Coun. Sage Colls. Served with USN, 1943-46. Recipient Paul J. Hallinan award Nat. Newman Chaplains Assn., 1967; arm. award Albany Arts League, 1977; Disting. Community Service award Rensselaer Poly. Inst., 1979; Edward Fox Demers medal Alumni Assn. Rensselaer Poly. Inst., 1986; Disting. Service award Hudson-Mohawk Consortium of Colls. and Univs., 1988; named Citizen Laureate of the State Univ. N.Y. Found. at Albany, 1988; Danforth Found. fellow, 1969-70; grantee Homeland Found., 1958-59; grantee Dorothy Thomas Found., 1969-70. Fellow Soc. Arts, Religion and Contemporary Culture; mem. Ch. Soc. Coll. Work (dir., exec. com. 1970—), Am. Conf. Acad. Deans, Liturgical Conf., Soc. Indsl. Archaeology, Assn. Internat. pour l'Etudes des Religions Prehistoriques et Ethnologiques, Cath. Campus Ministry Assn., Cath. Art Assn., Assn. for Religion and the Intellectual Life (bd. dirs. 1987—), Soc. History of Tech. Clubs: Ft. Orange, Troy Country; Squadron A (N.Y.). Home: 5 Whitman Ct Troy NY 12180-4732 Office: Rensselaer Poly Inst Troy NY 12180 *Service and community building have motivated most of my business and personal actions. I received these values from my parents and from the church. I work to make positive contributions towards a world in which there is more justice and consequent hope of peace.*

PHELPS, ARTHUR VAN RENSSELAER, physicist, consultant; b. Dover, N.H., July 20, 1923; s. George Osborne and Helen (Ketchum) P.; m. Gertrude Kanzius, July 21, 1956; children: Wayne Edward, Joan Susan. ScD in Physics, MIT, 1951. Cons. physicist rsch. labs. Westinghouse Elec. Corp., Pitts., 1951-70; sr. rsch. scientist Nat. Bur. Standards, Boulder, Colo., 1970-88; fellow Joint Inst. Lab. Astrophysics U. Colo., Boulder, 1970-88, adjoint fellow, 1988—, chmn., 1979-81; chmn. Gordon Rsch. Conf., Plasma Chemistry, 1990. Recipient Silver Medal award Dept. Commerce, 1978. Fellow Am. Phys. Soc. (Will Allis prize 1990). Achievements include patent for Schulz-Phelps ionization gauge; research on electron and atomic collision processes involving low energy electrons, molecules, ions, metastable atoms and resonance radiation; on laser processes and modeling; on gaseous electronics. Home: 3405 Endicott Dr Boulder CO 80303-6908 Office: U Colo Joint Inst Lab Astrophysics Campus Box 440 Boulder CO 80309-0440

PHELPS, ASHTON, JR., newspaper publisher; b. New Orleans, Nov. 4, 1945; s. Ashton Sr. and Jane Cary (George) P.; m. Mary Ella Sanders, Apr. 10, 1976; children—Cary Clifton, Mary Louise, Sanders. BA, Yale U., 1967; JD, Tulane U., 1970. Trainee Times-Picayune Pub. Corp., New Orleans, 1970-71; asst. to pub. Times-Picayune Pub. Corp., 1971-79, pres., pub., 1979—. Bd. dirs. Bur. Govtl. Rsch., New Orleans, 1973-89, Xavier U. of La., New Orleans, 1974-82, Coun. for Better La., 1982-85, Met. Area Com., New Orleans, Ochsner Found. Hosp., New Orleans, 1982—, Internat. House, New Orleans, 1981-83, Pub. Affairs Rsch., New Orleans, 1982-85, La. Children's Mus., New Orleans, 1983-90, Yale Alumni Assn. of La., 1985, Newspaper Advt. Bur. Future of Advt. Com., 1986-89; chmn. Audit Com. of Associated Press, 1986-90. Mem. So. Newspaper Pubs. Assn. (bd. dirs. 1982-85, found. bd. dirs. 1982-83, pres. 1990-91), La. Press Assn. (bd. dirs. 1984-93, v.p. 1989-90, pres. 1991-92). Avocation: tennis. Office: The Times-Picayune 3800 Howard Ave New Orleans LA 70140-1097

PHELPS, BARTON CHASE, architect, educator; b. Bklyn., June 27, 1946; s. Julian Orville and Elizabeth Willis (Faulk) P.; m. Karen Joy Simonson; 1 child, Charlotte Simonson Phelps. BA in Art with honors, Williams Coll., 1968; MArch, Yale U., 1973. Registered architect, Calif. With Colin St. John Wilson & Ptnrs., London, 1972-73, Frank O. Gehry and Assocs., Inc., Santa Monica, Calif., 1973-76; project architect Charles Moore/Urban Innovations Group, L.A., 1976-78; dir. architecture Urban Innovations Group, L.A., 1980-84; prin. Barton Phelps & Assocs., L.A., 1984—; asst. prof. architecture Rice U. Sch. of Architecture, Houston, 1977-79; asst. dean Grad. Sch. Architecture and Urban Planning, UCLA, 1980-83; prof. architecture Sch. Arts and Architecture UCLA; faculty mem. Nat. Endowment Arts, Mayor's Inst. for City Design, 1990, 92. Author, editor: Architecture California, 1988-92. Fellow Gramham Found. for Advanced Studies in Fine Art, 1989, Nat. Endowment for the Arts, 1988. Mem. AIA (Coll. of Fellows, chair com. on design, recipient design awards for Arrovo House, Kranz House, North Range Clark Libr. UCLA, D.W.P. Ctrl. Dist. Hdqrs., No. Hollywood Pump Sta., East Bldg. Seeds U. Elem. Sch., UCLA, Inst. Honor for Collaborative Design, Games XXIII Olympiad L.A. 1985). Democrat. Home: 10256 Lelia Ln Los Angeles CA 90077-3144 Office: Barton Phelps & Assocs 5514 Wilshire Blvd Los Angeles CA 90036-3829

PHELPS, CATHERINE, elementary school principal. Prin. Trinity Sch. Recipient Elem. Sch. Recognition award U.S. Dept. Edn., 1989-90. Office: Trinity Sch 4985 Ilchester Rd Ellicott City MD 21043-6837

PHELPS, CHARLOTTE MAE, health educator; b. Plymouth, Mass., Aug. 10, 1931; d. Lewis Edward and Eleanor (Buswell) Billings; m. Richard H. Phelps, Sept. 3, 1955; children: Elisabeth, Richard. BS, U. Vt., 1954; MS in Nursing, U. Md., 1973. Faculty instr. U. Vt., Burlington, 1954-57, St. Joseph's Sch. Nursing, Marshfield, Wis., 1961-63, St. Agnes Nursing Sch., Balt., 1963-65, Frederick (Md.) County Community Coll., 1968-72; faculty instr. Garland County Community Coll., Hot Springs, Ark. 1973-78, dir. health scis. dept., 1978—. Active ARC, YWCA, Hot Springs; also serves on numerous health delivery bds., state, local coms. Recipient Clara Barton Medal ARC, 1978. Mem. Am. Nurses Assn. (Polit. Action Com.), Ark. State Nurses Assn. (pres. 1978-80), Nat. League for Nursing (site visitor),

Sigma Theta Tau. Republican. Methodist. Avocations: walking, swimming, ceramics, needlework. Home: 113 Grand Ridge Ter Hot Springs National Park AR 71901-9219 Office: Garland County Community Coll 1 College Dr Hot Springs National Park AR 71913-9119

PHELPS, EDMUND STROTHER, economics educator; b. Evanston, Ill., July 26, 1933; s. Edmund Strother and Florence Esther (Stone) P.; m. Viviana Regina Montdor, Oct. 1, 1974. BA, Amherst Coll., 1955, DLitt (hon.), 1985; MA, Yale U., 1956, PhD, 1959. Economist Rand Corp., Santa Monica, Calif., 1959-60; asst. prof. Yale U., Cowles Found., 1960-62, assoc. prof., 1963-66; vis. assoc. prof. M.I.T., 1962-63; prof. econs. U. Pa., Phila., 1966-71; prof. econs. Columbia U., 1971-78, 79-82, McVickar prof. polit. economy, 1982—; scholar Russell Sage Found., 1993-94; prof. NYU, 1978-79; fellow Center for Advanced Study in Behavioral Scis., 1969-70; sr. advisor Brookings Inst., 1976—; econ. advisor European Bank for Reconstrn. and Devel., 1991—, econ. policy panel, OFCE, 1991—. Author: numerous books including Golden Rules of Economic Growth, 1966, Microeconomic Foundations of Employment and Inflation Theory, 1970, Economic Justice, 1973, Studies in Macroeconomic Theory, Vol. I, 1979, Vol. II, 1980, Political Economy, 1985, The Slump in Europe, 1988, Structural Slumps, 1994. Guggenheim fellow, 1978; Social Sci. Research Council fellow, 1966. Mem., NAS, Fellow Econometric Soc.; Fellow Am. Acad. Arts and Scis.; mem. Am. Econ. Assn. (mem. exec. com. 1976-78, v.p. 1983), Phi Beta Kappa. Home: 45 E 89th St New York NY 10128 Office: Columbia Univ Dept Economics New York NY 10027

PHELPS, FLORA L(OUISE) LEWIS, editor, anthropologist, photographer; b. San Francisco, July 28, 1917; d. George Chase and Louise (Manning) Lewis; m. C(lement) Russell Phelps, Jan. 15, 1944; children: Andrew Russell, Carol Lewis, Gail Bransford. Student, U. Mich.; AB cum laude, Bryn Mawr Coll., 1938; AM, Columbia U., 1954. Acting dean Cape Cod Inst. Music, East Brewster, Mass., summer 1940; assoc. social sci. analyst U.S. Govt., 1942-44; co-adj. staff instr. anthropology Univ. Coll. Rutgers U., 1954-55; mem. editorial bd. Américas mag. OAS, Washington, 1960-82; mng. editor, 1974-82, contbg. editor, 1982-89; N.J. vice chmn. Ams. Dem. Action, 1950; mem. Dem. County Com. N.J., 1948-49. Author articles in fields of anthropology, art, architecture, edn., travel; contbr. Latin Am. newspapers. Mem. AAAS, Am. Anthrop. Assn., Archaeological Inst. Am., Latin Am. Studies Assn., Soc. for Am. Archaeology, Soc. Woman Geographers. Home: Collington # 2212 10450 Lottsford Rd Mitchellville MD 20721-2748

PHELPS, JOSEPH WILLIAM, banker; b. Richmond, Ky., Jan. 6, 1927; s. Ben and Hannah (Blunschi) P.; m. Mary Margaret Culton, Jan. 2, 1954; children: Melanie Jean, Joseph William. Nat. bank examiner U.S. Treasury Dept., 1950-58; asst. cashier Liberty Nat. Bank & Trust Co., Louisville, 1958-59, asst. v.p., 1959-62, v.p., 1962-67, head corr. bank dept., sec. to bd., exec. com., 1967-68, sr. v.p., 1968-70, exec. v.p., 1971-73, pres., 1973—, also dir.; pres. Liberty-United Bancorp. (now named Liberty Bancorp.), 1983—; dir. Lincoln Income Life Ins. Co. Mem. exec. bd. Old Ky. Home council Boy Scouts Am.; Ky. Council Econ. Edn., Better Rds. Council Ky., Kidney Found. Ky., Spirit of Louisville Found.; bd. dirs. Ky. div. Am. Cancer Soc., Louisville Med. Research Found., YMCA, Assoc. Industries Ky.; gen. campaign chmn. Metro United Way, 1978; chmn. bd. regents Eastern Ky. U.; mem. Gov.'s Council Econ. Devel., Gov.'s Council Land Use Planning; chmn. Fund for Arts Campaign; mem. vis. com. Sch. Dentistry, U. Louisville; bd. dirs. Louisville Orch. Served with AUS, 1945. Mem. Am. Inst. Banking, Am. Bankers Assn., Ky. C. of C. (dir.), Louisville C. of C. (chmn. com. econ. edn.), Res. City Bankers, Filson Club, English Speaking Union, Newcomen Soc. Episcopalian (vestryman). Clubs: Pendennis (Louisville), Louisville Country (Louisville). Home: 5015 Dunvegan Rd Louisville KY 40222-6020 Office: Liberty Bancorp 416 W Jefferson St Louisville KY 40202-3244

PHELPS, JUDSON HEWETT, marketing sales executive; b. Evanston, Ill., Oct. 18, 1942; s. Sidney Norman and Mary Schyler (Coons) P.; m. Barbara Ann Ray, Dec. 21, 1963; children: Wyeth Hewett, Christopher Ashley, Whitney Magee. BA, Williams Coll., 1964; MS, Springfield Coll., 1993. Asst. brand mgr. Procter & Gamble Co., Cin., 1968-70; brand mgr. Memorex, Santa Clara, Calif., 1970-72; product mgr. Chesebrough Ponds Inc., Greenwich, Conn., 1972-76; v.p. mktg. L'Oreal subs. Cosmair, Inc., N.Y.C., 1976-77; v.p. sales Bio Products, Inc., Norwalk, Conn., 1978, exec. v.p., 1979, pres., 1980-86, corp. v.p. Ketchum & Co. parent co. Bio Products, Norwalk, 1982-86; mng. dir. Dameon Ptnrs. Inc., Wilton, Conn., 1987-88, pres. Theracom Corp., Rye, N.Y., 1988-89; v.p. Promotion Info. Bur., Norwalk, 1990; prin. Daniel Adams Co., Danbury, Conn., 1991-92; clin. coord., addictions therapist, counselor The Ctr., Bridgeport, Conn., 1993—. Pres. Camp Dudley (YMCA) Alumni Assn., Westport, N.Y., 1974-79; family counselor Caregivers, Assn. Religious Communities, Danbury, 1975-79; leader, treas. Ridgefield Emmaus Teenage Christian Retreats, Ridgefield, Conn., 1983-92; chmn. Ridgefield Alcohol and Drug Use Commn., 1992—. Lt. USNR, 1964-68. Home: 5 Wooster Heights Dr Ridgefield CT 06877-3109

PHELPS, ORME WHEELOCK, economics educator emeritus; b. Hobart, Okla., July 5, 1906; s. William Andrews and Kate Mae (Forman) P.; m. Jean Wright, Aug. 18, 1940; children—John Jackson, Sarah Hamilton; m. Barbara C. Green, July 25, 1981. A.B., U. Chgo., 1937, M.B.A., 1939, Ph.D., 1945. Asst. prof. bus. adminstrn. U. Chgo., 1942-47; prof. econs. Claremont (Calif.) Men's Coll. and Grad. Sch., 1947-63, sr. prof., 1963-76, emeritus, 1976—, dean faculty, 1970-74; vis. prof. UCLA, 1950, State U. N.Y. at Brockport, 1968-69; Fulbright research prof. Univ. Coll. of W.I., Kingston, Jamaica, 1957-58; Brookings research prof., Washington, 1962-63. Author: Introduction to Labor Economics, 4th edit, 1967, Discipline and Discharge in the Unionized Firm, 1959, Union Security, 1954, Legislative Background of the Fair Labor Standards Act, 1939; Contbr. articles, book revs. to profl. jours. Pub. mem., regional vice-chmn. Wage Stblzn. Bd., 1951-53; labor arbitrator, mem. various govt. bds. Ford found. fellow, 1953-54. Mem. Indsl. Relations Research Assn., Am., Western econ. assns., Am. Acad. Univ. Profs. Democrat. Episcopalian. Home: 1421 Rust Ct Claremont CA 91711-2732

PHELPS, PAUL MICHAEL, lawyer; b. Lake Forest, Ill., Sept. 19, 1933; s. Paul and Elizabeth Anne (Wilson) P.; m. Laura Elaine Pepe, Dec. 26, 1966; stepchildren: Kimberly A. Springer, Wendy L. Field, Gregory L. Field. B.A., Wesleyan U., Middletown, Conn., 1955; LL.B., Harvard U., 1958. Bar: Ill. 1958, U.S. Ct. Mil. Appeals 1959. Assoc. atty. Keck Mahin & Cate, Chgo., 1958, 63-65; atty. Ekco Products Co., Chgo., 1965-67, E. J. Brach & Sons, Chgo., 1967-69; asst. corp. sec. R. R. Donnelley & Sons Co., Chgo., 1969-73; asst. counsel Marsh & McLennan, Chgo., 1973-74; corp. sec. Morton-Norwich Products, Inc. (name changed to Morton Thiokol Inc., 1982, and to Thiokol Corp., 1989), Chgo., 1974-89; v.p., corp. sec. Morton Internat. Inc., Chgo., 1989—. Served to capt. JAGC U.S. Army, 1959-63. Mem. Am. Soc. Corp. Secs. (bd. dirs. 1987-93, chmn. 1991-92), Phi Beta Kappa, Psi Upsilon. Republican. Episcopalian. Clubs: University, Tower (Chgo.). Home: 222 E Chestnut St Apt 10B Chicago IL 60611-2351 Office: Morton Internat Inc 100 N Riverside Plz Chicago IL 60606-1518

PHELPS, PAULDING, rheumatologist, internist; b. Phila., June 5, 1933; s. Charles M. and Ann Paulding (Naile) P.; m. Susan M. Tyson, Dec. 22, 1956; children: Elizabeth Phelps Dorer, Geoffrey. BA, Haverford (Pa.) Coll., 1955; student, London Sch. of Econs., 1955-56; MD, Coll. of Physicians and Surgeons, 1961. Diplomate Am. Bd. Internal Medicine. Intern Phila. Gen. Hosp., 1960-61, resident in medicine, 1961-64, asst. clinic physician, 1965-67, asst. dir. gen. clin. rsch. ctr., 1965-71, attending physician medicine, Phila., 1964, jr. attending physician, 1964-67; assoc. in medicine dept. of medicine U. Pa. Sch. of Medicine, 1967-68; dir. rheumatology div. Maine Med. Ctr., 1978-86; clin. prof. Medicine U. Vt., Burlington, 1986—; attending physician Mercy Hosp., Portland, Maine, 1971-94; instr. medicine Hahnemann Med. Coll. and Hosp., Phila., 1964, sr. instr. medicine, 1966-67; asst. prof. medicine U. Pa. Sch. of Medicine, 1968-71; assoc. staff Portland City Hosp., 1972-94; Westbrook (Maine) Community Hosp., 1981-94; mem. bd. corporators Maine Med. Ctr., Haverford Coll. Bd. dirs. Arthritis Found. 1986-87, long range planning com., 1989-90, chmn. patient svcs. com., 1985-87; bd. trustees, mem. exec. com. Maine Arthritis Found., Found. for Blood Research,

1974-81, treas., 1975, mem. nominating com., 1980, chmn., 1981; mem. Nat. Arthritis Adv. Bd., 1985-87; bd. dirs. Portland Stage Co., 1989-94, chmn. strategic planning group, 1992; fleet surgeon Portland Yacht Club, 1986, 87. Fellow ACP; mem. Am. Coll. Rheumatology (pres. 1987-88, chmn. com. rheumatologic practice 1985, chmn. membership com. 1979-81, long range planning com. 1984-85), Maine Med. Assn., Arthritis Health Professions Assn. Democrat. Mem. Soc. of Friends. Avocations: sailing, gardening.

PHELPS, TIMOTHY MILLER, reporter; b. Newport, R.I., May 18, 1947; s. Walter Kane and Constance (Miller) P.; m. Helen Watson Winternitz; children: Constance, Paul. BA, U. Pa., Phila., 1969. Reporter Providence Jour., 1968-69, St. Petersburg (Fla.) Times, 1972-76, N.Y. Times, N.Y.C., 1980-81; freelance reporter Cairo, 1976-77; reporter Balt. Sun, 1977-80, state editor, 1981-85; Mid. East bur. chief Newsday, Cairo, 1985-91; Washington corr. Newsday, 1991—. Contbr. to book: Capitol Games: The Inside Story of Clarence Thomas, Anita Hill and a Supreme Court Nomination, 1992. With U.S. Army, 1969-72. Recipient Barnet Novelz award White House Correspondents Assn., 1992. Office: Newsday Ste 850 1730 Pennsylvania Ave NW Washington DC 20006

PHELPS, WILLARD, Canadian government official. Min. Edn., Health and Social Svcs., Can., 1993—. Office: Govt Yukon, PO Box 2703, Whitehorse, YK Canada Y1A 2C6

PHEMISTER, ROBERT DAVID, college dean; b. Framingham, Mass., July 15, 1936; s. Robert Irving and Georgia Nora (Savignac) P.; m. Ann Christine Lyon, June 14, 1960; children: Katherine, David, Susan. D.V.M., Cornell U., 1960; Ph.D., Colo. State U., Ft. Collins, 1967. Diplomate: Am. Coll. Vet. Pathologists. Research assoc. U. Calif., Davis, 1963-65; staff scientist Armed Forces Inst. Pathology, Washington, 1962-64; sect. leader to dir. collaborative radiol. health lab. Colo. State U., 1964-77; mem. faculty Coll. Vet. Medicine and Biomed. Scis., 1968-85, prof. vet. pathology, 1973-85, assoc. dean, 1976-77, assoc. dir. expt. sta., 1977-85, dean, 1977-85, interim acad. v.p., 1982, interim pres., 1983-84, spl. counselor to pres., 1984-85; prof. vet. pathology Cornell U., 1985—, dean Coll. Vet. Medicine, 1985—; vis. rsch. pathologist U. Calif., Davis, 1974-75; cons. Miss. State U., 1977-81; commr. Colo. Advanced Tech. Inst., 1983-84; mem. governing bd. N.Y. Sea Grant Inst., 1985—, vice chmn., 1990-92; mem. vet. medicine adv. com. FDA, 1984-88; mem. Joint Coun. on Food and Agrl. Scis. USDA, 1988-92, exec. com., 1989-92; chmn. Zweig Meml. Fund for Equine Rsch., 1985—; mem. adv. panel for vet. medicine Pew Health Professions Commn., 1991-93. Author papers in field. Served to comdr. USPHS, 1960-68. Recipient Charles A. Lory award and Disting. Univ. Leadership award Colo. State U., 1984, Disting. Practitioner award Nat. Acad. Practice, 1985, Regional Health Adminstr.'s award, 1985; named Honor Alumnus, Colo. State U., 1989. Mem. AVMA (coun. on edn. 1985-91), Assn. Am. Vet. Med. Colls. (pres. 1982-83), Colo. Vet. Med. Assn. (Disting. Svc. award 1985), N.Y. State Vet. Med. Soc. (Centennial award 1990), Sigma Xi, Phi Zeta, Phi Kappa Phi, Gamma Sigma Delta. Home: 536 Cayuga Heights Rd Ithaca NY 14853 Office: Coll Vet Medicine Cornell U Ithaca NY 14853

PHEMISTER, THOMAS ALEXANDER, lawyer; b. Framingham, Mass., June 2, 1940; s. Robert Irving and Georgia Nora (Savignac) P.; m. Lois Ann Devol, Dec. 28, 1963; children: Michael Anderson, Elizabeth Lynn, Mary Nicole, Virginia Noel. B.A., Carleton Coll., 1962; J.D., U. Chgo., 1965. Bar: Ill., Colo. 1965. Pvt. practice law Chgo., 1965-69; gen. atty. Western R.R. Assn., Chgo., 1969-71; in law practice with Richard J. Hardy, Washington, 1972-73; gen. atty. Assn. Am. R.R.s, Washington, 1973-79; dir. Bur. Explosives Assn. Am. Railroads, 1979-85; sole practice Washington, 1985-87; lead hazardous materials atty. Office Chief Counsel Fed. R.R. Adminstrn., Washington, 1987—; mem. dept. of transp. intermodal hazardous materials attys. group, 1989—; mem. com. on transp. of hazardous materials Transp. Rsch. Bd., 1980-86; mem. aut. motor carrier adv. com. Fed. Hwy. Adminstrn., 1982-86; mem. Can. Nat. Rail Task Force for Movements of Dangerous Commodities, 1985; mem. hazardous materials control course oversight com. Tex. A&M U., 1981-87. Pub.: Emergency Handling of Hazardous Materials in Surface Transportation, 1981, Hazardous Materials Regulations Excerpted for Railroad Employees, 1981, Emergency Action Guides, 1983; author: A Report on Tank Cars: Federal Oversight of Design Construction and Repair, 1990, Forward through the 90s: A Report on Selected Issues in the Transportation by Rail of Hazardous Materials, 1994. Treas. Ill. Lawyers for McCarthy, 1968; trustee First Congregational Ch., Western Springs, Ill., 1970-71; mem. program ministries council United Christian Parish of Reston, Va., 1980-82, mem. South Lakes vestry, 1984-87, mem. parish bd., 1, deacon, ministries com., 1987-93; bd. dirs. Upper Room Emmaus of nat. capital area, 1989-90, lay leader, 1990; mem. Fairfax County Drug Task Force chpt. Parents Alliance to Neutralize Drug and Alcohol Abuse (PANDAA), 1987-89; adult advisor Fairfax County 4-H Horse Forum. Mem. Hunters Valley Riding Club (bd. dirs., v.p. 1993-94). Home: 10802 Dayflower Ct Reston VA 22091-5110 Office: 400 7th St SW Washington DC 20590-0001 *Integrity is an absolute essential - both preserving my own and dealing with other people so that they, too, do not have to compromise on matters of principle.*

PHENIS, NANCY SUE, educational administrator; b. Anderson, Ind., Oct. 29, 1943; d. Wilma (Anderson) Baker; m. Richard W. Phenis, June 11, 1966; 1 child, Heidi L. BA, Ind. State U., 1965; MA, Ball State U., 1974, postgrad., 1985. Elem. tchr. Highland Park (N.J.) Schs., 1966-68, Anderson City Schs., 1969-71; elem. tchr., tchr. gifted and talented South Madison Schs., Pendleton, Ind., 1974-85, elem. prin., 1985—. Bd. dirs. South Madison Community Found., Pendleton, 1991, First Am. Bank FirstGrant. Recipient Outstanding Contbn. award Internat. Reading Assn., 1991. Mem. NAEPS, AAUW (pres. 1985-87), Ind. Assn. Sch. Prins. (bd. dirs. 1994—), First Am. (bd. dirs. 1992-95), Phi Delta Kappa (historian 1987), Delta Kappa Gamma (sec. 1990-92, pres. 1992-94, LEadership/Adminstr. award 1993). Office: East Elem Sch 893 E Us Highway 36 Pendleton IN 46064-9802

PHIBBS, CLIFFORD MATTHEW, surgeon, educator; b. Bemidji, Minn., Feb. 20, 1930; s. Clifford Matthew and Dorothy Jean (Wright) P.; m. Patricia Jean Palmer, June 27, 1953; children—Wayne Robert, Marc Stuart, Nancy Louise. B.S., Wash. State U., 1952; M.D., U. Wash., 1955; M.S., U. Minn., 1960. Diplomate Am. Bd. Surgery. Intern Ancker Hosp., St. Paul, 1955-56; resident in surgery U. Minn. Hosps., 1956-60; practice medicine specializing in surgery Oxboro Clinic, Mpls., 1962—, pres., 1985—. Mem. Children's Hosp. Ctr., Northwestern-Abbott Hosp., Fairview-Southdale Hosp., Fairview Ridges Hosp.; clin. asst. prof. U. Minn., Mpls., 1975-78, clin. assoc. prof. surgery, 1978—; med. dir. Minn. Protective Life Ins. Co. Contbr. articles to med. jours. Bd. dirs. Bloomington Bd. Edn., Minn., 1974—, treas., 1976, sec., 1977-78, chmn., 1981-83; mem. adv. com. jr. coll. study City of Bloomington, 1964-66, mem. community facilities com., 1966-67, advisor youth study commn., 1966-68; vice chmn. bd. Hillcrest Meth. Ch., 1970-71; mem. Bloomington Adv. and Rsch. Coun., 1969-71; bd. dirs. Bloomington Symphony Orch., 1976—, Wash. State U. Found., trustee, 1990—; dir. bd. mgmt. Minnesota Valley YMCA, 1970-75; bd. govs. Mpls. Met. YMCA, 1970—; bd. dirs. Bloomington Heart-Health Found., 1989—, Martin Luther Manor, 1989; pres. Oxboro Clinics, 1985—; bd. dirs. Bloomington History Clock Tower Assn., 1990—; bd. dirs. Fairview Hosp. Clinic, 1994—. Capt. M.C. U.S. Army, 1960-62. Mem. ACS, AMA (Physician Recognition awards 1969, 73, 76, 79, 82, 85, 88, 91, 94), Assn. Surg. Edn., Royal Soc. Medicine, Am. Coll. Sports Medicine, Minn. Med. Assn. (del. 1991-94), Minn. Surg. Soc., Mpls. Surg. Soc., Hennepin County Med. Soc., Pan-Pacific Surg. Assn., Jaycees, Bloomington C. of C. (chmn. bd. 1984, chmn. 1985-86). Home: 9613 Upton Rd Minneapolis MN 55431-2454 Office: 600 W 98th St Minneapolis MN 55420-4773

PHIBBS, HARRY ALBERT, interior designer, professional speaker, lecturer; b. Denver, Jan. 9, 1933; s. Harry Andrew and Mary May (Perriam) P.; m. Alice Conners Glynn, Oct. 23, 1957 (div. Jan. 1988); children: Kathleen Ann, Paul Robert, Mary Alice, Michael John, Peter James, Daniel Edward; m. Nevelle Haley Jones, Feb. 1988. B.A., U. Colo., 1954, B.F.A., 1957. Interior designer Howard Lorton, Inc., Denver, 1957-68; interior designer, v.p. Ronald Ansay Inc., Wheatridge, Colo., 1969-71; interior designer, pres. Phibbs Design Assos., Inc., Denver, 1972-78; interior designer, mgr. Howard Lorton, Inc., Colorado Springs, Colo., 1979-93; prin. Phibbs Design, Colorado Springs, 1993—; pres. Interior Designers Housing Devel. Corp., 1969-72. V.p. Arvada (Colo.) Hist. Soc., 1973; bd. dirs. Colo. Opera Fes-

tival, also pres., 1986; bd. dirs. Downtown Colorado Springs, Inc., also pres., 1984; chmn. bd. trustees Interior Design Inst. Denver, 1991-94. With U.S. Army, 1954-56. Fellow Am. Soc. Interior Designers (nat. pres. 1977); mem. Am. Arbitration Assn., Theta Xi (pres. Denver Area alumni club 1958-64). Democrat. Roman Catholic. Home: 91 W Boulder St Colorado Springs CO 80903-3371 Office: 10 Boulder Cres Colorado Springs CO 80903 *Each of God's infinite creations was carefully placed on earth with the same responsibility....to grow. Man has the unique role in that plan in that he can help other things and the people around him to grow. This process is contingent upon "loving your neighbor as yourself." Transposing the equation therefore requires that you love yourself. I wish I had learned at an earlier age to take what you do seriously, but not to take yourself too seriously.*

PHILBIN, EDWARD JAMES, federal agency commissioner, military officer, legal educator, engineer; b. N.Y.C., Aug. 7, 1932; s. Harry B. and Carlotta Isabel (Matthews-Kratz) P. BS in Engring., San Diego State U., 1957; JD summa cum laude, U. San Diego, 1965; disting. grad., Air War Coll., 1978. Commd. 2d lt. USAF, 1957, advanced through grades to maj. gen., 1986; rsch. dir. res. forces policy bd. Dept. Def., 1980, dep. asst. sec. def., res. affairs, 1981-84; commr. Fed. Maritime Commn., 1984-90; chmn. ICC, Washington, 1990-93, commr., 1993—; design research engr. Gen. Dynamics, San Diego, 1957-60, physicist, sr. physicist, 1960-66; atty. Hecsh, Hegner & Philbin, San Diego, 1966-70; assoc. prof., asst. dean Law Sch. U. San Diego, 1970-73, prof. law, 1973-85; vis. prof. internat. law Air War Coll., 1978-79. Contbr. articles to profl. jours. Trustee San Diego Aerospace Mus., 1968-70; pres. Air Force Assn., San Diego, 1968-70; bd. trustees Air War Coll. Alumni, 1993—. Decorated Air Force DSM, Legion of Merit; recipient Gen. Orvil A. Anderson award Nat. Geog. Soc., 1978; St. Thomas More scholar, 1963-65, Dean's scholar, 1963-65. Mem. Navy League U.S. (dir. 1974-77), Res. Officers Assn., Nat. Guard Assn. of U.S., Calif. Bar Assn., San Diego County Bar Assn., RAF Club, Army Navy Club, Internat. Club, Theta Chi. Republican. Roman Catholic. Office: ICC 12th and Constitution Ave Washington DC 20423-0001

PHILBIN, REGIS, television personality; b. N.Y.C.; s. Frank and Florence P.; m. Kay Faylan, 1957 (div.); children: Amy, Danny; m. Joy Senese, Mar. 1, 1970; children: Joanna, Jennifer. Student, U. Notre Dame. Hollywood stagehand, NBC page The Tonight Show; truck driver, newswriter, sportscaster. co-host The Joey Bishop Show, 1967-69, host KABC Am. L.A., WABC TV Morning Show, 1983-88 (with Kathy Lee Gifford in 1985); cohost (syndicated show) Live! With Regis and Kathie Lee, 1988—, Miss Am. Pageant, 1991, 92; co-author: Cooking with Regis and Kathie Lee, 1993, Entertaining with Regis and Kathie Lee, 1994. Office: Regis & Kathie Lee ABC-TV 77 W 66th St New York NY 10023-6201*

PHILBRICK, DONALD LOCKEY, lawyer; b. Portland, Maine, May 3, 1923; s. Donald Ward and Ruth (Lockey) P.; children: Deborah Palmer, Sarah Peyton; adopted children: Paul Sloat, Mark Whitfield, Andrew Hunter; m. Janet Mitchell Poole, Aug. 7, 1982. A.B., Bowdoin Coll., 1944; J.D., Harvard U., 1948. Bar: Maine 1948. Pvt. practice Portland; ptnr. Verrill & Dana, 1951-82. Selectman, Cape Elizabeth, Maine, 1957-63. Served with AUS, 1943-45; with USAF, 1951-53. Mem. Maine Hist. Soc. (past pres.), N.E. Hist. Gen. Soc., Delta Kappa Epsilon. Republican. Congregationalist. Club: Portland Country. Home: 39 Wildwood Dr Cape Elizabeth ME 04107-1160 Office: 80 Exchange St Portland ME 04101-5035

PHILBRICK, MARGARET ELDER, artist; b. Northampton, Mass., July 4, 1914; d. David and Mildred (Pattison) Elder; m. Otis Philbrick, May 23, 1941 (dec. Apr. 1973); 1 child, Otis. Grad., Mass. Sch. Art, Boston, 1937; student, De Cordova Mus., Lincoln, Mass., 1966-67. Juror art shows; exhibited one woman show, Bare Cove Gallery, Hingham, Mass., 1979, Greenwich Garden Ctr., Cos Cob, Conn., 1981; retrospective exhbn. graphics, Ainsworth Gallery, Boston, 1972; exhibited 40 yr. retrospective, Westenhook Gallery, Sheffield, Mass., 1977, 50 yr. retrospective, 1985; group shows, Boston Printmakers 1948—, USIA tour to Far East, 1958-59, Boston Watercolor Soc., 1956—, Pratt Graphic Art Ctr., N.Y.C., 1966, New Eng. Watercolor Soc., 1982—; represented in permanent collections Nat. Mus. Fine Arts, Hanoi, Library of Congress, Washington, Boston Pub. Library, Nat. Bezalel Mus., Jerusalem; artist, designer: Wedgwood Commemorative Plates, Stoke-on-Trent, Eng., 1944-55, Nat. Mus. of Women in the Arts, Washington, Wiggin Collection Boston Pub. Library, The Margaret Philbrick Collection Westwood (Mass.) Pub. Libr.; illustrator books; exhibited "The Book as Art" Nat. Mus. of Women in the Arts, 1987, "The Book as Art II", 1989. Recipient purchase Libr. of Congress, 1948; recipient 1st graphics Acad. Artist, Springfield, Mass., 1957, Multum in Parvo Pratt-2d Internat. Miniature Print Exhbn., 1966, 1st prize in floral Miniature Art Soc. Fla., 1986, Ralph Fabri award. Mem. NAD (Ralph Fabri 1977), Boston Printmakers Presentation Print (exec. bd. 1951—), Acad. Artists, New Eng. Watercolor Soc., Miniature Painters, Washington Sculptors and Gravers Soc. (Founders award), Miniature Art Soc. N.J., Miniature Art Soc. Home and Office: 47 Westwood Glen Rd Westwood MA 02090-1614

PHILBRICK, RALPH, botanist; b. San Francisco, Jan. 1, 1934; s. Howard R. and Elizabeth (Jauckens) P.; children—Lauren P. Lester, Winston H., Edward W. B.A., Pomona Coll., 1956; M.A., UCLA, 1958; Ph.D., Cornell U., 1963. Research assoc. Cornell U., 1957-63; assoc. in botany U. Calif., Santa Barbara, 1963-64; biosystematist Santa Barbara Botanic Garden, 1964-73, dir., 1974-87, biol. cons., 1987—; research assoc. U. Calif., Santa Barbara, 1964-82. Mem. Santa Barbara County Planning Commn., 1981-85. Mem. Sigma Xi, Phi Kappa Phi. Office: 29 San Marcos Trout Clb Santa Barbara CA 93105-9726

PHILION, NORMAN JOSEPH, III, lawyer; b. Colchester, Vt., Jan. 2, 1946; s. Norman Joseph and Concetta Ann (D'Orazio) P.; m. Diane Marcia Yeager, May 9, 1974. A.B., Ind. U., 1972; J.D., Duke U., 1975. Bar: D.C. 1976, U.S. Dist. Ct. D.C., U.S. Ct. Appeals (D.C. cir.). Mem. firm Thompson, Hine & Flory, Washington, 1975—. Served with USAF, 1965-69. Mem. Assn. Transp. Practitioners (chmn. D.C. chpt. 1985-86), Am. Hist. Assn., Inst. Early Am. History and Culture, Orgn. Am. Historians, Phi Beta Kappa. Office: Thompson Hine & Flory 1920 N St NW Ste 700 Washington DC 20036-1601

PHILIP, A. G. DAVIS, astronomer, editor, educator; b. N.Y.C., Jan. 9, 1929; s. Van Ness and Lillian (Davis) P.; m. Kristina Drobavicius, Apr. 25, 1964; 1 dau., Kristina Elizabeth Elanor. B.S., Union Coll., 1951; M.S., N.Mex. State U., 1959; Ph.D., Case Inst. Tech., 1964. Tchr. physics, math. and chemistry Brooks Sch., 1954-59; instr. Case Inst. Tech., 1962-64; asst. prof. astronomy U. N.Mex., 1964-66, asst. prof. astronomy SUNY-Albany, 1966-67, assoc. prof., 1967-76, mem. exec. com. Arts and Scis. Coun., 1975—; prof. astronomy Union Coll., Schenectady, 1976—, astronomer Dudley Obs., 1967-81, Frank L. Fullam chair astronomy, 1980-81, editor Dudley Obs. Reports, 1977-81; astronomer Van Vleck Obs. Wesleyan U., 1982-94; editor contbns. VVObs., 1982-94; vis. prof. Yale U., 1972, 73, La. State U., 1973, 76, 86, Acad. Scis. Lithuania, USSR, 1973, 76, 79, 86, Stellar Data Ctr., Strasbourg, France, 1978, 79, 80, 82, 85, 86; vis. astronomer Moletsi Obs., 1988, 94; bd. dirs., sec.-treas. N.Y. Astron Corp.; pres., treas. L. Davis Press, Inc.; Inst. Space Observations, 1986—; trustee, mem. grants award com. Fund Astrophys. Rsch. of Am. Astron. Soc., 1985—; dir. Shapley Lectureship Program, 1994—. Exhibited: 2d Ann. Photography Regional, Albany, 1980; author: (with M. Cullen and R.E. White) UBV Color - Magnitude Diagrams of Galactic Globular Clusters, 1976; (with A. Robucci, M. Frame, K.W. Philip) Mm, Fractal Series, Vol. 1, Midgets on the Spike, 1991; editor: The Evolution of Population II Stars, 1972, (with D.S. Hayes) Multicolor Photometry and the Theoretical HR Diagram, 1975, (with M.F. Mc Carthy) Galactic Structure in the Direction of the Galactic Polar Caps, 1977, (with D. H. DeVorkin In Memory of Henry Norris Russell, 1977, (with Hayes) The HR Diagram, 1978, Problems in Calibration of Multicolor Systems, 1979, (with M.F. McCarthy and G.V. Coyne) Spectral Classification of the Future, 1979, X-Ray Symposium, 1981, (with Hayes) Astrophysical Parameters for Globular Clusters 1981, (with A.R. Upgren) The Nearby Stars and the Stellar Luminosity Function, 1983, (with Hayes and L. Pasinetti) Calibration of Fundamental Stellar Quantities, 1985, (with D.W. Latham) Stellar Radial Velocities, Horizontal-Branch and UV-Bright Stars, 1985, Spectroscopic and Photometric Classification of Population II Stars, 1986, (with J. Grindley) IAU Symposium No. 126, Globular Cluster Systems in Galaxies, 1987, (with Hayes and Liebert) IAU Colloquium No.

95, The Second Conference on Faint Blue Stars, (with Hayes and Adelman) New Directions in Spectrophotometry, 1988, Calibration of Stellar Ages, 1988, (with A.R. Upgren) Star Catalogues; A Centennial Tribute to A.N. Vyssotsky, 1989, (with P. Lu) The Gravitational Force Perpendicular to the Galactic Plane, 1989, (with D.S. Hayes and S.J. Adelman) CCDs in Astronomy. II. New Methods and applications of CCD Technology, 1990, (with A. R. Upgren and K.A. Janes) Precision Photometry: Astrophysics of the Galaxy, 1991, (with Robucci, Frame and Philip K.) Midgets on the Spike, vol. I, 1991, (with A.R. Upgren) Objective-Prism and Other Surveys, 1991, N.Y. State Astronomy, 1992, (with B. Hauck and A.R. Upgren) Workshop on Databases for Galactic Structure, 1993, (with K. A. Janes and A. R. Upgren) IAU Symposium No. 167, New Developments in Array Technology and Applications, 1995; lectr. tours (with K.W. Philip) An Introduction to the Mandelbrot Set, 1988-91; contbr. chpts. to books, articles to profl. jours. Served with AUS, 1951-53. Yale U. vis. fellow, 1976; rsch. grantee Rsch. Corp., NSF, NASA, Nat. Rsch. Lab., NAS, am. Astron. Soc. Fellow AAAS, Royal Astron. Soc., Am. Phys. Soc.; mem. Am. Astron. Soc. (Harlow Shapley lectr. 1973-94, auditor 1977, 79-85), Am. Math. Soc., Can. Astron. Soc., Internat. Astron. Union (chmn., sec. various coms. and commns., pres. commn. 30 1982-85, chmn. working group on spectroscopic and photometric data 1985-94, chmn. sci. organizing com. symposium # 167), N.Y. Acad. Scis., Astron. Soc. Pacifistron. Soc. N.Y. (sec.-treas. 1969—, editor newsletter 1974—), Capital Computer Club (bd. dirs. 1990—, v.p. 1993—), Sigma Xi. Achievements include being 1st U.S. observer Soviet 6M telescope, 1980. Home: 1125 Oxford Pl Schenectady NY 12308-2913 Office: Union Coll Physics Dept Schenectady NY 12308

PHILIP, JAMES (PATE PHILIP), state senator; b. May 26, 1930; married; 4 children. Student, Kansas City Jr. Coll., Kans. State Coll. Ret. dist. sales mgr. Pepperidge Farm, Inc.; rep. State of Ill., 1967-74, senator, 1975—; asst. senate minority leader, 1979, senate minority leader, 1981-93, senate pres., 1993—; chmn. DuPage County Rep. Ctrl. Com.; committeeman Addison Twp. Precinct 52; past Jr. Nat. Rep. Committeeman. Past dir. Nat. Found. March of Dimes; past gen. chmn. Elmhurst March of Dimes; spl. events chmn. DuPage Heart Assn.; mem. DuPage Menl. Hosp. Century Club; dir. Ray Graham Assn. Handicapped Children; mem. bd. sponsors Easter Seal Treatment Ctr.; active Lombard YMCA; bd. dirs. Danada Sculpture Garden. With USMC, 1950-53. Recipient Ill. Coun. on Aging award, 1989, Leaders of 90's award Downers Grove Twp., 1989, Man of Yr. award United Hellenic Voters Am., 1989, Legis. of Yr. award Ill. County Treas.'s Assn., 1990, Tax$avers award Ill. Assn. County Auditors, 1990, Statesman of Yr. award Internat. Union of Operating Engrs. Local 150, 1991, Friend of Youth award Assn. Ill. Twp. Com. on Youth, 1991, Spl. Svc. award Serenity House, 1991, Recognition award DuPage Ctr. Independent Living, 1991. Mem. Am. Legion, Ill. Young Reps. (past pres.), DuPage County Young Rep. Fedn. (past chmn.), DuPage County Marine Corps League (life), DuPage Indsl. and Mfg. Assn. (past dir.), Suburban Bus. Mgmt. Coun. (past v.p.), Mil. Order Devil Dogs, Gravert Mgmt. and Sales Exec. Club Chgo., Exec. Club DuPage County, Shriners, Elks, Masons, Order of DeMolay (life), Moose. Office: Ill State Senate 327 S State St Springfield IL 62704-1756

PHILIP, PETER VAN NESS, former trust company executive; b. N.Y.C., Feb. 23, 1925; s. Van Ness and Lilian (Davis) P.; m. Sabina FitzGibbon, May 3, 1952; children: William Van Ness, Thomas Winslow, Peter Sandys. AB, Yale U., 1945W; MBA, NYU, 1950. With Price, Waterhouse & Co., N.Y.C., 1947-52; W.H. Morton & Co., Inc., N.Y.C., 1952-73; pres., CEO Equitable Securities, Morton & Co., Inc., 1970-73; sr. v.p., dir. White Weld & Co., Inc., N.Y.C., 1974-76; v.p. Morgan Guaranty Trust Co., N.Y.C., 1977-88, ret. With 86th inf. div. AUS, 1943-45. Decorated Purple Heart, Bronze Star. Clubs: Racquet and Tennis (N.Y.C.); Links; Yale (N.Y.C.), Downtown Assn. (N.Y.C.), Bond (N.Y.C.); Bedford ((N.Y.); Golf and Tennis; Ekwanok (Manchester, Vt.). Home: Guard Hill Rd Bedford NY 10506

PHILIP, THOMAS PETER, mining executive; b. Bellville, Cape, Republic South Africa, Feb. 5, 1933; came to U.S., 1984; s. David Henderson and Nora (VanWyk) P.; m. Adriana van Schalkwyk, Dec. 3, 1954 (div. 1982); children: Wayne, Lorinda, Lynette, Debra. BSMetE, U. Ariz., 1958. Asst. gen. mgr. Tsumeb Corp., Namibia, 1970-74; gen. mgr. O'okiep Copper Co., Nababeep, Republic South Africa, 1975-84; chief exec. officer O'okiep Copper Co., Nababeep, 1981-84, also bd. dirs.; exec. v.p., gen. mgr. Carlin (Nev.) Gold Mining Co., 1984-85; pres. Newmont Gold Co., Carlin, 1985—, also bd. dirs.; sr. v.p. Newmont Mining Corp., N.Y.C., 1986—; bd. dirs. Newmont Autstralia, Ltd., Melbourne. Fellow South Africa Inst. Mining and Metallurgy; mem. Soc. Mining Engring., Denver Club, Namutoni Club (master 1971). Avocations: sailing, golf, carpentry. Home: 5403 S Fulton Cir Englewood CO 80111-3660 Office: Newmont Mining Corp 1700 Lincoln St Denver CO 80203-4501

PHILIP, WILLIAM WARREN, banker; b. Tacoma, Oct. 26, 1926; s. Warren F. and Lillian (Lehman) P.; m. Dorothy Mary Mitchell, Oct. 14, 1954; children: Cynthia Ann, Susan Kelly. Student, U. Wash., 1946-47; grad., Pacific Coast Banking Sch., 1961; postgrad., Pacific Luth. U. 1987. With Puget Sound Nat. Bank, Tacoma, 1951—; pres. Puget Sound Nat. Bank, 1971—, chmn., 1979—; bd. Fed. Res. Bd. San Francisco; chmn. Pierce County, Savs. Bond div. Treasury Dept. Bd. dirs. Lakewood Water Dist., Tacoma Pierce County Econ. Devel.; chmn. Multicare Hosp. Tacoma; chmn. bus. adv. bd. Pacific Luth. U.; past chmn. bd. Mary Bridge Children's Hosp. Mem. Wash. Roundtable, Tacoma Golf and Country Club, Rainier Club, Columbia Tower Club, Canterwood Golf and Country Club. Office: Puget Sound Nat Bank 1119 Pacific Ave Tacoma WA 98402-4374

PHILIPP, FRED A., publishing executive; b. Detroit, Mar. 20, 1938; s. Frederick Philipp and Pauline Julia (Matzo) Fisher; m. Judith Ann Healy, June 28, 1959; children: Scott F., Terri L., Keith T. BS, Tri-State U., Angola, Inc., 1959. Various fin. positions U.S. Steel Corp., Gary, Ind. and Chgo., 1959-67; sr. v.p. Baker and Taylor Co. div. W.R. Grace and Co., N.Y.C., 1968-86; pres. Ingram Libr. Svc., pres. Ingram Internat. Nashville, 1987-89; pres., CEO Blackwell N.Am., Inc., Lake Oswego, Oreg., 1990—; dir. Book Industry Study Group, N.Y.C., 1980-83; v.p., dir. Friends of Librs. USA, Phila., 1986-90; dir. Blackwell N.A. Lake Oswego, 1990-95; advisor, cons. U.S. Info. Agy., Washington, 1990-92. Served to sgt. USAR, 1956-62. Recipient Disting. Svc. award Tri-State U., 1982, Spl. Merit award Friends of Librs. USA, 1990, Spl. Merit award U.S. Info. Agy., 1992. Mem. Am. Libr. Assn., Am. Bookseller Assn. Avocations: golf, swimming, reading, travel. Home: 6321 Chickering Woods Dr Nashville TN 34215 Office: Blackwell NAm Inc 6024 SW Jean Rd Lake Oswego OR 97035

PHILIP, WALTER VIKTOR, mathematician, educator; b. Vienna, Dec. 14, 1936; came to U.S., 1963, naturalized, 1974; s. Oskar and Anna Julie (Krasucky) P.; m. Ariane Randell, Dec. 10, 1984; children: Petra, Robert, Anthony, Andre. MS in Math. and Physics, PhD in Math., U. Vienna, 1960. Asst. U. Vienna, 1960-63, 65-67 dozent, 1967; asst. prof. U. Mont., 1963-64; vis. asst. prof. U. Ill., Urbana, 1964-65; mem. faculty U. Ill., 1967—, prof. math., 1973—, prof. stats. 1988—, chmn. dept. stats., 1990—; vis. prof. U. N.C., Chapel Hill, 1972, 88, MIT, 1980, Tufts U., 1981, U. Göttingen, 1982, 85, Imperial Coll., London, 1985; adv. bd. Monatshefte für Mathmatik, 1994—. Associate editor Annals of Probability, 1976-81. Fellow Inst. Math. Stats.; mem. Am. Math. Soc., Australian Math. Soc., Internat. Statis. Inst., Am. Statis. Assn., Australian Acad. Scis. (corr. mem.). Avocations: mountaineering. Home: 1922 Maynard Dr Champaign IL 61821-5265 Office: U Ill Champaign IL 61821

PHILIPPI, ERVIN WILLIAM, mortician; b. Lodi, Calif., June 4, 1922; s. William and Rebecca (Steinert) P.; m. Emma Grace Mosely, May 8, 1958 (div. Mar. 1979); m. Helen Jo Hunt, June 3, 1979. Grad., Calif. Coll. Motuary Sci., 1948. Embalmer, mortician, mgr. Salas Bros. Chapel, Modesto, Calif., 1946-92; dep. coroner Stanislaus County, Calif., 1955-75. With U.S. Army, 1942-46. Avocations: old car restoration, travel.

PHILIPPS, EDWARD WILLIAM, banker, real estate appraiser; b. N.Y.C., Dec. 19, 1938; s. Edward Charles and Eleanor Elizabeth (Eisenger) P.; m. Diane Rose DiCuffa, June 12, 1960; children: James Michael, Robert Christopher. Appraiser Dry Dock Savs., N.Y.C., 1956-70, Nat. Bank of West, White Plains, N.Y., 1970-72, Aires Real Estate, Yonkers, N.Y., 1972-74; sr.

v.p. Am. Savs. Bank (merger Empire Savs. Bank), N.Y.C., 1974-92; self employed real estate appraiser Yonkers, 1992-93; sr. v.p., chief lending officer Stamford (Conn.) Fed. Savs., 1993—; mem. mortgage com. Cmty. Preservation Corp., N.Y.C., 1990-92. Mem. Am. Inst. Real Estate Appraisers, Homebuilders Assn. Fairfield County (bd. dirs.). Avocations: wood working, fishing. Home: 261 Kimball Ave Yonkers NY 10704-3030 Office: 999 Bedford St Stamford CT 06905

PHILIPPS, LOUIS EDWARD, data systems manufacturing company executive; b. Duluth, Minn., Feb. 7, 1906; s. Carl Frederick Ferdin and Sarah Margueithe (Mortenson) P.; m. Gladys Victoria Monsen, Nov. 13, 1930. Student pub. schs., Duluth. Engr. Cleve. Radioelectric Co., 1946-48; v.p., gen. mgr. Radio Systems, Inc., Cleve., 1948-50, Royal Communications, Inc., Cleve., 1950-56; dir. engring. Auth Electric Co., N.Y.C., 1956-59; chief engr. hosp. products div. Motorola-Dahlberg Co., Mpls., 1959-63; founder, pres., chmn. bd. Medelco Inc., Schiller Park, Ill., 1964-74; founder, 1975; since chmn. bd., dir. Datx Corp., Chgo.; dir. sales, chmn. bd. Smart Controllers, Inc., Skokie, Ill., 1985—; cons. to health care industry. Contbr. to profl. jours. Named Father of Hosp. Systems Industry Am. Hosp. Assn., 1974. Sr. mem. IEEE. Republican. Presbyterian. Clubs: Anvil (E. Dundee, Ill.); Order Eastern Star (Robbinsdale, Minn.), Masons (Robbinsdale, Minn.); Masons (Chgo.), Shriners (Chgo.). Patentee pulsed audio signaling, radio nurse system, data handling system. Home: 31 W Diversey Ave Addison IL 60101-3527 Office: Datx Corp 303 E Ohio St Chicago IL 60611-3317 *My wife's faith and encouragement to use defeat as a stepping stone to success made it possible for me to reach my goals. Encouraging and teaching employees also played an important part.*

PHILIPS, DAVID EVAN, English language educator; b. Wilkes-Barre, Pa., Aug. 30, 1926; s. Jesse Evan and Edith Kathleen (Stone) P.; m. Janet Briggs Walker, Aug. 19, 1950; children: Evan Walker, Donald David, Kimberly Anne. B.A., Haverford Coll, 1950; M.A., Johns Hopkins U., 1952; postgrad., U. Pa., 1953-56. Instr. English Tufts U., 1956-62; asst. prof. English Ea. Conn. State U., Willimantic, 1962-68, assoc. prof. 1968-80, prof., 1980-90, prof. emeritus, 1990—; head dept., 1966-68, 81-83, dir. Office Pub. Affairs, 1965-67, dir. freshman writing program, 1978-79; profl. storyteller, 1984—. Co-author: A Guide to College Writing Skills, 1979; author: Legendary Connecticut: Traditional Tales from the Nutmeg State, 1984, paperback reprint, 1992; book and author citation Conn. Gen. Assembly, 1994; bbook rev. columnist: Down East, 1956-87, contbg. editor, 1979-87; assoc. editor: Conn. History, 1972-75, 82-85, editor, 1986-87. Chmn. Windham (Conn.) Devel. and Indsl. Commn., 1965-68; bd. dirs. Conn. Assn. Mcpl. Devel. Commns., 1965-68, Vis. Nurse Assn., Windham, 1968-72; mem. Windham Dem. Town Com., 1968-85, 90—, sec., 1972-74, 82-84, sec. 1978-82; mem. Windham Charter Commn., 1969-71, vice chmn., 1970-71; bd. dirs. Windham Sch. Dist., 1971-79, vice chmn., 1975-79; mem. Windham Zoning Commn., 1982-83; mem. Windham Planning Commn., 1983—, chmn., 1988—; mem. Windham Hist. Soc., 1985—, bd. dirs., 1991-94. With U.S. Merchant Marine, 1944-51; lt. USNR, 1951-53. Danforth Found. Tchr. Study grantee, 1960-61, summer 1963. Mem. AAUP (sec.-treas. Conn. State conf. 1963-65, sec. 1966-68, Emeritus Assembly 1990—, treas. 1991—), Conn. State Employees Assn. (sr. v.p. 1971-73), N.E. Folklore Soc., Conn. Hist. Soc. Democrat. Unitarian. Home: 7 Antrim Rd RFD 1 Willimantic CT 06226

PHILIPS, MALCOLM H., lawyer; b. Alexandria, La., Sept. 20, 1945. BS, U.S. Military Acad., 1967; MS, Iowa State U., 1971; JD, Georgetown U., 1978. Bar: D.C. 1978, Md. 1979; registered profl. engr. Tex., 1974. Plant mgr. SM-1 Nuclear Power Plant, 1973-74; mgr. program devel. dept. NUS Corp., 1974-78; ptnr. Winston & Strawn, Washington, 1978—; coun. govts. Transp. adv. com., 1976-77. With U.S. Army, 1967-74. Office: 5901 Serenity Ln Rockville MD 20855

PHILIPSBORN, JOHN DAVID, former banker, consultant; b. Chgo., Sept. 8, 1919; s. Martin Max and Amy (Dinkelspeil) P.; m. Edwige Auffret, Dec. 16, 1963; children: John Timothy, Christopher E. Grad., Francis W. Parker Sch., Chgo., 1938, Harvard U., 1942. With Office of Sec. Dept. State, 1947-49; joined U.S. fgn. service, 1949; vice consul Am. embassy, Paris, France, 1949-50; asst. commul. attache Am. embassy, 1950-51, asst. labor attach, 1951-55; 1st sec., 1958-64; assigned Dept. State, Washington, 1955-58; v.p. Chase-Manhattan Bank, N.Y.C., 1964-92; v.p. Geneva, Brussels, London Chase-Manhattan Bank, 1981-92, dir. internat. rels., 1981-92. Served to maj. USAAF, 1941-47. Mem. Harvard Club (N.Y.C.), Bucks Club (London). Office: Chase Manhattan Bank, Woolgate House Coleman St, London England EC2P 2HD

PHILIPSON, HERMAN LOUIS, JR., investment banker; b. Dallas, May 14, 1924; s. Herman Louis and Lillian (Adler) P.; m. Sonia Topletz, July 20, 1955; children: Cynthia Ann, Leslie, Nancy, Julie. B.S., Tex. A&M U. 1946; postgrad., Harvard Sch. Bus. Adminstrn., 1947-48. Pres. Philipson's, Inc., 1946-56; pres. Nat. Data Processing Corp., 1957-60, chmn. bd., 1960-61; chmn. bd. Techno-Growth Capital Corp., 1962-72; pres. Recognition Internat. Inc., Dallas, 1961-73; vice chmn. Recognition Equipment Inc., 1976-83; pres. Internat. Bus. Devel. Ltd., Dallas, 1973—, IBDL, Inc., Dallas, 1979—. Mem. Dallas Citizens Coun., also v.p. mem. exec. com.; bd. dirs. Dallas County Camp Fire Girls; trustee So. Meth. U. Found. for Sci. and Engring.; mem. engring. adv. and devel. coun. Tex. A&M U. 1st Lt. AUS, 1943-46. Decorated Bronze Star, Purple Heart with cluster; recipient Dallas Exporter of Yr. award, 1970, Ernest Thompson Seton award, 1975; named to Tex. A&M U. Acad. Disting. Mech. Engring. Grads. Mem. Dallas C. of C. (world trade com.), Japan-Tex. Assn. Lodges: Masons, Shriners. Patentee in field. Home: 9100 Rockbrook Dr Dallas TX 75220-3907 Office: Internat Bus Devel Ltd 1545 W Mockingbird Ln Dallas TX 75235-5014

PHILIPSON, WILLARD DALE, curriculum and instructional educator; b. Sleepy Eye, Minn., Mar. 18, 1930; s. Walter and Alice Anna (Rasmussen) P.; m. Sylvia Eileen Olson, Sept. 26, 1953; children: Andrew Will, Jennifer Dale, Pamela Elizabeth. B.S., U. Minn., 1953, M.A., 1959, Ph.D., 1967. Instr. agrl. engring. U. Minn., Morris, 1959; audio visual materials adv. Audio Visual Edn. Service, Mpls., 1960-63; assoc. prof., head mitl. film library No. Ill. U., DeKalb, 1963-66; mem. faculty U. Minn., Mpls., 1966-95, prof. emeritus, 1995—; prof. curriculum and instrn. systems U. Minn., 1978-94, dir. audio visual library services, 1966-78, architect microcomputer info. systems network, 1978-88; spl. projects dir. U. Minn., Mpls., 1988-93; mem. Minn. Civil Service Exec. Mgmt. Tng. Commn., 1969-71; mem. legis. com. Minn. Citizens for Libraries, 1976-91. Editor: Audi0-Visual Jour, 1966-78. Trustee Ramsey County Pub. Libr., 1992-95; active local Boy Scouts Am., 1972-75, chmn. fund dr., 1974-75. Capt. USNR, 1953-85. Recipient Gov. of Minn. Service award, 1969; Adult Educator of Yr. award Minn. Adult Edn., 1973; Silver Reel award Consortium U. Film Centers, 1979; Sears, Roebuck & Co. scholar, 1952. Mem. ASCD, Assn. Edni. Commun. and Tech., Adult Edn. Assn., Minn. Ednl. Media Orgn., Naval Res. Assn., Am. Legion (vice comdr., coun. local post 1991-95), Alpha Tau Alpha. Home: 1960 10th St Saint Paul MN 55110-6636 Office: U Minn Wesbrook Hall 77 Pleasant St SE Minneapolis MN 55455-0216

PHILLABAUM, LESLIE ERVIN, publisher; b. Cortland, N.Y., June 1, 1936; s. Vern Arthur and Beatrice Elizabeth (Butterfield) P.; m. Roberta Kimbrough Swarr, Mar. 17, 1962; children—Diane Melissa, Scott Christopher. B.S., Pa. State U., 1958, M.A., 1963. Editor Pa. State U. Press, 1961-63; editor-in-chief U. N.C. Press, 1963-70; assoc. dir., editor La. State U. Press, Baton Rouge, 1970-75; dir. La. State U. Press, 1975—. Served to 1st lt. AUS, 1959-61. Mem. Assn. Am. Univ. Presses (dir. 1978-80, 83-86, pres. 1984-85), So. Hist. assn., Acacia, Omicron Delta Kappa, Alpha Kappa Psi. Democrat. Home: 950 S Foster Dr Apt 48 Baton Rouge LA 70806-7150 Office: La State U Press Baton Rouge LA 70893

PHILLIPP, WENDELL CRANE, editor; b. Zionsville, Ind., July 4, 1918; s. Jesse F. and Bernice (Brock) P.; m. Georgiana Pittman, Jan. 10, 1942 (dec. July 10, 1978); children—Frank, Ann; m. Barbara Jean Caniff Howden, Oct. 30, 1980. A.B., Ind. U., 1940. Copy editor Indpls. News, 1940-46, state editor, 1946-47, city editor, 1947-52, asst. mng. editor, 1952-62, mng. editor, 1962-84; Pres. Ind. A.P., 1957; dir. Mid-Am. Press Inst., 1969-84; bd. dirs. A.P. Mng. Editors Assn., 1963-66, 69-72, v.p., 1971, pres., 1972; mem. Pulitzer Prize in Journalism Jury, 1971, 75, 76. Author: Dear Ike, 1991.

Pres. Ind. Armory Bd., 1968-73; bd. dirs. 500 Festival, v.p., 1963-65; mem. Ind. U. Daily Student Bd., 1968-77; sr. warden Episcopal Ch., 1966, 69, 71. Maj. AUS, 1941-45; maj. gen. Res. Decorated Silver Star, Bronze Star with cluster, Purple Heart. Mem. VFW, NG Assn. U.S. and Ind. (pres. 1953-55), Army Assn. Ind. (pres. 1957-58), Assn. U.S. Army, Indpls. C. of C., Am. Soc. Newspaper Editors, Am. Legion, Ind. U. Alumni Assn. (mag. bd. 1967-81), Soc. Ret. Execs., Econ. Club of Indpls., Indpls. Columbia, Ft. Harrison, Blue Key, Sigma Nu, Sigma Delta Chi. Episcopalian. Home: 2244 Rome Dr Indianapolis IN 46208-3240

PHILLIPS, ADRAN ABNER (ABE PHILLIPS), geologist, oil and gas exploration consultant; b. Sugden, Okla., Feb. 6, 1924; s. James M. and Jennie Elizabeth (Norman) P.; m. Carmel Darlene Pesterfield, Aug. 20, 1949 (div.); 1 son, John David. B.S. in Geology, U. Okla., 1949. With Exxon Corp. and affiliates, 1949-79, dist. geologist, Chico, Calif. 1959-64, ops. geologist, Sydney, Australia, 1964-67, exploration coordinator North Slope Alaska, Houston, 1968-70, div. geologist, Denver, 1970-71, exploration mgr. P.T. Inc., Stanvac, Jakarta, Indonesia, 1971-73, exploration mgr. ESSO exploration, Singapore, 1973-76; div. mgr. Exxon U.S.A., Denver, 1976-79; v.p. Coors Energy div., Golden, Colo., 1979-80, pres., 1980-92; oil and gas exploration cons., 1992—. Bd. dirs. Mountain States Legal Found., 1991—. Mem. Am. Assn. Petroleum Geologists, Ind. Petroleum Assn. Mountain States (past pres.), Ind. Petroleum Assn. Am. (dir.), Nat. Coal Council. Home and Office: 2194 S Augusta Dr Evergreen CO 80439-8923

PHILLIPS, ALMARIN, economics educator, consultant; b. Port Jervis, N.Y., Mar. 13, 1925; s. Wendell Edgar and Hazel (Billett) P.; m. Dorothy Kathryn Burns, June 14, 1947 (div. 1976); children: Almarin Paul, Frederick Peter, Thomas Rock, David John, Elizabeth Linett, Charles Samuel; m. Carole Cherry Greenberg, Dec. 19, 1976. B.S., U. Pa., 1948, M.A., 1949; Ph.D., Harvard, 1953. Instr. econs. U. Pa., 1948-50, 51-53, asst. prof. econs., 1953-56, prof. econs. and law, 1963-91; Hower prof. pub. policy U. Pa, 1981-91; chmn. dept. econs. U. Pa., 1968-71, 72-73, assoc. dean Wharton Sch., 1973-74, dean Sch. Pub. and Urban Policy, 1974-77, chair faculty senate, 1990-91; teaching fellow Harvard, 1950-51; assoc. prof. U. Va. 1956-61, prof., 1961-63; vis. prof. U. Hawaii, summer 1968, U. Warwick, London Grad. Sch. Bus. Studies, 1972, Ohio State U., McGill U., 1978, Calif. Inst. Tech, Northwestern U., 1980, Ariz. Coll. Law, 1987, Inst. Europeén d'Adminstrn. des Affairs (INSEAD), France, spring 1990; co-dir. Pres.'s Commn. Fin. Structure and Regulation, 1970-71; mem. Nat. Commn. Electronic Fund Transfers, 1976-77; chmn. bd. Econsult Corp., 1990—. Author: (with R.W. Cabell) Problems in Basic Operations Research Methods for Management, 1961, Market Structure, Organization and Performance, 1962, Technology and Market Structure: A Study of the Aircraft Industry, 1971, (with P. Phillips and T.R. Phillips) Biz Jets: Technology and Market Structure in the Corporate Jet Aircraft Industry, 1994; Editor: Perspectives on Antitrust Policy, 1965, (with O.E. Williamson) Prices: Issues in Theory, Practice and Policy, 1968, Promoting Competition in Regulated Markets, 1975 ; editor Jour. Indsl. Econs., 1974-90; Contbr. articles to tech. lit. Served with AUS, 1943-45. Decorated Purple Heart, Bronze Star. Fellow Am. Statis. Assn., AAAS; mem. Am. Econ. Assn., Econometric Soc., European Econ. Assn., Internat. Telecommunications Soc. (bd. dirs. 1990—). Home: 1115 Remington Rd Wynnewood PA 19096-4021

PHILLIPS, ANTHONY FRANCIS, lawyer; b. Hartford, Conn., May 18, 1937; s. Frank and Lena Phillips; m. Rosemary Karran McGowan, Jan. 28, 1967; children: Karran, Antonia, Justin. BA, U. Conn., 1959; JD, Cornell U., 1962. Bar: N.Y. 1964, U.S. Dist. Ct. (so. dist., ea. dist) N.Y. 1965, (ctrl. dist.) Calif. 1980, U.S. Tax Ct. 1981, U.S. Ct. Appeals (2nd cir.) 1967, (3d cir.) 1985, (4th cir.) 1983, (5th cir.) 1972, (7th cir.) 1987, (9th cir.) 1983, (10th cir.) 1983, U.S. Supreme Ct. 1971. Assoc. Willkie, Farr & Gallagher, N.Y.C., 1963-69, ptnr., 1969—. Mem. adv. com. Cornell U. Law Sch., 1994—. Internat. law chmn. mem. ABA, N.Y. State Bar Assn., N.Y. County Bar Assn. (bd. dirs. 1989-95), Assn. of Bar of City of N.Y. Home: 3 Elm Rock Rd Bronxville NY 10708-4202 Office: Willkie Farr & Gallagher 1 Citicorp Ctr 153 E 53rd St New York NY 10022-4611

PHILLIPS, ANTHONY GEORGE, neurobiology educator; b. Barrow, Cumbria, Eng., Jan. 30, 1943; came to Can., 1953; s. George William and Mabel Lilian (Wood) P. BA (hon.), U. Western Ont., London, Can., 1966, MA, 1967, PhD, 1970. Asst. prof. psychobiology U. British Columbia, Vancouver, Can., 1970-75, assoc. prof., 1975-80, prof., 1980—; head dept. psychology, 1994—; founder Quadra Logic Tech., Inc., Vancouver. Contbr. over 175 papers to scientific jours. Chmn. Can.-India Village Aid, Vancouver, 1981-86, bd. dirs. 1987—; bd. dirs. Tibetian Refuge Aid Soc., Vancouver, 1980—. Recipient Killam rsch. prize Can. Coun., 1977, Killam Rsch. prize U. B.C., 1986; Steacie fellow Nat. Scis. and Engring. Rsch. Coun. (Can.), 1980. Fellow Royal Soc. Can.; mem. Soc. Neurosci., Can. Soc. for Neurosci., Can. Coll. Neuropsychopharmacology. Office: U BC Dept Psychology, 2136 W Mall, Vancouver, BC Canada V6T 1Z4

PHILLIPS, ANTHONY MARK, auction house executive; b. London, Oct. 31, 1945; s. Eric Lawrance and Phyllis Mary (Bray) P.; m. Penelope Ann Davies, 1970 (div. 1974); m. Sara Prior, Dec. 31, 1976; children: Luke Alexander, Isobel Julia. BA, Oxford U., 1967. Asst. silver dept. Christie, Manson and Woods, London, 1967-72, asst. silver dept., head objects of vertu dept., 1972-76; head silver dept., v.p. Christie's, Internat., Inc., N.Y.C., 1976-79, v.p., dir., 1980-81, sr. v.p., dir., 1981—, dir. decorative arts dept., 1984-89, dir. specialist depts., 1990—. Author numerous sales catalogs including the Morgan Collection-Silver, 1982, The Firestone Collection-Gold Boxes, 1982; co-author: The Patino Collection-Silver, 1987. Mem. Freeman of City of London, Freeman of Worshipful Co. Goldsmiths. Office: Christies Internat Inc 502 Park Ave New York NY 10022-1108

PHILLIPS, ARTHUR WILLIAM, JR., biology educator; b. Claremont, N.H., Sept. 25, 1915; s. Arthur William and Jane Helen (Daley) P.; m. Mary Catherine Mich, Oct. 21, 1950; children: Marilynn, William (dec.). BS, U. Notre Dame, 1939, MS, 1941; DSc, MIT, 1947. Rsch. asst. Lobund lab. U. Notre Dame, Ind., 1937-41; rsch. scientist, 1943-45; rsch. assoc. MIT, 1947-49; rsch. assoc. prof., head biol. bioengring. Lobund lab. U. Notre Dame, 1949-54; rsch. scientist dept. biology and bioengring. MIT, Cambridge, 1942-43, rsch. fellow dept. food tech., 1945-47, rsch. assoc. dept. food tech., 1947-49; rsch. assoc. prof. dept. bacteriology Syracuse (N.Y.) U., 1954-58, prof. microbiology, 1959-86, prof. emeritus, 1986—, founder, dir. biol. rsch. labs., 1955-65, head radiation and isotope lab., 1956-63, dir. germ-free life rsch. lab., 1956-84; mem. Internat. Congress on Nutrition, Washington, 1960, Internat. Congress for Microbiology, Montreal, Can., 1962, Moscow, 1966, Internat. Congress for Germ-Free Life Rsch., Nagoya, Japan, 1967; mem. com. on nutrition NAS-NRC, Washington, 1964-66; mem. Conf. on Germ-Free Life and Gnobiotics, Madison, Wis., 1986, Internat. Conf. on Gnotobiology, Versailles, France, 1987; cons. NSF, Washington, Cradle Soc. Inc., Evanston, Ill., GE, Syracuse, Am. Cyanamid, Pearl River, N.Y., Carnation Co., L.A., C.V. Mosby, St. Louis, Can. Dry Corp., Greenwich, Conn., Chocolate Mfrs. Assn., Washington, Continental Can Co., Syracuse. Contbr. articles to profl. jours., chpts. to books. Refrigeration Rsch. Found. fellow, 1945-47; NIH grantee, 1956-84. Mem. Am. Soc. for Microbiology (placement com. 1968-78), Gnotobiotics Assn., Soc. for Gen. Microbiology. Avocations: history, genealogy, hiking. Home: Clark Hollow Rd East Poultney VT 05741-0604 Office: Syracuse U Dept Biology 108 College Pl Syracuse NY 13244-1270

PHILLIPS, BARNET, IV, lawyer; b. New York, N.Y., July 5, 1948; s. Barnet III and Isabelle (Auriema) P.; m. Sharon Walsted Packey, Jan. 2, 1981; children: Victoria Ilonka, Caroline Walsted. BA, Yale U., 1970; JD, Fordham U., 1973; LLM, NYU, 1977. Bar: N.Y. 1974. Assoc. Hughes Hubbard & Reed, N.Y.C., 1973-76; assoc. Skadden, Arps, Slate, Meagher & Flom, N.Y.C., 1977-81, ptnr., 1981—; adj. assoc. prof. Forham U., N.Y.C., 1987-88; articles editor The Tax Lawyer, 1989-91. Co-author: Structuring Corporate Acquisition - Tax Aspects. Bd. dirs Student/Sponsor Partnership N.Y.C.; bd. cons. Portsmouth (R.I.) Abbey Sch. Republican. Avocations: skiing, opera, triathlons. Home: 6 Hycliff Rd Greenwich CT 06831-3223 Office: Skadden Arps Slate Meagher & Flom 919 3d Ave New York NY 10022

PHILLIPS, BARRY, lawyer; b. Valdosta, Ga., Feb. 16, 1929; s. W. Otis and Gypsy (Mercer) P.; m. Grace Greer, Aug. 3, 1957; children: Mary

Grace, Barry Jr., Greer, Quinton. AB, U. Ga., 1949, LLB, 1954. Bar: Ga. 1951, D.C. 1977. Assoc. Kilpatrick & Cody, Atlanta, 1954-60, ptnr., 1960—; bd. dirs., mem. exec. com., credit com. Bank South Corp. Mem. bd. regents Univ. System Ga., 1988-94, vice chmn., 1991-93, chmn., 1993-94; trustee U. Ga. Found., Atlanta, 1983-87, treas. 1985-87; mem. bd. visitors U. Ga. Law Sch., 1983-87, chmn. 1985; dir. Cen. Atlanta Progress, 1985-86; dir. USA-ROC Econ. Coun., 1985-91; bd. dirs. Ga. Coun. Internat. Visitors, Atlanta, 1986-93, sec., 1986-87, pres., 1987-88; bd. dirs. Atlanta Conv. and Visitor's Bur., 1986-91, sec., 1986-87, v.p. 1987-88; bd. dirs. Ga. Region NCCJ, 1980—, co-chair, 1982-83; chmn. Met. Atlanta Olympic Games Authority, 1990-91; bd. dirs. Nat. High Sch. Football Hall of Fame, 1994—; Ga. Sports Hall of Fame, 1990—, vice chmn., 1993-95, chmn., 1995—; attache Can. Olympic Team for 1996 Olympics, 1995—. 1st lt. U.S. Army, 1951-53, Korea. Decorated Air medal; recipient Brotherhood-Sisterhood award Ga. Regional NCCJ, 1993. Fellow Am. Coll. Investment Counsel (bd. dirs. 1986-88), ABA, Ga. Bar Found., Soc. Internat. Bus. Fellows; mem. Ga. Bar Assn. (chmn. corp. and banking law sect. 1977-78), Atlanta Bar Assn., D.C. Bar Assn., Lawyers Club Atlanta, U. Ga. Law Sch. Alumni Assn. (trustee 1979-84, pres. 1982-83), Can. Am. Soc. (bd. dirs. 1981-90, pres. 1981-83), Brit. Am. Bus. Group (bd. dirs. 1982-90, sec. 1982-86), Atlanta C. of C. (bd. dirs. 1981-82), Ga. C. of C. (bd. dirs. 1985—), Sphinx, Gridiron, Phi Beta Kappa, Phi Kappa Phi, Omicron Delta Kappa. Democrat. Methodist. Avocations: reading, travel. Home: 4850 Tanglewood Ct NW Atlanta GA 30327-4558 Office: Kilpatrick & Cody 1100 Peachtree St NE Ste 2800 Atlanta GA 30309-4530

PHILLIPS, BETTIE MAE, elementary school educator; b. Ft. Worth, May 2, 1941; d. Robert Sr. and Charittie Barnes; m. George Vernon Phillips Sr., Aug. 29, 1960 (div. Aug. 1985); 1 child, George Vernon Jr. BS in Elem. Edn., Bishop Coll., 1967; MEd in Early Childhood Edn., East Tex. State U., 1976. Tchr. Dallas Ind. Sch. Dist., 1968—. Author: The Whole Armor, 1979, Petals, 1988, Lights in the Shadows, 1993; composer childen's songs Bettie's Songs, Vol. 1, 1987, God's Cloud and There's Love Everywhere, 1994 (recorded by Hilltop Records, included in album America). Mem. Classroom Tchrs. Dallas. Baptist. Avocations: singing in concerts for children and in church choir. Home: 1312 Mill Stream Dr Dallas TX 75232-4606 Office: Bayles Elem Sch 2444 Telegraph Dallas TX 75228

PHILLIPS, BETTY LOU (ELIZABETH LOUISE PHILLIPS), author, interior designer; b. Cleve.; d. Michael N. and Elizabeth D. (Materna) Suvak; m. John S. Phillips, Jan. 27, 1963 (div. Jan. 1981); children: Bruce, Bryce, Brian; m. John D.C. Roach, Aug. 28, 1982. BS, Syracuse U., 1960; postgrad. in English, Case Western Res. U., 1963-64. Cert. elem. and spl. edn. tchr., N.Y. Tchr. pub. schs. Shaker Heights, Ohio, 1960-66; sportswriter Cleve. Press, 1976-77; spl. features editor Pro Quarterback Mag., N.Y.C., 1976-79; freelance writer specializing in books for young people, 1976—; interior designer residential and comml.; bd. dirs. Cast Specialties Inc., Cleve. Author: Chris Evert: First Lady of Tennis, 1977; Picture Story of Dorothy Hamill (ALA Booklist selection), 1978; American Quarter Horse, 1979; Earl Campbell: Houston Oiler Superstar, 1979; Picture Story of Nancy Lopez, (ALA Notable book), 1980; Go! Fight! Win! The NCA Guide for Cheerleaders (ALA Booklist), 1981; Something for Nothing, 1981; Brush Up on Your Hair (ALA Booklist), 1981; Texas ... The Lone Star State, 1989, Who Needs Friends? We All Do!, 1989; also contbr. articles to young adult and sports mags. Bd. dirs. The Children's Mus., Denver; mem. Friends of Fine Arts Found., Denver Art Mus., Cen. City Opera Guild, Alameda County Cancer League. Mem. Soc. Children's Book Writers, Am. Soc. Interior Designers (profl. cert.), Internat. Interior Design Assn. (profl.), Delta, Delta, Delta. Republican. Roman Catholic. Home: 125 Guilford Rd Piedmont CA 94611-3804

PHILLIPS, CARTER GLASGOW, lawyer; b. Canton, Ohio, Sept. 11, 1952; s. Max Dean and Virginia Scott (Carter) P.; m. Sue Jane Henry, June 5, 1976; children: Jessica, Ryan. BA, Ohio State U., 1973; MA, Northwestern U., 1975, JD, 1977. Bar: Ill. 1977, D.C. 1979, U.S. Dist. Ct. (no. dist.) Ill., U.S. Dist. Ct. (D.C. dist.), U.S. Ct. Appeals (2d, 3d, 4th, 5th, 6th, 7th, 8th, 9th, 10th, 11th and D.C. cirs.). Law clk. U.S. Ct. Appeals (7th cir.), Chgo., 1977-78; law clk. to chief Justice Warren E. Burger U.S. Supreme Ct., Washington, 1978-79; asst. prof. law U Ill., Champaign, 1979-81; asst. solicitor gen. U.S. Dept. Justice, Washington, 1981-84; ptnr. Sidley & Austin, Washington, 1984—. Contbr. articles to profl. jours. Chief counsel Spina Bifida Assn. Am., Rockville, Md., 1987—; mem. bd. advisors state and local legal ctrs., Washington, 1985-91. Republican. Episcopalian. Office: Sidley & Austin 1722 I St NW Washington DC 20006-3705

PHILLIPS, CHARLES ALAN, accounting firm executive; b. Cin., Aug. 12, 1939; s. Charles Stanley and Mary Lucile (Kirkpatrick) P. BS in Bus. Adminstrn., Northwestern U., 1960, MBA, 1961. Cert. systems profl. Investment adviser Continental Ill. Bank, Chgo., 1960-65; asst. to pres. A.S. Hansen, Chgo., 1965-67; investment adviser Francis I. du Pont, N.Y.C., 1967-70; prof. North Central Coll., Mansfield, Ohio, 1970-73; prin. Peat, Marwick, Mitchell (now KPMG Peat Marwick), Cleve., Tulsa, Houston, 1973-88. Presbyterian. Avocations: classical music; natural history; gardening.

PHILLIPS, CHARLES FRANKLIN, economic consultant; b. Nelson, Pa., May 25, 1910; s. Frank G. and Emily Catherine (Stevens) P.; m. Evelyn Minard, June 22, 1932; children—Charles Franklin Jr., Carol Ann. A.B., Colgate U., 1931, LL.D., 1945; Ph.D. Harvard U., 1934; LL.D., Colby Coll., 1949, Bowdoin Coll., 1952, Northeastern U., 1953, Shaw U., 1966, Bates Coll., 1967; L.H.D., U. Maine, 1954; Litt.D., Western New Eng. Coll., 1959, Nasson Coll., 1959, Morehouse Coll., Atlanta, 1963. Asst. econs. Hobart Coll., Geneva, N.Y., 1933-34; instr. econs. Colgate U., 1934-36, asst. prof., 1936-39, prof., 1939-44; on leave of absence, 1941-44; to serve as cons. counsumers div. Nat. Def. Advy. Com., 1941; asst. price exec. OPA, 1941-42, chief tire rationing div., 1942-43; dir. automotive supply rationing div., 1943-44, dep. adminstr. charge rationing dept., 1944; pres. Bates Coll., 1944-67, pres. emeritus, 1967—; former pub. gov. Am. Stock Exch.; ret. dir. several corps. Author: Marketing, 1938, (with Jasper V. Garland) Government Spending and Economic Recovery, 1938, Discussion Methods, 1938, The American Neutrality Problem, 1939, (with Delbert J. Duncan and Stanley C. Hollander) Modern Retailing Management, rev. edit, 1972, (with others) Marketing Principles and Methods, rev. edit, 1973, Marketing by Manufacturers, rev. edit, 1951, A Tax Program to Encourage the Economic Growth of Puerto Rico, 1958; contbr. articles to acad., trade jours. Pres. New Eng. Colls. Fund, 1954. Mem. Phi Beta Kappa, Phi Delta Theta. Address: 117 Maple Hill Ln Auburn ME 04210

PHILLIPS, CHARLES FRANKLIN, JR., economist, educator; b. Geneva, N.Y., Nov. 5, 1934; s. Charles Franklin and Evelyn (Minard) P.; m. Marjorie Hancock, June 22, 1957; children: Charles Franklin, Susan Hancock, Anne Davis. B.A., U. N.H., 1956; Ph.D., Harvard U., 1960. Asst. prof. econs. Washington and Lee U., Lexington, Va., 1959-63; asso. prof. Washington and Lee U., 1963-66, prof., 1966—; mem. advy. bd. Lexington-Covington area, First Union, 1971—; econ. cons. pub. utilities. Author: Competition in the Synthetic Rubber Industry, 1963, The Economics of Regulation, 1965, rev. edit., 1969, The Regulation of Public Utilities, 1984, 3d edit., 1993; editor: Competition and Monopoly in the Domestic Telecommunications Industry, 1974, Competition and Regulation-Some Economic Concepts, 1976, Expanding Economic Concepts of Regulation in Health, Postal and Telecommunications Services, 1977, Regulation, Competition and Deregulation-An Economic Grab Bag, 1978, Regulation and the Future Economic Environment-Air to Ground, 1980. Mem. city coun., Lexington, 1969-71, mayor, 1971-88; trustee Hebron Acad., Maine, 1971-82, Presbyn. Ch., 1991—, elder, 1993—; mem. Commn. on Rev. of Nat. Policy Toward Gambling, 1972-76; chmn. Valley Program for Aging Svcs., 1993—; bd. dirs. Rockbridge Area Presbyn. Home, 1973—, Nat. Regulatory Rsch. Inst., 1992—; exec. com. mem. United Way of Lexington-Rockbridge County, 1994—. Recipient McKinsey Found. award, 1962; Outstanding Regional Dir. award Omicron Delta Epsilon, 1971. Mem. Am. Soc. econ. assns., Am. Mktg. Assn., Phi Beta Kappa, Omicron Delta Epsilon (pres. 1976-77, 78-79). Republican. Avoc. va. central com. 1974-76, 77—). Home: 414 Morningside Dr Lexington VA 24450-2739 Office: Washington and Lee U Dept Economics Lexington VA 24450

PHILLIPS, CHARLES GORHAM, lawyer; b. Glen Ridge, N.J., Apr. 27, 1921; s. Charles Swayne and Margaret Cook (Atwell) P.; m. Martha Hall Belden, Dec. 19, 1942; children: Webster B., Charles G. Jr., Tacey P. Carroll, Tyler A. AB magna cum laude, Williams Coll., 1943; JD cum laude, Harvard U., 1948. Bar: N.Y. 1949. Assoc. Cadwalader, Wickersham & Taft, N.Y.C., 1948-51; assoc. Dewey Ballantine and predecessor firm, N.Y.C., 1951-57, ptnr., 1958—, chmn. mgmt. com., 1984-88. Assoc. trustee Montclair (N.J.) Art Mus., 1988—. Cpl. USAAF, 1943-46. Mem. ABA, Montclair Golf Club, Riomar Bay Yacht Club, Riomar Country Club (Vero Beach, Fla.). Republican. Congregationalist. Avocations: golfing, bridge, needlepoint. Home: 746 Riomar Dr Vero Beach FL 32963-2013 also: 10 Crestmont Rd Montclair NJ 07042 Office: Dewey Ballantine 1301 Ave Of The Americas New York NY 10019-6092

PHILLIPS, CHRISTOPHER HALLOWELL, diplomat; b. The Hague, The Netherlands, Dec. 6, 1920; s. William and Caroline A. (Drayton) P.; m. Mabel B. Olsen, May 11, 1943; children: Victoria A. Phillips Corbett, Miriam O. Phillips Eley, David W. A.B., Harvard U., 1943. Reporter, Beverly (Mass.) Evening Times, 1947-48; mem. Mass. Senate, 1948-53; spl. asst. to asst. sec. UN affairs Dept. State, 1953; later dep. asst. sec. of state for internat. orgn. affairs; apptd. U.S. Civil Service commr.; vice chmn. U.S. Civil Service Commn., 1957; U.S. rep. on UN Econ. and Social Council, 1958-61; Chase Manhattan Bank rep. for UN affairs, 2d v.p., mgr. Canadian div., 1961-65; pres. U.S. council Internat. C. of C., 1965-69; ambassador, dep. U.S. rep. UN Security Council, 1969-70; ambassador, dep. permanent U.S. rep. to UN, 1970-73; pres. Nat. Council for U.S.-China Trade, Washington, 1973-86, now hon. mem. bd. dirs.; U.S. ambassador to Brunei Darussalam, 1989-91; presdl. appointee U.S. Inst. Peace, 1992—; mem. adv. coun. Sch. Advanced Internat. Studies, Johns Hopkins U. Mass. dist. del. Rep. Nat. Conv., 1952, 60. Served to capt. USAAF, 1942-46. Fellow Am. Acad. Arts and Scis.; mem. UN Assn. U.S.A., Coun. Fgn. Rels., Asia Soc., Coun. Am. Ambassadors (bd. dirs.), Met. Club Washington. Episcopalian. Home: 2801 New Mexico Ave NW Washington DC 20007

PHILLIPS, CLIFTON J., history educator; b. Olean, N.Y., Apr. 11, 1919; s. Charles Clifton and Edith (Grey) P.; m. Rachel Jacqueline Martin, July 19, 1952; children: Peter Martin, Elaine Abigail, Alexis Anne, Patience Cecily. B.A., Hiram Coll., 1941; Th.B., Starr King Sch. Religious Leadership, 1944; M.A., Harvard U., 1950, Ph.D., 1954. Civil edn. officer Dept. Def., Kobe, Japan, 1946-49; faculty history De Pauw U., 1954—, prof., 1965-85, sr. prof., 1985—, chmn. dept. history, 1969-72, 78—; lectr. Am. Studies, Korea, 1968-69. Author: Indiana in Transition: The Emergence of an Industrial Commonwealth, 1880-1920, 1968, Protestant America and the Pagan World: The First Half Century of the American Board of Commissioners for Foreign Missions, 1810-1860, 1969, (with others) The Missionary Enterprise in China and America, 1974, Missionary Ideologies in the Imperialist Era, 1880-1920, 1982; DePauw: A Pictorial History, 1987, From Frontier Circuit to Urban Church: The History of Greencastle Methodism, 1989. Served with inf. AUS, 1944-46, PTO. Fulbright-Hays fellow Chinese civilization Taiwan, summer 1962. Mem. Am. Hist. Assn., Assn. Asian Studies, Orgn. Am. Historians, Ind. Hist. Soc., Ind. Assn. Historians (past pres.). Home: 422 Anderson St Greencastle IN 46135-1727

PHILLIPS, CRAIG, aquarium administrator; b. Buffalo, May 23, 1922; s. Pressly Craig and Adelia Grace (Vergith) P.; m. Fanny Bradford Lee, Oct. 21, 1953. AB, U. Miami (Fla.), 1951; MS, U. Md., 1971. Asst. to curator Marineland of Fla., 1946-47; research aide U. Miami, Fla., 1951-53; curator Miami Seaquarium, 1954-59; asst. curator Nat. Aquarium, Washington, 1959-72; dir. Nat. Aquarium, 1976-82, ret., 1986; freelance illustrator, biol. cons. to ednl. publs., 1986—. Author and illustrator: (with Winfield Brady) Sea Pests, 1953, The Captive Sea, 1964; illustrator: The Desert Beneath the Sea, 1991; contbr. artwork to Nat. Geog. mag., 1952, 56, Websters Internat. Dictionary, 1960. Served with USN, 1942-46. Mem. Nat. Soc. Ichthyologists, Herpetologists, Fund for UFO Rsch., Zool. Parks, Aquariums, Internat. Apoid Soc. Home: 10109 Grant Ave Silver Spring MD 20910-1048

PHILLIPS, CYRUS EASTMAN, IV, lawyer; b. Charlottesville, Va., Oct. 2, 1944; s. Cyrus Eastman, III and Sue (Irving) P.; m. Shirley Ruth Hunter, June 11, 1967; children: Cyrus Eastman V, Kathryn G., Susan L., William H. A.B. with honors U. Ill., 1966; J.D., Coll. William and Mary, 1968. Bar: Va. 1968, U.S. Ct. Claims 1969, U.S. Supreme Ct. 1971, U.S. Ct. Appeals (4th cir.) 1976, U.S. Ct. Appeals (fed. cir.) 1982. Atty., adviser, trial atty. Def. Logistics Agy. Def. Constrn. Supply Ctr., Columbus, Ohio, 1968-80; adminstrv. judge Bd. Contract Appeals GSA, Washington, 1980-87, dep. vice chmn., 1984-86, vice chmn., 1986-87; of counsel, McGuire, Woods, Battle and Boothe, Washington, 1987-88, ptnr., 1989—; lectr. Legal Edn. Inst., Dept. Justice, Washington, 1982—; GSA Trail Boss Program, 1988—. Rsch. editor William and Mary Law Rev., 1968. Contbr. articles to profl. jours. Chmn. Plain Township Zoning Commn., New Albany, Ohio, 1978-80. Recipient Meritorious Civilian Svc. award Def. Logistics Agy., Dept. Def., 1980. Mem. ABA, Va. Bar Assn., Va. Trial Lawyers Assn., Fed. Bar Assn. (pres. Columbus chpt. 1974-75, vice chmn. bd. contracts appeals com. 1981), Nat. Conf. Bds. of Contract Appeal, Fed. Circuit Bar Assn., Computer Law Assn., Nat. Muzzle Loading Rifle Assn. (Friendship, Ind.). Republican. Presbyterian. Home: 608 Falmouth Dr Fredericksburg VA 22405-2014 Office: McGuire Woods Battle & Boothe Army and Navy Club Bldg 1627 I St NW Ste 1000 Washington DC 20006-4092

PHILLIPS, DANIEL ANTHONY, trust company executive; b. Boston, Feb. 24, 1938; s. Lyman Waldo and Harriet Anthony (Carlow) P.; m. Diana Walcott, Aug. 18, 1962; children: Lisa Walcott Phillips, Bradford Lyman, Phillips. AB cum laude, Harvard U., 1960, MBA, 1963. From v.p. to dir. to mem. exec. com. Fiduciary Trust Co., Boston, 1963-92, exec. v.p., dir., trust com. sec., trust officer, 1992—, exec. v.p., dir., trust com., trust officer, 1993-94, pres., CEO, 1993—. Bd. dirs. Family Svc. Am., chair fin. comm., 1993-95, treas., chair bd. dirs. 1995—; pres., bd. dirs. Am. Meml. Hosp., Reims, France; bd. dirs. Family Found., N.Am., 1993—, Grimes-King Found. for the Elderly, Inc.; v.p., treas Frederick E. Weber Charities Corp. Mem Boston Soc. Security Analysts, Harvard U. Alumni Assn. (past v.p.), Boston Econ. Club, Commercial Club. Home: 975 Memorial Dr Cambridge MA 02138-5753 Office: Fiduciary Trust Co 175 Federal St Boston MA 02110-2210

PHILLIPS, DANIEL MILLER, lawyer; b. Cleve., Mar. 21, 1933; s. Clovis H. and Lillian (Miller) P.; m. Joyce C. Hamilton, July 26, 1958; children: Meegan M., Sarah H., Anthony J. Student, Wesleyan U., Middletown, Conn., 1951-53; B.S., Ohio State U., 1958, J.D., 1961. Bar: Ohio 1961. Since practiced in Toledo; mem. firm Robison, Curphey & O'Connell, 1961-77, ptnr., 1967-77; dir. litigation Owens-Corning Fiberglas Corp., Toledo, 1977-86; spl. cons. Asbestos Claim Facility, Princeton, N.J., 1986-87, dir. adminstrn. and human resources, 1987-89, pres., 1990-92, trustee, 1985-86; cons. UNR Asbestos-Disease Claims Trust, 1991—; lectr. Ohio Legal Ctr. Inst., 1969-70, 73; pres. Found. for Practice Law in Pub. Interest, Toledo, 1976; legal rep. for unknown and future asbestos bodily injury persons Chpt. II Procs. Nat. Gypsum Co., 1992—; designated trustee Eagle-Pitcher Industries Chpt. II Procs. Pres. Toledo Florence Crittenton Services, 1971-72; mem. Lucas County Mental Health and Retardation Bd., 1975-76; trustee Toledo Legal Aid Soc., 1977-87, Community Planning Council of Northwestern Ohio, 1978-82; mem. working group on asbestos litigation Nat. Ctr. for State Cts. Jud. Adminstrn., 1982-83. Served with AUS, 1953-55. Mem. ABA, Ohio Bar Assn. (chmn. negligence law com. 1971-73, mem. ins. law com. 1974-79), Toledo Bar Assn. (exec. com. 1971-80, sec. 1974, pres. 1978-79), Toledo Jr. Bar Assn. (pres. 1970-71), Fedn. Ins. Counsel, Def. Rsch. Inst., Ohio Assn. Civil Trial Lawyers (pres. 1971-72), U.S. Jud. Conf. 6th Cir. (life). Home and Office: 439 Willowbrook Dr North Brunswick NJ 08902

PHILLIPS, DENIS CHARLES, education and philosophy educator; b. Melbourne, Victoria, Australia, Jan. 4, 1938; came to U.S., 1974; s. Charles Walter and Anne (Sherman) P.; m. Mara Jana Kallas, Dec. 19, 1962 (div. 1978); children: Russell, Darryl, Allison. BSc, U. Melbourne, 1958, BEd, 1961, MEd, 1963, PhD, 1968. Tchr. high sch. Victoria Edn. Dept., 1959-63; from lectr. to assoc. prof. Monash U., Melbourne, 1964-74; from assoc. prof. to prof. Stanford (Calif.) U., 1974—; vis. prof. Curtin U., Perth, Australia, 1991. Author: Holistic Thought in Social Science, 1976, Philosophy, Science and Social Inquiry, 1987, Evaluation and Education: At Quarter Century,

1991, Social Scientists Bestiary, 1992; editor book series Kluwer Pub., The Netherwlands, 1989—; sect. editor: International Encyclopedia of Education, England, 1991-93. Fellow Philosophy of Edn. Soc. (pres. 1990-91); mem. AAUP (chpt. pres. 1983-85, 91-92), Am. Ednl. Rsch. Assn., Philosophy of Sci. Assn. Avocation: magician. Office: Stanford U Sch Edn Stanford CA 94305

PHILLIPS, DERWYN FRASER, manufacturing company executive; b. St. Catharines, Ont., Can., Aug. 31, 1930; came to U.S., 1975; s. John Arthur and Margaret (Cameron) P.; m. Janice Irene Hunt, Sept. 24, 1955; children: John Timothy, Laurie Cameron, Jay Derwyn. B.A., U. Western Ont., London, 1954. V.p. mkgt. Rexall Drug Co. Unl., 1966-68; v.p., dir. mktg. Gillette-Can., Montreal, Que., 1969-71; pres. Gillette-Can., 1971-75; pres. toiletries div. Gillette Co., Boston, 1975-77; pres. personal care div. Gillette Co., 1977-81, exec. v.p., 1981-87, vice chmn., 1987—; dir. Can. Tire Corp., Toronto, 1984-86. Trustee New Eng. Colls. Fund, Boston, 1982—. Mem. Greater Boston C. of C. (dir. 1982—), Cosmetic Toiletry and Fragrance Assn. (dir. 1981-83). Office: Gillette Co 3900 Prudential Towers Bldg Boston MA 02199

PHILLIPS, DONALD WRIGHT, investment company executive; b. Streator, Ill., Apr. 24, 1948; s. Dale W. and Betty (Cronk) P.; m. Karen Phillips; children: David, Ryan. BA, Western Ill. U., 1970; MBA, No. Ill. U., 1974. Dir. employee benefits Beatrice Cos., Inc., Chgo., 1974-84; chief investment officer Ameritech, Chgo., 1984-90; pres. Nucorp, Inc., 1990-92; chmn. Consol. Fibres Co., 1991-93, Equity Instnl. Investors, Inc., Chgo., 1991—; exec. v.p. Equity Fin. and Mgmt. Co., Chgo., 1990—; bd. dirs. Capsure Holdings Corp. (formerly Nucorp), United Capitol Ins. Co., Sit New Beginning Mut. Fund Group, Mpls., Larimer and Co., Denver. With U.S. Army, 1970-72. Office: Equity Instnl Investors Inc 2 N Riverside Plz Ste 600 Chicago IL 60606-2606

PHILLIPS, DOROTHY KAY, lawyer; b. Camden, N.J., Nov. 2, 1945; d. Benjamin L. and Sadye (Levinsky) Phillips; children: Bethann P., David M. Schaffzin. BS in English Lit. magna cum laude, U. Pa., 1964; MA in Family Life and Marriage Counseling and Edn., NYU, 1975; JD, Villanova U., 1978. Bar: Pa. 1978, N.J. 1978, U.S. Dist. Ct. (ea. dist.) Pa. 1978, U.S. Dist. Ct. N.J., 1978, U.S. Ct. Appeals (3d cir.), 1984, U.S. Supreme Ct. 1984. Tchr., Haddon Twp. High Sch. (N.J.), and Haddon Heights High Sch. (N.J.), 1964-70; lectr., counselor Marriage Council of Phila.; lectr. U. Pa. and Hahnemann Med. Schs., Phila., 1970-75; atty. Adler, Barish, Daniels, Levin & Creskoff, Phila., 1978-79, Astor, Weiss & Newman, Phila., 1979-80; ptnr. Romisher & Phillips, P.C., Phila., 1981-86; prin. Law Office of Dorothy K. Phillips, 1986—; faculty Sch. of Law Temple U. Guest speaker on domestic rels. issues on radio and TV shows; featured in newspaper and mag. articles; contbr. articles to profl. jours. Rosenbach Found., Philadanco, Fedn. Allied Jewish Appeal (lawyers. div.), World Affairs Coun.; bd. mem. Anti-Defamation League of B'nai B'rith, Nat. Mus. Jewish History, mem. friends' circle, Athenaeum, Phila., shareholder. Mem. ABA, Assn. Trial Lawyers Am. (membership com. 1990-91), Pa. Trial Lawyers Assn. (chair membership com. family sect. 1989-90), Pa. Bar Assn. (continuing legal edn. com. 1990-92, faculty, lectr. Pa. Bar Inst. Continuing Legal Edn. 1990, panel mem. summer meeting 1991), N.J. Bar Assn., Phila. Bar Assn. (chmn. early settlement program 1983-84, mem. custody rules drafting com. for Supreme Ct. Pa., spl. events speaker on pensions, counsel fees, written fee agreements 1989-91, co-chair mandatory continuing legal edn. 1994), Phila. Trial Lawyers Assn., Montgomery County Bar Assn., Lawyers Club. Office: 1818 Market St Fl 35 Philadelphia PA 19103-3638

PHILLIPS, DOROTHY ORMES, elementary education educator; b. Denver, July 26, 1922; d. Jesse Edward and Belle (Noisette) Ormes; m. James Kermit Phillips, Apr. 28, 1945; children: William K., Dorothy E., Valerie A. BBA, Case Western Res. U., 1946, MA, 1959; PhD, U. Akron, 1989. Cert. tchr., adminstr., Ohio. Tchr. Cleve. Pub. Schs., 1955-68, math. cons., 1968-83, adminstrv. intern, 1970-73; grad. asst. U. Akron, Ohio, 1983-85, lectr. elem. edn., supr. student tchrs., 1985—; math. workshop presenter Norton (Ohio) Pub. Schs., 1986. Presenter Career Day, Cleve. Pub. Schs., 1992. Grantee NDEA, 1960, NSF, 1966. Mem. ASCD, Nat. Coun. Tchrs. Math., Ednl. Computer Consortium Ohio, Cleve. Pub. Schs. Math. Cons. (assoc.), Alpha Kappa Alpha, Pi Lambda Theta. Avocations: swimming, camping, reading. Home: 8746 Crackel Dr Chagrin Falls OH 44023

PHILLIPS, EARL NORFLEET, JR., financial services executive; b. High Point, N.C., May 5, 1940; s. Earl Norfleet Phillips and Lillian Jordan; m. Sarah Boyle, Oct. 19, 1971; children: Courtney Dorsett, Jordan Norfleet. BSBA, U. N.C., 1962; MBA, Harvard U., 1965. Security analyst Wertheim & Co., N.Y.C., 1965-67; exec. v.p. Factors Inc., High Point, N.C., 1967-71, exec. v.p. First Factors Corp., High Point, 1972-81, pres., 1982—; bd. dirs. Oakdale Cotton Mills, First Union Nat. Bank N.C.; bd. dirs., sec. N.C. Enterprise Corp. Bd. dirs. Culp, Inc. Trustee U. N.C., Chapel Hill, 1983-91, chmn. bd., 1989-91, chmn. endowment bd. U. N.C., 1989-91, U. N.C. Found., 1989-91, bd. govs., 1995—; bd. dirs. N.C. Bus. Found., N.C. Citizens for Bus. and Industry; mem. N.C. Econ. Devel. Bd., Raleigh, N.C., 1984-91; mem. nat. adv. coun. SBA, 1988-91; trustee High Point Regional Hosp., Asian Inst. Tech., Bangkok, Thailand, 1993—; mem. Piedmont Triad Airport Authority. Named Young Man of Yr., High Point Jaycees, 1971; named One of Five Outstanding Young Men, N.C. Jaycees, 1971. Mem. Nat. Comml. Fin. Assn. (bd. dirs.). Clubs: The Brook (N.Y.C.), Country of N.C. (Pinehurst), Willow Creek, String and Splinter (High Point), Linville (N.C.) Golf. Lodge: Gorgons Head. Office: First Factors Corp PO Box 2730 101 S Main St High Point NC 27261-2730

PHILLIPS, EDWARD JOHN, consulting firm executive; b. Phila., Sept. 8, 1940; s. Harold E. and Mary C. (Slatcher) P.; m. Kathleen A. Everett, July 23, 1960; children: Elizabeth J., Edward J. B of Mech. Engring., Villanova U., 1973; MBA, Widener U., 1975. Registered profl. engr., Ill., Kans., Mo., Pa., Ohio; chartered engr., U.K. Tech. ops. mgr. Motorola, Inc., Franklin Park, Ill., 1976-81; v.p. engring. Rival Mfg. Co., Kansas City, Mo., 1981-82; prin., sr. cons. Richard Muther & Assocs., Kansas City, 1982-85; chmn. KANDE, Inc., Overland Park, Kans., 1983-86; pres., CEO Sims Cons Group Inc., Lancaster, Ohio, 1986—; chmn. bd. dirs. Sims Consulting Group, Lancaster, Ohio; bd. dirs. KANDE, Inc., Wilmington, Del. Contbr. articles to profl. jours. Mem. NSPE, ASME (chmn. material handling sys. 1989-91, mem. internat. mgmt. com. 1977), MIMechE, Tau Beta Pi, Pi Tau Sigma. Office: Sims Cons Group Inc PO Box 968 111 N Broad St Lancaster OH 43130-0968

PHILLIPS, EDWIN ARTHUR, meteorologist; b. Alton, Ill., July 30, 1952; s. Edwin Charles and Ada Mae (Russell) P.; m. Anne Mildred Hasse, May 23, 1981; children: Alexander, Jacob. BA in Aeronautics, Parks Coll., 1973. bd. dirs. World Affairs Coun., Scottsdale, Ariz., 1992—, Clark Candy Co. Phoenix. Author: Koy/Ed Phillips Almanac, 1980-92, Ktar/Ed Phillips Almanac, 1983-93, Crisis in the Atmosphere, 1990. Mem. Am. Meteorological Soc., Nat. Assn. for the Advancement of Sci., Ariz. Pilots Assn. Republican. Jewish. Avocations: flying, golf, travel. Office: Arizona State Senate 1700 W Washington St Phoenix AZ 85007-2812

PHILLIPS, EDWIN CHARLES, gas transmission company executive; b. Saskatoon, Sask., Can., Oct. 19, 1917; s. Charles Henry and Beatrice Grace (Johnson) P.; m. Elizabeth Winnifred Johnston, June 27, 1942; children: Diane, Carol, Glen, Earl, Jane, Sue. Student, Lethbridge Collegiate Inst., 1931-35. Asst. buyer Loblaw Groceries Co. Ltd., Toronto, 1938-42; advt. mgr. Can. and Dominion Sugar Co., Chatham, Ont., 1945-47; asst. to gen. mgr. Consumers Gas Co., Toronto, 1947-52; with Trane Co. Can. Ltd., 1952-68, exec. v.p., gen. mgr., 1964-65, pres., Westcoast Transmission Co., Vancouver, 1968-70, exec. v.p., 1971-72, pres., 1972-82, chief exec. officer, 1976-83, chmn. bd., 1980-83, also dir.; dir. emeritus, 1989; chmn. bd. dirs. Cheni Resources Inc., dir. Balaclava Interprises Ltd., Emco Ltd., Future Shop Ltd., Weiser Inc. Served with RCAF, World War II. Home: 4458 W 2nd Ave, Vancouver, BC Canada V6R 1K5 also: 7210-C Carrara Pl San Diego CA 92122-5539

PHILLIPS, ELIZABETH JOAN, marketing executive; b. Cleve., July 8, 1938; d. George Tinl and Helen Walter; m. Erwin Phillips, June 1956 (div. 1960); 1 child, Michael A. B.A., Fordham U., 1980. Account exec. David Cogan Mgmt., N.Y.C., 1969-77; account exec. N.F.L. Films, N.Y.C., 1977-

78; mgr. sports programs Avon Products, N.Y.C., 1978-83; v.p. Needham, Harper & Steers (now Needham, Harper Worldwide), N.Y.C., 1983-86; v.p. Ted Bates Event Mktg., N.Y.C., 1986-87; pres. Custom Event Mktg. 1987—; adj. prof. NYU, N.Y.C., 1984—. Mem. exec. com. Vanderbilt YMCA, N.Y.C., 1976-84; ofcl. 1984 Olympic Games, L.A.; referee Women's Olympic Marathon, L.A., 1984; pres. Met. Athletics Congress, N.Y.C., 1980-83. Mem. Women's Sports Found. (bd. advisors 1983—), N.Y. Road Runners Club (v.p., mem. exec. com. 1976—, pres. 1970—, bd. dirs. 1992—), Road Runners Club of Am. (bd. dirs. 1992—). Office: Custom Event Mktg Inc 16 E 32nd St 12th Fl New York NY 10016

PHILLIPS, ELLIOTT HUNTER, lawyer; b. Birmingham, Mich., Feb. 14, 1919; s. Frank Elliott and Gertrude (Zacharias) P.; m. Gail Carolyn Isbey, Apr. 22, 1950; children—Elliott Hunter, Alexandra. A.B. cum laude, Harvard U., 1940, J.D., 1947. Bar: Mich. 1948. Since practiced in Detroit; ptnr. Hill Lewis (formerly Hill, Lewis, Adams, Goodrich & Tait), 1953-89, of counsel, 1989—; chmn. bd. dirs. Detroit & Can. Tunnel Corp.; pres., dir. Detroit and Windsor Subway Co.; mem. Mich. Bd. Accountancy, 1965-73. Contbr. to legal and accounting jours. Chmn. bd. dirs. Detroit chpt. ARC; pres., trustee McGregor Fund, Boys Republic, Detroit Inst. for Children, United Way Southeastern Mich., Univ. Liggett Sch.; mem. nat. major gifts com. Harvard U., Harvard Pres.'s Assocs., 1974—, Pres.'s Coun., 1990—, overseers com. to visit Law Sch., overseers com. univ. resources, Mich. chmn. Harvard Coll. fund; trustee, pres. Ch. Youth Svc.; mem. Detroit Area Coun. Boy Scouts Am. Lt. comdr. USNR, 1946. Recipient Spitzley award Detroit Inst. for Children, 1986, Harvard Alumni Assn. Disting. Svc. award, 1991. Fellow Mich. State Bar Found. (life), Am. Bar Found. (life); mem. ABA, State Bar Mich., Detroit Bar Assn., Lincoln's Inn Soc., Country Club Detroit, Detroit Club (pres. 1988-89), Yondotega Club, Leland Country Club, Grosse Pointe Club, Harvard Ea. Mich. Club (pres. 1955-56, Disting. Alumnus award 1992), Harvard Club N.Y.C., John's Island Club. Episcopalian (vestryman, sr. warden). Home: 193 Ridge Rd Grosse Pointe Farms MI 48236-3554 Office: 333 W Fort St Detroit MI 48226

PHILLIPS, ELLIS LAURIMORE, JR., legal educator, foundation executive; b. N.Y.C., Feb. 26, 1921; s. Ellis Laurimore and Kathryn (Sisson) P.; m. Marion Grumman, June 13, 1942; children: Valerie Phillips Parsegian, Elise Phillips Watts, Ellis Laurimore III, Kathryn Noel Phillips Zimmermann, Cynthia. AB, Princeton U., 1942; LLB, Columbia U., 1948; LLD, Keuka Coll.; N.Y., 1956; LLD (hon.), Adelphi U., 1979; LL.D. (hon.), L.I. U., 1980, Ithaca Coll., 1986. Bar: N.Y. 1948. With firm Burke & Burke, N.Y.C., 1948-53; mem. staff Pres.'s Com. Internat. Info. Activities, 1953; asst. dean Columbia Sch. Law, 1953-61, assoc. prof. law, 1953-56, prof., 1956-70, dir. univ. budget, 1961-64; pres. Ithaca (N.Y.) Coll., 1970-75; spl. asst. to U.S. amb. to Eng. Ct. St. James, 1957-58. Author: (with others) Cases and Materials in Accounting for Lawyers, 1964, The Legal Profession, 1970, Information Services for Academic Administration, 1971, Look Back from Forty, 1967, A New Approach to Academic Administration, 1969, Accounting and the Law: Cases and Materials, 1978. Pres. Bd. Edn. Union Free Sch. Dist. 15, Jericho, L.I., 1950-53, Ellis L. Phillips Found., 1959-93, v.p., 1993—; pres. Action Com. for L.I., Inc., 1978-81; trustee Inc. Village Brookville, L.I., 1958-64; Bangor Theol. Sem. With AUS, USAF, 1942-45. Republican. Home: 1855 Bay Rd # 302 Vero Beach FL 32963

PHILLIPS, ERICA EDELL, costume designer. Costume designer: (TV series) Charlie's Angels, 1976-81, Emerald Point N.A.S., 1983-84, (TV movies) A Long Way Home, 1981, Pray TV, 1982, M.A.D.D.: Mothers Against Drunk Drivers, 1983, One Cooks, the Other Doesn't, 1983, Princess Daisy, 1983, Cocaine and Blue Eyes, 1983, Peyton Place: The Next Generation, 1985, A Letter to Three Wives, 1985, Under the Influence, 1986, (films) How to Beat the High Cost of Living, 1980, Dead and Buried, 1981, Hadley's Rebellion, 1984, Twice in a Lifetime, 1985, Tough Guys, 1986, Robocop, 1987, Alien Nation, 1988, Major League, 1989, True Believer, 1989, Total Recall, 1990, Rapid Fire, 1992, Shattered, 1992, In the Line of Fire, 1993, A Perfect World, 1993, Little Big League, 1994. Office: Sandra Marsh Mgt 9150 Wilshire Blvd Ste 220 Beverly Hills CA 90210 also: 149 S Bedford Dr Beverly Hills CA 90212*

PHILLIPS, ETHEL C. (MRS. LLOYD J. PHILLIPS), writer; b. N.Y.C.; d. Henry and Minnie (Hirshfeld) Cohen; m. Lloyd Jay Phillips, 1930; children: Lloyd James, Anne. B.A., Vassar Coll.; M.A. in Pub. Law, Columbia U. Publs. dir. Am. Jewish Com., Inst. Human Relations, N.Y.C., 1939-65; bd. dirs., mem. exec. com. Nat. Charities Info. Bur., N.Y.C., 1966-90, vice-chmn., 1982-90. Author: Mind Your World, 1964, Record and the Vision, 1965, You in Human Rights, 1968; also pamphlets and media features on civil rights, internat. cooperation, human rights, volunteerism. Mem. N.Y. Soc. for Ethical Culture (trustee 1977-83), Nat. Council Women U.S. (pres. 1972-74, hon. pres. 1974-76, UN rep. 1976—). Clubs: Vassar (N.Y.C.), Women's City (N.Y.C.). Home: 120 E 79th St New York NY 10021-0319

PHILLIPS, EUAN HYWEL, publishing executive; b. Chipstead, Surrey, Eng., Mar. 31, 1928; s. Edgar Aneurin and Elsie Llewella (Davies) P.; m. Margaret June Savage, June 12, 1954; children: David John, Janet Margaret. B.A., Emmanuel Coll., Cambridge, Eng., 1949, M.A., 1965. Cost acct. J. Lyons & Co. Ltd., London, 1950-53; dispatch mgr. Pickerings Produce Canners Ltd., Manchester, Eng., 1953-56; mgmt. cons. P.A. Mgmt. Cons. Ltd., London, 1956-65; mng. dir. Unwin Bros. Ltd., Old Woking, Eng., 1965-73; univ. printer designate Cambridge (Eng.) U. Press, 1973-74, univ. printer, 1974-76; dir. Cambridge (Eng.) U. Press (Am. br.), N.Y.C., 1977-82; owner New Canaan Bibles and Manx Knitwear, Stamford, Conn., 1982-87; exec. dir. Assn. Am. Univ. Presses, 1987-90; gov. Guildford Sch. Art, 1966-69, Cambridge Coll. Arts and Tech., 1974-76; dir. East Asian History of Sci., Inc., 1978-81. Contbr. Scholarly Pub. Served with Royal Navy, 1946-48. Mem. Brit. Printing Industries Fedn. (mem. coun. 1966-73, pres. Home Counties Alliance 1970-71), Troupers Light Opera Co. Home: 289 Connestee Trl Brevard NC 28712-9009

PHILLIPS, FRANCES MARIE, history educator; b. Hale Center, Tex., Nov. 8, 1918; d. Clyde C. and Ada (Stutzman) P. B.A., West Tex. State Coll., 1940, M.A., 1946; Ph.D. (Univ. fellow), U. N.Mex., 1956; postgrad. (Fulbright scholar), U. London, 1954-55. Tchr. public schs. Channing, Tex., Miami, Tex., Palisade, Colo., Tucumcari, N.Mex., 1940-46; supr. State Tchrs. Coll. Campus High Sch., Wayne, Nebr., 1947-51; instr. U.Md. Overseas Program, Eng., 1955; grad. asst. U. N.Mex., 1955-56; asst., assoc. prof. history Sul Ross State Coll., Alpine, Tex., 1956-60; prof. history, dean grad. div. Sul Ross State Coll., 1962-71; program dir. sr. colls. Coordinating Bd. Tex. Coll. and Univ. System, Austin, 1971-85; asst. prof. Mankato (Minn.) State Coll., 1960-62. Editor: Dear Mother and Folks at Home: Iowa Farm to Clermont-Ferrand, 1917-1918, 1988. Chmn. bd. Carlsbad dist. Wesley Found., 1962-66; mem. Adv. Council for Ednl. Personnel Devel., 1972—, State Bd. Examiners for Tchr. Edn., 1972-79, Tex. Com. on Early Childhood Devel. Careers, 1976—. Mem. AAUW, N.Mex. Hist. Soc., Am. Assn. Higher Edn., Assn. Tex. Acad. Schs. (v.p. 1967-69, pres. 1969-70), Alpha Chi, Phi Kappa Phi, Phi Alpha Theta, Delta Kappa Gamma. Democrat. Methodist (past mem. N.Mex. Conf. Bd. Edn., nat. off. bd.) Research in Anglo-Am. relations, 1954-56, 1962. Home: 8700 Millway Dr Austin TX 78758-6832

PHILLIPS, FREDERICK FALLEY, architect; b. Evanston, Ill., June 18, 1946; s. David Cook and Katharine Edith (Falley) P.; m. Gay Fraker, Feb. 26, 1983 (div. Dec. 1993). BA, Lake Forest Coll., 1969; MArch, U. Pa., 1973. Registered architect, Ill., Wis. Draftsman, Harry Weese & Assocs., 1974, 75; pvt. practice architecture Frederick F. Phillips, Architect, Chgo., 1976-81; pres. Frederick Phillips and Assocs., Chgo., 1981—. Bd. dirs. Landmarks Preservation Coun., 1981-85, Chgo. Acad. Sci., 1988—, Friends of Ceuros de Escazu, Costa Rica, 1992—; mem. aux. bd. Chgo. Architecture Found., 1975-89; chmn. Task Group on Manufactured Housing, AIA Nat. Com. on Design, 1994—. Recipient award Townhouse for Logan Square Competition, AIA and Econ. Redevel. Corp. Logan Square, 1980, Gold medal award Willow St. Houses, Ill. Ind. Masonry Coun., 1981, Silver award for pvt. residence, 1989, 94 Archtl. Record, Three Record Houses awards, 1990, 95, award 2d Compact House Design Competition, 1990, award of exellence for pvt. residence AIA/Nat. Concrete Masonry Assn., 1992, award for pvt. residence Am. Wood Coun., 1993. Mem. AIA (Disting. Bldg. award for Willow St. Houses, Chgo. chpt. 1982 for Pinewood Farm 1983, for Pvt. Residences 1990, 92), Chgo. Archtl. Club, Racquet Club (bd. govs. 1983-89),

Arts Club, Cliff Dwellers Club (bd. govs. 1985-88). Office: Frederick F Phillips & Assocs 53 W Jackson Blvd Ste 1752 Chicago IL 60604-3705

PHILLIPS, GABRIEL, travel marketing executive; b. North Vandergrift, Pa., Aug. 3, 1933; s. Samuel and Margaret (Solomon) P.; m. Margaret Mednis, Sept. 5, 1965 (div. 1970). BS, U. Md., 1956; JD, George Washington U., 1962. Bar: D.C. 1963. Various positions CAB, Washington, 1956-66; dir. internat. programs Air Transport Assn., Washington, 1966-69, exec. sec. fin. and acctg., 1970, v.p. internat. programs, 1970-76, v.p. traffic svcs., 1976-79, sr. v.p. industry svcs., 1979-86, exec. v.p., 1986-91, acting pres., 1988-89, ret., 1991; exec. v.p. Holiday Mktg. Inc., Herndon, Va., 1991—; bd. dirs. Phillips Corp., Columbia, Md. Contbr. articles to profl. jours. Bd. dirs. Nat. Alliance of Sr. Citizens. With U.S. Army, 1956-58. Mem. Travel Industry Assn. Am. (bd. dirs., nat. chmn. 1985-86), Nat. Assn. Arab Ams. (bd. dirs., treas. 1985—, pres. 1990-92). Republican. Roman Catholic.

PHILLIPS, GAIL, state legislator; b. Juneau, Alaska; m. Walt Phillips; children: Robin, Kim. BA in Bus. Edn., U. Alaska. Mem. Homer (Alaska) City Coun., 1981-84, Kenai Peninsula Borough Assembly, 1986-87; chmn. legis. com. Alaska Mcpl. League; mem. Alaska Ho. of Reps., 1990, 92, 94, house majority leader, 1993-94, speaker, 1995—; high sch. bus. tchr., Fairbanks, Nome, Alaska; airline agt., exec. sec. and sta. mgr. Alaska Airlines, Western Airlines, Wien Air; owner, mgr. Quiet Sporting Goods; ptnr. Lindphil Mining Co.; pub. rels. cons.; legis. aide to Senate pres. Active Homer United Meth. Ch., Rep. Ctrl. Com. Alaska, Kenai Peninsula Coll. Coun.; past bd. dirs. Homer Soc. Natural History; past mem. com. bd. and race coord. Iditarod Trail Dog Sled Race. Mem. Western States Legis. Coun. (exec. com.), Am. Legis. Exch. Coun. (state chmn.), Resource Devel. Coun. Alaska, U. Alaska Coll. Fellows, Homer Emblem Club, Homer, Seldovia, Anchor Point, Soldotna and Kenai C. of C., Peninsula Coun. Chambers, Kachemak Bay Visitors Assn. Home: PO Box 3304 Homer AK 99603 Office: 126 W Pioneer Ave Homer AK 99603 also: Alaska House of Reps State Capitol Juneau AK 99811

PHILLIPS, GARY LYNN, wholesale grocery distribution company executive; b. Ford City, Mo., June 15, 1947; s. Elmo E. and Betty J. (Darby) P.; m. Marsha Elaine Wagner, May 3, 1965; children—Michael Alan, Scott Alan. Student bus. adminstrn., Draughon's Coll., Kansas City, Mo., 1965-70. Vice pres. mktg. Blackford Securities Corp., Kansas City, Mo., 1966-74; corp. acct. Assoc. Wholesale Grocers, Inc., Kansas City, Kans., 1974-77, dir. adminstrn., 1977-80, dir. procurement, 1980-83, sr. v.p., div. mgr., 1983—, also mem. exec. policy com. Mem. personnel com. 1st Baptist Ch. of Republic, Mo., 1984-85; group leader United Way of Ozarks, Springfield, Mo., 1984. Served with U.S. Army, 1968-70. Mem. Ozark Empire Grocers Assn., Mo. Retail Grocers Assn., Ark. Retail Grocers Assn. Republican. Home: RR 2 Box 164B Republic MO 65738-9538 Office: Assoc Wholesale Grocers Inc PO Box 2932 Kansas City KS 66110-2932

PHILLIPS, GEORGE L., prosecutor; b. Fulton, Miss., May 24, 1949; s. Gilbert L. and Grace (Staker) P. BS, U. So. Miss., 1971; JD, U. Miss., 1973. Bar: Miss. Assoc. Johnson, Pittman & Pittman, Hattiesburg, Miss., 1980-94; ptnr. Norris & Phillips, 1975-76; county pros. atty. Forrest County, Miss., 1976-80; U.S. atty. So. Dist. Miss., Jackson, Miss., 1980—; chmn. investigative agys. subcom. U.S. Atty. Gen.'s Adv. Com., 1983-86, mem. law enforcement coordination subcom. and budget subcom., 1986-88; spl. coun. U.S. Senator T. Cochran, 1995—; chmn. AGAC subcom. law enforcement cooperation and victim/witness assitance, 1989—; instr. Hattiesburg Police Acad., 1977. Bd. dirs. Forrest County Youth Ct.; pres. South Ctrl. chpt. ARC, 1980-81; bd. dirs. Pine Burr Area coun. Boy Scouts Am.; mem. Atty. Gen.'s Adv. Com., 1981-82, 89-91; bd. dirs. Jackson Zoo, 1989-91. Mem. Miss. Prosecutors Assn. (pres.), Fed. Bar Assn., Miss. Bar Assn. (v.p. southern region), Am. Criminal Justice Assn., Nat. Dist. Attys. Assn., Miss. Trial Lawyers, Miss. Quarter Horse Assn. (pres.), Kiwanis. Baptist. Office: Spl Counsel Office of US Sen T Cochran 188 E Capital Ste 614 Jackson MS 39201-2125

PHILLIPS, GEORGE MICHAEL, communications executive; b. New Kensington, Pa., Nov. 6, 1947; s. Samuel and Margaret (Solomon) P.; m. Juliana Marie Orkwis, Nov. 8, 1969; children: Christopher Michael, Kimberly Ann, Jill Michelle. BS in Acctg., U. Md., 1969; MBA, Suffolk U., 1973. Cert. investment adviser. Cost analyst Polaroid Corp., Cambridge Mass., 1969-73; mgr. fin. analysis Clorox Co., Oakland, Calif., 1973-75; pres., chief operating officer, dir. Acton (Mass.) Corp., 1975-85; chmn., chief exec. officer W.P. Ihrie and Sons, Inc., 1983-92, Chimill Corp., 1980—, Condor Corp., 1985—, Vesper Corp., 1988—. Bd. vis. U. Md. Served with U.S. Army, 1969-70. Republican. Roman Catholic. Club: Pres.'s U. Md.

PHILLIPS, GERALD BAER, internal medicine educator, scientist; b. Bethlehem, Pa., Mar. 20, 1925; s. Abel H. and Cecilia (Blum) P.; m. Maria Bonzi Lewis, July 15, 1970; children: Abigail, Elizabeth. AB, Princeton U., 1948; MD, Harvard U., 1948. Diplomate Am. Bd. Internal Medicine. Intern Presbyn. Hosp., N.Y.C., 1948-50; rsch. fellow Thorndike Meml. Lab. Med. Sch. Harvard U., Boston, 1950-53; vis. fellow biochemistry Columbia U. Coll. Physicians and Surgeons, N.Y.C., 1954-56, from assoc. in medicine to assoc. prof., 1956-73, prof., 1973—; sr. attending physician Roosevelt Hosp.; attending physician Presbyn. Hosp. Sr. asst. surgeon USPHS, 1952-54. Recipient Lederle Med. Faculty award, 1963-66. Mem. Am. Fedn. for Clin. Rsch., Am. Soc. for Clin. Investigation, Am. Soc. for Biochemistry and Molecular Biology, Alpha Omega Alpha. Home: 196 E 75th St New York NY 10021 Office: 428 W 59th St New York NY 10019-1105 I attribute any success I may have had to heredity and luck.

PHILLIPS, GLYNDA ANN, editor; b. Riverside, Calif.; d. Henry Grady and Patricia (Loflin) P. BA in English, Millsaps Coll., 1977; postgrad., Miss. Coll. News editor The Magee (Miss.) Courier, 1981-84; editor Miss. Farm Bur. News and MFB Producer Edition, Jackson, 1984—. Contbr. articles to profl. jours. Recipient first place personal column Nat. Fedn. Press Women, 1984, first place personal column Miss. Press Women's Assn., 1984, first place feature articles Miss. Press Women's Assn., 1984. Avocation; church organist.

PHILLIPS, GRAHAM HOLMES, advertising executive; b. London, Jan. 30, 1939; emigrated to U.S., 1965, naturalized, 1974; s. Leonard George and Mary Marjorie (Holmes) P.; m. Laurel Gilbert; 1 child, Debra Ann. Student, RAF Coll. Cranwell, 1957-58; M.B.A., London U., 1962. Mgmt. trainee Shell Internat. Petroleum, Ltd., London, 1957-59; aviation sales rep., 1960-63; aviation sales mgr. Shell Philippines, 1964; with Ogilvy & Mather (U.S.), N.Y.C., 1965—, account mgr., 1965-73; dep. mgr., account supr. Ogilvy & Mather (U.S.), Houston, 1970, v.p. 1971-72, sr. v.p. mgmt. supr., 1972-73; mng. dir. Ogilvy & Mather Inc., Amsterdam, 1973-75; former pres., then chief exec. officer Ogilvy & Mather (Can.) Ltd., Toronto, from 1975, former chmn. from 1979; dir. Ogilvy & Mather, 1978—; former chief fin. officer Ogilvy & Mather Internat., from 1983; former exec. v.p. Ogilvy & Mather (U.S.), N.Y.C., from 1979, former gen. mgr., from 1980, former mng. dir., chief fin. officer, from 1981; now vice chmn. Ogilvy & Mather Worldwide, N.Y.C.; former chmn. Ogilvy & Mather N.Am. Mem. N.Y. Yacht Club. Episcopalian. Office: Ogilvy & Mather Worldwide Inc Worldwide Plz 309 W 49th St # 12 New York NY 10019-7316*

PHILLIPS, GRETCHEN, clinical social worker; b. Erie, Pa., July 14, 1941; life ptnr. Beverly Campbell, June 10, 1989. BA, Mercyhurst Coll., 1966; MSW, Yeshiva U., 1972; postgrad., Advanced Ctr. Psychotherapy, 1972-73, Washington Sq. Inst., 1973-77. Bd. cert. diplomate clin. social work; lic. social worker, N.Y. Psychiat. social worker, forensic social worker Creedmoor Psychiat. Ctr., Queens Village, N.Y., 1972-80; Med. social worker Bellevue Hosp. Ctr., N.Y.C., 1980-83; intake probation officer N.Y.C. Probation, Family Court, Bklyn., 1983—. Mem. NASW, Am. Group Psychotherapy Assn. Home: 125 Radford St # 3C Yonkers NY 10705-3049 Office: Probation Intake Kings Family Ct 283 Adams St Brooklyn NY 11201-2898

PHILLIPS, HARVEY, musician, music educator, arts consultant; b. Aurora, Mo., Dec. 2, 1929; s. Jesse E. and Lottie A. (Chapman) P.; m. Carol A. Dorvel, Feb. 22, 1954; children: Jesse E., Harvey G., Thomas

A. Student, U. Mo., 1947-48, Juilliard Sch. Music, 1950-54, Manhattan Sch. Music, 1956-58; Mus.D. (hon.), New Eng. Conservatory of Music, 1971; HHD (hon.), U. Mo., Columbia, 1987. Founder, v.p. Mentor Music, Inc., N.Y.C., 1958-79; v.p. Wilder Music, Inc., N.Y.C., 1971—; Magellan Music, Inc., N.Y.C., 1971—; Peaslee Music Inc., 1971—; mem. faculty Aspen Sch. Music, summer 1962, U. Wis., summer 1963, Hartt Sch. Music, Hartford, Conn., 1962-64, Mannes Sch. Music, N.Y.C., 1964-65; exec. v.p. Orchestra USA, N.Y.C., 1962-65; exec. v.p., personnel mgr., tubist Symphony of the Air N.Y.C., 1957-66; v.p. Brass Artists, Inc., N.Y.C., 1964—; adminstrv. asst. to Julius Bloom, Rutgers U., New Brunswick, N.J., 1966-67; v.p. fin. affairs New Eng. Conservatory of Music, Boston, 1967-71; mem. faculty dept. music Ind. U., Bloomington, 1971-94, disting. prof. emeritus, 1994—, Disting. prof. music, trustee, 1979—; adv. bd. Am. Brass Chamber Music, Inc., 1971—; chmn. bd. Summit Brass/Keystone Brass Inst., 1986-92, Rafael Mendez Brass Inst., 1993—; cons. Margun Music, Inc., 1977—. Brass coach Festival at Sandpoint, Idaho, Faculty Joven Orch., Spain, Festival Casal Orch., San Juan, P.R., 1964-76, dir., 1st Internat. Tuba Symposium Workshop, 1973, Brass-Wind Music Studios, Carnegie Hall, N.Y.C., 1961-67, tubist, King Bros. Circus Band, 1947, Ringling Bros. & Barnum and Bailey Circus Band, 1948-50, N.Y.C. Ballet Orch., 1951-71, N.Y.C. Opera Orch., 1951-62, Voice of Firestone Orch., 1951-53, Sauter-Finegan Orch., 1952-53, Band of Am., 1952-54, NBC Opera Orch., 1956-65, Bell Telephone Hour Orch., 1956-66, Goldman Band, 1957-62, founding mem., tubist, N.Y. Brass Quintet, 1954-67, condr., co-producer, Burke-Phillips All Star Concert Band, 1960-62, co-founder, tubist, Matteson-Phillips Tubajazz Consort, 1976—, rec. artist, Crest Records, 1958—; originator: Octubafest TubaChristmas, Tubasantas, TubaJazz, Tubaeaster; exec. editor Instrumentalist mag. Founder, pres. Harvey Phillips Found., Inc., N.Y.C., 1977—; bd. dirs. Mid-Am. Festival of the Arts, 1982—, Bloomington Area Arts Council, 1983—; judge 1st internat. tuba competition of CIEM Internat. Competition for Musical Performers, Geneva, 1991. Served with Field Band U.S. Army, 1955-56. Recipient Disting. Service to Music award Kappa Kappa Psi, 1978, Community Service award City of Bloomington, 1978, Nat. Assn. Jazz Educators award, 1977, 78, Nat. Music Conf. award, 1977, T.U.B.A. award 1978, MI Hummel The Tuba Player award, 1990, Mentor Ideal award Assn. Concert Bands, 1994; Harvey Phillips Day proclaimed New Eng. Conservatory Music, 1971, Harvey Phillips Day proclaimed Marionville, Mo. Bicentennial, 1976. Mem. Am. Fedn. Musicians, Tubists Universal Brotherhood Assn. (bd. advs. 1973—, pres. 1984—; hon.), Hoagy Carmichael Jazz Soc. (founder, acting pres. 1983—), Tau Beta Sigma, Phi Mu Alpha Sinfonia, Kappa Gamma Psi. Home and Office: Tubaranch 4769 S Harrell Rd Bloomington IN 47401-9028 Office: Sch of Music Ind U Bloomington IN 47405 The role of a performer and teacher is to give, to share skills and knowledge. My primary goal in life is to create new opportunities in the music profession, to develop, expand, and preserve the music arts.

PHILLIPS, HERBERT ALVIN, JR., retired financial executive; b. Ft. Worth, June 14, 1928; s. Herbert Alvin and Nota May (Sanders) P.; m. Laura Elizabeth Fulton, June 2, 1956; 1 child, Tamara. BS, Tex. Wesleyan, 1950. Asst. contr. Equifax Inc., Atlanta, 1969-74, corp. contr., 1974-78, v.p., treas., 1978-85, sr. v.p, chief fin. officer, 1985-91, exec. v.p., 1990-91; retired, 1991; also bd. dirs. affiliated cos. Equifax Inc., 1992; vice chmn. Internat. Assn. Fin. Execs. Insts., 1990-91, chmn., 1991-92. Served to lt. (j.g.) USN, 1960. Mem. Fin. Execs. Inst. (past area v.p., exec. and nominating com., vice chmn. 1988-89, chmn. 1989-90), Fin. Execs. Rsch. Found. (trustee). Presbyterian. Home: 5461 Woodland Ct Atlanta GA 30338-3043 Office: Equifax Inc 1600 Peachtree St NW Atlanta GA 30309-2403

PHILLIPS, HOWARD MITCHELL, real estate developer; b. Atlanta, Aug. 23, 1943; s. Howard Mitchell and Frances (Dunn) P.; m. Bonnie Elizabeth Byrd, June 19, 1965; children: Howard Mitchell III, Walker Pearce. BA, Emory U., 1965; MA, Duke U., 1969. Grad. asst. history dept. Duke U., Durham, N.C., 1967-69, coord. Angier B. Duke scholarship program Admissions Office, 1967-69; v.p., ptnr. Inform, Inc., Hickory, N.C., 1970-73; exec. v.p., chief operating officer Faison & Assocs., Charlotte, N.C., 1973—; bd. dirs., v.p. Madd, Inc., Charlotte, 1975—, Mindboggle, Inc., Charlotte, 1984—; bd. dirs., pres. Harley-Davidson of Metrolina, Inc., Charlotte, 1987-89; bd. dirs. Cookies, Inc., Fayetteville, N.C. Active Berryhill Preservation Orgn., Charlotte, 1980—. Stipe scholar, 1964. Mem. Urban Land Inst., Bldg. Owners and Mgrs. Assn., Internat. Coun. Shopping Ctrs., Phi Beta Kappa. Democrat. Presbyterian. Avocations: hunting, fishing, water skiing, flying. Office: Faison & Assocs 122 E Stonewall St Charlotte NC 28202

PHILLIPS, HOWARD WILLIAM, investment banker; b. N.Y.C., May 16, 1930; s. Louis and Helen (Klein) P.; children: Jan Davis, Richard Louis; m. Carol Napack, June 9, 1985. B.A., Dartmouth Coll., 1951, M.B.A., 1952; J.D., Harvard U., 1957. Bar: N.Y. 1957. Asso. Cahill, Gordon, Reindel & Ohl, N.Y.C., 1957-64; v.p., gen. counsel McCall Corp., N.Y.C., 1964-68; sr. v.p. McCall Corp., 1968-69; partner Oppenheimer & Co., N.Y.C., 1969-81; chmn. Holmes, Phillips & Co., N.Y.C., 1981-83; dir. corp. fin. DH Blair & Co., Inc., 1983—; bd. dirs. Monaco Fin., Denver, Food Ct. Entertainment Network, Inc., N.Y.C., Telechips Corp., Reno. Served to lt. (j.g.) USNR, 1952-54. Mem. Easthampton (N.Y.) Tennis Club, Longboat Key Club (Sarasota, Fla.). Home: 885 Park Ave New York NY 10021-0325 Office: DH Blair & Co Inc 44 Wall St New York NY 10005-2401

PHILLIPS, JACK CARTER, educational administrator; b. Scottsboro, Ala., Jan. 27, 1935; s. Howard E. and Marie (Carter) P.; m. Frances Juanita Fortham, May 17, 1967; 1 dau., Annette. A.B., Birmingham So. Coll., 1960; M.Div., Vanderbilt U., 1963; LL.D., Union Coll., Ky., 1981. Dir. ch. relations Birmingham So. Coll., Ala., 1968-70, Fla. So. Coll., Lakeland, 1970-73; asst. to. pres. U. Ala., Huntsville, 1973-75; dir. Marshall U. Found., Huntington, W.Va., 1975-77; pres. Nat. Methodist Found., Nashville, 1977-83, Union Coll., Barbourville, Ky., 1983—; dir. funding Bach Festival, Carmel, Calif., 1977-82; mem. estate planning commn. Vanderbilt U. Sch. Religion, Nashville, 1980—; cons., pres. J. Phillips & Assocs., Nashville, 1981—. Author: National TV Presence Program and Ministry for United Methodist Church, 1980. Served with USMC, 1954-57. Apptd. Ambassador of Goodwill Govt. of Ky., 1983; apptd. hon. Ky. Col., 1983. Mem. Council for Support Edn., C. of C. Republican. Clubs: Lafayette (Lexington, Ky.); Richland Country (Nashville). Lodges: Rotary; Kiwanis. Office: Union College President's Office Barbourville KY 40906

PHILLIPS, JAMES CHARLES, physicist, educator; b. New Orleans, Mar. 9, 1933; s. William D. and Juanita (Hahn) P.; m. Joanna Vandenberg, July 4, 1993. B.A., U. Chgo., 1952, B.S., 1953, M.S., 1955, Ph.D., 1956. Mem. tech. staff Bell Labs., 1956-58; NSF fellow U. Calif. at Berkeley, 1958-59, Cambridge (Eng.) U., 1959-60; faculty U. Chgo., 1960-68, prof. physics, 1965-68; mem. tech. staff Bell Labs., 1968—. Sloan fellow, 1962-66; Guggenheim fellow, 1967. Fellow Am. Phys. Soc. (Buckley prize 1972), Minerals, Metals and Materials Soc. (William Hume-Rothery award 1992); mem. NAS. Home: 204 Springfield Ave Summit NJ 07901-3909

PHILLIPS, JAMES D., retired diplomat; b. Peoria, Ill., Feb. 23, 1933; s. James D. and (Hardy) P.; m. Rosemary Leeds, Mar. 30, 1957 (div. Dec. 1981); children: Michael, Madolyn, Catherine; m. Lucie Gallistel, Jan. 7, 1984; stepchildren: Paula David. B.A., Wichita State U., 1954, M.A., 1957; cert., U. Vienna, Austria, 1956; postgrad., Cornell U., 1958-61. Joined fgn. svc. Dept. State, 1961; served at Am. embassy Paris, before 1975; Am. Consulate Zaire, before 1975; Dept. State Washington, before 1975; dep. chief of mission Am. Embassy, Luxembourg, 1975-78; charge d'affaires Am. Embassy, Banjul, The Gambia, 1978-80; student Nat. War Coll., Washington, 1980-81; office dir. Dept. State, Washington, 1981-84; consul gen. Am. Consulate, Casablanca, Morocco, 1984-86; U.S. amb. to Burundi, 1986-90; U.S. amb. Republic of the Congo, 1990-93; diplomat in residence The Carter Ctr., Atlanta, 1993-94; ret., 1994; pres. Dan Phillips & Assocs., Arlington, Va., 1994—; bd. dirs. Gulf Resources, H.M. Salaam Found., pres. Ctrl. Africa Found. Contbr. articles to Fgn. Svc. Jour. Bd. dirs. Jane Goodall Inst., 1994—. Avocations: golf; tennis; skiing. Home: 3607 N Military Rd Arlington VA 22207 Office: 1101 30th St NW Ste 200 Washington DC 20007

PHILLIPS, JAMES DICKSON, JR., federal judge; b. Scotland County, N.C., Sept. 23, 1922; s. James Dickson and Helen (Shepherd) P.; m. Jean

Duff Nunalee, July 16, 1960; children: Evelyn, James Dickson, III, Elizabeth Duff, Ida Wills. BS cum laude, Davidson Coll., 1943; JD, U. N.C., 1948. Bar: N.C. 1948. Asst. dir. Inst. Govt., Chapel Hill, N.C., 1948-49; ptnr. firm Phillips & McCoy, Laurinburg, N.C., 1949-55, Sanford, Phillips, McCoy & Weaver, Fayetteville, N.C., 1955-60; from asst. prof. to prof. law U. N.C., 1960-78, dean Sch. Law, 1964-74; circuit judge U.S. Ct. Appeals (4th cir.), 1978—; Mem. N.C. Wildlife Resources Commn., 1961-63; mem. N.C. Cts. Commn., 1963-75; also vice chmn.; chmn. N.C. Bd. Ethics, 1977-78. Served with parachute inf. U.S. Army, 1943-46. Decorated Bronze Arrowhead, Bronze Star, Purple Heart; recipient John J. Parker Meml. award, Thomas Jefferson award, Disting. Alumnus award U. N.C., 1993. Mem. Am. Law Inst. Democrat. Presbyterian.

PHILLIPS, JAMES EDGAR, lawyer; b. N.Y.C., Aug. 30, 1947; s. Jack Louis Phillips and Jacqueline (Kasper) Ehrman; children: Zachary J., Mark H. BA, Boston U., 1971; JD, Case Western Reserve U., 1975. Bar: Ohio 1975, U.S. Supreme Ct. 1977, U.S. Dist. Ct. (so. dist.) 1978, U.S. Ct. Appeals (6th cir.) 1981, U.S. Dist. Ct. (no. dist.) 1982. Asst. prosecutor Franklin County Prosecutor Office, Columbus, Ohio, 1975-77; sr. asst. prosecutor Franklin County Prosecutor Office, Columbus, 1977-79; assoc. Vorys, Sater, Seymour & Pease, Columbus, 1979-84, ptnr., 1984—; gen. counsel Nat. Fraternal Order of Police, Washington, 1987—, Conrail Police # 1, U.S. Postal Police # 2; pres. Ohio Ctr. for Law-Related Edn., 1985—. Author: Civil Recovery in Ohio, 1986, Collective Bargaining in the Pub. Sector, 1988; editor Bar Briefs; contbr. articles Jours., 1987-89. Fellow Ohio Bar Found., Columbus Bar Found.; mem. ABA (youth edn. for citizenship spl. com.), Ohio Bar Assn. (chmn. com. law-related edn. 1982-86), Columbus Bar Assn., Am. Judicature Soc., Sixth Cir. Jud. Conf. (life). Office: Vorys Sater Seymour & Pease PO Box 1008 52 E Gay St Columbus OH 43215-3161

PHILLIPS, JAMES LINFORD, agricultural affairs journalist, editor; b. Bristol, Pa., Nov. 27, 1943; s. James Henry and Dorothy (Morgan) P.; m. Judith Lynne Bylund, May 31, 1968; children: James Bruce, Scott Linford, Mark Kevin, Deborah Eleanor, Rheanna Lynne. Student, Pa. State U., 1961-63; B.A., Brigham Young U., 1973. Missionary LDS Ch., Hong Kong, 1963-66; Editor Mich. Farm News, Lansing, 1974-76; asst. editor Mich. Farmer, Lansing, 1976-77; assoc. editor livestock Farm Jour. mag., Phila., 1977-80; assoc. editor Profl. Farmers Am., Cedar Falls, Iowa, 1980-83; Midwest regional editor Progressive Farmer Mag., Birmingham, Ala., 1983-88, sr. editor, 1988—. Mem. Am. Agrl. Editors Assn., Nat. Corn Growers Assn. (Communicator of Yr. 1991), Kappa Tau Alpha, Sigma Delta Chi. Office: Progressive Farmer Mag PO Box 2581 Birmingham AL 35202-2581

PHILLIPS, JAMES MACILDUFF, material handling company executive, engineering and manufacturing executive; b. Carrick, Pa., June 13, 1916; s. John MacFarlane and Harriet (Duff) P.; m., Majorie Watson, June 1940 (div. 1964); children: James M. Jr., William W.; m. Regina Leininger, Apr. 1964 (dec.); children: Jeffrey M., Molly M., Becky J., Thomas S. BSME, Carnegie Inst. of Tech., 1938; grad., Pitts. Inst. Aeronautics, 1939; ME refresher, Pa. State U. State Coll., 1960; grad., Internat. Corespondence Sch., Scranton, Pa., 1988. Profl. engr. Pa. Draftsmen; engr. Phillips Mine & Mill Supply Co., Pitts. 1933-40, v.p. 1941-77; v.p. engring. Salem Brosius, Inc., Carnegie, Pa., 1956-64; pres. Phillips Corp., Bridgeville, Pa., 1977-83, Phillips Jet Flight, Bridgeville, Pa., 1977-83, Phillips Mine & Mill Inc., Pitts., 1964—; also chmn. bd. Phillips Mine & Mill Inc. Inventor in field; contbr. articles to profl. mags. Bd. dirs. Brashear Assn., Pitts. Mem. Air Force Assn., Aero Club of Pitts., Pa. Pilots Coun. (pres.), Quiet Birdmen (pres.), Early Bird Pilots, Exptl. Aircraft Assn. Aircraft Owners and Pilots Assn. (founding), OX-5 Pioneer Airmen (pres. 1987), St. Clair County Club. Methodist. Avocations: airline transport pilot, flight instructor, golf, tennis. Office: Phillips Mine & Mill Inc 1738 N Highland Rd Pittsburgh PA 15241-1200

PHILLIPS, JAMES OSCAR, minister; b. Greenville, S.C., Sept. 9, 1920; s. James Henry and Ida Louise (Fortner) P.; m. Marie Burns, Jan. 31, 1943; children: Martha Phillips Henderson, Gwendolyn Phillips Mullinax, Linda Phillips Richey. Grad. bible langs., Missionary Bapt. Sem., 1948, M in bible langs., 1949, D in bible langs., 1961; DDiv (hon.), Carolina Missionary Bapt. Theol. Sem., 1959. Pastor Vilonia (Ark.) Bapt. Ch., 1946-48, Harmony Missionary Bapt. Ch., Stephens, Ark., 1948-50, Corinth Missionary Bapt. Ch., Stephens, Ark., 1948-50, East Union Missionary Bapt. Ch., Hensley, Ark., 1950-52, Glendale Bapt. Ch., Mauldin, S.C., 1952—; pres. Landmark Missionary Inst., Mauldin, 1954—. Sgt. USMC, 1942-45. Mem. Am. Bapt. Assn. (pres. 1992-94, v.p. 1990-91, mem. Bapt. Suncay Sch. com. 1955—). Office: Glendale Bapt Ch 212 E Butler Ave Mauldin SC 29662-2129

PHILLIPS, JANET COLLEEN, educational association executive, editor; b. Pittsfield, Ill., Apr. 29, 1933; d. Roy Lynn and Catherine Amelia (Wills) Barker; m. David Lee Phillips, Feb 7, 1954; children—Clay Cullen, Sean Vincent. B.S., U. Ill, 1954. Reporter Quincy (Ill.) Herald Whig, 1951, 52, soc. editor, 1953; editorial asst. Pub. Info. Office U. Ill.-Urbana, 1953-54, asst. editor libr., 1954-61; asst. editor Assn. for Libr. and Info. Sci. Edn., State College, Pa., 1960-61, mng. editor, 1961-89, exec. sec., 1970-89; adminstrv. dir. Interlibr. Delivery Svc. of Pa., 1990—. Mem. AAUW, Assn. for Libr. and Info. Sci. Edn., Embroiderer's Guild Am., Pa. State Blue Course Club, Pa. State U. Women's Club, Theta Sigma Phi, Delta Zeta. Presbyterian. Avocations: travel; golf; sewing; needlecraft. Address: 471 Park Ln State College PA 16803-3208

PHILLIPS, JERRY JUAN, law educator; b. Charlotte, N.C., June 16, 1935; s. Vergil Ernest and Mary Blanche (Wade) P.; m. Anne Butler Colville, June 6, 1959; children: Sherman Wade, Dorothy Colville. B.A., Yale U., 1956, J.D., 1961; B.A., Cambridge (Eng.) U., 1958, M.A. (hon.), 1964. Bar: Tenn. bar 1961. Assoc. firm Miller, Martin, Hitching, Tipton & Lenihan, Chattanooga, 1961-67; asst. prof. law U. Tenn., 1967-72, assoc. prof., 1972-73, prof., 1973—, W.P. Toms prof., 1980—; advisor Tenn. Law Revision Commn., 1968-70; mem. Tenn. Jud. Council, 1970-74; adv. Fed. Interagy. Task Force on Products Liability, 1976-77; lectr. in field. Author: Products Liability in a Nutshell, 4th edit., 1993, Products Liability Cases and Materials on Torts and Related Law, 1980, Products Liability Treatise, 3 vols., 1986, Cases and Materials on Tort Law, 1992, Products Liability-Cases, Materials, Problems, 1994; advisor Tenn. U. Law Rev., 1977—. U. Tenn. grantee, 1978. Mem. ABA, Am. Law Inst., Knoxville Bar Assn., Am. Assn. Law Schs., Order of Coif, Phi Beta Kappa. Democrat. Episcopalian. Club: Knoxville Racquet. Office: 1505 Cumberland Ave Knoxville TN 37996-1800

PHILLIPS, JILL META, novelist, critic, astrologer; b. Detroit, Oct. 22, 1952; d. Leyson Kirk and Leona Anna (Rasmussen) P. Student pub. schs., Calif. Lit. counselor Book Builders, Charter Oak, Calif., 1966-77; prin. Moon Dance Astro Graphics, Covina, Calif., 1994—. Author: (with Leona Phillips) A Directory of American Film Scholars, 1975, The Good Morning Cookbook, 1976, G.B. Shaw: A Review of the Literature, 1976, T.E. Lawrence: Portrait of the Artist as Hero, 1977, The Archaeology of the Collective East, 1977, The Occult, 1977, D.H. Lawrence: A Review of the Literature and Biographies, 1978, Film Appreciation: A College Guide Book, 1979, Annus Mirabilis: Europe in the Dark and Middle Centuries, 1979, (with Leona Rasmussen Phillips) The Dark Frame: Occult Cinema, 1979, Misfit: The Films of Montgomery Clift, 1979, Butterflies in the Mind: A Précis of Dreams and Dreamers, 1980; The Rain Maiden: A Novel of History, 1987, Walford's Oak: A Novel, 1990, The Fate Weaver: A Novel in Two Centuries, 1991, Saturn Falls: A Novel of the Apocalypse, 1993; contbr. book revs. to New Guard mag., 1974-76; contbr. numerous articles to profl. jours. Mem. Young Ams. for Freedom, Am. Conservative Union, Elmer Bernstein's Film Music Collection, Ghost Club London, Count Dracula Soc., Dracula Soc. London, Richard III Soc. Republican. Home: 851 N Garsden Ave Covina CA 91724-2636 Office: Moon Dancer Astro Graphics 1037 N Grand Ave Ste 202 Covina CA 91724

PHILLIPS, JOHN DAVID, management consultant; b. Exeland, Wis., June 29, 1920; s. Mathew Frank and Iva (Bryant) P.; m. Estelle Margaret Pautsch, July 19, 1941; 1 son, John David. B.S., U. Wis., 1937. Partner Miss Wis. Cheese, 1946-56; dir. marketing Armour & Co., 1956-60; v.p. Am. Home Corp., 1960-66; founder, pres. R.J. Reynolds Foods, Inc., 1966-72; pres., dir. CBS/Columbia Group, N.Y.C., 1973-81; vice chmn. Nat. Exec. Service Corp., N.Y.C., 1981-94, dir., 1981—; ptnr. Edjon Ltd., Ft. Washington, Pa., 1990—; pres. Intercity Oil & Gas Corp., 1980—; bd. dirs.

Glenmore Distillers Co., Airwick Industries, Inc., subs. of Ciba-Geigy Corp., Tex. Internat. Co.; founder, chmn. Sr. Careers Planning and Placement Svc., 1987-94. Past trustee N.Y.C. Pub. Libr., Juniata Coll., Mt. Senario Coll., Greenwich Coun. Boy Scouts Am.; adv. bd. Howard U.; trustee Safe Streets, Washington, 1992—. With USAAF, 1944-46; adminstr. Am. Armenian Diocese, 1994—. Mem. Assn. Corp. Growth (past pres. N.Y.C.), Hamilton Coll. Parents Assn. Conglist (past pres., trustee). Clubs: Greenwich Country, Riverside Yacht, N.Y. Yacht; Links (N.Y.C.); Petroleum (Corpus Christi, Tex.). Home: Pilot Rock Riverside CT 06878 Office: 630 2d Ave New York NY 10016

PHILLIPS, JOHN DAVID, communications executive; b. Charlotte, N.C., Nov. 27, 1942; s. Louis and A. Viola (Pack) P.; m. Cheryl Helen Rudd; children: Hunter, Scott, Andrew, Lauren. Student, U. Va., 1962-63. Pres. RMS Distbg., Frankfurt, West Germany, 1965-66, NGK Spark Plugs, Atlanta, 1967-82; pres., chief exec. officer Advanced Telecommunication, Atlanta, 1982-88, also bd. dirs., 1982-88; owner Specialized Hauling Trucking Co., 1987-89; pres., CEO Resurgens Comm. Group, Inc., Atlanta, 1989-93; pres., CEO, bd. dirs. Actava Group, Inc., Atlanta, 1994-95; pres., CEO Metromedia Group Internat. Inc., 1995—. Served to capt. USMC, 1963-64. Republican. Methodist. Avocations: fishing, automobiles, flying, boating.

PHILLIPS, JOHN DAVISSON, retired lawyer; b. Clarksburg, W.Va., Aug. 21, 1906; s. Robert Bruce and Lela (Davisson) P.; m. Virginia Maxwell, Nov. 12, 1932; children: John Davisson, Julia Anne. Student, Washington and Lee U., 1924-25; A.B., W.Va. U., 1928, LL.B., 1930; postgrad., Oxford U., 1930-32. Bar: W.Va. 1932. Gen. practice law Wheeling, W.Va., 1932-91; of counsel Phillips, Gardill, Kaiser, Boos & Altmeyer; ret., 1991; asst. pros. atty. Ohio County, 1937-40; city solicitor City of Wheeling, 1942-47. Past mem. W.Va. State Bd. Law Examiners. Served as capt. USMCR, World War II. Fellow Am. Bar Founds.; mem. ABA, W.Va. Bar Assn. (pres. 1955-56), Am. Judicature Soc., Phi Kappa Psi, Phi Beta Phi, Fort Henry Club. Episcopalian. Home: 4 Arlington Dr Howard Pl Wheeling WV 26003 Office: 61 14th St Wheeling WV 26003-3411

PHILLIPS, JOHN EDWARD, zoologist, educator; b. Montréal, Que., Can., Dec. 20, 1934; s. William Charles and Violet Mildred (Lewis) P.; m. Eleanor Mae Richardson, Sept. 8, 1956; children: Heather Anne, Jayne Elizabeth, Jonathan David, Catherine Melinda, Wendy Susannah. BSc with honors, Dalhousie U., Halifax, N.S., 1956, MSc, 1957; PhD, Cambridge U., Eng., 1961. Asst. prof. Dalhousie U., Halifax, N.S., 1960-64; assoc. prof. U. B.C., Vancouver, Can., 1964-71, prof., 1971—; head dept. zoology, 1991—; vis. rschr. Cambridge (Eng.) U., 1972, 76, 81; chair grant selection com. Nat. Rsch. Coun. Can., Ottawa, Ont., 1969-71; mem. coun. Nat. Sci. and Engring. Rsch. Coun., Ottawa, 1983-87. Mem. editorial bd.: Can. Jour. Zoology, 1971-75, Am. Jour. Physiology, 1978-93, Jour. Experimental Biology, 1981-85; contbr. articles to profl. jours. Mem. grant selection com. Can. Cystic Fibrosis Found., Toronto, 1989-91; active Vancouver Bach Choir. Named to James chair St. Francis Xavier U., Antigonish, N.S., 1993. Fellow Royal Soc. Can.; mem. Can. Soc. Zoologists (sec. 1972-76, v.p 1976-78, pres. 1979), Am. Soc. Zoologists (exec. 1983-85, chair chron. comp. physiol. biochemistry 1983-85). Avocations: music, choir. Home: 12908-22 B Ave, White Rock, BC Canada V4A 6Z3 Office: U BC, Dept Zoology, Vancouver, BC Canada V6T 1Z4

PHILLIPS, JOHN F., air force officer; b. Neches, Tex., Sept. 3, 1942; s. Obie Lee and Sadie Louise (Perpener) P.; m. Blanche Evelyn Moore, July 3, 1963; children: Yulanda N. Phillips-Andrews, Ursula E. Phillips-Lindsley, Cheryl A. BS in Biology, Chemistry, Jarvis Christian Coll., 1963; M in Logsitics Mgmt., USAF Inst. Tech., 1975. Commd. 2d lt. USAF, 1965, advanced through grades to maj. gen., 1991—; sr. mil. advisor Air Force Communications and Electronics Assn., 1988-91. Contbr. articles to profl. jours. Bd. dirs. Bus. Sch., Ctrl. State U. Wilberforce, Ohio, 1990, Dayton (Ohio) Contemporary Dance Co., 1990. Decorated Legion of Merit, 1987. Mem. Am. Legion (chartered), Soc. Logistics Engrs., Moraine Country Club, Dayton Racquet Club. Home: 5309 Arnold Ave North Highlands CA 95660-4660 Office: USAF Jt Log Sys Ctr Afmc Wright Patter OH 45433

PHILLIPS, JOHN RICHARD, engineering educator; b. Albany, Calif., Jan. 30, 1934; s. Eric Lester and Adele Catherine (Rengel) P.; m. Joan Elizabeth Soyster, Mar. 23, 1957; children: Elizabeth Huntley, Sarah Rengel, Catherine Hale. BS, U. Calif., Berkeley, 1956; M in Engring., Yale U., 1958, PhD in Engring., 1960. Registered profl. engr., Calif. Chem. engr. Stanford Rsch. Inst., Menlo Park, Calif., 1960; rsch. engr. Chevron Rsch. Co., Richmond, Calif., 1962-66; mem. faculty Harvey Mudd Coll., Claremont, Calif., 1966—, prof. engring., 1974—, James Howard Kindleberger prof. engring., 1991—, dir. engring. clinic, 1977-93, chmn. engring. dept., 1993—; vis. prof. U. Edinburgh, Scotland, 1975, Cambridge (Eng.) U., 1981, ESIEE, France, 1981, Naval Postgrad. Sch., 1984-85, Calif. Poly. U., San Luis Obispo, 1992; vis. scientist So. Calif. Edison Co., 1980; founder Claremont Engring., 1973; cons. in field. Contbr. articles to profl. jours. 1st lt. AUS, 1960-62. Mem. Am. Inst. Chem. Engrs., Sigma Xi, Alpha Delta Phi, Tau Beta Pi. Home: 911 W Maryhurst Dr Claremont CA 91711-3320

PHILLIPS, JOHN ROBERT, college dean, educator; b. Henderson, Ky., Dec. 16, 1942; s. Leander Armstead and Ann Reid (Brown) P. Diploma, Lang. Inst., Chateauroux, France, 1966; BA, Centre Coll., Danville, Ky., 1969; MA, Western Ky. U., Bowling Green, 1973. Instr. Drury Coll., Springfield, Mo., 1971-73, Western Ky. U., Bowling Green, 1975-79; asst. prof. Thiel Coll., Greenville, Pa., 1979-83; scholar-in-residence, 1983-85; pvt. cons. Henderson, Ky., 1985-87; adj. prof. Lockyear Coll., Evansville, Ind., 1987-88, acad. dean, 1988-90, v.p. acad. affairs, 1990-91; exec. dir. human rels. commn Henderson (Ky.) Mcpl. Ctr., 1991-93; dean acad. affairs, prof. political studies/govt. Springfield (Ill.) Coll., 1993—; adj. prof. pub. administrn. Ind. State U., Terre Haute; field investigator on religion and culture in ancient city of Taxila, 1968, on indsl. pollution of hist. bldgs. and monuments, France, Italy, Austria, 1969; rschr. on nationalism, Scotland, 1972, on local govt. and urban devels., 1993; participant in internat. confs. on The Future of a United Germany, 1991; mem. adv. coun. St. John's Hosp. Sch. Respiratory Therapy, 1993, fin. com. Ursuline Acad. Sch. Bd., 1993—. Mem. editorial bd. Jour. Urban Affairs, 1985-89; manuscript referee Pub. Adminstrn. Rev., 1985-87; contbr. chpts. to multi-vol. reference series The Small City and Regional Community, 1981, 85, 87; contbr. articles on urban affairs, policy planning and federalism/intergovtl. rels. to profl. jours. Policy advisor Lt. Gov.'s Office, Frankfort, Ky., 1985-86; cons. Commn. on Ky.'s Future, Frankfort, 1985-87; mem. Bd. Cath. Edn., Diocese of Springfield, 1994—. Sgt. USAF, 1963-68. Mem. Am. Polit. Sci. Assn. (Leon Weaver Disting. Rsch. Award com. 1990-93), Am. Soc. Pub. Adminstrn. (publs. com. 1984-88, 92-95), Urban Affairs Assn. (publs. com. 1985-89, nominating com. 1984-85, 88-89), Am. Philatelic Soc., Am. Guild Organists, Pi Sigma Alpha. Democrat. Episcopalian. Avocations: reading, classical music, philately. Home: 2605 Delaware Dr Springfield IL 62702

PHILLIPS, JOSEF CLAYTON, insurance and investment company executive; b. Seattle, June 27, 1908; s. Joseph Clinton and Margaret Janet (Branlund) P.; m. Ada May Gummer, Sept. 24, 1931; 1 dau., Barbara Lee (Mrs. Richard Angus). Student, U. Wash., 1925-28, U. Paris, France, 1928-29. With Merrill, Lynch, Pierce, Fenner & Bean, Seattle, 1930-35; with United Pacific Corp., 1936—, pres., 1960-63, chmn. bd., 1963-67; dir., chmn. exec. com. United Pacific Ins. Co., 1957-72, N.W. Bldg. Co., M.G. Norton Corp., Pelican Seafoods. Clubs: Seattle Golf (Seattle); Wailea Golf (Maui, Hawaii). Home: Apt 2 12523 Greenwood Ave N Seattle WA 98133-8001

PHILLIPS, JOSEPH ROBERT, museum director; b. Utica, N.Y., Mar. 14, 1950; m. Dixie Anne Stedman, June 25, 1988. BS in Marine Transp., SUNY, 1972; MA in Mus. Studies, SUNY, Cooperstown, 1981; MBA, New Hampshire Coll., 1990. Capt., exec. dir. Hudson River Sloop Clearwater, Poughkeepsie, N.Y., 1972-75; capt., assoc. project dir. N.Y. Bicentennial Barge, Albany, 1975-76; mgr. hist. shipyard Maine Maritime Mus., Bath, 1978-81; various mgmt. positions Bath Iron Works Corp., 1982-86, various mktg. positions 1986-92; mus. dir. Maine State Mus., Augusta, 1992—; mktg. cons. Australian Warships Systems, Sydney, 1988; chmn. indsl. engring. panel Soc. Naval Architects Marine Engrs., 1984-86, chmn. shipbuilding standards panel, 1984-86. Bd. dirs. Maine Community Cultural Alliance, 1992—, Friends of Maine State Mus., 1992—; mem. Maine Cultural Affairs

Coun., 1992—, State House and Capital Park Commn., 1992—, Blaine House Commn., 1994—. Office: Maine State Mus State House Station 83 Augusta ME 04333

PHILLIPS, JOYCE MARTHA, human resources executive; b. Bridgeport, Conn., Dec. 18, 1952; d. Stephen and Shirley B. (Howard) Tabory; m. Glenn L. Phillips, July 14, 1974. BA in English, Fairfield (Conn.) U., 1974; MS in Indsl. Rels., U. New Haven, 1982. Tchr. English and Reading Fairfield Woods Jr. High Sch., 1975; asst. to v.p. mktg. Bunker Ramo Corp., Trumbull, Conn., 1975-76; rep. in investor rels. Gen. Electric Co., Fairfield, 1976-77, specialist in manpower rels., 1977-79; specialist in employee benefits Gen. Electric Co., Bridgeport, Conn., 1979-80, specialist in employee rels., orgn. and staffing, 1980-84; mgr. hdqrs. personnel and office svcs. Armtek Corp., New Haven, 1984-87, dir. compensation and benefits, 1987-89; v.p. human resources (div. sr. human resources officer) Citibank, N.Y.C., 1989-91, v.p. compensation global fin., 1991—. Counsel Fairfield U. Alumni Adv. Coun. Avocations: tennis, piano, dance, boating. Office: Citibank 399 Park Ave Fl 3 New York NY 10043

PHILLIPS, JULIA MILLER, film producer; b. N.Y.C., Apr. 7, 1944; d. Adolph and Tanya Miller; m. Michael Phillips (div.); 1 dau., Kate Elizabeth. B.A., Mt. Holyoke Coll., 1965. Former prodn. asst. McCall's Mag.; later advt. copywriter Macmillan Publs.; editorial asst. Ladies Home Journal, 1965-69; later assoc. editor; East Coast story editor Paramount Pictures, N.Y.C., 1969; head Mirisch Prodns., N.Y., 1970; creative exec. First Artists Prodns., N.Y.C., 1971; founded (with Tony Bill and Michael Phillips) Bill/Phillips Prodns., 1971; founder, producer Ruthless Prodns., Los Angeles, 1971—. Author: You'll Never Eat Lunch in this Town Again, 1990, Driving Under the Influence, 1995; films include Steelyard Blues, 1972, The Sting, 1973 (Acad. award for best picture of yr.), Taxi Driver, 1976 (Palme d'or for best picture), The Big Bus, 1976, Close Encounters of the Third Kind, 1977, (co-producer) The Beat, 1988; dir. The Estate of Billy Buckner, for Women Dirs. Workshop, Am. Film Inst., 1974. Recipient Katherine McFarland Short Story award, 1963, Short Story award Phi Beta Kappa, 1964. Mem. Acad. Motion Picture Arts and Scis., Writers Guild. Office: care Writers Guild 8955 Beverly Blvd Los Angeles CA 90048-2420*

PHILLIPS, KAREN BORLAUG, economist, association executive; b. Long Beach, Calif., Oct. 1, 1956; d. Paul Vincent and Wilma (Tish) Borlaug. Student Cath. U. P.R., 1973-74; B.A., U. N.D., 1977, B.S., 1977; postgrad. George Washington U., 1978-80. Research asst. research and spl. programs adminstrn. U.S. Dept. Transp., Washington, 1977-78, economist, office of sec., Washington, 1978-82; profl. staff mem. (majority) Com. Commerce, Sci., Transp., U.S. Senate, Washington, 1982-85, tax economist (majority) com. on fin., 1985-87, chief economist (minority) senate com. on fin., 1987-88; commr. Interstate Commerce Commn., 1988-94; v.p. legislation Assn. Am. Railroads, Washington, 1994—. Contbg. author studies, publs. in field. Recipient award for Meritorious Achievement, Sec. Transp., 1980, Spl. Achievement awards, 1978, 80, Outstanding Performance awards, 1978, 80, 81. Mem. Am. Econ. Assn., Women's Transp. Seminar (Woman of Yr. award 1994), Transp. Research Forum, Tax Coalition, Assn. Transp. Law, Logistics, and Policy, Blue Key, Phi Beta Kappa, Omicron Delta Epsilon. Republican. Lutheran. Office: Assn Am Railroads 50 F St NW Washington DC 20001

PHILLIPS, KAY RANDELLE, association executive; b. St. Louis, Nov. 13, 1947; d. Clyde Randol and Esther (Moore) P.; m. Murvel D. Pretorius, Aug. 17, 1968; 1 dau., Jennifer Marie; m. 2d A. Fred Timmerman, Apr. 1, 1980. Student Knox Coll., 1966-68; B.A. in Sociology, U. Ill., 1971; M.A. in Pub. Adminstrn., Sangamon State U., 1978. Juvenile probation officer, program coordinator DRI-Roads Program, Peoria County (Ill.), 1971-76; sales rep. Xerox Corp., Peoria, 1976; personnel coordinator, staff devel. and tng. mgr. Methodist Med. Ctr., Peoria, 1977; adminstrv. asst. Lutheran Med. Ctr., Wheat Ridge, Colo., 1978; assoc. dir. planning Swedish Med. Ctr., Englewood, Colo., 1979; v.p. planning, mktg. and pub. affairs Colo. Hosp. Assn., Denver, 1980—; cons. in field. Bd. dirs. Parent Tchr. League, University Hills Luth. Sch., 1982-83; fund raiser United Way; Mem. Am. Coll. Hosp. Adminstrs., Colo. Code of Cooperation (sec.), Pub. Relations Soc. Am., Am. Soc. Hosp. Pub. Relations, Colo. Soc. Hosp. Pub. Relations, Soc. for Hosp. Planning. Republican. Presbyterian. Office: Spaldin Rehab Hosp 4500 E Iliff Ave Denver CO 80222

PHILLIPS, KEITH WENDALL, minister; b. Portland, Oreg., Oct. 21, 1946; s. Frank Clark and Velma Georgina (Black) P.; m. Mary Katherine Garland, July 16, 1973; children: Joshua, Paul, David. BA, UCLA, 1968; MDiv, Fuller Theology Sem., 1971, D. of Ministries, 1972; LHD (hon.), John Brown U., 1990. Dir. Youth For Christ Clubs, L.A., 1965-71; pres. World Impact, L.A., 1971—; mem. urban ministries resources svcs. editorial adv. bd. Zondervan Pub. House; commencement speaker Tabor Coll., 1969, 91, John Brown U., 1990. Author: Everybody's Afraid in the Ghetto, 1973, They Dare to Love the Ghetto, 1975, The Making of a Disciple, 1981, No Quick Fix, 1985. Chmn. L.A. Mayor's Prayer Breakfast Com., 1985—. Named Disting. Staley lectr., 1969. Mem. Evangelistic Com. of Newark (pres. 1976—), World Impact of Can. (pres. 1978—), The Oaks (pres. 1985—), Faith Works (pres. 1987—). Baptist. Office: World Impact 2001 S Vermont Ave Los Angeles CA 90007 *Our knowledge of God's Word outruns our obedience. The challenge for Christians is to live what we know.*

PHILLIPS, KENNETH HIGBIE, association executive; b. Newark, Mar. 5, 1940; s. William Lewis and Mary (Higbie) P.; m. Belinda Rinker, June 16, 1962, (div. May 1982); children: Karlton Allen, Tania Rinker, Larissa Jennifer Cornell; m. Rebecca Ann Stiles, Sept. 1, 1989. BA, Princeton U., 1962; MA in English Lang. and Lit., U. Mich., 1963; MA in Econs., NYU, 1972. Pres. Assn. Internat. des Etudiants en Sciences Economiques et Commerciales-U.S., N.Y.C., 1964-66; coord., planning and project devel. Inst. Internat. Edn., N.Y.C., 1966-72; dir. devel. Save the Children, Westport, Conn., 1972-78, v.p. 1978-82; nat. exec. dir. Childreach, Warwick, R.I., 1982-93, pres., 1988-93; dir. European program Christian Children's Fund, Geneva, 1993—; chmn., bd. dirs. Internat. Svc. Agys., Washington, 1978-84; adv. com. on standards Philanthrophic Adv. Svc. Coun., Better Bus. Bur., Washington, 1978-82; chmn., mem. adv. group Brown U. Rsch. Briefing Exch., Providence, 1987-90; vice chmn., bd. dirs. Sharing Internat., Washington, 1984-88; chmn. InterAction Working Group on Conv. on the Rights of the Child, Washington, 1989-92; chmn. InterAction Com. on Industry Standards, Washington, 1989-93. Contbr. articles on philanthropic mktg., mgmt. and ethics to profl. jours. Bd. dirs. , Common Cause R.I. Providence, 1987-91, Internat. Assn. Surgical Contraception, N.Y.C., 1977-82; Dist. 11 candidate R.I. Ho. of Reps., Providence, 1986; del. Constl. Conv. R.I. Dist. 11, Providence, 1985-86; dir. AIESEC Congress Com., N.Y.C., 1987-88; adv. bd. Caring for Children, San Francisco, 1987-93; co-founder, chmn., bd. dirs. AIESEC-US Alumni Soc. (Internat. Assn. Students Econs. and Commerce-U.S.), N.Y.C., 1967-70; expert witness Congl. Com. on Fgn. Assistance, charitable codes; mem. Iota Class Leadership R.I., Providence, 1989; chmn. West Broadway Neighborhood Assn., 1992-93. Ford Found. grantee, Lausanne, Switzerland, 1966; Brown U. fellow, 1985-92; recipient Spirit of Youth award Father Flannigan's Boys Town. Mem. InterAction: Am. Coun. for Voluntary Internat. Action (bd. dirs., exec. com. 1984-92, sec. 1985-89, vice chair 1989-90, chair, 1990-92, chmn. nominating com. 1984-85). Avocations: historic preservation of Victorian homes, photography.

PHILLIPS, KEVIN PRICE, columnist, author; b. N.Y.C., Nov. 30, 1940; s. William Edward and Dorothy Virginia (Price) P.; m. Martha Eleanor Henderson, Sept. 28, 1968; children: Andrew, Alexander. A.B., Colgate U., 1961; postgrad. U. Edinburgh, Scotland, 1959-60; LL.B., Harvard U., 1964. Bar: N.Y. 1965, D.C. 1965. Adminstrv. asst. to Congressman Paul Fino, 1964-68; spl. asst. atty. gen. 1965-69; newspaper columnist syndicated King Features, 1970-83; pres. Am. Polit. Rsch. Corp., 1971; commentator Nat. Pub. Radio, 1984—; spl. asst. to campaign mgr. Nixon for Pres. Com., 1968. Author: The Emerging Republican Majority, 1969, Electoral Reform and Voter Participation, 1975, Mediacracy, 1975, Post-Conservative America, 1982, The Business Case for a National Industrial Strategy, 1984, The Politics of Rich and Poor, 1990, Boiling Point: Democrats, Republicans and the Decline of Middle-Class Prosperity, 1993, Arrogant Capital: Washington, Wall Street and The Frustration of American Politics, 1994; editor, pub.: The American Political Report, 1971—; contbg. columnist L.A. Tim.

Mem. N.Y., D.C. bars, Phi Beta Kappa. Home: 5115 Moorland Ln Bethesda MD 20814-6117 Office: 7316 Wisconsin Ave Bethesda MD 20814-2925

PHILLIPS, LARRY EDWARD, lawyer; b. Pitts., July 5, 1942; s. Jack F. and Jean H. (Houghtelin) P.; m. Karla Ann Hennings, June 5, 1976; 1 son, Andrew H.; 1 stepson, John W. Dean IV. B.A., Hamilton Coll., 1964; J.D., U. Mich., 1967. Bars: Pa. 1967, U.S. Dist. Ct. (we. dist.) Pa. 1967, U.S. Tax Ct. 1969. Assoc. Buchanan, Ingersoll, Rodewald, Kyle & Buerger, P.C. (now Buchanan Ingersoll P.C.), Pitts., 1967-73, mem., 1973—. Mem. Am. Coll. Tax Counsel, Tax Mgmt. Inc. (adv. bd.), Pitts. Tax Club, ABA (sect. taxation, com. on corp. tax and sect. real property, probate and trust law), Allegheny County Bar Assn., Pa. Bar Assn. Republican. Presbyterian. Clubs: Duquesne, St. Clair County. Contbr. articles to profl. jours. Office: Buchanan Ingersoll 600 Grant St Ste 5800 Pittsburgh PA 15219-2703

PHILLIPS, LAUGHLIN, museum president, former magazine editor; b. Washington, Oct. 20, 1924; s. Duncan and Marjorie Grant (Acker) P.; m. Elizabeth Hood, 1956 (div. 1975); children: Duncan Vance, Elizabeth Laughlin; m. Jennifer Stats Cafritz, 1975. Student, Yale U., 1942-43; M.A., U. Chgo., 1949. Fgn. service officer, 1949-64; vice consul Hanoi, Vietnam, 1950-53; 2d sec. Tehran, Iran, 1957-59; co-founder Washingtonian mag., 1965, editor, 1965-74, editor-in-chief, 1974-79; pres. Washington Mag., Inc., 1965-79; dir. Phillips Collection, 1972-92, pres., chmn. of bd., 1967—; bd. dirs. Nat. Capital Area div. UN Assn. Am. (nat. coun. mem.). Bd. trustee MacDowell Colony, 1977-79, Nat. Com. for an Effective Congress, 1966—. Served with AUS, 1943-46, PTO. Decorated Bronze Star; comendador Orden de Mayo al Mérito (Argentina); chevalier de l'Ordre de la Couronne (Belgium), knight's cross 1st class Order of Danebrog (Denmark); officier Arts et Lettres (France). Mem. Nat. Coun., UN Assn. Am. Clubs: Cosmos (Washington), Metropolitan (Washington), Rolling Rock (Ligonier, Pa.). Home: 3044 O St NW Washington DC 20007-3107

PHILLIPS, LAWRENCE H., II, neurologist; b. Clarksburg, W.Va., Dec. 30, 1947; m. Elayne K. Phillips; children: Joshua, Melanie. AB in Biology, Princeton U., 1970; MD, W.Va. U., 1974. Diplomate Am. Bd. Psychiatry and Neurology (test com. 1990—), Am. Bd. Electrodiagnostic Medicine; lic. Minn., Va. Intern U. Wis. Hosps., Madison, 1974-75; resident in neurology Mayo Clinic, Rochester, Minn., 1975-78, rsch. fellow in neurophysiology, 1978-79; instr. neurology Mayo med. sch. U. Minn., Rochester, 1979-80; asst. prof. U. Va. Med. Sch., Charlottesville, 1981-87, assoc. prof., 1987—; dir. electromyography lab. U. Va. Med. Ctr., Charlottesville, 1981—, dir. neuromuscular ctr, Muscular Dystrophy Assn. clinic, 1983—; cons. neurology, Mayo Clinic, Rochester, 1979-80, VA Hosp. Salem, Va., 1981—; cons. panel AMA Diagnostic and Therapeutic Tech. Assessment, 1989—, arbitrator panel, 1990—; expert panel mem. NIH, 1991; med. adv. com. Diabetes Rsch. and Training Ctr., U. Va., 1981-88; com. for respiratory intensive care unit U. Va. Hosp., 1988; various coms. Nat. Bd. Med. Examiners. Editorial reviewer Jour. Urology, 1986—, Western Jour. Medicine, 1990—, Jour. Applied Physiology, 1990—, Jour. Neurosurgery, 1990—, So. Med. Jour., 1993—; contbr. articles to profl. jours. Active med. adv. bd. Myasthenia Gravis Found., 1983—, bd. dirs. 1986—; bd. dirs. ARC Ctrl. Va. Chpt., 1985-91, exec. com. 1990-91. Recipient Young Investigator Travel award Internat. Congress Electromyography, 1979. Mem. Am. Neurological Assn., Am. Acad. Neurology (neuroepidemiology sect. 1978—, chmn. edn. com. 1992—), clin. neurophysiology sect. 1992—), Am. Assn. Electrodiagnostic Medicine (chmn. course com. 1992—, annual meeting coord. com. 1992—, and other coms.), Assn. Univ. Profs. Neurology (undregraduate edn. com. 1993—), Va. Neurological Soc. (pres. 1993—), Sigma Xi. Home: 1405 Wendover Dr Charlottesville VA 22901 Office: U Va Med Ctr Dept Neurology Box 394 Charlottesville VA 22908

PHILLIPS, LAWRENCE S., apparel company executive; b. 1927; s. Seymour J. P.; married. B.A., Princeton U., 1948. With Phillips-Van Heusen Corp., N.Y.C., 1948—, v.p., 1951-59, exec. v.p., 1959-68, pres., 1968-87, past chief exec. officer, dir., chmn., 1987—. Mem. Am. Apparel Mfrs. (dir.) Office: Phillips-Van Heusen Corp 1290 Avenue Of The Americas New York NY 10104-0012*

PHILLIPS, LAYN R., lawyer; b. Oklahoma City, Jan. 2, 1952; s. James Arthur Cole and Eloise (Gulick) P.; m. Kathryn Hale, Aug. 17, 1986; children: Amanda, Parker, Graham. BS, U. Tulsa, 1974, JD, 1977; postgrad., Georgetown U., 1978-79. Bar: Okla. 1977, D.C. 1978, Calif. 1981, Tex. 1991. Asst. U.S. atty. Miami, 1980-81, L.A., 1980-83; trial atty. Bur. of Competition, Washington, 1977-80; U.S. atty. U.S. Dist. Ct. (no. dist.) Okla., Tulsa, 1983-87; judge U.S. Dist. Ct. (we. dist.) Okla., Oklahoma City, 1987-91; litigation ptnr. Irell & Manella, Newport Beach, Calif., 1991—; tchr. trial practice U. Tulsa Coll. Law, Okla. City U. Law Sch.; lectr. Attys. Gen's. Adv. Inst., Washington. Pres. Am. Inn of Ct. XXIII, Sch. Law, Okla. U., 1989-90; pres. Am. Inn of Ct. CVIII, Sch. Law., Okla. City U. 1990-91. Named one of Outstanding Young Ams., U.S. Jaycees, 1989. Office: Irell & Manella 840 Newport Ctr Dr Newport Beach CA 92660

PHILLIPS, LOYAL, newspaper executive; b. Cullman, Ala., Apr. 11, 1905; s. Monroe and Lucy Ann (Bailey) P.; m. Evelyn Caldwell, Apr. 8, 1928; children: Sharon Kay, Terry Lynn. B.A., Howard Coll. (now Samford U.), 1928. Promotion mgr. Atlanta Georgian-Am., 1929; classified advt. mgr. Birmingham (Ala.) Post, 1930, Nashville Banner, 1931-32, Omaha World-Herald, 1933-34; classified advt. mgr. Washington Daily News, 1936, acting advt. dir., 1937-38; co-founder, partner, editor Parish-Phillips Newspaper Advt. Syndicate, Miami, Fla., 1939-43; also spl. cons. Tampa Times, Miami News, Washington Post; columnist Editor and Pub. mag., N.Y.C., 1940; advt. dir. New Orleans Item, 1945-49; gen. mgr.; treas. St. Petersburg Ind., Inc., 1950-59, editor, pub., sec., treas., 1952-59, pres., 1959-62; pres. Petersburg (Va.) Newspaper Corp., 1959-62; sec-treas. Punta Gorda Herald and Clewiston News, 1953—; gen. mgr. Southwest Citizen; pres. Laurel (Miss.) Leader-Call, 1959-62, Independent, Inc., 1962—, WCCF radio sta., 1960; pub., v.p. Ocala (Fla.) Star-Banner, 1963-67; gen. mgr. Elizabeth City (N.C.) Daily Advance, 1967—, co-pub., 1970—; asst. to pres. Dear Publ. & Radio, Inc., 1971-72; gen. mgr. Seabag Newspaper for Norfolk Navy Base, 1967—; roving columnist Gannett Fla. Newspapers, 1973; dir. Citizens Pub. Co. Author: Newspaper Advertising, 1946, Fifty Successful Advertising Ideas, 1948. Active ARC, Goodwill Industries, Childrens Service Bur., Salvation Army, Boy Scouts Am.; treas. New Orleans Art Acad.; chmn. Gov.'s Traffic Safety Adv. Com. State Fla., 1956; chmn. Elizabeth City United Fund, 1969, pres., 1970; Bd. dirs. Greater New Orleans. Served as lt. (j.g.) USNR, 1943-47. Named VFW Man of Yr., Elizabeth City (N.C.), 1971, Man of Yr. City of Fort Walton Beach (Fla.), 1981, Cullman, 1982, Alumnus of Yr. Samford U., 1981. Mem. Nat. Newspaper Classified Advt. Mgrs. (v.p. 1933—), So. Newspaper Pubs. Assn. (dir., chmn. pub. relations), Sales Exec. Council, Assn. Commerce, Newspaper Advt. Execs. Assn., Internat. House, Elizabeth City C. of C. (pres. 1971), Lambda Chi Alpha. Clubs: Metairie Country, Quarterback, New Orleans Advertising (pres. 1945-46). Lodge: Rotary. Home: 102 4th Ave NE Fort Walton Beach FL 32547-2507

PHILLIPS, LYMAN C., utility company executive; b. 1939. BBA, U. Toledo, 1962. With Toledo Edison Co., 1962-88, v.p., 1976-84, sr. v.p., 1984-87, exec. v.p., 1987-88; exec. v.p. Centerior Energy Corp., Cleve., 1988—; also pres., dir. Cleve. Electric Illuminating Co. Office: Centerior Energy Corp 6200 Oak Tree Blvd Cleveland OH 44131-2510 Office: The Ceico Co 55 Public Sq Cleveland OH 44113-1913

PHILLIPS, MARGARET CROUSE, gifted and talented educator; b. Denton, Md., Oct. 19, 1937; d. Earl Monroe and Ida Ruth (Jones) Crouse; m. Bobby Jack Phillips, July 5, 1960. BS, Towson State U., 1959; postgrad., U. Md., 1961-65; cert. gifted edn., U. Fla., 1968. Lic. tchr., Fla. Tchr. 5th grade Caroline County Bd. Edn., Denton, Md., 1959-60; tchr. 1st grade Talbot County Bd. Edn., Easton, Md., 1960-64; tchr. 4th grade Caroline County Bd. Edn., Denton, 1964-65, tchr. 5th grade, 1965-69; tchr. 5th grade Marion County Bd. Edn., Ocala, Fla., 1969-77, tchr. 1st grade, 1977-80, tchr. gifted, 1980—; lead tchr. Peer Tchr. Program, Marion County, 1985-89; elem. rep. Comprehensive Health Coun. State Fla., 1976; tchr., coord. Parents Aid Sch. Success, Ocala, 1978-79; del. to Russia for gifted edn. People to People Internat., 1991. Bd. dirs. Ocala Community Concerts, 1982-83; choir mem. Ctrl. Bapt. Ch., Ocala, 1969-92, Sunday Sch. decoration com.; dir. Community Concert Assn., 1992-93. Named Tchr. of Yr. Marion County Coun. Exceptional Edn., Ocala, 1983, Tchr. of Yr. Gifted Marion County Exeptional Student Edn., Ocala, 1991, Woman of Yr. Marion County Woman's Club, Ocala, 1990. Mem. Exceptional Student Edn., Fla. Talented and Gifted (Tchr. of Yr. Marion County 1992), Greater Ocala Woman's Club (bd. dirs. 1989-92), Ocala Woman's Club (evening div. pres. 1979-89), Gifted Orgn. Moscow, Alpha Delta Kappa. Democrat. Avocations: music, art, travel, reading. Home: 1851 NE 40th Cir Ocala FL 34470-5039

PHILLIPS, OLIVER, botany educator. Prof. dept. biology Washington U., St. Louis. Recipient Edmund H. Fulling award Soc. Econ. Botany, 1992. Office: Wash Univ Box 1137 Biology Department Saint Louis MO 63130*

PHILLIPS, OLIVER C., classics educator; b. Kansas City, Mo., Oct. 23, 1929; s. Oliver Clyde and Blanche (Campbell) P.; m. Shirley Ann Liese, June 6, 1954; children—Stephen Oliver, Mark Clyde. Student, Kansas City Jr. Coll., 1946-48; B.S. in Edn., U. Kans., 1950; postgrad., Perkins Sch. Theology, So. Meth. U., 1951-53; M.A., U. Mo., 1954; Ph.D., U. Chgo., 1962. Tchr. Great Bend High Sch., Kans., 1950; tchr. Southeast High Sch., Kansas City, Mo., 1951, Northeast Jr. High Sch., Kansas City, Mo., 1954-55; from assoc. prof. to prof. William Jewell Coll., Liberty, Mo., 1955-64; dir. corr. study, prof. classics U. Kans., Lawrence, 1964-93; ret.; vis. prof. U. Cologne, Fed. Republic of Germany, 1983. Named Mortar Bd. Outstanding Educator, U. Kans., Lawrence, 1978; U. Chgo. Shorey fellow, 1958-59. Mem. Classical Assn. of Mid. West and South (Ovatio award 1993), Am. Philol. Assn., Am. Classical League, Vergilian Soc. Episcopalian. Home: 2235 Westchester Rd Lawrence KS 66049-1635

PHILLIPS, OWEN MARTIN, oceanographer, geophysicist, educator; b. Parramatta, Australia, Dec. 30, 1930; s. Richard Keith and Madeline (Lofts) P.; m. Merle Winifred Simons, Aug. 8, 1953; children: Lynette Michelle, Christopher Ian, Bronwyn Ann, Michael Stuart. B.Sc., Sydney (Australia) U., 1952; Ph.D., U. Cambridge (Eng.), 1955. Rsch. fellow Imperial Chem. Industries, U. Cambridge, 1955-57; asst. prof., then assoc. prof. Johns Hopkins, 1957-61; asst. dir. rsch. U. Cambridge, 1961-64; prof. geophys. mechanics Johns Hopkins, 1964—, chmn. dept. earth and planetary scis. 1971-77, 88-89, Decker prof. sci. and engring., 1975—; Cons. to industry, 1960—; Mem. council mems. Nat. Center Atmospheric Research, 1964-67, chmn. rev. and goals, 1965-67; mem. com. global atmospheric research project Nat. Acad. Sci., 1967-69; mem. Waterman award com. NSF, 1975-77. Author: The Dynamics of the Upper Ocean, 1966, 2d edit., 1968, 3d edit., 1977, Russian edit., 1969, 2d Russian edit., 1980, Chinese edit., 1986, The Heart of the Earth, 1968, Italian edit., 1970, 74, 77, The Last Chance Energy Book, 1979, 2d edit., 1980, Japanese edit., 1986; editor: Wave Dynamics and Radio Probing of the Ocean Surface, 1986, Flow and Reactions in Permeable Rocks, 1991; assoc. editor Jour. Fluid Mechanics, 1964-95; regional editor Proc. Royal Soc., 1990—; contbr. numerous articles to profl. jours. Trustee Roland Park Country Sch., 1974-81; trustee Chesapeake Research Consortium, 1972-76, sec., 1972. Recipient Adams prize U. Cambridge, 1965, Sverdrup Gold medal Am. Meteorol. Soc., 1974. Fellow Royal Soc. (London), Am. Meteorol. Soc. (publs. comm. 1971-77, planning com. 1983-84); mem. Am. Geophys. Union, Md. Acad. Sci. (sci. coun. 1974-85, pres. 1979-85, trustee 1985-87), Phi Beta Kappa, Sigma Xi, Pi Tau Sigma. Home: 23 Merrymount Rd Baltimore MD 21210-1908

PHILLIPS, PAMELA KIM, lawyer; b. San Diego, Feb. 23, 1958; d. John Gerald and Nancy Kimiko (Tabuchi) Phillips; m. R. Richard Zanghetti, Sept. 16, 1989. BA cum laude, The Am. U., 1978; JD, Georgetown U., 1982. Bar: N.Y. 1983, Fla. 1983, U.S. Dist. Ct. (so. dist.) N.Y. 1983, U.S. Dist. Ct. (mid. dist.) Fla. 1994. Assoc. Curtis, Mallet-Prevost, Colt & Mosle, N.Y.C., 1982-84; assoc. LeBoeuf, Lamb, Greene & MacRae, N.Y.C., 1984-90, ptnr., 1991—. Mng. editor The Tax Lawyer, Georgetown U. Law Sch., Washington, 1980-81. Coun. mem. The Fresh Air Fund, 1991-94. Am. Univ. scholar, Washington, 1976-78. Mem. ABA, Women's Bar Assn., Bar Assn. of City of N.Y. (sec. young lawyers com. 1987-89, chmn. 1989-91, second century com. 1990-93, banking law com. 1991-94), N.Y. Athletic Club, Jacksonville Bar Assn., The River Club. Democrat. Roman Catholic. Avocations: tennis, travel. Home: 108 Putters Way Ponte Vedra Beach FL 32082 Office: LeBoeuf Lamb Greene & MacRae 125 W 55th St New York NY 10019-5369 also: 50 N Laura St Ste 2800 Jacksonville FL 32202-3656

PHILLIPS, PATRICIA JEANNE, retired school administrator, consultant; b. Amarillo, Miss., Jan. 13, 1935; d. William Macon and Mary Ann (Cawthon) Patrick; m. William Henry Phillips, June 22, 1962; 1 child, Mary Jeanne. BA, Millsaps Coll., 1954; MA, Vanderbilt/Peabody U., 1957; EdD, U. So. Miss., 1978. Tchr. Jackson (Miss.) Pub. Schs., 1954-73, prin., 1973-75, asst. prin., 1975-77; dir. ednl. program Eden Prairie (Minn.) # 272, 1977-80; dir. elem. edn. Meridian (Miss.) Pub. Schs., 1980-91, asst. supt. curriculum, 1991, ret., 1991; prof. Miss. Coll., Clinton, part-time 1977, Miss. State U., Meridian, 1981-95; ednl. cons. in field. Co-author: (testing practice) Test Taking Tactics, 1987; contbr. articles to profl. jours. pres. Meridian Symphony Orch., 1987; v.p. Meridian Coun. Arts, 1986; bd. dirs. Meridian Art Mus. Named Boss of Yr., Meridian Secretarial Assn., 1985, Arts Education of Yr., Meridian Coun. Arts, 1991; recipient Excellence award Pub. Edn. Form, 1993. Mem. ASCD, Miss. ASCD, Miss. Assn. Women (pres.), Rotary, Phi Delta Kappa (pres. 1986-87). Republican. Methodist. Avocations: grant writing, computers, reading. Home: 322 51st St Meridian MS 39305-2013 Office: Miss State Univ Meridian Campus 1000 Hwy 19 S Meridian MS 39302

PHILLIPS, PAUL DAVID, JR., lawyer; b. Ft. Leavenworth, Kans., Oct. 16, 1950; s. Paul David Sr. and Rita Anne (Ruzicka) P.; m. Susan Zimmerman, May 25, 1974; children: Katherine, Helen, Alice, Mark. Student, Cambridge (Eng.) U., 1971-72; BA magna cum laude, Harvard U., 1973; JD, Yale U., 1976; postgrad., U. Sorbonne, 1976-77. Bar: Colo. 1977, U.S. Dist. Ct. Colo. 1977, U.S. Ct. Appeals (D.C., 5th, and 10th cirs.) 1977, U.S. Supreme Ct. Assoc. U.S. Customs, Washington, 1974; assoc. Holland & Hart, Denver, 1975, 77-83, ptnr., 1983—, chmn. environ law group, 1986; chmn. natural resources dept. Bogle & Gates, Seattle, 1990—. Editor: (jour.) Natural Resources and Environment. Mem. Colo. Bar Assn., Denver Bar Assn., Colo. Waste Soc., Colo. Mining Assn., Rocky Mountain Mineral Law Found. Avocations: running, skiing. Home: 593 Mt Evans Rd Golden CO 80401-9625 Office: Holland & Hart 555 17th St Ste 2900 Denver CO 80202-3979

PHILLIPS, PETER CHARLES BONEST, economist, educator, researcher; b. Weymouth, Dorset, Eng., Mar. 23, 1948; came to U.S., 1980; s. Charles Bonest and Gladys Eileen (Lade) P.; m. Emily Dowdell Birdling, Feb. 10, 1971 (div. 1980); 1 child, Daniel Lade; m. Deborah Jane Blood, June 13, 1981; children: Justin Bonest, Lara Kimberley. BA, Auckland (New Zealand) U., 1969, MA, 1971; PhD, London U., 1974; MA (hon.), Yale U. 1979. Teaching fellow U. Auckland, 1969-70, jr. lectr., 1970-71; lectr. in econs. U. Essex, Colchester, Eng., 1972-76; prof. econs. U. Birmingham, Eng., 1976-79; prof. econs. Yale U., New Haven, Conn., 1979-85, Stanley Resor prof. econs., 1985-89, Sterling prof. econs., 1989—; Alumni disting. prof. econs. U. Auckland, 1991—; pres. Predicta Software Inc., Madison, Conn., 1994—; vis. scholar Ecole Polytechnique, Paris 1977; univ. vis. prof. Monash U., Melbourne, Australia, 1986; vis. prof. Inst. Advanced Studies, Vienna, Austria, 1989; disting. visitor London Sch. Econs., 1989. Editor Econometric Theory jour., 1985; contbr. over 150 articles, book revs., notes to profl. jours. Recipient award for promotion of sci. Japan Soc., 1983; Commonwealth Grants Com. scholar, Eng., 1971, Guggenheim fellow, N.Y., 1984-85. Fellow Royal Soc. New Zealand (hon.), Econometric Soc., Jour. Econometrics, Am. Statis. Soc.; mem. Inst. Math. Stats. Avocations: building, poetry, reading. Home: 133 Concord Dr Madison CT 06443-1814 Office: Cowles Found PO Box 208281 New Haven CT 06520-8281 also Office: Predicta Software Inc 133 Concord Dr Madison CT 06443

PHILLIPS, RALPH SAUL, mathematics educator; b. Oakland, Calif., June 23, 1913; s. Isadore and Mary (Shaw) P.; m. Jean Adair, Oct. 11, 1942; 1 child, Xanthippe. A.B., UCLA, 1935; Ph.D., U. Mich., 1939. Instr. U. Wash., 1940-41, Harvard U., 1941-42; group leader Radiation Lab., Mass. Inst. Tech., 1942-46; asst. prof. math. NYU, 1946-47; assoc. prof. U. So. Calif., 1947-53, prof., 1953-58; prof. UCLA, 1958-60, Stanford U., 1960—; Rackham fellow Inst. Advanced Study, 1939-40, mem., 1950-51; research assoc. Yale U., 1953-54; Guggenheim fellow, 1954, 74; research asso. N.Y.

U., 1958; vis. prof. U. Aarhus, 1968; mem. interacad. exchange program mission to USSR, 1975. Co-author: Theory of Servomechanisms, 1947, Functional Analysis and Semigroups, 1957, Scattering Theory, 1967, Scattering Theory for Automorphic Functions, 1976; co-editor Jour. Functional Analysis. Mem. Am. Acad. Arts and Scis. Home: 1076 Cathcart Way Palo Alto CA 94305-1047 Office: Stanford U Stanford CA 94305

PHILLIPS, RANDALL CLINGER, minister, university administrator; b. Santa Maria, Calif., Dec. 3, 1924; s. Glenn Randall and Ruth (Clinger) P.; children—Ruth Ann Phillips McKercher, Janet Lee Phillips Kessler, Melinda Lee. B.S. cum laude, U. So. Calif., 1946, M.Th., 1951, Th.D., 1966; D.Arts, Willamette U., 1963; D.D., Calif. Western U., 1964. Ordained to ministry Meth. Ch., 1947; minister Sherman Oaks, Calif., 1949-55, Burbank, Calif., 1955-59; minister Wilshire United Meth. Ch., 1959-78; sr. v.p. U.S. Internat. U., San Diego, 1978—; mem. exec. com. nat. bd. publs. United Meth. Ch.; pres. Inter-religious Council Los Angeles. Vice pres. bd. trustees Sch. Theology, Claremont, Calif.; bd. dirs., v.p. Portals House, Los Angeles; pres., chmn. bd. dirs. Midnight Mission Los Angeles, Wilshire YMCA; chmn. bd. Pacific Homes. Served to lt. (j.g.) USNR, 1943-47. Recipient Freedoms Found. award, 1967, 68. Mem. L.A. Coun. Chs. (pres. 1970-71), People to People Internat. (pres., trustee San Diego chpt.), Sertoma (chaplain, pres. Wilshire area club), Rotary (pres. San Diego Scripps-Mesa club), Masons (33 degree), Shriners, Kappa Alpha. Republican. Home: 10347 Caminito Goma San Diego CA 92131-1628 Office: 10455 Pomerado Rd San Diego CA 92131-1717

PHILLIPS, RICHARD EDWARD, mathematics educator; b. Braddock, Pa., Dec. 3, 1936; s. Richard Edward and Romayne (Leddon) P.; m. Elizabeth Ann Difanis, Jan. 25, 1964; children: Anthony, Richard. BA, Otterbein Coll., 1961; PhD, U. Kans., 1965. Asst. prof. SUNY, Oneonta, 1962-63, U. Wis., Eau Claire, 1965-66, U. Kans., Lawrence, 1966-69; assoc. prof. Mich. State U., East Lansing, 1969-74, prof., 1974—, chairperson dept. math., 1991-94; vis. prof. U. Cambridge (Eng.), 1975-76, 82-83, U. Padova (Italy), 1983, 90; co-chair Coun. to Rev. Undergrad. Edn., East Lansing, 1988. Author: Opportunities for Renewal, 1988; contbr. articles to Jour. Algebra, Archiv der Mat., Cambridge Pilos. Soc. With USMC, 1966-68. Mem. Am. Math. Soc., Math. Assn. Am. (vice chair Mich. sect.), Centennial Rev. (bd. dirs.), Sigma Xi. Home: 5327 Park Lake Rd East Lansing MI 48823-3837 Office: Mich State U Dept Math East Lansing MI 48824

PHILLIPS, RICHARD HART, psychiatrist; b. Atlanta, June 23, 1922; s. Wendell Brooks and Margaret (Hart) P.; married Mar. 10, 1945; children: Valerie, Richard Jr., Hugh, Nancy, Mark. BS, U. N.C., 1943; MD, NYU, 1945. Intern U.S. Naval Hosp., Camp Lejeune, N.C., 1945-46; resident med.-surg. Harrisburg Hosp., Harrisburg, Pa., 1948; resident, chief resident psychiatry Duke U. Hosp., Durham, N.C., 1949-51; instr. psychiatry U. Pa., Phila., 1952-53; sr. psychiat. cons. Consolidated Industries Greater Syracuse, Syracuse, N.Y., 1976-89; from asst. prof. to prof. health sci. ctr. SUNY, Syracuse, 1953-92, prof. emeritus, 1992—; dir. adult psychiat. clinic health sci. ctr. SUNY, 1981-92. Author: (poetry) Bindweed, 1988; contbr. sci. and popular articles on psychology to jours. Pres. bd. dirs. Marcellus (N.Y.) Free Libr., 1968-75. Lt. (j.g.) USNR, 1943-48. Fellow Am. Psychiat. Assn. (life); mem. Soc. Children's Book Writers, Thursday Night Club. Republican. Avocations: poetry writing, sculpture, nature photography, bees, goats. Home: 4149 Bishop Hill Rd Marcellus NY 13108-9613 Office: SUNY Health Sci Ctr 750 E Adams St Syracuse NY 13210-2306

PHILLIPS, RICHARD L(OVERIDGE), marine corps officer; b. Sacramento, Nov. 27, 1939; s. Will D. and Lorraine (Richardson) P.; m. Linda Shughart; children: Rebecca, Richard. BS in Engring., Calif. Poly. Coll., 1961; MS in Computer Sci., Naval Postgrad. Sch., Monterey, Calif., 1973. Commd. 2d lt. USMC, 1961, advanced through grades to maj. gen., 1991; served in combat as squadron pilot and ground co. comdr. Vietnam, 1966-67, 70-71; project team leader Marine Corps Tactical Systems Support Activity, 1973-76; comdg. officer Marine Aircraft Group 39 and Marine Amphibious Units 11 and 17, Camp Pendleton and San Diego; dep. comdr. Naval Space Command, 1985-87; dep. asst. chief of staff, command, control, communications and computer, intelligence and interoperability Hdqrs. Marine Corps, Washington, 1987-89; dep. comdr. Fleet Marine Force, Pacific, Marine Corps Bases, Pacific, 1990-91; comdg. gen. 1st Marine Expeditionary Brig., Kaneohe Bay, Hawaii, 1989-91; comdr. U.S. Joint Task Force Cobra Gold, Thailand, 1990; dep. asst. sec. Navy Expeditionary Force Programs, Washington, 1992-93; insp. gen. USMC, Washington, 1993—. Decorated Legion of Merit, Meritorious Svc. medal, Air medal (26), numerous others. Republican. Presbyterian. Office: Marine Corps Insp Gen Hqmc Rm 2233 Washington DC 20380

PHILLIPS, RICHARD WENDELL, JR., air force officer; b. Harrisburg, Pa., Nov. 6, 1929; s. Richard Wendell Sr. and Mary Viola (Myers) P.; m. Betty Jo Teel, Mar. 7, 1954; children—David Wendell, Karen Marie, Terry Lee Phillips Woods. B.S. in Engring., U.S. Mil. Acad., 1953; grad., U.S. Air Force Exptl. Test Pilot Sch., Edwards AFB, Calif., 1960, Air Command and Staff Coll., Maxwell AFB, Ala., 1967, Air War Coll., Maxwell AFB, Ala., 1972; M.S. in Pub. Adminstrn., George Washington U., 1967. Commd. 2d lt. U.S. Air Force, 1953, advanced through grades to maj. gen., 1983; fighter pilot 51st Fighter Interceptor Wing, Naha Air Base,Okinawa, Japan, 1954-57; instr. pilot Laredo AFB, Tex., 1958-60; test pilot Eglm AFB, Fla., 1960-64; exchange officer to U.S. Navy Air Devel. Squadron Four/Point Mugu Naval Air Sta., Calif., 1964-66; chief of tactics 366th Tactical Fighter Wing, Da Nang AB, Vietnam, 1967-68; chief of fighter test 4950th Test Wing, Wright-Patterson AFB, Ohio, 1968-71; chief of operational test and eval. div. Hdqrs. U.S. Air Force, Washington, 1972-75; vice comdr. 51st Composite Wing (tactical) Osan AB, Korea, 1975-76; chief aero. systems div. Hdqrs. U.S. Air Force, Washington, 1977-78, dep. dir. requirements - gen. purpose forces, 1978-80; dir. electronic warfare during close air support joint test force Nellis AFB, Nev., 1980-82; comdr. Air Force Operational Test and Evaluation Ctr., Kirtland AFB, N.Mex., 1982-85; comdr. Sheppard Tech. Tng. Ctr., Sheppard AFB, Tex., 1985-87, ret., 1987. Mem. Soc. Exptl. Test Pilots. Avocations: sailing; golf; skiing. Home: 816 Weeden Island Dr Niceville FL 32578-3708

PHILLIPS, ROGER, steel company executive; b. Ottawa, Ont., Can., Dec. 17, 1939; s. Norman William Frederick and Elizabeth (Marshall) P.; m. Katherine Ann Wilson, June 9, 1962; 1 child, Andrée Claire. B.Sc., McGill U., Montreal, 1960. Vice pres. mill products Alcan Can. Products Ltd., Toronto, Ont., Can., 1969-70, exec. v.p., 1971-75; pres. Alcan Smelters and Chems. Ltd., Montreal, Que., Can., 1976-79; v.p. tech. Alcan Aluminium Ltd., Montreal, Que., Can., 1980-81; pres. Alcan Internat. Ltd., Montreal, Que., Can., 1980-81; pres., chief exec. officer IPSCO Inc., Regina, Sask., Can., 1982—; sr. mem. Conf. Bd. Inc., N.Y., 1987—; bd. dirs. Toronto Dominion Bank. Dir. Coun. for Can. Unity, Montreal, 1987—; bd. dirs. Conf. Bd. of Can., 1984-87, Inst. for Polit. Involvement, Toronto, 1982-88. Mem. Can. Assn. Physicists, Bus. Coun. on Nat. Issues, Am. Iron and Steel Inst. (bd. dirs. 1984—), Saskatchewan C. of C. (bd. dirs. 1984—), Que. C. of C. (pres. 1981), Inst. for Saskatchewan Enterprise (hon. chmn.), Pub. Policy Forum (bd. dirs.), Assiniboia Club (Regina), St. Denis Club, Univ. Club (Montreal). Home: 3220 Albert St, Regina, SK Canada S4S 3N9 Office: IPSCO Inc, Armour Rd, Regina, SK Canada S4P 3C7

PHILLIPS, RONALD EDWARD, artist, sales executive; b. Clovis, N.Mex., Apr. 10, 1937; s. Rodney Vernon and Ethel Edna (Huff) P.; m. May Frances Willingham, Aug. 27, 1957; children: Rhonda Louise, Russell Kent, Teresa Gail; m. Janet Irene Johnsonbaugh Smith, July 4, 1938; stepchildren: Steven, Gregg, Laura. Student, Ea. N.Mex. U., 1955-56, U. N.Mex., 1957, Famous Artist Schs., 1963-64, North Light Art Sch., 1989-90. Group merchandiser women's fashions J.C. Penney Inc., Albuquerque, 1957-64; chem. salesman Take Over Products, Clovis, N.Mex., 1964-65; with International Auto Leasing, Albuquerque, 1965; salesman Pennsalt Chems., N.Mex. div., Albuquerque, 1965-67; N.Mex. sales rep. W.W. Grainger Inc., Chgo. 1967-72; founder Pueblo Arts, Inc., Albuquerque, 1972—; mgr. Dairy Queen, Santa Rosa and Lovington, N.Mex., 1982-85; owner, mgr. Western Pit n Grill & Food Gallery, Lovington, 1985-88; owner Pueblo Arts Inc./Trailwest Gallery, Albuquerque, 1988—; tchr. quick draw, continuous line drawing, 1990; artist, guide Pueblo Arts Inc. Trailwest Paintouts, Guide for Artists, 1990-92; ind. sales cons. SWEPCO Bldg. Projects, 1993—. Artist, author sketchbooks Traveling Man's Old Town Sketchbook, 1990, The Shooting of

Wyatt Earp, 1994, also others; movie extra Whitesands, 1991, Next Fire on Earth, 1992, Wyatt Earp, 1993, Desperate Trails, 1993, Buffalo Girls, 1995. Pres. Albuquerque Wildlife and Conservation, 1963-64; active Albuquerque Conf. & Vis. Bur., 1988—, Albuquerque Arts Alliance, 1994-95, Tourism Assoc. of N.Mex., Albuquerque Film Commn. With N.Mex. Air Nat. Guard, 1955-61. Mem. N.Mex. Art League (hon. life, pres. 1964-65), Indian Arts and Crafts Assn. (mem. ethics com. 1973-74), Albuquerque Arts Alliance, Guild of Albuquerque Artist Models (advisor, bd. dirs. 1994-95). Republican. Avocations: art, sales and marketing. Office: Pueblo Arts Inc 5555 Zuni SE #154 Albuquerque NM 87108

PHILLIPS, RONALD FRANK, legal educator, law school dean; b. Houston, Nov. 25, 1934; s. Franklin Jackson and Maudie Ethel (Merrill) P.; m. Jamie Jo Bottoms, Apr. 5, 1957; children: Barbara Celeste Phillips Oliveira, Joel Jackson, Phil Edward. B.S., Abilene Christian U., 1955; J.D., U. Tex., 1965. Bar: Tex. 1965, Calif. 1972. Bldg. contractor Phillips Homes, Abilene, Tex., 1955-56; br. mgr. Phillips Weatherstripping Co., Midland and Austin, Tex., 1957-65; corp. staff atty. McWood Corp., Abilene, 1965-67; sole practice law Abilene, 1967-70; mem. adj. faculty Abilene Christian U., 1967-70; prof. law Pepperdine U. Sch. Law, Malibu, Calif., 1970—; dean Pepperdine U. Sch. Law, 1970—; bd. dirs. PNB Fin. Group. Deacon North A and Tenn. Ch. of Christ, Midland, 1959-62; deacon Highland Ch. of Christ, Abilene, 1965-70; elder Malibu Ch. of Christ, 1978-95; mgr., coach Little League Baseball, Abilene, Huntington Beach and Malibu, 1968-78, 90—; coach Youth Soccer, Huntington Beach, Westlake Village and Malibu, 1972-80, 85-86, 91. Recipient Alumni citation Abilene Christian U., 1974. Fellow Am. Bar Found.; mem. ABA, State Bar Tex., State Bar Calif. (com. on law sch. edn. 1970—), Christian Legal Soc., L.A. Bar Assn., Assn. Am. Law Schs. (chmn. sect. on adminstrn. law schs. 1982, com. on cts. 1985-87), Am. Law Inst., Nat. Conf. Commrs. on Uniform State Laws. Republican. Office: Pepperdine U Sch Law 24255 Pacific Coast Hwy Malibu CA 90263-0001

PHILLIPS, RONALD LEWIS, plant geneticist, educator; b. Huntington County, Ind., Jan. 1, 1940; s. Philemon Lewis and Louise Alpha (Walker) P.; m. Judith Lee Lind, Aug. 19, 1962; children: Brett, Angela. B.S. in Crop Sci., Purdue U., 1961, M.S. in Plant Breeding and Genetics, 1963; Ph.D. in Genetics, U. Minn., 1966; postgrad., Cornell U., 1966-67. Research and teaching asst. Purdue U., 1961-62; research and teaching asst. U. Minn., St. Paul, 1962-66; research assoc. U. Minn., 1967-68, asst. prof., 1968-72, assoc. prof., 1972-76, prof. genetics and plant breeding, 1976-93, Regents prof., 1993—; program dir. Competitive Rsch. Grants Office, USDA, Washington, 1979; mem. adv. grant panels NSF, USDA, AID; chmn. Gordon Conf. on Plant Cell and Tissue Culture, 1985; mem. sci. adv. coun. U. Calif. Plant Gene Expression Ctr., Berkeley, 1986-93; vis. prof., Italy, 1981, Can., 1983, China, 1986, Japan, 1990; dir. Plant Molecular Genetics Inst., 1991—; trustee Biol. Stain Commn.; mem. Nat. Plant Genetic Resources Bd. Co-editor: Cytogenetics, 1977, Molecular Genetic Modification of Eucaryotes, 1977, Molecular Biology of Plants, 1979, The Plant Seed: Development, Preservation and Germination, 1979, Genetic Improvement of Crops: Emergent Techniques, 1980, DNA-Based Markers in Plants, 1994; assoc. editor: Genetics, 1978-81, Can. Jour. Genetics and Cytology and Genome, 1985-90; mem. editl. bd. Maydica, 1978—, In Vitro Cellular and Developmental Biology, 1988-92, Cell Culture and Somatic Cell Genetics of Plants, 1983-91, Elaeis, 1994—; contbr. chpts. to Maize Breeding and Genetics, 1978, Staining Procedures, 1981, Cell Culture and Somatic Cell Genetics of Plants, 1984, Chromosome Structure and Function, 1987, Corn and Corn Improvement, 1988, Plant Transposable Elements, 1988, Chromosome Engring. in Plants, 1991, Maize Handbook, 1994; contbr. sci. articles to profl. jours. Mem. chmn. coun. on ministries, lay leader United Meth. Ch., 1968, dir. Project AgGrad, 1983—; Cub Scout Pack co-chmn. Boy Scouts Am., 1976-77; judge Minn. Regional and State Sci. Fair, 1970-80. Recipient Purdue Agrl. Alumni Achievement award, 1961, Purdue Disting. Agrl. Alumni award, 1993; NSF fellow, 1961; NIH fellow, 1966-67, Northrup King Oustanding Faculty Performance award, 1985, Crop Sci. Rsch. award, 1988. Fellow AAAS, Am. Soc. Agronomy, Crop Sci. Soc. Am. (awards com., div. chmn., bd. rep. 1988-91, rsch. award 1988); mem. NAS, Genetics Soc. Am., Am. Soc. Agronomy (award student sect., Caleb-Dorr award), Sigma Xi, Gamma Alpha (nat. treas.), Gamma Sigma Delta (award of merit 1994), Alpha Zeta. Office: U Minn Dept Agronomy & Plant Genetics Saint Paul MN 55108

PHILLIPS, ROSCOE WENDELL, JR., architect; b. Providence, Apr. 30, 1927; s. Roscoe Wendell and Esther Burr P.; ScB, Brown U., 1950; BArch, MIT, 1952; MS, U. Ill., 1953; m. Elizabeth Dewey Moss, June 18, 1955; children—Roscoe Wendell, James Moss, Eleanor Terry, Margaret Dewey. Draftsman, Perry Shaw Hepburn & Dean, 1956-58; draftsman Shepley, Bulfinch, Richardson & Abbott, Boston, 1958-59; asst. job capt. Sert, Jackson & Gourley, Architects, Cambridge, Mass., 1960-63; gen. practice architecture, Boston, 1963-68; partner Kent Cruise & Partners, Providence, also Boston, 1968-72; pres. R. Wendell Phillips & Assocs., Architects, Boston, 1972—; adj. prof. dept. arch. Tech. Wentworth Inst., Boston. Mem. exec. bd. Boston council Boy Scouts Am., 1958—; chmn., Dedham Bldg. Planning & Constrn. Com., 1982. Served to capt. USAF, 1952-56. Recipient USAF Design Excellence award, 1983. Mem. Boston Zool. Soc. (mem. bldg. com.), Boston Soc. Architects (design award), Mass. Assn. Architects, AIA (nat. housing com. 1979-93), Mayflower Soc. (gov. 1974), St. Botolph Club, Tau Beta Pi, Sigma Nu. Republican. Episcopalian. Home office: 173 County Rd New London NH 03257-5053

PHILLIPS, RUSSELL ALEXANDER, JR., foundation executive; b. Charlotte, N.C., Sept. 19, 1937; s. Russell Alexander and Robmae (Black) P. A.B., Duke U., 1959; LL.B. (Edward John Noble fellow), Yale U., 1962. Bar: N.C. 1962, D.C. 1966. Clk. to Sr. Judge, U.S. Ct. Appeals, 4th Circuit, 1962-63; legal adv. Ministry of Fin., Govt. No. Nigeria, 1963-65; asst. commr. income tax (legal) East African Common Services Orgn., Nairobi, Kenya, 1965-66; assoc. firm Wilmer, Cutler & Pickering, Washington, 1966-68; program officer Rockefeller Bros. Fund, N.Y.C., 1968-73, corp. sec., 1973-81; v.p. Rockefeller Bros. Fund, 1979-81, exec. v.p., 1982—, acting pres., 1987-88. Trustee Internat. Inst. for Rural Reconstrn., Lingnan Found.; trustee, v.p., sec. Asian Cultural Coun. Recipient Benjamin N. Cardozo prize Yale U., 1962. Mem. N.C. Bar Assn., D.C. Bar, Council Fgn. Relations, Phi Beta Kappa. Democrat. Presbyterian. Club: University (N.Y.C.), Century Assn. (N.Y.C.). Home: 40 E 88th St Apt 5D New York NY 10128-1116 Office: Rm 3450 1290 Avenue Of the Americas New York NY 10104-0012

PHILLIPS, SIDNEY FREDERICK, gastroenterologist; b. Melbourne, Australia, Sept. 4, 1933; s. Clifford and Eileen Frances (Fitch) P.; m. Decima Honora Jones, Mar. 29, 1957; children: Penelope Jane, Nichola Margaret, David Sidney. M.B.B.S., U. Melbourne, 1956, M.D., 1961. Resident med. officer Royal Melbourne Hosp., 1957-61, asst. sub-dean clin. sch., 1961-62; research assoc. Central Middlesex Hosp., London, 1962-63, Mayo Clinic, Rochester, Minn., 1963-66; cons. in gastroenterology Mayo Clinic, 1966—; prof. medicine Mayo Med. Sch., 1976—; dir. gastroenterology research unit, 1977-94; program dir. Mayo Gen. Clin. Research Ctr., 1974-87; dir. Mayo Digestive Diseases Core Ctr., 1984-90; Karl F. and Marjory Hasselman prof. rsch., 1994—. Editor: Digestive Diseases and Sciences, 1977-82, Gastroenterology International, 1990—; sr. assoc. editor: Gastroenterology, 1991—; contbr. chpts. to books, articles to profl. jours. Fellow ACP, Royal Coll. Physicians, Royal Australian Coll. Physicians; mem. Am. Soc. Clin. Investigation (emeritus), Gastroenterology Soc. Australia, Am. Gastroenterology Assn., Assn. Am. Physicians. Home: 524 14th Ave SW Rochester MN 55902-1956 Office: St Mary's Hosp Gastroenterology Unit 200 1st St SW Rochester MN 55905-0001

PHILLIPS, STANLEY F, restaurant company executive. V. chmn. Del. N. Co. Inc., Buffalo, 1990—. Office: Delaware North Copanies inc 438 Main St Buffalo NY 14202

PHILLIPS, SUSAN MEREDITH, financial economist, former university administrator; b. Richmond, Va., Dec. 23, 1944; d. William G. and Nancy (Meredith) P. BA in Math., Agnes Scott Coll., 1967; MS in Fin. and Ins., La. State U., 1971, PhD in Fin. and Economics, 1973. Asst. prof. La. State U., 1973-74, U. Iowa, 1974-78; Brookings Econ. Policy fellow, 1976-77; econ. fellow Directorate of Econ. and Policy Rsch., SEC, 1977-78; assoc. prof. fin.

dept. U. Iowa, 1978-83, assoc. v.p. fin. and univ. svcs., 1979-81; commr. Commodity Futures Trading Commn., 1981-83, chmn., 1983-87; prof. fin. dept., v.p. fin. and univ. svcs. U. Iowa, Iowa City, 1987-91; bd. govs. Fed. Res. Bd., Washington, 1991—. Author (with J. Richard Zecher): The SEC and the Public Interest; contbr. articles in field to profl. jours. Office: Fed Res System 20th Constitution St NW Washington DC 20551

PHILLIPS, T. STEPHEN, lawyer; b. Tennyson, Ind., Oct. 1, 1941. AB, DePauw U., 1963; LLB, Duke U., 1966. Bar: Ohio 1966, Ind. 1967. Assoc. Frost & Jacobs, Cin., 1966-72, ptnr., 1972—; adj. prof. North Ky. U. Chase Coll. Law, Highland Heights, 1983—. Contbg. editor: Ohio Probate Practice (Addams and Hosford), Page on Wills. Trustee Spring Grove Cemetery, Cin. Methodist. Office: Frost & Jacobs 2500 PNC Ct 201 E 5th St Cincinnati OH 45202

PHILLIPS, TED RAY, advertising agency executive; b. American Falls, Idaho, Oct. 27, 1948; s. Virn E. and Jessie N. (Aldous) P.; m. Dianne Jacqulynne Walker, May 28, 1971; children: Scott, Russell, Stephen, Michael. BA, Brigham Young U., 1972, MA, 1975. Account exec. David W. Evans, Inc., Salt Lake City, 1972-75; dir. advt. Div. Continuing Edn., U. Utah, Salt Lake City, 1975-78; sr. v.p. Evans/Lowe & Stevens, Inc., Atlanta, 1978, exec. v.p., 1979; pres., chief exec. officer David W. Evans/Atlanta, Inc., 1979-80; dir. advt. O.C. Tanner Co., Salt Lake City, 1980-82; pres. Thomas/Phillips/Clawson Advt., Inc., Salt Lake City, 1982-86; pres. Hurst & Phillips, Salt Lake City, 1986-94; pres., CEO Phillips Radley Advt., Inc., Salt Lake City, 1994—; advt. instr. div. continuing edn. Brigham Young U., 1983-85. Dir. publicity, promotion Western States Republican Con., 1976. Recipient Silver Beaver award Boy Scouts Am., 1994. Mem. Am. Advt. Fedn. (8 Best-in-West awards, 2 nat. Addy awards, Clio finalist 1984, Telly award 1991, 92), Utah Advt. Fedn. (bd. dirs. 1976-78, 80-87, pres. 1984-85). Mormon. Home: 1792 Cornwall Ct Sandy UT 84092-5436 Office: Phillips Radley Advt Inc 428 East 6400 South Salt Lake City UT 84107

PHILLIPS, THEODORE LOCKE, radiation oncologist, educator; b. Phila., June 4, 1933; s. Harry Webster and Margaret Amy (Locke) P.; m. Joan Cappello, June 23, 1956; children: Margaret, John, Sally. BSc, Dickinson Coll., 1955; MD, U. Pa., 1959. Intern Western Res. U., Cleve., 1960; resident in therapeutic radiology U. Calif., San Francisco, 1963, clin. instr., 1963-65, asst. prof. radiation oncology, 1965-68, assoc. prof., 1968-70, prof., 1970—, chmn. dept. radiation oncology, 1973—; rsch. radiobiologist U.S. Naval Radiologic Def. Lab., San Francisco, 1963-65; rsch. assoc. Cancer Rsch. Inst. and Lab. Radiobiology; rsch. physician Lawrence Berkeley Lab. and Donner Lab., U. Calif., Berkeley. Contbr. numerous articles to profl. publs. With USNR, 1963-65. Nat. Cancer Inst. grantee, 1970-94. Mem. Am. Soc. Therapeutic Radiologists (pres. 1984), Am. Soc. Clin. Oncology, Radiol. Soc. N.Am., Hyperthermia Soc. (pres.-elect 1993, pres. 1994), Am. Assn. Cancer Rsch., Calif. Med. Assn., Am. Coll. Radiology Radium Soc., No. Calif. Radiation Oncology Assn., Inst. Medicine, Phi Beta Kappa, Alpha Omega Alpha. Democrat. Home: 10 Marinita Ave San Rafael CA 94901-3431 Office: U Calif San Francisco Dept Radiation Oncology L-75 Box 0226 San Francisco CA 94143

PHILLIPS, THOMAS EDWORTH, JR., investment executive, consultant; b. Danville, Va., July 7, 1944; s. Thomas Edworth Sr. and Jean (Worley) P.; m. Claudia Mitchell, July 23, 1966; children: Kelly Marie, Melissa Joyce. BS in Econs., Va. Tech., 1966; cert. in investments, N.Y. Inst. Fin., 1969; MS in Bus., Va. Commonwealth U., 1973; postgrad., U. Pa., 1989. Cert. investment analyst; registered prin. NYSE and NASD. Edn. coord. Prince William County Schs., Manassas, Va., 1966-67; investment broker Conrad and Co., Richmond, Va., 1967-68; investment exec. Paine Webber, Inc., Richmond, 1968—, divisional v.p., 1980—; registered prin. NYSE, NASD, 1987—; mem. access program nat. com. PaineWebber, N.Y.C., 1989-90, mem. dir.'s coun., 1987-88, mem. managed accounts nat. adv. bd., 1991-93; bd. dirs. Madison Group, Inc., Richmond, Meadowbrook Assocs., Inc. Richmond; speaker in field. Bd. dirs. Va. Non-Profit Housing Coalition, pres., 1992—; chmn. bd. deacons. Mt. Olivet Ch., Hanover, Va., 1984-85; trustee Hanover Acad., Ashland, Va., 1980-84. Rotary Found. fellow, 1989. Mem. Investment Mgmt. Cons. Assn., Capital Soc., Melody Hills Property Owners Assn. (bd. dirs. 1980—), Va. Tech. Alumni Assn., Rotary, Bull and Bear Club, Omicron Delta Epsilon. Baptist. Avocations: horses, tennis, golf. Home: 15058 Melody Hills Dr Doswell VA 23047-9749 Office: PaineWebber Inc Two James Ctr Ste 1800 1021 E Cary St Richmond VA 23219-4023

PHILLIPS, THOMAS JOHN, lawyer; b. Mpls., Nov. 24, 1948. BA, U. Minn., 1970; JD, U. Utah, 1973; LLM in Taxation, NYU, 1974. Bar: Wis. 1974. Assoc. Whyte & Hirschboeck, S.C., Milw., 1974-78, Minahan & Peterson, S.C., Milw., 1978-91, Quarles & Brady, Milw., 1991—; law clk. Utah Supreme Ct., Salt Lake City, 1972-73. Mem. ABA, Wis. Bar Assn., Profl. Inst. Taxation, North Shore Country Club, Order of Coif. Avocations: gardening, golf, hockey, jogging, racquetball. Office: Quarles & Brady 411 E Wisconsin Ave Milwaukee WI 53202-4409

PHILLIPS, THOMAS L., corporate executive; b. Istanbul, Turkey, May 2, 1924. BSEE, Va. Poly. Inst., 1947, MSEE, 1948; hon. doctorates, Stonehill Coll., 1968, Northeastern U., 1968, U. Mass., Lowell, 1970, Gordon Coll., 1970, Boston Coll., 1974, Babson Coll., 1981, Suffolk U., 1986, U. Mass., Amherst, 1989. With Raytheon Co., Lexington, Mass., 1948-91, exec. v.p., 1961-64, chief operating officer, 1964-68, pres., 1964-75, chief exec. officer, 1968-91, chmn. bd., 1975-91, ret., 1991; bd. dirs. Raytheon Co., John Hancock Mut. Life Ins. Co., Knight-Ridder, Inc., Digital Equipment Corp. Trustee Gordon Coll., State Street Rsch. Funds, Northeastern U., Mass. Gen. Hosp.; mem. corp. Joslin Diabetes Ctr., Mus. Sci., Boston. Recipient Meritorious Pub. Service award for work in Sparrow III missile system, U.S. Navy, 1958. Mem. Nat. Acad. Engring., Bus. Coun., Am. Acad. Arts and Scis. Office: Raytheon Co 141 Spring St Lexington MA 02173-7899

PHILLIPS, THOMAS ROYAL, judge; b. Dallas, Oct. 23, 1949; s. George S. and Marguerite (Andrews) P.; m. Lyn Bracewell, June 26, 1982; 1 son, Daniel Austin Philips; 1 stepson, Thomas R. Kirkham. BA, Baylor U., 1971; JD, Harvard U., 1974. Bar: Tex. 1974; cert. in civil trial law Tex. Bd. Legal Specialization. Briefing atty. Supreme Ct. Tex., Austin, 1974-75; assoc. Baker & Botts, Houston, 1975-81; judge 280th Dist. Ct., Houston, 1981-88; chief justice Supreme Ct. Tex., Austin, 1988—; mem. com. on fed.-state rels. Jud. Conf. U.S., 1990—; chair Tex. Jud. Dists. Bd., 1988—; mem. State Judges Mass Tort Litigation Com., 1991—; bd. dirs. Elmo B. Hunter Citizens Ctr. for Jud. Selection, Southwestern Legal Found.; chair jud. pension plans task force Nat. Conf. Chief Justices, 1992—; chair Nat. Mass Tort Conf. Planning Com., 1993-94. Bd. advisors Ctr. for Pub. Policy Dispute Resolution, U. Tex. Law Sch., 1993—; mem. planning com. South Tex. Coll. of Law Ctr. for Creative Legal Solutions, 1993—. Recipient Outstanding Young Lawyer award Houston Young Lawyers Assn., 1986, award of excellence in govt. Tex. C. of C., 1992; named Appellate Judge of Yr., Tex. Assn. Civil Trial and Appellate Specialists, 1992-93. Mem. ABA, Am. Law Inst., State Bar Tex. (chmn. pattern jury charges IV com. 1985-87, vice chmn. adminstrn. justice com. 1986-87), Am. Judicature Soc. (bd. dirs. 1989—), Conf. Chief Justices (bd. dirs. 1992—), Tex. Philol. Soc., Houston Philol. Soc., Houston Bar Assn., Travis County Bar Assn. Republican. Methodist. Office: Tex Supreme Ct PO Box 12248 Austin TX 78711-2248

PHILLIPS, THOMAS WADE, lawyer; b. Oneida, Tenn., July 6, 1943; s. W.T. and Lucille (Lewallen) P.; m. Dorothy Mills, Jan. 2, 1971; children: Lori Ann, Wade Thomas. BA, Berea (Ky.) Coll., 1965; JD, Vanderbilt U., 1969; LLM in Labor Law, George Washington U., 1973. Bar: Tenn. 1969, U.S. Supreme Ct. 1972, U.S. Ct. Appeals (6th cir.) 1980. Assoc., ptnr. Baker, Worthington, Crosley, Stansberry & Wolfe, Huntsville, Tenn., 1973-77; ptnr. Phillips & Williams, P.C., Oneida, Tenn., 1977-91; U.S. magistrate judge ea. dist., Tenn., 1991—; county atty. Scott County, Huntsville, 1976-91; city atty. Town of Oneida, 1978-91. Capt. JAGC, U.S. Army, 1969-73. Mem. ABA, Tenn. Bar Assn. (ho. of dels. 1989-91), Scott County Bar Assn. Office: US District Court 333 US Courthouse 501 W Main St Knoxville TN 37902-2501

PHILLIPS, WALTER RAY, lawyer, educator; b. Democrat, N.C., Mar. 19, 1932; s. Walter Yancey and Bonnie (Wilson) P.; m. Patricia Ann Jones, Aug. 28, 1954; children: Bonnie Ann, Rebecca Lee. A.B., U. N.C., 1954; LL.B.,

Emory U., 1957, LL.M., 1962, J.D., 1970; postgrad., Yale U., 1965-66. Bar: Ga. 1957, Fla. 1958, U.S. Supreme Ct. 1962, Tex. 1969. With firm Jones, Adams, Paine & Foster, West Palm Beach, Fla., 1957-58; law clk. to chief judge U.S. Dist. Ct., Atlanta, 1958-59; with firm Powell, Goldstein, Frazer & Murphy, Atlanta, 1959-60; bankruptcy judge U.S. Cts., Atlanta, 1960-64; prof. law U. N.D., 1964-65; teaching fellow Yale U., 1965-66; prof. law Fla. State U., 1966-68, Tex. Tech. U., Lubbock, 1968-71; Disting. vis. prof. law Baylor U., 1971; atty. Commn. on Bankruptcy Laws of U.S. Washington, 1971-72; dep. dir. adminstrv. officer, 1972-73; prof. Sch. Law, U. Ga., 1973—, assoc. dean, 1975-83, acting dean, 1976, Joseph Henry Lumpkin prof., 1977-94, also dir. univ's self. study, 1978, Herman E. Talmadge prof., 1994—; Chapman disting. vis. prof. law U. Okla., 1985-86; vis. prof. law U. Okla., 1990, U. Mo., Columbia, 1993; reporter Gov.'s Legislation for Ga., 1973; v.p., dir. Killearn Estates, Inc.; mem. Conf. on Consumer Fin. Law. Author: Florida Law and Practice, 1960, Encyclopedia of Georgia Law, 1962, Seminar for Newly Appointed Referees in Bankruptcy, 1964, Damages: Cases and Materials, 1967, (with James William Moore) Debtors' and Creditors' Cases and Material, 1966, 5th edit., 1979, The Law of Debtor Relief, 1969, 2d edit., 1972, supplement, 1975, (with James William Moore) Rule 6, Moore's Federal Practice, 1969, Adjustment of Debts for Individuals, 1979, 2d edit., 1981, supplement, 1982, 84, 85, Liquidation Under the Bankruptcy Code, 3d edit., 1988, supplement, 1989, 90, 91, 92, 93, 94, Cases and Materials on Corporate Reorganization, 1983, 3d edit., 1986, 4th edit., 1988, 5th edit., 1990, 6th edit., 1993, Family Farmer and Adjustment of Individual Debts, 1987, supplement, 1988, 89, 90, 91, 92, 93, 94. Bd. dirs. Lubbock Day Nurseries, 1969, pres., 1970-71. Served with USAF, 1950. Mem. ABA (consumer bankruptcy com. 1973—, chmn. 1986-90), Fed. Bar Assn., Fla. Bar Assn., Tex. Bar Assn., Western Circuit Bar Assn., Ga. Bar Assn. (vice chmn. public com. 1977-89, com. on profl. responsibility 1983—), Am. Judicature Soc., Am. Trial Lawyers Assn., Phi Alpha Delta (chief tribune). Baptist. Home: 310 Red Fox Run Athens GA 30605-4409

PHILLIPS, WARREN HENRY, publisher; b. June 28, 1926; s. Abraham and Juliette (Rosenberg) P.; m. Barbara Anne Thomas, June 16, 1951; children: Lisa, Leslie, Nina. AB, Queens Coll., 1947, LHD (hon.), 1987; JD (hon.), U. Portland, 1973; LHD (hon.), Pace U., 1982, L.I. U., 1987. Copyreader Wall St. Jour., 1947-48; fgn. corr. Wall St. Jour., Germany, 1949-50; chief London bur. Wall St. Jour., 1950-51, fgn. editor, 1951-53, news editor, 1953-54, mng. editor Midwest edit., 1954-57, mng. editor, 1957-65, pub., 1975-88; exec. editor Dow Jones & Co., 1965-70, v.p., gen. mgr., 1970-71, exec. v.p., 1972, editorial dir., 1971-88, pres., 1972-79, CEO, 1975-90, also bd. dirs., past chmn.; co-pub. Bridge Works Pub. Co., 1992—; bd. dirs. Pub. Broadcasting Svc., 1991—; copyreader European edit. Stars & Stripes, 1949; pres. Am. Coun. Edn. for Journalism, 1971-73; mem. Pulitzer Prize Bd., 1977-87; adj. faculty Grad. Sch. Journalism Columbia U., 1992—, John F. Kennedy Sch. Govt. Harvard U., 1992. Author: (with Robert Keatley) China: Behind the Mask, 1973. Trustee Columbia U., 1980-93, trustee emeritus, 1993—; mem. vis. com. Kennedy Sch. Govt., Harvard U., 1984-90, 92—; mem. corp. adv. bd. Queens Coll., 1986-90, found. bd. trustees, 1990—. Named one of Ten Outstanding Young Men in U.S. U.S. Jaycees, 1958; inducted into the Info. Industry Assn's. Hall of Fame, 1984. Mem. Am. Newspaper Pubs. Assn. (bd. dirs. 1976-84), Am. Soc. Newspaper Editors (pres. 1975-76), Bridgehampton Club, River Club. Office: Bridge Works Publ PO Box 1798 Bridgehampton NY 11932-1798

PHILLIPS, WILLIAM, English language educator, editor, author; b. N.Y.C.; s. Edward and Marie (Berman) P.; m. Edna M. Greenblatt (dec.). BS, CCNY; MA, NYU; postgrad., Columbia U.; DHL, Adelphi U., 1991. Instr. Columbia U., N.Y.C., 1945; lectr. New Sch. Social Rsch., N.Y.C.; vis. lectr. Sarah Lawrence Coll., N.Y., 1951-54, 56-57, U. Minn., 1953; assoc. prof. NYU, 1960, 61-63; prof. English Rutgers U., New Jersey, 1963-78; prof. Boston U., 1978—. Author: A Sense of the Present, 1967, A Partisan View: Five Decades of the Literary Life, 1983; editor-in-chief Partisan Review, 1934—; editor Short Stories of Dostoyevsky; co-editor The Partisan Review Anthology, Literature and Psychoanalysis, 1983, Writers and Politics, 1983; former cons. editor Dial Press, Criterion Books, Random House, Chilmark Press. Mem. Gov. N.J. Com. Arts, 1964-66, Pres. Carter Task Force Arts and Humanities, arts adv. group Bus. Com. Arts. Rockefeller Found. grantee, 1977-78; NEH fellow, 1978-79, Guggenheim Found. fellow, 1977. Mem. PEN, Assn. Lit. Mags. Am., Author's League, Coord. Coun. Lit. Mags. Am. (chmn. 1967-75, hon. chmn. pres. 1975). Office: Partisan Review 236 Bay State Rd Boston MA 02215-1403

PHILLIPS, WILLIAM A., research animal scientist; b. Sept. 23, 1948; m. Barbara Moore, 1969; children: Jeffrey, Bradley, Jennifer. BS in Agr., Mid. Tenn. State U., 1971; MS in Animal Nutrition, Va. Poly. Inst. and State U., 1974, PhD in Animal Nutrition, 1976. Rsch. animal scientist Grazinglands Rsch. Lab., Agrl. Rsch. Svc., USDA, El Reno, Okla., 1976-85, 93—, rsch. leader, animal scientist, 1985-93; mem. adv. com. for agr. Redlands C.C. Mem. Maple Sch. Bd.; fundraiser, baseball coach YMCA; lay leader, pres. Men's Fellowship, Sunday sch. tchr., mem. fin. missions, long range planning, bldg. and pers. coms. Wesley United Meth. Ch. 2d lt. USAR, 1971-77. Mem. Am. Soc. Animala Sci. (program com., editl. bd.), Coun. for Agrl. Sci. and Tech., Okla. Grain and Stocker Prodrs., Am. Registry Profl. Animal Scientists, El Reno C. of C. (bd. dirs., exec. bd., v.p. for orgn.). Home: Rt 2 Box 38AA Calumet OK 73014 Office: USDA Agrl Rsch Svc Grazinglands Rsch Lab El Reno OK 73036

PHILLIPS, WILLIAM EUGENE, advertising agency executive; b. Chgo., Jan. 7, 1930; s. William E. and Alice P.; children: Michael, Tom, Sarah. B.S., Cornell U., 1951; M.B.A., Northwestern U., 1955. Brand mgr. Procter & Gamble, Cin., 1955-59; with Ogilvy & Mather, N.Y.C., 1959-90; chief exec. officer Ogilvy Group, 1981-88; exec. in residence, prof. Johnson Grad. Sch. Mgmt. Cornell U., 1989-90; bd. dirs. Lillian Vernon, Inc, Sun Glass Hut, Inc., D.S.M. Internat. Exec. Office Group. Chmn. Internat. Adv. Bd. Outward Bound; trustee Cornell U., Achilles Track Club, N.Y.C., Florence Griswold Mus., Old Lyme, Conn.; bd. dirs. Internat. Tennis Hall of Fame, Newport, R.I. Mem. Old Lyme Country Cub, Am. Alpine Club, Explorers Club, Cornell Club, Naval Mil. Club. Home: 200 N Cove Rd Old Saybrook CT 06475-2537

PHILLIPS, WILLIAM GEORGE, retired food products executive; b. Cleve., Mar. 3, 1920; s. Edward George and Ina Marie (Cottle) P.; m. Laverne Anne Evenden, Aug. 7, 1943; children—Karen Anne (Mrs. David F. Berry), Connie Allynette (Mrs. Richard Tressel), Scott William. A.B. Antioch Coll., 1942. Pub. acct. Price Waterhouse & Co., Cleve., 1944-48; tax acct. Glidden Co., Cleve., 1948-52, asst. treas., 1952, treas., dir., 1953-63, adminstrv. v.p., 1963-64, pres., 1964-67, chief exec. officer, 1967; pres. Glidden-Durkee div. SCM Corp., 1967-68; pres., chief exec. officer Internat. Multifoods Corp. (formerly Internat. Milling), Mpls., 1968-70, chmn. bd., chief exec. officer, 1970-85; dep. chmn. Mpls. Fed. Res. Bank, 1979-82, chmn., 1982-86; bd. dirs. Soo Line R.R. Co., No. States Power. Bd. overseers U. Minn. Coll. Bus. Adminstrn.; nat. corp. adv. bd. United Negro Coll. Fund; exec. com. U.S.-Iran Joint Bus. Coun.; adv. bd. Nat. Alliance Businessmen; bd. dirs. Mpls. Downtown Devel. Corp., Minn. State Coun. on Econ. Edn.; mem. Mpls. YMCA investment com.; mem. pres.'s adv. bd. Am. Diabetes Assn.; adv. bd. Inst. Internat. Edn.; trustee Baldwin-Wallace Coll., 1960-68, Hamline U., 1978-88; bd. dirs. Mpls. Found.; trustee Mpls. Soc. Fine Arts, Nat. Jewish Hosp. at Denver, Ednl. Rsch. Coun. Am.; conf. bd. mem. Community Ch.; chmn. bd. Sanibel Community Ch.; treas., dir., Barrier Island Group for the Arts. Lt., inf. AUS, 1942-45, ETO. Decorated Bronze star. Mem. Conf. Bd. C. of US., dir., mem. U.S.-Can. com.), Ohio Soc. CPAs, Grocery Mfrs. Am. (dir.), Dunes Country Club.

PHILLIPS, WILLIAM RAY, JR., shipbuilding executive; b. West Point, Va., Feb. 23, 1931; s. William Ray and Marjorie Evelyn (Treat) P.; m. Marian Belle Culbreth, Nov. 7, 1953; children: William Ray III, Dana Louise. Attended, Newport News (Va.) Shipbuilding Apprentice Sch., 1949-54; BS, Va. Poly. Inst., 1960; student advanced mgmt. program, Harvard U., 1975. Foreman machine shops and tool rm. Newport News (Va.) Shipbuilding Co., 1964-66, asst. supt. machine shops div., 1966-67, mgr. nuclear constrn., 1967-72, dir. waterfront ops., 1972-75, v.p. yard ops., 1975-79, v.p. mktg., 1979-83, v.p. engring., 1983-84, v.p. engring., 1984-87, exec. v.p., 1987-92, pres., CEO, 1992-94, chmn. CEO, 1994—; bd. dirs. Newport News Reactor Svcs., Idaho Falls, Idaho, pres.; bd. dirs. Newport News Indsl. Ohio, North Perry, Ohio, chmn., 1992—. Sgt. U.S. Army,

1955-57. Named Engr. of Yr., Peninsula Engrs. Com., 1986. Mem. Soc. Naval Architects and Marine Engrs. (pres.), Navy League U.S. (life), Naval Submarine League, Am. Soc. Naval Engrs., Propeller Club U.S., Seaford Yacht Club (Yorktown, Va., trustee). Republican. Presbyterian. Office: Newport News Shipbldg & Drydock 4101 Washington Ave Newport News VA 23607-2734

PHILLIPS, WINFRED MARSHALL, dean, mechanical engineer; b. Richmond, Va., Oct. 7, 1940; s. Claude Marshall and Gladys Marian (Barden) P.; children—Stephen, Sean. B.S.M.E., Va. Poly. Inst., 1963; M.A.E., U. Va., 1966, D.Sc., 1968. Mech. engr. U.S. Naval Weapons Lab., Dahlgren, Va., 1963; NSF trainee, teaching, research asst. dept. aerospace engring. U. Va., Charlottesville, 1963-67; research scientist, 1966-67; asst. prof. dept. aerospace engring. Pa. State U., University Park, 1968-74, from assoc. prof. to prof., 1974-80, assoc. dean research Coll. Engring., 1979-80; head Sch. Mech. Engring. Purdue U., West Lafayette, Ind., 1980-88; dean Coll. Engring. U. Fla., Gainesville, 1988—, assoc. v.p. engr. rsch., 1989—; chmn. bd. dirs. North Fla. Tech. Innovation Corp., 1995—; vis. prof. U. Paris, 1976-77; bd. dirs. Tokheim Corp., Fla. Innovation Partnership; adv. com. Nimbus Corp., 1985-90, Hong Kong U. Sci. and Tech., 1990-93, Fla. Bd. profl. Regulation, 1992—; co-founder, v.p., CEO Inc., 1990—; mem. acad. adv. coun. Indsl. Rsch. Inst., 1990-93; mem. sci. adv. com. electric Power Rsch. Inst., 1994—; chmn. bd. dirs. North Florida Tech. Innovation Corp., 1995—; bd. dirs. Southeastern Coalition for Minorities in Engring. Sect. editor Am. Soc. Artificial Internal Organs Jour.; contbr. more than 130 articles to profl. jours., chpts. to books. Bd. dirs. Cen. Pa. Heart Assn., 1974-80, U. Fla. Found., 1989-91; mem. Ind. Boiler and Pressure Vessel Code Bd., 1981-88. Named Disting. Hoosier Engr., 1987, Sagamore of the Wabash, 1988; recipient Laurel Rsch. award NIH, 1974-78, Surgery and Bioengring. Study sect., 1988-91, Fla. High Tech. and Industry Coun., 1990-94, So. Tech. Coun., 1991—. Fellow AAAS, AIAA (assoc.), ASME (sr. v.p. edn. 1986-88), Am. Astronautical Soc., Am. Inst. Med. and Biol. Engring. (founding fellow, chair coll. fellows 1994-95, pres.-elect 1995-96), Am. Soc. Engring. Edn. (past chmn. long range planning soc. awards 1990—, vice chmn. engring. deans coun. 1991-93, chair 1993—, bd. dirs. 1994—, 1st v.p. 1994—), Royal Soc. Arts; mem. Am. Soc. Artificial Internal Organs (trustee 1982-90, sec.-treas. 1986-87, pres. 1988-89), Nat. Assn. State Univs. and Land-Grant Colls. (com. quality of engring. edn.) Accreditation Bd. on Engring. and Tech. (bd. dirs. 1989—, exec. com. 1991—, mem. internat. revs. for univs. in Saudi Arabia, USSR, The Netherlands, Kuwait, pres.-elect 1994—), Univ. Programs in Computer-Aided Engring., Design and Mfg. (bd. dirs. 1985-91), Am. Phys. Soc., Biomed. Engring. Soc., N.Y. Acad. Scis., Internat. Soc. Biorheology, Fla. Engring. Soc., Cosmos Club, Fla. Blue Key, Rotary (pres. Lafayette chpt. 1987-88), Sigma Xi, Phi Kappa Phi, Pi Tau Sigma, Sigma Gamma Tau, Tau Beta Pi (eminent engr.). Achievements include development of artificial heart pumps; research on reentry aerodynamics, on blood rheology, on modelling blood flow, on fluid dynamics of artificial hearts, on the use of smooth blood contacting surfaces, on prosthetic valve fluid dynamics and on laser Doppler studies of unsteady biofluid dynamics. Home: 4140 NW 44th Ave Gainesville FL 32606-4518 Office: U Fla Coll Engineering 300 Weil Hall Gainesville FL 32611

PHILLIPS, ZAIGA ALKSNIS, pediatrician; b. Riga, Latvia, Sept. 13, 1934; came to U.S., 1949; d. Adolfs and Alma (Ozols) Alksnis; (div. 1972); children: Albert L., Lisa K., Sintija. BS, U. Wash., 1956, MD, 1959. Fellow Colo. Med. Ctr., Denver, 1961-62; sch. physician Bellevue and Issaquah (Wash.) Sch. Dists., 1970-77; pvt. practice Bellevue, 1977—; staff pediatrician Swedish Overlake Ctr., 1977—, Childrens Hosp. and Med. Ctr., Seattle, 1977—, Evergreen Med. Ctr., 1977—; cons. physician, Allergy Clinic, Childrens Hosp., Seattle, 1988—; cons. and contact to pediatricians in Latvia, 1988—. Mem. Am. Latvian Assn., 1972—, Wash. Latvian Assn., Seattle, 1972—; pres. Latvian Sorority Gundega, Seattle, 1990-93; bd. dirs. Sister Cities Assn.,Bellevue, 1992—. Fellow Am. Acad. Pediatricians; mem. Am. Latvian Physicians Assn., Wash. State and Puget Sound Pediatric Assn. Office: Pediatric Assn 2700 Northup Way Bellevue WA 98004-1461

PHILLIPSON, JOHN SAMUEL, retired English educator; b. Rochester, N.Y., Jan. 23, 1917; s. John Samuel and Mary Agnes (Price) P. B.A., U. Rochester, 1947; M.A., U. Wis., 1949, Ph.D., 1952. Editor Rochester Daily Record, 1944-47; teaching asst. U. Wis., 1947-52; instr. English U. Wis. Extension div., 1952-53; instr. Villanova U., 1953-54, asst. prof., 1954-61; asst. prof. English U. Akron, 1961-66, assoc. prof., 1966-78, prof., 1978-86. Author: Thomas Wolfe: A Reference Guide, 1977; Critical Essays on Thomas Wolfe, 1985. Founding editor: Thomas Wolfe Rev, 1977—. Mem. Modern Humanities Rsch. Assn. (bibliographer Annual Bibliography 1958-92), Thomas Wolfe Soc. (trustee 1980—, treas. 1980-87), MLA, Am. Soc. Eighteenth Century Studies, Soc. Study So. Lit., Johnson Soc. Cen. Region, Coll. English Assn. Home: 2597 24th St Cuyahoga Falls OH 44223-1650 Office: 302 Buchtel Commons Akron OH 44325-1906

PHILLIS, JOHN WHITFIELD, physiologist, educator; b. Port of Spain, Trinidad, Apr. 1, 1936; came to U.S., 1981; s. Ernest and Sarah Anne (Glover) P.; m. Pamela Julie Popple, 1958 (div. 1968); children: David, Simon, Susan; m. Shane Beverly Wright, Jan. 24, 1969. B in Vet. Sci., Sydney (Australia) U., 1958, D in Vet. Sci., 1976; PhD, Australian Nat. U., Canberra, 1961; DSc, Monash U., Melbourne, Australia, 1970. Lectr./sr. Monash U., 1963-69; vis. prof. Ind. U. Indpls., 1969; prof. physiology, assoc. dean rsch. U. Man., Winnipeg, Can., 1970-73; prof., chmn. dept. physiology U. Sask., Saskatoon, Can., 1973-81, asst. dean rsch., 1973-75; prof. physiology, chmn. dept. physiology Wayne State U., Detroit, 1981—; Wellcome vis. prof. Tulane U., 1986; mem. scholarship and grants com. Can. Med. Rsch. Coun., Ottawa, Ont., 1973-79; mem. sci. adv. bd. Dystonia Med. Rsch. Found., Beverly Hills, Calif., 1980-85; mem. sci. adv. panel World Soc. for Protection of Animals, 1982—. Author: Pharmacology of Synapses, 1970; editor: Veterinary Physiology, 1976, Physiology and Pharmacology of Adenosine Derivatives, 1983, Adenosine and Adenine Nucleotides as Regulators of Cellular Function, 1991, The Regulation of Cerebral Blood Flow, 1993; editor Can. Jour. Physiology and Pharmacology, 1978-81, Progress in Neurobiology, 1973—. Mem. grants com. Am. Heart Assn. of Mich., 1985-90, mem. rsch. coun., 1991-92, mem. rsch. forum com., 1991—, chair, 1992-93. Wellcome fellow London, 1961-62; Can. Med. Rsch. Found. grantee, 1970-81, rsch. prof., 1980; NIH grantee, 1983—. Mem. Brit. Pharmacol. Soc., Physiol. Soc., Can. Physiol. Soc. (pres. 1979-80), Am. Physiol. Soc., Soc. Neurosci., Internat. Brain Rsch. Orgn. Home: 25501 Circle Dr Southfield MI 48075-6127 Office: Wayne State U Dept Physiology 540 E Canfield St Detroit MI 48201-1998

PHILLIS, MARILYN HUGHEY, artist; b. Kent, Ohio, Feb. 1, 1927; d. Paul Jones and Helen Margaret (Miller) Hughey; m. Richard Waring Phillis, Mar. 19, 1949; children: Diane E., Hugh R., Randall W. Student, Kent State U., 1945; BS, Ohio State U., 1949. Chemist Battelle Meml. Inst., Columbus, Ohio, 1949-53; sec. Lakewood Park Cemetery, Rocky River, Ohio, 1972-75; illustrator periodical Western Res. Hist. Mag., Garrettsville, Ohio, 1974-78; illustrator book AAUW, Piqua, Ohio, 1976; art instr. Edison State C.C., Piqua, 1976; watermedia instr. Springfield (Ohio) Mus. Art, 1976-84; juror art exhbns. state and nat. art group, 1980—; nat. painting instr. state and nat. art. orgns., 1980—; dir. Nat. Creativity Seminars, Ohio Watercolor Soc., Fairborn, 1993, 95; lectr. art and healing Wheeling (W.Va.) Jesuit Coll., 1994. Author: Watermedia Techniques for Releasing the Creative Spirit, 1992; contbr. articles and illustrations to profl. jours.; one-man shows include Stifel Fine Art Ctr., Wheeling, W.Va., Springfield (Ohio) Art Mus., Zanesville (Ohio) Art Ctr., Cleve. Inst. Music, Columbus Mus. Art; exhibited in group shows at No. Ariz. U. Art Mus. Flagstaff, 1993, Taiwan Art Edn. Inst., Taipei, 1994; represented in permanent collections at Springfield Mus. Art, Ohio Watercolor Soc., also corp. collections. Gallery dir. Greene St. United Meth. Ch., Piqua, 1972-75; pres. Rocky River (Ohio) H.S. PTA, 1971; chmn. Community Health and Humor Porgram, Wheeling, 1992. Recipient First awards Watercolor West, Riverside, Calif., 1990, W.Va. Watercolor Soc., Morgantown, 1993, Hudson Soc. award Nat. Collage Soc., 1995. Mem. Internat. Soc. Study of Subtle Energies and Energy Medicine (art cons. sci. jour. 1992—), Am. Watercolor Soc. (dir. 1991-93, newsletter editor 1992—, Osborne award 1975), Soc. Layerists in Multi Media (nat. v.p. 1988-93), Ohio Watercolor Soc. (sec. 1979-82, v.p. 1982-89, pres. 1990—, Gold medal, Best of Show 1993), Nat. Watercolor Soc., Int. Noetic Sci., Western Ohio Watercolor Soc. (pres. 1979-80, 2nd award 1982), Allied Artists Ga., W.Va. Watercolor Soc., Ky. Watercolor Soc., Ga. Watercolor Soc.

Avocations: hiking, reading, genealogy, music, travel. Home and Office: Phillis Studio 72 Stamm Circle Wheeling WV 26003

PHILOGENE, BERNARD J. R., academic administrator, science educator; b. Beau-Bassin, Mauritius, May 4, 1940; came to Can., 1961; s. Raymond Pierre and Simone Marie (Ruffier) P.; m. Hélène Marie Lebreux, July 7, 1964; children: Simone, Catherine. BS, U. Montreal, 1964; MS, McGill U., 1966; PhD, U. Wis., 1970. Research officer Can. Forestry Service, Que., 1966-70, research scientist, 1970-71; asst. prof. U. B.C., Vancouver, 1971-74; asst. prof., assoc. prof., then prof. entomology U. Ottawa, Can., 1974—, vice dean sci. and engring., 1982-85, acting dean, 1985-86, dean faculty of sci., 1986-90, acad. vice rector, 1990—; pres. Can. Consortium of Sci. Scis., 1992-94; cons. OAS, Washington, 1979-80, Agence de Coop. Culture & Tech., Paris, 1982-83, Can. Internat. Devel. Agy., Ottawa, 1983-85, UN Environ. Program, Geneva, Switzerland, 1985-86, Internat. Devel. Research Ctr., Ottawa, 1985—. Mem. Ont. Pesticide Adv. Com., 1987-91. Decorated officier de l'Ordre des Palmes Académiques (France); knight of merit Order of St. John of Jerusalem. Fellow Entomol. Soc. Can. (bd. dirs. 1977-80); mem. Am. Inst. Biol. Scis., Entomol. Soc. Am., Can. Pest Mgmt. Soc., Assn. Can.-Française Advancement Sci. (bd. dirs. 1984-86). Office: U Ottawa, 550 Cumberland, Ottawa, ON Canada K1N 6N5

PHILP, RICHARD NILSON, writer, editor; b. Plainfield, N.J., July 7, 1943; s. Lester Perry and Gladys Emma Linea (Nilson) P. BA in English and Theater cum laude, U. N.C., 1965; MFA in Theater Lit. and Playwriting, Yale U., 1968. Lectr. in field. Author 8 plays, produced 1963-72; author: To Move, To Learn, 1973, Danseur: The Male in Ballet, 1977; editor and contbg. author: Memoirs of a Dancer: Shadows, Dreams, Memories, 1979, Alvin Ailey American Dance Theater, 1993; exec. editor: Dance Books subs. Dance Mag., 1978-83; founding bd. dirs., sec.-treas. Dance Mag. Found., 1984-93; founding bd. dirs. World Dance Alliance, 1993; chmn. Dance Mag. Prise for Reportage, Video Danse, 1992, 93; also numerous articles and dance/theater criticism; mng. editor: Dance Mag. 1970-88, editor-in-chief, 1989—; assoc. editor: Critic's Choice, 1969-70; assoc. editor: After Dark, The Magazine of Entertainment, 1970-75. Co-chmn. Internat. Adv. Bd. Jackson, Miss., Ballet Competition, 1989—; mem. selection com. ann. Astaire awards Dance Mag., 1989—; bd. dirs. Israel Dance Collection Libr., 1989—, Joffrey Ballet Sch., Video Danse, Paris; vestryman, 1979-82, 94—, lic. lay reader, chalice-bearer Christ Ch., Episcopal, Hudson, N.Y. Recipient Spl. citation Soc. Illustrators, Bronze medal 28th Internat. Film and TV Fest., N.Y.C., 1985, Silver medal Chgo. Internat. Film Festival, 1985, TV Documentary Writing award Am. Film Festival, 1986. Mem. Greene County Hist. Soc., Catskill Writer's Group (founder), Devon (Eng.) Beekeepers Assn. Home: The Towers Apt 22 33-15 80th St Jackson Heights NY 11372 also: 169 State Route 385 Catskill NY 12414-5027 Office: Dance Mag Inc 33 W 60th St New York NY 10023-7905

PHILPOTT, HARRY MELVIN, former university president; b. Bassett, Va., May 6, 1917; s. Benjamin Cabell and Daisy (Hundley) P.; m. Pauline Breck Moran, Sept. 15, 1943; children: Harry Melvin, Jean Todd, Benjamin Cabell II, Virginia Lee. A.B., Washington and Lee U., 1938, LL.D., 1966; Ph.D., Yale U., 1947; D.D., Stetson U., 1960; LL.D., U. Fla., 1969, U. Ala., 1970; H.H.D., Samford U., 1978, Montevallo U., 1980, Auburn U., 1981. Ordained to ministry Bapt. Ch., 1942; dir. religious activities Washington and Lee U., 1938-40; prof. religion U. Fla., 1947-52, v.p., 1957-65; dean, head dept. religion and philosophy Stephens Coll., 1952-57; pres. Auburn U., 1965-80. Mem. Regional Edn. Bd., 1966-82, vice chmn., 1973-75; chmn. Ala. Edn. Study Commn., 1967-69; pres. Southeastern Conf., 1972-74. Served to 1st lt. Chaplains Corps., USNR, 1943-46. Mem. Nat. Assn. State Univs. and Land-Grant Colls. (chmn. council presidents 1972-73, exec. com. 1973-78, pres. 1976-77), Fla. Blue Key, Kappa Alpha, Omicron Delta Kappa, Kappa Delta Pi, Phi Kappa Phi. Home: PO Box 3037 Auburn AL 36831-3037

PHILPOTT, JAMES ALVIN, JR., lawyer; b. Lexington, Va., Apr. 26, 1947; s. James Alvin and Helen (Gibbs) P.; m. Judy Mauze, June 10, 1968; children: John Harman, Jean Cameron, James Hundley. BS in Commerce, Washington & Lee U., 1969, JD summa cum laude, 1972. Bar: N.Y. 1974, KY. 1980, U.S. Dist. Ct. (so. dist.) N.Y. 1975, U.S. Dist. Ct. (ea. dist.) Ky. 1991, U.S. Ct. Appeals (4th cir.) 1973, (U.S. Ct. Appeals (6th cir.) 1993. Law clk. to justice U.S. Ct. Appeals (4th cir.) Asheville, N.C., 1972-73; assoc. Cravath, Swaine & Moore, N.Y.C., 1974-79; exec. v.p., gen. counsel Gainesway Farm, Lexington, Ky., 1980-85; dir., mem. exec. com., sec. Breeders' Cup Ltd., 1983—. Editor-in chief Washington & Lee U. Law Rev., 1972. Trustee The Lexington Sch., 1984-91. Served to capt. U.S. Army, 1972-73. Mem. ABA (corp., banking and bus. law sect.), Ky. Bar Assn., Ky. Thoroughbred Assn., Washington & Lee U. Law Sch. Assn. (mem. coun. 1986-91), Idle Hour Country Club, The Lexington Club, Omicron Delta Kappa. Presbyterian. Office: 1200 First National Bank Bldg Lexington KY 40507

PHILPOTT, LARRY LA FAYETTE, horn player; b. Alma, Ark., Apr. 5, 1937; s. Lester and Rena (Owens) P.; m. Elise Robichaud, Nov. 24, 1962 (div. June 1975); children: Daniel, Stacy; m. Anne Sokol, Feb. 14, 1984. B.S., Ga. So. Coll., 1962; Mus.M., Butler U., 1972. Instr. in horn Butler U., De Pauw U.; dir. music Cedarcrest Sch., Marysville, Wash., 1991—. Mem., N.C. Symphony, 1960, Savannah (Ga.) Symphony, L'Orchestre Symphonique de Quebec, Que., Can., 1962-64, prin. horn player, Indpls. Symphony Orch., 1964-89, Flagstaff Summer Festival, 1986—, artist-in-residence Ind.-Purdue Indpls.; appeared with Am. Shakespeare Theatre, summer 1965, Charlottetown Festival, summers 1967-68, Flagstaff Summer Festival, 1968-85, Marrowstone Music Festival, 1985—. Served with USN, 1956-60. Mem. Music Educators Nat. Conf., Am. Fedn. Musicians, Internat. Conf. Symphony and Opera Musicians, Internat. Horn Soc., Coll. Music Soc., Phi Mu Alpha Sinfonia. Home: 14925 63d Ave SE Snohomish WA 98290 Office: Cedarcrest Sch 6400 88th St NE Marysville WA 98270-2800

PHILYAW, A. ROGER, insurance company executive. Sr. v.p. Blue Cross Blue Shield of N.C., Durham, 1964—. Office: Blue Cross Blue Shield of NC 5901 Drham Chapel Hl Blvd Durham NC 27702

PHINNEY, JEAN SWIFT, psychology educator; b. Princeton, N.J., Mar. 12, 1933; d. Emerson H. and Anne (Davis) Swift; m. Bernard O. Phinney, Dec. 11, 1965; children: Peter, David. BA, Mass. Wellesley Coll., 1955; MA, UCLA, 1969, PhD, 1973. Asst. prof. psychology Calif. State U. L.A., 1977-81, assoc. prof. psychology, 1981-86, prof. psychology, 1986—. Editor: Children's Ethnic Socialization, 1987; asst. editor Jour. Adolescence; contbr. articles to profl. jours. NIH grantee. Mem. Am. Psychol. Assn., Soc. for Rsch. in Child Devel., Soc. for Rsch. in Adolescence. Avocations: skiing, hiking, travel, chamber music. Office: Calif State U Dept Psychology 5151 State University Dr Los Angeles CA 90032

PHINNEY, ROBERT ALDEN, geophysics educator; b. Rochester, N.Y., Oct. 7, 1936; s. Robert M. and Margaret (Smith) P.; m. Elizabeth Butler (div. 1973); children: Carolyn, Christopher; m. Caroline Roslia Manning, Dec. 29, 1977. SB, SM, MIT, 1959; PhD, Calif. Tech. U., 1961. Asst. prof. Calif. Tech. U., Pasadena, 1961-63; assoc. prof. Princeton (N.J.) U., 1963-68, prof., 1968—, chmn. dept. geol. and physical scis., 1982-88; pres. Inc. Rsch. Insts. for Seismology, Arlington, Va., 1989-91. Editor: History of the Earth's Crust., 1968. Trustee Waldorf Sch. Princeton, 1981—. Fellow Am. Geophysical Union, Geol. Soc. Am.; mem. Am. Assn. Petroleum Geologists, Seismological Soc. Am., Soc. Exploration Geophysicists. Avocations: piano, hiking. Office: Princeton U Dept Geol and Geophys Scis 416 Guyot Hall Princeton NJ 08540-1003

PHINNEY, WILLIAM CHARLES, retired geologist; b. South Portland, Maine, Nov. 16, 1939; s. Clement Woodbridge and Margaret Florence (Foster) P.; m. Colleen Dorothy Murphy, May 31, 1953; children—Glenn, Duane, John, Marla. B.S., MIT, 1953, M.S., 1956, Ph.D., 1959. Faculty geology U. Minn., 1959-70; chief geology br. NASA Lyndon B. Johnson Space Center, Houston, 1970-82; chief planetology br. NASA Lyndon B. Johnson Space Center, 1982-89, ret., 1994; NASA prin. investigator lunar samples. Contbr. articles to profl. jours. Served with C.E. AUS, 1953-55. Recipient NASA Exceptional Sci. Achievement medal, 1972, NASA Cert. of Commendation, 1987; NASA rsch. grantee, 1972-94, NSF rsch. grantee,

1960-70. Mem. Am. Geophys. Union, AAAS, Mineral. Soc. Am., Geol. Soc. Am., Minn. Acad. Sci. (dir.), Sigma Xi. Home: 18063 Judicial Way S Lakeville MN 55044

PHIPPS, ALLEN MAYHEW, management consultant; b. Seattle, Oct. 3, 1938; s. Donald Mayhew and Virginia (McGinn) P.; B.A. in Econs., U. Calif., Berkeley, 1961; M.B.A. with honors, Stanford U., 1969; m. Joyce Elisabeth Alberti, Aug. 21, 1971; children—Ramsey Mayhew, Justin Beckwith. Security analyst Morgan Guaranty Trust Co., 1968; with Boston Cons. Group, Inc., 1969—, mgr. 1971-74, mem. sr. team, Calif., 1974-77, corp. v.p., dir., 1975—; mgr. Boston Cons. Group, G.mbH, Munich. W. Ger., 1978-82, partner-in-charge West Coast client devel., Menlo Park, Calif, 1982-84; pres. Techno Digital Systems, Inc., 1984-86; pres., chief exec. officer, Techno Digital System (Sellectek, Inc.), 1984-85; exec. v.p., Regis McKenna Inc., Palo Alto, Calif., 1985-87; pvt. practice mgmt. cons., Menlo Pk., 1987-95; chief exec. officer Bio Electro Systems, Palo Alto, 1989-92; mng. dir., Bus. Engring. Inc., Menlo Park, Calif., 1992-95; sr. v.p. bus. and policy group SRI Internat., Menlo Park, Calif., 1995—. Served to capt. U.S. Army, 1961-67. Decorated Bronze Star, Army Commendation medal with 2 oak leaf clusters. Mem. Alpha Delta Phi. Republican. Presbyterian. Clubs: Bohemian (San Francisco); Sharon Heights Golf and Country (Menlo Park). Home: 33 Prado Secoya St Atherton CA 94027-4126 Office: SRI Internat 333 Ravenswood Ave Menlo Park CA 94025

PHIPPS, CLAUDE RAYMOND, research scientist; b. Ponca City, Okla., Mar. 15, 1940; s. Claude Raymond Louis and Deva Pauline (DeWitt) P.; m. Lynn Malarney, Dec. 1, 1962 (div. Feb. 1989); 1 child, David Andrew; life ptnr. Shanti E. Bannwart. BS, MIT, 1961, MS, 1963; PhD, Stanford U., 1972. Rsch. staff Lawrence Livermore (Calif.) Nat. Lab., 1972-74; rsch. staff Los Alamos (N.Mex.) Nat. Lab. 1974-95, project leader engine support sys. tech. program, 1993; assoc. dir. Alliance for Photonic Tech., Albuquerque, 1992-95; CEO Photonic Assocs., Santa Fe, 1995—; co-instr. (with Shanti E. Bannwart) "Pairs" Relationship Tng., Santa Fe, N.Mex., 1990—; dir. Santa Fe Investment Conf., 1987; mem. program com. MIT Workshop on High Temperature Superconductors, Cambridge, 1988; mem. Instl. R & D Com. Los Alamos Nat. Lab. 1990-92, project leader laser effects, 1982-87, mem. internat. rsch. tour, Australia, Japan, Scotland, 1988-89; invited discussion leader Gordon Conf. on Laser Particle Interactions, N.H., 1992. Co-author: Laser Ionization Mass Analysis, 1993; author internat. lecture series on laser surface interactions, Berlin, Antwerp, Marseilles, Xiamen, Cape Town, Durban, 1987—; contbr. articles to profl. jours. Lt. USN, 1963-65. Grad. fellow W. Alton Jones Found., N.Y.C., 1962-63. Avocations: writing poetry, reading, travel, photography. Home: 1621 Calle Torreon Santa Fe NM 87501 Office: Photonic Assocs 1621 Calle Torreon Santa Fe NM 87501

PHIPPS, JOHN RANDOLPH, retired army officer; b. Kansas, Ill, May 16, 1919; s. Charles Winslow and Kelsey Ethel (Torrence) P.; m. Pauline M. Prunty, Feb. 8, 1946; children: Charles W., Kelsey J. Phipps-Selander. B.S. in Econs. with honors, U. Ill., 1941; M.P.A., Sangamon State U., 1976; assoc. course, Command and Gen. Staff Coll., 1959, nuclear weapons employment course, 1962; course, U.S. Army War Coll., 1973, U.S. Nat. Def. U., 1978. Owner, operator chain shoe stores in Eastern Ill., 1946-70; commd. 2d lt. F.A. U.S. Army, 1941, advanced through grades to capt., 1943; service in Philippines and Japan; discharged as maj., 1946; organizer, comdr. Co. E, 130th Inf., Ill.; N.G., Mattoon, 1947; comdg. officer 2d Bn., 130th Inf. N.G., 1951, lt. col. 2d Bn., 130th Inf., 1951; called to fed. service, 1952; adv. (29th Regt., 9th Republic of Korea Div.), 1952-53; comdr. officer 1st Bn., 130th Inf., Ill. N.G., 1954, col.; 1959; comdg. officer 2d Brigade, 33d Div., 1963-67; asst. div. comdr. 33d Inf. Div., 1967, brig. gen., 1967; comdr. 33d Inf. Brigade, Chgo., 1967-70; comdr. Ill. Emergency Ops. Hdqrs., 1970, asst. adj. gen. Ill., 1970-77, acting adj. gen., 1977-78, adj. gen., 1978, promoted to maj. gen., 1978, now maj. gen. ret. Decorated Silver Star, Bronze Star, Disting. Service medal, Combat Infantry Badge, Army Disting. Service medal Ill., various Philippine and Korean decorations; State of Ill. Long and Honorable Service medal. Mem. VFW, Adj. Gens. Assn. U.S., N.G. Assn. U.S., N.G. Assn. Ill., Am. Legion, Amvets. Home: 100 Wabash Ave Mattoon IL 61938-4524 Office: Phipps 100 Wabash Ave Mattoon IL 61938-4524

PHIPPS, JOHN TOM, lawyer; b. Chgo., Sept. 20, 1937; s. J. Oliver and Jean C. (Kirkwood) P.; children: Anne Marie, John B., Karen Louise. BA, DePauw U., 1959; postgrad., Am. U.; JD, U. Ill., 1965. Bar: Ill. 1965, U.S. Dist. Ct. (cen. dist.) Ill. 1966. Pvt. practice, Champaign, Ill., 1965—; spl. prosecutor Champaign County, Ill., 1968; bd. dirs. Champaign County Legal Assistance Found., 1965-73, pres., 1971-73; incorporator Land of Lincoln Legal Assistance Found., 1973, bd. dirs., 1972—, chmn., 1981—; bd. dirs. Ill. Inst. for Continuing Legal Edn. Co-author: Going to Trial: A Step-by-Step Guide to Trial Practice and Procedure (ABA GP sect.), 1989; contbr. articles to profl. jours. and continuing legal edn. books. Bd. dirs. Clark-Lindsey Village, 1969-80, pres. 1973-75. Lt. USAF, 1959-62, capt. res., 1964-66. Fellow Ill. Bar Found. (charter), Am. Bar Found.; mem. ABA (gen. practice sect., vice-chmn. solo and small firms com. 1985-87, chmn. 1987-89, editor ABA gen. practice sect. newsletter The Briefcase 1990—), Champaign County Bar Assn. (bd. govs. 1972-74, v.p. 1973-74, gen. practice sect. counsel 1993—), Ill. Bar Assn. (mem. corp. and securities law sect. coun. 1976-78, law office tech. com. 1978-79, mem. mgmt. and econs. sect. coun. 1978-83, chmn. mgmt. and econs. of practice of law sect. 1980-82, family law sect. coun. 1985-90—, standing com. on alternative dispute resolution 1990—, vice chair 1993—, task force on ednl. bigotry 1990-92, pres. adv. com. mandatory CLE 1992—, Ill. Supreme Ct. alternative dispute resolution com. 1992—), Assn. Trial Lawyers Am., Ill. Trial Lawyers Assn., Phi Gamma Delta, Phi Alpha Delta. Office: 44 Main St Ste 303 Champaign IL 61820

PHIPPS, WILMA J., nursing educator, author; b. Detroit, Jan. 24, 1925; d. Walter and Inez M. (Steele) P. Diploma, Harper Hosp. Sch. Nursing, 1946; BSN, Wayne U., 1954; AM, U. Chego., 1956, PhD, 1977. Assoc. prof. med./surg. nursing Case Western Res. U., Cleve., 1970-76, prof. med./surg. nursing, 1976-87, prof. emeritus, 1987—. Editor: Medical-Surgical Nursing, Concepts and Clinical Practice, 1995, Medical-Surgical Nursing, A Nursing Process Approach, 1993. Mem. ANA, APHA, Am. Acad. Nursing, Nat. League Nursing, Sigma Theta Tau, Pi Lambda Theta. Home: 3701 Mayfield Rd Apt 302 Cleveland OH 44121-1750

PHISTER, MONTGOMERY, JR., computer engineering consultant, writer; b. San Pedro, Calif., Feb. 26, 1926; s. Montgomery and Helga Laurena (Winther) P.; m. Melinda Miles, Mar. 29, 1974; children—Montgomery, Julia Elizabeth, Roger Benjamin. Student, Stanford U., 1943-44, B.S., 1949, M.S., 1950; Ph.D., Cambridge (Eng.) U., 1953. Mem. tech. staff Hughes Aircraft Co., Culver City, Calif., 1953-55; dir. engring. TRW Products Co., Los Angeles, 1955-60; v.p. engring. Scantlin Electronics Inc. (later Quotron Systems), Los Angeles, 1960-66; v.p. devel. Xerox Data Systems, Los Angeles, 1966-72; pvt. practice cons., writer Santa Fe, 1972—; instr. UCLA, 1954-64, Harvard U., 1974, U. Sydney, Australia, 1975. Author: Logical Design of Digital Computers, 1958, Data Processing Technology and Economics, 1976. Served with USMCR, 1944-46. Fellow IEEE; mem. Assn. for Computing Machinery. Republican. Patentee. Home and Office: 414 Camino De Las Animas Santa Fe NM 87501-4535

PHLEGAR, BENJAMIN FOCHT, retired magazine editor; b. Salina, Kans., Nov. 21, 1921; s. Benjamin Gray and Frances Lucile (Focht) P.; m. Jane Fulton, Sept. 19, 1945 (dec. Sept. 1983); children: Janet Margaret, Benjamin Fulton. B.J., U. Mo., 1943. Reporter St. Louis Star-Times, 1943-44; with AP, 1944-63; newsman, then automotive editor AP, Detroit, 1955-63; Detroit bur. chief, assoc. editor, then asst. mng. editor U.S. News & World Report, Washington, 1963-92; exec. editor U.S. News & World Report, 1979-85. Mem. Am. Soc. Mag. Editors. Home: 4740 Connecticut Ave NW Washington DC 20008-5632

PHOCAS, GEORGE JOHN, international lawyer, business executive; b. N.Y.C., Dec. 1, 1927; m. Katrin Gorny, Feb. 26, 1966; 1 child, George Alexander. A.B., U. Chgo., 1950, J.D., 1953. Bar: N.Y. 1955, U.S. Supreme Ct. 1962. Assoc. Sullivan & Cromwell, N.Y.C., 1953-56; counsel Creole Petroleum Corp., Caracas, Venezuela, 1956-60; internat. negotiator Standard Oil Co. N.J. (Exxon), 1960-63; sr. ptnr. Casey, Lane & Mittendorf, London, 1963-72, counsel, 1972-76; exec. v.p. Occidental Petroleumm Corp., Los

Angeles, 1972-74; adv., U.S. del. UN, ECAFE, Teheran, 1963. Trustee Assn. Naval Aviation, Washington, Owl's Head Aviation Mus., Maine; mem. vis. bd. U. Chgo. Law Sch.; bd. visitors U. Chgo. Law Sch. Capt. U.S. Army. Mem. Law Soc. London, Brit. Inst. Comparative Law, Am. Soc. Internat. Law, ABA, Assn. Bar City N.Y. Clubs: Boodles (London); Metropolitan (N.Y.C.); Sleepy Hollow. Home: 28 Aubrey Walk, London W87JG, England Office: 5020 Goodridge Ave Riverdale NY 10471-2913

PHOENIX, PAUL JOSEPH, steel manufacturing company executive; b. Hamilton, Ont., Can., Feb. 13, 1928; s. Raymond Joseph and Marie (Hagerty) P.; m. Patricia Ruth Kearns, July 11, 1953; children: William, James, Marie, Margaret, Mary Ellen, Jane. B.A., U. Toronto, M.B.A. With Dofasco Inc., Hamilton 1941—; mgr. quality control, 1964-70, asst. dir. mfg. controls, from 1970, then task force chmn., computerized order entry and prodn. control, v.p. planning, 1973-82, exec. v.p., 1982-83, pres., chief operating officer, 1983-87, pres., chief exec. officer, 1987—, also bd. dirs.; dir. Aberford Resources Ltd., Calgary, Nat. Steel Car, Hamilton. Mem. adv. com. on indsl. mgmt. and tech., Mohawk Coll.; bd. dirs. St. Joseph's Villa, past chmn.; mem. Hamilton Philharm.; past pres. Children's Aid Soc. of Hamilton-Wentworth, 1972; dept. chmn. United Way Campaign. Mem. Am. Inst. Indsl. Engrs. (vis. 1964-65), Am. Mgmt. Assn., Am. Iron and Steel Inst., N.Am. Soc. Corp. Planning, Newman Alumni Soc. (pres. 1967-68), St. Michael's Coll. Alumni Soc. Roman Catholic. Clubs: Burlington Golf and Country; Hamilton Golf and Country, Ancaster. Avocation: golf. Home: Hamilton Can.

PHYPERS, DEAN PINNEY, retired computer company executive; b. Cleve., Jan. 13, 1929; s. Fordham S. and Grace Ellen (Pinney) P.; children: Dean A., Toni T., William C., Jonathan W., Katharine L. B.A. in Physics, Harvard U., 1950; postgrad., U. Mich. Sch. Bus., 1952. With IBM, 1955-87; v.p. bus. plans IBM, Armonk, N.Y., 1972-74; v.p. fin. and planning IBM, 1974-79, sr. v.p. fin. and planning, dir., 1979-82, sr. v.p., dir., 1982-87; bd. dirs. Bethlehem Steel, Am. Internat. Group, Church and Dwight Co., Inc., Cambrex Inc. Trustee Com. for Econ. Devel. Served with USNR, 1952-55. Home: 220 Rosebrook Rd New Canaan CT 06840-3727

PIAKER, PHILIP MARTIN, accountant, educator; b. N.Y.C., Oct. 26, 1921; s. Jacob and Sarah (Schloss) P.; m. Pauline Strum, Sept. 22, 1946; children: Susan, Alan, Matthew. BA, CCNY, 1943, MBA, 1949. Lectr. CCNY, 1949-52; asst. prof. acctg. SUNY, Binghamton, 1952-57, assoc. prof., 1957-62, prof., 1962—, Disting. Svc. prof. acctg., 1980—, chmn. dept. acctg., 1970-76, 77-89; chmn. bd. Endicott Rsch. Group, Inc., Johnson City, N.Y., 1983—; adv. dir. Endicott Bank N.Y.; mem. N.Y. State Bd. for Pub. Accountancy, 1973-83, chmn., 1982-83; v.p. Piaker, Lyons, P.C., CPA's; mem. Nat. Bd. to Evaluate CPA Exams., 1979-83; Danforth Seminar on Bus. Morality fellow Harvard U., 1959; Summer Study on Ethics in Bus. fellow U. So. Calif., 1982. Mem. editorial bd. Binghamton Reporter, 1975—. Bd. dirs. Broome chpt. Am. Cancer Soc., 1974-79, Tri-Cities Opera; trustee Temple Israel Binghamton, 1978—. With U.S. Army, 1943-46. SUNY SWANA fellow Jerusalem, 1966, Am. Profs. for Peace in Middle East fellow Jerusalem, 1974; recipient Chancellors award for teaching excellence, 1975, David Ben Gurion award State of Israel, 1979, Outstanding Contbn. to Acctg. award Found. for Acctg., 1979, Outstanding Educator award Found. for Acctg. Rsch., 1986. Mem. AICPA, N.Y. State Soc. CPA's (pres. Binghamton chpt. 1963-65), Am. Acctg. Assn., Acctg. Rsch. Assn., Nat. Assn. Accts., Bus. Ethics Soc., SUNY Alumni Assn. (Disting. Svc. award 1989), CHABAD (pres. 1989-92). Home: 301 Manchester Rd Vestal NY 13850-3604

PIAN, RULAN CHAO, musicologist, scholar; b. Cambridge, Mass., Apr. 20, 1922; d. Yuen Ren and Buwei (Yang) Chao; m. Theodore Hsueh-huang Pian, Oct. 3, 1945; 1 child, Chanta Chao-po. BA, Radcliffe Coll., 1944, MA, 1946, PhD, 1960. Teaching asst., instr. in modern Chinese Harvard U., 1947-60, lectr. Chinese and Chinese music, 1961-74, prof. E. Asian langs., and civilization and of music, 1974-92; prof. emerita, 1992—; coordinator modern Chinese lang. instrn. Harvard U., 1962-68, mem. council E. Asian studies, 1975-92, faculty mem. Com. on Degrees in Folklore and Mythology, 1976-92, master of South House, 1975-78; vis. prof. dept. music the chinese U. hong Kong, 1975, 78-79, 82, 94, inst. humanities Nat. Tsing Hua U., Taiwan, 1990, sch. humanities Nat. Cen. U., Taiwan, 1992; hon. prof. Cen. China U. of Sci. and Tech., Wuhan, 1990, Changsha, 1991, Southwest Jiaotong U., Chengdu, China, 1994; hon. rsch. fellow Shanghais China Acad. of Arts, Beijing, 1993; academician Academia Sinca, Taiwan, 1990. Author: A Syllabus for the Mandarin Primer, 1961, Sonq Dynasty Musical Sources and Their Interpretation, 1967; compiler: Complete Musical Works of Yuen Ren Chao, 1987; contbr. articles to scholarly jours. Recipient Caroline Wilby dissertation prize Radcliffe Coll., 1960, Radcliffe Grad. Soc. medal, 1980; NDEA Fulbright-Hayes research grantee Chinese Music Taiwan, 1964; NEH grantee Hong Kong, 1978-79. Mem. Am. Musicological Soc. (coun. 1993—, Otto Kindeldey book award 1968), Internat. Musicological Soc., Soc. Ethnomusicology (coun. 1968-75, 87-90), Conf. Chinese Oral and Performing Lit. (co-founder, pres. 1983-90, permanent hon. pres. 1995—), Assn. for Chinese Mus. Rsch. (co-founder). Home: 14 Brattle Cir Cambridge MA 02138-4625 Office: 2 Divinity Ave Cambridge MA 02138-2020

PIAN, THEODORE HSUEH-HUANG, engineering educator, consultant; b. Shanghai, China, Jan. 18, 1919; came to U.S., 1943; s. Chao-Hsin Shu-Cheng and Chih-Chuan (Yen) P.; m. Rulan Chao, Oct. 3, 1945; 1 child, Canta Chao-Po. B in Engring. Tsing Hua U., Kunming, China, 1940; MS, MIT, 1944, DSc, 1948; DSc (hon.), Beijing U. Aeros. and Astronautics, 1990; PhD (hon.), Shanghai U. of Tech., 1991, Shanghai U., 1994. Engr. Cen. Aircraft Mfg. Co., Loiwing, China, 1940-42, Chengtu Glider Mfg. Factory, 1942-43; stress analyst Curtis Aircraft Div., Buffalo, 1944-45; teaching asst. MIT, Cambridge, 1946-47; tech. assoc. Shanghai U. Tech. (renamed Shanghai U. 1993), Cambridge, 1947-52; assoc. prof. MIT, Cambridge, 1959-66, prof., 1966-89, prof. emeritus, 1989—; vis. assoc. Calif. Inst. Tech., Pasadena, 1965-66; vis. prof. U. Tokyo, 1974, Tech. U., Berlin, 1975; vis. chair prof. Nat. Tsing Hua U., Hsin Chu, Taiwan, 1990, Nat. Ctrl. U., ChungLi, Taiwan, 1992; hon. prof. Beijing U. Aero. and Astronautics, Beijing Inst. Aero. and Astronautics, Beijing Inst. Tech., Southwestern Jaiotong U., Dalian U. Tech., Huazhong U. Sci. and Tech., Changsha Rwy. U., Ctrl.-South U. Tech., Hohai U., Nanjing U. of Aero. and Astronautics, Dalian Rwy. U. Recipient von Karman Meml. prize TRE Corp., Beverly Hills, Calif., 1974. Fellow AAAS, AIAA (assoc. editor jour. 1973-75, Structures, Structural Dynamics and Materials award 1975); mem. ASME (hon.), Nat. Acad. Engring., Am. Soc. for Engring. Edn., Internat. Assn. for Computational Mechanics (hon. mem. gen. coun.). Home: 14 Brattle Cir Cambridge MA 02138-4625 Office: MIT Dept Aeronautics and Astronautics 77 Massachusetts Ave Cambridge MA 02139-4307

PIANALTO, SANDRA, bank executive; b. Vicenza, Italy, 1954. Graduate, U. Akron, 1976; Post graduate, George Washington U., 1985. First v.p., coo Fed. Reserve bank of Cleve. Office: Fed Reserve Bank Cleveland PO Box 6337 Cleveland OH 44101

PIANKA, URI, violinist, concertmaster; b. Tel-Aviv, Aug. 27, 1937; came to U.S., 1987; s. Eliezer and Sarah (Weinriber) P.; m. Sarah Seidman, July 25, 1961; children: Boaz, Ruth, Maya-Helen. Studies with Ivan Galamian and Dorothy DeLay, Julliard Sch. Music, diploma in violin, 1958. Teaching fellow, mem. quartet in residence Brandeis U., Waltham, Mass., 1958-59; mem. Israel Philharm. Orch., Tel-Aviv, 1959-69, concertmaster, 1969-88; violinist The Yuval Trio, Holon, Israel, 1969-89; concertmaster Houston Symphony Orch., Houston, 1987—; rec. artist Deutsche Grammophon, 1975, CBS Masterworks, 1978. Recipient prize Queen Elizabeth Internat. Violin Competition, Brussels, 1967. Avocation: photography. Office: Houston Symphony 615 Louisiana St Houston TX 77002-2715

PIANKO, THEODORE A., lawyer; b. Dennville, N.J., Sept. 5, 1955; s. Theodore and Pasqualina (Liguori) P.; m. Beatrice Maria Olivera (div. Dec. 1985); m. Kathryn Anne Lindley, Feb. 18, 1990; children: Matthew James, Samuel Wahoo. BA, SUNY, 1975; JD, U. Mich., 1978. Bar: Mich. 1978, Ill. 1979, Calif. 1980. Atty. Ford Motor Co., Dearborn, Mich., 1978-80; assoc. Lillick McHose & Charles, L.A., 1980-83; ptnr. Sidley & Austin, L.A.,

1983-94, Christie, Parker & Hale, Pasadena, Calif., 1994—. Office: Christie Parker & Hale 350 W Colorado Blvd 5th Fl Pasadena CA 91109-7068

PIANO, RENZO, architect; b. Genoa, Italy, Sept. 14, 1937; m. Magda Arduino, 1962; children: Carlo, Matteo, Lia. Dip.Arch., Poly. of Milan, 1964. Worked with Franco Albini, Milan, 1962-64, E. Piano, Genoa, 1964-65, Z.S. Makowsky, London, 1965-70; ptnr. Piano and Rogers Architects, London, Paris and Genoa, 1970—, Piano and Rice, Genoa, Paris and London, 1977—, Piano and Fitzgerald, Houston, 1980—; lectr. Poly. of Milan, 1965-68; vis. lectr. Columbia U., N.Y.C., 1967, U. Pa., Phila., 1967, U. Bucharest, Romania, 1968, Poly. of Delft, Netherlands, 1969, Unesco, Paris, 1973, Oslo Sch. Architecture, 1976; prof. architecture Archtl. Assn. Sch., London, 1971, Poly. Cen. London, 1971. Prin. works include Italian Industry Pavilion, Expo '70, Japan, 1970, Fitzroy St. Comml. Ctr., Cambridge, U.K., 1970, B&B Italia Offices, Como, 1971, Universal Oil Products U.K. Head Office and UOP Fragrances Ltd. Lab., Tadworth, Surrey, 1972, Aston Martin Lagonda Ltd. Offices, Showroom, Restaurant, etc., London, 1973, PATScentre, Cambridge, 1975, Inst. de Recherche et de Coordination Acoustique, Paris, 1977, Centre Beaubourg, Paris, 1977, Kronenbourg factory, Strasbourg, 1978, Quartiere Il Rigo housing estate, Corciano, Perugia, Italy, 1978-82, Civic Ctr. and Libr., Loano, Savona, Italy, 1980, Nationalgalerie extensions & housing, West Berlin, 1981, De Menil Collection bldg., Houston, 1981-83, Banca Agricola Comml. bldg., Reggio Emilia, Italy, 1981-83, IBM travelling exhbn. pavilions, 1982, Palazzo a Vela conversion, 1982, Centocelle/Torrespaccata Bus. Ctr., Rome, 1982, Banca Agricola Comml. br. bldg., Modena, Italy, 1982, 5 Met. Rwy. Stas., Genoa, 1983, Il Prometeo music rsch. lab., Venice, 1984, Centre Georges Pompidou cinema extensions, Paris, 1984, Comml. Ctr. office bldgs., Naples, Italy, 1984, Kenya Energy Tech. Inst., Nairobi, 1984, Leisure Ctr., Cremona, Italy, 1984, Columbus Expedition 500th Anniversary designs, Genoa, 1984, numerous others; exhbns. include Triennale, Milan, 1967, Archtl. Assn., London, 1970, Musée des Arts Decoratifs, Paris, 1973. Recipient 1st prize Place Beaubourg Competition, Paris, 1971, Auguste Perret prize Internat. Union Architects, 1978, Compasso d'Oro award, Milan, 1981, Arnold W. Brunner Memorial Prize in Architecture Am. Acad. of Arts and Letters, 1994, Erasmus prize, Netherlands, 1995. Fellow Am. Inst. Architects (hon.). Office: Atelier Piano, 14 Rue Ste Croix de la Bretonnerie, 75004 Paris France Office: Piano and Fitzgerald 5075 Westheimer Ste 1260 Houston TX 77056 also: Studio Piano and Rice, Viale G Modugno 22, 16156 Genoa Italy

PIANTINI, CARLOS, conductor; b. Santo Domingo, Dominican Republic, May 9, 1927; s. Alberto and Marina (Espinal) P.; m. Marianne Piantini (div. 1977); children: Susan, Vivian, Albert, Frank; m. Yolanda Trujillo, Dec. 5, 1982. MusB, NYU, 1968. Violinist 1st Recital, Santo Domingo, 1937-44, Mex. Symphony, 1944-47, Juilliard Sch., N.Y.C., 1947-50, N.Y. Philharm. Orch., N.Y.C., 1956-71; condr. Vienna (Austria) Acad. Music, 1971-73; artistic dir. Nat. Theatre, Santo Domingo, 1973-78; condr. Caracas (Venezuela) Philharm., 1979-83, Nat. Symphonic Orch., Santo Domingo, 1983—; Domican amb. to UN; head cultural affairs Dominican Rep. Govt., 1950-56. Contbr. articles to profl. jours. Cons. V Centennial Commemorative, Santo Domingo, 1988. Avocation: stamp collecting. Office: Nat Symphonic Orch, Palacio de Bellas Artes, Santo Domingo Dominican Republic

PIASSICK, JOEL BERNARD, lawyer; b. Atlanta, June 2, 1940; s. Louis S. and Sarah (Freeman) P.; m. Karen Pevow, Aug. 11, 1963; children: Joan, Louis. BA in Polit. Sci., Tulane U., 1962; LLB, U. Va., 1965. Bar: Va. 1965, Ga. 1966. Ptnr. Smith, Gambrell & Russell, Atlanta, 1967-90, Kilpatrick & Cody, Atlanta, 1990—; bd. dirs. Southeastern Bankruptcy Law Inst., Inc. Fellow Am. Coll. Bankruptcy. Office: Kilpatrick & Cody 1100 Peachtree St Ste 2800 Atlanta GA 30309-4530

PIATETSKI-SHAPIRO, ILYA, mathematics educator; b. Moscow, Mar. 30, 1929; arrived in Israel, 1976; s. Joseph and Sheina (Gurevitch) P.-S.; m. Edith Piatetski-Shapiro, 1978; children: Gregory, Vera, Shlomit. PhD, Moscow U., 1951, D, 1958. Prof. math. Moscow U., 1964-72, Tel Aviv U., 1976—, Yale U., New Haven, 1977—. Recipient Laureate of Israel prize in math., Wolf Found. Math. prize, 1990. Avocation: hiking. Office: Yale U Dept Math 10 Hillhouse Ave New Haven CT 06511-6814 also: Tel Aviv U Sch Math Scis, Ramat Aviv, Tel Aviv Israel

PIATT, JACK BOYD, manufacturing executive; b. Washington, Pa., Jan. 8, 1928; s. Harold Boyd and Violet Marie (Amos) P.; m. Thelma Jean Ritchie, Mar. 15, 1948 (div. 1974); children: Jack Boyd, Rebecca, Regina; m. Kathleen Mary Shattuck, May 4, 1975. Student schs. Washington, Pa. Chmn. Millcraft Industries, Washington, Pa., 1957—; bd. dirs. Pitts. br. Fed. Res. Bank Cleve. Pres., bd. dirs. Meadowcroft Found., Avella, Pa.; bd. dirs. Southeastern Found., Miami, Fla., 1983-84. Recipient Disting. Svc. award Greater Washington Area Jaycees, 1980; named Tri-State Entrepreneur of Yr. Arthur Young and INC. mag., 1989. Mem. Am. Iron and Steel Inst., Eastern States Blast Furnace Assn., Assn. Iron and Steel Engrs., Duquesne Club (Pitts.) Republican. Home: PO Box 396 Meadow Lands PA 15347-0396 Office: Millcraft Industries 90 W Chestnut St Washington PA 15301-4524

PIATT, WILLIAM MCKINNEY, III, consulting engineering executive; b. Durham, N.C., Nov. 17, 1918; s. William McKinney and Marion Adele (Sheppard) P.; m. Lois Jewel Keast, Apr. 22, 1943; children: William McKinney IV, Raymond Keast, Joseph Wood. B.S. in Elec. Engring. Lafayette Coll., 1940; postgrad., Rutgers U., 1940-42. Registered profl. engr., N.C., S.C., Ga., Va. Instr. elec. engring. Rutgers U., New Brunswick, N.J., 1942-44; with W.M. Piatt and Co. (Cons. Engrs., and predecessors), Durham, N.C., 1946—; elec. engr. W.M. Piatt and Co. (Cons. Engrs., and predecessors), 1946-57, ptnr., 1957-64, owner, 1964-66, pres., 1966—; guest lectr. water supply, waste treatment U. N.C., Duke U. Served to lt. comdr. USNR, 1944-46, 51-53. Fellow ASCE (life), Am. Cons. Engrs. Coun., N.C. Soc. Engrs. (life, pres. 1971, Outstanding Achievement award 1987), Am. Pub. Works Assn. (life); mem. ASTM, Instrument Soc. Am. (sr.), Water Environment Fedn. (life), New Eng. Waterworks Assn. (life), Am. Water Works Assn. (life), Cons. Engrs. Coun. N.C. (pres. 1973-74), N.C. Wildlife Fedn. (dir. 1966-69, v.p. 1970-76), Kiwanis (v.p. 1991, pres.-elect 1992, pres. 1993), Durham Engrs. Club (pres. 1962), Durham County Wildlife Club (pres. 1964-65). Democrat. Christian Scientist. Home: 5321 Lakeview Dr Durham NC 27712-1923 Office: W M Piatt and Company 216 Rigsbee Ave Durham NC 27701-3323

PIAZZA, JOHN, hosiery company executive. CEO Sara Lee Hosiery, Winston-Salem, N.C. Office: Sara Lee Hosiery 5660 University Pky Winston Salem NC 27105-1312

PIAZZA, MARGUERITE, opera singer, actress, entertainer; b. New Orleans, May 6, 1926; d. Albert William and Michaela (Piazza) Luft; m. William J. Condon, July 15, 1953 (dec. Mar. 1968); children: Gregory, James (dec.), Shirley, William J., Marguerite P., Anna Becky; m. Francis Harrison Bergtholdt, Nov. 8, 1970. MusB, Loyola U., New Orleans; MusM, La. State U.; MusD (hon.), Christian Bros. Coll., 1973; LHD honoris causa, Loyola U., Chgo., 1975. Singer N.Y.C. Ctr. Opera, 1948, Met. Opera Co., 1950; TV artist, regular singing star Your Show of Shows NBC, 1950-54; entertainer various supper clubs Cotillion Room, Hotel Pierre, N.Y.C., 1954, Las Vegas, Los Angeles, New Orleans, San Francisco, 1956—; ptnr. Sound Express Music Pub. Co., Memphis, 1987—; bd. dirs. Cemrel, Inc. Appeared as guest performer on numerous mus. TV shows. Nat. crusade chmn. Am. Cancer Soc., 1971; founder, bd. dirs. Marguerite Piazza Gala for the Benefit of St. Jude's Hosp., 1976; bd. dirs. Memphis Opera Co., World Literacy Found., NCCJ; v.p., life bd. dirs. Memphis Symphony Orch.; nat. chmn. Soc. for Cure Epilepsy. Decorated Mil. and Hospittaler Order of St Lazarus of Jerusalem; recipient service award Chgo. Heart Assn., 1956, service award Fedn. Jewish Philanthropies of N.Y., 1956, Sesquicentennial medal Carnegie Hall; named Queen of Memphis, Memphis Cotton Carnival, 1973, named Person of Yr. La. Council for Performing Arts, 1975, named Woman of Yr. Nat. Am. Legion, named Woman of Yr. Italian-Am. Soc. Mem. Nat. Speakers Assn., Women's Exchange, Memphis Country Club, Memphis Hunt and Polo Club, New Orleans Country Club, Summit Club, Beta Sigma Omicron, Phi Beta. Roman Catholic. Home: #301 Park Pl 5400 Park Ave # 301 Memphis TN 38119

PIAZZA, MICHAEL JOSEPH, professional baseball player; b. Norristown, Pa., Sept. 4, 1968. Student, Miami (Fla.)-Dade C.C. Player L.A. Dodgers, 1988—; mem. Nat. League All-Star Team, 1994. Named Nat. League Rookie Player of Yr. Sporting News, 1993, Catcher on the Sporting News N.L. All-Star Team, 1993-94, N.L. Silver Slugger Team, 1993-94, named to Nat. League Slugger Team, 1993; named Nat. League Rookie of Yr., Baseball Writers Assn., 1993. Office: LA Dodgers Dodger Stadium 100 Elysian Park Ave Los Angeles CA 90012*

PICARD, DENNIS J., electronics company executive; b. 1932. BBA, Northeastern Univ., 1962. With RCA, 1954-55; elec. engr. Raytheon Co., 1955-59, design engr., 1959-61, sect. mgr., 1961-69, dir. equipment div., data acquisition systems directorate, 1969-76, asst. gen. mgr. ops., equipment div., 1976-77, asst. gen. mgr. ops., equipment div., also corp. v.p., 1977-81, v.p. equipment div., 1981-1985, sr. v.p., gen. mgr. missile systems div., 1985-89, pres., 1989-90, chmn. bd., CEO, 1990—, also bd. dirs. Served USAF 1951-53. Mem. NAE. Office: Raytheon Co 141 Spring St Lexington MA 02173-7899*

PICARD, LAURENT A(UGUSTIN), management educator, administrator, consultant; b. Quebec, Que., Can., Oct. 27, 1927; s. Edouard and Alice (Gingras) P.; m. Therese Picard; children: Andre, Marc, Robert (dec.), Denys, Jean-Louis, François (dec.). BA, Laval U., Quebec, 1947, BS, 1954; DBA, Harvard U., 1964. Prof. U. Montreal, Que., Can., 1962-68, dir. bus. adminstrn. dept., 1964-68; exec. v.p. Can. Broadcasting Corp., Ottawa, Ont., 1968-72, pres., chief exec. officer, 1972-75; joint prof. McGill U. and U. Montreal, 1977-78; dean faculty mgmt. McGill U., Montreal, 1978-86, prof., 1986—; mem. Royal Commn. on Newspapers, Royal Commn. on Econ. Union and Devel. Prospects for Can.; conciliation commr. Maritime Employers Assn., Port of Montreal; bd. dirs. Lombard-Odier Trust Co., Jean Coutu Group, Dorel Ind. Inc.; cons. to industry; guest spkr. internat. meetings. Contbr. articles to profl. jours. Chmn. Nat. Book Festival, 1978-79; chmn. jury Prix Gerin Lajoie, Ministry Cultural Affairs, 1982. Recipient 125th Anniversary medal Can., 1992; decorated companion Order of Can. 1977. Mem. Commonwealth Broadcasting Assn. (1st chmn.). Home: 5602 Wilderton Ave, Montreal, PQ Canada H3T 1R9 Office: McGill U Faculty Mgmt, 1001 Sherbrooke St W, Montreal, PQ Canada H3A 1G5

PICCARD-KRONE, KAREN ALIOTTE, public relations executive, political consultant; b. La Jolla, Calif., Aug. 10, 1959; d. Peter Elliot and Connie (Anaya) Piccard; m. F. William Krone III, Aug., 1980. BA in History, Portland (Oreg.) State U., 1981; degree in law, U. West Los Angeles, 1985; grad. in polit. mgmt., U. Calif., Davis, 1992-94. Radio talk show host So. Calif. KPZE-AM, Anaheim, Calif., 1986-87; pres. Krones and Assocs., Inc., Portland, 1988—; mem. adv. bd. Pacific N.W. Grantmakers/Grantseekers Conf., 1990-92. Contbr. articles to profl. jours. Com. chmn., mem. adjustment com. Portland Planning Bur., 1991—; chmn. auction com. Oreg. Mus. Sci. and Industry, 1991, PSU "Ultimate Tailgate" Auction, 1994; chmn. steering com. Scanfair, Portland, 1989-90; mem. variance com., Portland, 1989-91; campaign mgr. numerous ballot measures, polit. candidates, 1990-94; exec. dir. Oreg. Non-Profits Assn., 1991—; dir. devel. Oreg. LWV, 1992—; dir. Columbia Symphony Orch., 1993—; chmn. vol. coun. Portland Art Mus., 1995—; dir. Loaves and Fishes, 1994—; pres. Friends of Mystery, 1995—. Charles S. Linderman scholar, 1992; recipient Pub. Svc. award Portland City Coun., 1991. Mem. Soc. Fund Raising Execs. (advocate, non-profit lobbyist, mem. exec. bd.), Portlandia Club, Inc. (bd. dirs., Woman of Yr. 1990), Oreg. Art Inst., Oreg. Nordic Coun. (pres. 1992—), Sherlock Holmes Soc. Portland, Scandinavian Heritage Found., Rotary, Optimist Club (pres. 1991-92), City Club Portland (com. mem.). Avocations: foreign travel, translating German works, chess, researching Victorian history. Office: 333 S State St Ste 166 Lake Oswego OR 97034-3959

PICCILLO, JOSEPH, artist; b. Buffalo, Jan. 9, 1941. B.S., Buffalo State U., 1961, M.S., 1964. Faculty Buffalo State U. Coll., 1967—, prof. art edn., 1980—. One-man shows include Banfer Gallery, N.Y.C., 1966, 68, 70, Krasner Gallery, N.Y.C., 1971-79, Housitanic (Conn.) Mus., 1977, Galerie Loyse Oppenheim, Geneva, 1978, 79, Monique Knowlton Gallery, N.Y.C., 1980, 81, 83, 84, Betsy Rosenfeld Gallery, Chgo., 1980, 83, 85, 87, 89, 91, 94, Albright-Knox Art Gallery, Buffalo, 1981, Galleria Forni, Bologna, Italy, 1983, Barbara Fendrick Gallery, N.Y.C., 1988, Brendan Walter Gallery, Santa Monica, Calif., 1990, 92; group shows include Fischer Fine Arts Ltd., London, 1977, 78, Galierie Isy Brachot, Brussels, 1977, Art 9'78, Basle, Switzerland, 1978, 79; represented in permanent collections, Mus. Modern Art, N.Y.C., Chgo. Art Inst., Albright-Knox Gallery, Bklyn. Mus., Rochester (N.Y.) Meml. Art Center, Minn. Mus. Art, Mpls., Little Rock Mus., Met. Mus. Art, N.Y.C., Butler Mus. Art, Youngstown, Ohio, San Francisco Mus. Modern Art, Ball State U., Muncie, Ind., So. Ill. U., Carbondale, SUNY, Buffalo, Fredonia, Alfred (N.Y.) U., St. Lawrence U., Canton, N.Y., Kutztown (Pa.) State Coll., Hamline U., St. Paul, 1st Nat. Bank Chgo., others; panelist, Visual Arts Panel, N.Y. State Council on Arts, 1976-78. SUNY fellow, 1968, 69, 72, 76, 79, 80; Creative Artists Pub. Service Program grantee, 1972, grantee Nat. Endowment Arts fellow, 1979. Home: 461 West Ave Buffalo NY 14213-2501

PICCININI, JANICE, state legislator; b. Balt., Dec. 16, 1945; d. Anthony Joseph and Irene (Knoedler) P. BS, Frostburg State U., 1967; MA, Johns Hopkins U., 1974. Lic. real estate agt., Md. Tchr. Baltimore County Pub. Sch., 1967-79; in real estate, 1974—; pres. Tchrs. Assn. Baltimore County, 1979-81, Md. State Tchrs. Assn., 1981-85; mem. Md. State Senate, Baltimore County's 10th Legis. Dist., 1991—, jud. proceedings com., joint com. on fed. rels., 1991-93; mem. budget and tax com., 1993-95; bd. dirs. Commn. on Infants and Toddlers; cons. in field. bd. dirs. Pub. Sector Labor Rels. Bd. of Md., 1983-85, Exec. Women's Network, 1987-90; mem. Congresswoman Helen D. Bentley's Mil. Acad. Rev. Com. and Edn. Com., 1984—; del. Dem. Nat. Conv., 1984; mem. Nat. Dem. Platform Com., 1984; apptd. mem. Md. Stadium Authority, 1986-88; apptd. mem. Md. State Dem. Ctrl. Com., 1987-90; chair legis. com. Women's Caucus, Md. Gen. Assembly, 1992. Named to Outstanding Young Women of Am., 1981, Educator of Yr., Md. Assn. Elem. Sch. Prins., 1985; recipient Outstanding Leadership award U. Md. Chpt. Phi Delta Kappa, 1983, Outstanding Contbns. to Minority Affairs award MSTA, 1985, Lille Carroll Jackson award, 1985, Am. Com. on Italian Migration award 1986, Shaare Zedek Med. Ctr. (Jerusalem) Pub. Svc. award 1994. Mem. NOW, Nat. Orgn. Women Legislators, Sons of Italy (exec. dir. Md. Order, Ameritan award 1983).

PICCININI, ROBERT M., grocery store chain executive. CEO, chmn. Save Mart Supermarkets, Modesto, Calif. Office: Save Mart Supermarkets 1800 Standiford Ave Modesto CA 95350-0180

PICCININO, ROCCO MICHAEL, librarian; b. Phila., Aug. 21, 1949; s. Rocco Anthony and Ida Marie (Minicozzi) P. BA in History magna cum laude, LaSalle Coll., 1971; postgrad., U. N.C., 1971-73; MSLS, Drexel U., 1981. Ednl. resources specialist C.C. of Phila., 1973-74; asst./assoc. libr. United Engrs. & Constructors Inc. (A Raytheon Co.) Libr., Phila., 1974-81; head libr. United Engrs. & Constructors Inc. (A Raytheon Co.) Libr., Boston, 1981-84; asst/assoc. dir. Wentworth Inst. of Tech. Libr., Boston, 1984-89; sci. libr. Smith Coll. Librs., Northampton, Mass., 1989-91, coord. br. and media svcs., sci. libr., 1991—. Mem. ALA (Assn. Coll. Rsch. Librs. divsn., Libr. Adminstrn. and Mgmt. Assn. divsn., Libr. and Info. Tech. Assn. divsn), Spl. Librs. Assn., Beta Phi Mu. Democrat. Roman Catholic. Avocations: travel, biking, reading, films. Home: 104 Woods Rd Northampton MA 01060-1517 Office: Smith Coll Young Sci Libr Northampton MA 01063

PICCIRILLI, ROBERT JAMES, JR., small business owner; b. Balt., Dec. 2, 1943; s. Robert J. Sr. and Frances Rita (Mazel) P.; m. Joyce Marie Cole, Nov. 21, 1964 (dec. Sept. 1991); children: Angela Thompson, Christina Dahlberg, Gina. BSEE, GM Inst., Flint, Mich., 1966; cert., Dale Carnegie, Detroit, 1986; exec. tng. cert., U. Mich., 1988. Asst. supt. and supt. mfg. engring. Volkswagen of Am., Westmoreland, Pa., 1976-78; supt. mfg. planning corp. hdqrs. Volkswagen of Am., Detroit, 1978-79, mgr. mfg. planning, 1979-80; dir. engring. and quality products Chrysler Corp., 1980-81, plant mgr. Belvidere Assembly Plant, 1981-83; plant mgr. assembly plant Chrysler Corp., Sterling Heights, Mich., 1983-84; dir. quality and product engring. mfg. ops. div. hdqrs. Chrysler Corp., Detroit, 1984-85, dir. mfg. engring., 1985-86, gen. mgr. advance mfg. ops., gen. mgr. stamping ops., 1986-89;

chmn. bd., pres. Performance Innovations Corp. Chgo. 1990—. Author: Practical Production Manual, 1991, Launch Manual, 1991. Century mem. Boy Scouts Am., Detroit, 1989. Mem. GM Inst. Alumni Assn. (bd. dirs. 1991—). Avocations: golf, bike riding, motorcycles, tennis, volleyball, dancing. Home and Office: Performance Innovations Corp 77 W Huron Apt 214 Chicago IL 60610

PICCOLO, C. A. LANCE, healthcare company executive; b. 1940. BS, Boston U., 1962; postgrad., Calif. State U. Pharm. rep. Riker Labs. Inc., 1965-68; territory mgr. parenteral products divsn., regional field asst., dist. mgr., ctrl. regional mgr., field sales mgr. Baxter Internat. Inc., Deerfield, Ill. 1968-77, dir. sales parenteral products divsn., 1977-78, v.p. sales parenteral products divsn., 1978-79, v.p. parenteral products divsn., 1979, pres. parenteral products divsn., 1979-81, v.p., 1981-85, group v.p. 1985-87, exec. v.p., 1987, dir. Crompton & Knowles Corp. & Orthomet Inc.; chmn., CEO, dir. Caremark Internat., Northbrook, Ill. Capt. USMC, 1962-65. Office: Caremark Internat 2215 Sanders Rd Northbrook IL 60062-6126*

PICHAL, HENRI THOMAS, electronics engineer, physicist, consultant; b. London, Feb. 14, 1923; came to the U.S., 1957; s. Henri and Mary (Conway) P.; m. Vida Eloise Collum Jones, Mar. 7, 1966; children: Chris C., Henri T. III, Thomas William Billingsley. MSc in Engring., U. London, 1953, PhD in Physics, 1955. Registered profl. engr., Wash., Fla. Product engr. John Fluke Mfg. Corp., Everett, Wash., 1970-73; engring. specialist Harris Corp., Melbourne, Fla., 1973-75; pres., prin. Profl. Engring. Co., Inc., Kissimmee, Fla., 1975-91. Contbr. articles to Electronics, Microwaves, and others. Named one of Two Thousand Men Achievement, 1972. Mem. Inst. Physics, Am. Phys. Soc., Fla. Engring. Soc. (sr.), Inst. Environ. Scis. (sr.), IEEE (past chmn. microwave theory and techniques communications systems), Aerospace/Navigational Electronics, Space Electronics and Telemetry, Mil. Electronics. Republican. Achievements include 69 patents in microwave RF, high frequency and high speed analog ultra linear technology, large dynamic range performance and intermodulation phenomena, noise, and congested area systems problems. Home: PO Box 969 Kingston WA 98346-0969

PICHETTE, CLAUDE, former banking executive, university rector, research executive; b. Sherbrooke, Que., Can., June 13, 1936; s. Donat and Juliette (Morin) P.; m. Renée Provencher, Sept. 5, 1959 (dec. 1994); children: Anne-Marie, Martin, Philippe. B.A., U. Sherbrooke, 1956; M.Sc.Soc. (Econ.), U. Laval, 1960; Doct. d'Etat es Sc. Econ, U. D'Aix-Marseille, France, 1970. Prof. U. Sherbrooke, 1960-70; civil servant Govt. Que., 1970-75; vice rector adminstrn. and fins. U. Que., Montreal, 1975-77; rector U. Que., 1977-86; pres., chief exec. officer La Financière prêts-épargne, 1986-90, La Financière Entraide-Cooperants (holding co.), 1987-90; pres. Que. Found. Econ. Edn., 1979-81; CEO Institut Armand-Frappier Rsch. Inst.; chmn. bd. La Financière crédit bail, 1989-90; bd. dirs. Shermag, Rona-Dismat, Montreal Exch. Author: Analyse micro-economique et cooperative, 1972. Can. Council grantee, 1958; Federation nationale des cooperatives de consommation de France grantee, 1973. Mem. Que. Assn. Econs. (pres. 1977-78). Club: St-Denis (Montreal). Home: 745 Hartland, Outremont, PQ Canada H2V 2X5 Office: Armand-Frappier Institute, 531 Blvd des Praires, Laval, PQ Canada H7N 4Z3

PICHLER, JOSEPH ANTON, food products executive; b. St. Louis, Oct. 3, 1939; s. Anton Dominick and Anita Marie (Hughes) P.; m. Susan Ellen Eyerly, Dec. 27, 1962; children: Gretchen, Christopher, Rebecca, Josh. BBA, U. Notre Dame, 1961; MBA, U. Chgo., 1963, PhD; PhD, 1966. Asst. prof. bus. U. Kans., 1964-68, assoc. prof., 1968-73, prof., 1973-80; dean U. Kans. (Sch. Bus.), 1974-80; exec. v.p. Dillon Cos. Inc., 1980-82, pres., 1982-86; exec. v.p. Kroger Co., 1985-86, pres., chief operating officer, 1986—, also bd. dirs., 1986-90, pres., chief exec. officer, 1990, chmn., chief exec. officer, 1990—, also dir.; spl. asst. to asst. sec. for manpower U.S. Dept. Labor, 1968-70; chmn. Kans. Manpower Svcs. Coun., 1974-78; bd. dirs. B.F. Goodrich Co.; indsl. cons. Author: (with Joseph McGuire) Inequality: The Poor and the Rich in America, 1969; contbg. author: Creativity and Innovation in Manpower Research and Action Programs, 1970, Contemporary Management: Issues and Viewpoints, 1973, Institutional Issues in Public Accounting, 1974, Co-Creation and Capitalism: John Paul II's Laborem Exercens, 1983; Co-editor, contbg. author: Ethics, Free Enterprise, and Public Policy, 1978; Contbr. articles to profl. jours. Bd. dirs. Kans. Charities, 1973-75, Benedictine Coll., Atchison, Kans., 1979-83, Cin. Opera; nat. bd. dirs. Boys Hope, 1983—; Tougaloo Coll., 1986—; chmn. nat. bd. Nat. Alliance of Bus. Recipient Performance award U.S. Dept. Labor Manpower Adminstrn., 1969, Disting. Svc. citation U. Kans., 1992; Woodrow Wilson fellow, Ford Found. fellow, Standard Oil Indsl. Rels. fellow, 1966, Woodrow Wilson fellow adv. com., 1990-93; named Disting. Alumnus U. Chgo., 1994. Mem. Bus. Roundtable, Queen City Club, Comml. Club of Cin. Office: Kroger Co 1014 Vine St Cincinnati OH 45202-1100

PICHOIS, CLAUDE P., classical studies educator; b. Paris, July 21, 1925; s. Léon and Renée (Bardou) P.; m. Vincenette Rey, Oct. 26, 1961. D ès L, U. Paris, 1963; D (hon.), U. Neuchâtel, Switzerland, 1983, Trinity Coll., Dublin, Ireland, 1984. Asst. prof. U. Aix-en-Provence, France, 1958-61; prof. U., Basel, Switzerland, 1961-70; vis. rsch. prof. U. Wis., Madison, 1968; prof. Vanderbilt U., Nashville, 1970-73, disting. prof., 1973—; prof. Sorbonne Nouvelle, Paris, 1981; bd. dirs. W.T. Bandy Ctr. for Baudelaire Studies, Vanderbilt U., Nashville, Centre de recherches Nerval/Baudelaire, Namur, Belgium, Paris. Author: L'Image de Jean-Paul Richter dans les Lettres Françaises, 1963, Ph. Chasles et la vie littéraire au temps du Romantisme, 1965, Baudelaire, 1987, Gérard de Nerval, 1995; editor: Baudelaire, Complete Works, 1975-76, Baudelaire, Correspondence, 1973, 93, Nerval, Complete Works, 1984, 89, 93, Colette, Works, 1984, 86, 91, Littérature Française (16 vols.), 1968-79. Recipient Prix de la critique Académie Française; Guggenheim fellow, 1978. Mem. MLA (hon.), Sté Hist. litt. de la France (hon.), Sté Etudes Romantiques, Nineteenth-Century French Studies (bd. dirs.), Lettres Romanes, Bull. Baudelairien, L'Année Baudelaire. Avocation: bibliophilia. Office: Vanderbilt U Station B Nashville TN 37235

PICIRILLI, ROBERT EUGENE, clergyman, college dean, writer; b. High Point, N.C., Oct. 6, 1932; s. Eugene and Lena (Harrell) P.; m. Clara Mae Lee, June 14, 1953; children: Annina Jean, Myra Jane, Mary June, Celina Joy, Roberta Jill. B.A., Free Will Bapt. Bible Coll., Nashville, 1953; M.A., Bob Jones U., 1955, Ph.D., 1963, D.D., 1967. Ordained to ministry Free Will Bapt. Ch., 1952; grad. asst. Bob Jones U., 1954-55; prof. N.T., Free Will Bapt. Bible Coll., 1955—, registrar, 1960-79, dean, 1979—, dean grad. sch., 1982-86; clk. Nat. Assn. Free Will Baptists, 1961-65, moderator, 1966-71, treas. hist. commn., 1974—, mem. bd. of retirement and ins., 1978-89, sec., 1979-89; mem. testing com. Am. Assn. Bible Colls., 1975-92, research commn., 1982-91, chmn., 1989-91; sec.-treas. So. region Evang. Theol. Soc., 1964-68, vice chmn., 1972-73, 84-85 chmn., 1973-74, 85-86. Author: Paul, the Apostle, 1986, 1, 2 Corinthians, 1987; co-author: The NKJV Greek English Interlinear New Testament, 1993. Pres. Ransom Elementary Sch. P.T.A., 1965-67. Fellow Inst. for Bibl. Rsch.; mem. AAHE, Am. Assn. Bible Colls. (v.p. 1992-94, pres. 1994—), Nashville Philatelic Soc. (treas. 1980-81, 92—, pres. 1981-82, 1st v.p. 1982-88), Delta Epsilon Chil. Home: 301 Greenway Ave Nashville TN 37205-2307

PICK, ARTHUR JOSEPH, JR., chamber of commerce executive; b. Louisville, Mar. 22, 1931. BS, U. Calif., Riverside, 1959; grad., Coro Found., L.A., 1960; MA in Urban Studies, Occidental Coll., 1969. Pres. Greater Riverside C. of C., 1972—; founding chair VCR Extension adv. bd. Mem. Riverside Monday Morning Group, 1991-94; pres. Riverside Symphony Orch. Soc., 1966-69; elected Riverside City Coun., 1967, 71; founder Friends of Calif. Bapt. Coll, 1978, Friends of La Sierra U., Riverside, 1978, Friends of Sherman Indian H.S., Calif. Sch. for the Deaf, Riverside, 1988; trustee LaSierra U., 1992—; mem. Calif.-Nev. Super Speed Train Commn., 1992—; v.p. Sunkist Orange Blossom Festival; treas. Calif. State Citrus Heritage Park Bd.; co-chair Mayor's Vision Com.; chair City/Univ. Task Force Com.; founding chair adv. bd. U. Calif.-Riverside Ext. With U.S. Army, 1953-55. Recipient Disting. Svc. award Riverside Jaycees, 1966, Patron of Arts award Cultural Arts Coun., 1977, Vernon Jordan Humanitarian award Riverside Area Urban League, 1989, Citizen of Yr. award Riverside Police Officers Assn., 1990, Atlas award Riverside YWCA, 1990, Community Svc. award, 1990; named Young Man of Yr. Riverside Jaycees, 1966, Citizen of Yr. Internat. Rels. Coun., 1992. Mem. Inland Area Urban League (founder, bd. dirs., Pacesetter award 1982), U. Calif. Riverside Alumni Assn. (bd. dirs. 1981-87), Riverside Jaycees (life), Riverside Raincross Club. Office: Greater Riverside C of C 3685 Main St Ste 350 Riverside CA 92501-3886

PICK, JAMES BLOCK, management and sociology educator; b. Chgo., July 29, 1943; s. Grant Julius and Helen (Block) P. BA, Northwestern U., 1966; MS in Edn., No. Ill. U., 1969; PhD, U. Calif., Irvine, 1974. Cert. computer profl. Asst. rsch. statistician, lectr. Grad. Sch. Mgmt. U. Calif., Riverside, 1975-91, dir. computing, 1984-91; co-dir. U.S.-Mex. Database Project, 1988-91; assoc. prof. mgmt. and bus., dir. info. mgmt. program U. Redlands, Calif., 1991-95, prof. mgmt. and bus. dept. chair 1995—; cons. U.S. Census Bur. Internat. Div., 1978: mem. Univ. Commons Bd., 1982-86; mem. bd. govs. PCCLAS, Assn. Borderlands Studies, 1989-92. Trustee Newport Harbor Art Mus., 1987-91, 88—, chmn. permanent collection com., 1987-91, v.p., 1991—. Recipient Thunderbird award Bus. Assn. Latin Am. Studies, 1993. Mem. AAAS, Assn. Computing Machinery, Assn. Systems Mgmt. (pres. Orange County chpt. 1978-79), Am. Statis. Assn., Population Assn. Am., Internat. Union for Sci. Study of Population, Soc. Info. Mgmt. Club, Standard (Chgo.). Author: Geothermal Energy Development, 1982, Computer Systems in Business, 1986, Atlas of Mexico, 1989, The Mexico Handbook, 1994; condr. research in info. systems, population, environ. studies; contbr. sci. articles to pubis. in fields.

PICK, MICHAEL CLAUDE, international exploration consultant; b. Stuttgart, Fed. Republic Germany, Sept. 17, 1931; came to Can., 1963; s. Manfred and Berti (Baer) P.; m. Jeanette Patrucia Zaharko, Mar. 13, 1965; children—David, Christopher. B.A., U. New Zealand, Wellington, 1952, M.A. with honors, 1954; Ph.D., U. Bristol, Eng., 1963. Sr. geologist Todd Bros. Ltd., Wellington, 1954-58; research assoc. Stanford U., Calif., 1958-60; geologist Chevron Standard Ltd., Calgary, Alta., Can., 1963-68; regional geologist BP Oil & Gas Ltd., Calgary, 1968-71; chief geologist, acting exploration mgr. Columbia Gas, Calgary, 1971-80; sr. v.p. Asamera, Inc., Calgary, 1980-87; pres. Terrenex Ventures Inc., Torwood Assocs. Ltd. Contbr. articles to profl. jours. Mem. Am. Assn. Petroleum Geologists, Can. Soc. Petroleum Geologists. Avocations: music; reading; model railroading. Home: 3359 Varna Crescent NW, Calgary, AB Canada T3A 0E4

PICK, ROBERT YEHUDA, orthopedic surgeon, consultant; b. Haifa, Israel, Dec. 24, 1945; came to U.S., 1957; s. Andre B. and Hanna (Gross) P.; m. Roni L. Kestenbaum, Sept. 25, 1977; children: Benjamin A., Joseph E., Jennifer L., Abigail I. BA, B in Hebrew Lit., Yeshiva U., 1967; MD, Albert Einstein Coll. Med., 1971; MPH, Harvard U., 1979. Diplomate Nat. Bd. Med. Examiners, Am. Bd. Orthopaedic Surgery. Intern Brookdale Hosp., Bklyn., 1971-72; resident in orthopedic surgery Albert Einstein-Bronx (N.Y.) Mcpl. Hosp. Ctr., 1972-74; resident in orthopedic surgery USPHS Hosp. Staten Island, N.Y., 1974-75, asst. chief orthopedic surgery, 1975-77; asst. chief orthopedic surgery USPHS Hosp., Boston, 1977-78; fellow orthopedic trauma Boston City Hosp., 1979-80, assoc. dir. orthopedic surgery, 1980-84, dir. pediatric orthopedics, 1981-83; practice medicine specializing in orthopedic surgery Newton Ctr., Mass., 1984—; instr. orthopedic surgery Boston U., 1980-82, asst. prof., 1982—; adj. asst. prof. health scis. and orthopedics Touro Coll., N.Y.C., 1976-78; dir. spinal screening program Dept. Health and Hosps., Boston, 1979-82; instr. med. advisor U.S. Dept. Labor, Boston, 1984—; cons. Boston Retirement Bd., 1983-84, New Eng. Telephone, Boston, 1985—, Commonwealth of Mass. Pub. Employee Retirement Adminstrn., Boston, 1985-90. Contbr. articles on med. issues to profl. jours. Trustee Young Israel Jackson Heights, Queens, N.Y., 1969-76, pres., 1976-77; sec. Young Israel Brookline, Mass., 1978-79; trustee Maimonides Sch., Brookline, 1990—. Served to lt. comdr. USPHS, 1975-78. Fellow Am. Acad. Orthopedic Surgeons; mem. Am. Physicians Fellowship for Medicine in Israel (trustee 1975—, exec. com. 1976—, asst. treas. 1987-90, treas. 1990—), Man of Yr. award 1977), Nat. Inst. Occupational Safety and Health (traineeship 1978-79), Mensa.

PICK, RUTH, research scientist, physician, educator; b. Carlsbad, Bohemia, Czechoslovakia, Nov. 13, 1913; came to U.S., 1949; d. Arthur and Paula (Lenk) Holub; m. Alfred Pick, May 28, 1938 (dec. Jan. 1982). M.D., German U., 1938. Resident in medicine Priessnitz Hosp., Graefenberg, Czechoslovakia, 1938; resident in psychiatry Hosp. Veleslavin, Prague, Czechoslovakia, 1945-47; extern in pathology State Hosp. Motol, Prague, 1948; research fellow cardiovascular dept. Michael Reese Hosp. & Med. Ctr., Chgo., 1949-50, research assoc., 1950-58, asst. dir. 1958-66, sr. investigator, 1966-71, chief exptl. atherosclerosis lab., 1971-83, attending physician div. cardiovascular diseases dept. medicine, 1964—; chief cardiac morphology lab. Cardiovascular Inst. Michael Reese Hosp. & Med. Ctr., 1983—; prof. emeritus medicine and pathology U. Chgo., 1973—; mem. research council Chgo. Heart Assn., 1979-84, bd. govs., 1983, pres., 1985-86. Fellow Am. Heart Assn. (coun. on arteriosclerosis, coun. on circulation, established investigator), AAAS; mem. Am. Assn. Pathologists and Bacteriologists, Chgo. Heart Assn. (past mem. 1985-86), Am. Fedn. Clin. rsch., Am. Physiol. Soc., Ctrl. Soc. Clin. Rsch. Home: 400 E Randolph St Chicago IL 60601-7329 Office: Michael Reese Hosp and Med Ctr 2929 S Ellis Ave Chicago IL 60616

PICKARD, FRANKLIN GEORGE THOMAS, mining company executive; b. Sudbury, Ont., Can., Sept. 10, 1933; s. Chester William and Margaret Christine (Downes) P.; m. Audrey Elaine Bull, Apr. 27, 1967; children: Barbara, Beverly. BA, Queen's U., Kingston, Ont., 1958. With Falconbridge Ltd., Toronto, Ont., 1957—, concentrator supt., 1967-75, chief metall. engr., 1975-82, v.p., 1982-89, v.p., 1989-90, pres., chief exec. officer, 1991—; also, bd. dirs.; bd. dirs. Falconbridge Ltd., Falconbridge Nikkelverk A/S (Norway), Falconbridge Dominicana C por A (Dominican Republic). Mem. AIME, Can. Inst. Mining and Metall. Engrs., Mining Assn.Can. (bd. dirs.), assn. Profl. Engrs. Ont., Nickel Devel. Inst. (bd. dirs., chmn. 1988-90), Ont. Club, Spring Lakes Golf Club, Keowee Key Golf and County Club. Avocations: fishing, golf, sports cars. Office: Falconbridge Ltd, 95 Wellington St W Ste 1200, Toronto, ON Canada M5J 2V4

PICKARD, GEORGE LAWSON, physics educator; b. Cardiff, Wales, July 5, 1913; came to Can., 1947; s. Harry Lawson and Phoebe P.; m. Lilian May Perry; children—Rosemary Ann, Andrew Lawson. B.A., Oxford U., 1935, M.A., 1947, D.Phil., 1937; D.M.S. (hon.), Royal Roads Mil. Coll., Victoria, B.C., Can., 1980. Sci. officer Royal Aircraft Establishment, Farnborough, Eng., 1937-42; sr. sci. officer ops. research sect. Coastal Command, RAF, 1942-46, prin. sci. officer ops. research sect., 1947; assoc. prof. dept. physics U. B.C., Vancouver, Can., 1947-54, prof. dept. physics, 1954-70, prof. emeritus, 1979—, dir. Inst. Oceanography, 1958-79; cons. Seaconsult Marine Research, Vancouver, Can., 1979—. Author: Descriptive Physical Oceanography, 1964, 5th edit., 1990; (with S. Pond) Introductory Dynamical Oceanography, 1978, 2d edit., 1983. Served with RAF, 1942-47. Decorated mem. Order Brit. Empire; recipient J.P. Tully medal Can. Meteorol. and Oceanographic Soc., 1987. Fellow AAAS, Royal Soc. Can. Club: Faculty Univ. B.C. Avocations: aviation; diving; coral reef oceanography. Home: 4546 W 5th Ave, Vancouver, BC Canada V6R 1S7

PICKARD, MARY ANN, senator; b. Cordele, Ga., Feb. 28, 1942; d. M.R. and Annie Claude Williams; m. Donald DeAltiet Pickard, Apr. 29, 1966; children: Donald D. Jr., Ronald D. BS, Hampton U., 1963; MEd, Savannah/Armstrong Coll., 1979. Tchr. Pub. Sch. System, St. Croix, U.S. Virgin Islands; senator St. Croix, U.S. Virgin Islands, 1992—. Sec. Law Revision Commn., St. Thomas, 1993; mem. Judicial Coun., St. Thomas, 1993; v.p. Virgin Islands Legislature, 1993. Mem. Delta Sigma Theta, Phi Delta Kappa. Democrat. Methodist. Office: VI Legislature 1 Lagoon St PO Box 4088 Frederiksted VI 00840

PICKARD, MYRNA RAE, college dean; b. Sulphur Springs, Tex., Oct. 10, 1935; d. George Wallace and Ellie (Williams) Swindell; m. Bobby Ray Pickard, May 17, 1957; 1 child, Bobby Dale. B.S. summa cum laude, Tex. Wesleyan Coll., 1961, M.Ed., 1964; M.S., Tex. Women's U., 1974; EdD, Nova U., 1976. Instr. John Peter Smith Hosp., Fort Worth, 1956-58; pub. health nurse Forest County Health Dept., Hattiesburg, Miss., 1958-60; asst. nurse adminstrn. John Peter Smith Hosp. Sch. Nursing, Fort Worth, 1960-70, nurse adminstr., 1970-73; assoc. dean, dean U. Tex. System Sch. Nursing, Fort Worth 1971-76; dean, prof. nursing U. Tex. Sch. Nursing, Arlington, 1976—; cons. in field; adv. com. Rural Health Rsch. Ctr., U. N.D., 1990.

Mem. editorial bd. Jour. Rural Health, 1985-92, 94; contbr. articles to profl. jours., chpt. in book. Pres. Tex. League for Nursing, 1986-89. Fellow Am. Acad. Nursing; mem. ANA, Nat. League Nursing, Nat. Rural Health Assn. (bd. dirs., treas. 1990-92), Sigma Theta Tau. Methodist. Avocations: jogging; gardening. Home: 8301 Anglin Dr Fort Worth TX 76140-4213 Office: U Tex Box 19407 Arlington TX 76019

PICKENPAUGH, THOMAS EDWARD, archaeologist; b. St. Clairsville, Ohio, Feb. 8, 1945; s. Douglas Giffin and Betty June (Brown) P. BA, Kent State U., 1970, MA, 1971; ABD, Cath. U., 1980. Anthropologist, instr. sociology and anthropology Wheeling (W.Va.) Coll., 1972-73; anthropologist, instr. asst. prof. anthropology Ohio U.-Eastern, 1972-74, 78; archaeologist, asst. prof. anthropology Ohio U., St. Clairsville, 1986-94; mus. technician U.S. Dept. Interior, Nat. Park Svc., Washington, 1983; mus. technican Nat. Mus. Natural History, Smithsonian Instn., Washington, 1984-87; mus. specialist, loan officer USN, Naval Hist. Ctr., Washington, 1987—; dir. archaeol. excavations Brokaw Village Site, St. Clairsville, Ohio, 1972-74, 76-78, 82, 86-94; mem. archaeol. staff Thunderbird Site, Front Royal, Va., Savannah River, Ga., S.C., Richard B. Russell Dam Project, 1980, El Mirador Site, Guatemala, 1980, Louis Berger Internat. Project, Trenton, N.J., 1983-84, Sully Plantation, Loudon County, Va., 1984, Fells Point Project, Balt., 1984; others. Contbr. articles to profl. pubis. Rsch. grantee U.S. Dept. Interior, Nat. Park Svc., 1978-79, Nat. Geog. Soc. rsch. grantee, 1992-93. Mem. Washington Assn. Profl. Anthropologists, Anthropol. Soc. Washington, Am. Assn. Museums, Internat. Platform Assn. Home: 3304 Chauncey Pl Mount Rainier MD 20712-1007 Office: Naval Hist Ctr 9th And M St SE Washington DC 20374

PICKENS, ALEXANDER LEGRAND, education educator; b. Waco, Tex., Aug. 31, 1921; s. Alex LeGrand and Elma L. (Johnson) P.; m. Frances M. Jenkins, Aug. 20, 1955. B.A., So. Methodist U., 1950; M.A., North Tex. State U., Denton, 1952; Ed.D., Columbia U., 1959. Tchr. art public schs. Dallas, 1950-53, Elizabeth, N.J., 1953-54; instr. Coll. Architecture and Design U. Mich., 1954-59; assoc. prof. dept. art U. Ga. Athens, 1959-62; assoc. prof. Coll. Edn. U. Hawaii, Honolulu, 1962—, prof. edn., 1968—; U. Hawaii; chmn. doctoral studies curriculum instrn. Coll. Edn. U. Hawaii, Honolulu, 1984-89, asst. to dean for coll. devel., 1989—; dir. children's classes Ft. Worth Children's Museum, 1951-53; head art Nat. Music Camp, Interlochen, Mich., summers 1957-58, U. Oreg., Portland, summers 1959-60, 62; cons. youth art activities Foremost Dairies, 1964-74; cons. art films United World Films, 1970-75; art edn. cons. Honolulu Paper Co., 1970-76, Kamehameha Sch., Bishop Estate, 1978—. Exhibited ceramics, Wichita Internat. Exhbn., Syracuse (N.Y.) Nat. Exhbn., St. Louis Mus., Dallas Mus., San Antonio Mus., Detroit Art Inst., Hawaii Craftsmen, also others; editorial bd.: Arts and Activities mag, 1955-82; editor: U. Hawaii Ednl. Perspectives, 1964—; contbr. articles to profl. jours. Memm. adult com. Dallas County chpt. Jr. ARC, 1951-53; exec. com. Dallas Crafts Guild, 1950-53; v.p. publicity chmn. U. Ga. Community Concert Assn., 1960-62, mem., program chmn. Gov.'s Commn. Observing 150 Yrs. Pub. Edn. in Hawaii, 1990-91. Served with USAAF. Recipient award merit, Tex. State Fair, 1957, All-Am. award, Ednl. Press Assn. Am., 1968, 70, 72, 75, 79, Regents' medal for excellence in teaching, U. Hawaii, 1989, Gov.'s Commn. Observance of 150 Yrs. Pub. Edn., 1990-91. Mem. AAUP, NEA, Internat. Soc. Edn., Nat. Art Edn. Assn., Coun. for Advancement and Support of Edn., Nat. Soc. Fundraising Execs., Hawaii Planned Giving Coun., Phi Delta Kappa, Kappa Delta Pi. Address: 1471 Kalaepohaku St Honolulu HI 96816

PICKENS, BUFORD LINDSAY, architectural educator, historian; b. Coffeyville, Kans., Jan. 15, 1906; s. Samuel Milton and Emily (Grigson) P.; m. Jenny Grönner Johnsen, June 2, 1934; children: Lindsay Lloyd, Grigson Buford. B.Arch., U. Ill., 1930; A.M. (fellow), U. Chgo., 1937. Archtl. work Chgo., 1925-28, 30-35; instr. Ohio U., 1937-38; pvt. practice residential architecture, community planning cons., 1938—; asst. prof. Wayne U., Detroit, 1938-45; prof., dir. Sch. Architecture, Tulane U., 1946-53; prof. Washington U., 1953-74, prof. emeritus, 1974—; dean Washington U. (Sch. Architecture), 1953-56, dir. campus planning, 1956-63; vis. lectr. U. Minn., summer 1940; cons. Detroit City Planning Commn., 1944-45; Mem. Vieux Carre Commn., New Orleans, 1947-52; mem. Fulbright Adv. Screening Com., 1958-60, Joint AIA/ACSA Award Com., 1973-74; author: (with others) Pueblo Style and Regional Architecture, 1990; sr. co-author: Washington University in St. Louis: Its Design and Architecture, 1978; editor: Jour. Archtl. Edn., 1955, The Missions of Northern Sonora, 1993; contbr. articles to Am., English, Italian jours. Hist. bldg. commr., Mo., 1960-73, hist. bldg. commr. St. Louis County, 1964-74. Served U.S. Army as instr. Univ. Tng. Command, 1945, Florence, Italy. Fellow AIA; mem. Soc. Archtl. Historians (pres. 1950), Assn. Collegiate Schs. Architecture (pres. 1957-59), Alpha Rho Chi. Home: 31 N Old Orchard Ave Apt 434 Saint Louis MO 63119-2656

PICKENS, DAVID RICHARD, JR., retired surgeon, educator; b. Nashville, Apr. 16, 1920; s. David Richard and Corinne (Waddey) P.; m. Harriet Palmer, May 12, 1945; children: David Richard III, Mary, John, Robert. BS, Vanderbilt U., 1941, MD, 1944. Diplomate Am. Bd. Surgery. Intern Western Res. U. Hosp., Cleve., 1944-45; resident in urol. surgery Roosevelt Hosp., N.Y.C., 1945-46; resident in gen. surgery St. Thomas Hosp., Nashville, 1946-47; resident in surgery Bellevue Hosp., N.Y.C., 1947-51; Nat. Tb Assn. fellow in chest surgery Triboro Hosp., N.Y.C., 1951-52, resident in thoracic surgery, 1951-52; practice medicine specializing in surgery, Nashville, 1952-53, 55-90, ret., 1990; mem. staffs St. Thomas Hosp., Bapt. Hosp.; asst. clin. prof. surgery Vanderbilt U. Hosp., 1968-90; retired; cons. social security. 1st lt. USAR, Army Specialized Tng. Program, 1944; capt. M.C., U.S. Army, 1953-55. Mem. AMA, ACS, Am. Soc. Colon and Rectal Surgeons, Southeastern Surg. Congress, Tenn. Med. Assn., Davidson County Med. Soc., Nashville Acad. Medicine, Piedmont Soc. Colon and Rectal Surgeons, So. Surg. Assn., So. Med. Assn., Soc. for Surgery Alimentary Tract, Delta Kappa Epsilon. Clubs: Belle Meade Country, University. Contbr. articles to profl. jours. Home: 17 Lynwood Ln Nashville TN 37205-2909

PICKENS, EARL, consumer products company executive. Sr. v.p. Hy-Vee Food stores Inc., Chariton, Iowa. Office: Hy-Vee Food Stores Inc 1801 Osceola Ave Chariton IA 50049-1503

PICKENS, FRANKLIN ACE, lawyer; b. Borger, Texas, Aug. 19, 1936; s. A.O. and Rhoda (Shaw) P.; m. Dianna Barnard, Dec. 17, 1966. BBA, U. Tex., 1958, JD, 1962. Bar: Tex. 1962, U.S. Dist. Ct. (no. dist.) Tex. 1964, U.S. Dist. Ct. (ea. dist.) Tex. 1983, U.S. Dist. Ct. (so. dist.) Tex. 1989; cert. adminstrv. law Tex. Bd. Legal Specialization. Pvt. practice Odessa, Tex., 1962-63; ptnr. McDonald and Pickens, Odessa, Tex., 1963-69; atty. Shafer, Gilliland, Davis, Bunton & McCollum, Odessa, Tex., 1969-71; rep. State of Texas, Odessa, 1964-73; pvt. practice Austin, Texas, 1973-76; ptnr. Brown McCarroll & Oaks Hartline, Austin, Texas, 1976—; bd. Ins. Adv. Com. HMOs; former gen. counsel Tex. State Bd. Nurse Examiners; former Washington counsel Tex. R.R.; mem. state bar com. Liason with Med. Profession, 1975-82; spkr. in field. Listed Naifeh and Smith, 1993-94; contbr. articles to profl. jours. Chmn. bd. trustees Shoal Creek Hosp., Austin; former mem. strategic planning task force Brackenridge Hosp., Austin; former mem. coun. advisors Austin Children's Cancer Ctr. Lt. comdr. USNR, 1958-60. Mem. ABA, Nat. Health Lawyers Assn., Am. Soc. Law and Medicine, State Bar Tex. (coll., coun., health law sect. 1980-82, legis. com. 1993), Travis County Bar Assn. (adminstrv. law sect., health law sect.). Episcopalian. Home: 713 Windsong Trail Austin TX 78746 Office: Brown McCarroll & Oaks Hartline 1400 Franklin Plz 111 Congress Ave Austin TX 78701

PICKENS, ROBERT BRUCE, accountant; b. Uniontown, Pa., May 20, 1926; s. Joseph Abraham and Margaret Gertrude (Brown) P.; m. Mary Ellen Evans, Sept. 9, 1950; children: Laura Gail Martin, Rachel Diane Rosen, David Bruce. B.S. in Bus. Adminstrn. Waynesburg Coll., 1950. C.P.A., Pa., Ill., Ind. Vice pres. Home Bottle Gas Corp., Uniontown, 1950-51; jr. accountant to sr. accountant Tenney & Co., Uniontown, 1951-56; mgr. Hosp. Service Assn. Western Pa., Pitts., 1956-57; auditor U. Pitts., 1957-58; sr. accountant Eugene A. Conniff Co., Pitts., 1958-59; mgr. Sheppard & Co., Pitts., 1959-63; supr. Alexander Grant & Co., Chgo., 1963-65; asst. to treas. CTS Corp., Elkhart, Ind., 1965, gen. auditor, controller, 1966-81; self-employed as acct., 1981-86; sec., controller, chief acctg. officer SEA Group, Inc. and SEA-ILAN, Inc., 1987-88; pvt. cons., 1989—. Mem. Bower Hill Civic

League, 1956-62; active Boy Scouts Am., 1938-62. Served to cpl. USAAF, 1944-45. Mem. AICPA, Pa. Inst. CPAs, Ill. CPA Soc., Ind. CPA Soc. Republican. Presbyn. (elder, trustee 1959-61, treas. 1960-61). Home and Office: 73 Rogers Rd Carmel IN 46032-1467

PICKENS, THOMAS BOONE, JR., oil company executive; b. Holdenville, Okla., May 22, 1928; s. Thomas Boone and Grace Molonson P.; m. Beatrice Louise Carr, Apr. 21, 1972. BS in Geology, Okla. State U., 1951. Geologist Phillips Petroleum Co., 1951-54; consulting geologist, 1954-56; with Petroleum Exploration, Inc., 1956, Altair Oil & Gas Co.; chmn. bd., pres., dir. Mesa Petroleum Co., Inc., 1964-85; gen. ptnr. Mesa, Inc., 1985—; mem. Nat. Petroleum Council, 1970—; founder, chmn. United Shareholders Assn., Washington. Author: Boone, 1987. Adviser Nat. Campaign for Drug Free Am. Home: 6909 Vassar Ave Dallas TX 75205-1257 Office: Mesa Inc 2001 Ross Ave Ste 2600 Dallas TX 75201-2920

PICKERELL, JAMES HOWARD, photojournalist; b. Dayton, Ohio, June 9, 1936; s. Howard and Frances (Harrison) P.; m. Mary Louise Fisher, June 26, 1965; children: Cheryl Elizabeth, Stacy Rae. Student, Ohio U., 1954-56; BA, UCLA, 1963. Comml. photographer, 1963—; ind. photographer Vietnam, 1963-67. Author: Vietnam in the Mud, 1966, Marketing Photography in the Digital Environment, 1994, Negotiating Stock Photo Prices, 3d edit., 1995; writer, pub. newsletter Taking Stock. With USNR, 1956-60. Mem. Nat. Press Photographers Assn. (1st Pl. Spot News award 1965), Am. Soc. Mag. Photographers (nat. bd. 1987-89), Beta Theta Pi. Address: 8104 Cindy Ln Bethesda MD 20817-6915

PICKERING, CHARLES W., federal judge; b. 1937. BA, U. Miss., 1959, JD, 1968; Hon. Doctorate, William Carey Coll. Ptnr. Gartin, Hester and Pickering, Laurel, Miss., 1961-71; judge Laurel Mcpl. Ct., 1969; pvt. practice Laurel, 1971-72, 80; ptnr. Pickering and McKenzie, Laurel, 1973-80, Pickering and Williamson, Laurel, 1981-90; judge U.S. Dist. Ct. (so. dist.) Miss., Hattiesburg, 1990—. Contbr. articles to Mississippi Law Journal. Mem. ABA, Miss. Bar Assn., Jones County Bar. Assn., State 4-H Adv. Coun. Assn. Trial Lawyers in Am., Miss. Trial Lawyers Assn., U. Miss. Alumni Assn., Jones County Jr. Coll., Jones County Farm Bur., Kiwanis Club. Office: US Courthouse 701 N Main St Ste 228 Hattiesburg MS 39401

PICKERING, HOWARD WILLIAM, metallurgy engineer, educator; b. Cleve., Dec. 15, 1935; s. Howard William and Marian (Vittes) P.; m. Judith Anne Burch, Apr. 20, 1963; children: John, Kim, Scott, Carolyn. BS in Metall. Engring., U. Cin., 1958; MS, Ohio State U., 1959, PhD, 1961. Scientist U.S. Steel Corp., Monroeville, Pa., 1962-69, sr. scientist, 1969-72; postdoctoral U.S. Steel fellow Max-Planck Inst., Gottingen, Fed. Republic Germany, 1964-65; assoc. prof. metall. engring. Pa. State U., University Park, 1972-76, chmn., 1975-80, prof., 1976-90, disting. prof., 1990—; cons. Ga. Pacific Corp., Newark, 1983-88, Argonne Nat. Lab., 1986-88, Allegheny Ludlum Corp., 1992—; mem. external adv. panel Corrosion Research Ctr., U. Minn., 1980-86. Co-author: Atom Probe Field Ion Microscopy and Its Applications, 1988; editor Corrosion Sci. Jour., 1975-95; contbr. numerous articles to profl. jours. Recipient Disting. Alumnus award Coll. Engring. U. Cin., 1988, Coll. Rsch. award Pa. State U., 1989, Disting. Alumnus award Coll. Engring. Ohio State U., 1990; numerous rsch. grants. Fellow Nat. Assn. Corrosion Engrs. (rsch. com. 1980-89, A.B. Campbell award 1964, Willis Rodney Whitney award 1985); mem. AAAS, Electrochem. Soc. (chmn. edn. com. 1979, Young Author award 1967, H.H. Uhlig award 1987), Metall. Soc. (edn. and profl. affairs com. 1979-83, corrosion resistant metals com. 1974—), Sigma Xi, Tau Beta Pi, Phi Lambda Upsilon.

PICKERING, JAMES HENRY, III, university president; b. N.Y.C., July 11, 1937; s. James H. and Anita (Felber) P.; m. Patricia Paterson, Aug. 18, 1962; children: David Scott, Susan Elizabeth. BA, Williams Coll., 1959; MA, Northwestern U., 1960, PhD, 1964. Instr. English Northwestern U., 1963-65; mem. faculty Mich. State U., East Lansing, 1965-81; prof. English Mich. State U., 1972-81, grad. and asso. chmn. dept., 1968-75, dir. Honors Coll., 1975-81; dean Coll. Humanities and Fine Arts U. Houston, 1981-90, sr. v.p., provost, 1990-92, pres., 1992—. Author: Fiction 100, 1974, 78, 82, 85, 88, 92, 95, The World Turned Upside Down: Prose and Poetry of the American Revolution, 1975, The Spy Unmasked, 1975, The City in American Literature, 1977, Concise Companion to Literature, 1981, Literature, 1982, 86, 90, 94, Mountaineering in Colorado, 1987, Wild Life on the Rockies, 1988, A Mountain Boyhood, 1988, The Spell of the Rockies, 1989, Purpose and Process, 1989, Poetry, 1990, In Beaver World, 1990, Rocky Mountain Wonderland, 1991, A Summer Vacation in the Parks and Mountains of Colorado, 1992, Fiction 50, 1993, Knocking Round the Rockies, 1994, Drama, 1994, Fredrick Chapin's Colorado, 1995. Mem. Coll. English Assn. (pres. 1980-81), Phi Beta Kappa, Phi Kappa Phi, Omicron Delta Kappa. Office: U Houston-University Park Office of the President Houston TX 77204

PICKERING, JOHN HAROLD, lawyer; b. Harrisburg, Ill., Feb. 27, 1916; s. John Leslie and Virginia Lee (Morris) P.; m. Elsa Victoria Mueller, Aug. 23, 1941 (dec. Nov., 1988); children: Leslie Ann, Victoria Lee; m. Helen Patton Wright, Feb. 3, 1990. AB, U. Mich., 1938, JD, 1940. Bar: N.Y. 1941, D.C. 1947. Practiced in N.Y.C., 1941, practiced in Washington, 1946—; assoc. Cravath, de Gersdorff, Swaine & Wood, 1941; law clk. to Justice Murphy, Supreme Ct. U.S., 1941-43; assoc. Wilmer & Broun, 1946-48, ptnr., 1949-62; ptnr. Wilmer, Cutler & Pickering, 1962-79, Wilmer & Pickering, 1979-81; ptnr. Wilmer, Cutler & Pickering, 1981-88, sr. counsel, 1989—; vis. lectr. U. Va. Law Sch., 1988; mem. com. visitors U. Mich. Law Sch., 1962-68, chmn. devel. com., 1973-81; mem. com. on administrn. of justice U.S. Ct. Appeals (D.C. cir.), 1966-72, chmn. adv. com. on procedures, 1976-82, chmn. mediation project, 1988—; adv. gov's. D.C. Bar, 1975-78, pres., 1979-80; dir. Nat. Ctr. for State Cts., 1987-93. Lt. comdr. USNR, 1943-46. Recipient Outstanding Achievement award U. Mich., 1978, Disting. Svc. award Nat. Ctr. for State Cts., 1985, 50 Yr. award from fellows Am. Bar Found., 1993, Paul C. Reardon award, 1994, Pro Bono award NAACP Legal Def. Fund, 1990, numerous other awards. Mem. ABA (state del. 1984-93, chmn. commn. on legal problems of elderly 1985-93, sr. advisor 1993—, vice chair sr. lawyers divsn. 1995—), D.C. Bar Assn., Am. Law Inst., Barristers Washington, Lawyers Club, Met. Club, Chevy Chase Club, Wianno Club, Order of Coif, Phi Beta Kappa, Phi Kappa Phi. Democrat. Mem. United Ch. Christ. Home: 5317 Blackistone Rd Bethesda MD 20816-1822 Office: 2445 M St NW 8th Fl Washington DC 20037-1420

PICKERING, ROBERT EARL, JR., airline executive, consultant; b. Ft. Riley, Kans., Jan. 10, 1952; s. Robert Earl and Elenore (Grossman) P.; m. Linda O. Pickering, Oct. 5, 1974 (div. May 1985); children: Robert Earl III, Lindsay Wave; m. Mary Neill, March 5, 1988; 1 child, David Neill. BBA, Baylor U., 1972, MBA, 1974. Ptnr. Arthur Andersen & Co., Houston, 1974-85; exec. v.p. First City Bancorporation, Houston, 1985-88; v.p. tech. Continental Airlines, Houston, 1988—. Mem. dean's adv. bd. Baylor Bus. Sch.; vice chmn. adminstrv. bd. Foundry United Meth. Ch., Houston, 1983, trustee, 1983. Office: Continental Airlines 2929 Allen Pky Ste 1900 Houston TX 77019-2120

PICKERING, SHELBIE JEAN, mortgage loan executive; b. Ellisville, Miss., Sept. 5, 1939; d. Robert Lee and Virgie Clyde (Shoemake) Smith; m. James Dale Pickering, Aug. 24, 1958; 1 child, James Stephen. BS in Bus. magna cum laude, William Carey Coll., 1990. Reg. mortgage underwriter; cert. appraisal reviewer. Bd. secretary Jones County Bd. Edn., Laurel, Miss., 1960-63; ins. underwriter Graves/Montgomery Ins. Agy., Laurel, 1963-65; office mgr. Kux Distributors, Laurel, 1965-66; adminstrv. asst. Gen. Electric, Bay St. Louis, Miss., 1966-71; mortgage loan officer Hancock Bank, Gulfport, Miss., 1971—; seminar leader Hancock Bank, Gulfport, 1988-92; panelist Miss. Mortgage Lenders, Jackson, 1988-91; cons. Equitrust Mortgage, Gulfport, 1988; Gulf Coast rep. Nat. Mortgage Lenders, Atlanta, 1978-91. Tutor Adult Literacy Progam of Gulfport, 1989-92; sponsor March of Dimes Walk-a-Thon, Gulfport, 1988-92. Mem. Miss. Gulf Coast Mortgage Lenders Assn. (bd. dirs. 1991-92), Nat. Assn. Reg. Mortgage Underwriters and Cert. Rev. Appraisers, Gulf Coast Bd. Realtors, Garden Park Hosp. Health Mgmt. Resources. Republican. Baptist. Avocations: boating, fishing, reading, camping, hiking. Office: Hancock Bank # 1 Hancock Plaza Gulfport MS 39501

PICKERING, THOMAS REEVE, diplomat; b. Orange, N.J., Nov. 5, 1931; s. Hamilton R. and Sarah C. (Chasteney) P.; m. Alice J. Stover, Nov. 24, 1955; children: Timothy R., Margaret S. A.B., Bowdoin Coll., 1953; M.A., Fletcher Sch. Law and Diplomacy, 1954, U. Melbourne, Australia, 1956. Joined U.S. Fgn. Svc., 1959; fgn. affairs officer ACDA, 1961; polit. adviser U.S. del. 18 Nation Disarmament Conf., Geneva, 1962-64; consul Zanzibar, 1965-67; counselor of embassy, dep. chief mission Am. embassy, Dar es Salaam, Tanzania, 1967-69; dep. dir. Bur. Politico-Mil. Affairs, State Dept., 1969-73; spl. asst. to Sec. of State; exec. sec. Dept. State, 1973-74; U.S. amb. to Jordan, 1974-78; asst. sec. for Bur. Oceans, Internat. Environ. and Sci. Affairs, Washington, 1978-81; U.S. amb. to Nigeria, 1981-83, U.S. amb. to El Salvador, 1983-85, U.S. amb. to Israel, 1985-88, U.S. permanent rep. to UN, 1989-92, U.S. amb. to India, 1992-93, U.S. amb. to Russia, 1993—. Served to lt. comdr. USNR, 1956-59. Mem. Council Fgn. Relations, Internat. Inst. Strategic Studies, Phi Beta Kappa. Office: American Embassy APO AE 09721

PICKERING, WILLIAM HAYWARD, physics educator, scientist; b. Wellington, N.Z., Dec. 24, 1910; s. Albert William and Elizabeth (Hayward) P.; m. Muriel Bowler, Dec. 30, 1932 (dec. Mar. 1992); children: William B., Anne E.; m. Inez Chapman, July 28, 1994. B.S., Calif. Inst. Tech., 1932, M.S., 1933, Ph.D. in Physics, 1936; hon. degrees, Clark U., 1966, Occidental Coll., 1966, U. Bologna, 1974. Mem. Cosmic Ray Expdn. to, India, 1939, Mexico, 1941; faculty Calif. Inst. Tech., 1940—, prof. elec. engring., 1946-80, prof. emeritus, 1980—, dir. jet propulsion lab., 1954-76; Mem. sci. adv. bd. USAF, 1945-48; chmn. panel on test range instrumentation (Research and Devel. Bd.), 1948-49; mem. U.S. nat. com. tech. panel Earth Satellite Program, 1955-60; mem. Army Sci. Adv. Panel, 1960-64; dir. rsch. inst. U. Petroleum and Minerals, Dharan, Saudi Arabia, 1977-79; pres. Pickering Rsch. Corp., 1980-91, Lignetics, Inc., 1983—. Decorated Order of Merit Italy; knight comdr. Order Brit. Empire; recipient James Wyld Meml. award Am. Rocket Soc., 1957; Columbus medal Genoa, 1964; Prix Galabert for Astronautics; Goddard trophy Nat. Space Club, 1965; NASA Disting. Service medal, 1965; Army Disting. Civilian Service award, 1959; Spirit of St. Louis medal, 1965; Crozier medal Am. Ordnance Assn., 1965; Man of Year award Indsl. Research Inst., 1968; Interprofl. Coop. award Soc. Mfg. Engrs., 1970; Marconi medal Marconi Found., 1974; Nat. Medal of Sci., 1976; Fahrney medal Franklin Inst., 1976; award of merit Am. Cons. Engrs. Council, 1976; Francois-Xavier Bagnoud Internat. award, 1993. Fellow AIAA (pres. 1963, Louis W. Hill Transp. award 1968, Aerospace Pioneer award 1986), AAAS, IEEE (Edison medal 1972); mem. NAS, Am. Geophys. Union, Internat. Astronautical Fedn. (pres. 1965-66), Am. Assn. Engring. Scis. (Nat. Engring. award 1984, Francois Bagnoud Aerospace Prize 1993, The Japan Prize 1994), Royal Soc. N.Z., NAE. Home: 292 St Katherine Dr La Canada Flintridge CA 91011-4109 Office: Lignetics Inc 1150 Foothill Blvd Ste E La Canada Flintridge CA 91011

PICKETT, BETTY HORENSTEIN, psychologist; b. Providence, R.I., Feb. 15, 1926; d. Isadore Samuel and Etta Lillian (Morrison) Horenstein; m. James McPherson Pickett, Mar. 10, 1952. A.B. magna cum laude, Brown U., 1945, Sc.M., 1947, Ph.D., 1949. Asst. prof. psychology U. Minn., Duluth, 1949-51; asst. prof. U. Nebr., 1951; lectr. U. Conn., 1952; profl. assoc. psychol. scis. Bio-Scis. Info. Exchange, Smithsonian Instn., Washington, 1953-58; exec. sec. behavioral scis. study sect. expl. psychology study sect. div. research grants NIH, Washington, 1958-61; research cons. to mental health unit HEW, Boston, 1962-63; exec. sec. research career program NIMH, 1963-66, chief cognition and learning sect. div. extramural research program, 1966-68, dep. dir., 1968-74, dir. div. spl. mental health programs, 1974-75, acting dir. div. extramural research program, 1975-77; assoc. dir. for extramural and collaborative research program Nat. Inst. Aging, 1977-79; dep. dir. Nat. Inst. Child Health and Human Devel., Bethesda, Md., 1979-81; acting dir. Nat. Inst. Child Health and Human Devel., 1981-82, dir. Div. Rsch. Resources, 1982-88; mem. health scientist adminstr. panel CSC Bd. Examiners, 1970-76, 81-88; mem. coun. on grad. edn. Brown U. Grad. Sch., 1989-91. Contbr. articles to profl. jours. Mem. APA, Am. Psychol Soc., Psychonomic Soc., Assn. Women in Sci., AAAS, Phi Beta Kappa, Sigma Xi. Home: Morgan Bay Rd PO Box 198 Surry ME 04684-0198

PICKETT, CALDER MARCUS, retired journalism educator; b. Providence, Utah, July 26, 1921; s. Leland M. and Julia (Gessel) P.; m. Nola Agricola, Mar. 20, 1947; children: Carolyn Zeligman, Kathleen Jenson. BS, Utah State U., 1944; MS in Journalism, Northwestern U., 1948; PhD, U. Minn., 1959. Copy editor Salt Lake (City) Tribune, 1946, Deseret News, Salt Lake City, 1948-49; instr. Utah State U., Logan, 1946-48, U. Denver, 1949-51; prof. U. Kans., Lawrence, 1951—; Oscar Stauffer prof. Journalism, 1973-77, Clyde M. Reed prof. Journalism, 1985-88, ret., 1988. Author: Ed Howe: Country Town Philosopher, 1968; author, editor: Voices of the Past, 1977; columnist Lawrence Jour.-World; writer, producer, narrator radio program The Am. Past; contbr. articles to profl. jours. Recipient Disting. Teaching award Standard Oil Found., 1967, Frank Luther Mott award, 1969, George Foster Peabody award, 1974, HOPE award U. Kans., 1975, Mortar Bd. award U. Kans., 1983, Armstrong Broadcasting award, 1983, Chancellor's Club Career Teaching award, 1987. Avocations: history, music. Home: 712 Lawrence Ave Lawrence KS 66049-4521

PICKETT, DONN PHILIP, lawyer; b. Chgo., May 3, 1952; s. Philip Gordon and Gloria Joan (Hansen) P.; m. Janet Benson, Aug. 25, 1973; children: Jessica Kelly, William Benson. BA, Carleton Coll., Minn., 1973; JD, Yale U., 1976. Bar: Calif. 1976, U.S. Dist. Ct. (no. dist.) Calif. 1976, (ctrl. dist.) Calif. 1980, (ea. dist.) Calif. 1983, U.S. Ct. Appeals (9th cir.) Calif. 1979, U.S. Ct. Appeals (5th cir.) Tex. 1984, U.S. Supreme Ct. 1991. Assoc. McCutchen, Doyle, Brown & Enersen, San Francisco, 1976-83, ptnr., 1983—. Mem. U.S. Dist. Ct. (no. dist. Calif.) Civil Justice Reform Act Adv. Group, State Bar Calif. (mem. com. on adminstrn. of justice 1988—, vice chmn. 1992-93, chmn. 1993-94, legis. chmn. 1994—), San Francisco Bar Assn. (mem. judiciary com. 1988-92, mem. exec. com. conf. of dels. 1993—), Phi Beta Kappa. Home: 25 Meadow Hill Dr Tiburon CA 94920-1638 Office: McCutchen Doyle Brown & Enersen Three Embarcadero Ctr San Francisco CA 94111

PICKETT, DOYLE CLAY, employment and training counselor, consultant; b. Greencastle, Ind., July 15, 1930; s. Joseph Virgil and Lora Clay (Phillips) P.; m. Judith Ann Marshall, 1956 (div. 1961); children: Brian Doyle, Marsha Ann; m. Dorothy Newgent McGinnis, 1964. AB, Wabash Coll., 1952; MBA, Ind. U., 1953. Exec. trainee, various staff and line exec. positions, asst. store mgr. L.S. Ayres & Co., Lafayette and Indpls., Ind., 1953-64; mgmt. analyst Cummins Engine Co., Columbus, Ind., 1964-67; adminstrv. asst. to pres., other exec. positions Baker & Taylor Co., 1967-80; v.p. mktg. Baker & Taylor Co. subs. W.R. Grace Co., N.Y.C., Somerville, N.J., 1980-82; pres. UNIPUB subs. Xerox Co., N.Y.C., 1982-86; mem. exec. com. R.R. Bowker Co., N.Y.C., 1982-86; pres. D.C. Pickett Assocs., 1986-93; counselor Project Reemployment Opportunities Sys. N.J. Dept. Labor, 1993—. Co-author: Approval Plans and Academic Libraries, 1977; mem. editorial adv. bd. Technicalities, 1980-81; contbr. articles to profl. jours. Mem. Dean's Assocs., Ind. U. Sch. of Bus., Bloomington, 1983-90. Mem. Am. Wabash Assn. (exec.), Assn. Coll. and Rsch. Librs. (mem. publs. com. 1983-87), World Future Soc., Japan Soc., Nat. Trust for Hist. Preservation, Soc. Logistics Engrs. (mem. adv. bd. 1988-91), Nat. Assn. Wabash Men (bd. dirs. 1983-90), Logistics Edn. Found., Caleb Mills Soc., Kiwanis (charter pres. N.W. Indpls. club 1958-59), Masons, Blue Key, Alpha Phi Omega, Delta Tau Delta (ednl. found.) Mem. Christian Ch. Home: 240 Great Hills Rd Bridgewater NJ 08807-1516

PICKETT, EDWIN GERALD, financial executive; b. Washington, Aug. 12, 1946; s. Clarence Edwin and Katherine (Molesworth) P.; m. Nancy Johnson, May 30, 1970; children: Karen, Andrew, Allison. BBA, W.Va. U., 1969; MBA, Loyola Coll. Balt., 1981. CPA, Md. Staff acct. Haskins and Sells CPA's, Balt., 1969-73; dir. internal audit Sun Life Ins. of Am., Balt., 1973-77; v.p., treas. Sun Life Group, Atlanta, 1977-80; v.p., treas. Md. Casualty Co., Balt., 1980-82; sr. v.p. fin., 1982-84; sr. v.p. exec. v.p., CFO Gen. Corp. Houston, 1984-86, CFO, 1986-89; exec. v.p., CFO USF&G Corp., Balt., 1990-93; sr. v.p., CFO TIG Holdings, Inc., Irving, Tex., 1993—. Treas. Poplar Springs (Md.) Meth. Ch., 1978-84; trustee Poplar Springs Meth. Ch., 1989—, Hood Coll., 1990—; Glenelg Country Sch., 1991—. Mem. Am. Inst. CPA's, Fin. Execs. Inst., Caves Valley Golf Club (bd. dirs. 1991—).

Republican. Methodist. Avocations: golf, outdoor activities. Office: TIG Holdings Inc 5205 N O'Connor Blvd Ste N1642 Irving TX 75015

PICKETT, GEORGE BIBB, JR., retired military officer; b. Montgomery, Ala., Mar. 20, 1918; s. George B. and Marie (Dow) P.; BS, U.S. Mil. Acad., 1941; student Nat. War Coll., 1959-60; m. Beryl Arlene Robinson, Dec. 27, 1941; children: Barbara Pickett Harrell, James, Kathleen, Thomas; m. 2d, Rachel Copeland Peeples, July 1981. Commd. 2d lt. U.S. Army, 1941, advanced through grades to maj. gen., 1966; instr. Inf. Sch., Fort Benning, Ga., 1947-50, instr. Armed Forces Staff Coll., Norfolk, Va., 1956-59; comdg. officer 2d Armored Cav. Regt., 1961-63; chief of staff Combat Devel. Command, 1963-66; comdg. gen. 2d inf. div., Korea, 1966-67; ret., 1973; field rep. Nat. Rifle Assn., 1973-85. Decorated Purple Heart with oak leaf cluster, D.S.M. with two oak leaf clusters, Bronze Star with two oak leaf clusters and V device, Silver Star, Legion of Merit with two oak leaf clusters, Commendation medal with two oak leaf clusters. Mem. SAR (pres. Ala. Soc. 1984), Old South Hist. Assn., Am. Legion, VFW. Episcopalian. Club: Kiwanis. Author: (with others) Joint and Combined Staff Officers Manual, 1959; contbr. articles on mil. affairs to profl. jours. Home: 3525 Flowers Dr Montgomery AL 36109-4719 Office: PO Box 4 Montgomery AL 36101-0004

PICKETT, LAWRENCE KIMBALL, physician, educator; b. Balt., Nov. 10, 1919; s. Herbert E. and Emily (Ames) P.; m. Pauline Ferguson, Dec. 17, 1943; children: Lawrence Kimball, Nancy Lee, Paul F., Stephen B. B.A., Yale U., 1941, M.D., 1944. Intern Peter Bent Brigham Hosp., Boston, 1945-46; resident surgery Boston Childrens Hosp., 1946-50; practice medicine specializing in pediatrics and surgery Syracuse, N.Y., 1950-64, New Haven, 1964-84; clin. assoc. prof. surgery Upstate Med. Center, 1953-64; prof. surgery and pediatrics Yale U. Sch. Medicine, 1964-84, prof. emeritus, 1984—, asso. dean, 1973-84; chief of staff Yale-New Haven Hosp., 1973-83; med. dir. Welch Allen Co., Inc., Skaneateles, N.Y., 1983-95. Served to capt. M.C. AUS, 1951-53. Fellow ACS, Am. Acad. Pediatrics (past sect. chmn.); mem. Am. Surg. Assn. Home and Office: PO Box 525 Skaneateles NY 13152-0525

PICKETT, MICHAEL D., computer hardware and software distributor; b. 1947. BSBA, U. So. Calif. With Deloitte Haskins & Sells, 1969-83; v.p. fin., chief fin. officer Merisel Internat. (formerly Softsel Computer Products), 1983-86, pres., chief oper. officer, 1986-88, now vice chmn., CEO. Office: Merisel Internat 200 Continental Blvd El Segundo CA 90245-4526*

PICKETT, OWEN B., congressman; b. Richmond, Va., Aug. 31, 1930. BS, Va. Poly. Inst., 1952; LLB, U. Richmond, 1955. Bar: Va. 1955; CPA. Lawyer, acct. Virginia Beach, Va., 1955-72; mem. Va. Ho. of Dels., Richmond, 1972-86, 100th-103rd Congresses from 2d Va. dist., Washington, D.C., 1987—; chmn. Va. Dem. State Cen. Com., 1980-82; ranking minority mem. Nat. Security Subcom. on mil. personnel. Mem. Va. Bar Assn., Virginia Beach Bar Assn. Office: US Ho of Reps 2430 Rayburn Washington DC 20515*

PICKETT, WILLIAM LEE, academic administrator; b. Kansas City, Mo., Jan. 28, 1941; s. William L. and Ruth Marie (Platt) P.; m. Patricia Jean Vincent, Dec. 26, 1964; children: Sean, Brian, Galen, Amy, Liam, Brendan, Erin. AB, Rockhurst Coll., 1962; MA, Duke U., 1963; MPA, U. Mo., 1973; PhD, U. Denver, 1977. Tchr. various high schs., 1963-66; dir. planning Rockhurst Coll., Kansas City, 1966-72; sr. analyst Midwest Research Inst., Kansas City, 1972-73; dir. devel. Regis Coll., Denver, 1973-77; v.p. U. Detroit, 1977-79, U. San Diego, 1979-86; pres. St. John Fisher Coll., Rochester, N.Y., 1986—. Democrat. Roman Catholic. Office: St John Fisher Coll 3690 East Ave Rochester NY 14618-3597

PICKHARDT, CARL EMILE, JR., artist; b. Westwood, Mass., May 28, 1908; s. Carl Emile and Louise (Fowler) P.; m. Marjorie Sachs, June 15, 1935 (div. 1952); children: Nancy Louise Arnold, Carl Emile III, Sally Anne Duncan; m. Rosamond Forbes Wyman, Mar. 28, 1953. BA, Harvard U., 1931; studied with Harold Zimmerman, 1931-37. Tchr. Fitchburg Art Mus., 1951-62, Worcester Mus. Sch., 1949-50, Sturbridge Art Sch., 1952-60. Author: Portfolio of Etchings, 1942; one-man shows, Berkshire Art Mus., 1941, Doris Meltzer Gallery, N.Y.C., 1961, 68, 70, 71, 72, Jacques Seligmann Gallery, N.Y.C., 1935, 51, 52, 54, Stuart Gallery, Boston, 1946, Margaret Brown Gallery, Boston, 1951, Fitchburg Art Mus., 1951, 91, Lawrence Gallery, Kansas City, Mo., 1955, Artek Gallery, Helsinki, Finland, 1995 Laguna Gloria Art Mus., Austin, Tex., 1966, Radcliffe Coll., 1983, Providence Art Club, 1986, Fitchburg Art Mus., 1991; exhibited in group shows at Carnegie Internat., 1951, Mus. Modern Art, N.Y.C., 1940, 63, 64, Whitney Mus., 1936, Nat. Acad., 1942, 49, Boston Inst. Contemporary Art, 1941, Internat. Exhbn., Japan., 1952, Exhbn. Am. Drawings, France, 1955, Art Inst. Chgo., Calif. Palace of Legion of Honor, 1953, Boston Arts Festival, 1950, Am. Drawing Biennial, Norfolk, 1964, Pa. Acad. Fine Arts, 1968, Laguna Gloria Art Mus., 1973, Fitchburg Art Mus., 1974, 91; represented in permanent collections, Mus. Modern Art, N.Y.C., Boston Mus. Fine Arts, Bklyn. Art Mus., Worcester Art Mus., Library of Congress, N.Y. Pub. Library, Newark Art Mus., Fogg Art Mus., Addison Gallery Finch Coll. Art Mus., Pa. Acad. Fine Arts, Boston Pub. Library, Fitchburg Art Mus., Wadsworth Atheneaum, De Cordova Mus. Served with USNR, 1942-45. Ford Found. and Am. Fedn. Arts artist-in-residence Laguna Gloria Art Mus. 1966; recipient Shope prize Nat. Acad. 1942. Address: 66 Forest St Sherborn MA 01770-1618 My life-long purpose has been to create in visual images a new language and to express order in asymetrical terms.

PICKHOLTZ, RAYMOND LEE, electrical engineering educator, consultant; b. N.Y.C., Apr. 12, 1932; s. Isidore and Rose (Turkish) P.; m. Eda Rebecca Mittler, June 30, 1957. BEE, CUNY, 1954, MEE, 1958; Ph.D. Poly. Inst. N.Y., 1966. Research engr. RCA Labs., Princeton, N.J., 1954-57, ITT Labs., Nutley, N.J., 1957-61; assoc. prof. Poly. Inst. Bklyn., 1962-71; prof. elec. engring., chmn. dept. George Washington U., Washington, 1977-80, prof., 1971—; pres. Telecommunication Assocs., Fairfax, Va., 1963—; cons. Inst. Def. Analyses, 1971-90, IBM Research, Yorktown Heights, N.Y., 1968-72; del. Union Radio Scientifique, Geneva, 1979—, vice chmn., 1987; del. NRC, Washington, 1980-83; vis. prof. U. Que., 1977; vis. scholar U. Calif., 1983; chmn. U.S. Nat. Commn. C, Union Radio Sci. Internat., 1990-92; mem. sci. and indsl. adv. bd. Telecom. Inst. Ont., Can. and Inst. Nacionale de la Recherches Scientique. Editor: book series Computer Science Press, 1979—; IEEE Trans., 1975-80; author: Local Area and Multiple Access Networks, 1986; contbr. articles to profl. jours.; patentee in field. Recipient rsch. award RCA Labs., 1955; rsch. grantee Office of Naval Research, Washington, 1982, E-Systems, Falls Church, Va., 1983, MCI, Falls Church, Va., Instelsat, Washington. Fellow IEEE (bd. govs. 1979-82, digital comm. com., Centennial medal 1984), AAAS, Washington Acad. Scis.; mem. IEEE Comm. Soc. (v.p. 1986-88, pres. 1990-92, Donald W. McLellan award, 1994), Math. Assn. Am., Cosmos Club, Sigma Xi, Eta Kappa Nu. Home: 3613 Glenbrook Rd Fairfax VA 22031-3210 Office: George Washington U Academic Ctr Washington DC 20052

PICKHOLZ, JEROME WALTER, advertising agency executive; b. N.Y.C., Sept. 11, 1932; s. Solomon and Miriam (Schussler) P.; m. Phyllis Rachelle Plump, July 11, 1954; children: Keith, Michelle. BBA, CCNY, 1953. CPA, N.Y. Sr. acct. Eisner & Lubin (CPAs), 1957-60; contr. Hodes-Daniel Co. Elmsford, N.Y., 1960-65; v.p. Hodes-Daniel Co., 1965-70; pres. mgr. direct mail ops. Cordura Corp. div. Hodes Daniel Co., Elmsford, 1970-74; exec. v.p Ogilvy & Mather Direct Response, Inc., N.Y.C., 1974-79, pres., 1979-86, chmn., chief exec. officer, 1986—; vice chmn. Ogilvy & Mather Worldwide, N.Y.C., 1991—; bd. dirs. Ogilvy & Mather U.S., Ogilvy & Mather Worldwide. Bd. dirs. ARC Greater N.Y., 1987—. Lt. (j.g.) USN, 1954-56. Recipient Eddy award Mail Advt. Sccs. Assn., 1988, Silver Apple award Direct Mktg. Club N.Y., 1989, Direct Marketer of Yr., 1992, Malcolm F. Dunn Leadership award, 1994. Mem. Direct Mktg. Assn. (bd. dirs. 1985—, mem. exec. com. 1986-88, chmn. 1991—). Office: Ogilvy & Mather Direct 309 W 49th St New York NY 10019-7316

PICKHOLZ, MARVIN G., lawyer; b. N.Y.C., Apr. 18, 1942; children—Jason, Michael. A.B., NYU, 1963, LL.B., 1966, LL.M., 1968. Bar: N.Y., D.C. trial atty. SEC, N.Y.C., 1967-69, chief atty. br. enforcement, 1969-72, spl. counsel div. enforcement, Washington, 1975-76, asst. chief trial atty., 1976-78, asst. dir., 1978-79; ptnr. Stroock, Stroock & Lavan, N.Y., Washington, 1988—; mem. adj. faculty Columbus Sch. Law, Cath. U.,

Washington; lectr. numerous legal assns., univs., profl. orgns. Author: (book) Securities Crimes, 1993. Mem. ABA (chmn. subcom. on legal compliance programs and preventive law 1981-82, chmn. govt. litigation com. 1982-84, chmn. com. on white collar crime 1984-89, coun. mem. criminal justice sect. 1985-89, mem. com. criminal laws and procedures, chmn. 1992—, mem. coord. com. on RICO, task force on SEC practice, task force on insider trading), Nat. Assn. Criminal Def. Lawyers (chmn. com. white collar crime), Assn. of Securities and Exchg. Commn. Alumni Inst. (founder, pres.). Mem. various editorial adv. bds.; contbr. articles to legal jours. Office: Stroock Stroock & Lavan 7 Hanover Sq New York NY 10004-2616

PICKITT, JOHN LEONARD, retired air force officer, association executive; b. Teague, Tex., July 30, 1933; s. Leonard Daily and Katherine (Davidson) P.; m. Mary Kay Oseland, Aug. 25, 1956; children—John Oseland, Mary Patricia Pickitt Farmer. B.S., U.S. Mil. Acad., 1955; M.S. in Aeros., Air Force Inst. Tech., 1961; grad. Air Force Command and Staff Coll. 1964, Indsl. Coll. of Armed Forces, 1973. Advanced through grades to lt. gen., 1983; instr. pilot 3505th Pilot Tng. Squadron Greenville AFB, Miss. 1956-60; chief liquid rocket sect., Air Force Systems Command Holloman AFB, N.Mex., 1961-64; ops. staff officer, Office of Dep. Chief of Staff, Plans, Hdqrs. Air Tng. Command Randolph AFB, Tex., 1965-67; aircraft comdr., 480th Tactical Fighter Squadron, 366th Tactical Fighter Wing Da Nang Air Base, Vietnam, 1967-68; staff officer, fighter div., Office of Asst. Chief of Staff, Studies and Analysis Washington, 1968-72; dep. comdr. ops., 474th Tactical Fighter Wing Nellis AFB, Nev., 1973-74, vice comdr. 474th Tactical Fighter Wing, 1975; spl. asst. to comdr. Tactical Air Command Langley AFB, Va., 1975-76, comdr. 2d Aircraft Delivery Group, 1976-77; comdr. 366th Tactical Fighter Wing Mountain Home AFB, Idaho, 1977-78; comdr. 832d Air Div. Luke AFB, Ariz., 1978-80; asst. dep. chief of staff plans, Hdqrs. Tactical Air Command Langley AFB, Va., 1980, dep. chief of staff for plans, 1980-81, comdr. 1st Air Force, 1981-83; dep. comdr. in chief UN Command Korea Seoul, 1983-85; dir. Def. Nuclear Agy. Washington, 1985-87; ret., 1987; pres. Computer and Bus. Equipment Mfrs. Assn., 1988-93; cons. S.C., 1993—. Bd. dirs. USO, Seoul, 1983-85, U.S./Republic of Korea Friendship Orgn., Seoul, 1983-85, Integrated Circuit Systems, 1994—. Decorated Def. D.S.M., Air Force D.S.M., Legion of Merit with oak leaf cluster, D.F.C. with 3 oak leaf clusters, Air medal with 12 oak leaf clusters; Republic of Korea Order of Nat. Merit Gugseon medal; Republic of Vietnam Gallantry Cross of palm. Mem. U.S. Air Force Assn. (cert. of honor 1977). Republican. Methodist. Avocations: golf; trap shooting; hunting; fishing. Office: River Hills Plantation 38 Sunrise Point Rd Lake Wylie SC 29710-9230

PICKLE, JAMES C., hospital administrator; b. Memphis, June 8, 1943; s. John Lott and Sarah Elizabeth (Adams) P.; m. Peggy Jean Massey, Dec. 18, 1965; children—Jeff, Matt. B.S. in Liberal Arts, Memphis State U., 1967, M.P.A., 1977. Asst. to pres. Store Devel. Corp., Memphis, 1967-69; investment analyst First Tenn. Adv. Corp., Memphis, 1972-73; v.p., dir. Care Inns Inc., Memphis, 1973-76; dir. shared services Meth. Hosps., Memphis, 1978, v.p. adminstrn., 1978-83, sr. v.p., 1983-84, exec. v.p., 1985-87. Mem. health and welfare ministry bd. Memphis Conf., United Meth. Ch., 1983-87; chief oper. officer Meth. Hosps., Memphis, 1983-87; pres., chief exec. officer Erlanger Med. Ctr., Chattanooga, Tenn., 1987-94; pres. Ky. divsn. Columbia/HCA Healthcare Corp., 1994—; mem. health adv. bd. Memphis State U., 1984-87; chmn. bd. dirs. Dogwood Village of Memphis and Shelby County Inc., 1984-87. Recipient Humanitarian award Am. Lung Assn., 1991, Mgr. of the Yr award Chattanooga Area Mgr. Assn., 1993. Mem. Am. Coll. Hosp. Adminstrs., Nat. Assn. Pub. Hosps. (bd. dirs., exec. com. 1991-94), Tenn. Hosp. Assn. (bd. dirs., numerous coms.), Memphis Hosp. Council (sec.-treas. 1985, pres. 1987), Tenn. Pub. and Teaching Hosp. Assn. (chmn. 1989-94). Republican. Methodist. Avocations: snow skiing; sailing. Home: 22 Brownsboro Hill Rd Louisville KY 40207-2009 Office: Columbia/HCA Healthcare Corp Ste 245 2000 Warrington Way Louisville KY 40222

PICKLE, JERRY RICHARD, lawyer; b. Paris, Tex., Feb. 2, 1947; s. Joseph Rambert and Martha Marie (Biggers) P.; m. Helen Leigh Russell, May 3, 1975; children: Jonathan Russell, Sarah Elizabeth. BA in History, U. Houston, 1969, JD, 1971. Bar: Tex. 1972, U.S. Dist. Ct. (no. dist.) Tex. 1974, U.S. Dist. Ct. (we. dist.) Tex. 1989. Mem. Luna, Ballard & Pickle, Garland, Tex., 1972-74; assoc. Hightower & Alexander, Dallas, 1974-76, Cuba & Johnson, Temple, Tex., 1976-77; assoc. gen. counsel Scott & White Clinic, Temple, 1977—; asst. prof. Tex. A&M U. Coll. of Medicine, Temple, 1986—. Contbr. articles to profl. jours. V.p. The Caring House, Temple, 1989, Tex. divsn. Am. Camcer Soc., Temple, 1976-77; adv. bd. R.R. & Pioneer Mus., Temple, 1982-84; historic preservation bd. City of Temple, 1979-90; chmn. Bell County Hist. Commn., 1980-82; bd. dirs. Bell County Mus., 1992—; Temple Coord. Child Care Coun., 1991-93, Sr. Citizens Activities, 1990-93, Cultural Activities Ctr., Temple, 1993—, pres., 1994-95. Mem. ABA, Am. Acad. Hosp. Attys., State Bar of Tex. (health law sect. councilman 1980-84, 85-87, chmn. 1983-84), Tex. Young Lawyers Assn., Bell-Lampasas-Mills Counties Bar Assn. (pres. 1988-89), Bell-Lampasas-Mills Counties Young Lawyers Assn. (pres. 1980-81), Nat. Health Lawyers Assn., Temple C.of C. (bd. dirs. 1983-85, 88-90), Rotary (chpt. dir. 1981-85, 86-87), Jaycees (chpt. dir. 1977-78). Democrat. Episcopalian. Avocations: reading, golf, music. Office: Scott & White Clinic 2401 S 31st St Temple TX 76508-0001

PICKLE, ROBERT DOUGLAS, lawyer, diversified industry executive; b. Knoxville, Tenn., May 22, 1937; s. Robert Lee and Beatrice Jewel (Douglas) P.; m. Rosemary Elaine Noser, May 9, 1964. AA, Schreiner Mil. Coll. Kerrville, Tex., 1957; BSBA, U. Tenn., 1959, JD, 1961; honor grad. seminar, Nat. Def. U., 1979. Bar: Tenn. 1961, Mo. 1964, U.S. Ct. Mil. Appeals 1962, U.S. Supreme Ct. 1970. Atty. Brown Shoe Co., Inc., St. Louis, 1963-69, asst. sec., atty., 1969-74; sec., gen. counsel Brown Group, Inc., St. Louis, 1974-85, v.p., gen. counsel, corp. sec., 1985—; indiv. mobilization augmentee, asst. army judge adv. civil law The Pentagon, Washington, 1984-89. Provisional judge Municipal Ct., Clayton, Mo., summer 1972; chmn. Clayton Region attys. sect., profl. div. United Fund Greater St. Louis Campaign, 1972-73, team capt., 1974-78; chmn. City of Clayton Parks and Recreation Commn., 1985-87; liaison admissions officer, regional and state coordinator U.S. Mil. Acad., 1980—. Col. JAGC, U.S. Army, 1961-63. Fellow Harry S. Truman Meml. Library; mem. ABA, Tenn. Bar Assn., Mo. Bar Assn., St. Louis County Bar Assn., Bar Assn. Met. St. Louis, St. Louis Bar Found. (bd. dirs. 1979-81), Am. Corp. Counsel Assn., Am. Soc. Corp. Secs. (treas. St. Louis regional group 1976-77, sec. 1977-78, v.p. 1978-79, pres. 1979-80), U. Tenn. Gen. Alumni Assn. (pres., bd. dirs. St. Louis chpt. 1974-76, 80-84, bd. govs. 1982-89), U.S. Trademark Assn. (bd. dirs. 1982-87), Tenn. Soc. St. Louis (bd. dirs. 1980-88, treas., sec., v.p. 1984-87, pres. 1987-88), Smithsonian Nat. Assocs., World Affairs Coun. St. Louis, Inc., Am. Legion, University Club (v.p., sec. St. Louis chpt. 1976-81, bd. dirs. 1976-81), Stadium Club, West Point Soc. St. Louis (hon. mem., bd. dirs. 1992—), Scabbard and Blade, Kappa Sigma, Phi Delta Phi, Phi Theta Kappa, Beta Gamma Sigma, Phi Kappa Phi. Republican. Presbyterian. Avocations: reading, spectator sports. Home: 214 Topton Way Saint Louis MO 63105-3638 Office: Brown Group Inc 8300 Maryland Ave Saint Louis MO 63105-3647

PICKREL, PAUL, English educator; b. Gilson, Ill., Feb. 2, 1917; s. Clayton and Inez (Murphy) P. A.B., Knox Coll., 1938; M.A., Yale U., 1942, Ph.D., 1944. Instr. English Lafayette Coll., 1941-42; instr. Yale U., 1943-45, asst. prof., 1945-50, lectr. English, 1954-66, chmn. Scholar of House Program, 1959-60, 61-66; fellow Morse Coll., 1962-66; adviser John Hay fellows, 1959-66; vis. prof. English Smith Coll., Northampton, Mass., 1966-67, prof., 1967-87, prof. emeritus, 1987—, chmn. dept., 1972-75, 81-82. Author: (novel) The Moving Stairs, 1984; also essays on fiction, numerous book revs.; mng. editor Yale Rev., 1949-66; chief book critic Harper's mag., 1954-65. Mem. Aurelian Honor Soc., Phi Beta Kappa. Clubs: Elizabethan (New Haven), Faculty (Northampton); Yale (N.Y.C.). Office: Smith Coll Wright Hall Northampton MA 01063

PICKRELL, THOMAS RICHARD, retired oil company executive; b. Jermyn, Tex., Dec. 30, 1926; s. Mont Bolt and Martha Alice (Dodson) P.; m. M. Earline Bowen, Sept. 9, 1950; children—Thomas Wayne, Michael Bowen, Kent Richard, Paul Keith. B.S., North Tex. State U., 1951, M.B.A., 1952; postgrad., Ohio State U., 1954-55; advanced mgmt. program, Harvard U., 1979. CPA, Tex. Auditor, acct. Conoco, Inc., Ponca City, Okla., 1955-62;

mgr. acctg. Conoco, Inc., Houston, 1965-67; asst. controller Conoco, Inc., Ponca City, 1967-81; v.p., controller Conoco, Inc., Stamford, Conn., 1982-83, Wilmington, Del., 1983-85; asst. prof. Okla. State U., Stillwater, Okla., 1962-63; controller Douglas Oil Co., Los Angeles, 1963-65; mem. adv. bd. Coll. Bus., Kansas State U., Manhattan, 1979-81. Bd. dirs. YMCA, Ponca City, 1976-78, Kay Guidance Clinic, Ponca City, 1971-74, United Way, Ponca City, 1979-81; chmn. Charter Rev. Com., Ponca City, 1971-72. Served to sgt. U.S. Army, 1944-46; ETO. Mem. AICPA, Fin. Execs. Inst. (pres. Okla. chpt. 1972), Am. Petroleum Inst. (acctg. com., gen. com.), Ponca City Country Club (pres. 1980-81), Rotary (pres. Ponca City club 1973-74), Beta Gamma Sigma, Beta Alpha Psi. Republican. Presbyterian. Home: 10 San Juan Ranch Rd Santa Fe NM 87501-9804

PICKRELL, TIMOTHY E., lawyer; b. Tucson, Apr. 23, 1949. AB, Wabash Coll., 1971; JD, Vanderbilt U., 1974. Bar: Ill. 1974, U.S. Dist. Ct. (no. dist.) Ill. 1974, Ariz. 1985, U.S. Dist. Ct. (Ariz. dist.) 1985. Ptnr. Snell & Wilmer, Tucson. Mem. ABA, Am. Water Resources Assn., Nat. Assn. Bond Lawyers, Ariz. Hydrol. Soc. Maricopa County Bar Assn. Office: Snell & Wilmer 1500 Citibank Tower 1 S Church Ave Tucson AZ 85701

PICOTTE, LEONARD FRANCIS, naval officer; b. Calumet, Mich., Dec. 8, 1939; s. Irving René and Maria (Tamborino) P.; m. Sandra Lees Whiteley, July 14, 1984; children from previous marriage: Mary Elizabeth, Lance, Michael. BS in Econs. cum laude, U. No. Mich., 1963; MA in Polit. Sci., San Diego State U., 1975; grad. with distinction, Armed Forces Staff Coll., Norfolk, Va., 1976; M in Strategic Studies, Naval War Coll., Newport, R.I., 1985. Commd. ensign USN, 1963, advanced through grades to rear adm., 1991; comdg. officer USS Marathon, Vietnam, 1971-73; exec. officer USS Point Defiance, San Diego, 1976-78; exec. officer, officer in charge Surface Warfare Officers' Sch., Coronado, Calif., 1978-80; exec. officer Naval Sta., San Diego, 1980; comdg. officer USS Alamo, San Diego, 1980-82; surface warfare detailer Bur. Naval Pers., Washington, 1982-84; comdg. officer USS Duluth, San Diego, 1986-88; 1st comdg. officer USS Wasp, 1988-90; insp. gen. Comdr. in Chief, US Atlantic Command, Comdr. in Chief, US Atlantic Fleet, Norfolk, 1990-92; comdr. Amphibious Group Two, Norfolk, 1992—. Decorated Legion of Merit (2). Mem. Surface Navy Assn., USS Wasp Assn. (hon.), Army and Navy Club, Town Point Club. Republican. Roman Catholic. Avocations: jogging, hunting, reading, gardening, chess. Home: 1914 Escadrille Pt Norfolk VA 23508-1267 Office: Naval Amphibious Base FPO AE 09501

PICOTTE, MICHAEL BERNARD, real estate developer; b. Albany, N.Y., Sept. 22, 1947; s. Bernard Francis and Kathleen (McManus) P.; m. Margaret Nelson Lindsay; children: Nicole Lindsay, Joseph McManus, Michelle Harrison. BBA, Villanova U., 1969; owner's and pres.'s mgmt. program, Harvard U., 1982. Exec. v.p. West Bradford Corp., Albany, N.Y., 1975-82; mng. ptnr. Picotte Cos., Albany, 1982-90, pres., chief exec. officer, 1990—; bd. dirs. Fleet Fin. Group. Trustee Coll. St. Rose, 1983-89, Albany Inst. History & Art, 1988—; chmn. St. Peter's Hosp., Albany, 1986—; cir. Ctr. for Econ. Growth, 1992. With USNG, 1969-74. Mem. Young Pres.'s Orgn., Schuyler Meadows Club, Ft. Orange Club (Albany). Avocations: skiing, golf, tennis. Office: Picotte Cos 20 Corporate Woods Blvd Albany NY 12211-2350

PICOWER, WARREN MICHAEL, magazine editor; b. N.Y.C., Aug. 21, 1934; s. Abraham and Nell (Bloom) P.; divorced; children: Jenny Emelia, Eve Julie. B.A., Queens Coll., 1956; M.A., New Sch. for Social Research, 1978; Psy.D. in Psychology, Heed U., Los Angeles, 1982. Editorial asst. Newsweek mag., N.Y.C., 1956-59; assoc. editor Supermarket Pub. Co., N.Y.C., 1961-63; assoc., mng. editor Fawcett Pubs., N.Y.C., 1963, 64-65; mng. editor Tuesday Publs., N.Y.C., 1965-67, exec. editor, v.p., 1967-73; sr. editor King Features Syndicate, N.Y.C., 1974-78; mng. editor Food & Wine Mag., N.Y.C., 1978-93; consulting editor Travel Holiday Mag., N.Y., 1993-94; mng. editor Zagat Survey Restaurant and Hotel Guides, N.Y.C., 1994—; cons. in field. Contbr. articles to profl. jours. Mem. Am. Soc. Mag. Editors, Overseas Press Club Am., Assn. of Food Journalists. Office: Zagat Survey 4 Columbus Cir New York NY 10019

PICOZZI, ANTHONY, dentistry educator, educational administrator; b. Bklyn., Dec. 24, 1917; s. Louis and Ida (DeRosa) P.; m. Gloria Margaret Patinella, Feb. 9, 1952; children—Kathryn, Lori. B.S., Columbia U., 1939; D.D.S., NYU, 1944. Section chief Lever Bros. Research, Edgewater, N.J., 1955-68; prof. dentistry NYU, N.Y.C., 1968-74; adminstr., researcher Fairleigh Dickinson U., Hackensack, N.J., 1974-89; rsch. cons. Warner Lambert Co., Morris Plains, N.J., 1989—; cons. Lever Research, Edgewater, 1968-74, W.R. Grace, Balt., 1979-81. Contbr. articles to profl. jours. Served to lt. col. USAR. Mem. ADA (mem. coun. on dental rsch. 1987-91), Am. Assn. Dental Research (councillor 1981, bd. dirs. 1988-90), Am. Assn. Dental Schs. (sect. chmn. 1980-81). Home: 21 Ridge Rd Ridgewood NJ 07450-3159 Office: Warner Lambert Co 170 Tabor Rd Morris Plains NJ 07950-2536

PICUS, MARK ANTHONY, broadcasting executive; b. Savannah, Ga., Oct. 1, 1953; s. Lawrence Roy and Phyllis Jane (Ortagus) P.; m. Debra Ann Decker, May 7, 1974 (div. Jan. 1976); m. Kimberly Thomas, Aug. 17, 1984; children: Lawrence, Kristen Michelle Foster. Announcer Sta. WPDQ, Jacksonville, Fla., 1968-75; announcer, gen. mgr. Sta. WKUE, Jacksonville, 1975-79; dir. programing Sta. WQMT, Dalton, Ga., 1979-81; gen. mgr. Sta. WENR, Athens, Tenn., 1981-82; asst. program dir. Sta. KXXY, Oklahoma City, 1982-83; gen. mgr., pres. Sta. WZAZ, Jacksonville, 1983-89; founder, pres., treas., gen. mgr. Picus Broadcasting Corp., Inc., Jacksonville, 1989-. Mem. Nat. Assn. Broadcasters, Fla. Assn. Broadcast. Democrat. Jewish. Office: Sta WZAZ 2611 Werd Radio Dr Jacksonville FL 32204-1751

PIDERIT, JOHN J., university educator; b. N.Y.C., Feb. 26, 1944. BA in Math. and Philosophy magna cum laude, Fordham U., 1967; Lic. in Sacred Theology cum laude, Philosophische und Theologische Hochschule Sankt Georgen, Frankfurt, West Germany, 1971; MPhil, Oxford U., 1974; MA, PhD in Econ., Princeton U., 1979. Ordained Jesuit priest Roman Cath. Ch., 1971. Tchr. math. Regis H.S., N.Y.C., 1967-68; asst. campus minister Fordham U., 1971-72; asst. campus minister Princeton U., 1975-78, preceptor, 1976-77; asst. chairperson grad. studies Fordham U., 1984-88, dir. program internat. polit. econ. and devel., 1981-83, 87-88, asst. chairperson dept. econs., 1979-82, 88-89, asst. prof. econs., 1978-89, assoc. prof. econs., 1989-90; corp. v.p. Marquette U., 1990-93; pres. Loyola U. Chgo., 1993—; vis. fellow Woodstock Theol. Ctr., Washington, summer 1982; sabbatical Santa Clara U., 1989-90; master Queen's Ct. Residential Coll., 1987-90; chmn. responsible investment com. N.Y. province SJ, 1986-88, mem. fin. com., 1986-88; mem. joint commn. govtl. rels. of Am. Coun. Edn., 1994—; mem. exec. com. Nat. Planning Com. Jesuit Assembly '89, 1988-90. Contbr. articles to profl. jours. Founder, moderator Friends of Loyola, 1987-90; pres. Univ. Neighborhood Housing Corp., 1986-90, Maroon Enterprises, Inc., 1986-90; trustee Canisius Coll., Buffalo, 1983-88, 89—; bd. dirs. Corp. Cmty. Schs. of Am., 1993—; organizer PIVOT H.S. and Middle Sch. with Milw. Pub. Schs., 1990—; mem. Greater Milw. Edn. Trust, 1990—; mem. steering com., chair edn. task force Milw. Cmty. Traffic Safety Com., 1991—; mem. steering com. Libr. Literacy Soc. Milw., 1991—; mem. scholarship com. Knitworkers Union Local 155, N.Y.C., 1982-90; mem. Princeton Schs. Com. N.Y. Region, 1985-88. Mellon grantee Fordham U., summer 1983, summer grantee Fordham U., 1979, Princeton U. fellow, 1974-78. Office: Loyola U Chgo 820 N Michigan Ave Chicago IL 60611

PIDGEON, JOHN ANDERSON, headmaster; b. Lawrence, Mass., Dec. 20, 1924; s. Alfred H. and Nora (Regan) P.; children: John Anderson, Regan S., Kelly; m. Barbara Hafer, May 1986. Grad., Phillips Acad., 1943; B.A., Bowdoin Coll., 1949; Ed.D., Bethany Coll., 1973; D.Litt., Washington and Jefferson Coll., 1979. Instr. Latin, adminstrv. asst. to headmaster Deerfield Acad., 1949-57; headmaster Kiskiminetas Springs Sch., Saltsburg, Pa., 1957—; dir. Saltburg Savs. & Trust. Served as ensign USNR, 1943-46. Mem. New Eng. Swimming Coaches Assn. (treas. 1957), Cum Laude Soc., Delta Upsilon. Home and Office: Kiski Sch 1888 Bret Ln Saltsburg PA 15681

PIDOT, WHITNEY DEAN, lawyer; b. N.Y.C., Mar. 2, 1944; s. George B. and Virginia (Ulrich) P.; m. Jeanne Stoddard, April 23, 1973; children:

Whitney Dean Jr., Philip Martin, Seth Thayer. AB, Harvard U., 1966; JD, Columbia U., 1970, MBA, 1970. Bar: N.Y. 1971. Ptnr. Shearman & Sterling, N.Y.C., 1971—; adv. bd. Barclays Bank N.Y., 1989-92, Molecular Tool, Inc. (biotech.) Balt., 1991—, Equine Genetic Rsch. Ptnrs., Balt., 1991—; trustee Winthrop Univ. Hosp., Mineola, N.Y. 1989—. Mayor, Village of Matinecock, Locust Valley, N.Y., 1977-92; vice chmn. North Shore Mayors Com., Long Island, N.Y., 1980-92; bd. dirs. Nassau County (N.Y.) Village Officials Assn., 1978-80; commr. Locust Valley Fire Dist., 1979—. Republican. Home: Piping Rock Rd Locust Valley NY 11560 Office: Shearman & Sterling 599 Lexington Ave New York NY 10022-6069

PIECEWICZ, WALTER MICHAEL, lawyer; b. Concord, Mass., Jan. 27, 1948; s. Benjamin Michael and Cecelia (Makuc) P.; A.B. magna cum laude, Colgate U., 1970; J.D., Columbia U., 1973; m. Anne T. Mikolajczyk, Oct. 28, 1978; children—Tiffany Anne, Stephanie Marie. Admitted to Ill. bar, 1973; mem. firm Leverhold, Sears, Giambalvo & Crowley, Chgo., 1978-73, Boodell, Sears, Giambalvo & Crowley, Chgo., 1978—; dir. No. Data Systems, Inc. Mem. Am. Bar Assn., Ill. Bar Assn., Chgo. Bar Assn., Chgo. Estate Planning Council, Internat. Bus. Council Midwest, Phi Beta Kappa. Democrat. Roman Catholic. Office: Peterson & Ross 200 E Randolph Dr Ste 7300 Chicago IL 60601-6969

PIECH, MARGARET ANN, mathematics educator; b. Bridgewater, N.S., Can., Apr. 6, 1942; d. Frederick Cecil and Margaret Florence (Laschinger) Garrett; m. Kenneth Robert Piech, June 19, 1965; children: Garrett Andrew, Marjorie Ann. BA, Mt. Allison U., Sackville, N.B., Can., 1962; PhD, Cornell U., 1967. Asst. prof. SUNY, Buffalo, 1967-72, assoc. prof., 1972-78, prof. math., 1978—; cons. NSF, Washington, 1980-81, Aspen Analytics, Buffalo, 1986—; v.p. Seventy Niagara Svcs., 1990—. Contbr. articles to profl. jours. Woodrow Wilson fellow, 1962-63; grantee NSF, 1976-85, U.S. Army Rsch. Office, 1985-89. Mem. IEEE, Am. Math. Soc., Assn. Computing Machinery, Greater Yellowstone Coalition, Henry's Fork Found. Avocation: fly fishing. Office: SUNY Diefendorf Hall Buffalo NY 14214

PIECUCH, JOHN M., manufacturing company executive; b. South Bend, Ind., 1949. BS, U. Notre Dame, 1965; postgrad., U. Chgo., 1983. Past pres., bd. dirs. Sun Metal Products, Warsaw, Ind., Sun Wheels Ltd., Warsaw; sr. v.p., pres. Great Lakes region LaFarge Corp., Reston, Va., 1987-89, exec. v.p., pres. Cement group, 1989-92, sr. v.p., 1992—. Office: LaFarge Corp 11130 Sunrise Valley Dr Reston VA 22091

PIEHL, DONALD HERBERT, chemist, consultant; b. Chgo., Jan. 18, 1939; s. Herbert Herman and Faye L. (Pentti) P.; m. Ann Elizabeth Guildner; children: Mark Donald, Jennifer Ann. BA in Chemistry, Carthage Coll., 1961; MS in Chemistry, U. Iowa, 1964, PhD in Chemistry, 1966; postgrad. Young Exec. Inst., U. N.C., 1974. Quality control chemist Bowey's, Inc., Chgo., 1961; polymer chemist Borg-Warner Corp., Des Plaines, Ill., 1962; sr. rsch. chemist R.J. Reynolds Tobacco Co., Winston-Salem, N.C., 1966-70, group leader, 1969-70; section head R.J. Reynolds Industries, Winston-Salem, 1970-76, rsch. mgr., 1976-80, dir. applied R & D, 1980-83; dir. tech. svcs. RJR Nabisco, Winston-Salem, 1983-85; v.p. R & D Heublein Inc., Hartford, Conn., 1985-89, v.p. tech. and brand devel., 1989-94; ret., 1994, tchr. mgmt. of tech. and total quality mgmt., quality cons., 1994—; instr. Am. Mgmt. Assn., organizer, chmn. Pub. Symposium on Energy and Environ, Greensboro, N.C., 1991; mem. adv. com. mgmt. of tech. program U. N.C., Chapel Hill, 1982-84; tchr. bus. inst. Mgmt. Devel., Inc., Chapel Hill, 1975-85. Contbr. articles to profl. jours. Bd. dirs. Sci. and Tech. Inst. of New Eng., Storrs, Conn., 1988—; Sci. Mus. Conn., Hartford, 1989—, Indsl. Rsch. Inst., 1983—; chmn. precoll. edn. com., 1993-94; pres. Optimist CLub, Winston-Salem, 1971. Recipient Outstanding Young Man of Am. award, 1970, Optimist of Yr. award Optimist Club, 1971, Spl. Teaching award U. N.C. Sch. Bus.; 1984; fellow Ethyl Corp., 1964-65. Fellow Conn. Acad. Edn.; mem. World Assn. of Alcohol Beverage Industry (v.p. and com. chair Conn. chpt. 1992-94), Am. Chem. Soc. (chmn. local sect. 1962—, Outstanding Svc. award 1974), Inst. Food Technologists, Conn. Quality Coun. (co-founder 1989—), N.C. Acad. Scis., Hartford Co. of C. (chmn. bd. tech. coun. 1986-89), Sigma Xi, Alpha Chi Sigma. Republican. Avocations: tennis, golf, skiing, photography.

PIEKARSKI, VICTOR J., lawyer; b. Lawrence, Mass., Feb. 20, 1950. BA cum laude, Boston Coll., 1971; MBA, U. Chgo., 1978; JD cum laude, Northwestern U., 1978. Bar: Ill. 1974, U.S. Ct. Appeals (7th cir.) 1977, U.S. Supreme Ct. 1978. Ptnr. Querrey & Harrow Ltd., Chgo. Mem. ABA, Ill. State Bar Assn., Chgo. Bar Assn., Ill. Assn. Def. Trial Counsel, Trial Lawyers Club Chgo., Def. Rsch. Inst. Office: Querrey & Harrow Ltd 180 N Stetson Ave Chicago IL 60601

PIEL, CAROLYN FORMAN, pediatrician, educator; b. Birmingham, Ala., Oct. 18, 1918; d. James R. and Mary Elizabeth (Dortch) Forman; m. John Joseph Piel, Aug. 3, 1951; children: John Joseph, Mary Dortch, Elizabeth Forman, William Scott. BA, Agnes Scott Coll., 1940; MS, Emory U., 1943; MD, Washington St. Louis, 1946. Diplomate Am. Bd. Pediatrics (examiner 1973-88, pres. 1986-87); diplomate Am. Bd. Pediatric Nephrology. Intern Phila. Gen. Hosp., 1946-47; resident Phila. Children's Hosp., 1947-49; fellow Cornell U. Med. Sch., N.Y.C., 1949-51; from instr. to assoc. clin. prof. Stanford U. Sch. Medicine, San Francisco, 1951-59; from asst. prof. to prof. Sch. Medicine, U. Calif., San Francisco, 1959-89, emeritus prof., 1989—. Author, co-author research articles in field. Bd. mem. San Francisco Home Health Service, 1977-83. Emeritus mem. Soc. for Pediatric Research, Am. Pediatric Soc., Am. Soc. for Pediatric Nephrology, Am. Soc. Nephrology, Western Soc. for Pediatric Nephrology (pres. 1960). Democrat. Presbyterian. Home: 2164 Hyde St San Francisco CA 94109-1701 Office: U Calif PO Box 748 San Francisco CA 94143

PIEL, GERARD, editor, publisher; b. Woodmere, L.I., N.Y., Mar. 1, 1915; s. William F.J. and Loretto (Scott) P.; m. Mary Tapp Bird, Feb. 4, 1938; children: Jonathan Bird, Samuel Bird (dec.); m. Eleanor Virden Jackson, June 24, 1955; child, Eleanor Jackson. A.B. magna cum laude, Harvard U., 1937; D.Sc., Lawrence Coll., 1956, Colby Coll., 1960; U. B.C., Brandeis U., 1965, Lebanon Valley Coll., 1977, L.I. U. 1978, Bard Coll., 1979, CUNY, 1979, U. Mo., 1985, Blackburn Coll., 1985; Litt.D., Rutgers U., 1961, Bates Coll., 1974; L.H.D., Columbia, 1962, Williams Coll., 1966, Rush U., 1979, Hahnemann Med. Coll., 1981, Mt. Sinai Med. Sch., 1985; LL.D., Tuskegee Inst., 1963, U. Bridgeport, 1964, Bklyn. Poly. Inst., 1965, Carnegie-Mellon U., 1968, Lowell U. 1986; Dr. (honoris causa), Moscow State (Lomonosov) U., 1985. Sci. editor Life mag., 1938-44; asst. to pres. Henry J. Kaiser Co. (and assoc. cos.), 1945-46; organizer (with Dennis Flanagan, Donald H. Miller, Jr.), pres. Sci. Am., Inc., 1946-84, chmn., 1984-87, chmn. emeritus, 1987—; pub. mag. Sci. Am., 1947-84. Translated editions: Le Scienze, 1968, Saiensu, 1971, Investigacion y Ciencia, 1976, Pour la Science, 1977, Spektrum der Wissenschaft, 1978, KeXue, 1979, V Mire Nauki, 1983, Tudomany, 1985, Majallat Al Oloom, 1986, Erde im Gleichgewicht, 1994; author: Science in the Cause of Man, 1961, The Acceleration of History, 1972, Only One World, 1992. Chmn. Commn. Delivery Personal Health Services City N.Y., 1967-68; trustee Am. Mus. Nat. History, N.Y. Bot. Garden, René Dubos Ctr.; trustee emeritus Radcliffe Coll., Phillips Acad., Mayo Clinic, Henry J. Kaiser Family Found., Found. for Child Devel.; pub. mem. Am. Bd. Med. Specialities; bd. overseers Harvard U., 1966-68, 73-79. Recipient George Polk award, 1961, Kalinga prize, 1962, Bradford Washburn award, 1966, Arches of Sci. award, 1969; Rosenberger medal U. Chgo., 1973, A.I. Djavakhishvili medal U. Tbilisi, 1985; named Pub. of Yr. Mag. Pubs. Assn., 1980. Fellow Am. Acad. Arts and Scis., AAAS (pres. 1985, chmn. 1986); mem. Coun. Fgn. Rels., Am. Philos. Soc., Nat. Acad. Sci. Inst. Medicine, Harvard Club, Century Club, Met. Opera Club, Cosmos Club, Somerset Club, Phi Beta Kappa, Sigma Xi. Home: 1115 Fifth Ave New York NY 10128-0100

PIEL, WILLIAM, JR., retired lawyer; b. N.Y.C., Nov. 28, 1989; s. William and Loretto (Scott) P.; m. Eleanor Green, Dec. 1, 1951; children by former marriage: Michael, Anthony, Thomas. AB, Princeton U., 1932; LLB, Harvard U., 1935. Bar: N.Y. 1935. Practiced in N.Y.C.; partner Sullivan & Cromwell, 1945-80; expert cons. mil. intelligence service War Dept. Gen. Staff, 1944-45; dir. emeritus Campbell Soup Co., Phillips Petroleum Co. Hon. dir. Greater N.Y.. coun. Girl Scouts Am.; hon. trustee Cancer Rsch. Inst.; trustee Internat. Crane Found., Baraboo, Wis. Fellow Am. Coll. Trial Lawyers, N.Y. State Bar Found.; mem. ABA, Assn. Bar City N.Y., Am.

Judicature Soc., Fed. Bar Coun., Squadron A Assn., Century Assn., Princeton Club (N.Y.C.). Home: Tree House 44 Briggs Hill Rd Sherman CT 06784

PIELE, PHILIP KERN, education infosystems educator; b. Portland, Oreg., May 14, 1935; s. Theodore R. and Helen D. (Hanson) P.; m. Sandra Jean Wright, Aug. 10, 1963; children: Melissa, Kathryn. BA, Wash. State U., 1957; student, U. Wash., 1960, San Jose State U., 1964; MS, U. Oreg., 1963, PhD, 1968. Prof. dept ednl. policy and mgmt. U. Oreg., Eugene, 1979—, mem. faculty applied info. mgmt. program, 1989—, dir. numerous ednl. orgns. and coms. Coll. Edn., 1968—, dir. Edn. Resources Info. Ctr. (ERIC) clearinghouse on ednl. mgmt., 1969—, assoc. dir. Ctr. for Ednl. Policy and Mgmt., 1973-76; vis. lectr. U. Western Australia, Monashe U., U. New S. Wales, and several other Australian Univs., 1973; vis. prof. Ontario Inst. for Studies in Edn., U. Toronto, 1974; vis. scholar Stanford U., 1984; exec. sec. Oreg. Sch. Study Coun., 1980—; dir. Networks and Comms. Ctr. for Advanced Tech. in Edn., 1984-92. Author numerous books, chpts., monographs; editor numerous books; contbr. articles to profl. jours. Bd. dirs. Oreg. Bach Festival, Eugene, 1980-83, Oreg. Mozart Players, Eugene, 1995—. Mem. Nat. Orgn. in Legal Problems in Edn. (pres. 1977-78), Nat. Sch. Devel. Coun. (pres. 1985-86), Am. Ednl. Rsch. Assn. (sec. adminstrn. divsn. 1991-93). Home: 2026 Morning View Dr Eugene OR 97405-1632 Office: U Oreg ERIC Clearinghouse on Ednl Mgmt 1787 Agate St Eugene OR 97403-1923

PIELOU, EVELYN C., biologist; m. Patrick Pielou, June 22, 1944; 3 children. B.Sc., U. London, 1950, Ph.D., 1962, DSc, 1975; LLD (hon.), Dalhousie U., 1993. Research scientist Can. Govt., 1963-67; vis. prof. N.C. State U., 1968, Yale, New Haven, 1969; prof. biology Queen's U., Kingston, Ont., 1969-71, Dalhousie U., Halifax, N.S., 1971-84; vis. prof. U. Sydney, Australia, 1975; oil sands environ. vis. research prof. U. Lethbridge, Alta. 1981-86. Author: Introduction to Mathematical Ecology, 1969, Population and Community Ecology, 1974, Ecological Diversity, 1975, Mathematical Ecology, 1977, Biogeography, 1979, Interpretation of Ecological Data, 1984, World of Northern Evergreens, 1988, After the Ice Age, 1991, Naturalist's Guide to the Arctic, 1994; contbr. articles to profl. jours. Recipient Lawson medal Can. Bot. Assn., 1984, Eminent Ecologist award Ecol. Soc. Am., 1986, Disting. Statis. Ecologist award Internat. Congress Ecology, Commemorative medal for 125th Anniversary of Confedn. of Can., 1992. Mem. Brit. Ecol. Soc. (hon. life).

PIEMONTE, ROBERT VICTOR, association executive; b. N.Y.C., July 28, 1934; s. Rosario and Carmela (Santoro) P. BS, L.I. U., 1967; MA, Columbia U., 1968, MEd, 1970, EdD, 1976; DSc (hon.), L.I. U., Bklyn., 1993. Asst. dir. nursing svc. ANA, 1962-69, dir. nursing svc., 1971-72, divsn. dir., 1983-85; asst. dir. nursing Univ. Hosp.-NYU, N.Y.C., 1970-71; assoc. dir. ops. N.Y.C. Health and Hosps. Corp., N.Y.C., 1972-76; assoc. prof. Tchr.'s Coll. Columbia U., N.Y.C., 1976-78; exec. dir. N.J. State Nurses Assn., Montclair, 1978-80; dep. exec. dir. Nat. Student Nurses Assn., N.Y.C., 1980-83, exec. dir., 1985—; adj. prof. nursing Tchr.'s Coll. Columbia U., 1990—; cons. Consensus Mgmt., N.Y.C., 1992—. Contbr. articles to profl. pubs.; mem. editl. adv. bd. Nursing and Health Care, 1985—. Area-wide chair nursing Greater N.Y. chpt. ARC, N.Y.C., 1990-93. Col. U.S. Army, 1987—. Recipient Disting. Alumni award L.I. U., 1984, Hon. Recognition award N.Y. State Nurses Assn., 1992. Fellow Am. Acad. Nursing (treas. 1993—); mem. Am. Soc. Assn. Execs. (cert., bd. dirs. 1993—), Am. Nurses Found. (trustee 1994—), Nursing House, Inc. (pres. 1993—), Nat. Adv. Coun. on Nurse Edn. and Practice, N.Y. Soc. Assn. Execs. (Outstanding Assn. Exec. 1991, pres. 1989-90). Democrat. Roman Catholic. Avocations: theatre, reading, travel. Home: 76 W 86th St New York NY 10024 Office: Nat Student Nurses Assn 555 W 57th St New York NY 10019

PIEN, FRANCIS D., internist, microbiologist; b. Detroit, Apr. 7, 1945; s. Chung Ling and Nung Chung (Lee) P.; m. Harriet Ho, Dec. 27, 1967; children: Brian, Ethan, Kevin. BA, Johns Hopkins U., Balt., 1965, MPH, 1971; MD, U. Chgo., 1969; MS in Microbiology, U. Minn., 1973. Diplomate Nat. Bd. Med. Examiners, Am. Bd. Internal Medicine, subspecialty in infectious disease, Am. Bd. Med. Microbiology. Intern U. Ill., 1969-70; fellow in microbiology, resident in internal medicine Mayo Grad. Sch. Medicine, Rochester, Minn., 1970-73; fellow in infectious disease Stanford (Calif.) U., 1973-74; assoc. program dir. integrated med. residency program U. Hawaii, Honolulu, 1977-90, assoc. prof. medicine, 1977-88, prof. medicine, 1988-93, chief infectious diseases, 1987-93, clin. prof. tropical medicine and med. microbiology, 1983—; infectious disease cons. Straub Clinic, Honolulu, 1974—; exchange prof. U. Osaka (Japan) Sch. Medicine, 1990; cons. in infection control Leahi Hosp., 1993—; bd. dirs. Rehab. Hosp. of Pacific, Honolulu, 1989-93, Interfaith Hosp. Chaplaincy Ministry, 1990—, Samaritan Counseling Ctr., 1992—, Straub Clinic and Hosp., 1990—. Reviewer Hawaii Med. Jour., Reviews of Infectious Diseases, Western Jour. Medicine, Straub Clinic Proceedings; contbr. over 150 articles to profl. jours. Fellow ACP, Am. Acad. Microbiology, Infectious Disease Soc. Am., Royal Soc. of Tropical Medicine and Hygiene; mem. AMA, Hawaii Med. Soc. (chmn. communicable disease com. 1979-83), Am. Soc. Tropical Medicine and Hygiene (mem. delegation to Mainland China 1978), Am. Soc. Microbiology (Hawaii br. pres. 1982-83), Christian Med. Soc., Assn. for Practitioners for Infection Control, Am. Thoracic Soc. (Tuberculosis Assembly), Am. Venereal Disease Assn., Soc. of Hosp. Epidemiologists of Am., European Soc. Clin. Microbiology. Republican. Presbyterian. Avocations: medical missions, research, travel. Office: Straub Clinic 888 S King St Honolulu HI 96813

PIEN, SHYH-JYE JOHN, mechanical engineer; b. Kaohsiung, Taiwan, Republic of China, July 14, 1956; came to U.S., 1980; s. Ke-Lee and Sue-Jean (Shen) P.; m. Fong-Ling Yang, July 15, 1982; children: Irene J., Jennifer M. BSME, Nat. Taiwan U., 1978; MSME, U. Ill., 1982, PhD, 1985. Asst. prof. U. Notre Dame, South Bend, Ind., 1985-89; sr. engr. Alcoa Tech. Ctr., Alcoa Ctr., Pa., 1989-91, staff engr., 1991-95, tech. specialist, 1995—; panelist on heat transfer in mfg. at profl. confs.; panel chmn. and panelist on spray forming tech. at profl. confs. Editor symposium proc.; contbr. articles to profl. publs. Co-chmn. Nat. Youth Day Assembly, Taiwan, 1977; pres. Chinese Inst. Engrs. in USA, U. Ill., Urbana, 1984; v.p. Orgn. Chinese Ams., Pitts., 1993—. Recipient Excellent Youth award Kashiung City Province, Taiwan, Nat. Coll. Excellent Youth award Govt. Taiwan, Rsch. Initiation award NSF, 1988. Mem. ASME (materials processing and mng. com. heat transfer div. 1990—, planning and devel. com. 1993—, chmn. indsl. liaison div.), Sigma Xi, Phi Kappa Phi. Roman Catholic. Achievements include 3 patents on continuous casting machine design, patents pending on roll casting device and twin-belt casting device; research on nuclear safety analysis, hysteresis effect in natural convection, thermal/fluid phenomena in continuous casting, electronic packaging, welding process control, extrusioon flow modeling, die casting, spray forming. Office: Aluminum Co Am Alcoa Tech Ctr Alcoa Center PA 15069

PIENE, OTTO, artist, educator; b. Laasphe, Westphalia, Germany, Apr. 18, 1928; s. Otto and Anne (Niemeyer) P.; children—Annette, Herbert, Claudia, Chloe. Student, Acad. Fine Arts, Munich, Germany, 1949-50, Acad. Fine Arts, Dusseldorf, Germany, 1950-52; Staatsexamen in Philosophy, U. Cologne, Germany, 1957. Co-founder Group Zero, Dusseldorf, Germany, 1957; vis. prof. Grad. Sch. Art, U. Pa., Phila., 1964; prof. environ. art Sch. Architecture and Planning, MIT, Cambridge, Mass., 1972-93, dir. Ctr. for Advanced Visual Studies, MIT, 1974-94; dir. emeritus Ctr. for Advanced Visual Studies MIT, 1994—; dir. Sky Art Conf. MIT, 1981, 82, 83, 86; vis. artist, guest prof. numerous univs.; mem. numerous archtl. and environ. art commns. and pub. celebrations. Author: (with Heinz Mack) Zero 1, 2, 3, 1958, 61, More Sky, 1970, Rainbows, 1971, Zero, 1973, More Sky, 1973, Sky Art Conf. Proc., 1981, 82, 83, Feuerbilder und Texte, 1988; one man exhbns. include, Galerie Heseler, Munich, 1971, 72, 75, 77, 78, 79, 83, 86, MIT, 1975, 93, Galerie Schoeller, Düsseldorf, Fed. Republic Germany, 1977, 79, 83, 87, 91, 95, Fitchburg (Mass.) Art Mus., 1977, Galerie Watari, Tokyo, 1983, Pat Hearn Gallery, N.Y.C., 1985, Gallery 360, Tokyo, 1991, 92, Galérie d'Art International, Paris, 1993, Gallery 360, Tokyo, 1995; numerous group exhbns. U.S. and abroad including, Guggenheim Mus., N.Y.C., 1964, 66, 84, Albright-Knox Gallery Buffalo, 1968, Nat. Mus. Modern Art, Tokyo, 1969, Tate Gallery, London, 1974, Smithsonian Instn., Washington, 1978, Royal Acad. Art, London, 1985, National Gallery, Berlin, 1986, Statsgalerie,

Stuttgart, 1986, Berlimische Galerie, Berlin, 1988-89, 91-92, MIT, 1994, Haus der Kunst, Munich, 1995, others; also represented in numerous permanent collections. (Recipient award Internat. Exhibition Graphic Art, Ljubljana, Yugoslavia 1967, 69, prize 8th Internat. Biennial Prints Nat. Mus. Modern Art, Tokyo, Japan 1972, Kohler-Maxwell prize 1987). Mem. Deutscher Kunstlerbund. Office: MIT Ctr Advanced Visual Studies 265 Massachusetts Ave Cambridge MA 02139-4312

PIEPER, DAROLD D., lawyer; b. Vallejo, Calif., Dec. 30, 1944; s. Walter A. H. and Vera Mae (Ellis) P.; m. Barbara Gillis, Dec. 20, 1969; 1 child, Christopher Radcliffe. AB, UCLA, 1967; JD, USC, 1970. Bar: Calif. 1971. Ops. rsch. analyst Naval Weapons Ctr., China Lake, Calif., 1966-69; assoc. Richards, Watson & Gershon, L.A., 1970-76, ptnr., 1976—; spl. counsel L.A. County Transp. Commn., 1984-93, L.A. County Met. Transp. Authority, 1993-94; commr. L.A. County Delinquency and Crime Commn., 1983—, pres., 1987—; chmn. L.A. County Delinquency Prevention Planning Coun., 1987-90. Contbr. articles to profl. jours. Peace officer Pasadena (Calif.) Police Res. Unit, 1972-87, dep. comdr., 1979-81, comdr., 1982-84; chmn. pub. safety commn. City of La Canada Flintridge, Calif., 1977-82, commr. 1977-88; bd. dirs. La Canada Flintridge Coordinating Council, 1975-82, pres. 1977-78; exec. dir. Cityhood Action Com., 1975-76; active Calif. Rep. Party, Appellate Circle of Legion Lex U. So. Calif.; chmn. Youth Opportunities United, Inc., 1990—, vice-chmn. 1988-89, bd. dirs. 1988—; mem. L.A. County Justice Systems Adv. Group, 1987-92; trustee Lanterman Hist. Mus. Found., 1989-94, Calif. City Mgmt. Found., 1992—. Recipient commendation for Community Service, L.A. County Bd. Suprs., 1978. Mem. La Canada Flintridge C. of C. and Cmty. Assn. (pres. 1981, bd. dirs. 1976-83), Navy League U.S., Pacific Legal Found., Peace Officers Assn., L.A. County, UCLA Alumni Assn. (life), U. So. Calif. Alumni Assn. (life), L.A. County Bar Assn., Calif. Bar Assn., ABA, U. So. Calif. Law Alumni Assn. Office: Richards Watson & Gershon 333 S Hope St 38th Fl Los Angeles CA 90071

PIEPER, HEINZ PAUL, physiology educator; b. Wuppertal, Germany, Mar. 24, 1920; came to U.S., 1957, naturalized, 1963; s. Heinrich Ludwig and Agnes Marie (Koehler) P.; m. Rose Irmgard Hackl, Apr. 23, 1945. M.D., U. Munich, Germany, 1948. Resident 2d Med. Clinic, U. Munich, 1948-50, asst. prof. dept. physiology, 1950-57; asst. prof. dept. physiology Coll. Medicine, Ohio State U., Columbus, 1957-60; assoc. prof. Coll. Medicine, Ohio State U., 1960-68, prof., 1968—, chmn. dept. physiology, 1974-85, prof. emeritus, 1985—; established investigator Am. Heart Assn., 1962-67. Mem. editorial bd.: Am. Jour. Physiology, 1973-82; contbr. articles on cardiovascular physiology to profl. jours. Mem. Am. Physiol. Soc., German Physiol. Soc., Ohio Acad. Scis., Biophys. Soc., Sigma Xi. Home: 2206 SE 36th St Cape Coral FL 33904-4434 Office: Ohio State U Coll Medicine 333 W 10th Ave Columbus OH 43210

PIEPER, PATRICIA RITA, artist, photographer; b. Paterson, N.J., Jan. 28, 1923; d. Francis William and Barbara Margareth (Ludwig) Farabaugh. Student, Baron von Palm, 1937-39, Deal (N.J.) Conservatory, 1939, 40, Utah State U., 1950-52; m. George F. Pieper, July 1, 1941 (dec. May 3, 1981); 1 child, Patricia Lynn; m. Russell W. Watson, Dec., 9, 1989. One-woman shows include Charles Russell Mus., Great Falls, Mont., 1955, Fisher Gallery, Washington, 1966, Tampa City Libr., 1977-81, 83, 84, Ctr. Pl. Art Ctr., Brandon, Fla., 1985; exhibited in group shows Davidson Art Gallery, Middletown, Conn., 1968, Helena (Mont.) Hist. Mus., 1955, Dept. Commerce Alaska Statehood Show, 1959, Joslyn Mus., Omaha, 1961, Denver Mus. Natural History, 1955, St. Joseph's Hosp. Gallery, 1980, 82, 84-86; represented in pvt. collections. Pres. Bell Lake Assn., 1976-78, 79. Winner photog. competition Gen. Tel. Co. of Fla., 1979; recipient Outstanding Svc. award Bell Lake Assn., 1987, Meml. award Land O' Lake Bd. of Realtors, 1989, Appreciation award Southwest Fla. Water Mgmt. Dist., 1993; photography winner in top 100 out of 8,000 Nat. Wildlife Fedn. competition, 1986; 1st place photography MacDill AFB, 1991. Mem. Pasco County (Fla.) Water Adv. Coun., 1978—, chmn., 1979-82, 83-84, 86-88, 92—; gov.'s appointee to S.W. Fla. Water Mgmt. Dist., Hillsborough River Basin Bd., 1981-82, 84-87, sec., 1988-91, vice chmn. 1992; active Save Our Rivers program, 1982-84, 85-86, 92—; ad hoc chmn., 1991-92; mem. adv. bd. Fla. Suncoast Expwy., 1988-90; pres. Bell Lake Assn., 1986, 87; mem. adv. bd. Tampa YMCA, 1979-80. Mem. Nat. League Am. Pen Women (v.p. Tampa 1976-78, Woman of Yr. award 1977-78), Tampa Art Mus., Ret. Officer's Wives Assn., Land O' Lakes C. of C. (bd. dir. 1981-82, Outstanding Svc. award 1980), Fla. Geneal. Soc., West State Archaeol. Soc. (distaff mem.), Ret. Officer's Assn., MacDill AFB, 1982—, Lutz Club, Land O' Lakes Women's Club, Moose. Home and Studio: 3304 E Derry Dr Sebastian FL 32958-8577

PIEPER, WYLIE BERNARD, diversified company executive; b. Beeville, Tex., 1932; married. BA, Rice U., 1953, BSCE, 1954. Engring. supr. Brown & Root Inc. (a co. of Halliburton Co.), Houston, 1957-72, v.p., 1972-74, sr. v.p., 1974-77, group v.p., from 1977, pres., CEO, also dir., 1977-92; vice chmn. Halliburton Co., Dallas, 1992—. Office: Halliburton Co 2500 Halliburton Ctr 5151 San Felipe Houston TX 77056

PIEPHO, (EDWARD) LEE, humanities educator; b. Detroit, Jan. 10, 1942; s. Edward Ernest and Dolores Faye (Dowis) P.; m. Susan Brand, June 13, 1964. AB, Kenyon Coll., 1964; MA, Columbia U., 1966; PhD, U. Va., 1972. Instr. Sweet Briar (Va.) Coll., 1969-72, asst. prof., 1972-78, assoc. prof., 1978-83, prof., 1983-94, Shallenberger Brown prof., 1994—, dept. chmn., 1983-86, coord. European civilization program, 1986-89. Translator, editor: Adulescentia: The Eclogues of Mantuan, 1989; contbr. articles to profl. jours. SIMRS fellow, 1979, Dulin fellow Folger Shakespeare Libr., 1989-90. Mem. Internat. Assn. for Neo-Latin Studies, Modern Lang. Assn. Am., Renaissance Soc. Am. Avocations: tennis, scuba diving. Home: Woodland Rd Sweet Briar VA 24595-9999 Office: Sweet Briar Coll Dept English Sweet Briar VA 24595

PIEPHO, ROBERT WALTER, pharmacy educator, researcher; b. Chgo., July 31, 1942; s. Walter August and Irene Elizabeth (Huybrecht) Apfel; m. Mary Lee Wilson, Dec. 10, 1981. BS in Pharmacy, U. Ill.-Chgo., 1965; PhD in Pharmacology, Loyola U., Maywood, Ill., 1972. Registered pharmacist, Ill., Colo. Assoc. prof. U. Nebr. Med. Ctr., Omaha, 1970-78; prof. pharmacy, assoc. dean Sch. Pharmacy U. Colo., Denver, 1978-86; prof. pharmacol., dean U. Mo. Sch. Pharmacy, Kansas City, 1987—. Contbr. articles to profl. jours., chpts. to books. Pres. Club Monaco Homeowners Assn., Denver, 1980-82. Named Outstanding Tchr. U. Nebr. Coll. Pharmacy, 1975; recipient Arthur Hassan Colo. Pharmacal Assn., 1983, Excellence in Teaching U. Colo. Med. Sch., 1983. Fellow Am. Coll. Clin. Pharmacology (regent 1983-88, 91-96), Am. Coll. Apothecaries; mem. Am. Soc. Hosp. Pharmacists, Am. Soc. Pharmacology and Exptl. Therapeutics, Rho Chi. Roman Catholic. Office: U Mo Sch Pharmacy 5005 Rockhill Rd Kansas City MO 64110-2239

PIERAS, JAIME, JR., federal judge; b. San Juan, P.R., May 19, 1924; s. Jaime Pieras and Ines Lopez-Cepero; m. Elsie Castaner, June 6, 1953; 1 child, Jaime Pieras Castaner. AB in Econs., Catholic U. Am., 1945; JD, Georgetown U., 1948. Bar: P.R. Pvt. practice San Juan, 1949-82; judge U.S. Dist. Ct. for P.R., San Juan, 1982—; mem. Com. on the Bicentennial of the Constitution, Judicial Conf. U.S.; mem. Puerto Rico Commn. on the Bicentennial of the U.S. Constituion. Contbr. article to Cath. U. Law Rev., 1986. Chmn. fin. Statehood Republican Party, San Juan, 1963-64; Rep. nat. committeeman for P.R., San Juan 1967-80. 2nd Lt. U.S. Army (Mediterranean) 1946-47, MTO; Res., 1949. Mem. ABA (exec. bd., Nat. Conf. Fed. Trial Judges), P.R. Bar Assn., D.C. Bar Assn. Lodge: Rotary. Office: US Dist Ct CH-111 Fed Bldg 150 Carlos Chardon Ave Hato Rey San Juan PR 00918-1761

PIERCE, ALLAN DALE, engineering educator, researcher; b. Clarinda, Iowa, Dec. 18, 1936; s. Franklin Dale and Ruth Pauline (Wright) P.; m. Penelope Claffey, Oct. 27, 1961; children: Jennifer Irene, Bradford Loren. BS, N.Mex. Coll. Agrl. and Mechanic Arts, 1957; PhD, MIT, 1962. Registered profl. engr.: Mass. Staff researcher Rand Corp., Santa Monica, Calif., 1961-63; sr. staff scientist Avco Corp., Wilmington, Mass., 1963-66; asst. prof. MIT, Cambridge, 1966-68, assoc. prof., 1968-73; prof. mech. engring. Ga. Inst. Tech., Atlanta, 1973-76, Regent's prof., 1976-88; Leonhard chair in engring. Pa. State U., University Park, 1988-93; chmn. dept

aerospace and mech. engring. Boston U., 1993—; vis. prof. Max Planck Inst., Goettingen, Fed. Republic Germany, 1976-77; cons. in field. Author: Acoustics: An Introduction to Its Physical Principles and Applications, 1981; editor phys. acoustics monograph series, 1988—; editor Jour. Computation Acoustics, 1992—; contbr. articles on acoustics, wave propagation, vibrations, solid and fluid mechanics to profl. jours. NSF fellow, 1957-60, Shell oil fellow, 1960-61, U.S Dept. Transp. faculty fellow, 1979-80; recipient Sr. U.S. Scientist award Alexander von Humboldt Found., 1976, Cert. of Recognition Nat. Aeronautics and Space Adminstrn., 1984. Fellow Acoustical Soc. Am. (Silver medal 1991), ASME (Raleigh Lectr. 1992); mem. IEEE, AIAA. Home: PO Box 339 East Sandwich MA 02537 Office: Boston U Dept Aerospace & Mech Engring 110 Cummington St Boston MA 02215-2407

PIERCE, ANNE-MARIE B., school system administrator; b. Grenoble, Isere, France, Sept. 9, 1943; came to U.S., 1961; d. Joseph and Andreé Georgette (Haguenauer) Bernheim; m. Robert L. Pierce, Mar. 21, 1964; 1 child, Eric. BA, U. Calif., Berkeley, 1965; MA, Hayward State U., 1973. Head fgn. lang. dept. Head-Royce Sch., Oakland, Calif., 1965-75; head fgn. lang. dept. San Francisco U. High Sch., 1975-79, dir. pub. events, 1979-80; headmistress Ecole Bilingue, Berkeley, 1980-89; cons. A.M.P. and Assocs., San Francisco, 1989-91; head Washington Internat. Sch., 1991—. Co-author radio instrn. A Touch of France, 1980—. Named to Cum Laude Soc. Head-Royce Schs., 1982. Mem. Assn. French Schs. in Am. (founder, pres. 1985-86. 87-88), Calif. Assn. Ind. Schs. (exec. bd. dirs. 1985-88, v.p. 1987-88), Internat. Sch. Assn. (exec. bd. dirs.), Assn. Ind. Schs. Greater Washington (sec.-treas.). Democrat. Avocation: skiing.

PIERCE, CHARLES ELIOT, library director, educator; b. Springfield, Mass., Dec. 25, 1941; s. C. Eliot and Dora Mason (Redway) P.; m. Barbara G. Hanson, Oct. 18, 1969; children: Sheila H., Charles Eliot III. B.A., Harvard U., 1964, M.A.T., 1966, Ph.D., 1970. Prof. English Vassar Coll., Poughkeepsie, N.Y., 1970-87; dir. Pierpont Morgan Library, N.Y.C., 1987—. Author: (literary criticism) The Religious Life of Samuel Johnson, 1983. Mem. Johnsonians, Century Assn., Grolier Club, Walpole Soc., Knickerbocker Club. Episcopalian. Home: Clinton Corners Rd Salt Point NY 12578 Office: Pierpont Morgan Libr 29 E 36th St New York NY 10016-3490

PIERCE, CHARLES R., electric company consultant; b. Bar Harbor, Maine, 1922. AB, Hofstra Coll., 1947; LLB, Columbia U., 1949. Bar: N.Y. 1950, U.S. Ct. Appeals (2nd cir.) 1951. Ret. chmn., chief exec. officer L.I. Lighting Co. Mem. Nassau County Bar Assn., Suffolk County Bar Assn., Nat. Assn. Securities Dealers N.Y. Stock Exch., Am. Arbitration Assn. Bds. of Arbitration. Office: 33 Walt Whitman Rd Huntington Station NY 11746-3627

PIERCE, CHESTER MIDDLEBROOK, psychiatrist, educator; b. Glen Cove, N.Y., Mar. 4, 1927; s. Samuel Riley and Hettie Elenor (Armstrong) P.; m. Jocelyn Patricia Blanchet, June 15, 1949; children: Diane Blanchet, Deirdre Anona. A.B., Harvard U., 1948, M.D., 1952; Sc.D. (hon.), Westfield Coll., 1977, Tufts U., 1984. Instr. psychiatry U. Cin., 1957-60; asst. prof. psychiatry U. Okla., 1960-62, 1965-69; prof. edn. and psychiatry Harvard U., 1969—; pres. Am. Bd. Psychiatry and Neurology, 1977-78; mem. Polar Research Bd.; cons. USAF. Author pubs. on sleep disturbances, media, polar medicine, sports medicine, racism; mem. editorial bds. Advisor Children's TV Workshop; chmn. Child Devel. Assn. Consortium; bd. dirs. Action Children's TV, Physicians for Human Rights. Served with M.C. USNR, 1953-55. Fellow Royal Australian and N.Z. Coll. Psychiatrists (hon.); mem. Inst. Medicine, Black Psychiatrists Am. (chmn.), Am. Orthopsychiat. Assn. (pres. 1983-84). Democrat. Home: 17 Prince St Jamaica Plain MA 02130-2725

PIERCE, DANIEL, investment company executive; b. Boston, Mar. 18, 1934; s. Roger and Ruth (Eliot) P.; m. May Parker Harding, June 20, 1955; children: Sara, Daniel Jr., Matthew V., Samuel. BA, Harvard U., 1956. Assoc. Scudder, Stevens & Clark, Boston, 1956-70, v.p. investments, 1970-77, sr. v.p., 1977-85, gen. ptnr., 1970-85, mng. dir., 1985—, chmn. bd. dirs., 1991—; pres., trustee Scudder Devel. Fund, N.Y.C., 1986—; v.p., trustee Scudder Cash Investment Trust, Boston, 1975-83, Scudder Managed Mcpl. Bonds, Boston, 1976—; v.p., bd. dirs. Scudder Investor Svcs., Boston, 1979—; v.p. Scudder Govt. Money Fund, Boston, 1980—; pres., bd. dirs. Scudder Income Fund, Inc., Boston, 1980—, Scudder Growth and Income Fund, Inc., Boston, 1980—, Scudder GNMA Fund, Boston, 1985—; pres. dir. Scudder Short Term Bond Fund; dir. Brazil Fund, 1991—, First Iberian Fund, 1992—; chmn. bd. dirs. Scudder New Europe Fund, 1991—; dir. Scudder New Asia Fund, 1991—, Scudder Global Fund, 1993—; bd. dirs. Fiduciary Trust Co., Boston, Fiduciary Co., Inc., Boston, Scudder Variable Life Investment Fund, trustee Scudder Internat. Fund, 1986—; pres., dir. Scudder Gold Fund, 1988—. Trustee The Trustees Reservations, 1992—; Milton Acad., 1974-75, New Eng. Aquarium, 1976—, bd. govs., 1978-83, 90—; trustee Dedham Country Day Sch., 1965-72, treas., 1966-69, pres., 1969-72; bd. overseers Brigham & Women's Hosp., 1969—; overseer W.G.B.H., 1994—; bd. mgrs., v.p. Hale Reservation Incorporator; chmn. Harvard U. 25th Reunion, 1980-81; bd. dirs. Am. Meml. Hosp., Reims, France, 1985—. Mem. Investment Counsel Assn. Am. (chartered), Harvard U. Alumni Assn. (bd. dirs. 1984-86), Somerset Club (Boston), The Country Club (Brookline, Mass.), The Harbor Club (Seal Harbor, Maine), The Links (N.Y.). Unitarian. Office: Scudder Stevens & Clark 2 International Pl Boston MA 02110-2210

PIERCE, DANIEL MARSHALL, lawyer, mayor; b. Chgo., Mar. 31, 1928; s. Hyman A. and Thelma (Udwin) P.; m. Rhoda Pierce; children: Andrew, Theodore, Anthony, Eric, Peter. AB, Harvard U., 1949, JD, 1952. Bar: Ill. 1952. Since practiced in Chgo.; partner firm Altheimer & Gray, 1966—; mem. Ill. Ho. of Reps. from 32d Dist., 1965-85, chmn. environ. com., 1975-77, chmn. revenue com., 1977-85; mem. Ill. Reapportionment Commn., 1963, Ill. Dem. Central Com., 1962-66, 70-82, 90—; chmn. Ill. Energy Resources Commn., 1979-82, Ill. Econ. and Fiscal Commn. 1980-83; v.p. Ill. Mcpl. League, 1988-95. Bd. dirs. Cove Sch., Evanston, Ill., 1975-83; trustee Highland Park Hosp. 1985—; mayor City of Highland Park, Ill., 1987-95. Served to 1st. lt. USAF, 1952-54. Mem. Am., Ill., Chgo. bar assns. Club: Harvard (Chgo.), Standard (Chgo.); Northmoor Country. Home: 675 Wake Robin Ln Highland Park IL 60035-5020 Office: Altheimer & Gray Ste 4000 10 S Wacker Dr Chicago IL 60606-7407

PIERCE, DANIEL THORNTON, physicist; b. L.A., July 16, 1940; s. Daniel Gordon Pierce and Celia Francis Thornton Thayer; m. Barbara Harrison, Nov. 19, 1988; children: Jed, Maia, Stephen. BS, Stanford U., 1962, PhD in Applied Physics, 1970; MA, Wesleyan U., Middletown, Conn., 1966. NSF rsch. asst. materials sci. dept. Stanford U., 1961; lectr in physics U.S. Peace Corps, Kathmandu, Nepal, 1962-64; rsch. asst. Wesleyan U., 1964-66; rsch. asst. Stanford Electronics Labs., 1966-70, rsch. assoc., 1970-71; rsch. staff Solid State Physics Lab., Swiss Fed. Inst. Tech., 1971-75; physicist Nat. Inst. Standards and Tech. (formerly Nat. Bur Standards), Gaithersburg, Md., 1975—. Contbr. chpts. to books, more than 150 articles to profl. jours. Trustee Unitarian Ch. of Rockville, Md., 1994—. Recipient IR-100 award R&D Mag., 1980, 85, Gold medal Dept. Commerce, 1987, William P. Schlichter award Nat. Inst. Standards and Tech., 1992. Fellow Am. Phys. Soc., Am. Vacuum Soc. (chair surface sci. exec. com. 1984-88, Gaede-Langmuir prize 1994). Achievements include patents for source of spin polarized electrons, absorbed current spin polarization detector; development of scanning electron microscopy with polarization analysis. Office: Nat Inst Standards and Tech Bldg 220 Rm B206 Gaithersburg MD 20899

PIERCE, DANNY PARCEL, artist, educator; b. Woodlake, Calif., Sept. 10, 1920; s. Frank Lester and Letitia Frances (Parcel) P.; m. Julia Ann Rasmussen, July 19, 1943; children: Julia Ann, Mary L., Danny L., Duane Nels. Student, Art Ctr. Sch., L.A., 1939, Chouinards Art Inst., L.A., 1940-41, 46-47, Am. Art Sch., N.Y.C., 1947-48, Bklyn. Mus. Art Sch., 1950-53; BFA, U. Alaska, 1963. Instr. Hunter Coll., N.Y.C., 1952-53, Burnley Sch. Art, Seattle, 1954-58, Seattle U., 1956-59; publ. Red Door Studio Press, Kent, Wash., 1959—; artist-in-res. U. Alaska, College, 1959-63; asst. prof. U. Wisc., Milw., 1964; head art dept. Cornish Sch. Allied Arts, Seattle, 1964-65; prof. art U. Wisc., Milw., 1965-84, prof. emeritus, 1984—. One person exhibition shows include Contemporaries Gallery, N.Y.C., 1953, Handforth Gallery, Tacoma, Washington, 1958, U. Alaska, College, 1959, 63, 73, 74,

Gonzaga U., Bradley Galleries, Milw., 1966, 68, 70, 72, 74, 76, 78-80, 82; represented in permanent collections Bibliothèque Nationale, Paris, Mus. Modern Art, N.Y.C., Libr. Congress, Washington, Smithsonian Instn. Washington, Seattle Art Mus., U. Washington Henry Art Gallery, Bklyn. Mus., Princeton U., U. Alaska, U. So. Calif., William and Mary Coll., Oostduinkerke (Belgium) Nat. Fishing Mus., Nat. Mus. Sweden, Stockholm, Johnson Wax Found., Racine, Wisc., Gen. Mills Collection Art, Mpls., Huntington Libr., San Marino, Calif., various pvt. collections. Recipient Best Oil Landscape Conn. Acad. Fine Arts, Hartford, 1st Prize oil Kohler Gallery, Seattle, 1974, others; chosen one of twelve artists to represent State Washington Expo 70, Osaka, Japan, rep. U.S. Internat. Sao Paulo Biannual Art Exhibition. Mem. Artist Equity Assn. (charter, pres. Seattle chpt. 1958), Am. Colorprint Soc., Internat. Arts and Letters (life). Office: Red Door Studio 330 Summit Ave N Kent WA 98031-4714

PIERCE, DAVID HYDE, actor; b. Albany, N.Y., Apr. 3, 1959. BA, Yale U., 1981. Appeared in plays Beyond Therapy, 1982, Holiday, 1982, Summer, 1983, That's It, Folks! 1983, Candida, 1984, The Seagull, 1984, The Grand Hysteric, 1984, The Three Zeks, 1984, Tartuffe, 1984, Donuts, 1985, Hamlet, 1986, The Author's Voice, 1987, The Maderati, 1987, Camille, 1987, The Cherry Orchard, 1988, Zero Positive, 1988, Much Ado About Nothing, 1988, The Heidi Chronicles, 1989, Elliot Loves, 1990, It's Only a Play, 1991; films include The Terminator, 1984, Moving Violations, 1985, Bright Lights, Big City, 1988, Crossing Delancey, 1988, Rocket Gibraltar, 1988, The Fisher King, 1991, Little Man Tate, 1991, Sleepless in Seattle, 1993, Wolf, 1994; TV series include The Powers That Be, 1993, Fraiser, 1993—.

PIERCE, DAVID R., educational administrator. AA in Math., Fullerton Coll., 1958; BA in Math., Long Beach State U., 1960, MA in Edn., 1961; MS in Math., Purdue U., 1965, PhD in Math. Edn., 1969. Math. instr. Orange Coast Coll., Costa Mesa, Calif., 1962-65; supr. math. student teaching Purdue U., Lafayette, Ind., 1965-66; chmn. natural scis. & math. divsn. Golden West Coll., Huntington Beach, Calif., 1966-67; dean instrn. Waubonsee C.C., Sugar Grove, Ill., 1967-70; supt., pres. North Iowa Area C.C., Mason City, 1970-80; exec. dir. Ill. C.C. Bd., Springfield, 1980-90; chancellor Va. C. C. Sys., Richmond, 1990-91; pres., chief exec. officer Am. Assn. C.C., Washington, 1991—; also joint Am. Assn. C.C./ACCT Comm. Fed. Rels. mem., 1984-86, 88-91; also bd. mem. Am. Assn. C.C., 1988-91, vice-chmn., 1990-91, chmn. task force on allied health, 1989-91, chmn. com. on fed. rels., 1990-91; mem. Nat. Coun. State Dirs. Cmty. and Jr. Colls., 1981-91 (chmn. 1984-85). Ill. Employment & Edn. Subcabinet, 1980-90; cons., evaluator North Ctrl. Assn. Commn. Insts. Higher Edn. (commr.-at-large 1977-83). mem. Ill. Econ. Devel. Subcabinet, 1980-90. Named Person of Yr. Nat. Coun. Cmty. Svcs. & Continuing Edn. Region 5, 1982, Nat. Person of Yr. Nat. Coun. Cmty. Svcs. & Continuing Edn., 1990; recipient Meritorious Svc. award Ill. C.C. Trustee Assn., 1988, Outstanding Ill. Citizen award Coll. Lake County, 1989, Outstanding Alumnus award Calif. C.C. League, 1991, Outstanding Alumnus award League for Innovation in the C.C., 1993. Mem. Nat. Policy Bd. Higher Edn. Instl. Accreditation, Washington Higher Edn. Secretariat, Nat. Alliance of Bus. Coun. on Workforce Excellence. Office: Am Assn of Community & Jr Colls 1 Dupont Cir NW Ste 410 Washington DC 20036-1110*

PIERCE, EDWARD FRANKLIN, college president; b. Cambridge, Mass., July 15, 1927; s. John and Kathleen (McCue) P.; m. Sandra Lea, June 8, 1958; children—Valerie, Marc, Adrienne. B.S., Boston Coll., 1949, M.A., 1950; Ph.D., Columbia U., 1959, Ed.D., 1959. Research chemist AEC, 1950-51; mem. faculty Skagit Valley Coll., Mt. Vernon, Wash., 1954; instr. chemistry SUNY, Geneseo, 1959-66; chmn. dept. SUNY, Chgo., dean, 1964; dean U. N.H. System, Keene, 1966-72; pres. Quincy (Mass.) Sr. Coll., 1972-82, Mt. Aloysius Coll., 1982—; mem. New Eng. Dist. Scholarship Com.; cons. in field, seminar lectr. Author: Selected Quantitative Studies in Physical Science, 1962, Modern Chemistry, 1960, Historical Perspectives in the Physical Sciences, 1964, also articles. Chmn. United Fund, 1968; dist. com. Boy Scouts Am., 1951-54, Council for Children, Quincy, 1972-82; pres., treas. South Shore Day Care Services, 1972-76. Served to ensign USNR, 1944-46. Fellow Am. Inst. Chemists; mem. AAAS, N.Y. Acad. Sci. Club: Quincy Kiwanis (past pres.). Lodge: Rotary (Altoona, Pa.). Home: 79 Circle Dr Hollidaysburg PA 16648 Office: Mt Aloysius Sr Coll Office of Pres Cresson PA 02169

PIERCE, FRANCIS CASIMIR, civil engineer; b. Warren, R.I., May 19, 1924; s. Frank J. and Eva (Soltys) Pierce; student U. Conn., 1943-44; B.S., U. R.I., 1948; M.S., Harvard U., 1950; postgrad. Northeastern U., 1951-52; m. Helen Lynette Steinouer, Apr. 24, 1954; children—Paul F., Kenneth J., Nancy L., Karen H., Charles E. Instr. civil engring. U. R.I., Kingston, 1948-49, U. Conn., Storrs, 1950-51; design engr. Praeger-Maguire & Ole Singstad, Boston, 1951-52; chief found. engr. C.A. Maguire & Assocs., Providence, 1952-59, assoc., 1959-69, v.p., 1969-72; sr. v.p. C.E. Maguire, Inc., 1972-76, officer-in-charge Honolulu office, 1976-78, exec. v.p., corp. dir. ops., 1975-87; dir. The Maguire Group, Inc., 1979—; gen. mgr. East Atlantic Casualty Co., Ltd., 1987-88; also dir.; pres. Magma, Inc., tech. ops. service co., 1986-88; lectr. found. engring. U.R.I., 1968-69, trustee, 1987—; mem. Coll. Engring. adv. council, 1986—, U.S. com. Internat. Commn. on Large Dams. Vice chmn. Planning Bd. East Providence, R.I., 1960-73; bd. dirs. R.I. Civic Chorale and Orch., 1986-90. Served with AUS, 1942-46. Recipient Chester H. Kirk Disting. Engr. award U. R.I. Coll. Engring., 1987. Mem. ASCE (chpt. past pres., dir.), R.I. Soc. Profl. Engrs. (nat. dir., engr. of year award 1973), Am. Soc. Engring. Edn., Soc. Am. Mil. Engrs., ASTM, Soc. Marine Engrs. and Naval Architects, Am. Soc. Planning Ofcls., Harvard Soc. Engrs., Scientists, Providence Engrs. Soc., R.I. Soc. Planning Agys. (past pres.). Contbr. articles to profl. jours. Recipient USCG Meritorious Pub. Service award, 1987. Home: 3830 St Girons Dr Punta Gorda FL 33950-7870 Office: 225 Foxborough Blvd Foxboro MA 02035

PIERCE, FREDERICK SMYTHE, envelope company executive; b. Buffalo, Aug. 19, 1918; s. Frederick Gaylord and Emily Victoria (Smythe) P.; m. Phyllis Eleanor Wendt; children; Phyllis Wendt, Frederick G. II. BS, Yale U., 1940. Trainee Niagara Envelope Co., Buffalo, 1946-48, asst. sec., 1948-52, v.p., 1952-56, pres., 1952-87, chmn., chief exec. officer, 1987—; bd. dirs. Marine Midland Band-Weston, Buffalo, Buffalo Forge Co. Dir. Med. Found. Buffalo, 1973—, U. Buffalo Found., 1976—; Capt. O.S.S., U.S. Army, 1941-45. Mem. Buffalo & Erie County Hist. Soc. (bd. mgrs. 1974—), Links Club, Buffalo Club. Presbyterian. Home: 150 Chapin Pky Buffalo NY 14209-1104 Office: Niagara Envelope Group 693 Seneca St Buffalo NY 14210-1395

PIERCE, GEORGE ADAMS, university administrator, educator; b. Carlsbad, N.Mex., May 21, 1943; s. Jack Colwell and Shirley (Adams) P.; m. Margaret Mary Brakel, Feb. 10, 1980; children: Christopher, Catherine Rose. BA in Polit. Sci., Fairleigh Dickinson U., 1969; MA in Polit. Sci., New Sch. Social Rsch., 1971; PhD in Higher Edn., Claremont Grad. Sch., 1976. Asst. dir. promotion Afco, N.Y.C., 1969-71; dir. spl. programs U. Calif., Riverside, 1971-73; asst. to pres. Claremont (Calif.) Grad. Sch., 1973-75; asst. to pres. Seattle U., 1975-78, dir. planning, 1978-83, v.p. administrn., 1983-87, v.p. planning, 1987-89; v.p. bus. and fin. affairs Western Wash. U., Bellingham, 1989—; chmn. regional rev. panel Truman Scholarship Found., 1977-90. Chmn. Seattle Ctr. Adv. Commn., 1977-83; bd. dirs. N.W. Kidney Found., Seattle, 1986—, YMCA, Bellingham, 1990—; chmn. pack 41 Boy Scouts Am., Bellingham, 1992-94. With USAF, 1963-65. Recipient Cert. Merit Riverside County Comprehensive Health Planning, 1972, Cert. Appreciation Office Mayor City of Seattle, 1983, Nat. Truman Scholarship Found., 1986. Mem. Am. Assn. Higher Edn., Assn. Instnl. Rsch. (regional pres. 1977), Nat. Assn. Coll. and Univ. Bus. Officers (chmn. pers. and benefits com. 1992-94), Rotary. Democrat. Roman Catholic. Avocations: backpacking, canoeing, swimming, tennis. Home: 421 Morey Ave Bellingham WA 98225-6606 Office: Western Wash U Old Main 300 Bellingham WA 98225

PIERCE, GEORGE FOSTER, JR., architect; b. Dallas, June 22, 1919; s. George Foster and Hallie Louise (Crutchfield) P.; m. Betty Jean Reistle, Oct. 17, 1942; children: Ann Louise Pierce Arnett, George Foster III, Nancy Reistle Pierce Brumback. Student, So. Meth. U., 1937-39; BA, Rice U., 1942, BS in Architecture, 1943; diplome d'architecture, Ecole des Beaux-

Arts, Fontainebleau, 1958. Pvt. practice architecture, 1946—; founding ptnr. Pierce, Goodwin, Alexander & Linville (architects, engrs. and planners), 1947-86, of counsel, 1987—; design cons. Dept. Army, 1966-70; instr. archtl. design Rice U., 1945, preceptor dept. architecture, 1962-67; past trustee, mem. exec. com. Rice Ctr. for Community Design and Rsch.; bd. dirs. Billboards Ltd. Prin. works include projects 8 bldgs., Rice U. Campus, Exxon Brook Hollow Bldg. Complex, Houston Mus. Natural Sci. and Planetarium, Michael Debakey Center Biomed. Edn. and Research, Baylor Coll. Medicine; 4 terminal bldgs., master plan Houston Intercontinental Airport; S.W. Bell Telephone Co. office bldg.; U. Tex. Med. Sch. Hosp., Galveston, U. Houston Conrad Hilton Sch. Hotel & Club Mgmt., U. Houston Univ. Center; 40 story office bldg. for Tex. Eastern Transmission Corp.; outpatient facility U. Tex. M.D. Anderson Cancer Hosp.; 44 story Marathon Oil Tower, others; contbr. articles to profl. jours. Mem. exec. adv. bd. Sam Houston Area Coun. Boy Scouts Am.; past mem. grad. coun. Rice U.; adv. coun. Rice Sch. Architecture, chmn. Houston Mcpl. Sign Control Bd.; past chmn. bd. trustee Contemporary Arts Mus., Houston; past trustee Houston Mus. Natural Sci.; trustee emeritus, past pres. Tex. Archtl. Found. With USNR, WWII. Recipient numerous nat., state, local archtl. awards for design, Silver Beaver award Boy Scouts Am.; named one of five Outstanding Young Texans Tex. Jr. C. of C., 1954; named Disting. R Man Rice U., 1992. Fellow AIAA (past nat. chmn. com. on aesthetics, student affairs and chpt. affairs, Golden Award Houston chpt. 1991), La Sociedad de Architectos Mexicanos (hon.); mem. Tex. Soc. Architects (past pres., L.W. Pitts award 1985), Houston C. of C. (past chmn. future studies), Rice U. Pres.'s Club (founding chmn. 1970-72), Rice U. Assocs., SAR, Tex. Golf Assn. (bd. dirs.), Kappa Alpha. Methodist. Home: 5555 Del Monte Dr Apt 1103 Houston TX 77056-4118 Office: 5555 San Felipe St Ste 1000 Houston TX 77056-2726 *I am pleased to have chosen architecture as my profession, whereby I have been able to influence the quality of life of my community and my country, not only in its physical form through building design and planning, but also toward its cultural, educational and political well being.*

PIERCE, HARVEY R., Insurance company executive. Pres. Am. Family Ins. Group, Madison, Wis. Office: Am Family Ins Group 6000 American Pky Madison WI 53783-0001

PIERCE, HILDA (HILDA HERTA HARMEL), painter; b. Vienna, Austria; came to U.S., 1940; 1 child, Diana Rubin Daly. Student, Art Inst. of Chgo.; studied with Oskar Kokoschka, Salzburg, Austria. Art tchr. Highland Park (Ill.) Art Ctr., Sandburg Village Art Workshop, Chgo., Old Town Art Center, Chgo.; owner, operator Hilda Pierce Art Gallery, Laguna Beach, Calif., 1981-85; guest lectr. major art mus. and Art Tours in France, Switzerland, Austria, Italy; guest lectr. Russian river cruise and major art mus. St. Petersburg and Moscow, 1994. One-woman shows include Fairweather Hardin Gallery, Chgo., Sherman Art Gallery, Chgo., Marshall Field Gallery, Chgo.; exhibited in group shows at Old Orchard Art Festival, Skokie, Ill., Union League Club (awards), North Shore Art League (awards), ARS Gallery of Art Inst. of Chgo.; represented in numerous private and corporate collections; commissioned for all art work including monoprints, oils, and murals for Carnival Cruise Lines megaliner M.S. Fantasy, 1990, 17 murals for megaliner M.S. Imagination, 1995, 49 paintings for megaliner M.S. Imagination, 1995; contbr. articles to Chgo. Tribune Mag., American Artist Mag., Southwest Art Mag., SRA publs., others. Recipient Outstanding Achievement award in Field of Art for Citizen Foreign Birth Chgo. Immigrant's Svc. League. Mem. Arts Club of Chgo. Studio: PO Box 7390 Laguna Niguel CA 92607-7390

PIERCE, ILONA LAMBSON, educational administrator; b. Blackfoot, Idaho, Dec. 3, 1941; d. Merlin A. Wright and Loa (Adams) Lambson; m. Sherman D. Pierce, Mar. 19, 1960. IBM cert., LDS Bus. Coll., Salt Lake City, 1960; BS, U. Utah, 1969, MEd, 1974, EdD, 1978. Cert. elem. tchr., administrv. endorsement, Utah; lic. real estate agt., Utah. Key punch operator Mountain Bell Telephone Co., Salt Lake City, 1960-61; key punch supr. Hercules Powder Co., Bacchus, Utah, 1961-66; tchr. Cottonwood Heights Elem. Sch., Jordan Sch. Dist., Sandy, 1969-74; tchr. Willow Canyon Elem. Sch., Jordan Sch. Dist., Sandy, Utah, 1974-76; postdoctoral fellow, grad. rsch. asst. U. Utah, Salt Lake City, 1976-78; tchr. Silver Mesa Elem. Sch. Jordan Sch. Dist., Sandy, Utah, 1978-79, tchr. specialist, 1979-80, asst. prin. Mt. Jordan Mid. Sch., 1980-84, prin. Union Mid. Sch., 1984-86, dir. instrnl. media and bilingual edn., 1986—; Mem. Utah Network Ednl. TV, 1986—; chmn. tech. adv. bd., chmn. bd. dirs. Math. Engring. Sci. Achievement, 1989, bd. dirs., 1987—; trustee. State Film Depository Consortium, 1986—; mem. Utah Info. Tech. Consortium, 1987—; mem. prin. mentor program Brigham Young U., 1986. Sch. dist. co-chmn. United Way, 1986—. Recipient recognition award Math Engring. Sci. Achievement, 1991, Valuable Svc. award Emergency Preparedness Action Com., 1988, Disting. Svc. award Utah Ednl. Libr. Media Assn., 1988. Mem. ASCD, Utah ASCD (bd. dirs., editor 1986-89), NEA (life), Utah Edn. Assn., Jžrdan Edn. Assn., Alpha Delta Kappa (state treas. 1980-84, state pres. 1984-86), Delta Kappa Gamma. Avocations: fossil hunting, travel, reading. Home: 8895 S 540 E Sandy UT 84070-1728 Office: Jordan Sch Dist 9361 S 300th E Sandy UT 84070

PIERCE, JACK, Olympic athlete, track and field. Olympic track and field participant Barcelona, Spain, 1992. Recipient 110m Hurdles Bronze medal Olympics, Barcelona, 1992. Office: US Olympic Com 1750 E Boulder St Colorado Springs CO 80909-5724*

PIERCE, JAMES CLARENCE, surgeon; b. Huron, S.D., Aug. 5, 1929; s. Henry Montraville and Carrie Bernice (Matson) P.; m. Carol Sue Wilson, 1967; children: Henry MacDonald, Richard Matson, Elizabeth Gail. B.A., Carleton Coll., 1951; M.D., Harvard U., 1955; M.S., U. Minn., 1963, Ph.D. in Surgery, 1966. Diplomate: Am. Bd. Surgery. Surg. intern Peter Bent Brigham Hosp., Boston, 1955-56; surg. fellow U. Minn., 1959-66; instr. surgery Med. Coll. Va., Richmond, 1966; prof. surgery and microbiology Med. Coll. Va., 1972-75; dir. Tissue Typing Lab., 1969-75; attending surgeon, dir. surg. research, dir. transplantation service St. Luke's Hosp. Center, N.Y.C., 1975-78; prof. surgery Columbia U., 1976, Ailsa Mellon Bruce prof. surgery, 1977-78; clin. prof. surgery Pa. State U. and, 1979-88; chmn. dept. surgery Geisinger Med. Center, Danville, Pa., 1979-90, chmn. emeritus, 1990—; clin. prof. surgery Jefferson U., 1990-93. Contbr. articles to profl. jours. Elder Presbyn. Ch. With M.C., USAF, 1957-59. NIH fellow, 1963-65; Royal Soc. Medicine Found. travelling fellow, 1971; James IV Assn. Surg. traveller, 1978. Mem. ACS (pres. Ctrl. Pa. chpt. 1981-82), Am. Assn. Pathologists, Transplant Soc., Am. Soc. Transplant Surgeons, Ea. Surg. Assn., N.Y. Cin. Soc., Soc. Univ. Surgeons, Sigma Chi. Republican. Home: 1906 Red Ln Danville PA 17821-8415

PIERCE, JAMES LEE, engineering and information systems company executive; b. Grove City, Pa., Nov. 22, 1936; s. Orrie C. and Ella M. (Williams) P.; m. Ellen Jane Crockett, June 5, 1958; children: David C., Laurie Pierce-Lyons. BS, U.S. Naval Acad., Annapolis, Md., 1958; MBA, U. Pa., 1982. Commd. 2d lt. USAF, 1958; pilot, ops. officer to capt., 1958-65, resigned, 1965; program contr. Hughes Aircraft, El Segundo, Calif., 1965-67; mktg. rep. IBM, Phila., 1967-70; pres. Columb Industries, West Chester, Pa., 1970-76; program mgr. GE, Valley Forge, Pa., 1976-87; v.p. Titan Electronics, Vienna, Va., 1987-88; pres., chief oper. officer ARINC Rsch Corp., Annapolis, Md., 1988—; also bd. dirs, 1993—; now pres., ceo. Bd. dirs. Profl. Svc. Coun., Vienna, 1990—, Def. Intelligence Coll. Found, Inc.; Washington, 1990—; Air N.G. 1991, Brig. gen. Del. Air N.G., 1990—. Mem. Air Force Assn., Armed Forces Communications and Electronics Assn., N.G. Assn. U.S., Nat. Space Club (bd. dirs. 1959—), Annapolis Yacht Club, Naval Acad. Sailing Assn. Avocation: sailing. Office: ARINC Rsch Corp 2551 Riva Rd Annapolis MD 21401-7465

PIERCE, JAMES ROBERT, magazine executive; b. Stockton, Ill., Apr. 15, 1933; s. Ellsworth B. and Mayme (Smythe) P.; m. Patricia Curran, May 14, 1960; children: Stacy, John Kelly, Shannon. B.A., U. Ill., 1955. Dist. mgr. McGraw Hill Pubs., N.Y.C., 1960-75; computer category mgr. Bus. Week mag., N.Y.C., 1976-79; pub. Aviation Week & Space Tech. mag., N.Y.C., 1979-82; v.p., pub. Bus. Week, 1982, sr. v.p., pub., 1983-84, exec. v.p., pub. 1984; pres., chief exec. officer James R. Pierce, Inc., 1985—; chief oper. officer Lotus Pub. Corp, 1986-88; pub. Investment Vision Mag. Fidelity Pub. Corp., 1988-91; pres., chief oper. officer Hunter Pub., Elk Grove Village, Ill. 1991-94; vice chmn. Adams Trade Press, Inc., 1995—. Served to 1st lt. SAC

USAF, 1956-59. Mem. Bus. and Profl. Advt. Assn., Worthington Country Club, LBS Golf Club. Roman Catholic.

PIERCE, JOEL FARWELL, lawyer; b. Evanston, Ill., Apr. 2, 1946; s. Alan Eugene and Barbara Louise (Wiggins) P.; m. Martha Amy Epstein, Nov. 24, 1977; children: Katharine, Caroline, Meredith, Mariana. AB, Carleton Coll., 1968; JD cum laude, U. Mich., 1975. Bar: Mass. 1975, U.S. Dist. Ct. Mass. 1976, U.S. Ct. Appeals (1st cir.) 1977. Assoc. Morrison, Mahoney & Miller, Boston, 1976-81, ptnr., 1981—; bd. dirs. Greater Boston Legal Svcs.; lectr. seminars various orgns., Boston, 1978—. Author: Product Liability Defense, 1993; contbr. articles to profl. jours. Pres. Beacon Hill Civic Assn., Boston, 1982-84, bd. dirs., 1980—; chmn. Beacon Hill Archtl. Commn., 1992—. Mem. ABA, Mass. Bar Assn., Boston Bar Assn., Am. Trial Lawyers Am., Defense Rsch. Inst., Boston Soc. Architects, Boston Preservation Alliance. Avocations: architecture, tennis, running, skiing, photography. Office: Morrison Mahoney & Miller 250 Summer St Boston MA 02210-1181

PIERCE, JOHN PATRICK, epidemiology educator; b. Melbourne, Australia, May 12, 1948; came to U.S., 1987; s. James and Valda Bernadette (Green) P.; m. Nuri Josefina Benet, Oct. 14, 1981; children: John Ramon, Nuri Teresa. BSc in Physiology, Monash U., Melbourne, 1972; MS in Epidemiology, McMaster U., Hamilton, Ont., Can., 1975; MA in Psychology, Stanford U., 1981, PhD comm. rsch., 1981. Asst. to dean Curtin U., Australia, 1976-79; sr. lectr. Sydney (Australia) U., 1983-85, acting dept. head, 1985-87; chief epidemiology br. Office on Smoking and Health, Ctrs. for Disease Control, Rockville, Md., 1987-89; assoc. prof. head cancer prevention-control U. Calif., San Diego, 1990-94, Sam M. Walton prof. for cancer rsch., 1994—. Contbr. articles on tobacco use and advt. to med. jours. Recipient Calif. Healthnet Wellness award Healthnet-U. Calif., 1993; Nat. Health and Med. Rsch. Australia fellow Stanford U., 1979-82; established investigator, fellow Am. Heart Assn., 1983—. Office: U Calif Cancer Ctr 0901 9500 Gilman Dr La Jolla CA 92093-0901

PIERCE, JOHN ROBINSON, electrical engineer, educator; b. Des Moines, Mar. 27, 1910; s. John Starr and Harriet Anne (Robinson) P.; m. Martha Peacock, Nov. 5, 1938 (div. Mar. 1964); children: John Jeremy, Elizabeth Anne; m. Ellen R. McKown, Apr. 1, 1964 (dec. Sept. 1986); m. Brenda K. Woodard, Oct. 17, 1987. BS, Calif. Inst. Tech., 1933, MS, 1934, PhD, 1936; D Engring., Newark Coll. Engring., 1961; DSc, Northwestern U., 1961, Poly. Inst. Bklyn, 1963, Yale U., 1963, Columbia U., 1965, U. Nev., 1970, UCLA, 1977; D. Engring., Carnegie Inst. Tech., 1964; D. Elec. Engring., U. Bologna, Italy, 1974; LLD, U. Pa., 1974; DSc, U. So. Calif., 1978. With Bell Telephone Labs., Inc., Murray Hill, N.J., 1936-71; mem. tech. staff, dir. electronics research, 1952-55, dir. research, communication principles, 1958-62, exec. dir. research, communications principles and systems div., 1963-65, exec. dir. research, communications scis. div., 1965-71; prof. engring. Calif. Inst. Tech., Pasadena, 1971-80; chief technologist Jet Propulsion Lab., 1979-82; vis. prof. music emeritus Stanford U., Calif., 1983—; past mem. Pres.'s Sci. Adv. Com., Pres.'s Com. of Nat. Medal of Sci. Author: Theory and Design of Electron Beams, rev. edit., 1954, Traveling Wave Tubes, 1950, Electrons, Waves and Messages, 1956, Man's World of Sound, 1958, Symbols, Signals and Noise, 1961, (with A.G. Tressler) The Research State: A History of Science in New Jersey, 1964, The Beginnings of Satellite Communications, 1968, Science, Art and Communication, 1968, Almost All About Waves, 1973; (with E.C. Posner) Introduction to Communication Science and Systems, 1980, Signals: The Telephone and Beyond, 1981, The Science of Musical Sound, 1983, rev. edit., 1992, (with Hiroshi Inose) Information Technology and Civilization, 1984, (with A. Michael Noll) Signals, The Science of Telecommunications, 1990; editor: (with M.V. Mathews) Current Directions in Computer Music Research, 1989; articles on popular sci.; short stories. Recipient Morris Liebmann meml. prize Inst. Radio Engrs., 1947; Stuart Ballantine medal 1960, Man of Yr., Air Force Assn., 1962; Golden Plate award Acad. Achievement, 1962; General Hoyt S. Vandenberg trophy Arnold Air Soc., 1963; Nat. Medal of Sci., 1963; Edison medal AIEE, 1963; Valdemar Poulsen Gold medal, 1963; H.T. Cedergren medal, 1964; Marconi award, 1974; John C. Scott award, 1975; Japan Prize, 1985; Arthur C. Clarke award, 1987; Pioneer award Internat. Telemetering Conf., 1990; Marconi Internat. fellow, 1979. Fellow IEEE (medal of honor 1976), Acoustical Soc. Am., Am. Phys. Soc.; mem. NAS, NAE (Founders award 1977), Am. Acad. Arts and Scis., Royal Acad. Sci. (Sweden), Inst. Electronics, Info. and Communication Engrs. of Japan (hon.), Inst. TV Engrs. Japan (hon.), Acad. Engring. of Japan (fgn. assoc.), Am. Philos. Soc. Home: 4008 El Cerrito Rd Palo Alto CA 94306-3114 Office: Stanford U Ctr for Computer Rsch in Music and Accoustics Stanford CA 94305

PIERCE, KENNETH RAY, veterinary medicine educator; b. Snyder, Tex., May 21, 1934; s. Clois Vernon and Ellen (Goolsby) P.; m. Anne Stasney, Aug. 31, 1956; children: Cynthia Cae, Mindy Rae. D.V.M., Tex. A&M U., 1957, M.S., 1962, Ph.D. (NSF fellow), 1965. Diplomate Am. Coll. Vet. Pathologists (pres. 1984). Instr. vet. anatomy Tex. A. and M. U., College Station, 1957-59; asst. prof. vet. pathology Tex. A and M. U., 1961-65, asso. prof., 1965-69, prof., 1969—, head dept., 1978-89, chief sect. vet. clin. pathology, 1967-75, 94—; comparative pathologist Inst. Comparative Medicine, Tex. A. and M. U.-Baylor Coll. Medicine, Houston, 1976-79; pvt. vet. practice San Angelo (Tex.) Vet. Hosp., 1959-61; adj. profl. dept. vet. medicine and surgery M.D. Anderson Tumor Inst. and Hosp., Houston, 1971-92; program dir continuing edn. C.L. Davis, D.V.M. Found., 1981-88; vis. scientist Nat. Inst. Environ. Health Scis., 1985. Co-editor: Vet. Pathology Jour, 1971-81; contbr. articles to profl. jours. Mem. AVMA, AAAS, Am. Soc. Vet. Clin. Pathologists, Am. Assn. of Avian Pathologists, U.S.-Can. Acad. Pathology, Tex. Vet. Med. Assn., Am. Assn. Vet. Med. Colls., N.Y. Acad. Scis., Sigma Xi, Phi Kappa Phi, Phi Zeta, Gamma Sigma Delta. Presbyterian (deacon, elder). Home: 12777 Hopes Creek Rd College Station TX 77845 Office: Dept Vet Pathobiology Tex A&M U College Station TX 77843

PIERCE, LAWRENCE WARREN, federal judge; b. Phila., Dec. 31, 1924; s. Harold Ernest and Leora (Bellinger) P.; m. Wilma Taylor (dec.); m. Cynthia Straker, July 8, 1979; children: Warren Wood, Michael Lawrence, Mark Taylor. BS, St. Joseph's U., Phila., 1948, DHL, 1967; JD, Fordham U., 1951, LLD, 1982; LLD, Fairfield U., 1972, Hamilton Coll., 1987, St. John's U., 1990. Bar: N.Y. State 1951, U.S. Supreme Ct. 1968. Civil law practice N.Y.C., 1951-61; asst. dist. atty. Kings County, N.Y., 1954-61; dep. police commr. N.Y.C., 1961-63; dir. N.Y. State Div. for Youth, Albany, 1963-66; chmn. N.Y. State Narcotic Addiction Control Commn., 1966-70; vis. prof. criminal justice SUNY, Albany, 1970-71; U.S. dist. judge So. dist. N.Y., 1971-81; judge U.S. Fgn. Intelligence Surveillance Ct., 1979-81; apptd. U.S. cir. judge for 2d Cir., 1981-89, sr. U.S. cir. judge for 2d Cir., 1990-95; apptd. Cambodian Ct. Tng. Project Internat. Human Rights Law Group, 1995—; former mem., bd. fellows Inst. Jud. Adminstrn.; former trustee Practising Law Inst.; former mem. Am. Law Inst. Former mem. bd. mgrs. Lincoln Hall for Boys; past trustee Fordham U., St. Joseph's U., Phila. With AUS, 1943-46, MTO. Mem. ABA (former alt. observer U.S.mission to UN), Nat. Bar Assn., Assn. Bar of City of N.Y. (past mem. com. on 2d century). Roman Catholic. Office: US Ct Appeals US Courthouse Foley Sq New York NY 10007-1501

PIERCE, LESTER LAURIN, retired pilot, aviation consultant; b. Merlin, Oreg., Sept. 26, 1907; s. Frank Arthur and Charlotte (Allen) P.; m. Helen Ramona Thomas, Mar. 22, 1937; children: Adrienne C. Freeman, Nancy E. Johnson. Grad. high sch., 1925. Theatre mgr. Redwood Theatres, Inc., Fortuna and Eureka, Calif., 1927-28; salesman, bookkeeper Thomas Furniture House, Eureka, 1930-39; pilot, mgr. Pierce Bros. Flying Svc., Eureka, 1934-41; aerial photographer Pierce Flying Svc., Eureka, 1934-75; chief flight instr. Govt. Approved Flight Sch., Eureka, 1947-60; aerial seeder, mgr., pres., salesman Pierce Flying Svc., Inc., Eureka, 1946-68; flight examiner FAA, Eureka, 1948-68, aircraft maintenance insp., 1950-68; mapping pilot Stand Aerial Surveys, Newark, 1948. Lt., flight tng., safety officer USNR, 1942, comdr., 1950. Mem. Soc. Aircraft Safety Investigators and Aviation Cons., OX-5 Club, Elks. Home and Office: 3428 Jacoby Creek Rd Bayside CA 95524-9304

PIERCE, MARGARET HUNTER, government official; b. Weedsport, N.Y., June 30, 1910; d. Thomas Murray and Ruby (Sanders) Hunter; m. John R. Pierce, Nov. 4, 1950 (div. May 1959); 1 dau., Barbara Hunter. B.A., Mt. Holyoke Coll., 1932; J.D., N.Y. U., 1939. Bar: N.Y. bar

1941, D.C. bar 1958. Atty. Office Alien Property Custodian, Washington, 1942-43, 45, Office Solicitor, Dept. Labor, 1943-45, NLRB, 1946, 47-48; atty.-adviser U.S. Ct. Claims, 1947-48, 48-59, reporter decisions, 1959-68; commr. U.S. Indian Claims Commn., 1968-78; pvt. practice Washington, 1978—. Mem. D.C. Bar Assn. (ct. claims com. 1958—, mil. law com. 1967), Fed. Bar Assn. (Indian law com. 1955—), ABA (sec. adminstrv. law-vets. com., mil. law com., immigration and nationality com.), Women's Bar Assn., Nat. Assn. Women Lawyers, Exec. Women in Govt., Bus. and Profl. Women (Cosmopolitan br.), Am. Women Composers, Zonta (Washington pres. 1977-78), Harvard Club (D.C.). Home: 3829 Garfield St NW Washington DC 20007-1319

PIERCE, MARTIN E., JR., fire commissioner; b. Boston, Nov. 13, 1940. Student, Boston Coll., 1958-60; cert. fire sci. program, Mass. Bay C.C., 1974. Fire fighter Boston Fire Dept., 1969-73, fire lt., 1973-76, fire capt., 1976-82, dist. fire chief, 1982-86, dep. fire chief, 1986-91, fire commr., chief dept., 1991—. Mem. Hyde Park Adv. Com.; coach varsity hockey Matignon High Sch., Cambridge, Mass., 1964—. With U.S. Army, 1962, with Res. 1962-68. Mem. Internat. Assn. of Fire Chiefs, Internat. Soc. for Respiratory Protection, Nat. Fire Protection Assn., Met. Fire Chiefs Assn., Urban Fire Forum, Fire Chiefs Assn. of Mass., Inc., Hundred Club of Mass., Inc. Avocation: golf. Office: Fire Dept 115 Southampton St Boston MA 02118-2713

PIERCE, MORTON ALLEN, lawyer; b. Liberec, Czechoslovakia, June 25, 1948; m. Nancy Washor, Dec. 14, 1975; children: Matthew J., Nicholas L. BA, Yale Coll., 1970; JD, U. Pa., 1974; postgrad. Oxford U., 1974-75. Bar: N.Y. 1975. Assoc. Reid & Priest, N.Y.C., 1975-83, ptnr., 1983-86; ptnr. Dewey Ballantine, N.Y.C., 1986—. Contbr. articles to profl. jours. Mem. Internat. Bar Assn., ABA (chairman subcom. internat. securities matters 1986-91), Assn. Bar City of N.Y. Home: 161 E 79th St New York NY 10021-0433 Office: Dewey Ballantine 1301 Ave Of The Americas New York NY 10019-6022

PIERCE, NAOMI ELLEN, biology educator, researcher; b. Denver, Oct. 19, 1954; d. Arthur Preble and Ruiko (Ishizaka) P. BS, Yale U., 1976; PhD, Harvard U., k1983. Fulbright postdoctoral fellow Griffith U., Brisbane, Australia, 1983-84; rsch. lectr. Christ Ch., U. Oxford, Eng., 1984-86; asst. prof. Princeton U., N.J., 1986-91; Sydney A. and John H. Hessel prof. biology, curator lepidoptera Harvard U. and Harvard Mus. Comparative Zoology, Cambridge, Mass., 1991—. Contbr. articles to profl. jours. MacArthur Found. fellow, Chgo., 1988-93. Office: Harvard U Museum Comparative Zoology Cambridge MA 02138

PIERCE, PONCHITTA ANNE, television host, producer, journalist; b. Chgo., Aug. 5, 1942; d. Alfred Leonard and Nora (Vincent) P. Student, Cambridge (Eng.) U., summer 1962; B.A. cum laude, U. So. Calif., 1964. Asst. editor Ebony mag., 1964-65, assoc. editor, 1965-67; editor Ebony mag. (N.Y.C. office), 1967-68; chief N.Y.C. editorial bur. Johnson Pub. Co., 1967-68; spl. corr. CBS news div., N.Y.C., 1968-71; contbg. editor McCall's mag., 1971-77; editorial cons. Philps Stokes Fund, 1971-78; staff writer Reader's Digest, 1976-77, roving editor, 1977-80; co-producer, host Today in New York Sta. WNBC-TV, N.Y.C., 1982-87; freelance writer, TV broadcaster; bd. govs. Overseas Press Club. WNBC-TV co-host: Sunday, 1973-77, The Prime of Your Life, 1976-80; author: Status of American Women Journalists on Magazines, 1968, History of the Phelps Stokes Fund 1911-1972; contbg. editor: Parade mag., 1993. Del. to WHO Conf., Geneva, 1973; bd. dirs. Casita Maria, Inc., Dance Theatre of Harlem, Voice Found., Third St. Music Sch. Settlement, Big Sisters, Inc., Unward, Inc., Inner-City Scholarship Fund, Sta. WNET-TV; mem. women's bd. Madison Sq. Boys and Girls Club; mem. Columbia U. Health Scis. Adv. Coun. Recipient Penney-Mo. mag. award excellence women's journalism, 1967; John Russwurm award N.Y.C. Urban League, 1968; AMITA Nat. Achievement award in communications, 1974. Mem. NATAS, Calif. Scholarship Fedn. (life), Nat. Honor Soc., Women in Communications (Woman Behind the News award 1969, Nat. Headliner award 1970), Fgn. Policy Assn. (bd. govs., bd. dirs.), Coun. on Fgn. Rels., Mortar Bd. Alumnae. Clubs: Econs. of N.Y., Lotos.

PIERCE, RICHARD HILTON, lawyer; b. Westerly, R.I., May 2, 1935; s. Ralph Wilson and Mildred (Clark) P.; m. Cynthia Nanian, Sept. 8, 1962; children: Stacey, Andrew, Hilary. AB cum laude, Bates Coll., 1957; JD, NYU, 1960. Bar: R.I. 1961, U.S. Dist. Ct. R.I. 1961, Mass. 1985. Assoc. Hinckley, Allen, Salisbury & Parsons, Providence, 1960-66; ptnr. Hinckley, Allen, & Snyder, Providence, 1966—. Councilman City of Cranston, R.I. 1967-68; libr. trustee Cranston Pub. Libr., 1969-85; mem. sch. com., Cranston, 1985-86; trustee St. Andrews Sch. Fellow Am. Coll. Trust and Estate coun.; mem. ABA, Mass. Bar Assn., R.I. Bar Assn., Vis. Nurses Assn. R.I. (bd. dirs.) Univ. Club. Office: Hinckley Allen Snyder 1500 Fleet Ctr Providence RI 02903

PIERCE, RICHARD JAMES, JR., legal educator, consultant; b. Norfolk, Va., July 15, 1943; s. Richard James Sr. and Julia Marie (Whitehurst) P.; m. Jill Read B, Aug. 21, 1965; children: Gabriel, Danielle. BS, Lehigh U., 1965; JD, U. of Va., 1972. Bar: D.C. 1972, U.S. Supreme Ct. 1972. Assoc. Sutherland, Asbill & Brennan, Washington, 1972-77; prof. U. Kans., Lawrence, 1977-80; vis. prof. U. of Va., Charlottesville, 1980-81; W. R. Irby prof. Tulane U., New Orleans, 1981-84; prof., dean U. Pitts., 1984-86; George W. Hutchison prof. So. Meth. U., Dallas, 1986-89; prof. Columbia U., N.Y., 1989—. Author: Natural Gas Regulation, 1980, Economic Regulation, 1980, Regulated Industries, 1982, Administrative Law and Process, 1985. Lt. comdr. USCG, 1966-69. Mem. ABA (adminstrv. sect., pub. utility sect., natural resources sect.), Fed. Energy Bar Assn., Order of Coif. Home: 260 Hillcrest Rd Ridgewood NJ 07450-2400 Office: Columbia U Sch of Law 435 W 116th St New York NY 10027-7201

PIERCE, RICKY CHARLES, professional basketball player; b. Dallas, Aug. 19, 1959; m. Joyce Wright. Student, Walla Walla (Wash.) Community Coll., 1978-79, Rice U., 1979-82. Player Detroit Pistons, 1982-83, San Diego (now L.A.) Clippers, 1983-84, Milw. Bucks, 1984-91, Seattle Super Sonics, 1991-94, Golden State Warriors, 1994—; player NBA All-Star Game, 1991. Recipient Sixth Man award NBA, 1987, 90. Office: care Golden State Warriors Oakland Coliseum Oakland CA 94621*

PIERCE, ROBERT BELL, English educator; b. Indiana, Pa., Nov. 19, 1934; s. William Elliott and Edna Todd (Bell) P.; m. Barbara Ann Bowman, Sept. 3, 1966; children Steven, Anne, Margaret. BA, Allegheny Coll., 1956; MA, Harvard U., 1957, PhD, 1964. Asst. prof. USAF Acad., Colorado Springs, Colo., 1957-60; asst. prof. to prof. Oberlin Coll., Ohio, 1964—. Author: Shakespeare's History Plays, 1971, The Design of Poetry, 1973. Lt. USAF, 1957-60. Danforth fellow Danforth Found., 1956, NEH fellow, 1970. Mem. Soc. for Values in Higher Edn., Modern Lang. Assn., Phi Beta Kappa. Democrat. Episcopalian. Home: 237 Oak St Oberlin OH 44074-1517 Office: Oberlin Coll English Dept Oberlin OH 44074

PIERCE, ROBERT LORNE, petrochemical, oil and gas company executive. Chmn. and chief exec. officer Foothills Pipe Lines Ltd., Calgary, Alta., Can.; bd. dirs. NOVA Corp. of Alta., Bank of N.S. Mem. Interstate Natural Gas Assn. Am. (bd. dirs.). Office: Foothills Pipe Lines Ltd, 3100 707 8th Ave SW, Calgary, AB Canada T2P 3W8

PIERCE, ROBERT NASH, writer; b. Greenville, Miss., Dec. 5, 1931. Student, Yale U., 1950; BA, Ark. State U., 1951; MJ, U. Tex., Austin, 1955; PhD, U. Minn., 1968. Reporter, asst. state editor, acting state editor Ark. Democrat, Little Rock, 1953-55; reporter, real estate editor San Angelo (Tex.) Standard-Times, 1955-56; news editor, assoc. editor Sarasota (Fla.) News, 1956-60; dir. public relations Fla. Presbyn. Coll., St. Petersburg, 1960-62; asst. city editor St Petersburg Evening Independent, 1962-63; asst. prof. La. State U., 1965-70; assoc. prof. U. Fla., Gainesville, 1970-76; legis. corr. La. Legislature Shreveport Jour., summer 1970; copy editor Miami Herald, 1972; prof. U. Fla., 1976-85, prof. emeritus, 1985—, dir. journalism grad. studies, 1978-83; Fulbright-Hays lectr. journalism U. Argentina de la Empresa, 1973; vis. lectr. Cath. U. Minas Gerais, Belo Horizonte, Brazil, 1973; vis. prof. Autonomous U., Barcelona, Spain, 1982-83, U. Yaounde, Cameroon, 1988; guest lectr. Panamanian Syndicate Journalists, Panama City, Colombian-Am. Cultural Inst., Medellin, Colombia, Guatemala

Chamber Journalism, Guatemala City. Author: Keeping the Flame: Media and Government in Latin America, 1979, A Sacred Trust: Nelson Poynter and the St. Petersburg Times, 1993; contbr. chpts. to Internat. Communication as a Field of Study, 1970, Mass Communication in Mexico, 1975, World Press Ency., 1981, Handbook of Latin Am. Popular Culture, 1985; contbr. monograph, articles to profl. publs. Research grantee Fulbright-Hays Faculty Research Abroad Program. Mem. Assn. for Edn. in Journalism, Kappa Tau Alpha. Office: U Fla Coll Journalism and Comms Gainesville FL 32611

PIERCE, ROY, political science educator; b. N.Y.C., June 24, 1923; s. Roy Alexander and Elizabeth (Scott) P.; m. Winnifred Poland, July 19, 1947. Ph.D., Cornell U., 1950. Instr. govt. Smith Coll., Northampton, Mass., 1950-51, asst. prof., 1951-56; asst. prof. polit. sci. U. Mich., Ann Arbor, 1956-59, assoc. prof., 1959-64, prof., 1964-94, prof. emeritus, 1993—; vis. prof. Columbia U., 1959, Stanford U., 1966, U. Oslo, 1976, Ecole des Hautes Etudes en Sciences Sociales, Paris, 1978. Author: Contemporary French Political Thought, 1966, French Politics and Political Institutions, 1968, 2d edit., 1973, (with Philip E. Converse) Political Representation in France, 1986, Choosing the Chief: Presidential Elections in France and the United States, 1995. Served with USAF, 1943-46. Mem. Am. Polit. Sci. Assn. (co-winner Woodrow Wilson Found. award 1987). Office: U Mich Dept Polit Sci Ann Arbor MI 48109

PIERCE, RUTH A., federal agency administrator. BS in English and History, U. Wis., 1962. Fin. mgmt. br. chief Bur. Retirement and Survivors Ins. Social Security Adminstrn., Balt., 1974-77, asst. dir. fgn. ops., 1977-78, dep. assoc. commr. for ctrl. ops., 1981-83, acting assoc. commr. for retirement and survivors ins., 1983, exec. staff dir. to acting commr., 1983-84, assoc. commr. for ctrl. ops., 1984-88, assoc. dep. commr. for regional ops., 1988-90, dep. commr. for human resources, 1990—; asst. dir. for program mgmt. Office Program Mgmt., Washington, 1978-80; instr. Office Program Mgmt. Seminars, Oak Ridge, Tenn. Mem. pastor's planning com. Queen's Chapel United Meth. Ch.; mem. human resources conf. Bd.; active NAACP, Pub. Employees Roundtable, Fed. Exec. Bd., Md. chpt. Balt., Black Human Resources Network, Washington. Mem. Sr. Exec. Assn., Profl. Black Women's Assn., Forsgate Neighborhood Assn. Office: Social Security Adminstrn 6401 Security Blvd Baltimore MD 21235

PIERCE, SAMUEL RILEY, JR., government official, lawyer; b. Glen Cove, L.I., N.Y., Sept. 8, 1922; s. Samuel R. and Hettie E. (Armstrong) P.; m. Barbara Penn Wright, Apr. 1, 1948; 1 child, Victoria Wright. AB with honors, Cornell U., 1947, JD, 1949; postgrad. (Ford Found. fellow), Yale U., 1957-58; LLM in Taxation, NYU, 1952, LLD, 1972; various other hon. degrees including LL.D., L.H.D., D.C.L., Litt.D. Bar: N.Y. 1949, Supreme Ct. 1956. Asst. dist. atty. County N.Y., 1949-53; asst. U.S. atty. So. Dist. N.Y., 1953-55; asst. to under sec. Dept. Labor, Washington, 1955-56; assoc. counsel, counsel Jud. Subcom. on Antitrust U.S. Ho. Reps., 1956-57; pvt. practice law, 1957-59, 61-70, 73-81, 89—; sec. HUD, 1981-89; faculty N.Y. U. Sch. Law, 1958-70; guest speaker colls., univs.; judge N.Y. Ct. Gen. Sessions, 1959-61; gen. counsel, head legal div. U.S. Treasury, Washington, 1970-73; cons. Fund Internat. Social and Econ. Edn., 1961-67; chmn. impartial disciplinary rev. bd. N.Y.C. Transit System, 1968-81; chmn. N.Y. State Minimum Wage Bd. Hotel Industry, 1961; mem. N.Y. State Banking Bd., 1961-70, N.Y.C. Bd. Edn., 1961, Adminstrv. Conf. U.S., 1968-70, Battery Park City Authority, 1968-70, N.Y.C. Spl. Commn. Inquiry into Energy Failures, 1977; mem. nat. adv. com. Comptroller of Currency, 1975-80; adv. group commr. IRS, 1974-76; mem. Nat. Wiretapping Commn., 1973-76; dir. N.Y. 1964-65 World's Fair Corp., Internat. Paper Co., Turner Corp.; former dir. Prudential Ins. Co., GE Corp., U.S. Industries, Inc., Rand Corp., 1st Nat. Boston Corp., 1st Nat. Bank Boston, Pub. Svc. Electric and Gas Co., Internat. Basic Economy Corp; gov. Am. Stock Exchange, 1977-80. Contbr. articles to profl. jours. Trustee Inst. Civil Justice, Mt. Holyoke Coll., 1965-75, Hampton Inst., Inst. Internat. Edn., Cornell U., Howard U., 1976-81; bd. dirs. Tax Found. U.S. del. Conf. on Coops., Georgetown, Brit. Guiana, 1956; mem. panel symposium Mil.-Indsl. Conf. on Atomic Energy, Chgo., 1956; fraternal del. All-African People's Conf., Accra, Ghana, 1958; mem. Nat. Def. Exec. Res., 1957-70; mem. nat. exec. bd. Boy Scouts Am., 1969-75; mem. N.Y.C. U.S.O. Com., 1959-61; mem. panel arbitrators Am. Arbitration Assn. and Fed. Mediation and Conciliation Service, 1957—; Bd. dirs. Louis T. Wright Meml. Fund, Inc., Nat. Parkinson Found., Inc., 1959-61; sec., dir. YMCA Greater N.Y., 1960-70; Mem. N.Y. State Republican Campaign Hdqrs. Staff, 1952, 58; gov. N.Y. Young Rep. Club, 1951-53. With AUS, 1943-46; as 1st lt. J.A.G.C. Res., 1950-52. Recipient N.Y.C. Jr. C. of C. Ann. Distinguished Svc. award, 1958, Alexander Hamilton award Treasury Dept., 1973, Disting. Alumnus award Cornell Law Sch., 1988, Disting. Svc. Medallion Nassau County Bar Assn., 1988, Reagan Revolution Medal of Honor, 1989, Presdl. Citizens medal, 1989, Salute to Greatness award Martin Luther King Jr. Ctr., 1989. Fellow Am. Coll. Trial Lawyers; mem. ABA, Assn. of Bar of City of N.Y., Cornell Assn. Class Secs., Telluride Assn. Alumni, Cornell U. Alumni Assn. N.Y.C. (gov.), C.I.D. Assn. (gov.), N.Y. County Lawyers Assn., Inst. Jud. Adminstrn., Phi Beta Kappa, Phi Kappa Phi, Alpha Phi Alpha, Alpha Phi Omega. Methodist (former mem. commn. on interjurisdictional relations United Meth. Ch.).

PIERCE, STANLEY, lawyer; b. June 1, 1933; m. Dorothy Pierce, Apr. 3, 1955; children: Leslie Ann, Amy Iris. BS in Biology, CUNY, 1955; MS, NYU, 1962, PhD in Biology, 1965; JD, Hofstra U., 1976. Bar: N.Y. 1977, U.S. Dist. Ct. (ea. and so. dists.) 1978, Fla. 1993. Rsch. assoc., rsch. fellow Am. Mus. Natural History, 1958-65; faculty dept. biology Queens Coll., CUNY, N.Y.C., 1965-81; prof. emeritus, 1981—; ptnr., head sci. causation team Rivkin, Radler & Kremer, Uniondale, N.Y., 1981-92, of counsel, 1993—; apptd. mem. USDA Agr. Biotech. Rsch. Adv. Commn., 1992, mem. nat. areas mgmt. adv. com., 1994—; chmn. legal sect. 1st Internat. Congress on Environ. Info., 1989, 92; chmn. litigation sect. 10th Internat. Meeting on Dioxin, 1990. Contbr. numerous articles to legal and sci. jours., including Jour. Nat. Cancer Inst., Human Pathology, Nat. Law Jour.; mem. editl. bd. sci. and legal jours. With U.S. Army, 1955-57. NSF grantee 1965-67, 68-70, 71-72. Mem. AAAS, ABA, Am. Assn. for Clin. Chemistry, Am. Chem. Soc. (chmn. torts group 1989-90), Am. Coll. Toxicology, Am. Microscopical Soc., Def. Rsch. Inst., Fla. Bar Assn., N.Y. Acad. Scis., N.Y. State Bar Assn., Palm Beach Bar Assn., Sigma Xi. Avocations: music, hiking, stamps. Office: Rivkin Radler & Kremer EAB Plaza Uniondale NY 11556-0111 also: 7412 Mandarin Dr Boca Raton FL 33433

PIERCE, SUSAN RESNECK, academic administrator, English educator; b. Janesville, Wis., Feb. 6, 1943; d. Elliott Jack and Dory (Block) Resneck; m. Kenneth H. Pierce; 1 child, Alexandra. AB, Wellesley Coll., 1965; MA, U. Chgo., 1966; PhD, U. Wis., 1972. Lectr. U. Wis., Rock County, 1970-71; from asst. prof. to prof. English Ithaca (N.Y.) Coll., 1973-83, chmn. dept., 1976-79, 81-82; dean Henry Kendall Coll. Arts and Scis., prof. English U. Tulsa, 1984-90; v.p. acad. affairs, prof. English Lewis and Clark Coll., Portland, Oreg., 1990-92; pres. U. of Puget Sound, Tacoma, 1992—; vis. assoc. prof. Princeton (N.J.) U., 1979; program officer div. ednl. programs NEH, 1982-83, asst. dir., 1983-84; bd. dirs. Janet Elson Scholarship Fund, 1984-1990, Tulsa Edn. Fund, Phillips Petroleum Scholarship Fund, 1985-90, Okla. Math. & Sci. High Sch., 1984-90, Hillcrest Med. Ctr., 1988-90, Portland Opera, 1990-92, St. Joseph's Hosp., 1992—, Seattle Symphony, 1993—; cons. U. Oreg., 1985, Drury Coll., Springfield, Mo., 1986; mem. Middle States and N. Cen. Accreditation Bds.; mem. adv. com. Women's Program, NEH, 1982-83; participant Summit Meeting on Higher Edn., Dept. Edn., Washington, 1985; speaker, participant numerous ednl. meetings, sems., commencements; chair Frederick Ness Book Award Com. Assn. Am. Colls., 1986; mem. award selection com. Dana Found., 1986, 87; mem. Acad. Affairs Council, Univ. Senate, dir. tchr. edn., adv. group for tchr. preparation, ex-officio mem. all Coll. Arts and Scis. coms. and Faculty Council on Internat. Studies, all U. Tulsa; bd. dirs. Am. Conf. Acad. Deans; bd. trustees Hillcrest Med. Ctr. Author: The Moral of the Story, 1982; also numerous essays, jour. articles, book sects., book revs.; co-editor: Approaches to Teaching "Invisible Man"; mem. editl. bd. dirs. Arts and Humanities Coun., Tulsa, 1984-90; trustee Hillcrest Hosp., Tulsa, 1986-90; mem. cultural series com., community rels. com. Jewish Fedn., Tulsa, 1986-90; bd. dirs. Tulsa chpt. NCCJ, 1986-90. Recipient Best Essay award Arix. Quar., 1979, Excellence in Teaching award N.Y. State Edn. Council, 1982, Superior Group Service award NEH, 1984, other teaching awards; Dana scholar, Ithaca Coll., 1980-81; Dana Research fellow, Ithaca Coll., 82-83; grantee Inst. for Ednl. Affairs, 1987, Ford Found., 1987, NEH, 1989.

Mem. MLA (adv. com: on job market 1973-74), South Ctrl. MLA, Soc. for Values in Higher Edn., Assn. Am. Colls. (bd. dirs.), Am. Conf. Acad. Deans (bd. dirs. 1988-91), Phi Beta Kappa, Phi Kappa Phi, Phi Gamma Kappa. Office: U of Puget Sound 1500 N Warner St Tacoma WA 98416-0001

PIERCE, WALTER S., architect; b. Bklyn., Feb. 10, 1920; s. Stanley Woodward and Sallie (Smith) P.; m. Marianne Fisker, Sept. 14, 1951; children—Steffen Fisker, Christian Smith. Student, Bowdoin Coll., 1937-38; BS in Archtl. Engring., Va. Poly. Inst. and State U., 1941; MArch., MIT, 1947. Registered architect, Mass. Architect Anderson & Beckwith, Boston, 1947-50; architect, principal Compton & Pierce, Cambridge, Mass., 1952-60, Peirce & Peirce, Boston, 1961-69; architect, prin. Pierce Pierce & Kramer, Boston, 1970-91, Walter S. Pierce, Architect, Lexington, Mass., 1992—; design studio instr. MIT Sch. Arch., 1947-50; instr. Kongelige Kunstakademiet, Copenhagen, 1951. Archtl. works include Avco Everett Research Lab. (AIA Honor award), Peacock Farms Housing Devel. (AIA First award), Duplicon Corp. Machine Tool Bldg. (Mass. AIA award of merit 1970). Mem. Design Adv. Com. Lexington, Mass., 1965-70, 85-87; mem. Historic Dist. Commn., Lexington, 1984—. Served to maj. U.S. Army, 1941-46; ETO; PTO. Fulbright fellow, 1950-51. Fellow AIA; mem. Boston Soc. Architects (dir. 1965-67). Home and Office: 16 Trotting Horse Dr Lexington MA 02173-6339

PIERCE, WILLIAM JAMES, law educator; b. Flint, Mich., Dec. 4, 1921; s. Francis Scott and Ellen (Pelton) P.; m. Betty Kathren Wise, Nov. 20, 1954; children—Darrell William, Margery Marie, Constance Ellen, Kathren Elizabeth. A.B. in Econs, U. Mich., 1947, J.D., 1949. Faculty U. Mich., 1953-89; emeritus prof. U. Mich., 1989—; prof. law, dir. Legis. Rsch. Ctr. U. Mich., 1958-89, asso. dean, 1971-79; exec. sec. Mich. Law Revision Commn., 1966-69; chmn. Citizens Adv. Com. Juvenile Ct., 1964-66; pres. Nat. Conf. Commrs. Uniform State Laws, 1966-69, exec. dir., 1969-92, emeritus exec. dir., 1992—. Author: (with Estep, Stason) Atomic Energy and the Law, 1957, (with Lamb, White) Apportionment and Representative Institutions, 1963, (with Read, MacDonald, Fordham) Materials on Legislation, 1973. Mem. Pres.'s Consumer Adv. Coun., 1967-69, Mich. Gov.'s Commn. on Mental Health Laws, 1969-72; mem. exec. com. Inst. Continuing Legal Edn., 1964-89. With AUS, 1943-45. Decorated Bronze Star medal. Mem. Am. Law Inst., Am. Bar Assn. (ho. of dels. 1966-69), State Bar Mich. Home: 1505 Roxbury Rd Ann Arbor MI 48104-4047 Office: U Mich Law Sch Ann Arbor MI 48109-1215

PIERCE, WILLIAM LUTHER, association executive, writer; b. Atlanta, Sept. 11, 1933; s. William Luther and Marguerite (Ferrell) P.; m. Susan Sarka, May 8, 1991. BS, Rice U., 1955; MA, U. Colo., 1958, PhD, 1962. Asst. prof. physics Oreg. State U., Corvallis, 1962-65; chmn. Nat. Youth Alliance, Arlington, Va., 1970-74, Nat. Alliance, Arlington, 1974—, Nat. Vanguard Books, Hillsboro, W.Va., 1988—. Author: The Turner Diaries, 1978, Hunter, 1989, Gun Control in Germany, 1928-1945, 1994; editor Nat. Vanguard mag., 1978—. Home and Office: Nat Vanguard Books PO Box 330 Hillsboro WV 24946-0330

PIERCE, WILLIAM SCHULER, cardiac surgeon, educator; b. Wilkes-Barre, Pa., Jan. 12, 1937; s. William Harold and Doris Louis (Schuler) P.; m. Peggy Jayne Stone, June 12, 1965; children: William Stone, Jonathan Drew. B.S., Lehigh U., 1958; M.D., U. Pa., 1962. Intern U. Pa., 1962-63; resident in surgery Hosp. U. Pa., 1963-70; asst. prof. M.S. Hershey Med. Ctr., Pa. State U. Coll. Medicine, Hershey, 1970-73, assoc. prof., 1973-77, prof. surgery, 1977—, chief div. cardiothoracic surgery, 1991—. Contbr. over 300 articles to profl. jours.; inventor cardiac valve, blood pump. Served with USPHS, 1965-67. Fellow ACS; mem. AMA, AAAS, Internat. Cardiovascular Soc., Am. Soc. Artificial Internal Organs, Soc. Vascular Surgery, Am. Heart Assn., Assn. Acad. Surgery, Inst. Medicine, So. Pa. Assn. Thoracic Surgery, Soc. Univ. Surgeons, Am. Surg. Assn., Soc. Clin. Surgery. Office: Milton S Hershey Med Ctr PO Box 850 Hershey PA 17033-0850

PIERCE-ROBERTS, TONY, cinematographer. Cinematographer: (TV movies) Tinker, Tailor, Soldier, Spy, 1979, Caught on a Train, 1980, A Voyage Round My Father, 1983, The Good Soldier, 1983, The Cold Room, 1984, (films) Moonlighting, 1982, Kipperbang, 1984, A Private Function, 1985, A Room with a View, 1986 (Academy award nomination best cinematography 1986), A Tiger's Tale, 1988, Slaves of New York, 1989, Out Cold, 1989, Mr. & Mrs. Bridge, 1990, White Fang, 1991, The Dark Half, 1993, The Remains of the Day, 1993, The Client, 1994. Office: care Am Soc of Cinematographers PO Box 2230 Los Angeles CA 90078*

PIERCY, GORDON CLAYTON, bank executive; b. Takoma Park, Md., Nov. 23, 1944; s. Gordon Clayton and Dorothy Florence (Brummer) P.; m. Roberta Margaret Walton, 1985; children: Elizabeth Anne, Kenneth Charles, Virginia Walton, Zachary Taylor Walton. BS, Syracuse U., 1966; MBA, Pace U., 1973. Mgmt. trainee Suburban Bank, Bethesda, Md., 1962-66; mktg. planning assoc. Chem. Bank, N.Y.C., 1966-70; sr. market devel. officer Seattle-First Nat. Bank, 1970-74; product expansion adminstr., mktg. planning mgr. VISA, Inc., San Francisco, 1974-76; v.p., dir. mktg. Wash. Mut. Savs. Bank, Seattle, 1976-82; v.p., mktg. dir. First Interstate Bank of Wash. N.A., 1983-86; sr. v.p. mktg., dir. Puget Sound Nat. Bank, Tacoma, 1986-92; sr. v.p., dir. mktg. and sales Key Bank, 1993-94; dir. corp. sales Kiro, Inc., 1994-95, dir. mktg., sales InterWest Bancorp, 1995—; Bd. dirs. Seattle BBB, Seattle Aquarium Soc., Concerts on the Cove. Mem. Am. Mktg. Assn. (bd. dirs.), Bank Mktg. Assn., Mktg. Communications Execs. Internat., Seattle Advt. Fedn., Sigma Nu, Alpha Kappa Psi, Delta Mu Delta. Episcopalian. Home: 750 Snowberry Ln Coupeville WA 98239 Office: PO Box 1649 Oak Harbor WA 98277

PIERCY, MARGE, poet, novelist, essayist; b. Detroit, Mar. 31, 1936; d. Robert Douglas and Bert Bernice (Bunnin) P.; m. Ira Wood, 1982. AB, U. Mich., 1957; MA, Northwestern U., 1958. Instr. Gary extension Ind. U., 1960-62; poet-in-residence U. Kans., 1971; disting. vis. lectr. Thomas Jefferson Coll., Grand Valley State Colls., fall 1975, 76, 78, 80; vis. faculty Women's Writers Conf., Cazenovia (N.Y.) Coll.; Elliston poetry fellow U. Cin., 1986; DeRoy Disting. vis. prof. U. Mich., 1992. Author: Breaking Camp, 1968, Hard Loving, 1969, Going Down Fast, 1969, Dance the Eagle to Sleep, 1970, Small Changes, 1973, To Be of Use, 1973, Living in the Open, 1976, Woman on the Edge of Time, 1976, The High Cost of Living, 1978, Vida, 1980, The Moon is Always Female, 1980, Braided Lives, 1982, Circles on the Water, 1982, Stone, Paper, Knife, 1983, My Mother's Body, 1985, Gone to Soldiers, 1988, Available Light, 1988 (May Sarton award 1991), Summer People, 1989, He, She and It, 1991, Body of Glass, 1991 (Arthur C. Clarke award 1993), Mars and Her Children, 1992, The Longings of Women, 1994. Cons. N.Y. State Coun. on Arts, 1971, Mass. Found. for Humanities and Coun. on Arts, 1974; mem. Writer Bd., 1985-86; bd. dirs. Transition House, Mass. Found. Humanities and Pub. Policy, 1978-85, Ha-Yam, 1988—; gov.'s appointee to Mass. Cultural Coun., 1990-91, Mass. Coun. on Arts and Humanities, 1986-89; artistic adv. bd. ALEPH Alliance for Jewish Renewal, Am. Poetry Ctr., 1988—; lit. adv. panel poetry NEA, 1989. Recipient Borenstone Mountain Poetry award, 1968, 74, Lit. award Gov. Mass. Commn. on Status of Women, 1974, Nat. Endowment of Arts award, 1978, Carolyn Kizer Poetry prize, 1986, 90, Shaeffer-Eaton-PEN New Eng. award, 1989, Golden Rose Poetry prize, 1990, Brit ha-Dorot award The Shalom Ctr., 1992. Mem. PEN, NOW, Authors Guild, Authors League, Writers Union, Am. Poetry Soc., Nat. Audubon Soc., Mass. Audubon Soc., New Eng. Poetry Club. Address: PO Box 1473 Wellfleet MA 02667

PIERESON, JAMES EUGENE, foundation administrator; b. Grand Rapids, Mich., Oct. 4, 1946; s. Lloyd Eugene and Katherine Louise (Graham) P.; Patricia Giles Leeds, Aug. 28, 1983; 1 child, James William. BA cum laude Polit. Sci., Mich. State U., 1968, PhD in Polit. Sci., 1973. Vis. faculty polit. sci. Ind. U., Bloomington, 1974-75; asst. prof. polit. sci. U. Pa., Phila., 1976-82; vis. faculty polit. sci. U. Minn., Mpls., 1979; program officer John M. Olin Found., N.Y.C., 1982-85; exec. dir. John M. Olin Found., 1986—; trustee John M. Olin Found., N.Y.C., 1987—; mem. adv. com. Simon Grad. Sch. Bus. Adminstrn., U. Rochester, Rochester, N.Y., 1986—. Co-author: Political Tolerance and American Democracy, 1981; contbr. articles to profl. jours. Trustee Adelphi U., 1991—. Evans scholar Evans Scholars Found., 1964-68; NDEA Grad. fellow, 1968-71, NSF Research fellow, 1978-79, U.S. Govt. Mem. Phila. Soc., Am. Hist. Assn.,

Union League Club. Republican. Roman Catholic. Office: John M Olin Found 100 Park Ave New York NY 10017-5516

PIERGALLINI, ALFRED A., food products executive; b. Easton, Pa., Aug. 1, 1946. BA, Lafayette Coll., 1968; MBA, U. Chgo., 1970. Regional dir. Beverage Mgmt. Inc.; sales mgr. Procter & Gamble Co., then brand mgr.; pres. Shasta Beverages Inc., Hayward, Calif., 1985-90; chmn., pres., chief exec. officer Gerber Prods. Co., Fremont, Mich., from 1985, also COO, dir. *

PIERLUISI, PEDRO RAFAEL, lawyer; b. San Juan, P.R., Apr. 26, 1959; s. Jorge A. and Doris (Urrutia) P.; m. Maria E. Rojo, June 20, 1981; children: Anthony, Michael, Jacqueline, Rafael. BA, Tulane U., 1981; JD, George Washington U., 1984. Bar: D.C. 1984, U.S. Dist. Ct. D.C. 1985, U.S. Ct. Appeals (D.C. cir.) 1985, P.R. 1990, U.S. Supreme Ct. 1990. Assoc. Verner, Liipfert, Bernhard, McPherson & Hand, Washington, 1984-85, Cole, Corette & Abrutyn, Washington, 1985-90; mem. Pierluisi & Pierluisi, San Juan, 1990—. Mem. ABA, Fed. Bar Assn., George Washington U. Internat. Law Soc. (pres. 1982-83), Country Club Fairfax, Rotary. Avocations: tennis, jogging. Office: Banco Popular Ste 1428 San Juan PR 00901-9203

PIERONI, LEONARD J., engineering and construction company executive; b. 1939. BSChemE, Notre Dame U., 1960; MSChemE, Northwestern U., 1961. With M.W. Kellogg Co., N.Y.C., 1961-70, Rust Engring., N.Y.C. 1970-72; with Parsons, Pasadena, Calif., 1972-77, 78—, exec. v.p., 1987-90, chmn., chief exec. officer, 1990—, also dir.; pres. SIP Engring. Inc. 1983-84; mng. dir. Ralph M Parsons Co. Ltd., London, 1984-85; pres., gen. mgr. Charles T. Main Inc., 1985-87; v.p. sales KTI Corp., 1977-78. Office: Parsons Corp 100 W Walnut St Pasadena CA 91124-0001*

PIEROTTI, JOHN WILLIAM, prosecutor; b. Memphis, Dec. 29, 1936; s. Harry C. and Alma (Folis) P.; m. Barbara Anne Dixon, Jan. 6, 1957; children: John Jr., Andrew, Thomas, Marianne. BS, Spring Hill Coll., 1958; JD, Memphis State U., 1968. Bar: Tenn. 1968. Asst. dist. atty. Dist. Atty.'s Office Shelby County, Memphis, 1968-90, dist. atty., 1990—. 1st lt. U.S. Army, 1958-60. Roman Catholic. Avocation: breeding, raising and racing thoroughbred horses. Office: Dist Atty Gen's Office 201 Poplar Ave Ste 301 Memphis TN 38103-1947

PIEROTTI, ROBERT AMEDEO, chemistry educator; b. Newark, Nov. 13, 1931; s. Amedeo and Maria-Pia (Pisani) P.; m. Dorothy Clare Soper, June 22, 1959; children: Margaret-Marie, Stephen Robert. B.A. in Chemistry, Pomona Coll., 1954; Ph.D. (Leonard and Rose Chudacoff scholar), U. Wash., 1958. Instr. U. Nev., Reno, 1958-60; faculty Ga. Inst. Tech., Atlanta, 1960—; prof. chemistry Ga. Inst. Tech., 1968—, dir. Sch. Chemistry, 1983—; dean. Coll. Scis. and Liberal Studies Ga. Inst. Tech., Atlanta, 1989, dean Coll. Scis., 1990—, dir. Ctr. for Edn. in Sci., Math. and Computing, 1990-94; NATO sr. fellow Bristol (Eng.) U., 1968. Mem. Am. Chem. Soc., Am. Phys. Soc., Faraday Soc., AAAS, AAUP, Sigma Xi (M.A. Ferst Research prize 1962). Home: 3689 Cochise Dr NW Atlanta GA 30339-4330

PIERPOINT, POWELL, lawyer; b. Phila., Apr. 30, 1922; s. James Reynolds and Ruth (Powell) P.; m. Margaret Shaw Sagar, Mar. 24, 1950; 1 child, Harriet Pierpoint Bos. B.A., Yale, 1944, LL.B., 1948. Bar: N.Y. bar 1949. Assoc. Hughes, Hubbard & Reed (and predecessors), N.Y.C., 1948-53; ptnr. Hughes, Hubbard & Reed (and predecessors), 1955-61, 63-93, of counsel, 1993—; asst. U.S. atty. So. Dist. N.Y., 1953-55; gen. counsel Dept. Army, 1961-63; dir. Legal Aid Soc., 1968-90, pres., 1979-81; mem. N.Y.C. Bd. Ethics, 1972-88, pres., 1983-89; spl. master appellate divsn. 1st Dept., 1992. Served with USNR, 1943-46. Fellow Am. Coll. Trial Lawyers; mem. ABA, N.Y. State Bar Assn., Assn. Bar City of N.Y. Home: 155 E 72nd St New York NY 10021-4371 Office: Hughes Hubbard & Reed 1 Battery Park Plz New York NY 10004-1403

PIERPONT, ROBERT, fund raising executive, consultant; b. Somers Point, N.J., Jan. 27, 1932; s. Robert E. and Elise E. (White) P.; m. Marion J. Welde, Oct. 11, 1958; children: Linda J. Staropoli, Nancy P. Oler, Robert W., Richard F. B.S. in Bus. Adminstrn. Pa. Mil. Coll., 1954; postgrad. Inst. Ednl. Mgmt. Harvard Grad. Sch. Bus. Adminstrn., 1970. Comml. sales rep. Atlantic City (N.J.) Electric Co., 1956-58; asst. dir. devel. Widener U. (formerly Pa. Mil. Coll.), Chester, 1958-61, asst. to pres., 1961-62, dir. devel., 1962-68, v.p. for devel., 1968-70; sr. cons. v.p. and dir. Brakeley, John Price Jones, Inc., N.Y.C., 1970-79; v.p. devel. Mt. Sinai Med. Center, N.Y.C., 1979-85; ptnr. Pierpont & Wilkerson, 1986—; guest faculty mem. Big 10 Fund Raisers Inst., Mackinac Island, Mich., 1971; mem. adv. com. on application of standards Philanthropic Adv. Service, Council of Better Bus. Burs., Washington, 1978-81; faculty The Fund Raising Sch., Ctr. on Philanthropy, Ind. U., 1989—. Mem. bishops adv. com. on stewardship Diocese of Pa., 1968-69; vestryman Trinity Episcopal Ch., Swarthmore, 1970-72; trustee Putnam Valley Free Library, 1986-92. Recipient Alumni Svc. award Widener U., 1989; named Disting. Alumnus in Econs., Widener U., 1986. Mem. Nat. Soc. Fund Raising Execs. (dir.-at-large 1970-78, pres. found. 1977-79, chmn. bd. 1979-82, chmn. cert. bd. 1982-87, presdl. search com. 1989, chmn. ethics com. 1993-95). Office: The Stone House PO Box 179 Rt 9 Garrison NY 10524

PIERPONT, WILBUR K., retired acounting educator; b. Winn, Mich., Mar. 15, 1914; s. Clarence N. and Ethel (Kent) P.; m. Maxine Sponseller, Feb. 7, 1941; children: Ann Pierpont Mack, James. AB, Central Mich. U., 1934; MBA (Univ. scholar), U. Mich., 1938, PhD, 1942; LLD, Central Mich. U., 1958, Hope Coll., 1977. Brookings Instn. fellow, 1941; price analyst Ordnance Dept., Washington, 1942-44; teaching fellow U. Mich., 1938-40, instr. Sch. Bus. Adminstrn., 1941-42, asst. prof., 1946-51, controller, 1947-51, v.p., chief fin. officer, prof., 1951-76, prof. acctg., 1977-81; bd. dirs. R and B Machine Tool Co., Chelsea Milling Co. Contbr. articles to numerous jours. Trustee Buhr Found. Served as lt. Bur. Ordnance, USNR, 1944-46. Recipient Outstanding Achievement award U. Mich., Alumni award U. Mich., Alumni award Cen. Mich. U. Mem. Delta Sigma Pi, Beta Gamma Sigma, Phi Kappa Phi. Methodist. Clubs: Golf and Outing (Ann Arbor), Rotary (Ann Arbor). Home: 2125 Nature Cove Ct Ann Arbor MI 48104-8325

PIERRE, JOSEPH HORACE, JR., commercial artist; b. Salem, Oreg., Oct. 3, 1929; s. Joseph Horace and Miriam Elizabeth (Holder) P.; m. June Anne Rice, Dec. 20, 1952; children: Joseph Horace III, Thomas E., Laurie E., Mark R., Ruth A. Grad., Advt. Art Sch., Portland, Oreg., 1954, Inst. Comml. Art, 1951-52. Lithographic printer Your Town Press, Inc., Salem, Oreg., 1955-58; correctional officer Oreg. State Correctional Instn., 1958-60; owner Illustrators Workshop, Inc., Salem, 1960-61; advt. mgr. North Pacific Lumber Co., Portland, 1961-63; vocat. instr. graphic arts Oreg. Correctional Instn., 1963-70; lithographic printer Lloyd's Printing, Monterey, Calif., 1971-72; illustrator McGraw Hill, 1972-73; owner Publishers Art Svc., Monterey, 1972-81; correctional officer Oreg. State Penitentiary, 1982-90; ret. Editor/publisher: The Pro Cartoonist & Gagwriter; author: The Road to Damascus, 1981, The Descendants of Thomas Pier, 1992, The Origin and History of the Callaway and Holder Families, 1992; author numerous OpEd eds. in Salem, Oreg. Statesman Jour., others; pub. cartoons nat. mags.; mural Mardi Gras Restaurant, Salem; cartoon strip Fabu, Oreg. Agr. mo. Mem. Rep. Nat. Com., Citizens Com. for Right to Keep and Bear Arms. Served with USN, 1946-51. Decorated Victory medal, China Svc. medal, Korea medal. Mem. U.S. Power Squadron, Nat. Rifle Assn., Acad. of Model Aeronautics, Oreg. Correctional Officers Assn. (co-founder, hon. mem.), Four Corners Rod and Gun Club. Republican. Avocations: sailing, flying, scuba, model aircraft building and flying. Home: 4822 Oak Park Dr NE Salem OR 97305-2931

PIERSKALLA, WILLIAM PETER, academic dean, management and engineering educator; b. St. Cloud, Minn., Oct. 22, 1934; s. Aloys R. and Hilda A. P.; m. Carol Spargo. Children: Nicholas, William, Michael. A.B. in Econs., Harvard U., 1956, M.B.A., 1958; M.S. in Math., U. Pitts., 1962; Ph.D. in Ops. Research, Stanford U., 1965; M.A., U. Pa., 1978. Assoc. prof. Case Western Res. U., Cleve., 1965-68, So. Meth. U., Dallas, 1968-70; prof. dept. indsl. engring. and mgmt. scis. Northwestern U., Evanston, Ill., 1970-78; exec. dir. Leonard Davis Inst., U. Pa., Phila., 1978-83; prof., chmn. health care systems dept. U. Pa., Phila., 1982-90, prof. decision sci. and

systems engring., dep. dean acad. affairs Wharton Sch., 1983-89, Ronald A. Rosenfield prof., 1986-93; dir. Huntsman Ctr. Global Competition and Leadership Wharton Sch., U. Pa., 1989-91; John E. Anderson prof. UCLA, 1993—, dean of John E. Anderson Grad Sch. of Mgmt., 1993—; cons. HHS, Bethesda, Md., 1974-87, MDAX, Chgo., 1985-91, MEDICUS, Evanston, 1970-75, Sisters of Charity, Dayton, Ohio, 1982-83, Project Hope, 1990—; bd. dirs. Huntsman Ctr. for Global Competition and Leadership, 1989, No. Wilderness Adventures, Griffin Funds, Inc., No. Trust Corp. Calif. Contbr. articles to various publs. Mem. adv. bd. Lehigh U., 1986-93, U. So. Calif. Bus. Sch., 1987-93. Recipient Harold Larnder Meml. prize Can. Oper. Rsch. Soc., 1993; grantee NSF, 1970-83, HHS, Washington, 1973-82, Office Naval Rsch., Arlington, Va., 1974-77. Mem. Ops. Rsch. Soc. Am. (pres. 1982-83, editor 1979-82, Kimball Disting. Svc. medal 1989), Inst. Mgmt. Scis. (assoc. editor 1970-77), Internat. Fedn. Operational Rsch. Socs. (pres. 1989-91). Office: Anderson Grad Sch. Management UCLA 405 Hilgard Avenue Los Angeles CA 90024

PIERSOL, LAWRENCE L., federal judge; b. Vermillion, S.D., Oct. 21, 1940; s. Ralph Nelson and Mildred Alice (Millette) P.; m. Catherine Anne Vogt, June 30, 1962; children: Leah C., William M., Elizabeth J. BA, U. S.D., 1962, JD summa cum laude, 1965. Bar: S.D. 1965, U.S. Ct. Mil. Appeals, 1965, U.S. Dist. Ct. S.D. 1968, U.S. Supreme Ct. 1972, U.S. Dist. Ct. Wyo. 1980, U.S. Dist. Ct. Nebr. 1986, U.S. Dist. Ct. Mont. 1988. Ptnr. Davenport, Evans, Hurwitz & Smith, Sioux Falls, S.D., 1968-93; judge U.S. Dist. Ct., Sioux Falls, 1993—. Majority leader S.D. Ho. of Reps., Pierre, 1973-74, minority whip, 1971-72; del. Dem. Nat. Conv., 1972, 76, 80; S.D. mem. del. select commn. Dem. Nat. Com., 1971-75. Capt. U.S. Army, 1965-68. Mem. ABA, State Bar S.D. Roman Catholic. Avocations: reading, running, sailing, mountaineering. Office: US Dist Ct 400 S Phillips Ave Sioux Falls SD 57102

PIERSON, ALBERT CHADWICK, business management educator; b. Pierson, Ill., Jan. 3, 1914; s. Charles Clevel and Gertrude Fannie (Gale) P.; m. Evelyn Matilda Swanson, Sept. 13, 1952; 1 stepson, Jay F. Lynch. B.A. in Liberal Arts and Scis, U. Ill., 1935; M.B.A. with distinction, Harvard U., 1947; Ph.D. Columbia U., 1963. Merchandiser Montgomery Ward & Co., Chgo., 1935-41; mgmt. cons. N.Y.C., 1947-53; prof. mgmt. San Diego State U., 1954—; cons. in field; pub. accountant, Calif.; research editor Jour. Travel Research, 1967—. Author: Trends in Lodging Enterprises, 1939-1963, 1963. Chmn. bd. Nat. Arts Found., N.Y.C.; mem. accreditation vis. teams Am. Assembly Collegiate Schs. Bus., 1977—. Served to col. AUS, 1941-46. Decorated Bronze Star. Fellow Soc. Applied Anthropology; mem. Acad. Mgmt. (pres. Western div. 1974-75), Western Council Travel Research (dir. 1965-67), Acad. Internat. Mgmt., Mil. Logistics Soc., James Joyce Soc., Beta Gamma Sigma, Sigma Iota Epsilon, Tau Sigma. Democrat. Methodist. Clubs: Harvard (Chgo.); Columbia (N.Y.C.); Marine Corps Officers (San Diego). Home: 1245 Park Row La Jolla CA 92037-3706 Office: Coll Bus San Diego State U San Diego CA 92182-0096

PIERSON, DAVID LOWELL, orchestra manager; b. Hamilton, Ohio, Jan. 21, 1949; s. Raymond Charles and Irma Lucille (Vizedom) P.; m. Deborah Pfleager, June 11, 1977; 1 child, Adam. B.Mus. Edn., Ind. U., 1972, M.A. in Arts Adminstrn., 1976. Music tchr. Lurnea High Sch., Liverpool, N.S.W. Australia, 1972-73; asst. mgr. Dayton Philharm. Orch. Assn., Inc., 1976-77, gen. mgr., 1977—; cons. Ohio Arts Council; bd. dirs. WDPR. Adv. com. music program Career Acad., Dayton Public Schs., 1979-81; mem. Leadership Dayton, 1986; bd. dirs. Dayton Boys Choir. Ind. U. Arts Adminstrn. Program fellow, 1974-76. Mem. Orgn. Ohio Orchs. (dir. 1980, pres. 1983), Am. Symphony Orch. League (Helen Thompson award 1984), Ohio Citizens Com. for Arts, Pi Kappa Lambda, Eta Sigma Pi. Lodge: Rotary. Avocations: swimming, gardening, reading. Home: 310 S Village Dr Dayton OH 45459-2130 Office: Jacksonville Symphony 128 E Forsyth St Ste 300 Jacksonville FL 32202-3332

PIERSON, DON, sports columnist. Tribune Pro Football columnist Chicago Tribune. Recipient Dick McCann Mem. Award, 1994. Office: Chicago Tribune Sports Dept 435 N Michigan Ave Chicago IL 60611

PIERSON, EDWARD SAMUEL, engineering educator, consultant; b. Syracuse, N.Y., June 27, 1937; s. Theodore and Marjorie O. (Bronner) P.; m. Elaine M. Grauer, June 6, 1971; 1 child, Alan. BS in Elec. Engring., Syracuse U., 1958; SM, MIT, 1960, ScD, 1964. Asst. prof., fellow MIT, 1965-66; assoc. prof., assoc. dept. head U. Ill., Chgo., 1966-75; program mgr. Argonne Nat. Labs., Ill., 1975-82; head dept. engring. Purdue U. Calumet, Hammond, Ind., 1982-95, spl. asst. to chancellor for environ. programs, 1995—; cons. Argonne Nat. Lab., 1972-75, 82—; Solmecs Corp., 1982-88, HMJ Corp., Washington, 1983-88. Contbr. numerous articles to profl. jours. NSF fellow, 1958-60. Mem. IEEE, Am. Soc. Engring. Edn., Am. Soc. Mech. Engrs. Office: Purdue U Calumet Hammond IN 46323

PIERSON, FRANK ROMER, screenwriter, director; b. Chappaqua, N.Y., May 12, 1925; s. Harold C. and Louise (Randall) P.; m. Polly Stokes, 1948 (div.); m. Dori Derfner, 1978 (div.); m. Helene Szamet, June 24, 1990; children: Michael, Eve. BS, Harvard U., 1946. Writer, corr. Time/Life mags., 1950-58; bd. trustees Los Angeles Theatre Ctr., 1984—. Screenwriter: (television) Naked City, 1962, Route 66, 1963, Nichols, 1971, Haywire, 1979, (feature films) Cat Ballou, 1965 (Academy award nomination best adapted screenplay 1965), The Happening, 1967, Cool Hand Luke, 1967 (Academy award nomination best adapted screenplay 1967), The Anderson Tapes, 1970, Dog Day Afternoon, 1975 (Academy award best original screenplay 1975), In Country, 1989, Presumed Innocent, 1990; screenwriter, dir.: The Looking Glass Wars, 1970, A Star is Born, 1976, King ofthe Gypsies, 1978; dir.: (television) The Neon Ceiling, 1972 (San Francisco Film Festival award 1972), Alfred Hitchcock Presents, 1985, Somebody Has to Shoot the Picture, HBO, 1990 (Cable ACE award for best direction 1990), Citizen Cohn, HBO, 1992 (Cable ACE award for best direction 1992), Emmy award nomination for direction 1993); dir., prodr.: (television series) Have Gun Will Travel, 1960-62. Served with U.S.A.A.F., 1943-46. Mem. Writers Guild Am. West (v.p. 1980-81, pres. 1981-83), Humanities Found. (pres. 1994). Office: UTA 9560 Wilshire Blvd Ste 500 Beverly Hills CA 90212-2427*

PIERSON, JOHN HERMAN GROESBECK, economist, writer; b. N.Y.C., Mar. 28, 1906; s. Charles Wheeler and Elizabeth Granville (Groesbeck) P.; m. Gertrude Trumbull Robinson, 1930 (div. 1942); children: Elizabeth P. Pierson, John Trumbull Robinson Pierson; m. Sherleigh Elizabeth Glad, June 16, 1948 (dec. 1991); m. Harriet-Anne Duell, Feb. 22, 1992. BA, Yale Coll., 1927, PhD in Econ., 1938. Tchr. St. Bernard's Sch., N.Y.C., 1928-29; spl. asst. to v.p. Consol. Gas Co. of N.Y., N.Y.C., 1929-33; instr. econ. Yale Coll., New Haven, 1933-38, Sterling rsch. fellow, 1938-39; assoc. dir. Inst. for Applied Social Analysis, N.Y.C., 1939-41; asst. chief, then chief of Postwar Labor Problems div. Bur. Labor Statistics, Washington, 1941-45, adviser to acting commr., 1945-46; econ. adviser, spl. asst. to asst. and Under Sec. of Labor Washington, 1946-48; econ. adviser to asst. to adminstr. Econ. Cooperation Adminstrn., Washington, 1949-50; econ. adviser, policy adviser Asia/Far East Aid in Econ. Cooperation Adminstrn. and Mutual Security Agy., 1950-53; founder, pres. Voices to Am., Inc., N.Y.C., 1953-54; dir. rsch., planning div. U.N. Econ. Commn. for Asia and the Far East, Bangkok, 1955-59; spl. cons. Bur. Social Affairs U.N., N.Y.C., 1959-61, spl. adviser to Under-Sec. for Econ. and Social Affairs, 1961-66, sec. adv. com. on application of sci. & tech. to devel., 1964-66; free-lance writer, 1966—; chmn. U.S. Govt. interdepartmental com. on full employment and econ. fgn. policy, 1946-48; adviser various other internat. meetings; active Nat. Environ. Leadership Coun., 1990-91. Author: (poems) The Circling Beast, 1941, (books) Full Employment, 1941, Full Employment and Free Enterprise, 1947, Insuring Full Employment: A United States Policy for Domestic Prosperity and World Development, 1964, Essays on Full Employment, 1942-72, Island in Breeze, 1973, Hubert Benoit's Reasoned Formulation of Zen, 1975, Full Employment Without Inflation: Papers on the Economic Performance Insurance Proposal, 1980; co-author: Guaranteed Full Employment: A Proposal for Achieving Continuous Work Opportunity for All, Without Inflation, through "Economic Performance Insurance", 1985; contbr. numerous articles to profl. jours. Mem. Am. Econ. Assn., Athens Soc. of the Friends of the Trees, Outrigger Canoe Club, Century Assn., Phi Beta Kappa. Home: 235 Walker St Lenox MA 01240-2762

PIERSON, JOHN THEODORE, JR., manufacturer; b. Kansas City, Mo., Oct. 13, 1931; s. John Theodore and Helen Marguerite (Sherman) P.; m. Susan K. Chadwick, Apr. 16, 1977; children by previous marriage—Merrill Sherman, Karen Louise, Kimberly Ann. B.S.E., Princeton U., 1953; M.B.A., Harvard U., 1958. With Vendo Co., Kansas City, Mo., 1960—, gen. automatic products salesman, 1960-61, mgr. new products, 1961-63; v.p. sales equipment for Coca-Cola, 1963-66; pres. Vendo Internat., 1966-69, exec. v.p., chief operating officer, 1969-71; pres., chief exec. officer, 1971-74; pres. Preco Industries, Inc., 1976-93; chmn. Internat. Trade and Exhbn. Ctr. Co-author: Linear Polyethylene and Polypropylene: Problems and Opportunities, 1958. Trustee Midwest Rsch. Inst.; bd. dirs. and chmn. Midland Mfg. Tech. Ctr.; bd. dirs. Johnson County Bus. Tech. Ctr., Youth Symphony Kansas City, 1965-69; past trustee Pembroke-Country Day Sch., Barstow Sch.; past mem. adv. coun. U.S.-Japan Econ. Rels. Coun.; mem. coun. chmn. for exploring Boy Scouts Am., mem. Nat. coun. Lt. M.I. USNR, 1953-56. Mem. Kansas City C. of C. (v.p. internat.), U.S. C. of C. (dir. 1970-74). Clubs: River (pres. 1994), Kansas City Country. Home: 2801 W 63rd St Shawnee Mission KS 66208-1866 Office: 9501 Dice Ln Shawnee Mission KS 66215-1158

PIERSON, RICHARD ALLEN, hospital administrator; b. Emporia, Kans., Dec. 17, 1944; s. Lea Ross and Irene (Loren) P.; m. LuJean Hiatt, June 24, 1967; children: Lindsey, Alyssa, Jedd, Amanda, Adam, Aaron, Spencer. BS, Kans. State Tchrs. Coll., 1966; MBA, U. Utah, 1971; MHA, U. Minn., 1974. Adminstrv. resident U. Minn. Hosp., Mpls., 1973-74, asst. dir., 1974-77, assoc. dir., 1977-81; hosp. dir. Univ. Hosp. Ark., Little Rock, 1981-86, exec. dir., 1986—; bd. dirs. Univ. Hosp. Consortium, Chgo. Vice chmn., mem. Ark. Kidney Disease Commn., Little Rock, 1982—. Capt. USAF, 1966-70. Mem. Am. Hosp. Assn. (governing coun. met. hosps. sect. 1988-90), Am. Coll. Healthcare Execs. (nominee). Mem. LDS Ch. Office: U Hosp Ark 4301 W Markham St Little Rock AR 72205-7101

PIERSON, RICHARD NORRIS, JR., medical educator; b. N.Y.C., Sept. 22, 1929; s. Richard Norris and Dorothy (Stewart) P.; m. Alice Roberts, Aug. 26, 1974; children by previous marriage: Richard N., Olivia Tiffany, Alexandra de Forest, Cordelia S.C.; stepchildren: Alice W. Dunn, Eric C.W. Dunn. BA, Princeton U., 1951; MD, Columbia U., 1955. Diplomate Am. Bd. Internal Medicine, Am. Bd. Nuclear Medicine. Resident St. Luke's Roosevelt Hosp., N.Y.C., 1955-61, assoc. dir., 1961-65, dir. div. nuclear medicine, 1965-89, dir. body composition unit, 1965—, attending physician 1975—; prof. clin. medicine Columbia U., 1980—; dir. medicine Hackensack Hosp., 1973-74; staff assoc. Brookhaven Nat. Lab., 1970—; research scholar Lawrence Radiation Lab., Berkeley, Calif., 1970-71, bioengring. inst. Columbia U., 1976—, chmn., 1989—. Editor: Quantitative Radiocardiography, 1975. Contbr. articles to profl. jours. Bd. dirs. Englewood Health Dept., N.J., 1966-74; warden St. Paul's Ch., 1980-82, bd. dirs. Empire Blue Cross/Blue Shield, N.Y., 1978-91, v.p., 1990-91. Lt. USNR, 1956-58. NIH grantee, 1973-76, 86—; John A. Hartford Found. grantee, 1967-70. Fellow N.Y. Acad. Medicine, ACP; mem. N.Y. County Med. Soc. (pres. 1978-79), N.Y. County Health Svc. Rev. Orgn. (chmn. 1980-82), Am. Bur. Med. Advancement in China (pres. 1979-87), Am. Med. Rev. Rsch. Ctr. (pres. 1985-89, N.Y. State del. to AMA 1978-90), Alliance for Continuing Med. Edn. (pres. 1985-89), Soc. Nuclear Medicine (greater N.Y. area pres. 1982-83, trustee 1991—, del. to AMA 1991—), P&S Alumni Assn. (pres. 1989-91), Century Club, Englewood Field Club. Home: 60 Lincoln St Englewood NJ 07631-3117 Office: St Lukes Roosevelt Hosp Ctr 1111 Amsterdam Ave New York NY 10025-1708

PIERSON, ROBERT DAVID, banker; b. Orange, N.J., Mar. 5, 1935; s. Carleton Wellington and Muriel Browning (Potter) P.; BA, Lehigh U., 1957; m. Virginia Duncan Knight, Apr. 30, 1960; children: Lisa Boles, Alexandra Mead, Robert Wellington. Exec. asst. 1st Nat. City Bank N.Y., N.Y.C., 1958-61; asst. to. pres. Cooper Labs. Inc., N.Y.C., 1961-65; dir. mktg. svcs. Arbrook div. Johnson & Johnson, Somerville, N.J., 1965-69; v.p. Klemtner Advt. Inc., N.Y.C., 1969-71; sr. v.p. Bowery Savs. Bank, N.Y.C., 1972-80; vice chmn., dir. Carteret Bancorp, Inc. Wilmington, Del., 1980-90 , Carteret Savs. Bank, F.A., Morristown, N.J., 1980-90; pres. Collective Fin. Svcs., Inc., (divsn. of Collective Bank, Montclair, N.J.), 1990—. With USCG, 1958-59. Republican. Presbyterian. Clubs: Morris County Golf, Morristown. Home: Green Hills Rd Mendham NJ 07945-3305 Office: Collective Bank 560 Valley Rd Montclair NJ 07042

PIERSON, WILLIAM ROY, chemist; b. Charleston, W.Va., Oct. 21, 1930; s. Roy H. Pierson and Gay Harris; m. Juliet T. Strong, May 20, 1961; children: Elizabeth T., Anne H. Veis. BSE, Princeton U., 1952; PhD, MIT, 1959. Rsch. assoc. Enrico Fermi Inst. for Nuclear Studies U. Chgo., 1959-62; rsch. scientist Ford Motor Co., Dearborn, Mich., 1962-87; exec. dir. Energy and Environ. Engring. Ctr. Desert Rsch. Inst., Reno, 1987—. Contbr. over 100 articles to profl. jours. Bd. dirs. Reno Chamber Orch., 1992—. Lt. USN, 1952-55. Fellow Air and Waste Mgmt. Assn. (Chambers award 1995); mem. AAAS, Am. Phys. Soc., Am. Chem. Soc., Am. Assn. for Aerosol Rsch. (bd. dirs. 1982-85). Office: Desert Rsch Inst 5625 Fox Ave PO Box 60220 Reno NV 89506

PIESTER, DAVID L(EE), magistrate judge; b. Lincoln, Nebr., Nov. 18, 1947; s. George P.; married; children. B.S., U. Nebr., 1969, J.D., 1972. Bar: Nebr. 1972, U.S. Dist. Ct. Nebr. 1972, U.S.Ct. Appeals (8th cir.) 1976, U.S. Supreme Ct. 1979. Staff atty. Legal Services S.E. Nebr., Lincoln, 1972-73, exec. dir., 1973-79; asst. U.S. atty. Dept. Justice, Lincoln, 1979-81; magistrate U.S. Dist. Ct. Nebr., Lincoln, 1981—; cons. Legal Services Corp., Nat. Legal Aid and Defender Assn., 1974-77. Mem. Lincoln Human Rights Commn., 1978-79. Mem. Nebr. State Bar Assn. (legal svcs./lawyers referral com., alt. dispute resolution com.), ABA (Jud. adminstrn. divsn., Nat. Conf. Fed. Trial Judges), Fed. Magistrate Judges Assn., Lincoln Bar Assn., Eighth cir. Jud. Coun. (edn. com., ex officio). Office: 538 Fed Bldg Lincoln NE 68508

PIETAK, RAYMOND ADAM, academic administrator; b. North Tonawanda, N.Y., June 3, 1933; s. Adam Stanley and Josephine Mary (Piwowarczyk) P.; m. Marie Alice Dettmer, Dec. 26, 1959; children: Lynn Marie, Raymond Jr., Scott Dettmer. AB, Niagara U., 1955; EdM, U. Buffalo, 1958; EdD, SUNY, Buffalo, 1966. Tchr. history Starpoint Cen. Sch., Pendleton, N.Y., 1958-60; dir. admissions Niagara County Community Coll., Niagara Falls, N.Y., 1963-65; assoc. dean, then dean Forest Park Community Coll., St. Louis, 1965-68; pres. Southwestern Mich. Coll., Dowagiac, 1968-69; provost Community Coll. Phila., 1969-85; pres. Joliet (Ill.) Jr. Coll. 1985—; bd. dirs. COMBASE; chmn. Mid. States Assn. Commn. Higher Edn. Accrediting Teams; cons. to community colls. Contbr. articles to ednl. publs. Bd. dirs. Joliet/Will County Coun. Econ. devel., 1986-90; adv. bd. St. Joseph's Hosp., Joliet, 1987-90. 1st lt. U.S. Army, 1955-57. Mem. Am. Assn. Higher Edn., Am. Assn. Community and Jr. Colls., Am. Coun. Edn., Nat. Coun. Occupational Edn. (past pres.), Ill. Coun. Pub. Community Coll. Pres. (past pres.), Rotary Internat., Joliet Region C. of C. (bd. dirs. 1988—), Phi Delta Kappa. Home: 214 Madison St Apt 3A Joliet IL 60435-8206 Office: Joliet Jr Coll 1216 Houbolt Ave Joliet IL 60436-9352

PIETERSEN, WILLIAM GERARD, pharmaceutical company executive; b. East London, Republic of South Africa, Sept. 24, 1937; came to U.S., 1980; s. Willem Gerhardus and Hester (Muller) P.; m. Bridget Marion Buchanan, Feb. 3, 1967; children: Christopher John, Sally Ann. BA, LLB, Rhodes U., Republic of South Africa, 1960; MA, Oxford U., Eng., 1963. Assoc. Fairbridge Arderne & Lawton, Capetown, 1965-68; mktg. and gen. mgmt. Unilever, Republic of South Africa and Eng., 1968-80; pres. foods div. Lever Bros. subs. Unilever, N.Y.C., 1980-86; pres. Guinness Am., N.Y.C., 1986-88, The House of Seagram, N.Y.C., 1988-89, Seagram USA, N.Y.C., 1989-91, The Seagram Beverage Group, N.Y.C., 1991-92, Tropicana Products, Inc., Bradenton, Fla., 1991-92; pres. Consumer Health Group Sterling Winthrop Inc., N.Y.C., 1993—. Trustee Inst. For The Future. Rhodes scholar, Eng., 1960. Mem. Inst. for the Future (trustee), Country Club New Canaan (Conn.), New Canaan Winter Club. Avocations: tennis, reading. Office: Sterling Winthrop Inc 90 Park Ave New York NY 10016

PIETRA, GIUSEPPE GIOVANNI, pathology educator; b. Piacenza, Italy, Dec. 30, 1930; came to U.S., 1957; s. Angelo and Emilia (Veratti) P.; m. Kathy Leuzinger, Nov. 23, 1957; children: Peter A., Philipp J. MD, U. Milan, 1955; BA (hon.), U. Pa., 1976. Diplomate Am. Bd. Pathology.

Oncology fellow Chgo. Med. Sch., 1957-60; resident pathology Mass. Gen. Hosp., Boston, 1962-63; prosector pathology U. Zurich, Switzerlaand, 1963-64; asst. prof. pathology Chgo. Med. Sch., 1965-66, U. Ill., Chgo., 1966-69; asst. prof. pathology U. Pa., Phila., 1969-72, assoc. prof., 1972-76, prof., 1976—; staff pathologist U. Pa. Hosp., 1969-76, dir. med. pathology, 1976-82, dir. anatomic pathology, 1982-94. Lt. M.C., Italian army, 1955-57. Fellow ACP; mem. Internat. Acad. Pathology, Microscopy Soc. Am. Office: U Pa Sch Medicine HUP 36th and Hamilton Walk Philadelphia PA 19104

PIETRINI, ANDREW GABRIEL, automotive aftermarket executive; b. Bryn Mawr, Pa., Feb. 27, 1937; s. Bernard and Irene (Norcini) P.; m. Pam Mari, Sept. 29, 1962; children: Darrin, Wayne. BS in Petroleum Engring., Stanford U., 1970; JD, U. Va., 1973. Bar: D.C. 1974, U.S. Supreme Ct. 1978. Assoc. Law Offices of Northcutt Ely, Washington, 1973-77, ptnr., 1977-84; ptnr. Bracewell & Patterson, Washington, 1984-89, Bryan, Cave, Washington and London, 1989-94, Coudert Bros., Washington and London, 1994—; mem. U.S. panel of arbitrators Internat. Ctr. for Settlement of Investment Disputes, 1988-94; chief counsel to Govt. Rep. of Guinea in Guinea-Bissau case, The Hague, 1984-85; arbitrator Pyramids Oasis case, 1984; legal advisor Ministry of Oil and Mineral Resources, Republic of Yemen, 1988—. Contbr. articles to profl. jours. Served to 1st lt. U.S. Army, 1966-69. Fellow Am. Bar Found.; mem. ABA, Am. Soc. Internat. Law, Internat. Bar Assn., Internat. Law Assn., Comml. Bar of U.K. (hon. overseas mem.), Union Internationale Des Avocats, Sigma Chi. Republican. Episcopalian. Clubs: Metropolitan, Cosmos (Washington); Farmington Country (Charlottesville, Va.); Guards Polo (Windsor, Eng.). Office: Coudert Brothers Ste 1200 1627 I St NW Washington DC 20006

PIETRUSKI, JOHN MICHAEL, JR., biotechnology company executive, pharmaceuticals executive; b. Sayreville, N.J., Mar. 12, 1933; m. Roberta Jeanne Talbot, July 3, 1954; children: Glenn David, Clifford John, Susan Jane. BS with honors, Rutgers U., 1954; LLD (hon.), Concordia Coll., 1993. With Proctor and Gamble Co., 1954-63; pres. med. products div. C.R. Bard, Inc., 1963-77; with Sterling Drug, Inc., N.Y.C., 1977-88; pres. Pharm. Group, 1977-81, corp. exec. v.p., 1981-83, pres., chief operating officer, 1983-85, chmn., chief exec. officer, 1985-88, ret., 1988; pres. Dansara Cons., 1988—; chmn. Tex. Biotech. Corp., 1990—; bd. dirs. Hershey Foods Corp., Gen. Pub. Utilities Corp., Lincoln Nat. Corp., McKesson Corp. Regent Concordia Coll. 1st lt. U.S. Army, 1955-57. Mem. Phi Beta Kappa. Club: Union League (N.Y.C.). Home: 27 Paddock Ln Colts Neck NJ 07722-1266 Office: One Penn Plaza Ste 3408 New York NY 10119

PIETRZAK, ALFRED ROBERT, lawyer; b. Glen Cove, N.Y., June 26, 1949; s. Alfred S. and Wanda M. (Wapniarski) P.; m. Sharon Esther Chizek, July 9, 1978; children: Eric A., Daniel J. BA, Fordham U., 1971; JD, Columbia U., 1974. Bar: N.Y. 1975, U.S. Dist. Ct. (so., ea., we. and no. dists.) N.Y. 1975, U.S. Dist. Ct. (no. dist.) Calif. 1983, U.S. Ct. Appeals (2d cir.) 1975, U.S. Ct. Appeals (9th cir.) 1983, U.S. Ct. Appeals (11th cir.) 1985, U.S. Supreme Ct. 1985. Assoc. Brown & Wood (formerly Brown, Wood, Ivey, Mitchell & Petty), N.Y.C., 1974-82, ptnr., 1983—; mem. policy com.; mem. fin. products adv. com. Commodity Futures Trading Commn.; mem. C.L.E. faculty Fordham U. Sch. Law.; Bd. editors Futures Internat. Law Letter; adv. bd. Fordham Internat. Law Jour.; contbr. articles to legal jours. Mem. ABA (litigation, bus law sect.), Assn. of Bar of City of N.Y. (securities regulation com., chair futures regulation com.), Am. Law Inst. (lectr.), Securities Industry Assn., Futures Industry Assn., Univ. Glee Club. Democrat. Roman Catholic. Home: 525 Monterey Ave Pelham Manor NY 10803-2513 Office: Brown & Wood 1 World Trade Ctr Fl 58 New York NY 10048-0001

PIETRZAK, LEONARD WALTER, accountant; b. Phila., Dec. 6, 1939; s. Walter Chester and Estelle Anne (Libucha) P.; m. Patricia Ann Cole, June 17, 1961; children: Stephen L., Diana L., Jeffrey S., Kristen M. BS, St. Joseph's U., Phila., 1961. Commd. officer USAF, Washington, 1961-64; audit mgr. Ernst & Young, Phila., 1964-77; corp. contr. Kleinert's Inc., Plymouth Meeting, Pa., 1977-81; v.p. fin. Jetronic Industries, Inc., Phila., 1981—; pres. NAA, So. Jersey, 1975-76. Mem. AICPA, Pa. Inst. CPA. Home: 60 Surrey Dr Southampton PA 18966-1224

PIETRZAK, TED S., art gallery director; b. Kitchener, Ont., Can., Sept. 18, 1952; m. Marlene C. Longdon, Aug. 26, 1990; 1 child, Christina. BA in Arts Mgmt., U. Guelph, Banff, Alta., Can. Asst. to dir. Art Gallery Hamilton, Ont., 1976-80; dir. Burlington Cultural Ctr., 1980-91, Art Gallery Hamilton, 1992—. Mem. Ont. Assn. Art Galleries (pres. 1983-84), Can. Art Museums' Dir.'s Orgn. (chair var. coms., treas. 1991—). Office: Art Gallery of Hamilton, 123 King St W, Hamilton, ON Canada L8P 4S8

PIETRZYK, DONALD JOHN, chemistry educator; b. Detroit, Jan. 20, 1934. B.S., Wayne State U., 1956; Ph.D., Iowa State U., 1960. Fellow MIT, 1960-61; from asst. prof. to assoc. T. Iowa, 1961-71; prof. chemistry U. Iowa, Iowa City. Office: Univ Iowa Chemistry Dept Iowa City IA 52242*

PIETTE, EDWARD JAMES, television executive; b. Detroit, Mar. 25, 1947; s. William Henry and Bernice Marie (Teeters) P.; m. Janet Lynn Aube, Feb. 5, 1977 (div. July 1980); 1 child, Kathryn; m. Eva Diane Carraway, Dec. 31, 1983; children: Jacquelyn, Marissa. BA, Mich. State U., 1969. Camera operator, dir. Sta. WXDN-TV, Detroit, 1969-71; producer, dir. Sta. WKBO-TV, Detroit, 1971-74; exec. producer Sta. WJXT-TV, Jacksonville, Fla., 1974-75, Sta. WFSB-TV, Hartford, Conn., 1975-79, Sta. WDIV-TV, Detroit, 1979-81; program dir. Sta. KWWL-TV, Waterloo, Iowa, 1981-83; gen. mgr. Sta. KTIV-TV, Sioux City, Iowa, 1983-84; dir. broadcast ops. Sta. KSDX-TV, St. Louis, 1984—. Served with U.S. Army, 1969. Roman Catholic. Office: WDAF TV Signal Hill Kansas City MO 64108

PIFER, ALAN (JAY PARRISH), former foundation executive; b. Boston, May 4, 1921; s. Claude Albert and Elizabeth (Parrish) P.; m. Erica Pringle, June 20, 1953 (div. 1994); children: Matthew, Nicholas, Daniel. AB, Harvard U., 1947; Lionel de Jersey Harvard student Emmanuel Coll., Cambridge (Eng.) U., 1947-48; LLD (hon.), Mich. State U., 1971, Hofstra U., 1974, Notre Dame U., 1975; DHL (hon.), Marymount Coll., 1983, Millsaps Coll., 1986; D of Univ. (hon.), Open U., Eng., 1974; JD (hon.), Atlanta U., 1980; DEd (hon.), U. Cape Town, South Africa, 1984. Exec. sec. U.S. Ednl. Commn. in U.K., London, 1948-53; program officer Carnegie Corp. N.Y., 1953-63, v.p., 1963-65, acting pres., 1965-67, pres., 1967-82, pres. emeritus, sr. cons., 1982-87; chmn., pres. Southport Inst. for Policy Analysis, 1987-91, chmn., 1991-94; v.p. Carnegie Found. for Advancement of Teaching, 1963-65, acting pres., 1965-67, pres., 1967-79, trustee, 1979-87; bd. dirs. Technoserve, Inc. Author: (with others) Our Aging Society, 1986, (with others) Women on the Front Lines: Meeting the Challenge of an Aging America, 1993; Government for the People, 1987. Mem. mgmt. com. U.S.-South Africa Leader Exch. Program, 1957—; pub. policy com. Adult Coun., 1987-91, adv. coun. Columbia U. Sch. Social Work, 1963-69, R & D ctr. panel U.S. Office Edn., 1963-65, adv. com. higher edn. U.S. Dept. Health Edn. and Welfare, 1967-68, bd. of overseers Harvard U., 1969-75, Charles Stark Draper Lab. bd. MIT, 1970-76, Commn. Pvt. Philanthropy and Pub. Needs, 1973-75; chmn. Consortium Advancement Pvt. Higher Edn., 1983-92, mayor's adv. com. Bd. Higher Edn. N.Y.C., 1966-69, Pres.'s Task Force on Edn., 1968, Aging Soc. Project, 1982-87, Nat. Conf. on Social Welfare Project, 1983-87; co-chmn. N.Y. State Nutrition Watch com., 1982; trustee U. Bridgeport, Conn., 1973—, Assn. Governing Bds. Colls. and Univs., 1985-91, African Am. Inst., 1957-71, Found. Libr. Ctr., 1967-71, Am. Ditchley Found., 1973-81; bd. dirs. Bus. Coun. Effective Literacy Inc., 1984-93, N.Y. Urban Coalition, 1967-71. Nat. Assembly for Social Policy and Devel., 1967-71, Coun. on Founds., Inc., 1970-76, Fed. Reserve Bank N.Y., 1970-76, Harry Frank Guggenheim Found., 1989—. Capt. U.S. Army, 1942-46, ETO. Recipient Barnard Coll. medal of distinction 1980, Cleve-

land E. Dodge medal of distinction Tchrs. Coll., Columbia U., 1982. Fellow Am. Acad. of Arts and Scis., African Studies Assn. (founding), Royal Soc. Arts (London); mem. Am. Assn. for Higher Edn. (bd. dirs. 1982-90), Council Fgn. Relations, Century Assn. Democrat. Episcopalian. Clubs: Harvard (N.Y.C.). Avocation: gardening.

PIGA, STEPHEN MULRY, lawyer; b. Bklyn., Apr. 9, 1929; s. Stephen Paul and Ella (Mulry) P.; married, Feb. 23, 1952 (div.); children: Maureen, Stephen, Susan, Elizabeth; m. Emilie Halliday, Aug. 1, 1975; 1 dau., Margaret. A.B., Princeton U., 1950; LL.B., Columbia u., 1955. Bar: N.J. 1955, N.Y. 1956. Assoc. White & Case, N.Y.C., 1955-63, ptnr., 1964-92; ret., 1992; lectr. Practicing Law Inst. N.Y. and various insts., bar assns. Served to capt. USMCR, 1951-53. Mem. ABA, N.Y. State Bar Assn. (exec. com. tax sect. 1981-89, chmn. employee benefits com.), Assn. of Bar of City N.Y., N.J. Bar Assn., Am. Contract Bridge League (life master), Profl. Bowlers' Assn. Am. Republican. Clubs: High Mt. Golf (Franklin Lakes, N.J.), Princeton (N.Y.C.). Avocations: bridge, golf, bowling.

PIGFORD, THOMAS HARRINGTON, nuclear engineering educator; b. Meridian, Miss., Apr. 21, 1922; s. Lamar and Zula Vivian (Harrington) P.; m. Catherine Kennedy Cathey, Dec. 31, 1948 (dec. 1992); children: Cynthia Pigford Naylor, Julie Pigford Brink; m. Elizabeth Hood Weekes, Nov. 12, 1994. B.S. in Chem. Engring., Ga. Inst. Tech., 1943; S.M. in Chem. Engring., M.I.T., 1948, Sc.D. in Chem. Engring., 1952. Asst. prof. chem. engring., dir. Sch. Engring. Practice, M.I.T., 1950-52; asst. prof. nuclear and chem. engring., 1952-55, assoc. prof., 1955-57; head engring., dir. nuclear reactor projects and asst. dir. research lab. Gen. Atomic Co., La Jolla, Calif., 1957-59; prof. nuclear engring., chmn. dept. nuclear engring. U. Calif., Berkeley, 1959—; sr. rsch. scientist Lawrence Berkeley Lab., 1959—; mem. panel Nat. Atomic Safety Licensing Bd. AEC-Nuclear Regulatory Commn., 1963-77; mem. Pres.'s Commn. on accident at 3-Mile Island, 1979; mem. bd. radioactive waste mgmt. and energy engring. bd., NAS-NAE, chmn. waste isolation systems panel, waste isolation pilot plant panel, fusion hybrid panel, separations and transmutations panel, transmutation of military plutonium panel, panel on health standard for radioactive waste disposal, chmn. adv. coun. Inst. Nuclear Power Op.; mem. Sec. of Energy's expert cons. group on Chernobyl accident; chmn. nuclear oversight com. Sacramento Mcpl. Utility Dist.; chmn. nuclear safety com. Gulf States Utilities Co.; mem. expert cons. group Swedish Nuclear Power Inspectorate; mem. peer rev. group for waste isolation pilot plant; mem. corp. rev. com. Oak Ridge Nat. Lab; lectr. Taiwan Nat. Sci. Found., 1990; vis. prof. Kyoto U., 1975, Kuwait U., 1976; cons. in field. Author: (with Manson Benedict) Nuclear Chemical Engineering, 1958, 2d edit., 1981; contbr. numerous articles to profl. jours. Served with USNR, 1944-46. Recipient John Wesley Powell award U.S. Geol. Survey, 1981; named Outstanding Young Man of Greater Boston, Boston Jaycees, 1955; E. I. DuPont DeNemours rsch. fellow, 1948-50; recipient Berkeley citation U. Calif., 1987; Japan Soc. for Promotion Sci. fellow, 1974-75; grantee NSF, 1960-75, EPA, 1973-78, Dept. Energy, 1979—, Ford Found., 1974-75, Electric Power Research Inst., 1974-75, Mitsubishi Metals Corp., 1989—. Fellow Am. Nuclear Soc. (bd. dirs., Arthur H. Compton award 1971); mem. AIME, NAE, Am. Chem. Soc., Am. Inst. Chem. Engrs. (Robert E. Wilson award 1980, Service to Society award 1985), Atomic Indsl. Forum (dir.), Sigma Xi, Phi Kappa Phi, Tau Beta Pi. Patentee in field. Home: 166 Alpine Ter Oakland CA 94618 Office: U Calif Dept Nuclear Engring Berkeley CA 94720

PIGGFORD, ROLAND RAYBURN, library and information services consultant; b. Monongahela, Pa., Jan. 28, 1926; s. Roland Rayburn and Emily Frances (Sanders) P.; m. Carole Meanor, Aug. 10, 1965; children—Eric, Susan. B.A., W.Va. Wesleyan Coll., Buckhannon, 1948; M.L.S., U. Pitts, 1964. Research assoc. Internat. Studies U. Pitts, 1964-66; librarian Internat. Studies Documentation Ctr., Oyster Bay, N.Y., 1966-67; asst. prof. SUNY, Albany, 1967-73; head planning and research Mass. Bd. Library Commrs., Boston, 1974-80, dir., 1980-91; cons. libr. and info. svcs., 1991—; cons. AID, Washington, 1967-70; bd. dirs. N.E. Document Conservation Ctr., Andover, Mass. 1980-89. Co-author: Book and Library Activities in Developing Countries, 1971; contbr. articles to profl. jours. Served to ensign USN, 1943-46; ETO. Mem. ALA, Mass. Libr. Assn. Home: 180 Oak St Shrewsbury MA 01545-5810

PIGNATARO, LOUIS JAMES, engineering educator; b. Bklyn., Nov. 30, 1923; s. Joseph and Rose (Capi) P.; m. Edith Hoffmann, Sept. 12, 1954; 1 child, Thea. B.C.E., Poly. Inst. Bklyn., 1951; M.S., Columbia U., 1954; Dr. Tech. Sci., Tech. U. Graz, Austria, 1961. Registered profl. engr., N.Y., Calif., Fla. Faculty Poly. Inst. N.Y., 1951-85, prof. civil engring., 1965—, dir. div. transp. planning, 1967—, head dept. transp. planning and engring., 1970, dir. Transp. Tng. and Research Center, 1975; Kayser prof. transp. engring. CCNY, N.Y.C., 1985-88; assoc. dir. Inst. for Transp. CCNY, 1985-88; mem. faculty N.J. Inst. Tech., 1988—, disting. prof. transp. engring., 1988—, dir. ctr. transp. studies and research, 1988-93; exec. dir. Inst. for Transp., 1994—; cons. govtl. agys., pvt. firms. Mem. Gov.'s Task Force Advisers on Transp. Problems, Gov.'s Task Force on Alcohol and Hwy. Safety; commr.'s council advisers N.Y. State Dept. Transp.; mem. adv. bd. freight services improvement conf. Port Authority N.Y. and N.J.; mem. adv. com. N.Y.C. Dept. Transp.; mem. rev. com. N.Y.C. Dept. City Planning; mem. Mayor's Transp. Commn., City of Newark. Sr. author: Traffic Engineering-Theory and Practice, 1973; contbr. over 70 papers to profl. jours. Served with AUS, 1943-46. Recipient Distinguished Tchr. citation Poly. Inst. Bklyn., 1965, Dedicated Alumnus award, 1971, Distinguished Alumnus award, 1972; citation for distinguished research Poly. Inst. Sigma Xi, 1975; named Engr. of Year N.Y. State Soc. Profl. Engrs., 1974. Fellow ASCE (dir.), Inst. Transp. Engrs. (Transp. Engr. of Yr. Met. sect. N.Y. and N.J. 1982); mem. Am. Rd. and Transp. Builders Assn. (div. dir.), Transp. Research Bd. (univ. liaison rep., Outstanding Paper award 1980 ann. meeting), Transp. Research Forum, Nat. Soc. Profl. Engrs., Sigma Xi, Chi Epsilon, Tau Beta Pi. Home: 230 Jay St Brooklyn NY 11201-1948 Office: NJ Inst Tech Inst for Transp 323 Martin Luther King Blvd Newark NJ 07102

PIGNATELLI, DEBORA BECKER, state legislator; b. Weehawken, N.J., Oct. 25, 1947; d. Edward and Frances (Fishman) Becker; m. Michael Albert Pignatelli, Aug. 22, 1971; children: Adam Becker, Benjamin Becker. AA, Vt. Coll., 1967; BA, U. Denver, 1969. Exec. dir. Girl's Club Greater Nashua, N.H., 1975-77; dir. tenant svcs. Nashua Housing Authority, 1979-80; vocat. counselor Comprehensive Rehab. Assocs., Bedford, N.H., 1982-85; specialist job placement Crawford & Co., Bedford, 1985-87; mem. appropriations com. N.H. Ho. of Reps., Concord, 1986-91, asst. minority leader, 1989-92; mem. N.H. State Senate, 1992—; Senate Dem. Whip; mem. environ., econ. devel., judiciary coms., fish and gam com., interstate coop. com.; del. Am. Coun. Young Polit. Leaders, Germany, 1987. Mem. Nashua Peace Ctr., 1980—; asst. coach Little League Baseball, Nashua, 1987-90; mem. steering com. Gephardt for Pres. Campaign, N.H., 1987-88; del. Dem. Nat. Conv., 1988; mem. Gov.'s Commn. on Domestic Violence. Mem. N.H. Children's Lobby, Women's Lobby. Jewish. Avocations: skiing, children, swimming, boating. Home: 22 Appletree Grn Nashua NH 03062-2252 Office: NH State Senate State House Rm 115 Concord NH 03301

PIGOTT, CHARLES MCGEE, transportation equipment manufacturing executive; b. Seattle, Apr. 21, 1929; s. Paul and Theiline (McGee) P.; m. Yvonne Flood, Apr. 18, 1953. B.S., Stanford U., 1951. With PACCAR Inc, Seattle, 1959—, exec. v.p., 1962-65, pres., 1965-86, chmn., pres., 1986-87, chmn., chief exec. officer, 1987—, also bd. dirs.; dir. The Seattle Times, Chevron Corp., The Boeing Co. Pres. Nat. Boy Scouts Am., 1986-88, mem. exec. bd. Mem. Bus. Council. Office: Paccar Inc 777 106th Ave NE Bellevue WA 98004*

PIGOTT, GEORGE MORRIS, food engineering educator, consulting engineer; b. Vancouver, Wash., Oct. 25, 1928; s. Alexander William and Moreita (Howard) P.; m. Joyce Burroughs (div. 1980); children: George Jr., Roy K., Randall E. Julie M., Becky P. Holm; m. Barbee W. Tucker. BS in Chem. Engring., U. Wash., 1950, MS in Chem. Engring., 1955, PhD in Food Sci. and Chemistry, 1962. Field engr. Continental Can Co., Seattle, 1951-53; rsch. engr. Fish and Wildlife Svc., Seattle, 1947-51, Nat. Canners Assn., Seattle, 1953-55, Boeing Corp., Seattle, 1957-60; prof. food engring. Inst. Food Sci. and Tech. U. Wash., Seattle, 1962—; pres. Sea Resources Engring. Inc., Bellevue, Wash., 1965—; also dir. various cos. Author: Pathway to a Healthy Heart, 1983, Fish and Shellfish in Human Nutrition, 1988; over 200

tech. papers; patentee in field. Served to lt. U.S. Army, 1951-53. Mem. NSPE, Am. Inst. Chem. Engrs., Am. Inst. Nutrition, Am. Chem. Soc., Inst. Food Technologists, Am. Inst. Chemistry, Am. Dietetic Assn., Am. Soc. Agrl. Engrs. Avocations: skiing, fishing, boating, scuba diving. Office: U Wash Inst for Food Sci and Tech HF-10 Seattle WA 98195 also: Sea Resources Engring Inc 10900 NE 8th Bellevue WA 98004

PIGOTT, RICHARD J., food company executive; b. Chgo., May 26, 1940; s. Charles Francis and Mary Barbara (Amberg) P.; m. Karen Victoria Nahigian, Aug. 22, 1964; children: Alicia, Christopher. B.B.A., U. Notre Dame, 1961; J.D., U. Wis., 1966. Law ptnr. Winston & Strawn, 1966-77; with Beatrice Foods Co., Chgo., 1977-88, sr. v.p., gen. counsel, 1977-80, exec. v.p., chief adminstrv. officer, 1981-88; merger and acquisition advisor, inventory, atty., 1988—; bd. dirs. Rodman & Renshaw Capital Group, Inc., Chgo., Ameriwood Industries, Grand Rapids, Mich. Trustee Chgo. Symphony Orch., 1983—; mem. bus. adv. coun. U. Ill., Chgo., 1983—. 1st lt. U.S. Army, 1961-63. Home: 1038 Longvalley Rd Glenview IL 60025-3414 Office: Three First Nat Plz 70 W Dearborn St Ste 3100 Chicago IL 60602

PIGOZZI, RAYMOND ANTHONY, architect; b. Chgo., Feb. 29, 1928; s. Mario and Milena (Kervin) P.; m. Judith M. Hays, Feb. 12, 1955; children: Raymond J., Thomas M., Robert J., Ellen A., Andrew H. BS in Architecture, U. Ill., 1951. Registered architect, Ill., Iowa, Wis., Mich., Ind., N.C. Designer Ganster & Henninghausen, Waukegan, Ill., 1954-58; prin. designer O'Donnell Wicklund Pigozzi & Peterson Architects, Inc., Deerfield, Ill., 1958—; juror Coun. Ednl. Facility Planners Internat., Chgo., 1977-78, Am. Assn. Sch. Adminstrs., Washington, 1982-83, honor awards program Masonry Inst. Mich., 1987, Am. Sch. and Univ. Award Winning Ednl. Bldg., 1989, Metal Constrn. Assn. Merit awards, 1993; cons. Ednl. Facilities Lab., N.Y.C., 1972-75; Ednl. Environ. Exhbn. Jury, Ill. Assn. Sch. Bds., 1993. Prin. works include Fairview South Elem. Sch. Auditorium and Learning Ctr., Skokie, Ill. (Chgo. Chpt. AIA Disting. Bldg. award 1968), Onwentsia Country Club Tennis and Squash Facility, Lake Forest, Ill. (Chgo. Chpt. AIA Disting. bldg. award 1971), Berkeley Elem. Sch., Arlington Heights, Ill. (Am. Assn. Sch. Adminstrs. citation 1971), Field Elem. Sch. Remodeling, Chgo. (Coun. Ednl. Facility Planners Modernization award 1973), Von Humboldt Child-Parent Ctr. (Assn. Sch. Bus. Ofcls. award of Merit 1981, Met. Chgo. Masonry Coun. Honor award for excellence in masonry 1981), Robert Crown Community Ctr., Evanston, Ill., Loyola U. Humanities Bldg., 1983, Crystal Lake Village Hall, 1987, Frank C. Whiteley Sch. Hoffman Estates, Ill., 1989, Arthur Anderson & Co. Campus Ctr. Expansion, St. Charles, Ill., 1990 (Gold medal Excellence in Masonry Awards), Science Wing Niles H.S., Skokie, Ill., 1993 (Disting. Bldg. award, Silver medal Exellence in Masonry AIA, 1994). mem. ednl. adv. com. Evanston Twp. High Sch., 1979-83; chmn. profl. svc. Evanston United Way, 1982; mem. state's fine arts rev. com. Northeastern Ill. U., 1987. Recipient Metal Construction Assn. Merit award, 1993, Ill. Assn. Sch. Bd. Award of Distinction, Homewood Floosmoor High Sch., 1993. Fellow AIA (mem. nat. com. on architecture for edn. 1980—, juror N.E. chpt. bldg. honor awards program 1989, Disting. Svc. award 1990, Disting. Svc. award Chgo. chpt. 1990); mem. Ill. Sch. Bus. Ofcls., Ill. Libr. Assn., Ill. Assn. Sch. Bus. Ednl. Environments (juror 1992), Coun. Ednl. Facility Planners (pres. Great Lakes region 1988-90), Landmarks Preservation Coun. Ill. Democrat. Roman Catholic. Home: 200 Lee St Evanston IL 60202-1450 Office: O'Donnell Wicklund Pigozzi and Peterson Architecs Inc 570 Lake Cook Rd Deerfield IL 60015-4910 also: 1 North Franklin Chicago IL 60601

PIGSLEY, DELORES ANN, tribal leader, educator; b. Toledo, Mar. 29, 1943; d. Alfred and Maude (Porter) Lane; m. Donald W. Pigsley, June 23, 1962; children: Timothy L., Troy A., Quanna M. Grad. h.s., Salem, Oreg. Tribal coun. mem. Conf. Tribes of Siletz, Oreg., 1975-80, 83-84, chmn., 1984—; chmn. Siletz Tribal Econ. Devel. Com., 1985-89, 94—; ops. supr. Social Security Adminstrn., Salem, 1974—; bd. dirs. Oreg. Health Sci. U., Portland. Fed. Recognition for Conf. Tribes of Siletz, 1975-79. Mem. Nat. Congress of Am. Indians. Democrat. Roman Catholic. Office: Siletz Tribal Council PO Box 549 Siletz OR 97380-0549

PIHL, JAMES MELVIN, electrical engineer; b. Seattle, May 29, 1943; s. Melvin Charles and Carrie Josephine (Cummings) P.; divorced; 1 child, Christopher James. AASEE, Seattle, 1971; postgrad., City Univ., Bellevue, Wash., 1982—. 1st class operators lic., FCC; lic. in real estate sales. Journeyman machinist Svc. Exch. Corp., Seattle, 1964-67; design engr. P.M. Electronics, Seattle, 1970-73, Physio Control Corp., Redmond, Wash., 1973-79; project engr. SeaMed Corp., Redmond, 1979-83; sr. design engr. Internat. Submarine Tech., Redmond, 1983-85; engring. mgr. First Med. Devices, Bellevue, Wash., 1985-89; rsch. engr. Pentco Products, Bothell, Wash., 1989—. Inventor, patentee protection system for preventing defibrillation with incorrect or improperly connected electrodes, impedance measurement circuit. With U.S. Army, 1961-64. Mem. N.Y. Acad. Scis. Avocations: boating, high-performance engine design and devel., target shooting, violin. Home: 14303 82nd Ave NE Bothell WA 98011-5016 Office: Pentco Products PO Box 403 Kenmore WA 98028-9999

PIHL, MARTIN, trust fund adminstrator. Pres. Ketchikan Pulp; ret., 1994; interim exec. dir. Alaska Permanent Fund Corp., Juneau, 1994—. Office: Alaksa Permanent Fund Corp 801 W 10th St Ste 302 Juneau AK 99801*

PIHLAJA, MAXINE MURIEL MEAD, orchestra executive; b. Windom, Minn., July 19, 1935; d. Julian Wright and Mildred Eleanor (Ray) Mead; m. Donald Francis Pihlaja, Jan. 4, 1963; children: Geoffrey Blake, Kirsten Louise, Jocelyn Erika. BA, Hamline U., 1957; postgrad., Columbia U., 1957-58. Group worker Fedn. of Chs., L.A., 1956; case worker St. Mary's Guild Floating Hosp. Ship, N.Y.C., 1957-59; Y-Teen program dir. YWCA, Elizabeth, N.J., 1957-60, Boulder, Colo., 1964-65; spl. svcs. program and club dir. U.S. Army, Ingrandes and Nancy, France, 1960-62; music buyer, salesperson Guinn's Music, Billings, Mont., 1977-78, N.W. Music, Billings, 1978-79; office adminstr. Am. Luth. Ch., Billings, 1979-84; gen. mgr. Billings Symphony Orchestra, 1984—; substitute tchr. Community Day Care and Enrichment Corp., Billings, 1971-76. Dir. Handbell choir 1st Presybn. Ch., Billings, 1972—, Am. Luth. Ch., 1981-84; 1st English Luth. Ch., 1982—; mem. Billings Symphony Chorale, 1965-91, Bellissimo!, 1983-93. Mem. Nat. Soc. Fund Raising Execs. (sec. Mont. 1988), Mont. Assn. Female Execs., Am. Guild English Handbell Ringers (state chmn., 1988-89, treas. Area X bd. dirs. 1990-94, membership chmn. 1994—), Mont Assn. Symphony Orchs. (treas, 1987-92). Lutheran. Office: Billings Symphony Orch 401 N 31st St Ste 530 Billings MT 59101-1200

PIIPPO, STEVE, educational program director. Dir. math. sci. tech. program Richland (Wash.) High Sch. Recipient A Sites Recognition award U.S. Dept. Edn. Office: Richland High Sch Math Sci Tech Program 930 Long Ave Richland WA 99352

PIIRMA, IRJA, chemist, educator; b. Tallinn, Estonia, Feb. 4, 1920; came to U.S., 1949; d. Voldemar Juri and Meta Wilhelmine (Lister) Tiits; m. Aleksander Piirma, Mar. 10, 1943; children: Margit Ene, Silvia Ann. Diploma in chemistry, Tech. U., Darmstadt, Fed. Republic of Germany, 1949; MS, U. Akron, 1957, PhD, 1960. Rsch. chemist U. Akron, Ohio, 1952-67, asst. prof., 1967-76, assoc. prof., 1976-81, prof., 1981-90; prof. emerita U. Akron, Ohio, 1990—; dept. head U. Akron, Ohio, 1982-85. Author: Polymeric Surfactants, 1992; editor: Emulsion Polymerization, 1982; contbr. articles to profl. jours. Recipient Extra Mural Rsch. award BP Am., Inc., 1989. Mem. Am. Chem. Soc. Avocations: swimming, skiing. Home: 3528 Adaline Dr Cuyahoga Falls OH 44224-3929 Office: U Akron Akron OH 44325-3909

PIKE, ALBERT LOUIS, JR., educational administrator, consultant; b. Somerville, Mass., June 26, 1942; s. Albert Louis and Mary Jeanette (Sullivan) P.; m. Barbara Antoinette Raymondi, Aug. 20, 1972. BA, Suffolk U., 1964; MA in French, Rivier Coll., 1975; postgrad., Boston Coll., 1983. Tchr. French, English and penmanship Western Jr. High Sch., Somerville (Mass.) Pub. Schs., 1964-69; tchr. French, Spanish and English Billerica (Mass.) Pub. Schs., 1969-81, chmn. dept. fgn. langs., 1981-91, teaching supr. fgn. langs., 1991-93, chmn. dept. fgn. langs., 1991—; ednl. cons. Holt, Rinehart, Winston, 1985-88; mem. world langs. curriculum framework com. Dept. of Edn., Commonwealth of Mass., 1994—. With U.S. Army, 1966-68.

Mem. ASCD, Mass. ASCD, Am. Coun. Teaching Fgn. Langs., Nat. Assn. Dist. Fgn. Lang. Administrs., Mass. Fgn. Lang. Assn., Ea. Mass. Fgn. Lang. Adminstr. (v.p. 1988-89). Democrat. Roman Catholic. Avocations: traveling, playing piano. Home: 9 Red Coat Ln Burlington MA 01803 Office: Billerica Pub Schs 35 River St Billerica MA 01821

PIKE, ALLEN W., supermarket company executive. Student, Carleton Coll.; grad., Harvard U., 1932. With Kroger Co., Cin., 1932-35; with Piggly-Wiggly Corp., Atlanta, 1935-41; with Almac's Inc., East Provident, R.I., 1941—, now chmn. bd., chief exec. officer, dir. Office: Almac's Inc 1 Noyes Ave Rumford RI 02916-3396

PIKE, DOUGLAS EUGENE, Indochina studies director; b. Cass Lake, Minn., July 27, 1924; s. Clarence Eugene and Esther (Jensen) P.; m. Myrna Louise Johnson, Sept. 15, 1956; children: Andrew Jefferson, Victoria Louise, Ethan Edward. BA, U. Calif., 1953; MA, Am. U., 1961; postgrad., MIT, 1963-64. Writer UN, Korea, 1950-52; fgn. service officer U.S. Govt. State Dept., Washington, Saigon, Hong Kong, Tokyo, and Taipei, Taiwan., 1958-82; dir. Indochina Studies Program, U. Calif., Berkeley, 1982—. Author: Viet Cong: The Organizational Techniques of the National Liberation Front of South Vietnam, 1965, War, Peace and the Viet Cong, 1969, History of Vietnamese Communism, 1978, PAVN: People's Army of Vietnam, 1986, Vietnam and the USSR: Anatomy of an Alliance, 1987, The Bunker Papers: Reports to the President from Vietnam, 1991; editor: Indochina Chronology, 1983—; contbr. numerous articles to profl. jours. Recipient Superior Honor award U.S. Info. Agy., 1976, Sec. Def. medal, U.S. Dept. Def., 1981. Mem. Author's Guild, Army-Navy Club (Washington), Fgn. Svc. Club, Faculty Club U. Calif. Methodist. Avocation: philately. Home: 2265 Alva Ave El Cerrito CA 94530-1857 Office: U Calif 6701 San Pablo Ave Berkeley CA 94720

PIKE, GEORGE HAROLD, JR., religious organization executive, clergyman; b. Summit, N.J., Jan. 14, 1933; s. George Harold and Ann Aurelia (Brewer) P.; m. Pauline Elizabeth Blair, Aug. 27, 1955; children: Elizabeth, George 3d, James. BA, Trinity Coll., Hartford, Conn., 1954; MDiv, Dubuque (Iowa) Theolog. Sch., 1957. Ordained to ministry Presbyn. Ch. USA., 1957. Pastor 1st PResbyn. Ch., Kasson, Minn., 1956-59, 3d Presbyn. Ch., Dubuque, 1959-64; sr. pastor Presbyn. Ch., Bettendorf, Iowa, 1964-68; sr. pastor 1st Presbyn. Ch., Vancouver, Wash., 1968-78, Cranford, N.J., 1978-88; exec. chair Presbyn. Ch. USA, Louisville, 1988-93; interim pastor 2d Presbyn. Ch., Kansas City, Mo., 1993-95; dir. sem. devel. U. Dubuque, Iowa, 1995—; mem. exec. com. Consultation on Ch. Union, Princeton, 1980-89, pres., 1984-88. Dir. Bettendorf Bd. Edn., 1964-68, pres. 1967-68; bd. dirs. Southwest Wash. Hosps., Vancouver, 1969-78. Named Citizen of Yr., Jaycees, Bettendorf, 1967, Citizen of Yr., B'nai B'rith, Cranford, 1988; named to Honorable Order of Ky. Cols., 1989. Avocations: golf, photography. Home: 3650 Keystone Dr Dubuque IA 52002 Office: U Dubuque 2000 University Dubuque IA 52001-5050

PIKE, JOHN NAZARIAN, optical engineering consultant; b. Boston, Feb. 13, 1929; s. Arthur Thorndike and Sarah Lucy (Nazarian) P.; m. Margaretta May Horner, Dec. 28, 1957; children: Sally Katharine, Susan Horner. AB, Princeton U., 1951; PhD in Physics and Optics, U. Rochester, 1958. Staff scientist Parma (Ohio) Rsch. Ctr., Union Carbide Corp., 1956-63; mem. physics faculty Baldwin-Wallace Coll., Berea, Ohio, 1961-63; sr. scientist Tarrytown (N.Y.) Tech. Ctr., Union Carbide Corp., 1963-85; pres. J.J. Pike & Co., Inc., Pleasantville, N.Y., 1986—. Patentee in applied indsl. optics; contbr. numerous articles to profl. jours. Bd. dirs. United Way Westchester, N.Y., 1979-85, 95—, chmn. planning com., 1989-95, chmn. planned giving, 1995—. Recipient Harold J. Marshall Citation for Cmty. Svc., United Way No. Westchester, 1976, Cmty. Svc. award Union Carbide Corp., 1982. Mem. Optical Soc. Am., Soc. Photo-Optical Instrument Engrs., Internat. Soc. for Optical Engring., Phi Beta Kappa, Sigma Xi. Home: 71 Cedar Ave Pleasantville NY 10570-1932 Office: JJ Pike & Co Inc PO Box 186 Pleasantville NY 10570-0186

PIKE, KENNETH LEE, linguist, educator; b. Conn., June 9, 1912; s. Ernest R. and Hattie (Granniss) P.; m. Evelyn Griset, Oct. 20, 1938; children: Judith, Barbara, Stephen. BTh, Gordon Coll., 1933, LHD (hon.), 1982; PhD, U. Mich., 1942; PhD (hon.), Huntington Coll., 1967, Wheaton Coll., Irian Jaya, 1975, René Descartes U., Sorbonne, 1978, Monterrey, Mex.; LHD (hon.), U. Chgo., 1974, Georgetown U., 1984. Assoc. prof. U. Mich., Ann Arbor, 1948-55, prof., 1955-79; adj. prof. U. Tex., Arlington, 1979—; researcher, cons. Summer Inst. Linguistics, Dallas; researcher, lectr. in Mex., Ecuador, Peru, Guatemala, Papua New Guinea, Ghana, Nigeria, Philippines, Irian Jaya, Nepal, Thailand, Chile, Brazil, Singapore, others. Author: Phonetics, 1943, Intonation of American English, 1945, Phonemics, 1947, Tone Languages, 1948, Language in Relation to a Unified Theory of the Structure of Human Behavior, 1954, 2d edit., 1967, (with R. Young and A. Becker) Rhetoric, Discovery and Change, 1971, (with Evelyn G. Pike) Grammatical Analysis, 1977, 2d edit., 1982, Linguistics Concepts--An Introduction to Tagmemics, 1982, (with Evelyn G. Pike) Text and Tagmeme, 1983, (with D. Stark and Angel Merecias) Translator: New Testament Mixtec, With Heart and Mind, 1962, Stir, Change, Create: Poems and Essays, 1961; editor: (with Thomas N. Headland, Marvin Harris) Emics and Etics--The Insider/Outsider Debate, 1990, Talk, Thought and Thing--The Emic Road Toward Conscious Knowledge, 1993. Bd. dirs. Wycliffe Bible Translators, Huntington Beach, Calif., 1942-79. Recipient Presdl. Medal Merit, Govt. of Philippines, 1974; named Hon. Prof., U. Trujillo, 1987. Mem. Summer Inst. Linguistics (pres. 1979), Linguistic Soc. Am. (pres. 1961), Linguistic Assn. Can. and U.S. (pres. 1978), Am. Anthrop. Assn., Internat. Phonetic Soc., Am. Acad. Arts and Sci., Nat. Acad. Sci. Republican. Presbyterian. Avocation: water polo. Home and Office: Summer Inst Linguistics 7500 W Camp Wisdom Rd Dallas TX 75236-5628

PIKE, KERMIT JEROME, library director; b. East Cleveland, June 19, 1941; s. Frank James and Pauline Frances (Prijatel) P.; m. Joyce Rita Massillo, June 27, 1964; children: Christopher James, Laura Elizabeth. BA, Case Western Res. U., 1963, MA, 1965. Rsch. asst. Western Res. Hist. Soc., Cleve., 1965-66, curator manuscripts, 1966-72, chief libr., 1969-75, dir. libr., 1976—; adj. prof. history, libr. sci. Case Western Res. U., 1975-84. Author: Guide to the Manuscripts and Archives, 1972, Guide to Shaker Manuscripts, 1974; editor: Guide to Jewish History Sources, 1983; Compiler: Guide to Major Manuscript Collections, 1987. Mem. Super Sesquicentennial Com., Cleve., 1971, Cleve. Bicentennial History Com., 1992—; trustee Nationalities Svc. Ctr., Clevel., 1979-86; chmn. vis. com. on humanites and arts, Cleve. State U., 1980-82. Recipient Achievement award No. Ohio Live, Cleve., 1987; Spl. Recognition award Gov. Richard F. Celeste of Ohio, 1990. Mem. Soc. Ohio Archivists (co-founder 1968, pres. 1971-72), Black History Archives (founder 1970), Orgn. Am. Historians, Soc. Am. Archivists, Manuscripts Soc., Midwest Archives Conf., Ohio Geneal. Soc., Early Settlers Assn. of the Western Res., Rowfant Club, Lake County Farmers' Conservation Club, Lambda Chi Alpha. Roman Catholic. Home: 3985 Orchard Rd Cleveland OH 44121-2411 Office: Western Res Hist Soc 10825 East Blvd Cleveland OH 44106-1788

PIKE, LARRY ROSS, insurance executive; b. Harrisburg, Pa., Aug. 14, 1935; m. Sandra Marie Thomas; children: Karen Lynn Aungst, Christine Elaine Frain. AB in Econs., Franklin & Marshall Coll., 1958; MBA, U. Del., 1974. CLU. Sr. life and health underwriter Provident Mutual Life Ins. Co., 1958-68; v.p. underwriting/issue Continental Life Ins. Co., 1968-79, Bankers Nat. Life Ins. Co., 1979-80; v.p. underwriting/issue Home Life Ins. Co., 1980-81, sr. v.p. ins. svcs., 1981-84, sr. v.p. corp. fin. info., 1984-87; exec. v.p. ind. ins. and annuities Union Cen. Life Ins. Co., Cin., 1987-89, pres., chief oper. officer, 1989-90, pres., chief exec. officer, chmn. bd. dirs., 1990—; chmn. bd. dirs., pres., chief exec. officer Manhattan Nat. Corp., Cin.; bd. dirs. Manhattan Life Ins. Co., Manhattan Nat. Pension Svc., Inc., Carillon Advisors, Inc., Carillon Investments, Inc., Carillon Mktg. Agy., Carillon Life Ins. Co. Fellow Life Mgmt. Inst.; mem. Cert. Life Underwriters., Bankers Club, Masons. Avocations: travel, Civil War history, walking. Home: 3598 Carpenters Creek Dr Cincinnati OH 45241-3819 Office: Union Cen Life Ins Co 1876 Waycross Rd Cincinnati OH 45240-2825

PIKE, LARRY SAMUEL, lawyer; b. Savannah, Ga., Feb. 23, 1939; s. Abram and Ida (Feinberg) P.; m. Bonnie Jo Haykin, June 21, 1959; children: Douglas, Stacey, Scott. BA, Emory U., 1960, LLB, 1963; postgrad., Leeds

(Eng.) U., 1960-61. Assoc. L. Jack Swertfeger Jr. Atty., Decatur, Ga., 1963-66; ptnr. Swertfeger, Scott, Pike & Simmons, Decatur, 1966-75, Simmons, Pike & Warren, Decatur, 1975-76, Lefkoff, Pike & Sims, Atlanta, 1976-85, Branch, Pike & Ganz, Atlanta, 1985—. Editor-in-chief law jour. and newspaper; contbr. numerous articles to profl. jours. Pres. Ansley Park Civic Assn., Atlanta, 1977-79, Northshore Homeowners Assn., Tybee Island, Ga., 1992—, The Temple, Atlanta, 1979-81, trustee, 1977—, Am. Cancer Soc., DeKalb County, Ga. unit, 1970-71, crusade chmn., 1969-70; trustee Ansley Park Beautification Found., Inc., Atlanta, 1984—, The Temple Endowment Fund, Atlanta, 1979-87, Atlanta Jewish Community Ctr., 1973-76; bd. overseers Hebrew Union Coll., Cin., 1987—; alumni coun. Emory U., Atlanta, 1966-72; bd. trustees Union of Am. Hebrew Congregations, 1991—. Fulbright fellow, 1960-61; named Outstanding Young Man of Yr. North DeKalb Jaycees, 1968. Mem. ABA, State Bar Ga. (exec. coun. Young Lawyers sect. 1968-72), Atlanta Bar Assn., Decatur-DeKalb Bar Assn. (sec. 1965-66), Atlanta Legal Aid Soc. (pres. 1974-75, past bd. dirs.), Atlanta Tax Forum, Lawyers Club Atlanta, B'nai B'rith (pres. Atlanta lodge 1970-71, Ga. pres. 1974-75, dist. 5 bd. govs. 1973-76, chair Youth Orgn. Bd. 1971-73), Phi Beta Kappa, Omicron Delta Kappa. Office: Branch Pike & Ganz 2 Midtown Plz Fl 15 Atlanta GA 30309

PIKE, LAURENCE BRUCE, retired lawyer; b. Brattleboro, Vt., Sept. 11, 1927; s. Lee Ernest and Alice Louise (Temple) P.; m. Norma I. Ecklund, Sept. 2, 1950; children: Barbara L., William T., Jeffrey O., Alan B. BA., U. Iowa, 1951; J.D., Columbia U., 1954. Bar: N.Y. 1955. Assoc. firm Simpson Thacher & Bartlett, N.Y.C., 1954-64, ptnr., 1964-87. Mem. Scarsdale Town Club, N.Y., 1964-68; mem. capt. Scarsdale Aux. Police, 1960-72. Served with USN, 1945-48. Mem. ABA, Bar Assn. City N.Y., N.Y. State Bar Assn., Ardsley Curling Club (N.Y., dir., sec. 1974-77), Phi Beta Kappa. Congregationalist. Home: 7 Guilford St Brattleboro VT 05301-2607 Office: Simpson Thacher & Bartlett 425 Lexington Ave New York NY 10017-3954

PIKE, RALPH WEBSTER, chemical engineer, educator, university official; b. Tampa, Fla., Nov. 10, 1935; s. Ralph Webster and Macey (Adams) P.; m. Patricia Jennings, Aug. 23, 1958. B Chem. Engring., Ga. Inst. Tech., 1957, PhD, 1962. Rsch. chem. engr. Exxon R & D Co., Baytown, Tex., 1962-64; prof. chem. engring. and systems sci. La. State U., Baton Rouge, 1964—, assoc. vice chancellor for rsch., 1975—, dir. La. Mineral Inst., 1979—; cons. to chem. and petroleum refining industry, fed. govt. and State of La., 1964—. Author: Formulation and Optimization of Mathematical Models, 1970, Optimization for Engineering Systems, 1986, Optimizacion en Ingenieria, 1989. Active various civic, ch. and community orgns., Baton Rouge, 1964—. 2d lt. U.S. Army, 1958-60. Recipient over 60 rsch. grants, including NASA, NSF, Dept. Interior, EPA, NOAA, state agys. and pvt. industry, 1964—. Fellow Am. Inst. Chem. Engrs. (chmn. nat. program com. 1984, local sect. 1985); mem. Am. Chem. Soc. (awards, univ. and profl.), Sigma Xi. Democrat. Methodist. Avocation: skiing. Home: 6063 Hibiscus Dr Baton Rouge LA 70808-8844 Office: La State U 210 Ctr Energy Studies Baton Rouge LA 70803

PIKE, WILLIAM EDWARD, business executive; b. Ft. Collins, Colo., Jan. 25, 1929; s. Harry H. and Alice Francis (Swinscoe) P.; m. Catherine Broward Crawford, June 26, 1965; children: Elizabeth Catherine, Robert Crawford, Daniel William. Student, U. Colo., 1947-48; B.S., U.S. Naval Acad., 1952; M.B.A., Harvard, 1960. Commd. ensign USN, 1952, advanced through grades to lt., 1958; ret., 1958; asst. treas. Morgan Guaranty Trust Co., N.Y.C., 1962-64; asst. v.p. Morgan Guaranty Trust Co., 1964-66, v.p., 1966-71, sr. v.p., 1971-74, chmn. credit policy com., 1974-86; exec. v.p. J.P. Morgan & Co., Inc., 1986-89; bd. dirs. VF Corp., Somat Corp., Am. States Ins. Co.; corp. dir., trustee, pvt. investor. Episcopalian. Club: Country (New Canaan, Conn.). Home: Indian Waters Dr New Canaan CT 06840 Office: 36 Grove St New Canaan CT 06840-5329

PIKLER, CHARLES, musician. Student violin, Norwich, Conn.; student, U. Conn., violin studies with Bronislaw Gimpel; BA in math., U. Minn. Violin soloist Chgo. Symphony Orch., 1987—; Appeared in summer festivals including Tanglewood Young Artist Program, Berkshire Music Ctr., 1965-71; prin. appearances include Hartford Symphony Orch., Ea. Conn. Symphony Orch. and Manchester Civic Orch.; substitute in Chgo. Symphony Orch. viola sect., violin soloist, solo performer on violin and viola; concertmaster of Chgo. Chamber Orch. Office: care Chgo Symphony Orch Orch Hall 220 S Michigan Ave Chicago IL 60604-2508*

PILAR, GUILLERMO ROMAN, physiology and neurobiology educator; came to U.S., 1961, naturalized; BA, Liceo Military Gen. San Martin, Argentina, 1948; MD, Nat. U. Buenos Aires, 1954. Intern, then resident in internal medicine Nat. U. Buenos Aires, 1954-55, 56-57, physician-in-residence, 1957-58; tng. dept. physiology Cath. U. Chile, Santiago, 1958, Nat. Inst. Cardiology, Mexico City, 1959-61; rsch. assoc. in physiology U. Utah, Lake Lake City, 1961-63; asst. rsch. prof., then assoc. rsch. prof. U. Utah, Salt Lake City, 1966-71; tng. dept. physiology Australian Nat. U., Canberra, 1963-64; vis. sr. lectr. Monash U., Melbourne, Australia, 1965-66; prof. physiology and neurobiology U. Conn., Storrs, 1971—, acting head, then head regulatory biology sect., 1972-77, head physiology sect., 1977-85, head dept. physiology and neurobiology, 1985—, mem. adv. bd. Biotech. Ctr., 1992—; vis. assoc. prof. dept. pharmacology UCLA, 1971, vis. prof., 1972; vis. rsch. assoc. div. biology Calif. Inst. Tech., Pasadena, 1989-90; vis. prof. dept. neurosci. Case Western U. Med. Sch., Cleve., 1993—; mem. nat. rev. bd. Ea. Pa. Psychiat. Inst., 1982-84; sr. cons. for high tech. State of Ariz., 1986-90; reviewer Life Sci., Brain Rsch., Am. Jour. Physiology, Sci., Jour. Physiology, Jour. Cell Physiology, Jour. Biol. Chemistry, Devel. Biology, Exptl. Neurology, Neurosci., Nature, Jour. Neurosci., Jour. Neurophysiology; reviewer rsch. grants NSF, 1973—; panel mem. for cellular and molecular neurobiology, 1984-86; external cons. NIH, 1971-81; mem. ad hoc peer rev. com. Conn. affiliate Am. Heart Assn., 1981-82; mem. behavioral neurosci. study sect. NIMH, 1992-96; participant numerous profl. meetings; invited lectr. numerous univs., including U. Sydney, Australia, Stanford U., U. Wash, U. Minn., U. Ill., Chgo., Harvard U., Boston, Washington U., St. Louis, U. Man., Winnipeg, Can., U. Md., Balt., U. N.C., Rochester U., SUNY, Albany, U. Colo., Denver, Med. Coll. Pa., U. Tex., Galveston, McGill U., Montreal, Que., Can., Yale U., U. Pa., Univ. Coll., London, U. Tex., Austin, U. Cin., U. Fla., U. Va., U. P.R. Assoc. editor Devel. Neurosci., 1977-81; contbr. numerous articles and abstracts to sci. jours. Squibb fellow U. Buenos Aires, 1956-57, Nat. Coun. for Sci. and Tech. Rsch. fellow Nat. Inst. Cardiology, Mex., 1959-61, Guggenheim fellow U. Utah, 1961-63; travel grantee Internat. Brain Rsch. Orgn., 1964, grantee NIH, 1967-93, U. Conn. Rsch. Found., 1971, 81, 93, Muscular Dystrophy Assn., 1980-82, NSF, 1984-87, Conn. Dept. Higher Edn., 1990. Mem. Am. Physiol. Soc. (steering com. sect. on nervous sys. 1979-83, neurophysiology steering com. 1979-83), Soc. for Neurosci. (minority selection com. 1985, 87, minority com. 1988-92), Soc. for Devel. Biology, Soc. for Advancement Chicanos and Native Ams. in Sci. (organizer, sec. Northeastern Sec. 1992). Office: U Conn Dept Physiology-Neurobiol 75 N Eagleville Rd Box U-42 Storrs CT 06269-3042

PILARCZYK, DANIEL EDWARD, archbishop; b. Dayton, Ohio, Aug. 12, 1934; s. Daniel Joseph and Frieda S. (Hilgefort) P. Student, St. Gregory Sem., Cin., 1948-53; PhB, Pontifical Urban U., Rome, 1955, PhL, 1956, STB, 1958, STL, 1960, STD, 1961; MA, Xavier U., 1965; PhD, U. Cin., 1969, LLD (hon.), Xavier U., 1975, Calumet Coll., 1982, U. Dayton, 1990, Marquette U., 1990, Thomas More Coll., 1991. Ordained priest Roman Catholic Ch., 1959; asst. chancellor Archdiocese of Cin., 1961-63; synodal judge Archdiocesan Tribunal, 1971-82; mem. faculty Athenaeum of Ohio, St. Gregory Sem., 1963-74; v.p. Athenaeum of Ohio, 1968-74, trustee, 1974—; also rector St. Gregory Sem., 1968-74; archdiocesan dir. ednl. services, 1974-82, aux. bishop of Cin., 1974-82, vicar gen., 1974-82, archbishop of Cin., 1982—; bd. dirs. Pope John Ctr., 1978-85; trustee Cath. Health Assn., 1982-85, Cath. U. Am., 1983-91, Pontifical Coll. Josephinum 1983-92; v.p. Nat. Conf. Cath. Bishops, 1986-89, pres., 1989-92; U.S. rep. Episc. Bd. Internat. Commn. on English in Liturgy 1987—; (mem.)—. Author: Praepositiani Cancellarii de Sacramentis et de Novissimis, 1964-65, Twelve Tough Issues, 1988, We Believe, 1989, Living in the Lord, 1990, The Parish: Where God's People Live, 1991, Forgiveness, 1992, What Must I Do?, 1993, Our Priests: Who They Are and What They Do, 1994, Lenten Lunches, 1995. Ohio Classical Conf. scholar to Athens, 1966. Mem. Am. Philol. Assn. Home and Office: 100 E 8th St Cincinnati OH 45202-2102

PILBEAM, DAVID ROGER, paleoanthropology educator; b. Brighton, Sussex, Eng., Nov. 21, 1940; came to U.S., 1968; s. Ernest Winton and Edith (Clack) P.; m. Maryellen Ruvolo, Dec. 18, 1982; 1 child, Katharine Alexandra. B.A., Cambridge U., 1962, M.A., 1966; Ph.D., Yale U., 1967; M.A. (hon.), Harvard U., 1982. Demonstrator in anthropology Cambridge U., Eng., 1965-68; asst. prof. anthropology Yale U., 1968-70, assoc. prof., 1970-74, prof., 1974-81, prof. anthropology, geology and geophysics, 1974-81, prof. anthropology, 1981-90; Henry Ford II prof. social sci. Harvard U., Cambridge, Mass., 1990—, dean undergrad. edn., 1987-92; Dir. Peabody Mus., 1990—. Author: Evolution of Man, 1970, Ascent of Man, 1972; co-author: Human Biology, 3d edit., 1988; co-editor: Cambridge Encyclopedia of Human Evolution, 1992. Fellow Am. Anthropol. Assn.; mem. Am. Acad. Arts and Scis., Nat. Acad. Scis. (fgn. assoc.). Office: Harvard U Peabody Mus 11 Divinity Ave Cambridge MA 02138-2019

PILCHER, WALTER HAROLD, apparel company executive; b. Washington, Oct. 21, 1941; s. Milton Alfred and Elizabeth (Haywood) P.; m. Carol Ann Beebe, July 17, 1965; children—Walter Todd, Jennifer Beebe, Carolyn Elizabeth. B.A., Wesleyan U., 1963; M.B.A., Stanford U., 1966. Product mgr. L'Eggs Products, Winston-Salem, N.C., 1969-73, v.p. mktg., 1979-83, pres., 1983-87; v.p. mktg. Hanes Knitwear, Winston-Salem, 1973-75; mktg. mgr. Wix Corp., Gastonia, N.C., 1975-77; v.p. mktg. L'Erin Cosmetics, Winston-Salem, 1977-79; pres., chief operating officer Sara Lee Hosiery, Sara Lee Corp., Winston-Salem, 1987-88; pres., chief exec. officer Kayser Roth Corp., Greensboro, N.C., 1989—. Mem. allocations com. Forsyth United Way, Winston-Salem, 1978; bd. dirs. United Way of Greater Greensboro, 1990—; mem. pres.'s council of advisors Regent U., 1986; bd. dirs. Regent U., 1991—. 1st lt. USAR, 1963-70. Republican. Presbyterian. Avocations: creative writing, photography. Office: Kayser-Roth Corp PO Box 77077 Greensboro NC 27417-7077

PILCHIK, ELY EMANUEL, rabbi, writer; b. Russia, June 12, 1913; came to U.S., 1920, naturalized, 1920; s. Abraham and Rebecca (Lipovitch) P.; m. Ruth Schuchat, Nov. 20, 1941 (dec. 1977); children: Susan Pilchik Rosenbaum, Judith Pilchik Zucker; m. Harriet Krichman Perlmutter, June, 1981. A.B., U. Cin., 1935; M.Hebrew Lit., Hebrew Union Coll., 1936, D.D., 1964. Ordained rabbi, 1939; founder, dir. Hillel Found. at U. Md., 1939-40; asst. rabbi Har Sinai Temple, Balt., 1940-41; rabbi Temple Israel, Tulsa, 1942-47, Temple B'nai Jeshurun, Short Hills, N.J., 1947-82; prof. Jewish Thought Upsala Coll., 1969—; pres. Jewish Book Council Am., 1957-58. Author: books, including Hillel, 1951, From the Beginning, 1956, Judaism Outside the Holy Land, 1964, Jeshurun Essays, 1967, A Psalm of David, 1967, Talmud Thought, 1983, Midrash Memoir, 1984, Touches of Einstein, 1987, Luzzatto on Loving Kindness, 1987, Prayer in History, 1989; author: play Toby, 1968; lyricist 6 cantatas; contbr. articles to profl. and gen. jours. Bd. dirs. Newark Mus.; mem. ethics com. N.J. Bar Assn. Served as chaplain USNR, 1944-46. Mem. N.J. Bd. Rabbis (pres. 1955-57), Central Conf. Am. Rabbis (pres. 1977-79). Office: 1025 S Orange Ave Short Hills NJ 07078-3135 I have been influenced by the teaching of the 1st sage Hillel who said: "If I am not for myself, who will be for me? And if I am for myself only, what am I? And if not now, when?".

PILCZ, MALETA, psychotherapist; b. Poland, June 5, 1945; came to U.S., 1949; s. Victor and Hana (Oks) P. BA in Psychology, Bklyn. Coll., 1967; MA in Social Work, U. Chgo., 1969. Diplomate Am. Bd. Examiners Clin. Social Work; cert. social worker, N.Y. Psychotherapist Scholarship and Guidance Assn., Chgo., 1969-71; family therapist, supr. Northwestern Meml. Hosp., Chgo., 1972-75; pvt. practice, psychotherapist, cons. Chgo., 1974-80, N.Y.C., 1980—; field work instr. U. Chgo. Sch. of Social Svcs., 1974-75; instr. dept. psychiatry Northwestern U. Med. Sch., 1973-75; cons. faculty Ctr. for Family Studies, Family Inst. Chgo., 1978-80; assoc. staff Ackerman Inst. Family Therapy, N.Y.C., 1983-88; part-time instr. Hunter Coll. Sch. of Social Work, N.Y.C., 1985-88; cons. N.Y.C. Bd. Edn., 1988—. Author: Understanding the Survivor Family, 1979; thematic cons. documentary film The Legacy, 1979 (Cigne Gold Eagle, Red Ribbon Am. Film Festival, 1980). Fellow Am. Orthopsychiat. Assn.; mem. NASW (diplomate clin. social work), Am. Group Psychotherapy Assn., Acad. Cert. Social Workers. Avocations: world travel, hiking, theater, the arts. Office: 330 E 46th St Apt 12D New York NY 10017-3076

PILE, ROBERT BENNETT, advertising executive, writer, consultant; b. Pierre, S.D., May 27, 1918; s. Homer Bennett and Ruth (Gleckler) P.; m. Cynthia Way, Feb. 28, 1953; children: Timothy, Benjamin, Robert, Michael, Cynthia, Anthony. B.A., U. Minn., 1941. Asst. advt. mgr. Red Owl Stores, Mpls., 1946-47; advt. mgr. Lactona, St. Paul, 1947-48; acct., ptnr. Olmsted & Foley Advt. Agy., Mpls., 1948-55; account exec. Campbell-Mithun, Inc., Mpls., 1955-59; v.p., group head Campbell-Mithun, Inc., 1960-69, sr. v.p., mgmt. rep., 1969-80; founder, pres., dir. mem. exec. com., chief exec. officer Bob's Wide World of Golf, 1980—; bd. dirs. Roberts-Hamilton Co., 1992; cons. in field; instr. St. Thomas Coll., St. Paul, 1980-86; mgr. 4-A Inst. Advt. Studies, 1981-87. Author: Letters from French Windmill, 1986, Panic in the Morning Mail, 1986, Crisis Every Fifteen Minutes, 1988, Top Entrepreneurs and Their Business, 1993; contbg. editor Active Lifestyles Mag.; writer Mpls. Tribune, T.C. Mag.; columnist Format mag., Skyway News. Bd. dirs. Big Bros. Mpls., Minn. Heart Assn., St. Mary's Hosp.; bd. dirs., chmn. 4-A's of Twin Cities, bd. govs. Ctrl. Region. Capt. USAAF, 1941-46. Recipient spl. award Mpls. Spruce Up Drive, 1965. Mem. Northwest Advt. Golf Assn. (pres. 1977-78, gov.), Am. Assn. ADvt. Agys. (chmn. Twin City coun.), Interlachen Country Club (bd. govs., chmn. house com. & food and beverage com., editor monthly newsletter Interocutor), Ham and Eggs Breakfast Club, Mpls. Club, Yo Yo's Club, Phi Kappa Psi. Home: 4315 E Lake Harriet Blvd Minneapolis MN 55409-1725

PILE, WALTER MITCHELL, JR., advertising agency executive; b. N.Y.C., Apr. 30, 1948; s. Walter Mitchell and Virginia M. (Schaefer) P.; m. Beth M. Harrigan, May 21, 1971; children—Andrew Patrick, Morgan Elizabeth. B.A., Villanova U., 1970. Media analyst Doyle, Dane Bernbach, N.Y.C., 1969; media planner Benton & Bowles, N.Y.C., 1970-72; media planner Hill, Holliday, Connors, Cosmopulos, Inc., Boston, 1972-84, exec. v.p., gen. mgr., 1984. Office: Pile & Company 45 Newbury St Boston MA 02116-3133

PILECKI, PAUL STEVEN, lawyer; b. Norristown, Pa., Sept. 12, 1950; m. Barbara Derrickson; children: Derek Steven, Christopher Drew. AB, St. Joseph's Coll., Phila., 1972; JD, Temple U., 1978. Bar: Pa. 1978, D.C. 1985. Sr. counsel Fed. Res. Bd., Washington, 1978-84; ptnr. Shaw, Pittman, Potts & Trowbridge, Washington, 1984—. Mem. ABA (banking law com.). Home: 11108 Deville Estates Dr Oakton VA 22124-1002 Office: Shaw Pittman Potts et al 2300 N St NW Washington DC 20037-1122

PILGRIM, DIANNE HAUSERMAN, art museum director; b. Cleve., July 9, 1941; d. John Martin and Norma Hauserman; divorced. BA, Pa. State U., 1963; MA, Inst. Fine Arts, NYU, 1965; postgrad., CUNY, 1971-74; LHD (hon.), Amherst Coll., 1991, Pratt Inst., 1994. Chester Dale fellow Am. wing. Met. Mus. Art, N.Y.C., 1966-68, researcher, 1971, rsch. cons. Am. paintings and sculpture, 1972-73; asst. to dir. Pyramid Galleries, Ltd., Washington, 1969-71, Finch Coll. Mus. Art, Washington, 1971; curator dept. decorative arts Bklyn. Mus., 1973-88, chmn. dept., 1988; dir. Cooper-Hewitt Mus., N.Y.C., 1988—; mem. adv. com. Gracie Mansion, N.Y.C., 1980; mem. design adv. com. Art Inst. Chgo., 1988—; mem. Hist. House Trust of N.Y.C., Mayor's Office, 1989—. Co-author, curator: (book and exhbn. catalogue) The American Renaissance 1876-1917, 1979, (book) The Machine Age in America 1918-1941, 1986 (Charles F. Montgomery prize Decorative Arts Soc.). Bd. dirs. Nat. Multiple Sclerosis Soc., 1989. Recipient Disting. Alumni award Pa. State U., 1991. Mem. Art Table, Decorative Arts Soc. (pres. 1977-79). Office: Smithsonian Instn Cooper-Hewitt Nat Design Mus 2 E 91st St New York NY 10128-0606

PILGRIM, LONNIE (BO PILGRIM), poultry production company executive; b. 1928; married. Ptnr. Pilgrims Pride Corp., Pittsburg, Tex., 1953-68, chmn., CEO, 1968—; chmn. First State Bank Pitts. Served with U.S. Armed Forces, 1951-53. Office: Pilgrim's Pride Corp 110 S Texas St Pittsburg TX 75686

PILGRIM, RICHARD D., engineering company executive; b. 1955. Pres. BRW Group Inc., Mpls. Office: BRW Group Inc 700 S 3rd St Minneapolis MN 55415*

PILIGUIAN, TRO, advertising executive. Pres. Ogilvy & Mather, N.Y.C. Office: Ogilvy & Mather New York Worldwide Plz 309 W 49th St New York NY 10019

PILISUK, MARC, community psychology educator; b. N.Y.C., Jan. 19, 1934; s. Louis and Charlotte (Feferholtz) P.; m. Phyllis E. Kamen, June 16, 1956; children: Tammy, Jeff. BA, Queens Coll., 1955; MA, U. Mich., 1956, PhD, 1961. Asst. prof., assoc. rsch. psychologist U. Mich., Ann Arbor, 1961-65, founder teach-in, 1965; assoc. prof. Purdue U., West Lafayette, Ind., 1965-67; prof.-in-residence U. Calif., Berkeley, 1967-77; prof. community psychology U. Calif., Davis, 1977—; vis. prof. U. Calif., Wright Inst., 1991—; cons. Ctr. for Self Help Rsch., Berkeley, Calif., 1991-93; prof. psychology Saybrook Inst. and Grad. Ctr., San Francisco, 1993—. Author: International Conflict and Social Policy, 1972, The Healing Web: Social Networks and Human Survival, 1986; editor: The Triple Revolution, 1969; Poor Americans, 1970; Triple Revolution Emerging, 1972; How We Lost the War on Poverty, 1973. NIMH fellow, 1959-60; NSF grantee, 1962-66; Nat. Inst. Alcoholism and Drug Abuse tng. grantee, 1973-77. Fellow Soc. for Community Rsch. and Action, Soc. for Psychol. Study Social Issues (council), Am. Psychol. Assn., Am. Orthopsychiat. Assn.; mem. ACLU, Am. Soc. on Aging, Am. Pub. Health Assn., Psychologists for Social Responsibility, Faculty for Human Rights in C.Am.

PILKEY, ORRIN H., geology educator; b. N.Y.C., Sept. 19, 1934; s. Orrin H. and Elizabeth (Street) P.; m. Sharlene M. Greenaa, Dec. 29, 1956; children—Charles, Linda, Diane, Keith, Kerry. B.S., Wash. State U., 1957; M.S., Mont. State U., 1959; Ph.D., Fla. State U., 1962. Research asso. U. Ga. Marine Inst., Sapelo Island, 1962-65; asso. prof. geology Duke U., 1965-72, prof., 1972—; James B. Duke prof. geology, 1983—; vis. prof. U. P.R. at, Mayaguez, 1972-73; sr. marine scientist U.S. Geol. Survey, Woods Hole, Mass., 1975-76. Editor: (with D.J. Swift and D.B. Duane) Shelf Sediment Transport, 1972, (with S. Fritz) Marine Atlas of Puerto Rico, 1976, Jour. Sedimentary Petrology, 1977-83, (with Larry J. Doyle) Geology of Continental Slopes, 1979, (with Nicholas Kraus) The Effects of Seawalls on Beaches, (with Charles Finkl) The Impact of Hurricane Hugo: September 10-22, 1989, (with Dag Nummedal) Sea Level Rise and Coastal Evolution, 1987, (with William Neal) Living with the Shore book series; co-author: (with O. Pilkey Sr., W.D. Pilkey and William Neal) Coastal Design, 1983; author: (with O.H. Pilkey and William Neal) How to Live with an Island, 1975, (with O.H. Pilkey Sr. and William Neal) Currituck to Calabash, 1978, (with Wallace Kaufman) The Beaches are Moving, 1979; author and/or editor with William Neal: Living With the Texas Shore, 1983, Living With the South Carolina Shore, 1984, Living With Long Island South Shore, 1984, Living With the West Florida Shore, 1984, Living With the East Florida Shore, 1984, Living With the Alabama-Mississippi Shore, 1985, Living With the New Jersey Shore, 1986, Living With the Lake Erie Shore, 1987, Living With the Chesapeake Bay Shore, 1989, Living with the Shore of Maine, 1992, Living with The Georgia Shore, 1992, A Moveable Shore: The Fate of the Connecticut Shore; contbr. articles to profl. jours. Active shoreline conservation. Recipient Francis Shepard medal for excellence in marine geology, 1987, Conservation Educator of the Yr award N.C. Wildlife Fedn., 1991. Mem. N.C. Acad. Sci. (pres. 1981-82), Soc. Econ. Paleontologists and Minerologists (pres. 1985-86), Geol. Soc. Am., Assn. Earth Sci. (editors), Am. Assn. Petroleum Geologists (George Cohee Pub. Svc. award 1992), Coastal Alliance (bd. dirs. 1985—), Soc. Study of Sediments (hon.), Am. Geol. Inst. (award for outstanding contbn. to pub. understanding of geology 1993), Nat. Assn. Geology Tchrs. (James H. Shea award 1993), Sigma Xi. Research on geol. oceanography, coastal geology and coastal conservation. Home: 3303 US Hwy 70 Hillsborough NC 27278-9547 Office: Duke U Dept Geology Durham NC 27708

PILKINGTON, ALAN RALPH, advertising executive; b. Yea, Victoria, Australia, Jan. 13, 1943; came to U.S., 1983; s. Reginald Ralph and Florence (Davies) P.; m. Carolyn Clayton Skate, Dec. 21, 1964; children—Emma Jane, Amy Louise. B.A. magna cum laude in econs. and Polit. Sci., Melbourn U., 1960-64; student, Scotch Coll., Melbourne, Australia, 1956-59. Gen. mgr. Masius Wynne Williams, Melbourne, Australia, 1970-72; mng. dir. D'Arcy MacManus Masius, Sydney, Australia, 1973-79, chmn. Australia-Far East, 1980-83; exec. v.p. DMM Worldwide, N.Y.C., 1983-85; mem. worldwide exec. com. D'Arcy MacManus Masius, N.Y.C., 1979-82, dir. 1977-85; pres. Asia/Pacific DDB Needham Worldwide Inc., N.Y.C. 1985-90; mng. dir. DDB Neeham Chgo., 1991-94, chmn., 1995—. Mem. Royal Sydney Yacht Squadron, Melbourne Cricket Club, Manursing Island Club, Pawling Mt. Club, Racquet Club of Chgo. Avocations: fly fishing, shotgunning, skiing. Office: DDB Needham Chgo 303 E Wacker Dr Chicago IL 60601-5212

PILKINGTON, THEO CLYDE, biomedical and electrical engineering educator; b. Durham, N.C., June 23, 1935. BEE, N.C. State U., 1958; MS, Duke U., 1960, PhD, 1963. Instr. Duke U., Durham, N.C., 1958-63, asst. prof. elec. engring., 1963-66, assoc. prof., 1966-69, prof. biomed. engring. and elec. engring., 1969—; dir. engring. rsch. ctr. Emerging Cardiovascular Techs., Durham. Co-author: (with Robert Plonsey) Biophysical Principles of Electrocardiography, 1982; contbr. numerous articles to tech. jours. Mem. task force for cardiovascular tng. Nat. Heart-Lung Inst., 1981-82; bd. dirs. NSF Engring. Rsch. Ctr., 1987—. With U.S. Army, 1961. Mem. IEEE, Am. Soc. Engring. Edn., Ridge Woode Beagles Club (master beagler 1980—). Home: 2932 Ridge Rd Durham NC 27705-5528 Office: Duke U Engring Rsch Ctr 301 School Of Engring Durham NC 27706

PILLA, ANTHONY MICHAEL, bishop; b. Cleve., Nov. 12, 1932; s. George and Libera (Nista) P. Student, St. Gregory Coll. Sem., 1952-53, Borromeo Coll. Sem., 1955, St. Mary Sem., 1954, 56-59; B.A. in Philosophy, John Carroll U., Cleve., 1961, M.A. in History, 1967. Ordained priest Roman Cath. Ch., 1959. Assoc. St. Bartholomew Parish, Middleburg Hts., Ohio, 1959-60; prof. Borromeo Sem., Wickliffe, Ohio, 1960-72; rector-pres. Borromeo Sem., 1972-75; mem. Diocese Cleve. Liturgical Commn., 1964-69, asst. dir., 1969-72; sec. for services to clergy and religious personnel Diocese Cleve., 1975-79; titular bishop Scardona; and aux. bishop of Cleve. and vicar Eastern region Diocese of Cleve., 1979-80, apostolic adminstr., from 1980; bishop of Cleve., from 1981; trustee Borromeo Sem., 1975-79. Cath. U., 1981-84; trustee, mem. bd. overseers St. Mary Sem., 1975-79; mem. adv. bd. permanent diaconate program Diocese of Cleve., 1975-79, hospitalization and ins. bd., 1979; bd. dirs. Cath. Communications Found., 1981—. Bd. dirs. NCCJ, 1986—. Mem. Nat. Cath. Edn. Assn. (dir. 1972-75), U.S. Cath. Conf., Nat. Conf. Cath. Bishops, Cath. Conf. Ohio., Greater Cleve. Roundtable (trustee from 1981). Home and Office: Chancery Office 350 Chancery Bldg 1027 Superior Ave Cleveland OH 44114-2503*

PILLA, FELIX MARIO, hospital administrator; b. Phila., Sept. 22, 1932; s. Domenick and Carmela (DiPalma) P.; m. Sally Irene Bixler, Oct. 2, 1953; children: Mark, Beth Ann, Michael, Matthew. Diploma profl. nursing, Pa. Hosp. Sch. Nursing, 1956; B.S. in Bus. Adminstrn, LaSalle Coll., Phila., 1959; M.S. in Hosp. Adminstrn, Columbia U., 1961. Various progressively responsible positions in health care field, 1957-70; exec. dir. Monmouth Med. Center, 1970-80; adminstrv. dir. U. Ariz. Health Scis. Center, Tucson, 1980-82; pres. Newton-Wellesley Hosp., Newton, Mass., 1982-85, Abington Meml. Hosp., Pa., 1985—; chmn. N.J. State Health Planning Council, 1976-77. USPHS tng. grantee, 1961. Fellow Am. Coll. Hosp. Adminstrs., Am. Pub. Health Assn.; mem. Am. Hosp. Assn. (life, mem. Ho. of Dels., governing coun. met. hosps. 1991-94), N.J. Hosp. Assn. (chmn. 1979-80), Hosp. Assn. of Pa. (trustee 1988-94), Del. Valley Hosp. Coun. (bd. dirs. 1986-94, chmn. bd. 1990-92). Office: Abington Meml Hosp 1200 Old York Rd Abington PA 19001-3788

PILLA, MARK DOMENICK, hospital administrator; b. Phila., July 2, 1954; married;. BA, LaSalle U., 1976; MA, Temple U., 1978. Adm. res. Frankford Hosp., Phila., 1977-78; asst. to v.p. West Jersey Hosp.-Voorhees, 1978-79, adminstrv. dir., 1979-80; v.p. adminstrn. Community Med. Ctr., Toms River, N.J., 1980-82, sr. v.p., 1982-87, pres., CEO, 1987—. Mem. Am. Coll. Healthcare Execs. (com. serv. community svc.). Office: Community Med Ctr 99 Hwy 37 W Toms River NJ 08755

PILLAERT, E(DNA) ELIZABETH, museum curator; b. Baytown, Tex., Nov. 19, 1931; d. Albert Jacob and Nettie Roseline (Kelley) P. B.A., U. St. Thomas, 1963; M.A., U. Okla., 1963; postgrad., U. Wis., 1962-67, 70-73. Asst. curator archaeology Stovall Mus., Norman, Okla., 1959-60, ednl. liaison officer, 1960-62; research asst. U. Wis., Madison, 1962-65, cons. archaeol. faunal analysis, 1965—; curator osteology Zool. Mus., Madison, 1965—, chief curator, 1967-92, assoc. dir., 1992—. Bd. dirs. Lysistrata Feminist Coop., Madison, 1977-81, Univ. YMCA, Madison, 1974-77. Mem. Soc. Vertebrate Paleontology, Wis. Archaeol. Soc., Okla. Anthrop. Soc., Am. Assn. Mus., NOW, Stoughton Hist. Soc., Am. Ornithological Union, Friends of Stoughton Libr., Friends of Stoughton Auditorium. Home: 216 N Prairie St Stoughton WI 53589-1647 Office: U Wis Zool Mus 434 Noland Bldg 250 N Mills Rd Madison WI 53706

PILLAI, A(RRACKAL) K(ASAVA) B., integral development therapist, anthropology educator; b. Changanacherry, Kerala, India, May 9, 1930; came to U.S., 1966; s. V. Potti and Amma (Narayani) P.; divorced; children: Gita, Prita. MA, Kerala (India) U., 1955, East Carolina U., 1968; MPhil, Columbia U., 1972, PhD, 1975. Cert. Am. Bd. Med. Psychotherapists. Prof., chair dept. English Sri Sankara Coll., Kalady, India, 1955-66; dir. Asian Studies, Hollywood Coll., Fla., 1966-67; prof., chair anthropology Ramapo Coll. of N.J., Mahwah, 1972—; co-chair East Asian studies Ramapo Coll. of N.J., 1988—; pvt. practice psychotherapist Riverdale, N.Y., 1986—; trainer psychotherapists, social workers, 1986—; founder Integral Devel. Therapy, Integral Devel. Social Work, Integral Human Devel.; assoc. univ. seminar Columbia U., N.Y.C., 1972—; co-chair nat. com. Anthropology and Social Work, 1988—; founder, chair N.Y. Inst. Integral Human Devel., Riverdale, 1987—. Author: (English) King Lear: A Study of Human Order, 1985, Transcendental Self, 1987, Culture of Social Stratification and Sexism: The Nayars, 1987; (Malayalam) Five volumes of short stories, two volumes of travelogues, two novels.s. Founder, chairperson Devel. Projects, India, 1955-66. Predoctoral fellowship NIMH, 1972-75. Fellow Am. Anthropol. Assn.; mem. Met. Med. Anthropology Assn. (subcom. chair 1980-83), Am. Assn. Counseling and Human Devel., Soc. Indian Academics Am. (chair ad hoc com.), Internat. Assn. Marriage and Family Counselors, World Malayalee Convention (exec. v.p.), World Malayalee Coun. (chair ad hoc com.), Assn. Multicultural Counseling and Devel., Assn. Asian Studies, Ramapo Anthropology Soc. (founder, dir.), India Devel. Inst. (chair). Avocations: travel field study, horticulture, bridge, poetry/music.

PILLAI, K. G. JAN, law educator, lawyer; b. Quilon, India, Jan. 23, 1936; came to U.S., 1966, naturalized, 1975; s. Raman and Janaky (Amma) P.; m. Sarada J., May 16, 1966; children: Jay J., Jan. BA, U. Kerala, India, 1957, LLB, 1959, LLM, 1965; LLM, Yale U., 1967, JSD, 1969. Bar: D.C. 1975, U.S. Dist. Ct. D.C. 1975, U.S. Ct. Appeals (D.C. cir.) 1975, U.S. Dist. Ct. (ea. dist.) Pa. 1982, U.S. Supreme Ct. 1982. Mgr. Indian affairs Overseas Nat. Airways, N.Y.C., 1970-71; exec. dir. Aviation Consumer Project, Washington, 1971-73; assoc. prof. law Temple U., Phila., 1973-75, prof., 1975-86, 87—; dir. office regulatory analysis Fed. Energy Regulatory Commn., 1986-87; mem. consumer adv. com. CAB, Washington, 1970-72; chmn. Temple U. Law Sch. Dean Search Com.. Author: The Air Net, 1969; contbr. articles to legal publs. Nat. chmn. Asian and Pacific Am. Civil Rights Alliance, Washington, 1987-90, Dole for Pres. com., Washington, 1987-88. Mem. ABA (chmn. adjudication com. adminstrv. law sect. 1991-94), Nat. Assn. Ams. of Asian Indian Descent (nat. chmn. 1980-85), Asian Indian C. of C. (nat. chmn 1983-85). Republican. Office: Sch Law Temple U 1719 N Broad St Philadelphia PA 19122-2504

PILLANS, CHARLES PALMER, III, lawyer; b. Orlando, Fla., Feb. 22, 1940; s. Charles Palmer Jr. and Helen (Scarborough) P.; m. Judith Hart, July 6, 1963; children: Charles Palmer IV, Helen Hart. BA, U. Fla., 1962, JD, 1966. Bar: Fla. 1967, U.S. Dist. Ct. (mid. dist.) Fla. 1967, U.S. Ct. Appeals (2d cir.) 1968, U.S. Supreme Ct. 1971, U.S. Ct. Appeals (3d cir.) 1976, U.S. Ct. Appeals (5th and 11th cirs.) 1981. Assoc. Bedell, Bedell, Dittmar, Smith & Zehmer, Jacksonville, Fla., 1966-70; asst. state atty. 4th jud. cir. Jacksonville, 1970-72; asst. gen. counsel City of Jacksonville, 1972; ptnr. Bedell, Dittmar, DeVault & Pillans, P.A., Jacksonville, 1972—; mem. Fla. Bd. Bar Examiners, Tallahassee, 1979-84, chmn., 1983-84; mem. Jud. Nominating Commn., 1988-92, chmn., 1990-91, 1st Dist. Ct. Appeal, Tallahassee, 1988-92, chmn., 1990-91. Master Chester Bedell Inn of Ct.; fellow Am. Coll. Trial Lawyers, ABA; mem. Am. Bar Found., Fla. Bar Assn. Methodist. Home: Villa 110 6740 Epping Forest Way N Jacksonville FL 32217-4322 Office: Bedell Dittmar DeVault & Pillans PA Bedell Bldg 101 E Adams St Jacksonville FL 32202

PILLITTERE, JOSEPH T., assemblyman; b. Buffalo, N.Y., June 26, 1932; s. Dominic and Grazia (Georginella) P.; m. Joan Bella; children: Donald, Michelle, Joseph, Georgine, Jennifer. BS in Mech. Engring., Detroit U. Mech. engr. Bell Aerospace, Niagara Falls, N.Y.; county legislator County of Niagara, Lewiston, N.Y.; state assemblyman N.Y. State Assembly, Albany. With USN, 1955-57. Mem. KC (3d degree), Kiwanis, Holy Name Soc. (usher), Casa Colombo, Elks. Democrat. Roman Catholic. Avocations: fishing, gardening, hunting, golf. Office: 1700 Pine Ave Niagara Falls NY 14301

PILLOT, GENE MERRILL, retired superintendent of schools; b. Canton, Ohio, Apr. 13, 1930; s. John D. Pillot and Vera R. Granstaff; m. Beverly Ann Shaw, June 4, 1982; children: Vera Kathleen Martin, Michael Gene, Patrick Merrill. BS in Math., Ohio State U., 1952; MEd in Adminstrn. and Supervision, Kent State U., 1957; EdD in Adminstrn. and Supervision, U. Fla., 1970. Asst. prin. North Royalton (Ohio) High Sch., 1959-61, prin., 1961-63; asst. prin. Sarasota (Fla.) Sr. High Sch., 1963-64, prin., 1964-68; dir. staff development Sarasota Dist. Schs., 1968-70, asst. supt., 1970-71, supt., 1971-80; dir. human resources Sarasota Meml Hosp., 1980-83; owner, broker Pillot Realty, Sarasota, 1986-90; commr. Sarasota City, 1989—, vice mayor, 1992-93, mayor, 1993-94; prof. Am. Assn. Sch. Adminstrn., Nat. Acad. Sch. Execs., 1969-73; adj. prof. U. South Fla., Tampa, 1978-81; pvt. cons. edn. orgns., 1969-76. Author (chpt.) Differentiated Staffing, Strategies for D.S., 1971; contbr. articles to profl. jours. Trustee Fla. Sch. Deaf/Blind, St. Augustine, Fla., 1980-89, chmn. bd. 1986-89; bd. dirs. Riverview Found., 1985-94, Girls Club, Sarasota, 1985-89, Hospice Found. bd. dirs., Sarasota Opera Assn.; mem. Civil Svc. Bd. Sarasota, 1984-89; mem. adv. bd. Cath. Social Svcs., 1987-89. Mem. Sara Bay Country Club (Sarasota), Phi Delta Kappa (Educator of Yr. 1980). Republican. Roman Catholic. Avocations: writing, Spanish language. Home: 1212 Hillview Dr Sarasota FL 34239-2020

PILLSBURY, EDMUND PENNINGTON, museum director; b. San Francisco, Apr. 28, 1943; s. Edmund Pennington and Priscilla Keator (Giesen) P.; m. Mireille Marie-Christine Bernard, Aug. 30, 1969; children: Christine Bullitt, Edmund Pennington III. B.A., Yale U., 1965; M.A., U. London, 1967, Ph.D. 1973. Curator European art Yale U. Art Gallery, New Haven, 1972-76; asst. dir. Yale U. Gallery, New Haven, 1975-76; dir. Yale Ctr. Brit. Art, New Haven, 1976-80; chief exec. officer Paul Mellon Ctr. Studies in Brit. Art, London, 1980—; dir. Kimbell Art Mus., Ft. Worth 1980—; founding chmn. Villa I Tatti Coun., Harvard U., 1979-84; adj. prof. Yale U., 1976-80, lectr., 1972-76. Author: Florence and the Arts, 1971, Sixteenth-Century Italian Drawings: Form and Function, 1974, David Hockney: Travels with Pen, Pencil and Ink, 1978, The Graphic Art of Federico Barocci, 1978. Trustee Ft. Worth Country Day Sch., 1982-87, 88-94, St. Paul's Sch., Concord, N.H., 1985—, Burlington Mag. Found., London, 1987—; bd. govs. Yale U. Art Gallery, 1990—; mem. art adv. panel indemnity program Nat. Endowment Arts, 1984-87; mem. vis. com. Sherman Fairchild Paintings Conservation Ctr., Met. Mus. Art, N.Y.C., 1982—; mem. bd. advisors art dept. U. North Tex., Denton, 1990—; mem. art adv. panel IRS, 1982-84. Decorated chevalier Ordre des Arts et des Lettres, 1985; David E. Finley fellow Nat. Gallery Art, Washington, 1970, Ford Found. fellow Cleve. Mus. Art, 1970-71, Nat. Endowment Arts rsch. fellow, 1974, Morse fellow Yale U., 1975. Mem. Assn. Art Mus. Dirs. (trustee 1989-90), Master Drawings Assn. (bd. dirs. 1987—), Coll. Art Assn., Century Club, Ft. Worth Club, Princeton Club. Episcopalian. Home: 1110 Broad Ave Fort Worth TX 76107-1529 Office: Kimbell Art Mus 3333 Camp Bowie Blvd Fort Worth TX 76107-2744

PILLSBURY, GEORGE STURGIS, investment adviser; b. Crystal Bay, Minn., July 17, 1921; s. John S. and Eleanor (Lawler) P.; m. Sally Whitney,

Jan. 4, 1947; children: Charles Alfred, George Sturgis, Sarah Kimball, Katharine Whitney. BA, Yale U., 1943. Chmn. Sargent Mgmt. Co. Clubs: Seminole Golf (North Palm Beach, Fla.), Woodhill, Minnetonka Yacht, Mpls. Athletic, Mpls. Club, River (N.Y.C.), Bath and Tennis, Everglades (Palm Beach, Fla.). Home: 1300 Bracketts Point Rd Wayzata MN 55391-9393 Office: 4800 First Bank Pl Minneapolis MN 55402

PILOUS, BETTY SCHEIBEL, nurse; b. Cleve., July 30, 1948; d. Raymond W. and Dorothy E. (Groth) S.; m. Lee Alan Pilous, Sept. 11, 1970; 1 child. Diploma in nursing, Huron Rd. Hosp., Cleve., 1970; BSBA, St. Joseph's Coll., 1989, postgrad., 1990—. RN, Ohio; cert. med.-surg. nurse, nursing adminstr. Nurse Huron Rd. Hosp., Cleve., 1970-71, Hillcrest Hosp., Cleve., 1974-77; head nurse, relief supr. Oak Park Hosp., Oakwood, Ohio, 1977-81; head nurse med.-surg. Bedford Hosp., Ohio, 1981-87; dir. inpatient svcs. Meridia Euclid Hosp., Euclid, Ohio, coord. hosp. info. system for nursing, chair nurse practice com., los com. nursing liason; dir. nursing Manor Care, Willoughby, Ohio. joint commn. Accreditation of Health Organizers. Former instr. ARC; chair nurse practice com. Am. Heart Assn.; mem. nursing standards com. Community Hosp. of Bedford; mem. health and safety com. Twinsburg Schs., Ohio, 1984, mem. curriculum com., 1981-83; chairperson standards com. Cmty. Hosp. of Bedford; former counselor jr. high youth 1st Congl. Ch., Twinsburg; chair adv. bd. chairperson Brecksville Rainbow Assembly for Girls, 1992; mem. Twinsburg Libr. Levy Com., 1991. Recipient Paradiam award, 1991. Mem. Ohio Citizen League Nursing Nurse Execs. Network (former sec.), Ohio Hosp. Assn., Ohio Orgn. Nurse Execs., Ohio Directors of Nursing Assocs. Long Term Care, Nat. League Nursing, Southeast Cleve. Mid Mgrs. Ohio Orgn. Nurse Exec., Acad. Med.-Surg. Nursing (charter mem.), Networking Group Nurse Mgrs. (initiated), Order Eastern Star, Sigma Theta Tau, Iota Psi. Avocations: aerobics, hiking. Office: Meridia Euclid Hosp 18901 Lake Shore Blvd Cleveland OH 44119-1078

PILSON, MICHAEL EDWARD QUINTON, oceanography educator; b. Ottawa, Ont., Can., Oct. 25, 1933; came to U.S., 1958; s. Edward Charles and Frances Amelia (Ferguson) P.; m. Joan Elaine Johnstone, July 6, 1957; children: Diana Jane, John Edward Quinton. BSc, Bishop's U., Lennoxville, Que., Can.; MSc, McGill U., Montreal, Que., Can., 1958; PhD, U. Calif., San Diego, 1964. Chemist Windsor Mills (Can.) Paper Co., 1954-55; asst. chemist Macdonaldl Coll. of McGill U., 1955-58; biologist Zool. Soc. San Diego, 1963-66; asst. prof. U. R.I., Narragansett, 1966-71, assoc. prof., 1971-78, prof., 1978—; dir. Marine Ecosystems Rsch. Lab., Narragansett, 1976—. Contbr. articles to profl. and popular jours.; author chpts. for 5 books. Grantee NSF, NOAA, EPA, NIH. Mem. AAAS, AGU, ASLO, Oceanography Soc., Am. Soc. Mammalogists, Saunderstown Yacht Club (bd. govs. 1974-87, commodore 1985-87). Home: PO Box 27 Saunderstown RI 02874-0027 Office: U RI Grad Sch Oceanography Narraganset RI 02882

PILZ, ALFRED NORMAN, manufacturing company executive; b. Evergreen Park, Ill., Oct. 12, 1931; s. Alfred and Erma Louise (Deane) P.; m. Constance Ney, Nov. 1957; children: Kerry, Kurt, Stephen, Matthew. B.S., Ill. Inst. Tech., 1953; M.B.A., Harvard U., 1960. Registered profl. engr., Mass. Indsl. engr. Harnischfeger Corp., Milw., 1956-58; cons. Arthur D. Little Co., Cambridge, Mass., 1959-60; asst. to exec. v.p., mgr. prodn. engring. Nat. Forge Co., Irvine, Pa., 1960-62; mgmt. cons. McKinsey & Co., N.Y.C. and Cleve., 1962-67; pres., gen. mgr. Ajax Iron Works div. Cooper Industries, Corry, Pa., 1967-72; pres., chief exec. officer WDP, Inc., 1972-79, Swank Refractories Co., Brookville, Pa., 1972-77, Hyde Park (Pa.) Foundry & Machine Co., 1974-79, Shepard-Niles Corp., Montour Falls, N.Y., 1979-82, Acco Babcock Materials Handling, Frederick, Md., 1982-85; ptnr. Fagan and Co., Ligonier, Pa.; bd. dirs. Acco Babcock, Inc., Babcock Internat., Chemung Foundry, Parnell Precision Products Co., Carre-Orban and Partners, Liberty Mut. Ins. Co., Ind. Steel and Engring. Corp., Bedford Crane Co., Shepard Niles Corp., Marine Bank, WDP, Inc.; chmn. Parnell Precision Products, 1980-82, Ind. Steeland Engring., Bedford Crane Co., 1981-82, pres., chmn., chief exec. officer, Greenway Products. Served with USN, 1953-56, Korea. Mem. Crane Mfrs. Assn., Hoist Mfrs. Assn., Conveyor Equipment Mfg. Assn., Nat. Trust Soc. Clubs: HYP (Pitts.). Auburn-Cord-Duesenberg. Home: 139 Ramsey Rd Ligonier PA 15658-0244 Office: 223 E Main Ligonier PA 15658-0611

PIMENTEL, DAVID, entomologist, educator; b. Fresno, Calif., May 24, 1925; s. Frank and Marion V. (Sylva) P.; m. Marcia R. Hutchins, July 16, 1949; children—Christina, Susan, Mark David. Student, St. John's U., Collegeville, Minn., 1943, Clark U., summer 1946; B.S., U. Mass., 1948; Ph.D., Cornell U., 1951; postdoctoral investigator, U. Chgo., winters 1954-55; postdoctoral investigator OEEC research fellow, Oxford (Eng.) U., 1961; postdoctoral investigator NSF computer scholar, MIT, summer 1961. Chief tropical research lab. USPHS, San Juan, P.R., 1951-54; project leader tech. devel. lab USPHS, Savannah, Ga., 1954-55; mem. faculty Cornell U., 1955—, prof. insect ecology, 1963—, head dept. entomology and limnology, 1963-69, prof. entomology, ecology and systematics, 1969-76, prof. insect ecology and agrl. scis., 1976—; prof., core faculty Center Environ. Quality Mgmt., 1973-74; cons. Office Sci. and Tech., Exec. Office Pres., 1964-67, 69-70, EPA, 1971; co-chmn. Commn. on Mosquito Control for Developing Countries, Nat. Acad. Sci., 1972-73; mem. comm. on pesticides and pest mgmt. in Inter-Am., 1973-77; mem. Nat. Adv. Council on Environ. Edn., 1973-74; chmn. panel on environ. impact of herbicides EPA, 1972-74, pesticide adv. council, 1975-78; nat. adv. council environ. edn. Office Edn., HEW, 1975-78, chmn., 1975; chmn. study team on interdependence of food, population, health, energy and environment World Food and Nutrition Study, Nat. Acad. Scis., 1976-77, chmn. environ. studies bd., 1980-83; mem. energy research adv. bd. Dept. Energy, 1979-85; mem. research adv. com. U.S. AID, 1979-82, chmn. panel on land productivity; mem. Office of Tech. Assessment, U.S. Congress, 1979-80. Assoc. editor: Am. Midland Naturalist; contbr. articles to profl. jours. Trustee Village of Cayuga Heights, 1974—. Served to 2d lt., pilot USAAF, 1943-45. Recipient Disting. Svc. award Rural Sociol. Coun., 1992. Mem. Entomol. Soc. Am. (governing bd., chmn. editorial bd., pres. Eastern br. 1974-75), Ecol. Soc. Am., Am. Soc. Naturalists, Soc. Study Evolution, Entomol. Soc. Can., Am. Soc. Zoologists, AAAS (climate com. 1979-92, population, resource and environment com. 1985-91, chmn. subcom. on food, population and resources 1986-87), NAS (chmn. panel biology and renewable resources, exec. bd. com. life scis. 1966-68, com. on world food, health and population 1974-75, chmn. panel on econ. and environ. aspects of pest mgmt. in C.Am. 1974-76, chmn. bd. on sci. and tech. for internat. devel. 1975-79, mem. com. on food and food prodn. 1974-76, mem. alternative agr. com. 1985-89, com. on role of alternative farming methods in modern productive agr. 1985-89), Nat. Geog. Soc. (mem. com. rsch & explorations 1993—), Internat. Union for Conservation of Nature and Natural Resources (commn. on ecology 1981—), Royal Swedish Acad. Scis. (mem. bd. dirs. Beijer Inst. 1994—), Sigma Xi, Phi Kappa Phi, Gamma Alpha (nat. recorder 1960-62). Office: Cornell U Dept Entomology Comstock Hall Ithaca NY 14853

PIMSLER, ALVIN J., artist; b. N.Y.C., May 17, 1918; s. Adolph and Jennie (Freedman) P.; m. Norma Moran, Aug. 3, 1947; children—Meade, Paul S. Grad., Pratt Inst. Sch. Fine and Applied Art, 1938, Art Students League, 1939-40. Tchr. fashion illustration Sch. Visual Arts, 1966-67; tchr. Parsons Sch. Design, 1974-76; mem. faculty Fashion Inst. Tech., 1975—, asst. prof., 1981—; evaluator, cons. masters degree program Empire State Coll., 1992; speaker on spl. educators Norman Rockwell Mus., 1995. Freelance illustrator, fashion artist; portrait painter: one-man show Soc. Illustrators Gallery, 1972; exhibited in group shows Art Students League, 1958, Art Dirs. Exhbn., 1956, Soc. Illustrators fashion illustration exhbn., 1964, portrait painting, 1967, Portraits, Inc., 1968, 11th, 12th, 16th, and 21st Ann. Exhbns.-Illustration, 1969, 70, 74, 76, 79, C.C. Price Gallery, 1970, N.Y. Hist. Soc., 1976, Soc. Ill. Ann., 1978, Smithsonian Instn., 1973, Salmagundi Club, 1973, NAD, 1986, Nat. Arts Club, 1986 (recipient William Collins award Hudson Valley Art Assn. 1971), Allied Artists of Am., 1986, Pratt Inst. Alumni, 1987, USAF, 1987, Art for the USAF, 1988-89, Portraits South Inc., 1989—, Monserrat Gallery, Soho, 1990, 94, print exhbn. Soc. Ill. Mus., 1990, faculty show Fashion Inst. Tech., 1993, 94. Served to capt. AUS, 1941-46, ETO. Decorated Combat Inf. Badge. Mem. Soc. Illustrators (v.p. 1970-73, pres. 1974-76, Fashion & Beauty Illustration show 1994), Artists Fellowship (trustee 1978, pres. 1985), West Side Tennis CClub, Lake Success Golf Club (pres. 1967-68). Home: 101 Central Park W New York NY 10023-4296

PINARD, GILBERT DANIEL, psychiatrist, educator; b. Montréal, Que., Can., July 19, 1940; s. Roland and Gabrielle (Laurendeau) P.; m. Andrée Pouliot, Aug. 17, 1963; children: Eric, Marc. BA, U. Montréal, 1961, MD, 1965, Spl. diploma in psychiatry, 1970. Intern Hôpital Maisonneuve, Montreal, 1965-66, resident in psychiatry, 1967-68; resident in psychiatry Hôpital Ste-Justine, Montreal, 1968-69, Hôpital St-Jean-de-Dieu, Montreal, 1969-70; asst. prof. research U. Montréal, 1975-76, assoc. prof., 1975-76; assoc. prof. U. Sherbrooke, Que., 1976-78, chmn. dept. psychiatry, 1976-82, prof., 1978, assoc. dean edn. and medicine, 1983-85; prof., chmn. dept. psychiatry McGill U., Montréal, 1986—; vis. prof. dept. psychiatry, U. Tex., Dallas, South Western Med. Sch., 1982-83; councillor, mem. nominating com. Can. Coll. Neuropsychopharmacology; mem. planning com. Fonds de la Recherche en Santé du Que. Contbr. numerous articles to profl. jours. and chpts. to books. Fellow Royal Coll. Physicians Can. (evaluation com. 1989—), Am. Psychiat. Assn. (Que. br. counsellor, chmn. pres.); mem. Can. Psychiat. Assn. (bd. adminstrs., liaison, edn. com., chmn. sci. program com., nominating com., R.O. Jones meml. vis. prof.), Que. Psychiat. Assn. (adv. com. for dean of medicine), Internat. Children's Found. Home: 3430 Peel Apt 11C, Montreal, PQ Canada H3A 3K8 Office: McGill U Dept Psychiatry, 1033 Pine Ave W, Montreal, PQ Canada H3A 1A1

PINARD, RAYMOND R., pulp and paper consultant; b. Trois-Rivieres, Que., Can., May 13, 1930; s. Albert and Mariette (Dufresne) P.; m. Estelle Frechette, Nov. 5, 1965; children: Robert, Andree. B.A., U. Laval, (Que., Can.), 1951; B.Eng., McGill U., Montreal, 1955. Registered profl. engr., Que. Process engring. plant mgr. Domtar Inc., East Augus, Que., 1955-68; gen. mgr. Domtar Kraft & Bd. Domtar Inc., Montreal, 1968-73, v.p., gen. mgr. Domtar Newspring & Pulp, 1974-79, pres. Domtar Pulp & Paper, 1979-81, exec. v.p., chief operating officer, 1981-90, also dir.; pres. South Shore Industries, E.F. Walter Ltd., United Auto Parts, Gen. Accident; bd. dirs. chmn. Centre Canadien de Fusion Magnetique; chmn. St. Laurent Paperboard Inc.; mem. Montreal adv. bd. Nat. Trust. Bd. dirs., past chmn. PPRIC; bd. dirs. Fondation de l'Universite' du Que., Montreal, 1979-92. Mem. TAPPI, Can. Pulp and Paper Assn. (chmn. 1982, bd. dirs.), Corp. Profl. Engrs. Que., Engring. Inst. Can., Can. Mfrs. Assn. (chmn. 1988-89), Can Pulp and Paper Tech. Assn. Office: R Pinard Cons Inc Ste 3000, 630 René-Lévesque Blvd W, Montreal, PQ Canada H3B 5C7

PINCAY, LAFFIT, JR., jockey; b. Panama City, Panama, 1946; s. Laffit and Rosario P.; m. Linda Pincay (dec.); children: Lisa, Laffit III. Jockey, 1964—. Winner Belmont Stakes, 1982, 84, 85, K. Derby, 1984, Preakness; leading money winner in thoroughbred horse racing, 1970-74, 79, 84; named Jockey of Yr., 1971, 72, 73, 79, 84, 85; inducted into Racing Hall of Fame. Office: care Jockey's Guild 20 E 46th St New York NY 10017-2417*

PINCH, JOHN G., radio executive; b. Milw., Oct. 28, 1948; s. Ken and Gwen Maud (Watkins) P.; m. Linda Diane Postles; children: Jodi, Lori, Michelle. BA, U. Wis., 1972. Sales mgr. Sta. WOKY, Milw., 1978-82; gen. mgr. Sta. WXJY, Milw., 1981-82, Sta. WFMR, Milw., 1982-83; pres., gen. mgr. Stas. WMTX & WHBO, Tampa, Fla., 1983—. Office: Sta WMTX-FM 18167 US Hwy 19 N Ste 500 Clearwater FL 34624

PINCHOT, BRONSON, actor; b. N.Y.C., 1959; s. Rosina Pinchot. BA with honors, Yale U., 1981. Ind. actor, 1981—. appeared in television series including Sara, 1985, Perfect Strangers, 1986-93, The Trouble With Larry, 1993; other TV appearances include George Burns Comedy Week, Amazing Stories, Saturday Night Live; films include Risky Business, 1983, The Flamingo Kid, 1984, Beverly Hills Cop, 1984, After Hours, 1985, Hot Resort, 1986, Second Sight, 1989, Blame It on the Bellboy, 1992, True Romance, 1993, Beverly Hills Cop III, 1994; television film Jury Duty, 1989, The Langoliers, 1995; appeared in Broadway play Zoya's Apartment, 1990; appeared in off-Broadway prodn. Poor Little Lambs. Office: ICM 8942 Wilshire Blvd Beverly Hills CA 90211*

PINCKNEY, C. COTESWORTH, lawyer; b. Richmond, Va., Oct. 23, 1939; s. Thomas and Charlotte (Kent) P.; m. Helen Raney, Aug. 13, 1966; children: Sarah Whitley, Thomas. BA, Yale U., 1961; LLB, U. Va., 1967. Bar: Va. 1967. Assoc. Mays, Valentine, Davenport & Moore, Richmond, 1967-72; ptnr. Mays & Valentine, Richmond, 1972—. Pres. Sheltering Arms Hosp., Richmond, 1986-87, bd. dirs. 1972—; trustee William H.-John G.-Emma Scott Found., 1974—. Mem. ABA, Va. Bar Assn., Richmond Bar Assn., Phila. Quarry Club (pres. 1984-92), Commonwealth Club (bd. govs. 1984-85, 87-92, pres. 1991-92). Republican. Episcopalian. Home: 2 Roslyn Rd Richmond VA 23226-1610 Office: Mays & Valentine 1111 E Main St 1111 E Main St PO Box 1122 Richmond VA 23208-1122

PINCKNEY, DARRYL, writer; b. Indpls., 1953. Student, Columbia U., Princeton U. Tchr. Columbia U., N.Y.C. Author: High Cotton, 1992 (Art Seidenbaum award L.A. Times 1992); contbr. to various periodicals including N.Y. Rev. of Books, Vanity Fair, Vogue, Granta, N.Y. Times. Hodder fellow Princeton U.; Ingram Merrill Found. grantee; Guggenheim Found. grantee; recipient Whiting Writers' award Mrs. Giles Whiting Found., 1986, Harold D. Vursell Meml. award in literature Am. Acad. Arts and Letters, 1994. *

PINCKNEY, NEAL THEODORE, psychologist, educator; b. N.Y.C., July 26, 1935; s. Leo Allen and Jean (Wiener) P.; children: Andrew Allen, Jennifer Elizabeth, Matthew Ian. Cert. polit. social and hist. issues, King's Coll., U. Durham, Eng., 1957; A.B., U. So. Calif., 1958, postgrad., 1958-61; Ph.D., Oxford U., 1966; postgrad., U. Vienna, U. Hiroshima, Stanford U. Mem. Pub. Welfare Commn., Los Angeles County, 1958-60; tchr. pub. schs., Los Angeles, 1960-61; tchr., counselor Las Vegas, 1961-62, adminstrt. therapist psychiat. clinic, 1962-63; educator, dir. guidance service Dept. Def. Overseas Dependent Schs., England and Japan, 1963-67; pvt. practice clin. psychology, 1967-87; lectr. Calif. State U., Sacramento, 1967-68, asst. prof., 1968-71, assoc. prof., 1971-77, prof. psychology and edn., 1977-87, prof. emeritus, 1987—, chmn. dept. behavioral scis., 1980-82, prof. counseling psychology, coordinator grad. studies, dept. adminstrn., counseling and policy studies, 1982—; founder, clin. dir. A Healing Heart, 1993—; vis. prof. U. Calif.-Davis, 1979—; psychologist, instr. enforcement psychology and human rels. Calif. Hwy. Patrol, 1967-80; dir. Univ. Software Evaluation Project, 1987; tech. cons., adv. Ministry Edn. and Culture, Goft. Brazil, Brasilia, 1974-76; cons. psychologist Calif. Med. Facility, Vacaville, various law enforcement agys.; prof. U. Hawaii, lectr. U. Hawaii Leeward C.C., 1992-93; founder, clin. dir. Healing Heart Found., 1993—. Author: Healthy Heart Handbook, 1994, Law and Ethics in Counseling and Psychotherapy, A Casebook, 1961, 86; pub. USER, a Software Report Card, 1987; editor: Incite Newsletter of Hawii Portable Computer Users Assn., 1987-88; editor: Ency. of Psychology, 2d edit. Served with 3d Armored Div. U.S. Army, 1954-55. Queen's scholar Eng., 1956-57; scholar Dept. State Fgn. Service Inst., 1964; fellow Ford Found., 1960-61. Mem. Am. Psychol. Assn., Brit. Psychol. Assn., Japanese Psychol. Assn., Brazilian Psychol. Assn., Am. Ednl. Research Assn., Am. Assn. Counseling and Devel., Am. Radio Relay League (life), Hawaii Portable Computer Users Assn., Hawaii Personal Computer Users Group (pres. 1989-91, system operator Electronic Bulletin Bd. Svc.), Quarter Century Wireless Assn. (life), Vegetarian Soc. Honolulu, No. Calif. DX Club, Hawaii DX Assn., Phi Delta Kappa, Delta Phi Epsilon. Clubs: Commonwealth (San Francisco); Oxonian (Tokyo); Toastmasters (area gov. 1962-63). Lodge: Masons. Home: 84-683 Upena St Waianae HI 96792-1935 Those who rush through life are merely hurrying toward their death. When one pauses to savor its many subtle varieties one begins to gain some insight and to be in awe of the wonder of it all. Then we begin to place ourselves in perspective and everything has meaning.

PINCO, ROBERT G., lawyer; b. L.A., Feb. 9, 1944. BS Pharmacy, U. Conn., 1966; JD, Georgetown U., 1969. Bar: Md. 1969, D.C. 1970, U.S. Claims Ct. 1971, U.S. Supreme Ct. 1973; registered pharmacist D.C. Atty. Dept. Justice, 1969-72; asst. gen. counsel spl. action office drug abuse prevention Exec. Office Pres., 1972-74; dir. over-the-counter drugs FDA, 1977—; ptnr. Akin, Gump, Strauss, Hauer & Feld, Washington, 1993—; adj. assoc. prof. pharmacy U. Md., 1978—; mem. bd. advisors U. Md. Sch. Pharmacy, 1994—. Contbr. articles to profl. jours. Mem. ABA, D.C. Bar Assn., Md. State Bar Assn., Fed. Bar Assn. (vice chair food and drug com 1977), Am. Soc. Pharmacy Law (Pres'. award 1986). Office: Akin Gump Strauss Hauer & Feld 1333 New Hampshire Ave NW Washington DC 20036

PINCOCK, DOUGLAS GEORGE, electronics company executive; b. Vancouver, B.C. Can., Sept. 29, 1940; s. George Leyland and Sadie McElvenna (Boyle) P.; m. Gloria Dawn Werth, Sept. 5, 1964 (div. 1985); children: Barrt, James, David, Lisa; m. Marilyn Marie Spearns, Oct. 28, 1990. BSEE, Man. (Winnipeg, Can.) U., 1963, MSEE, 1967; PhD, New Brunswick U., Fredericton, 1971. Registered profl. engr., N.S. Asst. prof. St. Francis Xavier U., Antigonish, N.S., 1969-70; from lectr. to asst. prof. to assoc. prof. U. N.B., 1970-75, 76-79; maitre de conf. U. Paris, 1975-76; prof. Tech. U. N.S., Halifax, 1979-82; pres., founder Applied Microelectronics Inc., Halifax, 1982—; bd. dirs. Can. Microelectronics Corp., Kingston, Ont., VEMCO, Shad Bay, N.S., Advanced Materials Eng. Ctr., Halifax; pres., bd. dirs. AMI Techs., Halifax, 1992—. Contbr. 25 papers to profl. jours. Head coach basketball Tech. U. N.S. With Can. Air Force, 1963-66. Achievements include co-invention weatherstar 4000, other inventions in underwater telemetry products. Office: Microelectronics Inc, 1046 Barrington St, Halifax, NS Canada B3H 2R1

PINCOCK, RICHARD EARL, chemistry educator; b. Ogden, Utah, Sept. 14, 1935; s. Earl Samuel and Virginia (Christenson) P.; m. Elke Gertrud Hermann, Aug. 20, 1960; children—Christina, Gordon, Jennifer. B.S., U. Utah, 1956; A.M., Harvard U., 1957, Ph.D., 1960. Postdoctoral research fellow Calif. Inst. Tech., 1959-60; faculty U. B.C., Vancouver, Can., 1960—; prof. U. B.C., 1969—. Mem. Phi Beta Kappa, Sigma Pi. Office: U BC, Chemistry Dept, Vancouver, BC Canada V6T 1Y6

PINCUS, ANN TERRY, federal agency administrator; b. Little Rock, Sept. 12, 1937; d. Fred William and Cornelia (Witsell) Terry; m. Walter Haskell Pincus, May 1, 1965; children: Ward, Adam, Cornelia Battle. BA, Vassar Coll., 1959. Editorial asst., writer Glamour Mag., 1963; reporter Ridder Pubs., Washington, 1963-66; freelance writer Washington, 1966-76; dir. info. select com. on U.S. population U.S. Ho. Reps., Washington, 1977-79; nat. publicist Nat. Pub. Radio, Washington, 1979-83; press sec. U.S. Sen. Charles Mathias, Washington, 1983-87; profl. staff mem. Senate Com. on Rules, Washington, 1983-87; v.p. communications Stas. WETA-TV/Radio, Washington, 1987-93; dir. Office of Rsch., U.S. Info. Agy., Washington, 1993—; bd. dirs. Wildfowl Trust of N. Am., Graysonville, Md., Fgn. Student Service Council, Washington, Woodley House. Editor: Kennedy Center Cookbook, 1977; contbr. articles to profl. jours. Avocations: politics, reading, walking, tennis. Home: 3202 Klingle Rd NW Washington DC 20008-3403 Office: Office of Rsch US Info Agy 301 4th St Rm 352 Washington DC 20547

PINCUS, GEORGE, university dean, engineering educator; b. Havana, Cuba, July 5, 1935; came to U.S., 1957, naturalized, 1966; s. Max and Ana (Slutzkaya) P.; m. Dora Dzubquevich, June 8, 1958; children: Cynthia Judith, David Nathan, Karen Joy. BSCE, Ga. Inst. Tech., 1959, MSCE, 1960; PhD, Cornell U., 1963; MBA, U. Houston, 1974. Registered profl. engr., Ky., Tex., Fla., Calif., N.J. Teaching asst. Cornell U., Ithaca, N.Y., 1959-61; rsch. assist. Cornell U. Ithaca, 1961-63; asst. prof. structural engring. U. Ky., Lexington, 1963-66; assoc. prof. civil engring. U. Ky., 1968-69; prof. civil engring. U. Houston, 1969-86, chmn. dept., 1976-80; prof. civil engring. N.J. Inst. Tech., Newark, 1986—, dean engring., 1986—; chief party grad. engring. program AID, Rio de Janeiro, Brazil, also prof. Fed. U., Rio de Janeiro, 1967-68. Author: Design of Structures and Foundations for Vibrating Machines, 1979, other books; contbr. articles to profl. jours. Recipient W.T. Kittinger Teaching Excellence award U. Houston, 1975. Fellow ASCE (D.V. Terrel award dist. 9, 1959); mem. AAUP, Am. Soc. for Engring. Edn., NSPE, N.J. Soc. Profl. Engrs. (N.J. Engr. of Yr. award 1990), Soc. Mfg. Engrs. (sr.), Order of Engr., Phi Kappa Phi, Omicron Delta Kappa, Tau Beta Pi, Chi Epsilon. Avocations: music, art. Office: NJ Inst Tech 323 Mill St Belleville NJ 07109-1673 It is surprising to find some who underestimate the value of living in this country with its principles of reward for hard work, full equal opportunity for all, personal liberty, and its tradition for world moral leadership. My primary goals have been: to show continued improvement and growth in my academic career and to prepare myself for greater administrative responsibilities in higher education. I hope that these goals will result in tangible benefits for my adopted country and in some way, repay my debt of gratitude to the United States of America.

PINCUS, HOWARD JONAH, geologist, engineer, educator; b. N.Y.C., June 24, 1922; s. Otto Max and Gertrude (Jankowsky) P.; m. Maud Lydia Roback, Sept. 6, 1953; children: Glenn David, Philip E. BS, CCNY, 1942; PhD, Columbia U., 1949. Mem. faculty Ohio State U., 1949-67, successively instr., asst. prof., assoc. prof., 1949-59, prof., 1959-67, chmn. dept. geology, 1960-65; rsch. geologist U. S. Bur. Mines, summers 1963-67; geologist, rsch. supr. U.S. Bur. Mines, 1967-68; prof. geol. sci. and civil engring. U. Wis., Milw., 1968-87, prof. emeritus, 1987—, dean Coll. Letters and Sci., 1969-72; rsch. assoc. Lamont Geol. Obs., Columbia, 1949, 50, 51; geologist Ohio Dept. Natural Resources, summers 1950-61; cons. geology and rock mechanics, 1954-67, 68—; mem. U.S. nat. com. on tunnelling tech. NAE, 1972-74, mem. U.S. nat. com. on rock mechanics NAS/NAE, 1975-78, 80-89, chmn., 1985-87; mem. U.S. com. Internat. Assn. Engring. Geology/NAS, chmn., 1987-90; sr. postdoctoral fellow NSF, 1962. Tech. editor: Geotech. Testing Jour., 1992—. Served to 1st lt. C.E. AUS, 1942-46. Recipient award for teaching excellence U. Wis-Milw. Alumni Assn., 1978. Fellow ASTM (Reinhart award 1987, Award of Merit 1989), AAAS, Geol. Soc. Am.; mem. NSPE, AAUP (pres. Ohio State U. chpt. 1955-56, mem. coun. 1965-67, pres. U. Wis.-Milw. chpt. 1976-77), Am. Geophys. Union, Geol. Soc. Am. (chmn. engring. geology divsn. 1973-74), Soc. Mining Engrs., Internat. Assn. Engring. Geology, Internat. Soc. Rock Mechanics, Assn. Engring. Geologists, Am. Inst. Profl. Geologists (pres. Ohio sect. 1965-66), Computer Oriented Geol. Soc., Phi Beta Kappa (pres. Ohio State U chpt. 1959-60, pres. U. Wis.-Milw. chpt. 1976-77), Sigma Xi. Home: 17523 Plaza Marlena San Diego CA 92128-1807 Office: PO Box 27598 San Diego CA 92198-1598

PINCUS, JILLIAN RUTH, physician; b. Bklyn., May 26, 1947; d. William and Elsa Bronson Pincus. BA, Radcliffe Coll., 1969; MD, Med. Coll. Pa., 1974. Cert. Am. Bd. Internal Medicine, Am. Bd. Nephrology. Intern, resident U. Medicine and Dentistry of N.J.-Robert Wood Johnson Med. Sch., 1974-77, nephrology fellow, 1978-79; nephrology fellow U. Miami Sch. Medicine, 1977-78; attending physician Jewish Inst. Geriatric Care, New Hyde Park, N.Y., 1979-80, L.I. Jewish Hosp.-Hillside Med. Ctr., New Hyde Park, 1980-82; from asst. to assoc. med. dir. Sandoz Pharm., East Hanover, N.J., 1982-88; med. dir. CIBA-Geigy Corp., Summit, N.J., 1988-90, exec. med. dir., 1990-92, clin. head, 1992-93, head, 1993—. Active Nat. Kidney Found. Mem. AMA, Am. Soc. Nephrology, Am. Med. Women's Assn., Women in Nephrology. Avocations: sports, reading, arts. Home: 1 Plymouth Rd Chatham NJ 07928 Office: CIBA-Geigy Corp 556 Morris Ave Summit NJ 07901

PINCUS, JOSEPH, economist, educator; b. N.Y.C., Apr. 17, 1919; s. Samuel and Lillian (Sirotkin) P.; m. Ethel Frances London, July 6, 1952; children: Terri Ellen Pincus Forman, Sally Neila, Robert Alan. BSS, CCNY, 1941; MA, Am. U., 1947, PhD, 1953. Internat. economist Latin Am. studies project U.S. Tariff Commn., Washington, 1946-47, 61-62; economist, fgn. affairs analyst Div. Research Am. Republics, Dept. State, Washington, 1949-58; tariff adviser ICA, USOM, Honduras, 1958-60; rep. with Continental Allied Co. to study indsl. devel., 1961; program officer, econ. adviser AID, Costa Rica, 1962-64; acting dir. mission AID, 1964; econ. adviser, pvt. enterprise adviser Am. Embassy, Asuncion, Paraguay, 1964-66, acting embassy econ. officer, 1967; pvt. enterprise devel. officer Am. Embassy, San Salvador, El Salvador, 1967-69, acting program officer, 1968, loan economist, 1968-69; dir. research Brokers Internat. Ltd., Miami, Fla., 1972-73; adj. prof. econs. Fla. Internat. U., also Embry-Riddle Aero. U., 1974-75; vis. prof. econs. U. Miami, 1974, 79, Fla. Meml. Coll., 1975; pres. Common Market Devel. Corp., Miami, 1975-86; ptnr., chief economist Brown and Pincus Assocs.; hon. fellow U. Asuncion Sch. Advanced Econ. Studies; dir. enterprise devel. program Ctr. for Advanced Internat. Studies, U. Miami; mem. Fla.-Colombia Ptnrs. Program. Mem. indsl. devel., promotion and retention task force Dade County Overall Econ. Devel. Program Com., 1983-85; senator Fla. Silver-Haired Legislature; mem. internat. bus. and commerce task force Beacon Council; founder South Dade-Kendall Rep. Club, Dade County, Fla. Mem. Am. Fgn. Svc. Assn., Nat. Assn. Ret. Fed. Employees, Latin Am. Studies Assn., Soc. Internat. Devel., Acad. for Internat. Bus., Caribbean Studies Assn., U. Miami Consortium on Hunger and Poverty, Omicron Delta Epsilon, Beta Gamma Sigma. Avocations: amateur

radio at Sta. KD6TCE. Home and Office: 50 Chumasero Dr San Francisco CA 94132-2338 To those involved in corporate or governmental bureaucracies, my advice is to exercise initiative, go as far as you can on your own, and then seek authority. If you're wrong, someone in authority will stop you eventually. But you could be RIGHT.

PINCUS, LIONEL IRWIN, venture banker; b. Phila., Mar. 2, 1931; s. Henry and Theresa Celia (Levit) P.; m. Suzanne Storrs Poulton. BA, U. Pa., 1953; MBA, Columbia U., 1956. Assoc. gen. ptnr. Ladenburg, Thalmann & Co., N.Y.C., 1955-63; pres. Lionel I. Pincus & Co., Inc., N.Y.C., 1964-66; pres., chief exec. officer E.M. Warburg & Co., Inc., N.Y.C., 1966-70; chmn., chief exec. officer E.M. Warburg, Pincus & Co., Inc., N.Y.C., 1970—. Bd. trustees Montefiore Hosp., N.Y.C.; trustee Ittleson Found., Inc., Columbia U., vice-chmn.; trustee Sch. Am. Ballet, Citizens Budget Commn., German Marshall Fund USA, 1982-88; mem. bd. overseers Columbia Grad. Sch. Bus. Mem. Council Fgn. Rels., N.Y.C. Partnership, Nat. Golf Links Am. Club, Meadow Club. Office: EM Warburg Pincus Co Inc 466 Lexington Ave New York NY 10017-3140

PINCUS, MICHAEL STERN, language educator; b. Atlanta, Jan. 18, 1936; s. Bernard M. and Amelia (Stern) P.; m. Jacqueline Kron, June 10, 1956; children: Jonathan D., Gregory K. BA, Union Coll., Schenectady, N.Y., 1957; MA, U. N.C., 1958, PhD, 1961; diploma, U. Madrid, 1960; postgrad., Fairleigh Dickinson U., 1987. Asst. prof. romance langs. Rutgers U., New Brunswick, N.J., 1961-67; assoc. prof. Spanish SUNY, New Paltz, 1967-69; chmn., assoc. prof. Spanish and classics U. N.H., Durham, 1969-72; acting v.p. acad. affairs Mansfield U. Pa., 1976, acting dean grad. studies, 1977, dean liberal arts, 1972-80; dean Mary Baldwin Coll., Staunton, Va., 1980-82; dean coll. liberal arts Fairleigh Dickinson U., Rutherford and Teaneck, N.J., 1982-87; prof., head divsn. classical and modern langs. Coll. of Charleston, S.C., 1987—; curriculum cons. Computer Horizons Corp., N.Y.C., 1985-86; program evaluation cons. to numerous state and regional accrediting agys., 1969-85. Contbr. numerous articles and reviews to newspapers and profl. jours. Coach Youth Baseball Assn., Mansfield, 1973-80. Mem. Am. Assn. Tchrs. Spanish and Portuguese, MLA, Am. Contract Bridge League (dir. unit 217 1978-80). Avocations: acting, tournament bridge, classical music, travel. Office: Coll of Charleston 66 George St Charleston SC 29424-0002

PINCUS, ROBERT LAWRENCE, art critic, cultural historian; b. Bridgeport, Conn., June 5, 1953; s. Jules Robert and Carol Sylvia (Rosen) P.; m. Georgianna Manly, June 20, 1981; 1 child, Matthew Manly. BA, U. Calif., Irvine, 1976; MA, U. So. Calif., 1980, PhD, 1987. Instr. U. So. Calif., L.A., 1978-83; art critic L.A. Times, 1981-85, San Diego Union, 1985-92, San Diego Union-Tribune, 1992—; vis. prof. San Diego State U., 1985-86, 92. Author: On A Scale That Competes with the World: The Art of Edward and Nancy Reddin Kienholz, 1990, (with others) West Coast Duchamp, 1991, But Is It Art: The Spirit of Art as Activism, 1994, Paradise, 1994; author introduction to W.D.'s Midnight Carnival, 1988. Recipient Chem. Bank award, 1994, Best Critical Writing award San Diego Press Club, 1994. Mem. Internat. Assn. Art Critics, Coll. Art Assn. Democrat. Office: San Diego Union-Tribune 350 Camino De La Reina San Diego CA 92108-3003

PINCUS, THEODORE, microbiologist, educator. AB, Columbia U., 1961; MD, Harvard U., 1966. Assoc. Sloan-Kettering Inst., N.Y.C., 1973-75; asst. prof. medicine-immunology Stanford (Calif.) U., 1975-76; adj. assoc. prof. medicine-rheumatology U. Pa., Phila., 1976-80; prof. medicine & microbiology Vanderbilt U., Nashville, 1980—; prof. Wistar Inst., Phila., 1976-80; dir. clin. immunology lab. Stanford U. Hosp., 1975-76. Fellow ACP, Am. Rheumatism Assn., Am. Soc. Microbiology. Achievements include research in morbidity and mortility of rheumatoid arthritis, host variables in chronic diseases, host genetic control of virus infection, psychological and economic consequences of chronic disease, socioeconomic status and chronic disease. Office: Vanderbilt U Arthritis & Lupus Ctr T-3219 MCN Nashville TN 37232

PINCUS, THEODORE HENRY, public relations executive; b. Chgo., Sept. 15, 1933; s. Jacob T. and J. (Engel) P.; m. Sharon Barr, Jan. 16, 1988; children: Laura, Mark, Susan, Anne, Jennifer. BS in Journalism, Ind. U., 1955. Free-lance bus. writer, 1955-58; sr. exec. Harshe Rotman & Druck, Chgo., 1958-62; dir. comm. Maremont Corp., Chgo., 1962-64; chmn., CEO, majority owner The Fin. Rels. Bd. Inc., N.Y.C., Chgo., L.A., San Francisco, 1964—; pub. affairs advisor to Nelson Rockefellen, N.Y.C., 1960, 68; advisor U.S. Info. Agy., 1993—. Author: Giveaway Day, 1977; contbr. articles to profl. jours. Active presdl. nomination campaigns; vice-chmn. Midwest region Am. Jewish Com.; mem. adv. bd. Ind. U. Bus. Sch. With USAF, 1955-57. Recipient numerous nat. awards for profl. excellence in investor rels. and corp.pub. rels. including Silver Anvil award Pub. Rels. Soc. Am., 1966, Civic Achievement award Am. Jewish Com., 1993. Mem. Young Pres.'s Orgn., Nat. Investor Relations Inst. (founding). Club: Union League. Office: The Financial Relations John Hancock Ctr 875 N Michigan Ave Chicago IL 60611-1779

PINCUS, WALTER HASKELL, editor; b. Bklyn., Dec. 24, 1932; s. Jonas and Clare (Glassman) P.; m. Betty Meskin, Sept. 12, 1954; 1 son, Andrew John; m. Ann Witsell Terry, May 1, 1965; children: Ward Haskell, Adam Witsell, Cornelia Battle Terry. B.A., Yale, 1954. Cons. Senate Fgn. Relations Com., 1962-63; spl. writer Washington Evening Star, 1963-66; editor, reporter Washington Post, 1966-69; chief cons. Symington subcom. Senate Fgn. Relations Com., 1969-70; asso. editor New Republic, 1972-74, exec. editor, 1974-75; spl. writer Washington Post, 1975—; Cons. NBC News, 1971-79, CBS News, 1979-86, NBC News, 1987-88, Washington Post Co., 1989—; vis. lectr. Yale U., Fall 1988; dir. N.Y. Rev. Corp., 1979-85. Trustee Shakespeare Theater at the Folger, 1988—, co-chmn. edn. com., 1989-91, chmn. nominating com., 1992—. Served with AUS, 1955-57. Recipient Page One award, 1960, George Orwell award, 1977, George Polk award, 1978, Emmy award, 1981. Mem. Council Fgn. Relations. Clubs: Federal City (Washington), Yale (Washington). Home: 3202 Klingle Rd NW Washington DC 20008-3403 Office: Washington Post 1150 15th St NW Washington DC 20071-0002

PINCZUK, ARON, physicist; b. San Martin, Argentina, Feb. 15, 1939; s. Faiwel and Ester (Wejeman) P.; m. Gladys Norma Teitelman, June 14, 1962; children: Ana Gabriela, Guillermo Fabian. Licenciado, U. Buenos Aires, Argentina, 1962; PhD, U. Pa., 1969. Staff mem. Nat. Rsch. Coun., Argentina, 1971-76; head physics dept. Faculty of Scis., U. Buenos Aires, Argentina, 1974; vis. scientist Max Planck Inst., Stuttgart, Germany, 1976, IBM Rsch., Yorktown Heights, N.Y., 1976-77; staff mem. AT&T Bell Labs., Murray Hill, N.J., 1978—; sec. Argentina Phys. Soc., Buenos Aires, 1972-75; editor Solid State Communications, 1989-92, assoc. editor in chief, 1992—. Contbr. over 180 articles to profl. jours. and numerous chpts. to books. Fellow Am. Phys. Soc. (Oliver E. Buckley prize 1994); mem. AAAS. Achievements include use and devel. novel optical methods in studies of structural phase transitions, semiconductor interfaces and interactions of free electrons in semiconductors; discovered novel phenomena in studies of quantum electron fluids. Office: AT&T Bell Labs 600 Mountain Ave Rm 1d-433 Murray Hill NJ 07974-0636

PINDELL, HOWARDENA DOREEN, artist; b. Phila., Apr. 14, 1943; s. Howard Douglas and Mildred Edith (Lewis) P. B.F.A., Boston U., 1965; M.F.A., Yale U., 1967. Curatorial asst. Mus. Modern Art, N.Y.C., 1969-71; asst. curator Mus. Modern Art, 1971-77, asso. curator dept. prints and illus. books, 1977-79; asso. prof. art SUNY, Stony Brook, 1979-84, prof. art, 1984—. Contbr. articles to profl. jours.; exhbns. include, Mus. Modern Art, Stockholm and 5 European mus., 1973, Fogg Art Mus., Cambridge, Mass., 1973, Indpls. Mus., Taft Mus., Cin., 1974, Gerald Piltzer Gallery, Paris, 1975, 9th Paris Biennale, Mus. Modern Art, Paris, 1975, Vassar Coll. Art Gallery, 1977; represented in permanent collections, Mus. Modern Art, N.Y.C., Fogg Art Mus., Met. Mus., N.Y.C., Whitney Mus. Am. Art; represented in travelling exhbns. Brandeis U., U. Calif. at Riverside, Cleve. Inst. Arts, SUNY, Potsdam, New Paltz, Wesleyan U., Davison Art Ctr., others. Recipient Artist award Studio Mus. of Harlem, 1994, Joan Mitchell Painting award Joan Mitchell Found. 1994/95; N.Y. Nat. Endowment Arts grantee, 1972-73, 83-84; Japan/U.S. Friendship fellow, 1981-82; recipient Boston U. Alumni award, 1983, Ariana Found. grant, 1984-85, Guggenheim fellowship, 1987-88. Mem. ACASA, Coll. Art Assn. (Best Exhbn./Performance award 1990), Internat. Assn. Art Critics, Internat.

Hous of Japan (acad.). Studio: PO Box 259 Inwood Station New York NY 10034 Office: SUNY Dept Art Stony Brook NY 11794

PINDER, GEORGE FRANCIS, engineering educator, scientist; b. Windsor, Ont., Can., Feb. 6, 1942; s. Percy Samuel and Stella Marie P.; m. Phyllis Marie Charlton, Sept. 14, 1963; children—Wendy Marie, Justin George. B.Sc., U. Western Ont., 1965; Ph.D., U. Ill., 1968. Research hydrologist U.S. Geol. Survey, 1968-72; mem. faculty dept. civil engring. Princeton U., 1972-89, prof., 1972-89, chmn. dept., from 1980, dir. water resources program, 1972-80; dean Coll. Engring. and Math. U. Vt., Burlington, 1989—. Recipient O.E. Meinzer award Geol. Soc. Am., 1975, WUC medal, 1992; U. Vt. Univ. scholar, 1993. Fellow Am. Geophys. Union (Robert E. Horton award 1969); mem. ASCE. Soc. Petroleum Engrs. Home: 7 Bishop Rd Shelburne VT 05482-7351 Office: U Vt Coll Engring and Math Burlington VT 05405

PINDERA, JERZY TADEUSZ, mechanical and aeronautical engineer; b. Czchow, Poland, Dec. 4, 1914; immigrated to Can., 1965, naturalized, 1975; s. Jan Stanislaw and Natalia Lucia (Knapik) P.; m. Aleksandra-Anna Szal, Oct. 29, 1949; children: Marek Jerzy, Maciej Zenon. BS in Mech. Engring. Tech. U., Warsaw, 1936; MS in Aero. Engring, Tech. U., Warsaw and Lodz, 1947; D in Applied Scis., Polish Acad. Scis., 1959; DS in Applied Mechanics, Tech. U., Cracow, 1962. Registered profl. engr., Ont. Asst. Lot Polish Airlines, Warsaw, 1947; head lab. Aero. Inst., Warsaw, 1947-52, Inst. Metallography, Warsaw, 1952-54; dep. prof., head lab. Polish Acad. Scis. 1954-59; head lab. Bldg. Research Inst., Warsaw, 1959-62; vis. prof. mechanics Mich. State U., East Lansing, 1963-65; prof. mechanics U. Waterloo (Ont. Can.), 1965-83, adj. prof., 1983-86, Disting. prof. emeritus, 1987—; pres. J.T. Pindera & Sons Engring. Services, Inc., Waterloo, 1980—; chmn. Internat. Symposium Exptl. Mechanics, U. Waterloo, 1972, dir. Inst. for Exptl. Mechanics, 1983-86; chmn. 10th Can. Fracture Conf., 1983; hon. adv. prof. Chongqing (Sichuan, China) U., 1988—; hon. prof. Shanghai (China) Coll. Archtl. and Mcpl. Engring., 1988—; hon. chmn. Internat. Conf. on Advanced Exptl. Mechanics, U. Tianjin, People's Republic of China, 1988; vis. prof. in France, Fed. Republic Germany, Slovenia, U.S.A., China; cons. in field. Bd. editors Mechanics Rsch. Communications, 1974—; Theoretical and Applied Fracture Mechanics, 1984—; mem. editorial adv. bd. Acta Mechanica Sinica, 1990—; patentee in field; contbr. tech. books, articles and chpts. in books. Served with Polish Army, 1939. Decorated Def. War 1939 medal (Poland), Cross of Oswiecim (Poland),; Comdr.'s Cross of Order of Merit (Fed. Republic Germany). Fellow Soc. Exptl. Mechanics (M.M. Frocht award 1978), Can. Soc. for Mech. Engring. (H.G. Duggan medal 1986); mem. Gesellschaft Angewandte Mathematik und Mechanik, N.Y. Acad. Scis., Soc. Engring. Sci., ASME, Assn. Profl. Engrs. Ont. Home: 310 Grant Crescent, Waterloo, ON Canada N2K 2A2 Office: U Waterloo Dept Civil Engring, 200 University Ave, Waterloo, ON Canada N2L 3G1 *It is true that "Nothing is more practical than a theory," provided however, that the assumptions on which the theory is founded are well understood. But, indeed, nothing can be more disastrous than a theory when applied to a real problem outside of the practical limits of the assumptions made, simply because of an homonymous identity with the problem under consideration!.*

PINDYCK, BRUCE EBEN, lawyer, corporate executive; b. N.Y.C., Sept. 21, 1945; s. Sylvester and Lillian (Breslow) P.; m. Mary Ellen Schwartz, Aug. 18, 1968; children: Ashley Beth, Eben Spencer, Blake Michael Lawrence. AB, Columbia U., 1967, JD, 1970, MBA, 1971. Bar: N.Y. 1971, Wis. 1987. Assoc. Olwine, Connelly, Chase, O'Donnell & Weyher, N.Y.C., 1971-80; asst. gen. counsel Peat, Marwick, Mitchell & Co., N.Y.C., 1980-82; ptnr. Hollyer, Jones, Pindyck, Brady & Chira, N.Y.C., 1983-87; pres., chief exec. officer Meridian Industries, Inc., Milw., 1985—; also chmn. bd. dirs. Meridian Industries, Inc.; chief exec. officer Majilite Corp., Dracut, Mass., 1987—; also chmn. bd. dirs. Majilite Corp.; mem. capital campaign com. Columbia U., 1984-87. Bd. dirs. Harambee Community Sch., 1991—, Milw. Ballet Co., 1993—, Milw. Pub. Mus., 1994—. Mem. Columbia Coll. Alumni Assn. (regional dir. 1988-94, v.p. 1994—, exec. com.), Young Pres.'s Orgn. Office: 100 E Wisconsin Ave Milwaukee WI 53202-4107

PINE, JEFFREY BARRY, state attorney general; b. N.Y.C., Jan. 10, 1955; s. Henry F. Pine and Irma (Goldberg) Nass; m. Faith Marcia Scavitti, May 20, 1984; children: Bethany Arielle, Jonathan Ian Lee. BA in Polit. Sci., Haverford Coll., 1976; JD, George Washington U., 1979. Bar: R.I. 1979, Mass. 1979, US. Dist. Ct. R.I. 1979. Asst. atty. gen., dep. chief criminal prosecution R.I. Dept. Atty. Gen., Providence, 1979-89; assoc. atty. Decof & Grimm, Providence, 1990-93; atty. gen. State of R.I., 1993—. Bd. dirs. Camp Jori, Providence, 1989—, Jewish Family Svcs., Providence, 1990-92; trustee Temple Beth El, Providence, 1990-92; mem. R.I. Criminal Bench Bar Com., 1979-90, MADD, 1987—, Bd. Bar Overseers Mass. Recipient Beta Rho Sigma award; named top prosecutor by R.I. Monthly. Mem. ABA, R.I. Bar Assn., Assn. Am. Trial Lawyers, R.I. Trial Lawyers Assn. Ledgemont Country Club. Home: 15 Westford Rd Providence RI 02906-4943 Office: Office of Attorney General 72 Pine St Providence RI 02903

PINEDA, MARIANNA, sculptor, educator; b. Evanston, Ill., May 10, 1925; d. George and Marianna (Dickinson) Packard; m. Harold Tovish, Jan. 14, 1946; children: Margo, Aaron, Nina. Student, Cranbrook Acad. Art, summer 1942, Bennington Coll., 1942-43, U. Calif.-Berkeley, 1943-45, Columbia U., 1945-46, Ossip Zadkine Sch. Drawing and Sculpture, Paris, 1949-50. instr. sculpture Newton Coll. Sacred Heart, 1972-75, Boston Coll., 1975-77; vis. assoc. prof. Boston U., 1974, 78, annually 83-87, 89-90; vis. sculptor Sch. of Mus. Fine Arts, Boston, 1990-91; vis. critic Boston U., 1992. One-woman shows include Slaughter Gallery, San Francisco, 1951, Walker Art Ctr., Mpls., 1952, Currier Gallery, Vt., 1954, De Cordova Mus., Lincoln, Mass., 1954, Premier Gallery, Mpls., 1963, Swetzoff Gallery, Boston, 1953, 56, 64, Honolulu Acad. Art, 1970, Alpha Gallery, Boston, 1972, Newton Coll., (Mass.) 1972, Bumpus Gallery, Duxbury, Mass., 1972, Contemporary Art Ctr., Honolulu, 1982, Hanalei Palace, Kona, Hawaii, 1982, Lyman House Mus., Hilo, Hawaii, 1982, Pine Manor Coll., Mass., 1984, Rotenberg Gallery, Boston, 1990, 93, 94, Coll. of William and Mary, 1992, Wiggin Gallery, Boston Libr., 1993, Rotenberg Gallery, Mass., 1994; group shows include Oakland (Calif.) Civic Mus., 1944, Village Art Ctr., N.Y.C., 1944, Albright Art Gallery, Buffalo, 1947, Bklyn. Mus., 1947, Galerie 8 Paris, 1950, Met. Mus. Art, N.Y.C., 1951, San Francisco Mus. of Art, 1955, Inst. Contemporary Art, Boston, 1958, 59, 61, Whitney Mus. Am. Art, N.Y.C., 1953, 54, 55, 57, 59, Boston Arts Festival, 1957, 58, 60, 62, 63, 65, 85, Silvermine Annual Exhibit, Conn., 1957, Pitts. Internat., 1958, Mus. Modern Art, N.Y.C., 1960 (traveling), Art Inst. Chgo., 1959, 61, Dallas Mus. Art, 1961, Nat. Inst. Arts & Letters, 1961, N.Y. World's Fair, 1964, De Cordova Mus., 1963, 64, 1972, 75, 87, Sculptors Guild, N.Y.C., 1967-95, Pine Manor Coll, Mass., Pa. State U., 1974, The Women's Bldg., L.A., 1976, Simmons Coll., Mass., 1980, Helen Schlein Gallery, Boston, 1982, SUNY-Buffalo, 1983, Fitchburg Mus. Art, Mass., 1984, Newton Art Ctr., Mass., 1985, Boston U. Art Gallery, 1986, Shulman Sculpture Pk., White Plains, N.Y., 1986, 87, 88, Alchemie Gallery, Boston, 1987, 93, Nat. Acad. Design, N.Y.C., 1988-89, 91, 92, 93, 94-95, Boston Visual Artist Union Invitational, 1986, Bunting Inst., Fed. Reserve Gallery, Boston, 1986, Port of History, Phila., 1987, Brockton Art Ctr., Mass., 1987, Judi Rotenberg Gallery, Boston, ann. 1987—, A.I.R. Gallery, N.Y.C., 1988, Boston Pub. Libr., 1988, Nat. Sculpture Soc., N.Y.C., 1986-89, 90-95, Holyoke Mus., Mass., 1989, Washington Art Assn., Conn., 1989, Bumpus Art Gallery, Duxbury, 1989, Page St. Gallery, San Francisco, 1989, Louis Ross Gallery, N.Y.C., 1990, Shidoni Galleries, 1990, The Contemporary Mus., Honolulu, 1990, Cast Iron Gallery, 1993, Kyoto (Japan) Civic Gallery, 1993, Walsh Art Gallery, Fairfield, Conn., 1991, Wingspread Gallery, Northeast Harbor, Maine, 1991, World Fin. Ctr. Gallery, 1992, Phila. Sculptors Guild, 1992, Kingsborough C.C., Bklyn., 1994, Womens Caucus for Arts, Staten Island, N.Y., 1995, FSS Gallery, N.Y.C., 1995, Danforth Mus., Framingham, Mass., 1995; represented permanent collections, Walker Art Ctr., Mus. Fine Arts, Boston Williams Coll., (Mass.), Dartmouth coll., Hanover, N.H., Addison Gallery, Andover, Mass., Munson-Williams-Proctor Inst., Ithaca, N.Y., Fogg Art Mus., Cambridge, Mass., Radcliff Coll., Boston Pub. Library, Wadsworth Athenaeum, Hartford, Conn. State of Hawaii, NAD, 1983, 84, 85, 87, 88, 90, 91, 92, 93, 94, Muscarelle Mus., Williamsburg, Va.; commd. work, Twirling, Bronze figure group, East Boston Housing for Elderly, The Spirit of Lili'uokalani bronze, Hawaii State Capitol. Recipient award Oakland Civic Mus., 1944, Mather prize Chgo. Art Inst., 1944, Margaret Brown award Ins. Contemporary Art, Boston, 1957, Grand prize Boston Arts Festival, 1960,

Lampston prize Nat. Sculpture Soc., N.Y.C., 1986, Gold medal Nat. Sculpture Soc., 1988, Taillx award, 1991; grantee Florsheim Art Fund, 1995, Mass. Found. for Humanities, 1995; Bunting Inst., Radcliffe Coll. fellow, 1962, 63. Fellow NAD (Gold medal 1987, Artists award 1988, 93). Home: 380 Marlborough St Boston MA 02115-1502 Office: care Judi Rotenberg 130 Newbury St Boston MA 02116-2904 *In a period of history such as ours where trend overtakes trend, the artist must somehow be true to her inner vision without shutting out the world or denying the human dilemma.*

PINES, ALEXANDER, chemistry educator, researcher; b. Tel Aviv, June 22, 1945; came to U.S., 1968.; s. Michael and Neima (Ratner) P.; m. Ayala Malach, Aug. 31, 1967 (div. 1988); children: Itai, Shani; m. Ditsa Kafry, May 5, 1983; children: Noami, Jonathan, Talia. BS, Hebrew U., Jerusalem, 1967; PhD, MIT, 1972. Asst. prof. chemistry U. Calif., Berkeley, 1972-75, assoc. prof., 1975-80, prof., 1980—, Pres.'s chair, 1993; faculty sr. scientist materials scis. div. Lawrence Berkeley Lab., 1975—; cons. Mobil Oil Co., Princeton, N.J., 1980-84, Shell Oil Co., Houston, 1981—; chmn. Bytel Corp., Berkeley, Calif., 1981-85; vis. prof. Weizmann Inst. Sci., 1982; adv. prof. East China Normal U., Shanghai, People's Rep. of China, 1985; sci. dir. Nalorac, Martinez, Calif., 1986—; Joliot-Curie prof. Ecole Superieure de Physique et Chemie, Paris, 1987; Walter J. Chute Disting. lectr. Dalhousie U., 1989, Charles A. McDowell lectr. U. B.C., 1989, E. Leon Watkins lectr. Wichita State U., 1990; Hinshelwood lectr., U. Oxford, 1990, A.R. Gordon Disting. lectr. U. Toronto, 1990, Venable lectr. U. N.C., 1990, Max Born lectr. Hebrew U. of Jerusalem, 1990; William Draper Harkins lectr. U. Chgo., 1991, Kolthoff lectr. U. Minn., 1991; Md.-Grace lectr. U. Md., 1992; mem. adv. bd. Nat. High Magnetic Field Lab., Inst. Theoretical Physics, U. Calif. Santa Barbara; mem. adv. panel chem. Nat. Sci. Found.; Randolph T. Major Disting. Lectr. U. Conn., 1992; Peter Smith lectr. Duke U., 1993, Arthur William Davidson lect. U. Kansas, 1992, Arthur Birch lect. Australian Nat. U., 1993, Richard C. Lord Meml. lect. MIT, 1993, Steacie lectr. Nat. Rsch. Coun. Can., 1993, Centenary lectr. Royal Soc. Chemistry, 1994, Morris Loeb lectr. Harvard U., 1994, Jesse Boot Found. Lectr., U. Nottingham, 1994. Editor Molecular Physics, 1987-91; mem. bd. editors Chem. Physics, Chem. Physics Letters, Nmr: Basic Principles and Progress, Advances in Magnetic Resonance; adv. editor Oxford U. Press; contbr. articles to profl. jours.; patentee in field. Recipient Strait award North Calif. Spectroscopy Soc., Outstanding Achievement award U.S. Dept. of Energy, 1983, 87, 89, R & D 100 awards, 1987, 89, Disting. Teaching award U. Calif., E.O. Lawrence award, 1988, Pitts. Spectroscopy award, 1989, Wolf Prize for chemistry, 1991, Donald Noyce Undergrad. Teaching award U. Calif., 1992, Robert Foster Cherry award for Great Tchrs. Baylor U., Pres.'s Chair for undergrad. edn. U. Calif., 1993; Guggenheim fellow, 1988, Christensen fellow St. Catherine's Coll., Oxford, 1990. Fellow Am. Phys. Soc. (chmn. divsn. chem. physics), Inst. Physics; mem. NAS, Am. Chem. soc. (mem. exec. com. divsn. phys. chemistry, Signature award, Baekeland medal, Harrison Howe award 1991), Royal soc. Chemistry (Bourke lectr.), Internat. Soc. Magnetic Resonance (v.p., pres.). Office: U Calif Chemistry Dept D 64 Hildebrand Hall Berkeley CA 94720

PINES, BURTON YALE, broadcasting executive; b. Chgo., Apr. 6, 1940; s. Hyman and Mary Pines; m. Helene Brenner, May 21, 1972. B.A., U. Wis., 1961, M.A., 1963. Instr. U. Wis., Madison, 1962-63; corr. Time mag., Bonn, Saigon and Vienna, 1966-73, editor, N.Y.C., 1973-81; sr. v.p. Heritage Found., Washington, 1981-92; chmn. Nat. Ctr. for Pub. Policy Rsch., Washington, 1982-94; co-founder, exec. v.p., COO Nat. Empowerment TV, Washington, 1992—; Disting. fellow Free Enterprise and Media Inst., Alexandria, Va., 1992—; bd. dirs. Media Rsch. Ctr., Alexandria, Va., Independence Inst., Denver. Author: Back to Basics, 1982, Out of Focus, 1994; editor: Mandate for Leadership II, 1984, Mandate for Leadership III, 1988. Recipient Page One award N.Y. Newspaper Guild, 1976, 77, 78, Freedom's Found. award, 1983. Jewish. Office: Nat Empowerment TV 717 Second St NE Washington DC 20002

PINES, HERMAN, chemistry educator, consultant; b. Lodz, Poland, Jan. 17, 1902; came to U.S., 1928; s. Isaac and Eugenia (Grynfeld) P.; m. Dorothy Mlotek, Aug. 13, 1927; 1 dau., Judith. Chem. engr., Ecole Superieure de Chimie Industrielle, Lyon, France, 1927; Ph.D., U. Chgo., 1935; docteur hon., Universite Claude Bernard, Lyon, 1983. Research chemist Universal Oil Product Co., Riverside, Ill., 1930-45; coordinator exploratory research Universal Oil Products Co., 1945-52; asst. prof. chemistry Northwestern U., 1941-50, assoc. prof., 1950-52, Ipatieff prof., 1953-70, dir. Ipatieff Lab., 1952-70, Ipatieff prof. emeritus, 1970—; adviser Israeli govt., 1951; chmn. Gordon Research Conf. in Catalysis, 1960; vis. prof. numerous univs. Author: Base-Catalyzed Reactions Chemistry of Hydrocarbons, 1977, The Chemistry of Catalytic Hydrocarbon Conversions, 1981, Genesis and Evolution of the Ipatieff Catalytic Laboratory, 1992; editor: (with D.D. Eley and P.B. Weisz) Advances in Catalysis, 1962-84; patentee in field. Recipient profl. achievement citation U. Chgo. Alumni Assn., 1986, Eugene J. Houdry award Catalysis Soc., 1981. Fellow Am. Inst. Chemists (recipient Chem. Pioneer 1982), Am. Chem. Soc. (recipient Fritzsche 1956, Midwest 1963, Petroleum Chemistry 1981, Murphree 1983), Sigma Xi, Phi Lambda Upsilon. Office: Northwestern U Dept Chemistry Evanston IL 60201

PINES, LOIS G., state legislator; b. Malden, Mass., 1940; m. Joseph Pines; 2 children. BA, Barnard Coll., 1960; JD, U. Cin. Law Sch., 1963. Corp. tax atty., 1964-72; alderman City of Newton, Mass., 1971-73; mem. Mass. Ho. of Reps., 1973-78; regional dir. New England Fed. Trade Commn., 1979-81; mem. Mass. State Senate, 1986—. Home: 40 Helene Rd Newton MA 02168-1025 Office: Mass State Senate State Capital Boston MA 02133

PINES, NANCY FREITAG, psychotherapist; b. Teaneck, N.J., Nov. 29, 1943; d. Arthur and Miriam L. (Johnson) Freitag; m. Wayne L. Pines, Apr. 16, 1966; children: Noah Morris, Jesse Mireth. BA, Douglass Coll., 1965; MA, George Washington U., 1972; MSW, Cath. U. of Am., 1980. Diplomate Am. Bd. Examiners. Psychotherapist Family Svcs. of Montgomery County, Rockville, Md., 1981-84; team social worker Psychiat. Inst. of Montgomery County, Rockville, 1984-85; psychotherapist Met. Psychiat. Group, Rockville, 1985-87; pvt. practice Rockville, 1987-88; admissions coord. Chestnut Lodge Hosp., Rockville, 1988-90; mental health therapist Montgomery Gen. Hosp., Olney, Md., 1991—. Mem. NASW, Am. Group Psychotherapy Assn., Greater Washington Soc. for Clin. Social Work. Home: 5821 Nevada Ave NW Washington DC 20015-2547 Office: Montgomery Gen Hosp 18101 Prince Philip Dr Olney MD 20832

PINES, WAYNE LLOYD, public relations counselor; b. Washington, Dec. 31, 1943; s. Jerome Martin and Ethel (Schnall) P.; B.A., Rutgers U., 1965; postgrad. George Washington U., 1969-71; m. Nancy Freitag, Apr. 16, 1966; children—Noah Morris, Jesse Mireth. Reporter, city editor Middletown (N.Y.) Times Herald-Record, 1965-68; copy editor Reuters News, 1968-69; assoc. editor FDC Reports, Washington, 1969-72; chief Consumer Edn. and Info., FDA, also editor FDA Consumer, 1972-74; exec. editor Product Safety Letter and Devices and Diagnostics Letter, Washington, 1974-75; dep. asst. commr. for pub. affairs, chief press relations FDA, Rockville, Md., 1975-78, assoc. commr. public affairs, 1978-82; adj. prof. Washington Public Affairs Center, U. So. Calif., 1980-81; instr. N.Y.U. Sch. Continuing Edn., 1982-84; instr. Profl. Devel. Inst., 1983-85; spl. asst. to dir. NIMH, 1982-83; sr. v.p., sr. counselor Burson-Marsteller, 1983-87; exec. v.p., dir. med. issues 1987-93; pres. healthcare practice APCO Assocs., Washington, 1993—, dir. crisis com.; sr. counselor Gross, Townsend, Frank, Hoffman, 1993—; bd. dirs. Transcell Techs., Inc.; columnist Med. Advt. News, 1985-90; mem. adv. bd. Nat. Orgn. Rare Disorders, Orphan Med.; mem. corp. adv. bd. ANA. Author: The Sermons of Jerome Martin Pines, FDA Advertising and Promotional Manual, When Lightning Strikes: A How-to Crisis Manual; contbr. numerous articles in field to profl. jours. Home: 5821 Nevada Ave NW Washington DC 20015-2547 Office: APCO Assocs 1615 L St NW Washington DC 20036

PINET, FRANK SAMUEL, former university dean; b. Topeka, Nov. 8, 1920; s. Frank Leo and Hattie Blanche (McClure) P.; m. Winifred Sarann Meyer, Jan. 27, 1956; children—Christopher Paul, Nancy Ann, Rosemary, Winifred Suzanne, Caroline Michele. B.S., U. Kans., 1942, M.B.A., 1947, Ph.D., 1955. Mem. faculty U. Kans., Lawrence, 1944—; prof. bus. adminstrn. U. Kans., 1970-80, Telecommunications Industry disting. teaching prof.; 1980-85, prof. emeritus, 1986—; asso. dean U. Kans. (Sch. Bus.), 1969-80; vis. prof. OEC, Italy, 1959-60; dir. Dold Foods, Inc.; cons. to

industry, 1955—. Author: Probated Estates in Kansas, 3d edit, 1956. Served to lt. comdr. USNR, 1942-46, 50-52. Recipient Standard Oil Co. (Ind.) Outstanding Teaching award, 1973, Henry A. Bubb Outstanding Teaching award, 1972, 84, Pacesetter award U.S. Ind. Telephone Assn., 1982; named Outstanding Educator Mortar Board, 1980; Ford Found. fellow, 1961-62. Mem. Am. Econ. Assn., Indsl. Relations Research Assn. Home: 704 W 12th St Lawrence KS 66044-3212 Office: Univ Kans 202 Summerfield Hall Lawrence KS 66044-7522

PING, CHARLES JACKSON, university administrator, educator; b. Phila., June 15, 1930; s. Cloudy J. and Mary M. (Marion) P.; m. Claire Oates, June 5, 1951; children—Andrew, Ann Shelton. B.A., Rhodes Coll., 1951; B.D., Louisville Presbyn. Theol. Sem., 1954; Ph.D., Duke, 1961. Asso. prof. philosophy Alma Coll., 1962-66; prof. philosophy Tusculum Coll., 1966-69, v.p., dean faculty, 1967-68, acting pres., 1968-69; provost Central Mich. U., Mt. Pleasant, 1969-75; pres. Ohio U., Athens, 1975-94, pres. emeritus, trustee, prof. philosophy and edn., 1994—; bd. dirs. Nationwide Corp.; mem. adv. bd. Ind. Coll. Program Northwest Area Found., Coun.for Advancement Experiential Learning, Inst. Ednl. Mgmt. of Harvard U.; chair Commn. Planning for Future of Higher Edn., Kingdom of Swaziland, Internat. Edn. Exchange; mem. Commn. on Higher Edn. Republic of Namibia. Author: Ohio University in Perspective, 1985, Meaningful Nonsense, 1966, also articles.; Editorial adv. bd.: Educational Record. Fulbright Sr. Rsch. scholar for So. Africa, 1995. Mem. Am Philos. Assn., Am. Coun. Acad. Deans, Am. Assn. Higher Edn., Nat. Assn. State U. and Land-Grant Colls., Coun. on Internat. Ednl. Exch. (chair bd), David C. Lam Inst. for East-West Studies. (bd.). Office: Ohio U Office of Pres Emeritus Athens OH 45701

PING, DAVID THOMAS, senior project engineer; b. Decatur, Ill., Sept. 2, 1942; s. Jesse Thomas and Ella Jane (Heckler) P.; m. Patricia Marie Quinn, Apr. 25, 1981; 1 child, Matthew Thomas. BS, Millikin U., 1972. Sr. project engr. Caterpillar, Inc., Decatur, Ill., 1965-77, Caterpillar Indsl., Inc., Mentor, Ohio, 1977-92, Drexel Industries Inc., Horsham, Pa., 1992—. Patentee in field. Mem. Our Shepherd Luth. Sch. Bd., Painesville, Ohio, 1992. Sgt. USAF, 1961-65. Mem. Am. Legion. Republican. Lutheran. Avocations: golf, tennis, model railroading, hiking, karate.

PINGEL, JOHN SPENCER, advertising executive; b. Mt. Clemens, Mich., Nov. 6, 1916; s. George F. and Margaret (Dalby) P.; m. Isabel Hardy, Dec. 12, 1939; children—John S., Roy Hardy. Student, U.S. Mil. Acad., 1936; B.A., Mich. State U., 1939. Asst. dir. truck merchandising Dodge div. Chrysler Corp., 1940-41, fleet sales rep., 1949; adminstrv. asst. Mich. State U., 1945-46; dir. advt. Reo Motors, Inc., 1947-48; with mdsg. dept. Brooke, Smith, French & Dorrance, Inc., 1949-55, v.p., account supr., 1955-57, v.p., asst. to pres., 1957-60, exec. v.p., 1960; exec. v.p. Ross Roy-BSF & D, Inc., Detroit, 1960-62; exec. v.p. Ross Roy, Inc., 1962-64, pres., 1964—, vice-chmn., 1979—. Exec. bd., pres., chmn. orgn. and extension com. Detroit area council Boy Scouts Am; pres. Inst. for Econ. Edn., 1971; mem. adv. bd. United Found., 1970-71; mem. Pres.'s Council on Phys. Fitness and Sports, 1975—; Trustee Alma Coll., New Detroit, Inc., Harper Grace Hosp., Oakland U. Found.; mem. exec. com. Grosse Pointe U. Sch., 1957-58, trustee, 1959—; bd. dirs Boys Republic, Inc., Greater Met. Detroit Project Hope, Greater Mich. Found.; trustee emeritus Mich. State U. Served from 2d lt. to lt. col. 95th Inf. Div. AUS, 1941-45. Decorated Bronze Star, Purple Heart; named to Nat. Football Hall of Fame, 1968, to Mich. Sports Hall of Fame, 1973, Mich. State U. Sports Hall of Fame, 1993. Mem. Detroit Sales Execs. Club (v.p. 1951), Am. Assn. Advt. Agys. (chmn. Mich. Dal. 1953, mem. 1978-79), Mich. C. of C. (dir.), Greater Detroit C of C. (dir. 1970-71, chmn. 1977-78). Presbyterian (elder). Clubs: Detroit Athletic, Country of Detroit, Adcraft (pres. 1960-61), Detroit, Economic, Yondotega (Detroit); Seminole Golf, Everglades (Palm Beach, Fla.); Jupiter Hills. Home: 582 Peachtree Ln Grosse Pointe MI 48236-2717 also: 80 Celestial Way Juno Beach FL 33408 Office: Ross Roy Inc 100 Bloomfield Hills Pky Bloomfield Hills MI 48304-2906

PINGREE, BRUCE DOUGLAS, lawyer; b. Salt Lake City, June 6, 1947; s. Howard W. and Lois (Ivie) P.; m. Lorraine Bertelli, Oct. 11, 1981; children: Christian James, Matthew David, Alexandra Elizabeth, Meredith Gillian, Lauren Ashley, Geoffrey Nicholas. BA in Philosophy, U. Utah, 1970, JD, 1973. Bar: Ariz. 1973, Tex. 1990. Ptnr. Snell & Wilmer, Phoenix, 1973-89; shareholder Johnson & Gibbs, Dallas, 1989-93; ptnr. Gardere & Wynne, Dallas, 1993-95; ptnr. Baker & Bihs, Dallas, 1995—; lectr. in field of taxation. Contbr. articles to profl. jours. Trustee Desert Bot. Garden, Phoenix, 1979-84; mem. Men's Art Council of Phoenix Art Mus., 1984-89. Served to capt. USAR. Mem. ABA (tax sect., past chair employee benefits com., past vice chair, past chmn. various sub-coms., 1993-94, chair joint com. on employee benefits 1994-95), Western Pension Conf., Southwest Benefits Conf., Order of Coif. Episcopalian. Home: 4065 Bryn Mawr Dallas TX 75225 Office: Baker & Bohs L.L.P. 2001 Ross Ave Dallas TX 75201-2980

PINGREE, DAVID EDWIN, ancient languages educator; b. New Haven, Conn., Jan. 2, 1933; s. Daniel and Elizabeth (Maconi) P.; m. Isabelle Sanchirico, June 20, 1963; 1 child, Amanda. AB, Harvard U., 1954, PhD, 1960; LittD (hon.), U. Chgo., 1992. Jr. fellow Harvard U., Cambridge, Mass., 1960-63; from asst. prof. to prof. U. Chgo., 1963-71; prof. history of math. Brown U., Providence, R.I., 1971—. Author: Census of the Exact Sciences in Sanskrit, series A, vols. 1-5, 1970-94, The Latin Picatrix, 1986. Recipient Abhinavavarahamihira award Gov. Uttar Pradesh, 1976. Fellow AAAS; mem. Am. Philos. Soc. Office: Brown U PO Box 1900 Providence RI 02912-1900

PINGS, ANTHONY CLAUDE, architect; b. Fresno, Calif., Dec. 16, 1951; s. Clarence Hubert and Mary (Murray) P.; m. Carole Clements, June 25, 1983; children: Adam Reed, Rebecca Mary. AA, Fresno City Coll., 1972; BArch, Calif. Poly. State U., San Luis Obispo, 1976. Lic. architect, Calif.; cert. Nat. Council Archtl. Registration Bds. Architect Aubrey Moore Jr., Fresno, 1976-81; architect, prin. Pings & Assocs., Fresno, 1981-83, 86—, Pings-Taylor Assocs., Fresno, 1983-85. Prin. works include Gollaher Profl. Office (Masonry Merit award 1985, Best Office Bldg. award 1986), Fresno Imaging Ctr. (Best Instnl. Project award 1986, Nat. Healthcare award Modern Health Care mag. 1986), Orthopedic Facility (award of honor Masonry Inst. 1987, award of merit San Joaquin chpt. AIA 1987), Modesto Imaging Ctr. (award of merit San Joaquin chpt. AIA 1991). Mem. Calif. Indsl. Tech. Edn. Consortium Calif. State Dept. Edn., 1983, 84. Mem. AIA (bd. dirs. Calif. chpt. 1983-84, v.p. San Joaquin chpt. 1982, pres. 1983, Calif. Coun. evaluation team 1983, team leader Coalinga Emergency Design Assistance team), Fresno Arts (bd. dirs., counsel 1989—, pres. 1990-93). Republican. Home: 4350 N Safford Ave Fresno CA 93704-3509 Office: 1640 W Shaw Ave Ste 107 Fresno CA 93711-3506

PINGS, CORNELIUS JOHN, educational association administrator; b. Conrad, Mont., Mar. 15, 1929; s. Cornelius John and Marjorie (O'Loughlin) P.; m. Marjorie Anna Cheney, June 25, 1960; children: John, Anne, Mary. B.S., Calif. Inst. Tech., 1951, M.S., 1952, Ph.D., 1955. John chem. engring. Stanford U., 1955-56, asst. prof., 1956-59; assoc. prof. chem. engring. Calif. Inst. Tech., 1959-64, prof., 1964-81, exec. officer chem. engring., 1969-73, vice-provost, dean grad. studies, 1970-81; provost, sr. v.p. acad. affairs U. So. Calif., 1981-93; pres. Assn. Am. Univs., Washington, 1993—; mem., dir. Nat. Commn. on Rsch., 1978-80; mem. bd. mgmt. Coun. on Govtl. Rels. 1980-83; bd. dirs Pacific Horizon Funds, Farmers Group, Inc., L.A.; pres. Assn. Grad. Schs., 1977-78; pres. Western Coll. Assn., 1988-90; mem. sci. engring. and pub. policy com. NAS, 1987-92, chmn., 1988-92; pres., Assn. Amer. Universities, 1993—. Contbr. articles to tech. jours. Mem., chmn. bd. trustees Mayfield Sr. Sch. Bd., 1979-85; mem. Pasadena Redevel. Agy., 1968-81, chmn., 1974-81; bd. dirs. Huntington Meml. Hosp., Pasadena; chmn. L.A. Ctrl. City Assn. Recipient Arthur Nobel medal, City of Pasadena, 1981, Disting. Alumni award Calif. Inst. Tech., 1989, Presdl. medallion U. So. Calif., 1993. Fellow AIChE, Am. Acad. Arts and Scis.; mem. NAE, Calif. Club, Twilight Club, Bohemian Club, Cosmos Club, Valley Hunt Club. Roman Catholic. Home: 2330 Massachusetts Ave NW Washington DC 20008 Office: Assn of Am Univs One Dupont Circle Ste 730 Washington DC 20036

PINHEY, FRANCES LOUISE, physical education educator; b. Canton, Ohio, Apr. 18, 1927; d. Frederick Otto and Rose June (Wolf) Sengleitner; m. Donald Charles Pinhey, June 13, 1952; children: Val Don, Shauna Rae, Kaye

Dorrell, Lon Pernell. BA, Muskingum Coll., 1949; MS, U. R.I., 1977; postgrad., Ind. U., 1958. Cert. tchr., Ohio. Tchr. Canton Pub. Schs., 1949-50; instr. Muskingum Coll., New Concord, Ohio, 1950-52; tchr. New Concord Pub. Schs., 1950-52, Barberton (Ohio) High Sch., 1952-53, Ottawa (Ont., Can.) Pub. Schs., 1954-57, Ottawa YMCA, 1954-57; instr. Dakota Wesleyan U., Mitchell, S.D., 1959-63, Wilmington (Ohio) Coll., 1963-67; tchr. New London (Conn.) Pub. Schs., 1967-68; asst. prof. phys. edn., coach Mitchell Coll., New London, 1968—; chair, mem. Conn. Sports Officiating Rating Bd., 1968-78. Nat. ofcl. women's volleyball & basketball, 1958-80; pres. PTA, Wilmington, 1967, PTA mem., New London, 1968-77; vol. New London Recreation Dept., 1986, Little League, 1970-75; vol. condr. CBA Badminton Tournaments. Inducted into Mitchell Coll. Hall of Fame, 1993. Mem. AAHPERD, Nat. Jr. Coll. Field Hockey Coaches Assn. (pres. 1991—), Nat. Jr. Coll. Men's Tennis Assn., U.S. Badminton Assn., Nat. Assn. Sport and Phys. Edn., Nat. Dance Assn., Nat. Dance-Exercise Instrs. Tng. Assn., Nat. Jr. Coll. Athletic Assn. (chmn. New Eng. region XXI field hockey com. 1975-89, women's field hockey Coach of Yr. region XXI 1975, 78, 79, 80, 81, 82, 83, 84, 90, nat. championships and Nat. Coach of Yr. 1979, 81, 83, 84, 90, Men's Tennis Coach of Yr. Region XXI 1983, 87, 89, 90). Avocations: badminton (ranked player, singles and doubles Conn. Badminton Assn. Top 10, 1981, 83, 84, 85, 86 and 87), tennis, gardening. Home: 43 Bellevue Pl New London CT 06320-4701 Office: Mitchell Coll 437 Pequot Ave New London CT 06320-4498

PINIELLA, LOUIS VICTOR, professional baseball team manager; b. Tampa, Fla., Aug. 28, 1943; m. Anita Garcia, Apr. 12, 1967; children: Lou, Kristi, Derrick. Student, U. Tampa. Baseball player various minor-league teams, 1962-68, Cleve. Indians, 1968, Kansas City Royals, 1969-73; baseball player N.Y. Yankees, 1974-84, coach, 1984-85, mgr., 1985-87, 1988, gen. mgr., 1987-88, spl. advisor, TV announcer, 1989; mgr. Cin. Reds, 1990-92, Seattle Mariners, 1992—. Named to Am. League All-Star Team, 1972; recipient Ellis Island Medal of Honor, 1990. Office: Seattle Mariners PO Box 4100 83 S King St Seattle WA 98104-2875*

PINKARD, WALTER DEVIER, JR., real estate executive; b. Balt., Nov. 21, 1950; s. Walter Devier Sr. and Anne (Merrick) P.; m. Dona Reisigl, July 17, 1976; children: Walter Devier III, Mary Casey. BA, Yale U., 1973; MBA, Harvard U., 1975. Rsch. analyst Beacon Cos., Boston, 1974-75; mgr. property W.C. Pinkard & Co., Inc., Balt., 1975-77, sec./treas., 1977-78, exec. v.p., 1978-82, pres., 1982—; mem. Greater Balt. Bd. Realtors, 1975; bd. sec. com. John Hanson Savs. Bank, Beltsville, Md., 1985—, chmn. exec. com., 1988—. Mem. editorial bd. Southeast Real Estate News, 1986. Mem. pub. policy coun. Greater Balt. Com., 1982—; bd. mgrs. Guildford Assn., Balt., 1983-87; trustee Gilman Sch., Balt., 1979-87, Md. Inst. Coll. Art, 1982—; Calvert Sch., Balt., 1984—; Jacob and Annita France Found., Balt., 1987—; Balt. Zool. Soc., 1983—; 1st v.p., 1985-88; bd. dirs. Balt. Reads, Inc., 1989—; mem. Yale Devel. Bd., 1989—. Mem. Bldg. Owners and Mgrs. Assn., Elkridge Club, Md. Club, Ctr. Club. Democrat. Roman Catholic. Office: WC Pinkard & Co Inc 7 E Redwood St Ste 1200 Baltimore MD 21202-1106

PINKEL, DONALD PAUL, pediatrician; b. Buffalo, Sept. 7, 1926; s. Lawrence William and Ann (Richardson) P.; m. Marita Donovan, Dec. 26, 1949 (div. 1981); children: Rebecca, Nancy, Christopher, Mary, Thomas, Anne, Sara, John, Ruth; m. Cathryn Barbara Howarth, May 16, 1981; 1 child, Michael. BS, Canisius Coll., 1947; MD, U. Buffalo, 1951. Diplomate Am. Bd. Pediatrics, Pediatric Hematology and Oncology, Nat. Bd. Med. Examiners. From intern to resident to chief resident Children's Hosp., Buffalo, 1951-54; research fellow Children's Hosp. Med. Ctr., Boston, 1955-56; chief. of pediatrics Roswell Park Meml. Inst., Buffalo, 1956-61; med. dir. St. Jude Children's Research Hosp., Memphis, 1961-73; chmn. pediatrics Med. Coll. Wis., Milw., 1974-78; pediatrician-in-chief Milw. Children's Hosp., 1974-78; chief. of pediatrics City of Hope Med. Ctr., Duarte, Calif., 1978-82; chmn. pediatrics Temple U. Sch. Medicine, Phila., 1982-85; prof., Kana Research chmn., dir. pediatric leukemia program U. Tex. System Cancer Ctr., M.D. Anderson Hosp. and Tumor Inst., Houston, 1985-93; prof. emeritus U. Tex.-M.D. Anderson Cancer Ctr., Houston, 1994—. Contbr. numerous articles to profl. jours. Bd. dirs. Lee County Coop. Clinic, Mariana, Ark., 1972-74. Served with USN, 1944-45, served to 1st lt. U.S. Army, 1954-55. Recipient Albert Lasker award for Med. Research Lasker Found., 1972, Windermere Lectureship Brit. Pediatric Assn., 1974, David Karnofsky award Am. Soc. Clin. Oncology, 1978, Zimmerman prize for Cancer Research Zimmerman Found., 1979, Charles Kettering prize Gen. Motors Cancer Research, 1986, Clin. Rsch. award Am. Cancer Soc., 1988, Return of the Child award Leukemia Soc. Am., 1992. Mem. Am. Pediatric Soc., Am. Assn. Cancer Rsch., Soc. Exptl. Biology and Medicine, Am. Soc. for Hematology, Pediatric Oncology Group. Democrat. Roman Catholic. Avocations: swimming, sailing. Home: 2501 Addison Rd Houston TX 77030-1811 Office: M D Anderson Hosp 1515 Holcombe Blvd Houston TX 77030-4095

PINKERTON, GUY CALVIN, savings and loan executive; b. Seattle, Aug. 1, 1934; s. John L. and Dorothy V. (Kock) P.; children: Deborah, Lisa. BA, U. Wash., 1959. CPA, Wash. Supr. Touche Ross & Co., Seattle, 1959-65; pres., CEO Wash. Fed. Savs., Seattle, 1965—. With USN, 1956-58. Mem. Fin. Mgrs. Soc. (dist. gov.), Fin. Execs. Inst. (sec.). Republican. Presbyterian. Office: Wash Fed Savs 425 Pike St Seattle WA 98101-2334

PINKERTON, LINDA F., lawyer; b. Phila., Dec. 4, 1949; d. Vicotr M. and Callie (Noland) Ferreri; m. Michael S. Foster, June 5, 1984. BA, Duke U., 1971; MA, NYU, 1973; JD, U. Tulsa, 1980. Bar: Calif. 1981, N.C. 1991, U.S. Dist. Ct. (all dists.) Calif. 1981, U.S. Ct. Appeals (9th and 10th cirs.). Atty. Exxon, Los Angeles, 1980-85; assoc. Pillsbury, Madison & Sutro, San Francisco, Calif., 1985-88; sec. gen. counsel J. Paul Getty Trust, L.A., 1988-94. Mem. Internat. Bar Assn. Office: 104 West St Black Mountain NC 28711-3142

PINKERTON, RICHARD LADOYT, management educator; b. Huron, S.D., Mar. 5, 1933; s. Abner Pyle and Orral Claudine (Arneson) P.; m. Sandra Louise Lee, Aug. 28, 1965 (div. 1992); children—Elizabeth, Patricia. B.A. (La Verne Noyes scholar 1952-55), U. Mich., 1955; M.B.A., Case Western Res. U., 1962; Ph.D. (Nat. Assn. Purchasing Mgmt. fellow 1967-68), U. Wis., 1969. Sr. market research analyst Harris-Intertype Corp., Cleve., 1957-61; mgr. sales devel. Triax Corp., Cleve., 1962-64; coordinator mktg. program Mgmt. Inst., U. Wis., 1964-67; dir. exec. programs Mgmt. Inst., U. Wis. (Grad. Sch. Bus.), also asst. prof. mktg., 1969-74; prof. mgmt., dean Grad. Sch. Adminstrn., Capital U., Columbus, Ohio, 1974-86; prof. mgmt., dir. Univ. Bus. Ctr. Sch. Bus. & Adminstrv. Scis. Univ. Bus. Ctr. Craig Sch. of Bus., Calif. State U., Fresno, 1986-89; prof. mktg. Calif. State U., Fresno, 1989—; mem. Gov. Wis. Exec. Conf. Mktg., Research and Devel., 1969-70; trustee Ohio Council Econ. Edn., 1976-86; bd. dirs. Univ. Bus. Ctr.; cons. to govt. and industry, 1960—. Author: Curriculum for Purchasing, 1969; co-author: Small Business Success: Operating and Executive Characteristics, 1963; contbr. articles to profl. jours. Bd. govs. Hannah Neil Home for Children, Columbus, 1975-78. Served as officer USAF, 1955-57; to lt. col. Res., 1957-78. Recipient Paul Harris fellow. Mem. Nat. Assn. Contract Mgmt. (chmn. validation cert. com. 1990), Nat. Assn. Purchasing Mgmt. (chmn. acad. planning 1979-84, rsch. symposium 1992), Am. Mktg. Assn. (chpt. pres. 1972-73), Western Mktg. Educators Assn., Res. Officers Assn., Air Force Assn., Beta Gamma Sigma, Alpha Kappa Psi, Phi Gamma Delta. Home: 4721 N Cedar Ave Apt 111 Fresno CA 93726-1007 Office: Calif State U Dept of Mktg Fresno CA 93740-0007

PINKERTON, ROBERT BRUCE, mechanical engineer; b. Detroit, Feb. 10, 1941; s. George Fulwell and Janet Lois (Hedke) P.; m. Barbara Ann Bandfield, Aug. 13, 1966; 1 child, Robert Brent. BSME, Detroit Inst. Tech., 1965; MA in Engring., Chrysler Inst. Engring., 1967; JD, Wayne State U., 1976. From mech. engr. to emissions and fuel economy planning specialist Chrysler Engring. Office Chrysler Corp., Highland Park, Mich., 1967-80; dir. engring. Replacement div. TRW, Inc., Cleve., 1980-83; v.p. engring. TRW Automotive Aftermarket Group, 1983-86; v.p. engring. and rsch. Blackstone Corp., Jamestown, N.Y., 1986-89; pres., CEO Blackstone Corp., Jamestown, 1989-90, Athena Corp., Beaufort, S.C., 1990—; Cedar Crest Corp., Beaufort, S.C., 1990—. Active oper. audit com. Beaufort County; bd. dirs. Village Renaissance, Inc., 1994—; exec. com. Greater Beaufort Com., 1994—. Mem.

Fripp Island Club, Rotary. Presbyterian. Home: 147 Sunset Blvd Beaufort SC 29902 Office: PO Box 4966 4300 Salt Creek Rd Beaufort SC 29902-7143

PINKHAM, DANIEL, composer; b. Lynn, Mass., June 5, 1923; s. Daniel R. and Olive C. (White) P. A.B., M.A., Harvard, 1944; Litt.D. (hon.), Nebr. Wesleyan U., 1976; Mus.D. (hon.), Adrian Coll., 1977, Westminster Choir Coll., 1979, New Eng. Conservatory, 1993, Ithaca Coll., 1994. Mem. faculty New Eng. Conservatory Music, 1959—; music dir. King's Chapel, Boston, 1958—; co-founder Cambridge Festival Orch., 1948. Composer: Sonatas for Organ and Strings, 1943, 54, 86, Piano Concertino, 1950, Concerto for Celesta and Harpsichord, 1954, Wedding Cantata, 1956, Christmas Cantata, 1958, Easter Cantata, 1961, Symphonies, 1961, 64, 85, Signs of the Zodiac, 1964, St. Mark Passion, 1965, Jonah, 1966, In the Beginning of Creation, 1970, Ascension Cantata, 1970, Organ Concerto, 1970, When the Morning Stars Sang Together, 1971, the Other Voices of the Trumpet, 1971, Safe in Their Alabaster Chambers, 1972, To Troubled Friends, 1972, Daniel in the Lions' Den, 1973, The Seven Deadly Sins, 1974, Four Elegies, 1974, The Passion of Judas, 1975, Garden Party, 1976, Blessings, 1977, Company at the Creche, 1977, Miracles, 1978, Epiphanies, 1978, Serenades, 1979, Proverbs, 1979, Diversions for Organ and Harp, 1980, Descent Into Hell, 1980, Before the Dust Returns, 1981, The Death of the Witch of Endor, 1981, Prelude and Scherzo for Wind Quintet, 1981, The Dreadful Dining Car, 1982, Brass Quintet, 1983, In Heaven Soaring Up, 1985, The Left-Behind Beasts, 1985, A Biblical Book of Beasts, 1985, Versets, 1985, A Mast for the Unicorn, 1986, A Crimson Flourish, 1986, Winter Nights, 1986, De Profundis, 1986, In the Isles of the Sea, 1986, Antiphons, 1987, Getting To Heaven, 1987, Angels Are Everywhere, 1987, Heav'n Must Go Home, 1988, Four Marian Antiphons, 1988, Alleluias, 1988, Sonata da Chiesa, 1988, Sonata da Camera, 1988, Petitions, 1988, Pedals, 1988, The Seasons Pass, 1988, Reeds, 1988, Concerto Piccolo, 1989, The Small Passion, 1989, Requiem Collects, 1989, The Saints Preserve Us!, 1989, String Quartet, 1989, Stabat Mater, 1990, Symphony Number 4, 1990, The Book of Hours, 1990, Carols and Cries, 1990, The Dryden Te Deum, 1990, Pentecost Cantata, 1991, Three Canticles from Luke, 1991, For Solace in Solitude, 1991, Advent Cantata, 1991, Smart Set, 1991, First Organbook, 1991, The Small Requiem, 1991, Second Organbook, 1992, Christmas Symphonies, 1992, Overture Concertante, 1992, Nocturnes for Flute and Guitar, 1992, Vowels, 1993, Adagietto for Organ and Strings, 1993, Wondrous Love, 1993, When Love Was Gone, 1993, Missa Domestica, 1993, Miserere mei Deus, 1993, The Guiding Star, 1994, The Creation of the World, 1994, Reed Trio, 1994, Organ Concerto Number Two, 1995, Preludes for Piano, 1995, Passion Music, 1995. Fellow Am. Acad. Arts and Scis.; mem. Am. Guild Organists (past dean Boston chpt.). Home: 150 Chilton St Cambridge MA 02138-1227

PINKHAM, FREDERICK OLIVER, foundation executive, consultant; b. Ann Arbor, Mich., June 16, 1920; s. Frederick Oliver and Leah Winifred (Hallett) P.; m. Helen Kostia, June 20, 1943; children: Peter James, Gail Louise, Steven Howard. AB, Kalamazoo Coll., 1942, LLD (hon.), 1958; MA, Stanford U., 1947, EdD, 1950; LLD (hon.), Lawrence U., 1957; DSc (hon.), Ripon Coll., 1990. Tchr., counselor Sequoia Union High Sch., Redwood City, Calif., 1947-49; researcher Stanford (Calif.) Consultation Service, 1949-50; asst. to pres. George Washington U., 1950-51; exec. sec. Nat. Commn. on Accrediting, 1951-55; pres. Ripon (Wis.) Coll., 1955-66; dir. The Yardstick Project, Cleve., 1966-67; v.p., dir. Western Pub. Co., 1967-70; founder, pres. Edn. Mgmt. Services, Inc., 1970-76; asst. adminstr. for population and humanitarian affairs AID, Dept. State, 1976-77; chmn., pres. Population Crisis Com., 1977-87; assoc. dir. Inst. for Population and Resource Studies, Stanford U., 1987-90; program officer David and Lucile Packard Found., 1988-92; cons. for population David and Lucille Packard Found., Los Altos, Calif., 1993—; cons. True North Found., 1993—, Mgmt. Scis. for Health, 1994—; v.p., dir. Rsch. Ednl. Recs. Bur., Darien, Conn., 1970-72; founder, pres. Edn. Mgmt. Svcs., Inc., 1970-76; v.p., co-founder World Bus. Coun., 1970-77; pres. Capital Higher Edn. Svc., 1975-76; pres., dir. The Omni Group, 1977-83; treas., co-founder Monterey Peninsula Coll. Found., 1994—. Chmn. Wisconsin adv. com. Nat. Commn. on Civil Rights.; bd. visitors Air U.; pres. Wis. Found of Ind. Colls.; chmn. Assn. Colls. Midwest, Midwest Coll. Council; sec., trustee, mem. exec. com. Young Pres.'s Found.; chmn. task force on fgn. assistance Pres.'s Pvt. Sector Survey on Cost Control (Grace Commn.); chmn. bd. Global Tomorrow Coalition, 1985-89; bd. dirs. Internat. Human Assistance Programs, N.Y.C., 1984-87, Mineral Fibre Internat. and Kings Mills Internat., 1986-90; v.p. Big Sur Land Trust, 1990—. Served with AUS, 1942-45, ETO. Decorated Bronze Star, Purple Heart. Mem. Young Pres. Orgn. (nat. sec., dir., mem. exec. com), Soc. Internat. Devel., Nat. Heritage Soc. (watchkeeper), Old Capital Club (Monterey, Calif.). Home and Office: 25715 Rio Vista Dr Carmel CA 93923-8811

PINKNEY, BETTY KATHRYN, lawyer; b. Cleve., Aug. 27; d. Emmett Maceo and Naomi Inez (Yates) Butts; m. Charles E. Pinkney; children: Jacqueline Pinkney-Royster, Pamela Merle. BA, Cen. State U., Wilberforce, Ohio, 1956; MA, Western Res. U., 1961; JD, Cleve. State U., 1976. Bar: Ohio 1977, U.S. Dist. Ct. (no. dist.) Ohio 1977, U.S. Ct. Appeals (D.C. cir.) 1979, U.S. Ct. Appeals (6th cir.) 1981, U.S. Supreme Ct. 1981. Tchr., adminstr. Cleve. Pub. Schs., 1961-77; assoc. Carl. J. Character Law Firm, Cleve., 1977-79; trial atty. EEOC, Cleve., 1979-81; atty. East Ohio Gas Co., Cleve., 1981—. Supt. adv. com. Cleve. Pub. Sch. System, 1987—; campaign chairwoman, mgr. jud. candidates Cuyahoga County, 1980, 84, 88; active county and state Dem. politics; supt. bd. trustees Judge Lloyd O. Brown Scholarship fund, Cleve., 1984—; trustee Cen. State U., Wilberforce, 1987—. Mem. ABA, Ohio State Bar Assn., Nat. Bar Assn., Cleve. Bar Assn. (vol. legal aid case program 1984—), Norman S. Minor Bar Assn., Ohio Self Insurers Assn., Delta Sigma Theta. Avocations: music, dance, reading, aerobics. Office: East Ohio Gas Co PO Box 5759 Cleveland OH 44101-0759

PINKNEY, D. TIMOTHY, investment company executive; b. Long Beach, Calif., June 6, 1948; s. Robert Patten and Mary (Chernus) P.; m. Nancy Dianne Fisher, Aug. 21, 1971; 1 child, Heather Anne. BA, Calif. Luth. U., 1970; MA, Pepperdine U., 1976. CFP. Membership mgr. Seattle C. of C., 1977-79; v.p. Bellevue, 1980; John L. Scott Investment, Bellevue, Wash., 1980-81, SRH Fin., Bellevue, 1981-82, Foster Investment Co., Bellevue, 1982-83; pres., CEO Footprint Fin. Planning, Bellevue, 1983-88, Sheppard & Assocs. Personal Fin. Advs., Bellevue, 1988-91; mgr. and v.p. asset mgmt. div. U.S. Bank, Tacoma, Wash., 1991-92; v.p., Calif. mgr. trust and investment mgmt. U.S. Bank of Calif., Sacramento, 1992—; founder, chief exec. officer Wealth Link Enterprises. Author: book, video and cassete series Pathways to Wealth, Yes IRA's Still Make Cent$?, 1988. Co-chmn. Fin. Independence Week, Western Wash., 1987; bd. dirs. Traveler's Aid Soc., A United Way Agy., Seattle, 1988, pacesetter United Way, 1988-91; alumni class steward Calif. Luth. U., 1992, 93; chmn., bd. dirs. Friends Scouting, Golden Empire council Boy Scouts Am.. Lt. USN, 1970-77, comdr. USNR, ret., 1992. Selected as Jr. Officer of Yr., USNR, 1984, 85. Mem. Nat. Speakers Assn. (bd. dirs. N.W. chpt. 1992), Internat. Assn. Find. Planning (chmn. West Region 1987-90, pres. Western Wash. chpt. 1986-87), Seattle Soc. CFPs (bd. dirs. 1985-86), Inst. CFPs, Real Estate Securities and Syndication Inst. (v.p. 1980-83), East King County and Pierce County Estate Planning Coun., Seattle Res. Officer Assn. (pres. and v.p. 1983-85), Puget Sound Naval Res. Assn. (v.p. 1985-90), Rotary (membership devel. com., chmn. edn. com., Sacramento, bd. dirs. Seattle). Avocations: flying gliders, pumpkin growing and sculpting, photography.

PINKNEY, JERRY, artist, educator; b. Phila., Dec. 22, 1939; s. James H. and Willemae (Landers) P.; m. Gloria Jean Maultsby, Mar. 19, 1959; children: Troy Bernardette, Jerry Brian, Scott Cannon, Myles Carter. Student, U. of the Arts, 1957-59. Designer, illustrator Rustcraft Pub. Co., Dedham, Mass., 1959-63, Barker/Black Studio, Boston, 1963-65, Kaleidoscope Studio, Boston, 1965-67, Jerry Pinkney Studio, Boston, 1967-70; illustrator, pres. Jerry Pinkney, Inc., Croton, N.Y., 1970—; assoc. prof. art U. Del., Newark, 1988-92; vis. critic R.I. Sch. Design, Providence, 1969-70; assoc. prof. Pratt Inst., Bklyn., 1986-87; disting. vis. prof. U. Del., 1986-88; vis. prof. art U. Buffalo, 1991. One-man retrospective shows include Northeastern U., Boston, 1983, Mass. Coll. Art, Boston, 1987, Mus. Nat. Ctr. African Am. Artists, Boston, 1987, U. Del., Newark, 1987, Phila. Afro-Am. Hist. and Cultural Mus., 1988, Johnson Mus. Art, Cornell U., Ithaca, N.Y., 1988, Schomburg Ctr. for Rsch. in Black Culture, N.Y., 1990, Bethune Hall, N.Y. Buffalo, 1991, Indpls. Mus. Art, 1991, Every Picture Tells a Story, L.A., 1991, Md. Inst. Art, Balt., 1992, ARt Inst. Chgo., 1993; internat. group shows Biennale Bratislace, Czechoslovakia, 1989, 91; illustrator Turtle in

Julu, 1989 (award N.Y. Times 1989, Time mag. 1989); included in Caldecott honor boof Mirandy and Brother Wind, 1989, The Talking Eggs, 1990, The Man Who Kept His Heart in a Bucket (Gold medal Soc. of Ill., N.Y. 1991), Homeplace, 1991 (Golden Kite award 1991), Caidecott Honor Book "John Henry", 1995. Mem. U.S. Citizens Stamp Adv. Com., Washington, 1982-92, U.S. Postal Svc. Quality Assurance Com., Washington, 1986-92. Recipient Alumni award Phila. Sch. Art & Design-U. Arts, 1992. Mem. N.Y. Soc. Illustrators (Hamilton King award 1993, gold medal 1993, 94). Avocation: music.

PINKSTON, RUSSELL FOUNTAIN, music composition educator; b. Beirut, Jan. 1, 1949; s. James Oliver and Margaret Louise (Fountain) P.; m. Margot Booth, Mar. 2, 1951; children: Malcolm B. Pinkston, Caroline B. Pinkston. BA in Music, Dartmouth Coll., 1974; M in Music Composition, Columbia U., 1979, DMA, 1984. Asst. prof. U. Tex., Austin, 1983-86, assoc. prof., 1987—; asst. prof. Columbia U., N.Y.C., 1986-87. Prin. works include string quartet Don't Look Now, 1991, Quartet for Four Horns, 1979, symphony Bellwether, 1984, Synthony for Flute, Piano and Tape, 1985. Charles Ives scholar and fellow Am. Acad. Arts and Letters, 1981, 87, Fulbright fellow, 1994-95. Mem. Soc. for Electro-Acoustic Music in U.S. (dir. archives 1985—), Computer Music Assn. Home: 1706 E 38 1/2 St Austin TX 78722-1212 Office: U Tex Dept Music Austin TX 78712

PIN-MEI, IGNATIUS KUNG (GONG) CARDINAL See KUNG (GONG) PIN-MEI, IGNATIUS CARDINAL

PINNEY, SIDNEY DILLINGHAM, JR., lawyer; b. Hartford, Conn., Nov. 17, 1924; s. Sydney Dillingham and Louisa (Griswold) Wells P.; m. Judith Munch, Sept. 30, 1990; children from previous marriage: William Griswold, David Rees. Student, Amherst Coll., 1941-43, Brown U., 1943; also, M.I.T., 1943-44; BA cum laude, Amherst Coll., 1947; LLB, Harvard U., 1950. Bar: Conn. 1950. Pvt. practice Hartford, 1950; assoc. Shepherd, Murtha and Merritt, Hartford, 1950-53; ptnr. Shepherd, Murtha and Merritt (name changed to Murtha, Cullina, Richter and Pinney 1967), 1953-92, of counsel, 1993—; lectr. on estate planning. Contbr. to: Estate Planning mag. Bd. dirs. Greater Hartford Area TB and Respiratory Diseases Health Soc., 1956-69, pres., 1966-67; mem. Wethersfield (Conn.) Town Coun., 1958-62; trustee Hartford Conservatory Music, 1967-71, 75-81; trustee, pres. Historic Wethersfield Found., 1961-81; bd. dirs. Hartford Hosp., 1971-80, adv. bd., 1980—; mem. adv. com. Jefferson House, 1978-82; corporator Hartford Pub. Libr., 1969—; Renbrook Sch., West Hartford, Conn., 1970-75. 1st lt. USAF, 1943-46. Fellow Am. Coll. Trust and Estate Counsel; mem. ABA, Nat. Acad. Elder Law Attys., Conn. Bar Assn. (exec. com. elder law sect.), Hartford County Bar Assn. Republican. Congregationalist. Office: City Place 185 Asylum St Hartford CT 06103-3469

PINNEY, THOMAS CLIVE, English language educator; b. Ottawa, Kans., Apr. 23, 1932; s. John James and Lorene Maude (Owen) P.; m. Sherrill Marie Ohman, Sept. 1, 1956; children—Anne, Jane, Sarah. B.A., Beloit Coll., Wis., 1954; Ph.D., Yale U., New Haven. 1960. Instr. Hamilton Coll., Clinton, N.Y., 1957-61; instr. English Yale U., New Haven, 1961-62; asst. prof. to prof., chmn. dept. English Pomona Coll., Claremont, Calif., 1962—. Editor: Essays of George Eliot, 1963, Selected Writings of Thomas Babington Macaulay, 1972, Letters of Macaulay, 1974-81, Kipling's India, 1986, A History of Wine in America, 1989, Kipling's Something of Myself, 1990, Letters of Rudyard Kipling, 1990, The Vineyards and Wine Cellars of California, 1994, The Wine of Santa Cruz Island, 1994. Guggenheim fellow, 1966, 84,Recipient Disting. Svc. citation Beloit Coll., 1984; fellow NEH, 1980; grantee Am. Coun. Learned Socs., 1974, 84, Am. Philos. Soc., 1968, 82, 94. Mem. MLA, Elizabethan Club (New Haven), Zamorano Club (L.A.), Phi Beta Kappa. Home: 228 W Harrison Ave Claremont CA 91711-4323 Office: Pomona Coll Claremont CA 91711

PINOTTI, JOSEPH R., light manufacturing executive. With BASF Corp., Parsippany, N.J., 1967-85; with Wacker Chem. Corp., Williamsburg, Va., now pres. Office: Wacker Chem Corp 460 McLaws Circle Ste 240 Williamsburg VA 23185*

PINSKER, PENNY COLLIAS (PANGEOTA PINSKER), television producer; b. Miami, Fla., Aug. 22, 1942; d. Theodore Peter and Agatha Madge (Bridgeman) Collias; m. Raymond Robert Elman, Feb. 19, 1962 (dec. 1967); 1 child, Alan; m. Lewis Harry Pinsker, Oct. 22, 1968. Grad. high sch., Miami, Fla. Operator So. Bell Telephone Co., Miami, 1960-67; asst. dir. pub. affairs Sta. WCKT-TV, Miami, 1968-70; dir. pub. affairs Sta. WOR-AM, N.Y.C., 1971-78; reporter documentary and consumer affairs Sta. WTFM, N.Y.C., 1978-81; dir. editorials and sta. svcs. Sta. WWOR-TV, N.Y.C. and Secaucus, N.J., 1981-87; mgr. community affairs and spl. projects Sta. WWOR-TV, Secaucus, 1987-91, dir. community affairs and spl. projects, 1991—. Author, editor: (resource directory) Sta. WOR on Crime, 1982 (recipient George Washington Medal Honor Freedom Found., Emmy award for Outstanding Editorial, 1981), The Changing Family, 1982 (recipient Broadcast Media award San Francisco State U., Emmy nominated), A Child is Missing, 1983 (recipient Broadcast Media award San Francisco State U., Emmy nominated), Taking the High Out of High School, 1984 (recipient Broadcast Media award San Francisco State U.; Angel award Religion Media, Bronze medal Internat. TV and Film Soc.); project mgr. A + For Kids (Emmy award 1989, also Emmy nomination, named 12th nat. Point of Light, 1989), At For Kids: Project Director National, (Emmy nominations 1989-91; N.Y. Emmy award 1989, 1991; Nat. Edn. Assn. award 1991). Media advisor N.J. Crime Prevention Officers Assn.; mem. comm. com. N.J. affiliation Am. Heart Assn., Am. Cancer Soc.; bd. dirs. Queensboro Soc. Prevention Cruelty to Children, 1978-83, Hoboken Chamber Orch., 1989-90, N.J. Edn. Found., 1991-92; pub. mem. N.J. Gov.'s Task Force on Child Abuse and Neglect, 1988—; trustee Assn. for Children of N.J., 1990—; mem. N.J. Coun. on Adult Edn. and Literacy, 1992-93. Recipient disting. svc. award N.J. Speech-Lang.-Hearing Assn., 1987, community svc. award Urban League Hudson County, 1986, media award for achievement in preventing child abuse N.J. Child Assault Prevention Project, 1993. Mem. NAFE, Nat. Broadcast Editl. Assn. (bd. dirs. 1986-87), Nat. Broadcast Assn. Cmty. Affairs, Advt. Coun. N.J. (bd. trustees 1986—), N.J. Broadcasters Assn. (bd. dirs. 1992), Meadowlands Regional C. of C. (bd. dirs. 1991-92). Avocation: breeder thoroughbred horses. Home: Winterwood Farm 449 Kingwood-Locktown Rd Flemington NJ 08822 Office: Sta WWOR-TV 9 Broadcast Plz Secaucus NJ 07094-2913

PINSKER, WALTER, allergist, immunologist; b. Bay Shore, N.Y., Mar. 27, 1933; s. Albert and Irene (Kuchlick) P.; m. Tillene Giller, June 15, 1958; children: Neil, Andrew, Susan. BA, U. Rochester, 1954; MD, Chgo. Med. Sch. U. Health Sci., 1958. Diplomate Am. Bd. Allergy and Immunology. Intern L.I. Jewish Hosp., New Hyde Park, N.Y., 1958-59; resident internal medicine Bklyn. VA Hosp., 1959-60; resident internal medicine Long Beach (Calif.) VA Hosp., 1960-61, resident allergy and immunology, 1961-62; chief of allergy Letterman Army Hosp., San Francisco, 1962-64; pres. Bay Shore Allergy Group, 1964—; attending physician Mather Hosp., Port Jefferson, N.Y., St. Charles Hosp., Port Jefferson 1981, Southside Hosp., Bay Shore, 1964—, Good Samaritan Hosp., West Islip, N.Y., 1964—, asst. clin. prof. medicine SUNY, Stony Brook, 1968—. Contbr. articles to profl. jours. Bd. visitors Pilgrim State Hosp., Brentwood, N.Y., 1974-77; pres. Suffolk Assn. Children with Learning Difficulties, N.Y., 1972-74; trustee Leeway Sch., Stony Brook, 1974-75, Bay Shore Jewish Ctr., 1974-84; com. for handicapped West Islip Schs., 1971—. Capt. U.S. Army, 1962-64. Named Co-Humanitarian of Yr. L.I. Adults and Children with Learning and Developmental Disabilities, 1994; recipient Physician's Recognition award AMA, 1969—. Fellow Am. Acad. Allergy and Immunology, Am. Coll. Allergy and Immunology, Am. Assn. Certified Allergists, Am. Coll. Chest Physicians, Am. Assn.- Study of Headaches, N.Y. Acad. Scis. Suffolk Acad. Medicine, Nassau-Suffolk Allergy Soc. (officer, bd. dirs. 1970—, pres. 1980-82). Avocations: golf, boating, photography. Office: Bay Shore Allergy Group P C 649 Montauk Hwy Bay Shore NY 11706-8542

PINSKY, LEONARD, geneticist; b. Montreal, Que., Can., July 2, 1935; married, 1960; 4 children. BSc, McGill U., 1956, MD, CM, 1960. Investigator somatic cell and molecular genetics, dir. divsn. Med. Genetics Lady Davis Inst. Med. Rsch. Jewish Gen. Hosp., Montreal, Que., 1967—; mem. oper. grants sect. Med. Rsch. Coun. Can., 1967—; asst. prof. McGill U., 1968-73, assoc. professor, 1973—; prof. pediatrics dept. Human Genetics,

1993—. Fellow Royal Coll. Physicians and Surgeons (Can.); mem. Am. Soc. Human Genetics, Soc. Pediatric Rsch., Can. Coll. Med. Geneticists (pres. 1978-80). Achievements include research in Androgen resistance, disorders of sexual development and nosology of malformation syndromes. Office: Lady Davis Inst Med Rsch, Jewish Gen Hosp, Dept Cell Genetics, Montreal, PQ Canada H3T 1E2*

PINSKY, ROBERT NEAL, poet, educator; b. Long Branch, N.J., Oct. 20, 1940; s. Milford Simon and Sylvia (Eisenberg) P.; m. EllenJane Bailey, Dec. 30, 1961; children: Nicole, Caroline, Elizabeth. B.A., Rutgers U., 1962; Ph.D., Stanford U., 1966. Mem. English faculty U. Chgo., 1967-68, Wellesley Coll., 1968-80; prof. English U. Calif., Berkeley, 1980-89; prof. Boston U., 1980-89, prof. creative writing, 1989—; poetry editor New Republic mag., 1978; vis. lectr. Harvard U.; Hurst prof. Washington U., St. Louis. Author: Landor's Poetry, 1968, Sadness and Happiness, 1975, The Situation of Poetry, 1977, An Explanation of America, 1980, History of My Heart, 1984, Poetry and the World, 1988, The Want Bone, 1990, The Inferno of Dante, 1994. Recipient Artists award Am. Acad. Arts and Letters, 1979; Saxifrage prize, 1980; William Carlos Williams prize, 1984; Guggenheim fellow, 1980. Mem. AAAS, PEN. Office: Boston U English Dept 236 Bay State Rd Boston MA 02215-1403

PINSOF, NATHAN, retired advertising executive; b. Havana, Cuba, July 16, 1926; came to U.S., 1928, naturalized, 1952; s. Oscar and Rose (Newman) P.; m. Barbara Cohn, Oct. 28, 1956; children—Ellen, Diane. Student, City Jr. Coll., Chgo., 1944-46; M.B.A., U. Chgo., 1949. Asst. controller Stineway Drugs, 1949-51; mgr. media dept. Weiss & Geller, 1953-60; sr. v.p., media dir. Edward H. Weiss & Co., 1960-67; v.p., mgr. media dept. J. Walter Thompson, 1967-69; sr. v.p., dir. media and fin. Grey-Chgo., Inc., Chgo., 1969-75; exec. v.p. Grey-Chgo., Inc., 1975-88, Lois/USA, Chgo., 1989-92; ret., 1992. Bd. dirs. Off The Street Club; trustee North Shore Cong. Israel.; Bd. dirs. Jewish Children's Bur.; chmn. communications div. Jewish United Fund, 1978-79. Served with U.S. Army, 1951-53. Clubs: B'nai B'rith, The Arts of Chicago. Home: 3900 S Mission Hills Rd Apt 101 Northbrook IL 60062

PINSON, ARTIE FRANCES, elementary school educator; b. Rusk, Tex., June 20, 1933; d. Tom and Minerva (McDuff) Neeley; m. Robert H. Pinson, Dec. 14, 1963 (div. Nov. 1967); 1 child, Deidre R. BA magna cum laude, Tex. Coll., 1953; postgrad., U. Tex., 1956, North Tex. U., 1958, 63, New Eng. Conservatory, 1955, 57, 59,62; MEd, U. Houston, 1970. Music tchr. Bullock High Sch., LaRue, Tex., 1953-59; music tchr., 9th grade English tchr. Story High Sch., Palestine, Tex., 1959-64; 6th grade tchr. Turner Elem. Sch., Houston, 1964-66; 3d, 5th and 6th grade tchr. Kay Elem. Sch., Houston, 1966-70; 6th grade tchr. Pilgrim Elem. Sch., Houston, 1970-75; 3d to 6th grade math. tchr. Pleasantville Elem. Sch., Houston, 1975-79; kindergarten to 5th grade computer/math. tchr. Betsy Ross Elem. Sch., Houston, 1979—, instrnl. coord.; lead tchr. math./sci. program Shell/Houston Ind. Sch. Dist., 1986-87, Say "Yes" program, 1988-89; math. tchr. summer potpourri St. Francis Xavier Cath. Ch., 1991; math. tchr. sci. and engring. awareness and coll. prep. program Tex. So. U., 1993, 94; presenter at confs. in field; conducts tchr. tng. workshops. Author computer software in field; contbr. articles to mags. Musician New Hope Bapt. Ch., Houston, 1991—; Sun. sch. tchr.; pianist Buckner Bapt. Haven Nursing Home, Houston, 1990-91. Recipient Excellence in Math. Teaching award Exxon Corp., 1990. Mem. Assn. African Am. Math. Educators (Salute to Math. Tchrs. award 1991, treas. 1991-93, sec. 1993—), Nat. Coun. Tchrs. Math., Tex. Coun. Tchrs. Math. (Excellence in Math. Tchg. award 1988), Houston Coun. Tchrs. of Math. (Excellence in Math. Tchg. award 1993), Heroines of Jericho. Avocations: needlework, number puzzles, piano, photography, gardening. Home: 5524 Makeig St Houston TX 77026 Office: Betsy Ross Elem Sch 2819 Bay St Houston TX 77026

PINSON, ELLIS REX, JR., chemist, consultant; b. Wichita, Kans., Oct. 23, 1925; s. Ellis Rex and Vivian (Neal) P.; m. Betty Ann Hogarth, Dec. 4, 1954; children: Matthew, Martha Pinson Salander, Thomas. B.Sc., U. of South, 1948; Ph.D., U. Rochester, 1951. Research chemist Pfizer Inc., Groton, Conn., 1951-59; project leader Pfizer Inc., 1959-61, sect. mgr., 1961-65, asst. dir. pharmacology research, 1965-67, dir. pharmacology research, 1967-71, dir. research, 1971-72, v.p. medicinal products research and devel., 1972-81; exec. v.p. Pfizer Cen. Research, 1981-86; cons., 1986—. Contbr. articles to profl. jours. Trustee Waterford Pub. Libr., 1980—, pres., 1988-93; bd. dirs., exec. com. Am. Indsl. Health Coun., 1980-86; bd. dirs. S.E. Area Tech. Devel. Ctr., 1992—. With USNR, 1943-46. Fellow N.Y. Acad. Scis.; mem. Am. Chem. Soc., AAAS, Am. Soc. Pharmacology and Exptl. Therapeutics, Phi Beta Kappa, Sigma Xi. Club: Baker Street Irregulars. Patentee in field. Office: Pfizer Inc Eastern Point Rd Groton CT 06340

PINSON, LARRY LEE, pharmacist; b. Van Nuys, Calif., Dec. 5, 1947; s. Leland J.and Audrey M. (Frett) P.; m. Margaret K., Mar. 18, 1972; children: Scott C., Kelly E. AA, Am. River Coll., Sacramento, 1969; PharmD, U. Calif., San Francisco 1973. Staff pharmacist/asst. dir. pharm. svcs. St. Mary's Hosp., Reno, 1973-77; chief pharmacist May Ang Base USAF, 1973-77; owner/chief pharmacist Silverada Pharmacy, Reno, 1979—; adj. prof. Idaho State U., Pocatello, 1989—; cons. pharmacist Physicians Hosp., 1974-, Reno Med. Plaza, 1973—; pharmacist coordinator Intensive Pharm. Svcs., 1986-87; cons. Calif. Dept. Health & Corrections, Susanville, 1975-76, Nev. Med. Care Adv. Bd., Carson City, 1984-87; provider and reviewer Nev. State Bd. Pharmacy, Reno, 1975-84; instr. We. Nev. Community Coll., 974-76; cons. Rural Calif. Hosp. Assn., 1973-74. Co-author: Care of Hickman Catheter, 1984. Mem. Nev. Arthritis Found.; bd. dirs. Am. Cancer Soc., 1986—; softball coach Reno/Sparks Recreation Dept.l 1973—; cubmaster Pack 153, Verdi, Nev.; scoutmaster com. chmn. Boy Scouts of Am. Reno troop 1, 1988—. Recipient Bow of Hygeia award (Pharmacist of the Year), 1984. Mem. Nev. Pharmacists Assn. (pres. 1981-82), Am. Pharm. Assn., Nev. Profl. Standards Rev. Orgn., Greater Nev. Health Sys. Agy., Kappa Psi. Avocations: skiing, fishing, backpacking, softball, golf. Home: PO Box 478 Verdi NV 89439-0478 Office: Silverada Pharmacy 2005 Silverada Blvd Ste 160 Reno NV 89512-2057

PINSON, RAY L., banking services holding company executive; b. 1956. Grad., Abilene (Tex.) Christian U., 1978. Sr. v.p. New Am. Holdings, Inc., Forth Worth, Tex., 1990—. Office: New American Holdings Inc 201 Main St Ste 2600 Fort Worth TX 76102*

PINSTRUP-ANDERSEN, PER, educational administrator; b. Bislev, Denmark, Apr. 7, 1939; came to U.S., 1965; s. Marinus and Alma (Pinstrup) Andersen; m. Birgit Lund, June 19, 1965; children: Charlotte, Tina. BS, Royal Vet. & Agrl. U., Copenhagen, 1965; MS, Okla. State U., 1967, PhD, 1969. Agrl. economist Centro Internacional de Agricultura Tropical, Cali, Colombia, 1969-72, head econ. unit, 1972-76; dir. agro.-econ. div. Internat. Fertilizer Devel. Ctr., Florence, Ala., 1976-77; sr. rsch. fellow, assoc. prof. Econ. Internat. Royal Vet. & Agr. U., 1977-80; rsch. fellow Internat. Food Policy Rsch. Inst., Washington, 1980, dir. food consumption and nutrition divsn., 1980-87, dir. gen., 1992—; dir. food and nutrition policy program, prof. food econs. Cornell U., Ithaca, N.Y., 1987-92; cons. The World Bank, Washington, 1978-92, Can. Internat. Devel. Agy., 1982-83, 86, UNICEF, N.Y.C.; cons. subcom. on nutrition UN, Rome, 1980-87; mem. bd. mng. editors Fertilizer Rsch., 1990—. Author: The World Food and Agricultural Situation, 1978, Agricultural Research and Economic Development, 1979, The Role of Fertilizer in World Food Supply, 1980, Agricultural Research and Technology in Economic Development, 1982; editor: (with Francis C. Byrnes) Methods for Allocating Resources in Applied Agricultural Research in Latin America, 1975, (with Margaret Biswas) Nutrition and Development, 1985, Food Subsidies in Developing Countries: Costs, Benefits, and Policy Options, 1988, Macroeconomic Policy Reforms, Poverty, and Nutrition: Analytical Methodologies, 1990, The Political Economy of Food and Nutrition Policies, 1993; (with David Pelletier and Harold Alderman) Child Growth and Nutrition in Developing Countries, 1995; mem. editl. com. various sci. jours.; contbr. numerous articles to profl. jours., chpts. to books. With Danish Army, 1958-59. Recipient Ford Internat. fellowship, 1965-66, People to People Cert. of Appreciation, 1967, Kellogg Travel fellowship, 1979, Competition prize Nordic Soc. Agrl. Rschrs. and Norsk Hydro, 1979, Cert. Merit, Gamma Sigma Delta, 1991, Disting. Alumnus award U. Colo., 1993. Mem. Am. Assn. Agrl. Econs. (PhD Thesis award 1970, Outstanding Jour. Article award 1977), Internat. Assn. Agrl. Econs., Columbian Nat.

Orgn. Profls. in Agr. (hon.). Home: 1451 Highwood Dr Mc Lean VA 22101 Office: Internat Food Policy Rsch Inst 1200 17th St NW Washington DC 20041

PINT, SISTER ROSE MARY, nun, religious order administrator, health care executive. BS in Nursing, Marillac Coll. Nursing, 1966; MA in Human Rels., St. Louis U., 1971, cert., 1977. Joined Franciscan Sisters, Daus. of Sacred Hearts of Jesus and Mary, Roman Cath. Ch., 1959. Staff nurse St. Anthony's Hosp., St. Louis, 1966-67, dir. staff devel., 1971-73; coord. alcohol outpatients dept. St. Michael Hosp., Milw., 1967-68, dir. outpatient clinic, 1968-69; with hosp. task force Franciscan Sisters, Wheaton, Ill., 1969-71; v.p. ops. St. Elizabeth Hosp., Appleton, Wis., 1973-76; v.p. clin. svcs. Marianjoy Rehab. Ctr., Wheaton, 1976-78; dir. Franciscan Sponsorship Commn., Wheaton, 1979-83; chairperson, chief exec. officer Wheaton Franciscan Svcs., Inc., 1983-86, chairperson bd., 1986—; provincial directress Franciscan Sisters, Daus. of Sacred Hearts of Jesus and Mary, Wheaton, 1988-92; mem. Chgo. Archdiocesan Collaboration Task Force, Commn. on Cath. Health Care Ministry Network. Author: (with others) Catholic Health Care Systems: A Prescription for Success, 1988. Recipient Harold M. Coon, MD Award of Merit Wis. Hosp. Assn., 1975; named Outstanding Young Woman of Yr., Appleton (Wis.) Jaycees, 1975, Outstanding Bus. and Profl. Woman Leader of DuPage County, DuPage YWCA, 1990. Fellow Am. Coll. Hosp. Adminstrs.; mem. Am. Hosp. Assn., Ill. Hosp. Assn., Cath. Health Assn. U.S. Address: PO Box 667 26w171 Roosevelt Rd Wheaton IL 60187-6078

PINTER, GABRIEL GEORGE, physiology educator; b. Bekes, Hungary, June 23, 1925; came to U.S., 1958; s. Lajos and Regina (Szilagyi-Farkas) P.; m. Berit Helgesen, Dec. 19, 1958 (dec. May 1980); children: Renee Astrid, Eva Ingelill; m. Vera Lederer, May 23, 1984. M.D., U. Sch. of Medicine, Budapest, Hungary, 1951. Asst. prof. U. Sch. Medicine, Budapest, 1951-56; rsch. assoc. U. Inst. Med. Rsch., Oslo, Norway, 1957-58; asst. prof. U. Tenn., Memphis, 1958-61; from asst. prof. to prof. U. Md., Balt., 1961-92, ret.; vis. prof. King's Coll., London, 1990-94. Contbr. articles to profl. jours. Recipient A.V. Humbolt prize Fed. Republic of Germany, 1980; Swedish Royal Med. Soc. fellow, Uppsala, Sweden, 1972. Mem. Am. Physiol. Soc., Physiol. Soc. Great Britain, Scandinavian Physiol. Soc., European Soc. Microcirculation.

PINTER, HAROLD, playwright; b. London, Oct. 10, 1930; s. Hyman and Frances (Mann) P.; m. Vivien Merchant, Sept. 14, 1956 (div. 1980); 1 son, Daniel; m. Antonia Fraser, Nov. 1980. Student, Brit. schs.; D.Litt. (hon.), U. Reading, 1970, U. Birmingham, 1971, U. Glasgow, 1974, U. East Anglia, 1974, U. Stirling, 1979, Brown U., 1982, U. Hull, 1986, Queen Niary Coll, London, 1986, U. Sussex, 1990, U Easthoudor, 1994, U. East London, London, 1994, U. Sofia, Bulgaria, 1995; D. Litt. (hon.), U. Sofia, Bulgaria, 1995. Actor in repertory theatres, 1949-57; dir. plays and films, 1970—; assoc. dir. Nat. Theatre, 1973-83; author: (plays) The Dumb Waiter, 1957, The Room, 1957, The Birthday Party, 1957, A Slight Ache, 1958, The Hothouse, 1958, A Night Out, 1959, The Caretaker, 1959, Night School, 1960, The Dwarfs, 1960, The Collection, 1961, The Lover, 1962 (Italia prize 1963), Tea Party, 1964, The Homecoming, 1964, The Basement, 1966, Landscape, 1967, Silence, 1968, Night, 1969, Old Times, 1970, Monologue, 1972, No Man's Land, 1974, Betrayal, 1978, Family Voices, 1980, A Kind of Alaska, 1982, Victoria Station, 1982, One for the Road, 1984, Mountain Language, 1988, The New World Order, 1991, Party Time, 1991, Moonlight, 1993; (screenplays) The Caretaker, 1962, The Servant, 1962, The Pumpkin Eater, 1963, The Quiller Memorandum, 1965, Accident, 1966, The Birthday Party, 1967, The Go-Between, 1969, The Homecoming, 1969, Langrishe Go Down, 1970, A la Recherche du Temps Perdu, 1972, The Last Tycoon, 1974, The French Lieutenant's Woman, 1980, Betrayal, 1981, Victory, 1982, Turtle Diary, 1984, The Handmaid's Tale, 1987, Reunion, 1988, The Heat of the Day, 1988, The Comfort of Strangers, 1989, The Trial, 1989; (pub.) The Dwarf, 1990 (novel), Collected Poems and Prose, 1990. Decorated comdr. Order Brit. Empire; recipient Shakespeare prize Hamburg, Germany, 1970, Austrian prize lit. 1973, Pirandello prize 1980, Commonwealth award, 1981, Donatello prize, 1982, Elmer H. Bobst award 1984, DAvid Cohen British Lit. prize, 1995; hon. fellow Queen Mary Coll., London, 1987. Office: care Judy Daish Assocs Ltd, 2 St Charles Pl, London W10 6EG, England

PINTO, LAWRENCE HENRY, neurobiologist, educator; b. Paterson, N.J., Feb. 9, 1943; s. Henry John and Mary Ada (Griffiths) P.; m. Maria Keiko Udo; children: Thomas, Michael, Kimi, Mark. MS, Northwestern U., 1966, PhD, 1970. Asst. prof. biology Purdue U., West Lafayette, Ind., 1970-75, assoc. prof., 1975-81, prof., 1981-87; prof. neurobiology and physiology Northwestern U., Evanston, Ill., 1987—; adv. panel NSF, Washington, 1986, 88; ad hoc study sect. NIH, Bethesda, Md., 1985, 91. Contbr. numerous articles to profl. jours. Recipient Rsch. award Marione Biol. Lab., Woods Hole, 1972, NIH Rsch. Career Devel. award, 1975-90. Mem. Biophys. Soc., Soc. for Neurosci., Assn. for Rsch. in Vision and Ophthalmology, AAAS. Office: Northwestern U Dept Neurobiology 2153 Sheridan Rd Evanston IL 60201-5503

PINTO, ROSALIND, retired educator, civic volunteer; b. N.Y.C.; d. Barney and Jenny Abrams; m. Jesse E. Pinto (dec.); children: Francine, Jerry, Evelyn. BA in Polit. Sci. cum laude, Hunter Coll.; MA in Polit. Sci., History, Columbia U.; postgrad., Queens Coll., LaGuardia Community Coll. Lic. social studies tchr. jr. high sch., N.Y., per diem lifetime substitute; cert. N.Y. State secondary sch. social studies grades 7-12. Substitute tchr., 1966-69, 90, 91—; tchr. social studies I.S. 126Q, L.I. City, N.Y., 1969-88, Jr. High Sch. 217 Briarwood, N.Y.C., 1988-89; ret. 1989; part-time cluster tchr. social studies and communication arts Pub. Sch. 140, Bronx, N.Y., 1990-91, 92; substitute tchr. I.S. 227Q, 1992-93; participant numerous personal and profl. devel. seminars and workshops. Author curriculum materials; contbr. chpt. to Study Guide for Regents Competency Test in U.S. History and Govt., 1990; contbr. poems to anthologies, include Tears of Fire, Dance on The Horizon, Outstanding Poets of 1995, Best Poems of 1994, Seasons to Come, poem to rec. The Sound of Poetry, Nat. Libr. of Poetry (editor's Choice award 1993, 94). Enrollment asst. Insight Heart Team, 1989; vol. receptionist Whitney Mus., Manhattan; mem. com. on history, 1990—, chmn. beautification com., 1992—; active Great Smokies Song Chase Warren-Wilson Coll., N.C., 1992; vol. local polit. campaigns; mem. Forest Hills Van Ct. Homeowners Assn., Cen. Queens Hist. Soc., Queens Hist. Soc. Recipient cert. of appreciation for participation in worksite sponsor program Dept. Probate Comty. Svc. Project, 1993, cert. of appreciation for participation in Make a Difference Day 1994, 1995. Mem. NAFE, Internat. Soc. Poets (lifetime mem. adv. panel, Internat. Poet of Merit award 1993), N.Y. Insight Alumni Assn., Forest Hills Van Ct. Homeowners Assn., Cen. Queens Hist. Soc. (bd. dirs. 1995—), Queens Hist. Soc., Columbia U. Grad. Sch. Arts and Scis. Alumni Assn., Hunter Coll. Alumni Assn., Mcpl. Art Soc. (hon. mention Design 2000 award), Robert F. Kennedy Dem. Assn. (bd. dirs.), Ctr. for Sci. in the Pub. Interest. Avocations: poetry and poetry contests, reading, long distance walking, art shows, plays. Home: 97-04 70th Ave Forest Hills NY 11375

PINTO, WILLIAM A., construction executive; b. 1947. B in Bldg. Cons., U. Fla., M in Bldg. Cons. With The Hardin Co., Inc., 1974—, group pres., exec. com., 1988—. Office: Hardin Constrn Group Inc 1380 W Paces Ferry Rd NW Atlanta GA 30327-2443*

PINTOZZI, CHESTALENE, librarian; b. Macomb, Okla., Apr. 4, 1947; d. Otis William and Edith Marie (Jordan) Bowerman; m. Nicola Francis Xavier Pintozzi, Aug. 2, 1967. Student, U. Okla., 1965-67; BA in English, No. Ill. U., 1969; MLS, U. Tex., 1981. Geology libr. U. Tex., Austin, 1982-84; environ. libr., Ann Marbut Environ. Libr. Sarasota (Fla.) County Pub. Libr. Sys., 1985-87; temporary reference libr. Sci.-Engring. Libr. U. Ariz., Tuscon, 1989-90, reference libr. Sci.-Engring. Libr., 1990—. Mem. ALA (chair Reference and Adult Svcs. Divsn. codes liaison with users group 1994—, Whitney-Carnegie award 1993), Ariz. State Libr. Assn., Arix. Online Users Group, N.Am. Serials Interest Group, Beta Phi Mu, Phi Kappa Phi. Democrat. Office: U Ariz Bldg 54 Rm 216 Tucson AZ 85720

PINZLER, ISABELLE KATZ, lawyer; b. New York, N.Y., May 2, 1945; d. Leon Sidney and Jeanne Eleanor (Sprung) K.; m. William Michael Pinzler, Mar. 29, 1970 (div. Dec. 5, 1985); children: Johanna Elisabeth, Andrew Howard; m. James Brook, Sept. 2, 1990. AB in History, Goucher Coll.,

1967; JD, Boston U., 1970. Bar: Mass. 1970, Ohio 1971, N.Y. 1974, U.S. Dist. Ct. Mass. 1971, (no. dist.) Ohio 1971, (so. dist.) N.Y. 1974, U.S. Ct. Appeals (6th cir.) 1973, (2nd cir.) 1975, (9th cir.) 1987, (11th cir.) 1992, U.S. Supreme Ct. 1977. Cons. staff atty. Lawyers Com. for Civil Rights Under Law, Boston, 1970-71; staff atty. Housing Svcs. Ctr., Fair Housing, Inc., Boston, 1970-71; staff atty. Law Reform Unit Legal Aid Soc. Cleveland, 1971-73; sr. staff atty. Nat. Employment Law Project, N.Y.C., 1973-78, dep. dir., 1977-78; dir.Women's Rights Project Am. Civil Liberties Union Found., N.Y.C., 1978-94; dep. asst. atty. gen.Civil Rights Divsn. U.S. Dept. of Justice, Washington, 1994—; adv. com. Women's Rsch. and Edn. Inst. project on women and the mil., 1991-94. Author: (with others) The Rights of Women, 1993; contbr. articles to profl. jours. Mem. Assn. of the Bar of the City of N.Y. (Com. on Sex and Law, 1984-87, Edn. and Law, 1989-92). Office: US Dept Justice Civil Rights Divsn 9th & Pennsylvania Ave Washington DC 20530

PIORE, EMANUEL RUBEN, physicist; b. Wilno, Russia, July 19, 1908; came to U.S.; 1917; s. Ruben and Olga (Gegusin) P.; m. E. Nora Kahn, Aug. 26, 1931; children—Michael Joseph, Margot Deborah, Jane Ann. A.B., U. Wis., 1930, Ph.D., 1935, D.Sc. (hon.), 1966; D.Sc. (hon.), Union U., 1962. Asst. instr. U. Wis., 1930-35; research physicist RCA, 1935-38; engr.-in-charge TV lab. CBS, 1938-42; head spl. weapons group, bur. ships U.S. Navy, 1942-44; head electronics br. Office Naval Research, 1946-47, dir. phys. sci., 1947-48, dep. for natural sci., 1949-51, chief sci., 1951-55; v.p., dir. Avco Mfg. Corp., 1955-56; dir. research IBM Corp., 1956-61, v.p. research and engring., 1961-63, v.p. group exec., 1963-65, v.p., chief scientist, 1965—; also dir.; physicist research lab. electronics MIT, 1948-49; dir. Sci. Research Assocs., Inc., Health Advancement, Inc., Paul Revere Investors, Guardian Mut. Fund.; adj. prof. Rockefeller U., 1974—. Mem. Pres.'s Sci. Adv. Com., 1959-62; mem. Nat. Sci. Bd., 1961—; bd. dirs. N.Y. State Found. for Sci.; past bd. dirs. NSF; chmn. vis. com. Nat. Bur. Standards; chmn. bd. Hall of Science, N.Y.C.; mem. corp. Woods Hole Oceanographic Instn.; mem. exec. com. Resources for Future; bd. dirs. Stark Draper Lab., Nat. Info. Bur., Meml. Cancer Hosp.; mem. vis. com. to elec. engring. dept. Mass. Inst. Tech., 1956-57; vis. com. Harvard Coll., 1958-70; trustee Sloan-Kettering Inst. Cancer Research; mem. N.Y.C. Bd. Higher Edn., 1976—. Served to lt. comdr. USNR, 1944-46. Recipient Indsl. Research Inst. award, 1967; Distinguished Civilian medal Dept. Navy; Kaplun award Hebrew U., 1975. Fellow AAAS, Royal Soc. Arts (London, Eng.), Am. Phys. Soc., IEEE, Am. Acad. Arts Scis.; mem. Sci. Research Soc. Am., Sci. Research Assn. (dir.). Nat. Acad. Sci., Nat. Acad. Engring., Am. Inst. Physics (dir.), Am. Philos. Soc. (sec. 1985—), Sigma Xi. Clubs: University (N.Y.C.), Cosmos (Washington), Century (N.Y.C.). Home: 2 Fifth Ave New York NY 10011

PIORE, MICHAEL JOSEPH, educator; b. N.Y.C., Aug. 14, 1940. BA magna cum laude, Harvard U., 1962, PhD in Econs., 1966. Asst. prof. labor econs. MIT, 1966-70, assoc. prof., 1970-75, prof. econs., 1975—, Mitsui prof. of Contemporary Tech., 1981-86; cons. NAACP Legal Def. and Edn. Fund, Inc., 1966-68, Boston Model Cities Adminstrn., 1960, U.S. Dept. of Labor, 1968-70, Labor, Manpower and Income Maintenance,Commonwealth of P.R., 1970-72, research coord., acting exec. dir., 1970-71, cons., 1977-86; mem. Nat. Manpower Policy Task Force Assocs., 1968-70; mem. Nat. Coun. on Employment Policy, 1977-79, cons. v.p. task force on youth employment, 1977—, labour studies ILO, 1987—; panel of factfinders, Bd. of Conciliation and Arbitration, Commonwealth of Mass. Author: Birds of Passage, Migrant Labor and Industrial Societies, 1979, (with Suzanne Berger) Dualism and Discontinuity in Industrial Society, 1980, (with B. Doeringer) Internal Labor Markets and Manpower Adjustment, 1981; (with Charles Sabel) The Second Industrial Divide, 1984; editor: Unemployment and Inflation: Institutionalist and Structuralist Views, 1979; editorial bd. Jour. of Econ. Lit., 1976—; contbr. articles to profl. jours. and publs. Recipient Harvard Coll. scholarship 1959-60, Detur Prize 1960, John Harvard scholarship 1960-61; Honorary Woodrow Wilson fellowship 1962-63, MacArthur Found. fellow 1984-89, research fellow John F. Kennedy Sch. Govt. Harvard U., 1968-69, 69-70, teaching fellow Harvard U., 1964-66. Mem. Am. Econ. Assn., Indsl. Relations Research Assn. Union of Radical Polit. Economists. Home: 295 Beacon St # 62 Boston MA 02116-1242 Office: MIT Dept Ecos Rm E52-271C Cambridge MA 02139

PIORE, NORA KAHN, economist, health policy analyst; b. N.Y.C., N.Y., Nov. 28, 1912; d. Alexander and Sara (Rosenbaum) Kahn; m. Emanuel R. Piore, Aug. 26, 1931; children: Michael Joseph, Margot Deborah, Jane Anne. B.A., U. Wis., 1933, MA, 1934. Research economist health legislation subcom. U.S. Senate, Washington, 1950-53; spl. asst. to commr. N.Y.C. Dept. Health, 1957-68; adj. prof. urban affairs Hunter Coll., N.Y.C., 1962-72; dir. N.Y.C. Urban Med. Econs. Research Ctr., 1960-68; vis. scientist Assn. Aid of Crippled Children, N.Y.C., 1968-72, study dir. hosp. ambulatory care svcs. in U.S., 1968-72; prof. pub. health econs. Columbia U. Sch. Pub. Health, N.Y.C., 1972-82; assoc. dir. Columbia U. Ctr. Community Health Systems, N.Y.C., 1971-82, cons. Health Services Research, 1982—; sr. program cons. Commonwealth Fund, N.Y.C., 1982-88; sr. fellow United Hosp. Fund, N.Y.C., 1982-90; dir. Health Svcs. Improvement Fund (Blue Cross-Blue Shield), 1984—, Sun Valley Health Forum, Boise, Idaho, 1978-88; active numerous coms., founds., task forces, funds in field; cons. Carnegie Corp. N.Y., R.I. Health Svcs. Rsch. Corp., Robert Wood Johnson Found., Pew Meml. Trust; mem. N.Y. State Hosp. Rev. and Planning Coun., 1976-84. Contbr. chpts. to books, articles to profl. jours. Recipient Merit award N.Y. Pub. Health Assn., 1977 Career Scientist award N.Y. Health Rsch. Coun., 1961-65, 66-71; Belding scholar Assn. Aid Crippled Children, 1968; grantee USPHS, 1980. Fellow Am. Pub. Health Assn., N.Y. Acad. Medicine; mem. Am. Econs. Assn., AAAS, Health Services Research Assn., Assn. Social Scientists in Health, Inst. Medicine, Nat. Acad. Sci., Phi Beta Kappa. Clubs: Cosmopolitan, Women's City (N.Y.C.).

PIOTROW, PHYLLIS TILSON, public health educator, international development specialist; b. N.Y.C., Mar. 16, 1933; d. Paul and Phyllis Tilson; children: Diana, Stephen. BA in History summa cum laude, Bryn Mawr Coll., 1954; BA in Modern History first class, Oxford U., England, 1956, MA, 1959; PhD in Pol. Sci. and Population Dynamics, Johns Hopkins U. 1971. Social sci. analyst history and govt. dvsn., legis. reference svc. Libr. Congress, 1956-57; writer Editorial Rsch. Reports (Congresl. quarterly), Washington, 1957-58; instr. St. Anne's Coll. Oxford (England) U., 1958-59; legis. asst. Senator Kenneth B. Keating of N.Y., Washington, 1960-64, Senator G. McGovern of S.D., Washington, 1965; first exec. dir. Population Crisis Com. Population Action Internat., Washington, 1965-69, 71-72, 75-78; adminstr. population info. program Dept. Med. and Pub. Affairs, George Washington U. Med. Ctr., Washington, 1972-75; prin. investigator Population Communication Svcs., Johns Hopkins U., Washington, 1982—; dir. Population Info. Program, Balt., 1978—, Ctr. Communication Programs, Johns Hopkins U., Balt., 1988—; bd. dirs., sec. Population Action Internat., 1969—, mem. exec. com., 1978—; bd. dirs. Ctr. Devel. and Population Activities, Washington, 1975-92, exec. com., 1978-92, sec., 1979-84, chmn., 1984-86; internat. cons. and presenter in field. Author: World Population Crisis: The United States Response, 1972, World Population: The Present and Future Crisis, 1980; (with G. Tapinos) Six Billion People: Demographic Dilemmas and World Politics, 1978; contbr. numerous articles to profl. jours. Advisor U.S. Del. to UN Population Comsn., 1969, 71, 73, 77, U.S. Del. to World Population Conf., Bucharest, 1974; mem. Internat. Adv. Coun. Bryn Mawr Coll., 1972-76, nat. adv. coun. Marshall Scholarship Comsn., 1972-80, Brit. Adv. Coun., 1973-84; mem. adv. com. UN POPIN database, 1987; mem. adv. New Directions, 1977-79; chmn. Informed Choice Task Force, 1988-91. European fellow Bryn Mawr Coll., 1954; Marshall scholar Oxford U., 1954-56; Ford mid-career fellow, 1969-71; recipient Charles A. Dana Found. award, 1991; U.S. AID grantee, 1978-84, 82-87, 84-87, 85-89, 86-91, 87-92, 88-92, 90—; POPLINE database grantee UN Population Fund, 1988. Mem. APHA (chairperson population and family planning sect. 1979-80, Carl Shultz award 1989), Population Assn. Am. Episcopalian. Avocations: tennis, gardening, hiking. Office: Johns Hopkins Univ Ctr for Comm Programs 111 Market Pl Ste 310 Baltimore MD 21202-4012

PIOTROWSKI, RICHARD FRANCIS, state agency administrator, council chairman; b. Manchester, N.H., Mar. 13, 1945; s. Stanley J. and Marion G. (Rubino) P.; m. Claudia H. Rund, Aug. 28, 1971; children: Richard Jr., Courtney. AAS in Civil Tech., Hartford (Conn.) State Tech. Coll., 1965; student, U. Conn., 1969. Registered profl. engr., Conn. Sr. engr. Henry N. Loomis and Assoc., New Hartford, Conn., 1970-77; quality control engr.

PIPAL 3302 WHO'S WHO IN AMERICA

Atlantic Pipe Corp., Plainville, Conn., 1977; sr. civil engr. C.E. Maguire, New Britain, Conn., 1977-80; chief civil engr. Anderson-Nichols and Co., Newington, Conn., 1980-83; project engr. Cahn Co., Wallingford, Conn. 1983-84; asst. chief engr. State of Conn. Dept. Pub. Works, Hartford, 1984-85, asst. dir. facilities, design and constrn., 1985-87; dep. commr. dept. pub. works State of Conn., Hartford, 1987—. Councilor Plainville Town Council, 1975-81, 85-87, council chmn./mayor, 1979-81, 1985-87; mem. adv. bd. Colonial Bank, Plainville, 1980-86; pres. Plainville Pre-Sch. Assn., 1984-85; corporator New Britain Gen. Hosp. Recipient Disting. Svc. award Plainville Jaycees, 1980, Conn. Engr. Recognition award, 1991, Dist. Mgr. Svc. award State of Conn., 1994. Mem. Nat. League of Cities (transp. and communications policy com. 1981, 87), Conn. Conf. Municipalities, Conn. Assn. Street and Hwy. Ofcls. Democrat. Roman Catholic. Home: 14 Peace Ct Plainville CT 06062-2836 Office: State of Conn Dept Pub Works 165 Capitol Ave Hartford CT 06106

PIPAL, FAUSTIN ANTHONY, savings bank executive; b. Chgo., Feb. 15, 1921; s. Frank J. and Agnes (Broz) P.; m. Florence C. Pipal; children by previous marriage: Nancy, Richard, Faustin A., David. J.D., Boston Coll. 1950. Bar: Ill. 1950. From office boy to sr. cost analyst Western Electric Co., 1939-46; with Talman Fed. Savs. & Loan Assn., Chgo., 1950-60; v.p., 1955-60, Gt. Western Savs. & Loan Assn., Calif., 1960-61; resident counsel, treas. LaGrange Fed. Savs. & Loan Assn., Chgo., 1962-86, vice chmn., 1986—; chmn. bd. St. Paul Bank for Savs., Chgo., 1962—; former chmn. bd. Renewal Effort Service Corp.; former bd. dirs. Fed. Savs. and Loan Council Ill. Chmn. bd. Cook County Council Urban Renewal; former trustee Ill. Benedictine Coll., Lisle; bd. dirs. Inst. Rehab. Engring., N.J., Austin Career Edn. Ctr., Nat. Housing Services, Alfred Adler Inst., Chgo., Neighborhood Housing Services of Chgo., Inc. Served with USNR, 1942-45. Mem. Order of Malta.

PIPAL, GEORGE HENRY, journalist; b. Lafayette, Ind., Oct. 14, 1916; s. Francis John and Belle (Kadavy) P.; m. Caroline Dunsmore, Aug. 17, 1946; children—John, Susan, Philip, Frank. B.A., U. Nebr., 1937; M.S., Columbia, 1939. Corr. various bureaus UPI, 1937-41; bur. mgr. UPI, Prague, 1946; mgr. for UPI, Eastern Europe, 1947, Germany, 1948; dir. European Services, 1949-51; gen. bus. mgr. Europe, Middle East, Africa, 1952-65; gen. sales exec. computer svcs. N.Y.C., 1966-68; gen. mgr. internat. features div., 1968-78; mng. dir. UPI (U.K.), Ltd., 1964-65; v.p. United Feature Syndicate, 1978-84, United Media Enterprises, 1985—. Served as lt. USNR, 1942-46. Office: United Media 1 Snoopy Pl Santa Rosa CA 95403-2665

PIPER, A. COLEMAN, retail executive; b. 1947. Exec. v.p. ops. Proffitt's Inc., 1972-93; exec. v.p. ops. & real estate Proffitt's Inc., Alcoa, Tenn., 1994—; tchr. Pa. Office: Proffitt's Inc Midland Shopping Ctr PO Box 388 Alcoa TN 37701-0388*

PIPER, ADDISON LEWIS, securities executive; b. Mpls., Oct. 10, 1946; s. Harry Cushing and Virginia (Lewis) P.; m. Louise Wakefield (div.); children: Gretchen, Tad, William; m. Cynthia Schuneman, Nov. 14, 1979; children: Elisabeth LaBelle, Richard LaBelle. BA in Econs., Williams Coll., 1968; MBA, Stanford U., 1972. Mktg. cons. Earl Savage and Co., Mpls., 1968-69; mem. capital market dept. Piper and Jaffray, Mpls., 1969-70; asst. syndicate mgr. Piper, Jaffray and Hopwood, Mpls., 1972-73, v.p., 1973-79, dir. trading, 1973-77, dir. sales, 1977-79, exec. v.p., dir. mktg., 1979-83, chief exec. officer, chmn. mgmt. com., 1983—, chmn. bd. dirs., 1988—; adv. com. N.Y. Stock Exch., 1986-90; bd. dirs. Minn. Pub. Radio, Mpls., Allina Health Systems, Minn. Comm. Group, Healthspan Corp., Mpls., Greenspring Corp., Mpls., Minn. Bus. Partnership, Mpls.; vice chair Abbott Northwestern Hosp., Mpls.; trustee CARE Found., Mpls. Fin. chmn. Senator Durenberger Fin. Com., Mpls., 1980-88. Mem. Securities Industry Assn. (bd. govs. 1986-90, tax policy com.), Woodhill Country Club (trustee), Country Club of the Rockies (Colo.), Mpls. Club. Republican. Episcopalian. Clubs: Woodhill Country (Wayzata); Minneapolis. Avocations: skiing, golfing, hunting, tennis, horses. Office: Piper Jaffray Cos. PO Box 28 222 S 9th St Minneapolis MN 55440

PIPER, ADRIAN MARGARET SMITH, philosopher, artist, educator; b. N.Y.C., Sept. 20, 1948; d. Daniel Robert and Olive Xavier (Smith) P.; m. Jeffrey Ernest Evans, June 27, 1982 (div. 1987). AA, Sch. Visual Arts, 1969; BA in Philosophy, CCNY, 1974; MA, Harvard U., 1977, PhD, 1981; student, U. Heidelberg, Germany, 1977-78; LHD (hon.), Calif. Inst. Arts, 1992, Mass. Coll. Art, 1994. Asst. prof. U. Mich., Ann Arbor, 1979-86; Mellon rsch. fellow Stanford (Calif.) U., 1982-83; assoc. prof. Georgetown U., Washington, 1986-88, U. Calif., San Diego, 1988; prof. philosophy Wellesley (Mass.) Coll., 1990—; speaker, lectr. on both philosophy and art. Artist: one-woman exhbns. include N.Y. Cultural Ctr., N.Y.C., 1971, Montclair (N.J.) State Coll., 1976, Wadsworth Atheneum, Hartford, Conn., 1980, Nexus COntemporary Art Ctr., Atlanta, 1987, The Alternative Mus., N.Y.C., 1987, Goldie Paley Gallery, Phila., 1989, Power Plant Gallery, Toronto, 1990, Lowe Art Mus., Coral Gables, Fla., 1990-91, Santa Monica (Calif.) Mus. Contemporary Art, 1991, John Weber Gallery, N.Y.C., 1989, 90, 91, 92, Whitney Mus. Am. Art, N.Y.C., 1990, Hirschorn Mus., Washington, 1991, Ikon Gallery, Birmingham, Eng., 1991, Cornerhouse, Manchester, Eng., 1992, Cartwright Hall, Bradford, Eng., 1992, Kunstverein, Munich, Germany, 1992, Indpls. Ctr. Contemporary Art, 1992, Manasterio de Santa Clara, Moguer, Spain, 1992, Grey Art Gallery, N.Y.C., 1992, Paula Cooper Art Galler, 1992; group exhbns. include Paula Cooper Gallery, 1969, Dwan Gallery, N.Y.C., 1969, 70, Seattle Art Mus., 1969, Stadtisches Mus., Leverkusen, Germany, 1969, Kunsthalle Berne, Berne, Switzerland, 1969, N.Y. Cultural Ctr., 1970, Allen Mus., Oberlin, Ohio, 1970, Musee d'Art Moderne, N.Y.C., 1970, 88, 91, Musee d'art Moderne, Paris, 1971, 77, 89, Inhibodress Gallery, New South Wales, Australia, 1972, Calif. Inst. Arts, Valencia, 1973, Samuel S. Fleischer Art Meml., Phila., 1974, Mus. Contemporary Art, Chgo., 1975, Newberger Mus., Purchase, N.Y., 1978, Mass. Coll. Art, Boston, 1979, Artemesia Gallery, Chgo., 1979, A.I.R. Gallery, N.Y.C., 1980, Inst. Contemporary Arts, London, 1980, The New Mus., N.Y.C., 1981, 83, 85, Kenkeleba Gallery, N.Y.C., 1983, The Studio Mus. Harlem, N.Y.C., 1985, 89, Mus. Moderner Kunst, Vienna, Austria, 1985, Intar Gallery, N.Y.C., 1988, Whitney Mus. Downtown, N.Y.C., 1988, Art Gallery Ont., Toronto, 1988, Long Beach (Calif.) Art Mus., 1989, Simon Watson Gallery, N.Y.C., 1990, Feigen Gallery, Chgo., 1990, Barbara Krakow Gallery, Boston, 1990, Milw. Art Mus., 1990, Contemporary Arts Ctr., Houston, 1991, John Weber Gallery, 1991, Anne Plumb Gallery, N.Y.C., 1991, Hirschorn Mus., 1991, The Albuquerque Mus. Art, 1991, The Toledo Mus. Art, 1991, Denver Art Mus., Fukui Fine Arts Mus., Fukyuiken, Japan, 1992-93, N.J. State Mus., Trenton, 1992-93, Philippe Staib Gallery, N.Y.C., 1992, New Loom House, London, 1992, Espace-Lyonnais D'Art Contemporain, Lyon, France, 1993, Am. Acad. Inst. Arts and Letters, N.Y.C., 1993; permanent collections include The Bklyn. Mus., Denver Art Mus., Kunstmusuem Berne, Musee d'Art Moderne, The Mus. Contemporary Art, Chgo., The Wadsworth Atheneum; art performances include RISD, 1973, The Whitney Mus. Am. Art, 1975, Kurfurstendamm, Berlin, 1977, Hauptstrasse, Heidelberg, Germany, 1978, Allen Meml. Mus., Oberlin, Ohio, 1980, Contemporary Art Inst. Detroit, 1980, San Francisco Art Inst., 1985, Calif. Inst. Art, 1984, The Studio Mus. Harlem, 1988; performances on video, 1987—; contbr. articles to profl. jours. NEH Travel fellow, 1979, NEA Visual Artists' fellow, 1979, 82, Andrew Mellon Postdoctoral fellow, 1982-84, Woodrow Wilson Internat. Scholars fellow, 1988-89, Guggenheim Meml. fellow, 1989; NEA Artists Forums grantee, 1987; recipient N.Y. State Coun. on Arts award, 1989, Visual Arts award, 1990. Mem. AAUP, Am. Philos. Assn. (mem. ea. divsn.), Am. Soc. Polit. and Legal Philosophy, N.Am. Kant. Soc. Avocations: medieval and renaissance music, fiction, poetry, yoga, German. Office: Wellesley Coll 10Central St Wellesley MA 02181-8203

PIPER, DON COURTNEY, political science educator; b. Washington, July 29, 1932; s. Don Carlos and Alice (Courtney) P.; m. Rowena Inez Wise, July 6, 1956; children: Sharon, Valarie. B.A., U. Md., 1954, M.A., 1958; Ph.D. (James B. Duke fellow), Duke U., 1961. Research assoc. Duke U., 1961-62; exec. sec. Commonwealth-Studies Center, 1962-64; asst. prof. dept. govt. and politics U. Md., College Park, 1964-67; assoc. prof. U. Md., 1967-69, prof., 1969—, head dept. govt. and politics, 1968-74, dir. grad. studies dept., 1982-95, mem. coun. of system faculty, 1989-90; chmn. teaching council College Park Faculty Assembly, 1974-75, chmn. campus senate, 1975-77, 89-90, univ. marshal, 1981—, mem. Athletic Council, 1986-93, mem. senate ad hoc com. on undergrad. edn., 1986-88, chmn. chancellor's ad hoc com. on campus ceremonies, 1986-87, chmn. acad. com. of Athletic Council, 1986-89; chmn. campaign for College Park, 1988-89; chmn. retention review com. U. Md., 1990-91, chmn. budget and facilities com. athletic coun., 1991-93, chmn. senate com. on programs courses and curriculi, 1991-93; teaching fellow Lilly Ctr. for Teaching Excellence, 1994-95; rsch. asst. Am. Coun. on Edn., 1966-68; faculty adv. com., planning adv. com. Md. State Bd. Higher Edn., 1977-82; chmn. com. on dept. chairmen Am. Polit. Sci. Assn., 1973-75; mem. coun. So. Polit. Sci. Assn., 1970-72, chmn. Chastain award com., 1973-75. Author: International Law of Great Lakes, 1967; contbg. author: International Law Standard and Commonwealth Developments, 1966, De Lege Pactorum, 1970, Foreign Policy Analysis, 1975; editor: (with R. Taylor Cole) Post-primary Education and Political and Economic Development, 1964; co-editor, contbg. author: (with Ronald Terchek) Interaction: Foreign Policy and Public Policy, 1983; bd. editors: World Affairs; editorial adv. com.: Internat. Legal Materials, 1977-78. Served to 1st lt. USAF, 1955-58. Recipient U. Md. Regents award for excellence in teaching, 1966, Teaching Excellence award Div. Behavioral and Social Scis., 1982-83, Outstanding Tchr. award Greek System, U. Md., 1982, Pres.'s medal, U. Md., 1992. Mem. Am. Soc. Internat. Law, Internat. Law Assn., Internat. Studies Assn. (chmn. internat. law sect. 1981-83), Am. Peace Soc. (bd. dirs.), UN Assn./ USA, Phi Beta Kappa (pres. Gamma chpt. 1978-79), Phi Kappa Phi (chpt. pres. 1982-83), Omicron Delta Kappa (faculty adviser 1990—), Pi Sigma Alpha. Methodist. Home: 4323 Woodberry St Hyattsville MD 20782-1174 Office: U Md Dept Govt & Politics College Park MD 20742

PIPER, FREDESSA MARY, school system administrator; b. Monroe, La., June 19, 1945; d. Floyd Preston and Zona Mary (Jones) P.; m. Robert John Parks, Mar. 20, 1969 (div. 1980). BS, Ill. State U., 1964; MEd with distinction, DePaul U., 1972; EdD, Loyola U., Chgo., 1984. Cert. tchr., gen. adminstr., sch. supt., Ill. Tchr. secondary schs. Chgo. Pub. Schs., 1964-73, staff asst., 1974-76, coord., 1977-83, tchr., coord., 1984-87; asst. supt. Ednl. Svc. Region Cook County, Chgo., 1987—; project coord. Malcolm X City Coll., Chgo., 1973-74; coord. Athletes for Better Edn., Chgo., 1975-77; cons. Community Reading is Rewarding Program, Chgo., 1989—; author radio scripts, speeches. Project coord. Local Ward Back to Sch. Fun-Fest, Chgo., 1983—; program coord. Pre-Thanksgiving Day Srs. Dinner, Chgo., 1983—; asst. to chmn. Re-election Campaign, Chgo., 1986, 88; promotional dir. Unity in Community Boat Cruise, Chgo., 1987—. Mem. ASCD, Nat. Alliance Black Sch. Educators, Am. Assn. Sch. Adminstrs., Phi Delta Kappa, Delta Epsilon Sigma. Baptist. Avocations: cooking, travel, gardening. Office: Ednl Svc Region Cook County 10220 S 76th Ave Bridgeview IL 60455

PIPER, GEORGE EARLE, retailing design and financial consulting company executive; b. Greenfield, Mass., Jan. 31, 1932; s. George B. and Elizabeth J. (Jones) P.; children: Sherri, Terri, Luanne. Mark B.E., Keene State Coll., 1959, postgrad., 1959-60; postgrad. U. Mass., 1959-60, Boston U., 1960-61; Harvard, 1984; Cert. Store Profl. Dir. aux. services Keene (N.H.) State Coll., 1959-61; dir. purchasing and aux. enterprises U. Vt., Burlington, 1961-64; dir. state univ. stores system U. Maine, Orono, 1964-68; pres. Store Ops. Services, Inc. and Creative Design Concepts, Franklin, Mass., 1968—; tchr. U. Maine, Orono, 1966-67; chmn. various profl. workshops, 1965-83; mem. various nat. merchandising coms. 1959-61, 69-71. Mem. sch. bd. Winchester, N.H., 1959-61; bd. selectmen, Edgartown, Mass., 1993—. Served with A.C., USN, 1951-55. Recipient 4 nat. merchandising awards, 1961-66, service awards Nat. Assn. Coll. Stores, 1969-70, 1984-85, Nat. Assn. Coll. Aux. Services, 1974-75; 2 week nat. tour award Nat. Assn. Aux. Enterprises, 1976; Pres.'s Svc. award Nat. Assn. Coll. Stores of New England, 1991. Mem. Inst. Store Planners, Am. Soc. Interior Designers, Boston Soc. Architects, Nat. Assn. Coll. Stores, Coll. Stores of New Eng. (pres. 1967-69), Mid-Atlantic Coll. Stores, Mass. Businessmen's Assn., Masons, Shriners, Martha's Vineyard Rod and Gun Club (dir. 1995—), Kappa Delta Phi. Designer more than 543 coll. univ. aux. service areas and bookstores, 5 malls; contbr. to profl. jours.; columnist for retail. jours. Home: 8 Smith Dr Edgartown MA 02539 Office: PO Box 1160 Edgartown MA 02539-1160

PIPER, JON KINGSBURY, ecologist, researcher; b. Keene, N.H., Sept. 6, 1957; s. Roy Kingsbury and Anne (Macechok) P.; m. Elizabeth Brown, Aug. 3, 1980; children: Joshua, Emily, Samuel. BS in Biology, Bates Coll., 1979; PhD in Botany, Wash. State U., 1984. Teaching asst., rsch. asst. Wash. State U., Pullman, 1980-84, technician, vis. faculty, 1985; rsch. assoc. The Land Inst., Salina, Kans., 1985—; adj. faculty Benedictine Coll., Salina, 1989; mem. Sand Prairie adv. bd. Bethel Coll., North Newton, Kans., 1989. Co-author: Farming in Nature's Image, 1991; contbr. articles to Ecology, Am. Jour. Botany, Oikos, Can. Jour. Botany, Am. Midland Naturalist. Grantee NSF, 1982, Eppley Found., 1988. Mem. Ecol. Soc. Am., Brit. Ecol. Soc., Soc. for Conservation Biology, Soil Sci. Soc. Am., Torrey Bot. Club. Achievements include research in natural ecosystem processes as models for sustainable agriculture. Office: The Land Inst 2440 E Water Well Rd Salina KS 67401-9051

PIPER, MARK HARRY, retired banker; b. Flint, Mich., Apr. 17, 1931; s. James U. and Dorothy (Weed) P.; m. Wanda L. Hubbard, June 20, 1953; children: Mark T., Kathryn L. BS, St. John's Mil. Acad., 1949; AB with distinction and honors in Econs, U. Mich., 1953, JD cum laude, 1956. Bar: Mich. 1956. With Clark, Klein, Winter, Parsons & Prewitt, Detroit, 1956-57; with Genesee Mchts. Bank & Trust Co., Flint, 1957-88, v.p., sr. trust officer, 1966-72, sr. v.p., 1972-88; sr. v.p. NBD Genesee Bank (formerly United Mich. Corp.), 1985-88, cashier, sec. bd. dirs., 1985-88; adj. instr. bus. adminstrn. U. Mich., Flint, 1976-80; pres. Flint Estate Planning Coun., 1969-70; mem. Flint citizens adv. coun. U. Mich., 1974-82; vice chmn., 1975-82. Bd. dir. Retirement Homes of Detroit Ann. Conf. Meth. Ch., 1968-76, vice chmn. profl. ministry and support, 1975, mem. bd. support systems, 1975, coun. fin. and adminstrn., 1976-84, chmn. coun. fin. and adminstrn., 1980-84; bd. dirs. United Meth. Devel. Fund, 1986-90; gen. bd. pensions United Meth. Ch., 1988—; trustee Flint YMCA Boysfarm Found., 1964-78, chmn., 1976-78; bd. mgmt. Flint YMCA Boysfarm, 1964-74; mem. Detroit Conf. Bd. P. United Meth. Ch., 1968-76, chmn., 1972-75, 88—, mem., 1986—; bd. dirs. U. Mich. Devel. Coun., 1980-82; bd. dirs., asst. treas. sec.-treas. Flint Area Young Life Found., 1979—, Mich. Area Young Life Com., 1980-88; bd. dirs., vice chmn. The Crim Road Race Inc., 1985-87. Mem. ABA, Mich. Bar Assn., Genesee County Bar Assn., Inst. Continuing Legal Edn., U. Mich.-Flint Club (bd. dirs., pres. 1973-74). Home: 1378 Ox Yoke Dr Flint MI 48532-2352 also: PO Box 3121 Estes Park CO 80517

PIPER, PAT KATHRYN, state senator; b. Delavan, Minn., July 16, 1934; d. Claire I. and Geneva R. (Tibodeau) P. BA, Coll. St. Teresa, Winona, Minn., 1962; MA, Cath. U., 1972. Tchr. St. Augustine Sch., Austin, Minn., 1956-58, St. Francis Sch., Rochester, Minn., 1958-60, St. James (Minn.) Sch., 1960-61; catechist St. Catherine Sch. Ctr., Luverne, Minn., 1961-63, catechist, dir., 1964-67; catechist Area Ctr., Hayfield, Minn., 1963-64; dir. St. Ann's Ctr., Slayton, Minn., 1967-69, Christian Edn. Ctr., Austin, 1969-94; mem. Minn. Ho. of Reps., 1982-84, 84-86, Senate State of Minn., 1986, 90, 92; chair Senate Family Svcs. Com. Contbr. articles to profl. jours. Active United Way, YMCA, Council for Handicapped, Salvation Army. Mem. LWV, Bus. and Profl. Women. Mem. Democrat Farmer Labor Party. Roman Catholic. Lodge: Zonta. Home: 800 1st Dr NW Austin MN 55912-3070 Office: Minn State Senate G-9 State Capitol Saint Paul MN 55155

PIPER, ROBERT JOHNSTON, architect, urban planner; b. Byron, Ill., Feb. 2, 1926; s. Leo Edward and Helen Anna (Johnston) P.; m. Carol Jane White, June 23, 1951; children—Christopher White, Brian Douglas, Eric Johnston. B.S. in Archtl. Engring. U. Ill., 1951; M. City and Regional Planning, Cornell U., 1953. Architect, planner Orput & Assos., Rockford, Ill., 1953-61; dir. profl. services AIA, Washington, 1961-67; partner, v.p. Perkins & Will, Chgo., 1967-74; dep. dir. Northeastern Ill. Planning Commn., Chgo., 1974-76; asso. Metz, Train, Olson & Youngren, Inc., Chgo., 1976-79; dir. community devel. City of Highland Park, Ill., 1980-91; ret. City of Highland Park, 1991; coord. Chicago '93 Chgo. Dept. Cultural Affairs, 1992—; pres. Landmarks Preservation Council Ill., Chgo., 1976-80. Author: Careers in Architecture, vocat. guidance manuals, 1967, 71, 75, 80, 85, 93; editor: Architect's Handbook of Professional Practice, 7th edit., 1963; prin. works include Regional Open Space Plan, Northeastern Ill., Spring Valley Operations Breakthrough Housing Complex, Kalamazoo, CBD Streetscape and Skokie Corridor Master Plan, Highland Park. Trustee Village of Winnetka, Ill., 1978-83; mem. Potomac Planning Task Force Dept. Interior, 1967-68, Commn. on Fed. Procurement, Washington, 1970-71; mem. nat. advisory bd. community characteristics HEW, 1970-78. Served with USNR, 1944-46, PTO. Fellow AIA (mem. Task Force Future of Inst. 1974-75, various coms., pres. AIA Ill. coun. 1986, Disting. Achievement awards AIA Ill., AIA Chgo. 1993); mem. Am. Inst. Cert. Planners (metro chpt. pres. 1971-72), Lambda Alpha. Episcopalian. Home: 972 Elm St Winnetka IL 60093-2207

PIPER, THOMAS LAURENCE, III, investment banker; b. Washington, June 20, 1941; s. Thomas Laurence and Edna (Milewski) P.; m. Ann Runnette, Apr. 8, 1967; children: Thomas Laurence IV, Andrew Kerr. Student, U. Va., 1959-61. Asso. Hodgdon & Co., Inc., Washington, 1962-65; sr. v.p. dir. Hayden Stone Inc., N.Y.C., 1966-73; mng. dir. New Court Securities Corp., N.Y.C., 1974-81, Dillon, Read & Co., Inc., N.Y.C., 1981—. Chmn. fund dr. New Canaan chpt. ARC, 1978; bd. dirs. Manhattan coun. Boy Scouts Am., Waveny Care Ctr., New Canaan. Mem. Investment Assn. N.Y. (pres. 1974), Bond Club N.Y. Clubs: Racquet and Tennis, Brook (N.Y.C.); Country of New Canaan. Home: Windrow Ln New Canaan CT 06840 Office: Dillon Read & Co Inc 535 Madison Ave New York NY 10022-4212

PIPES, DANIEL, writer, editor; b. Boston, Sept. 9, 1949; s. Richard and Irene (Roth) P.; children: Sarah, Anna. Student, U. Tunis, Institut Bourguiba des Langues Vivantes, 1970; BA in History Sci., Harvard U., 1971; student, U. Cairo, 1971-72, Al-Azhâr U., Cairo, 1971-72, U. Calif. (Berkeley) Ctr. for Arabic Studies Abroad, Cairo, 1971, 1971-72; reader, Orientalisches Sem., Freiburg U., 1976; PhD in History and Middle Eastern Studies, Harvard U., 1978; hon. degree, Am. Coll. of Switzerland, 1988. Vis. fellow Princeton U., 1977-78; Harper instr., rsch. assoc. U. Chgo., 1978-82; mem. policy planning staff, spl. advisor, Office of the Counselor U.S. State Dept., 1982-83; lectr. history Harvard U., 1983-84; assoc. prof., then prof. U.S. Naval War Coll., 1984-86; dir. Fgn. Policy Rsch. Inst., Phila., 1986-93; editor Mid. East Quar., 1994—. Author: Slave Soldiers and Islam, 1981, In the Path of God: Islam and Political Power, 1983, paperback edit., 1985, Spanish edit., 1987, tape rec. Libr. of Congress, An Arabist's Guide to Egyptian Colloquial, 1983, The Long Shadow: Culture and Politics in the Middle East, 1988, Greater Syria: The History of an Ambition, 1990, The Rushdie Affair, 1990; co-editor Friendly Tyrants: An American Dilemma, 1991, Damascus Courts The West, 1991, Syria Beyond The Peace Process, 1995; editor: Sandstorm, 1993, Syria Beyond the Peace Process, 1994, Orbis: A Journal of World Affairs 1986-1990, Middle East Quarterly, 1994—. Vice chmn. J. William Fulbright Scholarship Bd., 1992-95; mem. adv. com. Internat. Rep. Inst., 1993. Woodrow Wilson Nat. fellow, 1971-72, Harvard U. Grad. fellow, 1973-74, Nat. Def. Edn. Act Title VI fellow, 1974-76, Am. Rsch. Ctr. in Egypt fellow, 1976-77, Israel Inter-Univ. Rsch. grantee, 1979, Smith Richardson Found. rsch. grantee, 1980-82, 95-96, Coun. on Fgn. Rels. Internat. Affairs fellow, 1982-83, Heritage Found. vis. fellow, 1984, Fulbright Exch. grantee, 1984, Japan Soc. U.S.-Japan Leadership Program fellow, 1985, Nat. Inst. for Rsch. Advancement, Tokyo, vis. fellow, 1985, Washington Inst. for Near East Policy vis. fellow, 1986, 91, 94-95, Schumann Found. grantee, 1990-91, U.S. Inst. of Peace grantee, 1991, Ford Found. 1992-93, Scaife Found., 1995-97. Mem. Coun. on Fgn. Rels., Internat. Ho. of Japan. Office: Mid East Quar 1920 Chestnut St Ste 600 Philadelphia PA 19103

PIPES, RICHARD, historian, educator; b. Cieszyn, Poland, July 11, 1923; came to U.S., 1940, naturalized, 1943; s. Mark and Sophia (Haskelberg) P.; m. Irene Eugenia Roth, Sept. 1, 1946; children—Daniel, Steven. Student, Muskingum (Ohio) Coll., 1940-43; AB, Cornell U., 1945; PhD, Harvard U., 1950; LLD (hon.), Muskingum Coll., 1988; LHD (hon.), Adelphi U., 1991; Doctor honoris causa, U. Silesia, Poland, 1994. Mem. faculty Harvard U., 1950—, prof. history, 1958-75, Frank B. Baird Jr. prof. history, 1975—; assoc. dir. Russian Rsch. Ctr., 1962-64, dir., 1968-73; sr. cons. Stanford Research Inst., 1973-78; dir. East European and Soviet affairs NSC, 1981-82; cons. Ency. Britannica;. Author: Formation of the Soviet Union, rev. edit, 1964, Karamzin's Memoir on Ancient and Modern Russia, 1959, Social Democracy and the St. Petersburg Labor Movement, 1963, Europe Since 1815, 1970, Struve: Liberal on the Left, 1870-1905, 1970, Russia Under the Old Regime, 1974, Struve: Liberal on the Right, 1905-1944, 1980, U.S.-Soviet Relations in the Era of Detente, 1981, Survival Is Not Enough, 1984, Russia Observed, 1989, The Russian Revolution, 1990, Communism: The Vanished Specter, 1993, Russia Under the Bolshevik Regime, 1994; editor: Russian Intelligentsia, 1961, (with John Fine) Of the Russian Commonwealth (Giles Fletcher), 1966, Revolutionary Russia, 1968, Collected Works in Fifteen Volumes (P.B. Struve), 1970, Soviet Strategy in Europe, 1976; mem. editorial bd. Strategic Rev., Orbis, Comparative Strategy, Jour. Strategic Studies, Continuity, Arka. Mem. exec. com. on Present Danger, 1977-92; chmn. Govt. Team B to Rev. Intelligence Estimates, 1976; mem. Reagan transition team Dept. State, 1980. Served with USAAF, 1943-46. Guggenheim fellow, 1956, 65; fellow Am. Coun. Learned Socs., 1965; fellow Ctr. for Advanced Study in Behavioral Scis., Stanford, Calif., 1969-70; lectr. Spring lecture Nobel Inst., Oslo, 1993. Fellow Am. Acad. Arts and Scis.; mem. Council Fgn. Relations. Club: Cosmos (Washington). Home: 17 Berkeley St Cambridge MA 02138-3409

PIPES, ROBERT BYRON, academic administrator, mechanical engineer; b. Shreveport, La., Aug. 14, 1941; s. Walter H. and Mattye Mae (Wilson) P.; B.S., La. Poly. Inst., 1964, M.S., 1965; M.S.E., M.A., Princeton U., 1969; Ph.D., U. Tex., 1972; m. Ruth Ellen Franz, June 27, 1964; children: Christopher Franz, Mark Robert. Sr. structures engr. Gen. Dynamics Corp., 1969-72; asst. prof. mech. engring. Drexel U., 1972-74; assoc. prof. mech. and aerospace engring. U. Del., 1974-80, prof., 1980—, also dir. Center Composite Materials, 1974-80, dean Coll. Engring., 1985-91, provost, v.p. acad. affairs, 1991-93; pres. Rensselaer Polytech. Inst., N.Y., 1993—; dir. Nat. Ctr. Composites Mfg. Sci. and Engring., 1985; cons. in field; mem. com. NRC. Mem. ASME (Gustus Larson award 1983), Soc. Mfg. Engrs., Soc. Advancement of Material and Processing Engring., Nat. Acad. Engring. (elected 1987), Soc. Exptl. Stress Analysis (chaire Françqui-Belgium), Swedish Acad. Engring., Am. Soc. Composites (tech. rev. com. Air Force Composite Materials Design Guide—Analytical Methods), ASTM, Sigma Xi, Tau Beta Pi, Pi Tau Sigma, Omicron Delta Kappa. Methodist. Author: Experimental Mechanics of Fiber Reinforced Composite Materials, 1982, Characterization of Advanced Composite Materials, 1987; series editor 10 vols. Composite Materials; contbr. numerous articles to tech. jours. Home: 2005 Tibbits Ave Troy NY 12180-4269 Office: Rensselaer Polytech Inst Office of Pres Pittsburg Bldg Troy NY 12180-3590

PIPES, WESLEY O'FERAL, civil engineering educator; b. Dallas, Jan. 28, 1932; s. Wesley O'Feral and Lunnette (Waller) P.; children—Phylis, Victoria (dec.), Wesley, Susan, Gordon. B.S., N. Tex. State U., 1953, M.S., 1955; Ph.D., Northwestern U., 1959. Research engr. U. Calif.-Berkeley, 1955-57; asst. prof. Northwestern U., 1959-62, assoc. prof., 1962-67; prof. civil engring., 1967-74, prof. biol. scis., 1969-74; L. Drew Betz prof. ecology Drexel U., 1975-83, prof. civil engring., 1983—; head civil engring. dept., 1983-87; cons. water pollution and wastewater treatment Office of Drinking Water, EPA, 1986-91, P.R. Aquaduct and Sewer Authority, 1991, Malcolm Pirnie, Inc., 1991-92, Delaware County (Pa.) Regional Authority, 1992, environ. enforcement divsn. U.S. Dept. Justice, 1993-95, Ductile Iron Pipe Rsch. Assn., 1994, Smith & Loveless, Inc., 1994-95. Mem. tech. adv. com. on water resources Northeastern Ill. Planning Commn., 1968-74. Named one of 10 Outstanding Young Men of Chgo. Chgo. Jr. Assn. Commerce and Industry, 1963; recipient Rsch. award Pa. Water Pollution Control Assn., 1989. Mem. ASCE, Am. Assn. Environ. Engring. Profs. (dir. 1970-76, v.p. 1974, pres. 1975), Am. Water Works Assn., Water Pollutio Control Fedn., Am. Soc. Microbiology, Internat. Environmetrics Soc. (dir. 1994—), Sigma Xi, Tau Beta Pi. Research and publs. on microbiology of water and wastewater. Office: Drexel U Dept Civil Engring Philadelphia PA 19104

PIPKIN, JAMES HAROLD, JR., lawyer; b. Houston, Jan. 3, 1939; s. James Harold and Zenda Marie (Lewis) P. BA, Princeton U., 1960; JD, Harvard U., 1963; Diploma in Law, Oxford (Eng.) U., 1965. Bar: D.C. 1964, U.S. Supreme Ct. 1969, D.C. Ct. Appeals, 1972. Law clk. to assoc. justice U.S. Supreme Ct., Washington, 1963-64; assoc. Steptoe and Johnson, Washington, 1965-70, ptnr., 1971-93; counselor to The Sec. of the Interior U.S. Dept. of the Interior, 1993—; U.S. spl. negotiator for Pacific Salmon,

Dept. of State, 1994—; counsel Friends of Music, Smithsonian Inst., Washington, 1984-88; mem. Nat. Arbitration Panel, 1983-94. Author or coauthor: The English Country House: A Grand Tour, 1985, The Country House Garden: A Grand Tour, 1987, Places of Tranquility, 1990; contbr. photographs and articles to mags. including: House & Garden, Smithsonian mag., The Mag. Antiques, Art and Antiques, Archtl. Digest, Am. Illustrated. Grand officier Confrérie des Chevaliers du Tastevin, 1989. Mem. ABA, D.C. Bar Assn., Met. Club. Home: 6109 Davenport Ter Bethesda MD 20817-5827 Office: Office of The Secretary US Dept of the Interior Rm 6118 1849 C St NW Washington DC 20240

PIPPEN, SCOTTIE, professional basketball player; b. Hamburg, Ark., Sept. 25, 1965. Student, U. Cen. Ark., 1983-87. With Seattle Super Sonics, 1987; guard/forward Chgo. Bulls, 1987—; player NBA Championship Team, 1991, 92, 93, U.S. Olympic Basketball Team, 1992. Named to All-Star team, 1990, 92-93, NBA All-Defensive First team, 1992, 93, 94, NBA All-Star Team, 1992-94, NBA All-Star MVP, 1994, All-NBA First Team, 1994. Office: Chgo Bulls 1 Magnificent Mile 980 N Michigan Ave # 11600 Chicago IL 60611-4501*

PIPPIN, JOHN ELDON, electronics engineer, electronics company executive; b. Kinard, Fla., Oct. 7, 1927; s. Festus and Mary Elvie (Scott) P.; m. Barbara A. Pippin, June 15, 1952; children: Carol Jean Pippin Franklin, John F., Mary Christine Pippin Mobley. B.E.E., Ga. Inst. Tech., 1951, M.S.E.E., 1953; Ph.D. in Applied Physics, Harvard U., 1958. Research. engr. Ga. Inst. Tech. Expt. Sta., Atlanta, 1951-53; head research dept. Sperry Microwave Electronics Co., Clearwater, Fla., 1958-64; v.p., dir. research Scientific-Atlanta, Inc., 1964-68; pres. Electromagnetic Scis., Inc., Norcross, Ga., 1968—; adj. prof. U. Fla., 1962-64; cons. Cascade Research Corp., 1953-58. Contbr. articles to profl. jours. Served in USN, 1945-46. NSF fellow; Gen. Commns. fellow. Fellow IEEE (Outstanding Engr. Region III 1972, Engr. of Yr. 1972); mem. Briarean Soc., Am. Phys. Soc., Microwave Theory and Techniques Soc. (adminstrv. com.), Sigma Xi, Tau Beta Pi, Phi Kappa Phi, Eta Kappa Nu. Achievements include research in microwave physics; radar tracking problems. Home: 3760 River Summit Trl Duluth GA 30136-2278 Office: Electromagnetic Sci Inc 660 Engineering Dr Norcross GA 30092-2821

PIRAINO, THOMAS, writer, retired electrical engineer; b. Syracuse, N.Y., Apr. 2, 1912; s. Paul and Domenica (La Macchia) P.; m. Theodora M. Merzani, July 4, 1937; children: Maria Burnham, Paula Grimes, Joanne Dahlgren, Andrea Stidsen, Thomas A. Assoc. in liberal arts, Massasoit C.C., 1988; cert. in elec. engring., MIT, 1938, cert. in mech. engring., 1941. Registered profl. engr., Mass. Elec. engring. draftsman USN-Charlestown Navy Yard, Boston, 1940-42; elec. designer E.B. Badger & Sons, Boston, 1942-45; elec. engr. Jackson & Moreland, Engrs., Boston, 1945-51; sr./ project elec. engr. Chas. T. Main, Inc., Boston, 1951-78; freelance writer Braintree, Mass., 1979—. Author: The Sicilian Fisherman's Son, 1992. Vol. radio reader Talking Info. Ctr. Radio Sta., Marshfield, Mass., 1984-89; mem. Rep. Party, 1978—. Mem. IEEE (sr., life mem.), Am. Inst. Elec. Engrs. (sr. mem., chmn. pub. com. 1960-62, gen. meetings com. 1960-62). Roman Catholic. Home: 51 Brewster Ave Braintree MA 02184

PIRANI, CONRAD LEVI, pathologist, educator; b. Pisa, Italy, July 29, 1914; came to U.S., 1939, naturalized, 1945; s. Mario Giacomo Levi and Adriana P.; m. Luciana Nahmias, Mar. 12, 1955; children: Barbara, Sylvia, Robert. Diploma, Ginnasio-Liceo Beccaria, 1932; M.D., U. Milano, Italy, 1938. Intern Columbus Meml. Hosp., Chgo., 1940-42; resident Michael Reese Hosp., Chgo., 1942-45; instr. pathology U. Ill., Chgo., 1945-48; asst. prof. U. Ill., 1948-52, asso. prof., 1952-55, prof., 1955-70; chmn. dept. pathology Michael Reese Hosp., Chgo., 1965-72; prof. pathology Coll. Physicians and Surgeons, Columbia U., N.Y.C., 1972-85; prof. emeritus Coll. Physicians and Surgeons, Columbia U., 1985—; dir. Renal Pathology Lab., 1972-84; cons. Armed Forces Inst. Pathology; mem. sci. com. Kidney Found., N.Y., 1973-80. Contbg. author various books.; assoc. editor Lab. Investigation, 1972-82, Nephron, 1975-92, Clin. Nephrology, 1989-92; contbr. numerous articles to profl. jours. USPHS, NIH grantee. Mem. Am. Assn. Pathologists, AAAS, Internat. Acad. Pathology (counselor 1966-69), Am. Soc. Nephrology (John P. Peters award 1987), Internat. Soc. Nephrology. Home: 28 Bradford St Glen Rock NJ 07452-2102 Office: 630 W 168th St New York NY 10032-3702

PIRCHER, LEO JOSEPH, lawyer; b. Berkeley, Calif., Jan. 4, 1933; s. Leo Charles and Christine (Moore) P.; m. Phyllis McConnell, Aug. 4, 1956 (div. April 1981); children: Christopher, David, Eric; m. Nina Silverman, June 14, 1987; B.S., U. Calif.-Berkeley, 1954, J.D., 1957. Bar: Calif. 1958, N.Y. 1985; cert. specialist taxation law Calif. Bd. Legal Specialization. Assoc. Lawler, Felix & Hall, L.A., 1957-62, ptnr., 1962-65, sr. ptnr., 1965-83; sr. ptnr. Pircher, Nichols & Meeks, L.A., 1983—; adj. prof. Loyola U. Law Sch., L.A., 1959-61; corp. sec. Am. Metal Bearing Co., Gardena, Calif., 1975—, dir. Varco Internat. Inc., Orange, Calif.; speaker various law schs. and bar assns. edn. programs. Author: (with others) Definition and Utility of Leases, 1968. Chmn. pub. fin. and taxation sect. Calif. Town Hall, Los Angeles, 1970-71. Mem. Calif. State Bar, N.Y. State Bar, Los Angeles County Bar Assn. (exec. com. comml. law secton), ABA, Nat. Assn. Real Estate Investment Trusts Inc. (cert. specialist taxation law). Republican. Club: Regency (L.A.). Office: Pircher Nichols & Meeks 1999 Avenue Of The Stars Los Angeles CA 90067-6022

PIRES, MARY ANN, public relations consultant; b. Saginaw, Mich., May 6, 1944; d. Vincent Paul and Ann Catherine (Mainolfi) Kingry; m. Edward A. Pires, Oct. 21, 1973; 1 dau., Carrie Ann. B.A. in Sociology Nazareth Coll., 1966; M.S. in Pub. Relations, Boston U., 1973. Asst. to pres. Boston City Council, 1970-71; speechwriter Gov.'s Press Office, Boston, 1971-72; asst. editor John Hancock Ins. Co., Boston, 1970-72; pub. relations dir. Greater Boston C. of C., 1972-77; staff coordinator pub. relations Texaco Inc., White Plains, N.Y., 1977-79; mgr. planning, pub. relations, 1980-84; dir. corp. communication program Combustion Engring., Stamford, Conn., 1984-85; pub. relations cons., Armonk, N.Y., 1985—. Contbg. editor The Communicator, 1982; contbr. articles to profl. jours., newspapers. Mem. nat. alumni council, Boston U., 1977—. Recipient Young Am. medal for service Pres. John F. Kennedy, 1962. Mem. Pub. Relations Soc. Am. (nat. dir. 1983—, accredited), Women Exec. in Pub. Relations, Issues Mgmt. Assn. Roman Catholic. Office: The Pires Grp Inc 1055 Saw Mill River Rd Ardsley NY 10502-1045

PIRET, MARGUERITE ALICE, investment banker; b. St. Paul, May 10, 1948; d. E.L. and Alice P.; children: Andrew, Anne. AB, Radcliffe Coll., 1969; MBA, Harvard U., 1974. Comml. loan officer Bank New Eng. (now Fleet Bank), Boston, 1974-79; mng. dir. Kridel Securities, N.Y.C., 1979-81; pres., founder, dir. Newbury, Piret & Co., Inc., Boston, 1981—; trustee, chmn. audit com. Pioneer Mutual Funds, Boston. Vis. com. mem. Am. decorative arts and sculpture Mus. Fine Arts, Boston, 1982—; mem. nominating com. for candidates for overseer of Harvard U. and for candidates for dir. of Harvard Alumni Assn.; adv. com. on shareholder responsibility Harvard U., 1986-87; trustee, mem. exec. com. Boston U. Med. Ctr. Hosp., 1979—, chmn. fin. com.; trustee Mass. Hosp. Assn., 1983-86, Boston Ballet Ctr. for Dance Edn., 1989-93. Mem. Harvard Club. Office: Newbury Piret & Co Inc One Boston Pl Boston MA 02108

PIRIE, ROBERT BURNS, JR., defense analyst; b. San Diego, Sept. 10, 1933; s. Robert Burns and Gertrude May (Freeman) P.; m. Joan Adams, Dec. 23, 1960; children: John Winthrop, Carl Joseph Emil, Susan Gilman. Student, Princeton U., 1950-51; B.S., U.S. Naval Acad., 1955; B.A., Magdalen Coll., Oxford U., 1959, M.A., 1963. Commd. ensign U.S. Navy, 1955, advanced through grades to comdr., 1969; comdg. officer (U.S.S. Skipjack), 1969-72; dep. asst. dir. Congl. Budget Office, 1975-77; prin. dep. asst. sec. for manpower, res. affairs and logistics Dept. Def., Washington, 1977-79; asst. sec. Dept. Def., 1979-81; mgmt. cons., 1981—; def. analyst Ctr. for Naval Analyses, Alexandria, Va., 1981-83; asst. v.p. Inst. for Def. Analyses, Alexandria, Va., 1983-86, v.p., 1986-87; exec. v.p. Essex Corp., Alexandria, Va., 1987, pres., 1987-88; sr. economist Rand Corp., Washington, 1989; dir. strategic studies group U.S. Naval War Coll., 1989-92; v.p. Ctr. Naval Analyses, Alexandria, Va., 1992-94; asst. sec. of Navy for Installations and Environ. USN, Washington, 1994—. Vestryman St. John's Episcopal Ch., Chevy Chase, Md., 1973-76, 81, jr. warden, 1982-

84, sr. warden, 1984-87; trustee U.S. Naval Acad. Found., 1980-94. Rhodes scholar, 1956. Mem. U.S. Naval Inst., Internat. Inst. Strategic Studies, U.S. Naval Acad. Alumni Assn. (trustee 1967-70). Club: Vincent's. Office: 1000 Navy Pentagon Washington DC 20350-1000

PIRIE, ROBERT S., investment banker, lawyer; b. Chgo., 1934; m. Deirdre Howard. AB, Harvard U., 1956, LLB, 1962. Bar: Mass. 1962, N.Y. 1978. Law clk. to chief justice Mass. Supreme Ct., 1962-63; mem. Gaston, Snow, Motley & Holt, Boston, 1963-73; ptnr. Skadden, Arps, Slate, Meagher & Flom, Boston, 1973-82; pres., CEO Rothschild, Inc., N.Y.C., 1982-92, chmn., CEO, 1992-93; chmn., CEO Bear Stearns & Co., Inc., 1993—. Trustee Signet Soc., Asian Cultural Coun., N.Y., The Asia Soc., Rosenbach Mus., Howard Florey Biomed. Found., Am. Acad. in Rome; overseer Mus. Fine Arts, Boston. Fellow AAAS, Am. Antiquarian Soc.; mem. Brook Club, Century Club, Somerset Club, Odd Volumes Club, Roxburghe Club, Saturday Club, Zodiac Club, Manchester Yacht Club. Office: Rothschild Inc 1 Rockefeller Pla New York NY 10020

PIRKL, JAMES JOSEPH, industrial designer, educator; b. Nyack, N.Y., Dec. 27, 1930; s. James and Ida Bertha (Gigrich) P.; m. Sarah B. W. Woolsey, June 8, 1974; children: Theo, James, Philip. Cert. Advt. Design, Pratt Inst., 1951, B of Indsl. Design cum laude, 1958. With design staff Gen. Motors Corp., Warren, Mich., 1958-65; sr. designer Gen. Motors Corp., 1961-64, asst. chief designer, 1964-65; instr. indsl. design Center for Creative Studies, Detroit, 1963-65; faculty dept. design Syracuse (N.Y.) U., 1965-92, assoc. prof., 1969-73, prof. indsl. design, 1974-92, prof. emeritus, 1992—, coord. indsl. design program, 1979-84, chmn. dept. design, 1985-91; exec. council chmn. Sch. Art, 1976-78, 80-81; sr. rsch. fellow All-U. Gerontology Ctr., 1990—; prin. James J. Pirkl/Design, 1965—; cons. Brownlie Design, Inc., 1972—, Rolland Co., 1993, Arthritis Found., 1993—, GE Appliances, 1994, Prince Corp., 1991, Ford Motor Design Ctr., 1992, Loretto Geriatric Ctr., Sage Marcom Inc., 1988-90, Hazard Mgmt. Co., 1985, Marcom Switches Inc., 1977-82, Cazenovia Abroad Ltd., 1973-81, Holistic Mgmt. Group, Inc., 1981, Pulos Design Assocs., 1972-80, Beck Assocs., 1976, Fed. Prison Industries, 1974, Gen. Electric Co., 1967-70, Genesee Labs., Inc., 1968, N.Y. State Council on Arts, 1968-69, Stettner-Trush, Inc., 1972-78, Strathmore Chem. Coatings, Inc., 1969, 72, Village of Cazenovia, 1979-93, Xerox Corp., 1975, Age Wave, Inc., 1993—; chmn. accreditation council Design Found., 1982-84; interviewed on Nat. Pub. Radio. Author: Transgenerational Design: Products for an Aging Population, 1994; co-author: Guidelines and Strategies for Designing Transgenerational Products, 1988; co-editor: State of Art and Science of Design, 1971; co-designer: Gen. Motors Futurama Exhbn., N.Y. World's Fair, 1964-65; contbr. articles to profl. jours. including Mgmt. Jour., Jour. Indsl. Designers Soc. Am., Bus. Adminstrn. Jour., Design News, Design Perspectives, Indsl. Design. Mem. Everson Mus. Art, 1977-85; chmn. planning commn. Town of Cazenovia, N.Y., 1988-93; mem. senate Syracuse U., 1973-80; mem. adv. bd. SEARS Project, 1989-91; chmn. chancellor's citation com., 1988-92; mem. exhbns. com. Syracuse Cultural Resources Coun., 1992-93. With SeaBees USN, 1951-55. Recipient Gold Indsl. Design Excellence award Indsl. Designers Soc. Am. and Bus. Week Mag., 1994. Fellow Indsl. Designers Soc. Am. (chmn. universal design com. 1991-94, chmn. NASAD liaison com. 1984-88, mem. archives com. 1988-92, nat. bd. dirs. 1977-81, chmn. Central N.Y. chpt. 1977-78, v.p. Mid-East region 1978-80, dir., chmn. edn. com. 1980-81, U.S. rep., del. Internat. Congress Socs. Indsl. Design 1989); mem. The Design Found. (chmn. accreditation coun. 1982), Nat. Assn. Schs. Art and Design (accreditation evaluator 1985—), Nat. Ctr. for a Barrier Free Environment (adv. task force 1981), Human Factors Soc. (life mem.), Internat. Congress Socs. Indsl. Design (edn. com.), Author's Guild. Achievements include patent for 4-way handle. Home: 66 Camino Barranca Placitas NM 87043-9314

PIRKLE, EARL CHARNELL, geologist, educator; b. nr. Buckhead, Ga., Jan. 8, 1922; s. Early Charnell and Eva Lee (Collins) P.; m. Valda Nell Armistead, July 9, 1942; children: Betty Jean, William A., Fredric L. AB, Emory U., 1943; MS, 1947; postgrad., U. Tenn., 1947-50; PhD, U. Cin., 1956. Certified profl. geologist. Prodn. coordinator, research crystallographer Pan-Electronics Labs., Inc., Atlanta, 1942-45; instr. geology U. Tenn., 1947-50; mem. faculty dept. phys. scis. and geology U. Fla., Gainesville, 1950-93, prof. emeritus, 1993—; prof. U. Fla., 1963—, chmn. dept. phys. scis., 1972-79; dir. Phys. Scis., 1979-82; cons. in field; vis. prof. geology Emory U., summers, 1959-65; research cons. Fla. Dept. Natural Resources Bur. Geology. Author: Natural Regions of the United States, 1977, 4th edit., 1985; Editor: Physical Science- Our Environment, 1968, Our Physical Environment, 1980; Contbr. articles to profl. jours. Served with AUS, 1945-46. Fellow Geol. Soc. Am., Soc. Econ. Geologists; mem. Am. Assn. Petroleum Geologists, Am. Soc. Mining, Metall. and Petroleum Engrs., Fla. Acad. Scis., Southeastern Geol. Soc., Phi Beta Kappa, Sigma Gamma Epsilon, Gamma Theta Epsilon, Sigma Chi. Democrat. Methodist.

PIRKLE, GEORGE EMORY, television and film actor, director; b. Atlanta, Sept. 3, 1947; s. George Washington and Glanna Adeline (Palmer) P.; m. Karen Leigh Horn, Oct. 20, 1973; 1 child, Charity Caroline. Student North Ga. Coll., 1965-66; BA in Journalism, U. Ga., 1969, MA, 1971. Radio announcer, sportscaster for various radio stas., North Ga. area, 1968-70; TV producer, dir. Instructional Resources Ctr., Athens, Ga., 1969-70; info. officer, Southeastern Signal Sch., U.S. Army, 1971; producer, dir. DA MoPic Svc., Continental Army Command Network and Signal Corps TV Div., 1972-73; pub. info. officer Ga. Dept. Revenue, Atlanta, 1973-78; coord. TV prodn. svcs. Co. So. Svcs., Inc., Birmingham, Ala., 1978-88; exec. v.p. Mgmt. and Human Devel. Assocs., Inc., Birmingham, 1984-86; producer Prodn. Works, Birmingham, 1984-88; actor for various radio and TV commercials, corp. TV programs, radio dramas, stage plays, 1968—; owner Talking Rock Prodns., Cumming, Ga., 1989—. Editor monthly newsletter Ga. Revenews, 1973-78; editor, dir. Bankers TV Network, 1990-92; writer, producer, dir., exec. producer more than 500 corp. and pub. svc. TV and film programs. Recipient So. Superlative outstanding employee award, So. Co. Svcs., 1986. Mem. communications com. Birmingham Area Coun. Boy Scouts Am., 1983-85; Master of ceremonies gov.'s vet. awards presentation World Peace Luncheon, Birmingham, 1981, 82, 84; dir. campaign film Pensacola United Way, 1989; exec. producer videotape for Birmingham Film Coun., 1985; producer, dir. Highway in Crisis, 1986; writer, producer, dir. campaign film Birmingham Area United Way, 1981, 86, 87; writer, producer, narrator, 1987 campaign film; bd. dirs. Birmingham Internat. Ednl. Film Festival, 1987-91; chmn. Sadie award com., student video competition dir.; comml. acting instr. elan/Casablancas Modeling/Career Ctr., 1988-92; instr. Cliff Osmond Acting Program, 1989-92; anchor This Week in Banking, 1990-92; mem. tech. steering com. Forsyth Bd. Edn., 1995—. 1st lt. U.S. Army, 1971-73. Recipient Battles award, 1988, various others. Mem. Internat. TV Assn. (charter pres. Birmingham chpt. 1984-85, pres. pro tem 1984, editor newsletter Freeze Frame), So. Electric System Visual Communications Subcom. (founding), Ga. Hist. Soc., United Way of Forsyth County (bd. dirs., 1995—). Methodist. Avocations: photography, music, genealogy, hist. rsch., archaeology. Home and Office: 105 Brooks Farm Dr Cumming GA 30130

PIRKLE, WILLIAM H., chemistry educator; b. Shreveport, La., May 2, 1934; married, 1956; 4 children. BS, U. Calif., Berkeley, 1959; PhD in Chemistry, U. Rochester, 1963. NSF fellow Harvard U., 1963-64; asst. prof., 1964-69; assoc. prof. chemistry U. Ill., Urbana, 1969—; Alfred P. Sloan fellow, 1971-72. Mem. Am. Chem. Soc. (Am. Chem. Soc. award in Chromatography 1994). Office: U Illinois 161 Roger Adam Lab 1209 California Urbana IL 61801-3731*

PIRNER, DAVID, musician, songwriter; b. 1964. With Soul Asylum (formerly Loud Fast Rules), 1981—. Albums include (with Soul Asylum) Say What You Will, 1983, Made To Be Broken, 1986, While You Were Out, 1986, Time's Incinerator, 1986, Hang Time, 1988, Say What You Will, Clarence (Carl Sold the Truck), 1989, Clam Dip and Other Delights, 1989, Soul Asylum and the Horse They Rode in On, 1990, Grave Dancers Union, 1992 (Grammy award Best Rock Song 1994), Let Your Dim Light Shine, 1995; contributor to (albums): Free to Be...A Family, 1988, The Bridge, 1989, Sweet Relief, 1993, No Alternative, 1993; (soundtracks): Lost Angels, 1989, So I Married an Axe Murderer, 1993, Backbeat, 1993; film appearances include Reality Bites, 1994. Office: c/o Soul Asylum Columbia Records 51 W 52nd St New York NY 10019-6119*

PIRO, ANTHONY JOHN, radiologist; b. Boston, May 28, 1930; s. John Anthony and Josephine (Pepe) P.; m. Marian Giallombardo, Sept. 5, 1955; children—Anthony John, Janet, Jacquelyn. A.B., Boston U., 1952, M.D., 1956. Diplomate: Am. Bd. Internal Medicine, Am. Bd. Radiology. Intern Mass. Meml. Hosp., Boston, 1956-57; resident Boston VA Hosp., 1959-62; practice medicine specializing in internal medicine Framingham, Mass., 1962-63; staff physician Boston VA Hosp., 1963-66; sr. asso. Children's Cancer Research Found., 1966-70; radiotherapist Harvard Joint Center for Radiation Therapy, 1970-77; prof. therapeutic radiology, chmn. dept. therapeutic radiology Tufts-New Eng. Med. Center Hosp., 1977-79; radiation oncologist Salem (Mass.) Hosp., 1979—. Contbr. articles to profl. jours. Served with USAF, 1957-59. Nat. Cancer Inst. grantee, 1977-79. Fellow ACP, Am. Coll. Radiology; mem. AAAS, Am. Soc. Clin. Oncologists, Am. Soc. Therapeutic Radiologists, Am. Assn. Cancer Research, Radiation Research Soc., Phi Beta Kappa, Alpha Omega Alpha. Unitarian. Home: 6 Cider Mill Rd Lynnfield MA 01940-1132 Office: 81 Highland Ave Salem MA 01970-2768

PIRONE, THOMAS PASCAL, plant pathology educator; b. Ithaca, N.Y., Jan. 3, 1936; s. Pascal Pompey and Loretta Muriel (Kelly) P.; m. Sherrill Sevier, Aug. 1, 1961; children—John Sevier, Catherine Sherrill. B.S., Cornell U., 1957; Ph.D., U. Wis., 1960. Asst. prof. La. State U., Baton Rouge, 1960-63; asso. prof. La. State U., 1963-67, U. Ky., Lexington, 1967-71; prof. U. Ky., 1971—; chmn. plant pathology, 1978-86; mem. recombinant DNA adv. com. NIH, 1984-87. Contbr. articles on plant virology to profl. jours.; mem. editorial bd.: Virology, 1974-76, Phytopathology, 1971-73, sr. editor, 1977-78, Ann. Rev. Phytopathology, 1985-90. Sr. Fulbright research fellow U.K., 1974-75. Fellow Am. Phytopathol. Soc. (Ruth Allen award 1989); mem. AAAS, Internat. Soc. Plant Pathology, Am. Soc. Virology. Office: U Ky Dept Plant Pathology Lexington KY 40546

PIROS, CECILLE PATAO, business owner; b. Ilicos Sur, Philippines, July 7, 1944; came to U.S., 1972; d. Pedro Pinzon and Sinforosa (Pelayo) Patao; m. Rey T. Piros, June 24, 1972; 1 child, Ryan Patao. BS in Elem. Edn., St. Paul Coll., Vigan, Ilocos Sur, Philippines, 1966. Commd. Notary Public. Tchr. ESL, 1973-74; founder Rey-Cel Enterprises, Kahului, Hawaii, 1974—, v.p., sec., 1991—; travel cons. Diplomat Tour & Travel, Honolulu, 1976-81; founder Rey-Cel Travel Svc., 1986—; co-founder NR Filipino Variety Store, 1986—, R & C Philippine Food Imports, 1988-90; v.p. Rey Cel Broadcasting, Inc., 1993; newscaster Filipino program Sta. KMVI, 1974-78. Founder, dir. Maui Filipino Dramatic Club, 1976-80; v.p Kahului Sch. PTA, 1983-84. Mem. NAFE, Nat. Assn. Notaries Public, Saranay Maui Orgn., Sons & Daughters of Ilocano Region, Bantay Assn. Maui (auditor 1987), Santo Domingo Assn. Maui, Maui Filipino C. of C. (pres. 1994—). Office: Rey Cel Enterprises 230 Hana Hwy Kahului HI 96732

PIROUMIAN, FELIX ASHOT, Armenian government official; b. Tbilisi, Georgia, Aug. 27, 1954; s. Ashot Mnatsakan and Nina Sedrak (Mkrtichian) P.; m. Anahit Vladimir Bagdasarian, Sept. 21, 1991; 1 child, Ashot. Grad. in Civil Engring. Polytech. U., Yerevan, Armenia, 1976. From engr. to acting tech. dir. Haytransshin Engring. Co., USSR Ministry of Transport Engring., Yerevan, Armenia, 1976-83; tech. dir. HayTransShin Engring. Co., USSR Ministry of Transport Engring., Yerevan, 1983-87, mng. dir., 1987-92; mng. dir. HayTransShin Constrn. Corp., Yerevan, 1992-93; min. of constrn. Govt. of Armenia, Yerevan, 1993—. Office: Embassy of Republic of Armenia 1660 L St NW Ste 210 Washington DC 20036-5603

PIRSCH, CAROL MCBRIDE, state senator, community relations administrator; b. Omaha, Dec. 27, 1936; d. Lyle Erwin and Hilfrie Louise (Lebeck) McBride; student U. Miami, Oxford, Ohio, U. Nebr., Omaha; m. Allen I. Pirsch, Mar. 28, 1954; children—Pennie Elizabeth, Pamela Elaine, Patrice Eileen, Phyllis Erika, Peter Allen, Perry Andrew. Former mem. data processing staff Omaha Public Schs.; former mem. wage practices dept. Western Electric Co., Omaha; former legal sec. Omaha; former office mgr. Pirsch Food Brokerage Co., Inc., Omaha; former employment supr. U.S. West Communications, Omaha, now mgr. pub. policy; mem. Nebr. Senate, 1979—. mem. Omaha Pers. Bd.; founder, past pres., bd. dirs. Nebr. Coalition for Victims of Crime. Recipient Golden Elephant award; Outstanding Legis. Efforts award YWCA, Breaking the Rule of Thumb award Nebr. Domestic Violence Sexual Assault Coalition, Cert. of Appreciation award U.S. Dept. Justice. Mem. VASA, Nat. Orgn. Victim Assistance (Outstanding Legis. Leadership award), Freedom Found., Orgn. U.S. West Women, Nat. Order Women Legislators, Tangier Women's Aux., Footprinters Internat., Nebr. Hist. Soc., Nebr. Taxpayers Assn., Gretna Optimists, Springfield Boosters, Keystone Citizen Patrol (Keystoner of the Month award), Audubon Soc., Rotary Internat. (chmn. scholarship com.), N.W. Community Club, Benson Rep. Women's Club, Bus. and Profl. Rep. Women Club. Office: State Capitol Lincoln NE 68509

PIRSIG, ROBERT MAYNARD, author; b. Mpls., Sept. 6, 1928; s. Maynard Ernest and Harriet Marie (Sjobeck) P.; m. Nancy Ann James, May 10, 1954 (div. Aug. 1978); children—Christopher (dec. Nov. 17, 1979), Theodore; m. Wendy L. Kimball, Dec. 28, 1978; 1 dau., Nell. B.A., U. Minn., 1950, M.A., 1958. Author: Zen And The Art of Motorcycle Maintenance, 1974, Lila, 1991. Served with AUS, 1946-48. Recipient Award AAAL, 1979; Guggenheim fellow, 1974—. Mem. Soc. Tech. Communicators (sec. Minn. chpt. 1970-71, treas. 1971-72). Office: care Bantam Books 1540 Broadway New York NY 10036-4039

PISANI, JOSEPH MICHAEL, physician; b. N.Y.C., Mar. 22, 1919; s. Antonio David and Josephine Catherine (Walsh) P.; m. Agatha Rita Evaskitis, Nov. 11, 1942; children: Michael, Robert, Richard. A.B., Fordham Coll., 1938; M.D., N.Y.U., 1942; grad., Army Sch. Tropical Medicine, 1943. Intern Bellevue Hosp., 1942-43; resident medicine Bronx (N.Y.) VA Hosp., 1946-48, asst. chief chest service, 1948-49; dep. exec. dir. Com. on Med. Scis., Research and Devel. Bd., Washington, 1949-50; exec. dir. Com. on Med. Scis., Research and Devel. Bd., 1950-51; asst. dean and instr. medicine State U. Coll. of Medicine at N.Y., Bklyn., 1951-54; asst. dean, asst. prof. medicine State U. Coll. of Medicine at N.Y., 1954-57; asst. vis. physician Kings County Hosp., 1951-57; med. dir. Bankers Trust Co., N.Y.C., 1957-60, Union Family Med. Fund of Hotel Industry of N.Y.C., 1960-64; dep. med. dir. FDA, Dept. Health, Edn. and Welfare, Washington, 1964-66; industry liaison rep. FDA-OTC rev. panels, 1972-76; v.p. for med.-sci. affairs and med. dir. Proprietary Assn., Washington, 1966-84; clin. instr. medicine George Washington U. Sch. Medicine; asso. in medicine George Washington U. Hosp., 1949-51; adj. assoc. prof. adminstrv. medicine Columbia U., N.Y.C., 1960-64; assoc. clin. prof. adminstrv. medicine George Washington U., 1964-67, asso. clin. prof. medicine, 1968-84, assoc. professorial lectr. medicine, 1984-92, assoc. prof. emeritus clin. medicine, 1992—; domestic and internat. cons. on health affairs, 1984—; exec. sec. Spl. Com. on Med. Rsch., NSF, 1955, cons. on med.-sci. affairs, 1956; Del. U.S. Pharmacopeial Convs., 1970, 75, 80; mem. adv. bd. Physicians Desk Reference for Non-Prescription Drugs, 1979-88; mem. instl. rev. bd. G.H. Besselaar Assocs., 1989—. Contbr. articles on adminstrv. aspects med. care, med. edn. and med. research, drug evaluation. Served as capt. M.C. U.S. Army, 1943-46; NATOUSA and MTO with 5th Army, Field and Hosp. Med. Service. Recipient Alumni Achievement award in medicine Fordham U., 1959. Fellow Am. Pub. Health Assn., Indsl. Med. Assn.; mem. A.M.A., Am. Soc. Clin Pharmacology and Therapeutics, D.C. Med. Soc., N.Y. Acad. Scis., Soc. Alumni of Bellevue Hosp., Alumni Assn. N.Y. Univ. Coll Medicine, Celtic Med. Soc., Soc. Med. Cons. to Armed Forces., Am. Med. Tennis Assn. (bd. dirs. 1986-89). Roman Catholic. Home: 484 NE Plantation Rd Apt 4108 Stuart FL 34996-1751 Whatever small success I may have thus far achieved can be completely attributed to my good fortune in being blessed by a fine heritage, both past and present. The principles of conduct, discipline, ideals and goals in life to which my dear wife and I were exposed in our respective families, have guided us in our own family. No matter how trite it may seem to some, our basic philosophy of life is centered on the golden rule. This involves a fundamental interest in people and trust in them despite disappointments in this regard from time to time.

PISANKO, HENRY JONATHAN, command and control communications company executive; b. Trenton, N.J., Mar. 14, 1925; s. Isadore Stephen and Victoria (Gula) P.; m. Sophia Emily Zudnak, May 29, 1949; children: Barbara, Henry Jonathan, Jr., Michael. B in Naval Sci., U. Notre Dame, 1945, BA, 1947; cert. in Japanese, U. Colo. and Okla. State U., 1945; postgrad. Woodrow Wilson Sch., Columbia U., 1948-50. Constrn. reporter ea. div. F.W. Dodge div. McGraw-Hill, N.Y.C. and Phila., 1950-52; internat. affairs analyst Dept. Def., Washington, 1953-59; ops. officer Dept. Def., Pacific Rim, Japan and Hong Kong, 1960-63; sr. intelligence officer Internat. Security Affairs, Dept. Def., Washington, 1964-70; overseas adminstr. diplomatic telecommunications Dept. State, Asia, Africa, 1971-73; spl. advisor Def. Intelligence Coll., Washington, 1974-75; ctr. dep. chief, adminstrn. dir. Intelligence Community, Washington, 1976-82; exec. officer USA-EIGO Svcs. Co., Rockville, Md., 1983-87; exec. officer USA-EIGO Svcs. Co., Princeton, N.J., 1983-87, now bd. dirs.; pres. P.K. Co. Ltd., Bethesda, 1987—, Hong Kong, 1995—; bd. dirs. Asia Mgmt. Internat., Princeton; assoc. Bi-Lingual U.S.A. Corp., Bethesda, Md., 1984, Mgmt. Logistics Internat., Arlington, Va., 1983-86. Editor, translator: Yoshio Kodama, 1952; author: (monographs) Items of Inquiry Far East, 1983, Japenese Technology-Ancient Culture, 1985 (pamphlet) Fiber Optics Across the Pacific, 1989; editor (handbook) Japanese-English Proprietary Business Lexicon for Command Control Communications Intelligence, 1990-93. Sponsor, contbr. Pisanko-Kikan, 1982, Hotel Okura, Japan, 1983, Bungei Shunju, Japan, 1988. Lt. J.G., USN, 1942-46. Trenton Times scholar, 1942; recipient Moe Berg award Pub. Securtiy Investigation Agy.-Japan, Tokyo, 1961, telecommunications award Thai Gen. Staff, Bangkok, 1972. Mem. Asian Rsch. Svc., Bus. Devel. Africa, Internat. Inst. Japan, Bus. Execs. for Internat. Security, Internat. Platform Assn., Info. Processing Soc. Japan, Naval Res. Officers Tng. Corps, Unit Alumni Club, Boulder Boys-Japanese Club, Shek-O Club. Avocations: rare book collecting, cryptology, desert safaris. Office: PK Co Ltd Far East Hdqs, Peninsula New Business Ctr, Hong Kong Hong Kong

PISANO, A. ROBERT, entertainment company executive, lawyer; b. San Jose, Calif., Mar. 3, 1943; s. Anthony Edward and Carmen Jeanne (Morisoli) P.; m. Carolyn Joan Pollock, May 5, 1979; children: Catherine J., Anthony Daniel, Elizabeth A., Alexandra N. B.A. in Pub. Administrn., San Jose State U., 1965; J.D., U. Calif.-Berkeley, 1968. Bar: Calif. Assoc. O'Melveny & Myers, Los Angeles, 1968-75, ptnr., 1976-85, 92-93; exec. v.p. office of chmn., gen. counsel Paramount Pictures, Los Angeles, 1985-91; exec. v.p. Metro-Goldwyn-Mayer, Inc., Santa Monica, Calif., 1993—. Bd. dirs. Info. for Pub. Affairs, Sacramento, 1983—. Mem. Motion Picture Assn. Am. (bd. dirs. 1989-91, 93—), Acad. Motion Picture Arts and Scis. Office: Metro Goldwyn Mayer Inc 2500 Broadway St Santa Monica CA 90404-3061

PISANO, RONALD GEORGE, art consultant; b. N.Y.C., Dec. 19, 1948; s. Robert Louis and Mildred Jane (Willhelmi) P. BA, Adelphi U., 1971; postgrad., U. Del., 1971-73. Dir. exhbns. Baruch Coll. City U., N.Y., 1974-76; assoc. curator William Merritt Chase collection and archives Parrish Art Mus., Southampton, N.Y., 1976; curator mus. William Merritt Chase collection and archives Parrish Art Mus., 1977-78, dir., 1978-82; art cons., 1981—; guest curator Mus. at Stony Brook, N.Y., 1977-79, 85, 90, Henry Art Gallery U. Wash., 1982-83; cons. curator Am. art Heckscher Mus., Huntington, N.Y., 1977-77, guest curator, 1985, 90. Author: William Merritt Chase, 1979, The Heckscher Mus. Catalogue of the Am. Collection, 1979, An Am. Pl. Exhbn. Catalogue, 1981, A Leading Spirit in American Art: William Merritt Chase, 1849-1916, 1983, The Long Island Landscape, 1820-1920, 1985, The Art Students League; Selections from the Permanent Collection, 1987, A Centennial Celebration of the National association of Women Artists, 1988, Idle Hours: Americans at Leisure, 1865-1914, 1989, Long Island Landscape Painting in the 20th Century, 1990, Summer Afternoons: Landscape Paintings by William Merritt Chase, 1993, The League at the Cape, 1993, Parodying the American Masters: The Society of Fakirs, 1993, Gifford Beal; Picture Maker, 1993, Photographs from the William Merritt Chase Archives, 1993, William M. Chase and Irving R. Wiles: The Artist as Teacher, 1994, Henry and Edith Prellwitz and the Peconic Art Colony, 1995. Recipient A. Conger Goodyear award, 1971; Disting. Art Historian award Grand Central Art Galleries, 1979; Stebbins Family grantee, 1972-73. Mem. Coll. Art Assn., Am. Assn. Museums. Home: 6 Lakeview Trl Salisbury Mills NY 12577-5408 Office: Ronald G Pisano Inc 375 Riverside Dr Apt 13-b New York NY 10025-2149

PISCHL, ADOLPH JOHN, school administrator; b. East Orange, N.J., Mar. 28, 1920; s. Adolph and Anna (Ellerman) P.; m. Tennessee Wild, Sept. 9, 1947; 1 child, Sallyann. Certificate, Drake Coll., 1940. With Juilliard Sch. of Music, N.Y.C., 1962-86, asst. to concert mgr., 1962-66, dir. pub. relations, 1966-68, concert mgr., 1966-86; adminstr. The Sch. for Strings, N.Y.C., 1987-88; with The Dance Mart, N.Y.C., 1950—, pub. dir. Am. Dance Festival, Conn. Coll., 1964-68; mgr. Betty Jones Dances I Dance, 1966-68, Ruth Currier Dance Co., 1966-68, Anna Sokolow Dance Co., 1966-68, Julliard Sch. Bookstore, 1971-86. Founder, editor: Dance Perspectives, 1958-64, Dance Data, 1977; editor: Juilliard News Bull. and Rev. Ann, 1964-85; pub.: Dance Horizons, 1965-86; Contbr. articles to dance mags. Bd. dirs. Dance Notation Bur.; sec. bd. dirs. Walter W. Naumburg Found., Inc. Served with AUS, 1940-46. Home: 878 Warren Pky Teaneck NJ 07666-5640

PISCIOTTA, ANTHONY VITO, physician, educator; b. N.Y.C., Mar. 3, 1921; s. Andrew and Mary (Zinnanti) P.; m. Lorraine Gault, June 15, 1951; children: Robert Andrew, Nancy Marie, Anthony Vito. B.S., Fordham U., 1941; M.D., Marquette U., 1944, M.S., 1952. Diplomate: Am. Bd. Internal Medicine. Intern Jersey City Med. Center, 1944-45; resident pathology Fordham Hosp., N.Y.C., 1947-48; resident medicine Milwaukee County Gen. Hosp., 1948-51; rsch. fellow hematology New Eng. Center Hosp., 1951-52; instr. medicine Tufts U., 1951-52; mem. faculty Marquette U., 1952-81, prof., 1966-81; vice chmn. Radiation Effects Rsch. Found., Hiroshima, Japan, 1983; prof. medicine Med. Coll. Wis., Milw., 1983—, Robert A. Uihlein, Jr. prof. Hematologic Rsch., 1983—; dir. blood rsch. lab., staff hematologist John L. Doyne Hosp., 1952; cons. hematology U.S. Naval Hosp., Great Lakes, Ill., 1960; mem. hematology rsch. evaluation com. VA, 1968-70; vis. prof. Mayo Clinic, 1967. Mem. adv. editl. bd. of: Transfusion, 1960-67; mem. editl. bd. of: Jour. Lab. and Clin. Medicine, 1967-70. Served to capt. M.C. AUS, 1945-47. Named Alumnus of Yr. Med. Coll. Wis. Alumni Assn., 1977. Fellow A.C.P.; mem. AMA, Wis., Milw. County med. socs., Assn. Am. Physicians, AAAS, Am. Assn. Immunologists, Am. Soc. for Exptl. Pathology, Am. Soc. Hematology, Central Soc. Clin. Research, Internat. Soc. Hematology, Milw. Acad. Medicine (Achievement award 1987)i, Milw. Soc. Internal Medicine, N.Y. Acad. Sci., Soc. Exptl. Biology and Medicine, Nat. Blood Club (sec. 1970-71), Alpha Omega Alpha. Home: 12550 W Grove Ter Elm Grove WI 53122-1973 Office: Med Coll Wis 8700 W Wisconsin Ave Milwaukee WI 53226-3512

PISCOTTANO, ANN USCILLA, city official; b. New Haven, Feb. 5, 1954; d. Victor and Martha (Ianotti) Uscilla; m. Louis James Piscottano, Dec. 1, 1989; children: Martin, Louis, Daniel, Anthony, Joseph. Alderwoman City of New Haven; active Airport Adv. Bd., New Haven. Bd. dirs. People Against Violence Everywhere; mem. parish coun. St. Bernadette Ch., New Haven; mem. exec. bd., treas. St. Bernadette Sch.; founder Friends of East Shore. Avocations: reading, crafts. Home: 21 Ira St New Haven CT 06512 Office: Bd of Aldermen City Hall 165 Church St New Haven CT 06510

PISHKIN, VLADIMIR, psychologist, educator; b. Belgrade, Yugoslavia, Mar. 12, 1931; came to U.S., 1946, naturalized, 1951; s. Vasili and Olga (Bartosh) P.; m. Dorothy Louise Martin, Sept. 12, 1953; children—Gayle Ann, Mark Vladimir. B.A., Mont. State U., 1951, M.A., 1955; Ph.D., U. Utah, 1958. Dir. neuropsychiat. research labs. VA Hosp., Tomah, Wis., 1959-62; chief research psychologist Behavioral Sci. Labs., Oklahoma City, 1962-75; prof. psychiatry Coll. Medicine, U. Okla. Health Scis. Ctr., Oklahoma City, 1973-93, prof. emeritus, 1994; chmn. rsch. coun. dept. psychiatry and behavioral scis., 1972-75; bd. dirs. VA Med Ctr., Oklahoma City; dir. clin rsch. Willow View Hosp., Oklahoma City, 1987—. Author: (with Mathis and Pierce) Basic Psychiatry, rev. 3d edit, 1977; editor in chief: Jour. Clin. Psychology, 1974—; contbr. numerous articles to profl. jours. Served with USAF, 1952-54. Recipient Disting. Service award Jr. C. of C. Fellow Am. Psychol. Assn., Am. Psychol. Soc.; mem. Southwestern Psychol. Assn. (pres. 1973-74), Okla. Psychol. Assn.(Disting. Psychologist award 1986), Midwestern Psychol. Assn., AAAS, Psychonomics Soc. Clubs: Masons, Shriners. Home: 3113 NW 62nd St Oklahoma City OK 73112-4224 Office: 2601 Spencer Rd PO Box 11137 Oklahoma City OK 73136-0137

PISNEY, RAYMOND FRANK, international consulting services executive; b. Lime Springs, Iowa, June 2, 1940; s. Frank A. and Cora H. P. BA, Loras Coll., 1963; postgrad., Cath. U. Am., 1963; MA, U. Del., 1965. Asst.

adminstrn. and rsch. Mt. Vernon, Va., 1965-69; historic sites adminstr. N.C. Archives and Hist. Dept., Raleigh, 1969; asst. adminstr. div. historic sites and museums N.C. Dept. Art, Culture and History, Raleigh, 1969-72; cons. Cannon Mills Co., Kannapolis, N.C., 1972-73; exec. dir. Woodrow Wilson Birthplace Found., Staunton, Va., 1973-78, Mo. Hist. Soc., St. Louis, 1978-87; sr. v.p., cons. svcs. ETI Internat., Washington, 1987—; pres. Va. History and Museums Fedn., 1977-78; pres. Mo. Museums Assoc., 1982-84; cons. assoc. Battelle, Washington, 1994. Author: Historical Markers: A Bibliography, 1977, Historic Markers: Planning Local Programs, 1978, A Preview to Historical Marking, 1976, Old Buildings: New Resources for Work and Play, 1976; editor: Virginians Remember Woodrow Wilson, 1978, Woodrow Wilson in Retrospect, 1978, Woodrow Wilson: Idealism and Realty, 1977, Historic Preservation and Public Policy in Virginia, 1978. Bd. trustees James Clerk Maxwell Mus. and Found., Edinburgh, Scotland, 1993—, Internat. Human Rights Monument and Mus., Moscow, 1991—; sec., trustee Scotland WorldWide Heritage, Glasgow, 1993—; mem. internat. com. Charles A. Lindbergh Anniversary, Paris, 1987. Recipient Bertha Black Rhoda award NAACP, 1985; Hagley fellow U. Del., 1963-65; Seminar for Hist. Adminstrs. fellow, 1965. Mem. Washington Ind. Writers, Am. Assn. Museums, Nat. Trust Hist. Preservation U.S., Am. Assn. State and Local History, Can. Museums Assn., Brit. Museums Assn., Internat. Coun. Monuments and Sites, Internat. Coun. Museums, Lindbergh Anniversary Assn. (internat. com. 1987), Phi Alpha Theta. Roman Catholic.

PISTER, KARL STARK, engineering educator; b. Stockton, Calif., June 27, 1925; s. Edwin LeRoy and Mary Kimball (Smith) P.; m. Rita Olsen, Nov. 18, 1950; children: Francis, Therese, Anita, Jacinta, Claire, Kristofer. BS with honors, U. Calif., Berkeley, 1945, MS, 1948; PhD, U. Ill., 1952. Instr. theoretical and applied mechanics U. Ill., 1949-52; mem. faculty U. Calif., Berkeley, 1952-91, prof. engring. scis., 1962—, Roy W. Carlson prof. engring., 1985-90, dean Coll. Engring., 1980-90; chancellor U. Calif., Santa Cruz, 1991—, now pres., chancellor; Richard Merton guest prof. U. Stuttgart, W. Ger., 1978; cons. to govt. and industry; bd. dirs. Monterey Bay Aquarium Rsch. Inst.; bd. trustees Monterey Inst. Internat. Studies; chmn. bd. Calif. Coun. Sci. and Tech. Author research papers in field; assoc. editor: Computer Methods in Applied Mechanics and Engring, 1972, Jour. Optimization Theory and Applications, 1982; editorial adv. bd. Encyclopedia Phys. Sci. and Tech. Served with USNR, World War II. Recipient Wason rsch. medal Am. Concrete Inst., 1960, Vincent Bendix Minorities in Engring. award Am. Soc. for Engring. Edn., 1988, Lamme medal, 1993, Alumni Honor award U. Ill. Coll. Engring., Disting. Engring. Alumnus award U. Calif. Coll. Engring. Fellow ASME, AAAS, Am. Acad. Mechanics, Am. Acad. Arts and Scis., Calif. Acad. Scis. (hon.); mem. NAE, ASCE, Soc. Engring. Sci. Office: U Calif Santa Cruz Office of Chancellor 1156 High St Santa Cruz CA 95064-1077*

PISTILLI, PHILIP, hotel executive; b. N.Y.C., Aug. 10, 1926; m. Beverly Schubert, Apr. 5, 1947; children: Kevin M., Cynthia A. BS in Hotel Adminstrn., Cornell U., 1954. V.p., gen. mgr. Muehlebach Hotel, Kansas City, Mo., 1954-68; pres. Alameda Pla. Hotel, Kansas City, 1968-89; pres. The Raphael Hotel Group, Kansas City, 1989-92, chmn., 1992—; guest lectr. Cornell U.; past pres. Am. Hotel and Motel Assn.; pvt. industry cons. Pres. Harry S. Truman Good Neighbor Found.; vice chmn. bd. dirs. Edn. Inst., Mich. State U. Recipient Nat. Humanitarian award City of Hope, 1979. Mem. Mo. Restaurant Assn., Country Club Pla. Assn., Indian Hills Country Club, LaQuinta Country Club. Home: 400 W 49th Ter Kansas City MO 64112-2303 Office: 200 W 12th St Kansas City MO 64105-1637

PISTOLE, THOMAS GORDON, microbiology educator, researcher; b. Detroit, Sept. 17, 1942; s. Leotis Merton Pistole and Lillian Nell (Bosley) Besser; m. Donna Dulcie Straw, Sept. 11, 1965; children: James Alexander, Jennifer Katharine. PhB, Wayne State U., 1964, MS, 1966; PhD, U. Utah, 1969. Postdoctoral fellow U.S. Army, Frederick, Md., 1969-70; research assoc. U. Minn., Mpls., 1970-71; asst. prof. U. N.H., Durham, 1971-77, assoc. prof., 1977-83, prof., 1983—, chmn., 1983-92; vis. scientist Weizmann Inst., Rehovot, Israel, 1979; vis. prof. U. Edinburgh, Scotland, 1986. Co-editor: Biomedical Application of the Horseshoe Crab, 1979; mem. editorial bd. Jour. Invertebrate Pathology, 1988-90. NRC fellow, 1969-70, NIH sr. internat. fellow, 1986; grantee NIH, 1975-77, 89-93, NSF, 1981-84. Mem. Am. Soc. for Microbiology, Am. Assn. Immunologists, Internat. Soc. Devel. and Comparative Immunology, Soc. Leukocyte Biology. Avocations: singing, collecting old sheet music, walking, cooking. Office: U NH Dept Microbiology Durham NH 03824

PISTOR, CHARLES HERMAN, JR., former banker, academic administrator; b. St. Louis, Aug. 26, 1930; s. Charles Herman and Virginia (Brown) P.; m. Regina Prikryl, Sept. 20, 1952; children: Lori Ellen, Charles Herman III, Jeffrey Glenn. BBA, U. Tex., 1952; MBA, Harvard U., 1956, So. Meth. U., 1961. Chmn., chief exec. officer First RepublicBank Dallas, 1980-88, also bd. dirs.; chief exec. officer, chmn. bd. dirs. Northpark Nat. Bank, Dallas, 1988-90; vice chair So. Meth. U., Dallas, 1990—; bd. dirs. Am. Brands, AMR, Centex Corp., Oryx Corp. Trustee So. Meth. U., Dallas; elder Presbyn. Ch. Served to lt. USNR, 1952-54. Mem. Am. Bankers Assn. (past pres., bd. dirs.). Club: Dallas Country. Home: 4200 Belclaire Ave Dallas TX 75205-3033 Office: So Meth U Dallas TX 75275-0224

PISTORIUS, GEORGE, language educator; b. Prague, Czechoslovakia, Mar. 19, 1922; came to U.S. 1958, naturalized, 1964; s. Theodor and Blazena (Jiranek) P.; m. Marie Skokan, June 30, 1945; 1 dau., Erika. Student, Charles U., Prague, 1945-48; postgrad., Université de Paris, 1948-50; certificats d'etudes superieures, Université de Strasbourg, France, 1950, 1951; Ph.D., U. Pa., 1963. Asst. dept. comparative lit. Charles U., 1946-48; instr. Lafayette Coll., Easton, Pa., 1958-61; asst. prof. French Lafayette Coll., 1961-63; asso. prof. Williams Coll., 1963-68, prof. Romanic langs., 1968-92, chmn. dept., 1971-82, prof. emeritus, 1992—; instr. French, Colby Coll. Summer Sch. Lang., 1959-65. Author: Bibliography of the works of F.X. Salda, 1948, Destin de la culture francaise dans une democratie populaire, 1957, L'Image de l'Allemagne dans le roman francais entre les deux guerres (1919-1939), 1964, Marcel Proust and Deutschland, Eine Bibliographie, 1981, André Gide und Deutschland: Eine internationale Bibliographie, 1990. Mem. MLA, Am. Assn. Tchrs. of French, Assn. Internationale des Etudes Francaises. Home: 54 Cluett Dr Williamstown MA 01267-2805

PI-SUNYER, F. XAVIER, medical educator, medical investigator; b. Barcelona, Catalonia, Spain, Dec. 3, 1933; came to U.S., 1942; s. James and Mercedes (Diaz) Pi-S.; m. Penelope Wheeler; children: Andrea, Olivia, Joanna. BA, Oberlin (Ohio) Coll., 1955; MD, Columbia U., 1959, MPH, Harvard U., 1963. From instr. to asst. prof. Coll. of Physicians & Surgeons, Columbia U., N.Y.C., 1965-76, assoc. prof., 1976-85, prof. clin. medicine, 1985-91; prof. St. Luke's-Roosevelt Hosp. Ctr., N.Y.C., 1991—; from asst. to assoc. attending physician St. Luke's Hosp., N.Y.C., 1965-75; attending physician St. Luke's-Roosevelt Hosp. Ctr., N.Y.C., 1975—, chief div. endocrinology, diabetes and nutrition, 1988—, dir. Obesity Rsch. Ctr., 1988—; mem. adj. faculty Rockefeller U., 1984—; vis. physician Rockefeller U. Hosp., 1984—; attending physician Presbyn. Hosp., 1985—; sr. investigator N.Y. Heart Assn., 1968-73; Hsien Wu investigator St. Luke's-Roosevelt Hosp., 1982-90; Sigma Xi lectr. Pa. State U., 1989; Howard Heinz vis. prof. Med. Coll. Pa., 1987; mem. C study sect. Nat. Inst. Diabetes, Digestive and Kidney Disease, 1988-92, mem. task force on obesity, 1990—; mem. nutrition study sect., 1983-87; v.p. Am. Bd. Nutrition, 1987-88. Contbr. numerous articles to profl. jours. Fogarty Internat. fellow NIH, 1979-80. Mem. Am. Soc. for Clin. Nutrition (coun. 1987-90, pres. 1989-90), Am. Diabetes Assn. (exec. com. 1990-93, pres. 1992-93), N.Am. Assn. Study Obesity (v.p. 1992-93, pres. 1994-95), N.Y. State Health Rsch. Coun., N.Y. Acad. Medicine (com. on pub. health 1983—). Avocations: tennis, skiing, hiking, theater. Home: 305 Riverside Dr New York NY 10025 Office: St Luke's-Roosevelt Hosp Ctr Dept Medicine 1111 Amsterdam Ave New York NY 10025-1716

PITCHELL, ROBERT J., business executive; b. N.Y.C.; m. Louise Clark, Oct. 26, 1974; 1 dau., A.B., Fordham U., 1939; Ph.D., U. Calif., 1955. Mem. faculty Purdue U.; lectr. polit. sci. Butler U.; prof. Ind. U., to 1963; pres. Roosevelt U., 1963-65; formerly dep. adminstr. Fed. Extension Service, Dept. Agr.; later exec. dir. Nat. U. Extension Assn., Washington; pres. Hamden Enterprises Inc., Fairfax, Va.; cons., past dir. Ind. Tax Study

Commn. Author books on taxation and continuing edn. Assisted senatorial campaign Birch Bayh, 1962. Home and Office: 3134 Prosperity Ave Fairfax VA 22031-2820

PITCHER, GRIFFITH FONTAINE, lawyer; b. Balt., Nov. 1, 1937; s. William Henry and Virginia Griffith (Stein) P.; m. Sandra E. Barnett, Dec. 16, 1994; children: Virginia T. Pitcher Ballinger, L. Brooke Pitcher Fick, William T. B., Margaret W. Pitcher Lambino. B.A., Johns Hopkins U., 1960; J.D., U. Va., 1963. Bar: Ala. 1963, Fla. 1971. Assoc. Bradley, Arant, Rose & White, Birmingham, Ala., 1963-71; mem. Van den Berg, Gay & Burke, P.A., Orlando, Fla., 1971-76, Mahoney, Hadlow & Adams, P.A., Jacksonville, Fla., 1976-82; ptnr. Squire, Sanders & Dempsey, Miami, Fla., 1982-93; of counsel Mershon, Sawyer, Johnston, Dunwoody & Cole, Miami, 1994—. Vice-chmn. Winter Park (Fla.) Planning and Zoning Bd., 1974-75. Served with Army N.G., 1961-64. Mem. ABA, Nat. Assn. Bond Lawyers, The Fla. Bar, Fla. Econ. Devel. Coun., Fla. Mcpl. Attys. Assn., Fla. Acad. Hosp. Attys., Ala. State Bar Assn., Order of Coif, Delta Phi. Republican. Contbr. articles on law to profl. jours.

PITCHER, MAX GROW, exploration company executive, geologist; b. Calgary, Alta., Can., Apr. 22, 1935; s. Morgan Hinman and Favorite (Grow) P.; m. Diana Nutter, Feb. 12, 1960; children—Stephen, Shauna, Thomas, Andrea, Marcia. B.S. in Geology, Brigham Young U., 1959, M.S. in Geology, 1960; Ph.D. in Geology, Columbia U., 1964. Cert. petroleum geologist, Can. Rsch. scientist Conoco Inc., Ponca City, Okla., 1963-65, dir. geologic research, 1965-68; asst. to v.p. Conoco Inc., Houston, 1968-69, dir. geology Western hemisphere, 1973-76; Rocky Mountain div. geologist Conoco Inc., Denver, 1969-73; v.p., gen. mgr. N.Am. exploration Conoco Inc., Houston, 1976-86, v.p. internat. exploration, 1986-88, exec. v.p. worldwide exploration, 1988-90, exec. v.p. exploration and prodn., 1990—. Contbr. articles to profl. jours. Vice pres. Sandalwood Civic Assn., Houston, 1978-79, pres., 1979-80. Mem. Houston Geol. Soc., Am. Assn. Petroleum Geologists (grantee 1981-85, subcom. chmn., rsch. com. 1984-86, mem. selection com. future petroleum geologists 1985-86), Am. Petroleum Inst. (gen. com. exploration affairs 1984-86). Republican. Mem. Ch. of Jesus Christ of Latter-day Saints. Office: Conoco Inc 600 N Dairy Ashford St Houston TX 77079-1121

PITCHER, TONY JOHN, fishery science educator, author; b. Banbury, Eng., Oct. 23, 1944; arrived in Can., 1994; s. Ernest William and Winifred Nellie (Harris) P.; m. Marguerite Elizabeth Tinney; children: Susannah Jane, Tamsin Charlotte Lucy; m. Valerie Marie Gray, May 20, 1994. BA, Oxford (Eng.) U., 1966, DPhil, MA (hon.), 1970. Lectr. biology U. Ulster, Coleraine, Ireland, 1970-78; lectr. zoology U. Wales, Bangor, 1978-84, sr. lectr., 1984-87, reader, 1988-90; prof. fisheries Inst. für Meereskunde, Kiel, Germany, 1987; spl. rsch. fellow renewal resources assessment group Imperial Coll., London, 1990-93; prof., dir. Fisheries Ctr., U. B.C., Vancouver, Can., 1994—; cons. Marine Resources Assessment Ltd., London, 1990-93; hon. prof. U. Concepcion, Chile, 1994—; participant internat. devel. aid projects in fisheries in Angola, Cameroon, Chile, Ecuador, Shana, Indonesia, Kenya, Malawi, Mex., The Philippines, Sri Lanka, Tanzania, Thailand, Uganda, Zambia, Zimbabwe, Australia, Iceland, Italy, Norway, U.K., South Africa. Co-author: Fisheries Ecology, 1982; co-editor: Control Processes in Fish Physiology, 1983, The Behaviour of Fishes, 1986, Collected Reports on Fisheries Research in Malawi, Vol. 1, 1990, Hake: Fisheries Ecology and Markets, 1994, Molecular Genetics in Fisheries, 1994, The Impact of Species Changes in the African Lakes, 1995; editor: The Behaviour of Teleost Fishes, 1986, 2d edit., 1992; asst. editor Jour. Fish Biology, 1981-87; series editor Fish and Fisheries, 1990; founding editor Revs. in Fish Biology and Fisheries, 1991—; contbr. over 100 articles to sci. jours. Achievements include laboratory field and theoretical research on schooling behavior of fishes and its implications for human harvest. Office: U of British Columbia, Fisheries Ctr, Vancouver, BC Canada V6T 1Z4

PITCHUMONI, CAPECOMORIN SANKAR, gastroenterologist, educator; b. Madura, India, Jan. 20, 1938; came to U.S., 1967; s. Sankara and Jaya (Lekshmi) Iyer; m. Prema Iyer, Nov. 11, 1964; children: Sheila, Shoba, Suresh. Student, St. Xavier Coll., India, 1953-55; M.B. B.S., Trivandrum Med. Coll., India, 1959, M.D., 1965. Intern Med Coll., Trivandrum, India, 1961-63; resident in gastroenterology Yale U., 1967-69; N.Y. Med. Coll., 1969-72; practice medicine specializing in gastroenterology N.Y.C., 1972—; asst. prof. medicine Kottayam Med. Coll., India, 1967; asst. prof. medicine N.Y. Med. Coll., 1972-75, assoc. prof., 1975-80, prof. clin. medicine, 1980-85, prof. medicine, 1985—, assoc. prof. preventive and social medicine, 1975-86, prof. community and preventive medicine, 1986—; chief sect. gastroenterology Our Lady of Mercy Med. Ctr., N.Y., 1980—; assoc. dir. medicine Our Lady of Mercy Med. Ctr., N.Y.C., 1985—; program dir. internal medicine, 1987—; dir. medicine, 1992. Contbg author med. textbooks; contbr. articles to profl. jours. Recipient Om Prakash award Indian Soc. Gastroenterology, 1976, Outstanding Scientist of Yr. award MV Spltys., Madras, 1994, Oration award Thangavelu Endowment, 1994. Fellow Royal Coll. Physicians and Surgeons Can., ACP, Am. Coll. Gastroenterology, Am. Coll. Nutrition; mem. Am. Soc. for Gastrointestinal Endoscopy, Assn. Physicians India, Am. Coll. Nuitrition, Am. Gastroent. Assn., India Soc. Gastroenterology (life), Am. Inst. Nutrition, N.Y. Gastroent. Assn., N.Y. Acad. Scis., N.Y. Soc. Gastrointestinal Endoscopy, Am. Soc. for Clin. Nutrition. Home: 178 Fairmount Ave Glen Rock NJ 07452-3014 Office: 600 E 233d St Bronx NY 10466

PITCOCK, JAMES KENT, head and neck surgical oncologist; b. Tachikawa AFB, Japan, Nov. 18, 1951; s. James Kenneth and Helen (Robertson) P.; m. Cynthia H. Zipperly. Student, U. Houston, 1974; MD, Baylor U., 1979. Diplomate Am. Bd. Otolaryngology. Resident in gen. surgery Baylor Coll. Medicine, Houston, 1979-81, resident in otolaryngology, head and neck surgery, 1981-84; clinician Kelsey-Seybold Clinic, P.A., Houston, 1984-85; lectr. head and neck surgery Inst. Laryngology and Otology, U. London, 1985-86; instr., fellow head and neck surgery U. Chgo., 1986-88; asst. prof. dept. otolaryngology, head and neck surgery, chief div. head and neck surgical oncology U. Calif.-Irvine Med. Ctr., Orange, 1988-92; dir. head and neck oncology clin. & rsch. program Clin. Cancer Ctr. U. Calif., Irvine. Author: Oral and Maxillofacial Trauma, 1989, Musculocutaneous Flap Reconstruction of the Head and Neck, 1989, Surgery of the Skull Base, 1989. Fellow Am. Acad. Otolaryngology, Head and Neck Surgery; mem. ACS. Office: Dauphin W EENT Specialists 3701 Dauphin St Mobile AL 36608-1756

PITELKA, FRANK ALOIS, zoologist, educator; b. Chgo., Mar. 27, 1916; s. Frank Joseph and Frances (Laga) P.; m. Dorothy Getchell Riggs, Feb. 5, 1943; children: Louis Frank, Wenzel Karl, Vlasta Kazi Helen. B.S. with highest honors, U. Ill., 1939; summer student, U. Mich., 1938, U. Wash., 1940; Ph.D., U. Calif. at Berkeley, 1946. Mem. faculty U. Calif. at Berkeley, 1944—, prof. zoology, 1958—, chmn. dept., 1963-66, 69-71, Miller research prof., 1965-66; curator birds Mus. Vertebrate Zoology, 1945-63, assoc. dir., 1982—; exec. com. Miller Inst. Basic Rsch. in Sci., 1967-71, chmn., 1967-70; Panel environ. biology NSF, 1959-62, panel polar programs, 1978-80; mem. panel biol. and med. scis., com. polar research Nat. Acad. Scis., 1960-65; research assoc. Naval Arctic Research Lab., Barrow, Alaska, 1951-80; ecol. adv. com. AEC, 1956-1958; adv. coms. U.S. Internat. Biol. Program, 1965-69; mem. adv. com. U.S. Colo. Inst. Arctic and Alpine Research, 1968-73; mem. U.S. Tundra Biome Program, 1968-73, dir., 1968-69; vis. prof. U. Wash. Friday Harbor Labs, summer 1968; mem. U.S. Commn. for UNESCO, 1970-72. Contbr. research papers in field; Editorial bd.: Ecology, 1949-51, 60-62, editor, 1962-64; mem. editorial bd. U. Calif. Press, 1953-62, chmn., 1959-62; mem. editorial bd. Pacific Coast Avifauna, 1947-60, Ecol. Monographs, 1957-60, Systematic Zoology, 1961-64, The Veliger, 1961-85, Studies in Ecology, 1972-84, Current Ornithology, 1980-85; asst. editor Condor, 1943-45, assoc. editor, 1945-52; mem. editorial bd. Studies in Avian Biology, 1979-84, editor, 1984-87. Guggenheim fellow, 1949-50; NSF sr. postdoctoral fellow Oxford (Eng.) U., 1957-58; Research fellow Ctr. for Advanced Study in Behavioral Scis., Stanford, 1971; recipient Disting. Teaching award U. Calif.-Berkeley, 1984; The Berkeley citation, 1985, Alumnus Achievement award, U. Ill., 1993. Fellow Arctic Inst. N.Am., Am. Ornithologists Union (Brewster award 1980), Calif. Acad. Scis., AAAS, Animal Behavior Soc.; mem. Ecol. Soc. Am. (Mercer award 1953, Eminent Ecologist award 1992), Soc. Study Evolution, Cooper Ornithol. Soc. (hon. mem.; pres. 1948-50), Brit. Ecol. Soc., Am. Soc. Mammalogists, Am. Soc.

Naturalists, Am. Inst. Biol. Scis., Western Soc. Naturalists (pres. 1963-64), Nat. Audubon Soc., Sierra Club, Phi Beta Kappa, Sigma Xi. Home: PO Box 9278 Berkeley CA 94709-0278 *My ideas and goals reflect three important sources of influence: strong university teachers; the excellence of colleagues and the setting of my university base; and, most importantly, the unremitting stimulus and challenge of my graduate students to grow with them over years of dramatic changes in biology.*

PITERNICK, ANNE BREARLEY, librarian, educator; b. Blackburn, Eng.; emigrated to Can., 1956, naturalized, 1965; d. Walter and Ellen (Harris) Clayton; m. George Piternick, May 6, 1971. B.A., U. Manchester (Eng.), 1948, F.L.A., 1983. Mem. library staff U. B.C., Vancouver, Can., 1956-66; head sci. div. U. B.C., 1960-61, head social scis. div., 1965-66, prof. Sch. Library, Archival and Info. Studies, 1966-91, prof. emerita, 1991—, assoc. dean Faculty of Arts, 1985-90; mem. Nat. Com. Bibliog. Svcs. Can., 1975-80, chmn. com. on bibliography and info. services for social scis. and humanities, 1981-84; mem. adv. acad. panel Social Scis. and Humanities Research Council, 1981-84; mem. adv. bd. Nat. Libr. Can., 1978-84; mem. Nat. Adv. Com. Culture Stats., 1985-90; organizer Confs. on Can. Bibliography, 1974, 81; pres. Can. Assn. Spl. Librs. Info. Svcs., 1969-70, Can. Libr. Assn., 1976-77. Author articles on electronic info. svcs. and scholarly communication. Recipient Queen's Silver Jubilee medal, 1977, award for Spl. Librarianship Can. Assn. Spl. Librs. and Info. Svcs., 1987, 75th Anniversary medal U.B.C., 1990, Can. 125 medal, 1993. Fellow Council on Library Resources (1980). Home: 1849 W 63rd Ave, Vancouver, BC Canada V6P 2H9

PITINO, RICHARD, college basketball coach; b. N.Y.C., Sept. 18, 1952. Student, U. Mass. Asst. coach U. Hawaii, 1975-76, Syracuse U., 1976-78; coach Boston U., 1978-83; asst. coach N.Y. Knicks, 1983-85, coach, 1987-89; coach Providence U., 1986-87; basketball coach U. Ky., Lexington, 1989—. Author: (with Dick Weiss) Full Court Pressure: A Year in Kentucky Basketball, 1992. Named Coll. Coach of Yr., Sporting News, 1987. Office: U Ky Athletics Dept Basketball Office Lexington KY 40506*

PITKIN, EDWARD THADDEUS, aerospace engineer, consultant; b. Putnam, Conn., Dec. 14, 1930; s. Thaddeus Eugene and Florence Mabel (Brown) P.; m. Clara Lucy Modliszewski, June 13, 1953; children—Gayle Linda, Dale Edward. B.S., U. Conn., 1952; M.S. (Guggenheim fellow), Princeton, 1953; Ph.D. (NASA fellow), UCLA, 1964. Project engr. Astro Div. Marquardt Co., Los Angeles, 1956-59; mgr. space propulsion Astro Div. Marquardt Co., 1959-61; engring. cons. Los Angeles, 1961-64; asso. prof. aerospace engring. U. Conn., Storrs, 1964-70, prof. mech. and aerospace engring., 1970-90, prof. emeritus, 1990—; cons. engr., 1990—; asst. dean U. Conn., Storrs, 1977-87. Contbr. articles to tech. publs. Served as lt. USAF, 1953-55. Asso. fellow AIAA. Mem. Solar Energy Soc. Home: 115 Brookside Ln Mansfield Center CT 06250-1001 Office: U Conn Dep Mech Engring U-139 191 Auditorium Rd Storrs CT 06269

PITKIN, PATRICIA ALBANESE, library administrator; b. Rochester, N.Y., Oct. 6, 1951; d. Patrick and Marie E. (Perrotta) Albanese. B.A., SUNY-Geneseo, 1973, M.L.S., 1974. Database mgr., original cataloger Rochester Inst. Tech., 1974-75, head libr. systems dept., 1975-79, head automated and tech. svcs., 1979-81, acting dir. Wallace Meml. Libr., 1981-83, dir. Wallace Meml. Libr., 1983—; mem. SUNY/OCLC network adv. com. OCLC User Coun., 1992-93. Mem. ALA, NYSERNET (libr. steering com. 1991—), Dataphase Users Group (pres. 1985). Home: 800 E River Rd Rochester NY 14623-1134 Office: Rochester Inst Tech Wallace Meml Library 1 Lomb Memorial Dr Rochester NY 14623-5603

PITKIN, ROY MACBETH, physician, educator; b. Anthon, Iowa, May 24, 1934; s. Roy and Pauline Allie (McBeath) P.; m. Marcia Alice Jenkins, Aug. 17, 1957; children: Barbara, Robert Macbeth, Kathryn, William Charles. B.A. with highest distinction, U. Iowa, 1956, M.D., 1959. Diplomate Am. Bd. Obstetrics & Gynecology, 1967. Intern King County Hosp., Seattle, 1959-60; resident in ob-gyn U. Iowa Hosps. and Clinics, Iowa City, 1960-63; asst. prof. ob-gyn U. Ill., 1965-68; assoc. prof. ob-gyn U. Iowa, Iowa City, 1968-72; prof. U. Iowa, 1972-87, head dept. ob-gyn, 1977-87; prof. UCLA, 1987—, head dept. ob-gyn, 1987-95; mem. residency rev. com. ob-gyn, 1981-87, chmn. 1985-87. Editor-in-chief: Year Book of Obstetrics and Gynecology, 1975-86; editor-in-chief: Clinical Obstetrics and Gynecology, 1979; editor: Obstetrics and Gynecology, 1985. Contbr. articles to med. jours. Served to lt. comdr. M.C. USNR, 1963-65. NIH career awardee, 1972-77. Fellow Royal Obstetricians and Gynecologists (ad eundem); mem. AMA (Goldberger award in clin. nutrition 1982), Am. Coll. Obstetricians and Gynecologists, Am. Gynecol. and Obstet. Soc. (pres. 1994-95), German Soc. Gynecology and Obstetrics (hon. 1992), Ctrl. Assn. Obstetricians and Gynecologists, Soc. Gynecologic Investigation (pres. 1985-86), Soc. Perinatal Obstetricians, Am. Soc. Inst. of Medicine. Presbyterian. Office: UCLA Sch Med Dept Ob-Gyn Los Angeles CA 90024-1740

PITMAN, GROVER ALLEN, music educator; b. Corpus Christi, Tex., Nov. 16, 1943; s. John William and Mae Belle (Reese) P.; m. Jacqueline Kay Dunn, Aug. 29, 1966; children: William Dunn, Karen Joanne. BMus, U. Tex., 1965, MMus, 1967; PhD, Cath. U. Am., 1973. Tchr. Fredericksburg (Tex.) Pub. Schs., 1966-67; instr. Muskingum Coll. New Concord, Ohio, 1967-68; solo hornist U.S. Naval Acad. Band, Annapolis, Md., 1968-72; asst. prof. Winthrop Coll., Rock Hill, S.C., 1972-78; assoc. prof. Westminster Coll., New Wilmington, Pa., 1978—; prin. hornist Austin (Tex.) Symphony Orch., 1961-67, Annapolis (Md.) Symphony Orch., 1968-72; hornist Annapolis Brass Quintet, 1968-72, Youngstown (Ohio) Symphony Orch., 1988—. Grantee Winthrop Found., Rock Hill, 1977. Mem. Pa. Collegiate Bandmasters Assn. (pres. 1983-84), Pa. Music Educators Assn. (pres. dist. 5 1984-85), Rotary (pres. New Wilmington chpt. 1986). Episcopalian. Office: Westminster College New Wilmington PA 16172

PITOFSKY, ROBERT, lawyer, educator, university administrator; b. Paterson, N.J., Dec. 27, 1929; s. Morris and Sadye (Katz) P.; m. Sally Levy, June 4, 1961; children: Alexander, David, Elizabeth. BA, NYU, 1951; LLB, Columbia U., 1954; LLD (hon.), Georgetown U., 1989. Bar: N.Y. 1956, D.C. 1973, U.S. Supreme Ct. 1972. Atty. Dept. Justice, Washington, 1956-57; assoc. Dewey, Ballantine, Bushby, Palmer & Wood, N.Y.C., 1957-63; prof. law NYU, 1963-70; dir. Bur. Consumer Protection, FTC, 1970-73; prof. law Georgetown U. Law Ctr., Washington, 1973-83, 89—, dean, exec. v.p. law ctr. affairs, 1983-89; commr. FTC, 1978-81; of counsel Arnold & Porter, Washington, 1973-78, 81—; guest scholar Brookings Instn., Washington, 1989-90; vis. prof. law Harvard Law Sch., 1975-76; faculty mem. Salzburg (Austria) Seminar in Am. Studies, 1975. Co-author: Cases on Antitrust Law, 1967, Cases on Trade Regulation, 3d edit., 1990; co-editor: Revitalizing Antitrust in Its Second Century, 1991; contbr. articles on consumer protection and antitrust to profl. publs. Served with U.S. Army, 1954-56. Recipient Disting. Service award FTC, 1972; named One of Ten Outstanding Mid-Career Law Profs. Time Mag., 1977. Mem. ABA (mem. coun., antitrust sect. 1986-89), Am. Law Inst., Assn. Am. Law Schs. (anti-trust sect. 1971-72, 82—), Columbia U. Ctr. for Law Econ. Studies (adv. bd. 1975—). Democrat. Jewish. Home: 3809 Blackthorn St Bethesda MD 20815-4905 Office: Georgetown U Law Ctr 1507 Isherwood St NE # 1 Washington DC 20002-5564

PITONIAK, GREGORY EDWARD, state representative; b. Detroit, Mich., Aug. 12, 1954; s. Anthony Edward and Constance Elizabeth (Matuszak) P.; m. Denise Ruth Kadi, Apr. 21, 1979; children: Gregory, Mallory. BA, U. Mich., 1976; Masters, U. N.C., 1980. Adminstrv. asst. Taylor (Mich.) Neighborhood Devel. Com., 1977-78; pers. analyst Downriver Community Conf., Southgate, Mich., 1978-79; dir. client svcs. Econ. Devel. Corp. Wayne County, Dearborn, Mich., 1979-84; exec. dir. Econ. Devel. Corp. Wayne County, Livonia, Mich., 1984-88; dir. econ. dev. Downriver Community Conf., Southgate, Mich., 1988; state rep. Mich. Ho. Reps., Lansing, 1989—. Councilman Taylor City Coun., 1981-88, chmn., 1983-85, 87-88; pres. Mich. Young Dems., 1982-84; treas. 15th Congl. Dist. Dem. Orgn., Taylor, 1988-90. Named Outstanding Young Person, Taylor Jaycees, 1987, State Legislator of Yr., Mich. Credit Union League, 1993. Mem. Am. Econ. Devel. Coun. (cert. econ. developer 1984), Am. Soc. Pub. Adminstrn., Polish Am. Congress, Dem. Club Taylor, KC. Roman Catholic. Home: 9686 Rose St Taylor MI 48180-3046 Office: Mich Ho Rep PO Box 30014 Lansing MI 48909-7514

PITOT, HENRY CLEMENT, III, physician, educator; b. N.Y.C., May 12, 1930; s. Henry Clement and Bertha (Lowe) P.; m. Julie S. Schutten, July 29, 1954; children: Bertha, Anita, Jeanne, Catherine, Henry, Michelle, Lisa, Patrice. BS in Chemistry, Va. Mil. Inst., 1951; MD, Tulane U., 1955, PhD in Biochemistry, 1959, DSc (hon.), 1995. Instr. pathology Med. Sch. Tulane U., New Orleans, 1955-59; postdoctoral fellow McArdle Lab. U. Wis., Madison, 1959-60, mem. faculty Med. Sch., 1960—, prof. pathology and oncology, 1966—, chmn. dept. pathology, 1968-71, acting dean Med. Sch., 1971-73, dir. McArdle Lab., 1973-91. Recipient Borden undergrad. rsch. award, 1955, Lederle Faculty award, 1962, Career Devel. award Nat. Cancer Inst., NIH, 1965, Parke-Davis award in exptl. pathology, 1968, Noble Found. Rsch. award, 1984, Esther Langer award U. Chgo., 1984, Disting. Svc. award Am. Cancer Soc., 1989, Hilldale award U. Wis., 1991, Founders award Chem. Industry Inst. Toxicology, 1993. Fellow AAAS, N.Y. Acad. Scis.; mem. Am. Soc. Cell Biology, Am. Assn. Cancer Rsch., Am. Soc. Biochemistry and Molecular Biology, Am. Chem. Soc., Am. Soc. Investigative Pathology (pres. 1976-77), Soc. Exptl. Biology and Medicine (pres. 1991-93), Soc. Surg. Oncology (Lucy J. Wortham award 1981), Am. Soc. Preventive Oncology, Soc. Toxicology, Soc. Toxicologic Pathologists, Japanese Cancer Soc. (hon.). Roman Catholic. Home: 314 Robin Pkwy Madison WI 53705 Office: U Wis McArdle Lab Cancer Rsch 1400 University Ave Madison WI 53706-1599 *Where and who we are today is the result of those whom we have met and known and loved until now.*

PITSER, TOM G., manufacturing executive, heavy. V.p. Borg Warner at David Transmsm. Pdt., Chgo. Office: Borg Warner at Dvfd Transmsm Pdt 200 S Michigan Ave Chicago IL 60604*

PITSTICK, LESLIE JAMES, food products company executive; b. Jamestown, Ohio, Feb. 10, 1935; s. Harold B. and Helen L. (Gray) P.; m. Sharon N. Berg, Nov. 17, 1956; children: Michele, John. BS in Indsl. Mgmt., Miami U., Oxford, Ohio, 1957; MBA in Bus., Xavier U., Cin., 1970. Systems analyst IBM, Cin., 1957-59; data processing mgr. U.S. Shoe Corp., Cin., 1959-68, Dayco Corp., Dayton, Ohio, 1968-82; owner, mgr. CDCI, Dayton, 1982-83; corp. indsl. systems planner NCR Corp., Dayton, 1983-84; v.p. adminstrn. IAMS Co., Dayton, 1984-85, v.p. mktg. and adminstrn., 1986-87, sr. v.p. ops., 1988-90, sr. v.p. internat., 1991—.

PITT, BERTRAM, cardiologist, consultant; b. Kew Gardens, N.Y., Apr. 27, 1932; s. David and Shirley (Blum) P., m. Elaine Liberstein, Aug. 10, 1962; children—Geoffrey, Jessica, Jillian. BA, Cornell U., 1953; MD, U. Basel, Switzerland, 1959. Diplomate Am. Bd. Internal Medicine, Am. Bd. Cardiology. Intern Beth Israel Hosp., N.Y.C., 1959-60; resident Beth Israel Hosp., Boston, 1960-63; fellow in cardiology Johns Hopkins U., Balt., 1966-67; from instr. to prof. Johns Hopkins U., 1967-77; prof. medicine, dir. div. cardiology U. Mich., Ann Arbor, 1977-91, assoc. chmn. dept. medicine, 1991—. Author: Atlas of Cardiovascular Nuclear Medicine, 1977; editor: Cardiovascular Nuclear Medicine, 1974. Served to capt. U.S. Army, 1963-65. Mem. ACP, Am. Coll. Cardiology, Am. Soc. Clin. Investigation, Assn. Am. Physicians, Am. Physiol. Soc., Am. Heart Assn., Assn. Univ. Cardiologists, Am. Coll. Chest Physicians, Royal Soc. Mich. Home: 24 Ridgeway St Ann Arbor MI 48104-1739 Office: U Mich Divsn Cardiology 1500 E Medical Ctr Dr Ann Arbor MI 48109

PITT, BRAD, actor; b. Okla., Dec. 18, 1963; s. Bill and Jane P. Appearences include: (TV series) Dallas, Another World, Growing Pains, The Image(HBO), Glory Days, Two-Fisted Tales; (TV movie) Too Young To Die?, 1989; (films)Cutting Glass, Happy Together, 1989, Across the Tracks, 1990, Contact, Thelma and Louise, 1991, The Favor, 1992, Johnny Suede, 1992, Cool World, 1992, A River Runs Through It, 1992, Kalifornia, 1993, True Romance, 1993, Interview with the Vampire, 1994, Legends of the Fall, 1994. Office: Creative Artists Agy 9830 Wilshire Blvd Beverly Hills CA 90212*

PITT, EARLE WILLIAM, manufacturing company executive; b. Bklyn., June 4, 1923; s. Earle D. and Catherine T. (O'Neil) P.; B.S. in Mech. Engring., So. Meth. U., 1948; m. Alice M. Altman, Oct. 23, 1946; children—Linda, Karen, Earle, Alice Susan, Margaret. Gen. mgr. Foxboro Co. (Mass.), 1965-68, exec. v.p., 1968-70, pres., 1970-81, chief exec. officer, 1973-88, chmn., 1977—; also dir.; dir. Bank of New England, N.A., Boston, Wyman-Gordon, Worcester, Mass., GenRad, Concord, Mass., Liberty Mut. Ins. Co., Boston, Liberty Mut. Fire Ins. Co., Boston. Bd. dirs., v.p Neponset Valley Found., Norwood, Mass.; trustee St. Michael's Coll., Winooski, Vt.; trustee, past mem. exec. com. New Eng. Coll. Fund. Served with AC, U.S. Army, 1942-46. Mem. Sci. Apparatus Makers Assn., Elec. Mfrs. Club, Instrument Soc. Am. Office: The Foxboro Co Bristol Pk 38 Neponset Ave Foxboro MA 02035-2098

PITT, GEORGE, lawyer; b. Chgo., July 21, 1938; s. Cornelius George and Anastasia (Geocaris) P.; m. Barbara Lynn Goodrich, Dec. 21, 1963 (div. Apr. 1990); children: Elizabeth Nanette, Margaret Leigh; m. Pamela Ann Pittsford, May 19,1990. BA, Northwestern U., 1960, JD, 1963. Bar: Ill. 1963. Assoc. Chapman and Cutler, Chgo., 1963-67; ptnr. Borge and Pitt, and predecessor, 1968-87; ptnr. Katten Muchin & Zavis, Chgo., 1987—. Notes and Comments editor Northwestern U. Law Rev., 1962-63. Served to 1st lt. AUS, 1964. Mem. Ill. State Bar Assn., Eta Sigma Phi, Phi Delta Phi, Phi Gamma Delta. Home: 600 N McClurg Ct Chicago IL 60611-3044 Office: Katten Muchin & Zavis 525 W Monroe St Ste 1600 Chicago IL 60661-3693

PITT, HARVEY LLOYD, lawyer; b. Bklyn., Feb. 28, 1945; s. Morris Jacob and Sara (Sapir) P.; m. Saree Ruffin, Jan. 7, 1984; children: Robert Garrett, Sara Dillard; children from previous marriage: Emily Laura, Jonathan Bradley. BA, CUNY, 1965; JD with honors (Univ. scholar), St. John's U., N.Y.C., 1968. Bar: N.Y. 1969, U.S. Supreme Ct. 1972, D.C. 1979. With SEC, Washington, 1968-78; legal asst. to commr. SEC, 1969; editor Instl. Investor Study, 1970-71; spl. counsel Office Gen. Counsel, 1971-72, chief counsel div. market regulation, 1972-73, exec. asst. to chmn., 1973-75, gen. counsel, 1975-78; mng. ptnr. Fried, Frank, Harris, Shriver & Jacobson, Washington, 1978—; adj. prof. law George Washington U. Nat. Law Ctr., 1974-82, U. Pa. Law Sch., 1983-84, vis. practitioner, 1984, Georgetown U. Law Ctr., 1976-84; comml. arbitrator Am. Arbitration Assn. Contbr. articles to profl. jours. V.p. Glen Haven Civic Assn., Silver Spring, Md., 1972-73, pres., 1974. Recipient Learned Hand award Inst. for Human Rels., 1988. Mem. ABA (chmn. subcom. SEC practice and enforcement, past co-chmn. subcom. state takeover laws), Fed. Bar Assn. (Outstanding Young Lawyer award 1975), Adminstrv. Conf. U.S., Am. Law Inst. (project advisor on restatement law on corp. governance 1981—), Eldwick Homes Assn. (sec. bd. dirs.), Delta Sigma Rho, Tau Kappa Alpha, Phi Delta Phi. Home: 2404 Wyoming Ave NW Washington DC 20008-1643 Office: Fried Frank Harris Shriver & Jacobson 1001 Pennsylvania Ave NW Washington DC 20004-2505 also: Fried Frank Harris Shriver 1 New York Plz New York NY 10004

PITT, HELEN K., nurse, hospital administrator; b. N.Y.C., Oct. 12, 1935; d. Hermann and Cilly (Behr) Tietjen; m. Walter Pitt; children: Judith Frantz, Johanna Michehl, Walter, Albert, William. Diploma, Meth. Hosp. Bklyn., 1956; BA, Met. State U., St. Paul, 1979; MPH, U. Minn., 1981. Asst. dir. Fairview Deaconess Hosp., Mpls.; assoc. hosp. dir. U. Minn. Hosp., Mpls. Kellogg Found. fellow, 1981; Johnson and Johnson fellow to U. Pa. program for nurse execs., 1983. Mem. Am. Orgn. Nurse Execs., Minn. Orgn. Nurse Execs. (pres. 1991), Sigma Theta Tau. Home: 4200 Brunswick Ave S Minneapolis MN 55416-3146

PITT, JOSEPH CHARLES, philosophy educator; b. Hempstead, N.Y., Sept. 12, 1944; fs. Louis Antony and Miriam (Baumstein) P.; m. Donna Hanlon Smith, Feb. 25, 1946. AB in Philosophy, Coll. William and Mary, 1966; MA in Philosophy, U. We. Ont., London, Ont., Can., 1970; PhD, U. We. Ont., 1972. Instr. Va. Poly. Inst. and State U., Blacksburg, 1971-72; asst. prof. Va. Poly. Inst. and State U., 1972-78; vis. asst. prof. U. Pitts., 1974; assoc. prof. Va. Poly. Inst. and State U., 1978-83, prof. philosophy, 1983—; founding dir. Ctr. for Study of Sci. in Soc., Va. Poly. Inst. and State U., 1980-81, dir. humanities, sci. and tech. program, 1979-89, head dept. philosophy, 1992—. Author: Pictures, Images and Conceptual Change, 1981, Galileo, Human Knowledge and the Book of Nature, 1992; editor: New Perspectives on Galileo, 1978, Theories of Explanation, 1988; editor-in-chief Perspectives on Sci.; mem. bd. editors Phiosophy and Tech., 1985-94, Behaviorism, 1985—, History of Philosophy Quar., 1990—, Sci. and Edn.,

1992—; contbr. articles to profl. jours. U. Pitts. Ctr. for Philosophy of Sci. vis. sr. fellow, 1984. Mem. Philosophy of Sci. Assn., Soc. for Philosophy and Tech. (v.p., pres.-elect 1989-91, pres. 1991-93), History of Sci. Soc., Soc. for History of Tech., Am. Philos. Assn., Irish Wolfhound Club Am. (bd. dirs. 1987-95), Sigma Xi. Home: Gavagai Hollow Farm Newport VA 24128 Office: Va Poly Inst and State U Dept Philosophy Blacksburg VA 24061

PITTAWAY, DAVID BRUCE, investment banker, lawyer; b. Kansas City, Mo., Oct. 4, 1951; s. Alan Ralph and Joanne (Kenney) P. BA with highest distinction, U. Kans., 1972; JD, Harvard U., 1975, MBA with high distinction, 1982. Bar: Md., D.C., Pa. Assoc. Morgan, Lewis and Bockius, Washington, 1975-80; cons. Bain and Co., Boston, 1982-85; v.p. strategic planning, asst. to pres. Donaldson, Lufkin and Jenrette, N.Y.C., 1985-86; mng. dir. Castle Harlan, Inc., N.Y.C., 1986—; adj. prof. Columbia U., N.Y.C., 1986—; CFO Branford Chain, Inc., N.Y.C., 1987—; bd. dirs.; bd. dirs. Revere Nat. Corp., Balt., Quantum Restaurant Group, Inc., Roslyn Heights, N.Y., McCormick & Schmick Holdings, Inc., Portland, Oreg. Summerfield scholar, 1972, Baker scholar, 1982. Mem. Harvard Club N.Y., Harvard Club Boston, Phi Beta Kappa. Office: Castle Harlan Inc 150 E 58th St New York NY 10021

PITTELKOW, MARK ROBERT, dermatology educator, researcher; b. Milw., Dec. 16, 1952; s. Robert Bernard and Barbara Jean (Thomas) P.; m. Gail L. Gamble, Nov. 26, 1977; children: Thomas, Cameron, Robert. BA, Northwestern U., 1975; MD, Mayo Med. Sch., 1979. Intern then resident Mayo Grad. Sch., 1979-84; asst. prof. dermatology Mayo Med. Sch., Rochester, Minn., 1984-91, assoc. prof. dermatology, 1991—, assoc. prof. biochemistry and molecular biology, 1992; cons. Mayo Clinic/Found., Rochester, 1984—. Fellow Am. Acad. Dermatology; mem. AAAS, Am. Dermatol. Assn., Soc. Investigative Dermatology, Am. Burn Assn., Am. Soc. Cell Biology, N.Y. Acad. Scis., Chi Psi. Home: 721 12th Ave SW Rochester MN 55902-2027 Office: Mayo Clinic 200 1st St SW Rochester MN 55905-0001

PITTELKOW, RICHARD T., grain company executive; Pres. Lauhoff Grain Co., Danville, Ill. Office: Lauhoff Grain Co PO Box 571 Danville IL 61834-0571

PITTENDRIGH, COLIN STEPHENSON, retired biologist, educator; b. Whitley Bay, Eng., Oct. 13, 1918; came to U.S., 1945; s. Alexander and Florence Hemy (Stephenson) P.; married, May 1, 1943; children: Robin Ann., Sandy. BSc in Botany with 1st class honors, U. Durham, Newcastle, Eng., 1940; PhD in Zoology, Columbia U., 1948; DSc (hon.), U. Newcastle-Upon-Tyne, Eng., 1985. From asst. to prof. biology, prof. zoology Princeton (N.J.) U., 1947-69, dean acad. sch., 1965-69; Bing prof. human biology Stanford (Calif.) U., 1969-76, Miller prof. biology, 1980-84; dir. Hopkins Marine Sta. Stanford (Calif.) U., Pacific Grove, Calif., 1976-84; sr. fellow NSF Ctr. for Biol. Tng. U. Va., Charlottesville, 1992—. Author: (with G.G. Simpson) Textbook of Biology, 1957. Recipient Alexander von Humboldt prize Alexander von Humboldt Found., 1987, Gregor Mendel gold medal Czech Acad. Scis., 1994; Guggenheim fellow, 1959. Mem. NAS, Am. Philos. Soc., Am. Acad. Arts and Scis. Avocation: fly fishing. Home: 2309 Fairway Dr Bozeman MT 59715-5866

PITTI, DONALD ROBERT, financial service company executive; b. N.Y.C., Sept. 15, 1929; s. August and Mary (Vitaglione) P.; m. Grace Allen Curtis, Aug. 14, 1954; children: Gail, Robert. BA, NYU, 1959; postgrad., Adelphi U., 1963-65. Asst. v.p. Standard & Poor's Corp., N.Y.C., 1959-65; v.p. Quotron, Inc., N.Y.C., 1965-67; pres. Wiesenberger & Co., N.Y.C., 1967-76; v.p. John Nuveen & Co., Inc., N.Y.C., 1976-87; pres. Monarch Resources, Inc., N.Y.C., 1987-88; chmn., chief exec. officer Monarch Fin. Svcs., Inc., N.Y.C., 1988-89; pres., chief exec. officer Seligman Fin. Svcs. Inc., N.Y.C., 1989—; trustee Found. Fin. Planning, Atlanta, 1986—. Editor: Handbook of Financial Planning, 1988; contbr. articles to profl. publs. With USN, 1948-49, 50-52. Mem. Internat. Assn. Fin. Planning (pres.), Union League, Manhasset Bay Yacht Club, Met. Opera Club. Avocations: gardening, reading, swimming. Home: 169 Kensett Rd Manhasset NY 11030-2140 Office: Seligman Fin Svcs Inc 100 Park Ave New York NY 10017-5516

PITTINGER, WILBUR BARKE, medical center executive; b. Phila., Mar. 29, 1948; s. Wilbur Barke and Josephine Maria (Pagano) P.; m. Mary S. Manbeck, Sept. 13, 1980; children: Emily Barke, Trevor Manbeck. BA in Sociology with honors, Lycoming Coll., 1970; MA in Sociology, SUNY, Binghamton, 1973. Rsch. assoc. Albert Einstein Med. Ctr. Community Mental Health/Mental Retardation Ctr., Phila., 1973-74, coord. rsch. and evaluation unit, 1974-76; exec. dir. Clin. Faculty Practice Plan Office, Temple U. Sch. Medicine, Phila., 1976-79; chief oper. officer dept. medicine U. Mich. Med. Ctr., Ann Arbor, 1979-89; exec. dir. Hosp. U. Pa., Phila., 1989—; v.p U. Pa. Med. Ctr., Phila., 1989—; bd. dirs. Acad. Med. Ctr. Consortium, sec., treas. 1993; bd. dirs. Univ. Hosp. Consortium; cons. U. Tex. Med. Ch., 1980, U. Mich., 1984, Johns Hopkins Hosp., 1985, U. Calif. San Francisco, 1986; vis. lectr. U. Calif. Med. Ctr., Davis, 1989; speaker Assn. Profs. Medicine, 1989. Contbg. author: Textbook of Internal Medicine, 1989. Chmn. hosp. campaign United Way Southeastern Pa., 1991, 92. Mem. Coun. Teaching Hosps. (exec. com.), Assn. Am. Med. Colls. (speaker 1986), Delaware Valley Hosp. Coun., Hosp. Assn. Pa. Avocations: sailing, gardening. Office: Hosp U Pa 3400 Spruce St Philadelphia PA 19104-4283

PITTMAN, CAROLYN, artist. Recipient Outstanding Artistic Contbn. certificate City Coun. Balt., 1986, Certificate for devoted and caring way of artistically conveying arts to people of Md., 1986, certificate of hon. citizenship Annapolis, 1988, citizen citation City of Balt., 1986, Gov.'s citation Md., 1986; Carolyn Pittman Day proclaimed by City of Balt., 1986, Impressionist Paintings award Womens Power Inc., Md., 1986, Outstanding Achievements award Anne ARundel County, Md., 1988, Exec. citation, Md., 1988. Address: Character Art Inc 2301 Joplea Ave Baltimore MD 21225-1163

PITTMAN, DAVID JOSHUA, sociologist, educator, researcher, consultant; b. Rocky Mount, N.C., Sept. 18, 1927; s. Jay Washington and Laura Frances (Edwards) P. BA, U. N.C., 1949, MA, 1950; postgrad., Columbia U., 1953; PhD, U. Chgo., 1956. Asst. prof. sociology Washington U., St. Louis, 1958-60, assoc. prof., 1960-64, prof., 1964-91, prof. sociology in psychology, 1991-92, prof. psychology, 1992-93, prof. emeritus, 1993—, chmn. dept. sociology, 1976-86, dir. Social Sci. Inst., 1963-76; cons. Jellinek Clinic, Amsterdam, The Netherlands, 1965-68, HEW, Washington, 1977-85, Wine Inst., 1985-94; mem. sci. adv. com. Distilled Spirits Coun., Washington, 1976-86; field editor social scis. Jour. Study Alcoholism, 1985-92, mem. editorial bd., 1992—; Dent Meml. lectr. U. London, 1989. Author: Revolving Door: A Study of Chronic Police Case Inebriates, 1958, The Drug Scene in Great Britain, 1967, Primary Prevention of Alcoholism, 1980; editor: Society, Culture and Drinking Patterns, 1962, Alcoholism, 1967, Society, Culture and Drinking Patterns Reexamined, 1991. Bd. dirs. Nat. Gay and Lesbian Task Force, 1993—; pres. N.Am. Assn. Alcoholism Programs, 1965-67; chmn. 28th Internat. Congress on Alcohol and Alcoholism, Washington, 1968, Mo. Adv. Coun. on Alcoholism and Drug Abuse, Jefferson City, 1972-75, 87-91; mem. Mo. Mental Health Commn., Jefferson City, 1975-78. Recipient Page One Civic award St. Louis Newspaper Guild, 1967, Bronze Key St. Louis Coun. on Alcoholism, 1976, Silver Key Nat. Coun. on Alcoholism, N.Y.C., 1978; spl. fellow NIMH, 1966. Fellow Am. Sociol. Soc.; mem. Soc. Study Social Problems (chmn. alcoholism com. 1957-59, Disting. Sr. Scholar award 1993), Internat. Coun. on Alcohol and Addictions (exec. com. 1968-84), Am. Sociol. Assn. (chmn. alcohol and drugs sect. 1992), Phi Beta Kappa, Sigma Xi, Omicron Delta Kappa. Episcopalian. Avocations: collecting elephant replicas, collecting political memorabilia. Office: Washington U Psychol Dept Box 1125 One Brookings Dr Saint Louis MO 63130

PITTMAN, EDWIN LLOYD, state supreme court justice; b. Hattiesburg, Miss., Jan. 2, 1935; s. Lloyd H. and Pauline P.; m. Barbara Peel, Aug. 24, 1957 (dec. Dec. 1984); children: Melanie, Win, Jennifer. B.S., U. So. Miss.; J.D., U. Miss. 1960. Bar: Miss. Practiced law until, 1964; mem. Miss. Senate, 1964-72; treas. State of Miss., Jackson, 1976-80, sec. of state, 1980-84; atty. gen. State of Miss., 1984-88; justice Supreme Ct. Miss., Jackson, 1989—. Served to 2d lt., Inf. U.S. Army. Mem. U. Miss. Alumni Assn., U. So. Miss. Alumni Assn., Miss. Jaycees (past state dir.), ABA, South Central

Miss. Bar Assn. Democrat. Baptist. Clubs: Lions, Masons. Office: Miss Supreme Ct PO Box 117 Jackson MS 39205-0117

PITTMAN, JACQUELYN, mental health nurse, nursing educator; b. Pensacola, Fla., Dec. 22, 1932; d. Edward Corry Sr. and Hettie Oean (Wilson) P. BS in Nursing Edn., Fla. State U., 1958; MA, Columbia U., 1959, EdD, 1974. Physician asst. Med. Ctr. Clinic, Pensacola, 1953-55; clin. instr., asst. dir. nursing svc. Sacred Heart Hosp., Pensacola, 1955-56; instr.psychiatric nurse Fla. State Hosp., Chattahoochee, 1958, Pensacola Community Coll., 1959-60, 62-63; chmn. div. nursing Gulf Coast Community Coll., Panama City, Fla., 1963-66; asst. prof. U. Tex., Austin, 1970-72, assoc. prof., 1972-80; prof. nursing, coord. curriculum and teaching Grad. Program La. State U. Med. Ctr. Sch. Nursing, New Orleans, 1980—; curriculum cons. Nicholls State U., Thibodaux, La., 1982, Our Lady of the Lake Sch. Nursing, Baton Rouge, 1983; rsch. liaison So. Bapt. Hosp., New Orleans, 1987-89, Med. Ctr. La., 1992—; mem. Sci. Misconduct Inquiry com. La. State U. Med. Ctr., 1992—; adv. bd. Sister Henrietta Guyot Professorship. Tchr. Christian edn. program for mentally retarded St. Ignatius Martyr Ch., 1979-80; tchr. initiation team Rite of Christian Initiation of Adults, Our Lady of the Lake Cath. Ch., Mandeville, La., 1983-86; ethics com., bd. trustee Hotel Dieu Hosp., New Orleans, 1987-91; v.p. bd. dirs. St. Tammany Guidance Ctr., Inc., Mandeville, 1987-91; mem. Dem. Nat. Comm., Presdl. Task Force, 1992, Ctr. for Study of Presidency; judge Internat. Sci. and Engring. Fair Assn. 1990, 92; del. La. State Nurses' Assn. State Conv., 1992, 94; assoc. Libr. of Congress. mem. ANA, LWV, N.Y. Acad. Scis., Acad. Polit. Sci., Libr. of Congress Assocs., Nat. Trust for Hist. Preservation, La. Endowment for Humanities, La. Nurses assn. (archivist 1987—, state task force com. to preserve hist. documents 1987—), So. Nursing Rsch. Soc., Nat. League Nursing, Boston U. Nursing Archives, Women's Inner Cir. Achievement N.Am. Cmtys., Internat. Order of Merit, World Found. Successful Women, Wilson Ctr. Assocs., Kappa Delta Pi, Sigma Theta Tau. Democrat. Roman Catholic. Avocations: swimming, golf, travel, reading, Louisiana history. Address: 204 Woodridge Blvd Mandeville LA 70471-2604 Office: La State U Med Ctr 1900 Gravier St New Orleans LA 70112-2262

PITTMAN, JAMES ALLEN, JR., endocrinologist, dean emeritus, educator; b. Orlando, Fla., Apr. 12, 1927; s. James Allen and June C. (Garretson) P.; m. Constance Ming-Chung Shen, Feb. 19, 1955; children—James Clinton, John Merrill. BS, Davidson Coll., 1948; MD, Harvard, 1952; DSc (hon.), Davidson Coll., 1980, U. Ala., Birmingham, 1984. Intern, asst. resident medicine Mass. Gen. Hosp., Boston, 1952-54; teaching fellow medicine Harvard U., 1953-54; clin. assoc. NIH, Bethesda, Md., 1954-56; instr. medicine George Washington U., 1955-56; chief resident U. Ala. Med. Ctr., Birmingham, 1956-58, instr. medicine, 1956-59, asst. prof., 1959-62, assoc. prof., 1962-64, prof. medicine, 1964—, dir. endocrinology and metabolism div., 1962-71, co-chmn. dept. medicine, 1969-73, prof. physiology and biophysics, 1967—; dean U. Ala. Med. Ctr. (Sch. Medicine), 1973-92; asst. chief med. dir. rsch. and edn. in medicine U.S.A. VA, 1971-73; prof. medicine Georgetown U. Med. Sch., Washington, 1971-73; mem. endocrinology study sect. NIH, 1963-67; mem. pharmacology, endocrinology fellowships rev. coms., 1967-68; chmn. Liaison Com. Grad. Med. Edn., 1976; mem. Grad. Med. Edn. Adv. Com., 1976-78, HHS Coun. on Grad. Med. Edn., 1986-90; mem. nat. adv. rsch. resources coun. NIH, 1991—. Author: Diagnosis and Treatment of Thyroid Diseases, 1963; Contbr. articles in field to profl. jours. Master ACP; fellow Am. Coll. Endocrinology; mem. Assn. Am. Physicians, Endocrine Soc., Am. Assn. Clin. EndocrinologyAm. Thyroid Assn., N.Y. Acad. Scis. (life), Soc. Nuclear Medicine, Am. Diabetes Assn., Am. Chem. Soc., Wilson Ornithol. Club (life), Am. Ornithologists Union, Am. Fedn. Clin. Research (pres. So. sect., mem. nat. council 1962-66), So. Soc. Clin. Investigation (Founder's medal 1993), Harvard U. Med Alumni Assn. (pres. 1986-88, mem. com. on grad. med. evaluation 1987-90), Phi Beta Kappa, Alpha Omega Alpha, Omicron Delta Kappa. Office: U Ala-Sch of Med Disting Prof CAMS 75 SDB Birmingham AL 35294-0007 *I hope that each person I meet leaves the encounter better for it.*

PITTMAN, RICHARD FRANK, JR., newspaper publisher; b. Tampa, Fla., Mar. 12, 1923; s. Richard Frank and Jette (Robinson) P.; m. Dada Andrews, Apr. 15, 1952; children: Richard Andrews, Dada Katherine. B.S. in Bus. Adminstrn., U. Fla., 1944. With IRS, 1946; with Tribune Co., Tampa, 1946—; bus. mgr. Tribune Co., 1965-69, v.p., gen. mgr., 1970-77; pub. Tampa Tribune and Tampa Times, 1978—. Also pres., dir. Elder 1st Presbyn. Ch., 1976-79; past pres. Tampa chpt. ARC; campaign chmn., pres., dir., treas. United Way of Greater Tampa; past v.p. bd. dirs. United Cerebral Palsy; vice chmn. S.W. Fla. Blood Bank; bd. dirs. Community Coordinating Council, Fla. Gulf Coast Symphony Assn., Family Service Assn., Sta. WEDU, Fla. Council of 100; trustee St. Joseph's Hosp. Served to 1st lt., Tank Corps, AUS, 1942-46, PTO. Recipient Vol. Activist award, 1977, Citizen of Yr. award, 1982, Sales & Mktg. Execs. award, 1982. Mem. Am. Newspaper Pubs. Assn., So. Newspaper Pubs. Assn., Fla. Press Assn., Inst. Newspaper Controllers and Finance Officers, Tampa C. of C. (dir., mem. exec. com.), Pi Kappa Alpha. Clubs: Rotary (Tampa) (past pres.), Tampa Yacht and Country (Tampa) (commodore), Univ. (Tampa) (past pres.), Merrymakers (Tampa) (past pres.), Tower (Tampa) (dir.); Ye Mystic Krewe of Gasparilla (past king and capt.). Home: 2405 S Ardson Pl Apt 703A Tampa FL 33629-7326 Office: Tribune Co 202 S Parker St Tampa FL 33606-2308

PITTMAN, ROBERT TURNER, retired newspaper editor; b. Gates, N.C., Sept. 24, 1929; s. Thomas Everett and Lillian (Turner) P.; m. Ruth Fike, Aug. 25, 1956; children—Laura Emily, Mary Ann, Lillian Elizabeth. B.A., Washington and Lee U., 1951; M.A., U. N.C., 1957. Reporter Times Dispatch, Richmond, Va., 1951; editor, pub. Daily Ranger, Glendive, Mont., 1957-58; writer editorials Times Union, Jacksonville, Fla., 1958-63; editorial editor Times, St. Petersburg, Fla., 1963-92; dir. Times Pub. Co., 1968-92; trustee Poynter Inst. Media Studies, St. Petersburg, 1978-92. Editor (jour.) Masthead, 1980, 81. Active St. Petersburg Charter Revision Com., 1992-93; dir. Fla. Bar Found., 1994-96; Lt. (j.g.) USNR, 1951-55. Recipient Pinellas Civil Liberties award, 1993; U. N.C.-Chapel Hill scholarship established in honor, 1994. Mem. Am. Soc. Newspaper Editors, Nat. Conf. Editorial Writers (pres. 1978, life), Nat. Conf. Editorial Writers Found. Inc. (pres. 1984). Methodist. Home: 736 18th Ave NE Saint Petersburg FL 33704

PITTMAN, ROBERT WARREN, entertainment executive; b. Jackson, Miss., Dec. 28, 1953; s. Warren E. and Lanita (Hurdle) P.; m. Sandra Hill, July 27, 1979; 1 son, Robert Thomas. Student, Millsaps Coll., 1971-72, Oakland U., 1972-73, U. Pitts., 1973-74; AMP, Harvard U., 1984-85. Disc jockey Sta. WJDX-FM, Jackson, Miss., 1970-72, Sta. WRIT, Milw., 1972; research dir. Sta. WDRQ, Detroit, 1972-73; program dir. Sta. WPEZ, Pitts., 1973-74, Stas. WMAQ-WKRZ, NBC Radio, Chgo., 1974-74; Sta. WNBC, N.Y.C., 1977-79; exec. producer Album Tracks, NBC TV, N.Y.C., 1977-78; dir., v.p., then sr. v.p. Warner Amex Satellite Entertainment Co. (now MTV Networks, Inc.), N.Y.C., 1979-82; exec. v.p., chief oper. officer Warner Amex Satellite Entertainment Co., N.Y.C., 1983-85, pres., chief exec. officer, 1985-86; pres., chief exec. officer Quantum Media, Inc., N.Y.C., 1986-89; exec. advisor Warner Communications, Inc., N.Y.C., 1989-90; pres., chief exec. officer Time Warner Enterprises, N.Y.C., 1990—, chmn. Ct. TV, 1991—; chmn., CEO, Six Flags Entertainment, 1992—; bd. dirs. Atari Games Corp., 3-Do. Bd. dirs. One to One Found., N.J. Performing Arts Ctr., N.Y.C. Ballet, Hospitality Franchise Systems, Inc., N.Y. Shakespeare Festival, chmn., 1987-94. Recipient Program Mgr. of Yr. Billboard, 1977, Program Dir. of Yr. Hall Radio Report, 1978, Entrepreneur award White House SB Conf., 1986, Golden Plate award Am. Acad. Achievement, 1990, medal of Excellence Miss. U. Women, 1992, Vision award Retinitis Pigmentosa International, 1992, Lifetime Achievement Internat. Monitor award Internat. Teleproduction Soc., 1993; named Innovator of Yr. Performance Mag., 1981, Humanitarian of Yr., AMC, 1984, Time Mag. Man of Yr. runner-up, 1984, Esquire Mag. Under 40 Leadership, 1985; named one of Pioneers of New Am. Start-Up, Success mag., one of five Original Thinkers of 80s, Life mag. Methodist. Office: Time Warner Enterprises 75 Rockefeller Plz New York NY 10019 also: NY Shakespeare Festival Joseph Papp Pub Theater 425 Lafayette St New York NY 10003

PITTMAN, STEUART LANSING, lawyer; b. Albany, N.Y., June 6, 1919; s. Ernest Wetmore and Estelle Young (Romeyn) P.; children by previous marriage—Andrew Pinchot, Nancy Steuart, Rosamond Pinchot, Tamara Pickering; m. Barbara Milburn White, Mar. 29, 1958; children—Patricia Milburn, Steuart Lansing, Anne Romeyn. Grad., St. Paul's Sch., Concord,

N.H., 1937; B.A., Yale U., 1941, LL.B., 1948. Bar: N.Y. 1948, D.C. 1954. With Pan Am. Airways Africa Ltd., Cairo, 1941-42, China Nat. Aviation Co., Calcutta, India, 1942; with firm Cravath, Swaine & Moore, N.Y.C., 1948-50; with govt. agys. ECA, Mut. Security Agy. and FOA, 1950-54; ptnr. Shaw, Pittman, Potts & Trowbridge (and predecessors), Washington, 1954-61, 64—; asst. sec. of def., 1961-64; Cons. 2d Hoover Commn., 1954-55, Dept. State, 1955, Devel. Loan Fund, 1958-59; sr. fellow Inst. of Def. Analysis. Bd. dirs. HudsonInst., Chesapeake Environ. Protection Assn.; mem. Atlantic Coun. Served to 1st lt. USMCR, World War II, CBI. Decorated Silver Star. Mem. Met. Club (Washington). Office: Shaw Pittman Potts & Trowbridge 2300 N St NW Washington DC 20037-1122

PITTMAN, VIRGIL, federal judge; b. Enterprise, Ala., Mar. 28, 1916; s. Walter Oscar and Annie Lee (Logan) P.; m. Floy Lasseter, 1944; children—Karen Pittman Gordy, Walter Lee. B.S., U. Ala., 1939, LL.B., 1940. Bar: Ala. bar 1940. Spl. agt. FBI, 1940-44; practice law Gadsden, Ala., 1946-51; judge Ala. Circuit Ct., Circuit 16, 1951-66; U.S. dist. judge Middle and So. Dist. Ala., 1966-71; chief judge U.S. Dist. Ct. for Ala. So. Dist. 1971-81, sr. judge, 1981—; periodically sits as judge U.S. Ct. Appeals 11th Cir., 1981—; lectr. bus. law, econs. and polit. sci. U. Ala. Center, Gadsden, 1948-66. Author: Circuit Court Proceedings in Acquisition of a Tract of Right of Way, 1959, A Judge Looks at Right of Way Condemnation Proceedings, 1960, Technical Pitfalls in Right of Way Proceedings, 1961. Mem. Ala. Bd. Edn., 1951; trustee Samford U., 1974-90, 92—. Lt. (j.g.) USN, 1944-46. Mem. Ala. State Bar, Etowah County Bar Assn. (pres. 1949), Omicron Delta Kappa. Democrat. Baptist. Office: US Dist Ct PO Box 465 Mobile AL 36601-0465

PITTMAN, WILLIAM CLAUDE, electrical engineer; b. Pontotoc, Miss., Apr. 22, 1921; s. William Claude and Maude Ella (Bennett) P.; m. Eloise Savage, Apr. 20, 1952; children: Patricia A. Pittman Ready, William Claude III, Thomas Allen. BSEE, Miss. State Coll., 1951, MSEE, 1957. From electronic engr. to supr. elec. engring. dept. U.S. Army Labs., Redstone Arsenal, Ala., 1951-59; supr. electronic engr. to aero. engring. supr. NASA/Marshall Space Flight Ctr., 1960; electronic engr. Army Missile Labs., 1962-82; program mgr. Army Labs. and R&D Ctr., Redstone Arsenal, 1982—; organizer numerous sci. and tech. confs. Author patents, reports, papers. Sgt. USMC, 1940-46, PTO. Recipient Medal of Honor, DAR, Meritorious Civilian Svc. award Dept. Army, 1993. Fellow IEEE (assoc.; chmn. Miss.-Ala. chpt. 1981-82, Martin Schilling award 1980); mem. IEEE (sr.), NSPE, First Marine Div. Assn., DAV, IRE (chmn. Huntsville sect. 1957-58), Madison Hist. Soc., SAR (pres. Tenn. Valley chpt. 1984-85, Ala. Soc. 1990-91, Cert. 1991, Patriot medal), Tau Beta Pi, Phi Kappa Phi, Kappa Mu Epsilon. Avocations: history, genealogy. Home: 704 Desoto Rd SE Huntsville AL 35801-2032 Office: US Army Missile Command Redstone Arsenal AL 38598-5253

PITTS, BARBARA TOWLE, accountant; b. St. Paul, Minn., Nov. 8, 1944; d. James Francis and Helen (Gorman) Towle; m. E.R. Pitts, Oct. 19, 1965; 1 child, Paris Tucker Pitts. BSBA, U. Ala., 1980. CPA, Wash., Tenn. Prin. Barbara M. Pitts Assocs., Fayetteville, Tenn., 1982-90, Barbara M. Pitts CPA, Seattle, 1990—. Bd. dirs. United Way Lincoln County, Fayetteville, 1989, Lincoln County Bd. Edn., Fayetteville, 1988-90; mem. planning com. Tenn. Hist. Soc., Nashville, 1989. Recipient Cert. of Recognition Tenn. Main St. Program, 1989; named Woman of Yr. Fayetteville Bus. and Profl. Women, 1988. Mem. AICPA, Wash. Soc. CPA, Northwest Watercolor Soc. (treas.). Home: 3515 E Marion St Seattle WA 98122-5258

PITTS, BILL, museum director; b. Castleton, Kans., Jan. 7, 1934. BA, Northwestern State Coll., Alva, Okla., 1957; postgrad., Northwestern State Coll., We. Wash. Coll. Edn., Portland (Oreg.) State Coll. Curator Northwestrn State Coll. Mus., Alva, Okla., 1964-74; dir., curator Santa Fe Trail Ctr., Larned, Kans., 1974-83; dir. State Mus. of Okla. Hist. Soc., Oklahoma City, 1983—; adj. instr. Emporia (Kans.) State U., 1978-83; grant evaluator Inst. Mus. Services, 1980—. Mem. coordinating com. Promotion of Kans. History, 1979-83; mem. council Kans. Com. for Humanities, 1980-83; panel mem. Okla. Arts and Humanities Council, 1966-73; mem. Okla. Hist. Soc. Mem. Am. Assn. Mus. (past Okla. rep.), Am. Assn. State and Local History, Mountain-Plains Mus. Conf., Okla. Mus. Assn. (regional rep. 1984-85, past pres.), Kans. Mus. Assn. (past pres.), Santa Fe Trail Assn. (pres. 1991—), Westerners Internat., Toastmasters Internat. Home: 3824 N Oak Grove Dr # 841 Midwest City OK 73110-3558 Office: Okla Hist Soc Hist Bldg 2100 N Lincoln Blvd Oklahoma City OK 73105-4915

PITTS, JAMES ATWATER, financial executive; b. Greenwich, Conn., Apr. 8, 1940; s. Jeremiah Patrick and Mary Louise (McGregor) P.; m. Noreen Mary Kiggins, July 20, 1963; children: Paul, Andrew, Sarah. BBA with honors, Niagara U., 1962; MBA, U. Conn., 1971. CPA, N.Y. Staff acct. Price Waterhouse, Stamford, Conn., 1962; tax specialist Deloitte Haskins & Sells, Rochester, N.Y., 1965-68; div. contr. Xerox Corp., Stamford, 1968-76; asst. corp. contr. Digital Equipment Corp., Maynard, Mass., 1976-81; v.p., corp. contr. Data Gen. Corp., Westboro, Mass., 1981-86; exec. v.p. fin. adminstrn. and strategic planning Cullinet Software, Inc., Westwood, 1986-88; v.p., chief fin. officer Bain & Co. Inc., Boston, 1988-91; sr. v.p. fin. and adminstrn., treas., and chief fin. officer Clean Harbors Inc., 1992. Chmn. Sudbury (Mass.) Town Fin. Com., 1984; v.p., mem. exec. com. Children's Mus. Boston, 1984—; bd. dirs. Mus. Wharf Inc., 1988—, Lake Winniepesaukee Assn., Wolfeboro, N.H.; chmn. Sudbury Long Range Capital Expenditures Com., 1981; trustee Regional Conservation Trust, Meridith, N.H. With U.S. Army, 1963-64, USAR, 1965-90, Desert Storm, 1991. Decorated Meritorious Svc. medal, 1991; recipient Internat. Exec. Mgmt. award Internat. Mgmt. Inst. U. Geneva, 1980. Mem. AICPA, Conn. CPA Soc., N.Y. Soc. CPA, Fin. Execs. Inst., Harvard Bus. Sch. Assn. Boston (bd. govs. 1992, pres. 1992), Res. Officers Assn. (life), Soc. Mil. Compts., Algonquin Club, Bald Peak Colony Club, Officers Club. Home: 282 Beacon St Boston MA 02116-1152 Office: Clean Harbors PO Box 9137 1200 Crown Colony Dr Quincy MA 02269-9137

PITTS, LEONARD GARVEY, JR., columnist, writer; b. Orange, Calif., Oct. 11, 1957; s. Leonard Garvey and Agnes (Rowan) P.; m. Marilyn Vernice Pickens, June 27, 1981; children: Markise Pickens, Monique Pickens; (stepchildren) Marlon, Leonard, Onjél. BA English, U. So. Calif., 1977. Editor, writer Soul Mag., L.A., 1976-80; writer KFWB Radio, L.A., 1980-83; editor Radioscope, L.A., 1983-86; writer Westwood One Inc., Culver City, Calif., 1989-91; columnist, writer Miami (Fla.) Herald, 1991—. Writer, co-producer (broadcast) King: From Atlanta to the Mountaintop, 1986 (CEBA award 1987), (documentary) Young Black Men: A Lost Generation?, 1990 (Armstrong award 1991); writer, producer (documentary) Who We Are, 1988 (CEBA award 1989). Recipient Internat. Radio Festival award, 1991, Nat. Headliner award Arts critcism, 1991. Mem. Fla. Soc. Newspaper Editors (award arts criticism), Nat. Headliners, Am. Assn. Sunday and Feature Editors (award arts criticism 1991). Democrat. Baptist. Avocations: computer strategy games, reading. Office: Miami Herald One Herald Plaza Miami FL 33132

PITTS, ROBERT EUGENE, JR., marketing educator, consultant; b. Griffin, Ga., Feb. 12, 1948; s. Robert Eugene and Oree Francis (Brown) P.; m. Cheryl Ann Belew, May 31, 1968. BBA, Ga. State U., 1970, M in Bus. Info. Systems, 1972; PhD, U. S.C., 1977. Account sect. leader Gen. Electric Corp., Atlanta, 1970-72; instr. mktg. Jacksonville (Ala.) State U., 1972-74; assoc. dir. consumer panel U. S.C., Columbia, 1974-77; asst. prof. mktg. U. Notre Dame, South Bend, Ind., 1977-82; assoc. prof. mktg. U. Miss., Oxford, 1982-83, dir. bur. bus. and econ. research, 1983-85; prof., chmn. dept. mktg. DePaul U., Chgo., 1985—, dir. Kellstadt Ctr. Mktg. Analysis and Planning; cons. in mktg. strategy; expert legal witness in mktg. Author books on bank mktg.; contbr. articles on personal values in mktg. and pub. policy issues to profl. jours. Fellow Am. Mktg. Assn., Assn. Mktg. Sci.; mem. Decision Sci. Inst., So. Mktg. Assn. Avocations: running, akido. Office: DePaul U 243 S Wabash Ave Chicago IL 60604-2302

PITTS, ROBERT LYNN, automotive company executive; b. Los Angeles, Feb. 7, 1948; s. Leo Willard and Jane Ann (Rawson) P.; m. Helen Frances Donohoe, May 3, 1969; children: Brian M., Laura D. BBA, Calif. State U., Long Beach, 1970, MBA, 1973. Fin. mgr. Toyota Motor Sales, USA, Inc., Torrance, Calif., 1971-84; gen. mgr. Toyota Motor Credit Corp., Torrance, 1984—. Mem. Nat. Assn. Accts., Beta Gamma Sigma. Republican. Roman

Catholic. Avocations: camping, skiing, motorcycling, windsurfing. Home: 4123 Quinlin Dr Palos Verdes Peninsula CA 90274-3945 Office: Toyota Motor Sales USA Inc 19001 S Western Ave Torrance CA 90509

PITTS, TERENCE RANDOLPH, curator, museum director; b. St. Louis, Feb. 5, 1950; s. Benjamin Randolph and Barbara Avalon (Gilliam) P.; m. Judith Ellen Brown, Oct. 21, 1979; children: Jacob Richard, Rebecca Suzanne. BA, U. Ill., 1972, MLS, 1974, MA in Art History U. Ariz., 1986. Registrar Ctr. for Creative Photography, Tucson, 1976-77, curator, 1978-88, dir., 1989—; cons. Art and Architecture Thesaurus, Getty Mus., 1984—. Author: (with others) George Fiske: Yosemite Photographer, 1981, Edward Weston: Color Photography; book reviews Picturescope Mag., 1983-86; author: exhibition catalogs: Four Spanish Photographers, 100 Years of Photography in the American West, Photography in the American Grain; contbr. reviews to mags. NEA fellow, 1983; travel grantee Nat. Mus. Act, 1979, rsch. grantee U. Ariz., 1983.

PITTS, THOMAS E., lawyer; b. Providence, R.I., May 21, 1947. BA magna cum laude, Yale U., 1969; JD magna cum laude, U. Pa., 1976. Bar: R.I. 1976, U.S. Dist. Ct. R.I. 1976, U.S. Ct. Appeals (1st cir.) 1978, N.Y. 1984, U.S. Dist. Ct. (so. dist.) N.Y. 1985. Ptnr. Sidley & Austin, N.Y.C. Contbr. articles to profl. jours. Mem. N.Y. County Lawyers Assn. (com. bankruptcy 1985—), R.I. Bar Assn. (debtor's and creditor's rights com. 1984—), Order of Coif, Phi Beta Kappa. Office: Sidley & Austin 875 3rd Ave New York NY 10022-6225

PITTS, VIRGINIA M., human resources executive; b. Boston, Nov. 22, 1953; d. Harold Francis and Connie (Caico) Cummings; m. Daniel J. Pitts, Mar. 12, 1977. Student, Northeastern U., 1985, Lesley Coll. Adminstrv. asst. J. Baker Inc., Hyde Park, Mass., 1980-82, fin. adminstr., 1982-84, dir. human resources, 1984—, 1st sr. v.p., 1991—; trustee New Eng. Joint Bd. AFL-CIO, Quincy, Mass., 1984-89; guest lectr. Aquinas Jr. Coll.; mem. bd. dirs. Boston Crusaders, Drum & Bugle Corps. Instr. Boston Crusaders Drum and Bugle Corps, other marching bands, Mass., R.I., Maine, N.H., 1973-85; regional v.p. 210 Charitable Assn. Watertown, Mass., 1989-90; bd. dirs. Handi-Kids, Boston Crusaders Drum and Bugle Corps; guest lectr. Aquinas Jr. Coll., Milton, Mass. Mem. Am. Mgmt. Assn., Am. Compensation Assn. (cert. profl.), Soc. Human Resource Mgrs. Avocations: competitive horseback riding, gardening. Office: J Baker Inc 555 Turnpike St Canton MA 02021-2724

PITZER, KENNETH SANBORN, chemist, educator; b. Pomona, Calif., Jan. 6, 1914; s. Russell K. and Flora (Sanborn) P.; m. Jean Mosher, July 1935; children—Ann, Russell, John. B.S., Calif. Inst. Tech., 1935; Ph.D., U. Calif., 1937; D.Sc., Wesleyan U., 1962; LL.D., U. Calif. at Berkeley, 1963, Mills Coll., 1969. Instr. chemistry U. Calif., 1937-39, asst. prof., 1939-42, asso. prof., 1942-45, prof., 1945-61, asst. dean letters and sci., 1947-48, dean coll. chemistry, 1951-60; pres., prof. chemistry Rice U., Houston, 1961-68, Stanford, Calif., 1968-70; prof. chemistry U. Calif. at Berkeley, 1971—; tech. dir. Md. Rsch. Lab. for OSRD, 1943-44; dir. research U.S. AEC, 1949-51, mem. gen. adv. coun., 1958-65, chmn., 1960-62; Centenary lectr. Chem. Soc. Gt. Britain, 1978; mem. adv. bd. U.S. Naval Ordnance Test Sta., 1956-59, chmn., 1958-59; mem. commn. chem. thermo-dynamics Internat. Union Pure and Applied Chemistry, 1953-61; mem. Pres.'s Sci. Adv. Com., 1965-68; dir. Owens-Ill., Inc., 1967-86. Author: (with others) Selected Values of Properties of Hydocarbons, 1947, Quantum Chemistry, 1953, (with L. Brewer) Thermodynamics, 2d edit., 1961, Activity Coefficients in Electrolyte Solutions, 2d edit., 1992, Molecular Structure and Statistical Thermodynamics, 1993, Thermodynamics, 3rd edit., 1995; editor: Prentice-Hall Chemistry series, 1955-61; contbr. articles to profl. jours. Trustee Pitzer Coll., 1966—; Mem. program com. for phys. scis. Sloan Found., 1955-60. Recipient Precision Sci. Co. award in petroleum chemistry, 1950, Clayton prize Instn. Mech. Engrs., London, 1958, Priestley medal Am. Chem. Soc., 1969, Nat. medal for sci., 1975, Robert A. Welch award, 1984, Clark Kerr award U. Calif., Berkeley, 1991; named to Outstanding Young Men, U.S. Jaycees, 1950; named to Hall of Fame of Alpha Chi Sigma, 1994; Guggenheim fellow, 1951. Fellow Am. Nuclear Soc., Am. Inst. Chemists (Gold Medal award 1976), Am. Acad. Arts and Scis., Am. Phys. Soc.; mem. AAAS, NAS (councilor 1964-67, 73-76), Am. Chem. Soc. (award pure chemistry 1943, Gilbert N. Lewis medal 1965, Williard Gibbs medal 1976), Faraday Soc., Geochem. Soc., Am. Philos. Soc., Chem. Soc. (London), Am. Coun. Edn., Chemists Club (hon.), Bohemian Club, Cosmos Club of Washington. Clubs: Chemists (hon.), Bohemian; Cosmos (Washington). Home: 12 Eagle Hl Kensington CA 94707-1408 Office: U Calif Dept Chemistry Berkeley CA 94720

PIVEN, FRANCES FOX, political scientist, educator; b. Calgary, Alta., Can., Oct. 10, 1932; came to U.S., 1933, naturalized, 1953; d. Albert and Rachel (Paperny) F.; 1 dau., Sarah. B.A., U. Chgo., 1953, M.A., 1956, Ph.D., 1962; L.H.D. (hon.), Adelphi U., 1985. Mem. faculty Columbia, 1966-72; prof. polit. sci. Boston U., 1972-82, Grad. Ctr., CUNY, 1982—. Co-author: Regulating the Poor: The Functions of Public Welfare, 1971, 2d edit., 1993, The Politics of Turmoil: Essays on Poverty, Race and the Urban Crisis, 1974, Poor People's Movements, 1977, New Class War, 1982, The Mean Season, 1987, Why Americans Don't Vote, 1988; editor: Labor Parties in Post Industrial Societies, 1992. Recipient C. Wright Mills award Soc. Study Social Problems, 1971; Guggenheim fellow, 1973-74; Am. Council Learned Socs. awardee, 1982. Mem. Am. Polit. Sci. Assn. (v.p. 1981-82), Soc. Study Social Problems (pres. 1980-81, Lee founders award 1992), ACLU (dir.). Home: 35 Claremont Ave New York NY 10027-6823 Office: 33 W 42nd St New York NY 10036-8003

PIVEN, PETER ANTHONY, architect, management consultant; b. Bklyn., Jan. 3, 1939; s. William Meyer and Sylvia Lee (Greenberg) P.; m. Caroline Cooper, July 9, 1961; children: Leslie Ann, Joshua Lawrence. A.B., Colgate U., 1960; M.Arch., U. Pa., 1963; M.S., Columbia U., 1964. Diplomate: cert. Nat. Council Archtl. Registration Bds.; registered architect, N.Y., Pa., N.J. Architect Westermann-Miller Assocs., N.Y.C., 1964-66, Bernard Rothzeid, A.I.A., N.Y.C., 1967-68; v.p. Caudill Rowlett Scott, N.Y.C., 1968-72; prin. Geddes Brecher Qualls Cunningham, Phila., 1972-87; pres. The Coxe Group, Inc., Phila. 1980-90, dir., prin. cons., 1980—; adj. prof. U. Pa. Grad. Sch. Fine Arts, 1989—, Rensselaer Poly. Inst. Sch. Architecture, 1994—. Author: Compensation Management: A Guideline for Small Firms, 1982; co-author: Success Strategies for Design Professionals, 1987; contbr. editor Archtl. Record; contbg. author: Architects Handbook of Professional Practice, 1994. Mem. N.Y.C. Community Planning Bd., 1969-72. Fellow AIA (chmn. fin. mgmt. com. 1976-80, pres. Phila. chpt. 1980); mem. Phila. C. of C. (dir. 1980-81), The Carpenters Co. of City and County of Phila. (mng. com. 1989-91). Home: 112 N Lambert St Philadelphia PA 19103-1107 Office: The Coxe Group Inc 1218 Third Ave Seattle WA 98101

PIVER, M. STEVEN, gynecologic oncologist; b. Washington, Sept. 29, 1934; s. Harry Samuel and Sonia (Bard) P.; m. Susan Myers, June 25, 1958; children: Debra Ellen, Carolyn Jan, Kenneth Stuart. BS, Gettysburg Coll., 1957; MD, Temple U., 1961. Diplomate Am. Bd. Ob-Gyn, Am. Coll. Surgeons. Intern Nazareth Hosp., Phila., 1961-62; resident Johns Hopkins U. Hosp., Balt., 1962; resident ob-gyn. Pa. Hosp., U. Pa., Phila., 1965-68; fellow gynecologic oncology U. Tex., Hosp. and Tumor Inst., Houston, 1968-70; asst. prof. gynecologic oncology U. N.C. Sch. Medicine, 1970-71; assoc. chief gynecologic oncology Roswell Park Cancer Inst., Buffalo, 1972-83, founder, dir. Gilda Radner Familial Ovarian Cancer Registry, 1981—; chief gynecologic oncology, 1984—; clin. prof., dir. gynecologic oncology SUNY, Buffalo, 1986—. Cons. editor Yearbook of Cancer, 1972-88; assoc. editor Nat. Cancer Inst. PDQ, 1984—; mem. editl. bd. The Female Patient, 1989—, Oncology Reports, 1993—; author: Ovarian Malignancies: Clinical Care of Adults and Adolescents, 1983; editor: Ovarian Malignancies: Diagnostic and Therapeutic Advances, 1987, Manual of Gynecologic Oncology/Gynecology, 1989, Conversations About Cancer, 1989; author 287 articles to Handbook of Gynecol. Oncology. Bd. dirs. United Way of Buffalo and Erie County, 1986-91; trustee D'Youville Coll., Buffalo, 1989—; pres. Friends of the Night People (homeless shelter), Buffalo, 1988—. Capt. USAF, 1962-64. Hon. fellow Phi Beta Kappa, Gettysburg Coll., 1956, Tex. Assn. Obstetricians and Gynecologists, 1983, Alpha Omega Alpha, Temple U. Sch. Medicine, 1995; named Citizen of Yr., Buffalo News, 1989; recipient YMCA Leadership award Buffalo YMCA, 1990, Brotherhood/Sisterhood Award in Medicine (Western N.Y. Region), NCCJ, 1991, St. Marguerite D'Youville Coll. Community Svc. award, 1992. Fellow ACS, Am. Coll. Ob-

Gyn.; mem. Am. Soc. Clin. Oncology, Soc. Gynecologic Oncologists, Soc. Surg. Oncology, Am. Radium Soc., Phi Beta Kappa, Alpha Omega Alpha. Achievements include documentation of hydroxyurea as a radiation sensitizer in cervix cancer that significantly improves cure rate and that ovarian cancer can be inherited. Home: 315 Lincoln Pky Buffalo NY 14216-3127 Office: Roswell Park Cancer Inst Elm And Carlton St Buffalo NY 14263

PIVIK, ROBERT WILLIAM, accounting executive; b. Renton, Pa., Oct. 29, 1937; s. George and Amelia (Kern) P.; m. Yvonne C. Pivik, Aug. 6, 1960; children: Keith, Sharon, Tracey. BS, Pa. State U., 1959. CPA, D.C. Staff acct. Deloitte Haskins & Sells, Pitts., 1959-67; mgr. Deloitte Haskins & Sells, N.Y.C., 1967-72, ptnr., 1972, various positions, 1967-83; ptnr.-in-charge Deloitte Haskins & Sells, Washington, 1983-86; area mng. ptnr. Deloitte Haskins & Sells, Md., Va. and Washington, 1986-89; group mng. ptnr. Deloitte and Touche, Md., Va., Pa., Washington, 1989—; also bd. dirs. chief fin. officer Deloitte & Touche, 1993—; mem. Greater Washington bd. Trade, 1983, tax policy task force, 1985, chmn. mktg. com., 1989-90. Legacy com. Md. civ. Am. Cancer Soc., Silver Spring, 1984; adv. com. DeSales Sch. Theology, Washington, 1986; trustee Fed. City Coun., 1990—; adv. com. mayor of Washington, 1991, mem. subcom. Mgmt. System. & Tech. Mem. AICPA, Columbia Inst. CPAs, Washington-Balt. Regional Assn. (bd. dirs.), Econ. Club Washington, Tournament Players Club, Univ. Club, City Club, Beta Gamma Sigma, Phi Kappa Phi, Alpha Psi. Republican. Roman Catholic. Avocation: golf. Office: Deloitte and Touche 1900 M St NW Ste 350 Washington DC 20036-3508

PIVIROTTO, RICHARD ROY, former retail executive; b. Youngstown, Ohio, May 26, 1930; s. Arthur M. and Ruth (Erhardt) P.; m. Mary Burchfield, June 27, 1953; children: Mary B., Richard Roy, Susan W., Nancy P., David H., Jennifer P. A.B., Princeton U., 1952; M.B.A., Harvard U., 1954. Pres. Joseph Horne Co., Pitts., 1954-70; vice chmn. Associated Dry Goods Corp., N.Y.C., 1970-72; pres. Associated Dry Goods Corp., 1972-76, chmn. bd., 1976-81, also dir.; bd. dirs. Westinghouse Electric Corp., Pitts., Gen. Am. Investors Co., N.Y.C., N.Y. Life Ins. Co., Gillette Corp., Immunomedics Inc., Morris Plains, N.J. Trustee Princeton U., 1977—; chmn. bd., trustee Greenwich Hosp.; bd. dirs. Gen. Theol. Sem., N.Y.C. Served with AUS, 1955-56. Mem. Am. Retail Fedn. (dir. 1968-81). Clubs: Union League, Princeton (N.Y.C.); Duquesne, Rolling Rock, Fox Chapel Golf (Pitts.); Greenwich, Country, Field of Greenwich; Bald Peak Colony (Melvin Village, N.H.). Office: 111 Clapboard Ridge Rd Greenwich CT 06830-3405

PIVONKA, LEONARD DANIEL, priest; b. Bryan, Tex., Oct. 19, 1951; s. Herbert Daniel and Geraldine (Schoppe) P. Student, Tex. A&M U., 1969-70, Del Mar Coll., 1970-71; BA, Pontifical Coll. Josephinum, Columbus, Ohio, 1973; MDiv, Josephinum Sch. Theology, Columbus, 1977; JCD, Cath. U. Am., 1982. Ordained priest Roman Cath. Ch., 1977, named monsignor, 1985. Mem. faculty Corpus Christi (Tex.) Minor Sem., 1982-84; administr. St. Philip the Apostle Parish, Corpus Christi, 1983-85, pastor, 1985-91; adj. jud. vicar Diocesan Tribunal, Corpus Christi, 1984-88, bishop's sec. for canonical affairs, 1983—; episcopal vicar for synod and coun. Chancery, Corpus Christi, 1985-88, chancellor, 1987-88, jud. vicar Diocesan Tribunal, 1988—; rector Corpus Christi Cathedral, 1991—; mem. administrv. coun. Diocese of Corpus Christi, 1985—, Coll. of Consultors, 1985—; chaplain Natural Family Planning Office, Corpus Christi, 1991—; bishop's rep. Spohn Hosp. Coun. on Human Values; treas. Corpus Christi Ministerial Alliance, 1983-84; diocesan chaplain Legion of Mary, 1993—. Avocations: golf, tennis, cycling. Office: Diocese of Corpus Christi 620 Lipan St Corpus Christi TX 78401-2434

PIXLEY, JOHN SHERMAN, SR., research company executive; b. Detroit, Aug. 24, 1929; s. Rex Arthur and Louise (Sherman) P.; B.A., U. Wis., 1951; postgrad. Pa. State U., 1958-59; m. Peggy Marie Payne, Oct. 16, 1949; children—John Sherman, Steven, Lou Ann. Asst. cashier Old Dominion Bank, Arlington, Va., 1953-56; tech. dir. John I. Thompson & Co., research and engring. firm, Bellefonte, Pa., 1956-65; co-founder, exec. v.p. Potomac Research Inc., Alexandria, Va., 1965-80; v.p. Gov. Sevs. Div. Electronic Data Systems, 1980-81; co-founder, pres. Potomac Research Inc. Inc., Alexandria, Va., 1981—. Owner Edgeworth Farm, Orlean, Va. Mem. Fairfax County Republican Com., Annandale, Va., 1964-72; mem. fin. com. for U.S. Rep. Joel T. Broyhill, Republican, Va., 1970-72. Served to 1st lt. AUS 1952-53; maj. Res. ret. Decorated Army Commendation medal. Mem. IEEE, Am. Radio Relay League, Sleepy Hollow Woods Civic Assn. (v.p., pres. 1969-71). Episcopalian. Club: Quantico (Va.) Flying (charter mem.). Home: 3711 Sleepy Hollow Rd Falls Church VA 22041-1021 Office: Potomac Rsch Inc 11320 Random Hills Rd Ste 300 Fairfax VA 22030

PIZER, DONALD, author, educator; b. N.Y.C., Apr. 5, 1929; s. Morris and Helen (Rosenfeld) P.; m. Carol Hart, Apr. 7, 1966; children—Karin, Ann, Margaret. B.A., UCLA, 1951, M.A., 1952, Ph.D., 1955. Mem. faculty Tulane U., 1957—, prof. English, 1964-72, Pierce Butler prof. English, 1972—, Mellon prof. humanities, 1978-79. Author: Hamlin Garland's Early Work and Career, 1960, Realism and Naturalism in Nineteenth-Century American Literature, 1966, The Novels of Frank Norris, 1966, The Novels of Theodore Dreiser, 1976, Twentieth-Century American Literary Naturalism: An Interpretation, 1982, Dos Passos "USA": A Critical Study, 1988, The Theory and Practice of American Literary Naturalism, 1993. Served with AUS, 1955-57. Guggenheim fellow, 1962; Am. Council Learned Socs. fellow, 1971-72; Nat. Endowment Humanities fellow, 1978-79. Mem. MLA. Home: 6320 Story St New Orleans LA 70118-6340

PIZER, HOWARD CHARLES, professional baseball team executive, lawyer; b. Chgo., Oct. 23, 1941; s. Edwin and Estyr (Seeder) P.; m. Sheila Graff, June 14, 1964; children: Jacqueline, Rachel. B.B.A., U. Wis., 1963; J.D. magna cum laude, Northwestern U., 1966. Assoc. McDermott, Will & Emery, Chgo., 1966-72; ptnr. Katten, Muchin, Zavis, Chgo., 1972-74; exec. v.p., gen. counsel Balcor Co., Skokie, Ill., 1975-80; exec. v.p. Chgo. White Sox, Chgo., 1981—; exec. v.p. United Ctr. Joint Venture. Bd. dirs. Chgo. Conv. and Tourism Bur., Inc., 1983—, Spl. Children's Charities, 1984—, Chgo. Baseball Cancer Charities, 1983—, Near West Side Cmty. Devel. Corp. Mem. Chgo. Bar Assn., Standard Club Chgo., Briarwood Country. Office: Chgo White Sox 333 W 35th St Chicago IL 60616-3622

PIZITZ, RICHARD ALAN, retail and real estate group executive; b. Birmingham, Ala., Feb. 24, 1930; s. Isadore and Hortense (Hirsch) P.; m. Joan Black; children: Richard Alan Jr., Jill Carole, Susan Lyn. BA, Washington & Lee U., 1951; MBA, Harvard U., 1953. Mdse. mgr. Pizitz Dept. Stores, Birmingham, 1953-59, v.p., 1959-66, pres. 1966-86, chmn. bd., 1986-87; chmn. Pizitz Mgmt. Group, Birmingham, 1987—. Pres. United Way, Birmingham, 1988, Ala. Commn. on Higher Edn., 1987-95; pres. Better Bus. Bur., Birmingham, 1962; mem. Ala adv. commn. U.S. Commn. on Civil Rights, 1985. Recipient Erskine Ramsay award, 1974; named Mktg. Man of Yr., Am. Mktg. Assn., 1966, Man of Yr., Young Men's Bus. Club, 1970. Mem. Ala. Commn. on Higher Edn., Birmingham C. of C. (pres. 1970), Ala. Retail Assn. (pres. 1965). Avocations: pvt. pilot, skiing, tennis, scuba diving. Home: 2716 Hanover Cir S Birmingham AL 35205-1733 Office: Pizitz Mgmt Group 2140 11th Ave S Birmingham AL 35205-2832

PIZZAGALLI, ANGELO, construction company executive; b. Lugano, Switzerland, July 1, 1934; came to U.S., 1937; s. Angelo and Theresa Pizzagalli; m. Patricia Haron, Jan. 19, 1935; children: Lisa, Mia, Jon. BSBA, U. Vt., 1956. Pres. Pizzagalli Constrn. Co., South Burlington, Vt., 1958—; bd. dirs. The Howard Bank, Burlington, Vt., Cen. Vt. Ry., Detroit. Past chmn. bd. trustees U. Vt.; active Vt. Indsl. Devel. Authority; past gov. Med. Ctr. Hosp. Vt., past trustee. Served to capt. USAF. Mem. Chief Execs. Orgn. Home: PO Box 2009 S Burlington VT 05407-2009 Office: Pizzagalli Constrn Co 50 Joy Dr South Burlington VT 05403

PIZZAGALLI, JAMES, construction executive; b. Burlington, Vt., Nov. 23, 1944; s. Angelo and Theresa (Moalli) P.; m. Judy Nock, June 21, 1969; 1 child, Michael. BS, U. Vt., 1966; JD, Boston U., 1969. Treas. Pizzagalli Constrn. Co., Burlington, Vt., 1969-76, v.p., 1976-91, chmn., chief exec. officer, 1991—; dir. Chittenden Corp., Burlington, 1982, AGC Edn. Found., Washington, 1992—, Shelburne (Vt.) Mus., 1983-92; life dir. Assn. Gen. Contractors, Washington, 1976—, atty.-at-law. Mem. TheMoles, Ethan Allen Club. Republican. Roman Catholic. Office: Pizzagalli Constrn Co PO Box 2009 South Burlington VT 05407

PIZZURO, SALVATORE NICHOLAS, special education educator; b. Passaic, N.J., Jan. 25, 1945; s. John G. and Mary F. (Interdonato) P. BA, Jersey City State Coll., 1970, MA, 1973; profl. diploma, Fordham U., 1980; EdD, Columbia U., 1991. Tchr. spl. edn. Garfield (N.J.) Pub. Schs., 1970-71, Lodi (N.J.) Pub. Schs., 1971-75, 76-78; learning cons. Mt. Carmel Guild, Newark, 1976-76; instr. Columbia U., N.Y.C., 1988-91; asst. prof. spl. edn. Jersey City State Coll., 1990—; post-doctoral fellow U. Ky., 1993-94; dir. Learning Consultation Svcs., N.Y.C., 1990—; coord. pre-svcs. program in mental Retardation Tchrs. Coll., Columbia U., 1990-91; rsch. assoc. U. Ill., 1991-92; chmn. Early Childhood Inclusion Conf., Phila., 1993; dir. United Learning Cons., 1994—, Lectr. in Edn., Georgian Ct. Coll., N.J., 1994—; chmn. nat. ad hoc com. on the reauthorization of the Individuals with Disabilities Edn. Act, 1994—. Editor: Learning Consultant Jour., 1994—. Chmn. Walk for Hunger, 1979, NE Regional Legis. Coalition, 1984-86, Nat. AD HOC Comm. on the Reauthorization of the Individuals with DIsabilities Edn. Act. Recipient award for dedication to mentally retarded Mt. Carmel Guild, 1972. Mem. Coun. for Exceptional Children, N.J. Coun. for Exceptional Children (pres. 1984-85), N.J. Div. on Mental Retardation (pres. 1986-87), Jersey City State Coll. Alumni Assn. (pres. 1974-75), Tchrs. Coll. Christian Fellowship (pres. 1988-90). Roman Catholic. Avocations: writing nonfiction, jogging.

PLAA, GABRIEL LEON, toxicologist, educator; b. San Francisco, May 15, 1930; arrived in Can., 1968; s. Jean and Lucienne (Chalopin) P.; m. Colleen Neva Brasefield, May 19, 1951; children: Ernest (dec.), Steven, Kenneth, Gregory, Andrew, John, Denise, David. BS, U. Calif., Berkeley, 1952; PhD, U. Calif., San Francisco, 1958. Diplomate Am. Bd. Toxicology. Asst. toxicologist City/County San Francisco, 1954-58; asst. prof. Sch. Medicine Tulane U., New Orleans, 1958-61; assoc. prof. U. Iowa, Iowa City, 1961-68; prof. U. Montreal, Que., Can., 1968—, chmn. Dept. Pharmacology, 1968-80, vice-dean Faculty Medicine, 1982-89, dir. Interuniv. Ctr. Rsch. in Toxicology, 1991-95; Dorothy Snider disting. lectr. U. Ark., 1995; chmn. Can. Coun. Animal Care, Ottawa, Ont., Can., 1985-88. Editor Toxicology and Applied Pharmacology, 1972-80; contbr. over 200 articles to profl. jours. 1st lt. U.S. Army, 1952-53, Korea. Recipient Thienes award Am. Acad. Clin. Toxicology, 1977. Mem. Am. Soc. Pharmacology, Soc. Toxicology Can. (pres. 1981-83, Henderson award 1969, award of distinction 1994), Pharm. Soc. Can. (pres. 1973-74), Soc. Toxicology (pres. 1983-84, Achievement award 1967, Lehman award 1977, Edn. award 1987). Roman Catholic. Home: 236 Meredith Ave, Dorval, PQ Canada H9S 2Y7 Office: U Montreal Dept Pharmacology, PO Box 6128 Sta A, Montreal, PQ Canada H3C 3J7

PLACE, DAVID ELLIOTT, lawyer; b. N.Y.C., June 10, 1921; s. Henry Coe Place and Mary Bickford (Elliott) Garceau; m. Penelope Griswold, June 16, 1952 (div. 1985); children: David Elliott Jr., Richard Merrill, Penelope Parkman, Josiah Richardson; m. Susanna Badgley, June 21, 1985; children: Louise Verriest, Alexander Francis Badgley. B.S., Harvard U., 1943, JD, 1948. Bar: Mass. 1949, U.S. Dist. Ct. Mass. 1950, U.S. Ct. Appeals (1st cir.) 1951, U.S. Tax Ct. 1954, U.S. Ct. Mil. Appeals 1981. Asst. U.S. atty. U.S. Dist. Ct. Mass., Boston, 1953-55; spl. asst. to U.S. atty. gen. U.S. Dept. Justice, Boston, 1955; mem. Gaston Snow & Ely Bartlett, Boston, 1948-53; gen. counsel U.S. Dept. Air Force, Washington, 1981-84; dep. commnr. U.S. Govt. Standing Arms Control Commn., Washington, 1984-86; ptnr. Gaston & Snow, Boston, 1956-81, 84-91, Choate, Hall & Stewart, Boston, 1991—; trustee McCrillis Land Assn., Bangor, Maine, 1965—; chmn. Jud. Nominating Coun. of Mass., 1991—; bd. dirs. Greylock Corp., Forté Dupee Sawyer Co. Warden St. Stephen's Episcopal Ch., Cohasset, Mass., 1955-60; trustee, sec. Jackson Lab., Bar Harbor, Maine, 1966-92; trustee Mass Trustees of Reservations, 1968-92; town moderator Cohasset, 1969-81; trustee, pres. Dana Hall Sch., Wellesley, 1972-81. Served with U.S. Army, 1943-45. Recipient Meritorious Civilian Svc. medal Dept. Def., 1984. Mem. ABA, Mass. Bar Assn., Boston Bar Assn., Fed. Bar Assn., Somerset Boston Club, Harvard Club Boston, Drifters Club (Jackson, N.H.), Cohasset Yacht Club. Republican. Home: 224 Adams St Milton MA 02186-4201

PLACE, GEOFFREY, consumer goods manufacturing company executive; b. Accrington, Eng., Mar. 11, 1931; came to U.S., 1968; s. Harry and Edith (Salthouse) P.; m. Margaret Janice Entwistle, Aug. 9, 1955; children: Fiona, Andrew, Nicholas, Susan. BA, Kings Coll., Cambridge, Eng., 1953, MA, 1958. With Procter & Gamble Co., 1954—, v.p. research and devel., 1977—; mem. acad. corp. liaison program adv. com. Nat. Acad. Scis. Trustee, chmn. research com. Children's Hosp. Med. Ctr., Children's Hosp., 1979—; trustee Internat. Child Health Found. Served to maj. Brit. Army. Mem. Indsl. Rsch. Inst. Inc. (past pres.), Dirs. Indsl. Rsch., Coun. for Chem. Rsch. Inc. (Procter & Gamble rep.), Nat. Wildlife Fedn. (mem. corp. conservation coun.), Nat. Recycling Coalition (recycling adv. coun.). Episcopalian. Clubs: Queen City, Cowan Lake Sailing Assn. Office: Procter & Gamble Co 2131 La Cuesta Dr Santa Ana CA 92705-2522

PLACHTA, LEONARD E., academic administrator. Pres. Ctrl. Mich. U., Mt. Pleasant, Mich. Office: Ctrl Mich U Office of Pres Mount Pleasant MI 48859

PLACIER, PHILIP R., lawyer; b. Chillicothe, Ohio, Mar. 7, 1933; s. Don Harold and Ruth (Hartmann) P.; m. Nancy Kay Young, July 27, 1963; children—David Lane, Thomas Alan, Elizabeth Ann. A.B., Ohio Wesleyan U., 1955; LL.B., U. Mich., 1958. Bar: Calif. 1959. Assoc. Thelen, Marrin, Johnson & Bridges, San Francisco, 1962-69, ptnr., 1970—, chmn. mgmt. com., 1984-92. Contbr. chpt. to book. Elder United Presbyterian Ch., Lafayette, Calif.; trustee San Francisco Theological Seminary. Served to lt. JAGC, USN, 1958-62. Mem. ABA, Calif. State Bar Assn., Orinda County Club (Calif.), World Trade Club (San Francisco). Republican. Avocations: golf; skiing. Office: Thelen Marrin Johnson & Bridges 2 Embarcadero Ctr San Francisco CA 94111-3807

PLACKE, JAMES A(NTHONY), foreign service officer, international affairs consultant; b. Grand Island, Nebr., June 14, 1935; s. Gerhard F. and Florence E. (McCormick) P.; m. Mary Sabina Shea, July 25, 1959; children—Elizabeth, Stephen, Carolyn. B.Sc., U. Nebr., 1957, M.A., 1959. Commd. fgn. service officer Dept. State, 1958; econ. counselor Am. embassy, Tripoli, Libya, 1970-71; fgn. service insp. Dept. State, Washington, 1971-73, dir. office food policy, 1974-76; econ. counselor Am. embassy, Ottawa, Ont., Can., 1977-79; minister Am. embassy, Jidda, Saudi Arabia, 1979-82; dep. asst. sec. Nr. Eastern and South Asian Affairs Bur., Dept. State, Washington, 1982-85, ret., 1986; internat. affairs cons., 1986-90; dir. Cambridge Energy Rsch. Assoc., 1991; del. UN World Food Conf., 1974. Recipient Meritorious Honor award Dept. State, 1969, 71; Presdl. Meritorious Service award, 1985. Office: Ste 1000W 1299 Pennsylvania Ave NW Washington DC 20004-2400

PLACZEK, ADOLF KURT, librarian; b. Vienna, Austria, Mar. 9, 1913; came to U.S., 1940, naturalized, 1943; s. Oswald and Pauline (Selinko) P.; m. Jan Struther, Mar. 1, 1948 (dec. July 1953); m. Laura Beverley Robinson, Jan. 5, 1957. Student, U. Vienna Med. Sch., 1933-34, Inst. Fine Arts, U. Vienna, 1934-38; B.L.S., Columbia U. 1942; diploma of honor, U. Vienna, 1993. Asst. librarian Avery Archtl. Library, Columbia U., 1948-60; Avery librarian Avery Archtl. Library, 1960-80, emeritus, 1980—; adj. prof. architecture, 1971-80, prof. emeritus, 1980—; commr. N.Y.C. Landmarks Preservation Commn., 1984-93. Editor in chief Macmillan Ency. Architects, 1982, Bldgs. of the U.S., Oxford Press, 1984-90; contbr. articles to Columbia Ency., Ency. Brit., also to books and mags. Served with AUS, 1943-46. Decorated Austrian Cross of Honor for Sci. and Art 1st class, 1993; recipient Honor award AIA, 1986. Mem. Soc. Archtl. Historians (sec. 1963-67, dir. 1968-71, 2d v.p. 1974-75, 1st v.p. 1976-77, pres. 1978-80), Am. Council Learned Socs. (del. 1971-74). Home: 176 W 87th St New York NY 10024-2902

PLAEGER, FREDERICK JOSEPH, II, lawyer; b. New Orleans, Sept. 10, 1953; s. Edgar Leonard and Bernice Virginia (Schwetz) P.; m. Kathleen Helen Bickon, Nov. 19, 1977; children: Douglas A., Catherine E. BS, La. State U., 1976, JD, 1977. Bar: La. 1978, U.S. Dist. Ct. (ea. dist.) La. 1978, U.S. Ct. Appeals (5th cir.) 1981, U.S. Dist. Ct. (mid. dist.) La. 1985, (we. dist.) La. 1987. Law clk. U.S. Dist. Ct. (ea. dist.) La., New Orleans, 1977-79; assoc. Milling, Benson, Woodward, Hillyer, Pierson & Miller, New Orleans, 1979-85, ptnr., 1985-89; gen. counsel, corp. sec. La. Land and Exploration Co., New Orleans, 1989—. Bd. dirs. New Orleans Speech and Hearing Ctr., 1985-91, pres., 1988-90; bd. dirs. Children's Oncology Svcs. La. (Ronald McDonald House of New Orleans), 1987-90; selected mem. Met. Area Com. Leadership Forum, 1986; leader Cub Scouts--Boy Scouts Am., 1988-91; bd. dirs. Soc. Environ. Edn., La. Nature and Sci. Ctr., 1992—. Recipient Service to Mankind award Sertoma, 1989. Mem. ABA, La. Bar Assn., Am. Corp. Counsel Assn., Am. Soc. Corp. Secs., Am. Petroleum Inst. (mem. gen. commn. law), Pickwick Club, Petroleum Club. Republican. Avocations: golf, hunting, fishing. Home: 4632 Neyrey Dr Metairie LA 70002-1423 Office: La Land & Exploration Co 909 Poydras St Ste 3600 New Orleans LA 70112-1017

PLAGENZ, GEORGE RICHARD, minister, journalist, columnist; b. Lakewood, Ohio, Dec. 11, 1923; s. George William and Edith Louise (Fenner) P.; m. Faith Hanna, Sept. 12, 1953 (div.); children—Joel, George William II, Nicole, Sarah. B.A. cum laude, Western Res. U., 1945; S.T.B., Harvard, 1949. Ordained to ministry Unitarian Ch., 1951. Sports writer Cleve. Press, 1943-46; asst. minister King's Chapel, Boston, 1951-54; news broadcaster Radio Sta. WEEI, Boston, 1955-63; writer Boston Sunday Advertiser, 1963-70; religion editor Cleve. Press, 1970-82; syndicated columnist Scripps-Howard Newspapers, 1974-80, Newspaper Enterprise Assn., 1980—. Mem. Beta Theta Pi. Club: Harvard (Boston). Home: 239B E Beck St Columbus OH 43206-1210

PLAGER, S. JAY, federal judge; b. Long Branch, N.J., May 16, 1931; s. A.L. and Clara L. (Matross) P.; m. Ilene H. Nagel; children—Anna Katherine, David Alan, Daniel Tyler. A.B., U. N.C., 1952; J.D., U. Fla., 1958; LL.M., Columbia U., 1961. Bar: Fla. 1958, Ill. 1964. Asst. prof. law U. Fla., 1958-62, assoc. prof., 1962-64; assoc. prof. law U. Ill., Champaign-Urbana, 1964-65, prof., 1965-77; dir. Office Environ. and Planning Studies, 1972-74, 75-77; dean, prof. law Ind. U. Sch. Law, Bloomington, 1977-84; prof. law Ind. U. Sch. Law, 1984-90; counselor to undersec. U.S. Dept. Health and Human Svcs., 1986-87; assoc. dir. Office of Mgmt. and Budget Office of Mgmt. and Budget, 1987-88; administr. info. and regulatory affairs Exec. Office of the Pres. 1988-89; cir. judge U.S. Ct. Appeals (fed. cir.), 1989—; vis. research prof. law U. Wis., 1967-68; vis. scholar Stanford U., 1984-85. Author: (with others) Water Law and Administration, 1968, Social Justice Through Law-New Approaches in the Law of Property, 1970, (with others) Florida Water Law, 1980. Chmn. Gainesville (Fla.) Planning Commn., 1962-63; mem. Urbana Plan Commn., 1966-70; mem. nat. air pollution manpower devel. adv. com., 1971-75; cons. Ill. Inst. for Environ. Quality, U.S. EPA; chmn. Ill. Task Force on Noise, 1972-76; vice chmn. Nat. Commn. on Jud. Discipline and Removal, 1991-93. With USN, 1952-55. Office: US Ct Appeals for Fed Cir The National Courts Bldg 717 Madison Pl NW Washington DC 20439-0002

PLAGMAN, RALPH, principal. Prin. George Washington High Sch., Cedar Rapids, Iowa. Recipient Blue Ribbon Sch. award Dept. Edn., 1990-91. Office: George Washington High Sch 2205 Forest Dr SE Cedar Rapids IA 52403

PLAIN, BELVA, writer; b. N.Y.C., Oct. 9, 1919; d. Oscar and Eleanor Offenberg; m. Irving Plain, June 14, 1941 (dec. 1982); 3 children. Grad., Barnard Coll. Author: Evergreen, 1978, Random Winds, 1980, Eden Burning, 1982, Crescent City, 1984, The Golden Cup, 1987, Tapestry, 1988, Blessings, 1989, Harvest, 1990, Treasures, 1992, Whispers, 1993, Daybreak, 1994, The Carousel, 1995. Office: care Delacorte Press 1540 Broadway New York NY 10036-4094

PLAINE, DANIEL J., lawyer; b. Washington, Aug. 23, 1943; s. Herzel H.E. and Norma (Stein) P.; m. Susan Ambrose, Oct. 5, 1985; children: Caroline, Meredith. BA magna cum laude, Williams Coll., 1965; LLB, Cambridge U., Eng., 1967; JD, Yale U., 1970. Bar: D.C. 1970, U.S. Dist. Ct. DC 1970, U.S. Ct. Appeals (D.C. cir.) 1970, U.S. Ct. Appeals (fed. cir.), 1985, U.S. Supreme Ct., 1974. Ptnr. Steptoe & Johnson, Washington, 1970—. Marshall scholar, 1967. Mem. ABA, Am. Soc. Internat. Law, Washington Inst. Internat. Law. Office: Steptoe & Johnson 1330 Connecticut Ave NW Washington DC 20036-1795

PLAISTED, HARRIS MERRILL, III, real estate executive; b. Portland, Maine, June 3, 1935; s. Harris Merrill and Elizabeth Parsons (Hatch) P.; m. Patricia Walker, Feb. 20, 1982; children: Frederick William II, Parker Bennett; stepchildren: William H. Nau Jr., Mary Beth Nau. BA in Econs., Washington and Lee U. 1957. With Morton G. Thalhimer, Inc., Richmond, Va., 1960-66, v.p., 1966-80, sr. v.p., 1980-86, pres., 1986-92, vice chmn., 1992—; bd. dirs. Morton G. Thalhimer Realty Advisors, Inc., Richmond, MGT Svcs. Corp., Richmond. Pres. Ridgetop Recreation Assn., 1967, Big Bros. of Richmond, Inc., 1970; bd. dirs. Robert E. Lee coun. Boy Scouts Am., 1981; state dir. Internat. Coun. Shopping Ctrs., 1974-77. Capt. U.S. Army, 1957-59. Mem. Va. Assn. Realtors (bd. dirs. 1973-82), Richmond Bd. Realtors (pres. 1975, Realtor of Yr. 1975), Richmond Real Estate Group (pres. 1987), Richmond Jaycees (life, Key Man Club), Soc. Indsl. and Office Realtors (dist. v.p. 1979-80, regional v.p. 1984-85), Sons of the Revolution (sec. 1994, 2d v.p. 1995), Ships Watch Assn. (bd. dirs. 1994, pres. 1995), Kiwanis Club Richmond (bd. dirs. 1978-79). Episcopalian. Avocations: golf, sailing. Home: 9013 Wood Sorrel Ct Richmond VA 23229-7072 Office: Morton G Thalhimer Inc 1313 E Main St Richmond VA 23219-3600

PLAISTED, JOAN M., diplomat; b. St. Peter, Minn., Aug. 29, 1945; d. Gerald A. and Lola May (Peters) P. Student, U. Grenoble, France, 1965-66, U. Calif., Berkeley, 1966; BA in Internat. Rels., Am. U., 1967, MA in Asian Studies, 1969; graduate, Nat. War Coll., 1988. Korea desk officer Commerce Dept., Washington, 1969-72, Japan desk officer, 1972-73; commercial officer Am. Embassy, Paris, 1973-78; internat. economist Orgn. Econ. Cooperation & Devel., Paris, 1978-80; econ. officer Am. Consulate Gen., Hong Kong, 1980-83; trade negotiator White House Office of Spl. Trade Rep., Geneva, 1983-85; deputy dir. China desk State Dept., Washington, 1985-87; acting deputy chief of mission, chief econ./commercial sect. Am. Inst. in Taiwan, Taipei, 1988-91; chargé d'affaires, deputy chief of mission Am. Embassy, Rabat, Morocco, 1991-94; dir. Thai and Burma affairs Dept. of State, Washington, 1994—. Recipient Lodestar award Am. U., 1993. Mem. Am. Fgn. Svc. Assn., Hong Kong Wine Soc. (founding). Avocations: wine tasting, gastronomy, history, skiing, travelling. Office: Dept of State EAP/TB Rm 4312 Washington DC 20520

PLAISTED, ROBERT LEROY, plant breeder, educator; b. Hornell, N.Y., Jan. 1, 1929; s. Robert A. and Eva B. (Gitchell) P.; m. Ellen B. Overbaugh, Feb. 10, 1951; children: Deborah (dec.), Kathleen, Thomas, Diane. B.S., Cornell U., 1950; M.S., Ia. State U., 1954, Ph.D., 1956. Grad. asst. Ia. State U., 1953-56; asst. prof. Cornell U., 1956-60, assoc. prof., 1960-64, prof., 1964—, chmn. dept. plant breeding and biometry, 1964-79. Served with AUS, 1951-53. Mem. European Assn. Potato Research, Potato Assn. Am. (pres. 1971). Home: 536 Ellis Hollow Creek Rd Ithaca NY 14850-9623

PLANCHER, ROBERT LAWRENCE, manufacturing company executive; b. N.Y.C., Feb. 21, 1932; s. Murray Leon and Pearl P.; m. Ellen Roslyn, Feb. 14, 1954; children: Kevin, Daryn. B.B.A., CCNY, 1954. With American Brands, Inc., N.Y.C., 1963—; asst. tax dir. American Brands, Inc., 1967, tax dir., 1971, controller, 1978, dir. v.p., controller, 1981-86, sr. v.p., chief acctg. officer, 1986—; bd. dirs. AACO World Corp., Acushnet Co., Am. Brands Internat. Corp., Am. Tobacco Internat. Corp., Jim Beam Brands Co., Gallaher Ltd., MasterBrand Industries, Inc., Mid Atlantic Metro Region Adv. Bd. Arkwright Mut. Ins. Co. Served with U.S. Army, 1954-56. Mem. Fin. Execs. Inst., Tax Execs. Inst. Inst. Mgmt. Accts. Office: Am Brands Inc 1700 E Putnam Ave Old Greenwich CT 06870-1321

PLANE, DONALD RAY, management science educator; b. Evansville, Ind. July 17, 1938; s. Edward L. and Margaret I. (Downen) P.; m. Rosemary Bieber, Sept. 4, 1961; children: Brian Russell, Dennis Lowell, Margaret Diane. M.E., U. Cin., 1961; M.B.A. (NDEA fellow), U. Ind., 1963, D.B.A. (NDEA fellow), 1966. Instr. econs. U.S. Air Force Acad., 1965-67, asst. prof. econs., 1967-68; assoc. prof. mgmt. sci. U. Colo., Boulder, 1968-72; prof. mgmt. sci. and info. systems U. Colo., 1972-84, head div. mgmt. sci., 1976-84; prof. mgmt. sci. Crummer Grad. Sch. Bus., Rollins Coll., Winter Park, Fla., 1984—, pres. Crummer grad. faculty, 1992-93; vis. Fulbright prof. mgmt. sci. U. Nairobi, 1978-79; cons. in field. Co-author 6 books, including (with E.B. Oppermann) Business and Economic Statistics, 3d edit., 1986, (with J. Dinkel and G. Kochenberger) Management Science: Text and Applications, 1978, Quantitative Tools for Decision Support Using IFPS, 1986, Management Science: A Spreadsheet Approach, 1994. Served with USAF, 1965-68. Ford Found. fellow, 1965. Mem. Decision Scis. Inst. (mem. council 1977-81). Research, publs. in field. Home: 980 S Lake Sybelia Dr Maitland FL 32751-5403 Office: Rollins College Crummer Grad Sch Bus Winter Park FL 32789

PLANGERE, JULES L., III, newspaper company executive; b. Neptune, N.J., Nov. 4, 1944; s. Jules L. and Virginia May (Polhemus) P.; m. Nona Helen Chadwick, Nov. 20, 1971 (div. Mar. 25, 1985). B.A., Lafayette Coll., 1966. Reporter, photographer Asbury Park Press, Asbury Park, N.J., 1970-72, account exec., 1972-74, asst. prodn. mgr., 1974-80, dir. ops., 1980-82, v.p. ops., 1982-85, v.p. pub., 1986-89, exec. v.p., 1989—. Served to lt. comdr. USNR, 1966-69. Mem. N.J. Press Assn. Methodist. Home: 2805 Williamburg Dr Wall NJ 07719-9516 Office: Asbury Pk Press 3601 Hwy 66 PO Box 1550 Neptune NJ 07754

PLANGERE, JULES LEON, JR., media company executive; b. Spring Lake, N.J., Dec. 30, 1920; s. Jules Leon and Jesse Alene (Davidson) P.; student Rutgers U., 1942; m. Jane Wallhauser, Feb. 5, 1978; 1 son, Jules L. III; stepchildren: Mrs. John Bickart, John C. Conover III, Jeffrey Conover. With Asbury Park (N.J.) Press, 1947—, pub., 1977-91, chief exec. officer, 1980-91, chmn. bd., 1991—; former dir. N.J. Bell Telephone Co. Former chmn. bd. trustees Monmouth Coll., West Long Branch, N.J.; past pres. Welfare Council Monmouth County. Lt. U.S. Army, 1942-46. Mem. Asbury Park C. of C. (past pres.), N.J. Press Assn. (past pres.). Am. Newspaper Pubs. Assn., N.J. State C. of C. (bd. dirs.). Clubs: Spring Lake Bath and Tennis, Nassau, Quail Ridge Country, Metedeconk Nat. Golf.

PLANITZER, RUSSELL E., computer company executive; b. 1944. Student, U.S. Naval Acad, 1966, Harvard U., 1974. Chmn. bd. dirs. Computervision Corp., Bedford, Mass., 1974—; gen. ptnr. J.H. Whitney & Co., N.Y.C., 1981—; chmn. bd. dirs., CFO DR Holdings Inc. of Del., 1990—. Office: DR Holdings Inc of Delaware Prime Park Natick MA 01760*

PLANK, BETSY ANN (MRS. SHERMAN V. ROSENFIELD), public relations counsel; b. Tuscaloosa, Ala., Apr. 3, 1924; d. Richard Jeremiah and Bettye (Hood) P.; m. Sherman V. Rosenfield, Apr. 10, 1954. Student, Bethany (W.Va.) Coll., 1940-43; A.B., U. Ala., 1944. Continuity dir. radio sta. KQV, Pitts., 1944-47; account exec. Mitchell McKeown Orgn., Chgo., 1947-54; pub. relations counsel Chgo. chpt. A.R.C., 1954-57; dir. pub. relations Chgo. Council on Fgn. Relations, 1957-58; v.p. Ronald Goodman Pub. Relations Counsel, Chgo., 1958-61; exec. v.p., treas., dir. Daniel J. Edelman, Inc., Chgo., 1961-73; dir. pub. relations planning Am. Tel. & Tel. Co., N.Y.C., 1973-74; asst. v.p. corp. communications Ill. Bell, Chgo., 1974-90; prin. Betsy Plank Pub. Rels., Chgo., 1990—; dep. chmn. VII World Congress on Pub. Rels., 1976; co-chmn. nat. commn. on Pub. Rels. Edn., 1984-86; mem. adv. bd. Ill. Issues. Bd. dirs. United Way Chgo., 1986-90; chmn. Citizenship Coun. Met. Chgo., Betsy Plank chpt. Pub. Rels. Students Soc. Am., No. Ill. U.; trustee Found. for Pub. Rels. Rsch. and Edn., 1975-80; nat. bd. dirs. Girl Scouts U.S.A., 1975-85. Recipient medal of merit Pi Delta Epsilon; named One of World's 40 Leading Pub. Relations Profls., 1984. Fellow Pub. Rels. Soc. Am. (accredited, nat. pres. 1973, chmn. pub. utilities sect. 1977, Outstanding Profl. award 1977, Outstanding Community Svc. award 1989); mem. Pub. Rels. Clinic (pres. 1979), Publicity Club Chgo. (pres. 1963-64, Outstanding Profl. award 1961), Ill. Coun. on Econ. Edn. (past chmn. bd. trustees), Welfare Pub. Rels. Forum Chgo. (pres. 1966-67), Internat. Pub. Rels. Assn., Chgo. Network (chmn. 1980-81), Nat. Pub. Rels. Coun. (bd. dirs. 1973-75), Union League Club of Chgo., Bon Vivant Soc., Econ. Club Chgo., Zeta Tau Alpha. Presbyterian. Home and Office: 421 W Melrose St Chicago IL 60657-3848

PLANK, (ETHEL) FAYE, editor, photographer, writer; b. St. Francisville, Ill., Oct. 15, 1912; d. Perry Austin and Nellie Sarah (Hardin) Winget; m. Edward Earl Plank, July 10, 1934 (dec. Mar. 1986); children: Earleen F., Eugene Earl, Richard J. Student, Tex. Wesleyan U., West Tex. State U., N.Mex. U., San Antonio Coll., U. So. Miss., Ea. N.Mex. U., N.Mex. Drake U., Rutgers U., Dartmouth U. U. Colo., Amarillo Coll., Frank Phillips Coll., Permaian Basin Jr. Coll. Pvt. tchr. art Hereford, Tex., 1960-64; office mgr., bookkeeper West Tex. Devel. Co., Hereford, 1964-70; publicity writer Cowbelles, 1970-74; mng. editor Curry County Times, Clovis, N.Mex., 1974-77; writer advertising and news State Line Tribune, Farwell, Tex., 1977-82; corresp. Lubbock (Tex.) Avalanche Jour., 1977-82, Amarillo (Tex.) Globe News, 1977-86; owner, mgr. Ideas Unltd. (pub. rels. firm), 1977-82; owner, editor, pub. Your Paper, N.Mex., 1977-82; women's editor, photographer Dalhart (Tex.) Daily Texan, 1983—; former writer advt. Spl. Roping and Rodeo, Clovis, Pioneer Days, Clovis, Curry County Fair, Clovis; mem. spl. commr. on publicity and promotion Mesa Redonda Cowboy Camp Mtg., N.Mex., 1980-82, with publicity Federated Rep. Women's Club, Clovis, 1976-82, Clovis Bus. and Profl. Women's Club, 1977-82; with publicity and promotion Miss Rodeo N.Mex. Pageant, 1977-82, Curry County Farm and Livestock Bur., 1977-82; spl. assignments, photographer N.Mex. Stockman, Albuquerque, N.Mex. Farm and Ranch Mag. Publicity chmn., bd. dirs. Keep Dalhart Beautiful; publicity chmn., v.p. Dalhart Ctrl. United Meth. Women; v.p., program chmn., pres. Dalhart Wesleyan Group, Ctrl. United Meth. Ch.; publicity chmn. Dalhart Youth Ctr. Bd.; bd. dirs., task force Dalhart Sr. Citizens; chmn. Dalhart Writer's Group; leader 4-H Club, Hereford, Camp Fire Club, Hereford; active sch. bd. Hereford Red Cross (Gray Lady, chmn.), Hereford Art Guild, Hereford Meth. Ch. Recipient 4-H Leaders award, 1952, Citizen of Yr. award Hereford Lions Club, 1960, appreciation award Am. Nat. Red Cross, 1965, N.Mex. Cowbelle of Yr. award, 1973, Community Leaders and Noteworthy Am. award, 1975-76, award of merit Miss Rodeo N.Mex. Pageant, appreciation award FFA, Pvt. Enterprise award Federated Club Women Am., 1978, Cert. Appreciation, Nat. Heart Edn. Assn., 1979, Golden Quill award N.Mex. Farm and Livestock Bur., 1981, Woman of Achievment award N.Mex. Press Women, 1981, Woman of Achievement award Nat. Fedn. Press Women, 1981, N.Mex. Friend of 4-H award Curry County, 1984, Dallam, Tex., County, 1984, Disting. Proud Ptnr. award Keep Tex. Beautiful, 1988, 89, Cert. merit, O. P. Schnabel Status Citizen, 1992, Outstanding Spl. Promotion award Am. Cancer Soc., ACE award 1990-91, 91-92, Recognition award 1991-92, Pace Setter award 1993, Edn. award 1993, Tex. Sch. Bell award Distinction, Tex. Retired Tchrs. Assn., 1991, Appreciation award Tex. Press Women, 1993, Merit award Kcet Tex. Beautiful Individual Leadership, 1994, Appreciation cert. Tex. Press Women, 1994-95, Merit award HOSTS, 1995; named Citizen of Yr., Dalhart (Tex.) Area C. of C., 1993. Mem. Nat. Fedn. Press Women (bd. dirs., regional chmn.-Tex., N.Mex., Colo., Okla., La.), Panhandle Press Assn., Tex. Press Assn., Soc. Profl. Journalists, N.Mex. Press Women (past pres.), Ea. N.Mex. Press Women (past pres.), N.Mex. Farm and Livestock Bur. (info. dir., former bd. dirs.), Am. Nat. Cowbelles (chmn. beef edn.), N.Mex. Cowbelles (state bd., legis. chmn., publicity, news media, TV dir.), Cattle Capital Cowbelles (local pres.), Bus. and Profl. Women's Club (v.p., pres.), Republican Women's Club (publicity chmn., Curry County Rep. Ctrl. com.), Pilot Club, PTA (pres.). Republican. Methodist. Avocations: reading, writing, travel, photography.

PLANO, RICHARD JAMES, physicist, educator; b. Merrill, Wis., Apr. 15, 1929; s. Victor James and Minnie (Hass) P.; m. Louise Sylvia Grevillius, July 3, 1956; children—Linda Sylvia, Robert James. A.B., U. Chgo., 1949, B.S., 1951, M.S., 1953, Ph.D., 1956. Faculty Columbia, 1956-60; faculty Rutgers U., New Brunswick, N.J., 1960—; prof. physics Rutgers U., 1962-81, prof. II, 1981—. Mem. Am. Inst. Physics, Am. Assn. Physics Tchrs., AAUP. Studies on properties of elementary particles. Home: PO Box 5306 Somerset NJ 08875-5306 Office: Physics Dept Rutgers U New Brunswick NJ 08903

PLANT, ALBIN MACDONOUGH, lawyer; b. Balt., July 30, 1937; s. Albin Joseph and Ruth E. (Frech) P.; m. Anne Warwick Brown, June 17, 1961; children: Katherine, Albin Macdonough Jr., Elizabeth Ashby. BA, Princeton U., 1959; LLB, U. Va., 1963; MLA, Johns Hopkins U., 1975. Bar: Md. 1963, U.S. Dist. Ct. Md. 1963, U.S. Ct. Appeals 1970. Assoc. Semmes, Bowen & Semmes, Balt., 1963-71, ptnr., 1971-91; ptnr. Stewart, Plant & Blumenthal, Balt., 1991—; adj. prof. law U. Balt., 1979, U. Md.,

1979-83, 84-85. Co-author Md. Estate Planning, Will Drafting and Estate Administn. Forms Practice Ann. Bd. dirs. Ctr. Stage, Episc. Social Ministries, T. Rowe Price Renaissance Fund, Ltd., T. Rowe Price Spectrum Fund, New Age Media Fund. Mem. Am. Coll. Probate Counsel (regent) Lawyers Roundtable, Md. Club, Wednesday Law Club. Democrat. Office: 7 St Paul St Baltimore MD 21202-1626

PLANT, DAVID WILLIAM, lawyer; b. Ottawa, Ill., Apr. 22, 1931; s. Arthur Percival and Margery Elmina (Flick) P.; children: Susan W. BME, Cornell U., 1953, LLB, 1957. Bar: N.Y. 1957, U.S. Dist. Ct. (ea. and so. dists.) N.Y., U.S. Supreme Ct., 1968, U.S. Patent Office 1982. Assoc. Fish & Neave, N.Y.C., 1957-70; ptnr. Fish & Neave, 1970—, mng. ptnr. 1981-84; panel mem., arbitration cons. com. World Intellectual Property Orgn., 1994—; mem. panels of neutrals Internat. C. of C., 1992—, London Ct. Internat. Arbitration, 1992—, EDNY, SDNY; lectr. in field. Contbr. articles to profl. jours. Bd. dirs. Cornell Rsch. Found. Mem. ABA, Assn. Bar City N.Y. (com. on patents 1980-83, chmn. 1983-86, com. on arbitration and alternative dispute resolution 1987-90, 91-94, chmn. 1994—), Am. Arbitration Assn. (various coms. and panels), N.Y. Intellectual Property Law Assn. (chmn. arbitration com. 1989-91, dir. 1994—), Am. Intellectual Property Law Assn. (alternative dispute resolution com. 1993—), Ctr. Pub. Resources (co-chmn. tech. com., mem. panels), Internat. C. of C., Cornell Law Assn. (exec. com., pres. 1994—). Home: 7 George Langeloh Ct Rye NY 10580 Office: Fish & Neave 49th Flr 1251 Ave of the Americas New York NY 10020

PLANT, FORREST ALBERT, lawyer; b. Sacramento, Dec. 17, 1924; s. Forrest A. and Marie (Phleger) P.; m. Shirley J. Boles, Oct. 15, 1949; children: Forrest Albert Jr., Randall B., Gregory M., Brian J. AB, U. Calif., Berkeley, 1944, JD, 1949. Bar: Calif. 1950. Ptnr. Diepenbrock, Wulff, Plant & Hannegan, Sacramento, 1950—; prof. law McGeorge Coll. Law, 1952-61; mem. Jud. Coun. State Calif., 1972-76; mem. Calif. Law Revision Commn., 1988-94, chmn., 1988-89. Chmn. bd. editors: Calif. Lawyer, 1981-82. Trustee, dir. Golden Empire Council Boy Scouts Am., 1963-67; pres. Legal Aid Soc. Sacramento County, 1961-62; former bd. dirs. Sacramento Children's Home; former trustee and mem. exec. com. Sutter Community Hosps., Sutter Health Systems; trustee, pres. Crocker Art Mus. Found.; Sacramento Symphony Found., U. Calif.-Berkeley Found., 1980-86; former bd. dirs., v.p. exec. com. Sacramento Symphony Assn.; trustee Calif. Mus. Assn., pres., 1968-69, Sacramento Regional Found., (treas. 1993—), bd. visitors Stanford Law Sch., 1971-74; bd. regents U. Calif., 1978-79. Served with USNR, World War II. Recipient Disting. Svc. award Boalt Law Sch. Alumni, 1989; U. Calif. Berkeley fellow. Fellow Am. Bar Found., Am. Coll. Trust and Estate Counsel, Am. Coll. Trial Lawyers (bd. regents 1977-81); mem. State Bar of Calif. (bd. govs. 1968-71, pres. 1970-71), Sacramento County Bar Assn. (pres. 1966, mem. coun.), U. Calif. Alumni Assn. (pres. 1977-79, Alumni citation 1980), Sutter club (past bd. dirs.), Del Paso Country Club, Roberts Country Club (past pres., bd. dirs. Sacramento Club, Paul Harris fellow), Phi Beta Kappa. Home: 1515 13th Ave Sacramento CA 95818-4148 Office: 455 Capitol Mall Sacramento CA 95814-4404

PLANTE, WILLIAM MADDEN, news correspondent; b. Chgo., Jan. 14, 1938; s. Regis Louis and Jane Elizabeth (Madden) Plante; m. Barbara A. Barnes Orteig, Jan. 18, 1965 (div. 1975); children—Patrick, Michael, Daniel, Christopher, Brian, David; m. Robin L. Smith, May 23, 1987. B.S., Loyola U., 1959; student Columbia U., 1964. Asst. news dir. WISN-TV, Milw., 1960-63; news correspondent CBS News, N.Y.C., Chgo., Washington, 1964—. CBS fellow, 1963-64; recipient Emmy award for news coverage Acad. TV Arts and Scis., 1972, 85, 87, Radio News reporting award Overseas Press Club, 70, 75. Mem. Soc. Profl. Journalists, White House Corrs. Assn. Roman Catholic. Avocations: wine, music, running. Office: CBS News 2020 M St NW Washington DC 20036

PLANTINGA, ALVIN, philosophy educator, author; b. Ann Arbor, Mich., Nov. 15, 1932; s. Cornelius A. and Lettie Gertrude (Bossenbroek) P.; m. Kathleen Ann DeBoer, June 16, 1955; children: Carl, Jane, Harry, Ann. A.B., Calvin Coll., 1954; M.A., U. Mich., 1955; Ph.D., Yale U., 1958; several hon. degrees. Instr. Yale U., New Haven, 1957-58; assoc. prof. Wayne State U., Detroit, 1958-63; prof. Calvin Coll., Grand Rapids, Mich., 1963-82; John A. O'Brien prof. philosophy U. Notre Dame, Ind., 1982—, dir. Ctr. for Philosophy of Religion, 1983—; dir. summer seminar Coun. Philosophic Studies, Grand Rapids, 1973; dir. summer seminars NEH, Grand Rapids, 1975, 76, 78, co-dir., 1984; dir. Notre Dame Ctr. Philosophy of Religion. Author: God and Other Minds, 1967, The Nature of Necessity, 1974, God, Freedom and Evil, 1974, Does God Have A Nature?, 1980, Faith and Rationality, 1983, Warrant: The Current Debate, 1993, Warrant and Proper Function, 1993. Fellow Ctr. Advanced Study in Behavioral Scis., 1968-69, NEH, 1975-76, 87, 95-96, Guggenheim fellow, 1971-72, vis. fellow Balliol Coll., Oxford, Eng., 1975-76; Gifford lectr., 1987, Wilde lectr., 1988. Mem. Am. Philos. Assn. (pres. cen. divsn. 1982), Soc. Christian Philosophers (pres. 1983-86). Home: 50505 Hollyhock Rd South Bend IN 46637-2021 Office: U Notre Dame Dept Philosophy Notre Dame IN 46556

PLANTS, WALTER DALE, elementary education educator, minister; b. Middlefield, Ohio, June 8, 1942; s. William E. and Hazel A. Plants; m. Sarah A. Gaddis, July 5, 1962; children: Dale Anthony, Jeanette Marie. BD, Azusa Pacific U., 1967; MEd, U. Nev., 1970. Cert. elem. tchr., ednl. administr. Elem. tchr. Churchill County Sch. Dist., Fallon, Nev., 1967-69, 70-72, 81—; grad. asst. U. Nev., Reno, 1969-70; tchr. Kingman (Ariz.) Elem. Sch. Dist. #4, 1972-77; head sci. program E. C. Best Elem. Sch., Fallon, 1988—; adj. instr. Ariz. State U., Tempe, 1977-77; cons. sci. Ariz. State Dept. Edn., 1975-77. Bd. dirs. Solar Energy Commn. Mohave County, Ariz., 1974; coord. County Sci. Fair, 1988-93; active Western Regional Sci. Fair Com.; sci. fair coord. Churchill County, 1989-94; mem. com. Regional Sci. Fair 1992-94. HEW fellow, 1969; NSF grantee, 1973; AIMS Found. scholar, 1988; recipient Ariz. State PTA award, 1977, Ruth Neldon award Ariz. State Dept., 1977, Conservation award Big Sandy Natural Resources Conservation Dist. Ariz., 1976, Community Builder Svc. award Masons, Fallon, 1991, Disting. Leadership award, 1991, 92, 93; named State Tchr. of Yr. Nev. PTA, 1991, Conservation Tchr. of Yr., 1991; named to Congl. Select Edn. panel U.S. Congress, 1993. Mem. NEA, AAAS, Nat. Sci. Tchrs. Assn., Nat. Coun. Tchrs. Math., Internat. Reading Assn., Nat. State Tchr. of Yr., Churchill County Edn. Assn. (Tchr. of Yr. 1989), Internat. Platform Assn., Nat. Arbor Day Found., World Wildlife Fund, Nat. Parks and Conservation Assn., Nat. Audubon Soc., Nev. State Tchrs. of Yr. (pres. 1994-95), Phi Delta Kappa. Office: E C Best Mid Sch 750 E Williams Ave Fallon NV 89406-3096

PLAPP, BRYCE VERNON, biochemistry educator; b. DeKalb, Ill., Sept. 11, 1939; s. Vernon Edgar and Eleanor Barbara (Kautz) P.; m. Rosemary Kuhn, June 13, 1962; children—Brendan Bryce, Laurel Andrea. B.S., Mich. State U., East Lansing, 1961; Ph.D., U. Calif.-Berkeley, 1966. Research assoc. J.W. Goethe U., Frankfurt/Main, Fed. Republic Germany, 1966-68; research assoc. Rockefeller U., N.Y.C., 1968-70; faculty U. Iowa, Iowa City, 1970—, prof. biochemistry, 1979—. Contbr. articles to profl. jours.; mem. editorial bd. Jour. Biol. Chemistry, Archives Biochemistry and Biophysics. Am. Cancer Soc. fellow, 1966-68. Mem. Am. Soc. for Biochemistry and Molecular Biology, Am. Chem. Soc., Sigma Xi. Avocations: travel, sports. Office: U Iowa Dept Biochemistry 4-370 BSB Iowa City IA 52242

PLASIL, FRANZ, physicist; b. Prague, Czechoslovakia, May 17, 1939; came to U.S., 1960; s. Frank and Eva (Wenger) P.; m. Catherine Logan, Feb. 15, 1964 (div. Sept. 1979); 1 child, Maia; m. Carol Baratz, Apr. 12, 1980. BS, Queen Mary Coll., U. London, 1960; PhD, U. Calif., Berkeley, 1964. Chemist Lawrence Berkeley (Calif.) Lab., 1964-65; rsch. assoc. Brookhaven Nat. Lab., Upton, N.Y., 1965-67; rsch. staff physics div. Oak Ridge (Tenn.) Nat. Lab., 1967-78, group leader physics div., 1978-86, sect. head physics div., 1986—. Contbr. articles to Annals of Physics, Phys. Rev., Phys. Rev. Letters. Recipient Alexander von Humboldt award 1985. Fellow Am. Phys. Soc. Achievements include definition of angular-momentum-imposed limits on the stability of rotating nuclei. Home: 964 W Outer Dr Oak Ridge TN 37830-8607 Office: Oak Ridge Nat Lab PO Box 2008 Oak Ridge TN 37831-6001

PLASKETT, THOMAS G., transportation company executive; b. Raytown, Mo., Dec. 24, 1943; s. Warren E. and Frances S. (Winegar) P.; m. Linda Lee

Maxey, June 8, 1968; children—Kimberly, Keith. B.I.E., Gen. Motors Inst.; M.B.A., Harvard U. Supr. indsl. engring. Gen. Motors, Flint, Mich., 1968, supt. indsl. engring., 1969-73; sr. staff asst., treas Gen. Motors, N.Y.C., 1973; asst. controller Am. Airlines, N.Y.C., 1974, v.p. mktg. adminstrn., 1975-76, sr. v.p. fin., 1976-80; sr. v.p. mktg. Am. Airlines, Dallas, from 1980; pres., chief exec. officer Continental Airlines Inc., Houston, Tex., until 1988; chmn., chief exec. officer, pres. Pan Am Corp., N.Y.C., 1988-91; mng. dir. Fox Run Capital Assocs., 1991—; dir., interim pres., CEO, acting CFO Greyhound Lines, Inc., Dallas, 1994-95, chmn., dir., 1995—; bd. dirs. Tandy Corp., Ft. Worth. Mem. visitors com. Edwin L. Cox Sch. Bus.; mem. bus. adv. com. Northwestern U. Transp. Ctr.; trustee GMI Engring. and Mgmt. Inst., Flint, Mich. Avocations: golf, skiing, squash. Office: Pan Am Corp 9 King Rd Rockleigh NJ 07647-2501*

PLAT, RICHARD VERTIN, corporate finance executive; b. San Jose, Calif., July 14, 1929; s. Gaston and Frances (Vertin) P.; children from previous marriage: Julie, Carl, Marsha; m. Janet Toll Davidson, Dec. 19, 1992. BEE, U. Santa Clara, 1951; MBA, Washington U., St. Louis, 1957. Sr. ind. econ. Stanford Rsch. Inst., Menlo Park, Calif., 1959-65; dir. planning Litton Industries, Inc., Beverly Hills, Calif., 1965-70; v.p. Waltham Industries, N.Y.C., 1970-71, Computer Machinery Corp., L.A., 1971-77; exec. v.p. Pacific Scientific Co., Newport Beach, Calif., 1978—; bd. dirs. Powertec Indsl. Corp., Rock Hill, S.C., Automation Intelligence, Inc., Duluth, Ga., High Yield Tech., Inc., Sunnyvale, Calif., Helisys, Inc., Torrance, Calif., Pacific Sci. Ltd., Royce Thompson Ltd., Eng., Pacific Sci. S.A.R.L., France, Pacific Sci. GmbH, Eduard Bautz GmbH, Fed. Republic of Germany, Pacific Sci. Internat., Inc., U.S., V.I. 1st lt. U.S. Army, 1951-54. Mem. Fin. Execs. Inst. (bd. dirs., v.p. 1984—). Republican. Club: Jonathan (L.A.), Balboa Bay (Newport Beach, Calif.). Home: 2027 Bayside Dr Corona Del Mar CA 92625-1707 Office: Pacific Scientific Co 620 Newport Center Dr Newport Beach CA 92660-6420

PLATE, THOMAS GORDON, newspaper editor; b. N.Y.C., May 17, 1944; s. John William and Irene (Henry) P.; m. Andrea I. Margolis, Sept. 22, 1979; 1 child, Ashley Alexandra. AB, Amherst Coll., 1966; MPA, Princeton U., 1968. Writer Newsweek, N.Y.C., 1968-70; editor Newsday, L.I., N.Y., 1970-72; sr. editor N.Y. Mag., N.Y.C., 1972-75; editor edit. page L.A. Herald Examiner, 1978-82; sr. editor Time Mag., N.Y.C., 1982-83; editor in chief Family Weekly, N.Y.C., 1984-85; editor edit. pages N.Y. Newsday, N.Y.C., 1986-89, L.A. Times, 1990—; vis. asst. prof. UCLA. Author: Understanding Doomsday, 1971, Crime Pays!, 1975, Secret Police, 1981; co-author: Commissioner, 1978. Recipient Best Deadline Writing award Am. Soc. Newspaper Editors, 1981, Best Edit. awards L.A. Press Club, 1979, 80, 81. Mem. Century Assn. (N.Y.), UCLA Faculty Assn., Phi Beta Kappa. Avocations: tennis, fiction writing, computer games. Office: LA Times Times Mirror Sq Los Angeles CA 90053

PLATER, WILLIAM MARMADUKE, English language educator, academic administrator; b. East St. Louis, Ill., July 26, 1945; s. Everett Marmaduke and Marguerite (McBride) P.; m. Gail Maxwell, Oct. 16, 1971; children: Elizabeth Rachel, David Matthew. BA, U. Ill., 1967, MA in English, 1969, PhD in English, 1973. Asst. dir. Unit One, asst. to dean Coll. Liberal Arts and Scis. U. Ill., Urbana, 1971-72, acting dir. Unit One, 1972-73, asst. dean Coll. Arts and Scis., 1973-74, asst. dir. Sch. Humanities, 1974-77, dir., 1977-83, assoc. coordinator interdisciplinary programs, 1977-83; prof. English, dean Sch. Liberal Arts Ind. U., Indpls., 1983-87; dean of faculties Ind. U.-Purdue U., Indpls., 1987—, exec. vice chancellor, 1988—; cons. in field. Author: The Grim Phoenix: Reconstructing Thomas Pynchon, 1978, also articles, revs., poetry. Bd. dirs. Ind. Com. for Humanities, 1986-92, Ind. Repertory Theatre, 1987-93, Children's Mus., 1992—, U. Ill. YMCA, Urbana, 1982-83, Herron Gallery Contemporary Art, 1987—. Recipient Program Innovation prize Am. Acad. Ednl. Devel., 1982. Mem. MLA, Midwest MLA. Home: 3919 Cooper Ln Indianapolis IN 46208-3136 Office: Ind U-Purdue U Adminstrn Bldg Indianapolis IN 46202

PLATER-ZYBERK, ELIZABETH MARIA, architectural educator; b. Bryn Mawr, Pa., Dec. 20, 1950; d. Josaphat and Maria (Meysztowicz) P.-Z.; m. Andres M. Duany, June 12, 1976. BA in Architecture, Princeton U., 1972; MArch, Yale U., 1974. Registered architect, Fla. Architect, prin. Andres Duany & Elizabeth Plater-Zyberk, Architects, Miami, Fla., 1979—; prof. U. Miami, 1979—; dean Sch. Architecture U. Miami, 1995—. Contbr. numerous articles to profl. jours. and popular publs. Mem. adv. coun. Princeton (N.J.) U. Sch. Architecture, 1982—, trustee 1987-91, 93-2003; mem. vis. com. MIT Sch. Architecture, 1990—. Mem. AIA, Archtl. Club Miami (pres. 1982-87). Office: 1023 SW 25th Ave Miami FL 33135-4824

PLATIS, JAMES G., secondary education educator; b. Detroit, Mar. 23, 1927; s. Sam and Myra (Theodore) P.; m. Mary Lou Campbell, Aug. 16, 1974. BS in Physical Edn., Ind. U., 1955, MS in Edn., 1965; postgrad., Ind. State U., 1967. Cert. physical edn. tchr., Ind. Foreman Cast Armor, Inc., East Chicago, Ind., 1951-53; Youngstown Sheet & Tube, East Chicago, 1953-54; dir., tchr. East Chicago Pub. Schs., 1955—; sports editor East Chicago Globe/Calumet News, 1973-78, Herald Newspapers, Merrillville, Ind., 1973-78. Contbr. articles to newspapers, jours. Founder East Chicago Hall of Fame, 1975, Little Olympics, East Chicago, 1956; pres. Ind. Am. Amateur Baseball Congress, 1954-57, commr., 1984-95; dir. No. Ind. State Sports Mus., 1988-95. Named to Ind. Amateur Baseball Hall of Fame, 1962, East Chgo. Hall of Fame, 1976, All-Am. Amateur Baseball Congress, 1955, 56, The Athletic Congress Masters All-Am., 1986, 87, 88, 89, 90, 91, 92, 93, 94; selected to 90 Yr. Greatest Athletes in East Chgo. History, Nat. Athletic Congress, 1990; named Amateur Coach of Yr., U.S. Baseball Fedn. Ind., 1990, Amateur Runner-up Coach of Yr., 1988; recipient 16 World and 24 Nat. No. 1 track rankings, Athletic Congress Masters, 1989, 90, 91, 92, 93-94, 95, 14 League Batting Titles, 12 MV League Player awards; mem. team won 48 League Championships, 49 Playoff championships, 35 Ind. State Baseball Championships, 7 World Regional Titles, 5 World Finalist, 2 runner-up World Champions, Nat. C.I.O. Baseball Championship. Fellow Nat. Assn. Basketball Coaches, Am. Assn. Health, Phys. Edn. and Recreation; mem. Athletic Dirs. Assn. Sportswriters Guild, VFW, Am. Legion. Republican. Avocations: reading, running, baseball, writing. Home: 427 Fisher St Munster IN 46321 Office: E Chgo Pub Schs 2700 Cardinal Dr East Chicago IN 46312-3150

PLATIS, TOM GUST, lawyer, oil company executive; b. Price, Utah, Dec. 8, 1939; s. Gust Nick and Matilda (Hvala) P.; m. Helen J. Rasmussen, July 3, 1964; children: Tiffany, Christopher, John, Andrea. AS, Coll. Ea. Utah, 1960; JD, U. Utah, 1964. Bar: Utah 1964, Calif. 1975, Kans. 1978. Law clk. to presiding justice Utah Supreme Ct., Salt Lake City, 1963-65; pvt. practice law Salt Lake City, 1965-68; asst. atty. gen. State of Utah, 1964-68; judge City of Price, 1968-72; adminstrv. law judge Calif. Bd. of Unemployment and Appeals, Sacramento and Fresno, Calif., 1972-77; sr. adminstrv. law judge Calif. Bd. of Unemployment and Appeals, Fresno, 1977-78; pres., gen. counsel Hwy. Oil, Inc., Topeka, 1978—. Active Crimestoppers of Topeka, Inc. Mem. ABA, Topeka Bar Assn., California State Bar, Utah State Bar. Office: Hwy Oil Inc 534 S Kansas Ave Ste 1200 Topeka KS 66603-3434*

PLATNER, JOHN LELAND, process equipment company executive; b. Palmyra, Wis., Oct. 13, 1932; s. Lyle K. and Irma Amelia (Mundshau) P. m. Mary Lois Singer, June 19, 1954; children: Teresa Ann, Karen Jean, Susan Marie, Thomas Charles, Jean Marie, Patricia Ann. BSME, U. Wis., Madison, 1954; postgrad., U. Wis., Milw. Registered profl. engr., Wis. Corp. v.p. Allis-Chalmers Corp., Milw., 1976-88, v.p. strategic planning and bus. devel., 1982-83, v.p. tech., 1983-84, pres. Allis. Chalmers Energy and Minerals Co., 1984-88, pres. Allis-Chalmers Solids Process Equipment Co., 1986-88; pres. Boliden Allis, Inc., Milw., 1988-90, Svedala Inc., Milw., 1991—; also bd. dirs. Svedala Inc., Waukesha, Wis. Served to capt. USAF, 1954-57. Mem. Am. Mining Congress (bd. govs. mfrs. div.), Am. Mgmt. Assn., Am. So. Mech. Engrs., Soc. Mining Engrs. Republican. Avocation: commercial instrument pilot. Office: Svedala Inc 20965 Crossroads Cir Waukesha WI 53186*

PLATNER, WARREN, architect; b. Balt., June 18, 1919; s. Warren Kelly and Alice Darling (Chapman) P.; m. Joan Payne, 1945; children: Bronson, Joan, Sharon, Madeleine. B.Arch., Cornell U., 1941. Assoc. Eero Saarinen and Assocs. (architects), 1950-65; propr. Warren Platner Assocs. (architects),

New Haven, 1965—; vis. lectr. archtl. schs. Prin. works include Kent Meml. Library, Suffield, Conn., 1972, Princeton U. Prospect Center, 1970, MGIC Hdqrs, Milw., 1973, Am. Restaurant, Kansas City, Mo., 1974; malls at Water Tower Pl., Chgo., 1975, Windows on the World, N.Y.C., 1976, Standard Brands Research Center, Wilton, Conn., 1979, Providence Athenaeum, 1980; Sea Containers Hdqrs., London, 1983, Wildflower Restaurant Lodge, Vail, Colo., 1985, Porter, Wright, Morris & Arthur Headqrs., Columbus, Ohio, 1986, Pan Am Bldg. additions, N.Y.C., 1987, ships Fantasia and Fiesta, 1990, Carlyle Hotel additions, 1990, Fair Residence, 1990, Friedman Residence, 1993. Recipient Rome prize architecture, 1955; advanced research Fulbright award architecture, 1955; Graham Found. award advanced studies fine arts, 1962; 1st ann. award Designers Lighting Forum, 1975; Pres.'s fellow R.I. Sch. Design, 1980; Interior Design Hall of Fame award, 1985; also several internat. design awards. Fellow AIA, Am. Acad. in Rome. Address: 18 Mitchell Dr New Haven CT 06511-2516

PLATNICK, NORMAN I., curator, arachnologist; b. Bluefield, W.Va., Dec. 30, 1951; s. Philip and Fannie (Kascenewsky) P.; m. Nancy Stewart Price, June 14, 1970; 1 child, William Durin. BS in Biology, Concord Coll., 1968; MS in Zoology, Mich. State U., 1970; PhD in Biology, Harvard U., 1973. Asst. curator Am. Natural History, N.Y.C., 1973-77, assoc. curator, 1977-82, curator, 1982—, chmn. dept. entomology, 1987-94; sci. attaché Consulate of Gondwana, N.Y.C., 1976—. Author: Advances in Spider Taxonomy, 1989, 93; co-author: Systematics and Biogeography, 1981; co-editor: Advances in Cladistics, 1983. V.p. Ctr. Internat. de Documentation Arachnologie, 1986-89. Fellow Willi Hennig Soc. (founder, pres. 1990-92); mem. Am. Arachnological Soc. (charter, membership sec. 1976—). Office: Am Mus Natural History Central Pk W At 79th St W New York NY 10024

PLATOU, JOANNE (DODE), museum director; b. Mpls., Jan. 6, 1919; d. Wesley Richmond and Catherine Harriet (Fisher) Pierson; m. Ralph Victor Platou, Jan. 23, 1942 (dec. Sept. 1968); children: Peter Erling, Thomas Stoud, Mary Kirk Platou Marloff. BS, U. Minn., 1939; MFA, Tulane U., 1959. Columnist Mpls. Tribune, 1939-42; med. photographer Ochsner Clinic, New Orleans, 1943-46; tchr. photography Metairie (La.) Pk. Country Day Sch., 1946-51; free lance artist New Orleans, 1953-68; curator edn. New Orleans Mus. Art, 1969-75; chief curator Historic New Orleans Collection, 1976-86, dir., 1986-92, dir. emerita, 1992—; bd. dirs. Arts Coun. New Orleans, 1972-88, Long Vue House and Gardens, New Orleans, 1982-88; tchr. mus. career course Tulane U., New Orleans, 1983-87. Curator exhbns. The Wit of It, 1972, The Art Works, 1972, The Camera, 1974; author catalogue, curator exhbn. Alfred R. Waud, 1979. NEH grantee, New Orleans Mus. Art, 1975. Mem. Am. Mus. Assn., Friends of the Cabildo, Coll. Art Assn., Am. Assn. State and Local History. Avocations: travel, gardening.

PLATT, CHARLES ADAMS, architect, planner; b. N.Y.C., May 16, 1932; s. William and Margaret (Littell) P.; m. Joan Mathieson, June 20, 1958; children—Sylvia, Ethan, Virginia Lippincott. A.B., Harvard, 1954, M.Arch., 1960. Gen. ptnr. Smotrich & Platt, N.Y.C., 1965-85, Charles A. Platt Ptnrs., N.Y.C., 1985-89; ptnr. Platt Byard Dovell, 1989—; assoc. prof. Columbia U. Grad. Sch. Architecture and Planning, 1988—. Mem. nat. panel arbitrators Am. Arbitration Assn.; bd. dirs. Pub. Health Research Inst., N.Y.C., 1982-92, The New 42nd Street, 1990—; Municipal Art Soc., N.Y.C., 1966-78, 85—; pres. bd. trustees Augustus St.-Gaudens Meml., 1977-91; commr. N.Y.C. Landmarks Preservation Commn., 1979-84. Recipient nat. honor award for excellence in architecture AIA, 1969, Bard award for civic architecture and urban design, 1969, 85, Record Interiors award, 1970, 73, 75, Record House awards, 1971, 78. Mem. AIA. Club: Century (N.Y.C.). Home: 1261 Madison Ave New York NY 10128-0569 Office: Platt Byard Dovell 19 Union Sq W New York NY 10003-3304

PLATT, FRANKLIN DEWITT, history educator; b. Marion, La., Nov. 15, 1932; s. Robert Baxter and Ethel Estelle (White) P.; m. Dixie Ferguson, Aug. 4, 1956; 1 dau. Dixie. B.A., La. State U., 1955; Rockefeller Bros. Theol. fellow, Union Theol. Sem., 1955-56; A.M., Washington U., St. Louis, 1963, Ph.D., 1969. Instr. dept. humanities Wash. State U., 1964-69, asst. prof., 1969-72, assoc. prof., 1972-77, prof., 1977-89, asst. chmn. dept. humanities, 1971-78, chmn., 1978-80, prof. dept. history, 1989—. Co-author: The Western Humanities, 1991 (named Best Coll. Textbook Bookbuilders West 1991), Readings in the Western Humanities, 1994. Served with USNR, 1956-60. Home: 1134 Southlawn Ave East Lansing MI 48823-3041 Office: Mich State U Dept History East Lansing MI 48824

PLATT, JAN KAMINIS, former county official; b. St. Petersburg, Fla., Sept. 27, 1936; d. Peter Clifton and Adele (Diamond) Kaminis; m. William R. Platt, Feb. 8, 1962; 1 son, Kevin Peter. B.A., Fla. State U., 1958; postgrad. U. Fla. Law Sch., 1958-59, U. Va., 1962, Vanderbilt U., 1964. Pub. sch. tchr. Hillsborough County, Tampa, Fla., 1959-60; field dir. Girl Scouts Suncoast Coun., Tampa, 1960-62; city councilman Tampa City Council, 1974-78; county commr. Hillsborough County, 1978-94; chmn. Hillsborough County Bd. County commrs., 1980-81, 83-84, ret., 1994; chmn. Tampa Bay Regional Planning Council, 1982; chmn. West Coast Regional Water Supply Authority, Tampa, 1985; chmn. Hillsborough County Council of Govts., 1976, 79; chmn. Sunshine Amendment Drive 7th Congrl. Dist., Tampa, 1976; chmn. Community Action Agy., Tampa, 1980-81, 83-84; chmn. Tampa Charter Revision Commn., 1975; chmn. Prison Sitting Task Force, Tampa, 1983, Tampa Housing Study Com., 1983, Met. Planning Orgn., Tampa, 1984, Bd. Tax Adjustment, Tampa, 1984; appointee Constitution Revision Commn., Fla., 1977, HRS Dist. IV Adv. Council, Fla.; mem. Hillsborough County Expressway Authority, Taxicab Commn.; vice chmn. steering com. Nat. Assn. Counties Environ. Task Force; Bd. dirs. March of Dimes, Tampa, The Fla. Orchestra, Tampa; trustee Hillsborough County Hosp. Authority, Tampa, 1984-94; pres. Suncoast Girl Scout Council, Citizens Alert, Tampa, Bay View Garden Club; v.p. Hillsborough County Bar Aux.; mem. adv. bd. Northside Community Mental Health Ctr.: Access House, Tampa; active mem. Arts Council of Tampa-Hillsborough County, 1983-85, Drug Abuse Coordinating Council Orgn., Tampa, Bd. Criminal Justice, Tampa, Fla. Council on Aging, Inebriate Task Force, Tampa, Tampa Downtown Devel. Authority Task Force, Tampa Sports Authority, Tampa Area Mental Health Bd., Children's Study Commn., Manahill Area Agy. on Aging, Tampa, Athena Soc., Tampa Area Com. on Foreign Affairs, League of Women Voters. Recipient Outstanding Community Athena Soc. Service award, 1976, First Annual Humanitarian award Nat. Orgn. for Prevention of Animal Suffering, 1981, Spessard Holland Meml. award Tampa Bay Com. for Good Govt., 1979, First Lady of Yr. award Beta Sigma Phi, 1980, Women Helping Women award Soroptimist Internat. Tampa, 1983, Eliza Wolff award Tampa United Methodist Ctrs., 1982, Good Govt. award Tampa Jaycees, 1983, Good Govt. award League of Women Voters, 1983. Mem. Judicature Soc., State Assn. County Commrs. Fla. (at-large dir.), AAUW (bd. dirs.), Mortar Bd., Garnet Key, Phi Beta Kappa, Phi Kappa Phi. Democrat. Episcopalian. Home and Office: 3531 Village Way Tampa FL 33629-8950

PLATT, JOSEPH BEAVEN, former college president; b. Portland, Oreg., Aug. 12, 1915; s. William Bradbury and Mary (Beaven) P.; m. Jean Ferguson Rusk, Feb. 9, 1946; children: Ann Ferguson Walker, Elizabeth Beaven Garrow. BA, U. Rochester, 1937; PhD, Cornell U., 1942; LLD, U. So. Calif., 1969, Claremont McKenna Coll., 1982; DSc, Harvey Mudd Coll. 1981. Instr. physics U. Rochester, N.Y., 1941-43, from asst. prof. to prof., 1946-56, assoc. chmn. dept. physics, 1954-56; staff mem. radiation lab. MIT, Cambridge, 1943-46; pres. Harvey Mudd Coll., Claremont, Calif., 1956-76, now part-time sr. prof. physics; pres. Claremont U. Ctr., 1976-81; trustee Aerospace Corp., 1972-85, Consortium for Advancement of Pvt. Higher Edn., 1985-92 (First Lady); dir. AEC, 1949-51; cons. U.S. Office Ordnance Rsch. NSF, 1953-56; mem. com. on sci. in UNESCO, Nat. Acad. Scis.-NRC, 1960-62, mem. com. on internat. orgns. and programs, 1962-64; sci. advisor U.S. Del., UNESCO Gen. Conf., Paris, 1960, alt. del. 1962; mem. panel on internat. sci. Pres.'s Sci. Adv. Com., 1961; chmn. Subcom. on Sino-Am. Sci. Cooperation, 1965-79; trustee Analytic Svcs., Inc., 1958-89, chmn., 1961-89; mem. adv. com. on sci. edn. NSF, 1965-70, 72-76, chmn., 1969-70, 73-74, 74-75; bd. dirs. Lincoln Found., 1979-85, Bell & Howell Corp., 1978-88, Am. Mut. Fund, 1981-88, DeVry, Inc., 1984-87, Sigma Rsch., 1983-87, Jacobs Engring. Co., 1978-86. Author: Harvey Mudd College: The First Twenty YEars, 1994. Trustee China Found. for Promotion of Edn. and Culture, 1966—, Carnegie Found. for Advancement Tchg., 1970-78; chmn. scholar

com. Master Plan for Higher Edn. Calif., 1971-73; mem. Carnegie Coun. for Policy Studies in Higher Edn., 1975-80. Fellow Am. Phys. Soc.; mem. IEEE, Automobile Club So. Calif. (bd. dirs. 1973-90, chmn. bd. dirs. 1986-87), Calif. Club, Sunset Club, Twilight Club, Cosmos Club, Bohemian Club, Phi Beta Kappa, Sigma Xi, Phi Kappa Phi. Home: 452 W 11th St Claremont CA 91711-3833

PLATT, LEWIS EMMETT, electronics company executive; b. Johnson City, N.Y., Apr. 11, 1941; s. Norval Lewis and Margaret Dora (Williams) P.; m. Joan Ellen Redmund, Jan. 15, 1983; children: Caryn, Laura, Amanda, Hillary. BME, Cornell U., 1964; MBA, U. Pa., 1966. With Hewlett Packard, Waltham, Mass., 1966-71, engring. mgr., 1971-74, ops. mgr., 1976-77, div. gen. mgr., 1974-80, group gen. mgr., Palo Alto, Calif., 1980-84, v.p., 1983-85, exec. v.p., 1987-92, pres., CEO, chmn., 1993—; dir. Molex Inc., Lisle, Ill.; trustee Pacific Telesis. Trustee Waltham Hosp., 1978-80, Wharton Sch. Bd. Overseers, 1993; mem. Mid-Peninsula YMCA, 1980-86; mem. Mid-Peninsula YMCA, 1980—, Cornell U. Coun., 1992, Computer Sys. Policy Project, 1993, Calif. Bus. Roundtable, 1993, Bus. Coun., 1993, Bay Area Coun., 1993, Bus. Roundtable, 1993; vice chmn. Y Coun., 1989. Recipient Red Triangle award Min-Peninsula YMCA, 1992, Internat. Citizens award World Forum Silicon Valley, San Jose, Calif., 1994. Mem. IEEE, Sci. Apparatus Mfg. Assn. (dir. 1978-80). Office: Hewlett Packard Co 3000 Hanover St Palo Alto CA 94303

PLATT, LUCIAN BREWSTER, geology educator; b. Syracuse, N.Y., Apr. 9, 1931; s. Washington and Emily (Kent) P.; m. Kathrin Straumann, May 27, 1957; children: David W., Martin B. B.S., Yale U., 1953, M.S., 1957, Ph.D., 1960. Asst. prof. Villanova U., 1961-64; assoc. prof. George Washington U., 1964-70; assoc. prof. geology Bryn Mawr (Pa.) Coll., 1970-80, prof. geology, 1980—; with U.S. Geol. Survey, Denver, 1965-85. Mem. Commn. on Sci. and the Arts, Franklin Inst., Phila., 1982-92, chmn. 1990-92; trustee Phila. Coll. Pharmacy and Sci., 1988—. Fellow Geol. Soc. Am.; mem. Am. Assn. Petroleum Geologists, Am. Geophys. Union. Club: Cosmos. Office: Bryn Mawr Coll Dept Geology Bryn Mawr PA 19010

PLATT, MARK E., motion picture company executive. Pres. Orion Pictures Prodns., L.A. Office: Orion Pictures Prodns 1888 Century Park E Los Angeles CA 90067-1702

PLATT, NICHOLAS, Asian affairs specialist, ambassador; b. N.Y.C., Mar. 10, 1936; s. Geoffrey and Helen (Choate) P.; m. Sheila Maynard, June 28, 1957; children: Adam, Oliver, Nicholas. B.A. cum laude, Harvard U., 1957; M.A., Johns Hopkins U., 1959. Commd. fgn. service officer Dept. State, 1959; vice consul Windsor, Ont., Can., 1959-61; Chinese lang. trainee, 1962-63; polit. officer consulate gen. Hong Kong, 1964-68; chief Asian Communist areas div. Bur. Intelligence and Research, Dept. State, Washington, 1969, chief North Asia div., 1970, dept. dir. Exec. Secretariat staff, 1971, dir. staff, 1972-73; chief polit. sect. U.S. Liaison Office, Peking, China, 1973-74; 1st sec. Am. embassy, Tokyo, 1974-77; dir. Office of Japanese Affairs, Dept. State, 1977-78; mem. staff Nat. Security Council, White House, 1978-79; dep. asst. sec. for internat. security affairs Dept. Def., 1980-81; dep. asst. sec. for internat. orgn. affairs Dept. State, 1981-82; amb. Lusaka, Zambia, 1982-84; exec. sec., psl. asst. to sec. state Dept. State, 1985-87; amb. Manila, The Philippines, 1987-91, Pakistan, 1991-92; pres. Asia Soc., N.Y.C., 1992—. Recipient Meritorious award exemplary achievement pub. adminstrn. William A. Jump Found., 1973, Disting. Civilian Svc. medal Dept. Def., 1981, Presdl. Merit award, 1985, 87, Disting. Honor award U.S. Dept. State, 1987, 91, Wilbur Carr award, 1992. Mem. N.Y. Council Fgn. Relations. Clubs: Metropolitan (Washington); Century (N.Y.C.). Home: 131 E 69th St New York NY 10021-5158

PLATT, PETER GODFREY, lawyer; b. Battle Creek, Mich., May 11, 1937; s. Frank Kenneth and Louise Joy (Godfrey) P.; children: Peter G. Jr., Geoffrey B. BA, Yale U., 1959, JD, 1962. Bar: Calif. 1962. Assoc. Brobeck, Phleger & Harrison, San Francisco, 1962-68, ptnr., 1969-90; ptnr. Coudert Bros., San Francisco, 1990—. Trustee Grace Cathedral, San Francisco, 1976—, chmn. bd. trustees, 1985-89; mem. bd. govs. San Francisco Symphony, 1981—, v.p., 1993—; bd. dirs. Arthritis Found., San Francisco, 1983-86; chancellor Episcopal Diocese of Calif., 1989—. Mem. Calif. Bar Assn., San Francisco Bar Assn. Republican. Episcopalian. Clubs: San Francisco Golf, Pacific Union (San Francisco), Burlingame Country (Hillsborough, Calif.) (sec. 1980), Links (N.Y.C.). Avocation: golf. Office: Coudert Bros Ste 3300 Four Embarcadero Ctr San Francisco CA 94111

PLATT, SHERMAN PHELPS, JR., publishing consultant; b. N.Y.C., Mar. 29, 1918; s. Sherman Phelps and Penelope (Sears) P.; m. Leila Bronson, Jan. 11, 1941 (div. 1968); children: Sherman Phelps III, John, Bronson; m. Margaret McClure Smithers, 1968. Grad., Taft Sch., 1936; B.A., Yale, 1940. With Dodd, Mead & Co., N.Y.C., 1940-82, beginning as editor, successively salesman, prodn. mgr., sec., dir., exec. v.p., then pres., until 1982; v.p. dir. Apollo Edits., Inc., N.Y.C., 1962-72; pub. cons., 1982—. Served as 1st lt. inf. U.S. Army, 1943-46. Mem. Yale Club (N.Y.C.). Home: 38 Aylesbury Circle Madison CT 06443-3434

PLATT, THOMAS COLLIER, JR., federal judge; b. N.Y.C., N.Y., May 29, 1925; s. Thomas Collier and Louise Platt; m. Ann Byrd Symington, June 25, 1948; children: Ann Byrd, Charles Collier, Thomas Collier, III, Elizabeth Louise. B.A., Yale U., 1947, LL.B., 1950. Bar: N.Y. 1950. Assoc. Root, Ballantine, Harlan, Bushby & Palmer, N.Y.C., 1950-53; asst. U.S. atty. Bklyn., 1953-56; assoc. Bleakley, Platt, Schmidt, Hart & Fritz, N.Y.C., 1956-60, ptnr., 1960-74; judge U.S. Dist. Ct. (ea. dist.) N.Y., Bklyn., 1974-88, chief judge, 1988-95; former dir. Phoenix Mut. Life Ins. Co., RAC Corp., McIntyre Aviation, Inc.; atty. Village of Laurel Hollow, N.Y., 1958-74; acting police justice Village of Lloyd Harbor, N.Y., 1958-63. Alt. del. Republican Nat. Conv., 1964, 68, 72; del. N.Y. State Rep. Conv., 1966; trustee Brooks Sch., North Andover, Mass., 1968-82, pres., 1970-74. Served with USN, 1943-46. Mem. Fed. Judges Assn. (sec., bd. dirs. 1982-91). Episcopalian. Clubs: Phelps Assn. (New Haven) (bd. govs. 1960—); Cold Spring Harbor Beach (N.Y.) (bd. mgrs. 1964-70); Yale of N.Y.C. Office: US Dist Ct Uniondale Ave at Hempstead Tpke Uniondale NY 11553

PLATT, TREVOR CHARLES, oceanographer, scientist; b. Salford, Eng., Aug. 12, 1942; arrived in Can., 1963; s. John and Lily (Hibbert) P.; m. Shubha Sathyendranath, Feb. 24, 1988. BSc, U. Nottingham, U.K., 1963; MA, U. Toronto, Ont., Can., 1965; PhD, Dalhousie U., Halifax, N.S., Can., 1970. Rsch. scientist Bedford Inst. Oceanography, Dartmouth, N.S., 1965-72, chief biol. oceanography, 1972—; chmn. Joint Global Ocean Flux Study, 1991-93. Recipient Rosenstiel medal U. Miami, 1984, A.G. Huntsman medal A.G. Huntsman Found., 1992. Fellow Royal Soc. Can., Acad. Sci. Can.; mem. Am. Soc. Limnology and Oceanography (pres. 1990-92, G.E. Hutchinson medal 1988). Home: 33 Crichton Park Rd, Dartmouth, NS Canada B3A 2N9 Office: Bedford Inst Oceanography, Dartmouth, NS Canada B2Y 4A2

PLATT, WILLIAM HENRY, lawyer; b. Allentown, Pa., Jan. 25, 1940; s. Henry and Genevieve (McElroy) P.; m. Maureen Hart, Nov. 29, 1969; children: Meredith H., William H., James H. AB, Dickinson Coll., 1961; JD, U. Pa., 1964. Bar: Pa. 1967, U.S. Supreme Ct. 1971. Ptnr. Yarus and Platt, Allentown, 1967-77; asst. pub. defender Lehigh County (Pa.), 1972-75, chief pub. defender, 1975-76, dist. atty., 1976-91; ptnr. Eckert, Seamans, Cherin & Mellott, 1991—; mem. criminal procedural rules com. Supreme Ct. Pa. 1982-92, chmn., 1986-92. Mem. Gov.'s Trial Ct. Nominating Commn. Lehigh County, 1984-87; mem. Pa. Commn. on Crime and Delinquency Victim Services Adv. Com., 1983-91. Served with M.P., U.S. Army, 1964-66. Mem. ABA, Pa. Bar Assn., Lehigh County Bar Assn., Nat. Assn. Dist. Attys. (state dir. 1982-84), Pa. Bar Assn. (pres. 1983-84, exec. com. 1980-86, tng. inst. chmn. 1986-91), Pa. Bar Inst. (bd. dirs. 1989—, treas. 1994-95). Home: 435 Iroquois St Emmaus PA 18049-1718 Office: Eckert Seamans Cherin & Mellott Sovereign Bldg 609 Hamilton Mall Allentown PA 18101

PLATT, WILLIAM RADY, pathology educator; b. Balt., July 25, 1915; s. Louis Abraham and Ida Selma (Rady) P.; m. Shirley Ades, June 26, 1949 (dec. 1972); children: Karen J., Lois A., James R.; m. Jeanette Krulevitz Fineman, Mar. 4, 1979. BS in Pharmacy, U. Md., 1936, MD, 1940.

Diplomate Am. Bd. Pathology. Intern St. Joseph's Hosp., Lexington, Ky., 1940-41; resident in pathology Emory U. Hosp., Atlanta, 1941-44; instr. in pathology Yale U. Sch. Medicine, New Haven, 1944-45, Washington U., St. Louis, 1945-46, U. Pa., Phila., 1948-52; dir. lab. Norton Meml. Hosp., Louisville, 1946-48, West Jersey Hosp., Camden, N.J., 1948-52, Mo. Bapt. Hosp., St. Louis, 1952-76, U.S. Pub. Health Service Hosp., Batl., 1977-81; profl. Southwestern Med. Sch., Dallas, 1976-77, prof., 1976-77; lectr. Johns Hopkins U., Balt., 1977—; profl. Chinese U., Hong Kong, 1985-86. Author: Color Atlas and Textbook of Hematology, 1975, 2d edit., 1979; editor-in-chief Pathology Update, 1972-87. Fellow cytology Cornell U. 1946, radioisotope research AEC, 1947, tropical diseases Tulane U., 1943. Fellow ACP; mem., Coll. Am. Pathologist, Am. Soc. Hematology, Am. Soc. Clin. Pathology, Internat. Acad. Pathology, Rho Chi., Johns Hopkins Club, U. Club. Clubs: Johns Hopkins; Univ. (Balt.). Home and Office: 12 Hamlet Hill Rd Baltimore MD 21210-1501

PLATTEN, PETER MICHAEL, III, bank holding company executive; b. Green Bay, Wis., July 25, 1939; s. Peter M. and Helen V. (Brown) P.; m. Bonnie Anna Lipps, June 27, 1964; children: Carolyn, Peter, Christopher. BBA in Acctg. and Fin., U.Wis., Green Bay, 1962; postgrad., Northwestern U., 1970. Mgmt. trainee Continental Bank, Chgo., 1964-65; with West Side State Bank, Green Bay, 1965-67, asst. v.p., 1967-73; exec. v.p. West Bank and Trust, Green Bay, 1973-80, pres., chief exec. officer, 1980-83; pres. United Bankshares, Inc. (merged with Valley Bancorp), Green Bay, 1973-83; chmn., CEO M&I Bank Northeast (formerly West Bank and Trust), Green Bay, 1983-94; also bd. dirs. Valley Bank, N.E. (formerly West Bank and Trust), Green Bay; vice chmn., dir. Marshall & Isley Corp., Milw., Wis., 1989-94; chief oper. officer Valley Bancorp., Appleton, Wis., 1983-89, chief exec. officer, 1989-94, also bd. dirs.; chmn. Valley Bank Northeast, Green Bay, 1993—; bd. dirs. Pro-Drive, Inc., Green Bay; mem. Carter Golembe Assocs., mgmt. seminars; vice chmn. Marshall & Isley Corp., 1994—, also bd. dirs. B. dirs. U. Wis. Found.; capital campaign chmn., adv. dir. St. Mary's Hosp., adv. dir. and profl. care com. St Vincent Hosp., vp., dir. Ft. Howard Cemetery Assn.; treas., bd. dirs. Tri-High Sch. Found., Assn. for Retarded Children; mem. Gov.'s Task Force on Edn., Taxation; mem. Green Bay Park Bd., bus. adv. bd. St. Norbert Coll., Chmn. Town of Hobart Planning Com.; bd. dirs. St. Joseph Acad., co-chmn. capital fund campaign; bd. dirs. Jr. Achievement, Green Bay Comty. Found.; bd. visitors U. Wis. Mem. Wis. Taxpayers Alliance (bd. dirs.), World Bus. Coun., The Bankers Roundtable Emerging Issues Com., Chief Exec. Orgn., Bascom Hill Soc. Avocations: sailing, skiing, football, fitness, manufacturing maple syrup. Home: 1555 Arapahoe Trail Green Way WI 54313 Office: Valley Bancorp PO Box 1061 100 W Lawrence St Appleton WI 54912-1061

PLATTHY, JENO, cultural association executive; b. Dunapataj, Hungary, Aug. 13, 1920; s. Joseph K. and Maria (Dobor) P.; m. Carol Louise Abell, Sept. 25, 1976. Diploma, Peter Pazmany U., Budapest, Hungary, 1942; PhD, Ferencz J., U. Kolozsvar, Hungary, 1944; MS, Cath. U., 1965; PhD (hon.), Yangmingshan U., Taiwan, 1975; DLitt (hon.), U. Libre Asie, Philippines, 1977. Lectr. various univs., 1956-59; sec. Internat. Inst. Boston, 1959-62; adminstrv. asst. Trustees of Harvard U., Washington, 1962-85; exec. dir. Fedn. Internat. Poetry Assns., UNESCO, 1976—; pub. New Muses Quar., 1976—. Author: Winter Tunes, 1974, Ch'u Yuan, His Life and Works, 1975; Springtide, 1976 (opera) Bamboo, Collected Poems, 1981, The Poems of Jesus, 1982, Holliness in a Worldly Garment, 1984, Ut Pictures Poeta, 1984, European Odes, 1985, The Muthocal Poets of Greece, 1985, Book of Dithyrambs, 1986, Asian Elegies, 1987, Space Eclogues, 1988, Cosmograms, 1988, Nova Comoedia, 1988, vols. II-III, 1992, Bartok: A Critical Biography, 1988, Plato: A Critical Biography, 1990, Near-Death Experiences in Antiquity, 1992, Celebration of Life, 1992, Idylls, 1992, Elegies Asiatiques, 1992, Paeans, 1993, Rhapsodies, 1994, Prosodia, 1994, Visions, 1994, Prophecies, 1994, Epyllia, 1994, Budapestitol Tokyoig, 1994, 2d edit., 1995, Walking Two Feet Above the Earth, 1995; numerous others, transactions; editor in chief Monumenta Classica Perennia, 1967-84. Named Poet Laureate 2d World Congress of Poets, 1973; recipient Confucius award Chinese Poetry Soc., 1974, Yunus Emre award 12th Internat. Congress of Poets, Istanbul, Turkey, 1991, Jacques Raphael-Leygues prize Société des Poètes Français, 1992, French Ordre des Arts et des Lettres (officer) 1992. Mem. Internat. Soc. Lit., PEN, Die Literariscke Union, ASCAP, Internat. Poetry Soc., Melbourne Shakespeare Soc., 3d Internat. Congress Poets (pres. 1976, poet laureate 1976). Office: UNESCO Fedn Internat Poetry Assns PO Box 579 Santa Claus IN 47579-0579

PLATTI, RITA JANE, educator, draftsman, author, inventor; b. Stockton, Calif., Aug. 29, 1925; d. Umbert Ferdinand and Concettina Maria (Natoli) Strangio; m. Elvin Carl Platti, July 27, 1955; 1 child, Kimberley Jane. Student, Dominican Coll., 1943-45; AB in Math, U. Pacific, 1947, postgrad., 1947-52, 68. Cert. sec. tchr., Calif.; lic. real estate agt., Calif. Farmer Escalon, Calif., 1943—; tchr. math St. Mary's High Sch., Stockton, 1947-49, 52, 54; chem. analyst Petri Winery, Escalon, 1949; draftsman Kyle Steel Co., Stockton, 1950-52; pvt. practice as draftsman Stockton, 1952-66; tchr. math Montezuma Sch., Stockton, 1956-57, Davis Elem. Sch., Stockton, 1957-58; with rental bus., 1958-81; tchr. math Amos Alonzo Stagg High Sch., 1961-80, Humphreys Coll., 1981-83, Hamilton Jr. High Sch., 1984-90; owner, involved in prodn. and mktg. R.J. Creations, 1991—; speaker workshops Stanislaus State U., 1992, Calif. Math. Coun., Fresno State U., 1992, Nat. Sci. Found. Conf., 1993; speaker math./sci. conf. Calif. State U., Bakersfield, 1994, 95; evaluator Math. Framework (K-12) Calif. State Dept. Edn. Author: Math Proficiency Plateaus, 1979, Preparing Fundamentals of The Use of Sound in the Teaching of Mathematics, 1994; author, pub. series, 1979-86; 3 patents in field. Mem. NEA, Calif. Tchrs. Assn. Democrat. Roman Catholic. Avocations: inventing, mathematics theoretical development, poetry, piano, environmental clean up.

PLATTO, CHARLES, lawyer; b. Bklyn., Nov. 19, 1945; s. Irving and Mollie Platto; m. Leslie Joan Stoller, Mar. 19, 1969; children: Jamie, Carey, Jody, Terry. BA, U. Pa., 1966; JD, U. Mich., 1969; LLM, NYU, 1974. Bar: N.Y. 1970, Vt. 1992, N.H. 1992, U.S. Dist. Ct. (so. and ea. dists.) N.Y. 1972, U.S. Ct. Appeals (2d cir.) 1974, U.S. Supreme Ct. 1974, U.S. Tax Ct. 1989, U.S. Ct. Appeals (9th cir.) 1990, U.S. Dist. Ct. N.H., Vt., 1992. Atty. Community Legal Services, Phila., 1969-71; assoc. Cahill, Gordon & Reindel, N.Y.C. and Paris, 1971-79; ptnr. Cahill, Gordon & Reindel, N.Y.C., 1980-91, Brooks, McNally, Whittington, Platto & Vitt, Norwich, Vt., 1991—; adj. assoc. prof. NYU Law Sch., Vt. Law Sch. Mem. N.Y. State Bar Assn. (mem. exec. com. bus. law sect., rep. ho. dels.), Internat. Bar Assn. (chmn. internat. litigation com.). Office: Brooks McNally Whittington Platto & Vitt PO Box 200 Norwich VT 05055-0200

PLATTS, FRANCIS HOLBROOK, plastics engineer; b. Brunson, S.C., Sept. 15, 1939; s. Holbrook Trowbridge and Mildred Ruth (Thomar) P.; m. Martha Ann Price, July 1963; children: Martha Susan Platts Gilliam, David Holbrook. BS in Chem. Engring., U.S.C., 1962. Chem. engr. U.S. Naval Weapons Lab., Dahlgren, Va., 1962-64; engr. Westinghouse Electric Corp., Hampton, S.C., 1964-74, sr. engr., 1974-89, mgr. engring. and quality assurance, 1989-91, mgr. design and mktg. svcs., 1991-93, div. engr. mgr. 1993—; chmn. NEMA DLATC Engring. Com., Washington, 1991—; chairholder Color Marketing Group, Alexandria, Va., 1991—. Pres., mem. Hampton Jaycees, 1964-74; chmn., bd. dirs. Hampton County Watermelon Festival, 1965-76; mem., chmn. blood bank bd. South Atlantic region ARC, Savannah, Ga., 1974—; mem. Western Carolina Higher Edn. Com., Allendale, 1982—. Mem. ASTM, Hampton Rotary (sr., pres. 1981-82, Oustanding Mem. award 1975-82), Hampton Gamecock Club (pres. 1966—). Methodist. Achievements include development of decorative high-pressure laminate specialty product, research on color and design trends for interior finish applications. Office: Westinghouse Electric Corp PO Box 248 Hampton SC 29924-0248

PLATTS-MILLS, THOMAS ALEXANDER E., immunologist, educator, researcher; b. Colchester, Essex, Eng., Nov. 22, 1941; came to U.S., 1982; s. John Faithful F. and Janet Katherine (Cree) P-M.; m. Roberta Rosenstock, Apr. 9, 1970; children: Eliza, Timothy, James, Oliver. BA, Balliol Coll., Oxford (Eng.) U., 1963; MB, BChir, Oxford U., 1967; PhD, London U., 1982. Registrar in medicine Bury St. Edmunds, and New Market, Suffolk, Eng. 1968-71; fellow in medicine Johns Hopkins U. Balt., 1971-74; staff mem. Med. Rsch. Coun., U.K., 1976-82; hon. cons. physician Northwick Park Hosp., London, 1978-82; prof. medicine, head div. allergy and clin.

immunology U. Va., Charlottesville, 1982—; mem. immunological scis. study sect. NIH, 1988. Mem. editorial bd. Jour. Allergy Clin. Immunology, Clin. and Exptl. Immunology, Clin. Allergy, Jour. Immunological Methods; contbr. articles to profl. jours. Grantee NIH. Fellow Royal Coll. Physicians, Am. Acad. Allergy; mem. Assn. Am. Physicians, Southeastern Allergy Assn. (Hal Davidson award 1986, pres. 1987-88), Brit. Soc. Allergy and Clin. Office: U Va Dept Medicine PO Box 225 Charlottesville VA 22902-0225

PLATZ, GEORGE ARTHUR, III, lawyer; b. Safford, Ariz., Sept. 12, 1939; s. George Arthur and Dickey Azalea (Slagle) P.; m. Mary Condon, Sept. 20, 1963; m. Andrea Maxwell, Oct. 25, 1979; children—Susan, Stephanie. B.S., Northwestern U., 1960; LL.B., Harvard U., 1963. Bar: Ill. 1964, U.S. Dist. Ct. (no. dist.) Ill. 1964, U.S. C. Appeals (7th cir.) 1964, U.S. Tax Ct. 1981, U.S. Supreme Ct. 1981. Assoc Sidley & Austin, Chgo., 1964-71, ptnr., 1972—. Mem. ABA, Chgo. Bar Assn., Chikaming Country Club, Mid-Day Club. Office: Sidley & Austin 1 First Nat Plz Chicago IL 60603

PLATZ, TERRANCE OSCAR, utilities company executive; b. Cadillac, Mich., Jan. 20, 1943; s. Jay and Gladys Pearl (Bigelow) P.; m. Nellie Mae Cross, Dec. 15, 1961 (div. Oct. 1977); children: Michael, Christopher, Michelle; m. Dorothy Fay Beasley, Aug. 4, 1984. AS in Electronics Engring. Tech., Pensacola Jr. Coll., 1972. Enlisted USN, 1962, resigned, 1981; adj. instr. in electronics Pensacola (Fla.) Jr. Coll., 1981—; instrument/elec. control technician Escambia County Utilities Authority, Pensacola, 1981-87, instrument/elec. control supr., 1987-94, instrument/elec. mgr., elec. engr., 1994—; instrument controls advisor/cons. to various engring. firms, 1987—. Mem. Instrument Soc. Am. Democrat. Mem. Ch. of God. Achievements include design of cost saving variable speed drive systems, instrument control systems, SCADA systems, wastewater treatment plants, water wells, sewage lift stations, continuous emissions monitoring systems, data acquisition systems. Home: 5045 Bankhead Dr Pensacola FL 32526-9413 Office: Escambia County Utilities Authority 401 W Government St Pensacola FL 32501-5572

PLATZMAN, GEORGE WILLIAM, geophysicist, educator; b. Chgo., Apr. 19, 1920; s. Alfred and Rose I. (Kaufman) P.; m. Harriet M. Herschberger, Feb. 19, 1945 (dec. 1985). B.S., U. Chgo., 1940, Ph.D, 1948; M.S., U. Ariz., 1941. Instr. U. Chgo., 1942-45, research asso., 1947-48, mem. faculty, 1949—, head phys. scis. in coll., 1959-60, prof. meteorology, 1960-90, chmn. dept. geophys. scis., 1971-74, emeritus prof., 1990—; cons. Inst. Advanced Study, Princeton, 1950-53. Contbr. articles to profl. jours. Hydrologic engr. C.E., U.S. Army, 1945-46. Guggenheim fellow, 1967-68. Fellow AAAS, Am. Geophys. Union, Am. Meteorol. Soc. (editor jour. 1948-49, mem. publs. com. 1966-70, Meisinger award 1966). Office: Dept Geophys Scis U Chgo 5734 Ellis Ave Chicago IL 60637

PLAUT, ERIC ALFRED, psychiatrist, educator; b. N.Y.C., Nov. 16, 1927; s. Alfred and Margaret (Blumenfeld) P.; m. Eloine Raab, Sept. 5, 1976. B.S., Columbia U., 1949, M.D., 1953. Diplomate: Am. Bd. Psychiatry and Neurology. Intern Montefiore Hosp., Bronx, N.Y., 1953-54; psychiat. resident State Hosp., Worcester, Mass., 1954-55, Mass. Meml. Hosp., Boston, 1956-57; cons. psychiatrist Mass. Dept. Corrections, 1957; fellow student health psychiatry U. Calif., Berkeley, 1957-58; practice medicine specializing in psychiatry Berkeley, 1958-74; staff psychiatrist Kaiser Hosp., Oakland, Calif., 1958-62, Cowell Meml. Hosp., U. Calif., Berkeley, 1958-62; cons. psychiatrist Bur. Indian Affairs, Dept. Interior, 1967-68; program chief Berkeley Mental Health Services, 1968-71; dep. commr. Ind. Dept. Mental Health, Indpls., 1974-76; commr. Conn. Dept. Mental Health, Hartford, 1976-81; prof. Northwestern U. Med. Sch., Chgo., 1981-93; asst. clin. prof. psychiatry U. Calif. Med. Sch., San Francisco, 1958-74; asso. clin. prof. psychiatry U. Ind. Med. Sch., Indpls., 1975-76; clin. prof. psychiatry U. Conn. Med. Sch., Farmington, 1978-81, Yale U. Med. Sch., 1979-81; cons. Assembly Sci. Adv. Coun., Calif. Legislature, 1970; chmn. Bay Area region Calif. Conf. Local Mental Health Dirs., 1970-71; gen. ptnr. Vanguard Investments, Berkeley, 1971-78. Author: Grand Opera: Mirror of the Western Mind, 1993; mem. editl. bd. Yale Psychiat. Quar., 1976-81; contbr. articles to profl. jours. Bd. dirs. ACLU, Berkeley, 1960-65; mem. task force on acess and barriers Pres.'s Commn. on Mental Health, 1977; mem. psychiatry panel Grad. Med. Edn. Nat. Adv. Com., 1979-81. With USN, 1944-46. Fellow Am. Psychiat. Assn. (cons. task force on govt. rels. 1973-76, chmn. com. public info. 1975-76, mem. com. cert. in adminstrv. psychiatry 1979-82, chmn. task force on problems of Americans overseas 1984-88, chmn. task force on joint meeting with German Psychiat. Soc. 1989-90); mem. com. Chron. Ment. Ill; mem. No. Calif. Psychiat. Soc. (chmn. com. law and legis. 1968-72, fed. legis. rep. 1972-74, councillor 1972-73, pres.-elect 1973-74), Calif. Med. Assn. (alt. del. 1968-71), Alameda-Contra Costa Med. Assn. (chmn. mental health com. 1972), Conn. Med. Soc., Nat. Assn. State Mental Health Program Dirs. (dir.). Address: 912 Michigan Ave Evanston IL 60202 Office: Rm 203 2530 Ridge Evanston IL 60201

PLAUT, JAMES SACHS, foundation executive; b. Cin., Feb. 1, 1912; s. Jacob M. and Alice S. (Sachs) P.; m. Mary E. Friedlander, May 24, 1933; children—Susan, Thomas. Student, Auteuil Day Sch., Paris, 1925-26, Taft Sch., Watertown, Conn., 1927-28; A.B., Harvard, 1933, A.M., 1935; D.F.A. (hon.), Wheaton Coll., 1974. Asst. dept. of fine arts Harvard U., 1934-35; asst. to curator of paintings Mus. Fine Arts, Boston, 1935-39; dir. Inst. Contemporary Art, Boston, 1938-56; trustee and dir. emeritus Inst. Contemporary Art, 1956-61; cons. indsl. design for State of Israel; chmn. Exhbn. Services Internat.; dir. devel., trustee New Eng. Aquarium, Boston, New Eng. Conservatory Music; sec. gen. World Crafts Council, 1964-76; pres. Aid to Artisans, Inc., 1976—; dep. commr. gen. of U.S. to Brussels World Expn. 1958. Author: Steuben Glass, 1948, Oskar Kokoschka, 1948, (with Octavio Paz) In Praise of Hands, 1974; also catalogues for exhbns.; Contbr. to bulls. of art museums, Atlantic Monthly. Vice pres. Old Sturbridge Village, Mass., 1959-61; Gen. chmn. Cambridge Community Fund, 1950 campaign; mem. vis. com. Mus. Fine Arts, Boston Sch. Artisanry, Boston U.; chmn. vis. com. Wheaton Coll.; mem. council for arts Mass. Inst. Tech. Served with USNR, 1942-46, ETO, North Africa; lt. comdr. Res. Decorated Legion of Merit; Chevalier, Legion d'Honneur; knight 1st Class Order of St. Olav, Norway; comdr. Royal Order of Leopold, Belgium. Clubs: Country (Boston), Badminton and Tennis (Boston); Harvard (N.Y.C.), Century Assn. (N.Y.C.). Home: 10 Longwood Dr Westwood MA 02090

PLAUT, JONATHAN VICTOR, rabbi; b. Chgo., Oct. 7, 1942; s. W. Gunther and Elizabeth (Strauss) P.; m. Carol Ann Fainstein, July 5, 1965; children: Daniel Abraham, Deborah Maxine. BA, Macalester Coll., 1964; postgrad., Hebrew Union Coll., Jerusalem, 1967-68; BHL, Hebrew Union Coll., Cin., 1968, MA, 1970, DHL, 1995; DD, Hebrew Union Coll., 1995. Ordained rabbi, 1970. Rabbi Congregation Beth-El, Windsor, Ont., Can., 1970-84; sr. rabbi Temple Emanu-El, San Jose, Calif., 1985-93; dir. comty. outreach and involvement Jewish Fed. of Met. Detroit, 1993-95; vis. Rabbinic scholar Temple Beth El, Bloomfield Hills, Mich., 1995—; pres. JUP Fund Raising Cons., Inc., Farmington Hills, Mich., 1994—; lectr. Assumption Coll., 1972-84, St. Clair Coll., 1982-84. Aid to Handicapped Scouts Sch., 1972-84, St. Clair Coll., 1982; adj. asst. prof. Santa Clara U., 1985-93; vis. Rabbinic scholar Temple Beth El, 1993—; pres. JVP Fund Raising Cons., 1994—. Contbg. author: Reform Judaism in America: A Biographical Dictionary and Sourcebook, 1993; editor: Through the Sound of Many Voices, 1982, Jour. Can. Jewish Hist. Soc., 1976-83; also articles; host weekly program Religious Scope, Sta. CBET-TV, Religion in News, Sta. CKWW, 1971-84. Pres. Jewish Nat. Fund Windsor, 1978-81, chmn. bd. dirs., 1981-84; chmn. United Jewish Appeal Windsor, 1981-83, State of Israel Bonds, Windsor, 1980; nat. bd. dirs. Jewish Nat. Fund Can., 1972-84; pres. Reform Rabbis of Can., 1982-84; bd. dirs. Can. Jewish Congress, 1978-84, Jewish Family Svc. Santa Clara County, 1987-90, Jewish Fedn. Greater San Jose, 1986-93; chaplain San Jose Fire Dept., 1987-93; mem. exec. cabinet United Jewish Appeal, Windsor, 1971-84, mem. nat. rabbinic cabinet, 1993—; mem. exec. com. Windsor Jewish Community Coun., 1970-84, chmn. 1975-84; mem. adv. coun. Riverview unit Windsor Hosp. Ctr., 1972-81; pres. Credit Counselling Svc. Met. Windsor 1977-79. Mem. NCCJ, Can. Jewish Congress (nat. exec. bd. 1978-84), Can. Jewish Hist. Soc. (nat. v.p. 1974-84), Calif. Bd. Rabbis, Rabbinic Assn. Greater San Jose (chmn. 1986-87), Ctrl. Conf. Am. Rabbis, Nat. Assn. Temple Educators. Home: 30208 Kingsway Dr Farmington Hills MI 48331-1648 Office: Temple Beth El 7400 Telegraph at 14 Mile Bloomfield Hills MI 48010

PLAUT, NATHAN MICHAEL, retired lawyer; b. Cin., Nov. 25, 1917; s. Jacob Michael and Alice (Sachs) P.; m. Mary Hollis, Aug. 16, 1945; children—Alison P. Palmer, James Hollis. A.B., Harvard U., 1939, spl. student Law Sch., 1946; LL.B., U. Mich., 1941. Bar: Ohio 1941, Mass. 1946, N.H. 1947, U.S. Dist. Ct. N.H. 1947. Ptnr. Faulkner, Plaut, Hanna, Freund & Worthen P.C., Keene, N.H., 1953-82, ret., 1982; mem. visitor's com. U. Mich. Law Sch., 1962-68. Del., N.H. Constl. Conv., 1947—. Served to maj. USMCR, 1942-45. Fellow Am. Coll. Estate and Trust Counsel (ret.), Am. Bar Found., N.H. Bar Found. (hon. life fellow); mem. ABA (ho. of dels. 1972-89, state del. 1979-84, bd. govs. 1984-87, coun. sr. lawyers divsn. 1985-91, mil. law com. 1987-93, bd. elections 1990-92), N.H. Bar Assn. (pres. 1971-72, hon. inactive), Boston Bar Assn. (ret.), Cheshire County Bar Assn., Harvard Club (Boston), Rotary (Paul Harris fellow). Home: Peg Shop Rd Keene NH 03431-5502 Office: c/o Faulkner Plaut Hanna Freund and Worthen PC 91 Court St Keene NH 03431-0527

PLAUT, WOLF GUNTHER, minister, author; b. Muenster, Germany, Nov. 1, 1912; emigrated to U.S., 1935, arrived in Canada, 1961; s. Jonas and Selma (Gumprich) P.; m. Elizabeth Strauss, Nov. 10, 1938; children: Jonathan, Judith. LLB, U. Berlin, 1933, JD, 1934; MHL, Hebrew Union Coll., Cin., 1939, DD, 1964; LLD, U. Toronto, 1978; DLitt, Cleve. Coll. Jewish Studies, 1979; LLD, York U., 1987. Ordained rabbi, 1939. Rabbi B'nai Abraham Zion, Chgo., 1939-48, Mt. Zion Temple, St. Paul, 1948-61; sr. rabbi Holy Blossom Temple, Toronto, Ont., Can., 1961-77; sr. scholar Holy Blossom Temple, 1978—; adj. prof. York U., 1991—. Author: Mount Zion, 1956, The Jews in Minnesota, 1959, The Book of Proverbs: A Commentary, 1961, Judaism and the Scientific Spirit, 1962, The Rise of Reform Judaism, 1963, The Growth of Reform Judaism, 1964, The Case for the Chosen People, 1965, Your Neighbour Is a Jew, 1967, Page 2, 1971, Genesis: A Modern Commentary, 1974, Time to Think, 1977, Hanging Threads, 1978, (U.S. title) The Man in the Blue Vest, 1980, Numbers: A Modern Commentary, 1979; editor, chief author: The Torah: A Modern Commentary, 1981, 9th edit., 1994, Unfinished Business (autobiography), 1981, Refugee Determination in Canada, 1985, The Letter, 1986, The Magen David: How the Six Pointed Star Became the Jewish Symbol, 1991, The Man Who Would Be Messiah, 1988, 2d edit., 1990, Asylum--A Moral Dilemma, 1995; co-author: The Rabbi's Manual, 1988; editor: Affirmation, 1981-87; editl. contbr. Toronto Globe and Mail, 1962-94, Can. Jewish News; bibliography pub. in Through the Sound of Many Voices, 1982; contbr. to encys., anthologies, other books, articles to mags., newspapers. Chmn. Minn. Gov.'s Commn. on Ethics in Govt., 1958-61; pres. St. Paul Gallery and Sch. Art (name changed to Minn. Mus.), 1953-59, World Federalists Can., 1966-68; nat. pres. Can. Jewish Congress, 1977-82; vice chmn. Ont. Human Rights Commn., 1978-85; bd. govs. World Union for Progressive Judaism, 1970— pres. Central Conf. Am. Rabbis, 1983-85, bd. inquiry human rights cases, 1987—. Capt. AUS, 1943-46. Decorated Bronze Star; named officer Order of Can.; awarded Order of Ont.; Plaut Chair for Project Mgmt. established in his honor at Ben-Gurion U., Israel, 1991, Plaut Manor (pub.-assisted housing project) named in his and his wife's honor, Toronto. Clubs: York Racquets, Oakdale Golf and Country. Office: 1950 Bathurst St, Toronto, ON Canada M5P 3K9

PLAVOUKOS, SPENCER, advertising executive; b. N.Y.C., May 30, 1936; s. George and Elva (Murzi) P.; m. Harriet Phylis Gladstone, Jan. 9, 1964; children: Stacy, Matthew. B.S., Syracuse U., 1961. Account exec. SSC&B, Inc., N.Y.C., 1961-64; account exec. Grey Advt., 1964-67; v.p., dir. account service Manoff Advt., N.Y.C., 1967-79; exec. v.p. SSC&B, N.Y.C. 1979; chmn., chief exec. officer Lintas: N.Y. (formerly SSC&B), N.Y.C., until 1991; formerly vice chmn. Lintas: USA; pres., Lintas: Worldwide, chmn., Lintas: Americas, 1991—. Clubs: Country of New Canaan, Marco Polo (N.Y.C.), St. James (London). Office: Lintas Worldwide 1 Dag Hammarskjold Plz New York NY 10017-2201

PLAVSIC, BRANKO MILENKO, radiology educator; b. Zagreb, Yugoslavia, Croatia, Feb. 14, 1947; came to U.S. 1989; s. Milenko and Nevenka P.; m. Valerie H. Drnovsek, Aug. 26, 1991. MD, U. Zagreb, 1972, MS, 1974, PhD, 1975. Asst. prof. U. Zagreb, 1986, prof. radiology, chief abdominal radiology, 1988; prof. radiology, vice-chmn., dir. abdominal radiol./rsch. Tulane U., New Orleans, 1991—. Co-author: (with A.E. Robinson, R.B. Jeffrey) Gastrointestinal Radiology: A Concise Text, 1992; contbr. articles to profl. jours. Avocations: poetry, music. Home: 4460 Lennox Bl New Orleans LA 70131 Office: Tulane U Med Ctr Dept Radiology 1430 Tulane Ave New Orleans LA 70112

PLAWECKI, JUDITH ANN, nursing educator; b. East Chicago, Ind., June 5, 1943; d. Joseph Lawrence and Anne Marilyn (Hamnik) Curosh; m. Henry Martin Plawecki, June 10, 1967; children: Martin H., Lawrence H. BS, St. Xavier Coll., Chgo., 1965; MA, U. Iowa, 1971; PhD, 1974. Asst. prof. Mt. Mercy Coll., Cedar Rapids, Iowa, 1971-73; asst. dept. chmn., assoc. prof., 1974-75; assoc. prof. U. Iowa, 1975-76; asst. dean, assoc. prof. U. Minn. 1976-81; acting dean, assoc. dean and prof. U. N.D., Grand Forks, 1981-82, dean and prof. nursing, 1982-83; dean and prof. nursing Lewis U., Romeoville, Ill., 1983-87; prof. nursing U. South Fla., Tampa, 1987—, dean, 1987-95. Univ. Iowa Fellow, 1973. Mem. ANA, AHNA, Nat. League for Nursing, Older Women's League, Sigma Xi, Sigma Phi Omega, Sigma Theta Tau, Phi Lambda Theta. Office: U South Fla Coll Nursing MDC 22 12901 Bruce B Downs Blvd Tampa FL 33612-4742

PLAYER, GARY JIM, professional golfer; b. Johannesburg, South Africa, Nov. 1, 1935; s. Francis Harry Audley and Muriel (Ferguson) P; m. Vivienne Verwey, 1955; children: Jennifer, Marc, Wayne, Michele, Theresa, Amanda. Ed., King Edward Sch., Johannesburg. Profl. golfer, 1953—; joined PGA, 1957—; winner East Rand Open, Republic of South Africa, 1955-56, Egyptian Matchplay, 1955, South African Open, 1956, 60, 65-69, 72, 75-77, 79, 81, Dunlop Tournament, Eng., 1956, Ampol Tournament, Australia, 1956, 58, 61, Australian PGA, 1957, Coughs Harbour Tournament, Australia, 1957-58, Natal Open, South Africa, 1958-60, 62, 66, 68, Ky. Derby Open, 1958, Australian Open, 1958, 62-63, 65, 69-70, 74, Transvaal Open, South Africa, 1959, 60, 62, 63, 66, South African PGA, 1959-60, 69, 79, 82, Western Province Open, South Africa, 1959-60, 68, 71-72, Dunlop Masters, South Africa, 1959-60, 63-64, 67, 71-74, 76-77, Brit. Open, 1959, 68, 74, Victoria Open, Australia, 1959, Masters Tournament, U.S., 1961, 74, 78, Lucky Internat. Open, U.S., 1961, Sunshine Open, U.S., 1961, Yomiuri Open, Japan, 1961, PGA Championship, U.S., 1962, 72, Sponsored 5000, South Africa, 1963, Liquid Air Tournament, South Africa, 1963; winner Richelieu Grand Prix, Capetown, 1963, Johannesburg, 1963; winner San Diego Open, 1963, Pensacola Open, 1964, 500 Festival Open, U.S., 1964, U.S. Open (1st foreigner to win in 45 yrs.), 1965, Piccadilly World Match Play, Eng., 1965, 66, 68, 71, 73, NTL Challenge Cup, Can., 1965, World Series of Golf, U.S., 1965, 68, 72, World Cup Internat., 1965, Australian Wills Masters, 1968, 69, Tournament of Champions, U.S., 1969, 78, Greater Greensboro Open, 1970, Dunlop Internat., Australia, 1970, Gen. Motors Open, South Africa, 1971, 73, 74, 75, 76, Jacksonville Open, 1971, Nat. Airlines Open, U.S., 1971, New Orleans Open, 1972, Japan Airlines Open, 1972, Brazilian Open, 1972, 74, So. Open, U.S., 1973, Rand Internat. Open, South Africa, 1974, Gen. Motors Internat. Classic, South Africa, 1974, Memphis Classic, 1974, Ibergolf Tournament, Spain, 1974, La Manga Tournament, Spain, 1974, Gen. Motors Classic, 1975, ICL Transvaal, South Africa, 1977, World Cup Individual, Philippines, 1977, Houston Open, 1978, Kronenbrau Masters, South Africa, 1979, Sun City, S. Am., 1979, Trophee Boigny, Ivory Coast, 1980, Chilean Open, S. Am., 1980, Australian Tooth Gold Coast Classic, 1981, Johnnie Walker Trophy, Spain, 1984, Quadel Srs. Classic, 1985, PGA Srs. Championship, 1986, 1990, Northville Srs., 1987, Sr. Tournament, 1987, U.S. Sr. Open, 1987; PGA Srs. Championship, 1988, Aetna Challenge, 1988, Southwestern Bell Classic, 1988, USGA Srs., 1988, Sr. British Open, 1988. Named Christian Athlete of Yr. So. Bapt. Conv., 1967; Richardson award Golf Writers Assn. Am., 1975; named to World Golf Hall of Fame; hon. mem. R&A, 1994, Skills Challenge, 1994. Office: Gary Player Group 3300 P G A Blvd Ste 100 Palm Beach Gardens FL 33410 Office: PO Box 785629, Sandton 2146, South Africa

PLEASANT, JAMES SCOTT, lawyer; b. Anniston, Ala., July 14, 1943; s. James C. and Barbara (Scott) P.; m. Susan M. Pleasant, May 17, 1966; children: Deborah Kaye, Carol Ann, Julie Ruth. BS, Oreg. State U., 1965; JD summa cum laude, Williamette U., 1972. Bar: Tex. 1972, U.S. Dist. Ct. (no. dist.) Tex. 1973, U.S. Ct. Appeals (5th cir.) 1975, U.S. Supreme Ct.

1977. Ptnr. Gardere & Wynne LLP, Dallas, 1972—. Mem. Smithsonian Assn., Washington, 1985—, Dallas Mus. of Art 1987—. Capt. U.S. Army, 1966-69, Vietnam. Mem. ABA (partnership law sect. 1969—), Tex. Bar Assn. (partnership law sect. 1989—), Vietnam Pilots Assn., Dustoff Assn. Office: Gardere & Wynne LLP 1601 Elm St Ste 3000 Dallas TX 75201-4761

PLEASANTS, HENRY, music critic; b. Wayne, Penn., May 12, 1910; s. Henry and Elizabeth Washington (Smith) P.; m. Virginia V. Duffey, Aug. 31, 1940. Student, Phila. Music Acad., Curtis Inst. Music; D.M. (hon.), Curtis Inst. Music, 1977. Music critic Phila. Evening Bulletin, 1930-42; Central European music corr. N.Y. Times, 1945-55; with U.S. Fgn. Service, Munich, 1950-52, Bern, 1952-56, Bonn, 1956-64; London music critic Internat. Herald Tribune, Paris, 1967—; London editor Stereo Review, N.Y.C., 1967—; lectr. in field. Appearances on T.V., U.K., U.S.A., Europe.; Author: The Agony of Modern Music, 1955, Death of a Music?, 1961, The Great Singers, 1966, Serious Music-And All That Jazz!, 1969, The Great American Popular Singers, 1974; translator, editor various books in field; contbr. articles to musical, lit. jours. Served in U.S. Army, 1942-50, Alaska, ETO, NATOUSA. Decorated Bronze Star (twice). Mem. Authors Guild. Home: 95 Roebuck House, Palace St, London SW1E 5BE, England

PLEDGER, THOMAS ROLON, holding company executive; b. Piedmont, Ala., Jan. 13, 1938; s. John Edward and Mary Susan (Wright) P.; m. Phyllis Rounell Reeves, Oct. 23, 1959; children: Susanne Sheree, Thomas Rolon Jr. Student, U.S. Armed Forces Inst., 1956-58, U. Ala., 1958-59, Pensacola Jr. Coll., 1959-62. With Burnup & Sims, West Palm Beach, Fla., 1960-76; v.p., asst. dir. overseas operations Burnup & Sims, 1967-68, v.p., 1968-69, exec. v.p., 1969-70, pres., gen. mgr., 1970-76, also chief exec. officer, dir., until 1976; chmn. bd., chief exec. officer Rubin Constrn. Co., West Palm Beach, 1976-81; pres., chief exec. officer VCC, West Palm Beach, 1981-83, Dycom Industries, Inc., 1983—; bd. dirs. First Union Bank, Davis Water & Waste Industries, Inc. Served with USNR, 1956-59. Republican. Southern Baptist. Clubs: Mason (32 deg.), Fla. Council of 100; Mayacoo Country, Sailfish of Fla. Home: 16561 Jupiter Farms Rd Jupiter FL 33478 Office: Dycom Industries Inc 450 S Australian Ave West Palm Beach FL 33401-3524

PLENTY, ROYAL HOMER, writer; b. Phila., Aug. 28, 1918; s. Royal Homer and Florence (Gehman) P.; m. Evelyn Treaster, Dec. 15, 1945 (dec. 1958); 1 dau., Evelyn Ann; m. Mildred Craig, Sept. 12, 1959 (div. 1970); m. Gladys Ann Muller, Nov. 14, 1970. B.S. in Econs, U. Pa., 1941. Clk. H.M. Byllesby & Co. (investment bankers), 1941; jr. underwriter New Amsterdam Casualty Co., 1941-42; reporter Phila. office Wall St. Jour., 1942-46; mem. staff Phila. Inquirer, 1946-72, financial editor, 1957-72; dir. pub. relations Levitz Furniture Corp., 1972-73; pub. relations account exec. Aitkin-Kynett Co., Inc., Phila., 1973-75; dir. pub. info. Securities Industry Assn., N.Y.C., 1975-77; corporate relations Merrill Lynch & Co., 1977-78; free-lance editor, writer, 1978—. Mem. Phila. Econ. Assn., Phila. Press Assn., Phila. Investment Traders Assn., Sigma Delta Chi. Unitarian. Home: Harrison Towers Apt 7P Somerset NJ 08873

PLESEC, WILLIAM THOMAS, lawyer; b. Cleve., June 14, 1942. AB, John Carroll U., 1966; JD, Cleve. State U., 1971. Bar: Ohio 1971, D.C. 1981. Trial atty. Antitrust divsn., U.S. Dept. Justice, 1971-75; ptnr. Jones, Day, Reavis & Pogue, Cleve. Office: Jones Day Reavis & Pogue North Point 901 Lakeside Ave Cleveland OH 44114

PLESHETTE, SUZANNE, actress, writer; b. N.Y.C., Jan. 31; d. Eugene and Geraldine; m. Thomas Joseph Gallagher III, Mar. 16, 1968. Student, Sch. Performing Arts, Syracuse U., Finch Coll., Neighborhood Playhouse Sch. of Theatre. Founder, prin. The Bedside Manor (later div. of J.P. Stevens). Theatre debut in Truckline Cafe; star in Broadway prodns. Compulsion, The Cold Wind and the Warm, The Golden Fleecing, The Miracle Worker, Special Occasions; star TV series Bob Newhart Show, 1972-78, Suzanne Pleshette is Maggie Briggs, 1984; starred in TV series Bridges to Cross, 1986-87, Nightingales, 1988-89, The Boys Are Back, 1994-95; star 30 feature films including The Birds, Forty Pounds of Trouble, If It's Tuesday This Must Be Belgium, Nevada Smith, Support Your Local Gunfighter, Hot Stuff, Oh God! Book II; TV movies include Flesh and Blood, Starmaker, Fantasies, If Things Were Different, Help-Wanted Male, Dixie Changing Habits, One Cooks, The Other Doesn't, For Love or Money, Kojak, The Belarus File, A Stranger Waits, Alone In The Neon Jungle, Leona Helmsley: The Queen of Mean, 1990, Battling for Baby, 1991-92, A Twist of the Knife, 1993; writer, co-creator, producer two TV series; published author.

PLESKOW, ERIC ROY, motion picture company executive; b. Vienna, Austria; came to U.S., 1939; Film officer U.S. War Dept., 1946-48; asst. gen. mgr. Motion Picture Export Assn., Germany, 1948-50; continental rep. for Sol Lesser Prodns., 1950-51; with United Artists Corp., Far Eastern sales mgr., 1951-52, South African mgr., 1952-53, German mgr., 1953-58, exec. asst. to continental mgr., 1958-59, asst. continental mgr., 1959-60, continental mgr., 1960-62, v.p. in charge fgn. distbn., 1962, exec. v.p., chief operating officer, 1973, pres., chief exec. officer, 1973-78; pres., chief exec. officer Orion Pictures Co., N.Y.C., 1978-82; pres., chief exec. officer Orion Pictures Corp., N.Y.C., 1982-92, also chmn. bd. dirs., until 1992; ptnr. Pleskow/Spikings Partnership, Beverly Hills, Calif., 1992—. Office: Pleskow/Spikings Partnership 335 N Maple Dr Ste 135 Beverly Hills CA 90210

PLESS, JOHN EDWARD, forensic pathologist, educator; b. Bedford, Ind., 1938. BA, Ind. U., 1960, MD, 1963. Intern South Bend (Ind.) Med. Found. Hosps., 1963-64, resident in anatomy and clin. pathology, 1966-70; instr. pathology Ind. U. Sch. Medicine, South Bend, 1967-70; fellow Forensic Pathology Oka, U. Med. Ctr., 1970-71; asst. prof. Ind. U. Sch. Medicine, Bloomington, 1973-83, prof. pathology, 1983—, now Culbertson prof. pathology. Capt. USMC, 1964-66. Am. Am So. of Farenisc Science, Am. Soc. of Clinicic Pathologist, Coll. of Am. Pathologist, Nat. Assn. of Med. Examiners. Office: Ind U Med Ctr Pathology Med Scien Bldg M 157 Indianapolis IN 46202*

PLESS, VERA, mathematics and computer science educator; b. Chgo., Mar. 5, 1931; d. Lyman and Helen (Blinder) Stepen; m. Irwin Pless, June 15, 1952 (div. 1980); children: Naomi, Benjamin, Daniel. PhB, U. Chgo., 1952; PhD, Northwestern U., 1957. Mathematician USAF, Lincoln, Mass., 1962-72; rsch. assoc. MIT, Cambridge, Mass., 1972-75; prof. math. U. Ill., Chgo., 1975—. Author: The Theory of Error Correcting Codes, 1989; contbr. articles to profl. publs. U. Ill. scholar, 1989-92; recipient Tempo All-Professor Team, Sciences, Chicago Tribune, 1993. Mem. Am. Math. Soc. (chair nominating com. 1984), Math. Assn. Am., IEEE (bd. govs. 1985-89), Assn. Women in Math. Office: UIC MSCS (M/C 249) 851 S Morgan 322 SEO Chicago IL 60607-7045

PLETCHER, DAVID MITCHELL, history educator; b. Faribault, Minn., June 14, 1920; s. Nuba Mitchel and Jean (Hutchinson) P. B.A., U. Chgo., 1941, MA, 1941, PhD, 1946. Asst. U. Chgo., 1943; instr. history U. Iowa, 1944-46; asso. prof. Knox Coll., Galesburg, Ill., 1946-56; asso. prof., then prof. Hamline U., St. Paul, 1956-65; prof. history Ind. U., 1965-90, prof. emeritus, 1990—. Author: Rails, Mines and Progress, Seven American Promoters in Mexico, 1867-1911, 1958, The Awkward Years, American Foreign Relations Under Garfield and Arthur, 1962, The Diplomacy of Annexation, Texas, Oregon and the American War, 1973. Recipient McKnight Found. award, 1962; grantee Social Sci. Research Found., 1950-51, 62-63; grantee Nat. Archives, 1972; Fulbright sr. research fellow, 1953-54. Mem. Orgn. Am. Historians, Am. Hist. Assn. (Albert J. Beveridge award 1957), Soc. Historians Am. Fgn. Relations (v.p. 1979, pres. 1980). Home: 509 N Fess Ave Bloomington IN 47408-3821 Office: Indiana Univ Dept History Ballantine Hall Bloomington IN 47405

PLETCHER, ELDON, editorial cartoonist; b. Goshen, Ind., Sept. 10, 1922; s. Arthur and Dora (Cripe) P.; m. Barbara Jeanne Jones, Jan. 29, 1948; children—Thomas Lee, Ellen Irene. Student, Chgo. Acad. Fine Arts, 1941-42, U. Aberdeen, Scotland, 1945, John Herron Art Sch., Indpls., 1946-47. Editorial cartoonist Sioux City (Iowa) Jour., 1949-66; editorial cartoonist The Times-Picayune, 1966-85; free-lance gag cartoonist Sat. Eve. Post, Rotarian. Nat. Enquirer, other publs. Rep. permanent exhbns., Syracuse U.,

U. South Miss., U. Cin., Boston Mus. Art, Harry S. Truman Library, Lyndon B. Johnson Library, Wichita State U., John F. Kennedy Libr., Richard M. Nixon Libr. Served with AUS, 1943-46. Recipient Christopher award, 1955, Freedoms Found. award, 12 years. Mem. Assn. Am. Editorial Cartoonists. Democrat. Presbyterian.

PLETCHER, JOHN HAROLD, JR., air force officer; b. Findlay, Ohio, May 26, 1945; s. John H. and Bernadette (Gerschutz) P.; m. Phyllis G. Morrin, Jun. 7, 1968; children: Eric, Mary. BS in Aerospace Engring., USAF Acad., 1967; MS in Aerospace Engring., Ill. Inst. Tech. 1969; PhD in Mech. and Aerospace Engring., AF Inst. Tech., 1979. Registered prof. engr., Colo. Commd. 2d lt. USAF, 1967, advanced through grades to col.; pilot 39th Rescue and Recovery Squadron, Cam Ranh AB, Vietnam, 1970-71; pilot and wing air ops. officer 41st Rescue and Recovery Wing, Hickam AFB, Hawaii, 1971-75; assoc. prof. aero., dir. academic ops. USAF Acad., Colorado Springs, Colo., 1978-82; chief systems engr. Aero. Systems Div., Wright Patterson AFB, Ohio, 1982-85; comdr. Frank J. Seiler Rsch. Lab., Colorado Springs, 1985-87; asst. dep. engring. Strategic Def. Initiative, Washington, 1987-90; dir. Armament Directorate, Eglin AFB, Fla., 1990-94; comdr. European Office of Aerospace Rsch. and Devel., London, 1994—. Youth soccer, T-ball coach Dayton, 1982-85. Mem. AIAA, AF Assn., AF Acad. Assn. of Grads. Roman Catholic. Avocations: squash, tennis, chess, gardening, fishing. Home: European Office Aerospace R & D PSC #802 Box 14 FPO AE 09499-0200

PLEWES, THOMAS JEFFREY, economic statistician, government executive; b. Zeeland, Mich., Dec. 15, 1940; s. Lloyd Angus and Joyce (Wicht) P.; m. Elizabeth Marie Hall Feb. 20, 1971; children: Jeffrey Charles, Melissa Joy. BA, Hope Coll., Holland, Mich., 1962; MA in Econs., George Washington U., 1972. Economist U.S. Dept. Labor, Washington, 1962-66, Bur. Labor Standards, Washington, 1969-81; assoc. commr. Bur. Labor Stats., Washington, 1981—. Served to U.S. Army, 1966-69, maj. gen. Res., 1993-94. Decorated Legion of Merit. Fellow Am. Statis. Assn.; mem. U.S. Army, Res. Officers Assn. Home: 4510 Banff St Annandale VA 22003 Office: Dept of Labor Employment & Unemployment Stats 2 Massachusetts Ave NE Washington DC 20212

PLIMPTON, CALVIN HASTINGS, physician, university president; b. Boston, Oct. 7, 1918; s. George Arthur and Fanny (Hastings) P.; m. Ruth Talbot, Sept. 6, 1941; children: David, Thomas, George (dec.), Anne, Edward. B.A. cum laude, Amherst Coll., 1939; M.D. cum laude, Harvard, 1943, M.A., 1947; Med. Sci.D., Columbia, 1951; LL.D., Williams Coll., 1960, Wesleyan U., 1961, Doshisha U., Kyoto, Japan, 1962, St. Lawrence U., 1963, Amherst U., 1971; L.H.D., U. Mass., 1962; D.Sc., Rockford Coll., 1962, St. Mary's, 1963, Trinity Coll., 1966, Grinnell (Iowa) Coll., 1967; Litt.D., Am. Internat. Coll., 1965, Mich. State Coll., 1969; DSc, N.Y. Med. Coll., 1986. Diplomate: Nat. Bd. Med. Examiners, Am. Bd. Internal Medicine. Intern, asst. resident, resident medicine Presbyn. Hosp., N.Y.C., 1947-50; asst. attending physician Columbia-Presbyn. Med. Center, 1950-60; asso. medicine (Coll. Phys. and Surg.), 1950-59, asst. prof. clin. medicine, 1959-60; prof. medicine, chmn. dept. Am. U. Beirut, Am. U. Hosp., Beirut, Lebanon, 1957-59; pres. Amherst Coll., 1960-71; pres. Downstate Med. Center, SUNY, 1971-79, dean med. sch., 1971-74, 76-79, prof. medicine, 1971-82, prof. emeritus, 1982—; pres. Am. U., Beirut, 1984-87; vis. prof. Columbia Presbyn. Med. Center, 1976-77. Trustee Am. U., Beirut, 1960-90, trustee emeritus, 1990—, chmn. bd., 1965-82; trustee World Peace Found., 1962-77, Phillips Exeter Acad., 1963-76, Commonwealth Fund, 1962-83, Hampshire Coll., 1963-71, U. Mass., 1962-70, L.I. U., 1972-82, N.Y. Law Sch., 1976-84; mem. Harvard Bd. Overseers, 1969-75. Capt. U.S. Army, 1944-46, ETO. Decorated comdr. Order of Cedars Lebanon; recipient award Nat. Geog. Soc.; award New Eng. Soc., John Phillips award Phillip Exeter Acad. Fellow ACP; mem. Am. Acad. Arts and Scis., Coun. Fgn. Rels., Soc. Mayflower Descs., Harvey Soc., Alpha Omega Alpha, Sigma Xi. Clubs: Century, Univ. (N.Y.C.), Charaka (N.Y.C.), Riverdale Yacht (N.Y.C.), Pilgrims (N.Y.C.); Tavern Boston.

PLIMPTON, GEORGE AMES, writer, editor, television host; b. N.Y.C., Mar. 18, 1927; s. Francis T.P. and Pauline (Ames) P.; m. Freddy Medora Espy, 1968 (div. 1988); children: Medora Ames, Taylor Ames; m. Sarah Whitehead Dudley, 1991; children: Olivia Hartley, Laura Dudley. Student, Phillips Exeter Acad., 1944; A.B., Harvard U., 1948; M.A., Cambridge (Eng.) U., 1952; L.H.D. (hon.), Franklin Pierce Coll., 1968; Litt.D. (hon.), Hobart Smith Coll., 1978, Stonehill Coll., 1982, L.I.U., 1984, U. S.C., 1986, Pine Manor Coll., 1988. Editor in chief Paris Rev., 1953—, Paris Rev. Edits. (subs. Doubleday and Co.), 1965-72; editor-in-chief Paris Rev. Edits. (subs. Brit. Am. Pubs.), 1987—; instr. Barnard Coll., 1956-58; assoc. editor Horizon mag., 1959-61; dir. Am. Lit. Anthology program, 1967-71; assoc. editor Harper's mag., 1972-81; contbg. editor Food and Wine Mag., 1978; editorial adv. bd. Realities, 1978; TV host Dupont Plimpton Spls., 1967-69, Greatest Sports Legends, 1979-81, The Ultimate High, 1980, Survival Anglia, 1980—, Writers' Workshop, 1982, Masterpiece Theater, 1983—, Challenge, 1987; spl. contbr. Sports Illustrated, 1968—; bd. dirs. Int. Film Investors, 1979-82, Leisure Dynamics, 1983-85; curator Tennis Week, 1990—. Author: Rabbit's Umbrella, 1956, Out of My League, 1961, Paper Lion, 1966, The Bogey Man, 1968, Mad Ducks and Bears, 1973, One for the Record, 1974, Shadow-Box, 1976, One More July, 1976, (with Neil Leifer) Sports!, 1978, (with Arnold Roth) A Sports Bestiary, 1982, Fireworks, 1984, Open Net, 1985, The Curious Case of Sidd Finch, 1987, The X-Factor, 1990, The Best of Plimpton, 1990; also numerous articles.; editor: Writers at Work, Vol. 1, 1957, Vol. 11, 1963, Vol. 111, 1967, Vol. IV, 1976, Vol. V, 1981, Vol. VI, 1984, Vol. VII, 1987, Vol. VIII, 1989, Vol. IX, 1992, (with Jean Stein) American Journey: The Times of Robert Kennedy, 1970, Pierre's Book, 1971, The Fancy, 1973, (with Jean Stein) Edie, An American Biography, 1982, (with Christopher Hemphill) D.V., 1984; The Paris Review Anthology, 1989, The Writer's Chapbook, 1989, Women Writers at Work, 1989, Poets at Work, 1989, The Norton Book of Sports, 1992, (with Jean Kennedy Smith) Chronicles of Courage, 1992; contbg. editor Gentlemen's Quar., 1983-85, Smart mag., 1988-90, Esquire mag., 1990. Commr. fireworks, N.Y.C., 1973—; trustee WNET, 1973-81, Nat. Art Mus. Sport, 1967—, Police Athletic League, 1976-90, African Wildlife Leadership Found., 1980—, Guild Hall, East Hampton, 1980—, N.Y. Zool. Soc., 1985—; bd. dirs. Dynamite Mus., Nat. Tennis Found., 1979—, Squaw Valley Center for Written and Dramatic Arts, 1979—, Authors Trust Am., 1979, Friends of the Masai Mara, 1986, Friends of Conservation, 1988—, Roger Tory Peterson Inst., The Carnegie Cook Ctr. for the Arts; chmn. Books Across the Sea, English Speaking Union, 1988—; bd. dirs., pres. N.Y. Philomusica, Pen/Faulkner, 1995; mem. adv. bd. Coordinating Council Lit. Mags., 1979, Yoknapatawpha Press, Am. Chess Found., East Harlem Tutorial, Boy's Harbor. Served to 2d lt. AUS, 1945-48. Assoc. fellow Trumbull Coll., Yale, 1967; recipient Disting. Achievement award U. So. Calif., 1967, Blue Pencil award Columbia Spectator, 1981, Mark Twain award Internat. Platform Assn., 1982, Chancellor's award L.I. U., 1986, l'Ordre des Arts et des Lettres, France, 1994. Mem. NFL Alumni Assn., Am. Pyrotechnics Assn., Pyrotechnics Guild Internat., Explorers Club., Linnean Soc., PEN, Mayflower Descendants Soc. Clubs: Century Assn, Racquet and Tennis, Brook, Piping Rock, Dutch Treat, River, Coffee House, Devon Yacht, Travellers (Paris). Address: Paris Review Inc 541 E 72nd St New York NY 10021-4010

PLISCHKE, ELMER, political science educator; b. Milw., July 15, 1914; s. Louis and Louise (Peterleus) P.; m. Audrey Alice Siehr, May 30, 1941; children: Lowell Robert, Julianne. Ph.B. cum laude, Marquette U., 1937; M.A., Am. U., 1938; certificate Carnegie summer session internat. law, U. Mich., 1938; Ph.D. (fellow), Clark U., 1943; certificate, Naval Sch. Mil. Govt. and Civil Affairs, Columbia, 1944. Instr. Springfield Coll., 1940; dist. supr., state dir. Wis. Hist. Records Survey, 1940-42; exec. sec. War Records Commn., Wis. Council Def., 1942; asst. prof. DePauw U., 1946-48, U. Md., College Park, 1948-49; assoc. prof. U. Md., 1949-52, prof., 1952-79, prof. emeritus, 1979—, head dept. govt. and politics, 1954-68; adj. prof. Gettysburg (Pa.) Coll., 1979-85; spl. historian Office U.S. High Commr. for Germany, 1950-52; cons. Dept. State, summer 1952; adj. scholar Am. Enterprise Inst. Pub. Policy Research, 1978—; lectr. Air War Coll., Armed Forces Staff Coll., Army War Coll., Def. Intelligence Sch., Indsl. Coll. Armed Forces, Inter-Am. Def. Coll., Nat. War Coll.; lectr. Sr. Officers Seminar Fgn. Service Inst. Dept. State; lectr. Institut de Altos Estudios Nacionales, Quito, Ecuador.; mem. adv. com. fgn. relations of U.S. Dept. State, 1967-72, chmn., 1969-70; assoc. fellow Gettysburg Coll., 1993—.

Author 28 books and monographs including: Conduct of American Diplomacy, 3d edit, 1967, reissued, 1974, (with Robert G. Dixon, Jr.) American Government: Basic Documents and Materials, 1950, reissued, 1971, Berlin: Development of Its Government and Administration, 1952, reissued, 1970, The Allied High Commission for Germany, 1953, International Relations: Basic Documents, rev, 1962, American Foreign Relations: A Bibliography of Official Sources, 1955, reissued, 1966, American Diplomacy: A Bibliography of Biographies, Autobiographies, and Commentaries, 1957, Summit Diplomacy: Personal Diplomacy of the President of the United States, 1958, reissued, 1974, Contemporary Governments of Germany, 1961, rev. edit., 1969, Government and Politics of Contemporary Berlin, 1963, Foreign Relations Decisionmaking: Options Analysis, 1973, United States Diplomats and Their Missions: A Profile of American Diplomatic Emissaries Since 1778, 1975, Microstates in World Affairs: Policy Problems and Options, 1977, Neutralization as an American Strategic Option, 1978, Modern Diplomacy: The Art and the Artisans, 1979, U.S. Foreign Relations: A Guide to Information Sources, 1980, Presidential Diplomacy: A Chronology of Summit Visits, Trips and Meetings, 1986, Diplomat in Chief: The President at the Summit, 1986, Foreign Relations: Analysis of Its Anatomy, 1988, Contemporary United States Foreign Policy: Documents and Commentary, 1991, others; contbr. more than 80 articles to profl. and lit. jours., and encyclopaedias; Americana Ann., 1972-83; also editorials in newspapers; editor, contbr. Systems of Integrating the International Community, 1964; mem. bd. editors Jour. Politics, 1966-68. Served from ensign to lt. USNR, 1943-46; exec. asst., then exec. officer Civil Affairs div., comdr. U.S. Naval Forces for Europe, London, 1944-45; charge de- Nazification policy coordination Office Dir. Polit. Affairs, Office Mil. Govt. for Germany 1945. Recipient research awards U. Md. Gen. Research Bd., 1956, 58, 69; research grantee Earhart Found., 1982-83, 86-87; book Interaction: Foreign Policy and Public Policy (Piper and Terchek) dedicated in honor, 1983; elected knight Mark Twain, Mark Twain Jour., 1970. Mem. AAUP, Am. Soc. Internat. Law, Am. Polit. Sci. Assn. (coun.), D.C. Polit. Sci. Assn. (coun. pres. 1961), So. Polit. Sci. Assn. (coun.), Internat. Studies Assn., Com. Study Diplomacy, Inst. Study Diplomacy, Internat. Torch Club (sec. Gettysburg club 1989-91, archivist 1991—), Eclectic Club, Phi Beta Kappa, Phi Kappa Phi, Pi Sigma Alpha, Sigma Tau Delta. Home: 227 Ewell Ave Gettysburg PA 17325-3108

PLISCHKE, LE MOYNE WILFRED, research chemist; b. Greensburg, Pa., Dec. 11, 1922; s. Fred and Ruth Naomi (Rumbaugh) P.; m. Joan Harper, Mar. 11, 1966. BS, Waynesburg Coll., 1948; MS, W.Va. U., 1952. Rsch. chemist U.S. Naval Ordinance Test Sta., China Lake, Calif., 1952-53; asst. prof. chemistry Commonwealth U., Richmond, Va., 1953-54; rsch. chemist E.I. du Pont, Gibbstown, N.J., 1955-57, Monsanto Chem. Co., Pensacola, Fla., 1957—. Mem. Am. Chem. Soc. Achievements include 16 U.S. patents and 48 foreign patents in field. Home: 2100 Clubhouse Dr Lillian AL 36549-5402 Office: Monsanto Co The Chem Group PO Box 97 Gonzalez FL 32560-0097

PLISHNER, MICHAEL JON, lawyer; b. Rockville Centre, N.Y., Jan. 22, 1948; s. Meyer J. and Lillian (Gold) P.; m. Rosalind F. Schein, Jan. 26, 1969; children: Aaron, Alexander, Elias. BA summa cum laude, Yale U., 1969, JD, 1972. Bar: Calif. 1972, U.S. Dist. Ct. (no. dist.) Calif. 1972, U.S. Ct. Appeals (9th cir.) 1972. Assoc. McCutchen, Doyle, Brown & Enersen, San Francisco, 1972-79, ptnr., 1979—. Mem. Phi Beta Kappa. Home: 114 St Albans Rd Kensington CA 94708-1035 Office: McCutchen Doyle Brown & Enersen 3 Embarcadero Ctr San Francisco CA 94111-4003

PLISKIN, MARVIN ROBERT, lawyer; b. Akron, Ohio, Nov. 7, 1938; s. Abraham David and Roselle (Cohen) P.; m. Suzanne Schreiber, Aug. 27, 1961; children: Daniel, Lawrence. BS, Ohio State U., 1960, JD, 1963. Bar: Ohio 1963. Assoc. Murphey, Young & Smith, Columbus, Ohio, 1963-69; ptnr. Murphey, Young & Smith, Columbus, 1970-88, Squire, Sanders & Dempsey, Columbus, 1988-90, Porter, Wright, Morris & Arthur, Columbus, 1990—. Contbr. articles to profl. jours. Active Columbus Jewish Found. Legal and Tax Adv. Com., 1982—, Columbus Found. Legal Adv. Com., 1991—; mem. planning com. Columbus Estate Planning Coun. II, 1975—. Fellow Am. Coll. Trust & Estate Coun. (state chmn. Ohio 1991-95); mem. ABA, Ohio State Bar Assn. (bd. govs. probate and trust sect. 1979—, state chmn. 1987-88), Columbus Bar Assn. (mem. probate law com. 1971—, chmn. 1975-76, mem. estate and gift tax com. 1975—), Columbus Met. Club (mem. nominating com. 1991-94). Avocations: music, sports, travel. Home: 255 S Roosevelt Ave Columbus OH 43209 Office: Porter Wright Morris & Arthur 41 S High St Columbus OH 43215-3609

PLISKIN, WILLIAM AARON, physicist; b. Akron, Ohio, Aug. 9, 1920; s. Max and Lena (Slavin) P.; m. Miriam Jaffee, Mar. 15, 1944; children: Karen, Michael, Bina. B.S., Kent State U., 1941; M.S., Ohio U., 1943; Ph.D., Ohio State U., 1949. Rsch. physicist Texaco Rsch. Ctr., Beacon, N.Y., 1949-59; staff physicist IBM, Poughkeepsie, N.Y., 1959-60; adv. physicist IBM, 1960-63; sr. physicist, mgr. IBM, East Fishkill, N.Y., 1964-79; sr. staff mem. IBM, 1979-82, mgr., sr. tech. staff mem., 1982-87, sr. tech. staff mem., 1987-90; cons. characterization and measurement of dielectric films, 1990—. Contbr. numerous articles to profl. jours., chpts. in books; patentee in field. Served to 1st lt. U.S. Army, 1943-46, PTO. Fellow IEEE, Electrochem Soc. (ann. award electronics div. 1973); mem. Am. Phys. Soc., Am. Chem. Soc. (ann. award Mid Hudson sect. 1964), Sigma Xi, Pi Mu Epsilon, Sigma Pi Sigma. Jewish. Home: 31 Greenvale Farms Rd Poughkeepsie NY 12603-4201

PLISKOW, VITA SARI, anesthesiologist; b. Tel Aviv, Israel, Sept. 13, 1942; arrived in Can., 1951; came to U.S., 1967; d. Henry Norman and Renee (Mushkatel) Stahl; m. Raymond Joel Pliskow, June 30, 1968; children: Tia, Kami. MD, U. B.C., Vancouver, 1967. Diplomate Am. Bd. Anesthesiology. Anesthesiologist Olympic Anesthesia, Bremerton, Wash., 1971-74, ptnr., anesthesiologist, 1974-84; pres., co-founder Olympic Ambulatory Surgery Ctr., Bremerton, 1977-83; ptnr., anesthesiologist Allenmore Anesthesia Assocs., Tacoma, 1983—; staff anesthesiologist Harrison Meml. Hosp., Bremerton, 1971—, Allenmore Hosp., Tacoma, 1983—. Trustee Tacoma Youth Symphony Assn., 1994—; active Nat. Coun. Jewish Women, 1972—. Fellow Am. Coll. Anesthesiologists, Am. Coll. Chest Physicians; mem. Am. Soc. Anesthesiologists (del. Wash. State 1987—), Wash. State Med. Assn. (del. Pierce County 1993-94), Wash. State Soc. Anesthesiologists (pres. 1985-87), Pierce County Med. Soc. (sec.-treas. 1992). Avocations: classical music, opera, singing (mezzo soprano). Office: 900 Sheridan Rd Bremerton WA 98310

PLOGER, ROBERT RIIS, retired military officer, engineer; b. Mackay, Idaho, Aug. 12, 1915; s. Robert and Elfrieda (Riis) P.; m. Marguerite Anne Fiehrer, June 13, 1939 (dec. Feb. 1982); children: Wayne David, Robert Riis III, Daniel Bruce, Marguerite Anne, Marianne Ploger Hill, Gregory Fiehrer; m. Jeanne Allys Pray, Nov. 20, 1982. BS, U.S. Mil. Acad., 1939; MS in Engring., Cornell U., 1947; MBA, George Washington U., 1963. Registered civil engr., D.C. Commd. 2d lt. U.S. Army, 1939; served in corps of engrs. U.S. Army, ETO, Okinawa, 1939-65; advanced through grades to maj. gen. U.S. Army, 1966, div. engr. New England div., 1965, comdg. gen. 18th engr. brigade, 1965-66, comdg. gen. engr. command, Vietnam, 1966-67; dir. topography and mil. engring., Office Chief Engrs. U.S. Army, Washington, 1967-70; comdg. gen. Ft. Belvoir and commandant U.S. Army Engr. Sch. Va., 1970-73; ret. U.S. Army, 1973; engr. specialist Bechtel Power Corp., Ann Arbor, 1974-80, mgr. adminstrv. services, 1980-81; counselor SCORE, Ann Arbor, Mich., 1984—; lectr. Indsl. Coll. Armed Forces, 1962-65. Author: Vietnam Studies, U.S. Army Engineers 1965-70; contbr. numerous articles on war and mil. engring. to profl. jours. Chmn. gift com. Class of 1939 50th Reunion of U.S. Mil. Acad., 1985-89. Decorated DSM with oak leaf cluster, Legion of Merit, Silver Star with oak leaf cluster, Bronze Star with oak leaf cluster, Air medal, Purple Heart, Korean Order Mil. Merit Chung Mu, Nat. Order 5th Class Republic of Vietnam; recipient George Washington medal ICAF, 1965, Wheeler medal Soc. Am. Mil. Engrs., 1966, Silver Beaver award Boy Scouts Am., 1973, Médaille du Jubilé, Vire, France, 1994. Fellow Am. Soc. Mil. Engrs.; mem. NSPE (privileged; chpt. pres. 1979-80), 29th Inf. Divsn. Assn. (Phila. award 1985), West Point Soc. Mich. (pres. 1981-84), SCORE (at-large exec. com. 1991, counselor chpt. 18), Ann Arbor C. of C. (counselor svc. corps ret. execs.), Army Engr. Assn. (life, Silver Order de Fleury medal 1995), SHAPE Officers Assn. (life). Baptist. Avocations: tennis, skiing, sailboarding. Home: 2475 Adare Rd Ann Arbor MI 48104-4021

PLOMGREN, RONALD ARTHUR, retail executive; b. Oakland, Calif., Apr. 1, 1934; s. Arthur Ivar and Augusta W. (Nelson) P.; m. Sharon Jensen, May 15, 1959; children: David, Susan, Karen. B.S., U. Calif.-Berkeley, 1956. Clk. Longs Drug Stores, Walnut Creek, Calif., 1948-56; clk. to store mgr. Long Drug Stores, Walnut Creek, Calif., 1957-68; property supr., constrn. mgr. Longs Drug Stores, Walnut Creek, Calif., 1968-74, v.p., 1974-76, sr. v.p., 1976—; dir.; dir. APS, Oakland. Vice chmn. Orinda Parks and Recreation Dist., Calif., 1974-78; vice chmn. Orinda Found., 1978-83; chmn. Orinda Planning Commn.; co-chmn. U. Calif.-Berkeley Engring. Fund. Mem. Nat. Assn. Corp. Real Estate Execs. (sec. No. Calif. chpt.). Office: Longs Drug Stores Inc 141 N Civic Dr Walnut Creek CA 94596-3858

PLOMP, TEUNIS (TONY PLOMP), minister; b. Rotterdam, The Netherlands, Jan. 28, 1938; arrived in Can., 1951; s. Teunis and Cornelia (Pietersma) P.; m. Margaret Louise Bone, July 21, 1962; children: Jennifer Anne, Deborah Adele. BA, U. B.C. (Can.), Vancouver, 1960; BD, Knox Coll., Toronto, Ont., Can., 1963, DD (hon.), 1988. Ordained to ministry Presbyn. Ch., 1963. Minister Goforth Meml. Presbyn. Ch., Saskatoon, Sask., Can., 1963-68, Richmond (B.C.) Presbyn. Ch., 1968—; clerk Presbytery of Westminster, Vancouver, 1969—; moderator 113th Gen. Assembly Presbyn. Ch. Can., 1987-88, dep. clk., 1987—; chaplain New Haven Correctional Centre, Burnaby, B.C. Contbr. mag. column You Were Asking, 1982-89. Avocations: record collecting, audiophile, biking, swimming. Office: Richmond Presbyn Ch, 7111 #2 Rd, Richmond, BC Canada V7C 3L7

PLONSEY, ROBERT, electrical and biomedical engineer; b. N.Y.C., July 17, 1924; s. Louis B. and Betty (Vinograd) P.; m. Vivian V. Vucker, Oct. 1, 1948; 1 child, Daniel. BEE, Cooper Union, 1943; MSEE, N.Y.U., 1948; PhD, U. Calif., Berkeley, 1955; postgrad. med. sch., Case Western Res. U., 1969-71. Registered prof. engr., Ohio. Asst. prof. elec. engring. U. Calif., Berkeley, 1955-57; asst. prof. elec. engring. Case Inst. Tech., Cleve., 1957-60, assoc. prof., 1960-66, prof., 1966-68, dir. bioengring. group, 1962-68; prof. biomed. engring. Sch. Engring. and Sch. Medicine Case Western Res. U., 1968-83, chmn. dept., 1976-80; vis. prof. biomed. engring. Duke U., Durham, N.C., 1980-81, prof., 1983—, prof. biomed. engring., Hudson prof. engring., 1990-93, Pfizer-Inc.-Edmond T. Pratt Jr. Univ. prof. biomed. engring., 1993—; mem. biomed. fellowships rev. com. NIH, 1966-70; mem. tng. com. Engrs. in Medicine and Biology, 1972-73, cons., 1974—; cons. NSF, 1973-93; mem. internat. sci. adv. com. Ragnar Granit Inst., Tampere (Finland) U. Tech., 1992—; ad hoc mem. sci. adv. com. Whitaker Found., 1989-91. Author: (with R. Collin) Principles and Applications of Electromagnetic Fields, 1961, Bioelectric Phenomena, 1969, (with J. Liebman and P. Gillette) Pediatric Electrocardiography, 1982, (with T. Pilkington) Engineering Contributions to Biophysical Electrocardiography, 1982, (with J. Liebman and Y. Rudy) Pediatric and Fundamental Electrocardiography, (with R.C. Barr) Bioelectricity: A Quantitative Approach, 1988, (with J. Malmivuo) Bioelectromagnetism, 1995; mem. editorial bd. Trans. IEEE, Biomed. Engring, 1965-70; assoc. editor, 1977-79, editorial bd. TIT Jour. 1971-81, Electrocardiology Jour., 1974—, Medical and Biological Engineering and Computing, 1987—; proc. editor Engring. in Medicine and Biology, 17th Ann., Conf., 1965. Mem. com. on electrocardiography Am. Heart Assn., 1976-82; v.p. Your Schs., Cleveland Heights, ohio, 1968-69, 73-75; provisional trustee Am. Bd. Clin. Engrs., 1973-74, pres. 1975, trustee, 1976-85. With AUS, 1944-46. Recipient sr. postdoctoral award NIH, 1980-81. Fellow AAAS, IEEE (chmn. Cleve. chpt. group on biomed. electronics 1962-63, chmn. publs. com. group on engring. in medicine and biology 1968-70, v.p. adminstr. com. 1970-72, pres. 1973-74, chmn. fellows com. Engring. in Medicine and Biology Society 1986-87-88, v.p. tech. and conf. activities 1991, William S. Morlock award 1979, Centennial medal 1984, co-program chair annual conf., Paris 1992); mem. AAUP, NAE (bioengring. peer com. 1988-91, chair, 1990-91, nominating com. 1991-92, mem. com. 1992-94, NRC postdoctoral rsch. associateships evaluation panel 1987-90), Am. Inst. Med. and Biological Engring. (founding fellow 1992—), Alliance for Engring. in Medicine and Biology (treas. 1976-78), Biomed. Engring. Soc. (bd. dir. 1975-78, 79-83, pres. 1981-82, chmn. affiliations com. 1987-89, ALZA Disting. lectr. 1988), Am. Physiol. Soc., Am. Soc. Engring. Edn. (bd. dir. biomed. engring. div. 1978-83, chmn. 1982-83). Office: Duke U Dept Biomed Engring Durham NC 27706 *External recognition of success is not nearly so important as the inner awareness of coming to full grips with life, to be fully involved, bending all strengths to fulfill one's goals and philosophies. And of all involvements, those with people are most meaningful (to be aware of and share the feelings of colleagues, students, friends, and family—and to enrich these relationships)—and for me most difficult.*

PLONUS, MARTIN ALGIRDAS, electrical engineering educator; b. Trumpininkan, Lithuania, Dec. 21, 1933; came to U.S. 1949, naturalized, 1955; s. Christopher and Anna (Sliupas) P.; m. Martina Rauer, Feb. 20, 1965; children—Sabine, Jacqueline, Marcus, Michelle. B.S., U. Ill., 1956, M.S., 1957; Ph.D., U. Mich., 1961. Asst. prof. elec. engring. Northwestern U., Evanston, Ill., 1961-64, assoc. prof., 1964-69, prof., 1969—; dir. grad. program Northwestern U., 1989—; research mathematician U. Mich., summers 1964-66; bd. dirs. Ctr. Integrated Microelectronic Systems. Author: Applied Electromagnetics, 1978; contbr. articles to profl. jours. Grantee OSRD, 1964, NSF, 1967, 75-77, 94—, U.S. Air Force, 1980-85. Fellow IEEE (chmn. group antennas and propagation Chgo. sect. 1966-67, spl. recognition award 1971); mem. Internat. Sci. Radio Union, AAUP, U. Mich. Rsch. Club., Electromagnetics Acad., Sigma Xi, Eta Kappa Nu, Sigma Tau, Tau Beta Pi. Nat. sailing champion Shields class. Home: 2525 Orrington Ave Evanston IL 60201-2427 Office: Northwestern U Dept Elec Engring Comp S Evanston IL 60201

PLOPPER, CHARLES GEORGE, anatomist, cell biologist; b. Oakland, Calif., June 16, 1944; s. George Eli and Josephine Viola (Gates) P.; m. Suzanne May, Nov. 9, 1969. AB, U. Calif., Davis, 1967, PhD, 1972. Chief electron microscopy br. U.S. Army Med. Research Nutrition Lab., Denver, 1972-73; vis. scientist Calif. Primate Research Ctr., Davis, 1974-75; chief electron microscopy div. Letterman Army Inst. Research, San Francisco, 1974-75; asst. prof. U. Hawaii Sch. Medicine, Honolulu, 1975-77; assoc. prof. Kuwait U. Sch. Medicine, 1977-78; sr. staff fellow Nat. Inst. Environ. Health Sci. Research, Triangle Park, N.C., 1978-79; from asst. to assoc. prof. U. Calif. Sch. Vet. Medicine, Davis, 1979-86, dept. chmn., 1984-88; prof. anatomy, physiology and cell biology, Sch. Vet. Medicine U. Calif., Davis, 1986—; mem. study sect. NIH div. Research Grants, Bethesda, Md., 1986-90; Paley vis. prof. Boston U. Sch. Medicine, 1985; vis. pulmonary scholar Duke U., N.C., N.C. State U., 1991. Served to capt. U.S. Army, 1972-75. Mem. Am. Soc. Cell Biology, Am. Thoracic Soc., Am. Assn. Antomists, Am. Assn. Pathologists, Anat. Soc. Great Britain and Ireland, Davis Aquatic Masters (bd. dirs.). Democrat. Club: Davis Aquatic Masters. Avocations: swimming, hiking, tennis. Home: 511 Hubble St Davis CA 95616-2720 Office: Univ Calif Sch Vet Medicine Dept Anatomy Physiol Cell Biology Davis CA 95616

PLOSSER, CHARLES IRVING, dean, economics educator; b. Birmingham, Ala., Sept. 19, 1948; s. George Gray and Dorothy (Irving) P.; m. Janet Schwert, June 26, 1976; children: Matthew, Kevin, Allison. B.E. cum laude, Vanderbilt U., 1970; MBA, U. Chgo., 1972, PhD, 1976. Cons. Citicorp Realty Cons., N.Y.C., 1972-73; lectr. Grad. Sch. Bus., U. Chgo., 1975-76; asst. prof. Grad. Sch. Bus. Stanford (Calif.) U., 1976-78; asst. prof. econs. W.E. Simon Grad. Sch. Bus., U. Rochester (N.Y.), 1978-82, assoc. prof., 1982-86, prof., 1986-89; Fred H. Gowen prof. econs. U. Rochester, N.Y., 1989-92, John M. Olin Disting. prof. econs. and pub. policy, 1992—, acting dean W.E. Simon Grad. Sch. Bus., 1990-91, 92-93; dean W.E. Simon Grad. Sch. Bus., 1993—; bd. dirs. Genesee Health Sys., Inc. Editor, Jour. Monetary Econs., 1983—, Carnegie-Rochester Conference Series on Public Policy, 1989—; contbr. articles to profl. jours. 1st lt. U.S. Army, 1972-75. NSF research grantee, 1982, 84. Mem. Am. Econs. Assn., Econometrics Soc., Am. Fin. Assn., Am. Statis. Assn., Tau Beta Pi, Beta Gamma Sigma. Home: 95 Ambassador Dr Rochester NY 14610-3402 Office: U Rochester Dean Of Simon Grad Sch Rochester NY 14627

PLOSSU, BERNARD PIERRE, photographer; b. Dalat, South Vietnam, Feb. 26, 1945; s. Albert Fernand and Bernadett (Petot) P.; children: Shane Albert, Joaquim Fernand. Baccalauréat, U. Paris, 1962. Books of photographs include: Surbanalism, 1972, Go West, 1976, Le Voyage Mexicain, 1979, Egypte, 1979, New Mexico Revisited, 1983, The African Desert, 1987; monographs Les Paysages Intermediares, Gardens of Dust;

photographs in collections Amon Carter Mus., Tex., Bibliotheque Nationale, France, Eastman House U.S.A., Center for Creative Photography, Tucson, Cantini Mus., France, Stedelijk Mus., Netherlands Chateau d'eau, France, Australian Nat. Gallery, Sheldon Meml. Gallery, Internat. Pollaroid Collection, Paris Courthouse, France, Bernard Plossu 1963-85, 1986; exhibited in collections Library of Congress, San Franicsco Mus. Modern Art, Royal Museums of Belgium; exhbn. tour of photographs The African Desert to Eaton/Shoen Gallery, San Francisco, San Francisco Internat. Airport, Albuquerque Mus. Art, City Los Angeles Photography Ctr., Mus. Contemporary Photography, Chgo., Wilderness Park Mus., El Paso, Tex., Goddard Art Ctr., Ardmore, Okla., Sierra Nev. Mus. Art, Reno, Balt. Mus. Art, Nat. Mus. African Art, Smithsonian Inst., Washington; retrospective exhbn. include Centre Georges Pompidou, France. Recipient Grand Prix de la Photography, France, 1988. Roman Catholic. Office: Eaton Galleries 52 Spanish River Dr Boynton Beach FL 33435-3322

PLOSZAJ, STEPHEN CHARLES, lawyer; b. Hartford, Conn., Aug. 16, 1949; s. John Francis and Irene (Duval) P.; m. Faith Marion Margolis, May 21, 1972; children: Sara Lynne, Laura Beth. BS, USCG Acad., New London, Conn., 1971; JD with honors, George Washington U., 1978; LLM in Taxation, Boston U., 1984. Bar: Md. 1978, Mass. 1984. Commd. ensign USCG, 1971, advanced through grades to lt. comdr., 1980; officer USCGC Vigilant (WMEC-617), New Bedford, Mass., 1971-73; commanding officer USCG Loran Sta., Pt. Clarence, Alaska, 1973-74, CMDJ (G-PO), Washington, 1974-75, CMDJ (G-PTE), Washington, 1975-78, Commandant (GL) CGHQ, Washington, 1978-80, Commander 1st CG Dist., Boston, 1980-84; ptnr. Hale and Dorr, Boston, 1984-92, McDermott, Will & Emery, Boston, 1992—; mil. magistrate 1st Coast Guard Dist., Boston, 1980-84. Mem. ABA, Boston Bar Assn. Avocations: golf, racquetball, scuba diving. Office: McDermott Will & Emery Ste 1700 75 State St Boston MA 02109-1807

PLOTCH, WALTER, management consultant, fund-raising counselor; b. N.Y.C., July 19, 1932; s. Harry and Belle (Lebowsky) P.; AB, Queens Coll., 1957; MA, Harvard U., 1959, postgrad., 1959-61; m. Yvette Gabrielle Lambert, Mar. 15, 1956; children: Allison, Jennifer, Adrienne. Instr. history Pine Manor Jr. Coll., Wellesley, Mass., 1960-62; analyst L.F. Rothschild & Co., N.Y.C. and Boston, 1962-64; community cons., N.Y.C. and Boston, dir. for New Eng., Anti-Defamation League of B'nai B'rith, 1965-68, nat. edn. dir., 1968-76; v.p. Brakeley, John Price Jones Inc., N.Y.C., 1976-79, sr. v.p., dir., 1979-89; sr. v.p. The Oram Group, Inc., N.Y.C., 1989-92, exec. v.p.; pres. and CEO Walter Plotch Assocs., Inc., Croton-On-Hudson, N.Y., 1992—; mem. faculty Grad. Sch. Mgmt. and Urban Affairs, New Sch. Social Rsch.; lectr. Harvard U. Grad. Sch. Edn.; cons. Harcourt, Brace, Plenum Pubs. Bd. dirs. Schizophrenia Found., 1975-90; nat. bd. dirs. NCCJ, 1980-84, Nat. Charitable Info. Bur., mem. exec. com., 1986-94. Served with USCGR, 1953-55; Korea. Grantee, U.S. Office Edn., Dept. Labor, N.Y. Council Humanities; teaching fellow Harvard U., 1959-61. Mem. Princeton Club, U. Washington Club, Phi Alpha Theta. Democrat. Jewish. Co-editor: Pluralism in a Democratic Society, 1977; gen. editor: The Job Corps Intergroup Relations Series, 1974; author articles in field, contbg. editor Grants mag., Jour. Sponsored Research 1978-82. Office: 39 Furnace Dock Rd Croton On Hudson NY 10520-1406

PLOTKIN, HARRY MORRIS, lawyer; b. Athol, Mass., May 18, 1913; s. Louis and Fannie (Coffman) P.; m. Esther Lipsez, Dec. 25, 1937; children—Ira L., Judith Deborah (Mrs. Jonathan Wilkenfeld). A.B. magna cum laude, Harvard, 1934, LL.B. magna cum laude, 1937. Bar: Ill. 1937, D.C. 1951. Assoc. firm Topliff & Horween, Chgo., 1937-39; atty. FCC, 1940-51, asst. gen. counsel, 1943-51; ptnr. Arnold, Fortas & Porter, Washington, 1951-56, Arent, Fox, Kintmer, Plotkin & Kahn, Washington, 1956-82; of counsel Arent, Fox, Kintmer, Plotkin & Kahn, 1983—. Trustee Washington United Jewish Appeal Found.—. Mem. ABA, Fed. Bar Assn., Fed. Communications Bar Assn., D.C. Bar Assn., Phi Beta Kappa. Clubs: Harvard, Nat. Lawyers (Washington). Home: 3719 Harrison St NW Washington DC 20015-1815 Office: 1050 Connecticut Ave NW Washington DC 20036-5303

PLOTKIN, MANUEL D., management consultant, educator, former corporate executive and government official; s. Jacob and Bella (Katz) P.; m. Diane Fern Weiss, Dec. 17, 1967; 1 child, Lori Ann. B.S. with honors, Northwestern U., 1948; M.B.A., U. Chgo., 1949. Price economist, survey coordinator U.S. Bur. Labor Statistics, Washington, 1949-51, Chgo., 1951-53; sr. economist Sears Roebuck & Co., Chgo., 1953-61; mgr. market research Sears Roebuck & Co., 1961-66, chief economist, mgr. mktg. rsch., 1966-73, dir. corp. planning and research, 1973-77, exec. corp. planner, 1979-80; dir. U.S. Bur. Census, Washington, 1977-79; v.p., dir. group practice Divsn. Mgmt. Cons. Austin Co., Evanston, Ill., 1981-85; pres. M.D. Plotkin Research & Planning Co., Chgo., 1985—; tchr. statistics Ind. U., 1953-54; tchr. econs. Wilson Jr. Coll., Chgo., 1954-55; tchr. quantitative methods and managerial econs. Northwestern U., 1955-63; tchr. contemporary mktg. and mktg. mgmt. DePaul U., Chgo., 1992—; mem. Conf. Bd. Mktg. Rsch. Adv. Coun., 1968-77, chmn.-elect, 1977; chmn. adv. com. U.S. Census Bur., 1974-75; trustee Mktg. Sci. Inst., 1968-77; mem. Nat. Commn. Employment and Unemployment Stats., 1978-79, Adv. Coun. Edn. Stats., 1977-79, Interagy. Com. Population Rsch., 1977-79; mem. adv. coun. Kellstadt Ctr., DePaul U., 1987-92; trustee U.S. Travel Data Ctr., 1977-79. Contbr. articles to profl. jours. Served with AUS, 1943-46, ETO. Decorated Bronze Star medal with oak leaf cluster. Mem. Am. Mktg. Assn. (pres. Chgo. 1968-69, nat. dir. 1969-70, nat. v.p. mktg. rsch. 1970-72, nat. v.p mktg. mgmt 1981-83, pres., CEO 1985-86), Am. Statis. Assn. (pres. Chgo. 1966-67, Forecasting award 1963), Am. Econ. Assn., Nat. Assn. Bus. Economists, Planning Execs. Inst., World Future Soc., Midwest Planning Assn., U. Ill. Businessmen Rsch. Adv. Group, Chgo. Assn. Commerce and Industry, Beta Gamma Sigma, Alpha Sigma Lambda, Delta Mu Delta. Office: 2650 N Lakeview Ave Apt 3910 Chicago IL 60614-1831

PLOTKIN, MARTIN, retired electrical engineer; b. Bklyn., July 22, 1922; s. David and Tessie (Esris) P.; m. Beverly Ferber, July 2, 1949; 1 child, George Michael. BEE, CCNY, 1943; MEE, Poly. Inst. Bklyn., 1951. Electronic engr. Bendix Aviation Corp., Bklyn., 1943-44; sr. elec. engr. Brookhaven Nat. Lab., Upton, N.Y., 1946-84, ret., 1984, cons., 1986—. Inventor alternating gradient synchrotron radio frequency system, 1960. Lt. (j.g.) USNR, 1944-46. Fellow IEEE; mem. Nuclear and Plasma Scis. Soc. (pres. 1977-78), Trans. on Med. Imaging (mem. steering com. 1981-90, chmn. steering com. 1981-84, 86-90). Avocations: mineralogy; philately. Home: 117 Clover Dr Massapequa Park NY 11762

PLOTNICK, HARVEY BARRY, publishing executive; b. Detroit, Aug. 5, 1941; s. Isadore and Esther (Sher) P.; m. Susan Regnery, Aug. 16, 1964 (div. Apr. 1977); children: Andrew, Alice; m. Elizabeth Allen, May 2, 1982; children: Teresa, Samuel. B.A., U. Chgo., 1963. Editor Contemporary Books, Inc., Chgo., 1964-66; pres. Contemporary Books, Inc., 1964-94; with Paradigm Holdings, Inc., Chgo., 1994—. Trustee U. Chgo., 1990—. Office: Paradigm Holdings Inc 2 Prudential Plz Ste 1550 Chicago IL 60601-6790

PLOTNICK, ROBERT DAVID, academic administrator, economic consultant; b. Washington, Aug. 3, 1949; s. Theodore and Jean (Hirshfeld) P.; m. Gay Lee Jensen, Dec. 22, 1972. BA, Princeton U., 1971; MA, U. Calif., Berkeley, 1973, PhD, 1976. Research assoc. Inst. Research on Poverty, Madison, Wis., 1973-75; asst. prof. Bates Coll., Lewiston, Maine, 1975-77, Dartmouth Coll., Hanover, N.H., 1977-84; assoc. prof. U. Wash., Seattle, 1984-90, prof., 1990—; assoc. dean, 1990-95, acting dean, 1994-95; vis. scholar Russell Sage Found., 1990; cons. Wash. Dept. Social and Health svcs., Olympia, 1984-86, 90-91, 95; cons. numerous pub. and non-profit orgns. Author: Progress Against Poverty, 1975; also numerous articles. Recipient Teaching Excellence award U. Wash., 1985, 89. Mem. Am. Econ. Assn., Assn. Policy Analysis and Mgmt., Population Assn. Am. Avocations: tennis, hiking, bird watching. Office: U Wash Grad Sch Pub Affairs Box 353055 Seattle WA 98195-3055

PLOTNICKI, STEVEN JOEL, record company executive; b. Bklyn., May 22, 1954; s. Harry and Lillian (Jones) P.; m. Linda Sherry Sokoloff; children: Norah Issac, Gideon Maxwell (twins). Grad. high sch., Bayside, N.Y. Freelance songwriter, musician N.Y.C.X, 1969-79; sales rep. Musical Maze N.Y.C.X, 1979-80, Win Inc., Long Island City, N.Y., 1980-81; v.p., coowner Profile Records Inc., N.Y.C., 1981—. Composer: Love Insurance,

---

1979. Mem. ASCAP. Democrat. Jewish. Office: Profile Records Inc 740 Broadway # 7flr New York NY 10003-9518

PLOTNIK, ARTHUR, publishing executive; b. White Plains, N.Y., Oct. 1, 1937; s. Michael and Annabelle (Taub) P.; m. Meta Von Borstel, Sept. 6, 1960 (div. 1979); children: Julia Nicole, Katya Michelle.; m. Mary Phelan, Dec. 2, 1983. B.A., State U. N.Y., Binghamton, 1960; M.A., U. Iowa, 1961; M.S. in L.S, Columbia U., 1966. Gen. reporter, reviewer Albany (N.Y.) Times Union, 1963-64; freelance writer, 1964-66; editor Librarians Office, Library of Congress, 1966-69; assoc. editor Wilson Library Bull., Bronx, N.Y., 1969-74; editor-in-chief Am. Libraries, Chgo., 1975-89; assoc. pub. ALA, 1989—; edit. dir. ALA Editions, 1993—; adj. instr. journalism Columbia Coll., Chgo., 1988-89; speaker in field. Author: The Elements of Editing; A Modern Guide for Editors and Journalists, 1982, Jacob Shallus, Calligrapher of the Constitution, 1987, Honk If You're a Writer, 1992; also fiction, articles, television scripts, photography; exec. producer Library Video Mag., 1986-91. Bd. dirs. Am. Book Awards, 1979-82; bd. advs. Univ. Press of Am., 1982—. Served with USAR, 1962-67. Fellow Iowa Writers Workshop Creative Writing, 1961; recipient award Edni. Press Assn. Am., 1973 (3), 77, 82, 83; cert. of excellence Internat. Reading Assn., 1970, First Pl. award Verbatim essay competition, 1986, award Am. Soc. Bus. Press Editors, 1987. Mem. ALA. Home: 2120 W Pensacola Ave Chicago IL 60618-1718 Office: ALA 50 E Huron St Chicago IL 60611-2795 also: N E Pub Assocs Literary Agents PO Box 5 Chester CT 06412

PLOTT, CHARLES R., economics educator; b. Frederick, Okla., July 8, 1938; s. James Charles and Flossie Ann (Bowman) P.; m. Marianna Brown Cloninger, May 30, 1961; children: Rebecca Ann, Charles Hugh. B.S., Okla. State U., 1961, MS, 1964; Ph.D., U.Va., 1965. Asst. prof. econs. Purdue U., 1965-68, assoc. prof., 1968-70; vis. prof. econs. Stanford U., 1968-69; Edward S. Harkness prof. econs. and polit. sci. Calif. Inst. Tech., Pasadena, 1970—, dir. Program for Study of Enterprise and Public Policy, 1979—, dir. Lab. for Exptl. Econs. and Polit. Sci., 1987—; vis. prof. law U. So. Calif. Law Center, 1976; vis. prof. U. Chgo., 1980; dir. Lee Pharms. Author works in fields of econs., polit. sci., philosophy, exptl. methods, math. methods; contbr. articles to profl. jours.; bd. editors: Social Sci. Research, 1976-77, Public Choice, 1973—, Jour. Econ. Behavior, 1983—. Named to Coll. Bus. Hall of Fame Okla. State U.; Ford Found. fellow, 1968, Guggenheim fellow, 1981, fellow Ctr. for Advanced Studies in Behavioral Scis., 1981; NSF grantee, 1972, 74, 78, 79, 80, 83, 86, 88, 92. Fellow Am. Acad. Arts and Scis., Econometric Soc., Huntington Library and Art Gallery; mem. Am. Econ. Assn., Econ. Sci. Assn. (pres. 1987), So. Econ. Assn. (exec. com. 1978-79, v.p. 1985-87, pres. 1989-90), Pub. Choice Soc. (pres. 1977-78), Royal Econ. Assn., Am. Polit. Sci. Assn., Econs. Sci. Assn. (pres. 1987-88). Clubs: Cosmos, Mont Pelerin Soc. Home: 881 El Campo Dr Pasadena CA 91107-5565 Office: Calif Inst Tech Divsn Humanities & Social Scis Pasadena CA 91125

PLOTTEL, JEANINE PARISIER, foreign language educator; b. Paris, Sept. 21, 1934; came to U.S. 1943; m. Roland Plottel, 1956; children: Claudia S., Michael E., Philip B. Baccalauréat lettres, Lycée Française de N.Y., 1952, BA with honors, Barnard Coll., 1954; MA, Columbia U., 1955, PhD with distinction, 1959. Lectr. dept. French and Romance philology Columbia U., N.Y.C., 1955-59; rsch. assoc. fgn. lang. program MLA of Am., N.Y.C., 1959-60; lectr. dept. romance langs. CUNY, N.Y.C., 1960; asst. prof. div. humanities Julliard Sch. Music, N.Y.C., 1960-65; dir. lang. labs. Hunter Coll. CUNY, N.Y.C., 1965-69; asst. prof. dept. romance langs. Hunter Coll. CUNY, N.Y.C., 1965-69, assoc. prof. dept. romance langs., 1969-81, prof. dept. romance langs., 1981—, assoc. prof. French doctoral program grad. sch., univ. ctr., 1980-81, prof. French doctoral program grad. sch., univ. ctr., 1981—; extensive adminstrv. experience in CUNY including chairperson Dept. Romance Langs. Author: Les Dialogues de Paul Valéry, 1960; pub., editor N.Y. Literary Forum, 1978-88; contbr. articles to profl. jours., chpts. to books. Pres. Maurice I. Parisier Found., Inc. Named Chevalier des Palmes Acad., 1982; recipient NEH fellowship, 1979; grantee N.Y. Coun. for the Humanities, 1986, Helena Rubenstein Found., 1986, Florence J. Gould Found., 1986, N.Y. Times Found., 1986. Mem. Maison (bd. dirs. Columbia U.). Home: 50 E 77th St Apt 14a New York NY 10021-1836

PLOTZ, CHARLES MINDELL, physician; b. N.Y.C., Dec. 6, 1921; s. Isaac and Rose (Bluestone) P.; m. Lucille Weckstein, Aug. 5, 1945; children: Richard, Thomas, Robert. B.A., Columbia U., 1941, D.Sc., 1951; M.D., L.I. Coll. Medicine, 1944. Diplomate: Am. Bd. Internal Medicine. Intern New Haven Hosp., 1944-45; resident internal medicine Kings County Hosp., 1945-46, Maimonides Hosp., 1948-49; postdoctoral research fellow USPHS, Columbia Coll. Phys. and Surgs., 1949-50; practice medicine, specializing in internal medicine Bklyn., 1950—; chief Arthritis Clinic, attending physician Kings County Hosp. Center, 1950-85; chief L.I. Coll. Hosp. (Arthritis Clinic), 1950-65; asst. attending physician Mt. Sinai Hosp., 1955—; chief Mt. Sinai Hosp. (Arthritis Clinic), 1955-65, Arthritis Clinic, State U., Hosp., 1967-85; asst. physician Columbia-Presbyn. Med. Center, 1949-71; attending physician Bklyn. State Hosp.; dir. ambulatory care Bklyn. Hosp.Ctr., 1991-93; emeritus prof. medicine SUNY, 1991—; professorial lectr. Mt. Sinai Sch. Medicine, 1992—; emeritus prof. in medicine SUNY, 1991—; cons. physician Peninsula Gen. Hosp., Jamaica Hosp.; cons. on rheumatology VA Hosp., Bklyn., L.I. Coll. Hosp.; cons. family practice Luth. Med. Ctr.; vis. cons. internal medicine Jewish Gen. Hosp., Mont., Que., Can., 1965; cons. internal medicine Avicenna Hosp. and Wazir Akbar Hosp., Kabul, Afganistan, 1965; prof. medicine, dir. continuing edn., chmn. dept. family practice SUNY Downstate Med. Ctr., 1967-91, prof. emeritus medicine and family practice, 1991—; Fulbright lectr. U. Paris, 1984, 91; professorial lectr. Mt. Sinai Sch. Medicine, 1992—. Editorial adv. bd.: Pakistan Med. Forum; editor-in-chief: Clin. Rheumatology in Practice, 1981—; editor-in-chief: Advances in Rheumatology, 1986—. Mem. nat. bd. govs. Arthritis Found., 1964-82, bd. govs. N.Y. chpt., 1965—, v.p. 1971-83, trustee, 1977-82, N.Y. chpt. sr. v.p., 1977-82, vice chmn. bd. trustees, 1985, 87—, pres., 1985-87; trustee Leo N. Levi Meml. Nat. Arthritis Hosp., Alumni Fund-Alumni Assn. SUNY Downstate Med. Center, Bklyn. Inst. Arts and Scis., Bklyn. Bot. Garden; mem. adv. bd. MEDICO, corp. mem., 1977—; treas. Internat. League Against Rheumatism, 1981-89; trustee Internat. League Against Rheumatism Trust, 1981-89. Served to capt. AUS, 1946-48. WHO fellow U. Negev, 1974; master Am. Coll. Rheumatology, 1991—; recipient Gold medal Am. Coll. Rheumatology, 1992. Master Am. Coll. Rheumatology (Gold medal 1992), fellow ACP, Am. Acad. Family Physicians (charter), N.Y. Acad. Medicine (chmn. edn. com. 1976-78); mem. AMA, (N.Y. chpt.), AAUP, Internat. Soc. for Rheumatic Therapy (chmn. 1987-89), Am. Fedn. Clin. Rsch., Am. Rheumatism Assn. (past sec.-treas.), N.Y. Rheumatism Assn. (past pres., exec. com.), Harvey Soc., (N.Y. chpt.), Kings County med. socs., Bklyn. socs. internal medicine, Soc. Tchrs. Family Medicine, N.Y. State Acads. Family Physicians, Soc. Urban Physicians, Mystery Writers Am., Sigma Xi, Alpha Omega Alpha; hon. mem. Rheumatology Soc. France, Rheumatology Soc. Japan, Rheumatology Soc. Mex., Rheumatology Soc. Brazil, Rheumatology Soc. Yugoslavia, Rheumatology Soc. Norway, Rheumatology Soc. Egypt, Med. Soc. Czechoslovakia. Club: Heights Casino. Home: 184 Columbia Hts Brooklyn NY 11201-2186 also: 450 Clarkson Ave Brooklyn NY 11203-2012

PLOUFFE, JEAN-LOUIS, bishop. Address: Bishop's Residence, 480 McIntyre StW, PO Box 510, North Bay, ON Canada P1B 8J1

PLOURDE, GERARD, company executive; b. Joliette, Que., Can., Feb. 12, 1916; s. Louis-George and Rose de Lima (Jolicoeur) P.; m. Jeannine Martineau, Dec. 4, 1943; children: Monique, Pierre, Marc-André. BA, Brébeuf Coll., 1936; M in Commerce, U. Montreal, Que., 1939, D. Honoris Causa, 1971. Accountant UAP Inc., Montreal, from 1941; pres., gen. mgr. UAP Inc., 1951-70, chmn. bd., chief exec. officer, 1970-80, chmn. bd., 1980-86, hon. dir., 1986—; hon. dir. Molson Cos., Northern Telecom; vice-chmn. bd. Cambior, Inc. Decorated Order of Can. Mem. Soc. Automotive Engrs., Laval-sur-le-Lac Club, Saint Denis Club, Mt. Bruno Country Club. Office: 1010 Sherbrooke W #2012, Montreal, PQ Canada H3A 2R7

PLOWDEN, DAVID, photographer; b. Boston, Oct. 9, 1932; s. Roger and Mary Russell (Butler) P.; m. Pleasance Coggeshall, June 20, 1962 (div. 1976); children: John, Daniel; m. Sandra Oakes Schoellkopf, July 8th, 1977; children: Philip, Karen. BA Econs., Yale U., 1955; pvt. study with Minor

---

White, Rochester, N.Y., 1959-60. Asst. O. Winston Link Studio, N.Y.C., 1958-59, George Meluso Studio, N.Y.C., 1960-62; photographer, writer, 1962—; assoc. prof. Inst. Design, Ill. Inst. Tech., Chgo., 1978-86; lectr. U. Iowa Sch. Journalism, 1985-88; vis. prof. Grand Valley State Univ., 1988-90, 91—; artist-in-residence U. Balt., 1990-91. Author and photographer: Farewell to Steam, 1968, Lincoln and His America, 1970 (Benjamin Barondess award 1971), The Hand of Man on America, 1971, 2d edit, 1974, The Floor of the Sky: the Great Plains, 1972, Bridges: the Spans of North America, 1974, 2d edit. 1984, Commonplace, 1974, Tugboat, 1976 (notable Children's books ALA 1976, Children's Book Showcase 1976), Steel, 1981, An American Chronology, 1982 (Notable Books ALA 1982, Booklist's Best of the 80s 1989), Industrial Landscape, 1985, A Time of Trains, 1987, A Sense of Place, 1988, End of an Era: The Last of the Great Lakes Steamboats, 1992, Small Town America, 1994; co-author, photographer, Nantucket, 1970, Cape May to Montauk, 1973, Desert and Plains, the Mountains and the River, 1975, The Iron Road, 1978 (notable children's books 1978, Honor list Horn Books 1979), Wayne County: the Aesthetic Heritage of a Rural Area, 1979; introduction The Gallery of World Photography/the Country, 1983; commd. illustrator Gems, 1967, The Freeway in the City, 1968, America the Vanishing, 1969, New Jersey, 1977, North Dakota, 1977, Vermont, 1979, New York, 1981, A Place of Sense, 1988; contbr. articles to numerous jours.; one-man shows include Columbia U., 1965, Smithsonian Instn., 1970, 71, 75, 76, 81, 89, Internat. Ctr. Photography, N.Y., 1976, Witkin Gallery, N.Y., 1979, Cin. Art Acad., 1979, The Gilbert Gallery, Chgo., 1980, 81, Chgo. Ctr. Contemporary Photography, 1982, Fed. Hall Mus., N.Y.C., 1982, Calif. Mus. Photography, Riverside, 1982, Chgo. Hist. Soc., 1985, Martin Gallery, Washington, 1987, Kunstmuseum, Luzern, Switzerland, 1987, Burchfield Ctr., Buffalo, 1987-88, Iowa State Mus., Des Moines, 1988-89, Catherine Edelman Gallery, Chgo., 1990, Grand Valley State U., 1993, Ewing Gallery, Washington, 1994; exhibited in group shows at Met. Mus. Art, N.Y.C., 1967, Kodak Gallery, N.Y.C., 1976, Currier Gallery Art, Manchester, N.H., 1978, Whitney Mus., 1979, Art Inst. Chgo., 1983-86, 87, Witkin Gallery, N.Y.C., 1988, Davenport (Iowa) Mus. Art, 1992; represented in permanent collections Art Inst. Chgo., Calif. Mus. Photography, Ctr. Creative Photography, Chgo. Hist. Soc., Libr. Congress, Smithsonian Instn., U. Md., J.B. Speed Mus., Iowa Humanities Bd., Iowa State Hist. Dept., Burchfield Art Ctr., Buffalo and Erie County Hist. Soc., Am. Soc. Media Photographers Archives Internat. Mus. Photography George Eastman House, Internat. Ctr. Photography, Ekstrom Libr. U. Louisville. John Simon Guggenheim fellow, 1968; grantee N.Y. State Coun. Arts, 1966, 87, Smithsonian Inst., 1970-71, Dept. Transp. and Smithsonian Inst., 1975-76, H. E. Butt Found., 1977, United Bd. Homeland Ministries, 1976, Chgo. Hist. Soc., 1980-84, Seymour H. Knox Found., 1987, Baird Found., 1987, State Hist. Soc. Iowa, 1987-88, Iowa Humanities Bd., 1987-88; recipient Railroad History award, 1989. Mem. Am. Soc. Media Photographers. Home and Office: 609 Cherry St Winnetka IL 60093-2614

PLOWMAN, JACK WESLEY, lawyer; b. Blairsville, Pa., Sept. 12, 1929; s. Ralph Waldo, Sr., and Ethel Beatrice (Nicely) P.; m. Barbara Ellen Brown, Apr. 5, 1952; children: Linda Ellen, Judith Lynn. A.B., U. Pitts., 1951, LL.B. with honors, 1956. Bar: Pa. 1956, U.S. Dist. Ct. (we. dist.) Pa. 1956, U.S. Ct. Appeals 1960, U.S. Supreme Ct. 1978. Assoc. Campbell, Houck & Thomas, Pitts., 1956-57; ptnr. Rose, Houston, Cooper & Schmidt, Pitts., 1957-63, Plowman, Spiegel & Lewis, Pitts., 1963—; adj. prof. Duquesne U. Sch. Law, 1963-70, 83—. Editor-in-chief Pitts. Legal Jour., 1971-81, U. Pitts. Law Rev., 1955-56. Trustee, sec. Allegheny County Bar Found.; bd. dirs. United Meth. Pub. House, 1984—, Ward Home for Children, United Meth. Ch. Union, 1977-83, Wesley Inst., 1977-81, Neighborhood Legal Svcs. Assn., 1969-74; chancellor Western Pa. Ann. Conf., United Meth. Ch. Capt. USAF, 1951-53. Fellow Am. Bar Found. (life mem.), Am. Coll. Trial Lawyers; mem. ABA, Pa. Bar Assn., Allegheny County Bar Assn. (pres. 1982), Pa. Bar Inst. (bd. dirs. 1988-92), Supreme Ct. Pa. Hist. Soc. (trustee, pres.). Republican. Home: 1025 Lakemont Dr Pittsburgh PA 15243-1817 Office: 925 Grant Building Pittsburgh PA 15219-2200

PLOWMAN, R. DEAN, federal agriculture agency administrator; b. Smithfield, Utah, Aug. 25, 1928; s. Ronald O. and LaRue B. Plowman; m. Kathleen Simmons, 1950; children: Kenneth, Stephen, Maurine, Douglas, Anne. BS in Agr., Utah State U., 1951; MS, U. Minn., St. Paul, 1955, PhD, 1956. Rsch. asst. U. Minn., 1954-56; head dept. animal dairy and vet. scis. Utah State U., Logan, 1984-88; dairy rsch. scientist Agrl. Rsch. Svc., USDA, Beltsville, Md., 1957-63, investigations leader dairy rsch. bd., 1963-68, chief dairy cattle rsch. br., 1968-72; area dir. for Utah, Idaho and Mont. USDA, Logan, Utah, 1972-80, area dir. for Utah, Ariz., Nev. and N.Mex., 1980-83, area dir. for Utah, Colo., Wyo., Nev., Ariz. and N.Mex., 1983-84; adminstr. USDA, Washington, 1988-92, asst. sec. agrl. for sci. and edn., 1992—. Contbr. over 75 articles to sci. jours. Sgt. U.S. Army, 1946-47. Recipient Disting. Svc. award USDA, 1991, Alumnus of Yr. award Utah State U., 1993. Office: USDA Agrl Rsch Svc 12th St & Independence Ave SW Washington DC 20250

PLOWRIGHT, JOAN ANNE, actress; b. Brigg, Lancashire, Eng., Oct. 28, 1929; d. William and Daisy (Burton) P.; m. Roger Gage, 1953 (div.); m. Sir Laurence Olivier, 1961 (dec.); 3 children. Student Old Vic Theatre Sch. Mem. Old Vic Co., toured South Africa, 1952-53; 1st leading role in The Country Wife, London, 1956; mem. English Stage Co., 1956, Nat. Theatre, 1963-74. Appearances include (plays) The Chairs, 1957, The Entertainer, 1958, Major Barbara and Roots, 1959, A Taste of Honey, 1960 (Tony Best Actress award 1960), Uncle Vanya, 1962-64, St. Joan, 1963 (London Evening Standard Best Actress award 1964), Hobson's Choice, 1964, The Master Builder, 1965, Much Ado About Nothing, 1967, Tartuffe, 1967, Three Sisters, 1967, 69, The Advertisement, 1968, 69, Love's Labour's Lost, 1968, 69, The Merchant of Venice, 1970, 71-72, Rules of the Game, 1971-72, Woman Killed with Kindness, 1971-72, Taming of the Shrew, 1972, Doctor's Dilemma, 1972, Rosmersholm, 1973, Saturday Sunday Monday, 1973, Eden's End, 1974, The Sea Gull, 1975, The Bed Before Yesterday, 1975 (Variety award 1976), Filumena, 1977 (Soc. West End Theatres Best Actress award 1978), Enjoy, 1980, Who's Afraid of Virginia Woolf?, 1981, Cavell, 1982, The Cherry Orchard, 1983; The Way of the World, 1985, The House of Bernada Alba, 1986-87, Uncle Vanya, 1988, Time and The Conways, 1991, (films) Much Ado About Nothing, 1969, Equus, 1976, Richard Wagner, 1982, Brimstone and Treacle, 1982, Brittania Hospital, 1983, Revolution, 1985, The Dressmaker, 1987, Drowning By Numbers, 1987, The Divider, Conquest of the South Pole, 1989, I Love You To Death, 1990, Avalon, 1990, Enchanted April, 1991, Dennis the Menace, 1993, Last Action Hero, 1993, The Summer House, 1993, Widows' Peak, 1994, Pyromaniacs: A Love Story, 1995, The Grass Harp, 1995, Hotel Sorrento, 1995; (TV films) Merchant of Venice, 1973, Daphne, Laureola, 1977, Saturday Sunday Monday, 1977, The Importance of Being Earnest, 1988, The Birthday Party, 1987, House of Bernarda Alba, A Nightingale Sang, 1989, Stalin, 1992 (Emmy nomination, Supporting Actress - Miniseries, 1993), A Place for Annie, 1994, On Promised Land, 1994. Office: LOP Ltd, 33-34 Chancery Ln, London WC2A 1EN, England*

PLUCINSKY, CONSTANCE MARIE, school counselor, supervisor; b. Passaic, N.J., Sept. 17, 1937; d. Stephen and Beatrice (Ruby) Goralski; m. William Plucinsky, June 29, 1957; 1 child, Carolyn. BS, Paterson State Coll., 1959; MA, Seton Hall U., 1970, postgrad., 1975; postgrad., William Paterson Coll., 1989—. Tchr. Garfield (N.J.) Bd. Edn., 1959-61, Paramus (N.J.) Bd. Edn., 1961-71, Bergen Gifted Child Soc., Ridgewood, N.J., 1965-71; guidance counselor grades 9-12 Paramus Bd. Edn., 1971-89, 91—, adminstrv. asst. to supt., 1989-91, counselor, coord. sex equity grades 7-12, 1990—; S.A.T. program supr. Ednl. Testing Svc., Princeton, N.J., 1992—; mem. adv. bd., 1990—, project dir. 1993—. Editor: (newsletter) PEN, 1989-94 (pub. rels. asst., 1991—); author: (brochure) All That You Can BEEEEEE, 1991, 92, 93; contbr. articles to profl. jours. Mem. steering com. Bergen County Intercultural Task Force, 1992—; facilitator trainer Achieving Sex Equity Through Students, 1991. Named Guidance Counselor of Yr., Bergen County Profl. Guidance Assn., 1989, N.J. Equity Hall of Fame, 1993; recipient N.J. Dept. Edn. Best Practices award Paramus Acad. Sex Equity, 1993-94; N.J. Exemplary Equity Program grantee divsn. vocat. edn. N.J. Dept. Edn., 1991-93. Mem. AAUW, N.J. Edn. Assn., Bergen County Profl. Guidance Assn. (exec. com. 1994-95), Edn. Assn. Paramus. Democrat. Roman Catholic. Avocations: equestrian competitive rider, instructor, horse trainer. Home: 1030 Ramapo Valley Rd Mahwah NJ 07430 Office: Paramus High Sch E-99 Century Rd Paramus NJ 07652

PLUIMER, EDWARD J., lawyer; b. Rapid City, S.D., 1949. BA cum laude, U. S.D., 1971; JD cum laude, NYU, 1974. Bar: Minn. 1975. Law clk. to Hon. Robert A. Ainsworth, Jr. U.S. Ct. Appeals (5th cir.), 1974-75; ptnr. Dorsey & Whitney, Mpls.; mem. Minn. Supreme Ct. ADR Task Force, 1988-92. Editor N.Y. U. Law Rev. Mem. Order of the Coif. Office: Dorsey & Whitney PLLP 220 S 6th St Minneapolis MN 55402-4500

PLUM, CHARLES WALDEN, retired business executive and educator; b. Circleville, Ohio, Apr. 13, 1914; s. Horace Walden and Anna Frances (Eaton) P.; m. Margaret E. McCollister, Sept. 17, 1939; children: David Walden, Donald Alan (dec.). B.S., Ohio State U., 1936; M.B.A., Case Western Res. U., 1951; postgrad., Advanced Mgmt. Program, Harvard, 1954. CPA, N.Y., Tex. Sr. accountant Coopers and Lybrand, N.Y.C., 1936-42; supr. acctg. Amertorp Corp., Naval Ordnance Plant, St. Louis, 1942-45; various positions to v.p. acctg. and mgmt. systems Standard Oil Co. (Ohio), Cleve., 1945-78; prof. bus. adminstrn. Western Res. U., College Station, 1978-89; dir., chmn. audit com. Hospitality Motor Inns, Inc., Cleve., 1976-79; sec.-treas., dir., mem. mgmt. com. Am. Assembly Collegiate Schs. Bus., 1977-78; lectr. acctg. Western Res. U., 1946-54; bus. exec. in residence, disting. lectr. Tex. A. and M. U., 1976; Mem. bus. adv. council Kent State U., 1967-77. Mem. AICPA, Fin. Execs. Inst., Am. Petroleum Inst. (chmn. com. on cooperation with AICPA 1955-68), Tex. Soc. CPAs, Sigma Phi Epsilon, Beta Gamma Sigma, Beta Alpha Psi. Home: 5 Forest Dr College Station TX 77840-2312

PLUM, FRED, neurologist; b. Atlantic City, Jan. 10, 1924; s. Fred and Frances (Alexander) P.; children—Michael, Christopher, Carol; m. Susan Butler, Apr. 23, 1990. BA, Dartmouth Coll., 1944, postgrad., 1944-45; MD, Cornell U., 1947; MD (hon.), Karolinska Inst., Stockholm, 1982; DSc (hon.), L.I. U., 1990. Resident N.Y. Hosp., 1947-50, physician to outpatients, 1950-53, neurologist-in-chief, 1963—; instr. neurology Sch. Medicine Cornell U., 1950-53, Anne Parrish Titzell prof. neurology, 1963—, chmn. dept. neurology, 1963—; head neurology sect. U.S. Naval Hosp., St. Albans, N.Y., 1951-53; from asst. prof. to prof. neurology Sch. Medicine U. Wash., 1953-63; vis. scientist U. Lund, Sweden, 1970-71; vis. physician Rockefeller U. Hosp., 1975-85; assoc. neurosci. research program MIT and Rockefeller U., 1977-87; mem. neurology study sect., 1964-68, grad. tng. com., 1959-63, 71, nat. adv. council, 1977-81, Nat. Inst. Neurol., Communicative Disorders and Stroke, 84-86; past pres. McKnight Endowment Fund for Neurosci., 1986-90. Author: Diagnosis of Stupor and Coma, 1966, 3d edit., 1980, Clinical Management of Seizures, 1976, 2d edit., 1983, (with others) Cecil Essentials of Medicine, 1986, 2d edit., 1990; editor, contbg. author: Cecil's Textbook of Medicine, 1968, 8th edit., 1991; chief editor neurology sect. Contemporary Neurology series; editor: Recent Trends in Neurology, 1969, 2d edit., 1989, Brain Dysfunction in Metabolic Disorders, 1974; mem. editorial bd. Archives Neurology, 1958-68; chief editor, 1972-76; founding editor Annals of Neurology, 1977—; contbr. articles to scientific and profl. jours. Mem. Inst. of Medicine, Nat. Acad. Sci., Am. Neurol. Assn. (v.p. 1974-75, pres. 1976-77, Jacoby award 1984), Am. Acad. Neurology (past mem. council), Soc. Neurosci., Am. Soc. Clin. Investigation, Assn. Rsch. Nervous Mental Diseases (pres. 1973, 87), Assn. Am. Physicians, Alpha Omega Alpha; hon. mem. Can., Brit., French, Italian, Swiss neurol. socs. Rsch. in consciousness, coma and stroke. Office: Cornell U Medical Coll 1300 York Ave New York NY 10021-4873

PLUMB, PAMELA PELTON, consulting company executive, former mayor and councilwoman; b. St. Louis, Oct. 26, 1943; d. Frank E. and Dorothey-Lee (Culver) Pelton; m. Peter Scott Plumb, June 11, 1966; children: Jessica Culver, David Scott. BA, Smith Coll., 1965; MA, NYU, 1967. Tchr., Master's Sch., Dobbs Ferry, N.Y., 1967-69; exec. dir. Greater Portland (Maine) Landmarks, 1969-71; engaged in civic and vol. work, 1971-79; mem. Portland City Council, 1979-90, mayor, 1981-82; prin. Pamela Plumb & Assocs., 1990—; vice chmn. Peoples Heritage Savs. Bank, Peoples Heritage Fin. Group. Bd. dirs. Tom's of Maine; pres. Nat. League Cities, 1987-88. Recipient Doric Dames's Bullfinch award for preservation, 1979, Greater Portland Landmark's Preservation award, 1980, Deborah Morton award Westbrook Coll., Portland, 1982, Neal W. Allen award Greater Portland C. of C., 1982, Disting. Svc. award Kiwanis Club of Portland, 1990; named Portland and Maine Outstanding Young Woman, Jaycees, 1979. Democrat.

PLUMEZ, JEAN PAUL, advertising agency executive, consultant; b. N.Y.C., Oct. 31, 1939; s. Jean Paul and Marie Antoinette (Compagne) P.; m. Jacqueline Hornor, Feb. 20, 1965; children: Jean Paul, Nicole. B.S. in Chem. Engring., Bucknell U., 1962, B.A. in Chemistry, 1962; M.B.A., U. Pa., 1968. Product engr. Mobil Oil Co., Paulsboro, N.J., 1965-66; account mgr. Dancer Fitzgerald, Sample, Inc., N.Y.C., 1968-86, exec. v.p., 1979-86; pres. Leadership on Paper, Larchmont, N.Y., 1986—; founding ptnr. The Right Direction, 1987—. Served to capt. Signal Corps U.S. Army, 1962-64. Mem. Alpha Chi Sigma, Beta Gamma Sigma, Kappa Delta Rho. Clubs: Larchmont Yacht, Wharton of N.Y., Princeton of N.Y. Home and Office: 90 Beechtree Dr Larchmont NY 10538-1202

PLUMLEY, JOSEPH PINKNEY, JR., public relations educator; b. Atlanta, Sept. 3, 1944; s. Joseph Pinkney Sr. and Julia (West) P.; m. Patricia Susan Stone, June 10, 1967 (div. Aug. 1983); m. Laurie Ann Gray, June 30, 1984; children: Bradford Christian, Jennifer Elizabeth, Stephanie Anne. BA in Journalism, U. Ga., 1967; student Air. Def. Officer basic course, U.S. Army, 1969, U.S. Army, 1968; student Aviation Sch., U.S. Army, 1969, student Air Def. officer advanced course, 1974; MEd, U. Ga., 1975, EdS, 1976, EdD, 1978. Commd. 2nd lt. U.S. Army, 1968, advanced through grades to lt. col., 1984, student officer basic course, 1968, student aviation course, 1969; served Vietnam, 1970-71; commdg. officer HHB 31st Air Def. Bde U.S. Army, 1972-73; asst. prof. mil. sci. U. Ga., 1974-78; commdg. officer U.S. Army Missile Control Ctr., Wurzburg, Germany, 1978-79; exec. officer 37th Air Def. Bn., Schweinfurt, Germany, 1979-81; tech. dir. U.S. Army Pers. and Fin. Ctr., Ft. Benjamin Harrison, Ind., 1981-84; dep. chief of staff U.S. Army Combined Arms Ctr., Ft. Leavenworth, Kans., 1984-85, insp. gen., 1985-86; ret. U.S. Army, 1988; prof. mil. sci. U. Ala., Tuscaloosa, 1987-88, asst. prof. pub. rels., 1988—; owner, pres. Plumley & Assocs. Pub. Rels. Cons., Tuscaloosa, 1988—. Author: Writing for Mass Communication, 1994; editor So. Pub. Rels. Jour., 1993-94; contbr. articles to profl. jours. Bd. dirs. YMCA Tuscaloosa, 1989—, Black Warrior coun. Boy Scouts Am., 1986-90. Decorated Bronze Star, Cross of Gallantry, 21 Combat Air medals; recipient Spirit of Freedom award Exch. Club Ala., Montgomery, 1989; named Sr. Practitioner, So. Pub. Rels. Fedn., 1994. Mem. Pub. Rels. Soc. Am., Pub. Rels. Coun. Ala. (pres. 1992, state v.p. 1993, state treas. 1991, bd. dirs. 1991-92), Exch. Club Tuscaloosa (pres. 1989, bd. dirs. 1989-95), Sigma Nu (faculty advisor 1986-94). Republican. Episcopalian. Avocations: sailing, aviation, tennis. Home: 415 Vantage Pt Tuscaloosa AL 35406-2381 Office: Univ Ala Coll Comm PO Box 870172 Tuscaloosa AL 35487-0172

PLUMMER, AMANDA, actress; b. N.Y.C., Mar. 23, 1957; d. Christopher and Tammy (Grimes) Plummer. Student, Middlebury Coll. Has appeared in theatre roles: A Taste of Honey, 1981; A Month in the Country, 1980; N.Y.C. debut: Artichoke, 1979; The Glass Menagerie, 1983-84; motion picture debut: Cattle Annie and Little Britches, 1981, The World According to Garp, 1982, Daniel, 1983, Hotel New Hampshire, 1984, The Fisher King, 1991, Freejack, 1991, Pulp Fiction, 1994, Search and Destroy, 1995; other theatre roles include: Agnes of God (Tony, Drama Desk award, Outer Circle Critics award), 1982; A Lie of the Mind, 1985; TV appearances include Hallmark Hall of Fame: Miss Rose White (Emmy award supporting actress, 1992). Office: The Gersh Agency 232 N Canon Dr Beverly Hills CA 90210*

PLUMMER, CHARLES MCDONALD, retired community college administrator; b. Garibaldi, Oreg., Mar. 21, 1934; s. Earl Carlos and Florence Elta (Lamb) P.; m. Diane Hansen, July 7, 1957; children: Jeffrey Earl, Susan Lynn Plummer Johnson. BS in Edn., So. Oreg. State Coll. 1957; MEd, U. Oreg., 1967. Tchr. Canyonville (Oreg.) High Sch., 1957-59, Glendale (Oreg.) High Sch., 1959-60; tchr. Roseburg (Oreg.) High Sch., 1960-66, dir. student activities, pub. info., 1963-66; registrar Umpqua C.C., Roseburg, 1966-68, dean admissions and records, 1968-74, dean instrn., 1974-86, v.p. instructional svcs., 1986-94; ret., 1994; exec. bd. N.W. Student Success Conf., Portland, 1989-92; co-founder, staff Pacific NW Great Tchrs. Seminar, Portland, 1979-94. Pres. Greater Douglas United Way, 1989, bd. dirs. 1983-94; pres. Roseburg Concert Chorale, 1982-94; bd. dirs. Roseburg Community Concert Assn., 1989—. Mem. Kiwanis Club (pres. 1979, bd.

dirs. 1973-79), Oreg. Coun. of Instrnl. Adminstrs. (chair 1990), Roseburg Area C. of C. (bd. dirs. 1982-85, Roseburg First Citizen 1991), Phi Delta Kappa. Presbyterian. Avocations: golf, vintage singers, church choir, community service. Home: 567 NE Winchester St Roseburg OR 97470-3259

PLUMMER, (ARTHUR) CHRISTOPHER (ORME), actor; b. Toronto, Ont., Can., Dec. 13, 1929; s. John and Isabella Mary (Abbott) P.; m. Tammy Grimes (div.); 1 child, Amanda; m. Patricia Audrew Lewis, May 4, 1962 (div.); m. Elaine Taylor. Ed. pub. and pvt. schs., Can.; pupil, Iris Warren, C. Herbertcasari. Stage debut in The Rivals with Can. Repertory Theatre, 1950; Broadway debut in Starcross Story, 1954; London debut in Becket, 1961; leading actor Am. Shakespeare Theatre, Stratford, Conn., 1955, Royal Shakespeare Co., London and Stratford, Avon, Eng., 1961-62, Stratford (Ont.) Shakespeare Festival, 1956, 57, 58, 60, 62, 67, Nat. Theatre Co. London; radio roles include Shakespeare, Canada; plays include Home is the Hero, 1954, Twelfth Night, 1954, 70-71, Dark is Light Enough, The Lark, Julius Caesar, The Tempest, 1955, Henry VI, 1956, Hamlet, 1957, Winter's Tale, 1958, Much Ado About Nothing, 1958, J.B., 1958, King John, 1960, Romeo and Juliet, 1960, Richard III, 1961, Arturo Ui, 1963, The Royal Hunt of the Sun, 1965, Antony and Cleopatra, 1967, Danton's Death, 1971, Amphitryon 38, 1971; (musicals) Cyrano, 1973, The Good Doctor, 1973, Love and Master Will, 1975; Othello, 1982, Macbeth, 1988, No Man's Land, 1993; made TV debut 1953; TV prodns. include Little Moon of Alban, Johnny Belinda, 1958, Cyrano de Bergerac, 1962, Oedipus Rex, After the Fall, 1974, The Doll's House, The Prince and the Pauper, Prisoner of Zenda, Hamlet at Elsinore, BBC, 1964, Time Remembered, Capt. Brassbound's Conversion, The Shadow Box, 1981, The Thorn Birds, 1983, Little Gloria-Happy at Last, A Hazard of Hearts, 1987, Crossings, 1986, Danielle Steele's Secrets, 1992, Liar's Edge, 1992; star TV series The Moneychangers, 1977; made film debut in 1957; films include Stage Struck, 1957, Wind Across the Everglades, 1958, The Fall of the Roman Empire, 1963, Inside Daisy Clover, 1965, Sound of Music, 1965, Triple Cross, 1967, Nobody Runs Forever, 1969, The Battle of Britain, 1969, The Royal Hunt of the Sun, 1969, Lock up your Daughters, 1969, The Phyx, 1970, Waterloo, 1971, The Man Who Would Be King, 1975, The Return of the Pink Panther, 1975, Conduct Unbecoming, 1975, International Velvet, 1978, Murder By Decree, 1979, Starcrash, 1979, The Silent Partner, 1979, Hanover Street, 1979, Somewhere in Time, 1980, Eye witness, 1981, The Disappearance, 1981, The Amateur, 1982, Dreamscape, 1984, Ordeal by Innocence, 1984, Lily in Love, 1985, The Boss' Wife, 1986, The Boy In Blue, 1986, An American Tail, 1986 (voice), Souvenir, 1987, Dragnet, 1987, Light Years (voice), 1988, Where the Heart Is, 1989, Fire Head, 1991, Star Trek: VI: The Undiscovered Country, 1991, Rock a Doodle, 1992 (voice), Malcolm X, 1992, Wolf, 1994, Dolores Claiborne, 1994. Decorated companion Order of Can., 1968; recipient Theatre World award, 1955, Evening Standard award, 1961, Delia Austrian medal, 1973, 2 Drama Desk awards, 1973, 82, Antoinette Perry award, 1974, Emmy award Nat. Acad. TV Arts and Scis., 1977, Genie award, Can., 1980, Golden Badge of Honor, Austria, 1982, Maple Leaf award Nat. Acad. Arts and Letters. Mem. Theatre's Hall of Fame. Office: KM 8942 Wilshire Blvd Beverly Hills CA 90211*

PLUMMER, DANIEL CLARENCE, III, insurance consultant; b. Chgo., Apr. 30, 1927; s. Daniel C. and Ida May (Hayden) P.; m. Margaret Louise Marshall, Apr. 30, 1955; children: Daniel C., Judith Ann, David Marshall. B.S., Northwestern U., 1950. C.P.A., Ill. Sales rep. Sunbeam Corp., Chgo. and Phila., 1950-51; sr. acct. Touche Ross & Co., Chgo., 1952-56; adminstrv. mgr. Consol. Foundries & Mfg. Corp., Rockford, Ill., 1956-59; dir. internal audit Continental Casualty Co., Chgo., 1959-63; sec.-treas. Moline Malleable Iron Co., St. Charles, Ill., 1963-64; v.p. Allstate Ins. Cos., Northbrook, Ill., 1964-90, ret.; cons. re fin. regulation and mgmt. of insurers Lake Forest, Ill., 1990—; mem. acctg. com. Nat. Assn. Ind. Insurers, 1966-89, chmn., 1984-85; mem. acctg. prins. adv. com. Nat. Assn. Ins. Commrs., 1983-85, emerging acctg. issues com., 1985-93, chmn. data sys. adv. com., 1986-90. Co-author: Property-Liability Insurance Accounting, 1991. Bd. dirs. Chgo. coun. Boy Scouts Am., 1979-87, mem. fin. com., 1979-87, chmn. audit com., 1983-87, mem. exec. com., 1979-81, asst. treas., 1979-81, chmn. ins. com. 1986, adv. bd., 1987-90; mem. acctg. prins. adv. com. Nat. Assn. Ins. Commrs., 1983-85, emerging acctg. issues com., 1985-93, chmn. data sys. adv. com. 1986-90. With USN, 1945-46. Mem. Ill. Soc. CPAs (chmn. ins. industry com. 1976-77), Torch Lake Yacht Club Mich. Avocations: tennis; sailing; fishing.

PLUMMER, DIRK ARNOLD, electrical engineer; b. Stamford, Conn., Apr. 18, 1930; s. Charles Arnold Plummer and Edwina Woodling Johnson; m. Janis Susan Lowery Stuart, Feb. 18, 1967 (div. 1973); 1 child, Julie. B-SChEngr, MIT, 1952; BSEE, U. Calif., Berkeley, 1961; MSEE, Monmouth Coll., 1985. Cert. nondestructive test examiner of inspectors for radiography, magnetic particle, liquid penetrant and ultrasonic testing methods; cert. comml. pilot. Chem. engr. Foster Wheeler Corp., N.Y.C., 1952; engr. The M.W. Kellogg Co., N.Y.C., 1954; project engr. Am. Machine & Fdry. Co., Greenwich, Conn., 1955-56; devel. engr. Aerojet-Gen. Corp., Azusa, Sacramento, San Ramon, Calif., 1956-61; sr. mem. tech. staff Aerospace Comms. & Controls divsn. RCA, Burlington, Mass., 1961-62; engr. Elec. Boat Div. Gen. Dynamics Corp., Groton, Conn., 1963; electronics engr. U.S. Civil Svc., various locations, 1963-83; pvt. practice profl. engring. Sea Bright, N.J., 1988—. Contbr. articles to profl. jours. Archtl. control officer Sea Bright Village Assn., 1991. 1st lt. U.S. Army, 1952-54. Recipient Meritorious Svc. medal Pres. of U.S., 1982, Cert. for Commendable Svc. Def. Supply Agy., 1972. Mem. AAAS, ASCE, NSPE, AICE (profl. devel. officer 1990), IEEE (chmn. nuclear and plasma sci. chpt. 1990), Am. Consulting Engrs. Coun., Am. Phys. Soc., Am. Math. Soc., Math. Assn. Am. Home and Office: 45 Village Rd Sea Bright NJ 07760-2233

PLUMMER, EDWARD BRUCE, college librarian; b. Toledo, Feb. 27, 1938; s. Paul Abel and Mabel Bernardine (Wert) P.; m. Mary Louise Girsch, Sept. 9, 1967; children: Andrew Brooks, Jonathan Tad. BA, Ohio Wesleyan U., 1960; MLS, Kent State U., 1967. Tchr., adult tutor Clin. Pub. Schs., 1960-65; dir. br. libr. Kent (Ohio) State U., 1967-70; assoc. dir. Worcester (Mass.) State Coll., 1971-80, dir., libr., 1980—; dir. Citizens for Edn. Resources, Worcester, 1994; pres. Cen./Western Mass. Automated Resource Sharing, Paxton, Mass., 1991-92; treas. Mass. Coun. Chief Librs. of Pub. Higher Edn. Instn., Amherst, Mass., 1991-93. Author: (book of poetry) Innovations, 1993. Bd. dirs. Talking Books, Worcester, 1991-94, Unitarian Universalist Ch., Worcester, 1991-94; mem. Libr. Pub. Sch. Power Group, Worcester, 1994—; bd. dirs., tutor Literacy Vols. of Am., Worcester, 1989—; del. to nat. conf., 1991; pres. Friends of the Worcester Pub. Libr. Club, 1989-91. Mem. Mass. Libr. Assn., Life Info. for Edn., Ferry Beach Park Assn. (bd. dirs. 1993-96), New England Libr. Assn., Assoc. of Coll. and Rsch. Libr., New Eng. (city commr. 1999—), Worcester Cult. Commn. Avocations: photography, gardening, painting. Home: 66 Navasota Ave Worcester MA 01602 Office: Worcester State Coll Learning Resources Ctr 486 Chandler St Worcester MA 01602

PLUMMER, GAYTHER L(YNN), climatologist, ecologist, researcher; b. Indpls., Jan. 27, 1925; s. Conley L. and Rowena H. (Huber) P.; m. H. Eileen Barr, June 3, 1950. BS, Butler U., 1948; MS, Kans. State U., 1950; PhD, Purdue U., 1954. Instr. biology Knox Coll., Galesburg, Ill., 1950-51; naturalist Ind. Dept. Conservation, various locations, 1947-52; asst. prof. biology Antioch Coll., Yellow Springs, Ohio, 1954-55; prof. botany U. Ga., Athens, 1955-95, state climatologist, 1978-95; rsch. fellow Oak Ridge (Tenn.) Inst. Nuclear Studies, 1958-62. Author: Georgia Weather Watchers, 1991, Georgia Temperatures, 1993; cartographer 160 vegetation maps of Ga., 1972-74; editor Ga. Jour. Sci., 1977-84; author over 200 rsch. reports. 2d lt. USAAF, 1943-46. Fellow AAAS; mem. Ecol. Soc. Am., Ind. Acad. Sci., Ga. Acad. Sci., Soil Sci. Soc. Am., Crop Sci. Soc., Agron. Soc. Am., Sigma Xi, Phi Kappa Phi. Achievements include research in droughts in S.E. U.S. relating to astrogeophysical processes via geomagnetics; lightning history in Piedmont for over 70 million years etched in Stone Mountain granite. Office: Ga Climatology Assoc Inc 995 Timothy Rd Athens GA 30606-3818

PLUMMER, JAMES D., electrical engineering educator. Fluke profl elec. engring. Stanford (Calif.) U. Fellow IEEE. Office: Stanford U Dept Of Elec Engring Stanford CA 94305

PLUMMER, MARCIE STERN, real estate broker; b. Plymouth, Mass., Oct. 28, 1950; d. Jacob and Rosalie (Adelman) Stern; m. John Dillon

McHugh II, Oct. 8, 1974 (div.); 1 child, Joshua Stern; m. Louis Freeman Plummer Jr., Sept. 25, 1982; children: Jessica Price, Denelle Boothe. BA, Am. Internat. Coll., 1972, MAT in English, 1973, postgrad., 1974; postgrad., U. Conn., 1974; lic. real estate broker, Anthony Sch. Real Estate, Walnut Creek, Calif., 1985. Educator, chair dept. Windsor Locks (Conn.) Sch. Dist., 1972-74; educator, placement dir. Heald Bus. Coll., San Francisco, 1974-77; educator evening and day divs. Diablo Valley Coll., Pleasant Hill, Calif., 1975-77; real estate agt. Morrison Homes, Pleasant Hill, 1977-78; real estate agt., tract mgr. Dividend Devel., Santa Clara, Calif., 1978-81; real estate agt. Valley Realty, 1981-84; broker, owner Better Homes Realty, 1984-89; real estate broker, owner The Presád Co. Inc. subs. Better Homes Realty, Danville, Calif., 1984-90; owner The Mktg. Group, 1989—. Better Homes Realty rep. for orgn. of Danville 4th of July Parade, City of Danville, 1984-88; publicist San Ramon Valley Little League, Alamo, Calif., 1986—; active Battered Women's Found., Contra Costa County, Calif., 1986—, Yosemite Fund, 1992—, Safe Home Teen Program, 1991—; active rep. voter registration, Walnut Creek, Calif., 1987—; mem. Civic Arts Coun., Walnut Creek, 1988—; drama coach, dir. Advanced Drama Ensemble, 1993-94. Recipient numerous nat., state and regional awards in field, $400 million closed vol. in real estate sales achievement award, 1991. Mem. Bldg. Industry Assn. (Sales vol. award 1978-93), Sales & Mktg. Coun. (sponsor MAME awards banquet 1978-89, Gold sponsor 1986-88), Calif. Assn. Realtors, Contra Costa Bd. Realtors. Jewish. Avocations: playing piano, horseback riding, writing poetry and prose. Home: 123 Erselia Trl Alamo CA 94507-1311 Office: Better Homes Realty PO Box 939 Danville CA 94526

PLUMMER, PATRICIA LYNNE MOORE, chemistry and physics educator; b. Tyler, Tex., Feb. 26; d. Robert Lee and Jewell Ovelia (Jones) Moore; m. Otho Raymond Plummer, Apr. 10, 1965; children: Patrick William Otho, Christina Elisa Lynne. BA, Tex. Christian U., Ft. Worth, Tex., 1960; postgrad., U. N.C., 1960-61; PhD, U. Tex., 1964; grad., Bryn Mawr Summer Inst., 1992. Instr. Welch postdoctoral fellow U. Tex., Austin, 1964-66; postdoctoral fellow Dept. Chemistry, U. Ark., Fayetteville, 1966-68; rsch. assoc. Grad. Ctr., Cloud Phys. Rsch., Rolla, Mo., 1968-73; asst. prof. physics U. Mo., Rolla, 1973-77; assoc. dir. Grad. Ctr. Cloud Phys. Rsch., 1977-79, sr. investigator, 1980-85; assoc. prof. physics U. Mo., 1977-85; prof. dept. chemistry and physics U. Mo., Columbia, 1986—; internat. sci. advisor Symposium on Chemistry and Physics of Ice, 1982—; chair of Faculty Sen., 1995—, pres. U. of Mo. Intercampo Fac. Sen., 1994-95. Assoc. editor Jour. of Colloid and Interface Sci., 1980-83; contbr. articles to profl. jours., chpts. to books. Rsch. grantee IBM, 1990-92, Air Force Office Rsch., 1989-91, NSF, 1976-86, NASA, 1973-78; Air Force Office Rsch. summer fellow, 1988, Bryn Mawr Summer Inst., 1992. Mem. Am. Chem. Soc., Am. Phys. Soc., Am. Geophys. Union, Sigma Xi (past pres.). Democrat. Baptist. Avocations: sailing, gardening, tennis, photography. Office: Univ of Missouri 314 Physics Bldg Columbia MO 65211

PLUMMER, RAYMOND J., furniture manufacturing executive. BA, St. Francis Coll., Loretto, Pa., 1952. With Plummer Furniture Co., Cresson, Pa., 1954-69, Wolf Furniture Co., Altoona, Pa., 1966-89; exec. v.p. Van Art Furniture Inc., Warren, Mich., 1989-90, pres., 1991—; now chief operating officer. With USN, 1952-54. Office: Van Art Furniture Inc 6500 E 14 Mile Rd Warren MI 48092*

PLUMMER, RISQUE WILSON, lawyer; b. Mobile, Ala., Oct. 13, 1910; s. Frederick Harvey and Caroline (Wilson) P.; m. Constance M. Burch, Feb. 21, 1939; children: Risque Wilson Jr., Richard Randolph. J.D., U. Va., 1933. Bar: Va. 1932, Md. 1938. Atty. in charge of litigation HOLC, 1933-38; pvt. practice law, 1938—; counsel U.S. Maritime Commn., 1942; partner firm Griffin & Plummer, 1951-73; counsel O'Connor, Preston, Glenn & Smith, Balt., 1979—; prof. law Am. Inst. Banking, 1948-52. Contbr. articles to profl. jours. Exec. sec. Md. Commn. on Anti-Subversive Activities, 1949-50; co-founder, pres. Roland Park Baseball Leagues, Inc., 1956-57; co-founder, pres. Wyndhurst Improvement Assn., Inc., 1957-59; mem. Selective Service Adv. Bd., 1940-42. Served to lt. USNR, 1943-46, ATO, PTO. Fellow Internat. Acad. Law and Sci.; mem. Am. Judicature Soc., ABA (council sect. of family law 1966-70), Md. Bar Assn. (council sect. of family and juvenile law 1968-70), Md. Assn. Trial Lawyers (gov. 1966-67), Bar Assn. Baltimore City (com. on grievances 1966-69, chmn. com. on profl. ethics 1969-70, exec. com. 1969-70), Am. Contract Bridge League (Bronze life master, cert. dir., author The Small Club), Soc. Colonial Wars, Delta Tau Delta (pres. U. Va. chpt.), Phi Delta Phi. Episcopalian. Home: Highfield House 4000 N Charles St Unit 512 Baltimore MD 21218-1735 Office: Law Bldg 425 St Paul Pl Baltimore MD 21202-2107

PLUMMER, STEVEN TSOSIE, bishop; b. Coalmine, N. Mex., Aug. 14, 1944; m. Catherine B. Tso; children: Brian Tso, Byron Tso, Steven, Jr., Cathlena. Student, San Juan Community Coll., Farmington, N. Mex., Phoenix (Ariz.) Jr. Coll., Ch. Divinity Sch. of the Pacific, San Francisco. Ordained deacon, The Episc. Ch., 1975, priest, 1976. Deacon, priest Good Shepherd Mission, Fort Defiance, Ariz., 1976-77; vicar St. John the Baptizer, Montezuma Creek, Utah, 1977-83; regional vicar for Utah Bluff, Utah, from 1983; consecrated bishop Episc. Ch. in Navajoland, Farmington, N. Mex., 1990; mem. Episc. Council of Indian Ministries. Office: The Episcopal Ch Navajoland Area Mission PO Box 720 Farmington NM 87499-0720

PLUMSTEAD, WILLIAM CHARLES, quality engineer, consultant; b. Two Rivers, Wis., Nov. 2, 1938; m. Peggy Bass, July 19, 1959 (div. July 1968); children: William Jr., Jennifer; m. Vicki Newton, June 27, 1981. Student, U. Fla., 1956-58, Temple U., 1966-72, Albright Coll., 1973-75; BSBA, Calif. Coast U., 1985, MBA, 1989. Registered profl. engr., Calif. V.p. U.S. Testing Co., Inc., Hoboken, N.J., 1963-76; div. mgr. Daniel Internat., Inc., Greenville, S.C., 1976-83; group mgr. Bechtel Group, Inc., San Francisco, 1983-89; prin. engr. Fluor Daniel, Inc., Greenville, 1989-94; v.p. cons. Plumstead Quality and Tech. Svcs., Greenville, S.C., 1994—. Author: (with others) Code/Specification Syndrome, 1976, NDT Laboratories Update, 1991, NDT in Construction, 1991, NDT-A Partner in Excellence, 1994; contbr. articles to profl. jours. Fellow Am. Soc. for Nondestructive Testing (coun. chmn. 1985-88, nat. sec./treas. 1992-93, nat. v.p. 1993-94, pres. 1994—); mem. ASTM (sec. 1989-93, vice chmn. 1994—), Toastmasters Internat. (pres. local chpt. 1990-91, Competent Toastmaster award 1986, Able Toastmaster award 1993). Avocations: sports, wine tasting. Home and Office: Plumstead Quality Tech Svcs 806 Botany Rd Greenville SC 29615-1608

PLUNGIS, BARBARA MARIE, health facility nursing administrator; b. Bridgeport, Conn., Aug. 3, 1938; d. John Jr. and Elizabeth E. (Ando) George; m. James D. Plungis, Aug. 28, 1978. Diploma in nursing summa cum laude, Bridgeport Hosp. Sch. Nursing, 1959; BS, St. Joseph's Coll., 1984, postgrad. RN, Fla. Nurse mgr. telemetry, pediatrcs North Miami (Fla.) Med. Ctr.; nurse recruiter North Miami Med. Ctr., asst. DON, 1976-85, DON, 1985-88; nurse adminstr. Parkway Reg. Med. Ctr., North Miami Beach, Fla., 1988-92; staffing br. mgr. Kimberly Quality Care, Ft. Lauderdale, Fla., 1991; dir. profl. svcs. Staffbuilders Home Health, Miami Lakes, Fla., 1992-94; asst. adminstr., patient care svcs. Hollywood Med. Ctr.; asst. adminstr. patient care svcs. Hollywood (Fla.) Med. Ctr., 1994—. Mem. No. Miami Mayors Task Force. Named Nurse Adminstr. of Yr., So. Fla. Med. Bus. Rev., 1991. Mem. Nat. Assn. Nurse Recruiters, South Fla. Nurse Adminstrs. Assn., North Miami Disaster Preparedness Com., North Dade C. of C., Fla. Hosp. Assn. Home: 1060 NE 141st St Miami FL 33161-3312

PLUNK, ROBERT MALCOME, insurance company executive; b. Bethel Springs, Tenn., Oct. 12, 1932; s. William E. and Pearl (Wilkes) P.; m. Carolyn Elizabeth Garland; children: Kathy, Sharon. BA, MA, Memphis State U., 1962; JD, Western State U., Fullerton, Calif., 1973. Agt. Preferred Risk Ins. Co., Tenn., 1962-63; career agy. mgr. Tenn., 1963-65; sales mgr. Atlanta, 1965-68; asst. regional mgr. Calif. 1968-71, regional mgr., 1971-73; mgr. preferred abstrs. West Des Moines, 1973-78, dir. corp. responsibilities, 1978-82, v.p., 1982-85, exec. v.p., 1985-87, pres., chief exec. officer, 1987—; also bd. dirs.; bd. dirs. Midwest Mut. Ins. Co., West Des Moines, Preferred Risk Life, West Des Moines. Founding dir. Mothers Against Drunk Driving, Dallas. Mem. ABA, Calif. Bar Assn. Office: Preferred Risk Ins Co 1111 Ashworth Rd West Des Moines IA 50265-3544

PLUNKET, DANIEL CLARK, pediatrician; b. Birmingham, Ala., May 7, 1929; s. Henry Clark and Carolyn Clark (Langford) P.; m. Lillian C. Barrington, Dec. 31, 1971; children: Dennis, Beth, Ann, Brenda, Scott. B.S., Emory U., 1949, M.D., 1952. Diplomate Am. Bd. Pediatrics. Intern Med. Coll. Va. Hosp., Richmond, 1952-53; resident in pediatrics Med. Coll. Va. Hosp., 1953-54, Tripler Army Med. Center, Honolulu, 1958-59, Walter Reed Army Inst., 1962-64; pediatrician, pediatric hematologist/oncologist acad. medicine, chief pediatric service William Beaumont Gen. Hosp., El Paso, Tex., 1959-62; commd. 1st lt. U.S. Army, 1955, advanced through grades to col., 1967; asst. chief dept. pediatrics Letterman Army Med. Center, San Francisco, 1964-65; chmn. dept. pediatrics Fitzsimons Army Med. Center, Denver, 1965-75; prof., chmn. dept. pediatrics U. Okla. Coll. Medicine, Tulsa, 1975—; sr. assoc. dean for clin. affairs U. Okla. Health Scis. Ctr., Tulsa, 1993—; clin. prof. pediatrics U. Colo., Denver, 1974-75. Mem. adv. chmn. March of Dimes, Tulsa chpt., 1975-92; bd. dirs. ARC, Tulsa chpt., 1981—. Decorated Legion of Merit; Walter Reed Inst. Research fellow hematology and research, 1962-64. Mem. Am. Acad. Pediatrics, Am. Pediatric Soc., Am. Soc. Hematology, AMA, So. Soc. Pediatric Rsch. Episcopalian. Home: 2436 E 33rd St Tulsa OK 74105-2316 Office: 2815 S Sheridan Rd Tulsa OK 74129-1000

PLUNKETT, MARYANN, actress; b. Lowell, Mass., 1953; m. Jay O. Sanders; 1 child, James Plunkett. Student, U. N.H. Co-founder Portland (Maine) Stage Co. Broadway debut in Agnes of God, 1983; other Broadway appearances include Sunday in the Park with George, Me and My Girl (Tony award for best actress in a mus. 1987), (off Broadway) Aristocrats, (stage) The Crucible (Belasco Theatre, N.Y.), 1991, Little Hotel on the Side (Belasco Theatre, N.Y.) 1992, The Seagull, 1992, St. Joan, 1993 (nominated Best Actress Drama Desk). Office: Davis/Spylios 244 W 54th St Rm 707 New York NY 10019

PLUNKETT, PAUL EDWARD, federal judge; b. Boston, July 9, 1935; s. Paul M. and Mary Cecilia (Erbacher) P.; m. Martha Milan, Sept. 30, 1958; children: Paul Scott, Steven, Andrew, Kevin. BA, Harvard U., 1957, LLB, 1960. Asst. atty. U.S. Atty.'s Office, Chgo., 1963-66; ptnr. Plunkett Nisin et al, Chgo., 1966-78, Mayer Brown & Platt, Chgo., 1960-63, 78-83; judge U.S. Dist. Ct. (no. dist.) Ill., Chgo., 1983—; adj. faculty John Marshall Law Sch., Chgo., 1964-76, 82—, Loyola U. Law Sch., Chgo., 1977-82. Mem. Fed. Bar Assn. Clubs: Legal, Law, Union League (Chgo.). Office: US Dist Ct 219 S Dearborn St Chicago IL 60604-1702

PLUSK, RONALD FRANK, manufacturing company executive; b. Chgo., Mar. 30, 1933; s. Frank and Ann (Petrauskas) P.; m. Rose Marie Pawlikowski, May 25, 1957; children—Frank A., Ronald S., Cynthia Marie. B.S.C., Loyola U., Chgo., 1954; postgrad., Northwestern U., 1957-59. Mgmt. cons. Peat, Marwick, Mitchell & Co., Chgo., 1963-66; corp. controller Varo, Inc., Garland, Tex., 1966-69; dir. planning and mgmt. systems Rucker Co., Oakland, Calif., 1969-72; dir. ops., audit and systems Rucker Co., 1972-76, v.p. ops., audit and systems, 1976-77; v.p. fin. adminstrn. Rucker Co. (merged with NL Petroleum Svcs. Co.), Houston, 1977-79; v.p. fin. treas. Cobe Labs., Inc., Lakewood, Colo., 1979-92. Contbr. articles to profl. jours. Served to 1st lt. AUS, 1954-56, ETO. Mem. Am. Mgmt. Assn., Planning Execs. Inst., Fin. Execs. Inst. Roman Catholic. Home: 6151 Middlefield Rd Littleton CO 80123-6620

PLUSQUELLIC, DONALD L., mayor; b. Akron, Ohio, July 3, 1949; m. Mary Plusquellic; children: Dave, Michelle. BS, Bowling Green State U., 1972; JD, U. Akron, 1981. Councilman Akron City Council, 1973-81, councilman-at-large, 1982-86, council pres., 1984-86; mayor City of Akron, 1987—. Home: 2785 Nesmith Lake Blvd Akron OH 44314-3427 Office: Office of the Mayor 200 Municipal Bldg 166 S High St Akron OH 44308-1626

PLUZYNSKI, EDWARD DALE, advertising executive; b. Chgo., July 23, 1941; s. Sylvester and Helen (Huenink) P.; m. Claudine C. Harris, Sept. 5, 1943; 1 child, Scott Harris. BS in Journalism, So. Ill. U., 1964. Account exec. Erwin Wasey, Inc., L.A., 1964-70; account supr. Needhan, Harper & Steers, L.A., 1971-73; sales mgmt. Simmel & Assocs., Inc., L.A., 1974-75; owner Pluzynski & Assocs., Inc., N.Y.C., 1976—; guest lectr. Parsons, N.Y.C., 1988. Catalog producer Coach Leathwear, 1984-94, Community Kitchens, 1982-88, American Express, 1983-94, Godiva Chocolates, 1986-89. With U.S. Army, 1966-68. Mem. Dir. Mktg. Assn. (speaker, N.Y.C. 1980, 88), Retail Advt. Assn., Conn. Golf Club, Bermuda Surf Assn. (bd. dirs.). Avocations: golf, skiing, tennis, traveling. Office: Pluzynski & Assocs Inc 26 W 17th St # 10 New York NY 10011-5710

PLYLER, JOHN LANEY, JR., healthcare management professional; b. Greenville, S.C., Jan. 31, 1934; s. John Laney and Beatrice Elizabeth (Dennis) P.; m. Caroline Rasor Williams, June 26, 1959; children: Sharon, John III, James (dec.). Student, U.S. Naval Acad., 1953-54; BA, Furman U., 1956; MHA, Duke U., 1970. Prodn. planner J. P. Stevens & Co., Greenville, 1958-65; mgmt. engr., outpatient mgr. Greenville Hosp. Sys., 1967-68; assoc. dir. Cleveland Meml. Hosp., Shelby, N.C., 1970-79; exec. v.p., COO Bapt. Med. Ctr., Oklahoma City, 1979-85; group v.p. SunHealth Alliance, Charlotte, N.C., 1985-86, sr. v.p., 1986—. 2d lt. U.S. Army, 1957, capt. USAR, 1957-65. Fellow Am. Coll. Healthcare Execs. (mem. ethics com. 1990-93, chair 1992-93), Okla. Hosp. Assn. (mem. coun. on edn.), N.C. Hosp. Assn. (coun. on pers.). Avocations: travel, sailing, photography. Home: SunHealth Inc PO Box 909 Davidson NC 28036 Office: SunHealth Alliance PO Box 668800 Charlotte NC 28266

POBEREZNY, THOMAS, museum adminstrator. Ceo., pres. EAA Air Adventure Mus., Oshkosh, Wis. Recipient Laurels award for aeronautics/propulsion Aviation Week & Space Tech., 1993. Office: EAA Air Adventure Museum EAA Aviation Center PO Box 3065 Oshkosh WI 54903-3065*

POCH, STEPHEN, metallurgical engineer, consultant; b. Homestead, Pa., June 17, 1909; s. George and Mary (Banyas) P.; m. Elizabeth Alberta Mrasko, Feb. 1, 1941 (dec. Sept. 1994); 1 child, Pamela Elizabeth. Student, Geneva Coll., Beaver Falls, Pa., 1930-31; BS in Metall. Engring., U. Pitts., 1939, postgrad., 1942-44, 46-47. Registered profl. engr., N.J., Pa., Conn. Metall. observer Carnegie-Ill. Steel Corp., Homestead, 1936-39; devel. engr. Irvin (Pa.) Works, U.S. Steel Corp., 1940-41; commentator N.Y. World's Fair, U.S. Steel, Homestead, 1941; chief metall. observer Farrell (Pa.) Works, U.S. Steel, 1942; rsch. engr. Acid Open Hearth Rsch., U. Pitts., 1942-44, 46-47; supt. processes Driver Harris Co., Harrison, N.J., 1947-58; v.p. dir. R&D Molecu Wire Corp., Farmingdale, N.J., 1958-69; asst. prof. N.Y.C. Tech. Coll., Bklyn., 1969-74; metall. cons. in pvt. practice, 1974—; fine wire cons. C.O. Jelliff Co., Southport, Conn., 1970-72; cons. Kanthal Corp., Bethel, Conn., 1972-75, Marcal Paper Mills, Inc., Elmwood Park, N.J., 1979-80. Co-author monographs; patentee in field. Judge of elections Republican Party, Homestead, 1935-39; bd. dirs. Whitaker Depression Coll., Munhall, Pa., 1934-35. Lt. (s.g.) USN, 1944-46, PTO. Mem. AIME (sr., life), NSPE, ASTM (chmn. com. B-4, 1954), Metal Sci. Club, Am. Soc. for Metals.

POCHI, PETER ERNEST, physician; b. Boston, Mar. 8, 1929; s. Anesti and Alice (Peterson) P.; m. Barbara Orlob, June 11, 1955; children: Alan, Rena. A.B. cum laude, Harvard Coll., 1950; M.D., Boston U., 1955. Diplomate Am. Bd. Dermatology. Intern Boston City Hosp., 1955-56, vis. dermatologist, 1978-91, assoc. dir., 1964-74, 78-84, acting chief dermatology, 1984-85; resident in dermatology Boston U. Hosp., 1958-61, vis. dermatologist, 1977-91, acting chief dermatology, 1984-85; assoc. in medicine Peter Bent Brigham Hosp., Boston, 1972-78; sr. cons. in dermatology Lemuel Shattuck Hosp., Boston, 1975-91; Herbert Mescon prof. dermatology Sch. Medicine, Boston U., 1988-91, prof. emeritus, 1991—; interim chmn. dept. dermatology, 1984-85; cons. med. service in dermatology Boston VA Hosp., 1978-82; lectr. dermatology Sch. Medicine, Tufts U., 1980-91; assoc. staff New Eng. Med. Ctr. Hosp., 1981-91. Assoc. editor Jour. Investigative Dermatology, 1968-73; contbg. editor Year Book of Dermatology, 1983-90; mem. editorial bd.: Archives of Dermatology, 1979-84, Jour. Am. Acad. Dermatology, 1981-90; contbr. articles to med. jours. Bd. dirs. Cmty. Music Ctr., 1973-77, corp. mem., 1994—. With USN, 1956-58. USPHS fellow, 1960-62, 62-63; USPHS grantee, 1965-84. Fellow Am. Acad. Dermatology (bd. dirs. 1981-85); mem. Am. Fedn. Clin. Research, AMA, Boston Dermatological Club (sec.-treas. 1967-69), Boston U. Sch. Medicine Alumni

Assn. (pres. 1979-80), Boston U. Nat. Alumni Council, Dermatology Found., Evans Med. Found. (dir., sec.), Internat. Soc. Dermatology, Mass. Acad. Dermatology, Mass. Med. Soc. (chmn. sect. dermatology 1977-78), New Eng. Dermatol. Soc., Soc. Investigative Dermatology (bd. dirs. 1976-81, v.p. 1986-87). Home: 333 Commonwealth Ave Boston MA 02115-1931

POCHYLY, DONALD FREDERICK, physician, hospital administrator; b. Chgo., June 3, 1934; s. Frank J. and Vlasta (Bezdek) P.; m. Diane Dilelio, May 11, 1957; children: Christopher, Jonathan, David. M.D., Loyola U., 1959; M.Ed., U. Ill., 1971. Diplomate Am. Bd. Internal Medicine, Am. Bd. Geriatrics. Fellow ACP, 1966-67; asst. prof. med. edn. U. Ill., 1967-72, asso. prof., 1972-74; chmn. dept. health scis. edn. U. of Health Scis., Chgo. Med. Sch., 1975-77, provost, acting pres., 1977-79; prof. clin. medicine Loyola U., Chgo., 1980—; v.p. med. affairs N.W. Community Hosp., Arlington Heights, Ill.; chmn. com. rev. and recognition Am. Coun. Continuing Med. Edn., 1993; cons. Nat. Libr. Medicine, WHO. Contbr. articles to med. jours. Mem. AMA, Ill. Geriatrics Soc. (pres. Chgo. chpt. 1988-89), Ill. Med. Soc., Chgo. Med. Soc., Alpha Omega Alpha. Roman Catholic. Office: Northwest Community Hosp 800 W Central Rd Arlington Heights IL 60005-2392

POCKELL, LESLIE M., publishing company executive; b. Norwalk, Conn., June 19, 1942; s. Abe and Mildred (Shapiro) P.; m. Noriko Maejima, June 23, 1967. A.B., Columbia Coll., 1964. Articles editor Avant-Garde Mag., N.Y.C., 1967-70; dir. trade dept. St. Martin's Press, N.Y.C., 1970-84; exec. editor, dir. spl. interest group Doubleday & Co. Inc., N.Y.C., 1984-88; editorial dir. Kodansha Internat., 1988-94; dir. book devel. Book-Of-The-Month Club, Inc. N.Y.C., 1994—; adj. lectr. NYU, 1984-86. Served with U.S. Army, 1964-67.

POCKER, YESHAYAU, chemistry, biochemistry educator; b. Kishinev, Romania, Oct. 10, 1928; came to U.S., 1961; naturalized, 1967.; s. Benzion Israel and Esther Sarah (Sudit) P.; m. Anna Goldenberg, Aug. 8, 1950; children: Rona, Elon I. MSc, Hebrew U., Jerusalem, 1949; PhD, Univ. Coll., London, Eng., 1953; DSc, U. London, 1960. Rsch. assoc. Weizmann Inst. Sci., Rehovot, Israel, 1949-50; humanitarian trust fellow Univ. Coll., 1951-52, asst. lectr., 1952-54, lectr., 1954-61; vis. assoc. prof. Ind. U., Bloomington, 1960-61; prof. U. Washington, Seattle, 1961—; bicentennial lectr. Mont. State U., Bozeman, 1976, U. N.C., Chapel Hill, 1977, guest lectr. U. Kyoto, Japan, 1984; Edward A. Doisy vis. prof. biochemistry St. Louis U. Med. Sch., 1990; plenary lectr. N.Y. Acad. Sci., 1983, Fast Reactions in Biol. Systems, Kyoto, Japan, 1984, NATO, 1989, Consiglio nat. delle Richerche, U. Bari, Italy, 1989, Sigma Tau, Spoleto, Italy, 1990; Internat. lectr. Purdue U., 1990; cons. NIH, 1984, 86, 88; Spl. Topic lectr. on photosynthesis, Leibniz House, Hanover, Fed. Republic Germany, 1991; enzymology, molecular biology lectr., Dublin, Ireland, 1992. Mem. editorial adv. bd. Inorganica Chimica Acta-Bioinorganic Chemistry, 1981-89; bd. reviewing editors Sci., 1985—; contbr. numerous articles to profl. jours.; pub. over 220 papers and 12 revs. Numerous awards worldwide, 1983-90. Mem. Royal Soc. Chemistry, Am. Chem. Soc. (nat. spkr. 1970, 74, 84, chmn. Pauling award com. 1978, plaque awards 1970, 74, 84, Outstanding Svc. award 1979), Soc. Exptl. Biology, Am. Soc. Biol. Chemists, N.Y. Acad. Scis., Sigma Xi (nat. lectr. 1971). Avocations: Aramaic, etymology, history, philology, poetry. Office: U Wash Dept Chemistry Campus Box 351700 Seattle WA 98195-1700

POCKLINGTON, PETER H., business executive; b. Regina, Sask., Can., Nov. 18, 1941; s. Basil B. and Eileen (Dempsey) P.; m. Eva d. Jack McAvoy, June 2, 1974; 4 children. Pres. Westown Ford, Tilbury, Ont., Can., 1967-69; pres. Chatham, Ont., 1969-71, Edmonton, Alta., Can., 1971-82; chmn. Pocklington Fin. Corp., Edmonton, 1982—; owner, gov. Edmonton Oiler Hockey Club, 1976—; owner Edmonton Trapper Triple A Baseball Club, 1981—; formed Hartford Properties, Inc., 1985, Edmonton, Club Fit Inc., 1990; purchased Superior Furniture Systems Mfg., Inc., 1987, Canbra Foods Ltd., 1988, Green Acre Farms, Sabastool, Miss., 1988, Green Acre Foods Inc., Nacadoches, Tex., 1988. Mem. Mayfair Golf and Country Club, Edmonton Golf and Country Club, Vintage Golf Club, Indian Wells, Calif. Avocations: golf, skiiing, fishing. Office: Pocklington Fin Corp Ltd, 2500 Sun Life Pl 10123-99 St, Edmonton, AB Canada T5J 3H1 also: Edmonton Oilers, Edmonton, AB Canada T5B 4M9

POCOCK, FREDERICK JAMES, scientist, consultant; b. Canton, Ohio, May 28, 1923; s. Frederick Stanley and Mary Elizabeth (Tinker) P.; m. Lois Jean Rice, Jan. 12, 1952; children—Kathleen Jean, David Walter. B.S. in Chemistry, Mt. Union Coll., 1950; grad., Lincoln Aero. Inst. Akron U., 1942, postgrad., 1953. Registered profl. engr., Calif. Aircraft insp. Bell Aircraft Corp., 1942; in tech. sales Republic Steel Corp., 1949-50; with Babcock & Wilcox Co., Alliance, Ohio, 1950-88; sr. scientist Alliance Research Center, 1974-88; cons. water technology. Contbr. articles to profl jours. Past precinct committeeman Louisville Republican Com., Ohio. Served with USAAF, 1943-46. Recipient recognition for 30 yrs. rsch. Ohio Ho. of Reps., 1980, award of merit Internat. Water Conf., 1985; co-recipient Pau; Cohen Meml. award, 1993, Engrs. award for disting. svc. Soc. Profl. Engrs., 1987. Fellow ASME (co-recipient Prime Movers award 1962, Disting. Svc. award 1987, Dedicated Svc. award 1987); mem. ASTM, Am. Chem. Soc. (Cert. of Merit award 1967), Nat. Assn. Corrosion Engrs. (cert.).

POCOCK, JOHN GREVILLE AGARD, historian, educator; b. London, Mar. 7, 1924; came to U.S. in 1966; s. Lewis Greville and Antoinette (Legros) P.; m. Felicity Willis-Fleming, Mar. 27, 1958; children: Stephen Greville, Hugh Edward. BA, U. N.Z., 1945, MA, 1946; PhD, Cambridge (Eng.) U., 1952; LittD (hon.), U. Canterbury, N.Z., 1973. Lectr. history U. Otago, N.Z., 1953-55; research fellow St. John's Coll. Cambridge U., 1956-58; from sr. lectr. to prof. polit. sci. U. Canterbury, 1959-66; prof. history and polit. sci. Washington U., St. Louis, 1966-74; Harry C. Black prof. history Johns Hopkins U., Balt., 1974-94, prof. emeritus, 1994—; vis. fellow Australian Nat. U., 1973. Author: The Ancient Constitution and The Feudal Law, 1957, 2nd expanded edit., 1987, Politics, Language and Time, 1971, The Machiavellian Moment, 1975, The Political Works of James Harrington, 1977, Virtue, Commerce and History: Essays on Political Thought and History, Chiefly in the Eighteenth Century, 1985, Politica, Linguaggio e Storia, 1992, Die Andere Burgergesellschaft: Zur Dialektik von Tugend und Korruption, 1993. Overseas fellow Churchill Coll., Cambridge U., 1969; sr. fellow Am. Council Learned Socs., 1969. Mem. Am. Soc. 18th Century Studies (pres. 1977-78), Am. Acad. Arts and Scis., Royal Hist. Soc., Am. Hist. Assn., Am. Polit. Sci. Assn., Conf. Study Polit. Thought, Conf. Brit. Studies. Office: John Hopkins U Dept History Baltimore MD 21218

PODBERESKY, SAMUEL, lawyer; b. Cremona, Italy, Mar. 16, 1946; came to U.S., 1947; s. Noah and Mina (Milikowsky) P.; m. Rosita Rubinstein, March 8, 1970; children: Daniel J., Michael J. BS in Aeronautical Engring., U. Md., 1967; JD, U. Md., Balt., 1971. Bar: Md. 1972. Flight test engr. Vertol div. Boeing Co., Phila., 1967-68; regulatory atty. FAA, Washington, 1971-78; dep. asst. gen. counsel U.S. Dept. Transp., Washington, 1978-86, asst. gen. counsel aviation enforcement and proceedings, 1986—. Office: US Dept Transp 400 7th St SW Washington DC 20590-0001

PODBOY, ALVIN MICHAEL, JR., lawyer, law library director; b. Cleve., Feb. 10, 1947; s. Alvin Michael and Josephine Esther (Nagode) P.; m. Mary Ann Gloria Esposito, Aug. 21, 1971; children: Allison Marie, Melissa Ann. AB cum laude, Ohio U., 1969; JD, Case Western Res. U., 1972, MLS, 1977. Bar: Ohio 1972, U.S. Dist. Ct. (no. dist.) Ohio 1973, U.S. Supreme Ct. 1992. Assoc. Joseph T. Svete Co. LPA, Chardon, Ohio, 1972-76; dir. pub. services Case Western Res. Sch. Law Libr., Cleve., 1974-77, assoc. law libr., 1977-78; libr. Baker & Hostetler, Cleve. 1978-88, dir. librs., 1988—; instr. Notre Dame Coll. of Ohio, Cleve., 1991—, Am. Inst. Paralegal Studies, Cleve., 1991—. Bd. overseers Case Western Res. U., 1981-87, mem. vis. com. sch. librc. sci., 1980-86, mem. Westlaw adv. bd., 1987-92, bd. govs. law sch. alumni assn., 1992—; West's Legal Directory Ohio Adv. Panel, 1990-91; chmn. Case Western Res. Libr. Sch. Alumni Fund, 1979-80. Rep. precinct committeeman Cuyahoga County, Cleve., 1981—, exec. com., 1984-87. 1st lt. USAF, 1972. Mem. ABA (chmn. libraries com. 1989-91), Cleve. Bar Assn., Am. Assn. Law Librs. (cert., chmn. pvt. law librs. spl. interest sect. 1994—), Ohio Regional Assn. Law Librs. (pres. 1985), Case Western Res. U. Sch. Library Alumni Assn. (pres. 1981), Arnold Air Soc., Am. Legion, Pi Gamma Mu, Phi Alpha Theta. Roman Catholic. Lodge: K.C. Avocations: alpine skiing, boating. Home: 4637 Anderson Rd

Cleveland OH 44121-3868 Office: Baker & Hostetler 3200 National City Ctr Cleveland OH 44114-3485

PODD, ANN, newspaper editor; b. Buffalo, Jan. 15, 1954; d. Edward and Florence (Bojan) P.; m. Timothy Murray, 1980; children: Laura, Gregory. AB, Syracuse U., 1976; MBA, SUNY, Buffalo, 1981. Reporter AP, 1977; reporter Buffalo Courier-Express, 1977-78, bus. reporter, 1978-80, bus. editor, 1980-82; bus. editor Bergen (N.J.) Record, 1982-88; bus. editor New York Daily News, 1988-90, assoc. editor, 1990-92, assoc. editor, dir. human resources, 1992-93; dep. spot news editor Wall St. Jour., N.Y.C., 1993-94, New York news editor, 1994—. Office: Wall St Journal 200 Liberty St New York NY 10281*

PODELL, RICHARD JAY, lawyer; b. Milw., Nov. 22, 1943; s. Ralph J. and Ruth L. (Sherkow) P.; m. Penny E. Mayerson, Sept. 4, 1966; children: Todd, Tasha. BA, Colgate U., 1966; JD, U. Wis., 1969. Bar: Wis. 1969, U.S. Dist. Ct. (we. dist.) Wis. 1969, U.S. Dist. Ct. (ea. dist.) Wis. 1971, U.S. Supreme Ct. 1974, U.S. Ct. Appeals (7th cir.) 1977. Asst. dist. atty. Office Milwaukee County Dist. Atty., Milw., 1969-71; pres. Richard J. Podell & Assocs., Milw., 1971—; lectr. on family law topics at nat. and internat. symposiums. Editor Wis. Jour. Family Law, 1987-89. Mem. ABA (chmn. family law sect. 1988-89), State Bar Wis. (chmn. family law sect. 1985-86), Milw. Bar Assn. (chmn. family law sect. 1979-84), Am. Acad. Matrimonial Lawyers (pres. Wis. chpt. 1986-87). Office: 100 E Wisconsin Ave Ste 2800 Milwaukee WI 53202-4107

PODESTA, ROBERT ANGELO, investment banker; b. Chgo., Oct. 7, 1912; s. Angelo D. and Agnes (Fraser) P.; m. Corrine A. Murnighan, Dec. 26, 1936; children: Carol Ann (Mrs. Brian F. Foley), Mary Ellen (Mrs. C. Kevin Burke), Kathleen (Mrs. John T. Mehigan), Robert Anthony. B.S., B.A., Northwestern U., 1944; LL.D., St. Mary's Coll., 1969. V.p., treas., dir. Julien Collins & Co., 1945-49; mng. ptnr. Cruttenden, Podesta & Miller, 1949-63; sr. v.p., dir. Walston & Co., Inc., 1963-65; sr. v.p., treas., dir. Chgo. Corp., 1965-69, 73-79; chmn. exec. com. Altorfer, Podesta, Woolard & Co., 1979-81; v.p. Stifel, Nicolaus & Co., Inc., 1981-82; prin. Podesta & Co., 1982—; asst. sec. for econ. devel. Dept. Commerce, 1969-73; dir. Pettibone Corp.; bd. govs. Am. Stock Exch., 1962-64, Midwest Stock Exch., 1954-57. Pres. Grant Park Concerts Soc. Mem. Nat. Assn. Securities Dealers. Roman Catholic. Clubs: Chicago, Mid-Day, Mid-Am. (Chgo.); Bohemian (San Francisco). Home: 111 E Chestnut St Chicago IL 60611-2051 Office: Podesta & Co. 135 S La Salle St Chicago IL 60603-4101

PODGORNY, GEORGE, emergency physician; b. Tehran, Iran, Mar. 17, 1934; s. Emanuel and Helen (Parsian) P.; came to U.S., 1954, naturalized, 1973. B.S., Maryville Coll., 1958; postgrad. Bowman Gray Sch. Medicine, 1958; M.D., Wake Forest U., 1962; m. Ernestine Koury, Oct. 20, 1962; children: Adele, Emanuel II, George, Gregory. Intern in surgery N.C. Bapt. Hosp., Winston-Salem, 1962-63, chief resident in gen. surgery, 1966-67, in cardiothoracic surgery, 1967-69; sr. med. examiner Forsyth County, N.C., 1972—; dir. dept. emergency medicine Forsyth Meml. Hosp., Winston-Salem, 1970-80; sec.-treas. Forsyth Emergency Services, Winston-Salem, 1970-80; clin. prof. emergency medicine East Carolina U. Sch. Medicine, Greenville, 1984—, chmn. residency rev. com. on emergency medicine, 1980-88; mem. Accreditation Coun. for Grad. Med. Edn. Dir. Emergency Med. Svcs. Project Region II of N.C., 1975—; chmn. bd. trustees Emergency Medicine Found.; chmn. residency rev. com. emergency medicine Accreditation Coun. Grad. Med. Edn.; founder Western Piedmont Emergency Med. Svcs. Coun., 1973; mem. N.C. Emergency Med. Svcs. Adv. Coun., 1976-81; assoc. prof. clin. surgery Bowman Gray Sch. Medicine, Wake Forest U., Winston-Salem, 1979—. Bd. dirs. Piedmont Health Systems Agy., 1975-84; trustee Forsyth County Hosp., Authority, 1974-75; bd. dirs. N.C. Health Coordinating Coun. 1975-82, Medic Alert Found. Internat. Fellow Internat. Coll. Surgeons, Internat. Coll. Angiology, Royal Soc. Health (Great Britain), Royal Soc. Medicine, Southeastern Surg. Congress; mem. Am. Coll. Emergency Physicians (charter, pres. 1978-79), AMA, (chmn. coun. of sect. emergency medicine 1978-90, alt. del. for Am. Coll. Emergency Physicians, 1990—), Am. Bd. Emergency Medicine (pres. 1976-81). Contbr. articles to profl. publs. on trauma, snake bite and history of medicine; editorial bd. Annals of Emergency Medicine, Med. Meetings. Home and Office: 2115 Georgia Ave Winston Salem NC 27104-1917

PODGORNY, RICHARD JOSEPH, biologist, science administrator; b. Chgo., Jan. 27, 1944; s. Leon and Mary Agatha (Gryzik) P.; m. Dorothy Mary Doreca, June 11, 1966; 1 child, Nicole Marie. BA, St. Mary's Coll., 1966; MS, Am. U., 1971; PhD, Georgetown U., 1975; postgrad., Fed. Exec. Inst., 1989. Quality control supr. Capital Aerosol Packaging Co., Melrose Park, Ill., 1965-66; Peace Corps vol., Adi Teclesan, Ethiopia, 1966-68; sci. dept. chmn. and tchr. Western Sr. High Sch., Washington, 1968-76; dir. marine scis. D.C. Pub. Sch. Systems, 1976-79; mgr. nat. sanctuaries programs U.S. Dept. Commerce, NOAA, Washington, 1979-82, chief user affairs/mktg. unit, external affairs staff, 1983-86, chief internat. affairs Nat. Ocean Service, 1986-94, sr. advisor, pres. Coun. Sustainable Devel., 1994—; U.S. del. to Intergovtl. Oceanographic Commn., 1986—, South Pacific Commn., 1989—; bd. dirs. Pacific Congress Internat., 1987—; lectr. in field; cons. in field. Author: Introduction to Marine Science, 1977; Ocean Ecology, 1978; contbr. articles to profl. jours. Vice pres., bd. dirs. Friends of Arlington County Parks, 1982-86; chmn. bd. dirs. planning com. Burgundy Farm Country Day Sch., Inc., 1980-86. NSF scholar, 1969-71; Georgetown U. fellow, 1972-75; recipient service commendation Emperor Haile Sallassie, 1967. Mem. AAAS, Oceanography Soc., Marine Tech. Soc., Sigma Xi. Roman Catholic. Clubs: Capital Yacht, Skyline Health and Racquet. Home: 4858 28th St S Arlington VA 22206-1370 Office: US Dept Commerce NOAA Office of Sustainable Devel 14th & Constitution Ave NW Room 5222 Washington DC 20230

PODGORSAK, ERVIN B., medical physicist, educator, administrator; b. Vienna, Austria, Sept. 28, 1943; arrived in Slovenia, 1946, came to U.S., 1968, Can., 1973; s. Franc and Gabriella (Cukale) P.; m. Marjana Ambrozic, Oct. 23, 1965; children: Matthew, Gregor. Dipl.Ing. in Physics, U. Ljubljana, Slovenia, 1968; MSc in Physics, U. Wis., 1970, PhD in Physics, 1973. Diplomate Am. Bd. Med. Physics. Rsch. asst. U. Ljubljana, 1965-68, U. Wis., Madison, 1968-73; postdoctoral fellow U. Toronto, Ont., Can., 1973-74; asst. prof. McGill U., Montreal, Que., Can., 1975-79, assoc. prof., 1980-84, prof. med. physics, 1985—, dir. med. physics unit, 1991—; dir. dept. med. physics Montreal Gen. Hosp., 1979—; presenter in field. Contbr. over 130 articles to sci. jours., books. Fellow Can. Coll. Physicists in Medicine (bd. dirs. 1981-89, v.p. 1984-87, pres. 1987-89); mem. Am. Assn. Physicists in Medicine (bd. dirs. 1990-93, assoc. editor Med. Physics Jour., 1989—, radiother. com. 1994—), Am. Coll. Med. Physics, Can. Orgn. Med. Physics, Can. Assn. Physicists, Can. Assn. Radiation Oncologists, Can. Radiation Protection Assn., Internat. Stereotactic Radiosurgery Soc. (bd. dirs. 1991—). Home: 1540 croissant Seville, Brossard, PQ Canada J4X 1J4 Office: Montreal Gen Hosp Dept Med Physics, 1650 Cedar Ave, Montreal, PQ Canada H3G 1A4

PODHAJSKI, BLANCHE RITA, language foundation administrator; b. New Britain, Conn., Sept. 4, 1945; d. Charles Anthony and Blanche Margaret (Poplawski) P.; m. Kenneth R. Kreiling, June 22, 1990. BS in Speech and Hearing, Boston U., 1967; MS in Speech Pathology, U. Vt., 1969; PhD in Learning Disabilities, Northwestern U., 1980. Speech/lang. pathologist Ctr. Disorders of Comm. Med. Ctr. Hosp. of Vt., Burlington, 1968-70, acting dir. Ctr. Disorders of Comm., 1970-71, dir. Ctr. Disorders of Comm., 1971-78; asst. prof. learning disabilities Northwestern U., Evanston, Ill., 1980-81; pvt. practice as lang. and learning disabilities specialist Aesculapius Med. Ctr., South Burlington, Vt., 1981-83; founder, dir. Stern Ctr. for Lang. and Learning, Winooski, Vt., 1983—; clin. assoc. prof. neurology dept. neurology U. Vt. Med. Sch., Burlington, 1971—; field faculty Goddard Coll., Plainfield, Vt., 1973-76, summer vis. prof., 1980; adj. faculty Johnson (Vt.) State Coll., 1975-79; adj. faculty dept. comm. sci. and disorders, 1988—. mem. Vt. State Dept. Edn. Task Force, Vt. Spl. Edn. Evaluation Project, 1985; exec. bd. dirs. Vt. New Eng. br. Orton Dyslexia Soc., 1986; presenter in field. Contbr. articles to profl. jours. Commencement speaker Pine Ridge Sch., Williston, 1991, bd. dirs., edn. com. chair, 1989. Grantee Found. for Children with Learning Disabilities, 1985, Vt. Dept. Spl. Edn., 1986, Vt. Dept. Vocat. Rehab., 1992, Kresge Found., 1994, Freeman Found., 1994, Alma Gibbs Donchian Found., 1995; Turrell scholar, 1994-95. Mem. Am. Speech and

Hearing Assn. (cert. clin. competence), Coun. for Exceptional Children (divsn. for children with communicative disorders, divsn. for children with learning disabilities), Vt. Speech and Hearing Assn. (pres.-elect 1977-78, Clin. Achievement award 1989), Vt. Assn. for Learning Disabilites (lifetime hon., Outstanding Leadership award for contbns. to learning disabled 1978, Lamp of Knowledge award 1983), Orton Soc. Office: Stern Ctr Language & Learning 20 Allen Brook Ln Williston VT 05495

PODHORETZ, NORMAN, magazine editor, writer; b. Bklyn., Jan. 16, 1930; s. Julius and Helen (Woliner) P.; m. Midge Rosenthal Decter, Oct. 21, 1956; children: Rachel, Naomi, Ruth, John. A.B., Columbia, 1950; B.H.L., Jewish Theol. Sem., 1950, LL.D. (hon.), 1980; B.A. (Kellett fellow), Cambridge (Eng.) U., 1952, M.A., 1957; LHD (hon.), Hamilton Coll., 1969, Yeshiva U., 1991, Boston U., 1995. Assoc. editor Commentary, 1956-58, editor in chief, 1960-95, editor-at-large, 1995—; editor in chief Looking Glass Library, 1959-60; sr. fellow Hudson Inst., 1995—; Mem. U. Seminar Am. Civilization, Columbia, 1958. Author: Doings and Undoings, The Fifties and After in American Writing, 1964, Making It, 1968, Breaking Ranks, 1979, The Present Danger, 1980, Why We Were in Vietnam, 1982; The Bloody Crossroads, 1986; editor: The Commentary Reader, 1966. Chmn. new directions adv. com. USIA, 1981-87. Served with AUS, 1953-55. Fulbright fellow, 1950-51. Mem. Coun. on Fgn. Rels. Office: Commentary Am Jewish Com 165 E 56th St New York NY 10022-2709

PODLES, ELEANOR PAULINE, state senator; b. Dudley, Mass., June 6, 1920; d. Francis and Pauline Magiera; student U. N.H.; m. Francis J. Podles, June 28, 1941; children: L. Patricia Podles Barrett Fogleman, Elizabeth Lee Podles Keegan. Mem. N.H. Ho. of Reps., Concord, 1976-80; selectman City of Manchester, N.H., 1976-81, v.p., 1978—; mem. N.H. State Senate, Concord, 1980—; asst. majority whip, mem. fin. com., chmn. public affairs com., public instns. health and welfare com. Del., N.H. Republican Conv., 1976, 78, N.H. Constl. Conv., 1984; pres. pro tem N.H. Senate, 1986—, chair jud. com., vice chair exec. com., senate fin. com., senate edn. com., health and human services for pub. insts. com.; pres. Manchester Rep. Women's Club, 1979—; bd. dirs. St. Joseph's Community Service, Manchester Vis. Nurse Assn., Mental Health Ctr. Manchester, Senate Edn. Com.; state chmn. Am. Legis. Exchange Council; mem. sen. fin. com., 1995—; sen. pres. pro tem, 1995—. Bd. dirs. Mental Health Ctr. Greater Manchester; mem. N.H. Childrens Trust Fund, 1986—. Mem. Am Legis. Exch. Coun. (state chmn.), Orgn. Women Legislators, Manchester Vis. Nurse Assn., Manchester Country Club. Club: Manchester Country. Home: 185 Walnut Hill Ave Manchester NH 03104-2136 Office: N H State Senate State Capitol Concord NH 03301

PODOLAK, DOUGLAS JOHN, marketing consultant; b. Oakes, N.D., May 4, 1948; s. Ernest John and Marlys (Christensen) P.; m. Rita M. Podolak, Nov. 15, 1969. BS in Bus. Adminstrn., U. N.D., 1972. Dir. charter sales N.W. Airlines, St. Paul, 1976-78, dir. petroleum adminstrn., purchasing, 1978-82; mgr. aviation sales Langham Hill Petroleum, Houston, 1982-85; v.p. aviation sales Europe JSH Petroleum Ltd., London, 1985; mgr. aviation sales Langham Hill Petroleum, Charlottesville, Va., 1986-87; pres. Energy Mgmt. Internat., Charlottesville, 1988-91; v.p.; gen. mgr. NWA Fuel Svcs. Corp., 1991-94, pres., 1994—. Mem. Farmington Country Club, Hazeltine Country Club. Avocations: flying, golf. Home: 20985 Channel Dr Excelsior MN 55331-8659 Office: NWA Fuel Svcs Corp 5101 Northwest Dr Saint Paul MN 55111

PODOLSKY, RICHARD JAMES, biophysicist; b. Chgo., Aug. 20, 1923; s. Peter Peter and Esther Hanna (Seidman) P.; m. Kay Steele, 1961 (dec. 1974); children: Alex Nicholas, Paul Gregory. BS in Math., U. Chgo., 1946, PhD in Biophysics, 1952. Biophysicist Naval Med. Rsch. Inst., Bethesda, Md., 1956-62; lab. sect. chief Nat. Inst. Arthritis and Metabolic Diseases, Bethesda, 1962-74; lab. chief, Lab. Phys. Biology Nat. Inst. Arthritis, Metabolism and Digestive Diseases, Bethesda, 1974-86, Nat. Inst. Arthritis and Musculoskeletal and Skin Diseases, Bethesda, 1986; mem. Physiology Study Sect., NIH, 1965-69; mem. Biophysical Soc. coun., exec. bd., 1966-80; mem. coun., pres., Soc. Gen. Physiologists, 1967-72. Editor: Contractibility of Muscle Cells, 1971; contbr. articles to profl. jours. 1st lt. USAF, 1943-46, PTO. Recipient NIH Dir.'s award, 1978, Carter-Wallace lectureship Princeton U., 1967, Bottazzi lectureship Italian Physiol. Soc., 1990. Achievements include patent on apparatus and method for measuring muscle sarcomere length in vivo. Home: 5905 32d St NW Washington DC 20015 Office: NIH Bldg 6 Rm 114 Bethesda MD 20892

PODOS-UNTERMEYER, SALLE, lawyer; b. Bklyn., Oct. 1, 1938; d. David Meyer and Rose (Ifshin) Garber; m. Steven Maurice Podos, June 20, 1959 (div. Dec. 1978); children: Richard Lance Podos, Lisa Beth Podos; m. Walter Untermeyer, Jr., May 2, 1982. BA, Vassar Coll., 1959; MA, Brandeis U., 1960; JD, Columbia U., 1977. Bar: N.Y. 1978. Assoc. Paul, Weiss, Rifkind, Wharton & Garrison, N.Y.C., 1977-79; gen. counsel, v.p.; sec. MacAndrews & Forbes Group, Inc., N.Y.C., 1979-81; sr. assoc. Sage Gray Todd & Sims, N.Y.C., 1981-84, Proskauer Rose Goetz & Mendelsohn, N.Y.C., 1984-87; pres., gen. counsel Untermeyer Mace Ptnrs., 1987-89; of counsel Mazur Carp & Rubin, 1989-91; mem. fin. com. Congresswoman Carolyn Maloney, 1994—. Class fund-raising chmn. Vassar Coll., 1977-80; bd. dirs. Vassar Club N.Y., 1978-80; chmn. women's div. U.S. Senate Campaign, 1970; regional chmn. U.S. Presdl. Campaign, 1972; chmn. State Rep.'s Campaign, 1973; del.-elect Interim Dem. Conv., 1974, Lawyers Com. for Gov. Carey, 1978; chmn. Mo. state legis. Nat. Coun. Jewish Women, 1969-75, mem. nat. affairs com., 1969-77, chmn. Mo. juvenile justice project, 1970-75, mem. legis. coordinating com. Midwestern region, 1971-75, mem. nat. task force on constl. rights, 1974-77; v.p., bd. dirs. St. Louis Jewish Community Rels. Coun., 1970-75, chmn. ch.-state and Black Jack Amicus Curiae coms.; v.p. bd. dirs. St. Louis chpt. Am. Jewish Com., 1969-75, chmn. urban affairs and placement for ex-offenders coms., mem. com. on status of women, 1974-77; mem. legis. liaison Coalition for Environment, St. Louis, 1970-74; bd. dirs. St. Louis Jewish Community Ctrs. Assn., 1970-74, chmn. urban affairs and legis. affairs coms.; bd. dirs. St. Louis Jewish Family and Children's Svc., 1972-74, chmn. welfare rights and health svcs. coms.; bd. dirs. Glaucoma Found., 1986—; vol. coord. Poor People's Campaign, 1968; founder, bd. dirs. Consumer's Assn., 1967-69; founder, chmn. Urban Corps program St. Louis Mayor's Com. on Youth, 1969-72; panelist White House Conf. on Children and Youth, 1970, 72, White House Conf. on Aging, 1974; founder, bd. dirs. Mo. chpt. PEARL (Pub. Edn. and Religious Liberty), 1972-75; fundraising chmn. N.Y. Found. Arts, 1992-94; bd. dirs. N.Y. Found. Sr. Citizens. Woodrow Wilson Found. fellow, 1959, NDEA fellow, 1959. Mem. ABA, Assn. of Bar of City of N.Y. (mem. continuing legal edn. com., com. on lecture), N.Y. State Bar Assn., Womens Prison Assn. (bd. dirs.). Home: 950 Park Ave New York NY 10028-0320

PODUSKA, JOHN WILLIAM, SR., computer company executive; b. Memphis, Dec. 30, 1937; s. Ben F. and Lily Mae (Reid) P.; m. Susan McElaney, Oct. 1, 1983; 1 child, Lily; children by previous marriage: Alice Casey, Margaret Kay, John Jr., Mary Beth Pandiscio. BS, MS, MIT, 1960, ScD, 1962; LHD (hon.), U. Lowell, 1986. Dir. Honeywell Info. Systems, Cambridge, Mass., 1970-72; v.p. research and devel. Prime Computer, Framingham, Mass., 1972-79; chmn., chief exec. officer, pres. Apollo Computer, Chelmsford, Mass., 1980-85; chmn., chief exec. officer, founder Stellar Computer Inc., Newton, Mass., 1986-89; CEO Stardent Computer, Inc., Newton, 1989-92; chmn. bd. dirs., founder Advanced Visual Systems Inc., Waltham, Mass., 1992—; dir. Safeguard Sci., Pa.,Cambridge (Mass.) Tech. Ptnrs., Xylogics, Mass., XLvision, Melbourne, Fla. Trustee Bentley Coll., U. Mass., Rice U., Boston Ballet; ind. advisor. Recipient Ah Wang award C. of C., North Middlesex, Mass., 1985; named Man of Yr., Boy Scouts Am. 1983. Fellow IEEE; mem. Nat. Acad. Engrs. Office: Advanced Visual Systems Inc 300 5th Ave Waltham MA 02154

POE, DOUGLAS ALLAN, lawyer; b. Chicago Heights, Ill., Nov. 14, 1942; s. Armand Leslie and Marcella Elizabeth (Grote) P. BA, DePauw U., 1964; JD, Duke U., 1967; LLM, Yale U., 1968. Bar: Ill. 1967, U.S. Ct. Appeals (4th cir.) 1968, U.S. Supreme Ct. 1972, U.S. Ct. Appeals (7th cir.) 1973. Clk. U.S. Ct. Appeals (4th cir.), Balt., 1968-69; law clk. to Chief Justice Warren E. Burger U.S. Supreme Ct., 1969, to Hon. William J. Brennan, Jr., 1970; assoc. Mayer, Brown & Wolner) P., 1970-74, ptnr., 1974—. Mem. ABA, Am. Law Inst., Chgo. Council Lawyers, Order of Coif. Office: Mayer Brown & Platt 190 S La Salle St Chicago IL 60603-3410

POE, H. SADLER, lawyer; b. Rock Hill, S.C., Oct. 17, 1944; s. Alvis Bynum and Frances Guy (Sadler) P.; m. Justina Lasley, Aug. 12, 1972; children: Justina Lasley, Julia Rives, Abigail Sadler. AB, Princeton U., 1967; LLB, U. Va., 1971. Bar: Ga. 1971, U.S. Dist. Ct. (no. dist.) Ga. 1976. Assoc. Alston, Miller & Gaines, Atlanta, 1971-77, ptnr., 1977-82; ptnr. Alston & Bird, Atlanta, 1982—, chmn. bus. and fin. dept., 1988-93; bd. dirs., pres. Hillside, Inc., Atlanta. Presenter in field. Elder Trinity Presbyn. Ch., Atlanta, 1977-80, 92—; active Leadership Atlanta, 1988, mem. exec. com., 1991-92, 93-94; trustee Ga. Assn. Pastoral Care, Atlanta, 1991—. Mem. State Bar Ga. (chmn. securities com. 1981-88, bus. and banking law sect. 1990-91), Am. Coll. Investment Counsel. Avocations: woodworking, water skiing. Office: Alston & Bird One Atlantic Ctr 1201 W Peachtree St NW Atlanta GA 30309-3400

POE, JERRY B., financial educator; b. Springfield, Mo., Oct. 3, 1931; s. Carlyle and Eunice P.; m. Carol J. Mussler, Sept. 9, 1959; children: Cheryl Marie, Jennifer Brenna. A.B., Drury Coll., 1953; M.B.A. (Weinheimer fellow), Washington U., St. Louis, 1957; D.B.A. (Ford Found. fellow), Harvard U., 1963. Instr. U. Ark., spring 1957; indsl. engr. McDonnell Aircraft Corp., St. Louis, 1957; lectr. on fin. Boston U., 1959-61; asst. prof. bus. adminstrn. Drury Coll., 1961-64, assoc. prof., 1964-68, prof., 1968-74; dir. Breech Sch. Bus. Adminstrn., 1968-74; prof. fin. Ariz. State U., 1974—, chmn. dept. fin., 1974-82; vis. prof. Fla. Tech. U., 1971; examiner, commr. North Central Assn. Colls. and Schs.; dir. NDEA Inst. Econs.; cons. in field. Author: Essentials of Finance: An Integrated Approach, 1995, An Introduction to the American Business Enterprise, 1969, 7th rev. edit., 1989, Cases in Financial Management, 1977, 3d rev. edit., 1987. Mem. Regional Manpower Adv. Com.; mem. bus. and profl. adv. council Empire Bank. Served to lt. commdr. USNR, 1953-55. Mem. Fin. Mgmt. Assn., Kappa Alpha, Beta Gamma Sigma, Omicron Delta Kappa. Methodist. Office: Ariz State U Coll Bus Dept Fin Tempe AZ 85287-3906

POE, LUKE HARVEY, JR., lawyer; b. Richmond, Va., Jan. 29, 1916; s. Luke Harvey and Alice Colburn (Reddy) P. BS in Math, U. Va., 1938, JD, 1941; postgrad. (Rhodes scholar), Oxford (Eng.) U., 1939; D.Phil., Christ Ch., 1957. Bar: Va. bar 1940, D.C. bar and D.C. Ct. Appeals bar 1967, U.S. Supreme Ct. bar 1969, Md. bar 1974. Asso. firm Cravath, Swaine & Moore, N.Y.C., 1941-42; tutor St. John's Coll., Annapolis, Md., 1946-50; asst. dean St. John's Coll., 1947-49, tenure tutor, 1953-60, dir. physics and chemistry lab., 1959-60; asst. chmn. Nat. Citizens Com. for Kennedy and Johnson and chmn. Citizens Com., Pres.'s Inaugural Com., 1960-61; asst. to chmn. bd. Aerojet-Gen. Corp., El Monte, Calif., 1961-63; div. pres. Internat. Tech. Assistance and Devel. Co., Washington, 1963-66; ptnr. Howard, Poe & Bastian, Washington, 1966-83; pvt. practice law, 1983—; bd. dirs. First Am. Bank of Md.; cons. Dept. Transp., Dept. State, NEH; lect. War Coll. of USAF, Gen. Studies program U. Va.; seminar leader Aspen Inst. Humanistic Studies; guest panelist Panel on Sci. and Tech. of Com. on Sci. and Astronautics, U.S. Ho. of Reps., 1970; pres. bd. dirs. Watergate East, Inc., 1976-79, 90-92. Author: The Combat History of the Battleship U.S.S. Mississippi, 1947, The Transition From Natural Law to Natural Rights, 1957; (with others) lab. manuals Einstein's Theory of Relativity, 1957, Electro-Magnetic Theory, 1959; editor: (with others) Va. Mag., 1936-38, U. Va. Law Rev., 1940-41. Dean's adv. coun. Lehigh U., 1962-65, mem. Seminar on Sci., Tech. and Pub. Policy, Brookings Instn., 1964-66; coun. on trends and perspectives U.S. C. of C., 1966-69; chmn. bd. Bristol Property Mgmt. and Svcs., Inc., 1967-88; chmn. Annapolis Bd. Zoning Appeals, 1966-75; mem. Annapolis Mayor's Task Force, 1967-74, Md. Gov.'s Commn. on Capital City, 1970-76. Lt. commdr. USNR, 1942-46. Mem. Am. Law Inst., AAUP, Raven Soc. (pres.), Soc. Cin., Phi Beta Kappa, Phi Delta Phi, Met. Club (Washington), Travellers Club (London), Brook Club (N.Y.C.), New Providence Club (Annapolis), Vincent's Club (Oxford). Episcopalian. Home: 139 Market St Annapolis MD 21401-2628 also: 2500 Virginia Ave NW Washington DC 20037-1901 Office: 2600 Virginia Ave NW Washington DC 20037-1905

POE, (LYDIA) VIRGINIA, reading educator; b. Bklyn., Jan. 19, 1932; d. Harold Waldemar and Lydia Beatrice (Doswell) Lind; m. Harold Weller Poe, Sept. 11, 1954; children: Michael Lind, David Harold, Timothy Claude. BA, Beloit Coll., 1954; MEd, U. Southwestern La., 1961, EdS, 1972; EdD, U. So. Miss., 1983. Cert. tchr., Fla., La., Ill., Wis. Elem. tchr. Caroline Brevard Sch., Tallahassee, 1961-64; supervising tchr. Fla. State U., Tallahassee, 1962-64; elem., supervising tchr. Hamilton Lab. Sch., Lafayette, La., 1965-67; prof. reading U. Southwestern La., Lafayette, 1968—, head Dept. Curriculum and Instrn., 1986-91, assoc. dir. Hawthorne Ctr. Spl. Edn. and communicative disorders, 1988—; co-originator field experiences U. Southwestern La., 1970—; observer in elem. sch. Ecole de Charlemagne, Nancy, France, 1967; cons. Lafayette Parish Schs., 1968—. Editorial review panel The Ednl. Forum, 1992—; contbr. to book: Reading Research Review, 1984; contbr. articles profl. jours., 1985—; presenter papers to profl. orgns. 1968—. Organizer Conf. on Women in Politics, Lafayette, 1976 (recipient scholarship 1974); treas. State of La. ERA United, 1977; organizer, pres. First Luth. Ch. Day Care Ctr., Lafayette, 1977-80; chair quality edn. svcs. Lafayette Parish Year Round Schs. Study Com. Recipient research grant, U. Southwestern U., 1986-87. Mem. ASCD, Internat. Reading Assn., Am. Reading Assn., Coll. Reading Assn., AAUW, (fellowship contribution 1976), United Fedn. Coll. Tchrs., Nat. Assn. Yr. Round Edn., Phi Delta Kappa, Phi Kappa Phi, Kappa Delta Pi, Beta Sigma Phi. Democrat. Lutheran. Office: U Southwestern La PO Box 42051 Lafayette LA 70504-2051

POE, WILLIAM FREDERICK, insurance agency executive, former mayor; b. Tampa, Fla., July 22, 1931; s. Fred Holland and Zula Blanche (Willoughby) P.; m. Elizabeth Ann Blackburn, June 21, 1954; children—William, Keren, Janice, Marilyn, Charles. Student, Duke U., 1950; B.S., U. Fla., 1953. Founder, pres. Poe & Assocs. (Ins. Agency), Tampa, 1956-74, chmn., 1979-87, chmn. bd., 1987-93; bd. Poe and Brown, Inc. (formerly Poe & Assocs.), Tampa, 1993—; mayor City of Tampa, 1974-79. Mem. Hillsborough County Port Authority, 1961, chmn., 1963; mem. chpt. ARC, United Way of Greater Tampa. Served with USAF, 1955-56. Mem. Tampa Assn. Ins. Agents, Chief Execs. Orgn. Democrat. Baptist. Club: Yacht. Office: Poe Investments Inc 1000 N Ashley St Ste 504 Tampa FL 33602-9999

POEDTKE, CARL HENRY GEORGE, JR., management consultant; b. Chgo., Jan. 12, 1938; s. Carl H. Sr. and Irene F. (Eskilson) P.; m. Marie-Paule M. Thiriet, Mar. 10, 1962 (dec.); children: Gislaine Canavan, Carl Henry George III; m. Janice M. Barron, Aug. 26, 1991. BS, MIT, 1959. Mgr. value engring. Chgo. Rawhide Mfg. Co., Chgo., 1962-66; ptnr. Price Waterhouse, Chgo., Paris, N.Y.C., 1966-91; ret. Price Waterhouse, Chgo., 1991. Author: Managing and Accounting for Inventories, 1980; contbr. articles to profl. jours. Bd. dir. Guild Bd. Lyric Opera, Chgo., 1984-92; mem. vis. adv. com. sch. acctg. De Paul U., Chgo., 1986-91. 1st lt. U.S. Army, 1959-62. Fellow Am. Prodn. and Inventory Control Soc.; mem. AIIE (sr., cert.) Inst. Mgmt. Cons. (bd. dirs. 1987-90, life mem.), Coun. Cons. Orgns. (bd. dirs. 1989-90), Union League Club, Masons. Home: PO Box 677 Tesuque NM 87574-0677

POEHLEIN, GARY WAYNE, chemical engineering educator; b. Tell City, Ind., Oct. 17, 1936; s. Oscar Raymond and Eva Lee (Dickman) P.; m. Sharon Eileen Wood., Jan. 1, 1958; children: Steven Ray, Timothy Wayne, Valorie Ann, Sandra Lee. BSChemE, Purdue U., 1958, MSChemE, 1961, PhD, 1966. Design engr. Proctor & Gamble, Cin., 1958-61; from asst. prof. to assoc. prof. Lehigh U., Bethlehem, Pa., 1965-75, prof. chem. engring., 1975-78, co-dir. emulsion polymers inst., 1973-78; dir. sch. chem. engring. Ga. Inst. Tech., Atlanta, 1978-86, assoc. v.p. rsch., dean grad. studies, 1986-91, v.p. interdisciplinary programs, prof. chem. engring., 1991—; bd. dirs. Flexible Products Co., Mariettam Ga. Contbr. over 100 articles to tech. publs. Mem. sch. bd. Bethlehem Area Sch. Dist., 1969-75. Recipient Honor Scroll award Phila. Am. Inst. Chemists, 1977, Mac Pruitt award Coun. for Chem. Rsch., 1989. Fellow AICE; mem. Am. Chem. Soc., Sigma Xi. Avocations: woodworking, beekeeping. Home: 3147 Habersham Rd NW Atlanta GA 30305-2060 Office: Ga Inst Tech Office Interdisciplinary Programs/CRB 400 10th St Atlanta GA 30332-0370

POEHLING, ROBERT EDWARD, plumbing supply company executive; b. LaCrosse, Wis., May 6, 1944; s. Gerhard George and Anne Elizabeth (Schwartz) P. BA, Marquette U., 1968. Mgr. data processing LaCrosse Plumbing, 1968-74, v.p.; 1974-80, pres., 1980-90, vice chair, 1990—; dir. Norwest Bank-La Crosse. Pres. LaCrosse Symphony Orch., 1984-90; bd. dirs. United Fund for the Arts, LaCrosse, 1983-90, Viterbo Coll. LaCrosse; mem. LaCrosse County Harbor Commn., 1986—. Republican. Roman Catholic. Home: 1900 La Salle Ave Minneapolis MN 55403 Office: La Crosse Plumbing Supply Co 1904 La Salle Ave Minneapolis MN 55403

POEHLMANN, CARL JOHN, agronomist, researcher; b. Calif., Mo., Jan. 29, 1950; s. Edwin William and Lucille Albina (Neu) P.; m. Linda Kay Garner, Dec. 29, 1973; children: Anthony, Kimberly. BS, U. Mo., 1972, MS, 1978. Farmer Jamestown, Mo., 1972-73; vocat. agrl. tchr. Linn (Mo.) Pub. Schs., 1973-75, Columbia (Mo.) Pub. Schs., 1975-78; dir., mgr. agronomy rsch. ctr. U. Mo., Columbia, 1978—. Mem. Am. Soc. Agronomy (div. A-7 chair 1985-86, bd. mem. 1991-94, cert. crop advisor 1993), Crop Sci. Soc. Am., Soil Sci. Soc. Am. Mem. Christian Ch. (Disciples of Christ). Office: U Mo 4968 S Rangeline Rd Columbia MO 65201-8973[*]

POEHLMANN, JOANNA, artist, illustrator, designer; b. Milw., Sept. 5, 1932; d. Herbert Emil and Lucille (Conover) P. Attended, Layton Sch. Art, 1950-54, K.C. (Mo.) Art Inst., 1954, Marquette U., 1958, U. Wis., 1965, 1985. Solo exhbns. include St. James Gallery, Milw., 1963, (retrospective) Milw. Art Mus., 1966, Bradley Galleries, Milw., 1982, Signature Gallery, John Michael Kohler Art Ctr., Sheboygan, Wis., 1979, 84, Woodland Pattern Book Ctr., Milw., 1988, The Cell Gallery, Rochester, N.Y., 1988, 89, Charles Allis Art Mus., Milw., 1991, Layton Gallery at Cardinal Stritch Coll., Milw., 1993, Univ. Meml. Libr., Madison, Wis., 1993, Wustum Mus. Fine Arts, Racine, Wis., 1994; two-man shows include Bradley Galleries, 1964, 69, 80, 91, Cardinal Stritch Coll., Milw., 1980; invitational group shows include Cudahy Gallery of Wis. Art, Milw. Art Mus., 1962-85, 92, Bradley Galleries, 1967-79, Lakefront Festival of Art, Milw. Art Mus., 1962-63, 70-72, 76-79, Country Art Gallery, Long Island, N.Y., 1963-71, Mount Mary Coll., Milw., 1979, 83, Chosy Gallery, 1980, 81, 86, U. Dallas, 1987, Frick Gallery, Germany, 1991, Spertus Mus. Judaica, Chgo., 1986, World Fin. Ctr., N.Y.C., 1992, Istvan Kiraly Muzeum, Budapest, Hungary, 1992, Artspace, Richmond, Va., 1994, Va. Ctr. For Craft Arts, Richmond, 1994, many others; juried group shows include Milw. Art Mus., 1963, 75, 78, Chgo. Art Inst., 1978, 81, Milw. Fine Arts Gallery, 1980, U. Wis. Fine Arts Gallery, Milw., 1980, The West Pub. Co., St. Paul, 1982, Auburn U., 1983, Zaner Gallery, Rochester, N.Y., 1984, Pratt Graphics Ctr., N.Y.C., 1985, Art 54 Gallery, N.Y.C., 1987, Boston Art Inst., 1987, Bradley U., Peoria, Ill., 1989, Wustum Mus. Fine Arts, 1989, 1992, Trenton State Coll., 1991, numerous others; represented in collections including Victoria & Albert Mus., London, N.Y. Pub. Libr., Mus. Kunsthandwerk, Frankfurt, Germany, Milw. Art Mus., Milw. Pub. Libr., U. Dallas, Orchard Corp. Am., St. Louis McDonald's Corp., GE Med. Systems Bldgs., Waukesha, Goldhirsh Group, Boston, Marquette U.-Haggerty Mus. Art; others; subject of articles; author: Love Letters, Food for Thought, Cancelling Out. Recipient Merit award Art Dir.'s Club, Milw., 1962, 100 Best award, 1967, 100 Best award Milw. Soc. Communicating Arts, 1973, 76, MGIC award Wis. Painters & Sculptors, 1981, Merit award Illustration Milw. Advt. Club, 1983, 2d award Wustum Mus. Fine Arts, 1983, 4th Purchase Prize award McDonald's Fine Art Collection Competition, 1983, Juror's award Zaner Gallery, 1984, Hopper/ Koch award Wustum Mus. Fine Arts, 1985, spl. mention, Purchase award Bradley U., 1985, Purchase award Moravian Coll., 1985, Jack Richeson award Wustum Mus. Fine Arts, 1985, Purchase award U. Del., 1986, Strathmore Paper Co. award Wustum Mus. Fine Arts, 1986, Purchase award U. N.Dak., 1987, Award of Excellence miniature art Metro Internat. Competition, N.Y.C., 1987, 3d award Wustum Mus. Fine Arts, 1987, Purchase award U. Dallas, 1988, Award of Excellence Wustum Mus. Fine Arts, 1992, Individual Art fellowship Milw. County, 1993; Arts Midwest/NEA Regional Visual Artist fellow, 1994—. Roman Catholic. Home and Studio: 1231 N Prospect Ave Milwaukee WI 53202

POEL, ROBERT WALTER, career officer, physician; b. Muskegon, Mich., July 24, 1934; s. Abel John and Fannie M. (Vanderwall) P.; m. Carol Anne Noordeloos, June 24, 1960; children: Kathryn Anne Poel Engle, James Robert, Sharon Kay Poel Thompson. BS, Calvin Coll., 1957; MD, U. Mich., 1959. Diplomate Am. Bd. Surgery. Commd. capt. USAF, 1962, advanced through grades to brig. gen., 1988, ret., 1993; comdr. Hosp. Malmstrom AFB, Great Falls, Mont., 1971-73; dir. profl. svcs. Hdqrs. Tactical Air Command Command Surgeon's Office, Langley AFB, Va., 1973-74; div. chief, med. plans Office of Air Force Surgeon Gen., Wash., 1974-78; comdr. regional hosp. Sheppard AFB, Wichita Falls, Tex., 1978-83; dir. profl. svcs. Office of Air Force Logistics Command Surgeon, Wright-Patterson AFB, Ohio, 1983-85; vice-comdr. Wilford Hall USAF Med. Ctr., San Antonio, 1985-87; chief, quality assurance, dir. plans and resources Air Force Surgeon Gen., Bolling AFB, Washington, 1987-89; hosp. comdr. Malcolm Grow Med. Ctr., Andrews AFB, Washington, 1989-93; v.p. med. affairs, med. dir. Burdette Tomlin Meml. Hosp., Cape May Court House, N.J., 1993—; dir. Andrews Fed. Credit Union, 1991—, vice-chmn. bd. dirs., 1992—. Advisor, bd. regents Uniformed Svcs. U. the Health Scis., Bethesda, Md., 1989-93; mem. press. coun. Calvin Coll., 1990. Named Disting. alumnus, Calvin Coll., 1990; Paul Harris fellow Rotary Club of Wichita Falls, 1982. Mem. AMA, Air Force Soc. Clin. Surgeons (sr.), Assn. Mil. Surgeons of U.S., Am. Coll. Physician Execs. Republican. Mem. Christian Reformed Ch. Home: Ten Wyncroft Dr Petersburg NJ 08270 Office: Burdette Tomlin Meml Hosp Two Stone Harbor Blvd Cape May Court House NJ 08210

POEN, MONTE M., history educator, researcher; b. Lake city, Iowa, Nov. 25, 1930; s. John and Garnette (Montgomery) P.; m. Bonnie L. Diehl, July 15, 1952 (div. Feb. 1972); children: John M., Gregory E., Mark A.; m. Kathryn Lomen, May 22, 1982. AA, San Jose (Calif.) City Coll., 1959; BA, San Jose State U., 1961; MA, U. Mo., 1963, PhD, 1967. Instr. U. Mo., Columbia, 1964-66; with No. Ariz. U., Flagstaff, 1966—, prof., 1979-90, regents prof., 1990—; cons. McFarland papers Earnest W. McFarland Estate, Florence, Ariz., 1987. Author: Harry S. Truman Versus the Medical Lobby, 1979; editor: Strictly Personal & Confidential: Letters Harry Truman Never Mailed, 1982, Letters Home by Harry Truman, 1984. Mem. Coccnino County Dem. Cen. Com., Flagstaff, 1988—. Sgt. USAF, 1950-54, PTO. Truman Libr. Inst. scholar, 1987. Fellow Harry S. Truman Libr. Inst.; mem. Orgn. Am. Historians, Oral History Assn., Ariz. Humanities Coun., Ctr. for Study of the Presidency. Democrat. Avocations: camping, fishing, travel, gardening, hiking. Home: 3703 N Grandview Dr Flagstaff AZ 86004-1601 Office: No Ariz U Dept of History Flagstaff AZ 86011

POEPPELMEIER, KENNETH REINHARD, chemistry educator; b. St. Louis, Mo., Oct. 6, 1949. BS in Chemistry, U. Mo., 1971; PhD in Inorganic Chemistry, Iowa State U., 1978. Rsch. chemist, corp. rsch. sci. labs. Exxon Rsch. & Engring. Co., Annandale, N.J., 1978-80, sr. chemist, corp. rsch. sci. labs., 1980-81, staff chemist, corp. rsch. sci. labs., 1981-84, sr. staff chemist, corp. rsch. sci. labs., 1984; assoc. prof. chemistry Northwestern U., Evanston, Ill., 1984-88, assoc. dir. sci. and tech. ctr. for superconductivity 1989—, prof., 1988-92, Dow prof. chemistry, 1992—; lectr., cons. in field; organizer, chmn. nat. symposium on solid state chemistry of heterogeneous oxide catalysis including new microporous solids ACS, New Orleans, 1987; cons. Exxon Chemicals, Air Products and Chemicals, Inc., Shell, FMC Corp.; assoc. dir. NSF Sci. and Tech. Ctr. for Superconductivity; vice-chair, chair-elect, Gordon Conf. on Solid State Chem. Contbr. articles to numerous chemistry publications; patentee in field. Iowa State U. fellow, 1977-78; Iowa State scholar, 1975-76. Mem. Am. Assn. for the Advancement of Sci., ACS (chmn. Solid State Subdiv. of Div. Inorganic Chemistry 1988-89), AAAS, Am. Phys. Soc., Materials Rsch. Soc., Catalysis Club (Chgo.), Sigma Xi. Office: Northwestern U Dept Chemistry 2145 Sheridan Rd Evanston IL 60208-0834

POESCH, JESSIE JEAN, art historian; b. Postville, Iowa, May 19, 1922; parents: Edward H. and Vina (Meier) P. BA, Antioch Coll., 1944; MA, U. Del., 1956; PhD, U. Pa., 1966. Relief worker Am. Friends Svc. Com., Phila., also, France, Germany, 1946-54; curatorial asst. H.F. DuPont Winterthur (Del.) Mus., 1956-58; from asst. prof. to prof. art history Tulane U., New Orleans, 1963-92, Maxine and Ford Graham chair in fine arts, 1988-92; guest curator "Painting in the South", Va. Mus. Fine Arts, Richmond, 1980-84; curator "Newcomb Pottery: An Enterprise for So. Women, 1895-1940", Newcomb Coll. Tulane U. and Smithsonian Instn. traveling exhbn. svc., 1980-87. Author: Titian Ramsay Peale, 1799-1885, and His Journals of the

Wilkes Expedition, 1961, The Art of the Old South: Painting, Sculpture, Architecture and the Products of Craftsmen, 1560-1860, 1983; (book/exhbn. catalogue) The Early Furniture of Louisiana, 1972, Newcomb Pottery: An Enterprise for Southern Women 1895-1940, 1984, Will Henry Stevens, 1987; also numerous articles and book revs. Fellow U. Del., 1954-56; Fulbright scholar U. London, 1960-62; NEH grantee, London, 1969-70. Mem. Soc. Archtl. Historians (bd. dirs. 1986-89), Coll. Art Assn., Am. Antiquarian Soc., La. Endowment for the Humanities (bd. dirs. 1984-90, La. Humanist of Yr. 1992), Victorian Soc. Am. (bd. dirs. 1988-92). Office: Tulane U Newcomb Art Dept New Orleans LA 70118

POETHIG, RICHARD SCOTT, geneticist, biology educator; b. Buffalo, July 17, 1953; m. Maya Bucan, 1989; 1 child, Luke R. BA, Coll. Wooster, 1974; MPhil, Yale U., 1981, PhD in Biology, 1981. Fellow Stanford (Calif.) U., 1981, U. Mo., Columbia, 1981-83; asst. prof. U. Pa., Phila., 1983-89, assoc. prof. biology dept. biology, 1989—. Assoc. editor Devel. Biology, 1993—. Recipient Nickerson prize in biology, 1981, Pelton award Bot. Soc. Am., 1993. Mem. Soc. Devel. Biology, Genetics Soc. Am. Office: U Pa Biology Dept Philadelphia PA 19104-6018*

POETTCKER, HENRY, retired seminary president; b. Rudnerweide, Russia, Mar. 27, 1925; s. John and Margaretha (Voth) P.; m. Agenetha Baergen, July 4, 1946; children: Victoria, Ronald, Martin. A.B., Bethel Coll., North Newton, Kans., 1950; B.D., Mennonite Bibl. Sem., Chgo., 1953; Th.D., Princeton Theol. Sem., 1961, converted Ph.D., 1973. Ordained to ministry Mennonite Ch., 1948; instr. Can. Mennonite Bible Coll., Winnipeg, Man., 1954-59; pres. Can. Mennonite Bible Coll., 1959-78; pres. Mennonite Bibl. Sem., Elkhart, Ind., 1978-90, assoc. for devel., 1991-93; 1993; interim dean Bluffton (Ohio) Coll., 1965-66; vis. lectr. Taiwan Theol. Coll. and Tainan Theol. Coll., Taiwan, 1973-74. Editor: (with Rudy A. Regehr) Call to Faithfulness, 1972, Alumni Bull. Can. Mennonite Bible Coll, 1960-73. Pres. Gen. Conf. Mennonite Ch., Newton, Kans., 1968-74. Mem. Soc. Bibl. Lit. and Exegesis. Home: 80 Plaza Dr Ste 2502, Winnipeg, MB Canada R3T 5S2 *The secret of happiness lies not in doing what one likes, but in liking what one does.*

POETTMANN, FREDERICK HEINZ, retired petroleum engineering educator; b. Germany, Dec. 20, 1919; s. Fritz and Kate (Hussen) P.; m. Anna Bell Hall, May 29, 1952; children—Susan Trudy, Phillip Mark. B.S., Case Western Res. U., 1942; M.S., U. Mich., 1944, Sc.D., 1946; grad., Advanced Mgmt. Program, Harvard U., 1966; PhD in Mining Scis. (hon.), Mining U. Leoben, Austria, 1992. Registered profl. engr., Colo., Okla. Research chemist Lubrizol Corp., Wickliffe, Ohio, 1942-43; mgr. production research Phillips Petroleum Co., Bartlesville, Okla., 1946-55; asso. research dir. Marathon Oil Co., 1955-72; mgr. comml. devel. Marathon Oil Co., Littleton, Colo., 1972-83; prof. petroleum engineering Colo. Sch. Mines, 1983-90; retired; cons. in field. Contbr. articles to numerous publs.; co-author, editor 10 books in field; patentee in field. Chmn. S. Suburban Met. Recreation and Park Dist., 1966-71; chmn. Littleton Press Council, 1967-71; bd. dirs. Hancock Recreation Center, Findlay, Ohio, 1973-77. Recipient Halliburton award for outstanding profl. achievement, 1986, Katz medal Gas Processors' Assn., 1993. Fellow AIChE; mem. AIME (hon. mem. 1984, Charles F. Rand Meml. Gold medal 1992, Nat. Acad. Engring. Soc. Petroleum Engrs. (DeGolyer Disting. Svc. medal 1990), Am. Chem. Soc., Am. Petroleum Inst., Sigma Xi, Tau Beta Pi, Alpha Chi Sigma, Phi Kappa Phi, Pi Epsilon Tau. Republican. Home: 47 S Eagle Dr Littleton CO 80123-6644 Office: Colo Sch Mines Dept Petroleum Engring Golden CO 80401

POFF, RICHARD HARDING, state supreme court justice; b. Radford, Va., Oct. 19, 1923; s. Beecher David and Irene Louise (Nunley) P.; m. Jo Ann R. Topper, June 24, 1945 (dec. Jan. 1978); children: Rebecca, Thomas, Richard Harding; m. Jean Murphy, Oct. 26, 1980. Student, Roanoke Coll., 1941-43; LL.B., U. Va., 1948, LL.D., 1969. Bar: Va. 1947. Partner law firm Dalton, Poff, Turk & Stone, Radford, 1949-70; mem. 83d-92d congresses, 6th Dist. Va.; justice Supreme Ct. Va., 1972-89, sr. justice, 1989—; Vice chmn. Nat. Commn. on Reform Fed. Crime Laws; chmn. Republican Task Force on Crime; sec. Rep. Conf., House Rep. Leadership. Named Va.'s Outstanding Young Man of Year Jr. C. of C., 1954; recipient Nat. Collegiate Athletic Assn. award, 1966, Roanoke Coll. medal, 1967, Distinguished Virginian award Va. Dist. Exchange Clubs, 1970, Presdl. certificate of appreciation for legislative contbn., 1971, legislative citation Assn. Fed. Investigators, 1969, Thomas Jefferson Pub. Sesquicentennial award U. Va., 1969, Japanese Am. Citizens League award, 1972; named to Hall of Fame, Am. Legion Boys State, 1985. Mem. Bar Assn., VFW, Am. Legion, Pi Kappa Phi, Sigma Nu Phi. Clubs: Mason, Moose, Lion. Office: Va Supreme Ct 100 N 9th St Richmond VA 23219-2335 *When you know you are right, fight. When you are in doubt, wait. When you know you are wrong, admit your mistake and correct it.*

POGGIO, TOMASO ARMANDO, physicist, educator, computer scientist, researcher; b. Genoa, Italy, Sept. 11, 1947; came to U.S., 1981; s. Angelo and Maria Adele (Moro) P.; m. Barbara Venturini-Guerrini, July 29, 1972; children: Martino, Allegra. D in Physics summa cum laude, U. Genoa, 1971. Researcher Max Planck Inst., Federal Republic of Germany, 1971-82; assoc. prof. to prof. MIT, Cambridge, 1982-88, Uncas and Helen Whitaker prof., dept. brain and cognitive scis., 1988—; corp. fellow Thinking Machines Corp., Cambridge, 1985—; adv. bd. MIT/Bradford Press series on Computational Models of Cognition and Perception, 1984, VNY Sci. Press series of monographs in neuroinformatics and robotics, 1984. Contbr. over 250 sci. paper to profl. publs.; assoc. editor Systems and Control Letters, 1984 mem. editorial bd. Synapse, 1986, Visual Neurosci., 1987, Neural Computation, 1988, Network, 1989, others; adv. bd. Jour. Math. Biology, 1977, Lecture Notes in Biomathematics, 1979. Recipient Cassa di Risparmio di Genoa award, 1966, Otto-Hahn-Medaille award Max-Planck Soc., 1979, Columbus prize Instituto Internazionale delle Communicazioni Genoa, 1982, Premio Luigi Carlo Rossi award (with V. Torre) Elsag Elettronica, Italy, 1984, Max-Planck-Forschungs Preis Alexander von Humboldt-Stiftung, 1992; Angelo delle Riccia grad. fellow, 1969-70, fellow CNR Lab. Biophysics and Cybernetics, Italy, 1971. Mem. IEEE, Am. Math. Soc., Optical Soc. Am. Office: MIT Artificial Intelligence Lab Cambridge MA 02139

POGO, BEATRIZ TERESA GARCIA-TUNON, cell biologist, virologist, educator; b. Buenos Aires, Argentina, Dec. 24, 1932; came to U.S., 1964, naturalized, 1976; d. Dario and Maria Teresa (Vergnory) Garcia-Tunon; m. Angel Oscar Pogo, Jan. 13, 1956; children: Gustavo, Gabriela. B.S., Lycee No. 1, Buenos Aires, 1950; M.D., Sch. Medicine, Buenos Aires, 1956; D.M.Sci., 1961. Intern Univ. Hosp., Buenos Aires, 1956-57; asst. Inst. Histology and Embryology, Buenos Aires U., 1957-59; fellow Sloan Kettering Meml. Hosp., N.Y.C., 1959-60, Rockefeller U., N.Y.C., 1960-61; asst. prof. cell biology Inst. Cell Biology, Cordoba U., Argentina, 1962-64; research assoc. Rockefeller U., N.Y.C., 1964-67; asst. Pub. Health Research Inst., N.Y.C., 1967-69, assoc., 1969-73, assoc. mem, 1973-78; prof. exptl. cell biology and microbiology Mt. Sinai Sch. Medicine, CUNY, 1978—, acting dir. ctr. for exptl. cell biology, 1987-89, prof. neoplastic diseases, 1989—. Contbr. articles to profl. jours. Damon Runyon Fund fellow, 1964-65; grantee Am. Cancer Soc., 1970-73, 79-80, 84-85, 94-95, NIH, 1975—. Fellow N.Y. Acad. Scis.; mem. Am. Assn. for Cancer Rsch., N.Y. Acad. Sci., Am. Soc. Cell Biology, Harvey Soc., Am. Soc. Virology, Assn. for Women in Sci. (v.p. met. N.Y. chpt. 1981-83, pres. 1984-86), Am. Microbiol. Soc., Sigma Xi. Home: 237 Nyac Ave Pelham NY 10803-1907 Office: Mt Sinai Sch Medicine 1 Gustave L Levy Pl New York NY 10029-6504

POGORELEC, STEVEN MARTIN, fraternal organization administrator; b. Passaic, N.J., Nov. 9, 1946; s. Albert Joseph and Anna (Paciga) P.; m. Anne G. Boyle, Oct. 21, 1971; children: Jennifer Anne, Steven Jr., Scott Thomas. Air traffic controller FAA, Washington, 1970-81; custodian Slovak Cath. Sch. Sokol, Passaic, N.J., 1981-83; bookkeeper Slovak Cath. Sch. Passaic, N.J., 1983-86, office mgr. 1986-91, CEO, 1992—. Staff Sgt. USAF, 1965-69. Roman Catholic. Avocations: bowling, golf, softball, track & field. OFfice: Slovak Cath Sch Sokol 205 Madison St PO Box 899 Passaic NJ 07055

POGREBIN, LETTY COTTIN, writer, lecturer; b. N.Y.C., June 9, 1939; d. Jacob and Cyral (Halpern) Cottin; m. Bertrand B. Pogrebin, Dec. 8, 1963; children: Abigail and Robin (twins), David. A.B. cum laude with spl. distinction in English and Am. Lit, Brandeis U., 1959. V.p. Bernard Geis

Assocs. (book pubs.), N.Y.C., 1960-70; columnist The Working Woman column Ladies Home Jour., 1971-81; editor Ms mag., N.Y.C., 1971-87, columnist, editor at large, 1987-89, contbg. editor, 1990—; columnist The N.Y. Times, Newsday, Moment Mag., Wasington Post, Moment Mag., Washington, 1990—; contbg. editor Family Circle, Ms. mag., Tikkun mag.; cons. Free to Be, You and Me projects, 1972—; lectr. women's issues and family politics, changing roles of men and women, friendship in Am., nonsexist child rearing and edn., Judaism and feminism, Mid-East politics. Author: How to Make It in a Man's World, 1970, Getting Yours: How to Make the System Work for the Working Woman, 1975, Growing Up Free, 1980, Stories for Free Children, 1982, Family Politics, 1983, Among Friends, 1986, Deborah, Golda, and Me: Being Female and Jewish in America, 1991; mem. editorial bd. Tikkun Mag.; contbr. articles to N.Y. Times, Washington Post, Boston Globe, The Nation, TV Guide, also other mags., newspapers. Sec. bd. Author's Guild; bd. dirs. Ms. Found., Ams. for Peace Now, New Israel Fund, Jewish Fund for Justice, Commn. on Women's Equality, Am. Jewish Congress, PEN Am.; mem. Task Force on Women Fedn. Jewish Philanthropies, N.Y.C. Commn. on Status of Women. Pointer fellow Yale U., 1982, MacDowell Colony fellow, 1979, 89, 94, Cummigton Colony Arts fellow 1985, Edna St. Vincent Millay Colony fellow, 1985. Mem. Nat. Women's Polit. Caucus (a founder), Women's Forum of N.Y. (bd. dirs.). Address: 33 W 67th St New York NY 10023-6224

POGUE, FORREST CARLISLE, retired historian; b. Eddyville, Ky., Sept. 17, 1912; s. Forrest Carlisle and Frances (Carter) P.; m. Christine Brown, Sept. 4, 1954. AB, Murray (Ky.) State Coll., 1931, LLD, 1970; MA, U. Ky., 1932, LittD, 1983; PhD, Clark U., 1939, LHD, 1975; LittD, Washington and Lee U., 1970. Instr. history Western Ky. State Coll., 1933; instr. to assoc. prof. Murray State Coll., 1933-42, prof., 1954-56; with Office Chief Mil. History U.S. Dept. Army, 1946-52; ops. rsch. analyst Johns Hopkins U., U.S. Army Hdqrs., Heidelberg, Fed. Republic of Germany, 1952-54; dir. George C. Marshall Rsch. Ctr., Lexington, Va., 1956-64, George C. Marshall Rsch. Libr., Lexington, 1964-74; Harmon Meml. lectr. U.S. Air Acad., 1968; disting. Bicentennial lectr. U.S. Mil. Acad., 1974; disting. vis. prof. Va. Mil. Inst., 1972; professorial lectr. George Washington U., 1948, 49, 50; past chmn. Am. Commn. on History 2d World War; former mem. adv. groups U.S. Army, USAF and Navy Hist. Office; chmn. adv. com. Senate Hist. Office; mem. adv. bd. Former Mems. Congress, Ky. Oral History Commn.; mem. adv. com. on Eisenhower papers; adj. fellow Woodrow Wilson Internat. Ctr. Scholars, 1974-77; mem. Hist. Found., Centennial Adv. Com. on the History of the Eisenhower Era; dir. Dwight D. Eisenhower Inst. Hist. Rsch., Nat. Mus. Am. History, Smithsonian Inst., 1974-84; mem. Marine Corps Hist. Found. Author: The Supreme Command, 1954, George C. Marshall: Education of a General, Vol. 1, 1963, Ordeal and Hope, 1939-42, Vol. 2, 1966, Organizer of Victory, 1943-45, Vol. 3, 1973, Statesman, 1945-59, Vol. 4, 1987; author: (with others) The Meaning of Yalta, 1956; contbr. to books including Command Decisions, 1960, Total War and Cold War, 1962, D Day: The Normandy Invasion in Retrospect, 1970, America's Continuing Revolution, 1975, The War Lords, 1976, Bicentennial History of the United States, 1976, (with others) The Marshall Plan in Germany, 1991; contbg. editor: Guide to American Foreign Relations Since 1700, 1983. Trustee Harry S. Truman Inst. Libr.; mem. adv. com. Nat. Hist. Soc. With U.S. Army, 1942-45, ETO. Decorated Bronze Star, Croix de Guerre, France; recipient Disting. Alumni Centennial award U. Ky., 1965, Samuel Eliot Morison award Am. Mil. Inst., 1988; U. Paris Inst. des Hautes Etudes Internationales Am. Exchange fellow, 1937-38. Fellow U.S. Army History Rsch. Inst. (adv. group), Am. Mil. Inst. (past pres.); mem. Assn. U.S. Army (Disting. Svc. award 1990), Oral History Assn. (past pres.), U.S. Commn. on Mil. History (trustee), Am. Hist. Assn., So. Hist. Assn., Orgn. Am. Historians, Soc. Am. Historians (Francis Parkman medal 1988), NEA (life), English Speaking Union, Am. Legion, Murray State U. Alumni Assn. (past pres.), Cosmos Club. Democrat. Presbyterian. Address: 1405 B Valleywood Murray KY 42071

POGUE, LLOYD WELCH, lawyer; b. Grant, Iowa, Oct. 21, 1899; s. Leander Welch and Myrtle Viola (Casey) P.; m. Mary Ellen Edgerton, Sept. 8, 1926; children: Richard Welch, William Lloyd, John Marshall. A.B., U. Nebr., 1924; LL.B., U. Mich., 1926; S.J.D., Harvard Law Sch., 1927. Bar: Mass., N.Y., D.C., Ohio, U.S. Supreme Ct. bars. Assoc. Ropes, Gray, Boyden and Perkins, 1927-33; ptnr. firm Searle, James and Crawford, N.Y.C., 1933-38; asst. gen. counsel CAB, 1938-39, gen. counsel, through 1941, chmn. bd., 1942-46; mng. ptnr. Pogue & Neal, Washington, 1946-67; Washington mng. ptnr. Jones, Day, Reavis & Pogue, Washington, 1967-79, ret., 1981; Lindbergh Meml. lectr. Nat. Air and Space Mus., 1991; presenter essay 50th Ann. Internat. Civil Aviation Orgn., Montreal, 1994; spkr. in field. Author: International Civil Air Transport Transition Following WW II, 1979, Pogue/Pollock/Polk Genealogy as Mirrored in History, 1990 (1st pl. in Anna Ford Family history book contest 1992, Nat. Genealogical Soc. award for excellence genealogy and family history 1992, William H. and Benjamin Harrison Book award Coun. Ohio Genealogists, Outstanding Achievement award County and Regional History category Ohio Assn. Hist. Socs. and Mus., 1st place award Iowa Washington County Genealogical Soc. 1994, cert. commendation Am. Assn. State and Local History 1994). Mem. U.S. dels. Chgo. Internat. Civil Aviation Conf., 1944; mem. U.S. dels., vice chmn. del. Bermuda United Kingdom-U.S. Conf., 1946; vice chmn., del. Interim Assembly ICAO, 1947. With AUS, 1918. Recipient Elder Statesman of Aviation award Nat. Aeronautic Assn., Golden Eagle award Soc. Sr. Aerospace Execs.; fellow Am. Helicopter Soc., Benjamin Franklin fellow Royal Soc. Arts. Fellow Royal Aero. Soc.; mem. AIA (hon.), Can. Aeronautics and Space Inst., Nat. Geneal. Soc., Nassau Genealogical Soc. (life, former trustee), Ohio Geneal. Soc. (life), First Families of Ohio, Helicopter Assn. Internat. (hon. mem. for life), Met. Club, Univ. Club, Wings Club (hon., N.Y.C.), Bohemian Club (San Francisco), Cosmos Club, Masons. Home: 5204 Kenwood Ave Bethesda MD 20815-6604 Office: Metropolitan Sq 1450 G St NW Washington DC 20005-2088

POGUE, MACK, real estate company executive; b. 1934. Real estate salesman Majors & Majors, Dallas, 1955-65; with Lincoln Property Co. (partnership with Trammell Crow), Dallas, 1965—, chmn. bd. dirs., pres., CEO, 1968—. Office: Lincoln Property Co 500 N Akard St Dallas TX 75201-3302

POGUE, MARY ELLEN E. (MRS. L. WELCH POGUE), youth and community worker; b. Fremont, Nebr., Oct. 27, 1904; d. Frank E. and Mary (Coe) Edgerton; m. L. Welch Pogue, Sept. 8, 1926; children: Richard Welch, William Lloyd, John Marshall. BFA, U. Nebr., 1926; studied violin with Harrison Keller, Boston, 1926-28, Kemp Stillings Master Class, N.Y.C., 1935-37. Mem. Potomac String Ensemble, 1939-80. Historian, Gov. William Bradford Compact, 1966—; vice chmn. Montgomery County (Md.) Victory Garden Ctr., 1946-47; pres. Bethesda Community Garden Club, 1947-48; founder, bd. dirs. Montgomery County YWCA, 1946-50, 52-55; founder Welcome to Washington Music Group, 1947—. Recipient Outstanding Service award Bethesda United Meth. Ch., 1984, Bethesda Community Garden Club, 1985, 93, Devoted Svc. award D.C. Mayflower Soc., 1985, 89. Mem. Soc. Mayflower Descs. D.C. (dir. D.C. 1954—, elder 1971-91, elder emeritus), PEO Sisterhood (pres. 1957-59), Mortar Bd. Alumnae (pres. 1965-67, Mortar Bd. award, 1986), Nat. Cap. Area Fedn. Garden Clubs, Bethesda United Meth. Women, Nat. Geneal. Soc., New Eng. Historic Geneal. Soc. (life), Ohio Geneal. Soc. (life), Md. Geneal. Soc., Md. Hist. Soc., Conn. Soc. Genealogists, First Families of Ohio, Pilgrim Soc. (life), Plimoth Plantation, Hereditary Order of Descs. Colonial Govs., Nat. Soc. Magna Charta Dames, Colonial Order of Crown, Sovereign Colonial Soc. Ams. Royal Descent, Order of Descs. Colonial Physicians and Chirurgiens, Nat. Soc. Women Descs. Ancient and Hon. Arty. Co., First Families of Ohio, Welcome to Washington Internat. Club, Ind. Agy. Women (assoc.), Capital Speakers Club, The Plantagenet Soc., Soc. Descs. of Knights of the Most Noble Order of the Garter, DAR, Order Ams. Armorial Ancestry, Saybrook Colony Founders Assn., Soc. Founders of Norwich, Conn., Kenwood Country Club, Delta Omicron Music (life). Methodist. Compiler, editor: Favorite Recipes of Mary Edgerton of Aurora, Nebraska, 1963, Edgerton-Coe History, 1965. Home: 5204 Kenwood Ave Bethesda MD 20815-6604

POGUE, RICHARD WELCH, lawyer; b. Cambridge, Mass., Apr. 26, 1928; s. Lloyd Welch and Mary Ellen (Edgerton) P.; m. Patricia Ruth Raney, July 10, 1954; children: Mark, Tracy, David. B.A., Cornell U., 1950; J.D., Mich. Law Sch., 1953. Bar: Mich. 1953, Ohio 1957, U.S. Dist. Ct. (no. dist.) Ohio 1960, U.S. Ct. Appeals (6th cir.) 1972, U.S. Ct. Appeals (D.C. and 9th cirs.)

1979. Assoc. Jones, Day, Reavis & Pogue, Cleve., 1957-60, ptnr., 1961—, mng. ptnr., 1984-92, sr. ptnr., 1993-94; sr. advisor Dix & Eaton, Cleve., 1994—; vis. prof. Mich. Law Sch., 1993—; bd. dirs. Derlan Industries Toronto, Continental Airlines, Inc., Houston, OHM Corp., Findlay, Ohio, M.A. Hanna Co., Cleve., Redland PLC, Reigate, Eng., Rotek Inc., Aurora, Ohio, Key Corp., Cleve, TRW Inc. Cleve. Chmn. Cleve. Found, 1985-89, Greater Cleve. Roundtable, 1986-89, Greater Cleve. Growth Assn., 1991-93; mem. Adminstrv. Conf. U.S., 1974-80; chmn. Cleve. Ballet, 1983-85; chmn. United Negro Coll. Fund, Cleve., 1979; trustee Univ. Hosps., 1976—, vice chmn., 1988-94, chmn., 1994—; vice chmn. Cleve. Tomorrow, 1988-93; pres. 50 Club Cleve., 1988-89; trustee Case Western Res. U.; gen. campaign chmn. United Way, Cleve., 1989; active Coun. Fgn. Rels., 1989—, Am./EC Assn. Bus. Adv. Coun., 1988-93; trustee, vic chmn. Rock and Roll Hall of Fame and Mus., 1986—; co-chmn 1996 Cleve. Bicentennial Commn., interim chmn. Cleve. Inst. Music, 1994. Army, 1954-57. Recipient Outstanding Alumnus award U. Mich. Club., Cleve., 1983, Torch of Liberty award Anti-Defamation League, 1989, Leadership Cleve. Vol. of Yr. award, 1990, 1st Econ. Devel. Workshop award Nat. Coun. on Urban Econ. Devel., 1992, Humanitarian award Nat. Conf. Christians and Jews, 1992. Mem. ABA (chmn. antitrust sect. 1983-84), Ohio State Bar Assn. (chmn. antitrust sect. 1969-73). Republican. Mem. United Ch. of Christ. Clubs: Bohemian (San Francisco), Soc. Union (Cleve.), Metropolitan (Washington), Links (N.Y.C.). Office: Dix & Eaton 1301 E 9th St Ste 1300 Cleveland OH 44114

POGUE, WILLIAM REID, former astronaut, foundation executive, business and aerospace consultant; b. Okemah, Okla., Jan. 23, 1930; s. Alex W. and Margaret (McDow) P.; m. Jean Ann Pogue; children: William Richard, Layna Sue, Thomas Reid. B.S. in Secondary Edn., Okla. Bapt. U., 1951, D.Sc. (hon.), 1974; M.S. in Math., Okla. State U., 1960. Commd. 2d lt. USAF, 1952, advanced through grades to col., 1973; combat fighter pilot Korea, 1953; gunnery instr. Luke AFB, Ariz., 1954; mem. acrobatic team USAF Thunderbirds, Luke AFB and Nellis AFB, Nev., 1955-57; asst. prof. math. USAF Acad., 1960-63; exchange test pilot Brit. Royal Aircraft Establishment, Ministry Aviation, Farnborough, Eng., 1964-65; instr. USAF Aerospace Research Pilots Sch., Edwards AFB, Calif., 1965-66; astronaut NASA Manned Spacecraft Center, Houston, 1966-75; pilot 3d manned visit to Skylab space sta.; now with Vutara Services of Springdale, Ark. Decorated Air medal with oak leaf cluster, Air Force Commendation medal, D.S.M. USAF; named to Five Civilized Tribes Hall of Fame, Choctaw descent; recipient Distinguished Service medal NASA, Collier trophy Nat. Aero. Assn.; Robert H. Goddard medal Nat. Space Club; Gen. Thomas D. White USAF Space Trophy Nat. Geog. Soc.; Halley Astronautics award, 1975; de la Vaalx medal Fedn. Aeronautique Internat., 1974; V.M. Komarov diploma, 1974. Fellow Acad. Arts and Scis. of Okla. State U., Am. Astron. Soc.; mem. Soc. Exptl. Test Pilots, Explorers Club, Sigma Xi, Pi Mu Epsilon. Baptist (deacon). Office: Vutara Services 1039 Fir St Springdale AR 72764

POHL, FREDERIK, writer; b. N.Y.C., Nov. 26, 1919; s. Fred George and Anna Jane (Mason) P.; m. Carol Ulf, Sept. 15, 1953 (div. 1981); children—Ann, Karen, Frederik, Kathy; m. Elizabeth Anne Hull, July 27, 1984. Editor Popular Pubs., N.Y.C., 1939-43; editor Popular Sci., N.Y.C., 1946-49; freelance writer N.Y.C., 1950-60, 80—; editor Galaxy Pubs., N.Y.C., 1961-69, Bantam Books, N.Y.C., 1973-80. Author: Man Plus, 1977 (Nebula award), Gateway, 1978 (Nebula, Hugo, Campbell awards, Prix Apollo award), Jem, 1979 (Am. Book award), The Years of the City (Campbell award 1985). Served to sgt. USAAF, 1943-45; Italy. Recipient Popular Culture Assn. award, 1982. Fellow AAAS, Brit. Interplanetary Soc.; mem. Sci. Fiction Writers of Am. (pres. 1974-76, Grand Master award 1993), World Sci. Fiction (pres. 1980-82), Authors Guild, N.Y. Acad. Scis., Astron. Soc. Pacific. Democrat. Unitarian. Home: 855 Harvard Dr Palatine IL 60067-7026

POHL, GUNTHER ERICH, retired library administrator; b. Berlin, July 22, 1925; came to U.S., 1927; s. Erich Ernst and Martha (Seidel) P.; m. Dorothy Edna Beck, Aug. 21, 1949; children: Christine, Louise, Elizabeth, Ronald. BA, NYU, 1947, MA, 1950; MLS, Columbia U., 1951. Librarian local history and genealogy div. N.Y. Pub. Library, N.Y.C., 1948-69, chief local history and genealogy div., 1969-80, chief U.S. history and local history and genealogy div., 1980-85; ret. Compiler: N.Y. State Biographical Genealogical and Portrait Index. Fellow N.Y. Geneal. and Biog. Soc.; mem. ALA (chmn. genealogy com. 1971-73, 76-78), N.Y. Geneal. and Biog. Soc. (libr., trustee 1982-92), Sigma Phi Epsilon (trustee local chpt. 1978—). Republican. Avocations: stamps, opera; collecting New Yorkiana. Home: 24 Walden Pl Great Neck NY 11020

POHL, JOHN HENNING, chemical engineer, consultant; b. Ft. Riley, Kans., May 29, 1944; s. Herbert Otto and Ellen Irene (Henning) P.; m. Judith Lynn Sykes, Aug. 10, 1968; children: J. Otto, Clint. AA, Sacramento City Coll., 1964; BS, U. Calif., Berkeley, 1966; MS, MIT, 1973, DSci, 1976. Inspector constrn. C.O. Henning Cons. Engrs., Sacramento, 1965; engr. E.I. du Pont Nemours, Wilmington, Del., 1966-70; tech. asst. MIT, Cambridge, 1971-75, lectr., 1975-76; mem. tech. staff Sandia Nat. Labs., Livermore, Calif., 1976-81; dir. fossil fuels Energy and Environ. Rsch., Irvine, Calif. 1981-86; dir. R & D Energy Systems Assocs., Tustin, Calif., 1986-89; sr. scientist energy W.J. Schafer Assocs., Irvine, 1989-91; pres. Energy Internat., Laguna Hills, Calif., 1988—; sr. cons. ESA Engring., Laguna Hills, 1989—; v.p. Advanced Combustion Tech. Co., Hsinchu, Taiwan, 1993—; v.p. Technology Energeo, San Francisco, 1995—. Contbr. articles to profl. jours.; patentee in field. Treas. Headstart, Cambridge, 1975-76. Recipient Sci. and Tech. Achievement award U.S. EPA, 1987, Best Energy Projects award Energy Commn., Taiwan, coal evaluation, 1989, Low NOx Burner, 1992. Mem. ASME (advisor corrosion and deposits com. 1989—, rsch. program subcom. 1994—), AIChE (combustion advisor 1988-92), Am. Flame Rsch. Com., Am. Chem. Soc., Combustion Inst. Western States (exec. com. 1988-95), Combustion Inst. (program subcom. 1994—). Engring. Found. (steering com. on ash deposits 1989—). Home: 26632 Cortina Dr Mission Viejo CA 92691-5429

POHL, PAUL MICHAEL, lawyer; b. Erie, Pa., July 17, 1948; s. Joseph Paul and Mary (Strenio) P.; m. Kaya Lynn Gavriloff, Aug. 13, 1970; children: Thomas Michael, Mary Elizabeth, Michael David. AB, Princeton U., 1970; JD, U. Pitts., 1975. Bar: Pa. 1975, U.S Dist. Ct. (we. dist.) Pa. 1975, Ohio 1976, U.S. Dist. Ct. Ino. dist.) Ohio 1976, U.S.C. Ct. Appeals (5th cir.) 1980, U.S. Ct. Appeals (11th cir.) 1983, U.S. Ct. Appeals (1st, 3d and 6th cirs.) 1993, U.S. Ct. Appeals (D.C. cir.) 1995. Reporter Erie Daily Times, 1970-71; law clk. to presiding justice Pa. Supreme Ct., 1975-76; assoc. Jones, Day, Reavis & Pogue, Cleve., 1976-82, ptnr., 1982—; ptnr.-in-charge Jones, Day, Reavis & Pogue, Pitts., 1989—; guest mem. faculty Sch. Law, Hofstra U., Hempstead, N.Y., 1982, 84; mem. trial advocacy program Sch. Law, Emory U., Atlanta, 1983—; bd. dirs. JURA Corp., Erie, Amsco Internat. Corp., Pitts., Lord Corp., Erie. Co-author: Conflicts of Interest—A Trial Lawyers Guide, 1984. Bd. dirs. Franciscan U., Steubenville, Ohio, 1991—, vice chmn., 1994—; bd. dirs. Gannon U., Erie, Cath. Charities, Diocese of Pits., Inc. With USMC, 1971-72. Named one of Cleve.'s 78 Most Interesting People, Cleve. mag., 1978. Mem. ABA (chmn. best evidence symposium 1983), Pa. Bar Assn., Allegheny County Bar Assn., Am. Law Inst. Roman Catholic. Office: Jones Day Reavis & Pogue 500 Grant St Pittsburgh PA 15219-2502 also: Jones Day Reavis & Pogue 901 Lakeside Ave E Cleveland OH 44114-1190

POHL, ROBERT OTTO, physics educator; b. Gottingen, Fed. Republic of Germany, Dec. 17, 1929; came to U.S., 1958; s. Robert Wichard and Auguste Eleonore (Madelung) P.; m. Karin Ursula Koehler, May 6, 1961; children: Helen M., Robert S., Otto C. Vordiplom, U. Freiburg, Fed. Rep. Germany, 1951; diploma, U. Erlangen, Fed. Rep. Germany, 1955, Dr. rer. nat., 1957. Asst. U. Erlangen, 1957-58; research assoc. Cornell U., Ithaca, NY, 1958-60, asst. prof., 1960-63, assoc. prof., 1963-68, prof., 1968—; vis. prof. Tech. Hochschule Stuttgart, 1966-67, Tech. U. Munchen, 1973-74, Konstanz U., Regensburg U., 1987-88, all Fed. Republic Germany; vis. scientist Nuc. Research Ctr., Juelich, Fed. Rep. Germany, 1980-81, Hahn-Meitner Inst., Berlin, 1995. Contbr. articles on solid state physics to profl. jours. Recipient Sr. Scientist award Alexander von Humboldt Found., 1980; Guggenheim Found. fellow, 1973, Erskine fellow U. Canterbury, New Zealand, 1988. Fellow AAAS, Am. Inst. Physics (O.E. Buckley award 1985), Internat. Thermal Conductivity Confs. Office: Cornell U Physics Dept Ithaca NY 14853-2501

POHLAD, CARL R., professional baseball team executive, bottling company executive; b. West Des Moines, Iowa. Ed., Gonzaga U. With MEI Diversified, Inc., Mpls., 1959—, chmn. bd., 1976—; pres. Marquette Bank Mpls., N.A., pres., dir.; pres., dir. Bank Shares, Inc.; owner Minn. Twins, 1985—; dir. Meth. Hosp. Adminstrv. Group, T.G.I. Friday's, Tex. Air Corp., Ea. Airlines, Continental Air Lines, Inc., Carlson Cos. Inc. Office: MEI Diversified Inc 527 Marquette Ave Ste 400 Minneapolis MN 55402-1327 Office: Bank Shares Inc PO Box 1467 777 Marquette Ave Minneapolis MN 55402-2302*

POHLAND, FREDERICK GEORGE, environmental engineering educator, researcher; b. Oconomowoc, Wis., May 3, 1931; s. Arnold Ernest and Eda Karoline (Petermann) P.; m. Virginia Ruth Simmons, Sept. 10, 1966; 1 child, Elizabeth Eda. BS in Civil Engring., Valparaiso U., 1953; MS in Civil Engring., Purdue U., 1958, PhD, 1961. Profl. engr.: diplomate Am. Acad. Environ. Engrs. Civil engr. Erie Railroad Co., Huntingdon, Ind., 1953; preventive medicine specialist U.S. Army, Ft. Bragg, N.C., 1953-56; grad. rsch. asst. Purdue U., West Lafayette, Ind., 1956-61; asst. prof. Ga. Inst. Tech., Atlanta, 1961-64, assoc. prof., 1964-71, prof., 1971-88; Weidlein prof. U. Pitts., 1989—; vis. scholar U. Mich., Ann Arbor, 1967-68; guest prof. Delft Univ. Tech., The Netherlands, 1976-77; mem. EPA Sci. Adv. Bd., Washington, 1989-92; mem. sci. adv. com. Gulf Coast Hazardous Substance Rsch. Ctr., Beaumont, Tex., 1989—; mem. EPRI Sci. Adv. Com., Palo Alto, Calif., 1990-94; mem. adv. coun. Purdue U., West Lafayette, 1990-94; active NRC Com. on Water Rsch. and Innovative Techs., 1993—, NIER Sci. Adv. Com., 1995—, Dept. Def. Adv. Applications Tech. Demon Facility Ind. Adv. Com., 1994—. Author: Emerging Technologies in Hazardous Waste Management, 1990, 91, 93, Design of Anaerobic Processes for the Treatment of Industrial and Municipal Waste, 1992; editor (jour.) Water Rsch., 1983—; author over 130 publs. in field. Served with U.S. Army, 1953-56. Recipient Harrison Prescott Eddy medal Water Pollution Control Fedn., 1964, Charles Alvin Emerson medal, 1983, Gordon Maskew Fair medal, 1989; recipient Rsch. award Water Pollution Control Assn. Pa., 1991. Fellow Am. Soc. Civil Engrs.; mem. NAE, NSPE, AIChE, Am. Acad. Environ. Engrs. (diplomate; pres. 1992-93, Stanley E. Kappe award), Assn. Environ. Engring. Profs. (sec.-treas. 1970-71, Disting. lectr. 1992), Solid Waste Assn. N.Am. (Lawrence lectr. 1992), Am. Water Works Assn. (life mem.), Water Environ. Fedn. (hon.), Am. Chem. Soc., Am. Soc. for Microbiology, Ga. Soc. Profl. Engrs., Internat. Assn. Water Quality, Pa. Soc. Profl. Engrs., Pa. Water & Pollution Control Assn., Sigma Xi, Tau Beta Pi, Chi Epsilon, others. Achievements include major contributions to phase separation in anaerobic treatment processes; originated concept of leachate recirculation for accelerated stabilization in landfill bioreactors. Home: 118 Millstone Ln Pittsburgh PA 15238 Office: U Pitts Dept Civil and Environ Engring Pittsburgh PA 15260

POHLMAN, JAMES ERWIN, lawyer; b. Iowa City, Apr. 10, 1932; s. Erwin Christian and Agnes Freda (Johanns) P.; m. Patricia Anne Likert, Sept. 6, 1958; children: William James, John David, Bruce Likert. AB, Oberlin Coll., 1954; LLB, U. Mich., 1957. Bar: Ohio 1957. Assoc. Wright, Harlor, Purpus, Morris & Arnold, Columbus, Ohio, 1957-62; ptnr. Wright, Harlor, Morris & Arnold, Columbus, 1962-77; ptnr. Porter, Wright, Morris & Arthur, Columbus, 1977—, chmn. litigation dept., 1986—; bd. dirs. Physicians Ins. Co. Ohio, Pickerington. Trustee Oberlin (Ohio) Coll., 1986—, Columbus Children's Hosp., 1976-91; pres. John Frederick Oberlin Soc., 1983-86. Served with Air N.G., 1957-60. Fellow NEH seminar Yale U., summer 1977. Fellow Am. Coll. Trial Lawyers; mem. Am. Soc. Med. Assn. Counsel (pres. 1982-85), Internat. Assn. Def. Counsel (exec. com. 1984-87, sec.-treas. 1993—), Barristers Soc. (pres Columbus club 1963-64). Republican. Congregationalist. Clubs: Golf (New Albany, Ohio); Rocky Fork Country (Gahanna, Ohio) (trustee 1980-83). Office: Porter Wright Morris & Arthur 2900 Huntington Ctr Columbus OH 43215

POHLMAN, RANDOLPH ALLEN, business administration educator, dean; b. Topeka, Jan. 25, 1944; s. Clarence Alvin and Martha Melissa (McElheny) P.; m. Jeanne Lucille Gebhart, Aug. 22, 1965; children—Kristina, Lisa. B.S., Kans. State U., 1967, M.S., 1969; Ph.D., Okla. State U., 1976. Asst. prof., assoc. prof. fin. Kans. State U., Manhattan, 1976-82, assoc. prof., head dept. fin., 1982-84, prof., dean Coll. Bus. Adminstrn., 1984-90; dir. employee devel. Koch Industries, 1990-91, dir. human resources, 1991—; vis. rsch. scholar UCLA, 1983; holder L.L. McAninch Chair of Entrepreneurship, 1988-90; bd. dirs. Union Nat. Bank, Manhattan, mem. investment com., 1986-87, mem. trust mgmt. com., 1988. Author: International Investment, 1977, Financial Statement Analysis and Forecasting for the Non-Financial Executive, 1990, Understanding the Bottom Line: Finance for Non-financial Managers and Supervisors. Chmn. Kans. State U., United Way, 1982; trustee Meml. Hosp., Manhattan, 1984-90; treas. Kans. State U. Found., 1980-90, mem. investments com., 1988; mem. Ctr. for Workforce Mgmt. Steering Com., Sedgwick County Med. Soc. Cost Containment Roundtable, Wichita/Sedgwick County Partnership for Growth Employment and Tng. Bd. With USAF, 1971-73. Recipient Outstanding Tchr. award Coll. of Bus., Kans. State U., 1977, All-Univ. Disting. Teaching award Kans. State U., 1977; investments research grantee Kans. State U., 1978. Mem. Fin. Execs. Inst., Am. Fin. Assn., Am. Econ. Assn., Fin. Mgmt. Assn., Midwest Fin. Assn., Kans. State U. Alumni Assn. (treas. 1980-90, trustee 1983-90, bd. dirs.), Manhattan C. of C. (bd. dirs. 1987-90). Republican. Club: Manhattan Country (bd. dirs. 1983-85). Lodge: Rotary (bd. dirs. Manhattan club, 1986—, pres.-elect Manhattan chpt.). Avocations: golf; guitar playing; reading. Office: Koch Industries PO Box 2256 Wichita KS 67201-2256

POHLSANDER, HANS ACHIM, classics educator; b. Celle, Germany, Oct. 10, 1927, came to U.S., 1947, naturalized, 1953; m. Navee Newby, Aug. 20, 1956; children—Dianne, Eileen, Margaret. B.A. with high honors, U. Utah, 1954; M.A., U. Calif.-Berkeley, 1955; Ph.D., U. Mich., 1961. Tchr. Carmel High Sch., Calif., 1956-58; asst. prof. Washington U., St. Louis, 1961-62; asst. to assoc. prof. SUNY, Albany, 1962-71, prof. classics, 1971—, prof. religious studies, 1991—, chmn. dept. classics, 1972-78; vis. assoc. prof. Am. U. Beirut, 1968-69; vis. prof. Ohio State U., Columbus, 1983-84; lectr. Aegean Inst., Greece, summers 1969, 72, 75, 78, 83, Anatolia Coll., Greece, summer 1981. Contbr. articles to profl. jours. Served to cpl. U.S. Army, 1950-52. Grantee NEH, 1979, German Acad. Exchange Service, 1982, Am. Philos. Soc., 1983, 88, Am. Coun. Learned Socs., 1963. Mem. Archaeol. Inst. Am., Am. Philol. Assn., Hagiographic Soc. Home: 52 Wellington Rd Delmar NY 12054-3322 Office: SUNY at Albany Dept Classics 1400 Washington Ave Albany NY 12222-0001

POIANI, EILEEN LOUISE, mathematics educator, college administrator, higher education planner; b. Newark, Dec. 17, 1943; d. Hugo Francis and Eileen Louise (Crecca) P. BA in Math., Douglass Coll., 1965; MS in Math., Rutgers U., 1967, PhD in Math., 1971. Teaching asst., grad. preceptor Rutgers U., New Brunswick, N.J., 1966-67; asst. counselor Douglass Coll., New Brunswick, 1967, 69-70; instr. math. St. Peter's Coll., Jersey City, 1967-70, asst. prof., 1970-74, dir. of self-study, 1974-76, assoc. prof., 1974-80, prof., 1980—, asst. to pres., 1976-80; asst. to pres. for planning St. Peter's Coll., 1980—; chairwoman U.S. Commn. on Math. Instrn., NRC of NAS, Washington, 1983-90; founding nat. dir. Women and Math. Lectureship Program, Washington, 1975-81, mem. adv. bd., 1981—; project dir. Consortium for Advancement of Pvt. Higher Edn., Washington, 1986-88; mem. N.J. Math. Coalition, 1991—, Nat. Seminar on Jesuit Higher Edn., 1990-94, mem. strategic planning com. N.J. Assn. Ind. Colls. and Univs., 1990-92; charter trustee Rutgers U., 1992—. Author: (with others) Mathematics Tomorrow, 1981; contbr. articles to profl. jours. Mem. Newark Mus., Nutley (N.J.) Hist. Soc., Friends of Newark Libr.; trustee Nutley Free Pub. Libr., 1974-77, St. Peter's Prep. Sch., Jersey City, 1986-92; active fee arbitration commn. N.J. Supreme Ct., 1983-86, ct. ethics com., 1986-90; U.S. nat. rep. Internat. Congress Math. Edn., Budapest, Hungary, 1988; mem. statewide planning com. NCCJ, 1988-92; chair evaluation teams Mid. States Assn. Coll. and Schs.; mem. U.S. delegation to Internat. Congress on Math; trustee The Cath. Advocate, 1993—. Recipient Douglass Soc. award Douglass Coll., 1982, Outstanding Civic Svc. award Christopher Columbus Found., 1994, Outstanding Svc. award Middle States Assn. Colls. and Schs., 1994, Christopher Columbus award N.J. Columbus Found.; named Danforth Assoc., Danforth Found., 1972-86. Mem. AAUP, Math. Assn. Am. (bd. dirs. lectureship program, gov. N.J. chpt. 1972-79, chair human resources coun. 1991—, Outstanding Coll. Teaching award 1993), Am. Math. Soc., Nat. Coun. Tchrs. Math. (speaker 1974—), Soc. Coll. and Univ. Planning

---

(program com. 1989—, speaker nat. confs. 1986, 88, 89, 90, judge grad. paper competition), Pi Mu Epsilon (1st woman pres. in 75 yrs. 1987-90). Roman Catholic. Avocations: gourmet cook, traveling, biking. Office: St Peter's Coll 2641 Kennedy Blvd Jersey City NJ 07306

POILE, DAVID ROBERT, professional hockey team executive; b. Toronto, Ont., Can., Feb. 14, 1949; s. Norman Robert and Margaret (Elizabeth) P.; m. Elizabeth Ramey, July 4, 1971; children: Brian Robert, Lauren Elizabeth. B.S., Northeastern U., 1971. Asst. mgr. Atlanta Flames, 1971-80, Calgary Flames, Alta., Can., 1980-82; gen. mgr., v.p. Washington Capitals, Landover, Md., 1982—. Office: Washington Capitals Usair Arena Landover MD 20785

POINDEXTER, BUSTER See JOHANSEN, DAVID

POINDEXTER, CHRISTIAN HERNDON, utility company executive; b. Evansville, Ind., Sept. 20, 1938; s. Marlan Glenn and Ellen Mabelle (Sommers) P.; m. Marilyn Ann Mills, June 12, 1960; children: Scott H., Todd S. B.S. in Engring., U.S. Naval Acad., 1960; M.B.A. in Fin., Loyola Coll., Balt., 1976. With Balt. Gas & Electric Co., 1967—, gen. supr. fin. dept., 1976-78, treas., asst. sec., 1978-79, v.p. engring. and constrn., 1980-85; pres., chief exec. officer, dir. Constellation Holdings, Inc. subs. Balt. Gas & Electric Co., 1985-89; vice chmn. bd. Balt. Gas & Electric Co., 1989-93, chmn., CEO, 1993—; chmn. bd., chief exec. officer Constellation Biogas Inc., Constellation Investments Inc., Constellation Properties Inc.; bd. dirs. The KMS Group, Inc., 1986—. Bd. dirs., sec. YMCA of Anne Arundel County, Md., 1985—; bd. dirs., pres. Scholarships for Scholars, Inc.; exec. bd. Balt. Area council Boy Scouts Am.; trustee Md. Acad. Scis., 1984—, Villa Julie Coll., 1986—. Served to lt. USN, 1960-67. Mem. Engring. Soc. Balt., IEEE. Republican. Home: 413 Cornwall Ct Severna Park MD 21146-1619 Office: Balt Gas & Electric Co PO Box 1475 Baltimore MD 21203-1475*

POINDEXTER, JOHN BRUCE, entrepreneur; b. Houston, Oct. 7, 1944; s. George Emerson and Rose Ellen (McDowell) P.; B.S.B.A. with honors, U. Ark., 1966; M.B.A., N.Y. U., 1971, Ph.D. in Econs. and Fin., 1976. Assoc. Salomon Bros., N.Y.C., 1971-72; v.p. Lombard, Nelson & McKenna, N.Y.C., 1972-73; v.p., registered prin. Dominick & Dominick, Inc., N.Y.C., 1973-76; sr. v.p. Smith Barney Venture Corp., N.Y.C., 1976-83; gen. partner First Century Partnership, N.Y.C., 1980-83; mng. partner KD/P Equities, ptnr. Kellner, DiLeo & Co., N.Y.C., 1983-85; mng. ptnr., J.B. Poindexter and Co., L.P., 1985-94; chmn. bd. dirs. J.B. Poindexter & Co., Inc., 1994—; chmn. bd. dirs. EFP Corp., Leer Holdings, Inc., Morgan Holdings Inc., Southwestern Holdings, Inc., Lowy Group, Inc., Magnetic Instruments Inc., Gem Top, Inc.; adj. assoc. prof. L.I. U. Author various monographs. Served to capt. U.S. Army, 1966-70; Vietnam. Decorated Silver Star, Bronze Star (2), Purple Heart (2), Soldier's medal, others. Mem. Beta Gamma Sigma, Alpha Kappa Psi. Club: Metropolitan, N.Y.C., Argyle (San Antonio), Coronado (Houston). Office: 1100 Louisiana St Houston TX 77002-5211

POINDEXTER, KENNETH WAYNE, automobile executive; b. Gladewater, Tex., July 31, 1937; s. Chester Earl and Mildred (Holt) P.; m. Ellen Landers, Jan. 21, 1972; 1 child, Kenna Marie Kempton. Grad. high sch., Stephens, Ark. Editor The Ouachita Citizen, Camden, Ark., 1960-62; advt. mgr. The Camden News, 1962-66; ops. mgr. Cam-Tel Co., Camden, 1967-79; owner Am. Pulpwood Co., Ogemaw, Ark., 1979-90; propertion Poindexter Gen. Mercantile, Ogemaw, 1983-90; pres., dealer prin. Ken Poindexter Autoplex, Inc., Marshall, Tex., 1991—; pres. Ark. Cable TV Assn., 1976. Editor Ouachita County Hist. Quar. (Best in Ark. 1988-90). Elected Justice of the Peace, Ouachita County, 1962-82; chmn. Ouachita County Election Commn., 1984-86, Ouachita County Dem. Ctrl. Com., 1984-86; bd.dirs. Ouachita County Hist. Soc., Camden, 1991; elder Eastern Hills Ch. of Christ, Marshall, Tex. Mem. Stephens C. of C. (pres. 1985-87, Citizen of Yr. 1986), Buena Vista/Ogemaw Water Assn. (charter pres., bd. dirs. 1982-90), Stephens Lions Club (pres. 1982), Nat. Soc. of Sons of Am. Revolution. Mem. Ch. of Christ. Avocations: reading, old movie video collector, gardening. Home: 603 Ambassador Marshall TX 75670 Office: Ken Poindexter Autoplex Inc 1083 E Grand Ave Marshall TX 75670

POINDEXTER, WILLIAM MERSEREAU, lawyer; b. Los Angeles, June 16, 1925; s. Robert Wade and Irene M. (Mersereau) P.; m. Cynthia Converse Pastushin, Nov. 10, 1979; children: James Wade, David Graham, Honour Hêlenê, Timothy John. B.A., Yale U., 1946; postgrad., U. Chgo., 1946-47; LL.B., U. Calif., Berkeley, 1949. Bar: Calif. 1952. Practiced in San Francisco, 1952-54, Los Angeles, 1954—; mem. firm Poindexter & Doutre, Inc., 1964—; Pres. Consol. Brazing & Mfg. Co., Riverside, Calif. 1949-52. Pres. South Pasadena-San Marino (Calif.) YMCA, 1963; Mem. San Marino Sch. Bd., 1965-69, pres., 1967; pres. Conf. of Ins. Counsel, 1975. Served with USMCR, 1943. Fellow Am. Coll. Probate Counsel; mem. Am., Los Angeles County bar assns., State Bar Calif. Republican. Presbyterian. Clubs: Yale of So. Calif. (pres. 1961), California. Office: 1 Wilshire Bldg Suite 2420 Los Angeles CA 90017

POINTER, PETER LEON, investment executive; b. Erie, Pa., Aug. 3, 1934; s. Leon Royce and Katherine (Hermen) P.; m. Linda Milla Jensen, Sept. 21, 1957; children: Philip Leon, David Andrew. BS in Econs., U. Pa., 1956; MBA, U. Mo., 1968. V.p. Roose-Wade & Co. Inc., Toledo, 1976-78; br. mgr. Wm. C. Roney & Co., Detroit, 1978-79; v.p. Lowe & Assocs., Columbus, Ohio, 1979-88; pres. Pointer Investment Co., Columbus, 1988—; arbitrator Nat. Assn. Security Dealers, Washington, 1987—; adv. com. mem. Dept. Commerce Div. of Securities, Columbus, 1988—. Trustee, sec.-treas. Univ. Urology Ednl. and Rsch. Found., 1993—. Lt. col. USAF, 1956-76. Mem. Brookside Golf and Country Club (treas., trustee 1991-94), Sigma Nu (treas. 1955-56). Republican. Methodist. Avocations: aviation, golf, gardening. Home: 2290 Haverford Rd Columbus OH 43220-4320 Office: Pointer Investment Co Ste N 152 1550 Old Henderson Rd Columbus OH 43220

POINTER, SAM CLYDE, JR., federal judge; b. Birmingham, Ala., Nov. 15, 1934; s. Sam Clyde and Elizabeth Inzer (Brown) P.; m. Paula Purse, Oct. 18, 1958; children: Minge, Sam Clyde III. A.B., Vanderbilt U., 1955; J.D., U. Ala., 1957; LL.M., NYU, 1958. Bar: Ala. 1957. Ptnr. Brown, Pointer & Pointer, 1958-70; judge U.S. Dist. Ct. (no. dist.) Ala., Birmingham, 1970-82, chief judge, 1982—; judge Temp. Emergency Ct. Appeals, 1980-87; mem. Jud. Panel Multi-dist. Litigation, 1980-87; mem. Jud. Conf. U.S., 1987-90; mem. Jud. Coun. 11th Cir., 1987-90, mem. standing com. on rules, 1988-90, chmn. adv. com. on civil rules, 1990-93. Bd. editors: Manual for Complex Litigation, 1979-91. Mem. ABA, Ala. Bar Asn., Birmingham Bar Assn., Am. Law Inst., Am. Judicature Soc., Farrah Order of Jurisprudence, Phi Beta Kappa. Episcopalian. Office: US Dist Ct 882 US Courthouse 1729 5th Ave N Birmingham AL 35203-2000

POINTS, ROY WILSON, municipal official; b. Quincy, Ill., Oct. 21, 1940; s. Jess C. and Gladys (Wilson) P.; m. Karen Lee Olsen, July 23, 1966; children: Eric, Holly. BBA, Culver Stockton Coll., 1968. Tchr., coach Lewis County C-1, Ewing, Mo., 1968-69, Community Unit 3, Camp Point, Ill., 1969-78; real estate salesman Landmark, Quincy, 1978-80; supr. of assessment County of Adams, Quincy, 1980-90; assessor City Twp. of Quincy, 1990—; mem., chmn. Adams County Bd. Rev., 1977-80. Bd. dirs., 1st v.p., sec. Quincy Jaycees, 1970-76, Quincy Rotary East, 1980. Mem. Cert. Ill. Assessing Officers, Internat. Assn. Assessing Officers (cert. ednl. recognition 1988), Ill. Assessors Assn. (bd. dirs. 1992—), Tri-Twp. Ofcls. Ill. Democrat. Avocations: fishing, hunting, jogging, raising cattle. Office: Quincy Twp Assessor City Hall Annex 706 Maine St Quincy IL 62301-4042

POIRIER, FRANK EUGENE, physical anthropology educator; b. Paterson, N.J., Aug. 7, 1940; s. Frank Eugene and Alice (Apelian) P.; m. Darlene Matsko, July 6, 1963; children—Alyson, Sevanne Cara. B.A., Paterson State Coll., Wayne, N.J., 1962; M.A., U. Oreg., 1964, Ph.D., 1967. Asst. prof. dept. psychiatry U. Fla., 1967-68; prof., chair anthropology Ohio State U., Columbus, 1968—. Co-author: Human Evolution in China, 1995, In Search of Ourselves, 5th edit., 1993, An Introduction to Physical Anthropology and the Archaeological Record, 1982, Understanding Human Evolution, 3d edit., 1993; editor: Primate Socialization, 1972, (with others) Primate Bio-Social Development, 1977; contbr. articles to profl. jours., chpts. to books. Fellow NIH, 1963-67, NIMH, 1969-70, Fulbright, 1986. Mem. AAAS, Internat.

Primatological Soc., Am. Assn. Phys. Anthropologists, Current Anthropology, Am. Soc. Primatologists, Internat. Soc. Cryptozoology, Explorers Club, Sigma Xi. Democrat. Home: 420 Greenglade Ave Columbus OH 43085-2206 Office: Ohio State U Dept Anthropology 124 W 17th Ave Columbus OH 43210-1316

POIRIER, LOUIS JOSEPH, neurology educator; b. Montreal, Que., Can., Dec. 30, 1918; s. Gustave Joseph and Calixta (Brault) P.; m. Liliane Archambault, June 11, 1947; children—Guy, Michel, Louise, Esther. B.Sc., U. Montreal, 1942, M.D., 1947; Ph.D., U. Mich., 1950; D. (hon.), U. Rennes, France, 1973. Asst. prof. U. Montreal, 1950-55, assoc. prof., 1955-58, prof., faculty of medicine, 1958-65; chmn. dept. anatomy Faculty of Medicine, Laval U., Cité Universitaire, 1962—; prof. exptl. neurology Faculty of Medicine, Laval U., Cité Universitaire, 1970-83; dir. Centre de Research in Neurobiology, Laval U. and Hosp. de l'Enfant-Jesus, 1977-85, prof. emeritus, 1985—. Contbr. articles to profl. jours.; editor the extrapyramidal system and its disorders in: Advances in Neurology, vol. 24, 1979. Pres. Que. Health Scis. Research Council, 1978-81. Decorated Order of Can.; recipient Que. sci. award, 1975; Killam commemorative scholar, 1977, 78. Mem. Royal Soc. Belgium (hon.), Neurol. Soc. France (hon.), AAAS, Am. Assn. Anatomists, Am. Physiol. Soc., Soc. for Neuroscis., Internat. Brain Research Orgn. Address: 603 Chemin Caron, Lac Simon, Montpellier, PQ Canada J0V 1M0

POIRIER, RICHARD, English educator, literary critic; b. Gloucester, Mass., Sept. 9, 1925; s. Philip and Annie (Kiley) P. A.B., Amherst Coll., 1949; M.A., Yale U., 1951; Ph.D., Harvard U., 1959; student, U. Paris, France, 1944-45; H.H.D., Amherst Coll., 1978. Mem. faculty Williams Coll., 1950-52, Harvard U., 1953-63; Disting. prof. English Rutgers U., 1963—; bd. dirs., co-founder, chmn. bd. Libr. of Am.; Beckman prof. U. Calif., Berkeley, 1973; chmn. adv. English com. Harvard U., 1988-91; delivered Gauss Seminars, Princeton U., 1990, T.S. Eliot lectures, U. Kent, 1991, Henry James lectures, NYU, 1992. Editor: Partisan Rev, 1963-73, O Henry Prize Stories, 1961-65; editor/founder Raritan Quar., 1981—; author: The Comic Sense of Henry James, 1960, In Defense of Reading, 1962, A World Elsewhere, 1966, The Performing Self, 1971, Norman Mailer, 1973, Robert Frost: The Work of Knowing, 1977, The Renewal of Literature, 1987, Poetry and Pragmatism, 1992; contbr. author numerous articles, revs. to profl. jours. Served with AUS, 1943-46. Recipient achievement award AAAL, 1978, Jay B. Hubbell award, 1988, Lit. Lion award N.Y. Pub. Libr., 1992; Fulbright scholar, Cambridge, Eng., 1952-53; Bollinger fellow, 1962-63, Guggenheim fellow, 1974-75, fellow NEH, 1978-79. Mem. Am. Acad. Arts and Scis., P.E.N. (exec. bd. 1986), PMLA (editorial bd. 1977-79), nominating com. Nat. Medal for Lit., 1986, 87, Nat. Book Critics Cir., 1977-85, Phi Beta Kappa. Club: Century. Home: 104 W 70th St Apt 9B New York NY 10023-4457 Office: Raritan Quarterly Rutgers University 31 Mine St New Brunswick NJ 08901-1111

POIRION, DANIEL, foreign language educator; b. Amiens, France, Jan. 22, 1927; came to U.S., 1987; s. Michel and Marie-Louise (Martigny) P.; m. Jacqueline Dokier, Dec. 11, 1980; children: Jean-Marc, Karen; children from previous marriage: Fabrice, Marie-Christine. Student, Ecole Normale Supérieure, 1947-50; Agrégé des Lettres, Université de Paris-Sorbonne, 1950, Docteur-ès-Lettres, 1965. Prof. Lycée, Nevers, Dijon, France, 1951-53; asst. Faculté des Lettres, Paris, 1953-58; asst. prof. Yale U., New Haven, 1958-61, prof. French, 1970-71, 87—; prof. medieval lit. Université de Grenoble, France, 1961-68; dir. French Inst., Naples, Italy, 1968-70; prof. Université de Paris-Sorbonne, 1974-87; chmn. medieval studies YaleU., New Haven, Conn., 1993—; dir. Département d'Etudes Medievales, Paris, 1981-87; cons. Editions Gallimard, Paris, 1987—, Editions Garnier-Bordas, Paris, 1987-91. Author: Le Poéte et le prince, 1965, Le Lexique de Ch. d'Orléans, 1967, Le Roman de la Rose, 1973, Résurgences, 1986, Tristan et Yseut, 1989; editor: Chrétien de Troyes Oeuvres Completes, 1994. Lt. inf., French Army, 1950-51. Decorated chevalier Légion d'Honneur, Palmes Académiques (France). Fellow Am. Acad. Arts and Scis.; mem. Arthurian Soc. (treas. 1974-84), Acad. des Inscriptions et Belles Lettres, Inst. de France (corr.), European Medieval Acad. (pres.). Home: 175 Mill Plain Rd Branford CT 06405-2712 Office: Yale U PO Box 208313 New Haven CT 06520-8313

POIROT, JAMES WESLEY, engineering company executive; b. Douglas, Wyo., 1931; m. Raeda Poirot. BCE, Oreg. State U., 1953. With various constrn. firms, Alaska and Oreg.; with CH2M Hill Inc., 1955, v.p., Seattle and Atlanta, from 1967; chmn. bd. CH2M Hill Ltd., Englewood, Colo., 1983-93; former chmn. Western Regional Coun., Design Profls. Coalition, Accreditation Bd. Engring. and Tech., Indsl. Adv. Coun.; former mem. Oreg. Joint Grad. Schs. Engring., Engring. Coun. Named ENR Constrn. Man of Yr., 1988. Fellow ASCE (pres. 1993-94, chmn. steering com. quality manual 1985-90), Am. Cons. Engrs. Coun. (pres. 1989-90); mem. Am. Acad. Environ. Engrs. (diplomate), Am. Assn Engring. Socs. (vice chmn. 1995), Nat. Acad. Engring. Partnership for Sustainable Devel. (founding dir.). Office: CH2M Hill Inc PO Box 22508 Denver CO 80222-0508

POIS, JOSEPH, lawyer, educator; b. N.Y.C., Dec. 25, 1905; s. Adolph and Augusta (Lesser) P.; m. Rose Tomarkin, June 24, 1928 (dec. May 1981); children: Richard Adolph (dec.), Robert August, Marc Howard; m. Ruth Livingston, Nov. 27, 1983 (div. 1984). A.B., U. Wis., 1926; M.A., U. Chgo., 1927, Ph.D., 1929; J.D., Chgo.-Kent Coll. Law, 1934. Bar: Ill. 1934, Pa. 1978. Staff mem. J.L. Jacobs & Co., Chgo., 1929-35; jr. partner J.L. Jacobs & Co., 1946-47; gen. field supr. Pub. Adminstrn. Service, Chgo., 1935-38; chief adminstrv. studies sect. U.S. Bur. Old Age and Survivors Ins., 1938-39; chief adminstrv. and fiscal reorgn. sect. U.S. Bur. Budget Exec. Office of Pres., 1939-42; dir. finance State of Ill., 1951-53; counsel, asst. to pres., v.p., treas., dir. Signode Corp., 1947-61; prof. U. Pitts., 1961-76, emeritus, 1976—; chmn. dept. pub. adminstrn., 1961-71, assoc. dean, 1973-75; dir. Vision Service Plan of Pa., 1984-85; cons. ECA, 1948, Dept. State, 1949, 62-65, U.S. Dept. Def., 1954, Brookings Instn., 1962-63, AID, 1965, Indian Inst. Pub. Adminstrn., 1972, Commn. on Operation Senate, 1976, Pitts. Citizens' Task Force on Refuse Disposal, 1976-78; mem. cons. panel Comptroller Gen. of U.S., 1967-75. Author: The School Board Crisis: a Chicago Case Study, 1964, Financial Administration in the Michigan State Government, 1938, Kentucky, Handbook of Financial Administration, 1937, Public Personnel Administration in the City of Cincinnati, 1936, (with Edward M. Martin and Lyman S. Moore) The Merit System in Illinois, 1935, Watchdog on the Potomac: A Study of the Comptroller General of the United States, 1979; contbg. author: The New Political Economy, 1975, State Audit-Developments in Public Accountability, 1979. Mem. Chgo. Bd. Edn., 1956-61; pres. Chgo. Met. Housing and Planning Council, 1956-57, Immigrants Service League, Chgo., 1960-61; dir. Pitts. Council Pub. Edn., 1965-67; mem. citizens bd. U. Chgo., 1958-78; mem. Pitts. Bd. Pub. Edn., 1973-76; bd. dirs. Pitts. Center for Arts, 1977-85, World Federalist Assn. Pitts., 1984—, Pitts. dist. Zionist Orgn. Am., 1979-81, mem. Hunger Action Coalition, Pitts., 1985-86; mem. Allegheny County Bd. Assistance, 1981-90, chmn. 1981-87. Served from comdr. to capt. USCGR, 1942-46. Decorated Navy Commendation medal; recipient alumni citation for pub. service U. Chgo., 1960; award for pub. service U.S. Gen. Accounting Office, 1971. Mem. ABA, Chgo. Bar Assn., Fed. Bar Assn., Allegheny County Bar Assn., Am. Politt. Sci. Assn., Am. Soc. Pub. Adminstrn. (award for pub. svc. Pitts. area chpt. 1985), Ctr. for Study of the Presidency, Govt. Fin. Officers Assn., Fin. Execs. Inst., Inst. Mgmt. Accts., U. Chgo. Alumni Club. (Pres. chpt. 1981-84), Army and Navy Club (Washington), Phi Beta Kappa, Pi Lambda Phi, Phi Delta Phi. Home: 825 Morewood Ave Pittsburgh PA 15213-2950

POISKER, KAREN COONS, nursing administrator; b. Crisfield, Md., Apr. 11, 1949; d. Broadus Henderson Coons and June (Vessey) Larson; m. Ronald John Henderson Coons and June (Vessey) Larson; m. Ronald John Poisker, Aug. 9, 1967; children: Tanya, Ian. BSN, U. Md., Balt., 1978, MSN, 1981; MBA, Wilmington Coll., 1992. Mem. Am. Heart Assn. RN special care unit Peninsula Gen. Hosp. Med. Ctr., Salisbury, Md., 1975-77, RN ICU, 1977-78; sr. level instr. Peninsula Gen. Hosp. Sch. Nursing, Salisbury, Md., 1978; staff devel. instr. Peninsula Gen. Hosp. Med. Ctr., Salisbury, Md., 1978-81, supr. emergency dept., 1981-83, asst. dir. nursing, 1983-84, assoc. dir. nursing, 1984-85, asst. v.p. nursing, 1985-87, v.p. nursing, 1987-92; v.p. patient care Peninsula Regional Med. Ctr., Salisbury, Md., 1992—. Active Bus. and Profl. Women's Orgn., 1985-87; bd. dirs. Jr. Achievement Easter Shore, Salisbury, 1992—. Mem. Am. Orgn. Nurse Execs., Md. Orgn. Nurse Execs., Sigma Theta Tau. Democrat. Mem. Religious Soc. Friends. Avocations: horseback riding, reading, gardening.

swimming. Home: 27733 Oriole Rd Princess Anne MD 21853-2537 Office: Peninsula Regional Med Ctr 100 E Carroll St Salisbury MD 21801-5447

POISSANT, CHARLES-ALBERT, paper manufacturing company executive; b. Montréal, Que., Can., Sept. 13, 1925; m. Florence Drouin, June 12, 1951; children: Louise, Marc-André Hélène, Isabelle. Chartered acct., U. Montréal, 1953. Chartered acct. Que. Ptnr., pres. Poissant Thibault affiliate Peat Marwick Thorne, Montréal, 1947-87; chmn., CEO Donohue, Inc., Québec City, Que., 1987-92, chmn. bd., 1992—; bd. dirs., mem. exec. com. Quebecor, Inc., Montreal, Premier Choix: TVEC, Inc., Orchestre Metropolitain, l'Association des Manufacuriers de Que, Hopital du Sané-Coeur de Montreal; bd. dirs. Nat. Bank Can., Montreal, Foundation de L'Université de Que., Montreal, Can, Pulp and Paper Assn. Author: Taxation in Canada of Non-residents, 1976, Commentary on Canada-Germany Tax Agreement, 1976, How to Think Like a Millionaire, 1985 (transl. into 7 langs.). Mem. Club St. Denis, Laval sur-le-Lac. Roman Catholic. Avocations: golf, downhill skiing. Home: 333 Somerville, Ahuntsic, PQ Canada H3L 1A4 Office: Donohue Inc, 612 St-Jacques, Montreal, PQ Canada H3C 4N8

POITEVENT, EDWARD BUTTS, II, lawyer; b. New Orleans, Oct. 19, 1949; s. Eads and Elizabeth (Schramm) P.; m. Julia Dunbar Baños, Dec. 29, 1972; children: Sarah Dunbar,Elizabeth Grehan, Edward Scott, Mary McCutchen. BA, Tulane U., 1971, JD, 1974. Assoc. Jones, Walker, Waechter, Poitevent, Carrere & Denegre, New Orleans, 1974-79, ptnr., 1979-91; prnr. Phelps Dunbar, New Orleans, 1991—; mem. ad hoc com. Pipeline div. La. Office of Conservation; mem. adv. coun. La. Mineral Law Inst. Mem. editorial bd. Oil and Gas Law and Taxation Rev.; contbr. articles to profl. jours.; presenter in field. Pres. La. chpt. Leukemia Soc. Am., Inc., New Orleans, 1991; trustee Ea. Mineral Law Found., 1988-93; co-chmn. oil and gas sect. Rocky Mountain Mineral Law Found. 36th Ann. Inst., Santa Fe. MEm. ABA (sect. on natural resources, energy and environ. law natural gas and oil coms., litigation sect. energy litigation com., chair program com., editor energy litigation com. newsletter, chair energy litigation com. natural gas mktg. and trans. com., mem. coun. 1994—), La. State Bar Assn., Fed. Energy Bar Assn., Am. Assn. Petroleum Landmen (chair ad hoc com. on model form gas Balancing Agreement). Republican. Roman Catholic. Office: Phelps Dunbar 28th Fl 400 Poydras St Fl 28 New Orleans LA 70130-3245

POITIER, SIDNEY, actor, director; b. Miami, Fla., Feb. 20, 1927; s. Reginald and Evelyn (Outten) P.; m. Juanita Hardy (div.); children: Beverly, Pamela, Sherri, Gina; m. Joanna Shimkus; children: Anika, Sydney. Ed. pub. schs., The Bahamas. Ind. stage, screen, TV actor, 1948—. Appeared in Am. Negro Theater in numerous prodns. including: Days of Our Youth, Strivers Road, You Can't Take It With You; various roles in Broadway prodns. including: Anna Lucasta, 1948, A Raisin in the Sun, 1959; films include: No Way Out, 1950, Cry, the Beloved Country, 1951, Red Ball Express, 1952, Blackboard Jungle, 1955, Something of Value, 1957, Edge of the City, Band of Angels, 1958, The Defiant Ones, 1958; film adaptation of Porgy and Bess, 1959, A Raisin in Sun, 1960, Paris Blues, 1960, Pressure Point, 1962, The Long Ships, 1964, Lilies of theField, 1963 (Acad. award Best Actor), The Greatest Story Ever Told, 1965, Slender Thread, 1965, Duel of Diablo, To Sir With Love, 1967, In the Heat of the Night, 1967, Guess Who's Coming to Dinner, 1967, The Lost Man, 1968, For the Love of Ivy, 1968, They Call Me Mr. Tibbs, 1969, The Organization, 1971, Brother John, 1971, The Wilby Conspiracy, 1975, Little Nikita, 1987, Shoot to Kill, 1988, Sneakers, 1992; star, dir.: Buck and the Preacher, 1972, A Warm December, 1973, Uptown Saturday Night, 1974, Let's Do It Again, 1975, A Piece of the Action, 1977; dir.: Stir Crazy, 1980, Hanky Panky, 1982, Fast Forward 1984, Ghost Dad, 1990; TV mini series Separate But Equal, 1991, Children of the Dust, 1995; author: This Life, 1981. Served with 1267th Med. Detachment AUS, 1944-45. Decorated knight comdr. Order Brit. Empire; recipient Silver Bear award Berlin Film Festival, 1958, N.Y. Film Critics award and Acad. award nomination for The Defiant Ones, 1958, Best Actor award For Love of Ivy, San Sebastian Film Festival, 1968, Am. Film Inst. Lifetime Achievement Award, 1992. Office: CAA 9830 Wilshire Blvd Beverly Hills CA 90212*

POJETA, JOHN, JR., geologist; b. N.Y.C., Sept. 9, 1935; s. John and Emilie (Pilat) P.; m. Mary Louise Eberz, June 23, 1957; children: Kim Louise, John Martin. B.S., Capital U., Columbus, Ohio, 1957; M.S., U. Cin., 1961, Ph.D., 1963. Teaching fellow U. Cin., 1957-63; geologist U.S. Geol. Survey, 1963—; chief lower paleozoic studies unit, 1969-74, chief br. paleontology and stratigraphy, 1989-94; assoc. prof., lectr. George Washington U., 1965-74; research assoc. Smithsonian Instn., 1969—; U.S. Geol. Survey-Australian Bur. Mineral Resources exchange scientist, 1974-75. Author papers in field. Pres. Potomac Woods Citizens Assn.; mem. area 4 council Montgomery County (Md.) Bd. Edn.; mem. bd. Citizens for Good Govt.; trustee Paleontol. Research Instn., 1976-85, v.p., 1978-79, pres., 1980-82. Fellow Geol. Soc. Am., AAAS (coun.); mem. Paleontol. Soc. (sec. 1982-88, pres. 1989-90), Assn. Australasian Paleontologists. Home: 1492 Dunster Ln Rockville MD 20854-6119 Office: US Geol Survey Rm E-308 MRC137 Mus Natural History Washington DC 20560

POKELWALDT, ROBERT N., manufacturing company executive; b. North Tonawanda, N.Y.. BS, SUNY, Buffalo, 1960. With York Internat. Corp., 1983—, pres., chief exec. officer, 1991—, now also chmn., dir. Office: York Internat Corp 631 S Richard Ave York PA 17403*

POKEMPNER, JOSEPH KRES, lawyer; b. Monessen, Pa., June 11, 1936; s. Leonard and Ethel Lee (Kres) P.; m. Judith Montague Stephens, Aug. 23, 1970; children: Elizabeth, Jennifer, Amy. AB, Johns Hopkins U., 1957; LLB, U. Md., 1962. Bar: Md. 1962. Law clk. to judge Supreme Bench Balt., 1960-62; field atty. 5th region NLRB, 1962-64; pvt. practice labor law Balt., 1964—; ptnr. Wolf, Pokempner & Hillman, Balt., 1972-86, Whiteford, Taylor & Preston, Balt., 1986—. Contbr. articles to legal jours. Capt. AUS, 1969-74. Mem. ABA, Fed. Bar Assn. (pres. Balt. chpt. 1979-80), Md. Bar Assn., Balt. Bar Assn. (pres. 1984-85), Serjeant's Inn Law Club. Jewish. Home: 6002 Charlesmead Rd Baltimore MD 21212-2413

POKORNY, VIRGINIA ANNE, elementary education educator; b. Ashland, Ky., Sept. 27, 1941; d. Law Gibson and Dorothy (Schleicher) Weiner; children: Juliann, Richard. BEd, Nat. Louis U., Evanston, Ill., 1963; M Guidance and Counseling, Northeastern Ill. U., Chgo., 1982. 1st and 2nd grade tchr. West Elem. Sch., Lake Bluff, Ill., 1963-65, West Ridge Sch., Highland Park, Ill., 1965-68; 5th grade tchr. Sherwood Sch., Highland Park, Ill., 1970-71, tchr. combined 2nd to 4th grades and 3rd grade, 1976—. Mem. Deerfield Area Hist. Soc. (bd. dirs. 1991—), Optimist Club Deerfield (bd.dirs. 1992—, co-v.p. 1992-94). Avocations: singing, gardening, antiquing, hiking, working with youth. Home: 1033 Springfield Ave Deerfield IL 60015-3030 Office: Sherwood Sch 1900 Stratford Rd Highland Park IL 60035-3797

POKOTILOW, MANNY DAVID, lawyer; b. Patterson, N.J., June 26, 1938; s. Samuel Morris and Ruth (Fuchs) P.; children: Mali, Charyse, Mona, Andrew. BEE, Newark Coll. Engring., 1960; LLB, Am. U., 1964. Bar: Pa. 1964, U.S. Supreme Ct. 1969. Examiner Patent Office, Washington, 1960-64; ptnr. Caesar, Rivise, Bernstein, Cohen & Pokotilow Ltd., Phila., 1965—; lectr. Dickinson Law Sch., various trade assns., expert witness on protection of computer software, patents, trademarks, trade secrets and copyrights; faculty Temple U. Sch. Law, 1985—. Vol. Support Ctr. for Child Advs., Phila., 1979—; bd. dir., organizer Phila. Bar-Diabetes 10k Race, Phila., 1980—; Packard Press Road Run Grand Prix, 1986; bd. dirs. Hist. Soc. U.S. Dist. Ct. (ea. dist.) Pa., 1989—. Recipient Chair award for vol. excellence Am. Diabetes Assn., 1991; honored by Support Ctr. for Child Advocates, 1992. Mem. ABA (chmn. proprietary rights in software com., coun. sci. and tech. sect. 1989—), IEEE, Assn. Trial Lawyers Am., Phila. Bar Assn. (bd. govs. 1982-84, chmn. sports and recreation com. 1977—, hon. trustee campaign for qualified judges 1993), Phila. Patent Law Assn. (bd. govs. 1982-84, chmn. fed. practice and procedure com. 1983—), Phila. Trial Lawyers (chmn. fed. cts. com. 1986—), Lawyers Club Phila. (bd. govs. 1984—), Pa. Trial Lawyers, Tau Epsilon Rho (vice chancellor Phila. grad. chpt. 1986-88, chancellor 1988-90). Office: Caesar Rivise Bernstein Cohen & Pokotilow Ltd 1635 Market St Philadelphia PA 19103-2217

POKRAS, SHEILA FRANCES, judge; b. Newark, Aug. 5, 1935; m. Norman M. Pokras, 1954; children: Allison, Andrea, Larry. Student, Beaver Coll., 1953-54; BS in Edn., Temple U., 1957; JD cum laude, Pepperdine U., 1969. Bar: Calif. 1970, U.S. Dist. Ct. D.C. 1970, U.S. Dist. Ct. Calif. 1970, U.S. Supreme Ct. 1975. Tchr. elem. and secondary schs. Phila. and Newark, 1957-59; pvt. practice law Long Beach, Calif., 1970-78; city councilwoman Lakewood, Calif., 1972-76; judge Long Beach Mcpl. Ct., 1978-80, L.A. Superior Ct., 1980—; supervising judge, 1986; del. Calif. State Dem. Cen. Com., 1975, Calif. State Conv., 1975; mem. Com. on Gender Bias in Calif. Courts, 1986-89. Advisor Jr. League, 1980-85; mem. early childhood adv. bd. Long Beach City Coll.; bd. dirs. Long Beach Alcoholism Coun., 1979-80, Boys and Girls Club Am., 1981-89, Long Beach Symphony, 1985, Jewish Community Fedn., 1982-86, past mem. community rels. com.; active Nat. Women's Polit. Caucus, LWV. Named Woman of Yr. NOW, Long Beach, 1984; recipient Torch of Liberty award B'nai B'rith Anti-Defamation League, 1974; honoree Nat. Conf. Christians and Jews, 1986. Mem. ABA, AAUW, Nat. Assn. Women Judges (dist. supr. 1986), Calif. Bar Assn. (judges div.), Calif. Judges Assn. (mem. ann. seminar com. 1981-89), Mcpl. Cts. Judges Assn. (mem. Marshall com. 1978-80), L.A. County Bar Assn. (judges div., mem. arbitration com.), Women Lawyers Assn. L.A. (judges sect.), Women Lawyers Assn. Long Beach, Long Beach Legal Aid Found. (v.p. 1976-78), Long Beach Bar Assn. (active various coms., bd. govs. 1977-78, Judge of Yr. 1987), Long Beach C. of C. (bd. dirs.). Avocations: swimming, golf, jogging, classical music, movies. Office: So Dist Superior Ct 415 W Ocean Blvd Long Beach CA 90802-4512

POLACCO, PATRICIA, children's author, illustrator. Works include (juvenile) Meteor!, 1987, Rechenka's Eggs, 1988, The Keeping Quilt, 1988, Uncle Vova's Tree, 1989, Boatride with Lillian Two-Blossom, 1989, Thunder Cake, 1990, Just Plain Fancy, 1990, Babushka's Doll, 1990, Some Birthday!, 1991, Appelemando's Dreams, 1991, Picnic at Mudsock Meadow, 1992, Mrs. Katz & Tush, 1992, Chicken Sunday, 1992, The Bee Tree, 1993, Babushka Baba Yaga, 1993, Tikvah Means Hope, 1994, Pink & Say, 1994, My Rotten, Redheaded, Older Brother, 1994, Firetalking, 1994, My Ol' Man, 1995, Babushka's Mother Goose, 1995; illustrator: Casey at the Bat, 1990. Office: Putnam Pub Group 200 Madison Ave New York NY 10016-3901*

POLAK, ELIJAH, engineering educator, computer scientist; b. Bialystok, Poland, Aug. 11, 1931; came to U.S. 1957, naturalized, 1959; s. Isaac and Fruma (Friedman) P.; m. Virginia Ann Gray, June 11, 1961; children: Oren, Sharon. B.S.E.E., U. Melbourne, Australia, 1957; M.S.E.E., U. Calif., Berkeley, 1959, Ph.D., 1961. Instrument engr. ICIANZ, Melbourne, Australia, 1956-57; summer student IBM Research Labs., San Jose, Calif., 1959-60; vis. asst. prof. M.I.T., fall 1964; asso. dept elec. engring. and computer scis. U. Calif., Berkeley, 1958-61; asst. prof. elec. engring. and computer scis. U. Calif., 1961-66, asso. prof., 1966-69, prof., 1969-94, prof. Grad. Sch., 1994—. Author: (with L.A. Zadeh) System Theory, 1969, (with E. Wong) Notes for a First Course on Linear Systems, 1970, (with others) Theory of Optimal Control and Mathematical Programming, 1970, Computational Methods in Optimization, 1971. Guggenheim fellow, 1968; U.K. Sci. Research Council sr. fellow, 1972, 76, 79, 82. Fellow IEEE; mem. Soc. Indsl. and Applied Math. (asso. editor Jour. Theory and Applications Optimization 1972—), Soc. Math. Programming. Home: 38 Fairlawn Dr Berkeley CA 94708-2106 Office: U Calif Dept Elec Engring Comp S Berkeley CA 94720

POLAK, JACQUES JACOBUS, economist, foundation administrator; b. Rotterdam, The Netherlands, Apr. 25, 1914; came to U.S. 1940; s. James and Elisabeth F. Polak; m. Josephine Weening, Dec. 21, 1937; children: H. Joost, Willem L. MA in Econs., U. Amsterdam, 1936, PhD in Econs., 1937; PhD in Econs. (hon.); Erasmus U. Rotterdam, 1972. Economist League of Nations, Geneva, Switzerland and Princeton, N.J., 1937-43, Netherlands Embassy, Washington, 1943-44; advisor UN Relief & Rehab. Adminstrn., Washington, 1943-44; from div. chief, asst. dir. to dir. rsch. dept. IMF, Washington, 1947-80, exec. dir., 1981-86; fin. cons. World Bank, Washington, 1987-89, Orgn. Econ. Coop. and Devel., Paris, 1987-89; pres. Per Jacobsson Found., Washington, 1987—; profl. lectr. Johns Hopkins U., Balt., 1949-50, George Washington U., 1950-55. Author: (with J. Tinbergen) The Dynamics of Business Cycles, 1950; author: An International Economic System, 1953, Finanical Policies and Development, 1989, Economic Theory and Financial Policy-The Selected Essays of Jacques J. Polak, 1994; contbr. articles to profl. jours. Fellow Econometric Soc., Royal Netherlands Acad. Sci. (corr.); mem. Cosmos Club (Washington). Home: 3420 Porter St NW Washington DC 20016-3126 Office: care Internat Monetary Fund Washington DC 20431

POLAK, VIVIAN LOUISE, lawyer; b. N.Y.C., Nov. 1, 1952; d. Henri and Greta Etty (Querido) P. BA, Barnard Coll., 1974; JD, Harvard U., 1977. Bar: N.Y. 1978, D.C. 1978, U.S. Dist. Ct. (ea. and so. dists.) N.Y. 1978. Assoc. Donovan, Leisure, Newton and Irvine, N.Y.C., 1977-86; ptnr. LeBoeuf, Lamb, Greene & MacRae, N.Y.C., 1986—. Mem. N.Y. Bar Assn. (sec. antitrust sect. 1991-92, mem. exec. com. 1993—, chmn. internat. trade com. 1985-90). Office: LeBoeuf Lamb Greene and MacRae 125 W 55th St New York NY 10019-4513

POLAK, WERNER L., lawyer; b. Bremen, Germany, May 19, 1936; came to U.S., 1946, naturalized, 1955; s. Ludwig and Hilde (Schultz) P.; m. Evelyn F. Ruhmann, June 21, 1959; children—Douglas H., Deborah L. B.A., Columbia U., 1960, LL.B., 1963. Bar: N.Y. 1963. Assoc., Shearman & Sterling, N.Y.C., 1963-72, ptnr., 1972—. Served with U.S. Army, 1954-56. Mem. Trustee Practicing Law Inst. Office: 153 E 53rd St New York NY 10022-4611

POLAKOFF, ABE, baritone; b. Bucharest, Rumania; s. Sam and Mary P. Ousherenkova; children: David Fred, Mark Evan, Robert Ira; m. Judyth Kanner, Dec. 5, 1992. Civil engring. student, CCNY; profl. tng. program, Am. Theater Wing, 1952-54; student, N.Y. Coll. Music, 1955-57. Dir. Island Opera Players; opera lectr. Arts Couns. (municipalities and schs.); cantor Progressive Shayat Zedek synagogue, Bklyn., 1971-77, Temple Emanuel, Denver, 1984-94. Debuts include Marcello in La Boheme, Milan, Florence, 1960; leading baritone Zurich Opera, 1961-63, numerous appearances with N.Y. Met. Opera, City Opera N.Y., Phila. Lyric Opera, Pitts. Opera, Seattle Opera, Berlin Deutsche Opera, Frankfurt Opera, Cinn. Opera, Hamburg, Munich Staatsoper, Stuttgart Staatsoper, The Netherlands Opera, Cin. Opera, Kansas City Lyric Opera, Canadian Opera Co., others; soloist with Mex. State Symphony Orch., Kalamazoo Symphony Orch., Winston-Salem (N.C.) Symphony, numerous concert and recital appearances. 1st prize winner Am. Theatre Wing Vocal Profl. Scholarship award, 1954, 1st prize winner Am. Opera Auditions, 1960, Silver medal Vercelli (Italy) Internat. singing contest, 1960; Rockefeller Found. grantee, 1961-62; Bayreuth Festival Masterclass scholar. Mem. Cen. Opera Service, Am. Guild Musical Artists (bd. govs.), Actors Equity Assn. Address: 11132 76th Ave Apt 7H Forest Hills NY 11375-6409

POLAKOFF, KEITH IAN, historian, university administrator; b. N.Y.C., Dec. 12, 1941; s. Irwin L. and Edna (Sopkin) P.; m. Carol J. Gershuny, June 21, 1964; children: Amy Ellen, Adam Matthew. BA magna cum laude, Clark U., 1963; MA, Northwestern U., Evanston, Ill., 1966, PhD, 1968. Lectr. Herbert H. Lehman Coll., CUNY, 1967-69; asst. prof. history Calif. State U., Long Beach, 1969-73, assoc. prof. 1973-78, prof., 1978—; assoc. dean instrnl. support Sch. Social and Behavioral Scis., 1980-81, assoc. dean ednl. policy, 1981-84, dean, 1985-86; dean Sch. Fine Arts, 1984-85, asst. v.p. acad. affairs, dean grad. studies, 1986-90, assoc. v.p. acad. affairs, dean grad. studies, 1991—; co-chair Calif. Minority Grad. Edn. Forum, 1990—; mem. coun. Big West Conf. (formerly Pacific Coast Athletic Assn.), 1982-90, Western Collegiate Athletic Assn., 1982-85. Author: The Politics of Inertia, 1973, (with others) Generations of Americans, 1976, Political Parties in American History, 1981; contbg. author: The Presidents: A Reference History, 1984; editor: The History Tchr., 1972-77, prodn. mgr., 1977-80. Mem., clk. bd. trustees Los Alamitos Sch. Dist., 1980-81; mem. Los Alamitos Unified Sch. Dist. Bd. Edn., 1990-94, pres. 1992-93; chmn. adv. com. on facilities, Los Alamitos Sch. Dist., 1989, chair steering com. for measure K for kids, 1990; bd. dirs. Long Beach Opera Assn., 1981-89, pres. 1982-83, treas. 1987-88; bd. dirs. Los Alamitos Jr. Baseball, 1988-90, Los Alamitos Basball, 1990-92. Avocations: travel, photography. Home: 2971 Druid Ln

Los Alamitos CA 90720-4948 Office: Calif State U 1250 N Bellflower Blvd Long Beach CA 90840-0004

POLAKOFF, MURRAY EMANUEL, university dean, economics and finance educator; b. N.Y.C., Dec. 18, 1922; s. Joseph and Elizabeth (Zimmerman) P.; m. Sheila Doreen Brazil, Dec. 23, 1951; children: Michael Anton, Toni. BA summa cum laude, NYU, 1946; MA, Columbia U., 1951, PhD, 1955. Asst. prof. econs. U. Tex., Austin, 1951-57, assoc. prof. econs., 1957-61; prof. econs. and fin. U. Rochester, N.Y., 1961-63; prof., chmn., vice dean Grad. Sch. Bus. Adminstrn. NYU, 1968-71; leading prof., dean Sch. Mgmt. SUNY, Binghamton, 1971-77; prof. econs. and fin., provost U. Md., College Park, 1977-86, dean, 1986-91, dir. internat. devel. and conflict mgmt., 1991-92, prof. emeritus, 1993—; cons. U.S. House Com. on Banking and Currency, Washington, 1964; lectr. and cons. Brazilian Central Banking, Dept. State, São Paulo, 1966-68; chmn. bd. advisors of joint ventures Cen. Inst. Mathematical and Econ. Modelling of Soviet Acad. Scis., USSR and U. Md., College Park, 1989. Editor, contbg. author: Financial Institutions and Markets, 2d edit., 1981; contbr. articles to profl. jours. Scholar Sch. Law Columbia U., N.Y.C., 1946; Fund for Advancement Edn. faculty grantee, 1955-56; Found. Econ. Edn. fellow, summer 1956; Social Sci. Research Council fellow, 1957; Ford Found. faculty research grantee, 1961-62. Mem. Fin. Mgmt. Assn., Phi Beta Kappa. Jewish. Avocations: squash, theater. Office: Ctr Intl Dev & Conflict Mgmt Univ MD Tydings Hall College Park MD 20742

POLAN, ANNETTE LEWIS, artist; b. Huntington, W.Va., Dec. 8, 1944; d. Lake and Dorothy (Lewis) P.; m. Arthur Lowell Fox Jr., Aug. 31, 1969 (div. 1994); children: Courtney Van Winkle Fox, Arthur Lowell Fox III. 1st degree, Inst. des Profs. de Francaise, Paris, 1965; BA, Hollins Coll., 1967; postgrad., Corcoran Sch. Art, 1968-69. Vis. artist Art Therapy Italia, Vignale, Italy, 1986; dir. summer program La Napoule Art Found., Chateau de la Napoule, France, 1987, 88, 90; guest lectr. China, Japan, 1989; prof. Corcoran Sch. Art, Washington, 1974—; chmn. painting dept. Corcoran Coll. Art, Washington, 1991—; dir. Washington Project for the Arts. Illustrator: Say What I Am, 1989, Relearning the Dark, 1991; cover designer Doers of the Word, 1995. Bd. dirs. Washington Project for the Arts, 1994—. Mem. Corcoran Faculty Assn. (pres. 1988-89). Avocations: equitation, skiing. Office: Corcoran Sch Art 1680 Wisconsin Ave NW Washington DC 20007

POLAN, MARY LAKE, obstetrics and gynecology educator; b. July 17, 1943. Student, Smith Coll., Paris, 1963-64; BA cum laude, Conn. Coll., 1965; PhD in Biophysics and Biochemistry, Yale U., 1970, MD, 1975. Diplomate Am. Bd. Ob-Gyn., Am. Bd. Reproductive Endocrinology, Nat. Bd. Med. Examiners. Postdoctoral fellow dept. biology, NIH postdoctoral fellow Yale U., New Haven, 1970-72, resident dept. ob-gyn. So. Medicine, 1975-78, fellow in oncology, then fellow in endocrinology-infertility, 1978-80, asst. instr., then lectr. molecular biophysics-biochemistry, 1970-72, instr., then asst. prof. ob-gyn., 1978-79, 80-85, assoc. prof., 1985-90; clin. clk. in ob-gyn. and pediat. Radcliffe Infirmary, Oxford (Eng.) U. Med. Sch., 1974; instr. Pahlavi U., Shiraz, Iran, 1978; Katharine Dexter McCormick and Stanley McCormick Meml. prof. Stanford (Calif.) Sch. Medicine, 1990—, chmn. dept. gynecology and obstetrics, 1990—; vis. prof. Hunan Med. Coll., Changsha, China, 1986; mem. med. bd. Yale-China Assn.. 1987-90; liaison com. on ethics in modern med. Conn. Med., New London, 1988-90; mem. med. adv. bd. Ova-Med Corp., Palo Alto, Calif., 1992—, Vivus, Menlo Park, Calif., 1993—; bd. dirs. Metra Biosys., Palo Alto, Quidel, San Diego, LipoMatrix, Palo Alto, Stanford Health Svcs., 1994—; mem. reproductive endocrinology study sect. NIH, 1989-90, co-chmn. task force on opportunities for rsch. on woman's health, 1991. Author: Second Seed, 1997; guest editor: Seminars in Reproductive Endocrinology, 1984, Infertility and Reproductive Medicine Clinics of North America: GnRH Analogues, Vol. 4, 1993; editor; (with A.H. DeCherney) Surgery in Reproductive Endocrinology, 1987, (with DeCherney, S. Boyers and R. Lee) Decision Making in Infertility; ad hoc reviewer Jour. Clin. Endocrinology and Metabolism, Fertility and Sterility, Ob-Gyn., also others; contbr. numerous articles to med. jours., chpts. to books. Fellow NRSA, 1981-82; grantee NIRA, 1082-85, HD, 1985-90, NRSA, 1987-88, Johnson & Johnson, 1993-96; scholar Assn. Acad. Health Ctrs., 1993—. Fellow ACOG (PROLOG task force for reproductive endocrinology and infertility 1988-89, rep. to CREOG coun. 1994-97); mem. Am. Fertility Soc., Soc. for Gynecologic Investigation, Soc. for Reproductive Endocrinologists, Am. Gynecologic and Obstetric Soc., Inst. Medicine (com. on rsch. capabilities of acad. depts. ob-gyn. 1990-91, bd. on health scis. policy 1992—), San Francisco Gynecologic Soc., Bay Area Reproductive Endocrine Soc., Phi Beta Kappa. Home: 4251 Manuela Ct Palo Alto CA 94306 Office: Stanford U Sch Medicine 300 Pasteur Dr Rm HH333 Stanford CA 94305-5317

POLAN, MORRIS, librarian; b. St. Louis, Jan. 24, 1924; s. Jacob and Fannie (Poe) P.; m. Cecelia Hassan, Nov. 16, 1947 (div. 1974); children: Miriam, Ruth. Student, So. Ill. U., 1941-42; B.A., UCLA, 1949; postgrad., 1949-50; M.S. in L.S, U. So. Calif., 1951. Libr. Mcpl. Reference Libr., L.A., 1951-52; serials and reference libr. Hancock Libr. of Biology and Oceanography, U. So. Calif., L.A., 1952-55; periodicals libr. Calif. State U., LA, 1955, supervising reference libr., 1956-57, chief reader svcs., 1958-64, acting coll. libr., 1965, univ. libr., 1966-89, univ. libr. emeritus, 1989—; libr. and media resources com., 1990—; publs. coord. Edmund G. "Pat" Brown Inst. Pub. Affairs, 1992-94, pub. rels. com., 1995—; univ. adminstr. Ctr. Pub. Resources Calif. State U., 1980-86, mem. chancellor's library adv. com., 1984; lectr. library sci. U. So. Calif., 1967; mem. chancellor's library personnel study com. Calif. State Univs. and Colls., 1969, mem. adv. com. library devel., 1974; chmn. Council Calif. State Univ. and Colls. Library Dirs., 1967-68, 70, 74; mem. adv. bd. U. So. Calif. Library Sch., 1966-69, Productivity Council of Southwest, 1981-84; mem. library edn. adv. com. U. Calif. System, 1966-70; mem. U. Calif.-Calif. State Univ. and Colls. Task Force on Library Co-op., 1974-76; co-founder Los Angeles Coop. Library Consortium, 1983. Editor: California Librarian, 1971-74. Mem. Com. to Advise Gov. on State Librarian, 1972; mem. planning com. Calif. Library Authority for Systems and Services, 1973-75, adv. council, 1977-80, long range planning group, 1979-81, pres. congress of mems., 1979; mem. adv. bd. Arnold Schoenberg Ins., U. So. Calif., 1974-86, 89-92, Edmund G. (Pat) Brown Inst. Pub. Affairs, 1987-89; exec. com. Roy Harris Archive, 1978-86; mem. Mayor's Blue Ribbon Com. on L.A. Pub. Libr., 1976-77; mem. bd. scholars El Pueblo State Hist. Park, 1978-91; chmn. Calif. del. White House Conf. on Libraries and Info. Services, 1979; bd. dirs. ETHIKON: Inst. Study Ethical Diversity, 1981-88; Calif. state coord. Ctr. for the Book in Library of Congress, 1986-89; mem. adv. com. Ctr. for Study of Media and Values, 1988-90; treas. Frank Casado Meml. Scholarship Fund, 1992-95. With USAF, 1943-46. Mem. ALA, Calif. Library Assn. (pres. 1975, chmn. govt. relations com. 1977). Office: Calif State U 5151 State University Dr Los Angeles CA 90032-4221

POLAN, NANCY MOORE, artist; b. Newark, Ohio; d. William Tracy and Francis (Flesher) Moore; m. Lincoln Milton Polan, Mar. 28, 1934; children: Charles Edwin, William Joseph Marion. AB, Marshall U., 1936. One-man shows include Charleston Art Gallery, 1961, 67, 73, Greenbrier, 1963, Huntington Mus. Art, 1963, 66, 71, N.Y. World's Fair, 1965, W.Va. U., 1966, Carroll Reese Mus., 1967; exhibited in group shows Am. Watercolor Soc., Allied Artists of Am., Nat. Arts Club, 1968-74, 76-77, 86, 87, 91, 92, 93-94, Pa. Acad. Fine Arts, Opening of Creative Arts Center W.Va. U., 1969, Internat. Platform Assn. Art Exhbit, 1968-69, 72-74, 74, 79, 85-86, 88-90, (Gold medal Best of Show 1991, 2d award painting 1994), Allied Artists W.Va., 1968-69, 86, Joan Miro Graphic Traveling Exhbn., Barcelona, Spain, 1970-71, XXI Exhibit Contemporary Art, La Scala, Florence, Italy, 1971, Rassegna Internazionale d'Arte Grafica, Siena, Italy, 1973, 79, 82, Opening of Parkersburg (W.Va.) Art Center, 1975, Art Club Washington, 1992, Pen & Brush, 1992-93, others. Hon. v.p. Centro Studie Scambi Internazionale, Rome, Italy, 1977. Recipient Acad. of Italy with Gold medal, 1979, 86, Norton Meml. award 3d Nat. Jury Show Am. Art, Chautauqua, N.Y., 1960; Purchase prize, Jurors award, Watercolor award Huntington Galleries, 1960, 61; Nat. Arts Club for watercolor, 1969; Gold medal Masters of Modern Art exhbn., La Scala Gallery, Florence, 1975, gold medal Accademia Italia, 1984, 1986, diplomia Internat. Com. for World Culture and Arts, 1987, many others. Mem. AAUW, DAR, Nat. Mus. Women Artists (charter), Allied Artists W.va., internat. Platform Assn. (3rd award-painting in ann. art exhbn. 1977, Gold medal for Best of Show 1991, 2d award for painting 1995), Allied Artists Am. (assoc.), Huntington Mus. Fine Arts (life), Tri-

State Arts Assn. (Equal Merit award 1978), Sunrise Found., Composers, Authors, Artists Am., Inc., Pen and Brush (Watercolor exhbn. 1993, Grumbacher golden palette mem., Grumbacher award 1978), Am. Watercolor Soc. (assoc.), W.Va. Watercolor Soc. (charter mem.), Nat. Arts Club, Leonardo da Vinci Acad. (Rome), Accademia Italia, Vero Beach Arts Club, Riomer Bay Yacht Club, Guyan Golf and Country Club, Huntington Cotillion (charter mem.) Sigma Kappa. Episcopalian. Address: 2 Prospect Dr Huntington WV 25701-4860 also: 2106 Club Dr Vero Beach FL 32963-2154

POLAND, ROBERT PAUL, business educator, consultant; b. Bowling Green, Ohio, July 11, 1925; s. Donovan and Florence (Buck) P. BS, Bowling Green State U., 1949; MA, Columbia U., 1956; PhD, Mich. State U., 1962. Tchr. Mt. Edgecumbe Vocat. Sch., Alaska, 1949-53, Perrysburg High Sch., Ohio, 1954-58; prof. bus. edn. Mich. State U., East Lansing, 1960-92; cons. in field; leader seminars, presentations, workshops and confs. Contbr. numerous articles to profl. jours.; author texts on typewriting, including: (with others) Gregg Coll. Typing, 1979, 5th edit., 1984, 6th edit., 1989, Gregg College Keyboarding & Document Processing for Microcomputers, 7th edit., 1994, Gregg College Keyboarding & Document Processing for Electronic Typewriters, 7th edit., 1994, A Teaching-Learning System for Business Education, 1986; (audiovisual programs) Gregg Typing IPM, 1975, 2d edit., 1985. Served with USN, 1943-46; PTO. Recipient numerous grants in field; recipient John Robert Gregg award, 1986. Mem. Nat. Bus. Edn. Assn. (pres. 1978-79, exec. bd. dirs. 1969-70, 75-76, 77-80, Outstanding Teaching award 1981, Disting. Svc. award 1980), North-Central Bus. Edn. Assn. (pres. 1975, Disting. Svc. award 1972), Internat. Soc. Bus. Edn. (v.p. 1970-74, pres. U.S. chpt. 1967-69, Recognition of Significant Contbns. to internat. bus. edn. U.S. chpt. 1969), Mich. Bus. Edn. Assn. (pres. 1965-66, Recognition award 1970, Disting. Svc. award 1980), Delta Pi Epsilon , Phi Delta Kappa, Pi Omega Pi. Home: 901 N Harrison Rd East Lansing MI 48823-3020

POLAND, SUSAN LEE, lawyer; b. Washington, June 8, 1955; d. Sherman Swett and Nancy Ann (Leland) Poland. B.A., Sarah Lawrence Coll., 1977; B.A. in Law, Cambridge U. (Eng.) 1979; LL.M., N.Y.U., 1981. Bar: N.Y. 1982. Assoc., Weil, Gotshal & Manges, N.Y.C., 1981-86; atty. Nynex Credit Co., N.Y., 1987—. Mem. ABA. Democrat. Episcopalian. Office: GE Plastics 1 Plastics Ave Pittsfield MA 01201

POLANSKI, ROMAN, film director, writer, actor; b. Paris, Aug. 18, 1933; s. Ryszard and Bule (Katz-Przedborska) P.; m. Barbara Lass (div.); m. Sharon Tate (dec.); m. Emmanuelle Seigner. Student, Art Sch., Cracow, State Film Coll., Lodz. Appeared in children's radio show The Merry Gang, stage prodn. Son of the Regiment; dir. films Two Men and a Wardrobe, 1958, When Angels Fall, 1958, Le Gros et le Maigre, 1960, Knife in the Water, 1962 (Venice Film Festival award), The Mammals, 1963 (Tours Film Festival award), Repulsion, 1965 (Berlin Film Festival award), Cul-de-Sac, 1966 (Berlin Film Festival award), The Vampire Killers, 1967, Rosemary's Baby, 1968, Macbeth, 1971, What?, 1972, Chinatown, 1974 (Best dir. award, Soc. Film and TV Arts, Prix Raoul-Levy, 1975), The Tenant, 1976, Tess, 1980, Pirates, 1986, Frantic (also co-writer), 1988, Bitter Moon, 1994, Death and the Maiden, 1994, A Pure Formality, 1995 (actor only); actor: on stage The Metamorphosis, 1988; in films A Generation, The End of the Night, See You Tomorrow, The Innocent Sorcerers, Two Men and a Wardrobe, The Vampire Killers, What?, The Magic Christian and Andy Warhol's Dracula, Back in the U.S.S.R., A Pure Forality, Chinatown, The Tennant; star, dir. play Amadeus, Warsaw, 1981, Paris, 1982; dir. operas Lulu (Spoleto Festival), 1974, Rigoletto, 1976; author (autobiography): Roman, 1984. Office: Agents Associés, 5 rue de Ponthieu, 75008 Paris France also: ICM 8942 Wilshire Blvd Beverly Hills CA 90211*

POLANSKY, LARRY PAUL, court administrator, consultant; b. Blkyn., July 24, 1932; s. Harry and Ida (Gershengoren) P.; m. Eunice Kathryn Neun; children: Steven, Harriet, Bruce. BS in Acctg., Temple U., 1958, JD, 1973. Bar: Pa. 1973, U.S. Dist. Ct. (ea. dist.) Pa. 1973, U.S. Ct. Appeals (3d cir.) 1973, D.C. 1978, U.S. Supreme Ct. 1980. Acct., systems analyst City of Phila., 1956-63; data processing mgr. Jefferson Med. Coll. and Hosp., Phila., 1963-65; systems engr. IBM Corp., Phila., 1965-67; dep. ct. adminstr. Common Pleas Cts. of Phila., 1967-76; dep. state ct. adminstr. Pa. Supreme Ct., Phila., 1976-78; exec. officer D.C. Cts., Washington, 1979-90; presidential appointment to bd. dirs. State Justice Inst., 1985-89; bd. dirs. Search Group Inc.; mem. steering com. D.C. Bar, 1982-85; cons. in field. Author ct. info. systems monograph, 1978; contbr. articles to profl. jour. Served as cpl. U.S. Army, 1951-53, Korea. Fellow Inst. for Ct. Mgmt., Denver, 1984; recipient Reardon award Nat. Ctr. for State Cts., 1982, Disting. Svc. award Nat. Ctr. for State Cts., 1986, Justice Tom C. Clark award Nat. Conf. of Metro. Cts., 1991. Mem. ABA (jud. adminstrn. div., chmn. ct. adminstrn. com. 1984, exec. com. lawyers com. 1985—, chmn. 1991-92), Conf. State Ct. Adminstrs. (bd. dirs. 1980-86, pres. 1984-85). Republican. Jewish. Avocations: tennis, skiing, computers. Home and Office: PO Box 752 Lake Harmony PA 18624-0752

POLANYI, JOHN CHARLES, chemist, educator; b. Jan. 23, 1929; m. Anne Ferrar Davidson, 1958; 2 children. BSc, Manchester (Eng.) U., 1949, MSc, 1950, PhD, 1952, DSc, 1964; DSc (hon.), U. Waterloo, 1970, Meml. U., 1976, McMaster U., 1977, Carleton U., 1981, Harvard U., 1982, Rensselaer U., Brock U., 1984, Lethbridge U., Sherbrooke U., Laval U., Victoria U., Ottawa U., 1987, Manchester U. and York U., Eng., 1988. U. Montreal, Acadia U., 1989, Weizmann Inst., Israel, 1989, U. Bari, Italy, 1990, U. B.C., 1990, Concordia U., 1990, McGill U., 1990, Queen's U., 1992, Free U. Berlin, 1993, Free Univ. Berlin, 1993; LLD (hon.), Trent U., 1977, Dalhousie U., 1983, St. Francis-Xavier U., 1984, Calgary U., 1994. Bar: Queen's Privy Coun. Can. Mem. faculty dept. chemistry U. Toronto, Ont., Can., 1956—; prof. U. Toronto, 1962—; William D. Harkins lectr. U. Chgo., 1970; Reilly lectr. U. Notre Dame, 1970; Purves lectr. McGill U., 1971; F.J. Toole lectr. U. N.B., 1974; Philips lectr. Haverford Coll., 1974; Kistiakowsky lectr. Harvard U., 1975; Camille and Henry Dreyfus lectr. U. Kans., 1975; J.W.T. Spinks lectr. U. Sask., Can., 1976; Laird lectr. U. Western Ont., 1976; CIL Disting. lectr. Simon Fraser U., 1977; Gucker lectr. Ind. U., 1977; Jacob Bronowski meml. lectr. U. Toronto, 1978; Hutchinson lectr. U. Rochester, N.Y., 1979; Priestley lectr. Pa. State U., 1980; Barré lectr. U. Montreal, 1982; Sherman Fairchild disting. scholar Calif. Inst. Tech., 1982; Chute lectr. Dalhousie U., 1983; Redman lectr. McMaster U., 1983; Wiegand lectr. U. Toronto, 1984; Edward U. Condon lectr. U. Colo., 1984; John A. Allan lectr. U. Alta., 1984; John E. Willard lectr. U. Wis., 1984, Owen Holmes lectr. U. Lethbridge, 1985; Walker-Ames prof. U. Wash., 1986, John W. Cowper disting. vis. lectr. U. Buffalo, SUNY, 1986; vis. prof. chemistry Tex. A&M U., 1986; Disting. vis. speaker U. Calgary, 1987; Morino lectr. U. Japan, 1987; J.T. Wilson lectr. Ontario Sci. Ctr., 1987; Welsh lectr. U. Toronto, 1987; Spiers Meml. lectr. Faraday div. Royal Soc. Chemistry, 1987; Polanyi lectr. Internat. Union Pure & Applied Chemistry, 1988; W.B. Lewis lectr. Atomic Energy of Can. Ltd., 1988; Consol. Bathurst vis. lectr. Concordia U., 1988; Priestman lectr. U. N.B., 1988; Killam lectr. U. Windsor, 1988; Herzberg lectr. Carleton U., 1988; Falconbridge lectr. Lauretian U., 1988; DuPont lectr. Ind. U., 1989, C.R. Mueller lectr. Purdue U., 1989; Luther lectr. U. Regina, 1989; Franklin lectr. Rice U., 1990; Laurier lectr. Wilfred Laurier U., 1990; Pratt lectr. U. Va., 1990; Goodrich lectr. Case Western Res. U., 1990; Phillips lectr. U. Pitts., 1991; Albert Noyes lectr. U. Tex., 1992; John and Lois Dove Meml. lectr. U. Toronto, 1992, Fritz London lectr. Duke U., 1993; Castle lectr. U. South Fla., 1993; Linus Pauling lectr. Calif. Inst. Tech., 1994; mem. sci. adv. bd. Max Plank Inst. for Quantum Optics, Fed. Republic Germany, 1982-92; mem. nat. adv. bd. on Sci. and Tech., 1987-89; hon. cons. Inst. Molecular Sci., Okazaki, Japan, 1989-94; bd. dirs. Steacie Inst. Molecular Scis., Ottawa, Can., 1991—; founding mem. Can. Com. on Sci. and Scholars; Beam Disting. vis. prof. U. Iowa, 1992, Charles M. & Martha Hitchcock prof. U. Calif., Berkeley, 1994; Young Meml. visitor Royal Mil. Coll., 1994. Co-editor: (with F.G. Griffiths) The Dangers of Nuclear War, 1979; contbr. articles to jours., mags., newspapers; producer: film Concepts in Reaction Dynamics, 1970. Mem. Queen's Privy Coun. for Can., 1992; bd. dirs. Can. Ctr. for Arms Control and Environment; founding mem. Can. Pugwash Com., 1960. Decorated officer Order of Can., companion Order of Can., knight grand cross Order St. John of Jerusalem; Sloan Found. fellow, 1959-63, Guggenheim fellow, 1979-80; recipient Marlow medal Faraday Soc., 1962, Centenary medal Chem. Soc. Gt. Brit., 1965, N. Bartlett Steacie prize, 1965, Noranda award Chem. Inst. Can., 1967, award Brit. Chem. Soc., 1971, Mack award and lectureship Ohio State U., 1969, medal Chem. Inst. Can., 1976, Remsen

award and lectureship Am. Chem. Soc., 1978, Nobel Prize in chemistry, 1986, Isaac Walton Killam Meml. prize, 1988, John C. Polanyi award Can. Soc. Chemistry, 1992; co-recipient Wolf Prize in Chemistry, 1982. Fellow Royal Soc. Can. (founding mem., pres., com. on scholarly freedom, Marshall Tory medal 1977), Royal Soc. London (Royal medal 1989, Bakerian Lectr. and award 1994), Royal Soc. Edinburgh, Royal Soc. Chemistry (hon., Michael Polanyi medal 1989), Chem. Inst. Can. (hon.); mem. NAS (fgn.), Am. Acad. Arts and Sci. (hon. fgn., mem. com. on internat. security issues), Pontifical Acad. Scis., Rome. Office: U Toronto Dept Chemistry, 80 St George St, Toronto, ON Canada M5S 1A1*

POLASEK, EDWARD JOHN, electrical engineer, consultant; b. Cudahy, Wis., Oct. 12, 1927; s. John Vincent and Mary Ann (Totka) P.; m. Alice S. Nee (Harnecki), Aug. 18, 1948. BSEE, Marquette U., 1948. Registered profl. engr., Wis., Fla. Cons. engr. Eau Claire, Wis., Gainesville, Fla., 1955-60, various countries, Korea, Vietnam, Nicaragua, 1960-72; v.p., dir. Finley Engring. Co., Eau Claire, 1972-78; pres. Chippewa Devel. Co., Eau Claire, 1978-82; planning engr. Harza Engring. Co. in Cairo, Egypt and Dominican Rep., 1982-86; cons. engr. Gainesville, 1986—; cons. Lake Altoona Rehab. Dist., Eau Claire, 1974. Author: Planning Methods, 1982, Feasibility Study, 1984; editor: Field Engineer's Handbook, 1982. Chmn. Eau Claire chpt. Am. Cancer Soc.; master adventer U. Fla. Ext. Svc., Gainesville, 1990. With USN, 1944-46, PTO. Mem. Nat. Soc. Profl. Engrs. (pres. 1956), IEEE, Audobon Soc., Tau Beta Pi, Eta Kappa Nu. Avocations: mycology, fishing, arts.

POLASKI, ANNE SPENCER, lawyer; b. Pittsfield, Mass., Nov. 13, 1952; d. John Harold and Marjorie Ruth (Hackett) Spencer; m. James Joseph Polaski, Sept. 14, 1985. BA in Psychology, Allegheny Coll., 1974; MSW, U. Pa., 1976; JD, George Washington U., 1979. Bar: D.C. 1979, U.S. Dist. Ct. (D.C. dist.) 1980, U.S. Ct. Appeals (D.C. cir.) 1980, Ill. 1982, U.S. Dist. Ct. (no. dist.) Ill. 1982, U.S. Ct. Appeals (7th cir.) 1982. Law clk. to assoc. judge D.C. Ct., Washington, 1979-80; staff atty. Commodity Futures Trading Commn. Chgo., 1980-84, sr. trial atty., 1984, dep. regional counsel, 1984-88; assoc. Gottlieb and Schwartz, Chgo., 1988-91; staff atty. Chgo. Bd. of Trade, 1991-92, sr. atty., 1992-94, asst. gen. counsel, 1994—. Mem. ABA, Chgo. Bar Assn. Office: Chgo Bd of Trade 141 W Jackson Blvd Chicago IL 60604-2904

POLAYES, IRVING MARVIN, plastic surgeon; b. New Haven, Sept. 2, 1927; s. Abraham Noah and Ida (Stern) P.; m. Marcia Kresel, July 1, 1951 (dec. Apr. 1985); children: Roy Peter, Amy Lynn. BA, Duke U., 1948; DDS, Columbia U., 1953; MD, Albany Med. Coll., 1959. Diplomate Am. Bd. Plastic Surgery. Intern Albany (N.Y.) Med. Ctr., 1959-60, fellow plastic surgery, 1963-65; pvt. practice medicine specializing in plastic and reconstructive surgery Albany (N.Y.) Med. Ctr., New Haven, 1965—; attending plastic surgeon Yale New Haven Med. Ctr., 1965—, assoc. chief plastic surgery, 1969—; attending plastic surgeon St. Raphael's Hosp., New Haven; cons. plastic surgeon West Haven (Conn.) VA Hosp., Gaylord Hosp., Wallingford; clin. prof. plastic and reconstructive surgery Yale Med. Sch., 1977-86. Co-author: Diseases of the Salivary Glands, 1976. Concertmaster, violinist New Haven Civic Symphony Orch., 1970-84—; v.p. New Haven Symphony Orch., 1977—. Lt. comdr. USNR, 1954-56. Fellow ACS; mem. N.E. Soc. Plastic Surgeons (founding mem.), Am. Assn. Plastic Surgeons, Am. Soc. Plastic and Reconstructive Surgeons, Am. Trauma Soc., N.Y. Regional Soc. Plastic and Reconstructive Surgeons (bd. dirs.), New Eng. Soc. Plastic and Reconstructive Surgeons (pres. 1979-80), Am. Soc. Maxillofacial Surgeons (pres. 1979-80, lectr. syllabus-maxillofacial basic course), Soc. Head and Neck Surgeons, Am. Soc. Aesthetic Plastic Surgery, Conn. Med. Soc., New Haven County Med. Soc., Alpha Omega Alpha. Home: 49 N Racebrook Rd Woodbridge CT 06525-1407 Office: 60 Temple St New Haven CT 06510-2716

POLEBAUM, ELLIOT EDWARD, lawyer; b. Lowell, Mass., Sept. 8, 1950; s. Eugene Harvey and Phyllis Diane (Sherman) P.; m. Gilda Brancato, June 24, 1979; children: Danielle, David. BA, Middlebury Coll., 1972; MPA, Harvard U., 1975; JD, NYU, 1977. Bar: Mass. 1978, N.Y. 1978, D.C. 1981. Law clk. to Judge James L. Oakes, U.S. Ct. Ct., Brattleboro, Vt., 1977-78; assoc. Goodwin, Procter & Hoar, Boston, 1979-80; law clk. to Justice William J. Brennan, Jr., U.S. Supreme Ct., Washington, 1980-81; assoc. Cleary Gottlieb Steen & Hamilton, Washington, 1981-82, 85-86, Brussels, 1982-85; assoc. Fried, Frank, Harris, Shriver, Washington, 1986-89; ptnr. Fried, Frank, Harris, Shriver & Jacobson, Washington, 1989—; arbitrator Am. Arbitration Assn.; speaker on internat. litigation and arbitration issues to profl. programs throughout U.S. and fgn. countries. Contbr. articles to legal jours. Mem. ABA, Internat. Bar Assn. Office: Fried Frank Harris Shriver 1001 Pennsylvania Ave NW Washington DC 20004-2505

POLEDOURIS, BASIL K., composer; b. Kansas City, Mo., Aug. 21, 1945; s. Konstantine John and Helen Poledouris; m. Barbara Renée Godfrey, Aug. 15, 1969; children: Zoë Renée, Alexis Elene. BA in Music and Cinema, U. So. Calif., 1967, postgrad., 1967-69. Intern Am. Film Inst., L.A., 1969; freelance composer Hollywood, Calif., 1970—; pres. Basil Poledouris, Inc., Encino, Calif., 1987—; bd. dirs. Blowtorch Flats, Venice, Calif.; mem. adv. bd. Soc. for Preservation Film Music, L.A., 1985—. Composer music for films 90028, 1971, Extreme Close-Up, 1973, Tintorerra, 1977, Bid Wednesday, 1979, Defiance, 1979, The Blue Lagoon, 1988, The House of God, 1988, Conan the Barbarian, 1981, Summer Lovers, 1982, Making the Grade, 1984, Conan the Destroyer, 1984, Red Dawn, 1984, Protocol, 1984, Flesh and Blood, 1985, Cherry 2000, 1986, Iron Eagle, 1986, Robocop, 1987 (BMI award 1988), No Man's Land, 1987, Split Decisions, 1988, Spellbinder, 1988, Farewell to the King, 1989, Wired, 1989, Hunt for Red October, 1990 (BMI award 1991), Quigley Down Under, 1990, Flight of the Intruder, 1991, White Fang, 1992, Return to the Blue Lagoon, 1991, Harley Davidson and the Marlboro Man, 1991, Robocop III, 1992, Free Willy, 1992 (BMI award 1994, gold record 1994), Hot Shots! Part Deux, 1993, Serial Mom, 1993, On Deadly Ground, 1994, Lassie, 1994, Jungle Book, 1994, Free Willy II, 1995, Under Seige II, 1995; composer music for TV films Congratulations It's A Boy, 1973, A Whale for the Killing, 1981, Fire on the Mountain, 1981, Amazons, 1984, Single Women, Single Bars, 1984, Amerika, 1987, Intrigue, 1988, Lonesome Dove, 1989 (Emmy award 1988, BMI award 1989), Nasty Boys, 1989, Lone Justice, 1990, Return to Lonesome Dove, 1993, TV pilots Alfred Hitchcock Presents, 1985, Misfits of Science, 1986, Island Sons, 1987, Murphy's Law, L.A. Takedown, 1989, The Life and Times of Ned Blessing, 1991. Recipient nomination Calif. Legislature, 1990, Orange County Bd. Suprs., 1990, Key to City, Garden Grove City Coun., 1990, Disting. Artist award Calif. State U., Long Beach, 1992. Mem. NARAS, BMI, Am. Fedn. Musicians, Acad. Motion Picture Arts and Scis., Soc. Lyricists and Composers. Avocations: sailing, surfing.

POLENBERG, RICHARD, history educator; b. N.Y.C., July 21, 1937; married, 1988; 1 child; 3 children from previous marriage. BA, Blkyn. Coll., 1958; MA, Columbia U., 1959, PhD in history, 1966. Lectr. history Queens Coll., 1960-61; lectr. history Blkyn. Coll., 1961-64, from instr. to asst. prof., 1964-66; from asst. prof. to prof. Cornell U., Ithaca, N.Y., 1966-86, Goldwin Smith prof. Am. history, 1986—. Author: Reorganizing Roosevelt's Government, 1936-39, 1966, , War and Society: The United States, 1941-45, 1972, One Nation Divisible: Class, Race and Ethnicity in the United States since 1938, 1980, Fighting Faiths: The Abrams Case, The Supreme Court and Free Speech, 1987; co-author: The American Century, 1975; editor: America at War: The Home Front, 1941-45, 1968, Radicalism and Reform in the New Deal, 1972. Recipient Clark Disting. Teaching award Cornell U., 1979, Silver Gavel award ABA, 1988; grantee Soc. Sci. Rsch. Coun., Am. Coun. Learned Socs., 1970-71; Fulbright vis. prof. Hebrew U., Jerusalem, 1988-89. Office: Cornell U Dept Am History McGraw Hall Ithaca NY 14853-0001

POLENSKE, KAREN ROSEL, economics educator; b. Lewiston, Idaho, Mar. 20, 1937; d. Albert T. and Helen M. Polenske. BA in Home Econs. Oreg. State U., 1959; MA in Pub. Adminstrn. and Econs., Syracuse U., 1961; PhD in Econs., Harvard U., 1966. Instr., lectr. Harvard U., Cambridge, Mass., 1966-70, rsch. assoc. econ. rsch. project, 1966-72; sr. visitor faculty of econs. King's Coll., Cambridge U., Cambridge, Eng., 1970-71; assoc. prof. dept. urban studies and planning MIT, Cambridge, Mass., 1972-81, prof. dept. urban studies and planning 1981—; sr. econs. cons. World Bank (in China), Washington, 1988-90, CMT (in Kuwait), Cambridge, 1987-88,

Devel. Alternatives Inc. (in Pakistan), Washington, 1987-88, Asian Devel. Bank (in China), Manila, 1988, 92, Boston Inst. for Developing Econs., Washington, 1990-91, UN Devel. Programme (in India), 1993; del. System of Nat. Accounts Revisions, UN, Vienna, Austria, 1988; vis. scholar exch. program NAS, Beijing, 1986; vis. prof. U. Queensland, Brisbane, Australia, 1983, U. Montpellier, France, 1985, Chinese Acad. Scis., 1988, 90-92, 94; dir. Spl. Program in Urban and Regional Studies (SPURS), 1991—. Co-author: (with mem. of rsch. staff) State Estimates of the Gross National Product, 1947, 58, 63, State Estimates of Technology, 1963; author: The U.S. Multiregional Input-Output Accounts and Model, 1980; editor: Multiregional Input-Output Analysis, 1972, 73; co-editor: (with Jiri V. Skolka) Advances in Input-Output Analysis, 1976, (with Ronald E. Miller, Adam Z. Rose), Frontiers of Input-Output Analysis, 1989, (with Chen Xi Kang) Chinese Economic Planning and Input-Output Analysis, 1991. Mem. Cambridge (Mass.) Com. on the Status of Women, 1978-80. Netherlands Inst. for Advanced Study fellow, 1980. Mem. Am. Econ. Assn., Regional Sci. Assn. (councillor at large 1990-93), Internat. Assn. for Rsch. in Income and Wealth, Internat. Input-Output Assn. (v.p. 1992—). Avocations: birding, photography. Office: MIT Rm 9-535 77 Massachusetts Ave Cambridge MA 02139-4307

POLENZ, JOANNA MAGDA, psychiatrist; b. Cracow, Poland, Oct. 20, 1936; came to U.S., 1961; d. Mieczyslaw and Nusia (Goldberger) Uberall; m. Daryl Louis Polenz, July 8, 1962 (div. 1991); children: Teresa Ann, Daryl Philip, Elizabeth Sophia. MD, U. Sydney, Australia, 1960; MPH, Columbia U., 1992. Diplomate Am. Bd. Psychiatry and Neurology. Intern Blkyn. Hosp., 1961-62; resident Mt. Sinai Med. Ctr., N.Y.C., 1962-65; edln. fellow Mt. Sinai Med. Ctr., 1965-66, rsch. assoc., 1966-67; med. dir. Tappan Zee clin. Phelps Meml. Hosp., Tarrytown, N.Y., 1968-71, dir. dept. psychiatry, 1972-77; sr. attending psychiatrist Meml. Hosp. Ctr., 1972-93; pvt. practice Briarcliff Manor, N.Y., 1971-91; physician Joint Commn. Accreditation of Healthcare Orgns., Oakbrook Terrace, Ill., 1993—; lectr. in field. Author: In Defense of marriage, 1981; (with other) Test Your Marriage IQ, 1984, Test Your Success IQ, 1985; contbr. articles to profl. jours.; numerous TV appearances including Phil Donahue, 1988, Oprah Winfrey 1984. Grant Found. grantee, 1970. Fellow Am. psychiatric Assn., Royal Soc. for Health; mem. AMA, N.Y. Acad. Scis., Pan Am. Med. Assn., Westchester Psychiatric Assn. (sec. 1982-85, chair person fellowship com. 1989). Avocations: travel, international affairs.

POLESKIE, STEPHEN FRANCIS, artist, educator; b. Pringle, Pa., June 3, 1938; s. Stephen Francis and Antoinette Elizabeth (Chludzinski) P.; m. Jeanne Mackin, 1979. B.S., Wilkes Coll., 1959; postgrad., New Sch. for Social Research, 1961. Owner Chiron Press, N.Y.C., 1961-68; instr. Sch. Visual Arts, N.Y.C., 1968; prof. art Cornell U., Ithaca, N.Y., 1969—; vis. critic Pratt Graphic Arts Center, N.Y.C., 1965-68; vis. artist Colgate U., Hamilton, N.Y., 1973, USSR, 1979, Escuela de Bellas Artes, Honduras, 1980, Loughborough Coll. Art and Design, Eng., 1989; vis. prof. U. Calif., Berkeley, 1976. One-man shows include Louis K. Meisel Gallery, N.Y.C., 1978-80, Galerie Kupinski, Stuttgart, Germany, 1979, Palace of Culture and Sci., Warsaw, Poland, 1979, Sky Art Presentation, MIT, 1981, Am. Ctr., Belgrade, 1981, William and Mary Coll., 1983, McPherson Art Gallery, Victoria, B.C., Can., 1984, Studio D'Ars, Milan, 1985, Gallery Flaviana, Locarno, Switzerland, 1985, Il Salatto Gallery, Como, Italy, 1985, Galleria Schneider, Rome, 1987, Mus. Sztuki Lodz, Poland, 1987, Alternative Mus., Lido di Spina, Italy, 1987, Galerie Klaus Lea, Munich, 1987, Patricia Carega Gallery, Washington, 1988, Nine Columns Gallery, Palermo, Italy, 1988, John Hansard Gallery, Southampton, Eng., 1989, Quai Art Gallery, Isle of Wight, Eng., 1989, Lee Art Gallery, Clemson (S.C.) U., 1990, Apogeeairway, N.Y.C., 1991, Nine Columns Gallery, Brescia, Italy, 1991, Glenn Curtiss Mus., Hammondsport, N.Y., 1993, Caproni Mus., Trento, Italy, 1993, Temple U., Rome, 1995, Gallery of Modern Art, Maribor, Slovenia, 1995, Palazzo Communale, Todi, Italy, 1995; works represented in collections at Met. Mus., N.Y.C., Mus. Modern Art, N.Y.C., Victoria and Albert Mus., London, Whitney Mus., N.Y.C., Walker Art Center, Mpls., Tate Gallery, London, Fort Worth Art Center, Nat. Collection, Washington, others. Am. Fedn. of Arts grantee, 1965; Carnegie Found. grantee, 1967; Nat. Endowment for Arts grantee, 1973; N.Y. State Council on Arts grantee, 1973; Creative Artists Public Service Program grantee, 1978; Best Found. grantee, 1985. Mem. Exptl. Aircraft Assn., Aircraft Owners and Pilots Assn., Polish Acad. Sci. and Art, Internat. Aerobatic Club. Home: 306 Stone Quarry Rd Ithaca NY 14850-5308 Office: Cornell U Tjaden Hall Ithaca NY 14853 *I have taken my artwork out of the museums and galleries into the sky. I use an aerobatic bi-plane which I build and fly to make large works in space. The airplane is flown through a series of complex maneuvers while trailing smoke in order to make a four-dimensional piece visible to the spectators for only a few short moments. The work of art has no existence other than in the memory or in documentation.*

POLETTI, CHARLES, lawyer; b. Barre, Vt., July 2, 1903; s. Dino and Carolina (Gervasini) P.; m. Jean Knox Ellis, June 2, 1934 (dec. Feb. 1974); children: Carla Knox Poletti Tidmarsh, Charles Ellis, Joanna Shattuck Poletti Todisco; m. Elizabeth Munn Vanderloo, Sept. 1, 1975. A.B. summa cum laude, Harvard U., 1924, LL.B. cum laude, 1928; Eleanor Duse fellow, U. Rome, 1924-25; student, U. Madrid, 1928; LL.D., U. Palermo, U. Rome. Bar: N.Y. 1930. Assoc. Davis, Polk, Wardwell, Gardiner & Reed, N.Y., 1928-33; legal asst. St. Lawrence Power Devel. Commn., 1930; counsel to gov. N.Y., 1933-37; justice N.Y. Supreme Ct., 1937, resigned to run for lt. gov., 1938; lt. gov. State of N.Y., 1939-42, gov., 1942; spl. asst. sec. war, 1943; allied mil. gov. Sicily, 1943, Naples, Italy, 1944, Rome, Italy, 1944-45, Milan, Italy, 1945-46; counsel to Poletti, Freidin, Prashker & Gartner, 1966-85; v.p. charge internat. relations and exhibits N.Y. World's Fair Corp., 1960-66; counsel N.Y. State Commn. on Ednl. Finances, 1955-56; vice chmn. N.Y. State Commn. on Constl. Conv., 1956-58; chmn. Gov.'s Conf. on Crime, Criminal and Soc., 1935; mem. N.Y. Bd. Social Welfare, 1936; chmn. N.Y. Constl. Conv. Com., 1937-38; del.-at-large N.Y. Constl. Com., 1938; vice chmn. N.Y. State Def. Council and State War Coordinator, 1941-42; impartial chmn. Coat and Suit Industry, N.Y.C., 1946-48. Editor: Reports of N.Y. State Constitutional Conv. Com., 12 vols., 1938. Editor: Reports of N.Y. State Constl. Conv. Com., 12 vols., 1938, Oral History Interview, 1979. Decorated Legion of Merit, Bronze Star with 2 oak leaf clusters; Hist. Gold medal City of Rome, knight Order Grand Cross Crown (Italy); comdr. Papal Order St. Gregory the Great; officer Brit. Empire; Star of Jordan 1st Order; named hon. citizen of Naples, Rome, Milan, Varese. Mem. Council Fgn. Relations, Atlantic Council U.S., Council Against Intolerance in Am. (exec. com.), Italian Welfare League (adv. com.), Nat. Urban League (treas.), Am., N.Y. State bar assns., Assn. Bar City N.Y., N.Y. Law Soc., Phi Beta Kappa. Democrat. Presbyterian. Address: PO Box 428 Marco Island FL 33969-0428

POLI, KENNETH JOSEPH, editor; b. Blkyn., June 8, 1921; s. Joseph H. and Irene (Seeman) P.; m. Virginia Osk, Dec. 14, 1946; 1 child, Bruce. Student, Goddard Coll., 1938-40. Writer, photographer North Atlantic Area Office ARC, N.Y.C., 1946-49; Editorial cons., 1965—. Author Critical Focus Column, 1972-83; editor: External House Mags., Internat. Nickel Co., N.Y.C., 1949-53, Leica Photography mag., E. Leitz, Inc., N.Y.C., 1953-65; assoc. editor Popular Photography mag., Ziff-Davis Pub. Co., N.Y.C., 1965-69, sr. editor, 1969-70, editor, 1970-83, cons. editor, 1983-87; cons. editor Photography Ann., 35-mm Photography, Photography Directory and Buying Guide, 1970-83; contbr. articles to photog. jours. and encys. with inf. U.S. Army, 1942-45, PTO. Decorated Purple Heart medal. Mem. Am. Photog. Hist. Soc., Photographic Adminstrs., Circle of Confusion, Mensa. Home & Office: 362 Middle Rd Bayport NY 11705-1904

POLICANO, ANDREW J., university dean; b. July 4, 1949; m. Susanne Policano; children: Emily, Keith. BS in Math, SUNY, Stony Brook, 1971; MA in Econs., Brown U., 1973, PhD in Econs., 1976. Asst. prof. U. Iowa, Iowa City, 1975-79, assoc. prof. dept. econs. 1979-81, prof., chair dept. econs., 1984-87, sr. assoc. dean academic affairs 1987-88; prof. dept. econs. Fordham U. N.Y.C., 1981-84, asst. chair. dir. grad. studies, 1982-83; rsch. assoc. Ctr. for Study of Futures Markets Columbia U., N.Y.C., 1982-86; dean divsn. social & behavioral sci. SUNY, 1988-91; dean Sch. Bus. U. Wis., Madison, 1991—; guest prof. Inst. Advanced Studies, Vienna, Austria, 1985; dir. Nat. Guardian Life, Madison, 1991—; mem. Nat. Total Quality Forum Steering Com., Schaumburg, Ill., 1992—; Am. Assembly Collegiate Sch. Bus. Diversity Com., St. Louis, 1993—. Contbr. articles profl. jours. Recipient

Disting. Alumnus award SUNY, Stony Brook, 1994. Mem. Rotary. Office: U Wis Sch Bus Grainger Hall 975 University Ave Madison WI 53706-1323

POLICANO, JOSEPH DANIEL, import company executive; b. Bklyn., Dec. 15, 1933; s. Angelo Marie and Marie Ann (Galardi) P.; m. Kathleen Inez Larregui, June 22, 1957; children: Christopher Dante, Lisa Bernadette, Matthew Joseph. BA, Bklyn. Coll.; postgrad., NYU, New Sch. Corr. Wall St. Jour., 1955-57; sr. assoc. editor, bur. chief Washington Cen. Feature News, Inc., 1957-61; pub. relations dir. M.J. Jacobs, Inc., 1961; pres. Joseph D. Policano, Inc., 1961-70, Policano/Pace, Inc., N.Y.C., 1968-70; chmn. bd. Policano/Rothholz, Inc., N.Y.C., 1970-77; pres. Policano, Inc., N.Y.C. 1977—. Author: Martin Monti, GI Traitor, 1962, Franz Kafka Lived in Prague, 1964, Leos Janacek, His Life and Music, 1965. Vol. Peace Corps, Mali, West Africa, 1988; pres. Kennedy King Dem. Club, 1969-71; commr. Mayor's Commn. for Protocol, N.Y.C., 1979-85; bd. advisors Mcpl. Broadcasting Sys., 1979-85; bd. dirs. Queens Child Guidance Ctr.; mem. Arab-Am. Anti-Discrimination Com. Served with AUS, 1954-55. Recipient Columbus award Fedn. Italian-Am. Dem. Orgns., 1974. Mem. ACLU, U.S. Navy League, Circolo Italiano de Puerto Rico, Nat. Arts Club. Roman Catholic.

POLICH, JAMES W., environmental services consultant; b. 1941. Degree, Purdue U., 1966. With USPHS, Washington, 1966-68; ind. civil engr. Detroit, 1968-72; with Gen. Motors Co., Detroit, 1972-82, Environ, Deerfield, Ill., 1982—; now pres. Environ. Office: Environ 540 Lake Cook Rd Ste 300 Deerfield IL 60015*

POLICINSKI, EUGENE FRANCIS, newspaper editor; b. South Bend, Ind., Aug. 31, 1950; s. E.T. and Margaret C. (O'Neill) P.; m. Kathleen Beta O'Donnell Powell, Aug. 19, 1972; children: Ryan, David. Degree in journalism and polit. sci., Ball State U., 1972. Corr. Gannett News Svc., Washington, 1979-82; Washington editor USA Today, Arlington, Va., 1982-83, page one editor, 1983-89, mng. editor sports, 1989—; host, commentator USA Today Sky Radio, Arlington, 1992—. Founding editor USA Today Baseball Weekly, 1991. Named one of 100 Most Powerful People in Sports Sporting News, 1992, 93; inducted to Ball State U. Journalism Hall of Fame, 1989. Mem. Am. Soc. Newspaper Editors (com. chmn. 1989—), Associated Press Sports Editors (com. chmn. 1989—). Avocations: sailing, tennis, bicycling. Office: USA Today 1000 Wilson Blvd Arlington VA 22229

POLICOFF, LEONARD DAVID, physician, educator; b. Wilmington, Del., Apr. 22, 1918; s. David and Rosalie (Rochkind) P.; m. Naomi Lewis, June 25, 1942; children: Susan, Stephen. B.S., U. Richmond, 1938; M.D., Med. Coll. Va., 1942. Diplomate Am. Bd. Internal Medicine, Am. Bd. Phys. Medicine and Rehab. (mem. 1968-80). Asst. prof. Med. Coll. Va., 1948-55; prof., chmn. dept. phys. medicine and rehab. Albany Med. Coll., Union U., 1955-67, Temple U., Phila., 1967-70; prof., chmn. Hahnemann Med. Coll., Phila., 1970-71; prof. clin. phys. medicine U. Pa.; chmn. dept. rehab. medicine Princeton (N.J.) Hosp., 1971-75, cons., 1975-78; dir. rehab. medicine Somerset Hosp., Somerville, N.J., 1975-78; acting chmn., prof. clin. phys. medicine Rutgers Med. Sch., 1976-78; clin. prof. phys. medicine and rehab. U. Calif.-Davis Sch. Medicine, 1980-86; chmn. dept. rehab. medicine Pacific Med. Center, San Francisco, 1978-81; med. cons. Dept. Health Svcs., State of Calif., 1987-91; chief rehab. medicine svc. VA Med. Ctr., Martinez, Calif., 1983-85; med. dir. Rehab. Ctr., John Muir Meml. Hosp., Walnut Creek, Calif., 1985-87; mem. Bd. Med. Examiners, N.Y. State, 1962-67; chief of staff VA Hosp., Livermore, Calif., 1987-88. Contbr. articles to profl. jours., textbooks. Bd. dirs. Commn. on Edn. in Phys. Medicine and Rehab., 1968-80, com. for Handicapped People-to-People Program, 1967-75. Served to maj. M.C., AUS, 1943-46. Nat. Inst. Neurologic Diseases fellow, 1953-55. Fellow ACP, Am. Acad. Phys. Medicine and Rehab., Am. Acad. Cerebral Palsy; mem. Am. Congress Rehab. Medicine (pres. 1971), Assn. Acad. Physiatrists, AMA (chmn. phys. medicine sect. 1965-66), Phi Beta Kappa, Alpha Omega Alpha, Sigma Zeta. Home: 1462 Scenic Ave Berkeley CA 94708-1834

POLIKOFF, BENET, JR., lawyer; b. Winston-Salem, N.C., Nov. 25, 1936; s. Benet and Margaret (New) P.; m. Jean Troubh, June 26, 1959 (div. Mar. 1971); children—Elisabeth, Benet Steven, Lee; m. Florence Davis, June 11, 1971. B.A., Yale U., 1959; LL.B., Harvard U., 1962. Ptnr. Marshall, Bratter, Greene, Allison & Tucker, N.Y.C., 1969-82; Ptnr. Rosenman and Colin, N.Y.C., 1982-90, of counsel, 1990—. Bd. dirs. Lexington Ctr. for Hearing Impaired, Jackson Heights, N.Y. Mem. Assn. of Bar of City of N.Y. (chmn. real property law com. 1981-84), N.Y. State Bar Assn.

POLIMENO, LAWRENCE A., computer softwear company executive. Pres., COO Med. Info. Tech. Westwood, Mass. Office: Medical Info Tech Meditech Cir Westwood MA 02090*

POLIN, CLAIRE, musician; b. Phila.; d. Josef and Celia (Dolgien) P.; m. Merle Schaff (dec.); children—Josef, Gabriel. B.Mus., Phila. Conservatory Music, 1948, M.Mus., 1950, D.Mus., 1955; Mus.D., Temple U., Juilliard Sch. Music, Dropsie U., Gratz Coll., Berkshire Music Center. Mem. faculty Phila. Conservatory-Phila. Mus. Acad., 1955-65; mem. faculty Rutgers U., 1957-91, prof. emeritus music dept., 1991—; dir. Rutgers U. (Univ. Exchange Concerts), 1960—; free-lance flutist, 1955—; Leverhulme fellow to, U.K., 1968-69; vis. lectr., composer, performer, musicologist, Gt. Britain, France, Israel, U.S., Russia. Mem. Pan Orphic Duo, flute and harp; author: Music of the Ancient Near East, 1954, (with William Kincaid) Flute Method, 5 vols., 1967—, The Ap Huw Ms, 1982; also articles on Welsh, Hebrew, early Am. music, contemporary music, Russian music.; composer: brass quintet Cader Idris (Ga. State U. award 1970), The Journey of Owain Madoc, Infinito: saxophone, soprano, chorus, narrator-dancer, 1972, Aderyn Pur, 1972, flute, saxophone, tape Eligmos Archaios, solo harp, 1973, Procrisfor flute and tuba, 1973, Paraselene: song cycle for soprano, flute, piano, 1976, Ma'alot: viola and percussion, 1976, Klockwerk: saxophone, horn, bassoon, 1977, Gilgamesh: flute, string orch., 1967, Windsongs: voice and guitar, 1978, Isaiah Syndrome, (choral) 1980, Res Naturae: woodwind quintet, 1981, Georgics: solo flute, 1981, Kuequenaku: piano and percussion, 1983, Mythos Harp Concerto, 1984, Walum Olum: clarinet, viola, piano, 1985, Hortus Nardiensis: solo harp, 1986, Freltic Sonata: violin and piano, 1986, Garden of Earthly Delights: wind and sax quintet, Mystic Rondo: tenor, violin, piano, Shirilidang: for solo piano, 1988, Phantasmagoria: piano (4 hands), 1989, Taliesin for flute, oboe and cello with small percussion instruments, 1993; numerous solo works, recs. Recipient award-commn. Ga. Brass Symposium, 1970, numerous prizes for composition.; Faculty Study grant Rutgers U., 1973-74, 76-77, 82, 84, 88; City Phila. Tricentennial Commn., 1982; Pa. Council on Arts grantee, 1987. Mem. AAUP, Am. Soc. Composers, Soc. Ethnomusicology, Am. Music Center, Phila. Art Alliance, Am. Musicol. Soc., Composers Guild Gt. Britain, Bibliotheque Internat. de Musique Contemporaine, Welsh Guild, ASCAP, Delta Omicron (award 1953, 59). Home: Dragon Hill Baird and Heath Rds Merion PA 19066 Office: Rutgers U Dept Music Camden NJ 08102

POLIN, JANE LOUISE, foundation official; b. N.Y.C., Sept. 30, 1958; d. Raymond and Constance F. (Caplan) P. BA, Wesleyan U., Middletown, Conn., 1980; MBA, Columbia U., 1988. Asst. dir. ann. giving Wesleyan U., 1980-82; centennial fund assoc. Met. Opera Assn., N.Y.C., 1982-84; devel. officer Columbia U., N.Y.C., 1984-88; program mgr., compt. GE Founds., Fairfield, Conn., 1988—. Panelist arts-in-edn. Nat. Endowment for Arts, Washington, 1989-90, 94; adv. bd. mem. Carnegie Hall, N.Y.C., 1992—, Nat. Corp. Theatre Fund, N.Y.C., 1991—, Young Audiences, N.Y.C. 1991—. Mem. Alpha Delta Phi. Office: General Electric Fund 3135 Easton Tpke Fairfield CT 06431-0002

POLING, HAROLD ARTHUR, retired automobile company executive; b. Troy, Mich., Oct. 14, 1925; s. Plesant Arthur and Laura Elizabeth (Thompson) P.; m. Marian Sarita Lee, 1957; children—Pamela Lee, Kathryn Lynn, Douglas Lee. BA, Monmouth (Ill.) Coll., 1949, LHD (hon.), 1981; MBA, Ind. U., 1951, LHD (hon.), 1990; LHD (hon.), Hofstra U., 1986, U. Detroit 1990, Mich. State U., 1992. Cost analyst, supr. steel divsn. Ford Motor Co. Deaborn, Mich., 1951-59, fin. analyst, mgr. transmission and chassis divsn., 1960-64; asst. contr. transmission and chassis divsn. Ford Motor Co., Dearborn, Mich., 1964-66, contr. transmission and chassis divsns, 1966-67, contr. engine and foundry divsns., 1967-68, contr. product devel. group, 1968-72; v.p fin. Ford of Europe, Inc., 1972-75; pres. Ford of Europe, Inc., Brentwood, Eng., 1975-77; chmn. bd. Ford of Europe, Inc., 1977-79; exec.

v.p. Ford Motor Co., Dearborn, Mich., 1979, exec. v.p N.Am. automotive ops., 1980-85, mem. office of chief exec., 1984, pres., COO, 1985-87, vice-chmn., COO, 1987-90, chmn., CEO, 1990-93, chmn., 1993-94, also bd. dirs.; mem. Pres.' Commn. on Environ. Quality, The Bus. Coun., The Conf. Bd., The Bus. Roundtable, BHP Minerals Internat. Adv. Coun.; bd. dirs. Shell Oil Co., Detroit Renaissance Inc. Bd. dirs. Monmouth (Ill.) Coll. Senate; mem. dean's adv. coun. Ind. U. Sch. Bus.; mem. Nat. 4-H Coun.; bd. visitors Sch. Econs. and Mgmt. Oakland (Mich.) U., Grad. Sch. Bus., U. Pitts.; v.p. Boys and Girls Club S.E. Mich.; chmn.-elect Bus.-Higher Edn. Forum, The Brookings Coun. With USNR, 1943-45. Recipient Disting. Svc. Citation award Auto. Hall Fame, 1986, Leadership award Engring. Soc. Detroit, 1987, Horatio Alger award, 1991. Mem. Am. Auto Mfg. Assn., Hwy. Users Fedn. Office: Ford Motor Co PO Box 1899 Dearborn MI 48121-1899

POLING, KERMIT WILLIAM, minister; b. Elkins, W.Va., Oct. 1, 1941; s. Durward Willis and Della Mae (Boyles) P.; m. Patricia Ann Groves, June 12, 1965; children: David Edward Elson, Mikael Erik. Diploma in Bible, Am. Bible Sch., 1966; BRE, Am. Bible Coll., 1991; BA in Bible, Reed Coll. Religion, 1968; AA, W.Va. U., 1970; ThD, Zion Theol. Sem., 1971; postgrad., Wesley Theol. Sem., 1974; LLD, Geneva Theol. Coll., 1980; DSL (hon.), Berean Christian Coll., 1981; postgrad., Mansfield Coll., U. Oxford, Eng., 1986, 90, 91; D Ecumenical Rsch., St. Ephrem's Inst. for Oriental Studies, 1989; M of Herbology, Emerison Coll., 1994. Ordained to ministry United Meth. Ch., 1967. Pastor Parkersburg-Crossroads (W.Va.) Cir., 1967-70; asst. sec. W.Va. Ann. Conf., 1967-69; pastor Hope-Halleck Morgantown Cir., 1970-76, Trinity-Warren Grafton (W.Va.) Charge, 1976-83, 1st Trinity Pennsboro (W.Va.) Charge, 1983—; editor local ch. news; instr. Bible Bodkin Bible Inst., 1975-75, United Meth. Lay Acad., 1992—; mem. staff Taylor County Coop. Parish, 1976-83; coord. Hughes River Coop. Parish, 19836; mem. chaplains com. Grafton City Hosp., 1976-82; mem. coun. Ctr. d'Etudes et d'Action Oecumeniques, 1972-74. Author: A Crown of Thorns, 1963, A Silver Message, 1964, History of the Halleck Church, 1970, Eastern Rite Catholicism, 1971, From Brahmin to Bishop, 1976, Cult and Occult: Data and Doctrine, 1978, The Value of Religious Education in Ancient Traditional Churches, 1993; contbr. articles and poems to religious jours. Decorated Royal Afghanistan Order of Crown of Amanullah, Byzantine Order of Leo th earmenian, Order of Polonia Presituta, Mystical ORder of St. Peter, knight Grand Cross of the Order of St. Dennis of Zante, 1990; recipient Good Citizenship award Doddridge County, 1954, Silver medal Ordre Universel du Merit Humain, Geneva, 1973, Commendation for Outstanding Achievement in Ministry Ohio Ho. Reps., 1988; named Chief of Dynastic Ho. of Polanie-Patrikios, 1988. Mem. SAR, Assn. Bible Tchrs. (founder), Internat. Platform Assn., Sovereign Order St. John Jerusalem, Ritchie County Ministerial Assn. (pres. 1984—), Order Sacred Cup, Knights of Malta. Home: 118 Ray Ave Pennsboro WV 26415-1155 Office: 302 Lincoln St Grafton WV 26354-1530

POLING, WESLEY HENRY, college president; b. Akron, Ohio, May 22, 1945; s. Elmer Francis and Norma May (Flickinger) P.; m. Carol Ann Young, Aug. 17, 1968; children: Jason Alder, Todd Wesley. BA, Ohio Wesleyan U., 1968; MDiv, Yale U., 1971; PhD, U. Conn., 1983. Dir. parents program Yale U., New Haven, 1971-73, dir. alumni records, 1973-86; v.p. for devel. and alumni rels. Goucher Coll., Towson, Md., 1986-94; pres. Ky. Wesleyan Coll., Owensboro, 1994—; treas. Dist. I CASE, 1985-86, program chair Conf., 1984-85. Chmn. bd. mgr. Ctrl. br. YMCA of New Haven, 1976-83; v.p., treas. Balt. Choral Arts Soc., 1989-93, pres., 1993-94; bd. dirs. Roland Park Place, Balt., 1991-94; mem. Citizens Com. on Edn., Owensboro, 1994—. Berkeley Coll., Yale U. fellow. Mem. Owensboro C. of C. (bd. dirs. 1994—), Williams Club, Rotary, Phi Delta Kappa. Avocations: squash, running, music. Home: 3100 Frederica St Owensboro KY 42301-6059 Office: Ky Wesleyan Coll PO Box 1039 Owensboro KY 42302-1039

POLINGER, IRIS SANDRA, dermatologist; b. N.Y.C., Feb. 10, 1943; m. Harvey I. Hyman, Feb. 6, 1972. AB, Barnard Coll., 1964; PhD, Johns Hopkins U., 1969; MD, SUNY Downstate, Bklyn., 1975. Diplomate Am. Bd. Dermatology. Teaching positions various schs. including NYU Coll. Dentistry and Harvard Med. Sch., 1969-73; med. intern Baylor Coll. Medicine, 1975-76, resident in dermatology, 1976-79; pvt. practice dermatology Houston, 1979—. Bd. dirs. Ft. Bend County Women's Ctr., Richmond, Tex., 1993—. Mem. Am. Bus. Women's Assn. (chair scholarship com. 1986—, chair scholarship event com. 1993—). Office: 4915 S Main # 104 Stafford TX 77477

POLINSKY, A. MITCHELL, law and economics educator; b. 1948. A.B., Harvard U., 1970; Ph.D., MIT, 1973; M.S.L., Yale U., 1976. Asst. prof. econs. Harvard U., Cambridge, Mass., 1973-79, asst. prof. econs. and law, 1977-79; assoc. prof. econs., prof. law Stanford (Calif.) U., 1979-84, Josephine Scott Crocker prof. law and econs., 1984—; rsch. assoc., Nat. Bur. of Econ. Rsch., 1978—. Mem. editorial bd. Jour. Law, Econs. and Orgn.; 1983—, Internat. Rev. Law Econs., 1987—; adv. editor Jour. Risk and Uncertainty, 1987—. Office: Stanford U Law Sch Nathan Abbott Way Stanford CA 94305

POLINSKY, JANET NABOICHECK, state official, former state legislator; b. Hartford, Conn., Dec. 6, 1930; d. Louis H. and Lillian S. Naboicheck; BA, U. Conn., 1953; postgrad. Harvard U., 1954; m. Hubert N. Polinsky, Sept. 21, 1958; children: Gerald, David, Beth. Mem. Waterford 2d Charter Commn. (Conn.), 1967-68, Waterford Conservation Commn., 1968-69; Waterford rep. Town Meeting, 1969-71, SE Conn. Regional Planning Agy., 1971-73; mem. Waterford Planning and Zoning Commn., 1970-76, chmn., 1973-76; mem. Waterford Dem. Town Com., 1976-92, del. State Dem. Conv., 1976, 78, 80, 82, 84, 86, 90, 92; mem. Conn. Ho. of Reps. from 38th Dist., 1977-92, asst. majority leader, 1981-83, chmn. appropriations com., 1983-85, 87-89, ranking mem., 1985-87, minority whip, 1985-86, dep. speaker, 1989-92; dep. commr. dept. adminstrv. svcs., State of Conn., 1993-94, commr., 1994-95, asst. sec. of state, 1995; commr. utilities ctrl. auth. State of Conn., 1995—. Trustee Eugene O'Neill Meml. Theatre Ctr., 1973-76, 81-92; corporator, Lawrence and Meml. Hosps., 1987—; mem. New Eng. Bd. Higher Edn., 1981-83; mem. fiscal affairs com. Eastern Conf. Council of State Govts., 1983-88. Named Woman of Yr., Waterford Jr. Women's Club, 1977, Nehantic Women's Bus. and Profl. Club, 1979, Legislator of Yr., Conn. Library Assn., 1980. Mem. Order Women Legislators, Delta Kappa Gamma (hon.). Home: 15 Gardner Cir New London CT 06320 Office: 30 Trinity St Hartford CT 06106

POLIS, MICHAEL PHILIP, academic administrator, electrical engineering educator; b. N.Y.C., Oct. 24, 1943; s. Max and Sylvia (Goldner) P.; m. Claudette Martin, May 28, 1966; children: Melanie, Pascal, Karine. BSEE, U. Fla., 1966; MSEE, Purdue U., 1968, PhD, 1972. Grad. instr. Purdue U. 1966-71; postdoctoral fellow Ecole Polytechnique de Montreal, P.C., Can., 1972-73, asst. prof., 1973-74, assoc. prof., 1974-82, 1982-86; prof., chair dept. elec. and computer engring. Wayne State U., Detroit, 1987-93; dean Sch. Engring. and Computer Sci. Oakland U., Rochester, Mich., 1993—; vis. rsch. assoc. Laboratoire d'Automatique et d'Analyse des Systems, Toulouse, France, 1978; program dir. NSF, Washington, 1983-87; cons. Met. Transit Bur., Montreal, 1973-77, Quebec Bur. Planning and Devel., Quebec City, 1976-78, Transports Can., Montreal, 1979-80, ICAM Techs. Inc., Montreal, 1981-83. Contbr. chpts. to textbooks, articles to sci. jours. Grantee Natural Scis. and Engring. Rsch. Coun. Can. 1973-86, NSF 1989—. Sr. mem. IEEE (Best Paper award 1975); mem. Sigma Xi, Tau Beta Pi, Eta Kappa Nu. Office: Sch Engring & Computer Sci Oakland U Rochester MI 48309-4401

POLISHAN, PAUL FRANK, clothing company executive; b. Scranton, Pa., Dec. 20, 1945; s. Frank and Josephine (Logsong) P.; m. Gloria Sokolowsky, June 1967; children: Paul, Tim, Lisa, Robert, Tiffany. BS in Acctg., U. Scranton, 1968. Now sr. v.p. fin., chief fin. officer Leslie Fay Cos. N.Y.C. Avocations: fishing, hunting, hiking. Home: 383 S Main Rd Wilkes Barre PA 18707-1907 Office: Leslie Fay Cos Inc World Adminstrv Ctr 400 Stewart Rd Hanover Indsl Est Wilkes Barre PA 18706

POLISI, JOSEPH W(ILLIAM), college administrator; b. N.Y.C., Dec. 30, 1947; s. William Charles and Pauline (Kaplan) P.; m. Elizabeth Marlowe. BA in Polit. Sci., U. Conn., 1969; MA in Internat. Relations Tufts U., 1970, MusM, 1973, M of Mus. Arts, 1975; DMA, Yale U., 1980; DHL (hon.), Ursinus Coll., Collegetown, Pa., 1986; MusD (hon.), Curtis

Inst. Music, 1990. Exec. officer Yale Sch. of Music, New Haven, 1976-80; dean of faculty Manhattan Sch. of Music, N.Y.C., 1980-83; dean Coll. Conservatory of Music U. Cin., 1983-84; pres. The Juilliard Sch., N.Y.C., 1984—. Performances as bassoonist throughout the U.S.; contbr. articles to various publs. in U.S. and France. Office: Juilliard Sch Office of the Pres 60 Lincoln Ctr Plz New York NY 10023

POLITAN, NICHOLAS H., federal judge; b. Newark, Nov. 13, 1935; m. Marian E. Politan; children: Nicholas H. Jr., Vincent J. Bar: N.J. 1961, U.S. Dist. Ct. N.J. 1961, U.S. Ct. Appeals (2d cir.) 1969, U.S. Ct. Appeals (3d cir.) 1971, U.S. Tax Ct. 1972, U.S. Supreme Ct. 1973. Law clk. to Hon. Gerald McLaughlin U.S. Ct. Appeals (3d cir.), Newark, 1960-61; sr. ptnr. Cecchi and Politan, Lyndhurst, N.J., 1961-64, 72-87; litigation ptnr. Krieger, Chodash & Politan, Jersey City, 1964-72; ptr., chmn. exec. com. County Trust Co., Lyndhurst, 1980-87; judge U.S. Dist. Ct. N.J., 1987—; instr. legal rsch. and writing Rutgers U. Law Sch., 1963. Mng. editor Rutgers Law Rev., 1959; contbr. articles to profl. jours. Office: US Dist Ct Box 999 King Bldg Newark NJ 07101-0999

POLITANO, VICTOR ANTHONY, urology educator, physician; b. Point Marion, Pa., Jan. 13, 1919; s. Anthony and Elizabeth (Parco) P.; m. Aida Miskhin, June 20, 1969; children: Victor, Michael, Rebecca, Betty Frances, Jonathan. B.S., Marshall U., 1940; M.D., Duke U., 1944. Asso. urologist Mass. Gen. Hosp.; instr. surgery Harvard U., 1955-58; asso. prof. surgery div. urology Duke U., 1958-62; prof., chmn. dept. urology U. Miami, 1962—, chmn. emeritus Dept. Urology, 1992. Served with USN, 1945-47, 53-55. Recipient Disting. scholar award U. Miami, 1995; Victor A. Politano chair in urology established at U. Miami Sch. Medicine, 1982. Mem. Am. Urol. Assn. (pres.-elect 1984-85, pres. 1985-86), Soc. Univ. Urologists (pres.), Pediatric Urol. Soc. (pres.), Fla. Urol. Soc. (pres.), AMA, ACS (internat. relations com.), Am. Assn. Genito-urinary Surgeons, Clin. Soc. Genito-urinary Surgeons, Internat. Soc. Urology, Confederacion Americana de Urologia (pres. 1986-87), Fla. Med. Assn., Dade County Med. Assn., Greater Miami Urol. Soc. Developed technique for anti-reflux ureteral reimplantation, technique for teflon injection to correct urinary incontinence; developed periureteral Polytef paste injection for vesicoureteral reflux. Office: U Miami Jackson Meml Med Ctr 1611 NW 12th Ave Miami FL 33136-1005

POLITES, MICHAEL EDWARD, aerospace research engineer; b. Belleville, Ill., Mar. 19, 1944; s. Matthew Charles and Edith Louise (Schwarz) P. BS in Sys. and Automatic Controls, Washington U., St. Louis, 1967; MSEE, U. Ala., 1971; PhD in Elec. Engring., Vanderbilt U., 1986. Aerospace rsch. engr. guidance, navigation and control sys. NASA/Marshall Space Flt. Ctr. Structures & Dynamics Lab, Huntsville, Ala., 1967—. Contbr. numerous articles to profl. jours.; referee various jours. and confs. Recipient 45 NASA awards in field. Fellow AIAA (assoc., guidance navigation and control tech. com. 1990-95); mem. IEEE (sr. mem., Engr. of Yr. Huntsville sect. 1995), ASME, Am. Astron. Soc. (session co-chmn. 1995 Guidance and Control Conf.), Mensa, Tau Beta Pi, Eta Kappa Nu, Pi Tau Sigma. Achievements include patents for rotating unbalanced-mass devices for scanning and a suspension system for scanning payloads; contr. to the pointing control systems on Skylab, the High Energy Astronomical Observatory and the Hubble Space Telescope. Office: NASA/Marshall Space Flight Ctr Structures & Dynamics Lab Control Systems Divsn Huntsville AL 35812

POLITIS, TIMOTHY JUDE, insurance company executive; b. Manchester, Eng., Nov. 21, 1944; came to U.S. 1946; s. Joseph Paul and Dorothy (McGurk) P.; m. Deborah Dyer, Dec. 23, 1967 (div. 1975); children: Wendy Ellen, Holly Lynn; m. Elaine Bishop, Mar. 10, 1979; children: John Joseph, Alexandra Marcy, Daphne Earl. BS, Castleton (Vt.) Coll., 1967; student, Siena Coll., Loudenville, N.Y., 1962-63, Dartmouth Coll., 1963-65. CLU. Agt. Conn. Mutual Life, Rutland, Vt., 1971-74; mktg. cons. Conn. Mutual Life, Hartford, Conn., 1974-76; agy. supr. Conn. Mutual Life, Portland, Maine, 1976-78; dir. tng. Union Mutual Life Ins. Co., Portland, 1978-82; chartered life underwriter Mass. Mutual Life, Portland, 1982—. Vice chmn. Scarborough Rep. Town Com., 1989—; mem. Maine Estate Planning Coun., 1982—, Waterfowl Adv. Com., Maine, 1986-88, Com. on Fgn. Rels., Portland, 1979—, Maine State Rep. Com., 1992—; regional dir. Nat. Ski Patrol Sys., Maine, 1984-88, 1993-94; mem. Maine State Rep. coms., 1992—. Capt. USMC, 1967-71. Recipient Disting. Svc. award, Ducks Unltd., Inc., Long Grove, Ill., 1984, 88, Carl Horner award, 1987. Mem. Atlantic Salmon Fedn., Purpoodock Country Club, Auburn Skeet Club, Scarborough Rod and Gun Club, Sugarloaf/USA Ski Patrol, Shawnee Peak Ski Patrol. Republican. Avocations: skiing, bird and duck hunting, salmon and trout fishing. Home: 1 Milliken Rd Scarborough ME 04074-8989 Office: Massachusetts Mutual Life 93 Exchange St Portland ME 04101-5001

POLITZ, HENRY ANTHONY, federal judge; b. Napoleonville, La., May 9, 1932; s. Anthony and Virginia (Russo) P.; m. Jane Marie Simoneaux, Apr. 29, 1952; children: Nynette, Bennett, Mark, Angela, Scott, Jane, Michael, Henry, Alisa, John, Nina. B.A., La. State U., 1958, J.D., 1959. Bar: La. 1959. Assoc., then ptnr. firm Booth, Lockard, Jack, Pleasant & LeSage, Shreveport, 1959-79; judge U.S. Ct. Appeals (5th cir.), Shreveport, 1979—, chief judge, 1992—; vis. prof. La. State U. Law Center; bd. dirs. Am. Prepaid Legal Services Inst., 1975—; mem. La. Judiciary Commn., 1978-79. Mem. editorial bd. La. State U. Law Rev., 1958-59. Mem. Shreveport Airport Authority, 1973-79, chmn., 1977; bd. dirs. Rutherford House, Shreveport, 1975—, pres., 1978; pres. Caddo Parish Bd. Election Suprs., 1975-79; mem. Electoral Coll., 1976. Served with USAF, 1951-55. Named Outstanding Young Lawyer in La., 1971. Mem. Am. Bar Assn., Am. Judicature Soc., Internat. Soc. Barristers, La. Bar Assn., La. Trial Lawyers Assn., Shreveport Bar Assn., Justinian Soc., Omicron Delta Kappa. Democrat. Roman Catholic. Club: K.C. Office: US Ct Appeals 500 Fannin St Rm 2b04 Shreveport LA 71101-3000

POLITZER, HUGH DAVID, physicist, educator; b. N.Y.C., Aug. 31, 1949; s. Alan A. and Valerie T. (Diamant) P. B.S., U. Mich., 1969; Ph.D., Harvard U., 1974. Jr. fellow Harvard U. Soc. Fellows, 1974-77; mem. faculty Calif. Inst. Tech., 1977—, prof. theoretical physics, 1979—, exec. officer for physics 1986-88. Recipient J.J. Sakurai prize, 1986. Fellow NSF, 1969-74; Sloan Found., 1977-81; Woodrow Wilson grad. fellow, 1969-74. Mem. Phi Beta Kappa. Address: 452-48 Calif Inst Tech Pasadena CA 91125

POLIVNICK, PAUL, conductor, music director; b. Atlantic City, N.J., July 7, 1947; s. Sidney and Beatrice Ann (Craven) P.; m. Kathleen Lenski, Jan. 19, 1970 (div. 1976); m. Marsha Hooks, June 20, 1980. MusB, Juilliard Sch., N.Y.C, 1969; MusD (hon.), U. Montevallo, 1987. Condr. Debut Orch., L.A., 1969-73; mem. faculty UCLA, 1973-79; assoc. condr. Indpls. Symphony, 1977-80, Milw. Symphony, 1981-85; dir. music Ala. Symphony, Birmingham, 1985-93; music dir. N.H. Music Festival, 1993—; guest condr. various symphony and opera cos., worldwide. Avocations: backpacking, working out, traveling, cooking. Address: 1 Saint Joseph Rd Birmingham AL 35243-2209

POLJAK, ROBERTO J(UAN), research director, biotechnology educator; b. Buenos Aires, Argentina, Sept. 17, 1932; s. Giovanni P. and Josephine (Zorzut) P.; m. Mabel Amelia Iglesias, Dec. 28, 1956; children: Leonora, Gustavo. BSc, Coll. Nat. Quilmes, Argentina, 1949; PhD, U. de la Plata, Argentina, 1956. Teaching assoc. Instituto de Fisica, Bariloche, Argentina, 1957; fellow Sch. for Advanced Studies MIT, Boston, 1958-60; postdoctoral fellow Davy Faraday Rsch. Lab., Royal Instn., London, 1960-62; postdoctoral fielow MRC Unit for Molecular Biology, Cambridge, Eng., 1962; assot. prof. biophysics Johns Hopkins Sch. Medicine, Balt., 1963, assoc. prof. biophysics, 1966, prof. biophysics, 1972-81; prof. Institut Pasteur, Paris, 1981-92; dir. rsch. CNRS, Paris, 1981-92; prof., dir. CIM Advanced Rsch. in Biotech. U. Md./Nat. Inst. Stds. and Tech., Balt., 1992—; W.H. Elkins prof. U. Md., 1994—. Contbr. over 140 rsch. papers to profl. jours. Recipient Rsch. Career Devel. award USPHS, 1972-77, gold medal Soc. d'Encouragement au Progres, Paris, 1986, Jacques Monod prize Fondation de France, 1986, Disting. Scientist award S.W. Found. for Biomed. Rsch., 1987, Louis Jeantet Found. Medicine prize, Geneva, 1989, Gold medal Jimenez Diaz Found., 1991; Macy Faculty scholar, 1977-78. Mem. European Molecular Biology Orgn., Am. Assn. Immunologists. Office: Ctr for Advanced Rsch Biotech 9600 Gudelsky Dr Rockville MD 20850-3479

POLK, BENJAMIN KAUFFMAN, retired architect, composer, educator; b. Des Moines, May 18, 1916; s. Harry Herndon and Alice (Kauffman) P.; m. Emily Despain Isaacs, Aug. 23, 1946. Student, Amherst Coll., 1933-35, U. Chgo., 1935-36, Iowa State Coll., 1936-38. Ptnr. Polk and Malone, San Francisco, 1948-53; propr. Benjamin Polk, Architect & Planner, New Delhi, Calcutta, Karachi, 1952-64; assoc. W.R. Ewald Jr., Regional Planning, Washington, 1965-66; mem. architecture & planning faculty Calif. Poly. State U., San Luis Obispo, 1966-80; ret., 1980. Author: Architecture and the Spirit of the Place, 1961, Building for South Asia, An Architectural Autobiography, 1992, (with Emily Polk) India Notebook, 1986, (with Seneviratna) Buddhist Monastic Architecture, 1992, A Figure in a Landscape, 1993, Christchurch Priory, Dorset, 1994; Sturcture for Music and Synthesized Orchestrations, 1995; also booklets, articles; prin. works include Am. Lib., Times of India Press, New Delhi, Jallian Wala Bagh Amritsar India, Utkal U., Orissa, Gwalior Rayons Factories and Town Calicut, Birla Mus., Rajasthan, Woodlands, Calcutta , India, Palace for the king of Nepal, Buddhist Lib., Rangoon. Vice-pres. Service Civile Internat., East India, 1957-63; advisor Small Wilderness Area Preservation, Calif., 1970-80. Tech. sgt. U.S. Army, 1942-46. Recipient Gold medal Prime Min. of Burma, 1961. Republican. Presbyterian. Avocations: writing, sketching, hiking. Home: 2361 Claranita Ave Los Osos CA 93402 Office: Ind Quaker Gardens 12151 Dale St Stanton CA 90680

POLK, CHARLES, electrical engineer, educator, biophysicist; b. Vienna, Austria, Jan. 15, 1920; came to U.S., 1940, naturalized, 1943; s. Heinrich and Amalie (Canar) P.; m. Dorothy R. Lemp, Apr. 27, 1946; children: Dean F., Gerald W. Student, U. Paris-Sorbonne, 1939; BS, Washington U., 1948; MS, U. Pa., 1953, PhD, 1956. Engr. RCA Victor div., Camden, N.J., 1948-52; rsch. and teaching assoc. U. Pa., 1952-57; prof. elec. engring. Drexel Inst. Tech., Phila., 1957-59; tech. staff RCA Labs., Princeton, N.J., 1957-59; prof. elec. engring. U. R.I., 1959-90, prof. emeritus, 1990—, chmn. dept., 1959-79; head elec. scis. and analysis sect. engring. div. NSF, Washington, 1975-76; acting dir. engring. div. NSF, 1976-77; vis. prof. elec. engring. Stanford U., 1968-69, U. Wis., Madison, 1983-84; cons. Oak Ridge Nat. Lab., 1993—. Editor Handbook of Biologial Effects of Electromagnetic Fields; contbr. articles to profl. publs. Mem. R.I. Legis. Commn. on Electricity Rates, 1974-75. With AUS, 1943-46. NSF Superior Accomplishment award, 1977. Fellow IEEE (chmn. Phila. chpt. profl. group antennas and propagation 1954-55, chmn. Providence sect. 1964-65, mem. adminstrn. com., com. on man and radiation 1987—, chair subcom. biol. effects of power frequency fields 1989—, engring. in med. and biology soc.); mem. AAAS, AAUP, Am. Geophys. Union (nat. com. on space electricity 1974-75), Am. Soc. for Engring. Edn., N.Y. Acad. Scis., Internat. Sci. Radio Union, Bioelectromagnetics Soc. (pres. 1988-89), Bioelec. Repair and Growth Soc. (coun. mem. 1990-92), Sigma Xi, Tau Beta Pi. Organized 1st microwave closed circuit television link for grad. edn. in U.S., 1962. Home: 53 Springhill Rd Kingston RI 02881-1805

POLK, HIRAM CAREY, JR., surgeon, educator; b. Jackson, Miss., Mar. 23, 1936; s. Hiram Carey and Dorris (Hemby) P.; m. Susan Galandiuk; children: Susan Elizabeth, Hiram Cary. BS, Millsaps Coll., 1956; MD, Harvard U., 1960. Intern Barnes Hosp., St. Louis, 1960-61; resident Barnes Hosp., 1961-65; instr. in surgery Washington U., St. Louis, 1964-65; asst. prof. surgery U. Miami, Fla., 1965-69; assoc. prof. U. Miami, 1969-71; prof. chmn. dept. surgery U. Louisville, 1971—; pres., chmn. bd. Univ. Surg. Assocs., P.S.C., 1971—; chmn. bd. Clin. Services Assn., Inc.; mem. merit rev. bd. for surgery VA, 1983-85. Author: (with H.H. Stone) Contemporary Burn Management, 1971, Hospital-Acquired Infections in Surgery, 1977; (with B. Gardner, H.H. Stone and W.L. Sugg) Basic Surgery, 1978, (with H.H. Stone and B. Gardner) 2d edit., 1983, 3d edit., 1987, 4th edit., 1992; (with D.C. Carter) Trauma, 1982; (with J.E. Conte Jr. and L.S. Jacob) Antibiotic Prophylaxis in Surgery: A Comprehensive Review, 1984; (with J.D. Richardson and L.M. Flint Jr.) Trauma: Clinical Care and Pathophysiology, 1987; contbr. numerous articles to profl. publs.; mem. editorial bd. So. Med. Jour, 1970-72, Jour. Surg. Research, 1970-72, 75-77, 78-80, Current Problems in Surgery, 1973—, Surgery, 1975-85, Current Surgery, 1977—, Current Surg. Techniques, 1977—; Emergency Surgery: A Weekly Update, 1977—, Collected Letters in Surgery, 1978—, Brit. Jour. Surgery, 1981-94; chief editor Am. Jour. Surgery, 1986—. Bd. govs. Trover Clinic Found., Madisonville, Ky. Mem. ACS (gov. 1972-80, commn. on cancer 1975-80), AMA, Allen O. Whipple Soc. (exec. coun. 1977-80), Am. Assn. Cancer Edn. (exec. coun. 1968-72), Am. Assn. Surgery of Trauma, Am. Burn Assn., Am. Cancer Soc. (pres. Ky. div. 1989-90, nat. del. dir. 1989-92, 93-95), Am. Surg. Assn. (sec. 1984-89), Acad. Surgery (pres. 1975-76), Cen. Surg. Assn., Assn. Am. Med. Colls. (chmn. ad hoc com. on Medicare and Medicaid 1978-79), Collegium Internationale Chirurgiae Digestivae (sec.-treas. 1981-86, pres. 1986-87), Council on Public Higher Edn. (task group on health scis.), Halsted Soc., Jefferson County Med. Soc., Ky. Med. Assn., Ky. Surg. Soc. (pres. 1982-83), Louisville Surg. Soc. (pres. 1989-90), Residency Rev. Com. for Surgery (vice chmn. 1981-83, chmn. 1983-85), Société Internationale de Chirurgie, Soc. Surgery Alimentary Tract (treas. 1975-78, pres. 1985-86), Soc. Clin. Surgery, Soc. Surg. Chairmen, Soc. Surg. Oncology (pres. 1984-85), Soc. Univ. Surgeons (treas. 1971-74, pres. 1979-80), Southeastern Surg. Congress (exec. coun. for Ky. 1985-86, pres. 1994-95), So. Med. Assn. (vice chmn. sect. on surgery 1969-70, chmn. sect. 1972-73, sec. 1970-72, exec. coun. for Ky. 1971-77, 89-90), So. Surg. Assn. (sec. 1988-89), Alpha Omega Alpha. Home: 12 Poplar Hill Rd Louisville KY 40207 Office: U Louisville Dept Surgery Louisville KY 40292

POLK, JAMES RAY, journalist; b. Oaktown, Ind., Sept. 12, 1937; s. Raymond S. and Oeta (Fleener) P.; m. Bonnie Becker, Nov. 4, 1962; children: Geoffrey, Amy; m. Cara Bryn Saylor, June 21, 1980; 1 child, Abigail. B.A., Ind. U., 1962. With A.P., Indpls., 1962-65, Milw., 1965, Madison, Wis., 1966-67, Washington, 1967-71; investigative reporter Washington Star, 1971-75; correspondent NBC News, Washington, 1975-92; sr. producer CNN Spl. Assignment, 1992—; pres. Investigative Reporters and Editors, Inc., 1978-80, chmn. bd., 1980-82, nat. coll. chmn., 1983-90. Recipient Raymond Clapper Meml. award, 1972, 74; Pulitzer prize for nat. reporting, 1974; Sigma Delta Chi award, 1974; Ind. U. Disting. Alumni award. Mem. Phi Kappa Psi.

POLK, ROBERT FORREST, banker; b. Oshkosh, Wis., Jan. 14, 1947; s. Robert R. and Mary Ann (Witzel) P.; m. Joyce Elaine Peterson, Aug. 28, 1969; children: Sandra L., Jeremy R. BEE, U. Wis., Madison, 1969; MBA in Fin., U. Wis., Whitewater, 1973. Design engr. Honeywell Inc., St. Petersburg, Fla., 1969-71; sales rep. T&T Tech. Inc., McFarland, Wis., 1971-72; lending officer, asst. v.p. Firstar Bank Madison, N.A., 1973-81; dept. mgr., sr. v.p. 1st City Nat. Bank Houston, 1981-87; exec. v.p., chief lending officer Altus Bank, Mobile, Ala., 1987-89; v.p. Firstar Bank Milw., N.A., 1989-91; 1st v.p. Firstar Bank Oshkosh N.A., 1991-94; v.p. Firstar Bank Milw. N.A., 1994—. Avocations: travel, electronics, music, hiking, bicycling.

POLK, WILLIAM MERRILL, architect; b. Cleburne, Tex., July 26, 1935; s. William Merrill and Lucille (Ray) P.; m. Karla Leopold, July 26, 1958; children: Lucy Jennifer, Elizabeth Helene, Andrew James. B.A. in Architecture, Cornell U., Ithaca, N.Y., 1958. Registered architect, Wash., Hawaii, Idaho, Oreg., Mont., Calif., Nev., Wyo., Ariz., Ky., Tex., Utah. Architect NBBJ Group, Seattle, 1962-64; exec. v.p., ptnr. Waldron, Pomeroy, Polk & Smith, Seattle, 1964-81; ptnr., chief operating officer John Graham and Co., Seattle, 1981-85; prin. William Polk Assocs., Seattle; treas. Cornish Coll. Arts, Seattle, 1986-92. Author: (with others) The Architect's Handbook of Professional Practice, 1988. Mem. Wash. State Ho. of Reps., 1971-82, Speaker of house, 1981-83, Wash. State Redistricting Commn., 1991; trustee Hist. Soc. Seattle and King County, 1986-88; vice chmn. Washington Inst. for Policy Studies; bd. dirs. Met. Bd.-YMCA, Seattle, 1972-76, Ryther Child Ctr., 1977-90, Am. Legis. Exchange Council, Washington 1977-83; bd. govs. Council on Nat. Policy, Washington, 1981-86; bd. dirs Providence Health Found., Seattle, 1984—, vice chmn., 1986, 87, chmn., 1988-90. Served to 1st lt. U.S. Army, 1958-60, to capt. Wash. N.G. Named Citizen of Yr. Wash. State Young Republicans, 1981. Fellow AIA (mem. govt. affairs adv. bd. 1982), Seattle C. of C. (1982). Mem. Evangelical Covenant Ch. Am. Clubs: Rainier, Bellevue Athletic. Lodge: Rotary. Home: 7220 92D Ave SE Mercer Island WA 98040 Office: William Polk Assocs 1120 Post Ave Seattle WA 98101-2915

POLKE, SIGMAR, artist; b. Olesnicka, German Democratic Republic, Feb. 13, 1941; arrived in West Germany, 1953.; Student glass painting, Dusseldorf-Kaiserwerth, 1959-60; student painting, Gerald Hoehme, Karl-Otto Goetz Staatliche Kunstakademie, Dusseldorf, 1961-67. Founder with Konrad Fischer-Lueg, Gerhard Richter Capitalist realist painting group, Dusseldorf, 1963; painter Dusseldorf, 1967-70, Willich bei Krefeld, 1971-79, Cologne, 1980—; guest instr. Akademie der bildenden Kunste, Hamburg, Germany, 1970-71, prof. 1977—. One man shows include Galerie René Block, West Berlin, 1966, 68, 69, Galerie Heiner Friedrich, Munich, 1967, 70, Galerie Rudolph Zwirner, Cologne, Galerie Konrad Fischer, Dusseldorf, 1970, 71, 73, Kabinett fur Aktuelle Kunst, Bremerhaven, West Germany, 1970, Galerie Michel Werner, Cologne, 1971, 75, 83, Galerie Toni Gerber, 1971, 76, 81, Galerie Ernst, Hannover, 1971, Rochus Kowallek, Frankfurt, 1972, Galerie Grafikmeyer, Karlsruhe, 1972, Goethe-Inst., Amsterdam, 1972, Galeria Dorothea Loehr, Frankfurt, 1974, Galerie Klein, Bonn, 1974, 75, 80, 86, Kunsthalle, Kiel, 1975, 76, Kunstverein Kassel, West Germany, 1977, Halle fur Internationale Neue Kunst, Zurich, 1978, Galerie Bama, Paris, 1982, Holly Solomon Gallery, N.Y., 1982, Studio d'Arte Cannaviello, Milan, 1983, Marian Goodman Gallery, N.Y., 1983, Mary Boone Gallery, N.Y., 1985, 86, David Nolan Gallery, N.Y., 1987, others; exhibited in group shows at Kaiserstrasse, Dusseldorf, 1963, Stadtisches Mus., Trier, West Germany, 1965, 69, Whitechapel Art Gallery, London, 1970, Kassel, West Germany, 1972, Sao Paulo, 1975, Wurttembergischer Kunstrverein, Stuttgart, 1982, L.A. County Mus. Art, 1987; represented in permanent collections Stadtisches Kunstmuseum, Bonn, Kunstmuseum der Stadt, Dusseldorf, Kunsthalle, Tubingen, Landesmuseum, Darmstadt, Mus. Boymans-van Beuningen, Rotterdam, Stedelijk, Van Abbemuseum, Eindhoven, Centre Georges pompidou, Paris, Mus. Modern Art, N.Y.C.; author: Hohere Wesen befelhlen, 1968, der ganze Korper fuhlt sich leicht und mochte fliegen, 1969, (with others) Die Grafik der Kapitalistischen Realismus, 1971, Bizarre, 1972, (with Achim Duchow) Original und Falschung, 1973. Recipient painting prize Bienal, Sao Paulo, 1975. Office: Galerie Toni Gerber, Gerechtigkeitsgasse 74, 3011 Berne Switzerland also: c/o Michael Werner Gallery 21 E 67th St New York NY 10021

POLKINGHORN, JAMES B., architectural firm executive. Student, North Tex. U., East Tex. Bapt. U.; BArch, U. Tex., 1960. Lic. architect, Tex. Founder, sr. ptnr., prin.-in-charge The Polkingham/Cline Partnership, Austin, Tex.; mem. adv. coun. personal care facilities Tex. State Bd. Health, chmn. phys. environment com., mem. adv. coun. hosp. licensing code revision. Prin. works include Austin Retina Clinic, Ctrl. Plains Hosp., Plainview, Tex., colonial Hosp., Terrell, Tex., Dimmitt County Hosp., Carrizo Springs, Tex., East Dallas Hosp., El Paso (Tex.) Psychiat. Hosp., Fannin Regional Hosp., Blue Ridge, Ga., 1st Tex. Med. Facility, Lewisville, Tex., Iraan (Tex.) Gen. Hosp., Jackson County Hosp., Johnson County Hosp., Cleburne, Tex., La Paz Psychiat. Hosp., Austin, Lee Meml. Hosp., Giddings, Tex., Meml. Hosp., Palestine, Tex., Mother Frances Hosp., Tyler, Tex., Pearsall (Tex.) Hosp., VA Hosp., Kerrville, Tex., others; editor newsletter Austin chpt. Constrn. Specifications Inst. Mem. vestry St. David's Episcopal Ch.; bd. dirs. Westbank Community Libr.; trustee Eanes Ind. Sch. Dist. Mem. AIA, Am. Hosp. Assn., Tex. Soc. Architects (mem. profl. liability ins. com., chmn. com. architecture health, mem. com. edn.), Tex. Hosp. Assn., Tex. Assn. Sch. Bds., Tex. Health Assn., Coun. Ednl. Facility Planners, Austin C. of C., Rotary (past pres.). Office: The Polkinghorn Cline Part 3901 S Lamar 300 Austin TX 78704

POLK-MATTHEWS, JOSEPHINE ELSEY, school psychologist; b. Roselle, N.J., Sept. 24, 1930; d. Charles Carrington and Olive Mae (Bond) Polk; m. Donald Roger Matthews, Aug. 29, 1959 (div. 1974); children: John Roger, Alison Olivia; m. William Y. Delaney, Sept. 17, 1994. AB, Mt. Holyoke Coll., 1952; credential in occupational therapy, Columbia U., 1954; MA, U. So. Calif., L.A., 1957; Cert. Advanced Study, Harvard U., 1979, MS, 1980. Cert. elem. edn. life teaching credential, Calif; cert. ednl. adminstrn. life credential, Calif.; cert. pupil personnel svcs., counseling life credential, sch. psychology credential, Calif.; sch. psychology credential, Nev. Occupational therapist VA Hosp., Northport, N.Y., 1953-55, L.A., 1955-57; health svcs. adminstr. John Wesley County Hosp., L.A., 1957-59; elem. tchr. L.A. (Calif.) City Schs., 1959-60, Santa Clara (Calif.) Unified Sch. Dist., 1960-65, 71-74; asst. prof. Sch. Edn., San Jose (Calif.) State U., 1971; asst. prin. Berryessa Union Sch. Dist., San Jose, Calif., 1974-77, 85-86; ednl. cons. Boston (Mass.) U. Sch. Medicine, 1981-83; asst. prin. Inglewood (Calif.) Unified Sch. Dist., 1986-90; sch. psychologist Clark County Sch. Dist., Las Vegas, 1990-94; med. facility developer Commonwealth Mass., Dept. Mental Health, Boston, 1980-81, ednl. liaison Roxbury Juvenile Ct., 1979. Author: (with others) The New Our Bodies Ourselves, 1983; prodr.: (video) Individualized Rsch., 1971. Commr. Commn. on the Status of Women, Cambridge, Mass., 1981-83; hostess Ctr. for Internat. Visitors, Boston, 1983-84; pers. recruiter L.A. (Calif.) Olympic Organizing Com., 1984; vol. tutor Las Vegas (Nev.) Libr., 1992. Mem. Nat. Assn. Sch. Psychologists, Calif. Assn. Sch. Psychologists, Nev. Assn. Sch. Psychologists, Clark County Assn. Sch. Psychologists, Assn. Black Psychologists, Phi Delta Kappa, Alpha Kappa Alpha. Home and Office: 127 Sandpiper St Newport News VA 23602-6336

POLL, HEINZ, choreographer, artistic director; b. Oberhausen, Germany, Mar. 18, 1926; came to U.S., 1964, naturalized, 1975; s. Heinrich and Anna Margareta (Winkels) P. Co-founder, dir. The Dance Inst., U. Akron, 1967-77; founder, artistic dir., choreographer Ohio Ballet, Akron, 1968—; tchr. Chilean Instituto de Extension Musical, 1951-61, N.Y. Nat. Acad., 1965-66. Dancer Göttingen Mcpl. Theatre, 1947-49, Deutsches Theatre Konstanz, 1949-50, East Berlin State Opera, 1950-51, Nat. Ballet Chile, 1951-62, Ballet de la Jeunesse Musicales de France, 1963-64; guest appearances with Nat. Ballet Chile, 1964, Am. Dance Festival, 1965; choreographer works for Nat. Ballet Chile, Paris Festival Ballet, Ballet Jeunesse de la Musicales de France, Nat. Ballet Can., Pa. Ballet, Ohio Ballet, Limon Dance Co. Recipient Ohio Dance award, 1983, 88-89, Achievement Dance award No. Ohio Live Mag., 1985-86, 88-89, 93-94, 94-95; Nat. Endowment for Arts grantee, 1974-75. Mem. NEA (dance panelist 1987-89, 92-93). Office: Ohio Ballet U Akron Akron OH 44325-2501

POLL, MARTIN HARVEY, film producer; b. N.Y.C.; s. David and Fay (Tamber) P.; m. Lee Lindenberg, May 21, 1954 (div. Oct. 10, 1967); children: Mark, Jonathan; m. Gladys Peltz Jaffe, Oct. 31, 1976; 1 son, Anthony. B.S., Wharton Sch. Bus. U. Pa., 1943. Pres. Inter-Continental TV Films Inc., N.Y.C., 1952; exec. producer Theatre Network TV Inc., N.Y.C., 1953; pres. Gold Medal Studios, Bronx, N.Y., 1954-62; ind. producer, 1962—. (Named Hon. Commr. Motion Picture Arts N.Y.C. 1958, recipient David Di Donatello Best Film Producer award Pres. Italy 1968, N.Y. Film Critics award 1968, Hollywood Fgn. Press Assn. Golden Globe award 1968, Brit. Acad. award 1968); films include Love is a Ball, 1962, Sylvia, 1964, The Appointment, 1968, The Lion in Winter, 1968 (Best Picture award), The Magic Garden of Stanley Sweetheart, 1970, Night Watch, 1972, The Man Who Loved Cat Dancing, 1973, Love and Death, 1975, The Sailor Who Fell From Grace with The Sea, 1976, The Dain Curse, Somebody Killed Her Husband, 1978, Nighthawks, 1981, Arthur the King, 1984, Gimme An F, 1984, Haunted Summer, 1987, My Heroes Have Always Been Cowboys, 1991, (TV miniseries) Diana—Her True Story, 1993. Served with AUS, 1944-47. Mem. Producers Guild of Am., Acad. Motion Picture Arts and Scis., Cinema Circulus, Friends of Library U. So. Calif.

POLL, MAX HENRY, hospital administrator; b. Fremont, Mich., Sept. 10, 1946; s. Henry and Margaret Poll; m. Judith Poll; children: Melanie, Amy. BA, Western Mich. U., 1964; M of Hosp. Adminstrn., U. Minn., 1972. Adminstrv. resident St. Luke's Hosp., Kansas City, Mo., 1973-74, asst. dir., 1974-77; adminstr., chief exec. officer Boone Hosp. Ctr., Columbia, Mo., 1977-82; exec. v.p. Barnes Hosp., St. Louis, 1982-86, pres., chief exec. officer, 1986—; founding pres. First Tier Healthcare, Inc.; exec. com., founder, chmn. Vol. Hosps. Am.-Mid-America, Inc.; mem. Health Insights, Inc.; clin. faculty, preceptor Washington U. Sch. Medicine Health Adminstrn. and Planning Program, St. Louis, U. Minn. Hosp. and Health Care Adminstrn., U. Mo. Health Services Mgmt. Studies Program, Columbia, St. Louis U. Dept. Hosp. and Health Care Adminstrn. Bd. dirs., exec. com. Washington U. Med. Ctr., St. Louis; mem. Joint Senate-Ho. Reps. Interim Com. on Mo. Health Care Systems, 1987; sponsor-rep. St. Louis Sr. Olympics. With M.C., U.S. Army, 1968-70, Vietnam. Mem. Am. Hosp. Assn. (governing council for Assembly Hosps. Schs. Nursing), Mo. Hosp. Assn. (trustee 1985-87, 88—), Assn. Am. Med. Colls. (rep. 1987—),

Am. Coll. Healthcare Execs. Office: Scottsdale Mem Health Systems 3621 Wells Fargo Ave Scottsdale AZ 85251

POLL, ROBERT EUGENE, JR., bank executive; b. Urbana, Ill., Apr. 16, 1948; s. Robert E. Sr. and Dorothy (Baker) P.; m. Leslie Tompkins, Aug. 8, 1970 (div. Mar. 1980); m. Virginia O'Donnell, July 17, 1982; children: Alexandra, Bianca, Paulo Felipe Kos. BA, Kenyon Coll., 1970; MBA, Ind. U., 1972. V.p. Chase Manhattan Bank, N.Y.C., 1970-78; assoc. Lazard Freres & Co., N.Y.C., 1978-82, gen. ptnr., mgr. municipal divsn., 1985—; gen. ptnr. William Blair & Co., Chgo., 1982-84; mem. adv. bd. Ind. Small Bus. Assistance Corp., Bloomington, 1971, Pub. Fin. Inst., N.Y.C., 1976. Mem. Am. Mktg. Assn. N.Y. Acad. Sci., Am. Assn. Polit. and Social Scis., Acad. Polit. Sci., Chgo. Econ. Forum. Clubs: Tavern (Chgo.); N.Y. Athletic. Office: Lazard Freres & Co 1 Rockefeller Pla New York NY 10020

POLLACK, BERNIE, costume designer. Costume designer: (films) Bobby Deerfield, 1977, Straight Time, 1978, The Electric Horseman, 1979, Ordinary People, 1980, Absence of Malice, 1981, (with Gloria Gresham) The Natural, 1984, Twice in a Lifetime, 1982, Police Academy 2: Their First Assignment, 1985, (with Gail Bixby and Albert Wolsky) Legal Eagles, 1986, Touch and Go, 1987, Rain Man, 1988, Bright Lights, Big City, 1988, The Milagro Beanfield War, 1988, Tango & Cash, 1989, Lock-Up, 1989, Havana, 1990, What About Bob?, 1991, A River Runs Through It, 1992, Sneakers, 1992, Blue Chips, 1993. Office: care Costume Designer's Guild 13949 Ventura Blvd Ste 309 Sherman Oaks CA 91423*

POLLACK, BRUCE, banker, real estate consultant; b. Bklyn., June 15, 1951; s. Bernard and Grace (Mishanie) P.; children: Gennifer Ellen, Gregory Adam, Erica Dawn. BS, L.I. U., Bklyn., 1973, MBA with honors, 1979. Sr. appraiser Citizens Savs. & Loan Assn., Woodside, N.Y., 1973-77; chief appraiser Walter Oertly Assocs., N.Y.C., 1978, Flushing (N.Y.) Savs. Bank, 1978-81; v.p. real estate specialist Citibank, N.A., N.Y.C., 1981-90; pres. Met. Realty Solutions, Bklyn., 1990—. Contbr. to The Appraisal Jour., Real Estate Rev., Multi-Housing News, other publs. Recipient Pub./Pvt. Partnership award Ocean Pkwy. Community Devel. Corp., 1984, award Consolidated Edison, 1986. Mem. Young Mortgage Bankers Assn., N.Y. State Soc. Real Estate Appraisers, Bklyn. Bd. Realtors (bd. dirs.), Rho Epsilon. Avocations: traveling, sports, reading, numismatics, fishing. Home: 15 Mackay Pl Brooklyn NY 11209-1040 Office: Met Realty Solutions 15 Mackay Pl Brooklyn NY 11209-1040

POLLACK, DANIEL, concert pianist; b. Los Angeles, Jan. 23, 1935. MS in Music, Juilliard Sch., 1957, Acad. Musik, Vienna, Austria, 1958. Asst. prof. U. Hartford, Conn., 1966-70; prof. piano U. So. Calif., Los Angeles, 1971—. Concert performances in U.S., USSR, Europe, Far East, South Am. Recipient prize Internat. Tschaikowsky Piano Competition, Moscow, USSR, 1958; Fulbright grantee, 1957-58; Martha Baird Rockefeller Found. grantee, 1963. Mem. Am. Fedn. Musicians, Kosciuszko Found., Chopin Found., Music Tchrs. Nat. Assn. (nat. exec. bd.). Office: U So Calif Dept Music Los Angeles CA 90089*

POLLACK, FLORENCE ZAKS, management consultant; b. Washington, Pa.; d. Charles and Ruth (Isaacson) Zaks; divorced; children: Melissa, Stephanie. BA, Flora Stone Mather Coll., Western Res. U., 1961. Pres., treas. Exec. Arrangements, Inc., Cleve., 1978—. Lobbyist Ohio Citizens Com. for Arts, Columbus, 1975-83; mem. Leadership Cleve., 1978-79; trustee jr. com. Cleve. Orch., mem. pub. rels. adv. com.; trustee Great Lakes Theatre Festival, 1989-90; mem. pub. rels. adv. com., Cleve. Ballet, Dance Cleve., Jr. Com. of No. Ohio Opera Assn., Cleve. Opera, Shakers Lakes Regional Nature Ctr., Cleve. Music Sch. Settlement, Playhouse Sq. Cabinet, Cleve. Ctr. Econ. Edn., ARC, Cleve. Conv. and Visitors Bur., domed stadium adv. com. Named Idea Woman of Yr. Cleve. Plain Dealer, 1975, to Au Courrant list Cleve. Mag., 1979, one of Cleve.'s 100 Most Influential Women, 1985, one of 1988 Trendsetters Cleve. Woman mag. Mem. Cleve. Area Meeting Planning, Skating Club, Univ. Club, Women's City Club, Playhouse Club, Shoreby Club. Avocations: arts, travel, reading. Office: Exec Arrangements Inc 13221 Shaker Sq Cleveland OH 44120-2314

POLLACK, GERALD ALEXANDER, economist, government official; b. Vienna, Austria, Jan. 14, 1929; came to U.S. 1938; s. Stephen J. and Tini (Herschel) P.; m. Patricia S. Sisterson; children: Nora S., Carol A. BA, Swarthmore (Pa.) Coll., 1951; MA, MPA, Princeton U., 1953, PhD, 1958. Corp. economist Leeds & Northrup Co., Phila., 1958-62; officer in charge internat. payments U.S. Dept. State, Washington, 1962-63; internat. economist Joint Econ. Com. of Congress, Washington, 1963-65; chief economist Office Spl. Rep. for Trade Negotiations, 1964; dep. asst. sec. U.S. Dept. Commerce, Washington, 1965-68; v.p. Loeb, Rhoades & Co., N.Y.C., 1968-69, Bendix Corp., Southfield, Mich., 1969-70, Citibank, N.Y.C., 1970-71; internat. economist Exxon Corp., N.Y.C., 1971-86; v.p., chief economist Overseas Shipholding Group, N.Y.C., 1986-89; assoc. prof. fin. Pace U., N.Y.C., 1990-94; assoc. dir. for internat. econs. Bur. Econ. Analysis, U.S. Dept. Commerce, 1994—. Contbr. articles to profl. jours. Bd. dirs. Jamaica Estates Assn., 1976-80, Oakwood Sch., Poughkeepsie, N.Y., 1979-89; trustee Lindley Murray Fund, 1990-94; mem. Greenwich Dem. Town Com., 1992-94; clk. Flushing Friends monthly meeting Soc. of Friends, 1990-94. With U.S. Army, 1953-55. Mem. Am. Econ. Assn., Nat. Assn. Bus. Economists, Coun. on Fgn. Rels., Forecasters Club N.Y., Downtown Economists Club, Phi Beta Kappa. Soc. of Friends. Avocations: cello, classical music, photography, hiking, bicycling.

POLLACK, GERALD HARVEY, bioengineering educator; b. Bklyn., May 20, 1940; s. Max and Helen (Solomon) P.; m. Sylvia A. Byrne, Aug. 12, 1966 (div. 1982); children: Seth Benjamin, Ethan David, Mia Raphaella. BS, Poly. Inst. Bklyn., 1961; PhD, U. Pa., 1968. Mem. faculty U. Wash. Med. Sch., Seattle, 1968—; prof. bioengring. U. Wash. Med. Sch., 1977—. Author: Muscles and Molecules: Uncovering the Principles of Biological Motion, 1990 (Excellence award Soc. for Tech. Communication 1992); coeditor: Ballistocardiography and Cardiac Performance, 1967, Cross-bridge Mechanism of Muscle Contraction, 1979, Contractile Mechanisms in Muscle, 1983, Molecular Mechanism of Muscle Contraction, 1988, Mechanism of Sliding in Muscle Contraction, 1993; mem. editorial bd. Jour. Molecular and Cellular Cardiology, 1975-80, Am. Jour. Physiology, 1976-80, Circulation Rsch., 1982-89; contbr. articles to profl. jours. Established investigator Am. Heart Assn., 1974-79. Recipient Kulka award Poly. Inst. Bklyn., 1961; grantee NIH, 1970—; grantee Am. Heart Assn., 1973—; grantee Muscular Dystrophy Assn. Am., 1980. Fellow Am. Inst. Med. and Biol. Engring. (founding); mem. Bioengring. Soc. (dir. 1976-79), Biophys. Soc., Am. Heart Assn. (exec. com. Basic Sci. Coun. 1982-86), Eta Kappa Nu, Tau Beta Pi, Alpha Epsilon Pi. Address: 3714 48th Ave NE Seattle WA 98105-5250

POLLACK, GERALD J., financial executive; b. N.Y.C., Jan. 20, 1942; s. Charles and Reba P.; m. Diane Pollack, Aug. 30, 1964; children: Suzanne, Jennifer, John. BS in Physics, Rensselaer Poly Inst., 1963; MBA, Dartmouth Coll., 1965. Comptroller trainee Exxon Corp., N.Y.C., 1965-67; asst. ops. comptroller Amerada Hess, Woodbridge, N.J., 1967-68; mgr. customer svc. Arthur Young & Co., N.Y.C., 1969-73; dir. mgmt. svc. Arthur Young & Co., Stamford, Conn., 1973-74; v.p., controller Avis Inc., Garden City, L.I., 1975-81; sr. v.p., chief fin. officer Rayonier, Stamford, 1982—. Mem. N.Y. Adv. Bd. Allendale Ins. Co., Fin. Exec. Inst. Office: Rayonier Inc 1177 Summer St Stamford CT 06905-5522

POLLACK, GERALD LESLIE, physicist, educator; b. Bklyn., July 8, 1933; s. Herman and Jennie (Tenenbaum) P.; m. Antoinette Amparo Velasquez, Dec. 22, 1958; children: Harvey Anton, Samuela Juliet, Margolita Mia, Violet Amata. BS, Bklyn. Coll., 1954; Fulbright scholar, U. Gottingen, 1954-55; MS, Calif. Inst. Tech., 1957, PhD, 1962. Physics student trainee Nat. Bur. Standards, Washington, 1954-58, solid state physicist, 1961-65; cons. Nat. Bur. Standards, Boulder, Colo., 1965-70; assoc. prof. dept. physics Mich. State U., East Lansing, 1965-69, prof., 1969—; cons. NRC, Ill. Dept. Nuclear Safety; physicist Naval Med. Rsch. Inst., Bethesda, Md., summer 1979; physicist USAF Sch. Aerospace Medicine, San Antonio, Tex., summer 1987. Contbr. articles to profl. jours. Fellow Am. Phys. Soc., AAAS, Am. Assn. Physics Tchrs. Office: Mich State U Dept Physics and Astronomy East Lansing MI 48824-1116

POLLACK, HENRY NATHAN, geophysics educator; b. Omaha, July 13, 1936; s. Harold Myron and Sylvia (Chait) P.; m. Lana Beth Schoenberger, Jan. 29, 1963; children—Sara Beth (dec.) John David. A.B., Cornell U., 1958; M.S., U. Nebr., 1960; Ph.D., U. Mich., 1963. Lectr. U. Mich., 1962, asst. prof., asso. prof. geophysics, 1964—, assoc. dean for research, 1982-85, chmn. dept. geol. scis., 1988-91; rsch. fellow Harvard U., 1963-64; sr. lectr. U. Zambia, 1970-71; vis. scientist U. Durham, U. Newcastle-on-Tyne, Eng., 1977-78, U. Western Ont., 1985-86; chmn. Internat. Heat Flow Commn., 1991-95. Fellow AAAS, Geol. Soc. Am.; mem. Am. Geophys. Union. Achievements include research on thermal evolution of the earth, recent climate change. Office: U Mich Dept Geol Scis Ann Arbor MI 48109

POLLACK, HERBERT WILLIAM, electronics executive; b. N.Y.C., Mar. 27, 1927; s. Benjamin and Shirley (Fine) P.; m. Sandra Rowe, March 26, 1950; children: Jill C., Mindy L. BEE, CCNY, 1950; MEE, NYU, 1953. Electronic engr. A.B. Dumont Co., Clifton, N.J., 1950-51; rsch. assoc. NYU, N.Y.C., 1951-54; electronic engr. CBS - Columbia, N.Y.C., 1954-55; v.p., dir. Polarad Electronics Inc., N.Y.C., 1955-65; group div. mgr. Sanders Assocs., Nashua, N.H., 1965-70; chmn., pres. Parlex Corp., Methuen, Mass., 1970—; pres., dir. Inst. for Interconnecting and Packaging Electronic Cirs., Lincolnwood, Ill., 1984-86. With USN, 1945-46. Fellow IEEE; mem. Am. Arbitration Assn. (arbitrator), Tau Beta Pi, Eta Kappa Nu. Avocations: reading, music, tennis. Office: Parlex Corp 145 Milk St Methuen MA 01844-4699

POLLACK, IRWIN WILLIAM, psychiatrist, educator; b. Phila., Aug. 14, 1927; s. Nathan and Rose (Bergman) P.; m. Barbara Jean Callaway, Oct. 9, 1988; children from previous marriage: Nathaniel Edward, Joshua Frank, Jonathan Daniel. A.B., Temple U., 1950; M.A., Columbia, 1951; student, U. Pa., 1951-52; M.D., U. Vt., 1956. Diplomate: Am. Bd. Psychiatry and Neurology. Intern Grad. Hosp. U. Pa., 1956-57; asst. resident psychiatry Henry Phipps Psychiat. Clinic (John Hopkins Hosp.), 1957-60; chief resident psychiatry Johns Hopkins Hosp., 1960-61, administr. psychosomatic clinic, psychiat. liaison service, 1961-64; psychiatrist-in-chief Sinai Hosp., Balt., 1964-68; mem. faculty psychiatry Coll. Medicine and Dentistry N.J. (Rutgers Med. Sch.), 1968-87; U. Medicine and Dentistry N.J., Robert Wood Johnson Med. Sch., 1987—; asso. prof. psychiatry, 1968-70, prof. psychiatry, 1970—; chmn. dept. Univ. Medicine and Dentistry, prof. neurology, dir. Ctr. for Cognitive Rehab.; exec. dir. Coll. Medicine and Dentistry (Community Mental Health Ctr.), 1970-77. Served with USNR, 1945-46. Fellow Am. Psychiat. Assn. (life); mem. N.J. Psychiat. Assn., Am. Psychosomatic Soc., Am. Congress Rehab. Medicine, Alpha Omega Alpha. Rsch. research on problems of time and space perception, psychology of phys. disability, doctor-patient relationships, cognitive retraining of brain-injured persons. Home: 324 Lincoln Ave Highland Park NJ 08904-1827 Office: Robert Wood Johnson Med Sch U Medicine and Dentistry NJ Hoes Ln Piscataway NJ 08854

POLLACK, JOE, newspaper critic and columnist, free-lance writer; b. Bklyn., Feb. 3, 1931; s. Samuel H. and Anna (Weisman) P.; m. Joan S., Mar. 6, 1952 (div. 1964); children: Wendy, Dara, Sharon; m. Carol Atchison, Dec. 1, 1964 (dec. 1993); m. Ann Lemons, Nov. 20, 1994. BJ, U. Mo., 1952. Sports writer St. Louis Globe-Democrat, 1955-61; dir. pub. rels. St. Louis Football Cardinals, 1961-72; critic, columnist St. Louis Post-Dispatch, 1972—; critic Sta. KSDK-TV, St. Louis, 1973-88, Sta. KMOV-TV, St. Louis, 1988-92; commentator Sta. KMOX, St. Louis, 1960-85, Sta. KWMU, St. Louis, 1994—. Author: Joe Pollack's Guide to St. Louis Restaurants, 1988, updated, 1992; contbr. numerous articles to mags. Mem. Am. Theatre Critics Assn., Profl. Football Writers Assn., Am. Soc. Profl. Journalists, Internat. Writers Ctr. (adv. bd. St. Louis). Home: 7417 Oxford Dr Saint Louis MO 63105 Office: St Louis Post-Dispatch 900 N Tucker Blvd Saint Louis MO 63101-1069

POLLACK, JOSEPH, diversified company executive; b. Bklyn., Jan. 7, 1939; s. Soloman and Sophie (Kaufman) P.; m. Larissa Humeniuk, Feb. 27, 1985. BA, Bklyn. Coll., 1960; JD, NYU, 1964, LLM, 1965. Bar: N.Y. 1965. V.p. taxes AMF Inc., White Plains, N.Y., 1965-85; exec. v.p. taxes Grand Met. Inc., Mpls., 1985-93; tax cons. to pvt. clients, 1993—. Fulbright scholar, 1963. Mem. ABA, N.Y. State Bar Assn., Assn. of Bar of City of N.Y., Order of Coif. Republican. Avocation: landscape gardening. Home: 310 Disney Rd Nondland WA 98358

POLLACK, JOSEPH, retired labor union official; b. N.Y.C., Nov. 21, 1917; s. George and Martha (Miller) P.; m. Theresa Keenan, Dec. 17, 1941; 1 son, Terry. Student pub. schs., N.Y.C. Agt. Prudential Ins. Co., N.Y.C., 1946-52; pres. Local 19, Ins. Workers Internat. Union AFL-CIO, N.Y.C., 1952-61; v.p. Ins. Workers Internat. Union AFL-CIO, Washington, 1961-76, pres., 1976-83; assoc. dir. profl. ins., fin. and healthcare div. United Food and Comml. Workers Internat. Union, AFL-CIO, 1983-88, ret., 1988; mem. exec. bd. dept. profl. employees AFL-CIO.; bd. dirs., Labor Inst. Human Enrichment. Editor: Insurance Worker, 1976. Mem. Pres.'s Com. Employment Handicapped. Served with AUS, 1941-45. Democrat. Jewish. *The price of leadership is hard work and a willingness to accept responsibility. The main attribute of continued elected leadership is total fairness and under all circumstances. Dignity in leadership and a dedication to the dignity of all mankind makes for a worthwhile organization.*

POLLACK, LOUIS, telecommunications company executive; b. N.Y.C., Nov. 4, 1920; s. Benjamin and Lena (Woloshen) P.; m. Dorothy Silverman, Feb. 4, 1945; children: Annette Pollack Rachlin, Barbara Pollack Held, Lawrence. BEE, CCNY, 1953; postgrad., Stevens Inst. Tech., 1954-55. Registered profl. engr. Dir. transmission system ops. ITT Fed. Labs., Nutley, N.J., 1943-67; exec. dir. Comsat Labs., Clarksburg, Md., 1967-80; v.p. world systems div. Communications Satellite Corp., Washington, 1980-84; cons. Satellite System design, 1984—; del. XVIII Gen. Assembly Nat. Acad. Sci. Contbr. articles to profl. jours.; patentee in field. Fellow IEEE; mem. AIAA (asso. fellow), Nat. Soc. Profl. Engrs., Sigma Xi. Office: 15321 Delphinium Ln Rockville MD 20853-1725

POLLACK, MICHAEL, lawyer; b. N.Y.C., July 14, 1946; s. Irving and Bertha (Horowitz) P.; m. Barbara Linda Shore, Aug. 23, 1970; children: Matthew, Ilana. BEng, Cooper Union, 1967; MS, U. Pa., 1970; JD, Temple U., 1974. Bar: Pa. 1974, U.S. Dist. Ct. (ea. dist.) Pa. 1974. Rsch. scientist Pa. Rsch. Assocs., Phila., 1968-69; engr. GE Co., Valley Forge, Pa., 1969-70, Burroughs Corp., Great Valley, Pa., 1970-71; assoc. Blank, Rome, Comisky & McCauley, Phila., Pa., 1974-82; ptnr. Blank, Rome, Comisky & McCauley, Phila., 1982—; lectr., course planner Pa. Bar Inst., Phila., chmn. legal edn. com. for R.E. Dept. Mem. ABA, Pa. Bar Assn., Phila. Bar Assn., Eta Kappa Nu, Tau Beta Pi. Republican. Avocations: music, tennis. Office: Blank Rome Comisky & McCauley 4 Penn Center Plz Philadelphia PA 19103-2521

POLLACK, MILTON, federal judge; b. N.Y.C., Sept. 29, 1906; s. Julius and Betty (Schwartz) P.; m. Lillian Klein, Dec. 18, 1932 (dec. July 1967); children—Stephanie Pollack Singer, Daniel A.; m. Moselle Baum Erlich, Oct. 24, 1971. A.B., Columbia U., 1927, J.D., 1929. Bar: N.Y. 1930. Assoc. Gilman & Unger, N.Y.C., 1929-38; ptnr. Unger & Pollack, N.Y.C., 1938-44; propr. Milton Pollack, N.Y.C., 1945-67; dist. judge U.S. Dist. Ct. (so. dist.) N.Y., 1967—, sr. status, 1983; mem. com. ct. adminstrn. Jud. Conf. 1968-87, mem. Jud. Panel on Multi-dist. Litigation, 1986. Mem. Prospect Park So. Assn., Bklyn., pres., 1948-50, counsel, 1950-60, trustee, 1954-60; mem. local SSS, 1952-60; chmn. lawyers div. Fedn. Jewish Philanthropies, 1957-61, vice chmn., 1954-57; chmn. lawyers div. Am. Jewish Com., 1967, bd. dirs., from 1967; hon. dir. Beth Isreal Hosp.; trustee Temple Emanu-El, from 1977, v.p., from 1978. Recipient Learned Hand award Am. Jewish Com., 1967, Proskauer medal lawyers divsn. Fedn. Jewish Philanthropies, 1968, Disting. Svc. medal N.Y. County Lawyers Assn., 1991, Fordham-Stein Prize award, 1994, Devitt award Disting. Svc. to Justice, 1995; decorated chevalier Legion of Honor (France). Mem. ABA, N.Y. State Bar Assn., Assn. of Bar of City of N.Y., Columbia Law Sch. Alumni Assn. (pres. 1970-72), Harmonie Club (bd. trustees). Office: US Dist Ct US Courthouse Foley Sq New York NY 10007-1501

POLLACK, NORMAN, history educator; b. Bridgeport, Conn., May 29, 1933; s. Benjamin and Mary (Beimel) P.; m. Nancy Bassing, Feb. 2, 1957; 1 son, Peter Franklin. B.A., U. Fla., 1954; M.A., Harvard U., 1957, Ph.D.,

1961. Instr. history Yale, 1961-62, asst. prof., 1962-65; asso. prof. Wayne State U., 1965-68; prof. Mich. State U., 1968—. Author: The Populist Response to Industrial America, 1962, The Populist Mind, 1967, The Just Polity, 1987, The Humane Economy, 1990. Guggenheim fellow, 1968-69. Home: 929 Roxburgh Ave East Lansing MI 48823-3130 Office: Dept of History Mich State U East Lansing MI 48824

POLLACK, PAUL ROBERT, airline service company executive; b. N.Y.C., Nov. 17, 1941; s. Harry and Hilda (Tepper) P.; m. Linda Weinstein, Aug. 14, 1965; children: Mark, Melissa. BBA, CCNY, 1962; MBA, L.I. U., Greenvale, N.Y., 1993. CPA, N.Y. Staff acct. Seidman & Seidman, N.Y.C., 1962-68; with Hudson Gen. Corp., Great Neck, N.Y., 1968—, exec. v.p., chief oper. officer, 1990—. With U.S. Army, 1962. Mem. AICPA, N.Y. State Soc. CPAs (Haskins award 1966). Office: Hudson Gen Corp 111 Great Neck Rd Great Neck NY 11021-5402

POLLACK, REGINALD MURRAY, painter, sculptor; b. Middle Village, L.I., N.Y., July 29, 1924; m. Kerstin Birgitta Soederlund; children by previous marriage: Jane Olivia, Maia Jaquine. Grad., High Sch. Music and Art, N.Y.C., 1941; student with, Wallace Harrison, Moses Soyer, Boardman Robinson; student, Academie de la Grande Chaumiere, 1948-52. Occasional asst. to Constantin Brancusi; vis. critic Yale U., 1962-63, Cooper Union, 1963-64; mem. staff Human Rels. Tng. Ctr., UCLA, 1966; artistic dir. The Gallery, Washington Collection Fine Arts, Leesburg, Va., 1991—; chmn. artists adv. com. Loudon Arts Coun., Va., 1990-93. One-man shows include Charles Fourth Gallery, N.Y.C., 1948, Peridot Gallery, 1949, 52, 55-57, 59, 60, 62, 63, 65, 67, 69, Galerie Saint-Placide, Paris, 1952, Dwan Gallery, 1960, Jefferson Gallery, LaJolla, Calif., 1963, 68, 69, Goldwach Gallery, Chgo., 1964, 65, 66, Gallery Z, Beverly Hills, Calif., 1973, David Alexander Gallery, 1974, Washington Gallery Arts, 1974, Cosmos Club, Washington, 1976, Washington Project for Arts, 1976, Everhart Mus., Scranton, Pa., 1977, Pa. State U., 1977, Jack Rasmussen gallery, 1978, 79, 80, 81, 82, Art Washington, 1979, 81, Corcoran Mus., 1980, Zenith Gallery, Washington, 1982, Summit Gallery, N.Y., 1982, Tartt Gallery, Washington, 1986, Arctic Images Gallery, Aspen, Colo., 1987, Loudoun County Adminstrn. Bldg., 1988, Susan Conway Carroll Gallery, Washington, 1990, The Gallery, Leesburg, 1992, Loudoun Valley Vineyard, Waterford, Va., 1992-93, The Natural Light Art School Gallery, Lynchberg, Va., 1995; exhibited group shows including Whitney Mus. Am. Art, 1953, 55, 56, 58, 62, U. Nebr., 1951, 56, 57, 60, 63, Chgo. Art Inst., Carnegie, Pitts., Salon du Mai, Paris, U. Ill., Salon des Artistes Independants, Paris, 1955-58, NAS, 1990, NIH, 1990, Elaine Benson Gallery, Bridgehampton, L.I., 1991, numerous others; multimedia theatrical prodns. The War of The Angels, 1974; The Twelve Gifts of Christmas, 1974; comms. include Jacob's Ladder painting, Washington Cathedral, bronze sculpture, The World Bank, awarded to King of Thailand; represented in permanent collections, Bezalel Mus., Bklyn. Mus., Collection de L'Etat, France, U. Glasgow, Haifa, Mus. Modern Art, U. Nebr., Newark Mus., Rockefeller Inst., Whitney Mus. Am. Art, Worcester Art Mus., Nat. Mus. Am. Art, Ft. Lauderdale (Fla.) Mus., Loew Mus. U. Miami, Fla., Met. Mus., N.Y., numerous other pub. and pvt. collections.; author and illustrator: The Magician and the Child, 1971; illustrator: Get a Horse (Steven Price), 1974, Visions from the Ramble (John Hollander), 1964, The Quest of the Gole (John Hollander), 1966, O is for Overkill, A Survival Alphabet (Merrill Pollack), 1968, The Blessed Ones (Ulla Isaksson), 1970, Oedipus (Seneca, transl. Ted Hughes), 1973, The Enjoyment of Music (Joseph Machlis). Instr. Quaker Half-way House, Los Angeles, 1968; cons. staff Lighthouse Child Guidance Center Presbyn. Hosp., 1966-69; pvt. instr., 1966-69; vis. artist Materials Research Lab., Pa. State U., 1977; trustee Washington Project for Arts, 1976-80. Served with AUS, 1941-45. Recipient Prix Neumann Paris, 1952, Prix Othon Friesz Paris, mention, 1954, 57, Prix de Peintres Etrangeres, 2d prize Paris Moderne, 1958; Ingram-Merrill Found. grantee, 1964, 70-71. Address: Rt 1 Box 955 Waterford VA 22190

POLLACK, RICHARD W., lawyer. Pub. defender Honolulu. Office: Pub Defender Ste A135 1130 N Nimitz Hwy Rm A135 Honolulu HI 96817-4580

POLLACK, ROBERT ELLIOT, biological sciences educator, writer, scientist; b. Bklyn., Sept. 2, 1940; s. Hyman Ephraim and Molly (Pollack) P.; m. Amy Louise Steinberg, Dec. 23, 1961; 1 child, Marya. B.A. in Physics, Columbia U., 1961; Ph.D. in Biology, Brandeis U., 1966. Asst. prof. pathology Med. Sch. NYU, N.Y.C., 1969-70; sr. scientist Cold Spring Harbor Lab., N.Y., 1971-75; prof. microbiology Med. Sch., SUNY-Stony Brook, 1975-78; prof. biol. sci. Columbia U., N.Y.C., 1978—; dean Columbia Coll., N.Y.C., 1982-89; bd. dirs. Applied Microbiology, Inc.; instr. Pratt Archtl. Sch., Bklyn., 1970; vis. prof. pharmacology Albert Einstein Coll. Medicine, Bronx, N.Y., 1977-92; lectr. Rosenthal Colloquium, March of Dimes, 1989; McGregory lectr. Colgate U., 1979; du Vigneaud lectr. Med. Sch., Cornell U., 1983. Co-editor: Readings in Mammalian Cell Culture, 19734, 3d rev. edit., 1981, Signs of Life, 1984 (translations in 4 langs., Lionel Trilling award 1995); mng. editor BBA Revs. on Cancer 1980-86; contbr. numerous rsch. articles on molecular cell biology to profl. jours. Trustee N.Y. Found., 1986—, Brandeis U., 1989-94. Recipient Rsch. Career Devel. award NIH, 1974, Alexander Hamilton medal Columbia U., 1989; NIH spl. fellow Weizmann Inst., Rehovot, Israel, 1970-71; grantee Nat. Cancer Inst., NIH, 1968-92, Am. Cancer Soc., 1985-94; John Simon Guggenheim fellow, 1993. Fellow AAAS; mem. N.Y. Acad. Scis., Am. Soc. Microbiology. Jewish. Office: Columbia U Dept Biol Scis 813 Fairchild Hall New York NY 10027

POLLACK, RONALD F(RANK), foundation executive, lawyer; b. N.Y.C., Feb. 21, 1944; s. Max Louis and Hanna Esther (Borchardt) Pollack Baruch; m. Rebecca Lucy Bolling, Jan. 8, 1972; children: Sarah Shoshana, Abraham Max, Martin Landrum. B.A., Queens Coll., 1965; J.D., NYU, 1968. Bar: N.Y. 1968, D.C. 1978, U.S. Ct. Appeals (D.C. cir) 1970, U.S. Ct. Appeals (5th cir) 1971, U.S. Ct. Appeals (6th cir) 1974, U.S. Supreme Ct. 1973. Atty. Ctr. on Social Welfare Policy and Law, N.Y.C., 1968-73; founder, exec. dir. Food Research and Action Ctr., N.Y.C., 1970-80; dean Antioch Sch. Law, Washington, 1980-83; exec. dir. Families U.S.A., Washington, 1983—; Families U.S.A Found., Washington, 1983—; sec. treas., bd. dirs. Food Research and Action Ctr., Washington, 1980—; mem. civil legal services D.C. Jud. Conf. Com., 1980-83. Author: If We Had Ham, We Could Have Ham and Eggs...If We Had Eggs: A Study of the National School Breakfast Program, 1972, Out to Lunch: A Study of USDA's Child Care Feeding and Summer Feeding Programs, 1974; co-author: On the Other Side of Easy Street: Myths and Facts About the Economics of Old Age, 1987. Treas. Jewish Fund for Justice, 1985-88, bd. dirs., 1985-93; bd. dirs. Am. Jewish World Service, Self-Help Community Services, 1974-77; mem. domestic adv. bd., project rev. bd. U.S.A. for Africa/Hands Across Am., 1986-88; v.p. of bd. dirs. Burgundy Farm Country Day Sch., 1988-90, pres. 1990-91; bd. dirs. Americans for Health, 1986-81. Arthur Garfield Hays Civil Liberties fellow, 1967; research fellow Legal Services Corp., Washington, 1978-80.

POLLACK, SEYMOUR VICTOR, computer science educator; b. Bklyn., Aug. 3, 1933; s. Max and Sylvia (Harrison) P.; m. Sydell Altman, Jan. 23, 1955; children: Mark, Sherie. BChemE, Pratt Inst., 1954; MChemE, Bklyn. Poly. Inst., 1960. Lic. chem. engr., Ohio. Engr. Schwarz Labs., Mt. Vernon, N.Y., 1954-55; design engr. Curtiss-Wright, Wood-Ridge, N.J., 1955-57, Fairchild Engines, Deer Park, N.Y., 1957-59, GE, Evendale, Ohio, 1959-62; rsch. assoc. U. Cin., 1962-66; prof. computer sci. Washington U., St. Louis, 1966—; cons. Mo. Auto Club, St. Louis, 1969-82, United Van Lines, Fenton, Mo., 1984-86. Computer Sci. Accreditation Bd., N.Y.C., 1985—. Author: Structured Fortran, 1982, UCSD Pascal, 1984, Studies in Computer Science, 1983, The DOS Book, 1985, Turbo Pascal Programming, 1991; cons. editor Holt Rinehart & Winston, N.Y.C., 1979-86. Bd. dirs. Hillel orgn., Washington U., 1983-84. Recipient Alumni Achievement award Pratt Inst., 1966, Outstanding Teaching award Burlington Northern Found., 1987. Mem. Assns. for Computing Machinery, Am. Assn. for Engring. Edn. Jewish. Avocations: classical and jazz piano, jogging. Office: Campus Box 1045 Washington U Saint Louis MO 63130

POLLACK, SOLOMON ROBERT, bioengineering educator; b. Phila., May 7, 1934; s. Henry and Hannah (Segal) P.; married; children: Michael, Andrea, Carolyn. A.B. in Physics, U. Pa., 1955, M.S., 1957, Ph.D. 1961. Rsch. scientist Univac (div. Sperry Rand), Blue Bell, Pa., 1960-64; asst. prof. dept. materials sci. and engring. U. Pa., Phila., 1964-67; assoc. prof. U. Pa., 1967-75, prof., 1975—, prof., chmn. dept. bioengring., 1977-81, assoc. dean

grad. edn. and rsch. (Sch. Engring and Applied Sci.), 1981-86; pres. Cara Corp., Phila., 1971-85, chmn. bd., 1986-90. Editor: (with C. Brighton and J. Black) Electrical Properties of Bone and Cartilage, 1979; editor, contbr. to Ency. of Materials Sci. and Engring, 1981—; contbr. articles to profl. jours. Recipient Lindback award for disting. teaching, 1968, award for disting. rsch. Kappa Delta, 1985, bronze medal in honor of Luigi Galvani for disting. rsch. U. Bologna, 1989, S. Reid Warren award for disting. rsch., 1991, Clemson award for applied rsch., 1993. Fellow Am. Inst. Med. and Biol. Engring (pres. 1st World Congress in Electricity and Magnetism); mem. Soc. for Biomaterials (pres. 1981), Bioelectric Repair and Growth Soc. (pres. 1985), Orthopaedic Rsch. Soc., Bioelectromagnetics Soc., Engring. in Medicine and Biology, Sigma Xi. Jewish. Patentee in field. Home: 3213 Ayr Ln Fort Washington PA 19025-1603 Office: 116 Hayden Hall U Pa Philadelphia PA 19104

POLLACK, STANLEY P., lawyer; b. N.Y.C., Apr. 23, 1928; s. Isidor and Anna (Shulman) P.; m. Susan Aronowitz, June 16, 1974; 1 child, Jane. BA, NYU, 1948; JD, Harvard U., 1951; LLM in Taxation, NYU, 1959. Bar: N.Y. 1951, U.S. Dist. Ct. (so. dist.) N.Y. 1955. Sole practice N.Y.C., 1955-61; v.p., gen. counsel James Talcott, Inc., N.Y.C., 1961-73; exec. v.p., gen. counsel Rosenthal & Rosenthal Inc., N.Y.C., 1973—. Served to j.g. lt. USNR, 1951-54. Mem. Bklyn. Bar Assn. (banking com., bankruptcy com.), Fed. Bar Council, Assn. Comml. Fin. Atty.'s (pres. 1968). Club: Harvard (N.Y.C.). Home: 6 Peter Cooper Rd New York NY 10010-6701 Office: Rosenthal & Rosenthal Inc 1370 Broadway # 2 New York NY 10018-7302

POLLACK, STEPHEN J., stockbroker; b. N.Y.C., Aug. 25, 1937; s. Harold S. and Gladys H. Pollack; m. Barbara Jane Podgur, May, 1992; B.S. in Econs., U. Pa., 1960. Vice pres. retail sales Drexel Burnham Lambert, N.Y.C., 1960-77; v.p. retail sales, Drexel Burnham Lambert, N.Y.C., 1960-77, 1st v.p. investments Dean Witter Reynolds Inc., N.Y.C., 1978—; pres. Bnai Brith Gothem, N.Y.C.; exec. v.p. Cosmpolitan League of City of Hope; v.p., circle mem. Whitney Mus., N.Y.C.; treas. Sutton Pl. Synagogue, pres. Havurah Group. Served with USAR, 1966. Recipient Double Chai Citation, State of Israel Bonds, 1984; Appreciation award City of Hope, 1984, Kiter Key Club award Franklin Funds, Million Dollar Club Svc. award City of Hope, Bnai Brith Internat. award. Mem. Internat. Assn. Fin. Planners, Assn. Investment Brokers (dir.), Youngmen's Philanthropic League (bd. dirs.), Am. Biog. Inst. (life), Internat. Study & Research Inst, Dean Witter Pres. Club. Jewish. Clubs: Town, Atrium, Schuylkill Country, Wharton Sch., U. Pa., Yale, East River Tennis, Schuylkill Country, Matterhorn Sports, East Side Republican, Knickerbocker Republican, Friars, Penn (charter). Home: 245 E 40th St Apt 14E New York NY 10016-1714 Office: Dean Witter Reynolds Inc 900 3d Ave New York NY 10022

POLLACK, SYDNEY, film director; b. Lafayette, Ind., July 1, 1934; s. David and Rebecca (Miller) P.; m. Claire Griswold, Sept. 22, 1958; children: Steven, Rebecca, Rachel. Grad., Neighborhood Playhouse Theatre Sch., N.Y.C., 1954. Asst. to Sanford Meisner, Neighborhood Playhouse Theatre, 1954, instr. acting, 1954-60; exec. dir. West Coast br. The Actors Studio. Appeared in Broadway prodns.: The Dark Is Light Enough, 1954, A Stone For Danny Fisher, 1955; appeared on live TV programs: Alcoa Presents, others; toured in Stalag 17; dir. TV programs: The Chrysler Theatre, Ben Casey, 1962-63, Something About Lee Wiley, 1963-64; Films include: (dir.) The Slender Thread, 1965, This Property is Condemned, 1966, The Scalphunters, 1968, Castle Keep, 1969, Jeremiah Johnson, 1972, Three Days of the Condor, 1975, The Electric Horseman, 1979, The Firm, 1993; (dir., prodr.) They Shoot Horses, Don't They?, 1969, The Way We Were, 1973, The Yakuza, 1975, Bobby Deerfield, 1977, Absence of Malice, 1981, Tootsie, 1982 (also actor), Out of Africa, 1985 (Academy Award for Best Picture and Dir.), Havana, 1990; (prodr.) Songwriter, 1984, Bright Lights, Big City, 1988, The Fabulous Baker Boys, 1989, Presumed Innocent, 1990, The Firm, 1993; (exec. prodr.) Honeysuckle Rose, 1980, White Palace, 1990, King Ralph, 1991, Dead Again, 1991, Leaving Normal, 1992, Searching for Bobby Fischer, 1993; (actor) The Player, 1992, Death Becomes Her, 1992, Husbands and Wives, 1992, The Firm, 1993. Served with U.S. Army, 1957-59. Recipient Acad. award for best pic. and best picture, 1986. Office: Mirage Enterprises De Mille Bldg # 110 5555 Melrose Ave Hollywood CA 90038 also: CAA 9830 Wilshire Blvd Beverly Hills CA 90212-1804

POLLACK, SYLVIA BYRNE, educator, researcher, counselor; b. Ithaca, N.Y., Oct. 18, 1940; d. Raymond Tandy and Elsie Frances (Snell) Byrne; divorced; children: Seth Benjamin, Ethan David. BA, Syracuse U., 1962; PhD, U. Pa., 1967; MA, Antioch U., 1993. Instr. Women's Med. Coll. Pa., Phila., 1967-68; rsch. assoc. U. Wash., Seattle, 1968-73, rsch. asst. prof., 1973-77, rsch. assoc. prof., 1977-85, rsch. prof., 1985—, counselor Sch. Nursing, 1993—; asst. mem. Fred Hutchinson Cancer Ctr., Seattle, 1975-79, assoc. mem., 1979-81; mem. study sect. NIH, Washington, 1978-79, 83-85. Contbr. numerous articles to profl. jours.; reviewer for profl. jours. Recipient rsch. grants Am. Cancer Soc., 1969-79, Nat. Cancer Inst., 1973—, Chugai Pharm. Co., Japan, 1985-91. Mem. Am. Counsel Assn., Am. Assn. Immunologists, Soc. Devel. Biology, Soc. Leuc. Biology. Office: U Wash Box 357420 Seattle WA 98195-7420

POLLAK, BARTH, mathematics educator; b. Chgo., Aug. 14, 1928; s. Samuel and Esther (Hirschberg) P.; m. Helen Charlotte Schiller, Aug. 22, 1954; children: Martin Russell, Eleanor Susan. BS, Ill. Inst. Tech., 1950, MS, 1951; PhD, Princeton U., 1957. Instr. math. Ill. Inst. Tech., Chgo., 1956-58; assoc. prof. math. Syracuse (N.Y.) U., 1958-63; assoc. prof. U. Notre Dame, Ind., 1963-67, prof., 1967—. Office: U Notre Dame Dept Math Notre Dame IN 46556

POLLAK, EDWARD BARRY, chemical manufacturing company executive; b. N.Y.C., Sept. 6, 1934; s. Ben N. and Harriet E. (Springer) P.; m. Marianne E. Modi, Feb. 27, 1960; children—David, Anne, Kari. B.Chem. Eng., Cornell U., 1956, M.B.A., 1957. 1957-94 Olin Corp., 1957-94; bus. mgr. specialty and consumer products Olin Corp., Stamford, Conn., 1970-72; v.p. Olin Corp. (internat. Chems. Group), 1973-76, v.p., gen. mgr. designed products dept., 1976-80, corp. v.p., internat., 1980-86, pres., chief exec. officer Olin Hunt Specialty Products, Inc., 1986-93; chmn. OCG Microelectronic Materials Inc., 1991-93; v.p. internat. Olin Specialties Inc. 1994—; dir. Etoxyl C.A., Venezuela, Asahi-Olin Ltd., Japan; mem. steering com. internat. affairs group Chem. Mfrs. Assn. 1979-81, SRI adv. coun., 1994—. Bd. dirs. Stamford Symphony, U. Wyo. Inst. for Environment and Natural Resources. Mem. Synthetic Organic Chem. Mfrs. Assn. (gov. 1977-81, v.p. 1978, pres. 1979-80, steering com. internat. affairs group 1979-81), Internat. Isocyanate Inst. (bd. dirs. 1979-81), Cornell Soc. Engrs. (bd. dirs. 1967-72, v.p. 1971-72), Cornell Club For Fairfield County, Japan Soc.

POLLAK, HENRY OTTO, retired utility research executive, educator; b. Vienna, Austria, Dec. 13, 1927; came to U.S., 1940, naturalized, 1945; s. Ludwig and Olga (Weil) P.; m. Ida Jeanne Tobias, May 7, 1949; children: Katherine, James. BA, Yale, 1947; MA, Harvard U., 1948, PhD, 1951; DSc, Rose Poly. Inst., 1964; DSc (hon.), Monmouth Coll., 1975, Bowdoin Coll., 1977, Technol. U. Eindhoven, 1981; LLD (hon.), Montclair State Coll., 1984; DSc (hon.), Laval U., Que., 1992. With Bell Telephone Labs., Murray Hill, N.J., 1951-83; mem. tech. staff Bell Telephone Labs., 1951-59, head dept. communications fundamentals II, 1959-61, acting dir. math. and mechanics research center, 1961-62, dir. math. and statistics research center, 1962-83; asst. v.p. math., communications, computer scis. research Bell Communications Research, Morristown, N.J., 1984-86; mem. sch. math. study group, com. on undergrad. program in math. Internat. Commn. on Math. Instrn. 1970-74, 82-86, mem. adv. bd. Unified Sci. and Maths. for Elem. Schs., 1969-77; mem. adv. com. for sci. edn. NSF, 1977-80, 85-89, chmn., 1978-80; program chmn. 4th Internat. Congress Math. edn., 1980; bd. dirs. Math. Inst. Woodrow Wilson Found.; vis. prof. Tchrs. Coll., Columbia U., 1987—. Trustee N.C. Sch. for Sci. and Math, Durham, 1979-89; bd. dirs. COMAP, 1987—. Mem. Am. Math. Soc., Math. Assn. Am. (pres. 1975-76, Yueh-Gin Gung & Dr. Charles Y. Hu award for Disting. Svc. to Math. 1993), Nat. Coun. Tchrs. Math., Phi Beta Kappa, Sigma Xi. Mem. Christ Ch. Home: 40 Edgewood Rd Summit NJ 07901-3988

POLLAK, LOUIS HEILPRIN, federal judge, educator; b. N.Y.C., Dec. 7, 1922; s. Walter and Marion (Heilprin) P.; m. Katherine Weiss, July 25, 1952; children: Nancy, Elizabeth, Susan, Sarah, Deborah. A.B., Harvard, 1943; LL.B., Yale, 1948. Bar: N.Y. bar 1949, Conn. bar 1956, Pa. bar 1976. Law clk. to U.S. Supreme Ct. Justice Rutledge, 1948-49; with firm Paul, Weiss, Rifkind, Wharton & Garrison, N.Y.C., 1949-51; atty., spl. asst. to Dept. State, 1951-53; asst. counsel Amalgmated Clothing Workers Am., 1954-55; mem. faculty Yale Law Sch., 1955-74, dean, 1965-70; Greenfield prof. U. Pa., 1974-78, dean Law Sch., 1975-78, lectr., 1980—; U.S. dist. judge for Eastern dist. Pa., 1978—; vis. lectr. Howard U. Sch. Law, 1953; vis. prof. U. Mich. Law Sch., 1961, Columbia Law Sch., 1962. Author: The Constitution and the Supreme Court: A Documentary History, 1966. Mem. New Haven Bd. Edn., 1962-68; chmn. Conn. adv. com. U.S. Civil Rights Commn., 1962-63; mem. bd. NAACP Legal Def. Fund, 1960-78, v.p., 1971-78; chmn. New Haven Human Rights Com., 1963-64. Served with AUS, 1943-46. Mem. ABA (chmn. sec. individual rights 1970-71), Assn. Bar City N.Y., Fed. Bar Assn., Phila. Bar Assn., Am. Law Inst. (coun. 1978—). Office: US Dist Ct 16613 US Courthouse 601 Market St Philadelphia PA 19106-1510

POLLAK, MARK, lawyer; b. Paris, July 16, 1947; came to U.S., 1955; s. Joseph and Zofia (Berkowitz) P.; m. Joanne Elizabeth Harris, Dec. 26, 1976; children: Joshua David, Jonathan Stephen, Benjamin Eric, Rebecca Lynn. BA, Bklyn. Coll., 1968; MA in City Planning, U. Pa., 1972, JD, 1972. Bar: Md. 1972. Assoc. Piper & Marbury, Balt., 1972-81, ptnr., 1981—; pres. Balt. Corp. for Housing Partnerships; bd. dirs. Balt. Regional Community Devel. Corp. Bd. dirs. Balt. Children's Mus., Downtown Partnership of Balt., Inc. Mem. ABA, Md. Bar Assn., Am. Coll. Real Estate Lawyers, Am. Planning Assn., Nat. Assn. Bond Lawyers. Office: Piper & Marbury 36 S Charles St Baltimore MD 21201-3020

POLLAK, MARTIN MARSHALL, patent development company executive; b. N.Y.C., July 31, 1927; s. Edward and Jennie (Horowitz) P.; m. Ellen R. Spiegel, Sept. 16, 1929; children: David W., Richard M., Barbara S. AB, Syracuse U., 1950; LLB, St. John's U., Bklyn., 1953. Bar: N.Y. 1953, U.S. Dist. Ct. (ea. and so. dists.) N.Y. 1957, U.S. Supreme Ct. 1959. Ptnr. Feldman & Pollak, Attys., N.Y.C., 1953-59; atty. N.Y. State, 1953—; founder, exec. v.p., treas. Nat. Patent Devel. Corp., N.Y.C., 1959—; pres. Internat. Hydron Corp., Woodbury, N.Y., 1981-88; chmn. bd. Interferon Scis. Corp., New Brunswick, N.J., 1981—, Gen. Physics Corp., Columbia, Md., 1987—; trustee Worcester Found. for Exptl. Rsch., Shrewsbury, Mass., 1977—; bd. dirs. Duratek Corp., Silver Spring, Md., Brandon Corp., Secaucus, N.J.; cons. Allergan Optical Corp., Irvine, Calif., 1988-89; chmn. bd. Czechoslovak-U.S. Econ. Coun., Washington, 1987—; pres. NPO Trading USA, Inc., N.Y.C., Washington, Prague, Czechoslovakia, 1990—, Am. Drug Co., Washington, N.Y., Moscow, 1993—. With USN, 1945-47. Recipient gold medal Czechoslovakian Rep. C. of C., 1984. Office: Nat Patent Devel Corp 9 W 57th St New York NY 10019-2600 also: Gen Physics Corp 6700 Alexander Bell Dr Columbia MD 21046

POLLAK, RICHARD, writer, editor; b. Chgo., Apr. 5, 1934; s. Robert and Janet (Spitzer) P.; m. Merle Ann Winer, Mar. 26, 1961 (div. 1979); 1 dau., Amanda.; m. Diane Walsh, Mar. 6, 1982. Student, Knox Coll., 1952-54; B.A. in English, Amherst Coll., 1957. Reporter Worcester (Mass.) Telegram & Gazette, 1957; polit. reporter Evening Sun, Balt., 1959-64; assoc. editor Newsweek, N.Y.C., 1964-67; asst. editor Honolulu Star Bull., 1967-68; freelance writer N.Y.C., 1968-71; co-founder, editor More mag., N.Y.C., 1971-76; lit. editor The Nation, 1980-81, exec. editor, 1988-89; editor-at-large, 1989—; tchr. Yale U., spring 1977, NYU, fall 1977, 82-86; cons. Ford Found., 1970-72. Author: Up Against Apartheid, 1981, The Episode, 1986; editor: Stop The Presses, I Want To Get Off!, 1975. Served with AUS, 1957-59. Poynter fellow Yale U., 1977. Mem. Authors Guild. Home and Office: 404 Riverside Dr New York NY 10025-1861

POLLAK, SAM, sports editor, columnist; b. Queens, N.Y., May 18, 1950; s. Harry Jacob and Hannah (Brodsky) P.; m. Julie Ann Anderson, Aug. 27, 1978; children: Rachel, Deborah, Sarah, Joseph. Attended, U. Tex., El Paso. Reporter/slot Hollywood (Fla.) Sun-Tattler, 1976-77; slot/desk Miami (Fla.) News, 1977-78, Dallas Times Herald, 1978-80; sports editor The Ariz. Daily Star, Tucson, 1980-85; sports copy desk chief Dallas Morning News, 1985-86; sports mng. editor New Orleans Times-Picayune, 1986-90; dep. sports editor The Plain Dealer, Cleve., 1990-91; sports editor The Fresno (Calif.) Bee, 1991-93; asst. mng. editor Thomson L.A. News Group, West Covina, Calif., 1993—. Mem. AP Sports Editors. Democrat. Jewish. Avocations: reading, sports, politics, history. Office: Thomson LA News Group 1210 N Azusa Canyon Rd West Covina CA 91790

POLLAK, TIM, advertising agency executive. Exec. v.p. Young & Rubicam N.Y., 1987; pres., CEO D,Y&R Worldwide (formerly HDM Worldwide), 1987—; corp. CEO HDM Worldwide; pres., CEO HDM USA, N.Y.C., 1987-90, Young & Rubicam NY, N.Y.C., 1990-91; vice chmn. Young & Rubicam Advt., N.Y.C., 1991—; mem. exec. com., bd. dirs. Young & Rubicam, Inc.; mem. exec. com., bd. dirs. Dentsu, Young & Rubicam. Mem. Internat. Advt. Assn. (pres. N.Y. chpt. 1988-90, mem. worldwide bd. dirs.). Office: Young & Rubicam NY 285 Madison Ave New York NY 10017-6402

POLLAK, WILLIAM L., newspaper publishing executive. Exec. v.p. sales The New York Times, N.Y.C. Office: The New York Times 229 W 43rd St New York NY 10036-3913*

POLLAN, CAROLYN JOAN, state legislator; b. Houston, July 12, 1937; d. Rex and Faith (Basye) Clark; B.S. in Radio and TV, Univ. Brown U., 1959; postgrad. NYU, 1959; PhD in Edn., Walden U., 1993. m. George A. Pollan, Jan. 6, 1962; children—Cee Cee, Todd (dec.), Robert. Mem. Ark. Ho. of Reps., 1974—, now sr. Republican mem., asst. speaker pro-tempore, 1993; apptd. by Gov. numerous coms., commns.; ex-officio mem. Workplace Literacy Project Adv. Bd. U.S. Dept. Labor & Ednl. Testing Svc., 1990-93, Nat. Adult Literacy Survey, 1990-93; del. Am. Soviet Seminar, Am. Council Young Polit. Leaders, Exeter, N.H., 1976; co-developer Total Touch Test; owner Patent Model Mus. Vice chmn. Ark. Rep. Com., 1972-76; del. Rep. Nat. Conv., 1976; bd. dirs. Ark. Cancer Soc., Ark. Easter Seals Soc.; bd. dirs. Greg Kistler Treatment Center for Physically Handicapped, Ark. Found. Assoc. Colls., 4-H Found. for Sebastian County; trustee John Brown U.; mem. legis. adv. com. So. Regional Edn. Bd. Recipient Conservation Legislator of Yr. award Ark. Wildlife Fedn., Nat. Wildlife Fedn., Sears Roebuck & Co., 1976, Outstanding State Legislator of Yr. award Ark. Pub. Employees Assn., 1979, Lifetime Mem. award Ark. PTA, 1994, many others; named 1 of 10 Outstanding Legislators, Assembly of Govtl. Employees, 1980, Legislator of Yr., Ark. Human Service Providers Assn., 1982, Citizen of Yr. by Ark. Social Workers, 1993, Outstanding Women in Ark. Politics by Ark. Dem., 1990, One of 10 Top Legislators in 1993 Ark. Dem. Gazette, 1993, one of Top 100 Women in Ark., Ark. Bus. Publ., 1995; voted 1 of Ft. Smith's 10 Most Influential Citizens, S.W. Times Record Readers, 1979. Mem. Ark. Internat. Woman's Forum (founding mem.), Ft. Smith Car Restoration Assn. Baptist. Address: House of Reps State Capitol Little Rock AR 72201 Office: 400 N 8th St Fort Smith AR 72901-2204

POLLARA, BERNARD, immunologist, pediatrician; b. Chgo.; s. Joseph and Mamie P. PhB, Northwestern U., 1951, MS, 1954; MD, U. Minn., 1960, PhD, 1963. Intern USPHS Hosp., Seattle, 1960; resident in pediatrics U. Minn. Hosps., 1960-69; rsch. assoc. pediatrics U. Minn., 1960-63, assoc. prof. biochemistry and pediatrics, 1969; prof. pediatrics Albany (N.Y.) Med. Coll., 1969-94, chmn. dept., 1979-93; pediatrician in chief Albany Med. Ctr. Hosp., 1979-93; sabbatical leave, pediatrician Yukon Kuskokwim Regional Hosp., 1992-93; John and Aliese prof. pediatrics and adolescent medicine U. South Fla., Tampa, 1994—; v.p. for rsch. affairs Albany Med. Ctr., 1986-89. Dir. N.Y. State Kidney Disease Inst., 1969-79. With USN, 1945-46. Recipient Acad. Laureate award SUNY, Albany, 1991; Arthritis and Rheumatism Found. fellow, 1961-64. Fellow Am. Acad. Pediatrics; mem. AAAS, Am. Assn. Immunologists, Am. Pediatric Soc., Am. Soc. Cell Biology, Clin. Immunology Soc. Fla. Pediatric Soc., Sigma Xi, Phi Lambda Upsilon, Alpha Omega Alpha. Office: U South Fla Sch Medicine Dept Pediatrics 17 Davis Blvd 2d Fl Tampa FL 33606

POLLARD, CARL F., health insurance company executive; b. Lancaster, Ky., 1938. Grad., Univ. Ky., 1960. With Yeager Ford & Warren, Louisville, 1960-68; sr. exec. v.p. Humana Inc., Louisville. Office: Galen Health Care Inc 201 W Main St Louisville KY 40202

POLLARD, CHARLES W., transportation services executive; b. 1957. Student, 1977-83. With Skadden, Arps, Slate, Meagher & Flom, Washington, 1983-87; sec., gen. counsel World Airways, Inc., Herndon, Va., pres. Office: World Airways Inc 13873 Park Ctr Rd Herndon VA 22071*

POLLARD, CHARLES WILLIAM, diversified services company executive; b. Chgo., June 8, 1938; s. Charles W. and Ruth Ann (Humphrey) P.; m. Judith Ann, June 8, 1959; children: Julie Ann, Charles W., Brian, Amy. A.B., Wheaton Coll., 1960; J.D., Northwestern U., 1963. Bar: Ill. 1963. Mem. firm Wilson and McIlvaine, 1963-67, Vesculus, Perry & Pollard, Wheaton, Ill., 1968-72; prof., v.p. fin. Wheaton Coll., 1972-77; sr. v.p. ServiceMaster Industries, Downers Grove, Ill., 1977-80, exec. v.p., 1980-81, pres., 1981-83; pres., COO ServiceMaster Industries, 1981-83; pres., CEO ServiceMaster Co., Downers Grove, Ill., 1983-93, chmn. bd. dirs., mem. exec. com., 1994—; bd. dirs. Wheaton Coll., Herman Miller, Inc., Provident Life and Accident Ins. Co. Office: Servicemaster LP 1 ServiceMaster Way 2300 Warrenville Rd Downers Grove IL 60515-1765

POLLARD, CHARLES WILLIAM, lawyer; b. St. Mary's City, Md., June 1, 1957; s. Lyle H. and Teresa V. (Lavelle) P.; m. Lynna P. Maidman, Aug. 14, 1983; children: Louisa Ray, Katherine Allissa. AB magna cum laude, St. Anselm Coll., 1979; MPA, Syracuse U., 1980; JD, George Washington U., 1983. Bar: D.C. 1983, U.S. Dist. Ct. D.C. 1983. Law clk. Am. Petroleum Inst., Washington, 1981-83; assoc. Skadden, Arps, Slate, Meagher & Flom, Washington, 1983-87; gen. counsel WorldCorp, Herndon, Va., 1987-90, v.p. adminstrn. and legal affairs, 1990-92; pres. World Airways, Inc., 1992—; chmn. bd. trustees The Kingsbury Ctr., Washington, 1992—; bd. dirs. Found. Capital Ptnrs., Inc., Washington, Nat. Air Carrier Assn. Vol. counsel Reagan-Bush Campaign, Washington, 1984. Grad. fellow Maxwell Sch., Syracuse U., 1979-80. Mem. ABA, St. Anselm Coll. Alumni Assn. (pres. Washington chpt. 1988), Chesapeake Bay Yacht Racing Assn. Republican. Avocations: sailing, skeet shooting, backpacking. Office: World Airways Washington Dulles Internat Airport 13873 Park Center Rd # 400 Herndon VA 22071

POLLARD, DAVID EDWARD, editor; b. Columbus, Ohio, Oct. 7, 1927; s. James Edward and Marjorie Olive (Pearson) P.; m. Ilse Knack, Dec. 24, 1960; children: Walter Thomas, Marcus Andreas, Michael David, Christopher James. B.S., Ohio State U., 1950; postgrad. in cotton econs. Memphis State U., 1967. With Columbus Citizen, 1943-50; with Army Times Pub. Co., 1952-60; mng. editor U.S. Coast Guard Mag., Washington, 1956-57; asso. editor Am. Weekend, Washington, also Frankfurt, Ger., 1957-60; info. specialist Air Forces Europe Exchange, Wiesbaden, Ger., 1961-63; reporter Comml. Appeal, Memphis, 1963-66; fin. writer Comml. Appeal, 1967-68; news-desk editor U.S. News & World Report, Washington, 1968-76; chief news desk U.S. News & World Report, Herndon, 1976-91; pres. U.S. Moose Co., Inc., Boothbay Harbor, Maine, 1993—. Patentee garden implement. Served with USMC, 1945-46, 51-52. Mem. Legion of Mary, Sigma Delta Chi, Alpha Delta Sigma, Alpha Tau Omega. Roman Catholic. Home: 8405 Tobin Rd Annandale VA 22003-1103 and: Capitol Island ME 04538

POLLARD, FRED DON, finance company executive; b. Proctorsville, Vt., Sept. 15, 1931; s. Bryant Frank and Millie Viola (Brobst) P.; m. Sandra Jean Norton, Oct. 19, 1957; children: Fred Don, Bruce Gardiner, Mark Bryant. BA, Dartmouth Coll., 1953, MBA, 1954. C.P.A., N.Y. Staff auditor Touche, Niven, Bailey & Smart, Chgo., 1954-55, 57-58; with Hertz Corp., Chgo., 1958-60, London, 1960-62, Paris, France, 1962-64, N.Y.C., 1964-65; European controller Avis Rent A Car, London, 1965-69; internat. treas. Avis Rent A Car, 1969-71; asst. v.p., fin dir. Avis Rent A Car, Garden City, N.Y., 1971-72; asst. treas. Avis Rent A Car, 1972-75; treas. Garcia Corp., Teaneck, N.J., 1975-78; v.p. fin., treas. Augsbury Orgn., Inc., Ogdensburg, N.Y., 1978-79; sr. v.p. fin., treas. Augsbury Orgn., Inc., 1979-83, also dir.; pres. Corp. Fin. Assocs. No. N.Y., Canton, 1983—, Agrl. Processing Corp., Canton, 1983—; dir. Augsbury Corp., Halco Inc., Montreal, Que., Can., 1978-83, Carlton Holding Co./N.Y. Casualty, Watertown, N.Y., 1978-82, Creg System Inc., Watertown, Whalen, Daley & Looney (CPAs), Ogdenburg, N.Y., 1989—; Mem. adv. bd. Clarkson Sch. Mgmt., Potsdam, N.Y., 1979-83; vis. lectr. sch. of mgmt. Clarkson U., Potsdam, 1986-87; vis. lectr. dept. econs. St. Lawrence U., Canton, N.Y., 1987-88. Mem. exec. bd. Seaway Valley coun. Boy Scouts Am., 1980-86, adv. bd., 1986—. With U.S. Army, 1955-57. Mem. N.Y. State Soc. CPAs, Am. Inst. CPAs. Presbyterian. Lodges: Masons; Shriners. Home: Old Stone House 1129 County Rd 25 Canton NY 13617 Office: Russell Rd Canton NY 13617

POLLARD, GEORGE MARVIN, economist; b. St. Joseph, Mo., Oct. 5, 1909; s. James Coleman and Ethel (Mallory) P.; m. Jean Mary Campion, Apr. 15, 1939; 1 child, Elizabeth G. A.B. George Washington U., 1934, A.M., 1939; student, Columbia, 1940-41, sch. mil. govt. U. Va., 1944, Stanford, 1944-45. Mem. staff U.S. Dept. Agr., 1928-41, WPB, 1941-43; sr. economist U.S. Dept. Army, 1946-49; internat. economist, 1949-51; fgn. service officer Dept. State, 1955-64, internat. economist, 1951-55, 64—; consul, chief polit. and econ. affairs Am. Consulate Gen., Düsseldorf, Fed. Republic Germany, 1956-58; 1st sec. econ. affairs U.S. Mission to European Communities, Luxembourg, 1958-61; supervisory officer econ. affairs Bur. Internat. Orgn. Affairs, Dept. State, Washington, 1961-63; assigned to Bur. Internat. Commerce, U.S. Dept. Commerce, Washington, 1964-76; Mem. planning and zoning commn., Vienna, Va., 1953-56. Served as lt. USNR, 1943-46; mil. govt. officer Occupation of Japan 1945-46; mem. U.S. rep. Far Eastern Commn. 1947-49, Washington; lt. col. U.S. Army Res., 1949-63; ret. Mem. Phi Theta Kappa, Phi Sigma Kappa, Alpha Kappa Psi. Club: DACOR. Home: 2017 Dundee Rd Rockville MD 20850-3066

POLLARD, HARVEY B., physician, neuroscientist; b. San Antonio, May 26, 1943. BA in Biology, Rice U., 1964; MS in Biochemistry, U. Chgo., 1969, MD, 1969, PhD, 1973. Rsch. assoc. NIH-Nat. Inst. Arthritis and Metabolic Diseases, Bethesda, Md., 1969-71, sr. investigator, 1972-74, 1977-79, sect. chief, 1979-81; lab. chief Nat. Inst. Diabetes, Digestive and Kidney Diseases, Bethesda, 1981—. Contbr. over 200 articles to profl. jours. With USPHS, 1969—. Recipient Commendation medal USPHS, 1982, Alumni award for Disting. Svc., U. Chigo. Alumni Assn., 1989, NIH Inventor's award, 1991. Mem. Biophys. Soc., Am. Soc. for Neurosci., Am. Soc. for Pharmacology and Exptl. Therapeutics, Soc. for Cell Biology. Office: Nat Inst Diabetes Digestive & Kidney Disease 9000 Rockville Pike Blg 8 Rm 403 Bethesda MD 20892

POLLARD, HENRY, lawyer; b. N.Y.C., Jan. 10, 1931; s. Charles and Sarah (Lanster) P.; m. Adele Ruth Brodie, June 16, 1954; children: Paul A., Lydia S. AB, CCNY, 1953; JD, Columbia U., 1954. Bar: N.Y. 1954, Calif. 1962. Assoc. Sullivan & Cromwell, N.Y.C., 1954, 56-61; ptnr. Kaplan, Llvingston, Goodwin, Berkowitz & Selvin, Beverly Hills, 1962-81, Pollard, Bauman, Slome & McIntosh, Beverly Hills, Calif., 1981-87, Seyfarth, Shaw, Fairweather & Geraldson, L.A., 1987-95; of counsel Oberstein, Doniger, Fetter, Kibre & Horwitz, L.A., 1995—; judge pro tem L.A. County Mcpl. Ct.; arbitrator/mediator, mem. large complex case program Am. Arbitration Assn.; arbitrator Nat. Assn. Securities Dealers, N.Y. Stock Exch., Am. Stock Exch., Pacific Stick Exch., L.A. County Dispute Resolution Svcs. Editor Columbia U. Law Rev., 1953-54. Served with U.S. Army, 1954-56. Harlan Fiske Stone scholar, 1953-54. Mem. ABA, Calif. Bar Assn., Los Angeles County Bar Assn., Beverly Hills Bar Assn.

POLLARD, JOSEPH AUGUSTINE, advertising and public relations consultant; b. N.Y.C., June 22, 1924; s. Joseph Michael and Mary Theresa (Sheerin) P.; m. Helen Frances O'Neill, Jan. 18, 1947 (dec.); children: Christopher (dec.), Kenneth, Eugene, Daniel, Theresa, Michael; m. 2d, Lee Sharon Rivkins, Jan. 1, 1981. Student Pratt Inst., 1946-50. Advt. mgr. Boston Store, Utica, N.Y., 1951-53; sales promotion dir. Interstate Stores, N.Y., 1954-60, 67-70; v.p. sales Community Discount Stores, Chgo., 1960-63; dir. sales S. Klein, N.Y., 1964-66; v.p. advt. and pub. relations Peoples Drug Stores, Alexandria, Va., 1970-89; ret. Bd. dirs. Nat. Am. Cancer Soc., 1992—, trustee D.C. div., pres. 1985-86, nat. del., 1991-92; pres. Modern Retailers III., 1962. With USAF, 1943-46, 50-51. Recipient Am. Advt. Fedn. Silver medal award, 1982, St. George's medal Am. Cancer Soc., 1984. Mem. Advt. Club Met. Washington (pres. 1975-76), Country Club of Fairfax (pres. 1994, bd. dirs. 1992—). Home and Office: 5848 Kara Pl Burke VA 22015-3331

POLLARD, MORRIS, microbiologist, educator; b. Hartford, Conn., May 24, 1916; s. Harry and Sarah (Hoffman) P.; m. Mildred Klein, Dec. 29, 1938; children: Harvey, Carol, Jonathan. D.V.M., Ohio State U., 1938; M.S., Va. Poly. Inst., 1939; Ph.D. (Nat. Found. Infantile Paralysis fellow), U. Calif.-Berkeley, 1950; D.Sc. (hon.) Miami U., Ohio, 1981. Mem. staff Animal Disease Sta., Nat. Agrl. Research Center, Beltsville, Md., 1939-42; asst. prof. preventive medicine Med. br. U. Tex., Galveston, 1946-48; assoc. prof. U. Tex., 1948-50, prof., 1950-61; prof. biology U. Notre Dame, Ind., 1961-66; prof., chmn. microbiology U. Notre Dame, 1966-81, prof. emeritus, 1981—, dir. Lobund Lab., 1961-85, Coleman dir. Lobund Lab., 1985—; vis. prof. Fed. U. Rio de Janeiro, Brazil, 1977; vis. prof. Katholieke U., Leuven, Belgium, 1981; mem. tng. grant com. NIH, 1965-70; mem. adv. bd. Inst. Lab. Animal Resources NRC, 1965-68; mem. adv. com. microbiology Office Naval Research, 1966-68, chmn., 1968-70; mem. sci. adv. com. United Health Found., 1966-70; cons. U. Tex., M.D. Anderson Hosp. and Tumor Inst., 1958-66; mem. colon cancer com. Nat. Cancer Inst., 1972-76, chmn. tumor immunology com., 1976-79; mem. com. cancer cause and prevention NIH, 1979-81; program rev. com. Argonne Nat. Lab., 1979-85, chmn., 1983-84; lectr. Found. Microbiology, 1978. Editor: Perspectives in Virology Vol. I to XI, 1959-80; contbr. articles to profl. jours. Served from 1st lt. to lt. col. Vet. Corps, AUS, 1942-46. Recipient Disting. Alumnus award Ohio State U., 1979, Army Commendation medal, Presdl. citation; named Hon. Alumnus U. Notre Dame, 1989; McLaughlin Faculty fellow Cambridge U., 1956; Raine Found. prof. U. Western Australia, 1975; vis. scientist Chinese Acad. Med. Scis., 1979, 81; hon. prof. Chinese Acad. Med. Scis., 1982. Mem. Am. Acad. Microbiology (charter), Brazilian Acad. Scis., Soc. Exptl. Biology and Medicine, Am. Soc. Microbiology (Acad. Sci. Achievement award 1990), Am. Assn. Pathologists, Am. Assn. Cancer Rsch., Am. Soc. Lab. Animal Sci., Assn. Gnotobiotics (pres.), Internat. Commn. Lab. Animal Sci., AAAS, Internat. Assn. Gnotobiology (pres.), Internat. Assn. Gnotobiotics (hon. pres. 1987), Sigma Xi, Phi Delta Epsilon (hon.), Phi Zeta (hon.). Home: 3540 Hanover Ct South Bend IN 46614-2331 Office: Lobund Lab Notre Dame IN 46556

POLLARD, OVERTON PRICE, state agency executive, lawyer; b. Ashland, Va., Mar. 26, 1933; s. James Madison and Annie Elizabeth (Hutchinson) P.; m. Anne Aloysia Meyer, Oct. 1, 1960; children—Mary O., Price, John, Anne, Charles, Andrew, David. A.B. in Econs., Washington and Lee U., 1954, J.D., 1957. Bar: Va. Claims supr. Travelers Ins. Co., Richmond, Va., 1964-67; asst. atty. gen. State of Va., Richmond, 1967, 70-72; spl. asst. Va. Supreme Ct., Richmond, 1968-70; exec. dir. Pub. Defender Commn., Richmond, 1972—; ptnr. Pollard & Boice and predecessor firms, Richmond, 1972-87; bd. govs. Va. Criminal Law Sect., Richmond, 1970-72, 91-93; chmn. prepaid legal services com. Va. State Bar, Richmond, 1982-85; pres. Met. Legal Aid, Richmond, 1978. Del. to State Dem. Cong., Richmond, 1985; mem. Va. Commn. on Family Violence Prevention, 1995. With USN, 1957-59. Recipient service award Criminal Law Bd. of Govs. for Pub. Defender Study, 1971. Mem. ABA, Va. Bar Assn. (chmn. criminal law sect. 1991-93), Richmond Bar Assn., Nat. Legal Aid and Defender Assn. (Reginald Heber Smith award 1991). Democrat. Baptist. Avocation: fishing. Home: 7726 Sweetbriar Rd Richmond VA 23229-6622 Office: Pub Defender Commn 701 E Franklin St Ste 1416 Richmond VA 23219-2503

POLLARD, SHIRLEY, employment training director, consultant; b. Brunswick City, Va., July 8, 1939; 1 child, Darryl. Degree in bus. adminstrn., Upper Iowa U., 1978. Adminstr. East. Balt. Community Corp.; tng. coord. Balt. County Concentrated Employment Tng. Program; exec. dir. Park Heights Community Corp., Balt.; dir. Linkages, Inc., Balt. Contbr. articles to Afro Am. newspaper. Pres. Park Hghts. Cmty. Devel. Corp.; active Balt. Urban League, Balt. Welfare Rights Orgn.; pres. United Black Fund Balt., 1989—, Presdl. Task Force, 1992; founder, pres. Balt. County Polit. Action Coalition, 1982—; founder, dir. Linkages, Inc., 1980; founder, dir. Tng. and Placement Svcs., 1989; active United Svc. Orgn., Md. Minority Contractors Assn., U.S. Civil rights Mus. and Hall of Fame, Smithsonian Instn.; founder African Am. Culture Ctr.; co-founder Project Lou, Inc.; founder The Afro Fund, Inc.; active Fund for a Free South Africa's Founding Assocs. Leadership Coun., Nat. Women's Hall of Fame, Nat. Abortion Rights Action League, Srs. Coalition, Md. Edn. Coalition, CORE, So. Christian Leadership Conf, Nat. Trust for Hist. Preservation; presdl. appointment Md. Selective Svc. Bd., 1993, Exec. Coun. of Am. Friends Svc. Com. Recipient Outstanding Achievement award Md. Minority Contractors Assn., Mayor's Citation, Martin Luther King Civil Rights award, 1987, Md. State Dept. Edn. award, 1987, Congl. Achievement award, Kool Achiever awards, 1990, Nat. Black Caucus Spl. award, 1990, Congrssional Achievement award, 1988, Svc. award The Writers Club, 1991, USO Meritorious Svc. award, 1991, Gov.'s Vol. award, 1992, Acad. of Excellence award, 1992, Signs of Hope award, 1995; Mayor's citation, 1984. Mem. Am. Soc. Pers. Adminstrn., Am. Soc. Health/Manpower/Edn./Tng., Assn. for Providers Employment and Tng., NAACP (founder, pres. Randallstown chpt. 1988-95, Signs of Hope award), Balt. Coun. on Fgn. Affairs, Transafrica, USO, Md. Minority Contractors Assn. (Achievement award 1986, bd. dirs. 1984-89), Smithsonian Assoc., Md. C. of C. (greater Balt. com. 1985). Office: PO Box 32051 Baltimore MD 21208-8051

POLLARD, THOMAS DEAN, biologist, educator; b. Pasadena, Calif., July 7, 1942; s. Dean Randall and Florence Alma (Dierker) P.; m. Patricia Elizabeth Snowden, Feb. 7, 1964; children: Katherine, Daniel. BA, Pomona Coll., Claremont, Calif., 1964; MD, Harvard U., 1968. Intern Mass. Gen. Hosp., Boston, 1968-69; staff assoc. NIH, Bethesda, Md., 1969-72; from asst. prof. to assoc. prof. Harvard Med. Sch., Boston, 1972-78; prof., dir. dept. cell biology and anatomy Johns Hopkins Sch. Medicine, Balt., 1977—; chmn. Commn. on Life Sci., Nat. Rsch. Coun., 1993—. Guggenheim fellow, 1984. Fellow Am. Acad. Arts and Scis.; mem. NAS, Am. Soc. Cell Biology (pres. 1987-88, K.R. Porter lectr. 1989), NRC (commn. on life scis. 1990—), Biophys. Soc. (pres. 1992-93), Marine Biol. Lab. (trustee 1991—). Office: Johns Hopkins Med Sch Dept Cell Biology-Anatomy 725 N Wolfe St Baltimore MD 21205-2105

POLLARD, WILLIAM SHERMAN, JR., civil engineer, educator; b. Oak Grove, La., Jan. 1, 1925; s. William Sherman and Carrie Lois (Hornor) P.; m. Gloria Louise Ponder, June 29, 1946; children: William Sherman, III, Katherine Lynn. B.S. in Civil Engring. Purdue U., 1946, M.S., 1948. Instr. civil engring. Purdue U., 1948-49; instr. U. Ill., 1949-51, assoc. prof., 1951-55; with Harland Bartholomew & Assos., St. Louis, 1955-71; assoc. partner, chief civil engr. Harland Bartholomew & Assos., 1956-58; partner Harland Bartholomew & Assos., Memphis, 1958-71; head ops. Harland Bartholomew & Assos., 1958-60; head Harland Bartholomew & Assos. (Memphis office), 1960-71; pres. William S. Pollard Cons., Inc., Memphis, 1971-81; prof. civil engring. U. Colo., Denver, 1981—; adj. prof. urban planning Memphis State U., 1973-81; dir. Ctr. Urban Transp. Studies, U. Colo.; chmn. WKNO-TV, Memphis. Served with USMC, 1942-46. Named Distinguished Engring. Alumnus Purdue U., 1969. Fellow Am. Cons. Engrs. Council, ASCE (state of the art award 1970), Inst. Transp. Engrs.; mem. Am. Rd. Builders Assn., Nat. Soc. Profl. Engrs., Soc. Am. Mil. Engrs., Urban Land Inst., Transp. Research Bd., Lambda Alpha. Presbyterian. Lodge: Rotary (pres. 1979-80). Office: U Colo PO Box 173364 Denver CO 80217-3364

POLLART, DALE F(LAVIAN), petroleum company research executive; b. Holly, Colo., Jan. 7, 1932; s. Flavian J. and Agnes E. (Reedy) P.; m. Mary Galvin, Aug. 14, 1954; children: John, Susan, Daniel, Eileen, James. BS, Regis Coll., 1952; PhD in Organic Chemistry, Northwestern U., 1956. Research chemist, group leader, assoc. dir., tech. mgr. Union Carbide Corp., 1956-74, product mgr., 1974-76, dir. research and devel., 1976-79, bus. mgr., 1979-81; v.p. tech. Occidental Chem. Co., 1981-82; dir. strategic research Texaco Inc., Beacon, N.Y., 1982-85, dir. research and environ. affairs, 1985-89, gen. mgr. R&D, 1989—; Texaco rep. Indsl. Rsch. Inst., Washington, 1985—, bd. dirs., 1989-92. Contbr. articles to profl. jours.; patentee in field. Bd. dirs. United Way, Poughkeepsie, N.Y., 1985-89, Vassar Bros. Hosp. Found., Poughkeepsie, 1985—. Recipient Forrestal award Regis Coll., 1952, Phi Lambda Upsilon award Northwestern U., 1956. Mem. AAAS, Am. Chem. Soc., Chemist's Club, Dirs. Indsl. Rsch., Darien Boat Club (Conn.), Ischoda Yacht Club (Conn.), Sigma Xi. Roman Catholic. Avocations: tennis, boating. Office: Texaco Inc R & D PO Box 509 Beacon NY 12508-0509

POLLAY, RICHARD L., real estate title insurance company executive; b. 1932. BS, JD, U. Mich. Atty. Chgo. Title Ins. Co., 1965-66, asst. counsel, 1966-67, div. v.p., 1967-74, v.p., 1974-78, sr. v.p., 1978-81, exec. v.p., 1981-

84, pres., chief oper. officer, 1984—. Office: Chgo Title Ins Co 171 N Clark St Chicago IL 60601-2703

POLLAY, RICHARD L., title company executive; b. 1932. With Chgo. Title and Trust Co., 1958-91; with Ticor Title Ins. Co., Rosemead, Calif., 1991—, pres. Office: Ticor Title Ins Co 17171 Walnut Grove Ave Rosemead CA 91770*

POLLAZZI, ROGER G., transportation executive; b. 1937. BS, Lawrence Inst. Tech.; MBA, Mich. Rackum Meml. Campus, 1972. With ExCello Corp., Houston, 1964-70; with Joy Mfg. Co., Pitts., 1970-83, pres., 1983-88; founder Atlantic Products and Fa-Presto, Pitts., 1988-91; pres., CEO Pullman Co., Lebanon, N.J., 1990—. Office: Pullman Co 3 Werner Way Lebanon NJ 08833

POLLEY, DALE WHITCOMB, bank executive; b. Madisonville, Ky., May 5, 1949; s. Carl Mason and Sarah (Beazley) P.; m. Nancy Jo Weeks, Dec. 27, 1970; children: Lucinda Lynn, Dale Whitcomb Jr. B.B.A., Memphis State U., 1971. C.P.A., Tenn., Ky. Auditor Touche Ross & Co., Memphis, Tenn., 1971-73; auditor Schotte & Taylor, Paducah, Ky., 1973; acct. Commerce Union Corp., Nashville, 1973-78, contr., 1978-84, exec. v.p., chief fin. officer, 1984-87; exec. v.p., chief adminstrv. and fin. officer Sovran Fin. Corp./Cen. South, 1987; chief fin. officer, treas. Sovran Fin. Corp., Norfolk, Va., 1988, exec. v.p., CFO, 1989-91; vice chmn., chief adminstrv. officer First Am., Nashville, 1991-94; pres. First Am. Nat. Bank, Nashville, 1994—. Pres., U. Ky. Alumni Assn., Nashville, 1984—; vice chmn. United Way-Allocations Panel 10, Nashville, 1984—. Mem. Fin. Execs. Inst. (v.p. 1984—), Am. Inst. C.P.A.s, Tenn. Soc. C.P.A.s. Republican. Methodist. Office: First American Corp 1 American Ctr Nashville TN 37237

POLLEY, DAVID E., textile manufacturing executive; b. Bklyn., May 3, 1934; s. Henry M. and Mildred (Brown) P.; m. Nancy Sind, May 2, 1965 (div. Aug. 1985); children: Douglas Mark, Diana Hope; m. Virginia Lucile Cobb Spangler, Mar. 29, 1986; 1 child, Frank Henry Spangler. BS in Econs., U. Pa., 1955; MS, Columbia U., 1956. Buyer Abraham & Straus, Bklyn., 1956-66; div. mgr. Korvettes, N.Y.C., 1966-69; exec. v.p. Stephen Leedom, N.Y.C., 1969-72; chmn. David Industries, Dalton, Ga., 1972-81; pres. Lees Carpets (div. Burlington Industries), N.Y.C., 1981-86, Burlington Residential Carpet Group, Valley Forge, Pa., 1986—. Avocations: reading, tennis, math puzzles, model ship bldg. Office: Lees & Burlington House Carpets 3330 W Friendly Ave Greensboro NC 27410-4806

POLLEY, EDWARD HERMAN, anatomist, educator; b. Chgo., Sept. 20, 1923; s. Sam and Anna (Revzin) P.; m. Jo Ann Welsh, Aug. 11, 1953; children: Lisa, Eric. B.A., DePauw U., Greencastle, Ind., 1947; M.S., St. Louis U., 1949, Ph.D., 1951. USPHS postdoctoral research fellow Washington U., St. Louis, 1951-53; Instr., then asst. prof. anatomy Hahnemann Med. Coll., Phila., 1953-59; asst. prof., then asso. prof. U. Md. Med. Sch., 1964-70; research biologist Edgewood (Md.) Arsenal, 1959-70; prof. anatomy, neurosurgery and ophthalmology U. Ill. Med. Sch., Chgo., 1970—; vis. prof. dept. pharm. and physiol. scis. U. Chgo., 1979-80. Served to lt. (j.g.) USNR, 1942-46. Mem. Am. Assn. Anatomists, Assn. for Research in Vision and Ophthalmology, AAAS, Am. Soc. Neurosci., Sigma Xi. Club: Cajal. Office: U Ill Dept Anat Cell Biol M/C 512 808 S Wood St Chicago IL 60612-7300*

POLLEY, HARVEY LEE, retired missionary and educator; b. Wapato, Wash., Aug. 14, 1924; s. Edward Prestley and Alda June Polley; m. Corinne Weber; children: Catherine, David, Corinne, Robert. BA, Whitworth Coll., Spokane, Wash., 1951; postgrad., East Wash. Coll., 1953, Berkeley Bapt. Div. Sch., 1958-59; MEd, Cen. Wash. Coll., 1958; postgrad., Ecole d'Adminstrn. des Affaires Africaines, Brussels, 1959-60. Tchr. Quincy (Wash.) Pub. Schs., 1953-57, N.W. Christian Schs., Spokane, 1958; missionary Am. Bapt. Fgn. Missionary Soc., Zaire, 1958-89; tchr. Evang. Pedagogical Inst., Kimpese, Zaire, 1961-69; asst. legal rep., dir., prin., supt., 1969-72; dir. BIM Hostel, Kinshasa, Zaire, 1972-73; mem. staff Ctr. for Agrl. Devel. Lusekele, Zaire, 1975-85, dir., 1976-79, 83-85; dir. Plateau Bateke Devel. Program, Kinshasa, 1985-89; ret., 1989. Author: Rural Development Guide, 1989. Mem. Coun. Elders, Kimpese, 1969-72; pres. bd. adminstrn. Vanga (Zaire) Hosp., 1981-83; mem. exec. com. Nat. Human Nutrition Planning Coun. Govt. Zaire-USAID, Kikwit, 1983-85. Home: W2405 W Johansen Rd Spokane WA 99208-9616

POLLEY, HOWARD FREEMAN, physician; b. Columbus, Ohio, Nov. 12, 1913; s. David William Latimer and Mary Ann (Lakin) P.; m. Georgiana Alice Redrup, June 5, 1938 (dec. Feb. 1981); children: Alice Lynne, Mary Ann (Mrs. Dale McCoy), William Redrup. A.B., Ohio Wesleyan U., 1934, Sc.D., 1965; M.D., Ohio State U., 1938; M.S., U. Minn., 1945. Intern St. Luke's Hosp., Chgo., 1938-39; resident medicine St. Luke's Hosp., 1939-40; fellow medicine Mayo Grad. Sch. Medicine, 1940-43; cons. in medicine Mayo Clinic, 1943-83, emeritus, 1983—, head sect., 1962-66, chmn. div. rheumatology and internal medicine, 1966-76, sr. cons., 1976-83; instr. U. Minn., 1946-50, asst. prof. medicine, 1950-54, asso. prof. medicine, 1954-60, prof. medicine, 1960-83; prof. medicine Ind. U. Sch. Medicine, 1983-89; asso. Doctors Hench, Kendall and Slocumb (in original clin. research cortisone and ACTH for rheumatoid arthritis, rheumatic fever.); Bd. dirs. Arthritis Found., 1963-69, exec. com., 1963-68, v.p., 1966-68; trustee Ohio Wesleyan U., 1967—, exec. bd., 1970-72. Sr. author: Rheumatologic Interviewing and Physical Examination of Joints, 2d edit., 1978; assoc. editor: Arthritis and Rheumatism, 1960-64; co-author: Physical Examinations of Joints, 1965; internat. adv. bd. Japanese Jour. Rheumatology, 1985-94; contbr. articles to profl. jours. Mem. adv. council Nat. Inst. Arthritis, Metabolism and Digestive Diseases, NIH, 1972-76; mem. Nat. Arthritis Commn., 1975-76, Nat. Arthritis Adv. Bd., 1981-85; sec. gen. Internat. League Against Rheumatism, 1981-85. Recipient Alumni Achievement award Ohio State U., 1958; Fellow A.C.P. Mem. AMA (spl. cons. council phys. medicine and rehab. 1946-50), Central Soc. Clin. Research, Am. Rheumatism Assn. (v.p. 1962-64, pres. 1964-65, master charter group 1987—), Uruguay Soc. Rheumatology (hon. mem.), All-Union (USSR) Rheumatol. Soc. (hon.), Indian Rheumatism Assn. (hon. mem.), Japan Rheumatism Assn., (hon. mem.), French Rheumatism Assn. (hon. mem.), Sigma Xi, Alpha Omega Alpha, Omicron Delta Kappa, Phi Mu Alpha, Pi Delta Epsilon, Phi Delta Theta, Alpha Kappa Kappa. Home: 211 2nd St NW Rochester MN 55901-2897 Office: Mayo Clinic 200 First St SW Rochester MN 55905

POLLEY, RICHARD DONALD, microbiologist, polymer chemist; b. Bklyn., Feb. 23, 1937; s. George Weston and Evelyn (Tuttle) P.; m. Linda B. Radford, Sept. 21, 1991; children from previous marriage: Gordon MacHeath, Jennifer Elizabeth, Tabitha Isabelle, Sean Sullivan; m. Linda R. Radford, 1991. Student, Trinity Coll., 1954-57; BS, BA, Hofstra U., 1960. Asst. advt. mgr. tech. Permatex Chem. Corp., Huntington, N.Y., 1960-61, Sun Chem. Corp., 1961-63; advt. mgr. Celanese Plastics Co., Newark, 1963-67; account dir. McCann Indsl. Tech. Sci. Mktg., N.Y.C., 1967-68, v.p., gen. mgr., Miami, 1968-70; pres. Intercapital Belgium S.A., Brussels, 1970-72; pres., tech. dir. Iodinamics Corp., Lancaster, Pa., El Paso, Tex., 1972-76; tech. dir. Hydrodine Corp., Miami, 1976—, chmn., CEO, 1986—, also bd. dirs., chmn., CEO, COO, tech. dir. Polymorphic Polymers Corp., Miami, 1978-90; COO Omnidine Corp., Miami, 1980—, bd. dirs.; pres. Skin Care Labs., Inc., Miami, 1979-90; dir. microbiology, tech. dir. Pure H2O Biotechnology, Inc., Boca Raton, Fla., 1992—; chief exec. officer Polllabs, São Paulo, Brazil, 1990—; tech. dir. Ecology Tech. do Brasil, São Paulo, 1993—; bd. dirs., tech. dir. Hydrodine Biotech (Far East) Ltd., Bangkok, Thailand and Hong Kong, 1992—; tech. dir., chief scientist Biocer Boreal S.A., Bogotá and Medellin, Colombia, 1995—; chmn. Peer Group Influencers, Ltd. London, also Miami, Fla., 1988—; bd. dirs., v.p. Internat. Airlines, Long Beach, Calif., 1984—; tech. dir, v.p. bd. dirs. Swiver Corp., Miami, Fla., 1994—; overseas dir. Field Iodine Goiter Med. Demonstration Projects, Tremos East Hosp.-Harvard Med. Sch., 1977—; tech. dir. and chief scientist Tremos Ltd., Turks and Caicos, B.W.I. and Buenos Aires, Argentina, 1993—; cons. water microbiology and disinfection control Pan Am. Health Orgn., others. Mem. editorial adv. bd. Chem. Week, 1988; contbr. articles to profl. jours.; patentee in field. Mem. AAAS, Am. Concrete Inst., Water Quality Assn., N.Y. Acad. Scis., Internat. Iodine Inst. (chmn. bd.), Associaçao de Ciencia e Tecnologia Ambiental (bd. dirs. São Paulo 1993—). Republican. Office: Hydrodine Corp/Omnidine Corp/Swiver Corp 1472 NE 130th St North Miami FL 33161-4411

POLLICINO, JOSEPH ANTHONY, investment company executive; b. N.Y.C., Dec. 22, 1939; s. Paul and Carmela (Iudici) P.; m. Margaret Ryan, Nov. 29, 1957; children: Joseph, John, Kerry. Cert., Am. Inst. Banking, 1967; exec. cert. Grad. Sch. Credit & Fin. Mgmt., Dartmouth Coll., 1977. Various tng. and mgmt. positions Mfrs. Hanover Trust, N.Y.C., 1957-73, v.p., officer in charge, 1973-77; sr. v.p. Mfrs. Hanover Comml. Corp., N.Y.C., 1980-82, exec. v.p., 1982-84; pres. CIT Group, Inc. subs. Mfrs. Hanover Corp., N.Y.C., 1984-88; vice chmn. CIT Group Holdings, Inc., N.Y.C., 1988—; bd. dirs. CIT Group, Inc., Livingston, N.J. Recipient Community Leadership award Am. Jewish Congress, N.Y.C., 1982, Disting. Community Service award Brandeis U., 1986. Republican. Roman Catholic. Clubs: 475; Esquire Credit; Plandome (N.Y.) Country. Office: The CIT Group Holdings Inc 135 W 50th St New York NY 10020-2014

POLLICK, G. DAVID, college president, philosopher; b. Kansas City, Mo., Oct. 13, 1947; m. Janice Pollick, 1975; 2 children, Dayna, Landon. BA, philosophy, U. San Diego, 1971; Ph.L., philosophy, St. Paul U., Ont., Can., 1973; MA, philosophy, U. Ottawa, Can., 1973, Ph.D., philosophy, 1981. Lecturer, philosophy U. San Diego, San Diego, Calif., 1972-73; tchr.-counselor, neurologically and physically handicapped Aseltine Sch. Neurol. Handicapped, 1972-73; dir. heroin rehab. ctr. Imperial County Diversion Program, El Centro, Calif., 1973-74; tchr.-counselor, emotionally handicapped Finley Elem Sch. Holtville, Calif., 1974-75; lecturer, philosophy U. Ottawa, Ottawa, ON, Canada, 1975-77; asst. prof. philosopy, dept. chrm., acad. coordinator St. John's U., Collegeville, Minn., 1977-84; assoc. prof., dean coll. arts and scis. Seattle U., 1984-89; provost, v.p. for acad. affairs SUNY, Cortland, 1989-93; acting pres., 1991-93; co-CEO, pres. Art Inst. Chgo., Sch. of Art Inst. of Chgo., 1993—. Author: The Work of Roman Ingarden, 1977, (with others) The Aesthetics of Roman Ingarden, 1982; co-editor Supplementary Volume on Aesthetics, 1977. Served with USN. Fellow philosophy and fine arts, Inst. Ecumenical and Culture Rsch., 1976-77; Koscjusko Foundation awd., 1978. Avocations: sculpture, art history, archaeology. Office: Sch of Art Inst Chicago Office of the President 37 S Wabash Ave Chicago IL 60603-3103

POLLIHAN, THOMAS HENRY, lawyer; b. St. Louis, Nov. 15, 1949; s. C.H. and Patricia Ann (O'Brien) P.; m. Donna M. Bickhaus, Aug. 25, 1973; 1 child, Emily Christine. BA in Sociology, Quincy U., 1972; JD, U. Notre Dame, 1975; Exec. Masters in Internat. Bus., St. Louis U., 1992. Bar: Mo. 1975, U.S. Dist. Ct. (ea. dist.) Mo. 1975, Ill. 1976, U.S. Dist. (so. dist.) Ill. 1976. Jud. law clk. to judge Mo. Ct. of Appeals, St. Louis, 1975-76; from assoc. to ptnr. Greenfield, Davidson, Mandelstamm & Voorhees, St. Louis, 1976-82; asst. gen. counsel Kellwood Co., St. Louis, 1982-89, gen. counsel, sec., 1989-93, v.p., sec., gen. counsel, 1993—. Trustee Quincy (Ill.) U., 1987-93, pres. alumni bd., 1986-87; pres. S.W. Neighborhood Improvement Assn., St. Louis, 1984. Mem. Bar Assn. Met. St. Louis. Roman Catholic. Avocations: soccer, cycling. Home: 4934 Magnolia Ave Saint Louis MO 63139-1026 Office: Kellwood Co 600 Kellwood Pky Chesterfield MO 63017-5800

POLLIN, ABE, professional basketball team executive, builder; b. Phila., Dec. 3, 1923; s. Morris and Jennie (Sack) P.; m. Irene S. Kerchek, May 27, 1945; children: Robert Norman, James Edward. B.A., George Washington U., 1945; student, U. Md., 1941-44. Engaged in home bldg. bus., 1945—; pres. Abe Pollin Inc., Balt., 1962—; chmn. Balt. Bullets Basketball Club, Inc. (now Washington Bullets), 1964—; dir. County Fed. Savs. & Loan Assn., Rockville, Md. Bd. dirs. United Jewish Appeal, Nat. Jewish Hosp., Jewish Community Center; bd. dirs., adv. com. John F. Kennedy Cultural Center. Mem. Nat. Assn. Home Builders, Asso. Builders and Contractors Md., Washington Bd. Trade. Jewish. Office: Washington Bullets US Air Arena Landover MD 20785 also: Washington Capitals US Air Arena Landover MD 20785*

POLLINGER, WILLIAM JOSHUA, lawyer; b. Passaic, N.J., Dec. 14, 1944; s. Irving R. and Ethel (Groudan) P.; m. Helen Rizzo, May 30, 1977; children: Samantha, Zachary. BA, Rutgers U., 1966; JD, Am. U., 1969. Bar: N.J. 1969, U.S. Dist. Ct. N.J. 1969, N.Y. 1981, U.S. Supreme Ct. 1982, U.S. Ct. Appeals (3d cir.) 1986; cert. Civil Trial Atty. N.J. Supreme Ct. 1983. Assoc. Krieger & Klein, Passaic, 1969-75; ptnr. Delorenzo & Pollinger, Hackensack, N.J., 1975-84; pres. William J. Pollinger, P.A., Hackensack, 1984-88, Pollinger, Fearns & Kemezis, P.A., 1988-90, Pollinger & Fearns, P.A., Hackensack, 1990-92, William J. Pollinger P.A., Hackensack, N.J., 1992—; mem. Bergen County Ethics Com., N.J., 1984-88. Arbitrator Better Bus. Bur. of Bergen and Rockland Counties, Paramus, N.J., 1983-89, Am. Arbitration Assn., 1983—. Assoc. of Yr. award Builders Assn. No. N.J., Paramus, 1981. Mem. N.J. State Bar Assn., Passaic County Bar Assn., Bergen County Bar Assn., Assn. Trial Lawyers Am., Trial Attys. N.J., Am. Arbitration Assn., Def. Research Inst., Phi Delta Phi. Lodge: Masons (past master). Avocation: stamp and coin collecting. Office: 302 Union St Hackensack NJ 07601-4303

POLLINI, FRANCIS, author; b. West Wyoming, Pa., Sept. 9, 1930; s. Sam and Assunta (Ciani) P.; m. Gloria Ann Swann, Sept. 12, 1959; children: Susanne, Lisa. BA in Psychology, Pa. State U., 1951. Author: Night, 1959, Glover, 1965, Excursion, 1966, The Crown, 1967, Three Plays, 1967, Pretty Maids All In a Row, 1968, Dubonnet, 1973, The Hall, 1975. 1st lt. USAF, 1952-57. Home: 14 Oak Ln, Hingham NR9 4JY Norfolk, England

POLLITT, JEROME JORDAN, art history educator; b. Fair Lawn, N.J., Nov. 26, 1934; s. John Kendall and Doris B. (Jordan) P.; m. Susan Baker Matheson, Feb. 10, 1977. B.A., Yale U., 1957; Ph.D., Columbia U., 1963. Instr. history of art Yale U., New Haven, 1962-64; asst. prof. Yale U., 1964-68, assoc. prof., 1969-73, prof., 1973—, chmn. dept. classics, 1975-77, chmn. dept. history of art, 1981-84, dean, 1986-91. Author: Art and Experience in Classical Greece, 1972, The Ancient View of Greek Art, 1975, Art in the Hellenistic Age, 1986; editor-in-chief: Am. Jour. Archaeology, 1973-77; contbr. articles to profl. jours. Mem. Archaeol. Inst. Am., Coll. Art Assn. Home: 48 Dillon Rd Woodbridge CT 06525-1219 Office: Dept History of Art Yale U PO Box 208272 New Haven CT 06520-2009

POLLITT, KATHA, writer, poet, educator; b. N.Y.C., Oct. 14, 1949; d. Basil Riddiford and Leonora (Levine) P.; div.; 1 child, Sophie Pollitt-Cohen. BA, Harvard U., 1972; MFA, Columbia U., 1975. Lit. editor The Nation, N.Y.C., 1982-84, contbg. editor, 1986-92, assoc. editor, 1992—; jr. fellow council of humanities Princeton (N.J.) U., 1984; lectr. The New Sch., N.Y.C., 1986-90, Poetry Ctr. 92d St YMHA and YWHA, N.Y.C., 1986-88. Author: Antarctic Traveller, 1982 (Circle award Nat. Book Critics 1983), Reasonable Creatures: Essays on Women and Feminism, 1994; poetry appeared in The New Yorker, The New Republic, Poetry, and others; contbr. articles to jours. Whiting fellow, 1993; recipient I.B. Lavan Younger Poet's award Acad. Am. Poets, 1984; Fulbright grantee, 1985; grantee N.Y. Found. of the Arts, 1987, Nat. Endowment for Arts, 1984; Guggenheim fellow, 1987. Mem. Am. PEN Club. Democrat. Home: 317 W 93rd St New York NY 10025-7236

POLLITZER, WILLIAM SPROTT, anatomy educator; b. Charleston, S.C., May 6, 1923; s. Richard Morris and Cora (Sprott) P.; m. Margaret Buhlig, Aug. 29, 1955; children—Virginia, Patricia. A.B., Emory U., 1944, M.A., 1947; Ph.D., Columbia U., 1957. Instr. anatomy U. N.C., Chapel Hill, 1957-59, asst. prof., 1959-67, assoc. prof., 1967-73, prof., 1973-87, emeritus prof., 1987—. Contbr. articles to profl. jours. Served with U.S. Army, 1944-47. Mem. Am. Assn. Phys. Anthropologists (v.p. 1978-79, pres 1978-81, editor jour. 1970-77), Human Biology Council (pres. 1986-88). Democrat. Avocations: tennis; cycling. Home: 513 Morgan Creek Rd Chapel Hill NC 27514-4931 Office: U NC Dept Cell Biology & Anatomy Chapel Hill NC 27599-7090

POLLOCK, ALEXANDER JOHN, banker; b. Indpls., Jan. 28, 1943; s. Alex S. and Doris L. (VanHorn) P.; m. Anne M. Fryfogle, Jan. 27, 1968; children: Elizabeth, Alexander, Evelyn, James. B.A., Williams Coll., 1965; M.A., U. Chgo., 1966; M.P.A., Princeton U., 1969. Instr. philosophy Lake Forest Coll., (Ill.), 1967; with internat. banking dept. Continental Ill. Nat. Bank, Chgo., 1969-77, v.p. 1977-82, sr. v.p., 1982-85; prin. Nolan Norton & Co., Chgo., 1985-86; chief fin. officer The Marine Corp., Milw., 1986-87; pres. Marine Bank N.A., Milw., 1987; pres., chief exec. officer Community Fed. Savs., St. Louis, 1988-90; vis. scholar Fed. Res. Bank of St. Louis, 1991; pres., CEO Fed. Home Loan Bank Chgo., 1991—; bd. advisors Banking Rsch. Ctr.; bd. dirs. Great Lakes Higher Edn. Corp.; exec. com. Internat. Union of Housing Fin. Instns. Mem. Union League Club, Phi Beta Kappa. Office: Fed Home Loan Bank Chgo 111 E Wacker Dr Chicago IL 60601 *Omnia superans vi rationis et arte loquendi.*

POLLOCK, EARL EDWARD, lawyer; b. Decatur, Nebr., Feb. 24, 1928; s. Herman and Della (Rosenthal) P.; m. Betty Sokol, Sept. 8, 1951; children: Stephen, Della, Naomi. B.A., U. Minn., 1948; J.D., Northwestern U., 1953. Bar: D.C. 1955, Va. 1955, Ill. 1959, U.S. Supreme Ct. 1960. Law clk., chief justices Vinson and Warren, U.S. Supreme Ct. Washington, 1953-55; atty. antitrust div. Dept. Justice, Washington, 1955-56, asst. to solicitor gen., 1956-59; ptnr. Sonnenschein Carlin Nath & Rosenthal, Chgo., 1959—. Trustee Loyola U., Chgo., 1983-92; life trustee Northwestern Meml. Hosp. Mem. Chgo. Bar Assn. (chmn. antitrust law com. 1967-68), ABA (chmn. antitrust law sect. 1979-80), Alumni Assn. Northwestern U. Sch. Law (pres. 1974-75, svc. award 1976). Office: Sonnenschein Nath Ste 8000 233 S Wacker Dr Chicago IL 60606

POLLOCK, GEORGE HOWARD, psychiatrist, psychoanalyst; b. Chgo., June 19, 1923; s. Harry J. and Belle (Lurie) P.; m. Beverly Yufit, July 3, 1946; children: Beth L. Pollock Ungar, Raphael E., Daniel A., Benjamin B., Naomi R. Pollock Sneider. B.S., U. Ill., 1944, M.D. cum laude, 1945, M.S., 1948, Ph.D., 1951. Diplomate Am. Bd. Psychiatry and Neurology. Intern Cook County Hosp., Chgo., 1945-46; resident Ill. Neuropsychiat. Inst., Chgo., 1948-51; practice medicine, specializing in psychiatry Chgo., 1948-91; clin. assoc. prof. dept. psychiatry Coll. Medicine, U. Ill., 1955-64, clin. prof., 1964-72; prof. psychiatry Northwestern U., 1972-93, emeritus, 1993—, dir. rsch. dept. psychiatry/behavioral scis., 1988-93, emeritus, 1993—; faculty Inst. for Psychoanalysis, Chgo., 1956-92, asst. dean edn., 1960-67, tng. analyst 1961-92, supervising analyst, 1962-92, dir. rsch., 1963-71, pres., 1971-89; exch. program participant Hampstead Child Therapy Clinic, 1962-63; pres. Ctr. Psychosocial Studies, 1972-90. Chmn. bd. editors Annals of Psychoanalysis, 1971-89; mem. editorial bd. Jour. Am. Psychoanalytic Assn., 1971-74; mem. editorial bd. sect. psychoanalysis Psychiat. Jour. U. Ottawa Faculty Medicine, 1976—; corr. editor Jour. Geriatric Psychiatry, 1975—; Med. Problems of Performing Artists, Psychoanalytic Edn., Psychoanalytic Psychology, Internat. Forum for Psychoanalysis, Internat. Jour. Behavioral Scis. and the Law, Internat. Psychogeriatrics, Depression and Stress. Mem. med. adv. com. Planned Parenthood Assn., 1966-70; pres. governing bd. Parents Assn. Lab. Schs., U. Chgo., 1966-70; mem. med. adv. coun. Asthma and Allergy Found. for Greater Chgo. Capt. U.S. Army, 1946-48. Commonwealth fellow, 1951; research grantee Founds. Fund for Research in Psychiatry, 1960-65. Fellow Am. Coll. Psychiatrists, Am. Orthopsychiat. Assn., Am. Psychiat. Assn. (treas. 1980-86, pres. 1987-88), Am. Coll. Psychoanalysts (pres. 1985-86); mem. Internat. Psychogeriatrics (mem. editorial bds.), Am. Acad. Polit. and Social Sci., Am. Anthrop. Assn., Nat. Council on Family Relations, AAAS, AAUP, Profs., Am. Electroencephalographic Soc., Am. Heart Assn., Assn. for Research in Nervous and Mental Disease, Soc. for Exptl. Biology and Medicine, Ill., N.Y. acads. scis., Chgo. Psychoanalytic Soc. (pres. 1984-85), Soc. for Gen. Systems Research, AMA, World Med. Assn., Am. Name Soc., Am. Psychoanalytic Assn. (pres. 1974-75), Am. Psychol. Assn., Am. Psychosomatic Soc., Am. Pub. Health Assn., Am. Sociol. Assn., Assn. Am. Med. Colls., Ill. Psychiat. Soc. (pres. 1973-74), Sigma Xi, Alpha Omega Alpha, numerous others. Home: 5759 S Dorchester Ave Chicago IL 60637-1726 Office: 30 N Michigan Ave Chicago IL 60602-3402

POLLOCK, JOHN ALBON, broadcasting and manufacturing company executive; b. Kitchener, Ont., Can., Jan. 18, 1936; s. Carl Arthur and Helen Isabel (Chestnut) P.; m. Joyce Mary Smethurst, Apr. 13, 1963; children—Kimberlee, Kristen, Nichola, Graham. B.A.Sc., U. Toronto, Can., 1959; M.B.A., Harvard U., 1962. Tng. positions Electrohome Ltd., Kitchener, 1962-69, v.p., 1969-71, exec. v.p., 1971-74, pres., 1974-80, chmn., pres., CEO, 1980-92, chmn., CEO, 1992—; bd. dirs. Budd Can. Inc., S.C. Johnson & Sons, Ltd., Can. Gen. Tower, Waterloo Sci. Inc.; dir. Electrohome Ltd., CAP Comm. Ltd., CTV; past mem. Sci. Coun. Can., Past chmn. adv. bd. U. Western Ont.; bd. dirs. Trillium Found., Can. Clay and Glass Gallery, Jr. Achievement; past pres. K-W Art Gallery; past mem. bd. govs. U. Waterloo; past chmn. bd. govs. St. John's Sch., Elora; bd. govs. Grand Valley Conservation Found., Freeport Hosp. Mem. XPO Forum Group, Muskoka Lakes Golf and Country Club, Univ. Club Toronto, K-W Gyro Club, Rotary. Office: Electrohome Ltd, 809 Wellington St N, Kitchener, ON Canada N2G 4J6

POLLOCK, JOHN CROTHERS, III, educator, opinion research executive; b. Tacoma, Jan. 26, 1943; s. John Crothers, Jr. and Harriet Jane (Reib) P.; children: Christopher Frasier, Maxwell Crothers. BA, Swarthmore Coll., 1964; MPA, Syracuse U., 1966; postgrad. Sch. Advanced Internat. Studies, Johns Hopkins U., 1966-67; PhD, Stanford U., 1974. Asst. prof. Rutgers U., New Brunswick, N.J., 1971-78, Queens Coll., CUNY, N.Y.C., 1978-79, assoc. prof., 1979-80; dir. rsch. Rsch. & Forecasts, N.Y.C., 1979-81, pres., 1981-84; pres. New World Decisions, Princeton, N.J., 1984-90; sr. analyst Opinion Rsch. Corp., 1990; pres. J.C. Pollock Assocs., 1990—; Comm. Studies Dept. Trenton State Coll. Trenton, N.J., 1992—; dir. Latin Am. Inst., Rutgers U., 1974-76. Author: Aging in America, 1980, America Afraid (4 vols.) 1980-83, American Values in the Eighties: The Impact of Belief, 1981, Leisure in America, 1982, The Politics of Crisis Reporting, 1982, American Attitudes Toward Sports, 1983, America's Search for Quality, 1983, Women in Sports, 1985, Black Community Leaders in America, 1988, Retirement Planning: How 2 Generations View Their Financial Future, 1988, Perspectives on Middle Age, 1990, The Family: Surviving Tough Times in the 90s, 1991; numerous other books; sr. author survey reports in field, 1980-83; contbr. articles to mags. including N.Y. Times, Industry Week, Public Opinion, Society, The Nation, Journalism Quar., Venture; appearances on TV including: The Today Show, Nightline, Fin. News Network, Cable News Network); invited witness U.S. Congress. Mem. Am. Assn. Pub. Opinion Researchers, Assn. Ednl. Journalism and Mass Comm., Internat. Assn. Bus. Communicators, Internat. Comm. Assn., Speech Comm. Assn. Office: 80 Colleen Cir Trenton NJ 08638-1724

POLLOCK, JOHN GLENNON, facilities management services company executive; b. St. Louis, Aug. 9, 1943; s. Joseph A. and Eleanor K. (Donahue) P.; m. Susan M. Weber, July 10, 1965; children: Jennifer, John Jr., Rebecca, Donna, Nancy. BS, St. Louis U., 1965. Sales rep. Proctor & Gamble, Cin., 1965-68; comptrollership mgr. ServiceMaster, Downers Grove, Ill., regional mgr., area mgr., div. mgr., sales rep., div. v.p. group pres., 1968-89; pres. subs. co. ServiceMaster, Downers Grove, 1989-91, exec. v.p. mgmt. svc., 1992-94; pres. bus. & industry group, 1994—; chmn. ClassiCare Inc. Chgo. 1992—, Exec. Touch., Inc., Naples, Fla., 1994—, Mid-Am. Paralegal Inst., St. Louis, 1986—. Bd. dirs. St Andrews Episcopalian/Presbyn. Found., St. Louis, 1987—. Republican. Roman Catholic. Office: ServiceMaster Co One ServiceMaster Way Downers Grove IL 60515

POLLOCK, JOHN PHLEGER, lawyer; b. Sacramento, Apr. 28, 1920; s. George Gordon and Irma (Phleger) P.; m. Juanita Irene Gossman, Oct. 26, 1945; children: Linda Pollock Harrison, Madeline Pollock Chiotti, John, Gordon. A.B., Stanford U., 1942; J.D., Harvard U., 1948. Bar: Calif. 1949, U.S. Supreme Ct. 1954. Ptnr. Musick, Peeler & Garrett, L.A., 1953-60, Pollock, Williams & Berwanger, L.A., 1960-80; ptnr. Rodi, Pollock, Pettker, Galbraith & Phillips, L.A. 1980-89, of counsel, 1989—. Contbr. articles to profl. publs. Active Boy Scouts Am.; former trustee Pitser Coll., Claremont, Calif., 1968-76, Pacific Legal Found., 1981-91; trustee Fletcher Jones Found., Good Hope Med. Found. With AUS, 1942-45. Fellow Am. Coll. Trial Lawyers; mem. ABA, L.A. County Bar Assn. (trustee 1964-66). Home: 30602 Paseo del Valle Laguna Niguel CA 92677-2317 Office: 801 S Grand Ave Los Angeles CA 90017-4613

POLLOCK, MARC, educational media administrator, consultant; b. Pitts., Mar. 27, 1945; s. Hyman Disney and Beatrice (Berman) P.; m. Marjorie Ann Ginsburg, Dec. 16, 1967; 1 child, Brian Seth Ginsburg-Pollock. ABD in Eng., U. Pitts., 1973; BA in Eng. and Chemistry, Washington & Jefferson, 1966; MA in Eng., U. Pitts, 1969. Teaching fellow Eng. U. Pitts., 1968-74; instr. Eng. Chatham Coll., Pitts., 1972-79; exec. asst. to pres. Sta. WQED/Pitts., 1979-81, mgr. ednl. project devel., dir. edn., media and devel. cons., 1993—, cons. media and devel., 1993—. Lectr., presenter in field. Vol. March of Dimes, Pitts., 1990-92; cons. Am. Heart Assn., 1992-94.

Recipient NAGC Gold Screen award Nat. Assn. Govt. Communications, 1991, 2 Gold Screen awards, 1993, 2 CINE Golden Eagle awards, 1994. Mem. Acad. of TV Arts and Scis. (Emmy award Info. Series 1986), Modern Lang. Assn., Am. Assn. for Tng. and Devel., Melville Soc., Phi Beta Kappa. Avocations: tennis, skiing.

POLLOCK, MARVIN ERWIN, lawyer; b. N.Y.C., June 3, 1931; s. Benjamin and Roslyn (Dolman) P.; m. Helen Toby Schwartz, May 26, 1967; children: Jennifer, John. AB, U. Pa., 1953; JD, U. Chgo., 1956. Bar: Ill. 1956, N.Y. 1959, N.Mex. 1993, U.S. Dist. Ct. (no. dist.) Ill. 1956, U.S. Dist. Ct. (so. dist.) N.Y. 1960, U.S. Supreme Ct. 1967. Assoc. Altheimer & Gray, Chgo., 1956-58; assoc. Guggenheimer & Untermyer, N.Y.C., 1959-68, ptnr., 1968-85; mem. Herzfeld & Rubin, P.C., N.Y.C., 1986-92; of counsel Montgomery and Andrews, P.A., Santa Fe, 1993—. Author: Resale of Restricted Securities Under SEC Rules 144 and 144A, 1991; author monewspaper column, Art and the Law. Mem. ABA, N.Y. State Bar Assn. Home: 811 Gonzales Rd Santa Fe NM 87501 Office: Montgomery and Andrews PA 325 Paseo de Peralta Santa Fe NM 87501

POLLOCK, ROBERT ELWOOD, nuclear physicist; b. Regina, Sask., Can., Mar. 2, 1936; s. Elwood Thomas and Harriet Lillian (Rooney) P.; m. Jean Elizabeth Virtue, Sept. 12, 1959; children—Bryan Thomas, Heather Lynn, Jeffrey Parker, Jennifer Lee. B.Sc. (Hons.), U. Man., Can., 1957; M.A., Princeton U., 1959, Ph.D., 1963. Instr. Princeton U., 1961-63; Nat. Research Council Can. postdoctoral fellow Harwell, Eng., 1963-64; asst. prof. Princeton U., 1964-69, research physicist, 1969-70; asso. prof. Ind. U., 1970-73, prof., 1973-84, disting. prof., 1984—, dir. Cyclotron Facility, 1973-79, mem. Nuclear Sci. Adv. Com., 1977-80; Recipient Alexander von Humboldt sr. U.S. scientist award, 1985-87. Fellow Am. Phys. Soc. (Bonner prize 1992); mem. Can. Assn. Physicists. Home: 1261 Winfield Rd Bloomington IN 47401-6147 Office: West Ind U Swain Hall Dept of Physics Bloomington IN 47405

POLLOCK, ROY VAN HORN, pharmaceutical company animal health researcher; b. Detroit, Dec. 23, 1949; s. Alexander Samuel and Doris Louise (Van Horn) P.; m. Barbara Kathleen James, Aug. 22, 1970; children: Roy Alexander, Irene Eva, Sarah Helen. BA, Williams Coll., 1972; DVM, Cornell U., 1978, PhD, 1981. Asst. dean Coll. Vet. Medicine, Cornell U., Ithaca, N.Y., 1981-85, dir. med. informatics, 1985-89; dir. tech. svcs. SmithKline Beecham Animal Health, Exton, Pa., 1989-93; v.p. strategic product devel. SmithKline Beecham Animal Health, West Chester, Pa., 1993-94; v.p. companion animal divsn. Pfizer Animal Health, West Chester, Pa., 1995—; adj. prof. vet. pathobiology Purdue U., 1990—; cons. Impromed Computer Systems, Oshkosh, Wis., 1989—; mem. adv. bd. Cornell Feline Health Ctr., 1990—. Author: (with others) Provides Computer Aided Diagnosis, 1987; also articles; editor: (computer program) Active Learning, 1989; editor Animal Health Newsletter, 1985-89. Cubmaster local chpt. Boy Scouts Am., Ithaca, 1988-89. Recipient Small Animal Rsch. award Ralston-Purina, 1981; Kellogg Nat. fellow, 1987. Mem. AVMA (student advisor 1987-89, Gaines award 1989), N.Y. Acad. Sci., Am. Animal Hosp. Assn. (Veterinarian of Yr. award 1987), Phi Beta Kappa, Phi Zeta. Avocations: photography, creative writing. Office: Pfizer Animal Health 1600 Paoli Pike West Chester PA 19380-6014

POLLOCK, SHELDON IVAN, language professional, educator; b. Cleve., Feb. 16, 1948; s. Abraham and Elsie (Russ) P.; m. Estera Milman, Dec. 21, 1968 (div. May 1985); children: Niria, Mica; m. Ute Gregorius, 1991. AB, Harvard U., 1971, AM, 1973, PhD, 1975. Instr. Harvard U., Cambridge, Mass., 1974-75; asst. prof. U. Iowa, Iowa City, 1975-79, assoc. prof., 1979-85, prof., 1985-89; George V. Bobrinskoy prof. Sanskrit and Indian Studies U. Chgo., 1989—, chmn. Dept. S. Asian Langs. and Civilizations, 1991—; vis. prof. Collège de France, Paris, 1991. Author: Aspects of Versification in Sanskrit Lyric Poetry, 1977, Ramayana of Valmiki, Vol. II, 1986, Vol. III, 1991; regional editor: Harper Collins World Reader; contbr. articles to profl. jours. Am. Inst. Indian Studies sr. and short-term fellow, 1979, 84, 87, 94; Maharaja of Cochin Meml. lectr., Sanskrit Coll., Tripunithura, Kerala, 1989. Mem. Am. Oriental Soc., Assn. Asian Studies, Social Sci. Rsch. Coun. (Joint Com. on South Asia 1990—). Home: 5532 S South Shore Dr Chicago IL 60637-1904 Office: U Chgo Dept S Asian Langs 1130 E 59th St Chicago IL 60637-1543

POLLOCK, STEPHEN MICHAEL, industrial engineering educator, consultant; b. N.Y.C., Feb. 15, 1936; s. Meyer and Frances R. Pollock; m. Bettina Dorn, Nov. 22, 1962; children: Joshua, Aaron, Ethan. B in Engring. Physics, Cornell U., 1958; SM, MIT, 1960, PhD in Physics and Ops. Research, 1964. Mem. tech. staff Arthur D. Little Inc., Cambridge, Mass., 1964-65; asst. prof. Naval Postgrad. Sch., Monterey, Calif., 1965-68, assoc. prof., 1968-69; assoc. prof. U. Mich., Ann Arbor, 1969-73, prof., dept. indsl. and ops. engring., 1974—, chmn. dept., 1980-90; research scientist Inst. Pub. Policy Studies, Ann Arbor, 1972—; cons. to over 25 orgns. Area editor Ops. Rsch. Jour., 1977-82; sr. editor Inst. Indsl. Engrs. Trans., 1985-89, Army Sci. Bd., 1994—; contbr. more than 60 tech. papers to profl. jours. Fellow, Space Tech. Labs., 1960; sr. fellow NSF, 1975. Fellow AAAS; mem. Inst. Mgmt. Scis., Ops. Research Soc. Am. (pres. 1986-87). Home: 2694 Wayside Dr Ann Arbor MI 48103 Office: U of Mich Dept Indsl Ops Engring Ann Arbor MI 48109-2117

POLLOCK, STEWART GLASSON, state supreme court justice; b. East Orange, N.J., Dec. 21, 1932. BA, Hamilton Coll., 1954; LLB, NYU, 1957; LLM, U. Va., 1988. Bar: N.J. 1958. Asst. U.S. atty. Newark, 1958-60; ptnr. Schenck, Price, Smith & King, Morristown, N.J., 1960-74, 76-78; commr. N.J. Dept. Pub. Utilities; counsel to gov. State of N.J., Trenton, 1978-79; assoc. justice N.J. Supreme Ct., 1979—; mem. N.J. Commn. of Investigation, 1976-78; chmn. coordinating coun. on life-sustaining med. treatment decision making Nat. Ctr. for State Cts., 1994—; bd. dirs. Law Ctr. Found. Asso. editor: N.J. Law Jour; contbr. articles to legal jours. Trustee Coll. Medicine and Dentistry, N.J., 1976. Mem. ABA (chmn. appellate judges conf. 1991-92), N.J. Bar Assn. (trustee 1973-78), Am. Judicature Soc. (dir. 1984-88), Morris County Bar Assn. (pres. 1973). Office: NJ Supreme Ct Morris County Courthouse Morristown NJ 07963-0900

POLLOCK, THOMAS P., motion picture company executive; b. L.A., Apr. 10, 1943; m. Peggy Pollock; children: Alexandra, Allegra, Luke. BA, Stanford U., 1964; JD, Columbia U., 1967. With Pollock Bloom & Dekon, 1970-86, sr. ptnr.; v.p., chmn. bd. motion picture group MCA/Universal, Universal City, Calif., 1986-89; exec. v.p., chmn. motion picture group MCA, Inc., Universal City, 1989—. Trustee Am. Film Inst., L.A. Music Ctr., Am. Mus. of Moving Image. Mem. Calif. Bar Assn. Office: MCA Inc 100 Universal City Plz Universal City CA 91608*

POLLOCK, WILLIAM JOHN, secondary school administrator; b. N.Y.C., Nov. 25, 1943; s. Edward and Rose (Favero) P.; m. Jennie Ann Taccetta, Jan. 28, 1967; children: John-Paul, Elizabeth. BSEd, CCNY, 1967; MSEd, Trenton State Coll., 1985; EdD, Nova U., 1993; postgrad., Harvard Graduate Sch., 1992. Tchr. N.Y.C. Pub. Schs., 1967-69; tchr. electronics Howell High Sch., Farmingdale, N.J., 1970-85, dept. supr., 1985-89; vice-prin. Monmouth County Vocat. Schs., Middletown, N.J., 1989-90; prin. High Tech. High Sch., Brookdale Community Coll. Campus, Lincroft, N.J., 1990—; pres. suprs.' assn. Freehold (N.J.) Regional High Sch. Dist., 1988-89; pres. exec. bd. Region V Libr. Coop., Freehold, 1989-92. Asst. scout master Jackson (N.J.) area Boy Scouts Am., 1987-92; pres. exec. bd. St. Mary Acad., Lakewood, N.J., 1987-89; mem. Ocean County Agrl. Devel. Bd., Toms River, N.J., 1989—. 1st lt. U.S. Army, 1969-70, Vietnam. Decorated Bronze Star medal, 1970; Geraldine R. Dodge Fdn. Fellowship award, 1993. Mem. ASCD, Nat. Assn. Secondary Sch. Prins., N.J. Assn. Supervision and Curriculum Devel., Internat. Tech. Edn. Assn., Am. Vocat. Edn. Assn., Prins. and Suprs. Assn., K.C., Garden State Prin.'s Ctr. (charter mem.). Avocations: farming, growing Christmas trees, photography, pottery, solar energy. Office: High Tech High Sch PO Box 119 Lincroft NJ 07738-0119

POLLOCK, WILSON F., architectural firm executive. BArch, Pa. State U.; MS in Architecture, Columbia U. Cert. Nat. Coun. Archtl. Registration Bds.; registered architect, 15 states. Formerly with Sert, Jackson Assocs., Cambridge, Mass., Cambridge Seven Assocs., Eshback Pullinger, Phila., Emo Goldfinger, London; founder, pres. ADD Inc., Cambridge; lectr. in field. Prin. works include One Federal Street Renovation, Boston, Hewlett Packard's Med. Products Group Expansion, Andover, Mass., 404 Wyman Street, Waltham, Mass. Bd. trustees Boston Found. for Architects; bd. dirs. Newton Community Devel. Found., Jackson Homestead Mus.; frequent sem. leader Build Boston. Recipient Alumni Achievement award Pa. State U., 1991. Fellow AIA; mem. I.D.R.C., Nat. Assn. Indsl. and Office Parks (assoc.), Boston Soc. Architects (past pres.), Urban Land Inst. Office: ADD Inc 80 Prospect St Cambridge MA 02139-2599

POLLOCK-O'BRIEN, LOUISE MARY, public relations executive; b. Tarentum, Pa., Mar. 14, 1948; d. Louis P. and Amelia M. (Ballay) Pollock; m. Vincent Miles O'Brien. BS, Ind. U. of Pa., 1970. Tchr. Archbishop Wood High Sch., Warminster, Pa., 1970-75; spokesperson, publicist Calif. Olive Industry, Fresno, 1976-78; account exec. Ketchum Pub. Rels., N.Y.C., 1979-81, account supr., 1982-83, v.p., 1984—, group mgr., 1985-88, sr. v.p., group mgr., 1988-89, assoc. dir., dir. food mktg., sr. v.p., 1990-91; chmn. Aronow & Pollock Communications, Inc., N.Y.C., 1991—; mem. pub. relations adv. com. Mayor's Vol. Action Com., N.Y.C., 1986; mem. food service adv. bd. L.I. City Coll., Bklyn., 1987-88. V.p.: fundraiser West 76th St. Block Assn., N.Y.C., 1982. Mem. Internat. Foodservice Editorial Council (v.p., bd. dirs. 1984-85). Avocations: watercolor painting, skiing. Office: Aronow & Pollock Communications Inc 524 Broadway New York NY 10012

POLOMÉ, EDGAR CHARLES, foreign language educator; b. Brussels, Belgium, July 31, 1920; came to U.S. 1961, naturalized, 1966; s. Marcel Félicien and Berthe (Henry) P.; m. Julia Joséphine Schwindt, June 22, 1944 (dec. May 1975); children: Monique Laure (Mrs. John Ellsworth), André Robert; m. Barbara Baker Harris, July 13, 1980 (div. Jan. 1991); m. Sharon Looper Rankin, Feb. 8, 1991. B.A., Université Libre de Bruxelles, 1941, Ph.D., 1949; M.A., Cath. U. Louvain, 1943. Prof. Germanic lang. Athénée Ville de Bruxelles, 1942-56; prof. Dutch Belgian Nat. Broadcasting Corp., Brussels, 1954-56; prof. linguistics U. Belgian Congo (now Zaire), 1956-61; prof. Germanic, Oriental, African langs. and lits. U. Tex., Austin, 1961—, dir. Ctr. for Asian Studies, 1962-72, Christie and Stanley Adams Jr. Centennial prof. liberal arts, 1984—; chmn. dept. U. Tex., 1969-76. Author: Swahili Language Handbook, 1967, Language in Tanzania, 1980, Language, Society and Paleoculture: Essays, 1982, Essays on Germanic Religion, 1989; editor: Old Norse Literature and Mythology, 1969, The Indo-Europeans in the 4th and 3rd Millennia, 1982, Guide to Language Change, 1990, Reconstructing Languages and Cultures, 1992; co-editor Jour. Indo-European Studies, 1973—, The Mankind Quar., 1980—; mng. editor Jour. Indo-European Studies, 1987—. Served with Belgian Aux. Aerodrome Police, 1945. Fulbright prof. U. Kiel, 1968; Ford Found. team dir. Tanzania survey, 1969-70. Mem. Linguistics Soc. Am., Am. Oriental Soc., MLA, African Studies Assn., Am. Anthrop. Assn., Indogermanische Gesellschaft, Societas Linguistica Europea, Société de Linguistique de Paris, Am. Inst. Indian Studies (chmn. lang. com. 1972-78). Home: 2701 Rock Terrace Dr Austin TX 78704-3843 Office: U Tex Dept Germanic Langs EPS 3 102 Austin TX 78712 *Having taught and done research on four continents—Europe, Africa, America and Asia—I feel gratitude that my experience has enabled me to discover the richness of man's intellectual and artistic heritage. It has especially allowed better appreciation of the perennial aesthetic, ethical and social values that make us all part of the great human brotherhood, whatever our language, creed or ethnic background.*

POLONIS, DOUGLAS HUGH, engineering educator; b. North Vancouver, B.C., Can., Sept. 2, 1928; came to U.S. 1955, naturalized, 1963; s. William and Ada (Burrows) P.; m. Vera Christine Brown, Jan. 30, 1953; children: Steven Philip, Malcolm Eric, Douglas Hugh, Christine Virginia. B.A.Sc., U. B.C., 1951, Ph.D., 1955; M.A.Sc., U. Toronto, 1953. Metall. engr. Steel Co. Can., Hamilton, Ont., 1951-52; mem. faculty U. Wash., Seattle, 1955—; prof. metall. engring., materials sci. & engring. U. Wash., 1962—, chmn. dept. mining, metall. and ceramic engring., 1969-71, 73-82; metall. cons., 1955—. Contbr. articles to profl. jours. Fellow Am. Soc. Metals; mem. AIME, Sigma Xi, Tau Beta Pi, Alpha Sigma Mu, Sigma Phi Delta. Home: 19227 46th Ave NE Seattle WA 98155-2909

POLONSKY, ARTHUR, artist, educator; b. Lynn, Mass., June 6, 1925; s. Benjamin and Celia (Hurwitz) P.; children: Eli, D.L., Gabriel. Diploma with highest honors, Sch. of Mus. Fine Arts, Boston, 1948. Instr. painting dept. Sch. Mus. Fine Arts, Boston, 1950-60; asst. prof. dept. fine arts Brandeis U., 1954-65; assoc. prof. Boston U., 1965-90, prof. emeritus, 1990—. One-man shows, Boris Mirski Gallery, Boston, 1950, 54, 56, 64, 66, Boston Public Library, 1969, 90, 93, Durlacher Gallery, N.Y.C., 1965, Mickelson Gallery, Washington, 1966, 74, Boston Ctr. for Arts, 1983, Starr Gallery, Boston, 1987, Fitchburg Art Mus., 1990; group shows include, Met. Mus., N.Y.C., 1950, Stedelijk Mus., Amsterdam, The Netherlands, 1950, Carnegie Internat. Expn., 1951, Inst. Contemporary Art, Boston, 1960, Mus. Fine Arts, Boston, 1976, Boston Arts Festival, 1985, Expressionism in Boston, Decordova Mus., Lincoln, Mass., 1986, Decordova Mus., Lincoln, 1987, Palais Universitaire de Strasbourg, France, 1992; represented in permanent collections, Mus. Fine Arts, Boston, Fogg Mus., Harvard U., Addison Gallery of Am. Art, Andover, Mass., Stedelijk Mus., Walker Art Center, Mpls. Recipient Louis Comfort Tiffany award for painting, 1951, 1st prize Boston Arts Festival, 1954; European travelling fellow Sch. Mus. Fine Art, Boston, 1948-50. Mem. AAUP, Artists Equity Assn., Inc. (founding, former dir. New Eng. chpt.). Address: 364 Cabot St Newtonville MA 02160

POLOZOLA, FRANK JOSEPH, federal judge; b. Baton Rouge, Jan. 15, 1942; s. Steve A. Sr. and Caroline C. (Lucito) P.; m. Linda Kay White, June 9, 1962; children: Gregory Dean, Sheri Elizabeth, Gordon Damian. Student bus. adminstrn., La. State U., 1959-62; JD, 1965. Bar: La. 1965. Law clk. to U.S. Dist. Ct. Judge E. Gordon West, 1965-66; assoc. Seale, Smith & Phelps, Baton Rouge, 1966-68, ptnr., 1968-73; part-time magistrate U.S. Dist. Ct. (mid. dist.) La., Baton Rouge, 1972-73, magistrate, 1973-80, judge, 1980—; adj. prof. Law Ctr., La. State U., 1977—. Bd. dirs. Cath. High Sch. Mem. La. Bar Assn., Fed. Bar Assn., Baton Rouge Bar Assn., Fifth Circuit Dist. Judges Assn., L.A. Law Inst., Omicron Delta Kappa. Roman Catholic. Clubs: KC, La. State U. L Club. Office: US Dist Ct Russell B Long Fed Bldg & US Courthouse 777 Florida St Ste 313 Baton Rouge LA 70801-1712

POLSBY, DANIEL D., law educator; b. 1945. BA, Oakland U., 1964; JD, Minn. State U., 1971. Bar: Minn. 1971, D.C. 1972, Ill. 1977, N.Y. 1982. Law clk. to presiding justice U.S. Ct. Appeals (D.C. cir.), 1971-72; assoc. Wilmer, Cutler & Pickering, D.C., 1972-74; legal adviser to commr. FCC, D.C., 1974-76; asst. prof. law Northwestern U., Chgo., 1976-78, assoc. prof., 1978-79, prof., 1979—, Kirkland & Ellis prof., 1990—; vis. prof. Cornell U., 1981-82, U. Mich., 1982, U. So. Calif., 1990. Pres. Minn. Law Rev. Bd. Mem. ABA, Order of Coif. Office: Northwestern U Law Sch 357 E Chicago Ave Chicago IL 60611

POLSHEK, JAMES STEWART, architect; b. Akron, Ohio, Feb. 11, 1930; s. Alex and Pearl (Beyer) P.; m. Ellyn May Margolis, June 29, 1952; children—Peter, Jennifer. BS, Case Western Res. U., 1951; BArch, Yale U., 1955. With I.M. Pei & Assocs., N.Y.C., 1955-56, Ulrich Frazen & Assocs., N.Y.C., 1957-60, Westermann & Miller & Assocs., N.Y.C., 1960-61; pvt. practice architecture N.Y.C., 1962-80; dean Sch. Architecture and Planning, spl. advisor to pres. for design and planning Columbia U., N.Y.C., 1972-87; prin. James Stewart Polshek & Ptnrs., N.Y.C., 1988—. Trustee Mcpl. Art Soc., N.Y.C. Fulbright fellow, 1956-57. Mem. AIA (1st. v.p. 1971, pres.-elect 1972). Clubs: Yale of N.Y, Century Assn. Office: Polshek & Partners 161 W 16th St 19B New York NY 10011

POLSKY, DONALD PERRY, architect; b. Milw., Sept. 30, 1928; s. Lew and Dorothy (Geisenfeld) P.; m. Corinne Shirley Neer, Aug. 25, 1957; children: Jeffrey David, Debra Lynn. BArch, U. Nebr., Lincoln, 1951; postgrad., U. So. Calif., 1956, U. Calif., Los Angeles, 1957, U. Nebr., Omaha, 1964, U. Ill., 1965. Project architect Richard Neutra, Architect, Los Angeles, 1953-56, Daniel Dworsky, Architect, Los Angeles, 1956; prin. Polsky, AIA & Assocs., Los Angeles, 1956-62, Omaha, 1964—; dir. dept. architecture MCA, Inc., Universal City, Calif., 1962-64. Prin. works include Mills residence, 1958, apt. bldgs., 1960, Polsky residence, 1961, Milder residence, 1965. Chmn. Design Control I480 Study Mayor's Riverfront Devel., Omaha, 1969, 71; pres. Swanson Sch. Community Club, Omaha, 1972; mem. Mayor's Adv. Panel Design Services, Omaha, 1974; vice chmn. Omaha Zoning Bd. Appeals, 1976. Recipient archtl. awards Canyon Crier Newspaper, Los Angeles, 1960, House and Home Mag., Santa Barbara, Calif., 1960. Mem. AIA (pres. Omaha chpt. 1968, numerous awards 1956-87), Nebr. Soc. Architects (pres. 1975, award 1965, 87). Office: Donald P Polsky AIA & Assocs 8723 Oak St Omaha NE 68124-3051

POLSTON, MARK FRANKLIN, minister; b. Indpls., Feb. 9, 1960; s. Albert Franklin and Mildred (Wiggington) P.; m. Lisa Kaye Polston, July 21, 1984; 1 child, Jordan Franklin. AS, Somerset (Ky.) C. C., 1981; BS, Campbellsville Coll., 1984; JD, Ind. Sch. Law, 1995. Real estate agt. Homestead Real Estate, Somerset, 1978-89; pastor Trace Fork Separate Bapt. Ch., Liberty, Ky., 1979-81, Calvary Separate Bapt. Ch., Nancy, Ky., 1980-84, Harmony Separate Bapt. Ch., Jacksonville, Fla., 1984-85, Fairview Separate Bapt. Ch., Russell Springs, Ky., 1985-89, Calvary Separate Bapt. Ch., Nancy, Ky., 1989-91, Edinburgh (Ind.) Separate Bapt. Ch., 1992—; sales rep. Sentry Ins., Somerset, 1989-91; law clk. Ind. Atty. Gen., Indpls., 1992—; clk. Gen. Assn. Separate Bapt., 1988—; bd. dirs. Separate Bapt. Missions., Inc., 1988-92; adj. prof. Ind. Vocat. Tech. Coll., Indpls., 1993—. Home: 787 Kitchen Rd Mooresville IN 46158 Office: Ind Atty Gen 402 W Washington St Indianapolis IN 46204 also: Edinburgh Separate Bapt Ch 1010 S Main St Edinburgh IN 46124

POLSTRA, LARRY JOHN, lawyer; b. Lafayette, Ind., June 28, 1945; s. John Edward and Elizabeth (Vandergraff) P.; m. Joan Marie Blair Rozier, Sept. 2, 1972 (dec.); 1 stepchild, Shawn M. Rozier; m. Barbara Dominy, March 18, 1988; stepchildren: Tobi Shawn Porter, Teri Lane Porter. BS in Bus. Mgmt., Bob Jones U., 1968; JD, Atlanta Law Sch., 1976, LLM, 1977. Bar: Ga. 1976, U.S. Dist. Ct. (no. dist.) Ga. 1976, U.S. Ct. Appeals (11th cir.) 1990, U.S. Supreme Ct. 1994. Mktg. dir. N.Am. Security, Atlanta, 1972-73; acctg. supr. Allstate Ins. Co., Atlanta, 1973-76; sole practice Atlanta, 1976-77; ptnr. Law Smith (formerly Smith & Polstra), Atlanta, 1977-94, of counsel, 1995—; arbitrator Fulton County Superior Ct., Atlanta, 1986. Served to 1st lt. USMC, 1968-71, Vietnam. Mem. ATLA, Atlanta Bar Assn., Ga. Assn. Trial Lawyers, Ga. Assn. Criminal Def. Lawyers, Marine Corps Assn. Ga. Lawyers. Avocations: golf, softball. Home: 1311 Golf Link Dr Stone Mountain GA 30088-3727 Office: PO Box 450909 3550 Habersham at Northlake Atlanta GA 31145-0909

POLUNIN, NICHOLAS, environmentalist, author, editor; b. Checkendon, Oxfordshire, Eng.; s. Vladimir and Elizabeth Violet (Hart) P.; m. Helen Lovat Fraser, 1939 (dec.); 1 child, Michael; m. Helen Eugenie Campbell, Jan. 3, 1948; children: April Xenia, Nicholas V. C., Douglas H. H. Open scholar, Christ Ch., 1928-32; BA (1st class honors), U. Oxford, 1932, MA, 1935, DPhil, 1935, DSc, 1942; MS, Yale U., 1934. Participant or leader numerous sci. expdns., 1930-65, primarily in arctic regions, including Spitsbergen, Greenland, Ala., Can. western, eastern Arctic, North Pole; curator, tutor, demonstrator, lectr. various instns., especially Oxford U., 1933-47; vis. prof. botany McGill U., 1946-47, Macdonald prof. botany, 1947-52; Guggenheim fellow, rsch. assoc. Harvard U., 1950-53; earlier fgn. research asso., USAF botanical Ice-island research project dir., lectr. plant sci. Yale, also biology Brandeis U., 1953-55; prof. plant ecology and taxonomy, head dept. botany, dir. U. Herbarium and Botanic Garden, Baghdad, Iraq, 1955-58; guest prof. U. Geneva, 1959-61, 75-76; adviser establishment, founding prof. botany, dean faculty sci. U. Ife, Nigeria, 1962-66; founding editor Plant Sci. Monographs and World Crops Books, 1954-78, Biol. Conservation, 1967-74, Environ. Conservation, 1974—; chmn. internat. steering com., organizer, editor procs. Internat. Conf. Environ. Future, Finland, 1971; chmn. internat. steering com., sec. gen., editor proc. 2d Internat. Conf. Environ. Future, Reykjavik, Iceland, 1977, 3d Internat. Conf. Environ. Future, Edinburgh, Scotland, 1987; sec.-gen., joint editor procs. 4th Internat. Conf. Environ. Future, Budapest, Hungary, 1990; pres. Found. for Environ. Conservation, 1975—; participant Internat. Bot. Congresses, Stockholm, 1950, Paris, 1954, Edinburgh, 1964, Seattle, 1969, Leningrad, 1975, Sydney, 1981; councillor (pres.) World Council For The Biosphere, 1984—. Author: Russian Waters, 1931, The Isle of Auks, 1932, Botany of the Canadian Eastern Arctic, 3 vols., 1940-48, Arctic Unfolding, 1949, Circumpolar Arctic Flora, 1959, Introduction to Plant Geography and Some Related Sciences, 1960 (various fgn. edits), Eléments de Géographie Botanique, 1967; editor: The Environmental Future, 1972, Environmental Monographs and Symposia, 1979-88, Growth Without Ecodisasters?, 1980, Ecosystem Theory and Application, 1986, (with Sir John Burnett) Maintainance of The Biosphere, 1990, Surviving With The Biosphere, 1993, (with Mohammad Nazim) Environmental Challenges I: From Stockholm to Rio and Beyond, 1993, II: Population and Global Security, 1994; founding chmn. edit. bd. Cambridge Studies in Environmental Policy, 1984—; contbr. to various jours. Decorated comdr. Order Brit. Empire, 1975; recipient undergrad., grad. student scholarships, fellowships, rsch. associateships Yale U., 1933-34, Harvard U., 1936-37; Rolleston Meml. prize, 1938; D.S.I.R. spl. investigator, 1938; Leverhulme Rsch. award, 1941; from sr. scholar to sr. rsch. fellow New Coll., Oxford, 1934-47; Arctic Inst. N.A. rsch. fellow, 1946-47; Guggenheim fellow, 1950-52; recipient Ford Found. award Scandinavia, USSR, 1966-67, Canadien Marie-Victorin medal, 1957, Indian Ramdeo medal, 1986, Internat. Sasakawa Environ. prize, 1987, USSR Vernadsky commemoration, 1988, Chinese Academia Sinica medal, 1988, Vernadsky medal USSR Acad. Scis., 1988, 89, Founder's (Zéchenyi) medal Hungarian Acad. of Scis., 1990; named to Netherlands Order of the Golden Ark, 1990 (officer), UN Environ. Programme Global 500 Roll of Honour, 1991. Fellow Royal Geog. Soc., Royal Hort. Soc., Linnean Soc. London, AAAS, Arctic Inst. N.A., INSONA (v.p.), NECA (India); assoc. fellow Pierson Coll., Yale U.; mem. Internat. Soc. for Environ. Edn. (life), Internat. Acad. Environment Geneva (mem. conseil de fondation), Torrey Bot. Club (life), Bot. Soc. Am. (life), N.Am. Assn. for Environ. Edn. (life), Asian Soc. Environ. Protection (life), various fgn. and nat. profl. and sci. socs. Clubs: Harvard (N.Y.C.) (life); Canadian Field Naturalists (Ottawa, life); Reform (London) (life). Achievements include confirming existence of Spicer Islands in Foxe Basin and made world's last major land discovery, Can. Arctic, 1946; past rsch. plant life and ecology of arctic, subarctic and high-altitude regions; present occupation environ. conservation at the global level; initiator of ann. worldwide Biosphere Day, 1991, plans for Biosphere Fund and Prizes, 1992, Biosphere Clubs, 1993. Address: Found Environ Conservation, 7 Ch Taverney 7th & 8th Fls, 1218 Grand-Saconnex Geneva Switzerland

POLUNSKY, BOB A., movie critic, talk show host; b. San Antonio, Dec. 3, 1931; s. Maurice Bernard and Ethel (Mazur) P.; m. Paulina Norman, June 12, 1960; children: Julianne, Laurianne, Adrianne. BFA, U. Tex., 1953. Traffic mgr. KABC Radio, San Antonio, 1953-55; Yellow Pages sales S.W. Bell Telephone, 1957-60; sales exec. mgr. KONO/KSAT, San Antonio, 1960-68; sales mgr. KENS-TV, San Antonio, 1968-85; movie critic San Antonio Express-News, 1968—, KENS-TV and WDAI RAdio, San Antonio, 1968—. With U.S. Army, 1950-57. Home: 619 Briar Oak San Antonio TX 78216 Office: The Express News Corp Ave E & 3rd St PO Box 2171-7297 # 3rd St San Antonio TX 78205

POLZIN, JOHN THEODORE, lawyer; b. Rock Island, Ill., Dec. 23, 1919; s. Max August and Charlotte Barbara (Trenkenschuh) P.; m. Helen Louise Hosford, Nov. 27, 1969. A.B., U. Ill., 1941, J.D. 1943. Bar: Ill. 1943. Sole practice, Galva, Ill., 1946-55, Chgo., 1975—; city atty., Galva, 1950-54; assoc. Langner, Parry, Card & Langner, Chgo., 1955-75; lectr. Ill. Inst. for Continuing Legal Edn., 1978. Served to lt. USNR, 1943-46. Mem. ABA, Ill. State Bar Assn. (chmn. patent, trademark and copyright law sect. 1981-82), Patent Law Assn. (chmn. fgn. trademark com. 1972, 74). Republican. Home and Office: 1503 Oak Ave Evanston IL 60201-4260

POMBO, RICHARD, congressman, rancher, farmer; b. Tracy, Calif., 1961; m. Annette, 1983; children: Richard Jr., Rena. Student, Calif. State U., Pomona, 1981-83. Councilman City of Tracy, 1991-92; mayor pro-tem Tracy City Coun., 1992; mem. 103rd-104th Congresses from 11th Calif. dist., 1993—; mem. Agrl. Com., Resources Com. Co-founder San Joaquin County Citizen's Land Alliance, Calif., 1986—; active San Joaquin County Econ. Devel. Assn., Tracy Bus. Improvement Dist., City Coun. (vice chmn. Cmty. Devel. Agy., Cmty. Parks Com., and Waste Mgmt. Com.), San Joaquin County Rep. Ctrl. Com. Mem. Rotary Club. Roman Catholic. Office: US Ho of Reps 1519 Longworth HOB Washington DC 20515-0511*

POMERANCE, NORMAN, publishing company executive; b. Greensburg, Pa., June 24, 1926; s. Isaac and Esther (Cohen) P.; m. Paula Diamond, Aug. 2, 1985; children—John, Jane, Jason. BS (Evan Pugh scholar), Pa. State U., 1950; MS, Ohio State U., 1951; JD, Yeshiva U., 1990. Dir. planning and analysis Gen. Precision, Inc., Tarrytown, N.Y., 1954-66; dir. bus. planning IT&T, N.Y.C., 1966-69; sr. v.p. Macmillan, Inc.; pres., dir. Macmillan Pub. Co., N.Y.C., 1969-74; group v.p. Arlen Realty and Devel. Corp., N.Y.C., 1974-76; v.p., dir. Am. Optical Corp., Southbridge, Mass., 1976-79; pres. internat. div. Am. Optical Corp., 1976-79; group v.p. Harper & Row (Pubs., Inc.), 1980-87; ret.; strategic planning advisor CARE, N.Y.C., 1991—. Served with USNR, 1944-46. Mem. Tau Beta Pi, Eta Kappa Nu, Pi Mu Epsilon, Phi Kappa Phi, Phi Eta Sigma. Home: 60 Gramercy Park N Apt 4A New York NY 10010-5435

POMERANCE, RALPH, retired architect; b. N.Y.C., Sept. 1, 1907; s. Harry and Esther (Perlstein) P.; m. Josephine A. Wertheim, June 8, 1934 (dec. 1980); children: Pamela (Mrs. Henry Steiner), Stephen M., Ralph.; m. Marilyn S. Selver, May 6, 1984. B.Arch., Carnegie Inst. Tech., 1930. Archtl. practice as Ralph Pomerance, 1933-38, Pomerance & Breines, N.Y.C., 1938-93. Prin. works include Bronx Municipal Hosp. Center, N.Y.C., 1955, Rose Fitzgerald Kennedy Research Center at Albert Einstein Coll. Medicine, 1969, Riis Houses Plaza and Amphitheatre, N.Y.C., 1966, Bellevue Hosp, 1970, NYU Dental Coll., 1976, NYU Hosp. offices, 1986. Chmn. Greenwich (Conn.) Housing Authority, 1947-53. Served to capt. AUS, 1942-45. Decorated knight 1st class Royal Order Vasa, Sweden, 1939. Fellow AIA (treas. N.Y. chpt. 1950-51, exec. com. 1954-57). Home: 101 Orchard St Cos Cob CT 06807-0112

POMERANTZ, CHARLOTTE, writer; b. Bklyn., July 24, 1930; d. Abraham L. and Phyllis (Cohen) P.; m. Carl Marzani, Nov. 12, 1966; children: Gabrielle Rose, Daniel Avram. B.A., Sarah Lawrence Coll., 1953. Children's books include The Bear Who Couldn't Sleep, 1965, The Moon Pony, 1967, Ask the Windy Sea, 1968, Why You Look Like You Whereas I Look Like Me, 1968, The Day They Parachuted Cats on Borneo, 1971 (chosen for Internat. Year of the Child 1977-78), The Princess and the Admiral, 1974 (Jane Addams Children's Book award), The Piggy in the Puddle, 1974 (Featured on Reading Rainbow in Claymation, 1992), NYT Outstanding Picture Book of the Year award 1974), The Ballad of the Long Tailed Rat, 1975, Detective Poufy's First Case, 1976, The Mango Tooth, 1977 (Jr. Literary Guild Selection), The Downtown Fairy Godmother, 1978, The Tamarindo Puppy and Other Poems, 1980 (an ALA Notable Book), Noah's and Namah's Ark, 1980, If I Had a Paka, 1982 (Jane Addams Honor award 1983), Buffy and Albert, 1982, Posy, 1983 (1984 Christopher award), Whiff, Sniff, Nibble and Chew, 1984, Where's the Bear?, 1984, The Half-Birthday Party (Jr. Literary Guild Selection), 1984, All Asleep, 1984, One Duck, Another Duck, 1984, How Many Trucks Can a Tow Truck Tow? (Children's Book of the Year Libr. of Congress 1991) 1987, Timothy Tall Feather, 1987, The Chalk Doll (Top 10 Picture Books of 1989 Boston Globe, Parents Choice award, 1990) 1989, Flap Your Wings and Try, 1989, Serena Katz, 1992, The Outside Dog (One of 100 Books Recommended by the N.Y. Pub. Libr., 1993, ALA Notable) 1993, Halfway to Your House, 1993, Mangaboom, 1994, You're Not My Friend Any More, 1994, Here Comes Henny, 1994; Lyricist: (children's musical) Eureka!, 1964; contbr. stories to mags.; spl. editorial asst.: Einstein on Peace, 1960; editor: A Quarter Century of Un-Americana, 1963. Address: 260 W 21st St New York NY 10011-3447

POMERANTZ, JAMES ROBERT, psychology educator, academic administrator; b. N.Y.C., Aug. 21, 1946; s. Mihiel Charles and Elizabeth (Solheim) P.; m. Sandra Elaine Jablonski, Oct. 1, 1945; children: Andrew Emil, William James. BA., U. Mich., 1968; PhD, Yale U., 1974. Prize teaching fellow Yale U., New Haven, 1973-74; asst. prof. psychology Johns Hopkins U., Balt., 1974-77; assoc. prof. SUNY, Buffalo, 1977-83, prof., 1983-88, chmn. dept. psychology, 1986-88, assoc. dean, 1983-86; dean social scis., Elma W. Schneider prof. psychology Rice U., Houston, 1988—; adj. prof. Baylor Coll. Medicine, 1992—. Editor: Perceptual Organization, 1981, The Perception of Structure, 1991. Fellow APA, Am. Psychol. Soc.; mem. Psychonomic Soc. Office: Rice U Sch Social Scis Houston TX 77251-1892

POMERANTZ, JOHN J., manufacturing executive; b. N.Y.C., July 4, 1933; s. Fred P. and Greta (Grainsky) P.; m. Laura H. Herman; children: Andrea, Susan, Marnie. BS in Econs., U. Pa., 1955. With Leslie Fay Cos., Inc., N.Y.C., 1955—, exec. v.p., 1968-71, pres., 1971-87, chmn., chief exec. officer, 1987—; bd. trustees Fashion Inst. Tech., pres. ednl. found. F.I.T. Bd. dirs. Am. Com. for Shenkar Coll. Textile Tech. and Fashion in Israel, Inc.; founder Albert Einstein Coll. Medicine, N.Y., Nat. Jewish Hosp. and Research Ctr., Denver, Israel Bonds Century Club; fundraising com. Am. Cancer Soc.; past chmn. Greater N.Y. Council Boy Scouts Am. Recipient award of Merit, Jack Martin Fund, Champion of Youth award Internat. Officers of B'nai B'rith, Humanitarian award Albert Einstein Coll. Medicine. Clubs: Quaker Ridge (Scarsdale, N.Y.); Palm Beach (Fla.) Country. Office: Leslie Fay Cos 1400 Broadway New York NY 10018-5203*

POMERANTZ, LAURA, apparel company executive; b. 1948. V.p. Leslie Fay Cos., N.Y.C. Office: Leslie Fay Cos 1400 Broadway New York NY 10018-5203

POMERANTZ, MARTIN, chemistry educator, researcher; b. N.Y.C., May 3, 1939; s. Harry and Pauline (Sietz) P.; m. Maxine Miller, June 4, 1961; children: Lee Allan, Wendy Jane, Heidi Lauren. B.S., CCNY, 1959; M.S., Yale U., 1961, Ph.D., 1964. NSF postdoctoral fellow U. Wis.-Madison, 1963-64; asst. prof. Case Western Res. U., Cleve., 1964-69; assoc. prof. chemistry Yeshiva U., N.Y.C., 1969-74; prof. Yeshiva U., 1974-76, chmn. dept., 1971-72, 73-76; prof. chemistry U. Tex.-Arlington, 1976—; co-dir. Ctr. for Advanced Polymer Rsch., 1988-91, dir. Ctr. for Advanced Polymer Rsch., 1991—; vis. assoc. prof. U. Wis.-Madison, 1972; vis. prof. Columbia U., N.Y.C., 1970-75, Ben Gurion U. of the Negev, Beer Sheva, Israel, summers 1981, 85. Contbr. articles to sci. jours. Fellow Alfred P. Sloan Found., 1971-76, NSF and Sterling, 1962-63, Leeds and Northrup Found., 1960-62, Woodrow Wilson fellow, 1959-60; grantee NSF, Robert A. Welch Found., Def. Adv. Rsch. Projects Agy., Air Force Office Sci. Rsch., Dept. Energy, Petroleum Rsch. Fund, Tex. Advanced Tech. program, also others. Mem. Am. Chem. Soc., Royal Soc. Chemistry, Phi Beta Kappa, Sigma Xi. Jewish. Home: 5521 Williamstown Rd Dallas TX 75230-2127 Office: U Tex Dept Chemistry & Biochemistry Box 19065 Arlington TX 76019

POMERANTZ, MARVIN, thoracic surgeon; b. Suffern, N.Y., June 16, 1934; s. Julius and Sophie (Luksin) P.; m. Margaret Twigg, Feb. 26, 1966; children: Ben, Julie. AB, Colgate U., 1955; MD, U. Rochester, 1959. Diplomate Nat. Bd. Med. Examiners, Am. Bd. Surgery, Am. Bd. Thoracic Surgery (dir. 1989—). Intern Duke U. Med. Ctr., Durham, N.C., 1959-60, resident, 1960-61, 63-67; instr. surgery, 1966-67; asst. prof. surgery U. Colo. Med. Sch., Denver, 1967-71, assoc. prof. surgery, 1971-74, assoc. clin. prof. surgery, 1974-93, prof. surgery, chief gen. thoracic surgery, 1992—; chief thoracic and cardiovascular surgery Denver Gen. Hosp., 1967-73, asst. dir. surgery, 1967-70, assoc.dir. surgery, 1970-73; pvt. practice Arapahoe CV Assocs., Denver, 1974-92; clin. assoc. surgery br. Nat. Cancer Inst., 1961-63; mem. staff Univ. Hosp., Denver, Denver Gen. Hosp., Rose Med. Ctr., Denver, St. Joseph's Hosp., Denver, Presbyn. Hosp., Denver, Craig Rehab. Hosp., Englewood, Colo., Porter Meml. Hosp., Denver, Swedish Med. Ctr., Englewood, Denver VA Med. Ctr., Children's Hosp., Denver, U. Coll. Health Sci. Ctr., 1992—; bd. dirs. Am. Bd. Thoracic Surgery, 1989—, chmn. in-svc. exam. com.; mem. dir. Cardiac Ctr. of Excellence Porter Meml. Hosp., 1987-92. Guest editor Chest Surgery Clinics N.Am., 1993; contbr. numerous articles to profl. publs.; chpts. to books. Fellow ACS, Am. Coll. Chest Surgeons; mem. AMA, Western Thoracic Soc. Assn. (v.p. 1992, Pres. 1993-94), counselor-at-large 1988-90), Am. Assn. Thoracic Surgeons (program com. 1991—), Am. Heart Assn. (bd. dirs. Colo. chpt. 1993), Arapahoe Med. Soc., Colo. Med. Soc., Denver Acad. Surgery (pres. 1980), Internat. Cardiovascular Soc., Rocky Mountain Cardiac Surg. Soc., Rocky Mountain Traumatologic Soc., Soc. Thoracic Surgeons (nomenclature/coding com. 1991—), stds. and ethics com., govt. rels. com.), Soc. Vascular Surgeons. Office: UCHSC Divsn CTS 4200 E 9th Ave # C310 Denver CO 80262

POMERANTZ, MARVIN ALVIN, corporate executive; b. Des Moines, Aug. 6, 1930; s. Alex and Minnie (Landy) P.; m. Rose Lee Lipsey, Nov. 12, 1950; children: Sandy Sager, Marcie Kuperman, Vickie Ginsberg,
Lori Wolnerman. BS in Commerce, U. Iowa, 1952. Exec. v.p. Midwest Bag Co., Des Moines, 1952-60; founder, pres., gen. mgr. Gt. Plains Bag Corp., Des Moines, 1961-75; v.p. Continental Can Co. Inc., Greenwich, Conn., 1971-75; v.p., gen. mgr. Forest Products Brown Systems Operation (div. Continental Can Co. Inc.), Greenwich, Conn., 1975-77; pres. Diversified Group Internat. Harvester, Chgo., 1980-81, ex. v.p., 1981-82; pres., chmn., chief exec. officer The Mid-Am. Group, Des Moines, 1981—; chmn., chief exec. officer Gaylord Container Corp., Deerfield, Ill., 1986—. Mem. Greater Des Moines Comn.; trustee Drake U., 1978—; pres. Iowa State Bd. Regents, 1987-93; mem. U.S. Olympic Budget and Audit Commn., Colorado Springs, Colo., 1989-92. Republican. Avocations: golf, tennis. Office: Gaylord Container Corp 4700 Westown Pky Ste 303 West Des Moines IA 50266-6728

POMERANTZ, RHODA SILVERSTEIN, geriatrician, internist, health center executive; b. Phila., May 6, 1937; d. Alexander Silverstein and Bertha (Joffe) Solomon; m. Marc A. Pomerantz, Aug. 14, 1958 (div. Jan. 1986); children: Lauren, Susan; m. Irwin I. Feinberg, Nov. 16, 1986; stepchildren: Susan, Michael, Jonathan, David, Steven. AB, U. Pa., 1958; MD, Women's Med. Coll., Phila., 1963; MPH, U. Ill., 1976. Diplomate Am. Bd. Internal Medicine, Am. Bd. Geriatric Medicine. Intern Presbyn. St. Luke's Hosp., Chgo., 1963-64, resident in internal medicine, 1964-66, 68-69; mem. attending staff Tri-City Hosp., Oceanside, Calif., 1967, Mile Square Health Ctr., Chgo., 1969-72; med. dir. attending staff Presbyn. St. Luke's Hosp., Chgo., 1969-70, med. dir., assoc. adminstr. ambulatory care, 1969-72, asst. attending staff dept. internal medicine, 1970-74, assoc. attending staff internal medicine and preventive care, 1974-82; project dir. Johnston R. Bowman Health Ctr., 1972-76, med. dir., 1976-82; chief Sect. of Geriatric Medicine St. Joseph Health Ctrs. and Hosps., Chgo., 1982—. Editor Geriatric Rehab. Series, 1980-81; mem. editorial bd. The Pharos, 1976-94, Ambulatory Medicine Alert, 1987. Fellow ACP, Gerontol. Soc. Am., Am. Geriatrics Soc. (del. to AMA 1983-90); mem. AMA, Am. Med. Dirs. Assn. (alt. del. to AMA 1990—, cert.), Ill. Geriatrics Soc., Phi Beta Kappa, Alpha Omega Alpha, Delta Omega. Home: 1315 N Sutton Pl Chicago IL 60610-2007 Office: St Joseph Health Ctrs and Hosp 2900 N Lake Shore Dr Chicago IL 60657

POMERANZ, FELIX, accounting educator; b. Vienna, Austria, Mar. 28, 1926; s. Joseph and Irene (Meninger) P.; m. Rita Lewin, June 14, 1953; children: Jeffrey Arthur, Andrew Joseph. BBA, CCNY, 1948; MS, Columbia U., 1949; PhD, U. Birmingham, Eng., 1992. CPA, N.Y., Va., La., N.C.; cert. computer profl., fraud examiner, govt. fin. mgr. Audit staff Coopers & Lybrand, CPAs, N.Y.C., 1949-56; mgr. Marks, Grey & Shron (now Ernst & Young, CPA's), N.Y.C., 1956-58; asst. chief auditor Am.-Standard, N.Y.C., 1958-62; mgr. systems Westvaco Corp., N.Y.C., 1962-66; dir. operational auditing Coopers & Lybrand, CPAs, N.Y.C., 1966-68, ptnr., 1968-85; disting. lectr. and dir. Ctr. for Acctg., Auditing and Tax Studies Fla. Internat. U., Miami, 1985-93, prof. acctg., 1993—, assoc. dir. sch. acctg., 1993—. Author: Managing Capital Budget Projects, 1984; The Successful Audit: New Ways to Reduce Risk Exposure and Increase Efficiency, 1992; co-author: Pensions-An Accounting and Management Guide, 1976; Auditing in the Public Sector: Efficiency, Economy, and Program Results, 1976; Comparative International Auditing Standards, 1985; contbr. articles to profl. jours. Emeritus trustee Nat. Ctr. for Automated Info. Rsch. 1st lt. AUS, 1944-46, 51-52. Recipient Spear Safer Harmon faculty fellow, 1987. Mem. AICPAs, N.Y. State Soc. CPAs, Assn. Systems Mgmt., Acad. Acctg. Historians, Assn. Govt. Accts., N.Y. Acad. Scis., Am. Acctg. Assn., Inter-Am. Acctg. Assn., Assn. Cert. Fraud Examiners, Beta Gamma Sigma, Beta Alpha Psi (Most Disting. and Most Outstanding Prof. awards 1993), Alpha Kappa Psi. Home: 250 Jacaranda Dr Apt 406 Plantation FL 33324 Office: Fla Internat U Sch Acctg University Park Miami FL 33199

POMERANZ, YESHAJAHU, research chemist, technologist; b. Tlumacz, Poland, Nov. 28, 1922; came to U.S., 1959, naturalized, 1967; s. David and Rysia (Bildner) P.; m. Ada Waisberg, Oct. 27, 1948; children: Shlomo, David. B.S., Israeli Inst. Tech., Haifa, 1946; Chem. Engr., Israeli Inst. Tech., 1947; student, U. London, 1954-55; Ph.D., Kans. State U., 1959-62. Dir. Central Food Testing Lab., Haifa, 1948-59; research chemist Agrl. Research Service, U.S. Dept. Agr., Manhattan, Kans., 1962-69; dir. Barley and Malt Lab. Agrl. Research Service, U.S. Dept. Agr., Madison, Wis., 1969-73; dir. U.S. Grain Mktg. Research Ctr. Agrl. Research Service, U.S. Dept. Agr., Manhattan, 1973-86; research prof. dept. food sci. Wash. State U., Pullman, 1986—; vis. prof. U.S. and abroad. Sci. editor, Am. Assn. Cereal Chemists; author, co-author, editor numerous book, symposia procs. in cereal sci., tech., food sci. tech. analysis; patentee high protein bread lipid syntheses and uses. Von Humboldt awardee, 1981; recipient Wiley award, 1980, Osborne award, 1981, W.F. Geddes medal, 1982, Disting. Svc. award U.S. Dept. Agr., 1983, Nat. Assn. Wheat Growers, 1990. Fellow AAAS, Inst. Food Technologists, Assn. Cereal Chemists; mem. Am. Chem. Soc. (Food Agr. award 1984), Assn. Ofcl. Analytical Chemists, Sigma Xi, Gamma Sigma Delta. Home: 1405 SW Wadleigh Dr Pullman WA 99163-2048 Office: Wash State Univ Dept Food Sci & Human Nutrition Pullman WA 99164-6376

POMERENE, JAMES HERBERT, retired computer engineer; b. Yonkers, N.Y., June 22, 1920; s. Joel Pomerene and Elsie Bower; m. Edythe R. Schwenn, Dec. 1, 1944; children: James Bennett, Katherine Ellen, Andrew Thomas Stewart. BSEE, Northwestern U., 1942; postgrad., Princeton U., 1950. Elec. engr. Hazeltine Corp., Little Neck, N.Y., 1942-46; mem. staff electronic computer project Inst. for Advanced Study, Princeton, N.J., 1946-51; chief engr. Inst. for Advanced Study, Princeton, 1951-56; sr. engr. IBM Corp., Poughkeepsie, N.Y., 1956-67; sr. staff mem. IBM Corp., Armonk, N.Y., 1967-76; cons. in field. Patentee in field. IBM fellow T.J. Watson Rsch. Ctr., 1976—. Fellow IEEE (Computer Pioneer award Computer Soc. 1986, Edison medal 1993); mem. NAE, Sigma Xi, Tau Beta Pi. Episcopalian. Home: 403 Bedford Rd N Chappaqua NY 10514-2207

POMEROY, EARL R., congressman, former state insurance commissioner; b. Valley City, N.D., Sept. 2, 1952; s. Ralph and Myrtle Pomeroy; m. Laurie Kirby, Dec. 26, 1986. BA, U. N.D., 1974, JD, 1979. Atty. Sproul, Lenaburg, Fitzner and Walker, Valley City, 1979-84; commr. of ins. State of N.D., Valley City, 1984-92; mem. 103rd Congress from N.D. (at large), Washington, D.C., 1993—; mem. coms.: budget, agriculture. State rep. N.D. Legis. Assembly, 1980-84. Recipient Found. award Rotary, 1975; named Outstanding Young North Dakotan N.D. Jaycees, 1982. Mem. Nat. Assn. of Ins. Commrs. (chmn. midwest zone 1987-88, exec. com. 1987-88), Phi Beta Kappa. Democrat. Presbyterian. Office: US Ho Rep 1533 Longworth Washington DC 20515-3401*

POMEROY, HARLAN, lawyer; b. Cleve., May 7, 1923; s. Lawrence Alson and Frances (Macdonald) P.; m. Barbara Lesser, Aug. 24, 1962; children: Robert Charles, Caroline Macdonald, Harlan III. BS, Yale U., 1944; LLB, Harvard U., 1948. Bar: Conn. 1949, U.S. Supreme Ct. 1954, U.S. Ct. Appeals (fed. cir.) 1954, Ohio 1958, U.S. Dist. Ct. (no. dist.) Ohio 1958, U.S. Claims Ct. 1958, U.S. Ct. Appeals (6th cir.) 1958, U.S. Tax Ct. 1958, D.C. 1975, Md. 1981, U.S. Dist. Ct. (D.C. dist.) 1984, U.S. Ct. Internat. Trade 1984, U.S. Ct. Appeals (D.C. cir.) 1986. Atty. trial sect. tax div. Dept. Justice, Washington, 1952-58; assoc. Baker & Hostetler, Cleve., 1958-62, ptnr., 1962-75; ptnr. Baker & Hostetler, Washington, 1975-92; gen. chmn. Cleve. Tax Inst., 1971; lectr. in field. Author: (monographs) The Privatization Process in Bulgaria, Bulgarian Government Structure and Operation—An Overview; contbr. articles to profl. jours. Treas. Shaker Heights (Ohio) Dem. Club, 1972-76; trustee, mem. exec. com. First Unitarian Ch. Cleve., 1965-68; trustee River Rd. Unitarian Ch., 1989-90; gen. counsel, former asst. treas. John Glenn Presdl. Com., 1983-87; participant Vol. Lawyers Project, Legal Counsel for Elderly, Washington, 1983-92; vol. Guardian Ad Litem Program, Sarasota, Fla., 1990-92, GED-H.S. Equivalency Program, Sarasota, 1990-92; resident liaison in Sofia, Bulgaria for Ctrl. and Ea. European Law Initiative, 1992-93; vol. execc., fgn. legal advisor Internat. Exec. Svc. Corps with Privatization Ministry, Prague, Czech Republic, 1994-95; mem. U.S. Treasury Dept. Spl. Mission to Bulgarian Ministry of Fin., 1995. Mem. ABA, D.C. Bar Assn., Am. Arbitration Assn. (arbitrator 1992—), Yale Club, Harvard Club, Ivy League Club, Columbia Country Club (Bethesda, Md.), Country Club of Sarasota Tennis Ctr. Home: 7336 Villa d'Este Dr Sarasota FL 34238 Office: Baker & Hostetler 11th Fl 1050 Connecticut Ave NW Washington DC 20036-5304 also: 3200 National City Ctr Cleveland OH 44414

POMEROY, HORACE BURTON, III, accountant, corporate executive; b. Bronxville, N.Y., July 11, 1937; s. Horace Burton Jr. and Juhn (McCalla) P.; m. Margarita Maria Benavidez, July 14, 1973; children: Josephine, Emily. BS in Bus Administrn., U. Ariz., 1964; MBA, Boise State U., 1982. Comml. bank officer Continental Bank, Chgo., 1964-67; cons. Morgan Olmstead Kennedy Gardner, L.A., 1967-74; mgr. cash and banking Morrison Knudsen Corp., Boise, Idaho, 1974—; rep. Idaho State Legistature Dist. 16, 1988—. With U.S. Army, 1959-60. Mem. Nat. Assn. Accts., Nat. Corp. Cash Mgrs. Assn., Nat. Philatelic Assn., Masons. Republican. Episcopalian. Avocations: stamp collecting, fishing, golf, tennis. Home: 6822 Kingsdale Dr Boise ID 83704-7343 Office: Morrison Knudsen Corp 1 Mk Plz Boise ID 83729

POMEROY, JOHN ERIC, electronics company executive; b. South Bend, Ind., Sept. 2, 1941; s. Wardell Baxter and Martha Cathrin (Sindlinger) P.; m. Karen Lee Fahlstrom, Mar. 30, 1968; children: Jeffrey John, Jay Michael. BSEE, Purdue U., 1963. V.p. mktg. Strippit/Houdaille, Akron, N.Y., 1968-75; pres. Excellon Industries, Torrance, Calif., 1975-85, Universal Instruments, Binghamton, N.Y., 1985-87, Dover Technologies, Binghamton, 1987—. Served to 1st lt. U.S. Army, 1964-66. Mem. Am. Electronics Assn. (bd. dirs. 1984-85), Torrance C. of C. (v.p. 1983), Broome County C. of C. Office: Dover Techs Corp 1 Marine Midland Pla PO Box 825 Binghamton NY 13902-0825

POMEROY, KENT LYTLE, physical medicine and rehabilitation physician; b. Phoenix, Apr. 21, 1935; s. Benjamin Kent and LaVerne (Hamblin) P.; m. Karen Jodelle Thomas (dec. Dec. 1962); 1 child, Charlotte Ann; m. Margo Delilah Tuttle, Mar. 27, 1964 (div. Jan. 1990); children: Benjamin Kent II, Janel Elise, Jonathan Barrett, Kimberly Eve; m. Brenda Pauline North, Sept. 1, 1990. BS in Phys. Sci., Ariz. State U., 1960; MD, U. Utah, 1963. Diplomate Am. Bd. Phys. Medicine and Rehab. Rotating intern Good Samaritan Hosp., Phoenix, 1963-64; resident in phys. medicine and rehab. Good Samaritan Hosp., 1966-69, asst. tng. dir. Inst. Rehab. Medicine, 1970-74, dir. residency tng., 1974-76, asst. med. dir., 1973-76; dir. Phoenix Phys. Medicine Ctr., 1980-85, Ariz. Found. on Study Pain, Phoenix, 1980-85; pvt. practice, Scottsdale, Ariz., 1988—; lectr. in field. Contbr. articles to med. jours. Leader Theodore Roosevelt coun. Boy Scouts Am.; mem. exec. posse Maricopa County Sheriff's Office, Phoenix, 1981—, posse comdr., 1992-94, qualified armed posseman; mem. med. adv. bd. Grand Canyon-Saguaro chpt. Nat. Found. March of Dimes, 1970-78. Recipient Scouter's Tng. award Theodore Roosevelt coun. Boy Scouts Am., 1984, Scouter's Woodbadge, 1985. Mem. AMA, Am. Acad. Phys. Medicine and Rehab., Internat. Rehab. Medicine Assn., Am. Acad. Orthopaedic Medicine (co-founder, sec.-treas. 1982-88, pres. 1988-90), Pan Am. Med. Assn. (diplomate), Prolotherapy Assn. (pres. 1981-83), Am. Pain Soc., Western Pain Soc., Am. Assn. for Study Headache, Am. Thermographic Soc. (charter), Am. Soc. Addiction Medicine (sec. Ariz. chpt.), Am. Acad. Pain Medicine, Nat. Eagle Scout Assn., Acad. Clin. Neurophysiology, Ariz. Soc. Phys. Medicine (pres. 1977-78), Ariz. Med. Assn., Maricopa County Med. Soc., others, Nat. Sheriff's Assn., Law Enforcement Alliance of Am. Mem. LDS Ch. Avocations: camping, drawing, painting, writing poetry, music. Office: Royal Orthopedic & Pain Rehab Assocs 9755 N 90th St Ste A-205 Scottsdale AZ 85258-5046 also: 2536 N 3rd St Ste 3 Phoenix AZ 85004-1308

POMEROY, LEE HARRIS, architect; b. N.Y.C., Nov. 19, 1932; s. Alfred and Florence Pomeroy; m. Sarah Pomeroy; children: Jordana, Jeremy, Alexandra. BArch, Rensselaer Poly. Inst., 1955; MArch, Yale U., 1961. Registered architect N.Y., Conn., Mass., Vt., N.J., Fla., Pa., Maine. Architect William Tabler, N.Y.C., 1958-59, The Architects Collaborative, Cambridge, Mass., 1959-60; assist. prof. CCNY, 1962-64; pres. Lee Harris Pomeroy Associates, N.Y.C., 1965-87; adj. prof. Sch. Architecture, CUNY, 1964-87; prin. solar rsch. group ECOSOL, Conn., Eng., Spain, 1965-84; dir. Project for Pub. Spaces, Inc., N.Y.C., 1982-88; dean's adv. coun. Sch. Architecture, Resselaer Poly. Inst., 1991—, adv. to pres., 1994—. Prin. works include Swiss Bank Tower and Saks Fifth Ave. extension, N.Y.C., restoration of Plaza Hotel, N.Y., Sch. Art and Dance City Coll., N.Y.C., 1989, New Rochelle Pub. Libr., 1980 (AIA-ALA design award 1980, N.Y. State AIA and Urban Design awards 1980), Dutchess County Jail, Poughkeepsie, N.Y. (AIA-ACA design award 1981), HBO Satellite Communications Ctr., 1983 (N.Y. State AIA Design award 1984), Manitou Sta. planned community, 1973 (AIA and Progressive Architecture awards 1973), Henry Street studios artists housing (Progressive Architecture mag. design award 1963, AIA design award 1975), Bedford Mews housing (AIA, Owens Corning energy conservation and Record Homes design awards 1980), Fulton Mall, Bklyn., 1985 (City Club of N.Y.C. Bard award for design 1985), Trinity Ch. Bridge (AIA design award 1991). Mem. Community Bd. 5, Midtown Manhattan, N.Y.C., 1980-91; bd. dirs. Bellview Assn., Bellview Hosp., N.Y.C., 1992—. Recipient Mcpl. Arts Soc. award, N.Y.C., 1982; Nat. Endowment for Arts grantee, N.Y.C., 1983. Fellow AIA (bd. dirs. 1979-81); mem. Mcpl. Arts Soc., Regional Plan Assn., Yale Club, Century Club, City Club N.Y. (co-chmn. Bard award program for excellence in urban design 1988-90, 94). Avocations: tennis, photography, travel. Home: 285 Central Park W New York NY 10024-3006 Office: 462 Broadway New York NY 10013-2618

POMEROY, ROBERT CORTTIS, lawyer; b. Syracuse, N.Y., Sept. 17, 1943; s. Stuart E. and Elizabeth (Corttis) P.; m. Sandra Campbell; children: Lisa, Robert Jr., Heather. AB, Hamilton Coll., 1965; LLB, Harvard U., 1968. Bar: Mass. 1968, Fla. 1981. Assoc. Goodwin, Procter & Hoar, Boston, 1968-76, ptnr., 1977—. Mem. Am. Coll. Trust & Estate Counsel. Avocations: skiing, golf, sailing. Home: 3 Pier 7 Charlestown MA 02129 Office: Goodwin Procter & Hoar Exchange Pl Boston MA 02109-2881

POMEROY, ROBERT LEE, food distribution executive; b. Lakewood, Ohio, Dec. 25, 1938; s. Robert Chester and Helen (Paddock) P.; m. Mary V. Sitera, Mar. 3, 1984; children: Jane, Jim, Robert. BS, U. Okla., 1960, MBA, 1961. Mktg. engr. IBM Corp., Houston, 1962-67; v.p. distbn. Uniroyal Corp., Houston, 1967-72; sr. v.p. store ops W.E. Walker Stores, Jackson, Miss., 1972-77; sr. v.p. distbn. Wetterau Inc. St. Louis, 1977—. Contbr. articles to profl. jours. Avocations: boating, skiing. Home: 14535 Amstell Ct Chesterfield MO 63017-5607 Office: Wetterau Inc 345 Dunn Rd Florissant MO 63031-7929

POMEROY, THOMAS WILSON, JR., lawyer, former state supreme court justice; b. Crafton, Pa., Nov. 20, 1998; s. Thomas Wilson and Marion Elizabeth (Bradbury) P.; m. Maria Frances Whitten, July 6, 1935 (dec. Dec. 1994); children: Anne Whitten Pomeroy Martin, George Robinson, Helen F. Pomeroy Hopkins, Benjamin Bradbury. A.B., Lafayette Coll., 1929; LL.B., Harvard U., 1933; LLD (hon.), Lafayette Coll., 1962, Wilson Coll., 1988. Bar: Pa. 1933. Instr. pub. speaking Lafayette Coll., 1929-30; practiced in (Pitts.); ptnr. Kirkpatrick, Pomeroy, Lockhart & Johnson, 1946-68; gen. counsel Pitts. & W.Va. Ry. Co., 1946-65; justice Supreme Ct., Pa., 1968-78; of counsel firm Kirkpatrick & Lockhart, Pitts., 1979—; chmn. Pa. Joint Council's Com. to Study Unified Jud. System in Pa., 1980-85. Pres. Pitts. Council Intercultural Edn., 1943-44; pres. Pitts. YMCA, 1964-66, now emeritus dir.; chmn. Pa. Gov.'s Commn. to Investigate Charges of Excessive Use of Force by Police in Chester, Pa., 1964; mem. Pa. Gov.'s Commn. on Three Mile Island, 1979, Commonwealth Commn. on Bicentennial of U.S. Constn., 1986-88; former mem. bd. Christian edn. United Presbyn. Ch. U.S.A.; trustee emeritus Lafayette Coll. Served to lt. comdr. USNR, 1944-46. Fellow Am. Bar Found., Pa. Bar Found.; mem. ABA, Pa. Bar Assn. (pres. 1961), Allegheny County Bar Assn. (pres. 1959), Am. Law Inst., Am. Judicature Soc., Inst. Jud. Adminstrn., World Affairs Coun. Pitts. (pres. 1940-44), Scotch-Irish Soc. U.S. (pres. 1962-64), Phi Kappa Psi, Tau Kappa Alpha. Clubs: Harvard-Yale-Princeton (Pitts.), Duquesne (Pitts.). Office: 1500 Oliver Building Bldg Pittsburgh PA 15222-2300

POMMERVILLE, ROBERT W., corporate lawyer. BA, Occidental Coll., 1965; JD, U. Utah, 1968. Trial atty. Safeco Ins. Co., 1969-70; sr. v.p., gen. counsel, sec. Beverly Enterprises, Ft. Smith, Ark., 1970-76; v.p. gen. counsel Beverly Enterprises, Pasadena, Calif., 1984—; with Currie & Kendall, 1976—, pres., 1980-84. Office: Beverly Enterprises PO Box 3324 Fort Smith AR 72913-3324

POMORSKI, STANISLAW, lawyer, educator; b. Lwow, Poland, Nov. 23, 1934; came to U.S., 1972, naturalized, 1983; s. Juliusz and Maria (Ziemba) P.; m. Patricia Smith; children—Lukasz, Christopher, Maria. M.Law, U.

Warsaw, 1956, D.Law. 1968. Law clk., 1958-61; pvt. practice law Warsaw, 1961-64; vis. scholar Harvard U. Law Sch., 1964-66; rsch. assoc. Polish Acad. Scis., 1966-72; mem. faculty Rutgers U. Law Sch., Camden, N.J., 1973—; prof. law Rutgers U. Law Sch., 1977-81, Disting. prof. law, 1981—; fellow Soviet law U., Leyden, Netherlands, 1980-81; trustee Nat. Coun. Soviet and East European Rsch., Washington, 1988-94. Author: American Common Law and the Principle Nullum Crimen Sine Lege, 2d edit, 1975, Restructuring the System of Ownership in the USSR, 1991; co-author: A Profile of the Soviet Constitution of 1977, 1979. Ford Found. fellow, 1972-73. Office: Rutgers U Law Sch 5th And Penn St Camden NJ 08102

POMPA, JAMES ROBERT, computer industry executive; b. Aurora, Ill., Nov. 8, 1937; s. Leroy Henrey and Eleanor (Michels) P.; m. Julianne Robinson, Mar. 8, 1958 (div. May 1988); children: Jeffrey, Michael, Linda, Sarah. BBA, Quincy U., 1959. V.p.e fed. systems Honeywell Info. Systems, Washington, 1970-77; v.p., gen. mgr. small systems Honeywell Info. Systems, Billerica, Mass., 1977-83; sr. v.p. mktg. Honeywell Info. Systems, Waltham, Mass., 1983-85; pres. Encore Computer Corp., Marlborough, Mass., 1985-88; pres., chief exec. officer Hadron, Inc., Fairfax, Va., 1989-90; prin. J.R. Pompa & Assocs., 1991—. Republican. Avocation: golf. Home: 8014 Rising Ridge Rd Bethesda MD 20817-6960

POMPADUR, I. MARTIN, communications executive; b. Bkln., June 25, 1935; s. Jack and Florence (Raitbord) P.; m. Joan Lynn Krassner, Dec. 18, 1960 (div. 1986); children: F. Douglas (dec.), Jana Sue; m. Mahan Hackett, Dec. 23, 1987; 1 child, Chelsea Rae. BA, Williams Coll., 1955; LLB, U. Mich., 1958. Bar: Conn. 1958, N.Y. 1961. Atty. ABC-TV Network, N.Y.C., 1960-61, 61-66, chief adminstrv. officer, 1966-68, gen. mgr., 1968-70, v.p. broadcast div., 1970-72, corp. v.p.; 1972; pres. ABC Leisure Group I, 1973-75, asst. to pres. parent co., 1975-76; also dir. parent co.; sr. v.p. Ziff Corp., 1977-78, pres., 1978-82; chmn., chief exec. officer GP Sta. Ptnrs., 1982; mng. gen. ptnr. TV Sta. Ptnrs., 1982—; chmn., chief exec. officer PBTV, Inc., 1984—; mng. gen. ptnr. Northeastern TV Investors Ltd. Partnership, 1984—; prin. owner, sec. Caribbean Internat. News Corp., 1985—, also bd. dirs.; CEO, COO RP Media Mgmt., Inc., 1986-93; chief exec. officer ML Media Ptnrs., L.P., 1986—; chief exec. officer, chief oper. officer RP Opportunity Mgmt.; chief exec. officer ML Media Opportunity Ptnrs., L.P., 1988—; prin. shareholder Hispanic Media Inc., 1986-90; prin. shareholder, vice-chmn. Hunter Pub. L.P., 1986-94; co-trustee Lidan Trust, 1983—; atty. Young & Rubicam, Inc., advt. agy., N.Y.C., summer 1961. Mem. Stamford bd. reps., chmn. legis. and rules com., 1959-60. Home: 10 Highland Farm Rd Greenwich CT 06831-2606 Office: RP Cos Inc 350 Park Ave Fl 16 New York NY 10022-6022

POMPER, PHILIP, history educator; b. Chgo., Apr. 18, 1936; s. Solomon and Rebecca (Fenigstein) P.; m. Alice N. Epstein, Aug. 27, 1961 (div.); children: Erica, Stephen, Karen; m. Emily Meyer, June 26, 1994. B.A., U. Chgo., 1959, M.A., 1961, Ph.D., 1965. Instr. history Wesleyan U., Middletown, Conn., 1964-65, asst. prof., 1965-71, assoc. prof., 1971-76, prof., 1976—, chmn. dept. history, 1981-84; William F. Armstrong prof. history, 1992—. Author: The Russian Revolutionary Intelligentsia, 1970, 2nd edit., 1993, Peter Lavrov and the Russian Revolutionary Movement, 1972, Sergei Nechaev, 1979 (Choice award 1979), The Structure of Mind in History: Five Major Figures in Psychohistory, 1985, Trotsky's Notebooks, 1933-35: Writings on Lenin, Dialectics and Evolutionism, 1986, Lenin, Trotsky, and Stalin: The Intelligentsia and Power, 1990; assoc. editor History and Theory, 1991—; contbr. articles on Russian history and theory of history to profl. jours. Fellow, Ford Found., 1963-64, Social Scis. Rsch. Coun., 1968, Hoover Instn., 1987, Wilson Ctr., 1988; Russian Rsch. Ctr. scholar, 1987—. Mem. Am. Hist. Assn., Am. Assn. for Advancement Slavic Studies, Conn. Acad. Arts and Scis. Home: 13 Red Orange Rd Middletown CT 06457 Office: Wesleyan U Middletown CT 06457

POMRANING, GERALD CARLTON, engineering educator; b. Oshkosh, Wis., Feb. 23, 1936; s. Carlton Chester and Lorraine Helen (Volkman) P.; m. Gayle Ann Burkitt, May 27, 1961 (div. 1983); children: Linda Marie, Sandra Lee. BS, U. Wis., 1957; cert., Technische Hogeschool, Delft, Holland, 1958; Ph.D. (NSF fellow), MIT, 1962. Mgr. GE, Pleasanton, Calif., 1962-64; group leader Gen. Atomic Co., La Jolla, Calif., 1964-69; v.p. Sci. Applications, La Jolla, 1969-76; prof. engring. UCLA, 1976—; cons. to govt. and industry. Author: Radiation Hydrodynamics, 1973, Transport in Stochastic Mixtures, 1991; editor: Reactor Physics, 1966; contbr. articles to profl. jours. Fulbright fellow, 1957-58. Fellow AAAS, Am. Nuclear Soc. (Mark Mills award 1963), Am. Phys. Soc.; mem. Math. Assn. Am., Soc. Indsl. Applied Math., Am. Math. Soc., Sigma Xi, Alpha Xi Sigma, Phi Eta Sigma, Phi Kappa Phi, Tau Beta Pi, Phi Lambda Upsilon.

PONCE DE LEON, MICHAEL, artist, lecturer, educator; b. Miami, Fla., July 4, 1922; s. Manuel and Joan (Cobos) P. de L. Student, U. Mexico, 1939, NAD, 1942, Art Students League, N.Y.C., 1947, Bklyn. Mus. Art Sch., also in Europe., 1949. Cartoonist Saturday Evening Post, Colliers, New Yorker mags., 1942-49, Yank Army mag., 1943-45; tchr. Vassar Coll., 1953, Pratt Graphic Art Center, 1957-71, Cooper Union, 1962-67, Hunter Coll., 1959-67, U. Pa., 1966—, Art Students League, 1966-86, Pratt Inst., 1968-86, Calif. State Coll., 1969, Hayward State Coll., 1970, Columbia U., 1972, NYU, 1976-77; v.p. Nelson Rockefeller Collection, Shah of Iran collection, John F. Kennedy collection; lectr. U.S., Europe, Asia, judge 50 art competitions, presenter demonstrations. Commd. by P.O. Dept. to design U.S. stamp honoring fine arts, 1964; USIA cultural missions to Yugoslavia, 1965, Pakistan, India, 1967, Venezuela, 1966, 82, Spain, 1971; Contbr. to: 16 books on printmaking, including Printmaking, 1971, Printmaking Today, 1972, Etching, 1973, Mexican-American Artists, 1973, History of Pictorial Illusion, 1975, the Art of the Print, 1976, Printmaking, 1977, History of Prints, 1980, Prints and Printmakers, 1980; 14 books on printmaking, including History of an Art, 1981, others; one-man shows include Corcoran Gallery, Washington, 1966, Salambo S.A. Gallery, Paris, 1988, Geneva, 1988; exhibited in group shows at Doma Gallery, N.Y.C., 1989, 40 prints So. Graphics Coun. U. Ala., Birmingham, Les Editions arts et images du monde, Paris, 1992, exhibition of prints, U. Ala., Birmingham; exhibited numerous cities throughout Can., S.Am., Mexico, Middle East, Russia, Europe, India, Australia, Japan, Korea, Taiwan; represented in permanent collections, Whitney Mus., Jewish Mus., NAD, Mus. Modern Art, Met. Mus. Art, Bklyn. Mus., Pa. Acad., Dallas Mus., Cin. Art Mus., U. Ill., U. Mich., U. Nebr., U. N.C, Norfolk Mus. Smithsonian Instn., Library of Congress, Phila. Mus., NYU, Acherbach Found., San Francisco, Cleve. Mus., Columbia (S.C.) Mus., UN, Nat. Gallery, Washington, Boston Mus., Sarasota (Fla.) Art Mus., Walker Art Ctr., Mpls., Auckland (New Zealand) Art Mus., Nat. Gallery, Stockholm, Oslo, Musee de l'Art Moderne, Paris, Victoria and Albert Mus., London, Am. embassies in Bonn, Germany, Belgrade, Moscow, Prague, New Delhi, White House, Washington; show by mems. Atelier Ponce de Leon at Doma Gallery, N.Y.; exhbn. of 40 prints and plates, 3 talks at U. Ala., 1991. Represented U.S. at Symposium of 1st Indian Triannial of Art in New Delhi; represented Venice Biennale, 1970, Bienal of P.R., 1981. Served with USAAF, 1943-44. Recipient Gold medal Oakland Art Mus., 1958, Nat. Acad. Design prize, 1963, 78, Medal of Honor Audubon Artists, 1964, 66, 67, 68, 70, 83, 84, Gold Medal of Honor, 1994, Alice McFadden Eyre medal Pa. Acad. Design, 1965, 65 purchase prizes from U.S. museums and colls.; Included in Archives Am. Art; Tiffany fellow, 1953-55; Fulbright fellow, 1955-57; Guggenheim fellow, 1967. Mem. Soc. Am. Graphic Artists (past. press.). *Every creative artist is a unique individual who has his feet firmly planted in mid-air. He uses all his negative energies—tensions, anxieties and other vulnerabilities and transforms them into rich reservoirs of positive forces, from which his art emerges carrying with it the mystery and wonder of the unknown.*

POND, BYRON O., manufacturing company executive; b. 1936. BSBA, Wayne State U. With Fed. Mogul Corp., Detroit, Mich.; with Maremont Corp., Chgo., 1968—, dir. sales exhaust systems div., 1970-74, corp. v.p.; 1974-76, sr. v.p. nat. accounts, 1976-78, exec. v.p., 1978-79, pres., chief exec. officer, from 1979, now pres., chmn. bd. dirs., chief exec. officer. Office: Maremont Corp 250 Kehoe Blvd Carol Stream IL 60188-1888 Also: Arvin Industries Inc PO Box 3000 Columbus IN 47202-3000

POND, DANIEL JAMES, industrial technology administrator; b. Bklyn., Oct. 24, 1949; s. Jack Jacob and Helen (Bartholomew) P.; m. Diane Louise Lippman, Sept. 5, 1971 (div. Oct. 1982); children: David Alan, Steven

Douglas; m. Linda Rae Smith, June 18, 1983; stepchildren: Timothy Joseph Wood, Melissa Jill Wood. AA, Nassau Community Coll., Garden City, N.Y., 1969; BS in Psychology, Adelphi U., 1971; MS in Counselor Edn., L.I. Univ., 1975; PhD in Ergonomics, N.C. State U., 1981. Operating engr. for several indsl. firms, 1968-77; assoc. prin. engr. Harris Govt. Systems, Melbourne, Fla., 1981-83; sr. human factors engr. Lockheed-Ga. Co., Marietta, Ga., 1983-84; chmn. engring. psychology Fla. Inst. Tech., Melbourne, 1984-90; chief adminstr. Ctr. for Interdisciplinary Rsch. on Aging, Fla. Inst. Tech., Melbourne, 1988-89; cons. Grumman, Melbourne, 1990; sr. program mgr., human factors tech. group leader Pacific N.W. Lab., Richland, Wash., 1990—; cons. Fla. Power & Light Nuclear Tng., Ft. Pierce, 1987-90; mem. Dept. Def. Human Factors Engring. Tech. Adv. Group Tech. Soc./Industry Group rep. of Assn. of Aviation Psychologists. Reviewer Ergonomics, Human Factors Engrs. Mem. Human Factors Soc. (rep. to the edn. com. AAAS, 1985-91, profl. standards com. 1985-91, chmn. 1988-91, chmn. tech. adv. group, 1991-93, coun. tech. groups chmn. 1987-88, educators' profl. group chmn. 1985-87, Paul M. Fitts educators' award com. chmn. 1985-87, edn. com.-internship subcom. chmn. 1984-85, pub. rels. com. 1983-85), chair, Energy Facilities Contractors Group, Human Factors/ Ergonomics Working Group, Assn. Aviation Psychologists, Sigma Xi. Home: RR 3 Box 3885 Prosser WA 99350-9541 Office: Pacific NW Lab Tech Planning & Analysis Ctr PO Box 999 MS K8-04 Richland WA 99352-0999

POND, KENNETH W., title company executive. Pres. Lawyers Title of Ariz., Phoenix. Office: Lawyers Title of Ariz 40 E Mitchell Dr Ste 100 Phoenix AZ 85012*

POND, PATRICIA BROWN, library science educator, university administrator; b. Mankato, Minn., Jan. 17, 1930; d. Patrick H. and Florence M. (Ruehle) Brown; m. Judson S. Pond, Aug. 24, 1959. BA, Coll. St. Catherine, St. Paul, 1952; MA, U. Minn., 1955; PhD, U. Chgo., 1982. Sch. libr. Minn., N.Y., 1952-62; asst. prof. libr. sci. U. Minn., 1962-63; reference libr. U. Mont., 1963-65; asst. prof. U. Oreg., 1967-72, assoc. prof., 1972-77; prof., assoc. dean Sch. Libr. and Info. Sci. U. Pitts., 1977-85. Mem. ALA (life), Phi Beta Kappa, Beta Phi Mu, Delta Phi Lambda, Kappa Gamma Pi. Home: 14740 SW Forest Dr Beaverton OR 97007-5117

POND, PHYLLIS JOAN, state legislator; b. Warren, Ind., Oct. 25, 1930; d. Clifford E. and Rosa E. (Hunnicutt) Ruble; m. George W. Pond, June 10, 1951; children: William, Douglas, Jean Ann. BS, Ball State U., Muncie, Ind., 1951; MS, Ind. U., 1963. Tchr. home econs., 1951-54; kindergarten tchr., 1961—; mem. Ind. Ho. of Reps. from 15th dist., 1978-82, from 20th dist., 1982-92, from 85th dist., 1992—, majority asst. caucus chmn., vice chmn. ways and means com., 1995. Del. Ind. State Rep. Conv., 1976, 80, 84, del. 1986, 88; alt. del. Rep. Nat. Conv., 1980. Mem. AAUW, New Haven Woman's Club. Lutheran.

POND, THOMAS ALEXANDER, physics educator; b. L.A., Dec. 4, 1924; s. Arthur Francis and Florence (Alexander) P.; m. Barbara Eileen Newman, Sept. 6, 1958; children: Arthur Phillip Ward, Florence Alexandra. A.B., Princeton U., 1947, A.M., 1949, Ph.D., 1953. Instr. physics Princeton U., 1951-53; asst. prof., then assoc. prof. physics Washington U., St. Louis, 1953-62; prof. physics SUNY, Stony Brook, 1962-81, chmn. dept., 1962-68, exec. v.p., 1967-79, acting pres., 1970, 75, 78; prof. physics Rutgers U., New Brunswick, N.J., exec. v.p., chief acad. officer, 1982-91, acting pres., 1990, univ. prof., 1991—; bd. dirs. Action Com. for L.I., 1978-80, Tri-State Regional Planning Commn., 1979-82; trustee Univs. Research Assn., 1985-87; bd. dirs. Fermilab, 1987-89. Served to major USNR, 1943-46. Mem. Am. Phys. Soc., Phi Beta Kappa, Sigma Xi. Home: 8 Campbells Brook Rd White House Station NJ 08889-9469 Office: Rutgers Univ Dept Physics and Astronomy Piscataway NJ 08855-0849

PONDER, ALONZA, church administrator. Vice-chief bishop Ch. of the Living God Exec. Bd. Office: Church of The Living God 5609 N Terry Oklahoma City OK 73111

PONDER, HERMAN, geologist; b. Light, Ark., Jan. 31, 1928; s. Herman Cook and Sylvia Adell (Cameron) P.; m. Barbara Elaine Sando, May 10, 1947; children: Teresa Elaine, David Mark. BA, U. Mo., 1955, PhD, 1959. Registered profl. engr., Colo. Rsch. engr. A.P. Green Refractories Co., Mexico, Mo., 1959-61, lab mgr., 1961-63; project engr., then mgr. mining div. Colo. Sch. Mines Rsch. Inst., Golden, 1963-67, dir. rsch., 1967-70, pres., 1970-85; pres. ATI Exploration, Golden, Colo., 1985-90; chmn. bd. dirs. Analytica, Inc.; bd. dirs. Sterling Springs Water Co.; v.p. Copper Range Co., White Pine, Mich., 1985-89. Served with USN, 1946-47. Recipient Disting. Alumnus award U. Mo., 1993. Mem. AIME. Home: 7214 Lupine St Golden CO 80403-7863

PONDER, LESTER MCCONNICO, lawyer, educator; b. Walnut Ridge, Ark., Dec. 10, 1912; s. Harry Lee and Clyde (Gant) P.; m. Sallie Mowry Clover, Nov. 7, 1942; children—Melinda, Constance; m. Phyllis Gretchen Harting, Oct. 14, 1978. B.S. summa cum laude in Commerce, Northwestern U., 1934; J.D. with honors, George Washington U., 1938. Bar: Ark. 1937, Ind. 1948. Atty. Ark. Dept. Revenue, Little Rock, 1939-41; atty. IRS, Chgo. and Indpls., 1941-51; ptnr. Barnes & Thornburg and predecessor Barnes, Hickam, Pantzer & Boyd, Indpls., 1952—; adj. prof. Sch. Law, Ind. U., Bloomington, 1951-54, Sch. Law, Ind. U., Indpls., 1954-63; lectr. polit. sci. Ind. U., Indpls., 1982-85. Author: United States Tax Court Practice & Procedure, 1976. Bd. dirs., vice chmn., chmn. fed. chpt. The Nature Conservancy, 1981-89; mem. adv. coun. Ind. Dept. Natural Resources, 1986—; past bd. mem. Sigma Chi Found. Served with USN, 1942. Fellow Am. Bar Found., Ind. State Bar Found., Ind. Bar Found., Am. Coll. Tax Counsel; mem. ABA (coun., taxation sect. 1970-73, chair sr. lawyers div. 1993-94, adv. coun. Commr. Internal Revenue 1964—), Ind. State Bar Assn., Indpls. Bar Assn., Assn. of Seventh Fed. Cir. Republican. Presbyterian. Club: Meridian Hills Country (Indpls.). Lodge: Rotary (past bd. dirs.). Office: Barnes & Thornburg Ste 1313 Merchants Bank Bldg Indianapolis IN 46204

PONDROM, LEE GIRARD, physicist, educator; b. Dallas, Dec. 26, 1933; s. Levi Girard and Guinevere (Miller) P.; m. Cyrena Jo Norman, Aug. 25, 1961. B.S., So. Meth. U., 1953; M.S., U. Chgo., 1956, Ph.D, 1958. Instr. dept. physics Columbia U., N.Y.C., 1960-63; assoc. prof. dept. physics U. Wis., Madison, 1963-69; prof. physics U. Wis., 1969—, Robert Williams Wood prof., 1992—; mem. high energy adv. com. Brookhaven Nat. Lab., 1973-75, chmn. Associated Universities, Inc., vis. com., 1987; mem. physics adv. com. Fermi Nat. Accelerator Lab., 1979-82, chmn., 1981-82; adv. com. for physics NSF, 1981-84; mem. high energy adv. panel (physics) U.S. Dept. Energy, 1981-84, 87-88, chmn. subcom. on detectors, 1987-88, mem. subpanel on future facilities, high energy physics, 1983, mem. subpanel on future modes of exptl. research in high energy physics, 1987; trustee Univs. Research Assn., 1973-76, 82-85; mem. sci. policy com. Stanford Linear Accelerator Ctr., 1984-88; mem. Internat. Com. Future Accelerators, 1984-90; chmn. Snowmass 1986 Summer Study on the SSC; chmn. User's Orgn. for the SSC, 1987-89, mem. sci. policy com. SSC Lab., 1992. Contbr. articles to profl. jours. Served to 1st lt. USAF, 1958-60. J.S. Guggenheim Meml. fellow, 1971-72, Japan Soc. for Promotion of Sci. fellow; recipient Disting. Alumni award So. Meth. U., 1983, W.K.H. Panofsky award Am. Phys. Soc., 1994. Fellow Am. Phys. Soc. (divan. particles and fields 1987, com. on status of women in physics 1989—, chmn. com. to award the Panofsky prize 1991); mem. AAAS. Episcopalian. Home: 210 Prospect Ave Madison WI 53705-4077 Office: U Wis Dept Physics Madison WI 53706 *I have been fortunate to pursue a career in research and teaching at a university and at various U.S. national laboratories, where the individual has much freedom to do whatever he or she wants. Close association with many colleagues and my work with younger people in physics have been sources of stimulation.*

PONEMAN, DANIEL BRUCE, federal official; b. Toledo, Mar. 12, 1956; s. Meyer and Delores Suzanne (Shapiro) P.; m. Susan Anne Danoff, Aug. 12, 1984; children: Claire Gillian, Michael Bruder, William Meyer. AB in Govt. and Econs. magna cum laude, Harvard Coll., 1978; MLitt in Politics, Lincoln Coll., Oxford, Eng., 1981; JD cum laude, Harvard U., 1984. Bar: D.C. 1985. Vis. fellow Internat. Inst. Strategic Studies, London, 1980-81; rsch. fellow ctr. sci. and internat. affairs Kennedy sch. govt. Harvard U., 1981-84; assoc. Covington & Burling, 1985-89; White House fellow Dept. of Energy, 1989-90; dir. def. policy and arms control Nat. Security Coun.,

Washington, 1990-93, spl. asst. to the Pres., sr. dir. nonproliferation and export controls, 1993—. Author: Nuclear Power in the Developing World, 1982, Argentina: Democracy on Trial, 1987; contbr. articles to profl. jours. and newspapers including N.Y. Times, Washington Post, L.A. Times, Boston Globe. Grantee Corp. Pub. Broadcasting; Lord Crewe scholar. Mem. D.C. Bar, Coun. Fgn. Rels., Phi Beta Kappa. Home: 2109 Mason Hill Dr Alexandria VA 22306 Office: Nat Security Coun 1600 Pennsylvania Ave NW Washington DC 20506

PONIEWAZ, KENNETH ANTHONY, banker; b. Milw., Oct. 31, 1949; s. Alex Walter and Gertrude (Jaszewski) P.; m. Sharon Lorraine Radke, July 29, 1972; children—Keith Alan, Scott Andrew. B.B.A. in Acctg., U. Wis., 1972. C.P.A.—Wis. Staff auditor First Wis. Corp., Milw., 1972-74, sr. auditor, 1974, Madison, 1974-79, audit officer, 1979-81, asst. v.p., 1981-82; v.p. Firstar Bank Madison NA, 1982-86, sr. v.p., controller, cashier, 1986—. Bd. dirs. Madison Children's Mus. Mem. AICPA, Wis. CPAs., Wis. United Ath. Club (bd. dirs.). Roman Catholic. Office: Firstar Bank Madison NA 1 S Pinckney St Madison WI 53703

PONITZ, DAVID H., academic administrator; b. Royal Oak, Mich., Jan. 21, 1931; s. Henry John and Jeanette (Bauman) P.; m. Doris Jean Humes, Aug. 5, 1956; children: Catherine Anne, David Robinson. BA, U. Mich., 1952, MA, 1954; EdD, Harvard U., 1964. Prin. Waldron (Mich.) Area Schs., 1956-58, supt., 1958-60; cons. Harvard U., Boston Sch. Survey, 1961-63; supt. Freeport (Ill.) Pub. Schs., 1962-65; pres. Freeport C.C., 1962-65, Washtenaw C.C., 1965-75, Sinclair C.C., 1975—; cons. to community colls.; chmn., pres. Ohi Advanced Tech. Ctr. Mem. editorial adv. bd. Nations Schs., 1963-70; chmn. adv. bd. Community Coll. Rev, 1978-89. Past chmn. Dayton Mayor's Coun. on Econ. Devel.; 1977-85; mem. Nat. Adv. Coun. on Nursing; former co-chair Performing Arts Edn. Task Force; bd. dirs. Alliance for Edn.; former campaign chmn. Ann Arbor and Dayton United Way; past vice chmn. Dayton Citizens Adv. Coun. for Desegregation Implementation; v.p. Miami Valley Rsch. Park; mem., past chmn. Area Progress Coun., Dayton; bd. dirs. Dayton Devel. Coun.; mem. F.S.B. bd. Citizens Fed. Banks, Universal Energy Systems Bd.; past chmn. Miami Valley Joint Labor/Mgmt. Profls., Area Progress Coun.; bd. dirs Ctr. Occupational R & D; chmn. Human Svcs. Levy, Tech-Prep Coll. H.S. Consortium; vice chair Miami Valley Rsch. Found.; bd. dirs. League Innovation C.C., Miami Valley Regional Planning Commn. Served with U.S. Army, 1954-56. Named Outstanding Alumnus U. Mich., One of Top 100 Pres. in U.S. Council for Advancement and Support of Edn., Exec. of Yr., Bd. Realtors, Presdl. medallion Patron emeritus Horry-Georgetown Tech. Coll.; recipient Bogie Buster Red Jacket award, 1987, Thomas J. Peters award for Excellence Assn. Community and Jr. Colls. 1988, Marie N. Martin Chief Exec. Officer award, ACCT, 1989, The Living Legend award Martin Luther King Jr. Holiday Celebration Com., 1991, Sinclair Hon. Alumnus award, 1991, India Found. Honor, 1992, Disting. Eagle Scout award Nat. Eagle Scout Assn., 1993. Mem. Am. Assn. Community and Jr. Colls. (nat. future commn., bd. dirs., chmn. 1988-89), Ohio Tech. and Community Coll. Assn. (pres. 1979-80), Rotary. Methodist. Office: Sinclair Community Coll 4444 W 3rd St Dayton OH 45417

PONITZ, JOHN ALLAN, lawyer; b. Battle Creek, Mich., Sept. 7, 1949; m. Nancy J. Roberts, Aug. 14, 1971; children: Amy, Matthew, Julie. BA, Albion Coll., 1971; JD, Wayne State U., 1974. Bar: Mich. 1974, U.S. Dist. Ct. (ea. dist.) Mich. 1975, (we. dist.) Mich. 1986, U.S. Ct. Appeals (6th cir.) Mich. 1981, U.S. Supreme Ct. 1992. Assoc. McMachan & Kaichen, Birmingham, Mich., 1973-75; atty. Grand Trunk Western R.R., Detroit, 1975-80, trial atty., 1980-89; gen. counsel, 1990—. V.p. Beverly Hills (Mich.) Jaycees, 1981. Served to capt. USAR, 1974-82. Mem. Mich. Bar Assn., Detroit Bar Assn., Nat. Assn. R.R. Trial Counsel. Lutheran. Avocations: golf, sailing. Office: Grand Trunk Co 1333 Brewery Park Blvd Detroit MI 48207

PONKO, WILLIAM REUBEN, architect; b. Wausau, Wis., Apr. 4, 1948; s. Reuben Harrison and Ora Marie (Ranke) P.; m. Kathleen Ann Hilt, May 5, 1973; children—William Benjamin, Sarah Elizabeth. B.Arch. magna cum laude, U. Notre Dame, 1971. Cert. Nat. Council Archl. Registration Bds. V.p., architect, dir. ednl./instl. specialty LeRoy Troyer & Assocs. (now The Troyer Group), Mishawaka, Ind., 1971—; design instr. dept. architecture U. Notre Dame, 1976; mem. Ind. State Bd. Registration for Architects, 1990—; mem. registration exam com. Nat. Coun. Archtl. Registration Bds., 1992, 93, 94. Leonard M. Anson Meml. scholar, 1966-70. Mem. AIA (gold medal for excellence in archtl. edn. 1971), Ind. Soc. Architects (design excellence award 1978, chpt. pres. 1985). Prin. archtl. works include: St. Peter Luth. Ch., Mishawaka, Ind., 1979, 4 brs. for South Bend Pub. Library, 1983; Edward J. Funk & Sons office bldg., Kentland, Ind., 1976; Music Edn. bldg. Taylor U., Upland, Ind., 1982, Taylor U. Library, carillon tower, 1985. Office: The Troyer Group Inc 415 Lincolnway E Mishawaka IN 46544

PONSETI, IGNACIO VIVES, orthopaedic surgery educator; b. Cuidadela, Balearic Islands, Spain, June 3, 1914; s. Miguel and Margarita (Vives) P.; 1 child, William Edward; m. Helena Percas, 1961. BS, U. Barcelona, 1930, MD, 1936, D honoris causa, 1984. Instr. dept. orthopaedic surgery State U. Iowa, 1944-57, prof., 1957—. Author papers on cogenital and developmental skeletal deformities. Capt. M.C. Spanish Army, 1936-39. Recipient Kappa Delta award for orthopaedic rsch., 1955. Mem. Assn. Bone and Joint Surgeons, Am. Acad. Cerebral Palsy, Soc. Exptl. Biology and Medicine, Internat. Coll. Surgeons, N.Y. Acad. Sci., AMA (Ketoen gold medal 1960), Am. Acad. Orthopedic Surgeons, ACS, Am. Orthopedic Assn., Pediatric Orthopaedic Soc. (hon.), Iowa Med. Soc., Orthopedic Rsch. Soc. (Shands award 1975), Sigma Xi, Asociacion Argentina de Cirugia (hon.), Asociacion Balear de Cirugia (hon.), Sociedad de Cirujanos de Chile (hon.), Sociedad Espanola de Cirugia Ortopedica (hon.), Sociedad Brasilera de Ortopedia e Traumatologia (hon.). Home: 110 Oakridge Ave Iowa City IA 52246-2935 Office: Carver Pavilion U Iowa Hosps Iowa City IA 52242

PONSOR, MICHAEL A., federal judge; b. Chgo., Aug. 13, 1946; s. Frederick Ward and Helen Yvonne (Richardson) P.; m. Carol Booth, June 20, 1981 (div. Mar. 1993); children: Anne, Joseph; 1 stepchild, Christian Walker. BA magna cum laude, Harvard Coll., 1969; BA second class honors, Oxford U., 1971, MA, 1979; JD, Yale U., 1975. Bar: Mass., U.S. Dist. Ct. Mass., U.S. Ct. Appeals (1st cir.), U.S. Supreme Ct. Tchr. Kenya Inst. Administrn., Nairobi, 1967-68; law clk. U.S. Dist. Ct., Boston, 1975-76; assoc. Homans, Hamilton, Dahmen & Lamson, Boston, 1976-78; ptnr. Brown, Hart & Ponsor, Amherst, Mass., 1978-83; U.S. magistrate judge U.S. Dist. Ct., Springfield, Mass., 1984-94, judge, 1994—; adj. prof. Western N.E. Coll. Sch. Law, Springfield, 1988—, Yale Law Sch., New Haven, 1989-91; presenter in field. Rhodes scholar Oxford U., 1969. Mem. Mass. Bar Assn., Hampshire County Bar Assn., Boston Bar Assn. Office: US Dist Ct 1550 Main St Springfield MA 01130

PONT, JOHN, football coach, educator; b. Canton, Ohio, Nov. 13, 1927; s. Bautista and Susie (Sikurinec) P.; m. H. Sandra Stoutt, June 23, 1956; children: John W., Jennifer Ann, Jeffrey David. B.S., Miami U., Oxford, Ohio, 1952, M.S., 1956. Profl. football player Can., 1952-53; instr., freshman football and basketball coach Miami U., 1953-55, asst. prof., head football coach, 1955-62; head football coach Yale U., 1963-65; prof., head football coach Ind. U., Bloomington, 1965-73; head football coach Northwestern U., Evanston, Ill., 1973-77, athletic dir., 1974-79; head football coach, athletic dir. Hamilton, Ohio; head football coach, tennis coach, asst. athletic dir. Coll. Mt. St. Joseph, Mt. St. Joseph, Ohio; now head football coach Gakusei-Engo-Kai Inc., Tokyo, Japan; agt. Equitable Assurance Soc., U.S., 1981-82; v.p. Fin. Leasing Corp., 1983-85; Splty. Brush, Inc.; athletic dir. Jewish Community Center, Canton, 1953; v.p. NCAA Coun., 1979-80; mem. bd. dirs. Cin. chpt. Nat. Football Found. Hall of Fame. Mem. Pres.'s Coun. on Phys. Fitness; chmn. Ind. Easter Seal, 1968-69, Ind. div. Cancer Crusade, 1969; bd. dirs. Multiple Sclerosis, N.E. Ill. counc. Boy Scouts Am., Boys Hope. Served with USN, 1945-47. Named Coach of Year Coaches Assn., 1967, Coach of Year Football Writers, 1967, Coach of Yr. Washington Touchdown Club, 1968, Coach of Yr. Walter Camp Found.; recipient Significant Sig award, 1968, Disting. Am. award Nat. Football Found.; charter mem. Miami U. Hall of Fame, 1968; elected Ind. Football Hall of Fame, 1984, Butler County Hall of Fame, 1986, Mid-Am. Conf. Hall of Fame, 1992, Ind. U. Sports Hall of Fame, 1992. Mem. Am. Football Coaches Assn. (chmn. ethics com.), Am. Legion, Blue Key, Sigma Chi, Phi

Epsilon Kappa, Omicron Delta Kappa. Republican. Home: 482 White Oak Dr Oxford OH 45056-9272

PONT, MARISARA, public relations executive; b. Río Piedras, P.R., Oct. 29, 1941; d. Rafael Pont and Sara Marchese. BA in Humanities cum laude, U. P.R., 1962-63; MS in Libr. Sci., Columbia U., 1971. Asst. to libr. med. scis. campus U. P.R., Río Piedras, 1964-72; spl. aide to Pres. Senate Commonwealth of P.R., San Juan, 1972; dep. aide in mgmt. Office of Gov. of P.R., San Juan, 1973, exec. aide to dir. of communications, 1973-74; dir. communications, 1974-76; pres. Plus Image Devel. and Pub. Rels., San Juan, 1977-86, Comstat/Rowland Pub. Rels., San Juan, 1986—. Mem. Assn. Profl. Pub. Rels. Practitioners of P.R. (pres. 1984-86), Pub. Rels. Soc. Am. Overseas Press Club P.R. (co-chmn. ann. award program 1981-89), P.R. Mfrs. Assn., P.R.C. of C. (pub. rels. award 1985), Bankers Club. Roman Catholic. Office: Comstat/Rowland Caparra Heights Sta 1506 FD Roosevelt Ave Caparra PR 00922

PONTIKES, WILLIAM N., computer rental and leasing company executive; b. 1941. BA, So. Ill. U., 1968. With Ill. Police Dept., 1963-65; with Comdisco, DesPlaines, Ill., 1973—, v.p. ops., 1975-76, sr. v.p. ops., 1976-77, dir., 1977—. With U.S. Army, 1963-65. Office: Comdisco Inc 6111 N River Rd Des Plaines IL 60018-5158*

PONTOLILLO, BROTHER PETER A., school system administrator. Supt. schs. Archdiocese of San Antonio. Office: Archdiocesan Schs Office PO Box 28410 San Antonio TX 78228-0410

PONTY, JEAN-LUC, violinist, composer, producer; b. Avranches, Normandy, France, Sept. 29, 1942; came to U.S., 1973; Grad., Conservatoire National Superieur de Musique, Paris, 1960. Classical violinist to 1964, played with Concerts Lamoureux Symphony Orch.; jazz violinist in Europe, 1964-69, night club and music festivals with George Duke Trio, U.S., 1969, toured with own group, Europe, 1970-72, recorded with Elton John, Honky Chateau, 1972; with Frank Zappa and the Mothers of Invention, 1973, Mahavishnu Orch., 1974-75, pioneer of electric violin, Jazz innovator, headlining internat. concerts with own group since 1975; appearances at music festivals in the U.S. including Meadowbrook, Artpark, Wolf Trap, and in Europe Montreux, North Sea Festival, Paris Jazz Festival; spl. appearance as guest soloist with Montreal Symphony Orch., 1984, Toronto Symphony Orch., 1986, New Japan Philharm., 1987; European tour with Stanley Clarke and Al DiMeola The Rite of Strings, 1994; own-produced albums include: Upon the Wings of Music, Aurora, Imaginary Voyage, Enigmatic Ocean, Cosmic Messenger, Jean-Luc Ponty: Live, Civilized Evil, A Taste for Passion, Mystical Adventures, Individual Choice, Open Mind, Fables, The Gift of Time, Storytelling, Tchokola (with African musicians), No Absolute Time; television appearances include: (with Doug Kershaw and Itzhak Perlman) Fiddlers Three, Soundstage, Rock Concert, The Tonight Show, The Merv Griffin Show, Solid Gold, Pat Sajak Show CNN Entertainment; TV show appearances throughout Europe, Brazil, Chile and Venezuela. Recipient numerous internat. awards. Office: care Bob Zievers ICM 8942 Wilshire Blvd Beverly Hills CA 90211-1908*

POOL, MARY JANE, design consultant, author, lecturer; d. Earl Lee Pool and Dorothy (Matthews) Evans. Grad., St. de Chantal Acad., 1942; BA in Art with honors, Drury Coll., 1946. Mem. staff Vogue mag., N.Y.C., 1946-68; assoc. merchandising editor Vogue mag., 1948-57, promotion dir., 1958-66, exec. editor, 1966-68; editor House and Garden mag., 1969, editor-in-chief, 1970-80; cons. Baker Furniture Co., 1980-81, Aves Advt., Inc., 1981-94, bd. dirs.; mem. bd. govs. Decorative Arts Trust; past mem. bd. govs. Fashion Group, Inc., N.Y.C. Co-author: The Angel Tree, 1984, The Gardens of Venice, 1989, The Gardens of Florence, 1992, The Angel Tree-A Christmas Celebration, 1993; editor: 20th Century Decorating, Architecture, Gardens, Billy Baldwin Decorates, 26 Easy Little Gardens. Mem. bus. com. N.Y. Zool. Soc., 1979-86; trustee Drury Coll., 1971—; bd. dirs. Isabel O'Neil Found., 1978—. Recipient award Nat. Soc. Interior Designers, Disting. Alumni award Drury Coll., 1961. Address: 1 E 66th St New York NY 10021-5852

POOL, PHILIP BEMIS, JR., investment banker; b. N.Y.C., Apr. 11, 1954; s. Philip B. and Virginia Middleton (French) P.; m. Joan H. Barnes, May 19, 1978; children: Elliott Livingston, Victoria Middleton. BS in Commerce, U. Va., 1976; MBA, Columbia U., 1980. Asst. treas. The Bank of N.Y., N.Y.C., 1976-78; v.p. Kidder Peabody & Co., Inc., N.Y.C., 1980-85; mng. dir. Merrill Lynch & Co., N.Y.C., 1985-94, Donaldson, Lufkin & Jenrette, N.Y.C., 1994—. Mem. Piping Rock Club (gov. 1989—), Meadow Brook Club, Lyford Cay Club, Racquet and Tennis Club. Republican. Episcopalian. Avocations: golf, squash.

POOLE, CECIL F., federal judge; b. Birmingham, Ala.; children: Gayle, Patricia. LL.B., U. Mich.; LL.M., Harvard U., 1939. Practice of law San Francisco, former asst. dist. atty., 1951-58; clemency sec. to Gov. Brown of Calif., 1958-61; U.S. atty. No. Dist. Calif., 1961-70; Regents prof. Law U. Calif., Berkeley, 1970; counsel firm Jacobs, Sills & Coblentz, San Francisco, 1970-76; judge U.S. Dist. Ct., No. Dist. Calif., 1976-79, U.S. Ct. of Appeals for 9th Circuit, 1979—; adj. prof. Golden Gate U. Sch. Law, 1953-58; mem. adv. com. Nat. Commn. for Reform Fed. Criminal Laws, 1968-70. Served to 2d lt. AUS, World War II. Mem. ABA (chmn. sect. individual rights 1971-72, ho. of dels. 1972-74), San Francisco Bar Assn. (dir. 1975-76). Office: US Ct Appeals 9th Cir PO Box 193939 San Francisco CA 94119-3939*

POOLE, D. BRUCE, lawyer; b. Hagerstown, Md., June 17, 1959; s. David Kreigh Jr. and Janice Marie (Zaiser) P. BA, Washington & Lee U., 1981, JD, 1985. Bar: Md. 1985. Ptnr. Poole & Poole, P.A., Hagerstown, 1985-89, Snyder & Poole, P.A., Hagerstown and Frederick, Md., 1989-95, Poole & Poole, P.A., Hagerstown, Md., 1995—; state legis. Md. Ho. of Dels., Annapolis, 1987—, house majority leader, 1991—. Assoc. mem., bd. dirs. March of Dimes of Washington County, Hagerstown, 1986-91; pres. United Dems. Washington County, Hagerstown, 1985-86; mem. Gov.'s Commn. on Drug & Alcohol Abuse and Truck Safety, Annapolis, 1989-93. Mem. Sons of American Legion, Jaycees (named one of Ten Outstanding Marylanders 1991), Elks, Rotary (fellow U. Melbourne, Australia 1981). Lutheran. Avocations: tennis, travel, history, hunting. Office: Poole & Poole PA 92 W Washington St Hagerstown MD 21740-4813

POOLE, EARLE GOWER, clothing manufacturing company executive; b. Dundalk, Ont., Can., b. 1929; s. Lawrence Gower and Ethel Virginia (LeGarrie) P.; m. Fern McFarlane, Mar. 21, 1951; children: Leslie, Lorraine. Supr. Gulf Oil, Toronto, 1950-62; mgr. systems and EDP Work Wear Corp. Can., Toronto, 1962-67, controller, 1967-70, gen. mgr. adminstrv. services, 1970-74, group gen. mgr., 1974-81, exec. v.p., chief operating officer Rental div., 1981-84, pres., chief exec. officer, 1984—, chmn. bd., 1986—; pres., chief exec. officer Work Wear Corp. Inc., Cleve., 1986—; lectr. Ryerson Poly. Inst., Toronto, York U., Humber Coll. Active mem. Variety Village Tent 28, Toronto. Mem. Toronto Bd. Trade. Avocations: tennis, racquetball, biking, skiing, early Can. antiques. Office: Work Wear Corp Inc PO Box 19009 Greensboro NC 27419-9009

POOLE, EVA DURAINE, librarian; b. Farrell, Pa., Dec. 20, 1952; d. Leonard Milton and Polly Mae (Flint) Harris; m. Tommy Lynn Cole, May 15, 1970 (div. Sept. 1984); 1 child, Tommy Lynn Cole; m. Earnest Theodore Poole, Sept. 22, 1990; 1 child, Aleece Remelle Poole. BA in LS, Tex. Woman's U., 1974, MLS, 1976; postgrad., U. Houston, 1989. Libr. asst. Emily Fowler Pub. Libr., Denton, Tex., 1970-74; children's libr. Houston Pub. Libr., 1974-75, 1st asst. libr., 1976-77; children's libr. Ector County Libr., Odessa, Tex., 1977-80; head pub. svcs. Lee Davis Libr. San Jacinto Coll., Pasadena, Tex., 1980-84; libr. dir. San Jacinto Coll. South, Houston, 1984-90; libr. svcs. mgr. Emily Fowler Pub. Libr., Denton, 1990-93, interim dir., 1993, libr. dir., 1993—. Named to Outstanding Young Women of Am., 1991. Mem. ALA (libr. adminstrn. and mgmt. assn. edn. com. 1993—, conf. program com. 1994—), Pub. Libr. Assn. (conf. program com., 1995), Tex. Libr. Assn. (by-laws com. pub. libr. div. 1993—, ad hoc leadership inst. com. 1995, alumnae 1st class Tex. Accelerated Libr. Leaders 1994), Pub. Libr. Adminstrs. North Tex. (vice chair 1994-95, chair 1995—, pres. 1995), Tex. Mcpl. Libr. Dirs. Assn. (v.p./pres. elect 1994-95, grantee 1993), Denton Rotary Club. Office: Denton Pub Libr 502 Oakland St Denton TX 76201

POOLE, GORDON LEICESTER, lawyer; b. Mpls., Dec. 25, 1926; s. Arthur Bensell and Mildred Loyal (Wood) P.; m. Lois Claire Teasdale, Oct. 30, 1954; children—David Wilson, Edward Gray, Elisabeth Claire. A.B., Harvard U., 1949, LL.B., 1952. Assoc. Treadwell & Laughlin, San Francisco, 1953-54; assoc. Lillick, McHose & Charles, San Francisco, 1955-63, ptnr., 1963—, mem. exec. com., 1977-81, chmn. mgmt. com., 1981-84, chmn., 1984—. Contbr. articles to profl. jours. Pres. Young Republicans, San Mateo County, Calif., 1958-59; vestryman Trinity Episcopal Parish, Menlo Park, Calif., 1968, 70, 76-78, sr. warden, 1970. Served as sgt. U.S. Army, 1944-47, Korea. Mem. Calif. Bar Assn., San Francisco Bar Assn., Maritime Law Assn. (com. on marine financing), Maritime Adminstry. Bar Assn., ABA, Mng. Ptnrs. Assn. Clubs: Bohemian, World Trade (San Francisco); Ladera Oaks (Menlo Park). Avocations: stamp collecting; marine paintings, prints and memorabilia. Home: 2280 Stockbridge Ave Redwood City CA 94062-1130 Office: Lillick & Charles 2280 Stockbridge Ave Woodside CA 94062

POOLE, JOHN JORDAN, lawyer; b. Fulton County, Ga., May 19, 1906; s. James Stubbs and Etta Ida Lou (Porter) P.; m. Jeannette Harper, July 21, 1931. Ph.B., Emory U., 1927, J.D., 1929. Bar: Ga. 1929. Ptnr. Poole, Pearce, Cooper & Smith Civil law, Atlanta, from 1934; dir. Bass Furniture Co., Peachtree on Peachtree Inn, Simons-Eastern Internat., Inc. Bd. dirs. Atlanta Union Mission Corp. Served as lt. comdr. USNR, 1942-45. Decorated Letter of Commendation. Mem. Am., Ga., Atlanta bar assns. Baptist. Clubs: Optimists (pres. 1949, sec.-treas. 21st dist. 1957), 13, Lawyers, Atlanta Athletic, Commerce (Atlanta). Lodges: Masons, Shriners. Home: 203 Kings Brg NE Atlanta GA 30329-2549 Office: 2970 Clairmont Rd NE Ste 600 Atlanta GA 30329

POOLE, MONTE LARUE, sports columnist, consultant; b. Oakland, Calif., Nov. 30, 1955. AA, Chabot Coll., 1983; BA, San Jose State U., 1985. Dist. mgr. Mervyn's, Hayward, Calif., 1979-81; sports writer Oakland Tribune, 1982-91, Oakland Tribune/Alameda Newspaper Group, Oakland, 1991—; host talk show Sta. KSFO, San Francisco, 1992; instr. New Coll. Calif., 1994. Mem. com. U. Calif. Hall of Fame, Berkeley, 1993—. Mem. Nat. Assn. Black Journalists, Baseball Writers' Assn. Am. Avocations: reading, exercise, jazz music. Office: Oakland Tribune PO Box 28884 66 Jack London Sq Oakland CA 94607

POOLE, NANCY GEDDES, art gallery director, writer; b. London, Ont., Can., May 10, 1930; d. John Hardy and Kathleen Edwards (Robinson) G.; m. William Robert Poole, Aug. 15, 1952; 1 child, Andrea Mary. BA, U. Western Ont., 1956, LLD, 1990. Owner, dir. Nancy Poole's Studio, Toronto, Ont., Can., 1969-78; acting dir. London Regional Art Gallery, Ont., Can., 1981—; exec. dir., 1985-89; dir. London Regional Art and Hist. Museums, Ont., Can., 1989—; chair governing coun. Ont. Coll. Art, 1972-73. Author: The Art of London 1939-1980, 1984; editor Jack Chambers, 1978, The Collection, 1990. Bd. govs. U. Western Ont., 1974-85. Fellow Ont. Coll. Art. Office: London Reg Art & Historical Mus, 421 Ridout St N, London, ON Canada N6A 5H4

POOLE, NORMAN A., retail executive. Exec. v.p., coo L.L. Bean Inc, Freeport, Maine. Office: L L Bean Inc Casco St Freeport ME 04033-0002

POOLE, RICHARD WILLIAM, economics educator; b. Oklahoma City, Dec. 4, 1927; s. William Robert and Lois (Spicer) P.; m. Bertha Lynn Mehr, July 28, 1950; children: Richard William, Laura Lynne, Mark Stephen. B.S., U. Okla., 1951, M.B.A., 1952; postgrad., George Washington U., 1957-58; Ph.D., Okla. State U., 1960. Research analyst Okla. Gas & Electric Co., Oklahoma City, 1952- 54; mgr. scis. and mfg. devel. dept. Oklahoma City U. of C., 1954-57; mgr. Office of J.E. Webb, Washington, 1957-58; instr., asst. prof., assoc. prof., prof. econs. Okla. State U., Stillwater, 1960-65; prof. econs., dean Coll. Bus. Adminstrn. Okla. State U., 1965-72, v.p., prof. econs., 1972-88, Regents Disting. Svc. prof., 1988-93, emeritus v.p., dean, Regents Disting. Svc. prof./prof. econ., 1993—; cons. to adminstr. NASA, Washington, 1961-69; adviser subcom. on govt. rsch. U.S. Senate, 1966-69; lectr. Intermediate Sch. Banking, Ops. Mgmt. Sch., Okla. Bankers Assn., 1968-89; lectr. internat. off-campus programs, Okla. City U., 1994—. Author: (with others) The Oklahoma Economy, 1963, County Building Block Data for Regional Analysis, 1965. Mem. Gov.' Com. on Devel. Ark.-Verdigris Waterway, 1970-71, Gov.'s Five-Yr. Econ. Devel. Plan, 1993; past v.p., bd. dirs., past chmn. Mid-Continent Rsch. and Devel. Coun. 2d lt., arty. U.S. Army, 1946-48. Recipient Delta Sigma Pi Gold Key award Coll. Bus. Adminstrn., U. Okla., 1951, Merrick Found. tchg. award on Am. Free Enterprise Sys., 1992; inductee Coll. Bus. Adminstrn. Hall of Fame, Okla. State U., 1993. Mem. Southwestern Econ. Assn. (past pres.), Am. Assembly Collegiate Schs. Bus. (past bd. dirs.), Nat. Assn. State Univs. and Land Grant Colls. (past chmn. commn. on edn. for bus. professions), Southwestern Bus. Adminstrn. Assn. (past pres.), Okla. C. of C. (past bd. dirs.), Stillwater C. of C. (past bd. dirs. and pres.), Beta Gamma Sigma (past bd. dirs.), Phi Kappa Phi, Phi Eta Sigma, Omicron Delta Kappa. Home: 124 W Georgia Ave Stillwater OK 74075-3706

POOLE, ROBERT ANTHONY, journalist; b. St. Austell, Cornwall, Eng., Dec. 17, 1944; arrived in Can., 1977; m. Valerie Avril Taggart, Apr. 14, 1973; children—Claire Lucy, Emma Louise. Irish editor Press Assn., Belfast, Northern Ireland, 1977-79; gen. reporter Calgary Herald, Alta., Can., 1977-79; city editor Calgary Albertan, 1979-80; city editor Calgary Sun, 1980-81, mng. editor, 1981-84, editor-in-chief, 1984—. Office: Calgary Sun, 2615 12th St NE, Calgary, AB Canada T2E 7W9

POOLE, WILLIAM, economics educator, consultant; b. Wilmington, Del., June 19, 1937; s. William and Louise (Hiller) P.; m. Mary Lynne Ahroon, June 26, 1960; children—William, Lester Allen, Jonathan Carl. AB, Swarthmore Coll., 1959, LLD (hon.), 1989; MBA, U. Chgo., 1963, PhD, 1966. Asst. prof. polit. economy Johns Hopkins U., Balt., 1963-69; professorial lectr. Am. U., Washington, 1970-71; assoc. professorial lectr. George Washington U., Washington, 1971-73; lectr. Georgetown U., Washington, 1972, Harvard U., Cambridge, Mass., 1973; vis. lectr. MIT, Cambridge, 1974, 77; Bank Mees and Hope vis. prof. econs. Erasmus U. Rotterdam, 1991; prof. econs. Brown U., Providence, R.I., 1974, 85—, dir. ctr. for the study fin. markets and insts., 1987-92, prof., chmn. econs. dept., 1981-82, 85-86; economist Bd. Govs. of FRS, Washington, 1964, 1969-70, sr. economist, 1970-74; vis. scholar Fed. Res. Bank, San Francisco, 1977; adviser Fed. Res. Bank, Boston, 1973-74, cons., 1974-81; vis. economist Res. Bank of Australia, 1980-81; mem. Council Econ. Advisers, 1982-85; adj. scholar Cato Inst., 1985—. Mem. Am. Econ. Assn., Am. Fin. Assn. (mem. nominating com. 1979), Western Econ. Assn. Office: Brown U Dept Econs 64 Waterman St Providence RI 02912-9029

POOLEY, BEVERLEY JOHN, law educator, librarian; b. London, Eng., Apr. 4, 1934; came to U.S., 1957; U.S. citizen, 1993; s. William Vincent and Christine Beatrice (Coleman) P.; m. Patricia Joan Ray, June 8, 1958; children—Christopher Jonathan, Rachel Vanessa. BA, Cambridge U., Eng., 1956, LLB, 1957; LLM, U. Mich., Ann Arbor, 1958, SJD, 1961, MLS, 1964. Legis. analyst U. Mich. Law Sch., Ann Arbor, 1958-60; lectr. U. Ghana Law Sch., 1960-62; instr. U. Mich. Law Sch., Ann Arbor, 1962-63, asst. prof., 1963-66, assoc. prof., 1966-70, dir. law library, 1966-84, prof., 1970—, assoc. dean law library, 1984—. Author: The Evolution of British Planning Legislation, 1960; Planning and Zoning in the United States, 1961. Scholar, King's Coll., Cambridge, Eng., 1956; Blackstone Scholar, Middle Temple, London, 1957. Democrat. Avocations: Acting; musical comedy; food preparation.

POOLEY, JAMES HENRY ANDERSON, lawyer, author; b. Dayton, Ohio, Oct. 4, 1948; s. Howard Carl and Daisy Frances (Lindsley) P.; children by previous marriage: Jefferson Douglas, Christopher James; m. Laura Anderson, Oct. 13, 1984; 1 child, Catherine Lindsley. BA, Lafayette Coll., 1970; JD, Columbia U., 1973. Bar: Calif. 1973, U.S. Dist. Ct. (no. dist.) Calif. 1973, U.S. Ct. Appeals (9th cir.) 1974, U.S. Supreme Ct. 1977, U.S. Dist. Ct. (cen. dist.) Calif. 1978. Assoc. Wilson, Mosher & Sonsini, Palo Alto, Calif., 1973-78; ptnr. Mosher, Pooley & Sullivan, Palo Alto, 1978-88, Graham and James, 1988-93, Fish & Richardson, Menlo Park, 1993—; lectr. Practicing Law Inst., N.Y.C., 1983, 85-86, 88, 95, Santa Clara U. Sch. Law, 1985-87. Author: Trade Secrets, 1982, Protecting Technology, 1983, Trying the High Technology Case, 1984, Trade Secrets: A Guide to Protecting Proprietary Business Information, 1989; contbr. articles to profl. jours.; editor-in-chief Trade Secret Law Reporter, 1984-85; bd. advisors Santa Clara Computer and High Tech. Law Jour., 1984—; chair Nat. Trade Secret Law Inst., 1994. Arbitrator, spl. master U.S. Dist. Ct. (no. dist.) Calif., Santa Clara County Superior Ct., San Jose, 1979—. Mem. ABA (intellectual property sect.), Computer Law Assn., Am. Intellectual Property Lawyers' Assn., Am. Electronics Assn. (chmn. lawyers' com. 1981-82). Republican. Office: Fish & Richardson 2200 Sand Hill Rd Ste 100 Menlo Park CA 94025-6936

POOLMAN, JIM, state legislator; b. Fargo, N.D., May 15, 1970; s. Robert Francis and Susan Faye (Brown) P. BBA, U. N.D., 1992, postgrad., 1994—. Sales cons. Straus Co., Grand Forks, N.D., 1987—; state representative N.D. State Ho. of Reps., 1992—. Task force State of N.D., Grand Forks, 1992; mem. United Hosp. Corp. United Health, Grand Forks, 1992—, Presdl. Search Com., U. N.D., 1992. Mem. Toastmasters Internat. (sec.), Phi Delta Theta Alumni (varsity bachelors club scholarship ednl. found. 1992). Republican. Lutheran. Avocations: fishing, water sports, golf. Home: 529 Oxford St # 4 Grand Forks ND 58203-2846

POONS, LARRY, artist; b. Tokyo, Oct. 1, 1937; came to U.S., 1938; Student, New Eng. Conservatory Music, 1955-57, Boston Mus. Fine Arts Sch., 1958. Mem. vis. faculty N.Y. Studio Sch., 1967. Author: The Structure of Color, 1971; exhbns. include, Green Gallery, N.Y.C., 1963-65, Art Inst. Chgo., 1966, Corcoran Gallery Art, Carnegie Inst., 1967, Leo Castelli Gallery, 1967-68, Documenta IV, Kassel, W. Ger., 1968, Whitney Mus. Am. Art Ann., 1968, 72, Lawrence Rubin Gallery, 1970-73, Whitney Biennial, 1973, Knoedler & Co., 1973-78, Knoedler Contemporary Art, N.Y.C., 1974-78, Andre Emmerlich Gallery, N.Y.C., 1979-87, Albright-Knox Art Gallery, Buffalo, 1968, 70, Pasadena Art Mus., 1969, Gallery 99, Bar Harbor Islands, Fla., 1981, Mus. Fine Arts, Boston, 1981-82, Galerie Montaigne, Paris, 1990, Helander Gallery, Palm Beach, Fla., 1990, Salander-O'Reilly Galleries, N.Y.C., 1990, Beverly Hills, Calif., 1990, Berlin, 1990, Gallery Afinsa, Madrid, 1991; represented in permanent collection, Mus. Modern Art, N.Y.C., Allen Meml. Art Mus., Oberlin Coll., Cleve. Mus. Art, Hirschhorn Mus. and Sculpture Garden, Washington, Milw. Art Ctr., Solomon R. Guggenheim Mus., N.Y.C., Tate Gallery, London, Whitney Mus. Am. Art, Met. Mus. Art, Chgo. Art Inst., Denver Mus., Boston Mus. Fine Arts, Albright-Knox Art Gallery, Stedelijk Mus., Amsterdam, Woodward Found., Washington, David Mirvish Gallery, Toronto; artist-in-residence, Inst. Humanistic Studies, Aspen, Colo., 1966-67. Address: Salander O'Reilly Galleries 20 E 79th St New York NY 10021-0106

POOR, ANNE, artist; b. N.Y.C., Jan. 2, 1918; d. Henry Varnum and Bessie (Breuer) P. Student, Bennington Coll., 1936, 38, Art Students League, 1935, Acad. Julien, Paris. trustee, gov. Skowhegan Sch. Painting and Sculpture, 1947-61, 89; artist corr. WAC, 1943-45. Illustrator: Greece, 1964. Works exhibited: Am. Brit. Art Ctr., 1944, 45, 48, Maynard Walker Gallery, 1950, Graham Gallery, 1957-59, 62, 68-71, 85, Rockland Ctr. for Arts, West Nyack, N.Y., 1982, 83, Terry Distenfass Gallery, N.Y.C.; executed murals, P.O., Gleason, Tenn., DePew, N.Y., South Solon (Maine) Free Meeting House, 1957, others; represented permanent collections, Whitney Mus., Bklyn. Mus., Wichita Mus., Art Inst. Chgo. Edwin Austin Abbey Meml. fellow, 1948; grantee Nat. Inst. Arts and Letters, 1957; recipient Benjamin Altman 1st prize landscape painting N.A.D., 1971, 86, Childe Hassam award, 1972, 77. Mem. Artists Equity Assn., Nat. Inst. Arts and Letters. Office: Terry Distenfass Gallery 50 W 57th St New York NY 10019-3914

POOR, HAROLD VINCENT, electrical engineering educator; b. Columbus, Ga., Oct. 2, 1951; s. Harold Edgar and Virginia (Hardin) P.; m. Connie Irene Hazelwood, Sept. 1, 1973; children: Kristin Elizabeth, Lauren Alissa. BEE with highest honors, Auburn U., 1972; PhD, Princeton U., 1977. Asst. prof. U. Ill., Urbana, 1977-81, assoc. prof., 1981-84, prof., 1984-90; prof. dept. elec. engring. Princeton (N.J.) U., 1990—; acad. visitor Imperial Coll. London U., 1985; vis. prof. Newcastle (Australia) U., 1987; sr. visiting fellow Imperial Coll., London U., 1993; cons. numerous orgns., 1978—. Author: An Introduction to Signal Detection and Estimation, 1988, 2d edit., 1994; contbr. more than 80 articles to profl. jours. Grantee NSF, Office of Naval Rsch., Army Rsch. Office, 1978—; recipient Terman award Am. Soc. Engring. Edn., 1992, Centennial certificate Am. Soc. for Engring. Edn., 1993. Fellow IEEE (bd. dirs. 1991-92), AAAS, Acoustical Soc. Am.; mem. Info. Theory Soc. of IEEE (pres. 1990), IEEE Control Sys. Soc. (Disting. Mem. award 1994). Office: Princeton Univ Dept Elec Engring Princeton NJ 08544

POOR, JANET MEAKIN, landscape designer; b. Cin., Nov. 27, 1929; d. Cyrus Lee and Helen Keats (Meakin) Lee-Hofer; m. Edward King Poor III, June 23, 1951; children: Edward King IV, Thomas Meakin. Student, Stephens Coll., 1947-48, U. Cinn., 1949-51, Triton Coll., 1973-76. Pres. Janet Meakin Poor Landscape Design, Winnetka, Ill., 1975—; chmn. bd. dirs. Cgho. Horticultural Soc., Chgo. Botanic Garden. Author, editor: Plants That Merit Attention Vol. I: Trees, 1984; contbr. articles to profl. jours. Participant in longe range planning City of Winnetka, 1978-82, archtl. and environ. bd., 1980-84, beautification commn., 1978-84, garden coun., 1978-82; adv. coun., sec. of agr. Nat. Arboretum, Washington; nat. adv. bd. Filoli, San Francisco; trustee Ctr. Plant Conservation at Mo. Botanical Garden, St. Louis, also mem. exec. com.; mem. adv. coun. The Garden Conservancy, 1989—; trustee Winnetka Congl. Ch., 1978-80. Recipient merit award Hadley Sch. Blind, 1972; named Vol. of Yr. Hadley Sch. Blind. Mem. Chgo. Hort. Soc. (chmn. bd. dirs. 1987-93, medal 1984, gold medal garden design, exec. com., chmn. rsch. com., women's bd., designer herb garden Farwell Gardens at Chgo. Botanic Garden, Hutchinson medal 1994), Am. Hort. Soc. (bd. dirs. Catherine H. Sweeney award 1985), Garden Club Am. (chmn. nat. plant exchange 1980-81, chmn. hort. com. 1981-83, bd. dirs., 1983-85, corresponding sec. 1985-87, Horticulture award Zone X1 1981, Creative Leadership award 1986), Fortnightly Club, Garden Guild (bd. dirs.), Garden Club Am. (v.p. 1987-89, medal awards chmn. 1991-93, Honor medal 1994). Republican. Avocations: gardening, writing, music, hort. rsch., lecturing.

POOR, PETER VARNUM, producer, director; b. N.Y.C., May 17, 1926; s. Henry Varnum and Bessie Breuer (Freedman) P.; m. Eloise Marcovicci Miller, Sept. 27, 1950; children: Candida Eustacia, Anna Maria, Graham Varnum. BA, Harvard U., 1947; postgrad., Centro Sperimentale di Cinematografia, Rome, 1951-52. Prodn. asst. New World Films, N.Y.C., 1948; editor, dir. Willard Pictures, N.Y.C., 1948-51; film editor, dir. and producer CBS News-Airpower, 1954-57, 7 Lively Arts, 1957-58, Twentieth Century, 1958-66, 21st Century, 1966-69, 60 Minutes, 1970-71, CBS Reports, 1971-75; sr. producer NBC News, Monitor, First Camera, White Paper, 1977-87; freelance producer and dir. Crow House Prodns., N.Y.C., 1988—; instr. in TV journalism Fordham U., 1976-78; mem. Screening Com. for Fulbright Grants in Film, TV and Radio, 1965-67, chmn., 1967, 70; adj. assoc. history of documentary Columbia U. Grad. Sch. Journalism, 1987; adj. asst. prof. visual arts NYU, 1991-92. Producer-dir.: (TV documentary films) What's New at School, 1972, The IQ Myth, 1975, The Biggest Lump of Money in the World, 1985, The Japan They Don't Talk About, 1986 Nuclear Power in France, 1987, The Cronkite Report, 1993. Served with USAF, 1944-45. Recipient Emmy award Acad. TV Arts and Sci., 1961, 62, 67, Lasker TV award Lasker Found., 1968, 69, U.S. CEA Forum award, 1967, 87; hon. mention Robert Kennedy Journalism Award in TV, 1976, Fulbright scholar, 1951-52. Mem. Dirs. Guild Am. (coun. 1980-90), Film Editors Union, Writers Guild Am. East. Club: Phoenix S-K (Cambridge, Mass.). Avocations: bicycling, reading, photography, gardening. Home and Office: 1150 Fifth Ave New York NY 10128-0724

POORE, JAMES ALBERT, III, lawyer; b. Butte, Mont., June 28, 1943; s. James A. Jr. and Jesse (Wild) P.; m. Shelley A. Borgstede, Feb. 12, 1989; children: James IV, Jeffrey. AB, Stanford U., 1965; JD with honors, U. Mont., 1968. Bar: Mont. 1968, U.S. Dist. Ct. Mont. 1968, U.S. Ct. Appeals (9th cir.) 1972, U.S. Supreme Ct. 1973. Assoc. Poore, Poore, McKenzie & Roth, Butte, 1968-74; ptnr., v.p. Poore, Roth & Robinson, P.C., Butte, 1974—; speaker in field. Assoc. editor U. Mont. Law Rev., 1967-68; contbg. editor Product Liability Desk Reference, 1995; contbr. articles to profl. publs. Dist. dir. Boy Scouts Am., S.W. Mont., 1969; dir. YMCA, Butte, 1981-83; founding bd. dirs. Hospice of Butte, 1982-85, Butte Community Theater, 1977-80; pres. Butte Uptown Assn., 1974; dir. Butte Silverbow Am. Cancer Soc. Bd., 1992—. Fellow Am. Bar Found.; mem. ABA, State Bar

Mont., Am. Judicature Soc., Silver Bow Bar Assn., Phi Delta Phi. Home: 6 Cedar Lake Dr Butte MT 59701-4338 Office: Poore Roth & Robinson PC 1341 Harrison Ave Butte MT 59701-4898

POORMAN, PAUL ARTHUR, educator, media consultant; b. Lock Haven, Pa., Aug. 29, 1930; s. Wilson Paul and and Margaret (Heylmun) P.; m. Sylvia Elizabeth Powers, Nov. 22, 1952; children: Pamela (Mrs. Robert Phillips), Cynthia (Mrs. Donald Paul), Peter, Stephen, Thomas, Andrew, Robert, William. B.A., Pa. State U., 1952. Reporter State College (Pa.) Centre Daily Times, 1953-57, news editor, 1957-62; news editor Harrisburg (Pa.) Patriot, 1962-63, Phila. Bulletin, 1963-66; asst. mng. editor Detroit News, 1966-69, mng. editor, 1969-75; vis. prof. Northwestern U., Evanston, Ill., 1975-76; editor Akron (Ohio) Beacon Jour., 1976-86; prof. journalism, spl. asst. to pres. Kent (Ohio) State U., 1986—. Served with USAF 1951-53. Mem. Am. Soc. Newspaper Editors, AP Mng. Editors (regent). Office: Kent State U 2D Fl Libr Kent OH 44242

POORMAN, ROBERT LEWIS, education educator, consultant, academic administrator; b. Germantown, Ohio, Dec. 9, 1926; s. Dale Lowell and Bernice Velma (Krick) P.; m. Lois May Romer, Dec. 26, 1949; children: Paula Beth, Janice Marie, Mark Leon, John Alex, Lisa Ann, Daniel Romer. Student, Ohio Wesleyan U., 1944-45, U. Va., 1945-46; B.S.Ed., Ohio State U., 1948, M.A., 1950; postgrad., U. So. Calif., 1951-53; Ed.D. (Kellogg fellow 1960-62, Disting. Scholar Tuition grantee 1960-62), UCLA, 1964. Tchr., counselor, adminstr., secondary schs. Colo., Mo., Ariz., 1948-57; registrar Phoenix Coll., 1957-60; intern Bakersfield Coll., 1960-63, asst. to pres., 1963-64, asso. dean instrn., 1964-65, dean students, 1965-67; founding pres. Lincoln Land Community Coll., 1967-88, pres. emeritus; edn. cons. MARA of Malaysia, 1983; higher edn. cons. Springfield, Ill., 1988—; interim pres. Parkland Coll., Champaign, Ill., 1989-90; Fulbright lectr., cons. to Lithuania, 1993; vis. assoc. prof. Fla. Internat. U., 1994-95. Contbr. articles to profl. jours. Bd. dirs. United Way of Springfield, Urban League of Springfield, Good Will Industries of Springfield, Springfield (Ill.) Symphony, Catholic Youth Orgn., Springfield, Ill., Gov.'s Prayer Breakfast, Springfield Mental Health, Griffin High School Bd., Diocesan Sem.; mem. adv. bd. Sacred Heart Acad., Springfield Commn. on Internat. Visitors, Sisters Cities Assn. Served with USNR, 1944-46. Recipient Midwest region Chief Exec. Officer of Yr. Assn. Community Coll. Trustees, 1988, recognition Ill. Community Coll. Trustees Assn., 1988; named an Outstanding Chief Exec. Officer for Ill. Community Colls. U. Tex. Leadership Program, 1987; Phi Theta Kappa fellow, 1981. Mem. Am. Assn. Community and Jr. Colls., Ill. Council Public Community Coll. Pres. (sec. 1973-74, vice chmn. 1974-75, chmn. 1975-76), Council North Central Community and Jr. Colls. (exec. bd. 1979-81), North Central Assn. (cons., evaluator 1984-88). Republican. Roman Catholic. Home and Office: 2324 S Willemore Ave Springfield IL 62704-4362

POP, IGGY (JAMES NEWELL OSTERBERG), composer, singer, musician; b. Muskegon, Mich., Apr. 21, 1947; s. James Newell and Louella Kristine (Christensen) Osterberg. Student, U. Mich., 1963-64. Drummer, lead singer, composer The Iguanas, 1966-67; lead singer, composer The Stooges, 1967-74; solo artist, 1975—, toured extensively with David Bowie and others. composer music and lyrics for over 90 songs including China Girl (recorded by David Bowie); rec. artist, albums include The Stooges, 1970, Funhouse, 1972, Raw Power, 1973, Kill City, 1976, The Idiot, 1977, Lust for Life, 1977, TV Eye, 1977, New Values, 1979, Soldier, 1980, Party, 1982, Zombie Birdhouse, 1983, Blah, Blah, Blah, 1986, Instinct (Grammy nomination 1988), 1988, BrickXBricks, 1990, ArizonaDream, 1992, American Caesar, 1993; has recorded for Elektra, Columbia; RCA, solo albums for Arista, Chrysallis, A&M; guest appearances on television and prodns.; known as Godfather of Punk; appeared in films The Color of Money, Cry-Baby, 1990, Coffey and Cigarettes (Palme d'Or 1993). Named Punk of the Yr. Creem Mag. Office: care Floyd Peluce 449 S Beverly Dr # 102 Beverly Hills CA 90212-4428*

POPCHAK, SISTER BARBARA JO, private school director; b. Clairton, Pa., Feb. 12, 1941; d. John Francis and Barbara Lucille (Demchak) P. BS, Carlow Coll., 1969; MEd, Xavier U., Cin., 1976. Mem. Vincentian Sisters of Charity; cert. Montessori tchr., Pa. Tchr. parochial schs. Pitts., 1962-76; founder, dir., adminstr. Mt. Lebanon Montessori Sch., Pitts., 1976—; vis. supervising tchr. Montessori Tchr. Tng., N.Y.C., Boston, Pitts., also Ind. 1980—; founder Master Degree Tchr. Tng. Ctr., 1979; workshop presenter various parents groups, Pitts., 1975—; developer Montessori assts. work-shop, 1991—; founder Mt. Lebanon Montessori Acad., 1994—. Recipient award for 10 Yrs. Excellence, Mt. Lebanon Parents Group; Cath. Daus. Am. grantee, 1972; featured in Good Shepherd, Slovak Cath. Fedn., 1995. Mem. Am. Montessori Soc. (cons. 1979—), Great Pitts. Montessori Soc. (chair 1988-90), Nat. Assn. for Edn. Young Children, Pa. Assn. for Edn. Young Children, Montessori Internationale, N.Am. Montessori Tchrs. Assn., Assn. for Childhood Edn. Internat., Nat. Ctr. for Montessori Info. Republican. Roman Catholic. Avocations: golf, fishing, reading, extensive travel to Europe and Slovakia. Home: 1817 Mary St Pittsburgh PA 15203-1821

POPE, ALEXANDER H., lawyer, former county official; b. N.Y.C., June 4, 1929; s. Clifford H. and and Sarah H. (Davis) P.; m. Katherine Mackinlay, Sept. 14, 1985; children by previous marriage: Stephen C., Virginia L., Daniel M. A.B. with honors, U. Chgo., 1948, J.D., 1952. Bar: Ill. 1952, Republic of Korea 1953, Calif. 1955, U.S. Supreme Ct. 1970. Pvt. practice L.A., 1955-77, 87—; assoc. David Ziskind, L.A., 1955; ptnr. Shadle, Kennedy & Pope, L.A., 1956, Fine & Pope, L.A., 1957-77; legis. sec. to Gov. State of Calif., 1959-61; county assessor Los Angeles County, L.A., 1978-86; ptnr. Mayer, Brown & Platt, L.A., 1987-88, Barash & Hill, L.A., 1989-92; of counsel Seyforth, Shaw, Fairweather & Geraldson, 1993—. Pres. Westchester Mental Health Clinic, 1963; nat. bd. mem. Vols. for Stevenson, 1952; vice-chmn. L.A. County Dem. Cen. Com., 1958-59; mem. Calif. Hwy. Commn., 1966-70; mem. L.A. Bd. Airport Commrs., 1973-77, v.p., 1973-75, pres., 1975-76; trustee, sec. L.A. Theatre Ctr., 1984-89. With U.S. Army, 1952-54, Korea. Mem. ACLU, Calif. State Bar Assn. (state and local tax com. 1991—, chair 1993-94), L.A. County Bar Assn. (state and local tax com. 1987—), U. Chgo. Alumni Club Greater L.A. (pres. 1970-71), Zero Population Growth, Ams. United, Common Cause, Order of Coif, Phi Beta Kappa. Democrat. Unitarian. Home: Unit 2205 800 W 1st St Los Angeles CA 90012-2430

POPE, ANDREW JACKSON, JR. (JACK POPE), retired state supreme court chief justice; b. Abilene, Tex., Apr. 18, 1913; s. Andrew Jackson and Ruth Adelia (Taylor) P.; m. Allene Esther Nichols, June 11, 1938; children: Andrew Jackson III, Walter Allen. BA, Abilene Christian U., 1934, LLD (hon.), 1980; LLB, U. Tex., 1937; LLD (hon.), Pepperdine U., 1981, St. Mary's U., San Antonio, 1982, Okla. Christian U., 1983. Bar: Tex. 1937. Practice law Corpus Christi, 1937-46; judge 94th Dist. Ct., Corpus Christi, 1946-50; justice Ct. Civil Appeals, San Antonio, 1950-65; justice Supreme Ct. of Tex., Austin, 1965-82, chief justice, 1982-85. Author: John Berry & His Children, 1988; chmn. bd. editors Appellate Procedure in Tex., 1974; author numerous articles in law revs. and profl. jours. Pres. Met. YMCA, San Antonio, 1956-57; chmn. Tex. State Law Libr. Bd., 1973-80; trustee Abilene Christian U., 1958—. Seaman USNR, 1944-46. Recipient Silver Beaver award Alamo council Boy Scouts Am., 1961, Distinguished Eagle award, 1983; Rosewood Gavel award, 1962, St. Thomas More award, St. Mary's U., San Antonio, 1982; Outstanding Alumnus award Abilene Christian U., 1965; Greenhill Jud. award Mcpl. Judges Assn., 1980; Houston Bar Found. citation, 1985; San Antonio Bar Found. award, 1985; Disting. Jurist award Jefferson County Bar, 1985; Outstanding Alumnus award U. Tex. Law Alumni Assn., 1988; George Washington Honor medal Freedom Found., 1988; Disting. Lawyer award Travis County, 1992. Fellow Tex. Bar Found. (Law Rev. award 1979, 80, 81); mem. ABA, State Bar Tex. (pres. jud. sect. 1962, Outstanding Fifty Years Lawyer award 1994), Order of Coif, Nueces County (pres. 1946), Travis County Bar Assn., Bexar County Bar Assn., Tex. Philos. Soc., Austin Knife and Fork (pres. 1980), Am. Judicature Soc., Tex. State Hist. Assn., Tex. Supreme Ct. Hist. Soc. (v.p.), Sons of Republic of Tex., Christian Chronicle Coun. (chmn.), Masons, K.P. (grand chancellor 1946), Alpha Chi, Phi Delta Phi, Pi Sigma Alpha. Mem. Ch. of Christ. Home: 2803 Stratford Dr Austin TX 78746-4626

POPE, BILL JORDAN, chemical engineering educator, business executive; b. Salt Lake City, Sept. 12, 1922; s. Louis Albert and Ruth (Jordan) P.; m.

Margaret McConkie, Sept. 10, 1943; children: Louis, Leslie (Mrs. Alan S. Layton), Kathryn (Mrs. Richard D. Hoopes), Patrice (Mrs. Wayne L. Tew). B.S. in Chem. Engring., U. Utah, 1947; M.S., U. Wash., 1949, Ph.D., 1959. Project chem. engr. Utah Oil Refining Co., 1951-58; mem. faculty Brigham Young U., 1958-59, 62-78, prof. chem. engring., 1962-78, prof. emeritus, 1978—, chmn. dept., 1966-78; prof. chem. engring., acting pres. Abadan (Iran) Inst. Tech., 1959-62; v.p. Megadiamond Corp., Provo, 1966-70, exec. v.p., 1970-73, pres., 1973-78; pres. Megadiamond Industries N.Y., 1976-78; pres. U.S. Synthetic Corp., 1978-92, chmn. bd. , 1988—; cons. to industry; specialist in ultra high pressure processes and equipment, diamond synthesis, diamond sintering. Del. Utah Republican Conv., 1958, 74. Served to 1st lt., C.E. AUS, 1942-46. Research fellow U. Wash., 1947-49; Keysor Chem. Research grantee, 1946-70. Mem. Am. Inst. Chem. Engrs., Am. Chem. Soc., Am. Soc. Profl. Engrs., Am. Soc. Engring. Edn., Utah Acad. Arts and Scis., Utah Soc. Profl. Engrs., Sigma Xi, Tau Beta Pi. Mem. Ch. of Jesus Christ of Latter Day Saints (bishop 1965-72, stake pres., counsellor 1972-76, stake pres. 1976-81, regional rep. 1981-87). Home: 1866 N 1450th E Provo UT 84604

POPE, DANIEL JAMES, lawyer; b. Chgo. Nov. 22, 1948. BA, Loyola U., Chgo., 1972; JD cum laude, John Marshall Law Sch., 1975; postgrad., U. Chgo., 1977-78. Bar: Ill. 1975, U.S. Dist. Ct. (no. dist.) Ill. 1982, N.Y. 1983, U.S. Tax Ct. 1985. Corp. trust adminstr. Continental Bank, Chgo., 1972-74; assoc. Haskell & Perrin, Chgo., 1975-77; assoc. Coffield, Ungaretti, Harris & Slavin, Chgo., 1977-81, ptnr., 1981-90, head litigation dept., 1988-90; ptnr. Seyfarth Shaw Fairweather & Geraldson, Chgo., 1990—; instr. John Marshall Law Sch., Chgo., 1978-79; appointed panel atty. Fed. Defender Program, Chgo., 1983. Mem. ABA, Ill. Bar Assn., Chgo. Bar Assn. (chmn. aviation law com. 1979, jud. evaluation com. 1982-87), Pub. Initiative Law Inst. (dir. 1989-91), Chgo. Athletic Club, Tavern Club, Oak Park Country Club. Home: 146 N Taylor Ave Oak Park IL 60302-2524 Office: Seyfarth Shaw Fairweather & Geraldson 55 E Monroe St Ste 4200 Chicago IL 60603-5803

POPE, DAVID E., geologist, micropaleontologist; b. Forrest City, Ark., Dec. 20, 1920; s. Jesse Ellis and Mary Ruth (Remley) P.; m. Dorothy Angeline Salario, June 8, 1947 (dec. Jan. 1982); children: David Brian, Mark Alan; m. Alice Duke Akins, June 1, 1990. BS, La. State U., 1947, MS, 1948; grad. U.S. Army Command and Gen. Staff Coll., 1967. Paleontologist, Union Producing Co., Houston, 1948-49, New Orleans, 1949-55, dist. paleontologist, New Orleans, 1955-63, Lafayette, La., 1963-67; cons., Lafayette, La., 1967-75; sr. rsch. geologist, La. Geol. Survey, Baton Rouge, 1975—; lectr. La. State U., 1979, 80, N.E. La. U., 1983. Mem. nat. adv. bd. Am. Security Coun., 1983—; bd. dirs. La. State U. Mus. Geosci. Assocs., 1980—, pres. 1981-82, 1987—. Capt. U.S. Army, 1942-46, to lt. col. USAR, 1945-70. Contbr. articles to profl. jours. Decorated Silver Star medal with oak leaf cluster, Purple Heart, Combat Inf. badge. Mem. Am. Assn. Petroleum Geologists (cert., mem. ho. of dels. 1981—), Am. Inst. Profl. Geologists, Gulf Coast sect. SEPM (pres. 1959-60, hon. mem., 1987), New Orleans Geol. Soc. (v.p. 1962-63), Lafayette Geol. Soc., Baton Rouge Geol. Soc. (pres. 1980-81, hon. mem. 1989), Gulf Coast Assn. Geol. Socs. (bd. dirs 1980-87, historian 1983—, pres. 1985-86), Res. Officers Assn. (life), Mil. Order World Wars, La. State U. Sch. Geology Alumni Assn. (pres. 1958-59, 84-85), La. Petroleum Coun. Home: 12026 Pecan Grove Ct Baton Rouge LA 70810-4835 Office: La Geol Survey Univ Sta PO Box G Baton Rouge LA 70893

POPE, DURAND L., opera manager; b. Akron, Ohio, Aug. 15, 1946; s. Doyle Chester and M. Jo Ann (Barlow) P.; m. Nancy Newman, Sept. 26, 1970. AB in English Lit., Brown U., 1968; postgrad., U. Akron, 1969-72; MA in Theatre, Case Western Res. U., 1974; postgrad., Ind. U., 1974-79. Tchr. Sagamore Hills Children's Hosp., Cleve., 1968-73; adminstv. dir. dept. theatre, lectr. Ind. U., Bloomington, 1975-87; gen. mgr. Indpls. Opera, 1987-1993; adminstrv. dir. Brown County Playhouse, Nashville, Ind., 1975-87; mng. dir. Peninsula (Ohio) Playhouse, 1968-73. Dir. over 25 plays and musicals, 1968—.

POPE, G. PHILLIP, insurance company executive. Sr. v.p. fin., cfo Blue Cross Blue Shield of Ala., Birmingham, 1970—. Office: Blue Cross Blue Shield of Ala 450 Riverchase Pky E Birmingham AL 35244

POPE, HARRISON GRAHAM, JR., psychiatrist, educator; b. Lynn, Mass., Dec. 26, 1947; s. H. Graham and Alice (Rider) P.; m. Mary M. Quinn, June 7, 1974; children: Kimberly, Hilary, Courtney. AB summa cum laude, Harvard U., 1969, MPH, 1972, MD, 1974. Diplomate Am. Bd. Psychiatry and Neurology. Resident in psychiatry McLean Hosp., Belmont, Mass., 1974-77, clin. rsch. fellow Mailman Rsch. Ctr., 1977-79, asst. psychiatrist, 1979-84, assoc. psychiatrist, 1984-92, psychiatrist, 1992—, chief biol. psychiatry lab., 1984—; Dupont-Warren rsch. fellow Harvard Med. Sch., Boston, 1976-77; instr. psychiatry Harvard Med. Sch., Boston, 1977-82, asst. prof., 1982-85, assoc. prof., 1985—; staff psychiatrist Hampstead (N.H.) Hosp., 1976-80; vis. fellow The Maudsley Hosp., London, 1977, Hôp. Ste. Anne, Paris, 1977; mem. Am. Psychiat. Assn., 1976-80, adv. com. on schizophrenic, paranoid and affective disorders, 1979, adv. com. on preparation of DSM-III-R, 1984, task force on nomenclature and stats., 1979, 84. Author: Voices from the Drug Culture, 1971, The Road East, 1974, (with Hudson J.I.) New Hope for Binge Eaters: Advances in the Understanding and Treatment of Bulimia, 1984; co-editor: The Psychobiology of Bulimia, 1987, Use of Anticonvulsants in Psychiatry: Recent Advances, 1988; contbr. over 250 papers on biol. psychiatry, with particular emphasis on diagnosis of psychotic disorders, treatment of mood disorders and eating disorders, and substance abuse, particularly abuse of anabolic steroids by athletes; mem. editorial bd. European Psychiatry, Paris, 1984—, Internat. Jour. of Eating Disorders, 1984—. Named one of Outstanding Americans under 40 Esquire mag., 1984; fellow Scottish Rite Schizophrenia Program, No. Masonic Jurisdiction, 1977-81, Charles A. King Trust, Boston, 1977-79. Avocation: weightlifting. Office: McLean Hosp 115 Mill St Belmont MA 02178-1048

POPE, INGRID BLOOMQUIST, sculptor, lecturer, poet; b. Arvika, Sweden, Apr. 2, 1918; came to U.S. 1928; d. Oscar Emanuel and Gerda (Henningson) Brostrom; m. Howard Richard Bloomquist, Feb. 14, 1941 (dec. Nov. 1982); children: Dennis Howard, Diane Cecile Connelly, Laurel Ann Shields; m. Marvin Hoyle Pope, Mar. 9, 1985. BA cum laude, Manhattanville Coll., 1979, MA in Humanities, 1981; MA in Religion, Yale Div. Sch. Yale U., 1984. lectr. Nat. Assn. Am. Pen Women, Greenwich, Soroptimist Club, Greenwich, Greenwich Travel Club, Ch. Women United Greenwich, 1st Congl. Ch., Scarsdale, N.Y., 2d Congl. Ch., Greenwich, 1st Congl. Ch., Stamford, Conn., 1st Ch. of Round Hill, St. Mary Ch., Greenwich. Exhbns. include Manhattanville Coll., Purchase, N.Y., Yale Div. Sch., Ch. of Sweden in N.Y.C., Greenwich Arts Coun., Greenwich Arts Soc., First Ch. of Round Hill; author: (poems) Musings, 1994. Past bd. dirs. N.Y.C. Mission Soc., Greenwich YWCA, Greenwich Acad. Mother's Assn.; past trustee First Ch. Round Hill, Greenwich, mem.; pres. Ch. Women United, Greenwich, 1989-91; bd. dirs. Greenwich Chaplaincy. Mem. AAUW, Nat. Assn. Pen Women (v.p.), English Speaking Union, Yale Club N.Y.C. and Greenwich, Stanwich Club, Acad. Am. Poets, Nat. Mus. of Women in the Arts, Travel Club. Home: 538 Round Hill Rd Greenwich CT 06831-2641

POPE, JEROME W., lawyer; b. Chgo., July 30, 1951. BS summa cum laude, Bradley U., 1973; JD with honors, DePaul U., 1976. Bar: Ill. 1976, U.S. Dist. Ct. (no. dist.) Ill. 1977, U.S. Ct. Appeals (7th cir.) 1978. Ptnr. Winston & Strawn, Chgo. Mem. ABA, Ill. State Bar Assn., Chgo. Bar Assn. Office: Winston & Strawn 35 W Wacker Dr Chicago IL 60601-1614

POPE, JOHN CHARLES, airline financial executive; b. Newark, Mar. 30, 1949; s. John Aris Coutant and Eleanor Laura (Hillman) P. BA, Yale U., 1971; MBA, Harvard U., 1973. Dir. profit analysis and capital analysis GM, N.Y.C., 1973-77; sr. v.p. fin., treas., chief fin. officer Am. Airlines, Inc., AMR Corp., Dallas-Fort Worth, 1977-88; exec. v.p., chief fin. officer UAL Corp., United Airlines (subs.), Chgo., 1988-91, pres., COO, 1991—; bd. dirs. Fed. Mogul Corp., Detroit; trustee Sta. WTTW, Chgo. Mem. Air Transport Assn. (chmn. fin. com.). Home: 810 S Ridge Rd Lake Forest IL 60045-2756 Office: United Airlines Inc PO Box 66100 AMF Ohare IL 60666-0100

POPE, JOHN EDWIN, III, newspaper sports editor; b. Athens, Ga., Apr. 11, 1928; s. Henry Louis and Rose (McAfee) P. B.A. in Journalism, U. Ga., 1948. Sports editor Banner-Herald, Athens, Ga., 1944-48; So. sports editor

UPI, Atlanta, 1948-50; sports writer Atlanta Constn., 1950-54; exec. sports editor Atlanta Jour., 1954-56; asst. sports editor Miami (Fla.) Herald, 1956-67, sports editor, 1967—. Author: Football's Greatest Coaches, 1956, Baseball's Greatest Managers, 1960, Encyclopedia of American Greyhound Racing, 1963, Ted Williams: The Golden Year, 1970, (with Norm Evans) On the Line, 1976, The Edwin Pope Collection, 1988; contbr. articles to popular mags. and Ency. Brittanica, World Book. Recipient Bill Corum Meml. award Thoroughbred Racing Assn., 1962, Top Sports Column award Nat. Headliners Club, 1962, 79, 86, Eclipse award Thoroughbred Racing Assn., 1976, 82, 86, Red Smith award AP Sports Editors, 1989; named to Internat. Churchmen's Sports Hall of Fame, 1976, Nat. Sportwriters and Sportcasters Assn. Hall of Fame, 1994. Mem. Profl. Football Writers Am. (pres. 1968-69), Football Writers Assn. Am., Golf Writers Am., U.S. Basketball Writers, Basketball Writers Am., Nat. Turf Writers, U.S. Tennis Writers. Presbyterian. Office: Miami Herald 1 Herald Plz Miami FL 33132-1693

POPE, JOHN M., journalist; b. Hattiesburg, Miss., Nov. 5, 1948; s. Paul M. Jr. and Mary Lee (Scott) P.; m. Diana Pinckley, May 19, 1984. BA cum laude, U. Tex., 1970, MA, 1972. Copy editor The States-Item, New Orleans, 1972-73, reporter, 1973-80; reporter The Times-Picayune, New Orleans, 1980-86, med.-health reporter, 1986—. Co-author: American First Ladies: Their Livves and Their Legacy, 1995. Recipient Frank Allen award La.-Miss. AP, 1989, Med. Writing award La. State Med. Soc., 1990. Mem. Soc. Profl. Journalists, Nat. Assn. Sci. Writers, Press Club New Orleans (4 1st pl. awards 1978-87, Alex Waller award 1987), Phi Beta Kappa. Avocations: running, travel, aerobics. Office: The Times-Picayune 3800 Howard Ave New Orleans LA 70140

POPE, JOHN W., retail executive; b. 1924. With Pope's 5$5 Stores, 1944-57; with Variety Wholesalers, Inc., Raleigh, N.C., pres. Office: Variety Wholesalers Inc 3401 Gresham Lake Rd Raleigh NC 27615*

POPE, KERIG RODGERS, magazine executive; b. Waukesha, Wis., Sept. 30, 1935; s. Kerig James Pope and Mildred (Offerman) Troemel; m. Claudia T. Koralewski, Nov. 1961 (div. 1975); children—Kerig William, Giles Thomas; m. Beth Leslie Kasik, May 24, 1980; children: Kolin Jared, Zoe Alissa. Grad., Art Inst. Chgo., 1958. Designer Jack Denst Wallpaper Designs, Chgo., 1958-60; designer Continental Casualty Ins. Co., Chgo., 1960-62, Leo Burnett Advt. Agy., Chgo., 1962-63; art dir. Mercury Records Corp., Chgo., 1963-66; mng. art dir. Playboy mag., Chgo., 1966—. Exhibited in group shows Whitney Mus. Am. Art, N.Y.C., 1969, Mus. Contemporary Art, Chgo., 1972, Bienal de Sao Paulo, Brazil, 1973, Museo de Arte Moderno, Mexico City, 1974, Nat. Collection Fine Arts, Washington, 1979, Moderno, Mexico City, 1974; represented in permanent collections Nat. Collection Fine Arts, Washington, Mus. Contemporary Art, Chgo., Smart Mus., U. Chgo. Recipient silver medal Communigraphics, N.Y.C., 1971, gold medal, 1971, 72; award of excellence Soc. Publ. Designers, 1979, 4 awards of excellence Design Ann., 1984, Silver medal Illustrators 29, 1986, Silver medal Soc. of Illustrators, 1988. Mem. Soc. Illustrators (gold medal 1981, 84, 91), Art Dirs. Club N.Y., Soc. Typog. Arts, Soc. Publ. Arts (3 Silver awards 1987). Club: Arts (Chgo.). Office: Playboy Enterprises Inc 680 N Lake Shore Dr Chicago IL 60611-3057

POPE, LAURENCE E., II, ambassador; b. New Haven, Conn., Sept. 24, 1945; m. Elizabeth Harris; 2 children. BA, Bowdoin Coll. Joined Fgn. Svc., Dept. State, 1969; vice consul Fgn. Svc., Dept. State, Saigon, Vietnam, 1970-72; polit. officer Fgn. Svc., Dept. State, Rabat, 1973, Tripoli, 1973-76; desk officer Fgn. Svc., Dept. State, Lebanon, 1977-78; Mid. East specialist Bur. Internat. Orgn. Affairs Dept. State, 1979-81; polit. counselor Dept. State, Tunis, 1981; dep. chief of mission Dept. State, Manama, 1985-86; dir. office No. Gulf affairs Dept. State, 1987-90; assoc. coordinator for counterterrorism, 1991-93; U.S. amb. to Chad N'Djamena, 1993—. Contbr. articles on Mid. East policy to profl. jours. Una Chapman Cox fellow. Mem. Am. Fgn. Svc. Assn. Office: Ave Felix Eboue BP 413, N'Djamena Chad

POPE, MARK ANDREW, lawyer; b. Munster, Ind., May 22, 1952; s. Thomas A. and Eleanor E. (Miklos) P.; m. Julia Risk Pope, June 15, 1974; children: Brent Andrew, Bradley James. BA, Purdue U., 1974; JD cum laude, Ind. U., 1977. Bar: Ind. 1977, U.S. Dist. Ct. (so. dist.) Ind. 1977, U.S. Ct. Appeals (7th cir.) 1984. Assoc. Johnson & Weaver, Indpls., 1977-79, Rocap, Rocap, Reese & Young, Indpls., 1980-82, Dutton & Overman, Indpls., 1982-88; ptnr. Dutton & Overman, 1988-89; asst. gen. counsel Lincoln Nat. Corp., 1989-91; sr. counsel Lincoln Nat. Corp., Fort Wayne, Ind., 1991—; bd. dirs. Ft. Wayne Bicentennial Coun.; pres., bd. dirs. ARCH, Inc., 1994—. Bd. editors, devel. editor Ind. U. Law Rev., 1976-77. Mem. pres.'s coun. Purdue U., 1977—; applied econ. cons. Jr. Achievement, 1989-95; bd. dirs. Jr. Achievement of No. Ind., 1992-94. Named Disting. Hoosier, Gov. of Ind., 1974. Fellow Ind. Bar Found., Indpls. Bar Found. (disting.); mem. ABA (dist. rep. young lawyers divsn. 1981-83, dir. 1983-84, liaison coord. 1985-86, 87-88, exec. coun. 1981-88, cabinet 1982-88, gen. practice sect. coun. mem. 1986—; membership chmn. 1987-89, chmn. career and family com. 1990-92, dir. 1991—), Indpls. Bar Assn. (v.p. 1983, chmn. young lawyers divsn. 1981), 500 Festival Assocs. (vice-chmn. of 500 festival parade 1985-89). Avocations: tennis, golf, running. Home: 11116 Bittersweet Dells Ln Fort Wayne IN 46804-8156 Office: Lincoln Nat Corp PO Box 1110 Fort Wayne IN 46801-1110

POPE, MARVIN HOYLE, language educator, writer; b. Durham, N.C., June 23, 1916; s. Charles Edgar and Bessie Cleveland Sorrell Pope; m. Helen Thompson, Sept. 4, 1948 (dec. Feb. 1979); m. Ingrid Brostrom Bloomquist, Mar. 9, 1985. AB, Duke U., 1938, AM, 1939; PhD, Yale U., 1949. Instr. dept. religion Duke U., Durham, 1947-49; asst. prof. Hebrew Yale U., New Haven, 1949-55, assoc. prof., 1955-64, prof. Semitic langs. and lit., 1964-86, prof. emeritus, sr. rsch. scholar, 1986—; Haskell lectr. Oberlin Coll., 1971, vis. lectr. Cath. U. Lublin, Poland, 1977, Fulbright lectr. U. Aleppo, Syria, 1980; Wickenden lectrs. Miami U., Oxford, Ohio, 1982; Fulbright Rsch. scholar Inst. Ugaritische U. Muenster, Germany, 1986, 90; Hooker disting. vis. prof. McMaster U., Hamilton, Ont. Can., 1986; dir. Hebrew Union Coll. Bibl. and Archeol. Sch., Jerusalem, 1966-67; trustee Albright Inst. Archeol. Rsch., Jerusalem; fellow Pierson Coll. Yale U. Author: El in the Ugaritic Texts, 1955; The Book of Job, 1973, Song of Songs, 1977 (Nat. Religious Book award 1978), Syrien Die Mythologie der Ugariter und Phoenizier, 1962, Collected Essays, 1994; contbr. articles to scholarly jours. and dictionaries. Mem. rev. standard version Bible com. Nat. Coun. of Chs., 1960—; mem. 1st Ch. Round Hill. With USAAF, 1941-45, PTO. Nat. Endowment for Humanities Rsch. grantee, 1980—. Mem. Am. Oriental Soc., Am. Schs. Oriental Rsch., Soc. Bibl. Lit., Am. Soc. Study Religions, Columbia U. Seminar for Study of Hebrew Bible, Yale Club, Oriental Club New Haven, Mory's Club, Stanwich Country Club, Phi Beta Kappa. Home: 538 Round Hill Rd Greenwich CT 06831-2641

POPE, MICHAEL THOR, chemistry educator; b. Exeter, Devon, Eng., Apr. 14, 1933; came to U.S. 1962; naturalized, 1992; s. Hector Maurice and Edith Mary (Hewett) P.; m. Ann Mavis Potter, Aug 12, 1957; children—Gregory, Lucy. B.A., Oxford U., 1954, D.Phil., 1957. Postdoctoral, Boston U., Mass., 1957-59; research chemist Laporte Chems., Luton, Eng., 1959-62; asst. prof. Georgetown U., Washington, 1962-67, assoc. prof., 1967-73, prof., 1973—, dept. chair, 1990—; vis. prof. Tech. U., Vienna, Austria, 1970-71, Free U. of Berlin, 1979, Northeast Normal U., Changchun, China, 1985, U. Umeå, U. Bielefeld, Germany; prof. associé U. Pierre et Marie Curie, Paris, 1979. Author: Heteropoly and Isopoly Oxometalates, 1983, Polyoxometalates: From Platonic Solids to Anti-Retroviral Activity, 1994; contbr. articles to profl. publs. Recipient Sr. U.S. Scientist award Alexander von Humboldt Found., 1989-90; Petroleum Research Fund Internat. award fellow, 1970-71; Research grantee NSF, NIH, Petroleum Research Fund, Office Naval Research, Army Research Office, Air Force Office of Sci. Research. Mem. Royal Soc. Chemistry (London), Am. Chem. Soc., Sigma Xi (chpt. pres. 1969-70). Episcopalian. Avocations: music, art. Office: Georgetown Univ Chemistry Dept Washington DC 20057-2222

POPE, PETER T., forest and paper products company executive; b. 1934; married. BA, Stanford U., 1957, MBA, 1959. With Pope & Talbot Inc., Portland, Oreg., 1960—, asst. sec., 1964-68, v.p., 1968-69, v.p., gen. mgr., 1969-71, chmn. bd. chief exec. officer, 1971-90, chmn., pres., chief exec. officer, 1990—. With USAR, 1957-58. Office: Pope & Talbot Inc 1500 SW 1st Ave Portland OR 97201-5815

POPE, RANDALL RAY, retired national park superintendent; b. Durham, Kans., Oct. 15, 1932; s. Reuben S. and Enid Lillian (Powers) P.; m. Kathleen V. Higer, Feb. 23, 1958; children: Mark Randall, Renee Lynn Pope Polenske. BS in Landscape Architecture, Kans. State U., 1959. Cert. landscape arch., Nebr. State Bd. Landscape Archs., 1968. Landscape architect Midwest regional office Nat. Pk. Svc., Omaha, 1959-61, 65-69; pk. landscape architect Grand Teton Nat. Pk. Nat. Pk. Svc., Moose, Wyo., 1961-65; supt. Herbert Hoover Nat. Hist. Site Nat. Pk. Svc., West Branch, Iowa, 1969-71; supt. Ozark Nat. Scenic Riverway Nat. Pk. Svc., Van Buren, Mo., 1971-76; dep. regional dir. Midwest regional office Nat. Pk. Svc., Omaha, 1976-87; supt. Great Smoky Mountains Nat. Pk. Nat. Pk. Svc., Gatlinburg, Tenn., 1987-93; ret., 1993. Counselor Boy Scouts Am., West Branch, Van Buren, 1970-76; bd. dirs. Foothills Land Conservancy, 1994—. With USN, 1951-55. Mem. Am. Soc. Landscape Archs., Rotary (Gatlinburg), Lions (instl. rep. 1970-71, 1st, 2d, 3d v.p., pres. Sunrise club 1986-87), Gamma Sigma Delta. Avocations: hiking, photography, gardening, fishing. Home: 845 Vixen Run Gatlinburg TN 37738

POPE, RICHARD M., rheumatologist; b. Chgo., Jan. 10, 1946. Student, Procopius Coll., 1963-65, U. Ill., 1965-66; MD, Loyola U., 1970. Diplomate Am. Bd. Internal Medicine. Intern in medicine Med. Ctr. Michael Reese Hosp., Chgo., 1970-71, resident in internal medicine, 1971-72; fellow in rheumatology U. Wash., Seattle, 1972-74; asst. clin. prof. medicine U. Hawaii, 1974-77; asst. prof. medicine U. Tex. Health Sci. Ctr., San Antonio, 1976-81, assoc. prof. medicine, 1981-85; assoc. prof. medicine Northwestern U. Med. Sch., 1985-88, prof. medicine, 1988—; attending physician Northwestern Meml. Hosp., Chgo., 1985—, VA Lakeside Med. Ctr., Chgo., 1985—, Rehab. Inst. Chgo., 1985—; chief divsn. rheumatology VA Lakeside Med. Ctr., 1985-91, divsn. arthritis-connective tissue diseases Northwestern U. and Northwestern Meml. Hosp., 1989—, Northwestern Med. Faculty Found., 1989—; mem. program com. Ctrl. Soc. Clin. Rsch., 1987, ctrl. region Am. Rheumatism Assn., 1987; mem. sci. com. Ill. chpt. Arthritis Found., 1988-1992, bd. dirs., 1990—; mem. chpt. review grants subcom., 1983-88, chmn. chpt. rsch. grant subcom., 1986-88, mem. rsch. com. 1986-88; mem. site visit teams NIH, 1986, 87, 89; cons. reviewer VA Merit Review Bd., 1984, 87, 91; cons. reviewer Arthritis Soc. Can., 1986, 87; mem. editorial adv. bd. Arthritis and Rheumatism Jour. Lab. and Clin. Medicine, 1992—. Author: (with others) The Science and Practice of Clinical Medicine, 1979, Proceedings of the University of South Florida International Symposium in the Biomedical Sciences, 1984, Concepts in Immunopathology, 1985, Biology Based Immunomodulators in the Therapy of Rheumatic Diseases, 1986, Primer on the Rheumatic Diseases, 1988; contbr. numerous articles to profl. jours. With U.S. Army, 1974-76. Anglo-Am. Rheumatology fellow, 1983. Mem. Am. Coll. Physicians, Am. Coll. Rheumatology (councillor ctrl. region coun. 1990—, program com. 1983-86, 91), Am. Assn. Immunologists, Am. Fedn. Clin. Rsch., Am. Soc. Clin. Investigation, Lupus Found. Ill. (mem. adv. bd. 1990-93), Chgo. Rheumatism Assn. (pres. 1991-93), Ctrl. Soc. Clin. Investigation, Soc. Irish and Am. Rheumatologists (sec., treas. 1989-93), Univ. Rheumatology Coun. Chgo., Alpha Omega Alpha. Achievements include research in pathophysiology of rheumatoid arthritis, T cell activation, T cell receptor, macrophage gene expression. Office: Northwestern U Multipurpose Arthritis Ctr 303 E Chicago Ave Chicago IL 60611-3008

POPE, ROBERT DEAN, lawyer; b. Memphis, Mar. 10, 1945; s. Ben Duncan and Phyllis (Drenner) P.; m. Elizabeth Dante Cohen, June 26, 1971; 1 child, Justin Nicholas Nathanson. AB, Princeton U., 1967; Diploma in Hist. Studies, Cambridge U., 1971; JD, Yale U., 1972, PhD, 1976. Bar: Va. 1974, D.C. 1980. Assoc. Hunton & Williams, Richmond, Va., 1974-80; ptnr. Hunton & Williams, Richmond, 1980—. Contbg. author: Disclosure Rules of Counsel in State and Local Government Securities Offerings, 2d edit., 1994. Mem. adv. com. Va. Sec. of Health and Human Svcs. on Continuing Care Legislation, 1992—; mem. Anthony Commn. on Pub. Fin.; adv. coun. dept. history Princeton U., 1987-91. Mem. Govt. Fin. Officers Assn. (com. on govtl. debt and fiscal policy), Va. Bar Assn. (chmn. legal problems of the elderly 1982-88). Am. Assn. Bond Lawyers (treas. 1984-85, sec. 1985-86, pres. 1987-88, bd. dirs. 1982-89, Bernard P. Friel medal for contbns. to pub. fin. 1994), Am. Acad. Hosp. Attys., Yale Law Sch. Assn. (exec. com. 1985-88), Bond Club Va. (bd. dirs. 1990—, v.p. 1993-94, pres. 1994—), NCCJ (Richmond area bd.), Phi Beta Kappa. Republican. Episcopalian. Avocations: history, golf, music, book reviews. Home: 8707 Ruggles Rd Richmond VA 23229-7918 Office: Hunton & Williams PO Box 1535 951 E Byrd St Richmond VA 23219-4040

POPE, ROBERT EUGENE, fraternal organization administrator; b. Wellington, Kans., Sept. 10, 1931; s. Samuel E. and Opal Irene (Davis) P. BSChemE, U. Kans., 1952, MS, 1958. Registered profl. engr., Kans. Asst. instr. U. Kans., Lawrence, 1952-56; lab. technician Monsanto Co., St. Louis, 1952; project engr. Mallinckrodt, Inc., St. Louis, 1953-59; traveling sec. Theta Tau, St. Louis, 1959-62, exec. sec., 1963-84, exec. dir., 1984—. Author: Years of Progress, 1995; (with C.E. Wales) Designing a Rush Program, 2d edit., 1981; mem. bd. editors (mag.) The Gear of Theta Tau, 1993—. Carillonneur, Grace United Meth. Ch., St. Louis, 1985—, chmn. adminstrv. coun., 1991—. Mem. Am. Soc. Assn. Execs., St. Louis Soc. Assn. Execs., Profl. Fraternity Assn. (exec. sec. 1977-86), Engrs. Club St. Louis, Creve Coeur Country Club, Tau Beta Pi, Phi Lambda Upsilon, Omicron Delta Kappa. Democrat. Methodist. Avocations: physical fitness, sports, photography. Home: 13 Sona Ln Saint Louis MO 63141-7742 Office: Theta Tau Ctrl Office 655 Craig Rd Ste 128 Saint Louis MO 63141-7168

POPE, ROBERT GLYNN, telecommunications executive; b. Greenville, Tex., Dec. 5, 1935; s. Edwin R. P.; m. Shirley Hall, Dec. 30, 1958; children: Kenneth, Richard, David. BSME, So. Meth. U., 1958. Registered profl. engr. Chief engr. Southwestern Bell Telephone Co., Houston, 1973-77; v.p. staff Tex. Southwestern Bell Telephone Co., Dallas, 1977-78, v.p. centralized svcs., 1978-80; v.p. residence and pub. svcs. Southwestern Bell Telephone Co., St. Louis, 1980-81, v.p. transition, 1981-83, v.p. strategic planning, 1983; v.p. corp. devel. Southwestern Bell Corp., St. Louis, 1984-86, vice-chmn. corp. devel., 1986-88, vice chmn. corp. devel., chief fin. officer, 1988-90, vice chmn., chief fin. officer, 1990-94, ret., 1994; mem. Adv. Bd. Battery Ventures; bd. dirs. Southwestern Bell Corp., Boatmen's Bancshares Corp. Trustee Maryville U.; mem. governing bd. Luth. Med. Ctr. With U.S Army, 1959. Mem. NSPE, Mo. Soc. Profl. Engrs., Media Club St. Louis, Univ. Club, Golf Club Okla., Old Warson Country Club, St. Louis Club. Avocations: golf, coin collecting, fishing.

POPE, SARAH ANN, elementary education educator; b. Granite City, Ill., Dec. 4, 1938; d. Vance Guy and Lily Lovinia (Fischer) Morgan; m. Thomas E. Pope; children: Robert, Susan, James, John, William. BS in Edn., So. Ill. U., Edwardsville, 1970, MS in Edn., 1976. Lang. arts, humanities, sci., English, reading, math. tchr. Madison (Ill.) Community South Dist., 1970—. Co-founder libr. Harris Elem. Sch., 1990. Fellow Old Six Mile Hist. Soc.; mem. Am. Hemerocallis Soc. Avocations: reading, growing flowers, visiting historical sites, swimming. Office: Madison Community Unit Sch 1707 4th St Madison IL 62060-1505

POPE, STEPHEN BAILEY, engineering educator; b. Nottingham, England, Nov. 26, 1949; came to U.S., 1977; s. Joseph Albert and Evelyn Alice (Gallagher) P.; m. Linda Ann Syatt, Aug. 16, 1979; children: Sarah Evelyn, Samuel Joseph. BS in Engring., Imperial Coll., London, 1971; MS, Imperial Coll., 1972, PhD, 1976, DSc in Engring., U. London, 1986. Rsch. asst. Imperial Coll., London, 1972-77; rsch. fellow Calif. Inst. Tech., Pasadena, 1977-78; asst. prof. MIT, Cambridge, Mass., 1978-81; assoc. prof. MIT, 1981, Cornell U., Ithaca, N.Y., 1982-87; prof. engring. Cornell U., 1987—; cons. GE, Schenectady, N.Y., 1984—; GM, Warren, Mich., 1985—, Allison Engine Co., Indpls., 1986—. Assoc. editor Physics of Fluids A; contbr. articles to profl. jours. Overseas fellow Churchill Coll, Cambridge, Eng., 1989; awards NSF, Army Rsch. Office, Air Force Office Sci. Rsch., U.S. Dept. Energy. Fellow Am. Phys. Soc., Combustion Inst. Office: Cornell U Upson Hall Ithaca NY 14853

POPE, STEVEN FRANCOIS, association executive; b. Chgo., Nov. 2, 1948; s. Frank and Lucille (Pelchan) P.; m. Louise Few, Feb. 27, 1971 (div. May 1984); children: David, Susan; m. Maryann Oprondek, May 25, 1991. BA, DePauw U., 1970; MBA, Northwestern U., Evanston, 1976. Communications cons. Ill. Bell, Chgo., 1970-74; sales mgr. Geocaris & Co., Chgo., 1974-78; nat. sales mgr. Tenex Corp., Elk Grove Village, Ill., 1978-80;

v.p. mktg. Realtors Nat. Mktg. Inst., Chgo., 1980-84; regional sales mgr. ERA Real Estate/Control Data Corp., Schaumburg, Ill., 1984-85; exec. v.p. Commercial-Investment Real Estate Inst., Chgo., 1985—. Bd. dirs. Abraham Lincoln Ctr., Chgo., 1976-78; pres. jr. bd. Travelers Aid Soc., Immigrant Svc. League, 1977-78. Mem. Am. Soc. Assn. Execs., Chgo. Soc. Assn. Execs., Trevian Soccer Club (Winnetka, Ill.). Avocations: soccer, tennis. Office: Comml Investment Real 430 N Michigan Ave Chicago IL 60611-4002

POPE, THEODORE CAMPBELL, JR., utilities executive, consultant; b. Sanford, Fla., Oct. 28, 1932; s. Theodore Campbell and Mary (Cook) P.; m. Edith L. Carlton; children: Theodore, Jeffrey, Laura; m. Jeris Julia Dawson, Nov. 21, 1973. BSME, U. Fla., 1954, MBA, 1959. Registered profl. engr., Fla.; diplomate Am. Acad. Environ. Engrs. Chief mech. engr. Orlando Utilities, 1959-64, plant supt., 1964-67, dir. elec. generation, 1967-70, asst. mgr. elec. ops., 1970-72, mgr water ops., 1972-84, asst. gen. mgr., 1984-86, gen. mgr., 1986-92; pres. Ted Pope Enterprises, Orlando, 1992—. Contbr. articles to profl. jours.; patentee water treatment process. Bd. dirs. United Fund Brevard County; bd. dirs. Econ. Devel. Commn. of Mid-Fla., Orlando; bd. dirs., pres. Ctrl. Fla. Fair; trustee United Arts of Ctrl. Fla. 1st lt. U.S. Army, 1955-57. Recipient Abel Waldman award InterAm. Assn. San. Engrs., 1982. Mem. Am. Water Works Assn. (hon.; Disting. Pub. Svc. award 1991, George Warren Fuller award, chair emeritus Rsch. Found.), Greater Orlando Area C. of C. (pres. 1990-91), Fla. Engring. Soc. (Engr. of Yr.), Fla. Conservation Assn., Rotary Club of Orlando, Smyrna Yacht Club, Country Club of Orlando, Univ. Club, Delta Sigma Pi. Democrat. Avocations: sailing, golfing, travel, hunting, fishing. Home: 723 Baxter Ave Orlando FL 32806

POPE, THOMAS HARRINGTON, JR., lawyer; b. Kinards, S.C., July 28, 1913; s. Thomas H. and Marie (Gary) P.; m. Mary Waties Lumpkin, Jan. 3, 1940; children: Mary Waties (Mrs. Robert H. Kennedy Jr.), Thomas Harrington III, Gary Tusten. A.B., The Citadel, 1935, LL.D., 1977; LL.B., U. S.C., 1938; grad., Command and Gen. Staff Coll., 1951; LL.D., Newberry Coll., 1969. Bar: S.C. 1938, U.S. Supreme Ct. 1962. Practice in Newberry, 1938—; sr. ptnr. Pope and Hudgens, P.A.; spl. circuit judge Richland and Lexington counties, 1955-56; dir. emeritus The Citizens and So. Nat. Bank S.C.; bd. dirs. Carolina Motor Club, Newberry Fed. Savs. Bank; mem. S.C. Ports Authority, 1957-65; mem. Jud. Coun. S.C., 1957—, chmn., 1979-83; mem. S.C. Archives Commn., 1965-75, vice chmn., 1974-75. Author: The History of Newberry County, South Carolina, Vol. I, 1973, Vol. 2, 1992; co-author: The History of the 107th Separate Coast Artillery Battalion (AA) 1982. Chmn. Newberry County Sesqui-Centennial Commn., 1939; Mem. S.C. Ho. of Reps. from Newberry County, 1936-40, 45-50, speaker, 1949-50; chmn. S.C. Democratic Party, 1958-60; del. at large Dem. Nat. Conv., 1956, 60; pres. S.C. Dem. Conv., 1958, 62; Mem. S.C. Tricentennial Commn., 1966-71; Trustee U. of South, 1965-70, Newberry Coll., 1965-75; chmn. S.C. Found. Ind. Colls.; bd. visitors The Citadel, 1939-40, 46. Served to lt. col. AUS, 1941-45, ETO; brig. gen. ret. S.C. N.G. Recipient Algernon Sydney Sullivan award Newberry Coll., 1976, Durant Disting. Pub. Svc. award S.C. Bar Found., 1983, The Compleat Lawyer award Law Sch., U. S.C., 1992, U. S.C. Disting. Alumnus, 1994. Fellow Am. Coll. Trial Lawyers, Am. Bar Found., S.C. Bar Found.; mem. ABA, S.C. Bar Assn. (pres. 1964, chmn. exec. com. 1956-58), Newberry County Bar Assn. (pres. 1951), Am. Law Inst. (life), John Belton O'Neall Inn of Ct., So. Hist. Assn., Soc. Colonial Wars, Nat. Trust Historic Preservation (adv. bd. 1967-72), U. S.C. Soc. (curator 1968-72), S.C. Hist. Soc. (curator 1968-74), Newberry County Hist. Soc. (pres. 1966), Mason (grand master S.C. 1958-60, Albert Gallatin Mackey medal Grand Lodge S.C. 1965, Henry Price medal Grand Lodge Mass. 1960), Newberry Country Club, Palmetto Club (Columbia), Pine Tree Hunt Club (Columbia), Phi Beta Kappa, Omicron Delta Kappa, Phi Delta Phi, Phi Kappa Phi, Alpha Tau Omega. Episcopalian (sr. warden 1963-65, 70). Home: 1700 Boundary St Newberry SC 29108-3912 Office: 1508 College St Newberry SC 29108-2749

POPE, TIM L., state legislator, consultant; b. Mooresville, Ind., Oct. 2, 1957; s. Eugene L. and Mary L. (Clark) P.; m. LaDonna K. Freeman, Aug. 6, 1976; children: Melissa, Andrea, Erica. Sales mgr. Generay Sales, Martinsville, Ind., 1976-80, Royal Mobile Homes, Oklahoma City, 1980-86; counselor Draughon Coll., Oklahoma City, 1986-88; mem. Okla. Ho. of Reps., Oklahoma City, 1988—. County chmn. Canadian County (Okla.) Reps., 1992; bd. dirs. Mustang (Okla.) Handicapped Assn., 1989—. Recipient Taxpayers Friend award Okla. Taxpayers Union, 1993. Mem. Mustang Kiwanis. Home: 11503 Belle Blvd Mustang OK 73064-9795 Office: 504 State Capital Bldg Oklahoma City OK 73105

POPEIL, RON, consumer products company executive; b. Chgo., 1936; s. Sam and Julia P.; children: Kathryn, Shannon, Lauren. Owner Ronco, Inc.; bd. dirs. Mirage Hotel & Casino, Las Vegas. Office: Mirage Resort Inc PO Box 7777 Las Vegas NV 89177-0777

POPEJOY, WILLIAM J., savings and loan association executive; b. 1938; married. A.B., Calif. State U., 1961, M.A., 1962. Pres. Fed. Home Loan Mortgage Corp., 1971-74; pres. Am. Savs. & Loan Assn. subs. Fin. Corp. Am., Los Angeles, 1974-80; chmn., pres., chief exec. officer Am. Savs. & Loan Assn. subs. Fin. Corp. Am., Irving, Calif., 1984-89, also bd. dirs.; pres. Far West Savs. & Loan Assn., 1980-81; pres., chief fin. officer Fin. Fedn. Inc., Culver City, Calif., from 1981; chmn., pres., chief exec. officer Fin. Corp. Am., Irvine, 1984-89; limited ptnr. Western Financial Printing Co., Santa Fe Springs, 1990—; chief executive Orange County, Calif., 1995—. Office: Western Financial Printing Co 10036 Freeman Ave Santa Fe Springs CA 90670

POPEL, ALEKSANDER S., engineering educator; b. Moscow, Oct. 8, 1945; came to U.S., 1975; s. Samson Popel and Mary Gellershtein; m. Natalya Kalnitskaya, Sept. 17, 1966; 1 child, Julie. MS, Moscow State U., 1967, PhD, 1972. Rsch. scientist Inst. Mechanics, Moscow State U., 1970-75; asst. prof. Tulane U., New Orleans, 1976; rsch. assoc. prof. U. Ariz., Tucson, 1976-80; assoc. prof. U. Houston, 1980-84; assoc. prof. Johns Hopkins U., Balt., 1984-88, prof., 1988—. Editor 2 books; contbr. articles to profl. jours. NIH, NSF grantee. Fellow ASME, Am. Inst. Med. & Biol. Engring.; mem AAAS, Biomed. Engring. Soc. (sr.), Am. Physiol. Soc. Soc. for Indsl. and Applied Math. Office: Johns Hopkins U Sch Medicine Dept Biomed Engring Baltimore MD 21205

POPENOE, HUGH LLYWELYN, soils educator; b. Tela, Honduras, Aug. 28, 1929; s. Frederick Wilson and Dorothy (Hughes) P. BS, U. Calif., Davis, 1951; PhD, U. Fla., 1960. Mem. faculty U. Fla., Gainesville, 1960—; dir. ctr. tropical agr., 1965—, dir. internat. programs, 1966-92, dir. Fla. Sea Grant Coll., 1971-81; bd. dirs. Escuela Agricola Panamericana, Zamorano, Honduras, Orgn. Tropical Studies. Contbr. numerous articles to profl. jours. Chair Assn. U.S. Univ. Dirs. Internat. Agrl. Programs, 1969-70, Joint Rsch. Com. Bd. Internat. Food and Agrl. Devel., 1977-82, Joint Com. Agrl. Rsch. and Devel., 1982-86; chair numerous reports Bd. Sci. and Tech. in Devel., 1979-84; trustee Internat. Found. for Sci., Stockholm, 1984-87; mem. sci. liaison officer Internat. Inst. for Tropical Agr., Nigeria, 1983-88; mem. adv. com. internat. programs NSF, 1985-87; bd. dirs. League for Internat. Food Edn., 1976-87. With U.S. Army, 1952-54. Recipient Sci. Pioneer prize Egyptian Vet. Assn. for Buffalo Devel., 1985. Fellow AAAS, Am. Soc. Agronomy, Am. Geog. Soc., Internat. Soil Sci. Soc., Am. Water Buffalo Assn. (pres. 1988—), Cosmos Club. Office: U Fla 3028 McCarty Gainesville FL 32611

POPENOE, JOHN, horticultural consultant, retired botanical garden administrator; b. L.A., Jan. 24, 1929; s. Paul and Betty (Stankowitch) P.; m. Geraldine V. Mann, June 29, 1952; children: Deborah Irene, Natalie, Juanita, Jennifer. B.S., UCLA, 1950; M.S. U. Md., 1952, Ph.D., 1955. Asst. horticulturist U.S. Dept. Agr., Miami, 1955-58; asso. prof. horticulture Ala. Poly. Inst., 1958-59; assoc. horticulturist U. Fla. Subtropical Experiment Sta., 1960-63; dir. Fairchild Tropical Garden, Miami, 1963-91; horticultural cons., 1991—. Served with U.S. Army, 1952-54. Mem. Am. Soc. Hort. Sci. Home: 113 Washington St Hancock MD 21750-1127

POPEO, R. ROBERT, lawyer; b. Boston, Apr. 9, 1938. AB, Northeastern U., 1958; JD, boston Coll., 1961. Bar: Mass. 1961, D.C. 1972. Law clerk U.S. Dist. Ct. Mass., 1961-63; instr. Sch. Law Boston U., 1964-67; U.S.

Commr., 1967-71; asst. atty. gen. Commonwealth of Mass., 1970-74; chmn. Mintz, Levin, Cohn, Ferris, Glovsky and Popeo, P.C., Boston, 1974—. Editor Boston Coll. Indsl. and Comml. Law Rev., 1960-61; student editor Ann. Survey Mass. Law, 1960-61. Fellow Am. Coll. Trial Laywers; mem. ABA, Practising Law Inst., Mass. Bar Assn., Boston Bar Assn. (chmn. com. on state ct. study 1991—). Office: Mintz Levin Cohn Ferris Glovsky & Popeo PC One Financial Center Boston MA 02111

POPHAM, ARTHUR COBB, JR., lawyer; b. Louisville, Mar. 31, 1915; s. Arthur C. and Ethel (Estes) P.; m. Mary Corzine, July 6, 1939; children: Carole Popham McKnight, Melinda Popham Benton, Arthur C. III; m. Phoebe T. Kennedy, Nov. 13, 1969. BA, U. Ariz., 1937; JD, U. Mo., 1939. Bar: Mo. 1939, U.S. Dist. Ct. (we. dist.) Mo. 1940. Assoc. Cowgill & Popham, Kansas City, Mo., 1939-40; ptnr. in successive firms to Popham Law Firm, P.C., Kansas City, 1940—, also bd. dirs. Author: Stalking Game From Desert to Tundra, 1986; contbr. articles on various topics to outdoor mags. Collector, PLanner Natural History Habitat Groups, Kansas City Mus., 1951-63; pres., bd. dirs. Kansas City Mus. History and Sci., 1952-85. Served ti 1st lt. USAAFA, 1942-45. Mem. ABA, Mo. Bar Assn., Kansas City Bar Assn., Boone and Crockett Club (v.p 1970-86) (Missoula, Mont.), Shikar Safari Internat. Club, Camp Fire Club of America (Chappaqua, N.Y.), Sigma Nu, Phi Delta Phi. Avocations: hunting, conservation groups. Home: 5521 Mission Dr Shawnee Mission KS 66208-1133 Office: Commerce Trust Bldg 922 Walnut St Kansas City MO 64106-1809

POPHAM, LEWIS CHARLES, III, hotel corporation executive, former university dean; b. N.Y.C., Sept. 18, 1928; s. Lewis Charles and Harriet (Andreas) P. Student, Trinity Sch., N.Y.C., 1946, East Stroudsburg U., 1946-48; BS, Am. U., 1950; AM, Harvard U., 1951. Lectr., asst. to dir. bus. affairs Am. U., Washington, 1951-54; asst. to pres. So. Conn. State U., New Haven, 1954-60; asst. to v.p. Cen. Mich. U., Mt. Pleasant, 1960-61; dir. gen. studies Dakota State Coll., Madison, S.D., 1961-63; chmn. div. social scis. Prince George's Community Coll., Largo, Md., 1963-64, acting pres., 1964-65; dean continuing edn. Orange County Community Coll., SUNY, Middletown, 1965-73, dean continuing edn. SUNY, Oswego, 1973-87, dean emeritus, 1987—; bd. dirs. sec. Sky Top Lodges, Inc. and Pocono Hotels Corp. Producer, historian: (TV series) Explorations: The World and its Peoples, Sta. WNHC-TV, New Haven, 1956; host: (radio series) The College Speaks, Sta. KJAM, Madison, S.D., 1962-63. Chmn. Conn. br. Am. Ch. Union, 1958-60, nat. v.p., 1972-73. Fletcher scholar. Mem. New Eng. Tchr. Preparation Assn. (sec. 1957-60), Orgn. Am. Historians Assn., N.Y. state hist. assns., Western History Assn., Broadcast Edn. Assn., Assn. Higher Edn., Am. Assn. Sch. Adminstrs., Assn. Continuing Higher Edn. (dir., pres. 1978-79), Assn. Univ. Evening Colls. (former chmn. jr. coll. com.), Continuing Edn. Assn. N.Y. (past pres.), Nat. Univ. Extension Assn. (former regional chmn.), Omicron Delta Kappa, Soc. of Cincinnati, Alpha Sigma Phi, Delta Kappa Kappa. Republican. Episcopalian (past mem. council N.Y. diocese). Clubs: Elks, Kiwanis (past club pres.); Skytop (bd. govs.), Squadron A. Office: Sky Top Lodges Inc PO Box 11 Skytop PA 18357-0011

POPKIN, ROY SANDOR, emergency management consultant, writer, researcher; b. N.Y.C., Mar. 4, 1921; s. Louis and Zelda (Feinberg) P.; m. Dorothy R. Popkin, Apr. 28, 1943 (div. June 1971); children: Gail Popkin Ohnsman, Raymond Louis; m. Mary O'Rourke, June 26, 1971. Student, U. N.C., 1938-39, NYU, 1939-41. Various pub. relations and mgmt. positions ARC, Bklyn. and Washington, 1942-59; disaster dir. N.Y.C. chpt. ARC, 1959-60; asst. nat. dir. disaster services ARC, Washington, 1960-81, dep. nat. dir. disaster services, 1981-84; ret.; sr. environ. specialist, cons., researcher, writer, editor EPA, Washington, 1984—; sr. assoc. Rsch. Alternatives, Rockville, Md., 1968—; mem. task force Pres.'s Commn. on Three Mile Island, Washington, 1979-80; mem. task force to study recovery Hurricane Hugo NOAA and George Washington U. Author: History of ESSA, 1966, Desalination, Water For The World's Future, 1968, Technology of Necessity, 1970; corr. Bklyn. Eagle newspaper, 1943-44, reporter various publs., N.Y.C., 1942-59; contbr. editor Hazard Monthly (now Hazard Tech.); contbr. numerous articles to mags. Fire commr. S. Hempstead (N.Y) Fire Dist., 1959-60; bd. dirs. Garrett Park (Md.) Pub. Library, 1965-68, Community Psychiat. Clinic, Bethesda, Md., 1963-65, Natural Hazards Rsch. and Applications Ctr., U. Colo.; mem. adv. bd. Cumberland Hosp., Bklyn., 1959-60, 81—. Recipient Pub. Svc. award U.S. Weather Svc., Washington, 1984; fellow hazard assessment lab. Colo. State U., 1984—. Mem. Assn. States Flood Plains Mgrs., Internat. Desalination Assn., Nat. Water Supply Improvement Assn. Avocations: gardening, traveling. Home and Office: 2111 Hanover St Silver Spring MD 20910-2108

POPLE, JOHN ANTHONY, chemistry educator; b. Burnham, Somerset, Eng., Oct. 31, 1925; s. Herbert Keith and Mary Frances (Jones) P.; m. Joy Cynthia, Sept. 22, 1952; children: Hilary Jane, Adrian John, Mark Stephen, Andrew Keith. B.A. in Math., Cambridge U., Eng., 1946, M.A. in Math., 1950; Ph.D in Math., Cambridge U., 1951. Research fellow Trinity Coll., Cambridge U., Eng., 1951-54, lectr. in math., 1954-58; Ford vis. prof. chemistry Carnegie Inst. Tech., Pitts., 1961-62; Carnegie prof. chem. physics Carnegie-Mellon U., Pitts., 1964-74, J.C. Warner prof., 1974-91; prof. Northwestern U., Evanston, Ill., 1986—. Recipient Wolf Found. prize in chemistry, 1992. Fellow Royal Soc. London, AAAS; fgn. mem. NAS. Office: Northwestern U Sheridan Rd Evanston IL 60202

POPOFF, FRANK PETER, chemical company executive; b. Sofia, Bulgaria, Oct. 27, 1935; came to U.S. 1940; s. Eftim and Stoyanka (Kossoroff) P.; m. Jean Urse; children: John V., Thomas F., Steven M. B.S. in Chemistry, Ind. U., 1957, M.B.A., 1959. With The Dow Chem. Co., Midland, Mich., 1959—, exec. v.p., 1985-87, dir., pres., chief executive officer, 1987-92; chmn., CEO, dir. Dow Chemical Corp., Midland, Mich., 1992—; exec. v.p., then pres. Dow Chem. Europe subs., Horgen, Switzerland, 1976-85; bd. dirs. Dow Corning Corp., Am. Express, Chem. Bank & Trust Co., Chem. Fin. Corp., Midland. Mem. dean's adv. coun. Ind. U.; mem. vis. com. U. Mich. Sch. Bus.; mem. Pres.' Commn. Environ. Quality. Recipient Internat. Palladium medal, 1994, Société de Chimie Industrielle (Am. Section). Mem. Chem. Mfrs. Assn. (bd. dirs.), U.S. Coun. for Internat. Bus., Bus. Roundtable, Conf. Bd., Am. Chem. Soc. Office: Dow Chem Co 2030 Dow Ctr Midland MI 48674*

POPOFSKY, MELVIN LAURENCE, lawyer; b. Oskaloosa, Iowa, Feb. 16, 1936; s. Samuel and Fannye Charlotte (Rosenthal) P.; m. Linda Jane Seltzer, Nov. 25, 1962; children: Mark Samuel, Kaye Sylvia. BA in History summa cum laude, U. Iowa, 1958; BA in Jurisprudence (first class honors), Oxford U., Eng., 1960; LLB cum laude, Harvard U., 1962. Bar: Calif. 1962. Assoc. Heller, Ehrman, White & McAuliffe, San Francisco, 1962-69, ptnr., 1969—, mem. exec. com., 1980-93, chair, 1988-93. Contbr. articles to law jours. Bd. dirs. Mt. Zion Hosp., San Francisco, 1982-88, U.S. Dist. Ct. (no. dist.) Calif. Hist. Soc., 1988—, Jewish Home for Aged, San Francisco, 1989—, Rhodes scholar, 1958. Fellow Am. Bar Found., Am. Coll. Trial Lawyers; mem. ABA, Calif. Bar Assn., San Francisco Bar Assn., Bur. Nat. Affairs (adv. bd. antitrust sect.), Calif. Acad. Appellate Lawyers. Democrat. Jewish. Home: Apt 10 1940 Broadway St San Francisco CA 94109-2299 Office: Heller Ehrman 333 Bush St San Francisco CA 94104-2878

POPOV, EGOR PAUL, engineering educator; b. Kiev, Russia, Feb. 19, 1913; s. Paul T. and Zoe (Derabin) P.; m. Irene Zofia Jozefowski, Feb. 18, 1939; children—Katherine, Alexander. B.S., U. Calif., 1933; M.S., Mass. Inst. Tech., 1934; Ph.D., Stanford, 1946. Registered civil, structural and mech. engr., Calif. Structural engr., bldg. designer Los Angeles, 1935-39; asst. prodn. engr. Southwestern Portland Cement Co., Los Angeles, 1939-42; machine designer Goodyear Tire & Rubber Co., Los Angeles, 1942-43; design engr. Aerojet Corp., Calif., 1943-45; asst. prof. civil engring. U. Calif. at Berkeley, 1946-48, assoc. prof., 1948-53, prof., 1953-83, prof. emeritus, 1983—, chmn. structural engring. and structural mechanics div. structural engring. lab., 1956-60; Miller rsch. prof. Miller Inst. Basic Rsch. in Sci., 1968-69. Author: Mechanics of Materials, 1952, 2d edit. 1976, Introduction to Mechanics of Solids, 1968, Engineering Mechanics of Solids, 1990; Contbr. articles profl. jours. Recipient Disting. Tchr. award U. Calif.-Berkeley, 1976-77, Berkeley citation U. Calif.-Berkeley, 1983, Disting. Lectr. award Earthquake Engring. Rsch. Inst., 1993. Fellow AAAS (assoc.); mem. NAE, Am. Soc. Metals, Internat. Assn. Shell Structures (hon. mem.), ASCE (hon. mem., Ernst E. Howard award 1976, J. James R. Croes medal 1979, 82, Nathan M. Newmark medal 1981, Raymond C. Reese research prize

1986, Norman medal 1987, von Karman medal 1989), Soc. Exptl. Stress Analysis (Hetenyi award 1967, William M. Murray medallion 1986), Am. Soc. Engring. Edn. (Western Electric Fund award 1976-77, Disting. Educator award 1979), Am. Concrete Inst., Soc. Engring. Sci., Internat. Assn. Bridge and Structural Engring., Am. Inst. Steel Constrn. (adv. com. specifications, chmn. subcom. on seismic design), Sigma Xi, Chi Epsilon, Tau Beta Pi. Home: 2600 Virginia St Berkeley CA 94709-1031

POPOVA, NINA, dancer, choreographer, director; b. Novorossisk, USSR, 1922. Ed. in Paris, studied ballet with Olga Preobrajenska, Lubov Egorova, Anatole Vilzak, Anatole Oboukhov, Igor Schwezoff. Ballet debut with Ballet de la Jeunesse, Paris, London, 1937-39; soloist Original Ballet Russe, 1939-41, Ballet Theatre (now Am. Ballet), 1941-42, Ballet Russe de Monte Carlo, 1943, 47, Ballet Alicia Alonso, Cuba; mem. faculty Sch. Performing Arts, N.Y.C., from 1954; later artistic dir. Houston Ballet, 1975; tchr. Nat. Acad. Arts, Champaign, Ill., also N.Y.C., 1975—, now Eglevsky Ballet Sch., L.I.; tchr. ballet Mexico City, Mex.; asst. choreographer mus. comedy Birmingham So. Coll., Ala., 1960; numerous appearances on Broadway stage, TV; former mem. regular cast Your Show of Shows; currently teaching N.Y.C. Address: 33 Adams Sea Cliff NY 11579

POPOVICH, HELEN HOUSER, university administrator; b. El Paso, Tex., Nov. 19, 1935; m. James E. Popovich, Oct. 4, 1967 (dec. Apr. 1976); 1 son, Peter Edward; m. Donald G. MacConnel, Oct. 14, 1984. B.A., U. Tex., El Paso, 1955; M.A., U. Tex.-El Paso, 1958; Ph.D., U. Kans., 1965. Asst. prof. to assoc. prof., assoc. dean U. South Fla., Tampa, 1965-78; dean, v.p., acting pres. Winona (Minn.) State U., 1978-83; pres. Fla. Atlantic U., Boca Raton, 1983-89; pres. Ferris State U., Big Rapids, Mich., 1989-94, univ. advancement officer, 1994—. Bd. dirs. Winona LWV, 1980-82, Boca Raton United Way, 1983-89, Med. Investment Trust Fund, 1985-89, Rsch. and Tech. Inst. Amerikam; mem. Minn. Humanities Commn., St. Paul, 1980-83; v.p. Grand Rapids Econ. Coun., 1991. Mem. Am. Assn. Higher Edn., Am. Assn. State Colls. and Univs. (bd. dirs. 1988-93, sec.-treas. 1990-93), Grand Rapids Econ. Club (vice chairperson 1991-92, chairperson 1992-93), Delta Kappa Gamma, Omicron Delta Kappa, Phi Delta Kappa. Office: Ferris State University Big Rapids MI 49307

POPOVICH, PETER STEPHEN, lawyer, former state supreme court chief justice; b. Crosby, Minn., Nov. 27, 1920; s. Peter and Rose Mary (Mehelich) P.; children: Victoria, Dorothy, Stephen, Susan Jane; stepchildren: Michelle, Paul, Stephen; m. Gail Prince Javorina, July 5, 1985. AA, Hibbing (Minn.) Jr. Coll., 1940; BA, U. Minn., 1942; LLB, St. Paul Coll. of Law, 1947; LLD (hon.), William Mitchell Coll. Law, 1991. Bar: Minn. 1947, U.S. Dist. Ct. Minn. 1947, U.S. Supreme Ct. 1956, U.S. Ct. Appeals (8th cir.) 1975. Sr. ptnr. Peterson & Popovich, St. Paul, 1947-83; chief judge Minn. Ct. Appeals, St. Paul, 1983-87; assoc. justice Minn. Supreme Ct., St. Paul, 1987-89, chief justice, 1989-90; ptnr. Briggs & Morgan, St. Paul, 1991—. Chmn. Minn. Statehood Centennial Com., 1955-59; rep. Minn. State Legis., St. Paul, 1953-63. Named Outstanding Minnesotan, Minn. Broadcasters Assn., 1983; recipient Dist. Svc. to Journalism award Minn. Newspaper Assn., 1991, John Finnegan Freedom of Info. award, 1991. Mem. ABA, Minn. Bar Assn. Minn. Hist. Soc. (hon. council). Roman Catholic. Avocations: boating, reading. Home: 2301 River Rd S Lakeland MN 55043-9777 Office: Briggs & Morgan 2200 1st Nat Bank Bldg Saint Paul MN 55101

POPOVICH, ROBERT P., biochemical engineer, educator; b. Sheboygan, Wis., Jan. 9, 1939. BS, U. Wis., 1963; MS, U. Wash., 1968, PhD in Chemical Engring., 1970. Chem. engr. Battelle Meml. Inst. Pacific Northwest Labs., 1963-65; teaching asst. chem. engring. U. Wash., 1965-70, asst. prof., 1970-72, from assoc. prof. to prof., 1970-83; prof. chem. and biochem. engring. U. Tex., 1983—; cons. chem. and biochem. engring. various pvt., pub. and govt. agys., 1972—; pres. Hemotherapy Instruments, Inc., 1974—; co-dir. Moncriet-Popovich Rsch. Inst. Inc., 1977—; biomed. engring. cons. Baxter-Travenol Labs. Inc., 1977—. Recipient Dialysis Pioneering award Nat. Kidney Found., 1983. Mem. AICE, Am. Soc. Artificial Internal Organs, Nat. Soc. Profl. Engrs., Am. Soc. Nephrol., European Dialysis & Transplant Assn., Internat. Soc. Peritoneal Dialysis. Achievements include research in industrial and biomedical applications of membrane systems, development of artificial internal organs, transport phenomena and biomedical instrumentation, continuous ambulatory peritoneal dialysis. Office: U Tex Austin Biomed Transport Lab ENS-610 Austin TX 78712

POPOVICI, ADRIAN, law educator; b. Bucharest, Rumania, Sept. 6, 1942; came to Can., 1951; s. Adrian and Alice (Moruzi) P.; children—Adrian, Alexandra. B.A., Stanislas Coll., Montreal, 1959; B.C.L., McGill U., 1962; D.E.S., U. Paris, 1965. Bar: Que. 1963. Prof. law U. Montreal, Que., Can., 1968—. Author: L'Outrage au Tribunal, 1977, La Couleur du Mandat, 1985; editor: Problèmes de Droit Contemporain, 1974. Roman Catholic. Home: 5589 Canterbury, Montreal, PQ Canada H3T 1S8 Office: U Montreal Faculte de Droit, CP 6128 Succursale A, Montreal, PQ Canada H3C 3J7

POPOVICS, SANDOR, civil engineer, educator, researcher; b. Budapest, Hungary, Dec. 24, 1921; came to U.S., 1957; s. Milan and Erzsebet (Droppa) P.; m. Lea M. Virtanen, Aug. 29, 1960; children: John, Lisa. 1st Degree in Civil Engring., Poly. U., Budapest, Hungary, 1944; Advanced Degree in Civil Engring., Poly. U., 1956; PhD, Purdue U., 1961. Registered profl. engr., Ala., Ariz., Pa. Rsch. engr. Met. Lab., Budapest, 1944-48; adj. prof. Tech. Coll., Budapest, 1949-52; rsch. engr., mgr. Inst. for Bldg. Scis., Budapest, 1949-56; grad. asst. Purdue U., Lafayette, Ind., 1957-59; prof. engring. Auburn (Ala.) U., 1959-69; prof. civil engring. No. Ariz. U., Flagstaff, 1968-76; prof. engring. King Abdulazziz U., Jeddah, Saudi Arabia, 1977-78; Samuel S. Baxter prof. civil engring. Drexel U., Phila., 1979-92, rsch. prof., 1992—; pres. Optimum Engring. Rsch. Author: Fundamentals of Pc Concrete, 1982, Concrete Materials, 1992, others; author more than 200 tech. papers in various langs. Recipient numerous grants and awards. Fellow ASCE (life), Am. Concrete Inst.; mem. ASTM, Ala. Acad. Scis., Ariz. Acad. Scis., Sigma Xi, Chi Epsilon. Avocations: jogging, music, fine art. Home and Office: 283 Congress Ave Lansdowne PA 19050-1206 Office: Drexel U Dept Civil Engring 32d and Chestnut Philadelphia PA 19104

POPP, JAMES ALAN, toxicologist, toxicology executive; b. Salem, Ohio, Mar. 13, 1945; s. John W. and Florence H. (Rowley) P.; m. Gloria Jean Paxton, Aug. 20, 1966; 1 child, Candice Renee. DVM summa cum laude, Ohio State U., 1968; PhD, U. Calif., Davis, 1972. Postdoctoral rsch. fellow Temple U. Sch. Medicine, Phila., 1972-74; asst. prof. U. Fla., Gainesville, 1974-78; scientist Chem. Industry Inst. Toxicology, Research Triangle Park, N.C., 1978-84, dept. head, 1984-93, v.p., 1989-93; v.p. Sterling Winthrop Inc., Collegeville, Pa., 1993-94, Sanofi Winthrop Inc., Collegeville, Pa., 1994—; mem. bd. sci. counselors Nat. Inst. Environ. Health Scis., Research Triangle Park. Editor mouse liver neoplasia Current Perspectives, 1984, mouse liver carcinogenesis Mechanisms and Species Comparisons, 1990. Recipient George H. Scott award Toxicology Forum, 1992; Borden scholar. Mem. Am. Soc. for Investigative Pathology, Am. Assn. Cancer Rsch., Am. Coll. Vet. Pathologists (councilor), Soc. for Toxicology, Phi Eta Sigma, Phi Zeta, Phi Kappa Phi. Office: Sanofi Winthrop Inc PO Box 8000 5250 S Collegeville Rd Collegeville PA 19426-0900

POPP, NATHANIEL, bishop; b. Aurora, Ill., June 12, 1940; s. Joseph and Vera (Boytor) P. BA, Ill. Benedictine U., 1962; ThM, Pontifical Gregorian U., 1966. Ordained priest, 1966, bishop, 1980. Parish priest Holy Cross Romanian Orthodox Ch., Hermitage, Pa., 1975-80; aux. bishop Romanian Orthodox Episcopate of Am., Orthodox Ch. in Am., Jackson, Mich., 1980-84, ruling bishop, 1984—; mem. Holy Synod, Orthodox Ch. in Am., Syosset, N.Y., 1980—; participant Monastic Consultation, WCC, Cairo, 1979, 7th Assembly, Vancouver, Can., 1983. Author: Holy Icons, 1969; working editor: (monthly newspaper) Solia. Chmn. bd. Romanian-Am. Heritage Ctr., Grass Lake, Mich. Mem. Mineral and Rock Soc. Mich. Home: 2522 Grey Tower Rd Jackson MI 49201-9120 Address: PO Box 309 Grass Lake MI 49240-0309

POPP, PENELOPE JEAN, health facility administrator; b. Buffalo, Jan. 22, 1938; d. Arthur Morris and Edith Clara (Ireland) P. BSN, U. Buffalo, 1960; MS in Nursing, Wayne State U., 1977. RN, Pa. Asst. chief evenings night svcs. VA Med. Ctr., Buffalo; asst. chief nursing svc. VA Med. Ctr., Allen Park, Mich.; assoc. med. ctr. dir. for nursing programs VA Med. Ctr., Wilkes-Barre, Pa.; adj. prof. nursing Coll. Misericordia. Mem. Nurse

Adminstrs. Forum N.E. Pa., Sigma Theta Tau (Zeta Psi chpt., Excellence in Leadership award 1989). Home: 45 Yorktown Rd Wilkes Barre PA 18707-2242

POPPA, RYAL ROBERT, manufacturing company executive; b. Wahpeton, N.D., Nov. 7, 1933; s. Ray Edward and Annabelle (Phillips) P.; m. Ruth Ann Curry, June 21, 1952; children: Sheryl Lynn, Kimberly Marie. BBA, Claremont Men's Coll., 1957. Sales trainee IBM, L.A., 1957-59, sales rep. 1959-62, product mktg. rep., 1963, sales mgr., 1964-66; v.p., gen. mgr. Comml. Computers Inc., L.A., 1966-67; v.p. Greyhound Computer Corp., Chgo., 1967-68, pres., chief exec. officer, bd. dirs. 1969-70; pres., chief exec. officer, bd. dirs., mem. exec. com. Data Processing Fin. & Gen., Hartsdale, N.Y., 1970-72; exec. v.p., chief fin. officer, bd. dirs., mem. exec. com. Mohawk Data Sci. Corp., Utica, N.Y., 1972-73; pres., chief exec. officer Pertec Computer Corp., L.A., 1973-81, BMC Industries, Inc., St. Paul, 1982-85; pres., chmn., chief exec. officer Storage Tech. Corp., Louisville, Colo., 1985—; founder Charles Babbage Inst. Trustee Claremont Men's Coll.; mem. Chmn.'s Circle Colo. Reps.; past mem. Pres. Com. Nat. Medal of Sci. Recipient Exec. of Yr. award U. Colo. MBA Alum Assn. 1986, Community Svc. award Inst. Human Rels. Am. Jewish Com., 1980, Colo. Bus. Leader of Yr. award CACI, 1991. Mem. Computer and Comm. Industry Assn. (chmn., past bd. dirs., mem. exec. com., vice chmn.), Am. Electronics Assn. (past bd. dirs., mem. exec. com. Colo. chpt.), Electronic Mfrs. Club, Boulder Country Club. Office: Storage Tech Corp 2270 S 88th St Louisville CO 80027-9717

POPPE, FRED CHRISTOPH, advertising agency executive; b. Bklyn., Dec. 26, 1923; s. Fred G. and Laura (Funk) P.; m. Inez Hanssen, Oct. 2, 1952; children: Steven Hammond, Ellen Jane. Student, Adm. Farragut Acad., Toms River, NJ, 1940-41, Bklyn. Poly. Inst., 1941-42; A.B., Princeton U., 1948. Copywriter Fuller & Smith & Ross, Inc., N.Y.C., 1948-51; advt. mgr. Yale & Towne Mfg. Co., 1951-53; group account supr. G.M. Basford Co., N.Y.C., 1953-59; mgr. account devel. Donahue & Coe, Inc., N.Y.C., 1959-60; exec. v.p. T.N. Palmer, Inc., N.Y.C., 1960-63; pres. Complan, Inc., N.Y.C., 1963-74; pres., chmn. emeritus Poppe Tyson Inc., N.Y.C., 1986—; bd. dirs. Inter-Ad Ltd., Skills Unlimited Inc. Author: The Hundred Greatest Corporate and Industrial Ads, 1983, 50 Rules to Keep a Client Happy, 1987, 100 New Greatest Corporate Ads, 1993. Served with USNR, 1941-46. Named Advt. Agy. Man of Yr., N.Y. Bus./Mktg. Assn., 1966-67. Mem. Bus./Mktg. Assn. (past pres., G.C. Crain award, Advt. Hall of Fame 1981, Communicator of Yr. 1983), Gt. South Bay Yacht Racing Assn., Princeton Club (N.Y.C.), Stuart Yacht and Country Club (Fla.), Elm Club (Princeton, N.J.), Southward Ho Country Club (Bay Shore, N.Y.), Magoun Landing Yacht Club (West Islip, N.Y.), Babylon Yacht Club (N.Y.). Republican. Home: 3713 SE Fairway E Stuart FL 34997-6117 also: 133 Tahlulah Ln West Islip New York NY 11795 Office: Poppe Tyson 40 W 23rd St New York NY 10010-5200

POPPE, KENNETH C., school system administrator. Supt. Wall (S.D.) Sch. Dist. 51-5; del. Am. Assn. Sch. Adminstrs. Nat. Conf., 1995. State finalist Nat. Supt. Yr., 1993. Mem. S.D. Sch. Supts. Assn. (pres. 1994-95). Office: Wall Sch Dist 51-5 512 Norris St Wall SD 57790

POPPEL, HARVEY LEE, management consultant; b. Bklyn., Dec. 18, 1937; s. Frank M. and Fannie (Axenzow) P.; m. Emily A. Daigneault, Jan. 2, 1959; children: Marc F., Clinton S. BS, Rensselaer Poly. Inst., 1958, MS, 1959. Sr. info. systems analyst Westinghouse Electric Corp., Pitts., 1959-65; mgr. industry systems Western Union, Paramus, N.J., 1965-67; assoc., cons. Booz, Allen & Hamilton, N.Y.C., 1967-69, v.p., 1969-72, sr. v.p., 1972-84, mem. operating council, 1973-84; pres. Poptech, Inc., Sarasota, Fla., 1984—; mng. dir. Broadview Assocs., Ft. Lee, 1984—; mem. panel, lectr. on computers, comms. and info. industry; judge Entrepreneur of Yr., 1991, 93, 94, 95. Co-author: Information Technology: The Trillion Dollar Opportunity, 1987; contbr. articles to profl. jours. Mem. Aspen Inst. Fellows, Inst. Mgmt. Cons., Soc. Mgmt. Info. Systems (exec. council), Zeta Psi. Club: Road Runners. Office: 1875 S Grant St San Mateo CA 94402

POPPEL, SETH RAPHAEL, business executive; b. Bklyn., Mar. 17, 1944; s. Frank M. and Fritzi R. (Axenzow) P.; BS magna cum laude, L.I. U., 1965; MBA, Columbia U., 1967; m. Danine Vokt, Jan. 5, 1974; children: Clarysa, Jared, Stacy. Asst. prof. L.I. U., Greenvale, N.Y., 1967-68; v.p. Synergistic Systems Corp., N.Y.C., 1968-77; v.p., dir. corp. planning Chase Manhattan Corp., N.Y.C., 1977-90; chmn., pres. Am. Vision Ctrs., N.Y.C., 1990—; owner harness horses Seth Poppel Stables, 1983—; founder, owner, operator Seth Poppel Yearbook Archives, 1986—. E.I. DuPont fellow, 1965-67; Downie Muir fellow, 1965-66; recipient Claire F. Adler award in math., 1964-65, Mepham High Sch. Hall of Fame award, 1993. Mem. Am. Statis. Assn., Ops. Research Soc. Am., Inst. Mgmt. Sci., Nat. Assn. Bus. Economy, N.Am. Soc. Corp. Planning, U.S. Trotting Assn., Beta Gamma Sigma, Psi Chi, Omega Epsilon. Home: 38 Range Dr Merrick NY 11566-3233 Office: 90 John St New York NY 10038-3202

POPPELIERS, JOHN CHARLES, architectural historian; b. Binghamton, N.Y., Oct. 5, 1935; s. Johannes Marinus and Irene (Marx) P.; m. Julia Margaret Tatnell, Dec. 16, 1967. AB, Hamilton Coll., 1957; MA, U. Pa., 1962; PhD, Cath. U. of Am., 1975. Instr. history and English various high schs., Binghamton, Johnson City, 1957-58, 60-62; sr. editor, architectural historian Historic Am. Bldgs. Survey, Dept. Interior, 1962-72, chief, 1972-80; chief ops. and tng. Divsn. Cultural Heritage, Unesco, 1980-86; internat. liaison Officer for Cultural Resources, U.S. Nat. Park Svc., 1986—; rep. for exec. and consultative coms. for internat. campaigns to safeguard Moenjodaro (Pakistan), Göreme and Istanbul (Turkey), Tyr (Lebanon) Unesco; curator Smithsonian Traveling Exhbns. on Archtl. History. Author: HABS Massachusetts Catalog, 1965; author: (with Nancy B. Schwartz and S. Allen Chambers) What Style Is It?; contbr. articles to profl. jour.; editor many tech. reports. Fulbright-Hays rsch. grantee, U. Vienna, 1968-69; grad. fellow U. Pa., 1960-62, Catholic U. Am., 1966-68; recipient History Dept. award Hamilton Coll., 1957. Fellow Internat. Coun. on Monuments and Sites (U.S. com. 1990, bd. trustees, asst. sec.-treas.); mem. AIA (cons. mem. com. on historic resources), Nat. Trust for Hist. Preservation, Cosmos Club, Soc. of Arch. Historians (com. on arch. preservation, former pres. Latrobe chpt.), Com. for the Preservation of Architectural Records, Nat. Preservation Inst. (dir. for edn. 1988-92), Nat. Trust Libr. (bd. advisors 1988—), Secular Franciscan Order. Roman Catholic. Avocations: vol. charitable causes, ecology, painting, music. Home: 2939 Van Ness St NW # 606 Washington DC 20008-4622 Office: US Nat Park Svc PO Box 37127 Washington DC 20013-7127

POPPEN, ALVIN J., religious organization administrator. Dir., office ministry and pers. svcs. Reformed Ch. in Am., N.Y.C. Office: Reformed Church in Am 475 Riverside Dr Rm 1811 New York NY 10115-0001

POPPENHAGEN, RONALD WILLIAM, newspaper editor, publishing executive; b. Chgo., Feb. 23, 1948; s. Andrew Charles and Elaine Edith (Larson) P.; m. Judy Diane Wagenblast, July 25, 1981. BA. in History and Lit., Augustana Coll., 1970. Reporter Sta. KBUR, Burlington, Iowa, 1970-71, Sta. KROS, Clinton, Iowa, 1971-72; reporter Sta. WDWS, Champaign, Ill., 1972-73, news dir., 1973-77; reporter The Morning Courier, Urbana, Ill., 1977-79; mng. editor The Daily Journal, Wheaton, Ill., 1979-80; met. editor The Southern Illinoisan, Carbondale, Ill., 1980-83; editor Green Bay (Wis.) News Chronicle, 1983-86, editor, general mgr., 1986—. Recipient Best Editorials award Wis. Newspaper Assn., 1985, 88, 93, UPS, 1983-86, Best Local Column award, 1993. Avocation: railroads. Office: Green Bay News Chronicle 133 S Monroe Ave Green Bay WI 54301-4056

POPPENSIEK, GEORGE CHARLES, veterinary scientist, educator; b. N.Y.C., June 18, 1918; s. George Frederick and Emily Amelia (Miller) P.; m. Edith M. Wallace, July 3, 1943; children: Neil Allen, Leslie Marion. Student, Cornell U., 1936-37, M.S., 1951; student, U. Pa., 1937-42, V.M.D., 1942. Diplomate Am. Bd. Microbiology, Am. Coll. Vet. Microbiology (charter), Am. Coll. Vet. Preventive Medicine (hon.). Asst. instr. medicine U. Pa. Sch. Vet. Medicine, 1943; asst. prof. vet. sci. U. Md., 1943-44; head dept. vet. virus vaccine prodn. Lederle Labs. div. Am. Cyanamid Co., 1944-49; dir. diagnostic lab. N.Y. State Coll. Vet. Medicine Cornell U., 1949-51, research assoc. Vet. Virus Research Inst., 1951-55; veterinarian Plum Island Animal Disease Ctr., animal disease and parasite research div.

Agrl. Research Service, U.S. Dept. Agr., 1955-56, acting-in-charge diagnostic investigations, 1956-58, charge immunological investigations, 1958-59; dean and prof. microbiology N.Y. State Coll. Vet. Medicine, Cornell U., 1959-74, James Law prof. comparative medicine, 1974-88, dean emeritus, James Law prof. comparative medicine emeritus, 1988—; guest prof. U. Bern, Switzerland, 1975; mem. exam. com. Nat. Bd. Vet. Med. Examiners, 1976-79; bd. dirs. Cornell Research Found., 1963-74; chmn. bd. dirs. Cornell Veterinarian, Inc., 1976-86. Recipient Certificate of Merit award U.S. Dept. Agr., 1958; citation Sch. Vet. Med., U. Pa., 1978, Centennial medals U. Pa., 1984, Ohio State U., 1985; others. Charter fellow Am. Acad. Microbiology; fellow AAAS; charter mem. Am. Soc. Virology; mem. AVMA, N.Y. State Vet. Med. Soc. (disting. life), Am. Bd. Microbiology, U.S Animal Health Assn., Assn. Am. Vet. Med. Colls. (pres. 1970-71), So. Tier Vet. Med. Assn., Am. Vet. Radiology Soc., Am. Soc. for Microbiology, N.Y. Agrl. Soc. (life), Argentine Nat. Acad. Agronomy and Vet. Medicine (hon.), Societas Polona Medicinae Veterinariae (hon.), Sigma Xi, Phi Kappa Phi, Alpha Psi, Omega Tau Sigma, Phi Zeta. Congregationalist. Home: 122 E Remington Rd Ithaca NY 14850-1456

POPPER, ARTHUR N., zoology educator; b. N.Y.C., May 9, 1943; s. Martin and Evelyn (Levine) P.; m. Helen Apfel, Nov. 30, 1968; children: Michelle, Melissa. BA, NYU, 1964; PhD, CUNY, 1969. Asst. prof. zoology U. Hawaii, Honolulu, 1969-72; assoc. prof. zoology U. Hawaii, 1972-78; assoc. prof. dept. anatomy & cell biology Georgetown U., Washington, 1978-83; prof. dept. anatomy & cell biology Georgetown U., 1983-87; prof., chmn. dept. zoology U. Md., College Park, 1987—; adj. sr. scientist Mote Marine Lab., Sarasota, Fla., 1979—. Editor: Comparative Studies of Hearing in Vertebrates, 1980, Hearing and Sound Communication in Fishes, 1981, Sensory Biology of Aquatic Animals, 1988, Evolutionary Biology of Hearing, 1992, Springer Handbook of Auditory Research, 1992. Recipient Research Career Devel. award NIH, 1978-83. Fellow AAAS; mem. Soc. for Neurosci., Acoustical Soc. Am., Assn. for Rsch. in Otolaryngology, Internat. Soc. Neurothology, Sigma Xi. Office: U Md Dept Zoology College Park MD 20742

POPPER, ROBERT, law educator, former dean; b. N.Y.C., May 22, 1932; s. Walter G. and Dorothy B. (Kluger) P.; m. Mary Ann Schaefer, July 12, 1963; children: Julianne, Robert Gregory. BS, U. Wis., 1953; LLB, Harvard U., 1956; LLM, NYU, 1963. Bar: N.Y. 1957, U.S. Dist. Ct. (so. dist.) N.Y. 1962, U.S. Ct. Appeals (2d cir.) 1962, U.S. Supreme Ct. 1962, U.S. Dist. Ct. (ea. dist.) N.Y. 1969, U.S. Ct. Appeals (7th cir.) 1970, U.S. Ct. Appeals (8th cir.) 1971, Mo. 1971, U.S. Dist. Ct. (we. dist.) Mo. 1973. Trial atty. criminal br. N.Y.C. Legal Aid Soc., 1960-61; asst. dist. atty. N.Y. County, 1961-64; assoc. Seligson & Morris, N.Y.C., 1964-69; mem. faculty School of Law, U. Mo., Kansas City, 1969—, prof., 1973—, acting dean, 1983-84, dean, 1984-93, cons. and lectr. in field. Author: Post Conviction Remedies in a Nutshell, 1978, De-Nationalizing the Bill of Rights, 1979; contbr. articles to profl. jours. Mem. N.Y. State Bar Assn., Mo. Bar Assn., Kansas City Met. Bar Assn., Lawyers Assn. Kansas City. Office: U Mo Kansas City Sch Law 500 E 52nd St Kansas City MO 64110-2467

POPPER, ROBERT DAVID, computer and management consultant; b. Budapest, Hungary, Dec. 10, 1927; came to U.S., 1950; s. Eugene Andrew and Ilona Angela (Nagy) P.; m. Mary Elizabeth Metzel, June 26, 1956; children: Ilona, Robert, Thomas, Margaret, Emily, John, Edward. BA, George Washington U., 1959, MA, 1961; postgrad., Yale U., 1961-64. Assoc. rsch. scientist Human Scis. Rsch., Inc., Washington, 1959-62; cons. Dunlap and Assocs., Darien, Conn., 1962-65; dir. ops. rsch. and systems devel. Glidden Co., Cleve., 1965-70; dir. corp. MIS Sandoz, Basle, Switzerland, 1970-72; sr. v.p. strategic planning and MIS U.S. Trust Co., N.Y.C., 1972-80; sr. v.p. MIS J. Walter Thompson Co., N.Y.C., 1980-82; pres. info. products group Squibb Corp., Lawrenceville, N.J., 1982-87; chief exec. officer New Dimensions Cons., Princeton, N.J., 1982—. Trustee Buxton Sch., Williamstown, Mass., 1987—. With U.S. Army, 1956-58. Co-author: The Physical Effects of Nuclear Attack, 1961. Mem. Am. Econ. Assn., Am. Statis. Assn., Am. Math. Assn., Data Processing Mgmt. Assn., Am. Arbitration Assn., Yale Club (N.Y.C.). Republican. Roman Catholic. Avocations: hunting, chess, reading. Office: New Dimensions Cons Inc 539 Kingston Rd Princeton NJ 08540-4058

POPPER, VIRGINIA SOWELL, education educator; b. Macon, Ga., Sept. 10, 1945; d. Clifford E. and Hazel (Sewell) Sowell; m. James Clarence Sikes, June 24, 1967 (div. 1989); children: Zachary Andrew, Cristen Elizabeth; m. Joseph W. Popper, Jr., Dec. 28, 1992. AB, Wesleyan Coll., Macon, 1967; MEd, U. North Fla., 1973; PhD, Ga. State U., 1991. Tchr. 6th grade Jones County Schs., Gray, Ga., 1966-67; tchr. 12th grade Richmond County Schs., Augusta, Ga., 1967-68; guidance counselor Aiken County Schs., North Augusta, S.C., 1968-69, asst. prin., 1969-71; dir. Durham (N.C.) campus Kings Coll., 1974-77; rsch. asst. Ga. Dept. Edn., Atlanta, 1983-85; assoc. prof. tchr. edn. Mercer U., Macon, 1989—; tchr. cultural studies exch. program Scinanto Gakuin Coll. of Kitakusha, Japan-Mercer U. Contbg. author: Business in Literature, 1980; contbr. articles, reports to profl. publs. Chmn. Mid. Ga. Regional Libr. System, Macon, 1989-91; bd. dirs. Jr. League Macon, Macon YWCA, Macon Intown, Macon Heritage Found., Bibb County Am. Cancer Soc., March of Dimes, Macon Ballet, Friends of Libr., Gladys Lasky Weller Scholarship Found., Mayor's Lit. Task Force. Mem. ASCD, Assn. Tchr. Educators, Ga. Coun. Social Studies, Kappa Delta Lambda, Pi Lambda Theta. Republican. Episcopalian. Home: 798 Saint Andrews Dr Macon GA 31210-4769 Office: Univ Coll Mercer Tift College Dr Forsyth GA 31029

POPPERS, PAUL JULES, anesthesiologist, educator; b. Enschede, Netherlands, June 30, 1929; came to U.S., 1958; naturalized, 1963; s. Meyer and Minca (Ginsburg) P.; m. Ann Feinberg, June 3, 1969; children: David Matthew, Jeremy Samuel. MD, U. Amsterdam, 1955. Diplomate Am. Bd. Anesthesiology. Instr. anesthesiology Columbia U., N.Y.C., 1962-63, assoc., 1963-65, asst. prof. anesthesiology, 1965-71, assoc. prof. anesthesiology, 1971-74; prof., vice chmn. dept. anesthesiology NYU, 1974-79; prof., chmn. dept. anesthesiology SUNY, Stony Brook, 1979—; cons. Brookdale Med. Ctr., Bklyn., 1975—, VA Med. Ctr., Northport, N.Y., 1979—, The N.Y. Hosp. Med. Ctr. of Queens (formerly Booth Meml. Hosp.), Flushing, N.Y., 1979—, L.I. Jewish Med. Ctr., New Hyde Park, N.Y., 1980—, Eastern L.I. Hosp., Greenport, N.Y., 1995—, Am. Hosp. Paris, 1989-93; cons., lectr. USN Regional Med. Ctr., Portsmouth, Va., 1975-83. Author: Regional Anesthesia, 1977; editor: Beta Blockade and Anaesthesia, 1979; sect. editor Jour. Clin. Anesthesia, 1990—; mem. editorial bd. Internat. Jour. Clin. Monitoring and Computing, 1990—; internat. bd. editors Anaesthesiology Digest, 1991-94; contbr. numerous articles to profl. jours. NIH postdoctoral rsch. fellow, 1961; recipient medal Polish Acad. Scis., Poland, 1987, Univ. medal Jagiellonian U., Krakow, Poland, 1987, 1st Sci. award Post-grad. Assembly in Anesthesiology; named Hon. Prof. Anesthesiology, U. Leiden, The Netherlands, 1977. Fellow Am. Coll. Anesthesiology, Am. Coll. Ob-Gyns., Royal Soc. Medicine, Post-Grad. Assembly in Anesthesiology (hon. chmn. 1989—); mem. Am. Soc. Anesthesiologists, Assn. Univ. Anesthesiologists, Soc. Acad. Anesthesia Chmn., Internat. Anesthesia Rsch. Soc., Soc. Obstetric Anesthesia and Perinatology, Am. Soc. Regional Anesthesia, Jerusalem Acad. Medicine, Am. Soc. Pharmacology and Exptl. Therapeutics, Fedn. Am. Soc. Exptl. Biology, Sigma Xi. Office: Health Scis Ctr Suny Sch Medicine Stony Brook NY 11794-8480

POPPLER, DORIS SWORDS, lawyer; b. Billings, Mont., Nov. 10, 1924; d. Lloyd William and Edna (Mowre) Swords; m. Louis E. Poppler, June 11, 1949; children: Louis William, Kristine, Mark J., Blaine, Claire Arminda. Student, U. Minn., 1942-44; JD, Mont. State U., 1948. Bar: Mont. 1948, U.S. Dist. Ct. Mont. 1948, U.S. Ct. Appeals (9th cir.) 1990. Pvt. practice law Billings, 1948-49; sec., treas. Wonderpark Corp., Billings, 1959-62; atty. Yellowstone County Attys. Office, Billings, 1972-75; ptnr. Poppler and Barz, Billings, 1972-79, Davidson, Veeder, Baugh, Broeder and Poppler, Billings, 1979-84, Davidson and Poppler, P.C., Billings, 1984-90; U.S. atty. Dist. of Mont., Billings, 1990-93; field rep. Nat. Indian Gaming Commn., Washington, 1993—. Pres. Jr. League, 1964-65; bd. dirs., pres. Yellowstone County Metre Bd. 1982; trustee Rocky Mt. Coll., 1989-90, mem. nat. adv. bd., 1993—; mem. Mont. Human Rights Commn., 1988-90. Recipient Mont. Salute to Women award, Mont. Woman of Achievement award, 1975, Disting. Svc. award Rocky Mt. Coll., 1990. Mem. AAUW, Mont. Bar Assn., Nat. Assn. Former U.S. Attys., Nat. Rep. Lawyers Assn.,

Internat. Women's Forum, Yellowstone County Bar Assn. (pres. 1990), Alpha Chi Omega. Republican. Office: Nat Indian Gaming Commn 1850 M St NW Ste 210 Washington DC 20005

POP-STOJANOVIC, ZORAN RISTA, mathematics educator; b. Belgrade, Yugoslavia, May 30, 1935; arrived in U.S., 1965; s. Rista and Cveta (Lazarevic) P-S.; Mary Frances Torraca, Dec. 15, 1966 (div. 1973) 1 child, Diana Lynn. BS in Math., U. Belgrade, Yugoslavia, 1958, PhD in Math., 1964. Instr. math. U. Belgrade, 1958-62, docent for math., 1963-65; rsch. fellow Hebrew U., Jerusalem, 1962-63; asst. prof. math. U. Fla., Gainesville, 1965-68, assoc. prof., 1968-72, prof., 1972—; co-dir. Ctr. Applied Math. U. Fla., 1991—. Contbr. papers to profl. jours. Mem. Am. Math. Soc. Office: U Fla Ctr Applied Math 201 Walker Hall Gainesville FL 32611

PORAY, JOHN LAWRENCE, professional association executive; b. Rochester, N.Y., Nov. 9, 1955; s. Jack Loysen and Jane Ann (Williams) P.; m. Rebecca Sue Wells, June 16, 1979 (div. Jan. 1993); children: John Lawrence Jr., David Scott. AA in Liberal Arts, Monroe C.C., Rochester, 1975; BA in Human Rels., Salem (W.Va.) Coll., 1977. Sr. dist. exec. Ctrl. Ohio Coun. Boy Scouts Am., Columbus, 1977-83; asst. exec. dir. Columbus Apt. Assn., 1983-88, Apt. Assn. Ind., Indpls., 1988-92; exec. dir. Soc. Broadcast Engrs., Indpls., 1992—. Youth coach Plainfield (Ind.) Optimist Club, 1988-95; moderator 1st Bapt. Ch., Plainfield, 1995—. Mem. Am. Soc. Assn. Execs. (cert.), Ind. Soc. Assn. Execs. Office: Soc Broadcast Engrs Inc 8445 Keystone Crossing Ste 140 Indianapolis IN 46240

PORCELLO, LEONARD JOSEPH, engineering research and development executive; b. Mar. 1, 1934; s. Stephen James and Mary Josephine (Bacchi) P.; m. Patricia Lucille Berger, July 7, 1962 (dec. Sept. 1991); children—John Joseph, Thomas Gregory. B.A. in Physics, Cornell U., 1955; M.S. in Physics, U. Mich., 1957, M.S. in Elec. Engring, 1959, Ph.D. in Elec. Engring, 1963. Research asst. U. Mich., Ann Arbor, 1955-58; instr. elec. engring. U. Mich., 1958-61; research engr. Radar & Optics Lab., 1968-72; asso. dir. Willow Run Labs., 1970-72, asso. prof., 1969-72, prof., 1972-73, adj. prof., 1973-75; dir. radar and optics div. Environ. Rsch. Inst. of Mich., Ann Arbor 1973-76, v.p., 1973-76, trustee, 1975; asst. v.p., mgr. sensor systems operation Sci. Applications Internat. Corp., Tucson, 1976-79, v.p., 1979-85, corp. v.p., 1985-87, mgr. def. systems group, 1986-94, sr. v.p., 1987—, dep. mgr. tech. and advanced systems sector, 1993—, mgr. Applied Systems Group, 1995—. Bd. dirs. Tucson Jr. Strings, 1977-79, chmn., 1978-79. Fellow IEEE; mem. Optical Soc. Am., AAAS, Sigma Xi, Eta Kappa Nu. Roman Catholic. Research on imaging radar, synthetic aperture radar systems and radar remote sensing. Home: 13190 E Camino La Cebadilla Tucson AZ 85749-9324 Office: Sci Applications Internat Corp 5151 E Broadway Blvd Ste 900 Tucson AZ 85711-3713

PORFELI, JOSEPH J., computer and software development company, computer leasing company executive; b. 1947. BS in Bus. Administrn. and Mktg., Point Park Coll., 1969. With sales dept. Comshare, Inc., Bala Cymwyd, Pa., 1969-73; v.p. comms. svcs. Compuserve, Inc., Pitts., 1973-83; v.p. sales and mktg. Telenet Comms. Corp.-US Sprint, Plymouth Meeting, Pa., 1983-87; exec. v.p. Centex Telemanagement Corp., Pitts., 1987-89; with Electronic Info. Syss., Inc., Stamford, Conn., 1989—; now pres., CEO, chmn. bd. EIS Internat., Stamford, Conn. Office: EIS Internat Inc 1351 Washington Blvd Stamford CT 06902*

PORGES, WALTER RUDOLF, television news executive; b. Vienna, Nov. 26, 1931; s. Paul and Charlotte (Posamentier) P.; m. Jean Belle Mlotok, Dec. 22, 1953; children: Donald F., Marian E., Lawrence M. B.A., CCNY, 1953. News writer radio sta. WOR, N.Y.C., 1955-56, WCBS Radio and TV, N.Y.C., 1956-57; news writer ABC Radio Network, N.Y.C., 1958-60; news editor ABC Radio Network, 1960-63, asst. dir. radio news, 1963-65; asst. assignment mgr. ABC-TV, 1965-68; asso. producer ABC-TV Evening News, 1968-70, sr. producer, 1973-75; European producer ABC News, London, 1970-73; producer ABC-TV spl. events, N.Y.C., 1975-76; coordinating producer ABC News (Republican Nat. Conv.), 1976; editorial producer, chief writer ABC Evening News, 1976-77, sr. producer, 1977-80; sr. producer ABC World News Tonight, 1978-83; fgn. news dir. ABC News, N.Y.C., 1983-89, v.p. news practices, 1989-93; assoc. Exec. TV, 1993. Served with U.S. Army, 1953-55.

PORIES, WALTER JULIUS, surgeon, educator; b. Munich, Germany, Jan. 18, 1930; came to U.S., 1940; s. Theodore Francis and Frances (Lowin) P.; m. Muriel Helen Aronson, Aug. 18, 1951; children: Susan E., Mary Jane, Carolyn A., Kathy G.; m. Mary Ann Rose McCarthy, June 4, 1977; children: Mary Lisa, Michael McCarthy. BA, Wesleyan U., Middletown, Conn., 1952; MD with honors, U. Rochester, 1955. Diplomate: Am. Bd. Surgery, Am. Bd. Thoracic Surgery. Intern Strong Meml. Hosp., Rochester, N.Y., 1955-56, resident, 1958-62; chmn. dept. surgery Wright-Patterson AFB, Ohio, 1952-67; asst. prof. surgery and oncology U. Rochester, 1967-69; prof. surgery and assoc. chmn. dept. surgery U. Cleve., 1969-77; prof. surgery East Carolina U., Greenville, N.C., 1977—, chmn. dept. surgery, 1977—; chief surgery Pitt County Meml. Hosp., 1977—; prof. surgery U. Health Scis. of Uniformed Svcs., 1982—; founder, assoc. dir. Rochester Cancer Ctr., 1967-69; founder, dir. Cleve. Cancer Ctr., 1972-77, Hospice of Cleve., 1975; founder, chmn. bd. Hospice of Greenville, 1981; med. dir. Home Health Care of Greenville, 1978-83; founder, chmn. bd. Ctr. for Creative Living, 1985-91. Author: Clinical Applications of Zinc Metabolism, 1974; editor: Operative Surgery series, vols. 1-4, 1979-83, Office Surgery for Family Physicians, 1985; editor in chief Current Surgery, 1990—; editor Nat. Curriculum for Residency in Surgery, 1988—, mem. residency rev. com., 1992—; contbr. articles to profl. jours. Bd. dirs. Boy Scouts Am., Cleve., 1974-77, Greenville Arts Mus., 1980-82; pres., CEO, chmn. bd. dirs. Ea. Carolina Health Orgn. Maj. USAF, 1955-67; col. USAR, 1979-91, comdr. USAF Hosp., Durham, N.C.; activated Desert Shield, 1990. Decorated Legion of Merit; Thorndyke scholar, 1948-51; recipient McLester award USAF, 1966, Miss. Magnolia Cross, 1989, Presdl. citation for Desert Shield, 1994; named to Hon. Order of Ky. Cols., 1965. Fellow ACS, Am. Coll. Cardiology, Am. Coll. Chest Physicians; mem. Soc. for Vascular Surgery, Soc. Surg. Oncology, Soc. Univ. Surgeons, Am. Surg. Assn., Soc. Environ. Geochemistry (past pres.), Residency Rev. Com. for Surgery, So. Surg. Assn., Soc. for Thoracic Surgery, Ea. Carolina Health Orgn. (pres., chmn.), Assn. Program Dirs. in Surgery (pres.), N.C. Surg. Assn. (pres.), Phi Kappa Phi. Republican. Roman Catholic. Club: Country (Greenville). Home: Deep Sun Farm Rte 1 Box 427 Macclesfield NC 27852 Office: East Carolina U Dept Surgery Greenville NC 27858

PORILE, NORBERT THOMAS, chemistry educator; b. Vienna, Austria, May 18, 1932; came to U.S., 1947, naturalized, 1953; s. Irving and Emma (Intrator) P.; m. Miriam Eisen, June 16, 1957; 1 son, James. B.A., U. Chgo., 1952, M.S., 1954, Ph.D., 1957. Rsch. assoc. Brookhaven Nat. Lab., Upton, N.Y., 1957-59; assoc. chemist Brookhaven Nat. Lab., 1959-63, chemist, 1963-64; vis. prof. chemistry McGill U., 1963-65; assoc. prof. chemistry Purdue U., West Lafayette, Ind., 1965-69; prof. chemistry Purdue U., 1969—; rsch. collaborator Brookhaven Nat. Lab., Argonne Nat. Lab., Los Alamos Sci. Lab., Lawrence Berkeley Lab.; vis. prof. Facultes des Scis., Orsay, France; fellow Soc. Promotion of Sci. in Japan, Inst. Nuclear Study, U. Kyoto, 1961. Editor: Radiochemistry of the Elements and Radiochemical Techniques, 1986-90. John Simon Guggenheim meml. fellow Institut de Physique Nucleaire Orsay, 1971-72; recipient F.D. Martin Undergrad. Teaching award, 1977; Von Humboldt Sr. U.S. Scientist award Philipps U., Marburg, W. Ger., 1982. Mem. Am. Chem. Soc., Am. Phys. Soc. Office: Purdue U Dept Chemistry Chemistry Bldg Lafayette IN 47907

PORITZ, DEBORAH T., state attorney general. Atty. gen. State of N.J. Office: Law & Pub Safety Dept Justice Complex CN 080 Trenton NJ 08625-0080

PORIZKOVA, PAULINA, model, actress; b. Czechoslovakia, Apr. 9, 1965; came to U.S., 1982; m. Ric Ocasek; 1 child. Ind. model Europe and U.S., 1980-88; became model for Estee Lauder, 1988. Cover girl for numerous mags. including Cosmopolitan, Vogue, Women's Day, Sports Illustrated, Playboy; film acting debut: Anna, 1987, also appeared in Portfolio, 1987, Her Alibi, 1989. Office: Elite Model Management Corp 111 E 22d St 2d Fl New York NY 10010

POROSKY, MICHAEL HANNY, real estate and investment company executive; b. Detroit, Mar. 28, 1930; s. Walter Michael and Ruth (Hanny) P.; m. Paula Lea Dickinson; children: Michael Winston, Patrick Dickens, Wendy Christine. BA in Journalism, U. Wash., 1953. Agt. Phoenix Mut. Life Ins. Co., Seattle, 1957-66; pres. Profl. Cons. Cos., Seattle, 1967—. V.p. N.W. region Pacific N.W. Lawn Tennis Assn., 1974-78. Lt. commdr. USN, 1952-57; USNR, '57-68. Mem. Seattle Tennis Club. Republican. Avocation: competitive tennis.

POROSOFF, HAROLD, chemist, research and development director; b. Bklyn., Apr. 3, 1946; s. Solomon and Ruth (Goldberg) P.; m. Leslie Pamela Freiman, May 19, 1948; children: Lauren, Stephen, Marc. BS, MIT, 1966; PhD, Brown U., 1970. Various rsch. and mgmt. positions fibers div. Am. Cyanamid Co., Stamford, Conn. and Milton, Fla., 1970-78; various mgmt. positions Shulton Rsch. div. Am. Cyanamid Co., Clifton, N.J., 1978-83, dir., 1983-88; v.p. R & D chem. rsch. divsn Am. Cyanamid Co., Stamford, 1989-93; v.p. R & D Cytec Industries Inc., Stamford, 1993—. Patentee in field. Mem. AAAS, Am. Chem. Soc., N.Y. Acad. Scis. Office: Cytec Industries Inc PO Box 60 Stamford CT 06904-0060

POROW, MARIE-CARL, mental health nurse; b. Haiti, W.I., Mar. 14, 1941; m. Melvin Porow, Apr. 12, 1969; children: Marc Antoine, Monique Anne. Diploma, Montreal Gen. Hosp., 1967; BS, St. Francis Coll., Bklyn., 1976. RN, N.Y.; cert. mental health nurse. Staff nurse Kings County Hosp., Bklyn.; unit care coord. Gracie Square Hosp., N.Y.C. Recipient Naomi Graham Meml. prize Montreal Gen. Hosp. Mem. N.Y. State Nurses Assn. (co-chmn.).

PORRETTA, EMANUELE PETER, banker; b. N.Y.C., Aug. 4, 1942; s. Joseph Edward and Italia (Sesti) P.; m. Mary Valanzano, Apr. 18, 1964; children: Denise, Robert, Janice. Student, N.Y. Tech. Coll., 1960-61. Transfer clk. Mfrs. Trust Co., N.Y.C., 1961; sr. v.p. U.S. Trust Co., N.Y.C., 1984—; now sr. v.p., dir. adminstrv. services for instn. asst. services div. U.S. Trust Co.; mem. payment system com. N.Y. Clearing House, 1978-80, chmn. Bank Ops. Conf., 1981-82. Treas. Manalapan, N.J. Rep. campaign, 1980; mem. adv. com. Williams Coll. Exec. Program. Mem. Am. Mgmt. Assn., Am. Bankers Assn. Roman Catholic. Avocations: running, reading, golf. Office: US Trust Co of NY 770 Broadway New York NY 07726

PORT, SIDNEY CHARLES, mathematician, educator; b. Chgo., Nov. 27, 1935; s. Isadore and Sarah (Landy) P.; m. Idelle Jackson, Mar. 24, 1957; children—Ethan, Jonathan, Daniel. A.B., Northwestern U., 1957, M.S., 1958, Ph.D., 1962. Staff mathematician Rand Corp., 1962-66; assoc. prof. math. U. Calif. at Los Angeles, 1966-69, prof., 1969—. Author: (with P. Hoel and C. Stone) Probability, Statistics and Stochastic Processes, 1971, (with C. Stone) Brownian Motion and Classical Potential Theory, 1978, Theoretical Probability for Applications, 1993; contbr. articles to profl. jours. Fellow Inst. Math. Statistics; mem. Am. Math. Soc. Home: 680 Kingman Ave Santa Monica CA 90402-1334 Office: Univ Calif Los Angeles Los Angeles CA 90024

PORTAL, GILBERT MARCEL ADRIEN, oil company executive; b. Paris, Aug. 2, 1930; came to U.S., 1981; s. Emmanuel Jules and Henriette Josephine (Bonnard) P.; m. Monique Janine Adam, July 12, 1951; children: Dominique, Veronique, Marc-Emmanuel. Baccalaureate, Lycee Charlemagne U., Paris, 1949; Ingenieur Civil des Mines, Sch. of Mines, St. Etienne, 1955; diplome du C.P.A., Ctr. Advanced Bus., Paris, 1969; auditeur 30 eme session IHEDN, Higher Studies Nat. Defense, Paris, 1978. Geophysicist Societe Nationale Elf Aquitaine, Sahara, Algeria, 1957-63; exploration mgr. north sea Societe Nationale Elf Aquitaine, 1963-65, dep. exec. v.p. Europe, 1965-68, dep. exec. v.p. North and South Am., 1968-70; chief exec. officer Societe Nationale Elf Aquitaine, Iraq, 1970-72; dir., chief exec. officer Societe Nationale Elf Aquitaine, Gabon, Africa, 1972-76; dep. exec. v.p. hydrocarbons Societe Nationale Elf Aquitaine, 1976-78, exec. v.p. North Africa, Mid. East, Far East, 1978-82; pres. Elf Aquitaine Petroleum, Houston, 1982-89; chmn., chief exec. officer Elf Exploration, Inc., Houston, 1989-90; sec.-gen. European Petroleum Industry Assn., 1990—; bd. dirs. Sterling Chems., Houston, Sonat Offshore, Inc., Houston. Served to lt. French army, 1955-57. Decorated Legion of Honor (France), Nat. Merit Order (France); Equatorial Star (Gabon). Mem. Cercle Royal Gaulois Artistique et Littéraire. Roman Catholic. Office: European Petroleum Industry Assn, Madou Plaza 1 Place Madou, B-1030 Brussels Belgium

PORTAS, JOSE, oil industry executive. Sec., treas. PDV Am. Inc., N.Y.C. Office: PDV Am Inc 750 Lexington Ave Fl 10 New York NY 10022*

PORTE, DANIEL, JR., physician, educator, health facility administrator; b. N.Y.C., Aug. 13, 1931; s. Daniel and Marjorie Veronica (Clark) P.; m. Eunice Claire Ungerleider, Mar. 21, 1951; children—Jeffrey, Michael, Kenneth. B.A., Brown U., 1953; M.D., U. Chgo., 1957. Assoc. prof. medicine U. Wash., Seattle, 1969-73; prof. medicine U. Wash., 1973—; dir. U. Wash. Diabetes-Endocrinology Rsch. Ctr., 1977—; ACOS for research and devel. VA Med. Ctr., Seattle, 1971—; chief div. endocrinology and metabolism VA Med. Ctr., 1975—; chmn. med. sci. adv. bd. Juvenile Diabetes Found., N.Y.C., 1977-78; cons. Scripps Clinic and Research Found., San Diego, 1978-81; Connaught lectr. Can. Diabetes Assn., Toronto, Ont., 1984. Assoc. editor Am. Jour. Physiology, 1976-78, Jour. Diabetes, 1984—; contbr. numerous articles, chpts. to profl. publs., 1965—. Served to lt. comdr. USN, 1959-61. Recipient Career Devel. award NIH, 1968-70, David Rumbaugh award Juvenile Diabetes Found., 1984; Guggenheim fellow, 1985. Fellow ACP; mem. Assn. Am. Physicians, Am. Soc. Clin. Investigation, Am. Diabetes Assn. (pres. 1986-87, Eli Lilly award 1970), Am. Diabetes Assn. (Wash. affiliate) (pres. 1984-85), Western Assn. Physicians (councillor 1982-85). Avocation: skiing. Home: 2707 Boyer Ave E Seattle WA 98102-3931 Office: U Wash Diabetes-Endocrinology Rsch Ctr-VA Med Ctr 2B-21 1660 S Columbian Way Seattle WA 98108-1597

PORTE, JOEL MILES, English educator; b. Bklyn., Nov. 13, 1933; s. Jacob I. and Frances (Derison) P.; m. Ilana D'Ancona, June 17, 1962 (div. 1977); 1 child, Susanna Maria; m. Helene Sophrin, Oct. 18, 1985. A.B. magna cum laude, CCNY, 1957; A.M., Harvard U., 1958, Ph.D., 1962. Instr. English Harvard U., Cambridge, Mass., 1962-64, asst. prof., 1964-68, assoc. prof., 1968-69, prof., 1969-82, Bernbaum prof. of lit., 1982-87, chmn. English and Am. Lit. Dept., 1985-87; Frederic J. Whiton prof. of English Cornell U., Ithaca, N.Y., 1987-89, Ernest I. White prof. Am. Studies and Humane Letters, 1989—; vis. lectr. Am. Studies Research Ctr., Hyderabad, India, spring 1976. Author: Emerson and Thoreau: Transcendentalists in Conflict, 1966, The Romance in America: Studies in Cooper, Poe, Hawthorne, Melville and James, 1969, Representative Man: Ralph Waldo Emerson in His Time, 1979, In Respect to Egotism: Studies in American Romantic Writing, 1991; editor: Emerson in His Journals, 1982, Emerson: Prospect and Retrospect, 1982, Emerson: Essays and Lectures, 1983, New Essays on Portrait of a Lady, 1990. Scholar in Residence, Rockefeller Found., Bellagio, Italy, 1979; fellow John Simon Guggenheim Found., 1981-82. Mem. Am. Studies Assn., Am. Lit. Assn., Phi Beta Kappa. Home: 1405 Hanshaw Rd Ithaca NY 14850-2730 Office: Cornell U Dept Eng Rockefeller Hall Ithaca NY 14853

PORTENIER, WALTER JAMES, aerospace engineer; b. Davenport, Iowa, Oct. 9, 1927; s. Walter Cleveland and Doris Lucile (Williams) P.; m. Martha L. Dallam, Aug. 26, 1950 (dec. Apr. 1986); children: Andrea Ellen, Renee Suzanne; m. Patty Grosskopf Caldwell, Oct. 3, 1992. B in Aero Engring., U. Minn., 1950; MS in Aero Engring., U. So. Calif., 1958, Engr. in Aerospace Engring., 1969. Sr. engr. aerodynamics N. Am. Aviation, L.A., 1951-61; MTS project engr., mgr. The Aerospace Corp., El Segundo, Calif., 1961-85; instr. U. So. Calif., L.A., 1979; cons. L-Systems, Inc., El Segundo, 1985-89. Pres., bd. dirs. First United Meth. Ch., Santa Monica, Calif., 1988-90; judge, range officer Internat. Shooting Union, 1989—. Recipient Bronze Medal Internat. Shooting Union, 1990. Fellow Am. Inst. Aeronautics and Astronautics (assoc.). Republican. Achievements include discovery of F-100 wing transonic buffet solution, blowing definition and test, design definition and test of area variation, F-108 mach 3 cruise canard and shock lift effectiveness, XB-70 transport wing definition for subsonic lift and supersonic cruise; re-entry systems analysis of vehicle design, payload, observables for systems procurement and technical direction; development of re-entry technology support for nosetip shape change, boundary layer transition, flow

field codes, maneuvering technology; DoD-space transportation system support for space transportation system management (program definitions, manpower); launch on demand requirements; support of new booster systems performance options; reliability review of current systems; re-entry systems test in arms control environment; definition of space transportation system DoD reference missions and mission modeling for cost effectiveness, effective V/STOL aircraft implementation options. Home and Office: 2443 La Condessa Dr Los Angeles CA 90049-1221

PORTEOUS, TIMOTHY, academic administrator; b. Montreal, Que., Can., Aug. 31, 1933; s. John Geoffrey and Cora Ann (Kennedy) P.; m. Wendy Elizabeth Farris, June 28, 1968 (div. Dec. 1986); 1 child, Vanessa Bell; m. Beatrice Donald, Feb. 7, 1987; 1 child, Nicholas William. B.A., McGill U., Montréal, 1954, B.C.L., 1957; postgrad., Université de Montréal, 1957-58, Université de Paris Inst. de Droit Comparé, 1958-59; LLD (hon.), Trent (Ont.) U., 1986. Called to Que. bar 1958. Assoc. firm Bourgeois, Doheny, Day & Mackenzie, Montreal, 1958-66; exec. asst. to Minister of Industry of Can., Ottawa, Ont., 1966-68; spl. asst. to Prime Minister, Ottawa, 1968-73, exec. asst.; 1970-73; assoc. dir. Can. Council, Ottawa, 1973-82, dir., 1982-85; assoc. dir. Can. Ctr. for Architecture, Montreal, 1986-88; pres. Ont. Coll. Art, 1988—. Co-author, assoc. producer: My Fur Lady, 1957-58. Mem. adv. coun. Coop. Programme in Arts Adminstrn., U. Toronto; mem. dairy products com. Royal Agrl. Winter Fair; mem. adv. bd. Laidlaw Found. Mem. Soc. Authors, Composers and Music Pubs. Can., Can. Conf. of the Arts, Toronto Arts Coun. (bd. dirs.), Coun. Ghanaian-Canadians (chair, hon. bd. govs.). Avocations: skiing, tennis, scuba diving, wind surfing.

PORTER, ALAN LESLIE, industrial and systems engineering educator; b. Jersey City, June 22, 1945; s. Leslie Frank and Alice Mae (Kaufman) P.; m. Claudia Loy Ferrey, June 14, 1968; children: Brett, Doug, Lynn. BSChemE, Calif. Inst. Tech., 1967; MS, UCLA, 1968, PhD in Psychology, 1972. Research assoc., asst. prof. program social mgmt. tech. U. Wash., Seattle, 1972-74; asst. prof. indsl. and systems engring. Ga. Inst. Tech., Atlanta, 1975-78, assoc. prof., 1979-85, prof., 1986—, dir., tech. policy and assessment ctr., 1989—; cons. Dept. Commerce, State of Md., Search Tech., IBM, Coca Cola. Author, editor: (with others) A Guidebook for Technology Assessment and Impact Analysis, 1980, (with T.J. Kuehn) Science Technology and National Policy, 1981, (with F.A. Rossini) Integrated Impact Assessment, Impact Assessment Bull., 1981-84, Methods and Experience in Impact Assessment, 1986, Interdisciplinary, 1986, Impact of Office Automation on Clerical Employment, 1985—, Forecasting and Management of Technology, 1991. NIH fellow, 1968; NSF grantee, 1974-75, 78-86, 89—, Dept. Transp. grantee, 1977-79, Fund for Improvement Post Secondary Edn. grantee, 1977-79, Dept. Labor grantee, 1973-74. Mem. Internat. Assn. Impact Assessment (co-founder, sec. 1981-87, exec. dir. 1987-90, pres. 1995-96), IEEE Systems Man and Cybernetics Soc. (chmn. tech. forecasting com.), Am. Soc. Engr. Edn. (chmn. engrs. and pub. policy div. 1982-83, Bellcore adv. coun.). Home: 110 Lake Top Ct Roswell GA 30076-3017 Office: Sch Indsl and Systems Engring Ga Tech Atlanta GA 30332

PORTER, AMY R., lawyer; b. Memphis, Jan. 30, 1944. BA magna cum laude, Memphis State U., 1965; JD, Ariz. State U., 1975. Bar: Ariz. 1975. Ptnr. Lewis and Roca, Phoenix; judge pro tempore Ariz. Ct. Appeals, Phoenix, 1985; instr. Ariz. State U. 1987-88. Mem. ABA, Air and Waste Mgmt. Assn., Def. Rsch. Inst. Office: Lewis & Roca 40 N Central Ave Phoenix AZ 85004

PORTER, ANDREW CALVIN, educational administrator, psychology educator; b. Huntington, Pa., July 10, 1942; s. Rutherford and Grace (Johnson) P.; m. Susan Porter, June 5, 1967; children: Matthew, Anna, John, Joe, Kate. BS, Ind. State U., 1963; MS, U. Wis., 1965, PhD, 1967. Prof., co-dir. inst. rsch. on teaching Mich. State U., East Lansing, 1967-88; assoc. dir. basic skills group Nat. Inst. Edn., Washington, 1975-76; prof. ednl. psychology, dir. Wis. Ctr. Edn. Rsch. U. Wis., Madison, 1988—; vis. asst. prof. Ind. State U., Terre Haute, 1967; mem. adv. bd. Am. Jour. Edn., 1988—; mem. bd. Internat. Studies, Nat. Acad. Scis., Nat. Rsch. Coun., 1993—; chmn. U.S. Dept. Edn., adv. coun. on edn. stats, 1994—. Author: Creating a System of School Process Indicators, 1991. Bd. dirs. Madison Urban League, 1992—. Recipient Ctr. Policy Rsch. in Edn. award OERI U.S. Dept. Edn., 1987—; Inst. Sci. Edn. award NSF, 1995—, Indicators of Content Instruction Project award Nat. Ctr. Edn. Stats., 1994—. Mem. Am. Ednl. Rsch. Assn. (mem.-at-large), Nat. Coun. Edn. Measurement, Nat. Coun. Tchrs. Math., Psychometric Soc., Nat. Acad. Edn., Phi Delta Kappa (life). Office: U Wis Madison Wis Ctr Edn Rsch 1025 W Johnson St Madison WI 53706-1706

PORTER, ARTHUR RENO, economist, arbitrator; b. Poland, Ohio, Nov. 14, 1918; s. Arthur Reno and Grace (Schoeller) P.; m. Ruth Stottler, June 23, 1945; children—Stephen Warren, Mark Schoeller, David Rankin, Malcolm James. BS, Washington and Lee U., 1940; MA, U. Pa., 1948, PhD, 1955; LLD (hon.), Hanover Coll., 1993. Instr. econs. U. Pa., Phila., 1940-42, 45-48; mem. staff regional WLB, Phila., 1943-45; prof. econs. Hanover (Ind.) Coll., 1948-67; prof. econs., dean coll. Heidelberg Coll., Tiffin, Ohio, 1967-79; Arbitrator labor disputes. Author: Job Property Rights, 1954; Contbr. articles to Labor Law Jour. Mem. Nat. Acad. Arbitrators, Am. Arbitration Assn., Phi Beta Kappa., U.P. Ch. Office: Apt 7 192 St Francis Ave Tiffin OH 44883-4407

PORTER, ARTHUR T., oncologist, educator; b. June 11, 1956; m. Pamela Porter; 3 children. Student, U. Sierra Leone, 1974-75; BA in Anatomy, Cambridge U., 1978, M.B.B.Chir./M.D., 1980, MA, 1984; DMRT, Royal Coll. Radiologists, Eng., 1985; postgrad., U. Alta., 1984-86; FRCPC, Royal Coll. Physicians and Surgeons, Can., 1986; cert. for physicians mgr. program, U. Toronto, 1990; postgrad., LaSalle U. Lic., bd. cert., Mich., Can., Eng. House physician gen. medicine Norfolk and Norwich Hosp., Eng., 1981; house sugeon gen. surgery New Addenbrookes Hosp., Cambridge, Eng., 1981-82; house officer clin. hematology No. Gen. Hosp., Sheffield, Eng., 1982; sr. house officer gen. medicine Huntington County Hosp., Hinchingbrooke Hosp., Eng., 1982-83; sr. house officer radiotherapy and oncology Norfolk and Norwich Hosp., Norwich, 1983-84; chief resident radiation oncology Cross Cancer Inst., Edmonton, Alta., Can., 1984-86, radiation oncologist, 1986-87; sr. radiation oncologist, 1987; asst. prof. faculty medicine U. Alta., Edmonton, 1987, assoc. clin. prof. dept. surgery faculty medicine, 1988; head divsn. radiation oncology U. Western Ont., London, Can., 1988; cons. radiation oncologist, chief dept. radiation oncology London Regional Cancer Ctr., 1988, program dir. radiation oncology, 1989-91; chmn. dept. oncology Victoria Hosp. Corp., London, 1990; assoc. prof. dept. oncology U. Western Ont., 1990; program dir. radiation oncology Wayne State U., Detroit, 1991-92, prof., chmn. dept. radiation oncology Sch. Medicine, 1991—; chief Gershenson Radiation Oncology Ctr. Harper Hosp., Detroit, 1991—; radiation oncologist-in-chief Detroit Med. Ctr., 1991—; pres., CEO Radiation Oncology R & D Center, Detroit, 1991—; dir. multidisciplinary svcs. Meyer L. Prentice Comprehensive Cancer Ctr., Detroit, 1992—; chmn. radiation oncology Grace Hosp., Detroit, 1993—; vis. prof. U. London, Eng., 1990, U. Mich., 1991, U. Ky., 1992, U. Rochester, 1992; cons. neutron therapy Dept. Health Govt. of U.K., 1990; mem. editorial bd. Endocurietherapy/Hyperthermia Oncology, 1991—, Cambridge Cancer Series, 1991—, Baxter Adminstrv. Manual, 1991—, Oncore, 1989-91, Internat. Monitor Oncology, 1992—; mem. genito-urinary com. Radiation Therapy Oncology Group, 1986—, new investigators com., 1986-87, bladder task force, 1986-88, time dose and fractionation, 1987—, large field working group, 1987—, full mem. com., 1987-91, exec. com., 1991; mem. radiation oncology com. Nat. Cancer Inst. Can., 1987-90, radiation quality assurance subcom., 1987-90, G.U. com., 1987-90; prin. investigator Radiation Therapy Oncology Group, U. Alta., 1987-88, U. Western Ont., 1989-91; mem. working group on bladder cancer Internat. Consensus, 1988, working group on prostate cancer, 1988; mem. Can. Uro-Oncology Group, 1990; chmn. brachytherapy subcom. Radiation Therapy Oncology Group, 1990-92, spl. populations com., 1991, systemic radionucleides com., 1991; mem. G.U. com. Southwest Oncology Group, 1991, selection com. Windsor Cancer Ctr., 1992; mem. cancer grant review conf. Nat. Cancer Inst., 1992; mem. NIH Sub-Saharan African Health Rsch. Initiative, 1993; chmn. South Western Ont. Uro-Oncology Group, 1988-91, Profl. Adv. Com. Radiation Oncology, 1990-91, Site Com. for Prostate Cancer, 1990-91; mem. Ont. Commn. Radiation Oncology, 1989-91, Cancer 2000 Com., 1990-91, PET com. Children's

Hosp. Mich., 1991—, adv. com. dept. radiology Detroit Receiving Hosp., 1991—; dir. Univ. Physicians, Inc., 1991—; bd. dirs. MLPCCCMD, Biomide Corp., Vetrogen Corp., MedCyc, Med. Knowledge Systems, Am. Cancer Soc.; bd. trustees Fund Med. Rsch. Edn., 1991—, Meyer L. Prentice Comprehensive Cancer Ctr., 1992—; mem. exec. com. Am. Cancer Soc., Wayne County, 1992—; mem. Amersham Internat. Adv. Bd., 1992—; co-chmn. regional advi. bd. Am. Cancer Soc., 1992—, v.p., pres. elect, 1993—; mem. Medi-Pysics Adv. Bd., 1992—; pres. Biomide Corp. Bd., 1993—; lectr. in field. Author: (with others) Fundamental Problems in Breast Cancer, ss in Urological Cancers, 1988, Proceedings of the Consensus Meeting of the Treatment of Bladder Cancer-1987, 1988, Brachytherapy, 1989, High and Low Dose Rate Brachytherapy, 1989, Brachytherapy of Prostate Cancer, 1991; co-editor Treatment of Cancer, 1991—; assoc. editor Can. Jour. Oncology, 1990—, Antibody and Radiopharmaceuticals, 1992—; contbr. articles to profl. jours. Recipient Nat. award Sierra Leone, 1975-80, Commonwealth Found. scholarship, 1980, Best Doctor in Am. award, 1992, Testimonial Resolution, City of Detroit, 1991, Testimonial Resolution, County of Wayne, 1993. Fellow Am. Coll. Angiology, Detroit Acad. Medicine, Royal Soc. Medicine; mem. Am. Soc. Therapeutic Radiation Oncology, Am. Radium Soc., Am. Soc. Clin. Oncology, Am. Coll. Radiology, Am. Med. Assn. (Physicians Recognition award 1986), Am. Acad. Med. Adminstrs., Am. Acad. Oncology Adminstrs., Am. Endocurietherapy Soc. (sec. Can. chpt. 1988, sec.), Mich. State Med. Soc., Mich. Soc. Therapeutic Radiation Oncology, Mich. Radiol. Soc., Detroit Med. Soc. (Ann. award for Excellence 1993), Wayne County Med. Soc., European Soc. Therapeutic Radiation Oncology, Brit. Inst. Radiology, Can. Oncology Soc., Can. Assn. Radiation Oncology, Royal Coll. Radiologists, Sierra Leone Med. and Dental Assn., Greater Detroit C. of C., Sigma Xi. Achievements include patent in a perineal applicator; research in novel methods in delivery dose, brachytherapy, intraoperative therapy, unsealed source therapy, verification and dosimetry, real time portal imaging, three-dimensional and planning, unsealed source dosimetry, the design of perineal applicators. Office: Radiation Oncology Rsch & Dev Ctr 4201 St Antoine Detroit MI 48201

PORTER, BERNARD HARDEN, consulting physicist, author, publisher; b. Porter Settlement, Maine, Feb. 14, 1911; s. Lewis Harden and Etta Flora (Rogers) P.; m. Helen Elaine Hendron, July 15, 1946 (div. Aug. 1947); m. Margaret Eudine Preston, Aug. 27, 1955 (dec. April 1975); m. Lula Mae Blom, Sept. 9, 1976 (div. Nov. 1986). BS, Colby Coll., 1932; MS, Brown U., 1933; DSc (hon.), Inst. Advanced Thinking, Calais, Maine, 1959. Physicist Acheson Colloids Corp., Port Huron, Mich., 1935-40; rsch. physicist Manhattan Dist. Engrs., Princeton, N.J., Berkeley, Calif. and Oak Ridge, 1940-45; cons. physicist San Francisco and Pasadena, Calif., Waldwick, N.J., Rockland, Belfast, Maine, 1945—; chmn. bd. Bern Porter Inc., Pasadena, Rockland, Belfast, 1945—; pres. Bern Porter Books, Pasadena, Rockland, Belfast, 1929—, Bern Porter Internat., Belfast, 1974—; cons. Internat. Exec. Service Corps, 1968, SBA, 1968-88. Author: The 14th of February, 1971, I've Left, 1971, Founds, 1972, Hand Coated Chocolates, 1972, Contemporary Italian Painters, 1973, Trattoria Due Forni, 1973, The Book of Do's, 1974, The Manhattan Telephone Book, 1975, Run-On, 1975, Where, 1975, Selected Founds, 1975, Gee-Whizzles, 1976, Don't Book, 1981, Last Acts, 1985, My, My, 1985, Left Leg, 1988, Neverends, 1988, Numbers, 1989, Sweetend, 1989, Bern Porter and Fa Gaga, 1990, Sounds That Arouse Me, 1992, Less Than Overweight, 1992, Mothering Time, 1993; contbr. numerous articles to profl. jours. Rep. candidate for gov. Maine, 1969; bd. dirs. Inst. Advanced Thinking, Belfast, chmn. bd., 1959—. Recipient awards PEN, 1975, 76, 77, Authors League, 1977; Carnegie author, 1975; diploma merit Centro Studi E Scambi Internazionale, Rome, 1976; Nat. Endowment for Arts lit. award, 1979. Fellow Am. Astronautical Soc., Tech. Pub. Soc., Am. Rocket Soc. (assoc.), Soc. Tech. Writers and Pubs. (assoc.), Internat. Acad. Poets (London) (founding); mem. Am. Phys. Soc., Soc. Internat. Devel., Nat. Soc. Programmed Instrn., Phi Beta Kappa, Sigma Xi, Kappa Phi Kappa, Chi Gamma Sigma. Methodist. Clubs: Fenway (Boston); Algonquin, St. Andrews (N.B., Can.). Address: 22 Salmond Rd Belfast ME 04915

PORTER, BLAINE ROBERT MILTON, psychology/sociology educator; b. Morgan, Utah, Feb. 24, 1922; s. Brigham Ernest and Edna (Brough) P.; m. Elizabeth Taylor, Sept 27, 1943 (dec.); children: Claudia Black, Roger B., David T., Patricia A. Hintze, Corinna; m. Myrna Katherine Kennedy, Feb. 26, 1988. Student, Utah State U., 1940-41; BS, Brigham Young U., 1947, MA, 1949; PhD (Grant Found. fellow family life edn. 1951-52), Cornell U., 1952. Instr. sociology Iowa State Coll., 1949-51; asst. prof. sociology and child devel. Iowa State U., 1952-55; prof., chmn. dept. human devel. and family relationships Brigham Young U., 1955-65, dean Coll. Family Living, 1966-80, Univ. prof., 1980-87; vis. prof. Fulbright rsch. scholar U. London, 1965-66; vis. prof. U. Wurzberg, 1980, 81, 83; facilitator human rels. workshops for the Human Devel. Inst., Denver, 1988-90. Editor: The Latter-day Saint Family, 1963, rev. edit., 1966; editor quar. jour.: Family Perspective, 1966-82; contbr. articles to profl. jours. Pres. elect Iowa Coun. Family Rels., 1954-55; pres. Utah Coun. Family Rels., 1957-58; chmn. sect. marriage counseling Nat. Coun. Family Rels., 1958-59, bd. dirs., 1957-60, exec. com., 1958-72, pres., 1963-64; bd. dirs. Am. Family Soc., 1975-85. Pilot USAAF, 1942-45. Recipient Prof. of Yr. award Brigham Young U., 1964. Mem. Am. Home Econs. Assn. (vice chmn. sect. family relations and child devel. 1955-56), Am. Sociol. Assn. (sec. sect. on family 1964-67), Am. Assn. Marriage and Family Therapy, Am. Psychol. Assn., Soc. Research in Child Devel., Sigma Xi, Phi Kappa Phi (chpt. pres. 1969-71). Home: 1675 Pine Ln Provo UT 84604-2163 Office: Brigham Young U 4505 Hbll Provo UT 84602-1035

PORTER, BRIAN STANLEY, police chief; b. Seattle, May 2, 1938; s. Jack D. and Margaret I. (Tuter) P.; grad. U. Alaska, 1970, Northwestern U. Traffic Inst., 1970-71, FBI Nat. Exec. Inst., 1981; m. Bette K. Schakohl, Apr. 26, 1958; children—Kelle, Kerry, Kory. With Anchorage Police Dept., 1960—, chief of police, 1980—; chmn. Alaska Police Standards Council, 1978-80. Served with U.S. Army, 1957-58. Office: House of Reps 3430 Fordham Dr Anchorage AK 99508

PORTER, BRUCE DOUGLAS, educator, federal agency administrator, writer; b. Albuquerque, Sept. 18, 1952; s. Lyle Kay and Wilma (Holmes) P.; m. Susan Elizabeth Holland, Feb. 2, 1977; children: David William, Christopher Jonathan, Lisa Jennette, Jennifer Rachel. BA in History, Brigham Young U., 1976; AM in Soviet Studies, Harvard U., 1978, PhD in Polit. Sci., 1979. Sr. rsch. analyst Radio Free Europe/Radio Liberty, Inc., Munich, 1980-83; profl. staff mem. armed svcs. com. U.S. Senate, Washington, 1983-84; sr. analyst Northrop Corp. Analysis Ctr., Washington, 1984-86; exec. dir. Bd. for Internat. Broadcasting, Washington, 1986-90; Bradley sr. rsch. assoc. Harvard U., Cambridge, Mass., 1990-93; assoc. prof. Brigham Young U., Provo, Utah, 1993-95; min. LDS Ch., 1995—. Author: The USSR in Third World Conflicts, 1976, Red Armies in Crisis, 1991, War and the Rise of the State, 1993; co-author: The Polish Drama: 1980-82, 1983; contbr. articles to profl. jours. Lay min. Ch. Jesus Christ Latter-day Saints, bishop, 1985-90, missionary, Düsseldorf, Fed. Republic Germany, 1971-73. Post doctoral fellow Harvard Ctr. for Internat. Affairs, 1979-80, Danforth fellow, 1976-79, David O. McKay scholar Brigham Young U., 1970-71, 74-76; recipient Meritorious Svc. award Pres. of U.S., 1990. Mem. Am. Polit. Sci. Assn., Am. Assn. Advancement Slavic Studies, Internat. Studies Assn. Avocations: swimming, creative writing. Office: Brigham Young U 784 Swkt Provo UT 84602-1130

PORTER, BURTON FREDERICK, philosophy educator, author; b. N.Y.C., June 22, 1936; s. John and Doris (Neloway) P.; m. Susan Jane Porter, May 10, 1966 (div. 1974); 1 child, Anastasia; m. Barbara Taylor Metcalf, Dec. 31, 1980; 1 child, Mark Graham Bevan. B.A. in Philosophy cum laude with spl. hons. in lit., U. Md., 1959; PhD, St. Andrews U., Scotland, 1968; postgrad., Oxford (Eng.) U., Scotland, 1968. Asst. prof. philosophy U. Md., London, 1966-69; assoc. prof. philosophy King's Coll., Wilkes-Barre, Pa., 1969-71; prof. philosophy, chmn. dept. Russell Sage Coll., Troy, N.Y., 1971-87; prof. philosophy, head Dept. Humanities-Communications Drexel U., Phila., 1987-91; dean arts and scis. Western New Eng. Coll., Springfield, Mass., 1991—. Author: Deity and Morality, 1968, Philosophy, A Literary and Conceptual Approach, 1974, 80, 95, Personal Philosophy: Perspectives on Living, 1976, The Good Life, Alternatives in Ethics, 1980, 91, 94, Reasons for Living: A Basic Ethics, 1988, Religion and Reason, 1993; also articles and book revs. Named Outstanding Educator of Am., NEA, 1975. Mem. Am. Philos. Assn., MLA. Home: 30 Fearing St Amherst MA 01002 Office: Western New Eng Coll Arts & Scis Dean's Office Springfield MA 01119

PORTER, CHARLES ALLAN, French language educator, educational administrator; b. Chgo., May 31, 1932; s. Charles Augustin and Emma Catherine (Fliege) P.; m. Elizabeth Anne Robinson, Nov. 24, 1956. A.A., North Park Coll., 1951; B.S., Northwestern U., 1953, M.A., 1954; Ph.D., Yale U., 1962. Inst. to assoc. prof. Yale U., New Haven, 1960-75, prof. French, 1975—, dir. summer and spl. programs, 1978-88, chmn. dept. French, 1979-83. Author: Restif's Novels, 1967, Chateaubriand: Composition, Imagination, and Poetry, 1978. Fellow Am. Council Learned Socs.; mem. MLA, Am. Assn. Tchrs. French, Am. Soc. Eighteenth Century Studies, Societe Francaise d'etude du XVIII siecle, Societe Chateaubriand. Club: Yale (N.Y.C.). Home: 188 Bishop St New Haven CT 06511-3718 Office: Yale U PO Box 2504A Yale Sta New Haven CT 06520-2504

PORTER, CHARLES KING, advertising executive; b. Mpls., Oct. 10, 1945; s. King E. and Bernetta Porter Andrews; m. Margit Gammeltoft, Feb. 26, 1972; children: Kristin, Catherine, James. BS in Journalism, U. Minn., 1967. Ptnr. Breen & Porter Co., Miami, Fla., 1974-85; pres. Porter Creative Svcs., Miami, 1985-88, Crispin & Porter Advt., Miami, 1988—; dir. Miami Ad Sch. Trustee Beacon Coun., Miami, 1988—. Recipient Nat. Addy award Am. Advt. Fedn., 1991, 92, Andy award Advt. Club N.Y., 1993, 94. Mem. Am. Assn. Advt. Agys. (forum, Nat. A award 1991, 94, 95). Presbyterian. Avocations: skiing, travel, history. Office: Crispin & Porter Advt 2699 S Bayshore Dr Miami FL 33133-5408

PORTER, CLOYD ALLEN, state representative; b. Huntley, Ill., May 22, 1935; s. Cecil and Myrtle (Fischer) P.; m. Joan Hawkins, July 25, 1959; children: Ellen, LeeAnn, Jay, Joli. Grad. high sch., Burlington, Wis. Ptnr. Cecil W. Porter & Son Trucking, 1955-70; treas. Burlington Sand and Gravel, 1964-70; owner Cloyd A. Porter Trucking, Burlington, 1970-72; state rep. 43d dist. Wis. State Assembly, Madison, 1972-82; state rep. 66th dist. Wis. State Assembly, 1982—; mem. coun. on recycling, Wis., 1991—, fire svc. legis. adv. com., 1987—, legis. coun. com. on fire inspections and fire dues, 1991, legis. coun. spl. com. on emergency med. svcs., 1992-93. Contbr. articles to profl. jours. Chmn. Town of Burlington, 1971-75; state and met. affairs chmn. Jaycees, Wis., 1963, state v.p., 1969, adminstrv. asst., 1970, exec. v.p., 1971; mem. Wis. Conservation Congress for Natural Resources Leadership and Support in the State Assembly, 1994. Recipient many awards and honors including being named hon. mem. State Fire Chiefs Assn., Wis., 1992, Guardian of Small Bus., NFIB, Wis., 1991, Friend of Agr., Farm Bur. of Wis., 1992, 94; recipient Mission Impossible award Consumer Packaging Coun., Wis., 1990, Cert. of Appreciation, Wis. Counties Assn., 1993, others. Mem. Wis. Alliance for Fire Safety. Republican. Roman Catholic. Home: 28322 Durand Ave Burlington WI 53105 Office: State Capitol PO Box 8953 309 North Madison WI 53708

PORTER, DANIEL REED, III, museum director; b. Northampton, Mass., July 2, 1930; s. Daniel Reed and Eleanor (Parsons) P.; m. Joan Joyce Dornfeld, Nov. 22, 1958; children: Leslie Marie, Andrew Gregory. BA, U. Mass., 1952; MA, U. Mich., 1956. Asst. to dir. State Hist. Soc. Wis., Madison, 1956-58; dir. Hist. Soc. York County, Pa., 1958-61; asst. dir., dir. Ohio Hist. Soc., Columbus, 1961-74; exec. dir. Preservation Soc. Newport County, R.I., 1974-78; dir., prof. Cooperstown (N.Y.) Grad. Programs, 1978-82; dir. N.Y. State Hist. Assn. Farmer's Mus. Cooperstown, Cooperstown, 1982-92; hist. preservation officer State of Ohio, Columbus, 1967-74. Editor: N.Y. Heritage, 1984-92; contbr. articles to publs. in field. With U.S. Army, 1952-54, Korea. Recipient Spl. award of Merit Ohio Hist. Socs., 1970. Mem. Am. Assn. Mus. (accreditation commn. 1982-88, councillor-at-large 1981-84), Am. Assn. State and Local History (coun., Nashville 1971-73, councillor 1985-87). Congregationalist.

PORTER, DARWIN FRED, writer; b. Greensboro, N.C., Sept. 13, 1937; s. Numie Rowan and Hazel Lee (Phillips) P. B.A., U. Miami, 1959. Bur. chief Miami Herald, 1959-60; v.p. Haggart Assocs., N.Y.C., 1961-64; editor, author Arthur Frommer Inc., N.Y.C., 1964-67, Frommer/Pasmantier Pub. Corp., N.Y.C., 1967-86, Prentice Hall Press, N.Y.C., 1987-90, Simon & Schuster, N.Y.C., 1991—. Author: Frommer Travel Guides to Eng., 1964, Frommer Travel Guides to Spain, 1966, Frommer Travel Guides to Scandinavia, 1967, Frommer Travel to Los Angeles, 1969, Frommer Travel Guide to London, 1970, Frommer Travel Guide to Lisbon/Madrid, 1972, Frommer Travel Guide to Paris, 1972, Frommer Travel Guide To Morocco, 1974, Frommer Travel Guide to Rome, 1974, Frommer Travel Guide to Portugal, 1968, Frommer Travel Guide to England, 1969, Frommer Travel Guide to Italy, 1969, Frommer Travel Guide to Germany, 1970, Frommer Travel Guide to France, 1970, Frommer Travel Guide to Caribbean, Bermuda, the Bahamas, 1980, Frommer Travel Guide To Switzerland, 1984, Frommer Travel Guide to Austria and Hungary, 1984, Frommer Travel Guide to Bermuda and the Bahamas, 1985, Frommer Travel Guide to Scotland and Wales, 1985, Frommer Travel Guide to the Virgin Islands, 1991, Frommer Travel Guide to Scotland, 1992, Frommer Travel Guide to Jamaica/Barbados, 1992, Frommer Travel Guide to Puerto Rico, 1992, Frommer Travel Guide to the Caribbean, 1993, Frommer Travel Guide to Bermuda, 1993, Frommer Travel Guide to the Bahamas, 1993, Frommer Travel Guide to Austria, 1993, Frommer Travel Guide to Madrid & the Costa del Sol, 1993; (novels) Butterflies in Heat, 1976, Marika, 1977, Venus, 1982. Recipient Silver award Internat. Film and TV Festival N.Y., 1977. Mem. Soc. Am. Travel Writers, Smithsonian Assocs., Nat. Trust for Historic Preservation, Sigma Delta Chi. Home: 75 St Marks Pl Staten Island NY 10301-1606

PORTER, DAVID BRUCE, air force officer, behavioral scientist, educator; b. Lexington, Ky., June 17, 1949; m. Sharon Jo Mahood, June 9, 1971; children: David Damien, Kristin Jillian. BS, USAF Acad., 1971; MS, UCLA, 1972; DPhil, Oxford U., 1986. Commd. 2d lt. USAF, 1967, advanced through grades to col.; chief orgnl. maintenance, functional check flight pilot USAF, Hickam AFB, Hawaii, 1976-79; instr. behavioral sci., leadership USAF Acad. USAF, Colorado Springs, Colo., 1979-81, assoc. prof., dept. head USAF Acad., 1986—; exec. officer USAF, RAF Woodbridge, U.K., 1981-83. Contbr. to profl. publs. including Jour. Coll. Reading and Learning, Current Psychology Rsch. and Revs. Bd. dirs. Citizens Project, Colorado Springs, 1991-92; dir. leadership devel. Mountain Desert dist. Unitarian Universalist Assn. Leadership Sch., St. Malo, Colo., 1991—. Home: 1402 N Weber St Colorado Springs CO 80907-7516 Office: USAF Acad Dept Behavioral Scis 6L67 Fairchild Hall U S A F Academy CO 80840

PORTER, DAVID HUGH, pianist, classicist, academic administrator, liberal arts educator; b. N.Y.C., Oct. 29, 1935; s. Hugh B. and Ethel K. (Flentye) P.; m. Laudie Ernestine Dimmette, June 21, 1958 (dec. Nov., 1986); children: Hugh, Everett, Helen, David; m. Helen Louise Nelson, Aug. 24, 1987. BA with highest honors, Swarthmore Coll., 1958; PhD (Danforth Grad. fellow, Woodrow Wilson Grad. fellow), Princeton U., 1962; student, Phila. Conservatory Music, 1955-61. Instr. in classics and music Carleton Coll., Northfield, Minn., 1962-63, asst. prof., 1963-68, assoc. prof., 1968-73, prof., 1973-87, William H. Laird prof. liberal arts, 1974-87, pres. faculty, 1980-82, coll. pres., 1986-87; pres. Skidmore Coll., Saratoga Springs, N.Y., 1987—, prof. classics, 1987—; Phi Beta Kappa vis. lectr., 1979-92, vis. scholar, 1994—; vis. prof. classics Princeton U., 1986; recitalist, lectr.; especially on contemporary music, at colls., univs. throughout U.S., Europe, on radio and TV; bd. dirs. Adirondack Trust Co.; chmn. Hudson-Mohawk Assn., 1990-92. Author: Only Connect: Three Studies in Greek Tragedy, 1987, Horace's Poetic Journey: A Reading of Odes I-III, 1987; editor: Carleton Remembered, 1909-86, 1987, The Not Quite Innocent Bystander: Writings of Edward Steuermann, 1989; contbr. articles on classics, music and edn. to profl. jours. NEH research fellow, 1969-70, 83-84; Am. Council Learned Socs. research fellow, 1976-77. Mem. Am. Philological Assn., Classical Assn. Atlantic States. Democrat. Mem. United Ch. Christ. Avocations: hiking, fishing, reading, collecting rugs and books. Home: 791 N Broadway Saratoga Springs NY 12866-1601 Office: Skidmore Coll Office of Pres Saratoga Springs NY 12866

PORTER, DAVID LINDSEY, history and political science educator; author; b. Holyoke, Mass., Feb. 18, 1941; s. Willis Hubert and Lura Frances (Bowen) P.; m. Marilyn Esther Platt, Nov. 28, 1970; children: Kevin, Andrea. BA magna cum laude, Franklin Coll., 1963; MA, Ohio U., 1965; PhD, Pa. State U., 1970. Asst. prof. history Rensselaer Poly. Inst., Troy, N.Y., 1970-75, co-dir. Am. studies program, 1972-74; ednl. adminstrv. asst. Civil

Svc. Office State of N.Y., Troy, 1975-76; asst. prof. history William Penn Coll., Oskaloosa, Iowa, 1976-77, assoc. prof. history, 1977-82, prof. history and polit. sci., 1982-86, Louis Tuttle Shangle prof. history and polit. sci., 1986—, chmn. Sperry & Hutchinson Found. lectureship series, 1980-82; supr. legis. internship program Iowa Gen. Assembly, 1978—, records inventory project Mahaska County, 1978-79, internship program Washington Ctr., 1985—. Author: The Seventy-sixth Congress and World War II, 1939-40, 1979, Congress and the Waning of the New Deal, 1980; contbr. to Dictionary of American Biography, 1981, 88, 94, Directory of Teaching Innovations in History, 1981, The Book of Lists #3, 1983, Biographical Dictionary of Internationalists, 1983, The Hero in Transition, 1983, Herbert Hoover and the Republican Era: A Reconsideration, 1984, The History of Mahaska County, Iowa, 1984, Franklin D. Roosevelt, His Life and Times: An Encyclopedic View, 1985, The Rating Game in American Politics: An Interdisciplinary Approach, 1987, Sport History, 1987, Book of Days, 1988, Sports Encyclopedia North America, 1988, The Harry S. Truman Encyclopedia, 1989, Encyclopedia of Major League Baseball Team Histories: The National League, 1991, Twentieth Century Sports Champions, 1992, Statesmen Who Changed the World, 1993; editor, contbr.: Biographical Dictionary of American Sports: vols. Baseball, 1987, Football, 1987, Outdoor Sports, 1988, Basketball and Other Indoor Sports, 1989, 1989-92 Supplement for Baseball, Football, Basketball and Other Sports, 1992, 1992-95, Supplement for Baseball, Football, Basketball and Other Sports, 1995, African-American Sports Greats, 1995; compiler, A Cumulative Index to the Biographical Dictionary of American Sports, 1993; assoc. editor: (with others) American National Biography, 20 vols.; contbr. weekly column to Oskaloosa Herald, 1994—, numerous articles to various dictionaries, directories, encys., jours., revs., newspapers, commentary to Nat. Pub. Radio. Grantee NSF, 1967, NEH, 1974, Rensselaer Poly. Inst., 1974, Eleanor Roosevelt Inst., 1981, William Penn Coll., 1986, 89, 92; recipient Choice Outstanding Acad. Book awards, 1989. Mem. AAUP, Am. Hist. Assn., Orgn. Am. Historians, N.Am. Soc. for Sport History, Soc. History Am. Fgn. Rels., Ctr. for Study of the Presidency, Soc. Am. Baseball Rsch., Popular Culture Assn., Profl. Football Researchers Assn., Coll. Football Researchers Assn., Coll. Football Hist. Soc., State Hist. Soc. Iowa, Mahaska County Hist. Soc., Iowa State UN Assn. (chmn. ann. assembly 1982, nat. soc. Disting. Svc. award 1981), Mahaska County UN Assn., Oskaloosa Babe Ruth League (bd. dirs.), Oskaloosa Community Choir, Friends of Oskaloosa Pub. Libr. (nominating com.), Phi Alpha Theta, Kappa Delta Pi. Mem. United Meth. Ch. Home: 2314 Ridgeway Ave Oskaloosa IA 52577-9109 Office: William Penn Coll Dept Social Sci 201 Trueblood Ave Oskaloosa IA 52577-1799

PORTER, DEAN ALLEN, art museum director, art historian, educator; b. Gouverneur, N.Y., June 13, 1939; s. Arnold W. and Gertrude V. Porter; m. Carol DuBrava, July 27, 1963; children: Kellie Ann, Tracie Ann. BA, Harpur Coll., 1961; MA in Art History, SUNY, Binghamton, 1966. PhD in Art History, 1974. curator Art Gallery, U. Notre Dame, 1966-74, dir. Snite Mus. Art, 1974—, prof. art history, 1994—; bd. dirs. Southwest Art History Coun.; mem. mus. coun. Harwood Found., U. N.Mex.; mem. adv. bd. Ind. U. Art Mus.; mem. nat. adv. coun. Valparaiso (Ind.) Mus. Art. Samuel H. Kress fellow. Mem. Coll. Art Assn., Am. Assn. Mus., Assn. Art Mus. Dirs. Author exhbn. catalogues, including: Janos Scholz, Musician and Collector, 1980, A Guide to The Snite Museum of Art, 1980, Selected Works from the Snite Museum of Art, 1987, Victor Higgins: An Am. Master, 1990, The Univ. Notre Dame Friends and Alumni Collect: A Sesquicentennial Celebration, 1992. Office: Snite Mus of Art University of Notre Dame Notre Dame IN 46556

PORTER, DENNIS DUDLEY, foreign language educator; b. Rayleigh, Essex, Eng., Dec. 3, 1933; came to U.S. 1961; s. William Arthur and Annie (Prangley) P.; m. Annick F. Leitner, Dec. 22, 1960; children: Gregory Y., Thomas A., Benjamin W. BA, MA, U. Cambridge (Eng.), 1957; PhD, U. Calif., Berkeley, 1966. Asst. prof. U. Calif., Berkeley, 1966-71; from assoc. to full prof. modern European lit. and theory, dept. French and Italian U. Mass., Amherst, 1971—, dir. Ctr. for Studies in Contemporary Culture, 1988-91. Author: Pursuit of Crime, 1981, Haunted Journeys, 1991, Rousseau's Legacy, 1995; translator: Ethics of Psychoanalysis (Jacques Lacan), 1992; contbr. numerous articles to profl. jours. Pilot RAF, 1952-54. Rsch. fellow NEH, 1977-78, Am. Coun. Learned Socs., 1985-86, Humanities Rsch. Ctr., Australian Nat. U., 1994. Mem. MLA, Am. Acad. Lit. Studies. Avocations: garden design. Office: U Mass Amherst MA 01003

PORTER, DON E., sports administrator; b. Oklahoma City, Okla. Exec. dir. Amateur Softball Assn., 1963; sec. gen. Internat. Softball Fedn., 1965-87; officiator Big Eight Conf., 1970-75; NFL, 1976-79; pres. Internat. Softball Fedn., 1987—; bd. dirs. U.S. Olympic Com., chmn. Transp. Com., 1985, Olympic Festival Com., 1989, 93, U.S. Olympic Congress Site Selection Com., 1991, Sooner State Games Com., Okla., 1983-89, Gov's. Coun. on Physical Fitness and Sports, 1988, 91, pres., 1995; co-chmn. U.S. Olympic Com. Games Site and Nat. Tng. Ctrs. Com., 1980; sec. gen. World Games I, 1981; sec. Assn. Internat. Olympic Com. Recognized Sports Fedns., 1984; rep. U.S. Olympic Com. Nat. Governing Bodies Hall of Fame Oversight Com., 1987, Special Ethics Oversight Com., 1992; apptd. U.S. State Dept. Adv. Com. Internat. Athletics, 1975, Gov's. Task Force on Physical Fitness and Sports,Okla., 1980, U.S. Olympic Com. Internat. Rels. Com., 1980, 95, Eligibility Com., 1986, Task Force Olympic Festivals, 1990, Internat. Olympic Com. Press Commn., 1994. Hearing panel Ethics Commn., Okla., 1979; Mayor's adv. coun., Okla. City, 1985; Riverfront Devel. Authority, 1985, 91. With U.S. Army, 1950-52. Recipient Medal of Honor Italian Olympic Com., 1977, Chinese Taipei Olympic Com., 1991; named Hall of Fame, Internat. Softball Assn., 1982. Office: Nat Softball Hall of Fame & Mus 2801 NE 50th Oklahoma City OK 73111

PORTER, DONALD JAMES, federal judge; b. Madison, S.D., Mar. 24, 1921; s. Donald Irving and Lela Ann (Slack) P.; m. Harriet J. Whitney, Aug. 22, 1948; children: Donald A., Mary Lela, William W., Carolyn S., Elizabeth C. Student, Eastern Normal Coll., 1938-39; B.S., U. S.D., 1942, LL.B., 1943. Bar: S.D. 1943. Pvt. practice law Chamberlain, S.D., 1947-59; ptnr. May, Porter, Adam, Gerdes & Thompson, and (predecessor), Pierre, S.D., 1959-77; assoc. justice S.D. Supreme Ct., Pierre, 1977-79; judge U.S. Dist. Ct. S.D., Pierre, 1979—, former chief judge; S.D. commr. Nat. Conf. Commrs. on Uniform State Laws, 1973-76; mem. S.D. Ho. of Reps., 1955-56. Served with U.S. Army, 1943-46, ETO. Mem. ABA, S.D. Bar Assn., Am. Bd. Trial Advocates (charter mem. S.D. chpt.). Roman Catholic. Office: US Dist Ct 413 US Courthouse Pierre SD 57501

PORTER, DUDLEY, JR., environmentalist, foundation executive, lawyer; b. Paris, Tenn., May 10, 1915; s. Dudley and Mary (Bolling) P.; m. Mary Rhoda Montague, Oct. 21, 1950. Student, Murray (Ky.) State Coll., 1933-34; LL.B., Cumberland U. 1936. Bar: Tenn. 1937. Asst. atty. gen. Tenn., 1937-40; mem. firm Tyne, Peebles, Henry & Tyne, Nashville, 1940-49; with law dept. Nat. Life & Accident Ins. Co., Nashville, 1940-49; assoc. gen. counsel Nat. Life & Accident Ins. Co., 1949; with Provident Life & Accident Ins. Co., Chattanooga, 1949—; gen. counsel Provident Life & Accident Ins. Co., 1954-72, v.p., 1955-72, sec., 1965-72, vice chmn., sr. counsel, 1972-76; of counsel Chambliss, Bahner, Crutchfield, Gaston & Irvine, Chattanooga, 1977—. Mem. Hamilton County Juvenile Ct. Commn., 1958-64, chmn., 1964; mem. Tenn. Health Planning Council, 1968-76, Tenn. Hist. Commn., 1976-86; trustee Hermitage Assn., Nashville, 1983-90; an incorporator, mem. bd. Sr. Neighbors Chattanooga, 1960-66; vice chmn., trustee Maclellan Charitable Trust. With AUS, 1942-46; judge adv. 100th Inf. Div. ETO. Mem. Am., Tenn., Chattanooga bar assns., Am. Life Conv. (chmn. legal sect. 1958), Assn. Life Ins. Counsel (exec. com. 1970—, pres. 1974-75), Nature Conservancy (life, co-founder and trustee Tenn. chpt.), Sigma Alpha Epsilon. Presbyterian. Clubs: Mountain City (Chattanooga); Belle Meade Country (Nashville). Home: 1125 Healing Springs Rd Elder Mountain Chattanooga TN 37419 Office: 1125 Healing Springs Rd Chattanooga TN 37419-1043 *My environmentalist credo: O Lord, how manifold are thy works! In wisdom hast thou made them all; the earth is full of thy riches. (Psalm 104, verse 24).*

PORTER, DWIGHT JOHNSON, former electric company executive, foreign affairs consultant; b. Shawnee, Okla., Apr. 12, 1916; s. Dwight Ernest and Gertrude (Johnson) P.; m. Adele Ritchie, Oct. 6, 1942; children—Dwight A., James G., Ellen Jean, Barbara Adele, Joan Anne. Ritchie Johnson. A.B., Grinnell Coll., 1938, LL.D., 1968; student, Am. U., 1938-40,

46-48, Nat. War Coll., 1957-58. Govt. intern Nat. Inst. Pub. Affairs, Washington, 1938-39; personnel officer U.S. Housing Authority, 1939-41; exec. officer Dept. Agr., San Francisco, 1941-42; asst. personnel dir. Bd. Econ. Warfare, 1942; dir. adminstrv. services Rural Electrification Adminstrn., 1946-48; mgmt. officer Dept. State, 1948; dep. dir. Displaced Persons Commn., 1949; adminstrv. officer U.S. High Commn., Germany, 1949-54; 1st sec. Am. embassy, London, 1954-56; exec. officer econ. area Dept. State, 1956-57; coordinator Hungarian Refugee Relief, 1957, spl. asst. to dep. under-sec., and under-sec. state, 1958-59; counsellor Am. embassy, Vienna, 1959-62; minister Am. embassy, 1962, dep. chief of mission, 1962-63; asst. sec. of state for adminstrn., 1963-65; ambassador to Lebanon, 1965-70; permanent U.S. rep. IAEA, Vienna, 1970-75; v.p. internat. affairs Westinghouse Electric Corp., Washington, 1975-85; fgn. affairs cons., 1986—. Served to capt. USMCR, 1942-45. Recipient alumni award Grinnell Coll., 1958. Home: 15100 Interlachen Dr #526 Silver Spring MD 20906

PORTER, ELISABETH SCOTT (LEEZEE PORTER), political worker; b. Mar. 23, 1942; d. Buford and Mary (Lowe) Scott; 1 child, Erin Lee; m. Paul Henry Nitze, Jan. 1993. Student, Sweet Briar Coll., Pan Am. Bus. Sch. Pres. Antique and Contemporary Leasing, Inc., Washington; founder, dir. Adams Nat. Bank, Washington; mem. Bd. Trade, Washington, Allied Bd. Trade, N.Y.C. Mem. fin. com. Diocese of Washington; mem. adv. bd. WAMU-FM, Washington; founder, profl. mem. Potomac chpt. Inst. Bus. Designers; active PTA; vestry mem. Grace Episcopal Ch., Washington; mem. Georgetown Citizens Assn., Leadership Washington, 1989—; mem. adv. bd. Elk Hill Farm, Va., Urban League; Dem. co-chmn. Women's Campaign Fund, Washington; mem. Dem. Women's Coun.; mem. bd. Women's Campaign Research Fund; v.p. bd. trustees Maret Sch., Washington; v.p. Champs Found.; mem. Leadership Washington, 1989-90. Mem. Washington C. of C., Nat. Assn. Women Bus. Owners, Georgetown Bus. and Profl. Orgn., Capitol Hill Assn. Bus. and Profls. Office: Antique and Contemporary Leasing Inc 709 12th St SE Washington DC 20003-2962

PORTER, ELSA ALLGOOD, writer, lecturer; b. Amoy, China, Dec. 19, 1928; d. Roy and Petra (Johnsen) Allgood; m. Raeford B. Liles, Mar. 19, 1949 (div. 1959); children: Barbara, Janet; m. G. Hinckley Porter, Nov. 22, 1962; children: David, Brian, Wendy. BA, Birmingham-So. Coll., 1949; MA, U. Ala., 1959; M in Pub. Adminstrn., Harvard U., 1971; LHD (hon.), U. Ala., 1986. With HEW, Washington, 1960-73; with U.S. CSC, Washington, 1973-77; asst. sec. Dept. Commerce, Washington, 1977-81; disting. practitioner in residence Washington Pub. Affairs Ctr., U. So. Calif., Washington, 1982-84; sr. mgmt. assoc. The Prodn. Group, Alexandria, Va., 1985-87; project dir. Cathedral Coll. of the Laity, Washington, 1987-89; v.p. R & D The Maccoby Group, Washington, 1990—. Bd. dirs. Delphi Internat. Group, 1981—. Fellow Nat. Acad. Pub. Adminstrs.; mem. Women's Nat. Dem. Club. Home: 1250 S Washington St Alexandria VA 22314-4454

PORTER, GARY LYNN, investment manager; b. Kinston, N.C., Mar. 25, 1959; s. Ola L. and Jean S. Porter; m. Eileen Maria Sampson, Aug. 3, 1985. BS in Bus., U. N.C., 1981; MBA, East Carolina U., 1983. Chartered fin. analyst. Asst. finance officer City of Greenville, N.C., 1986-87; investment officer North State Savs. and Loan, Greenville, 1983-86, Mecklenburg County, Charlotte, N.C., 1987—. Vol. Davidson Habitat for Humanity, Adult Basic Literacy Edn., Charlotte, 1990. Mem. Assn. Investment Mgmt. and Rsch. (former bd. dirs.), N.C. Soc. Fin. Analysts, N.C. Local Govt. Investment Assn. (past pres.). Avocations: reading, golf. Office: Mecklenburg County 600 E 4th St Fl 11 Charlotte NC 28202-2836

PORTER, GERALD JOSEPH, mathematician, educator; b. Elizabeth, N.J., Feb. 27, 1937; s. Fred and Tillie Florence (Friedman) P.; m. Judith Deborah Revitch, June 26, 1960; children: Daniel, Rebecca, Michael. AB, Princeton U., 1958; PhD, Cornell U., 1963; MA (hon.), U. Pa., 1971. Instr. MIT, 1963-65; asst. prof. math. U. Pa., Phila., 1965-69; assoc. prof. U. Pa., 1969-75, prof., 1975—, chmn. undergrad. affairs dept. math., 1971-73, assoc. dean computing Sch. Arts and Scis., 1981-91, dir. Interactive Math. Text Project, 1991—; bd. dirs. Com. Concerned Scientists; chair-elect faculty senate U. Pa., 1992-93, chair, 1993-94, past chair, 1994-95. Mem. Dem. Com., Haverford Twp., Pa., 1976-82, ward leader, 1980-84, treas., 1984-87. Postdoctoral fellow Office Naval Rsch., 1965-66. Mem. AAUP, Am. Math. Soc., Math. Assn. Am. (chmn. com. computers in math. edn. 1983-86, chmn. investment com. 1986—, bd. govs. 1980-83, 86—, mem. fin. com. 1986—, exec. com. 1992—, chmn. audit and budget com. 1988-90, 92, treas. 1992—), Assn. for Women in Math., AAAS, Nat. Assn. Mathematicians, Nat. Coun. Tchrs. Math., Joint Policy Bd. for Math., Am. Math. Assn. of Two Year Colls. Democrat. Jewish. Home: 161 Whitemarsh Rd Ardmore PA 19003-1698 Office: U Pa 4N69 DRL 209 S 33d St Philadelphia PA 19104-6395

PORTER, GLENN, museum and library administrator; b. New Boston, Tex., Apr. 2, 1944; s. Pat Paul and Mary Lee (Sanders) P.; m. K.T. Wimberly, June 1, 1968 (div. 1986); m. Barbara H. Butler, Dec. 18, 1987. BA, Rice U., 1966; MA, Johns Hopkins U., 1968, PhD, 1970. Asst. prof. bus. history Harvard Bus. Sch., Boston, 1970-76; dir. regional econ. history research ctr. Hagley Mus. & Library, Wilmington, Del., 1976-83, dir., 1984—. Editor Bus. History Rev., 1970-76; editorial bd. Jour. Am. History, 1977-80, Del. History, 1982—, Bus. History Rev., 1983-92; author: (with Harold C. Livesay) Merchants and Manufacturers, 1971; Rise of Big Business, 1860-1910, 1973, rev. edit., 1992; The Workers World at Hagley, 1981; gen. editor: Ency. of Am. Econ. History, 1980, The Papers of John D. Rockefeller, 1991. Mem. com. com. Nat. Survey of Historic Sites and Bldgs., Washington, 1976-79; council mem. Del. Humanities Council, 1981-83; trustee Worldesign Found., 1993-95, Andalusia Found., 1994—. pres., Ind. Rsch. Libr. Assn., 1994—. bd. dirs., Nat. Humanities Alliance, 1994—. Recipient Cultural Achievement award, U.S. Dept. Interior, 1979; NEH grantee, 1977-82, 81-83, 85-92, 93—. Mem. Bus. History Conf. (pres.1987), Soc. for History of Tech., Soc. Archtl. Historians, Independent Rsch. Librs. Assn. (pres.1994—), Nat. Humanities Alliance (bd. dirs. 1994—), Am. Assn. Mus., Mid-Atlantic Assn. Mus., Phi Beta Kappa. Office: Hagley Mus & Libr PO Box 3630 Wilmington DE 19807-0630

PORTER, HELEN VINEY (MRS. LEWIS M. PORTER, JR.), lawyer; b. Logansport, Ind., Sept. 7, 1935; d. Charles Lowry Viney and Florence Helen (Kunkel) V.; m. Lewis Morgan Porter, Jr., Dec. 26, 1966; children: Alicia Michelle, Andrew Morgan. A.B., Ind. U., 1957; J.D., U. Louisville, 1961. Bar: Ind. and Ill. 1961, U.S. Supreme Ct. 1971. Atty. office chief counsel Midwest regional office IRS, Chgo., 1961-73; assoc. regional atty. litigation center Equal Employment Opportunity Commn., Chgo., 1973-74; practice in Northbrook, Ill., 1974-79, 80-86; ptnr. Porter & Andersen, Chgo., 1979-80, Porter & Porter, Northfield, Ill., 1986—; lectr. Law in Am. Found., Chgo., summer, 1973, 74; assoc. prof. No Ill Coll Law (formerly Lewis U. Coll. Law), Glen Ellyn, Ill., 1975-79. Lectr. women's rights and fed. taxation to bar assns., civic groups. Recipient Disting. Alumni award U. Louisville Sch. of Law, 1986, President's Award Nat. Assn. of Women Lawyers, 1985. Fellow Am. Bar Found., Ill. State Bar Found.; mem. Women's Bar Assn. Ill. (pres. 1972-73), ABA (chmn. standing com. award 1983-85, bd. editors jour. 1984-90, mem. standing com. assn. comm. 1990-93), Fed. Bar Assn. (pres. Chgo. chpt. 1974-75), Ill. Bar Assn. (assembly del. 1972-78), Nat. Assn. Women Lawyers (pres. 1973-74). Home and Office: 225 Maple Row Northfield IL 60093-1037

PORTER, HENRY HOMES, JR., investor; b. Chgo., Nov. 13, 1934; s. Henry H. and Mary (Kinney) P.; m. Louisa Catherine Perkins, June 10, 1961; children: Mary Porter Johnson, Catherine. A.B., Yale U., 1956; M.B.A., Harvard U., 1962. With Gen. Mills, Inc., Mpls., 1962-76; asst. treas. Gen. Mills, Inc., 1964-67, treas., 1967-76, v.p. fin., treas., 1969-76; sr. v.p., chief fin. officer, dir. Brown & Williamson Industries, Inc., 1977-79, Batus, Inc., 1980; pres., dir. Promain Holdings, Inc., 1980—; chmn. bd. Louisville Nat. Records Mgmt. Corp.; active Ankle Systems, Inc., Mid. Continent Computer Group, Inc.; bd. dirs. SEI Corp., Dame Inc., Droll Inc., Caldwell & Orkin Funds, Inc. Lt. (j.g.) USNR, 1957-60. Home and Office: 5806 River Knolls Dr Louisville KY 40222-5914

PORTER, IRWIN W., food store chain executive; b. 1912; married. Chmn., dir. Giant Eagle, Inc. (formerly Giant Eagle Markets Inc.), Pitts. Office: Giant Eagle Inc 101 Kappa Dr Pittsburgh PA 15238-2833*

PORTER, IVAN, company executive; b. U.K., 1947. Acct. trainee, fin. Brit. Rys., 1963-68; mgmt. acct. Geest Industries Ltd., 1971-72; with Massey-Ferguson Ltd., 1969-71, 72—; with Perkins Engines, 1969-71, 72-80, comptroller, 1978-79, dir. group fin., 1979-80; corp. v.p. and comptroller Massey Ferguson Ltd, Toronto, Ont., Can., 1980-81, corp. v.p. fin. comptroller, 1981-83, pres. combines div., 1983-88; pres. diversified products group Jarrock Ltd., 1988-89; chief exec. officer Canron Inc., Toronto, 1989—. Office: Canron Inc, 145 King St W, Toronto, ON Canada M5H 1J8

PORTER, JACK NUSAN, writer, sociologist; b. Rovno, Ukraine, USSR, Dec. 2, 1944; came to U.S. 1946; s. Irving Puchtik and Faye (Merin) P.; m. Miriam Almuly, Sept. 18, 1977; children: Gabriel, Danielle. Cert., Machon Inst., Jerusalem, 1963; BAS cum laude, U. Wis., Milw., 1967; MA, PhD, Northwestern U., 1971; lic.real estate, Lee Inst., Brookline, Mass. 1982. Rsch. assoc. Harvard U. Ukrainian Rsch. Inst., Cambridge, Mass., 1982-84; pres. The Spencer Group (Real Estate Devel. and Cons.), Newton, Mass., 1984—; dir. The Spencer Sch. Real Estate, Newton, 1986—; dir. The Spencer Inst. for Bus. and Soc., Newton, 1984—; asst. prof. Coll. of Basic Studies Boston U., 1989-90; vis. lectr. Boston U. Met. Coll., 1987, 88, Bryant Coll., Smithfield, R.I., 1991; adj. lectr. U. Mass., Lowell, 1994-95; presenter White House Conf. on Family, 1980; mem. Gov. Dukakis' Adv. Coun., 1982-84; panelist on Comparative Genocide, the Oxford (Eng.) Conf., 1988; sr. rsch. assoc. Ctr. for Atomic Rsch. Studies, Brookline. Author or editor 25 books and anthologies including Confronting History and Holocaust, Sexual Politics in Nazi Germany, Kids in Cults, Jews and the Cults, Genocide and Human Rights, Conflict and Conflict Resolution, Jewish Partisans (2 vols.), The Jew as Outsider, The Sociology of Business, The Sociology of Jewry, An Historical Bibliography , Forclosed Property (with George Glazer), The Agunah: A Sourcebook, Handbook on Cults and Sects, curriculum guides in various fields; contbr. over 300 articles and revs. to jours. in field; founder, editor Jour. of the History of Sociology, 1977-85, The Sociology of Bus. Newsletter, 1977-79. Founder Holocaust Survival Video Project, Newton, Mass., 1992—; judge Nat. Jewish Book Awards, 1993-95; mem. Jewish Radical Edn. Project. John Atherton fellow Breadloaf Writers Conf., Middlebury, Vt., 1976; recipient Spl. award Boston Police Dept., 1986. Mem. PEN (newsletter com. 1992-95), Am. Sociol. Assn., Ea. Sociol. Soc., Am. Philos. Soc., New Eng. Soc., Tikkun. Avocations: collecting Jewish baseball cards and memorablia, reading, spiritual thinking. Home and Office: 8 Burnside Rd Newton MA 02161-1401 The older I get the important things in life are my wife, my children, good health, a few good friends, my brother and sister and Mom, of course, a good meal, and lastly - some money and fame.

PORTER, JAMES ALEXANDER, lawyer; b. Nashville, Sept. 17, 1942; s. Samuel Mann and Frances Van Sant (Scobee) P.; m. Harriet Ann Watkins, Nov. 26, 1966; children: Christopher Clayton, John McWilliams, Samuel Watkins. BA, Vanderbilt U., 1964, JD, 1971. Bar: Ga. 1971, U.S. Ct. Appeals (5th cir.) 1972, U.S. Supreme Ct. 1975, U.S. Ct. Appeals (11th cir.) 1983. Assoc. Swift, Currie, McGhee & Hiers, Atlanta, 1971-76, ptnr., 1976-80; ptnr. Porter, Davis, & Saunders, Atlanta, 1980-83, Asbill, Porter, Churchill & Nellis, Atlanta, 1983-86, Porter & Doster, Atlanta, 1986—. Pres. Buckhead Little League Baseball, Atlanta, 1988-89. Lt. (j.g.), USNR, 1964-68. Mem. ABA, State Bar Ga., Atlanta Bar Assn. Episcopalian. Avocations: fishing, hunting, skiing, running, sports. Office: Porter & Doster 3525 Piedmont Rd NE Atlanta GA 30305

PORTER, JAMES H., chemical engineering executive; b. Port Chester, N.Y., Nov. 11, 1933; s. George James and Josephine (Hall) P.; m. Sandra Adrienne Knox, Sept. 8, 1958 (div. Dec. 1969); children: Michael Brandon, Adrienne Michelle, Lynn Sharon; m. Jennifer Anne Waterhouse, Feb. 26, 1978. BSChemE, Rensselaer Poly. Inst., 1955; ScD, MIT, 1963. Tech. svc. engr. Exxon, Linden, N.J., 1955-58; rsch. engr. Chevron Rsch. Corp., Richmond, Calif., 1963-67; mgr. process design Abcor Inc., Cambridge, Mass., 1967-71; assoc. prof. MIT, Cambridge, 1971-76; v.p. energy div. Energy Resources Co. Inc., Cambridge, 1976-79; pres. Energy and Environ. Engring. Inc., Somerville, Mass., 1979—; sci. adv. bd. U.S. EPA, Washington, 1976-83. Author: Chemical Equilibria in C.H.O. Systems, 1976; patentee in field. Bd. dirs. Tisbury Waterways Inc., Vineyard Haven, Mass., 1990, Trustees of Reservation, Boston, 1991, Cambridge Adult Edn. Ctr., Cambridge, 1988, sec., 1991. Mem. Am. Inst. Chem. Engrs., Nat. Orgn. Black Chemists and Chem. Engrs. (pres. 1978-79, bd. dirs., Founders award 1983), Sigma Xi, Pi Delta Epsilon. Avocations: sportsfishing, bridge. Home: PO Box 1131 Vineyard Haven MA 02568 Office: Energy & Environ Engring Inc PO Box 215 Malden MA 02148

PORTER, JAMES MORRIS, state judge; b. Cleve., Sept. 14, 1931; s. Emmett Thomas and Mary (Connell) P.; m. Helen Marie Adams, May 31, 1952; children: James E., Thomas W., William M., Daniel J. A.B., John Carroll U., 1953; J.D., U. Mich., 1957. Bar: Ohio 1957. Assoc. firm M.B. & H.H. Johnson, Cleve., 1957-62, McAfee, Hanning, Newcomer, Hazlett & Wheeler, Cleve., 1962-67; ptnr. firm Squire, Sanders & Dempsey, Cleve., 1967-92; judge Ohio Ct. Appeals, 8th Dist., Cleve., 1993—. 1st lt. U.S. Army, 1953-55. Fellow Am. Coll. Trial Lawyers; mem. Best Lawyers in Am., Union Club, The Club, The Country Club (Cleve.). Republican. Roman Catholic. Office: Lakeside Courthouse Ct Appeals Lakeside Ave Cleveland OH 44113-1082

PORTER, JAMES R., computer company executive; b. 1936. With IBM Corp., 1961-68, Tracor Computer, 1968-70, United Sys., 1970-72, Informatics Gen. Corp., 1972-85; with Triad Sys. Corp., Livermore, Calif., 1985—, pres., chief exec. officer. With USAF, 1958-61. Office: Triad Systems Corp 3055 Triad Dr Livermore CA 94550-9206*

PORTER, JILL, journalist; b. Phila., Aug. 5, 1946; d. Sidney and Mae (Merion) Chalfin; m. Eric Porter, Mar. 7, 1970 (div. 1975); m. Fred Hamilton, Oct. 28, 1983; 1 child, Zachary. BA, Temple U., 1968. Pub. rels. Manning Smith P.R., Phila., 1968-69; reporter Norristown Times Herald, Norristown, Pa., 1969-72, The Trentonian, Trenton, N.J., 1972-75; reporter The Phila. Daily News, Phila., 1975-79, columnist, 1979—; instr. Temple U., 1976-80. Contbr. articles to numerous mags. Vol. Phila. Futures, 1994. Recipient Keystone Press award Pa. Newspaper Publisher's Assn., 1985. Avocations: reading, gardening. Home: 715 Stradone Rd Bala Cynwyd PA 19004-2113 Office: Phila Newspapers Inc Phila Daily News 400 N Broad St Philadelphia PA 19130-4015

PORTER, JOHN EDWARD, congressman; b. Evanston, Ill., June 1, 1935; s. Harry H. and Beatrice V. P.; m. Kathryn Cameron; 5 children. Attended, MIT, BSBA, Northwestern U., 1958; JD with distinction, U. Mich., 1961; DHL, Barat Coll., 1988; LLD (hon.), Kendall Coll., 1992. Bar: Ill. 1961, U.S. Supreme Ct. 1968. Former honor law grad. atty., appellate div. Dept. Justice, Washington; mem. Ill. Ho. of Reps., 1973-79; mem. house appropriations com., subcoms. on labor, health & human svcs., edn., fgn. ops. 96-103rd Congresses from 10th Ill. Dist., Ill., 1980—; mem. legis. select com. on aging, 1980-92; founder, co-chmn. Congl. Human Rights Caucus; founder Congl. Coalition on Population and Devel. Past editor: Mich. Law Rev. Recipient Best Legislator award League of Conservation Voters, 1973, Ind. Voters Ill., 1974, Chgo. Crime Commn., 1976, Lorax award Global Tomorrow Coalition, 1989, Spirit of Enterprise award U.S. C. of C., 1988, 89, 90, Golden Bulldog award Watchdogs of the Treasury, 11 times, Taxpayer's Friend award Nat. Taxpayers Union, Taxpayer Superhero award Grace Commn.'s Citizens Against Government Waste. Republican. Office: US Ho of Reps 2373 Rayburn House Bldg Washington DC 20515-1310

PORTER, JOHN FINLEY, JR., physicist, conservationist, retired educator; b. Birmingham, Ala., Aug. 22, 1927; s. John Finley and Janice (Nowell) P.; m. Jacqueline Christine Harbin, Dec. 27, 1949; children: Gayle P. Barnett, John Finley III, Paul William, Adam Michael, David Wade. BS, U. Ala., 1950, MS, 1956, PhD, Johns Hopkins U., 1966. Rsch. staff asst. Radiation Lab., Johns Hopkins U., 1956-59; rsch. assoc. Carlyle Barton Lab. Johns Hopkins U., 1959-66, rsch. scientist, 1966, lectr. elec. engring., 1965-66; assoc. prof. physics U. Ala., Huntsville, 1966-69, chmn. physics faculty, 1968-69, prof., 1969-72; dean faculty Johns Hopkins U., 1969-70, dean grad. programs and rsch., 1970-72; dep. exec. dir. Ala. Commn. on Higher Edn., 1972-73, exec. dir., 1973-81; vis. prof. adminstrn. and higher edn. U.Ala. Coll. Edn., 1981-83, prof., 1983-92, acting dir. Office Instl. Rsch., 1984-91, dir. Office Instl. Rsch., 1991-92, prof. emeritus, 1992—; cons. Catalyst Rsch.

Corp., Balt., Environ. Sci. Svc. Adminstrn., Washington; chmn. State Coun. Grad. Deans, 1971-72; mem. planning bd. Edn. Commn. of States, 1975-77; mem. adv. coun. Ala. Right to Read, 1974-76; mem. Ala. Post Secondary Edn. Planning Commn., 1974-76, Gov.'s Budget Adv. Com. 1976-77. Contbr. articles to profl. jours. Bd. dirs., v.p. Tuscaloosa County Preservation Soc., 1988-89, 1990-91; v.p. Ala. Ornithol. Soc., 1990-91, pres., 1991-93; bd. dirs Tuscaloosa Audubon Soc., 1989-92, Ala. Coastal Found., 1994—, Mobile Bay Audubon Soc., 1993—; mem. Ala. Audubon Coun., 1990—; pres. Friends of Dauphin Island Audubon Sanctuary Inc., 1992—. Methodist. Home: 1404 Cadillac Ave PO Box 848 Dauphin Island AL 36528-0848

PORTER, JOHN FRANCIS, III, banker; b. Wilmington, Del., Sept. 17, 1934; s. John Francis, Jr. and Eloise Wilhelmina (Berlinger) P.; m. Ann Mayfield, Sept. 8, 1956; children: Leslie Gibson, Nina Porter Winfield, Sophie Porter Rohrer. BA, U. Va., 1956; MBA, U. Del., 1965. With Del. Trust Co., Wilmington, 1958—; asst. treas. Del. Trust Co., 1960-66, sec., 1966-68, v.p., sec., 1968-72, sr. v.p., 1972-75, exec. v.p., 1975-79, pres., 1979-88, chmn., chief exec. officer, 1988—; vice chmn. BANKPAC, 1982-86, chmn., 1986-88. Mem. bank adv. bd. State of Del., 1969-71; mem. Council on Banking for State of Del., 1970—, chmn., 1976—; trustee Alfred I. duPont Testamentary Trust, 1995—, Alfred I. duPont Inst. Nemours Found., 1971—, chmn. bd. mgrs., 1990-94; chmn. exec. coun. Thomas Jefferson U. Med. Ctr., Del./AIDI Affiliation , 1990-92, mem., 1990—; pres. Wilmington and Brandywine Cemetery, 1974—; bd. dirs., trustee, mem. fin. com. mem. exec. com. Med. Ctr. Del., 1985—; bd. dirs. Penjerdel, 1989—, State v.p., 1990—; bd. gov. Winterthur Corp. Coun., 1989—, chmn., 1993-95. Capt. arty., U.S. Army, 1957. Mem. Am. Bankers Assn. (govt. rels. coun. 1984-88), Del. Bankers Assn. (pres. 1984-85, bd. dirs. 1981-87), Del. Bus. Roundtable (vice chmn. exec. com., 1989-92, chmn. exec. com. 1993-94), Court on Judiciary Preliminary Investigatory Com. (Panel B 1991—), Clubs: Wilmington Country (bd. dir.), Wilmington (bd. govs 1980-89), Vicmead Hunt; Nassau (Princeton, N.J.). Home: 4821 Kennett Pike Wilmington DE 19807-1813 Office: Del Trust Co 900 N Market St Wilmington DE 19801-3026

PORTER, JOHN ROBERT, art history educator, curator, writer; b. Lévis, Que., Can., Apr. 28, 1949; s. John William and Irène (Bernier) P.; m. Martine Tremblay, July 26, 1975; children: Isabelle, Jean-Olivier. LèsL, Laval U., 1971, Ma, 1972; PhD, U. Montreal, 1982. Asst. curator Can. art Nat. Gallery Can., 1972-78; prof. art history Laval U., 1978—; chief curator Montreal Mus. Fine Arts, 1990-93; dir. Musée du Que., 1993—; mem. programming and acquisition coms. for various mus. Author various books, catalogues and articles in field. Office: Musée du Québec, Parc des Champs-de-Bataille, Quebec, PQ Canada G1R 5H3

PORTER, JOHN ROBERT, JR., space technology company executive, geochemist; b. Oklahoma City, Feb. 27, 1935; s. John Robert and Margaret Florence (Nicholson) P.; m. Amelie Alexanderson Wallace, June 2, 1963; children: Jennifer A. Porter Dowling, Amelie M. BA, Dartmouth Coll., 1957; MS, Okla. U., 1964. Cert. petroleum geologist. Am. Assn. Petroleum Geologists. Analyst CIA, Washington, 1962-66; chief Earth Resources Program NASA, Washington, 1966-69; pres., chmn. Earth Satellite Corp., Rockville, Md., 1969—; bd. dirs. Stauffer Communications, Inc., Topeka; mem. space applications bd. NRC, Washington, 1983-86, GEOSAT Com., Norman, Okla., 1972—. Trustee Washington Gallery Modern Art, 1966-67. 1st lt. U.S. Army, 1960-62. Mem. Am. Assn. Petroleum Geologists, Chevy Chase Club. Republican. Presbyterian. Avocations: tennis, squash, skiing, jogging. Home: 3407 36th St NW Washington DC 20016-3147 Office: Earth Satellite Corp 6011 Executive Blvd # 400 Rockville MD 20852-3804

PORTER, JOHN STEPHEN, television executive; b. Avoca, N.Y., Sept. 2, 1932; s. Frank R. and Margaret H. (McGreel) P.; m. Marie C. Eiffert, Sept. 6, 1958; children: Stephen, David, Mark, Kevin, Matthew. B.A. in English, St. John Fisher U., 1958; M.S. in Radio/TV, Syracuse U., 1959; postgrad. in Edn, U. Rochester, 1960-61. Producer, broadcaster weekly news analysis N.Y. State Empire State FM Sch. of Air, 1962-64; producer, narrator weekly series sta. WROC-FM, Rochester, N.Y., 1964-65; pres., gen. mgr. sta. WXXI-TV, Rochester, 1966-69; trustee Eastern Ednl. TV Network, Boston, 1966-68, mem. exec. com., 1967-68, exec. dir., 1969-89, pres., mem. exec. com., 1989-92; pres., mem. exec. com. Am. Program Svc. (formerly Ea. Ednl. TV Network), Boston, 1992—. Served to 1st lt. USAR, 1958. Mem. N.Y. State Ednl. Radio/TV Assn. (treas. 1962-64), Pub. TV Sta. Mgrs. New York State (chmn. 1968-69), Nat. Assn. Ednl. Broadcasters (adv. com.). Home: 1001 Marina Point Dr # 307 North Quincy MA 02171

PORTER, JOHN T., health facility administrator; b. 1948. Grad., U. S.D. With Presentation Health Sys., Sioux Falls, S.D., 1980—, pres.; pvt. practice as lawyer, Yankton, S.D., 1973-80. Office: Presentation Health System 1301 S 9th Ave Sioux Falls SD 57105*

PORTER, JOHN WILSON, education executive; b. Ft. Wayne, Ind., Aug. 13, 1931; s. James Richard and Ola (Phillips) P.; m. Lois Helen French, May 27, 1961; children: Stephen James, Donna Agnes. BA, Albion Coll., 1953; MA, Mich. State U., 1957, PhD, 1962; D in Pub. Adminstrn. (hon.), Albion Coll., LLD (hon.), Mich. State U., 1977, Cleary Coll., 1987; LHD, Adrian Coll., 1970, U. Detroit, 1979; LLD, Western Mich. U., 1971, Eastern Mich. U., 1975, HHD, Kalamazoo Coll., 1973, Detroit Coll. Bus., 1975, Madonna Coll., Livonia, Mich., 1977; DEd, Detroit Inst. Tech., 1978; AA, Schoolcraft Coll., Livonia, Mich., 1979; DBA, Lawrence Inst. Tech., 1988; LLD, Cleary Coll., 1989. Counselor Lansing (Mich.) Pub. Schs., 1953-58; cons. Mich. Dept. Pub. Instrn., 1958-61; dir. Mich. Higher Edn. Assistance Authority, 1961-65; assoc. supt. for higher edn. Mich. Dept. Edn. 1966-69, state supt. schs., 1969-79; pres. Ea. Mich. U., Ypsilanti, 1979-89; CEO Urban Edn. Alliance Inc., Ann Arbor, Mich., 1988—; v.p. Nat. Bd. for Profl. Teaching Standards, 1989; gen. supt. Detroit Pub. Schs., 1989-91; CEO Urban Edn. Alliance, Inc., Ypsilanti, Mich., 1991—; mem. numerous profl. commns. and bds., 1959—, including; Commn. on Financing Postsecondary Edn., 1972-74, Commn. for Reform Secondary Edn., Kettering Found., 1972-75, Edn. Commn. of States, 1973-79, Nat. Commn. on Performance-Based Edn., 1974-76, Nat. Commn. on Manpower Policy, 1974-79, Mich. Employment and Tng. Svcs. Coun., 1976-79, Nat. Adv. Coun. on Social Security, 1977-79, Commn. on Ednl. Credit, Am. Coun. on Edn., 1977-80; task panel on mental health of family Commn. on Mental Health, 1977-80; mem. Nat. Coun. for Career Edn. (HEW), 1974-76; pres. bd. dirs. Chief State Sch. Officers, 1974-79; pres. Coun. Chief State Sch. Officers, 1977-78; bd. dirs. Comerica Bank; former chmn. bd. Coll. Entrance Exam. Bd., 1984-86. Trustee Nat. Urban League, 1973-79, Charles Stewart Mott Found., 1981—, Albion Coll., 1989—; bd. dirs. Mich. Internat. Council, 1977—, Mich. Congress Parents and Tchrs.; mem. bd. overseers com. for Grad. Sch., Harvard U., 1980-88; mem. edn. com. NAACP; convener grad 6 Nat. Edn. Goals Panel, 1990—; mem. East Lansing Human Relations Commn.; chmn. Am. Assn. State Colls. and U.'s Task Force on Excellence in Edn.; mem. Mich. Martin Luther King, Jr. Holiday Commn., Gov.'s Blue Ribbon Commn. on Welfare Reform; trustee East Lansing Edgewood United Ch.; mem. Catherine McAuley Health Systems Bd., 1990—. Recipient numerous awards including Disting. Svc. award Mich. Congress Parents and Tchrs., 1963, Disting. Svc. award NAACP, Lansing, 1968; cert. of outstanding achievement Delta Kappa chpt. Phi Beta Sigma, 1970; award for disting. svc. Assn. Ind. Colls. and Univs. Mich., 1974; Disting. Alumni award Coll. Edn., Mich. State U., 1974; award for disting. svc. to edn Mich. State U., 1974; Disting. Alumni award, 1979; award for disting. svc. to edn. in Mich. Mich. Assn. Secondary Sch. Prins., 1974; President's award as disting. educator Nat. Alliance Black Sch. Educators, 1977; Marcus Foster Disting. Educator award, 1979; recognition award Mich. Ednl. Rsch. Assn., 1978; recognition award Mich. Assn. Secondary Sch. Prins., 1978; recognition award Mich. Assn. Intermediate Sch. Adminstrs., 1979; recognition award Mich. Assn. Sch. Adminstrs., 1979; Mich. Sch. Bus. Ofcls., 1979; resolution Mich. State Legislature, 1978; Anthony Wayne award Coll. Edn., Wayne State U., 1979; Educator of Decade award Mich. Assn. State and Fed. Program Specialists, 1979; Spirit of Detroit award Detroit City Coun., 1981; Disting. Svc. award Ypsilanti Area C. of C., 1988; Philip A. Hart award Mich. Women's Hall of Fame, 1988; Summit award Greater Detroit C. of C., 1991; Mich. State C. of C. award 1991; inducted Mich. Edn. Hall of Fame, 1992. Mem. Am. Assn. Sch. Adminstrs., Am. Assn. State Colls. and Univs. (president's council, chmn. task force on excellence in edn.), Nat.

Measurement Council, NAACP (life), Greater Detroit C. of C. (Summit 1991), Mich. State C. of C. (Disting. Svc. and Leadership award 1991), Tuskeegee Airmen (Disting. Svc. award 1991), Mich. PTA (hon. life), Econ. Club (dir. 1979), Sigma Pi Phi, Phi Delta Kappa. Office: Urban Edn Alliance Inc 900 Victors Way Ste 210 Ann Arbor MI 48108-1779

PORTER, JUDITH DEBORAH REVITCH, sociologist, educator; b. Phila., Mar. 26, 1940; d. Eugene and Esther (Tulchinsky) Revitch; m. Gerald Joseph Porter, June 26, 1960; children—Daniel, Rebecca, Michael. Student, Vassar Coll., 1958-60; BA, Cornell U., 1962, MA, 1963; PhD, Harvard U., 1967. Lectr. Bryn Mawr (Pa.) Coll., 1966-67, asst. prof., 1967-73, assoc. prof., 1973-79, prof. sociology, 1979—, chair dept. sociology, 1987—. Author: Black Child, White Child: The Development of Racial Attitudes, 1971; contbr. articles to profl. jours. Committeeperson Haverford Twp. Democratic Party, 1976—. Ford Found. fellow, 1973-74; NSF fellow, 1967. Mem. Am. Sociol. Assn., Soc Psychol. Study Social Issues, Phi Beta Kappa, Phi Kappa Phi. Jewish. Home: 161 Whitemarsh Rd Ardmore PA 19003-1698 Office: Bryn Mawr Coll Dept Sociology Bryn Mawr PA 19010

PORTER, KARL HAMPTON, orchestra musical director, conductor; b. Pitts., Apr. 25, 1939; s. Reginald and Naomi Arzetta (Mitchell) P. Student, Carnegie-Mellon U., 1957-60, Peabody Conservatory, 1960-62, Juilliard Sch. Music, 1962-63, Domaine Sch. Condrs., 1961-63, Am. Symphony Orch. League/Tanglewood, 1962-72; student Polit. Sci., Fordham U., 1978; student Bus. Computer Tng., SUNY, 1986. judge for Congress of Strings, BMI Composers Competition, 1970-74; instr. theory Mt. Morris Park, 1969-73; instr. woodwind L.I. Inst. Music, 1969-75, U. Denver, 1963-64, Coll. New Rochelle, 1980; tchr. bassoon Newark Community Arts Center, 1969-71; instr. music N.Y.C. Tech. Coll., 1972-90; pres. Finale Prodns. Mem., Denver Symphony Orch., 1963-64, Met. Opera Nat. Co., 1965-67, Gil Evans Band, 1967-69, formed, Harlem Youth Symphony, 1968, Harlem Philharmonic Orch., 1969—, New Breed Brass Ensemble, Harlem String Quartet, Harlem Woodwind Quintet, 1970, condr., Balt. Symphony, 1970, mus. dir., condr., Harlem Philharmonic Orch., 1970—, N.Y.C. Housing Authority Orch., 1972-86, Massapequa (N.Y.) Symphony Soc., 1974-80, condr., Park West Symphony, Northeastern Philharmonic of Pa., Scranton Philharmonic, Ridgefield Symphonette, 1971, mus. dir. for Josephine Baker, 1972, free lance bassoonist, Am. Symphony, Bklyn. Philharmonic, N.J. Symphony, 1967—; min. of music St. Thomas the Apostle, 1989—; dir. Independent Communty Ctr., 1993—; dir. counselor Elmcor Youth Ctr., 1991-93. Mem. nat. adv. bd. Dance Theatre of Harlem, Air Force Assn., Mental Health Assn.; bd. dirs. Empire Trust; hon. bd. dirs. Sickle Cell, Baton Rouge, La.; performing arts coord. Afro-Acad. Cultural Tech. Sci. Olympics; cons. N.Y. State Coun. Arts; dir. Ind. Cmty. Ctr., 1993—; field ops. supr.; U.S. Bur. Census. Recipient Martha Baird Rockefeller Found. grant, 1969, Nat. Endowment grant, 1970. Mem. NAACP, Nat. Soc. Lit. and Arts, N.Y. State Assn. Jr. Colls., Am. Symphony Orch. League, Performing Arts Assn. N.Y., Soc. Black Composers, Nat. Soc. Symphony Condrs. Club: The Bohemians. Home: 425 Central Park W New York NY 10025 Office: PO Box 445 New York NY 10025-0445

PORTER, LILIANA ALICIA, artist, printmaker; b. Buenos Aires, Argentina, Oct. 6, 1941; came to U.S., 1964, naturalized, 1982; d. Julio and Margarita (Galetar) P.; m. Luis Camnitzer, 1965 (div. 1978); m. Alan B. Wiener, May 28, 1980 (div. 1991). Grad., Nat. Sch. Fine Arts, Argentina, 1963. Co-dir. and instr. Studio Camnitzer-Porter summer workshops, Lucca, Italy, 1974, 75, 76, 77; assoc. prof. art Queens Coll., N.Y.C., 1991—; adj. lectr. SUNY Coll., Old Westbury, N.Y., 1974-76, Purchase N.Y., 1987; co-dir. Studio Porter-Wiener, N.Y.C., 1979-87. One-woman shows of prints and/or paintings include Galeria Artemultiple, Buenos Aires, Argentina, 1977, 78, Galleria Arte Comunale, Adro, Brescia, Italy, 1977, Hundred Acres Gallery, N.Y.C., 1977, Mus. Modern Art, Cali, Colombia, 1978, Center for Interamerican Relations, N.Y.C., 1980, Galeria Arte Nuevo, Buenos Aires, 1980, Barbara Toll Fine Arts, N.Y.C., 1979, 81, 82, 84, Galerie Jolliet, Montreal, 1983, Museo de Arte Contemporaneo, Panama City, Panama, 1984, Dolan/Maxwell Gallery, Phila., 1985, U. Alta., Edmonton, 1985, Dolan/Maxwell Gallery, Phila., 1985, Galería Luigi Marrozzini, San Juan, P.R., 1986, Galería-Taller, Museo de Arte Moderno, Cali, Colombia, 1987, The Space, Boston, 1988, Syracuse U., N.Y., 1990, retrospective exhibit 1968-90 Fundacion San Telmo, Buenos Aires, 1990, Museo Nacional de Artes Plasticas, Montevideo, Uruguay, 1991, Centro de Recepciones del Gobierno, San Juan, P.R., 1991, Bronx Mus. Art, N.Y.C., 1992, retrospective exhibit Archer Huntington Art Gallery U. Tex. Austin, 1993, Steinbaum-Krauss Gallery, N.Y.C., 1993, Galeria Ruth Benzacar, Buenos Aires, 1994; numerous group shows, 1963—, latest being Center for Interamerican Relations, N.Y.C., 1978, Chateau de L'Hermitage, Belgium, 1978, Mus. Fine Arts, Buenos Aires, 1978, Alternative Center for Internat. Arts, N.Y.C., 1978, Ben Shah Gallery, N.J., 1979, Everson Mus., Syracuse, N.Y., 1979, Alternative Mus., N.Y.C., 1980, Bronx Mus. Fine Arts, 1982, Musee d'Art Contemporain, Montreal, 1983, Queens Coll., Flushing, N.Y., 1983, Mus. Modern Art, San Francisco, 1983, Galeria Epoca, Santiago, Chile, 1986, Centro Wilfredo Lam, Cuba, 1986, Mus. Contemporary Spanish Art, N.Y.C., 1987, MOMA, N.Y.C., 1993; represented in permanent collections Mus. Phila., Mus. Modern Art, N.Y.C., RCA Corp., N.Y.C., N.Y. Public Library, N.Y.C., La Biblioteque Nationale, Paris, France, Museo del Grabado, Buenos Aires, Museo Universitario, Mexico City, Mexico, Museo de Art Moderno, Cali, Colombia, Museo de Bellas Artes, Caracas, Venezuela, Met. Mus. Art, N.Y.C. Recipient 1st prize Argentinian Art 78 Mus. Fine Arts, Buenos Aires, 1978, Grand Prix XI, Internat. Print Biennial, Cracow, Poland, 1986, 1st prize VII Latin Am. Print Biennial, San Juan, Puerto Rico, 1986; fellow Guggenheim Found., 1980-81, N.Y. Found. for the Arts, 1985. Address: 178 Franklin St 5th Floor New York NY 10013

PORTER, MAX L., engineering educator; b. Hamburg, Iowa, Oct. 25, 1942; s. Harry E. and Mary O. P.; m. Monica G, Munyer, Aug. 2, 1969; 1 child. Nathan A. BS in Civil Engring., Iowa State U., 1965, MS in Structural Engring., 1968, PhD in Structural Engring., 1974. Registered structural engr., Iowa. Party chief survey crew Iowa Dept. Transp. (formerly Iowa State Hwy. Commn.), Atlantic, Iowa, 1965; instr. Iowa State U., Ames, 1966-74, asst. prof., 1974-77, assoc. prof., 1977-81, prof., assoc. engr. Ames Lab., 1981—; civil engring. asst. bridge dept. County of L.A., 1966; tech. subcom. 5 Masonry Bldg. Seismic Safety Coun., 1989-92; mem. Iowa State Bd. Engring. Examiners Peer Review Com., 1991, 92; mem. tech. adv. bd. Espeland Mktg. and Rsch., 1992-93; cons. Pitney, Hardin, Kipp, Szuch, Interstate Power, Associated Engrs., Otto-Culver, Chuck Barnes, Am. Iron and Steel Inst., Computerized Designs, Inc., Teltech, Inc., Skinner, Beattie & Wilson, Wheeling Corrugating Co. Wheeling-Pittsburg Steel Corp, City of Dubuque, Iowa, Gen. Svcs. Adminstrn., Edwards Precast, Allison, McCormac & Nicholaus, White & Johnson, Nady Engring., Engring. Tech. Assistance Program, Teltech Svcs., Midwest Planners, David Koench, Architect, City of Ames, City of Spencer, Iowa Mut. Ins., ASC Pacific Corp, others; expert witness in field; presenter numerous seminars; participant numerous nat. confs. Co-author: Commentary on the Specifications for the Design and Construction of Composite Slabs, 1985, Specifications for the Design and Construction of Composite Slabs, 1985, Form and Style Manual for ASCE Codes and Standards, 1990, Commentary on Specifications for Masonry Structures, 1988, Commentary on Building Code Requirements for Masonry Structures, 1988, Specifications for Masonry Structures, 1988, Building Code Requirements for Masonry Structures, 1988, Introduction to the Codes and Standards Development, 1991, Commentary to Chapter 24, Masonry of the Uniform Building Code 1988 Edition, 1990, Commentary on Specifications for the Construction and Inspection of Composite Slabs, 1992, Commentary on Building Standard for Structural Design of Composite Slabs, 1992, Commentary on Chapter 24, Masonry of the Uniform Building Code 1991 Edition, 1992, Specifications for Masonry Structures, 1992, Building Code Requirements for Masonry Structures, 1992, State-of-the-Art-Report on Fiber Reinforced Concrete, 1993, Commentary on the Standard for the Structural Design of Composite Slabs, 1993, Commentary on the Standard Practice for the Construction and Inspection of Composite Slabs, 1993, Standard Practice for the Construction and Inspection of Composite Slabs, 1993, Standard for Structural Design of Composite Slabs, 1993; contbr. articles to profl. jours. Vice chmn. King-Am Neighborhood Assn., 1982-88, pres. 1991—; bd. dirs. Ames Econ. Devel. Commn., 1987-89; trustee Presbyn. Ch., 1989-91, deacon, 1992—,. Fred Loy Meml. scholar in Civil Engring., 1964; recipient Citation of Merit Enerpac hydraulic divsn. Applied Power Industries, Inc., 1974; grantee Agy. Internat. Devel., Masonry Inst. Iowa, Masons Union Iowa, Civil Engring. Rsch. Assistant-

ship, Engring. Project Devel. Funding, 1981-84, Wheeling Corrigating Co.divsn. Wheeling-Pittsburg Steel Co., 1985-90, 87, 89-92, Vulcraft divsn. Nucor Corp., 1985-88, 86-90, U.S. Nuclear Regulatory Commn., 1984, Carter-Waters, Monarch Cement Co., Mac-Fab Corp. St. Louis, 1985-87, Thermomass Tech. Inc., 1986-87, Amoco Foam Products Co., 1986-87, NSF, 1987-90, 92—, Iowa Tech. Coun., 1988, Walker divsn. Butler Mfg., 1989, Dow Chem. Co., Shafer Fiberglass Co., 1989-90, Ctr. Advanced Tech. and Devel., 1990-92, Iowa Hwy. Rsch. Bd., 1990-93, Hammer's Plastic Recycling Corp., Composite Tech. Corp., 1990-92, DUR-O-WAL, Inc., 1991-92, DEHA, Martin Marietta Energy Systems, Inc., 1992, Wallace Techs., 1992-93, Espeland Mktg. & Rsch., Inc., 1992—; others; named Most Valuable Player Sixth Internat. Specialty Conf. Cold Steel Structures, 1982. Mem. ASCE (png coms. 1978-79, moderator student conf. 1978, com. composite constrn. divsn. structures 1977-84, 86-90, chmn. 1979-82, exec. com. tech. coun. codes and standards 1986-89, vice-chmn. 1988-89, adminstrv. com. bldg. codes 1987-93, steel deck & concrete com. 1977-92, standards com. design loads for structures during constrn. 1989-92, chmn. subcom. devel. mgmt. group plan 1988-90, task group oper. procedures and ops. manual 1989-90, masonry limit states standards com. 1989-92, chmn. structural standards exec. com. 1989-93, chmn. design subcom. allowable stress and empirical design 1990-93, vice chair nat. masonry standards joint com. 1990-93, nat. earthquake hazard reduction program adv. com. 1990-93, mgmt. group F 1991—, chair subcom. design composite deck slabs 1992—), NSPE (budget com. 1982-84, parliamentarian nat. convs. 1982-84, 85-86, 89, 90), chmn. constn. & bylaws com. 1983-84), AAUP (Iowa State U. chpt., chmn. faculty appeals grievance com. 1988-91), Am. Concrete Inst. (Iowa-Minn. chpt. com. 530 new masonry bldg. code standards 1988-89, bd. dirs. 1985-88, chpt. v.p. 1988-89, chpt. pres. 1989-90, immediate past pres., bd. dirs., chair nominations 1990-91, vice chair com. 530 masonry standards 1990-92, chair design subcom. 1990-92, com. fiber reinforced plastic 1991-93, com. fiber reinforced concrete 1991-93, subcom. bond and devel. 1991-93), Am. Inst. Parliamentarians, Nat. Assn. Parliamentarians, Nat. Inst. Bldg. Scis. (reviewer gen. svcs. adminstrn. model codes implementation study project com. 1989), Nat. Inst. Engring. Ethics, Iowa State Assn. Parliamentarians, Assn. Internat. Cooperation and Rsch. Steel-Concrete Composite Structures, Iowa Engring. Soc. (Anson Marston chpt. bd. dirs. 1978-79, chmn. young engrs. com. 1977-78, chmn. profl. devel. com., membership com. 1979-81, activities com. 1979-80, v.p. 1980-82, chmn. nominations com. 1982-86, pres.-elect 1982-83, co-chair matthcounts 1983-85, pres. 1983-84), Bldg. Seismic Safety Coun., Earthquake Engring. Rsch. Inst., Structural Engrs. Assn. Ctrl. Iowa (bd. dirs. 1977-79), Concrete Reinforcing Steel Inst., Soc. Exptl. Stress Analysis, Internat. Conf. Bldg. Officials, N.Y. Acad. Scis., Masonry Soc. (rsch. com. 1986-92, bd. dirs. Ctrl. Region 1987-92, codes com. 1988-92, masonry limit states standards com. 1989-92, vice chair, chair design subcom. and nat. masonry standards joint com. 1990-92, assoc. editor The Masonry Soc. Jour. 1990-93, chair pubs. com. 1991-92, editor The Masonry Soc. News 1992-93), Precast/Prestressed Concrete Inst., Rotary (Paul Harris sustaining 1986—, chmn. fellowship and brotherhood com. 1987-89), Iowa State Meml. Union (life), Scabbard & Blade, Order Knoll, Sigma Xi, Phi Kappa Phi, Tau Beta Pi, Chi Epsilon, Phi Eta Sigma. Office: Iowa State U Dept Civil Constrn Eng Ames IA 50011

PORTER, MICHAEL PELL, lawyer; b. Indpls., Mar. 31, 1940; s. Harold Troxel and Mildred Maxine (Pell) P.; m. Alliene Laura Jenkins, Sept. 23, 1967 (div.); children: Genevieve Natalie, Porter Eason; m. Janet Kay Smith Hayes, Feb. 13, 1983 (div.). Student, DePauw U., 1957-58; BA, Tulane U., 1961, LLB, 1963. Bar: La. 1963, U.S. Ct. Mil. Appeals 1964, N.Y. 1969, Hawaii 1971. Clk. U.S. Ct. Appeals (5th cir.), New Orleans, 1963; assoc. Sullivan & Cromwell, N.Y.C., 1968-71, Cades Schutte Fleming & Wright, Honolulu, 1971-74, prnr., 1975-94; mem. faculty Addis Ababa (Ethiopia) U. Sch Law, 1995—; mem. deans coun. Law Sch. Tulane U., 1981-88; dep. vice chancellor Episcopal Diocese Hawaii, 1980-88, chancellor, 1988-94; chancellor Episcopal Ch., Micronesia, 1988-95. Author: Hawaii Corporation Law & Practice, 1989, Nat. Corp. Law Series, 1989; Hawaii reporter: State Limited Partnership Laws, 1992-94. Bd. dirs. Jr. Achievement Hawaii, Inc., 1974-84, Inst. Human Svcs., Inc., 1980-88; donor Michael P. Porter Dean's Scholastic award U. Hawaii Law Sch., 1977—; lectorship named in his honor, Addis Abba, Etheopia, 1994—; established Michael P. Porter Prizes on Ethnic Harmony and Religious Tolerance in a Dem. Soc. at Addis Ababa U., 1995. With JAGC, U.S. Army, 1963-66, Vietnam. Tulane U. fellow, 1981. Mem. ABA, Assn. of Bar of City of N.Y., Hawaii State Bar Assn. Republican. Office: Cades Schutte Fleming & Wright 1000 Bishop St Honolulu HI 96813-4212

PORTER, MICHAEL R., manufacturing executive; b. Allentown, Pa., May 19, 1946; s. Edwin W. and Elizabeth M. (Kremus) P.; m. Patty L. Mutter, July 6, 1968; children: Amy, Casey. BS, Cornell U., 1971, M in Indsl. Engring., 1972. Gen. mgr. Borg Warner, Simcoe, Ont., Can., 1974-80; div. mgr. Borg Warner, Ithaca, N.Y., 1978-80, v.p. ops., 1980-84; v.p., gen. mgr. Borg Warner Automotive, Ithaca, N.Y., 1984—; bd. dirs. Tempkin County Trust Co., Ithaca. Chmn. bd. trustees 1st Congl. Ch., Ithaca, 1980—; bd. dirs. Ithacare, 1985—. Served in U.S. Army, 1966-68, Vietnam. Democrat. Congregationalist. Home: 104 Juniper Dr Ithaca NY 14850-6058 Office: Transmission & Engine Components 770 Warren Rd Ithaca NY 14850-1242

PORTER, MILTON, investment executive; b. Charleroi, Pa., Mar. 2, 1911; s. Harry S. and Jennie (Mitnick) P.; m. Adrienne Foster, Nov. 11, 1938. B.A. in Bus. Adminstrn., U. Pitts., 1932. With L.B. Foster Co., Pitts., 1945-89, v.p., 1955, bd. dirs., 1958, pres., CEO, 1968, chmn. bd., CEO, 1981-84, now bd. dirs.; chmn. bd., CEO Foster Industries, Inc., Pitts. Past pres., life bd. dirs. Jewish Health Care Found. of Pitts.; bd. dirs. Pitts. Symphony; dir. United Jewish Fedn., United Way Southwestern Pa.; chmn. emeritus Health Edn. Ctr., Pitts.; trustee emeritus The Carnegie Inst.; dir. emeritus Carnegie-Mellon U. Recipient Benjamin Rush award Pa. Med. Soc., 1984; recognition award N. Am. Soc. for Corp. Planning, Inc. Mem. Duquesne Club, Westmoreland Country Club (life dir.), Concordia Club, Rivers Club (Pitts.) (dir.). Home: Gateway Towers 320 Fort Duquesne Blvd Pittsburgh PA 15222 Office: Foster Industries Inc 681 Andersen Dr Pittsburgh PA 15220-2747

PORTER, NICOLAS CHRISTOPHER, healthcare executive; b. Norfolk, Va.; s. Oswald Bland and Miriam Jewel (Dorris) P.; m. Patricia Ellen Quinn, June 19, 1971; children: Nicolas Quinn, Shaun Christopher. BA, U. Balt., 1969; MEd, Loyola Coll., Balt., 1971. Adminstrv. asst. medicine Johns Hopkins Hosp., Balt., 1972-74, adminstr. dept. neurology, neurosurgery, 1974-83, exec. v.p., 1987—; adminstr. Johns Hopkins Oncology Ctr., Balt., 1983-87; vice-chmn. Johns Hopkins Fed. Credit Union, 1984-88, chmn., 1988—; co-dir. strike planning Johns Hopkins Hosp., 1982, 84, 86; cons. Nat. Inst. Neurol. and Communicative Disorders and Stroke, 1980-87, Nat. Cancer Inst., 1980-87. Mem. Assn. Am. Cancer Inst. (chmn. 1983-87), Cancer Ctr. Adminstrs. Forum (exec. com. mem. 1983-87), JoAnne Rockwell Found. (bd. dirs. 1985—), Hackerman/Patz Found. (bd. dirs. 1986—), Hosp. Exec. Assn., Md. Hosp. Laundry (bd. dirs. 1987—). Democrat. Club: Bottom Draggers Trading (Balt.) (treas. 1983-85). Avocations: cooking, making wine, golf, racquetball. Office: H Lee Moffitt Cancer Ctr 12902 Magnolia Dr Tampa FL 33612-9416

PORTER, PHILIP THOMAS, retired electrical engineer; b. Clinton, Ky., Mar. 18, 1930; s. Philip Henry and Ruth Frances (Pennebaker) P.; m. Louise Monroe Jett, July 3, 1957; children: Philip C., Sara Shelby Porter Taylor. BA in Physics, Vanderbilt U., 1952, MA in Physics, 1953. Mem. tech. staff Bell Telephone Labs., Murray Hill, N.J., 1953-62; mem. tech. staff Bell Telephone Labs., Holmdel, N.J., 1962-70, supr., 1971-78; supr. Bell Telephone Labs., West Long Branch, N.J., 1979-83; dir. wireless and wireline network compatibility studies Bell Communications Rsch., Red Bank, N.J., 1984-94; retr., 1994; U.S. del. Consultative Com. for Internat. Radio, Geneva, 1984-93. Contbg. author: Electronics Engineers' Handbook, 1982, History of Science and Technology in the Bell System, 1985, Digital Communications, 1986; patentee in field. Fellow IEEE. Unitarian. Avocations: group singing, bridge, sailing.

PORTER, PHILIP WAYLAND, geography educator; b. Hanover, N.H., July 9, 1928; s. Wayland Robinson and Bertha Maria (LaPlante) P.; m. Patricia Elizabeth Garrigus, Sept. 5, 1950; children: Janet Elizabeth, Sara Louise, Alice Catherine. A.B., Middlebury Coll. 1950; M.A., Syracuse U.,

1955; Ph.D., U. London, 1957. Instr. geography U. Minn., Mpls., 1957-58; asst. prof. U. Minn., 1958-64, asso. prof., 1964-66, prof., 1966—, chmn. dept., 1969-71; asso. to v.p. acad. affairs, also dir. Office Internat. Programs, 1979-83; Mem. geography panel Com. on Space Programs for Earth Observations Nat. Acad. Scis., 1967-71; bd. dirs., liaison officer Midwest Univs. Consortium for Internat. Activities, 1979-83. Contbr. articles, monographs to profl. lit. Served with AUS, 1952-54. Ctrl. Rsch. Fund (London) grantee, 1955-56, NSF grantee, 1961-62, 78-80, 92-93, Social Sci. Rsch. Coun. grantee, 1966-67, Rockfeller Found. grantee, 1969, 71-73, Gen. Svc. Found. grantee, 1981-83, Exxon Edn. Found. grantee, 1983-84, Fulbright grantee, 1992-93; Bush Sabbatical fellow, 1985-86. Mem. Assn. Am. Geographers, Am. Anthrop. Assn., African Studies Assn. Home: 86 Arthur Ave SE Minneapolis MN 55414-3410 Office: U Minn Dept Geography Minneapolis MN 55455

PORTER, RICHARD HOWARD, lawyer; b. Fitchburg, Mass., Nov. 5, 1942; s. Howard W. and Dorthy (Flinton) P.; m. Joyce A. Catalini, Aug. 6, 1966; children: Tracy A., Jennifer E., Jeffrey R. BSBA, Georgetown U., 1964, JD, 1967. Bar: U.S. Dist. Ct. D.C., U.S. Ct. Claims, U.S. Ct. Appeals (D.C. cir.), U.S. Supreme Ct. Asst. Senator Edward M. Kennedy, Washington, 1967-68; prtnr. Steptoe & Johnson, Washington, 1971—. Capt. U.S. Army, 1968-71. Mem. ABA (litigation sect., antitrust sect.), Georgetown U. Alumni Assn. (bd. govs., alumni senate pres.). Avocations: tennis, baseball. Office: 1330 Connecticut Ave NW Washington DC 20036-1704

PORTER, RICHARD STERLING, retired metal processing company executive, lawyer; b. Newton, Mass., May 14, 1929; s. William Edwin Jr. and Mabel Elizabeth (Saunders) P.; m. Sara Patten McCrum, June 15, 1955; children: Edwin Ross, John Sterling. AB, Princeton U., 1952; LLB, U. Va., 1957. Various positions Alcan Aluminium Ltd., Montreal, Que. and Cleve., 1957-85; sec., corp. counsel Alcan Aluminium Ltd., Montreal, 1985-88. Served to 1st lt. U.S. Army, 1952-54, Korea. Home: 206 Woodside Rd Brunswick ME 04011-7442

PORTER, ROBERT HUGH, economics educator; b. London, Ont., Can., Jan. 25, 1955; came to U.S., 1976; s. Hugh Donald and Olive Marie (Anderson) P.; m. Therese Jane McGuire, June 20, 1981. BA with honors, U. Western Ont., London, 1976; PhD, Princeton U., 1981. Asst. prof. econs. U. Minn., Mpls., 1980-84; post doctoral fellow Bell Labs., Murray Hill, N.J., 1982-83; assoc. prof. SUNY, Stony Brook, 1984-87; mem. tech. staff Bell Communications Rsch., Morristown, N.J., 1986-88; prof. Northwestern U., Evanston, Ill., 1987—. Mem. bd. editors Am. Econ. Rev., 1988-92, 94—; assoc. editor Internat. Jour. Indsl. Orgn., 1989—; co-editor Econometrica, 1988-93, Rand Jour. Econs., 1995—; contbr. articles to profl. jours. NSF grantee, 1985, 88, 93. Fellow Econometric Soc.; mem. Am. Econ. Assn., Can. Econs. Assn. Home: 904 Michigan Ave # 1 Evanston IL 60202-1416 Office: Northwestern U Dept Econs 2003 Sheridan Rd Evanston IL 60208-2600

PORTER, ROGER BLAINE, government official, educator; b. Provo, Utah, June 19, 1946; s. Blaine Robert and Elizabeth M. (Taylor) P.; m. Ann Robinson, Jan. 6, 1972; children: Robert Roger, Stacy Ann, David R., Rachel Elizabeth. B.A. in History and Polit. Sci., Brigham Young U., 1969; B.Phil, Oxford U., 1971; M.A., Harvard U., 1978, Ph.D., 1978. Asst. dean, tutor in politics Queen's Coll., Oxford U., 1971-72; spl. asst. to pres. The White House, 1974-77; research assoc. Kennedy Sch. Govt. and Grad. Sch. Bus., Harvard U., 1977-79, asst. prof. pub. policy, 1979-81, assoc. prof., 1981, prof. govt. and bus., 1985—; spl. asst. to Pres. of U.S., 1981-82, dep. asst. to Pres., 1982-85; dir. White Ho. Office of Policy Devel., Washington, 1982-85; counselor to sec. U.S. Treasury, 1981-85; exec. sec. Nat. Productivity Adv. Com., 1981-85, Cabinet Coun. on Econ. Affairs, 1981-85, Econ. Policy Coun., 1985; asst. to Pres. for Econ. and Domestic Policy, 1989-93; exec. sec. President's Econ. Policy Bd., 1974-77; guest scholar Brookings Instn., 1977; sr. scholar Woodrow Wilson Internat. Ctr. for Scholars, 1993—; mem. President's Commn. on White House Fellowships, 1976—. Author: Presidential Decision Making, 1980, U.S.-U.S.S.R. Grain Agreement, 1984; asst. editor: Public Policy, 1979-81. Mem. Utahns for Effective Govt., Salt Lake City, 1971-72; mem. Republican Nat. Com. Econ. Adv. Com., 1977-81. Rhodes scholar, 1969; Woodrow Wilson fellow, 1969; White House fellow, 1974; recipient spl. citation U.S. Sec. Treasury, 1977; named One of 10 Outstanding Young Men in Am., 1981. Fellow Nat. Acad. Pub. Adminstrn.; mem. Phi Kappa Phi, Pi Sigma Alpha, Phi Eta Sigma, Phi Alpha Theta. Mem. LDS Ch. Avocations: classical music, basketball, tennis, travel. Home: 12 Clifton St Belmont MA 02178 Office: Harvard U Kennedy Sch Govt 79 JFK St Cambridge MA 02138

PORTER, ROGER JEFFREY, literature educator; b. Newark, May 25, 1936; s. Joseph Alvin and Anita (Silverman) P.; m. Mancy Maxwell, Aug. 5, 1961 (div. 1969). B.A., Amherst U., 1958; M.A., Yale U., 1959, Ph.D., 1967. From instr. to prof. lit. Reed Coll., Portland, Oreg., 1961—; vis. prof. SUNY-Buffalo, 1976, Inst. Renaissance Studies, 1971, Emory U., Atlanta, 1981, Aristotelian U. Greece, 1979-80; artist in residence Cairo Am. Coll., Egypt, 1983. Author: The Voice Within, 1973; contbr. articles to newspapers and mags. Founder, artistic dir. Portland Conservatory. Mem. MLA. Democrat. Jewish. Avocations: theatre; cooking. Home: 7200 SW La View Dr Portland OR 97219-3006 Office: Reed Coll 3203 SE Woodstock Blvd Portland OR 97202-8199

PORTER, ROGER JOHN, medical research administrator, neurologist, pharmacologist; b. Pitts., Apr. 4, 1942; s. John Keaggy and Margaret (Parker) P.; m. Candace Marie Leland, Feb. 17, 1968; children: David, Stacey. BS, Eckerd Coll., 1964; MD, Duke U., 1968. Diplomate Nat. Bd. Med. Examiners, Am. Bd. Neurology, Am. Bd. Electroencephalography. Intern U. Calif. at San Diego, 1968-69; resident in neurology U. Calif. at San Francisco, 1971-74; fellow Rsch. Tng. Program Duke U., Durham, N.C., 1966-67; staff assoc. sect. epilepsy Nat. Inst. Neurol. Diseases and Stroke, NIH, Bethesda, Md., 1969-71; investigator U. Calif., San Francisco, 1972-73; sr. rsch. assoc. epilepsy br., Neurol. Disorders Program Nat. Inst. Neurol. and Communicative Disorders and Stroke, NIH, Bethesda, 1974-78, assoc. chief epilepsy br., 1977-79, acting chief, 1979-80, acting chief clin. epilepsy sect., IRP, 1979-84, chief epilepsy br., Neurol. Disorders Program, 1980-84, chief med. neurology br. and clin. epilepsy sect. IRP, 1984-87; dep. dir. Nat. Inst. Neurol. Disorders and Stroke, NIH, Bethesda, 1987-93; v.p., clin. pharmacology Wyeth-Ayerst Rsch., Radnor, Pa., 1992—; adj. prof. neurology U. Pa., 1993—; prof. neurology Uniformed Svcs. U. Health Scis., Bethesda, 1980-93, adj. prof. pharmacology, 1982—; cons. neurology Nat. Naval Med. Ctr., Bethesda, 1978-93; chmn. White House Subcom. on Brain and Behavioral Scis., 1990-92. Author/editor: 10 books; contbr. numerous papers, book chpts., abstracts to profl. publs.; writer/contbr. 5 motion pictures, 1 exhibit. With USPHS, 1969-92. Recipient USPHS Commendation medal, 1977, MacArthur Outstanding Alumnus award Eckerd Coll., 1977, Fulbright Disting. Prof. award, 1985, USPHS Meritorious Svc. medal, 1986, Dept. Def. Meritorious Svc. medal, 1989, Disting. Alumnus award Duke Duke U. Med. Ctr., 1989, USN Commendation medal, 1991, USPHS Disting. Svc. medal, 1991; scholar in residence Assn. Am. Med. Colls., Washington, 1989-90. Fellow Am. Acad. Neurology, Am. Neurol. Assn.; mem. Am. Electroencephalographic Soc., Am. Epilepsy Soc. (pres. 1989-90), Soc. Neurosci., Am. Soc. Clin. Pharmacology and Therapeutics, Am. Soc. Neurologic Investigation (hon.), Internat. League Against Epilepsy (sec.-gen. 1989-93). Home: 461 Timber Ln Devon PA 19333-1232 Office: Wyeth-Ayerst Rsch PO Box 8299 Philadelphia PA 19101

PORTER, ROGER STEPHEN, chemistry educator; b. Windom, Minn., June 2, 1928; s. Sherman Clarence and Cora Ruth (Rogers) P.; m. Catharine Crow, Aug. 3, 1968; children: Margaret Davis, Stephen Cady; children by previous marriage: Laura Jean, Ruth Anne. B.S. in Chemistry, U. Calif., Los Angeles, 1950; Ph.D., U. Wash., 1956. Sr. research assoc. Chevron Research Co. Richmond, Calif., 1956-66; prof., dept. polymer sci. and engring. U. Mass., Amherst, 1966—; head dept. U. Mass., 1966-76, asst. to pres. for research, 1979-81; plastics cons. to maj. U.S. cos.; co-dir. NSF Materials Lab., 1972-82; study group head U./USSR Commn. on Sci.; mem. Nat. Acad. Scis. coms., 1969—; mem. adv. panels NSF; mem. adv. bds. for various sci. jours.; lectr. Russian, Brazilian and Romanian acads. scis.; bd. dirs. Plastics Inst. Am.; trustee Gordon Research Confs. Editor: Polymer Engineering and Science, Polymer Composites; co-editor books. Recipient Polyolefins award Internat. Plastics Edn. award Soc. Plastics Engring., 1977,

Internat. award in plastics sci. and engring. Soc. Plastics Engring., 1981, Disting. mem. award Soc. Plastics Engring., 1993, Mettler award, 1983, Bingham medal Soc. Rheology, 1985; named to Plastics Hall of Fame, 1991. Fellow Am. Phys. Soc., N.Am. Thermal Analysis Soc. (pres. 1987); mem. Am. Chem. Soc. (award in plastics 1979), Sigma Xi, Alpha Chi Sigma, Phi Gamma Delta. Home: 220 Rolling Ridge Rd Amherst MA 01002-1423

PORTER, STEPHEN CUMMINGS, geologist, educator; b. Santa Barbara, Calif., Apr. 18, 1934; s. Lawrence Johnson Porter Jr. and Frances (Cummings) Seger; m. Anne Mary Higgins, Apr. 2, 1959; children: John, Maria, Susannah. BS, Yale U., 1955, MS, 1958, PhD, 1962. Asst. prof. geology U. Wash., Seattle, 1962-66, assoc. prof., 1966-71, prof., 1971—; dir. Quaternary Research Ctr., 1982—; mem. bd. earth scis. Nat. Acad. Sci., Washington, 1983-85; mem. advisory com. div. polar programs NSF, Washington, 1983-84; vis. fellow Clare Hall Cambridge (Eng.) U., 1980-81; guest prof. Academia Sinica, People's Rep. of China, 1987—; v.p. Internat. Union Quaternary Rsch., 1992—; pres. Am. Quaternary Assn., 1992-94. Co-author: Physical Geology, 1987, The Dynamic Earth, 1989, 92, 95, The Blue Planet, 1985; editor: Late Quaternary Environments of the United States, 1983, (jour.) Quaternary Research, 1976—; assoc. editor (jour.) Radiocarbon, 1982-89: editorial bd.: Quaternary Science Reviews, 1988—, Quaternary International, 1989—. Served to lt. USNR, 1955-57. Recipient Benjamin Silliman prize Yale U., New Haven, 1962, Willis M. Tate Lectr., So. Meth. U., Dallas, 1984; Fulbright-Hays Sr. Research fellow New Zealand, 1973-74. Fellow Geol. Soc. Am., Arctic Inst. N.Am. (bd. govs.); mem. Am. Quaternary Assn. (coun., pres. 1992-94), Am. Alpine Club (N.Y.C.). Avocations: photography, mountaineering. Home: 18034 15th Ave NW Seattle WA 98177-3305 Office: U Wash Quaternary Rsch Ctr AK-60 Seattle WA 98195

PORTER, STEPHEN WINTHROP, stage director; b. Ogdensburg, N.Y., July 24, 1925; s. Charles T. and Anna (Newton) P. B.A., Yale U., 1945, M.F.A., 1948. Asst. prof. English in charge of drama McGill U., Montreal, 1949-56. Stage dir. plays on Broadway Right You Are, Wild Duck, 1966, The Show Off, 1967, The Misanthrope, 1968, 83, The Wrong Way Light Bulb, Private Lives, 1969, Harvey, 1970, The School for Wives, 1971, Captain Brassbound's Conversion, 1972, Don Juan, 1973, Chemin de Fer, 1974, Rules of the Game, 1975, They Knew What They Wanted, 1976, Days in the Trees, 1976, The Importance of Being Earnest, 1977, Tartuffe, 1977, Man and Superman, 1978, Major Barbara, The Man Who Came to Dinner, 1980, You Never Can Tell, 1986, The Devil's Disciple, 1988, The Miser, 1990, Getting Married, 1991. Address: 25 W 54 St New York NY 10019

PORTER, TERRY, professional basketball player; b. Milw., Apr. 8, 1963. Student, U. Wis., Stevens Point, 1981-85. With Portland Trail Blazers, 1985—. Recipient Citizenship award, 1993; named to NBA All-Star team, 1991, 93. Holds single game record for most three point field goals without a miss-7, 1992. Office: Portland Trail Blazers 700 NE Multnomah St Ste 600 Portland OR 97232-4106*

PORTER, THOMAS JOSEPH, writer, songwriter; b. Macon, Ga., July 18, 1941; s. Thomas Joseph and Mary Leanora (McClellan) P.; 1 child, Thomas Joseph III. AB, U.Ga., 1967. Singer, guitarist, songwriter Warner, Porter & Warner group Warner, Porter & Warner, Status Cymbal groups, 1966-69; co-owner Tandem Pubs., Macon, 1967; mng. dir. The Grand Opera House, Macon, 1969-71; pres. Asterisk Music Pubs, Charleston, S.C., 1971; editor Gateway mag., Charleston, 1971-73; TV critic, columnist Charleston Post-Courier newspapers, 1971-93; ptnr. New Departure Records, 1972-76. Composer: (film scores) The Farewell Performance of Little Mary Sunshine, 1967, Charleston, Room for a Way of Life, 1972; freelance scriptwriter: (TV series) Simon & Simon, Lobo, 1980-83; writer, host: (documentary) Praise House Spirit; author: Animal Crackers, 1988. Recipient Gold and Silver Addy awards, 1988, S.C. Press Assn. award, 1989, nat. finalist Silver Microphone award for radio advt. scripts, 1989, Iris award runner-up for TV documentary, 1992. Mem. Nat. Acad. Rec. Arts and Scis., Writers Guild Am. (West chpt.). Club: Sea Island Yacht (Rockville, S.C.). Office: Asterisk Music Pubs PO Box 34 Charleston SC 29402

PORTER, VERNA LOUISE, lawyer; b. L.A., May 31, 1941. B.A., Calif. State U., 1963; JD, Southwestern U., 1977. Bar: Calif. 1977, U.S. Dist. Ct. (cen. dist.) Calif. 1978, U.S. Ct. Appeals (9th cir.) 1978. Ptnr. Eisler & Porter, L.A., 1978-79, mng. ptnr., 1979-86, pvt. practice law, 1986—; judge pro-tempore L.A. Mcpl. Ct., 1983—; L.A. Superior Ct., 1989—, Beverly Hills Mcpl. Ct., 1992—; mem. state of Calif. subcom. on landlord tenant law, panelist conv., mem. real property law sect. Calif. State Bar, 1983; speaker on landlord-tenant law to real estate profls., including San Fernando Bd. Realtors; vol. atty. L.A. County Bar Dispute Resolution, mem. client rels. panel, fee arbitrator. Mem. adv. coun. Freddie Mac Vendor, 1995—. Editl. asst., contbr. Apt. Owner Builder; contbr. to Apt. Bus. Outlook, Real Property News, Apt. Age; mem. World Affairs Coun. Fre Mem. ABA, L.A. County Bar Assn. (client-rels. vol. dispute resolution and fee arbitration, 1981—), L.A. Trial Lawyers Assn., Wilshire Bar Assn., Women Lawyer's Assn., Landlord Trial Lawyers Assn. (founding mem., pres.), Freddie Mac Vendor Adv. Coun., da Camera Soc. Republican. Office: 2500 Wilshire Blvd Fl 1226 Los Angeles CA 90057-4317

PORTER, W. ARTHUR, research center executive; b. Irving, Tex., Mar. 29, 1941; s. Marvin Henry and Rosalie Rebecca (Black) P.; m. Billie Greene, June 1, 1963; children: Arthur Brent, Paige Nicole. BS in Physics, N. Tex. State U., 1963, MS, 1964; PhD, Tex. A&M U., 1970. From instr. to assoc. prof. physics, math., elec. engring. Tex. A&M U., 1964-76, prof. elec. engring., 1976—, asst., then dir. Tex. Engring. Expt. Sta., 1979-80; pres. Houston Advanced Rsch. Ctr., 1985—, also bd. dirs.; adj. prof. elec. and comp. engring. Rice U., 1989—; dir. Inst. for Solid-State Electronics, Tex. A&M, 1972-79; cons. Tex. Instruments Inc., Electro Sci. Industries, 1980, bd. dirs. 1980—; chmn. bd., 1987-92; bd. dirs. RepublicBank A&M 1982-89, Tex. Lyceum Assn. 1983—, Stewart Info. Svcs. Corp., 1993—; tech. adv. bd. Keplinger Cos. 1985-88; mem. adv. bd. Tex. Acad. Math. and Sci., North Tex. State U., 1988—; cons. U. of Petroleum and Minerals, Dhahran, Saudi Arabia, 1983; served on various edml. coms. Tex. A&M; appointed mem. Tex. Partnership Econ. Devel., 1992—. Contbr. numerous articles on sci. and tech. to profl. journals; patentee in field. Trustee S.W. Research Inst.; bd. regents U. Portland, 1985-89. Mem. AAAS, IEEE (del. USSR, Japan, India, editor newsletter 1976, chmn. Electronic Components Conf. 1981, recipient numerous awards), Electrochem. Soc., Cosmos Club (Washington), Sigma Xi (internat. com. 1989—). Office: Houston Advanced Rsch Ctr 4802 Research Forest Dr The Woodlands TX 77381-4142

PORTER, W. L., bishop. Bishop of Cen. Tenn., Ch. of God in Christ, Memphis. Office: Ch of God in Christ 1235 E Parkway S Memphis TN 38114-6728

PORTER, WALTER ARTHUR, judge; b. Dayton, Ohio, June 6, 1924; s. Claude and Estella (Raymond) P.; m. Patricia Reeves Higdon, Dec. 3, 1947; children—Scott Paul, David Bryant. B.S. in Engring, U. Cin., 1948, LL.B., 1949. Bar: Ohio 1949. Legal dep. Montgomery County Probate Ct., 1949-51; asst. pros. atty. Montgomery County, 1951-56; with Albert H. Scharner (atty.), Dayton, 1956-61; mem. firm Smith & Schnacke, Dayton, 1962-85; pres. Smith & Schnacke, 1980-85; judge Montgomery County Common Pleas Ct., 1985—. Served with inf. U.S. Army, 1943-45, ETO. Mem. ABA, Ohio Bar Assn. (pres. 1973-74), Dayton Bar Assn., Am. Coll. Trial Lawyers, Am. Coll. Probate Counsel, Phi Alpha Delta, Omicron Delta Kappa. Democrat. Presbyterian. Club: Mason. Home: 785 E Schantz Ave Dayton OH 45419-3818 Office: Montgomery County Cts Dayton OH 45422

PORTER, WALTER THOMAS, JR., bank executive; b. Corning, N.Y., Jan. 8, 1934; s. Walter Thomas and Mary Rebecca (Brookes) P.; m. Dixie Jo Thompson, Apr. 3, 1959; children: Kimberlee Paige, Douglas Thompson, Jane-Amy Elizabeth. BS, Rutgers U., 1954; MBA, U. Wash., 1959; PhD, Columbia U., 1964. CPA, Wash., N.Y. Staff cons. Touche Ross & Co., Seattle, 1959-61; NDEA fellow Columbia U., 1961-64; dir. edn. Touche Ross & Co., N.Y.C., 1964-66; assoc. prof. U. Wash., 1966-70, prof., 1970-74; vis. prof. N. European Mgmt. Inst., Oslo, Norway, 1974-75; nat. dir. planning Touche Ross & Co., Seattle, 1975-78, dir. exec. fin. counseling, 1978-84, exec. v.p., mgr. pvt. banking, Rainier Nat. Bank, 1984-87, exec. v.p., mgr. capital mgmt. and pvt. banking, 1987-88, vice chmn. 1988-89; vice chmn. Security

Pacific Bank Washington, 1989-92; exec. v.p., mgr. capital mgmt. group Seafirst Bank, Seattle, 1992—; vis. lectr. taxation U. Wash., 1978-85; bd. dirs. AEI, Inc. Mem. Seattle adv. bd. Salvation Army, 1975-83, 89—, pres. 1993-95; trustee Ryther Child Ctr., 1975-85, pres., 1979-81; trustee Lakeside Sch., 1977-87, treas., 1980-81, 1st v.p. 1982-84, pres. 1984-86; trustee Va. Mason Med. Ctr., 1986—, chair, bd. govs. 1994—; Va. Mason Rsch. Ctr., 1982-87, Mus. History and Industry, 1982-83. Served with U.S. Army, 1955-57. Author: Auditing Electronic System, 1966; (with William Perry) EDP: Controls and Auditing, 1970, 5th edit., 1987; (with John Burton) Auditing A Conceptual Approach, 1974; (with D. Alkire) Wealth: How to Achieve It, 1976; Touche Ross Guide to Personal Financial Management, 1984, 3d edit., 1989; (with D. Porter) The Personal Financial Planner's Practice Sourcebook, 1986. Mem. Am. Inst. CPA's. Congregationalist. Club: Wash. Athletic, Sand Point Country, Rainer Club, Sand Point Golf Club. Office: Seafirst Bank PO Box 3586 701 5th Ave 56th Fl Seattle WA 98124

PORTER, WILLIAM EMME, state legislator, small business owner; b. Lucknow, India, Mar. 29, 1925; (parents Am. citizens); s. Ruben Boring and Lenore Carolyn (Emme) P.; m. E. Caryl Wilbur, June 3, 1947; children: Elisabeth, Katherine, Kristin. Student, Doane Coll., 1945-47; AB, Albion Coll., 1949; MS, Kans. State U., 1950. Tchr. Garden City (Kans.) Pub. Schs., 1951-53; prin. pub. schs. Wilson, Kans., 1953-55; tchr., head sci. dept.pub. schs. Las Cruces, N.Mex., 1955-84, farmer-mgr., 1975—; mem. N.Mex. Ho. Reps., Santa Fe, 1990—; Mem. agriculture and water com., N.Mex. State Ho. Reps., 1990—, tax and revenue com., 1990—, tax equalization com., 1990—, border devel. com., 1992—, internat. spaceport com., 1992—, agriculture and forestry com. Nat. Conf. State Legis., 1993-95, vice chair capital outlay com. Contbr. articles to newspapers; patentee Porter Bermuda Grass. Founder Friends of Fort Selden, N.Mex., 1988. With U.S. Army, 1943-45, ETO. Mem. N.Mex. Acad. Sci. (pres. 1960-61), Beta Beta Beta. Democrat. Home and Office: 5200 N Highway 85 Las Cruces NM 88005-6847

PORTER, WILLIAM L., electrical engineer; b. Leeds, N.D., July 2, 1929; s. Ernest Cecil and Dena Grace (Thompson) P.; m. Mary Lynn Lindsey, Oct. 9, 1948; children: Belinda Joyce, William Harry, Terry Jane, Derek Lewis, Michael Ronald. AA, Springfield Coll., 1960; BSEE, U. Ill., 1963. Registered profl. engr., Ill., Minn., Iowa, N.D., S.D., Ohio, Mich., Wis., Ind., Nebr. Lineman City Water, Light and Power, Springfield, Ill., 1947-54, troubleshooter, 1954-62, gen. supt. elec. divsn., 1962-76; prin. engr. R.W. Beck and Assocs., Columbus, Nebr., 1976-77; engring. mgr. R.W. Beck and Assocs., Mpls., 1977-80, ptnr., mgr., 1980-90, sr. cons., 1990—; speaker on engring. and utilities; cons. to electric utilities. Author numerous engring. reports and engring. and utilities papers. Street light com. chair City of Springfield, 1964, mem. CATV com., 1966; mem. Planning Commn. Spring Park (Minn.), 1978-79; chair environ. quality com. region IV Ill. Soc. Profl. Engrs., chair ethics and practices com. Capital chpt.; mem. tech. adv. com. Fed. Power Commn's Nat. Power Survey; chair engring. and ops. com. Am. Pub. Power Assn., 1967-70, chair power supply planning com., 1973-74. Named Engr. of Yr., Capital chpt.-TS Soc. Profl. Engrs., 1975. Mem. NSPE, IEEE (chmn. Cen. Ill. sect. 1974-75), Minn. Soc. Profl. Engrs., Cons. Engrs. Coun., Am. Bus. Club, Eta Kappa Nu. Republican. Home: 4349 Channel Rd Spring Park MN 55384-9734 Office: R W Beck and Assocs 8300 Norman Center Dr Ste 860 Minneapolis MN 55437-1030

PORTER, WILLIAM LYMAN, architect, educator; b. Poughkeepsie, N.Y., Feb. 19, 1934; s. William Quincy and Lois (Brown) P.; m. Lynn Rogers Porter; children: Quayny Lyman, Zoe Lynn, Eve Lyman. B.A., Yale U., 1955, M.Arch., 1957; Ph.D., MIT, 1969. Designer, job capt. Louis I. Kahn (architect), Phila., 1960-62; urban designer, asst. chief of design Ciudad Guayana project Joint Center for Urban Studies of Harvard and MIT, Caracas, Venezuela, 1962-64; Mellon fellow dept. urban studies and planning MIT, 1964-65; Samuel Stouffer fellow Joint Center for Urban Studies, Harvard and MIT, 1966-67; asst. prof. urban design, depts. architecture and urban studies and planning MIT, 1968-70, assoc. prof. urban design, 1970-71, prof. architecture and planning, 1971—, Norman B. and Muriel Leventhal prof. architecture and planning, 1988—, head. dept. architecture, 1987-91, dean Sch. Architecture and Planning, 1971-81; co-dir. Aga Khan Program for Islamic Architecture Harvard U.-MIT, 1979-85; cons. in field; mem. Nat. Archtl. Accrediting Bd., 1978-80, pres., 1979; mem. Mass. Designer Selection Bd. 1978-79, chmn., 1979; mem. steering com. Aga Khan Award for Architecture, 1977-86, mem. master jury, 1989. Co-founder, co-editor Places: A Quarterly Jour. Environ. Design, 1982-88. Trustee Milton (Mass.) Acad., 1989—; mem. bd. overseers Coll. Fine Arts, U. Pa., 1984-90, Mus. Fine Arts, Boston, 1992-94. Fellow AIA; mem. Boston Soc. Architects (dir. 1969-73, 77-81). Clubs: Harvard Musical Assn. (Boston). Home: 410 Memorial Dr Cambridge MA 02139-4318 Office: MIT Sch Architecture & Planning 77 Massachusetts Ave Cambridge MA 02139-4307

PORTER, WILMA JEAN, university administrator; b. Sylacauga, Ala., May 30, 1931; d. Harrison Samuel and Blanche Leonard Butcher; m. Douglas Taylor Porter, Apr. 18, 1953; children: Daria Cerise, Blanche Evette, Douglas Vincent. BS, Tuskegee U., 1953; MS, Mich. State U., 1966; PhD, Iowa State U., 1980. Asst. dietitian Miss. State Tb Sanatorium, 1951-52; therapeutic dietitian dept. of hosp. City of N.Y., S.I., 1952-53; libr. asst. Mississippi Valley State Coll., Itta Bena, Miss., 1963-65; asst. prof. Grambling (La.) State U., 1966-75, Howard U., Washington, 1976-80; country dir. U.S. Peace Corps, Tonga, 1980-82; asst. dir. internat. programs Ft. Valley (Ga.) Coll., 1983-84, dir. Inst. Advancement, 1984-88; dir. Sch. Home Econs., Tenn. Technol. U., Cookeville, 1989—; project dir. Capitol Hill Health and Homemaker, Washington, 1982-83; interim dir. Inst. Advancement Alcorn State U., Lorman, Miss., 1988-89. Author lab. manual for quantity foods, 1977; editor: (cookbook) Some Christmas Foods and Their Origins from Around the World, 1983. Convenor Nat. Issues Forums, Ga. and Tenn., 1985—; bd. dirs. Leadership Putnam, Cookeville, 1990-94; chmn. Tenn. Technol. U. campaign United Way, 1989; mem. devel. and planning com. Peach County, Ft. Valley, 1985-87; mem. Peach County Heart Fund Dr., 1986-88. Title III grantee U.S. Dept. Edn., 1986, 87; Tenn. Dept. Human Svcs. grantee, 1993, 94. Mem. AAUW (program chairperson 1991-92; pres. Cookeville br. 1994—), Am. Home Econs. Assn., Am. Dietetic Assn., Nat. Coun. Adminstrs. Home.Econs., Tenn. Home Econs. Assn., Tenn. Dietetic Assn. Democrat. Roman Catholic. Avocations: writing, vegetable and flower gardening. Home: 512 Fisk Rd Cookeville TN 38501-2925

PORTERFIELD, JAMES TEMPLE STARKE, business administration educator; b. Annapolis, Md., July 7, 1920; s. Lewis Broughton and Maud Paxton (Starke) P.; m. Betty Gold, Apr. 23, 1949 (dec. 1985); m. Janet Patricia Gardiner Roggeveen, Oct. 5, 1986. AB, U. Calif., Berkeley, 1942; MBA, Stanford U., 1948, PhD, 1955. From asst. to assoc. prof. Harvard U. Bus. Sch., Boston, 1955-59; prof. fin. Stanford (Calif.) U. Grad. Sch. Bus., 1959-79, James Irvin Miller Prof. fin., 1979-90, prof. emeritus, 1990—; prof. IMEDE Mgmt. Devel. Inst., Lausanne, Switzerland, 1962-63. Author: Life Insurance Stocks as Investments, 1955, Investment Decisions and Capital Costs, 1965; co-author: Case Problems in Finance, 1959. Served as lt. USNR, 1941-46. Recipient Salgo Noren award Stanford U., 1966. Home: 295 Golden Oak Dr Portola Vally CA 94028-7730 Office: Stanford U Grad Sch Bus Stanford CA 94305

PORTERFIELD, NEIL HARRY, landscape architect, planner; b. Murrysville, Pa., Aug. 15, 1936; s. Phil Frank and Alvira Clare (Rea) P.; m. Sandra Jean Beswarick, Aug. 9, 1958; children: Eric Jon, Jennifer Jane, Garrett Andrew. BS in Landscape Architecture, Pa. State U., 1958; M in Landscape Architecture, U. Pa., 1964. Landscape architect Pitts. Dept. Parks and Recreation, 1958-59; land planner Neil H. Porterfield & Assocs., Murrysville, 1961-64; dir. landscape architecture and planning Hellmuth, Obata & Kassabaum, Inc., St. Louis, 1964-70; exec. v.p. HOK Assocs., St. Louis, 1970-72, pres., 1972-85; prin., v.p., dir. Hellmuth, Obata & Kassabaum, Inc., 1977-80, corp. dir. planning, sr. v.p., dir., 1980-85; prof., head dept. land-scape architecture Pa. State U., University Park, 1985-93, dean Coll. Arts and Architecture, 1993—; lectr. in field; prof. Washington U., 1979; chmn. Landscape Archtl. Accreditation Bd. Contbr. articles to profl. orgns., anthologies. Bd. dirs. Landscape Architecture Found., 1983-85; adv. coun. Coll. Architecture and Urban Studies, Va. Poly. Inst. and State U., Blacksburg, 1984-86; vice-chmn. The Commn. Fine Arts, Washington, 1985-93. Recipient honor award Married Student Housing, U. Mich., honor award

Am. Soc. Landscape Architects, 1969, Merit award Parkside Campus Study U. Wis. at Kenosha, Merit award Am. Soc. Landscape Architects, 1969, Outstanding Alumnus award Coll. Arts and Architecture, Pa. State U., 1983, others. Fellow Am. Soc. Landscape Architects (v.p. 1985-87); mem. Coun. of Edn. Presbyterian. Home: RR 1 Centre Hall PA 16828-9801 Office: Pa State U Coll Arts and Architecture 111 Arts Bldg University Park PA 16802

PORTERFIELD, PATRICIA ROUGH, education educator; b. Poplar Bluff, Mo., Aug. 9, 1946; m. Lyndel H. Porterfield, Feb. 11, 1976; children: Robert Eugene, Karen Paige, Robert Benjamin. Student, Sparks Sch. Nursing, Fort Smith, Ark., 1967; BSN, Southwest Mo. State U., 1981; MSN, U. Mo. Columbia, 1984. Charge nurse Ark. Children's Colony, Conway, 1967-68; staff nurse U. Mo. Med. Ctr., Columbia, 1970, head nurse, 1970-71, staff dev. coordinator, 1971-73; dir. edn. Ellis Fischel State Cancer Hosp., Columbia, 1973-75; staff devel. coordinator St. John's Regional Health Ctr., Mo., 1975-80; instr. sch. nursing St. John's Regional Health Ctr., Springfield, 1981-82; asst. dir. nursing Chas. E. Still Hosp., Jefferson City, 1983-85; asst. prof. nursing St. Mary's Coll., O'Fallon, Mo., 1985-88; instr. St. Charles County Community Coll., O'Fallon, Mo., 1988—; item writer U. N.Y. Bd. Regents, 1987—, state faculty Mo. League for Nursing, Jefferson City 1987—. Mem. Mo. Assn. Community and Junior Colleges, Mo. Orgn. for Advancement Assoc. Degree Nursing (pres. 1986-89), Mo. Nurses Assn., Bus. and Profl. Women (bd. dir. 1986-88), Sigma Theta Tau. Avocations: camping, genealogy. Home: 313 Oriole Dr Saint Charles MO 63301-3908

PORTERFIELD, WILLIAM WENDELL, chemist, educator; b. Winchester, Va., Aug. 24, 1936; s. Donald Kennedy and Adelyn (Miller) P.; m. Dorothy Elizabeth Dail, Aug. 24, 1957; children—Allan Kennedy, Douglas Hunter. B.S., U. N.C., 1957, Ph.D., 1962; M.S., Calif. Inst. Tech., 1960. Sr. research chemist Hercules, Inc., Cumberland, Md., 1962-64; asst. prof. chemistry Hampden-Sydney (Va.) Coll., 1964-65, assoc. prof., 1965-68, prof. chemistry, 1968—, Charles Scott Venable prof. chemistry, 1989—, chmn. natural sci. div., 1973-77, chmn. dept. chemistry, 1982-85, 93—; vis. fellow U. Durham (U.K.), 1984. Author: Concepts of Chemistry, 1972, Inorganic Chemistry, 1984, 2d edit., 1993; contbr. articles to profl. jours. Mem. Am. Chem. Soc., Royal Chem. Soc. (London, Eng.), Phi Beta Kappa. Home: PO Box 697 Hampden Sydney VA 23943

PORTES, ALEJANDRO, sociologist, educator; b. Havana, Cuba, Oct. 13, 1944; came to U.S., 1960; s. Helio B. Portes and Eulalia Cortada; m. Nancy Brazie, Jan. 28, 1966 (div. Dec. 1974); children: Elizabeth, Charles A., Audred; m. Patricia Fernandez Kelly, Mar. 31, 1985. BA summa cum laude, Creighton U., 1965; MA, U. Wis., 1967, PhD, 1970. Lectr. U. Wis., Madison, 1969-70; asst. prof. U. Ill., Urbana, 1970-71; assoc. prof. U. Tex., Austin, 1971-75; prof. Duke U., Durham, N.C., 1975-80; prof. Johns Hopkins U., Balt., 1980-87, John Dewey prof., 1987—; Frost disting. vis. prof. Fla. Internat. U., Miami, 1988—; cons. Ford Found., 1977, 79, 89, U.S. Congress Com. for Study of Immigration, 1988-90, Ministries of Labor and Social Welfare of Spain, Immigration Policy, 1990—. Author: Urban Latin America, 1976, Labor, Class, and the International System, 1981, Latin Journey, 1985, Immigrant America, a Portrait, 1990; editorial bd. mem. Johns Hopkins U. Press, Balt., 1989—, Annual Rev. Sociology, Palo Alto, Calif., 1988-91. Guest Witness U.S. Congress Sub-com. on Immigration, 1983, 86; del. Internat. Sociol. Assn., Madrid, Spain, 1990—. Fellow Heinz Internat. Studies (rev. bd. mem. 1988-90); mem. Am. Sociol. Assn., Latin Am. Studies Assn. (mem. jt. com. Social Sci. Rsch. Coun. 1985-88). Avocations: sailing, motor boating. Office: Johns Hopkins U Dept Sociol Baltimore MD 21218

PORTIS, ALAN MARK, physicist, educator; b. Chgo., July 17, 1926; s. Lyon and Ruth (Libman) P.; m. Beverly Aline Levin, Sept. 5, 1948; children: Jonathan Marc, Stephen Robert, Lori Ann, Frederick Sean. Ph.B., U. Chgo., 1948; A.B., U. Calif., Berkeley, 1949, Ph.D., 1953. Mem. faculty U. Pitts., 1953-56; Mem. faculty U. Calif.-Berkeley, 1956—, prof. physics, 1964-95, prof. emeritus, 1995—, asst. to chancellor for research, 1966-67, asso. dean grad. div., 1967-68, dir. Lawrence Hall Sci., 1969-72, univ. ombudsman, 1981-83, 92-94, assoc. dean Coll. Engring., 1983-87, 94-95. Author: Electromagnetic Fields/Sources and Media, 1978, Electrodynamics of High-Temperature Superconductors, 1993; contbg. author: Berkeley Physics Laboratory, 1964, 65, 66, 71. Fulbright fellow, 1961, 67, Guggenheim fellow, 1965, SERC sr. fellow, U.K., 1991-92. Fellow Am. Phys. Soc.; mem. Am. Assn. Physics Tchrs. (Robert Andrews Millikan award 1966).

PORTIS, CHARLES MCCOLL, reporter, writer; b. El Dorado, Ark., Dec. 28, 1933; s. Samuel Palmer and Alice (Waddell) P. BA, U. Ark., 1958. Reporter The Comml. Appeal, Memphis, 1958, Ark. Gazette, Little Rock, 1959-60, N.Y. Herald Tribune, N.Y.C., 1960-64. Author: Norwood, 1966, True Grit, 1968, The Dog of the South, 1979, Masters of Atlantis, 1985, Gringos, 1991. Sgt. USMC, 1952-55, Korea. Presbyterian. Home: 7417 Kingwood Rd Little Rock AR 72207-1734

PORTMAN, GLENN ARTHUR, lawyer; b. Cleve., Dec. 26, 1949; s. Alvin B. and Lenore (Marsh) P.; m. Katherine Seaborn, Aug. 3, 1974 (div. 1984); m. Susan Newell, Jan. 3, 1987. BA in History, Case Western Res. U., 1968; JD, So. Meth. U., 1975. Bar: Tex. 1975, U.S. Dist. Ct. (no. dist.) Tex. 1975, U.S. Dist. Ct. (so. dist.) Tex. 1983, U.S. Dist. Ct. (we. and ea. dists.) Tex. 1988. Assoc. Johnson, Bromberg & Leeds, Dallas, 1975-80, ptnr., 1980-92; ptnr. Arter, Hadden, Johnson & Bromberg, Dallas, 1992—; chmn. bd. dirs. Physicians Regional Hosp., 1994—; mem. exec. bd. So. Meth. U. Sch. Law, 1994—; lectr. bankruptcy topics South Tex. Coll. Law, State Bar Tex. Asst. editor-in-chief Southwestern Law Jour., 1974-75; contbr. articles to profl. jours. Firm rep. United Way Met. Dallas, 1982-92; treas. Lake Highlands Square Homeowners Assn., 1990-93. Mem. ABA, Am. Bankruptcy Inst., State Bar Tex. Assn., Dallas Bar Assn., So. Meth. U. Law Alumni Assn. (council bd. dirs., v.p. 1980-86, chmn. admissions com., chmn. class agt. program 1986-89, chmn. fund raising 1989-91), 500 Club Inc., Assemblage Club. Republican. Methodist. Home: 9503 Winding Ridge Dr Dallas TX 75238-1451 Office: Arter Hadden Johnson & Bromberg 1717 Main St Ste 4100 Dallas TX 75201

PORTMAN, JOHN C., JR., architect, developer; b. Walhalla, S.C., Dec. 4, 1924; s. John Calvin and Edna (Rochester) P.; m. Joan Newton, Dec. 23, 1944; children: Michael Wayne, John Calvin III, Jae Phillip, Jeffrey Lin, Jana Lee, Jarel Penn. Midshipman, U.S. Naval Acad., 1944; B.S. in Architecture, Ga. Inst. Tech., 1950, DFA, 1993; DFA, Emory U., 1993, Atlanta Coll. Art, 1993. Diplomate: Registered architect, Ga. With Ketchum, Gina and Sharp, H.M. Heatly, Asso. (Architects), N.Y.C. and Atlanta, 1945-49, Stevens & Wilkinson, Atlanta, 1950-53; individual practice Atlanta, 1953-56; partner Edwards and Portman (Architects), Atlanta, 1956-68; prin. John Portman and Assocs., 1968—; chmn., CEO The Portman Cos., Atlanta, 1971—; bd. dirs. Nations Bank.; pres. Central Atlanta Progress, 1970-72. Prin. works include: The Regent Hotel, Marina Sq., both Singapore, Embarcadero Center, The Pan Pacific-San Francisco, San Francisco Fashion Ctr., Hyatt Regency O'Hare Hotel, Chgo., Peachtree Center, Atlanta; George W. Woodruff Phys. Edn. Ctr. R. Howard Dobbs Student Ctr., both Emory U., Atlanta, Atlanta Merchandise Mart, Atlanta Apparel Mart, Atlanta Decorative Arts Center, Atlanta Gift Mart, Inforum, One Peachtree Ctr., Kennedy Community Center and Middle Sch, Hyatt Regency Hotel, Westin Peachtree Plaza Hotel, Atlanta Marriott Marquis, Northpark Town Ctr., Riverwood, Greenbriar Shopping Ctr., Olympic Village Housing, all Atlanta, Blue Cross-Blue Shield Bldg, Chattanooga, Ft. Worth Nat. Bank Bldg. and Garage, Brussels Internat. Trade Mart, Dana Fine Arts Bldg. at Agnes Scott Coll, Decatur, Ga., Renaissance Center, Detroit, Bonaventure Hotel, Los Angeles, N.Y. Marriott Marquis, Rockefeller Ctr. renovation, N.Y.C., Shanghai Centre, Dream Lake Villas, Hangzhou Qiantang River City, Shandong Bldg., Guomai Bldg., BAODA Bldg., Senfuli Bldg., S Renzhill Complex, Peoples Republic of China, Capital Sq., Kuala Lumpur, Malaysia. Co-author: The Architect as Developer, 1990. Hon. consul, Denmark; sponsor Atlanta Symphony; mem. nat. adv. bd. Ga. Inst. Tech. Found. Bd. Inc.; trustee Atlanta Arts Alliance, Nat. Jewish Hosp. and Research Center; Dean's adv. coun. Harvard U. Sch. Bus.; dir. Atlanta C. of C. (named famous Georgian 1991). Served with USNR, 1942-44. Decorated knight Royal Order Knights of Dannebrog, Denmark; officer Royal Order of the Crown, Belgium; recipient Ivan Allen award N. Ga. chpt. AIA, 1964; award excellence Am. Inst. Steel Constrn., 1973; Design in Steel award Am. Iron and Steel Inst., 1975; medal for hotel design AIA, 1978; Silver medal for innovative design Ga. chpt. AIA, 1981, Community Devel. award Atlanta Bus. League, 1986, others; named Outstanding Young Man of Year, Ga. Jr. C. of C., 1959; Salesman of Year, Sales and Mktg. Execs., Atlanta, 1968; recipient Exceptional Achievement award Ga. Inst. Tech. Alumni Assn., 1985, Disting. Service award Empire Real Estate Bd., Atlanta, 1991, Martin Luther King Salute to Greatness, 1993, Disting. Community Svc. award Atlanta Urban League Inc., 1991, Atlanta Downtown Partnership's Resurgens award Design of Peachtree Plz. Park, 1991, Altanta Downtown Partnership's Resurgens award Design of One Peachtree Ctr., 1993, Horatio Alger award Horatio Alger Assn., 1990, Nat. Home Furnishings Assn. Disting. Svc. award, 1990, Shaping the City award Atlanta Convention and Visitors Bureau, 1988, Trendsetter award Foodsvc. Cons. Soc. Internat., 1987, Torch of Liberty award Anti-Defamation League, 1994; named Man of Yr. Danish Am. Soc., 1986, Father of Yr. Southeast Father's Day Council, 1986; named to Bus. Hall of Fame Coll. Bus. Adminstrn. Ga. State U., 1987, Atlanta Bus. Chronicle, 1991, Atlanta Entrepreneurs Hall of Fame Atlanta Entrepreneurs Network, 1990; named Famous Georgian, Atlanta C. of C.; Paul Harris fellow Rotary Found. Rotary Internat., 1991. Fellow AIA (Atlanta Svc. to Profession award 1992); mem. Nat. Council Archtl. Registration Bds., Am. Inst. Interior Designers (hon.), Soc. Internat. Bus. Fellows (hon.), World Trade Club (founding), Ga. Archtl. and Engring. Soc., Atlanta Rotary Club, Atlanta Action Forum, Omicron Delta Kappa, Tau Sigma Delta. Club: Commerce (bd. dirs.). Office: John Portman & Assocs 225 Peachtree St NE Ste 200 Atlanta GA 30303-1727

PORTMAN, RACHEL MARY BERKELEY, composer; b. Eng., Dec. 11, 1960. BA, Oxford Univ. Scores include (films) Sharma and Beyond, 1986, Antonia and Jane, 1991, Life Is Sweet, 1991, Where Angels Fear to Tread, 1991, Rebecca's Daughters, 1992, Used People, 1992, Ethan Frome, 1993, Benny and Joon, 1993, Friends, 1993, The Joy Luck Club, 1993, (TV movies) Young Charlie Chaplin, 1989, The Cloning of Joanna May, 1992, (documentaries) Elizabeth R: A Year In the Life of the Queen, 1992; compositions include Fantasy for Cello and Piano, 1985. Named Composer of Yr. British Film Inst., 1988. Office: The Kraft-Benjamin Agency 8491 Sunset Blvd Ste 492 West Hollywood CA 90069*

PORTMAN, ROB, congressman; b. Cin., Dec. 19, 1955; m. Jane Portman; children: Jed, Will. BA, Dartmouth Coll., 1979; JD, U. Mich., 1984. Ptnr. Graydon, Head & Ritchie, Cin., 1986-89; assoc. counsel to President of U.S., then dep. asst. to President, dir. Office Legis. Affairs White House, Washington, 1989-92; mem. U.S. Del. to UN Subcom. on Human Rights, 1992, 103d-104th Congresses from 2nd Ohio dist., 1993—; mem. ways and means com., mem. Leaders' Econ. Task Force. Bd. trustees Springer Sch., The United Way, Hyde Park Community United Meth. Ch.; founding trustee Cin.-China Sister City Com.; former bd. dirs. United Home Care; vice chmn. Hamilton County George Bush for Pres. Campaign, 1988, 92; chmn. Rep. Early Bird Campaign com., 1992; del. Rep. Nat. Conv., 1988, 92; active Hamilton County Rep. Party Exec. com., Hamilton County Rep. Party Fin. Com. Mem. Cin. World Trade Assn. Office: US Ho of Reps 238 Cannon HOB Washington DC 20515-0509*

PORTNOY, IAN KARL, lawyer; b. Phila., Aug. 27, 1943; s. Joseph and Florence Portnoy; m. Judith Kobak; children: Michael, Beth. BA, U. Mich., 1965; JD, Villanova U., 1968. Bar: Pa. 1969, D.C. 1970, U.S. Supreme Ct. 1973. Corp. counsel Villager Industries, Phila.; assoc. Danzansky, Dickey, Tydings, Quint and Gordon, Washington, 1970-88; ptnr. Laxalt, Washington, Perito & Dubuc, Washington, 1988-90, Proskauer, Rose, Goetz & Mendelsohn, Washington, 1991—. Dr. editor Digest Environ. Law, Nat. Property Law Digests, Nat. Financing Law Digest; bd. dirs. The Dial Mag., WETA pub. TV and radio sta.; author numerous legal articles. Chmn. bd. dirs. Dumbarton Concert Series, Washington, Live Music Now; devel. bd. Capitol campaign steering and auction com. Georgetown Day Sch.; bd. dirs. Big Brothers, Washington, chmn. annual gourmet dinner. Mem. Am. Arbitration Assn. (comml. com.), Leadership Washington. Home: 6018 Onondaga Rd Bethesda MD 20816-2152 Office: Proskauer Rose Goetz & Mendelsohn 1233 20th St NW Ste 800 Washington DC 20036-2304

PORTNOY, SARA S., lawyer; b. N.Y.C., Jan. 11, 1926; d. Marcus and Gussie (Raphael) Spiro; m. Alexander Portnoy, Dec. 13, 1959 (dec. 1976); children—William, Lawrence. B.A., Radcliffe Coll., 1946; LL.B., Columbia U., 1949. Bar: N.Y. 1949, U.S. Dist. Ct. (so. dist.) N.Y. 1952, U.S. Dist. Ct. (ea. dist.) N.Y. 1975, U.S. Ct. Appeals (2d cir.) 1975, U.S. Supreme Ct. 1975. Assoc. Seligsberg, Friedman & Berliner, N.Y.C., 1949-51; atty. AT & T, N.Y.C., 1951-61; assoc. Proskauer Rose Goetz & Mendelsohn, N.Y.C., 1974-78, ptnr., 1978-94, retired 1994. Mem. Commn. on Human Rights, White Plains, N.Y., 1973-78; bd. dirs. Legal Aid Soc. of Westchester County, N.Y., 1975-83, Columbia Law Sch. Assn., 1990-94; mem. Pres.'s Coun. Yaddo. Mem. Assn. of Bar of City of N.Y. (chair com. legal support staff 1994—). Democrat. Office: Proskauer Rose et al 1585 Broadway New York NY 10036-8200

PORTNOY, WILLIAM MANOS, electrical engineering educator; b. Chgo., Oct. 28, 1930; s. Joseph and Bella (Saltzman) P.; m. Alice Catherine Walker, Sept. 9, 1956; children: Catherine Anne, Michael Benjamin. B.S., U. Ill., 1952, M.S., 1952; Ph.D., 1959. Registered profl. engr., Tex. Mem. tech. staff Hughes Aircraft Co., Newport Beach, Calif., 1959-61, Tex. Instruments Inc., Dallas, 1961-67; mem. faculty Tex. Tech. U., Lubbock, 1967—, prof. biomed. engring., 1973-85, prof. physics, 1985—, prof. elec. engring., 1972; adj. assoc. prof. Baylor Coll. Medicine and Inst. Health Svcs. Rsch., Houston, 1969-73; cons. Hughes Rsch. Labs., Malibu, Calif., 1972, NDM Corp., 1974-76, Los Alamos Nat. Lab., 1980-81, 91, Battelle Rsch. Inst., 1980-81, Westinghouse, 1984, SRI Internat., 1986-88, Lawrence Livermore Nat. Lab., 1986-93, W.J. Shafer Assocs., 1988-91, Sandia Nat. Lab., 1989—, Gen. Rsch. Corp., 1990-92, STI Optronics, 1991-92. Contbr. articles to profl. jours.; patentee in field. Bd. dirs. Am. Heart Assn., Lubbock County, 1972-75. Nat. Heart Inst. postdoctoral trainee, 1969; NASA sr. postdoctoral resident, research assoc. Manned Spacecraft Center, Houston, 1968; Fulbright prof., 1975; recipient Abell faculty award, 1984. Fellow IEEE; mem. Am. Soc. Engring. Edn. (Western Electric Fund award for excellence in instrn. engring. students 1980), Am. Phys. Soc., Sigma Xi. Office: Tex Tech U Dept Elec Engring Lubbock TX 79409

PORTOGHESE, PHILIP SALVATORE, medicinal chemist, educator; b. N.Y.C., June 4, 1931; s. Philip A. and Constance (Antonelli) P.; m. Christine L. Phillips, June 11, 1960; children—Stephen, Stuart, Philip. B.S., Columbia U., 1953, M.S., 1958; Ph.D., U. Wis., 1961; Dr. honoris causa, U. Catania, Italy, 1986, Royal Danish Sch. Pharmacy, Copenhagen, 1992. Asst. prof. Coll. Pharmacy, U. Minn., Mpls., 1961-64; prof. medicinal chemistry Coll. Pharmacy, U. Minn., 1964-69, prof. medicinal chemistry, 1969—, prof. pharmacology, 1987—, dir. grad. study in medicinal chemistry, 1974-86, head dept., 1974-83; cons. NIMH., 1971-72; mem. med. chemistry B sect. NIH, 1972-76; mem. pharmacology, substance abuse and environ. toxicology interdisciplinary cluster President's Biomed. Research Panel, 1975; mem. expert panel of Flavor and Extract Mfrs. Assn. of U.S., 1984—. Mem. editorial adv. bd. Jour. Med. Chemistry, 1969-71; editor-in-chief, 1972—; mem. editorial adv. bd. Med. Chem. series, 1972—. Served with U.S. Army, 1954-56. Recipient Research Achievement award in med. chemistry Am. Pharm. Assn. Found./Acad. Pharm. Sci., 1980; Ernest H. Volwiler award for outstanding contbns. to pharm. scis. Am. Assn. Colls. of Pharmacy, 1984, N.B. Eddy Meml. award Coll. on Problems of Drug Dependence-NAS NRC, 1991. Fellow AAAS, Acad. Pharm. Scis., Am. Assn. Pharm. Scientists (Rsch. Achievement award 1990); mem. Am. Chem. Soc. (Medicinal Chemistry award 1990, E.E. Smissman-Bristol-Meyers-Squibb award 1991), Am. Soc. Pharm. Exptl. Therapeutics, Internat. Union Pure and Applied Chemistry (commn. on medicinal chemistry 1978-82, internat. com. med. chemistry 1982-85), Soc. Neurosci., Sigma Xi, Rho Chi, Phi Lambda Upsilon. Home: 17 Oriole Ln Saint Paul MN 55127-6334 Office: U Minn Coll of Pharmacy 308 Harvard St SE Minneapolis MN 55455-0353

PORTWOOD, JOHN HARDING, lawyer, electric products manufacturing executive; b. Port Huron, Mich., June 5, 1928; s. George Harding and Nina Louise (Powrie) P.; m. Anne Elizabeth Beck, Aug. 28, 1954; children—Elizabeth A. Portwood Bieber, Steven D., Susan E. B.A., Ohio State U., 1953, J.D., 1955. Bar: Ohio 1955. Corp. counsel Toledo Scale Corp., 1955-66, legal counsel, asst. sec., 1967-69; counsel, asst. sec. Reliance Electric Co.,

Cleve., 1969-75; asst. gen. counsel Reliance Electric Co., 1976-83, v.p., sec., gen. counsel, 1983—. Served as cpl. U.S. Army, 1950-54. Mem. Ohio State Bar Assn. Republican. Avocations: golf; reading. Office: Reliance Electric Co 6065 Parkland Blvd Cleveland OH 44124-6106

PORZAK, GLENN E., lawyer; b. Ill., Aug. 22, 1948; m. Judy Lea McGinnis, Dec. 19, 1970; children: Lindsay and Austin. BA with distinction, U. Colo., 1970, JD, 1973. Bar: Colo. 1973. Assoc. Holme Roberts & Owen, Denver, 1973-80, ptnr., 1980-85, mng. ptnr. Boulder office, 1985—; bd. dirs. Norwest Bank Boulder, 1993—. Contbr. articles to profl. jours. 1st Lt. U.S. Army, 1970-78. Fellow Explorers Club; mem. Am. Alpine Club (pres. 1988-91), Colo. Mtn. Club (pres. 1983, hon. mem. 1983—), Colo. Outward Bound (trustee 1992—), Phi Beta Kappa. Achievements include reaching summit of Mt. Everest, climbing highest peak on all seven continents. Home: 771 7th St Boulder CO 80302-7402 Office: Holme Roberts & Owen 1401 Pearl St Boulder CO 80302-5319

POSAMENTIER, ALFRED STEVEN, mathematics educator, university administrator; b. N.Y.C., N.Y., Oct. 18, 1942; s. Ernest and Alice (Pisk) P.; children—Lisa Joan, David Richard. A.B., Hunter Coll., 1964; M.A., CCNY, 1966; postgrad., Yeshiva U., N.Y.C., 1967-69; Ph.D., Fordham U., 1973. Tchr. math Theodore Roosevelt High Sch., Bronx, 1964-70; asst. prof. math. edn. CCNY, N.Y.C., 1970-76, assoc. prof., 1977-80, prof., 1981—, dept. chmn. dept. secondary and continuing edn., 1974-80, chmn., 1980-86; assoc. dean Sch. Edn. CCNY, 1986—, dir. select program in sci. and engring., 1978—; dir. CCNY, U.K., iniatives program dir., 1983—; dir. Germany/CCNY Exch. Program CCNY, 1985—, dir. Austria/CCNY Exch. Program, 1987—, dir. Czechoslovakia/CCNY Exch. Program, 1989—, dir. sci. lectr. program, 1981—, dir. Ctr. for Sci. and Maths. Edn., 1986—; chmn. bd. dirs. Salvadori Ednl. Ctr. on Built Environ., 1988—; supr. math. and sci. Mamaroneck H.S., N.Y., 1976-79; project dir. Math Proficiency Workship, Ossining, N.Y., 1976-79, NSF math. devel. program for secondary sch. tchrs. math., 1978-82, N.Y.C. Profl. Preparation of Math. and Sci. Tchrs., 1978-79; project dir. numerous NSF sponsored math./sci. tchr. devel. insts., 1976—; cons. Inst. Ednl. Devel. N.Y.C., 1970-73, Croft Ednl. Svcs., New London, 1971, Design and Evaluation, 1973, N.Y.C. Bd. Edn., 1973-75, N.Y.C. Bd. Edn. Office of Evaluation, 1974-80, N.Y.C. Bd. Edn. Examiners, 1979-92, Ossining Bd. Edn., 1975-83, numerous others; coord. NSF N.E. Resource Ctr. Sci. and Engring., 1981-90; lectr. various convs. and meetings; vis. prof. U. Vienna, Austria, 1985, 87, 88, 90, Tech. U., Berlin, 1989, Tech. U., Vienna, 1993—, Pedagogical Inst., Vienna, 1993—, Fed. Pedagogical Acad., Vienna, 1995—. Author: Geometric Constructions, 1973, Geometry, Its Elements and Structure, 1972, rev. edit., 1977, Challenging Problems in Geometry, 2 vols., 1970, Challenging Problems in Algebra, 2 vols., 1970, A Study Guide for the Scholastic Aptitude Test in Math., 1969, rev. edit., 1983, Excursions in Advanced Euclidean Geometry, 1980, 2d edit., 1984, Teaching Secondary School Mathematics: Techniques and Enrichment Units, 1981, 3d edit., 1990, 4th edit., 1995, Uncommon Problems for Common Topics in Algebra, 1981, Unusual Problems for Usual Topics in Algebra, 1981, Using Computers in Mathematics, 1983, 2d edit., 1986, Math Motivators: Investigations in Pre-Algebra, 1982, Math Motivators: Investigations in Geometry, 1982, Math Motivators: Investigations in Algebra, 1983, Using Computers: Programming and Problem Solving, 1984, 2d edit., 1989, Advanced Geometric Constructions, 1988, Challenging Problems in Algebra, 1988, Challenging Problems in Geometry, 1988, The Art of Problem Solving: A Resource for the Mathematics Teacher; contbr. numerous articles to profl. jours. Trustee Demarest Bd. Edn., 1977-80. Decorated Grosse Ehrenzeichen für Verdienste (Medal of Honor, Austria); named Tchr. of Yr., CCNY Alumni Assn., 1993; hon. fellow U. South Bank, London, 1988; Fulbright scholar U. Vienna, 1990. Mem. Math. Assn. Am., Sch. Sci. and Math. Assn., Nat. Council Tchrs. Math., (reviewer new publs., referee articles Math. Tchr. Jour.), Assn. Tchrs. Math. N.Y.C. (exec. bd. 1966-67, referee articles assn. jour.), Assn. Tchrs. of Math. of N.Y. State, Assn. Tchrs. Math. N.J. (editorial bd. N.J. Math. Tchr. Jour. 1981-84), Nat. Council of Suprs. of Maths. Home: 634 Caruso Ln River Vale NJ 07675-6210 Office: CCNY New York NY 10031

POSCOVER, MAURY B., lawyer; b. St. Louis, Jan. 13, 1944; s. Edward and Ann (Chapnick) P.; m. Lorraine Wexler, Aug. 14, 1966; children: Michael, Daniel, Joanna. BA, Lehigh U., 1966; JD, Washington U., 1969. Bar: Mo. 1969. Assoc. Husch & Eppenberger, St. Louis, 1969-75, ptnr., 1975—; lectr. Washington U., St. Louis, 1972-79. Editor-in-chief: Business Lawyer; contbr. articles to profl. jours. Bd. dirs. Childhaven, St. Louis, 1978-92, pres. 1986; pres. Jewish Community Rels. Coun., 1990-92. Mem. ABA (chmn. comml. fin. svcs. com. bus law sect. coun., vice chair bus. law sect., editor-in-chief mag.), Bar Assn. Met. St. Louis (pres. 1983-84), Mo. Bar Assn. (bd. govs. 1979-81), Am. Judicature Soc. (dir. 1981-87), Washington U. Alumni Law Assn. (pres. 1980-81), Mo. Athletic Club. Jewish. Office: Husch & Eppenberger 100 N Broadway Ste 1300 Saint Louis MO 63102-2706

POSEN, SUSAN ORZACK, lawyer; b. N.Y.C., Nov. 5, 1945. BA, Sarah Lawrence Coll., 1967; JD, Bklyn. Law Sch., 1978. Bar: N.Y. 1979. Assoc. Stroock & Stroock & Lavan, N.Y.C., 1978-83, 84-86; ptnr. Stroock, Stroock & Lavan, N.Y.C., 1987—; asst. gen. counsel Cablevision Systems Corp., Woodbury, N.Y., 1983-84. Office: Stroock & Stroock & Lavan 7 Hanover Sq New York NY 10004-2616

POSER, CHARLES MARCEL, neurology educator; b. Antwerp, Belgium, Dec. 30, 1923; s. Maurice and Sadye (Gleitsman) P.; m. Joan Doris Crawford, Sept. 3, 1950; children: William John, Nicholas Charles. B.S., CCNY, 1947; M.D., Columbia U., 1951. Diplomate Am. Bd. Psychiatry and Neurology. Resident in neurology Neurol. Inst. Columbia-Presbyn. Med. Center, N.Y., 1952-55; Fulbright scholar Neuropathology Inst. Bunge, Antwerp, Belgium, 1955-56; instr. through assoc. prof. neurology U. Kans. Sch. Medicine, 1955-64; prof., head div. neurology U. Mo. Sch. Medicine, Kansas City, 1964-68; prof., chmn. dept. neurology U. Vt. Coll. Medicine, 1968-81; prof. neurology Boston U. Sch. Medicine, 1981-84, lectr., 1984—; sr. neurologist Beth Israel Hosp.; cons. prof. Tex. Tech. U. Sch. Medicine, Lubbock, 1981-90; lectr. on neurology Harvard Med. Sch., 1982, Tufts U. Sch. Medicine, 1982-90; cons. in neurology U.S. Army and U.S. Navy, 1963—; Cross lectr. U. Witwatersrand, Johannesburg, Republic of South Africa, 1990. Editor-in-chief Jour. Tropical and Geog. Neurology, 1989-92, Neurol. Infections and Epidemiology, 1995—; contbr. numerous articles to med. jours. Served with U.S. Army, 1943-46. Decorated officer Order of Leopold II Belgium; recipient Silver Bicentennial medal Coll. of Physicians and Surgeons, 1967; named Luis Guerrero Meml. lectr. U. Santo Tomás, Manila, 1979, Wilder Penfield lectr. Am. U., Beirut, 1983, Salmon James lectr. London Med. Soc., 1987, Kroc lectr. Rush Med. Coll., Chgo., 1987; Wu Ho-Su Meml. Lectr. Taipei, Taiwan, 1994. Fellow ACP, Am. Acad. Neurology, Am. Acad. Pediatr., Royal Soc. Medicine (London), Royal Soc. Tropical Medicine and Hygiene London; hon. fellow Japanese, Belgian, Cuban, French, Icelandic, Filipino, and Colombian Socs. Neurology, All-Russian Soc. Neurol. Sci., Neurol. Soc. India, Asian Brit. Neurologists; mem. Am. Neurol. Assn. (sr.), Am. Assn. Neuropathologists, Am. Soc. for Rsch. in Nervous and Mental Diseases, Nat. Acad. Medicine Colombia (hon.). Home: 11 Rutland Sq Boston MA 02118-3105 Office: Beth Israel Hosp Dept Neurology Harvard Med Sch 330 Brookline Ave Boston MA 02215

POSER, ERNEST GEORGE, psychologist, educator; b. Vienna, Austria, Mar. 2, 1921; emigrated to Can., 1942, naturalized, 1946; s. Paul and Blanche (Faust) P.; m. Maria Jutta Cahn, July 3, 1953; children: Yvonne, Carol, Michael. B.A., Queen's U. Kingston, Ont., 1946, M.A., 1949; Ph.D., U. London, 1952. Diplomate: Am. Bd. Profl. Psychologists; registered psychologist, B.C. Asst. prof. U. N.B., 1946-48; chief psychologist N.B. Dept. Health, 1952-54; prof. psychology McGill U., Montreal, 1954-83; assoc. prof. psychiatry Faculty Medicine McGill U., 1963-83; adj. dept. psychology U. B.C., 1984—; dir. behavior therapy unit Douglas Hosp. Center, Montreal, 1966-83. Author: Adaptive Learning: Behavior Modification with Children, 1973, Behavior Therapy in Clinical Practice, 1977. hon. fellow Middlesex Hosp., London, 1964. Fellow Canadian Psychol. Assn., Am. Psychol. Assn.

POSER, NORMAN STANLEY, law educator; b. London, May 28, 1928; came to U.S., 1939, naturalized, 1946; s. Jack and Margaret (Salomon) P.; m. Miriam Kugelman, Sept. 1, 1957 (div. 1979); children: Samuel Marc,

Susan; m. Judith Eiseman Cohn, Aug. 11, 1985. A.B. cum laude, Harvard U., 1948, LL.B. cum laude, 1958. Bar: N.Y. 1958. Asso. Greenbaum, Wolff & Ernst, N.Y.C., 1958-61; atty. SEC, Washington, 1961-64; asst. dir. div. trading and markets SEC, 1964-67; asso. Rosenman, Colin, Kaye, Petschek, Freund & Emil, N.Y.C., 1967-68; v.p. Am. Stock Exchange, N.Y.C., 1968-72; sr. v.p. Am. Stock Exchange, 1972-75, exec. v.p., 1975-80; adj. prof. law NYU, 1975-80; prof. law Bklyn. Law Sch., 1980—; cons. World Bank, SEC, OAS, various stock exchs.; spl. counsel N.Y. Stock Exch., 1987—. Mem. adv. bd.: BNA Securities Regulation & Law Report, 1979—, Rev. Securities and Commodities Regulation, 1975—; author: International Securities Regulation: London's "Big Bang" and the European Securities Markets, 1991, Broker-Dealer Law and Regulation: Private Rights of Action, 1995. Served with U.S. Army, 1951-53. Mem. Am. Law Inst., ABA, N.Y.C. Bar Assn., Nat. Futures Assn. (arbitrator 1987—). Club: Harvard (N.Y.C.). Office: 250 Joralemon St Brooklyn NY 11201-3700

POSEY, CLYDE LEE, business administration and accounting educator; b. Tucumcari, New Mex., Dec. 27, 1940; s. Rollah P. and Opal (Patterson) P.; m. Dora Diane Vassar; children: Amanda Fox, Julia, Rebecca; m. Judith James Jerry, July 31, 1991; stepchildren: David Jerry, Georgia Kenyan. BBA, U. Tex., El Paso, 1963; MBA, U. Tex., 1965; postgrad., U. So. Calif., 1968; PhD, Okla. State U., 1978. CPA, Calif., La., Tex. Lab. aide FBI, Washington, 1959-60; acct. Lipson, Cox & Colton (now Deloitte & Touche), El Paso, Tex., 1962; auditor Main & Co. (now KPMG Peat Marwick), El Paso, 1963; teaching asst. U. Tex., Austin, 1963-65; tax cons. Peat, Marwick, Mitchell & Co., Dallas, 1965-66; cons. Roberson, Martin, Horg and Ryckman, Fresno, Calif., 1967; CPA pvt. practice Fresno, Ruston, Calif., La, 1966—; asst. prof. Calif. State U., Fresno, 1966-76; assoc. prof. La. Tech. U., Ruston, 1978-84, prof., 1984—; vis. assoc. prof. Ctrl. State U., Edmond, Okla., 1971-72, U. Okla., Norman, 1976-78; cons. J. David Spence Accountancy Corp., Fresno, 1974-76; many coms. at La. Tech. U. including acad. senator, new faculty welcoming com., acctg. scholarship chmn.; faculty senate rep.; Faculty Consortium, St. Charles, Ill., 1993; expert witness Superior Ct. Calif. Contbr. numerous articles to profl. jours., bus. mags., newspapers, also book reviews; presentations to profl. meetings. Past bd. dirs. Goodwill, Inc. Ctrl. Calif.; ch. deacon and mem. many coms.; pres., treas. Gideons Internat. Ruston Camp; rep. United Way La. Tech. U., Ruston. With U.S. Coast Guard, 1965. Recipient El Paso CPA's Outstanding Jr. scholarship, Standard Oil scholarship, Price Waterhouse scholarship, Outstanding Educator award Gamma Beta Phi, 1986. Mem. AICPA, Am. Acctg. Assn. (La. membership com. chmn.), Am. Inst. for Decision Scis. (program com. chmn. acctg. track), Tex. Soc. CPAs, Am. Tax Assn. (internat. tax policy subcom.), Beta Gamma Sigma (pres.), Beta Alpha Psi. Baptist. Avocations: bicycle racing, golf, tennis, gardening. Home: 2700 Foxxwood Dr Ruston LA 71270 Office: La Tech U CAB 129A Ruston LA 71272

POSEY, EDWIN DALFIELD, librarian; b. Dallas, Jan. 8, 1927; s. Jonathan R. and Illa I. (Golden) P.; m. Erica Grace Krumm, Apr. 9, 1962; children—Reba Alison, Michael John. B.A., U. Houston, 1967; M.S., Drexel U., 1969. Engr., Texteam Corp., Houston, 1960-68; librarian Princeton U., N.J., 1968-69, Purdue U., West Lafayette, Ind., 1969—. Author: Approval Plans, 1977; also articles. Served with USN, 1944-45. Mem. ALA, Am. Soc. Engring. Edn., Am. Soc. Info. Sci., Beta Phi Mu. Democrat. Avocations: book collecting; golf; auto racing. Home: 237 Schilling St West Lafayette IN 47906-2448 Office: Purdue U Libraries West Lafayette IN 47907

POSEY, ELDON EUGENE, mathematician, educator; b. Oneida, Tenn., Jan. 25, 1921; s. Daniel M. and Eva (Owens) P.; m. Christine K. Johnson, Dec. 25, 1943; children—Margaret Posey McQuain, Daniel Marion. B.S., East Tenn. State U., 1947; M.A., U. Tenn., 1949, Ph.D., 1954. Instr. W.Va. U., 1954-55, asst. prof., 1955-59; asso. prof. Va. Poly. Inst., 1959-61, prof., 1961-64; prof. math. U. N.C., Greensboro, 1964-88, prof. emeritus, 1988—; head dept. math. U. N.C., 1964-80. Served to capt. USAAF, 1941-46. Decorated Air medal with 18 oak leaf clusters, D.F.C., Silver Star, Purple Heart. Mem. Am. Math. Soc., Math. Assn. Am., Sigma Xi, Pi Mu Epsilon. Home: 4311 Dogwood Dr Greensboro NC 27410-5611

POSEY, SANDRA DALTON, special education educator; b. Phoenix, Az., May 7, 1945; d. Ruth (Privett) Dalton; children: Melinda Ruth, Clay McDowell. BA, Northeast La. U., 1966; MEd, Vanderbilt U., 1981, Trevecca Nazarene Coll., 1989. Tchr. 8th grade Caddo Parish Sch. system, Shreveport, La., 1967; tchr. 7th and 8th grades Monroe (La.) City Sch. System, 1969; tchr. 7th grade Rocky Mt. (N.C.) Sch. System, 1971-73; grad. asst. Peabody Coll. Vanderbilt U., Nashville, 1980-81; resource tchr. Williamson County Sch. System, Franklin, Tenn., 1981-87, gifted coord., 1987—; asst. dir. Tenn. Acad. for Tchrs. of the Gifted, Nashville, 1989—; mid. Tenn. regional dir. Odyssey of the Mind, 1990, 92; adj. faculty mem. Belmont Coll., Nashville, 1989-93. Mem. Nat. Assn. for the Gifted, Tenn. Assn. for Gifted, Williamson County Assn. for Gifted, Williamson County Assn. for Retarded Citizens, Delta Kappa Gamma, Phi Delta Kappa (v.p. for programs 1991-92, pres. 1992-93). Office: Westwood Elem Sch Springdale AR 72764

POSHARD, GLENN W., congressman; b. Herald, Ill., Oct. 31, 1945. BA, So. Ill. U., 1970, MS, 1974, PhD, 1984. Tchr. high sch.; asst. dir. then dir. Ill. State Regional Edn. Svc. Ctr.; mem. Ill. State Senate, 1984-88, 101st-104th Congresses from 22nd (now 19th) Ill. Dist., 1989—; ranking minority mem. small bus. subcom. on govt. programs, mem. transp. and infrastructure com. Served with U.S. Army. Democrat. Office: US Ho of Reps 2334 Rayburn HOB Washington DC 20515*

POSIN, DANIEL Q., physics educator, television lecturer; b. Turkestan, Aug. 13, 1909; came to U.S., 1918, naturalized, 1927; s. Abram and Anna (Izritz) P.; m. Frances Schweitzer, 1934; children: Dan, Kathryn. A.B., U. Cal., 1932, A.M., 1934, Ph.D., 1935. Instr. U. Cal., 1932-37; prof. U. Panama, 1937-41; dean natural scis. U. Mont., prof., 1941-44, chmn. dept. physics and math., 1942-44; staff Mass. Inst. Tech., 1944-46; prof. physics, chmn. dept. N.D. State Coll., Fargo, 1946-55; prof. dept. physics DePaul U., 1956-67; prof. phys. sci. dept. Calif. State U., San Francisco, 1967—; chmn. dept. interdisciplinary scis. Calif. State U., 1969—; dir. Schwab Sci. Lecture Series, Atoms for Peace exhibit Mus. Sci. and Industry, Chgo.; Chief cons. Borg Warner Sci. Hall and Allied Chem. Sci. Hall, Times Square; scientific cons. CBS-TV. (Recipient 6 Emmy awards for best educator on TV in Chgo., and best ednl. TV programs). Author: Trigonometria, 1937-41, Fisica Experimental, Fisica, 1937-41, Mendeleyev—The Story of a Great Scientist, 1948, I Have Been to the Village, with Introduction by Einstein, 1948, rev. edit., 1974, Out of This World, 1959, What is a Star, 1961, What is Chemistry, 1961, What is a Dinosaur, 1961, The Marvels of Physics, 1961, Find Out, 1961, Chemistry for the Space Age, 1961, Experiments and Exercises in Chemistry, 1961, What is Matter, 1962, What is Electronic Communication, 1962, What is Energy, Dr. Posin's Giants, 1962, Life Beyond our Planet, 1962, Man and the Sea, 1962, Man and the Earth, 1962, Man and the Jungle, 1962, Man and the Desert, 1962, Science in the Age of Space, 1965, Rockets and Satellites, Our Solar System, The Next Billion Years, 1973; contbr. to: Today's Health; sci. cons.: Compton's Yearbook; contbr. to: feature articles Chgo. Tribune, (book) After Einstein-Remembering Einstein, 1981; co-contbr. to book The Courage to Grow Old, 1989; appearances, CBS Radio-TV, WTTW-WGN-TV, 1956-67, NET; ABC TV series Dr. Posin's Universe. Chmn. edn. com. Chgo. Heart Assn., 1963-67; Trustee Leukemia Soc. James T. Grady award Am. Chem. Soc., 1972. Fellow Am. Phys. Soc.; mem. A.A.A.S., Phi Beta Kappa, Sigma Xi. Office: Calif State Univ San Francisco CA 94132

POSLER, GERRY LYNN, agronomist, educator; b. Cainsville, Mo., July 24, 1942; s. Glen L. and Helen R. (Maroney) P.; m. O. Shirley Weeda, June 23, 1963; children: Mark L., Steven C., Brian D. BS, U. Mo., 1964, MS, 1966; PhD, Iowa State U., 1969. Asst. prof. Western (Macomb) Ill. U., 1969-74; assoc. Kans. State U., Manhattan, 1974-80, prof., 1980—, asst. dept. head, 1982-90, dept. head, 1990—. Contbr. articles to profl. jours. and popular pubs., abstracts, book reviews. Fellow Am. Soc. Agronomy, Crop Sci. Soc. Am.; mem. Am. Forage Grassland Coun., Crop Science Soc. Am. (C-3 div. chmn. 1991), Coun. Agrl. Science Tech. (Cornerstone club), Nat. Assn. Colls. Tchrs. Agr. (tchr. fellow award 1978, ensminger interstate dist. teaching award, 1987, north cen. region dir. 1989, v.p. 1990, pres.; life mem.), Kans. Assn. Colls. Tchrs. Agr. (pres. 1983-85),

Kans. Forage Grassland Coun. (bd. dirs. 1989-92), Gamma Sigma Delta (Outstanding Faculty award 1991, pres. 1987). Home: 3001 Montana Ct Manhattan KS 66502-2300 Office: Kans State U Dept Agronomy Throckmorton Hall Manhattan KS 66506

POSLUNS, WILFRED M., manufacturing and retailing company executive; b. Toronto, Ont., Can., Apr. 4, 1932; s. Louis H. and Leah (Granatstein) P.; m. Joyce Eleanor Cohen, June 16, 1953; children: Wendy Carol, Lynn Susan, David Howard. B.Com., U. Toronto, 1955. With Superior Fin. Co. Ltd., Toronto, 1955; customs man Burns Bros. & Denton, 1955-59; dir. R. A. Daly & Co., 1959-61; fin. mgr. Irving Posluns Sportswear and Jack Posluns & Co., Toronto, 1961-67; sec.-treas. Dylex Ltd, Toronto, 1967-76, dir. 1967—, pres., CEO, 1976-88, chmn. bd. dirs., CEO, 1988—, chmn. bd., dir., 1972—; sec.-treas. WET Seal, Pacific Linen. Pres. Jewish Community Ctr., Toronto, 1974-78, chmn. bd. dirs., 1978-82; pres. Can. Friends Hebrew U., 1977—; asst. sec. Toronto Jewish congress; bd. govs. Mount Sinai Hosp.; trustee United Community Fund of Greater Toronto; bd. dirs. United Jewish Appeal Toronto, Nat. Jewish Welfare Bd., Baycrest Centre Geriatric Care, Jewish Camp Council YMHA, Can.-Israel Cultural Found. Mem. Oakdale Golf and Country Club. Office: Dylex Ltd, 637 Lake Shore Blvd W, Toronto, ON Canada M5V 1A8

POSNANSKY, MERRICK, history and archaeology educator; b. Bolton, Lancashire, Eng., Mar. 8, 1931; came to U.S., 1977; s. Simon and Dora (Cohen) P.; m. Eunice Sarah Lubega, Feb. 10, 1962; children: Sheba, Tessa, Helen. B.A., U. Nottingham, Eng., 1952, Ph.D., 1956; Dip. Arch., Peterhouse, Cambridge U., Eng., 1953. Warden of prehist. sites Royal Nat. Parks, Nairobi, Kenya, 1956-58; curator Uganda Museum, Kampala, 1958-62; asst. dir. Brit. Inst. in Eastern Africa, Kampala, 1962-64; dir. African studies Makerere U. Coll., Kampala, 1964-67; prof. archaeology U. Ghana, Legon, 1967-76; prof. history and anthropology UCLA, 1976—, chmn. archaeology program, 1979-81, chmn. adv. com. James S. Coleman African Studies Ctr., 1983-88, dir. Inst. Archaeology, 1984-87, dir. African Studies Ctr., 1988-92; chmn. Hist. Monuments Commn. Uganda, 1964-67. Editor: Nile Quest, 1962, Prelude to East African History, 1966; joint editor: The Archaeological and Linguistic Reconstruction of African History, 1982; guest editor: Jour. New World Archaeology, 1982, 86. Grantee UNESCO, Brit. Acad., Leverhulme Trust, L.S.B. Leakey Found., Valco Found., Wenner-Gren Found., Nat. Geog. Soc., Fulbright Program, Rotary Found.; hon. fellow Brit. Inst. in Eastern Africa, 1964; vis. fellow Clare Hall, Cambridge U., 1974. Fellow Soc. Antiquaries of London; mem. Uganda Soc. (editor jour. 1962-67, pres. 1964), Soc. Hist. Archeology, African Studies Assn., UCLA Friends of Archaeology, Mus. Assn. Middle Africa (founding pres. 1959-61), Soc. African Archaeology (pres. 1990-92). Home: 5107 Rubio Ave Encino CA 91436-1124

POSNER, DONALD, art historian; b. N.Y.C., Aug. 30, 1931; s. Murray and Frances (Teitel) P.; 1 dau., Anne Tyre. A.B., Queens Coll., 1956; M.A., Harvard U., 1957; Ph.D., NYU, 1962. Lectr. Queens Coll., 1957; asst. prof. art history Columbia U., 1961-62; mem. faculty Inst. Fine Arts, NYU, 1962—, Ailsa Mellon Bruce prof. fine arts, 1975—, acting dir. Inst. Fine Arts, 1978-79, now dep. dir.; Robert Sterling Clark prof. Williams Coll., 1973; William R. Kenan, Jr. prof. U. Va., 1976-77; vis. prof. U. Wash., 1991. Author: Annibale Carracci, 1971, Watteau: A Lady at Her Toilet, 1973, Seventeenth and Eighteenth Century Art, 1971, Antoine Watteau, 1984; editor-in-chief: The Art Bull, 1968-71. Served with USAF, 1951-55. Am. Acad. in Rome fellow, 1959-61; Inst. for Advanced Study fellow, 1976; recipient Charles Rufus Morey award, 1972. Mem. Coll. Art Assn. Am. (dir. 1970-74), Am. Soc. 18th Century Studies. Office: Inst Fine Arts 1 E 78th St New York NY 10021-0102

POSNER, EDWARD MARK, stock brokerage company executive; b. Bklyn., Aug. 19, 1938; s. Morris and Edith Posner; student Bklyn. Coll. 1956-58, N.Y.U. 1958-59; m. Karen, Dec. 4, 1960; children—Michele, Charles. Clerk, Walston Co., N.Y.C. 1960; securities trader Meade Co., N.Y.C. 1961-63, Lee Higginson Corp. N.Y.C. 1963-66; with Rauscher Pierce Refsnes, Inc., N.Y.C. 1966-85, now sr. v.p., dir. equity trading Cowen & Co., 1985—; sr. v.p. equity trading and resident mgr. N.Y. office. Bd. dirs. Central Synagogue, Nassau County, N.Y. 1976-83; treas. Rockville Centre Boys Basketball League 1981—. Mem. Phila. Stock Exchange, Security Traders Assn. N.Y. (pres. 1983-84), Nat. Security Traders Assn. (bd. govs., sec. 1987—). Home: 199 N Forest Ave Rockville Centre NY 11570-3009 Office: 1 Battery Park New York NY 10004-1412

POSNER, EDWARD MARTIN, lawyer; b. Phila., Oct. 20, 1946. BA, Amherst Coll., 1968; JD, Harvard U., 1974. Bar: Pa. 1974. Exec. asst. to sec. of pub. welfare Commonwealth of Pa., Harrisburg, 1971-72; assoc. Drinker, Biddle & Reath, Phila., 1974-80, ptnr., 1980—. Democrat. Avocation: fly fishing. Office: Drinker Biddle & Reath 1345 Chestnut St Philadelphia PA 19107-3496

POSNER, ERNEST GARY, lawyer; b. Nashville, July 2, 1937; s. Alvin Joseph and Bertha (Halpern) P.; m. Gretel Roberta Tishler, Dec. 22, 1963; children: Suzanne Lyn, Deborah Ariel. BChE, Vanderbilt U., 1959; postgrad., Suffolk U., 1963-64; JD, Am. U., 1967. Bar: Va. 1967, Pa. 1968, U.S. Dist. Ct. (ea. dist.) Pa. 1969, U.S. Patent Office 1970, U.S. Supreme Ct. 1975. Advanced through grades to lt. comdr., 1967; commd. U.S. Navy, 1959, ret., 1967; staff Interagy. Com. Oceanography, Washington, 1967-68; patent lawyer Atlantic Richfield Co., Phila., 1968-72; v.p., gen. counsel, corp. sec. PQ Corp., Valley Forge, Pa., 1972—. Commr., vice chmn. Govt. Study Commn., Upper Merion, Pa., 1975-76. Mem. ABA, Soap & Detergent Assn. (legal com. 1974—), Am. Intellectual Property Law Assn., Internat. Bus. Forum (speaker), Lic. Exec. Soc. (trustee 1993—), Am. Corp. Counsel Assn., Masons, B'nai B'rith. Office: PQ Corp Swedesford Rd PO Box 840 Valley Forge PA 19482-0840

POSNER, GARY HERBERT, chemist, educator; b. N.Y.C., June 2, 1943; s. Joseph M. and Rose (Klein) P.; children: Joseph, Michael. BA, Brandeis U., 1965; MA, Harvard U., 1965, PhD, 1968. Asst. prof. Johns Hopkins U., Balt., 1969-74, assoc. prof., 1974-79, prof. dept. chemistry, 1979—, Scowe prof. chemistry, 1989—; prof. dept. environ. chemistry Johns Hopkins U., 1982—, chmn. dept. of chemistry, 1987-90; cons. Batelle Meml. Inst., Columbus, Ohio, 1983, S.W. Rsch. Inst., San Antonio, Nova Pharm. Co., Balt.; mem. Fulbright-Hays Adv. Screening Com. in Chemistry, 1978-81; Fulbright lectr. U. Paris, 1976; Michael vis. prof. Weizmann Inst. Sci., Rehovot, Israel, 1983; leader Round Table discussion Welch Found. Conf. Chem. Rsch., Houston, 1973, 83; Plenary lectr. Nobel Symposium on Asymmetric Synthesis, Sweden, 1984. Author: Introduction to Organic Synthesis Using Organocopper Reagents, 1980; mem. editorial bd. Organic Reactions, 1976-89. Named Chemist of Yr., State of Md., 1987; fellow Japan Soc. for Promotion Sci., 1991; recipient Johns Hopkins U. Disting. Tchng. award, 1994. Mem. Am. Chem. Soc., AAUP, NIH (medicinal chemistry study sect. 1986-89), Phi Beta Kappa. Office: Johns Hopkins U Dept Chemistry 3300 N Charles St Baltimore MD 21218

POSNER, GERALD, author, lawyer; b. San Francisco, May 20, 1954; s. Gerald Gerard and Gloria Lillian (Pagannini) P.; m. Trisha Denise Levene, Apr. 27, 1984. BA, U. Calif., Berkeley, 1975; JD cum laude, U. Calif., San Francisco, 1978. Litigation assoc. Cravath, Swaine & Moore, N.Y.C., 1978-80; ptnr. Posner & Ferrara, N.Y.C., 1981-86, of counsel, 1985—; author, freelance journalist, 1986—. Author: Mengele: The Complete Story, 1986, Warlords of Crime: Chinese Secret Societies-The New Mafia, 1988, Bio-Assassins, 1989, Hitler's Children: Sons and Daughters of Leaders of the Third Reich Talk About Themselves and Their Fathers, 1991, Case Closed: Lee Harvey Oswald and the Assassination of JFK, 1993; contbr. articles to newspapers and jours. Recipient Polit. Book award Washington Monthly, 1993; finalist Pulitzer prize in history, 1993. Mem. PEN, Authors Guild, Nat. Writers Union (mem. exec. bd.), Com. to Protect Journalists, Phi Beta Kappa. Office: Posner & Ferrara 515 Madison Ave Ste 905 New York NY 10022

POSNER, JEROME BEEBE, neurologist, educator; b. Cin., Mar. 20, 1932; s. Philip and Rose (Goldberg) P.; m. Gerta Grunen, Aug. 29, 1954; children: Roslyn, Joel, P.J. B.S., u. Wash., 1951; M.D., U. Wash., 1955. Intern King County Hosp., Seattle, 1955-56; asst. resident in neurology U. Wash. Affiliated Hosps., Seattle, 1956-59; fellow in neurology U. Wash. Affiliated

Hosps., 1958-59; spl. fellow NIH, U. Wash., 1961-63; instr. medicine U. Louisville Sch. Medicine, 1959-61; attending neurologist King County Hosp., 1962-63; asst. prof. neurology Cornell U. Med. Coll., N.Y.C., 1963-67; assoc. prof. Cornell U. Med. Coll., 1967-70, prof., 1970—, vice chmn. dept. neurology, 1978-87; asst. attending neurologist N.Y. Hosp., 1963-67, asso. attending neurologist, 1967-70, attending neurologist, 1970—; asso. Cotzias Lab. of Neuro-Oncology, Sloan Kettering Inst. Cancer Research, N.Y.C., 1967-76; mem. Cotzias Lab. of Neuro-Oncology, Sloan Kettering Inst. Cancer Research, 1976—; chief neuropsychiat. service, attending physician dept. medicine Meml. Hosp. for Cancer and Allied Diseases, 1967-75, attending physician, 1975—, chmn. dept. neurology, 1975-87, 89—, Cotzias chair neuro-oncology, 1986; med. med. adv. bd. Burke Rehab. Ctr., White Plains, N.Y., 1973—; adj. prof. vis. physician Rockefeller U. Hosp., N.Y.C., 1973-75; vis. physician Rockefeller U. Hosp., 1980—; mem. med. adv. bd. Assn. for Brain Tumor Rsch., 1974-93; mem. neurology B study sect. NIH, 1972-76. Author: (with F. Plum) Diagnosis of Stupor and Coma, 3d edit., 1980, (with H. Gilbert and L. Weiss) Brain Metastasis, 1980, Neurologic Complications of Cancer, 1995; mem. editorial bd. Archives of Neurology, 1971-76, Annals of Neurology, 1976-80, Am. Jour. Medicine, 1978-93, Neurology, 1992—; contbr. articles to med. jours. Served with M.C. U.S. Army, 1959-61. Fellow AAAS; mem. AMA, Am. Acad. Neurology (Farber Brain Tumor award 1988), Am. Assn. Cancer Rsch., Am. Fedn. Clin. Rsch., Am. Neurol. Assn., Am. Physiol. Soc., Assn. Am. Physicians, Harvey Soc., N.Y. Acad. Sci. Inst. of Medicine, Soc. Neuroscis., Can. Neurol. Soc. (hon.), Alpha Omega Alpha. Office: Meml Sloan-Kettering Cancer 1275 York Ave New York NY 10021-6007

POSNER, KENNETH ROBERT, hotel corporation executive; b. Chgo., Sept. 2, 1947; m. Arlene Lynn Robinson, June 21, 1970; children—Zachary, Brennan. B.S. in Acctg., So. Ill. U., 1970. C.P.A., Ill. Acctg. mgr. Jewel Cos., Inc., Melrose Park, Ill., 1970-72; audit ptnr. Laventhol & Horwath, Chgo., 1972-81; v.p. fin. Hyatt Corp., Chgo., 1981—.

POSNER, RICHARD ALLEN, federal judge; b. N.Y.C., Jan. 11, 1939; s. Max and Blanche Posner; m. Charlene Ruth Horn, Aug. 13, 1962; children: Kenneth A., Eric A. AB, Yale U., 1959; LLB, Harvard U., 1962; LLD (hon.), Syracuse U., 1986, Duquesne U., 1987, Georgetown U., 1992; Dr. hon. causa, U. Ghent, 1995. Bar: N.Y. 1963, U.S. Supreme Ct. 1966. Law clk. Justice William J. Brennan Jr. U.S. Supreme Ct., Washington, 1962-63; asst. to commnr. FTC, Washington, 1963-65; asst. to solicitor gen. U.S. Dept. Justice, Washington, 1965-67; gen. counsel Pres.'s Task Force on Communications Policy, Washington, 1967-68; assoc. prof. Stanford U. Law Sch., Calif., 1968-69; prof. U. Chgo. Law Sch., 1969-78, Lee and Brena Freeman prof., 1978-81, sr. lectr., 1981—; circuit judge U.S. Ct. Appeals (7th cir.), Chgo., 1981—, chief judge, 1993—; research assoc. Nat. Bur. Econ. Research, Cambridge, Mass., 1971-81; pres. Lexecon Inc., Chgo., 1977-81. Author: Antitrust Law: An Economic Perspective, 1976, Economic Analysis of Law, 4th edit., 1992, The Economics of Justice, 1981, The Federal Courts: Crisis and Reform, 1985 (with William M. Landes) The Economic Structure of Tort Law, 1987, Law and Literature: A Misunderstood Relation, 1988, The Problems of Jurisprudence, 1990, Cardozo: A Study in Reputation, 1990, Sex and Reason, 1992, The Essential Holmes, 1992 (with Tomas J. Philipson) Private Choices and Public Health: The AIDS Epidemic in Economic Perspective, 1993, Overcoming Law, 1995; pres. Harvard Law Rev., 1961-62; editor: Jour. Legal Studies, 1972-81. Fellow AAAS, Am. Law Inst., British Acad.; mem. Am. Econ. Assn., Am. Phil. Assn. Office: US Ct Appeals 7th Cir 219 S Dearborn St Chicago IL 60604-1702

POSNER, ROY EDWARD, finance executive; b. Chgo., Aug. 24, 1933; s. Lew and Julia (Cvetan) P.; m. Donna Lea Williams, June 9, 1956 (div. May 1991); children: Karen Lee, Sheryl Lynn. Student, U. Ill., 1951-53, Internat. Accountants Soc., 1956-59, Loyola U., Chgo., 1959; grad., Advanced Mgmt. Program, Harvard U., 1976. CPA, Ill. Pub. acct. Frank W. Dibble Co., Chgo., 1956-61; supr. Harris, Kerr, Forster & Co. (C.P.A.s), Chgo., 1961-66; with Loews Corp. N.Y.C., 1966—; v.p. fin. svcs., chief fin. officer Loews Corp., 1973-86, sr. v.p., chief fin. officer, 1986—; find. cons. N.Y. Football Giants, Inc., Rutherford, N.J.; bd. dirs. Bulova Italy S.P.A., Milan, Bulova Systems and Instruments Corp., N.Y.C., Loews Hotels Monaco S.A.M., Monte Carlo, Monaco, Loews Internat. Svcs. S.A., Switzerland, G F Corp., Youngstown, Ohio, Taj Mahal Holding Corp., Atlantic City. Mem. editorial com.: Uniform System of Accounting for Hotels, 7th edit. Pres. No. Regional Valley High Sch. Music Parents Assn., 1979; trustee Loews Found., N.Y.C. With U.S. Army, 1953-55. Mem. AICPA, Fin. Execs. Inst., Ins. Acctg. and Stats. Assn., Internat. Hospitality Accts. Assn., Am. Hotel and Motel Assn., Ill. Soc. CPAs, N.Y. State CPAs (chmn. com. on hotel restaurant and club acctg. 1980-82), Tri-County Golf Assn. (treas. 1985-88, v.p. 1988-89), Alpine Country Club (bd. govs. 1982-94, exec. com. 1982-90, pres. 1988-90), Delta Tau Delta. Home: 273 Whitman St Haworth NJ 07641-1315 Office: Loews Corp 667 Madison Ave New York NY 10021-8029

POSNER, SIDNEY, advertising executive; b. Syracuse, N.Y., Jan. 14, 1924; s. Harry and Fannie (Hoffman) P.; m. Miriam Frances Kaplowitz, June 8, 1952; children: Steven Charles, Peter Scott, Robert Keith. BS, Syracuse U., 1947. Asst. advt. mgr. Rudolph Bros., Syracuse, 1947-48; copy chief Kaletski Advt. Agy., Syracuse, 1948-50; promotion mgr. Photo Trade News, N.Y.C., 1950-53; asst. to pres. Dobin Advt. Agy., N.Y.C.; pres. S. Posner & Co. Advt. Agy., N.Y.C., 1955-59, Constellation Art Corp., 1959-76, Communicorp, N.Y.C., 1959-76, Bus. Counselors Corp., N.Y.C., 1959-76, Newmark, Posner & Mitchell Inc.. N.Y.C., 1959-92, Posner Comm. Inc., Boca Raton, Fla., 1993-94. Office: Posner Comm Assocs Inc 17547 Bocaire Way Boca Raton FL 33487-1109

POSOKHOV, IOURI, ballet dancer, educator; b. Lougansk, Ukraine, July 20, 1964; came to U.S., 1994; s. Mikail and Alla (Korotkova) P.; m. Anna Yurievna Titova, July 9, 1988; 1 child, Danila Yurievich. Student, Choreographic Acad. Bolshoi, Moscow, 1982. Dancer Bolshoi Ballet, 1982-92, mem. corps de ballet, soloist, 1982-87, prin. dancer, 1987-92; prin. dancer Royal Danish Ballet, Copenhagen, 1992-94, San Francisco Ballet, 1994—. Home: 643 Spruce St San Francisco CA 94118 Office: San Francisco Ballet 455 Franklin St San Francisco CA 94102

POSPISIL, GEORGE CURTIS, biomedical research administrator; b. Thomas, Okla., Aug. 8, 1945; s. George Frank and Zelpha Earline (Hensley) P.; children: Heather Elizabeth, Derek Curtis. Student Wheaton Coll., 1963-64; BA, U. Okla., 1968, MA, 1971. Peace Corps tchr., Maseru, Lesotho, Southern Africa, 1973-74; dir. health services fin. project State of Wis., Madison, 1975-76; pub. health advisor USPHS, Rockville, Md., 1972-73, program/policy analyst, 1977-81, contract mgr., 1982-84, program/policy analyst, 1984-86; dir. Services Crime Victims/Witnesses Project, Tioga County, N.Y., 1986—; guest lectr. U. Wis., Summer Inst., Carthage Coll.; sci. editor The Johns Hopkins U. Krieger Mind/Brain Inst., 1993-95. Mem. Rockville Humanities Commn., 1981-83; spokesperson Neighborhood Planning Com., 1980-82; coordinator mental health services Cuban Refugee Project, Ft. McCoy, Wis., 1980; sec. community adv. com. mental health program Montgomery House, 1982-86; rsch. and tng. administr. Cornell U., Ithaca, N.Y., 1986-89; analyst biomed. rsch. program NIH, 1989—; bd. dirs. Family Svc. Montgomery County, 1984-86; legis. fellow U.S. Senate Labor and Human Resources Com./Health Office, 1991; mem. county Spl. Olympics Com., 1982-86; mem. Citizens' Planning Subcom. Carroll County, Md., 1992-93; mem. Am. Friends Svc. Com. Mem. Soc. Rsch. Administrs., Nat. Coun. Univ. Rsch. Administrs; mem. exec. coun. NIH Recreation and Welfare Assn.; bd. dir. Westminster Ch. of the Brethren. Editor: Decade of the Brain, 1990, Maximizing Human Potential: Decade of the Brain, 1991. Office: Nat Inst Neurol Disorders NIH 9000 Rockville Pike Rm 8a03 Bethesda MD 20892-0001

POSPISIL, LEOPOLD JAROSLAV, anthropology educator; b. Olomouc, Czechoslovakia, Apr. 26, 1923; came to U.S., 1949, naturalized, 1954; s. Leopold and Ludmila (Petrlak) P.; m. Zdenka Smyd, Jan. 31, 1945; children: Zdenka, Mira. Juris Universae Candidatus, Charles U., Prague, Czechoslovakia, 1947, Juris Universae Dr., 1991; BA in Sociology, Willamette U., Salem, Oreg., 1950; MA in Anthropology, U. Oreg., 1952; PhD, Yale U., 1956; ScD (hon.), Willamette U., 1969; PhD (hon.), Charles U., Prague, Czech Rep., 1994. Instr. Yale U., New Haven, 1956-57, asst. prof., 1957-60; asst. curator Peabody Mus., 1956-60, assoc. prof., 1960-65, prof., curator,

1965—, dir. divsn. anthropology, 1966-93; prof. anthropology, 1966-93, prof. emeritus, 1993—. Author: Kapauku Papuans and Their Law, 1958, Kapauku Papuan Economy, 1963, Kapauk Papuans of West New Guinea, 1963, Anthropology of Law, 1971, Ethnology of Law, 1972, Anthropologie des Rechts, 1981, Obernberg: Quantitative Analysis of a Tyrolean Economy, 1995; contbr. articles to profl. jours. Guggenheim fellow, NSF fellow, 1962, 64-65, 67-71, NIMH fellow, 1973-79; Social Sci. Rsch. Coun. grantee, 1966. Fellow AAAS, N.Y. Acad. Scis., Am. Anthrop. Assn.; mem. NAS, Explorers Club, Czechoslovakian Acad. Arts and Scis. (past pres.), Coun. Free Czechoslovakia, Assn. for Polit. and Legal Anthropology (pres.-at-large), Assn. for Social Anthropology in Oceania, Soc. for Econ. Anthropology, Sigma Xi. Home: 554 Orange St New Haven CT 06511-3819 Office: Yale U Dept Anthropology 51 Hillhouse Ave New Haven CT 06520-3703

POSS, JEFFERY SCOTT, architect, educator; b. Harvey, Ill., May 20, 1956. BAS, U. Ill., 1978, MArch, 1980. Intern architect Charles Kober Assocs., Chgo., 1980-81, Skidmore, Owings and Merrill, Chgo., 1981; designer Newman/Lustig and Assocs., Chgo., 1983-84; design assoc. Kevin Roche John Dinkeloo and Assocs., Hamden, Conn., 1985-87; project architect and designer Tai Soo Kim Assocs., Hartford, Conn., 1987-89; pvt. practice architect Urbana, Ill., 1989—; assoc. prof. U. Ill., Champaign-Urbana, 1989—; invited juror and lectr. in field. Contbr. articles to profl. jours. Recipient First Alt. prize Nat. Inst. for Archtl. Edn., 1981, First Place award Champaign Park Dist./AIA, 1989, Nat. Design award Concrete Steel Reinforcing Inst./AIA, 1992. Mem. AIA (Corp. Ill., Ctrl. Ill. and Champaign-Urbana chpts., Excellence in Edn. Honors award 1993, Ctrl. Ill. award for design excellence, 1993), Am. Soc. Archtl. Perspectives (Excellence in Graphic Representation Architecture award 1990, 93). Office: 909 E Water St Urbana IL 61801-2841

POST, AUGUST ALAN, economist, artist; b. Alhambra, Calif., Sept. 17, 1914; s. Edwin R. and Edna (Stickney) P.; m. Helen E. Wills, Nov. 21, 1940; 1 child, David Wills. AB, Occidental Coll., 1938; student Chouinard Inst. Art, 1938; MA, Princeton, 1940; LLD, Golden Gate U., 1972, Occidental Coll., 1974, Claremont Grad. Sch., 1978. In banking bus., 1933-36; instr. econs. Occidental Coll., 1940-42; asst. prof. Am. U., 1943; economist Dept. State, 1944-45; rsch. dir. Utah Found., 1945-46; chief economist, adminstrv. analyst State of Calif., 1946-50, state legis. analyst, 1950-77; cons. Com. Higher Edn. and State, 1964; mem. Nat. Com. Support of Public Schs., 1967; mem. nat. adv. panel Nat. Center Higher Edn. Mgmt. Systems, 1971-72; chmn. Calif. Gov.'s Commn. on Govt. Reform, 1978—; mem. faculty U. So. Calif. Grad. Sch. Pub. Adminstrn., 1978-80; Regents' prof. U. Calif., Davis, 1983, vis. prof., 1984-85; spl. cons. Touche Ross and Co., 1977-87; cons., interim exec. dir. Calif. Commn. for Rev. of Master Plan for Higher Edn., 1985; mem. adv. bd. Calif. Tomorrow nat. shows and one-man shows; dir. Crocker Art Gallery Assn., pres., 1966-67. Trustee U. Calif., Berkeley, Art Mus., 1986-91; mem. adv. com. on future ops. Coun. State Govts., 1965; bd. mgrs., pres. YMCA; bd. dirs. Sacramento Civic Ballet Assn.; trustee Calif. Coll. Arts and Crafts, 1982-86; chmn. Calif. State Task Force on Water Future, 1981-82, Sacramento Regional Found., bd. dirs., 1983-91; bd. dirs. Calif. Mus. Assn., pres., 1976-77, Policy Analysis for Calif. Edn., 1985—, Senate Adv. Commn. on Control of Cost of State Govt., 1986—, Ctrl. Valley Found., 1994—, Pub. Policy Inst. Calif., 1994—; co-chmn. Calif. Citizen's Budget Commn., 1992; chmn. Citizens Commn. on Ballot Initiatives, 1992—, Catalonia Sister State Task Force, 1988—, Commn. on Innovation, Calif. Community Colls., 1992, Californians for Pension Protection, 1992, Judicial Coun. Select com. on Judicial Retirement, 1993—; bd. dirs. Central Valley Found., 1994—, Pub. Policy Inst. Calif., 1994—. With USNR, 1943-44. Mem. Nat. Acad. Public Adminstrn., Phi Beta Kappa, Kappa Sigma. Home: 1900 Rockwood Dr Sacramento CA 95864-1527

POST, AVERY DENISON, church official; b. Norwich, Conn., July 29, 1924; s. John Palmer and Dorothy (Church) P.; m. Margaret Jane Rowland, June 8, 1946; children: Susan Macalister Post Ross, Jennifer Campbell, Elizabeth Post Elliott, Anne Denison Post Roy. B.A., Ohio Wesleyan U., 1945; B.D., Yale U., 1949, S.T.M., 1952; L.H.D. (hon.), Lakeland Coll., Sheboygan, Wis., 1977; D.D. (hon.), Chgo. Theol. Sem., 1978, Middlebury Coll. (Vt.), 1978, Defiance Coll. (Ohio), 1979; LL.D. (hon.), Heidelberg Coll. (Ohio), 1982, Chapman Coll.; Litt.D. (hon.), Elmhurst Coll. Ordained to ministry, 1949; pastor chs. in Vt, Ohio, Conn. and N.Y., 1946-63; sr. minister Scarsdale (N.Y.) Congl. Ch., 1963-70; minister, pres. Mass. conf. United Ch. Christ, 1970-77; pres. United Ch. Christ, N.Y.C., 1977-89; mem. central com. World Council Chs., 1978-91; exec. com., bd. govs. Nat. Council Chs., 1977-89; moderator, planning com. 7th Gen. Assembly World Coun. Chs.; lectr. Bible Adelphi Coll., Garden City, N.Y., 1958-59; Luccock lectr. Yale U. Div. Sch., 1961; lectr. homiletics Union Sem., N.Y.C., 1967-69, bd. dirs., 1967-77; trustee Andover Newton Theol. Sem., 1970-80; del. numerous internat. ch. meetings; sr. fellow Hartford Sem., 1989-93. Bd. dirs. Bridges for Peace, 1990—; exec. dir. Bangor Theol. Sem., Hanover, N.H., 1991-93; life mem. PTA, Norwich, N.Y. With USNR, 1943-45. Decorated Comdr.'s Cross (Federal Republic Germany), 1990; recipient 1st Ecumenical award Mass. Coun. Chs., 1976; Disting. Achievement award Ohio Wesleyan U., 1983. mem. Randolph (N.H.) Mountain Club, Phi Beta Kappa, Omicron Delta Kappa. Democrat. Home: PO Box 344 Beaver Meadow Rd Norwich VT 05055

POST, BOYD WALLACE, forester; b. Glouster, Ohio, Oct. 5, 1928; s. Herbert Dwight and Fern Hazel (Wallace) P.; m. Vivian Joan Baker, July 19, 1952; children: Rebecca Jane, Martha Eleanor, Boyd Wallace, Charles Christopher. BS, Ohio U., 1950; M in Forestry, Duke U., 1958, D in Forestry, 1962. Weather observer US Weather Bur., 1948; soil conservationist trainee, Soil Conservation Service USDA, 1948, firefighting laborer Forest Service, 1949; weather observer USAF, 1950, pers. officer, 1952; asst. ranger Ohio Div. Forestry, 1953; asst. prof., asst. forester U. Vermont, Burlington, 1959-61, assoc. prof., assoc. forester, 1967-69; forest biologist CSRS USDA, Washington, 1969-80, 80-81, asst. dept. administr., 1981-82, program coordinator, 1982-83, forest biologist, 1984—; group leader nat. resources USDA Sci. & Edn. Administrn., Washington, 1980; asst. dir. Hawaii Inst. Tropical Agr. & Human Resources, Honolulu, 1983-84. Contbr. articles to profl. jours.; editorial bd. Internat. Jour. Forest Ecology & Mgmt., 1976-90. Co-pres. Juvenile Diabetes Found., N.Va. chpt., 1984-86; scoutmaster Boy Scouts Am., Vienna, Va., 1978-83, asst., 1984—, mem. camping com. Nat. Capital Area Coun., 1987—. Fellow AAAS, Soc. Am. Foresters; mem. Internat. Union Foresty Research Orgns., Internat. Soc. Tropical Foresters, Sigma Xi. Lodge: Masons. Avocations: fishing, canoeing, gardening, acting, singing. Office: Coop State Rsch Edn and Extension Svc USDA Washington DC 20250-2210

POST, EMILY (ELIZABETH LINDLEY POST), author; b. Englewood, N.J., May 7, 1920; d. Allen L. and Elizabeth (Ellsworth) Lindley; m. George E. Cookman, 1941 (dec. 1943); 1 child, Allen C.; m. William G. Post, Aug. 5, 1944; children: William G., Lucinda Post Senning, Peter L. Grad. high sch. Dir. Emily Post Inst., 1965—. Author: Emily Post's Book of Etiquette for Young People, 1968, Wonderful World of Weddings, 1970, Please Say Please, 1972, Emily Post's Etiquette, 1965, rev. edit. 1992, The Complete Book of Entertaining, 1981, Emily Post's Complete Book of Wedding Etiquette, 1982, rev. edit., 1991, Emily Post Talks with Teens about Manners and Etiquette, 1986, Emily Post on Weddings, 1987, Emily Post on Entertaining, 1987, Emily Post on Etiquette, 1987, Emily Post on Invitations and Letters, 1990, Emily Post on Business Etiquette, 1990, Emily Post on Second Weddings, 1991, Emily Post's Wedding Planner, rev. edit., 1991, Emily Post's Table Manners For Today: Advice For Every Dining Occasion, 1994, Emily Post on Guests and Hosts, 1994; contbg. editor: Good Housekeeping Mag. Republican. Episcopalian. Office: Good Housekeeping Hearst Corp 959 8th Ave New York NY 10019-3737*

POST, GAINES, JR., college educator, dean, administrator; b. Madison, Wis., Sept. 22, 1937; s. Gaines and Katherine (Rike) P.; m. Jean Wetherbee Bowers, July 19, 1969; children—Katherine Doris, Daniel Lawrence. B.A., Cornell U., 1959; B.A., Oxford U., 1963; M.A., Stanford U., 1964, Ph.D., 1969. Instr. Stanford U., 1966-69; asst. prof. history U. Tex., Austin, 1969-74, assoc. prof., 1974-83; dean faculty, sr. v.p. Claremont McKenna Coll., Calif., 1983-88, prof., 1988—; exec. dir. Rockefeller Found. Commn. on Humanities, 1978-81; fellow Interuniv. Seminar on Armed Forces and Society. Author: The Civil Military Fabric of Weimar Foreign Policy, 1973; (with others) The Humanities in American Life, 1980, Dilemmas of Appeasement: British Deterrence and Defense, 1934-37, 1993; Editor: German Unification: Problems and Prospects, 1992. Mem. exec. com. Forming the Future Project, Austin Ind. Sch. Dist., 1982; mem. Tex. Com. for Humanities, 1981-83; mem. council Calif. Congl. Recognition Program, 1984-88, Calif. Coun. Humanities, 1995—. Rhodes scholar, 1961-63; Am. Council Learned Socs. fellow, 1982-83; Am. Philos. Soc. grantee, 1974. Mem. Community Coll. Humanities Assn. (bd. dirs. 1981-89), Am. Hist. Assn. Home: 2254 N Navarro Dr Claremont CA 91711-1758 Office: Claremont McKenna Coll Dept History 850 Columbia Ave Claremont CA 91711-3901

POST, GERALD JOSEPH, retired banker, retired air force officer; b. Braintree, Mass., Sept. 27, 1925; s. Robert Z. and Marjorie F. (Dunn) P.; m. Jane Stewart Curry, May 4, 1945; children: Sharyn, Gerald, J., Steven M., Richard J., Sean C., David D., Tracy Post Krupa. M.B.A., U. Chgo., 1958. Commd. 2d lt. U.S. Air Force, 1945, advanced through grades to lt. gen., 1978; comptroller, dir. materiel mgmt. San Antonio Air Materiel Area, 1970-73; dep. chief of Staff for Materiel Mgmt., Wright-Patterson AFB, Ohio, 1973-75; chief of staff Air Force Logistics Command, Wright-Patterson AFB, 1975-77; asst. dep. chief of staff for systems and logistics Hdqrs. USAF, 1977-78, dir. Def. Logistics Agy., 1978-81; ret., 1981; pres. Lackland Nat. Bank, 1981-82. Decorated Def. Disting. Service medal, Legion of Merit with oak leaf cluster, D.F.C., Air medal with 2 oak leaf clusters, others. Mem. Am. Soc. Mil. Comptrollers, Air Force Assn., Am. Inst. Aeros. and Astronautics, Am. Def. Preparedness Assn., Phi Beta Kappa, Beta Gamma Sigma. Home: 12534 Misty Creek San Antonio TX 78232

POST, HOWARD ALLEN, forest industry specialist; b. Mpls., June 14, 1916; s. William Noble and Eva Victoria (Hanson) P.; m. Doloras Clair Nordland, Dec. 6, 1941; children: Philip Noble, Stephen Edward, William Noble, Peter Bentley. BS in Forestry, U. Minn., 1939; MF in Forest Mgmt. and Silviculture, Harvard U., 1942. Forester Colville Indian Reservation, Washington, 1937; with U.S. Forest Svc., various locations, 1939, 64; civil svc. examiner in agriculture and forestry State of Minn., 1939-41; chief materials div. position classifications system War Prodn. Bd., 1942-43; chief China pers. recruitment UN Relief and Rehab. Adminstrn., 1946-47; asst. sec. Soc. Am. Foresters, 1947; adminstrv. forester Minn. and Ont. Paper Co., 1947-57; forester and nat. resources specialist U.S.C. of C., 1957-63; forest industries specialist and team leader Bus. and Def. Svcs. Adminstrn./ Internat. Trade Adminstrn. U.S. Dept. Commerce, Washington, 1965-84; forest industries cons. forest Industries com. on timber valuation and taxation, other Nat. Lumber Mfrs. Assn., 1984—; owner Post Enterprises, Forest Industry Cons.; lectr. in field various univs. U.S. editor World Paper jour. (Britain), Wood Based Panels Internat., 1984—, Xilon Internat. and Perini Jour. (Italy), 1992—; contbr. articles to profl. jours. Com. chmn., scoutmaster, counselor Boy Scouts Am.; mem. vestry Episcopal Ch., 1949-57, others. With USAAF, 1943-46, ret. USAFR, 1976. Decorated Air Force Commendation medal; recipient Bronze medal U.S. Dept. Commerce, 1976; named Boy Scouts of Am. Scouter of Yr., 1973. Mem. Tech. Assn. Pulp and Paper Industry, Soc. Am. Foresters, Assn. Cons. Foresters, Internat. Soc. Tropical Foresters, Retired Officers Assn., Forest Products Rsch. Soc., Harvard Club (Washington), Mil. Dist. of Washington Club, Nat. Press Club (Harvard group), Am. Legion, Rotary, Alpha Zeta. Republican. Home: 6203 Colmac Dr Falls Church VA 22044-1811

POST, MARKIE, actress; b. Palo Alto, Calif., Nov. 4, 1950; d. Richard and Marylee Post; m. Michael Ross; 1 child, Kate. BA, Lewis and Clark Coll. Researcher TV game show Split Second; assoc. producer game show Double Dare, 1976-77; actress, 1977—. Actress: (stage prodns.) Joe Egg, The Fantastiks, The Hairy Ape, Guys and Dolls, (TV shows) Masquerade Party, Frankie and Annette - the Second Time Around, (TV series) Semi-Tough, 1980, The Gangster Chronicles, 1981, The Fall Guy, 1982-85, Night Court, 1985-92, Hearts Afire, 1992-95, (TV movies) Not Just Another Affair, 1982, Triple Cross, 1986, Glitz, 1988, Tricks of the Trade, 1988. Mem. AFTRA, Screen Actors Guild. Office: care Jon Carrasco Sterling/Withers Co 4044 Melrose Ave 3d Flr Los Angeles CA 90069*

POST, MIKE, composer; b. San Fernando Valley, Calif.; children: Jennifer, Aaron. Founder Wellingbrook Singers, First Edition; backup guitar for Dick and Dee, Sammy Davis Jr., Dean Martin; played in Sonny and Cher's band; producer single I Just Dropped In (To See What Condition My Condition Was In); producer/arranger The Mason Williams Phonograph Album (Grammy award); mus. dir. The Andy Williams Show; producer Mac Davis Show; designer various stage shows; composer numerous music scores for TV including (with Pete Carpenter) Toma, The Rockford Files (Grammy award), Baa Baa Black Sheep, Hunter and Magnum P.I., 1968-87, also composer scores for L.A. Law (Grammy award), Doogie Howser, M.D., Wiseguy, Law and Order, Quantum Leap, The A-Team, The White Shadow, Riptide, Hardcastle & McCormick, Hill Street Blues (Grammy award), Hooperman, Sonny Spoon, The Joan Rivers Show, The Hat Squad, NYPD Blue, NewsRadio; composer TV movies Gidget Gets Married, 1972, The Morning After, 1974, Locusts, 1974, The Invasion of Johnson County, 1976, Scott Free, 1976, Richie Brockelman: Missing 24 Hours, 1976, Dr. Scorpion, 1978, Captain America, 1979, The Night Rider, 1979, Captain America II, 1979, Scouts Honor, 1980, Coach of the Year, 1980, Willy G. Gordon Liddy, 1982, Adam, 1982, Hard Knox, 1984, No Man's Land, 1984, Heart of a Champion, 1985, Stingray, 1985, The Last Precinct, 1986, Adam: His Song Continues, 1986, Destination: America, 1987, Wiseguy, 1987, J.J. Starbuck, 1987, The Ryan White Story, 1989, B.L. Stryker: The Dancer's Touch, 1989, Unspeakable Acts, 1990, Without Her Consent, 1990, The Great Pretender, 1991; (motion pictures) Rabbit Test, 1978, Deep in the Heart, 1981, Running Brave, 1983, Hadley's Rebellion, 1984, Rhinestone, 1984, The River Rat, 1984; producer, arranger, co-writer (with Stephen Geyer) the theme from The Greatest American Hero (Grammy award); music producer, songwriter TV series Cop Rock; arranger various Ray Charles LP's; record producer Dolly Parton's Nine To Five, Peter Allen's I Could've Been A Sailor; album releases include Music from L.A., Law & Otherwise. Established with BMI Found. Pete Carpenter Meml. Fund, 1989. Avocations: golf, running, arm wrestling. Office: c/o Gorfaine Schwartz Agy 3301 Barham Blvd Ste 201 Los Angeles CA 90068-1477 also: Mike Post Prodns 1007 W Olive Ave Burbank CA 91506-2296*

POST, PETER DAVID, lawyer; b. Reading, Pa., Jan. 2, 1947; s. Carl B. and Frances (Gaughan) P.; m. Anne Gage, Feb. 5, 1972; children: Michael, Elizabeth. BS, Pa. State U., 1968; JD, Harvard U., 1971. Bar: Pa. 1971, La. 1974. Assoc. Reed, Smith, Shaw & McClay, Pitts., 1975-81, ptnr., 1982—, dept. head, 1992—; Commr. Upper St. Clair (Pa.) Twp., 1989—. Lt. USN, 1971-75. Avocations: golf, skiing. Office: Reed Smith Shaw & McClay 435 6th Ave Pittsburgh PA 15219-1886

POST, RICHARD, real estate company executive. Pres. US West Real Estate Inc., Denver. Office: US West Real Estate Inc 1999 Broadway Ste 2000 Denver CO 80202*

POST, RICHARD BENNETT, retired human resources executive; b. Clyde, Ohio, July 5, 1936; s. Robert Irving and Elinor May (Bennett) P.; m. Nancy Jane Wardlow, Aug. 31, 1956; children: David Bennett, Todd McKinley, Amy Ellen, Brett Richard, Brina Marie. BS in Psychology, Iowa State U., 1958; student, Ohio U., Athens, 1954-56; postgrad., George Washington U., 1959-60, St. Ill. U., Edwardsville, 1972-74. With U.S. Civil Svc. Commn., 1958-79; chief evaluation div. U.S. Civil Svc. Commn., St. Louis, 1967-71; chief staffing div. U.S. Civil Svc. Commn., 1971-74, dep. reg. dir., 1974-79; dep. assoc. dir. staffing U.S. Office Pers. Mgmt., Washington, 1979-81, assoc. dir. staffing, 1982-86; dir. Washington area svc. ctr. U.S. Office Pers. Mgmt., 1986-94; retired, 1994. Recipient Dirs.' Disting. Svc. award U.S. Office Pers. Mgmt., 1986, Dirs.' citation for Exemplary Pub. Svc., 1994. Mem. ASPA, Sr. Execs. Assn. (life), Fed. Exec. Inst. Alumni Assn., Vienna Choral Soc. (pres. 1987-89), Assn. Quality and Participation. Avocations: woodworking, singing, gardening, photography, stamp collecting.

POST, ROBERT CHARLES, law educator; b. Bklyn., Oct. 17, 1947; s. Ted and Thelma (Feifel) P.; m. Fran Layton, Jan. 22, 1981; children: Alexander, Amelia. AB, Harvard U., 1969, PhD, 1980; JD, Yale U., 1977. Bar: D.C. 1979, Calif. 1983. Law clk. to chief judge U.S. Ct. Appeals (D.C. cir.), 1977-78; law clk. to justice William Brennen Jr. U.S. Supreme Ct. D.C., 1978-79; assoc. Williams & Connelly, Washington, 1980-82; acting prof. law U. Calif., Berkeley, 1983-87, prof. law, 1987—. Editor: Law and the Order of Culture,

1991; author: Constitutional Domains, 1995. fellow Guggenheim Found., 1990-91, Am. Coun. Gen. Socs., 1990-91. Mem. AAUP, Am. Acad. Arts and Scis., Law & Soc. Assn. Office: U Calif Sch Law Boalt Hall Berkeley CA 94720

POST, ROBERT M., psychiatrist; b. New Haven, Conn., Sept. 16, 1942; s. William B. and Esther (Stolzman) P.; m. Susan W. Post; children: Laura, David. BA, Yale U., 1964; MD, U. Pa., 1968. Resident in psychiatry Mass. Gen. Hosp., Boston, 1969-70; clin. assoc. sect. on psychiatry lab. clin. sci. NIMH, Bethesda, Md., 1970-72, rsch. fellow sect. on psychiatry lab. clin. sci., 1972-73, chief 3-West clin. rsch. unit sect. on psychobiology BPB, 1973-77, chief sect. on psychobiology BPB, 1977-81, chief. biol. psychiatry br., 1981—. Author: Neurobiology of Mood Disorders, 1984; assoc. editor Psychiatry Rsch. Jour.; mem. editorial bd. and com. Biol. Psychiatry; mem. editorial bd. Clin. Neuropharmacology; contbr. over 500 articles to sci. jours. With USPHS, 1970-72. Recipient Internat. Anna Monika Psychiat. Rsch. award, 1989. Fellow Am. Coll. Neuropsychopharmacology (Efron Excellence in Rsch. award 1985); mem. Am. Psychiat. Assn. (Found.'s Fund Rsch. award 1983), Soc. Biol. Psychiatry (Bennett Neuropsychiatric Rsch. award 1973), Collegium Internat. Neuro-Psychopharmacologicum. Achievements include co-invention of treatment for cocaine addiction. Home: 3502 Turner Ln Bethesda MD 20815-3214 Office: NIMH Biol Psychiatry Br Bldg 10 9000 Rockville Pike Rm 3n212 Bethesda MD 20892-0001

POSTE, GEORGE HENRY, pharmaceutical company executive; b. Polegate, Sussex, Eng., Apr. 30, 1944; came to U.S., 1972; s. John H. and Kathleen B. (Brooke) P.; m. Mary E. Mudge, Mar. 9, 1968 (div. 1992); 1 child, Eleanor Kathy; m. Linda C. Suhler Lopez, Nov. 21, 1992; stepchildren: John Robert, Lisa Carolyn. DVM, U. Bristol, 1966, PhD, 1969, DSc, 1987. Lectr. Univ. London, 1969-72; assoc. prof. SUNY, Buffalo, 1972-76; prof. pathology Roswell Park Meml. Inst., Buffalo, 1976-80; v.p. rsch. SmithKline Beckman, Phila., 1980-82, v.p. rsch. and devel., 1982-86, v.p. worldwide rsch. and pre-clin. devel., 1987-88, pres. rsch. and devel., 1988-89; pres. rsch. and devel. techs. SmithKline Beecham, King of Prussia, Pa., 1989-90, vice chmn., exec. v.p. rsch. and devel., 1990-91, pres. and chmn. rsch. and devel., 1992—; also bd. dirs., 1992—; mem. pathology B study sect. NIH, Bethesda, Md., 1978-82; chairperson Gordon Conf., N.H., 1985, 86; pres. coun. U. Tex. M.D. Anderson Cancer Ctr.; mem. adv. coun. Beckman Ctr. for Molecular and Genetic Medicine, Stanford U.; mem. coun. Oxford Internat. Biomedical Centre. Editor: Cell Surface Revs., New Horizons in Therapeutics, Cancer Metastasis Revs., Advanced Drug Delivery Revs., 15 books; contbr. numerous articles to profl. jours. Mem. governing bd. UCLA Symposia, Life Sci. Rsch. Found.; mem. bd. Overseers Sch. Vet. Medicine, U. Penn., Gov.'s adv. com. Sci. and Tech., Pa.; mem. adv. bd. Natural Sci. Assn., U. Pa. Fellow Royal Coll. Veterinary Surgeons, Royal Coll. Pathologists; mem. AAAS, Am. Soc. Cell Biology, Pathol. Soc., Nat. Assn. Biomed. Rsch. (bd. govs. 1984), Univ. Assn. Space Rsch. (mem. coun. 1984), Pharm. Mfrs. Assn. (former chmn. rsch. and devel. section 1988). Avocations: military history, foreign affairs, photography, auto racing. Office: SmithKline Beecham Pharms PO Box 1539 King Of Prussia PA 19406-0939

POSTEL, JOACHIM MICHAEL, cardiac surgeon; b. Tuebingen, Germany, Mar. 9, 1944; came to U.S., 1974; s. Frederick Charles and Berta P.; m. Deborah Ann Darr, Aug. 4, 1990; 1 child, Mackenzie. BS in Math. summa cum laude, Dr. Richter Coll., Kelkheim, West Germany, 1965; MD, Johann Wolfgang Goethe U., Frankfurt, West Germany, 1970, PhD in Biochemistry, 1971. Diplomate Am. Bd. Thoracic Surgery, Am. Bd. Surgery; lic. surgeon Calif., Colo., Fla., Kans., Mass., Tex. Intern Johann Wolfgang Goethe U., Frankfurt, 1971-72; resident in gen. surgery U. Basel, Switzerland, 1972-74; chief resident, resident gen. surgery U. Kans., Kansas City, 1974-78; chief resident, resident cardiothoracic surgery Harvard Med. Sch./ 5th Harvard Surg. Svc., Boston, 1978-80; spl. fellow cardiac surgery Tex. Heart Inst. St. Luke's Episcopal & Tex. Childrens Hosp., Houston, 1981; chief cardiothoracic surgery, asst. prof. surgery U. South Fla. and James A. Haley VA Med. Ctr., Tampa, 1982-86; chief cardiothoracic surgery, assoc. prof. surgery Denver Gen. Hosp./U. Colo., 1986; dir. cardiac surgery Desert Hosp., Palm Springs, Calif., 1986-91; chief cardiac surgery Cedars Med. Ctr., Miami, 1991—; cons. on cardiac surgery to surgeon gen. USN, 1984; presenter in field. Contbr. articles to profl. jours. Active Rep. Nat. Commn., Washington, 1993. Comdr. USNR, 1992. Named Outstanding Resident, U. Kans., 1977; merit rev. grantee NIH-VA, 1974-76. Fellow Am. Coll. Chest Physicians; mem. AMA, Soc. Thoracic Surgeons, Am. Heart Assn. (coun. mem. cardiac surgery), Assn. for Acad. Surgeons, Assn. Mil. Surgeons the U.S., Am. Fedn. for Clin. Rsch., Internat. Soc. for Heart Transplantation, N.Y. Acad. Scis., Riverside County Med. Assn., Calif. Med. Assn. Republican. Roman Catholic. Avocations: oil painting, classical music. Office: Cedars Medical Ctr 1400 NW 12th Ave Miami FL 33136-1087

POSTER, JUNE, performing company executive; b. New York, May 6, 1949. BFA, SUNY, Buffalo, 1970; MA, U. Calif., Berkeley, 1975. Exec. dir. San Francisco Camerawork, 1981-87; dir. devel. Meredith Monk/The House, N.Y.C., 1984-87; dir. fin., domestic booking Merce Cunningham Dance Found., N.Y.C., 1987-90; mng. dir. David Gordon Pick Up co., N.Y.C., 1991—; devel. con. various ind. film projects, N.Y.C., 1991. Office: Pick Up Co 131 Varick St Rm 901 New York NY 10013-1410

POSTER, STEVEN BARRY, publisher, photographer, digital imaging consultant; b. Chgo., Mar. 1, 1944; s. David and Lillian Violet (Diamondstone) P. Student, So. Ill. U., 1962-64, L.A Art Ctr. Coll. Design, 1964-66; BS, Ill. Inst. Tech., 1967. Pres. Posters Internat. Ltd., L.A., 1980; dir. photography, pub. Am. Cinematographer Mag.; cons. NHK, Tokyo, 1990—. Dir. photography (films) Strange Brew, 1983, Testament, 1984, Heavenly Kid, 1985, Blue City, 1986, The Boy Who Could Fly, 1986, Someone to Watch Over Me, 1986, (Am. Soc. Cinematographers nomination 1987), Big Top Pee Wee, 1987, Next of Kin, 1988, Opportunity Knocks, 1989, Rocky V, 1990, Life Stinks, 1991, Cemetery Club, 1993, Roswell, 1994. Mem. Am. Soc. Cinematographers (2d v.p.), Leica Hist. Soc. Am., Acad. Motion Picture Arts and Scis., Can. Soc. Cinematographers, Internat. Assn. Panoramic Photographers, Behind the Lens (assoc.), Internat. Alliance of Theatrical and Stage Employees. Democrat. Jewish. Avocations: still photography, computers, bicycles.

POST-GORDEN, JOAN CAROLYN, psychology educator; b. Oak Park, Ill., July 3, 1932; d. DeWitt T. and Mary Jane (Lewellen) Post; children: Gregrey Wayne, Jeffrey Scott, Kayle Lynn, Tamara Anne. BS, Manchester (Ind.) Coll., 1964; MS, U. Ga., 1967, PhD, 1970. Lic. psychologist, Colo. Tchr. Clarke County Schs., Athens, Ga., 1964-65; part-time asst. prof. Tex. Tech U., Lubbock, 1968-69; instr. So. Colo. State Coll., Pueblo, 1970-71; asst. prof. U. So. Colo., Pueblo, 1971-76, assoc. prof., 1976-81, prof., 1981—, chmn. dept., 1991—; asst. to city mgr., Champaign, Ill., 1980-81; psychologist So. Ctrl. Ill. Devel. Dist., Flora, 1979-80; dir. scholarly and creative activities U. So. Colo., 1988-91. Contbr. chpt. to book and articles to profl. jours. NDEA fellow, 1964-66, Danforth teaching fellow, 1978, faculty fellow Colo. State Div. Mental Health, 1986-87. Mem. APA, Soc. for Rsch. in Child Devel., Rocky Mountain Psychol. Assn., Colo. Psychol. Assn., Psi Chi, Sigma Xi, Alpha Omicron Pi. Avocation: scuba diving. Home: 1021 Ruppel St Apt 31 Pueblo CO 81001-2559 Office: U So Colo Dept Psychology Pueblo CO 81001

POSTLEWAIT, HARRY OWEN, chemical company executive; b. Pitts., Nov. 17, 1933; s. George Russell and Emma Ellen (Hickenbottom) P.; m. Sandra Anne Anderson, June 18, 1955; children: Alyssa Walker, Jordan Lindsay, Tammy Towen, Heather Anderson. BS in Indsl. Adminstrn., Yale U., 1955; MBA, Harvard U., 1961. Mfg. engr. W.R. Grace Co., Cambridge, Mass., 1955-56; project engr. Standard Oil Co., Cleve., 1959-60; cons. Booz, Allen & Hamilton, Cleve., 1961-64; exec. v.p. Raychem Corp., Menlo Park, Calif., 1964—. Served to capt. USAF, 1956-59. Home: 130 Southwood Dr Palo Alto CA 94301-3134 Office: Raychem Corp Office Exec V P 300 Constitution Dr Menlo Park CA 94025-1111

POSTLEWAITE, ANDREW WILLIAM, economics and public policy educator; b. Harvey, Ill., Aug. 23, 1943; s. Edward Homer and Margaret (Hostetler) P.; m. Elaine Sharon Kavelaras, April 1, 1966; children: Justin, Kevin. BA, Ill. Wesleyan U., 1965; MS, DePaul U., 1969; PhD, Northwes-

tern U., 1974. Tchr. St. George H.S., Evanston, Ill., 1966-68, Evanston Twp. H.S., 1968-70; lectr. DePaul U., Chgo., 1970-73; rsch. fellow CORE, Louvain, Belgium, 1973-74; asst. prof. econs. U. Ill., Urbana, 1974-75; assoc. prof. econs. U. Ill., Urbana, 1976-80; prof. econs. U. Pa., Phila., 1980-82, prof. econs. fin., pub. mgmt., 1982—, chmn. dept. econs., 1982-87, 90—; bd. dirs. Nat. Bur. Econ. Rsch., Cambridge, Mass.; cons. in field. Contbr. articles to profl. jours. NSF grantee, 1975—. Fellow Econometric Soc.; mem. Am. Econ. Assn. Home: 6 Hampton Ter Bala Cynwyd PA 19004 Office: U Pa Dept Econs 3718 Locust Walk Philadelphia PA 19104-6209

POSTLEWAITE, PHILIP FREDERICK, law educator. JD, U. Calif., Berkeley, 1970; LLM in Taxation, NYU, 1971. Bar: Wis. 1970, Wash. 1973. Assoc. Foley & Lardner, Milw., 1970-71; instr. in taxation NYU, N.Y.C., 1971-73; assoc. prof. law U. Notre Dame, South Bend, Ind., 1976-81; prof. law Northwestern U., Chgo., 1981—. Author: Policy Readings in Individual Taxation, 1980, International Corporate Taxation, 1980; co-author: Partnership Taxation, 3d ed., vols. I, II and III, 1981, Partnership Taxation Problems and Answers, 1982, International Individual Taxation, 1982, Problems and Materials in Federal Income Taxation, 1986; contbr. articles to profl. jours. Home: 417 Abbotsford Rd Kenilworth IL 60043-1106 Office: Northwestern U Sch Law 357 E Chicago Ave Chicago IL 60611-3069

POSTMA, HERMAN, physicist, consultant; b. Wilmington, N.C., Mar. 29, 1933; s. Gilbert and Sophia Postma; m. Patricia Dunigan, Nov. 25, 1960; children: Peter, Pamela. BS summa cum laude, Duke U., 1955; MS, Harvard U., 1957, PhD, 1959. Registered profl. engr., Calif. Summer staff Oak Ridge Nat. Lab., 1954-57, physicist thermonuclear div., 1959-62, co-leader DCX-1 group, 1962-66, asst. dir. thermonuclear div., 1966, asso. dir. div., 1967, dir. div., 1967-73, dir. nat. lab., from 1974; v.p. Martin Marietta, 1984-88, sr. v.p., 1988-91; vis. scientist FOM-Inst. for Plasma Physics, The Netherlands, 1963; cons. Lab. Laser Energetics, U. Rochester; mem. energy rsch. adv. bd. spl. panel Dept. Energy; bd. dirs. Nashville br. Fed. Res. Bank Atlanta, ICS Corp., PAI Corp., ORAS, Inc., M4 Corp. Mem. editorial bd. Nuclear Fusion, 1968-74; contbr. numerous articles to profl. jours. Bd. dirs. The Nucleus; chmn. bd. trustees Hosp. of Meth. Ch.; mem. adv. bd. Coll. Bus. Adminstrn., U. Tenn., 1976-84, Energy Inst., State of N.C.; bd. dirs., exec. com. Tenn. Tech. Found., 1982-88, Venture Capital Fund; vice chmn., commr. Tenn. Higher Edn. Commn., 1984-92; trustee Duke U., 1987—, Pellissippi State Coll., 1991—; chmn. Meth. Hosp. Found., 1990; mem. adv. bd. Inst. Pub. Policy Vanderbilt U., 1986-88, conf. chmn. 1987. Fellow Am. Phys. Soc. (exec. com. div. plasma physics), AAAS, Am. Nuclear Soc. (dir.); mem. C. of C. (v.p. 1981-83, chmn. 1987), Indsl. Rsch. Inst., Gas Rsch. Inst. (adv. bd. 1986-88), Phi Beta Kappa, Beta Gamma Sigma, Sigma Pi Sigma, Omicron Delta Kappa, Sigma Xi, Pi Mu Epsilon, Phi Eta Sigma. Home: 104 Berea Rd Oak Ridge TN 37830-7829

POSTOL, LAWRENCE PHILIP, lawyer; b. Bridgeport, Conn., Oct. 18, 1951; s. Sidney Samuel and Eunice Ruth (Schine) P.; m. Ellen Margaret Russell, Mar. 22, 1975; children: Raymond Russell, Stephen Russell, Carolyn Russell. BS, Cornell U., 1973, JD, 1976. Bar: Conn. 1976, D.C. 1977, U.S. Dist. Ct. D.C. 1977, U.S.C. Appeals (D.C. cir.) 1977, U.S. Supreme Ct. 1980, Va. 1982, U.S.C. Appeals (4th cir.) 1982, U.S. Dist. Ct. (ea. dist.) Va. 1985, U.S. Dist. Ct. Md. 1989, U.S. Dist. Ct. Conn. 1990. Assoc. Arent, Fox, Kintner & Plotkin, Washington, 1976-80; assoc. Seyfarth, Shaw, Fairweather & Geraldson, Washington, 1980-83, ptnr., 1985—; assoc. Jones, Day, Reavis and Pogue, Washington, 1983-85; lectr. Loyola U., New Orleans, 1983—, Ga. Inst. Tech., Atlanta, 1985—, U. Cin., 1987—; bd. advisers The Environ. Counselor Jour.; spl. counsel Greater Washington Bd. Trade, 1991-93. Author: Legal Guide to Handling Toxic Substances in the Workplace, 1990, Americans with Disabilities Act - A Compliance Manual for Employers, 1993. Jewish. Avocation: sports. Home: 6340 Chowning Pl Mc Lean VA 22101-4129 Office: Seyfarth Shaw Fairweather & Geraldson 815 Connecticut Ave NW Washington DC 20006-4004

POSTON, TOM, actor; b. Columbus, Ohio, Oct. 17, 1927; s. George and Margaret P.; m. Jean Sullivan, 1955; m. Kay Hudson, June 8, 1968; children: Francesca, Hudson, Jason. Student, Bethany Coll., 1938-40. First appeared on stage as a tumbler with The Flying Zeblevs; acting and Broadway debuts in Cyrano de Bergerac, 1947; appeared on Broadway, regional theaters, and summer stock; stage appearances include: The Insect Comedy, King Lear, Will Success Spoil Rock Hunter?, Goodbye Again, Best of Burlesque, Romanoff and Juliet, Drink to Me Only, Golden Fleecing, The Conquering Hero, Come Blow Your Horn, Mary, Mary, Forty Carats, But Seriously..., A Funny Thing Happened on the Way to the Forum, The Odd Couple, Bye Bye Birdie, Mother Courage, host WABC-TV series Entertainment, 1955; regular on TV show The Steve Allen Show, 1956-58 (Emmy award for best supporting actor in comedy series 1959); host TV show Split Personality, 1959-60; panelist TV show To Tell the Truth; appeared in TV series On the Rocks, 1975-76, We've Got Each Other, 1977, Mork and Mindy, 1978-82, Newhart, 1982-90; numerous TV appearances include The Bob Newhart Show; film appearances include: The Tempest, The City That Never Sleeps, 1953, Zotz, 1962, Soldier in the Rain, 1963, The Old Dark House, 1963, Cold Turkey, 1970, The Happy Hooker, 1975, Rabbit Test, 1978, Up the Academy, 1980, Carbon Copy, 1981. Served with USAAF, World War II. *

POSUNKO, BARBARA, elementary education educator; b. Newark, July 17, 1938; d. Joseph and Mary (Prystauk) P. BA, Rutgers U., Newark, 1960; MA, Kean Coll., Union, N.J., 1973; teaching cert., Seton Hall U., Newark, 1966. Cert. elem. tchr., reading specialist, N.J. Social case worker Newark City Hosp., 1960-65; elem. tchr. Plainfield (N.J.) Bd. Edn., 1966; elem., jr. and sr. high sch. tchr. minimum basic skills and reading Sayreville (N.J.) Bd. Edn., 1966-82; tchr. Chpt. I and minimum basic skills Sayreville (N.J.) Bd. Edn., Parlin, 1982—, cooperating tchr. to student tchrs., 1983—, coord. testing, 1984—; sch. coord. for congressionally mandated study of ednl. growth and opportunity, 1991—; mem. numerous reading coms. Recipient Outstanding Tchr. award N.J. Gov.'s Tchr. Recognition Program, 1988. Mem. NEA, Internat. Reading Assn., N.J. Reading Assn., N.J. Edn. Assn. Home: 17 Drake Rd Mendham NJ 07945-1805

POSUNKO, LINDA MARY, elementary education educator; b. Newark, Dec. 24, 1942; d. Joseph and Mary (Prystauk) P. BA, Newark State Coll., Union, N.J., 1964; MA, Kean Coll., Union, 1974. Cert. permanent elem. tchr., supr., prin., N.J. Elem. tchr. Roselle (N.J.) Bd. Edn., 1964-65; elem. tchr. Garwood (N.J.) Bd. Edn., 1965-92, head tchr., 1974-76, 79-81, head tchr. elem. and early childhood edn., tchr. 1st grade, 1992—; cooperating tchr. to student tchrs.; instr. non-English speaking students and children with learning problems; mem. affirmative action, sch. resource coms.; conductor in-svc. workshops on early childhood devel. practices, 1993. Recipient honor cert. Union County Conf. Tchrs. Assn., 1972-73, Garwood Tchr. of Yr. award, 1983, Outstanding Tchr. award N.J. Gov.'s Tchr. Recognition Program, 1988; nominee Gov.'s Tchr. Recognition award 1993-94. Mem. ASCD, NEA, Internat. Reading Assn. (bd. dirs. suburban coun.), N.J. Edn. Assn., Garwood Tchrs. Assn. (sec., v.p., pres.), High/Scope Ednl. Found. Home: 17 Drake Rd Mendham NJ 07945-1805

POTAMKIN, MEYER P., mortgage banker; b. Phila., Nov. 11, 1909; s. Jacob and Ida (Soloman) P.; m. Vivian Orleans, July 27, 1940; children—Macy Ann Potamkin Lasky, Marshall F. Ph.B., Dickinson Coll., 1932; Ed.M., Temple U., 1941; D.F.A., Dickinson Coll., 1972. Social worker, dir. agy. Crime Prevention Assn., Phila., 1935-40; ptnr. Orleans Constrn. Co., Phila., 1940-54; pres. Blvd. Mortgage Co., Phila., 1954—. Pres. Phila. coun. Boys Clubs Am., 1962-82; nat. assoc. Boys Clubs Am. 1972-80; chmn. bd. trustees Camp William Penn, 1964-82; bd. dirs. Glen Mills Sch. for Delinquent Boys, 1960-77, v.p. 1976-77; bd. dirs. Phila. Coll. Art, 1970-75, Phila. Art Commn., 1974-82; mem. Juvenile Task Force Gov.'s Justice Commn. and L.E.A.A. Coun. 1974-80; bd. dirs. Mann Music Ctr., 1982—, Settlement Music Sch., 1962—; trustee Bklyn. Mus., Crime Prevention Assn. (pres., chmn. bd. trustees 1977-87), Phila. Mus. Art; 1960-75, 1981—; Richmond Coll., Eng., 1982-87; bd. dirs., co-founder Sarah Allen Nursing Home for Blacks; mem. adv. com. to bd. trustees Dickinson Coll., 1976—; trustee, mem. exec. com. Nat'l Stage Workshops Am., 1977-82; bd. dirs. Phila. Ctr. for Older People, 1980-83; pres. Phila. Art Alliance, 1991-92. Recipient AME Mother Bethel award, 1977, Silver Keystone award Boys Clubs Am., 1977, Recognition award Boys Clubs Am., 1986, Jewish Basketball League award, 1990, Achievement award Perkiomen Sch., 1990,

Alumni award Perkiomen Sch., 1990. Alumni Achievement award Dickinson Coll., 1991; Israel Bond honoree, 1973. Mem. Home Builders Assn., Mortgage Bankers Assn. Am., Phila. Mortgage Bankers Assn. (pres. 1985-86), Pa. Mortgage Bankers Assn. (pres. 1985-86, award 1990), Locust Club, Union League, Bala Golf Club, Squires golf Club, Phi Epsilon Pi (bd. trustees found., Achievement award 1967), Zeta Beta Tau (grand coun. mem., 1978). Office: Blvd Mortgage Co 2620 Cottman Ave Philadelphia PA 19149-1395

POTASH, JEREMY WARNER, public relations executive; b. Monrovia, Calif., June 30, 1946; d. Fenwick Bryson and Joan Antony (Blair) Warner; m. Stephen Jon Potash, Oct. 19, 1969; 1 child, Aaron Warner. AA, Citrus Coll., 1965; BA, Pomona Coll., 1967. With Forbes Mag., N.Y.C., 1967-69, Japan External Trade Orgn., San Francisco, 1970-75; v.p., co-founder Potash & Co. Pub. Rels., Oakland, Calif., 1980-87; pres. Potash & Co. Pub. Rels., San Francisco, 1987—; founding exec. dir. Calif.-S.E. Asia Bus. Coun., Oakland, 1992—; exec. dir. Customs Brokers and Forwarders Assn., San Francisco, 1990—; bd. dirs. Temple Sinai, Oakland, 1984-86. Mem. Am. Soc. Assn. Execs., World Trade Club San Francisco, Book Club Calif., Oakland Women's Lit. Soc. Office: Potash & Co Pub Rels 1946 Embarcadero Oakland CA 94606-5213

POTASH, STEPHEN JON, international public relations practitioner; b. Houston, Feb. 25, 1945; s. Melvin L. and Petrice (Edelstein) P.; m. Jeremy Warner, Oct. 19, 1969; 1 son, Aaron Warner. BA in Internat. Rels., Pomona Coll., 1967. Account exec. Charles von Loewenfeldt, Inc., San Francisco, 1969-74, v.p., 1974-80; founder, pres. Potash & Co., Pub. Rels., Oakland, Calif., 1980-87; pres. Am. Pres. Lines and Am. Pres. Cos., 1979-87; exec. dir. Calif. Coun. Internat. Trade, 1970-87; v.p. corp. communications Am. Pres. Cos., Oakland, 1987-90; chmn. Potash & Co., Oakland, 1990—. Bd. dirs. Calif. Coun. Internat. Trade, 1987-94, Calif.-Southeast Asia Bus. Coun., 1992—, Temple Sinai, Oakland, 1979-81. Mem. Pub. Rels. Soc. Am., Commonwealth Club of Calif., World Trade Club San Francisco. Office: Potash & Co 1946 Embarcadero Oakland CA 94606-5213

POTATE, JOHN SPENCER, SR., engineering company executive, consultant; b. Temple, Ga., Mar. 19, 1934; s. Harold Clyde and Eugenia Marie (McClung) P.; m. Barbara Jean Moorefield; children: Pamela, Vivian, Brenda, John Jr. BS in Indsl. Engring., Ga. Inst. Tech., 1959; MS in Aerospace Engring., Fla. Inst. Tech., 1965; MS in Mgmt., MIT, 1975. Program mgr. NASA, Cape Kennedy, Fla., 1961-70; exec. NASA, Washington, 1970-72; exec. Marshall Space Flight Ctr. NASA, Huntsville, Ala., 1973-82; v.p. System Devel. Corp. (now subs. Unisys), Santa Monica, Calif., 1982-84, Unisys, Camarillo, Calif., 1984-89; pres. AC Engring., Huntsville, Ala., 1989-92, ret., 1993; prin. John Potate Assocs., Huntsville, Ala., 1993—. With USCG, 1951-54; engr. USAF, 1959-61. Sloan fellow, MIT, 1972; recipient NASA Exceptional Svc. medal, 1969 (Apollo), NASA Leadership medal, 1980 (shuttle). Home: 1319 Blevins Gap Rd SE Huntsville AL 35802-2709

POTCHEN, E. JAMES, radiology educator; b. Queens County, N.Y., Dec. 12, 1932; s. Joseph Anton and Eleanore Joyce P.; children: Michelle, Kathleen, Michael, Joseph. BS, Mich. State U., East Lansing, 1954; MD, Wayne State U., 1958; MS, MIT, 1953; JD U. Mich., 1984. Diplomate Am. Bd. Nuclear Medicine, Am. Bd. Radiology (examiner 1968-78). Intern Butterworth Hosp., Grand Rapids, Mich., 1958-59; resident Peter Bent Brigham Hosp., Boston, 1961-64; gen. practice medicine, Grand Rapids, 1959-61; chief resident radiologist Peter Bent Brigham Hosp., Children's Hosp., Pondville State Cancer Hosp., 1964; jr. assoc. radiology Peter Bent Brigham Hosp., 1965; dir. div. Nuclear Medicine, Harvard Med. Sch., dept. radiology, Peter Bent Brigham Hosp., 1965-66; dir. nuclear medicine div. Mallinckrodt Inst. Radiology, Washington U. Sch. Medicine, 1966-73, chief diagnostic radiology, 1971-72; asst. prof. radiology Washington U. St. Louis, 1966, assoc. prof. radiology, 1967-70, prof. radiology, 1970-73; prof. radiology, dean mgmt. resources Johns Hopkins U., Balt., 1973-75; mem. faculty Mich. State U., East Lansing, 1975—, prof. radiology Coll. Human Medicine, prof. mgmt. Coll. Bus., Univ. Disting. prof., 1990, chmn. radiology, chmn. faculty group practice Mich. State U.; chmn. Liaison Com. Med. Edn., 1980-86; mem. Bur. Radiologic Health-Med. Radiation Adv. Com. FDA, 1982-85; mem. med. necessity in diagnostic imaging adv. com. Nat. Blue Cross/Blue Shield, 1981. Assoc. editor Investigative Radiology, 1968-72, Jour. Nuclear Medicine, 1969-74, Jour. Microvascular Rsch., 1970-78, Radiology, 1970-90, Internat. Jour. Radiation Oncology, 1977-86, Biology and Physics, Continuing Edn. Radiology; mem. editorial bd. Radiology, 1970-71; editor-in-chief The Radiology Resident, 1992-94. Contbr. articles to various pubs. Recipient awards including Dist. Alumni award Wayne State U., 1970; Scholar in Radiologic Rsch. James Picker Found., 1967-68; Advanced fellow Academic Radiology, James Picker Found., Nat. Acad. Scis.-NRC, 1965-66; John J. Larkin award for basic med. research, 1963, Disting. Alumnus award Brigham Women's Hosp., 1993. Fellow ACP, Am. Coll. Chest Physicians; mem. Acad. Mgmt. (div. sec. 1977-78), Am. Cancer Soc. (div. bd. trustees 1977-78), AMA (council med. edn. 1979-88), ABA, Am. Physiologic Soc., Am. Radium Soc., Am. Roentgen Ray Soc., Am. Soc. Clin. Investigation, Assn. Am. Med. Colls., Assn. U. Radiologists (mem. exec. com. 1970-72; mem. com. 1971-72), Central Soc. Clin. Rsch., Fleischner Soc. (pres. 1993), Interam. Coll. Radiology, Ingham County Med. Soc. (mem. com. 1977—), Mich. State Med. Soc. (mem. adv. com. med. edn. 1980—), Nat. Inst. Health Found. Advanced Edn. Scis., Radiologic Soc. N.Am., Soc. Chmn. of Acad. Radiology Depts. (mem. exec. com.), Soc. Nuclear Medicine (nat. pres. 1975-76), Soc. Health and Human Values, Soc. Med. Decision Making (founding mem. 1979), Soc. Thoracic Radiology (founding mem., 1982—), Sigma Xi, Alpha Omega Alpha. Office: Mich State U Dept Radiology B-220 Clinical Ctr East Lansing MI 48824

POTE, HAROLD WILLIAM, banker; b. Phila., Sept. 18, 1946; s. Frank Lafferty and Lucille (Bock) P.; m. Judy Elizabeth Constantine, Oct. 12, 1968. A.B., Princeton U., 1968; M.B.A., Harvard U., 1972. Dir. investor relations Fidelcor/Fidelity Bank, Phila., 1974-76, v.p., head corp. devel. dept., 1976-78, sr. v.p., head corp. devel. dept., 1978-80, exec. v.p., treas. fin. and planning dept., 1980-83; vice chmn., treas. fin. and planning dept., 1983-84; chmn. bd., chief exec. officer Fidelity Bank, Phila., 1984-88; pres., chief exec. officer Fidelcor, Inc., 1986-88; pres. and chief exec. officer First Fidelity Bancorp, Phila., 1988; chief exec. officer Spl. Situation Fund, N.Y.C., 1988-93; ptnr. The Beacon Group, N.Y.C., 1993—; asst. prof. La Salle Coll., Phila., 1972-79; bd. dirs. Norfolk So. Corp. Trustee Pa. Ballet Assn., Phila., 1976-92; mem. exec. coun. Harvard Bus. Sch. Assn., 1980—. Mem. AICPA, Merion Golf Club, Locust Club.

POTEET, DANIEL P(OWELL), II, college provost; b. Dallas, Dec. 22, 1940; s. Daniel Powell and Helene (Van der Veer) P.; m. Nancy Heusinkveld, Mar. 13, 1971; 1 child, Daniel C. BA, Harvard U., 1963; MA, U. Ill., 1965, PhD, 1969. Asst. prof. U. Del., Newark, 1969-76, West Chester (Pa.) State Coll., 1976-77; dean faculty Hampden-Sydney (Va.) Coll., 1978-81, provost, 1981-85; provost Albion (Mich.) Coll., 1985-91, Guilford (N.C.) Coll., 1991—. Co-author: Rise of the Realists, 1979; also articles and revs. Mem. AAUP, Am. Conf. Acad. Deans, Am. Assn. Higher Edn. Episcopalian. Avocation: sailing. Office: Guilford Coll Office of Provost 5800 W Friendly Ave Greensboro NC 27410-4108

POTEETE, ROBERT ARTHUR, editor; b. Perry, Ark., Aug. 29, 1926; s. Arthur and Ruby (Farish) P.; m. Frances Reynolds, Feb. 15, 1951 (dec. Mar. 1969); children: Anthony R., Julia Anne, Richard A.R. (dec. Sept. 1973). B.A., U. Central Ark., 1948; postgrad., Medill Sch. Journalism, Northwestern U., 1948-49. Reporter Ark. Gazette, 1949; reporter, day city editor, asst. news editor, asst. Sunday editor N.Y. Herald Tribune, 1950-66; mng. editor N.Y. Herald Tribune (European edit.), Paris, 1963-65; sr. editor Saturday Evening Post, N.Y.C., 1966-69; mng. editor, editor Psychology Today, Del Mar, Calif., 1969-73; mng. editor New Publs., Playboy Enterprises, Inc., Chgo., 1973-74; sr. editor Money mag., 1974-76; editor in chief Am. Illustrated mag. USIA, Washington, 1976-91; freelance editor, writer Washington, 1991—; editorial cons. Episcopal Diocese L.I., Garden City, N.Y., 1967-68. Contbr. articles popular mags. Mem. bd. United Youth Ministry, La Jolla, Cal., 1971-72. Served with U.S. Army, PTO, 1945-46. Recipient Citizens Budget Commn. citation for articles on N.Y.C. govt. purchase of real estate, 1958; named Disting. Alumnus, U. Ctrl. Ark., 1993. Mem. Am. Soc. Mag. Editors, Inner Circle. Home: 2500 Q St NW Apt 644 Washington DC 20007-4366

POTERBA, JAMES MICHAEL, economist, educator; b. Flushing, N.Y., July 13, 1958; s. William Samuel and Margaret Mary (Toale) P.; m. Nancy Lin Rose, June 23, 1984; children: Matthew Robert, Timothy James, Margaret Rose. AB, Harvard U., 1980; MPhil, Oxford U., Eng., 1982, DPhil, 1983. From asst. to assoc. prof. MIT, Cambridge, Mass., 1983-88, prof., 1988—; dir. pub. econs. rsch. program Nat. Bur. Econ. Rsch., Cambridge, 1990—; fellow Ctr. Advanced Study in Behavioral Scis., 1993-94. Editor: Economic Policy Responses to Global Warming, 1991, International Comparisons of Household Saving, 1994; contbr. articles to profl. jours. Marshall scholar, 1980-83. Fellow Econometric Soc.; mem. Am. Fin. Assn. (bd. dirs.), Phi Beta Kappa. Office: MIT 50 Memorial Dr Rm E52-350 Cambridge MA 02139-4307

POTH, EDWARD CORNELIUS, construction company executive; b. Chgo., Aug. 19, 1927; s. John Henry and Cecelia Kathryn (Kuijer) P.; m. Eve Elsie Kaisto, June 25, 1953; children: Susan, Sharon, Cathy. BSCE, Bradley U., 1951. Project mgr. Paschen Contractors, Inc., Chgo., 1955-65, v.p., 1965-70, exec. v.p., 1970-80, pres., 1980-83, also bd. dirs.; exec. v.p. Mellon Stuart Co., Pitts., 1984-85, pres., 1986-88; vice chmn. Case Group, J. H. Pomeroy & Co. Inc., and Pomco, Inc., 1988—, also bd. dirs.; pres., bd. dirs. PCI Ins. Co., Chgo., 1978-83; pres. PCI Aviation Co., Chgo., 1978-83; treas., bd. dirs. Mid Am. Elevator Co., Chgo., 1976-83. Bd. dirs. Dist. 89 Sch. System, Glen Ellyn, Ill., 1970-76, Chgo. Builders Assn., 1978-83; mem. Econ. Devel. Bd., Glen Ellyn, 1991—. Served to sgt. C.E. U.S. Army, 1945-47. Recipient Value Engring. award Gen. Service Adminstrn., Chgo., 1971. Episcopalian. Clubs: Medinah Golf, Mid Am., Ground Hog Club (v.p), Beavers (Chgo.); Duquesne (Pitts.). Avocations: tennis, golf, skiing, fishing, hunting. Home: 591 Hill Ave Glen Ellyn IL 60137-5033 Office: JH Pomeroy & Co Inc 850 E Algonquin Rd # 102A Schaumburg IL 60173-3855

POTH, STEFAN MICHAEL, retired sales financing company executive; b. Detroit, Dec. 9, 1933; s. Stefan and Anna (Mayer) P.; m. Eileen T. McClimon, May 28, 1966; 1 child, Stefan Michael Jr. Cert. in acctg., Walsh Inst., Detroit, 1954. CPA, Mich.; cert. consumer credit exec. Sr. acct. Lybrand, Ross Bros. & Montgomery, Detroit, 1953-56, 58-61; with Ford Motor Credit Co., Dearborn, Mich., 1961-91; v.p. leasing truck and recreational products and tractor financing Ford Motor Credit Co., Dearborn, 1973-77; v.p. cen. and western U.S. ops. Ford Motor Credit CO., Dearborn, 1977-79; v.p. mktg. and ops. svcs. Ford Motor Credit Co., Dearborn, 1979-85, v.p. bus. planning, 1985-90, v.p. credit policy, 1990-91; bd. dirs. GE Credit Auto Resale Svcs., Inc.; adv. coun. Credit Rsch. Ctr., Krannert Grad. Sch. Mgmt., Purdue U., 1984-91. Chmn. adv. coun. Credit Rsch. Ctr. Krannert Grad. Sch. Mgmt., Purdue U., 1989-90; mem. bd. dirs. Internat. Credit Assoc., 1989-91. With AUS, 1956-58. Roman Catholic. Home: 7230 Mohansic Dr Bloomfield Hills MI 48301-3550

POTKIN, HARVEY, food company executive; b. Bklyn., Dec. 17, 1935; s. Samuel Jack and Mollie (Krinick) P.; m. Lois Millicent Schenfield, June 17, 1956 (dec. May 1993); children: Jill, Susan, Scott. BS in Mktg. and Acctg., NYU, 1957. Pres. Pokur Packing Co., Bklyn., 1957-81; v.p. Nat. Foods, Inc., Queens, N.Y., 1981-90, pres., COO, 1990—. Office: Nat Foods Inc 600 Food Center Dr Bronx NY 10474-7037

POTOK, CHAIM, author, artist, editor; b. N.Y.C., Feb. 17, 1929; s. Benjamin Max and Mollie (Friedman) P.; m. Adena S. Mosevitzky, June 8, 1958; children: Rena, Naama, Akiva. BA summa cum laude, Yeshiva Coll., 1950; MHL, Jewish Theol. Sem., 1954; PhD, U. Pa., 1965. Ordained rabbi, 1954. Nat. dir. Leaders Tng. Fellowship, 1954-55; dir. Camp Ramah, Ojai, Cal., 1957-59; scholar-in-residence Har Zion Temple, Phila., 1959-63; mem. faculty Tchrs. Inst., Jewish Theol. Sem., 1963-64; editor Jewish Publ. Soc., 1965-74, spl. projects editor, 1974—; vis. prof. U. Pa., 1983, 92, 93, 94, 95; vis. lectr. Bryn Mawr Coll., 1985. Author: The Chosen, 1967 (Edward Lewis Wallant award), The Promise, 1969 (Athenaeum award), My Name is Asher Lev, 1972, In The Beginning, 1975, Wanderings, 1975, The Book of Lights, 1981, Davita's Harp, 1985, Tobiasse: Artist in Exile, 1986, The Gift of Asher Lev, 1990 (Nat. Jewish Book award), I Am the Clay, 1992, (children's book with Tony Auth) The Tree of Here, 1993, (plays) Out of the Depths, 1990, Sins of the Father, 1991, The Play of Lights, 1992, also short stories; works translated into more than a dozen fgn. langs. Served as chaplain AUS, 1955-57, Korea. Mem. P.E.N., Artists' Equity, Author's Guild, Dramatists Guild, Rabbinical Assembly.

POTOKAR, RICHARD ALBERT, architect; b. Berwyn, Ill., Jan. 10, 1951; s. Edward H. and Josephine T. (Schram) P.; m. Patricia J. Cherney, Sept. 13, 1975; children: Christopher Jon, Elizabeth Ann. BArch, U. Ill., 1974. Registered Architect, Ill., Iowa. Architect Gelick/Caron, Chgo., 1974-75, Skidmore, Owings & Merrill, Chgo., 1975-76; project designer Perkins & Will, Chgo., 1976-77, 1978-80; project architect Booth, Nagle & Hartray, Ltd., Chgo., 1977-78; project mgr. Krussinski Gelick Foran, Ltd., Chgo., 1980-81; prin. Hansen Lind Meyer, Inc., Chgo., 1981-87; pres. Richard A.M. Potokar, Inc., Riverside, Ill., 1987—. Recipient Design award Women's Archtl. League, 1973, Design award Chgo. Bar Assn., 1985; hon. Mention Graham Found., 1978. Mem. AIA (Interior award 1986), Nat. Assn. Indsl. and Office Parks, Urban Land Inst., Chgo. Archtl. Club. Avocations: gardening, guitar. Home: 77 Herrick Rd Riverside IL 60546-2014 Office: Richard A M Potokar Inc 241 A E Burlington Riverside IL 60546

POTOKER, EDWARD MARTIN, English language educator, author; b. Newark, June 13, 1931; s. Benjamin and Bessie (Linn) P.; m. Berit Maria Arneberg, Sept. 3, 1958; 1 son, Eric Benjamin. A.B., Dartmouth Coll., 1953; M.A., Columbia U., 1955, Ph.D, 1964; postgrad., U. Munich, Germany, 1955-56. Mem. editorial staff New Yorker Mag., 1957-58; instr. English U. Rochester, 1958-59; lectr. English Hunter Coll., 1960; mem. faculty CCNY, 1960—, asst. prof. English, 1966—; asst. prof. English Bernard M. Baruch Coll., N.Y.C., 1968-72, assoc. prof., 1972-79, prof., 1979—, chmn. dept. English, 1971, 76—; faculty mem. coll. senate Baruch Sch. Edn. Author: The Corn Grain, 1956, Ronald Firbank, 1969, John Brain, 1978; contbr.: Ency. World Lit. in the 20th Century, Groliers Ency. Internat., The Dartmouth Alumni mag., Ramparts; book reviewer: N.Y. Times Book Rev., 1962—, Saturday Rev., 1965—; editor: The Ronald Firbank-Carl Van Vechten Correspondence, A Tragedy in Green and When Widows Love: Two Stories by Donald Firbank, 1978; founding mem.: Jour. Critical Analysis, 1969. Charter mem. USS Constn. Mus., 1991. Recipient John Edgar Hoover award for disting. pub. svc., The Untouchables Meml. award, Eliot Ness Cert. Appreciation, award Venerable Order of Justice; named a Knight of Justice, Michael the Archangel. Mem. AAUP, MLA, U.S. Justice Found., Ams. for a Sound Fgn. Policy, Council Inter-Am. Security, Young Ams. for Freedom, Congl. Policy Inst., Am. Council for Free Asia, Citizens for the Republic, Internat. Platform Assn., Vietnam Vets Am., Nat. Eagle Scout Assn., Heritage Found., Hale Found., U.S. Def. Com., Council Vol. Ams., Coalition for Freedom, Am. Security Council, Ctr. for Free Soc., Nat. Congl. Club, Nat. Right to Work Com., Am. Immigration Control Found., Council Nat. Def., Battle of Normandy Found. (charter), Navy League U.S., Nat. Assn. Chiefs of Police/Am. Police Hall of Fame (hon. chief 1991-92), Am. Legion, DAV, Amvets, The Am. Legion, Vietnam Vets. of Am., Vietnam Vets. Inc., Phi Beta Kappa. Club: Andiron (N.Y.C.). Home: 13 Dovas Path Southampton NY 11968-2830 also: 186 Riverside Dr New York NY 10024-1007 Office: Baruch Coll 17 Lexington Ave New York NY 10010

POTRA, FLORIAN ALEXANDER, mathematics educator; b. Cluj, Romania, Dec. 7, 1950; came to the U.S., 1982; s. Ioan and Ana (Popa) P.; m. ELena Lavric, Nov. 15, 1973; 1 child, Valentin. MS, Babes-Bolyai U., Cluj, 1973; PhD, U. Bucharest, 1980. Analyst IPGGH, Bucharest, Romania, 1974-78; researcher INCREST, Bucharest, 1978-82; postdoctoral researcher U. Pitts., 1982-83, asst. prof., 1983-84; assoc. prof. U. Iowa, Iowa City, 1984-90, prof., 1990—; vis. researcher Lawrence Livermore Nat. Lab., Rice U. U. Catania, Italy, Konrad Zuse Zentrum, Berlin, U. Darmstadt, Germany, 1990, U. Karlsruhe, Germany, 1987-91, Argonne Nat. Lab., 1991, U. Geneva, 1993. Assoc. editor: SIAM Jour. on Optimization, 1991—, Jour. Optimization Theory and Applications, 1991—; co-author: Research Notes in Mathematics 103, 1984; contbr. articles to profl. jours. Andrew Mellon fellow, 1982, Old Gold fellow, 1984, James Van Allen fellow in natural scis., 1991; NSF grantee, 1985-87, 94—. Home: 4029 W Overlook Rd NE Iowa City IA 52240-7942 Office: U Iowa Mathematics Iowa City IA 52242

POTSIC, WILLIAM PAUL, physician, educator; b. Berwyn, Ill., May 22, 1943; s. Andrew M. and Estella (Buschak) P.; m. Roberta I. Kite; children: Amie, Jordan. B.S., U. Ill., 1965; M.D. cum laude, Emory U., 1969; postgrad., U. Pa. Intern, resident U. Chgo., 1969-74; practice medicine specializing in pediatric otolaryngology Phila., 1974—; mem. staff Presbyn. Hosp., Pa. Hosp., Children's Seashore House; assoc. prof. otorhinolaryngology and human communication U. Pa., 1974-93, prof. otorhinolaryngology and human communication, 1993—; dir. div. otorhinolaryngology and human communication Children's Hosp., Phila., 1975—; sec.-treas. med. staff Children's Hosp., 1980—, pres. med. staff, 1982-84. Author book on pediatric otolaryngology; contbr. articles to profl. jours. Recipient 1st prize for clin. research Am. Acad. Ophthalmology and Otolaryngology, 1977; NIH grantee. Mem. Am. Acad. Otolaryngology Head and Neck Surgery, AMA, Am. Laryngology, Otolgy and Rhinology Soc., Internat. Acad. Cosmetic Surgery, Pa. Med. Soc., Phila. Coll. Physicians, Phila. County Med. Soc., Phila. Laryngol. Soc. (treas. 1983), Phila. Pediatric Soc., Phila. Laryngol. Soc. (pres. 1984), Phila. Soc. Facial Plastic Surgeons, Politzer Soc., Soc. Ear, Nose and Throat Advances in Children (pres. 1983), Am. Soc. Pediatric Otolaryngology (pres. 1991), Soc. Univ. Otolaryngologists, Am. Acad. Pediatrics, Am. Coll. of Physician Exec., Alpha Omega Alpha, Phi Chi. Home: 1057 Beaumont Rd Berwyn PA 19312-2007 Office: Children's Hosp Phila 34th And Civic Center Blvd Philadelphia PA 19104

POTTASH, A. CARTER, psychiatrist, hospital executive; b. Phila., Nov. 30, 1948; s. R Robert and Elizabeth (Braunschweig) P. BS with high honors, Trinity Coll., Hartford, Conn., 1970; MD, Yale U., 1974. Intern in internal medicine Tufts U. Sch. Medicine, Springfield, Mass., 1974-75; clin. fellow Yale-New Haven Hosp., 1977-78; postdoctoral fellow Yale U., New Haven, 1975-78; med. dir. Psychiatric Diagnostic Labs. Am., Summit, N.J., 1979-83; lectr. in field; cons. in field; vis. prof. St. Elizabeth Med. Ctr., Northeastern Ohio U. Coll Medicine, 1979; clin. prof. NYU, 1989—; pres. Psychiatric Assocs. N.J., P.A., Summit, N.J., 1978-93, Met. Med. Group P.C., N.J., 1981—, So. Fla. Med. Group P.A., Delray Beach, 1984-93, Stony Lodge Hosp., Inc., Briarcliff Manor, N.Y., 1985—, Hampton Med. Group, P.A., Rancocas, N.J., 1986—; exec. med. dir. Fair Oaks Hosp., Summit, 1978-92, The Regent Hosp., N.Y.C., 1981-92, Lake Hosp of the Palm Beaches, Lake Worth, Fla., 1984-92, Fair Oaks Hosp. at Boca/Delray, Fla., 1984-92, Stony Lodge Hosp., Briarcliff Manor, N.Y., 1985—, Hampton Hosp., Rancocas, N.J., 1986—. Editor Psychiatry Letter, 1980-91; mem. editl. bd. Internat. Jour. Psychiatry in Medicine, 1978-87, The Psychiatric Hosp., 1982—, Jour. Nat. Assn. Pvt. Psychiatric Hosps., 1980-81, Fla. Psychiatry Newsletter, 1992—; reviewer Jour. Nervous and Mental Disorders, Alcoholism, Clin. and Exptl. Rsch., JAMA, Hosp. and Cmty. Psychiatry; contbr. numerous articles to profl. jours. Mem. adv. bd. Mothers for More Halfway Houses, N.Y.C., 1986—; cons. com. on women and alcoholism Jr. League of N.Y.C., 1987; bd. dirs. Met. Soc. Arts, N.Y.C., 1984-87. Fellow Am. Coll. Clin. Pharmacology, Assn. Clin. Scientists, Nat. Acad. Clin. Biochemistry, Am. Psychiat. Assn., The Acad. Medicine N.J.; mem. AMA, Soc. Neurosci., Nat. Acad. Clin. Biochemistry, Palm Beach County Med. Soc., Am. Acad. Clin. Psychiatrists, British Brain Research Assn. (hon.), European Brain and Behavioral Soc. (hon.), Am. Med. Soc. on Alcoholism and Other Drug Dependencies, Am. Acad. Psychiatrists in Alcoholism and Addictions (founding mem. 1987), Am. Psychiatric Assn., Fla. Med. Soc., Palm Beach County Psychiatric Soc., Med. Soc. State N.Y., Med. Soc. N.J., Union County Med. Soc., N.Y. Athletic Club, Canoe Brook Country Club, Beacon Hill Club, Phi Beta Kappa, Delta Phi Alpha. Office: PO Box 511 West Palm Beach FL 33402-0511

POTTER, BARRETT GEORGE, historian, educator; b. Cortland, N.Y., Oct. 28, 1929; s. Leo Barrett and Charlotte May (Hazen) P.; B.A., Hobart Coll., 1952, M.S. in Edn., 1955; M.A., Cornell U. 1959; Ph.D. in History, SUNY, Buffalo, 1973; postgrad. SUNY, Cortland, 1952, Syracuse U., 1962; m. Beverly Ann Platts, Aug. 6, 1961; children—Barrett George, Heather Gaye. Instr., Hobart Coll., Geneva, N.Y., 1952-54; lectr. SUNY, New Paltz, 1955-57, summer 1960; high sch. tchr., Bayport, N.Y., 1957-58; asst. mgr. 1000 Acres Ranch Resort, Stony Creek, N.Y., 1958-59; asst. prof. history SUNY Tech. Coll., Alfred, 1959-64, prof., 1965-92, prof. emeritus, 1992—; chmn. dept., 1965-71; teaching asst. SUNY, Buffalo, 1964-65; adj. prof. Elmira Coll., 1978, Rochester Inst. Tech., 1979, Alfred U., 1985; tutor Empire State Coll., 1985. Mem. Alfred-Almond Central Sch. Bd. Edn., 1971-74, pres., 1973; trustee Alfred Rural Cemetery Assn., 1973-81, pres., 1979-80; trustee Alfred Hist. Soc., 1974-76, 85-88, Union U. Ch., Alfred, 1977-80, Alfred Village, 1987—; acting mayor City of Alfred, 1990-92; vice chmn. Alfred Community Chest, 1983-90. Coe Found. fellow in Am. Studies, 1961. Mem. Am. Fedn. Musicians, Phi Beta Kappa. Republican. Episcopalian. Clubs: Elks, Masons, Foster Lake (exec. com. 1972-74). Contbr. articles to profl. jours. Home: 76 S Main St Alfred NY 14802-1323 Office: Social Science Dept SUNY Alfred NY 14802

POTTER, CARY NICHOLAS, banker; b. N.Y.C., May 15, 1939; s. Cary and Julia Macy (Thompson) P.; m. Clare Ellsworth Prentice, Oct. 6, 1962; children: Cary, Christopher, Jennifer. BA, Yale U., 1961. With Morgan Guaranty Trust Co., N.Y.C., 1965—, sr. v.p., head research, trust and investment div., 1979-80, sr. v.p., chief investment officer trust and investment div., 1981-84; chmn. J.P. Morgan Investment Mgmt., Inc., N.Y.C., 1984-90, chmn., 1990—; mng. dir. J.P. Morgan & Co., N.Y.C., 1990—; bd. dirs. Munich Am. Reins. Co. Trustee Manhattan Eye, Ear and Throat Hosp., 1980-84, St. Mark's Sch., 1983—. Served with USNR, 1961-65. Office: JP Morgan & Co Inc 9 West 57th St New York NY 10019

POTTER, CHARLES ARTHUR, JR., trust company executive; b. St. Charles, Ill., July 25, 1925; s. Charles Arthur and Althea Mae (Whitney) P.; m. Joan Patricia Shannon, June 12, 1948; 1 child, Charles Arthur. Student, Western Mich. Coll., 1943, Officers Candidate Sch., U.S. Marine Corps, Quantico, Va., 1945; B.S., U. Ill., 1948, J.D., 1949; postgrad. Northwestern U., 1956. Bar: Ill. 1949. Mem. firm Gately & Burns, Chgo., 1949-50; spl. agt. FBI, Washington, Boston, N.Y.C. and Chgo., 1951-54; asst. trust officer Elmhurst Nat. Bank, Ill., 1955-59, United Calif. Bank, Los Angeles, 1959-61; v.p. trust officer First Am. Title and Trust Co., Santa Ana, Calif., 1961-68, also dir.; pres. First Am. Trust Co., Santa Ana, Calif., 1968—; treas., bd. dirs. Orange County Estate Planning Coun., 1966-69, Mansfield Ctr. Pacific Affairs, Helena, Mont., 1984-87; chmn. Nat. Def. U. Found., Washington, 1985-88; bd. dirs. Eldorado Bank, Tustin, Calif., First Am. Title Co. of Nev. Bd. dirs. Orange County Sports Celebrities, 1971-80, Providence Speech and Hearing Ctr., Orange County chpt. Multiple Sclerosis Soc., 1978—, Orange County area AMC Cancer Research Ctr., 1985—, Children's Hosp. Orange County Found., 1980—; mem. adv. bd. Salvation Army, Santa Ana, 1980—; trustee Calif. Med. Coll., U. Calif., Irvine, 1985—. Served with USMC, 1943-45. Recipient County of Los Angeles Cert. Commendation for pub. service, 1975. Mem. Soc. Former Spl. Agts. FBI (Western regional v.p 1976-77), Calif. Bankers Assn. (chmn. trust div. 1982-83, 1982-83), So. Calif. Trust Officers Assn. (pres. 1973-74), ABA, Ill. Bar Assn., Orange County Bar Assn., Def. Orientation Conf. Assn. (pres. 1982-84, dir., 1975—, chmn. 1985-86), Big Canyon Country Club (Newport Beach, Calif.), Indian Wells Country Club, Center Club (Costa Mesa, Calif.), PGA West Club (La Quinta, Calif.), Phi Delta Phi, Alpha Delta Phi. Home: 47 Pinewood Irvine CA 92714-3239 Office: 421 N Main St Santa Ana CA 92701-4617

POTTER, CHARLOTTE ANN, health education educator, physical education educator; b. Sept. 21, 1943; d. Charles Douglas and Jessie (Lewallen) Faulkner; m. Gary D. Potter, Dec. 24, 1962; 1 child, Bill Douglas. BS in Health and Phys. Edn., Tex. A&M U., 1972, MS in Health and Phys. Edn., 1975. With Westinghouse Corp., 1965; sec. dept. microbiology U. Ky., 1966-67; sec. dept. poultry sci. Tex. A&M U., 1968-69, tchr. dept. phys. edn., 1973; tchr. health and phys. edn. dept. College Station Ind. Schs., A&M Consolidated High Sch., 1973—, dept. head health and phys. edn., coord. intramurals, 1973—, student tchr. supr., 1974—; guest lectr. Tex. A&M U., College Station, 1993—. Adult leader Equestrian 4-H Club, 1971-83; vol. College Station Little League Baseball, 1971-81; vol. sch. health College Station Ind. Sch. Dist., 1972, com. chmn. PTO South Knoll, 1972-76; cardiopulmonary resuscitation instr. vol., 1972—; vol. Tex. A&M U. Horseman's Assn., 1982—; vol. Phoebe's Home Toy, 1989—. Mem. AAHPER, NEA, Nat. Assn. Secondary Sch. Prins., Am. Heart Assn., Assn. for Advancement Health Edn., Tex. AHPERD, Tex. Edn. Assn., College Station Edn. Assn., Ctrl. Tex. Assn. Student Coun. Sponsors, Tex. Assn. Student Coun. Sponsors, Tex. A&M Assn. Former Students, Am. Sch. Health Assn., Tex. Sch. Health Assn., Ctrl. Tex. Long Ears Assn., Am.

Donkey and Mule Assn., S.W. Donkey and Mule Assn., Gulf Coast Donkey and Mule Assn., Delta Psi Kappa, Delta Kappa Gamma. Avocation: training and showing mules in driving events. Home: 5609 Straub Rd College Station TX 77845-6966

POTTER, CLARKSON NOTT, publishing consultant; b. Mendham, N.J., May 17, 1928; s. John Howard Nott and Margaretta (Wood) P.; m. Ruth Delafield, June 14, 1949 (div. Aug. 1965); children—Howard Alonzo, Christian, Margaretta, Edward Eliphalet; m. Pamela Howard, Nov. 26, 1973 (div. Apr. 1976); 1 son, Jack Rohe Howard-Potter; m. Helga Maass, Oct. 31, 1981. B.A., Union Coll., 1950. With Doubleday & Co., N.Y.C., 1950-57; sr. editor, advt. mgr., mng. editor Dial Press, N.Y.C., 1958-59; founder, editor-in-chief Clarkson N. Potter Inc., N.Y.C., 1959-76; dir., editor-in-chief Barre Pub. Co. Inc., Mass., 1974-76; pres. The Brandywine Press, N.Y.C., 1976-80; lit. agt., publishing cons. Jamestown, R.I., 1980-86; pres. The Kestrel Press, Inc., 1992—; bd. dirs. Beckham House Pubs., Inc., Hampton, Va.; trustee Newport (R.I.) Art Mus., 1994—. Author: Writing for Publication, 1990, Who Does What and Why in Book Publishing, 1990. Mem. Century Club (N.Y.C.), Newport Reading Room. Home and office: 5 Westwood Rd Jamestown RI 02835-1165

POTTER, CORINNE JEAN, librarian; b. Edmonton, Alta., Can., Feb. 2, 1930; d. Vernon Harcourt and Beatrice A. (Demaray) MacNeill; m. William B. Potter, Aug. 11, 1951 (div. Jan. 1978); children—Caroline, Melanie, Theodore, William, Ellen. B.A., Augustana Coll., 1952; M.S., U. Ill., 1976. Br. librarian Rock Island (Ill.) Pub. Library, 1967-73, children's work supr., 1973-74; dir. St. Ambrose U. Library, Davenport, Iowa, 1978—; chairperson Quad City Library Dir.'s Publicity Com., 1984-88. Chairperson Com. of the Whole for Local Automated Circulation and Online Catalog System, 1989-90. Mem. ALA, Assn. Coll. and Research Libraries (sec., v.p., pres. Iowa chpt. 1979-82), Iowa Library Assn. (com. chmn. 1983-84), Iowa Pvt. Academic Libraries Consortium (sec.-treas. 1986-89), Iowa Oline Computer Libr. Ctr. Users Group (v.p.-pres. elect 1988-89, pres. 1989-90). Office: St Ambrose Coll McMullen Libr 518 W Locust St Davenport IA 52803-2898

POTTER, DAVID SAMUEL, former automotive company executive; b. Seattle, Jan. 16, 1925; children: Diana (Mrs. Paul Bankston), Janice (Mrs. Robert Meadows), Tom, Bill; m. Nancy Shaar, Dec. 1979. B.S., Yale U., 1945; Ph.D., U. Wash., 1951. Mem. staff Applied Physics Lab., U. Wash., 1946-60, asst. dir. research, 1950-60; with Gen. Motors Corp., 1960-73; chief engr. Milw. ops. GM Delco Electronics div., 1970-73; dir. research and devel. Detroit Diesel Allison div., 1973; asst. sec. for research and devel. Dept. Navy, 1973-74, under sec., 1974-76; v.p. environ. activities staff Gen. Motors Corp., Detroit, 1976-78; v.p. and group exec. public affairs group Gen. Motors Corp., 1978-83, v.p. in charge power products and def. ops. group, 1983-85; ret., 1985; Mem. Gov. Calif. Adv. Commn. Ocean Resources, 1964-68; mem. adv. panel Nat. Sea Grant Program, 1966; adv. bd. Naval Postgrad. Sch., Dept. Energy; bd. dirs. Sanders Assocs. Inc., Sci. Applications Internat. Co., John Fluke Mfg. Co., Lockheed Corp. Served to ensign USNR, 1943-46. Mem. Nat. Acad. Engring., NSF, Marine Tech. Soc., Am. Phys. Soc., AIAA, Am. Acoustical Soc., Nat. Oceanographic Assn. (v.p. 1966), Soc. Automotive Engrs. (chmn. tech. bd. 1978-79, dir. 1981-83), Cosmos Club (Washington), Detroit Club, Birmingham Athletic Club (Mich.), Birnam Wood Country Club (Montecito, Calif.), Santa Barbara Club. Research cosmic rays, magnetics, underwater acoustics. Home: 877 Lilac Dr Santa Barbara CA 93108-1438

POTTER, DEBORAH ANN, news correspondent, educator; b. Hagerstown, Md., June 10, 1951; d. Peter R. and H. Louise (McDevitt) P.; m. Robert H. Witten, May 1, 1982; children: Cameron, Evan. BA, U. N.C., 1972; MA, Am. U., 1977. Assignment editor Sta. WMAL-TV, Washington, 1972-73, prodr., 1973-74; reporter Voice of Am., Washington, 1974-77; anchor Sta. KYW, Phila., 1977-78, CBS Radio, N.Y.C., 1978-81; White House corr. CBS News, Washington, 1981-85, state dept. corr., 1985-87, congl. corr., 1987-89, environ. corr., 1989-91; contbg. corr. 48 Hours, 1989-90; host Nightwatch CBS News, Washington, 1991; Washington corr. Cable News Network, Washington, 1991-94; asst. prof. Sch. Comm. Am. U., Washington, 1994—; vis. faculty Poynter Inst. Media Studies. Host (video prodn.) Beyond the Spotted Owl, 1993, Health Beat, 1994, Risk Reporting, 1995. Mem. adv. coun. Environ. Journalism Ctr., Radio and TV News Dirs. Found., Washington, 1994—; lay reader St. Alban's Episc. Ch., Washington, 1988-89. Mem. U. N.C. Alumni Assn. (bd. dirs. 1990-93, Disting. Young Alumna award 1990). Office: Am U Sch Comm 4400 Massachusetts Ave NW Washington DC 20015

POTTER, DELCOUR S., finance company executive; b. 1935. AB, Bowdoin Coll., 1957. With Gen. Electric Corp., N.Y.C., 1957-65, asst. treas., 1965-72; v.p. fin. Chase Manhattan Mortgage and Realty Trust, N.Y.C., 1972-75, resigned; sec.-treas. Pvt. Export Funding Corp., N.Y.C., 1975—, pres. chief exec. officer. With U.S. Army, 1958. Office: Private Export Funding Corp 747 3rd Ave New York NY 10017*

POTTER, ERNEST LUTHER, lawyer; b. Anniston, Ala., Apr. 30, 1940; s. Ernest Luther and Dorothy (Stamps) P.; m. Gwyn Johnston, June 28, 1958; children: Bradley S., Lauren D. A.B., U. Ala., 1961, LL.B., 1963, LL.M., 1979. Bar: Ala. 1963, U.S. Dist. Ct. (no. dist.) Ala. 1964, U.S. Ct. Appeals (5th cir.) 1965, U.S. Supreme Ct. 1972, U.S. Ct. Appeals (11th cir.) 1982. Assoc. Burnham & Klinefelter, Anniston, Ala., 1963-64; assoc. Bell, Richardson, Cleary, McLain & Tucker, Huntsville, Ala., 1964-66, ptnr., 1967-70; ptnr. Butler & Potter, Huntsville, 1971-82; pvt. practice, Huntsville, 1983—; bd. dirs. VME Microsystems Internat. Corp., Inc.; mem. faculty Inst. Bus. Law and Polit. Sci., U. Ala.-Huntsville, 1965-67. Contbg. author: Marital Law, 1976, 2d edit. 1985. V.p. No. Ala. Kidney Found., 1976-77; treas. Madison County Dem. Exec. Com., 1974-78; bd. dirs. United Way Madison County, 1982-87, Girls Inc., Huntsville, 1988—, pres., 1991. Mem. Ala. Law Inst., ABA, Ala. Bar Assn., Madison County Bar Assn., Phi Beta Kappa, Order of Coif. Episcopalian. Home: 1284 Becket Dr SE Huntsville AL 35801-1670 Office: 200 Clinton Ave W Huntsville AL 35801-4918

POTTER, GLENN EDWARD, hospital administrator; b. Canton, Ill., July 4, 1943; married. BA, Ottawa U., 1965; MA, Washington U., 1972. Bus. mgr. Graham Hosp., Canton, 1966-70; adm. res. Samaritan Health Svc., Phoenix, 1971-72; asst. adminstr. Desert Samaritan Hosp., Mesa, Ariz., 1972-73; dir. profl. svcs. N.C. Meml. Hosp., Chapel Hill, 1973-77; sr. v.p. Iowa Methodist Med. Ctr., Des Moines, 1982; v.p. ops. Cuyahoga County Hosp., Cleve., 1977-82; exec. v.p. adminstr. Iowa Methodist Med. Ctr., Des Moines, 1983-90; vice chancelor Kans. U. Med. Ctr., Kansas City, 1990—; adj. prof. in field. Fellow HF Med. Assn., Kans. Hosp. Assn. Office: U of Kansas Hospital 3901 Rainbow Blvd Kansas City KS 66160

POTTER, GUY DILL, radiologist, educator; b. Greensboro, N.C., Jan. 24, 1928; s. Guy Dill and Frances Tanner (Potter) P.; m. Pearl Bear, May 11, 1951. B.S., U. Chgo., 1957, M.D., 1960. Intern Blodgett Meml. Hosp., Grand Rapids, Mich., 1960-61; resident U. Chgo. Clinics, 1961-64; instr. to prof. radiology Coll. Physicians and Surgeons, Columbia U., N.Y.C., 1964—; asst. to attending radiologist Presbyn. Hosp., N.Y.C., 1964-78; dir. dept. radiology Lenox Hill Hosp., N.Y.C., 1979-81; dir. dept. radiology St. Luke's-Roosevelt Hosp. Ctr., N.Y.C., 1981—; guest lectr. Royal Australasian Soc. Radiologists, 1979; cons. USPHS, 1966—, VA, 1975. Author: Sectional Anatomy and Tomography of the Head, 1971; co-author: Radiology of the Ear, Nose and Throat, 1982; Author numerous articles on radiology of the ear, sinuses and skull; editor: Radiology of the Ear, 1974, Disorders of the Head and Neck, 3d series, 1985, CT of the Head and Neck, 1984; co-editor: Ear Nose and Throat Radiology, 1980; editorial adv. bd.: Radiology. Served with AUS, 1946-47. Named Hickey Lectr. Mich. Radiol. Soc., 1973. Fellow Am. Coll. Radiology (head and neck evaluation com.); mem. Radiol. Soc. N.Am. (chmn. audiovisual com.), Am. Soc. Head and Neck Radiology (past pres.), AMA, N.Y. Otol. Soc., N.Y. State Med. Soc., N.Y. County Med. Soc., N.Y. Roentgen Soc., Am. Roentgen Soc. Office: 428 W 59th St New York NY 10019-1105

POTTER, HAMILTON FISH, JR., lawyer, consultant, author; b. Bklyn., Dec. 21, 1928; s. Hamilton Fish and Alma Virginia (Murray) P.; m. Virginia Fox Patterson, Sept. 17, 1953 (div. May 1979); children: Virginia Patterson, Hamilton Fish III, Robert Burnside, Elizabeth Stuyvesant; m. Maureen Ellen Cotter, Nov. 28, 1981; children: Nicholas Fish, Warwick Alonzo. B.A.,

Harvard U., 1950, LL.B., 1956. Bar: N.Y. 1957, U.S. Supreme Ct. 1961. Assoc. Sullivan & Cromwell, N.Y.C., 1956-65, ptnr., 1965-91. Bd. dirs. Berkshire Farm for Boys, N.Y., 1962-71, Alice and Hamilton Fish Libr., Garrison-on-Hudson, N.Y., 1980—; mem. Bd. Correction, N.Y.C., 1963-71; warden Ch. of Resurrection, 1972-74; trustee Episcopal Sch. of N.Y., 1969-76, Chapin Sch., 1975-81, Knox Sch. 1985—; warden All Saints Episcopal Ch., 1982-90; bd. dirs. Dutch Am. West Indies Found., 1984-89, The Netherlands Am. Found., 1989-92. Lt. (j.g.) USN, 1950-53, Korea. Mem. ABA (chmn. banking law com. 1975-80), Am. Bar Found., N.Y. State Bar Assn. (ho.of dels. 1978-80), N.Y. Bar Found., Assn. of Bar of City of N.Y. (chmn. banking law com. 1972-74), Am. Law Inst. (3-4-8 com. 1975-83), Mystery Writers Am. (assoc.). Home: 325 E 65th St New York NY 10021-6863 Office: c/o Sullivan and Cromwell 250 Park Ave 21st Flr New York NY 10177-0001

POTTER, JAMES DOUGLAS, pharmacology educator; b. Waterbury, Conn., Sept. 26, 1944; s. Herbert Eugene and Jean Gladys (Troske) P.; m. Priscilla F. Strang, Aug. 9, 1985; children: Liesse, Andrew, Ian Brown. BS, George Washington U., 1965; PhD, U. Conn., 1970; postgrad. (fellow) Boston Biomed. Rsch. Inst., 1970-74. Staff scientist Boston Biomed. Research Inst., 1974-75; assoc. in neurology Harvard U. Med. Sch., 1974-75; asst. prof. cell biophysics Baylor Coll. Medicine, 1975-77; assoc. prof. pharmacology U. Cin., 1977-81, prof., 1981-83; chmn., prof. dept. molecular and cellular pharmacology U. Miami, 1983—; grant reviewer in field. Grantee NIH, 1978-81, 83—, Nat. Heart Lung and Blood Inst., 1978— (Merit award 1989—), Muscular Dystrophy Assn., 1983-94. Fellow Muscular Dystrophy Assn.; mem. AAAS, Am. Chem. Soc., Am. Soc. Pharmacology and Exptl. Therapeutics, Assn. for Med. Sch. Pharmacology (chmn.), Internat. Soc. Heart Rsch., Am. Heart Assn. (established investigator 1974-79), Am. Soc. Biochem. and Molecular Biologists, Cardiac Muscle Soc. (sec.-treas. 1992-94, pres. 1994—), Biophys. Soc., Sigma Xi. Contbr. articles to profl. jours. Home: 7240 SW 127th St Miami FL 33156-5336 Office: U Miami Sch Medicine Dept of Molecular & Cellular Pharm 1600 NW 10th Ave Miami FL 33136

POTTER, JAMES EARL, retired international hotel management company executive; b. Utica, N.Y., July 25, 1933; s. Earl Moses and Helen May (Cruikshank) P. BS in Hotel Mgmt. with distinction, Cornell U., 1954, postgrad., 1955-56. Owner, propr. Old Drovers Inn, Dover Plains, N.Y., 1956-89; various acctg. positions Inter-Continental Hotels Corp., N.Y.C., 1960-62, fin. dir. for Asia and Pacific, 1963-69; v.p. Overseas Nat. Airways Hotels, N.Y., 1972; sr. v.p. Inter-Continental Hotels Corp., N.Y.C., 1972-89, London, 1990-92; instr. acctg. Cornell U., Ithaca, N.Y., 1957-59. Trustee Opera Co. Boston, 1978-85; mem. coun. Cornell U., 1988-91. Mem. Culinary Inst. Am. (trustees com. on acad. policy 1980-90), Met. Opera Club (N.Y.C., house com.), Cornell Soc. Hotelmen, Cornell Club (N.Y.C.). Presbyterian. Avocation: opera.

POTTER, J(EFFREY) STEWART, property manager; b. Ft. Worth, July 8, 1943; s. Gerald Robert Potter and Marion June (Mustain) Tombler; m. Dianne Eileen Roberb, Dec. 31, 1970 (div. Aug. 1983); 1 child, Christopher Stewart; m. Deborah Ann Blevins, Oct. 20, 1991. AA, San Diego Mesa Coll., 1967. Cert. apartment mgr., apartment property supr., housing adminstr. Sales mgr. Sta. KJLM, La Jolla, Calif., 1964-67; mgr. inflight catering Host Internat., San Diego, 1967-69; lead aircraft refueler Lockheed Co., San Diego, 1969-70; property mgr. Internat. Devel. and Fin Corp., La Jolla, 1970-72; mgr. bus. property BWY Constn. Co., San Diego, 1972-73; mgr. residents Coldwell Banker, San Diego, 1973-74; mgr. Grove Investments, Carlsbad, Calif., 1974-76, Villa Granada, Villa Seville Properties Ltd., Don Cohn, Chula Vista, Calif., 1976-83; gen. mgr. AFL-CIO Bldg. Trades Corp., National City, Calif., 1983—; instr., Cert. Apt. Mgmt. San Diego Apt. Assn. Bd. dirs. San Diego County Apt. Assn., 1995—. Fellow Internat. Platform Assn., Nat. City C. of C., Toastmasters, Founding Families San Diego Hist. Soc., Am. Assn. Retired Persons, San Diego County Apt. Assn. (bd. dirs.), La Jolla Monday Night Club (treas. 1984-89). Roman Catholic. Avocations: golf, tennis, snow skiing. Home: 4616 Granger St San Diego CA 92107-4012 Office: AFL-CIO Bldg Trades Corp 2323 D Ave National City CA 91950-6730

POTTER, JOHN FRANCIS, surgical oncologist, educator; b. N.Y.C., July 26, 1925; s. John Albert and Isabelle Cecelia (Sullivan) P.; m. Tanya Agnes Kristof, Nov. 19, 1955; children—Tanya Jean, Miriam Isabelle, John Mark. Student, Holy Cross Coll., 1943-45; M.D. Georgetown Med. Sch., 1949. Intern Grasslands Hosp., Valhalla, N.Y., 1949-50; surg. resident Grasslands Hosp., Valhalla, 1949-50, Georgetown U. Hosp., Washington, 1953-56; sr. investigator Nat. Cancer Inst., Bethesda, Md., 1957-60; chief div. surgical oncology Georgetown Med. Ctr., Washington, 1960-85; prof. of surgery Georgetown Med. Ctr., 1969—; dir. Vincent T. Lombardi Cancer Rsch. Ctr., Washington, 1967-87. hon. prof. Universidad Cayetano Heredia, Lima, Peru, 1980. Served to lt. j.g. USNR, 1951-53. Recipient Pres.'s medal Georgetown U., 1991. Mem. Soc. Surg. Oncology (rep. adv. bd.), ACS, Assn. Am. Cancer Insts. (bd. dirs. 1982, v.p. 1985-86, pres. 1986-87, chmn. bd. dirs. 1987-88), So. Surg. Assn., Peruvian Cancer Soc. (hon.), Knights of Malta. Lodge: Knights of Malta. Office: Georgetown U Med Ctr 3800 Reservoir Rd NW Washington DC 20007-2196

POTTER, JOHN LEITH, mechanical and aerospace engineer, educator, consultant; b. Metz, Mo., Feb. 5, 1923; s. Jay Francis Lee and Pearl Delores (Leeth) P.; m. Dorothy Jean Williams, Dec. 15, 1957; children: Stephen, Anne, Carol. BS in Aerospace Engring., U. Ala., Tuscaloosa, 1944, MS in Engring., 1949; MS in Engring. Mgmt., Vanderbilt U., 1976, PhD in Mech. Engring., 1974. Engr., educator various indsl., ednl. and govt. orgns., 1944-52; chief, flight and aerodyns. lab. Redstone Arsenal, Ala., 1952-56; mgr. div. chief, dep. tech. dir., sr. staff scientist Sverdrup Tech., Inc., Tullahoma, Tenn., 1956-83; research prof. Vanderbilt U., Nashville, 1983-92, prof. emeritus, 1992—; cons. engr. Nashville, 1983—; convener NATO-AGARD, U.S. and Eng., 1980-82, mem. working group, 1984-88; mem. adv. com. Internat. Symposium on Rarefied Gasdynamics, 1970—; invited lectr. USSR Acad. Scis., 1967; mem. NRC com. on assessment nat. aeronautical wind tunnel facilities, 1987-88; mem. NASA working groups, 1987—; mem. Engring. Accreditation Commn., 1985-90. Editor: Rarefied Gas Dynamics, 1977. Contbr. articles to profl. publs., chpts. to books. Chmn. bd. dirs. Coffee County Hist. Soc., Tenn., 1971-72; bd. dirs. Southeastern Amateur Athletic Union, 1972-73; pres. Tullahoma Swim Club, 1972-73; Sheffield Homeowners Assn., Nashville, 1983—. Recipient Outstanding Fellow award U. Ala. Aerospace Engring. Dept., 1987; elected 150th Anniversary Disting. Engring. Fellow U. Ala. Coll. Engring., 1988; USAF Arnold Engring. Devel. Ctr. fellow, 1993. Fellow AIAA (assoc. editor jour. 1970-73, publs. com. 1973-78, assoc. editor Progress in Astronautics and Aeronautics 1981-85, Gen. H.H. Arnold award Tenn. chpt. 1964); mem. Capstone Engring. Soc. (regional bd. dirs. 1972-77), Sigma Xi, Tau Beta Pi, Theta Tau, Pi Tau Sigma, Sigma Gamma Tau. Home: 200 Sheffield Pl Nashville TN 37215-3235 Office: Vanderbilt U Box 1592 Sta B Nashville TN 37235

POTTER, JOHN WILLIAM, federal judge; b. Toledo, Ohio, Oct. 25, 1918; s. Charles and Mary Elizabeth (Baker) P.; m. Phyllis May Bihn, Apr. 14, 1944; children: John William, Carolyn Diane, Kathryn Susan. PhB cum laude, U. Toledo, 1940; JD, U. Mich., 1946. Bar: Ohio 1947. Assoc. Zachman, Boxell, Schroeder & Torbet, Toledo, 1946-51; ptnr. Boxell, Bebout, Torbet & Potter, Toledo, 1951-69; mayor City of Toledo, 1961-67; asst. atty. gen. State of Ohio, 1968-69; judge 6th Dist. Ct. Appeals, 1969-82; judge U.S. Dist. Ct., Toledo, 1982—, sr. judge, 1992—; presenter in field. Sr. editor U. Mich. Law Rev., 1946. Pres. Ohio Mcpl. League, 1965; past assoc. pub. mem. Toledo Labor Mgmt. Commn.; past pres., bd. dirs. Commn. on Rels. with Toledo (Spain); past bd. dirs. Cummings Sch. Toledo Opera Assn.; Conlon Ctr.; past trustee Epworth United Meth. Ch.; hon. chmn. Toledo Festival Arts, 1980. Capt. F.A., U.S. Army, 1942-46. Decorated Bronze Star; recipient Leadership award Toledo Bldg. Congress, 1965, Outstanding Alumnus award U. Toledo, 1966, Merit award Toledo Bd. Realtors, 1967, Resolution of Recognition award Ohio Ho. of Reps., 1982. Fellow Am. Bar Found., Am. Judicature Soc., 6th Jud. Cir. Dist. Judges Assn., Fed. Judges Assn.; mem. ABA, Ohio Bar Assn., Toledo Bar Assn. (exec. com. 1962-64), Lucas County Bar Assn., Toledo Area C. of C. (former mem., v.p. 1973-74), U. Toledo Alumni Assn. (past pres), Toledo Zool. Soc. (former Bd. dirs.), Old Newsboys Club, Toledo Club, Kiwanis (past pres.), Phi Kappa Phi. Home: 2418 Middlesex Dr Toledo OH 43606-

3114 Office: US Dist Ct 210 US Courthouse 1716 Spielbusch Ave Toledo OH 43624-1332

POTTER, KARL HARRINGTON, philosophy educator; b. Oakland, Calif., Aug. 19, 1927; s. George Reuben and Mabel (Harrington) P.; m. Antonia Fleak, June 26, 1957; children: David Fleak, Julie Ann. Grad., Taft Sch., 1945; AB, U. Calif. at Berkeley, 1950; MA, Harvard U., 1952, PhD, 1955. Instr. philosophy Carleton Coll., 1955-56; mem. faculty U. Minn., 1956-71, prof. philosophy, 1965-70, chmn. dept., 1964-67, dir., 1967-70; prof. philosophy and South Asian studies U. Wash., Seattle, 1971—, chmn. South Asia program, 1972-86, chmn. dept. philosophy, 1986-91. Author: The Padarthatattvanirupanam of Raghunatha Siromani, 1957, Presuppositions of India's Philosophies, 1963, Ency. of Indian Philosophies, 1970, 77, 81, 94, Guide to Indian Philosophy, 1988. With USNR, 1945-46. Fulbright fellow, India, 1952-53, 59-60, 81; Am. Inst. Indian Studies fellow, India, 1963-64. Mem. Assn. Asian Studies (bd. dirs., mem. South Asia regional coun. 1971-74, chmn. coun. 1972-74), Am. Philos. Assn. Univ. Profs., Am. Oriental Soc., Soc. Asian and Comparative Philosophy (pres. 1968-70). Home: 19548 47th Ave NE Seattle WA 98155-1720 Office: U Washington Dept Philosophy Seattle WA 98105

POTTER, LILLIAN FLORENCE, business executive secretary; b. Montreal, Que., Can., Oct. 19, 1912; came to U.S., 1934; naturalized citizen.; d. Thomas Joseph and Lily Rose (Robertson) Quirk; m. Theodore Edward Potter, July 20, 1932 (dec. Apr. 1980); children: Peter Edward, Stephen Thomas. Grad. high sch., Montreal, 1929, grad., 1931. Sr. sec. S.D. Warren div. Scott Paper Co., Westbrook, Maine, 1955-69, editor indsl. publ. S.D. Warren div., 1969-72; editor Nat. Antiques Rev. mag., Portland, Maine, 1972-77; exec. sec. Humboldt Portland Litho div. Humboldt Nat. Graphics, Inc., Fortuna, Calif., 1977—; free lance writer Guy Gannett Pub. Co., Portland, 1960-64. Author: (children's book) Once Upon an Autumn, 1984 (state 1st pl. award, nat. 3d pl. award), (antiques and collectibles) A Re-Introduction to Silver Overlay on Glass and Ceramics, 1992; co-author: (textbook, tchrs. manual) Foundations of Patient Care, 1981; asst. editor, N.E. dist. The Secretary mag., Profl. Secs. Internat., 1960-62; editor Maine Chpt. Bull., 1963-64. Recipient George Washington Honors medal Freedoms Found., Valley Forge, Pa., 1964, Sec. of Yr. award Portland chpt. Profl. Secs. Internat., 1967, Outstanding Svc. award State of Maine Sesquicentennial, 1970, Outstanding Svc. award Island Pond (Vt.) Hist. Soc. 1978. Mem. Maine Media Women (pres. 1970-71, Woman of Yr. 1973, Communicator of Achievement plaque and prize 1991), Maine Writers and Pubs. Alliance, Women's Lit. Union, Portland Lyric Theater, Island Pond Hist. Soc., Jones Mus. Glass and Ceramics, Westbrook Women's Club, Order Eastern Star (past matron, past pres.). Republican. Episcopalian. Avocations: reading, researching, antiques, swimming, gardening. Home: 80 Payson St Portland ME 04102-2851

POTTER, MICHAEL, genetics researcher, medical researcher; b. East Orange, N.J., Feb. 27, 1924. AB, Princeton U., 1945; MD, U. Va., 1949. Research asst. dept. microbiology U. Va. Med. Sch., 1952-54, biologist, 1954-70, head immunochemistry sect. Lab. Cell Biology, 1970-82; head genetics lab., cancer biology and diagnosis div. Nat. Cancer Inst., Bethesda, Md., 1982—. Recipient Paul-Ehrlick & Ludwig-Darmstaedter prize, 1983, Lasker award in basic med. research, 1984. Mem. Nat. Acad. Scis., Am. Assn. Cancer Research, Am. Assn. Immunologists. Office: Nat Cancer Inst 9000 Rockville Pike Bldg 31 Bethesda MD 20892-0001

POTTER, RALPH BENAJAH, JR., theology and social ethics educator; b. Los Angeles, May 19, 1931; s. Ralph Benajah and Vivian Irene MacNabb (Borden) P.; m. Jean Ishbel MacCormick, Aug. 15, 1953; children: Anne Elizabeth, Ralph Andrew, James David, Margaret Jean; m. Christine Iva Mitchell, Aug. 25, 1985 (div. 1995); children: Charles Benajah Mitchell Potter, Christopher Ralph Mitchell Potter. B.A., Occidental Coll., 1952; postgrad., Pacific St. Religion, 1952-53; B.D., McCormick Theol. Sem., 1955; Th.D. (Presbyn. Grad. fellow 1958-63, Rockefeller fellow 1961-62, Kent fellow 1963-64), Harvard, 1965. Ordained to ministry Presbyn. Ch., 1955; dir., pastor Clay County Presbyn. Larger Parish, Manchester, Ky., 1955-58; sec. social edn. Bd. Christian Edn. United Presbyn. Ch. in U.S.A., Phila., 1963-67; asst. prof. social ethics Harvard Div. Sch.; mem. Center for Population Studies, Harvard U, Cambridge, Mass., 1965-69; prof. social ethics Harvard U., 1969-89; theologian-in-residence Am. Ch. in Paris, 1975; sr. rsch. scholar Kennedy Inst. for Bio-ethics Georgetown U., 1974; assoc. Lowell House, Harvard U.; founding fellow Hastings Ctr. Author: War and Moral Discourse, 1969; contbr. chpts. to The Religious Situation, 1968, 1968, Religion and the Public Order, 1968, Toward a Discipline of Social Ethics, 1972, The Population Crisis and Moral Responsibility, 1973, Community in America, 1988, also scholarly articles. Mem. Soc. Christian Ethics, Soc. for Values in Higher Edn., Société Européene de Culture, Am. Acad. Religion, Tocqueville Soc. Home: 7 Swan St Arlington MA 02174 Office: 45 Francis Ave Cambridge MA 02138-1994

POTTER, ROBERT DANIEL, federal judge; b. Wilmington, N.C., Apr. 4, 1923; s. Elisha Lindsey and Emma Louise (McLean) P.; m. Mary Catherine Neilson, Feb. 13, 1954; children: Robert Daniel, Mary Louise, Catherine Ann. AB in Chemistry, Duke U., 1947, LLB, 1950; LLD (hon.), Sacred Heart Coll., Belmont, N.C., 1982. Bar: N.C. 1951. Pvt. practice law Charlotte, N.C., 1951-81; chief judge U.S. Dist. Ct. (we. dist.) N.C., 1981-90, dist. judge, 1990—, now sr. judge. Commr. Mecklenburg County, Charlotte, 1966-68. Served to 2d lt. U.S. Army, 1944-47, ETO. Mem. N.C. Bar Assn. Republican. Roman Catholic. Club: Charlotte City. Home: 2710 Coltsgate Rd Charlotte NC 28211-3503 Office: US Courthouse 250 Federal Bldg 401 W Trade St Charlotte NC 28202

POTTER, ROBERT JOSEPH, technical research and business executive; b. N.Y.C., Oct. 29, 1932; s. Mack and Ida (Bernstein) P.; married; children: Diane Gail, Suzanne Lee, David Craig. BS cum laude, Lafayette Coll., 1954; MA in Physics, U. Rochester, 1957, PhD in Optics, 1960. Cons. ANPA Research Inst., AEC Brookhaven Nat. Lab., RCA Labs., U.S. Naval Research Labs., 1952-60; mgr. optical physics and optical pattern recognition IBM Thomas J. Watson Research Center, Yorktown Heights, N.Y., 1960-65; assoc. dir. Applied Research Lab., Xerox Corp., Rochester, N.Y., 1965-67; v.p. advanced engring. Xerox Corp., 1967-68, v.p. devel. and engring., 1968-69, v.p., gen. mgr. Spl. Products and Systems div. Spl. Products and Sys. divsn. Xerox Corp., Stamford, Conn. and Pasadena, Calif., 1969-71; v.p. info. tech. group Xerox Corp., Rochester, 1971-73; v.p. info. tech. group Xerox Corp., Dallas, 1973-75, pres. Office Sys. divsn., 1975-78; sr. v.p., chief tech. officer Internat. Harvester Co., Chgo., 1978-82; with R.J. Potter & Co., 1983-84; group v.p. integrated office sys. No. Telecom Inc., Richardson, Tex., 1985-87; pres., CEO Datapoint Corp., San Antonio, 1987-89, R.J. Potter Co., Dallas, 1990—; dir. Molex Inc. Contbr. articles to profl. jours. Trustee Ill. Inst. Tech. Recipient IBM Outstanding Tech. Contbr. award, 1964, Disting. Achievement award Soc. Mfg. Engrs., 1981; Kroner scholar Lafayette Coll., 1954; Disting. Rochester scholar U. Rochester, 1995. Fellow Optical Soc. Am., Am. Phys. Soc.; mem. Phi Beta Kappa, Sigma Xi. Office: R J Potter Co 5215 N O'Connor Rd Ste 975 Irving TX 75039

POTTER, TREVOR ALEXANDER MCCLURG, lawyer; b. Chgo., Oct. 24, 1955; s. Charles Steele and Barbara (McClurg) P. AB, Harvard Coll., 1978; JD, U. Va., 1982. Bar: Ill. 1983, D.C. 1988. Counsel office of legal policy U.S. Dept. Justice, Washington, 1982-84; asst. gen. counsel FCC, Washington, 1984-85; assoc. Wiley, Rein & Fielding, Washington, 1985-88, ptnr., 1988-91; commr. Fed. Election Commn., Washington, 1991—, vice chmn., 1993, chmn., 1994—. Republican. Episcopalian. Mem. ABA (chmn. com. on election law, adminstrv. law sect. 1993—). Office: Fed Election Commn 999 E St NW 9th Fl Washington DC 20463

POTTER, WILLIAM BARTLETT, business executive; b. Washington, Jan. 4, 1938; s. George Holland and Virginia (Bartlett) P.; m. Simone Robert, June 6, 1964; children: Eva Simone, William Bartlett. A.B., Princeton U., 1960; M.B.A., Emory U., 1962. With Merc.-Safe Deposit & Trust Co., Balt., 1962—; asst. sec., asst. treas. Merc.-Safe Deposit & Trust Co., 1964-66, asst. v.p., 1966-68, v.p., 1968-69, sr. v.p., 1969-76, exec. v.p., 1976; assoc. v.p. Preston Trucking Co., 1976-77, pres., 1977-86; chmn., pres. Preston Trucking, 1986-92; Preston Corp., 1986-93, chmn., 1994—; bd. dirs.

Trinidad Nat. Bank. Trustee Aspen Inst. Mem. Md. Club. Home: PO Box 614 Trinidad CO 81082-0614

POTTER, WILLIAM GRAY, JR., library director; b. Duluth, Minn., Feb. 18, 1950; s. William Gray and Kathryn Martha (Scheuer) P.; m. Marsha Ann Maune, Sept. 23, 1982. BA, So. Ill. U., 1973; MLS, U. Ill., 1975, MA, 1975, PhD, 1984. Ref. libr., cataloger, systems libr. U. Wis.-Whitewater, 1975-78; asst. dir. gen. svcs. U. Ill.-Urbana, 1978-85; assoc dean librs. for tech. svcs., automation and systems Ariz. State U., Tempe, 1985-89; dir. librs. U. Ga., Athens, 1989—. Editor: Serials Automation, 1980, Libr. Trends, 1981, Info. Tech. and Librs., 1984-89; mem. editl. bd. Multi-Media, Rev., 1989-92, Libr. Hi-Tech., 1992—, OCLC Micro, 1990—; contbr. articles to profl. jours. Bd. dirs Richard B. Russell Found., 1989—, sec. 1990—; mem. adv. com. Ga. Libr. Svcs. and Constrn. Act; bd. trustees OCLC, 1994—. Mem. ALA, Libr. and Info. Tech. Assn. (pres. 1987-88), OCLC Users Coun. (del. 1990-94, pres. 1991-92), IBM (info. steering com. 1994-95, higher edn. adv. coun. 1995—), Beta Phi Mu. Home: 6 Dearing Pl 420 Waddell St Athens GA 30605-1070 Office: Univ of Georgia Libraries Athens GA 30602

POTTER, WILLIAM JAMES, investment banker; b. Toronto, Ont., Can., Aug. 11, 1948; s. William Wakely and Ruby Loretta (Skidmore) P.; m. Linda Lee, Nov. 25, 1972; children: Meredith Lee, Andrew David. AB, Colgate U., 1970; MBA, Harvard U., 1974. With White Weld & Co., Inc., N.Y.C., 1974-75; Toronto Dominion Bank, Toronto (Can.) and N.Y., 1975-78; group mgr. Toronto Dominion Bank, Toronto, 1979-82; 1st v.p. Barclays Bank PLC, N.Y.C., 1982-84; mng. dir. Prudential-Bache Securities, Inc., N.Y.C., 1984-89; pres. Ridgewood Ptnrs. Ltd., N.Y.C., 1989—; advisor Ladenberg Thalman Internat., 1990-92, Laidlaw Holdings, Inc., 1992-93; bd. dirs. 1st Australia Fund Inc., Md., 1st Australia Prime Income Fund Inc., Md., 1st Australia Prime Income Co. Ltd., New Zealand, Heartland Fin. Corp., Impulsora del Fondo Mex., Mexico City, Alexandria Bancorp, Can., Battery Techs. Inc., Can., 1st Commonwealth Fund, Md., Compuflex Inc., Del. Author: Finance for the Minerals Industry, 1985. Bd. dirs. Glen Ridge (N.J.) Community Fund, 1985—; fin. mem. Glen Ridge Congl. Ch., 1985—; trustee Glen Ridge Ednl. Found., 1994—. Mem. Nat. Fgn. Trade Coun. (bd. dirs., chmn. fin. com.), Harvard Club, Williams Club (N.Y.C.), Nat. Club (Toronto), Glen Ridge Country Club (N.J.), Buck Hill Country Club (Pa.), Capitol Hill Club (Washington), Internat. Platform Assn. (Washington). Congregationalist. Avocations: golf, tennis. Office: Ridgewood Ptnrs Ltd 156 W 56th St New York NY 10019-3800

POTTIE, ROSWELL FRANCIS, science and technology consultant; b. St. Peter's, N.S., Can., Oct. 28, 1933; s. John Henry and Margaret Mary (Landry) P.; m. Huguette Lacoste, Aug. 18, 1989; children: Michael F., Gregory J., Lisa M., David S. BS in Chemistry summa cum laude, St. Francis Xavier Univ., 1954; PhD in Chemistry, Notre Dame U., 1958. Postdoctoral fellow Notre Dame (Ind.) U., 1957-58, E.I. Du Pont de Nemours, Inc., Wilmington, Del., 1960-64; postdoctoral fellow NRC Can., Ottawa, 1958-60, research officer, 1964-74, asst. to sr. v.p., 1976-80; Atlantic regional dir. NRC Can., Halifax, N.S., 1980-83; v.p. regional labs. NRC Can., Ottawa, 1983-84, v.p. physical scis. and engring., 1984-86, sr. v.p. labs., 1986-87, exec. v.p. 1987-91; pvt. cons., 1991—; program officer Ministry of State for Sci. and Tech. (secondment), Ottawa, 1974-75; program analyst Treasury Bd. Can. (secondment), Ottawa, 1975-76; bd. govs. Ctr. for Cold Regions Resources Engring., St. John's; mem. N.B. (Can.) Research and Productivity Council, Fredericton, 1981—. Contbr. articles to profl. jours. Coach, exec. baseball, swimming and soccer clubs, Gloucester, Ont., 1970-76; pres. Gloucester Swim Club, 1973-75; exec. North Gloucester Recreation Assn. 1971-74. Recipient Gov. Gen.'s medal, St. Francis Xavier U., 1954. Mem. Can. Research Mgmt. Assn., St. Francis Xavier Alumni Assn. (Ottawa pres. 1970-73), Sigma Xi. Roman Catholic. Avocations: swimming, badminton, carpentry, ancient history. Home: RR 1, Head of Jeddore, NS Canada B0J 1P0

POTTORFF, JO ANN, state legislator; b. Wichita, Kans., Mar. 7, 1936; d. John Edward McCluggage and Helen Elizabeth (Alexander) Ryan; m. Gary Nial Pottorff; children: Michael Lee, George Nial. BA, Kansas State U., 1957; MA, St. Louis U., 1969. Elem. tchr. Pub. Sch., Keats and St. George, 1957-59; cons., elem. specialist Mid Continent Regional Edn. Lab., Kansas City, Mo., 1971-73; cons. Poindexter Assocs., Wichita, 1975; campaign mgr. Garner Shriver Congl. Camp, Wichita, 1976; interim dir. Wichita Area Rape Ctr., 1977; conf. coord. Biomedical Synergistics Inst., Wichita 1977-79; real estate sales asst. Chester Kappelman Group, Wichita, 1979—; state rep. State of Kans., Topeka, 1985—. Mem. sch. bd. Wichita Pub. Schs., 1977-85; bd. dirs. Edn. Consol. and Improvement Act Adv. com., Kans. Found. for the Handicapped; mem. Children and Youth Adv. com. (bd. dirs.); active Leadership Kans.; chairperson women's network Nat. Conf., State Legislators; mem. Wichita Children's Home Bd. Recipient Disting. Svc. award Kans. Assn. Sch. Bds., 1983, Outstanding Svc. to Sch. Children of Nation award Coun. Urban Bds., 1984, awards Gov.'s Conf. for Prevention of Child Abuse and Neglect, Kans. Assn. Reading. Mem. Leadership Am. Alumnae (bd. dirs., sec.), Found. for Agrl. in Classroom (bd. dirs.), Jr. League, Vet. Aux. (pres.), Bd. Nat. State Art Agys., Rotary, Chi Omega (pres.). Avocations: politics, traveling. Office: Chester Kappelman Group PO Box 8036 Wichita KS 67208-0036

POTTRUCK, DAVID STEVEN, brokerage house executive; b. 1948. BA, U. Pa., 1970, MBA, 1972. Now pres., CEO U.S. Govt., 1972-74; with Arthur Young & Co., 1974-76, sr. cons.; with Citibank N.Am., 1976-81, v.p.; with Shearson/Am. Express, 1981-84, sr. v.p. consumer mktg. and advt.; with Charles Schwab & Co., San Francisco, 1984—; exec. v.p. mktg., dir. adminstr. Charles Schwab and Co., Inc.; pres., CEO The Charles Corp., Charles Schwab & Co.; pres., COO The Charles Schwab Corp. Office: Charles Schwab & Co Inc 101 Montgomery St San Francisco CA 94104-4122

POTTS, ANNIE, actress; b. Nashville, Oct. 28, 1952. Student, Calif. Inst. of Arts; BFA, Stephens Coll. Appeared in films including Corvette Summer, 1978, King of the Gypsies, 1978, Heartaches, 1982, Crime of Passion, 1984, Ghostbusters, 1984, Stick, 1985, Pretty in Pink, 1986, Jumpin' Jack Flash, 1986, Pass the Ammo, 1988, Who's Harry Crumb, 1989, Ghostbusters II, 1989, Texasville, 1990, Breaking the Rules, 1992; plays include Richard III, Charley's Aunt, Cymbeline; TV appearances include Black Market Baby, 1977, Flatbed Annie and Sweetie Pie: Lady Truckers, 1979, Cowboy, 1983, Why Me?, 1984, Ladies in Waiting; TV series include Goodtime Girls, 1980, Designing Women, 1986-1993, Love and War, 1993-95 (Emmy nomination, Lead Actress - Comedy Series, 1994). Spokesperson Women for the Arthritis Found.; mem. aux. bd. MADD. Office: care Erwin Stoff 7920 Sunset Blvd Ste 350 Los Angeles CA 90046*

POTTS, BARBARA JOYCE, historical society executive; b. L.A., Feb. 18, 1932; d. Theodore Thomas and Helen Mae (Kelley) Elledge; m. Donald A. Potts, Dec. 27, 1953; children: Tedd, Douglas, Dwight, Laura. AA, Graceland Coll., 1951; grad. Radiol. Tech. Sch., 1953; grad. program for sr. execs. in state and local govt., Harvard U., 1989. Radiol. technician Independence (Mo.) Sanitarium and Hosp., 1953, 58-59, Mercy Hosp., Balt., 1954-55; city coun. mem.-at-large City of Independence, 1978-82, mayor, 1982-90; exec. dir. Jackson County Hist. Soc., 1991—; chmn. Mid-Am. Regional Coun., Kansas City, Mo., 1984-85; bd. dirs. Mo. Mcpl. League, Jefferson City, 1982-90, v.p., 1986-87, pres., 1987, 88; chmn. Mo. Commn. on Local Govt. Cooperation, 1985-90. Author: Independence, 1985. Mem. Mo. Gov.'s Conf. Edn., 1976, Independence Charter Rev. Bd., 1977; bd. dirs. Hope House Shelter Abused Women, Independence, 1982—; Vis. Nurses Assn., 1990-93, Mid-Continent Coun. U.S. Girl Scouts, 1991-95; pres. Child Placement Svcs., Independence 1972-89, Greater Kans. City region NCCJ, 1990—; trustee Independence Regional Health Ctr., 1982-90, 94—, Park Coll., 1989—, chmn. bd. trustees, 1995—; mem. Nat. Women's Polit. Caucus, 1978—; mem. adv. bd. Greater Mo. Focus on Leadership, mem. steering com., 1989—; bd. mem. Independence Cmty. Found., 1990—. Recipient George Lehr Meml. award for community svc., 1989, Woman of Achievement award Mid-Continent coun. Girl Scouts U.S.A., 1983, 75th Anniversary Women of Achievement award Mid-Continent coun. Girl Scouts, 1987, Jane Adams award Hope House 1984, Community Leadership award Comprehensive Mental Health Svcs., Inc., 1984, 90, Graceland Coll. Alumni Disting. Svc. award 1991, Disting. Citizen award Independence C. of

C., 1993, Outstanding Community Svc. award Jackson County Inter-Agy. Coun., 1994; named Friend of Edn. Indpendence NEA, 1990. Mem. LWV (Community Svc. award 1990), Am. Inst. Pub. Svc. (mem. bd. nominators), Nat. Trust for Hist. Preservation. Mem. Reorganized LDS Ch. Home: 18508 E 30th Ter S Independence MO 64057-1904

POTTS, DAVID MALCOLM, population specialist, administrator; b. Sunderland, Durham, Eng., Jan. 8, 1935; came to U.S., 1978; S. Ronald Windle and Kathleen Annie (Cole) P.; m. Carolina Mervia Days (div. 1979); children: Oliver, Sarah, Henry; m. Marcia Jaffe (dec. 1993); m. Martha Madison Campbell, Mar. 1995. M.A., St. Catherine's Coll., Cambridge, Eng., 1960; M.B., B.Chir., Univ. Coll. Hosp., London, 1962; Ph.D., Sidney Sussex Coll., Cambridge U., 1965. Intern North Middlesex Hosp., London, 1962-64; fellow Sidney Sussex Coll., Cambridge, 1964-67; med. dir. Internat. Planned Parenthood Fedn., London, 1968-78; pres. Family Health Internat., Research Triangle Park, N.C., 1978-91; Bixby prof. of Fam. Planning and Population U of Calif., Berkeley, Calif., 1991—; dir. Population Services Internat., Washington, Alan Guttmacher Inst., N.Y.C.; Tracey Maund lectr. Women's Hosp., Melbourne, Australia, 1989. Author: Abortion, 1977, Society and Fertility, 1979, Childbirth in Developing Countries, 1983, Textbook of Contraceptive Practice, 1984; mem. editorial bd. Jour. Biosocial Sci. Recipient Hugh Moore award Population Crisis Com., 1972. Fellow Zool. Soc. Eng.; mem. Internat. Union for Sci. Study of Population. Avocations: history; writing. Home: 3416 Chris Ln San Mateo CA 94403

POTTS, DOUGLAS GORDON, neuroradiologist; b. New Zealand, Jan. 27, 1927; came to U.S., 1960, naturalized, 1966; s. Leslie Andrew and Vera (Morgan) P.; m. Ann Jean Frank, June 16, 1962; children: David Andrew, Kenneth Morgan, Alison Jean. B.Sc., Canterbury Univ. Coll., Christchurch, New Zealand, 1946; M.B., Ch.B., U. Otago, Dunedin, New Zealand, 1951; M.D., U. New Zealand, 1960. Intern Auckland (New Zealand) Hosp., 1952-53, resident radiology, 1957-58; resident Central Middlesex Hosp., London, Eng., 1957-58; sr. registrar Atkinson Morley's Hosp., London, Eng., 1958-59, Nat. Hosp., London, Eng., 1959-60; radiologist Presbyn. Hosp., N.Y.C., 1960-67, N.Y. Hosp., 1967-85; prof. radiology Cornell U. Med. Coll., 1970-85; prof., chmn. dept. radiology U. Toronto, Ont., Can., 1985-91; ret., 1992. Author: (with Pool) Aneurysms and Arteiovenous Anomalies of the Brain, 1965; Editor: (with T.H. Newton) Radiology of the Skull and Brain, Vol. 1, 1971, Vol. 2, 1974, Vol. 3, 1977, Vol. 4, 1978, Vol. 5, 1981, Modern Neuroradiology, Vols. 1 and 2, 1983. Mem. Am. Soc. Neuroradiology (pres. 1970-71).

POTTS, ERWIN REA, newspaper executive; b. Pineville, N.C., Apr. 20, 1932; s. Jennings Bryan and Edith Maxine (Matthews) P.; m. Silvia Antuna Montalbo, Feb. 18, 1961; children: Matthew Kingsley, Jeffrey Manuel, Bryan Erwin (dec.). Student, Mars Hill (N.C.) Jr. Coll., 1950-52; A.B. in Journalism, U. N.C., 1954. Reporter, editor Knight Newspapers, Miami, Fla., 1958-70; city editor Miami Herald, 1967-70; v.p., gen. mgr. Tallahassee Democrat, 1970-73, Charlotte (N.C.) Observer, News, 1973-75; pres. McClatchy Newspapers (Sacramento Bee, Fresno Bee, Modesto Bee, Anchorage Daily News, Tri-City Herald, Tacoma News Tribune, Rock Hill Herald, Beaufort Gazette, Hilton Head Island Packet, 10 other newspapers), Sacramento, Calif., Wash., S.C., 1975—; chief exec. officer McClatchy Newspapers (Sacramento Bee, Fresno Bee, Modesto Bee, Anchorage Daily News, Tri-City Herald, Tacoma News Tribune, 13 other newspapers), Sacramento, Calif., Wash., S.C., 1989—. Bd. dirs. Nespaper Advt. Bur.; bd. visitors U. N.C. Sch. Journalism, Stanford U. Knight fellowships. With USMC, 1955-58. Mem. Calif. Newspaper Pubs. Assn., Am. Newspaper Assn. (govt. affairs com.), API (regional adv. bd.). Office: Mc Clatchy Newspapers PO Box 15779 2100 Q St Sacramento CA 95852 also: The Modesto Bee PO Box 3928 1325 H St Modesto CA 95354-2427*

POTTS, GERALD NEAL, manufacturing company executive; b. Franklin, N.C., Apr. 10, 1933; s. Joseph Thomas and Virgie (Bryant) P.; m. Ann Eliza Underwood, Dec. 21, 1956 (div. 1991); children: Catherine, Thomas, Alice. B.S., U. N.C., 1954; grad., Advanced Mgmt. Program, Harvard, 1973. With Vulcan Mold & Iron Co., Chgo., 1957-59; sales engr. Vulcan Mold & Iron Co., 1959-62; gen. sales mgr. Vulcan Mold & Iron Co., Latrobe, Pa., 1963-65; v.p. sales Vulcan Mold & Iron Co., 1965-68; v.p. Vulcan, Inc., Latrobe, 1968-72; exec. v.p. Vulcan, Inc., 1972-73, pres., 1973-85, chief exec. officer, 1977-85, chmn., 1981-85; group exec. Teledyne Inc., 1985-92; pres. Woodings Verona Tool Works Inc., 1993—; Active Young Pres.'s Orgn., 1973-83. Bd. dirs. Latrobe Area Hosp., 1967—, chmn., 1985-88; trustee Greater Latrobe Community Chest, 1970-87, pres., 1978-79; adv. bd. U. Pitts. at Greensburg, 1974-80; trustee Seton Hill Coll., Greensburg, 1978-80. Served with AUS, 1954-56. Mem. Laurel Valley Golf Club, Rolling Rock Club, Duquesne Club (Pa.), Masons (32 deg.), Shriners, Chi Phi. Office: PO Box 126 Verona PA 15147

POTTS, JOHN THOMAS, JR., physician, educator; b. Phila., Jan. 19, 1932; married; 3 children. B.A., LaSalle Coll, Phila., 1953; M.D., U. Pa., Phila., 1957. From intern to asst. resident in medicine Mass. Gen. Hosp., Boston, 1957-59; resident Nat. Heart Inst., 1959-60, research fellow in medicine, 1960-63, sr. research staff, 1963-66, head sect. polypeptide hormones, 1966-68; chief endocrine unit Mass. Gen. Hosp., Boston, 1968-81, chief gen med. svc., 1981—; from asst. to assoc. prof. medicine Harvard U. Med. Sch., Boston, 1968-75, prof., 1975-81, Jackson prof. clin. medicine, 1981—; chief endocrine unit Mass. Gen. Hosp., Boston, 1968-81, chief gen. med., 1981—. Recipient Ernest Oppenheimer award, Andre Lichwitz prize Endocrine Soc., 1968, Fred Conrad Koch award Endocrine Soc., 1991, William F. Neumann award Am. Soc. Bone and Mineral Rsch. Fellow AAAS; mem. Am. Soc. Biol. Chemistry, Endocrine Soc. (pres. 1987), Assn. Am. Physicians, Am. Fedn. Clin. Research, Am. Soc. Clin. Investigation, Inst. Medicine. Office: Mass Gen Hosp Med Svcs Med Svcs Fruit St Boston MA 02114-2620

POTTS, KEVIN T., emeritus chemistry educator; b. Sydney, Australia, Oct. 26, 1928; married; children: Mary Ellen, Jeannette, Karen, Susan. B.Sc., U. Sydney, 1950, M.Sc., 1951; D. of Philosophy in Organic Chemistry, Oxford U., Eng., 1954, D.Sc., 1973. Demonstrator chemistry U. Sydney, 1950, teaching fellow, 1951; research asst. organic chemistry Oxford U., 1951-54; scientist Med. Research Council of Eng., 1954-56; research asst. organic chemistry Harvard, 1956-58; lectr. Adelaide, 1958-61; asso. prof. chemistry U. Louisville, 1961-65; assoc. prof. Rensselaer Poly. Inst., 1965-66; prof. chemistry Rensselaer Poly. Inst., 1966-94; prof. emeritus Rensselaer Poly Inst., 1994—; chmn. dept. Rensselaer Poly. Inst., 1973-80. Contbr. articles in field organic chemistry to sci. jours. Grantee Nat. Cancer Inst., Nat. Heart Inst., Dept. Energy, NSF, Am. Chem. Soc.-Petroleum Rsch. Fund. Mem. AAAS, Am. Chem. Soc., Brit. Chem. Soc., Royal Soc. Chemistry. Home: 102 Pelican Cove Sneads Ferry NC 28460-9520 Office: Rensselaer Poly Inst Dept Chemistry 110 Eighth Troy NY 12180

POTTS, RAMSAY DOUGLAS, lawyer, aviator; b. Memphis, Oct. 24, 1916; s. Ramsay Douglas and Ann Clifton (VanDyke) P.; m. Veronica Hamilton Raynor, Dec. 22, 1945 (dec. May 1993); children: Ramsay Douglas, David Hamilton, Lesley Ann, Lindsay Veronica. B.S., U. N.C., 1941; LL.B., Harvard U., 1948. Bar: Tenn. 1948, D.C. 1954, U.S. Supreme Ct. 1957. Commd. 2d lt. USAAF, 1941, advanced through grades to maj. gen. Res., 1961; various combat and operational assignments (8th Air Force and Air Force Res.), 1942-60; chmn. Air Force Res. Policy Com., 1967-68; practice of law Washington, 1955—; spl. asst. to chmn. Nat. Security Resources Bd., 1951; pres. Ind. Mil. Air Transport Assn., 1952-55; ptnr. Shaw, Pittman, Potts & Trowbridge, 1956-86; sr. counsel Shaw, Pittman, Potts & Trowbridge, Washington, 1986—. Publisher: Air Power History, 1989-93; contbr. articles to profl. jours. Mem. State Council Higher Edn. for Va., 1968-71; Trustee Air Force Hist. Found., pres., 1971-75; pres. Washington Area Tennis Patrons Found., 1984-87; vice-chmn. Physicians for Peace 1989—. Decorated D.S.C., other combat decorations. Mem. Am., D.C. bar assns., Phi Beta Kappa. Clubs: City Tavern (Washington), Metropolitan (Washington); Harvard (N.Y.C.); Army Navy Country (Arlington, Va.); Internat. Lawn Tennis Club of U.S., Gt. Brit., India. Home: 21808 27th St N Arlington VA 22207-4921 Office: Shaw Pittman Potts & Trowbridge 2300 N St NW Washington DC 20037-1122

POTTS, ROBERT LESLIE, academic administrator; b. Huntsville, Ala., Jan. 30, 1944; s. Frank Vines and Helen Ruth (Butler) P.; m. Irene Elisabeth

Johansson, Aug. 22, 1965; children: Julie Anna, Robert Leslie. Student Newbold Coll., Eng., 1963-64; BA, So. Coll., 1966; JD, U. Ala., 1969; LLM, Harvard U., 1971. Law clk. to chief judge U.S. Dist. Ct. (no. dist.) Ala., 1969-70; researcher Herrick, Smith, Donald, Farley & Ketchum, Boston, 1970-71; lectr. Boston U., 1971, U. Ala., 1973-75, 88; ptnr. Potts & Young, Florence, Ala., 1971-84; gen. counsel U. Ala. System, 1984-89, pres. U. North Ala., 1990—; active Nat. Adv. Com. on Instnl. Quality and Integrity, 1994—; bd. dirs. Bank Ind., Florence, 1975-85; adv. com. Rules Civil Procedure, Ala. Supreme Ct., 1973-88; mem. Ala. Bd. Bar Examiners, 1973-79, chmn., 1983-86; trustee Nat. Conf. Bar Examiners, 1986—, chmn., 1994—, Ala. State U., 1976-79, Oakwood Coll., 1978-81; pres. Ala. Higher Edn. Loan Corp., 1988-93. Mem. ABA, Ala. Bar Assn. (pres. young lawyers sect. 1979-80). Contbr. numerous articles to profl. jours., edn. and schs. Office: U North Ala University Station Florence AL 35632

POTTS, SIMON, record company executive; b. Newcastle-upon-Tyne, Tyne and Wear, Eng., Jan. 26, 1953; came to U.S., 1987; s. Alan and Doreen Helen (Etheridge) P. Diploma in art and design, Newcastle Art Coll., 1972. Sales rep. ABC Records, London, 1978-79; promotion mgr. Arista Records, London, 1979, div. dir., 1980-85; mng. dir. Elektra Records, London, 1985-86; sr. divisional v.p. Capitol Records, Los Angeles, 1987—. Anglican. Home: 8700 Hollywood Blvd West Hollywood CA 90069-1418 Office: Capitol Records 1750 Vine St Los Angeles CA 90028-5247

POTTS, STEPHEN DEADERICK, lawyer; b. Memphis, Nov. 20, 1930; s. Ramsay Douglas and Anne (Van Dyke) P.; m. Irene Potter, Mar. 14, 1953; children: Lori Potts-Dupre, Stephen Deaderick Jr., Stacy Potts Krogh. AB, Vanderbilt U., 1952, LLB, 1954. Bar: Tenn. 1954, D.C. 1961. Assoc. Farris, Evans & Evans, Nashville, 1957-61; ptnr. Shaw, Pittman, Potts & Trowbridge, Washington, 1961-90; dir. U.S. Office Gov. Ethics, Washington, 1990—; mem. Pres.'s Coun. on Integrity and Efficiency; mem. Adminstrv. Conf. of U.S. Past pres. Washington Tennis Patrons Found., 1970-72, Wood Acres Sch. PTA, 1972. 1st U. S. Army, 1954-57. Mem. ABA, U.S. Supreme Ct. Bar Assn., D.C. Bar Assn., Tenn. Bar Assn., Chevy Chase Club (bd. govs. 1982-86), Met. Club, U.S. Tennis Assn. (bd. dirs. won 5 nat., 1 internat. father/son championships, twice ranked 1st in U.S.). Methodist. Office: Of of Government Ethics 1201 New York Ave NW Washington DC 20005

POTTS, THOMAS H., trust company executive; b. 1949. BA, Princeton U., 1971; MBA, Stanford U., 1976. With Weyerhaeuser Co., Tacoma, 1976-79, Weyerhaeuser Real Estate, Tacoma, 1979-81; exec. v.p. CFO Am. Southwest Fin. Corp., Tucson, 1981-83; treas., v.p. Ryland Group, Columbia, Md., 1984-87; pres., CEO Resource Mortgage Capital, Columbia, Md., 1987—. Office: Resource Mortgage Capital 10500 Little Patuxent Pky Columbia MD 21044*

POTUZNIK, CHARLES LADDY, lawyer; b. Chgo., Feb. 11, 1947; s. Charles William and Laverne Frances (Zdenek) P.; m. Mary Margaret Quady, Jan. 2, 1988; children: Kylie Brommell, Kathryn Mary. BA with high honors, U. Ill., 1969; JD cum laude, Harvard U., 1973. Bar: Minn. 1973. Assoc. Dorsey & Whitney, Mpls., 1973-78, ptnr., 1979—. Mem. Minn. State Bar Assn. (chmn. state securities law subcom., 1987—), Hennepin County Bar Assn., Minn. Securities Adv. Com., Phi Beta Kappa. Mem. Evang. Free Ch. Avocations: hunting, fishing, camping, canoeing, foreign travel. Office: Dorsey & Whitney Pillsbury Ctr S 220 S 6th St Minneapolis MN 55402-4500

POTVIN, ALFRED RAOUL, engineering executive; b. Worcester, Mass., Feb. 5, 1942; s. Alfred Armand and Jacqueline (Morin) P.; m. Janet Holm, Mar. 20, 1965. BEE, Worcester Poly. Inst., 1964; MEE, Stanford U., 1965, Engr. in EE, 1967; MS in Bioengring., U. Mich., 1970, M.S. in Psychology, 1970, PhD in Bioengring., 1971. Registered profl. engr., Tex. Asst. prof. elec. engring. U. Tex., Arlington, 1968-69, assoc. prof. biomed. engring. and elec. engring., 1971-76, prof., 1976-84; chmn. biomed. engring. U. Tex., 1972-84; dir. med. instrumentation systems research div. Eli Lilly & Co., Indpls., 1984-90, dir. tech. assessment and project mgmt., 1990-92; dir. engring., med. devices and diagnostics divsn., 1992-93; prof. elec. engring. Purdue Sch. Engring. and Tech., Ind. U.-Purdue U., Indpls., 1993—; dean Ind. U.-Purdue U., Indpls., 1993—; faculty fellow, life scientist, cons. NASA, Houston, 1972-76, NASA and Moffett Field, 1974-76; clin. prof. biophysics U. Tex. Health Sci. Ctr., Dallas, 1967-84; mem. phys. med. device panel FDA, Washington, 1978-84; mem. adv. bd., reviewer Biomed. Engring. NSF, Washington, 1983-89, 92—; founding dir. Ctr. Advanced Rehab. Engring., 1983-84, mem. adv. bd., 1984-88; mem. adv. bd. Engring. Rsch. Ctrs. NSF, Washington, 1988-92, Biomed. Engr. Worcester Polytech. Inst., Mass., 1987—, Coll. Engrs. Duke U., Durham, N.C., 1987-94, U. Calif., Berkeley, 1989-92, Coll. Engrs. U. Denver, 1990-93, Sch. Engr. and Tech. Ind. U.-Purdue U., Indpls, 1992-93, med. engring. Jet Propulsion Lab., Pasadena, Calif., 1989; chmn. NIH Resource Ctr. Case Western Res. U., Cleve., 1988—; bd. advisors Sch. of Health and Rehab. Sci., U. Pitts., 1993—; mem. adv. com. NIH, 1993. Author: (with W.W. Tourtellotte) Quantitative Examination of Neurologic Functions, 1985; editl. bd. IEEE Spectrum, 1987-90, 92-95, Biomed. Sci. and Tech., 1990-93; co-editor spl. issue on biosensors IEEE Trans. on Biomed. Engring., 1986, spl. issue on status and future directions in biomed. engring. Medicine and Biol. Mag., 1989; mem. editl. bd. Biomed. Sci. and Tech., 1990-92. Mem. Masthead Property Owners Assn., Indpls., 1984—; Manasota Key Property Owners Assn., Englewood, Fla., 1985—. Recipient Life Scientist award NASA, 1974; spl. fellow NIH, 1968. Fellow IEEE (pres. Engring. in Medicine and Biology Soc. 1983, reelected 1984, gen. chmn. annual conf. 1982, chmn. health care engring. com. 1986, mem. editorial bd. spectrum 1987-89, 92-94, founding mem. steering com. symposium on computer based med. systems 1988-94, Centennial award 1984, co-editor spl. issue Medicine and Biology, 1989), Am. Inst. Med. and Biol. Engring. (bd. dirs. 1991-94, v.p. pub. awareness 1993-94, elected founding fellow 1992, co-pres. world congress on med. biological engring. in Chgo in the yr. 2000, 1993—), Houston Soc. Engrs. in Medicine and Biology (Career Achievement award 1993), Assn. Advancement of Med. Instrumentation; mem. Am. Soc. Engring. Edn. (chmn. biomed. engring. div. 1979-80), Biomed. Engring. Soc. (sr. mem. 1972-88, chmn. edn. and pub. affairs com. 1979-83), Alliance Engrs. in Medicine and Biology (v.p. nat. affairs 1987-89, pres. 1989-92), Assn. Advancement of Med. Instrumentation, Ind. Elec. Mfg. Assn. (bd. dirs. 1993—). Avocations: boating, travel, gourmet dining, skiing.

POTVIN, FELIX, professional hockey player; b. Anjou, Que., Canada, July 23, 1971. Goalie Chicoutimi, QMJHL, 1988-91, St. John's, AHL, 1991-92, Toronto Maple Leafs, 1991—. Recipient Goaltender of the Year Award, Can. Hockey League, 1990-91, Hap Emms Mem. Trophy, 1990-91, Jacques Plante Trophy, 1990-91, Shell Cup, 1990-91, Guy Lafleur Trophy, 1990-91, Baz Bastien Trophy, 1990-91, Dudley Garrett Mem. Trophy, 1991-92. All-Star first team goalie, QMJHL, 1990-91, All-Star first team goalie, AHL, 1991-92, All-Rookie Team, NHL, 1992-93. Office: Toronto Maple Leafs, 60 Carlton St, Toronto, ON Canada M5B 1L1

POTVIN, PIERRE, physiologist, educator; b. Quebec City, Que., Can., Jan. 5, 1932; s. Rosario and Eva (Montreuil) P.; m. Louise Dube, Aug. 31, 1963; children: Aline, Bernard. BA, Laval U., 1950, MD, 1955; PhD, U. Toronto, 1962. Asst. prof. Faculty of Medicine Laval U., Quebec City, 1956-63, assoc. prof., 1963-68, prof., 1968—; vice dean exec., 1977-86, dean, 1986-94; v.p. Internat. Conf. of Deans of French-Speaking Faculties of Medicine, 1992—; hon. prof. Norman Bethune U. Med. Scis., Changchun, China, 1992. Assoc. editor Modern Medicine Can., 1958-61, Laval Med., 1962-70. Decorated comdr. Ordre Nat. des Palmes académiques (France), officer Ordre Nat. du Lion (Senegal). Fellow Royal Coll. Physicians and Surgeons Can.; mem. Can. Soc. Physiology. Roman Catholic. Avocation: painting. Home: 1915 Bourbonniere, Sillery, PQ Canada G1S 1N3 Office: Laval U Faculty of Medicine, Dept Physiology, Quebec, PQ Canada G1K 7P4

POTVIN, RAYMOND HERVE, sociology educator, author; b. Southbridge, Mass., Oct. 28, 1924; s. Cleophas R. and Eva (Beauvais) P. S.T.B., U. Montreal, 1948; Ph.D., Catholic U. Am., 1958; DHL (hon.), Assumption Coll., 1993. Ordained priest Roman Cath. Ch., 1948; asst. pastor Springfield, Mass.; resrch team mem. faculty Cath. U., 1958—; prof. sociology, 1967—, chmn. dept., 1968-71, 77-83, asst. acad. v.p. for grad. programs, 1985-88; dir. Inst. Social and Behavioral Research, 1972-74; sr. researcher

Boys Town Center, 1974-88; Trustee Population Reference Bur., 1981-87, Center for Applied Research in the Apostolate, 1981-85; Fellow Population Council, 1966-67. Author: (with Charles Westoff) College Women and Fertility Values, 1967, (with Antanas Suziedelis) Seminarians of the Sixties, 1970, Vocational Challenge and Seminary Response, 1971, (with D. Hoge and H. Nelson) Religion and American Youth, 1976, (with Hart Nelson and Joseph Shields) The Religion of Children, 1977, Seminarians of the Eighties, 1986, (with P. Mucada) Seminary Outcomes: Perseverance and Withdrawal, 1990. Fellow Am. Sociol. Assn., Population Assn.; mem. Soc. Sci. Study of Religion. Office: Cath Univ Dept Sociology Washington DC 20064

POTVIN, SUZANNE HILDA, chief nurse; b. New Bedford, Mass., July 3, 1949; d. Wilfred E. and Irene L. (Bourgeois) P. BSN, St. Anselm's Coll.; MSN, Boston U. Cert. med.-surg. clin. specialist Am. Nurses Assn. Staff nurse R.G. Hosp., Providence, 1970—; staff nurse Calvary Hosp., Bronx, N.Y.; head nurse R.J. Hosp., Providence 1979; clin. specialist VA Med. Ctr., Brockton, Mass., 1979—; clin. coord. VA Med. Ctr.; assoc. prof. Stonehill Coll., Brockton; assoc. chief nurse trainee Nashville VA Med. Ctr., 1983-84; assoc. chief nurse VA Med. Ctr., Louisville, 1984-85; chief nurse VA Med. Ctr., 1985—; adj. faculty U. Louisville, 1984—, Spalding U., Louisville, 1984—. Mem. AONE, Greater Louisville Nurse Adminstrs., Sigma Theta Tau. Roman Catholic. Avocations: art, music, sports. Office: VA Med Ctr 800 Zorn Ave Louisville KY 40206-1499

POUGH, FREDERICK HARVEY, mineralogist; b. Bklyn., June 26, 1906; s. Francis H. and Alice H. (Beckler) P.; m. Eleanor C. Hodge, Oct. 14, 1938 (dec. May 1966); children: Frederick Harvey, Barbara Hodge. SB, Harvard, 1928, PhD, 1935; MS, Washington U., 1932; student, Ruperto Carola, Heidelberg, Germany, 1932-33. Asst. curator mineralogy Am. Mus. Natural History, N.Y.C., 1935-40; acting curator Am. Mus. Natural History, 1941, curator, 1942-44, curator phys. geology and mineralogy, 1942-52, cons. mineralogist, 1953-64, 66—; gem cons. Jewelers Circular-Keystone, 1940-85; dir. Santa Barbara Mus. Natural History, 1965-66; pres. Mineralogy, Inc., 1978—. Author: Jewelers Dictionary, 1945, 50, 76, Field Guide to Rocks and Minerals, 1953, 76, 95, All About Volcanoes and Earthquakes, 1953, Hindi translation, 1958, Persian translation, 1959, Bengali translation, 1959, Italian translation, 1960, Arabic translation, 1962, Portuguese translation, 1964, Our Earth, 1961, The Story of Gems and Semi-Precious Stones, 1967, Guide des Roches et Mineraux, 1969, 79, First Guide to Rocks and Minerals, 1991; contbg. editor: Lapidary jour., 1984—. Recipient Bronze medal Royal Geol. Soc., Belgium, 1948, Derby medal Brazilian Geol. Survey, Hanneman award for outstanding contbns. in lit. of mineralogy and gemology, 1988, Mineral. award Carnegie Mus. Nat. History, Pitts., 1989, Lifetime Achievement award Accredited Gemologist Assn., 1993; named Mineralogist of Yr., Am. Fedn. Mineral Soc., 1966. Fellow Mineral Soc. Am., Geol. Soc. Am.; mem. Mineral Soc. Gt. Britain, Gemmological Assn. All Japan (Am. rep. 1985—). Clubs: Harvard (N.Y.C.); Explorers. Address: PO Box 7004 Reno NV 89510-7004

POUL, FRANKLIN, lawyer; b. Phila., Nov. 6, 1924; s. Boris and Anna P.; m. Shirley Weissman, June 26, 1949; children—Leslie Paul Melman, Alan M., Laurie. Student, U. Pa., 1942-43, Haverford Coll. 1943-44; LL.B. cum laude, U. Pa., 1946. Bar: Pa. 1949, U.S. Supreme Ct. 1955. Asso. firm Gray, Anderson, Schaffer & Rome, Phila., 1948-56, Wolf, Block, Schorr and Solis-Cohen, Phila., 1956-60; partner Wolf, Block, Schorr and Solis-Cohen, 1960-93. Bd. dirs. ACLU, Phila., 1955-80, pres., 1975-76. Served with AUS, 1943-46. Mem. ABA, Am. Law Inst., Order of Coif. Office: Wolf Block Shorr & Solis-Cohen 12th Fl Packard Bldg SE Corner 15 Chestnut St Philadelphia PA 19122

POULIN, MARIE-PAULE, Canadian government official; b. Sudbury, Ont., Can., June 21, 1945; d. Alphonse-Emile and Lucille (Ménard) Charette; m. Bernard A. Poulin, May 21, 1977; children: Elaine, Valérie. BA, Laurentian U., Sudbury, 1966; MSW, U. Montréal, Que., Can., 1969; PhD (hon.), Laurentian U., Sudbury, 1995. Lectr. U. Montreal, 1969-70, Coll. of Gen. and Profl. Instrn., Hull, Que., 1972-73; rschr. Ctr. Social Svcs., Hull, 1972-73; interviewer, rschr. French Radio and TV, Ottawa, Ont., 1973-74; prodr. Sta. CBOF-CBC, Ottawa, 1974-78; founder and dir. svcs. in N.E. and N.W. Ont. Sta. CBON (French Network-CBC), Sudbury, 1978-83; exec. dir. regional programming CBC, Ottawa, 1983-84, assoc. v.p. regional broadcasting, 1984-88, sec. gen., 1988-90, v.p. human resources, 1990-92; dep. sec. for comm. and consultation The Privy Coun. Govt. of Can., Ottawa, 1992-93; chmn. Can. Artists and Prodrs. Profl. Rels. Tribunal, Ottawa, 1993—; bd. dirs. Cité Collégiale, Ottawa, 1988-91. Commr. for French lang. svcs. Province of Ont., 1986-89; regent U. Sudbury, 1981-83; bd. dirs. Laurentian Hosp., Sudbury, 1980-88, Cambrian Coll.Found., Sudbury, 1983-88; v.p. Art Ctr., Ottawa, 1988-90; pres. Regroupement gens d'affaires, Ottawa, 1991-92. Recipient medal for contbn. to Can. Culture, Coun. of French-Am. Life, 1987, Prix Marcel-Blouin for best morning program in Can., 1983, Profl. Woman of Yr. award Reseau des femmes d'affaires professionnelles, 1990. Mem. Assn. Grads. of U. Montréal, Can. Circle (exec.). Avocations: running, reading, swimming. Home: 100 Pretoria Ave, Ottawa, ON Canada K1S 1W9 Office: 240 Sparks St 8th Fl W, Ottawa, ON Canada K1A 1A1

POULIN, THOMAS EDWARD, marine engineer, state legislator, retail business owner; b. Waterville, Maine, Apr. 23, 1956; s. Donald Richard and Beatrice Delores (Berard) P.; m. Kim E. Marston, July 3, 1981; children: Elizabeth, Brittany, Chanelle. BS in Marine Engring., Maine Maritime Acad., 1978; cert. in tchg., U. Maine, Farmington, 1985. Various marine engring. positions Keystone, Sealand, Maritime Overseas Corp., and U.S. Lines, 1978—; math. tchr. Messalonshee H.S., Oakland, Maine, 1986-90; mem. Maine Ho. of Reps., Oakland and Sidney, 1990—. Mem. budget and adv. coms. Town of Oakland, 1988—, mem. recycling com., 1990—. Roman Catholic. Home: R 3 Box 1060 Oakland ME 04963

POULIOT, ASSUNTA GALLUCCI, business school owner and director; b. West Warwick, R.I., Aug. 14, 1937; d. Michael and Angelina (DeCesare) Gallucci; m. Joseph F. Pouliot Jr., July 4, 1961; children: Brenda, Mark, Jill, Michele. BS, U. R.I., 1959, MS, 1971. Bus. tchr. Cranston High Sch., R.I., 1959-61; bus. dept. chmn. Chariho Regional High Sch., Wood River Junction, R.I., 1961-73; instr. U. R.I., Kingston, 1973-78; founder, dir. Ocean State Bus. Inst., Wakefield, R.I., 1977—; dir. Fleet Nat. Bank, 1985-91; bd. mgrs. Bank of New Eng., 1984-85; commr. Accrediting Coun. Ind. Colls. and Schs., 1995—; speaker in field. Pres. St. Francis Women's Club, Wakefield, 1975; sec. St. Francis Parish Coun., Wakefield, 1980; mem. Econ. Devel. Commn., Wakefield, 1981-85; mem. South County Hosp. Corp., Wakefield, 1978—; fin. dir. Bus and Profl. Women's Club, Wakefield, 1982-84; chmn. Ladies Golf Charity, 1985-91; mem. Computer Info. Systems Com., Chariho Regional Career and Tech. Ctr.; bd. dirs., treas. Galilee Beach Club Assn. Mem. R.I. Bus. Edn. Assn. (newsletter editor 1979-81), New Eng. Bus. Coll. Assn. (sec. 1984-86, pres. 1985-87), R.I. Assn. Career and Tech. Schs. (treas., bd. dirs. 1979-), Eastern Bus. Edn. Assn. (conf. leader), Nat. Bus. Edn. Assn. (conf. leader), Career Coll. Assn. (conv. speaker, pub. rels. com., govt. rels. com., membership com., key mem., nominating com., evaluator), Assn. Colls. and Schs. (COPSA commr. 1994—), R.I. Women's Golf Assn. Am. Cancer Soc. (R.I. Alumi Assn. (Excellence Bus. award 1992), Phi Kappa Phi, Delta Pi Epsilon (pres., newsletter editor). Roman Catholic. Club: Point Judith Country (past ladies golf chmn.). Avocations: golf, gardening. Home: 137 Kenyon Ave Wakefield RI 02879-4242 Office: Ocean State Bus Inst Mariner Sq Boxes 1&2 140 Point Judith Rd Narragansett RI 02882

POULOS, GARY PETER, school system administrator. Dir. Union High Sch. Dist., San Mateo, Calif. Recipient Blue Ribbon Sch. award U.S. Dept. Edn., 1990-91. Office: Union High Sch Dist 605 N Delaware St San Mateo CA 94401-1731

POULOS, MICHAEL JAMES, insurance company executive; b. Glens Falls, N.Y., Feb. 13, 1931; s. James A. and Mary Poulos; m. Mary Kay Leslie; children: Denise, Peter. Ba, Colgate U., 1953; MBA, NYU, 1963. CLU, 1970. With sales and mgmt. U.S. Life Ins. Co., N.Y.C., 1958-70, sec., treas. dir. 1968, v.p adminstrn., 1969, mem. exec. com., 1970; with Calif.-Western States Life Ins. Co., Sacramento, 1970-79, pres., chief exec. officer, 1975-79, dir., 1975; with Am. Gen. Corp., Houston, 1979-83, sr. v.p. div. head life ins., 1979-81, pres., 1981-91; mem. exec. com., dir. Am. Gen. Corp., 1981-93, vice chmn., 1991-93. Mem. Sam Houston Area coun. Boy Scouts

Am. Mem. Am. Soc. CLU's, Nat. Assn. Life Underwriters, Houston Assn. Life Underwriters, Am. Mgmt. Assn., Heritage Club, The Houstonian Club. Greek Orthodox. Office: Am Gen Corp PO Box 3247 2929 Allen Pky Houston TX 77019-2119

POULOS-WOOLLEY, PAIGE M., public relations executive; b. Woodland, Calif., Apr. 26, 1958; d. Paul William Jr. and Frances Marie (Gibson) Poulos; m. John Stuart Woolley, Jr., Feb. 3, 1990. Student, U. Calif., Davis, 1977-80. Mgr. pub. rels. Somerset Wine Co. N.Y.C. and San Martin, Calif., 1982-88; dir. comm. The Beverage Source, San Francisco, 1988-89, Rutherford (Calif.) Hill Winery, 1989-90; pres. Paige Poulos Comm. Berkeley, Calif., 1990—; founder, chmn. WINECOM, 1992—. Pub. rels. editor: Practical Winery & Vineyards, 1994—; wine editor Focus Mag. Mem. Pub. Rels. Soc. Am. (bd. dirs. 1993—, sec. 1994, pres.-elect East Bay chpt. 1994-95, editor newsletter food and beverage sect. 1993-94), Women in Comm., Acad. Wine Comm. (program chair 1994), Internat. Assn. Bus. Communicators. Republican. Episcopalian. Avocations: horseback riding, needlework, skiing, gardening. Office: Paige Poulos Comm PO Box 8087 Berkeley CA 94707

POULSON, HOWARD D., agricultural products company executive. Vice chmn. bd. Growmark, Inc., Bloomington, Ill. Office: Growmark Inc 1701 N Towanda Ave Bloomington IL 61701-2040

POULSON, RICHARD JASPER METCALFE, lawyer; b. Elizabeth City, N.C., Sept. 4, 1938; s. Richard Jasper and Dorothy (Morse) P.; m. Anne Keenan, Dec. 21, 1963 (div. 1976); m. Anne Dare Wrenn, Sept. 25, 1993. BA, U. Va., 1960; JD, Am. U., 1968; ML in Taxation, Georgetown U., 1970. Bar: Va. 1968, D.C. 1969, U.S. Supreme Ct. 1976. V.p. Am. Security & Trust Co., Washington, 1968-70; assoc. Hogan & Hartson, Washington, 1970-73, ptnr., 1973-94; sr. ptnr. Hogan & Hartson, London, 1990-93; chmn. Rapidan Capital Ptnrs., 1994—; CEO, sr. mng. dir. The Appian Group, Washington, 1995—; adj. prof. Georgetown U. Law Ctr., 1971-78; lectr. Law and Fgn. Svc. Schs. Georgetown U.; internat. advisor in field; active Euro-Arab Conciliation and Arbitration System. Trustee, bd. mgrs., U. Va., Charlottesville, 1992—, v.p., 1994-95, pres., 1995—; dir., chmn. exec. com. Mary & Daniel Loughran Found., Washington, 1976—; chmn., dir. Montpelier Steeplechase Found., Orange, Va., 1991—; chmn., trustee U.S. Rugby Football Found., Boston, 1988—. 1st lt. USAR, 1961-63. Mem. Law Society of England and Wales, Metro. Club, Farmington Country Club, Norfolk Yacht Club, Keswick Country Club. Republican. Episcopalian. Avocations: horseback riding, hunting, steeplechase racing, thoroughbred breeding. Home: Hare Forest Farm Orange VA 22960 Office: The Appian Group 9th Fl 1455 Pennsylvania Ave NW Washington DC 20004

POULSON, ROBERT DEAN, lawyer; b. Valparaiso, Ind., June 10, 1927; s. Frank Ferlin and Esther Marie P.; m. Betty Lou Caroline Mercer, Aug. 19, 1950 (dec.); children: Richard D., Thomas C., John R. LL.B., Drake U., 1953, J.D., 1974. Bar: Iowa 1953, Ill. 1954, Colo. 1957. Staff atty. Texaco, Chgo. and Denver, 1953-59; divisional atty. Superior Oil Co., Denver, 1959-64; sr. ptnr. firm Poulson, Odell & Peterson, Denver, 1964—. Mem. Bow Mar City Council, Colo., 1968-72. Served with USN, 1945-47. Mem. Denver, Arapahoe County (Colo.), Colo., Am. bar assns., Rocky Mountain Mineral Law Found. (pres. 1975-76, trustee 1965—), Rocky Mountain Oil and Gas Assn. (chmn. gen. legal com. 1963-66, trustee 1963—), Ind. Petroleum Assn. Am. (dir.), Phi Alpha Delta. Masons. Methodist. Clubs: Univ. (Denver); Masons. Home: 5455 Lakeshore Dr Littleton CO 80123-1542 Office: 1775 Sherman St Ste 1400 Denver CO 80203-4316

POULTER, CHARLES DALE, chemist, educator, consultant; b. Monroe, La., Aug. 29, 1942; s. Erwin and Mary Helen Poulter; m. Susan Raetzsch, Aug. 24, 1964; children: Mary Christa, Gregory Thomas. BS, La. State U., Baton Rouge, 1964; PhD, U. Calif., Berkeley, 1967. NIH postdoctoral fellow UCLA, 1967-68; asst. prof. chemistry U. Utah, Salt Lake City, 1969-75, assoc. prof., 1975-78, prof., 1978-94, John A. Wittsoe prof. chemistry, 1994—; cons. Amoco Rsch. Ctr., Naperville, Ill., 1985-90, Merck Sharp & Dohme, Rahway, N.J., 1986-90, Bristol-Myers Squibb, Princeton, N.J., 1989-93, Zeneca Ag Products, Richmond, Calif., 1993—. Fellow AAAS; mem. Am. Chem. Soc. (organic exec. com. 1983-86, biol. div. councillor 1993-95, Ernest Guenther award 1991, Utah award 1992). Office: U Utah Dept Chemistry Salt Lake City UT 84112-1102

POULTON, BRUCE ROBERT, former university chancellor; b. Yonkers, N.Y., Mar. 7, 1927; s. Alfred Vincent and Ella Marie (Scanlon) P.; m. Elizabeth Charlotte Jerothe, Aug. 26, 1950; children: Randall Lee, Jeffrey Jon, Cynthia Sue, Peter Gregory. B.S. with honors, Rutgers U., 1950, M.S., 1952, Ph.D., 1956; LL.D., U. N.H. Research instr., then asst. prof. Rutgers U., 1952-56; assoc. prof., then prof., chmn. dept. animal and vet. sci. U. Maine, 1958-66, dir. Bangor Campus, 1967-68, dean, dir. Coll. Life Scis. and Agr., 1968-71, v.p. research and pub. service, 1971-75; chancellor Univ. System N.H., 1975-82, also trustee; chancellor N.C. State U., Raleigh, 1982-89; vis. prof. Mich. State U., 1966-67; mem. regional adv. com. Farm and Home Administrn.; mem. exec. com., council on research policy and grad. edn. Nat. Assn. State Univs. and Land Grant Colls.; also mem. senate; mem. Gov.'s Econ. Advisory Council, N.H.; mem. selection com. Kellogg Found.; Lectureship in agr.; chmn. Rhodes scholarship com. for. N.H.; mem. policy devel. com. New Eng. Innovation Group; adv. com. U.S. Command and Gen. Staff Coll. Author articles in field. Bd. dirs. Research Triangle Inst., Microelectronic Ctr., Triangle Univs. Ctr. Advanced Studies, Aubrey Brooks Found. Served with AUS, 1944-46. Am. Council Edn. fellow acad. adminstrn., 1966-67. Mem. Am Inst. Nutrition, Brit. Nutrition Soc., Fedn. Am. Soc. Exptl. Biology, Am. Soc. Exptl. Biology, Am. Soc. Animal Sci., Am. Dairy Sci. Assn. (past pres. Eastern div.), AAAS, Sigma Xi, Alpha Zeta. Office: NC State U Office of Chancellor Raleigh NC 27695

POULTON, CHARLES EDGAR, natural resources consultant; b. Oakley, Idaho, Aug. 2, 1917; s. Richard and Narrie Jane (Queen) P.; m. Marcile Belle McCoy, Sept. 29, 1939; children: Richard C., Robert J., Mary Jane Poulton Morris, Betty Jean Poulton Strong. B.S. with high honors, U. Idaho, 1939, M.S., 1948; postgrad., Mont. State Coll., 1946-47; Ph.D., Wash. State U., 1955; postdoctoral, U. Calif. at Berkeley, 1967-68. Administr., researcher U.S. Forest Service, Western states, 1937-46; dist. forest ranger U.S. Forest Service, 1941-46; cons. forest ecology U.S. Forest Service, Ala., Fla., 1958-59; asst. prof. range mgmt. Mont. State Coll., Bozeman, 1946-47; instr. range mgmt. U. Idaho, Moscow, 1947-49; prof., dir. range mgmt. program Oreg. State U., Corvallis, 1949-70; prof. range ecology Oreg. State U., 1970-73; dir. Environ. Remote Sensing Applications Lab., 1972-73; dir. range and resource ecology div. Earth Satellite Corp., Berkeley, Calif., 1974-75; sr. officer Rangeland Resources and Pasture, Food and Agr. Orgn. UN, Rome, Italy, 1976-77, 81; Cons., Benton County, Oreg.; (in land use planning), 1972-73, NASA, 1967-71; tng. officer, remote sensing of natural resources NASA-Ames Research Center, 1978-81; cons. natural resource mgmt., bus. devel., 1978—; developed new MS program in interdisciplinary natural resources devel. Asian Inst. of Tech., Bangkok, Thailand, 1986-87, coord. of program, 1987, project work in developing countries. Assoc. editor: Range Mgmt. Jour. Forestry, 1956-62; mem. editorial bd. Ecology, 1965-67; author chpts. to books, articles to profl. jours. Served with USNR, 1945-46. Recipient merit certificate for outstanding service to grassland agr. Am. Grassland Council, 1963. Fellow Soc. Range Mgmt. (charter, pres. Pacific N.W. sect. 1962, Outstanding Achievement award 1986); Mem. (nat. dir. 1965-68, com. on accreditation 1980-83, chmn. com. on internat. affairs 1983), Soc. Am. Foresters (chmn. range mgmt. div. 1955), Nat. Acad. Sci. (panels 1969, 73-74), Sigma Xi, Phi Eta Sigma, Xi Sigma Pi. Mem. Christian Ch. Home: PO Box 2081 Gresham OR 97030-0601

POUNCEY, PETER RICHARD, college president, classics educator; b. Tsingtao, Shantung, China, Oct. 1, 1937; came to U.S., 1964; s. Cecil Alan and Eugenie Marde (Lintilhac) P.; m. Bethanne McNally, June 25, 1966; 1 son, Christian; m. Susan Rieger, Mar. 21, 1973; 1 dau., Margaret; m. Katherine Dalsimer, June 9, 1990. Lic. Phil., Heythrop Coll., Eng. (1960); B.A., Oxford U., Eng. 1964, M.A., 1967; Ph.D., Columbia U., 1969; AM (hon.), Amherst Coll., 1985; LLD (hon.), Williams Coll., 1985; LHD (hon.), Doshisha U., 1987; LLD (hon.), Wesleyan U., Mass., 1989; LHD (hon.), Trinity Coll., 1990. Instr. classics Fordham U., Bronx, N.Y., 1964-67; asst. prof. Columbia U., N.Y.C., 1969-71, dean Columbia Coll., 1972-76, assoc.

prof., 1977-83, prof. classics, 1983-84; pres. Amherst (Mass.) Coll., Mass., 1984-94; pres. emeritus Amherst (Mass.) Coll., 1994—, prof. classics, 1994—; cons. classical lit. Columbia Ency., 1970-73; trustee Columbia Univ. Press, 1972-75. Author: The Necessities of War: A Study of Thucydides' Pessimism, 1980 (Lionel Trilling award 1981). Trustee Brit.-Am. Edn. Found., N.Y.C., 1971-75. Recipient Great Tchr. award Soc. Columbia Grads., 1983. Mem. Am. Philol. Assn., Phi Beta Kappa.

POUNCY, MARVA NELL, elementary education educator; b. Ft. Worth, Dec. 17, 1944; d. Lenzy Kert Pouncy and Lavada Cole. BS, Prairie View A&M U., 1967; student, Tex. Wesleyan Coll., Ft. Worth, 1968-69; MEd, Wayne State U., 1974; EdS, Ea. Mich. U., 1993. Cert. elem. tchr., Tex., Mich. Customer svc. clk. Ft. Worth Water Dept., 1968-69; tchr. Port Huron (Mich.) Area Schs., 1970-78; tchr. 6th grade Detroit Pub. Schs., 1978—. Mem. Justice, Unity, Generosity and Svc., Detroit, 1989; precinct del. Dem. Party, Detroit, 1990. Recipient Dedicted Tchr. award Bd. Edn., Detroit, 1988-89, Cert. of Appreicaiton, Gov. of Mich., 1990; recipient mini-grants, 1989, 90, 91, 92, 93; Renaissance Writign fellow, 1985. Mem. Met. Alliance of Black Sch. Educators, Nat. Assn. Negro Bus. and Profl. Women, Optimist Club, Phi Delta Kappa (exec. bd.), Dalta Kappa Gamma. Avocations: skating, planning social activities, dancing. Home: 1321 Orleans St Detroit MI 48207-2908

POUND, RICHARD WILLIAM DUNCAN, lawyer, accountant; b. St. Catharines, Ont., Can., Mar. 22, 1942; s. William Thomas and Jessie Edith Duncan (Thom) P.; m. Julie Houghton Keith, Nov. 4, 1977. B.Commerce, McGill U., Montreal, 1962, B.C.L., 1967; B.A.; Sir George Williams U. (now Concordia U.), Montreal, 1963; PhD (hon.), U.S. Sports Acad., 1989. Bar: called to Que. bar 1968, Ont. bar 1980; chartered accountant, 1964. Auditor Riddell, Stead, Graham & Hutchinson, Montreal, 1963-65; law clk., then atty. firm Laing, Weldon, Courtois, Clarkson, Parsons & Tétrault, Montreal, 1965-71; mem. firm Stikeman, Elliott, Montreal, Toronto, Ottawa, Vancouver, London, N.Y.C. Hong Kong, Taipei, Budapest, Paris, 1972—; lectr. taxation McGill U. Faculty Law; lectr. Que. Real Estate Assn.; mem. Ct. of Arbitration of Sport, Lausanne, 1991—; officer Order of Can., officer Order nat. du Quebec, Queen's Coun. Author: Five Rings Over Korea, 1994; editor-in-chief: Doing Business in Canada, Canada Tax Cases, Stikeman Income Tax Act (annotated); mem. editl. bd. Can. Tax Svc.; editor Tax Case Notes, Legal Notes, CGA mag. Pres. Canadian Olympic Assn., 1977-82, sec., 1968-76, mem. Internat. Olympic Com., 1978—, exec. bd., 1983-87, 92—, v.p., 1987-91; bd. govs. McGill U., 1986—, chmn., 1994—; trustee Martlet Found.; former trustee Stanstead Wesleyan Coll.; chmn. McGill U. Athletic Bd.; chmn. McGill U. Fund Coun. Named to Canadian Swimming Hall of Fame, 1969, Sports Fedn. Can. Hall of Fame, 1976. Mem. Can. Bar Assn., Can. Tax Found., Internat. Fiscal Assn., Internat. Assn. Practicing Lawyers, Can. Squash Racquets Assn., Royal Life Savs. Soc., Grads. Soc. McGill U. (former pres.). Clubs: Montreal Amateur Athletic Assn. (pres. 1987-88), Badminton and Squash (Montreal); Hillside Tennis, Jesters, Mt. Bruno Country. Home: 87 Arlington Ave, Westmount, PQ Canada H3Y 2W5 Office: Ste 3900, 1155 Rene Levesque Blvd W, Montreal, PQ Canada H3B 3V2

POUND, ROBERT VIVIAN, physics educator; b. Ridgeway, Ont., Can., May 16, 1919; came to U.S., 1923, naturalized, 1932; s. Vivian Ellsworth and Gertrude C. (Prout) P.; m. Betty Yde Andersen, June 20, 1941; 1 son, John Andrew. BA, U. Buffalo, 1941; AM (hon.), Harvard Coll., 1950; DSc (hon.), SUNY, Buffalo, 1994. Rsch. physicist Submarine Signal Co., 1941-42; staff mem. Radiation Lab. MIT, Cambridge, 1942-46; Soc. Fellows jr. fellow Harvard Coll., Cambridge, 1945-48, asst. prof. physics, 1948-50, assoc. prof., 1950-56, prof., 1956-68; chmn. dept. physics, 1968-72, Mallinckrodt prof. emeritus, 1989—; dir. Physics Lab. Harvard U., Cambridge, 1975-83; Fulbright rsch. scholar Oxford (Eng.) U., 1951, vis. rsch. fellow Merton Coll., 1980; Fulbright lectr. Paris, 1958; vis. prof. Coll. de France, 1973; vis. fellow Joint Inst. Lab. Astrophysics, U. Colo., 1979-80; Zernike vis. prof. U. Groningen, The Netherlands, 1982; vis. sr. scientist Brookhaven Nat. Lab., 1986-87; vis. prof. U. Fla., 1987; W.G. Brickwedde lectr. Johns Hopkins U., Balt., 1992; Julian Mack lectr. U. Wis., 1992. Author, editor: Microwave Mixers, 1948; Contbr. articles to profl. jours. Trustee Associated Univs., Inc., 1976—. Recipient B.J. Thompson Meml. award Inst. Radio Engrs., 1948, Eddington medal Royal Astron. Soc., 1965, Nat. Medal Sci., NSF 1990; John Simon Guggenheim fellow,1957-58, 72-73. Fellow AAAS, Am. Phys. Soc.; Am. Acad. Arts and Scis.; mem. NAS, French Phys. Soc. (mem coun. 1958-61), Acad. Scis. (France, fgn. assoc.), Phi Beta Kappa, Sigma Xi.

POUNDER, RICHARD A., advertising executive; b. Jackson Heights, N.Y., Nov. 12, 1946; s. Albert George and Elizabeth (Leonhardt) P.; m. Amy Caroline Maricarian, Sept. 20, 1986; children: Scott Ashton, Lindsay Caroline. BA in Polit. Sci., Middlebury Coll., 1967; MBA, Columbia U., 1973. With Dancer, Fitzgerald, Sample (acquired by Saatchi & Saatchi), N.Y.C., 1973—; v.p. Saatchi & Saatchi, N.Y.C., 1977-80, sr. v.p., 1980-85, exec. v.p., from 1985, now vice chmn. bd. Lt. USN, 1968-71. Mem. Am. Philatelic Soc., Beta Gamma Sigma (Columbia chpt.). Avocations: philately, antique clocks. Office: Saatchi & Saatchi Worldwide 375 Hudson St New York NY 10014-3658

POUNDS, WILLIAM FRANK, management educator; b. Fayette County, Pa., Apr. 9, 1928; s. Joseph Frank and Helen (Fry) P.; m. Helen Anne Means, Mar. 6, 1954; children: Thomas Mcclure, Julia Elizabeth. B.S. in Chem. Engring., Carnegie Inst. Tech., 1950, M.S. in Math. Econs., 1959, Ph.D. in Indsl. Adminstrn., 1964. Indsl. engr. Eastman Kodak Co., 1950-51, 55-57; cons. Pitts. Plate Glass Co., 1958-59, asst. to gen. mgr. Forbes finishes div., 1960-61; mem. faculty Sloan Sch. Mgmt., MIT, 1961—, prof. mgmt., 1966—, dean, 1966-80; cons. to industry, 1958—; sr. adv. Rockefeller Family and Assocs., 1981-91; bd. dirs. EG&G, Inc., Putnam Funds, Sun Co., Inc., M/A COM, Inc., Idexx Labs., Inc., Mgmt. Scis. for Health, Inc., Perseptive Biosystems, Inc. Trustee Boston Mus. Fine Arts; overseer WGBH Found. Served as aviator lt. (j.g.) USNR, 1951-55. Fellow Am. Acad. Arts and Scis. Home: 83 Cambridge Pky #W1101 Cambridge MA 02142-1241 Office: MIT 50 Memorial Dr Cambridge MA 02139-1347

POUNDSTONE, SALLY, library director; m. Robert Bruce Poundstone; children: Nancy Katrina, Holly Megan, Angus Bruce, Alice Heather. BA, U. Ky., 1954, MA in Libr. Sci., 1955. Asst. head ref. dept. Louisville (Ky.) Free Pub. Libr., 1955-59; libr. Folger Shakespeare Libr., Washington, 1959-60; chief acquisition dept. White Plains (N.Y.) Pub. Libr., 1960-62; libr. Bedford Hills (N.Y.) Pub. Elem. Sch., 1965-66; dir. Mamaroneck (N.Y.) Free Libr. and Emelin Theatre, 1966—; instr. libr. sci. N.Y. U., 1968-69, Coll. of New Rochelle (N.Y.), 1970-71; adv. coun. mem. Pratt Inst. Grad Sch. of Libr. and Info. Sci., 1978-87; adminstrv. svcs. chmn. N.Y. Met. Ref. and Res. Libr. Agy., 1977-79, bd. trustees, 1979-88, 2d b.p. and chair, 1984-85, pres., 1985-88; planning and devel. com. mem. Bibliomation, Inc., 1988-90; chair Conn. State Adv. Coun. for Libr. Planning and Devel., 1988-90. Pres. Garden Club of Mamaroneck, 1969-70, Larchmont-Mamaroneck Film Coun., 1971-72, Mamaroneck Hist. soc., 1976-77, bd. mem., 1976-87; vice chmn. Village of Upper Nyack Planning Bd., 1988-89; leadership com. and task force mem. Westchester 2,000, 1984-87; com. mem. Rotary Club of Westport, 1987—; bulletin chair, 1988-90; active Downtown Westport Adv. Com., 1989-90, Rep. Town. Com., Weston, Conn., 1990-93, Westport Bridge & Traffic Com., 1989-90; Westports of the World Com., 1991, Westport Telecomm. Com., 1994—, and others. Mem. ALA, Conn. Libr. Assn., Fairfield Libr. Adminstrs. Group, Archons of Colophon, Pub. Libr. Dirs. Assn. Westchester County (various offices and chairs), N.Y. Libr. Assn. (sec. treas. adult librs. assn. 1970-72, pres. pub. librs. sect. 1981-82, chair planning com.). Home: 48 Sharp Hill Rd Wilton CT 06897 Office: Westport Lib Assn PO Box 5020 Westport CT 06881-5020

POUPARD, JAMES J., controller; b. Monroe, Mich., Mar. 21, 1932; s. Edmund Lawrence and Ruth Mary (Soleau) P.; m. E. Ruth Gilmer, Aug. 21, 1954; children: Michelle, Brenda, Dennis, Gary. PhB in Econs., U. Detroit, 1964. Systems analyst Mercury div. Ford Motor Co., Detroit, 1956-57; acct., analyst Chrysler Corp., Detroit, 1957-67; internat. controller airtemp div. Chrysler Corp., Dayton, Ohio, 1970-72; div. controller Allis Chalmers Corp., Matteson, Ill., 1972-80; v.p. controller Komatsu Dresser Co., Peoria, Ill., 1980—. Bd. dirs. Heart of Ill. United Way, Peoria, 1981-89; bd. dirs. Peoria YMCA, 1983-84, mem. adv. bd., 1990—; bd. dirs. Tri-County

Women Strength, 1990—; chmn. FEMA local bd. Emergency Food and Shelter, 1983-93; past coach Jr. League Football, past football ofcl. With USAF, 1951-55. Roman Catholic. Clubs: Holiday Boat (Rome, Ill.) (vice commodore 1985-86, commodore 1986-87, bd. dirs. 1988—). Avocation: power yachting. Home: 11918 N Windcrest Dr Dunlap IL 61525-9509 Office: Komatsu Dresser Co Haulpak Div 2300 NE Adams St Peoria IL 61639-0001

POUPART-LAFARGE, OLIVIER MARIE, financial executive; b. Angers, France, Oct. 26, 1942; s. Henri M. and Edith M. (LaFarge) Poupart; m. Benedicte M. Gentin, Feb. 12, 1965; children: Arnaud, Bertrand, Henri, Domitille, Astrid. MBA, Hautes Etudes Commerciales, Paris, 1964; BA, U. Paris, 1965. Fin. analyst Credit Lyonnais, London, 1967-68; fin. exec. Roussel Uclaf, Paris, 1968-74; fin. mgr. Bouygues, Paris, 1974-84, CFO, 1984—. Lt. French Air Force, 1964-65. Decorated chevalier Ordre Nat. du Mérite, Legion of Honor (France). Roman Catholic. Home: 4 Imp Nattier, 78000 Versailles France Office: Bouygues, 1 Ave Eugene Freyssinet, 78061 Saint Quentin France

POURCIAU, LESTER JOHN, librarian; b. Baton Rouge, La., Sept. 6, 1936; s. Lester John and Pearlie M. (Hogan) P.; m. Rebecca Anne Thomas, 1975; 1 son, Lester John III. B.A., La. State U., 1962, M.S., 1964; Ph.D. (Higher Edn. Act fellow), Ind. U., 1975. Asst. reference librarian U. S.C., Columbia, 1963-64; reference librarian Florence County Pub. Library, Florence, S.C., 1964-65; reference services coordinator U. Fla., Gainesville, 1966-67; dir. libraries Memphis State U., 1970—, assoc. v.p. for acad. affairs, dir. libraries, 1987—; chmn. coun. of head librarians State Univ. and C.C. System Tenn., 1980, 87; acad. assoc. Atlantic Coun. of U.S., Memphis State U.; fgn. expert, vis. lectr. Beijing U. of Posts & Telecomms., Beijing Normal U., Peking U., Renmen U., Qinghua U., Chingqing Inst. Posts & Telcomms., Guizhou Normal U., Republic of China, 1993; fgn. expert/vis. lectr. Beijing U. Posts and Telecom, 1993, Beijing Normal U., 1993, Peking U., 1993, RenMen U., 1993, Tsinghua U., 1993, Chongqing Inst. Posts and Telecom., 1993, Guizhou Normal U., 1993; fgn. expert, vis. lectr. Nanjing U. Posts and Telecom., Anhui Normal U., Beijing U. Posts and Telecom., 1994, Nanjing U. Posts & Telecomms., Anhui Normal U., Republic of China, 1994. Contbr. articles to profl. jours. Served with USAF, 1955-59. Recipient Adminstrv. Staff award Memphis State U., 1981, Commendation Boy Scouts Am., 1985, Commendation Tenn. Sec. State, 1989, Honor award Tenn. Libr. Assn., 1990; named Outstanding Alumnus, La. State U., 1988; named Libr. of Yr., Memphis Public Libr. Coun., 1989. Mem. Am. Library Assn., Am. Soc. for Info. Sci., Nat. Assn. Watch and Clock Collectors (chpt. pres. 1983, sec.-treas. 1988, 89), Antique Automobile Am., Mid-Am. Old Time Automobile Assn., Memphis Old Time Car (sec. 1981, pres. 1982, 89), Delta Phi Alpha, Omicron Delta Kappa (Order of Omega), Phi Kappa Phi. Office: Memphis State U U Libr Memphis TN 38152

POUR-EL, MARIAN BOYKAN, mathematician, educator; b. N.Y.C.; d. Joseph and Mattie (Caspe) Boykan; m. Akiva Pour-El; 1 dau., Ina. A.B., Hunter Coll.; A.M., Harvard U., 1951, Ph.D., 1958. Asst. prof. math. Pa. State U., 1958-62, assoc. prof., 1962-64; mem. faculty U. Minn., Mpls., 1964—; prof. math. U. Minn., 1968—; mem. Inst. Advanced Study, Princeton, N.J., 1962-64; mem. coun. Conf. Bd. Math. Scis., 1977-82, trustee, 1978-81, mem. nominating com., 1980-82, chmn., 1981-82; lectr. internat. congresses in logic and computer sci., Eng., 1971, Hungary, 1967, Czechoslovakia, 1973, Germany, 1983, Japan, 1985, 88, China, 1987; lectr. Polish Acad. Sci., 1974; lecture series throughout Fed. Republic of Germany, 1980, 87, 89, 91, Japan, 1985, 87, 90, 93, China, 1987, Sweden, 1983, 94, Finland, 1991, Estonia, 1991, Moscow, 1992, Amsterdam, 1992; mem. Fulbright Com. on Maths., 1986-89. Author: (with I. Richards) Computability in Analysis and Physics, 1989; author numerous articles on mathematical logic (theoretical computer sci.) and applications to mathematical and physical theory. named to Hunter Coll. Hall of Fame, 1975; NAS grantee, 1966. Fellow AAAS, Japan Soc. for Promotion of Sci.; mem. Am. Math. Soc. (coun. 1980-88, numerous coms., lectr. nat. meeting 1976, also spl. sessions 1971, 78, 82, 84, chmn. spl. sessions on recursion theory 1975, 84), Assn. Symbolic Logic, Math. Assn. Am. (nat. panel vis. lectrs. 1977—, lectr. nat. meetings 1982, 89), Phi Beta Kappa, Sigma Xi, Pi Mu Epsilon, Sigma Pi Sigma. Achievements include research in mathematical logic (theoretical computer science) and in computability and noncomputability in physical theory—wave, heat, potential equations, eigenvalues, eigenvectors. Office: U Minn Sch Math Vincent Hall Minneapolis MN 55455 *In order to practice our careers our family has evolved a pattern of life at variance with the norm. For more than twenty years we have lived apart most of the time. Our strong emotional and personal ties were intensified by this absence of continuous physical nearness. It is my belief that one can succeed personally, socially and professionally without having to accept the constraints of an existing social order.*

POURFARROKH, ALI, ballet company artistic director. Dancer, choreographer with Harkness Ballet, Joffrey Ballet, Am. Ballet, Am. Ballet Theatre, Alvin Ailey Dance Theatre; co-dir., resident choreographer Essen Ballet Co., Germany; owner dance sch., Long Island, N.Y.; artistic dir. Alta. Ballet, Edmonton, 1988—. Office: care Alta Ballet Co, 10210 108 Ave # 253, Edmonton, AB Canada T5H 1A8

POURNELLE, JERRY EUGENE, author; b. Shreveport, La., Aug. 7, 1933; s. P. Eugene and Ruth (Lewis) P.; m. M. Roberta Jane Isdell, July 17, 1959; children: Jennifer, Alexander, Francis Russell, Phillip Eugene, Richard Stefan. BS, U. Wash., 1954, MS, 1957, PhD, Inst. U. Wash., Seattle, 1956-57; research engr., aviation psychologist Boeing Co., Seattle, 1958-64; mgr. spl. studies Aerospace Corp., San Bernardino, Calif., 1964; prof., dir. research inst. Pepperdine U., Los Angeles, 1965-69; exec. asst. to mayor City Los Angeles, 1969; author, lectr., cons. Studio City, Calif., 1970—; cons. Directorate of Plans USAF, 1968; chief cons. Profl. Educators Los Angeles, 1970; cons. to chancellor Calif. State Colls., 1970—. Author: Human Temperature Tolerance in Astronautic Environments, 1959, Stability and National Security, 1968, (with Stefan Possony) The Stategy of Technology, 1970, Congress Debates Viet Nam, 1971, The Right to Read, 1971, Red Heroin, Red Dragon, 1971; (with Larry Niven) The Mote in God's Eye, 1974, (with Larry Niven) Inferno, 1976; West of Honor, 1976, The Mercenary, 1977, High Justice, 1977, (with Larry Niven) Lucifer's Hammer, 1977, Janissaries, 1979, King David's Spaceship, 1980, (with Larry Niven) Oath of Fealty, 1981, Prince of Mercenaries, 1989, (with Roland Green) Janissaries: Clan and Crown, 1982, (with Dean Ing) Mutual Assured Survival, 1984, (with Larry Niven) Footfall, 1985, (with Larry Niven, Stephan Barnes) Legacy of Heorot, 1987, (with Roland Green) Storms of Victory, 1987, Prince of Mercenaries, 1989, Falkenberg's Legion, 1990; (with S.M. Stirling) Go Tell the Spartans, 1991, (with S.M. Stirling) The Children's Hour, 1991; (with Larry Niven and Michael Flynn) Fallen Angels, 1991, (with S.M. Stirling) Prince of Sparta, 1992, (with Larry Niven) The Gripping Hand, 1993, (with Larry Niven and Stepha Barnes) Children of Beowulf; editor: 2020 Vision; sci. editor, columnist Galaxy Sci. Fiction, 1975-78, Byte mag., 1978—; (anthologies) (with John F. Carr) Black Holes, 1978, Endless Frontier, 1979, Survival of Freedom, 1982, Endless Frontier Vol. II, 1982, There Will Be War, 1983, Men At War, 1984, Blood and Iron, 1984, Day of The Tyrant, 1985, Warrior, 1986, Imperial Stars, 1986, Guns of Darkness, 1987, Imperial Stars: Republic and Empire, Vol. II; InfoWorld columnist, 1986-92, War World, 1988, There Will Be War: Call to Battle, 1988, Imperial Stars: Clash of Empire Vol. III, 1989, Armageddon!, 1989, After Armageddon, 1990, War World: Death's Head Mutiny, Vol. II, 1990, (with John F. Carr) Endless Frontier III: Cities in Space, 1991, War World: Sauron Dominion, Vol. III, 1991; editor: (with John F. Carr) Codomium: Revolt on War World, 1992, Endless Frontier IV: Life in the Asteroid Belt, 1992, War World IV: Invasion. Scoutmaster Boy Scouts Am., 1958; chmn. bd. dirs. Seattle Civic Playhouse Assn., 1963-6; asst. chmn. San Bernardino County Rep. Com., 1964; assoc. dir. Sam Yorty for Mayor Campaign, 1969; bd. dirs. Pepperdine Research Inst., 1966-69. Served with AUS, 1950-52; mem. Rep. Bd. Govs., 1962-63. Decorated Bronze medal; recipient Excellence award Am. Security Council, 1969, John W. Campbell award 1973. Fellow AAAS; mem. Inst. Strategic Studies, AIAA, Ops. Research Soc. Am., Univ. Prof. for Acad. Order (bd. dirs. 1971), Sci. Fiction Writers Am. (pres. 1973-74). Episcopalian. Home and Office: 12190 1/2 Ventura Blvd Studio City CA 91604-2517

POUSSAINT, ALVIN FRANCIS, psychiatrist, educator; b. N.Y.C., May 15, 1934; s. Christopher Thomas V. and Harriet (Johnston) P. BA, Columbia U., 1956; MD, Cornell U., 1960; MS, UCLA, 1964. Intern UCLA Ctr. for Health Sci., 1960-61, resident in psychiatry Neuropsychiat. Inst., 1961-64, chief resident, 1964-65; So. field dir. Med. Com. Human Rights, Jackson, Miss., 1965-66; asst. prof. psychiatry Tufts U. Med. Sch., 1966-69; assoc. prof. psychiatry, assoc. dean students Harvard Med. Sch., 1969-75, 78—, prof. psychiatry, 1993—, dean students, 1975-78; cons. HEW, 1969-73; chmn. select com. on Edn. of Black Youth. Author numerous articles in field. Nat. treas. Black Acad. Arts and Letters, 1969-70, Med. Com. Human Rights, 1966—. Recipient Michael Schwerner award, 1968, Am. Black Achievement award in Bus. and the Professions Johnson Pub. Co., Inc., 1986, John Jay award for Disting. Profl. Achievement Columbia Coll. N.Y., 1987, Medgar Evers Medal of Honor Beverly Hills/Hollywood chpt. NAACP, Hollywood, Calif., 1988, and numerous hon. degrees. Fellow AAAS, Am. Orthopsychiatric Assn., Am. Psychiat. Assn. (mem. com. on Black Psychiatrists 1970-75); mem. Nat. Med. Assn., Am. Acad. of Child Psychiatry, Children's Longwood. Office: Judge Baker Ctr 295 Longwood Ave Boston MA 02115

POUSSAINT, RENEE FRANCINE, journalist; b. N.Y.C., Aug. 12, 1944; d. Christopher Wallace and Bobbie (Vance) P.; m. Henry J. Richardson III, Sept. 10, 1977. B.A., Sarah Lawrence Coll., 1966; M.A., UCLA, 1971; postgrad., Yale Law Sch., 1966-67, Ind. U., 1971-72; student, Sorbonne, Paris, 1964-65; hon. doctorate, Mt. Vernon Coll., Washington, 1985; cert., Columbia U. Journalism Sch., Michele Clark Fellowship Program for Minority Journalists, 1972. Program dir. AIESEC, N.Y.C., 1968-69; editor African Arts Mag., Los Angeles 1969-71; reporter WBBM-TV, Chgo., 1974-76, CBS Network News, Chgo., Washington, 1976-78; became anchorperson WJLA-TV, Washington, 1978; now correspondent PrimeTime Live, ABC News, New York; dancer Jean Leon Destine Troupe, N.Y.C., 1966; translator U. Calif. Press, Los Angeles, 1970; tutor Operation Rescue, Washington, 1981—. Hon. dir. Nat. Kidney Found., Washington, 1981—; citizen advisor YWCA Nat. Capitol Area, 1983—; co-chmn. Nat. Capital Area Lung Assn., 1982; membership chmn. Arthritis Found., 1981-82. Recipient Reporting award Ill. Mental Health Assn., 1976; recipient Reporting award Nat. Assn. Media Women, 1977, Broadcasting Excellence award AAUW, 1979, Emmy awards, 1979, 80, 81, 82, Broadcast award NAACP, 1980, Whitney Young Meml. award Washington Urban League, 1983. Mem. AFTRA, NAACP (life), Capitol Press Club. Office: PrimeTime Live 147 Columbus Ave 3rd Fl New York NY 10023-5900*

POUSSART, DENIS JEAN-MARIE, electrical engineering educator, consultant; b. St. Denis D'Oleron, France, Oct. 3, 1940; arrived in Can., 1952; s. Jean and Anne (Gerardin) P.; m. Nicole Dorion, Dec. 19, 1964; children: Caroline, Brigitte, Pascale. BS, Laval U., Que., Can., 1963; MS, MIT, 1965, PhD, 1968. Registered profl. engr., Que. Prof. elec. engring. Laval U., Quebec, Can., 1968—, chmn. dept. elec. engring., 1988-91; coord. Inst. for Robotics and Intelligent Systems, Can., 1990—; v.p. R & D Centre de Recherche Informatique de Montreal, Can., 1991—; chmn. bd. dirs. elec. engring. Coun. Can., 1986-88; bd. dirs. Centre de Recherche Industrielle du Qie., 1985-89; mem. engring. grant com. Fonds Formation Chercheurs, 1989-91, mem. ctr. grant com., 1993—. Assoc. editor Indsl. Meteorology, 1988, Can. Jour. Elec. and Computer Engring., 1988; contbr. numerous papers to profl. jours. Mem. IEEE, Internat. Soc. Optical Engring., Sigma Xi. Office: Dept Elec Engring, Laval U, Quebec, PQ Canada G1K 7P4

POUTSMA, MARVIN L., chemical research administration; b. Grand Rapids, Mich., Aug. 7, 1937; m. Yolanda Arco, July 20, 1968; children: John C., Julie A. BS, Calvin Coll., 1958; PhD, U. Ill., 1962. Staff scientist corp. rsch. Union Carbide, Tarrytown, N.Y., 1961-65, group leader corp. rsch., 1965-68, sr. scientist corp. rsch., 1968-73, sr. group leader corp. rsch., 1972-78; group leader chemistry divsn. Oak Ridge (Tenn.) Nat. Lab., 1978-80, sect. head chemistry divsn., 1980-83, dir. chemistry divsn., 1984-93, dir. chem. & analytical scis. divsn., 1994—. Contbr. chpts. to books and articles to profl. jours. Fellow AAAS; mem. Am. Chem. Soc. Office: Oak Ridge Nat Lab PO Box 2008 Oak Ridge TN 37831-6129

POVELL, ROY ALBERT, lawyer; b. Bklyn., Mar. 23, 1929; s. Roy and Antonina (Zebrauskas) P.; m. Ann Wallace MacKinnon, July 20, 1957; children: Roy Dickson, Maryann Wallace, Elizabeth Ona. A.B., Harvard U., 1951, J.D., 1957; LL.M., NYU, 1963. Bar: N.Y. 1958, Fla. 1979. Assoc. Cadwalader, Wickersham & Taft, N.Y.C., 1957-65, ptnr., 1965-89, of counsel, 1989—; lectr. Practising Law Inst., 1960—, World Trade Inst., 1970—. Author: Practising Law Inst. Handbook Series, 1970—, Foreign Tax Havens, 1973, Foreign Tax Planning, 1983. bd. dirs. Harvard Legal Aid Bur., Cambridge, Mass., 1956-57. Served to commdr. USNR, 1951-54, Korea. Mem. ABA, N.Y. State Bar Assn., Fla. Bar Assn., Internat. Tax Assn. (pres. 1968-69). Clubs: Hasty Pudding (Cambridge); NYU (N.Y.C.). Office: Cadwalader Wickersham & Taft 100 Maiden Ln New York NY 10038-4892 also: 440 Royal Palm Way Palm Beach FL 33480-4138

POVEY, THOMAS GEORGE, office systems company executive; b. Norristown, Pa., Dec. 27, 1920; s. Thomas and Blanche (Groff) P.; B.S., Temple U., 1948; m. Bettina O. Houghton, June 2, 1945; children: Bettina C., Denise E. With Sperry Remington div. Sperry Rand Corp., Phila., also Newark, N.Y.C., 1948-76, eastern regional gen. sales mgr., Phila., asst. gen. sales mgr., N.Y.C., 1966-67, dir. mktg., Marietta, Ohio, 1968-71, v.p. mktg., 1972-73, v.p. fed. govt. mktg., Washington, 1973-76; pres. Remco Bus. Systems, Inc., Washington, 1976—, also chmn. bd.; lectr. Newark High Sch., 1954-56, Belleville (N.J.) High Sch., 1956-58, Fairleigh Dickinson Coll., Paterson, N.J., 1957-58, Pace Coll., N.Y.C., 1965—, Georgetown U., 1974, ednl. TV N.Y.C., 1965—. Dir. Community Fund, Essex Fells, N.J., 1967. Served as 1st lt. with USAF, 1942-45. Decorated Air medal; named Remington Dartnell Salesman of Yr. 1950. Mem. Smithsonian Assocs., Internat. Systems Dealer Assn. (bd. dirs. 1977-78, Founders award 1991), Office Systems Equipment Corp. (pres. 1978-80), Pi Delta Epsilon (pres. 1948). Republican. Methodist. Home: 227 Cape St John Rd Annapolis MD 21401 Office: 8000 Parston Dr Forestville MD 20747

POVICH, DAVID, lawyer; b. Washington, June 8, 1935; s. Shirley Lewis and Ethyl (Friedman) P.; m. Constance Enid Tobriner, June 14, 1959; children: Douglas, Johanna, Judith, Andrew. B.A., Yale U., 1958; LL.B., Columbia U., 1962. Bar: D.C. 1962. Law clk. to assoc. judge D.C. Ct. Appeals, Washington, 1962-63; ptnr. Williams & Connolly, Washington, 1963—, mem. exec. com., 1986-87; speaker Georgetown U. Criminal Practice Inst., Harvard Law Sch. Trial Advocacy Workshop. Bd. dirs. officer Lisner Home for Aged. Mem. D.C. Bar Assn., ABA, Bar Assn. D.C., Barristers (exec. com. 1992-93). Office: Williams & Connolly 725 12th St NW Washington DC 20005

POVICH, (MAURICE) MAURY RICHARD, broadcast journalist, talk show host, television producer; b. Washington, Jan. 17, 1939; s. Shirley and Ethel Povich; m. Constance "Connie" Y. Chung, Dec. 2, 1984; children from previous marriage, Susan, Amy. BA, U. Pa., 1962. Reporter WWDC Radio, Washington, 1962-66; gen. assignment and sports report Sta. WTTG-TV, Washington, 1966; co-anchor Panorama, Washington, 1967-70, host, 1973-76, host and anchor 1983-86; host People and Povich Sta. WTTG, Washington, 1970-72; news anchor Sta. WMAQ-TV, Chgo., 1977, Sta. KNXT-TV, L.A., 1977-78; anchor Sta. KGO-TV, San Francisco, 1978-79, Sta. KYW-TV, Phila., 1980-83, Sta. WTTG-TV, Washington, 1983-86; host A Current Affair 1986-90; host, anchor WTTG-TV News, 1983-86; host Maury Povich Show, 1991—; guest on Carol Leifter show, 1989, Donahue show with Connie Chung, 1989, John MacLaughlin show, 1989, Dick Cavett show, 1989, others; guest speaker Am. Agrl. Editors Assn. Communication Clinic, 1989, ASTA Conf., N.Y.C., 1990, Assn. Broadcast Exec. of Tex., 1990; speaker on tabloid TV, the media and Israel, entertainer blacklists; host Forbes 400, CBS-TV Special, 1992. Author: Current Affairs: A Life on the Edge, 1991. Office: The Maury Povich Show 221 W 26th St New York NY 10001-6703

POVICH, SHIRLEY LEWIS, columnist, former sports editor; b. Bar Harbor, Me., July 15, 1905; s. Nathan and Rosa (Orlovich) P.; m. Ethyl Friedman, Feb. 21, 1932; children: David, Maurice R., Lynn. Student, Georgetown U., 1922-24. Reporter Washington Post, 1923-25, sports editor, 1926-33, columnist, 1933-45; war corr. Washington Post, PTO, 1945;

columnist Washington Post, 1946—; adj. prof. communications Am. U., 1975—. Author: The Washington Senators, 1954, All These Mornings, 1969; also articles in mags. Recipient citation for outstanding service as war corr., 1945; Nat. Headliners Grantland Rice award for sportswriting, 1964; elected to Baseball Hall of Fame, Cooperstown writers div., 1976; recipient Red Smith award, 1983. Mem. Baseball Writers Assn. Am. (pres. 1955). Home: 2801 New Mexico Ave NW Washington DC 20007-3921 Office: Washington Post 1515 L St NW Washington DC 20005-1601

POVISH, KENNETH JOSEPH, bishop; b. Alpena, Mich., Apr. 19, 1924; s. Joseph Francis and Elizabeth (Jachcik) P. A.B., Sacred Heart Sem., Detroit, 1946; M.A., Cath. U. Am., 1950; postgrad., No. Mich. U., 1961, 63. Ordained priest Roman Catholic Ch., 1950; asst. pastorships, 1950-56; pastor in Port Sanilac Mich., 1956-57, Munger, Mich., 1957-60, Bay City, Mich., 1966-70; dean St. Paul Sem., Saginaw, Mich., 1960-66; vice rector St. Paul Sem., 1962-66; bishop of Crookston Minn., 1970-75; bishop of Lansing Mich., 1975—; bd. consulators Diocese of Saginaw, 1966-70; instr. Latin and U.S. history St. Paul Sem., 1960-66. Weekly columnist Saginaw and Lansing diocesan newspapers. Bd. dirs. Cath. Charities Diocese Saginaw, 1969-70. Mem. Mich., Bay County hist. socs., Lions Club, KC (pres. Mich. Cath. Conf. 1985—), Kiwanis. Office: Chancery Office 300 W Ottawa St Lansing MI 48933-1577

POWDERLY, WILLIAM H., III, lawyer; b. Pitts., Feb. 23, 1930. BS, Georgetown U., 1953; LLB, U. Pitts., 1956. Bar: Pa. 1956. Ptnr. Jones, Day, Reavis & Pogue, Pitts. Office: Jones Day Reavis & Pogue 1 Mellon Bank Ctr 500 Grant St Pittsburgh PA 15219-2502

POWE, L. A. SCOT, JR., law educator; b. 1943. BA, Yale U., 1965, JD 1968. Bar: Wash. 1968, Tex. 1980. Law clk. to Hon. William O. Douglas U.S. Supreme Ct., 1970-71; asst. prof. U. B.C., 1968-70; asst. prof. U. Tex., Austin, 1971-74, prof. law, 1974—, prof. govt., 1989—; vis. prof. Georgetown U., 1977-78, U. Calif., Berkeley, 1983-84, U. Conn., fall 1986. Mem. Am. Law Inst. Office: U Tex Sch Law 727 E 26th St Austin TX 78705-3224

POWE, RALPH ELWARD, university administrator; b. Tylertown, Miss., July 27, 1944; s. Roy Elward and Virginia Alyne (Bradley) P.; m. Sharon Eve Sandifer, May 20, 1962; children: Deborah Lynn, Ryan Elward, Melanie Colleen. BS in Mech. Engring., Miss. State U., 1967, MS in Mech. Engring., 1968; PhD in Mech. Engring., Mont. State U., 1970. Student trainee NASA, 1962-65; research asst. lab. instr. Miss. State U., 1968, instr. dept. mech. engring., 1968; research asst., teaching asst. Mont. State U., Bozeman, 1968-70, asst. prof. dept. mech. engring., 1970-74; assoc. prof. Miss. State U. 1974-78, prof., 1979-80, assoc. dean engring., dir. engring. and indsl. research sta., 1979-80, assoc. v.p. research, 1980-86, v.p., 1986—; chmn. bd. dirs. Coalition of Experimental Program to Stimulate Competitive Rsch. States, 1994—; bd. dirs. Gulf Univs. Rsch. Consortium, Tenn.-Tombigbee Project Area Coun.; rep. rsch. coun. Nat. Assn. State Univs. and Land Grant Colls., So. Growth Policies Bd.; Miss. Mineral Resources Inst., Sci. and Tech. Coun. States. Disting. Engring. fellow Coll. Engring.; active Miss. Univ. Res. Authority, Coun. on Rsch. Policy, So. Growth Policies Bd.; rep. Miss. Mineral Resources Inst.; gov. rep. Sci. and Tech. Coun. of States; cons. energy conservation programs, coal fired power plants, torsional vibrations, accident analysis; dir. Miss. Energy Rsch. Ctr., 1979-81, Ctr. for Environ. Studies, 1980—; univ. rep. on lignite task force, rep. on bd. dirs. Miss.-Ala. Sea Grant Consortium, chmn. of Council Oak Ridge Associated Univs., rep. to Tenn.-Tombigbee project area coun.; chmn. Miss. Rsch. Consortium; mem. S.E. Univs. Rsch. Assn. Named Outstanding Engr., Engring. Socs. Contbr. articles to profl. jours. Mem. Miss. Econ. Coun., univ. coord. United Way, 1983, 85; tchr. adult Sunday Sch. class 1st Bapt. Ch. Recipient Ralph E. Teeter award Soc. Automotive Engrs.; named Outstanding Engr. in No. Miss. Joint Engr. Soc. Fellow ASME; mem. Nat. Assn. State Universities and Land Grant Colls., Starkville Community Theatre Wing. Edn., Wind Energy Soc. Am., Miss. Acad. Scis., Miss. Engring. Soc., Toastmasters, Starkville Quarterback Club, Rotary, Starkville C. of C. (bd. dirs.), Blue Key, Sigma Xi (Miss. State U. research award), Tau Beta Pi, Kappa Mu Epsilon, Pi Tau Sigma, Phi Kappa Phi, Omicron Delta Kappa. Baptist. Lodge: Rotary. Avocations: hunting, fishing, gardening. Home: 110 Pinewood Rd Starkville MS 39759-4128 Office: Miss State U PO Box 6343 Mississippi State MS 39762-6343

POWELL, ALAN, engineer, scientist, educator; b. Buxton, Derbyshire, Eng., Feb. 17, 1928; came to U.S., 1956; s. Frank and Gwendolen Marie (Walker) P.; m. June Sinclair, Mar. 28, 1956. Student, Buxton Coll., 1939-45; diploma in aeros., Loughborough Coll., 1948; B.Sc. in Engring. with 1st class honors, London U., 1949; honours diploma 1st class, Loughborough Coll., 1949; D.Tech. (hon.), Loughborough U. Tech., 1980; Ph.D., U. Southampton, 1953. Chartered aero. engr., mech. engr. Engr. Percival Aircraft Co., Luton, Eng., 1949-51; research asst. U. Southampton, Eng., 1951-53; lectr. U. Southampton, 1953-56; research fellow Calif. Inst. Tech., Pasadena, 1956-57; engr. Douglas Aircraft Co., 1956; assoc. tech. dir., head acoustics and vibration lab. David Taylor Model Basin, Dept. Navy, Washington, 1965-66; tech. dir. David Taylor Model Basin, Dept. Navy, 1966-67, David Taylor Naval Ship Research & Devel. Center, Bethesda, Md., 1967-85; mem. Undersea Warfare Research & Devel. Council, 1966-76, chmn., 1971-72; mem. council on Fed. Labs., 1972-85; prof. mech. engring. U. Houston, 1985—, chmn., 1985-87; mem. com. on hearing bioacoustics and biomechs. NAS-NRC, 1961-85, advisor, 1985—, exec. council, 1963-65, chmn., 1965-66, mem. naval studies bd., 1990—; advisor Chinese U. Devel. Project, NAS, 1989-91; cons. Douglas Aircraft Co., various aerospace and acoustics cos. 1956-65; mem. adv. council Internat. Towing Tank Conf., 1981-85; mem. sci. com. Internat. Union Theoretical and Applied Mechanics, 1983-85; advisor U.S-Japan Program Natural Resources, 1987—, mem. 1979-86; chmn. internat. conf. ComputerAided Design, Manufacture and Ops. in Marine and Offshore Industries, 1987-88; cons. Scientific Applications Internat., Inc., 1987-90. Contbr. articles to profl. jours. Recipient Navy Meritorious Civilian Service award, 1970; Brit. Empire scholar, 1945, Per Bruel gold medal, 1991; named Meritorious Exec. Pres. of U.S., 1982; Capt. Robert Dexter Conrad gold medal for sci. achievement Sec. Navy, 1984. Fellow Royal Aero. Soc. London (Baden-Powell prize 1948, Wilbur Wright prize 1953), Acoustical Soc. Am. (biennial award 1962, assoc. editor Jour. 1962-67, chmn. exec. coun. 1964-66, exec. coun. 1966-69, chmn. medals and awards com. 1978-81, v.p. elect 1981-82, v.p 1982-83, pres. elect 1989-90, pres. 1990-91, past pres. 1991-92, Silver medal in engring acoustics 1992, designated Nat. Spkr. on Engring. Acoustics 1994—), Instn. Mech. Engrs., Inst. Acoustics U.K.; mem. AIAA (assoc. fellow, Aeroacoustics award 1980), ASME (Rayleigh lectr. 1988, Per Bruel Gold medal for noise control and acoustics 1991), Inst. Noise Control Engrs. (initial mem., dir. 1974-77, Disting. lectr. 1975, 83, v.p. 1981-84, bd. cert. 1993), Acoustics, Speech and Signal Processing Soc. (sr., exec. com. 1969-72, awards com. 1971-73, bylaws com. 1973-75), Am. Soc. Naval Engrs. (life), Tau Beta Pi (hon. life). Office: U Houston Dept Mech Engring Houston TX 77204-4792

POWELL, ALLEN ROYAL, bishop; b. Beaumont, Tex., June 9, 1922; s. Millard and Annie (Surrey) P.; m. Mary Louise Barclay, Dec. 9, 1940; children: Allen R. Jr., Gloria P. Russell, Raymond L., Gwendolyn P. Robinson. Student, Bishop Coll., 1949-51. Pastor Ch. of Living God, Lukin, Tex., 1946-49, Dallas, 1949-51, Kansas City, Kans., 1951-62; dist. overseer Ch. of Living God, Tenn., 1960-66, bishop, 1964-74; bishop Ch. of Living God, Miss., 1974—; pastor Ch. of Living God, Chgo., 1961—, revivalist, counselor, nat. youth instr., exec. bd., Cin., 1966—. Chaplain U.S. Army, 1944-46. Named hon. bishop Five Chs. of Monrovia, 1992. Avocations: printing, singing. Home: 8557 S Wabash Ave Chicago IL 60619-5617 Office: Ch of Living God 14 E 45th St Chicago IL 60653-3111

POWELL, ANICE CARPENTER, librarian; b. Moorhead, Miss., Dec. 2, 1928; d. Horace Aubrey and Celeste (Brian) Carpenter; student Sunflower Jr. Coll., 1945-47, Miss. State Coll. Women, 1947-48; B.S., Delta State Coll., 1961, M.L.S., 1974; m. Robert Wainwright Powell, July 19, 1948 (dec. 1979); children: Penelope Elizabeth, Deborah Alma. Librarian, Sunflower (Miss.) Pub. Library, 1958-61; tchr. English, Isola (Miss.) High Sch., 1961-62; dir. Sunflower County Library, Indianola, Miss., 1962—; mem. adv. coun. State Instl. Library Services, 1967-71; mem. adv. bd. library services and constrn.

act com. Miss. Library Commn., 1978-80, mem. pub. library task force, 1986—; mem. Pub. Library Standards Com., 1988—; mem. state adv. coun. adult edn., 1988-92; mem. steering com. NASA community involvement program Miss. Delta Community Coll., 1990, adult edn. adv. com.; mem. Dist. Workforce Coun., 1994—. Mem. AAUW, NOW, ALA (speaker senate subcom. on illiteracy 1989), Miss. Library Assn. (exec. dir. Nat. Library Week 1975, steering com. 1976, chmn. Right to Read com. 1976, co-chmn., 1987, chmn. legis. com. 1979, chmn. intellectual freedom com. 1975, 80, mem. legis. com. 1973-86, chmn membership com. 1982, pres. 1984, chmn. nominating com. 1986, chmn. election com. 1989, mem. legis com., mem. registration com. 1991—, mem. membership com., mem. nominating com. 1994, Peggy May award 1981), Sunflower County Hist. Soc. (pres. 1983-87), Miss. Literacy Assn., Delta Coun., Sunflower County Literacy Coun. (treas.). Methodist. Home: PO Box 310 Sunflower MS 38778-0310 Office: Sunflower County Libr 201 Cypress Dr Indianola MS 38751-2415

POWELL, ANNE ELIZABETH, editor; b. Cheverly, Md., Nov. 11, 1951; d. Arthur Gorman and Barbara Anne (MacAran) P.; m. John Alan Ebeling Jr., 1972 (div. 1983). BS, U. Md., 1972. Reporter Fayetteville (N.C.) Times, 1973-75; home editor Columbus (Ga.) Ledger-Enquirer, 1976; assoc. editor Builder mag., Washington, 1977-78; architecture editor House Beautiful's Spl. Publs., N.Y.C., 1979-81; editor Traditional Home mag., Des Moines, 1982-87, Mid-Atlantic Country mag., Alexandria, Va., 1987-89; editor in chief publs. Nat. Trust for Hist. Preservation, Washington, 1989—. Author: The New England Colonial, 1988. Mem. Nat. Press Club, Am. Soc. Mag. Editors. Home: 707 S Royal St Alexandria VA 22314-4309 Office: Nat Trust for Hist Preservation 1785 Massachusetts Ave NW Washington DC 20036-2117

POWELL, ANTHONY, costume designer, set designer. Diploma (with honors), Central Sch. of Art & Design, London, England, 1958. Costume designer, lecturer Central Sch. of Art & Design, London, England, 1958-71; lectr. Central Sch. of Art and Design, London, 1958-71. Costume designer, set designer: (stage) The School for Scandal, 1963 (Tony award best costume design 1963); set designer: Private Lives, 1975; prodn. designer: Ring Round the Moon, 1975; costume designer: (films) The Royal Hunt of the Sun, 1969, Travels with My Aunt, 1972 (Academy award best costume design 1972), Papillon, 1973, Buffalo Bill and the Indians, or Sitting Bull's History Lesson, 1976, Sorcerer, 1977, Death on the Nile, 1978 (Academy award best costume design 1978), Tess, 1980 (Academy award best costume design 1980), Priest of Love, 1981, Evil under the Sun, 1982, Indiana Jones and the Temple of Doom, 1984, Pirates, 1986, Ishtar, 1987, Frantic, 1988, (with Joanna Johnston) Indiana Jones and the Last Crusade, 1989, Hook, 1991 (Acad. award nomination best costume design 1991), (theatre) Lettice and Lovage, 1990, Senset Boulevard, 1993 (Tony award nomination best costume design 1995). Office: care Costume Designer's Guild 13949 Ventura Blvd Ste 309 Sherman Oaks CA 91423*

POWELL, AUDREY LEE, nursing administrator, critical care nurse; b. Trimble County, Ky., June 21, 1947; d. Albert Louis and Florence Wilma (Fitzgerald) Rosell; m. James DeVon Powell, Feb. 21, 1970. ADN, Ind. U.-Purdue U., Indpls., 1974; BSN, Marian Coll., Indpls., 1981; postgrad., Ind. U., Indpls., 1983. RN, Ind. Staff nurse, head nurse, clin. specialist, supr. St. Francis Hosp., Beech Grove, Ind., coord. nursing standards; dir. nursing Clay County Hosp., Brazil, Ind., Winona Meml. Hosp., Indpls. Mem. Ind. Nurses Assn., Ind. Nursing Diagnosis Assn. (past pres.), Sigma Theta Tau. Home: Box 333 RR 1 Box 333 Reelsville IN 46171-9783

POWELL, BARRY BRUCE, classicist; b. Sacramento, Apr. 30, 1942; s. Barrett Robert and Anita Louise (Burns) P.; m. Patricia Ann Cox; children: Elena Melissa, Adam Vincent. BA in Classics, U. Calif., Berkeley, 1963, PhD, 1971; MA, Harvard U., 1965. Asst. prof. Northern Ariz. U., Flagstaff, 1970-73; asst. prof. to prof. U. Wis., Madison, 1973—, chmn. dept. classics, 1985-92, chmn. program integrated liberal studies. Author: Composition by Theme in the Odyssey, 1973, Homer and the Origin of the Greek Alphabet, 1991, Classical Myth, 1995; contbr. articles to profl. jours. Woodrow Wilson fellow, 1965. Mem. Am. Philol. Assn., Am. Sch. Classical Studies at Athens (mng. com), Archeol. Inst. of Am., Classical Assn. of Midwest and South, Am. Academy in Rome, Phi Beta Kappa (former pres. Madison chpt.). Home: 1210 Sweetbriar Rd Madison WI 53705-2228 Office: Univ Wis Dept Classics Madison WI 53707

POWELL, BILL JAKE, newspaper executive; b. Pottsboro, Tex., July 12, 1936; s. Murlan Weaver and Irene (Jones) P.; m. Theresa Leverette, Feb. 3, 1955; children—Richard, Kerry, Eileen, Joanna. Grad. high sch., Dallas. Ind. dealer Dallas Times Herald, 1954-70, circulation dir., 1970-80, sr. v.p., 1984-87; circulation dir. Phila. Bull., 1980-82; exec. circulation dir. San Antonio Light, 1982-84; exec. v.p. circulation MediaNews Group, Inc., 1987-89; circulation dir. Ft. Worth Star-Telegram, 1989-90; cons., 1990-92; CFO McBride & Powell Inc., Carrollton, Tex., 1992—. Contbr. articles to profl. jours. Mem. Tex. Circulation Mgrs. Assn. (bd. dirs. 1978-79), Internat. Circulation Mgrs. Assn. (bd. dirs. 1979—). Avocations: skiing; softball; tennis. Home: 159 Highland Meadow Cir Coppell TX 75019-5735 Office: McBride & Powell Inc 1303 E Belt Line Rd Carrollton TX 75006-6278

POWELL, BOLLING RAINES, JR., lawyer, educator; b. Florala, Ala., Aug. 10, 1910; s. Bolling Raines and Marie (Arnold) P.; m. Mary Vilette Spaulding, Dec. 10, 1949; children: Bolling Raines, James Spaulding. B.A., Birmingham-So. Coll., 1930; M.A., LL.B., J.D., U. Va., 1934. Asst. prof. law U. Va., 1938-39; partner Paul V. McNutt, Washington and N.Y.C., 1947-50, Powell, Dorsey and Blum, Washington, 1950-62, Powell, Horkan and Powell, Washington, 1962-75; prof. Wythe Sch. Law, Coll. William and Mary, 1969-80; sole practice Gloucester, Va., 1975—; spl. trial counsel to bd. govs. FRS, 1956-62; bd. advisors Ct. Practice Inst., 1973-78. Editor-in-chief: Va. Law Rev., 1934. Chmn. Gloucester United Taxpayers, 1978—; dir. Boy Scouts Am. Fund Raising Campaign, Gloucester County, 1965. Served to lt. col. AUS, 1942-46. Decorated Legion of Merit. Mem. Va. State Bar (bd. govs. adminstrv. law sect.), Ala. Bar Assn., D.C. Bar Assn., ABA, Raven Soc. U. Va., Phi Beta Kappa, Omicron Delta Kappa. Episcopalian. Clubs: Metropolitan (Washington); Farmington Country (Charlottesville, Va.). Home: Warner Hall Plantation Gloucester VA 23061 Office: PO Box 800 Gloucester VA 23061-0800

POWELL, BOONE, JR., hospital administrator; b. Knoxville, Tenn., Feb. 9, 1937; married. BA, Baylor U., 1959; MA, U. Calif., 1960. Adm. intern Marin Gen. Hosp., Greenbrae, Calif., 1959; adm. resident Baptist Meml. Hosp., Memphis, 1960-61; asst. administr. Hendrick Med. Ctr., Abilene, Tex., 1961-69, assoc. administr., 1969-70, administr., 1970-73, pres., 1973-80; pres. Baylor U. Med. Ctr., Dallas, 1980—. Contbr. articles to profl. jours. Mem. Am. Coll. Healthcare Execs., Tex. Hosp. Assn. (chair community svc., trustee). Office: Baylor U Med Ctr 3500 Gaston Ave Dallas TX 75246-2088

POWELL, BURNELE VENABLE, law educator; b. Kansas City, Kans., Mar. 5, 1947; s. Lorenzo Roland and Teola (Sykes) P.; m. Brenda Joyce Venable, June 30, 1973; children: Bradley Venable, Berkeley Venable. BA, U. Mo., Kansas City, 1970; JD, U. Wis., 1973; LLM, Harvard U., 1979. Bar: Wis. 1973, Mass. 1977. Assoc. regional counsel HUD, Boston, 1973-77; grad. law teaching fellow Harvard U. Law Sch., Cambridge, Mass., 1977-79; asst. prof. U. N.C. Sch. Law, Chapel Hill, 1979-84, assoc. prof., 1984-88, prof., 1988—, assoc. dean, 1990-93; vis. assoc. prof. law U. Oreg. Sch. Law, Eugene, 1987; vis. prof. law Washington U., St. Louis, summer 1990; cons. Administrv. Conf. U.S., Washington, 1983-86; arbitrator Nat. Future Adminstrn., Chgo., 1990. Bd. dirs. Consumers Union, 1993—, Planned Parenthood of Orange and Durham Counties, 1992—. Mem. ABA (coms. 1987—, chmn. standing com. on profl. discipline 1991—, N.C. ethics com. 1990-92), AAUP (chpt. pres. 1990-91), ALI, Am. Bar Found., Assn. Am. Law Schs. (coms. 1981—). Democrat. Unitarian. Home: 2003 S Hawick Ct Chapel Hill NC 27516-1607 Office: U of NC Sch of Law Van Hecke Wettach Hall CB 3380 Rm 210 Chapel Hill NC 27599-3380

POWELL, CAROLYN WILKERSON, music educator; b. Hamburg, Ark., Oct. 9, 1920; d. Claude Kelly and Mildred (Hall) Wilkerson; m. Charles Luke Powell, Dec. 12, 1923; children: Charles Luke Jr., James Davis, Mark Wilkerson, Robert Hall. AB, Cen. Methodist, Fayette, Mo., 1942; MAT, U. N.C., Chapel Hill, 1970. Life Teaching Cert. Mo. Teaching Cert. N.C. Choral dir. Maplewood Richmond Heights Sch., St. Louis, 1943-45; pvt.

piano tchr. Greensboro N.C. Area, Greensboro, 1951-63; organist Presbyterian and Methodist Ch., Greensboro, 1950-61; dir. Ch. Youth Choirs, Greensboro, 1958-61; choral and humanities tchr. Page High Sch., Greensboro, 1963-67; choral dir. Githens Jr. High Sch., Durham, N.C., 1967-80; organist St. Peter's Episcopal Ch., Altavista, Va., 1981-83; chmn. Dist. Choral Festival N.C. Dist., 1968-78; accompanist and music dir. Altavista Little Theatre Altavista, Va., 1981-83. Sunday and vacation schs. tchr., organist Grace Meth. Ch., Greensboro; den mother Boy Scouts Am., Greensboro, 1951-57; mem. Chapel Hill Preservation Soc., 1985—; vol., chapel organist, pediat. tutor U. N.C. Hosps., Chapel Hill, 1984-89. Mem. NEA, AAUW, Music Educators Nat. Conf., Am. Organists Guild, Class-room Tchrs. Assn., Ackland Art Mus. Assn., Chapel Hill Preservation Soc., Nat. Federated Music Club Euterpe, Chapel Hill Country Club, U. Woman's Club, The Carolina Club, Delta Kappa Gamma. Avocations: reading, golf, needlework, gardening, travel and antiques. Home: 2446 Honeysuckle Rd Chapel Hill NC 27514-6821

POWELL, CHARLES ROLAND, financial services company executive; b. Durham, N.C., Sept. 10, 1940; s. George Dowell and Anna Freances (Redfern) P.; m. Dorothy Laverne Vandegrift, Aug. 25, 1963; children: Kimberly Anne Powell Lloyd, Susan Elizabeth Powell Courtney, Charls Vandegrift. B Indsl. Engring., Ga. Inst. Tech., 1962; MBA, Harvard U., 1964. Registered profl. engr., Ga. Mgmt. cons. Arthur Andersen & Co., Atlanta, 1966-76; sr. v.p. Barclays Comml. Corp. (formerly BarcalysAm./Comml.), Charlotte, N.C., 1976—. Deacon, treas., Carmel Presbyn. Ch., Charlotte, 1981-83. 1st lt. U.S. Army, 1964-66. Mem. Charlotte C. of C. (mem. fgn. trade com. 1980, team leader for membership drive 1989), Carmel Country Club. Democrat. Avocations: tennis, reading. Office: Barclays Comml Corp 201 S Tryon St Charlotte NC 28202-3201

POWELL, CLINTON COBB, radiologist, physician, former university administrator; b. Hartford, Conn., Mar. 9, 1918; s. Harry Havey and Nita Florence (Nass) P.; m. Frances Arlene Collins, Apr. 2, 1944; children: Pamela Powell Kellogg, Brenda Joyce, Donna Sue Powell Mason. B.S., Mass. Inst. Tech., 1940; M.D., Boston U., 1944; student, U. Chgo., 1947-48. Diplomate: Am. Bd. Radiology, Nat. Bd. Med. Examiners. Intern U.S. Marine Hosp., Boston, 1944-45; commd. asst. surgeon USPHS, 1946, med. dir., 1956; staff mem. indsl. hygiene research lab. NIH, 1946-47, radiation safety officer, 1948-51; resident radiology USPHS Hosp., Balt., 1951-52; fellow radiology U. Pa. Hosp., 1952-54; staff physician radiation therapy, clin. center NIH, 1954-55; grants analyst, research grants and fellowship br. Nat. Cancer Inst., 1955-56; chief radiol. health med. program, div. spl. health services USPHS, 1956-58; exec. sec. radio and surgery study sect., div. research grants NIH, 1958-59, asst. chief research grants rev. br., div. research grants, 1959-60, dep. chief div., 1960-61; asst. dir. Nat. Inst. Allergy and Infectious Diseases, 1961-62; dir. Nat. Inst. Gen. Med. Scis., NIH, 1962-64; assoc. coordinator med. and health scis. U. Calif., 1964-66, coordinator, 1966-71, spl. asst. to pres. for health affairs, 1971-79, spl. asst. emeritus, 1979—; Mem. Internat. Commn. Radiol. Protection, 1965-68; mem. com. Nat. Com. Radiation Protection, 1956-68, exec. com., 1957-67, ad hoc subcom. wide-spread radioactive contamination, 1958-60, subcom. 1, 1960—; mem. radiol. physics fellowship bd. AEC, 1958-63; com. radiation effects Am. Thoracic Soc., 1957—; com. use radioisotopes in hosps. Am. Hosp. Assn., 1953—; subcom. radiol. health Assn. State and Territorial Health Officers, 1956-58. Contbr. numerous articles profl. jours. Served with USNR, 1945-46. Fellow AAAS; mem. Am. Coll. Radiology (commn. radiol. units, standards and protection 1957—, chmn. com. radiation exposure of women), AMA, Am. Pub. Health Assn. (program area com. radiol. health 1959), Radiol. Soc. N.Am., Radiation Research Soc., Health Physics Soc., Assn. for Acad. Health Centers (dir. 1969-70).

POWELL, COLIN LUTHER, army officer; b. N.Y.C., Apr. 5, 1937; s. Luther and Maud Ariel (McKoy) P.; m. Alma V. Johnson, Aug. 25, 1962; children: Michael, Linda, Annemarie. B.S., CUNY, 1958; M.B.A., George Washington U., 1971. Commd. 2d lt. U.S. Army, 1958; advanced through grades to gen., 1989; comdr. 2d Brigade, 101st Airborne Div., 1976-77; exec. asst. to sec. Dept. Energy, 1979; sr. mil. asst. to sec. Dept. Def., 1979-81; asst. div. comdr. 4th Inf. Div. Dept. Def., Ft. Carson, Colo., 1981-83; mil. asst. to Sec. of Def. Dept. Def., Washington, 1983-86; assigned to U.S. V Corps, Europe, 1986-87; dep. asst. to the pres. for nat. security affairs The White House, Washington, 1987; asst. to Pres. for nat. security affairs Washington, 1987-89; comdr.-in-chief Forces Command, Ft. McPherson, Ga., 1989—; chmn. Joint Chiefs of Staff The Pentagon, Washington, 1989-93. Decorated Legion of Merit, Bronze Star, Air medal, Purple Heart; recipient Medalof Freedom (2); named hon. knight comdr. Most Honorable Order of the Bath QueenElizabeth II, 1993; The White House fellow, 1972-73. Mem. Assn. U.S. Army. Episcopalian. Office: Ste 767 909 N Washington St Alexandria VA 22314

POWELL, DAVID, manufacturing company executive. Chmn., chief exec. officer A.B. Dick Co., Chgo. Office: Gec Incorporated 5700 W Touhy Ave Niles IL 60648-4606

POWELL, DAVID GREATOREX, public affairs executive; b. Princeton, N.J., Apr. 7, 1933; s. Richard Chew P. and Clare Davis Todd; m. Joan Van Nostrand Hitch, Mar. 27, 1956; children: Katherine Dexter Wood, Clare Davis Pitney, Elizabeth Todd. A.B. cum laude, Princeton U., 1954. Asst. mgr. pub. relations Esso Europe Inc., London, 1966-68; asst. to pres. Esso Iberia, Madrid, 1968-70; sr. pub. affairs adv. Exxon Corp., N.Y.C., 1970-74, mgr. pub. info., 1974-76; mgr. pub. affairs Exxon Chem. Co., 1976-79; sr. v.p. pub. affairs AlliedSignal Inc., Morristown, N.J., 1979—; chmn. conf. bd. Pub. Affairs Research Council, 1985-88, mem. exec. com., 1985—. Trustee Ind. Coll. Fund, N.J., 1981-87, Centenary Coll., 1986—, The Seeing Eye Inc., 1988—; bd. dirs. Nat. Fgn. Trade Coun., 1988—, exec. com., 1990—; bd. dirs. United Way Morris County, 1980-87; dir. Pub. Affairs Coun., 1985, vice chmn. 1988—, chmn., 1991-92; membership corp. of Morristown Meml. Hosp., 1984, bd. dirs., 1988—. Mem. N.J. C. of C. (bd. dirs. 1985). Clubs: Somerset Hills Country, Somerset Lake & Game (N.J.); Adirondack League (N.Y.). Office: AlliedSignal Inc PO Box 3000 Morristown NJ 07962-2301

POWELL, DON WATSON, medical educator, physiology researcher; b. Gadsden, Ala., Aug. 29, 1938; s. Gordon C. and Ruth (Bennett) P.; children: Mary Paige, Drew Watson, Shawnee Margaret. BS with honors, Auburn U., 1960; MD with highest honors, Med. Coll. Ala., Birmingham, 1963. Diplomate Am. Bd. Internal Medicine, Am. Bd. Gastroenterology. Intern, resident P.B. Brigham Hosp., Boston, 1963-65; resident Yale U. Sch. Med., New Haven, 1968-69, spl. NIH fellow in physiology, 1969-71; asst. prof. medicine U N.C., Chapel Hill, 1971-74, assoc. prof., 1974-78, prof., 1978-91; chief divsn. Digestive Diseases U. N.C., 1977-91; dir. Ctr. Gastrointestinal Biol. Diseases, U. N.C., 1985-91, assoc. chmn. for clin. affairs dept. medicine, 1989-91; prof., chmn. dept. internal medicine, prof. dept. physiol. and biophysics U. Tex. Med. Br., Galveston, 1991—; cons. WHO, Geneva, 1980-82, Burroughs-Wellcome, Inc., Research Triangle Park, N.C., 1981-82, Hoffmann-LaRoche, Inc., Nutley, N.J., 1982-93; mem. merit rev. bd. in gastroenterology VA, 1977-80; mem. gen. medicine A-2 study sect. NIH, 1985-89. Assoc. editor: Textbook of Gastroenterology, Atlas of Gastroenterology; mem. editorial bd. Am. Jour. Physiology, 1979—, Am. Jour. Med. Sci., 1984-92, Regulatory Peptide Letter, 1990—, Annals of Internal Medicine, 1993—; contbr. more than 100 articles to profl. jours. Capt. U.S. Army Med. Corps, 1965-68. Recipient Rsch. Career Devel. award NIH, 1973-78, Merit award NIH/NIDDK, 1987; named Outstanding Physician of Yr. Gulf Coast chpt. Crohn's Colitis Found. Am., 1994. Fellow ACP (mem. knowledge self-assessment program VII gastroenterology com. 1983-85); mem. Am. Physiol. Soc., Am. Gastroenterol. Assn. (v.p. 1991-92, pres.-elect 1992-93, pres. 1993-94), Gastroenterology Rsch. Group (chmn. 1988-89), So. Soc. Clin. Investigation, Assn. Am. Physicians, Assn. Prof. Medicine, Am. Clin. and Climatological Assn. Avocation: singing. Office: U Tex Med Br 4.108 John Sealy Annex 301 University Blvd Galveston TX 77555-0567

POWELL, DREXEL DWANE, JR., editorial cartoonist; b. Lake Village, Ark., Nov. 7, 1944; s. Drexel Dwane and Minnie Louise (Ruth) P.; m. Janice Sue Lovell, Apr. 10, 1971. B.S. in Agri-Bus, U. Ark. at Monticello, 1970. Cartoonist Sentinel Record, Hot Springs, Ark., 1970-72, San Antonio Light, 1973-74; editorial cartoonist Cin. Enquirer, 1974-75, News and Observer, Raleigh, N.C., 1975—; syndicated L.A. Times Syndicate, 1979—; lectr. in field. Author: Is That All You Do?, 1979, Surely SOMEONE Can Still Sing

Bass!, 1981, The Reagan Chronicles, 1987. One Hundred Per Cent Pure Old Jess, 1993; freelance artist; designer book jackets. Served with N.G., 1967-68. Recipient Overseas Press Club citation, 1978, Headliners Club award, 1978; named Disting. Alumnus U. Ark. at Monticello, 1999. Mem. Assn. Am. Editorial Cartoonists. Office: 215 S Mcdowell St Raleigh NC 27601-1331

POWELL, DURWOOD ROYCE, lawyer; b. Raleigh, N.C., Nov. 21, 1951; s. Albert Royce and Ruby Rader (Lowery) P.; m. Leej Ida Copperfield, Mar. 1, 1980. BS, U. N.C., 1974, JD, 1979; LLM in Taxation, Emory U., 1985. Bar: N.C. 1979, U.S. Dist. Ct. (ea., mid. and we. dists.) N.C. 1981, U.S. Tax Ct. 1981, U.S. Ct. Appeals (4th cir.) 1984, U.S. Ct. Claims 1984, U.S. Supreme Ct. 1984, D.C. 1988, U.S. Ct. Appeals (D.C. cir.) 1988, N.Y. 1989. Mgmt. analyst GAO, Norfolk, Va., 1974-76; mem. tax staff Arthur Andersen & Co., Washington, 1979-80; assoc. Biggs, Meadows, Etheridge & Johnson, Rocky Mount, N.C., 1980-82; Biggs Law Firm, Rocky Mount, 1982-83; ptnr. Maupin, Taylor, Ellis & Adams, Raleigh, N.C., 1985—; also bd. dirs.; adj. prof. corp. taxation Grad. Sch. Bus., U. N.C.-Chapel Hill, 1989-92; faculty Duke U. Tax and Estate Planning Conf., 1991; mem. negotiation project Harvard U., Cambridge, Mass., 1992. Contbr. articles to profl. publs. mem. tax reform com. Duke U., Washington, 1988. Mem. ABA (tax, corp., banking and securities sects.), N.C. Bar Assn. (tax and corp. sects.), Phi Beta Kappa, Phi Eta Sigma. Home: 4917 Rembert Dr Raleigh NC 27612-6239 Office: Maupin Taylor Ellis & Adams 3200 Beech Leaf Ct Raleigh NC 27604-1063

POWELL, EARL ALEXANDER, III, art museum director; b. Spartanburg, S.C., Oct. 24, 1943; s. Earl Alexander and Elizabeth (Duckworth) P.; m. Nancy Landry Powell, July 17, 1971; children—Cortney, Channing, Sumner. AB with honors, William Coll., 1966; AM, Harvard U., 1970, PhD, 1974. Teaching fellow in fine arts Harvard U., 1970-74; curator Michener Collection U. Tex., Austin, 1974-76, asst. prof. art history, 1974-76; mus. curator, sr. staff asst. to asst. dir. and chief curator Nat. Gallery Art, Washington, 1976-78, exec. curator, 1979-80; dir. Los Angeles County Mus. Art, 1980-92, Nat. Gallery Art, Washington, 1992—; career advisor Harvard U.; mem. fine arts adv. panel Fed. Res. Bank, Commn. Pres. of White House, Pres.' Commn. on Arts and Humanities, Coun. Arts and Humanities, Fed. Coun. on Arts and Humanities, Nat. Portrait Gallery Commn., Pennsylvania Ave. Devel. Corp., Scholarly Adv. Coun., Japan Am. Nat. Mus. Author: American Art at Harvard, 1973, Selections from the James Michener Collection, 1975, Abstract Expressionists and Imagists: A Retrospective View, 1976, Milton Avery, 1976, The James A. Michener Collection: Twentieth Century American Painting, catalogue raisonne, 1978, Thomas Cole monograph, 1990. Trustee Pitzer Coll.; mem. vis. com. Williams Coll. Mus. Art. Served with U.S. Navy, 1966-69, comdr. Res., 1976-80. Harvard U. traveling fellow, 1973-74; recipient King Olav medal, 1978, Bicentennial medal Williams Coll., 1995; decorated chevalier Arts and Letters. Mem. Walpole Soc., Am. Assn. Mus. (co-chmn. commn. on mus. for a new century), Am. Assn. Mus. Dirs. (trustee), Am. Fedn. Arts (trustee), White House Hist. Assn. (trustee), Nat. Trust Hist. Preservation, Thomas Jefferson Meml. Found.

POWELL, EARL W., chemicals executive; b. 1939. Ptnr. Peat, Marwick, Mitchell & Co., CPAs, Miami, 1965-85; chmn., chief exec. officer Atlantis Plastics, Inc., Miami, 1984—; also pres. Atlantis Plastics, Inc. *

POWELL, EDMUND WILLIAM, lawyer; b. St. Paul, Dec. 23, 1922; s. George L. and Mary (Sexton) P.; m. Ellen M. Williams, May 7, 1949; children—Susan Marie, Sarah Ann, Daniel. Student, St. Thomas Coll., St. Paul, 1941-43, U. Minn., 1943, 46; LL.B., Marquette U. 1948. Bar: Wis. bar 1948. Pvt. practice Milw., 1948—; pres. firm Borgelt, Powell, Peterson & Frauen and predecessors, 1948-90. Served with USNR, 1943-45; to capt. USMCR, 1945-46, 52-53. Fellow Am. Coll. Trial Lawyers; mem. State Bar Wis. (sec. 1964-65, bd. govs. 1961-63, 65-67, sec., dir. ins. sect. 1962-69), Marquette Law Alumni Assn. (pres., dir. 1957-60). Club: Town (Milw.). Home: 4611 N Lake Dr Milwaukee WI 53211-1255 Office: 735 N Water St Milwaukee WI 53202-4100

POWELL, ERNESTINE BREISCH, retired lawyer; b. Moundsville, W.Va., Feb. 16, 1906; d. Ernest Elmer and Belle (Wallace) Breisch; student Dayton YMCA Law Sch., 1929; m. Roger K. Powell, Nov. 15, 1935; children—R. Keith (dec.), Diane L.D., Bruce W. Admitted to Ohio bar, 1929; tax analyst tax dept. Wall, Cassell & Groneweg, Dayton, Ohio, 1929-31; practiced law, 1931-42; gen. counsel for Dayton Jobbers and Mfrs. Assn., 1931-41; mem. firm Powell, Powell & Powell, Columbus, Ohio, 1944-86, ret. Ohio chmn. Nat. Woman's Party, Washington, 1950-51, nat. chmn., 1953, hon. nat. chmn. Pres. vol. activities com. Columbus State Sch., 1960-61, mem. bd. trustees, 1957-59. Mem. Nat. Assn. Women Lawyers, Am., Ohio, Columbus bar assns., Nat. Soc. Arts and Letters (pres. Columbus chpt. 1963-64), Nat. Lawyers Club (charter mem.). Co-author: Tax Ideas, 1955; Estate Tax Techniques, 1956-90. Editor-in-chief: Women Lawyers Jour., 1943-45. Office: 103 Charleston Ave Columbus OH 43214-1101

POWELL, GEORGE EVERETT, JR., motor freight company executive; b. Kansas City, Mo., June 12, 1926; s. George Everett and Hilda (Brown) P.; m. Mary Catherine Kuehn, Aug. 26, 1947; children: George Everett III, Nicholas K., Richardson K., Peter E. Student, Northwestern U. With Riss & Co., Inc., Kansas City, Mo., 1947-52, treas., 1950-52; with Yellow Freight System, Inc., Kansas City, Mo., 1952—, pres., 1957-68, chmn. bd., 1968—; pres. Yellow Freight Systems, Inc. of Del., Overland Park, Kans., 1987-88; dir. 1st Nat. Charter Corp., Butler Mfg. Co. Trustee, mem. exec. com. Mid-West Research Inst., Kansas City, Mo., from 1961, chmn. bd. trustees, from 1968; bd. govs. Kansas City Art Inst., from 1964, chmn. bd. trustees, 1973-75. Served with USNR, 1944-46. Mem. Kansas City C. of C. (bd. dirs. 1964-68). Office: Yellow Corp 10777 Barkley St Overland Park KS 66211-1161

POWELL, GEORGE EVERETT, III, trucking company executive; b. Kansas City, Mo., Oct. 18, 1948; s. George Everett Jr. and Mary Catherine (Kuehn) P.; m. Wendy Jarman, July 29, 1972; children: Jessica Jarman, Ashley Sinclair. BSBA, Ind. U., 1970. From planning analyst trainee to pres., chief exec. officer Yellow Freight System Inc. of Del. (now Yellow Corp.), Overland Park, Kans., 1971—; also chmn. bd. dirs. Yellow Freight System, Inc., Overland Park, Kans.; pres., CEO Yellow Freight System, Inc. of Del. Trustee Midwest Rsch. Inst.; mem. Powell Family Found., Kansas City Pub. TV. Mem. Young Pres.'s Orgn. Home: 5801 Ward Pky Kansas City MO 64113-1155 Office: Yellow Corp 10777 Barkley PO Box 7563 Overland Park KS 66211

POWELL, GEORGE VAN TUYL, lawyer; b. Seattle, May 14, 1910; s. John Havard and Elizabeth Sargent (Gastman) P.; m. Katherine Jaynes, Aug. 22, 1933; children—Jane Powell Thomas, George Van Tuyl, Lisa Katherine. Grad., Phillips Exeter Acad., 1927; A.B., Princeton, 1931; LL.B., U. Wash., 1934. Bar: Wash. bar 1935. Pvt. practice Seattle; counsel Lane Powell Spears Lubersky. Mem. Wash. Ho. of Reps., 1947-53; Commr. Uniform State Laws, 1952-64; Regent U. Wash., 1965-77. Served to lt. USNR, 1944-46. Mem. ABA (past del.), Wash. Bar Assn. (past bd. govs.). Clubs: Seattle Golf (Seattle) (past pres.), University (Seattle) (past pres.), Rainier (Seattle). Home: 1620 43rd Ave E Apt 2C Seattle WA 98112-3202 also: 13947 Silven Ave NE Bainbridge Is WA 98110-4275 Office: 1420 5th Ave Ste 4100 Seattle WA 98101-2338

POWELL, H. JEFFERSON, law educator; b. 1954. BA, U. Wales, A.M. 1977; MDiv, Duke U., 1979, JD, 1982. Bar: N.C. Law clk. to Hon. Sam J. Ervin, III U.S. Ct. Appeals (4th cir.), Morganton, N.C., 1982-83; rsch. assoc. Yale U., 1983-84; assoc. prof. Iowa U., 1984-88, prof., 1988-89; prof. law and divinity Duke U., Durham, N.C., 1989—. Office: Duke U Sch Law Durham NC 27706

POWELL, HAROLD FRYBURG, food products executive; b. Corry, Pa., Oct. 18, 1932; s. Harold K. and Freda (Fryburg) P.; m. Jacqueline Williams, May 14, 1955; children: Jeffery, Stephen. BS in Econs., U. Pa., 1954; post-grad., Western Res. U. Securities analyst Cen. Nat. Bank, Cleve., 1955-61; asst. treas. Carling Brewing Co., Cleve., 1961-63; div. contr. Carling Brewing Co., St. Louis, 1963-67; mgr. corp. planning Philip Morris Inc., N.Y.C.,

1967-69, asst. to corp. pres., 1969-71; v.p. Benson & Hedges (Can.) Ltd., Toronto, Ont., Can., 1971-74; v.p. fin. Standard Brands Ltd., Montreal, Que., Can., 1974-76; Internat. Standard Brands Inc., N.Y.C., 1976-77; p.s., treas. Standard Brands Inc., N.Y.C., 1977-79, v.p., corp. comptr., 1979-80, sr. v.p., chief fin. officer, 1980-81; pres., chief exec. officer Nabisco Brands Ltd., Toronto, 1982-83; exec. v.p., chief fin. officer Nabisco Brands Inc., N.Y.C., 1984; exec. v.p. Internat. Nabisco Brands Inc., N.Y.C., 1983-84, pres., 1986—. Home: 1062 Smith Ridge Rd New Canaan CT 06840-2330

POWELL, HARVARD WENDELL, former air force officer, business executive; b. Duluth, Minn., Feb. 1, 1915; s. Edgar S. and Leona (Bush) P.; m. Audrey Barker, June 18, 1941; children: Mark Horton, Anne Bush. B.S., U. Minn., 1950, J.D., 1951; grad., Indsl. Coll. Armed Forces, 1956. Commd. 2d lt. USAAF, 1940; advanced through grades to brig. gen. USAF, 1959; command pilot, comdr. China, 1943-45; dir. procurement and prodn. USAF, 1958; vice comdr. Air Force Space Systems Div., 1960, ret., 1963; v.p. mgmt. planning and service N.Am. Rockwell, 1963-70; pres., chief exec. officer A.J. Industries, Inc., Los Angeles, 1970—; also dir.; pres. A.J. Land Co.; Juneau Hydroelectric, Inc.; dir. Devel. Services, Inc., Sargent Engring. Co., Roberts-Gordon Appliance Ltd., Calif. Bankers Trust Corp.; Mem. Gov. Calif. Commn. Ednl. Reform; dir. small bus. and econ. utilization policy Office Sec. Def., 1971-77; internat. bus. cons., 1977—. Decorated D.F.C., Air medal with 2 oak leaf clusters, Legion of merit with oak leaf cluster. Mem. Fed. Bar Assn., State Bar Minn., Air Force Assn.

POWELL, JAMES BOBBITT, biomedical laboratories executive, pathologist; b. Burlington, N.C., Aug. 28, 1938; s. Thomas Edward and Sophia (Sharpe) P.; m. Pamela Oughton, Sept. 12, 1969 (div. Sept. 1979); 1 child, Daphne Oughton; m. Anne Ellington, Oct. 20, 1984; children: James Bobbitt (dec.), John Banks, James Rosser, Helen Bobbitt. BA, Va. Mil. Inst., 1960; MD, Duke U., 1964. Diplomate Am. Bd. Pathology. Intern, Duke U. Med. Ctr., Durham, N.C., 1964-65; resident Cornell Med. Ctr., N.Y.C., 1965-67, Englewood Hosp., N.J., 1967-69; founder Biomed. Labs., Burlington, 1969—; pres. Roche Biomed. Labs., 1982—, Warren Land Co.; bd. dirs. First South Bank, Burlington, N.C. Trust Co. Contbr. articles to sci. publs. Trustee Elon Coll. (N.C.), 1981—, N.C. Sch. Sci. and Math.; mem. bd. visitors Duke U. Med. Ctr.; chmn. Alamance Found. Served as maj. M.C., U.S. Army, 1969-72. Fellow Am. Soc. Clin. Pathologists, Coll. Am. Pathologists; mem. Alamance Country Club. Republican. Methodist. Avocations: tennis, walking, military history. Home: 2307 York Rd Burlington NC 27215-3360 Office: Roche Biomed Labs Inc 358 S Main St Burlington NC 27215-5837

POWELL, JAMES HENRY, lawyer; b. N.Y.C., May 1, 1928; s. Milton Jerome and Doris (Unterberg) P.; m. Connie Lu Egger, Oct. 5, 1958; children: David E., Andrew J., Jeffrey K. AB, Harvard U., 1949; LLB, Yale U., 1952. Bar: N.Y. 1952. Assoc. McLaughlin and Stern, N.Y.C., 1955-69; atty. ABC, N.Y.C., 1969-72; assoc. Fried Frank Harris Shriver & Jacobson, N.Y.C., 1972-76; assoc. Patterson Belknap Webb & Tyler, N.Y.C., 1976-80, ptnr., 1980—. Mem. exec. com. Lexington Dem. Club, 1961-63. With U.S. Army, 1953-55. Mem. Assn. Bar City N.Y., City Athletic Club N.Y.C. (bd. govs. 1973-81), Phi Beta Kappa. Office: Patterson Belknap Webb & Tyler 1133 Ave of the Americas New York NY 10036

POWELL, JAMES LAWRENCE, museum president; b. Berea, Ky., July 17, 1936; s. Robert Lain and Lizena (Davis) P.; m. Joan Hartmann; children: Marla, Dirk, Joanna. AB, Berea Coll., 1958; PhD, MIT, 1962; DSc (hon.), Oberlin Coll., 1983; LHD (hon.), Tohoku Gakuin U., 1986; DSc (hon.), Beaver Coll., 1992. Mem. faculty Oberlin Coll., Ohio, 1962-83, also prof. geology, asso. dean, 1973-75, v.p., provost, 1976-83; pres. Franklin and Marshall Coll., Lancaster, Pa., 1983-88, Reed Coll., Portland, Oreg., 1988-91; pres., chief exec. officer The Franklin Inst., Phila., 1991-94; pres., dir. Los Angeles County Mus. Natural History, L.A., 1994—; mem. Nat. Sci. Bd., 1986—. Author: Strontium Isotope Geology, 1972. Fellow Geol. Soc. Am. Home: 150 S Muirfield Rd Los Angeles CA 90004 Office: LA County Mus Natural Histo 900 Exposition Blvd Los Angeles CA 90007

POWELL, JAMES MATTHEW, history educator; b. Cin., June 9, 1930; s. Matthew James and Mary Loretta (Weaver) P.; m. Judith Catherine Davidorf, May 29, 1954 (dec. 1992); children: James, Michael, Mark, Mary Helen, Miriam, John. B.A., Xavier U., Cin., 1953, M.A., 1955; postgrad., U. Cin., 1955-57; Ph.D., Ind. U., 1960. Instr. Kent State U., Ohio, 1959-61; asst. prof. U. Ill., Urbana, 1961-65; asst. prof. Syracuse U., N.Y., 1965-67, assoc. prof., 1967-72, prof. history, 1972—; dir. Ranke Cataloging Project, 1977—. Author: Medieval Monarchy and Trade, 1962, Civilization of the West, 1967, Anatomy of a Crusade, 1213-1221, 1986, 2d edit., 1990, Albertanus of Brescia: The Pursuit of Happiness in the Early Thirteenth Century, 1992; translator: Liber Augustalis, 1971; editor: Innocent III: Vicar of Christ or Lord of the World, 1963, revised and enlarged 2d edit., 1994, Medieval Studies, 1976, 2d edit., 1992; (with George G. Iggers) Leopold von Ranke and the Shaping of the Historical Discipline, 1989, Muslims Under Latin Rule, 1100-1300, 1990; contbr. articles to profl. jours. NEH grantee, 1977-84, 86; Fritz Thyssen Stiftung, 1986, 89; John Gilmary Shea prize Am. Cath. Hist. Assn., 1987; grantee Inst. for Advanced Study, Princeton, N.J., 1989-90. Mem. Am. Hist. Assn., Am. Cath. Hist. Assn., Medieval Acad. Am., Soc. for Italian Hist. Studies (coun. 1976-79, v., 1991-92, pres. 1993-95), Midwest Medieval Conf. (pres. 1965-66), Soc. for Study of the Crusades and the Latin East (sec. 1989—). Democrat. Roman Catholic. Home: 114 Doll Pky Syracuse NY 13214-1428 Office: Syracuse U Maxwell School Syracuse NY 13244

POWELL, JOSEPH HERBERT, hospital administrator; b. Etowah, Tenn., Oct. 5, 1926; s. Newton Carter and Savannah (Smith) P.; m. Ann Marie Lockeman, Mar. 10, 1956; children: Charlotte Marie, Margaret Annabelle, Susan Lea. BS, U. Tenn., 1950; MHA, U. Minn., 1955; LHD (hon.), Union U., Jackson, Tenn., 1986. Cert. hosp. adminstr., Tenn. Adminstrv. resident Bapt. Meml. Hosp., Memphis, 1954-55, adminstrv. asst., 1955-58, asst. adminstr., 1958-72, v.p., 1972-75, exec. v.p., 1975-80, pres., chief exec. officer, 1980-92; pres., chief exec. officer Bapt. Meml. Healthcare System, Memphis, 1981—; bd. dirs., vice chmn. Blue Cross-Blue Shield, Memphis; trustee Nat. Com. for Quality Healthcare, Washington, 1985—; mem. Hosp. Rsch. and Devel. Inst. bd. dirs. 1985-91, Pensacola, Fla. Bd. dirs. Nations Bank, Memphis, 1986—, NCCJ, Memphis, 1988—; bd. dirs., vice chmn. Future Memphis, 1991—; mem. devel. coun. U. Tenn., 1989-92. 1st lt. U.S. Army, 1945-46, 51-53. Recipient Silver Hope award Multiple Sclerosis Soc., Memphis, 1989, L.M. Graves award Outstanding Achievement Community Health, 1992. Fellow Am. Coll. Healthcare Execs. (Regent 1978-84, Regents Disting. Svc. award 1987); mem. Am. Hosp. Assn. (bd. trustees 1984-88), Internat. Hosp. Fedn., Tenn. Hosp. Assn. (chmn. 1975-76, Disting. Svc. award 1981), Memphis C. of C. (bd. dirs., vice chmn. 1989—), Crescent Club, Econ. Club, Rotary, Omicron Delta Kappa. Home: 4656 Peppertree Ln Memphis TN 38117-3905 Office: Bapt Meml Health Care System 899 Madison Ave Memphis TN 38146

POWELL, JOSEPH LESTER (JODY POWELL), public relations executive; b. Vienna, Ga., Sept. 30, 1943; s. Joseph Lester and June Marie (Williamson) P.; m. Nan Sue Jared, Apr. 23, 1966; 1 child, Emily Claire. Student, U.S. Air Force Acad., 1961-64; BA in Polit. Sci., Ga. State U., 1966; post grad., Emory U., 1967-70. Press sec. Gov. Jimmy Carter, Atlanta, 1971-74, 75-76, Pres. Jimmy Carter, Washington, 1977-81; columnist Los Angeles Times Syndicate, 1982-87; news analyst ABC News, Washington, 1982-87; prof. Boston Coll., 1985-86; chmn., CEO Powell Adams & Rinehart, Washington, 1987-91, Powell Tate, Washington, 1991—. Author: The Other Side of the Story, 1984. Baptist. Avocations: golf, tennis, hunting, fishing, Civil War history. Office: Powell Tate 700 13th St NW 10th Fl Washington DC 20005-3960

POWELL, KENNETH EDWARD, investment banker; b. Danville, Va., Oct. 5, 1952; s. Terry Edward and C. Anne (Wooten) P.; m. Cicely Grandin Moorman, Jan. 3, 1976; children: Tanner, Priscilla. Student, Hampden-Sydney Coll., 1971-73; BA in Polit. Sci., U. Colo., 1975; JD, U. Richmond, 1978; LLM in Taxation, Coll. of William and Mary, 1982. Bar: Va. 1978, U.S. Dist. Ct. (ea. dist.) Va. 1979, U.S. Tax Ct. 1980. Ptnr. Maloney, Yeatts & Barr, Richmond, Va., 1978-87; ptnr., owner Hazel & Thomas, P.C., Richmond, 1987-94, mem. bus./tax team, internat. bus. team; v.p. Legg Mason, Richmond, Va., 1994—. Vice chmn. Sci. Mus. Va., Richmond,

1984-91; chmn. Va. Police Found., Inc., 1987; bd. dirs. State Edn. Assistance Authority, 1991—; mem. adv. bd. Va. Opera, 1991—; candidate U.S. Congress, Va., 1986. Recipient Disting. Svc. award Fraternal Order of Police, 1986; named Outstanding Young Man of the Yr., Jaycees, 1981, Outstanding Young Alumni, U. Colo., 1982. Mem. ABA, Va. Bar Assn. (chmn. profl. responsibility com. 1989-92, chmn. com. on legal edn. and admission to the Bar 1991—), Richmond Bar Assn., Richmond C. of C. (bd. dirs. 1988), Va. Econ. Developers Assn. (gen. counsel), Va. Bridge Initiative. Presbyterian. Office: Legg Mason Wood Walker Inc Riverfront Plz East Tower 951 E Byrd St Ste 810 Richmond VA 23219

POWELL, LARRY R., chemicals executive. Pres., CEO DSM Copolymer, Inc., Baton Rouge, La. Office: DSM Copolymer Inc 5955 Scenic Hwy Baton Rouge LA 70805*

POWELL, LARRY RANDALL, columnist; b. Texarkana, Tex., Nov. 7, 1948; s. John Calvin and Pearl Mae (Thatcher) P.; m. Martha Jon Muse, Dec. 15, 1991; children: Bret Allen, Bart Randall (twins). AA in Journalism (hon.), Texarkana Community Coll., 1991. Reporter, editor Texarkana Gazette, 1965-68, reporter, asst. mng. editor, 1969-71; sportswriter Shreveport (La.) Times, 1968-69; feature writer Tyler (Tex.) Morning Telegraph, 1969; reporter, editor Fort Worth Press, 1971-75; editor Grand Prairie (Tex.) Daily News, 1975-76; copy editor, page layout editor, nat. editor Dallas Morning News, 1976—, features editor, columnist, 1976—; adj. prof. U. Tex., Arlington, 1982-83. Bd. dirs. Great Pretenders Theatre, Carrollton, Tex., 1981-83, Theatre of the Hill, Cedar Hill, Tex., 1987-88. Recipient 1st pl. headline writing Tex. Gridiron Club, 1974, 1st pl. page one design Tex. UPI Editors assn., 1980, 3rd pl. spot news reporting, 1975, 2nd pl. page layout, 1975, 2nd pl. page layout Tex. AP Mng. Editors, 1972. Home: 1011 Tarryall Dr Dallas TX 75224-4920 Office: The Dallas Morning News Communications Ctr PO Box 655237 Dallas TX 75265-5237

POWELL, LARSON MERRILL, investment advisory service executive; b. Pittsfield, Mass., Mar. 8, 1932; s. Harry LeRoy and Elsie Madeline (Larson) P.; m. Anne C. Millett, Dec. 8, 1956 (div. Oct. 1993); children: Larson Merrill, Anne Coleman, Miles Sloan. AB Harvard U., 1954; student Columbia U. Law Sch., 1957-59. News editor, reporter Boston Daily Globe, 1954, 56-57; security analyst Moody's Investors Service, N.Y.C., 1959-62, regional mgr., 1964-67, v.p., 1967-68; pres. instl. investment mgmt. div. Anchor Corp., Elizabeth, N.J., 1968-70; pres. Res. Research, Ltd., N.Y.C., 1971—, Powell Publs. Corp., N.Y.C., 1980-88. Bd. mgrs. W.Side br. YMCA of Greater N.Y., 1970-79, mem.-at-large citywide bd., 1976-79; chmn. men's com. Am. Mus. Natural History, 1970-72; mem. Boro of Manhattan Community Planning Bd. 7, 1966-69; bd. dirs. Children's Home of Portland, 1986-92, Sweetser Children's Svcs., 1988—; Episcopal Camp and Conf. Center, 1978-80; pres. Wiscasset, Waterville & Farmington Railway Mus., 1994—. With AUS, 1954-56. Fellow Fin. Analysts Fedn.; mem. Internat. Soc. Fin. Analysts, N.Y. Soc. Security Analysts. Episcopalian. Club: Harvard (N.Y.C.); Cumberland (Portland, Maine). Editor, pub. Powell Monetary Analyst, 1971—, Powell Gold Industry Guide and Internat. Mining Analyst, 1976—, Powell Alert, 1980-88. Home: 836 Washington Ave Portland ME 04103 Office: PO Box 4135 Portland ME 04101-0335

POWELL, LESLIE CHARLES, JR., obstetrics and gynecology educator; b. Beaumont, Tex., Dec. 13, 1927; s. Leslie Charles and Tillie Bee (Wallace) P.; m. Jeanne LeBarron Easton, July 30, 1983; children: Jeffrey Johns, Randall Gardner, Daniel Charles, Gerard Paul. B.S., So. Meth. U., 1948; M.D., Johns Hopkins U., 1952. Diplomate: Am. Bd. Ob-Gyn. Intern, then resident U. Tex., Galveston, 1952-55, instr. ob-gyn, 1957-59, asst. prof., 1959-63, assoc. prof., 1963-68, prof., 1968—; cons. Richmond State Sch. 1969—; vis. prof. ob-gyn Moi U., Eldoret, Kenya, 1993-94. Editorial cons.: Tex. Reports Biology and Medicine, 1975, Psychosomatics, 1977, Tex. Medicine, 1978-88; contbr. articles to profl. jours. Pres. Am. Cancer Soc., Galveston County, 1972-73; dir. S.W. conf. Unitarian Ch. Served with M.C., AUS, 1955-57. Recipient Hannah award Tex. Assn. Ob-Gyn, 1955; research grantee HEW, 1966-71; Fulbright scholar Burma, 1975. Mem. Alpha Tau Omega, Phi Beta Pi. Republican. Home: 1906 Back Bay Dr Galveston TX 77551-1211 Office: 800 Ave B U Tex Med Sch Galveston TX 77550

POWELL, LEWIS FRANKLIN, JR., retired U.S. supreme court justice; b. Suffolk, Va., Sept. 19, 1907; s. Lewis Franklin and Mary Lewis (Gwathmey) P.; m. Josephine M. Rucker, May 2, 1936; children: Josephine Powell Smith, Ann Pendleton Powell Carmody, Mary Lewis Gwathmey Powell Sumner, Lewis Franklin, III. B.S., Washington and Lee U., 1929, LL.B., 1931, LL.D., 1960; LL.M., Harvard, 1932. Bar: Va. 1931, U.S. Supreme Ct. 1937. Practiced law in Richmond, 1932-71; mem. firm Hunton, Williams, Gay, Powell and Gibson, 1937-71; assoc. justice U.S. Supreme Ct., 1972-87; chmn. emeritus Colonial Williamsburg Found.; mem. Nat. Commn. on Law Enforcement and Adminstrn. Justice, 1965-67, Blue Ribbon Def. Panel to study Def. Dept., 1969-70. Served to col. USAAF, 1942-46, 32 months overseas. Decorated Legion of Merit, Bronze Star; Croix de Guerre with palms (France); Trustee emeritus Washington and Lee U.; hon. bencher Lincoln's Inn. Fellow Am. Bar Found. (pres. 1969-71), Am. Coll. Trial Lawyers (pres. 1969-70); mem. ABA (gov., pres. 1964-65), Va. Bar Assn., Richmond Bar Assn. (pres. 1947-48), Bar Assn. City N.Y., Nat. Legal Aid and Defender Assn. (v.p. 1964-65), Am. Law Inst., Soc. Cin., Sons Colonial Wars, Commonwealth Club (Richmond), Phi Beta Kappa, Phi Delta Phi, Omicron Delta Kappa, Phi Kappa Sigma. Presbyterian. Office: care US Supreme Ct 1 First St NE Washington DC 20543

POWELL, LEWIS FRANKLIN, III, lawyer; b. Richmond, Va., Sept. 14, 1952; s. Lewis F. Jr. and Josephine (Rucker) P.; m. Lisa T. LaFata; 1 child, Emily. Ba, Washington & Lee U., 1974; JD, U. Va., 1978. Bar: Va. 1978, U.S. Dist. Ct. (ea. and we. dists.) Va. 1979, U.S. Ct. Appeals (4th cir.) 1979, U.S. Ct. Appeals (2d cir.) 1983, U.S. Ct. Appeals (11th cir.) 1992, U.S. Supreme Ct. 1985. Law clk. to judge U.S. Dist. Ct. (ea. dist.), Richmond, 1978-79; from assoc. to ptnr. Hunton & Williams, Richmond, 1979—; pres. young lawyers conf. Va. State Bar, 1986-87. Bd. dirs. William Byrd Cmty. Ho., Richmond, 1982-87, Boys Club of Richmond, 1984-90, Maymont Found., Richmond, 1987-92, St. Christopher's Sch., Richmond, 1989—. Mem. Richmond Bar Assn. (chmn. improvement justice com. 1982-83), 4th Cir. Jud. Conf., Am. Law Inst. Avocations: skiing, mountaineering, backpacking, fishing, duck hunting. Office: Hunton & Williams Riverfront Plz East Tower 951 E Byrd St Richmond VA 23219-4040

POWELL, LINDA, state education official. Commr. of edn. Minn. Dept. Edn. Office: Edn Dept 712 Capitol Sq Bldg 550 Cedar St Saint Paul MN 55101-2233

POWELL, LINDA RAE, educational healthcare consultant; b. Youngstown, Ohio, Sept. 1, 1947; d. Roger Gene and Beverly (Dahlke) P.; m. James Ronald Taylor, Aug. 14, 1985. BSN, Madonna Coll., 1980; MA in Adult Edn., U. Mich., 1988. RN; cert. profl. healthcare quality. Adminstrv. nurse U. Mich., Ann Arbor, 1970-86; coord. exec. spouse program U. Mich. Bus. Sch., Ann Arbor, 1987, 89, exec. dir. Mich. individual entrepreneurial project, 1986-88, bd. dirs. Mich. Individual Entrepreneurial Project, 1991—; ednl. cons. Quality Mgmt. in Healthcare, Ann Arbor, 1988-91; pres., founder Quality Mgmt. Edn. Cons., Ann Arbor, 1991—; nat. healthcare speaker on quality assessment and improvement. Mag. columnist, 1990-92. Mem. Ronald McDonald House of Ann Arbor, 1988—. Mem. Am. Soc. Healthcare Edn. and Tng., Nat. Assn. Healthcare Quality, Assn. Quality and Participation, Am. Soc. Quality Control, Health Alumni Assn. U. Mich. Avocations: cooking, bicycling, dance. Office: Quality Mgmt Ednl Cons Inc 380 Windycrest Dr Ann Arbor MI 48105-3014

POWELL, LOUISE FOX, real estate developer; b. Hickory, N.C., June 14, 1925; d. Lester Lee and Vesta Boliek Fox; m. Nelson Sherril Powell, May 23, 1953 (dec.); children: Cynthia Louise, Joan Marie, Suzanne Jayne. Grad. in Bus., King's Coll., Charlotte, N.C., 1942. Time study engr. Glenn L. Martin Co., Balt., 1942-44; owner, mgr. isenhour Fabric Co., Lenoir, N.C., 1949-53; rsch. mgr. Alfred Politz Rsch., Tampa, Fla., 1957-63; cemetary sales mgr. Southea. Advt. and Sales, Hickory and Atlanta, 1954-56; owner, mgr. Louise Powell Realty, Hickory, 1964—; pres., owner Benson-Fox Assocs., Ltd., Hickory, 1986—; owner, mgr. Fairway Shopping Ctrs., Inc., Hickory, 1989—. Leader Girl Scouts U.S., Hickory and Tampa, 1967—; active First United Meth. Ch., Hickory; mem. Hickory Mus. Arts, 1983—, Am. Legion

Aux., Hickory, 1973—, Hickory Cmty. Theatre. Avocations: helping others, dolls, quilting, dancing, music. Home: 1235 10th St Blvd NW Hickory NC 28601

POWELL, MEL, composer; b. N.Y.C., Feb. 12, 1923. Studied piano from age 4; studied composition with Ernst Toch, L.A., 1946-48; with Paul Hindemith, Yale U., from 1948, MusB, 1952. Mem., chmn. faculty composition Yale U., 1957-69; mem. staff, head faculty composition, formerly dean Calif. Inst. Arts, Valencia, provost, 1972-76, now Inst. fellow, Roy E. Disney chair in mus. composition. Albums include Six Recent Works, 1982-88; composer: Duplicates: A Concerto for Two Pianos and Orchestra (premier L.A. Philharm. 1990, Pulitzer prize for music 1990), Modules for chamber orch. (recorded L.A. Philharm. 1991), Woodwind Quintet (recorded 1991), Setting for Two Pianos (recorded 1992), Settings for Small Orch., 1992 (commissioned by chamber orchs. of St. Paul, L.A., N.J.), Settings for Guitar (recorded 1993), numerous other compositions; subject of profile in New Yorker mag. Recipient Creative Arts medal Brandeis U., 1989; Pulitzer Prize for music, 1990; Guggenheim fellow; Nat. Inst. Arts and Letters grantee. Mem. Arnold Schoenberg Inst. (hon. life). Office: Calif Arts Inst Dept Composition 24700 Mcbean Pky Santa Clarita CA 91355-2340

POWELL, MIKE, olympic athlete, track and field; b. Phila., Pa., 1964. Grad., UCLA. Olympic track and field participant Seoul, South Korea, 1988; set world record for long jump at World Track and Field Championships, Tokyo, 1991; Olympic track and field participant Barcelona, Spain, 1992. Recipient Long Jump Silver medal Olympics, Seoul, South Korea, 1988, Long Jump Silver medal Olympics, Barcelona, 1992. Office: Footlocker Track Club 233 Broadway 4th fl New York NY 10279*

POWELL, NANCY EGAN, elementary education educator; b. Galesburg, Ill., Nov. 5, 1944; d. Robert Matthew and Eva (Fullerton) Egan; m. Dennis Lynn Powell, May 26, 1973; children: Matthew, Susan. BE, Washburn U., 1968; postgrad., Emporia State U., 1973-78, Ottawa U., 1979-85, Avilia U., 1985-89, Portland State U., 1987-88. Cert. K-8, Kans. Tchr. grade 2, permanent substitute tchr. Kansas City Dist. 500, Kans., 1968-69; kindergarten tchr. Kansas City (Kans.) Dist. 500, 1969-91, collaborative kindergarten tchr., 1991—; instr. Math Learning Ctr., Portland State U., 1989—; tchr.'s adv. bd. Kansas Children's Mus., Kansas City, 1988—; presenter S.W. Regional Conf. Kans. Assn. Tchrs. Math., 1989, 90, 92, mem. Kindergarten Curriculum Guide Com., 1988, Math Curriculum Guide Com., 1990, U.S. Russian Joint Conf. Math. Edn., Moscow, 1993, Scope Sequence Writing Team, 1993, Kans. City Math Cadre. Troop leader, trainer Santa Fe Trail coun. Girl Scouts U.S., 1982—; troop leader Mid Am. coun. Boy Scouts Am., 1983—. Grantee Kansas City, Kans. Profl. Devel. Coun. Spl. Edn. Dept., 1990, N.E. Kans. Elem. Sch. Math. Dissemination Project, 1993, 94. Mem. NEA, Internat. Reading Assn., Assn. Childhood Edn. Internat., Nat. Coun. PTA, Nat. Assn. Tchrs. Math., Nat. Assn. Edn. Young Children, Profl. Devel. Coun. Kansas City, Alpha Delta Kappa (v.p. 1986-88, pres. 1988-90, state courtesy chmn. 1992-94). Republican. Methodist. Avocations: art, travel, cooking, reading. Home: 7924 Armstrong Ave Kansas City KS 66112-2547 also: Kansas City Pub Schs Libr Bldg 625 Minnesota Ave Kansas City KS 66101

POWELL, NORBORNE BERKELEY, urologist; b. Montgomery, Ala., July 24, 1914; s. Floyd Berkeley and Eloise (Sadler) P.; m. Elizabeth Mary Balas, Dec. 18, 1939; children—Norborne Berkeley, Barbara Key. M.D., Baylor U., 1938. Diplomate: Am. Bd. Urology. Intern Duke Hosp., Durham, N.C., 1938-39, Charity Hosp., New Orleans, 1939-40; resident Tulane Service, Charity Hosp., 1940-42; practice medicine, specializing in urology Houston, 1942-90; mem. staff Ben Taub Gen. Hosp., Twelve Oaks Hosp., Houston; chief staff Twelve Oaks Hosp., 1974; mem. cons. staff Meth. Hosp., St. Luke's Episc. Hosp.; clin. prof. urology Baylor Coll. Medicine, 1964-90; ret., 1990; Trustee Baylor Med. Found., 1945-55; pres. Twelve Oaks Med. Found., 1976-90. Contbr. articles to profl. jours. Recipient continuing med. edn. award AMA, 1980. Fellow A.C.S., Internat. Coll. Surgeons; mem. Mexican Urol. Assn. (corr.), Am. Urol. Assn. (Sci. Exhbn. 1st prize 1951, continuing med. edn. award 1980), Houston Urol. Soc. (pres. 1955), Can. Urol. Assn. Home: 23 Cedar Cliff Rd Asheville NC 28803-2905

POWELL, REBECCA ANN, secondary education educator; b. Bluffton, Ohio, Oct. 5, 1944; d. Paul Richard and Clara Lucille (Niswander) McDowell; m. William Dean Powell, June 17, 1967; children: Timothy William, Deborah Ann.; AB, Asbury Coll., 1966; MA, Eastern Mich. U., 1978. Cert. tchr. Tchr., history/english Columbus (Ohio) Pub. Schs., 1966-67; tchr., english Lawton (Okla.) Pub. Schs., 1967-68; tchr., social studies Flint (Mich.) Community Schs., 1971-79, Midland (Mich.) Pub. Schs., 1979—; tchr. cons. Mich. Geographic Alliance, 1991—; curriculum developer Midland Pub. Schs., 1985—; insvc. presenter Mich. Coun. for the Social Studies, 1984—; Britton humanities chair Midland County Britton Com., 1992-94. Steering com. mem. Global Emphasis Midland League of Women's Voters, 1992; precinct del. Genessee County, 1974-78. Recipient Apple for the Tchr. award Midland Law Aux., 1988, Fulbright-Hays Seminar Abroad Brazil award Dept. of Edn., 1989, Fulbright-Hays Seminar Abroad Egypt and Zimbabwe award, 1993. Mem. NEA, Nat. Coun. for the Social Studies, Nat. Coun. for Geog. Edn., Mich. Coun. for the Social Studies (dist. rep, awards chair 1983—, Mich Outstanding Social Studies Educator of the Yr. award 1989), Mich. Edn. Assn., Midland City Edn. Assn. (bldg. rep.), Assn. for Supervision and Curriculum Devel. Avocations: traveling, reading, walking, collecting mushrooms and trivets. Office: Midland Pub Schs-Jefferson Intermediate 800 W Chapel Ln Midland MI 48640-2966

POWELL, RICHARD C., physicist, educator, researcher; b. Lincoln, Nebr., Dec. 20, 1939; s. William Charles and Allis (Conger) P.; m. Gwendolyn Cline Powell, June 24, 1962; children: Douglas W., David M. BS in Engring., U.S. Naval Acad., 1962; MS in Physics, Arizona State U., 1964, PhD in Physics, 1967. Staff scientist Air Force Cambridge Rsch. Labs., Bedford, Mass., 1964-68, Sandia Nat. Lab., Albuquerque, 1968-71; prof. Okla. State U., 1971-92; prof. dir. optical sci. ctr. U. Ariz., Tucson, 1992—; reviewer numerous physics jours. and funding agys.; cons. laser rsch. with several indsl. and govt. agys. Editor-in-chief Jour. Optical Materials, 1992&; patents include Holographic Gratings in Rare Earth Doped Glasses, with Okla. State U., 1988; contbr. numerous articles to profl. jours. Recipient over 40 grants for rsch. support, 1971—. Fellow Am. Phys. Soc. (co-chmn. Internat. Laser Sci. Conf. 1985, chmn. 1986, vice chmn. Topical Group on Laser Sci., 1986, chmn. 1987, APS rep. Joint Coun. on Quantum Electronics, 1986-90), Optical Soc. Am. (mem. bd. dirs. 1993—, mem. program com. OSA Photoacoustic Spectroscopy Mtg., 1979, mem. nom. com. 1982, organizer Laser Tech. Group Session 1985, com. mem. Meggers award, 1986, 89, 90, chmn. program com. CLEO, 1988, mem. book pub. com., 1992—, mem. awards com., 1994—, mem. organizing coun. Adv. Solid State Laser Conf., 1992—, OSA rep. Internat. Coun. on Optics, 1994—); mem. IEEE (mem. solid state lasers adv. com., 1987—, program com. mem. Nonlinear Optical Materials Mtg., 1994), Sigma Xi (hon. lectr. 1983-84). Episcopalian. Avocations: skiing, fishing, softball, jogging, hiking. Office: U Ariz Optical Scis Ctr Tucson AZ 85721

POWELL, RICHARD GORDON, retired lawyer; b. Rochester, N.Y., Jan. 7, 1918. B.S., Harvard U., 1938; LL.B., Columbia U., 1941. Bar: N.Y. 1941, U.S. Supreme Ct. 1955. Assoc. Sullivan & Cromwell, N.Y., 1941-52; ptnr. Sullivan & Cromwell, 1952-85. Former mem. bd. mgrs. Englewood (N.J.) Community Chest; trustee, elder 1st Presbyterian Ch. Mem. ABA, Assn. Bar City of N.Y., Am. Law Inst. Home: 200 E 65th St # 33N New York NY 10021-6603

POWELL, RICHARD PITTS, writer; b. Phila., Nov. 28, 1908; s. Richard Percival and Lida Catherine (Pitts) P.; m. Marian Carleton Roberts, Sept. 6, 1932 (dec. Nov. 1979); children: Stephen Barnes, Dorothy Louise; m. Margaret M. Cooper, 1980. Grad., Episcopal Acad., 1926; A.B., Princeton, 1930. Reporter Phila. Evening Ledger, 1930-40; with N.W. Ayer & Son, Phila., 1940-58; mem. pub. relations dept. N.W. Ayer & Son, 1940-42, charge info. services, 1949-58, v.p., 1951-58. Author: mystery books Don't Catch Me, 1944, All Over but the Shooting, 1944, Lay That Pistol Down, 1945, Shoot If You Must, 1946, And Hope to Die, 1947, Shark River, 1950, Shell Game, 1950, A Shot in the Dark, 1952, Say It with Bullets, 1953, False Colors, 1955; novels The Philadelphian, 1957, Pioneer, Go Home, 1959, The Soldier, 1960, I Take This Land, 1963, Daily and Sunday, 1965, Don

Quixote, U.S.A, 1966, Tickets to the Devil, 1968, Whom the Gods Would Destroy, 1970, Florida: A Picture Tour, 1972; novel under pen name Jeremy Kirk The Build-Up Boys, 1951; Contbr. short stories, articles, serials to mags. Served as lt. AUS, 1942-46; chief news censor 1945, S.W. Pacific Theatre. Home: 1201 Carlene Ave Fort Myers FL 33901-8715

POWELL, ROBERT BARROWS, architectural firm executive; b. Rochester, N.Y., Jan. 29, 1938. BArch, U. Mich., 1960; postgrad., U. Pa., 1960. Registered arch. Arch. Glen Paulsen & Assocs., Bloomfield Hills, 1961-63, Albert Kahn Assocs., Detroit, 1963-66; joined Jickling Lyman Powell Assocs., Inc., Birmingham, Mich., 1966—, prin., 1972—, pres., 1987—; mem. faculty Lawrence Tech. U., 1971—. Prin. work include Woodfield Mall, Bentley Hist. Libr., Taubman Libr., Gerald R. Ford Presdl. Libr., High Tech. Ctr., UAW-GM Human Resources Ctr., First Nat. Bldg., U. Mich. Med. Rsch. Complex, many others. Treas. exec. com. Bentley Hist. Libr.; active Friends of Terra Cotta. Mem. ALA, AIA (Detroit chpt., Mich. chpt.), Nat. Trust Hist. Preservation, Mich. Archival Assn. Office: Jickling Lyman Powell Assoc Ste 210 2900 W Maple Troy MI 48084

POWELL, ROBERT ELLIS, mathematics educator, former college dean; b. Lansing, Mich., Mar. 16, 1936; s. James Ellis and Mary Frances (Deming) P.; children: Carl Robert, Glenn Arthur, Charles Addison; m. Lisbeth Nilsen, Nov. 21, 1992. B.A. Mich. State U., 1958, M.A., 1959; Ph.D. Lehigh U., 1966. Instr. math. Lehigh U., 1964-66; asst. prof. math. U. Kans., Lawrence, 1966-69; vis. asst. research prof. U. Ky., Lexington, 1967-68; vis. asst. prof. math. Ind. U., Bloomington, summer 1969; assoc. prof. math. Kent State U., Ohio, 1969-74, prof. math., 1974—, dean Grad. Coll., 1980-92; bd. dirs. Kent State U. Found., 1981-91, Coun. Grad. Schs., 1990-91; mem. Ohio Bd. Regents' Adv. Com. on Grad. Study, 1980-92, chmn., 1983-84. Co-author: Summability Theory, 1973, rev. edit., 1988, Intuitive Calculus, 1973; contbr. numerous articles to profl. jours. NSF summer grantee, 1964, 65, Fulbright award, 1988. Mem. Math. Assn. Am., Midwest Assn. Grad. Schs. (vice chair 1989-90, chair 1990-91, past chair 1991-92). Home: 94 Ridge Side Ct Munroe Falls OH 44262-1076 Office: Kent State U Dept Math and Computer Sci Kent OH 44242

POWELL, ROSALIE, home economist; b. Milw., Oct. 24, 1947; d. William and Daisy P.; BS in Home Econ. Bus., U. Wis., Stout, 1969, MS in Home Econs. Edn., 1974. Extension home economist U. Wis. Extension, Langlade County, 1969-74, Waukesha County, 1976-91, Milw. and Waukesha Counties, 1992-93, family resource mgmt. agent, Milwaukee County, 1994—; instr. U. Wis.-Stout, Menomonie, 1975-76; asst. prof. dept. family devel. U. Wis. Extension, 1976-81, assoc. prof., 1981-87, chmn. family devel. dept., 1984-94, prof., 1987—. Mem. Am. Assn. Family and Consumer Scis., Wis. Assn. Family and Consumer Scis., Nat. Coalition Consumer Edn., Nat. Assn. Extension Home Economists, Wis. Assn. Extension Home Economists, Soc. Nutrition Edn., Wis. Consumers League, Bus. and Profl. Women (chpt. pres. 1970-72), Am. Council on Consumer Interests, Gamma Sigma Sigma (nat. pres. 1975-77), Epsilon Sigma Phi. Home: 403 Sheffield Rd Waukesha WI 53186-6361 Office: 1304 S 70th St West Allis WI 53214

POWELL, SANDRA THERESA, timber company executive; b. Orofino, Idaho, Jan. 9, 1944; s. Harold L. and Margaret E. (Thompson) P. B.S. in Bus./Acctg., U. Idaho, 1966. CPA, Idaho. Acct., Weyerhaeuser Co., Tacoma, Wash., 1966-67; with Potlatch Corp., 1967—, asst. sec., San Francisco, 1981, sec., asst. treas., 1981-89, treas. 1989-92; v.p. fin. svcs., sec., 1993—. Mem. AICPA, Idaho State Bd. Accountancy, Idaho Soc. CPAs. Office: Potlatch Corp PO Box 193591 San Francisco CA 94119-3591

POWELL, SANDY, costume designer. Costumer designer for films including Caravaggio, 1986, Stormy Monday, 1988, The Miracle, 1991, The Crying Game, 1992, Orlando, 1993 (Acad. award nomination best costume design 1993), Being Human, 1994, Interview with the Vampire, 1994, Rob Roy, 1995. Office: care Costume Designer's Guild 13949 Ventura Blvd Ste 309 Sherman Oaks CA 91423*

POWELL, SARA JORDAN, musician, religious worker; b. Waller, Tex., Oct. 6, 1938; d. Samuel Arthur and Mable Ruth (Ponder) Jordan; m. John Atkins Powell, June 24, 1967; 1 child, Marc Benet. B.A., Tex. So. U., 1960; M.R.E., U. St. Thomas, Houston, 1979. Tchr., Chgo. Bd. Edn., 1961-68, Houston Ind. Sch. Dist., 1968-73; youth dir. Gospel Music Workshop Am., Detroit, 1972-76; dir. talent and fine arts Ch. of God in Christ, Memphis, 1974—, dir., cons. ch. hist. mus. and fine arts center, 1980—; mem. nat. reference com. One Nation Under God, Virginia Beach, Va., 1979—; regional sponsor Yr. of the Bible, Washington, 1983; soloist Savoy Record Co., 1972-79; counselor Mike Barber Prison Ministries, 1987—. Bd. dirs. talent coordinator Charles Harrison Mason Edn. Found., 1975—; bd. dirs. James Oglethorpe Patterson Fine Arts Scholarships, 1974—; music and talent dir. Juneteenth U.S.A., 1985—; acad. advisor Oral Roberts U., 1991-92. Recipient 1st Pl. award Record Album, Savoy Record Co., 1972. Best Female Vocalist, Gospel Music Workshop Am., 1973, 74, 75, Gold record, 1978; letter of appreciation Cook County Dept. Corrections, Chgo., 1978; Silver Plate award Assembly of God Ch., Calcutta, India, 1978; letter of appreciation for White House performance, Washington, 1979. Mem. Houston PTA, Houston Peoples Workshop (dir. 1981—), Women in Leadership (adv. bd. 1985—). Home: 7114 S Victor Ave #C Tulsa OK 74136*

POWELL, SHARON LEE, social welfare organization administrator; b. Portland, Oreg., July 25, 1940; d. James Edward Carson and Betty Jane (Singleton) Powell. BS, Oreg. State U., 1962; MEd, Seattle U., 1971. Dir. outdoor edn. Mapleton (Oreg.) Pub. Schs., 1962-63; field dir. Totem Girl Scout Council, Seattle, 1963-68, asst. dir. field services, 1968-70, dir. field services, 1970-72; dir. pub. rels. and program Girl Scout Council of Tropical Fla., Miami, 1972-74; exec. dir. Homestead Girl Scout Council, Lincoln, Nebr., 1974-78, Moingona Girl Scout Coun., Des Moines, 1978—. Pres. agy. dirs. assn. United Way Cen. Iowa, Des Moines, 1987-88, mem. priorities com., 1986-90, chairperson agy. rels., 1994—, chairperson agy. issues, 1989-90; mem. priority goals task group United Way Found., Des Moines, 1985-92; capt. Drake U. Basketball Ticket Drive, Des Moines, 1983-87; sec. Urbandale Citizens Scholarship Found., 1989-93; mem. ad hoc long-range planning com. Urbandale Schs., 1989, mem. budget rev. task group, mem. year-round sch. task group, 1992-93; mem. gender equity task force State of Iowa, 1993—. Mem. AAUW (mem. gender equity task group), Assn. Girl Scouts Execs. (chair nat. conv. 1985-90, nat. bd. dirs. 1985-87, nat. nominating com. 1982-84, nat. treas. 1987-90, nat. pres. 1991—), Urbandale C. of C. (bd. dirs., chair edn. com.), Animal Rescue League of Iowa (bd. dirs. 1992—, shelter chair 1992—), Des Moines Obedience Tng. Club (pres. 1987-89), Des Moines Golden Retriever Club (bd. dirs., pres. 1992—), Altrusa (treas. Des Moines chpt. 1983-85, cmty. svc. chair 1986-87), Des Moines Kennel Club. Democrat. Avocations: sailing, dog showing, obedience and conformation. Office: Moingona Girl Scout Coun 10715 Hickman Rd Des Moines IA 50322-3798

POWELL, THOMAS EDWARD, III, biological supply company executive; physician; b. Elon College, N.C., Aug. 1, 1936; s. Thomas Edward, Jr., and Sophia Maude (Sharpe) P.; m. Betty Durham Yeager, June 19, 1965; children: Frances Powell Barnes, Thomas Edward IV, Caroline Yeager. A.B. in Biology, Va. Mil. Inst., 1957; M.D., Duke U., 1961; M.A., Harvard U., 1966. Surgeon USPHS, 1966-68; co-founder Biomed. Reference Labs., Inc., Burlington, N.C., 1969, exec. v.p., 1969-75, chmn. exec. com., 1979-82, also dir.; exec. v.p. Carolina Biol. Supply Co., Burlington, N.C., 1968-80, chmn., 1977-94, pres., 1980-94; pres. Wolfe Sales Corp., Burlington, 1980-84, Waubun Labs. Inc., Schriever, La., 1980—, Bobbitt Labs., Inc., Burlington, 1983-94; bd. mgrs. Wachovia Bank and Trust Co. N.A., Burlington. Contbr. articles to profl. jours. Bd. dirs. United Way Alamance County, Burlington, 1968—; bd. dirs. Elon Coll., N.C., 1968—, sec., 1975—; bd. dirs. Am. Cancer Soc., Burlington, 1971-81; bd. dirs. Burlington Day Sch., 1973—, pres., 1974-78, 80-84; bd. dirs. N.C. Citizens for Bus. and Industry, Raleigh, 1983-87, Nat. Found. for Study of Religion and Econs., Greensboro, 1984-88, Blue Ridge Sch., Dyke, Va., 1985-90. Served to capt. USAR, 1957-66. Recipient Citizens Service award Elon Coll. Alumni Assn., 1980. Mem. Assn. Biology Lab. Edn., N.C. Acad. Sci., Alamance-Caswell Med. Soc., N.C. Med. Soc. Assn. Venture Founders, Newcomen Soc. Democrat. Mem. United Ch. of Christ. Clubs: Alamance Country (Burlington); Capital City

(Raleigh, N.C.); Congl. Country (Washington); Country of N.C. (Pinehurst); Hope Valley Country (Durham, N.C.); Greensboro City.

POWELL, TREVOR JOHN DAVID, archivist; b. Hamilton, Ont., Can., Feb. 3, 1948; s. David Albert and Morvydd Ann May (Williams) P.; m. Marian Jean McKillop, May 1, 1976. BA, U. Sask., Regina, 1971; MA, U. Regina, Sask., Can., 1980. Staff archivist Sask. Archives Bd., Regina, Sask., 1973-80, dir., 1980-86, acting provincial archivist, 1986-87, provincial archivist, 1988—. Co-author: Living Faith: A Pictorial History of Diocese of Qu'Appelle; author: From Tent to Cathedral: A History of St. Paul's Cathedral, Regina. Archivist Diocese of Qu'Appelle, Regina, Sask., 1971—; registrar, 1979—; archivist, eccles. Province of Rupert's Land, Winnipeg, Man., 1988—; mem. adv. coun. Sask. Order of Merit, 1988—. Mem. Soc. Am. Archivists, Can. Hist. Assn., Commonwealth Archivists Assn., Sask. Coun. Archives (sec.-treas. 1987-88, 90-92, pres. 1994—, Can. Coun. Archives rep. 1994—), Assn. Can. Archivists (bd. dirs. 1979-81), Inst. Pub. Adminstrn. Can. Anglican. Avocations: gardening, walking, reading, music, bird watching. Home: 241 Orchard Cres, Regina, SK Canada S4S 5B9 Office: Sask Archives Bd, 3303 Hillsdale St-Univ of Regina, Regina, SK Canada S4S 0A2

POWELL, VIRGINIA W., lawyer; b. Spartanburg, S.C., Feb. 9, 1948. BA, Queens Coll., U. S.C, 1970; JD, U. N.D., 1974. Bar: N.D. 1974, Calif. 1974, Va. 1975, D.C. 1982. Ptnr. Hunton & Williams, Richmond, Va.; adj. instr. trial advocacy Coll. William and Mary, 1982-90, 92—. Mem. Order of Coif, Phi Beta Kappa. Office: Hunton & Williams Riverfront Plz East Tower 951 E Byrd St Richmond VA 23219-4074

POWELL, WALTER HECHT, labor arbitrator; b. N.Y.C., Apr. 13, 1915; s. Arthur Lee and Stella (Hecht) P.; m. Dorothy Meyer, June 15, 1945; children: Lawrence L., Alan W., Lesley A., Steven H. BS, NYU, 1938, JD, 1940; MA, U. Pa., 1948. Bar: N.Y. 1940, Pa. 1956. Asst. prof. Temple U., Phila., 1946-51, v.p. for pers. resources, 1973-78; asst. dir. pers. Am. Safety Razor, Kingsbury, Ind., 1951-53; v.p., dir. ops. Internat. Resistance Co, Phila., 1953-69, v.p., dir. indsl. rels., 1956-69; sr. v.p. 1st Pa. Banking & Trust Co., Phila., 1969-73; v.p. human resources Temple U., 1973-77; ind. labor arbitrator Phila., 1978—; mem. panel Am. Arbitration Assn., Fed. Mediation and Conciliation Svc., Pa., N.J. labor rels. bds.; lectr. U. Pitts., Temple U., U. Richmond, Vanderbilt U., Am. U., others.; bd. dirs. Auerbach Corp., Phila. Contbr. book chpts., articles to profl. jours. Commr. Phila. Commn. on Human Rels., 1969—; bd. dirs. Opportunities Industrialization Ctr. Capt. AUS, 1942-46. Recipient award Phila. C. of C., 1968. Mem. Am. Mgmt. Assn. (adv. coun. 1963—), Indsl. Rels. Assn., Indsl. Rels. Rsch. Assn. (pres. local chpt. 1966), Nat. Acad. Arbitrators. Home and Office: 2401 Pennsylvania Ave Apt 9-A-7 Philadelphia PA 19130-3027

POWELL, WATSON (SCOT) W., III, insurance company executive; b. 1947. Grad., Simpson Coll., 1969. With Am. Rep. Ins. Co, Des Moines, 1969—, vice-chmn., chief exec. officer. Office: Am Rep Ins co 601 6th Ave Des Moines IA 50309*

POWELL, WATSON W., JR., insurance executive; b. 1917. Chmn. bd. dirs. Am. Rep. Ins. Co., Des Moines, Iowa. Office: Am Rep Ins Co 601 6th Ave Des Moines IA 50309*

POWELL, WILLIAM ARNOLD, JR., retired banker; b. Verbena, Ala., July 7, 1929; s. William Arnold and Sarah Frances (Baxter) P.; m. Barbara Ann O'Donnell, June 16, 1956; children: William Arnold III, Barbara Calhoun, Susan Thomas, Patricia Crain. BSBA, U. Ala., 1953; grad., La. State U. Sch. Banking of South, 1966. With Am. South Bank, N.A., Birmingham, Ala., 1953—, asst. v.p., 1966, v.p., 1967, v.p., br. supr., 1968-72, sr. v.p., br. supr., 1972-73, exec. v.p., 1973-79, pres., 1979-83, vice chmn. bd., 1983-93, also bd. dirs.; pres. AmSouth Bancorp., 1979—; bd. dirs. AmSouth Bank Fla., AmSouth Bancorp. Bd. dirs. Salvation Army, United Way Found.; trustee Ala. Hist. Soc., Ala. Ind. Colls.; bd. visitors U. Ala.; past pres. United Way, campaign chmn., 1987; mem. pres.'s coun. U. Ala., Birmingham; bd. dirs., sec.-treas. Warrior-Tombigbee Devel. Assn., Birmingham Mus. Art, Brookwood Med. Ctr.-AMI, Big Bros./Big Sisters of Greater Birmingham. Lt. AUS, 1954-56. Mem. Birmingham Area C. of C. (bd. dirs.), The Club, Mountain Brook, AmSouth Banking Country Club, Green Valley Country Club (Birmingham), Rotary Internat. Home: 2114 Hickory Ridge Cir Birmingham AL 35243

POWELL, WILLIAM ROSSELL, JR., retired judge; b. Evansville, Ind., Aug. 4, 1926; s. William R. and Nellie M. (Springer) P.; m. Jeri Lacy, Apr. 30, 1955. B.A., Western Ky. U., 1950; J.D., South Tex. Coll. Law, 1961. Bar: Tex. 1961. Mgr. claims Agrl. Ins. Group, Houston, 1954-61; assoc. Foreman, Dyess, Prewett, Henderson & Cantey, Houston, 1961-67; ptnr. Schulman & Powell, Houston, 1967-69, Prappas, Caldwell & Moncure, Houston, 1969-73, Funderburk, Powell & Gibson, Houston, 1973-76; dist. judge Harris County Civil Ct., Houston, 1984-92. Contbr. articles to profl. jours. Served with USAAF, 1944-46; Served with USAF, 1950-51. Mem. Houston, Tex. bar assns., Houston Assn. Claims Men, Tex. Assn. Def. Counsel. Home: 2025 South Blvd Houston TX 77098-5333

POWER, DENNIS MICHAEL, museum director; b. Pasadena, Calif., Feb. 18, 1941; s. John Dennis Power and Ruth Augusta (Mott) Zwicky; m. Kristine Moneva Fisher, Feb. 14, 1965 (div. Aug. 1984); children: Michael Lawrence, Matthew David; m. Leslie Gabrielle Baldwin, July 6, 1985; 1 stepchild, Katherine G. Petrosky. B.A., Occidental Coll., 1962, M.A., 1964; Ph.D. (NSF fellow), U. Kans., 1967. Asst. curator ornithology Royal Ont. Mus.; also asst. prof. zoology U. Toronto, 1967-71; asso. curator Royal Ont. Mus., Toronto, 1971-72; exec. dir. Santa Barbara (Calif.) Mus. Natural History, 1972-94, Oakland (Calif.) Mus., 1994—; biol. researcher; cons. ecology. Editor: The California Islands: Proceedings of a Multidisciplinary Symposium, 1981, Current Ornithology, vol. 6, 1989, vol. 7, 1990, vol. 8, 1991, vol. 9, 1992, vol. 10, 1993, vol. 11, 1993, vol. 12, 1995; contbr. articles to sci. jours. Bd. dirs. Univ. Club Santa Barbara, 1989-92, v.p., 1991-92; bd. dirs. Santa Barbara Chamber Orch., 1990-94, v.p., 1991-94; mem. adv. coun. Santa Cruz Island Found., 1989—; mem. discipline adv. com. for museology Coun. fo rInternat. Exch. of Scholars, 1991-95. Grantee NRC Can., 1968-72, 1974-78. Fellow Am. Ornithologists Union (life, sec. 1981-83, v.p. 1988-89), Am. Assn. Mus. (coun. 1980-83); mem. Cooper Ornithol. Soc. (dir. 1976-79, pres. 1978-81, hon. mem. 1993), Calif. Assn. Mus. (dir. 1990-94, chmn. 1987-89), Western Mus. Conf. (dir. 1977-83, pres. 1981-83), AAAS, Am. Soc. Naturalists, Assn. Sic. Mus. Dirs., Ecol. Soc. Am. Soc. Study of Evolution, Soc. Systematic Zoology, Sigma Xi. Office: The Oakland Mus 1000 Oak St Oakland CA 94607-4892

POWER, EDWARD FRANCIS, newspaper editor; b. Norfolk, Va., Oct. 18, 1953; s. Edward Vincent and Elinor (Kuester) P.; m. Marguerite Ulmer, July 25, 1980; children: Edward Graham, Nicholas Conrad. BA, U. Va., 1976, MA, 1978; postgrad., Columbia U., 1979-80. Staff writer The Virginian Pilot/The Ledger-Star, Norfolk, 1983-85, The Phila. Inquirer, 1985-89; from coord. metro editor to dep. mng. editor The Virginian Pilot/The Ledger-Star, 1989—; guest lectr. U. Va., Old Dominion U. Tidewater C.C. Trustee Virginia Beach Ctr. for the Arts; bd. dirs. World Affairs Coun. Greater Hampton Roads; fundraiser Hampton Roads Com. for Prevention of Child Abuse, 1990-94; chmn. United Way Keel Club, 1991-92, 92-93. Mem. Va. Press Assn. (numerous awards). Avocations: surfing, skiing, sailing, running. Office: Va Pilot/Landmark Comms 150 W Brambleton Ave Norfolk VA 23510

POWER, FRANCIS WILLIAM, newspaper publisher; b. Webster, S.D., Aug. 12, 1925; s. Frank B. and Esther C. (Fowler) P.; m. Margaret Jean Atkinson, Mar. 24, 1951; children: Patricia Ann, John Michael, Kerry Jean. B.B.A., U. N.Mex., 1948. Display advt. sales rep. The Register, Santa Ana, Calif., 1948-51; advt. mgr. Valley Morning Star, Harlingen, Tex., 1951-62; gen. mgr. Pampa (Tex.) Daily News, 1962-69; bus. mgr. Brownsville (Tex.) Herald, 1969-75; pub. The Lima (Ohio) News, 1975-91; v.p. Freedom Comm., Inc. until 1991; ret. 1991; dir. Huntington Nat. Bank, Lima. Served with USNR, 1943-46. Roman Catholic. Clubs: Shawnee Country, Rotary, Elks. Office: Freedom Comm Inc 17666 Fitch Irvine CA 92714-6022

POWER, FRANK RAYMOND, transportation company executive; b. N.Y.C., Aug. 12, 1938; s. Frank and Kathleen Bridget (Raymond) P.; m. Marie Frances Lynch, Oct. 27, 1962; children: Kathleen, Elizabeth, Edward. BCE, Manhattan Coll., 1960; MS, Cornell U., 1964; LLB, NYU, 1966, postgrad., 1968-70. Bar: N.Y. 1966; registered profl. engr. Project engr. Foster Wheeler Corp., Livingston, N.J., 1962-65; lawyer Am. Ind. Oil Co., Livingston, 1966-70; gen. mgr. Japan ops. Am. Ind. Oil Co., Tokyo, 1970-73; mgr. mktg. planning Am. Ind. Oil Co. N.Y.C., 1973-75, mgr. bus. planning, 1976-78; dir. devel. R.J. Reynolds Industries, Winston-Salem, N.C., 1976; v.p. bus. planning Aminoil Inc., Houston, 1978-84; v.p. corp. planning Sea-Land Corp., Edison, N.J., 1985—; lectr. Sophia U., Tokyo, 1971-73, U. Houston, 1984-85, MIT, 1987. Contbr. articles to profl. jours. Mem. Houston Planning Forum, Asia Soc., Japan Soc., Petroleum Club, Tau Beta Pi, Chi Epsilon, Phi Kappa Theta. Republican. Avocations: Oriental art, history. Home: 13208 Glen Mill Rd Rockville MD 20850-3708 Office: Sea Land Corp PO Box 2555 Elizabeth NJ 07207-2555

POWER, JOHN BRUCE, lawyer; b. Glendale, Calif., Nov. 11, 1936; m. Ann Power, June 17, 1961 (div. 1982); children: Grant, Mark, Boyd. AB magna cum laude, Occidental Coll., 1958; JD, NYU, 1961; postdoctoral, Columbia U., 1972. Bar: Calif. 1962. Assoc. O'Melveny & Myers, Los Angeles, 1961-69, ptnr., 1969—; resident ptnr. O'Melveny & Myers, Paris, 1973-75; mem. Social Svcs. Commn., City of L.A., 1993, pres., 1993; lectr. in field. Contbr. articles to profl. jours. Dir. Met. L.A. YMCA, 1988—; mem. bd. mgrs. Stuart Ketchum Downtown YMCA, 1985-92, pres., 1989-90; mem. Los Angeles County Rep. Ctrl. Com., 1962-63; trustee Occidental Coll., 1992—. Root Tilden scholar. Mem. ABA (vice chmn. internat. fin. subcom. 1984-91, comml. fin. svcs. com., com. 3rd party legal opinions, bus. law sect.), Am. Bar Found. (life), Calif. Bar Assn. (chmn. partnerships and unincorp. assns. com. 1982-83, chmn. uniform commn. code com. 1984-85, exec. com. 1987-91, treas. bus. law sect. 1988-89, vice chmn. 1989-90, chmn. 1990-91, chmn. coun. sect. chairs 1992-93, liaison to state bar commn. on the future of the legal profession and the state bar), L.A. County Bar Assn. (exec. com. comml. law and bankruptcy sect. 1970-73, 86-89), Internat. Bar Assn., Fin. Lawyers Conf. (bd. govs., pres. 1984-85), Exec. Svc. Corps. (sec. 1985—), Occidental Coll. Alumni Assn. (pres. 1967-68, pres. circle, exec. com. 1979-82, 91—, vice chair 1992-93, chair 1993-94), Phi Beta Kappa (pres. 1988-90 So. Calif.). Club: California. Office: O'Melveny & Myers 400 S Hope St Los Angeles CA 90071

POWER, JOHN JAY, labor union official; b. Chgo., Sept. 2, 1946; s. Joseph Thomas and Mary Elizabeth (Powers) P.; m. Janet Lynn Pickett, June 20, 1970 (div. Oct. 1977); 1 child, Bevin Mary; m. Joyce Marie Palermo, June 6, 1981. A Bus. Adminstrn., No. Va. C.C., 1968; BSBA, Va. Commonwealth U., 1970. Legis. asst. United Brotherhood Carpenters, Washington, 1973-75, dir. legis., 1975-80; legis. rep. AFL-CIO, Washington, 1980—. With U.S. Army, 1970-72. Democrat. Avocations: reading, theatre. Office: AFL-CIO 815 16th NW Washington DC 20006

POWER, JOSEPH EDWARD, lawyer; b. Peoria, Ill., Dec. 2, 1938; s. Joseph Edward and Margaret Elizabeth (Birkett) P.; m. Camille June Repass, Aug. 1, 1964; children—Joseph Edward, David William, James Repass. Student, Knox Coll., Galesburg, Ill., 1956-58; B.A., U. Iowa, 1960, J.D., 1964. Bar: Iowa 1964. Law clk. to judge U.S. Dist. Ct., 1964-65; mem. Bradshaw, Fowler, Proctor & Fairgrave, P.C, Des Moines, 1965—. Bd. dirs. Moingona coun. Girl Scouts U.S.A., 1968-77, pres., 1971-74; mem. Des Moines CSC, 1971-73; bd. dirs. Des Moines United Way, 1976-82, v.p., 1979-81; trustee Am. Inst. Bus., 1987—, chmn., 1992—; bd. dirs. Iowa Law Sch. Found., 1992—, Plymouth Ch. Found., 1991—, Hawley Found., 1994—; mem. Des Moines Civil War Roundtable. Comdr. USNR, 1965-81. Fellow Am. Coll. Trust and Estate Counsel (state chair 1994—), Am. Coll. Real Estate Lawyers; mem. ABA, Iowa Bar Assn. (chmn. probate, property and trust law com. 1983-87), Polk County Bar Assn., Des Moines Estate Planners Forum (pres. 1982-83). Republican. Mem. United Ch. of Christ. Clubs: Des Moines, Rotary. Home: 4244 Foster Dr Des Moines IA 50312-2542 Office: Bradshaw Fowler Proctor & Fairgrave 801 Grand Ave Ste 3700 Des Moines IA 50309-2727

POWER, JULES, television producer; b. Hammond, Ind., Oct. 19, 1921; m. Dorothy Kutchinsky; children—Robert, Robin. Grad. with honors (Hardy scholar in speech and communications), Northwestern U., 1944. chmn. Power-Rector Prodns., Inc.; pres. Jules Power Prodns. Sr. producer AM America, ABC-TV; former producer TV show Watch Mr. Wizard, NBC-TV; exec. producer TV show ABC-TV News and Pub. Affairs; creator, exec. producer TV prodn. Discovery, 1962-71; TV spl. How Life Begins, 1968, The Unseen World, 1970; producer ABC-TV series AM America, 1975; exec. producer TV series Over Easy, Pub. Broadcasting System, 1976-83; sr. program cons. Pub. Broadcasting System 1987—; producer The Scheme of Things, Disney TV Channel, 1983, ednl. films for ABC-McGraw-Hill, Bits, Bytes and Buzzwords, PBS, 1983, State of the Lang., PBS, 1983; exec producer Take Charge, Pub. Broadcasting System; exec. producer for Mary Martin; author: How Life Begins. Pub. info. advisor Buck Ctr. for Aging Rsch. Served with USAAF, World War II. Emmy award, 11 Emmy nominations; Peabody award (2); Thomas Alva Edison award (3); Ohio State award (6); Am. Film Festival 1st place award (2), Internat. Film and TV Festival award (4); Hammond (Ind.) Ann. Achievement award, 1985. Mem. NATAS (past nat. vice-chmn., past pres. N.Y. chpt.), Writers Guild Am. East, Phi Beta Kappa. Home: 78 Red Hill Cir Belvedere Tiburon CA 94920-1773

POWER, KENNETH D., utilities company executive; b. Weeping Water, Nebr., Dec. 12, 1927; m. Jane Ann Osborne, June 20, 1953; children: Joan, Mary, John. BA in Bus., Cornell Coll., 1952. Installer Northwestern Bell, Davenport, Iowa, 1952-53, traffic chief, 1953-56; dist. supr. Northwestern Bell, Waterlo, Iowa, 1956-58, Mason City, Iowa, 1958-59; dist. mgr. Northwestern Bell, Sioux City, Iowa, 1959-60; bus. office supr. Northwestern Bell, Omaha, 1960-63; staff rep. AT&T, N.Y.C., 1961-63; div. mgr. Northwestern Bell, Mpls., 1963-64; gen. collecting employment coord. Northwestern Bell, Omaha, 1966-67; gen. comml. mgr. Northwestern Bell, Mpls., 1967-68, gen. ops. mgr., 1968-72, sec., treas. Northwestern Bell, Omaha, 1972-78, v.p. support svcs., 1978-81, v.p. residence, 1981, v.p. distbn. svcs., 1981-83, v.p. personnel, 1983-84, v.p. corp. and H.R., 1984-87, v.p., chief exec. officer, 1987-90; ret., 1990; bd. councillor Al-Sar-Ban; bd. dirs. Belluvue Coll., FirsTier Nat. Bank. Mem. United Way of the Midlands; bd. dirs. Western Heritage Mus. With USN, 1946-48. Mem. NCCJ, Nebraskans for Pub. TV, Nebr. Telephone Assn., Nebr. C. of C. (pres. local chpt.), Nebr. Futures, Omaha Club, Plaza Club, Happy Hollow County Club. Office: Northwestern Bell 100 S 19th St Omaha NE 68102-1379

POWER, MARK, journalist, photographer, educator; b. Washington, Mar. 6, 1937; s. Francis C. and Mary H. P.; m. Virginia North; children: Nancy, John, Rachel, Shelagh. Student, Bowdoin Coll., 1957, student Art Ctr. Coll. Design, 1960-61. Asst. prof. art Corcoran Sch. Art, Washington, 1971-83, assoc. prof. art, 1983—, prof. art, 1989—; art critic Washington Post, 1974-76, 85-87; lectr. in field. Curatorial work exhbns. include Icon Gallery, 1969-71, Corcoran Gallery Art, Dupont Ctr., Washington, 1972, 1985; exhibitor (photographs) one-man shows, Dartmouth Coll., 1967, Corcoran Gallery Art, Washington, 1970, 74, 79, Jefferson Pl. Gallery, Washington, 1974, Columbia (Mo.) Gallery, 1974, Diane Brown Gallery, Washington, 1977, Kathleen Ewing Gallery, Washington, 1978, 85, 92, Contrast Gallery, London, 1981, Galerie Chambre de la Claire, Paris, 1983; numerous group shows, permanent collections, Library of Congress, Smithsonian Institution, Iowa Mus. Art, New Orleans Mus. Art, Balt. Mus. Art, Bibliotheque Nationale, Nat. Mus. Am. Art; contbr. over 100 articles on art, film and photography to newspapers and mags. including Washington Post, Washington Star, Afterimage, Photographies, Art in America, Museum Art, Fotographies Views, San Francisco Camera, Times Lit. Supplement; contbg. editor Photo Review, Washington Review. Mem. Soc. Photog. Educators. Home: Murray's Ford Farm RR 1 Box 417 Leesburg VA 22075-8918 Office: Corcoran Sch Art 500 17th St NW Washington DC 20006-4804

POWER, MARY SUSAN, political science educator; b. Hazleton, Pa., July 5, 1935; d. Younger L. and Cleo (Boock) P.; 1 dau., Catherine Laverne. B.A., Wells Coll., 1957; postgrad., Exeter U. (Eng.), 1954-55, Yale U., 1958-59; M.A., Stanford U., 1959-60; Ph.D., U. Ill., 1959-61. Asst. prof. Susquehanna U. (Pa.), 1961-64; assoc. prof. U. Ark., Fayetteville, 1965-68;

assoc. prof. polit. sci. Ark. State U., State University, 1968-79; prof. Ark. State U., 1979—. Author: Before the Convention, Religion and the Founding Fathers, 1984, Jacques Maritsen and the Quest for a New Commonwealth, 1992; contbr. articles to profl. jours. Mem. State com. Ark. Rep. Com., 1968—, sec., 1978-80; alt. del. Rep. Nat. Conv., 1972, 76, 88; mem. Fed. Edn. Commn. of States, 1982-84, Craighead County Election Commn., chmn. Craighead County GOP, 1986-88, vice chmn. 1990—; N.E. regional chmn., 1988—; chmn. Craighead County Sheffeld for Gov., 1990; mem. exec. com. Ark. Rep. party, 1990—, N.E. regional chair, 1988-93; N.E. chair Arkansans for Progress, 1990—. Relm Found. fellow, 1960, NSF-Am. Polit. Sci. Assn. fellow, 1963, Nat. Def. Seminar, Nat. War Coll. fellow, 1973, NEH fellow, 1978, Pres.'s fellow Ark. State U., 1988-89. Mem. AAUP (pres. 1983—, state sec. 1978-80), Ark. Polit. Sci. Assn. (bd. dirs., v.p. 1992-93, pres. 1993—), Am. Polit. Sci. Assn., So. Polit. Sci. Assn., Phi Sigma Alpha, Phi Gamma Mu, Phi Kappa Phi (pres. 1991). Republican. Roman Catholic. Office: Ark State U Dept Polit Sci State University AR 72467

POWER, RICHARD D., manufacturing executive; b. 1949. MBA, Boston Coll., 1970. Acct. Price Waterhouse, Boston, 1970-79; with Tyco Labs. Inc., Exeter, N.H., 1979—; officer Mueller Holdings Corp., Exeter, 1988—, now v.p., CFO. Office: Mueller Holdings Corp 1 Tyco Park Exeter NH 03833*

POWER, THOMAS MICHAEL, economist, educator; b. Milw., May 12, 1940; s. Paul C. and Edith (Thomas) P.; m. Pamela Shore, June 13, 1977; children: Donovan, Kate. BA, Lehigh U., 1962; MA, Princeton U., 1965, PhD, 1971. Instr. Lehigh U., Bethlehem, Pa., 1966-67, Princeton (N.J.) U., 1967-68; from asst. to assoc. prof. U. Mont., Missoula, 1968-78, prof. econ., chmn., 1978—. Author: Economic Value of Quality of Life, 1980, The Economic Pursuit of Quality, 1987, Extraction and the Environment, 1995. Chmn. bd. dirs. Sussex Sch. Bd., Missoula, 1984-93. Woodrow Wilson Nat. fellow, 1963. Mem. Phi Beta Kappa. Avocations: mountaineering, long distance running, skiing. Office: U of Montana Dept Of Econs Missoula MT 59812

POWERS, ANTHONY RICHARD, JR., educational sales professional; b. Chgo., June 14, 1942; s. Anthony Richard and Bernadine Rene (Schwenke) P.; m. Marianne Fugiel, Mar. 15, 1980; children: Kathleen Mary, Anthony Richard III. BA, Quincy Coll., 1964; MS, U. Notre Dame, 1974. Cert. tchr., Ill. Sci. tchr. St. Rene Sch., Chgo., 1964-70; sci. coord. Queen of All Saints Sch., Chgo., 1970-76; sci. and math. product mgr. Ideal Sch. Supply Co., Oak Lawn, Ill., 1976-79, customer svc. mgr., 1980-83, Midwest sales mgr., 1983-85; nat. sales mgr. Ednl. Teaching Aids, Vernon Hills, Ill., 1985-89, v.p., 1989—; lectr., De Lourdes Coll., Des Plaines, Ill., 1970-78; sci. adviser, Archdiocese of Chgo., 1969-76. Author sci. materials. Pres. Orchard Estates Condominium Assn., 1986-87. Mem. Northeastern Ill. Sci. Assn. (pres. 1970-75), U.S. Golf Assn., Internat. Brotherhood Magicians, K.C. Roman Catholic. Avocations: magic, music, golf. Home: 241 Tally Ho Dr Vernon Hills IL 60061 Office: Ednl Teaching Aids 620 Lakeview Pky Vernon Hills IL 60061-1828

POWERS, BRUCE RAYMOND, writer, academic administrator; b. Bklyn., Dec. 10, 1927; s. George Osborne and Gertrude Joan (Bangs) P.; m. Dolores Anne Dawson, July 25, 1969; children: Christopher, Patricia. Student U. Conn., 1947-49; AB, Brown U., 1951, MA, (tuition scholar 61-62), 1965; postgrad. U. Pa., 1966-67. Announcer/mgr. Sta. WNLC, New London, Conn., 1946-47; tng. officer CIA, Dept. Def., 1951-55; TV sales/service rep. NBC, 1955; TV news writer and reporter Movietone News, United Press Assns., Inc., 1955-56; asst. to pres. Gotham-Vladimir Advt., Inc., 1956-57; asst. account exec. D'Arcy Advt. Co., 1957-58; asst. campaign dir. Community Counselling Services, Inc., 1958-59; fund-raising campaign dir. Tamblyn & Brown, Inc., 1959-60; instr. Brown U., Providence, 1963-65, Ryerson Poly. Inst., Toronto, 1966, Nazareth Coll., Rochester, N.Y., 1966-67; asst. prof. English and communication studies Niagara U., Lewiston, N.Y., 1967-86, assoc. prof., 1986-92, prof. emeritus, 1992, chmn. permanent curriculum com. English dept., 1970-71, dir. Film Repertory Center, 1971-92, dir. communication studies program, 1973-87; producer-mgn. dir. Exptl. Film retrospective, N.Y. State Coun. of the Arts, Buffalo, 1972; panelist-judge Artists Com. 2d World Festival of Animated Films, Zagreb, Yugoslavia, 1974; lectr., vis. artist ARTPARK, Lewiston, N.Y., 1975; project dir. Bicentennial Symposium, N.Y. State Am. Revolution Bicentennial Commn., Buffalo, N.Y., 1975-76; research assoc. Center Culture and Tech., U. Toronto, 1977-81; keynote speaker Dupont de Nemours & Co. Health and Safety Conf., Buffalo, 1990. Co-author (with Marshall McLuhan): The Global Village, Oxford, 1989; editor The Film and Study Guide, 1973-74. Served with USNR, 1945-46, PTO. Recipient Carpenter prize in elocution, Brown U., 1951. Mem. MLA, Broadcast Edn. Assn., Soc. Cinema Studies, Am. Soc. Journalism Sch. Adminstrs., Assn. for Edn. in Journalism and Mass Communication, Internat. Exptl. Film Soc. (founding pres. 1971-73), Western N.Y. Audio-Visual Assn., N.Y. Coll. English Assn., Phi Beta Kappa. Roman Catholic. Home: 915 Sun Valley Dr North Tonawanda NY 14120-1952 Office: 105 Main St Niagara Falls NY 14303

POWERS, CHARLES WILLIAM, environmental ethicist; b. Chgo., Sept. 29, 1941; s. Raymond Allen and Elizabeth Browne (Miller) P.; m. Barbara Ley Toffler, Apr. 17, 1982; children: Samuel Bruce Toffler, Anna Laura Elizabeth Powers, Aaron Michael Toffler, Catherine Linnea Powers, Judith Nell Toffler. BA with honors, Haverford (Pa.) Coll., 1963; MDiv with honors, Union Theol. Sem., 1966; diploma, Oxford (U.), 1965; MPhil, Yale U., 1968, PhD, 1969. Instr. Princeton (N.J.) U., 1968-69, Haverford Coll., Pa., 1969; asst. prof. Yale U., New Haven, 1969-73, assoc. prof., 1972-75; dir. pub. responsibility Cummins Engine Co., Columbus, Ind., 1975-76, exec. dir. corp. responsibility 1976-78, v.p. pub. policy, 1978-80; founding exec. dir. The Health Effects Inst., Cambridge, Mass., 1980-84; founding pres. Clean Sites, Inc., Alexandria, Va., 1984-87; founding prin. Resources for Responsible Mgmt., Boston, 1987—; cons. hazardous waste mgmt. Appropriations Com. U.S. Ho. of Reps., Washington, 1987-88; pres. Resources for Responsible Site Mgmt., Boston, 1989-93, Inst. for Responsible Mgmt., Boston, 1985—; founding exec dir. Inst. for Evaluating Health Risks, Irvine Calif., also Washington, 1989; founding exec. dir. Consortium for Risk Edn. and Stakeholder Participation, Piscataway, N.J.; lectr. ethics Tufts U., 1989-92; mem. editorial bds. Environ. Bus. Jour., 1989—, Jour. Indsl. Ecology, 1995—. Author: State Brownfields Policy and Practice, 1995; co-author: The Ethical Investor, 1972, Can the Market Sustain an Ethic?, 1978, Ethics in the Education of Business Managers, 1980; mem. editl. bd. Environ. Bus. Jour., 1989—, Jour. Indsl. Ecology, 1995—. Mem. adv. coun. The Carnegie Commn. on Sci., Tech. and Govt., 1989-93; bd. dirs. The Climate Inst., 1987-93; mem. adv. com. Environ. and Occupational Health Scis., Inc. 1988—; bd. dirs. Sites, Inc., 1984—, Health Effects Inst. Asbestos Sch., 1989-93; counselor U.S. Senator Bill Bradley, 1993. Recipient Rene Dubos Environ. Award Rene Dubos Ctr. for Human Environments, 1991; Inst. of Politics fellow Kennedy Sch. Govt., 1980; Kent fellow Danforth Found., 1966; Columbia U. Internat. fellow, 1965; recipient The Haverford award Haverford Coll., 1972. Office: Resources for Responsible Mgmt 575 Boylston St Boston MA 02116-1236

POWERS, CLAUDIA MCKENNA, state government official; b. Key West, Fla., May 28, 1950; d. James Edward and Claudia (Antrim) McKenna; m. Richard Garland Powers, Dec. 27, 1971; children: Gregory, Theodore, Matthew, Thurston. BA in Edn., U. Hawaii, 1972; MA, Columbia U., 1975. Cert. tchr., N.Y. Rep. Greenwich (Conn.) Rep. Town Meeting, 1979-93, sec. bldg. com., 1982-84, sec. legis. com., 1986-88, 90-93; mem. Conn. Ho. of Reps., 1993—, ranking mem. govt. adminstrn. and elections com., 1995—. Campaign chmn. Greenwich Rep. Town Com., 1984, 85, chmn., 1986-90; sec. Rep. Round Table, Greenwich, 1988-90; bd. govs. Riverside Assn., Greenwich, 1987-91, sec., 1991-92; class mother Riverside Sch., Greenwich, 1984-90; mem. altar guild Christ Ch., Greenwich, 1990—; adminstrv. coord. Greenwich Teen Ctr., 1990-91; alt. del. Rep. Nat. Conv., New Orleans, 1984—; v.p. LWV of Greenwich, 1990-91. Episcopalian. Home and Office: 15 Hendrie Ave Riverside CT 06878-1808

POWERS, DAVID RICHARD, educational administrator; b. Cambridge Springs, Pa., Apr. 5, 1939; s. William Herman and Elouise Fancheon (Fink) P.; m. Mary Julia Ferguson, June 11, 1960. Student, Pa. State U., 1957-60; BA, U. Pitts., 1963, MA, 1965, PhD, 1971. Dir. CAS advising ctr. U. Pitts., 1966-68, asst. dean faculty, 1968-70, asst. to chancellor, 1970-76, assoc.

provost, 1976-78, vice provost, 1978-79; v.p. for acad. affairs George Mason U., Fairfax, Va., 1979-82; vice chancellor for acad. affairs W.Va. Bd. Regents, Charleston, 1982-88; exec. dir. Minn. Higher Edn. Coord. Bd., St. Paul, 1989-94, Nebr. Coord. Commn. Post-secondary Edn., Lincoln, 1994—. Prin. author: Making Participatory Management Work, 1983, Higher Education in Partnership with Industry, 1988; contbr. articles to Ednl. Record, Adult Learning, Forum for Applied Rsch. on Pub. Policy. Grantee USOE Faculty Seminar, Taiwan, 1967, ARC Ctr. for Edn. & Rsch. with Industry Appalachian Regional Commn., 1983, Republic of China Sino-Am. Seminar, 1985; recipient Award for Acad. Quality W.Va. Coun. Faculty, 1986. Mem. Am. Assn. for Higher Edn., Am. Soc. for Pub. Adminstrn., State Higher Edn. Exec. Officers, Minn. Polit. Sci. Assn., Civil Air Patrol, Pi Sigma Alpha. Avocation: flying. Home: 1928 High St Lincoln NE 68502 Office: Nebr Coord Comm Postsecondary Edn PO Box 95005 Lincoln NE 68509-5005

POWERS, DENNIS ALPHA, biology educator; b. Detroit, May 4, 1938; s. Virginia (Ward) P.; m. Dianne Williamson, 1963 (div. 1993); children: Kathy M., Wendy R., Julie A. BA, Ottawa U., 1963; PhD, U. Kans., 1970. AEC postdoctoral fellow Argonne (Ill.) Nat. Lab.; NSF postdoctoral fellow Marine Biol. Lab., Woods Hole, Mass., 1971-72, SUNY, Stony Brook, 1971-72; asst. prof. biology Johns Hopkins U., Balt., 1973-79, assoc. prof., 1979-82, prof. biology, McCollum-Pratt prof., 1982-89, dir. McCollum-Pratt Inst., chmn. dept. biology, 1983-88; acting dir. Chesapeake Bay Inst., Shady Side, Md., 1984-87; Harold A. Miller prof. biol. sci., dir. Hopkins Marine Sta. Stanford (Calif.) U., 1989—; sci. adv. com. Chesapeake Bay Inst., Shady Side, Md.; prin. rsch. scientist Ctr. Marine Biotech., U. Md., Balt., 1986-89; bd. advisors Nat. Aquarium, Balt. Mem. editl. bd. Sci., Molecular Biology and Evolution, Molecular Phylogenetics and Evolution, Physiol. Zoology, Zool. Studies; mem. editl. adv. bd. Advances in Genetics, Advances in Marine Biotechnology; contbr. over 200 articles to sci. jours. Trustee Monterey Bay Aquarium; bd. dirs. Montery Bay Aquarium Rsch. Inst. Cpl. USMC, 1957-59. Grantee NSF, NIH, NOAA, others, 1970—; numerous honors and awards. Fellow AAAS; mem. Am. Chem. Soc., Am. Soc. Molecular Marine Biology and Biotechnology (pres., editor-in-chief jour.), Soc. Study Evolution, Genetics Soc., Am. Soc. Zoologists, Biophysical Soc., N.Y. Acad. Sci., The Protein Soc., Am. Soc. Biol. Chemists, Sigma Xi. Office: Stanford U Hopkins Marine Sta Pacific Grove CA 93950

POWERS, DORIS HURT, engineering company executive; b. Indpls., Jan. 17, 1927; d. James Wallace Hurt Sr. and Mildred (Johnson) Devine; m. Patrick W. Powers, Nov. 12, 1950 (dec. 1989); children: Robert W. Powers, Jaye P., Laura S. Powers. Student, So. Meth. U., 1944-45; BS in Engring., Purdue U., 1949; postgrad., U. Tex., W. Tex., 1952-53, Ecole Normale Du Musique, Paris, 1965-68; grad., Harford County Leadership Acad., 1991. Flight instr. Red Leg Flying Club, El Paso, Lawton, Okla., 1951-57; check pilot Civil Air Patrol, El Paso, Lawton, Okla., 1952-57; ground instr. Civil Air Patrol, Washington, Tex., Okla, 1957-61; exec. v.p. T&E Internat., Inc., Bel Air, Md., 1979-88, pres., 1989-91; exec. v.p. T.E.I.S, Inc., Bel Air, 1979-88, pres., 1989-91; pres. Shielding Technologies, Inc., Bel Air, 1987—. Mem. Northeastern Md. Tech. Coun., 1991—; bd. dirs. Leadership Acad., 1991-94. Recipient Svc. award U.S. Army, 1978, Cert. of Appreciation U.S. Army Test and Evaluation Command, 1988. Mem. CAP (lt. maj. 1951-58), Soc. of Women Engrs. (sr., v.p. 1977, treas. 1979, sec. rep. 1986-88, mentor 1986—, speaker 1978—, selected to Coll. of Fellows 1993), Engring. Soc. Balt. (speaker 1980—), 99's (pres. 1951-53), Am. Soc. Indsl. Security, Am. Def. Preparedness Assn., Hartford County Econ. Devel. Coun., Assn. of U.S. Army, Northeastern Md. Tech. Coun. Avocations: ice dancing, music. Home: 11 Glen Gate Ct Bel Air MD 21014

POWERS, DUDLEY, musician; b. Moorhead, Minn., June 25, 1911; s. James Harold and Mary Phoebe (Brainard) P.; m. Dorothy Louise Dasch, May 14, 1935; children: Jean Powers Todd, Eileen Powers Buchanan, Arthur, Anita Powers Palant. Student, Juilliard Mus. Found., 1926-30; MusB, Northwestern U., 1942, MusM, 1945. Cellist Little Symphony of Chgo., 1930-33; cellist Chgo. Symphony, 1933-43, solo cellist, 1943-53; prof. cello Northwestern U., 1931-80; vis. prof. cello U. South Fla., Tampa, 1980-86. Mem. Mischakoff String Quartet, 1935-38, Chgo. Symphony Quartet, 1940-53, Sheridan String Quartet, 1960-72; condr. Youth Symphony Greater Chgo., 1958-80, Eckstein String Quartet, 1972-80; cello recitalist. Home: 5644 Long Common Cir Sarasota FL 34235-2420

POWERS, EDWARD ALTON, minister, educator; b. Jamestown, N.Y., Oct. 26, 1927; s. Leslie Edgar and Mabelle Florence (Alton) P.; children: Randall Edward, Christopher Alan, Ann Lynn. BA, Coll. of Wooster, 1948; MDiv, Yale U., 1952; EdD, Columbia U., 1973. Ordained to ministry Congregational Ch., 1951; pastor Hamden, Conn., 1949-53, Pleasant Hill, Ohio, 1953-56; sec. dept. youth work Congl. Christian Ch. Bd. Home Missions, 1956-60; gen. sec. div. Christian edn., bd. home missions Congl. and Christian Chs., 1960-61; div. Christian edn., bd. homeland ministries United Ch. of Christ, 1962-73; gen. sec., div. evangelism, edn., ch. extension United Ch. Bd. Homeland Ministries, 1973-79; mem. faculty Inst. Mgmt. Competency, Am. Mgmt. Assn., N.Y.C., 1980-87; vis. lectr. Grad. Sch. Mgmt. New Sch. for Social Research, 1981—; mem. program bd. div. edn. and ministry Nat. Council Chs., 1963-80; mem. edn. working group World Council Chs.; chmn. Peace Priority Team, United Ch. of Christ, 1970-75, adminstr., editor sexuality study, 1977; ptnr. Cane Powers Cons., and Powers, Wayno & Assocs. Author: Journey Into Faith, 1964, Signs of Shalom, 1973, (with Rey O'Day) Theatre of the Spirit, 1980, In Essentials Unity, 1982, Youth in the Global Village, 1982; also articles. Home: 7 Gramercy Park W Apt 5B New York NY 10003-1759 Office: Graybar Bldg 420 Lexington Ave Ste 300 New York NY 10170-0001

POWERS, EDWARD LATELL, accountant; b. Birmingham, Ala., Jan. 21, 1919; s. Jesse Franklin and Clara (Kircus) P.; m. Frances Gail Watters, Aug. 2, 1939; children: Karen Sue Powers Hoss, Linda Gail Powers Nix. Student, Wayne State U., 1944-45, U. Ala., 1952-53. C.P.A., Ala., N.Y., La., N.C. Accountant So. Cotton Oil Co., Birmingham, 1937-42; examiner pub. accounts Ala. Dept. Examiners Pub. Accounts, 1942; chief accountant Refuge Cotton Oil Co., Columbus, Miss., 1942-43; chief warrant officer, auditor Detroit Ordnance Dist., 1943-46; pub. accountant Screven, Turner & Co., Birmingham, 1946-48, Scarborough, Thomas & Co., Birmingham, 1948-49; sr. ptnr. Blankenship & Powers, Birmingham, 1950-51, Scarborough & Powers, Birmingham, 1951-56; mng. ptnr. Birmingham office, Haskins & Sells (now Deloitte & Touche), 1956-79; Mem., former chmn. Ala. Bd. Pub. Accountancy. Contbr. articles profl. jours. Mem. Mayor's Fact Finding Com., Birmingham, 1964-65; former trustee Bapt. Med.Ctrs.; treas. Lenox Owners Assn. Recipient Army Commendation award Detroit Ordnance Dist., 1945. Mem. AICPA, Ala. Soc. CPAs (past pres.), Soc. States Conf. CPAs (past mem. exec. com.), N.Y. Soc. of CPAs, Beta Alpha Psi. Baptist (deacon). Clubs: Downtown, The Club. Home: 905 Linkside Way Birmingham AL 35242-6430 Office: 3800 Colonnade Pky Birmingham AL 35243-2363

POWERS, EDWIN MALVIN, consulting engineer; b. Denver, July 20, 1915; s. Emmett and Bertha Malvina (Guido) P.; m. Dorothy Lavane Debler, Jan. 18, 1941; children: Dennis M., Kenneth E., James M., Steven R. BS in Chem. Engring., U. Denver, 1939, MS, 1940. Registered profl. engr., N.J., Colo., Fall Out Analysts Engr., U.S. Fed. Emergency Mgmt. Agency, 1975-87. Prodn. supr. Nat. Aniline Div., Buffalo, 1940-45; engr., project supr. Merck & Co., Rahway, N.J., 1945-67, chief project coordinator, 1967-72, purchasing engr., 1972-82; ret., 1982; cons. engr. Conifer, Colo., 1982—; Capt. Air Raid Wardens, River dist., Buffalo, 1942-45. Mem., del. Conifer Home Owners Assns. Protect Our Single Homes, 1984-86, Regional Environ. Assn. Concerned Home Owners, 1985-86, task force area devel. Hwy. 285/ Conifer Area County Planning Bd. Community, 1986-88. Mem. NSPE, Am. Chem. Soc. (emeritus), Am. Inst. Chem. Engrs. (emeritus, treas. N.J. 1960, exec. com. 1961-63). Home and Office: 26106 Amy Cir Dr Conifer CO 80433-6102

POWERS, HARRIS PAT, broadcasting executive; b. Junction City, Kans., Oct. 29, 1934; s. Horace Pierce and Margaret (Harris) P.; m. Jerry Biles, Sept. 23, 1976; children: Rebecca, Randal, Mark, Shawn, Shannon, John. BA, Kans. State U., 1956. From salesman to mgr. Sta. KJCK, Junction City, 1957-73; mgr. Sta. KOYY, Eldorado, Kans., 1974-76; pres., CEO Sta. KTPK-FM, Topeka, 1976—; pres., chief exec. officer Stas. KINA

and KQNS, Salina, Kans., 1979-87—; mem. bd. pub. adv. coun. Sta. KTWU, Topeka, 1979-87; pres., CEO Twenty First Century Broadcasting, Inc., Topeka, 1994—; bd. dirs. State Savs. & Loan Assn., Topeka; ptnr. Reichs Fgn. Cars and Parts, Topeka and Junction City. Mem. exec. com. Jayhawk Area coun. Boy Scouts Am., 1979-82; bd. dirs. Topeka Big Bros./ Big Sisters, local chpt. ARC, Downtown Topeka, Inc.; past chmn. Downtown Topeka, Inc.; mem. Radio-TV-Film Curriculum adv. coun. Kans. U., adv. bd. Channel 11 Pub. TV; bd. dirs. Topeka Community Found., Pub. Schs. Found. Recipient numerous C. of C. and Jaycee awards, Disting. Svc. award Topeka Sales and Mktg. Execs., 1983, Grover Cobb award Kans. U., Silver award Profl. Advt. Club. Mem. Nat. Assn. Broadcasters, Internat. Broadcasters Soc., Mid-Am. Broadcasters (past chmn.), Kans. Assn. Broadcasters (past pres., Disting. Svc. award 1993), Kans. Assn. Commerce and Industry, (pres., bd. dirs. 1980-83), Sales and Mktg. Execs. Internat. (past pres. Topeka chpt.), Greater Topeka C. of C. (past vice chmn. devel. com., past v.p. pub. rels.), Kans. C. of C. (bd. dirs.), Topeka Town Club, Elks, Kiwanis (life mem. found.). Republican. Home: 2120 SW Brooklyn Ave Topeka KS 66611-1612 Office: 3003 SW Van Buren St Topeka KS 66611-2293

POWERS, HENRY MARTIN, JR., oil company executive; b. Bath, Maine, July 18, 1932; s. Henry Martin and Eva (Saunders) P.; m. Hepzibah Hinchey Reed, June 20, 1959; children—Henry Martin III, Carlton Reed. B.S., Maine Maritime Acad., 1954. Marine engr. Am. Export Lines, N.Y.C., 1954-58; staff engr. Bull & Roberts Inc., N.Y.C., 1958-59; gen. sales mgr. Williams Bros., Inc., Portland, Maine, 1959-61; v.p. C.H. Sprague & Son Co., Boston, 1961-72; pres. C.H. Sprague & Son Co., 1972—, chmn. bd., 1987—, also bd. dirs.; chmn. Pease Devel. Authority, 1990-93; bd. dirs. Shanley Corp., Strawbery Banke Inc., First N.H. Banks, Seaward Constrn. Co. Vice pres. Seacoast United Fund, 1967-69; chmn. fuels, energy com. New England Council, 1974-75; pres. Portsmouth Council, 1966-67; bd. visitors Maine Maritime Acad. Served to lt. USNR, 1956-58. Mem. Navy League, Mechanic Fire Soc., Algonquin Club (Boston), Cumberland Club (Portland), Masons. Home: 68 River Rd Box 261 Stratham NH 03885 Office: C H Sprague & Son Co 1 Parade Mall Portsmouth NH 03801-3749

POWERS, HUGH WILLIAM, newspaper executive; b. Slaton, Tex., Dec. 20, 1926; s. James Jerome and Myrtle (Black) P.; m. Constance Margaret Cornwall, Aug. 30, 1952; children: Nan Margaret, Sarah Ann. Student, W.Va. U., 1943-47. Mng. editor AGC News Svc., Houston, 1949-56; city editor Houston Press, 1956-64; asst. city editor Houston Chronicle, 1964-65, bus. editor, 1965-67, feature editor, 1973-75, assoc. editor, 1973-95; dir. Taping for the Blind, 1995—. Mem. Press Club of Houston (pres., dir. 1968-72), Ducks Unltd. (dir. Houston chpt. 1989—, chmn. 1995), Phi Kappa Psi. Home: 10818 Hillcroft St Houston TX 77096-6031

POWERS, JAMES, engineering company executive. Pres. Envirodyne Engring, Chgo., 1967—; exec. v.p. Consoer Townsend, Chgo., 1967—. Office: Envirodyne Engring 168 N Clinton St 6th Fl Chicago IL 60661 also: Consoer Townsend Envirodyne 303 E Wacker Dr Ste 600 Chicago IL 60601*

POWERS, JAMES, record and tape company executive; married. With Handleman Co., Troy, Mich., 1956—, sr. v.p. sales, 1976-86, exec. v.p., 1987—. Served with AUS, 1952-54. Office: Handleman Co 500 Kirts Dr Troy MI 48084-5225

POWERS, JAMES BASCOM, banker; b. Laurens, S.C., May 30, 1924; s. John Bascom and Ollie Esther (Ellenburg) P.; m. Julia Weskett, Dec. 7, 1963; children: James S., Deborah Powers Dickens, John W. BA, Furman U., 1955; postgrad. in banking, U. N.C., 1958, postgrad. bus. edn., 1971; postgrad. in banking, La. State U., 1961. Acct. Daniel Constrn. Co., Greenville, S.C., 1945-50; v.p. Wachovia Bank and Trust Co., Raleigh, N.C., 1954-67; chmn., chief exec. officer, dir. chmn. exec. com. Planters Corp. and Planters Nat. Bank and Trust Co., Rocky Mount, N.C., 1967-89; chmn. exec. com. Planters Corp. and Planters Nat. Bank and Trust Co., 1989-90; past vice chmn. dir. Atlantic States Bankcard Assn., Atlantic States Bankcard Properties, Atlantic States Svcs. Assn. Bd. dirs. Bus. Found. N.C., Independent Coll. Fund, past mem. N.C. Mus. History Assocs.; past mem. Econ Devel. Bd. N.C., past chmn. indsl. devel. com.; past mem. N.C. Mil. Affairs Commn.; mem. adv. coun. Furman U.; mem. Gov.'s Bus. Com. for Math./Sci. Edn., past mem. Gov.'s Bus. Coun. on Arts and Humanities; past dir. Rocky Mount YMCA, United Community Svcs.; past trustee Peace Coll., N.C. Wesleyan Coll.; former pres., dir. N.C. Wesleyan Coll. Area Found.; former trustee, chmn. bd., mem. exec. com. N.C. Bapt. Hosps., Inc.; former trustee N.C. Bapt. Homes; former chmn. Nash County Med. Devel. Authority; past dir. Nash Health Care Systems, Inc.; former mem. Bd. Disting. Visitors N.C. Wesleyan Coll.; past del. White Ho. Conf. on Small Bus.; former pres. Rocky Mount C. of C. Served with USN, 1942-45, 50-52. Mem. Am. Bankers Assn. (former chmn. edn. policy and devel. coun., past v.p. N.C. chpt., past mem. govt. rels. coun. adminstrv. com.), N.C. Bankers Assn. (former bd. dirs., past pres., past chmn. membership com., past chmn. Carolina Sch. Banking), Benvenue Country Club. Home: 307 Shady Circle Dr Rocky Mount NC 27803-1712 Office: Centura Bank 307 Shady Circle Dr Rocky Mount NC 27803

POWERS, JOE L., publishing executive; b. 1945. With TVA, Knoxville, 1966-69; with Thomas Nelson Inc., Nashville, 1969—, v.p., sec. Office: Thomas Nelson Inc Nelson Pl At Elm Hl Pike Nashville TN 37214*

POWERS, JOHN AUSTIN, alcoholic beverage company executive; b. N.Y.C., Oct. 24, 1926; s. Francis A. and Meta Marie (Touwsma) P.; m. Eileen Herlihy, Mar. 23, 1962; children: Maribeth, John Austin, Jennifer, Cecilia. B.A., St. Peters Coll., 1950; A.M.P., Harvard U., 1980. With McCann-Erickson, Inc., 1957-73; chmn. McCann-Erickson, Inc., U.K., 1967-70; pres. McCann-Erickson, Inc., Europe, 1967-71; v.p. internat. McCann-Erickson, Inc., 1968-70; pres. McCann-Erickson, Inc., U.S.A., 1971-73; v.p. Heublein, Inc., Farmington, Conn., 1973-78; group exec. wines group Heublein, Inc., 1975-78, sr. v.p. alcoholic beverages, 1979-81, pres., chief exec. officer, 1982-86, chmn., chief exec. officer, 1986-87, chmn. bd., 1987—; chmn., chief exec. officer United Vintners, Inc., San Francisco, 1973-78; sr. v.p. alcoholic beverages United Vintners, Inc., 1978-81; bd. dirs. Hartford Nat. Corp., Hartford Steam Boiler and Inspection Co., The Pillsbury Co.; dep. chmn. Internat Distillers & Vintners, Ltd. Bd. dirs. Hosp.; regent U. Hartford; trustee Hartford Grad. Ctr., Bus. Advisory Council, Skidmore Coll., Saratoga Springs, N.Y.; dir. San Francisco Ballet, 1975-77. Served to 2d lt. U.S. Army, 1944-46. Mem. Conn. Bus. and Industries Assn. (bd. dirs.). Clubs: Meadow (Southampton, N.Y.); Hartford Golf (West Hartford, Conn.). Office: Heublein Inc Munson Rd Farmington CT 06032

POWERS, JOHN GLENN, JR., manufacturing company executive; b. Evanston, Ill., Nov. 7, 1930; s. John G. and Marjories (McShane) P.; m. Joan M. Dougherty; children: John, Daniel, Anne, William, James, Kathleen, Paula, Nancy, John S. BSME, Marquette U., 1952. With Signode Industries, Inc., Glenview, Ill., 1958—, chief oper. officer, v.p. packaging div., 1983-86, pres. packaging div., 1986—; now also pres. Signode Corp.; with Ill. Tool Works, Inc., 1958—, exec. v.p. Bd. dirs. Evanston Hosp. Corp., 1989. Sgt. U.S. Army, 1952-54. Mem. Park Ridge (Ill.) Country Club. Office: Signode Corp 3610 W Lake Ave Glenview IL 60025

POWERS, JOHN H., school system administrator. Supt. Oyster River Sch. Dist., Durham, N.H. Recipient Nat. Superintendent of the Yr. awd., New Hampshire, Am. Assn. of School Administrators, 1992. Office: Oyster River Sch Dist Sau 5 36 Coe Dr Durham NH 03824

POWERS, JOHN Y., federal judge; b. Lake Orion, Mich., Aug. 1, 1929; s. Henry Stephen and Bertha Mae (Youngerman) P.; m. Barbara Mathilda Levero, Aug. 25, 1958; children: Joshua A., Lucas A., John Matthew, Samuel David. Student, Union U., 1947-48; BA, Vanderbilt U., 1951, LLB, 1953. Bar: Tenn. 1954. Enlisted man U.S. Army, Ft. Holabird, Md., 1954; 1st Lt. Judge Adv. Gen. Corps, Charlottesville, Va., 1955-57; with Claims Divsn. Office of the Judge Advocate General, Ft. Holabird, Md., 1955-57; with Adminstrv. divsn. U.S. Dept. Justice, 1957-58; claims rep. State Farm Ins. Co., Miami, Fla., 1958-59; atty. Spears, Moore, Rebman & Wms, Chattanooga, Tenn. 1959-70; ptnr. Hargraves, Curtis & Powers, Chattanooga, Tenn., 1970-74, Noone, Stringer & Powers, Chattanooga, Tenn., 1974-78,

Reingold, Powers & Schulman, Chattanooga, Tenn., 1978-84; U.S. magistrate judge ea. dist. Tenn. U.S. Dist. Ct., Chattanooga, Tenn., 1984—. Mem. Tenn. Bar. Assn., Chatanooga Bar Assn. Office: US District Court US Courthouse 900 Georgia Ave Rm 102 Chattanooga TN 37402-2257

POWERS, JOSEPH EDWARD, marine biologist; b. Gustine, Calif., Feb. 19, 1949; married, 1973. AB, U. Calif., Davis, 1971; MS, Calif. State U., Humboldt, 1973; PhD in Fish & Wildlife, Va. Polytech. Inst. & State U., 1975. Systems analyst fisheries dept. fisheries & wildlife sci. Va. Polytech. Inst. & State U., 1975; ops. rsch. analyst fisheries S.W. fisheries ctr. Nat. Marine Fisheries Svc., 1975-80; mem. staff nat. marine fisheries svc. S.E. Fisheries Ctr., 1980—. Mem. Am. Fisheries Soc., Soc. Computer Simulation, Ops. Rsch. Soc. Office: Nat Marine Fisheries Svc SE Fisheries Sci Ctr Miami Lab 75 Virginia Beach Dr Miami FL 33149-1003*

POWERS, MARCUS EUGENE, lawyer; b. Cedarville, Ohio, Apr. 7, 1929; s. Frederick Armajo and Elizabeth Isabel (Rumbaugh) P. B.A., Ohio Wesleyan U., 1951; J.D. (Root-Tilden scholar), NYU, 1954, LL.M., 1958. Bar: Ohio 1954, N.Y. 1959, Calif. 1964. Asst. prof. law NYU Sch. Law, 1956-60; atty. Am. Brake Shoe Co., N.Y.C., 1959-63; asst. gen. counsel Dart Industries Inc., Los Angeles, 1963-81; sr. v.p., gen. counsel Nat. Med. Enterprises, Inc., Los Angeles, 1981-93; exec. v.p., sec. Health Care Property Investors Inc., Santa Monica, Calif., 1985-87; cons. Nat. Med. Enterprises, Inc., Los Angeles, 1993—. Served with U.S. Army, 1954-56. Mem. ABA (mem. com. on corp. law depts. 1985-93), Los Angeles County Bar Assn. (past chmn. corp. law depts. sect., Outstanding Corp. Counsel 1990), Inst. Corp. Counsel (bd. dirs. 1979-92, chmn. 1984-86), Assn. Bar City N.Y., Calif. State Coastal Conservancy, Phi Beta Kappa, Omicron Delta Kappa, Phi Delta Theta, Kappa Sigma, Pi Sigma Alpha, Theta Alpha Phi. Office: Nat Med Enterprises Inc 2700 Colorado Ave PO Box 4070 Santa Monica CA 90404

POWERS, MARGARET A., nursing administrator; b. Dec. 11, 1945; m. Joseph F. Powers. BS, Mich. State U., 1967; MS, U. Mich., 1975. Dir. med.-surg. nursing Anne Arundel Gen. Hosp., Annapolis, Md.; St. Joseph Mercy Hosp., Ann Arbor, Mich.; asst. prof. dept. nursing edn. Ea. Mich. U., Ypsilanti; clin. dir. surg.-critical care nursing Greater Balt. Med. Ctr. Mem. Am. Orgn. Nurse Execs., Nat. League for Nursing, Md. Orgn. Nurse Execs., Sigma Theta Tau. Home: 405 Berkshire Dr Riva MD 21140-1428

POWERS, MICHAEL KEVIN, architectural and engineering executive; b. Boston, Feb. 3, 1948; s. Albert Thomas and Claire Marie (Sullivan) P.; m. Patricia Marie Collins, July 10, 1971; children: Kristin Michelle, Jennifer Anne. BSCE, Northeastern U., 1971. Registered profl. engr. N.Y., Vt., Minn., Maine, Mass., N.H., Ky., D.C., R.I. Staff engr. Edwards and Kelcey, Boston, 1967-70; project mgr. DeLeuw Cather & Co., Boston, 1971-80; exec. v.p., dir. engring Symmes Maini & McKee Assocs., Cambridge, Mass., 1980—; guest spkr. Tradeline Forum on Bus. and Tech., Boston, 1986-88, Microcontamination Conf. and Exposition, Santa Clara, Calif., 1987, Ocean Rooms Conf., Balt., 1995; lectr. facility design MIT, 1989, 92, 93, Wentworth Inst., 1993, 94, Pa. State, 1995. Contbr. articles to profl. jours. Mem. ASCE, NSPE, Inst. Environ. Scis. (sr.), Internat. Soc. Pharm. Engrs., Parenteral Drug Assn., Mt. River East Condominium Assn. (past trustee). Roman Catholic. Avocations: Alpine skiing, tennis, golf, music. Office: Symmes Maini & McKee Assocs Inc 1000 Massachusetts Ave Cambridge MA 02138-5397

POWERS, PAUL J., manufacturing company executive; b. Boston, Feb. 5, 1935; s. Joseph W. and Mary T. Powers; m. Barbara Ross, June 3, 1961; children: Briana, Gregory, Jeffrey. BA in Econs., Merrimack Coll., 1956; MBA, George Washington U., 1962. Various mfg. and fin. positions with Chrysler Corp., Detroit and overseas, 1963-69; v.p., gen. mgr. Am. Standard, Dearborn, Mich., 1970-78; pres. Abex-Dennison, Columbus, Ohio, 1978-82; group v.p. Comml. Intertech Corp., Youngstown, Ohio, 1982-84, pres., chief ops. officer, 1984-87, chmn., CEO, 1987—; bd. dirs. Acme-Cleve. Corp., Ohio Edison Co., Twin Disc, Inc. bd. dirs. Youngstown Symphony, 1984-88. Lt. USNR, 1957-63. Mem. NAM (bd. dir. 1986-93, 95—), Nat. Fluid Power Assn. (bd. dirs. 1984-87), Machinery and Allied Products Inst., Youngstown Area C. of C. (bd. dirs. 1990—). Office: Comml Intertech Corp 1775 Logan Ave # 239 Youngstown OH 44505-2661

POWERS, PIKE, JR., lawyer; b. Houston, May 1, 1941. BA, Lamar U., 1962; JD, U. Tex., 1965. Bar: Tex. 1965. Mem. Tex. House Reps., 1972-79; exec. asst. to gov. Tex., 1983; ptnr. Fulbright & Jaworski LLP, Austin. Fellow Am. Bar Found., Tex. Bar Found.; mem. ABA, Am. Judicature Soc., Travis County Bar Assn., State Bar Tex., Maritime Law Assn., Fedn. Ins. and Corp. Counsel, Tex. Assn. Defense Counsel, Phi Delta Phi. Office: Fulbright & Jaworski 600 Congress Ave Ste 2400 Austin TX 78701-3271

POWERS, RAMON SIDNEY, historical society administrator, historian; b. Gove County, Kans., Sept. 24, 1939; s. Sanford and Gladys Fern (Williams) P.; m. Eva Redin, Apr. 11, 1963; children: Elisabeth, Christina. AB, Ft. Hays (Kans.) State U., 1961, MA, 1963; PhD, U. Kans., 1971. Instr. western civilization U. Kans., Lawrence, 1963-67; asst. prof. history U. Mo. Kansas City, 1967-71; instr. Haskell Indian Jr. Coll., Lawrence, 1971-73; rsch. asst. Kans. Legis. Rsch. Dept., Topeka, 1973-77, rsch. analyst, 1977-78, prin. analyst, 1978-88; asst. exec. dir. Kansas State Hist. Soc., Topeka, 1988, exec. dir., 1988—. Contbr. articles to various jours. Chair Eisenhower Centennial Adv. Com., Topeka, 1988-90, Kans. Antiquities Commn., 1988—, State Records Bd., 1988—, Sante Fe Hist. Trail Adv. Bd., 1988—; mem. bd. review Kans. Hist. Sites, 1988—; mem. State Hist. Records Adv. Bd., 1988—, Gov.'s Commn. on Travel and Tourism, 1988—; mem. Charles F. Menninger Soc., Kans. Bus. Hall of Fame, 1988—; mem. bd. dirs. Nat. Conf. of State Historic Preservation Officers, 1991—. Recipient regional award Col. Dames Am., 1965, Disting. Alumni award Ft. Hays State U. and Hays Rotary Club, 1978; travel grantee N.J. Hist. Commn., 1971, summer grantee NEH, 1973. Mem. Am. Assn. State and Local History, Kans. Corral of the Westerns, Kans. History Tchrs. Assn., Western History Assn., Travel Industry Assn. (bd. dirs. 1991-93), Greater Topeka C. of C., Topeka Heritage League, Sat. Night Literary Club. Office: Kans History Ctr 6425 SW 6th Ave Topeka KS 66615-1004

POWERS, RICHARD AUGUSTINE, III, judge, lecturer; b. Phila., Sept. 22, 1932; s. Richard Augustine and Evelyn Lenore (Clark) P.; m. Helen Regina Penza, Aug. 30, 1958; children: Mary, Helen, Joan, Grace, Patricia, Theodore, Robert. BS in Econs., LaSalle Coll., 1958; J.D., Temple U., 1962. Bar: U.S. Dist. Ct. (ea. dist.) Pa. 1962; U.S. Supreme Ct., 1993. Assoc., Leo Francis Doyle, Phila., 1962; law clk. to judges US Dist. Ct. (ea. dist.) Pa., 1962-71; U.S. Magistrate judge U.S. Dist. (ea. dist.) Pa., Phila., 1971—; chief U.S. Magistrate judge, 1994—. lectr. in law Fed. Jud. Center, Washington; lectr. in civil litigation Main Line Paralegal Inst. Contbr. articles to profl. jours. Served with USAR, 1957-63. Recipient award Temple Law Alumni, 1979, LaSalle Law Alumni, 1979. Mem. Nat. Council Fed. Magistrates Judges, Phila. Bar Assn., Pa. Hist. Soc., Genealogical Soc. Pa., Brehon Law Soc., Phila. Museum Art, Smithsonian Contributory Assn., Pa. Hort. Soc., SAR. Roman Catholic. Office: US District Court 2716 US Courthouse Ind Mall W 601 Market St Philadelphia PA 19106

POWERS, RICHARD F., III, finance company executive; b. Boston, Feb. 2, 1946; s. Richard Francis Jr. and Mary Frances (Sullivan) P.; m. Colleen Teresa Cullen, Apr. 8, 1980; 1 child, Alicia Quilty. BS, Boston Coll., 1967; MBA, Columbia Sch. Bus., 1972. Asst. v.p., v.p., 1st v.p., exec. v.p., vice chmn., dir. Dean Witter, 1972—. Lt. USN, 1967-72. Office: Dean Witter Reynolds Inc Two World Trade Center 66th Fl New York NY 10048

POWERS, RICHARD P., pharmaceutical executive. Sr. v.p., CFO Syntex Corp., Palo Alto, Calif., 1979—. Office: Syntex Corp 3401 Hillview Ave Palo Alto CA 94304-1397*

POWERS, SHIRLEY MARIE, banker; b. Miles City, Mont., Feb. 27, 1930; d. Emil Henry and Karen Elizabeth (Topp) Swanson; m. William Howard Powers Jr., Apr. 5,1952; children: Michael Howard, Thomas Mark. AAS, Coastal Carolina Community Coll, 1969; cert. Sch. Banking, U. N.C., Chapel Hill, 1978. Lic. real estate broker, N.C. Adminstrv. asst. Bank of N.C., Jacksonville, 1974-77; mortgage loan officer Bank of N.C., Raleigh, 1977-82; real estate lending officer N.C. Nat. Bank, Raleigh, 1983;

asst. v.p. So. Nat. Bank N.C., Raleigh and Charlotte, 1983-86; v.p. So. Nat. Bank N.C., Charlotte, 1987—. Mem. Home Builders Assn. Charlotte (treas. women's coun. 1988). Democrat. Lutheran. Avocations: dancing, swimming, travel. Office: So Nat Bank NC 1263 Arrowpine Dr Ste 301 Charlotte NC 28273-5508

POWERS, STEFANIE (STEFANIE FEDERKIEWICZ), actress; b. Hollywood, Calif., Nov. 2, 1945; m. Patrick de la Chenais, April 1, 1993. Film appearances include Among the Thorns, Experiment in Terror, 1962, McClintock, 1963, Fanatic, 1964, Warning Shot, 1967, Herbie Rides Again, 1973, Escape to Athena, 1979, Invisible Stranger, 1984, Mother's Day, 1984; TV movie appearances include Five Desperate Women, 1971, Sweet Sweet Rachel, 1971, Paper Man, 1971, Ellery Queen: Don't Look Behind You, 1971, Hardcase, 1972, Sky Heist, 1975, Return to Earth, 1976, Washington: Behind Closed Doors, 1977, Nowhere to Run, 1978, A Death in Canaan, 1978, Family Secrets, 1984, Mistral's Daughter, 1984, Hollywood Wives, 1985, Deceptions, 1985, At Mother's Request, 1987, (co-producer) Beryl Markham: A Shadow on the Sun, 1988, She Was Marked for Murder, 1988, Love and Betrayal, 1989, When Will I Be Loved?, 1990, The Burden of Proff, 1992, Survive The Night, 1993, Hart to Hart: Old Friends Never Die, 1994; TV series The Girl from U.N.C.L.E., 1966, The Feather and the Father Gang, 1977, Hart to Hart, 1979-84. *

POWERS, THOMAS MOORE, author; b. N.Y.C., Dec. 12, 1940; s. Joshua Bryant and Susan (Moore) P.; m. Candace Molloy, Aug. 21, 1965; children: Amanda, Susan, Cassandra. B.A., Yale U., 1964. Reporter Rome (Italy) Daily American, 1965-67, U.P.I., N.Y.C., 1967-70; freelance writer, 1970—; contbg. editor The Atlantic mag., L.A. Times Opinion; editor, founding ptnr. Steerforth Press, So. Royalton, Vt., 1993—. Author: Diana: The Making of a Terrorist, 1971, The War at Home, 1973, The Man Who Kept the Secrets: Richard Helms and the CIA, 1979, Thinking About the Next War, 1982, Total War: What It Is, How It Got That Way, 1988, Heisenberg's War: The Secret History of the German Bomb, 1993. Recipient Pulitzer prize for nat. reporting, 1971. Mem. PEN Am. Center, Council on Fgn. Relations. Office: care Susan P Urstadt PO Box 1676 New Canaan CT 06840-1676

POWERS, WILLIAM CHARLES, JR., law educator; b. 1946. AB, U. Calif., Berkeley, 1967; JD, Harvard U., 1973. Bar: Wash. 1974, Tex. 1980. Law clk. to Hon. E. A. Wright U.S. Ct. Appeals (9th cir.), Seattle, 1973-74; asst. prof. Wash. U., Seattle, 1974-77, assoc. prof., 1977-78; prof. law U. Tex., Austin, 1978—, assoc. dean acad. affairs, 1985-87. Office: U Tex Sch Law 727 E 26th St Austin TX 78705-3224

POWERS, WILLIAM FRANCIS, automobile manufacturing company executive; b. Phila., Dec. 11, 1940; s. Francis Simpson and Kathryn Emily (Thoroughgood) P.; m. Linda Nell Shelton, Sept.7, 1963; children—Stephen, Leigh. B.S. in Aerospace Engring., U. Fla., 1963; M.S., U. Tex., 1966, Ph.D., 1968. Aerospace engr. NASA Marshall Space Flight Ctr., Huntsville, Ala., 1960-65; faculty mem. U. Mich., Ann Arbor, 1968-79, prof. aerospace engring., 1976-79; research mgr. Ford Motor Co., Dearborn, Mich., 1980-86, rsch. dir., 1986-87, dir. computer ops. N.Am., 1987-89, program mgr., 1989-91, exec dir. rsch., 1991-94, exec. dir IS and rsch., 1994—; cons. NASA Johnson Space Ctr., Houston, 1971-79, other cos., 1978-90. Contbr. articles to profl. jours. Editor: Astrodynamics, 1975, Jour. Astron. Scis., 1977-80. USSR research exchange scientist U.S. Nat. Acad. Scis., 1976. Fellow AIAA (assoc.), IEEE; mem. ASME, NAE, Soc. Automotive Engrs., Am. Automatic Control Council (v.p. 1986-87, pres. 1988-89), Royal Swedish Acad. Engring. Scis. (fgn.). Home: 2032 Greenview Dr Ann Arbor MI 48103-6110 Office: Ford Motor Company Ford Research Laboratory PO Box 1603 Rm 3153/srl Dearborn MI 48121-1603

POWIS, ALFRED, natural resources company executive; b. Montreal, Que. Can., Sept. 16, 1930; s. Alfred and Sarah Champe (McCulloch) P.; m. Louise Finlayson, Nov. 1977; children: Timothy Alfred, Nancy Alison, Charles Robert. B in Commerce, McGill U., 1951. Mem. staff investment dept. Sun Life Assurance Co. Can., 1951-55, now dir.; with Noranda Inc. (formerly Noranda Mines Ltd.), Toronto, 1956—, asst. treas., 1958-62, asst. to pres., 1962-63, exec. asst. to pres., 1963-66, v.p., 1966-67, exec. v.p., 1967-68, pres., 1968-82, chmn., chief exec. officer, 1977—, chmn., 1990—, dir., 1964—; bd. dirs. Noranda subsidiaries, Noranda Forest Inc., Can. Imperial Bank Commerce, Ford Motor Co. Can. Ltd., Norcen Energy Resources Ltd., Noranda Forest Inc., Sears Can. Inc., Kerr Addison Mines Ltd., Sun Life Assurance Co. Can., Brascan Ltd., Dal-Tile Group Inc.; mem. Brit. N.Am. Com.; dir. Canadian Inst. Internat. Affairs. Trustee Toronto Gen. Hosp. Recipient Inco medal Can. Inst. Mining and Metallurg., 1991. Mem. Conf. Bd., Conf. Bd. Can. (chmn.), Order of Can., York Club, Toronto Club, Mount Royal Club (Montreal). Anglican. Office: Noranda Inc, 181 Bay St Ste 4100BCE Box 755, Toronto, ON Canada M5J 2T3

POWLEDGE, FRED ARLIUS, freelance writer; b. N.C., Feb. 23, 1935; s. Arlius Raymond and Pauline (Stearns) P.; m. Tabitha Morrison, Dec. 21, 1957; 1 child, Pauline Stearns. AB in English, U. N.C., 1957. Writer, editor AP, New Haven, 1958-60; reporter Atlanta Jour., 1960-63, N.Y. Times, N.Y.C., 1963-66; freelance journalist, 1966—; lectr. New Sch., N.Y.C., 1967-69, 80-82; narrator, co-producer, writer WNET-TV/13, N.Y.C., 1972. Author: Black Power/White Resistance: Notes on the New Civil War, 1967, To Change a Child: A Report on the Institute for Developmental Studies, 1967, Model City: A Test of American Liberalism: One Town's Efforts to Rebuild Itself, 1970, Mud Show: A Circus Season, 1976, Born on the Circus, 1976, The Backpacker's Budget Food Book, 1977, Journeys Through the South, 1979, So You're Adopted: A Book About the Experience of Being Adopted, 1982, Water: The Nature, Uses and Future of Our Most Precious and Abused Resource, 1982, A Forgiving Wind: On Becoming a Sailor, 1983, Fat of the Land, 1984, The New Adoption Maze: And How to Get Through It, 1985, You'll Survive, 1986, Free at Last? The Civil Rights Movement and the People Who Made It, 1991, We Shall Overcome: The Heroes of the Civil Rights Movement, 1993, Working River, 1995. Mem. Bd. Library Trustees, St. Mary's County, Md. With USAR, 1957. Russell Sage fellow Russell Sage Found., 1966-67; travel and study grantee Ford Found., 1971, 93-94. Mem. Nat. Writer's Union.

POWLEN, DAVID MICHAEL, lawyer; b. Logansport, Ind., May 28, 1953; s. Daniel Thomas and Bertha Frances (Cappa) P.; m. Karen Lamb Gentleman, Aug. 5, 1978 (div. Jan. 1984); 1 child, Brooks Ryan. AB, Harvard U., 1975, JD, 1978. Bar: Ind. 1978, U.S. Dist. Ct. (so. dist.) Ind. 1978, U.S. Ct. Appeals (7th cir.) 1985. Assoc. Barnes & Thornburg, Indpls., 1978-84, ptnr., 1985—, chmn. creditors rights dept. Contbr. articles to profl. jours. Mem. ABA (bus. bankruptcy com., secured creditors and chpt. 11 subcom., comml. fin. svcs. com., creditors rights subcom.), Seventh Cir. Bar Assn., Ind. Bar Assn. (chmn. bankruptcy and creditors rights sect. 1990-91), Indpls. Bar Assn. (chmn. edn. com. 1984, chmn. ct. liaison com. 1985, bankruptcy and comml. law sect.), Am. Bankruptcy Inst. (regional programs and seminars subcom.), Comml. Law League Am. (bankruptcy and insolvency sect.), Harvard Club, Indpls. Sailing Club. Republican. Home: 1450 Preston Tr Carmel IN 46032-8971 Office: Barnes & Thornburg 11 S Meridian St Ste 1313 Indianapolis IN 46204

POWLES, PETER B., lawyer; b. Kenya, Feb. 19, 1936. BA, Cambridge U., Eng., 1957, MA, 1962, LLB, 1958. Bar: Eng. 1958, Victoria, Australia 1962, New South Wales, Australia 1963, Ill. 1966, St. Lucia, Windward and Leeward Islands 1966. Ptnr. Baker & McKenzie, Chgo. Office: Baker & McKenzie 1 Prudential Plz 130 E Randolph St Chicago IL 60601

POWNALL, MALCOLM WILMOR, mathematics educator; b. Coatesville, Pa., Jan. 6, 1933; s. Malcolm and Elizabeth (Moore) P.; m. Gertrude Decker, June 3, 1961; children: Joseph, Elizabeth, Kathryn, Thomas. A.B., Princeton U., 1954; M.A., U. Pa., 1958, Ph.D., 1960. Instr. to prof. math. Colgate U., Hamilton, N.Y., 1959—. Author: Prelude to the Calculus, 1967, Functions and Graphs, 1983, Real Analysis, A First Course with Foundations, 1994. Mem. Math. Assn. Am. (exec. dir. com. on undergrad. program 1966-68, chmn. com. on vis. lectrs. and cons. 1969-83). Democrat. Mem. Soc. of Friends. Office: Colgate Univ Dept Math 13 Oak Dr Hamilton NY 13346

POWSNER, EDWARD RAPHAEL, physician; b. N.Y.C., Mar. 17, 1926; m. Rhoda Lee Moscovitz , June 8, 1950; children: Seth, Rachel, Ethan, David. SB in Elec. Engring., MIT, 1948, SM in Biology, 1949; MD, Yale U., 1953; MS in Internal Medicine, Wayne State U., 1957. Diplomate Am. Bd. Nuclear Medicine, Am. Bd. Pathology in clin. pathology and anatomic pathology, Am. Bd. Internal Medicine; lic. physician, Mich., Calif., N.Y. Intern Wayne County Gen. Hosp., Eloise, Mich., 1953-54, resident internal medicine, 1954-55; resident internal medicine Detroit Receiving Hosp., 1955-56; fellow in hematology Wayne State U. and Detroit Receiving Hosp., 1957-58; clin. investigator VA Hosp., Allen Park, Mich., 1958-61, chief nuclear medicine svc., 1961-78; dir. clin. labs. Mich. State U., East Lansing, 1978-81; staff pathologist Ingham Med. Ctr., Lansing, Mich., 1978-81; dir. nuclear medicine St. John Hosp., Detroit, 1982—; rsch. assoc. biology MIT, 1948-49, 50; asst. instr. medicine Wayne State U. Coll. Medicine, 1954-56, instr. 1959-61; assoc. prof. pathology Wayne State U. Sch. Medicine, 1961-68, assoc. medicine, 1961, prof. pathology, 1968-78; prof. pathology Mich. State U., 1978-81, assoc. chairperson, 1980-81, clin. prof., 1981-82; chief clin. labs. Detroit Gen. Hosp., 1969-73; chief lab. svcs. Health Care Inst., 1974-78; prof. pathology Wayne State U., 1976-78; mem. adv. coun. Nuclear Medicine Tech. Cert. Bd., 1990-91. Bd. editors Am. Jour. Clin. Pathology, 1963-76, 83-88; author 1 textbook, 10 chpts., 48 peer reviewed papers, 19 abstracts and other publs. With U.S. Army, 1944-47. Mem. AMA (sect. coun. on pathology), Am. Soc. Clin. Pathologists (rep. 1987-89, 93—), govt. rels. com. 1993—, mem. coun. nuclear medicine 1978-82, chmn. 1982-84), Am. Coll. Nuclear Physicians, Am. Soc. Nuclear Cardiology, Coll. Am. Pathologists, Detroit Acad. Medicine, Mich. Soc. Pathologists, Mich. State Med. Soc., Soc. Nuclear Medicine, Washtenaw County Med. Soc., Sigma Xi, Tau Beta Pi. Office: St John Hosp Nuclear Med Detroit MI 48236 also: St John Hosp & Med Ctr 22101 Moross Rd Detroit MI 48236

POYNER, JAMES MARION, retired lawyer; b. Raleigh, N.C., Sept. 18, 1914; s. James Marion and Mary (Smedes) P.; m. Florence I Chan, Feb. 24, 1945; children: Susan Poyner Moore, Chan Poyner Pike, Margaret Poyner Galbraith, Edythe Poyner Lumdsen, James Marion III. B.S. in Chem. Engring, N.C. State U., 1935, M.S., 1937; J.D., Duke U., 1940. Bar: N.C. 1940. Pvt. practice Raleigh, 1946-51; ptnr. Poyner, Geraghty, Hartsfield & Townsend, Raleigh, 1951-86; of counsel Poyner & Spruill, Raleigh, 1986-95, ret., 1995; co-founder Cameron-Brown Co. (now 1st Union Mortgage Co.); life dir. 1st Union Corp., 1st Union Nat. Bank; chmn. bd. dirs. Eastern Standard Ins. Co., George Smedes Poyner Founds. Inc. Orch. leader, trombonist, arranger, Jimmy Poyner and His Orch., 1933-38. Mem. N.C. Senate, 1955-59; Past chmn. bd. trustees St. Mary's Coll.; past chmn. bd. World Golf Hall of Fame; past chmn. trustees N.C. Symphony Soc. Served with Chem. Warfare Service, AUS, 1942-46. Decorated Legion of Merit. Mem. ABA, N.C. Bar Assn. (pres. 1967-68, dir. 1963-67), Am. Judicature Soc. (dir. 1973-77), Raleigh C. of C. (past pres.), Phi Kappa Phi. Episcopalian. Home: 710 Smedes Pl Raleigh NC 27605-1141 Office: 3600 Glenwood Ave Raleigh NC 27612-4945

POYNOR, ROBERT ALLEN, JR., guidance counselor; b. Franklin, Tenn., Aug. 2, 1939; s. Robert Allen and Agnes Elizabeth (Gillespie) P.; divorced; 1 child, Melissa Dawn Hay. BA, Belmont Coll., Nashville, 1967; MEd, Middle Tenn. State U., 1972, EdS, 1975; postgrad., Tenn. State U. Cert. elem. tchr., elem. guidance counselor, elem. prin.-advanced, Tenn. Teller, mgmt. trainee Third Nat. Bank, Nashville, 1962-67; employment rep. S.S. Bd. of the S.B.C., Nashville, 1967-68; tchr. Sumner County Bd. Edn., Gallatin, Tenn., 1968-69; asst. sec.-treas., br. mgr. Security Fed. Savs. and Loan Assn., Nashville, 1969-71; tchr. Sumner County Bd. Edn., Gallatin, 1971-79, 83-85, prin., 1979-83, guidance counselor, 1985—; mem. textbook adoption com. Sumner County bd. Edn., 1968-69, gifted com., 1980-82. Charter sec. 100 Oaks Sertoma Club, Nashville, 1970; treas. Am. Savs. and Loan Inst., Nashville, 1970. With U.S. Army, 1957-59, France. Mem. ASCD, Tenn. ASCD, Tenn. Assn. Counselor Devel., Mid. Tenn. Assn. for Counselor Devel., United Teaching Profession, Sumner County Elem. Prins. (past pres. 1982-83), Sumner County Edn. Assn. (past pres. 1978-79), Phi Delta Kappa. Baptist. Avocations: jogging, reading, yard work, spectator sports, art. Home: 288 Indian Lake Rd Hendersonville TN 37075-4344

POYNTER, JAMES MORRISON, travel educator, travel company executive; b. Kansas City, Mo., July 27, 1939; s. Lewis Alderson and Patricia Connely (Dunn) P.; m. Sorore; children: Lewis, Robert, Michael. BA, George Washington U., 1969, MA, 1975. Cert. travel counselor (honorary). Adminstrv. dir. Inst. Cert. Travel Agents, Arlington, Va., 1967-72; ednl. cons. Saudi Arabian Airlines, Jeddah, 1972-77; specialist employment and tng. Leon County Dept. Human Resources, Tallahassee, 1977-79; pres., CEO Fla. Profl. and Econ. Devel. Corp., Tallahassee, 1979-81; mgr., co-owner The Travel Ctr., Tallahassee, 1979-82, Adventures in Travel, Tallahassee, 1979-82; assoc. prof. travel adminstrn. Met. State Coll. Denver, 1982—; pres. Travel Analysis, Denver, 1988—. Author: Foreign Independent Tours, 1989, Corporate Travel Management, 1990, Travel Agency Accounting Procedures, 1991, Tour Design Marketing and Management, 1992, Travel and Tourism Books in Print, 1992, How to Research and Write A Thesis in Hospitality and Tourism, 1993, (with others) Travel Industry Business Management, 1986; compiler, editor: Proceedings of the Colloquium on Corporate Travel Curricula Development, 1994, Travel and Tourism Books in Print, 1994. With U.S. Army, 1957-60. Mem. Am. Soc. Travel Agts., Assn. Corp. Travel Execs. (edn. coms. 1988-89, bd. govs. 1993—, v.p. edn. 1994—, Edn. award 1992, Educator of Yr. award 1993), Soc. Travel and Tourism Educators (bd. dirs. 1989-91, 93—), Profl. Guides Assn. Am. Rocky Mountain Bus. Travel Assn. (bd. dirs. 1986-87), Rocky Mountain Profl. Guides Assn. (bd. dirs. 1989-90, v.p. 1989-90), Colo. Author's League (treas. 1992). Republican. Presbyterian. Office: Met State Coll Denver HMTA Dept PO Box 60 Denver CO 80210

POYTHRESS, DAVID BRYAN, state commissioner, lawyer; b. Macon, Ga., Oct. 24, 1943; s. John M. and Dorothy (Bayne) P. BA, Emory U., 1964, JD, 1967. Bar: Supreme Ct. Ga. 1967, U.S. Supreme Ct. 1971. Asst. atty. gen. Dept. Law, State of Ga., Atlanta, 1971-72; dep. commr. Ga. Dept. Revenue, Atlanta, 1972-76; commr. Ga. Dept. Med. Assistance, Atlanta, 1976-79; sec. of state State of Ga., Atlanta, 1979-83; ptnr. Kutak Rock & Huie, Atlanta, 1983-84; pvt. practice Atlanta, 1984-86; exec. dir. Ga. Health Network, Atlanta, 1986-89; atty. Chilivis & Grindler, Atlanta, 1989-92; commr. Ga. Dept. Labor, Atlanta, 1992—. With USAF, 1967-71. Mem. State Bar Ga. Democrat. Methodist. Office: Labor Dept 148 Internat Blvd NE Atlanta GA 30303

POZDRO, JOHN WALTER, music educator, composer; b. Chgo., Aug. 14, 1923; s. John and Rose Anna (Mossman) P.; m. Shirley Allison Winans, June 12, 1954; children—John Winans, Nancy Allison. B.M. in Music, Northwestern U.-Evanston, Ill., 1948, M.M. in Music, 1949; Ph.D. in Music, Eastman Sch. Music, 1958. Instr. Iowa State Tchrs. Coll., Cedar Falls, 1949-50; instr. to assoc. prof. U. Kans., Lawrence, 1950-64, prof. music, 1964—; prof. theory and composition U. Kans., 1961—; teaching fellow Eastman Sch. Music, Rochester, NY, 1956-57; chmn. symposium com. U. Kans., Lawrence, 1958-69. Representative works include: Third Symphony, 1960, Piano Sonata Number 4, 1976, Malooley & Fear Monster, 1977, Impressions, Winds, Piano, 1984, Tryptich for Carillon and the Spirit of Mt. Oread, 1989. Served with U.S. Army, 1943-46. Recipient U. Calif. Berkeley medal for Disting. Svc., 1993; grantee Ford Found., 1960. Nat. Endowment Arts, 1976; nominated for Pulitzer prize in Music, 1960. Mem. ASCAP (award 1965-92), Pi Kappa Lambda. Presbyterian. Avocations: golf; photography; reading. Home: 4700 Muirfield Dr Lawrence KS 66047

POZEN, WALTER, lawyer; b. East Orange, N.J., Oct. 17, 1933; s. Irving Joseph and Berte (Protter) P.; m. Elizabeth Klupt, June 19, 1955 (div. 1967); children: Agatha Elizabeth, Jonathan Walter, Thorn Lord; m. Joan Kennan, Apr. 24, 1971 (div. Apr. 1988). B.A., U. Chgo., 1952, grad. student, 1952-53; J.D., 1956. Bar: Md. 1963. With Strasser, Spiegelberg, Fried & Frank, Washington and N.Y.C., 1956-58; mem. campaign staff Harrison A. Williams for U.S. Senator, 1958; legis. counsel Home Rule Com., Inc., Washington, 1959-60; counsel, assoc. dir. Fgn. Policy Clearing House, Washington, 1960-61; asst. to sec. interior, 1961-67; ptnr. Stroock & Stroock & Lavan, N.Y.C., 1967—, in charge Washington office; ofcl. rep. U.S. del. GATT Ministerial Meeting, Geneva, 1963; mem. Gov.'s Commn. on Historic Preservation, Md.; mem. D.C. Bd. Elections and Ethics; del. Democratic Nat. Conv., 1964, counsel credentials com., 1968; counsel compliance rev.

com. Dem. Nat. Com.; vis. prof. Irving B. Harris Sch. Pub. Policy Studies U. Chgo., 1993—. Author: (with Dr. J.H. Cerf) Strategy for the Sixties, 1960; also articles, book reviews. Bd. dirs. Nat. Symphony Orch.; mem. vis. com. Harris Sch. Pub. Policy Studies, U. Chgo. Mem. D.C. Bar Assn., Md. Bar Assn., Harmonie Club, Fed. City Club. Home: 3806 Klingle Pl NW Washington DC 20016-5433 also: PO Box 121 West Halifax VT 05358-0121 Office: Stroock & Stroock & Lavan 1150 17th St NW Ste 600 Washington DC 20036-4603

POZNANSKI, ANDREW KAROL, pediatric radiologist; b. Czestochowa, Poland, Oct. 11, 1931; came to U.S., 1957, naturalized, 1964; s. Edmund Maurycy and Hanna Maria (Ceranka) P.; children: Diana Jean, Suzanne Christine. B.Sc., McGill U., 1952, M.D.C.M., 1956. Diplomate: Am. Bd. Radiology, Royal Coll. Physicians and Surgeons Can. Intern Montreal (Que., Can.) Hosp., 1956-57; resident Henry Ford Hosp., Detroit, 1957-60; staff radiologist Henry Ford Hosp., 1960-68, U. Mich. Med. Center, Ann Arbor, 1968-79; co.-dir. pediatric radiology C.S. Mott Children's Hosp., Ann Arbor, 1971-79; radiologist-in-chief Children's Meml. Hosp., Chgo., 1979—; prof. radiology U. Mich., 1971-79, Northwestern U. Med. Sch., 1979—; bd. dirs. Nat. Coun. on Radiation Protection, 1983-90; mem. Internat. Commn. on Radiologic Protection, 1981-89; mem. adv. panel on radiologic devices FDA, 1975-77, chmn., 1976-77; trustee Am. Bd. Radiology, 1993—. Author: The Hand in Radiologic Diagnosis, 1974, 2d edit., 1983, Practical Approaches to Pediatric Radiology, 1976; bd. editors: Skeletal Radiology, 1975—, Radiographics, 1980-84, Pediatric Radiology, 1986-91. Fellow Am. Coll. Radiology; mem. AMA, Am. Roentgen Ray Soc. (pres. 1993-94), Soc. Pediatric Radiology (pres. 1980-81), Radiol. Soc. N.Am., Assn. Univ. Radiologists, John Caffey Soc., Am. Assn. Phys. Anthropologists, Internat. Skeletal Soc. (founding, pres. 1992-94), Can. Assn. Radiologists (hon.). Teratology Soc., Alpha Omega Alpha. Home: 2400 N Lakeview Ave Chicago IL 60614-2747 Office: Childrens Meml Hosp 2300 N Childrens Plz Chicago IL 60614-3318

POZNANSKY, MARK J., research institute administrator, educator; b. Montreal, Que., Can., Apr. 25, 1946; s. Eric and Ruth Poznansky; m. Esther Goldberg, Dec. 18, 1981; children: Shoshana, Mirit. BSc in Physiology, McGill U., Montreal, 1967, PhD in Physiology, 1970. Postdoctoral fellow Biophys. Lab., Harvard Med. Sch., Boston, 1970-72, instr., 1972-74, lectr., 1974-76; assoc. prof. dept. physiology U. Alta., Edmonton, Can., 1976-81, prof. lipid and lipoprotein rsch. group, 1982-93, mem. Robarts Rsch. Inst., London, Ont., Can., 1993—; prof. dept. biochemistry U. Western Ont. Faculty Medicine, London, 1993—; in charge rsch. dept. physiology Coll. de France, Paris, 1973-74; rsch. on superoxide dismutase, oxygen free radicals and control of post-reperfusion injury, relating biotech. univ. rsch. to pvt. sector. Home: 80 Sherwood Ave, London, ON Canada N6A 2E2 Office: John P Robarts Rsch Inst, 100 Perth Dr PO Box 5015, London, ON Canada N6A 5K8

POZO, SANTIAGO, marketing executive; b. Logrono, Rioja, Spain, Nov. 4, 1957; came to U.S., 1983; s. Santiago Pozo and Asuncion Arenas. MFA, U. So. Calif., 1986; PhD, Univ. Complutense, Madrid, 1982. Mgr. spl. mkts. Universal Pictures, MCA, L.A., 1985-88; pres., founder The Arenas Group, L.A., 1988—. Author: The Spanish Film Industry, 1983 (Best Cinema Book of Yr. 1983); dir., writer The First Meters, 1977; producer: Argos, 1984 (1st prize Internat. Film Festival Huesca, 1984); responsible for U.S. Hispanic mktg. campaigns for An. American Tail, Born in East L.A., Milagro Beanfield War, Colors, My Stepmother is an Alien. Mem. Hispanic Acad. Arts, Publicists Guild. Office: The Arenas Group 8833 W Sunset Blvd Ste 408 West Hollywood CA 90069-2110

POZZATTI, RUDY OTTO, artist; b. Telluride, Colo., Jan. 14, 1925; s. Innocente and Mary L. (Mimiolla) P.; m. Dorothy I. Pozzatti, May 20, 1946; children—Valri Marie, Rudy Otto, Gina Maria, Mia Ines, Illica Lara. B.F.A., U. Colo., 1948, M.F.A., 1950, D.H.L., 1973. Mem. faculty dept. art U. Nebr., Lincoln, 1950-52, 53-56; mem. faculty dept. art Ind. U., Bloomington, 1956-91, prof. fine arts, 1964-91, disting. prof., 1975-91; ret., 1991; dir. Echo Press, Bloomington, 1979—; artist-in-residence Roswell Mus. and Art Ctr.; bd. dirs. Echo Press, Bloomington, Ind. One-man exhbns. include Cleve. Mus. Art, 1955, Whitney Mus. Am. Arts, N.Y.C., 1961, Tyler Sch. Art, Rome, 1969, Sheldon Meml. Art Gallery U. Nebr., 1969, Mitchell Mus. Art, Mt. Vernon, Ill., 4 other sites, 1992-93; represented in permanent collections, Mus. Modern Art, N.Y.C., Libr. Congress, Washington, Art Inst. Chgo., Cleve. Mus. Art. Served with AUS, 1943-46. Recipient George Norlin silver medal U. Colo., 1974; Fulbright grantee, 1952-53, 63-64, grantee U.S. Dept. State, USSR, 1961, Yugoslavia, 1965, Brazil, 1974, Hungary, 1986; Guggenheim fellow, 1963-64; Fellow Ford Found., 1963, grantee, Japan, 1981. Mem. Soc. Am. Graphic Artists, Am. Color Print Soc., Coll. Art Assn. (bd. dirs.), Artists Equity Assn. Roman Catholic. Office: Echo Press 1901 E 10th St Bloomington IN 47408-3978

P'POOL, GERALD W., manufacturing executive; b. Princeton, Ky., Mar. 1, 1933; s. Herbert Claude and Laura Lucille (Adams) P'P.; m. Peggy Simons (div. Sept. 1960); m. Jo Mercer; children: Deborah, Elisha, Jill. Student, Murray (Ky.) State U. Sales rep. Thomas Industries, Inc., Ky., Tenn., N.C. and Fla., 1956-62; mgr. div. Thomas Industries, Inc., Atlanta, 1964-71; mgr. merchandising Thomas Industries, Inc., Louisville, 1971-72, mgr. nat. sales, 1972-78; pres. Paint Applicators div. Thomas Industries, Inc., Johnson City, Tenn., 1978-81, v.p. group mgr., paint applicator, tool and fastener, beni. div., 1981-83; sr. v.p. mktg. Thomas Industries, Inc., Louisville, 1983-84, exec. v.p., 1984-87, exec. v.p., mgr. light group, 1987—. Avocations: hunting, fishing. Home: 317 S Jefferson St Princeton KY 42445-2111 Office: Thomas Industries Inc PO Box 35120 Louisville KY 40232-5120

PRABHAKAR, ARATI, federal administration research director, electrical engineer; b. New Delhi, Feb. 2, 1959; came to U.S., 1962; d. Jagdish Chandra and Raj (Madan) P. BSEE, Tex. Tech U., 1979; MSEE, Calif. Inst. Tech., 1980, PhD in Applied Physics, 1984. Congl. fellow Office Tech. Assessment U.S. Cong., Washington, 1984-86; program mgr. electronic sci. divsn. DARPA, Arlington, Va., 1986-90, dep. dir. defense sci. office, 1990-91, dir. microelectroncs tech. office, 1991-93; dir. Nat. Inst. Standards & Tech., Gaithersburg, Md., 1993—. Contbr. articles to profl. jours. Rsch. fellow, 1979-84, Disting. Alumni award, 1995, Calif. Inst. Tech.; grad.rsch. program for women Bell Labs., 1979, 80; named Disting. Engr. of 1994, Tex. Tech. U.; elected to Tex. Tech. Elec. Engring. Acad., 1994. Mem. IEEE, Eta Kappa Nu, Tau Beta Pi. Office: Nat Inst Stds & Tech US Dept of Commerce Rte 270 Bldg 101 Rm A1134 Gaithersburg MD 20899

PRABHUDESAI, MUKUND M., pathology administrator, director, researcher, administrator; b. Lolyem, Goa, India, Mar. 17, 1942; came to U.S., 1967; s. Madhav R. and Kusum M. Prabhudesai; m. Sarita Mukund Usha, Feb. 8, 1972; 1 child, Nitin M. MB, BS (MD), G.S. Med., Bombay, 1967, postgrad., 1973-75. Diplomate Am. Bd. Pathology. Asst. pathologist Fordham Hosp., Bronx, N.Y., 1973-74, assoc. pathologist, 1974-76; assoc. dir. clin. pathology Lincoln Med., Bronx, 1976, dep. dir. pathology, 1977-79; chief pathology and lab. medicine svc., coord. R&D VA Med. Ctr., Danville, Ill., 1979—, dir. electron microscopy lab., 1987—; senator U. Ill. Chgo.; co-investigator U. Ill. Coll. Medicine, Urbana/Champaign, clin. assoc. prof. pathology and medicine Rsch., Rehab., Nutrition, Alcohol, 1982—. Contbr. articles to Am. Jour. Clin. Nutrition, Jour. AMA, Am. Jour. Clin. Pathology. Member Gifted Student Adv. Bd., Danville, 1984-86; U. Am. Cancer Soc. Vermilion County chpt., 1982, pres., 1986-88. VA rsch. grantee, 1980-82, 82-85, 83. Fellow Coll. Am. Pathology (inspector 1981—; Ill. state del. to C.A.P. Ho. Dels. 1992—; mem. reference com. 1993); mem. AAAS, Am. Coll. Physician Execs., Ill. State Soc. Pathologists; bd. dirs. 1990—, chmn. membership com. 1990—). Achievements include development of cancer of bladder following portocaval shunting; research in adverse effects of alcohol on liver structure and metabolism; on effects of soy and bran on cholesterol, endocrine response to soy protein, in induction and reversibility of atherosclerosis in trout, effects of ethanol on Vitamin A, lymphatics in atherosclerosis, iron in atherosclerosis. Office: VA Med Ctr Pathology and Lab Med Svcs 1900 E Main St Danville IL 61832-5198

PRADO, EDWARD CHARLES, federal judge; b. San Antonio, June 7, 1947; s. Edward L. and Bertha (Cadena) P.; m. Maria Anita Jung, Nov. 10, 1973; 1 child, Edward C. AA, San Antonio Coll., 1967; B.A., U. Tex., 1969, JD, 1972. Bar: Tex. 1972. Asst. dist. atty. Bexar County Dist. Atty.'s Office, San Antonio, 1972-76; asst. pub. defender U.S. Pub. Defender's Office, San Antonio, 1976-80; judge U.S. Dist. Ct. Tex., San Antonio, 1980; U.S. atty. Dept. Justice, San Antonio, 1980-85; judge U.S. Dist. Ct. (we. dist.) Tex., 1984—. Served to capt. U.S. Army. Named Outstanding Young Lawyer of Bexar County, 1980. Mem. ABA, Tex. Bar Assn., San Antonio Bar Assn., San Antonio Young Lawyers Assn., Fed. Bar Assn. Republican. Roman Catholic. Office: US Courthouse 655 E Durango Blvd San Antonio TX 78206-1101

PRADO, GERALD M., investment banker; b. Langeloth, Pa., Jan. 19, 1946; s. Caesar S. and Anita A. P.; m. Judith A. Pompe, May 20, 1967; children—Dennis, Eric, Lynn, Christopher. B.A., Washington and Jefferson Coll., 1963-67; M.B.A., U. Pitts., 1983. Sr. acct. Haskins and Sells, Pitts., 1967-72; auditor G.C. Murphy Co., McKeesport, Pa., 1972-76, asst. controller, 1976-78, treas., 1979-80, asst. v.p., treas., 1980-82, v.p., treas., 1982-85; v.p., treas. Russell, Rea & Zappala, Pitts., 1986-87, sr. v.p., 1987-90; pres. Westinghouse Mcht. Banking, Inc., Pitts., 1990-94; prin. Main St. Capital Holdings L.L.C, Pitts., 1994—. Mem. Pa. Inst. CPA's, Am. Inst. CPA's, Washington and Jefferson Alumni Assn., Assn. for Corp. Growth. Roman Catholic. Home: 205 Overlook Dr McMurray PA 15317-2657 Office: Main St Capital Holdings LLC 600 Corant St 42d flr Pittsburgh PA 15219-1400

PRADOS, JOHN WILLIAM, educational administrator; b. Spring Hill, Tenn., Oct. 12, 1929; s. Gustave Olivier and Elizabeth (Branham) P.; m. Ruth Lynn Baird, Sept. 2, 1951; children: Elizabeth Prados Bowman, Laura Lynn, Anne Prados Lynch. B.S. in Chem. Engring. U. Miss., 1951; M.S., U. Tenn., 1954, Ph.D., 1957. Registered profl. engr., Tenn. Asst. prof. U. Tenn., Knoxville, 1956-59, asso. prof., 1959-64, prof. chem. engring., 1964—, Univ. prof., 1989—, asso. dean engring., 1969-71, dean admissions and records, 1971-73, acting chancellor Knoxville campus, 1973, acting chancellor Martin campus, 1979; v.p. acad. affairs statewide U. Tenn. System, 1973-81, v.p. acad. affairs and rsch., 1981-88, v.p. emeritus, 1989—, head chem. engring. dept., 1990-93; cons. nuclear divsn. Union Carbide Corp., Oak Ridge, 1957-84, Martin Marietta Energy Sys., Inc., 1984-86; sr. edn. assoc. NSF, Arlington, Va., 1994-95. Served with USAF, 1951-53. Recipient Outstanding Tchr. award U. Tenn., 1967, 92. Fellow Am. Inst. Chem. Engrs. (mem. council 1975-77, Knoxville-Oak Ridge Chem. Engr. of Yr. 1977), Am. Inst. Chemists; mem. Am. Chem. Soc., Am. Soc. Engring. Edn., Engring. Accreditation Commn. Accreditation Bd. Engring. and Tech., Inc. (vice chmn. 1981-84, chmn. 1984-85, bd. dirs. 1988—, sec. 1989-90, pres. 1991-92, L.E. Grinter award 1993), So. Assn. Colls. and Schs. (commn. on colls. 1986-92, exec. coun. 1986-89), Sigma Xi (dir. at large, chmn. com. 1976—, pres. 1983-84, treas. 1990—), Torch Club, Tau Beta Pi (exec. coun. 1986-90), Alpha Tau Omega. Roman Catholic. Home: 7021 Stagecoach Trl Knoxville TN 37909-1112 Office: U Tenn Knoxville TN 37996-2200

PRADY, NORMAN, advertising executive, writer, marketing consultant; b. Detroit, Sept. 19, 1933; s. Calvin and Mildred Prady; m. Susan Frank, July 5, 1959 (div. Nov. 1991); children: William Scott, Anne Elizabeth Prady Sheehan. Student, Wayne State U., 1951-53, Fordham U., 1952. Reporter, feature writer Detroit Times, 1955-60; writer various advt. agys. Detroit, 1960-65, creative dir. various advt. agys., 1965-80; exec. v.p., creative dir., prin. Stone, August & Co., Birmingham, Mich., 1980-84; pres. The Norman Prady Co., Farmington Hills, 1985—. Contbr. features various newspapers. Bd. dirs. ARC, Detroit, 1983—, exec. com., 1987—, vice-chmn. pub. affairs com., 1986—, fin. devel. com., 1987—. Office: The Norman Prady Co Ste 314 35526 Grand River Ave Farmington Hills MI 48335

PRADZYNSKI, ANDRZEJ HENRYK, chemist; b. Plock, Poland, Jan. 1, 1924; came to U.S., 1969; s. Maurycy and Frania (Goldkind) Nejman; m. Halina Romana Bromberger, Apr. 1, 1946; children: Richard E. Neuman, Zgibniew Jacek. BS, U. Wroclaw, Poland, 1949, MS, 1951. Asst. prof. crystallography, chmn. dept. U. Wroclaw, 1948-51; sect. mgr. materials testing Inst. Aviation, Warsaw, Poland, 1951-57; adj. prof. Polish Acad. Scis., Warsaw, 1957-68; dept. dir. Atomic Energy Commn. Poland, Warsaw, 1959-68; rsch. assoc. IV nuclear reactor U. Tex., Austin, 1969-80; exec. v.p. Halinco Skin Care Products, Inc., Austin, 1980—; cons. IAEA, Vienna, Austria, 1968-69. Author: Industrial Radiography (in Polish), 1957; also over 3o articles in IAEA Conf. Procs., Nukleonika, ISA Trans., also others. Mem. Am. Chem. Soc., Soc. Cosmetic Chemists, N.Y. Acad. Scis. Achievements include patent for method and apparatus for collection and analysis of mercury in the atmosphere; developer method of photo-nuclear activation analysis of copper in ores and concentrates, synthetic standards for EDX-ray analysis, method of collection and analysis of mercury in air, method of nondestructive X-ray analysis of heavy metals in toys. Developed pre-concentration methods of trace elements in water for EDX-ray analysis. Office: Halinco Skin Care Products PO Box 9405 Austin TX 78766-9405

PRAEGER, SANDY, state legislator; b. Oct. 21, 1944; m. Mark A. Praeger. Student, U. Kans., 1966. V.p. Douglas County Bank; mem. Kans. Ho. of Reps. Vice chmn. Douglas County Rep. Cent. Com.; chmn. Leadership Kans.; pres. bd. dirs. United Way. Home: 3601 Quail Creek Ct Lawrence KS 66047-2134 Office: Kans State Senate State Capitol Topeka KS 66612

PRAETORIUS, WILLIAM ALBERT, SR., artist, former advertising and real estate executive; b. Forty-Fort, Pa., Oct. 7, 1924; s. George Albert and Elizabeth (Madden) P.; m. Theresa M. Barnes, June 25, 1949; children: Kathleen Ann, William Albert, Gregg Douglas. Student, Biaritz (France) Am. U., 1945-46, N.Y. U., 1947-48. With L.W. Frohlich Intercon Internat., Inc., 1946-72, sr. v.p., dir. ops., 1969-71, chmn. operating com., 1972; sr. v.p., dir. ops. Deltakos div. J. Walter Thompson Co., N.Y.C., 1972-73; sr. v.p. administrn. J.W.T. Affiliated Cos., 1973-75; pres. Healthmark Communications, Inc., N.Y.C., 1975-77; dir. Clause Comml. div. Donald J. Clause, Southampton, N.Y., 1977-78; dir. comml. div. Meadow Real Estate, 1978-86; artist, 1987—. Author, pub.: Concepts in Leadership, 1982; contbr. column to East End Bus. Rev, articles to profl. jours; exhbns. of paintings include East Hampton Town Hall, Edwin Winfield Gallery, Sag Harbor. Served with AUS, 1943-46. Mem. Barns Landing Assn. Democrat. Catholic. Home and Studio: 30 Captains Walk East Hampton NY 11937-3169

PRAGER, ALICE HEINECKE, music company executive; b. N.Y.C., Aug. 2, 1930; d. Paul and Ruth (Collin) Heinecke; m. George L. Dresser, 1963. BA, Russell Sage Coll., 1951; postgrad., NYU, 1952-55. V.p. SESAC Inc., N.Y.C., 1956-73, pres., 1973-78, pres., chmn. bd., 1978-92; chmn. bd. Personal Touch Music, Personal Touch, Inc. Mem. Internat. Radio and TV Soc., Am. Women in Radio and TV, Am. Inst. of Mgmt., Advt. Women of N.Y., Nat. Acad. Recording Arts and Scis., Broadcast Pioneers, Country Music Assn. (bd. dirs., 1986), Gospel Music Assn., Vets. Bedside Network (bd. dirs.). Office: The Personal Touch Inc 68-34 Fleet St Forest Hills NY 11375

PRAGER, DAVID, retired state supreme court chief justice; b. Ft. Scott, Kans., Oct. 30, 1918; s. Walter and Helen (Kishler) P.; m. Dorothy Schroeter, Sept. 8, 1945; children: Diane, David III. AB, U. Kans., 1939, JD, 1942. Bar: Kans. 1942. Practiced in Topeka, 1946-59; dist. judge Shawnee County (Kans.) Dist. Ct., 1959-71; assoc. justice Kans. Supreme Ct., Topeka, 1971-87, chief justice, 1987-88; ret., 1988; lectr. Washburn Law Sch., 1948-68. Served to lt. USNR, 1942-46, ETO, PTO. Mem. Kans. Dist. Judges Assn. (past pres.). Order of Coif, Phi Beta Kappa, Phi Delta Theta, Lions Lodge, Arab Shrine Lodge.

PRAGER, ELLIOT DAVID, surgeon, educator; b. N.Y.C., Sept. 10, 1941; s. Benjamin and Sadye Zelda (Newman) P.; m. Phyllis Damon Warner, July 1, 1967; children: Rebecca, Sarah, Katherine. AB, Dartmouth Coll., 1962; MD, Harvard U., 1966. Diplomate Am. Bd. Surgery, Am. Bd. Colon and Rectal Surgery. Surg. resident Roosevelt Hosp., N.Y.C., 1966-71; colon-rectal fellow Lahey Clinic, Boston, 1971-72; staff surgeon Sansum Clinic, Santa Barbara, Calif., 1974—; dir. colorectal fellowship Sansum Clinic, Santa Barbara, 1982—; chief of surgery, 1986-94; dir. surg. edn. Cottage Hosp., Santa Barbara, 1994—; mem., vice chair Residency Rev. Com., 1992—. Author: (with others) Operative Colorectal Surgery, 1994, Current Therapy in Colon and Rectal Surgery, 1990; contbr. articles to profl. jours. Lt. comdr. USN, 1972-74. Fellow Am. Coll. Surgeons (adv. coun. 1992—), Am. Soc. of Colon and Rectal Surgeons (v.p. 1992, sec. of program dirs., 1990—).

Achievements include 5 patents for colostomy control devices. Office: Sansum Clinic 317 W Pueblo Santa Barbara CA 93102

PRAGER, STEPHEN, chemistry educator; b. Darmstadt, Germany, July 20, 1928; came to U.S., 1941, naturalized, 1950; s. William and Gertrude Ann (Heyer) P.; m. Julianne Heller, June 7, 1948. B.Sc., Brown, 1947; Ph.D., Cornell, 1951. Mem. faculty U. Minn., Mpls., 1952—, assoc. prof. chemistry, 1956-62, prof., 1962-90, prof. emeritus, 1990—; cons. Union Carbide Corp., Oak Ridge, 1954-74. Asso. editor Jour. Phys. Chemistry, 1970-79. Fulbright scholar and Guggenheim fellow, 1958, 59; Fulbright lectr. and Guggenheim fellow, 1966-67. Mem. Am. Chem. Soc., Am. Phys. Soc. Home: 3320 Dunlap St N Saint Paul MN 55112-3709 Office: Chemistry Dept U Minn Minneapolis MN 55455

PRAGER, SUSAN WESTERBERG, dean, law educator; b. Sacramento, Dec. 14, 1942; d. Percy Foster Westerberg and Aileen M. (McKinley) P.; m. James Martin Prager, Mar. 24, 1973; children: McKinley Ann, Case Mahone. AB, Stanford U., 1964, MA, 1967; JD, UCLA, 1971. Bar: N.C. 1971, Calif. 1972. Atty. Powe, Porter & Alphin, Durham, N.C., 1971-72; acting prof. law UCLA, 1972-77, prof. Sch. Law, 1977—; Arjay and Frances Fearing Miller prof. of law, 1992—, assoc. dean Sch. Law, 1979-82, dean, 1982—; bd. dirs. Pacific Mut. Life Ins. Co., Newport Beach, Calif. Editor-in-chief, UCLA Law Rev., 1970-71. Trustee Stanford U., 1976-80, 87—. Mem. ABA (council of sect. on legal edn. and admissions to the bar 1983-85), Assn. Am. Law Schs. (pres. 1986), Order of Coif. Office: UCLA Sch Law 405 Hilgard Ave Los Angeles CA 90095-1476

PRAH, PAMELA MARIE, journalist; b. Latrobe, Pa., June 22, 1963; d. Lonnie Joseph and Eleanor Ruth (Stefl) P. BS in Journalism, Ohio U., 1985; postgrad., Am. U., 1987. Assoc. editor McGraw-Hill Pub., Washington, 1986-87; editor Internat. Pubs., Washington, 1987—; staff editor Bur. Nat. Affairs, Washington, 1989-91, 93—; spl. corr. Bur. Nat. Affairs, Heidelberg, Germany, 1991-92; intern 13-30 Pub. Co., Knoxville, Tenn., 1985, Tribune Rev., Greensburg, Pa., 1985, McGraw-Hill World News, London, 1985; editor Athens Mags., 1985, mng. editor, 1984, The Awakening, 1985. Scholar Ohio U., Athens, 1981-85. Mem. Soc. Profl. Jounalists (Washington chpt.), Women Communications, Kappa Tau Alpha. Roman Catholic. Avocations: tennis, reading, theater, travel. Home: Apt 301 2901 Connecticut Ave NW Washington DC 20008-1419

PRAISNER, JAN A., electronics executive; b. 1951. MBA, So. Meth. U. CPA. With Price Waterhouse, Digital Equipment Corp.; v.p., contr. Monolithic Memories, Inc.; worldwide mfg. contr. Advanced Micro Devices, Sunnyvale, Calif., 1987-88; v.p. mktg. Aspect Telecomm. Corp., San Jose, Calif., 1988—. Office: Aspect Telecommunications Corp 1730 Fox Dr San Jose CA 95131*

PRAKAPAS, EUGENE JOSEPH, art gallery director; b. Lowell, Mass., July 29, 1932; s. Joseph S. Prakapas and Viola Schensnol; m. Dorothy A. Seitner, Dec. 1, 1971. BA, Yale U., 1953; MA, Oxford U., Balliol, 1959. Vice-pres., editor-in-chief Trident Press and Pocket Books div. Simon & Schuster, Inc., N.Y.C., 1960-70; co-dir. Carus Gallery, N.Y.C., 1973-75; dir. Prakapas Gallery, N.Y.C., 1976—; vis. curator San Francisco Mus. Modern Art, 1986. Author: Bauhaus Photography, 1985. Lt. (s.g.) USNR, 1953-57. Fulbright fellow, 1957-59; Yale U. scholar, 1949-53. Mem. Art Dealers Assn. Am., Assn. Internat. Photography Art Dealers. Home and Office: 1 Northgate Apt 6B Bronxville NY 10708-2656

PRAKASH, RAVI, physician, educator; b. Meerut, U.P., India, Feb. 22, 1941; s. Daya Ram and Ramkali Devi Bansal; m. Odette Agustin, June 10, 1978; children: Gennifer Gita, John Paul Ravi, Jonathan Dayaram. BSc, Agra U., 1958; MD, All India Inst. Med. Scis., New Delhi, 1963. Diplomate: Diplomate Am. Bd. Internal Medicine. Fellow in cardiology Cedars-Sinai Med. Center, 1970-71; asst. prof. medicine U. Ill., 1971-73; asst. prof., then assoc. prof. medicine U. Calif., Irvine, 1973-79; prof. medicine UCLA Sch. Medicine, 1981-92, vice chmn. dept. medicine, 1989-90; chmn. dept. medicine Charles R. Drew U. Medicine and Sci., L.A., 1989-90; chief cardiology King-Drew Med. Ctr., L.A., 1979-90; pres. Am. Heart Inst., 1987—. Contbr. articles to profl. jours. Capt. M.C. Indian Army, 1963-66. Recipient Outstanding Tchr. award Long Beach VA Hosp., 1974, 76. Fellow ACP, Am. Coll. Cardiology; mem. Am. Heart Assn. Office: 4305 Torrance Blvd Ste 405 Torrance CA 90503-4404

PRAKASH, SATYA, biology educator; b. Pilkhuwa, U.P., India, July 8, 1938; came to U.S., 1962; s. Suraj Bali and Atar Kali; m. Louise Burlant; children: Ulka, Ravi, Anita. PhD, Washington U., St. Louis, 1966. Asst. prof. biology U. Rochester, N.Y., 1969-74, assoc. prof., 1974-80, prof., 1980-93; prof. U. Tex. Med. Branch, Galveston, 1993—. NIH grantee, 1972—. Mem. Genetics Soc. Am., Am. Soc. Biochemistry and Molecular Biology. Hindu. Office: U Tex Med Branch Sealy Ctr Molecular Sci Galveston TX 77555

PRAMER, DAVID, microbiologist, educator, research administrator; b. Mt. Vernon, N.Y., Mar. 25, 1923; s. Coleman and Ethel (Toback) P.; m. Rhoda Lifschutz, Sept. 6, 1950; children—Andrew, Stacey. Student, St. John's U., 1940, Tex. A&M Coll., 1941; B.S. cum laude, Rutgers U., 1948, Ph.D., 1952. Vis. investigator Butterwich Research Labs., Welwyn, Eng., 1952-54; from asst. to assoc. prof. microbiology Rutgers U., New Brunswick, N.J., 1954-60; prof. Rutgers U., 1960-67, disting. prof., 1967—, dir. biological scis., 1969-73, dir. univ. research, 1973-75, assoc. v.p. research, 1973-80; dir. Waksman Inst. Microbiology, 1980-88, assoc. v.p. corp. liaison, 1988-93; exec. asst. and disting. prof. emeritus, exec. asst. Rutgers U., New Brunswick, N.J., 1993—; cons. various fed. agys., 1965—; dir. New Brunswick Sci. Co., Edison, R&D Coun. of N.J., Nanodyne, Inc., New Brunswick, Organica, Inc., Great Neck, N.Y.; served on numerous chmn., com. and adv. posts. Author: Life in the Soil, 1964, Experimental Soil Microbiology, 1965, The Microbes, 1971, Engineered Organisms in the Environment, 1985; also over 250 articles in profl. jours; regional editor World Jour. Soil and Biology and Biochemistry; mem. editl. bd. Soil Sci., BioSci., Applied Microbiology and Biotech. Bd. dirs. Library, Highland Park, N.J., 1966-75, chmn., 1976-78; committeeman Democratic Party, Highland Park, 1958-66. Served to cpl. USAF, 1943-46. Fulbright-Hays Sr. Research fellow, 1969. Fellow Am. Acad. Microbiology; mem. Am. Soc. Microbiology, Internat. Commn. Microbial Ecology (chmn.). Internat. Cell Rsch. Orgn., Phi Beta Kappa, Alpha Zeta, Sigma Xi. Jewish. Avocations: jogging, travel. Home: 208 Hampshire Ct Piscataway NJ 08854-6218 Office: Rutgers Univ Office Rsch & Sponsord Programs Adminstrv Svc Bldg Annex II Piscataway NJ 08855-1179

PRANCKUN, JOHN, manufacturing executive; b. 1947. Grad., Marquette U., 1969. V.p. fin. and adminstrn. Kimble Glass Inc., Vineland, N.J., 1972—. With U.S. Army, 1969-72. Office: Kimble Glass Inc 537 Crystal Ave Vineland NJ 08360*

PRANGE, ARTHUR JERGEN, JR., psychiatrist, neurobiologist, educator; b. Grand Rapids, Mich., Sept. 19, 1926; s. Arthur Jergen and Martha Frances (Elliott) P.; m. Sarah Elizabeth Bowen, Feb. 4, 1950; children—Christine Anne, Martha Louise, Laura Beth, David Elliott. B.S., U. Mich., 1947, M.D., 1950. Intern Wayne County Gen. Hosp., Eloise, Mich., 1950-51; resident in psychiatry U. N.C., Chapel Hill, 1954-57; instr. U. N.C., 1957-60, asst. prof., 1960-64, asso. prof., 1964-68, prof. psychiatry, 1968-83, Boshamer prof. psychiatry, 1983—, acting chmn. dept. psychiatry, 1983-85, dir. NIMH Clin. Rsch. Ctr., 1979—; vis. scientist Med. Rsch. Coun. Unit, Epson, Surrey, Eng., 1968-69; chmn. clin. projects rsch. rev. com. HEW, NIMH, 1975-76, chmn. bd. sci. counselors, 1986-87; mem. psychopharmacologic drugs adv. com. HEW, FDA, 1979-82. Editor: The Thyroid Axis, Drugs and Behavior, 74; Contbr. articles to med. jours. Recipient NIMH Career Devel. award, 1961-69, Career scientist award, 1969—. Fellow Am. Psychiat. Assn. (life), Am. Coll. Neuropsychopharmacology (life, pres. 1987); mem. Internat. Soc. Psychoneuroendocrinology (founding mem.), N.C. Neuropsychiat. Assn. Collegium Internationale Neuropsychopharmacologicum, Royal Coll. Psychiatrists (London). Home: 218-6 Conner Dr Chapel Hill NC 27514-7070 Office: Univ NC Sch Medicine Dept Psychiatry Chapel Hill NC 27599-7160

PRANGE, ROY LEONARD, JR., lawyer; b. Chgo., Sept. 12, 1945; s. Roy Leonard and Marjorie Rose (Kauppi) P.; m. Carol Lynn Poels, June 5, 1971; children: David, Ellen, Susan. BA, U. Iowa, 1967; MA, Ohio State U., 1968; JD, U. Wis.-Madison, 1975. Bar: Wis. 1975, U.S. Dist. Ct. (we. and ea. dists.) Wis. 1975, U.S. Ct. Appeals (7th cir.) 1978, U.S. Supreme Ct. 1978. Assoc. Ross & Stevens, Svc. Corp., Madison, Wis., 1975-79; prin. Ross & Stevens, Svc. Corp., 1979-90, Quarles & Brady, Madison, 1990—; lectr. bankruptcy, debtor-creditor rights, U. Wis., Madison, 1982--. Contbr.: Wisconsin Lawyer's Desk Reference Manual, 1987, Commercial Litigation in Wisconsin Practice Handbook, 1995. 1st lt. U.S. Army, 1969-72. Fellow Am. Coll. Bankruptcy; mem. ABA, Wis. State Bar (dir. bankruptcy, insolvency, creditors rights sect. 1985-91, chair 1990-92, mem. continuing legal edn. com. 1990—), Am. Bankruptcy Inst., Dickens Fellowship (v.p. 1980-84). Avocations: running, soccer, karate, golf. Office: Quarles & Brady 1 S Pinckney St PO Box 2113 Madison WI 53703

PRANSES, ANTHONY LOUIS, retired electric company executive, organization executive; b. Claracq, France, May 3, 1920; s. Anthony Kasimer and Georgette (Pilon) F.; m. Margaret Louise Hamill, July 24, 1943; children—Anthony Randolph, Terry Jay, Renee Louise. Student, Sorbonne, Paris, France, 1937-39; B.S. in Metall. Engring, Carnegie Inst. Tech., 1942, grad. student, 1946-48. With Westinghouse Electric Corp., 1945-86; mgr. mfg. planning Westinghouse Electric Corp., Lima, Ohio, 1954-57; plant mgr. Westinghouse Electric Corp., Lima, 1958-59, mgr. mfg. services, 1959-72; mgr. mfg. Westinghouse Electric Corp., 1972-80, cons., 1980-86. Joined Am. Youth Hostels, 1935, founder Pitts. council, 1947, pres. council, 1947-50, mem. nat. bd. dirs., 1954-72, Midwest regional v.p., 1957-59, nat. pres., 1959-62, pres. Lima council, 1962-75, 87-91, chmn. nat. bd. dirs., 1963-67. Served to capt., C.E. AUS, 1942- 45. Home: Rural Route 2 6005 Poling Rd Lima OH 45807-9452

PRAS, ROBERT THOMAS, hotel executive; b. Newark, Dec. 14, 1941; s. Leon Lewis and Helen (McCully) P.; m. Constance Wilson, Nov. 30, 1968; children: Andrew, Douglas, Allison. BS, Delaware Valley Coll., 1965. Sanitarian Phila. Dept. Pub. Health, 1965-66; dir. quality assurance Acme Markets, Phila., 1966-68; merchandiser Alpha Beta Acme Markets, LaHabra, Calif., 1968-72; dir. Wakefern Food Corp., Elizabeth, N.J., 1972-79; exec. v.p. Marriott Internat., Washington, 1979—. Mayor Hillsborough (N.J.) Twp., 1979, mem. twp. council, 1976-77. Mem. Am. Mgmt. Assn., Nat. Restaurant Assn. Office: Marriott Internat 10400 Fernwood Rd Bethesda MD 20817-1109

PRASAD, ANANDA SHIVA, medical educator; b. Buxar, Bihar, India, Jan. 1, 1928; came to U.S., 1952, naturalized, 1968; s. Radha Krishna and Mahesha (Kaur) Lall; m. Aryabala Ray, Jan. 6, 1952; children: Rita, Sheila, Ashok, Audrey. BSc, Patna (India) Sci. Coll., 1946, MB, BChir, 1951; PhD, U. Minn., 1957. Intern Patna Med. Coll. Hosp., 1951-52; resident St. Paul's Hosp., Dallas, 1952-53, U. Minn., 1953-56, VA Hosp., Mpls., 1956; instr. dept. medicine Univ. Hosp., U. Minn., Mpls., 1957-58; vis. assoc. prof. medicine Shiraz Med. Faculty, Nemazee Hosp., Shiraz, Iran, 1960; asst. prof. medicine and nutrition Vanderbilt U., 1961-63; mem. faculty, dir. div. hematology dept. medicine Wayne State U., Detroit, 1963-84; assoc. prof. Wayne State U., 1964-68, prof., 1968—, dir. research dept. medicine, 1984—; mem. staff Harper-Grace Hosps., VA Hosp., Allen Park, Mich.; mem. trace elements subcom. Food and Nutrition Bd., NRC-Nat. Acad. Scis., 1965-68; chmn. trace elements com. Internat. Union Nutritional Scis.; mem. Am. Bd. Nutrition; pres. Am. Coll. Nutrition, 1991-93. Author: Zinc Metabolism, 1966, Trace Elements in Human Health and Disease, 1976, Trace Elements and Iron in Human Metabolism, 1978, Zinc in Human Nutrition, 1979, Biochemistry of Zinc, 1993; editor: Clinical, Biochemical and Nutritional Aspects of Trace Elements, 1982, Am. Jour. Hematology, Jour. Trace Elements in Exptl. Medicine; editor: Zinc Metabolism, Current Aspects in Health and Disease, 1977; co-editor: Clinical Applications of Recent Advances in Zinc Metabolism, 1982, Zinc Deficiency in Human Subjects, 1983, Essential and Toxic Trace Elements in Human Health and Disease, 1988, Essential and Toxic Trace Elements in Human Health and Disease: An Update, 1993; mem. editorial bd. Jour. Micro Nutrient Analysis, Jour. Am. Coll. Nutrition; contbr. articles to profl. jours., also reviewer. Trustee Detroit Internat. Inst., Detroit Gen. Hosp. Research Corp., 1969-72. Recipient Rsch. Recognition award Wayne State U., 1964, award Am. Coll. Nutrition, 1976, Disting. Faculty Fellowship award Wayne State U., 1986, Acad. Scholars, Wayne State U., 1992, Medal of Honor, City of Lyon, France, 1989; Pfizer scholar, 1955-56. Master Am. Coll. Nutrition; fellow ACP (recipient Mich. Laureate award), AAAS, Am. Inst. Nutrition, Internat. Soc. Hematology; mem. AMA (Goldberger award 1975), Internat. Soc. Trace Element Rsch. in Humans (pres. 1986-92, chmn. steering com. 1985-86, Raulin award 1989), Am. Soc. Clin. Nutrition (awards com. 1969-70), Am. Fedn. Clin. Rsch. (pres. Mich. 1969-70), Am. Inst. Nutrition (trace elements panel), Am. Physiol. Soc., Am. Soc. Clin. Investigation, Am. Soc. Hematology, Assn. Am. Physicians, Ctrl. Soc. Clin. Rsch., Soc. Exptl. Biology and Medicine (Councillor Mich. 1967-71), Wayne County Med. Soc., Internat. Soc. Internal Medicine, Am. Soc. Clin. Nutrition (Robert H. Herman award 1984), Nutrition Soc. India (Gopalan oration award 1988), Cosmos Club (Washington), Sigma Xi. Home: 4710 Cove Rd West Bloomfield MI 48323-3604 Office: Univ Health Ctr 5-C 4201 St Antoine Detroit MI 48201

PRATHER, DENZIL LEWIS, petroleum engineer; b. Elizabeth, W.Va., Mar. 18, 1921; s. Elias Hugh and Mary Deborah (Lewis) P.; m. Madeline Shimer, May 13, 1945; children: Denzil Jr., Kathy Taylor, Linda Holtgrewe, Mary Smith, Anne Scarbro, David. Student, Potomac State U., 1941-42; BS in Petroleum Engring., Marietta Coll., 1945. Registered profl. engr., W.Va. Supt. Weva Oil Co., Elizabeth, 1945-50; pvt. practice as cons. Midland, Tex., 1950-57; div. mgr. Southwestern Devel. Co., Parkersburg, W.Va., 1957-70; ptnr. Loper and Prather, Parkersburg, 1970-80; pres. Adena Petroleum, Inc., Parkersburg, 1980—. Pres. PTA, Belpre, Ohio, 1961-63; active Congl. Ch., Belpre, 1957-90. 1st lt. USAF, 1942-45. Mem. Soc. Petroleum Engrs. (sr. mem.), Appalachian Geol. Soc., Ohio Acad. Sci., Ohio Acad. History. Democrat. Congregationalist. Home: 814 Boulevard Dr Belpre OH 45714 Office: Adena Petroleum Inc PO Box 250 Mineral Wells WV 26150

PRATHER, DONNA LYNN, psychiatrist; b. Charlotte, N.C., Nov. 4, 1946; d. James Boyd and Ann (Joyner) P. BA, Queens Coll., Charlotte, 1968; MD, U. N.C., 1978. Supr. Meckenburg County Dept. Social Svcs., Charlotte, 1971-74; family practice intern Charlotte Meml. Hosp., 1978-79, resident in family practice, 1979-81; fellow in family medicine U. N.C., Chapel Hill, 1981-82; resident in psychiatry N.C. Meml. Hosp., Chapel Hill, 1982-85; pvt. practice psychiatry Chapel Hill, N.C., 1985—; psychiatrist Person Counceling Ctr., Roxboro, N.C., 1983-92; med. dir. Orange-Person-Chatam Mental Health Ctr., Chapel Hill, 1992—; clin. asst. prof. U. N.C., Chapel Hill, 1985—. Mem. N.C. Psychiat. Assn., N.C. Med. Soc., Am. Psychiat. Assn., N.C. Psychiat. Assn. (chmn., com. for women 1990-91). Avocation: music. Office: The Courtyard Ste 27 Chapel Hill NC 27514

PRATHER, GERALD LUTHER, management consultant, retired air force officer, judge; b. LaGrange, Ga., Apr. 7, 1935; s. Luther Pate and Hazel Belle (McCullough) P.; m. Carolyn Pearson, Nov. 22, 1956; children—Dean Allen, Bryan Pate, Jeri Lynn, Angela. B.S.E.E., Auburn U., 1966; M.S. in Mgmt., Air Force Inst. Tech., 1972; postgrad. advanced mgmt., U. Houston, 1978; grad., SQ Officer Sch., Maxwell AFB, 1963, ICAF, Washington, 1974. Enlisted USAF, 1954-56, commd. 2d lt., 1956, advanced through grades to maj. gen., 1981, various assignments as pilot, 1956-68, served in Vietnam, 1967-68; commandt. 1963d Comm. Squadron USAF, Chanute AFB, Ill., 1968-69; comdr. 1918th Comm. Squadron USAF, Scott AFB, Ill., 1969-70; dep. dir. comm.-electronics for 15th Air Force USAF, March AFB, Calif., 1970-72; chief comm. ops. div. hdqrs. USAF, Washington, 1972-75; comdr. strategic comm. div. USAF, Offutt AFB, Nebr., 1975-77; comdr. European Comm. Div. USAF, Ramstein AFB, W. Ger., 1977-80; dir. Command Control, Comm. & Computer Systems, Hdqrs. U.S. Readiness Command USAF, MacDill AFB, Fla., 1980-81; asst. chief of staff of Info. Systems Hdqrs. USAF, Washington, 1981-84; comdr. Air Force Comm. Command USAF, Scott AFB, Ill., 1984-86; ret. USAF, 1986; pvt. practice mgmt. cons. Del Rio, Tex., 1986—; Justice of the Peace Val Verde County, Tex.; lectr. in field; also air traffic controller, parachutist. speech writer Team America 1983 (Freedom Found. nat. award 1984). Scout master Boy Scouts Am., Sacramento, 1963, chmn. com., Sacramento, 1964, cub master, Auburn, Ala.,

1965; sponsor Explorer Troop, Boy Scouts Am., Scott AFB, Ill., 1969; alumni Boy Scouts Am., 1984-85; chmn. Amistad Dist. Boy Scouts Am., 1988; chmn. Val Verde County United Way Campaign, 1989, pres., bd. dirs. 1990. Decorated DSM with oak leaf cluster, Legion of Merit with one oak leaf cluster, DFC, Bronze Star with V device, Air medal with two oak leaf clusters, Republic of Vietnam Gallantry Cross with Palm; recipient Gen. Edwin W. Rawlings award Air Force Inst. Tech., 1972, Comdt.'s award, 1972, also numerous other decorations and awards. Mem. VFW (life), Vietnam Vet. Assn. (life), Armed Forces Comm. - Electronics Assn. (assoc. 1984—, internat. v.p. 1982-84, chmn. ethics com. 1982-83, mem. com. 1981-82, Meritorious Gold medal 1976, 83), Air Traffic Control Assn., Soc. Am. Mil. Engrs., Del Rio C. of C. (bd. dirs. 1990-91, v.p. 1991-92), Soc. Logistics Engrs., Telephone Pioneers of Am., Order of Daedalians, Air Force Assn., Air Force Sgts. Assn. (hon.), Non-Commd. Officers Assn. (hon.), Vietnam Vets. of Am., Ret. Officers Assn., Am. Legion, Lions Internat., Del Rio Club (v.p. 1989-90), Civitan Internat. Club (Auburn U.). Avocations: gardening, racquetball, sketching, automotive mechanics, private pilot.

PRATHER, LENORE LOVING, state supreme court presiding justice; b. West Point, Miss., Sept. 17, 1931; d. Byron Herald and Hattie Hearn (Morris) Loving; m. Robert Brooks Prather, May 30, 1957; children: Pamela, Valerie Jo, Malinda Wayne. B.S., Miss. State Coll. Women, 1953; JD, U. Miss., 1955. Bar: Miss. 1955. Practice with B. H. Loving, West Point, 1955-60, sole practice, 1960-62, 65-71, assoc. practice, 1962-65; mcpl. judge City of West Point, 1965-71; chancery ct. judge 14th dist. State of Miss., Columbus, 1971-82; supreme ct. justice State of Miss., Jackson, 1982-92; presiding justice State of Miss., 1992—; v.p. Conf. Local Bar Assn., 1956-58; sec. Clay County Bar Assn., 1956-71. 1st woman in Miss. to become chancery judge, 1971, and supreme ct. justice, 1982. Mem. ABA, Miss. State Bar Assn., Miss. Conf. Judges, DAR, Rotary, Pilot Club, Jr. Aux. Columbus Club. Episcopalian. Office: Miss Supreme Ct PO Box 117 Jackson MS 39205-0117 also: PO Box 903 Columbus MS 39703-0903

PRATHER, THOMAS LEVI, JR., army officer; b. Washington, June 25, 1940; s. Thomas Levi Prather and Jestina Mae (Jones) Stewart; m. Beulah Mae Sullivan, Nov. 3, 1962; children: Delia, Marcia, Thomas III. BS in Music Edn., Morgan State U., 1962; MS in Procurement and Contract Mgmt., Fla. Inst. Tech., 1974. Commd. 2d lt. U.S. Army, 1962, advanced through grades to maj. gen., 1992; mil. asst. Office Asst. Sec. Army for Installation and Logistics, Washington, 1975-77; comdr. Materiel Mgmt. Ctr., 8th Div., Bad Kreuznach, Fed. Republic Germany, 1977-79, Combat Equipment Bn. West, Kaiserslautern, Fed. Republic Germany, 1979-81; student Army War Coll., Carlisle, Pa., 1981-82; dir. materiel mgmt. Communications Command, Ft. Monmouth, N.J., 1982-85; comdr. Tobyhanna (Pa.) Army Depot, 1985-87; dep. comdr. 2d Corps Support Command, Stuttgart, Fed. Republic Germany, 1987-89; dep. comdg. gen. Armament, Munitions and Chem. Command, Rock Island, Ill., 1989-90; comdg. gen. Troop Support Command, St. Louis, 1990—. Decorated Def. Superior Svc. medal, Legion of Merit, Bronze Star, Meritorious Svc. medal. Mem. Assn. U.S. Army, Ordnance Assn. Avocation: sports. Home: 53 Fairfax Dr Fort Belvoir VA 22060-2107 Office: US Army Troop Support Command 4300 Goodfellow Blvd Saint Louis MO 63120-1703

PRATS, MICHAEL, petroleum engineer, educator; b. Tampa, Fla., Dec. 18, 1925; s. Miguel and Maria (Carbó) P.; m. Mary Blanche Flaherty, Apr. 7, 1951; children: Delicia Anne, Barbara Eileen, Teresa Kaye, Steven Michael. BS in Physics, U. Tex., 1949, MA in Physics, 1951. With Shell Devel. Co., Houston, 1950—, cons. research engr., then sr. research assoc., 1972-89; pres. Michael Prats & Assocs., Houston, 1989—; adj. prof. dept. petroleum engring. U. Tex., Austin, 1991—; participant scientist exchange Royal/Dutch Shell Lab., Amsterdam, The Netherlands, 1954, 55, Shell Internat. Petroleum, The Hague, The Netherlands, 1981, Maraven, S.A., Caracas, Venezuela, 1981-83. Author: Thermal Recovery, 1982, Spanish transl., 1987; contbr. articles to profl. jours.; 21 patents in field. Served to staff sgt. USAAF, 1944-46, PTO. Recipient Diploma of Honor Pi Epsilon Tau, 1986, Disting. Svc. award Rep. Honduras, 1989, Thermal Recovery Disting. Achievement award SPE Thermal Ops. Symposium, 1991, KAPITSA medal Acad. Natural Scis. (Moscow), 1995; named to Internat. Hall of Fame, 1989. Mem. AIME (hon.), NAE, Soc. Petroleum Engrs. (hon., bd. dirs. 1976-79, sr. tech. editor 1987-90, Enhanced Oil Recovery Pioneer 1986, Uren award 1974, Disting. Mem. award 1983, Anthony F. Lucas Gold medal 1993), Soc. Venezolana de Ingenieros de Petroleo, Can. Inst. Mining, Mex. Nat. Acad. Engring. (corr.), Acad. Engring. Armenia (fgn. mem.), Pi Epsilon Tau (hon.). Avocation: travel. Address: 2834 Bellefontaine Houston TX 77025-1610

PRATT, ALBERT, financial consultant, trustee; b. Newton, Mass., May 23, 1911; s. Frederick Sanford and Ella Winifred (Nickerson) P.; m. Alice Mathea Lee, May 24, 1940 (dec. 1976); children—Alice Mathea, Cornelia S., Nina L. (Mrs. Timothy W. Casey), Frederick H., Kate Nickerson (Mrs. Barry E. Lapping); m. Fanny Gray Little Morgan, Jan. 2, 1977. Grad., Country Day Sch., Newton, 1929; A.B., Harvard, 1933, J.D., 1936. Bar: Mass. bar 1936. With firm Goodwin, Procter & Hoar, Boston, 1936-40; with Paine, Webber, Jackson & Curtis, Inc., Boston, 1946-80; vice chmn. Paine, Webber, Jackson & Curtis, Inc., 1970-76, cons., 1976-80, gen. partner, 1950-54, 57-70, ltd. partner, 1954-57; adv. dir. Blyth, Eastman Paine Webber Inc., Boston, 1980-83; dir., chmn. investment com. Paine Webber Properties, Inc., 1980-84, pres., 1984, cons., 1985—; ptnr. F.S. Pratt & Son, 1946-87; asst. sec. navy, 1954-57; bd. govs. N.Y. Stock Exchange, 1963-66. Pres. United Fund Boston, 1962-64. Served to comdr. USNR, 1940-45. Mem. Investment Bankers Assn. (chmn. N.E. group 1952-53, gov. 1957-60, 64-67, chmn. securities act com. 1959-63, pres. 1965-66), Assn. Harvard Alumni (dir. 1964-70), Boston C. of C. (dir. 1958-61), Assn. Harvard Clubs (pres. 1962-63), Harvard Alumni Assn. (dir. 1958-63), Cruising Club Am., N.Y. Yacht Club, Wianno Club (Osterville, Mass.). Home: Key Largo Anglers Club 50 Clubhouse Rd Key Largo FL 33037 Office: care PaineWebber Properties 265 Franklin St Fl 16 Boston MA 02110-3113

PRATT, ARTHUR D., printing company executive; b. Indpls., May 7, 1924; s. Arthur D. and Helen L. (Rikhoff) P.; m. Marjorie M. Zwally May 19, 1967 (div. Mar. 1974); m. Amal Marcos, Apr. 11, 1987; children: Margaret, Michael, Sarah, Andrew. Student, Sorbonne U., Paris, 1947. Pres. Found. Internat. Econ. Devel., 1949-56, Pratt Printing Co., Indpls., 1972-93; with Life Effectiveness Tng., Indpls., 1982-94. Author: The Party's Over, 1976, Christ and America's Survival, 1977, The Great Idea of God, 1984, How to Help and Understand the Alcoholic, 1987, (poetry) (with Amal Pratt) The Meeting of East and West. Pres. Flynn Christian Fellowship Houses Inc., 1956-94, Christ. Interfaith Housing Inc., 1966-73, Madras Coun., 1974-79. Mem. Athenaeum Club. Episcopalian. Home: 2621 Sutherland Ave Indianapolis IN 46205-4270 Office: Life Effectiveness Tng 1505 N Delaware Indianapolis IN 46202

PRATT, BRIAN, heavy manufacturing executive; b. 1952. Graduate, Calif. State Poly. U., 1974. With ARB, Inc., Bakersfield, Calif., 1974—, ARB Fabricated Syss., Inc. affiliate, Bakersfield, Calif., 1983-92; pres. ARB, Inc., Bakersfield, Calif., 1992—. Office: ARB Inc 4042 Patton Way Bakersfield CA 93308-5030*

PRATT, DAN EDWIN, chemistry educator; b. High Point, N.C., Feb. 7, 1924; s. C. Daniel and Carol Druscilla (Wyatt) P.; m. Mana Clariece Peacock, Aug. 29, 1959; 1 child, Mana Lisa. BS, U. Ga., 1950, MS, 1951; PhD (nuclear sci. fellow 1960), Fla. State U., 1962; postgrad. in food sci., U. Mass. Asst. prof. chemistry U. Ga., 1955-61; assoc. prof., research scientist food sci. and nutrition U. Wis., Madison, 1964-69; research scientist, assoc. prof. Purdue U., 1969-76, prof. chemistry, 1976—; vis. prof. food law Emory U., 1954; vis. rsch. scientist Natick R & D Command, 1980; vis. lectr. U. Viscosa, Brazil, 1982, Harvard U., 1980; vis. scientist Am. Oil Chemists, Cannes, France, 1985; vis. rsch. scientist in lipid chemistry FDA, Washington, 1987, lectr., 1988; cons. to food industry, Taiwan, 1981, Nat. Poultry Industry, Lipid Chemistry, 1990; rsch. scientist Am. Oil Chemists, 1992; rsch. com., rep. Inst. Food Technologists, 1986-89. Contbr. numerous articles profl. jours. Del. Internat. Congress Food Scientists, Tokyo, 1978. With USMCR, 1942-45. Recipient Disting. Scientist Research award Ind. Inst. Food Sci., 1982. Fellow Am. Inst. Chemists, Inst. Food Technologists; mem. Nat. Inst. Food Scientists, Am. Acad. Scis., N.Y. Acad. Scis., Sigma Xi, Phi Kappa Phi, Pi Mu Epsilon, Phi Tau Sigma (exec. sec. 1969) Gamma

Sigma Delta. Club: Lafayette Toastmasters (pres. 1975). Home: 1600 Northwestern Ave West Lafayette IN 47906-2269 Office: Purdue U Dept Foods And Nutriti West Lafayette IN 47906

PRATT, DANA JOSEPH, publishing consultant; b. Cambridge, Mass., Dec. 9, 1926; s. Carroll Cornelius and Marjory (Bates) P.; m. Therese Louis, July 14, 1957; children—Joseph Caldwell, Michael Louis, Benjamin Lyon. B.Naval Sci., Tufts U., 1946, B.A., 1948. Mgmt. trainee N.J. Bell Telephone Co., Newark, 1948-50; sales asst. Princeton U. Press, N.J., 1950-53; sales mgr. U. Ill. Press, Urbana, 1953-55; field cons. Franklin Book Programs, N.Y.C., 1955-59; staff assoc. Am. Book Pubs. Council, N.Y.C., 1959-62; exec. sec. Assn. Am. Univ. Presses, N.Y.C., 1962-66; asst. dir. Yale U. Press, New Haven, 1966-78; dir. pub. Library of Congress, Washington, 1978-93. Contbr. articles to profl. jours. Served as ensign USNR, comdg. officer PC 566, 1946-47. Mem. Washington Book Pubs. (pres. 1984-85), Soc. for Scholarly Pub. (bd. dirs. 1982-86), Washington Map Soc., Washington Rare Book Group. Home and Office: 7514 Old Chester Rd Bethesda MD 20817-6163

PRATT, DAVID TERRY, mechanical engineering educator, combustion researcher; b. Shelley, Idaho, Sept. 14, 1934; s. Eugene Francis and Bernice (Montague) P.; m. Marilyn Jean Thackston, Dec. 22, 1956; children: Douglas Montague, Elizabeth Joann, Brian Stephens. BSc. M.E., U. Wash., 1956; M.Sc., U. Calif., Berkeley, 1962, Ph.D., 1968. Asst. prof. marine engring. U.S. Naval Acad., Annapolis, Md., 1961-64; prof. mech. engring., asst. dean Wash. State U., Pullman, 1968-76; prof. mech. engring. U. Utah, Salt Lake City, 1976-78; prof., chmn. mech. engring. and applied mechanics U. Mich., Ann Arbor, 1978-81; prof., chmn. mech. engring. U. Wash., Seattle, 1981-86, prof. mech. engring., 1987—; research dir. supercomputing Aerojet Propulsion Research Inst., Sacramento, 1986-87. Author (with W.H. Heiser) Hypersonic Airbreathing Propulsion, 1994; editor (with L.D. Smoot) Combustion and Gasification of Pulverized Coal, 1976; contbr. articles to profl. jours. Served to 1st lt. USMC, 1956-60. NSF sci. faculty fellow, 1965-66; Fulbright-Hays sr. research fellow Imperial Coll., 1974-75; David Pierpont Gardner faculty fellow U. Utah, 1976. Mem. ASME, AIAA, Combustion Inst., Am. Soc. Engring. Edn. Lutheran. Office: U Washington Dept Mech Engring M-S FU-10 Seattle WA 98195

PRATT, DIANE ADELE, elementary education educator; b. Battle Creek, Mich., Oct. 24, 1951; d. John Robert and Kathleen Adele (Cooper) Dickert; m. Stephen Howard Pratt, Apr. 29, 1972; children: Eric Stephen, Elizabeth Adele. BS, Western Mich. U., 1972. Cert. elem. tchr., Ohio, Iowa, Mich. Elem. tchr. Berea (Ohio) Cmty. Schs., 1973-76; ednl. cons. Kolbe Products, Inc., Phoenix and Scottsdale, Ariz., 1982-84; tchr. Lemon Tree Nursery Sch., Battle Creek, 1985-88; instr. Jr. Great Books, 1984-87; elem. tchr. Ft. Dodge (Iowa) Cmty. Schs., 1976-78, 90, substitute tchr., 1988-90, middle sch. tchr., 1990—, team leader, 1994—; exec. sec. Born Free Safari Club, Dodgen Industries, Humboldt, Iowa, 1988; advt. exec. Ft. Dodge Today mag., 1989-92; ednl. tutor, Battle Creek, Ft. Dodge, 1986—; mem. adv. bd. Inst. for Instrn. Svcs., Battle Creek, 1984-88; dir., instr. Battle Creek Presch. Enrichment Program, 1984; chmn. Ft. Dodge Supr.'s Comty. Com. to Study K-8 Curriculum, 1988-89, facilitator K-3 human growth and devel. curriculum, 1989-92; mem. standing com. early childhood needs assessment com. Ft. Dodge Comty. Schs., 1989—; mem. adv. bd., instr. Kids on Kampus Iowa Cen. C.C., Ft. Dodge, 1990—; speaker State Conv. Childbirth Educators, Lansing, Mich., 1982; trustee Ft. Dodge Comty. Sch. Found. Bd., 1992—; mem. pub. rels. com. Ft. Dodge Comty. Sch. Dist., 1992-94, mem. ednl. outcomes standing com., 1993-94. Author, editor various newsletters. Mem., past chmn. bd. Christian edn. 1st Bapt. Ch., Ft. Dodge, 1978-79, 89—, music cons., 1992-94, dir. children's choirs, 1988-90, mem. bell choir, 1990-91, ch. sch. supt. 1993—; membership chmn. Battle Creek Parents, 1981-83; neighborhood coord. mothers' march March of Dimes, Battle Creek, 1981-83; troop leader Lakota coun. Girl Scouts U.S., 1988-90; pres. La Mora Park PTA, 1985-87, Phillips Mid Sch. PTA, Ft. Dodge, 1990-91; bd. dirs. Main Stage Players, jr. theater, Ft. Dodge, 1990-91; sec., pres. Jr. Women's Club, Ft. Dodge, 1977-80; mem. kickoff com. United Way, 1991; membership co-chair Ft. Dodge Athletic Booster Club, 1994—. Recipient Mem. of Yr. award La Mora Park PTA, 1987. Mem. NEA, AAUW (sec., pres. Battle Creek br. 1986-88), PEO (N.J. chpt., Ft. Dodge chpt. 1990—), Iowa Edn. Assn., Ft. Dodge Edn. Assn., Iowa Assn. Middle Level Educators, Iowa Coun. Tchrs. English. Avocations: educational research, cross-country skiing, tennis. Home: 1851 9th Ave N Fort Dodge IA 50501

PRATT, DONALD HENRY, manufacturing company executive; b. Hays, Kans., Dec. 2, 1937; s. Donald Edwin and Ida Marjorie (Dreiling) P.; m. George-Ann Hinkle, June 7, 1960; children—Jacqueline, Donald. B.S.I.E., Wichita State U., 1960; M.B.A., Harvard U., 1965. With Butler Mfg. Co., Galesburg, Ill, 1965-67; with Butler Mfg. Co., Kansas City, MO, 1967—; sr. v.p., gen. mgr. bldgs. div. Butler Mfg. Co., 1978-80, exec. v.p., gen. mgr. bldgs. div., 1980-82, exec. v.p., pres. bldgs. div., 1982-86, pres., 1986—; bd. dirs. Union Nat. Bank, Wichita, Kans., Commerce Bank, Kansas City. Trustee Midwest Research Inst.; bd. dirs. Kansas City Art Inst., Mo. Served to capt. USAF, 1960-63. Mem. Metal Bldg. Mfrs. Assn. (chmn. 1983), Am. Royal of Kansas City (bd. dirs.). Republican. Roman Catholic. Avocation: tennis. Home: 433 Ward Pky Kansas City MO 64112-2128 Office: Butler Mfg Co PO Box 917 Kansas City MO 64141

PRATT, EDMUND TAYLOR, JR., pharmaceutical company executive; b. Savannah, Ga., Feb. 22, 1927; s. Edmund T. and Rose (Miller) P.; m. Jeanette Louise Carneale, Feb. 10, 1951; children: Randolf Ryland, Keith Taylor. BSEE magna cum laude, Duke U., 1947; MBA, U. Pa., 1949; hon. degrees, L.I. U., Marymount Manhattan Coll., Poly. U. of N.Y., St. Francis Coll. With IBM Corp., 1949-51, 54-57, asst. to exec. v.p., 1956-57; with IBM World Trade Corp., 1958-62, contr., 1958-62; asst. sec. fin. mgmt. Dept. Army, 1962-64; contr. Pfizer, Inc., N.Y.C., 1964-67, v.p. ops. internat. subs., 1967-69, chmn. bd., pres. internat. subs., 1969-71, exec. v.p., 1970-71, pres., 1971-72, chmn., chief exec. officer, 1972-90, chmn., 1972-92, chmn. emeritus, 1992—, also bd. dirs.; bd. dirs. Chase Manhattan Corp., Internat. Paper Co., GM, Minerals Techs., Inc.; trustee Logistics Mgmt. Inst. Lt. (j.g.) USNR, 1952-54. Mem. Bus. Coun., Bus. Roundtable (past chmn., mem. policy com.), Phi Beta Kappa.

PRATT, EDWARD TAYLOR, JR., real estate company executive; b. Joplin, Mo., Aug. 12, 1923; s. Edward Taylor Sr. and Etner (Peek) P.; m. Maria Alma Valenzuela, Mar. 20, 1947; children: Carolyn Hickey, Diana Heisler, Edward Taylor III, Sharon Neftal. Grad. high sch., Joplin. Ptnr. Pratt & Co., Dallas, 1952—; vice chmn. Pratt Hotel Corp., Dallas, 1965—; bd. dirs., chmn. audit. com., 1981—; bd. dirs. Bay Hotel & Casino (Sands Hotel and Casino), Atlantic City. Chmn. Planning & Zoning Commn., Mineral Wells, Tex., 1969-78. Mem. Old Port Yacht Club (Palm Beach, Fla.), Club de Yates (Acapulco, Mex.). Republican. Avocation: boating. Home: 5200 Keller Springs Rd Apt 1430 Dallas TX 75248-2753 Office: Pratt Hotel Corp 2 Galleria Tower SW 2200 13455 Noel Rd Lock Box 48 Dallas TX 75240

PRATT, GEORGE CHENEY, law educator, retired federal judge; b. Corning, N.Y., May 22, 1928; s. George Wollage and Muriel (Cheney) P.; m. Carol June Hoffman, Aug. 16, 1952; children: George W., Lise M., Marcia S., William T. B.A., Yale U., 1950, JD, 1953. Bar: N.Y. 1953, U.S. Supreme Ct. 1964, U.S. Ct. Appeals 1974. Law clk. to Charles W. Froessel (Judge of N.Y. Ct. Appeals), 1953-55; assoc. then ptnr. Sprague & Stern, Mineola, N.Y., 1956-60; ptnr. Andromidas, Pratt & Pitcher, Mineola, 1960-65, Pratt, Caemmerer & Cleary, Mineola, 1965-75; partner Farrell, Fritz, Pratt, Caemmerer & Cleary, 1975-76; judge U.S. Dist. Ct. (Eastern Dist. of N.Y.), 1976-82, U.S. Circuit Ct. Appeals for 2d circuit (Uniondale), N.Y., 1982-93; sr. circ. judge U.S Cir. of Appeals for 2d Cir., N.Y., 1993-95; prof. Touro Law Sch., Huntington, N.Y., 1993—; counsel Parnon & Pratt L.L.P., N.Y.C., 1995—. Mem. ABA, N.Y. State Bar Assn., Nassau County Bar Assn. Mem. United Ch. of Christ. Office: Touro Law Ctr 300 Nassau Rd Huntington NY 11743

PRATT, JACK E., SR., hotel executive; b. 1927. Commd. USAF, 1942, advanced through grades, resigned, 1951; ptnr. Wes-Tex Vending Co., 1951—; founder, ptnr. Dairy Queen, Mineral Wells, Tex., 1954-64, Bonanza Steakhouse Restaurants, Tex., 1964-68; chmn., CEO Pratt Hotel Corp.,

Dallas, 1968—. Office: Pratt Hotel Corp 13455 Noel Rd Ste 48 Dallas TX 75240-6620*

PRATT, JOHN HELM, federal judge; b. Portsmouth, N.H., Nov. 17, 1910; s. Harold Boswell and Marguerite (Rockwell) R.; m. Bernice G. Safford, Oct. 25, 1938; children: Clare, Lucinda (Mrs. Daniel D. Pearlman), John Helm Jr., Patricia (Mrs. George Moriarty), Mary (Mrs. John Bruadenburg). AB cum laude, Harvard U., 1930, LLB, 1934. Bar: D.C. 1934. Pvt. practice law Washington; ptnr. Morris, Pearce, Gardner & Pratt, 1954-68; asst. counsel Boys Club Greater Washington, 1948-68; U.S. dist. judge, Washington, 1968—. Chmn. Montgomery County (Md.) Housing Authority, 1950-53; chmn. bd. trustees D.C. Legal Aid Agy., 1967-68; chmn. U.S. Jud. Conf. Com. on Jud. Ethics, 1985-90. Capt. USMCR, 1942-46, PTO. Decorated Bronze Star, Purple Heart; recipient Army citation for civilian svc. in field prosthetics, 1948. Mem. ABA (ho dels. 1963-64), Am. Bar Found., Bar Assn. D.C. (pres. 1963-64), Harvard Law Sch. Assn. (pres. Washington 1952-53), Assoc. Harvard Clubs (pres. 1952-53), Marine Corps Res. Officers Assn. (judge adv. gen. 1961-68), Barristers Club (pres. 1969), Lawyers (pres. 1987), Harvard Club (pres. 1949-51), Chevy Chase Club. Democrat. Roman Catholic. Office: US Dist Ct US Courthouse 3rd & Constitution Ave NW Washington DC 20001

PRATT, JOHN SHERMAN, lawyer; b. Bloomsburgh, Pa., Feb. 7, 1952; s. B.D. and Frances Marie (Quinn) P.; m. Teresa Gayle Plemmons, June 14, 1975; children: Andrew, Caroline, Alexander. BS, Clemson U., 1974; JD, Harvard U., 1977. Bar: Ga. 1977, U.S. Dist. Ct. (no. dist.) Ga. 1977, U.S. Patent and Trademark Office 1979, U.S. Ct. Appeals (5th and 11th cirs.) 1981, U.S. Ct. Appeals (fed. cir.) 1985. Bd. dirs. Wesley Woods Geriatric Hosp. at Emory U., Atlanta, 1991, Ga. Biomed. Partnership, Atlanta, 1991-94. Mem. Am. Intellectual Property Law Assn., Licensing Execs. Soc. Avocation: woodworking. Office: Kilpatrick & Cody 1100 Peachtree St Ste 2800 Atlanta GA 30309

PRATT, JOHN WINSOR, statistics educator; b. Boston, Sept. 11, 1931; s. Frederic Wolsey and Theresa (Winsor) P.; m. Joy A. Wilmunen, Nov. 15, 1958; children: Maria Theresa Winsor, Samuel Frederick Wolsey. AB, Princeton U., 1952; PhD, Stanford U., 1956; MA (hon.), Harvard U., 1966. Rsch. assoc. U. Chgo., 1955-57; mem. faculty Harvard U. Cambridge, Mass., 1957—; prof. bus. adminstrn., 1966—; dir. Social Sci. Rsch. Coun. 1971-76; vis. rsch. prof. Kyoto U., Japan, 1972-73; vis. lectr. Keio U. Bus. Sch., Japan, 1982; Yamaichi vis. prof. fin. Tokyo U., 1989-90; chmn. study group on environment monitoring NRC, 1975-77, chmn. panel on decennial census methodology NRC, 1983-87, mem. com. nat. stats., 1982-88. Coauthor: Introduction to Statistical Decision Theory, 1965, rev. edit., 1995, Social Experimentation: A Method for Planning and Evaluating Social Intervention, 1974, Concepts of Nonparametric Theory, 1981; editor: Statistical and Mathematical Aspects of Pollution Problems, 1974; co-editor: Principals and Agents: The Structure of Business, 1985. Trustee Middlesex Sch., Concord, Mass., 1964-67. Guggenheim fellow, 1971. Fellow AAAS (chmn. sect. U. 1977), Am. Statis. Assn. (editor jour. 1965-69, chmn. bus. and econs. sect. 1983), Inst. Math. Stats., Econometric Soc., Am. Acad. arts and Scis.; mem. Internat. Statis. Inst., Bernoulli Soc. Math. Stats. and Probability, Math. Assn. Am. Home: 2 Gray Gdns E Cambridge MA 02138-1402 Office: Harvard Bus Sch Boston MA 02163

PRATT, JOSEPH HYDE, JR., surgeon; b. Chapel Hill, N.C., Mar. 9, 1911; s. Joseph Hyde and Mary (Bayley) P.; m. Hazel Housman, Dec. 11, 1943; children: Judith Housman, Lisa Mary, Joseph Hyde. AB, U. N.C. 1933; MD, Harvrad U., 1937; MS, U. Minn., 1947. Diplomate Am. Bd. Surgery, Am. Bd. Ob-gyn. Intern Boston City Hosp., 1938-39; fellow surgery Mayo Found., Rochester, Minn., 1940-43; mem. staff Mayo Clinic, Rochester, 1943—, head sect. in surgery, 1945-77, sr. gynecol. surgeon, 1958—; prof. clin. surgery Mayo Grad. Sch. Medicine U. Minn., 1963—; prof. surgery Mayo Med. Sch., 1973—. Contbr. articles to med. jours. Mem. ACS (bd. govs. 1966-71, bd. regents 1971-80), AMA, ACOG, Ctrl. Assn. Ob-Gyn., Minn. Ob-Gyn. Soc., Western Surg. Assn., soc. Vaginal Surgeons (pres. 1979-80), Soc. Pelvic Surgeons (pres. 1968), So. Surg. Assn., Ob-Gyn. Travel Club (pres. 1993—), Sigma Xi, Nu Sigma Nu. Republican. Episcopalian. Home: 1159 Plummer Cir SW Rochester MN 55902-2035 Office: 200 1st St SW Rochester MN 55905-0001

PRATT, LAWRENCE ARTHUR, thoracic surgeon, foreign service officer; b. Paris, Ill., Dec. 20, 1907; s. Luther F. and Katherine (Kaufman) P.; m. Mai Thi NgocSuong, May 7, 1974; children: Elizabeth, Lawrie Porter, D. Jane. B.S., Wayne State U., Detroit, 1930, M.B., M.A., M.D., 1934, M.Ed., 1960; LL.B., Woodrow Wilson Coll. Law, Atlanta, 1943. Diplomate: Am. Bd. Surgery, Am. Bd. Thoracic Surgeons. Intern Grace Hosp., 1934-35; practice thoracic surgery Detroit, 1935-41, 46-63; attending thoracic surgeon Grace, Detroit Meml. hosps.; courtesy staff St John's Hosp.; cons. thoracic surgeon Holy Cross, Highland Park Gen. hosps., Detroit; U.S. fgn. svc. officer, 1963—; vis. prof. medicine U. Saigon, Vietnam, 1963-75; med. dir. Urban Health Clinic of Orange County, Calif., 1981—; exec. v.p. Am. Fedn. Med. Ctrs., Inc., 1953-54; chief med. dental edn. divsn. AID/PH, Vietnam; cons. Vietnam Min. Edn., 1974-75; assoc. dean Minh Duc. Med. Sch., Saigon, 1974-75; cons. HEW, 1975-77; spl. asst. HEW (Divsn. Medicine Bur. Health Manpower), 1976; cons., mem. White House Task Force Internat. Health Policy, 1977; mem. World Bank Task Force Internat. Health Policy and Manpower, 1977, U.S. Pub. Health Assn.; leader design team Health Care Program, Mauritania, West Africa, 1978; physician in charge Refugee Transit Camps, Malaysia, 1980; med. dir. Urban Health Clinic, Orange County, Calif., 1981-84, Spl. Disease Specialist 1981—; cons. physician overseas ops. World Cons., Irvine, Calif., 1984-85; cons. to min. health, Rabat, Morocco, 1986; sr. cons. World Care Inc., 1988—; mem. Nat. Coun. for Internat. Health, 1988—. Author: Total Development for Survival, 1986. bd. dirs. Sun Yet Middle Sch., Zhongshan, Quandong Province, People's Republic of China, 1986—; med. dir. 100 For 1 Systems Corp., 1986—. Lt. col., M.C. AUS, 1941-46. Active Nat. Coun. on Internat. Health , 1984—, U.S.-Mexican Border Health Assn., 1986—. Recipient Unit citation; medal of Culture and Edn.; medal of Merit Vietnam. Fellow ACS (life), Am. Coll. Chest Physicians; mem. AMA, Mich. Med. Soc., Wayne County Med. Soc., Internat. Bronchoesophagol. Assn. (founder), Am. Bronchoesophagol. Assn., 4th Aux. Surg. Group Assn. (pres. 1955-56), Wayne State U. Med. Alumni Assn. (pres. 1956-57), Ga. Bar Assn., Am. Bd. of Surgery (diplomat), Am. Bd. of Thoracic Surgery (diplomat). Clubs: Essex Cricket (Eng.); Lambs (N.Y.C.); Scarab (Detroit), Detroit Skating (Detroit); Grosse Pointe Yacht, Grosse Pointe Hunt. Am. Radio Relay League, El Cajon (Calif.). Radio. Home: 2302 Lowell Ln Santa Ana CA 92706-1932

PRATT, LEIGHTON CALVIN, state legislator; b. Hartford, Conn., Apr. 23, 1923; s. Calvin and Jessie (White) P.; m. Sally Burgess, Oct. 21, 1961; children: Randall Leighton, Bruce Charles. BS, U. Vt., 1951; MS, U. R.I., 1953. Plant pathologist Vt. Dept. Agr., Montpelier, 1952-62; tchr. sci. Cabot (Vt.) H.S. and J. H.S., 1962-65; tchr. biology, asst. prin. Newport (Vt.) H.S., 1965-67; tchr. biology North Country Union H.S., Newport, 1967-79; Coos agrl. ext. agt. U. N.H., Durham, 1969-88, prof. emeritus ext. edn., 1988—; mem. N.H. Ho. of Reps., Concord, 1991—. Named hon. state farmer Future Farmers Am., 1986. Mem. Rotary (dir. exch. to Brazil dist. 1986, pres. Lancaster, N.H.), Epsilon Sigma Phi. Republican. Congregationalist. Avocations: travel, gardening. Home: 63 Water St Lancaster NH 03584-1804

PRATT, MICHAEL THEODORE, book publishing company executive, marketing, sales and publishing specialist; b. Troy, Ohio, May 30, 1943; s. James Alden and Dorothy (Kennedy) P.; m. Helen Diane Biddle, Oct. 24, 1964 (div. Sept. 1983); children: Nicole Christine, Jason Alan. Student, Muskingum Coll., New Concord, Ohio, 1961-62, Ashland Coll., Ohio, 1962-63, Temple U., 1963-64, Wharton Sch. (U. Pa.), 1964. Corp. sr. v.p. Random House, Inc., N.Y.C., 1969-90; pres., chief exec. officer Corinthian Internat., Inc., Spring Valley, N.Y., 1990, also bd. dirs.; sr. v.p. St. Martin's Press, N.Y.C., 1991—; bd. dirs. Shambhala Pubs., Inc., J. Alden Pratt, Inc. Mem. Am. Mgmt. Assn. Democrat. Presbyterian. Club: University (Larchmont, N.Y.). Home: 50 Judges Hollow Fairfield CT 06430 Office: St Martin's Press 175 Fifth Ave New York NY 10010-7703

PRATT, PHILIP CHASE, pathologist, educator; b. Livermore Falls, Maine, Oct. 19, 1920; s. Harold Sewell and Cora Johnson (Chase) P.; m.

Helen Clarke Deitz, Feb. 4, 1945; children: William Clarke (dec.), Charles Chase (dec.). A.B., Bowdoin Coll., 1941; M.D., Johns Hopkins U., 1944. Diplomate: Am. Bd. Pathology. Intern in pathology Johns Hopkins Hosp., 1944-45, asst. resident in pathology, 1945-46; pathologist Saranac Lab., Saranac Lake, N.Y., 1946-52; asst. dir. Saranac Lab., 1952-55; instr. Ohio State U., 1955-57, asst. prof. pathology, 1957-62, asso. prof., 1962-66; asso. prof. Duke U. Med. Center, 1966-71, prof., 1971—. Contbr. numerous articles to profl. publs. Fellow Am. Coll. Chest Physicians, Coll. Am. Pathologists; mem. AAAS, Am. Thoracic Soc., Am. Soc. Exptl. Pathology, Am. Assn. Pathologists and Bacteriologists, Internat. Acad. Pathology, Royal Soc. Health. Unitarian. Office: PO Box 3712 Davison Bldg Durham NC 27710 *The innovative idea is the essential commodity of the academic life. Origins of such ideas are varied but for me usually begin with realization that an existing concept does not adequately explain observed phenomena. When direct reasoning does not produce a new, better concept, the problem is put aside. Weeks later a return to the question often promptly reveals a logical new solution which has arisen without conscious effort. Of course, this must then be subjected to investigation to be either confirmed or refuted.*

PRATT, RICHARD HOUGHTON, physics educator; b. N.Y.C., May 5, 1934; s. Karl Chapman and Gertrude (Gennis) P.; m. Elizabeth Ann Glass, Nov. 1, 1958; children—Jonathan Peter, Kathryn Eileen, Mary Caroline, Paul Chapman. A.B., U. Chgo., 1952, S.M., 1955, Ph.D., 1959. Rsch. assoc. Stanford U., 1959-61, asst. prof., 1961-64; assoc. prof. physics U. Pitts., 1964-69, prof., 1969—, acad. dean semester at sea, fall 1984, adminstrv. dean, spring 1990; program dir. theoretical physics NSF, Washington, 1987-89; cons. Lawrence Livermore Nat. Lab.; prin. investigator Dept. Energy, NSF. Fellow Am. Phys. Soc. (chmn. com. internat. sci. affairs), AAAS; mem. Sierra Club (chmn. Pa. chpt. 1976-80, v.p. Appalachian region 1982-84), European Phys. Soc., Internat. Radiation Physics Soc. (sec. 1985—), Phi Beta Kappa. Achievements include research in atomic theory, including photoelectric effect, bremsstrahlung, x-ray scattering; applications to atomic processes in plasmas. Home: 1131 Shady Ave Pittsburgh PA 15232-2809

PRATT, RICHARDSON, JR., retired college president; b. N.Y.C., Mar. 25, 1923; s. Richardson and Laura C. (Parsons) P.; m. Mary Esterbrook Offutt, Aug. 12, 1944; children: Laura Pratt Gregg, Thomas R., David. O. A.B., Williams Coll., 1946, LL.D. (hon.), 1978; M.B.A., Harvard U., 1948; LL.D. (hon.), St Joseph, 1984. Econ. analyst, sec. com. on human relations Exxon Co., 1948-52, distr. mktg. mgr., 1953-63, mktg. planning and evaluation, 1964-71; chmn. Charles Pratt & Co., Inc., 1971—; pres. Pratt Inst., Bklyn., 1972-90; bd. dirs. Dime Savs. Bank N.Y., Bklyn. Union Gas Co.; mayor Village of Lloyd Harbor (N.Y.), 1983—. Trustee Near East Found., Fedn. Protestant Welfare Agys.; mem. governing bd. Bklyn. Bot. Gardens; chmn. bd. dirs. Greenwood Cemetary. With USNR, 1943-46. Presbyterian. Home: 30 Dock Hollow Rd Cold Spring Harbor NY 11724-1002 Office: Charles Pratt & Co Inc 355 Lexington Ave New York NY 10017-6601

PRATT, ROBERT CRANFORD, political scientist, educator; b. Montreal, Que., Can., Oct. 8, 1926; s. Robert Goodwin and Henrietta (Freeman) P.; m. Renate Hecht, July 15, 1956; children—Gerhard, Marcus, Anna. BA, McGill U., Montreal, 1947; postgrad., Inst. Etudes Politique, Paris, 1948; M. Phil. (Rhodes scholar), Oxford U., Eng., 1952. Lectr. McGill U., 1952-54, 56-58, Makerere U., Uganda, 1954-56; research officer Oxford Inst. Commonwealth Studies, 1958-60; prin. Univ. Coll., Dar-es-Salaam, Tanzania, 1961-65; chmn. internat. studies program U. Toronto, Ont., Can., 1966-71; prof. polit. sci. U Toronto, 1966—; spl. asst. to pres., Tanzania, 1965, 69; research fellow Internat. Devel. Research Centre, 1978; commonwealth vis. prof. U. London, 1979-80; dir. Research Project on Western Middle Powers and Global Poverty, 1985-89; vis. fellow Devel. Ctr. Orgn. for Econ. Cooperation and Devel., Paris, 1986-87. Author: (with Anthony Low) Buganda and British Overrule, 1960, The Critical Phase in Tanzania, Nyerere and the Emergence of a Socialist Strategy, 1976, Towards Socialism in Tanzania, 1979, (with Robert Matthews) Human Rights in Canadian Foreign Policy, 1988, Internationalism Under Strain: The North-South Policies of Canada, The Netherlands, Norway and Sweden, 1989; (with Roger Hutchinson) Christian Faith and Economic Justice: A Canadian Perspective, 1989); Middle Power Internationalism: The North-South Dimension, 1990, Canadian International Development Assistance Policies: An Appraisal, 1994. Recipient Killam award Can. Council, 1968. Fellow Royal Soc. Can.; mem. Can. Polit. Sci. Assn., Can. African Studies Assn. (past pres.), Can. Assn. for Study of Internat. Devel. (exec. coun.), Ecumenical Forum Can. (past chmn.). Mem. New Democratic Party. Mem. United Ch. Canada. Home: 205 Cottingham St, Toronto, ON Canada M4V 1C4 Office: U Toronto, Dept Polit Sci, Toronto, ON Canada M5S 1A1

PRATT, ROBERT WINDSOR, lawyer; b. Findlay, Ohio, Mar. 6, 1950; s. John Windsor and Isabelle (Vance) P.; m. Catherine Camak Baker, Sept. 3, 1977; children: Andrew Windsor, David Camak, James Robert. AB, Wittenberg U., Springfield, Ohio, 1972; JD, Yale U., 1975. Bar: Ill. 1975, U.S. Dist. Ct. (no. dist.) Ill. 1976, U.S. Ct. Appeals (fed. cir.) 1984, U.S. Dist. Ct. (we. dist.) Mich. 1995. Assoc. Keck, Mahin & Cate, Chgo., 1975-81, ptnr., 1981—. Bd. dirs. Chgo. region ARC, 1985—, vice chmn., 1988-92, chmn., 1992—, bd. dirs. Mid-Am. chpt., 1992—. Mem. ABA, Chgo. Bar Assn. Clubs: Yale (Chgo.). Office: Keck Mahin & Cate 77 W Wacker Dr Ste 4900 Chicago IL 60601

PRATT, TERRENCE WENDALL, information research scientist; b. Mpls., Mar. 9, 1940; s. Wendall Ballou and Beth (Meyer) P.; m. Margaret Ruth Hammond; m. 2d, Barbara Anne Kraft; children: Kirsten Elizabeth, Robert Randall, Laurelyn Kathleen. Asst. prof. Mich. State U., East Lansing, 1965-66; asst. prof. U. Tex., Austin, 1966-71, assoc. prof., 1972-77; assoc. prof. U. Va., Charlottesville, 1977-81, prof., 1982-86, rsch. prof., 1986-92, dir. Inst. Parallel Computation, 1989-90; assoc. dir. Ctr. Excellence in Space Data and Info. Scis., NASA Goddard Space Flight Ctr., Greenbelt, Md., 1992-94, acting dir., 1993-94; cons. Inst. Computer Applications in Sci. and Engring./NASA Langley Rsch. Ctr., Hampton, Va., 1978-92. Author: Programming Languages, 1975, 2d edit., 1984, Pascal, 1990. Mem. IEEE, Assn. for Computing Machinery, Soc. for Indsl. and Applied Math.

PRATT, VAUGHAN RONALD, computer engineering educator; b. Melbourne, Australia, Apr. 12, 1944; s. Ronald Victor and Marjorie (Mirams) P.; m. Margot Frances Koster, Feb. 2, 1969; children: Jennifer Katherine, Jacqueline Andrea. BSc with honors, Sydney U., Australia, 1967, MSc, 1970; PhD, Stanford U., 1972. From asst. to assoc. prof. MIT, Cambridge, 1972-82; head of research Sun Microsystems Inc., Mountain View, Calif., 1983-85; prof. Stanford (Calif.) U., 1981—; pres. Triangle Concepts Inc., Palo Alto, Calif., 1988—. Author: Shellsort and Sorting Networks, 1979. Mem. IEEE, Am. Math. Soc., Assn. for Computing Machinery, Assn. for Symbolic Logic. Office: Stanford U Dept Computer Sci Stanford CA 94305

PRATT, WILLIAM CROUCH, JR., English language educator; b. Shawnee, Okla., Oct. 5, 1927; s. William Crouch and Irene (Johnston) P.; m. Anne Cullen Rich, Oct. 2, 1954; children: Catherine Cullen, William Stuart, Randall Johnston. B.A., U. Okla., 1949; M.A., Vanderbilt U., 1951, Ph.D., 1957. Rotary Internat. fellow U. Glasgow, Scotland, 1951-52; instr. English Vanderbilt U., 1955-57, Miami U., Oxford, Ohio, 1957-59; asst. prof. Miami U., 1959-64, assoc. prof., dir. Freshman English, 1964-68, prof., 1968—; adviser Ohio Poetry Cir., 1964—; Fulbright-Hays lectr. Am. lit., prof. Am. lit. Univ. Coll., Dublin, Eire, 1975-76; resident scholar Miami U. European Ctr., Luxembourg, fall 1976; lectr. Yeats Internat. Summer Sch., Sligo, Eire, 1979, 81, 82, 83; writer-in-residence Tyrone Guthrie Ctr., County Monaghan, Ireland, summer 1992. Author: The Imagist Poem, 1963, The Fugitive Poets, 1965, rev. edit., 1991, The College Writer, 1969, College Days at Old Miami, 1984, The Influence of French Symbolism on Modern American Poetry, 1985, Miami Poets, 1988, Homage to Imagism, 1992; contbr. essays, translations, poems, rev.s to lit. jours.; books. Served to lt. USNR, 1953-55. Mem. MLA, Nat. Coun. Tchrs. English (Ohio awards chmn. 1967-69), Coll. Conf. on Composition, Communication, Internat. Contemporary Lit. and Theatre Soc. (program chmn. 1983, 88), Soc. Study So. Lit. (sec. 15th Ezra Pound Internat. Conf. 1993), Phi Beta Kappa, Sigma Alpha Epsilon, Omicron Delta Kappa. Republican. Home: 212 Oakhill Dr Oxford OH 45056-2710 *True happiness is to live in the understanding of what we love, the pursuit of what we believe in.*

PRATT, WILLIAM HUNTER, insurance agent, small business owner; b. Inverness, Miss., May 18, 1913; s. William Henry and Sallie Belle (Bradley) P.; m. Ara Mullen, June 18, 1940; children: William Stanley, Hunter De-Lap. BS in Bus., Miss. State U., 1935. Chief acct. Sheriff Sunflower County, Indianola, Miss., 1939-44; sec./treas. Duncan Gin Inc., Inverness, Miss. 1944-71; pres. Duncan Gin Inc., Inverness, Inverness, 1971-88; solicitor Inverness Ins. Agy., Inc., Inverness, 1988—; owner W. Hunter Pratt, Farm, Inverness, 1991; dir. Miss. Chemical Corp., Yazoo City, Miss., 1975-84, Yazoo Valley Oil Mill, Greenwood, Miss., 1976—, Miss. Agr. & Forestry Found., Jackson, Miss., 1970—. Alderman-vice mayor Town of Inverness, 1960-73; pres. Sunflower County Sch. Bd.,Indianola, 1954-68; trustee Miss. Delta Community Coll., Moorhead, 1956-66; trustee & deacon First Bapt. Ch., 1988—; vice-chmn. Sunflower County Econ. Dist., 1981. Recipient Nat. Cotton Ginner of Yr. award Nat. Ginners Assn., 1987, Miss. Ginner of Yr. So. Ginners Assn., 1985; Alumnae of Yr. dist. 9, Miss. State U., 1978. Mem. Nat. Cotton Coun. (dir., exec. com. 1979), Delta Coun. (v.p. 1950, Achievemnt award 1981-82), Oscar Johnson Found. (trustee 1982), T.J. Catchings Lodge (Master), Inverness Rotary Club (pres. 1946). Baptist. Home: 806 Lamar PO Box # 111 Inverness MS 38753 Office: Inverness Ins Agy Inc 806 E Grand Ave Inverness MS 38753-9731

PRATTE, LISE, lawyer, corporate secretary; b. Laval, Que., Can., May 16, 1950. LLB, Laval U., 1976; MBA, Montreal U., Que., Can., 1988. Bar: Que. Asst. sec. Malouf Inquiry Commn. on 21st Olympiad, 1977-79, Des Manoirs Sch. Bd., Terrebonne, Que., 1979-82; legal counsel for various corps., mgmt. cons., 1981-82; corp. sec., legal counsel Can. Arsenals Ltd., Le Gardeur, Que., 1982-85; asst. sec., legal counsel Imasco Ltd., Montreal, 1985-88; corp. sec. Bombardier Inc., Montreal, 1988—. Bd. dirs. La Fondation de L'Universite Laval. Mem. Can. Bar Assn., Que. Bar Assn., Inst. Chartered Secs. and Adminstrs., Can. Shareholders Svcs. Assn. (bd. dirs.), Am. Soc. Corp. Secs., Order of Chartered Adminstrs. Avocation: management. Office: Bombardier Inc/29th FL, 800 René-Lévesque Blvd W, Montreal, PQ Canada H3B 1Y8

PRATTE, LOUIS, judge; b. Quebec City, Que., Can., Nov. 29, 1926; s. Garon and Georgine (Rivard) P.; m. Charlotte Tremblay, July 2, 1953; children—Marie, Francois. Grad. Faculte de droit et des scis economiques, Laval U.; diplome d'etudes superieures en droit prive, U. Paris. Bar: Que. 1950. Mem. trial div. Fed. Ct. Can., 1971-73; judge Fed. Ct. Appeal, Ottawa, Ont., 1973—. Office: Fed Ct Appeal, Kent & Wellington Sts, Ottawa, ON Canada K1A OH9

PRATTE, ROBERT JOHN, lawyer; b. Victoria, B.C., Can., Feb. 14, 1948; s. Arthur Louis Jr. and Marie Bertha (Latremouille) P.; children from previous marriage: Merie Elise, Jessica Louise, Allison Adele; m. Erica Catherine Street, Oct. 20, 1984; 1 child, Chelsea Nicole. BA, Northwestern U., 1970; JD, Tulane U., 1976. Bar: Minn. 1976. Ptnr. Best & Flanagan, Mpls., 1976-84; ptnr. Briggs & Morgan, Mpls., 1985—, head mortgage banking group. Editor: Mortgage Lending in Minnesota—A Desktop Reference Guide, 1990. Ex-officio mem. Wilderness Inquiry, Minn.; pres. Twin Cities Northwestern U. Alumni Assn., 1978; active Westminster Presbyn. Ch., Mpls. Fellow Am. Coll. Mortgage Attys.; mem. ABA (real estate financing com., real property sect., bus. law and internat. law and practice sects.), Minn. State Bar Assn. (banking law com., real property, bus. law, internat. law and practice sects.), Hennepin County Bar Assn., Mortgage Bankers Assn. Am. (legal issues, regulatory compliance and secondary and capital markets coms.), Mortgage Bankers Assn. Minn. (chmn. legal issues com. 1989—), Calhoun Beach Club (exec. mem.), Minnetonka Country Club. Office: Briggs & Morgan 2400 IDS Ctr 80 S 8th St Minneapolis MN 55402-2113

PRATTER, GENE E. K., lawyer; b. Chgo., Feb. 25, 1949; d. Eugene Anthony and Laurel Marilyn (Dauer) Kreyche; m. Robert Lawrence Pratter, Oct. 21, 1978; children: Virginia Paige, Matthew Robert. BA, Stanford U., 1971; JD, U. Pa., 1975. Bar: Pa. 1975, U.S. Dist. Ct. (ea. dist.) Pa. 1975, U.S. Ct. Appeals (3d cir.) 1981. Admissions officer U. Pa., Phila., 1972-73; assoc. Duane, Morris & Heckscher, Phila., 1975-83, ptnr., 1983—; judge pro tem Phila. Ct. Common Pleas, 1994—. Bd. overseers U. Pa. Law Sch., Phila., 1994—, lectr. Ctr. on Professionalism. Contbr. articles to profl. jours. Mem. ABA, Def. Research Inst., Pa. Bar Assn., Phila. Bar Assn., Stanford U. Alumni Club (fund raiser, officer 1976-83). Republican. Roman Catholic. Office: Duane Morris & Heckscher Ste 4200 One Liberty Pl Philadelphia PA 19103

PRAUSNITZ, JOHN MICHAEL, chemical engineer, educator; b. Berlin, Jan. 7, 1928; came to U.S. 1937, naturalized, 1944; s. Paul Georg and Susi Prausnitz; m. Susan PRausnitz, June 10, 1956; children: Stephanie, Mark Robert. B Chem. Engring., Cornell U., 1950; MS, U. Rochester, 1951; Ph.D., Princeton, 1955; DSc (hon.), Princeton U., 1995; Dr. Ing., U. L'Aquila, 1983, Tech. U. Berlin, 1989; DSc, Princeton U., 1995. Mem. faculty U. Calif., Berkeley, 1955—, prof. chem. engring., 1963—; cons. to cryogenic, polymer, petroleum and petrochem. industries. Author: (with others) Computer Calculations for Multicomponent Vapor-Liquid Equilibria, 1967, (with P.L. Chueh) Computer Calculations for High-Pressure Vapor-Liquid Equilibria, 1968, Molecular Thermodynamics of Fluid-Phase Equilibria, 1969, 2d edit., 1986, (with others) Regular and Related Solutions, 1970, Properties of Gases and Liquids, 3d edit., 1977, 4th edit., 1987, Computer Calculations for Multicomponent Vapor-Liquid and Liquid-Liquid Equilibria, 1980; contbr. to profl. jours. Recipient Alexander von Humboldt Sr. Scientist award, 1976, Carl von Linde Gold Meml. medal German Inst. for Cryogenics, 1987, Solvay prize Solvay Found. for chem. Scis., 1990, Corcoran award Am. Soc. for Engring. Edn., 1991, D.L. Katz award Gas Processors Assn., 1992; named W.K. Lewis lectr. MIT, 1993; Guggenheim fellow, 1962, 73, fellow Inst. Advanced Study, Berlin, 1985; Miller rsch. prof., 1966, 78; Chistensen fellow St. Catherine's Coll. Oxford U., 1994. Mem. AIChE (Colburn award 1962, Walker award 1967, Inst. Lectr. award 1994), Am. Chem. Soc. (E.V. Murphree award 1979, Petroleum Chemistry Rsch. award 1995), NAE, NAS, Am. Acad. Arts and Scis. Office: U Calif 308 Gilman Hall Berkeley CA 94720

PRAVEL, BERNARR ROE, lawyer; b. Detroit, Feb. 10, 1924; s. William Frank and Edythe (Roe) P.; m. Retta Atkinson, June 3, 1946; children: Mark, Bonnie, Ann, Jim. BSChemE, Rice U., 1947; JD, George Washington U., 1951. Bar: D.C. 1951, Tex. 1951, U.S. Supreme Ct. 1951. Ptnr. Pravel, Hewitt, Kimball and Krieger, Houston, 1970—. Patent editor George Washington U. Law Rev., 1950. Precinct chmn. Houston Rep. Com., 1972-74. Served to lt. (j.g.) USNR. Fellow Am. Bar Found., Tex. Bar Found.; mem. Tex. Bar Assn. (chmn. patent, trademark sect. 1968-69, bd. dirs. 1976-79, Outstanding Contbn. 1982), Nat. Coun. of Patent Law (chmn. 1970-71), Am. Intellectual Property Law Assn. (pres. 1983-84), ABA (chair intellectual property sect. 1991-92), Houston Intellectual Property Law Assn. (pres. 1983-84, Outstanding Svc. award 1986), Order of Coif, Kiwanis, Masons, Tau Beta Pi. Republican. Presbyterian. Home: 10806 Oak Hollow St Houston TX 77024-3017 Office: Pravel Hewitt Kimball and Krieger 1177 West Loop S Fl 10 Houston TX 77027-9010

PRAW, ALBERT Z., lawyer; b. L.A., Apr. 9, 1948. AB, U. Calif., Berkeley, 1969; JD, UCLA, 1972. Bar: Calif. 1972, U.S. Dist. Ct. (ctrl. dist.) Calif. 1972. Ptnr. Hayutin, Rubinstein, Praw & Gopeitzky, 1979-87, Sidley & Austin, 1987-89, 92-94; sr. v.p., gen. counsel Kaufman and Broad Home Corp., L.A., 1994—. Mem. ABA (mem. corp., banking and bus. law sects., real property, probate and trust law sects.), mem. REA rev. subcom. on real property fin. 1982-83), State Bar Calif. (sr. v.p. and gen. counsel), L.A. County Bar Assn. (mem. bus. and corp., real property sects.), Beverly Hills Bar Assn. Office: Kaufman & Broad Home Corp 12th Fl 10990 Wilshire Blvd 7th Fl Los Angeles CA 90024

PRAY, DONALD GEORGE, aerospace engineer; b. Troy, N.Y., Jan. 19, 1928; s. George Emerson and Jansje Cornelia (Ouwejan) P.; m. Betty Ann Williams, Oct. 1, 1950; children: Jennifer Loie, Jonathan Cornelius, Judy Karen, Jeffrey Donald. BA in Physics, Tex. Christian U., 1955; MS in Mech. Engring., So. Meth. U., 1979. Sr. structures engr. Gen. Dynamics Corp., Ft. Worth, 1955-62, 67-84; engring. specialist LTV Astronautics Corp., Dallas, 1962-65, sr. engring. specialist 1989-91; aero. group engr. space div. Chrysler Corp., New Orleans, 1965-67; V-22 group engr. Bell

Helicopter Textron, Ft. Worth, 1984-89; E-3 structural integrity program mgr. Tinker AFB, 1991—; prin. Donald G. Pray, Con., Ft. Worth, 1959-61. Contbr. articles to tech. publs. Chmn. bd. trustees Cope Cemetery Assn., Johnson County, Tex., 1987—; corps comdr., v.p. bd. dirs. Masqueraders Drum and Bugle Corps, New Orleans, 1965-67; scoutmaster, cubmaster, explorer advisor, dist. com. chmn. Longhorn coun. Boy Scouts Am., Ft. Worth, 1967-75. Recipient Grand Championship Mardi Gras award, 1966. Mem. ASME, NSPE, NRA, Acoustical Soc. Am., Soc. Mayflower Descendants Tex. (sec. 1983-85, 88-91, gov. 1991-93, dep. gov. gen. 1993—), mem. gen. soc. edn. com. 1990—, chmn. Dallas colony scholarship com. 1988—), Ft. Worth Rifle and Pistol Club (marksman 1980), Train Collectors Assn., Ft. Worth Geneal. Soc. (bd. dirs. 1983-84), Masons, Scottish Rite, Shriners, Sigma Pi Sigma, Pi Mu Epsilon. Baptist. Achievements include analytical engineering contributions to numerous aircraft and spacecraft programs including B-36, B-58, NX-2, Robot, Dynasoar, Scout, Apollo, F/ FB-111, F-16, V-22 Osprey, C-17, E-3 AWACS. Home: 3628 Wedgway Dr Fort Worth TX 76133-2135 also: Lazy Acres Farm 5750 Lazy Bend Rd Brock TX 76066 Office: Oklahoma City Air Logistics OC-ALC/LAKRA Tinker AFB OK 73145

PRAY, LLOYD CHARLES, geologist, educator; b. Chgo., June 25, 1919; s. Allan Theron and Helen (Palmer) P.; m. Carrel Myers, Sept. 14, 1946; children: Lawrence Myers, John Allan, Kenneth Palmer, Douglas Carrel. B.A., Carleton Coll., 1941; M.S., Calif. Inst. Tech., 1943, Ph.D. (NRC fellow 1946-49), 1952. Geologist Magnolia Petroleum Co., summer 1942, U.S. Geol. Survey, 1943-44; hydrographic officer USN, 1944-46; Geologist U.S. Geol. Survey, 1946-56 part time; instr. to assoc. prof. geology Calif. Inst. Tech., 1949-56; sr. research geologist Denver Research Ctr., Marathon Oil Co., 1956-62, research assoc., 1962-68; prof. geology U. Wis., Madison, 1968-88; emeritus prof. geology, 1989—; short course vis. prof. U. Tex., 1964, U. Colo., 1967, U. Miami, 1971, U. Alta., 1969, Colo. Sch. Mines, 1985; vis. scientist Imperial Coll. Sci. and Tech., London, 1977, U. Calif. Santa Cruz, 1987. Author articles sedimentary carbonates, the Permian Reef complex, stratigraphy and structural geology So. N.M. and W. Tex., porosity of carbonate facies, Calif. rare earth mineral deposits. Pres. Colo. Diabetes Assn., 1963-67, v.p., 1968; mem. adv. panel earth scis. NSF, 1973-76. Served as hydrographic officer USNR, 1944-46. Named Layman of Year Am. Diabetes Assn., 1968; recipient Disting. Teaching award U. Wis. Madison, 1988; Disting. Achievement citation Carleton Coll., 1991. Fellow Geol. Soc. Am. (rsch. grants com. 1965-67, com. on nominations 1973, com.Penrose medal 1979-81); mem. Am. Assn. Petroleum Geologists (rsch. com. 1958-61, lectr. continuing edn. program 1966-69, Matson trophy 1967, continuing edn. com. 1978-80, disting. lectr. 1986-87, 87-88), Soc. Sedimentary Geologists (hon. life mem. Permian Basin sect., hon. mem. internat. soc., sec.-treas. 1961-63, v.p. 1966-67, pres. 1969-70), Am. Geol. Inst. (edn. com. 1966-68, ho. bd. dels. 1970-72), Phi Beta Kappa. Office: U Wis Madison WI 53706

PRAY, RALPH MARBLE, III, lawyer; b. San Diego, June 7, 1938; s. Ralph Marble Jr. and Doris (Thomson) P.; m. Karen L. Pray (div. May 1988); children: Matthew Thomson, Kristen Leigh; m. Sandra Anne Shaw, June 7, 1988. BS, U. Redlands, 1960; JD, U. Calif., San Francisco, 1967. Bar: Calif. 1967, U.S. Dist. Ct. (so. dist.) Calif. 1968, U.S. Supreme Ct. 1972, U.S. Dist. Ct. (ea. dist.) Calif. 1985, U.S. Dist. Ct. (ctrl. dist.) Calif. 1989, U.S. Dist. Ct. (no. dist.) Calif. 1992. Assoc. Gray, Cary, Ware & Friedenrich and predecessor, San Diego, 1967-73, ptnr., 1973—; mem. mgmt. com. Gray, Cary, Ames & Frye, San Diego, 1975-80; arbiter Superior Ct., San. Diego, 1984—. Lt. USN, 1960-64. Mem. ABA, SAR, NRA, Calif. Bar Assn., Am. Arbitration Soc. (arbiter), San Diego Zool. Soc., Ducks Unltd., Thurston Soc., Rotary Club of Coronado, Calif., Order of Coif. Republican. Episcopalian. Home: 535 C Ave Coronado CA 92118-1824 Office: Gray Cary Ware & Friedenrich 1700 1st Interstate Plz 401 B St San Diego CA 92101-4223

PRAYSON, ALEX STEPHEN, drafting and mechanical design educator; b. Tulsa, Okla., June 24, 1939; s. Stephen Alexander and Frances Prayson; children: Stephen, David, Timothy, Anthony. AS, Edison Tech., 1967; DC, Cleveland Coll., 1972. Diplomate Am. Bd. Chiropractic Examiners. Owner Prayson Candies Co., Tulsa, 1960-63; cartographer Howard Needles Tammen and Bergendoff, Kansas City, Mo., 1968-71; supr. M. J. Harden Assocs., Kansas City, 1971-81; asst. prof. Tulsa Jr. Coll., 1981—; disting. advisor Phi Theta Kappa, Tulsa, 1991—. Author: A Love-Hate Anthology, 1993; inventor Taffy-Pull. Mem. selection com. Ahepa Civic Youth Svc. Award, Tulsa, 1992—. Mem. Am. Design and Drafting Assn., Okla. Tech. Soc., Tulsa Jr. Coll. Faculty Assn. Avocations: croquet, bridge, travel. Home: 2534 E 20th St Tulsa OK 74104-5810

PREATE, ERNEST D., SR., lawyer; b. Pescopagano, Italy, Jan. 10, 1909; s. Dominick J. and Theresa B. (Manzo) P.; m. Anne R. Smith, Feb. 11, 1939; children: Ernest D., Donald L., Robert A., Carlon. AB, Columbia U., 1931; JD, U. Pa., 1934; LHD (hon.), U. Scranton, 1969. Bar: Pa. 1934, U.S. Ct. Appeals (3d cir.) 1957. Ptnr. Levy, Mattes, Preate &McNulty, Scranton, Pa., 1958-66, Levy & Preate, Scranton, 1966—; dir., gen. counsel Scranton Lackawanna Indsl. Bldg. Co., Lackawanna Indsl. Fund Enterprises, 1982; chmn. Pocono N.E. Devel. Fund, 1984; bd. dir. First Ea. Bank. Pres. Econ.Devel. Coun. N.E. Pa. 1977, MetroAction, Inc., 1981; cited by Greater Scranton Chamber of Commerce for dedicated commitment as Founder and First President (1977) of MetroAction, Inc, a community development corp., June 8, 1983; mem. adv. bd., counsel U Scranton, 1981; trustee Scranton Prep. Sch., 1982; chmn. bd. dirs. Scranton State Gen. Hosp., 1991-93; bd. dirs. gen. counsel Pa. Devel. Credit Corp., 1963—; "Man of the Year Award", Columbus Day Assn. of Lacka. Co., Pa., 1984; Jesuit "Ignation Award" for outstanding civic business and religious community service, Scranton Preparatory School, 1985; citation from Commonwealth of Pa. House of Reps. for outstanding civic leadership in Northeastern Pa., 1986; chmn. Gov.'s Trial Ct. Nominating Commn., 1986-87. Recipient Lifetime Achievement award Pa. and Am. Planning Assns., 1991; named Disting. Pennsylvanian, William Penn Soc., 1980; named to Bus. Hall of Fame, Jr. Achievement of Northeastern Pa., 1991. Mem. ABA, Pa. Bar Assn. (professionalism com. 1990), Am. Judicature Soc., Lackawanna County Bar Assn., Community Assn. Inst., Scranton C. of C. (bd. dir.), Jud. Conf. 3rd Cir. of U.S. Republican. Roman Catholic. Clubs: Scranton Country, Scranton. Coauthor: Pennsylvania Industrial Development Authority Law, 1956. Contbr. articles to profl. jours. Home: 216 E Morton St Old Forge PA 18518 Office: Levy & Preate Scranton Elec Bldg 507 Linden St Scranton PA 18503

PREATE, ERNEST D., JR., state attorney general; b. Scranton, Pa., Nov. 22, 1940; s. Ernest D. Sr. and Anne (Janeczek) P.; children: Elizabeth D., Alexandra V. BS in Econs., U. Pa., 1962, JD, 1965. Dist. atty. Lackawana County, 1977-89; atty. gen. State of Pa., Harrisburg, 1989—. Capt. USMC, 1966-69, Vietnam. Recipient Outstanding Svc. to Edn. award Pa. Sch. Bds. Assn., 1990, Law Enforcement Achievement award Nat. Italian Am. Found., 1989, Dist. Svc. to Law Enforcement award Pa. County Detectives and State Investigators Assn., 1985, ADL of B'nai B'rith Americanism award 1991, First Ann. Law and Justice award Sons of Italy, 1989, Gold Medal Man of the Yr. award Pa. State Lodge Sons of Italy, 1991, Dist. Svc. award Marine Corps League, 1991; named Man of Yr. Phila. chpt. Nat. Italian-Am. Sports Hall of Fame, 1992, Citizen of Yr. Valley Forge Coun. Boy Scouts Am., 1993. Mem. Nat. Assn. Attys. Gen. (chair criminal law com. 1991-93, co-chair fed. crime bill leadership, vice-chair telecom. subcom., rep. to ABA), Assn. Govt. Attys. in Capital Litigation, Exec. Working Group of U.S. Dept. Justice, Am. Legion, Marine Corps League, VFW, Kiwanis, Sigma Chi. Republican. Office: Office of Atty Gen 16th Fl Strawberry Sq Harrisburg PA 17120

PREBLE, JAMES J., banker; b. 1923; married. With United Bank & Trust Co., Hartford, Conn., now chmn. bd.

PREBLE, LAURENCE GEORGE, lawyer; b. Denver, Apr. 24, 1939; s. George Enos and Ruth (Jewett) P.; m. Deborah Joan Horton, Aug. 24, 1963; children—Robin Lee, Randall Laurence. B in Petroleum Refining Engring., Colo. Sch. Mines, 1961; J.D. cum laude, Loyola U., Los Angeles, 1966. Bar: Calif. 1966, N.Y. 1987, U.S. Dist. Ct. (cen. dist.) Calif. 1983. Assoc. firm O'Melveny & Myers, Los Angeles, 1968-76; ptnr. O'Melveny & Myers, 1976—; adj. prof. law Southwestern U., 1970-75, Loyola U. of L.A. Sch. Law, 1984-92, Fordham Sch. Law, 1992—, Calif. Continuing Edn. of the Bar; lectr., author Practicing Law Inst. Trustee Harvey Mudd Coll.

1991-94. Mem. Los Angeles County Bar Assn. (chmn. real property sect. 1979-80), Calif. Bar Assn. (mem. exec. com. real property sect.), ABA, Am. Coll. Real Estate Lawyers (bd. govs. 1986—), Anglo-Am. Real Property Inst., La Canada-Flintridge C. of C. (pres. 1974-75), Loyola Law Sch. Alumni Assn. (pres. 1978). Office: O'Melveny & Myers 153 E 53rd St Fl 54 New York NY 10022-4611

PREBLE, LOU-ANN M., state legislator; m. Bill Preble. Grad., Tuomey Hosp. Sch. Nursing, 1950, Prima C.C., 1978. RN S.C., 1951-77; physical evaluator Medi-Quik, Tucson, 1978-82; co-owner, mgr. retail apparel store, 1972-75, ret.; mem. Ariz. Ho. of Reps., mem. assignments com. former precinct committeeman, dep. registr.; state committeeman, 1974-92; rep. at large State Exec. Com., 1991-92. Republican. Roman Catholic. Address: 2100 S Cathy Ave Tucson AZ 85710 Office: House of Representatives 1700 W Washington Phoenix AZ 85007

PRECOPIO, FRANK MARIO, chemical company executive; b. Providence, Mar. 12, 1925; s. Domenic and Antonetta (Altomari) P.; m. Rita Marie Carr, Apr. 28, 1956; children—Thomas J., Frank J., Michael J. B.Sc. in Chemistry summa cum laude, Brown U., 1948; Ph.D., Yale U., 1952. Research assoc. Gen. Electric Research Ctr., Schenectady, 1951-55; mgr. research and devel. Gen. Electric Co., Erie, Pa., 1955-61; dir. research and devel. wire and cable dept. Gen. Electric Co., Bridgeport, Conn., 1961-66; v.p. tech. Amchem Products, Ambler, Pa., 1966-83; exec. v.p. Henkel Corp., Ambler, 1983-89; ret., 1989. Patentee in field of organic chemistry and high temperature polymers. Trustee Alfred and Mary Douty Found., Phila., 1972-91, William Jeanes Meml. Library, Whitemarsh, Pa., 1968-74. Served to lt. (j.g.) USNR, 1943-46. Recipient Mordica award Wire Assn. Internat., 1983. Fellow Am. Inst. Chemists; mem. Am. Chem. Soc. (chmn. Erie sect. 1958), Sigma Xi. Republican. Roman Catholic. Avocations: antique pewter collecting; antique furniture refinishing; sailing; gardening.

PRECOURT, GEORGE AUGUSTINE, government official; b. Hartford, Conn., Oct. 26, 1934; s. Charles A. and Antoinette (Gauthier) P.; m. Alma E. Hall, Aug. 28, 1954; children: Debra Ann, Carol Anne, David Charles, Kenneth George. Student, LaSalle U., 1952-55. Prodn. and inventory mgr. Beacon Machine Co., E. Hartford, Conn., 1960-65; purchasing/prodn. control mgr. Redington Counters, Windsor, Conn., 1965-73; gen. mgr. Able Coil & Electronics, Kensington, Conn., 1973-74; chief industries Conn. Svcs. for the Blind, Wethersfield, 1974—, commr., exec. dir., 1989—; regional dir. Nat. Industry for the Blind, Wayne, N.J., 1983—; chmn. New Eng. Conf. Vending Facility Dirs., 1982—; v.p. sales Bernstein Leibstone Assocs., Inc., N.Y.C.; exec. v.p. Tech. Mktg., Inc., Plantation, Fla. Inventor in field; contbr. articles to profl. jours. Vice chmn. E. Hartford Pub. Bldg. Commn., 1971—; chmn. Dem. Town Com. Dist. 6, E. Hartford, 1970-74; del. Dem. State Conv., 1960. With U.S. Army, 1950-52. Named Lion of the Yr., 1972; Spl. Citation, U.S. Pres., 1974. Mem. Am. Assn. Workers for the Blind, Prodn. and Inventory Control Soc., C. of C., Career Edn. Placement Assn. (bd. dir.), Lions, Financo War Vets. Episcopalian. Home: 29 Laurel Ter Manchester CT 06040-6833 Office: State Svcs for the Blind Office of Exec Dir 170 Ridge Rd Wethersfield CT 06109-1044

PRECOURT, LYMAN ARTHUR, lawyer; b. Milw., Aug. 30, 1926; s. Bernard Antoine and Blanche Elizabeth (Plaisted) P.; m. Patricia Louise Edlredge, Jan. 20, 1947; children: Susan, Dianne, Bruce, Laura. BS, U. Wis., 1950, JD, 1952. Bar: Wis. 1952, Fla. 1974. Assoc. Foley & Lardner, Milw., 1952-61, ptnr., 1961—. Mem. ABA, Fla. Bar Assn., Am. Coll. Real Estate Lawyers, Milw. Country Club. Office: Foley & Lardner 777 E Wisconsin Ave Milwaukee WI 53202-5367

PREDDY, RAYMOND RANDALL, newspaper publisher; b. Texarkana, Ark., Feb. 1, 1940; s. Raymond Watson and Dorothy Belle (Long) P.; m. Sarah Elizabeth Mitchell, Nov. 20, 1965; children: Lewis, Tiffany. B.S., Northwestern U., 1961, M.S. in Journalism, 1962. Copy editor Louisville Courier-Jour., 1965-69; with Dayton (Ohio) Daily News, 1969-74, asst. city editor, 1971, met. editor, 1971-74; systems mgr. Dayton Newspapers, Inc., 1974-76; bus. mgr. Waco (Tex.) Tribune-Herald, 1976-77, asst. pub., 1977-78; pub. Waco Tribune-Herald, 1978—. Pres. Waco United Way, 1986, Waco Found., 1984-86, Waco Symphony Assn., 1985-86. Served with USN, 1962-65; capt. Res. Presbyterian. Club: Rotary. Office: Waco-Tribune-Herald 900 Franklin Ave Waco TX 76701-1906

PREECE, WARREN EVERSLEIGH, editor; b. Norwalk, Conn., Apr. 17, 1921; s. Everett Lowe and Ethel (Miles) P.; m. Deborah Weeks, July 12, 1947; children: Scott Everett, Mark William, Thayer Evelyn. BA cum laude, Dartmouth Coll., 1943; MA, Columbia U., 1947. Instr. English, U. Chgo., 1947-49; reporter Norwalk Hour, 1949-50, writer, copy editor, 1952-56; campaign aide, publicity dir. to U.S. Senator Dodd, 1956-57; exec. sec. bd. editors Ency. Brit., 1957-64, editor, 1964-65, editor-in-chief, 1965-68, gen. editor, 1968-70, editor, 1970-75, vice chmn. bd. editors, 1974-79, bd. editors, 1979—; cons. Center Study Democratic Instns.; hon't man C.N. Williamson lectr. Peabody Coll., Nashville. Author: (with others) The Technological Order, 1962; editor: Encyclopaedia Britannica College Preparatory Series, 1964; bd. editorial advisors Internat. Ency., Tokyo, 1974-88. Bd. dirs., sec. Conn. chpt. ARC, 1955-57; pres. Mass. Protestant Social Svcs. Inc., 1977-78; bd. dirs. Protestant Youth Homes, Baldwinville, Mass., 1976-78; mem. Standing Commn. on Peace with Justice, Episcopal Ch., 1989-94. Served with arty. U.S. Army, 1943-46, 50-52. Mem. Phi Beta Kappa Assos., Phi Beta Kappa, Sigma Nu. Democrat. Episcopalian. Home: 10 N Main St Orange MA 01364-1016

PREEG, ERNEST HENRY, strategic and international studies center executive; b. Englewood, N.J., July 5, 1934; s. Ernest W. and Claudia T. Preeg; m. Florence L. Tate, May 12, 1962; 1 child, Terri E. BS in Marine Transp., N.Y. State Maritime Coll., 1956; MA in Econs., New Sch. for Social Rsch., 1961, PhD, 1964. Officer Mcht. Marine, 1956-61; lectr. Export Lines, 1956-61; lectr. econs. Bklyn. Coll., 1962-63; fgn. svc. officer Dept. State, Washington, 1963-88; amb. to Haiti, 1981-83; now William M. Scholl chair internat. bus. Ctr. for Strategic and Internat. Studies, Washington. Author: Traders and Diplomats, 1969, Economic Blocs and U.S. Foreign Policy, 1974, The Evolution of a Revolution, 1981, Haiti and the CBI, 1984, The American Challenge in World Trade, 1988, The Tied Aid and Credit Issue, 1989, Neither Fish Nor Foul: U.S. Economic Aid to the Philippines, 1991, Cuba and the New Caribbean Economic Order, 1993. Coun. Fgn. Rels. fellow, 1967-68. Mem. Am. Fgn. Svc. Assn. Office: CSIS 1800 K St NW Washington DC 20006-2202

PREEG, WILLIAM EDWARD, oil company executive; b. N.Y.C., Oct. 16, 1942; s. Ernest Winfield and Claudia Teresa (Casper) P. BE in Marine Engring., SUNY, 1964; MS in Nuclear Sci. and Engring., Columbia U., 1967, PhD in Nuclear Sci. and Engring., 1970. Project engr. U.S. AEC, N.Y.C., 1964-67; physics specialist Aerojet Nuclear Systems Co., Sacramento, Calif., 1971-80; group leader Los Alamos (N.Mex.) Sci. Lab., 1971-80; dir. fluid-mechanics-nuclear dept. Schlumberger-Doll Rsch., Ridgefield, Conn., 1980-85, v.p., dir. rsch., 1990-94; mgr. nuclear dept. Schlumberger Well Svcs., Houston, 1985-87, v.p. engring., 1987-90; v.p., dir. rsch. Schlumberger Austin Rsch., Austin, 1994—; instr. mech. engring. CCNY, N.Y.C., 1968-70; cons. AEC, Gamma Process Co., Los Alamos Sci. Lab., Lawrence Livermore Lab. Mem. Am. Nuclear Soc., Am. Physics Soc., Am. Inst. Physics (adv. com on corp. assocs.), Soc. Profl. Well Log Analysts, Soc. Petroleum Engrs. Office: 203 Hurst Creek Austin TX 78734 Office: Schlumberger Austin Rsch 8311 North RR 620 Austin TX 78726

PREER, JEAN LYON, university administrator, educator; b. Rochester, N.Y., June 25, 1944; d. Henry Gould and Helen Corinne (McTarnaghan) Lyon; m. James Randolph Preer, June 24, 1967; children: Genevieve, Stephen. BA in History with honors, Swarthmore Coll., 1966; MLS, U. Calif., Berkeley, 1967; JD with highest honors, George Washington U., 1974, PhD, 1980. Bar: D.C. 1975. With Henry E. Huntington Libr., San Marino, Calif., 1967-69; Woodrow Wilson Found. teaching intrn Fed. City Coll., Washington, 1969-70; cons. Inst. for Svcs. to Edn., Silver Spring, Md., 1981-82; vol. edn. divsn Nat. Archives, Washington, 1981-89; adj. prof. U. D.C., 1984-85; adj. prof. Cath. U. Am., Washington, 1985-87, asst. prof. sch. libr. and info. sci., 1987-92, assoc. prof., 1992—; assoc. dean, 1991-93, 94—, acting dean, 1993-94; adj. assoc. prof. George Washington U., 1985-87. Contbr. articles to profl. jours. Mem. governing bd. Nat. Cathedral Sch.,

Washington, 1987-91. Fellow Nat. Acad. Edn., 1984-85; grantee Nat. Endowment for Humanities. Mem. Order of Coif, Beta Phi Mu. Home: 2900 Rittenhouse St NW Washington DC 20015-1524 Office: Cath U Am Sch Libr and Info Sci Washington DC 20064

PREER, JOHN RANDOLPH, JR., biology educator; b. Ocala, Fla., Apr. 4, 1918; s. John Randolph Sr. and Ruth (Williams) P.; m. Louise Bertha Brandau; children: James Randolph, Robert William. BS with highest honors, U. Fla., 1939; PhD, Ind. U., 1947. From asst. prof. to assoc. prof. to prof. depts. zoology and biology U. Pa., Phila., 1947-67, chmn. grad. group depts. zoology and biology, 1958-67, admissions officer grad. sch. arts and scis., 1960-61; prof. depts. zoology and biology Ind. U., Bloomington, 1968-77, chmn. dept. biology, 1977-79, disting. prof. depts. zoology and biology, 1977—, disting. prof. emeritus, 1988—. Contbr. 85 articles to profl. jours. and chpts. to books. Served to 1st lt. USAF, 1942-45, ETO. NSF sr. postdoctoral fellow, 1967-68, Guggenheim fellow 1976-77. Mem. AAAS, Nat. Acad. Scis. (elected 1976), Am. Inst. Biol. Scis., Am. Soc. Cell Biology, Am. Soc. Protozoology (pres. 1986-87), Phi Beta Kappa. Democrat. Methodist. Home: 1414 E Maxwell Ln Bloomington IN 47401-5143 Office: Ind Univ care Dept of Biology Bloomington IN 47405

PREGERSON, HARRY, federal judge; b. L.A., Oct. 13, 1923; s. Abraham and Bessie (Rubin) P.; m. Bernardine Seyma Chapkis, June 28, 1947; children: Dean Douglas, Kathryn Ann. B.A., UCLA, 1947; LL.B., U. Calif.-Berkeley, 1950. Bar: Calif. 1951. Pvt. practice Los Angeles, 1951-52; Assoc. Morris D. Coppersmith, 1952; ptnr. Pregerson & Costley, Van Nuys, 1953-65; judge Los Angeles Mcpl. Ct., 1965-66, Los Angeles Superior Ct., 1966-67, U.S. Dist. Ct. Central Dist. Calif., 1967-79, U.S. Ct. Appeals for 9th Circuit, Los Angeles, 1979—; faculty mem., seminar for newly appointed distr. Judges Fed. Jud. Center, Washington, 1970-72; mem. faculty Am. Soc. Pub. Adminstrn., Inst. for Ct. Mgmt., Denver, 1973—; panelist Fed. Bar Assn., L.A. chpt., 1989, Calif. Continuing Edn. of Bar, 9th Ann. Fed. Practice Inst., San Francisco, 1986, Internat. Acad. Trial Lawyers, L.A., 1983; lect. seminars for newly-appointed Fed. judges, 1970-71. Author over 450 published legal opinions. Mem. Community Rels. Com., Jewish Fedn. Coun., 1984—, Temple Judea, Encino, 1955—; bd. dirs. Marine Corps Res. Toys for Tots Program, 1965—; Greater Los Angeles Partnership for the Homeless, 1988—; bd. trustees Devil Pups Inc., 1988—; adv. bd. Internat. Orphans Inc., 1966—, Jewish Big Brothers Assn., 1970—, Salvation Army, Los Angeles Met. area, 1988—; worked with U.S. Govt. Agy. Svcs. to establish the Bell Shelter for the homeless, the Child Day Care Ctr., the Food Partnership and Westwood Transitional Village, 1988. 1st lt. USMCR, 1944-46. Decorated Purple Heart, Medal of Valor Apache Tribe, 1989; recipient Promotion of Justice Civic award, City of San Fernando, 1965, award San Fernando Valley Jewish Fedn. Coun., 1966, Profl. Achievement award Los Angeles Athletic Club, 1980, Profl. Achievement award UCLA Alumni Assn., 1985, Louis D. Brandeis award Am. Friends of Hebrew U., 1987, award of merit Inner City Law Ctr., 1987, Appreciation award Navajo Nation and USMC for Toys for Tots program, 1987, Humanitarian award Los Angeles Fed. Exec. Bd., 1987-88, Grateful Acknowledgement award Bet Tzedek Legal Svcs., 1988, Commendation award Bd. Suprs. Los Angeles County, 1988, Others award Salvation Army, 1988, numerous others. Mem. ABA (vice-chmn., com. on fed. rules of criminal procedure and evidence sect. of criminal 1972—, panelist Advocacy Inst., Phoenix, 1988), L.A. County Bar Assn., San Fernando Valley Bar Assn. (program chmn. 1964-65), State Bar Calif., Marines Corps Res. Officers Assn. (pres. San Fernando Valley 1966—), DAV (Birmingham chpt.), Am. Legion (Van Nuys Post),. Office: US Ct Appeals 9th Cir 21800 Oxnard St Ste 1140 Woodland Hills CA 91367-3633*

PREHEIM, JOHN S., secondary education educator; b. Marion, S.D., July 18, 1941; s. Peter P. and Edith (Wenger) P.; m. Jo Ann Doerksen, June 1, 1963; children: Scott, David. BS in Elem. Edn., Bethel Coll., 1963; MS in Elem. Edn., Ind. U., 1968; postgrad., Ind. U., South Bend, 1972-92, U. Notre Dame, 1980, 86. Cert. tchr., Ind., emotionally handicapped tchr., Ind. Dir. indsl. therapy LaRue Carter Hosp., Indpls., 1963-65; 6th grade tchr. Speedway (Ind.) Schs., 1965-72; asst. prin. Allison Elem. Sch., 1968-72; coord treehouse program for emotionally handicapped children Oaklawn Mental Health Ctr./Elkhart (Ind.) Community Schs., 1972-78; 6th grade tchr. Elkhart Community Schs., 1978-81, emotionally handicapped resource tchr., 1981-84, 7th grade math. tchr., 1984—, chmn. math dept., 1987—; cons. Elkhart Community Day Care Ctr., 1975-78. Bd. pres. Hively Ave Presch., Elkhart, 1978-82; bd. dirs., bd. pres. Camp Friedenswald, Cassopolis, Mich., 1980-86. Named Disting. Vol., Christian Camping Internat., 1986. Mem. NEA, Ind. Tchrs. Assn., Elkhart Tchrs. Assn. (bd. dirs. 1987-91), Nat. Coun. Tchrs. Math. Mennonite. Avocations: visiting state capital buildings, travel, running, genealogy, gardening. Home: 22967 Chestnut Ln Goshen IN 46526-9534 Office: West Side Mid Sch 101 S Nappanee St Elkhart IN 46514-1955

PREHEIM, VERN QUINCY, religious organization administrator, minister; b. Hurley, S.D., June 27, 1935; s. Jacob Roy and Selma (Miller) P.; m. Marion Kathryn Keeney, Aug. 28, 1958; children: Jay, Janette, Beth, Brian, Lorie. AA, Freeman Jr. Coll., 1956; BA, Bethel Coll., 1957; BD, Mennonite Bibl. Sem., 1960. Algeria program dir. Mennonite Cen. Com. Mennonite Ch., Algiers, 1960-62; Peace sec. Gen. Conf. Mennonite Ch., Newton, Kans., 1962-65, gen. sec., 1980—, dir. Africa and Middle East, 1965-75, Asia dir., 1975-80; mission bd. sec. Gen. Conf. Mennonite Ch., 1968-72, chmn. gen. bd. dirs., 1974-80. Home: 1112 Lorna Ln Newton KS 67114-1643 Office: Gen Conf Mennonite Ch 722 N Main St Newton KS 67114-1819 To maintain a sense of direction with a vibrant hope in an uncertain world is imperative for the religious community. Our challenge is also to help others find direction and maintain hope.

PREISER, WOLFGANG FRIEDRICH ERNST, architect, educator, consultant, researcher; b. Freiburg, Germany, June 26, 1941; came to U.S., 1967; s. Gerhard Friedrich and Ursula Helene (von Huelsen) P.; m. Cecilia M. Fenoglio, Feb. 16, 1985; children: Johanna, Timothy, Andreas, Nicholas. Student, Vienna Tech. U., 1963; diploma in Engring. Architecture, U. Karlsruhe, 1967; M.Arch., Va. Poly. Inst. and State U., 1969; Ph.D. in Man-Environ. Relations, Pa. State U., 1973. Architect Germany, Austria, Eng., 1960-66; prof. architecture Va. Poly. Inst. and State U., Pa. State U., Ill., U. N.Mex., U. Cin., 1970—; research architect constrn. engring. research lab. U.S. Army, 1973-76; co-dir. Inst. Environ. Edn., U. N.Mex., 1976-86; dir. Ctr. for R & D, U. N.Mex., Albuquerque, 1986-90; dir. research Archtl. Research Cons. Inc., 1976—; lectr. estdni., profl. and civic groups worldwide; v.p. faculty club U.N.Mex., 1976-78; pres. Internat. Club, Va. Poly. Inst. and State U., 1968-69. Editor, author 10 books on programming, post-occupancy evaluation and design rsch.; contbr. over 75 articles in field to profl. jours. Trustee Cin. Chamber Orch., 1992—. Recipient Faculty Devel. Award for Rsch., U. Cin., 1992, Pogue/Wheeler Traveling award, 1993, Dean's Spl. award, 1994, Finland's Inst. Tech. award, 1966, awards Am. Iron and Steel Inst., 1968, Progressive Arch. Ann., 1985, 89, undergrad. teaching award U. Ill., 1976, hon. mention 1st Kyoto award Internat. Coun. of Soc. Indsl. Design, 1979; Fulbright fellow, 1967, 87, Found Found. fellow, 1968, Nat. Endowment for Arts fellow, 1979, 82. Mem. Soc. Human Ecology (pres. 1980-86), Environ. Design Research Assn. (vice chmn. 1974-76, sec. 1973-74), Nat. Acad. Scis. (chmn. com. on programming and post-occupancy evaluation, bldg. research fellow 1985), Phi Kappa Phi. Research in field. Office: U Cin Coll DAAP Sch Architecture Cincinnati OH 45221-0016

PREISKEL, BARBARA SCOTT, lawyer, association executive; b. Washington, July 6, 1924; d. James and B. Beatrix Scott; m. Robert H. Preiskel, Oct. 28, 1950; children: John S., Richard A. BA, Wellesley Coll., 1945; LLB, Yale U., 1947. Bar: D.C. 1948, N.Y. 1948, U.S. Supreme Ct. 1960. Law clk. U.S. Dist. Ct., Boston, 1948-49; assoc. Poletti, Diamond, Roosevelt, Freidin & Mackay, N.Y.C., 1949-50; assoc. Dwight, Royall, Harris, Hoegel & Caskey, N.Y.C., 1950-54, legal cons., 1954-59; cons. Ford Found. Fund for the Republic, N.Y.C., 1954; dep. atty. Motion Picture Assn. Am., Inc., N.Y.C., 1959-71, v.p., legis. counsel, 1971-77, sr. v.p., gen. atty., 1977-83; pvt. practice N.Y.C., 1983—; bd. dirs. GE, Fairfield, Conn., Mass. Mut. Life Ins. Co., Springfield, Textron, Inc., Providence, Am. Stores Co., Salt Lake City, The Washington (D.C.) Post Co. Mem. Pres.'s Commn. on Obscenity and Pornography, 1968-70, Am. Arbitration Assn., 1971-87, N.Y. Bd. Ethics, 1976-89, Inst. Civil Justice, 1984-86, Citizens Com. for Children,

N.Y.C., 1966-72, 85-91, Child Adoptive Service of State Charities Aid Assn., N.Y.C., 1961-68, Hillcrest Ctr. for Children, N.Y.C., 1958-61, Fedn. Protestant Welfare Agys., N.Y.C., 1959-61, 64-92, N.Y. Philharm. Soc., 1971—; Am. Women's Econ. Devel. Corp., 1981-93, Med. Edn. for South African Blacks, Inc., Washington, 1985-89; bd. dirs. Wiltwyck Sch., N.Y.C., 1968-78, chmn. bd. dirs. 1950; successor trustee Yale Corp., New Haven, 1977-89; trustee Ford Found., N.Y.C., 1982-94, Am. Mus. of Moving Image, 1986—, Wellesley Coll., 1988—; mem. distbn. com. N.Y. Community Trust, Inc., N.Y.C., 1978—, chmn. dist. com. N.Y. Community Trust, 1990—; chmn. council advisors Hunter Coll. Sch. Social Work, 1985-89; mem. Dumpson chair com., Fordham U., N.Y.C., 1981-89; bd. dirs. Tougaloo Coll. Econ. Devel. Corp., 1991—. Recipient Meritorious award Nat. Assn. Theatre Owners, 1970, 72, Alumni Achievement award Wellesley Coll., 1975, Tribute to Women in Internat. Industry award YWCA, 1984, Elizabeth Cutter Morrow award, 1985, Outstanding Contbrs. award Am. Women's Econ. Devel., 1985, Dirs. Choice award Nat. Women's Econ. Alliance Found., 1989, Keystone award Fedn. Protestant Welfare Agys., 1991. Mem. ABA, Assn. of Bar of City of N.Y. (mem. exec. com. 1972-76), ACLU (bd. dirs.), Century Assn., Cosmopolitan Club, Yale Club, Wellesley Club. Episcopalian. Office: 36 W 44th St New York NY 10036-8102 office: New York Community Trust 2 Park Avenue New York NY 10016

PREISS, JACK, biochemistry educator; b. Bklyn., June 2, 1932; s. Erool and Gilda (Friedman) P.; m. Judith Weil Rosen, June 10, 1959; children: Jennifer Ellen, Jeremy Oscar, Jessica Michelle. BS in Chemistry, CCNY, 1953; PhD in Biochemistry, Duke U., 1957. Scientist NIH, Bethesda, 1960-62; asst. prof. dept. biochemistry, biophysics U. Calif., Davis, 1962-65, assoc. prof., 1965-68, prof., 1968-85, chair dept. biochemistry, 1971-74, 77-81; prof. dept. biochemistry Mich. State U., East Lansing, 1985—, chair dept., 1985-89; Mem. physiol. chemistry study panel NIH, Bethesda, 1967-71, study panel Metabolic Biology Div., NSF, 1972-75, study sect. biochemistry and molecular biology carcinogenesis Am. Cancer Soc., 1989-92. Mem. editl. bd. Jour. Bacteriology, 1969-74, Arch. Biochem. Biophysics, 1969—, Plant Physiology, 1969-74, 77-80, assoc. editor, 1980-92, editor, 1993—; editor Jour. Biol. Chemistry, 1971-76, 78-83, 94—. Recipient Camille and Henry Dreyfus Disting. scholar award Calif. State U., 1983, Alexander von Humboldt Stiftung Sr. U.S. Scientist award 1984, Alsberg-Schoch Meml. Lectr. award Am. Assn. Cereal Chemists, 1990, Nat. Sci. Coun. lectr. Republic of China, 1988, award of merit Japanese Soc. Starch Sci., 1992; Guggenheim Meml. fellow, 1969-70; grantee NIH, 1963—, NSF, 1978-89; Japan Soc. for Promotion of Sci. fellow, 1992-93. Mem. AAAS, Am. Chem. Soc. (Charles Pfizer award in enzyme chemistry 1971), Biochem. Soc., Am. Soc. Biol. Chemists and Molecular Biology, N.Y. Acad. Scis., Am. Soc. Microbiologists, Am. Soc. Plant Physiologists, Soc. for Complex Carbohydrates, Protein Soc. Office: Mich State Univ Dept Of Biochemistry East Lansing MI 48824

PREISTER, DONALD GEORGE, greeting card manufacturer, state senator; b. Columbus, Nebr., Dec. 23, 1946; s. Maurice J. Preister and Leona T. (Dusel) Chereck. BS in Edn., U. Nebr., 1977. Unit dir. Boys' Clubs of Omaha, 1973-83; dep. city clk. City of Omaha, 1984-85; tchr. The Great Peace March, U.S., 1986; founder, owner Joy Creations, Co., Omaha, 1988—; instr. Metro C.C., Omaha, 1979-80. Author: (sect.) Drug Abuse Prevention, 1977. Troop leader Boy Scouts Am., Omaha, 1973-83. Served with U.S. Army, 1966-68, Vietnam. Decorated Bronze Star. Mem. Vets. for Peace, Nebr. Sustainable Agr. Soc., Optimist. Democrat. Roman Catholic. Avocations: gardening, running, horses. Home: 3937 W St Omaha NE 68107 Office: State Capitol Dist # 5 Lincoln NE 68509

PREKOP, MARTIN D., art educator, artist; b. Toledo, July 2, 1940; s. Martin W. and Laurel (Rohr) P.; m. Martha McIntosh, Oct. 4, 1963; children—Sam, John, Zachary. Student, Cleve. Inst. of Art, 1958-60; BFA, Cranbrook Acad. Art, 1962; MFA, R.I. Sch. Design, 1964; postgrad., Slade Sch. Art, London, 1964-65. Chmn. freshman found. Sch. Art Inst. of Chgo., 1968-72, chmn. dept. painting, 1977-80, grad. div., 1972-76, prof., chmn. undergrad. div., 1981—, dean, 1987—; vis. prof. Newcastle Poly., Newcastle-upon-Tyne, Eng., 1980-81; cons. artists adv. council Liquidtex div. Binney & Smith, 1986—. Exhibited at group shows Cicero Gallery, Chgo., 1975—; one man show Cicero Gallery, 1975, 83, 85. Fulbright Found. fellow, 1964; Nat. Endowment for the Arts fellow, 1987; recipient Ill. Artists award 1985. Office: Sch Art Inst Chgo 37 S Wabash Ave Chicago IL 60603-3103

PRELL, JOEL JAMES, medical group administrator; b. L.A., Aug. 16, 1944; s. Samuel and Mary Devorah (Schwartz) P.; children: Vanessa S., Matthew. BA, U. So. Calif., L.A., 1967; cert. fin. mgmt., Ohio State U., 1979; M. Pub. Health, UCLA, 1981. Various positions, 1967-72; chief adminstrv. office sr. adminstrv. analyst L.A. County, 1972-73; dep. regional dir. for planning and community rels. L.A. County Dept. Health Svcs. Region, 1973-75; adminstr. ambulatory care L.A. County Harbro Gen. Hosp., 1975-76; assoc. dir. hosp. and clinics ambulatory care svcs. U. Calif.-Irvine Med. Ctr., 1976-78; asst. to the dir. rsch. and analysis unit U. Calif., Davis, 1978-80; v.p. profl. svcs. San Pedro Peninsula Hosp., 1981-84; sr. v.p. South Coast Med. Ctr., 1984-87; pres., CEO Harbor Health Systems, Inc., 1987-90; CEO Santa Monica (Calif.) Plz. Med. Group, Inc., 1990-93; administrator Pathology Cons. Med. Group, Torrance, Calif., 1993—; splt. asst. to the contr. UCLA Hosp. and Clinics, 1980-81, adminstr. emergency medicine ctr., 1981. Mem. Hosp. Coun .So. Calif. (polit. action steering com., chmn. legis. affairs com.), Calif. Hosp. Polit. Action Com. (bd. dirs.), Health Care Execs. So. Calif., UCLA Health Svcs. Adminstrs. Alumni Assn. (pres.), Med. Group Mgmt. Assn., Am. Coll. Health Care Adminstrs., Friends of Castle Heights. Office: Pathology Cons Med Group 20221 Hamilton Ave Torrance CA 90502-1321

PRELL, MICHAEL JACK, economist; b. Ft. Worth, Nov. 2, 1944; s. Martin and Ruth Dorothy (Sosin) P.; m. Terri Lynne Hume, Nov. 30, 1969; 1 child, Marisa Hume. AB, U. Calif., Berkeley, 1966, MA, 1967, PhD, 1971. Fin. economist Fed. Res. Bank, Kansas City, Mo., 1970-73; with div. rsch. and stats. Bd. Govs. of Fed. Res. System, Washington, 1973—; economist capital mkts. sect., 1973-74, banking sect., 1974-75; sr. economist govt. fin. sect., 1975-77; chief capital mkts. sect., 1977-78; assoc. dir. div. rsch. and stats., 1978-83, dep. dir., 1983-87, dir., 1987—; assoc. economist Fed. Open Market Com., 1981-87, economist, 1987—; U.S. del. OECD Com. on Fin. Mkts., Paris, 1982—; bd. dirs. Securities Investor Protection Corp., Washington. Mem. Conf. Bus. Economists. Office: Fed Res Bd Rsch & Stats Div 20th Constitution Ave NE Washington DC 20551

PREM, F. HERBERT, JR., lawyer; b. N.Y.C., Jan. 14, 1932; s. F. Herbert and Sybil Gertrude (Nichols) P.; m. Patricia Ryan, Nov. 18, 1978; children from previous marriage: Julia Nichols, F. Herbert III. AB, Yale U., 1953; JD, Harvard U., 1959. Bar: N.Y. 1960. Assoc. Whitman & Ransom, N.Y.C., 1959-66, ptnr., 1967-93, co-chmn. exec. com., 1988-92, chmn., 1993; chmn. Whitman Breed Abbott & Morgan, N.Y.C., 1993—; bd. dirs. Fuji Photo Film U.S.A., Inc., Fuji Med. Sys. U.S.A., Inc., Noritake Co., Inc., Seiko Instruments U.S.A., Inc., Cmty. Action for Legal Svc. Inc., 1967-70, treas.; bd. dirs. Legal Aid Soc., N.Y.C., 1969-73. Bd. dirs. Bagaduce Music Lending Libr., Inc., 1988—, pres., 1989-93. Lt. (j.g.) USNR, 1953-56. Mem. ABA, Assn. of Bar of City of N.Y. (sec. 1967-69), N.Y. State Bar Assn., Am. Law Inst., Am. Soc. Internat. Law, Univ. Club, Yale Club. Episcopalian. Office: Whitman Breed Abbott & Morgan 200 Park Ave New York NY 10166-0005

PREM, KONALD ARTHUR, physician, educator; b. St. Cloud, Minn., Nov. 6, 1920; s. Joseph E. and Theresa M. (Willing) P.; m. Phyllis Edelbrock, June 14, 1947; children: Mary Kristen, Stephanie, Timothy. B.S., U. Minn., 1947; M.B., 1950, M.D., 1951. Diplomate: Am. Bd. Ob-Gyn (with spl. competence in gynecologic oncology). Intern Mpls. gen. Hosp., 1950-51; fellow dept. obstetrics and gynecology U. Minn., Mpls., 1951-54; instr. U. Minn., 1955-58, asst. prof., 1958-60, assoc. prof., 1960-69, prof., 1969-93, dir. div. gynecologic oncology, 1969-83, head dept. obstetrics and gynecology, 1976-84; prof. dept. surgery, 1993—. Served to capt. USAR, 1941-46, brig. gen. M.C. USAR (Ret.). Decorated Legion of Merit. Mem. Am. Coll. Ob-Gyn, Am. Gynec. and Obstet. Soc., Central Assn. Ob-Gyn, Hennepin County Med. Soc., Soc. Pelvic Surgeons, Minn. Ob-Gyn Soc., Soc. Gynecologic Oncologists, Internat. Soc. Gynecologic Pathologists, Soc. Gynecologic Surgery, Minn. Acad. Medicine, Am. Radium Soc., Mpls. Surg. Soc., Soc.

Med. Cons. to Armed Forces, Am. Assn. Pro-Life Ob-Gyn. Roman Catholic. Home: 4806 Sunnyside Rd Minneapolis MN 55424-1108 Office: PO Box 395 Mayo Bldg 420 Delaware St SE Minneapolis MN 55455-0374

PREMACK, DAVID, psychologist; b. Aberdeen, S.D., Oct. 26, 1925; s. Leonard B. and Sonja (Liese) P.; m. Ann M. James, Oct. 26, 1951; children: Ben, Lisa, Timothy. B.A., U. Minn., 1949, Ph.D., 1955. Research assoc. Yerkes Labs. Primate Biology, Orange Park, Fla., 1955; research assoc., asst. prof. psychology U. Mo., Columbia, 1956-58; assoc. prof. U. Mo., 1959-62, prof., 1963-64; prof. U. Calif., Santa Barbara, 1965-75; vis. prof. Harvard U., 1970-71; prof. U. Pa., 1975—; artist-in-residence Yaddo, Saratoga Springs, N.Y., 1955; fellow Van Leer Jerusalem Inst., 1980, Inst. for Advanced Study, Berlin, 1985-86; vis. scientist Japan Soc. for Promotion Sci., 1980; univ. rsch. lectr. U. Calif., Santa Barbara, 1973; mem. sci. gov. bd. Fyssen Found., Paris, 1989—; assoc. neurosci. rsch. program, La. Jolla, Calif., 1991—. Author: Intelligence in Ape and Man, 1976, (with Ann James Premack) The Mind of an Ape, 1983, Gavagai! Or the Future History of the Animal Language Controversy, 1986; mem. editl. bd. Jour. Exptl. Psychology: Animal Processes, 1976—, Cognition, 1977—, Brain and Behavior Sci., 1978—, Jour. Cognitive Neurosci. Served with U.S. Army, 1943-46. Ford Found. teaching intern, 1954; USPHS postdoctoral fellow, 1956-59; Social Sci. Research Council fellow, summer 1963; Center for Advanced Study in Behavioral Scis. fellow, 1972-73; Guggenheim fellow, 1979-80; grantee NSF, 1961—, USPHS, 1960-80; recipient Kenneth Craik Research award St. John's Coll.-Cambridge U., 1987, Internat. Sci. prize Fyssen Found., Paris, 1987. Fellow AAAS; mem. Soc. Exptl. Psychologists. Office: 3815 Walnut St Philadelphia PA 19104-3604 also: CREA, Ecole Polytechnique, 1 rue Descartes, 75005 Paris France

PREMO, PAUL MARK, oil company executive; b. Syracuse, N.Y., Nov. 20, 1942; s. Matthias George and Kathryn (Whitbread) P.; m. Mary Catherine Hennessy, June 19, 1965; children—Deborah, Mark. B.S. in Chem. Engring., Manhattan Coll., Riverdale, N.Y., 1964; S.M. in Chem. Engring., MIT, 1965. Chem. engr. Chevron Research, Richmond, Calif., 1965-69; fin. analyst Chevron Corp., San Francisco, 1969-72, coordinator, mgr. supply and distbn., 1972-79; mgr. petroleum regulations Chevron USA, San Francisco 1979-81, sec.-treas., 1981-85, mgr. property tax adminstrn., 1985-86, mgr. natural gas regulatory affairs, 1986-92; exec. cons. Resource Mgmt. Internat., San Rafael, Calif., 1992—; dir. Ky. Agrl. Energy Corp., Franklin. Trustee Calif. Tax Found., 1985—. Mem. Calif. State C. of C. (tax com.), Western Oil and Gas Assn., Am. Petroleum Inst. (property tax com.), Natural Gas Supply Assn., Inst. Property Taxation, Calif. Taxpayers Assn. (bd. dirs. 1985—), MIT Alumni Assn., Commonwealth (San Francisco), Sigma Xi, Tau Beta Pi. Avocations: sailing, personal computing, woodworking. Home: 310 Hazel Ave Mill Valley CA 94941-5054 Office: Resource Mgmt Internat 4346 Redwood Hwy # B San Rafael CA 94903

PREMPREE, THONGBLIEW, oncology radiologist; b. Thailand, Feb. 1, 1935; s. Korn and Kam (T.) P.; m. Amporn Lohsuwand, Apr. 27, 1963. Pre-Med., Chulalongkorn U., Thailand, 1954; MD, Siriraj U. of Med. Sci., Thailand, 1958; PhD in Radiobiology, John Hopkins U., 1968. Diplomate Am. Bd. Radiology; Fellow in Am. Coll. Radiology. Instr. Dept. Radiology John Hopkins U., Balt., 1968-69; asst. prof. John Hopkins U. Dept. Radiol. Scis., Balt., 1969; staff mem. Dept. of Radiology Ramathibodi Hosp. Mahidol U., Bankok, Thailand, 1969-70; dir. radiobiology Dept. Therapeutic Radiology Tuft New England Med. Ctr., Boston, 1970; asst. prof. sch. of medicine John Hopkins U., Balt., 1971-74; assoc. prof. dept. radiology U. Md. Hosp., Balt., 1974, acting dir., assoc. prof., 1977-79, prof., chief, div. radiation oncology, 1979-83; prof., chmn. dept. radiation oncology U. Hosp., Jacksonville, Fla., 1983—. Recipient PhD Fellowship awards John Hopkins U., 1963-68. Mem. Am. Soc. Therapeutic Radiobiologists, Am. Coll. Radiology, AAAS, AMA, Radiation Research Soc., Fedn. Am. Scientists, Radiol. Soc. N. Am., The John Hopkins Med. & Surgical Assn. Home: 104 Lamplighter Island Ct Ponte Vedra Beach FL 32082-1940 Office: U Fla 655 W 8th St Jacksonville FL 32209-6511

PRENDERGAST, JOHN PATRICK, accounting company executive; b. Jersey City, Dec. 13, 1927; s. William James and Hannah (Conmy) P.; m. Peg Prendergast, Dec. 27, 1952; children—Kevin, William, Mary Kay, Brian, Sheila; m. Margaret Teresa McGrath. A.B., Fordham U., 1950; M.B.A., NYU, 1957. Ptnr., cons. Arthur Young & Co., N.Y.C., 1961-63, mng. assoc., 1963-66; prin. Arthur Young, N.Y.C., 1966-68, ptnr., 1968—. Track and field ofcl. Olympic Games, Los Angeles, 1984; mem. adv. council Fordham U., Pace U., N.C. Central U. Durham, 1985. Served to lt. USN, 1950-53, Korea; capt. USNR (ret.). Roman Catholic. Clubs: Fordham (pres. 1970-75) (N.Y.C.); Spiked Shoe. Home: 167 Godwin Ave Wyckoff NJ 07481-2004 Office: Arthur Young 277 Park Ave New York NY 10172-0003

PRENDERGAST, ROBERT A., pathologist educator; b. Bklyn., Nov. 6, 1931. BA, Columbia U., 1953; MD, Boston U., 1957. Intern Bellevue Hosp., 1957-58; resident Boston City Hosp., 1958-59, Meml. Sloan-Kettering Hosp., 1959-61; vis. physician Rockefeller U., 1963-65, asst. prof., 1965-70; Assoc. prof. opthamology and pathology, sch. medicine Johns Hopkins U., 1970—; prof. Rsch. Prevent Blindness, 1971—. Mem. Am. Assn. Immunology, Am. Soc. Exp. Pathology, Transplantation Soc., Reticuloendothelial Soc. Achievements include research in delayed hypersensitivity and cellular immunology, ontogeny of the immune response, transplantation immunology, immunology of neoplasia, viral immunopathology, immunopathology of ocular inflammatory diseases. Office: Johns Hopkins U Oscular Immunology Lab Baltimore MD 21205

PRENDERGAST, THOMAS A., investments and management consultant; b. Dec. 10, 1933; m. Mary Alice Peinado; children: Elizabeth Jane, Laura Ann Gordon. BS, Fordham U., 1955; postgrad., U. Tex., El Paso, 1960. CPA, Tex. Pvt. practice acctg., 1957-61; v.p. fin. Farah Mfg., Inc., 1961-71; chmn. bd. Billy the Kid, Inc., 1971-81, Jetco, 1972-74, Fashion Enterprises, Inc., 1982-84; chmn. bd. Air Cargo Equipment Corp., 1983-88, investments, mgmt. cons.; chmn. bd. El Paso Gibson's, Inc., 1988—; chmn. Sunland Audio Ltd. Co., 1994—; chmn. bd. dirs. Baron Chem., Inc., Clinitech, Inc., 1986-91, Steel Corp. Tex., Texzona Industries, Inc., True Blue Sky, Inc.; bd. dirs. APL Corp., DWG Corp., Graniteville Co., Inc., Pa. Engring. Corp., Southeastern Pub. Svc. Co., Wilson Bros., Triarc. Founder, pres. bd. trustees El Paso Community Coll, 1969-82. Office: Ste 210 501 Executive Center Blvd El Paso TX 79902-1037

PRENDERGAST, THOMAS F., railroad executive; b. Chgo., June 6, 1952; s. Francis V. and Julia M. Prendergast; m. Christine L. Prendergast, Oct. 1, 1994; 1 child, Kelly. BS in Socio-Technol. Sys., U. Ill., Chgo., 1974. Sys. safety engr. Chgo. Transit Authority, 1975-79; transit safety sys. specialist Fed. Transit Adminstrn., Washington, 1979-82; dir. sys. safety N.Y.C. Transit, 1982-84, asst. v.p. sys. safety, 1984-87, gen. mgr. S.I. divsn., 1987-90, sr. v.p. subways, 1990-94; pres. L.I. R.R., Jamaica, 1994—. Office: LIRR Jamaica Station Jamaica NY 11435

PRENG, DAVID EDWARD, management consultant; b. Chgo., Sept. 30, 1946; s. Edward M. and Frances (Maras) P.; m. JoAnne Ferzoco, Dec. 6, 1969; children: Mark, Laura, Stephen, Michael. BS, Marquette U., 1969; MBA, DePaul U., 1973. Supr. Shell Oil Co., Houston and Chgo., 1969-73; controller Litton Office Products, Houston, 1973-74; v.p. Addington & Assocs., Houston, 1974-76; exec. v.p. Mantech S.W., Inc., Houston, 1976-77; sr. asso. Energy div. Korn/Ferry Internat., Houston, 1977-78; v.p. Korn Marlar & Assocs., 1978-80; pres. Preng & Assocs., 1980-85; pres. Preng Zant & Assocs., 1985-87, Preng & Assocs., 1987—; bd. dirs. Citizens Nat. Bank of Tex., Brit. Am. Bus. Assn. Mem. Sugar Creek Country Club (pres.). Home: 607 Chevy Chase Cir Sugar Land TX 77478-3601

PRENSKY, ARTHUR LAWRENCE, pediatric neurologist, educator; b. N.Y.C., Aug. 31, 1930; s. Herman and Pearl (Newman) P.; m. Sheila Carr, Nov. 13, 1969. A.B., Cornell U., 1951; M.D., N.Y. U., 1955. Diplomate: Am. Bd. Psychiatry and Neurology. Intern Barnes Hosp., St. Louis, 1955-56; resident and research fellow in neurology Harvard U., Mass. Gen. Hosp., Boston, 1959-66; instr. neurology Harvard Med. Sch., 1966-67; mem. faculty Washington U. Sch. Medicine, St. Louis, 1967—; prof. pediatrics and neurology Washington U. Sch. Medicine, to 1975, Allen P. and Josephine B. Green prof. pediatric neurology, 1975—; pediatrician St. Louis Children's Hosp.; neurologist Barnes and Allied Hosps., Jewish Hosp., St. Louis.

Author: (with others) Nutrition and the Developing Nervous System, 1975; editor: (with others) Neurological Pathophysiology, 2d edit, 1978, Advances in Neurology, 1976; mem. editorial bd. Pediatric Neurology, 1984-90, Jour. Child Neurology, 1985—. Served with USAF, 1957-59. Fellow Am. Acad. Neurology; mem. Am. Neurol. Assn., Am. Soc. Neurochemistry (mem. council 1973-77), Central Soc. Neurol. Research (pres. 1977-78), Child Neurology Soc. (pres. 1979-80), Am. Pediatric Soc., Internat. Child Neurology Assn., Japanese Soc. Child Neurology, Profs. Child Neurology (pres. 1984-86). Home: 15 Monarch Hill Ct Chesterfield MO 63005-4004 Office: 400 S Kingshighway Blvd Saint Louis MO 63110-1014

PRENTICE, ANN ETHELYND, academic adminstrator; b. Grafton, Vt., July 19, 1933; d. Homer Orville and Helen (Cooke) Hurlbut; divorced; children: David, Melody, Holly, Wayne. AB, U. Rochester, 1954; MLS, SUNY, Albany, 1964; DLS, Columbia U., 1972; LittD (hon.), Keuka Coll., 1979. Lectr. sch. info. sci. and policy SUNY, Albany, 1971-72, asst. prof., 1972-78; prof., dir. grad. sch. library and info. sci. U. Tenn., Knoxville, 1978-88; assoc. v.p. info. resources U. South Fla., Tampa, 1988-93; dean Coll. of Libr. and Info. Svcs. U. Md., 1993—. Author: Strategies for Survival, Library Financial Management Today, 1979, The Library Trustee, 1973, Public Library Finance, 1977, Financial Planning for Libraries, 1983, Professional Ethics for Librarians, 1985; editor Pub. Library Quar., 1978-81; co-editor: Info. Sci. in its Disciplinary Context, 1990; assoc. editor Library and Info. Sci. Ann., 1987-90. Cons. long-range planning and pers. Knox County Libr. System, 1980, 85-86, Richland County S.C. Libr. System, 1981, Upper Hudson Libr. Fedn., N.Y., State Libr. Ohio, 1986; trustee Hyde Park (N.Y.) Free Libr., treas., 1973-75, pres., 1976; trustee Mid-Hudson Libr. System, Poughkeepsie, N.Y., 1975-78; trustee adv. bd. Hillsborough County Libr., 1991-93. Recipient Disting. Alumni award SUNY, Albany, 1987, Columbia U., 1991. Mem. ALA, Am. Soc. Info. Sci. (exec. bd. 1986-89, conf. chmn. 1989, pres. 1992-93, chmn. info. policy com. 1994-95), Assn. for Libr. and Info. Sci. Edn. (pres. 1986). Office: Univ Md Coll Libr and Info Svcs 4105 Hornbake Bldg College Park MD 20742

PRENTICE, EUGENE MILES, III, lawyer; b. Glen Ridge, N.J., Aug. 27, 1942; s. Eugene Miles and Anna Margaret (Kiernan) P.; m. Katharine Kirby Culbertson, Sept. 18, 1976; children: Eugene Miles IV, Jessie Kirby, John Francis. BA, Washington and Jefferson Coll., Pa., 1964; JD, U. Mich., 1967. Bar: N.Y. 1973, U.S. Dist. Ct. (so. dist.) N.Y. 1973, U.S. Dist. Ct. (ea. dist.) N.Y. 1974, U.S. Ct. Appeals (2d cir.) 1974, N.Y. Supreme Ct. 1973. With Morgan Guaranty Trust, N.Y.C., 1967-68, 71-73; assoc. White & Case, N.Y.C., 1973-78; assoc. Windels, Marx et al, N.Y.C., 1978-80, ptnr., 1980-84; ptnr. Brown & Wood, N.Y.C., 1984-93, Piper & Marbury, N.Y.C., 1993—; pres. Midland (Tex.) Sports, Inc., 1990—; bd. dirs. Nat. Life Ins. Co., Montpelier, Vt., Tex. League Profl. Baseball, 1990—. Trustee Vt. Law Sch., 1984—, Washington and Jefferson Coll., Pa., 1985—, Nat. Assn. Profl. Baseball Leagues, 1992—, St. Hilda's and St. Hugh's Sch., N.Y.C., 1993—. Capt. U.S. Army, 1968-70. Mem. ABA, Assn. of Bar of City of N.Y., Links Club, Union League Club, N.Y. Athletic Club, Spring Lake Bath & Tennis Club, Lake Mansfield Trout Club (Vt.). Republican. Home: 34 W 95th St New York NY 10025-6701 Office: Piper & Marbury 53 Wall St New York NY 10005

PRENTICE, FREDERICK SHELDON, lawyer; b. Summit, N.J., May 7, 1950; s. Eugene Miles and Anna Margaret (Kiernan) P.; m. Barbara Mary Mayzik, Aug. 13, 1977; children: Hilary Jeanne, Amanda Mary, Julie Ellen. AB, Dartmouth Coll., 1972; JD, Fordham U., 1977. Bar: N.Y. 1978, U.S. Dist. Ct. (ea. and so. dists.) N.Y. 1978, Vt. 1980, U.S. Ct. Appeals (2d dist.) 1980, U.S. Dist. Ct. Vt. 1982, U.S. Supreme Ct. 1986. Assoc. Davis Polk & Wardwell, N.Y.C., 1977-80; asst. counsel Nat. Life Ins., Montpelier, Vt., 1980-85; adj. prof. Vt. Law Sch., S. Royalton, 1982—; sr. v.p., gen. counsel, sec. Chittenden Corp., Burlington, Vt., 1985—; dir. Vt. Green Up Inc. Campaign mgr. Cheney for Atty. Gen., Vt., 1974; chmn. alumni council nominating and trustee search Dartmouth Coll., 1985; trustee Vt. Legal Aid Inc., Vt. Municipal Retirement Bd. Mem. ABA, Vt. Bar Assn., Vt. Bankers Assn., Nat. Assn. Securities Dealers, Inc. (bd. arbitrators). Club: Dartmouth Cen. Vt. (dist. enrollment dir. 1980—). Lodge: Rotary. Avocations: reading, running. Office: Chittenden Corp 2 Burlington Sq Burlington VT 05401-4442

PRENTICE, JAMES STUART, energy company executive, chemical engineer; b. Louisville, Feb. 4, 1944; s. John Edward and Helen (Staples) P.; m. Mary Joan Kelly, July 24, 1965; children: Holly Michelle, Craig Edward, Brian Andrew. B in Chem. Engring., U. Louisville, 1966; MS, Northwestern U., 1967. Research engr. Esso Research and Engring. Co., Baytown, Tex., 1967-71; engr., supr. ops., mkt. mgr. to plant mgr. No. Petrochem. Co., Morris and Des Plaines, Ill., 1971-82; v.p. mfg. No. Petrochem. Co., Omaha, 1982-85; sr. v.p. corp. planning HNG/Internorth, Omaha, 1985-86; sr. v.p. adminstrn. and human resources Enron Corp., Houston, 1986-87; exec. v.p. Enron Liquid Fuels, Houston, 1987-89; sr. v.p. Enron Gas Pipeline Group, Houston, 1989-93; sr. v.p., chief tech. officer Enron Ops. Corp., Houston, 1993-95, sr. v.p. human resources, 1995—. Patentee in field. Bd. dirs. St. Joseph Hosp. Found., The Houston Symphony. Mem. Am. Inst. Chem. Engrs., Gas Rsch. Inst., Interstate Natural Gas Assn. of Am., Inst. Gas Tech., Lakeside Country Club, Petroleum Club of Houston. Roman Catholic. Avocations: tennis, golf. Office: Enron Corp EB4903 PO Box 1188 Houston TX 77251-1188

PRENTICE, NORMAN MACDONALD, clinical psychologist; b. Yonkers, N.Y., Feb. 25, 1925; s. Lester M. and Islay (Macdonald) P.; m. Marilyn E. Shepherd, Dec. 24, 1953 (dec. July 14, 1979); children: Wendy Elizabeth, Lisa Shepherd; m. Joyce Marie Broyles, June 25, 1987. A.B. in Psychology, Princeton U., 1949; M.A. in Clin. Psychology, Harvard U., 1952, Ph.D. 1956. Diplomate Am. Bd. Profl. Psychology. Research fellow child psychiat. unit Mass. Gen. Hosp., Boston 1953-55; NIMH fellow Judge Baker Guidance Center, Boston, 1955-57; chief adolescent sect. psychologist Children's Hosp., Boston, 1957-58; staff psychologist to coordinator of training Judge Baker Guidance Center, 1958-65; asso. prof. psychology U. Tex., Austin, 1965-68; prof. psychology and ednl. psychology U. Tex., 1968—, dir. clin. psychology tng. program, 1974-76; cons. VA, 1966-80. Contbr. articles to profl. jours. Bd. dirs. Austin Community Nursery Sch., 1966-69, Austin Child Guidance and Evaluation Ctr., 1981-84; trustee Austin-Travis County Mental Retardation Ctr., 1971-73, Art Inst. Boston, 1968-90. With AUS, 1943-45. Decorated Purple Heart. Fellow Am. Psychol. Assn., Am. Orthopsychiat. Assn. (v.p. 1979-80), Soc. for Personality Assessment; mem. Phi Beta Kappa. Office: U Tex Dept Psychology Austin TX 78712-1157

PRENTICE, TIM, sculptor, architect; b. N.Y.C., Nov. 5, 1930; s. T. Merrill and Theodora (Machado) P.; m. Marie Truesdale Bissell, Aug. 23, 1960; children: Nora L., Phoebe A. BA, Yale U., 1953, M.Arch., 1960. Gen. partner Prentice & Chan, Ohlhausen, Architects and predecessor, N.Y.C., 1966-74; adj. prof. archtl. design Columbia U., 1974-80. One-man shows include Inst. Architecture and Urban Studies, N.Y.C., 1975, Paul Mellon Arts Ctr., Wallingford, Conn., 1983, Aldrich Mus., Ridgefield, Conn., 1989, Bruce Mus., Greenwich, Conn., 1989, Maxwell Davidson Gallery, N.Y.C., 1990, 94, Mattatuck Mus., Waterbury, Conn., 1990, Neville Sargent Gallery, Chgo., 1991, Maxwell Davidson Gallery, N.Y.C., 1992; group shows, New Britain Mus. Am. Art, 1978, Carlson Art Gallery U. Bridgeport, 1978, Indpls. Mus. Art, 1978, Conn. Painting, Drawing and Sculpture Today, 1977, Parsons-Dreyfuss Gallery, N.Y.C., 1980, Allan Stone Gallery, N.Y.C., 1984, Am. Acad. and Inst. Arts and Letters, N.Y.C., 1991, Soma Gallery, San Diego, 1993, Chgo. Cultural Ctr., 1993; kinetic sculpture represented in permanent collections Am. Express Co., N.Y.C., AT&T Long Lines, Bedminster, N.Y., Henry St. Settlement, N.Y.C.; major commns. include CBS Bldg., N.Y.C., 1979, Conn. Natural Gas Co., Hartford, 1980, Mobil Oil, Fairfax, Va., 1982, Tex. Commerce Bank, Houston, 1982, INA CIGNA Corp., Wilmington, Del., 1983, Bank Am. Plaza, N.Y.C., 1984, United Va. Bank, Richmond, 1984, Bradley Internat. Airport, Windsor Locks, Conn., 1987, Hollister Inc., Libertyville, Ill., 1988, Mattatuck Mus., Waterbury, Conn., 1989, Summit Office Bldg., Raleigh, N.C., 1989, Sioux City (Iowa) Pub. Libr., 1990, Tempozan Market Place, Osaka, Japan, 1990, Irving (Tex.) Arts Ctr., 1991, Fed. Res. Bank of N.Y., East Rutherford, N.J. 1992, Math. Lib. Univ. Colo., Boulder, 1992, World Population Coun., N.Y.C., 1993, Peak Galleria, Hong Kong, 1993, Civic Ctr. Torroti, Japan, 1993, Hewlett Packard, Andover, Mass., Nat. Inventors Hall of Fame, 1995, Los Cerritos

(Calif.) Ctr., 1995. Served to lt. (j.g.) USNR, 1954-58. Dept. State cultural exchange grantee, 1963-64. Fellow AIA (pres. N.Y. chpt. 1973-74); mem. Nat. Council Archtl. Registration Bds., Mcpl. Arts Soc. N.Y. (pres. 1974-76). Club: Century Assn. Studio: 129 Lake Rd West Cornwall CT 06796-1402

PRENTISS, CHARLES GARY, museum director; b. Astoria, Oreg., June 29, 1942; s. Donald Crane and Marian Caroline (Gary) P.; m. Dianne Ritner, June 18, 1966 (div. 1980); children: Carlos, Katherine; m. Nikki Silva, July 3, 1982; children: Molly, Grace. BS in Zoology, U. Calif., 1966. Curator, dir. Santa Cruz (Calif.) City Mus., 1969—. Editor: Fossils of Santa Cruz County, 1977. Served with USAR, 1963-69. Recipient Civic Improvement award SCOPE, 1982, Craftsman Exhibit award Santa Cruz Hist. Soc., 1983. Mem. Am. Assn. Mus. Home: 89 Spring Valley Rd # D Watsonville CA 95076-9638 Office: Santa Cruz City Mus 1305 E Cliff Dr Santa Cruz CA 95062-3722

PRENTISS, C.J., state legislator. BA in Edn., Cleve. State U., 1969, MEd, 1975; cert., Kent State U., 1976; grad. Weatherhead Sch. Mgmt., Case Western Res. U., 1978. Mem. Ohio Ho. of Reps., Columbus, 1991—; chair edn. policy Black Elected Dem. of Ohio; vice-chair edn. com. Nat. Conf. State Legislatures; past vice-chair House Edn. com., ways and means; ins. mem. State Bd. Edn., 1984-90, chair lit. and youth-at-risk com., legis. stds. com., past chair joint select com. on infant health and family support. Past Vice-chair Black Leadership Cleve. Alumni; past mem. gov.'s com. Socially Disadvantaged Black Males. Office: 77 S High St Columbus OH 43266

PRENTISS, PAUL E., lawyer; b. Milford, Mass., June 8, 1943. AB, Middlebury Coll., 1965; JD, Duke U., 1971. Bar: Wis. 1971. Mem. Michael Best & Friedrich, Milw. Mem. editorial bd. Duke Law Jour., 1970-71. Mem. ABA. Office: Michael Best & Friedrich 100 E Wisconsin Ave Milwaukee WI 53202-4108*

PRENTKE, RICHARD OTTESEN, lawyer; b. Cleve., Sept. 8, 1945; s. Herbert E. and Melva B. (Horbury) P.; m. Susan Ottesen, June 9, 1974; children: Catherine, Elizabeth. BSE, Princeton U., 1967; JD, Harvard U., 1974. Assoc. Perkins Coie, Seattle, 1974-80, prtnr., 1981—, chief fin. officer, 1989—. Author: School Construction Law Deskbook, 1989; contbr. articles to profl. jours. Pres., trustee Princeton U. Rowing Assn., 1976—; pres., trustee Seattle Country Day Sch., 1990—. With USN, 1967-70. Fellow Leadership Tomorrow, Seattle, 1985-86. Mem. ABA, Wash. State Bar Assn. (jud. screening com. 1985-91, chmn. 1987-91), Seattle-King County Bar Assn. (chmn. jud. task force 1990-93), Rainier Club, Tower Club, Princeton Club of Wash. (trustee 1986—, pres. 1990-92), Seattle Tennis Club, AAA (arbitrator 1988—). Avocations: art, carpentry, travel, rowing, sports. Office: Perkins Coie 1201 3d Ave 40th Fl Seattle WA 98101

PREONAS, GEORGE ELIAS, lawyer; b. Dayton, Ohio, Oct. 5, 1943; s. Louis D. and Mary (Drakos) P.; m. Aileen Strike, June 1, 1944; children—Annemarie, Michael, Stephen. B.A., Stanford U., 1965; J.D., U. Mich., 1968. Bar: Ill. 1968, Nev. 1969, Calif. 1974. Ptnr., Seyfarth, Shaw, Fairweather & Geraldson, Los Angeles, 1968—. Mem. Los Angeles County Bar Assn., Calif. Bar Assn., ABA, Ill. Bar Assn., Nev. Bar Assn. Office: Seyfarth Shaw Fairweather 2029 Century Park E # 3300 Los Angeles CA 90067-3063

PREOVOLOS, PENELOPE ATHENE, lawyer; b. San Francisco, Sept. 16, 1955; d. James Peter and Lorraine Lucille (Tiscornia) P.; m. Richard Gonzalo Katerndahl, Mar. 24, 1984. AB, U. Calif., Berkeley, 1976; JD, Harvard U., 1979. Bar: Calif. 1979, U.S. Dist. Ct. (no. dist.) Calif. 1979, U.S. Ct. Appeals (9th cir.) 1979. Law clk. to Hon. Charles M. Merrill U.S. Ct. Appeals (9th cir.), San Francisco, 1979-80; assoc. Morrison & Foerster, San Francisco, 1980-85; ptnr. Morrison & Foerster, San Francisco, 1985—; mng. ptnr. San Francisco office Morrison & Foerster, San Francisco, 1995—. Contbr. articles to profl. jours. Bd. dirs. San Francisco Neighborhood Legal Assistance Found., 1990—. Mem. ABA (antitrust sect.), State Bar of Calif. (chair antitrust and trade regulation law sect. 1994-95). Democrat. Roman Catholic. Avocations: riding (dressage), classical music. Home: 225 Evergreen Dr Kentfield CA 94904-2707 Office: Morrison & Foerster 345 California St San Francisco CA 94104-2606

PREPARATA, FRANCO PAOLO, computer science and engineering educator; b. Reggio E, Italy, Dec. 29, 1935; came to U.S., 1965, naturalized, 1977; s. Vincenzo and Stefania P.; m. Rosamaria Cupi, Apr. 30, 1964; children: Paola, Claudia. Dr.Ing., U. Rome, 1959; Libera Docenza, Italian U. System, 1969. System analyst, tech. mgr. Univac, Rome, 1960-63; sr. designer Selenia S.p.A., Rome, 1963-65; professorial staff U. Ill., Urbana, 1965-90, prof. elec. engring. and computer sci., 1970-90; An Wang prof. computer sci. Brown U., Providence, 1991—. Author: (with Raymond T. Yeh) Introduction to Discrete Structures, 1972, Introduction to Computer Engineering, 1985, (with M.I. Shamos) Computational Geometry, 1985; assoc. editor: IEEE Trans. on Computers, 1978-82, also 9 other jours.; contbr. articles to profl. jours. Fellow IEEE (Darlington award 1993), Assn. Computing Machinery; mem. European Assn. Theoretical Computer Sci. Office: 115 Waterman St Providence RI 02912-9016

PRESANT, SANFORD CALVIN, lawyer, educator, author, lecturer; b. Buffalo, Nov. 15, 1952; s. Allen Norman and Reeta (Coplon) P.; m. Ilene Beth Shendell, Dec. 2, 1984; 1 child, Jarrett Matthew. B.A., Cornell U., 1973; J.D. cum laude, SUNY-Buffalo, 1976; LL.M. in Taxation, Georgetown U., 1981. Bar: N.Y. 1977, D.C. 1977, U.S. Ct. Claims 1978, U.S. Tax Ct. 1977, U.S. Supreme Ct. 1982. Staff atty. SEC options task force, Washington, 1976-78; assoc. Barrett Smith Schapiro, N.Y.C., 1978-80, Trubin Sillcocks, N.Y.C., 1980-81; ptnr. Carro, Spanbock, Fass, Geller, Kaster, N.Y.C., 1981-86, Finley, Kumble, Wagner, Heine, Underberg, Manley, Myerson & Casey, N.Y.C., 1987—; adj. assoc. prof. real estate NYU, 1983—; frequent lectr. in tax law; regular TV appearances on Nightly Business Report, Pub. Broadcasting System, 1986—; co-chmn. NYU Conf. Fed. Taxation of Real Estate Transactions, 1987, 88. Author: (with others) Tax Aspects of Real Investments, 1987, Understanding Estate Partnership Tax Allocations, 1987, Realty Joint Ventures, 1980-86, Tax Sheltered Investments Handbook-Special Update on Tax Reform Act of 1984, Real Estate Syndication Handbook, 1985, Real Estate Syndication Tax Handbook, 1986, The Tax Reform Act of 1986, 1986, The Final Partnership Nonrecourse Debt Allocation Regulations, 1987, Taxation of Real Estate Investments, 1987, Understanding Partnership Tax Allocations, 1987. Kripke Securities law fellow NYU, 1976. Mem. ABA (nat. chmn. audit subcom. of tax sect. partnership com. 1984-86, partnership tax allocation subcom. chmn. 1986—), N.Y. State Bar Assn. (tax sect. partnership com. 1980—), Assn. of Bar of City of N.Y. Republican. Jewish. Office: Kaye Scholer Fierman Hays 1999 Ave of the Stars Ste 1600 Los Angeles CA 90067

PRESBY, J. THOMAS, financial advisor; b. Newark, Feb. 15, 1940; s. George and Shirley (Kandel) P.; m. Elaine Merle Smith, Aug. 19, 1961; children: Philip, Terry, Mona. BSEE, Rutgers U., 1961; MS in Indsl. Adminstrn., Carnegie-Mellon U., 1963. CPA, Ohio, N.Y. Ptnr. Deloitte & Touche, N.Y.C., 1972-76; regional ptnr. Touche Ross Internat., Paris, 1976-79, nat. dir. client svcs., 1979-81, exec. dir., 1981-82, ptnr.-in-charge fin. svcs. ctr., 1982-90, mng. ptnr. Ea. Europe, Brussels, 1991—; chief exec. officer Europe, Paris, 1991-95; COO Deloitte Touche Tohmatsu Internat., N.Y.C., 1995—. Mem. bus. adv. council Grad. Sch. Indsl. Adminstrn., Carnegie-Mellon U., Pitts., 1984—; trustee Rutgers U., New Brunswick, N.J., 1985-90, Coll. Ins., N.Y.C., 1986-89. Mem. AICPA, Ohio Soc. CPAs, N.Y. Soc. CPAs, Harmonie Club, N.Y. Athletic Club, Tennis Club of Paris. Avocations: antique autos; racquetball; squash. Home: 6 HOlton Ln Essex Fells NJ 07021 Office: Deloitte Touche 1633 Broadway New York NY 10019

PRESCHLACK, JOHN EDWARD, management consultant; b. N.Y.C., May 30, 1933; s. William and Anna M. (Hrubesch) P.; m. Lynn A. Stanley, Dec. 29, 1962; children: John Edward Jr., James S., David C. B.S.E.E., M.I.T., 1954; M.B.A., Harvard U., 1958. Ptnr. McKinsey & Co., Inc., N.Y.C., London, Dusseldorf, W. Ger., 1958-73; pres. ITEK Graphic Products Co., Lexington, Mass., 1973-77; pres., CEO Gen. Binding Corp., Northbrook, Ill., 1977-83, Roberts & Porter, Inc., Des Plaines, Ill., 1984-86; ptnr., sr. dir. Spencer Stuart, Chgo., 1987—; bd. dirs. Blyth Industries,

Greenwich, Conn., 1989—. Trustee Chgo. Hort. Soc., 1979—; chmn. Lake Forest (Ill.) Planning Commn., 1982-88; alderman City of Lake Forest, 1989—; mem. devel. com. MIT, 1986-92. With USAF, 1954-56. Decorated Air Force Commendation medal; recipient Corp. Leadership award M.I.T., 1978. Mem. Onwentsia Club, Chgo. Club, Harvard Club of N.Y.C. Republican. Roman Catholic. Avocations: tennis, skiing, travel. Office: Spencer Stuart 401 N Michigan Ave Chicago IL 60611-4212 *Focus on what's right, not who's right; be honest and candid in dealing with others; don't get hung up on who gets credit for what you've done; select and reward outstanding people.*

PRESCOTT, DAVID MARSHALL, biology educator; b. Clearwater, Fla., Aug. 3, 1926; s. Clifford Raymond and Lillian (Moore) P.; m. Gayle Edna Demery; children: Lavonne, Jason, Ryan. BA, Wesleyan U., 1950; PhD, U. Calif., Berkeley, 1954. Asst. prof. UCLA Med. Sch., 1955-59; biologist Oak Ridge (Tenn.) Nat. Lab., 1959-63; prof. U. Colo. Sch. Medicine, Denver, 1963-66; prof. molecular, cell and devel. biology U. Colo., Boulder, 1966—, Disting. prof., 1980—; pres. Am. Soc. Cell Biology, 1966. Author: Cell Reproduction, 1976, Cancer: The Misguided Cell, 1986, Cells, 1988; also numerous rsch. reports; editor: Methods in Cell Biology, 15 vols., 1963-78. Adv. com. March of Dimes, 1979-90. Recipient von Humboldt prize Fed. Republic Germany, 1979; grantee NIH, 1985-95, Nat. Found. Cancer Rsch., 1985-89, NSF, 1990-91, 95—; John Simon Guggenheim Meml. Found. fellow, 1990-91. Fellow Am. Acad. Arts and Scis.; mem. NAS, Soc. Protozoologists (pres. 1995—). Avocation: numismatics. Home: 285 Brook Pl Boulder CO 80302-8031 Office: Univ Colo Dept Biology Boulder CO 80309

PRESCOTT, JOHN HERNAGE, aquarium executive; b. Corona, Calif., Mar. 16, 1935; s. Arthur James and Henrietta (Hernage) P.; m. Sandra Baker, Sept. 26, 1985; children by previous marriage—Craig C., Blane R. B.A., UCLA, 1957; postgrad., U. So. Calif., Los Angeles, 1958-60; cert. advanced mgmt. program, Harvard U. Curator Marineland of the Pacific, Palos Verdes, Calif., 1957-70, v.p., 1966-70, gen. mgr., 1970-72; exec. dir., v.p. New Eng. Aquarium, Boston, 1972-95; dir. emeritus, 1995—; corporator Woods Hole (Mass.) Oceanographic Inst., 1976-90; chmn. mem. sci. advisers Marine Mammal Commn., Washington, 1977-80; dir. Mus. Inst. Teaching Sci. Boston, 1987-93; chmn. Humpback Whale Recovery Team NOAA, Washington, 1987-93; mem. U.S. del. Internat. Whaling Commn., 1989-94. Author: Aquarium Fishes of the World, 1976. Editor: Georges Bank: Past, Present, Future, 1981, Right Whales: Past and Present Status, 1986. Bd. dirs. Boston Mcpl. Rsch. Bur., 1981-95, Boston Am. Heart Assn., 1983-86, NOAA, Washington, 1987-92; mem. Marine Fisheries Adv. Com., 1991-93, Artery Bus. Com., 1993-95. Recipient commendation for efforts to conserve whales U.S. Ho. of Reps., 1971, Ann. Sci. award for Conservation, Am. Cetacean Soc., 1969. Fellow Am. Assn. Zool. Parks and Aquariums (bd. dirs. 1985-95); mem. AAAS, Soc. Marine Mammalogy, Am. Assn. Mus., Sea Life Assn. (trustee 1986-92), Explorers Club (chmn. New Eng. sect. 1981-85). Office: New Eng Aquarium Corp Central Wharf Boston MA 02110-3399

PRESCOTT, JOHN MACK, biochemist, retired university administrator; b. San Marcos, Tex., Jan. 22, 1921; s. John Mack and Maude (Raborn) P.; m. Kathryn Ann Kelly, June 8, 1946; children: Stephen Michael, Donald Wyatt. B.S. in Chemistry, S.W. Tex. State Coll., 1941; M.S. in Biochemistry and Nutrition, Tex. A&M U., 1949; Ph.D. in Biochemistry, U. Wis., 1952. Lab. asst. Dow Chem. Co., Freeport, Tex., 1942-43; faculty Tex. A&M U., College Station, 1946-49, 52-85, prof. biochemistry, 1959-85, dean Coll. Sci., 1970-77, v.p. for acad. affairs, 1977-81, dir. Inst. Occupational and Environ. Medicine, 1981-87, prof. med. biochemistry, 1981-85, prof. emeritus, 1985—, spl. asst. to dep. chancellor for biotech. devel., 1987-88; research asst. U. Wis.-Madison, 1949-51, U. Tex., Austin, 1951-52; vis. prof. Harvard Med. Sch., 1982. Contbr. articles profl. jours. Mem. Tex. Bd. Examiners in Basic Scis., 1974-79, mem. Tex. State Bd. Edn., 1978-85. Served to lt. USAAF, 1943-46; lt. col. USAF Res., 1946-68. Mem. Am. Soc. for Biochemistry and Molecular Biology, Soc. for Exptl. Biology and Medicine, Sigma Xi, Phi Lambda Upsilon. Home: 31 Forest Dr College Station TX 77840-2312

PRESCOTT, PETER SHERWIN, writer; b. N.Y.C., July 15, 1935; s. Orville and Lilias (Ward-Smith) P.; m. Anne Courthope Kirsopp Lake, June 22, 1957; children: David Sherwin, Antonia Courthope. A.B. magna cum laude, Harvard, 1957. Editor E.P. Dutton Co., N.Y.C., 1958-67; lit. editor, syndicated columnist Women's Wear Daily, N.Y.C., 1964-68; mem. faculty Pubs. Sch. for Writers, N.Y.C., 1965-66; lit. editor, columnist Look mag., 1968-71; book critic Newsweek mag., N.Y.C., 1971-91; sr. writer Newsweek mag., 1978-91; lectr. U.S. State Dept., 1978; adj. prof. Grad. Sch. Journalism, Columbia U., 1979-86. Author: A World of Our Own: Notes on Life and Learning in a Boys' Preparatory School, 1970, Soundings: Encounters with Contemporary Books, 1972, A Darkening Green: Notes from the Silent Generation, 1974, The Child Savers: Juvenile Justice Observed, 1981, Never in Doubt: Critical Essays on American Books, 1972-85, 1986, The Norton Book of American Short Stories, 1988. Mem. Democratic Town Com., New Canaan, 1969-72; constable Town of New Canaan, 1969-73; dir. Authors Guild Found., pres., 1971-93; exec. bd. Authors League Fund, 1st v.p., 1994—. Served with USAR, 1958-64. Recipient George Polk award criticism, 1978, 1st prize Robert F. Kennedy Books Awards, 1981; Guggenheim fellow, 1977, NEH fellow, 1993. Mem. PEN Am. Center (exec. bd. 1974-76), Authors League Am. (exec. bd. 1974-76), Assn. Literary Scholars and Critics, Authors Guild (exec. bd. 1971-91), Nat. Book Critics Circle (exec. bd. 1973-75, 92-93), Century Assn., Harvard Club (N.Y.C.), Phi Beta Kappa. Home and Office: 81 Benedict Hill Rd New Canaan CT 06840-2904

PRESCOTT, RICHARD PAUL, JR., computer company consultant; b. Bloomington, Ill., Apr. 20, 1939; s. Richard Paul Sr. and Kathern Grace (Rhodus) P.; m. Winifred Luce Rockefeller, June 15, 1962 (dec. 1966); children: Paul Luce and Peter Grace (dec.). Bus., Ill. Wesleyan U., 1960; MBA, U. Chgo., 1963; PhD, London Sch. Econ., 1966; lic. real estate sales, Ill. State U., 1992. Systems analyst Honeywell EDP, Chgo., 1963-67; info. specialist IBM, White Plains, N.Y., 1967-68; sr. project dir. United Artists, N.Y.C., 1969-70; info. mgr. Blue Cross Assn., Chgo., 1971-72; software cons. Bloomington, Ill., 1973-92; Referral Co. of McLean County, 1992; founding mem., owner Software Info. Svc. Bd., 1993; cons. Gen. Acct. Office, Washington, Sec. of State, Washington, Econ. Devel. Peru, Lima, 1990—. Author: SSA and Blue Cross Instruction Manual, 1970, (software) Easy Tran-sort, 1971, Operating System, 1974. Mem. Rep. Nat. Com., Pres.'s Conf. Econ. Advisor, 1990—. Lt. comdr. USN, 1963—. Decorated Navy Cross, Silver Star, Purple Heart. Mem. DAV, Chgo. Econ. Coun., Am. Legion, Smithsonian Instn., Chgo. Art Inst., Bloomington Symphony, Theta Chi (chpt. pres.). Methodist. Avocations: sailing, collecting U.S. stamps, reading, computers. Home and Office: 1128 N Colton Ave Bloomington IL 61701-1922

PRESECAN, NICHOLAS LEE, civil, environmental engineer, consultant; b. Indpls., Sept. 4, 1940; s. Nicholas Eli and Dorothy Lee (Moore) P.; m. Joan Westin, Nov. 11, 1940; children: Julie Marie, Mary Lee, Anne Westin. BSCE, Purdue U., 1963; MS in Engring., U. Calif., Berkeley, 1967. Cert. profl. engr., 31 states. Project engr. San Bernardino County (Calif.) Flood Control, 1963, Engring. Sci. Inc., Arcadia, Calif., 1968-70; office mgr. Engring. Sci. Inc., Cleve., 1970-72, v.p., chief engr., 1972-81; v.p. internat. divsn. Engring. Sci. Inc., Arcadia, 1981-84, group v.p., 1984-87; sr. v.p. Engring. Sci. Inc., Pasadena, Calif., 1987—; mem. industry adv. bd. Sch. Engring. and Tech. Calif. State U., L.A., 1986—. Contbr. articles to profl. jours. Commr. Archtl. Commn., Claremont, Calif., 1980-86; councilman Claremont City Coun., 1986-94; mayor City of Claremont, 1989-92; mem. Pasadena Tournament of Roses Assn., 1980—, L.A. 2000 Environ. Com. 1987-88. With USMC, 1963-67. Recipient Disting. Engring. Achievement award Inst. for Advancement of Engring., 1993. Fellow ASCE (mem. internat. adv. com. 1987-90); mem. NSPE, Am. Acad. Environ. Engrs., Am. Water Works Assn. (life), Water Environ. Fedn., Soc. Am. Value Engrs., Rotary. Republican. Avocations: skiing, hiking, fishing, boating, writing. Home: 727 E Alamosa Dr Claremont CA 91711-2008 Office: Parsons Engring Sci Inc 100 W Walnut St Pasadena CA 91124-0001

PRESKA, LORETTA A., federal judge; b. 1949. BA, Coll. St. Rose, 1970; JD, Fordham U., 1973; LLM, NYU, 1978. Assoc. Cahill, Gordon & Reindel, N.Y.C., 1973-82; ptnr. Herzog, Calamari & Gleason, N.Y.C., 1982-92;

fed. judge U.S. Dist. Ct. (so. dist.) N.Y., N.Y.C., 1992—. Active The Parents League. Mem. ABA, N.Y. State Bar Assn., N.Y. County Lawyers Assn., Assn. Bar City N.Y., Fed. Bar Coun., Fordham Law Alumni Assn. (v.p.). Office: US Courthouse Foley Sq New York NY 10007

PRESKA, MARGARET LOUISE ROBINSON, education educator, institute executive; b. Parma, N.Y., Jan. 23, 1938; d. Ralph Craven and Ellen Elvira (Niemi) Robinson; m. Daniel C. Preska, Jan. 24, 1959; children: Robert, William, Ellen Preska Steck. B.S. summa cum laude, SUNY, 1957; M.A., Pa. State U., 1961; Ph.D., Claremont Grad. Sch., 1969; postgrad., Manchester Coll., Oxford U., 1973. Instr. LaVerne (Calif.) Coll., 1968-75, asst. prof., asso. prof., acad. dean, 1972-75; instr. Starr King Sch. for Ministry, Berkeley, Calif., summer, 1975; v.p. acad. affairs, equal opportunity officer Mankato (Minn.) State U., 1975-79, pres., 1979-92; project dir. Kaliningrad (Russia) Mil. Re-Tng., 1992—; Disting. svc. prof. Minn. State U., Winona, 1993—, pres. Inst. for Effective Tchg., 1993—; bd. dirs. No. States Power Co., Norwest Corp., Mankato, Minn. Pres. Pomona Valley chpt. UN Assn., 1968-69, Unitarian Soc. Pomona Valley, 1968-69, PTA Lincoln Elem. Sch., Pomona, 1973-74, Campfire Boys and Girls, 1986-88; mem. Pomona City Charter Revision Commn., 1972; chmn. The Fielding Inst., Santa Barbara, 1983-86; bd. dirs. Elderhostel Internat., 1983-87, Minn. Agrl. Interpretive Ctr. (Farmam.), 1983-92, Am. Assn. State Colls. and Univs., Moscow on the Mississippi - Minn. Meets the Soviet Union; nat. pres. Campfire, Inc., 1985-87; chmn. Gov.'s Coun. on Youth, Minn., 1983-86, Minn. Edn. Forum, 1984; mem. Gov.'s Commn. on Econ. Future of Minn., 1985—, NCAA Pres. Commn., 1986-92, NCAA Cost Cutting Commn., Minn. Brainpower Compact, 1985; commr. Great Lakes Govs.' Econ. Devel. Coun., 1986, Minn Gov.'s Commn. on Forestry. Carnegie Found. grantee Am. Coun. Edn. Deans Inst.; 1974; recipient Outstanding Alumni award Pa. State, Outstanding Alumni award Claremont Grad. Sch., YWCA Leader award 1982, Exch. Club Book of Golden Deeds award, 1987; named one of top 100 alumni, SUNY, 1985, Hall of Heritage award, 1988, Wohelo Camp Fire award, 1989. Mem. AAUW (pres. Mankato 1990-92), LWV, Women's Econ. Roundtable, St. Paul/Mpls. Com. on Fgn. Rels., Am. Coun. on Edn., Am. Assn. Univ. Adminstrs., Zonta, Rotary, Benedicts Dance Club. Unitarian. Home: 476 W Broadway Winona MN 55987 Office: Minn State Univs Inst for Effective Teaching 1125 W Wabasha Winona MN 55987

PRESKILL, JOHN PHILLIP, physics educator; b. Highland Park, Ill., Jan. 19, 1953; m. Roberta M. Gross, June 22, 1975; children: Carina Lou, Micaela Marie. AB in Physics, Princeton U., 1975; AM in Physics, Harvard U., 1976, PhD in Physics, 1980. Jr. fellow Harvard Soc. Fellows, 1980-81; asst. prof. physics Harvard U., Cambridge, Mass., 1981-82, assoc. prof., 1982-83; assoc. prof. theoretical physics Calif. Inst. Tech., Pasadena, 1983-90, prof., 1990—. Recipient Presdl. Young Investigator award NSF, 1984-89; fellow NSF, 1975-78, Alfred P. Sloan Found., 1982-86. Fellow Am. Phys. Soc. Home: 2110 Canyon Rd Arcadia CA 91006-1505 Office: Calif Inst of Tech Div Physics Math & Astronomy Pasadena CA 91125

PRESLAR, LEN BROUGHTON, JR., hospital administrator; b. Concord, N.C., Aug. 13, 1947; s. Len B. and Billie M. (James) P.; m. Joyce W. Whittington, July 11, 1971; children: Bradley E., Whitney A., Andrew C. BA, Wake Forest U., 1971; MBA, U. N.C., Greensboro, 1980. Admissions clk. N.C. Bapt. Hosp., Winston-Salem, 1969-71, systems analyst, 1971-72, budget mgr., 1973, contr., 1973-75, v.p. fin. mgmt., 1975-88, pres., chief exec. officer, 1988—; bd. dirs. Planters Nat. Bank, Winston-Salem, Amos Cottage, Inc. Co-chmn. cabinet United Way, Winston-Salem, 1989—; bd. dirs. N.C. chpt. ARC, 1989—; deacon local Bapt. ch. Fellow Hosp. Fin. Mgmt. Assn. Republican. Baptist. Avocations: gardening, racketball. Office: NC Bapt Hosp Medical Center Blvd Winston Salem NC 27157

PRESLEY, BRIAN, entrepreneur; b. Evansville, Ind., Dec. 28, 1941; s. Harry and Ruth P.; B.S. in Bus. Adminstrn., U. Evansville, 1963; M.B.A. Mich. State U., 1964; diploma Wahton Sch., U Pa., 1995, m. Mary Nell Minyard, Aug. 17, 1972; children—Debra, Cynthia, David, Jeffrey, Clark, Gregory, Steven. Market research analyst Stanley Works, New Britain, Conn., 1964-68; tax shelter coordinator F.I. Dupont, Memphis, 1973; v.p. Bullington Schas, Memphis, 1973-75; pres., mng. gen. ptnr. Presley Assocs., Memphis, 1965-93; pres., chief fin. officer CSG, Inc., Memphis, 1975—; gen. ptnr. various real estate and oil and gas partnerships, 1974-1986; pres. Cooper St. Group Securities, Inc., 1983-86; div. mgr. Advantage Capital Corp. (divsn. Travelers, Inc.), 1986-89, reg. v.p., 1989, CEO 1990-94, mng. dir., mkt. strategist, 1995—; instr. fin. div. continuing edn. Memphis State U. Bd. dirs. Apt. Council Tenn., 1980-86, sec.-treas., 1982-83; pres. Memphis Apt. Council, 1983; mem., U. Evansville Nat. Alumni Bd., 1988-91. Producer 2 daily radio stock market commentary shows, 1988. fin. commentator Sta. WEVU-TV (ABC), Ft. Myers/Naples, 1988-89. Mem. Internat. Assn. Fin. Planners (mem. broker dealer adv. coun., 1993—), Admirals Club (life), Naples Sailing and Yacht Club, Pi Sigma Epsilon, Beta Gamma Sigma, Tau Kappa Epsilon Alumni Assn. (pres. Memphis area 1979-80). Presbyterian. Host syndicated radio show for sr. citizens, 1979-81. Home: 425 17th Ave S Naples FL 33940-7404 Office: 2800 Post Oak Blvd Houston TX 77056-6106

PRESLEY, PRISCILLA, actress; b. Bklyn., May 24, 1945; m. Elvis Presley, 1967 (div. 1973). Studies with Milton Katselas; student, Steven Peck Theatre Art Sch., Chuck Norris Karate Sch. Prin. Bis and Beau; Co-executor Graceland, Memphis. Appearances include (films) The Naked Gun, 1988, The Adventures of Ford Fairlane, 1990, The Naked Gun 2 1/2, 1991, The Naked Gun 33 1/3, 1994, (TV series) Those Amazing Animals, 1980-81, Dallas, 1983-88, (TV movie) Love Is Forever, 1983; prodr. (TV movie) Elvis and Me, 1988. Office: Graceland PO Box 16508 Memphis TN 38186-0508*

PRESLEY, ROBERT BUEL, state senator; b. Tahlequah, Okla., Dec. 4, 1924; s. Doyle and Annie (Townsend) P.; grad. FBI Nat. Acad., Washington, 1962; student Riverside City Coll., 1960; A.A., UCLA, m. Ahni Ratliff, Aug. 20, 1944; children—Donna Thurber, Marilyn Raphael, Robert Buel. Various positions Riverside County Sheriff's Dept. (Calif.), 1950-62, undersheriff, 1962-74; mem. Calif. Senate, 36th Dist., 1974—; lectr. ethics. Served with U.S. Army, 1943-46. Decorated Bronze Star. Mem. FBI Nat. Acad. Assn. (pres. Calif. chpt. 1974). Baptist. Clubs: Lions, Elks, Am. Legion, V.F.W., Moose, Riverside County Democratic Century (pres. 1972-73). Home: 5508 Grassy Trail Dr Riverside CA 92504-1251 Office: Office of State Senate 5114 State Capital Sacramento CA 95814

PRESS, AIDA KABATZNICK, writer; b. Boston, Nov. 18, 1926; m. Newton Press, June 5, 1947; children: David, Dina Press Weber, Benjamin Presskreischer. BA, Radcliffe Coll., 1948. Reporter Waltham (Mass.) News-Tribune, 1960-63; freelance writer, 1960-63; editorial com. Mass. Dept. Mental Health, Boston, 1966-72; Waltham/Watertown reporter Boston Herald Traveler, 1963-70; dir. news and publs. Harvard Grad. Sch. Design, Cambridge, Mass., 1972-78; publs. editor Radcliffe Coll., Cambridge, 1978-81, dir., editor of publs., 1981-93, editor Radcliffe Quar., 1971-93, dir. pub. info., 1983-93; cons. editor Regis Coll. Alumnae Mag., Weston, Mass., 1994. Editor emerita Radcliffe Quar., 1993—; contbr. articles to newspapers and mags. Recipient Publs. Distinction award Am. Alumni Coun., 1974, Top 5 coll. Mag., Coun. for Advancement and Support of Edn., 1984, Top 10 Univ Mags., 1991, Gold medal Coll. Mags., 1991, Alumnae Achievement award Radcliffe Coll., 1997. Avocations: hiking, playing recorder.

PRESS, CHARLES, retired political science educator; b. St. Louis, Sept. 12, 1922; s. Otto Ernst and Laura (Irion) P.; m. Nancy Miller, June 10, 1950; children: Edward Paul, William David, Thomas Leigh, Laura Mary. Student, Elmhurst (Ill.) Coll.; B of Journalism, U. Mo., 1948; M.A., U. Minn., 1951, Ph.D., 1953. Faculty N.D. Agrl. Coll., 1954-56; dir. Grand Rapids Area Study, 1956-57; with Bur. Govt., U. Wis., 1957-58; faculty Mich. State U., East Lansing, 1958-91; prof. polit. sci. Mich State U., 1964-91; emeritus, 1991—; chmn. dept. Mich. State U., 1966-73; cons. Mich. Constl. Conv., 1962-63; supr. Ingham County, 1966-72; tchr. scamners, London: tchr. U. N.S.W., Sydney, Mich. State U. Author: Main Street Politics, 1962, (with Charles Adrian) The American Government Process, 1965, Governing Urban America, 1968, 5th edit., 1977, American Politics Reappraised, 1974, (with Kenneth VerBurg) States and Community Governments in a Federal System, 1979, 3d edit., 1991, American Policy Studies, 1981, The Political Cartoon, 1982, (with others) Michigan Political

Atlas 1984, (with Kenneth VerBurg) American Politicians and Journalists, 1988, (with Kenneth VerBurg) (weekly newspaper column) The Pros and Cons of Politics. Sec. Ingham County Bd. Health, 1983-93; chmn., mem. East Lansing Bd. Rev., 1966-86; bd. dirs. Urban League, 1971-73; mem. East Lansing Housing and Urban Devel. Commn., 1988-93. Served with AUS, 1943-45. Recipient Disting. Prof. award Mich. State U., 1980. Mem. Am. Polit. Sci. Assn., Midwest Polit. Sci. Assn. (pres. 1974-75), So. Polit. Sci. Assn., Mich. Conf. Polit. Scientists (pres. 1972-73), Nat. Municipal League. Home: 987 Lantern Hill Dr East Lansing MI 48823-2831 Office: Mich State U 315 S Kedzie Hall East Lansing MI 48824-1032

PRESS, EDWARD, consulting physician; b. N.Y.C., May 4, 1913; s. Louis and Anna (Karpas) P.; m. Ruth Scheffer, July 8, 1951; children: Stephen, Phyllis. B.A., Ohio U., 1934; M.D., NYU, 1937; M.P.H., Harvard U., 1947. Diplomate: Am. Bd. Pediatrics, Am. Bd. Preventive Medicine. Intern Beth Israel Hosp., N.Y.C., 1938-40; resident Lincoln Hosp., Bronx, N.Y., 1940; psychiatric resident E.P. Bradley Home, East Providence, R.I., 1940-41; asst. dir. maternal and child health div. W.Va. Health Dept., 1941-42; pediatric cons. Mich. Health Dept., 1946; regional med. dir. U.S. Children's Bur., Chgo., 1947-50; asso. dir. div. services crippled children U. Ill., 1950-55; field dir. Am. Public Health Assn., N.Y.C., 1955-59; dir. Dept. Public Health, Evanston, Ill., 1959-64; med. asst. to dir. Ill. Dept. Public Health, 1964-67; state health officer (Oreg. Health Div.), Portland, 1967-79; public health cons., 1979—; emeritus sec.-treas. Press Internat. Sales Corp., 1978—; asst. prof. preventive medicine U. Ill., 1950-55; asst. prof. pediatrics Northwestern U., 1964-67; clin. prof. pub. health, preventive medicine and pediatrics Med. Sch., Oreg. Health Scis. U., 1967-79, emeritus clin. prof., 1979—; vice chmn. Tech. Adv. Group for Fire Safe Cigarette Act of 1990-93. Mem. editorial adv. com. The Nation's Health, 1989-91; contbr. articles to profl. jours. Organizer Poison Control Ctr., Chgo., 1953; trustee Underwriters' Labs., Inc., 1969-79. Served to maj. USAAF, 1942-46. Recipient Clifford G. Grulee award Am. Acad. Pediatrics, 1961; recognition award Am. Assn. Poison Control Centers, 1975. Mem. AMA, Am. Pub. Health Assn. (founder and pres. Conf. Emeritus Mems. 1986-89, Excellence in Health Admintrn. award 1992), Nat. Soc. Prevention of Blindness, Am. Assn. Public Health Physicians (pres. 1971-72, Bronze medal 1979), Conf. State and Provincial Health Authorities N.Am. (pres. 1971-72), Assn. State and Territorial Health Officers (mem. exec. com. 1972-75, Arthur G. McCormack award 1978), Am. Assn. Sr. Physicians (pres. 1984-86), Oreg. Pub. Health Assn. (Leadership award 1986), Oreg. Med. Assn. (presdl. citation 1980), Portland City Club, Multnomah Athletic Club, Rotary. Home: 2211 SW 1st Ave Apt 905 Portland OR 97201-5013

PRESS, FRANK, geophysicist, educator; b. Bklyn., Dec. 4, 1924; s. Solomon and Dora (Steinholz) P.; m. Billie Kallick, June 9, 1946; children: William Henry, Paula Evelyn. BS, CCNY, 1944, LLD (hon.), 1972; MA, Columbia U., 1946, PhD, 1949; DSc (hon.), 28 univs. Rsch. assoc. Columbia U., 1946-49, instr. geology, 1949-51, asst. prof. geology, 1951-52, assoc. prof., 1952-55; prof. geophysics Calif. Inst. Tech., 1955-65, dir. seismol. lab., 1957-65; prof. geophysics, chmn. dept. earth and planetary scis. MIT, 1965-77; sci. advisor to pres., dir. Office Sci. and Tech. Policy, Washington, 1977-80; instr. prof. MIT, 1981; pres. Nat. Acad. Scis., 1981-93; Cecil & Ida Green sr. fellow Carnegie Inst. of Washington, Washington, DC, 1993—; mem. Pres.'s Sci. Adv. Com., 1961-64; mem. Com. on Anticipated Advances in Sci. and Tech., 1974-76; mem. Nat. Sci. Bd., 1970-76; mem. lunar and planetary missions bd. NASA; participant bilateral scis. agreement with Peoples Republic of China and USSR; mem. U.S. delegation to Nuclear Test Ban Negotiations, Geneva and Moscow. Author: (with M. Ewing, W.S. Jardetzky) Propagation of Elastic Waves in Layered Media, 1957, (with R. Siever) Earth, 1986, Understanding Earth, 1994; also over 160 publs.; co-editor: (with R. Siever) Physics and Chemistry of the Earth, 1957—. Decorated Cross of Merit (Germany), Legion of Honor (France); recipient Columbia medal for excellence, 1960, Pub. Svc. award U.S. Dept. Interior, 1972, Gold medal Royal Astron. Soc., 1972, Pub. Svc. medal NASA, 1973, Japan prize sci. and Tech. Found. Japan, 1993, Pupin medal Columbia U., 1993, Nat. Medal Sci. Pres. of U.S., 1994; named Sherman Fairchild Disting. scholar Calif. Inst. Tech., 1994. Mem. Am. Acad. Arts and Scis., Geol. Soc. Am. (councilor), Am. Geophys. Union (pres. 1973), Soc. Exploration Geophysicists, Seismol. Soc. Am. (pres. 1963), AAUP, NAS, NSF (Vannevar Bush Award, 1994), Am. Philos. Soc., French Acad. Scis., Royal Soc. (U.K.), Nat. Acad. Pub. Adminstrn., Acad. Scis. of USSR (fgn. mem.). Office: Carnegie Inst Washington 5241 Broad Branch Rd Washington DC 20015

PRESS, JEFFERY BRUCE, chemist; b. Rochester, N.Y., May 24, 1947; s. James Herbert and Mildred (Hau) P.; m. Linda Helen Seghers, Dec. 20, 1976; children: Samantha, Michael. BS, Bucknell U., 1969; PhD, Ohio State U., 1973; postgrad., Harvard U., 1973-75. Rsch. chemist Lederle Labs., Pearl River, N.Y., 1975-77, sr. rsch. chemist, 1977-81, group leader, 1981-83; rsch. mgr. Ortho Pharm. Corp., Raritan, N.J., 1983-89; asst. dir. R.W. Johnson Pharm. Rsch. Inst., Spring House, Pa., 1990-94; v.p. dir. rsch. Emisphere Tech. Inc., Hawthorne, N.Y., 1994—. Editor: Organic Reactions, 1983—, Chemtracts Organic 1988—; Current Opinion Therapeutic Patents, 1989—, Analgesia, 1993—; patentee in field; contbr. numerous articles to profl. jours. NIH fellow, 1974. Mem. AAAS, Am. Chem. Soc., N.Y. Acad. Scis., Internat. Soc. Heterocyclic Chemistry, Internat. Pure and Applied Chemistry, Drug Info. Assn., Mid-Atlantic Pharmacology Soc., Drug Info. Assn., Sedgewood Club, Tuxedo Club, Phi Beta Kappa, Sigma Xi, Alpha Chi Sigma. Episcopalian. Avocations: golf, building golf clubs, model railroads. Office: Emisphere Tech Inc Hawthorne NY 10532

PRESS, MICHELLE, editor; b. Memphis, Nov. 22, 1940; d. Sam and Rana (Cohen) Appelbaum; m. Robert Press, June 18, 1960 (div. 1965). B.A., New Sch. for Social Research, 1967. Tchr. U.S. Peace Corps, Malawi, Africa, 1962-64; copy editor Japan Quar., Tokyo, 1967-71; asst. editor Am. Scientist, New Haven, 1971-78, mng. editor, 1978-81, editor, 1981—. Office: Am Scientist PO Box 13975 Durham NC 27709-3975

PRESS, WILLIAM HENRY, astrophysicist, computer scientist; b. N.Y.C., N.Y., May 23, 1948; s. Frank and Billie (Kallick) P.; m. Margaret Ann Lauritsen, 1969 (div. 1982); 1 dau., Sara Linda; m. Jeffrey Foden Howell, Apr. 19, 1991; 1 son, James Howell. A.B., Harvard Coll., 1969; M.S., Calif. Inst. Tech., 1971, Ph.D., 1972. Asst. prof. theoretical physics Calif. Inst. Tech., 1973-74; assoc. prof. physics Princeton (N.J.) U., 1974-76; prof. astronomy and physics Harvard U., Cambridge, Mass., 1976—; chmn. dept. astronomy Harvard U., 1982-85; mem. numerous adv. coms. and panels NSF, NASA, NAS, NRC; vis. mem. Inst. Advanced Study, 1983—; mem. Def. Sci. Bd., 1985-89, sci. adv. com. Packard Found., 1988—; program com. Sloan Found., 1985-91; chmn. adv. bd. NSF Inst. Theoretical Physics, 1986-87; cons. MITRE Corp., 1977—; trustee Inst. Def. Analysis, 1988—; chief naval ops. Exec. Panel, 1994—. Author: Numerical Recipes, 1986; contbr. articles to profl. jours. Sloan Found. research fellow, 1974-78. Fellow Am. Acad. Arts and Scis., Am. Phys. Soc.; mem. NAS, Am. Astron. Soc. (Helen B. Warner prize 1981), Internat. Astron. Union, Internat. Soc. Relativity and Gravitation, Assn. for Computing Machinery. Office: Harvard U 60 Garden St Cambridge MA 02138-1596

PRESSER, HARRIET BETTY, sociology educator; b. Bklyn., Aug. 29, 1936; d. Phillip Rubinoff and Rose (Gudowitz) Jabish; m. Neil Nathan Presser, Dec. 16, 1956 (div.); 1 child, Sheryl Lynn. BA, George Washington U., 1959; MA, U. N.C., 1962; PhD, U. Calif., Berkeley, 1969. Statistician Bur. Census, Washington, 1959; research assoc. Inst. Life Ins., N.Y.C., 1962-64; lectr. demography U. Sussex, Brighton, England, 1967-68; staff assoc. Population Council, N.Y.C., 1968-69; asst. prof. sociomed. scis. Columbia U., N.Y.C., 1969-73, assoc. prof. sociomed. scis., 1973-76; prof. sociology U. Md., College Park, 1976—; dir. Ctr. on Population, Gender, and Social Inequality, 1988—; disting. faculty rsch. fellow, 1993-94; fellow in residence Netherlands Inst. for Advanced Study in Humanities & Social Sci., Wassenaar, The Netherlands, 1994-95; fellow Ctr. for Advanced Study in Behavioral Scis., Stanford, Calif., 1986-87, 91-92; bd. dirs. Population Reference Bur., 1993—; cons. Nat. Inst. for Child Health and Human Devel., 1975—. Editorial bd. Time and Soc., 1991—, Social Forces, 1984-87, Signs, 1975-85; assoc. editor Jour. Health and Social Behavior, 1975-78. Nat. Inst. for Child Health and Devel. grantee, 1972-78, 83-88, Population Coun. grantee, 1976-79, NSF grantee, 1983-85, 90-94, Rockefeller Found. grantee, 1983-85, 88-94, William and Flora Hewlett Found. grantee, 1989—, Andrew

W. Mellon Found. grantee, 1994—; named Disting. Alumni scholar George Washington U., 1992-93. Mem. Population Assn. Am. (bd. dirs. 1972-75, 2nd v.p. 1983, 1st v.p. 1985, pres.-elect 1988, pres. 1989), Am. Pub. Health Assn. (council mem. population sect. 1976-79), Am. Sociological Assn. (coun. mem. at large 1990-93, chmn., coun. mem. population sect. 1978-83), Sociological Research Assn. (elected). Office: U Md Dept Sociology College Park MD 20742

PRESSER, STANLEY, sociologist; b. Bklyn., Feb. 18, 1950; s. Sidney and Sydonia (Cohen) P. A.B., Brown U., 1971; Ph.D., U. Mich. 1977. Research investigator Survey Research Ctr. U. Mich., Ann Arbor, 1977-78, head of field office, 1981-83; research assoc. Inst. Research Social Sci.; U. N.C., 1978-81; dir. Detroit Area Study U. Mich., 1983-85; assoc. dir. sociology program NSF, 1985-87, dir., 1987-88; vis. prof. sociology U. Md., College Park, 1988-89, prof. of sociology, dir. Survey Rsch. Ctr., 1989—, dir.joint U Md. and U. Mich. program in Survey Methodology, 1992—; bd. overseers Nat. Opinion Rsch. Ctr. Gen. Social Survey, 1984-85, 93—; spl. cons. Nat. Econ. Research Assocs., 1986-89. Co-author: Questions and Answers in Attitude Surveys, 1981, Survey Questions: Handcrafting the Standardized Questionnaire, 1986; editor Pub. Opinion Quar., 1993—; co-editor: Sourcebook of Harris National Surveys, 1981, Survey Rsch. Methods, 1989. Mem. editorial bd. Pub. Opinion Quar., 1983-87 ; Sociol. Methods and Research, 1980-83, Social Psychology Quar., 1979-82. Contbr. articles to profl. jours. and books. Fellow Am. Assn. for Pub. Opinion Rsch. (pres. 1993-94), Am. Statis. Assn. Office: U of Md Survey Rsch Ctr 1103 Art-Sociology Bldg College Park MD 20742

PRESSER, STEPHEN BRUCE, lawyer, educator; b. Chattanooga, Aug. 10, 1946; s. Sidney and Estelle (Shapiro) P.; m. Carole Smith, June 18, 1968 (div. 1987); children: David Carter, Elisabeth Catherine; m. Arynn Leiber, Dec. 13, 1987; children: Joseph Leiber, Eastman Leiber. A.B., Harvard U., 1968, J.D., 1971. Bar: Mass. 1971, D.C. 1972. Law clk. to Judge Malcolm Richard Wilkey U.S. Ct. Appeals (D.C. cir.), 1971-72; assoc. Wilmer, Cutler & Pickering, Washington, 1972-74; asst. prof. law Rutgers U., Camden, N.J., 1974-76; vis. assoc. prof. U. Va., 1976-77; prof. Northwestern U., Chgo., 1977—, class 1940 rsch. prof., 1992-93, Raoul Berger prof. legal history, 1992—, assoc. dean acad. affairs Sch. Law, 1982-85. Author: (with Jamil S. Zainaldin) Law and Jurisprudence in American History, 1980, 3d edit., 1995, Studies in the History of the United States Courts of the Third Circuit, 1983, The Original Misunderstanding: The English, The Americans and the Dialetic of Federalist Jurisprudence, 1991, Piercing the Corporate Veil, 1991, (with Ralph Ferrara and Meredith Brown) Takeovers: A Strategist's Manual, 2d edit., 1993, Recapturing the Constitution, 1994; assoc. articles editor Guide to American Law, 1985. Mem. acad. adv. bd. Washington Legal Found. Recipient summer stipend NEH, 1975; Fulbright Sr. scholar Univ. Coll., London Sch. Econs. and Polit. Sci., 1983-84. Mem. Am. Soc. Legal History (bd. dirs. 1979-82), Am. Law Inst., Univ. Club Chgo., Legal Club Chgo. Home: 1015 Cherry St Winnetka IL 60093-2112 Office: Northwestern U Law Sch 357 E Chicago Ave Chicago IL 60611-3008

PRESSLER, LARRY, senator; b. Humboldt, S.D., Mar. 29, 1942; s. Antone Lewis and Loretta Geneive (Claussen) P.; m. Harriet Dent, 1982. B.A., U. S.D., 1964; diploma (Rhodes scholar), Oxford U., Eng., 1965; M.A., Kennedy Sch. Govt., Harvard U., 1971; J.D., Harvard U., 1971. Mem. 94th-95th Congresses from 1st S.D. Dist.; mem. U.S. Senate from S.D., 1979—; U.S. del. Inter-Parliamentary Union for 97th Congress; mem. bd. visitors all mil. svc. academies; now chmn. Commerce Com. U.S. Senate; mem. commerce, sci. and transp. com., spl. com. on aging, small bus.; chmn. Fin. Subcom. on Long-Term Growth, Debt and Deficit Reduction; mem. Senate Rep. Policy Com.; congl. del. to UN Gen. Assembly, 1986, 92; mem. U.S. Commn. on Improving the Effectiveness of UN, 1993. Author: U.S. Senators from the Prairie, 1982, Star Wars: The SDI Debates in Congress, 1986. All-Am. del. 4-H agrl. fair, Cairo, 1961, U.S. Rep. (appointed by Vice Pres.) to UN Fall Gen. Assembly, 1986. Served to 1st lt. AUS, 1966-68, Vietnam. Recipient Nat. 4-H Citizenship award, 1962, Report to the Pres. 4-H award, 1962. Mem. Am. Assn. Rhodes Scholars, VFW, ABA Phi Beta Kappa. Office: US Senate 283 Russell Senate Bldg Washington DC 20510*

PRESSLEY, FRED G., JR., lawyer; b. N.Y.C., June 19, 1953; s. Fred G. Sr. and Frances (Sanders) P.; m. Cynthia Denise Hill, Sept. 5, 1981. BA cum laude, Union Coll., 1975; JD, Northwestern U., 1978. Bar: Ohio 1978, U.S. Dist. Ct. (so. dist.) Ohio 1979, U.S. Dist. Ct. (no. dist.) Ohio 1985, U.S. Dist. Ct. (ea. dist.) Wis. 1980, U.S. Ct. Appeals (6th cir.). Assoc. Porter, Wright, Morris & Arthur, Columbus, Ohio, 1978-85, ptnr., 1985—. Bd. dirs. Columbus Area Leadership Program, 1981-84, Franklin County Bd. Mental Retardation and Devel. Disabilities, Columbus, 1989—, Union Coll., Schenectady, N.Y., 1992—. Recipient Civic Achievement award Ohio Ho. of Reps., 1988. Mem. ABA. Avocations: jogging, golf, basketball, military history. Office: Porter Wright Morris & Arthur 41 S High St Columbus OH 43215-6101

PRESSLY, BARBARA, state legislator; b. Chgo., May 13, 1937; d. C. David and Esther (Rustad) Brown; m. George Byrne Pressly, 1960; children: Patricia, George Jr., Robert. BS, U. Ill., 1960. Former mem. N.H. Ho. of Reps., Hillsborough County Exec. Com.; alderman-at-large Nashua, N.H.; mem. N.H. State Senate. Mem. Nashua Hist. Dist. Commn.; mem. adv. bd. Nashua Salvation Army; deaconess First Congl. Ch., Nashua, 1980-83. Mem. Kings Daus. Benevolent Soc. Democrat. Address: 80 Concord St Nashua NH 03060-1961

PRESSLY, THOMAS JAMES, history educator; b. Troy, Tenn., Jan. 18, 1919; s. James Wallace and Martha Belle (Bittick) P.; m. Lillian Cameron, Apr. 30, 1943; children—Thomas James II, Stephanie (Mrs. Kaoruhiko Suzuki). AB, Harvard U., 1940, AM, 1941, PhD, 1950; LLD (hon.), Whitman Coll., 1981. Instr. history Princeton U., 1946-49; asst. prof. U. Wash., 1949-54, assoc. prof., 1954-60, prof., 1960-87, prof. emeritus, 1987—; vis. assoc. prof. Princeton U., 1953-54, Johns Hopkins U., 1969-70. Author: Americans Interpret Their Civil War, 1954; editor: (with W. H. Scofield) Farm Real Estate Values in the United States, 1965, (with others) American Political Behavior, 1974, Diary of George Templeton Strong (abridged), 1988, (with Glenn M. Linden) Voices From the House Divided, 1995. Served with AUS, 1941-45. Ford Found. Faculty fellow, 1951-52; Center for Advanced Study in Behavioral Scis. fellow, 1955-56. Mem. Am. Hist. Assn., So. Hist. Assn. (editorial bd. Jour. So. History 1973-77), Orgn. Am. Historians. Home: 4545 E Laurel Dr NE Seattle WA 98105-3838 Office: U Wash Dept History Seattle WA 98195

PRESSMAN, EDWARD R., motion picture producer; b. N.Y.C. Grad., Stanford U.; student, London Sch. Econs. Co-founder Pressman-Williams Enterprises. Producer Out of It, 1969, The Revolutionary, 1970, Dealing: or the Berkeley to Boston Forty Brick Lost Bag Blues, 1972, Sisters, 1973, Plenty, 1985, Good Morning Babylon, 1986, Wall Street, 1987, Cherry 2000, 1988, Talk Radio, 1988, Blue Steel, 1989, Reversal of Fortune, 1990; exec. producer Badlands, 1973, Paradise Alley, 1978, Heartbeat, 1979, Half Moon Street, 1986, True Stories, 1986, Masters of the Universe, 1987, Walker, 1987, Paris By Night, 1988, Martians Go Home, 1990, To Sleep With Anger, 1990, Waiting for the Light, 1990; dir., producer Despair, 1978, The Hand, 1981, Das Boot, 1981, Conan the Barbarian, 1982, The Pirates of Penzance, 1982, Crimewave, 1985. Office: Edward R Pressman Film Corp 445 N Bedford Dr Penthouse Beverly Hills CA 90210

PRESSMAN, MICHAEL, film director; b. N.Y.C., July 1, 1950. Ed., Calif. Inst. Arts. Dir.: (films) The Great Texas Dynamite Chase, 1976, The Bad News Bears in Breaking Training, 1977, Boulevard Nights, 1979, Those Lips, Those Eyes, 1980, Some Kind of Hero, 1982, Doctor Detroit, 1983, Teenage Mutant Nija Turtles II: The Secret of the Oozie, 1991, (TV films) Like Mom, Like Me, 1978, The Imposter, 1984, And the Children Shall Lead, 1985, Private Sessions, 1985, Final Jeopardy, 1985, The Christmas Gift, 1986, Haunted By Her Past, 1987, Tp Heal A Nation, 1988, Shootdown, 1988. Incident at Dark River, 1989, Man Against The Mob: The Chinatown Murders, 1989, Joshua's Heart, 1990, Quicksand: No Escape, 1992, Miracle Child, 1993; co-exec. prod.: (TV series) Picket Fences, 1992— (Emmy award Outstanding Drama Series, 1993). Mem. Dirs. Guild Am. Office: William Morris Agency 151 El Camino Beverly Hills CA 90212*

PRESSMAN, THANE ANDREW, consumer products executive; b. San Diego, June 6, 1945; s. Harold Andrew and Audre Ethelyn (Negus) P.; m. Caroline Hannah Hood Snyder, Nov. 23, 1966; children: Sean, Steven. BS, Springfield (Mass.) Coll., 1967; MS, Syracuse U., 1969. Various to brand mgr. Procter & Gamble Co., Cin., 1968-76, assoc. mgr. advt., 1976-79; v.p. Lamalie Assocs., Inc. Chgo., 1979-81; dir. new products Alberto Culver Co., Melrose Park, Ill., 1981-84; group staff, v.p. Sara Lee Corp., Northbrook, Ill., 1984-85; pres., COO Kitchens of Sara Lee Can., Bramalee, Ont., 1986-88; exec. v.p. Sara Lee Bakery Co., Bramalee and Deerfield, Ill., 1988-90; pres., CEO Crestar Food Products, Inc. (affiliate of H.J. Heinz Co.), Eugene, Oreg., 1991-92, Crestar Food Products Inc. & Crestar Food Products Can. Ltd., Nashville and Mississauga, Ont., Can., 1992-93; pres. Labatt Ont. Breweries, Etobicoke, 1994—; guest lectr. U. Mich. Grad. Sch. Bus., Ann Arbor, 1977-79; bd. dirs. Brewers Retail Inc., Toronto; bd. dirs. Brewers of Ont., 1994—, chmn., 1995. Bd. dirs. Am. Field Svc. U.S.A., N.Y.C., 1986-91, trustee AFS intercultural programs, N.Y.C., 1988-93; trustee Springfield Coll., 1988—; campaign co-chmn. United Way Cin., Chgo., Bramalea, Deerfield, 1976-94. Mem. Assn. Governing Bds. Univs. and Colls., David Allen Reed Soc., Grocery Product Mfrs. Can., Internat. Dairy Deli Assn., Dixie Curling Club, Eugene Country Club, Richland Country Club, Mississauga Country Club.

PRESSON, ELLIS WYNN, health services executive; b. Electra, Tex., Mar. 28, 1940; s. Ellis Wilbur and Juanita M. (Morgan) P.; B.B.A., U. Tex., 1963; M.H.A., Washington U., St. Louis, 1965; m. Andrea L., July 5, 1969; children—Eric, Garett, Amber. Adminstrv. asst. Methodist Hosp. of Dallas, 1964-66; asst. adminstr. Dallas County Hosp., 1966-70; pres. Swedish Am. Hosp., Rockford, Ill., 1970-77, Research Med. Center, Kansas City, Mo., 1977-80, Research Health Services, Kansas City, 1980-91, Health Midwest, 1991—. Pres., Comprehensive Mental Health and Retardation, 1972-74; treas. bd. Rockford Med. Edn. Found., 1972-75; preceptor for adminstrn. extern U. Wis., 1975-76; search com. Rockford Sch. Medicine, U. Ill., 1975-76; regional com. mem. Hosp. Adminstrv. Surveillance Program, 1973-76; bd. dirs. Ill. Hosp. and Health Service, 1972-77, Midwest Bioethics Ctr., pres. 1988-89; mem. Health Planning NW Ill., 1973-77; licensing bd. mem. Ill. State Ambulatory Surgery Treatment Center, 1974-76. Mem. Am. Hosp. Assn. (chmn. healthcare systems bd. 1989—), Mo. Hosp. Assn. (chmn. bd., del. to Am. Hosp. Assn., mem. labor relations com., regional policy bd. 1988-90), Kansas City Area Hosp. Assn. (chmn. fin. council, dir.). Clubs: Rotary, Indian Hills Country. Home: 15613 Overbrook Rd Shawnee Mission KS 66224-9603 Office: 2304 E Meyer Blvd Kansas City MO 64132-4104

PRESTAGE, JAMES JORDAN, university chancellor; b. Deweyville, Tex., Apr. 29, 1926; s. James J. and Mona (Wilkins) P.; m. Jewel Limar, Aug. 12, 1953; children—Terri, James Grady, Eric, Karen, Jay. B.S. cum laude, So. U., Baton Rouge, 1950; M.S., U. Iowa, 1955, Ph.D., 1959. Instr. biology Prairie View Coll., Tex., 1955-56; asst. prof. So. U., Baton Rouge, 1959, assoc. prof. biology, 1959-61, prof. biology, 1961—, dir. computer sci. ctr., 1968-71, 72-73, dean acad. affairs, v.p. acad. affairs, 1973-81, exec. v.p., 1981-82, chancellor, 1982-85, univ. disting. prof., 1985—; univ. disting. prof. biology Dillard U., New Orleans, 1987—; chair divsn. natural sci. Dillard U., 1990—; asst. dir. La. Coordinating Council for Higher Edn., Baton Rouge, 1971-72; mem. commn. on scholars Ill. Bd. Higher Edn., 1975-82; mem. com. on off-campus instrn. La. Bd. Regents, 1975—; mem. La. Data Processing Council, Baton Rouge, 1979-82; vis. prof. biology Dillard U., New Orleans; trustee Am. Coll. Testing Program, 1983—. Mem. exec. bd. Istrouma council Boy Scouts Am.; vice chmn. bd. trustees Greater Mt. Carmel Baptist Ch., Baton Rouge; bd. dirs. Capital Area United Way, Baton Rouge. Served with USN, 1944-46, 50-52; ETO, Korea. Named Most Outstanding Faculty Mem., So. U., 1966-67; Nat. Med. Fellowships fellow U. Iowa, Iowa City, 1956-59; NIH grantee, 1960-65. Mem. Conf. Acad. Deans So. States. NAACP, Sigma Xi, Alpha Chi, Alpha Phi Alpha (chpt. pres.), Sigma Pi Phi. Democrat. Avocations: fishing; reading; gardening. Home: 2145 77th Ave Baton Rouge LA 70807-5508 Office: PO Box 9222 So Br PO Baton Rouge LA 70813

PRESTAGE, JEWEL LIMAR, political science educator; b. Hutton, La., Aug. 12, 1931; d. Brudis L. and Sallie Bell (Johnson) Limar; m. James J. Prestage, Aug. 12, 1953; children—Terri, James, Eric, Karen, Jay. B.A., So. U., Baton Rouge, 1951; M.A., U. Iowa, 1952, Ph.D., 1954; LHD (hon.), U. D.C., 1994. Assoc. prof. polit. sci. Prairie View (Tex.) Coll., 1954-55, 56; assoc. prof. polit. sci. So. U., 1956-57, 58-62, prof., 1962—, chairperson dept., 1965-83, dean pub. policy and urban affairs, 1983-89; Honors prof. polit. sci. Banneker Honors Coll., Prairie View U., 1989—, dean, 1990—; chmn. La. adv. com. to U.S. Commn. on Civil Rights, 1975-85; mem., chmn. nat. adv. coun. on women's edn. programs U.S. Dept. Edn., 1980-82; vis. prof. U. Iowa, 1987-88. Author: (with M. Githens) A Portrait of Marginality: Political Behavior of the American Woman, 1976; contbr. articles to profl. jours. Rockefeller fellow, 1951-52; NSF fellow, 1964; Ford Found. postdoctoral fellow, 1969-70. Mem. Am. Polit. Sci. Assn. (v.p. 1974-75), So. Polit. Sci. Assn. (pres. 1976-76), Nat. Conf. Black Polit. Scientists (pres. 1976-77), Nat. Assn. African Am. Honors Programs (pres. 1993-94), Am. Soc. for Pub. Adminstrn. (pres. La. chpt. 1988-89, mem. nat. coun. 1989-90), Links Inc., Alpha Kappa Alpha. Home: 2145 77th Ave Baton Rouge LA 70807-5508 Office: So Univ PO Box 125 Prairie View TX 77446-0125 Commitments which guide my life are: (1) maximum development of personal potential through pursuit of excellence in all endeavors; (2) fair play, respect, compassion and quest of community in relations with fellow human beings; (3) utilization of personal talents in the interest of removing impediments to the good life "for all persons"; (4) pursuit of truth as the pervasive concern in academia; and (5) transmission of the above as priority goals to all with whom I have contact.

PRESTBO, JOHN ANDREW, newspaper editor, journalist, author; b. Northwood, N.D., Sept. 26, 1941; s. Oscar Bernt and Jeanne (Schol) P.; m. Darlene Parrish, Aug. 14, 1965; children: Bradford Jonathan, Laura Christine. B.S., Northwestern U., 1963, M.S., 1964. Reporter, writer Wall Street Jour., Chgo., 1964-74; staff editor, Page 1 Wall Street Jour., N.Y.C., 1974-75, commodities editor, 1975-77; bur. chief Wall Street Jour., Cleve., 1977-81; markets editor Wall Street Jour., N.Y.C., 1984—, editor Dow Jones World Stock Index, 1993—; v.p. editorial Dow Jones Radio 2, Inc., Princeton, N.J., 1981-83. Author: Sleuthing, 1976; co-author: (with Frederick C. Klein) News and the Market, 1974, (with Douglas R. Sease) Barron's Guide to Making Investment Decisions, 1994; editor: This Abundant Land, 1975, Dow Jones Commodities Handbook, 1976-79, The Dow Jones Guide to the World Stock Market, 1994. Served with USAFR, 1966-73. Recipient Econ. Reporting award Ind. Natural Gas Assn., U. Mo., 1967; recipient Achievement-bur. writing award G.M. Loeb, 1968. Home: 14 Charleston Dr Skillman NJ 08558-1801 Office: Wall Street Jour 200 Liberty St New York NY 10281-1003

PRESTERA, LAURETTA ANNE, newspaper executive; b. Newark, Dec. 15, 1947; d. George Anthony and Carmela (Sallustro) P. BA in Communications, Bridgewater State Coll., 1976; MBA in Mgmt., Fairleigh Dickinson U., 1981. Advt. sales rep. The N.Y. Times, N.Y.C., 1980-81, circulation sales rep., 1981-82, asst. mgr. circulation, 1982-83; home delivery mgr. The N.Y. Times, Torrance, Calif., 1983-84; S.W. mgr. The N.Y. Times, Dallas, 1984-85; west coast mgr. The N.Y. Times, Torrance, 1985-87; nat. sales dir. The N.Y. Times, N.Y., 1987-92; home delivery dir. The N.Y. Times, N.Y.C., 1992-93, group dir. distbn., 1992—; treas. The N.Y. Times Distbn. Corp., N.Y. and Calif., 1984-89. Recipient Pub. award The N.Y. Time, 1984. Mem. People for Ethical Treatment of Animals, San Francisco SPCA, L.A. SPCA, Cal-Western Circulation Mgrs., Am. Newspapers Pubs. Assn. Roman Catholic. Avocations: animal rights, golf, tennis.

PRESTON, ALDA S., academic administrator, nursing educator; b. Kansas City, Kans., Aug. 25, 1949; d. Beryl LeFrance and Vivian Artneal (Wilson) P. Dabbing, Bethany Hosp. Sch. Nursing, Kansas City, 1970; BSN, Ft. Hays State U., Hays, Kans., 1972; MA in Curriculum and Instrn., U. Kans., 1981; MSN magna cum laude, U. Mo., Kansas City, 1989. RN, Kans., Mo., Wis. DON Hillcrest Manor, Hays, 1971-72; staff nurse various hosps., Met. Kansas City, Kans., 1970-72, 76-87; mem. faculty LPN program Kansas City (Mo.) Bd. Edn., 1976-77; instr. med.-surg. nursing, pediatrics nursing Penn Valley C.C., Kansas City, 1977-90, coord. LPN-ADN bridge program, 1985-89; assoc. dean health, human and protective svcs. div. Madison (Wis.) Area Tech. Coll., 1990—; instr. Cochran Sch. Nursing, Yonkers, N.Y., 1972-

76. Historian, reporter Pan Hellenic Coun. Greater Kansas City, 1987-90; treas. no. region Nat. Pan Hellenic Coun., 1988-90. Kellogg fellow League for Innovation in Community Coll., 1992. Mem. ANA, Wis. Nurses Assn., Mo. Assn. Health Occupations Educators (sec., policy com. 1984-87), Am. Assn. Women in Community Colls. (pres., chpt. charter mem.), Mo. Vocat. Assn., Kans. Nurses Assn., Sigma Theta Tau Internat., Delta Sigma Theta (life), Lambda Phi (charter Beta Eta chpt.), Links, Inc.

PRESTON, ANDREW JOSEPH, pharmacist, drug company executive; b. Bklyn., Apr. 19, 1922; s. Charles A. and Josephine (Rizzutto) Pumo; BSc, St. John U., 1943; m. Martha Jeanne Happ, Oct. 10, 1953; children: Andrew Joseph Jr., Charles Richard, Carolyn Louise, Frank Arthur, Joanne Marie, Barbara Jeanne. Cert. bus. intermediary. Mgr. Press Club, Bklyn. Nat. League Baseball Club, 1941-42; purchasing agt. Drug and Pharm. div. In-trassind, 1947; chief pharmacist Hendershot Pharmacy, Newton, N.J., 1949; agt. Bur. of Narcotics, U.S. Treasury Dept., 1948-49; owner Preston Drug & Surg. Co., Boonton, N.J., 1949-86; CEO Preston Pharmaceutics, Inc., Butler, N.J., 1970-80, Preston Bus. Cons., Inc., Kinnelon, N.J., 1987—; commr. N.J. State Bd. Pharmacy, 1970-72, pres., 1973; organizer State of N.J. Drug Abuse Speakers Program, 1970-76; chmn. Morris County Drug Abuse Coun., 1969-70; lectr. drug abuse and narcotic addiction various community orgns., 1968-78; mem. adv. bd. Nat. Community Bank, Boonton, N.J., 1973. Chmn. bldg. fund com. Riverside Hosp., Boonton, 1963; mem. Morris County (N.J.) Rep. Fin. Com., 1972; pres. Ronald Reagan N.J. Re-Election Adv. Bd., 1984; mem. exec. com. Gov. Tom Kean Annual Ball, 1985-86; mem. N.J. Congressman Dean Gallo adv. com. on Pres. Clinton's Health Security Plan, 1994; chmn. Pharmacists of N.J. for election of Pres. Ford, 1976, Pharmacists for Gov. Tom Kean, 1981-84, N.J. Pharmacists for Reagan/Bush '84; mem. exec. com. Morris County Overall Econ. Devel. Com., 1976-82; chmn. Pharmacists for Fenwick, 1982; v.p. Kinnelon Rep. Club, 1980, Rep. Com., Kinnelon, 1990; adv. com. to Congressman Dean Gallo on Pres. Clinton's Health Security Plan, 1994. Served to lt. (j.g.), USNR, 1943-46. Recipient Bowl Hygeia award Robbins Co., 1969, E.R. Squibb President's award, 1968, N.J. Pharm. Square Club award, 1969. Mem. Am. Pharm. Assn., N.J. Pharm. Assn. (mem. econs. com. 1960-65, pres. 1967-68, Oscar Singer Meml. award 1987, William H. McNeil award 1994), Nat. Assn. of Retail Druggists, Internat. Narcotic Enforcement Officers Assn., N.J. Narcotic Enforcement Officers Assn., Nat. Assn. Realtors, N.J. Assn. Realtors, Morris County Bd. Realtors, Internat. Bus. Brokers Assn. (cert. bus. intermediary), Internat. Bus. Appraisers, Pharmacists Guild Am. (pres. N.Y. div. 1946-47), Pharmacists Guild of N.J., N.J. Public Health Assn., Morris County Pharm. Assn., Morris-Sussex Pharmacists Soc., Am. Legion, St. John's Alumni Assn. Roman Catholic. Clubs: Elks, K.C., Smoke Rise. Contbr. editorials to profl. jours. Home and Office: 568A Pepperidge Tree Ln Kinnelon NJ 07405-2213

PRESTON, COLLEEN ANN, lawyer; b. Monterey, Calif., Oct. 11, 1955; d. Howard Houston and Catherine (Reid) Harrison; m. Raymond C. Preston Jr., June 12, 1982. BA, U. Fla., 1975, JD, 1978; LLM, Georgetown U., 1985. Bar: Fla. 1979, U.S. Ct. Claims 1979, U.S. Ct. Appeals (fed. cir.) 1979. Assoc. Akerman, Senterfitt & Eidson, Orlando, Fla., 1978-79; atty. advisor, office of gen. counsel Sec. USAF, 1979-83; counsel com. on armed svcs. U.S. Ho. Reps., Washington, 1983-89, gen. counsel, 1990-93; spl. asst. to Sec. Def. for legal matters Dept. Def., Washington, 1993, dep. under sec. of def. for acquisition reform, 1993—. Capt. USAF, 1979-83. Avocations: golf, tennis, cross country and downhill skiing, water skiing. Office: 3610 Defense Pentagon Washington DC 20301-3610

PRESTON, DAVID MICHAEL, lawyer; b. Detroit, Apr. 15, 1930; s. David Harold and Ruth (MacDonald) P.; m. Judith Ann Hillner, Aug. 19, 1961; children: Matthew MacDonald, Sarah Elizabeth Parker, Melissa Ann. B.A., U. Mich., 1952, J.D., 1955. Bar: Mich. 1955. Ptnr. firm Long, Preston, Kinnaird & Avant, Detroit and Bloomfield Hills, Mich., 1965-87; ptnr. Barnett, Knight, Preston, Falvay, Drolet & Freeman, Bloomfield Hills, 1987-89, Drolet, Freeman, Preston & Cotton, Bloomfield Hills, 1990—. Pres. Tim-Ro-Nan-Go Center for Emotionally Disturbed Children, Birmingham, 1972-74; trustee Oakland Community Coll., 1969-70, 83-84. Mem. Am., Mich., Oakland County bar assns., Beta Theta Pi, Phi Delta Phi. Club: Birmingham Athletic (pres. 1977-78). Home: 577 Westwood Dr Birmingham MI 48009-1129 Office: 33 Bloomfield Hills Pky Ste 100 Bloomfield Hills MI 48304-2945

PRESTON, EDGAR HARLAN, real estate broker; b. Emporia, Kans., July 11, 1931; s. Cecil Alvin and Grace Marie (Benedict) P.; m. Jean Ann Walker, Dec. 23, 1951 (div. June 1981); children: Blair W., Melissa A., Christy A.; m. Kate Kramer, Aug. 21, 1981. Student, Southwestern Coll., Winfield, Kans., 1949-50; BS in Polit. Sci., USN Post Grad. Sch., Monterey, Calif., 1967. Enlisted USN, 1950-51, commd. ensign, 1951, advanced to cmmdr., 1967, naval aviator various shipboard/land-based billets, 1951-73; commanding officer RECONRON 3, Agana, Guam, 1967-69; project mgr. SPECOMM U.S. Naval Air System Command, Washington, 1969-73; with flight test U.S. Naval Electronic System Command, Dallas, 1969-73; ret. USN, 1973; mng. dir. Collin Realty Ltd., Hong Kong, 1973-75; mgr., broker DBWF Andy Hughes Realty (GOH), Sedona, 1976-85; broker, owner Ed Preston Realty, Sedona, 1985—; pres. Sedona-Verde Valley Bd. Realtors, 1983. Treas., bd. dirs. Sedona C. of C., 1986-87; life. mem. Realtors Polit. Action Com., Washington, 1981—; pres. Keep Sedona Beautiful, 1986-87. Decorated Navy Commendation medal, Air medal; named Realtor of Yr. Sedona-Verde Valley Bd. Realtors, 1982. Mem. Ariz. Assn. Realtors (regional v.p., v.p. 1987-88, bd. dirs. subs. corp. 1987—, pres.-elect 1989, pres. 1990, honor soc. 1988-90), Realtors Nat. Mktg. Inst. (CRB award, CRS award 1984-90), Real Estate Securities & Syndication, Nat. Assn. Realtors (dir. 1990), Am. Legion, Kiwanis, Elks (local treas. 1978-83). Republican. Avocations: flying, traveling, reading. Home: PO Box 281 Sedona AZ 86339-0281 Office: Profl Realty Organization 45 S Sunset Dr Ste 195 Sedona AZ 86336-5422

PRESTON, FAITH, college president; b. Boston, Sept. 14, 1921; d. Howard Knowlton and Edith Smith (Wilson) P.; m. Winthrop Wadleigh, Dec. 19, 1970. B.A., Boston U., 1944; M.A., 1945; Ed.D., Columbia U. Tchrs. Coll., 1964. Tchr. Georgetown (Mass.) High Sch., 1945-47; tchr. Stoneham (Mass.) High Sch., 1947-50, Endicott Jr. Coll., Beverly, Mass., 1950-53; dir. research P.R. Jr. Coll., 1953-55; dean adminstrn., 1955-63, v.p. 1963-65; pres. White Pines Coll., 1965-91, pres. emerita, 1991—, also life trustee. Author: David and the Handcar, 1950, Jose's Miracle, 1955, The Silver Box, 1979, A Gift of Love, 1994. Mem. bd. incorporators Cath. Med. Ctr., Manchester, N.H., 1978-89; bd. dirs. Caregivers; pres. bd. dirs. N.H. Assn. for blind; trustee funds Chester Congl. Bapt. Ch., deacon, 1988—. Kellogg fellow, 1964. Mem. Am. Assn. Jr. Colls., Phi Lambda Theta, Kappa Delta Pi, Delta Kappa Gamma. Republican. Clubs: Univ. Women's (London); The College (Boston); Fortnightly. Home: PO Box 25 Chester NH 03036-0025 Office: White Pines Coll Office of the Pres 40 Chester St Chester NH 03036 *I am a teacher, and I yearn to impart a few non-textbook lessons. Two are simply said: care, endure.*

PRESTON, FRANCES W., performing rights organization executive; children: Kirk, David, Donald. Hon. degree, Lincoln (Ill.) Coll.; degree (hon.), Berklee Coll. Musicawrd. With BMI (Broadcast Music Inc.), Nashville, 1958—, v.p., 1964-85; sr. v.p. performing rights BMI, N.Y.C., 1985, exec. v.p., chief exec. officer, 1986, pres., chief exec. officer, 1986—; also bd. dirs. Mem. Film, Entertainment and Music Commn. Adv. Council State of Tenn., Leadership Nashville, John Work Meml. Found.; trustee Country Music Found., Inc.; mem. Commn. on White House Record Library, Carter adminstrn., Pres.'s Panama Canal Study Com., Carter adminstrn.; bd. dirs. Rock & Roll Hall of Fame; mem. adminstrv. council Confedn. of Internat. Socs. of Authors and Composers; v.p. Nat. Music Council; bd. dirs. Peabody Awards; hon. trustee Nat. Acad. Popular Music. Recipient achievement award Women's Equity Action League, spl. citation award NATAS, Golden Baton award Young Musicians Found.; named one of Am.'s 50 Most Powerful Women Ladies' Home Jour.; named to Country Music Hall of Fame. Mem. Country Music Assn. (life mem. bd. dirs., past chmn., past pres., Irving Waugh Award of Excellence), Nashville Symphony Assn. (past sec., bd. dirs.), NARAS (pres.'s adv. bd., past bd. dirs. Nashville chpt.), Nashville Songwriters Assn. (life mem.), Gospel Music Assn. (life mem. bd., past chmn., past pres.), Am. Women in Radio and TV (past bd. dirs.). Presbyterian. Lodge: Rotary (1st woman mem. Nashville club), Friars Club

(Friars Found. Applause award). Office: Broadcast Music Inc 320 W 57th St New York NY 10019-3705

PRESTON, FREDERICK WILLARD, surgeon; b. Chgo., June 27, 1912; s. Frederick Augustus and Margaret (Atwater) P.; m. Gertrude Eldred Bradford, June 23, 1942 (div. 1961); children: Frederick Willard Jr., David E. (dec. 1994), William B.; m. Barbara Gay Hess, July 30, 1961. BA, Yale U., 1935; MD, Northwestern U., 1940, MS, 1942; MS, U. Minn., 1947. Intern Presbyn. Hosp., Chgo., 1940-41; fellow surgery Mayo Clinic, Rochester, Minn., 1941-42, 46-48; pvt. practice surgery Chgo., 1968-75; mem. surg. faculty Northwestern U. Med. Sch., 1949-75, prof. surgery, 1960-75; assoc. attending surgeon Northwestern Meml. Hosp., 1950-75; attending surgeon Skokie Valley Community Hosp., 1964-75, Henrotin Hosp., 1950-75; chief surg. svc. VA Rsch. Hosp., Chgo., 1953-68; mem. Supreme Acad. Coun. Ofcl. U. Congo, Lubumbashi, 1965-71; chmn. dept. surgery Santa Barbara Gen. Hosp., 1975-78; dir. surg. edn. Santa Barbara Cottage Hosp., 1975-83; rsch. physiologist U. Calif., Santa Barbara, 1976-84. Author, editor: Basic Surgical Physiology, Loose-Leaf Practice of Surgery, Manual of Ambulatory Surgery; cons. editor Internat. Surg. Digest, 1969-70, contbr. numerous articles to profl. jours. Bd. dirs. Schweppe Found., Love Med. Rsch., English Speaking Union, Chgo. chpt., 1960-65; gov. mem., mem. planning com. Shedd Aquarium, 1968-75. 1st lt. to maj. M.C., AUS, 1942-46. Fellow ACS (chpt. pres. 1965-66); mem. AMA, AAAS, Chgo. Surg. Soc. (sec. 1961-64, pres. 1968-69), Chgo. Acad. Scis. (sec. 1963-67), Am. Assn. Cancer Research (pres. Chgo. sec. 1963-64), Am. Geriatrics Soc., Am. Fedn. Clin. Research, Am. Surg. Assn., Central Surg. Assn., Western Surg. Assn. (coun.), Pacific Coast Surg. Assn., Pan Pacific Surg. Assn., Société Internationale de Chirurgie, Soc. Surgery Alimentary Tract, Santa Barbara Club, La Cumbre Golf and Country Club, Chgo. Literary Club, Univ. Club (Chgo.), Sigma Xi. Republican. Episcopalian. Home: 755 Via Airosa Santa Barbara CA 93110-2302

PRESTON, JAMES E., cosmetics company executive; b. 1933. BS, Northwestern U., 1955. With Avon Products, Inc., N.Y.C., 1964—, from mgmt. trainee to dir. sales promotions, 1964-70, dir. personnel, 1970-71, v.p. corp. personnel, 1971-72, from group v.p. mktg. to sr. v.p. field ops. worldwide, 1972-77, exec. v.p., 1977-81, exec. corp. v.p., pres., 1981-88, pres., chief operating officer, 1988-89, chief exec. officer, 1988—, chmn. bd. dirs., 1989—; bd. dirs. ARA Svcs., Woolworth Corp. Mem. Reader's Digest Assn. (bd. dirs. 1994). Office: Avon Products Inc 9 W 57th St New York NY 10019-2600*

PRESTON, JANE, psychiatrist, educator. BS in Biology, Trinity U., 1949; MD, Baylor Coll. of Medicine, 1953. Intern St. Louis City Hosp., 1953-54; resident in internal medicine St. John's (Newfoundland, Can.) Gen. Hosp., 1955-56; resident in internal medicine Baylor Coll. of Medicine, Houston, 1956-57, resident in psychiatry, 1957-60, clin. assoc. prof., 1965—; mem. faculty Austin (Tex.) State Hosp. Residency Program, 1983—; bd. dirs. Samaritan Counseling Ctrs., 1987-90; mem. ad hoc ethics com. Shoal Creek Hosp., 1987-89, chair credentials com., 1987-90; presenter Carrier Found. Symposium, 1984; mem. Task Force on Revision of Insanity Sect. of Tex. State Criminal Code, 1973; chair med. evaluation team Richmond State Sch. for Retarded, 1975-76; mem. ad hoc com. Revisions Mental Health Code of Tex., 1976, 79, 82-85; mem. mental health adv. coun. Tex. Dept. Mental Health and Mental Retardation, 1979-84, mental adv. com., 1984—, chair med. adv. com. subcom. on community mental health ctrs., 1986—; examiner Am. Bd. Psychiatry and Neurology, 1983, 87; project dir. Tex. Telemedicine Project, 1989—; mem. adv. bd. Tex. Tech. Health Sci. Ctr. MedNet Project, 1989-90, cons., 1989—; speaker for medicine Bell Commn. Rsch., 1989, 90; pres. Telemed. Interactive Consultative Svcs., Inc., 1988—; pres. The Am. Telemedicine Assn.; mem. com. high performance computing and comm. Nat. Rsch. Coun.; bd. dirs. Friends of Nat. Libr. of Medicine. Author: The Telemedicine Handbook, 1993; contbr. articles to profl. jours. Elder Presbyn. Ch., USA; docent The Gov.'s Mansion, Austin; past docent The Bayou Bend Collection, Houston; cons. Cath. Charities, Gulf Coast Presbytery, Jewish Community Ctr., Houston, 1976-79. Recipient resolution honoring rural health contbn. Tex. Ho. of Reps. Fellow Am. Psychiat. Assn. (diplomate, budget com. 1976-82, chair 1981-82, cons. 1982-89, cons. resource and devel. com. 1987-89, chair long range planning com. 1981-82, com. info. systems 1984-87, cons. 1987-89, chair task force on telemedicine 1981, com. telemed. svcs. delivery 1984—, sci. exhibitor 1985, 86, 87, 88); mem. AMA, Am. Group Psychiat. Assn., Am. Coll. Psychiatry, Internat. Platform Assn., Nat. Alliance for the Mentally Ill, Mental Health Assn., Tex. Med. Assn. (sci. exhibitor 1988-90), Tex. Soc. Psychiat. Physicians (pres. 1970-80, chair sci. program devel. com. 1976-79, cons. com. allied disciplines 1976—, co-chair nat. affairs, govt. rels. com. 1977-79), Houston Psychiat. Soc. (pres. 1972), N.Y. Acad. Scis., Alpha Chi, Alpha Epsilon Iota, Alpha Omega Alpha. Office: Telemed Interactive Cons Svc Inc 204 E 4th St Austin TX 78701 also: 1700 One American Ctr 600 Congress Ave Austin TX 78701

PRESTON, JOHN THOMAS, engineering executive; b. Fullerton, Calif., Mar. 18, 1950; s. Seaton Tinsley and Aline Marie (Debbaut) P.; m. Gail Ellen Sandberg. BS, U. Wis., 1972; MBA, Northwestern U., 1976. Mng. dir. Polyscience Corp., Niles, Ill., 1971-77; assoc. dir. MIT, Cambridge, Mass., 1977-82; pres. Visual Comm. Network, Cambridge, Mass., 1982-86; dir. MIT, Cambridge, Mass., 1986-92, 1992—; dir. Molten Metal Tech., Waltham, Mass., 1989—, Energy Biosystems, The Woodlands, Tex., 1990—, MIT Enterprise Forum, Cambridge, 1993—, Mass. Microelectronics Ctr., Ctr. for Tech. Commercialization Inc., Clean Harbors Techs.; mem. adv. bd. Strategic Defende Initiative, Nat. Aeronautics and Space Adminstrn., Nat. Sci. and Tech. Bd., Singapore, So. Carolina U. Rsch. and Edn. Found., Technology Linkages, Inc., Nat. Tech. Transfer Ctr. Named Chevalier dans l'Order National du Mérite Pres. Rep. of France, 1993. Office: MIT Tech Licensing Office 77 Mass Ave Rm E32-300 Cambridge MA 02142

PRESTON, LEWIS THOMPSON, banker; b. N.Y.C., Aug. 5, 1926; s. Lewis Thompson and Priscilla (Baldwin) P.; m. Gladys Pulitzer, Apr. 17, 1959; children: Linda Pulitzer Bartlett, Victoria Maria Bartlett, Lucile Baldwin, Lewis Thompson, Priscilla Munn, Electra. Grad., Harvard U., 1951. With J.P. Morgan & Co. (merged with Guaranty Trust Co., named Morgan Guaranty Trust Co. 1959), N.Y.C., 1951—; vice chmn. bd., dir. J. P. Morgan & Co. and Morgan Guaranty Trust Co., N.Y.C., 1976-78, mem. corporate office, mem. exec. com., 1976-90; pres. J.P. Morgan and Morgan Guaranty Trust Co., N.Y.C., 1978-80; chmn. bd., chief exec. officer J. P. Morgan and Morgan Guaranty Trust Co., N.Y.C., 1980-90, chmn. exec. com., 1991; pres. Internat. Bank Reconstruction and Devel., Washington, 1991—; also pres. Internat. Finance Corp., Washington, DC, Multilateral Investment Guarantee Agency, Washington, DC. With USMC, 1944-46. Mem. Coun. Fgn. Rels., Assn. N.Y. City Bankers, Brook Club. Republican. Episcopalian. Office: IBRD 1818 H St NW Washington DC 20433 Also: IFC 1850 I Street NW Washington DC 20433

PRESTON, LOYCE ELAINE, retired social work educator; b. Texarkana, Ark., Feb. 25, 1929; d. Harvey Martin and Florence (Whitlock) P.; student Texarkana Jr. Coll., 1946-47; B.S. Henderson State Tchrs. Coll., 1950; certificate in social work La. State U., 1952; M.S.W., Columbia U. 1956. Tchr. pub. schs., Dierks, Ark., 1950-51; child welfare worker Ark. Dept. Public Welfare, Clark and Hot Spring counties, 1951-56, child welfare cons., 1956-58; casework dir. Ruth Sch. Girls, Burien, Wash., 1958-60; asst. prof. spl. edn. La. Poly. Inst., Ruston, 1960-63; asst. prof. Northwestern State Coll., Shreveport, La., 1963-73; asst. prof. La. State U., Shreveport, 1973-79; ret., 1979. Chpt. sec. La. Assn. Mental Health, 1965-67, Gov.'s adv. council, 1967-70; mem. Mayor's Com. for Community Improvement, 1972-76. Mem. AAUW (dir. Shreveport br. 1963-69), Acad. Cert. Social Workers, Nat. Assn. Social Workers (del. 1964-65, pres. North La. chpt., state-wide com. 1968-69), La Council for Social Welfare, La. Fedn. Council Exceptional Children (pres. 1970-71), La. Tchrs. Assn. Home: 9609 Hillsboro Dr Shreveport LA 71118-4804

PRESTON, MALCOLM, artist, art critic; b. N.J., May 25, 1919; s. Frank and Anniece (Landau) P.; m. Mary Alice Bales, Nov. 27, 1942; children: Jennifer, Amanda. BS, U. Wis., 1940; MA, Columbia U., 1945, PhD, 1951; student, New Sch. Social Rsch., N.Y.C., 1940-42. Display artist and designer, free lance artist, 1939-41; fellow, asst. instr. painting New Sch. Social Research, 1940-41; high sch. tchr., 1944-49; art supr. Manhasset pub.

schs., 1945; part-time instr. Adelphi Coll., 1947; chmn. dept. fine arts Hofstra Coll., 1949-74, prof. fine arts, 1954-74, chmn. div. humanities, 1959-74, coordinator arts, 1961-74; dir. Inst. Arts, 1962-74; art critic Newsday, 1968-86, Boston Herald Traveler, 1970-72. Contbr. articles to newspapers and mags.; radio, television shows Met. area; developed and carried out television series Ford Found. grant, Nat. Ednl. Radio and Television Center, Arts Around Us, Am. Art Today, 1956; one-man shows include Ward Eggleston Gallery, N.Y.C., 1950-51, 54, 56, A.C.A. Gallery, 1959, S.A.G., 1962, Palm Beach, 1968, St. Mary's Coll., 1978, Benson Gallery, 1979, The Gallery, Truro, Mass., 1980, 81, 82, Customs House Gallery, 1984, Country Art Gallery, 1986, Wenniger Gallery, 1988, Elaine Benson Gallery, 1991, Galerie Mourlot, Boston, 1992; group shows include New Art Gallery, 1948-49, Ward Eggleston Gallery, 1949-50, also, L.I. Artists Exhibit, Nat. Water Color Exhibit, San Diego, Am. Artists Assn. Gallery, 1951, Roosevelt Field Art Center, 1957, Art U.S.A., 1958, Hansa Gallery Group Show, 1958, Shore Studio Gallery, Provincetown, 1957-58, Kendall Art Gallery, Wellfleet, Mass., 1974, 75, 76, 77, 78, Roko Gallery, 1978, Himelfarb Gallery, 1978, Linden Gallery, 1981-82, Tower Gallery, 1983, Customs House Gallery, 1983, 84, 85, Grand Central Art Gallery, 1984, 85; work represented in permanent collections: Queens's Mus., Guild Hall Mus., Portland Mus., Cape Cod Mus. Fine Arts, Hofstra U., Living Arts Found., Winning Images, Columbus, Ohio, Country Art Gallery, Locust Valley, N.Y. Served as 2d lt. F.A. AUS, World War II. Lowe Found. research grantee, 1950; Ford Found. grantee, 1958; recipient Emily Lowe award, 1949, 50, 52, 54, 56; 1st prize oil Utica, N.Y.; Shell Research award, 1963. Home: PO Box 182 Truro MA 02666-0182 Office: care Galerie Mourlot 14 Newbury St Boston MA 02118-2907

PRESTON, MARK I., investment company executive; b. Schenectady, May 16, 1938; s. Samuel P. and Fay (Zelig) P.; children: Meredith, Laurence. BSBA, Syracuse U., 1959. Gen. mgr. AD-Allure Industries Inc., N.Y.C., 1962-64; pres. Marlin Mfg. Corp., 1965-68; asst. exec. Walston, Inc., 1969-72; v.p. DuPont, Walston, Inc., N.Y.C. and Washington, 1973, Legg Mason Wood Walker, Inc., Balt., 1974-81, sr. v.p. mktg., 1981-85, sr. v.p., dir. of sales, 1986-90, sr. v.p. dir. investor svcs., 1991—. Pres. Balt. County Gen. Hosp. Found., 1983-84; v.p. Safety First Club Md., 1982-90; trustee Balt. County Gen. Hosp., 1983-88; pres. parent bd. Balt. County Gen. Hosp., 1988-90; bd. dirs. blood svcs. bd. ARC, Md. Mem. Int. Assn. Fin. Planners (cert.). Club: Bond (Balt.) (pres. 1984). Home: 2365 Boston St Baltimore MD 21224-3656 Office: Legg Mason Wood Walker Inc 111 S Calvert St Baltimore MD 21202-6174

PRESTON, MELVIN ALEXANDER, physicist, educator; b. Toronto, Ont., Can., May 28, 1921; s. Gardener Alexander and Hazel (Melvin) P.; m. Mary Whittaker, Aug. 16, 1947; children: Jonathan, Richard; m. Eugene Shearer, June 25, 1966. B.A., U. Toronto, 1942, M.A., 1946; Ph.D., U. Birmingham, 1949; D.Sc., McMaster U., 1983. Asst. lectr. math. physics U. Birmingham, 1947-49, Nuffield fellow, 1957; faculty U. Toronto, 1949-53, McMaster U., Hamilton, Ont., 1953-77; prof. physics McMaster U., 1959-77, prof. applied math., 1967-77, chmn. dept., 1975-77, dean grad. studies, 1965-71; exec. vice chmn. adv. com. on acad. planning Council of Ont. Univs., 1971-75; prof. physics U. Sask., Saskatoon, 1977-86, acad. v.p., 1977-82; emeritus prof. physics McMaster U., 1986—; pres. Canadian Assn. Grad. Schs., 1971. Author: Physics of the Nucleus, 1962, Structure of the Nucleus, 1975; Contbr. articles to profl. jours. Decorated Can. Decoration, Centennial medal; NRC Sr. fellow U. Inst. Teoretisk Fysik, Copenhagen, 1963-64. Fellow Am. Phys. Soc., Royal Soc. Can., AAAS; mem. Sask. Sailing Clubs Assn. (pres. 1980-83), Can. Yachting Assn. (v.p. 1981-86). Office: McMaster U, Hamilton, ON Canada L8S 4M1

PRESTON, RICHARD ARTHUR, historian; b. Middlesbrough, England, Oct. 4, 1910; s. Frank and Florence Rachel (Carter) P.; m. Marjorie Fishwick, Sept. 2, 1939; children—David Frank, Carol Jane, Peter Eric. B.A., Leeds U., 1931, M.A., 1932, Dip.Ed.; Ph.D., Yale U., 1936; LL.D., Royal Mil. Coll. Can., 1977. Mem. faculty U. Toronto, 1936-38, U. Coll. South Wales, 1938-45, U. Toronto, 1945-48; mem. faculty Royal Mil. Coll. Can., Kingston, 1948-65; prof. history Royal Mil. Coll. Can., to 1965, Duke U., Durham, N.C., 1965-80; prof. emeritus Duke U., 1980—, dir. Can. studies, 1973-79. Author: Gorges of Plymouth Fort, 1953, Men in Arms, 1956-91, Royal Fort Frontenac, 1958, Kingston Before the War of 1812, 1958, Canada in World Affairs, 1959-61, 1965, Canada and Imperial Defense, 1967, Canada's R.M.C, 1969, For Friends at Home, 1974, Defence of the Undefended Border, 1977, Perspectives in the History of Military Education and Professionalism, 1980, the Squat Pyramid: Canadian Studies in the U.S, 1980, To Serve Canada, 1991. Served with RAF, 1940-45. Commonwealth Fund fellow, 1933-36; Can. Coun. fellow, 1963-64; Social Sci. Rsch. Coun. fellow, 1963-64; Guggenheim fellow, 1972-73; recipient Achievement award City Kingston, 1959; Can. Confedn. medal, 1967; Queen's Jubilee medal, 1975; Donner medal, 1977; No. Telecom. Internat. Can. Studies award and Gold medal, 1983, Kingston Hist. Soc. award, 1994. Mem. Can. Hist. Assn. (pres. 1961-62), Am. Can. Studies U.S. (founding pres. 1971-72), Am. Mil. Inst. Home: 25 Old Oak Ct Durham NC 27705-5644 Office: Duke U Carr Bldg Durham NC 27706

PRESTON, RICHARD MCCANN, creative company executive, writer; b. Cambridge, Mass., Aug. 5, 1954; s. Jerome and Dorothy (McCann) P. BA summa cum laude, Pomona Coll., 1977; PhD in English, Princeton U., 1983. Staff writer Princeton (N.J.) U., 1984-85; chmn., chief exec. officer Urania, Inc., 1986—. Author: First Light, 1987, American Steel, 1991; regular contbr. articles to The New Yorker mag. Award judge Am. Inst. Physics, N.Y.C., 1989-92. Recipient Sci. Writing award Am. Inst. Physics, 1988, Eugene McDermott award in the Arts MIT, 1992, Westinghouse award AAAS, 1993. Avocations: backpacking, whitewater canoeing, all-terrain bicycles, connoisseurship of whisky.

PRESTON, RICHARD MCKIM, lawyer; b. Balt., June 2, 1947; s. Wilbur Day Jr. and May Virginia (Honemann) P.; m. Trisa Jean Thompson, Apr. 28, 1961. BA, Washington & Lee U., 1969, JD cum laude, 1976; MA cum laude, Fairleigh Dickinson U., 1973. Assoc. vomBaur, Coburn, Simmons & Turtle, Washington, 1976-79; assoc. Seyfarth, Shaw, Fairweather & Geraldson, Washington, 1979-82, ptnr., 1982—; mng. ptnr. Constrn. Group, 1987—. Contbr. articles to profl. publs., chpt. to book. Bd. dirs. Jubilee Support Found., Washington, 1989—; mem. Washington & Lee Law Coun., Lexington, Va., 1986-93. Mem. Univ. Club D.C., River Bend Golf and Country Club, Sankaty Head Golf Club. Office: Seyfarth Shaw Fairweather 815 Connecticut Ave NW Washington DC 20006-4004

PRESTON, ROBERT BRUCE, retired lawyer; b. Cleve., Feb. 24, 1926; s. Robert Bruce and Erma May (Hunter) P.; m. Agnes Ellen Stanley, Jan. 29, 1949; children—Robert B., Patricia Ellen Preston Kiefer, Judith Helen Preston Yanover. A.B., Western Res. U., 1950, J.D., 1952. Bar: U.S. Dist. Ct. (no. dist.) Ohio 1953, U.S. Ct. Appeals (6th cir.) 1959, U.S. Supreme Ct. 1964. Assoc. Arter & Hadden, Cleve., 1952-63, ptnr., 1964-93; ret., 1994; dir. Service Stampings Inc., Willoughby, Ohio. Vice pres. Citizens League Cleve., 1965; chmn. Charter Rev. Com., Cleveland Heights, Ohio, 1972; mem. Zoning Bd. Appeals, Cleveland Heights, 1974-76. Mem. Ohio Bar Assn., Greater Cleve. Bar Assn., City Club. Republican. Presbyterian. Avocations: tennis, fishing, travel. Home: 117 Manorbrook Dr South Russell OH 44022-4163 Office: Arter & Hadden 1100 Huntington Bldg Cleveland OH 44115

PRESTON, ROBERT FRANCIS, state legislator; b. Lowell, Mass., May 11, 1929; m. Charlotte Keefe Preston; children: Robert, Charles, Martha, James, Mary Kaye. Student, Salem (Mass.) State Coll., 1963, St. Anselm Coll., N.H. N.H. state senator Dem. leader Concord, 1973—; owner Preston Real Estate, Seabrook and Hampton, N.H.; co-founder, bd. dirs. Seabrook Bank & Trust Co.; prin. Hampshire Motor Inn. Del. Dem. Nat. Conv., N.Y.C., 1980; mem. N.H. Dem. State Com.; chmn. Transp. Commn., N.H. Senate; commn. on rules, jud. capital budget and internal affairs; mem. hist. commn. various statutory coms. Served with U.S. Army, 1946-47, 50-51. Mem. Hampton C. of C. Home: 63 Ocean Blvd Hampton Beach NH 33301 Office: N H State Senate State Capital Concord NH 03301

PRESTON, SAMUEL HULSE, demographer; b. Morrisville, Pa., Dec. 2, 1943; s. Samuel H. and Dora (Berrell) P.; m. Winnifred de Witt, June 19, 1965; children: Samuel, Andrew, Benjamin, Leah. BA in Econs., Amherst

Coll., 1965; PhD in Econs., Princeton U., 1968. Asst. prof. demography U. Calif., Berkeley, 1968-72; dir. Ctr. for Demography U. Wash., Seattle, 1972-77; chief, population structure sect. UN, N.Y.C., 1977-79; dir. Population Studies Ctr. U. Pa., Phila., 1979-88. Author: Mortality Patterns in National Populations, 1976, Patterns of Urban and Rural Population Growth, 1980, (with M. Haines) Fatal Years, 1991. Fellow AAAS, Am. Acad. Arts and Scis, Am. Statis. Assn.; mem. NAS, Inst. Medicine, Am. Philos. Soc., Population Assn. Am. (pres. 1984, Irene B. Tauber award for Excellence in Demographic Research 1983), Internat. Union for Sci. Study of Population (council 1981-88). Democrat. Methodist. Home: 234 Walnut Ave Wayne PA 19087-3423 Office: Univ Pa Population Studies Ctr Philadelphia PA 19104

PRESTON, SEYMOUR STOTLER, III, manufacturing company executive; b. Media, Pa., Sept. 11, 1933; s. Seymour Stotler and Mary Alicia (Harper) P.; m. Jean Ellen Holman, Sept. 8, 1956; children: Courtney J., Katherine E., Alicia D., Shelley S. BA, Williams Coll., 1956; MBA, Harvard Coll., 1958. With Pennwalt Corp., Phila., 1961-89; exec. v.p. in charge of chems. and equipment ops., worldwide Pennwalt Corp., 1975-77, pres., COO, 1977-89; pres., CEO Elf Atochem N.Am., Inc. (formerly Atochem N.Am.), Phila., 1990-93; chmn. AAC Engineered Systems Inc., 1994—; bd. dirs. Core States Fin. Corp., Phila. Nat. Bank, Scott Specialty Gases, Inc., ADCO Technologies, Inc. Trustee Shipley Sch., Bryn Mawr, Pa., 1976-88, Acad. Natural Scis., 1981—, Phila. Orch. Assn., 1992—; mem. bd. mgrs. Franklin Inst., Phila., 1980-92; bd. dirs. Lawrenceville (N.J.) Sch., 1982—. 1st lt. USAF, 1958-61. Mem. Soc. for Chem. Industry, Greater Phila. C. of C. (bd. dirs. 1979-94), Radnor Hunt Club (Malvern, Pa.).

PRESTON, THOMAS RONALD, English language educator, researcher; b. Oct. 31, 1936; s. Thomas and Marie Katherine (Nettlow) P.; m. Mary Ruth Atkinson, June 4, 1960; children: Lorel, Mary, Thomas. BA, U. Detroit, 1958; MA, Rice U., 1960, PhD, 1962. Asst. prof. English U. Fla., Gainseville, 1963-67; assoc. prof., chmn. dept. Loyola U., New Orleans, 1967-69; prof., chmn. dept. U. Tenn., Chattanooga, 1969-73, U. Wyo., Laramie, 1973-82; prof., dean arts and scis. U. North Tex., Denton, 1982-92; prof. English, 1992—; chmn. Wyo. Council for Humanities, Laramie, 1976-77. Author: Not in Timon's Manner, 1975; editor U. Ga. edit. of Smollett's Humphry Clinker, 1990; contbr. articles on 18th century lit. to profl. jours. Recipient John W. Gardner award Rice U., 1962; George Duke Humphrey award U. Wyo., 1982; NEH grantee, 1979; Am. Council of Learned Socs. grantee, 1980. Mem. South Ctrl. MLA, Am. Soc. for 18th Century Studies. Coll. English Assn., South Ctrl. Soc. for 18th Century Studies (pres. 1986-87). Democrat. Anglican. Home: 11722 S Central Ln Winona TX 75792-6704 Office: U North Tex English Dept Denton TX 76203

PRESTON, WILLIAM HUBBARD, consultant to specialty businesses; b. Bklyn., July 24, 1920; s. Russell Jackson and Mary Louise (Yetman) P.; m. Marcia Whitney Emery, Dec. 18, 1943; children: William Hubbard, Craig Ryder. B.S.M.E. cum laude, Poly. Inst. N.Y., 1942. Asst. supt. Ball & Roller div. SKF Industries, Phila., 1946-51; cons. Booz, Allen & Hamilton, N.Y.C., 1951-53; gen. sales mgr. Joy Mfg. Co., Pitts., 1953-59; exec. v.p. Chase Brass/Kennecott, Waterbury, Conn., 1959-62; pres. Indsl. Group Joy Mfg. Co., Michigan City, Ind., 1962-67, Davis-Standard div., Pawcatuck, Conn., 1967-83; v.p. Crompton & Knowles Corp., N.Y.C., 1967-83; prin. Hubbard Assocs., Hopkinton, Mass., 1983—; bd. dirs. Lefebvre Ltd., Montreal. Served to lt. (j.g.) USNR, 1943-46. Unitarian. Home: 152 Hayden Rowe St Hopkinton MA 01748-2512

PRESTOWITZ, CLYDE VINCENT, economist, research administrator; b. Wilmington, Del., Sept. 14; s. Clyde Vincent and Lillian (Lang) P.; m. Carol Ann Jay, Mar. 29, 1964; children: Anne, Clyde, Brian. B.A., Swarthmore Coll., 1963; M.A., U. Hawaii, 1965; M.B.A., U. Pa., 1980. Mgr. market devel. Scott Paper Co., Phila., 1968-72; dir. planning Europe Scott Paper Co., Brussels, 1972-76; v.p. Japan Egon Zehnder Internat., Tokyo, 1976-78; dir. mktg. Am. Can Co., Greenwich, Conn., 1978-79; pres. Prestowitz Assocs., New Canaan, Conn., 1979-81; dep. asst. sec. internat. econ. policy U.S. Dept. Commerce, Washington, 1981-82, acting asst. sec. internat. econ. policy, 1982-83, counselor to sec., 1983-86; Wilson fellow, 1986-87; sr. assoc. Carnegie Endowment for Internat. Peace, Washington, 1987-89; pres. Econ. Strategy Inst., Washington, 1989—; bd. dirs. Lanxide Corp.; vice chmn. Pacific Basin Econ. Coun., 1989—. Republican. Presbyterian. Home: 10420 Masters Ter Potomac MD 20854 Office: Econ Strategy Inst 1401 H St NW Ste 750 Washington DC 20005

PRETO-RODAS, RICHARD ANTHONY, foreign language educator; b. N.Y.C., May 30, 1936; s. Manuel and Beatrice Alina (Carvalho) Preto-R. B.A., Fairfield U., 1958; M.A. in Philosophy, Boston Coll., 1960; M.A. in Spanish, U. Mich., 1962, Ph.D. in Romance Langs. (fellow Rackham Sch. Grad. Studies 1965), freq. Instr. U. Mich., Ann Arbor, 1964-66; asst. prof. U. Fla., 1966-70; assoc. prof. U. Ill., Urbana-Champaign, 1970-74; prof. U. Ill., 1974-81, chmn. Spanish, Italian, 1978-81; dir. lang. U. South Fla., Tampa, 1981-89, prof. lang., 1989—; cons. MLA; vis. prof. comparative lit. Université Stendhal, Grenoble, France, 1994—. Author: Negritude as A Theme in the Poetry of the Portuguese-Speaking World, 1971, Dialogue and Courtly Lore in Renaissance Portugal, 1971; co-author: Cronicas Brasileiras: A Portuguese Reader, 1980, rev. 1994 as Cronicas Brasileiras, Nova Fase, 40 Historinhas of C.D. de Andrade, 1983; co-editor, contbr: Empire in Transition: The Portuguese World in the Time of Camoes, 1985; contbg. editor: Handbook of Latin American Studies, 1983—; contbg. reviewer World Lit. Today, 1986—. NDEA fellow, 1965. Mem. MLA, Am. Council on Teaching Fgn. Langs., Am. Assn. Tchrs. of Spanish and Portuguese, Phi Beta Kappa. Democrat. Home: 4483 Vieux Carre Cir Tampa FL 33613-3057 Office: CPR-107 U South Fla Tampa FL 33620

PRETTI, BRADFORD JOSEPH, lay worker, insurance company executive; b. Glenwood Springs, Colo., Oct. 11, 1930; s. Joseph John and Ethel Elizabeth (Roe) P.; m. Nancy Ann Clayton, Mar. 30. 1951 (div. 1971); children: Kristi Pretti Micander, Terice Pretti Brownson, Bradford Joseph Holli; m. Sarah Jane Rupp, Aug. 8, 1974. B.A. U. Colo., 1952. Pres. Pub. Adv. Ins. Com., Chaves County, N.Mex., 1965-72; sr. warden St. Thomas á Beckett Ch., Roswell, N.Mex., 1978-79, St. Andrew's Ch., Roswell, N.Mex., 1991-92; mem. Progam Coun. Diocese of Rio Grande, Albuquerque, 1991-92, mem. Venture in Mission Commn., 1980-84; pres. Standing Commn., 1981-85, chmn. Bishop Search Commn., 1987, dep. to Gen. Conv., 1985-88; Cathedral chpt., 1988-91; pres. Roswell Ins. & Surety Agy., RBS Ins., 1974—; instr. Ea. N.Mex. U., Roswell, 1970—. Contbr. articles to jours. in field. Pres. Assurance Home Found., Roswell, 1984—; campaign chmn. United Way of Chaves County, Roswell, 1982, v.p., 1984; bd. dirs. Roswell Hospice Inc., 1984; trustee Roswell Mus. and Art Ctr., 1985, pres. bd. trustees, 1990-92; pres. bd. Roswell Mus. and Art Ctr. Found., 1995; bd. dirs. Sunny Acres, Inc. Mem. N.Mex. Ind. Ins. Agts. Assn. (Outstanding Svc. award 1964), Roswell C. of C. (treas. 1984, pres. elect 1985, pres. 1986, Pres.'s Club citation 1983), Mus. Trustees Assn., Am. Contract Bridge League (pres. #382 sect. 1965-68), C Club (Boulder, Colo.). Republican. Episcopalian. Avocation: duplicate bridge. Home: 317 Sherrill Ln Apt 14 Roswell NM 88201-5828 Office: RBS Ins PO Box 280 Roswell NM 88202-0280 Without a deep, abiding faith our lives are essentially meaningless.

PRETTYMAN, ELIJAH BARRETT, JR., lawyer; b. Washington, June 1, 1925; s. Elijah Barrett and Lucy Courtney (Hill) P.; children by previous marriage: Elijah Barrett III, Jill Savage. Grad., St. Albans Sch., Washington, 1943; BA, Yale U., 1949; LLB, U. Va., 1953. Bar: D.C. 1954, U.S. Supreme Ct. 1957. Pvt. practice Washington, 1955—; law clk. to Justices Jackson, Frankfurter and Harlan (U.S. Supreme Ct.), 1953-55; assoc. firm Hogan & Hartson, Washington, 1955-63; partner Hogan & Hartson, 1964—; spl. asst. to Atty. Gen. U.S., 1963, White House, 1963-64; also Pres.'s rep. to Interagy. Com. on Transport Mergers; spl. cons. subcom. to investigate problems connected with refugees and escapees U.S. Senate Judiciary Com., Vietnam, 1967-68; outside cons. to subcom on oversight and investigations, Ho. of Reps. com. on internal and fgn. commerce, 1978; spl. cons. for ABSCAM investigation to Com. on Standards of Ofcl. Conduct, U.S. Ho. of Reps., 1980-81; trustee emeritus, past mem. exec com. Am. U., Washington; past trustee, mem. exec. com. Washington Journalism Ctr.; past bd. dirs. Nat. Council on Crime and Delinquency; mem. adv. com. Media Law Reporter. Author: Death and the Supreme Court, 1961; Editor: (with William E. Jackson) The Supreme Court in the American System of Government

(Justice Robert H. Jackson), 1955; contbr. articles to profl. jours. Past corp. mem. Salvation Army; mem. adv. com. Procedures of Jud. Coun., D.C.; mem. adv. bd. Inst. Comm. Law Studies, Cath. U.; bd. govs. St. Albans Sch., 1957-63, 65-72, chmn., 1950-51; spl. agt. FBI, Washington, 1951-56; sales supr. Farmers Group Inc., Los Angeles, 1956-60, asst. mgr. sales, 1960-63, mgr. sales, 1963-65, regional mgr., 1966-69, v.p. profl. liability, 1978-84; pres., bd. dirs. Farmers Ins. Co. Oreg., 1984-89; ret.; v.p., gen. mgr. Farmers New World Life, Mercer Island, Wash., 1969-78. Pres. Northridge (Calif.) Townhome and Homeowners Assn., 1981-82; bd. dirs. St. Martin in the Fields Episc. Ch., Canoga Park, Calif., 1982-84. Lt. (j.g.) USN, 1942-46, PTO. Mem. Oreg. Ins. Mgrs. (bd. dirs. 1984-88), Oreg. Life and Health Guaranty Assn. (chmn., bd. dirs. 1984-89), Oreg. Ins. Guaranty Assn. (treas., bd. dirs. 1984-89), Oreg. Ins. Coun. (bd. dirs. 1984-89), Masons. Republican. Avocations: tennis, golf, travel. Home: 18235 Moria Ct Lake Oswego OR 97034-7349

PRETZINGER, DONALD LEONARD, retired insurance executive; b. Los Angeles, Sept. 17, 1923; s. Leonard K. and Beatrice K. (Haupt) P.; m. Beverly Helen Winnard, Aug. 30, 1946; children: Christine, Kathryn, Kerry. BS with honors, Oreg. State U., 1948; MS, U. So. Calif., 1949. CLU, chartered fin. cons. Secondary tchr. sci. Fillmore (Calif.) High Sch., 1949-50, Los Angeles City Schs., 1950-51; spl. agt. FBI, Washington, 1951-56; sales supr. Farmers Group Inc., Los Angeles, 1956-60, asst. mgr. sales, 1960-63, mgr. sales, 1963-65, regional mgr., 1966-69, v.p. profl. liability, 1978-84; pres., bd. dirs. Farmers Ins. Co. Oreg., 1984-89; ret.; v.p., gen. mgr. Farmers New World Life, Mercer Island, Wash., 1969-78. Pres. Northridge (Calif.) Townhome and Homeowners Assn., 1981-82; bd. dirs. St. Martin in the Fields Episc. Ch., Canoga Park, Calif., 1982-84. Lt. (j.g.) USN, 1942-46, PTO. Mem. Oreg. Ins. Mgrs. (bd. dirs. 1984-88), Oreg. Life and Health Guaranty Assn. (chmn., bd. dirs. 1984-89), Oreg. Ins. Guaranty Assn. (treas., bd. dirs. 1984-89), Oreg. Ins. Coun. (bd. dirs. 1984-89), Masons. Republican. Avocations: tennis, golf, travel. Home: 18235 Moria Ct Lake Oswego OR 97034-7349

PREUS, DAVID WALTER, bishop, minister; b. Madison, Wis., May 28, 1922; s. Ove Jacob Hjort and Magdalene (Forde) P.; m. Ann Madsen, June 26, 1951; children: Martha, David, Stephen, Louise, Laura. BA, Luther Coll., Decorah, Iowa, 1943, DD (hon.), 1969; postgrad., U. Minn. 1946-47; BTh, Luther Sem., St. Paul, 1950; postgrad., Union Sem. 1951, Edinburgh U., 1951-52; LLD (hon.), Wagner Coll., 1973, Gettysburg Coll., 1976; DD (hon.), Pacific Luth. Coll., 1974, St. Olaf Coll., 1974, Dana Coll., 1979, Tex. Luth. Coll., 1994; LHD (hon.), Macalester Coll., 1976. Ordained to ministry Luth. Ch., 1950; asst. pastor First Luth. Ch., Brookings, S.D., 1950-51; pastor Trinity Luth. Ch., Vermillion, S.D., 1952-57; campus pastor U. Minn., Mpls., 1957-58; pastor Univ. Luth. Ch. of Hope, Mpls., 1958-73; v.p. Am. Luth. Ch., 1968-73, pres., presiding bishop, 1973-87; exec. dir. Global Mission Inst. Luther Northwestern Theol. Sem., St. Paul; Disting. vis. prof. Luther-Northwestern Sem., St. Paul, 1988-94; Luccock vis. pastor Yale Div. Sch., 1969; chmn. bd. youth activity Am. Luth. Ch., 1960-68; mem. exec. com. Luth. Council U.S.A.; v.p. Luth. World Fedn., 1977-90; mem. cen. com. World Council Chs., 1973-75, 80-90; Luth. del. White House Conf. on Equal Opportunity. Chmn. Greater Mpls. Fair Housing Com., Mpls. Council Chs., 1960-64; Mem. Mpls. Planning Commn., 1965-67; mem. Mpls. Sch. Bd., 1965-74, chmn., 1967-69; mem. Mpls. Bd. Estimate and Taxation, 1968-73, Mpls. Urban Coalition; sr. public adv. U.S. del. Madrid Conf. of Conf. on Security and Cooperation in Europe, 1980-81; bd. dirs. Mpls. Inst. Art, Walker Art Center, Hennepin County United Fund, Ams. for Childrens Relief, Luth. Student Found., Research Council of St. City Schs., Urban League, NAACP; bd. regents Augsburg Coll., Mpls. Served with Signal Corps AUS, 1943-46, PTO. Decorated comdr.'s cross Royal Norwegian Order St. Olav, Order of St. George 1st deg. Orthodox Ch. of Georgia (USSR), 1989; recipient Regents medal Augustana Coll., Sioux Falls, S.D., 1973, Torch of Liberty award Anti-Defamation League, 1973, St. Thomas Aquinas award St. Thomas U. Office: 2481 Como Ave Saint Paul MN 55108-1445

PREUSS, ROGER E(MIL), artist; b. Waterville, Minn., Jan. 29, 1922; s. Emil W. and Edna (Rosenau) P.; m. MarDee Ann Germundson, Dec. 31, 1954 (dec. Mar. 1981). Student, Mankato Comml. Coll., Mpls. Sch. Art. instr. seminar Mpls. Coll. Art and Design, Mpls. Inst. Arts Speakers Bur.; former judge ann. Goodyear Nat. Conservation Awards Program. Painter of nature art; one-man shows include: St. Paul Fine Art Galleries, 1959, Albert Lea Art Center, 1963, Hist. Soc. Mont., Helena, 1964, Bicentennial exhbn., Le Sueur County Hist. Soc. Mus., Elysian, Minn., 1976, Merrill's Gallery of Fine Art, Taos, N.Mex., 1980; exhbns. include: Midwest Wildlife Conf. Exhbn., Kerr's Beverly Hills, Calif., 1947, Laguna Art Mus., Calif., 1947, Joslyn Meml. Mus., Omaha, 1948, Minn. Centennial, 1949, Federated Chaparral Authors, 1951, Nat. Wildlife Art, 1951, 52, N.Am. Wildlife Art, 1952, Ducks Unltd. Waterfowl exhibit, 1953, 54, St. Paul Winter Carnival, 1954, St. Paul Gallery Art Mart, 1954, Salmagundi Club, 1968, Galerie Internationale, N.Y.C., 1972, Holy Land Conservation Fund, N.Y.C., 1976, Faribault Art Ctr., 1981, Wildlife Artists of the World Exhbn., Bend, Oreg., 1984, U. Art Mus., U. Minn., Mpls., 1990, Rochester Art Ctr., 1991, Minn. Hist. Soc.-Hill House, 1992, Bemidji Art Ctr., 1992, Jack London Ctr., Dawson City, Yukon Territory, Can., 1992; represented in permanent collections: Demarest Meml. Mus., Hackensack, N.J., Smithsonian Instn., N.Y. Jour. Commerce, Mont. Hist. Soc., Inland Bird Banding Assn., Minn. Capitol Bldg., Mont State U., Wildlife Am. Collection, LeSueur Hist. Soc., Voyageurs Nat. Park Interpretive Ctr., Krause-Hartig VFW Post, Mpls., Nat. Wildlife Fedn. Collection, Minn. Ceremonial House, U.S. Wildlife Svc. Fed. Bldg., Fort Snelling, Minn., Crater Lake Nat. Park Visitors Ctr., Va. Mus., Mpls., Luxton Collection, Banff, Alta., Can., Internat. Inst. Arts, Geneva, Mont. Capitol Bldg., People of Century-Goldblatt Collection, Lyons, Ill., Harlem Savings Collection, N.Y.C., Weisman Art Mus., Mpls., Tex., Minn. Vets. Home, Mpls., Blauvelt Art Mus., Oradell, N.J., Roger Preuss Art Collection, Augustana Ctr. for Western Studies, Sioux Falls, S.D., Minn. Mus. Am. Art, St. Paul, U. Minn. Art Mus., C.M. Russell Mus., Great Falls, Mont., others, numerous galleries and pvt. collections; designer: Fed. Duck Stamp, U.S. Dept. Interior, 1949, Commemorative Centennial Pheasant Stamp, 1981, Gold Waterfowl medallion Franklin Mint, 1983, Gold Stamp medallion Wildlife Mint, 1983, 40th Anniverary Commemorative Fed. Duck Stamp etching, 1989; panelist: Sportsman's Roundtable, Sta. WTCN-TV, Mpls. (emeritus), from 1953; author: Is Wildlife Art Recognized Fine Art?, 1986; contbr.: Christmas Echos, 1955, Wing Shooting, Trap & Skeet, 1955, Along the Trout Stream, 1979; contbr. Art Impressions mag., Can., Wildlife Art, U.S.; also illustrations and articles in Nat. Wildlife and over 300 essays on North American animals, others.; assoc. editor: Out-of-Doors mag.; compiler and artist: Outdoor Horizons, 1957, Twilight over the Wilderness, 1972, 60 limited edition prints Wildlife of America, from 1970; contbr. paintings and text Minnesota Today; creator paintings and text Preuss Wildlife Calendar; inventor: paintings and text Wildlife Am. Calendar; featured artist Art West, 1980-84, Wildlife Art; featured in films Your BFA- Care and Maintenance, Black Ducks Along the Border. Del. Nat. Wildlife Conf.; bd. dirs. Voyageurs Nat. Park Assn., Deep-Portage Conservation Found., 1977—, Wetlands for Wildlife U.S.A.; active Wildlife Am.; co-organizer, v.p., bd. dirs. Minn. Conservation Fedn., 1952-54; mem. U.S. Hospitalized Vets. Venison Program, 1957—; trustee Liberty Bell Edn. Found.; hon. life mem. Faribault Art Ctr., Waseca Arts Coun.; founder, dir. Roger Preuss Conservation Preserve for Study of Nature, 1990—. With USNR, World War II. Recipient Stamp Design award U.S. Fish and Wildlife Service, 1949, Minn. Outdoor award, 1956, Patron of Conservation award, 1956, award for contbns. conservation Minn. Statehood Centennial Commn., 1958, 1st award Am. Indsl. Devel. Council, citation of merit V.F.W., Award of Merit Mil. Order Cootie, 1963, Merit award Minn. Waterfowl Assn., 1976, Silver medal Nat. S.A.R., 1978, Services to Arts and Environment award Faribault Art Ctr., 1981, Ptnrs. for Wildlife award U.S. Fish and Wildlife Svc., 1994; named Wildlife Conservationist of Yr., Sears Found.-Nat. Wildlife Fedn. Program, 1966, Am. Bicentennial Wildlife Artist, Am. Heritage Assn., 1976; hon. mem. Ont. Chippewa Nation of Can., 1957; named Knight of Mark Twain for contbns. to art Mark Twain Soc. 1978; named to Water, Woods and Wildlife Hall of Fame, named Dean of Wildfowl Artists, 1981, Hon. Ky. Col.; recipient Honor degree U.S. Vets. Venison Program, 1980, Western Art. award significant contbns. to preservation arts and history Northern Prairie Plains, Augustana Coll. Ctr. Western Prairie Studies, Sioux Falls, S.D., 1992; named creator first signed, numbered photolithographic print pub. in N.Am., 1959 documented Colo. Springs Fine Arts Ctr., 1993, Colleague of Frederick R. Weisman Mus., Mpls., 1994. Fellow Internat. Inst. Arts (life), Soc. Animal Artists (emer-

itus), N.Am. Mycol. Assn.; mem. Internat. Sci. Info. Service, Nat. Wildlife Fedn. (nat. wildlife week chmn. Minn.), Minn. Ducks Unltd. (bd. dirs.), Minn. Artists Assn. (v.p., bd. dirs. 1953-59), Soc. Artists and Art Dirs., Outdoor Writers Am., Am. Artists Profl. League (emeritus), Mpls. Soc., Fine Arts, Wildlife Soc., Minn. Mycol. Soc. (pres. emeritus, hon. life mem.), Le Sueur County Hist. Soc. (hon. life mem.), Minn. Conservation Fedn. (hon. life), Wildlife Artists World (charter mem., internat. v.p. 1986—, chmn. fine arts bd.), Internat. Platform Assn. (emeritus), Great Lakes Outdoor Writers (emeritus), The Prairie Chicken Soc. (patron), The Sharp-tailed Grouse Soc. (patron), Mission Oceanic Arctic, 1992. Clubs: Beaverbrook (hon. life), Minn. Press (emeritus); Explorers (N.Y.C., emeritus). Office: care Wildlife Am PO Box 580004-a Minneapolis MN 55458-0004 Studio: 2224 Grand Ave Minneapolis MN 55405-3412 *With a modicum of natural skills in painting and writing, my basic goal throughout all my work has been to help people appreciate and understand nature. If I as a naturalist am a small voice for our world's waters, woods, and wildlife, if I have influenced many children and adults to become more environment conscious, if my art brings to others a measure of joy, then my best aspirations for my creations have been fulfilled.*

PREUSSER, JOSEPH WILLIAM, academic administrator; b. Petersburg, Nebr., June 18, 1941; s. Louis Henry and Elizabeth Sophia (Oberbrocking) P.; m. Therese Marie Mahoney, Aug. 12, 1967; children: Scott, Michelle, Denise. BA in Social Scis., Wayne State Coll., 1965; MA in Geography, U. Nebr., Omaha, 1971; PhD in Adminstrn., U. Nebr., 1978. Coord. social studies Lewis Cen. Community Sch. Dist., Council bluffs, Iowa, 1967-71; chmn. social sci. div., instr. Platte Jr. Coll., Columbus, Nebr., 1972-73; dean instrn./Platte campus Cen. Community Coll., Columbus, 1973-82, v.p. ednl. planning community edn., pres. Platte campus, 1982-84; pres. Cen. Community Coll., Grand Island, Nebr., 1984—; mem. edit com. devel. Nebr. Tech. Community Coll., 1973-75, sec., dean instrn., 1974-76, chmn. coun. pres's., 1990-91; mem. Archdiocese Omaha Bd. Edn., 1980-84; chmn. bd. St. Bonaventure Bd. Edn., 1976-80; pub. speaker in field. Contbr. articles to profl. jours. Bd. dirs. Cen. Nebr. Goodwill Industries, Grand Island, 1987—, treas., 1990-91; chmn. sustaining membership enrollment campaign Overland Trails Boy Scouts Am., 1990; worker YMCA Fund Drive, Columbus, 1980; mem. Columbus City Planning Commn., 1979-84, chmn., 1981, 82; mem. adv. com. Camp Pawnee, Columbus, 1974-76; coach boys baseball and girls softball, Council Bluffs, Columbus and Grand Island, 1968—. With U.S. Army, 1959-61. Named one Outstanding Young Men of Am., 1976. Mem. Am. Assn. Community and Jr. Colls., Am. Vocat. Assn., Nebr. Vocat. Assn. (Outstanding Svc. award 1986), Am. Assn. Ret. People, Nat. Coun. Instructional Officers, Nat. Coun. Instructional Adminstrs., Saddle Club, Rotary (Columbus and Grand Island chpts.), KC, Greater Columbus Area C. of C., Phi Delta Kappa, Gamma Theta Epsilon. Democrat. Roman Catholic. Avocations: golfing, gardening, woodworking.

PREVIN, ANDRE, composer, conductor; b. Berlin, Apr. 6, 1930; came to U.S., 1938, naturalized, 1943; s. Jack and Charlotte (Epstein) P.; m. Mia Farrow, Sept. 10, 1970 (div. 1979); children: Matthew and Sascha (twins), Fletcher, Lark, Daisy; m. Heather Hales, Jan. 1982; 1 child, Lukas. Student, Berlin Conservatory, Paris Conservatory; privately with, Pierre Monteux, Mario Castelnuovo-Tedesco. Mem. faculty Guildhall Sch., London, Curtis Inst., Phila., Berkshire Music Ctr. Rec. artist classical music for RCA, EMI, Phillips, Telarc, Deutsche Gramophone, 1946—; composer chamber music, Cello Concerto, Guitar Concerto, piano music, serenades for violin, brass quintet, song cycle on poems by Philip Larkin Every Good Boy Deserves Favour, Principals, Reflections, Piano Concerto, Triolet for BBrass Ensemblbg, Haydn variations for piano solo, 4 lyrics of Toni Morrison for sporano, Cello Sonata, Violin Sonata, Trio for Piano Oboe and Bassoon, Billy the Kid (Songs for Soprano and Piano), film scores, 1950-59; condr.-in-chief Houston Symphony, 1967-69; prin. condr. London Symphony Orch., 1968-79, Royal Philharm. Orch., Eng., 1985-91; music dir. L.A. Philharm., 1985-89; condr. laureate London Symphony Orch., 1992—; guest condr. maj. symphony orchs. and festivals in U.S. and Europe including: festivals in Salzburg, Edinburgh, Flanders, Vienna, Osaka, Prague, Berlin, Bergen; music dir. South Bank Music Festival, London, 1972-74, Pitts. Symphony, 1976-84, Los Angeles Philharmonic, 1984-89; author: Music Face to Face, 1971, Orchestra, 1979, No Minor Chords, 1992. Served with AUS, 1950-51. awards Nat. Grammophone Soc., Acad. Motion Picture Arts & Scis. Mem. Acad. Motion Picture Arts and Scis., Dramatists Guild, Brit. Composers Guild, Nat. Composers and Condrs. League, Degrees Curtis Inst., Royal Acad., Guild Hall Sch./Duquesne U. Home: 6 Sherwood Ln Bedford Hills NY 10507 Address: care Columbia Artists 165 W 57th St New York NY 10019 also: Barbican Centre, Silk St, London England EC2Y8DS

PREVITE, RICHARD, computer company executive; b. Boston, 1935. BS, San Jose State U., 1956, MA. Contr. Sierra Elec. Corp., Menlo Park, Calif., 1961-69; with Advanced Micro Devices, Inc., Sunnyvale, Calif., 1969—, sr. v.p., treas., chief adminstrv. officer, pres., COO, bd. dirs.; bd. dirs. Robinson Nugent, Inc. Office: Advanced Micro Devices Inc PO Box 3453 Sunnyvale CA 94088-3453

PREVOR, RUTH CLAIRE, psychologist; b. N.Y.C., June 20, 1944; d. Gustav and Greta (Dreifuss) Strauss; m. Sydney Joseph P., July 4, 1963; children: Joy, Grant, Jed. BA, U. P.R., 1966; PhD, Caribbean Ctr. of Postgrad., Studies, San Juan, 1988. Cert. forensic psychologist, critical incidents stress debriefing and post-trauma symptoms. Asst. dean Caribbean Ctr. of Postgrad. Studies, 1986-87; dir. prenatal edn. Ashford Meml. Hosp., San Juan, 1987; pvt. practice San Juan, 1984—; advisor, field faculty Vt. Coll., Norwich U., 1990-91; trustee Caribbean Ctr. for Advanced Studies, San Juan, Miami, Fla., 1990—. Bd. dirs. Jewish Community Ctr., Miramar, P.R., 1986—; bd. dirs. pre-sch., 1990—; pres. Home and Sch./St. John's Prep., San Juan, 1980-81, P.R. chpt. Hadassah Sch., 1972-74; presdl. adv. com., 1990-92. Mem. Am. Psychol. Assn., Assn. of Psychology of P.R. (hon. award 1984), Caribbean Counselors Assn., Caribe Hilton Club, Nat. Assn. Children with Learning Disabilities, Nat. Register Health Svc. Providers in Psychology. Jewish. Office: Ashford Med Ctr San Juan PR 00907

PREVOST, EDWARD JAMES, paint manufacturing executive; b. Baie Comeau, Que., Can., May 26, 1941; s. Omer and Jeanne (Ouellet) P.; m. Anna Marie Murphy, June 20, 1964; children: Marc, Louise, Eric. Luc. BA in History with honors, Loyola Coll., Montreal, Que., 1962; MBA, U. Western Ont., London, 1964. Cert. Advt. Agy. Practitioner. Account exec. J. Walter Thompson Co. Ltd., Montreal, 1964-66; successively account exec., account supr., group mgr. and v.p. Cockfield Brown & Co. Ltd., Montreal, 1966-69; gen. mgr. CJRP Radio, Quebec City, 1969-71; exec. v.p., chief operating officer Mut. Broadcasting Ltd., 1971-72, pres., chief operating officer, 1973; chmn. bd. Stephens and Towndrow Co. Ltd., Toronto, 1973-74; exec. v.p. Civitas Corp. Ltd., Montreal, 1973-74, pres., chief exec. officer, 1974-82, also chmn. bd. operating cos., 1974-82; pres., chief exec. officer La Brasserie O'Keefe Limitée, Montreal, 1983-89; sr. v.p. Carling O'Keefe Breweries of Can. Ltd., 1983-89; pres., chief exec. officer, dir. SICO Inc., Longueuil, Can., 1989-91; pres., CEO Para Inc., Brampton, Can., 1991—; bd. dirs. BBM Bur. Broadcasting Measurement, 1971-78; mem. Montreal Bd. Trade; treas., vice chmn.-elect Can. Paint & Coatings Assn., 1994—. Gov. Can. Advt. Found., 1982. Chmn. Televifan Can., 1983-86; chmn. Montreal Heart Inst. Rsch. Fund, 1979-81, exec. com. 1981-86. Mem. Bd. L'Assn. des Brasseurs du Que. (chmn. 1984-86), Montreal C. of C. (dir. 1980, co-pres. cinematographic com. 1980-81), Province Que., Can., chambers commerce, Canadian Assn. Broadcasters (dir. 1975, vice chmn. radio 1976-77, chmn. 1978-79, past chmn., mem. exec. com. 1980-81), Inter-Am. Assn. Broadcasters Uruguay (sec., past treas), Young Pres. Orgn. (chmn. Que. chpt. 1987), Inst. Canadian Advt., Que. Diabetes Assn., Assn. des MBA du Que. (chmn. 1985-86). Clubs: St.-Denis (Montreal), Western Bus. Sch. (founding pres. 1972), Royal Montreal Golf. Office: Para Inc, 11 Kenview Blvd, Brampton, ON Canada L6T 5G5

PREVOZNIK, STEPHEN JOSEPH, anesthesiologist; b. McAdoo, Pa., June 21, 1929; s. John George and Mary Margaret (Ficek) P.; m. Rita Agnes Kellett, Aug. 20, 1955; children—Mary Therese, Stephen Joseph, John Cyril, Michael Edward, Margaret Anne, Rita Marie, Thomas William, Jean Marie. R.N., St. Joseph Hosp. Sch. Nursing, Phila., 1951; B.S., U. Notre Dame, 1955; M.D., U. Pa., 1959. Intern Fitzgerald Mercy Hosp., Darby, Pa., 1959-60; resident in anesthesia U. Pa., Phila., 1960-62; practice medicine specializing in anesthesiology Phila., 1962—; mem. staff U. Pa. Hosp.; prof.

anesthesia U. Pa., 1977-94, dir. clin. activities, 1971-89; Chmn. Residency Rev. Com. for Anesthesiology, 1991—. Contbr. to textbooks on anesthesiology. Mem. AMA, Am. Soc. Anesthesiologists, Pa. Soc. Anesthesiologists, Phila. Soc. Anesthesiologists (pres. 1975-77), Internat. Anesthesia Rsch. Soc., U. Anesthetists (exec. coun. 1977-79, sec. 1981-84, dir. anesthesiology pain mgmt. program 1992-94). Home: 474 Fairfax Rd Drexel Hill PA 19026-1209 Office: Dept Anesthesia Hosp U Pa Philadelphia PA 19104 *No one does everything by himself; someone is always there to provide a helping hand. As one progresses and matures, he finds many opportunities to repay what he has received. Without this repayment, the chain is broken and that life is without meaning.*

PREWITT, CHARLES THOMPSON, geochemist; b. Lexington, Ky., Mar. 3, 1933; s. John Burton and Margaret (Thompson) P.; m. Gretchen B. Hansen, Jan. 31, 1958; children: Daniel Hansen. SB, MIT, 1955, SM, 1960, PhD, 1962. Research scientist E.I. DuPont De Nemours & Co. Inc., Wilmington, Del., 1962-69; assoc. prof. SUNY, Stony Brook, 1969-71, prof., 1971-86, chmn. dept. earth and space scis., 1977-80; dir. Geophys. Lab., Carnegie Inst. of Washington, 1986—; sec.-treas. U.S. Nat. Com. for Crystallography, Washington, 1983-85; gen. chmn. 14th Meeting of Internat. Mineral. Assn., Stanford, Calif., 1986; chmn. NRC/Nat. Acad. Scis. com. on physics and chemistry of earth materials, 1985-87; mem. bd. govs. Consortium for Advanced Radiation Svcs. Editor: (jour.) Physics and Chemistry of Minerals, 1976-85; contbr. over 140 articles to profl. jours. Capt. USAR, 1956-65. NATO sr. postdoctoral fellowship, 1975, Churchill overseas fellowship, 1975, Japan Soc. for Promotion of Sci. fellowship, 1983; named Disting. Vis. Prof. Chemistry, Ariz. State U., 1983. Fellow Mineral. Soc. Am. (pres. 1983-84); mem. Geol. Soc. Am., Am. Crystallographic Assn., Materials Research Soc., Mineral. Soc. Gt. Britain and Ireland. Home: 2728 Unicorn Ln NW Washington DC 20015-2234 Office: Carnegie Inst Geophys Lab 5251 Broad Branch Rd NW Washington DC 20015-1305*

PREWITT, KENNETH, political science educator, foundation executive; b. Alton, Ill., Mar. 16, 1936; s. Carl Kenneth and Louise (Carpenter) P.; children: Jennifer Ann, Geoffrey Douglas. BA, So. Meth. U., 1958; MA, Washington U., St. Louis, 1959; PhD, Stanford U., 1963. Prof. polit. sci. U. Chgo., 1964-80, chmn. dept. polit. sci., 1975-76; dir. Nat. Opinion Research Center, 1976-79; pres. Social Sci. Research Council, N.Y.C., 1979-85; sr. v.p. Rockefeller Found., N.Y.C., 1985—; vis. scholar U. Nairobi, Kenya, 1968-71; adj. prof. polit sci. Columbia U., 1980-83; teaching and rsch. Stanford U., 1964-68; cons. Rockefeller Found, Zaire, 1972, Thailand, 1973; chmn. governing bd. Energy Found.; bd. dirs. Washington U., So. Meth. U., Ctr. Advanced Study Behavioral Scis. Author: Political Socialization, 1969, Ruling Elites, 1973, Labyrinths of Democracy, 1973, Introduction to American Government, 1983, 6th edit., 1991. Guggenheim fellow, 1983; fellow Center Advanced Study in Behavioral Scis., 1983. Fellow AAAS, Am. Acad. Arts and Scis. (v.p.); mem. Am. Polit. Sci. Assn. (v.p.), Coun. on Fgn. Rels. Office: Rockefeller Found 420 5th Ave New York NY 10018-2729

PREWOZNIK, JEROME FRANK, lawyer; b. Detroit, July 15, 1934; s. Frank Joseph and Loretta Ann (Parzych) P.; m. Marilyn Johnson, 1970; 1 son, Frank Joseph II. AB cum laude, U. Detroit, 1955; JD with distinction, U. Mich., 1958. Bar: Calif. 1959. Pvt. practice, Calif., 1960-91. Served with U.S. Army, 1958-60. Mem. ABA (bus. law sect., law and acctg. com., chmn. auditing standards subcom. 1981-86), State Bar Calif. (bus. law sect., exec. com. 1983-86), Order of Coif. Republican. Home and Office: 431 Georgina Ave Santa Monica CA 90402-1909

PREY, BARBARA ERNST, artist; b. Jamaica, N.Y., Apr. 17, 1957; d. Herbert Henry and Margaret (Joubert) Ernst; m. Jeffrey Drew Prey, Jan. 11, 1986; children: Austin William Ernst Prey, Emily Elizabeth Prey. BA with honors, Williams Coll., 1979; MDiv, Harvard U., 1986. Sales staff Tiffany and Co., N.Y.C., summer 1977; summer intern Met. Mus. Art, N.Y.C., summer 1979; personal asst. Prince Albrecht Castell, Castell, Germany, 1980-81; with modern painting dept. Sotheby's Auction House, N.Y.C., 1981-82; sales asst. Marlborough Gallery, N.Y.C., 1982; teaching asst. Boston Coll., 1984, Harvard U., Cambridge, Mass., 1984-85; vis. lectr. Tainan (Taiwan) Coll. and Sem., 1986-87; artist Prosperity, Pa., 1987—; art juror Washington and Jefferson Coll., Washington, Pa., 1990; presenter in field. Illustrator: (books) Boys Harbor Cookbook, 1988, A Dream Became You, (4 book series) A City Grows Up, 1991, (cover) Am. Artist Mag., summer 1994; exhibited paintings in group shows including Mus. of Fine Arts, Nassau County, N.Y., 1988, Nat. Arts Club, N.Y.C., 1988, Gallery One, Rockland, Maine, 1992, Williams Coll., Williamstown, Mass., 1993, Johnstown (Pa.) Art Mus., 1993, Blair Art Mus., Hollidaysburg, Pa., 1993, Phila. Mus. of Art Gallery, 1995; exhibited in one-woman shows including Harvard-Yale-Princeton Club, Pitts., 1991; represented in many pvt. collections. Class agt. Williams Coll., Williamstown, Mass., 1981-91; bd. mem. Citizens Libr., Washington, 1992-93; active Bethel Presbyn. Ch. Recipient Fulbright scholarship Fulbright Assn., Germany, 1979-80, grant Roothbert Fund, Chataugua, N.Y., 1982-84, Ch. History award Gordan-Conwell Sem., S. Hamilton, Mass., 1984, Henry Luce Found. grant Henry Luce Found., Taiwan, 1986-87. Mem. Pitts. Watercolor Soc. (Jean Thoburn award 1994), Nat. Mus. Women in the Arts. Republican. Avocations: tennis, skiing, bird watching, reading, cross county skiing.

PREYER, NORRIS WATSON, history educator; b. Greensboro, N.C., Feb. 9, 1926; s. William Yost Preyer and Mary Norris Richardson; m. Kathryn Jeanette Cobb, Dec. 15, 1950; children: Norris Watson Jr., Janet McFadyen Nelson. BA, U. N.C., 1947; MA, U. Va., 1950, PhD, 1954. Asst. prof. history Guilford Coll., Greensboro, N.C., 1953-57; asst. prof. history Queens Coll., Charlotte, N.C., 1957-58, prof. history, 1958-62, chair dept. history, 1959-90, Dana prof. history, 1962-90, Dana prof. emeritus, 1990—; bd. dirs. Piedmont Fin. Co. Author: Hezekiah Alexander and the Revolution in the Backcountry, 1987 (Book award N.C. Soc. Historians 1988); contbr. articles to profl. jours. Mem. Textile History Soc., 1962-65, Sci. Mus., Inc., Charlotte, 1973-79, Presbyn. Hist. Soc., 1985-91, Mecklenburg Hist. Soc., 1994—, Cons. Mus. New South, 1990—; bd. dirs. Latta Place, Inc. Charlotte, 1972-75, 85-91, 92—, pres., 1994-95; elder Myers Park Presbyn. Ch., Charlotte; mem. planning group Charlotte-Mecklenburg Cultural Task Force, 1974-75. Named Danforth Assoc., Danforth Found., 1962-68; NEH fellow Newberry Libr., Chgo., 1979. Mem. Am. Hist. Assn., Orgn. Am. Historians, So. Hist. Assn., Soc. for the History of the Early Am. Republic, N.C. Hist. Soc., Presbyn. Hist. Soc., Mecklenburg Hist. Assn. Democrat. Avocations: tennis, fishing, travel. Home: 2028 Roswell Ave Charlotte NC 28207-2735

PREYER, ROBERT OTTO, English literature educator; b. Greensboro, N.C., Nov. 11, 1922; s. William Yost and Mary Norris (Richardson) P.; m. Renee Haenel, June 14, 1947; children: Jill, Sally, Elizabeth; m. Kathryn Conway Turner, July 19, 1966. Grad., Choate Sch., 1939; student, Davidson Coll., 1939-40; AB, Princeton U., 1945; MA, Columbia U., 1948, PhD, 1954. Instr. Smith Coll., 1948-54; asst. prof. Brandeis U. Waltham, Mass., 1954-55, prof., chmn. dept. English and Am. lit., 1963-66, chmn. faculty senate, 1976-80, dir. univ. studies program, 1979—, prof. emeritus, 1988—; vis. lectr. Amherst Coll., 1952; vis. prof. Freiburg U., Germany, 1956-57; guest prof. Heidelberg U., Germany, 1973-74; bd. dirs. Peidmont Fin. Corp., Richardson Corp., Boston, Blacksides Inc., Boston conservancy, Earl Warren Legal Tng. Program Inc., N.Y.C.; mem. adv. bd. Eyes on the Prize, TV series, 1985. Author: Bentham, Coleridge and The Science of History, 1958; adv. editor: Victorian Studies, 1961—; editor: Victorian Literature; contbr. essays to profl. jours. Chmn. Mass Civil Liberties Fund, 1987-90; mem. bd. overseers humanities Tufts U., 1989-94; mem. adv. coun. dept. English, Princeton U., 1991—; bd. dirs. Mus. Afro-Am. History, Boston. Ensign USNR, 1940-43, PTO. Mem. MLA, ACLU (bd. dirs.), Legal Def. Found. (nat. bd. dirs. 1990—), Cottage Club, St. Botolph Club, Princeton Club, Keene Valley Country Club. Democrat. Home: 6 Maple Ave Cambridge MA 02139-1116

PREZZANO, WILBUR JOHN, photographic products company executive; b. Chappaqua, N.Y., Dec. 18, 1940; s. Wilbur J. and Adelaide J. Prezzano; m. Sheila Neary, Aug. 29, 1964; children: Timothy J., David N., E. Peter. Bs in Econs., U. Pa., 1962, M.B.A. in Indsl. Mgmt., 1964. Statistician Eastman Kodak Co., Rochester, N.Y., 1965-66, mem. treas.'s staff, 1966-67, fin. analyst, 1967-68, fin. analyst bus. systems markets div., 1968-

69, coordinator sales analysis and fin. info. systems, 1969-71, supr. fin. planning analysis, 1971-73, supt. acctg. analysis, 1973, staff asst. to gen. mgr. Customer Equipment Services Div., 1973-76, mgr. field ops., 1976-78, dir. copy products, mgr. field ops., 1978-79, dir. bus. mktg. planning mktg. div., 1979-80, asst. gen. mgr., 1980, v.p., 1980-82, gen. mgr. U.S. mktg. div., 1982-83, group v.p., gen. mgr. mktg., mgr. internat. photog. ops., 1983-84, gen. mgr. photog. products, 1985-90, gen. mgr. internat., 1990-91, pres. health, 1991-94, exec. v.p., chmn. and pres. Kodak greater China region, 1994—, also bd. dirs.; bd. dirs. First Fed. Savs. & Loan Assn., Rochester. Mem. Health Industry Mfrs. Assn., Nat. Action Coun. for Minorities in Engring., Inc., Genesee Valley Club (Rochester). Office: Eastman Kodak Co 343 State St Rochester NY 14650-0237

PRIAULX, A(LLAN), publishing executive; b. Eugene, Oreg., May 13, 1940; s. Arthur W. and Kathleen Dealtry (Bean) P.; m. Jacqueline Markham, Jan. 10, 1976; children—Sharmon, Elizabeth. Student, Dartmouth Coll., 1958-60, U. Southampton, Eng., 1960, New Sch. for Social Research, 1961-62. Corr. UPI, Buffalo, 1962-63; mgr. bur. UPI, Concord, N.H., 1963-65, Honolulu, 1965-66; news mgr. UPI, Paris, 1966-68; dir. spl. projects McLendon Corp., Dallas, 1968-70; v.p. Register & Tribune Syndicate, N.Y.C., 1970-76; dir. editor King Features Syndicate, N.Y.C., 1976-79, editor, 1979-81, v.p. gen. mgr., 1981-86; v.p. editorial dir. C.N.R. Ptnrs., 1986-87; pres. Resource Media Inc., 1988—; exec. v.p., pub. The Am. Banker Thomson Corp., 1990-92; chmn., chief exec. Resource Media Inc., 1992—; bd. dirs. Markham/Novell Comm. Author: (with S.J. Ungar) The Almost Revolution, 1969. V.p., chmn. pub. relations com. United Cerebral Palsy Assns.; mem. exec. vol. core Victim Services Agys. N.Y.C.; bd. dirs. Greyhound Friends Inc. Mem. Overseas Press Club Am., Advt. Club N.Y., Yale Club N.Y., Dartmouth Club N.Y. Episcopalian.

PRIBBLE, EASTON, artist; b. Falmouth, Ky., July 31, 1917; s. Thaddeus Sewell and Louise Ella (Parker) P. Student, U. Cin., 1941. Ind. tchr. N.Y.C., 1950-57; instr. painting and history of art Munson-Williams-Proctor Inst., Utica, N.Y., 1957—; instr. history of art Utica Coll., Syracuse U., 1960-74. One-man exhbns. include Pinacotheca Gallery, N.Y.C., 1947, 48, Alan Gallery, N.Y.C., 1953, 55, 59, Hamilton Coll., Clinton, N.Y., 1975, Munson-Williams-Proctor Inst. Mus. Art, 1957, 76, 82, Kirkland Art Ctr., Clinton, N.Y., 1988, Rome (N.Y.) Art Ctr., 1990; represented in permanent collections, Whitney Mus. Am. Art, Hirschorn Mus. and Sculpture Garden, Smithsonian Instn., Parrish Mus., Southampton, N.Y., Munson-Williams-Proctor Inst. Mus. Art., Fallingwater (Frank Lloyd Wright house), Mill Run, Pa., Hudson River Mus., Yonkers, N.Y. Fellow Yaddo, Saratoga Springs, N.Y., 1954, 55, 68. Mem. Artists Equity. Home: 24 Rose Pl Utica NY 13502-5614 Office: Munson-Williams-Proctor Inst 310 Genesee St Utica NY 13502-4764

PRIBBLE, EDWARD DAVID (LALOR), labor and employment arbitrator, lawyer; b. Madison, Wis., Jan. 29, 1944; s. Edward Richard and Viola (Byrne) Lalor; adopted mother: Helen Rose (Litney) P.; m. Paula Sue Tompkins, Aug. 12, 1978; children. BBA, U. Wis., 1966, JD, 1969. Bar: Wis., 1969, Minn., 1980, U.S. Dist. Ct. (we. dist.) Wis., 1969, U.S. Supreme Ct., 1979. Gen. atty. NLRB, Kansas City, Mo., Kans., 1969-80; trial specialist NLRB, Kansas City, 1977-80; arbitrator labor and employment, pres. Pribble Arbitration and Mediation Svcs., Inc., Mpls., 1980-85; arbitrator, pres. Pribble Arbitration and Mediation Svcs., Inc., St. Cloud, Minn., 1985-95; CEO, pres., arbitrator Lalor Arbitration and Mediation, Inc., St. Cloud, Minn., 1995—; atty. advice div. NLRB, Washington, 1973-74; mcpl. judge City Countryside (Kans.), 1979-80; mem. arbitration panels Fed. Mediation and Conciliation Svc., 1982—, Am. Arbitration Assn., 1984—, Nat. Mediation Bd., 1991—, Minn. Bur. Mediation Svcs., 1982—, Iowa Pub. Employment Rels. Bd., 1983—; pvt. panel Tenneco, J.I. Case Div. and I.A. Machinists and Aerospace Workers Local 2525, Fargo, N.D., 1985—; full-day moderator in arbitration, labor and employment law, discrimination, alternate dispute resolution, evidence, and family law programs Minn. Cont tinuing Legal Edn., 1989—; labor and employment arbitrator Minn. Alt. Dispute Resolution. Contbr. articles to profl. jours. Mem. Minn. Dem. Farm Labor State and Congl. Dist. Ctrl. Com., 1981—, Minn. State Platform Commn., Dem.-Farm-Labor Party, 1984-85, chmn. senate dist., 1984-85, fundraiser; initiator, co-founder Dr. Guy Stanton Ford Ednl. Found., 1964-69; co-founder Westport Free Health Clinic, Kansas City, Mo., 1970-79; active coun. Land of Lakes Girl Scouts, Minn., 1985—; Leadership Coun. So. Poverty Ctr., Habitat for Humanity Internat. Ptnrs. Coun.; coach Girls Youth Basketball League, St. Cloud, 1992—; bd. dirs. St. Cloud Symphony Orch. 1992-94. Mem. ABA (labor and employment law sects. 1978—), Fed. Bar Assn. (labor and employment law sects. 1974—), Minn. Bar Assn. (labor and employment law sects. 1980—), Nat. Youth Sports Coaches Assn. (cert.), Wis. Bar Assn. (labor and employment law sects. 1969—), Internat. Indsl. Rels. Assn., Soc. Profls. in Dispute Resolution, Indsl. Rels. Rsch. Assn., Theta Delta Chi. Roman Catholic. Avocations: reading, family history, fishing, stock investing. Office: Lalor Arbitration & Mediation Inc 1220 Thirteenth St North Saint Cloud MN 56303-2733

PRIBILLA, PETER, telecommunications industry executive. Degree in comms. engring., Tech. U. Munich, 1968. Pres. Siemens AG Private Comm. Sys. group, 1985—; mng. bd. Siemens AG, 1993—; pres., CEO Siemens Rolm Comms., Santa Clara, Calif., 1992—. Office: Rolm Company 4900 Old Ironside Dr Santa Clara CA 95054*

PRIBLE, LARRY R., insurance company executive; b. 1946. With IBM, Indpls., 1967-79; with Indpls. Life Ins., 1980—, now pres., CEO. Office: Indianapolis Life Ins Co 2960 N Meridian St Indianapolis IN 46208*

PRIBRAM, KARL HARRY, psychology educator, researcher; b. Feb. 25, 1919. BS, U. Chgo., 1938, MD, 1941; PhD in Psychology (hon.), U. Montreal, Can., 1992. Diplomate Am. Bd. Med. Psychotherapists. Lectr. Yale U., Hartford, Conn., 1951-58; dir. Inst of Living, Hartford, Conn., 1951-58; fellow Stanford (Va.) U., 1958-59, assoc. prof., 1959-62, rsch. career prof., 1962-89, prof. emeritus, 1989—; eminent scholar Radford (Va.) U., 1989—; vis. scholar, hon. lectr. MIT, 1954, Clark U., 1956, Harvard, 1956, Haverford Coll., 1961, U. So. Calif., 1961, U. Moscow, 1962, Beloit Coll., 1966-67, U. Alberta, Can., 1968, Ctr. for Study Dem. Insts., 1974-75, U Coll., London, 1972, U. Chgo., 1973, Menninger Sch. Psychiatry, 1973-76, Ohio State U., 1975, Inst. for Higher Studies, 1975 and numerous others, 1954—. Author: Brain and Behavior, vol. 1-4, 1969, What Makes Man Human, 1971, Languages of the Brain: Experimental Paradoxes and Principles in Neuropsychology, 1971; The Neurosciences: Third Study Program, 1974, Brain and Perception: Holonomy and Structure in Figural Processing, 1991; editor, mem. consulting bd. Neuropsychologia, Jour. Math. Biology, Internat. Jour. Neurosci., Behavioral and Brain Scis., Jour. Mental Imagery, Jour. Human Movement Studies, Jour. Social and Biol. Structures, ReVision, STSM Quarterly, Indian Jour. Psychophysiology, Interam Jour. Psychology, Internat. Jour. Psychophysiology, Cognition and Brain Theory; contbr. over 170 articles to profl. jours. Recipient Lifetime Rsch. Career award in neurosci. NIH, 1962-89, Humanitarian award INTA, 1980, Realia honor Inst. Advanced Philosophic Rsch., 1986, Outstanding Contbns. award Am. Bd. Med. Psychotherapists. Fellow Am. Acad. Arts and Scis., N.Y. Acad. Scis. (hon. life); mem. AAUP, AMA, AAAS, APA (pres. div. physiol. and comparative psychology 1967-68, pres. div. theoretical and philos. psychology 1979-80), Internat. Neuropsychol. Soc. (founding pres. 1967-69), Internat. Assn. Study of Pain, Soc. Exptl. Psychologists, Am. Psychol. Soc., Am. Psychopathological Assn. (Paul Hoch award 1975), Am. Acad. Psychoanalysis, Soc. Biol. psychiatry (Manfred Sakel award 1976), Soc. Clin. and Exptl. Hypnosis (Henry Guze award 1991), Soc. Neurosci., Profs. For World Peace (pres. 1982-85), Sigma Xi. Home: 102 Dogwood Ln Radford VA 24141 Office: Radford Univ Ctr Brain Rsch Box 6977 Radford VA 24142

PRICE, ALFRED LEE, lawyer, mining company executive; b. Little Rock, May 19, 1935; s. Dewey Ernest and Dorothy Ava (Cooper) P.; m. Magdalena Torres, June 20, 1958; children: Gregory L., Ana Maria. Ba, Hendrix Coll., 1956; JD, Tulane U., 1967. Bar: La. 1967, Miss. 1974, D.C. Office mgr., dir. personnel Petroleum Helicopters Co., Lafayette, La. and New Orleans, 1956-67; atty., office mgr. Offshore Navigation and Petroleum Helicopters Co., New Orleans, 1967-74; gen. counsel First Miss. Corp., Jackson, 1974—, corp. sec., 1988—. Mem. ABA, La. Bar Assn., Miss. Bar Assn., Hinds County Bar Assn., Miss. Mfrs. Assn. (bd. dirs.), Miss. Econ.

PRICE, ARTHUR D., food products executive; b. 1944. With Mid Valley Products, Inc., Taylors, S.C., 1964-76, pres.; with Global Trading, Inc., Greenville, S.C., 1976—, pres. Office: Global Trading Inc 14 Creekside Park Ct Greenville SC 29615*

PRICE, ARTHUR RICHARD, petroleum company executive; b. Calgary, Alta., Can., Oct. 22, 1951; married; 3 children. BSc, U. Alta., 1973. With NOVA Corp. of Alta., 1973-79; v.p. Husky Oil Ltd., Calgary, 1979-84, pres., 1984-93, CEO, 1987-93; pres. Husky Oil Ops. Ltd., Calgary, 1984-93; dir. Husky Oil Ltd., 1993—; spl. advisor internat. investment Hutchinson Whampoa Ltd. Bd. Dirs. Office: Husky Oil Ltd, 707 8th Ave SW, Calgary, AB Canada T2P 1H5

PRICE, B. BYRON, museum director. Dir. Panhandle-Plains Hist. Mus., Canyon, Tex., until 1987; exec. dir. Nat. Cowboy Hall of Fame and Western Heritage Ctr., Oklahoma City, 1987—. Office: Nat Cowboy Hall Fame & Western Heritage Ctr 1700 NE 63rd St Oklahoma City OK 73111-7997

PRICE, CHARLES GRATTAN, JR., retired insurance agency executive; b. Harrisonburg, Va., May 31, 1919; s. Charles Grattan and Julia Page (Pleasants) P.; m. Kathleen Violette Nutter Price, Mar. 15, 1940 (dec. 1992); children: Julia Kathleen, Melinda Marshall, Charles Grattan III. BS in Mech. Engring., Va. Poly. Inst., Blacksburg, 1940. Mech. engr. Chesapeake Western Ry., Harrisonburg, Va., 1940-41; officer U.S. Army, 1941-45; cons. pvt. practice, Vt., Pa., 1946; with ins. agy. C.G. Price & Sons, Inc., Harrisonburg, Va., 1946-78; ret., 1978; ind. railroad dieselization survey cons., 1946-47. Author: The Crooked and Weedy, 1992, Reminiscences of a Rambling Railroader, 1993, Robert E. Lee's Railroad, 1994. Maj. USAR, 1947-54. Mem. Rlwy. and Locomotive Hist. Soc., Nat. Rlwy. Hist. Soc., Railroadiana Collectors Assn., Elks (lodge 450), Am. Legion (post 27). Presbyterian. Avocations: reading, historical railroad research and writing. Home: 531 Ott St Harrisonburg VA 22801-3218

PRICE, CHARLES H., II, former ambassador; b. Kansas City, Mo., Apr. 1, 1931; s. Charles Harry and Virginia (Ogden) P.; m. Carol Ann Swanson, Jan. 10, 1969; children: Caroline Lee, Melissa Marie, Charles H., C. B., Pickette. Student, U. Mo., 1951-53; LLD (hon.), Westminster Coll., 1984; LLD (honoris causa), U. Mo., 1988; LHD, Baker U., 1991; DSc (hon.), U. Buckingham, Eng., 1993. Chmn. bd., dir. Price Candy Co., Kansas City, 1969-81, Am. Bancorp., Kansas City, 1973-81; chmn., chief exec. officer Am. Bank & Trust Co., Kansas City, 1973-81; Am. ambassador to Belgium Brussels, 1981-83; Am. ambassador to U.K. London, 1983-89; chmn. bd. Ameribanc, Inc., St. Joseph, Mo., 1989-92, pres., CEO, 1990-92; chmn. bd. Mercantile Bank Kansas City, Mo., 1992—; bd. dirs. Brit. Airways and Hanson PLC, London, N.Y. Times Co., Texaco, Inc., Sprint Corp., Kansas City, Mercantile Bancorp., Inc. Bd. dirs. St. Luke's Hosp., Kansas City, 1970-81, hon. dir., 1989—; advisor Heart Inst. com.; bd. dirs. Midwest Rsch. Inst., Kansas City, chmn., 1990-93. Hon. fellow Regent's Coll., London, 1986; recipient William Booth award Salvation Army, 1985, World Citizen of Yr. award Mayor of Kansas City, 1985, Trustee Citation award Midwest Rsch. Inst., 1987, Disting. Svc. award Internat. Rels. Coun., 1989, Mankind award Cystic Fibrosis Found., 1990, Gold Good Citizenship award SAR, 1991, Chancellor's medal U. Mo. Kansas City, 1992. Mem. Brook Club, Cypress Point Club, Eldorado Country Club, Castle Pines Country Club, Kansas City Country Club, River Club, Swinley Forest Golf Club, White's Club. Republican. Episcopalian. Office: 1 W Armour Blvd Ste 300 Kansas City MO 64111-2087

PRICE, CHARLES T., lawyer; b. Lansing, Mich., Feb. 11, 1944. BA, Ohio Wesleyan U., 1966; JD, Harvard U., 1969. Bar: Ohio 1969, U.S. Dist. Ct. (no. dist.) Ohio 1974, U.S. Ct. Appeals (6th cir) 1981, U.S. Supreme Ct. 1982, Ill. 1989. Ptnr. Baker & Hostetler, Cleve.; pres., pub. Chgo. Sun-Times, 1987-88; exec. v.p. Sun-Times Co., 1989-92. Office: Baker & Hostetler 3200 Nat City Ctr 1900 E 9th St Cleveland OH 44114-3303

PRICE, DALIAS ADOLPH, geography educator; b. Newtonville, Ind., June 28, 1913; s. Fred J. and Rose (Gillam) P.; m. Lillian O. Alexander, May 14, 1943; children—David, Curtis, Kent, Roger. B.A., U. Ill., 1937, M.A., 1938; Ph.D., U. Wis., 1954. Instr. geography U. Ill., 1938-40; acting head dept. S.W. Mo. State Coll., Springfield, 1940-45; asst. U. Wis., 1945-47; assoc. prof. geography So. Ill. U., 1947-58; prof. geography, head dept. Eastern Ill. U., 1958—. Author articles in field. Mem. Wabash Valley Interstate Commn., 1965—; Bd. suprs. Coles County, Ill., 1967, chmn., 1971-72; Bd. dirs. Charleston Community Hosp., 1966—, Inst. Urban and Regional Affairs, 1967—. Recipient Distng. Svc. award Nat. Weather Svc., 1988, 90.; hon. fellow U. Wis., 1953. Mem. AAUP (sec.-treas. Ill. conf. 1958-62), Ill. Geog. Soc. (sec. 1950, chmn. 1951,62, distinguished geographer award 1976), Charleston C. of C. (bd. dirs. 1961-64), Assn. Am. Geographers, Gamma Theta Upsilon. Democrat. Unitarian. Club: Rotarian (pres. Charleston 1952—). Home: 517 W Coolidge Ave Charleston IL 61920-3860

PRICE, DAVID, recreational facilities executive; b. 1933. With Am. Golf Corp., Santa Monica, Calif., 1972—, now chief exec. officer; chmn. Nat. Golf Properties, Santa Monica, Calif., 1993—. Office: Am Golf Corp 1633 26th St Santa Monica CA 90404-4023*

PRICE, DAVID ROBERT, construction company executive; b. Lafayette, Ind., June 16, 1940; s. James R. and Robert L. (Pierce) P.; m. Jane Hovde, Aug. 19, 1961; children: Rebecca L., James F. BS, Purdue U., 1962. Pres. Price Homes, INc., Kokomo, Ind., 1962-66, Nat. Home Constrn. Corp., Lafayette, 1966-72; exec. v.p. Nat. Homes Corp. (name changed to Nat. Enterprises, Inc. 1987), Lafayette, 1966-72, 1972-77, pres., 1977-87, chmn., 1987—, chief operating officer, 1977-78, chief exec. officer, 1978—, also bd. dirs.; bd. dirs. Bank One (formerly Purdue Nat. Bank), Lafayette. Past mem. bd. dirs. Jr. Achievement, Lafayette, St. Elizabeth Hosp., Lafayette. Mem. Young Pres. Orgn., Nat. Assn. Home Builders (past bd. dirs.), Nat. Housing Ctr. (past trustee), Coun. Housing Producers (past bd. dirs.), Ind. Home Builders Assn. (past bd. dirs., Pres. of Yr. award 1968). Presbyterian. Avocation: golf. Home: 8751 Jaffa Court East Dr Apt 2 Indianapolis IN 46260-2398 Office: Nat Enterprises Inc PO Box 4577 Lafayette IN 47903-4577

PRICE, DEBBIE MITCHELL, journalist, newspaper editor; b. Littlefield, Tex., June 3, 1959; d. Horace A. and Diane (Hall) Mitchell; m. Larry C. Price, May 2, 1981. BFA, So. Meth. U., 1980. Reporter Ft. Worth Star-Telegram, 1980-83, 91, Phila. Daily News, 1983-87, Washington Post, 1988-91; columnist Ft. Worth Star-Telegram, 1991-93, exec. editor, 1993—, v.p., 1994—; free-lance writer, Phila., 1987-88. Recipient 1st place Gen. Column Writing award Tex. AP Mng. Editors, 1991, 1st place Mag. Writing award Women's Sports Journalism, 1989, 1st place award Chesapeake Bay AP Mng. Editors, 1990. Mem. Am. Soc. Newspaper Editors, Soc. Profl. Journalists (Ft. Worth chpt.). Office: Ft Worth Star-Telegram Inc PO Box 1870 400 W 7th St Fort Worth TX 76102

PRICE, DENNIS LEE, industrial engineer, educator; b. Taber, Alberta, Can., Oct. 24, 1930; s. Walter and Wilma Harlan (Nance) P.; m. Barbara Ann Shelton; children: Denice Lynn Price Thomas, Philip Walter. BA, Bob Jones U., 1952; BD, MA, Am. Bapt. Sem. of the West, Berkeley, Calif., 1955; MA, Calif. State U., Long Beach, 1967; PhD in Indsl. Engring., Tex. A&M U., 1974. Cert. product safety mgr., hazard control mgr., human factors profl. Clergyman Am. Bapt. Conv., Calif., 1953-66; mem. tech. staff autonetics div. Rockwell Internat., Anaheim, Calif., 1966-69; sr. engr. Martin Marietta Aerospace, Orlando, Fla., 1969-72; rsch. assoc. Tex. A&M U., College Station, 1972-74; teaching asst. Calif. State U., Long Beach, 1963-66; asst. prof. dept. indsl. engring. and operations rsch. Va. Poly. Inst. and State U., Blacksburg, 1974-78, assoc. prof. dept. indsl. and systems engring., 1979-83, prof., 1984—, dir. safety projects office, 1975, coord. Human Factors Engring. Ctr., 1986; cons., expert witness in safety engring. and human factors, 1977—; mem. U.S. Nuclear Waste Tech. Rev. Bd., 1989—; mem. U.S. tech. adv. group Internat. Stds. Tech. Com. 159 Ergonomics, 1987-94; chmn. com. on transp. of hazardous materials NRC, 1981-87; chmn. group 3 coun. emerging issues subcom. Transp. Rsch. Bd., 1987-89; chmn. task force on pipeline safety NAS, 1986. Mem. editorial bd. Human Factors, Santa Monica, Calif., 1989—; author: (with K.B. Johns, J.W. Bain) Transportation of Hazardous Materials, 1983; contbr. chpts. to books, articles to profl. jours.; reviewer in field. Recipient Outstanding. Svc. award Nat. Rsch. Coun. NAS, 1987, 89, Outstanding Svc. commendation Transp. Rsch. Bd. NAS, 1981; grantee NIOSH, Va. Dept. Transp. and Safety, 1977-82, 86-87, IBM, 1981-84, USN Office of Naval Rsch., 1978-80, USN Naval Systems Weapons Command, 1978-79. Mem. Inst. Indsl. Engrs. (sr.), Am. Soc. Safety Engrs. (profl.), Human Factors Soc. (rep. to rev. panel Guideline for the Preparation of Material Safety Data Sheets), Systems Safety Soc. (Educator of Yr. 1993), Alpha Pi Mu. Avocation: flying. Home: 1011 Evergreen Way Blacksburg VA 24060-5366 Office: Va Poly Inst and State U Dept Indsl and Systems Engring 302 Whittemore Blacksburg VA 24061

PRICE, DON K., political science educator; b. Middlesboro, Ky., Jan. 23, 1910; s. Don K. and Nell (Rhorer) P.; m. Margaret Helen Gailbreath, Mar. 3, 1936 (dec. Feb. 1970); children—Don C, Linda; m. Harriet Sloane Fels, May 8, 1971. A.B., Vanderbilt U., 1931; B.A., Oxford U. (Rhodes scholar 1932), 1934, B. Litt., 1935; D.C.L. (hon.), Oxford U., 1983; L.H.D., Case Inst. Tech., 1967, Coll. Wooster, 1972; Litt.D., U. Pitts., 1968; LL.D., Centre Coll. Ky., 1961, Syracuse U., 1962, Bucknell U., Harvard U., 1970. Reporter, state editor Nashville Eve. Tennessean, 1930-32; research asst. H.O.L.C., asst. to chmn. Central Housing Com., 1935-37; staff mem., com. on pub. adminstrn. Social Sci. Research Council, 1937-39; editorial assoc. Pub. Adminstrn. Clearing House, 1939-41, asst. dir., 1941-43, assoc. dir., 1946-53; staff mem. U.S. Bur. Budget, 1945-46; dep. chmn. Research and Devel. Bd., U.S. Dept. Def., 1952-53; assoc. dir. The Ford Found., 1953-54, v.p., 1954-58; prof. govt. Kennedy Sch. Govt. Harvard, 1958-80, prof. emeritus, 1980—; Weatherhead prof. pub. mgmt., 1980, Weatherhead prof. emeritus, 1980—, dean, 1958-77; Eastman prof., fellow Balliol Coll., U. Oxford, Eng., 1985-86; trustee Twentieth Century Fund, 1965—, chmn. bd. trustees, 1977-82; bd. trust Vanderbilt U., 1964—; trustee Rand Corp., 1961-71; sr. mem. Inst. Medicine of Nat. Acad. Scis., 1979—; asst. to Herbert Hoover (on study of U.S. Presidency under auspices Commn. on Orgn. Exec. Br. Govt.), 1947-48; cons. Exec. Office of Pres., 1961-72; dir. Social Sci. Research Council, 1949-52, 64-69; staff dir. Committee on Dept. Def. Orgn., 1953; mem. Pres.'s adv. com. on government orgn., 1959-61; adviser to the King of Nepal, Kathmandu, Nepal, 1960. Author: (with Harold and Kathryn Stone) City Manager Government in the United States, 1940, Government and Science, 1954, The Scientific Estate, 1965, America's Un-written Constitution, 1983; Editor, co-author: The Secretary of State, 1960. Trustee Rhodes Trust, 1968-78, Weatherhead Found., 1973—. Served as lt. USCGR, 1943-45. Fellow Am. Acad. Arts and Scis.; mem. Am. Philos. Soc., AAAS (bd. dirs. 1959-64, 66-69, pres. 1967), Phi Beta Kappa. Club: Cosmos (Washington). Home: 984 Memorial Dr Cambridge MA 02138-5741 Office: 79 John F Kennedy St Cambridge MA 02138-5800

PRICE, DONALD, retail executive; b. 1933. Grad., U. Calif., Berkeley, 1956. With Batten, Barton, Durstne & Osborne, Inc., 1958-65; product mgr. mktg. divsn. Block Drug Co. Inc., 1965-67; dir. mktg. CPC Internat., Best Food Divsn., 1967-76; v.p. sales and mktg. mfg. group Great Atlantic and Pacific Tea Co., 1976-78; pres. Groves-Kelco, 1978-79; exec. v.p. WaWa Inc. Media, Pa., 1979—. With U.S. Army, 1956-58. Office: WaWa Inc 260 Baltimore Pike Media PA 19063

PRICE, DONALD ALBERT, veterinarian, consultant; b. Bridgeport, Ohio, Dec. 25, 1919; s. Arthur David and Louise Ann (Knellinger) P.; m. June Loree Fleming, July 17, 1946; children—Karen Price Privett, Benita Price Esposito, Donna. Grad., Elliott Sch. Bus., 1938; D.V.M., Ohio State U., 1950. Lic. veterinarian, Ohio, Ill., Tex. Adminstrv. asst. Wheeling Steel Corp., W.Va., 1938-41; counselor psychol. dept. Ohio State U. Columbus, 1946-48, lab. asst. vet. parasitology dept., 1948-50; mem. research faculty Tex. A&M U., Sonora, 1950-55; ptnr. San Angelo Vet. Hosp., Tex., 1955-58; assoc. editor AVMA, Chgo., 1958-59, editor in chief, 1959-72, exec. v.p. 1972-85; cons., adj. prof. Tex. A&M U., College Station, 1985—. Served to capt. USAAF, 1941-46. Recipient Disting. Alumnus award Coll. Vet. Medicine, Ohio State U., 1966. Fellow Am. Med. Writers Assn.; mem. AVMA (Service Commendation award 1984, Appreciation award, 1984, chief exec. officer 1972-85), Ill. Vet. Med. Assn. (hon. life), Mich. Vet. Med. Assn. (hon. life), Tex. Vet. Med. Assn. (disting. life), Am. Equine Practitioners Assn. (hon.), Am. Assn. Sheep and Goat Practioners (hon.), Am. Animal Hosp. Assn. (hon.) (Merit award 1983), Bexar County Vet. Med. Assn. (hon.), Phi Zeta Sigma, Phi Zeta, Alpha Psi. Republican. Presbyterian. Lodge: Masons. Avocations: woodworking; ranching. Home and Office: Rte 1, Box 174-A Hunt TX 78024

PRICE, DONALD RAY, university official, agricultural engineer; b. Rockville, Ind., July 20, 1939; s. Ernest M. and Violet Noreen (Measel) P.; m. Joyce Ann Gerald, Sept. 14, 1963; children—John Allen, Karen Sue, Kimberly Ann, Daniel Lee. B.S. in Agrl. Engring., Purdue U., 1961, Ph.D. in Agrl. Engring., 1971; M.S. in Agrl. Engring., Cornell U., 1963. Registered profl. engr., Fla. From asst. prof. to prof. Cornell U., Ithaca, N.Y., 1962-80, dir. energy programs, 1975-77, 78-80; program mgr. Dept Energy, Washington, 1977-78, cons.; assoc. dean research U. Fla., Gainesville, 1980-83; dean Grad. Sch., U. Fla., Gainesville, 1983-84; v.p. research U. Fla. Gainesville, 1984—; pres. U. Fla. Research Found., Inc.; chmn. bd. dirs. Progress Research, Inc.; cons. to Pres. Carter, Washington, 1978; bd. dirs. Nat. Food and Engring. Council, Columbia, Mo., 1978-85, S.E. Healthcare Found., Gainesville, Fla., 1985. Contbr. numerous articles on engring. to profl. jours.; patentee mech. device. Mem. Ithaca Sch. Bd., N.Y., 1979-80; deacon Ch. of Christ, Gainesville, Fla., 1983—. Recipient citation Pres. Carter, 1979, Disting. Alumnus award Purdue U., 1990. Fellow Am. Soc. Agrl. Engrs. (dir. 1990, paper awards 1963, 77, 78, Young Engr. of Yr. award 1980); mem. Soc. Research Adminstrs., Nat. Assn. Univ. Research Adminstrs., S.E. Univ. Research Assn., Research Univs. Network. Democrat. Lodge: Rotary. Avocations: tennis, jogging, woodworking. Home: 8507 SW 5th Pl Gainesville FL 32607-1468 Office: U Fla 223 Grinter Hall Gainesville FL 32611

PRICE, EDGAR HILLEARY, JR., business consultant; b. Jacksonville, Fla., Jan. 1, 1918; s. Edgar Hilleary and Mary Williams (Phillips) P.; m. Elise Ingram, June 24, 1947; 1 son, Jerald Steven. Student, U. Fla., 1937-38. Mgr. comml. flower farm, 1945-49, Fla. Gladiolus Growers Assn., 1949-55; exec. v.p. Tropicana Products, Inc., Bradenton, Fla., 1955-73, dir. div. govt. and industry regulations, to 1979; dir.; exec. v.p. Indsl. Glass Co., Inc., Bradenton, 1963-73; pres., chmn. bd. Price Co., Inc., Bradenton, cons., 1973—; dir. emeritus F.P.L. Group, Inc.; past chmn. Fla. Citrus Commn., Fla. Gov.'s Freeze Damage Survey Team, Spl. Commn. for Study Abolition Death Penalty; bd. dirs. Fla. Power and Light Co., Fla. Fair Assn., Fla. Citrus Expn., Fla. Fruit and Vegetable Assn.; past chmn. Joint Citrus Legis. Com.; past mem. Fla. Plant Bd., Fla. Bd. Control, Fla. Legis. Coun.; exec com. Growers and Shippers League Fla., Fla. Agrl. Council, Spl. Health Agrl. Research and Edn.; past pres., chmn. bd. Fla. Hort. Soc. Past chmn., commr. census 12th Jud. Circuit; mem. Gov. Fla. Com. Rehab. Handicapped, Fla. Commn. on Ethics, 1976-77, Presdl. Inaugural Fin. Com., 1977, Eastern 5th Circuit U.S. Jud. Nominating Commn., 1977—; Fla. Senate from 36th Dist., 1958-66; past chmn. Manatee County Bd. Sch. Dist. Trustees, Local Housing Authority Bradenton, Bradenton Sub-Standard Housing Bd., Bradenton Charter Adv. Com.; del. Democratic Nat. Conv., 1960, dist. del., 1964; past trustee, mem. exec. com. Stetson U.; former trustee Aurora Found. Served to 1st lt. USAAF, 1941-45. Named Boss of Yr., Nat. Secs. Assn., 1959, Man of Yr. for Fla. Agr., Progressive Farmer mag., 1961; recipient Merit award Am. Flag Assn., 1962, Merit award Gamma Sigma Delta, 1965; Leadership award Fla. Agrl. Extension Service, 1963; Outstanding Senator award Fla. Radio Broadcasters, 1965; Allen Morris award as most valuable mem. Fla. Legislature, 1965; Most Valuable Mem. Fla. Senate award St. Petersburg Times, 1965; Brotherhood award Sarasota chpt. NCCJ, 1966; Disting. Citizen award Manatee County, 1970; Disting. Alumnus award U. Fla., 1972; Service to Mankind award Sertoma Internat., 1976; Goodwill Disting. Citizen award, 1979; inducted into Fla. Agrl. Hall of Fame, 1992, Tampa Bay Bus. Hall of Fame, 1992. Mem. Manatee Co. C. (past pres.), Fla. C. of C. (dir. emeritus and past chmn.), Fla. Hort. Soc. (past pres., chmn. bd.), Fla. Flower Assn., Blue Key (hon.), Omicron Delta Kappa (hon.), Sigma Alpha Epsilon. Baptist (deacon 1953—). Club: Kiwanis (pres. 1955). Inducted into Fla. Agrl. Hall of Fame, 1992. Home: 3009 Riverview Blvd W Bradenton FL 34205-3420 Office: PO Box 9270

Bradenton FL 34206-9270 *The turning point in my life came at the age of 32 when I accepted Jesus Christ as my personal Lord and Saviour. I believe every person should live his life up to the fullest extent of his God-given talents and ability. I think we have a responsibility to "pay our dues" for the privilege of living in a free land by being actively involved in our government.*

PRICE, EDWARD DEAN, federal judge; b. Sanger, Calif., Feb. 12, 1919; s. Earl Trousdale and Daisy Shaw (Biggs) P.; m. Katherine S. Merritt, July 18, 1943; children: Katherine Price O'Brien, Edward M., Jane E. B.A., U. Calif., Berkeley, 1947, LL.B., 1949. Bar: Calif. 1949. Assoc. Cleary & Zeff, Modesto, Calif., 1949-51; assoc. Zeff & Halley, Modesto, Calif., 1951-54; ptnr. Zeff, Halley & Price, Modesto, Calif., 1954-63, Zeff & Price, Modesto, Calif., 1963-65, Price & Martin, Modesto, Calif., 1965-69, Price, Martin & Crabtree, Modesto, Calif., 1969-79; judge U.S. Dist. Ct., Fresno, Calif., 1980-90, sr. judge, 1990—; mem. adv. bd. governing com. Continuing Edn. of Bar, San Francisco, 1963-71, governing bd. Calif. State Bar, 1973-76; v.p. Jud. Council, Calif., 1978-79. Contbr. articles to profl. jours. Served with U.S. Army, 1943-46. Mem. ABA, Am. Coll. Trial Lawyers, Am. Bd. Trial Advocates. Democrat. Methodist. Home: 1012 Wellesley Ave Modesto CA 95350-5042 Office: US Dist Ct 5554 US Courthouse 1130 O St Fresno CA 93721-2201

PRICE, FRANK, motion picture and television company executive; b. Decatur, Ill., May 17, 1930; s. William F. and Winifred A. (Moran) P.; m. Katherine Huggins, May 15, 1965; children: Stephen, David, Roy, Frank. Student, Mich. State U., 1949-51. Writer, story editor CBS-TV, N.Y.C., 1951-53, Columbia Pictures, Hollywood, Calif., 1953-57, NBC-TV, Hollywood, Calif., 1957-58; producer, writer ZIV-TV, Hollywood, Calif., 1958; producer, writer Universal Television, Universal City, Calif., 1959-64, v.p., 1964-71, sr. v.p., 1971-73, exec. v.p. in charge of production, 1973-74, pres., 1974-78; v.p., dir. MCA, Inc., 1976-78; pres. Columbia Pictures Prodn., 1978-79; chmn., chief exec. officer Columbia Pictures, 1979-84, also bd. dirs.; chmn. MCA Motion Picture Group, 1984-86; chmn., chief exec. officer Price Entertainment Inc., 1987-90; chmn. Columbia Pictures, 1990-91; also bd. dirs. Sony Pictures Entertainment; chmn., chief exec. officer Price Entertainment, 1991—; bd. dirs. Savoy Pictures. With USN, 1948-49. Mem. Writers Guild Am., West. Office: Price Entertainment Inc 2425 Olympic Blvd Santa Monica CA 90404-4030

PRICE, GORDON A., brokerage house executive; b. Cleve., Dec. 20, 1947; s. Arthur Charles and Kathryn Nadine (Burk) P.; m. Christine M. Carroll; children: Ian, Kirk, Kim, Thomas, Megan, Kevin. Student, Dyke Coll., 1966-69. Registered fin. prin., Ohio. Supr. Ball Burge & Krales, Cleve., 1968-73; mgr. acctg. McDonald & Co., Cleve., 1973-80, ptnr., 1980-83; first v.p. McDonald & Co. Securities Inc., Cleve., 1983-84, sr. v.p., 1984-87, mng. dir., chief fin. officer, 1987—; bd. dirs. McDonald Capital Mgmt. Inc., Cleve. Mem. Fin. Execs. Inst. Avocation: sailing. Office: McDonald & Co Securities Inc Ste 2100 800 Superior Ave Cleveland OH 44114

PRICE, GRIFFITH BALEY, JR., lawyer; b. Lawrence, Kans., Aug. 15, 1942; s. Griffith Baley and Cora Lee (Beers) P.; m. Maria Helena Martin, June 29, 1968; children: Andrew Griffith, Alexandra Helena. AB (cum laude), Harvard U., 1964; LLB, NYU, 1967. Bar: N.Y. 1967, U.S. Ct. Appeals (6th cir.) 1975, U.S. Ct. Appeals (2nd cir.) 1978, U.S. Ct. Appeals (3d, 5th and 11th cirs.) 1981, U.S. Ct. Appeals (fed. cir.) 1984, D.C. 1991. Assoc. Dewey, Ballantine, Bushby, Palmer & Wood, N.Y.C., 1967-75; ptnr. Milgrim Thomajan & Lee, N.Y.C., 1976-86; of counsel, ptnr. Finnegan, Henderson, Farabow, Garrett & Dunner, Washington, 1987—; adj. prof., lectr. George Washington U. Law Ctr., Washington, 1989-93; frequent lectr. ABA, Practicing Law Inst., Law & Bus., 1982—. Author: (with others, treatise) Milgrim on Trade Secrets, 1986; contbr. articles to publs. Root-Tilden scholar NYU Law Sch., 1964-67. Mem. ABA (patent trademark copyright sect., com. chmn.), Internat. Trademark Assn. (bd. dirs., com. chmn.), Am. Intellectual Property Law Assn., Licensing Execs. Soc., N.Y. Athletic Club, Harvard Club (N.Y.C. and Washington). Presbyterian. Office: Finnegan Henderson Farabow Garrett & Dunner 1300 I St NW Ste 700 Washington DC 20005-3315

PRICE, HARRISON ALAN, business research company executive; b. Oregon City, Oreg., May 17, 1921; s. Harry I. and Isabel (Esson) P.; m. Anne Shaw, Apr. 29, 1944; children: Bret, David, Dana, Holly. B.S., Calif. Inst. Tech., 1942; M.B.A., Stanford U., 1951. Mgr. econ. research Stanford Research Inst., Los Angeles, 1951-55; gen. mgr. Def. Plant div. Harvey Aluminum, Torrance, Calif., 1955-58; founder, pres. Econ. Research Assocs., West Los Angeles, Calif., 1958-73; sr. v.p., mem. Planning Research Corp., Washington, 1973-76, chmn., 1976-78; pres. Harrison Price Co., Los Angeles, 1978—; dir. Air Conditioning of Calif., Electronic Scales Internat. Trustee Calif. Inst. of Arts., Calif. State Dominguez Found. Served with inf. U.S. Army, 1944-46. Club: California. Home: 2141 W Paseo Del Mar San Pedro CA 90732-4556

PRICE, HARRY STEELE, JR., construction materials company executive; b. East Jordan, Mich., Oct. 11, 1910; s. Harry S. and Grace B. (Beers) P.; m. Janet Smith, Apr. 7, 1934; children: Pamela, Harry Steele III, Marlay B. B.S., U. Mich., 1932. Office and field office on heavy constrn. Price Bros. Co., 1932-36, designer, constrn. and operation of gravel plant, 1936-38, in charge concrete sewer and culvert pipe operations, sand and gravel operations, gen. sec., 1938-45, v.p. in charge of pressure pipe div., 1945-67, exec. v.p., 1953-67, chmn., pres., 1967-73, chmn, 1973-80, vice chmn., 1980—; Past commr. Montgomery County Park Dist.; past pres. Dayton Art Inst.; bd. dirs. Sinclair Community Coll. Found. Mem. NSPE, ASCE (life), Am. Concrete Pipe Assn. (past pres.), Am. Water Works Assn. (life, past trustee). Clubs: Dayton City, Buz-Fuz, Moraine Country, 49 Club, Dayton Raquet; St. Andrews (Delray Beach, Fla.); Wequetonsino Golf Club (Harbor Springs, Mich.). Home: 333 Oakwood Ave Apt 2B Dayton OH 45409 Office: 367 W 2d St Dayton OH 45401

PRICE, HUGH B., foundation executive, lawyer; b. Washington, Nov. 22, 1941; s. Kline A. and Charlotte (Schuster) P.; m. Marilyn Lloyd, Dec. 29, 1963; children: Traer, Janeen, Lauren. BA, Amherst Coll., 1963; LLB, Yale U., 1966. Bar: Conn. 1966. Atty. New Haven Legal Assistance Assn., 1966-68; exec. dir. Black Coalition of New Haven, 1968-70; ptnr. Cogen, Holt & Assocs., New Haven, 1970-76; human resources adminstr. City of New Haven, 1977-78; editorial writer N.Y. Times, N.Y.C., 1978-82; sr. v.p. Sta. WNET-TV, N.Y.C., 1982-88; v.p. The Rockefeller Found., N.Y.C., 1988-94; pres. Nat. Urban League, 1994—; lectr. Yale U. Law Sch., New Haven, 1978. Bd. dirs. NAACP Legal Def. & Edn. Fund, N.Y.C., 1986-88, Cooper Union, N.Y.C., 1991—, Rockefeller Bros. Fund, N.Y.C., 1988. Mem. Boule (sire archon 1990-91), The Westchester Clubmen. Avocations: travel, tennis, reading. Home: 21 Trenor Dr New Rochelle NY 10804 Office: Nat Urban League 500 E 62nd St New York NY 10021

PRICE, JAMES GORDON, physician; b. Brush, Colo., June 20, 1926; s. John Hoover and Rachel Laurette (Dodds) P.; m. Janet Alice McSween, June 19, 1949; children: James Gordon II, Richard Christian, Mary Laurette, Janet Lynn. B.A., U. Colo., 1948, M.D., 1951. Diplomate: Charter diplomate Am. Bd. Family Practice (dir., pres. 1979). Intern Denver Gen. Hosp., 1951-52; private medicine specializing in family medicine Brush, 1952-78; prof. family practice U. Kans. Med. Center, 1978—, chmn. dept., 1978-90, exec. dean, 1990-93, prof. emeritus in family practice, 1993—; mem. Inst. Medicine, Nat. Acad. Scis., 1973—; med. editor Gen. Learning Corp. 1973-92. Editorial bd.: Med. World News, 1969-79; editor: Am. Acad. Family Physician Home Study Self Assessment Program, 1978-83; contbr.: (column) Your Family Physician, 1977-90. Trustee Family Health Found. Am., 1970-82. Served with USNR, 1943-46. Charter fellow Am. Acad. Family Physicians (pres. 1973-74); mem. Phi Beta Kappa, Alpha Omega Alpha. Home: 12205 Mohawk Rd Shawnee Mission KS 66209-2137

PRICE, JAMES MELFORD, physician; b. Onalaska, Wis., Apr. 3, 1921; s. Carl Robert and Hazel (Halderson) P.; m. Ethelyn Doreen Lee, Oct. 23, 1943 (div.); children: Alta Lee, Jean Marie, Veda Michele; m. Charlotte E. Schwenk, Sept. 27, 1986; children: Shirley S. Bunn, Cindy S. Davis, Irene S. McCumber. BS in Agr., U. Wis., 1943, MS in Biochemistry, 1944, PhD in Physiology, 1949, MD, 1951. Diplomate Am. Bd. Clin. Nutrition. Intern Cin. Gen. Hosp., 1951-52; mem. faculty U. Wis. Med. Sch., 1952—, prof.

clin. oncology, 1959—, Am. Cancer Soc.-Charles S. Hayden Found. prof. surgery in cancer research, 1957—; on leave as dir. exptl. therapy Abbott Labs., 1967—, v.p. exptl. therapy, 1968, v.p. corp. research and exptl. therapy, 1971—, v.p. corp. sci. devel., 1976-78; v.p. med. affairs Norwich-Eaton Pharms., 1978—, v.p. internat. R&D 1980-82; pres. RADAC Group, Inc., 1982-90, Biogest Products, Inc., 1984-88; mem. metabolism study sect. NIH 1959-62, pathology B study sect., 1964-68; sci. adv. com. PMA Found.; chmn. research adv. com. Ill. Dept. Mental Health; sci. com. Nat. Bladder Cancer program; mem. Drug Research Bd. Nat. Acad. Scis./NRC. Bd. dirs. Grandview Coll., Des Moines, 1977-78. Served with USNR, 1944-45. Fellow Am. Coll. Nutrition, Royal Soc. Medicine London; mem. Am. Soc. Pharmacology and Exptl. Therapeutics, Am. Assn. Cancer Research, Am. Cancer Soc. (com. etiology 1957-61), Pharm. Mfrs. Assn. (chmn. research and devel. sect. 1974-75), Am. Soc. Biol. Chemists, Am. Inst. Nutrition, Am. Soc. Clin. Nutrition, Research Dirs. Assn. Chgo., Soc. Exptl. Biology and Medicine, Soc. Toxicology. Spl. research trytophan metabolism, metabolism vitamin B complex, chem. carcinogenesis; research and devel. pharm., diagnostic and consumer products; licensing and bus. devel. Avocation: pvt. pilot. Home: PO Box 211 Edmeston NY 13335-0211

PRICE, JIM, engineering company executive, earth scientist. CFO, v.p. Geomatrix Consultants, Inc., San Francisco. Office: Geomatrix Consultants Inc 100 Pine St 10 San Francisco CA 94111*

PRICE, JOE (ALLEN), artist, former educator; b. Ferriday, La., Feb. 6, 1935; s. Edward Neill and Margaret (Hester) P. BS, Northwestern U., 1957; postgrad., Art Ctr. Coll., L.A., 1967-68; MA, Stanford U., 1970. Free-lance actor, artist N.Y.C., 1957-60; freelance illustrator, actor, L.A., 1960-68; free-lance comml. artist, San Carlos, Calif., 1968-69; package designer Container Corp. Am., Santa Clara, Calif., 1969; prof. studio art and filmmaking, chmn. dept. art Coll. San Mateo, Calif., 1970-94. One-man shows include Richard Sumner Gallery, Palo Alto, Calif., 1975, San Mateo County Cultural Ctr., 1976, 82, Tahir Galleries, New Orleans, 1977, 82, Kerwin Galleries, Burlingame, Calif., 1977, Edits. Gallery, Melbourne, Australia, 1977, Ankrum Gallery, Los Angeles, 1978, 84, Edits. Ltd. West Gallery, San Francisco, 1981, Miriam Perlman Gallery, Chgo., 1982, San Mateo County Arts Council Gallery, 1982, Candy Stick Gallery, Ferndale, Calif., 1984, Assoc. Am. Artists, N.Y.C. and Phila., 1984, Gallery 30, Burlingame, 1991, San Mateo, 1984, Triton Mus. Art, Santa Clara, Calif., 1986, Huntsville (Ala.) Mus. Art, 1987, Gallery 30, San Mateo, 1988-91, Concept Art Gallery, Pitts., 1991, Eleonore Austerer Gallery, San Francisco, 1995; exhibited in groups shows at Berkeley Art Ctr., Calif., 1976, Burlingame Civic Art Gallery, 1976, Syntex Gallery, Palo Alto, Calif., 1977, Gump's Gallery, San Francisco, 1976, 77, Nat. Gallery of Australia, 1978, Sonoma County Gallery, 1979, Gov. Dummer Acad. Art, Byfield, Mass., 1979, Miss. Mus. Art, 1982, C.A.A. Galleries, Chautauqua, N.Y., 1982, Huntsville Mus. Art, 1983, Tahir Gallery, New Orleans, 1983, Hunterdon Art Ctr., N.J., 1984, Editions Galleries, Melbourne, Australia, 1988, Van Stratten Gallery, Chgo., 1988, 6th Internat. Exhbn., Carnegie-Mellon U., Pa., 1988, Forum Gallery, Jamestown, N.Y., 1988, 5th Internat. Biennale Petite Format de Papier, Belgium, 1989, 4th Internat. Biennial Print Exhibit, Taipei Fine Arts Mus., People's Republic China, 1990, Interprint, Lviv '90, USSR, 1990, New Orleans Mus. Art, 1990, Internat. Print Triennale, Cracow, Poland, 1991, 15th Ann. Nat. Invitational Drawing Exhbn. Emporia State U., Kans., 1991, Haggar U. Gallery, U. Dallas, 1991, Directions in Bay Area Printmaking: Three Decades Palo Alto Cultural Ctr., 1992, Am. Prints: Last Half 20th Century, Jane Haslem Gallery, Washington, 1992, Wenniger Graphics, Boston, 1993, Eleonore Austerer Gallery, San Francisco, 1994, Triton Mus. Art, Santa Clara, 1994, Mobile Mus. Art, 1995; represented in permanent collections San Francisco Mus. Modern Art, Achenbach Found. Graphic Arts, San Francisco, Phila. Mus. Art, New Orleans Mus. Art, Portland Mus. Art, Maine, The Libr. of Congress, Washington. Huntsville Mus. Art, Midwest Mus. Am. Art, Ind., Cracow Nat. Mus., Poland, Cabo Frio Mus., Brazil, Nat. Mus. Am. Art, Smithsonian Inst., Washington. Recipient Kempshall Clark award Peoria Art Guild, 1981, Paul Lindsay Sample Meml. award 25th Chautauqua Nat. Exhbn. of Am. Art, 1982, 1st Ann. Creative Achievement award Calif. State Legislature/Arts Coun. San Mateo County, 1989. Mem. Am. Color Print Soc., Audubon Artists (Louis Lozowick Meml. award 1978, Silver medal of honor award 1991), Boston Printmakers (Ture Bengtz Meml. award 1987), Calif. Soc. Printmakers (mem. council 1979-81), Los Angeles Printmaking Soc., Phila. Print Club (Lessing J. Rosenwald prize 1979), Arts Council of San Mateo Count, Theta Chi. Democrat. Studio and Office: PO Box 3305 Sonora CA 95370-3305 *Personal philosophy: In being an artist, I do not wish to be just a "recorder" or my time, what I see, what I think. To me, the joy of art is in expressing the love of being an artist, for in loving without shame, without fear, and without doubt one transcends to the moment and speaks with integrity. For the rest of my life I wish to reflect on what life is, and to have the courage to create that which touches not only men's eyes, but their hearts and spirits. I seek the profound truth of what it is to be human and the universal truth of what it means to be creative in expressing the love of being.*

PRICE, JOHN ALEY, lawyer; b. Maryville, Mo., Oct. 7, 1947; s. Donald Leroy and Julia Catherine (Aley) P.; m. Julie Ann Seipel, Aug. 16, 1969 (div. June 1995); children: Theodore John, Joseph Andrew. BS, N.W. Mo. State U., 1969; JD, U. Kans., 1972. Bar: Kans. 1972, U.S. Dist. Ct. Kans. 1972, U.S. Ct. Appeals (10th cir.) 1972, Tex. 1984, U.S. Ct. Appeals (5th cir.) 1984, U.S. Supreme Ct., 1987; cert. civil trial law Tex. Bd. Legal Specialization, 1989—. Law clk. U.S. Dist. Ct. Kans., Wichita, 1972-74; assoc., then ptnr. firm Weeks, Thomas and Lysaught, Kansas City, Kans., 1974-82; ptnr. Winstead, Sechrest & Minick, Dallas, 1982—, litigation sect. coord., 1990-92, intellectual property sect. litigation coord., 1993—; spl. prosecutor Leavenworth County Dist. Atty., 1970-71, Sedgwick County Dist. Atty., Wichita, Kans., 1971-72. Author: Our Boundless Self (A Call to Awake), 1992, A Gathering of Light: Eternal Wisdom for a Time of Transformation, 1993; editor (mag.) Academic Analyst, 1968-69; assoc. editor U. Kans. Law Rev., 1971-72, Dallas Bus. Jour.; author legal publs. Co-dir. Douglas County Legal Aid Soc., Lawrence, Kans., 1971-72; co-pres. Northwood Hills PTA, Dallas, 1984, Westwood Jr. High Sch. PTA, 1989-90; founder New Frontiers Found., 1993. Mem. ABA, Kans. Bar Assn. (mem. task force for penal reform; Pres.'s Outstanding Svc. award 1981), Tex. Bar Assn., Pro Bono Coll., State Bar Tex., 1992—, World Bus. Acad., Inst. Noetic Scis., UN Assn. (humans rights com. Dallas chpt. 1991-93, bd. dirs. 1991-93), Campaign for the Earth (chpt. coord. Global Report 1991-92, coord. govt. and politics area 1991-92), Blue Key, Order of Coif, Phi Delta Phi, Sigma Tau Gamma (v.p. 1968-69). Mem. Unity Ch. Office: Winstead Sechrest & Minick 1201 Elm St 5400 Renaissance Tower Dallas TX 75270 *Individually, each person creates his or her reality every moment of existence. Collectively, we hold within ourselves a boundless capacity to co-create a world filled with love, compassion and abundance for all sentient beings. The key to a new order of the ages lies within our own hearts, minds and souls.*

PRICE, JOHN RANDOLPH, writer; b. Alice, Tex., Feb. 12, 1932; s. John Randolph and Eva Mae (Boney) P.; m. Janis Bryant Price, June 20, 1953; children: Susan Lynn, Leslie Anne. BS, U. Houston, 1957. Dir. advt. Gates Radio Corp., Quincy, Ill., 1957-62; v.p. Sander Rodkin, Ltd., Chgo., 1962-64; exec. v.p. Stewart, Price, Tomlin, Inc., Chgo., 1964-67; v.p. Goodwin, Dannenbaum, Littman & Wingfield, Inc., Houston, 1967-70; pres. O'Neill, Price, Anderson, Fouchard, Inc., Houston, 1970-74, John Price & Co., Houston, 1974-79, Arnan, Inc., Austin, 1979-81; chmn. bd. The Quartus Found. Inc., Boerne, Tex., 1981—; adv. bd. Global Family, Inc., Palo Alto, Calif., 1990—; Santi Found., Yucalpa, Calif., 1990—, Unity and Diversity World Coun., Inc. L.A., 1992—. Author: The Superbeings, 1981, The Manifestation Process, 1983, The Planetary Commission, 1984, Practical Spirituality, 1985, With Wings as Eagles, 1987, The Abundance Book, 1987, Prayer, Principles & Power, 1987, A Spiritual Philosophy for the New World, 1990, Empowerment, 1992, The Angels Within Us, 1993, Angel Energy, 1995. Chmn. Red Cross Drive, Quincy, Ill., 1960; cons. All Am. City campaign, Quincy, 1962. Staff sgt. USAF, 1952-56. Recipient Joseph S. Cullinan award U. Houston, 1956, Grand Prix Best Consumer Mag. Advt. award, 1970. Mem. Internat. New Though Alliance (Humanitarian award 1992, Joseph Muphy award 1994). Achievements include organizer of first annual World Peace day on December 31, 1986. Office: The Quartus Found Inc PO Box 1768 Boerne TX 78006

PRICE, JOHN ROY, JR., financial executive; b. N.Y.C., Dec. 20, 1938; s. John Roy and Pauline Bernice (Milnes) P.; m. Victoria Scott Pohle, Dec. 19,

1970 (div. 1982); 1 son, Matthew Roy; m. Marion Cobb Hardie, Oct. 1, 1988. B.A., Grinnell Coll., 1960, Queens Coll., Oxford (Eng.) U., 1962; M.A., Queens Coll., Oxford (Eng.) U., 1965; J.D., Harvard U., 1965. Assoc. Casey, Lane & Mittendorf, N.Y.C., 1965-67; v.p. Bedford-Stuyvesant D & S Corp., N.Y.C., 1967-68; spl. asst. to Pres. U.S., Washington, 1969-71; assoc. Donaldson, Lufkin & Jenrette, N.Y.C., 1971-72; v.p. Mfrs. Hanover Trust, N.Y.C., 1972-75; v.p. Mfrs. Hanover Corp., N.Y.C., 1975-80, sr. v.p. nonbank subs., 1980-83, sr v.p., sec., 1983-87; mng. dir. Mfrs. Hanover Trust Co., 1987-88, Mfrs. Hanover Securities Corp., 1988-92; mng. dir. govt. and community affairs Chem. Bank, 1992—; bd. dirs. Am. Trust for Oxford, 1990-94, chmn. Cmty. Devel., Inc., Prin. Fin. Group (formerly Bankers Life Co.), Transcell Techs. Corp., Bankers Assn. for Fgn. Trade, 1990—, pres., 1994—, Nat. Trade Coun., 1991—; pres. Am. for Oxford, 1987—; chmn. local devel. corp. Bklyn. Acad. Music, 1980-82. Nat. chmn. Ripon Soc., 1967-68; trustee Grinnell Coll., 1970—; bd. dirs. New Communities Corp., 1976-77; mem. exec. panel Chief of Naval Ops., 1972-79. Rhodes scholar. Mem. Council Fgn. Relations, Phi Beta Kappa. Club: Harvard (N.Y.C.). Home: 3144 Granite Rd Woodstock MD 21163-1004

PRICE, JONATHAN G., geologist; b. Danville, Pa., Feb. 1, 1950; s. A. Barney and Flora (Best) P.; m. Elisabeth McKinley, June 3, 1972; children: Alexander D., Argenta M. BA in Geology and German, Lehigh U., 1972; MA, U. Calif., Berkeley, 1975, PhD, 1977. Cert. profl. geologist. Geologist Anaconda Copper Co., Yerington, Nev., 1974-75; geologist U.S. Steel Corp., Salt Lake City, 1977, Corpus Christi, 1978-81; rsch. assoc. Bur. Econ. Geology, U. Tex., Austin, 1981-85, rsch. sci., 1984-88, program dir., 1987-88; dir. Tex. Mining & Mineral Resources Rsch. Inst., Austin, 1984-88; dir., state geologist Nev. Bur. Mines & Geology, U. Nev., Reno, 1988-92, 95—; staff dir. Bd. on Earth Scis. & Resources Nat. Rsch. Coun., Washington D.C., 1993-95; asst. prof. Bucknell U., Lewisburg, 1977-78. Author, editor: Igneous Geology of Trans-Pecos Texas, 1986. Vol. instr. CPR and 1st aid ARC, 1983—; bd. dirs. U. Heidelberg, Sierra Nev. chpt., 1991-92. German Acad. Exchange Svc. fellow U. Heidelberg, 1972-73. Fellow Geol. Soc. Am., Soc. Econ. Geologists; mem. Am. Assn. Profl. Geologists (Nev. sect. pres. 1992), Mineral. Soc. Am., Phi Beta Kappa. Office: Nev Bur Mines & Geology UNR/MS 178 Reno NV 89557-0088

PRICE, JOSEPH HUBBARD, lawyer; b. Montgomery, Ala., Jan. 31, 1939; s. Aaron Joseph and Minnie Jule (Reynolds) P.; m. Cynthia Winant Ramsey, Sept. 14, 1963 (div. 1980); children—Victoria Reynolds, Ramsey Winant; m. Courtney McFadden, Apr. 26, 1980. A.B., U. Ala., 1961; LL.B., Harvard U., 1964; postgrad. London Sch. Econs., 1964-65. Bar: Ala. 1964, D.C. 1968. Law clerk to justice Hugo L. Black, U.S. Supreme Ct., Washington, 1967-68; assoc. Leva, Hawes, Symington, Martin & Oppenheimer, Washington, 1968-71; v.p. Overseas Pvt. Investment Corp., Washington, 1971-73; ptnr. Leva, Hawes, et. al., Washington, 1973-83, Gibson, Dunn & Crutcher, Washington, 1983—. Mem. CARE Com. Washington; mem. adv. com. Hugo Black Meml. Library, Ashland, Ala. Served to capt. U.S. Army, 1966-67; Vietnam. Decorated Bronze Star; Frank Knox Meml. fellow London Sch. Econs., 1964-65. Mem. ABA, Am. Soc. Internat. Law, Supreme Ct. Hist. Soc., Phi Beta Kappa. Clubs: Metropolitan. Home: 3104 Cathedral Ave NW Washington DC 20008-3419 Office: Gibson Dunn & Crutcher 1050 Connecticut Ave NW Washington DC 20036-5303

PRICE, JOSEPH LEVERING, neuroscientist, educator; b. Mobile, Ala., Oct. 17, 1942; s. Benjamin Joseph and Virginia (Levering) P.; m. Elisabeth Uttenthal, June 23, 1967; children: Anna Elise, Virginia Sigrid, Paul Joseph. BA in Chemistry, U. of the South, 1963; BA in Physiology, U. Oxford, Eng., 1966, PhD in Anatomy, 1969. Instr. Washington U. Sch. Medicine, St. Louis, 1969-71, asst. prof., 1971-76, assoc. prof., 1976-83, prof., 1983—. Mem. editorial bd. Jour. of Comparative Neurology, 1983—; contbr. articles to profl. jours. Jr. warden Christ Ch. Cathedral, St. Louis, 1985-87. Rhodes scholar Oxford U., 1963-66; USPHS predoctoral fellow, 1966-68; recipient C.J. Herrick award Am. Assn. Anatomists, 1973, Javits Neurosci. Investigator award NIH, 1987. Mem. Soc. for Neurosci., Assn. for Chemoreception Scis., Phi Beta Kappa. Democrat. Episcopalian. Office: Washington U Sch Medicine Dept Anatomy and Neurobiology Saint Louis MO 63110

PRICE, JOSEPH MICHAEL, lawyer; b. St. Paul, Dec. 2, 1947; s. Leon and Rose (Kaufman) P.; m. Louise Rebecca Braunstein, Dec. 19, 1971; children—Lisa, Laurie, Julie. B.A., U. Minn., 1969, J.D., 1972. Bar: Minn. 1972, U.S. Dist. Ct. Minn. 1974. Ptnr., Faegre & Benson, Mpls., 1972—. Mem. Minn. Bar Assn., Hennepin County Bar Assn. Home: 4407 Country Club Rd Minneapolis MN 55424-1148 Office: Faegre & Benson 2200 Norwest Ctr 90 S 7th St Minneapolis MN 55402-3900

PRICE, LARRY C., photojournalist; b. Corpus Christi, Tex., Feb. 23, 1954; s. David Vernon and Martha C. (Tucker) P.; m. Debbie Mitchell, May 2, 1981. B.J., U. Tex., 1977. Mem. staff U. Tex. Daily Texan, Austin, 1976-77, El Paso Times, Tex., 1977-79, Ft. Worth Star-Telegram, Tex., 1979-83; asst. mng. editor Ft. Worth Star-Telegram, Tex., 1991-93; assoc. editor Ft. Worth Star-Telegram, 1993—; photojournalist Phila. Inquirer, 1983-90, dir. photography, 1987-88, photographer Washington Bur., 1988-90; freelance photographer Washington, 1990-91; vis. prof. U. Tex., Austin, 1983. Contbg. photographer: A Day in the Life of America, 1986, A Day in the Life of Spain, 1987, A Day in the Life of the Soviet Union, 1987, A Day in the Life of California, 1988, A Day in the Life of China, 1989, The Jews in America, 1989, The Power to Heal, 1989, A Day in the Life of Hollywood, 1992, The African Americans, 1993, A Day in the Life of Thailand, 1994, A Day in the Life of Israel, 1994, Jerusalem 3000, 1994. Recipient Pulitzer Prize in spot news photography Columbia U., N.Y.C., 1981, Pulitzer Prize in feature photography, 1985, Best Photographic Reporting From Abroad award Overseas Press Club, 1985, World Press Photo awards, 1987. Mem. Nat. Press Photographer's Assn. Methodist. Home: 2021 Windsor Pl Fort Worth TX 76110-1759

PRICE, LEIGH, banker; b. Malin, Oreg., Feb. 6, 1941; d. Clarence Loraine and Nina Ellen (Kamping) P.; m. Richard D. McNabb, 1958 (div. 1963); children: Brian, Leigh Ann; m. Ronald D. Stein, 1969 (div. 1988). BA magna cum laude in Psychology, UCLA, 1980, MBA in Mgmt., 1982. Analyst Standard Oil Co., Tulsa, 1967-69; programmer/analyst Honeywell, Inc., Mpls., 1969-73; sr. systems analyst Fabri-Tek, Inc., Mpls., 1974-77; pres. Price & Assocs., Mpls., 1978-79; sr. cons. MRG Assocs., L.A., 1981-83; exec. v.p., chief operating officer Prescription Health Svcs., L.A., 1984-85; v.p., mgr. First Interstate Bank, L.A., 1985-88; v.p. Md. Nat. Bank, Balt., 1988—. Del. Minn. Dem. Conv., 1972; chmn. Patent/Sci. Bd. Coun., Edina, Minn., 1975; pres. Friends of L.A. Opera, 1980-81; v.p. Guild Opera Co., L.A., 1983-85; exec. v.p. Opera Guild So. Calif., 1984-85, pres., 1985-87, parliamentarian, 1987-88; bd. dirs. Roland Park Community Assn., 1990—, treas., 1992. Unitarian. Avocations: reading, gardening. Office: MNC Info Svcs PO Box 987 Baltimore MD 21203-0987

PRICE, LEONTYNE, concert and opera singer, soprano; b. Laurel, Miss., Feb. 10, 1927; d. James A. and Kate (Baker) P.; m. William Warfield, Aug. 31, 1952 (div. 1973). BA, Central State Coll., Wilberforce, Ohio, 1949, DMus, 1968; student, Juilliard Sch. Music, 1949-52; pupil, Florence Page Kimball; LHD, Dartmouth Coll., 1962, Fordham U., 1969, Yale U., 1979, MusD, Howard U., 1962; Dr. Humanities, Rust Coll., 1968. Profl. opera debut in 4 Saints in 3 Acts, 1952; appeared as Bess in Porgy and Bess, Vienna, Berlin, London, under auspices U.S. State Dept., also N.Y.C. and U.S. tour, 1952-54; recitalist, soloist with symphonies, U.S., Can., Australia, Europe, 1954—; appeared concerts in India, 1956, 64; soloist, Hollywood Bowl, 1955-59, 66, Berlin Festival, 1960; role as Mme. Lidoine in Dialogues des Carmelites, San Francisco Opera, 1957; opera singer, NBC-TV, 1955-58, 60, 62, 64, San Francisco Opera Co., 1957-59, 60-61, 63, 65, 67, 68, 71, as Aida at La Scala, Milan, 1957, Vienna Staatsoper, 1958, 59-60, 61, Berlin Opera, 1964, Rome Opera, 1966, Paris Opera 1968, recital, Brussels Internat. Fair, auspices State Dept., 1958, Verona Opera Arena, 1958-59, recitals in Yugoslavia for State Dept., 1958; rec. artist, RCA-Victor, 1958—; appeared Covent Garden, London, 1958-59, 70, Chgo. Lyric Theatre, 1959, 60, 65, Oakland (Calif.) Symphony, 1980, soloist, Salzburg Festival, 1959-63, Tetro alla Scala, Milano, 1960-61, 63, 67, appeared Met. Opera, N.Y.C. 1961-62, 64, 66, 75, 76; since resident mem., until 1985; soloist, Salzburg Festival, 1950, 60, debut, Teatre Dell'Opera, Rome, 1967, Teatro Colon, Buenos Aires, Argentina, 1969, Hamburg Opera, 1970; recordings include A

Christmas Offering with Karajani, God Bless America with Charles Gerhardt, Arias from Don Giovanni, Turandot, Aida, Emani, Messa di Requiem, Trovatore, Live at Ordway, The Prima Donna Collection, A Program of Song with D. Garvey, Right as the Rain with André Previn. Hon. bd. dirs. Campfire Girls; hon. vice-chmn. U.S. com. UNESCO; cochmn. Rust Coll. Upward Thrust Campaign; trustee Internat. House. Decorated Order at Ment Italy; recipient Merit award for role of Tosca in NBC-TV Opera, Mademoiselle mag., 1955, 20 Grammy awards for classical vocal recs. Nat. Acad. Rec. Arts and Scis., citation YWCA, 1961, Spirit of Achievement award Albert Einstein Coll. Medicine, 1962, Presdl. medal of freedom, 1964, Springarn medal NAACP, 1965, Schwann Catalog award, 1968, Nat. Medal of Arts, 1985, Essence award, 1991, others; named Musician of Year, Mus. Am. mag., 1961. Fellow Am. Acad. Arts and Sci.; mem. AFTRA, Am. Guild Mus. Artists, Actors Equity Assn., Sigma Alpha Iota, Delta Sigma Theta. Office: Columbia Artists Mgmt Inc Walter Divsn 165 W 57th St New York NY 10019-2201 also: 1133 Broadway New York NY 10010*

PRICE, LEROY VERNON, secondary school educator; b. Christiansburg, Va., Apr. 30, 1942; s. Leroy Vernon and Nora Pauline (Grubb) P.; m. Vickie Lee Likens, Mar. 4, 1966; children: Amanda Lee, Alison Denise; 1 child by previous marriage, Paula Renee. BS in Indsl. Arts, Va. Poly. Inst. and State U., 1965. Cert. tchr., Va. Tchr. metals and drafting Warren County High Schs., Front Royal, Va., 1964-65; tchr. woodworking, drafting James River High Sch., Fincastle, Va., 1965-66, Northside High Sch., Salem, Va., 1966-74; tchr. power mechanics, photography, tech. systems Northside Jr. High Sch., Salem, 1974—; tchr. photography adult edn. program Roanoke County Schs., Salem; tchr. furniture restoration Warren County Schs., Front Royal. Author curriculum materials. Recipient vocat. edn. awards Va. Bd. Edn., 1991. Mem. NEA, Va. Edn. Assn., Roanoke County Edn. Assn., internat. Tech. Assn., Va. Mid. Sch. Assn., Va. Tech. Edn. Assn. (life), Epsilon Pi Tau. Presbyterian. Avocations: antique car restoration, woodworking, travel, camping. Home: 1580 Richland Hills Dr Salem VA 24153-1612 Office: Northside Jr High Sch 6810 Northside High School Rd Roanoke VA 24019-2830

PRICE, LIZA, entrepreneur; b. Pitts., Mar. 17, 1950; d. Paul David and Margaret (Cantor) P.; m. Donald M. Rappaport, July 7, 1973; children: Brian, Pam, Michael. MA, Pa. State U., 1971. Gen. mgr. Ed Burnett, Inc., N.J., 1973; founder, pres. Am. List Counsel, Inc., Princeton, N.J., 1978—. Cited in Inc. mag. list of fastest growing cos. in U.S., 1984, 85, 86. Avocations: skiing, horseback riding. Office: Am List Counsel Inc 88 Orchard Rd Ringoes NJ 08551-1504

PRICE, MARION WOODROW, journalist; b. Elizabeth City, N.C., Oct. 13, 1914; s. James Asa and Meddie (Divers) P.; m. Mary Dudley Pittman, Aug. 31, 1940; children—Wiley, Dudley, Mary, Catherine. Student, Wake Forest Coll., 1933-34. Reporter Daily Advance, Elizabeth City, 1935-39, Raleigh (N.C.) Times, 1939-41; mng. editor Kannapolis (N.C.) Ind., 1941-42; reporter AP, Raleigh, 1942-43, News and Observer, Raleigh, 1946-57; mng. editor News and Observer, 1957-72; outdoor editor, 1949-76. Mem. Kerr Reservoir Devel. Commn., 1950-52, Cape Hatteras Seashore Commn., 1949-50, N.C. Wildlife Resources Commn., 1977-89; chmn. N.C. Outer Banks Park Commn., 1962-63, N.C. Seashore Commn., 1963-69, N.C. State Ports Authority, 1969-73. Served with USAAF, 1943-45. Mem. AP Mng. Editors Assn., Outdoor Writers Am. Baptist. Home: Old Ferry Dock Rd Gloucester NC 28528

PRICE, (WILLIAM) MARK, professional basketball player; b. Bartlesville, Okla., Feb. 15, 1964. Student, Ga. Tech. With Dallas Mavericks, 1986; guard Cleve. Cavaliers, 1986—. Winner NBA Long Distance Shootout, 1993, 94; named to NBA All-Star team, 1989, 92, 93, 94, NBA First Team, 1993, Dream Team II, 1994. Holder career record for highest free-throw percentages during regular and playoff seasons. Office: Cleve Cavaliers The Coliseum 2923 Streetsboro Rd Richfield OH 44286-5000*

PRICE, MARK MICHAEL, building development consultant; b. Cleve., Jan. 20, 1920; s. Mark Michael and Sarah Ann (Moran) P.; ed. U. Detroit, 1940, Cleve. Coll., 1946; m. Ellen Elizabeth Hafford, June 3, 1948; children—Marilyn Michelle, Pamela Susan. Founder Desk Tops, Inc., Cleve., 1950, Vistron Door Corp., Cleve., 1962; pres., chief exec. officer Bldg. Devel. Counsel Inc., Washington; founder Desk Tops Inc., Vistron Door Corp. Mem. Cleve. Mayor's Bus. Men's Civic Com., 1977-78. Mem. Soc. Mktg. Profls. Democrat. Roman Catholic. Clubs: Army-Navy, Nat. Press, Capital Hill (Washington), University, Capitol. Office: Bldg Devel Counsel Inc 1225 Connecticut Ave NW Ste 300 Washington DC 20036-2604

PRICE, MICHAEL HOWARD, journalist, critic, composer, cartoonist; b. Amarillo, Tex., Sept. 14, 1947; s. John Andrew and Thelma Adeline (Wilson) P.; m. Christina Renteria, Aug. 31, 1980. BA in Journalism, West Tex. State U., 1970. Edn. writer Amarillo Globe-News, 1968-74, fin. editor, 1974-76, city editor, 1976-77; adminstr. Amarillo Coll., 1977-80; bur. chief Ft. Worth Star-Telegram, 1980-83, features editor, 1983-85, film critic, 1985—; cons. journalism West Tex. State U., Canyon, 1977-90, Tex. Tech U., Lubbock, 1982-85; dirs. The Harvey Group comic-book profls. awards, 1990—. Author: (albums) Cognitive Dissonance, 1994, The Last Temptation of Price, 1995, R. Crumb—the Musical, 1995; (books) Forgotten Horros, 1986, Human Monsters in the Movies, 1994, Jazz Guitars, 1995, Krime Duzzin't Pay, 1995; (novels) The Prowler, 1989, Holiday for Screams, 1992. Creative dir. Tex. Gridiron Show, Fort Worth, 1984-85, 92-93. Mem. Soc. Profl. Journalists (bd. dirs. 1992-94), Soc. Film Critics. Office: Ft Worth Star Telegram Inc 400 W 7th 3d Fl Fort Worth TX 76102

PRICE, NICK, professional golfer; b. Durban, South Africa, Jan. 28, 1957; m. Sue Price; children: Gregory, Robyn Frances. Winner PGA Championship, 1992, 1994, British Open, 1994, 3rd PGA Tour Money Leader, 1992, PGA Tour Money Leader, 1993, 10 USPGA Tour Victories, 26 World Wide Victories; recipient Vardon Trophy, 1993; named Player of Yr. 1993. Holds PGA Tournament record for lowest score (269), 1994. Address: care PGA Tour 112 TPC Blvd Ponte Vedra Beach FL 32082*

PRICE, PAUL BUFORD, physicist, educator; b. Memphis, Nov. 8, 1932; s. Paul Buford and Eva (Dupuy) P.; m. JoAnn Margaret Baum, June 28, 1958; children—Paul Buford III, Heather Alynn, Pamela Margaret, Alison Gaynor. BS summa cum laude, Davidson Coll., 1954, DSc, 1973; MS, U. Va., 1956, PhD, 1958. Fulbright scholar U. (Eng.) Bristol, 1958-59; NSF postdoctoral fellow Cambridge (Eng.) U., 1959-60; physicist R&D Ctr. GE, Schenectady, 1960-69; vis. prof. Tata Inst. Fundamental Rsch., Bombay, India, 1965-66; adj. prof. physics Rensselaer Poly. Inst., 1967-68; prof. physics U. Calif., Berkeley, 1969—, chmn. dept. physics, 1987-91, McAdams prof. physics, 1990-92, dean phys. scis., 1992—; dir. Space Scis. Lab., 1979-85; bd. dirs. Terradex Corp., Walnut Creek, Calif.; vis. com. Bartol Rsch. Inst., 1991-94; adv. bd. Indian Inst. Astrophysics, Bangalore, 1993—; cons. to lunar sample analysis planning team NASA; space sci. bd. Nat. Acad. Scis.; vis. prof. U. Rome, 1983, 92; sci. assoc. Ctr. d'Etude Rsch. Nuclear, 1984; Miller rsch. prof. U. Calif., Berkeley, 1972-73; researcher in space and astrophycs, nuclear physics. Author: (with others) Nuclear Tracks in Solids; Contbr. (with others) articles to profl. jours. Recipient Disting. Svc. award Am. Nuclear Soc., 1964, Indsl. Rsch. awards, 1964, 65, E.O. Lawrence Meml. award AEC, 1971, medal for exceptional sci. achievement NASA, 1973; John Simon Guggenheim fellow, 1976-77. Fellow Am. Phys. Soc., Am. Geophys. Union; mem. Nat. Acad. Scis. (chmn. geophysics sect. 1981-84, sec. class phys.-math. scis. 1985-88, chmn. 1988-91).

PRICE, PHILLIP S., retired adult education educator; b. Freestone County, Tex., May 17, 1914; s. James H. and Lula A. Price; m. Emma K., Apr. 30, 1943; 1 child, Charles A. BS, Tuskegee U., 1937; MS, Cornell U., 1947; postgrad., NYU. Cert. guidance counselor, supr., adminstr., N.Y. Tchr., sci. N.Y.C. Bd. Edn., 1946-50, tchr. of horticulture and animal husbandry, asst. prin., 1975-76; ret., 1977; vis. prof. Tuskeegee (Ala.) U. Counselor older adults; active Boy Scouts Am.; founder libr. and edni. found.; Streetman, Tex.; organizer of Tree Corps (Bklyn.) for Sch. Age Boys and Girls; other civic activities. Mem. Phi Delta Kappa.

PRICE, REYNOLDS, novelist, poet, playwright, essayist, educator; b. Macon, N.C., Feb. 1, 1933; s. William Solomon and Elizabeth (Rodwell) P. AB summa cum laude (Angier Duke scholar) Duke, 1955; BLitt (Rhodes scholar), Merton Coll., Oxford U., Eng., 1958; LittD, St. Andrews Presbyn. Coll., 1978, Wake Forest U., 1979, Washington and Lee U., 1991; Davidson Coll., 1992. Mem. faculty English Duke U., 1958—; asst. prof., 1961-68, assoc. prof., 1968-72, prof., 1972-77, James B. Duke prof., 1977—, acting chmn., 1983; writer in residence U.N.C., Chapel Hill, 1965, U. Kans., 1967, 69, 80, U.N.C., Greensboro, 1971; Glasgow prof. Washington and Lee U., 1971; faculty Salzburg Seminar, 1977. Author: A Long and Happy Life, 1962, The Names and Faces of Heroes, 1963, A Generous Man, 1966, Love and Work, 1968, Permanent Errors, 1970, Things Themselves, 1972, The Surface of Earth, 1975, Early Dark, 1977, A Palpable God, 1978, The Source of Light, 1981, Vital Provisions, 1982, Private Contentment, 1984, Kate Vaiden, 1986, The Laws of Ice, 1986, A Common Room, 1987, Good Hearts, 1988, Clear Pictures, 1989, The Tongues of Angels, 1990, The Use of Fire, 1990, New Music, 1990, The Foreseeable Future, 1991, Conversations with Reynolds Price, 1991, Blue Calhoun, 1992, Full Moon, 1993, The Collected Stories, 1993, A Whole New Life, 1994. Recipient William Faulkner Found. award notable 1st novel, 1962, Sir Walter Raleigh award, 1962, 76, 81, 84, 86, award Nat. Assn. Ind. Schs., 1964, Roanoke-Chowan Poetry award, 1982; Guggenheim fellow, 1964-65; fellow Nat. Endowment for Arts, 1967-68; lit. adv. panel, 1973-76, chmn., 1976; recipient Nat. Inst. Arts and Letters award, 1971, Bellamann Found. award, 1972, Lillian Smith award, 1976, N.C. award, 1977, Nat. Book Critics Circle award, 1986, Elmer H. Bobst award, 1988, R. Hunt Parker award N.C. Lit. and Hist. Soc., 1991. Mem. Am. Acad. Arts and Letters, Phi Beta Kappa, Phi Delta Theta. Home: Box 99014 Durham NC 27708 Office: care Harriet Wasserman Lit Agy Inc 137 E 36th St New York NY 10016-3528

PRICE, RICHARD, anthropologist, author; b. N.Y.C., Nov. 30, 1941; s. George Price and Gertrude (Swee) Jaffe; m. Sally Hamlin, 1963; children: Niko, Leah. AB in History and Lit. magna cum laude, Harvard U., 1963, PhD in Social Anthropology, 1970. From lectr. to assoc. prof. anthropology Yale U., New Haven, 1969-74; prof. anthropology Johns Hopkins U., Balt., 1974-87, chmn. dept., 1974-77, 79-85; Marta Sutton Weeks sr. fellow Stanford Humanities Ctr. Stanford (Calif.) U., 1989-90; fellow Shelby Cullom Davis Ctr. for Hist. Studies, Princeton U., 1992; Rockefeller fellow in humanities U. Fla., 1994; vis. prof. U. Paris, 1985-87, U. Minn., Mpls., 1987-88; George I. Miller vis. scholar U. Ill., 1994; Dittman prof. Am. Studies, anthropology and history Coll. William and Mary, 1994—. Author: Maroon Societies, 1973, Saramaka Social Structure, 1975, The Guiana Maroons, 1976, Afro-American Arts of the Suriname Rain Forest, 1980, First-Time: the Historical Vision of an Afro-American People, 1983, To Slay the Hydra, 1983, Stedman's Narrative of a Five Years Expedition, 1988, Alabi's World, 1990, Two Evenings in Saramaka, 1991, The Birth of African-American Culture, 1992, Stedman's Surinam, 1992, Equatoria, 1992, On the Mall, 1994, Enigma Variations, 1995; editor: GK Hall & Co., Boston, 1980. Recipient Elsie Clews Parsons prize Am. Folklore Soc., 1984, Albert J. Beveridge award Am. Hist. Assn., 1991, Gordon K. Lewis Mem. award for disting. Caribbean scholarship, 1992, J.I. Staley prize, 1993; NEH grantee, NSF grantee, Fulbright grantee; John Simon Guggenheim Meml. fellow. Fellow Am. Anthrop. Assn., Royal Anthrop. Inst. Gt. Britain and Ireland, Royal Dutch Inst. Anthropology; mem. Am. Ethnological Soc., Phi Beta Kappa. Home and Office: Anse Chaudière, 97217 Anses d'Arlet Martinique

PRICE, ROBERT, electronics consultant; b. West Chester, Pa., July 7, 1929; s. Llewellyn Robert and Elise Maclay (Mirkil) P.; m. Jennifer Ann Livingstone Martin, Apr. 19, 1958; children: Stephen Livingstone, Colin Llewellyn, Edmund Hazleton. A.B., Princeton U., 1950; Sc.D. (Indsl. fellow 1950-52), M.I.T., 1953. Engr. Philco Corp., Phila., 1950; mem. staff Lincoln Lab., M.I.T., 1951-65; mgr. Sperry Research Center, Sperry Corp., Sudbury, Mass., 1965-77; staff cons. communication scis. Sperry Research Center, Sperry Corp., 1977-83; chief scientist M/A-COM Govt. Systems Div., Burlington, Mass., 1983-87, cons., 1987-88; cons. scientist Research div. Raytheon Co., Lexington, Mass., 1988-93; pvt. practice cons. Lexington, Mass., 1993—; vis. lectr. U. Calif., Berkeley, 1962-63; adv. council dept. elec. engring. and computer sci. Princeton U., 1971-77; chmn. Mil. Communication Conf. Bd., 1985. Contbr. sci. and hist. articles on spread spectrum techs.; patentee in spread spectrum communications and magnetic recording. Recipient Edwin Howard Armstrong achievement award IEEE Communications Soc., 1981; Fulbright fellow in radio astronomy Australia, 1953-54. Fellow IEEE (gov. info. theory group 1967-70, 77-79); mem. Internat. Union Radio Sci., Nat. Acad. Engring., Franklin Inst., Phi Beta Kappa, Sigma Xi.

PRICE, ROBERT, lawyer, media executive, investment banker; b. N.Y.C., Aug. 27, 1932; s. Solomon and Frances (Berger) P.; m. Margery Beth Wiener, Dec. 18, 1955; children: Eileen Marcia, Steven. AB, NYU, 1953; LLD, Columbia U., 1958. Bar: N.Y. 1958, U.S. Dist. Ct. 1958, U.S. Ct. Appeals 1958, U.S. Supreme Ct 1958, ICC 1958, FCC 1958, IRS 1958. With R.H. Macy & Co., Inc., 1955-58; practiced in N.Y.C., 1958—; law clk. to judge U.S. Dist. Ct. (so. dist.) N.Y., 1958-59; asst. U.S. atty. So. Dist. N.Y., 1959-60; ptnr. Kupferman & Price, 1960-65; chmn. bd. pres. Atlantic States Ind. Inc., 1963-66; dep. mayor N.Y.C., 1965-66; exec. v.p., dir. Dreyfus Corp., N.Y.C., 1966-69; v.p., investment officer Dreyfus Fund, until 1969; chmn., pres., dir. Price Capital Corp., N.Y.C., 1969-72; gen. ptnr., spl. counsel Lazard, Freres & Co., 1972-82; pres. N.Y. Law Jour., Nat. Law Jour.; pres., treas., dir. Price Communications Corp., 1979—; pres., dir. PriCellular Corp., 1988—, TLM Corp., 1989—; adv. com. Bankers Trust Co. N.Y.; dir. Holly Sugar Corp., Lane Bryant, Inc., Graphic Scanning Corp.; chmn. N.Y.C. Port Authority Negotiating Com. for World Trade Ctr., 1965-66; spl. counsel N.Y. State Joint Legis. Com. on Ct. Reorgn; asst. counsel N.Y. State Joint Legis. Com. on N.Y. Banking Laws. Author articles. Chmn. govt. and civil svc. div. United Jewish Appeal Greater N.Y., 1966; co-chmn. Met. N.Y. Red Cross Blood Drive, 1966; mem. nat. exec. com. Columbia Law Sch. 16th Ann. Fund Drive, 1966-67; campaign mgr. John V. Lindsay campaigns for congressman, N.Y.C., 1958, 64; del. N.Y. Rep. State Conv., 1962, 66; del. Rep. Nat. Conv., 1988; campaign mgr. Nelson A. Rockefeller, Ore. Rep. presdl. primary campaign, 1964, Lindsay campaign for mayor, N.Y.C., 1965; lectr. Rep. Nat. Com., 1966—; bd. dirs. Am. Friends Hebrew U.; past trustee Columbia U. Sch. Pharm. Scis., Birch Wathen Sch. Served with AUS, 1953-55. Recipient Yeshiva U. Heritage award, Pub. Svc. award Queens Catholic War Vets. Mem. ABA, FCC Bar Assn., Assn. Bar City N.Y., N.Y. State Dist. Attys. Assn., Coun. Fgn. Rels., Columbia Law Sch. Alumni Assn. (dir.), Scribes, Tau Kappa Alpha. Home: 25 E 86th St New York NY 10028-0553 Office: Price Communications Corp 45 Rockefeller Plz New York NY 10020

PRICE, ROBERT E., manufacturing company executive; b. 1942. BA, Pomona Coll., 1964. V.p. Fed-Mart Corp., 1964-75; pres., chief exec. officer Price Corp., San Diego, 1976-89, pres., chmn. bd., chief exec. officer, 1989-91, chmn. bd., chief exec. officer, 1991—, also bd. dirs. Office: Price Co 4649 Morena Blvd San Diego CA 92112

PRICE, ROBERT EBEN, judge; b. Waco, Tex., Jan. 13, 1931; s. Robert Eben and Mary Hamilton (Barnett) P.; m. Ann Hodges, June 4, 1954; children—Eben, Mary, Ann, Emily. B.A., So. Methodist U., 1952, J.D., 1954, LL.M., 1972; postgrad. Air War Coll., 1976. Bar: Tex. 1954, U.S. Supreme Ct., U.S. Ct. Mil. Appeals, U.S. Ct. Claims, U.S. Dist. Ct. (no. dist.) Tex. 1954. Mem. firm Taylor, Mizell, Price, Corrigan & Smith, Dallas, 1956-86; judge Dallas County Probate Ct. No. 2, 1986—; lectr. continuing legal edn. program U. Houston Law Found., 1993—; lectr. law So. Meth. U. Law Sch., 1973—, faculty paralegal cert. Continuing Edn., 1987—; lectr. practice skills program State Bar Tex., 1974—. Editor-in-chief: Southwestern Law Jour., 1953-54. Trustee and sec. St. Michael and All Angels Found.; bd. dirs. Downtown Ministry, Diocese of Dallas Episcopal; chmn. legis. and legal awareness subcom., vice chmn. Tex. Gov.'s Com. on Employment of Handicapped, 1978-82. Served as legal officer USAF, 1954-56; col. JAGC Res. ret. Fellow Am. Coll. Trust and Estate Counsel (state membership com., fiduciary litigation com.); mem. ABA (nat. conf. spl. ct. judges com. on probate and surrogates cts. 1992—), Nat. Coll. Probate Judges, Coll. of State Bar Tex., Dallas Bar Assn., State Bar Tex. (lectr. profl. devel. program 1988—), Tex. Coll. Probate Judges (mem. faculty), Phi Alpha Delta, Phi Eta Sigma, Phi Delta Theta. Episcopalian. Home: 4300 Arcady Ave Dallas TX 75205-3704 Office: Probate Ct # 2 211 Records Bldg 500 Main St Dallas TX 75202-3504

PRICE, ROBERT IRA, coast guard officer; b. N.Y.C., Sept. 22, 1921; s. Alfred and Mary Edna (Schweitzer) P.; m. Virginia Louise Miller, June 20, 1946; children: Andrea Jean, Keven Virginia. B.B.A., CCNY, 1942; B.S., U.S. Coast Guard Acad., 1945; postgrad., M.I.T., 1950-53. Registered profl. engr., D.C. Commd. ensign U.S. Coast Guard, 1945, advanced through grades to vice adm., 1978; asst. chief Mcht. Marine Tech. Div., Washington, 1965-67; chief planning staff Office Mcht. Marine Safety, 1967-71; capt. Port of Phila., 1971-73; chief Office Marine Environ. Washington, 1974-76; comdr. 11th Coast Guard Dist. Long Beach, Calif., 1976-78; comdr. Atlantic Area and 3d Coast Guard Dist. N.Y.C., 1978-81; ret., 1981; sr. v.p. J.J. Henry Co. (marine engrs.), N.Y.C., 1981-86; maritime cons., 1986—; prin. U.S . negotiator to tech. programs Intergovtl. Maritime Consultative Orgn., UN, 1962-71. Contbg. author: Ship Design and Construction, 1980; Contbr. articles to profl. jours. Decorated D.S.M. with gold star, Legion of Merit with gold star, Meritorious Service medal with gold star, Coast Guard Commendation medal. Fellow Royal Instn. Naval Architects, Soc. Naval Architects (Land medalist 1982); mem. Sigma Xi. Clubs: Propeller, Army Navy, N.Y. Yacht.

PRICE, ROBERT O., mayor; b. Abilene, Kans., Jan. 4, 1932; s. Iru Paul and Irene Isabel (Parrish) P.; m. Dorothy Faye Price, Jan. 26, 1951; children: Fred Dennis, Donald Eugene. BA, U. Redlands, 1978. Patrolman, sgt., lt., capt. Bakersfield Police Dept., 1956-73; chief police, 1973-88; cons. troubleshooter, various cities, 1988-92; mayor City of Bakersfield, 1993—; pres. Secret Witness Bd., 1980-83. Mem. Calif. Coun. on Criminal Justice, Sacramento, 1983-93; chmn. State Adv. Group on Juvenile Justice, Sacramento, 1988-93, Citizens Adv. Com., Fresno, Calif., 1993—, Youth Devel. Coalition, Bakersfield, 1993—, Econ. Devel. Discussion Group, Bakersfield, 1993—; chmn. western region Nat. Coalition Juvenile Justice and Delinquency Prevention, 1988-93; founder, cons. Youth Adv. Coun., Bakersfield, 1993—; founder Bakersfield Action Team, 1994. Sgt. U.S. Army, 1952-54. Recipient John W. Doubenmier award Am. Soc. Pub. Admins., 1978, Califf Morris award Calif. Probation, Parole and Corrections Officers Assn., 1982. Mem. Internat. Assn. Chiefs Police, Calif. Police Chiefs Assn., Calif. Peace Officers Assn., Calif. Council Criminal Justice, Kern County Police Chiefs Assn. (pres. 1979), Kern County Law Enforcement Admin. Assn. (pres. 1974). Republican. Avocations: photography, fishing, travel. Office: City of Bakersfield 1501 Truxtun Ave Bakersfield CA 93301

PRICE, ROBERT STANLEY, lawyer; b. Phila., Jan. 21, 1937; s. Benjamin and Estelle B. (Muchnick) P.; m. Emilie W. Kirschbaum, June 27, 1965; children: Louise W., Marianna R. BA, Kenyon Coll., 1958; LLB, Yale U., 1961. Bar: Pa. 1963, U.S. Dist. Ct. (ea. dist.) Pa. 1963, U.S. Ct. Appeals (3d cir.) 1963, N.Y. 1993. Assoc. Dechert, Price & Rhoads, Phila., 1961-63; asst. tax atty. Smith Kline & French, Phila., 1963-67; tax atty. Pa. Central Transp. Co., Phila., 1967-70; tax counsel IU Internat., Phila., 1970-72; ptnr. Townsend, Elliott & Munson, Phila., 1972-76; ptnr. Pepper, Hamilton & Scheetz, Phila., 1977-86; ptnr. Saul, Ewing, Remick & Saul, 1986-93, spl. cons. 1994—; tax counsel Plunkett & Jaffe, P.C., 1994—. Served with U.S. Army, 1961-62. Mem. Phila. Bar Assn., Pa. Bar, ABA (tax exempt fin. com.), Alpha Delta Phi Internat. (pres. 1975-78). Club: Racquet of Phila. (v.p. 1987-88). Author ABCs of Industrial Development Bonds, 1981, 5th edit., 1990; contbr. articles to legal jours. Home: 1034 W Upsal St Philadelphia PA 19119-3715 Office: Saul Ewing Remick & Saul 3800 Centre Sq W Philadelphia PA 19102

PRICE, THEODORA HADZISTELIOU, individual and family therapist; b. Athens, Greece, Oct. 1, 1938; came to U.S. 1967; d. Ioannis and Evangelia (Emmanuel) Hadzisteliou; m. David C. Long Price, Dec. 26, 1966 (div. 1989); children: Morgan N., Alkes D.L. BA in History/Archaeology, U. Athens, 1961; DPhil, U. Oxford, Eng., 1966; MA in Clin. Social Work, U. Chgo., 1988; Diploma in Piano Teaching, Nat. Conservatory, Athens, 1958. Lic. clin. social worker; bd. cert. diplomate in clin. social work. Mus. asst. and resident tutor U. Sydney, Australia, 1966-67; instr. anthropology Adelphi U., N.Y.C., 1967-68; archaeologist Hebrew Union Coll., Gezer, Israel, 1968; asst. prof. classical archaeology/art U. Chgo., 1968-70; jr. rsch. fellow Harvard Ctr. Hellenic Studies, Washington, 1970-71; clin. social worker Harbor Light Ctr., Salvation Army, Chgo., 1988-89; therapist Inst. Motivational Devel., Lombard, Ill., 1989-90; caseworker Jewish Family & Community Svc., Chgo., 1989-90; staff therapist Family Svc. Ctrs. of South Cook County, Chicago Heights, 1990-91; pvt. practice child, adolescent, family therapy Bolingbrook, Ill., 1991—; clin. counseling svcs., clin. supr., psychotherapist The Family Link, Inc., Chgo., 1993; therapist children, adolescents and families dept. foster care Catholic Charities, Chgo., 1993-94; individual and family therapist South Ctrl. Cmty. Svcs. Individual-Family Counseling Svcs., Chgo., 1994—; staff therapist Cen. Bapt. Family Svcs., Chgo., 1991, Gracell Rehab., Chgo., 1991-92; casework supr., counselor Epilepsy Found. Greater Chgo., 1992-93; lectr. in field; bd. mem., cons. Naperville Sch. for Gifted and Talented, 1982-84. Author: (Monograph) Kourotrophos Cults and Representations of the Greek Nursing Dieties, 1978; contbr. articles to profl. jours. Meyerstein Traveling awardee, Oxford, Eng., 1963, 64; Sophocles Venizelos scholar, 1962-65. Mem. NASW, Nat. Acad. Clin. Social Workers, Ill. Clin. Social Workers (bd. cert. diplomate). Avocations: yoga, piano playing. Home and Office: 10 Pebble Ct Bolingbrook IL 60440

PRICE, THOMAS BENJAMIN, former textile company executive; b. W. Jefferson, N.C., Aug. 23, 1920; s. Avery Asper and Jenny L. (Goss) P.; m. Judith Ostberg, Jan. 28, 1950; children: Jonathan R., Gregory W., Timothy C. B.S. in Textile Engring., N.C. State U., 1941. With J.P. Stevens & Co., Inc., 1941-83, corp. v.p., 1964-68, pres. Domestics and Allied Products div., 1971-74, corporate group v.p., 1974-83, also dir.; mem. exec. com., chmn.'s office. Served to lt. comdr. USNR, World War II, Korean Conflict. Mem. Am. Arbitration Council, Sigma Tau Sigma, Phi Psi. Clubs: Pine Valley (Clemenon, N.J.); Royal Poinciania (Naples, Fla.); Lake Sunapee Golf, Lake Sunapee Yacht (New London, N.H.), U.S. Srs. Golf Assn. Home: 530 Turtle Hatch Rd Naples FL 33940-8541 also: PO Box 1245 New London NH 03257

PRICE, THOMAS EMILE, export and investment company executive; b. Cin., Nov. 4, 1921; s. Edwin Charles and Lillian Elizabeth (Werk) P.; BBA, U. Tex., 1943; postgrad. Harvard U., 1944; m. Lois Margaret Gahr Matthews, Dec. 21, 1970 (dec. Nov. 26, 1988); 1 child by previous marriage, Dorothy Elizabeth Wood Price; stepchildren: Bruce Albert, Mark Frederic, Scott Herbert, Eric William Matthews. Co-founder Price Y Cia, Inc., 1946—, sec., 1946-75, treas., 1946—, pres., 1975—, also dir.; co-founder Price Paper Products Corp. (merger Price Y Cia, Inc.), Cin., 1956, treas., 1956-75, pres., 1975-90, sec., 1956-75, also dir.; mem. Cin. Regional Export Expansion Com., 1961-63; dir. Cen. Acceptance Corp., 1954-55; founding mem. and dir. Cin. Royals Basketball Club Co., 1959-73. Referee Tri-State Tennis Championships, 1948-68, Western Tennis Championships, 1969-70, Nat. Father-Son Clay Court Championships, 1974—; Tennis Grand Masters Championships, 1975-77, 80; vol. coach Walnut Hills High Sch. Boys Team, Cin., 1970-81; chmn. and coach Greater Cin. Jr. Davis Cup, 1968-78; co-founder Tennis Patrons of Cin., Inc., 1951, trustee, 1951-79, pres., 1958-63, 68; co-founder Greater Cin. Tennis Club., 1979. Participant in fund raising drives Cin. Boys Amateur Baseball Fund; chmn. Greater Cin. YMCA World Svc. Fund Drive, 1962-64; trustee Cin. World Affairs Inst., 1957-60, gen. chmn., 1959. 1st lt. USAAF, 1943-46; ETO. Elected to Western Hills High Sch. Sport Hall of Honor; named hon. Almaden Grand Master, 1980. Cin. Met. Tennis Tournament renamed Thomas E. Price Cin. Met. Tennis Torunament, 1991. Mem. Cin. World Trade Club (pres. 1959), U.S. Trotting Assn., Cin. Hist. Soc., U.S. Lawn Tennis Assn. (trustee 1959-60, 62-64, chmn. Jr. Davis Cup com. 1960-62, founder of Col. James H. Bishop award 1962), Ohio Valley Tennis Assn. (trustee 1948—), Gillespie award 1957, Dredge award 1973, pres. 1952-53, Tom Price award named in his honor at Jr. Davis Cup 1988), Western Tennis Assn. (trustee 1951—), mem. championships adv. com. 1969-78, pres. 1959-60, Hall of Fame, 1994, Melvin R. Bergman Disting. Svc. award 1979), Greater Cin. Tennis Assn. (named after and recipient of Tom Price award 1987), Assn. Tennis Profls. (nat. championship adv. 1979—), Cin. Country CLub, Univ. Club, Cin. Tennis Club (hon. life, pres. 1957-58, adv. com. 1959—, Founders and Guardians award 1983), Indoor Tennis CLub, Ea. Hills Indoor Tennis Club, Cin. Rotary, Phi Gamma Delta. Republican. Presbyterian. Nationally ranked boys 15, 1936, jr. tennis player, 1939. History columnist Tennis Life Greater Cin., 1978-80. Home: 3249 Epworth Ave Cincinnati OH 45211-7037 Office: Dixie Terminal

Buildin Ste 216 Cincinnati OH 45202 *Personal philosophy: Follow the Ten Commandments and the Golden Rule.*

PRICE, THOMAS MUNRO, computer consultant; b. Madison, Wis., Oct. 2, 1937; s. John Edward and Georgia Winifred (Day) P.; m. Judith Ann Holm, Aug. 8, 1959; children: Scott Michael, Andrea Lynn. BS, Carroll Coll., Waukesha, Wis., 1959; MS, U. Wis., 1961, PhD, 1964. Prof. math. U. Iowa, 1964-77, U. Wyo., Laramie, 1978-79; computer user cons. U. Wyo., 1979-85, MIS prof., 1985-89; computer cons. Laramie, 1989-93; home rebuilder Pecos, N.Mex., 1994—. Contbr. articles to profl. jours. Home: HC 70 Box 235 Pecos NM 87552

PRICE, THOMAS RANSONE, neurologist, educator; b. Hampton, Va., July 31, 1934; s. William Spencer and Virginia (Ransone) P.; m. Nancy Worrell Franklin, June 28, 1958; children: Franklin Ransone, Catherine Blair. BA in Psychology, U. Va., 1956, MD, 1960. Diplomate Am. Bd. Psychiatry and Neurology. Chief resident in neurology U. Va. Hosp., Charlottesville, 1965-66; instr. U. Va. Hosp., 1966-67, U. Md. Sch. Medicine, Balt., 1967-68; asst. prof. U. Md. Sch. Medicine, 1969-72, assoc. prof., 1972-78, prof., 1978—. Editor: Cerebro Vascular Diseases, 1979; contbr. articles to profl. jours. Mem. Govs. Task Force on Alzheimers Disease, Md., 1984-88. Capt. USAF, 1961-63. Fellow Am. Neurological Assn., Am. Acad. Neurology (chmn. bylaws com. 1978-79, 83-85), Am. Heart Assn. (chmn. stroke sub-com. 1986-87); mem. Md. Neurologic Soc. (pres. 1979-80). Office: U Md Hosp 22 S Green St Baltimore MD 21201

PRICE, TOM, journalist; b. Pitts., May 26, 1946; s. H. Samuel and Anna Mae (Nicholson) P.; m. Susan Crites; 1 child, Julianna Margaret. BS Journalism, Ohio U., 1968. Reporter Athens (Ohio) Messenger, 1968-73; freelance writer, 1973-75; Wash. corrs. Dayton Daily News/Cox Newspapers, Washington, 1982—; urban affairs/politics writer Dayton Journal Herald, 1975-82. Co-author: (with Susan Crites Price) The Working Parents Help Book: Practical Advice for Dealing with the Day-to-Day Challenges of Kids and Careers, 1994 (Parent's Choice award, Scholastic Book Club selection). Presbyterian. Avocations: photography, hiking, travel, reading. Office: Cox Newspapers Washington Bur 2000 Pennsylvania Ave NW Washington DC 20006

PRICE, TREVOR ROBERT PRYCE, psychiatrist, educator; b. Concord, N.H., Nov. 29, 1943; s. Trevor Alaric and Beatrice (Dinsmore) Pryce; m. Margaret Ann Bowring, June 8, 1991; children: Meghan Jennifer, Sara Brittany; children by previous marriage: Trevor Breton, Elizabeth Anne. BA, Yale U., 1965; MD, Columbia U., 1969. Diplomate Am. Bd. Psychiatry and Neurology (examiner 1985—); Am. Bd. Internal Medicine, Nat. Bd. Med. Examiners. Intern in medicine Med. Ctr. U. Calif., San Francisco, 1969-70; resident in internal medicine Med. Ctr. of U. Calif. San Francisco, 1972-74; resident in psychiatry Dartmouth Med. Sch., Hanover, N.H., 1974-77, asst. prof., assoc. prof. psychiatry and medicine, 1977-85; assoc. prof., prof. psychiatry U. Pa. Sch. Medicine, Phila., 1985-88; dir. psychiat. in-patient svcs. Hosp. of U. Pa., 1985-88; prof. psychiatry Med. Coll. Pa. and Hahnemann U., Pitts., 1989-90, prof. psychiatry and medicine, 1991—; tenured prof. psychiatry Med. Coll. Pa., Pitts., 1993; chmn. dept. Med. Coll. Pa. and Hahnemann U., Pitts., 1989—; sr. assoc. dean, 1993—; pres. Allegheny Neuropsychiat. Inst. Med. Coll. Pa., Pitts., 1992-94; bd. dirs. Coll. Health Consortium, Inc., Phila., Allegheny Neuropsychiat. Inst., Highland Dr. Rsch. and Edn. Found., Yale Club Pitts., Pitts. Psychoanalytic Found.; mem. blue ribbon bd. Alzheimer's Disease Alliance, Western Pa., 1989—. Mem. editl. bd. Convulsive Therapy, 1984-94, Jour. Neuropsychiatry and Clin. Neurosci., 1992—, Allegheny Gen. Hosp. Jour. Neurosci., 1992—; Seminars in Neuropsychiatry, 1995—; editl. reviewer 12 psychiat. and med. jours., 1978—; contbr. chpts. to books and articles to profl. jours. Mem. N.H. Commn. on Laws Effecting Mental Health, 1974-75; bd. dirs. Advanced Studies Program, Friends of St. Paul's Sch., Concord, N.H., 1983-87. Recipient William C. Menninger award Ctrl. Neuropsychiat. Assn., 1977, Faculty Teaching award dept. psychiatry Dartmouth Med. Sch., 1984, Pres. award for Exceptional Achievement AHERF, 1994, numerous grants. Fellow Am. Psychiat. Assn.; mem. Pa. Psychiat. Assn., Soc. Biol. Psychiatry, Am. Neuropsychiat. Assn. (bd. dirs., exec. dir. 1995—), Assn. for Acad. Psychiatry, Am. Assn. Dirs. Psychiat. Residency Tng., Assn. Acad. Psychiatry, Assn. Conclusive Therapy, Assn. Medicine and Psychiatry, Yale Club Pitts., H-Y-P Club Pitts. Avocations: fly fishing, tennis, reading, piano. Office: Med Coll Pa Dept Psychiatry Allegheny Campus 320 E North Ave Pittsburgh PA 15212-4756 *Life at its best is being continually challenged and fully engaged, yet not self-absorbed.*

PRICE, VERLA BLANCHE, elementary education educator; b. Mannington, W.va., May 13, 1936; d. Paul Byron and Ida Martinia (Newbrough) Stewart; m. Harry Eugene Price, Oct. 20, 1959; 1 child, Dwight Eugene. AA, W.Va. No. C.C., Weirton, 1974; BA, W. Liberty State Coll., 1976; MA, W.Va. U., 1981. Cert. tchr., W.Va. Classroom tchr. Marion County Bd. Edn., Fairmont, W.Va., 1976-84; math. tchr. chpt. 1 Brooke County Bd. Edn., Wellsburg, W.Va., 1984—. Pianist Free Meth. Ch., Follansbee, W.Va., 1985. Recipient Am. Legion Scholastic award Am. Legion, Mannington, W.Va., 1954. Mem. NEA, Brooke County Edn. Assn. (sec. 1985-87), W.Va. Coun. Tchrs. Math., Phi Theta Kappa. Democrat. Methodist. Avocations: playing piano, gardening, walking, crocheting, knitting. Home: PO Box 208 Follansbee WV 26037-0208 Office: Wellsburg Primary Sch 14th and Main Sts Wellsburg WV 26070

PRICE, WESTCOTT WILKIN, III, health care company executive; b. Glendale, Calif., May 6, 1939; s. Westcott Wilkin Jr. and Edna Johnson P.; m. Hillary Clark Haney, Apr. 12, 1941; children: Christopher, Gretchen, Wendy. BS in Bus., U. Colo., 1961; MBA, U. So. Calif., 1967. V.p., chief operating officer Calif. Med. Ctrs., Los Angeles, 1970-73; pres., chief exec. officer Wm. Flaggs Inc., Commerce, Calif., 1973-80; pres., vice chmn. FHP Inc., Fountain Valley, Calif., 1981—. Bd. dirs. FHP Found., Long Beach, Calif., 1985—; bd. govs. U. So. Calif. Sch. Pub. Adminstrn., Los Angeles 1987—. Served to lt. (j.g.) USN, 1961-63. Republican. Episcopalian. Club: Calif. (Los Angeles). Office: FHP Internat Corp 9900 Talbert Ave Fountain Valley CA 92708-5153

PRICE, WILLIAM JAMES, organization executive; b. Alexandria, Ohio, Dec. 3, 1918; s. Lewis J. and Mary (Wright) P.; m. Betty Kistler, Aug. 22, 1943; children—Mary Barbara, Sarah Margaret, Lewis Charles. A.B., Denison U., 1940, Sc.D., 1969; M.S., Rensselaer Poly. Inst., 1941, Ph.D., 1948; DS of Anatomy, Davidson U., 1969. Research physicist Bendix Aviation Corp., 1942-45, Battelle Meml. Inst., Columbus, Ohio, 1948-50; head dept. physics Air Force Inst. Tech., Dayton, Ohio, 1950-57; chief modern physics br. Aero. Research Lab., Dayton, 1957-59; chief scientist Aero. Research Lab., 1959-63; exec. dir. Air Force Office Sci. Research, 1963-74; mgmt. cons. 1974-78; coordinator World Peacemakers, 1978—; instr. Rensselaer Poly. Inst., 1948; prof. Air Force Inst. Tech., Dayton, Ohio, 1950-57; An organizer Yokefellowship in Nation's Capital, 1964; fed. exec. fellow The Brookings Instn., 1967-68; chmn. Congl. Commn. Govt. Procurement Study Group Research and Devel., 1970-71. Author: Nuclear Radiation Detection, rev. edit, 1964; Co-author: National Security and Christian Faith, 1982, Building Christian Community Pursuing Peace with Justice, 1983, (handbook) World Peacemaker Groups, 1979; Author: also numerous articles. Mem. The Ch. of the Saviour, 1972—; Bd. dirs. Yokefellows Internat., 1967-71, Washington Lift, Inc., 1971-76, World Peacemaker, 1978—. Recipient Alumni citation Denison U., 1965, Outstanding Unit award citation Office Aerospace Research, 1965, Outstanding Unit award citation Air Force Inst. Tech., 1964. Mem. Am. Phys. Soc., A.A.A.S., Phi Beta Kappa, Sigma Xi, Tau Beta Pi (hon.). Home: 11427 Scottsbury Ter Germantown MD 20876-6010

PRICE, WILLIAM JAMES, IV, investment banker; b. Balt., Oct. 6, 1924; s. William James 3d and Frances (Robbins) P.; m. Marjorie Beard, Dec. 6, 1952; children: Marjorie, Jonathan Robbins, William James V, Juliet Robbins. B.S., Yale U., 1949. Propr. Price & Co., 1949-52; with Alex. Brown & Sons, Balt., 1952—; gen. partner, 1959—, mng. dir., 1984-89; bd. dirs. Alex Brown Cash Res. Fund, chmn., 1981—; bd. dirs. Flag Investors Tel. Income Fund, Emerging Growth Fund, Internat. Trust, Boca Rsch., Inc. Trustee Washington Coll., St. Paul's Sch. Served with inf. AUS, 1943-46, ETO. Decorated Bronze Star, Purple Heart with oak leaf cluster, Combat Infantry badge. Mem. Nat. Assn. Securities Dealers (bd. govs. 1964-66, vice chmn.

1966). Home: 6885 N Ocean Blvd Ocean Ridge FL 33435-3343 Office: Alex Brown & Sons Inc 222 Lakeview Ave West Palm Beach FL 33401-6145

PRICE, WILLIAM RAY, JR., state supreme court judge; b. Fairfield, Iowa, Jan. 30, 1952; s. William Ray and Evelyn Jean (Darnell) P.; m. Susan Marie Trainor, Jan. 4, 1975; children: Emily Margret, William Joseph Dodds. BA with high distinction, U. Iowa, 1974; student, Yale U., 1974-75; JD cum laude, Washington and Lee U., 1978. Bar: Mo. 1978, U.S. Dist. Ct. (we. dist.) Mo. 1978, U.S. Ct. Claims 1978, U.S. Ct. Appeals (8th cir.) 1985. Assoc. Lathrop & Norquist, Kansas City, Mo., 1978-84, ptnr., 1984-92, chmn. bus. litigation sect., 1987-88, 90-92, mem. exec. com., 1989-92; judge Supreme Ct. Mo., Jefferson City, 1992—; mem. G.L.V. Zumwalt monitoring com. U.S. Dist. Ct. (we. dist.) Mo., Kansas City. Pres. Kansas City Bd. Police Commrs.; mem. Together Ctr. & Family Devel. Ctr., Kansas City; chmn. merit selection com. U.S. marshall Western Dist. of Mo., Kansas City; bd. dirs. Truman Med. Ctr., Kansas City. Rockefeller fellow, 1974-75; Burks scholar Washington & Lee U., 1976. Mem. Christian Ch. Office: Supreme Ct Mo PO Box 150 Jefferson City MO 65102

PRICE, WILLIS JOSEPH, retired oil company executive; b. Louisville, Sept. 23, 1931; s. Zinn O'Hara and Geraldine Susan Violette P.; m. Gloria Rick, Sept. 5, 1970; children by previous marriage—Deborah, Barbara, Natalie. B.A. in English, Fla. State U., 1953. With Standard Oil Co. Ky., 1953-65, pres., 1970-77; with Standard Oil Co. of Calif., San Francisco, 1965-67; pres. Chevron Oil Co. East, 1967-70; sr. v.p. mfg., supply and mktg. Chevron U.S.A., San Francisco, 1977-87, pres., 1987—; v.p. Chevron Corp., San Francisco; 1987-91, retired, 1991. Bd. dirs. San Francisco Opera, Met. br. YMCA, San Francisco, United Way of Bay Area.; bd. advisers NCCJ, San Francisco; mem. bd. councillors Am. Cancer Soc., Bay Area Sci. Fair, Inc. Mem. NAM (bd. dirs.), Am. Petroleum Inst., Nat. Assn. Mfrs., Western States Petroleum Assn., Calif. C. of C., BIPAC. Republican. Office: Chevron USA Inc 225 Bush St PO Box 7137 San Francisco CA 94104

PRICE BODAY, MARY KATHRYN, choreographer, small business owner, educator; b. Fort Bragg, N.C., May 20, 1945; d. Max Edward and Katharine (Jordan) P.; m. Les Boday (div. 1982); children: Shawn Leon Boday, Irmali Ferecho Boday; m. Richard A. Weil, May 1, 1986. BFA, U. Okla., 1968, MFA, 1970; studies with David Howard, 1972-74. Soloist dancer Mary Anthony Dance Co., N.Y.C., 1971-74, Larry Richardson Dance Co., N.Y.C., 1971-73; dancer Pearl Lang Dance Co., N.Y.C., 1971-73, Gaku Dance Theater, N.Y.C., 1972-74; ballet mistress and soloist dancer St. Gallen Ballet, Switzerland, 1974-75; dancer, tchr. Zurich Ballet, Switzerland, 1975-76; asst. prof. U. Ill., Champaign-Urbana, 1976-79; artist-in-residence Cornish Inst., Seattle, 1979-80; pres. The Dance Works, Inc., Seattle, 1981-90; dir. Seahurst Ballet, 1982-84; pres. The Dance Works, Inc., Erie, Pa., 1990—; dir. dance dept., asst. prof. Mercyhurst Coll., Erie, Pa., 1990-94; dir. Peoria Ballet, 1994—; asst. prof. Bradley U., Peoria, 1994—; tchr. Harkness Ballet N.Y., Mary Anthony Dance Sch., Zurich Ballet, Nat. Acad. Arts Ill., Jefferson High Sch. Performing Arts Portland, also choreographer; tchr. Summer Dance Lab.; choreographer Mary K. Price Dance Co., U. Ill., Nat. Acad. Arts, Cornish Inst., Seahurst Ballet; tchr. Kneeland Workshops, Port Townsend, Wash., 1988; tchr., co-dir. Kneeland Seminars, Las Vegas, Nev., Port Townsend, summers 1989, 90, Oklahoma City U., summer 1990, Am. Coll. Dance Festival, 1991, 92, 93; tchr. Pa. Gov's. Sch. of the Arts, 1991, 92, 94, David Howard summer seminar Mercyhurst Coll., summer 1992, David Howard Summer Workshop with Tulsa Ballet Theatre, 1993, 94; guest artist, asst. prof. Slippery Rock U., 1994. Choreographer 3 ballets Ballet Co. St. Gallen, 1988, dance concert Mary & Friends, Seattle, 1990, The Nutcracker for Warner Theatre Erie; co-choreographer The Nutcracker Ballet, 1991-93, Coppelia, 1993, The Little Mermaid of Lake Erie at the Warner Theatre, 1994. Outstanding Dancer award U. Okla., 1968; named one of Outstanding Young Women of Am., 1977. Office: Mary Price Boday Dance Bradley Univ Communications/Fine Arts Peoria IL 61625

PRICER, WAYNE FRANCIS, counseling administrator; b. Bogue, Kans., Feb. 11, 1935; s. William C. and Lena I. (Hecke) P.; m. Alice M. Fitzpatrick, July 25, 1964; children: Wayne F. Jr., Elizabeth Anne. AB, Ft. Hays State U., 1957; MEd, U. N.D., 1963; postgrad., Wayne State U. Nat. cert. counselor; nat. cert. career counselor; nat. cert. sch. counselor; lic. profl. counselor Mich. Counselor Lamphere High Sch., Madison Heights, Mich., 1964-69, jr. high. Madison Heights, Mich., 1968-69; adj. counselor Oakland Community Coll., Bloomfield Hills, Mich., 1969—; dir. guidance Lamphere Schs., Madison Heights, Mich., 1975—. Contbr. articles to prof. jours. Mem. ACA, Assn. for Counselor Edn. and Supervision, Am. Coll. Pers. Assn., Am. Fedn. Tchrs., Am. Sch. Coun. Assn., Assn. for Adult Devel. and Aging, Assn. for Assessment in Counseling, Lamphere Fedn. Tchrs., Mich. Assn. for Adult Devel. and Aging, Mich. Assn. Coll. Admission Counselors, Mich. Counseling Assn., Mich. Assn. for Counselor Edn. and Supervision, Mich. Assn. for Measurement and Evaluation in Guidance (pres.), Mich. Assn. Specialists in Group Work, Mich. Career Devel. Assn. (treas. 1994—), Mich. Coll. Pers. Assn., Mich. Sch. Counselors Assn., Mich. Assn. for Humanistic Edn. and Develop., Mich. Assn. for Multi-Cultural Develop., Nat. Assn. Coll. Admission Counselors, Nat. Career Devel. Assn., Oakland Assn. for Counseling and Devel. (former pres.), Phi Delta Kappa. Office: 610 W 13 Mile Rd Madison Heights MI 48071-1893

PRICER, WILBUR DAVID, electrical engineer; b. Des Moines, July 22, 1935; s. Wilbur Ray and Mary Elizabeth (Berner) P.; m. Nancy Loizeaux, Oct. 10, 1964; children: Douglas, Amy, Timothy, Edward. AB in Physics, Middlebury Coll., 1959; BSEE, MIT, 1959, MSEE, 1959. Engr. IBM Corp., Poughkeepsie, 1959-70, sr. engr., East Fishkill, N.Y., 1970-83, sr. mem. tech. staff, Essex Junction, Vt., 1983—; adj. prof. elec. engring. U. Vt., 1984-90; pres. Solid State Circuits Council, 1980-81; mem. editorial bd. Spectrum Mag., 1990-92. Editor Jour. of Solid State Circuits, 1983-86. Patentee in field. Fellow, IEEE; mem. Internat. Solid State Circuits Conf. (program chmn. 1976, chmn. 1988—); program Evaluator Accreditation Bd. for Engring. and Tech., 1990-95, Sigma Xi. Methodist. Home: RR # 1 Box 1689 Charlotte VT 05445-9746 Office: IBM Dept N37 Bldg 863-2 Essex Junction VT 05452

PRICHARD, EDGAR ALLEN, lawyer; b. Brockton, Mont., Mar. 6, 1920; s. Clifford B. and Helen (Ouwersloat) P.; m. Nancy M. McCandlish, Apr. 7, 1945; children: Helen Montague (Mrs. Thomas C. Foster), Robert Walton, Thomas Morgan. Student, U. Tulsa, 1937-39, U. Okla., 1940-41; LL.B., U. Va., 1948. Bar: Va. 1947. Pvt. prac. Boothe, Prichard & Dudley, Fairfax, Va., 1948-87, McGuire, Woods, Battle & Boothe, Fairfax, 1987—; bd. dirs. George Mason Bank Shares, George Mason Bank; bd. editors Va. Law Rev., 1947-48. Mem. pub. bd. Nat. Coun. Chs., 1966-72; councilman, City of Fairfax, 1953-64, mayor, 1964-68; chmn. Fairfax Dem. Com., 1962-64, 69-72; mem. Va. Bd. Elections, 1970-75; mem. Lynch Found., pres., 1981-82; trustee Trinity Episcopal Sch. Ministry, 1977—, chmn., 1985—; bd. visitors George Mason U., 1982-91, rector, 1988-91; chmn. Fairfax Parking Authority, 1991—; mem. George Mason U. found., pres., 1971-72. Fellow ABA, Va. Bar Assn., Fairfax Bar Assn. (pres. 1964), Va. State Bar (v.p. 1969), Am. Law Inst., Diocesan Missionary Soc. Va. (pres. 1986-88), Urban Land Inst., 4th Cir. Jud. Conf., Order of Coif, Raven Soc.; mem. Lambda Alpha , Lambda Chi Alpha. Episcopalian (lay reader, warden). Clubs: Fairfax Racquet Club, Inc. (chmn.), Fairfax Country Club. Home: 3820 Chain Bridge Rd Fairfax VA 22030-3904 Office: McGuire Woods Battle & Boothe 8280 Greensboro Dr Mc Lean VA 22102-3807

PRICHARD, JOHN ROBERT STOBO, academic administrator, law educator; b. London, Jan. 17, 1949; arrived in Can., 1951; s. John Stobo and Joan Suzanne (Webber) P.; m. Ann Elizabeth Wilson, Dec. 19, 1975; children: Wilson, Kenneth, John. Honrs Econs. student, Swarthmore Coll., 1967-70; MBA, U. Chgo., 1971; LLB U. Toronto, Ont., Can., 1975; LLM, Yale U., 1976. Asst. prof. faculty of law U. Toronto, 1976-81, assoc. prof., 1981-88, prof., 1988—; assoc. Ctr. for Indsl. Rels., 1979—; dean faculty of law, 1984-1990, pres. univ., 1990—; vis. assoc. prof. Yale U. Law Sch., New Haven, Conn., 1982-83; vis. prof. Harvard U. Law Sch., Cambridge, Mass., 1983-84; mem. Law Reform Commn., Toronto, 1986-1990; chmn. Fed., Provincial and Territorial Review of Liability and Compensation on Health Care, Ottawa, Ont., 1987-90. Co-author: Canadian Business Corporations, 1977, Canadian Competition Policy, 1979, Choice of Governing Instrument, 1982; co-author, editor: Public Ownership: The Calculus of Instrument

Choice, 1983. Mem. Law Soc. Upper Can. Avocation: children, fishing. Office: U Toronto, 27 King's College Cir, Toronto, ON Canada M5S 1A1

PRICHARD, PETER S., newspaper editor; b. Auburn, Calif., Dec. 18, 1944; s. Jarvis B. and Floris C. (Smith) P.; m. Ann O'Donnell, Nov. 13, 1971; children: Oliver W., Lindsay M. AB, Dartmouth Coll., 1966. Wire editor Greenwich (Conn.) Time, 1970-72; reporter Democrat and Chronicle, Rochester, N.Y., 1972-75; assoc. news dir. WOKR TV, Rochester, N.Y., 1975-76; reporter Times Union, Rochester, 1976-78; asst. to chmn. communications Gannett Co. Inc., Rochester, 1980-82, dir. communications, Office of Chief Exec., 1980-82; columns editor USA Today, Washington, 1982-83, dep. assoc. editorial dir., 1983-84, assoc. editorial dir., 1984-86, mng. editor spl. projects, 1986-87, sr. editor, 1988, editor, sr. v.p., news, 1988—; sr. v.p. News Gannett Co. Inc., Washington, 1988—, chief news exec., 1990—. Author: The Making of McPaper: The Inside Story of USA Today, 1987 (Frank Luther Moh Rsch. award Kappa Tau Alpha 1987). Vice chmn., bd. trustees Washington Journalism Ctr., 1989—. With U.S. Army, 1967-69, Vietnam. Decorated Bronze Star. Mem. Nat. Press Club, Am. Soc. Newspaper Editors (Reston, Va.) (various coms. 1985—). Office: USA Today 1000 Wilson Blvd Arlington VA 22229*

PRICKETT, GORDON ODIN, mining, mineral and energy engineer; b. Morris, Minn., Nov. 26, 1935; s. Glenn Irvin and Edna Margaret (Erickson) P.; m. Jean Carolyn Strobush, Oct. 8, 1958; children: Karen Joan Keating, Laura Jean, Glenn Thomas. B Mining Engrg., U. Minn., 1958, MS in Mineral Engring. and Econs., 1965. Registered profl. engr., Mo., Ill. U.S. Steel fellow U. Minn., Mpls., 1963-65; rsch. mineral engr. Internat. Minerals & Chem. Corp., Skokie, Ill., 1965-68; mgmt. sci. cons. Computer Mgmt. Cons., Northfield, Ill., 1968-71; mgr. tech. systems Duval Corp., Tucson, Ariz., 1971-77; dir. mgmt. info. systems Arch Mineral Corp., St. Louis, 1977-78; supr. mine planning projects Peabody Coal Co., St. Louis, 1978-82; mgr. elec. tech. transfer, nuclear plant simulator, rsch. Union Electric Co., St. Louis, 1983—; presenter papers at industry confs. Contbr. articles to profl. jours. Co-founder, chmn. Lake Forest - Lake Bluff (Ill.) Com. for Equal Opportunity, 1968-71; com. Confluence St. Louis, 1987—; bd. dirs., officer ch. bds., polit. twp. orgn., Lake Forest, Tucson, St. Louis, 1968—. Lt. USN, 1958-63, Cuba; to comdr. USNR, 1963-79. Mem. AIME (chair programs 1958—), Assn. Quality and Participation (chair programs 1986-90), Norwegian Soc. St. Louis, Engrs. Club St. Louis (chair affiliated soscs. and pub. affairs 1987-88, 93—). Avocations: running, photography, Norwegian Singing Club, skiing. Home: 125 W Cedar Ave Saint Louis MO 63119-2905 Office: Union Electric Co 1901 Chouteau Ave Saint Louis MO 63103-3003

PRIDE, CHARLEY, singer; b. Sledge, Miss., Mar. 18, 1939; m. Rozene Pride, Dec. 28, 1956; children—Kraig, Dion, Angela. Grad. high sch. Formerly with constrn. cos., refining plants; profl. baseball player with Detroit, Memphis Red Sox, Birmingham Black Barons (all Negro Am. League), Los Angeles Angels (Am. League). Appeared with WSM Grand Ole Opry, Nashville, 1967, Lawrence Welk Show, ABC-TV; appeared on Joey Bishop Show, ABC-TV; appeared with Ralph Emery Show, WSM-TV, Nashville; appeared with Syndicated Bill Anderson, Bobby Lord and Wilburn Brothers, Hee Haw, Tom Jones Show, Flip Wilson Show, Johnny Cash Show, numerous other TV shows; recorded for RCA; albums include: Country Charley Pride, Charley Pride Sings Heart Songs, Charley, Happiness, She's Just Sunday, Happiness of Having You, Charley Pride IN Person, Christmas in My Hometown, Did You Think to Pray, Roll on Mississippi, There's a Little Bit of Hank in Me, You're My Jamaica, Best of Charley Pride, The Best There Is, Greatest Hits, Night Games, Power of Love, Country Feelin, Songs of Love, A Sunshiny Day, Charley Pride Live, 1994; recorded songs Kiss an Angel Good Mornin', Snakes Crawl at Night, Let the Chips Fall, Day You Stopped Loving Me, Does My Ring Hurt Your Finger, Let Me Help You Work It Out, Is Anyone Goin' to San Antone, Afraid of Losing You Again, Let Me Live, One of These Days, Whole Lotta Love; (Named Most Promising Male Artist, Country Song Roundup 1967, Male Vocalist of Year, Country Music Assn. 1971, 72, Entertainer of Yr. in Country Music 1971, winner Grammy awards for best sacred rec. 1971, for best country vocal 1972, Trendsetter award Billboard 1970, Top Male Vocalist award Cashbox, Photoplay Gold Medal award 1976). Served with U.S. Army, 1956-58. Address: care Chardon Inc 3198 Royal Ln Ste 204 Dallas TX 75229*

PRIDE, DOUGLAS SPENCER, minister; b. Latrobe, Pa., Jan. 13, 1959; s. Spencer MacVeagh and Kathleen (Tidd) P.; m. Elizabeth Armstrong, June 5, 1982; children: Kathryn Elizabeth and Jennifer Suzanne (twins), Pamela Campbell. BA, Westminster Coll., 1980; MDiv, Pitts. Theol. Sem., 1983, DMin, 1993. Ordained to ministry Presbyn. Ch., 1983. Asst. pastor Shadyside Presbyn. Ch., Pitts., 1983-85, assoc. pastor, 1985-91; pastor The Presbyn. Ch. of Clearfield, Clearfield, Pa., 1992—; chaplain palliative care program West Penn Hosp., 1983-86; chaplain Clearfield Hospice, 1992—. Bd. dirs. Theol. Sem., 1983-86; mem. alumni coun. Westminster Coll., New Wilmington, Pa., 1986-90, pres., 1989-90; bd. dirs. Bethesda Ctr., Pitts.; 1st v.p. Spina Bifida Assn., Pitts., 1987-89, pres., 1989-93, bd. dirs., 1984—; sec. bd., 1985-87. Mem. Huntingdon Presbytery, Clearfield Curwensville Country Club. Republican. Avocations: tennis, racquetball, reading. Home: 2538 Meadow Rd Clearfield PA 16830-1140

PRIDEAUX, GARY DEAN, linguistics educator; b. Muskogee, Okla., Apr. 21, 1939; arrived in Can., 1966; s. Ivor Dean and Lorene Gertrude (Molohan) P.; m. Pamela Joyce Asquith, Oct. 7, 1989. BA in Physics, Rice U., 1961; PhD in Linguistics, U. Tex., 1966. Asst. prof. linguistics U. Alta., Edmonton, Can., 1966-71; assoc. prof., 1971-78; prof., 1978—; Fulbright lectr. Tottori U., Shimane U., Japan, 1967-68. Author: Psycholinguistics: The Experimental Study of Language, 1985; co-author: Strategies and Structures, 1986; mem. editorial com. Can. Jour. Linguistics, 1983-86; contbr. articles to profl. jours. Grantee Social Scis. and Humanities Rsch. Coun. Can., 1978, 80-82, 90-92, 93-96. Mem. Can. Linguistics Assn. (exec. com. 1972-79), Linguistic Soc. Am., Western Conf. on Linguistics (pres. 1981-82), Linguistic Assn. of Can. and the U.S. Avocations: swimming, sailing. Office: U Alta, Dept Linguistics, Edmonton, AB Canada T6G 2E7

PRIDHAM, THOMAS GRENVILLE, research microbiologist; b. Chgo., Oct. 10, 1920; s. Grenville and Gladys Etheral (Sloss) P.; m. Phyllis Sue Hokamp, July 1, 1943 (dec.); children: Pamela Sue, Thomas Foster, Grenville Thomas, Rolf Thomas, Montgomery Thomas; m. Edna Lee Boudreaux, Mar. 6, 1995. BS in Chemistry, U. Ill., 1943, PhD in Bacteriology, 1949. Instr. bacteriology U. Ill., Champaign-Urbana, 1947; rsch. microbiologist No. Regional Rsch. Lab., USDA, Peoria, Ill., 1948-51, 53-65, U.S. Indsl. Chems., Balt., 1951-52; supr. tech. ops. Acme Vitamins, Inc., Joliet, Ill., 1952-53; sr. rsch. biologist U.S. Borax Rsch. Corp., Anaheim, Calif., 1965-67; supervisory rsch. microbiologist No. Regional Rsch. Ctr. USDA, Peoria, 1967-81, head agrl. rsch. culture collection No. Regional Rsch. Lab., 1967-81; ret., 1981; cons. Mycogen Corp., San Diego, 1985-87; U.S. sr. scientist Fed. Republic Germany, Darmstadt, 1977. Contbg. author: Actinomycetales: The Boundary Microorganisms, 1974, Bergey's Manual of Determinative Bacteriology, 1974, Synopsis and Classification of Living Organisms, 1982; mem. editorial bd. Jour. Antibiotics, 1969-81; contbr. articles to Jour. Bacteriology, Applied Microbiology, Phytopathology, Actinomycetes, Mycologia, Devel. Indsl. Microbiology, Jour. Antibiotics, Internat. Bull. Bacteriological Nomenclature Taxonomy, Antibiotics Ann., Antimicrobial Agts., Chemotherapy, also others. With USNR, 1943-45, with Rsch. Res., 1945-54, lt. ret. Fulbright scholar, Italy, 1952; grantee Soc. Am. Bacteriologists, 1957. Fellow Am. Acad. Microbiology (ASM state network 1991—); mem. Am. Soc. Microbiology (com. mem., workshop presenter), Soc. Indsl. Microbiology, Mycol. Soc. Am., U.S. Fedn. Culture Collections (v.p. 1981). Episcopalian. Achievements include patents in fermentative production of riboflavin and of antibiotics; research in microbial culture collection technology and management, systematics of streptomycetes, industrial microbiology, and air pollution. Home: 3020 Treasure Island Rd Las Vegas NV 89128-7075

PRIDMORE, ROY DAVIS, government official; b. Gaffney, S.C., May 18, 1925; s. Davis Bailey and Ethel (Hughes) P.; m. Doris Hedy Glatzl, July 16, 1960; children: Lisa Ann, David Michael. Cert., Columbus U. Washington, 1949, Am. Inst., Washington, 1953, U.S. Dept. Agr. Grad. Sch., Washington, 1957. Pers. asst. Dept. Army, Fort Myer, Va., 1955-58; staff asst. D.C. Hwy. Dept., Washington, 1962-67; adminstrv. asst. Dept. Transp.,

Washington, 1958-62, adminstrv. officer, 1967-94, ret., 1994. Vice pres. Springboard Swim Club, Springfield, Va., 1984-85. Served with U.S. Army, 1946-47; mem. Res. (ret.). Decorated Legion of Merit. Democrat. Roman Catholic. Avocation: swimming.

PRIEM, RICHARD GREGORY, writer, systems analyst, entertainment company executive; b. Munich, Sept. 18, 1949; came to U.S., 1953; s. Richard Stanley and Elizabeth Teresa (Thompson) P.; m. Janice Lynne Holland, July 27, 1976; children: Michael John, Matthew Warren, Kathryn Elizabeth. BS in Radio-TV-Film, U. Tex., 1970; grad. with Distinction, U.S. Mil. Police Sch., 1973, 77; MEd in Ednl. Tech., U. Ga., 1979; postgrad., Coll. William and Mary, 1981-82. Cert. fraud examiner. Radio personality, sales exec. KOKE, Inc., Austin, Tex., 1968-73; commd. 2d lt. U.S. Army, 1973, numerous positions including asst. prof. dept. behavioral scis. and leadership U.S. Mil. Acad.; staff officer anti terrorism and inspector gen., 1973-94; exec. v.p. It's Your Party, Herndon, Va., 1992—; sr. security systems analyst Sci. Applications Internat. Corp., McLean, Va., 1994—; cons. Dallas Cowboys Football Club, 1981; scouting coord. Army Football, 1983-85. Contbr. articles to profl. jours. Mem. ASTD, Assn. Cert. Fraud Examiners, Nat. Soc. for Performance and Instrn., Am. Soc. Indsl. Security Internat., Phi Kappa Phi, Kappa Delta Pi, Alpha Epsilon Rho. Home: 15386 Twin Creek Ct Centreville VA 22020-3742 Office: Sci Application Internat Corp 1710 Goodridge Dr Mc Lean VA 22102

PRIESAND, SALLY JANE, rabbi; b. Cleve., June 27, 1946; d. Irving Theodore and Rosetta Elizabeth (Welch) P. B.A. in English, U. Cin., 1968; B.Hebrew Letters, Hebrew Union Coll.-Jewish Inst. Religion, 1971, M.A. in Hebrew Letters, 1972; D.H.L. (hon.), Fla. Internat. U., 1973. Ordained rabbi, 1972. Student rabbi Sinai Temple, Champaign, Ill., 1968, Congregation B'nai Israel, Hattiesburg, Miss., 1969-70, Congregation Shalom, Milw., 1970, Temple Beth Israel, Jackson, Mich., 1970-71; rabbinic intern Isaac M. Wise Temple, Cin., 1971-72; asst. rabbi Stephen Wise Free Synagogue, N.Y.C., 1972-77; assoc. rabbi Stephen Wise Free Synagogue, 1977-79; rabbi Temple Beth El, Elizabeth, N.J., 1979-81, Monmouth Reform Temple, Tinton Falls, N.J., 1981—; chaplain Lenox Hill Hosp., N.Y.C., 1979-81. Author: Judaism and the New Woman, 1975. Mem. commn. on synagogue relations Fedn. Jewish Philanthropies N.Y., 1972-79, mem. com. on aged commn. synagogue relations, 1972-75; mem. task force on equality of women in Judaism pub. affairs com. N.Y. Fedn. Reform Synagogues, 1972-75; mem. com. on resolutions Central Conf. Am. Rabbis, 1975-77, com. on cults, 1976-78, admissions com., 1983-89; chmn. Task Force on women in rabbinate, 1977-83, chmn. 1977-79, mem. exec. bd., 1977-79, com. on resolutions, 1989-92, chmn. com. conv. program, 1993—; mem. joint commn. on Jewish edn. Central Conf. Am. Rabbis-Union Am. Hebrew Congregations, 1974-77; mem. task force on Jewish singles Commn. Synagogue Relations, 1975-77; mem. N.Y. Bd. Rabbis, 1975—, Shore Area Bd. Rabbis, 1981—; mem. interim steering com. Clergy and Laity Concerned, 1979-81; bd. dirs. NCCJ, N.Y.C., 1980-82, Jewish Fedn. Greater Monmouth County, trustee; trustee Planned Parenthood of Monmouth County, also chair religious affairs com., Brookdale Ctr. for Holocaust Studies, Monmouth Campaign for Nuclear Disarmament; v.p. Interfaith Neighbors, 1988—; mem. UAHC Task Force on Unaffiliated, 1992—; bd govs. Hebrew Union Coll.-Jewish Inst. Religion, 1993—; trustee Union Am. Hebrew Congregations, 1994—. Cited by B'nai Brith Women, 1971; named Woman of Yr. Temple Israel, Columbus, Ohio, 1972, Woman of Yr. Ladies Aux. N.Y. chpt. Jewish War Vets., 1973, Woman for All Seasons N. L.I. region Women's Am. ORT, 1973, Extraordinary Women of Achievement NCCJ, 1978, Woman of Achievement Monmouth County Adv. Commn. on Status Women, 1988; recipient Quality of Life award Dist. One chpt. B'nai B'rith Women, 1973, Medallion Judaic Heritage Soc., 1978, Eleanor Roosevelt Humanities award Women's div. State of Israel Bonds, 1980, Rabbinical award Coun. Jewish Fedn., 1988, Woman of Leadership award Monmouth Coun. Girl Scouts U.S., 1991, The Woman Who Dares award Nat. Coun. Jewish Women, 1993. Mem. Hadassah (life), Central Conf. Am. Rabbis, NOW, Am. Jewish Congress, Am. Jewish Com., Assn. Reform Zionists Am., B'nai B'rith Women (life), Jewish Peace Fellowship, Women's Rabbinc Network, Nat. Coun. Jewish Women, Nat. Breast Cancer Coalition. Home: 10 Wedgewood Cir Eatontown NJ 07724-1203 Office: 332 Hance Ave Tinton Falls NJ 07724-2730

PRIESMAN, ELINOR LEE SOLL, family dynamics administrator, mediator, educator; b. Mpls., Jan. 19, 1938; d. Arthur and Harriet Lucille (Premack) Soll; m. Ira Morton Priesman, Mar. 30, 1958; children: Phillip Sherman, Artyce-Joy Erin. PhD, Union Inst., 1993. Cert. mediator, Va.; cert. family life educator. Nursery sch. tchr. Altrusa Day Nursery, Santa Monica, Calif., 1958-59; head tchr. Altrusa Day Nursery, Battle Creek, Mich., 1959-60; prin. Arlington/Fairfax Jewish Ctr., Arlington, Va., 1966-67; tchr. grades 1-10 Congregation Olam Tikvah, Fairfax, Va., 1970-75; dir. Creative Play Nursery Sch., Fairfax, Va., 1970-71; tchr. high sch. Temple Sinai, Washington, Va., 1976-78; prin. Congregation Olam Tikvah, Fairfax, Va., 1975-76; asst. to pres.-emeritus Coun. for Advancement and Support of Edn., McLean, Va., 1987-90; cons. to univ. Union for Experimenting Colls. and Univs., McLean, Va., 1988-90; dir. family dynamics inst. Fairfax; mem. doctoral com. Union Inst., Cin., 1991-92, 92—; faculty mentor Ea. U., Albuquerque, 1993—. Author: The Empowered Parent, 1993, A New Perspective on Parenting, 1994, A New Perspective on Parenting for Attorneys and Mediators, 1995; editor: Empowered Printing newsletter, 1991-92. Pres. No. Va. Artistic Skating Club, Manassas, 1983-85; chair edn. com. Olam Tikvah Synagogue, Fairfax. Recipient Pres.'s award Olam Tikvah Synagogue, 1976. Mem. N.Am. Soc. Adlerian Psychology, Nat. Coun. on Family Rels. (children's rights coun.), Acad. Family Mediators, No. Va. Meditation Svc. (mediator), Hadassah (life, Alexandria chpt. pres. 1966-67, Esther award 1965). Jewish. Office: Family Dynamics Inst 9302 Swinburne Ct Fairfax VA 22031-3027

PRIEST, AARON MENDELL, publishing executive; b. Providence, Feb. 14, 1938; s. Herman Maurice and Bertha (Markoff) P.; m. Arleen Gradinger, Oct. 8, 1961; children: David, Michael. BA, Columbia U., 1959. Sales rep. Doubleday & Co., Rochester, N.Y., 1960-66; sales rep., mgr. Doubleday & Co., Dallas, 1966-74; founder, pres. Aaron M. Priest Lit. Agy. Inc., N.Y.C., 1974—; chmn. pub. div. UFA-Fedn. N.Y.; co-founder IPA. Chmn. pub. divsn. UJA-Jewish Welfare Orgn. With U.S. Army, 1960-61. Mem. Ind. Literacy Agts. Assn. (co-founder). Jewish. Avocations: tennis, chess, water skiing. Home: 41 Hampton Rd Scarsdale NY 10583-3026 Office: Aaron Priest Lit Agy Inc 708 3rd Ave 23rd Fl New York NY 10017

PRIEST, GEORGE L., law educator; b. 1947. BA, Yale U., 1969; JD, U. Chgo., 1973. Assoc. prof. U. Puget Sound, Tacoma, 1973-75; law and econ. fellow U. Chgo., 1975-77; prof. U. Buffalo, 1977-80; prof. UCLA, 1980-81, Yale U., New Haven, 1981—; dir. program in civil liability; John M. Olin prof. law and econs., 1986—. Mem. Pres.' Com. on Privatization, 1987-88. Office: PO Box 208215 New Haven CT 06520-8215

PRIEST, HARTWELL WYSE, artist; b. Brantford, Ont., Can., Jan. 1, 1901; d. John Frank Henry and Rachel Thayer (Gavet) Wyse; m. A.J. Gustin Priest, Aug. 4, 1927; children: Paul Lambert, Marianna Thayer. BA, Smith Coll. Former tchr. graphic art Va. Art Inst., Charlottesville; former lectr. on prints and lithography; juror art exhbn. Unitarian Ch., 1993. One-woman shows include Argent Gallery, N.Y.C., 1955, 58, 60, 73, 77, 81, Va., 1969, 71, Nantucket, Mass., 1956, Ft. Lauderdale, Fla. Art Ctr., 1956; Pen & Brush, N.Y.C., 1973, 91, invitational retrospective exhbn. McGuffey Art Ctr., Charlottesville, Va., 1984, Va., N.Y., 1984, 88; work represented in permanent collections Library of Congress Washington, Norton Gallery, Palm Beach, Fla., Soc. Am. Graphic Artists, Hunterdon County Art Ctr., Longwood Coll., Smith Coll., Va. Mus., Richmond, Carnegie Mellon U. and numerous others; solo exhbn. of prints McGuffey Art Ctr., Charlottesville, Va., 1988, 90, 93, Woodstock Artist Gallery, 1990, Soc. Am. Graphic Artists, 1988-89, 92, Bombay, 1989, U. Va. Hosp. Main Bus. Art and Sci., 1991; represented in group shows McGuffey Gallery, 1988, 94, Gallery Show, Richmond, Va., 1988, Nat. Assn. Women Artists, Florence, Italy, 1972, N.Y.C., 1989, ann. show Ojibway Hotel Club, Pointe au Baril, Georgian Bay, Ont., Can., 1991, Soc. Am. Graphic Srts, N.Y.C., 1989, 92, Woodstock, N.Y. Art Assoc., 1990, McGuffey Art Ctr., Charlottesville, Va., 1990, 94, Pen and Brush ann. Graphic Show, N.Y.C., 1991 (award for etching Spring, Ada Rosario Cecere Meml. award), Bergen Mus., N.J., 1991, Ojibway Club, Ont., Can., 1991; Pen and Brush Christmas exhbn., 1994-95,

Showing of a Video, Harrisonburg, Va.; represented in traveling group shows Nat. Assn. Women Artists, Puerto Rico, 1987, India, 1989, N.Y.C., 1989, pvt. collection U. Va. Hosp., Charlottesville, 1989; subject of TV documentary Hartwell Priest: Printmaker, 1995. Recipient awards for lithograph Field Flowers, Longwood Coll., 1965, Nat. Assn. Woman Artists, 1965, lithograph West Wind, A Buell award, 1961, print Streets of Silence, T. Giorgi Meml. award, 1973, lithograph Blue Lichen, Pen & Brush, 1984, award for collage, 1985; 1st award for graphics Blue Ridge Art Show, 1985, Gene A. Walker award for print Glacial Rocks, 1986, award for print Blue Ridge Show, 1987, Philip Isenburg award for graphic PreCambrian Rock Pattern, 1988, Ada R. Cecere Meml. award Pen and Brush, 1991, Art award Piedmont Coun. Arts, 1993. Mem. Nat. Assn. Women Artists (Travelling Printmaking Exhbn. 1987-89), Pen and Brush, Soc. Am. Graphic Artists, Washington Print Club, 2d St. Gallery, Charlottesville, McGuffey Art Ctr. Avocations: walking, singing in choir, gardening, playing Bach and Mozart, playing recorder and piano. Home: 41 Old Farm Rd Charlottesville VA 22903-4725

PRIEST, MELVILLE STANTON, retired consulting hydraulic engineer; b. Cassville, Mo., Oct. 16, 1912; s. William Tolliver and Mildred Alice (Messer) P.; m. Vivian Willingham, Mar. 22, 1941 (dec.); m. Virginia Young, Dec. 16, 1983. B.S., U. Mo., 1935; M.S., U. Colo., 1943; Ph.D., U. Mich., 1954. Registered profl. engr., Ala., La., Miss. Jr. engr. U.S. Engrs. Office, 1937-39; from jr. to asst. engr. Bur. Reclamation, 1939-41; from instr. to assoc. prof. civil engring. Cornell U., 1941-55; prof. hydraulics Auburn (Ala.) U., 1955-58, prof. civil engring., head dept., 1958-65; dir. Water Resources Research Inst., Miss. State U., 1965-77; UN adviser on hydraulics, Egypt, 1956, 57, 60; Mem. Ala. Bd. Registration Profl. Engrs., 1962-65. Contbr. articles to profl. jours. Fellow ASCE (pres. Ala. 1962, exec. com., pipeline div. 1971-74), Am. Water Resources Assn. (dir. 1973-75), Sigma Xi, Tau Beta Pi, Chi Epsilon, Pi Mu Epsilon. Address: PO Box 541 Starkville MS 39759

PRIEST, SHARON DEVLIN, state official; b. Montreal, Quebec, Can.; m. Bill Priest; 1 child, Adam. Tax preparer, instr. H & R Block, Little Rock, 1976-78; account exec. Greater Little Rock C. of C.; owner, founder Devlin Co.; mem. Little Rock Bd. Dirs., 1986—; vice mayor Little Rock, 1989-91, mayor, 1991-93; Sec. of State State of Arkansas, 1994—; bd. dirs. Invesco Inc., New Futures. Bd. dirs., past pres. Metroplan (Environ. Svc. award 1982), YMCA, Southwest Hosp.; mem. Advt. and Promotion commn., Ark. Internat. Visitors Coun., Pulaski Are Transp. Svc. Policy Com., St. Theresa's Parish Coun., Exec. com. for Ark. Mcpl. League, Nat. League of Cities Trans. and Communications Steering Com. and Policy Com., adv. bd. M.M. Cohn., Little Rock City Beautiful Commn., 1980-86; former bd. dirs. Downtown Partnership, Southwest YMCA, 1984, 86, sec.; former mem. Community Housing Resource Bd., 1984-86, Pub. Facilities Bd. Southwest Hosp., 1985-86, Southwest Merchants' Assn., 1985—, 2d v.p., 1985; chmn. Little Rock Arts and Humanities Promotion Commn.; led petition dr. for appropriation for Fourche Creek Plan 7A. Mem. Leadership Inst. Alumni Assn. (4 Bernard de la Harpe awards). Office: Office of Secretary of State State Capitol Bldg 256 Little Rock AR 72201-1411

PRIEST, WILLIAM WALLACE, JR., investment counselor; b. Pitts., Sept. 24, 1941; s. William Wallace and Helen (Blackmore) P.; m. Nancy Woods, Dec. 30, 1961; children—Jeffrey, Karen. A.B., Duke U., 1963; M.B.A., U. Pa., 1965. With Coopers & Lybrand, Phila., 1965, Commonwealth Mut. Funds, San Francisco, 1965-66, Anchor Corp., Elizabeth, N.J., 1966-72; dir. BEA Assocs., N.Y.C., 1972—. Author: Financial Reality of Pension Funding Under ERISA, 1976; contbr. articles to profl. publs. Pres. Philippian Found., Westfield, N.J.; trustee Presbyn. Ch., Westfield; bd. dirs. Duke U. Grad. Sch. Bus., Durham, N.C. Recipient Graham and Dodd award for article Fin. Analysts Fedn., 1968. Mem. Am. Inst. C.P.A.s, Chartered Fin. Analysts Assn. Home: 11 Kimball Cir Westfield NJ 07090-1809

PRIESTLEY, G. T. ERIC, manufacturing company executive; b. Belfast, Northern Ireland, May 7, 1942; came to U.S., 1990; s. Thomas John McKee P.; m. Carol Elizabeth Gingles Nelson, June 8, 1966; children: Peter, Gaye, Simon. BS, Queens U., 1963; postgrad., Harvard Bus. Sch., 1989. Sales trainee Burroughs Machines Ltd., 1963-64; dealer, sales devel. Regent Oil Co., 1964-66; ops. mgr. RMC (Ulster) Ltd., 1967-70; distbn. mgr. Bass Charrington, Ireland, 1970-71; dir., gen. mgr. Farrans Ltd., 1971-80; dir., CEO Redland plc/British Fuels/Cawoods, 1980-88; dir. Bowater plc, London, 1988-90; pres., CEO Rexham Inc., Charlotte, N.C., 1990—; bd. dirs. Rexham Inc., Bowater plc, MiTek Inc., St. Louis, Interprint Ltd., Sao Paulo, Brazil. Mem. Moortown Golf Club, Aloha Golf Club, Royal Ulster Yacht Club, Quail Hollow Golf & Country Club. Home: 9114 Winged Bourne Charlotte NC 28210-4205 Office: Rexham Inc 4201 Congress St Ste 340 Charlotte NC 28209-4621

PRIESTLEY, JASON, actor; b. Vancouver, BC, Can.. Actor: (TV series) Sister Kate, 1989-90, Beverly Hills, 90210, 1990—; (films) Calendar Girl, 1993, Tombstone, 1993; dir. (TV series) Beverly Hills, 90210, 1993-94. Office: c/o Wolf Kasteler 1033 Gayley Ave Ste 208 Los Angeles CA 90024-3417

PRIESTNER, EDWARD BERNARD, manufacturing company executive; b. Hamilton, Ont., Can., June 4, 1936; s. William Joseph and Helen Gladys (Osbaldeston) P.; m. Marianne Agnes Baker, May 23, 1959; children: Lorraine, Patricia, Nancy. BA in Econs., U. Western Ont., 1958. Supr., treas. Prudential Ins. Co. Am., Toronto, Ont., 1958-61; treasury asst. Westinghouse Can. Inc., Hamilton, 1961-64, asst. treas., 1964-71, treas., 1971-78, v.p., 1975-78, v.p. fin., 1978-81; v.p. ops. Westinghouse Can. Inc., Toronto, 1981-84, exec. v.p. ops., 1984-85, also bd. dirs.; pres., chief exec. officer Westinghouse Can. Inc., Hamilton, 1985-91, chmn. bd., 1991-93; bd. dirs. Allendale Ins. Co., Johnston, R.I. Mem. steering com. Hamilton dist. United Way, 1978-91; bd. govs. McMaster U., Hamilton, 1985—, chmn. bd. govs., 1991-93; mem. bd. govs. Jr. Achievement Hamilton, 1985-93; bd. dirs. Halton-Wentworth Alzheimer Found., Inc. Mem. Hamilton C. of C. (past pres.). Clubs: Hamilton; Hamilton Golf and Country (Ancaster, Ont.). Avocations: sailing, golf. Office: Westinghouse Can Inc, 120 King St W Box 2510, Hamilton, ON Canada L8N 3K2

PRIETO, CLAUDIO R., academic administrator, lawyer; b. Caguas, P.R., Aug. 17, 1933; s. Claudio Prieto and Carmen (Gutierrez) del Arroyo; m. Myrna Irizarry; children: Claudio, Carmen, Isabel, Rosa, Anna, Alfonso. BS, U. P.R., 1954, JD, 1971. Bar: P.R. Asst. prof. U. P.R., Rio Piedras, 1956-70, coord. student affairs, 1957-59, dir. extension div., 1959-61, assoc. prof. Sch. Law, 1970-71; dir. edn. press Commonwealth of Puerto Rico, Rio Piedras, 1961-65, asst. sec. edn., 1965-67; asst. to gov. Commonwealth of Puerto Rico, San Juan, 1967-68; asst. to dep. commr. Dept. Edn. State of N.Y., Albany, 1977-78, asst. commr., 1978-88; chancellor Turabo U., Gurabo, P.R., 1989-93; exec. dir. office of equity and acccess policy studies N.Y. State Dept. Edn., Albany, 1993—; cons. to chancellor U. P.R., 1969, legal plannning and adminstrn. Tech. Svcs. P.R., 1973-76. Columnist San Juan Star, 1973-76, 1992—. Trustee Ewald B. Nyquist Meml. Found, Albany, 1990—; bd. overseers Regents Coll., 1989-93. Named Edn. Exec. of Yr. Sales and Mktg. Assn., P.R., 1989. Mem. Intercollegiate Athletic League (bd. govs.). Democrat. Roman Catholic. Office: NY State Dept Edn Albany NY 12234

PRIEVE, E. ARTHUR, arts administration educator. BBA in Adminstrn. and Art History, U. of Wis., 1959, MBA in Mgmt. and Orgn. Behavior, 1961; DBA in Mgmt. and Psych., George Washington U., Washington, 1965. Asst. dean adminstrv. affairs Sch. Bus. U. Wis., Madison, 1966-69, prof. mgmt. Grad. Sch. Bus., 1969—, dir. exec. MBA program, 1993—; dir. Ctr. For Arts Adminstrn., Madison, 1969—; curriculum cons. for arts adminstrn.; cons. visual, performing and arts svc. orgns.; workshops and presentations on planning. bd. dirs. Mem. Assn. of Arts Adminstrn. Educators (chmn. U.S., Can.). Office: U Wis Ctr Arts Adminstrn 4171 Grainger Hall 975 University Ave Madison WI 53706-1323

PRIGMORE, CHARLES SAMUEL, social work educator; b. Lodge, Tenn., Mar. 21, 1919; s. Charles H. and Mary Lou (Raulston) P.; m. Shirley Melaine Buuck, June 7, 1947; 1 child, Philip Brand. A.B., U. Chattanooga, 1939; M.S., U. Wis., 1947, Ph.D., 1961; extension grad., Air War Coll., 1967, Indsl. Coll. Armed Forces, 1972. Social caseworker Children's Svc. Soc., Milw., 1947-48; social worker Wis. Sch. Boys, Waukesha, 1948-51; supr. tng.

Wis. Bur. Probation and Parole, Madison, 1951-56; supt. Tenn. Vocat. Tng. Sch. for Boys, Nashville, 1956-59; assoc. prof. La. State U., 1959-64; ednl. cons. Coun. Social Work Edn. N.Y., 1962-64; exec. dir. Joint Commn. Correctional Manpower and Tng., Washington, 1964-67; prof. Sch. Social Work, U. Ala., 1967-84, prof. emeritus, 1984—, chmn. com. on Korean relationships; Fulbright lectr., Iran, 1972-73; vis. lectr. U. Sydney, 1976; cons. Iranian Ministry Health and Welfare, 1976-78; frequent lectr., workshop leader. Author: Textbook on Social Problems, 1971, Social Work in Iran Since the White Revolution, 1976, Social Welfare Policy Analysis and Formulation, 1979, 2d edit., 1986; editor 2 books; contbr. articles to profl. jours. Adv. Com. for Former Prisoners of War Ala., 1981-83; chmn. Prisoner of War Ala., State of Ala., 1984-89; state comdr. Am. Ex-Prisoners of War, Ala., 1985-86, nat. legis. officer, 1985—, nat. dir., 1989-92, nat. sr. vice comdr., 1993—, nat comdr., 1994-95; gov.'s liaison U.S. Holocaust Meml. Coun., 1983-89; mem. Ala. Bd. Vets. Affairs, 1986-89, Ala. Bicentennial Commn. on Constn., 1987-90; bd. dirs. Community Svcs. Programs of W. Ala., 1985-89, others in past. Served to 2d lt. USAAF, 1940-45, prisoner of war, Germany, 1944-45; lt. col. Res., ret. Decorated Air medal with oak leaf cluster; recipient Conservation award Woodmen of the World, 1971; Fulbright rsch. fellow Norway, 1979-80. Fellow Am. Sociol. Assn., Royal Soc. Health; mem. Acad. Cert. Social Workers, Nat. Coun. Crime and Delinquency, Tuscaloosa Country Club, Capitol Hill Club, Alpha Kappa Delta, Beta Beta Beta. Home: 923 Overlook Rd N Tuscaloosa AL 35406-2122 Office: PO Box 870314 Tuscaloosa AL 35487-0314 *The following principles seem most related to my success: 1) From childhood I was encouraged to formulate specific vocational goals and work toward them; 2) support of friends and relatives is secondary, though important; more significant is one's own effort and planning. 3) Objectives and plans usually can be achieved only through persistence and determination. Usually one is forced to sacrifice a measure of peer fellowship and conviviality. 4) Belief in oneself and one's own potentialities makes for a self-fulfilling prophecy.*

PRIGOGINE, VICOMTE ILYA, physics educator; b. Moscow, Russia, Jan. 25, 1917; s. Roman and Julie (Wichmann) P.; m. Marina Prokopowicz, Feb. 25, 1961; children: Yves, Pascal. PhD, Free U. Brussels, 1942; hon. degree, U. Newcastle, Eng., 1966, U. Poitiers, France, 1966, U. Chgo., 1969, U. Bordeaux, France, 1972, U. de Liège, Belgium, 1977, U. Uppsala, Sweden, 1977, U de Droit, D'Economie et des Scis., d'Aix-Marseille, France, 1979, U. Georgetown, 1980, U. Cracovie, Poland, 1981, U. Rio de Janeiro, 1981, Stevens Inst. Tech., Hoboken, 1981, Heriot-Watt U., Scotland, 1985, Universidad Nacional de Educacion a Distancia, Madrid, 1985, U. Francois Rabelais de Tours, 1986, U. Peking, People's Republic of China, 1986, U. Buenos Aires, 1989, U. Cagliari, Sardinia, Italy, 1990, U. Sienne, Italy, 1990, DS (hon.), Gustavus Adolphus Coll., 1990; Membre d'Honneur, l'Academie Nationale d'Argenti, 1990, l'Academie des Sciences Nature, Iles de Republique Federale de Russie, 1991; Pres. d'Honneur, l'Acad. Nat. des Scis. de Republique de San Marino, 1991; Membre d'Honneur, l'Academie Chilienne des Scis., 1991, de l'Université de Nice-Sophia-Antipolis, Nice, France, 1991, de l'Univ. Philippines System, Quezon City, 1991, del'Université de Santiago, Chile, del'Université de Tucumán, Argentine, 1991; Docteur Honoris Causa, Université Lomonosov de Moscow, Russie, 1993, L'Universite de A L I. Cuza, Romania, 1994; Docteur Honoris Cause, Université de Sau Luis, Argentine, 1994, U. Palerno, Argentine, 1994, Inst. Nat. Polytech. Lorraine, France, 1994, SUNY, Binghamton, 1995, Vrije Univ. Brussel, 1995, Internat. Assn. Univs. Pres., Seoul, 1995, Inst. Royal Elites, Brussels, 1995. Prof. U. Brussels, 1947—; dir. Internat. Insts. Physics and Chemistry, Solvay, Belgium, 1959—; prof. physics and chem. engring. U. Tex., Austin, 1967—; dir. Ilya Prigogine Ctr. for Studies in Statis. Mechanics, Thermodynamics and Complex Systems, U. Tex., Austin, 1967—; hon. prof. U. Nankin, People's Republic of China, 1986, Banaras Hindu U., Varasani, India, 1988; Ashbel Smith regental prof. U. Tex., Austin, 1984—; Dir.'s Disting. visitor Inst. for Advanced Study, Princeton (N.J.) U., 1993; conseiller spl. Commn. des Corrulvhaute Europiennes, 1993. Author: (with R. Defay) Traite de Thermodynamique, conformement aux methodes de Gibbs et de De Donder, 1944, 50, Etude Thermodynamique des Phenomenes Irreversibles, 1947, Introduction to Thermodynamics of Irreversible Processes, 1954, 62, 67 (with A. Bellemans, V. Mathot) The Molecular Theory of Solutions, 1957, Statistical Mechanics of Irreversible Processes, 1954, 2nd edit. 1962, 3rd edit. 1967, (with others) Non Equilibrium Thermodynamics, Variational Techniques and Stability, 1966, (with R. Herman) Kinetic Theory of Vehicular Traffic, 1971, (with R. Glansdorff) Thermodynamic Theory of Structure, Stability and Fluctuations, 1971, (with G. Nicolis) Self-Organization in Nonequilibrium Systems, 1977, From Being to Becoming-Time and Complexity in Physical Sciences, 1979, French, German, Japanese, Russian, Chinese and Italian edits., (with I. Stengers), Order Out of Chaos, 1983, La Nouvelle Alliance, Les Métamorphoses de la Science, 1979, German, English, Italian, Spanish, Serbo-Croatian, Romanian, Swedish, Dutch, Danish, Russian, Japanese, Chinese, Portugese, Bulgarian, Korean and Polish edits., (with G. Nicolis) Die Erforschung des Komplexen, 1987, (with G. Nicolis) Exploring Complexity, 1989, Chinese, Russian, Italian, French and Spanish edits., (with I. Stengers) Entre le temps et l'Eternité, 1988, Dutch edit., 1989, Italian edit., 1989, Portuguese and Spanish edit., 1990, Le leggi del Caos, 1993, (with L. Heugers) Das Paradox der Leit, 1993; mem. editorial bur. Ukrainian Phys. Jour., 1990. Mem. sci. adv. bd. Internat. Acad. for Biomed. Drug Rsch., 1990. Fellow RGK Found. Centennial, U. Tex. 1989-90; decorated comdr. Légion d'Honneur, France, comdr. de l'Ordre de Leopold, comdr. de l'Ordre Leopold II, Grande Croix de l'Ordre de Leopold II, Médaille Civique de Premiere Classe, comdr. de l'Ordre National du Mérite, France, comdr. de l'Ordre des Arts et des Lettres, France; named Mem. d'Honneur de l'Acad. Nat. d'Argentine, 1990, de l'Acad. des. Scis. Naturelles de la République Fédérale de Russie, 1991, de l'Acad. Nat. des. Scis. de la République de San Marino, 1991, de l'Acad. Chilienne des Scis., 1991; recipient Prix Franqui, 1955, Prix Solvay, 1965, Nobel prize in chemistry, 1977, Honda Prize, 1983, Rumford gold medal Royal Soc. London, 1976, Karcher medal Am. Crystallographic Assn., 1978, Descartes medal U. Paris, 1979, Prix Umberto Biancamano, 1987, award recipient Gravity Rsch. Found., 1988, Artificial Intelligence Sci. Achievement award Internat. Found. for Artificial Intelligence, 1990, others. Fellow NAS India (hon.); mem. Royal Acad. Belgium, Am. Acad. Sci. (medal 1975), Royal Soc. Scis. Uppsala (Sweden), NAS U.S.A. (fgn. assoc.), Soc. Royale des Scis. Liège Belgium (corr.), Acad. Gottingen Germany, Deutscher Acad. der Naturforscher Leopoldina (Cothenius medal 1975), Österreichische Acad. der Wissenschaften (corr.), Academie Nationale des Sciences, des Letters et des Arts de Modine (Italy, hon.), Commn. Moudiale de la Culture et du Devel. de l'UNESCO, Chem. Soc. Poland (hon.), Internat. Soc. Gen. Systems Rsch. (pres.-elect 1988), Royal Soc. Chemistry Belgium (hon.), N.Y. Acad. Scis., Interant. Acad. Philosophy Sci., World Acad. Arts and Scis., Nat. Acad. Agentina (hon.), Acad. Natural Scis. Fed. Rep. Russia (hon.), NAS Republic San Marino (hon. pres.), Chilian Acad. Scis. (hon.), World Inst. Sci., others. Address: 67 Ave Fond Roy, 1180 Brussels Belgium Office: U Tex Ilya Prigogine Ctr Studies Statis Mechanics Austin TX 78712*

PRILL, ARNOLD, diversified metal repair company executive. Formerly exec. v.p Chromalloy Gas Turbine Corp., San Antonio, now sr. v.p. Office: Chromalloy Gas Turbine Corp 4430 Director Dr San Antonio TX 78219-3206

PRIMIS, LANCE ROY, newspaper executive; b. Bklyn., June 16, 1946; s. David and Sybil (Schiller) P.; m. Ellen Linda Wildman, June 16, 1946; children: Blair S., Ashley K. BA in English, U. Wis., 1968. Sales rep. Scott Paper Co., N.Y.C., 1968-69; with N.Y. Times, 1969—, retail advt. rep., 1969-72, asst. class advt. mgr., 1972-76, retail advt. mgr., 1976-79, dir. advt. promotion and rsch., 1979, advt. dir., 1979-80, v.p. advt., 1981-82, sr. v.p advt., from 1982, former v.p., gen. mgr., pres. mgr., 1989-92, pres., CEO, 1992—. Mem. Internat. Newspaper Advt. Execs. (chmn. nat. advertiser rels. com.), Am. Assn. Advt. Agys., Nat. Sales Assn. Proprietary Assn., Cosmetic Toiletry Fragrance Assn., Internat. Newspaper Promotion Assn., N.J. Advt. Club. Office: NY Times Co 229 W 43rd St New York NY 10036-3913

PRIMM, BENY JENE, addiction treatment foundation administrator; b. Williamson, W.Va., May 21, 1928; s. George Oliver and Willie Henrietta (Martin) P.; widowed; children: Annelle, Martine, Jeanine, Eraka. BS, W.Va. State Coll., 1950, DSc (hon.), 1994; cert. fin. studies, MD, U. Geneva, 1959. Lic. physician, Calif., N.Y., N.J., W.Va., Mass. Dir. med. affairs Interfaith Hosp., Jamaica, N.Y., 1965, 66; assoc. anesthesiologist Harlem Hosp. Ctr., N.Y.C., 1966-68; founder, dir. Narcotics Hosp. Orientation Ctr.

Harlem Hosp. Ctr., 1968, 69; exec. dir. Addiction Rsch. and Treatment, Bklyn., 1969—; dir. Nat. Ctr. For Substance Abuse Treatment Dept. Health & Human Svcs., Rockville, Md., 1989-93; pres. Urban Resource Inst., Bklyn., 1983—; U.S. speaker U.S. Info. Agy., East and West Africa, 1989; U.S. rep. World Summit on Substance Abuse and AIDS, HHS, London, 1990; presdl. appointee Presdl. Commn. on Human Immunodeficiency Virus, The White House, Washington, 1987-88. Bd. dirs. Meharry Med. Coll. Nashville, 1988—, W.Va. State Coll. Found., 1993—. 1st lt. U.S. Army, 1950-52. Recipient Cert. of Commendation, HHS, 1988. Mem. Coll. on Problems of Drug Dependence (bd. dirs. 1989-93, J. Michael Morrison award for sci. adminstrn. 1993), Nat. Med. Assn., Nat. Minority AIDS coun. (bd. dirs. 1994), Black Leadership Commn. on AIDS (bd. dirs. 1989). Avocations: tennis, golf. Office: Addiction Rsch & Treatment 22 Chapel St Brooklyn NY 11201

PRIMM, EARL RUSSELL, III, publishing executive; b. Rhinelander, Wis., Oct. 24, 1958; s. Earl Russell and Betty Joan (Dennis) P. AB in Classics (hon.), Loyola U. Chgo. 1980; MA in Libr. Sci., U. Chgo., 1990. Asst. to edn. dir. J.G. Ferguson Pub. Co., Chgo., 1981-84; prodn. mgr. Joint Commn. on Accreditation of Hosps., Chgo., 1984-85; sr. editor J.G. Ferguson Pub. Co., Chgo., 1985-87; asst. editor U. Chgo. Press., 1987-88; editorial dir. J.G. Ferguson Pub. Co., Chgo., 1988-89; project mgr. Children's Press, Chgo., 1989-92; exec. editor Franklin Watts, Inc., Chgo., N.Y.C., 1992-95; editorial dir. Grolier Children's Pub., Danbury, Conn., 1995—; mem. adv. bd. U. Chgo. Pub. Program, 1990—; judge Lambda Lit. awards, Washington, 1994—. Editorial chief: Career Discovery Encyclopedia, 1990; editor: Civil Rights Movement in America, 2nd edit., 1991, Extraordinary Hispanic Americans, 1991. Mem. crisis counselor Nat. Runaway Switchboard, Chgo., 1985-88; Horizon's hotline counselor, Chgo., 1987-88; bd. dirs. Gerber/Hart Libr. and Archives, Chgo., 1992-94. Named Honors Sr. of Yr., Loyola U. Chgo., 1980; recipient Mertz Latin Scholarship key Loyola U. Chgo., 1980. Mem. Pub. Triangle, Chgo. Book Clinic, Am. Libr. Assn. Democrat. Home: 358 W 23rd St # 2C New York NY 10011 Office: Grolier Inc Sherman Twp Danbury CT 06816

PRIMOSCH, JAMES THOMAS, music educator, composer, musician; b. Cleve., Oct. 29, 1956; s. Edward Joseph and Rose Marie (Potochar) P.; m. Mary Marguerite Murphy, April 5, 1986. BA in Composition magna cum laude, Cleve. State U., 1978; MA in Composition, U. Pa., 1980; DMA in Composition awarded with distinction, Columbia U., 1988; studied piano privately with Lambert Orkis, Phila., 1978-80; studied composition with John Harbison, Tanglewood, 1984. Asst. prof. music U. Penn., 1988-94, assoc. prof. music, 1994—; grad. assistantships Columbia-Princeton Electronic Music Ctr., 1982-84, 86-87, preceptorship Columbia U., 1984-85; residency Va. Ctr. Creative Arts, 1985, MacDowell Colony, 1988, Bellagio Conf. Ctr., 1992; regional vis. artist Am. Acad. in Rome, 1994; composer in residence Marlboro Music Festival, 1994. Composer of more than 30 compositions and 19 published works; compositions performed by L.A. Philharm., St. Paul Chamber Orch., Cleve. Chamber Symphony, N.Y. New Music Ensemble; compositions performed at Carnegie Hall, Dorothy Chandler Pavilion, Town Hall, Weill (Carnegie) Recital Hall, and many others; reviewer High Performance Rev. Mag., 1987—. Recipient 3rd prize, People's prize Internat. Gaudeamus Competition, The Netherlands, 1977, Helen L. Weiss prize U. Pa., 1979, David Halstead prize U. Penn., 1980, 3rd prize Shreveport Symphony Composer's Competition, 1980-81, John H. Bearns prize, 1981, 1st prize Holtkamp Organ Composition Contest, 1982, Eda and Boris Rappoport prize Columbia U., 1984, Tanglewood prize in Composition Berkshire Music Ctr., 1984, Cleve. Arts prize, 1992; recipient Mader Meml. Fund Recognition award, 1980, BMI Student Composers award, 1982; New Music Consort Composition Contest winner, 1987, League of Composers ISCM winner, 1988; Fine Arts scholar Cleve. State U., 1974-78, scholar Cleve. Fortnightly Music Club, 1976-78, Arthur Loesser Meml. scholar, 1977-78, Yale Composer's Workshop at Norfolk, 1981, Columbia U. scholar, 1981-82, Charles Ives scholar Am. Acad. Inst. Arts & Letters, 1985; U. fellow U. Penn., 1978-79, Composers Conf. Johnson Vt., 1979, 80, CBS Found. fellow U. Penn., 1979-80, Margaret Lee Crofts fellow Berkshire Music Ctr. Tanglewood, 1984, Guggenheim fellow, 1985, NEA, 1991-92, Goddard Lieberson fellow Am. Acad. Arts and Letters, 1993; ASCAP Found. Young Composers grant, 1984, 82, Meet The Composer grant 1980, 82, 85, 87, 89, 90, 94, Am. Music Ctr. Copying Assistance grant, 1985, 90, Penn. Coun. On The Arts, 1990, Presser Found. grant U. Penn. Mem. BMI, Pi Kappa Lambda. Roman Catholic. Avocation: reading.

PRIMPS, WILLIAM GUTHRIE, lawyer; b. Ossining, N.Y., Sept. 8, 1949; s. Richard Byrd and Mary Elizabeth (Guthrie) P.; m. Sophia Elizabeth Beutel, Aug. 25, 1973; children: Emily Ann, Elizabeth Armstrong, William Andrew. BA, Yale U., 1971; JD, Harvard U., 1974. Bar: N.Y., 1975. Assoc. LeBoeuf, Lamb, Leiby & MacRae, N.Y.C., 1974-82; ptnr. LeBoeuf, Lamb, Greene & MacRae, N.Y.C., 1983—; counsel to Bd. Zoning Appeals, Bronxville, 1988-89, chmn., 1989-91; bd. dirs. Nat. Integrity Life Ins. Co. Mem. class coun. Yale U., New Haven, 1986-91; trustee Village of Bronxville, 1991—, dep. mayor, 1995—; deacon Reformed Ch. Bronxville, 1989-94. Mem. ABA, N.Y. State Bar Assn., Assn. Yale Alumni (class rep. 1986-91), Yale Club, Bronxville Field Club. Republican. Home: 71 Summit Ave Bronxville NY 10708-1815 Office: LeBoeuf Lamb Greene & MacRae 125 W 55th St New York NY 10019-5389

PRINA, L(OUIS) EDGAR, journalist; b. West New York, N.J., Oct. 7, 1917; s. Louis Edgar and Marion (Duggan) P.; m. Frances Lee Lorick, Feb. 14, 1947; 1 dau., Lee Lorick II. A.B., Syracuse U., 1938, M.A. 1940. Copy editor, asst. night city editor N.Y. Sun, N.Y.C., 1946-48; Washington corr. N.Y. Sun, 1948-50; nat. affairs writer Washington Star, 1950-66; mil. affairs writer/editor Copley News Svc., Washington, 1966-77; bur. chief Copley News Svc., 1977-84, sr. corr.-1984-87; editor Navy mag., Washington, 1961-68; columnist Sea Power mag., 1968—. Author: The Political Virgin, 1958, Flew to South Pole for Overnight Visit, 1966. Served with USN, 1941-46, 51-53; capt. Res. (ret.). Recipient honorable mentionHeywood Broun award, 1956, Disting. Public Svc. award USN, 1965, Alfred Thayer Mahan award Navy League U.S., 1987, Copley Ring of Truth award, 1971, 74-76, 79, 80-81; nominated for Pulitzer Prize (twice). Mem. U.S. Naval Inst., Nat. Press Club (chmn. bd. govs.), White House Corrs. Assn., Explorers Club, Sigma Delta Chi (pres. Washington chpt.), Kappa Sigma, Phi Kappa Phi. Roman Catholic. Clubs: Gridiron, Chevy Chase, Met. of Washington. Home: 4813 Quebec St NW Washington DC 20016-3228 Office: National Press Bldg PO Box 2042 Washington DC 20045

PRINCE (PRINCE ROGERS NELSON), musician, actor; b. Mpls., June 7, 1958; s. John L. and Mattie D. (Shaw) Nelson. Singer, songwriter, actor. Albums include For You, 1978, Dirty Mind, 1979, Controversy, 1981, 1999, 1983, film star and soundtrack Purple Rain, 1984, Around the World in a Day, 1985 (Best Soul/Rhythm and Blues Album of the Yr., down beat Readers Poll, 1985), Parade, 1986, Sign O' the Times, 1987, Lovesexy, 1988, Batman: Motion Picture Soundtrack, 1989 (Soundtrack of Yr. award Playboy mag. readers' poll, Best Pop/Rock album downbeat mag. readers' poll), (with the New Power Generation) Diamonds and Pearls, 1991, (symbol), 1992, Come, 1994; films include Purple Rain, 1984 (Acad. award for best original score 1985), film star and soundtrack Under the Cherry Moon, 1986, film star and soundtrack Sign O' the Times, 1987; film appearance and soundtrack Graffiti Bridge, 1990; formerly mem. group Prince and the Revolution (Best Soul/Rhythm and Blues Group of Yr. downbeat mag. readers poll 1985). Recipient 3 Grammy awards, 1985, Am. Music Achievement award for infuence on look and sound of the 80's; named Rhythm and Blues Musician of Yr. Down Beat mag. readers' poll, 1984, 1992. *

PRINCE, ALAN THEODORE, former government official, engineering consultant; b. Toronto, Can., Feb. 15, 1915; s. Theodore and Sarah Helena (McMillan) P.; m. Virginia C. Lea, May 30, 1942; children: Linda Lea Prince Anderson, Mary Catherine Prince Kaschub. BA, U. Toronto, 1937, MA, 1938; PhD, U. Chgo., 1941. Registered profl. engr., Ont. With div. chemistry Nat. Research Council Can., Ottawa, 1940-43, Can. Refractories Ltd., Kilmar, Que., 1943-45; lectr. geology U. Man., 1945-46; with Canadian Dept. Mines and Tech. Surveys, 1946-67, dir. water research br., 1965-67; dir. inland waters br. Dept. Environment, 1967-73; asst. dep. minister planning and evaluation Dept. Energy, Mines and Resources, 1973-75; pres. Atomic Energy Control Bd., Ottawa, 1975-79; cons. Fellow Chem. Inst.

Can., Mineral. Soc. Am.; mem. Canadian Inst. Mining and Metallurgy, Assn. Profl. Engrs. Ont. Home: 5445 Riverside Dr, PO Box 106, Manotick, ON Canada K4M 1A2

PRINCE, ANDREW STEVEN, lawyer, former government official; b. Bklyn., Oct. 9, 1943; s. Milton S. and Beatrice M. (Ratkin) P.; m. Rochelle Moskowitz, July 4, 1973; children: Brett, Kenneth. B.S., U.S. Naval Acad., 1965; M.B.A., Harvard U., 1974, J.D., 1974. Bar: N.Y. 1975, U.S. Supreme Ct. 1980. Assoc. firm Shearman & Sterling, N.Y.C., 1974-81; dep. asst. sec. Navy Dept., Washington, 1981-86; exec. v.p fin., gen. counsel Urquhart and Co., Inc., McLean, Va., 1986-94; pres. BretKen Enterprises, McLean, Va., 1994—; sec. Potash Import & Chem. Corp., N.Y.C., 1979-81; mem. panel of arbitrators Am. Arbitration Assn., N.Y.C. 1979—. Bd. dirs. Harvard Coop. Soc., Cambridge, Mass., 1972-74; bd. dirs. USO, Washington, 1982—, N.Y.C., 1979-81. Served with USN, 1965-70; capt. Res. Mem. Harvard Bus. Sch. Club (v.p.), Mil Order World Wars (judge adv.), Naval Acad. Alumni Assn.

PRINCE, CARL E., historian, educator; b. Newark, Dec. 8, 1934; s. Phillip G. and Anne (Silver) P.; children: Elizabeth, Jonathan. B.A. with honors, Rutgers U., 1956, M.A., 1958, Ph.D. in History, 1963. Instr. history Fairleigh Dickinson U., 1960-63; asst. prof. history Seton Hall U., 1963-66, assoc. prof., 1966-68; assoc. prof. N.Y. U., 1968-74, prof., 1974—, chmn. dept. history, 1978-86. Author books: including New Jersey's Jeffersonian Republicans, 1789-1817, 1967, The Federalists and the Origns of the U.S. Civil Service, 1977, The Papers of William Livingston, 5 vols., 1979-88, the U.S. Customs Svc., 1989. Mem. exec. bd. N.J. Catholic Hist. Records Commn.; mem. N.J. Hist. Records Commn.; mem. exec. bd. United Negro Coll. Fund Archives; Chmn. West Orange (N.J.) Citizens Against the Vietnam War, 1965-70; county coord. Essex County (N.J.) Citizens for McCarthy, 1968. Younger scholar fellow NEH, 1968-69; Fulbright scholar, Israel, 1972-73. Fellow N.J. Hist. Soc.; mem. Soc. for Historians of Early Am. Republic (exec. bd. 1980-86, pres. 1983-84), Inst. Early Am. History and Culture (assoc.), Columbia U. Seminar in Early Am. History (assoc.). Jewish. Office: NYU Dept History 19 University Pl New York NY 10003-4501

PRINCE, CHARLES O., III, lawyer; b. 1950. BA, U. So. Calif., 1971, MA, JD, 1975. Bar: Pa. 1975, Md. 1979, Minn. 1982. Formerly gen. counsel Commercial Credit Co.; now sr. v.p., gen. counsel, sec. Primerica Corp., N.Y.C. Office: Commercial Credit Co 300 Saint Paul Pl Baltimore MD 21202-2120

PRINCE, DANIEL LLOYD, molecular biologist, virologist, validation scientist, industrial microbiologist, computer network administrator, consultant; b. Willamantic, Conn., Dec. 26, 1955; s. Herbert Norman and Leah Fanchen (Berman) P.; m. Teresa Lynn Williams. BA, Clark U., 1978; MS, Rutgers U., 1982, U. Medicine and Dentistry N.J.; PhD, Rutgers U., 1984. Electron microscopist Osborne Labs. Marine Sci., Coney Island, N.J., 1978; lab. technician Gibraltar Biol. Labs., Fairfield, N.J., 1978-84, asst. sci. dir., 1984-87; assoc. sci. dir. Gibraltar Biol. Labs., Fairfield, 1987—, acting pres., 1990, pres., 1991; mgr. Gibraltar Inst. Rsch. and Tng., Fairfield, 1984-87; lectr. Am. Soc. for Quality Control, Princeton, N.J., 1987—, Am. Soc. Microbiology, Washington; vis. scientist Rockefeller U., N.Y.C., 1987—; sci. adv. bd. Internat. Found. for Ethical Research, Boston, 1987—; expert U.S. Pharmacopeia, Rockville, Md., 1987—. Author poems and song lyrics; contbr. articles to profl. jours. Trustee Hills Master Assn., Bedminster, N.J., 1985-87. Mem. N.Y. Acad. Scis., Am. Soc. Microbiology, Am. Soc. Quality Control, Regulatory Affairs Profls. Soc., Soc. Cosmetic Chemists (in vitro toxicology group). Avocations: computer programming, sports, reading, cars, music. Office: Gibraltar Biol Labs Inc 122 Fairfield Rd Fairfield NJ 07004-2405

PRINCE, EDWARD R., JR., holding company; b. 1929. BS, UNC, 1955. Commd. 2d lt. USAF, 1951; resigned, 1961; with Tex. Instruments Inc., Dallas, 1961-65, chmn. bd., CEO, 1965—. Office: Digicon Inc 3701 Kirby Dr Ste 112 Houston TX 77098*

PRINCE, GARNETT B., JR., business executive; b. Chattanooga, Feb. 1, 1949; w. Garnett B. and Anna Mae (Elrod) P.; m. Deborah Roemer, Jan. 19, 1971 (div.); m. Charlotte V. McCauley, July 23, 1983; children: Shelly McCauley, Becky, Brandon. Student radio and TV broadcasting, Coastal Carolina Community Coll., Jacksonville, N.C., 1971; student, No. Va. Community Coll., Sterling, 1979-80. Dep. ct. clerk Criminal Ct., Chattanooga, 1971-73; dist. field rep. VA, Chattanooga, 1973-76; leadership tng. cons. Nat. Vocat.-Indsl. Clubs Am., Leesburg, Va., 1976-78, dir. tng. and govt. relations, 1978-84; spl. asst. to sec. U.S. Dept. Labor, Washington, 1984-85; dep. asst. sec. for vets. employment and tng. U.S. Dept. Labor, 1985-88; dep. dir. Nat. Drug Policy Bd., Office of Pres., Washington, 1988-89; regional mgr. state govt. affairs Parke-Davis div. Warner-Lambert Co., Atlanta, 1989—; dir. fed. health care policy Warner-Lambert Co., Washington, 1991—. Co-author: The Meetings Kit, 1985. Trustee U.S. Internat. Youth Yr. Com., Washington, 1985. Served with USMC, 1967-71. Mem. Mil. Order Purple Heart, DAV, VFW, Am. Legion. Republican. Lodge: Masons. Avocations: golf; bowling; swimming. Home and Office: 17 Uvilla Est Shenandoah Junction WV 25442-9538

PRINCE, GERALD JOSEPH, Romance languages educator; b. Alexandria, Egypt, Nov. 7, 1942; came to U.S., 1959, naturalized, 1964; s. Tully Rudolph and Marguerite (Bigio) P.; m. Ellen Friedman, June 25, 1967. B.A., Bklyn. Coll., 1963; M.A., U. Fla., 1963; Ph.D., Brown U., 1968. Instr. French lang. U. Pa., Phila., 1967-68, asst. prof., 1968-73, assoc. prof., 1973-81, prof. Romance langs., 1981—, chmn. comparative lang. program, 1984-87; co-dir. Ctr. Cultural Studies, 1987—. Author: Métaphysique et Technique dans l'Oeuvre Romanesque de Sartre, 1968, A Grammar of Stories, 1973, Narratology: The Form and Function of Narrative, 1992, A Dictionary of Narratology, 1987, Narrative as Theme, 1992. Contbr. articles and revs. to scholarly jours. Recipient award of honor, Bklyn. Coll., 1978, Lindback award for excellence in teaching U. Pa., 1974. Mem. MLA, N.E. MLA (officer 1983-86), Am. Comparative Lit. Assn. (adv. bd. 1983—), Phi Beta Kappa, Phi Kappa Phi, Pi Delta Phi. Office: Ctr Cultural Studies Univ Pa 521 Williams Hall Philadelphia PA 19104

PRINCE, GREGORY SMITH, JR., academic administrator; b. Washington, May 7, 1939; s. Gregory Smith and Margaret (Minor) P.; m. Toni Layton Brewer; children: Tara Wyndom, Gregory S. III. BA, Yale U., 1961, M in Philosophy, 1969, PhD, 1973; cert. in teaching English as a Second Language, Georgetown U., 1961; DHL (hon.), Amherst Coll., 1991, LLD (hon.), 1991. Instr. Near Asia Coll., Kowloon, Hong Kong, 1961-62, Chinese U., Kowloon, 1962-63, Yale China Assn., Kowloon, 1961-63, Woodberry Forest (Va.) Sch., 1963-65; dean summer programs Dartmouth Coll., Hanover, N.H., 1970-72, asst. dean faculty, 1972-78, assoc. dean faculty, 1978-89; pres. Hampshire Coll., Amherst, Mass., 1989—; mem. Coun. on Racial and Ethnic Justice, ABA. Producer: (film) A Way of Learning, 1988. Trustee Montshire Mus. Sci., Hanover, 1973-89, Washington Campus, 1978—; trustee, chmn. Univ. Press New Eng., Hanover, 1983-84; trustee, pres. Yale-China Assn., New Haven, 1969-84; bd. dirs., pres. Five Colls., Inc., Amherst, 1989—, chmn. of bd. Assn. Ind. Colls. and Univs. of Mass., 1994-95, common. on accreditation Am. Coun. Edn. Coe fellow Stanford U., 1965, Woodrow Wilson fellow Yale U., 1966, NDEA fellow, 1967-70. Mem. Internat. Assn. of Chiefs Police Found. (bd. dirs. 1991—). Democrat. Episcopalian. Home: 15 Middle St Amherst MA 01002-3009 Office: Hampshire Coll 893 West St Amherst MA 01002-3359

PRINCE, HAROLD, theatrical producer; b. N.Y.C., Jan. 30, 1928; s. Milton A. and Blanche (Stern) P.; m. Judith Chaplin, Oct. 26, 1962; children: Charles, Daisy. AB, U. Pa., 1948, DFA (hon.), 1971; LittD, Emerson Coll., 1971. chmn. Performing Arts Libr., N.Y.C. Co-producer Pajama Game, 1954-56 (Antoinette Perry award), Damn Yankees, 1955-57 (Antoinette Perry award), New Girl in Town, 1957-58, West Side Story, 1957-59, Fiorello, 1959-61 (Antoinette Perry award, Pulitzer prize), Tenderloin, 1960-61, A Call on Kuprin, 1961, They Might Be Giants, London, 1961, Side by Side by Sondheim, 1976; producer Take Her, She's Mine, 1961-62, A Funny Thing Happened on the Way to the Forum, 1962-64 (Antoinette Perry award), Fiddler on the Roof, 1964-72 (Antoinette Perry award), Poor Bitos, 1964, Flora the Red Menace, 1965; dir.-producer: She Loves Me, 1963-64

(London 1964), Superman, 1966, Cabaret, 1966-69 (Antoinette Perry award 1968), Zorba, 1968-69, Company, 1970-72 (Antoinette Perry award 1972), A Little Night Music, 1973-74 (Antoinette Perry award 1975), Pacific Overtures, 1976; co-dir., producer Follies, 1971-72, Faust; co-producer, dir. Candide, 1974-75, Merrily We Roll Along, 1981, A Doll's Life, 1982; dir. A Family Affair, 1962, Baker Street, 1965, Great God Brown, 1972-73, The Visit, 1973-74, Love for Love, 1974-75, Ashmedai, 1976, On The Twentieth Century, 1978, Evita (London, 1978, Broadway, 1979, L.A., 1980, Australia, 1980, Chgo., 1980, Detroit, 1982), Sweeney Todd, The Demon Barber of Fleet Street, Broadway, 1979, London, 1980, Silverlake, 1980, Willie Stark, 1981, Candide, 1982, Madama Butterfly, 1982, Turandot, 1983, Play Memory, 1984, End of the World, 1984, Diamonds, 1984, Grind, 1985, Cabaret Revival, 1987, Roza, 1987, Phantom of the Opera, London, 1986, N.Y.C., (Antoinette Perry award) 1988, La Fanciula del West, Don Giovanni, N.Y. City Opera, 1989, Faust, Met. Opera, 1990; adapter, dir. Grandchild of Kings, 1992, Kiss of the Spider Woman, the Musical, 1992 (London), 1993 Broadway, Show Boat, 1993 (Toronto), 1994 (Broadway, Antoinette Perry award, 1995); co-producer films The Pajama Game, 1957, Damn Yankees, 1958; dir. films Something for Everyone, 1970, A Little Night Music, 1978. Mem. coun. Nat. Endowment Arts; pres. League N.Y. Theatres, 1964-66; chmn. Performing Arts Libr., N.Y.C. Recipient 19 Antoinette Perry (Tony) Meml. awards, Critics Circle awards, Pulitzer prize, 1961, Best Mus. awards London Evening Standard, Kennedy Ctr. Honors, 1994. Office: 10 Rockefeller Plz New York NY 10020

PRINCE, JERRY LADD, engineering educator; b. Manchester, Conn., Aug. 10, 1957; s. Ralph Peery and Lela (Ladd) P.; m. Carol Ann Morello, June 12, 1982; children: Emily, Benjamin, Mark, David. SM, MIT, 1982, PhD, 1988. Rsch. asst. MIT, Cambridge, 1979-82; engr. Brigham and Women's Hosp., Boston, 1982-83; teaching asst. MIT, Cambridge, 1983-84, rsch. asst., 1984-88; mem. tech. staff The Analytical Scis. Corp., Reading, Mass., 1988; asst. prof. Johns Hopkins U., Balt., 1989-94, assoc. prof. elec. and computer engring., 1994—. Contbr. articles to profl. jours. Mem. IEEE (assoc. editor Transactions on Image Processing 1992—), Sigma Xi. Office: Johns Hopkins Univ 3400 N Charles St Baltimore MD 21218

PRINCE, JIMMIE DAN, retail food chain executive; b. Loco, Tex., Aug. 18, 1933; s. John Franklin and Maude Irene (Seay) P.; m. Deborah C. McKeever, Oct. 23, 1982; children: Janet Danette Povero, Paula Renee Drews. BS, Tex. Tech U., 1959; postgrad., UCLA, U. Tex. Plant supt. Safeway Stores, Oakland, Calif., 1959-65; area salesman Wyandotte Chem. Corp., Columbia, S.C., 1965-66; creamery supt. Alpha Beta Stores, La Habra, Calif., 1966-69; milk plant mgr. Lucky Stores Inc., Buena Park, Calif., 1969-78, mfg. mgr., 1978-79; corp. v.p. Lucky Stores Inc., Dublin, Calif., 1980—; bd. dirs. Milk Industry Found., Washington, Dairy Inst. Calif., Sacramento; mem. Calif. Milk Adv. Bd., Modesto, Calif., also new products adv. com. Served with USN Air Force, 1951-55. Republican. Office: Lucky Stores Inc 6300 Clark Ave Dublin CA 94568-3002 Office: Dairymans Cooperative Crmry 400 S M St Tulare CA 93274-5431

PRINCE, JOHN LUTHER, III, engineering educator; b. Austin, Tex., Nov. 13, 1941; s. John Luther and Glynda (Chollett) P.; m. Martha Ann Hight, Mar. 4, 1960; children: Cynthia Kay, John Luther IV, Alan Douglas, David William. BSEE, So. Meth. U., 1965; MEE, N.C. State U., 1968, PhD, 1969. Research engr. RTI, Res. Tri. Park, N.C., 1968-70; mem. tech. staff Tex. Instruments, Dallas, 1970-75; from assoc. prof. to prof. Clemson (S.C.) U., 1975-80; dir. R.A. Intermedics, Inc., Freeport, Tex., 1980-83; prof. U. Ariz., Tucson, 1983—; acting dir. packaging scis. Semiconductor Rsch. Corp., 1991-92; cons. numerous semi-conductor and electronics cos., 1983—; dir. Electronic Packaging Lab., 1984-91, Ctr. for Electronic Packaging Rsch., 1991—, SEMATECH Ctr. of Excellence for Contamination and Defect Control, 1988-90. Contbr. articles to profl. jours. Named Ariz. Innovator of the Yr., 1992; NSF fellow, 1965-68. Fellow IEEE; mem. Am. Philatelic Soc. Lutheran. Avocations: stamp collecting, classic cars, motorcycles. Home: 7542 N San Lorenzo Dr Tucson AZ 85704-3141 Office: U Ariz Tucson AZ 85721

PRINCE, JULIUS S. (BUD), retired foreign service reserve officer; b. Yonkers, N.Y., July 21, 1911; s. Julius and Clara B. (Rich) P.; m. Eleanora Molloy, July 6, 1943; children: Thomas Marc, Tod Ainslee (dec.), Richard M. Johnson. B.A., Yale U., 1932; M.D., Columbia U., 1938, M.P.H., 1948; Dr.P.H., Harvard, 1957. Intern Sinai Hosp., Balt., 1939-40; asst. resident medicine N.Y. U. div. Goldwater Meml. Hosp., 1941-42; dist. state health officer N.Y. State Dept. Health, Jamestown, 1948-58; chief pub. health div. USAID, Ethiopia, 1958-67; prin. investigator demonstration and evaluation project AID, Ethiopia, 1959-67; chief Africa div. Population and Humanitarian Affairs, Population Office, AID, Washington, 1967-73; dir. Africa Regional Population Office, Accra, Ghana, 1973-74; chief health, population and nutrition projects AID, Ghana, 1974-76; cons. internat. health APHA, 1977-78, Pacific Cons., Inc., 1978-82, RONCO Inc., 1982; pub. health specialist/sr. health advisor One Am., Inc., 1982-87; sr. pub. health and nutrition specialist Internat. Sci. and Tech. Inst. Inc., 1985-94; cons. on internat. health, 1985—; report on sustainability of AID supported health population and nutrition programs, Ghana, 1963-85, Ctr. Devel. Info. and Evaluation AID, 1988, Annotated History of AID-Supported Health and Nutrition Rsch.: From Outset to Present, Introduction and Background, AID Office Health, 1991, Compendium of Abstracts, 1985-92, rsch. by historically black colls. and univs. under AID Univ. Ctr./Rsch. and Univ. Devel. Linkages, 1985-92. Served from lt. to maj. M.C. Royal Canadian Army, 1942-46. Recipient Letter of Commendation, Adj. Gen. Can. Army, 1946, Superior honor award AID, 1968, Letter of Commendation, 1977. Fellow Am. Pub. Health Assn., Soc. Applied Anthropology, Wash. Acad. Scis., Royal Soc. Health; mem. AMA, N.Y. State Pub. Health Assn. (pres. 1957), Pan Am. Med. Assn., Am. Assn. World Health (emeritus mem. bd. dirs.), Internat. Soc. Hypertension in Blacks, Population Assn. Am., Soc. Internat. Devel., Nat. Coun. Internat. Health (award 1992), N.Y. Acad. Scis., World Med. Assn., Soc. Prospective Medicine, Am. Heart Assn., Can. Soc. Internat. Health. Home and Office: 7103 Pinehurst Pky Chevy Chase MD 20815-3144

PRINCE, KENNETH STEPHEN, lawyer; b. Newton, Mass., Jan. 28, 1950; s. Samuel and Edna L. Prince; m. Patricia Denning, Jan. 15, 1977 (dec. Nov. 1985); 1 child, Kenneth Stephen Jr.; m. Jane M. McCabe, Sept. 5, 1987; 1 child, Allison Pamela. BA, U. Pa., 1972; JD, Boston Coll., 1975. Bar: N.Y. 1976, Mass. 1975, U.S. Dist. Ct. (so. and ea. dists.) N.Y. 1978. Assoc. Shearman & Sterling, N.Y.C., 1975-83, ptnr., 1984—; antitrust group practice leader Shearman & Sterling, 1992—. Mem. N.Y. Law Inst. (exec. com. 1984—), Order of Coif. Office: Citicorp Ctr 153 E 53rd St New York NY 10022-4611 also: 599 Lexington Ave #53 New York NY 10022-6030

PRINCE, LARRY L., automotive parts and supplies company executive; b. 1937. With Genuine Parts Co., Atlanta, 1958—, v.p., then group v.p., 1977-83, exec. v.p., 1983-86, pres., chief oper. officer, 1986-90, chief exec. officer, 1989—, chmn. bd. dirs., 1990—, also bd. dirs. Office: Genuine Parts Co 2999 Circle 75 Pky NW Atlanta GA 30339-3073*

PRINCE, MILTON S., investment company executive; b. Bklyn., Jan. 20, 1912; s. Abraham and Frances (Raps) P.; m. Beatrice Ratzkin, Jan. 18, 1942; children: Andrew, Thomas. BS, Carnegie Inst. Tech., 1935; LLB, St. Johns U., Bklyn., 1938, JSD, 1939. Bar: N.Y. 1940, U.S. Dist. Ct. (ea. and so. dists.) N.Y. 1950, U.S. Ct. Mil. Appeals, U.S. Supreme Ct. 1954. Sole practice, Bklyn., 1940-41; mng. ptnr., gen. counsel Prince & Prince, Bklyn., 1946—. Trustee U.S. Naval Acad. Found., Annapolis, Md., 1964—; dir., excom. USO, N.Y.C., 1965—; nat. council mem., Bklyn. council officer, dir. Boy Scouts Am., Irving, Tex. and Bklyn.; state advisor U.S. Congl. Adv. Bd., 1982-88. Served with USN, 1941-45, to capt. USNR, to rear admiral N.Y. State Naval Militia, 1985—. Recipient USN Distng. Pub. Svc. award, 1972, Shofar award Boy Scouts Am., 1984, Bklyn. citation, 1990; decorated various medals Dept. Def. Mem. Navy League U.S. (nat. dir., officer 1962—), U.S. Naval Inst. (silver), ABA, Mil. Order World Wars (dir., past comdr. 1966-67, Meritorious Achievement award 1964), Naval Order U.S. (ex. com. 1960-88), Salmagundi Club (N.Y.C.), Coasters Harbor Yacht Club (Newport, R.I.), Mcpl. Club, Bklyn. Club, Army-Navy Club (Washington), Rotary. Avocations: sailing, golf, travel, pub. service.

PRINCE, MORTON BRONENBERG, physicist; b. Phila., Apr. 1, 1924; s. David H. and Jennie (Bronenberg) P.; m. Blanche E. Stern, June 15, 1947; 1 child, Judith Ann. A.B., Temple U., 1947; Ph.D., MIT, 1951. Mem. tech. staff Bell Telephone Labs., Inc., Murray Hill, N.J., 1951-56; v.p., gen. mgr. Hoffman Electronics Corp., El Monte, Calif., 1956-61; with electro optical systems div. Xerox, Pasadena, Calif., 1961-69; pres. SSR Instruments Co., Santa Monica, Calif., 1970-74; v.p., gen. mgr. Meret Inc., Santa Monica, 1974-75; with U.S. Dept. Energy, Washington, 1975-93. Contbr. chpts. to books, articles to profl. jours. Served with U.S. Army, 1943-46. Recipient Marconi premium Inst. Radio Engrs. Gt. Britain, 1959 (Becquerel prize 1994). Fellow IEEE; mem. Am. Phys. Soc., Internat. Solar Energy Soc. Club: Cosmos. Home: 7301 Coventry Ave Apt 601 Elkins Park PA 19027

PRINCE, ROBB LINCOLN, manufacturing company executive; b. Duluth, Minn., June 30, 1941; s. Milton H. and Katherine (Lincoln) P.; m. Jacqueline H. Marik, June 19, 1965; children: Daniel, Deborah. BA in Econs., Carleton Coll., 1963; MBA in Mktg., U. Pa., 1965. With mktg. planning United Airlines, Chgo., 1965-72; dir. planning Jostens Inc., Mpls., 1973-74, treas., 1975-79, v.p., treas., 1979—; dir. FORTIS Mut. Funds, Analysts Internat. Corp., Analysis Internat. Corp. With USN, 1966-69. Mem. Wharton Alumni Club (bd. dirs.). Office: 5108 Duggan Plz Edina MN 55439-1453

PRINCE, THOMAS E., bank executive; b. 1947. With Security Pacific Corp., L.A., 1968-92; exec. v.p., CFO, treas. Downey Savs Loan Assn., Newport Beach, Calif., 1992—. Office: Downey Savs Loan Assn 3501 Jamboree Rd Newport Beach CA 92660*

PRINCE, THOMAS RICHARD, accountant, educator; b. New Albany, Miss., Dec. 7, 1934; s. James Thompson and Callie Florence (Howell) P.; m. Eleanor Carol Polkoff, July 14, 1962; children—Thomas Andrew, John Michael, Adrienne Carol. B.S., Miss. State U., 1956, M.S., 1957; Ph.D. in Accountancy, U. Ill., 1962. C.P.A., Ill. Instr. U. Ill., 1960-62; mem. faculty Northwestern U., 1962—, prof. acctg. and info. systems, 1969—; chmn. dept. accounting and info. systems Northwestern U. (Grad. Sch. Mgmt.), 1968-75; cons. in field; dir. Applied Research Systems, Inc. Author: Extension of the Boundaries of Accounting Theory, 1962, Information Systems for Management Planning and Control, 3d edit, 1975, Financial Reporting and Cost Control for Health Care Entities, 1992. Served to 1st lt. AUS, 1957-60. Mem. Am. Accounting Assn., Am. Inst. C.P.A.s, Am. Econ. Assn., Inst. Mgmt. Scis., Fin. Execs. Inst., AAAS, Ill. Soc. C.P.A.s, Nat. Assn. Accts., Alpha Tau Omega, Phi Kappa Phi, Omicron Delta Kappa, Delta Sigma Pi, Beta Alpha Psi. Congregationalist. Home: 303 Richmond Rd Kenilworth IL 60043-1138 Office: Northwestern U Leverone Hall Evanston IL 60208

PRINCE, WARREN VICTOR, mechanical engineer; b. Kansas City, Mo., May 21, 1911; s. Charles William and Bertha (Lybarger) P.; m. Edna Skinner Scott, Aug. 31, 1975; children—Charlotte E. Prince Smith, Leslie Warren (dec.), Charles Allan, Charlene Diane Prince Tercovich. Student engring. Baker U., 1931-34, BS (hon.), 1995. Registered mech. engr., Calif. Design engr. Hoover Co., North Canton, Ohio, 1934-39; tool and machine design Thompson Products, Inc., Cleve., 1939-41; devel. engr. The Acrotorque Co., 1941-42; asst. chief devel. engr. The Weatherhead Co., 1942-45; pres. Prince Indsl. Plastics Corp., 1945-46; cons. engr., mech., plastics and plant prodn. problems, Kansas City and Los Angeles, 1946-50; project engr. Aerojet Gen. Corp., 1950-63, chief engr. Deposilube Mfg. Co., 1963-65; cons., 1965-66; sr. mech. engr. Avery Label Co., 1966-68; sr. project engr. machine design projects AMF, Inc., 1969-72; mech. cons. engr. as machine and product design specialist, 1972-80; pres. Contour Splitys., Inc., 1980-85; v.p. mech. engring. HEP Inc., 1985-88, mechanical cons. engr., 1988—; evening instr. Mt. San Antonio Coll., 1954-93, alternate pres., mgr. of rsch. and devel. Progressive Household Products, Inc. Recipient Soc. Plastics Engrs. 1948 Nat. award for establishing basic laws of plastic molding process, Commendable Recognition award First Internat. Conf. on Machine Tech., Hong Kong, 1991. Mem. ASME, ASTM (D28 com.), Kappa Sigma. Presbyterian. Lodges: Masons, Shriners, Rotary. Contbr. articles to profl. jours. Patentee in field. Achievements include an explanation of break through performance with a new principle of anti-friction. Office: 838 N West St Anaheim CA 92801-4302

PRINCE, WILLIAM J., church officer; m. Evelyn Imel; 1 child. 4th pres. Mt. Vernon Nazarene Coll., 1980-89; pres. So. Nazarene U., 1989; bd. gen. supts. Ch. of the Nazarene, Indpls., 1989—; former supt. Pitts. dist.; pres. European Nazarene Bible Coll., 1970-76; pastor Lone Pine, Reseda and Ventura, Calif., Mpls., and Dayton; min. teaching and preaching missions in Haiti, Guatemala, South Africa, Zambia, Zimbabwe, Swaziland, Kenya; leader preacher missions in Hawaii; participant European Congress on Evangelism, Amsterdam, The Netherlands; speaker to students, Shanghai, 1989; speaker commencement Luzon Nazarene Theol. Sem. Office: Church of Nazarene 6401 The Paseo Kansas City MO 64131

PRINCE, WILLIAM TALIAFERRO, federal judge; b. Norfolk, Va., Oct. 3, 1929; s. James Edward and Helen Marie (Taliaferro) P.; m. Anne Carroll Hannegan, Apr. 12, 1958; children: Sarah Carroll Prince Pishko, Emily Taliaferro, William Taliaferro, John Hannegan, Anne Martineau, Robert Harrison. Student, Coll. William and Mary, Norfolk, 1947-48, 49-50; AB, Williamsburg, 1955, BCL, 1957, MLT, 1959. Bar: Va. 1957. Lectr. acctg. Coll. William and Mary, 1955-57; lectr. law Marshall-Wythe Sch. Law, 1957-59; assoc. Williams, Kelly & Greer, Norfolk, 1959-63, ptnr., 1963-90; U.S. magistrate judge Eastern Dist. of Va., Norfolk, 1990—; pres. Am. Inn of Ct. XXVII, 1987-89. Bd. editors: The Virginia Lawyer, A Basic Practice Handbook, 1966. Bd. dirs. Madonna Home, Inc., 1978-93, Soc. Alumni of Coll. William and Mary, 1985-88. Fellow Am. Coll. Trial Lawyers, Am. Bar Found., Va. Law Found. (bd. dirs. 1976); mem. ABA (ho. of dels. 1984-90), Am. Judicature Soc. (bd. dirs. 1984-88), Va. State Bar (coun. 1973-77, exec. com. 1975-80, pres. 1978-79), Elks. Roman Catholic. Home: 1227 Graydon Ave Norfolk VA 23507-1006 Office: Walter E Hoffman US Courthouse 600 Granby St Rm 181 Norfolk VA 23510-1915

PRINCIPAL, VICTORIA, actress; b. Fukuoka, Japan, Jan. 3, 1950; d. Victor and Ree (Veal) P.; m. Harry Glassman, 1985. Attended, Miami-Dade Community Coll.; studied acting with Max Croft, Al Sacks and Estelle Harman, Jean Scott, Royal Acad. Dramatic Arts. Worked as model, including TV commls.; appearances include (film) The Life and Times of Judge Roy Bean, 1972, The Naked Ape, 1973, Earthquake, 1974, I Will I Will For Now, 1976, Vigilante Force, 1976; (TV movies) Last Hours Before Morning, 1975, Fantasy Island, 1977, The Night They Stole Miss Beautiful, 1977, Pleasure Palace, 1980, Not Just Another Affair, 1982, Mistress, 1987, The Burden of Proof, 1990, Just Life, 1992, Beyond Obsession, 1994; exec. prodr., actress Naked Lie, 1989, Blind Witness, 1989, Sparks: The Price of Passion, 1990, Don't Touch My Daughter, 1991, Seduction: Three Tales from the Inner Sanctum, 1993, River of Rage: The Taking of Maggie Keene, 1993; exec. prodr. Midnight's Child, 1992; (TV series) Dallas, 1978-87; (theatre) Love Letters, 1990; author: The Body Principal, 1983, The Beauty Principal, 1984, The Diet Principal, 1987. Office: care Alan Nierob 10000 Santa Monica Blvd Los Angeles CA 90067-7007*

PRINCIPI, ANTHONY JOSEPH, lawyer; b. N.Y.C., Apr. 16, 1944; s. Antonio Joseph and Theresa (Princiotta) P.; m. Elizabeth Ann Ahlering, June 26, 1971; children: Anthony, Ryan, John. B.S., U.S. Naval Acad., 1967; J.D., Seton Hall U., 1975. Commd. 2d lt. U.S. Navy, 1967, advanced through grades to comdr., 1984; line officer U.S. Navy, Washington, 1967-72; atty. JAGC, San Diego, 1975-80; counsel Com. on Armed Service U.S. Senate, Washington, 1980-83, staff dir. Com. on Vets. Affairs, 1984—; dep. administr. congl. and pub. affairs VA, Washington, 1983-84; dep. sec. Dept. of Veterans Affairs, 1989—. Dep. sec. Depart. Vets. Affairs, 1989—. Decorated Bronze Star with combat "V", Vietnamese Cross of Gallantry, Navy Commendation medal with combat "V" (3); recipient Meritorious Service medal VA, 1983. Mem. ABA (chmn. subcom. gen. practice sect. 1985—). Republican. Roman Catholic. Avocations: gardening, skiing. Home: 7002 Native Dancer Ct Fairfax VA 22039-1922 Office: Depart Vets Affairs 810 Vermont Ave NW Ste 1001 Washington DC 20420-0002

PRINCZ, JUDITH, publishing executive. BA, Wheaton Coll., 1974. Retail circulation asst. Family Media, 1975-76; asst. mgr. direct mail Redbook, 1977; subscription mgr. Women Sports, 1977; circulation mgr. Sport mag., 1978-79; circulation dir. Weight Watcher's, 1979-83; assoc. pub. Am. Baby

mag., N.Y.C., 1983-89, v.p., pub., 1989—; v.p., group pub. Cahners Child-care Group, 1992—. Office: American Baby/Healthy Kids 249 W 17th St New York NY 10011

PRINDIVILLE, ROBERT ANDREW, investment executive; b. Chgo., Aug. 18, 1935; s. James A. and Mary (Greening) P.; m. Kathleen Hardie, Aug. 8, 1959; children: Eleanor, Victoria, Christopher, Charles, Anne, Mary Alice, Genevieve. BS, Marquette U., 1958. With Thomson Adv. Group L.P., Stamford, Conn., 1958—; bd. dirs. Chgo. Bd. Option Exchange, 1978-82. Mem. City Midday Club, Baltusrol Golf Club. Office: Thomson Adv Group L P One Station Pl Stamford CT 06902

PRINDLE, WILLIAM ROSCOE, consultant, retired glass company executive; b. San Francisco, Dec. 19, 1926; s. Vivian Arthur and Harriette Alnora (Nickerson) P.; m. June Laverne Anderson, June 20, 1947; children—Carol Susan, William Alastair. B.S., U. Calif., Berkeley, 1948, M.S., 1950; Sc.D., M.I.T., 1955. Asst. tech. dir. Hazel-Atlas Glass Co., 1954-56; mgr. research Hazel-Atlas Glass div. Continental Can Co., Wheeling, W.Va., 1956-58, gen. mgr. research and devel., 1959-62; mgr. materials research Am. Optical Co., Southbridge, Mass., 1962-65; v.p. research Southbridge and Framingham, Mass., 1971-76; dir. research Ferro Corp., Cleve., 1966-67, v.p. research, 1967-71; exec. dir. Nat. Materials Adv. Bd., NRC-NAS, Washington, 1976-80; dir. adminstrv. and tech. svcs. R & D div. Corning Glass Works, N.Y., 1980-85, dir. materials rsch., 1985-87; assoc. dir. R & D, Engring. div. Corning Glass Works (now Corning, Inc.), N.Y., 1987-90; div. v.p. assoc. dir. tech. group Corning Inc., N.Y., 1990-92; ret.; pres. XII Internat. Glass Congress, 1990, Internat. Commn. on Glass, 1985-88. Served with U.S. Navy, 1944-46. Named Outstanding Ceramist of New Eng., New Eng. sect. Am. Ceramic Soc., 1974, Toledo Glass and Ceramic award NW Ohio sect., 1986, Albert Victor Bleininger Meml. award Pitts. sect., 1989; Friedberg Meml. lecture Nat. Inst. Ceramic Engrs., 1990. Fellow Am. Ceramic Soc. (disting. life, pres. 1980-81), Soc. Glass Tech., Am. Soc. for Metals Internat.; mem. NAE, AAAS, Cosmos Club (Washington), Sigma Xi, Phi Gamma Delta. Home and Office: 1556 Crestline Dr Santa Barbara CA 93105-4611

PRINE, CHARLES W., JR., construction executive; b. Pitts., Apr. 23, 1926; s. Charles W. and Mabel (Kerr) P.; m. Elizabeth Waite, July 23, 1983; children: Linda, Janet, Karen, Roger, Barbara, Alison. A.B., Princeton U., 1948. Journalist Pitts. Sun-Telegraph, 1948-56; pres. P.R. Counselors, Inc., Pitts., 1957-69; v.p. Ryan Homes, Inc., Pitts., 1969—. Chmn. Mt. Lebanon Joint Recreation Commn., 1968-70; bd. dirs. Grantmakers of Western Pa.; pres. Action Housing Inc.; bd. dirs., v.p. Health and Welfare Planning Assn.; chmn. adv. council YWCA Greater Pitts.; mem. strategic planning and resource mgmt. United Way Allegheny County; elder Bower Hill Community Presbyn. Ch. Served with USNR, 1944-46. Recipient Vol. of Yr. award United Way Allegheny County, 1987. Club: Harvard-Yale-Princeton (Pitts.). Office: Ryan Homes Inc 100 Ryan Ct Pittsburgh PA 15205-1370

PRINE, JOHN, singer, songwriter; b. Maywood, Ill., Oct. 10, 1946. Pres. Oh Boy Records, Nashville. Began performing original compositions, 1969; songs include Paradise, Sam. Stone, Hello in There, Dear Abby; albums include Bruised Orange, Common Sense, Diamonds in the Rough, John Prine, Pink Cadillac, Prime Prine, Storm Windows, Sweet Revenge, Aimless Love, German Afternoons, 1986, John Prine Live, 1988, The Missing Years, 1991 (Grammy award for best contemporary folk rec.), Great Days: The John Pride Anthology, 1993, Lost Dogs & Mixed Blessings, 1995. Served with U.S. Army. Address: Oh Boy Records 33 Music Sq W Ste 102-A Nashville TN 37203*

PRINEAS, RONALD JAMES, epidemiologist, educator; b. Junee, New South Wales, Australia, Sept. 19, 1937; came to U.S., 1973; s. Peter John and Nancy (MacDonald) P.; m. Julienne Swynny, Apr. 21, 1961; children: Matthew Leigh, Anna Mary, John Paul, Miranda Jane. MBBS, U. Sydney, Australia, 1960; PhD, U. London, 1969. Med. house officer Prince Henry Hosp., Sydney, 1961; sr. med. house officer Royal Perth Hosp., Australia, 1962; registrar in medicine Royal Glasgow Infirmary, Scotland, 1963-64; research fellow London Sch. Hygiene and Tropical Medicine, 1964-67, lectr., 1967-68; asst. in medicine U. Melbourne, Australia, 1968-72; prof. epidemiology U. Minn., Mpls., 1973-88, prof. medicine, 1974-88; prof., chair epidemiology and pub. health U Miami, Fla., 1988—; cons. WHO, Geneva, 1976—, Nat. Heart Lung and Blood Inst., 1976—; prin. investigator Nat. Health Lung and Blood Inst., 1973—. Author books, including; Blood Pressure Sounds; Their Measurement and Meaning, 1978; The Minnesota Code Manual of Electrocardiographic Findings, 1982; also numerous articles. Recipient numerous cardiovascular disease research grants and contracts. Mem. Fla. affiliate Am. Heart Assn., Mpls., 1973—, chmn. adv. groups, 1975—. Fellow Royal Coll. Physicians Edinburgh, Am. Coll. Cardiology, Am. Pub. Health Assn., Soc. Epidemiologic Research, Am. Heart Assn. Council on Epidemiology, Internat. Soc. Hypertension, Council on Human Biology, Internat. Soc. Cardiology, Soc. Controlled Clin. Trials, Am. Coll. Epidemiology, Am. Soc. Epidemiology, Internat. Soc. Human Biology; mem. Royal Coll. Physicians London. Avocations: reading; raising a family. Office: U Miami Sch Medicine Dept Epidemiology & Pub Health PO Box 669R Miami FL 33101-0116

PRINGLE, BARBARA CARROLL, state legislator; b. N.Y.C., Apr. 4, 1939; d. Nicholas Robert and Anna Joan (Woloshinovich) Terlesky; m. Richard D. Pringle, Nov. 28, 1959; children: Christopher, Rhonda. Student, Cuyahoga C.C. With Dunn & Bradstreet, 1957-60; precinct committeewoman City of Cleve., 1976-77; elected mem. Cleve. City Coun., 1977-81; mem. Ohio Ho. of Reps., Columbus, 1982—; vice chmn. pub. utilities com., energy and environment com., pub. safety and hwy. com., transp. and urban affairs com., interagy. coun. on Spanish speaking affairs, power siting bd., communicatively impaired program adv. bd., small bus. com., aging and housing com., fin. and references coms., edn. com. Vol. Cleve. Lupus Steering Com., various community orgns.; charter mem. Statue of Liberty Ellis Island Found. Recipient cert. of appreciation Cleve. Mcpl. Ct., 1977, Exch. Club Bklyn., 1978, Cmty. Recreation Appreciation award City of Cleve., 1978, Key to City of Cleve., 1979, Cleve. Area Soapbox Derby cert., 1976, 77, 81, cert. of appreciation Ward 9 Youth League, 1979-82, No. Ohio Patrolman's Benevolent Assn. award, 1983, Cuyahoga County Firefighters award, 1983, Outstanding Pub. Servant award for Outstanding Svc. to Hispanic Cmty., 1985, Nat. Sr. Citizen Hall of Fame award, 1987, cert. of appreciation Cleve. Coun. Unemployed Workers, 1987, Ohio Farmers Union award, 1990, award of appreciation United Labor Agy., 1993, Susan B. Anthony award, 1995. Mem. Nat. Order Women Legislators, Fedn. Dem. Women of Ohio, Nat. Alliance Czech Catholics, St. Michael Ch. Altar and Rosary Soc., Ward 15 Dem. Club, Polish Falcons. Democrat. Home: 708 Timothy Ln Cleveland OH 44109-3733

PRINGLE, BRUCE D., federal magistrate; b. Denver, June 17, 1944; s. Edward E. and Pauline (Judd) P.; children: Jeffrey, Jennifer; m. Gail G. Pringle, Jan. 5, 1992. Student, Northwestern U., 1962-63; BA, U. Colo., 1966, JD, 1969. Bar: U.S. Ct. Appeals (10th cir.), Colo. Supreme Ct. Law clk. to Hon. William Doyle U.S. Dist. Ct. (Colo. dist.), Denver, 1969-70; assoc. Winner, Berge, Martin & Clark, Denver, 1970-75; ptnr. Clark, Martin & Pringle, Denver, 1975-81, Baker & Hostetler, Denver, 1981-91; U.S. Magistrate Judge U.S. Dist. Ct., Denver, 1991—; instr. law, lectr. U. Denver Law Sch., Fed. Bar Assn., Aurora C.C., Met. State Coll. Author of treatise Colo. Law Annotated (7 vols.), 1984-88, (2 vols.), 91. Mem. com. conduct of U.S. Dist. Ct., 1981-84; mem. Colo. Supreme Ct. com. on Colo. Rules of Civil Procedure; former mem. Litigation Subcom. for Freedom of Info. Coun. Mem. ABA, Am. Judicature Soc., U.S. Magistrates Assn., Colo. Bar Assn., Aurora Bar Assn., Order of Coif. Office: US Dist Ct C-338 1929 Stout St Denver CO 80294-2900

PRINGLE, EDWARD E., legal educator, former state supreme court chief justice; b. Chgo., Apr. 12, 1914; s. Abraham J. and Lena (Oher) P.; m. Pauline Judd, Aug. 17, 1941; children: Bruce, Eric. LL.B., U. Colo., 1936, LL.D., 1976; LL.D., U. Denver, 1979. Bar: Colo. Practiced in Denver, 1936-42, 47-57; with fed. govt. service Washington, 1943-47; dist. judge Colo. Dist. Ct., Denver, 1957-61; justice Supreme Ct. Colo., Denver, 1961-79; chief justice Supreme Ct. Colo., 1970-78; dir. research and writing program U. Denver Coll. Law, 1979-90, prof. emeritus, 1990—. Contbr. articles to profl. jours. Bd. dirs. Am. Med. Center, Denver; mem. Nat.

Commn. for Establishment of Nat. Inst. Justice. Served with USAAF, 1942. Recipient William Lee Knous award U. Colo. Law Sch., 1975. Mem. Am., Colo., Denver bar assns., Conf. Chief Justices (chmn. 1973-74), Am. Judicature Soc. (Herbert Lincoln Harley award 1973, chmn. bd. 1974-76), Nat. Center State Cts. (pres. 1977-79). Jewish. Club: Masons (33 deg.). Office: U Denver Coll Law 1900 Olive St Denver CO 80220-1857

PRINGLE, JOHN D., ecological research administrator. Dir. Can. Dept. Fisheries & Oceans, Halifax Fisheries Rsch. Lab., NS, Canada. Office: Halifax Fisheries Rsch Lab, 1707 Lower Water St PO Box 550, Halifax, NS Canada B3J 2S7

PRINGLE, LAURENCE PATRICK, writer; b. Rochester, N.Y., Nov. 26, 1935; s. Laurence Erin and Marleah Elizabeth (Rosehill) P.; m. Judith Malanowicz, June 23, 1962 (div. 1970); children: Heidi Elizabeth Jeffrey Laurence, Sean Edmund; m. Susan Deborah Klein, Mar. 13, 1983; children: Jesse Erin, Rebecca Anne. BS in Wildlife Biology, Cornell U., 1958; MS in Wildlife Biology, U. Mass., 1961. Tchr. sci. Lima (N.Y.) Cen. Sch., 1961-62; editor Nature and Sci. mag. Am. Mus. Natural History, N.Y.C., 1963-70; free-lance writer, 1970—; writer-in-residence Kean College, Union, N.J., 1985-86. Author: (children's books) Dinosaurs and Their World, 1968, The Only Earth We Have, 1969, From Field to Forest, 1970, In a Beaver Valley, 1970, One Earth, Many People, 1971, Ecology: Science of Survival, 1971, Cockroaches: Here, There, Everywhere, 1971, From Pond to Prairie, 1972, This Is a River, 1972, Pests and People: The Search for Sensible Pest Control, 1972, Estuaries: Where Rivers Meet the Sea, 1973, Into the Woods: Exploring the Forest Ecosystem, 1973, Follow a Fisher, 1973, Twist, Wiggle and Squirm: A Book about Earthworms, 1973, Recycling Resources, 1974, Energy: Power for People, 1975, City and Suburb: Exploring an Ecosystem, 1975, Chains, Webs and Pyramids: The Flow of Energy in Nature, 1975, Water Plants, 1975, The Minnow Family: Chubs, Dace, Minnows and Shiners, 1987, Listen to the Crows, 1976, Our Hungry Earth: The World Food Crisis, 1976, Death is Natural, 1977, The Hidden World: Life under a Rock, 1977, The Controversial Coyote: Predation, Politics and Ecology, 1977, The Gentle Desert: Exploring an Ecosystem, 1977, Animals and Their Niches: How Species Share Resources, 1977, The Economic Growth Debate: Are There Limits to Growth?, 1978, Dinosaurs and People: Fossils, Facts and Fantasies, 1978, Wild Foods, 1978, Nuclear Power: From Physics to Politics, 1979, Natural Fire: Its Ecology in Forests, 1979, Lives at Stake: The Science and Politics of Environmental Health, 1980, What Shall We Do with the Land?: Choices for America, 1981, Frost Hollows and Other Microclimates, 1981, Vampire Bats, 1982, Water: The Next Great Resource Battle, 1982, Radiation: Waves and Particles/Benefits and Risks, 1983, Wolfman: Exploring the World of Wolves, 1983, Feral: Tame Animals Gone Wild, 1983, The Earth Is Flat—and Other Great Mistakes, 1983, Being a Plant, 1983, Nuclear War: From Hiroshima to Nuclear Winter, 1985, Animals at Play, 1985, Here Come the Killer Bees, 1986, Throwing Things Away: From Middens to Resource Recovery, 1986, Restoring Our Earth, 1987, Home: How Animals Find Comfort and Safety, 1987, Rain of Troubles: The Science and Politics of Acid Rain, 1988, Living in a Risky World, 1989, Nuclear Energy: Troubled Past, Uncertain Future, 1989, Bearman: Exploring the World of Black Bears, 1989, The Animal Rights Controversy, 1989, Saving Our Wildlife, 1990, Global Warming: Assessing the Greenhouse Threat, 1990, The Golden Book of Insects and Spiders, 1990, Killer Bees (rev. edit.) 1991, Batman: Exploring the World of Bats, 1991, Living Treasure: Saving Earth's Threatened Biodiversity, 1991, Antarctica: The Last Unspoiled Continent, 1992, The Golden Book of Volcanoes, Earthquakes, and Powerful Storms, 1992, Chemical and Biological Weapons: The Cruelest Weapons, 1993, Oil Spills: Damage, Recovery, and Prevention, 1993, Jackal Woman: Exploring the World of Jackals, 1993, Scorpion Man: Exploring the World of Scorpions, 1994, Dinosaurs! Strange and Wonderful, 1995, Vanishing Ozone: Protecting Earth from Ultraviolet Radiation, 1995, Coral Reefs: Earth's Undersea Treasures, 1995, Dolphin Man: Exploring the World of Dolphins, 1995, Fire in the Forest: A Cycle of Growth and Renewal, 1995; (fiction) Jesse Builds a Road, 1989, Octopus Hug, 1993; (adult books) Wild River, 1972, Rivers and Lakes, 1985. Recipient Spl. Conservation award Nat. Wildlife Fedn., 1978, Eva L. Gordon award Am. Nature Study Soc., 1983. Mem. the Authors Guild. Home and Office: PO Box 252 West Nyack NY 10994252

PRINGLE, LEWIS GORDON, international trade and investment company executive; b. Lansing, Mich., Feb. 13, 1941; s. Gordon Henry and Lucile Roxana (Drake) P.; children: Lewis Gordon Jr., William Davis, Thomas Benjamin. BA, Harvard U., 1963; M.S., M.I.T., 1965, Ph.D., 1969. Vice pres., dir. mktg. sci. BBDO, Inc., N.Y.C., 1968-73, exec. v.p., dir. rsch. svcs., corp. dir., 1978-91; exec. v.p. BBDO Worldwide, 1986-91; chmn. CEO BBDO Europe, 1986-91, LG Pringle and Assocs., 1992—; asst. prof. mktg. Carnegie-Mellon U., 1973-74. Author numerous articles in field. Active local Boy Scouts Am. Ford Found. fellow, 1967. Fellow Royal Statis. Soc.; mem. Market Research Council, Inst. Mgmt. Sci., Am. Psychol. Assn., European Soc. Mktg. and Opinion Research, Am. Mktg. Assn. Republican. Congregationalist. Home: 71 Hunting Ridge Rd Greenwich CT 06831-3122

PRINGLE, ORAN ALLAN, mechanical and aerospace engineering educator; b. Lawrence, Kan., Sept. 14, 1923; s. Oran Allan and Mae (McClell) P.; m. Billie Hansen, June 25, 1947; children—Allan, Billie, James, Rebecca. B.S. in Mech. Engring. U. Kan., 1947; M.S., U. Wis., 1948, Ph.D. 1967. Registered profl. engr., Mo. Mech. engr. Black and Veatch (cons. engrs.), Kansas City, Mo., 1947-48; engr. Boeing Airplane Co., Wichita, 1952—; prof. U. Mo., Columbia, 1948—. Co-author: Engineering Metallurgy, 1957; contbr. articles to profl. lit. Bd. dirs. United Cerebral Palsy Boone County, Mo. Served with AUS, 1943-45. Ford Found. grantee. Mem. Am. Soc. M.E. (chmn. fastening and joining com., design engring. div.), Sigma Xi. Home: 1820 University Ave Columbia MO 65201-6004 Office: Dept Mech and Aerospace Engring U Mo Columbia MO 65201

PRINGLE, ROBERT BERNARD, lawyer; b. Summit, N.J., Jan. 2, 1944; s. Edward Harvey and Caroline (Mazuco) P.; m. Rebecca Winslow, June 29, 1974; children: Robin Stevens, Parker Winslow, Edward Sterling. BS, U. N.C., 1966; JD, Duke U., 1969. Bar: Pa. 1970, Calif. 1971, U.S. Dist. Ct. (no. dist.) Calif. 1971, U.S. Ct. Appeals (9th cir.) Calif. 1970, U.S. Dist. Ct. (cen. dist.) Calif. 1975. Assoc. Thelen, Marrin, Johnson & Bridges, San Francisco, 1971-77, ptnr., 1978—. Mem. Tiburon (Calif.) Planning Commn., 1980-83, chmn., 1984; mem. bd. visitors Duke U. Sch. Law. Mem. ABA (anti-trust sect., civil practice and procedure com. 1977—, litigation sect., chair intellectual property litigation com.), Olympic Club (San Francisco), San Francisco Yacht Club (Belvedere, Calif.). Avocations: sailing, skiing, tennis, golf. Office: Thelen Marrin Johnson & Bridges 2 Embarcadero Ctr Ste 2100 San Francisco CA 94111-3807

PRINGLE, ROBERT MAXWELL, diplomat; b. N.Y.C., Nov. 12, 1936; s. Henry Fowles and Helena Huntington (Smith) P.; m. Barbara Ann Cade, Sept. 26, 1964; children: James Maxwell, Anne Elizabeth. BA, Harvard U., 1958; PhD, Cornell U., 1967. Dir. econ. policy staff Bur. African Affairs Dept. State, 1981-83; dep. chief mission Ouagadougou, Burkina Faso, 1983-85, Port Moresby, Papua New Guinea, 1985-87; ambassador to Mali, 1987-90; dir. cen. African affairs U.S. Dept. State, 1990-93; dir. ecology and terrestrial conservation U.S. Dept. of State, 1993—. Author: Rajahs and Rebels: The Ibans of Sarawak under Brooke Rule, 1970, Indonesia and the Philippines: American Interests in Island Southeast Asia, 1980. Mem. Assn. Asian Studies, African Studies Assn. Avocations: photography, gardening, scuba diving. Home: 216 Wolfe St Alexandria VA 22314

PRINS, DAVID, speech pathologist, educator; b. Herkimer, N.Y., Oct. 4, 1930; s. Tunis W. and Harriet Z. (Baker) P.; m. Gloria B. Fleming, June 4, 1955; children: Leslie, Steven, Douglas, Michael. B.A., Central Coll. Iowa, 1952; M.A., U. Mich., 1957, Ph.D., 1961. Tchr., Denison (Iowa) High Sch. 1954-55; instr. U. Mich., 1960-63, asst. prof., 1963-66, assoc. prof., 1966-69; asst. dir. U. Mich. Speech and Hearing Camp, 1960-64, dir., 1964-69; dir. program in speech and hearing scis. U. Wash., 1974-75, assoc. prof., 1969-72, prof., 1973-92, chmn. dept. speech and hearing scis., 1973-79, assoc. dean Coll. Arts & Scis., 1979-88, prof. emeritus, 1992—; vis. prof. U. Va. Contbr. articles in field of stuttering and articulation disorders to profl. jours. Served with U.S. Army, 1952-54. Mem. AAAS, Am. Speech and Hearing Assn. Wash. Speech and Hearing Assn., Mich. Speech and Hearing Assn. (past

pres.), Phi Beta Kappa, Phi Kappa Phi. Home: Waterford Ct # 4 131 8th Ln Kirkland WA 98033 Office: U Wash Dept Speech And Scis Seattle WA 98195

PRINS, ROBERT JACK, college administrator; b. Grand Rapids, Mich., Oct. 12, 1932; s. Jacob and Marie (Vanden Brink) P.; m. Ruth Ellen John, Oct. 10, 1950; children: Linda, Douglas, Debra, Nancy, Eric, Sarah. BA, Hope Coll., 1954; DBA, Coll. Emporia, 1974. With Mich. Bell Telephone Co., Detroit area, 1954-66; dir. devel. Bethesda Hosp., Denver, 1966-68; v.p. planning and devel. Park Coll., Parkville, Mo., 1969-70; chief adminstrv. officer Coll. of Emporia, Kans., 1970-75; dir. fin. and devel. The Abbey Sch., Canon City, Colo., 1975-79; dir. devel. Kirksville Coll. Osteo. Medicine, Mo., 1979-84; v.p. devel. McKendree Coll., Lebanon, Ill., 1984-86; pres. Iowa Weslyan Coll., Mt. Pleasant, 1986—; bd. dirs. Iowa Coll. Found., Iowa Commn. on Nat. and Cmty. Svc.; mem. adv. bd. Iowa Commn. on Status of Women, Iowa Assn. Ind. Colls. and Univs.; mem. adv. com. Potomak Internat., Taipei, Taiwan. Mem. Nat. Assn. Ind. Colls. and Univs., Coun. for Advancement and Support of Edn., Mt. Pleasant Mfrs. Assn., Mt. Pleasant C. of C.

PRINZO, FELIX J., chemicals executive. Sr. v.p., CFO, sec. Laroche Chem., Inc., Baton Rouge, La. Office: Laroche Chemicals Inc 1200 Airline Hwy Baton Rouge LA 70805*

PRIOR, BOYD THELMAN, management consultant; b. Tacoma, May 7, 1926; s. George Archie and Thelma Mary (Chambers) P. Student, U.S. Naval Acad., 1948-50; BA, Claremont Men's Coll., 1952; MBA, Harvard U., 1954. Sr. v.p., dir. The Lusk Corp., Tucson, 1954-60; v.p. sales & mktg. Horizon Land Corp., Tucson, 1960-62; sr. v.p., dir. Gen. Devel. Corp. Miami, Fla., 1962-71; chmn., pres. Prior Assocs., Phoenix, 1971-74; mgmt. cons., dir. Am. Solar King Corp., Waco, Tex., 1982-85; pvt. practice Kerrville, Tex. and Boca Raton, Fla., 1974-82, Burleson, Tex., 1985—; pvt. practice mgmt. cons. Burleson, Dallas/Ft. Worth, Phoenix, Miami, 1985—; cons. Cob Select Sand & Gravel, Inc., 1986—, Resolution Trust, 1989—. Recipient Cert. Appreciation Better Bus. Bur., 1971, 74. Republican. Episcopalian. Home and Office: 544 Post Oak Ct Burleson TX 76028-6515

PRIOR, GARY L., lawyer; b. Niagara Falls, N.Y., June 26, 1943; s. Harold D. and Adeline Thelma (Lee) P.; m. Nancy O'Shaughnessy, Aug. 12, 1975; children: Joseph Lee, Julia Elizabeth. BS, Tulane U., 1965; JD, U. Chgo., 1968. Bar: Ill. 1968, U.S. Dist. Ct. (no. dist.) Ill. 1968, U.S. Ct. Appeals (7th cir.) 1973, U.S. Ct. Appeals (3rd cir.) 1974, U.S. Trial Bar 1983, U.S. Supreme Ct. 1989, U.S. Dist. Ct. (we. dist.) Wis. 1992, U.S. Dist. Ct. (ea. dist.) Wis. 1993. Assoc. Rooks, Pitts & Poust, Chgo., 1968-71; assoc. McDermott, Will & Emery, Chgo., 1971-74, ptnr, 1974—, dir. trial dept. tng., 1980-85, mem. securities approval com., 1984—, mem. nominating com., chmn., 1988-89, partnership com., 1989-92, mem mgmt. com., 1991-93. Mem. Chgo. Bar Assn., Phi Delta Phi. Avocations: farming, sports, family. Home: 623 W Briar Pl Chicago IL 60657-4520 Office: McDermott Will & Emery 227 W Monroe St Chicago IL 60606-5096

PRIOR, RONALD L., animal scientist, nutritionist; b. McCook, Nebr., Mar. 9, 1945. BS, U. Nebr., 1967; PhD in Nutrition, Cornell U., 1971. NIH postdoctoral trainee N.Y. State Vet. Coll. Cornell U., 1971-73; rsch. chemist, asst. prof. meat animal rsch. ctr., Clay ctr., USDA U. Nebr., 1973-83; pres. Sunshine Audio, Inc., 1983-87; gen. ptnr. R&M Enterprises, 1983-87; sci. program officer, nutritionist USDA human nutrition rsch. ctr. aging Tufts U., 1987—; lectr. animal nutrition lab. Cornell U., 1968, U. Nebr. 1978-81; chmn. ruminant nutrition workshop U.S. Meat Animal Rsch. Ctr., 1977, 2d ann. ruminant nutrition conf. Fedn. Am. Soc. Exptl. Biology & Medicine, 1981; coop scientist spl. fgn. currency rsch. programs U. Alexandria, Egypt and Warsaw Agr. U., Poland. Contbr. over 70 articles to profl. jours. Mem. AAAS, Am. Soc. Animal Sci. (chmn. ruminant nutrition session 1973), Am. Inst. Nutrition, Sigma Xi. Office: USDA Human Nutrition Rsch Ctr Tufts U 711 Washington St Rm 919 Boston MA 02111

PRIORE, ROGER L., biostatistics educator, consultant; b. Buffalo, Apr. 21, 1938; s. Anthony J. and Linda M. (DeMarchi) P.; m. Carol A. Cooper, Sept. 3, 1960; children—Howard W., Susan L., John D. B.A., SUNY-Buffalo, 1960, M.S., 1962; Sc.D., Johns Hopkins U., 1965. Jr. cancer research scientist Roswell Park Meml. Inst., Buffalo, 1960-65, sr. cancer research scientist, 1965-67, assoc. cancer research scientist, 1967-69, prin. cancer research scientist, 1974-79, dir. computer sci., 1979-83, dir. dept. biomath., 1983-91, dir. mgmt. info. systems, 1988-91; asst. rsch. prof. SUNY, Buffalo, 1966-68, assoc. rsch. prof., 1968-69, rsch. prof., dir. grad. studies in biometry, 1980-91; rsch. prof. Niagara U., 1968-91; cons. in stats. and computing, 1991—; clin. prof. dept. social and preventive medicine SUNY, Buffalo, 1991—; pres. Compustat Assocs., Inc., Buffalo, 1993—; clin. prof. dept. statistics SUNY, Buffalo, 1995—; cons. Am. Joint Com. on Cancer, 1980-88. Contbr. articles to profl. jours. Mem. Am. Statis. Assn., Soc. for Epidemiol. Rsch., Sigma Xi. Office: 342 Dan Troy Dr Buffalo NY 14221

PRIORY, RICHARD BALDWIN, electric utility executive; b. Lakehurst, N.J., May 15, 1946; s. Joseph Albert Jr. and Betty (Baldwin) P.; m. Joan Ellen Rourke, May 30, 1968; children: Jennifer Joan, Richard Baldwin Jr. BS in Civil Engring. magna cum laude, W.Va. Inst. Tech., 1969; MS in Engring., Princeton U., 1973; grad. utility exec. program, U. Mich., 1982; grad. advanced mgmt. program, Harvard U., 1991. Registered profl. engr., N.C., S.C. Design engr., project engr. Union Carbide Corp., 1969-72; asst. prof. structural engring. U. N.C., Charlotte, 1973-76; design engr. Duke Power Co., Charlotte, N.C., 1976-78, prin. engr., 1978-81, mgr. project mgmt. divsn., 1981-84, v.p. design engring., 1984-88, sr. v.p. generation and info. svcs., 1988-91, exec. v.p. Power Generation Group, 1991-94, pres., COO, 1994—; mem. Duke Power Co., bd. dirs.; mem. Duke Fluor Daniel Mgmt. Com.; mem., bd. dirs. J.A. Jones Applied Rsch. Co.; mem. power generation com. Assn. of Edison Illuminating Cos.; mem. nuclear waste adv. com. Nuclear Energy Inst. Bd. visitors U. N.C., Charlotte; bd. dirs. N.C. State U. Engring. Found.; bd. trustees N.C. chpt. Nature Conservancy; mem., past chmn. bd. dirs. Charlotte-Mecklenburg Edn. Found.; pres., bd. trustees Discovery Place, Inc., 1992-93; past mem. Charlotte-Mecklenburg Pub. Broadcasting Found.; vice chmn. campaign drive United Way Ctrl. Carolinas, Inc., 1990; mem. adv. coun. N.C. Alliance for Competitive Technologies. Mem. ASCE, Nat. Acad. Engring, Charlotte Engrs. Club. Avocation: golf. Office: Duke Power Co 422 S Church St Charlotte NC 28242-0001

PRISBREY, REX PRINCE, insurance agent, underwriter, financial consultant; b. Washington, Utah, Mar. 18, 1922; s. Hyrum William and Susan (Prince) P.; m. Pinka Julieta Lucero, Nov. 16, 1943; children: Karol Sue Prisbey Lewallen, Pamela Blanche Prisbrey Ebert, Michael Rex. BA in Acctg., Denver U., 1949. CLU. Ptnr. Allen Stamm & Assocs., home builders, Farmington, N.Mex., 1949-52; acct. Linder Burke & Stevenson, Santa Fe, N.Mex., 1949-52; agt. State Farm Ins. Cos., Farmington, 1952-56; mgr. State Farm Ins. Cos., Phoenix, 1956-60; contractor, agt. State Farm Ins. Cos., Scottsdale, Ariz., 1960—; v.p., treas. Original Curio Store Inc., Santa Fe. Pres. Farmington Jr. C. of C., 1952; v.p. N.Mex. Jr. C. of C., 1953. 1st lt. USAAF, 1941-46, CBI. Decorated DFC, Air medal with oak leaf cluster; recipient Disting. Life Underwriter award Cen. Ariz. Mgrs. Assn., 1979. Mem. Am. Soc. CLU's, Scottsdale Assn. Life Underwriters (pres. 1980-81), Airplane Owners and Pilots Assn., Hump Pilots Assn. (life, speaker at meml. of Hump Flyers, Kunming, China 1993), Pinewood Country Club (bd. dirs., treas., v.p. 1985—), Civitans (pres. Scottsdale 1962-63). Avocations: flying, golf, photography. Home: 4011 N 65th St Scottsdale AZ 85251-4235 Office: State Farm Ins Cos 6730 E Mcdowell Rd Scottsdale AZ 85257-3141

PRITCHARD, ARTHUR OSBORN, retired business administrator; b. Scarsdale, N.Y., Oct. 7, 1910; m. Dorothy E. White (dec.); m. Virginia R. Cunningham (div.). AB, Pomona Coll., 1932; MA in Internat. Rels., Columbia U., 1934. With Dept. Agr. and Gen. Acctg. Office U.S. Govt., Washington, 1934-36, Berkeley, Calif., 1936-41; staff agt. Army Med. Corp. U.S. Army, 1941-45; pub. acctg. pvt. practice, 1945; acct. and office mgr. Talbot Bird & Co., SF, 1946-60; treas. and bus. mgr. No. Calif. Conf. of United Ch. of Christ, 1960-76; ret., 1976; participant UN Film Study Guide project, 1991-93, 94—. Mem. Outlook Club of Calif. 1948—, sec., 1967-93; bd. dirs, Berkeley City Club, 1977-83, pres., 1978-82; instr. of adult edn.

Berkeley YMCA; pres. 1989 program, City Commons Club of Berkeley; program dir., 1991—; active mem. First Congl. Ch. of Berkeley, 1938—; life mem. Commonwealth Club, 1939—. Decorated Bronze Star; Team Facilitator grantee U.S. Inst. of Peace, Washington, 1991-93. Mem. Am. Assn. for the UN, UN Assn. of the U.S. of Am. (pres. Alameda County chpt., 1956-59, No. Calif. Divsn. of UNA-USA, 1959-65, received citation), World Affairs Coun. of No. Calif. (charter mem. 1947). Address: care Berkeley City Club 2315 Durant Ave Berkeley CA 94704

PRITCHARD, CLAUDIUS HORNBY, JR., retired university president; b. Charleston, W.Va., June 28, 1927; s. Claudius Hornby and Katherine (Ellison) P.; m. Marjorie Walker Pullen, Aug. 9, 1952; children: Virginia Aiken, Katherine Winston, Olivia Reynolds, Claudius V. BA, Hampden-Sydney Coll., 1950; MA, Longwood Coll., 1965; PhD, Fla. State U., 1971. Comml. loan teller Am. Nat. Bank and Trust Co., Danville, Va., 1950-53; asst. cashier Planters Bank & Trust Co., Farmville, Va., 1953-55; asst. to pres. Hampden-Sydney (Va.) Coll., 1955-57, bus. mgr. and treas., 1957-67, v.p. devel., 1967-71; sr. budget analyst-edn. State of Fla., Tallahassee, 1971-72; pres. Sullins Coll., Bristol, Va., 1972-76; v.p. adminstrn. Maryville U., St. Louis, 1976-77, pres., 1977-92, pres. emeritus, 1992—; dir. Commerce Bank of St. Louis, 1982-92. Author: Col. D. Wyatt Aiken (1828-1887) South Carolina's Militant Agrarian, 1970; contbr. articles to profl. jours. Bd. dirs. West St. Louis County YMCA, Chesterfield, Mo., 1985-92; bd. visitors Charleston So. Univ., 1993—. Served with USNR, 1945-46. Fla. State U. fellow, 1969-70, Arthur Vining Davis fellow Am. Council on Edn., 1974. Mem. AAUP, Am. Assn. Higher Edn., So. Hist. Assn., S.C. Hist. Soc., Mo. Colls. Fund (bd. dirs., chmn. 1987-88), Ind. Colls. and Univs. Mo., Chesterfield C. of C. (pres. 1987, named Chesterfield Citizen of Yr. 1986), Rotary. Republican. Presbyterian.

PRITCHARD, CONSTANCE JENKINS, human resources specialist, trainer, consultant; b. Washington, May 6, 1950; d. William Morton and Marguerite Kathleen (Marshall) Jenkins; m. Paul Ralph Pritchard, June 30, 1973; children: Laura, Leslie. BA in English and History, Hiram (Ohio) Coll., 1972; MA in Linguistics, U. S.C., 1978, EdD in Student Pers. Svcs., 1991. Tchr. Sterling High Sch., Somerdale, N.J., 1972-76; instr. U. S.C., Aiken, 1982-93; dir. advisement ctr., 1984-89, asst. dean for career planning, placement and orientation, 1989-93; trainer, cons. Pritchard Group, North Augusta, S.C., 1989—; adminstr. Grace United Meth. Ch., North Augusta, S.C., 1993—. Scout leader Girl Scouts Am., S.C., 1987-89; trainer Leadership Aiken County, 1991—; bd. dirs. United Way of Aiken County, 1993—, Aiken County ARC, 1994—. Recipient citation for excellence in career programming Am. Assn. Career Edn., 1992; named Woman of Achievement, Miss. S.C. Pageant, 1993. Mem. Nat. Comty. Leadership Assn., Coll. Placement Coun. (Excellence award 1992, Award for Excellence in Rsch. 1992), Nat. Assn. Acad. Adminstrs. (newsletter editor 1987-89), Student Affairs Profl. Orgn., Cen. Savannah River Area Human Resource Assn. (sec. 1992-93), North Augusta Rotary (Rotarian of Yr. 1990-91), North Augusta C. of C. (bd. dirs. 1995—). Avocations: sailing, reading, family. Office: The Pritchard Group PO Box 6756 North Augusta SC 29841-0756

PRITCHARD, DALTON HAROLD, retired electronics research engineer; b. Crystal Springs, Miss., Sept. 1, 1921; s. Cecil Harold and Marvie Prudence (Lofton) P.; m. Caroline Ann Hnatuk, Apr. 27, 1947; 1 child, Mary Ann Pritchard Poole. B.S.E.E., Miss. State U., 1943; postgrad., Harvard, MIT Radar Sch., 1943-44. Mem. tech. staff RCA Labs, Riverhead, N.Y., 1946-50; mem. tech. staff RCA Labs., Princeton, N.J., 1950-75, fellow tech. staff, 1975-87; session chmn., mem. program com. Internat. Conf. on Consumer Electronics, Chgo., 1980-85. Contbr. articles to profl. jours.; patentee in field. mem. N.J. Gov.'s Sci. Adv. Council, Princeton, 1981-85. Served to capt. U.S. Army Signal Corps. Decorated Bronze Star; recipient Eduard Rhein prize Edward Rhein Found., Berlin, Fed. Republic of Germany, 1980; Disting. Engring. fellow Miss. State U., 1991. Fellow IEEE (Vladimir Zworykin award 1977, David Sarnoff award 1981), Soc. Info. Display, Nat. Assn. Engrs., Nat. Acad. Engring., Sigma Xi, Tau Beta Pi, Kappa Mu Epsilon. Republican. Baptist. Avocations: amatuer radio; tennis. Home: 3 Bent Tree Ln Hilton Head Island SC 29926-1906

PRITCHARD, DAVID EDWARD, physics educator; b. N.Y.C., Oct. 15, 1941; m. Andrea Hasler; children: Orion, Alexander. BS, Calif. Inst. Tech., 1962; PhD, Harvard U., 1968. Postdoctoral fellow MIT, Cambridge, Mass., 1968, instr., 1968-70, asst. prof., 1970-75, assoc. prof., 1975-80, prof., 1980—; vis. scientist Stanford Rsch. Inst., 1975; vis. prof. U. Pais Sud Orsay, 1983; disting. visitor Joint Inst. for Lab, Astrophysics, 1989, mem. subpanel, 1990-94, chmn. 1994. Div. assoc. editor Phys. Rev. Letters, 1983-88; contbr. articles to profl. jours. Polaroid fellow Harvard U., 1962-63, NSF predoctoral fellow, 1963-68. Fellow AAAS, Am. Acad. Arts and Scis., Am. Phys. Soc. (disting. traveling lectr. laser sci. topical group, 1992-94, rep. steering com. laser sci. topical group, rep. to joint coun. on quantum electronics, Broida prize 1991), Tiverton (R.I.) Yacht Club. Avocations: sailing, carpentry. Office: MIT Rm 26-237 Dept Physics Cambridge MA 02139

PRITCHARD, DAVID J., oil company executive; b. 1948. BA, Cambridge (Eng.) U., 1969, MA, 1969. With BP Pipelines (Alaska) Inc., Anchorage, 1969-93; pres., CEO Alyeska Pipeline Svc Co., Anchorage, 1993—. Office: Alyeska Pipeline Svc Co 1835 S Bragaw St Anchorage AK 99512-0001*

PRITCHARD, DONALD WILLIAM, oceanographer; b. Santa Ana, Calif., Oct. 20, 1922; s. Charles Lorenzo and Madeleine (Sievers) P.; m. Thelma Lydia Amling, Apr. 25, 1943; children—Marian Lydia, Jo Anne, Suzanne Louise, Donald William, Albert Charles. B.A., UCLA, 1942; M.S. Scripps Instn. Oceanography, La Jolla, 1948, Ph.D., 1951; D.Sc. (hon.), Coll. William and Mary, 1985. Research asst. Scripps Instn. Oceanography, 1946-47; oceanographer USN Electronics Lab., 1947-49; assoc. dir. Chesapeake Bay Inst., Johns Hopkins, Balt., 1949-51; dir. Chesapeake Bay Inst., Johns Hopkins, 1951-74, chief scientist, 1974-79, prof., 1958-79, chmn. dept. oceanography, 1951-68; assoc. dir. for research, prof. Marine Scis. Rsch. Ctr., SUNY at Stony Brook, 1979-86, acting dir., dean, 1986-87, assoc. dean, 1987-88, prof. emeritus, 1988—; cons. C.E., U.S. Army, USPHS, AEC, Internat. AEA, NSF, Adv. Panel Earth Scis.; mem. adv. bd. to Sec. Natural Resources, State of Md. Bd. editors Jour. Marine Rsch., 1953-70, Bull. Bingham Oceanographic Collection, 1960-70, Geophys. Monograph Bd. Am. Geophys. Union, 1959-70, Johns Hopkins Oceanographic Studies, 1967-78; contbr. articles to profl. jours. Served from 2d lt. to capt. USAAF, 1943-46. Recipient Mathias Sci. medal The Chespeake Rsch. Consortium, 1990. Fellow Am. Geophys. Union (past pres. oceanography sect.); mem. AAAS, Nat. Acad. Engring., Nat. Acad. Engring., Am. Soc. Limnology and Oceanography (past v.p.), Am. Meteorol. Soc., Sigma Xi (past chpt. pres.). Office: SUNY Marine Scis Rsch Ctr Stony Brook NY 11794

PRITCHARD, HUW OWEN, chemist, educator; b. Bangor, Wales, July 23, 1928; s. Owen and Lilian Venetia (McMurray) P.; m. Margaret Ramsden, Nov. 3, 1956; children—Karen, David. B.Sc., U. Manchester, 1948, M.Sc., 1949, Ph.D. 1951, D.Sc., 1964. Asst. lectr. chemistry Manchester (Eng.) U., 1951-54, lectr. 1954-65; prof. chemistry York U., Ont., Can., 1965—. Contbr. articles to profl. jours. Fellow Royal Soc. Can. Office: Chemistry Dept York Univ, Downsview, ON Canada M3J 1P3

PRITCHARD, JAMES BENNETT, archaeologist, educator, author; b. Louisville, Oct. 4, 1909; s. John Hayden and Mary (Bennett) P.; m. Anne Elizabeth Cassedy, June 30, 1937; children: Sarah Anne (Mrs. Robert F. Hayman), Mary Bennett (Mrs. Clifton Mitchell). AB, Asbury Coll., 1930; BD, Drew U., 1935; PhD, U. Pa., 1942, LHD (hon.), 1991; STD, Phila. Div. Sch., 1961; DD, Div. Sch. of Pacific, 1962; LHD (hon.), Swarthmore Coll., 1977; DD (hon.), U Uppsala, Sweden, 1977. Prof. O.T. lit. Crozer Theol. Sem., 1942-54; ann. prof. Am. Sch. Oriental Research, Jerusalem, 1950-51; archeol. dir. expdn. to Jericho, Jordan, 1951; vis. prof. Am. Sch. Oriental Research, 1956-57, 61-62; dir. expdns. to el-Jib, Jordan, 1956-62; to Tell es-Sa'idiyeh, Jordan, 1964-67, Am. Sch. Oriental Research, Sarafand, Lebanon, 1969, 70, 71, 72, 74; prof. O.T. lit. Div. Sch. Pacific 1954-62; curator Bib. archeology Univ. Mus., 1962-78, assoc. dir., 1967-76, dir., 1976-77; prof. religious thought U. Pa., 1962-78; Winslow lectr. Gen. Theol. Sem., 1960; Fulbright-Hays vis. prof. archaeology Am. U. Beirut, 1966-67; mem. Inst. Advanced Study, Princeton, N.J., 1978; Sec., Am. Schs. Oriental Research, 1963-71. Author: Palestinian Figurines, 1943, Ancient Near Eastern Texts, 1950, 55, 69, The Ancient Near East in Pictures, 1954, 69,

Archaeology and the Old Testament, 1958, The Excavation at Herodian Jericho, 1958, The Ancient Near East, 1958, vol. 2, 1975, Hebrew Inscriptions from Gibeon, 1959, The Water System at Gibeon, 1961, Gibeon, Where the Sun Stood Still, 1962, Bronze Age Cemetery at Gibeon, 1963, Winery, Defenses and Soundings at Gibeon, 1964, Sarepta, 1975, Recovering Sarepta, A Phoenician City, 1978, The Cemetery at Tell es-Sa'idiyeh, 1980, Excavations on the Tell, 1964-66, 1985, The Times Atlas of the Bible, 1987, The Times Concise Atlas of the Bible, 1991, Sarepta IV, 1988, The Harper Concise Atlas of the Bible, 1991; assoc. editor: Jour. Am. Oriental Soc, 1948-52; editor, 1952-54. Trustee Am. U. Beirut, 1970-79. Decorated Order of Istiqlal, 1st Class Jordan, 1964. Mem. Am. Philos. Soc. (Benjamin Franklin medal 1990), Am. Oriental Soc., Archeol. Inst. Am. (pres. 1973, 74, Disting. Archeol. Achievement award 1983). Clubs: Franklin Inn, Penn. Home: 108 Tunbridge Rd Haverford PA 19041-1038 Office: Univ Mus 33rd And Spruce St Philadelphia PA 19104

PRITCHARD, JOEL, state lieutenant governor; b. Seattle, May 5, 1925; children: Peggy, Frank, Anne, Jeanie. Student, Marietta Coll.; PhD (Hon.), Seattle U. Pres. Griffin Envelope Co., Seattle; mem. Wash. Ho. of Reps., Olympia, 1958-66, Wash. State Senate, 1966-70, U.S. Ho. of Reps., Washington, 1972-84; dir. govt. rels. Bogle & Gates, 1985-88; lt. gov. State of Wash., Olympia, 1989—; mem. Merchant Marine and Fisheries Com. U.S. Ho. of Reps., subcom. on Asia and the Pacific Fgn. Rels. Com., Panama Canal Consultative Commn., 1987-88; U.S. del. to UN Gen. Assembly, 1983. With U.S. Army, PTO, WWII. Office: Lt Gov's Office PO Box 40482 304 Legislative Bldg Olympia WA 98504-0482

PRITCHARD, PAUL CLEMENT, conservation association executive; b. Huntington, W.Va., Aug. 27, 1944; m. Susan Ford; children: Robin Elizabeth, Marcus, Stephen, Christopher. B.A. (scholar), U. Mo., 1966; M.S.P., U. Tenn., 1971; postgrad. in Bus. Mgmt, Harvard U., 1973-74, U. Mich., 1980. Chief natural resources planning Ga. Dept. Natural Resources, Atlanta, 1972-74; Pacific region coordinator NOAA, U.S. Dept Commerce, 1974-75; exec. dir. Appalachian Trial Conf., Inc., Harpers Ferry, W.Va., 1975-77; asst. to sec. U.S. Dept. Interior, Washington, 1977; dep. dir. Heritage Conservation and Recreation Service U.S. Dept Interior, 1977-80; pres. Nat. Parks and Conservation Assn., Washington, 1980—. Editor: Views of the Green, 1985; contbr. articles to profl. jours. Chmn. Nat. Park Trust; v.p. Resources for the Future, League of Conservation Voters. Recipient Spl. Achievement award Dept. Commerce, 1975; Meritorious Achievement award Dept. Interior, 1980; Gulf Conservation award; 1st recipient Schweitzer prize in Humanities. Office: Nat Parks & Conservation Assn 1776 Massachusetts Ave NW 2nd fl Washington DC 20036-1904

PRITCHARD, WILBUR LOUIS, telecommunications engineering executive; b. N.Y.C., May 31, 1923; s. Harmon and Jessie H. (Roth) P.; m. Kathleen H. Moss, Apr. 24, 1949; children: Hugh, Sarah, Ruth. BSEE, CCNY, 1943, ScD (hon.), 1993; postgrad., MIT, 1948-52. Registered profl. engr., Mass., Md. Microwave engr., mgr. Wayland Lab. Raytheon Co., Waltham, Mass., 1946-60; dir. engring. Europe Raytheon Co., Rome, 1960-62; group dir. satellite communication systems Aerospace Corp., El Segundo, Calif., 1962-67; v.p., dir. Comsat Labs., Clarksburg, Md., 1967-73; pres. Fairchild Space & Electronics Co., Germantown, Md., 1973-74, Satellite Systems Engring., Bethesda, Md., 1974-87, SSE Telecom, Inc., Bethesda, 1987-89, Direct Broadcast Satellite Corp., Bethesda, 1982-86, W.L. Pritchard & Co., Inc., Bethesda, 1989—; chmn. panel on broadcast satellites Nat. Acad. Scis., Falmouth, Mass., 1967; mem. space applications bd. Nat. Acad. Engring., Colo., 1968; mem. space applications adv. com. NASA, Washington, 1984, space and earth scis. adv. com., 1984-88, Nat. Acad. Engring. com. on Voice of Am., 1986-89. Author: (with others) China Space Report, 1980, Satellite Communication Systems Engineering, 1986, 2d edit., 1993; contbr. numerous articles to profl. jours.; holder 12 patents. Recipient Systems Command award USAF, 1967, Lloyd V. Berkner Space Utilization award Am. Astronautical Soc., 1983. Fellow IEEE, AIAA (Aerospace Comm. award 1972), Brit. Interplanetary Soc.; mem. Soc. Satellite Profls., Am. Astronautics Soc. (sr.), Nat. Acad. Engring., Internat. Acad. Astronautics. Club: Cosmos (Washington). Home: 9201 Laurel Oak Dr Bethesda MD 20817-1937 Office: WL Pritchard & Co Inc 7315 Wisconsin Ave Ste 520E Bethesda MD 20814-3209

PRITCHARD, WILLIAM ROY, former university system administrator; b. Portage, Wis., Nov. 15, 1924; s. William Roy and Lillian Edith (Roberts) P.; m. Deanna Elaine Pritchard; children: Rosan June, William Roy, Caryl Jean, Alyn Evan, Cynthia Bedeau. Student, U. Wis., 1942-43; D.V.M., Kans. State U., 1946, D.Sc. (hon.), 1970; D.Sc. (hon.), Tufts U., 1988; Ph.D., U. Minn., 1953; J.D., Ind. U., 1957; D.Sc. (hon.), Purdue U., 1977. Asst. prof. U. Wis., 1946-49; asso. prof. U. Minn., 1949-53; prof. Purdue U., 1953-57; prof., head vet. sci. U. Fla., 1957-61; asso. dir. Vet. Med. Research Inst., Ia. State U., 1961-62; prof. U. Calif.-Davis, 1962—, dean Sch. Vet. Medicine, 1962-82; asso. dir. Agrl. Expt. Sta., 1962-72; coordinator internat. agrl. programs U. Calif. system, 1977-81; vis. fellow Woodrow Wilson Sch. Pub and Internat. Affairs, Princeton, 1968-69; John Thomson lectr. U. Queensland, 1966; co-dir. nat. veterinary edn. program Duke U., 1987-92; spl. research hemmorrhagic diseases animals. Cons. Dept. Agr., Def. Dept., USPHS, VA, Calif. Dept. Health, FDA, 1962—; bd. cons. agr. Rockefeller Found., 1962-66; nat. med. cons. surgeon gen. USAF, 1962-64; mem. FAO/WHO Expert Panel Vet. Edn., President's Sci. Advisory Com. Panel World Food Supply, 1966-67, President's Sci. Advisory Com. Panel Biology and Med. Sci., 1969-70, Joint Research Com. Bd. Internat. Food and Agr. Aid, 1977-81. Served with U.S. Army, 1942-44. Recipient Gov. Fla. award, 1961, Disting. Svc. award Kans. State U., 1963, Outstanding Achievement award U. Minn., 1976, Disting. Pub. Svc. award U. Calif.-Davis, 1991, Gold Headed Cane award Am. Soc. Vet. Epidemiology, 1992. Mem. AAAS, APHA, Am. Vet. Med. Assn. (Internat. Vet. Congress award 1988), Am. Soc. Vet. Epidemiologists, Conf. of Pub. Health Vets. (hon. life), U.S. Animal Health Assn., Nat. Assn. State Univs. and Land-Grant Colls. (internat. affairs com. 1965-70), Order of Coif, Sigma Xi, Phi Zeta, Gamma Alpha. Home: 2409 Madrid Ct Davis CA 95616-0141

PRITCHARD, WILLIAM WINTHER, lawyer, drilling company executive; b. Bartlesville, Okla., Mar. 20, 1951; s. James Edward and Agnes Kathryn (Winther) P.; m. Susan Jane Parsons, Aug. 12, 1972; children—Jane, Kathryn, Robert. BA with honors, U. Kans., 1973; JD, U. Tulsa, 1976. Bar: Okla. 1976. With Parker Drilling Co., Tulsa, 1976—, v.p., gen. counsel, 1984—. Mem. ABA, Okla. Bar Assn., So. Hills Country Club (Tulsa). Republican. Presbyterian. Office: Parker Drilling Co 8 E 3rd St Tulsa OK 74103-3616

PRITCHARD SCHOCH, TERESA NOREEN, lawyer, law librarian, executive; b. Brackley, Eng., Apr. 2, 1953; came to U.S., Dec. 1953; d. Boston Forrest and Noreen PHyliss (Taylor) P.; m. Claude M. Schoch, 1992. BA magna cum laude, Oakland U., 1974; MLS, Wayne State U., 1976, JD cum laude, 1981. Bar: Fla. 1985, Mich. 1981. Law librarian Honigman Miller Schwartz & Cohn, Detroit, 1979-81; assoc. Honigman, Miller, Schwartz & Cohn, Detroit, 1981-83, Rumberger, Kirk et al, Orlando, Fla., 1984-85; dir. rsch. svcs. Gunster, Yoakley, Criser & Stewart, West Palm Beach, Fla., 1985-91; pres. Pritchard Info., Inc., Palm Beach Gardens, Fla., 1991-92; v.p. Digital Directory Assistance, Bethesda, Md., 1993—. Columnist Online, Database; contbr. articles to profl. jours. Mem. Am. Bar Assn., Mich. Bar Assn. (judicial and profl. ethics com. 1982-84), Am. Assn. Law Libraries (cert.). Protestant. Avocations: aerobics, gourmet cooking. Office: Digital Directory Assistance Ste 405 6931 Arlington Rd Bethesda MD 20814

PRITCHETT, CHARLES HERMAN, political science educator; b. Latham, Ill., Feb. 9, 1907; s. Charles and Anna Margaret (Nottelmann) P.; m. Marguerite A. Lentner, July 27, 1937; children: Jean Charla, Philip Lentner. AB, Millikin U., 1926; PhD, U. Chgo., 1937. Rsch. asst. U. Chgo., 1934, asst. prof. polit. sci., 1940-46, assoc. prof., 1946-52, prof., 1952-69, acting chmn. dept., 1948-49, chmn. dept., 49-55, 58-64; rsch. assoc. TVA, 1934-37; rsch. assoc. pub. adminstrn. com. Social Sci. Rsch. Coun., 1937-38, post-doctoral research fellow, 1938-39; Ford prof. govtl. affairs, 1958-59; Bacon lectr. constn. Boston U., 1957; Dillon lectr. law and govt. U. S.D. 1957; Guy Stanton Ford lectr. U. Minn., 1959; vis. prof. Stanford, 1966; prof. U.Calif. at Santa Barbara, 1965-67, 69-89; faculty rsch. lectr. U. Calif., 1975, emeritus prof., 1975-89. Author: The Tennessee Valley Authority: A Study in Public Administration, 1943, The Roosevelt Court, 1948, Civil

Liberties and the Vinson Court, 1954, The Political Offender and the Warren Court, 1958, The American Constitution, 3d edit, 1977, Congress Versus the Supreme Court, 1960, Courts Judges and Politics, 4th edit, 1986, American Constitutional Issues, 1962, The Third Branch of Government, 1963, The American Constitutional System, 5th edit, 1981; co-author: The Revolutionary Theme in Contemporary America, 1965, American Government in World Perspective, 5th edit, 1981, The Presidency Reappraised, 2d edit, 1977, The Federal System in Constitutional Law, 1978, Essays on the Constitution of the United States, 1978, Constitutional Civil Liberties, 1984; Contbr. articles to sci. revs. Dir. Nat. Endowment for Humanities summer seminar, 1975; Residential Fellowships seminar, 1977; adminstrv. analyst Dept. Labor, 1939; Staff Commn. Orgn. Exec. Branch Govt. (Hoover Commn.), 1948. Fellow Am. Acad. Arts and Scis.; mem. Am. Polit. Sci. Assn. (pres. 1963-64), Am. Bar Assn. (com. electoral col. reform 1966). Home: 900 Calle De Los Amigos Apt 6N Santa Barbara CA 93105-4436

PRITCHETT, SAMUEL TRAVIS, finance and insurance educator, researcher; b. Emporia, Va., Dec. 18, 1938; s. Harvey Eugene and Mary (Brown) P.; m. Bertha Yates, Feb. 20, 1960; children: John Travis, Meri Katherine. BS in Bus. Adminstrn., Va. Poly. Inst. and State U., 1960, MS in Bus. Adminstrn., 1967; DBA, Ind. U., 1969. CLU, ChFC, CPCU. Claim rep. Equitable Life Assurance Soc., Richmond, Va., 1960-64, asst. div. claim mgr., 1964-65; asst. prof. bus. adminstrn. U. Richmond, 1969-70; asst. prof. ins. Va. Commonwealth U., Richmond, 1970-72, assoc. prof. ins., 1972-73; assoc. prof. fin. and ins. U. S.C., Columbia, 1973-76, prof. fin. and ins., 1976—; J.H. Fellers prof., 1981-83, W.F. Hipp prof. ins., 1983—; acad. dir. MBA program, 1993—; chair Risk Theory Soc., Columbus, Ohio, 1987-88; acad. dir. internat. exec. devel. program Bamerindus Seguros, Curtiba, Brazil, 1995. Author: Risk and Insurance, 6th edit., 1989, Stock Life Insurance Company Profitability, 1986, Individual Annuities as a Source of Retirement Income, 2d edit., 1982, An Economic Analysis of Workers' Compensation in South Carolina, 1994; assoc. editor Jour. Risk and Ins. 1982-86, editor, 1987-91; assoc. editor Fin. Svcs. Rev., 1989—; mem. acad. rev. bd. Jour. Fin. Planning, 1990-91; mem. editorial bd. Jour. Bus. Rsch., 1976-83, Am. Jour. Small Bus., 1975-79; contbr. articles to profl. jours, asst. editor Jour. Am. Soc. of CLU & ChFC, 1993—; editorial adv. bd. Benefits Quarterly, 1993—. Mem. S.C. Joint Ins. Study Com., 1981-86, 89—. Mem. Am. Risk and Ins. Assn. (pres. 1980-81), Acad. Fin. Svcs. (pres. 1987-88), So. Risk and Ins. Assn. (pres. 1977-78), Fin. Mgmt. Assn., Profl. Ins. Agts. Found. (named Ins. Educator of Yr. 1989), Beta Gamma Sigma (pres. chpt. 1980-81), Gamma Iota Sigma (nat. trustee 1976-92). Home: 7740 Castleton Ln Columbia SC 29223-2508 Office: U SC Coll Bus Columbia SC 29208

PRITCHETT, THOMAS RONALD, retired metal and chemical company executive; b. Colorado City, Tex., Sept. 2, 1925; s. John Thomas and Meddie Omeira (Terry) P.; m. Mary Margaret Hallenbeck, Dec. 23, 1948; children: Rhonda Jean, Thomas Rand, Rebecca Ann. BS in Chemistry and ChemE., U. Tex., 1948, MS, 1949, PhD, 1951. Registered profl. engr. Calif. Rsch. chemist Def. Rsch. Lab., Austin, Tex., 1948-51, Monsanto Chem. Co., Dayton, Ohio, 1951-52; sect. head, rsch. investigator, asst. dir., tech. mgr. Kaiser Aluminum & Chem. Corp., Pleasanton, Calif., 1952-68, v.p., dir. rsch., 1968-89; cons. Alamo, Calif., 1989—. Contbr. articles to profl. jours. Mem. adv. bd. Sch. Engring. U. Calif.-Berkeley. Served with U.S. Army, 1944-46. Fellow Am. Soc. Metals; mem. AIME, Aluminum Assn. (chmn. tech. com. and acad. com.), Nat. Assn. Corrosion Engrs., Am. Chem. Soc., Electrochem. Soc., Materials Properties Council (bd. dirs.), Sigma Xi, Phi Lambda Upsilon. Home and Office: 1430 Laurenita Way Alamo CA 94507-1133

PRITCHETT, SIR VICTOR SAWDON, author; b. Ipswich, Eng., Dec. 16, 1900; s. Sawdon and Beatrice (Martin) P.; m. Dorothy Roberts, Oct. 2, 1936; children: Josephine, Oliver. Ed., Alleyn's Sch., Dulwich; D.Litt. (hon.), Leeds U., 1973, Columbia U., 1978, U. Sussex, 1980, Harvard U., 1985. Free-lance journalist France, Ireland, Spain and U.S., 1921-28; lit. critic New Statesman, London, 1928-78; dir. New Statesman, 1951-78; Christian Gauss lectr. Princeton U., 1953; Beckman prof. U. Calif., Berkeley, 1960; writer-in-residence Smith Coll., 1966-71; Zisskind prof. Brandeis U., Waltham, Mass., 1969; vis. prof. Sch. Fine Arts, Columbia U., 1972; Clark lectr. Cambridge (Eng.) U., 1969, Vanderbilt U., 1981. Author: Marching Spain, 1928, Clare Drummer, 1929, The Spanish Virgin, 1930, Elopement into Exile, 1932, Nothing Like Leather, 1935, You Make Your Own Life, 1938, It May Never Happen, 1945, The Living Novel, 1949, Mr. Beluncle, 1951, The Spanish Temper, 1954, Books in General, 1962, In My Good Books, 1953, The Working Novelist, 1965, When My Girl Comes Home, 1961, Dead Man Leading, 1949, The Key to My Heart, 1963, London Perceived, 1962, The Offensive Traveller, 1964, New York Proclaimed, 1965, (with Elizabeth Bowen and Graham Greene) Why Do I Write?, 1948, Dublin: A Portrait, 1967, A Cab at the Door, 1967, Blind Love, 1970, Meredith's English Comedy, 1970, Midnight Oil, 1971, Balzac, 1973, The Camberwell Beauty, 1974, The Gentle Barbarian: Turgenev: Selected Stories, 1978, The Myth Makers, 1979, On the Edge of the Cliff, 1980, The Tale Bearers (essays), 1980, Collected Stories, 1981, More Collected Stories, 1983, The Turn of the Year, 1984, The Oxford Book of Short Stories, 1981, Man of Letters (essays), 1986, Chekhov, 1987, A Careless Widow, 1989, At Home and Abroad, 1989, Lasting Impressions (essays), 1990, Complete Short Stories, 1990, Complete Essays, 1992; contbr. stories to leading mags. Decorated comdr. Order Brit. Empire, 1968, created knight, 1975, Companion of Honor, 1993; recipient Royal Soc. Lit. award, 1969, 87, W.H. Smith award, 1990, Elmer Holmes Bobst award NYU, 1991, Golden Pen award Internat. PEN, 1993. Mem. Soc. Authors (pres. 1978). Clubs: Savile (London), Beefsteak (London). Address: 12 Regents Park Terr, London NW1, England

PRITIKIN, DAVID T., lawyer; b. Freeport, Ill., May 2, 1949. AB summa cum laude, Cornell U., 1971; JD magna cum laude, Harvard U., 1974. Bar: Ill. 1974, U.S. Ct. Appeals (9th cir.) 1975, U.S. Ct. Appeals (7th cir.) 1976, U.S. Supreme Ct. 1977, U.S. Ct. Appeals (fed. cir.) 1993. Ptnr. Sidley & Austin, Chgo. Office: Sidley & Austin 1 First Nat Plz Chicago IL 60603

PRITIKIN, JAMES B., lawyer, employee benefits consultant; b. Chgo., Feb. 18, 1939; s. Stan and Anne (Schwartz) P.; m. Barbara Cheryl Demovsky, Apr. 20, 1968 (dec. 1988); children: Gregory, David, Randi; m. Mary Szatkowski, July 7, 1990; 1 child, Peyton. BS, U. Ill., 1961; JD, DePaul U., 1965. Bar: Ill. 1965, U.S. Dist. Ct. (no. dist.) Ill. 1965, U.S. Supreme Ct. 1988; cert. matrimonial arbitrator. Sole practice Chgo., 1965-68, 1984—; ptnr. Sudak, Grubman, Pritikin, Rosenthal & Feldman, Chgo., 1969-80, Pritikin & Sohn, Chgo., 1980-84; pres. Prepaid Benefits Plans Inc., Chgo., 1978—. Fellow Internat. Acad. Matrimonial Lawyers; mem. Acad. Matrimonial Lawyers; mem. ABA, Ill. Bar Assn., Chgo. Bar Assn. (cir. ct. Cook County liaison com.), Chgo. Pub. Schs. Alumni Assn. (v.p. 1984—). Office: 221 N La Salle St Chicago IL 60601-1206

PRITIKIN, ROLAND I., ophthalmologic surgeon, writer, lecturer; b. Chgo., Jan. 9, 1906; s. Edward and Bluma (Saval) P.; m. Jeanne DuPre Moore, May 25, 1940 (dec. May 1988); children: Gloria Anne, Karin (Mrs. Craig Howard Heiser). B.S., Loyola U., 1928; M.D. 1930; diploma, U.S. Army Command and Gen. Staff Coll., 1964. Diplomate: Am. Bd. Ophthalmology. Eye department Loyola U. School Medicine, 1933-35; resident Ill. Eye and Ear Infirmary, 1936-38, staff, 1939-48; vis. eye surgeon, Shikarpur, Sind, Pakistan, under Sir Henry Holland, 1939, 57, 60, 63, 66, 71, vis. eye surgeon Ethiopia, 1972; cons. Rockford industries, 1946—; pvt. practice ophthalmology Rockford, 1946—; pres. staff Winnebago County (Ill.) Hosp., 1950; lecture, research tour, Western Europe, Near and Middle East, 1951, vis. eye surgeon, Pakistan, 1960; cons. in ophthalmology HHS; hearing officer Social Security Adminstrn.; vis. eye clinics Vienna, Zurich, Paris, 1934. Author: Essentials of Ophthalmology, 1950, 3d edit., 1975, World War Three Is Inevitable, 1976; contbr. Americana supplements, 1946-80, reg. vols., 1955-72, articles on ophthalmology various med. jours., also sects. on spectacles and contact lenses to Acad. Am. Ency. Med. Res. Officers; chmn. meeting on computers in ophthalmology Internat. Symposium on Bio-Engring. in Ophthalmology, Haifa, Israel, 1975, Ctr. For Global Security, 1978—; life mem. Weizmann Inst., Sci. Served as col. M.C. AUS, 1941-45; brig. gen. Ill. N.G., ret. Recipient 1st award World Medical assn., 1964; Quetta Mission Medal, 1964; Physician's Recognition award AMA, 1972, 75, 77, 83, 86, 89, 92, Cert. award VFW, 1986, Cert. award Chapel of the Four Chaplains, 1980, Super Sr. award Winnebago County Coun. on Aging, 1991, Cert. Appreciation for 25 yrs. vol. cons. ophthalmology U.S.

Army Health Svcs. Command; named Commodore State of W.Va., 1980, Ky. Col., 1982; decorated Army Commendation medal, 1965, Order St. John of Jerusalem by Queen Elizabeth II, 1970; promoted to Comdr. by Queen Elizabeth II, 1993. Fellow Indsl. Med. Assn., Am. Med. Writers Assn., Soc. Mil. Ophthalmologists (bd. govs., 1st life), AMA, A.C.S., Internat. Coll. Surgeons, AAAS, Am. Geriatrics Soc., Royal Soc. Health, Am. Coll. Nuclear Medicine (distinguished mem., founding mem.), Instituto Barraquer, Barcelona; assoc. Royal Soc. Medicine London; mem. Internat. Assn. Secs. Ophthalmol. and Otolaryngol. Socs. (editor ophthalmology 1973-80), Ill., Winnebago County med. socs., Am. Nuclear Soc., Am. Acad. Ophthalmology and Otolaryngology, Chgo. Ophthal. Soc., Assn. Mil. Surgeons U.S., Rock River Valley Ophthalmology Assn. (sec. 1978—), World Med. Assn., Pan-Am. Assn. Ophthalmology, Am. Assn. History of Medicine, Assn. Am. Phys. and Surg., Internat. Assn. Prevention of Blindness, Joseph Waring Meml. Library Assn. History of Medicine, Soc. Med. Cons. to Armed Forces, N.Y. Acad. Scis., Contact Lens Soc. of Ophthalmologists, Nat. Soc. Prevention Blindness, Henry Holland Hosps. Alumni Assn. and Fund (pres.), Internat. Assn. Against Trachoma, Assn. Research Ophthalmology, Soc. Nuclear Medicine, Pan Am. Soc. Ophthalmic Microsurgery (charter), Ophthalmol. Soc. Canary Islands (hon.), Internat. Soc. History Medicine (hon.), Am. Coll. Eye Surgeons (life mem.), C. of C., 33d Div. War Vets. Assn. (surgeon 1975-85), Am. Legion, Res. Officers Assn. U.S., Internat. Agy. Prevention Blindness, Ophthalmol. Soc. Pakistan (life), others. Club: Univ. (Rockford). Inventor surg. and diagnostic equipment for the eye. Home: Independence Village 3655 N Alpine Rd Apt B-302 Rockford IL 61114-7324 Office: Talcott Bldg Rockford IL 61101

PRITSKER, A. ALAN B., engineering executive, educator; b. Phila., Feb. 5, 1933; s. Robert and Gertrude (Liebowitz) P.; m. Anne Gruner, 1956; children: Caryl DuBrock, Pamela Poteet, Kenneth, Jeffrey. B.S.E.E., Columbia U., 1955, M.S. in Indsl. Engring., 1956; Ph.D., Ohio State U., 1961; DSc (hon.), Ariz. State U., 1992. Registered profl. engr., Tex., Ariz. Engr. Battelle Inst., 1956-62; Prof. engring. Ariz. State U., Tempe, 1962-69; prof. engring. Va. Poly. Inst., Blacksburg, 1969-70; prof. engring. Purdue U., West Lafayette, Ind., 1970-81, adj. prof. engring., 1981—; pres. Pritsker Corp., West Lafayette, 1973-86, 91—, chmn., 1973—; cons. Rand Corp., Gen. Electric Co., Gen. Motors Corp., Bethlehem Steel Co. Author: Simulation With Gasp IV, 1974, Modeling and Analysis Using Q-Gert Networks, 1979, Management Decision Making, 1984, Introduction to Simulation and SLAM II, 1986, TESS: The Extended Simulation Support System, 1987, SLAM II Network Models for Decision Support, 1989, Papers, Experiences, Perspectives, 1990. Recipient Gilbreth Indsl. Engring. award Am. Inst. Indsl. Engrs., 1991. Fellow Inst. Indsl. Engrs. (Rsch. and Innovation award 1978, Gilbreth award 1991); mem. NAE, Inst. Mgmt. Scis. (coll. on simulation, Disting. Svc. award 1991), Ops. Rsch. Soc. Am. Office: Pritsker Corp PO Box 2413 West Lafayette IN 47906-0413

PRITZKER, JAY ARTHUR, lawyer; b. Chgo., Aug. 26, 1922; s. Abraham Nicholas and Fanny (Doppelt) P.; m. Marian Friend, Aug. 31, 1947; children: Nancy (dec.), Thomas, John, Daniel, Jean. BSc, Northwestern U., 1941, JD, 1947. Bar: Ill. 1947. Asst. custodian Alien Property Adminstrn., 1947; pvt. practice law Chgo.; ptnr. firm Pritzker & Pritzker, 1948—; chmn. bd. dirs. Hyatt Corp., Hyatt Internat., Marmon Group, Inc.; bd. dirs. Royal Caribbean Cruise Lines; ptnr. Chgo. Mill & Lumber Co., Mich.-Calif. Lumber Co. Life trustee U. Chgo. Lt. USN, WW II. Mem. ABA, Chgo. Bar Assn. Clubs: Standard (Chgo.), Comml. (Chgo.), Lake Shore (Chgo.), Arts (Chgo.), Vince (Chgo.). Office: Dalfort Corp 7701 Lemmon Ave Dallas TX 75209

PRITZKER, LEON, statistician, consultant; b. N.Y.C., June 26, 1922; s. Harry and Sophie (Greene) P.; m. Mary Anne Watts; children: William Earl, David Ronald, Paul Mark, Carol Ann, Phillip Joseph. BS, CCNY, 1942; MA, U. Pa., 1947. Statistician U.S. Bur. of Census, Washington, 1947-61, chief response rsch. br., 1961-67; dir. mktg. info. svcs. Anheuser-Busch Cos. St. Louis, 1967-73, dir. mgmt. systems, 1973-84; exec. v.p., staff ops. Campbell Taggart, Inc., Dallas, 1985-90; cons., 1990—; vis. faculty Case Inst. Tech., Cleve., 1954-55; cons. Cen. Statis. Bur., Govt. Israel, Jerusalem, 1961, Inst. Stats., Govt. Turkey, Ankara, 1967. Contbr. articles to profl. jours. With U.S. Army, 1943-46. Fellow Am. Statis. Assn.; mem. Ops. Rsch. Soc., Internat. Assn. Survey Statisticians.

PRITZKER, NICHOLAS J., diversified services corporation executive. Formerly exec. v.p. devel. Hyatt Corp., Chgo.; pres. Hyatt Devel. Corp., Chgo. Office: Hyatt Devel Corp 200 W Madison St Chicago IL 60606-3414

PRITZKER, ROBERT ALAN, manufacturing company executive; b. Chgo., June 30, 1926; s. Abram Nicholas and Fanny (Doppelt) P.; m. Mayari Sargent; children: James, Linda, Karen, Matthew , Liesel. B.S. in Indsl. Engring., Ill. Inst. Tech., Chgo., 1946; postgrad. in bus. adminstrn., U. Ill. Engaged in mfg., 1946—; chief exec. officer, pres., dir. Marmon Corp., Chgo., Marmon Indsl. Corp., Chgo.; pres., dir. The Colson Group, Inc., Marmon Holdings, Inc., Marmon Industries, Inc., Chgo.; bd. dirs. Hyatt Corp., Chgo., Dalfort Corp., Union Tank Car Co.; vis. prof. Oxford U.; chmn. Nat. Assn. Mfrs. Chmn. bd. Pritzker Found., Chgo.; trustee, chmn. Ill. Inst. Tech., Chgo. Symphony Orch.; immediate past chmn. Field Mus. of Natural History; bd. dirs. Rush-Presbyn.-St. Luke's Med. Ctr. Mem. NAE, Nat. Assn. Mfrs. (former chmn.). Office: Marmon Group Inc 225 W Washington St Chicago IL 60606-3418

PRITZKER, THOMAS JAY, lawyer, business executive; b. Chgo., June 6, 1950; s. Jay Arthur and Marian (Friend) P.; m. Margot Lyn Barrow-Sicree, Sept. 4, 1977; children—Jason, Benjamin, David. B.A., Claremont Men's Coll, 1971; M.B.A., U. Chgo., 1972, J.D., 1976. Assoc. Katten, Muchin, Zavis, Pearl and Galler, Chgo., 1976-77; exec. v.p. Hyatt Corp., Chgo., 1977-80, pres., 1980—; chmn. bd. Hyatt Hotels Corp., Chgo., 1980-86, 1988; chmn. exec. com. Hyatt Hotels Corp., 1986-88; ptnr. Pritzker & Pritzker, Chgo., 1976—; pres. Rosemont Shipping, Chgo., 1980-86; chmn. Health Care Compare Corp.; bd. dirs. Dalfort, Chgo. Trustee Art. Inst. Chgo., 1988—; chmn. Indo-U.S Subcommn. Mem. ABA, Ill. Bar Assn., Chgo. Bar Assn. Clubs: Standard (Chgo.); Lake Shore Country (Glencoe, Ill.). Office: Hyatt Corp 200 W Madison St Fl 38 Chicago IL 60606-3400

PRITZLAFF, JOHN CHARLES, JR., former state senator; b. Milw., May 10, 1925; s. John C. and Elinor (Gallun) P.; m. Mary Dell Olin, Feb. 10, 1951; children: Ann, John, Barbara, Richard. B.A., Princeton U., 1949. Pres., John Pritzlaff Hardware Co., Milw., 1957-59; v.p. Arrow Valve Co., Phoenix, 1959-60; exec. v.p. Oxford Life Ins. Co., Scottsdale, Ariz., 1960-63; v.p. Republic Properties, Scottsdale, 1961-67; chmn. bd. Republic Properties, 1963-67; pres. Rockmount Mgmt. Corp., 1967-86; treas. Seamair Farm Inc.; dir. Marshall & Ilsey Trust Co. Ariz.; U.S. ambassador to Malta, 1969-72; mem. Ariz. senate, 1975-82, minority whip, 1977-78, chmn. appropriations com., 1979-83; mem. Ariz. Ho. of Reps., 1963-69, chmn. appropriations com., 1966-69. Mem. Republican Nat. Fin. Com., 1968-69; bd. dirs. Santa Barbara Botanic Gardens, Ariz. nat. chpts. Nature Conservancy. Served with AUS, 1943-45. Home: PO Box 202 Scottsdale AZ 85252-0202 Office: 4419 N Scottsdale Rd Scottsdale AZ 85251-3334

PRIVALOV, PETER L., biology and biophysics educator; b. Tbilisi, Georgia, Russia, July 25, 1932; came to U.S., 1991; m.; 2 children. M of Physics, U. Tbilisi, 1956; postgrad. fellow in biophysics inst. physics, Gergian Acad. Scis., Tbilisi, 1956-59; PhD, Tbilisi U., 1964; DSc, Inst. Biophysics, Acad. Scis. USSR, 1971. Rsch. scientist inst. physics Georgian Acad. Scis., Tbilisi, 1959-64, sr. rsch. scientist, 1964-66; head lab. thermodynamics inst. protein rsch. Acad. Scis. USSR, Puschino, Moscow Region, 1966-91, prof., 1984, corr. mem., 1984; prof. biology and biophysics Johns Hopkins U., Balt., 1991—; vis. prof. Reginsburg U., Germany, 1990, dept. biology and inst. biophysical rsch. on macromolecular assemblies Johns Hopkins U., 1991; mem. scientific coun. inst. protein rsch. Acad. Scis. USSR, 1967—; inst. biophysics, 1972-85, scientific coun. molecular biology Moscow State U., 1985-91; internat. lectr. and PhD advisor in field. Mem. adv. bd. Jour. Biophysical Chem.; contbr. numerous articles to profl. jours.; 4 patents in microcalorimetry. Mem. Interunion Comsn. Biothermodynamics, 1976-84, Com. Lenin and State Prizes USSR, 1979-91. Grantee NIH, NSF; recipient State prize USSR, 1978, Alexander Humboldt Rsch. award 1989. Mem. Russian Acad. Scis., Am. Biophysical Soc., Biochemical Soc., Protein Soc.

Avocations: gardening, classical music. Office: Johns Hopkins U 3400 N Charles St Baltimore MD 21218-2608

PRIVAT, JEANNETTE MARY, bank librarian; b. Seattle, May 2, 1938; d. Glenn McKenzie and Katherine (VanDerveer) P. BA in Bus. Adminstrn., U. Wash., 1960, MLS, 1969. Asst. libr. United Control Corp., Redmond, Wash., 1960-64, libr., 1964-68; libr. Seattle-First National Bank, Seattle, 1968-75, asst. v.p. and mgr., 1975-93; exec. dir. King County Libr. System Found., Seattle, 1993—; mem. vis. com. U. Wash. Grad. Sch. Libr. and Info. Sci., 1981—, chmn., 1991—; mem. adv. bd. extension libr. mgmt. program U. Washington, 1989—. Bd. trustees Northwest Chamber Orch., Seattle, 1986—, pres. 1987-92, exec. com., 1992—. Named disting. alumnus Wash. Grad. Sch. Libr. and Info. Sci. Fellow Spl. Librs. Assn. (nat. bd. dirs. 1977-79, various offices 1966-89). Office: King County Libr Sys Found 300 8th Ave N Seattle WA 98109

PRIVETT, HOWARD J., lawyer; b. Monahans, Tex., Aug. 27, 1929. Student, Pepperdine U., 1946-50; LLB summa cum laude, U. Calif., San Francisco, 1957. Bar: Calif. 1958. Ptnr. Baker & Hostetler, L.A. Editor-in-chief Hastings Law Jour., 1956-57. Fellow Am. Coll. Trial Lawyers; mem. State Bar Calif., Chancery Club. Office: Baker & Hostetler 600 Wilshire Blvd Los Angeles CA 90017

PRIVOTT, W. J., agricultural products company executive; b. 1938. BS in Chem. Engring., N.C. State U., 1961, PhD, 1964. With Monsanto Co., St. Louis, 1964-91, pres., 1991-94; CEO, pres. Novus Internat. Inc., St. Louis, 1994—. Office: Novus Internat Inc 530 Maryville Centre Dr Saint Louis MO 63141*

PRIZER, CHARLES JOHN, chemical company executive; b. Lake Forest, Ill., Apr. 24, 1924; s. Charles Sumner and Josephine Mary (Jansz) P.; m. Dorothy Gore, June 15, 1944; children: John, Sharon Lee, Mark Sumner, Linda Ann. B.S., U. Ill., 1944; M.S., Drexel U., 1956. With Eastman Kodak Co., 1944-46, Edwal Labs., 1946-51; with Rohm & Haas Co., Phila., 1951-85; v.p., dir. Rohm & Haas Co., 1978-83, group v.p. corp. ops., 1983-85; exec. v.p. Clean Sites, Inc., Alexandria, Va., 1986; prin. Mill Creek Co., 1987-93, Prizer & Wilkinson, 1988-93, Dotsu Enterprises, Inc., 1991-93, CJP Enterprises, Inc., 1992—. Mem. Am. Inst. Chem. Engrs., Am. Chem. Soc. Office: 4325 Gulf of Mexico Dr Ste 307 Longboat Key FL 34228

PRIZZI, JACK ANTHONY, investment banking executive; b. Rochester, N.Y., July 5, 1935; s. Samuel Anthony and Mary Ann (Emanuele) P.; B.S. in Chemistry, Va. Mil. Inst., 1956; M.S. in Phys. Chemistry, U. Va., 1961, M.B.A., 1963; m. Geraldine A. Bias, Feb. 16, 1957 (div. 1971); children—Lynne Marie, Michael Vincent, Karen Annette. Chem. engr. E.I. du-Pont DeNemours & Co., Inc., Niagara Falls, N.Y., 1956-57; engr. Project Mercury, NASA, 1959; mgr. planning and devel. PPG Industries, Pitts., 1963-68; gen. mgr. Process Components Inc., Norfolk, Va., 1968-70; ptnr. Alan Patricof Assocs., N.Y.C., 1970-74, Beacon Ptnrs., N.Y.C., 1974-76, 77-79, Stuart Bros., N.Y.C., 1976-77; v.p. Walter E. Heller & Co., exec. v.p. Heller Capital Services Inc., N.Y.C., 1979-84; sr. v.p. DnC Am. Banking Corp., N.Y.C., 1984-86; mng. dir. DnC Capital Corp., 1986-89; pres., CEO Jack A. Prizzi & Co., 1989—; spl. ltd. ptnr. Harvest Ptnrs., 1993—; pres. U.S. Fin. Recoveries, Inc., 1995—; bd. dirs. Tex. Meridian Resources Corp.; instr. advanced grades N.Y. Power Squadron; chmn. bd., trustees Components Recs. Inc. Vol. Urban Cons. Group. Served to capt. U.S. Army, 1957-59. Grantee Office Naval Research, 1960, Calif. Research Corp., 1960-61. Mem. Assn. for Corp. Growth, Am. Chem. Soc., Raven Soc., N.Y. Athletic Club. Home: 21 W 58th St Apt 12E New York NY 10019-1634 Office: Harvest Ptnrs 767 3d Ave New York NY 10017

PRO, PHILIP MARTIN, federal judge, lawyer; b. Richmond, Calif., Dec. 12, 1946; s. Leo Martin and Mildred Louise (Beck) P.; m. Dori Sue Hallas, Nov. 13, 1982; 1 child, Brenda Kay. BA, San Francisco State U., 1968; JD Golden Gate U., 1972. Bar: Calif. 1972, Nev. 1973, U.S. Ct. Appeals (9th cir.) 1973, U.S. Dist. Ct. Nev. 1973, U.S. Supreme Ct. 1976. Pub. defender, Las Vegas, 1973-75; asst. U.S. atty., Dist. Nev., Las Vegas, 1975-78; ptnr. Semenza, Murphy & Pro, Reno, 1978-79; dep. atty. gen. State of Nev., Carson City, 1979-80; U.S. magistrate U.S. Dist. Ct. Nev., Las Vegas, 1980-87; U.S. dist. judge, 1987—; instr. Atty. Gen.'s Advocacy Inst., Nat. Inst. Trial Advocacy, 1992; chmn. com. adminstrn. of magistrate judge system Jud. Conf. U.S., 1993—. Bd. dirs. NCCJ, Las Vegas, 1982—, mem. program com. and issues in justice com. Mem. ABA, Fed. Judges Assn. (bd. dirs. 1992—), Nev. State Bar Assn., Calif. State Bar Assn., Nev. Judges Assn. (instr.), Assn. Trial Lawyers Am., Nev. Am. Inn Ct. (pres. 1989—), Ninth Cir. Jury (instructions com.), Nat. Conf. U.S. Magistrates (sec.), Nev. Am. Inn of Ct. (pres. 1989-91). Republican. Episcopalian. Office: US Dist Ct 341 Fed Bldg 300 Las Vegas Bldv S Las Vegas NV 89101

PROBASCO, CALVIN HENRY CHARLES, clergyman, college administrator; b. Petaluma, Calif., Apr. 5, 1926; s. Calvin Warren and Ruth Charlene (Winans) P.; m. Nixie June Farnsworth, Feb. 14, 1947; children—Calvin, Carol, David, Ruth. B.A. cum laude, Biola Bible Coll., La Mirada, Calif., 1953; D.D. (hon.), Talbot Theol. Sem., La Mirada, 1983. Ordained to ministry, 1950. Pastor Sharon Baptist Ch., El Monte, Calif., 1951-58, Carmichael Bible Ch., Calif., 1958—; pres. Sacramento Bible Inst., Carmichael, 1968—. Mem. nat. Ind. Fundamental Chs. Am. (rec. sec. 1978-81, pres. 1981-84, 1st v.p. 1987-88), Delta Epsilon Chi. Republican. Office: Carmichael Bible Ch 7100 Fair Oaks Blvd Carmichael CA 95608-6409

PROBERT, WALTER, lawyer, educator; b. Portland, Oreg., Jan. 13, 1925; s. Raymond and Mildred Marie (Pyburn) P.; m. Barbara Louise Stevenson, Mar. 22, 1952; children: Richard Walter, James Stevenson. Student, Alfred U., 1944; B.S., U. Oreg., 1948, J.D., 1951; J.S.D. (Grad. fellow), Yale U., 1957. Bar: Oreg. 1951. Practiced in Portland, 1951-52; asst. prof. Western Res. U., 1953-57, asso. prof., 1957-59; prof. U. Fla., Gainesville, 1959—; endowed prof. U. Fla., 1985—; vis. prof. Northwestern U., 1960-61, U. Tex., summer 1970, U. Wash., 1972-73; vis. research prof. U. Denver, 1966-67; lectr. Balliol Coll., Oxford U., 1968; dir. law and social sci. program NSF, 1973-74. Author: Law, Language, and Communication, 1972; faculty editor Western Res. U. Law Rev., 1953-59; contbr. articles to profl. jours. Served with AUS, 1943-47. Recipient grants for law-communication research. Mem. ATLA, Assn. Am. Law Schs. (mem. panel advocates), Oreg. Bar Assn., Internat. Philosophy of Law and Social Philosophy, Law and Soc. Assn., Am. Psychology-Law Soc., Am. Soc. Polit. and Legal Philosophy, Phi Beta Kappa, Order of Coif, Order of St. Ives, Delta Theta Phi. Home: 1522 SW 35th Pl Gainesville FL 32608-3530

PROBST, LAWRENCE F., III, computer company executive. BA, U. Del., 1972. Dist. sales mgr. Johnson & Johnson, 1972-80; nat. accounts mgr. The Clorox Co., 1980-82, Mediagenic (formerly Activision Inc.), 1982-84; pres., CEO Electronic Arts, San Mateo, Calif., 1984—. Office: Electronic Arts 1450 Fashion Island Blvd San Mateo CA 94404*

PROBSTEIN, RONALD FILMORE, mechanical engineering educator; b. N.Y.C., Mar. 11, 1928; s. Sidney and Sally (Rosenstein) P.; m. Irene Weindling, July 30, 1950; 1 child, Sidney. B.M.E., NYU, 1948; M.S.E., Princeton U., 1950, A.M., 1951, Ph.D., 1952; A.M. (hon.), Brown U., 1957. Research asst. physics N.Y. U., 1946-48, instr. engring. mechanics, 1947-48; research asst. dept. aero. engring. Princeton U., 1948-52, research assoc., 1952-53, asst. prof., 1953-54; asst. prof. divs. engring., applied math. Brown U., 1954-55, assoc. prof., 1955-59, prof., 1959-62; prof. mech. engring. M.I.T., 1962-89, Ford prof. engring., 1989—; Disting. prof. engring. U. Utah, 1973; sr. partner Water Purification Assos., Cambridge, 1974-82; chmn. bd. Water Gen. Corp., Cambridge, 1982-83; sr. corp. tech. advisor Foster-Miller, Inc., 1983—; commr. commn. on engring. and tech. systems NRC, 1980-83; sci. advisor to bd. Corrpro Cos., 1993—. Author: Hypersonic Flow Theory, 1959, Hypersonic Flow, Inviscid Flows, 1966, Water in Synthetic Fuel Production, 1978, Synthetic Fuels, 1982, Physicochemical Hydrodynamics, 1989, 2d edit., 1994; editor: Introduction to Hypersonic Flow, 1961, Physics of Shock Waves, 1966, Jour. PhysicoChem. Hydrodynamics, 1987-89; contbr. articles to profl. jours.; patentee in field. Guggenheim fellow, 1960-61. Fellow Am. Acad. Arts and Scis. (councilor 1975-79), Am. Phys. Soc., ASME (Freeman award 1971), AIAA, AAAS,

mem. NAE, Internat. Acad. Astronautics, Am. Inst. Chem. Engrs. Home: 5 Seaver St Brookline MA 02146-5714 Office: 77 Massachusetts Ave Cambridge MA 02139-4307

PROCHNOW, DOUGLAS LEE, lawyer; b. Omaha, Jan. 9, 1952; s. Albert Delmer and Betty Jean (Wood) P. BA with high distinction, U. Nebr., 1974; JD, Northwestern U., 1977. Bar: Ill. 1977, U.S. Dist. Ct. (no. dist.) Ill. 1977. Assoc. Wildman, Harrold, Allen & Dixon, Chgo., 1977-84, ptnr., 1985—. Spl. asst. corp. counsel City of Chgo., 1986-87. Mem. ABA, Ill. Bar Assn., Chgo. Bar Assn., Assn. Trial Lawyers Am. (assoc.), Ill. Trial Lawyers Assn., Soc. Trial Lawyers, Def. Rsch. Inst., Phi Beta Kappa, Phi Eta Sigma. Home: 1230 N State Pky Apt 6D Chicago IL 60610-2261 Office: Wildman Harrold Allen & Dixon 225 W Wacker Dr Chicago IL 60606-1229

PROCHNOW, HERBERT VICTOR, former government official, banker, author; b. Wilton, Wis., May 19, 1897; s. Adolph and Alvina (Liefke) P.; m. Laura Virginia Stinson, June 12, 1928 (dec. Aug. 1977); 1 child, Herbert Victor. BA, U. Wis., 1921, MA, 1922, LLD, 1956; PhD, Northwestern U., 1947, Northwestern U., 1963; LLD (hon.), LittD, Millikin U., 1952; LLD, Ripon Coll., Wis., 1950, Lake Forest Coll., 1964, Monmouth Coll., 1965, U. N.D., 1966; DHL, Thiel Coll., 1965. Prin. Kendall (Wis.) High Sch.; asst. prof. bus. adminstrn. Ind. U.; advt. mgr. Union Trust Co., Chgo.; officer First Nat. Bank of Chgo., pres., 1962-68, dir., 1960-68, hon. dir., 1968-73; former dir. Carter H. Golembe Assocs., Inc., 1972-76; dir. Banco di Roma, Chgo., 1973-87; columnist Chgo. Tribune, 1968-70; sec. fed. adv. coun. Fed. Res. System, 1945-94; apptd. spl. asst. to sec. of state, 1955, dep. under sec. of state for econ. affairs, 1955-56; alt. gov. for U.S. Internat. Bank and Internat. Monetary Fund, 1955-56; pres. Internat. Monetary Conf., 1968, now cons., hon mem. Co-author: The Next Century Is America's, 1938, Practical Bank Credit, 1963, (with Herbert V. Prochnow, Jr.) A Dictionary of Wit, Wisdom and Satire, 1962, The Public Speaker's Treasure Chest, 1976, rev. edit., 1986, The Successful Toastmaster, 1966, A Treasury of Humorous Quotations, 1969, The Changing World of Banking, 1973, The Toastmaster's Treasure Chest, 1979, rev. edit., 1988, A Treasure Chest of Quotations for All Occasions, 1983, (with Everett M. Dirksen) Quotation Finder, 1971; author: Great Stories from Great Lives (an anthology), 1944, Meditations on the Ten Commandments, 1944, The Toastmaster's Handbook, 1949, Term Loans and Theories of Bank Liquidity, 1949, Successful Speakers Handbook, 1951, 1001 Ways to Improve Your Conversations and Speeches, 1952, Meditations on the Beatitudes, 1952, The Speaker's Treasury of Stories for All Occasions, 1953, The Speaker's Handbook of Epigrams and Witticisms, 1955, Speakers Treasury for Sunday School Teachers, 1955, A Treasury of Stories, Illustrations, Epigrams and Quotations for Ministers and Teachers, 1956, The New Guide for Toastmasters, 1956, Meditations on The Lord's Prayer, 1957, The New Speaker's Treasury of Wit and Wisdom, 1958, A Family Treasury of Inspiration and Faith, 1958, The Complete Toastmaster, 1960, Speaker's Book of Illustrations, 1960, 1000 Tips and Quips for Speakers and Toastmasters, 1962, 1400 Ideas for Speakers and Toastmasters, 1964, Tree of Life, 1972, Speaker's Source Book, 1972, A Speaker's Treasury for Educators, Convocation Speakers, 1973, 1,000 Quips, Stories, and Illustrations for All Occasions, 1973, Toastmaster's Quips and Stories and How to Use Them, 1982; editor: American Financial Institutions, 1951, Determining the Business Outlook, 1954, The Federal Reserve System, 1960, World Economic Problems and Policies, 1965, The Five Year Outlook for Interest Rates, 1968, The One-Bank Holding Company, 1969, The Eurodollar, 1970, The Five Year Outlook for Interest Rates in the U.S. and Abroad, 1972, Dilemmas Facing the Nation, 1979, Bank Credit, 1981, Speaker's and Toastmaster's Handbook, 1990, 5100 Quotations for Speakers and Writers, 1992. Mem. O.S.S., 1942-45, U.S. delegation GATT, Geneva, 1956; del. Colombo Conf., Singapore, 1955, OECD, Paris, 1956; former lectr. Loyola U., Ind. U., Northwestern U.; bd. dir. grad. sch. of banking U. of Wis., 1945-81; trustee, cons. McCormick Theol. Sem.; hon. trustee Chgo. Sunday Evening Club. With AEF, 1918-19. Decorated Order of Vasa (Sweden), comdr. Cross Order of Merit (Fed. Republic of Germany); recipient Bus. Statesmanship award Harvard U. Bus. Sch. Assn. Chgo., 1965, Ayres Leadership award Stonier Grad. Sch. Banking, Rutgers U., 1966, Silver Plaque NCCJ, 1967. Mem. Chgo. Coun. on Fgn. Rels. (pres. 1966-67), Am. Econ. Assn., Chgo. Assn. Commerce and Industry (pres. 1964-65), Rotary, Beta Gamma Sigma (nat. honoree). Clubs: Comml., Glen View; Univ., Chgo., Union League (Chgo.), Bankers (past pres.). Home: 2950 Harrison St Evanston IL 60201-1249 Office: 1 First National Plz Chicago IL 60670

PROCHNOW, HERBERT VICTOR, JR., lawyer; b. Evanston, Ill., May 26, 1931; s. Herbert V. and Laura (Stinson) P.; m. Lucia Boyden, Aug. 6, 1966; children: Thomas Herbert, Laura. A.B., Harvard U., 1953, J.D., 1956; A.M., U. Chgo., 1958. Bar: Ill. 1957, U.S. Dist. Ct. (no. dist.) Ill. 1961. With 1st Nat. Bank Chgo., 1958-91, atty., 1961-70; sr. atty., 1971-73, counsel, 1973-91, adminstrv. asst. to chmn. bd., 1978-81; pvt. practice, 1991—. Author: (with Herbert V. Prochnow) A Treasury of Humorous Quotations, 1969, The Changing World of Banking, 1974, The Public Speaker's Treasure Chest, 1986, The Toastmaster's Treasure Chest, 1988; also articles in legal publs. Mem. ABA, Ill. Bar Assn., Chgo. Bar Assn. (chmn. com. internat. law 1970-71), Am. Soc. Internat. Law, Phi Beta Kappa. Clubs: Harvard (N.Y.C.); Chicago (Chgo.), Legal (Chgo.), Law (Chgo.), Onwentsia, Economic (Chgo.), University (Chgo.). Home: 949 Woodbine Pl Lake Forest IL 60045-2275 Office: 155 N Michigan Ave Chicago IL 60601-7511

PROCHNOW, JAMES R., lawyer; b. Hutchinson, Minn., Sept. 22, 1943. BA, Hamline U., 1965; JD, William Mitchell Law Sch., 1969. Bar: Minn. 1969, U.S. Supreme Ct. 1973, Colo. 1975. Staff civil divsn. Dept. Justice, Washington, 1973-74; legal counsel to Pres. The White House, Washington, 1974; ptnr. Baker & Hostetler, Denver. Editor in chief William Mitchell Opinion, 1968-69; antitrust notes editor The Barrister, 1978-81. Mem. ABA, Denver Bar Assn., Colo. Bar Assn., Assn. Trial Lawyers Am., Colo. Trial Lawyers Assn. Office: Baker & Hostetler 303 E 17th Ave Ste 1100 Denver CO 80203-1264

PROCKOP, DARWIN JOHNSON, biochemist, physician; b. Palmerton, Pa., Aug. 31, 1929; s. John and Sophie (Gurski) P.; m. Elinor Sacks, Apr. 15, 1961; children: Susan Elizabeth, David John. AB, Haverford Coll., 1951; MA, Oxford U., 1953; MD, U. Pa., 1956; PhD, George Washington U., 1962; DSc (hon.), U. Oulu, 1983, U. So. Fla., 1993. Investigator NIH, 1957-61; assoc., asst. prof., asso. prof. medicine and biochemistry U. Pa., Phila., 1961-72; prof., chmn. dept. biochemistry U. Medicine and Dentistry of N.J. (Rutgers Med. Sch.), Piscataway, N.J., 1972-86; prof., chmn. dept. biochemistry and molecular biology Jefferson Med. Coll., Phila., 1986—; dir. Jefferson Inst. Molecular Medicine. Contbr. articles to profl. jours.; research on collagen. Served with USPHS, 1958-61. Fulbright fellow Oxford U., 1951-53; NIH, grantee, 1961—; recipient Disting. Alumnus award George Wash. U., 1991, U. Pa., 1994. Mem. NAS, Inst. Medicine, Acad. Finland, Soc. Biol. Chemists, Am. Soc. Clin. Investigation, Am. Assn. Physicians, Phi Beta Kappa, Alpha Omega Alpha. Home: 291 Locust St Philadelphia PA 19106-3913 Office: Jefferson Med Coll 233 S 10th St Philadelphia PA 19107-5083

PROCTER, JOHN ERNEST, former publishing company executive; b. Gainesboro, Tenn., July 23, 1918; s. Leon and Mary (Poteet) P.; m. Jane Sprott, May 23, 1941; children: Mary Carol, Valere Kay. Student, Vanderbilt U., 1940-41, U. Miami (also extension div.), 1943-44, U. Tenn., 1946-50; LL.D. (hon.), Ohio No. U., 1971; D.L. (hon.), Ky. Wesleyan Coll., 1981. With Methodist Pub. House, Nashville, 1945-83; v.p., pub. Methodist Pub. House, 1964-70, pres., pub., 1970-83; dir. 3d Nat. Bank, Nashville. Bd. dirs. Tenn Council on Econ. Edn. Served to capt. USAAF and USAF, 1944-45, 50-52. Decorated Certificate of Valor; Air medal with 7 oak leaf clusters; D.F.C. Mem. Adminstrv. Mgmt. Soc. (past pres. Nashville, area. sec.-treas. 1967-68, Merit Key award 1961, Diamond Merit award 1967), Nashville C. of C. (past mem. bd. govs.), Assn. Am. Pubs. (past dir.). Clubs: Golf Club of Tenn., Belle Meade Golf & Country. *The modest success I have achieved is the result of an intense commitment to intellectual honesty, sensitivity to the needs of my associates, the setting of challenging and realistic goals, striving for efficiency by doing things right and being effective by doing the right things, always with faith in myself and my associates.*

PROCTOR, AMELIA DOLEMAN, mathematics educator; b. Occoquan, Va., Aug. 16, 1913; d. James Upshur and Mary Elveta (White) Doleman; m. Franklin Webster Proctor, Nov. 19, 1941. BS, Miner Tchrs. Coll., 1936; MA, NYU, 1953. Elem. tchr. Prince William County Pub. Sch., Quantico, Hickory Ridge and Dumfries, Va., 1937-40; sta. clk. Cencus Bur., Fed. Govt., Washington, 1940-41; jr. high math. tchr. D.C. Pub. Schs., Washington, 1941-63; spl. tchr. math. improvement program Dept. Math., Washington, 1963-65, asst. dir., 1965-70, ret., 1970; speaker and exhibitor in field. Inventor in field. Hon. fellow John F. Kennedy Libr. Found.; chmn. Girl Scouts U.S., Arlington, Va. and Washington; mem. Civic Assn. D.C. and Va., NAACP; founder Community Libr., Ebenezer Bapt. Ch., Occoquan, Va., 1973. Recipient trophy and cert. Ebenezer Bapt. Ch., 1961, 83, cert. No. Va. Mins. Wives, 1973, plaque Woodlawn United Meth. Ch., 1986, Woodlawn United Meth. Women and Men, 1985, St. James United Meth. Ch., 1989. Mem. Nat. Mus. Women in the Arts (charter 1988—). Democrat. Home: 7 Lansdown Cir Hampton VA 23666-1817

PROCTOR, BARBARA GARDNER, advertising agency executive, writer; b. Asheville, N.C.; d. William and Bernice (Baxter) Gardner; B.A. Talladega Coll., 1954; m. Carl L. Proctor, July 20, 1961 (div. Nov. 1963); 1 son, Morgan Eugene. Music critic, contbg. editor Down Beat Mag., Chgo., from 1958; internat. dir. Vee Jay Records, Chgo., 1961-64; copy supr. Post-Keyes-Gardner Advt., Inc., 1965-68, Gene Taylor Assos., 1968-69, North Advt. Agy., 1969-70; contbr. to gen. periodicals, from 1952; founder Proctor & Gardner Advt., Chgo., 1970—, now pres., chief exec. officer. Mem. Chgo. Urban League, Chgo. Econ. Devel. Corp. Bd. dirs. People United to Save Humanity, Better Bus. Bur. Cons. pub. relations and promotion, record industry. Recipient Armstrong Creative Writing award, 1954; awards Chgo. Fedn. Advt. Clubs, N.Y. Art Dirs. Club. Woman's Day; Frederick Douglass Humanitarian award, 1975; named Chgo. Advt. Woman of Year, 1974. Mem. Chgo. Media Women, Nat. Assn. Radio Arts and Sci., Women's Advt. Club, Cosmopolitan C. of C. (dir.), Female Execs. Assn., Internat. Platform Assn., Smithsonian Instn. Assos. Author TV documentary Blues for a Gardenia, 1963. Office: Proctor & Gardner Advt Inc 111 E Wacker Dr Ste 321 Chicago IL 60601

PROCTOR, CONRAD ARNOLD, physician; b. Ann Arbor, Mich., July 14, 1934; s. Bruce and Luena Marie (Crawford) P.; m. Phyllis Darlene Anderson, June 23, 1956; children: Sharon Darlene Proctor Heimbach, Barbara Jan Brown, David Conrad, Todd Bruce. MD, U. Mich., 1959, MS, 1964. Cert. Am. Bd. Otolaryngology. Intern St. Joseph Mercy Hosp., Ann Arbor, 1959-60; jr. clin. instr. Univ. Hosp., Ann Arbor, 1961-63, sr. clin. instr., 1963-65; chief dept. otolaryngology Munson Army Hosp., Ft. Leavenworth, Kans., 1965-67; mem. attending staff William Beaumont Hosp., Royal Oak, Mich., 1967—; instr. Am. Acad. Otolaryngology, Washington, 1968-82, guest examiner, Chgo., 1978-79; midwest dir. Macrocellular Cellular Phone Sys., 1990—. Author: Current Therapy in Otolaryngology, 1984-85; (booklet) Dietary Treatment of Meniere's Syndrome, 1983, Hyperinsulinemia and Tinnitus, 1988; (manual) Hereditary Sensorineural Hearing Loss, 1978, Etiology, Treatment of Fluid Retention in Meniere's Syndrome, 1992; (med. jour.) Abnormal Insulin Levels and Vertigo, 1981. Dir. Christian edn. Bloomfield Hills (Mich.) Bapt. Ch., 1969-72, fin. chmn., 1975-78, Sunday sch. tchr., 1967—. Served to capt. U.S. Army, 1965-67. Recipient 1st pl. award for med. rsch. Students Am. Med. Assn., 1959, Merit award Am. Acad. Otolaryngology, 1978; holder 4 world records Internat. Game Fish Assn. Mem. AMA, Mich. State Med. Assn., Oakland County Med. Assn., Am. Bd. Otolaryngology, ACS, Triological Soc., Otosclerosis Study Group, Internat. Game Fish Assn., Phi Eta Sigma, Phi Kappa Phi, Phi Beta Kappa. Republican. Clubs: Panangling Ltd. (Chgo.); Victors and Presidents (Ann Arbor). Avocations: baseball, football, tennis, fishing, basketball. Holder 4 Internat. Game Fish Assn. world records; veteran Arctic explorer. Home: 1645 Kirkway Ln Bloomfield Hills MI 48302-1360 Office: 3535 W 13 Mile Rd Royal Oak MI 48073-6700

PROCTOR, DONALD FREDERICK, otolaryngology educator, physician; b. Red Bank, N.J., Apr. 19, 1913; s. Frederick R. and Gertrude (Chauncey) P.; m. Janice Carson, June 10, 1937; children: Douglas, Nan. A.B., Johns Hopkins, 1933, M.D., 1937. Diplomate: Am. Bd. Otolaryngology. With otol. lab. Johns Hopkins Hosp., 1937-38, mem. clinical house staff, 1938-40; resident otolaryngology Balt. City Hosps., 1940-41; pvt. practice otolaryngology Med. Arts., Johns Hopkins, 1946-51, 58-73, prof. anesthesiology, 1951-55, 77-84, asst. prof. physiology, laryngology and otolaryngology, 1955-58, 77-84, prof. laryngology and otology, 1973-84, prof. environ. health sci., 1965-84, prof. emeritus, 1984—, chief bronchoscopic clinic, 1962-66, chief research program air hygiene, dept. environmental medicine, 1955—; with dept. physiology U. Rochester, 1946-47; fellow anesthesiology U. Pa., 1951-52. Author: Anesthesia and Otolaryngology, 1957, Tonsils and Adenoids in Childhood, 1960, Nose Paranasal Sinuses and Ears in Childhood, 1962, Breathing, Speech, and Song, 1980; editor: Respiratory Defense Mechanisms, 1977, The Nose, Upper Airway Physiology and Atmospheric Environment, 1982; author articles, book chpts. deafness, respiration, air hygiene, air pollution, mucous membrane. Fellow A.C.S., Am. Acad. Otolaryngology; mem. Am. Bronchoesophagol. Assn., Am. Indsl. Hygiene Assn., Air Pollution Control Assn., Am. Physiol. Soc., Phi Beta Pi, Sigma Xi. Club: 14 West Hamilton Street (Balt.). Home: 4300 N Charles St Apt 9-f Baltimore MD 21218-1052

PROCTOR, EDWARD GEORGE, lawyer; b. Chgo., July 16, 1929; s. Harold Proctor and Catherine Elliott; m. Kathleen Friend, Apr. 4, 1959; children: Brian, Diana, Edward, Laurel, Abigail, John. BS, Loyola U., Chgo., 1951; JD, Loyola U., 1953. Bar: Ill. 1953. From assoc. to ptnr. Kirkland & Ellis, Chgo., 1953-78; ptnr. Reuben & Proctor, Chgo., 1978-87, Isham, Lincoln, Beale (merger with Reuben & Proctor), Chgo., 1987-88, Hinshaw & Culbertson, Chgo., 1988—; adj. prof. Loyola U. Sch. of Law; trustee Loyola U.; chmn. bus. dept. Hinshaw & Culbertson. Co-chmn. Com. to Elect Mary Ann McMorrow to Ill. Supreme Ct., 1991-92; mem. Legal Assistance Found. Friends Com. Chgo.; former tchr. CCD classes St. Barnabas Ch., Chgo.; former fundraiser Mt. Carmel H.S., Morgan Park Acad., St. Ignatius Coll. Prep. Recipient Medal of Excellence Loyola U. Sch. Law, 1989, plaque of Appreciation Cath. Charities, 2 plaques of Appreciation Loyola Alumni Assn. Fellow ABA (life); mem. Ill. Bar Assn., Chgo. Bar Assn. (comml. fin. and transactions coms.), Bankruptcy Inst., Loyola Law Alumni Assn. (past pres.), Olympia Fields Country Club (past pres.), Lambda Alpha Internat. Roman Catholic. Avocation: golf. Office: Hinshaw & Culbertson 222 N LaSalle St Chicago IL 60601

PROCTOR, JESSE HARRIS, JR., political science educator; b. Durham, N.C., Sept. 3, 1924; s. Jesse Harris and Rosa Belle (Rogers) P.; m. Ella Jane Callahan, Mar. 27, 1948; children: Edward Sidney, Thomas Christopher, Kenneth Stuart. A.B., Duke U., 1948; M.A., Fletcher Sch. Law and Diplomacy, 1949; Ph.D., Harvard U., 1955. Instr., asst. prof. polit. sci. MIT, 1949-56; asst. prof., assoc. prof. polit. sci. Am. U. in Cairo, 1956-58, prof., 1991-92; asst. prof., then assoc. prof. and prof. polit. sci. Duke U., 1958-70; Charles A. Dana prof. polit. sci. Davidson (N.C.) Coll., 1970-91, prof. emeritus, 1991—, chmn. dept. polit. sci., 1972-89; vis. assoc. prof. polit. sci. U. Coll., Nairobi, Kenya, 1964-65; vis. prof. polit. sci., U. Dar es Salaam, Tanzania, 1969-70; Fulbright lectr. St. Stephen's Coll., Delhi U., India, 1982-83. Editor: Islam and International Relations, 1965; contbg. author: Federalism in the Commonwealth, 1963, The Aftermath of Sovereignty, 1973, Prospects for Constitutional Democracy, 1976; Contbr. articles to profl. jours. Served in USAAF, 1943-46. Mem. Phi Beta Kappa, Pi Sigma Alpha, Omicron Delta Kappa. Home: PO Box 567 Davidson NC 28036

PROCTOR, JOHN FRANKLIN, lawyer; b. Scottsboro, Ala., May 6, 1931; s. James Moody and Lucy (May) P.; m. Anne Esco, Dec. 3, 1988; children from previous marriage: James Moody, Laura. B.S., U. Ala., 1953, LL.B., 1957. Bar: Ala. bar 1957. Asst. atty. gen., 1957-59; pvt. practice Scottsboro, 1959-90; judge Jackson County, 1962-63; pvt. practice, 1963-66, 68—; judge 9th Jud. Circuit, 1966-68; fed. adminstrv. law judge, 1990—. Served with U.S. Army, 1953-55. Mem. Ala. Bar Assn. (commr. 1979-90), Sigma Chi, Phi Alpha Delta. Methodist. Clubs: Rotarian, Scottsboro Golf and Country. Home: 253 Whitehall Rd Chattanooga TN 37405-3741 Office: Office of Hearings and Appeals 5700 Brainerd Rd Chattanooga TN 37411-4012

PROCTOR, JOHN P., lawyer; b. Kewaunee, Wis., 1942. BA, Princeton U., 1964; LLB, U. Pa., 1967. Bar: D.C. 1968, U.S. Ct. Mil. Appeals 1970, U.S. Ct. Appeals (D.C. cir.) 1975, N.Y. 1984. Ptnr. Winston & Strawn, Washington. Mem. ABA (vice chmn. air quality com., nat. resources law sect. 1984—), Fed. Bar Assn. Office: Winston & Strawn 1400 L St NW Washington DC 20005

PROCTOR, KENNETH DONALD, lawyer; b. Balt., Apr. 28, 1944; s. Kenneth Chauncey and Sarah Elizabeth (Kent) P.; m. Judith Danner Harris, Aug. 2, 1969; children—Kenneth Scott, Kent Harris, Janet Cameron. B.S., Lehigh U., 1966; J.D., U. Md., 1969. Bar: Md. 1969, U.S. Dist. Ct. Md. 1970, U.S. Ct. Appeals (4th cir.) 1980, U.S. Supreme Ct. 1974. Law clk. to presiding judge Md. Ct. Appeals, 1969-70; assoc. Miles & Stockbridge, Balt., 1970-73, 74-76, ptnr., Balt., 1976-81, Towson, Md., 1981—; asst. atty. gen. Md., Balt., 1973-74; Trustee, Gilman Sch., Balt., 1982-85. Mem. ABA, Md. State Bar Assn., Balt. County Bar Assn. Democrat. Episcopalian. Office: Miles & Stockbridge 600 Washington Ave Baltimore MD 21204-3913

PROCTOR, NICK HOBERT, toxicologist; pharmacologist; b. Moscow, Idaho, Nov. 1, 1941; s. Hobert Basle and Cleo Evelyn (Rothwell) P.; m. Terry Ladd Whiting, June 27, 1964; children: Ken Lawrence, John David. B Pharmacy, Wash. State U., 1965; PhD in Comparative Pharmacology, U. Calif., San Francisco, 1973. Diplomate Am. Bd. Toxicology; registered pharmacist Wash., Calif. Toxicologist Kaiser Found. Internat, Oakland, Calif., 1975-76; toxicologist, dir. health Kaiser Aluminum & Chem. Corp., Oakland, Calif., 1976-84; dir. product safety Kimberly-Clark Corp., Neenah, Wis., 1984—. Co-author: Chemical Hazards of the Workplace, 1978, 2d edit., 1987, 3d edit., 1991. Lt. USPHS, 1966-68. Recipient Jean Spencer Felton award Western Occupational Med. Assn., 1978. Mem. Soc. Toxicology, Am. Coll. Toxicology. Home: 53 N Parkview Dr Appleton WI 54915-9509 Office: Kimberly-Clark Corp Box 999 2100 Winchester Rd Neenah WI 54957-0999

PROCTOR, PETER, pharmaceutical executive. V.p., fin. Syntex Labs, Inc., Palo Alto, Calif. Office: Syntex Labs Inc 3401 Hillview Ave Palo Alto CA 94304*

PROCTOR, RICHARD J., geologist, consultant; b. L.A., Aug. 2, 1931; s. George Arthur and Margaret Y. (Goodman) P.; m. Ena McLaren, Feb. 12, 1955; children: Mitchell, Jill, Randall. BA, Calif. State U., L.A., 1954; MA, UCLA, 1958. Engring. geologist, Calif.; cert. profl. geologist Am. Inst. Profl. Geologists. Chief geologist Met. Water Dist., L.A., 1958-80; pres., cons. geologist Richard J. Proctor, Inc., Arcadia, Calif., 1980—; vis. assoc. prof. Calif. Inst. Tech., Pasadena, 1975-78. Co-author: Citizens Guide to Geologic Hazards, 1993; editor: Professional Practice Guidelines, 1985, Engineering Geology Practice in Southern California, 1992. Pres., dir. Arcadia Hist. Soc., 1993-96. Fellow Geol. Soc. Am. (rep. 1989, Burwell Meml. award 1972); mem. Assn. Engring. Geologists (pres. 1979), Am. Inst. Profl. Geologists (pres. 1989, Van Couvering Meml. award 1990, hon. mem. 1992), Am. Geol. Inst. (sec.-treas. 1983).

PROCTOR, RICHARD OWEN, public health administrator, army officer; b. Austin, Tex., Nov. 18, 1935; s. William Owen and Arlene Gertrude (Holdeman) P.; m. Martha June Whitlock, Nov. 19, 1955; children: Tanya Marie, Sheilia Renee, Michael Lee, Terry Glen, Richard Lowell, Roger Owen. BA, Oklahoma City U., 1957; MS, Baylor U. Coll. Medicine, Houston, 1964, MD, 1964; MPH and TM, Tulane U., 1970; diploma, U.S. Army War Coll., 1983. Diplomate Am. Bd. Pediatrics, Am. Bd. Preventive Medicine. Commd. capt. U.S. Army, 1964, advanced through grades to brig. gen.; instr. Imperial Ethiopian Coll. A&M Arts, Alemaya, 1957-59; dep. comdr. U.S. Army Hosp., Kagnew Station, Ethiopia, 1967-69, U.S. Army Med. Lab., Ft. Sam Houston, Tex., 1973-75; instr. U.S. Army Acad. Health Scis., Ft. Sam Houston, 1975-77; surgeon U.S. Army VII Corps, Moeringen, Fed. Republic Germany, 1978-81; prof., chmn., comdt. of students Uniformed Svcs. U. of Health Scis., Bethesda, Md., 1981-82; comdr. Raymond Bliss Army Community Hosp., Ft. Huachuca, Ariz., 1983-85; surgeon U.S. Army Tng. and Doctrine Command, Ft. Monroe, Va., 1985-88; comdg. gen. William Beaumont Army Med. Ctr., El Paso, Tex., 1988-91; dir. pub. health Region 6 Tex. Dept. Health, Houston, 1991—; cons. WHO/PAHO, Bolivia, 1971; lectr. on medicine, anthropology, theology, history, substance abuse prevention; past adj. or clin. faculty positions Baylor U., Tulane U., U. Tex. Author: (with others) Principles of Pediatrics: Healthcare of the Young, 1978, Current Pediatrics Diagnosis and Treatment, 1978, 80, Primary Pediatric Care, 1987, 2d edit., 1992, Comprehensive Adolescent Health Care, 1992; author multiple articles on viremia with Sabin polio vaccines. Asst. scout master Boy Scouts Am., Bowie, Md., 1971-73; scout committeeman Boy Scouts Am., Moeringen, 1978-81. Decorated D.S.M., Legion of Merit (twice); recipient scholarship Broadhurst Found., Tulsa, 1953-57; rsch. fellow NIH, 1960-61; Tropical Medicine fellow La. State U. 1970. Fellow Am. Acad. Preventive Medicine, Am. Acad. Pediatrics, Royal Soc. Medicine; mem. Assn. Mil. Surgeons of U.S., Nat. Eagle Scout Assn. Methodist. Avocations: ranching, fitness training, lecturing. Home: RR 4 Box 1193 Paris TX 75462-9804 Office: 10500 Forum Place Dr Houston TX 77036-8502

PROCTOR, ROBERT SWOPE, retired petroleum company executive; b. Columbus, Ohio, June 15, 1922; s. William Edward and Elsie M. (Swope) P.; m. Mary M. Thornton, Dec. 31, 1945; children: Robert M., Jill, Mary, Ann, Kathleen. MSME, Oreg. State U., 1947. With Standard Oil Co. Calif., Inc., 1947-76; gen. mgr. El Segundo (Calif.) refinery, 1969-71; v.p., div. Western Operation Inc., San Francisco, 1971-76; v.p. mfg. Chevron U.S.A., San Francisco, 1976-84. Served to 1st lt., C.E. AUS, 1943-45. Mem. Calif. Mfrs. Assn. (dir.). Republican. Home: PO Box 1639 Zephyr Cove NV 89448-1639

PROCTOR, SAMUEL, history educator; b. Jacksonville, Fla., Mar. 29, 1919; s. Jack and Celia (Schneider) P.; m. Bessie Rubin, Sept. 8, 1948; children: Mark Julian, Alan Lowell. B.A., U. Fla., 1941, M.A., 1942, Ph.D. 1958. Mem. faculty U. Fla., Gainesville, 1946—, prof. history and social scis., 1963-74, disting. service prof. history, 1974—, Julien C. Yonge prof. Fla. history, 1976—, univ. historian, 1953—, dir. oral history program, 1968—; curator History Fla. State Mus.; dir. Doris Duke Southeastern Indian Oral History Program, Ctr. for Study of Fla. History and Humanities. Author: Napoleon Bonaparte Broward, Florida's Fighting Democrat, 1950, Florida Commemorates the Civil War Centennial, 1962, Florida One Hundred Years Ago, 1966, Florida History Preservation Planning, 1971, Gator History: History of the University of Florida, 1986, The University of Florida, 1990, N.B. Broward, 1993; editor, author introduction: Dickison and His Men: Reminiscences of the War in Florida, 1962; series editor: Bicentennial Floridiana Facsimile Series; editor: Eighteenth Century Florida and Its Borderlands, 1975, Eighteenth Century Florida and the Carribean, 1976, Eighteenth Century Florida, Life on the Frontier, 1976, Eighteenth Century Florida and the Revolutionary South, 1977, Eighteenth Century Florida and the Impact of The American Revolution, 1978, Tacachale, Essays on the Indians of Florida and Southeastern Georgia during the Historic Period, Jews of the South; assoc. editor: Fla. Hist. Quar., 1962-64, editor, 1963-93; contbr. articles to profl. jours. Served with U.S. Army, 1943-46. Mem. Fla. Blue Key, Phi Beta Kappa, Tau Epsilon Phi, Pi Kappa Phi, Phi Alpha Theta. Democrat. Jewish. Home: 2235 NW 9th Pl Gainesville FL 32605-5201 Office: Univ Fla Dept History Gainesville FL 32611

PROCTOR, WILLIAM LEE, college president; b. Atlanta, Jan. 27, 1933; s. Samuel Cook and Rose Elizabeth (Nottingham) P.; m. Pamela Evans Duke; children: Samuel Matthews (dec.), Priscilla Nottingham. BS, Fla. State U., 1956, MS, 1964, PhD, 1968. Tchr. Seminole County Pub. Schs., Longwood, Fla., 1956-57, 58-62, Orange County Fla. Pub. Schs., Orlando, Fla., 1957-58; athletic coach Fla. State U., Tallahassee, 1962-65, asst. dean men, 1965-67, grad. fellow, 1967-68; supt. of schs. Rock Hill (S.C.) Sch. Dist. #3, 1968-69; dean of men U. Cen. Fla., Orlando, 1969-71; pres. Flagler Coll. St. Augustine, Fla., 1971—; cons. higher edn. policy Heritage Found., Washington, 1983—; mem. commn. on Colls., So. Assn. Colls. and Schs., 1995—. Bd. dirs. Flagler Health Svcs., Inc., St. Augustine, 1977—, Fla. Ind. Coll. Fund, Lakeland, 1986—, Vickers Landing Retirement Cmty., pres. bd. dirs., 1994—; trustee Fla. Sch. for Deaf and Blind, St. Augustine, 1984—, also chmn. bd.; pres. St. Augustine Found., 1986—; bd. dirs. Penny Farms Retirement Cmty., 1990-91, pres., 1991—. Nat. Accrediting Coun. for Agys.

Serving the Blind, 1993—, Jacksonville Symphony Orch., 1994—; trustee WJCT pub. broadcasting, 1994—. Recipient Disting. Educator award Fla. State U. Coll. Edn., 1989, Phil Carrol award Soc. for Advancement Mgmt., 1990, Disting. Svc. award Fla. Sch. for Deaf and Blind, 1990, Patrick Henry Medallion patriotic achievement Mil. Order of World Wars, 1991, Stetson S Club Achievement award, 1993; named to Fla. State U. Athletic Hall of Fame, 1988. Mem. Am. Assn. Pres. of Ind. Colls., State Hist. Assn., Ind. Colls. and Univs. Fla. (legis. chmn. 1974-77, vice chmn. 1976-77, chmn. 1978-79), Nat. Assn. Ind. Colls. and Univs. (rep., tchr. edn.), St. Johns County C. of C. (dir.), Rotary (pres. 1978-79, govs. dist. 697 1988-89). Republican. Presbyterian. Avocations: history, jogging, karate. Office: Flagler Coll Office of the Pres PO Box 1027 Saint Augustine FL 32085-1027

PROCTOR, WILLIAM ZINSMASTER, lawyer; b. Des Moines, Nov. 30, 1902; s. Frank and Louise (Zinsmaster) P.; m. Alice S. Bowles, Nov. 24, 1944; children: David J. W., Mary Martha. Student, Drake U., 1920; J.D., U. Mich., 1925. Bar: Iowa 1925. Assoc. Bradshaw, Schenk & Fowler, 1925-35; ptnr. Bradshaw, Fowler, Proctor & Fairgrave, Des Moines, 1935-92; dir. emeritus and gen. counsel emeritus Employers Mut. Casualty Co., Employers Modern Life Co., Emcasco Ins. Co., EMC Ins. Group Inc., Dakota Fire Ins. Co., Bismarck, N.D., Am. Liberty Ins. Co., Birmingham, Ala., Union Mut. Ins. Co. Providence; dir. emeritus Norwest Des Moines N.A. Pres. Des Moines Community Chest, 1956, Des Moines United Community Services, 1957; mem. bd. SSS, 1942-55, Iowa appeal bd., 1955-67; Pres. Des Moines Roadside Settlement, 1950-53; trustee Hawley Welfare Found., 1968—, chmn., 1974-86; chmn. bd. trustees Preston Ednl. Trust, 1952-86. Mem. ABA, Iowa Bar Assn., Polk County Bar Assn. (pres. 1945), Internat. Bar Assn., Inter-Am. Bar Assn., Am. Judicature Soc., Assn. Bar City N.Y., Fedn. Ins. Counsel. Clubs: Mason (Shriner, Jester), Wakonda, Des Moines (pres. 1953); University (Chgo.). Home: 3401 Lincoln Place Dr Des Moines IA 50312-3007 Office: Bradshaw Fowler Proctor & Fairgrave 801 Grand Ave Ste 3700 Des Moines IA 50309-8006

PROCUNIER, RICHARD WERNER, environmental scientist, administrator; b. Dallas, Tex., Oct. 27, 1936; s. Werner Richard and Dorothy (Koch) P.; m. Janet Mesing, Sept. 5, 1958 (div. Aug. 28, 1984); children: Nancy, Carol, Ellen; m. Carolyn Harris, June 25, 1988. BSEE, MIT, 1958; PhD, Univ. Coll. London, 1966. Prof. U. London, 1966-68; rsch. scientist Lockheed, Palo Alto, Calif., 1968-72; mgr. Hewlett Packard, Santa Clara, Calif., 1972-74; chief of noise control U.S. EPA, San Francisco, 1974-82, sci. advisor, 1982-83, environ. scientist, 1990—; prof. U. Calif., Davis, 1984-85; adminstr. County Health Svcs., Martinez, Calif., 1986-89; mem. Nat. Edn. Com., Nat. Environ. Health Assn., Denver, 1980-87; enforcement coord., U.S. EPA, San Francisco, 1990. Contbr. many articles to profl. jours. Proponent to incorporate Orinda, Calif., 1984. Recipient Presidential citation, Nat. Environmental Health Assn., 1981. Fellow Royal Soc. London; mem. World Affairs Coun., Commonwealth Club, Kappa Sigma (Leadership award 1958). Avocation: golf.

PROCYK, JUDSON M., bishop. ordained priest May 19, 1957. Bishop Byzantine Metropolitan Diocese of Pittsburgh, 1994—. Office: 925 Liberty Ave Pittsburgh PA 15222*

PROEBSTING, EDWARD LOUIS, JR., retired research horticulturist; b. Woodland, Calif., Mar. 2, 1926; s. Edwrd Louis and Dorothy (Critzer) P.; m. Patricia Jean Connolly, June 28, 1947; children: William Martin, Patricia Louise, Thomas Alan (dec.). BS, U. Calif., Davis, 1948; PhD, Mich. State U., 1951. Asst. horticulturist Wash. State U., Prosser, 1951-57, assoc. horticulturist, 1957-63, horticulturist, 1963-93, superintendent irrigated agrl. rsch. and extension ctr., 1990-93; ret., 1993; vis. prof. Cornell U., Ithaca, N.Y., 1966; vis. scientist Hokkaido U., Sapporo, Japan, 1978, Victoria Dept. Agr., Tatura, Australia, 1986—. Contbr. numerous articles to profl. jours. Scoutmaster Boy Scouts Am., Prosser, 1963-76, dist. chmn., 1976-78. Served to lt. USNR, 1943-46, 52-54. Recipient Silver Beaver award Boy Scouts Am.; fellow Japan Soc. Promotion Sci., Sapporo, 1978, Res. Bank. Australia, 1986. Fellow AAAS, Am. Soc. Hort. Sci. (pres. 1983-84, sci. editor jour. 1993—). Methodist. Avocations: backpacking, native plants. Home: 1929 Miller Ave Prosser WA 99350-1532 Office: Wash State U Irrigated Agrl Rsch Ctr and Ext RR 2 Box 2953A Prosser WA 99350-9678

PROEFROCK, CARL KENNETH, academic medical administrator; b. Curtis, Ill., Mar. 30, 1928; s. Carl Robert and Anna Lorraine (Hagel) P.; m. Margaret Muntz (dec. 1984); children: Philip, Andrew, Elizabeth, Liesl; m. Janelle Dillon, Sept. 8, 1988. BA, Carthage Coll., Kenosha, Wis., 1949; MDiv, Chgo. Luth. Theol. Sem., 1953. Sr. com. orgn. specialist N.Y.C. Housing and Devel. Adminstrn., 1966-68; exec. dir. Model Cities Program, Manchester, N.H., 1968-70, Health Assn. Rochester and Monroe (N.Y.), 1970-73, Mahoning Shenango Area Health Ed. Network, Youngstown, Ohio, 1973-78; spl. asst. to dean Northeastern Ohio Univs. Coll. Medicine, Rootstown, 1978-79; v.p. Med. Coll. Ohio, Toledo, 1979-88, sr. v.p. govtl. affairs, 1988-93; pres. KPA Assocs., Inc., 1993—; v.p. Found. for Applied Rsch., Washington, 1976; chmn. adv. bd. Ohio AHEC, Columbus, 1976; program adminstr. Ohio Statewide Area Health Edn. Ctr., Toledo, 1988-93. Mem. budget allocation com. United Appeal, Youngstown, 1975-78; mem. dist. planning coun. Ohio Dept. Mental Health, Youngstown, 1977-78; chmn. Toledo Area Coun. Tech., 1986. Mem. Nat. Area Health Edn. Ctrs. Assn. (bd. dirs. 1988—), Nat. Assn. Univ. Rsch. Adminstrs., Soc. Rsch. Adminstrs., Internat. Assn. Univ. Rsch. Parks, Soc. Univ. Patent Adminstrs., Nat. Assn. Health Manpower Edn. Systems, Northeastern Ohio Med. Educators Assn. (bd. dirs.), Rotary. Lutheran. Home and Office: 4323A Nantucket Dr Toledo OH 43623-3111

PROFFITT, WILLIAM ROBERT, orthodontics educator; b. Harnett County, N.C., Apr. 19, 1936; s. Glenn Theodore and Edna Marie (Queener) P.; m. Sara Thomas, Sept. 20, 1953; children: Lola Ann, Edward Thomas, Glenn Theodore. BS, U. N.C., 1956, DDS, 1959; student, Campbell Coll., Buies Creek, N.C., 1952-53; PhD, Med. Coll. Va., 1962; MS, U. Wash., 1963; FDS, Royal Coll. Surgeons, 1990. Am. Bd. Orthodontics. Investigator Nat. Inst. Dental Research, Bethesda, Md., 1963-65; asst. prof. orthodontics U. Ky., Lexington, 1965-68, assoc. prof., 1968-71; prof. U.Ky., Lexington, 1971-73; prof. orthodontics U. Fla., Gainesville, 1973-75; prof., chmn. dept. orthodontics U. N.C., Chapel Hill, 1975—, Kenan prof., 1992; cons. NIH, Bethesda, 1974, 76—. Author: Contemporary Orthodontics, 1986, 2d edit., 1993; co-author: Surgical Correction of Dentofacial Deformity, 1980, Surgical-Orthodontic Treatment, 1990; contbr. articles to sci. jours. Served to lt. comdr. USPHS, 1963-65. Fulbright research scholar U. Adelaide, Australia, 1972. Mem. Am. Orthodontists (council on research 1970-76), ADA, Internat. Assn. Dental Research, Phi Beta Kappa. Democrat. Presbyterian. Home: 620 Rock Creek Rd Chapel Hill NC 27514-6716 Office: U NC Sch Dentistry Orthodontics Dept Chapel Hill NC 27599

PROFFITT, H. KEVIN, archivist; b. Hamilton, Ohio, Dec. 24, 1956; s. Henry C. and Marjorie O. (Elam) P.; m. Joan Moriarity, May 17, 1986. BA, Miami U., Oxford, Ohio, 1979; MA, Wright State U., 1980. Archivist Am. Jewish Archives, Cin., 1981—. Contbr. articles to profl. jours. Mem. Soc. Am. Archivists, Acad. Cert. Archivists (cert.), Midwest Archives Conf., Soc. Ohio Archivists (pres. 1987-89). Office: Am Jewish Archives 3101 Clifton Ave Cincinnati OH 45220

PROFFITT, JOHN RICHARD, investment banking executive; b. Grand Junction, Colo., Sept. 12, 1930; s. Hillus D. and Joy Elaine (Lindsay) P.; m. Claire Boyer Miller, May 8, 1965 (div. 1992); children: Cameron Lindsay, William Boyer. BA in Edn., U. Ky., 1953, MA in Polit. Sci., 1961; postgrad., U. Mich., 1959-65. Asst. dean of men, instr. polit. sci. profl. U. Ky., Lexington, 1957-59; teaching fellow U. Mich., Ann Arbor, 1961-63, 63-65; asst. dir. Nat. Commn. on Accrediting, Washington, 1966-68; dir. accreditation and eligibility staff U.S. Dept. HEW, Washington, 1968-75; dir. div. eligibility and agy. evaluation U.S. HEW, Washington, 1975-80; dir. div. instnl. and state incentive programs U.S. Dept. Edn., Washington, 1980-82; pres. The Clairion Corp., Bethesda, Md., 1982-84, Nat. Asbestos Removal, Inc., Beltsville, Md., 1985-90; pres. Commonwealth Environ. Svcs., Inc., Alexandria, Va., 1987-91, also chmn. bd. dirs.; chmn. Internat. Environ. Engrs., Inc., Alexandria, Va., 1991-92; pres. Canterbury Internat., Vienna, Va., 1992—; cons. Conn. State Commn. Higher Edn., Hartford, 1967, Am. Coun. Edn., Washington, 1970; cons. U.S. Dept. Hew, 1967, 68; mem. study steering com. Am. Vocat. Assn., Washington, 1968; exec. sec. Nat. Adv.

Com. on Accreditation and Instnl. Eligibility, Washington, 1968-80; mem. gen. com. Nat. Study Sch. evaluation, Alexandria, 1970-78; mem. task force Edn. Commn. of the States, Denver, 1972; subcom. chmn. Fed. Interagy. Com. on Edn., Washington, 1974-76; lectr., presenter profl. confs. Co-author: Accreditation and Certification in Relation to Allied Health Manpower, 1971; contbg. author: Health Manpower: Adapting in the Seventies, 1971, Accreditation in Teacher Education, 1975, Transferring Experiential Credit, 1979; contbr. articles to profl. and govtl. agy. publs., 1968-79. v.p. bd. dirs. Nat. Accreditation Coun. for Agys. Serving the Blind, N.Y.C., 1985; pres., chmn. bd. dirs. Found. for Advancement of Quality Svcs. for the Blind, Alexandria, 1988. 1st lt. USAF, 1953-55, Japan and Korea. Higher edn. fellow Univ. Mich., 1959. Mem. Club Internat. (Chgo.), Island Club (Hope Sound, Fla.), Thoroughbred Club Am. (Lexington, Ky.), Tower Club (Vienna, Va.), Sigma Nu. Democrat. Episcopalian. Avocations: conservation, animal welfare, travel, antiques, art. Home: 11008 Spring House Ct Potomac MD 20854-1452

PROFFITT, WALDO, JR., newspaper editor; b. Plainview, Tex., Oct. 8, 1924; s. Waldo and Susan Ann (Smith) P.; m. Marjorie Baltzegar, Sept. 14, 1946 (div. 1963); children: Ann Herbert, Deborah, Geoffrey Harrison, Laurence Scott; m. Anne Collier Greene, Feb. 6, 1966; 1 child, Herbert Waldo. BA cum laude, Harvard U., 1948. Reporter Bangor (Maine) Commercial, 1948-50; assoc. dir. Harvard News Office, Cambridge, Mass., 1952-54; city editor Charlotte (N.C.) News, 1954-58; mng. editor Journal, Lorain, Ohio, 1958-61; editorial dir. Sarasota (Fla.) Herald-Tribune, 1961-84; editor, 1984—. Lt. U.S. Army, 1943-46, ETO, lt. USAF, 1950-52. Mem. Am. Soc. Newspaper Editors, Fla. Soc. Newspaper Editors (pres. 1978). Democrat. Unitarian. Home: 1581 Hillview Dr Sarasota FL 34239-2047 Office: Sarasota Herald-Tribune PO Box 1719 Sarasota FL 34230-1719

PROFFITT, GLENN ARLISS, II, air force officer; b. Corbin, Ky., Apr. 3, 1942; s. Glenn Arliss and Jessie Louvena (Byrley) P.; m. Mary Louise Miller, Aug. 4, 1962 (div. Oct. 1976); children: Glenn Scott, David Spencer; m. Jane Ellenn, Nov. 26, 1983. BS in Ind. Econs., Purdue U., 1964; MA in Mgmt., Webster Coll., 1977. Commd. 2d lt. USAF, 1964, advanced through grades to maj. gen., 1992; flight comdr. Thailand, 1970-74; fighter resource mgr. Air Force Mil. Pers. Ctr., Randolph AFB, Tex., 1974-79; comdr. 78th Tactical Fighter Squadron USAF Europe, Bentwaters, U.K., 1979-82; student Nat. War Coll., Nat. Def. U., Washington, 1982-83; programming div. chief USAF Pentagon, 1983-85; comdr. 23 Tactical Fighter Wing, Alexandria, La., 1987-89, 14th Air Div., U.S. CENTAF, Saudi Arabia, 1990-91, Combined Task Force, Provide Comfort, Incirlik, Turkey, 1991—. Decorated Legion of Merit, DFC with 6 oak leaf clusters, Air medal with 29 oak leaf clusters. Republican. Methodist. Avocations: golf, tennis, flying. Home: Psci Box 4575 APO AE 09633 Office: USAF Hq USAF Washington DC 20330

PROFT, PAT, screenwriter, film producer; b. Mpls., Apr. 3, 1947; s. Bob and Marguerite (Hobl) P.; m. Karen Philipp; 1 child, Patrick. Writer: (T.V. series) The Jim Stafford Show, 1975, The Smothers Brothers Show, 1975, When Things Were Rotten, 1975, Cher, 1975-76, Welcome Back Kotter, 1975-79, Van Dyke and Company, 1976 (Emmy award nomination outstanding writing 1976), The Redd Foxx Comedy Hour, 1977-78, The Mary Tyler Moore Comedy Hour, 1979, Detective School, 1979, Police Squad!, 1982, (TV spls.) Bob Hope Special: Bob Hope's Christmas Party, 1975, Cher, 1975, Ringo, 1978, The Roy Clarke Special, 1979, All Commercials: A Steve Martin Special, 1980, Gary Owens All Nonsense News Network, 1982, (TV pilots) Ultra Quiz, 1981, Twilight Theatre II, 1982, High School, U.S.A., 1984, (films) (with Neal Israel) Bachelor Party, 1984, (with Israel and Hugh Wilson) Police Academy, 1984, (with Israel and Peter Torokvei) Real Genius, 1985, (with Jim Abrahams, David Zucker, and Jerry Zucker) The Naked Gun: From the Files of Police Squad!, 1988, (with D. Zucker) Naked Gun 2 1/2: The Smell of Fear, 1991, Brain Donors, 1992, (with D. Zucker and Robert LoCash) Naked Gun 33 1/3: The Final Insult, 1994; writer, exec. prodr.: (films) (with Israel) Moving Violations, 1985, Lucky Stiff, 1989, (with Abrahams) Hot Shots!, 1991, (with Abrahams) Hot Shots! Part Deux, 1993; writer, prodr.: (TV series) Marie, 1980, Buckshot, 1980; tech. advisor: Johnny Dangerously, 1984; appearances include (films) Modern Problems, 1981, Bachelor Party, 1984, (TV series) Madhouse 90, 1972, The Burns and Schreiber Comedy Hour, 1973, Joey & Dad, 1975, Van Dyke and Company, 1976, Detective School, 1979, (TV movies) Fast Friends, 1979, (TV pilots) Twilight Theatre, 1982. Office: 10202 W Washington Blvd Culver City CA 90232*

PROFUSEK, ROBERT ALAN, lawyer; b. Cleve., Jan. 14, 1950; s. George John and Geraldine (Hobl) P.; m. Linda Gail Schmidt, May 7, 1972; children: Robert Charles, Kathryn Anne. B.A., Cornell U., 1972; J.D., NYU, 1975. Bar: Ohio 1975, Tex. 1981, N.Y. 1994. Assoc. Jones, Day, Reavis & Pogue, Cleve., 1975-81, Dallas, 1981-82, ptnr., 1982—, N.Y., 1993. bd. dir. Maybelline, Inc. Contbr. articles to profl. jours. Mem. ABA, N.Y. Bar Assn., Assn. Bar City of N.Y., Tex. Bar Assn., Dallas Bar Assn., Exchange Club, Bent Tree Country Club, Tower Club (all Dallas). Republican. Episcopalian. Home: 20 Bobolink Ln Greenwich CT 06830 Office: Jones Day Reavis & Pogue 32nd Flr 599 Lexington Ave New York NY 10022

PROGAR, DOROTHY, retired library director; b. Bruceville, Tex., Sept. 14, 1924; d. Florence Scott and George Thomas Watkins; m. Walter L. Progar, Aug. 3, 1946; 1 child, James Scott. Student, Mich. State U.; BA, Baylor U.; postgrad., Tex. Woman's U. With Waco-McLennan County Libr., 1961-92, circulation libr., 1961-65, young adult libr., 1965-67, ref. libr., 1967-69, asst. dir., 1969-72, assoc. dir., 1972-78, dir. librs., 1978-92. Contbr. articles to profl. jours. Mem. Cen. Tex. Lit. Coalition; mem. Stercker Mus. Assocs. Bd. Recipient Waco-McLennan County Pathfinder in Pub. Svc. award, 1988, Silver Bridge award Cen. Tex. chpt. Pub. Rels. Soc. Am., 1990; Dorothy Progar Day proclaimed by City of Waco, 1986. Mem. ALA, Tex. Libr. Assn. (exec. bd. 1986-89), Tex. Mcpl. Libr. Dirs. Assn. (pres. 1987-88, Libr. Dir. of Yr. award 1989), Friends of Baylor Fine Arts Bd., Waco Family Y, Advt. Club Waco (Silver Medal award 1988), Rotary. Baptist. Avocations: reading, sports, people. Home: 1800 Trinity Dr Waco TX 76710-2842

PROIES, MICHAEL CONSTANTINE, apparel company executive; b. Bklyn., Feb. 12, 1947; s. Michael C. and Marcella E. (James) P.; B.S., Fordham U., 1969; m. Rita D. Gentleman, Sept. 30, 1972; children—Michael, Mark, Craig. With Main Hurdman & Cranston, N.Y.C., 1969-72; mgr. acctg. Gulf & Western Mfg. Co., N.Y.C., 1972-75; div. controller Kayser Roth Corp., N.Y.C., 1975-77, asst. corp. controller, 1980-81, corp. controller, 1981, v.p., chief fin. officer, 1982-86; sr. v.p. K.R. Hosiery Co., 1982-86, chmn. exec. co., 1986-87, pres., No-Nonsense Fashions, Inc., 1987—; acting pres. No Nonsense Fashions,Inc., 1986—; C.P.A., N.Y. Mem. Am. Inst. C.P.A.s, N.Y. State Soc. C.P.A.s. Republican. Office: Authentic Fitness Corp 6040 Bandini Blvd Los Angeles CA 90040

PROKASY, WILLIAM FREDERICK, academic administrator; b. Cleve., Nov. 27, 1930; s. William Frederick and Margaret Lovinia (Chapman) P.; m. Suzanne B. Canning; children: Kathi Lynn, Cheryl Anne, Benjamin Canning. B.A., Baldwin-Wallace Coll., 1952; M.A., Kent State U., 1954; Ph.D., U. Wis., 1957. Grad. asst. Kent State U., 1953-54; W.A.R.F. fellow U. Wis., 1954-55, teaching asst., 1955-57; asst. prof., then assoc. prof. Pa. State U. 1957-66; prof. psychology, chmn. dept. U. Utah, 1966-69. Disting. rsch. prof., 1971-72, dean social and behavioral sci., 1968-70; dean U. Utah (Coll. Social and Behavioral Sci.), 1970-79; acting dean U. Utah (Grad. Sch. Social Work), 1979-80; prof. psychology dean Coll. Liberal Arts and Scis., U. Ill., Champaign-Urbana, 1980-88; prof., v.p. for acad. affairs U. Ga., 1988—; cons. in field. Editor: Classical Conditioning, 1965, (with A.H. Black) Classical Conditioning II, 1971, (with D. Raskin) Electrodermal Responding in Psychological Research, 1973, Psychophysiology, 1974-77; editor (with I. Gormezano and R. Thompson) Classical Conditioning III, 1986; assoc. editor Learning and Motivation, 1969-76; cons. editor Jour. Exptl. Psychology, 1968-80. Del. Utah Dem. Conv., 1968-70, 72-74; trustee Utah Planned Parenthood Assn., 1977-80, Utah bd. dirs. ACLU, 1978-80; v.p., bd. dirs. Champaign-Urbana Symphony, 1986-88; bd. advis. Ga. Mus. of Art, 1989—. NSF sr. postdoctoral fellow, 1963-64; recipient Alumni Merit award Baldwin Wallace Coll., 1992. Fellow AAAS, Am. Psychol. Assn. (chmn. bd. sci. affairs 1977-78, coun. of reps. 1980-86, bd. dirs. 1983-86, bd. ednl. affairs 1993—); mem. Fedn. Behavioral, Psychol. and Cognitive Scis. (v.p. 1984-85, pres. 1985-87), Coun. of Sci. Soc. Pres.'s (exec. bd. 1987-91, chmn. 1990),

Psychonomic Soc., Coun. Rsch. Librs. (bd. dirs. 1990—), Am. Assn. Higher Edn., Soc. Psychophysiol. Rsch. (bd. dirs. 1978-84, pres. 1982-83), Utah Psychol. Assn. (exec. bd. 1968-70, pres. 1971-72), Assn. Advancement Psychology (bd. dirs. 1982-83), Sigma Xi (pres. U. Utah chpt. 1972-73), Phi Kappa Phi.

PROKOPIS, EMMANUEL CHARLES, communications company executive; b. Peabody, Mass., July 5, 1942; s. Charles Emmanuel and Stevia (Kassotis) P.; m. Mary Catherine Dudeck, Dec. 6, 1969; children: Peter Matthew, Christina Eve. BBA, U. Mass., 1966. Mgr., pricing, budgeting, acctg. The Mitre Corp., Mass., Va., 1969-74; mgr. contracts liaison Pratt & Whitney Aircraft div., Conn., Fla., 1974-78; mgr. fin. planning, corp. office United Techs. Corp., Hartford, Conn., 1978-81; contr. magnet wire and insulation div. United Techs. Corp., Fort Wayne, Ind., 1981-83; v.p. fin., chief fin. officer The Mostek Corp. (subs.) United Techs. Corp., Carrollton, Tex., 1983-85; sr. v.p. fin. and ops., chief fin. officer The Lotus Devel. Corp., Cambridge, Mass., 1985-87; fin. mgr. mfg. and engring. Digital Equipment Corp., 1987-91, v.p. budgeting, 1991-92; exec. v.p. MAST Industries, 1992, Ziff Comm., 1992-93; v.p. corp. contr. Digital Equipment Corp., 1994—. Served as 1st lt. U.S. Army, 1966-69, Vietnam. Decorated Bronze Star. Greek Orthodox.

PROKOPOFF, STEPHEN STEPHEN, art museum director, educator; b. Chgo., Dec. 24, 1929; s. Stephen George and Jadwiga M. (Borejszo) P.; m. Paula M. Delle Donne, Oct. 26, 1957 (div. 1981); children—Alexander, Ilya; m. Lois A. Craig, June 21, 1982. B.A., U. Calif.-Berkeley, 1951, M.A., 1952; Ph.D., NYU, 1963. Dir. Hathorn Gallery, Skidmore Coll., Saratoga Springs, NY, 1966-67; dir. Inst. Contemporary Art, U. Pa., Phila., 1967-71, Mus. Contemporary Art, Chgo., 1971-78, Inst. Contemporary Art, Boston, 1978-82, Krannert Art Mus., U. Ill., Champaign, 1982-92, Univ. Art Mus., U. Iowa, Iowa City, 1992—. Co-author and co-designer (with Joan Siegfried): 19th Century Architecture of Saratoga Springs, New York, 1972 (named 1 of 50 Best Designed Books of Yr.); co-author (with text by Marcel Franciscono) The Modern Dutch Poster: The First Fifty Years, 1986; contbr. articles to art periodicals. Grantee Fulbright, 1956-57, German Govt., 1958, U.S. State Dept., 1974, Am. Council on Germany, 1980, 82. Mem. Coll. Art Assn., Assn. Art Mus., Assn. Art Mus. Dirs. Avocations: music; reading; study of architecture. Home: 200 Ferson St Iowa City IA 52246 Office: U Iowa U Art Mus 150 N Riverside Dr Iowa City IA 52242

PROM, STEPHEN GEORGE, lawyer; b. Jacksonville, Fla., July 8, 1954; s. George W. and Bonnie M. (Porter) P.; divorced; children: Ashley Brooke, Aaron Jacob, Adam Glenn. AA in Polit. Sci. with high honors, Fla. Jr. Coll., 1974; BA in Polit. Sci. with high honors, U. Fla., 1977, JD with honors, 1979. Bar: Fla. 1980, U.S. Dist. Ct. (mid. dist.) Fla. 1980, U.S. Dist. Ct. (no. dist.) Fla. 1981, U.S. Tax Ct. 1982, U.S. Ct. Appeals (11th cir.) 1985, U.S. Supreme Ct. 1985. Assoc. Rogers, Towers, Bailey, Jones & Gay, Jacksonville, 1979-83, Foley & Lardner, Jacksonville, 1983-86; ptnr. Christian & Prom, Jacksonville, 1986-87, Prom, Korn & Zehmer, P.A., Jacksonville, 1987-95, Blant, Moore, Sapp, Macdonald & Wells, P.A., 1995—. Sr. mgmt. editor U. Fla. Law Rev., 1978-79. Mem. Leadership Jacksonville 1984, Jacksonville Community Coun. Inc., 1985-86; bd. dirs. Mental Health Resource Ctr., Jacksonville, 1984-87, Mental Health Resource Foun., Jacksonville, 1985-87, Mental Health Found., Inc., 1987-89, mem. community bd., 1989-91; bd. dirs. Youth Crisis Ctr., Jacksonville, 1984-86, Young Profls. Bd. Multiple Sclerosis Soc., 1988-89; bd. dirs. The Team, Inc., 1992—; vol. Jacksonville, Inc., 1993—, Jacksonville Found., Inc., 1993—, Positively Jacksonville!, Inc., 1994—. Mem. ABA (tax, corp. banking and bus. law, health law, mcpl. fin., local gov. law sects.), Fla. Bar Assn. (tax and corp. banking and bus. law sects., health law com., bd. govs. young lawyers sect. 1983-87), Jacksonville Bar Assn., Jacksonville Beaches Bar Assn., Am. Acad. Hosp. Attys., Am. Hosp. Assn., Nat. Health Lawyers Assn., Fla. Acad. Hosp. Attys. (dir. 1994—), Epping Forest Yacht Club, Ponte Vedra Club, North Fla. Cruising Club, Phi Beta Kappa, Phi Theta Kappa, Phi Kappa Phi. Republican. Baptist. Avocations: sailing, surfing, weightlifting, tennis, jogging. Office: Ste 3100 Barnett Ctr PO Box 4548 50 North Laura St Jacksonville FL 32201-4548

PROMISEL, NATHAN E., materials scientist, metallurgical engineer; b. Malden, Mass., June 20, 1908; s. Solomon and Lyna (Samwick) P.; m. Evelyn Sarah Davidoff, May, 17, 1931; children: David Mark, Larry Jay. B.S., M.I.T., 1929, M.S., 1930; postgrad., Yale U., 1932-33; D.Engring. (hon.), Mich. Tech. U., 1978. Asst. dir. lab. Internat Silver Co. Meriden, Conn., 1930-40; chief materials scientist and engr. Navy Dept., Washington, 1940-66; exec. dir. nat. materials advy. bd. Nat. Acad. Scis., Washington, 1966-74; cons. on materials and policy, internationally, Washington, 1974—, mem., chmn. NATO Aerospace Panel, 1959-71; U.S. rep. (materials) OECD, 1967-70; U.S. chmn. U.S./USSR Sci. Exch. Program (materials), 1973-77); hon. guest USSR Acad. Scis.; permanent hon. mem. Internat. Conf. Materials Behavior; mem. Nat. Materials Adv. Bd.; adv. com. Oak Ridge Nat. Lab., Lehigh U., U. Pa., U.S. Navy Dept. Labs., U.S. Congress Office Tech. Assessment. Contbr. 65 articles to profl. publs.; contbr., editor: Advances in Materials Research, 1963, Science and Technology of Refractory Metals, 1964, Science, Technology and Application of Titanium, 1970; other books. Named Nat. Capitol Engr. of Yr. Coun. Engring. and Archtl. Socs., 1974; recipient Outstanding Accomplishment awards Navy Dept., 1955-64, Nat. Materials Advancement award, Fedn. Materials Socs., 1994; annual hon. lectr. Electrochem. Soc., 1970. Fellow AIME (hon. mem., ann. disting. lectr. Metall. Soc. 1984), Soc. Advanced Materials and Process Engring., Am. Soc. Materials Internat. (hon. mem.), Carnegie Inst. 1967, ann. hon. lectr. 1984), Brit. Inst. Materials; mem. NAE, ASTM (hon., ann. disting. lectr. 1964), Fedn. Materials Soc. (pres. 1972-73, 1st Decennial award 1982), Soc. Automotive Engrs. (chmn. aerospace materials divsn. 1959-74), Alpha Sigma Mu (hon.). Inventor in electroplating, 1930-40; metall. devels., 1941-66. Home and Office: Hyatt Classic Residence 8100 Connecticut Ave Apt 1406 Chevy Chase MD 20815-2820 *Ten key words and phrases for a professional career: identified goals, long range vision, can-do attitude, integrity, objectivity, understanding and tolerance, faith and trust, professionalism, dedication and perseverance, sense of humor.*

PROMISLO, DANIEL, lawyer; b. Bryn Mawr, Pa., Nov. 15, 1932; s. Charles and Pearl (Backman) P.; m. Estelle Carasso, June 10, 1961; children: Mark, Jacqueline, Steven. BSBA, Drexel U., 1955; JD magna cum laude, U. Pa., 1966. Bar: Pa. 1966. Pres., owner Hist. Souvenir Co, Phila., 1957—; assoc. Wolf, Block, Schorr & Solis-Cohen, Phila., 1966-70, ptnr., 1977-94, mem. exec. com., 1987-89, of counsel, 1994—; founder, pres. dir. Inst. for Paralegal Tng., Phila., 1970-75, cons., 1975-77. Editor: Corporate Law, 1970, Real Estate Law, 1971, Estates and Trusts, 1971, Civil Litigation, 1972, Employee Benefit Plans, 1973, Criminal Law, 1974; contbr. articles in field to profl. jours. Bd. dirs. Phila. Drama Guild, 1977—, chmn., 1982-86; bd. dirs. Phila. Israel Econ. Devel. Program, 1983-88, Inst. for Arts in Edn., 1990-93, WHYY, Inc., 1994—, Cancer Recovery, Inc., 1995—. Mem. Order of Coif, Blue Key, Phi Kappa Phi. Democrat. Jewish. Avocations: movies, basketball, tennis. Office: Wolf Block Schorr & Solis-Cohen SE Corner 15 Chestnut St Philadelphia PA 19122

PRONKO, LEONARD CABELL, theater educator; b. Cebu, Philippines, Oct. 3, 1927; s. Stephen Michael and Alice Lee Ludwell (Beal) P. BA, Drury Coll., 1947; MA, Washington U., St. Louis, 1951; PhD, Tulane U. 1957. Asst. prof. langs. Lake Erie Coll., Painesville, Ohio, 1955-56; from asst. prof. to prof. romance langs. Pomona Coll., Claremont, Calif., 1957-84, prof. to theater, 1985—, chair theater dept., 1985-91; dir. kabuki Mixed Blood Theatre, Mpls., 1984. Author: The World of Jean Anouilh, 1961, Avante-Garde, 1962, Eugene Ionesco, 1965, Theatre East and West, 1967, Guide to Japanese Drama, 1973, George Feydeau, 1975, Eugene Labiche and Georges Feydeau, 1982; contbr. articles to profl. publs. Fellow Guggenheim Soc., 1963-64, Japan Found., 1976; recipient award L.A. Drama Critics Circle, 1972, award of excellence Am. Coll. Theatre Festival, 1974, Order of Sacred Treasure, Govt. of Japan, 1986. Democrat. Avocations: opera, music, graphic art, ceramics, travel. Home: 1543 N Bates Pl Claremont CA 91711-3107 Office: Pomona Coll Theater Dept 300 E Bonita 333 N College Way Claremont CA 91711

PRONZINI, BILL JOHN (WILLIAM PRONZINI), author; b. Petaluma, Calif., Apr. 13, 1943; s. Joseph and Helene (Guder) P. Coll. student, 2 years. Author: 50 novels (including under pseudonyms), 4 books of non-fiction, 6 collections of short stories, 1971—; first novel, The Stalker, 1971; editor 80 anthologies; contbr. numerous short stories to publs. Recipient Scroll award, Best First Novel, Mystery Writers Am., 1972, Life Achievement award Pvt. Eye Writers Am., 1987. Democrat. Office: PO Box 2536 Petaluma CA 94953

PROOPS, JAY D., agricultural products executive. Pres. Vigoro Corp., Chgo., Ill., until 1994, v. chmn., 1994—. Office: Vigoro 225 N Michigan Ave Chicago IL 60601-5918

PROPHET, MATTHEW WALLER, JR., school superintendent; b. Okolona, Miss., Apr. 4, 1930; s. Matthew Waller and Elzira Elise (Walker) P.; m. Freddye Maxine Adams, Jan. 17, 1954; children—Michael, Matthew, Tony Michelle. B.Gen. Edn., U. Omaha, 1960; M.A. in Ednl. Supervision and Adminstrn., Roosevelt U., 1970; Ph.D., Northwestern U., 1972. Enlisted U.S. Army, 1951; commd. 2d lt., 1952; advanced through grades to comdr.; various assignments in Germany, Korea, other countries; advisor to Ohio N.G., 1964-65; personnel mgmt. advisor, Vietnam, 1965-66; chief inf. tng. 5th U.S. Army, Fort Sheridan, Ill., 1967-71; dep. supt. Lansing Sch. Dist., Mich., 1972-1978, supt., 1978-82; supt. Portland Pub. Schs., Oreg., 1982—; adj. prof. Coll. Edn. Mich. State U., East Lansing, Mich., 1974-82; coordinator Edn. Policy Fellowship Program, Mich., 1975-82; dir. Inst. Ednl. Leadership, Inc., Washington. Active United Way, Jr. Achievement, Mich. Soc. to Prevent Blindness, others. Decorated Bronze Star, Air medal, Legion of Merit, others. Mem. Mich. Assn. Sch. Adminstrs. (former nat. del.), Am. Assn. Sch. Adminstrs., Nat. Program for Ednl. Leadership, Mich. Middle Cities Edn. Assn., Area Educators Committed to Cooperation (former chmn.), Roundtable (Ingham County), Edn. Policy Fellowship Program, Adv. Council for Equal Ednl. Opportunity, Ret. Officers Assn. (U.S. Army), Alpha Chi, Phi Delta Kappa. Office: Portland Pub Schs PO Box 3107 Portland OR 97208-3107

PROPST, CATHERINE LAMB, biotechnology company executive; b. Charlotte, N.C., Mar. 10, 1946; d. James Pinckney and Eliza Mayo (Mills) P. BA magna cum laude, Vanderbilt U., 1967; M of Philosophy, Yale U., 1970, PhD, 1973. Head microbiology dir. GTE Labs., Waltham, Mass., 1974-77; various mgmt. positions Abbott Labs, North Chgo., Ill., 1977-80; v.p. rsch. and devel. Ayerst Labs., Plainview, N.Y., 1980-83; v.p. rsch. and devel. worldwide Flow Gen. Inc., McLean, Va., 1983-85; pres. and chief exec. officer Affiliated Sci. Inc., Ingleside, Ill., 1985—; vis. prof. genetics U. Ill., Chgo., 1989-90; exec. dir. Ctr. for Biotech., Northwestern U., 1990—; faculty Grad. Sch. Biotech. and Kellogg Grad. Sch. Mgmt., Northwestern U., 1990—; bd. dirs. several cos. Author and editor: Computer-Aided Drug Design, 1989, Nucleic Acid Targeted Drug Design, 1992; contbr. articles to profl. jours. Named to Outstanding Working Women in the U.S., 1982; recipient many sci. and bus. awards. Fellow Soc. Indsl. Microbiology (bd. dirs. 1990—); mem. AAAS, Am. Chem. Soc., Nat. Wildlife Fedn., Phi Beta Kappa, Sigma Xi. Episcopalian. Avocations: horseback riding, skiing, raising German Shephard dogs. Office: Affiliated Sci Inc PO Box 437 Ingleside IL 60041-0437 also: Northwestern U Ctr for Biotech 2153 Sheridan Rd Evanston IL 60208

PROPST, HAROLD DEAN, retired university chancellor; b. Newton, N.C., Feb. 7, 1934; s. Charles Clayton and Sarah Isabel (Hilderbrand) P. B.A., Wake Forest Coll., 1956; M.A., Peabody Coll., 1959, Ph.D, 1964; LL.D., Mercer U., 1985. Tchr. Vandalia Pub. Schs., Ohio, 1959-60; instr. Wake Forest Coll., Winston-Salem, N.C., 1960-61; asst. prof. English, Radford Coll., Va., 1962-64, assoc. prof., 1964-65, prof., 1965-69, chmn. dept. English, 1965-66, 68-69; dean Armstrong State Coll., Savannah, Ga., 1969-76, v.p. for acad. affairs, 1976-79; vice chancellor for acad. devel. Univ. System Ga., Atlanta, 1979-81, exec. vice chancellor, 1981-85, chancellor, 1985-94. Editor: (novel) John Brent, 1970; contbr. articles to profl. jours., monographs, books. Bd. visitors Radford Coll. 1970-74; former pres. bd. Family Counseling Ctr., Savannah; former pres. bd. Family Counseling Ctr., Savannah; former bd. dirs. Savannah Symphony, Savannah Heart Assn., Alliance Theatre, Atlanta; mem. So. Region Edn. Bd., 1985-94. With USN, 1956-58. Fellow Carnegie Found., 1958, Ford Found., 1960; recipient Disting. Alumnus award Wake Forest U., 1986. Mem. Am. Assn. State Colls and Univs. (com. on accreditation 1982-86), Acad. for Ednl. Devel. (study com. on campus govt. 1976-77). Baptist.

PROPST, JOHN LEAKE, lawyer; b. Winnsboro, S.C., Apr. 7, 1914; s. Floyd Ernest and Jennie (Leake) P.; m. Marjorie Vilsack, Oct. 4, 1941; children: Marie T. Propst MacPhail, Pamela A. Propst Campbell, Suzanne L. Propst Honeycutt, Marjorie Louise Propst Bernard. A.B., Princeton U., 1935; LL.B., Duquesne U., 1940, LL.D. (hon.), 1970. With The Union Trust Co., Pitts., 1935-46; with Mellon Nat. Bank & Trust Co., 1946—, successively asst. trust officer, trust officer, asst. v., 1946-54, v.p. trust dept., 1954-65, v.p., sr. trust officer, 1965-70, sr. v.p., 1970-77; exec. Roldiva Inc., 1977-82; of counsel Reed Smith Shaw & McClay, 1982—. Treas. Pitts. Urban Redevel. Authority, 1957-71; sponsor Allegheny Conf. Tr. Kaufmann Found., Shadyside Hosp., Ellis Sch., 1960-87; trustee Pitts. Found., 1977—, chmn. distbn. com., 1982-87; trustee Mercy Hosp., 1960-95; bd. dirs. Duquesne U., 1960-86, Pitts. Boys Club, The Dreyfus Laurel Funds, 1988—. Lt. USNR, 1942-45. Mem. Pa. Bankers Assn. (past chmn. trust div.), Allegheny County Bar Assn., Fox Chapel Golf Club, Pitts. Law Club, Pitts. Golf Club, Duquesne Club. Home: 5521 Dunmoyle Ave Pittsburgh PA 15217-1014 Office: James Hay Reed Bldg 435 6th Ave Pittsburgh PA 15219-1809

PROPST, ROBERT BRUCE, federal judge; b. Onatchee, Ala., July 13, 1931; s. Franklin Glenn and Mildred (Moore) P.; m. Elma Jo Griffin, Dec. 29, 1962; children: Stephen, David, Joanne. B.S., U. Ala., 1953, J.D., 1957. Pvt. practice law Wilson, Propst, Isom, Jackson, Bailey & Bott, 1957-80; Judge U.S. Dist Ct. (no. dist.) Ala., Birmingham, 1980—. Served to 1st lt. U.S. Army, 1953-55. Mem. ABA, Ala. Bar Assn., Birmingham Bar Assn., Calhoun County Bar Assn., Jaycees (pres. 1954-60). Methodist. Club: Exchange (Anniston, Ala.). Avocation: golf. Home: 500 Webster Rd Apt 102 Auburn AL 36830-4214 Office: US Dist Ct 581 US Courthouse 1729 5th Ave N Birmingham AL 35203-2000

PROROK, ROBERT FRANCIS, lawyer; b. Pitts., Feb. 21, 1952; s. Stephen F. and Nellie (Mamula) P.; m. Joanne Marie Dolata, May 26, 1979; children: Matthew, Christine. BA, U. Pitts., 1974, JD, 1977. Bar: Pa. 1977, U.S. Dist. Ct. (we. dist.) Pa. 1977, U.S. Ct. Appeals (3d cir.) 1979, U.S. Supreme Ct. 1985, U.S. Dist. Ct. (ea. dist.) Mich. 1989, U.S. Tax Ct. 1989. Law clk. U.S. Dist. Ct. Western Dist. Pa., Pitts., 1977-80; ptnr. Reed Smith Shaw & McClay, Pitts., 1980—. Mem. Pa. Bar Assn. (continuing edn. com. 1990-91), Pitts. Pers. Assn. (program com. 1991). Republican. Roman Catholic. Avocation: golf. Office: Reed Smith Shaw & McClay Mellon Sq 435 6th Ave Pittsburgh PA 15219

PROSKIN, ARNOLD W., state assemblyman, lawyer; b. Albany, N.Y., Apr. 2, 1938; s. Betty (Levin) P.; m. Martha Pollack, June 4, 1960; children: Lisa, Heath, Wendy, Michael. Grad., SUNY, Albany; LLD, Boston Coll., 1964. Bar: N.Y. 1964. Pvt. practice Albany, N.Y., 1964—; dist. atty. Office of Dist. Atty. Albany County, N.Y., 1969-73; judge Albany County Ct., 1973-76; ptnr. The Proskin Law Firm, Albany, 1976—; mem. N.Y. State Assembly, Albany, 1984—; mem. judiciary, codes and ethics standing com., guidance standing com., racing and wagering standing com., chmn. steering com. minority conf.; mem. legis. ethics com.; mem. civil practice, property rights, estates and trusts, court ops. and constl. amendments subcoms.; past mem. ins., corps., authorities, commns., election law, labor and housing standing coms. Active Temple Ohav Shalom, Gov. Clinton Coun., Boy Scouts Am. Adv. Bd., Jewish War Vets., Adv. Bd. Barn Raisers. With USN, 1956-58. Recipient N.Y. State Vocat. Schs. award, 1971, Histradrut Pub. Svc. Coun. award, 1973; named Outstanding Young Man of Yr., N.Y. State Jaycees, 1972, Man of Yr., Internat. Order of Alhambra, 1975, Mem. of Yr., Independent Order of Off Fellows, 1985. Mem. ABA, Am. Judicature Soc., N.Y. State Bar Assn., N.Y. State Dist. Attys. Assn., Saratoga County Bar Assn., Albany Bar Assn., Nat. Dist. Attys. Assn., County Judge's Assn. State N.Y., Am. Legion, B'nai B'rith Gideon Lodge, Shiners, West Albany Athletic Assn., Latham Area C. of C. Office: The Proskin Law Firm 423 Loudon Rd Ballston Lake NY 12204

PROSKY, ROBERT JOSEPH, actor; b. Phila., Dec. 13, 1930; s. Joseph and Helen (Kuhn) Porzuczek; m. Ida Mae Hove, June 4, 1960, children—Stefan, John, Andrew. Student, Temple U., Am. Theatre. Appeared at Arena Stage, Washington, 23 years including roles in Death of a Salesman, Twelfth night, Enemy of the People, Galileo; appeared on Broadway in Moonchildren, View From the Bridge, Glengarry Glen Ross, A Walk in the Woods, 1988 (Tony award nomination 1988, Best Actor award Outer Critics Circle, toured USSR and Lithuania 1989); films include Thief, 1981, Lords of Discipline, 1983, Christine, 1983, The Natural, 1984, Broadcast News, 1987, Outrageous Fortune, 1987, Things Change, 1988, Gremlins II, 1988, Something About Love, 1990, Green Card, 1990, Life in the Food Chain, 1990, The Love She Sought, 1990, Far and Away, 1992, Hoffa, 1992, Life on the High Wire, 1992, Rudy, 1992, Last Action Hero, 1993, Mrs. Doubtfire, 1993, Miracle on 34th Street, 1994; TV appearances include role of Sgt. Jablonski in Hill Street Blues, The Murder of Mary Phagan, 1988, Home Fires Burning, 1988, From the Dead of Night, 1989, Heist, 1989, Dangerous Pursuit, 1990, Johnny Ryan, 1990, The Love She Sought, 1990, Double Edge, 1992, Teamster Boss: The Jackie Presser Story, 1992, narrator Lifestories; mem. first Am. co. to tour Soviet Union 1972. Recipient Tony award nomination for Glengarry Glen Ross, 1985; Joseph Jefferson award nomination, 1985; Drama Desk award, 1985. Office: care ICM 304 E 65th St Apt 5A New York NY 10021-6783

PROSPERI, DAVID PHILIP, public relations executive; b. Chgo., June 20, 1953. BSBA, U. Ill., 1975; MBA in Internat. Bus., George Washington U., 1983. Moving cons. Fed. Safety Moving & Storage, Elmhurst, Ill., 1975-79; press aide 1980 Reagan for Pres. campaign, Los Angeles, 1979-80, Reagan-Bush Campaign, Alexandria, Va., 1980-81; asst. press sec. to the Pres. White House, Washington, 1981-82; mgr. govt. affairs The Superior Oil Co., Washington, 1982-84; press sec. U.S. Dept. Energy, Washington, 1985; asst. to sec. dir. pub. affairs U.S. Dept. Interior, Washington, 1985-88; asst. sec. transp. U.S. Dept. Transp., Washington, 1989-90; v.p. Chgo. Bd. Trade, 1990—; prin. Coun. on Excellence in Govt. Republican. Roman Catholic. Avocations: basketball, tennis, spending time with family. Office: Chgo Bd Trade 141 W Jackson Blvd Ste 1740A Chicago IL 60604-2904

PROSPERI, LOUIS ANTHONY, lawyer; b. Altoona, Pa., Jan. 12, 1954; s. Louis Alfred and Ann Francis (DiDimenico) P.; m. Susan Lynn Irwin, Sept. 14, 1985. BS in Bus. Adminstrn. summa cum laude, Georgetown U., 1975; JD cum laude, Harvard U., 1978. Bar: Pa. 1978, U.S. Dist. Ct. (we. dist.) Pa. 1978, U.S. Ct. Appeals (Fed. cir.) 1985, U.S. Ct. Fed. Claims, 1985, U.S. Tax Ct. 1979. From assoc. to ptnr. Reed, Smith, Shaw & McClay, Pitts., 1978-94; pvt. practice Law Office Louis A. Prosperi, Pitts., 1994—. Mem. Allegheny County Bar Assn., Pitts. Tax Club. Republican. Roman Catholic. Club: Longue Vue (Verona, Pa.). Avocations: golf, tennis, paddle tennis, cross-country skiing. Home: 3036 Grassmere Ave Pittsburgh PA 15216-1862 Office: Law Office Louis A Prosperi Grant Bldg 310 Grant St Ste 3601 Pittsburgh PA 15219

PROSPERI, ROBERT, manufacturing company executive; b. Boston, Oct. 11, 1942; s. Amaddio and Josephine (Barra) P.; m. Carol J. Coholan, Sept. 22, 1966; children: David, Michelle. BSBA, Boston U., 1964. Trainee New Eng. Elec. Systems, Malden, Mass., 1964-65; prodn. mgr. Granite Rsch. Industries, Somerville, Mass., 1965-70, v.p., 1970-75; prodn. mgr. Lynn Sand & Stone Co., Swampscott, Mass., 1975-80, v.p., 1980-84, exec. v.p., 1988—; exec. v.p. Bardon Trimount, Burlington, Mass., 1988-92, also bd. dirs. Bd. dirs. Mass. Constrn. Industry Bd., 1986-88. With USMCR, 1964-70. Mem. Mass. Concrete and Aggregates (pres. 1988-90), Constrn. Industry of Mass., Assn. Gen. Contractors Mass., Mass. Concrete Assn. (v.p. 1986-88, pres. 1988-90). Roman Catholic. Home: 6 Charing Cross Lynnfield MA 01940 Office: Bardon Trimount 70 Blanchard Rd Burlington MA 01803

PROSSER, C. LADD, physiology educator, researcher; b. Avon, N.Y., May 12, 1907; s. Clifford James and Izora May (Ladd) P.; m. Hazel Blanchard, Aug. 25, 1934; children—Jane Ellen, Nancy Ladd, Loring Blanchard. A.B., U. Rochester, 1929; Ph.D., Johns Hopkins U., 1932; hon. degree, Clark U., 1975. Asst. prof. physiology Clark U., Worcester, Mass., 1934-39; asst. prof physiology U. Ill., Urbana, 1939-47, assoc. prof. physiology, 1947-52, prof. physiology, 1952-74, prof. emeritus, 1975—; asst. sect. chief Metallurgy Lab. U. Chgo., 1943-46; vis prof. U. Hawaii, U. Wash., U. Mass., Ariz. State U. Author: Adaptational Biology, 1986; author, editor: Comparative Animal Physiology, 1st edit., 1951, 4th edit. 1991; contbr. numerous articles to profl. jours. Guggenheim fellow, 1963-64; Fulbright fellow, 1971-72. Fellow Am. Acad. Arts and Scis.; mem. Nat. Acad. Scis., Soc. Gen. Physiologists (pres. 1958-59), AAAS (v.p. 1960), Am. Soc. Zoologists (pres. 1961), Am. Physiol. Soc. (pres. 1969-70), Bavarian Acad. Sci. Unitarian. Avocations: music; gardening. Home: 101 W Windsor Rd Urbana IL 61801-6663 Office: U Ill 524 Burrill Hall Urbana IL 61801

PROSSER, FRANKLIN PIERCE, computer scientist; b. Atlanta, July 4, 1935; s. Edward Theron and Eunice (McDaniel) P.; m. Brenda Mary Lau, June 16, 1960; children: Edward, Andrea. B.S., Ga. Inst. Tech., 1956, M.S., 1958; Ph.D., Pa. State U., 1961. Prof. computer sci. Ind. U., Bloomington, 1969—; asso. dir. Wrubel Computing Center, 1969-81, chmn. dept. computer sci., 1971-77, 87-93, spl. asst. for acad. computing, 1979-81; v.p. Logic Design, Inc., 1982-92; cons. Lockheed Theoretical Physics Lab., Palo Alto, Calif., 1967. Mem. AAAS, IEEE. Home: 1200 S Longwood Dr Bloomington IN 47401-6072 Office: Ind U Dept Computer Sci Bloomington IN 47405

PROSSER, JOHN MARTIN, architect, educator, university dean, urban design consultant; b. Wichita, Kans., Dec. 28, 1932; s. Francis Ware and Harriet Corinne (Osborne) P.; m. Judith Adams, Aug. 28, 1954 (dec. 1982); children: Thomas, Anne, Edward; m. Karen Ann Cleary, Dec. 30, 1983; children: Jennifer. B.Arch., U. Kans., 1955; M.Arch., Carnegie Mellon U., 1961. Registered architect, Kans., Colo. Architect, Robinson and Hissem, Wichita, 1954-56, Guirey, Srnka, and Arnold, Phoenix, 1961-62, James Sudler Assocs., Denver, 1962-68; ptnr., architect Nuzum, Prosser and Vetter, Boulder, 1969-73; from asst. prof. to prof. U. Colo., Boulder, Denver, 1968—, acting dean, 1980-84, dean, 1984; dir. environ. design U. Colo., Boulder, 1969-72, dir. urban design, 1972-85; cons. John M. Prosser Assoc., Boulder and Denver, 1974—; vis. prof. urban design Oxford Poly., Eng., 1979; vis. Critic Carnegie Mellon U., U. N.Mex., Colo. Coll.; pres. Denver chpt. AIA, 1983. Author, narrator PBS TV documentary Cities Are For Kids Too, 1984. Prin. works include (with others) hist. redesign Mus. Western Art, Denver (design honor 1984), Villa Italia, Lakewood, Colo., Denver, Auraria Higher Edn. Ctr., Pueblo C.C. campus plan and new acad. facilities, comprehensive campus plan Denver U., Lamar C.C., Ft. Lewis Coll., Pueblo City Ctr. Urban Design, Westminster Golf Course Community, Denver Botanic Gardens 20-Yr. Concept Plan, Colo. Coll. Historic Preservation Plan, Commerce City Golf Course Community. Bd. dirs. Denver Parks and Recreation Bd., 1987-93; chmn. design rev. bd. Univs. Colo., Boulder, Denver and Colorado Springs, 1981—; mem. archtl. control com. Denver Tech. Ctr., 1984—; Meridian Internat. Bus. Ctr., 1984—; DTC West, 1991—; Denver Internat. Bus. Ctr., 1993—; planning cons. Denver Internat. Airport Environs Devel. Projects. Capt. USAF, 1956-59. Co-recipient 2d place nat. award Am. Soc. Interior Designers, 1984, honor award Colo. Soc. Architects, 1984. Mem. Urban Land Inst. Republican. Club: Denver Country (pres. 1986-87). Avocation: Arlberg Ski. Home: 1620 Monaco Pky Denver CO 80220-1643 Office: U Colo 1200 Larimer St Denver CO 80204-5310

PROSSER, KATHY, state official; b. Canton, Ohio, Aug. 9, 1950; d. Ralph H. Prosser and Frances Elizabeth Vandall Copeland. MPA, Harvard U., 1987. Exec. asst., dep. treas. Office of Senator John Glenn, Washington, 1973-83, chief of staff, 1983-85; dir. scheduling and advance, campaign com. John Glenn for Pres., Washington, 1983-84; Washington rep. John F. Kennedy Sch. Govt., Harvard U., Cambridge, Mass., 1986; dep. commr. fin. and adminstrn. Mass. Dept. Environ. Mgmt., 1987-89; commr. Ind. Dept. Environ. Mgmt., Indpls., 1989—; bd. dirs. water quality Internat. Joint Commn., Washington, 1989—; chair Recycling Inst. Ind., Indpls., 1989—; Ind. State Emergency Planning Commn., Indpls., 1989—; bd. dirs. Econ. Devel. Coun. Indpls., 1989—. Mem. Dem. platform com. Mass., 1989. Named one of 100 Most Interesting Women, Boston Woman Mag., 1988, Woman of Distinction, Soroptimist Club Ind. 1993. Mem. Environ. Coun. States (founding, pres. 1993-94), Women Execs. in State Govt. (chair 1993-

94), Environ. Law Inst. (bd. dirs., exec. com.). Avocations: golf, tennis, skiing. Office: Ind Dept Environ Mgmt PO Box 6015 100 N Senate Ave Indianapolis IN 46206

PROSSER, MICHAEL HUBERT, communications educator; b. Indpls., Mar. 29, 1936; s. Marshall Herbert and Clydia Catharine (O'Dea) P.; m. Carol Mary Hogle, Nov. 27, 1958 (div. 1983); children: Michelle Ann Prosser-Evans, Leo Michael, Louis Mark; m. Joan Ann Kirkeby, Dec. 6, 1986. BA, Ball State U., 1958, MA, 1959; PhD, U. Ill., 1964. Tchr. Latin Urbana (Ill.) Jr. High Sch., 1960-63; asst. prof. speech SUNY, Buffalo, 1963-69; assoc. prof. speech Ind. U., Bloomington, 1969-72; prof. rhetoric and comm. U. Va., Charlottesville, 1972—, chair, 1972-77; William A. Kern prof. in comm. Rochester Inst. Tech., 1994—; chair AFS Global Awareness Day, U. Va., 1983-90, Global Awareness Day, The New South Africa, 25th Ann. of Intercultural Communication, The UN Gen. Assembly Security Coun. confts., Rochester Inst. Tech., 1995; vis. lectr. comm. Queens Coll. CUNY, 1966, 67; vis. assoc. prof. qpeech Calif. State U., Hayward, 1971; vis. prof. curriculum Meml. U. Newfoundland, St. John's, 1972, St. Paul U. and U. Ottawa (Can.). 1975; cons. intercultural comm. U.S. info. Agy., Washington1, 977; disting. vis. prof. speech Kent (Ohio) State U., 1978; Fulbright prof. English, U. Swaizilnad, Kwalusene, 1990-91, Am. U. of Bulgaria, 1994-95 (declined); fellow New Coll. U. Va., 1992—; Gannett Lecture Rochester Inst. Tech., 1995. Author: The Cultural Dialogue, 1978; editor: An Ethic for Survival, 1969, Sow the Wind, Reap the Whirlwind: Heads of State Address the United Nations (2 vols.), 1970, Intercommunication Among Nations and Peoples, 1973; co-editor: Readings in Classical Rhetoric, 1969, Readings in Medieval Rhetoric, 1973. Mem. Haiti commn. Cath. Diocese Richmond, 1989-93; bd. dirs. Rochester Assn. UN, 1995—; chair pro tem Rochester Area Fulbright Chpt., 1995. Recipient Disting. Alumnus award Ball State U., 1978. Mem. Internat. Soc. for Intercultural Edn., Tng. and Rsch. (founding mem., pres. 1984-86, Citizen of World 1986, Outstanding Sr. Interculturalinst 1990), Internat. Comm. Assn. (v.p. Disting. Svc. award 1978), Fulbright Assn., Am. Field Svc. (pres. intercultural program. Charlottesville, Va., 1982-86), Speech Comm. Assn. (chair comms. on intercultural and internat. comm. 1971-73), Midwest Univs. Consortium on Internat. Affairs (chair devel. comms. coun. 1971-75), N.Y. State African Studies Assn. Democrat. Roman Catholic. Avocations: social justice and peace advocacy, youth, travel. Office: Rochester Inst Tech Coll of Liberal Arts 92 Lomb Meml Dr Rochester NY 14623

PROSTERMAN, ROY L., law educator, development specialist; b. Chgo., July 13, 1935; s. Sidney and Natalie (Weisberg) P. A.B., U. Chgo., 1954; J.D., Harvard U., 1958. Bar: N.Y. 1958. Assoc. firm Sullivan & Cromwell, N.Y.C., 1959-65; asst. prof. law U. Wash., Seattle, 1965-68, assoc. prof., 1968-70, prof. law, 1970—, Corbally prof. pub. svc., 1991—; land law cons. Stanford Research Inst. project on South Vietnamese land tenure, 1967; cons. on land reform and devel. issues, various countries, 1967—; cons. to various mems. of Congress on fgn. aid and devel., 1968—; cons. on land reform Am. Inst. Free Labor Devel., El Salvador, 1980-85, World Bank, Ukraine, Kirghizstan, 1992—, Harvard Inst. Internat. Devel., Russia, 1993—. Author: textbook Surviving to 3000: An Introduction to the Study of Lethal Conflict, 1972, Land Reform and Democratic Development, 1987; editor: Agrarian Reform and Grassroots Development, 1990; contbr. articles in field to publs. Prin. adv. Magnuson-Humphrey-Packwood Criteria for Aid amendment to Fgn. Assistance Act, 1975; adv. council World Without War Council; bd. dirs. Hunger Project, 1980-90; pres. Rural Devel. Inst. Served with USAFR, 1958; res. 1958-64. Recipient 1st Ann. Ralph Bunche award Seattle-King County Bar Assn., 1973, Outstanding Pub. Svc. award U. Wash., 1990. Office: U Wash Sch Law JB-20 Seattle WA 98195

PROTAS, RON, dance company executive. Gen. dir. Martha Graham Ctr. Contemporary Dance, N.Y.C, assoc. artistic dir.; now artistic dir. Martha Graham Dance Co., N.Y.C. Office: Martha Graham Dance Co 316 E 63rd St New York NY 10021-7702*

PROTO, NEIL THOMAS, lawyer, educator; b. New Haven, Sept. 4, 1945; s. Matthew and Celeste Proto. BA, So. Conn. State U., New Haven, 1967; MA, George Washington U., 1969, JD, 1972. Bar D.C. 1973, Conn. 1983, U.S. Ct. Appeals (1st, 2d, 3d, 4th, 5th, 8th, 9th, 10th, 11th and D.C. cirs.), U.S. Supreme Ct. 1976. Atty. U.S. Dept. Justice, Washington, 1972-79; gen. counsel Pres.'s Nuclear Safety Oversight Com., Washington, 1980-81; of counsel Kelly, Drye and Warren, Stamford, Conn., 1983-89; ptnr. Verner Liipfert Bernhard McPherson & Hand, Washington, 1989—; adj. prof. Georgetown U., Washington, 1990—; vis. lectr. Yale U., 1978-79, Yale Law Sch., 1979. Contbr. articles to newspaper. Chair Am. Friends of Wilton Park, Washington and West Sussex, Eng., 1992; bd. dirs. Shubert Theater, New Haven, 1981-86, Long Wharf Theater, New Haven, 1980-90. Named. Disting. Alumnus So. Conn. State U., 1981. Office: Verner Liipfert Bernhard McPherson & Hand 901 15th St NE NW Ste 700 Washington DC 20005

PROUDFOOT, WAYNE LEE, religion educator; b. Peterborough, N.H., Nov. 17, 1939; s. Raymond Stanley and Sarah Alice (King) P. BS, Yale U., 1961; BD, Harvard U., 1964, ThM, 1966, PhD, 1972. Asst. prof. philosophy of religion Andover-Newton Theol. Sch., 1969-70; asst. prof. religion Fordham U., N.Y.C., 1970-72; prof. Columbia U., N.Y.C., 1972—; bd. dirs. Fund for Theol. Edn. Kent fellow, 1965-68. Mem. Am. Acad. Religion, Soc. for Values in Higher Edn. Home: 315 W 106th St New York NY 10025-3445 Office: Columbia U 506 Kent Hall New York NY 10028

PROUGH, RUSSELL ALLEN, biochemistry educator; b. Twin Falls, Idaho, Nov. 5, 1943; s. Elza Leroy and Beulah Elsie (Huddleston) P.; M. Betty Marie Ehlers, Dec. 26, 1965; children: Jennifer Sally, Kimberly Marie. BS in Chemistry, Coll. of Idaho, 1965; PhD in Biochemistry and Biophysics, Oreg. State U., 1969. Postdoctoral fellow VA Hosp., Kansas City, Mo., 1969-72; instr. biochemistry U. Tex. Southwestern Med. Sch., Dallas, 1972-73, asst. prof. biochemistry, 1973-77, assoc. prof. biochemistry, 1977-82, prof. biochemistry, 1982-86; prof., chmn. dept. biochemistry U. Louisville Sch. Med., 1986—; mem. NIH Toxicology Study Sect., 1984-88, State of Nebr. Smoking Disease and Cancer Rsch. Program, 1984-91. Assoc. editor Drug Metabolism and Disposition, 1994—. Recipient Rsch. Career Devel. award USPHS. Mem. Am. Soc. Biochemistry and Molecular Biology, Am. Assn. Cancer Rsch., Am. Soc. Pharmacology and Exptl. Therapeutics, Internat. Soc. for Study of Xenobiotics, Sigma Xi. Lutheran. Office: U of Louisville Dept of Biochemistry Louisville KY 40292

PROUGH, STEPHEN W., savings and loan executive; b. 1945. COO Westcorp, Irvine, Calif., 1983—; bd. dirs. Office: Downey Savs Loan Assn 3501 Jamboree Rd Newport Beach CA 92660

PROULX, EDNA ANNIE, writer; b. Norwich, Conn., Aug. 22, 1935; d. George Napolean and Lois Nelly (Gill) Proulx; m. James Hamilton Lang, June 22, 1969 (div. 1990); children: Jonathan Edward Lang, Gillis Crowell Lang, Morgan Hamilton Lang. BA cum laude, U. Vt., 1969; MA, Sir George Williams U., Montreal, Can., 1973; DHL (hon.), U. Maine, 1994. Author: Heart Songs and Other Stories, 1988, Postcards, 1992 (PEN/Faulkner award 1993), The Shipping News, 1993 (Nat. Book award for fiction 1993, Chgo. Tribune Heartland award 1993, Irish Times Internat. Fiction award 1993, Pulitzer Prize for fiction 1994); contbr. more than 50 articles to mags. and jours. Kress fellow Harvard U., 1974, fellow Vt. Coun. Arts, 1989, NEA, 1991, Guggenheim Found., 1992; rsch. grantee Inter.-U. Ctr., 1975; resident Ucross Found., 1990-92. Mem. PEN Am. Ctr., Phi Beta Kappa, Phi Alpha Theta. Avocations: canoeing, reading, fishing, carpentry. Office: c/o Scribners Pub Co 866 3rd Ave Fl 7 New York NY 10022-6221*

PROUT, GEORGE RUSSELL, JR., medical educator, urologist; b. Boston, July 23, 1924; s. George Russell and Marion (Snow) P.; m. Loa Katherine Wheatley, Oct. 17, 1950; children: George Russell III, Elizabeth Louise. Student, Union Coll., 1943, DSc (hon.), 1990; MD, Albany Med. Coll., 1947, DSc (hon.), 1988; MA (hon.), Harvard U., 1969. Intern Grasslands Hosp., Valhalla, N.Y., 1947-48; resident N.Y. Hosp., N.Y.C., 1952-56; asst. attending physician Meml. Ctr. for Cancer and Allied Disease, N.Y.C., 1956-57; assoc. prof., chmn. div. urology U. Miami, 1957-60; prof., chmn. div. urology Med. Coll. Va., 1960-69; chief urol. svc. Mass. Gen. Hosp., Boston, 1969-89; prof. surgery Harvard Med. Sch., 1969-89; emeritus prof. surgery Harvard Med. Sch., Boston, 1989—; hon. urologist Mass. Gen.

Hosp., Boston, 1993—; chmn. Adjuvants in Surg. Treatment of Bladder Cancer; mem. adv. task force to Nat. Cancer Inst., 1968—, expert cons. divsn. surveillance, 1991—, Finland coop. ATBC study, 1991—; chmn. Nat. Bladder Cancer Group, 1973-86. Editor: Urol. Oncology, 1994—. With USNR, 1950-52. Fellow ACS, Acad. Medicine Toronto (corr.); mem. AMA, AAUP, Am. Urol. Assn., Can. Urol. Assn., Am. Cancer Soc., Soc. Pelvic Surgeons, Soc. Surg. Oncology, Soc. Univ. Urologists, Dallas. So. Clin. Soc. (hon.), Am. Assn. Genitourinary Surgeons, Soc. Pediatric Urology, Soc. Urol. Oncology, Soc. Internat. Urologists, Soc. Basic Urol. Rsch., Alpha Omega Alpha. Home: 27 W Prospect Bay Dr Grasonville MD 21638-9668

PROUT, RALPH EUGENE, physician; b. Los Angeles, Feb. 27, 1933; s. Ralph Byron and Fern (Taylor) P.; m. Joanne Morris, Sept. 17, 1980; children: Michael, Michelle. BA, La Sierra Coll., 1953; MD, Loma Linda U., 1957; D of Nutri-Medicine (hon.), John F. Kennedy Coll., 1987. Diplomate: Nat. Bd. Med. Examiners. Intern Los Angeles County Hosp., 1957-58; resident internal medicine White Meml. Hosp., Los Angeles, 1958-60; resident psychiatry Harding Hosp., Worthington, Ohio, 1960-61; practice medicine specializing in internal medicine Napa, Calif., 1961-63; staff internist Calif. Med. Facility, Vacaville, 1963-68, chief med. officer, 1968-84; chief med. cons. Calif. Dept. Corrections, 1977-86, chief med. services, 1983; med. cons. Wellness Cons., Placerville, Calif., 1986—; pres. Addiction Medicine treatment Ctr., Placerville, Calif., 1991-95; instr. Sch. Medicine, Loma Linda U., 1965-66; clin. assoc. U. Calif.-Davis Sch. Medicine, 1978-84; med. cons. Substance Abuse Pine Grove Camp, 1985-90. Treas. Vacaville Republican Assembly, 1972-75; del. Republican Central Com. Solano County, 1975-78; Bd. dirs. Napa-Solano County United Crusade, Vallejo, Calif., 1969-71, v.p. 1970-71; bd. dirs. Project Clinic, Vacaville, 1974-77, Home Health Com. Inter-Community Hosp., Fairfield, 1978-80; pres. MotherLode Citizens for Drug-Free Youth, Amador County, 1985—. Named One of Outstanding Young Men of Am., 1968. Mem. AMA, Internat. Acad. Nutrition and Preventive Medicine, Calif. Soc. Internal Medicine, Am. Soc. Internal Medicine, Am. Assn. Sr. Physicians, Internat. Assn. New Sci., Union Concerned Scis., Mother Lode Citizens for Drug-Free Youth, Native Sons of Golden West, Alpha Omega Alpha. Republican. Home and Office: 24405 Shake Ridge Rd Volcano CA 95689-9728 *When we ask better questions, the answers will follow.*

PROUTY, NORMAN R., investment banker; b. N.Y.C., Feb. 4, 1939; s. Norman R. and Eleanor (Ryan) P.; m. Alden Finch, July 18, 1964 (div. Mar. 1989); children: Brooks Silliman, Nicholas Alden, Honor Howland; m. Allison LoveJoy Simmons, Jan. 27, 1990; 1 child, Annabel Scarlett LoveJoy. BA, Yale U., 1961. V.p., sr. credit officer Citibank, N.Y.C., 1961-81; gen. ptnr. Lazard Frères & Co., N.Y.C., 1981—. Trustee Pitzer Coll., Nature Conservancy of N.Y. State, 1992—; bd. overseers The Claremont Colls., 1990. Mem. Anglers' Club, The Brook, Racquet and Tennis Club, Bedford Golf and Tennis Club, Fishers Island Club. Avocations: fishing, shooting, skiing, sailing, tennis. Home: 120 E 80th St New York NY 10021-0306 Office: Lazard Freres & Co 1 Rockefeller Plz New York NY 10020

PROVENCHER, ROGER ARTHUR, international consultant; b. Manchester, N.H., June 20, 1923; s. Arthur J. and Rose Albina (Briere) P.; m. Josette Marguerite Camus, Jan. 3, 1946 (dec. 1976); children: Frances Provencher-Kambour, Carl; m. Mary Lou Sack, Mar. 17, 1989. BA, U. N.H., 1949; Doctorat D'Universite', U. Paris, 1950. Joined Dept. State, 1950; asst. commr. gen. Expo 67, Montreal, Que., Can., 1965-67; mgmt. analyst Washington, 1968; assigned to Nat. War Coll., 1969-70; 1st sec., counselor Am. embassy, Moscow, 1970-73; counselor for administrv. affairs Am. embassy, Vientiane, Laos, 1973-74, Tehran, Iran, 1974-77; sr. counsellor Internat. Telecommunication Union, Geneva, 1977-82; mng. dir. Pan African Airlines (Nigeria) Ltd., Lagos, 1962-63. V.p Rollingwood Community Assn. 1st lt. AUS, 1943-46, ETO. Recipient Meritorious Honor award Dept. State, 1958, 62, also Superior Honor award, 1975. Mem. Nat. War Coll. Alumni Assn., Am. Fgn. Service Assn. (dir.), Lambda Pi. Home and Office: PO Box 326 Ladysmith VA 22501-0326 *A public servant must never forget that his responsibility rests on serving the public. The public have contributed their trust and hope in their investments. Their aspirations must be honored even if at times, physical, ideological, conjugal or other personal stresses invite abdication.*

PROVENSEN, ALICE ROSE TWITCHELL, artist, author; b. Chgo.; d. Jay Horace and Kathryn (Zelanis) Twitchell; m. Martin Provensen, Apr. 17, 1944; 1 child, Karen Anna. Student, Art Inst. of Chgo., 1930-31, U. Calif., L.A., 1939, Art Student League, N.Y., 1940-41; D.H.L. (hon.), Marist Coll., 1986. With Walter Lanz Studios, Los Angeles, 1942-43; OSS, 1944-45. Exhibited (with Martin Provensen) Balt. Mus., 1954, Am. Inst. Graphic Arts, N.Y., 1959, Botolph Group, Boston, 1964; exhibited one person shows: Henry Feiwel Gallery, N.Y.C., 1991, Children's Mus., Washington, 1991, Moscarelle Mus. Art, Williamsburg, Va., 1991; books represented in Fifty Books of Yr. Selections, Am. Inst. Graphic Arts, 1947, 48, 52 (The Charge of the Light Brigade named Best Illustrated Children's Book of the Yr. N.Y. Times 1964, co-recipient Gold medal Soc. Illustrators 1960); author/illustrator: books including Karen's Opposites, 1963, Karen's Curiosity, 1963, What is a Color?, 1967, (with Martin Provensen) Who's In the Egg, 1970, The Provensen Book of Fairy Tales, 1971, Play on Words, 1972, My Little Hen, 1973, Roses are Red, 1973, Our Animal Friends, 1974, The Year at Maple Hill Farm, 1978, A Horse and a Hound, A Goat and a Gander, 1979, An Owl and Three Pussycats, 1981, Town and Country, 1984, Shaker Lane, 1987, The Buck Stops Here, 1990, Punch in New York, 1991 (Best Books N.Y. Times 1991), My Fellow Americans, 1995; illustrator: (with Martin Provensen) children's books including Mother Goose Book, 1976, Old Mother Hubbard, 1977, A Peaceable Kingdom, 1978, The Golden Serpent, 1980, A Visit to William Blake's Inn, 1981, Birds, Beasts and the Third Thing, 1982, The Glorious Flight, 1984 (Caldecott medal 1984), The Voyage of the Ludgate Hill, 1987; also textbooks.

PROVENZALE, MARYELLEN KIRBY, judge, educator; b. Chgo., Dec. 21, 1938; d. Cornelius A. and Hanora (O'Sullivan) Kirby; m. Richard Paul Doria; children: Donald J. Jr., James P., John G., Patrick L. BA, Mundelein Coll., 1960; JD, DePaul U., 1977. Bar: Ill. 1977, U.S. Dist. Ct. (no. dist.) Ill. 1978, U.S. Dist. Ct. Trial Bar (no. dist.) Ill. 1984. Asst. state's atty. DuPage County, Wheaton, Ill., 1977-85; assoc. judge Ill. 18th jud. cir. DuPage County, Wheaton, 1985—; adj. prof. U. Ill. Police Tng. Acad. 1985, Nat. Law Inst., FBI Acad., Quantico, Va., 1985; instr. criminal law Coll. of DuPage, 1987, Multi-Regional Police Tng., 1983-86. V.p. Oak Creek Homeowners Assn., Downers Grove, Ill., 1974; mem. criminal justice adv. com. Coll. DuPage, Glen Ellyn, 1984—. Recipient award Glen Ellyn Family Shelter, 1984, Excellence award State's Atty. DuPage County, 1979, Prosecutor of Yr. Outstanding Performance award, 1981. Mem. DuPage County Bar Assn., DuPage Assn. Women Lawyers. Roman Catholic. Home: 1225 Candlewood Dr Downers Grove IL 60515-1450 Office: DuPage County 18th Jud Cir 505 N County Farm Rd Wheaton IL 60187-4595

PROVINE, JOHN C., lawyer; b. Asheville, N.C., May 15, 1938; s. Robert Calhoun and Harriet Josephine (Thoms) P.; m. Martha Ann Monson, Aug. 26, 1966 (div. Jan. 1975); m. Nancy Frances Lunsford, Apr. 17, 1976; children: Robert, Frances, Harriet. AB, Harvard U., 1960; JD, U. Mich., 1966; MBA, NYU, 1972, LLM in Taxation, 1975. Bar: N.Y., Tenn., U.S. Dist. Ct. (so. and ea. dists.) N.Y., U.S. Ct. Appeals (2nd and 6th cirs.), U.S. Dist. Ct. (mid. dist.) Tenn., U.S. Supreme Ct. From assoc. to ptnr. White & Case, N.Y.C., 1966-74, ptnr., 1974-81, 92-94; ptnr. White & Case, Jakarta and Ankara, 1982-91; counsel Dearborn & Ewing, Nashville, Tenn., 1982. Lt. USN, 1960-63. Mem. ABA, N.Y. Bar Assn., Tenn. Bar Assn., Assn. of Bar of City of N.Y. Avocations: bluegrass music, rural activities. Home: 560 3rd St Brooklyn NY 11215-3003

PROVORNY, FREDERICK ALAN, lawyer; b. Bklyn., Sept. 7, 1946; s. Daniel and Anna (Wurm) P.; m. Nancy Ilene Wilkins, Nov. 21, 1971; children: Michelle C., Cheryl A., Lisa T., Robert D. BS summa cum laude, NYU, 1966; JD magna cum laude, Columbia U., 1969. Bar: N.Y. 1970, U.S. Supreme Ct. 1973, D.C. 1975, Mo. 1977, Md. 1987, Calif. 1989; CPA, Md., Mo. Law clk. to Judge Harold R. Medina U.S. Ct. Appeals (2d cir.), N.Y.C., 1969-70; asst. prof. law Syracuse (N.Y.) U., 1970-72; assoc. Debevoise, Plimpton, Lyons & Gates, N.Y.C., 1972-75, Cole & Groner P.C., Washington, 1975-76; with Monsanto Co., St. Louis, 1976-86, asst. co. counsel, 1978-86; pvt. practice Washington, 1986-89; ptnr. Provorny &

Jacoby, Washington, 1989-91; counsel Shaw, Pittman, Potts & Trowbridge, Washington, 1991-93; ptnr. Tydings & Rosenberg, Balt., 1993-94; pvt. practice Balt., 1994—; lectr. Bklyn Law Sch., 1973-74; pres. Sci. and Tech. Assocs., Inc., 1986-91. Contbr. articles to profl. jours. Trustee Christian Woman's Benevolent Assn. Youth Home, 1979-83. Mem. ABA, Am. Law Inst., Bar Assn. of Balt. City, Assn. of Bar of City of N.Y. (environ. law com 1985-88), Bar Assn. Met. St. Louis (trees. young lawyers sect. 1980-81), Am. Arbitration Assn. (panel comml. arbitrators), Philo-Mt. Sinai Lodge 968, Masons, Beta Gamma Sigma. Jewish. Home: 11803 Kemp Mill Rd Silver Spring MD 20902-1511 Office: Ste 806 201 N Charles St Baltimore MD 21201

PROVOST, DAVID EMILE, financial services executive; b. Detroit, Oct. 28, 1949; s. Emile L. and Terese M. (Disnard) P.; m. Nancy B. McCormick; children: Emilie N., Natalie E. BBA, Northeastern U., BS in Acctg., 1975; MBA, Boston U., 1981. Controller, Lion Precision Corp., Newton, Mass., 1973-76, Life Support Equipment, Woburn, Mass., 1976-80; treas. Nixdorf Computer, Burlington, Mass., 1980-82, pres. Nixdorf Leasing Inc., 1982-88; fin. v.p-treas. Unitarian Universalist Assn., Boston, 1988—; assoc. prof. Middlesex Coll., Bedford, Mass., 1982-86. Treas., First Parish, Dedham, Mass., 1981-86, Boston Ballet Soc., 1982-85; trustee Soc. Ministerial Relief, Boston, 1988—, Liberal Religious Charitable Soc., Boston, 1988—, Interfaith Ctr. Corp. Responsibility, N.Y.C., 1989—, Devel. Capital Inst., Washington, 1994—. Served with U.S. Army, 1970-72. Democrat. Unitarian-Universalist. Home: 93 Cedar St Lexington MA 02173-6651 Office: Unitarian Universalist Assn of Congregations 25 Beacon St Boston MA 02108-2824

PROVOST, THOMAS TAYLOR, dermatology educator, researcher; b. Pitts., Mar. 21, 1938; s. Charles Thomas and Marcelle K. (Taylor) P.; m. Carol Sara Christie, July 2, 1960; children: Charles T., Christie Lynn, Thomas Wright. AB, U. Pitts., 1958, MD, 1962. Resident in dermatology Dartmouth Med. Ctr., Hanover, N.H., 1966-67, U. Oreg. Med. Ctr., Portland, 1967-68; fellow in immunology SUNY, Buffalo, 1969-72, asst. prof. dermatology, 1972-75, assoc. prof., 1975-78; assoc. prof. Johns Hopkins U. Med. Sch., Balt., 1978-82, prof., dept. chmn., 1982—. Lt. commdr. USPHS, 1962-64. Mem. Soc. Investigative Dermatology, Soc. Clin. Investigation. Avocation: boating. Office: Johns Hopkins U Sch of Medicine 720 Rutland Ave Baltimore MD 21205

PROVUS, BARBARA LEE, executive search consultant; b. Washington, Nov. 20, 1949; d. Severn and Birdell (Eck) P.; m. Frederick W. Wackerle, Mar. 29, 1985. Student, NYU, 1969-70; BA in Sociology, Russell Sage Coll., 1971; MS in Indsl. Rels., Loyola U., Chgo., 1978; postgrad., Smith Coll., 1971. Sec. Booz, Allen & Hamilton, Chgo., 1973-74; mgr. tng., 1974-77, dir. rsch., 1977-79, cons. search, 1979-80; mgr. mgmt. devel. Federated Dept. Stores, Cin., 1980-82; v.p. Lamalie Assocs., Chgo., 1982-86; prin., founder Sweeney, Shepherd, Bueschel, Provus, Harbert & Mummert, Inc., Chgo., 1986-91; founder Shepherd Bueschel & Provus Inc., Chgo., 1992—. Bd. dirs. Anti Cruelty Soc., Chgo., 1990—. Mem. Chgo. Fin. Exch., Assn. Exec. Search Cons. (dir. 1989-92), Chgo. Network, Econ. Club Chgo. Avocations: collecting rubber bands, modern art, baseball. Home: 3750 N Lake Shore Dr Chicago IL 60613-4238 Office: Shepherd Bueschel & Provus Inc 1 S Wacker Dr Ste 2740 Chicago IL 60606-4617

PROWLER, DONALD MARC, architect, educator; b. N.Y.C., Nov. 10, 1950; s. Millard Edwin and Gloria (Brill) P.; m. Elaine Mady Kutsher, June 30, 1974; children—Matthew Lewis, Rachel Laura. B.A. cum laude, Princeton U., 1972; M. Arch., U. Pa., 1975. Registered architect, Pa. Prin. Donald Prowler, Architect, Phila., 1982—; adj. asst. prof. U. Pa., Phila., 1979-82, asst. prof., 1982—; vis. asst. prof. Princeton U., N.J., 1986—. Author: Modest Mansions, 1985; (with others) The Fuelsavers, 1978. Editor Proc. Second Nat. Passive Solar Conf., 1979. Contbr. chpt. to book in field. Recipient Citation award Progressive Architecture Mag., 1983, First Place award Monroeville, Pa., 1979. Mem. AIA (energy com. 1983-85), Nat. Acad. Scis. (com. 1985-86). Club: Dial Lodge (Princeton). Office: U Pa Dept Architecture Meyerson Hall Philadelphia PA 19104

PROWN, JULES DAVID, art historian educator; b. Freehold, N.J., Mar. 14, 1930; s. Max and Matilda (Cassileth) P.; m. Shirley Ann Martin, June 23, 1956; children: Elizabeth Anderson, David Martin, Jonathan, Peter Cassileth, Sarah Peiter. AB, Lafayette Coll., 1951, DFA (hon.), 1979; AM, U. Del., 1956, Harvard U., 1953; PhD, Harvard U., 1961. Dir. Hist. Soc. Old Newbury, Newburyport, Mass., 1957-58, Old Gaol Mus., York, Maine, 1958-59; asst. to dir. Harvard U., Fogg Art Mus., Cambridge, Mass., 1959-61; instr. to prof. history of art Yale U., New Haven, 1961—, curator collections, 1963-68; vis. lectr. Smith Coll., Northampton, Mass., 1966-67; dir. Yale Ctr. for Brit. Art, New Haven, 1968-76; assoc. dir. Nat. Humanities Inst., New Haven, 1977; trustee Whitney Mus., N.Y.C., 1975-94; mem. editorial adv. bd. Am. Art-Smithsonian, Washington, 1986—, On Common Ground, 1993—; mem. vis. com. Harvard U. Art Museums, 1993—. Author: John Singleton Copley, 2 Vols., 1966, American Painting from Its Beginnings to the Armory Show, 1969, The Architecture of the Yale Center for British Art, 1977, (catalogue) American Art from Alumni Collections, 1968. Recipient George Washington Kidd award Lafayette Coll., 1986. Fellow The Athenaeum of Phila. (hon.); mem. Am. Antiquarian Soc., Coll. Art Assn., Am. Studies Assn., Conn. Acad. Arts & Scis., Walpole Soc., Royal Soc. Arts. Office: Yale U History of Art Dept 56 High St New Haven CT 06520

PROXMIRE, WILLIAM, former senator; b. Lake Forest, Ill., Nov. 11, 1915; s. Theodore Stanley and Adele (Flanigan) P.; m. Ellen Hodges. Grad., Hill Sch., 1934; B.A., Yale, 1938; M.B.A., Harvard, 1940, M.P.A. in Pub. Adminstrn, 1948. Assemblyman Wis. Legislature, 1951; nominee gov. Wis., 1952, 54, 56; pres. Artcraft Press, Waterloo, Wis., 1953-57; U.S. senator from Wis., 1957-89; former chmn. Sen. Banking, Housing and Urban Affairs com., Cong. JointEcon. com. Author: Can Small Business Survive?, 1964, st of the Big Time Spenders, 1972, You Can Do It, 1977, The Fleecing of America, 1980, Your Joy Ride to Health, 1993. Democrat.

PRUCHA, JOHN JAMES, geologist, educator; b. River Falls, Wis., Sept. 22, 1924; s. Edward Joseph and Katharine (Schladweiler) P.; m. Mary Elizabeth Helfrich, June 12, 1948; children—David, Stephen, Katharine, Carol, Mark, Barbara, Margaret, Christopher, Anne, Andrew. Student, Wis. State U., River Falls, 1941-43; Ph.B., U. Wis., 1945, Ph.M, 1946; M.A., Princeton, 1948, Ph.D, 1950. Asst. prof. geology Rutgers U., 1948-51; sr. geologist N.Y. State Geol. Survey, 1951-56; rsch. geologist Shell Devel. Co., 1956-63; prof. geology Syracuse U., 1963-90, prof. emeritus, 1990—, chmn. dept., 1963-70, 88-89, dean Coll. Arts and Scis., 1970-72, vice chancellor acad. affairs, 1972-85; pres. Syracuse U. Press, 1973-85, bd. dirs., 1985-90. Author: Basement Tectonics of Rocky Mountains, 1965, Structural Behavior of Salt, 1967, Stratigraphy and Structure of Southeastern New York, 1959, Fracture Patterns, 1979, Zones of Structural Weakness, 1992, (with Norman A. Foss) Kinnickinnic Years, 1993. Trustee Le Moyne Coll., 1971-78; bd. dirs. Cultural Resources Council Syracuse, 1974—, pres., 1978-80; bd. dirs. Everson Mus. Art, Syracuse, 1977-83, v.p.; 1980-81; mem. Regents vis. com. N.Y.S. Mus., 1993. Fellow AAAS, Geol. Soc. Am.; mem. Am. Assn. Petroleum Geologists, Am. Geophys. Union. Home: 112 Ardsley Dr Syracuse NY 13214-2110 Office: Syracuse Univ 204 Heroy Geology Lab Syracuse NY 13244-1070

PRUDE, ELAINE S., principal. Prin. John S. Bradfield Elem. Sch., Dallas. Recipient Elem. Sch. Recognition award U.S. Dept. Edn., 1989-90. Office: John S Bradfield Elem Sch 4300 Southern Dallas TX 75205

PRUDEN, JAMES WESLEY, newspaper editor, columnist; b. Jackson, Miss., Dec. 18, 1935; s. James Wesley and Anne (Wilder) P.; m. Ann Fontaine Rice, Oct. 15, 1960 (div. 1961). Student, U. Ark.-Little Rock, Little Rock, 1954-55. Sportswriter Ark. Gazette, Little Rock, 1953; asst. state editor, 1954-56; reporter The Comml. Appeal, Memphis, 1956-63; fgn. corr. The Nat. Observer, Washington, 1963-77; free-lance journalist, 1977-82; chief polit. corr. The Washington Times, 1982-84, dep. mng. editor, 1984-87, mng. editor, 1987-92, editor-in-chief, 1992—. Author: Vietnam: The War, 1965. Ark. del. to Dem. Nat. Conv., L.A., 1960. With USAF, 1957-58, Ark. Air Nat. Guard, 1954-63. Recipient H.L. Mencken prize Balt. Sun,

1991. Mem. Sigma Delta Chi. So. Bapt. Office: The Washington Times 3600 New York Ave NE Washington DC 20002-1947

PRUD'HOMME, ROBERT KRAFFT, chemical engineering educator; b. Sacramento, Jan. 28, 1948; s. Earle Sutter and Adele E. (Wilkens) P.; m. N. Beth Morton, June 2, 1973; children: Wendy A., Graham C., Jodie B. BSChemE, Stanford U., 1969; Grad. Spl. Studies, Harvard U., 1973; PhD ChemE, U. Wis., 1978. Asst. prof. chem. engring. Princeton (N.J.) U., 1978-84, assoc. prof., 1984-91, prof., 1991—; rsch. engr. AT&T Bell Labs., Murray Hill, N.J., 1984-85; bd. dirs. Rheometrics Inc., Piscataway, N.J.; McCabe lectr. Dept. Chem. Engring. N.C. State U. Contbr. articles to profl. jours. Deacon Cornerstone Ch., Hopewell, N.J., 1989-92. Capt. U.S. Army, 1969-73. Decorated Bronze Star, Army Commendation Medal; recipient Presdl. Young Investigator award NSF. Mem. Am. Chem. Soc., Am. Inst. Chem. Engrs. (bd. dirs. material sci. and engring. div. 1982-93), U.S. Soc. Rheology (exec. com. 1989-91), Soc. Petroleum Engrs. Achievements include research in areas of polymer fluid mechanics, polymer characterization and transport phenomena. Office: Princeton U Dept Chem Engring Princeton NJ 08544

PRUETT, JAMES WORRELL, librarian, musicologist; b. Mt. Airy, N.C., Dec. 23, 1932; s. Samuel Richard and Gladys Dorne (Worrell) P.; m. Lilian Maria-Irene Pibernik, July 20, 1957; children—Mark, Ellen. BA., U. N.C., Chapel Hill, 1955, M.A., 1957, Ph.D., 1962. Mem. faculty U. N.C., Chapel Hill, 1961-87; prof. music U. N.C., 1974-87, music librarian, 1961-76, chmn. dept. music, 1976-86; chief music div. Library of Congress, Washington, 1987-94; vis. prof. U. Toronto, 1976. Editor: Studies in the History, Style and Bibliography of Music in Memory of Glen Haydon, 1969; author: Research Guide to Musicology, 1985. Contbr. profl. jours., encys. Newberry Library fellow, summer 1966. Mem. Internat. Musicol. Soc., Am. Musicol. Soc. (chpt. chmn. 1964-66, mem. coun. 1974-77), Music Libr. Assn. (pres. 1973-75, editor jour. 1974-77), Internat. Assn. Music Libraries, Cosmos Club (Washington). Home: 343 Wesley Dr Chapel Hill NC 27516-1520

PRUETT, JEANNE, singer, songwriter; m. Jack Pruett (div. 1982); children: Jack, Jael; m. Eddie Fulton. owner J Bar E Ranch, Franklin, Tenn. Debut on, Grand Ole Opry, 1964, regular appearances, 1974—; recs. include Hold on to My Unchanging Love, 1971, Satin Sheets, 1973, I'm Your Woman, Honey on His Hands, You Don't Need to Move a Mountain, Just Like Your Daddy, I'm Living a Lie, 1977, Back to Back, 1979, Temporarily Yours, 1980, It's Too Late, 1980; songwriter for recs. include, Marty Robbins. Office: Grand Ole Opry 2800 Opryland Dr Nashville TN 37214-1297*

PRUETT, KYLE DEAN, psychiatrist, writer, educator; b. Raton, N.Mex., Aug. 27, 1943; s. Ozie Douthitt Pruett and Velma Lorraine Smith; children: Elizabeth Storr, Emily Farrar. BA in History, Yale U., 1965; D of Medicine, Tufts U., 1969. Intern Mt. Auburn Hosp.-Harvard U., 1969-70; resident in psychiat. medicine Tufts-New England Med. Ctr., Boston, 1970-72; child psychiatry fellow Child Study Ctr., Yale U., New Haven, 1972-74, asst. clin. prof. psychiatry, 1975-79, assoc. clin. prof., 1979-87, clin. prof., 1987—; dir. child devel. unit Yale U., 1982—; attending physician dept. child psychiatry Yale-New Haven Hosp., 1972—; cons. psychiatrist Guilford (Conn.) Pub. Schs., 1977—; vis. scholar Sch. Medicine, U. Vt., 1987, Sch. Medicine, U. N.Mex., 1988; mem. editorial bd. Med. Problems of Performing Artists jour., 1983—, Fathers mag., 1987—; bd. dirs. Zero to Three: Nat. Ctr. for Clin. Infant Programs, Washington; cons. CBS News, Lifetime. Author: The Nurturing Father, 1988 (Am. Health Book award 1988); contbr. numerous articles to profl. jours.; host biweekly TV series Your Child 6 to 12 with Dr. Kyle Pruett Lifetime TV, 1993—. Mem. med. adv. bd. Conn. Multiple Sclerosis Soc., Hartford, 1985—, Scholastic, Inc., 1988—, Yale U. Program for Humanities in Medicine, 1989—, World Assn. for Infant Mental Health, 1979—; cons. Neighborhood Music Sch., New Haven, 1986—, CBS TV Family time, 1989—, Wellesley Child Study Ctr.; prin. tenor Conn. Chancel Opera Co., New Haven, 1983—. Vis. fellow Anna Freud Clinic, London, 1975; recipient Mayoral Citation, City of Indpls., 1987. Mem. Am. Acad. Child and Adolescent Psychiatry, Am. Psychiat. Assn., Soc. for Rsch. in Family Therapy, Physicians for Social Responsibility, Nat. Assn. Physician Broadcasters (CBS news cons. 1989—), Zero to Three (Nat. Ctr. for Clin. Infant Programs pres.-elect 1995—), Yale U. Glee Club Alumni Assn. (pres. 1985-89). Avocations: rowing, sailing, skiing, vocal chamber music, running. Home: 10 Fernwood Dr Guilford CT 06437-2349 Office: Yale Child Study Ctr 333 Cedar St New Haven CT 06510

PRUETT, SAMUEL H., manufacturing executive; b. Michigan City, Ind., Aug. 19, 1932; s. Samuel K. and Anne S. P.; m. Yvonne C. Jones; children: Carrie, Steven. BS in Bus., Ind. U., 1954. Staff asst. household soap products div. Procter & Gamble Co., 1957-59, with sales tng. household soap products div., 1959, asst. brand mgr. household soap products, 1959-61, brand mgr. household soap products div., 1961-65, assoc. brand promotion mgr. household soap products div., 1965-66, brand promotion mgr. bar soap and household cleaning products div., 1966-75, div. mgr. gen. advt. dept., 1975-81, gen. mgr. citrus products div., 1981-84, v.p. personnel citrus products div., 1984—. Trustee Deaconess Hosp., Cin., 1988—. Capt. USAF, 1954-57. Mem. Bus. Roundtable (employee relations com.), Cowdrick Group, Greater Cin. C. of C. (trustee, 1988), Ind. U. Sch. Bus. Alumni Assn. (bd. dirs.). Office: Procter & Gamble Co 1 Procter Gamble Plz Cincinnati OH 45202

PRUGH, GEORGE SHIPLEY, lawyer; b. Norfolk, Va., June 1, 1920; s. George Shipley and Florence (Hamilton) P.; m. Katherine Buchanan, Sept. 27, 1942; children: Stephanie Dean, Virginia Patton. A.B., U. Calif., Berkeley, 1941; J.D., U. Calif., San Francisco, 1948; postgrad., Army War Coll., 1961-62; M.A., George Washington U., 1963. Bar: Calif. 1949, U.S. Supreme Ct. 1954. Legal advisor U.S. Mil. Assistance Command, Vietnam, 1964-66; legal adviser U.S. European Command, Stuttgart, Ger., 1966-69; Judge Adv., U.S. Army Europe, Heidelberg, Ger., 1969-71; Judge Adv. Gen. Washington, 1971-75; ret., 1975; prof. law Hastings Coll. Law, U. Calif., San Francisco, 1975-82. Author: (with others) Law at War, 1971; (play) Solferino; contbr. articles to profl. jours. Mem. Sec. Def. Task Force on Racial Discrimination in Adminstrn. Mil. Justice, 1973; mem. U.S. del. Diplomatic Conf. on Law of War, Geneva, 1974, 75. 2d lt. U.S. Army; maj. gen. JAGC, 1971. Decorated D.S.M. with oak leaf cluster, Legion of Merit with oak leaf cluster. Mem. ABA, Am. Judicature Soc., Internat. Soc. Mil. Law and Law of War (hon. pres.), Civil Affairs Assn. (hon. dir.), Selden Soc., Calif. Bar, Order of Coif, Bohemian Club, Army and Navy Club (Washington), Phi Delta Phi. Episcopalian.

PRUGOVECKI, EDUARD, mathematical physicist, educator, author; b. Craiova, Romania, Mar. 19, 1937; emigrated to Can., 1965; s. Slavoljub and Helena (Piatkowsky) P.; m. Margaret Rachelle Loveys, July 19, 1973. Dipl. Phys., U. Zagreb, Croatia, 1959; Ph.D., Princeton U., 1964. Rsch. asst. Inst. Ruder Boskovic, Zagreb, 1959-61; rsch. asst. Princeton (N.J.) U., 1961-64, research associate., 1964-65; postdoctoral fellow Inst. Theoret. Physics, Edmonton, Alta., Can., 1965-67; lectr. U. Alta., Edmonton, 1966-67; asst. prof. math. U. Toronto, 1967-69, assoc. prof., 1969-75, prof., 1975—; vis. prof. Centre National de Recherche Scientifique, Marseille, France, 1974. Author: monographs Quantum Mechanics in Hilbert Space 1971, 2d rev. edit., 1981, Stochastic Quantum Mechanics and Quantum Spacetime, 1984, 2d rev. edit., 1986, Quantum Geometry, 1992, Principles of Quantum General Relativity, 1995; contbr. articles to profl. jours. Grantee NRC Can., 1971-79; grantee Nat. Sci. and Engring. Research Council, 1980—. Mem. Sci. for Peace. Office: U Toronto, 100 Saint George St, Toronto, ON Canada M5S 1A1

PRUIS, JOHN J., business executive; b. Borculo, Mich., Dec. 13, 1923; s. Ties J. and Trientje (Koop) P.; m. Angeline Rosemary Zull, Sept. 14, 1944; children: David Lofton, Daniel J., Dirk Thomas. B.S., Western Mich. U. 1947; M.A., Northwestern U., 1949, Ph.D., 1951; Litt.D. (hon.), Yeungnam U., Taegu, Korea, Ind. State U.; LL.D. (hon.), Ball State U., U. So. Ind. Tchr. pub. schs. Mich., 1942-43; supervising tchr. Campus Sch., Western Mich. U., 1947-48; instr. speech U No la., 1951-52; from asst. prof. to assoc. prof. speech So. Ill. U., 1952-55; mem. faculty Western Mich. U., 1955-68, sec. bd. trustees, 1964-68, v.p. administrn., 1966-68; pres. Ball State U., 1968-78; v.p. corp. rels. Ball Corp., 1978-88; Cons., examiner North Central Assn., 1959-78; also bd. dirs. N. Central Assn. V.p. Country dr. chmn. Kalamazoo Cmty. Chest, 1964; bd. dirs. Kalamazoo chpt. Am. Cancer Soc., 1963-68,

Del. County United Way, Muncie Symphony Assn., Ball Meml. Hosp., Big Bros./Big Sisters, Ind. Legal Found.; trustee U. So. Ind., 1985-90; exec. v.p. George and Frances Ball Found. With USNR, 1943-46; capt. Res., ret. Mem. Am. Assn. Higher Edn., Speech Communication Assn., Muncie C. of C., Blue Key, Rotary, Phi Delta Kappa, Omicron Delta Kappa, Beta Gamma Sigma. Presbyterian.

PRUITT, ALICE FAY, mathematician, engineer; b. Montgomery, Ala., Dec. 17, 1943; d. Virgil Edwin and Ocie Victoria (Mobley) Maye; m. Mickey Don Pruitt, Nov. 5, 1967; children: Derrell Gene, Christine Marie. BS in Math., U. Ala., Huntsville, 1977; postgrad. in engring., Calif. State U., Northridge, 1978-79. Instr. math. Antelope Valley Coll., Quartz Hill, Calif., 1977-78; space shuttle engr. Rockwell Internat., Palmdale, Calif., 1979-81; programmer, analyst Sci. Support Svcs. Combat Devel. and Experimentation Ctr., Ft. Hunter-Liggett, Calif., 1985-87; sr. engring. specialist Loral Vought Systems Corp., Dallas, 1985-92; mem. tech. staff Nichols Rsch. Corp., Huntsville, Ala., 1992—. Mem. DeSoto (Tex.) Coun. Cultural Arts, 1987-89. Mem. AAUW (sch. bd. rep. 1982, phone chmn. 1987-89, legal advocacy Fund Chairperson 1989-91), Toastmasters Internat., Phi Kappa Phi. Republican. Methodist. Avocations: dancing, gourmet cooking. Office: Nichols Rsch Corp PO Box 40002 4040 S Memorial Pkwy Huntsville AL 35815-1502

PRUITT, ANNE LORING, university administrator, educator; b. Bainbridge, Ga., Sept. 19, 1929; d. Loring Alphonzo and Anne Lee (Ward) Smith; m. Harold G. Logan; children: Leslie; stepchildren: Dianne, Pamela, Sharon, Ralph Pruitt Jr., Harold, Minda, Andrew Logan. BS, Howard U., Washington, 1949; MA, Tchrs. Coll. Columbia U., N.Y.C., 1950, EdD, 1964; HumD hon., Central State U. Wilberforce, Ohio, 1982. Counsel for women Howard U., 1950-52; tchr., dir. guidance Hutto High Sch., Bainbridge, 1952-55; dean students Albany State Coll., Ga., 1955-59, Fisk U., Nashville, 1959-61; prof. edn. Case Western Res. U., Cleve., 1963-79; prof. ednl. policy and leadership Ohio State U., Columbus, 1979—, assoc. dean Grad. Sch., 1979-84; assoc. provost Ohio State U., 1984-86, dir. Ctr. for Teaching Excellence, 1986-94; dean in residence Coun. Grad. Schs., Washington, 1994—; cons. So. Regional Edn. Bd., Atlanta, 1967-78, So. edn. Found., Atlanta, 1978-87. Author: New Students and Coordinated Counseling, 1973, Black Employees in Traditionally White Institutions in the Adams States 1975-1977, 1981, In Pursuit of Equality in Higher Education, 1987. Bd. trustees Urban League, Cleve., 1965-71, Central State U., 1973-82, Case Western Res. U., 1987—; Columbus Area Leadership Program, 1988-91; bd. dirs. ARC, Cleve., 1978-79, Am. West Airlines Found., 1992—; mem. adv. com. U.S. Coast Guard Acad., New London, Conn., 1980-83; Ohio State U. rep. to AAUW, 1989-94; univ. co-chair United Way, 1990-91; trustee Marburn Acad., 1991—; mem. Columbus 1992 Edn. Com., 1988-92, edn. subcom. Columbus Found. 1991—; exec. com. Renaissance League, 1992-94. Recipient Outstanding Alumnus award Howard U. Alumni Assn., 1975; Am. Council on Edn. fellow, 1977; named one of Am.'s Top 100 Black Bus. and Profl. Women Dollars & Sense Mag., 1986; recipient Disting. Affirmative Action award Ohio State U., 1988; named Sr. Scholar Am. Coll. Personnel Assn., 1989, Woman of Achievement award YMCA, 1993. Mem. NSF (com. equal opportunities in sci. and engring. 1989—), Am. Coll. Personnel Assn. (pres. 1976-77), Ohio Assn. Counselor Edn. (pres. 1966-67), Council of Grad. Schs. in U.S. (chairperson com. on minority grad. edn. 1980-84), Am. Ednl. Research Assn., Alpha Kappa Alpha. Club: Links, Inc. (Washington). Office: Coun Grad Schs 1 DuPont Cir NW Ste 430 Washington DC 20036

PRUITT, BASIL ARTHUR, JR., surgeon, army officer; b. Nyack, N.Y., Aug. 21, 1930; s. Basil Arthur and Myrtle Flo (Knowles) P.; m. Mary Sessions Gibson, Sept. 4, 1954; children: Scott Knowles, Laura Sessions, Jeffrey Hamilton. AB, Harvard U., 1952, postgrad., 1952-53; MD, Tufts U., 1957. Diplomate: Am. Bd. Surgery (bd. dirs. 1982-88); cert. surg. critical care. Intern Boston City Hosp., 1957-58, resident in surgery, 1958-59, 61-62; commd. capt., M.C. U.S. Army, 1959, advanced through grades to col., 1972; resident Brooke Gen. Hosp., Ft. Sam Houston, Tex., 1962-64; chief clin. div. Inst. Surg. Rsch., Ft. Sam Houston, Tex., 1965-67; chief profl. services 12th Evacuation Hosp., Vietnam, 1967-68; comdr., dir. U.S. Army Inst. Surg. Research, Brooke Army Med. Center, Ft. Sam Houston, 1968—; clin. prof. gen. surgery Med. Sch. U. Tex., San Antonio, 1975—; prof. gen. surgery uniformed svcs. U. of the Health Scis., Bethesda, Md., 1978—; mem. surgery, anaesthesiology and trauma study sect. NIH, 1978-82; mem. Shriners Burns Adv. Bd., 1985-92; mem. Shriners Med. Adv. Bd., 1992—; mem. rev. bd. for surgery, VA, 1990-93. Author med. books; contbr. chpts. to textbooks, articles to profl. jours.; assoc. editor: Jour. Trauma, 1975—; mem. edit. bd.: Archives Surgery, 1981-93, Consultations in Surgery, Correspondence Society of Surgeons, Collected Letters, 1978—, Circulatory Shock, 1985-93, Jour. Burn Care and Rehabilitation, 1984-87, Jour. Investigative Surgery, 1987—, Shock Research, 1993—, Current Opinion in Surgical Infections, 1993—. Decorated Bronze Star, Legion of Merit. Fellow ACS (gov. 1973-79, pre- and postoperative care com. 1973-79, com. on trauma 1974-84, internat. relats. com. 1983-93, chmn. 1987-89), fellow Am. Coll. of Critical Care Medicine; mem. Am. Burn Assn. (pres. 1975-76), Internat. Soc. Burn Injuries (nat. rep. 1974-82, co-chmn. disaster planning com. 1982-86, pres.-elect 1990-94, pres. 1994—), Smoke Burn and Fire Assn. (adv. council), Am. Trauma Soc. (dir., pres. Tex. div. 1974-75, sec. 1986-88, 2d v.p. 1988-90, pres. elect 1990-92, pres. 1992-94), Soc. Univ. Surgeons, Am. Surg. Assn. (2d v.p. 1980-81), Tex. Surg. Assn., Western Surg. Assn. (dist. rep. 1984-88, pres. 1993-94), So. Surg. Assn., Halsted Soc. (pres. 1985-86), Am. Assn. Surgery of Trauma (recorder 1976-80, pres. 1982-83), Surg. Biol. Club III, Societe Internat. de Chirurgie, Assn. Acad. Surgery, Surg. Infection Soc. (recorder 1980-84, pres. 1985-86), Internat. Surg. Group., North Am. Burn Soc. (pres. 1993-94). Home: 402 Tidecrest Dr San Antonio TX 78239-2517 Office: US Army Inst Surg Rsch Fort Sam Houston TX 78234-5012

PRUITT, CHARLES JOSEPH, lawyer; b. Portland, Oreg., Jan. 22, 1946; s. Harold Gilbert and Lena Elsie (Hummel) P.; m. Kathleen Eleanor Payne, Dec. 28, 1967; children: Henry C., Louis G. BA, U. Oreg., 1967; JD, Ohio State U., 1972. Bar: Oreg. 1973, Wash. 1984. Assoc. Lane Powell Spears Lubersky, Portland, 1973-78; ptnr. Lane Powell Spears Lubersky, Portland, 1978—. Contbr. articles to legal jours. 1st lt. U.S. Army, 1967-70, Vietnam. Mem. City Club Portland. Democrat. Episcopalian. Avocations: sailing, skiing, hiking. Home: 1842 SW Terrace Dr Portland OR 97201-1760 Office: Lane Powell Spears & Lubersky 520 SW Yamhill St Ste 800 Portland OR 97204-1331

PRUITT, CHARLES WILLIAM, JR., long term health care executive, educator; b. Jacksonville, Fla., Apr. 10, 1929; s. Charles William and Bertie Lee (Hamm) P. BSBA, U. Fla., 1951, MBA in Mgmt. and Indsl. Rels., 1957; postgrad., Cornell U., 1964, U. Birmingham, Eng., 1981. Grad. asst. to dean Grad. Sch., U. Fla., Gainesville, 1953-54, asst. to provost, 1955-57, asst. dir. Univ. Hosp. and Clinic, 1957-65, asst. prof. dept. health and hosp. adminstrn., 1963-65, dir. cmty. svcs. div. Ctr. for Health and Hosp. Adminstrn., 1965-66; pres., CEO, Cathedral Found. Jacksonville, Inc., 1966-73, Urban Jacksonville, Inc., 1968-73; pres. Tremont Mgmt. Co., Dallas, 1973-74; chief adminstrv. and operating officer Trinity Ch., N.Y.C., 1975-79; pres., CEO, bd. dirs. Presbyn. Assn. on Aging, Pitts., 1979—; speaker, lectr. at numerous local, state and nat. ednl., civic, bus. and govtl. orgns. on gerontol. subjects, 1954—; cons. on elderly housing, long term health care facilities and continuum of care, 1966—; lectr. U. Pitts. Grad. Sch. Pub. Health, 1981—, Carnegie-Mellon U. Sch. Architecture and Grad. Sch. Urban and Pub. Affairs, 1981—, Harvard U. Grad. Sch. Design, 1981—; mem. adv. com. to develop nat. exam. for licensure nursing home adminstrs. Profl. Exam. Svcs., N.Y.C., 1972-82; also others. Trustee Jacksonville Art Mus., 1969-73; pres. Jacksonville Urban Ministry Program, 1971-72, Alleghery Widows' Home Assn., 1983—, Southwestern Pa. Partnership on Aging, 1991—; mem. Alliance on Aging, 1988—; bd. dirs. Ea. Area Adult Svcs., 1987—, pres. 1988—; bd. dirs. Episcopal svcs. ministries Episcopal Diocese of Pitts., 1988-91; mem. com. on aging and continuum of care Hosp. Coun. Western Pa., 1989—; mem. Pa. Health Policy Bd., 1993—; others. 2d lt. USAF, 1951-53; lt. col. USAFR, 1953-79. Sloan fellow, summer 1964. Fellow Am. Coll. Healthcare Execs. (cert., spl. com. to develop program for long term care adminstrs. 1973); mem. Episcopal Soc. for Ministry on Aging (bd. dirs. 1966-89, treas. 1975-82, pres. 1982-86), Fla. Blue Key, Phi Kappa Psi, Alpha Kappa Psi, Beta Theta Pi. Episcopalian. Avocations: travel, exercise, reading, theatre, concerts. Home: 300 Fox Chapel Rd Apt 407

Pittsburgh PA 15238 Office: Presbyn Assn on Aging 1215 Hulton Rd Oakmont PA 15139-1135

PRUITT, DEAN GARNER, psychologist, educator; b. Phila., Dec. 26, 1930; s. Dudley McConnell and Grace Richards (Garner) P.; m. France Juliard, Dec. 27, 1959; children: Andre Juliard, Paul Dudley, Charles Alexandre. A.B., Oberlin Coll., 1952; M.S., Yale U., 1954, Ph.D., 1957. Postdoctoral fellow U. Mich., 1957-59; research assoc. Northwestern U., 1959-61; asst. prof., assoc. prof. U. Del., 1961-66; assoc. prof., prof., Disting. prof. SUNY-Buffalo, 1966—, dir. Grad. Program in Social Psychology, 1969-73, 76-77, 85-88. Author: Negotiation Behavior, 1981, (with J. Z. Rubin) Social Conflict, 1986, 94; (with P.J. Carnevale) Negotiation in Social Conflict, 1993; editor; (with R.C. Snyder) Theory and Research on the Causes of War, 1969, (with K. Kressel) Mediation Research, 1989. Grantee Office Naval Rsch., 1965, NIMH, 1967, NSF, 1969, 74, 76, 80, 83, 86, 88, 93, Guggenheim Found., 1978-79. Fellow Am. Psychol. Assn., Am. Psychol. Soc., Soc. for Psychol. Study Social Issues; mem. Internat. Assn. for Conflict Mgmt. (pres. 1990-92), Internat. Soc. Polit. Psychology (v.p. 1984-85, Harold D. Lasswell award 1992), Phi Beta Kappa, Sigma Xi. Home: 9006 Friars Rd Bethesda MD 20817-3320 Office: SUNY Buffalo Dept Psychology Buffalo NY 14260

PRUITT, DOROTHY J. GOOCH, home economics educator, educational administrator; b. Granville County, N.C., June 10, 1935; d. Edgar N. and Lorine (Henley) Gooch; m. William Leonard Pruitt, July 22, 1958. BS, East Carolina U., 1956, MEd, U. N.C.-Chapel Hill, 1971; sixth yr. cert. Nova U., 1984, EdD, 1985. Home econs. tcr. Granville County Schs., Oxford, N.C., 1956-69; cons. State Dept. Pub. Instrn., Raleigh, N.C., 1972-82; prin. Granville County Schs., Oxford, N.C., 1982-91, ret. 1991; part time instr. Vance Granville C.C., 1994—; mem. Bd. Edn. Bd. dirs. N.C. Sch. Bd. Assn., Raleigh, 1980-82; chmn. Granville County Bd. Edn., 1979-82; v.p. Jr. Woman's Club, Oxford, 1965-66 (named Club Woman of Yr. 1965). Named Granville County Prin. of Yr., 1987-88, 90-91. Mem. N.C. Assn. Sch. Adminstrs., Am. Sch. Curriculum Devel. Assn., Am. Sch. Curriculum Assn., Am. Ednl. Research Assn., N.C. Future Homakers of Am. (hon.), Alpha Delta Kappa (corr. sec. 1970). Baptist. Home and Office: 106 Country Club Dr Oxford NC 27565

PRUITT, GEORGE ALBERT, college president; b. Canton, Miss., July 9, 1946; s. Joseph Henry and Lillie Irene (Carmichael) P.; m. Delores Maxine Walker, Dec. 30, 1972; 1 dau., Shayla Nicole. BS, Ill. State U., 1968, MS, 1970; PhD, Union Grad. Sch., Cin., 1974; D Pub. Svc. (hon.), Bridgewater State Coll., 1990, MA (hon.), 1990. Asst. to v.p. for acad. affairs Ill. State U., Normal, 1968-70, dir. high potential students program, 1968-70; dean students Towson State U., 1970-72; v.p. exec. asst. to pres., assoc. prof. urban affairs Morgan State U., 1972-75; v.p., prof. Tenn. State U., 1975-81; exec. v.p. Council for Advancement Experiential Learning, Columbia, Md., 1981-82; pres. Thomas A. Edison State Coll., Trenton, 1982—; bd. mgrs. Trenton Savs. Bank; mem. commn. on ednl. credit and credentials, labor/higher edn. coun. Am. Coun. on Edn.; advisor group XII, Nat. Fellowship program W.K. Kellogg Found., 1990-94, advisor group XV, 1995—; bd. dirs. SEEDCO; bd. trustees Ctr. for Analysis of Pub. Issues, Princeton, N.J., 1993—; mem. nat. adv. com. on instnl. quality and integrity U.S. Dept. Edn., 1994—. Trustee Union Inst., Cin.; Mercer Med. Ctr.; bd. dirs. N.J. Assn. Colls. and Univs., N.J. div. Am. Cancer Soc., 1992—. Recipient Resolution of Commendation Bd. Trustees Morgan State U., 1975, Outstanding Svc. to Edn. award Tenn. State U., 1981, Gubernatorial citation Gov. of Tenn., 1981, Good Guy award George Washington coun. Boy Scouts Am., 1991, Humanitarian award NCCJ, 1992; apptd. hon. mem. Gen. Assembly Tenn., 1981, hon. mem. U.S. Congress from 5th Tenn. dist., 1981; named one of the Most Effective Coll. Pres. in U.S., Exxon Edn. Found. Study, 1986. Mem. Coun. for Advancement Exptl. Learning, Am. Assn. State Colls.and Univs., Coun. for Advancement and Support of Edn., Am. Coun. Edn., Mid. States Assn. Colls. and Schs. (accreditation evaluator commn. on higher edn.), Mercer County C. of C. (trustee). Office: Thomas Edison Coll 101 W State St Trenton NJ 08608-1176

PRUITT, J. DOUG, construction executive; b. Duncan, Okla., June 22, 1945; s. Mike E. and D. Ruth (Kaiser) P.; m. Rebecca L. Black, July 6, 1968; children: Joey Lynn, Jeffrey Michael. AS in Civil Tech., Okla. State U., 1965; BSBA, U. Phoenix, 1983; postgrad., Stanford U., 1987. Estimator, project coord. M.M. Sundt Constrn. Co., Phoenix, 1966-71, chief estimator, 1971-75, mgr. constrn. mgmt. svcs., 1975-80, Phoenix area mgr., 1980-82, group v.p., 1982-84; sr. v.p. Sundt Corp., Phoenix, 1984—, also bd. dirs.; vice chmn. John C. Lincoln Hosp. and Health Ctr., Phoenix. Contbr. articles to profl. publs. Pres. constrn. program adv. coun. Ariz. State U., 1988; bd. dirs. Phoenix Community Alliance, 1987—. With USAR, 1965-71. Mem. Associated Gen. Contractors Am. (project delivery systems com., chmn. AGC/ASA Joint com., 2d v.p., nat. dir. Ariz. bldg. chpt., legis com. 1980—, spl. contracts com. 1987—), Ariz. Assn. Indsl. Devel., Ariz. C. of C. (bd. dirs. 1987—), Phoenix Country Club, La Camarilla Club. Avocations: golf, tennis, skiing, water skiing. Office: Sundt Corp 2630 S 20th Pl Phoenix AZ 85034-6717

PRUITT, J. MICHAEL, real estate company executive. Pres. James H. Pruitt Real Estate, Melbourne, Fla. Office: James H Pruitt Real Estate 10 S Harbor City Blvd Melbourne FL 32901*

PRUITT, JAMES H., real estate company executive; b. 1917. Former mem. Fla. Ho. of Reps.; chmn., sec. James H. Pruitt Real Estate, Melbourne, Fla.; mem. Gov. Adv. Com. Former mayor City of Melbourne, Fla. Mem. Melbourne Area Bd. Realtors (v.p.). Office: James H Pruitt Real Estate 10 S Harbor City Blvd Melbourne FL 32901*

PRUITT, PETER TALIAFERRO, insurance company executive; b. Miami, Fla., Nov. 15, 1932; s. Frank Oliphant and Martha (Lowe) P.; m. Shirley Williams, Dec. 27, 1954; children: Peter T., Martha Catherine, John Sanders. B.S. in Bus. Adminstrn., U. Fla., 1954; B.S.B.A., Harvard Grad. Sch. Bus. Adminstrn., 1974. Account exec. to pres. Parker & Co., Miami, 1957-71; v.p. to exec. v.p. Frank B. Hall & Co., Inc., N.Y.C., 1971-85, pres., chief operating officer, 1985—; trustee Stamford Mus., 1986—, Coll. Ins., 1985—. Trustee Employee Benefit Research Inst., Washington, 1980—; pres. Crippled Children's Soc., Miami, 1974-76; mem. Orange Bowl Com., 1976—; chmn. Westchester County Tri-Centennial, Briarcliff, N.Y., 1982—. Served to maj. USAF, 1954-57. Clubs: University, Miami, Biscayne Bay Yacht (Miami); Metropolitan, Marco Polo (N.Y.C.). Office: Frank B Hall & Co Inc 549 Pleasantville Rd Briarcliff Manor NY 10510-1952

PRUITT, THOMAS P., JR., textiles executive; b. 1922. Grad., N.C. State U., 1945. With Springs Mills, Lancaster, S.C., 1945-52; with Carolina Mills, Maiden, N.C., 1952—, v.p., now exec. weaving ops. Office: Carolina Mills Inc 618 N Carolina Ave Maiden NC 28650*

PRUITT, WILLIAM CHARLES, JR., minister, educator; b. Reed, Okla., May 31, 1926; s. William Charles and Helen Irene (Sanders) P.; m. Ellen Ruth Palmer, Aug. 25, 1953; children: Philip, Suzanne, John. BS, Stephen F. Austin State U., 1956, MEd, 1958; BD, MRE, Bapt. Missionary Assn. Theol. Sem., 1959, DRE, 1963; MLS, East Tex. State U., 1963. Ordained to ministry Bapt. Missionary Assn. Am., 1955. Pastor Mt. Pleasant Bapt. Ch., Bedias, Tex., 1955-60, Calvary Bapt. Ch., Commerce, Tex., 1960-63, Glenfawn Bapt. Ch., Laneville, Tex., 1963-66, New Hope Bapt. Ch., Winkler, Tex., 1966-70, Pleasant Ridge Bapt. Ch., Centerville, Tex., 1970-74, Redland Bapt. Ch., Centerville, 1970-79, Concord (Tex.) Bapt. Ch., 1983—; dir. libr. svc., instr. Bapt. Missionary Assn. Theol. Sem., 1958-67, prof. missions and religious edn., 1967-72; instr. psychology Jacksonville Coll., 1971-76; asst. dir. East Tex. Adult Edn. Coop., 1973-93; supr. Adult Learning Ctr. Rusk State Hosp., 1988—. Tex. wing chaplain CAP, 1971-77; exec. dir. Armed Forces Chaplaincy Com., Bapt. Missionary Assn. Am., Jacksonville, Tex., 1965-95. Mem. Mil. Chaplains Assn. U.S., Lions. Home: Rte 8 Box 327 Jacksonville TX 75766 Office: PO Box 912 Jacksonville TX 75766-0912

PRUNTY, BERT SHERMAN, JR., lawyer; b. Des Moines, Jan. 4, 1924; s. Bert Sherman and Carrie Blanch (Quiner) P.; m. Lois Bernice Cummins, Nov. 27, 1946; children: Randall Charles, Mary Lou, Bert Sherman,

III. B.A., Drake U., 1947, J.D., 1950. Bar: Iowa 1950, N.Y. 1972, Maine 1973. Asst. prof. law NYU, 1951-53, assoc. prof., 1953-56, prof., 1956-73, assoc. dean., 1967-73; prof. U. Maine, 1973-79, dean, 1973-78; prof., dean Hastings Sch. Law U. Calif., San Francisco, 1979-87; vis. prof. Duke U., 1978-79, Hebrew U., Jerusalem, 1972—, U. Naples, Italy, 1967—, Tel Aviv U., 1982; cons. to numerous legis. and jud. bodies, N.Y., Maine. Author: Not-for-Profit Corporation Law, 3 vols, 1973; contbr. numerous articles to law jours. Served with U.S. Army, 1943-46. Mem. Am. Law Inst. Office: U Calif Hastings Coll Law 200 Mcallister St San Francisco CA 94102-4976

PRUS, FRANCIS VINCENT, tire company executive; b. Sewickley, Pa., 1927; s. Mark Phillip and Mary Agnes Prus; m. Catherine Frances Dumesic, Jan. 30, 1949; children: Cathy, Mark, Linda, David. B.S. in Elec. Engring., Carnegie Mellon U., 1949. Gen. mgr. Goodyear Aerospace Corp., Akron, Ohio, pres., chief exec. officer, until 1981; dir. mfg. services, then v.p. mfg. Goodyear Tire & Rubber Co., from 1981, now exec. v.p. research and devel.; formerly dir. prodn. Kelly Springfield Tire Co.; dir. mfg. services, then v.p. mfg. Goodyear Tire & Rubber Co., exec. v.p. corp. technology, bd. dirs., 1981—. Mem. Litchfield Park Sch. Bd., 1970-71; bd. dirs. Akron Jr. Achievement, 1974-80, pres., 1977-78. Served with USNR, 1945-46. Mem. Aerospace Industries Assn., Nat. Security Indsl. Assn., Am. Def. Preparedness Assn., Navy League U.S. Club: Portage Country (Akron). Office: Goodyear Tire & Rubber Co 1144 E Market St Akron OH 44316-0001

PRUS, VICTOR MARIUS, architect, urbanist; b. Poland, Apr. 19, 1917; s. Marien Raymond and Susanna (Hoffman) P.; m. Maria Fisz, Sept. 22, 1948. Diploma in architecture, Warsaw Tech. U., 1939; Ing.Arch., M.Arch., U. Liverpool, 1946. Sr. exec. officer Festival of Britain, London, 1948-51; prin. Victor Prus (Architect), London, 1948-52, Montreal, Que., Can., 1953-76; prin. Victor Prus & Assos. (Architects and Urbanists), Montreal, 1976—; asst. to Buckminster Fuller Princeton U., 1953; vis. prof. McGill U., 1953, 66, 72, Washington U., St. Louis, 1978. Works include New Internat. Airport, Barbados, Montreal Conv. Ctr., Observatory, Mauna Kea, Hawaii, Grand Théâtre de Québec, Conservatory of Music, Montreal Metro stas., Bonaventure, Langelier, Mt. Royal, Brudenell River Resort, P.E.I., Can., Place Longueuil Comml. Centre, Rockland Shopping Centre, Centaur Theatres, Expo '67 Stadium and James Lyng Sch., Montreal. Served with RAF, 1941-45. Decorated Polish Cross of Valour (2); recipient Massey medal, 1961, Can. Architect award, 1971, 1st prize for Que. Performing Arts Centre, 1964, 1st prize for RCAF Meml., 1969, 1st prize for Montreal Congress Center, 1978. Fellow Royal Archtl. Inst. Can., AIA (hon.); mem. Royal Can. Acad. Arts, Royal Inst. Brit. Architects, Can. Inst. Planners. Home: 108 Senneville Rd, Senneville, PQ Canada H9X 1B9 Office: Victor Prus & Assocs, 224 Place d'Youville, Montreal, PQ Canada H2Y 2B4

PRUSINER, STANLEY BEN, neurology and biochemistry educator, researcher; b. Des Moines, May 28, 1942; s. Lawrence Albert and Miriam (Spigel) P.; m. Sandra Lee Turk, Oct. 18, 1970; children: Helen Chloe, Leah Anne. AB cum laude, U. Pa., 1964, MD, 1968; PhD (hon.), Hebrew U., Jerusalem, 1995. Diplomate Am. Bd. Neurology. Intern in medicine U. Calif., San Francisco, 1968-69, resident in neurology, 1972-74, asst. prof. neurology, 1974-80, assoc. prof., 1980-84, prof., 1984—, prof. biochemistry, 1988—, acad. senate faculty rsch. lectr., 1989-90; prof. virology U. Calif. Berkeley, 1984—; mem. neurology com. Nat. Inst. Neurol. Disease and Strokes, NIH, Bethesda, Md., 1982-86, 90-92; mem. sci. adv. bd. French Fedn., L.A., 1985—; mem. sci. rev. com. Alzheimer's Disease Diagnostic Ctr. & Rsch. Grant Program, State of Calif., 1985-89; chmn. sci. adv. bd. Am. Health Assistance Found., Rockville, Md., 1986—. Editor: The Enzymes of Glutamine Metabolism, 1973, Slow Transmissible Diseases of the Nervous System, 2 vols., 1979, Prions - Novel Infectious Pathogens Causing Scrapie and CJD, 1987, Prion Diseases of Humans and Animals, 1992, Molecular and Genetic Basis of Neurologic Disease, 1993; contbr. over 200 rsch. articles to profl. jours. Mem. adv. bd. Family Survival Project for Adults with Chronic Brain Disorders, San Francisco, 1982—; San Francisco chpt. Alzheimer's Disease and Related Disorder Assn., 1985—. Lt. comdr. USPHS, 1969-72. Alfred P. Sloan Rsch. fellow U. Calif., 1976-78; Med. Investigator grantee Howard Hughes Med. Inst., 1976-81; grantee for excellence in neurosci. Senator Jacob Javits Ctr., NIH, 1985-1990; recipient Leadership and Excellence for Alzheimer's Disease award NIH, 1990—, Potamkin prize for Alzheimer's Disease Rsch., 1991, Presdl. award, 1993, Med. Rsch. award Met. Life Found., 1992, Christopher Columbus Discovery award NIH and Med. Soc. Genoa, Italy, 1992, Charles A. Dana award for pioneering achievements in health, 1992, Dickson prize for outstanding contbns. to medicine U. Pitts., 1992, Max Planck Rsch. award Alexander von Humboldt Found. and Max Planck Soc., 1992, Gairdner Found. Internat. award, 1993, Distin. Achievement in Neuroscience Rsch. award Bristol-Myers Squibb, 1994, Albert Lasker award for Basic Med. Rsch., 1994, Caledonian Rsch. Found. prize Royal Soc. Edinburgh, 1995, Paul Ehrlich and Ludwig Darmstaedter award Germany, 1995, Paul Hoch award Am. Psychopathological Assn., 1995. Mem. NAS (Inst. Medicine, Richard Lounsbery award for extraordinary achievements in biology and medicine 1993), Am. Acad. Arts and Scis., Am. Acad. Neurology (George Cotzias award for outstanding rsch. 1987, Presdl. award 1993), Am. Assn. Physicians, Am. Soc. Microbiology, Am. Soc. Neurochemistry, Internat. Soc. Neurochemistry, Am. Soc. Virology, Am. Neurol. Assn., Am. Soc. Clin. Investigation, Am. Soc. Cellular Biology, Am. Soc. Molecular Biol. Biochemistry, Protein Soc., Concordia Argonaut Clu.

PRUSINOWSKI, JULIE ELLEN, artistic director; b. Devon, Pa., Dec. 4, 1952; d. Joseph S. and Julia Marie (DeSimone) P. BS in Edn. Theater, West Chester U., 1974; MA in Acting and Directing, W.Va. U., 1978; postgrad., U. Pitts., 1978-81. Tng. facility coord. Am. Dance Machine, N.Y.C., 1981; prodn. asst. Night of 100 Stars, N.Y.C., 1982; producer informal series Equity Libr. Theatre, N.Y.C., 1981-83; producing dir. Foundation Theatre, Pemberton, N.J., 1983—; teaching fellow U. Pitts., 1978-81; asst. prof. in theater Burlington County Coll. Pemberton, 1983-85; cons. N.J. Theatre Group, Florham Park, N.J.; founding mem. West Chester Musical Theatre Co.,., 1973, Map of the New World Players, 1977; on-site reporter NEA. Dir. plays: The Other Side of Newark, 1987, Victim of an Assassination, 1988, Italian American Reconciliation, 1990, (world premiere) The Scarlet Letter, 1993. Mem. N.J. Young Playwrights Festival (selection com. 1985—), N.J. Theatre Group (pres. 1991—, mem. exec. com.). Avocations: reading, antiques, sailing, travel. Home: 1116 Nottinghill Ln Trenton NJ 08619-4013

PRUSOFF, WILLIAM HERMAN, biochemical pharmacologist, educator; b. N.Y.C., June 25, 1920; s. Samuel and Mary (Metrick) P.; m. Brigitte Auerbach, June 19, 1948 (dec. Apr. 1991); children—Alvin Saul, Laura Ann. B.A., U. Miami, Fla., 1941; M.A., Columbia U., 1947, Ph.D., 1949. Research assoc., instr. pharmacology Western Res. U., 1949-53; mem. faculty Yale Med. Sch., 1953—; prof. pharmacology, 1966-90, prof. emeritus. sr. rsch. scientist, 1990—, acting chmn. dept., 1968; cons. in field, 1965—. Mem. Am. Assn. Cancer Rsch., Am. Chem. Soc., Am. Soc. Biol. Chemists, Am. Soc. Pharmacology and Exptl. Therapeutics, Soc. Chinese Bioscientists in Am., Sigma Xi, Internat. Soc. for Antiviral Rsch. Achievements include rsch. in virology, photochemistry, mechanism drug action, synthesis potential drugs; synthesized Idoxuridine; developed (in collaboration with D.T.S. Lin) Stavudine for therapy of AIDS. Home: De Forest Dr Branford CT 06471 Office: Yale U Sch Medicine New Haven CT 06510

PRUSSING, LAUREL LUNT, state official, economist; b. N.Y.C., Feb. 21, 1941; d. Richard Valentine and Maria (Rinaldi) Lunt; m. John Edward Prussing, May 29, 1965; children: Heidi Elizabeth, Erica Stephanie, Victoria Nicole Johanna. AB, Wellesley Coll., 1962; MA, Boston U., 1964; postgrad., U. Calif., San Diego, 1968-69, U. Ill., 1970-76. Economist Arthur D. Little, Cambridge, Mass., 1963-67, U. Ill., Urbana, 1971-72; mem. county bd. Champaign County, Urbana, 1972-76, county auditor, 1976-92; mem. local audit adv. bd. Office Ill. Compt., Chgo., 1984-92. Contbr. to Illinois Local Government: A Handbook, 1990. Founder Com. for Intelligent Tax Reform, Urbana, 1982—, Com. for Elected County Exec., Urbana, 1986—; state rep. 103d dist. Ill. Gen. Assembly, 1993-95. Named Best Freshman Legislator Ind. Voters Ill., 1994; recipient Friend of Agriculture award Ill. Farm Bur., 1994; named to Legis. Honor Roll Ill. Environ. Coun., 1994. Mem. LWV, Govt. Fin. Officers Assn., U.S. and Can. (com. on acctg., auditing and fin. reporting 1980-88, Fin. Reporting award 1981-91, Disting. Budget award 1986), Nat. Assn. Local Govt. Auditors (charter), Ill. Assn.

County Auditors (pres. 1984-85). Democrat. Home: 2106 Grange Dr Urbana IL 61801

PRUTER, KARL HUGO, bishop; b. Poughkeepsie, N.Y., July 3, 1920; s. William Karl and Katherine (Rehling) P.; m. Nancy Lee Taylor, 1943; children: Hugo Jr., Robert, Karl, Stephen, Maurice, Katherine, Nancy Goodman. B.A., Northeastern U., 1943; M.Div., Lutheran Theol. Sem., Phila., 1945; M.A. in Edn., Roosevelt U., 1963; M.A. in History, Boston U., 1968. Guest lectr. Landerziehungsheim, Stein, West Germany, 1964-65; ordained priest Christ Catholic Ch., 1965; pastor Ch. of the Transfiguration, Boston, 1965-70; bishop Christ Cath. Ch. Author: The Theology of Congregationalism, 1953, The Teachings of the Great Mystics, 1969, A History of the Old Catholic Church, 1973, The People of God, 1975, The Jewish Christians in the United States, 1985. Address: Cathedral Ch Prince of Peace Highlandville MO 65669

PRUYN, WILLIAM J., energy industry executive; b. Boston, Aug. 25, 1922; s. William J. and Ida M. (Langan) P.; m. Mary Anton, May 19, 1945; children: William J., Barbara, Marilyn, Ann Marie, Stephen, Christopher. Student, Bentley Coll., 1939-41, Harvard U., 1944-45, 64; BBA, Northeastern U., 1948. Pub. acct. Meahl, McNamara & Co., 1946-51; with Eastern Gas & Fuel Assocs. (name changed to Eastern Enterprises 1989), Boston, 1951-91, sr. v.p., 1972-76, treasurer, 1973—, pres., chief adminstrv. officer, 1976-77, pres., chief exec. officer, 1977-85, chmn. bd., chief exec. officer, 1986-87, chmn. bd., 1987-91; ret., 1991. Bd. dirs. Med. Found., Inc.; trustee Northeastern U., New Eng. Aquarium; mem. pres.'s adv. council Bentley Coll. Served with USNR, 1943-45. Mem. Corinthian Yacht Club. Home: 17 Vassar Rd Marblehead MA 01945-3630

PRUZANSKY, JOSHUA MURDOCK, lawyer; b. N.Y.C., Mar. 16, 1940; s. Louis and Rose (Murdock) P.; m. Susan R. Bernstein, Aug. 31, 1980; 1 child, Dina Gabrielle. BA, Columbia Coll., 1960, JD, 1965. Bar: N.Y. 1965, U.S. Dist. Ct. (ea. and so. dists.) N.Y., 1968, U.S. Supreme Ct., 1980. Ptnr. Scheinberg, DePetris & Pruzansky, Riverhead, N.Y., 1965-85, Greshin, Ziegler & Pruzansky, Smithtown, 1985—; mem. exec. coun. N.Y. State Conf. Bar Leaders, 1984—, chmn. 88-89; mem. grievance com. Appellate Divsn. 10th Judicial Dist., 1992—; mem. adv. bd. Ticor Title Guarantee Co., 1992—. Trustee Evan Frankel Found., 1993—, Suffolk Acad. Law, Suffolk County, N.Y., 1979-89; dir. Planned Parenthood Suffolk County, Inc., 1995—; mem. secondary sch. adv. com. Columbia U.; mem. Suffolk adv. bd. Fund for Modern Cts. Fellow ABA Found., N.Y. State Bar Found. (bd. dirs. 1994—), mem. ABA (probate and real property sect.), N.Y. State Bar Assn. (ho. dels. 1982—, exec. com. del. 1991—, v.p. 1991-92, 95—, mem.-at-large exec. com. 1992-95, nominating com. 1986-91, spl. com. women and law 1986-91, task force on adminstrv. adjudication 1986—, task force on small firms 1991—, chair by-laws com. 1991—, trusts and estates sect.), Suffolk County Bar Assn. (bd. dirs. 1979-89, pres. 1985-86, recipient president's award 1995), N.Y. County Lawyers Assn., Nassau County Bar Assn., Suffolk Bar Pac (chmn. 1987-88), Columbia U. Law Alumni Assn. Suffolk County (dir. 1989—). Office: Greshin Ziegler & Pruzansky 199 E Main St Smithtown NY 11787-2899

PRYBIL, LAWRENCE DEWEY, health system executive; b. Iowa City, Iowa, July 24, 1940; s. Reynolds James and Vivian Margaret (Ford) P.; m. Marilyn M. Reed, Aug. 17, 1963; children: David Reed, Catherine Ford. BA, State U. of Iowa, 1962; MA, State U. Iowa, 1964; PhD, U. Iowa, 1970. Resident in health adminstrn. Jewish Hosp. St. Louis, St. Louis, 1964; asst. adminstr. Westover AFB Regional Hosp., Chicopee, Mass., 1965-67; doctoral student U. Iowa, Iowa City, Iowa, 1967-70; mem. faculty, chmn. dept. health adminstrn. Med. Coll. Va., Richmond, 1970-80; v.p. of adminstrn. Sisters of Mercy Health Corp., Farmington Hills, Mich., 1980-84; exec. v.p., COO Daus. of Charity Nat. Health System, East Cen., Evansville, Ind., 1984-88, CEO, 1988—; bd. dirs. Benedictine Health System, Duluth, Minn. Author numerous articles, book chpts. and rsch. reports. Fellow Am. Coll. Healthcare Execs.; mem. Am. Hosp. Assn. (bd. dirs.), Newcomen Soc., Phi Beta Kappa, Omicron Delta Kappa. Avocations: running, golf, mus. Home: 6405 Echo Hill Dr Evansville IN 47720-2507 Office: Daus Charity Nat Health Sys 9404 New Harmony Rd Evansville IN 47720-8939

PRYCE, DEBORAH D., congresswoman; b. Warren, Ohio, July 29, 1951. BA cum laude, Ohio State U., 1973; JD with honors, Capital U., 1976. Bar: Ohio 1976. Former asst. city prosecutor, asst. city atty., first asst. city prosecutor Columbus, Ohio; former judge Franklin County Mcpl. Ct., Columbus; mem. 103rd Congress from 15th Ohio dist., Washington, D.C., 1993—; mem. coms.: banking, fin. and urban affairs, housing and community devel., fin. instns. supervision, regulations and deposit ins., consumer credit and ins., govt. ops., environment, energy and natural resources. Republican. Presbyterian. Avocations: skiing, traveling.

PRYCE, EDWARD LYONS, landscape architect; b. Lake Charles, La., May 26, 1914; s. George Samuel and Dora (Cook) P.; m. Woodia Bernice Smith, Nov. 2, 1940; children—Marilyn C., Joellen G. B.S., Tuskegee Inst., 1937; B.L.A., Ohio State U., 1948; M.S. in Landscape Architecture, U. Calif., Berkeley, 1953. Head dept. ornamental horticulture Tuskegee Inst., 1948-55, supt. of bldgs. and grounds, 1955-69, prof. dept. architecture, 1969-77; pvt. practice landscape architecture Tuskegee, Ala., 1948—; chmn. Ala. State Bd. Examiners for Landscape Architects, 1981—. Mem. Tuskegee City Planning Commn., 1970-76; mem. Tuskegee Model Cities Commn., 1968-72, Ala. State Outdoor Recreation Planning Bd., 1978—. Recipient Alumni Merit award Tuskegee Inst., 1977, Disting. Alumnus award Ohio State U., 1980. Fellow Am. Soc. Landscape Architects. Baptist. Office: PO Box 246 1901 Montgomery Rd Tuskegee AL 36087

PRYCE, JONATHAN, actor; b. North Wales, June 1, 1947. Appearances include (stage) Liverpool Everyman, 1972, Nottinguam Playhouse-Comedians, Comedians, 1977 (Tony award, Theatre World award); Hamlet (Olivier award), Macbeth, Julius Caesar, The Caretaker, 1981, Accidental Death of an Anarchist, 1984, Miss Saigon, 1991 (Tony award), Oliver, 1995, (films) Voyage of the Damned, 1976, Breaking Glass, 1980, Loophole, 1981, Praying Mantis, 1982, The Plowman's Lunch, 1983, Something Wicked This Way Comes, 1983, Brazil, 1985, The Doctor and the Devils, 1985, Haunted Honeymoon, 1986, Jumpin Jack Flash, 1986, Hotel London, 1987, Man On Fire, 1987, The Adventures of Baron Munchausen, 1988, Consuming Passions, 1988, The Rachel Papers, 1989, Glengarry Glen Ross, 1992, The Age of Innocence, 1993, Carrington, 1995, (TV movie) Barbarians at the Gate, HBO, 1993 (Emmy nomination, Supporting Actor - Miniseries or Special, 1993). Office: Duval Flack and Assocs 200 W 57th St Ste 1407 New York NY 10019*

PRYCE, WILLIAM THORNTON, foreign service officer; b. San Diego, July 19, 1932; s. Roland Fremont and Katharine (Hartmann) P.; m. Joan MacClurg, Mar. 22, 1958; children: Kathy Ellen, Jeffrey Fremont, Scott Fisher. BA, Wesleyan U., 1953; MA, Tufts U., 1954. Joined Fgn. Svc., Dept. State, 1958; spl. asst. to under sec. of state for econ. affairs, asst. sec. for Latin Am. affairs Washington, 1964-65; polit. officer Am. ambassies in Moscow, Panama, Guatemala, 1966-74; dir. Soviet ednl. and cultural programs Dept. State, Washington, 1974-76; exec. asst. to amb.-at-large Ellsworth Bunker Washington, 1977-78; polit. counselor Am. Embassy, Mexico City, 1978-81; dep. chief of mission Am. Embassy, La Paz, Bolivia, 1981-82, Panama City, Panama, 1982-86; alt. U.S. rep. Orgn. Am. States, Washington, 1986-89; spl. asst. to pres. for nat. security affairs NSC, Washington, 1989-92; U.S. amb. to Honduras, 1993—. Lt. USN, 1955-58. Recipient Meritorious Honor award Dept. State, 1986, Superior Honor award, 1989, Sr. Performance award 1982-87, 89, 90, 92. Mem. Am. Fgn. Svc. Assn., City Tavern Club. Episcopalian. Home and Office: Am Embassy Honduras APO AA 34022

PRYOR, ALAN MARK, banker; b. Charleston, S.C., Apr. 4, 1949; s. Sidney and Grace (Buchstane) P.; m. Pamela Ray Pryor, Nov. 22, 1986; 2 children. BA in History, U. Mich., 1971, MA in Econs., 1974. Asst. mgr. internat. banking group Citibank, N.A., N.Y.C., 1975-78, mgr., v.p. internat. fin., 1978-82, v.p. internat. capital markets, 1983-85; from v.p. to exec. v.p., head swap and derivative products dept. Deutsche Bank Capital Corp., N.Y.C., 1985-91; dir., global head equity derivatives Deutsche Bank AG, Frankfurt, Fed. Republic Germany, 1992-93; mng. dir., head transaction devel. group Deutsche Bank Securities Corp., N.Y.C., 1994—; guest lectr.

Columbia U. Grad. Sch. Bus., N.Y.C., 1987, 89, adj. asst. prof. fin., 1990; speaker Inst. for Internat. Rsch., N.Y.C., 1986-87, Euromoney Confs., N.Y.C., 1988. Author: (with others), Cross Currency Swaps, 1992. Office: Deutsche Bank Securities Corp 1290 Ave Americas New York NY 10104-0101

PRYOR, CAROL GRAHAM, obstetrician-gynecologist; b. Savannah, Ga.; m. Louis O.J. Manganiello, June 11, 1950; children: Carol Helen, Victoria Manganiello Mudano. AB, Ga. Coll., 1943; MD, Med. Coll. Ga., 1947. Rotating intern City Hosps., Balt., 1947-48; asst. resident pathology Baroness Erlanger Hosp., Chattanooga, 1948; intern. obstetrics City Colls., Balt., 1949; coll. physician Ga. State Coll. for Women, Milledgeville, Ga., 1949-50; resident obstetrics City Hosps., Balt., 1950-51; asst. resident gynecology Univ. Hosp., Balt., 1951-52; sr. resident ob-gyn. Univ. Hosp., Augusta, Ga., 1952; pvt. practice ob-gyn. Augusta, 1952—. Mem., former pres. Iris Garden Club, Augusta; mem. coun. on maternal and infant health State of Ga., Atlanta, 1981-90; mem. edn. found. AAUW, 1961-63, state v.p. br. pres., 1963-65. Recipient Cert. of Achievement-Community Leadersip, Ga. div. AAUW, 1982; named Med. Woman of Yr., Ga. br. 51 Am. Med. Women's Assn., 1961. Fellow am. Coll. Surgeons (1st woman mem. Ga. chpt. 1956), Am. Coll. Ob-Gyn.; mem. AMA, Richmond County Med. Soc., So. Med. Assn., So. Surg. Congress, Delta Kappa Gamma. Democrat. Methodist. Office: 2316 Wrightboro Rd Augusta GA 30904

PRYOR, CHARLES WINGFIELD, JR., nuclear technology company executive; b. Lynchburg, Va., Dec. 31, 1944; s. Charles Winfield and Elizabeth (Baldock) P.; m. Mary Jane Meacham, Apr. 19, 1990; children: Chip, Blake Newton, Laurie, Reed Newton. BSCE with honors, Va. Inst. Tech. and State U., 1966, MS in Structural Engring., 1968, PhD in Structural Engring., 1970; postgrad., Northeastern U., 1980. Registered profl. engr., Va. Instr. engring. mechanics Va. Poly. Inst. and State U., Blacksburg, 1969-70; sr. engr. McDonnell Douglas Aerospace Co., 1970-72; various positions nuclear power generation div. Babcock & Wilcox Co., 1972-83; v.p., gen. mgr. nuclear power div., 1983-89, v.p., 1989-91; pres., CEO, B&W Nuclear Svc. Co.; chmn. bd. B&W Fuel Co., 1989-91; pres., CEO B&W Nuclear Techs., Inc., Lynchburg, Va., 1991—; numerous presentations in field; bd. dirs., mem. internat. adv. com. Nuclear Energy Inst., Washington; chmn. bd. Centra Health, Inc.; mem. com. of 100 engring. adv. bd. Va. Poly. Inst. and State U. Contbr. numerous articles to tech., profl. and managerial jours. Chmn. bd. Employee Assistance Ctrl. Va., Ctrl. Va. Ptnrs. in Edn.; bd. dirs. Va. Ctr. for Innovative Tech., Ctrl. Va. C.C. Found., Ctrl. Va. YMCA, NCCJ; trustee Lynchburg Coll.; mem. Blue Ridge Econ. Devel. Coun., Coun. for Va. Urban Renewal; past div. dir. United Way Ctrl. Va. Decorated chevalier Ordre Nat. du Merite (France); named Va. Outstanding Industralist, State of Va., 1993. Mem. Am. Nuclear Soc., Greater Lynchburg C. of C. (past pres.), Sigma XXi, Tau Beta Pi, Phi Kappa Phi, Chi Epsilon. Episcopalian. Home: Rt 4 Box 195C Lynchburg VA 24503 Office: B&W Nuclear Techs Inc PO Box 10 935 Lynchburg VA 24506

PRYOR, DAVID HAMPTON, senator; b. Camden, Ark., Aug. 29, 1934; s. Edgar and Susan (Newton) P.; m. Barbara Lunsford, Nov. 27, 1957; children—David, Mark, Scott. B.A. in Polit. Sci, U. Ark., 1957, LL.B., 1961. Bar: Ark. 1964. Practiced in Camden; mem. firm Pryor and Barnes; founder, pub. Ouachita Citizen newspaper, Camden, 1957-60; mem. Ark. Ho. of Reps., 1961-65, 89th-92d Congresses from 4th Ark. dist.; gov. of Ark., 1974-79, senator from Ark., 1979—; ranking min. mem. Select Com. On Aging, Nutrition and Forestry Subcom. on Prodn. and Price Competitiveness, Fin. Subcom. on Long Term Growth, Debt. and Deficit Reduction; mem. Govt. Affairs, Sen. Dem. Conf. Com., Sen. Dem. Steering and Coord. Com., Dem. Senatorial Campign Com. Office: US Senate 267 Russell Senate Bldg Washington DC 20510*

PRYOR, HAROLD S., retired college president; b. Overton County, Tenn., Oct. 3, 1920; s. Hubert S. and Ethel (Stockton) P.; m. LaRue Vaughn, June 26, 1946. B.S., Austin Peay State U., 1946; M.A., George Peabody Coll., 1947; Ed.D., U. Tenn., 1951. Instr. George Peabody Coll., Vanderbilt U., 1946-47, E. Tenn. State U., 1947-49, U. Tenn., Knoxville, 1949-51; head dept. edn. Austin Peay State U., 1952, dir. tchr. edn., 1954-68; pres. Columbia (Tenn.) State Community Coll., from 1968, now pres. emeritus; dir. First Farmers and Merchants Nat. Bank, Columbia, 1970—, First Farmers and Mchts. Corp., 1982—; Columbia State Found., 1971—. Contbr. articles to profl. jours. With U.S. Army, 1943-46. Grantee Dept. Labor; Grantee HEW. Mem. NEA, Tenn. Coll. Assn. (past pres.), Tenn. Edn. Assn., Am. Assn. Higher Edn., Comparative Edn. Soc., Graymere Country Club, Kiwanis, Kappa Delta Pi, Phi Delta Kappa. Democrat. Presbyterian.

PRYOR, HUBERT, editor, writer; b. Buenos Aires, Argentina, Mar. 18, 1916; (parents Am. citizens); s. John W. and Hilda A. (Cowes) P.; m. Ellen M. Ach, 1940 (div. 1959); children: Alan, Gerald, David. Grad., St. George's Coll., Argentina, 1932; student, U. London, Eng., 1934-36. Corr. in S.Am. for United Press, 1937-39; pub. relations rep. Pan Am. Airways in Buenos Aires, 1939-40; reporter N.Y. Herald Tribune, 1940-41; writer, dir. short-wave newsroom CBS, 1941-46; asst. mng. editor Knickerbocker Weekly, 1946-47; sr. editor Look mag., 1947-62; creative supr. Wilson, Haight & Welch (advt.), 1962-63; editor Science Digest, 1963-67; mng. editor Med. World News, 1967; editor NRTA Jour. Modern Maturity, 1967-82; editorial dir. Dynamic Years, 1977-82; publs. coordinator Modern Maturity, Dynamic Years, 1982-84; editorial coms., writer, 1985—. Author: Soul Talk, 1995. Served to lt. USNR, 1943-46. Mem. Am. Soc. Mag. Editors, Overseas Press Club. Home: 3560 S Ocean Blvd Palm Beach FL 33480-5772

PRYOR, JOSEPH EHRMAN, chemistry educator; b. Melber, Ky., Mar. 19, 1918; s. Lonnie Ernest and Quetro Desdemona (Rives) P.; m. Bessie Mae Ledbetter, Aug. 16, 1946; children: Beverly Jo, Joseph Byron, Susan Rebecca. B.A., B.S., Harding Coll., Searcy, Ark., 1937; M.A., La. State U., 1939, Ph.D., 1943; student, U. Minn., summers 1949, 55, U. Chgo., summer 1950. Teaching fellow math. La. State U., 1937-39, teaching fellow chemistry, 1939-41, Charles Edward Coates research fellow chemistry, 1941-42, instr. math., 1942-44; prof. phys. sci. Harding Coll., 1944-89, chmn. phys. sci. dept., 1944-62, dean coll., 1960-83, v.p. acad. affairs, 1973-83; prof. emeritus, 1989—; prof. physics Mid. Tenn. State U., summer 1959, Harding U., Florence, Italy, 1987; yearbook advisor Harding Coll., 1944-87 (29 ACP All-American books, ACP Hall of Fame, 1988); research chemist Lion Oil Co., El Dorado, Ark., summer 1957; mem. com. liberal arts edn. N. Central Assn., 1952-54, coordinator, 1963-69; faculty rep. Ark. Intercollegiate Athletic Conf., 1957-88, pres., 1967-68, 77-78, 87-88; broadcasting and recording engr., 1946-60. Bd. dirs. Camp Wyldewood, Searcy, 1948-51, So. Christian Home, Morrilton, Ark., 1978—; Zambia Christian Sch., 1975—; preacher, elder Ch. of Christ. Recipient Disting. Alumnus award Harding Coll., 1974, Golden Eagle award Am. Yearbook Co., 1969, Disting. Svc. Plaque for 15 yrs. chmn. ad hoc pubs., 1994; elected to Harding U. Athletic Hall of Fame, 1989, Nat. Assn. of Intercollegiate Athletics Hall of Fame, 1990; Harding U. Sci. Bldg. named the Joseph E. Pryor Sci. Ctr., 1989. Fellow AAAS; mem. Am. Chem. Soc. (chmn. central ark. sect. 1954-55, sect. councilor 1959-65, 50-yr. membership pin award 1991, Disting. Svc. plaque Cen. Ark. sect. 1991), Am. Sci. Affiliation, Ark. Acad. Sci. Nat. Edn. Assn., Ark. (2d v.p. dept. higher edn. 1964-65, pres. dept. 1965-66), Ark. Deans Assn. (past chmn.), Nat. Council Coll. Publs. Advisers (dist. chmn. 1973-75, disting. yearbook adviser award 1973), Assn. Coll. Honor Socs. (exec. com. 1976-80), Searcy C. of C, Alpha Phi Gamma, Sigma Xi, Alpha Chi (nat. council 1959-93, sec.-treas. region II 1959-71, nat. sec.-treas. 1970-83, exec. dir. 1983-93, installed 85 chpts., awarded outstanding svc. plaque 1993), Phi Kappa Phi, Alpha Psi Omega, Sigma Delta Psi, Alpha Chi Sigma, Phi Lambda Upsilon, Kappa Mu Epsilon, Pi Kappa Delta, Delta Mu Delta, Phi Eta Sigma. Home: 17 Magnolia Dr Searcy AR 72143-5608

PRYOR, RICHARD, actor, writer; b. Peoria, Ill., Dec. 1, 1940; s. Leroy and Gertrude (Thomas) P.; children: Elizabeth Ann, Richard, Rain, Renee. Grad. high sch. Appeared on: Ed Sullivan, Merv Griffin and Johnny Carson television shows in 1960s; appeared in motion pictures The Busy Body, 1967, The Green Berets, 1968, Wild In The Streets, 1968, The Phynx, 1970, Dynamite Chicken, 1970, Lady Sings the Blues, 1972, Hit, 1973, Wattstax, 1973, The Mack, 1973, Some Call It Loving, 1973, Uptown Saturday Night, 1974, Adios Amigos, 1976, The Bingo Long Travelling All-Stars and Motor Kings, 1976, Car Wash, 1976, Silver Streak, 1976, Greased Lightning, 1977,

Which Way is Up?, 1977, Blue Collar, 1978, California Suite, 1978, The Wiz, 1978, Richard Pryor Live in Concert, 1979, The Muppet Movie, 1979, Wholly Moses, 1980, In God We Trust, 1980, Stir Crazy, 1980, Bustin' Loose, 1981, Some Kind of Hero, 1982, The Toy, 1982, Superman III, 1983, Richard Pryor Here and Now, 1983, Brewster's Millions, 1985, Critical Condition, 1987, Moving, 1988, See No Evil, Hear No Evil, 1989, Another You, 1991; writer, producer, dir. Jo Jo Dancer Your Life Is Calling, 1986; writer scripts for Flip Wilson; co-writer TV spls. for Lily Tomlin, 1973 (Emmy award); movie script Blazing Saddles, 1973 (Am. Writers Guild award, Am. Acad. Humor award), Lily, 1974 (Am. Acad. Humor award); recorded That Nigger's Crazy, 1974 (Grammy award, certified Gold and Platinum album), Bicentennial Nigger, 1976 (Grammy award); star Richard Pryor Show, NBC-TV, 1977; owner Richard Pryor Enterprises, Inc., Los Angeles, 1975—. Served with U.S. Army, 1958-60. Mem. Nat. Acad. Rec. Arts and Scis., Writers Guild Am. Office: Indigo Prodns Columbia Plz Ste 110 Burbank CA 91505*

PRYOR, RICHARD WALTER, telecommunications executive, retired air force officer; b. Poplar Bluff, Mo., Nov. 6, 1932; s. Walter V. and Mary (Clifford) P.; m. Barbara LeCompte, Feb. 19, 1955; children: Richard, Susan Davis, Robert, William. B in Gen. Studies, U. Nebr., Omaha, 1972; MA, Webster Coll., St. Louis, 1975; grad., U. No. Colo., 1975. Commd. 2d lt USAF, 1953, advanced through grades to maj. gen., 1982, ret., 1982, instr. Acad., DVMT engr. space and missile systems, chief of staff Communication Services; mgr. worldwide def. communication system Def. Communications Agy., 1980-81; pres. ITT World Communications, N.Y.C., 1982-84, ITT Indsl. Transmission Co., N.Y.C.; sr. v.p. engring. ops. ITT Communication Services GP; pres., gen. mgr. ITT Christian Rovsing-Copenhagen DK, 1984-86; chmn. Christian-Rovsing Inc., Tulsa; exec. v.p. Electronic Data Systems (EDS) Comm. Corp., Dallas, 1986-89; pres., chief oper. officer IMM Corp., Phila., 1989-92; chmn., CEO. officer Ultranav Corp, Dallas; chmn. Prism Video, Dallas. Contbr. articles to tech. publs. Assoc. dir. Boy Soucts Am., N.Y.C., 1983. Recipient Cert. of Appreciation Okla. Mental Health Assn. 1979, Kansas City Lions Club, 1974. Mem. Armed Forces Communications and Electronics Assn. (pres. N.Y.C. 1983, nat. dir.), Air Force Assn., Oklahoma City Soc. Profl. Engrs., Phi Alpha Theta. Republican. Roman Catholic. Clubs: Bolling AFB Officers; Canoe Brook Country (Short Hills, N.J.); Army-Navy (Washington). Home: 17328 Village Ln Dallas TX 75248-6035 also: 17328 Village Ln Dallas TX 75248-6035 Office: 8th Floor 17304 Preston Rd Dallas TX 75252

PRYOR, WILLIAM AUSTIN, chemistry educator; b. St. Louis, Mar. 10, 1929; s. Saul Arnold and Adeline (Franzel) P. Ph.B., U. Chgo., 1948, B.S., 1951; Ph.D., U. Calif. at Berkeley, 1954. Chemist Calif. Research Corp. Richmond, 1954-60; lectr. U. Calif. at Berkeley, 1956-60; asst. prof. Purdue U., Lafayette, Ind., 1960-63; assoc. prof. La. State U., Baton Rouge, 1963-67; prof. La. State U., 1967-72, Thomas and David Boyd prof. chemistry and biochemistry, 1972—; mem. depts. chemistry and biochemistry Inst. Environ. Studies, La. State U. Med. Ctr., New Orleans; mem. depts. cehmistry, biochemistry Inst. Environ. Studies Pennington Biomed. Rsch. Ctr., Baton Rouge; dir. Biodynamics Inst. La. State U., 1985—; vis. prof. Washington U., St. Louis, 1968, UCLA, 1970, U. Calif., Berkeley, 1971, Duke U., 1978, U. Calif., Davis, 1978, U. Calif., San Deigo, 1978, U. Calif., Davis, 1994, Harvard U., 1995, Tufts U., 1995; cons. to chem. co., 1963—. Author: books including Free Radicals, 1966, (with Melvin Calvin) Organic Chemistry of Life, 1973, Organic Free Radicals, 1978, Frontiers of Free Radical Chemistry, 1980, Free Radicals in Biology, vols. I and II, 1976, vol. III, 1977, vol. IV, 1980, vol. V, 1982, vol. VI, 1984 (with L. Packer) Methods in Enzymology, vol. 105, 1984, (with A.T. Diplock, L.J. Macklin, L. Packer) Vitamin E: Biochemistry and Health Implications, 1989, (with L. Packer, A.N. Glazer), Methods in Enzymology, vol. 186, 1989, (with J. Diana) Tobacco Smoking and Nutrition: Influence of Nutrition on Tobacco Associated Health Risks, 1993, (with L. Packer) Methods in Enzymology, Vols. 233, 234, 1994; also numerous articles; editorial bd. internat. jours. in chemistry and gerontology; editor-in-chief Advances in Free Radical Biology and Medicine, 1985-87; co-editor-in-chief: Free Radical Biology and Medicine, 1987—. Grantee AEC, 1960-64, NIH, 1964—, NSF, 1964—, Air Force Office Sci. Research, 1964-68, Dow Chem. Co., 1964—, Du Pont, U.S. Army, 1965-69, Exxon Research and Devel. Co., 1966—, Owens-Corning Fiberglas, 1983—; Distinguished Faculty fellow La. State U. Found., 1969, NIH Spl. Postdoctoral fellow, 1970-71, John Simon Gugenheim fellow, 1970-71; recipient Merit award NIH, 1986, Harold Harper Meml. award Am. Council for Advancement of Medicine, 1987. Fellow Am. Inst. Chemists, AAAS; mem. Am. Chem. Soc. (S.W. sect. award 1975, Petroleum Chemistry award 1980, Southern Chemist award 1983, Charles E. Coates award 1989), Chem. Soc. London (VERIS award for nutrition rsch.), Faraday Soc., Gerontol. Soc., Radiation Rsch. Soc., Am. Aging Assn., Pan-Am. Med. Assn. (hon. life), Soc. for Free Radical Search (founding mem., internat. coun.), Oxygen Soc. (founding mem., pres.-elect 1995-96, pres. 1997-98). Patentee in field. Home: 3631 S Lakeshore Dr Baton Rouge LA 70808-3631 Office: La State U Biodynamics Inst 711 Choppin Baton Rouge LA 70803-1800

PRYOR, WILLIAM DANIEL LEE, humanities educator; b. Lakeland, Fla., Oct. 29, 1926; s. Dahl and Lottie Mae (Merchant) P. AB, Fla. So. Coll., 1949; MA, Fla. State U., 1950, PhD, 1959; postgrad. U. N.C., 1952-53. Pvt. art study with Florence Wilde; pvt. voice study with Colin O'More and Anna Kaskas; pvt. piano study with Waldemar Hille and audited piano master classes of Ernst von Dohnányi. Asst. prof. English, dir. drama Bridgewater Coll., 1950-52; vis. instr. English Fla. So. Coll., MacDill Army Air Base, summer 1951; grad. teaching fellow humanities Fla. State U., 1953-55, 57-58; instr. English, U. Houston, University Park, 1955-59, asst. prof., 1959-62, assoc. prof., 1962-71, prof., 1971—; assoc. editor Forum, 1967, editor, 1967-82; vis. instr. English, Tex. So. U., 1961-63; vis. instr. humanities, govt. U. Tex. Dental Br., Houston, 1962-63; lectr. The Women's Inst., Houston, 1967-72; lectr. humanities series Jewish Community Center, 1972-73; originator, moderator weekly television and radio program The Arts in Houston on Stas. KUHT-TV and KUHF-FM, 1956-57, 58-63. Contbg. author: National Poetry Anthology, 1952, Panorama das Literaturas das Americas, vol. 2, 1958-60; contbr. articles to scholarly jours.; dir. T.S. Eliot's Murder in the Cathedral, U. Houston, 1965 (Houston's first full-scale prodn.); performed in opera as Sir Edgar in Der Junge Lord (Henze), Houston Grand Opera Assn., 1967; played the title role in Aella (Chatterton), Am. premiere, U. Houston, 1970. Bd. dirs. Houston Shakespeare Soc., 1964-67; bd. dirs., program annotator Houston Chamber Orch. Soc., 1964-76 ; narrator Houston Symphony Orch., Houston Summer Symphony Orch., Houston Chamber Orch., U. Houston Symphony Orch., St. Stephen's Music Festival Symphony Orch., Ind.; narrator world premier of The Bells (Jerry McCathern), 1969, U. Houston Symphony Orch., 1969, Am. premier Symphony No. Seven, Antartica (Vaughn-Williams), Houston Symphony Orch., 1967, L'Histoire du Soldat (Stravinski), U. Houston Symphony Orch., 1957, Am. premier Babar the Elephant (Poulenc-Francais), Houston Chamber Orch., 1967, Le Roi David (Honegger), 1979, Voice of God in opera Noye's Fludde (Britten), St. Stephen's Music Festival, 1981; bd. dirs., program annotator Music Guild, Houston, 1960-67, v.p., 1963-67, adv. bd. 1967-70; bd. dirs. Contemporary Music Soc., Houston, 1963; mem.-at-large bd. dirs. Houston Grand Opera Guild, 1966-67; mem. repertory com. Houston Grand Opera Assn. 1967-70; bd. dirs. Houston Grand Opera, 1970-75, adv. bd., 1978-79; mem. cultural adv. com. Jewish Community Center, 1960-66; bd. dirs. Houston Friends Pub. Library, 1962-67, 73-75, 1st v.p., 1963-67; adv. mem. cultural affairs com. Houston C of C., 1972-75; adv. bd. dirs. The Wilhelm Schole, 1980—, Buffalo Bayou Support Com., 1985-87. Recipient Master Teaching award Coll. Humanities and Fine Arts U. Houston, 1980, Favorite Prof. award Bapt. Student Union, U. of Houston, 1991. Mem. MLA, Coll. English Assn., L'Alliance Francaise, English-Speaking Union, Alumni Assn. Fla. So. Coll., Fla. State U., Am. Assn. U. Profs., South Cen. Modern Lang. Assn., Conf. Editors Learned Jours., Coll. Conf. Tchrs. English, Nat. Council Tchrs. of English, Am. Studies Assn., Phi Beta (patron), Phi Mu Alpha Sinfonia, Alpha Psi Omega, Pi Kappa Alpha, Sigma Tau Delta (named an Outstanding Prof. of English U. Houston chpt. 1990), Tau Kappa Alpha, Phi Kappa Phi, Caledonian Club (London). Episcopalian. Avocations: tennis, racquetball, swimming, traveling. Home: 2625 Arbuckle St Houston TX 77005-3929 Office: 3801 Cullen Blvd Houston TX 77004

PRYSTOWSKY, HARRY, physician, educator; b. Charleston, S.C., May 18, 1925; s. Moses Manning and Raye (Karesh) P.; m. Rhalda Betsy Bressler, Mar. 8, 1951; children: Michael Wayne, Ray Ellen, Jay Bressler. BS, The Citadel, 1944, DSc (hon.), 1974; MD, Med. Coll. S.C. 1948, LHD (hon.), 1975; DSc (hon.), U. Fla., 1988. Diplomate: Am. Bd. Obstetrics and Gynecology (dir., asso. examiner). Intern Johns Hopkins Hosp. and Med. Sch., 1948-49, resident, 1950-51, 53-55, instr., 1955-56, asst. prof., 1956-58; research fellow U. Cin. Sch. Medicine, 1949; research fellow physiology Yale Med. Sch., 1955-56; prof., chmn. obstetrics and gynecology U. Fla. Coll. Medicine, 1958-73; provost Milton S. Hershey Med. Center, Pa. State U., 1973-84, sr. v.p. health affairs 1984-86; dean Coll. Medicine, 1973-86; sr. v.p. emeritus health affairs, dean emeritus Pa. State U., 1986—; bd. dirs. North Shore Med. Ctr. Inc., STV Group, Inc., North Shore Med. Ctr. Physician Hosp. Orgn. Inc.; bd. visitors faculty, chmn. exec. com. Ben Gurion U. of Negev, Israel. Contbr. articles to med. jours. Capt., M.C. U.S. Army, 1951-53. Named 1 of 10 Outstanding Young Men Am. U.S. Jaycees; recipient Alumni Centennial award Med. U. S.C. Mem. Soc. Gynecol. Investigation, Am. Assn. Obstetricians and Gynecologists, Am. Gynecol. Soc., Assn. Profs. Gynecology and Obstetrics (pres.), U. Fla. Alumni Assn. (hon.), Pa. State U. Alumni Assn. (hon.), Alpha Omega Alpha. Home: 8877 Collins Ave Apt 208 Surfside FL 33154-3519

PRYWES, NOAH SHMARYA, computer science educator and researcher; m. Ruth Weinstein; children—Menachem, Daniel, Ron. B.S., Technion, Israel, 1949; M.S. Carnegie Inst. Tech., 1951; Ph.D., Harvard U., 1954. Mgr. dept. Sperry Univac, Phila., 1956-58; prof. computer sci. U. Pa., Phila., 1958—, dir. Shanghai Jiao Tong U. program; founder, pres. Computer Command and Control Co., Phila., 1963-69, 73—, Comserv Corp., Phila., 1969-73; mem. Navy Audit Adv. Com. Contbr. articles to profl. jours. Fellow IEEE (chmn. various coms.). Jewish. Home: 416 Bryn Mawr Ave Bala Cynwyd PA 19004-2721 Office: U Pa Cis Dept D2 33rd and Walnut Sts Philadelphia PA 19104

PRZELOMSKI, ANASTASIA NEMENYI, retired newspaper editor; b. Cleve., Dec. 11, 1918; d. Ernest Nicholas and Anna (Ress) Nemenyi; m. Edward Adrian Przelomski, July 4, 1946. A.B., Youngstown State U., 1939; M.Ed., U. Pitts., 1942. Tchr. Youngstown Pub. Sch., Ohio, 1939-42; reporter Vindicator, Youngstown, 1942-57, asst. city editor, 1957-73, city editor, 1973-76, mng. editor, 1976-88, ret., 1988. Named Woman of Yr., Youngstown Bus. and Profl. Women's Club, 1977, bus. category Woman of Yr., YWCA, 1986; recipient Community Service award Youngstown Fedn. Women's Clubs, 1981, Woman of Yr. award YWCA, 1983; named to Ohio Woman's Hall of Fame, 1986. Mem. AP Mng. Editors Assn., UPI Ohio Editors Assn. (bd. dirs. 1984-88), Ohio Assn. AP, Ohio Soc. Newspaper Editors, Youngstown State U. Alumni Assn. (trustee 1978-83), Catholic Collegiate Assn., Phi Kappa Phi. Republican. Roman Catholic. Avocations: travel; golf. Home: 4000 Logangate Rd Youngstown OH 44505

PRZEMIENIECKI, JANUSZ STANISLAW, college dean, engineer; b. Lipno, Poland, Jan. 30, 1927; came to U.S., 1961, naturalized, 1967; s. Leon and Maria (Sarnacka) P.; m. Stefania (Fiona) Rudnicka, July 17, 1954; children: Anita, Christopher. B.S., U. London, 1949, Ph.D., 1953; diploma in Aeros., Imperial Coll. Sci. and Tech., 1953; D.Sc. in Engring., U. London, 1988. Registered profl. engr., Ohio. Head structural research and devel. sect. Bristol Aircraft Ltd., Eng., 1954-61; asso. prof. Sch. Engring., Air Force Inst. Tech., Wright-Patterson AFB, Ohio, 1961-64; prof. mechanics Sch. Engring., Air Force Inst. Tech., 1964-66, asst. dean, assoc. dean research, 1966-69, dean, 1969-89, Inst. sr. dean, 1978—; cons. in field. Author: Theory of Matrix Structural Analysis, 1968, Mathematical Methods in Defense Analyses, 1990, Defense Analyses Software, 1991; assoc. editor: Jour. Aircraft, 1970-71; editorial bd.: Internat. Jour. Numerical Methods in Engring., 1969-75; editor: Critical Technologies for Nat. Defense, 1991, Acquisition of Defense Systems, 1993; contbr. articles to profl. jours. Chmn. bd. trustees The Air Force Inst. Tech. Found., Ohio, 1987-88, trustee, 1993—; trustee Engring. and Sci. Found. of Dayton, 1984—. Decorated Polish Underground Army Cross, Armed Forces medal; recipient USAF superior performance award, 1965, exceptional civilian service decoration, 1978, Presdl. rank of Meritorious Exec., 1981, Disting. Exec., 1982, Outstanding Engr. award Dayton Engring. and Sci. Found., 1986. Fellow Royal Aeros. Soc. (Usborne Meml. prize 1959), AIAA (editor-in-chief ednl. series 1981—, Pendray medal 1992), City and Guilds of London Inst.; mem. Am. Soc. Engring. Edn., NSPE, Ohio Acad. Sci., Polish Inst. Arts and Scis., Tau Beta Pi. Home: 2535 Valdina Dr Beavercreek OH 45434-6706 Office: Wright-Patterson AFB Air Force Inst Tech Dayton OH 45433

PSALTIS, JOHN COSTAS, manufacturing company executive; b. Drama, Greece, Jan. 5, 1940; came to U.S., 1955; naturalized, 1961; s. Costas Dimitriou and Kay Psaltis; m. Dorothy May Coons, Sept. 18, 1961; children: Costas John, Kay Joanne. BSBA, Loyola U., Chgo., 1971; diploma corp. fin. mgmt, Harvard U., 1979, postgrad. internat. sr. mgrs. program, 1981. With Molex Inc., mfrs. electronic connectors, Lisle, Ill., 1973—; contr. internat. ops. Molex Inc., 1973-78, mem. corp. mgmt. com., 1978-91; mem. corp. exec. com., 1991—; treas. Molex Inc., 1978-79, v.p. treas., 1982-87, corp. v.p., treas., CFO, 1994—, pres. for Americas, 1982-87, treas., bd. dirs. Molex Internat. Inc., 1979—; sec.-treas., dir. Molex Far East Svcs. Ltd.; sec-treas. Molex Electronics Ltd.; sec., dir. Molex Electronics Ltd. U.K., Molex Euorpean Svcs. Ltd.; bd. dirs. Molex Japan, Molex Singapore Pte. Ltd., Molex Italia Spa, Molex Korea Co. Ltd., Molex Malaysia Ltd.; auditor Touche Ross & Co., 1971-72, sr. auditor, 1972-73. Mem. adv. com. Inst. for Internat. Mktg., Ill. Benedictine Coll. With USAR, 1958-66. Mem. Fin. Execs. Inst., Am. Mgmt. Assn. (fin. coun., briefing adv. bd.), Leading CFO's, Strategic Planning Inst., Pers. Inventory Mgmt. Sys. (coun. on value for 90's), Chicagoland C. of C. (bd. dirs. 1989—, exec. com., v.p. world trade div. 1994, past chmn. fin. and audit com.). Office: 2222 Wellington Ave Lisle IL 60532-1682

PSATHAS, GEORGE, sociologist, educator; b. New Haven, Feb. 22, 1929; s. Milton Emanuel and Melpa (Joannides) P.; m. Irma M. Amatruda, Feb. 5, 1951; children: Christine Ann, David George, Anthony Paul. BA, Yale U., 1950; MA, U. Mich., 1951; PhD, Yale U., 1956; diploma, N.E. Sch. Photography, 1979. Instr. to asst. prof. Ind. U., Bloomington, 1955-63; lectr. Harvard U., Cambridge, Mass., 1961-62; assoc. prof. Washington U., St. Louis, 1963-68, rsch. assoc. Social Sci. Inst., 1963-68; program dir. community mental health tng. program NIMH/Washington U., 1966-68; prof. sociology Boston (Mass.) U., 1968—; acting chair Boston U., Mass., 1968-69, assoc. chair, 1969-70, 76-78, chair, 1984-85; dir. Ctr. for Applied Social Sci., Boston (Mass.) U., 1970-73; co-dir. post-doctoral rsch. tng. program in sociology and mental health Nat. Inst. Mental Health, Boston U., 1976-79; co-dir. Sociology and Health Svcs. Rsch. Tng. Program NCHSR and Boston (Mass.) U., 1970-78; vis. lectr. MRC Med. Sociology-U. Aberdeen, Scotland, 1974, U. Colo., 1963, U. London, 1973; vis. prof. Panteios Sch. Polit. Sci., Athens, 1982, Internat. U. Japan, Yamato-Machi, 1988, Doshisha U., Kyoto, Japan, 1989; chair Mass. Interdisciplinary Discourse Analysis seminar, 1989-95; cons. NSF, 1978, 79, 89, 94, 95, Rsch. Coun. Can., 1983-84, Social Sci. Rsch. Coun. Eng., 1981-82; active Ctr. Advanced Rsch. in Phenomenology, 1980—; presenter 70 presentations at profl. and scholarly socs. Editor: Phenomenological Sociology, 1973, Everyday Language, 1979, Interaction Competence, 1990, Situated Order, 1994; editor-in-chief: Human Studies, Boston, 1978—; assoc. editor Social Problems, 1958-61, Visual Sociology, 1993—; author: Student Nurse in Diploma School of Nursing, 1968, Phenomenology & Sociology, 1989, Conversation Analysis, 1994; cons. editor Temple Univ. Press, Kluwer Academic Pubs., Qualitative Sociology; author 9 book chpts.; contbr. over 50 articles to profl. jours. Cons. Human Rels. Lab., Boston, Bethel, St. Louis, 1967, 69, Sch. for the Blind, Kallithea, Athens, Greece, 1982; tng. dirs. com. Nat. Ctr. for Health Svcs. Rsch., Washington, 1971-73; bd. dirs. Carroll Ctr. for the Blind, Newton, Mass., 1974-79. Named Post-Doctoral fellow NIMH Dept. Social Rels., Harvard U., Cambridge, 1961-62; recipient Sci. Faculty Devel. award NSF, 1978-79, Fulbright grant Fulbright Commn., Greece and Turkey, 1982. Mem. AAUP (sec. 1977-79, v.p. Boston U. chpt. 1979-80), Am. Sociol. Assn., Ea. Sociol. Assn., Internat. Visual Sociology Assn., Internat. Inst. for Ethnomethodology (chair 1990—), Soc. for Phenomenology & Existential Philosophy, Soc. for Phenomenology and Human Scis., Soc. Study Social Problems (treas., bus. mgr. 1959-61). Home: 150 Mt Vernon St Newtonville MA 02160 Office: Boston Univ Boston MA 02215

PSOMIADES, HARRY JOHN, political science educator; b. Boston, Sept. 8, 1928; s. John and Koula (Yalmanides) P.; m. Dorothy Smith, Aug. 18, 1962 (dec. Aug. 27, 1984); children—Kathy Alexis, Christine Anne. B.A., Boston U., 1953; M.Internat. Affairs, Columbia U., 1955; cert., Middle East Inst., 1956, Ph.D. (Ford Found. fellow), 1962; Litt.D. (hon.), Holy Cross/ Hellenic Coll., 1985. Lectr. govt. Columbia U., 1959-65, asst. dean Grad. Sch. Internat. Affairs, 1959-65, dir. Carnegie Endowment Fellowships in Diplomacy, 1959-71; assoc. prof. polit. sci. Queens Coll., City U. N.Y., 1965-69, prof., 1970—, chmn. dept. polit. sci., 1967-71, dep. exec. officer Ph.D program in polit. sci., 1975-76, program dir. seminar on the modern Greek state, 1976—; dir. Center Byzantine and Modern Greek Studies, 1976—; cons. faculty U.S. Army Command and Gen. Staff Coll., 1968-86; U.S. Dept. State Fgn. Service Inst., 1968-71; mem. screening com. Fgn. Area Fellowships Program for Asia and Middle East Joint Com., Social Sci. Research Council and Am. Council Learned Socs., 1967-69. Author: Greece and Turkey: Mutual Economic Interests, 1964, (with Thomas Spelios) A Pictorial History of the Greeks, 1967, The Eastern Question: The Last Phase, 1968, (with T.A. Couloumbis) Foreign Interference in Greek Politics: An Historical Perspective, 1976, (with A. Scourby) The Greek American Community in Transition, 1982, (with R.S. Orfanos) Education and Greek Americans: Process and Prospects, 1987, (with S. Thomadakes) Greece, The New Europe and the Changing International Order, 1993; editor: Jour. Modern Hellenism, 1984—; contbr. articles to profl. jours. Served with U.S. Army, 1946-50; to col. USAR, 1950-83. Hon. fellow Soc. Macedonian Studies, Thessaloniki, Greece, 1970—. Fellow Middle East Studies Assn. N.Am.; mem. Am. Polit. Sci. Assn., Middle East Inst., Modern Greek Studies Assn. (mem. exec. com. 1972-76), Phi Beta Kappa. Greek Orthodox. Home: 440 Riverside Dr New York NY 10027 Office: Dept Polit Sci Queens Coll Flushing NY 11367

PSUTY, NORBERT PHILLIP, marine sciences educator; b. Hamtramck, Mich., June 13, 1937; s. Phillip and Jessie (Proszykowski) P.; m. Sylvia Helen Zurinsky, June 13, 1959; children: Eric Anthony, Scott Patrick, Ross Phillip. BS, Wayne State U., 1959; MS, Miami U., Oxford, Ohio, 1960; PhD, La. State U., 1966. Rsch. assoc. Coastal Studies Inst., La. State U., Baton Rouge, 1962-64; instr. dept. geography and dept. geology U. Miami, Coral Gables, Fla., 1964-65; asst. prof. geography U. Wis., Madison, 1965-69; assoc. prof. geography and geol. scis. Rutgers U., New Brunswick, N.J., 1969-73, prof., 1973—, chmn. dept. marine and coastal scis., 1991—, dir. Marine Scis. Ctr., 1972-76, dir. Ctr. for Coastal and Environ. Studies, 1976-90; assoc. dir. Inst. Marine and Coastal Scis., New Brunswick, N.J., 1990—; mem. sci. com. Thalassas, Vigo, Spain, 1985—. Co-author: Living with the New Jersey Shore, 1986, Coastal Dunes, 1990; mem. editorial bd Coastal Mgmt., 1981—, Jour. Coastal Rsch., 1987—; contbr. numerous articles to scholarly jours., chpts. to books, monographs. Mem. Water Policy Bd., East Brunswick, N.J., 1981-83, N.J. Shoreline Adv. Bd., Trenton, 1984-86; chmn. N.J. Gov.'s Sea Level Rise Com., Trenton, 1987-90; mem. N.J. State Beach Erosion Commn., 1994—; referee U.S. Volleyball Assn. Recipient Disting. Pub. Svc. award Pres. of Rutgers U. 1988; numerous grants including NSF, Nat. Park Svc., EPA, Office Naval Rsch., Nat. Sea Grant Program, NOAA, 1961—. Mem. AAAS, Assn. Am. Geographers (Honors award 1993), Coastal Soc. (pres. 1980-82), Internat. Geog. Union (vice chair commn. on coastal environ. 1988-92, chmn. commn. on coastal systems, 1992-96, editor newsletter 1984-96), N.J. Acad. Sci. (pres. 1982). Avocations: gardening, reading. Office: Rutgers U Inst Marine & Coastal Scis Cook Campus New Brunswick NJ 08903

PTACEK, WILLIAM H., library director. BA in English and Psychology, U. Ill., 1972; MLS, SUNY, Geneseo, 1974; cert. of advanced study, U. Ill., Chgo., 1979. Reference libr. South Br. Chgo. Pub. Libr., 1974-75, head libr. Mt. Greenwood br., 1975-76, head system-wide circulation, 1976-77, asst. dir. personnel, 1977-78, chief Northeast Dist., 1978-79; dir. Idaho Falls Pub. Libr., 1979-83, Louisville Free Pub. Libr., 1984-89, King County Libr. System, Seattle, 1989—. Co-author: (with Peggy Sullivan) Public Libraries: Smart Practices in Personnel, 1982; contbr. articles to profl. jours. Office: King County Libr System 300 8th Ave N Seattle WA 98109-5191

PTAK, FRANK S., manufacturing executive; b. Chgo., Apr. 23, 1943; s. Frank J. and Stella R. (Los) P.; m. Karen M. Novoselsky, May 2, 1971; children: Jeffrey B., Jacquelyn F., Russell E. BS, De Paul U., 1965. CPA, Ill. Sr. auditor Arthur Young & Co., Chgo., 1965-69; sr. rsch. cons. Kemper Fin. Svcs., Chgo., 1969-71; asst. sec., mgr. acquisitions Sara Lee Corp., Chgo., 1971-73, asst. treas., 1973-74, asst. to chmn., 1974, v.p. planning, 1974-75; bus. devel. mgr. ITW Conex, Des Plaines, Ill., 1975-77; mktg. mgr. ITW Shakeproof, Elgin, Ill., 1977-78, group pres., 1977-78; group pres. ITW Metal Components Cos., Glenview, Ill., 1978-91; exec. v.p. Global Automotive Components ITW Corp., Glenview, 1991—. Patentee in field. Mem. AICPA, Assn. Corp. Growth, ITW Patent Soc. Jewish. Home: 849 Edgewood Ct Highland Park IL 60035-3714 Office: ITW Corp 3600 W Lake Ave Glenview IL 60025-1215

PTAK, JOHN A., talent agent; b. San Diego, Sept. 23, 1942; s. John and Doris Elizabeth P.; m. Margaret Elizabeth Black, May 21, 1981; 1 child, Hillary Elizabeth. BA, UCLA, 1967. Theatre mgr., booker Walter Reade Orgn., Beverly Hills, Calif., 1967-68; adminstrv. exec. Am. Film Inst., Beverly Hills, 1968-70; talent agent Internat. Famous Agy. (now ICM), L.A., 1971-75, William Morris Agy., Beverly Hills, 1976-91, Creative Artists Agy., Beverly Hills, 1991—; cons. Nat. Endowment for Arts, Washington, 1980—; co-chmn. Am. Film Inst. Ctr. for Film & Video Preservation, L.A., 1991—; mem. Nat. Film Preservation Bd., Washington, 1992—. Avocations: tennis, travel. Office: Creative Artists Agy 9830 Wilshire Blvd Beverly Hills CA 90212

PTASHNE, MARK STEVEN, biochemistry educator; b. Chicago, Ill., June 5, 1940; s. Fred and Mildred P. BA, Reed Coll., 1961; PhD, Harvard U., 1968. Lectr. biochemistry Harvard U., Cambridge, Mass., 1968-71, prof., 1971—, chmn. dept. biochemistry and molecular biology, 1980-83; Feodor Lynen lectr. James L. Knight Internat. Ctr. U. Miami, Fla., 1988. Author: A Genetic Switch, 1986; contbr. numerous articles to sci. jours. Recipient Eli Lilly award, 1975, Prix Charles-Leopold Mayer Acad. des Sciences, Inst. de France, 1977, Louise Gross Horwitz prize Bd. Trustees Columbia U., 1985, Gairdner Found. Internat. award, 1985; co-recipient Ledlie award Harvard U., 1968, GM Sloan prize, 1990. Fellow N.Y. Acad. Sci., Am. Acad. Sci.; mem. NAS, Fedn. Am. Soc. Biol. Soc. (bd. sponsors 1981). Avocations: opera, classical music. Office: Harvard U Dept Biochemistry & Molecular Biology 7 Divinity Ave Cambridge MA 02138-2019

PTASZEK, EDWARD GERALD, JR., lawyer; b. Cleve., Sept. 29, 1950; s. Edward Gerald and Roseanne (Venetta) P. BS in Fin., Bowling Green U., 1972; JD, Case Western Res. U., 1978. Bar: Ohio 1978, U.S. Dist. Ct. (no. dist.) Ohio, U.S. Tax Ct. Assoc. Baker & Hostetler, Cleve., 1978-85, ptnr., 1985—. Mem. ABA, Cleve. Bar Assn., Columbus Bar Assn., Lakewood Club, Club at Social Ctr. Office: Baker & Hostetler 3200 National City Ctr 1900 E 9th St Cleveland OH 44114-3485

PUCCIO, JOHN, hospital administrator; b. 1946. With Peat, Marwick, Mitchell & Co., N.Y.C., 1970-76; v.p. fin. Bklyn. Hosp. Ctr., 1976—. Office: Bklyn Hosp Ctr 121 Dekalb Ave Brooklyn NY 11201*

PUCEL, ROBERT ALBIN, electronics research engineer; b. Ely, Minn., Dec. 27, 1926; s. Joseph and Theresa (Francel) P.; m. Catherine Ann Silva, June 30, 1952; children: Robert W., James J., Valerie A. Marc R. Joseph J. BS, MIT, 1951, MS, 1951, DSc, 1955. With rsch. div. Research div. Raytheon Co., Lexington, Mass., 1955-93; staff mem. microwave tube group Research div. Raytheon Co., 1951-55, solid state physics group, 1955-65, project mgr. microwave semicondr. group, 1965-70, cons. to microwave semicondr. group, 1970-74, cons. scientist semicondr. group, 1974—; pres. RCP Cons., Needham, Mass., 1994—; lectr. on monolithic microwave integrated circuits. Editor: Monolithic Microwave Integrated Circuits, 1985; contbg. author: Advances in Electronics and Electron Physics, vol. 38, 1975, Gallium Arsenide Technology, 1985. Served with USNR, 1945-46. Recipient Excellence in Technology award Raytheon, 1988. Fellow IEEE (life); mem. Microwave Theory and Techniques Soc. (editorial rev. bd., nat. lectr. 1980-81, Microwave prize 1976, Microwave Career award 1990), Nat. Acad. Engring., Electron Devices Soc. Inventor low-distortion FET; co-inventor Spacistor, Overlay FET. Office: RCP Cons 427 South St Needham MA 02192

PUCHI, LINDA CAROL, elementary school principal; b. Midland, Tex., Aug. 2, 1944; d. Gonzalo Jr. and Lillian (Grimm) P.; divorced; children: Bianca Michelle Fontes Garcia, Adrian Paulino Fontes. BA in Elem. Edn., Ariz. State U., 1966; MEd in Elem. Edn., U. Ariz., 1972; EdD, No. Ariz. U., 1993. Cert. supt., prin., tchr. elem. edn., Ariz. Tchr. 1st grade Phoenix Elem. Sch. # 1, 1966-67; teaching prin. Santa Cruz Dist. # 28, Nogales, Ariz., 1967-68; tchr. bilingual elem. edn. Nogales Unified Schs., 1968-74, 76-77, 1978-80, grade level chair. tchr. bilingual elem. edn., 1980-88; tchr. bilingual edn. U. Ariz., Tucson, 1974-76, teaching asst., student tchr. supr., undergrad. advisor, 1977-78; tchr., asst. to pers. dir. Roosevelt Sch. Dist. # 66, Phoenix, 1989, asst. prin., 1989-91, prin., 1991—; coord. adult edn. Spanish as Second Lang., Nogales, 1968-70; tchr. adult ESL, Pima C.C., Tucson, 1970-72, 87-88, Luth. Social Svcs. Ministry, Phoenix, 1988-90. Scholar Marshall Found. Mem. ASCD, AAUW, Am. Assn. Sch. Adminstrs., Ariz. Sch. Adminstrs., Ariz. Hispanic Sch. Adminstrs. Assn., Nat. Assn. Elem. Sch. Prins., Ariz. AWARE, Phi Delta Kappa. Home: 1550 E University Dr Ste 0-1 Mesa AZ 85203-8136 Office: John R Davis Elem Sch 6209 S 15th Ave Phoenix AZ 85041-5500

PUCHTA, CHARLES GEORGE, lawyer; b. Cin., Feb. 19, 1918; s. Charles George and Kate (Carlisle) P.; m. Jean Geary, Dec. 12, 1959; children: Polly Carlisle Puchta Wells, Charles George, Jr. AB, U. Cin., 1940, LLD, 1943. Bar: Ohio 1943, Ky. 1964, U.S. Dist. Ct. (so. dist.) Ohio 1944, U.S. Ct. Appeals (6th cir.) 1960. Assoc. Frost & Jacobs, Cin., 1943-53, ptnr., 1953-83, chmn. exec. com., 1978-83, sr. ptnr., 1983—. Pres. The C. of C. 1978, C. of C. Found., 1978; pres. Cin. Nature Center, 1979-81, chmn., 1981-84; trustee U. Cin. Endowment Fund, 1979—; trustee U. Cin. Found., 1978-85, emeritus, 1989—, Greater Cin. Ctr. for Econ. Edn., 1981-93. Cin. Mus. Natural History, 1988-90, Jewish Hosp., 1992—; chmn. Bus. Mobilized for Xavier campaign, 1976; chmn. exec. com. Hebrew Union Coll Assoc. ann. Tribute Dinner, 1988-89; former trustee, sec. Cin. Country Day Sch.; former mem., pres., bd. dirs. Bradley U. Parents Assn.; mem. adv. bd. Juvenile Diabetes Found., 1982—. Mem. ABA, Ohio Bar Assn., Ky. Bar Assn., Cin. Bar Assn., Cin. Country Club, Queen City Club, Comml. Club (sec. 1983-85), Commonwealth Club (v.p. 1985-86), Queen City Optimists Club (past pres.). Republican. Episcopalian. Home: 2444 Madison Rd Apt 1402 Cincinnati OH 45208-1277 Office: Frost & Jacobs 25 PNC Ctr 201 E 5th St Cincinnati OH 45202-4117

PUCHTLER, HOLDE, histochemist, pathologist, educator; b. Kleinlosnitz, Germany, Jan. 1, 1920; came to U.S., 1955; d. Gottfried and Gunda (Thoma) P. Cand. med., U. Würzburg, 1944; Md, U. Köln, 1949; MD, U. Küln (Germany), 1951. Rsch. assoc. U. Köln, 1949-51, resident in pathology, 1951-55; rsch. fellow Damon Runyon Found., Montreal, Que., Can., 1955-58; rsch. assoc. Med. Coll. Ga., Augusta, 1959-60, asst. rsch. prof., 1960-62, assoc. rsch. prof., 1962-68, prof., 1968-90, prof. emerita, 1990—. Assoc. editor Jour. Histotechnology, 1982—; editl. bd. Histochemistry, 1977-90. Honored at Symposium on Connective Tissues in Arterial and Pulmonary Diseases, 1980. Fellow Am. Inst. Chemists, Royal Microscopical Soc.; mem. Royal Soc. Chemistry, Am. Chem. Soc., Histochem. Soc. Gesellschaft Histochemie, Anatomische Gesellschaft, Ga. Soc. Histotech. (hon.). Achievements include development of new techniques for light, polarization, visible and infrared flourescence based on theoretical and physical chemistry and x-ray diffraction data; demonstration of relations between dye configurations and selective affinity for certain components of human tissues, such as collagens, elastin, myosins, neurofibrils, and amyloids; application of molecular orbital theories to histochemistry. Avocations: archeology, history of science, folk medicine, comparative religion. Office: Med Coll Ga Dept Pathology Augusta GA 30912

PUCIE, CHARLES R., JR., public affairs executive; b. Asheville, N.C., Oct. 8, 1943. BSFS in Internat. Affairs, Georgetown U., 1965. Fin. analyst Chase Manhattan Bank, 1969-70; account exec. Doremus, 1970-73, v.p., 1973-80; sr. v.p., regional mgr. Doremus, Washington, 1980-85; sr. v.p., group dir., internat. counseling Hill and Knowlton, 1986-90, exec. v.p., 1991; mng. dir., sr. prin. Capitoline Internat. Group, Washington, 1991—; chmn., CEO C.I.H. Ltd., 1992—; CEO Capitoline/MS&L, G.P., 1995—. Capt. arty. U.S. Army, 1966-69. Mem. Nat. Press Soc. Am. (mem. exec. com. IR sect. 1977-80), Nat. Press Club, DPE (mem. nat. bd. govs. 1980-82, mem. DC corp. bd. 1987), Delta Phi Epsilon. Office: Capitoline/MS&L GP 1615 NW 1150 # L Washington DC 20036

PUCK, THEODORE THOMAS, geneticist, biophysicist, educator; b. Chgo., Sept. 24, 1916; s. Joseph and Bessie (Shapiro) Puckowitz; m. Mary Hill, Apr. 17, 1946; children: Stirling, Jennifer, Laurel. B.S., U. Chgo., 1937, Ph.D., 1940. Mem. commn. airborne infections Office Surgeon Gen., Army Epidemiol. Bd., 1944-46; asst. prof. depts. medicine and biochemistry U. Chgo., 1945-47; sr. fellow Am. Cancer Soc., Calif. Inst. Tech., Pasadena, 1947-48; prof. biophysics U. Colo. Med. Sch., 1948—, chmn. dept., 1948-67, disting. prof., 1986—; dir. Eleanor Roosevelt Inst. Cancer Research, 1962-95; Disting. research prof. Am. Cancer Soc., 1966—; nat. lectr. Sigma Xi, 1975-76. Author: The Mammalian Cell as a Microorganism: Genetic and Biochemical Studies in Vitro, 1972. Mem. Commn. on Physicians for the Future. Recipient Albert Lasker award, 1958, Borden award med. rsch., 1959, Louisa Gross Horwitz prize, 1973, Gordon Wilson medal Am. Clin. and Climatol. Assn., 1977, award Environ. Mutagen Soc., 1981, E.B. Wilson medal Am. Soc. Cell Biology, 1984, Bonfils-Stanton award in sci., 1984, U. Colo. Disting. Prof. award, 1987, Henry M. Porter medal, 1992; named to The Colo. 100, Historic Denver, 1992; Heritage Found. scholar, 1983; Phi Beta Kappa scholar, 1985. Fellow Am. Acad. Arts and Scis.; mem. Am. Chem. Soc., Soc. Exptl. Biology and Medicine, AAAS (Phi Beta Kappa award and lectr. 1983), Am. Assn. Immunologists, Radiation Research Soc., Biophys. Soc., Genetics Soc. Am., Nat. Acad. Sci., Tissue Culture Assn. (Hon. award 1987), Paideia Group, Santa Fe Inst. Sci. Bd., Phi Beta Kappa, Sigma Xi. Achievements include pioneering contributions to establishment of somatic cell approaches to mammalian cell genetics, to the identification and classification of the human chromosomes; measurement of mutation in mammalian cells; demonstration of the reverse transformation reaction and the genome exposure defect in cancer; development of quantitative approaches to mammalian cell radiobiology. Office: Eleanor Roosevelt Inst Cancer Rsch 1899 Gaylord St Denver CO 80206-1210 *Our age is threatened by distorted emphasis on power, material wealth, and competitiveness, and by an explosive increase in population which exceeds our traditional regulative capacities. But it also holds promise for new and profound understanding of ourselves - of our basic human biological intellectual and emotional needs. There is room for hope.*

PUCKET, SUSAN, newspaper editor. Exec. food editor features desk Atlanta Jour. and Constn. Office: Atlanta Jour and Constn 72 Marietta St NW Atlanta GA 30303*

PUCKETT, ALLEN EMERSON, aeronautical engineer; b. Springfield, Ohio, July 25, 1919; s. Roswell C. and Catherine C. (Morrill) P.; m. Betty J. Howlett; children—Allen W., Nancy L., Susan E.; m. Marilyn I. McFarland; children—Margaret A., James R. BS, Harvard U., 1939, MS, 1941; PhD, Calif. Inst. Tech., 1949. Lectr. aeronautics, chief wind tunnel sect. Jet Propulsion Lab., Calif. Inst. Tech., 1945-49; with Hughes Aircraft Co., Culver City, Calif., 1949—, exec. v.p., 1965-77, pres., 1977-78, chmn. bd., chief exec. officer, 1978-87; chmn. emeritus Hughes Aircraft Co., Culver City, 1987—; tech. cons. U.S. Army Ordnance, Aberdeen Proving Ground, Md., 1945-60; mem. sci. adv. com. Ballistic Rsch. Labs., 1958-65; bd. dirs. Gen. Dynamics, Fluor, Logicon Investment Co. of Am., Am. Mut. Fund, Lone Star Industries; mem. steering group OASD adv. panel on aeros.; cons. Pres.'s Sci. Adv. Com.; chmn. rsch. adv. com. control, guidance and navigation NASA, 1959-64; vice-chmn. Def. Sci. Bd., 1962-66; mem. Army Sci. Adv. Panel, 1965-69, NASA tech. and rsch. adv. com., 1968-72, space program adv. coun. 1974-78; Wilbur and Orville Meml. lectr. Royal Aero. Soc., London, 1981. Author: (with Hans W. Liepmann) Introduction to Aerodynamics of a Compressible Fluid, 1947; editor: (with Simon Ramo) Guided Missile Engineering, 1959; contbr. tech. papers on high-speed aerodynamics. Trustee U. So. Calif. Recipient Lawrence Sperry award Inst. Aero. Scis., 1949, Lloyd V. Berkner award Am. Astronautical Soc., 1974, Nat. Medal of Tech., 1985; named Calif. Mfr. of Yr., 1980. Fellow AIAA (pres. 1972); mem. NAS, NAE, AAAS, Aerospace Industries Assn. (chmn. 1979), L.A. World Affairs Coun. (pres.), Sigma Xi, Phi Beta Kappa. Office: Hughes Aircraft Co PO Box 80028 Los Angeles CA 90080-0028

PUCKETT, ALLEN WEARE, health care information systems executive; b. Pasadena, Calif., Mar. 17, 1942; s. Allen Emerson Puckett and Betty Jane (Howlett) Ward; m. Joan Adrienne Roth, Apr. 10, 1965 (div. 1980); children: Glenn A., Tod A.; m. Laura Treadgold, July 10, 1992. BS, U. Calif., Berkeley, 1963; JD, Harvard U., 1966. Bar: Calif. 1966. Prin. McKinsey & Co., San Francisco, 1966-78; pres. Atman Corp., San Francisco, 1979-83; v.p. VWR Sci., San Francisco 1980-83, Univar Corp., Seattle, 1984-85; sr. v.p. fin. VWR Corp., Seattle, 1986-90, Momentum Distbn. Inc., Seattle, 1990; v.p. cen. ops. Eldec Corp., Lynnwood, 1990-92; chmn., co-CEO Phycom Corp., 1993—. Recipient Nathan Burkan prize ASCAP, 1966. Democrat. Club: Rainier (Seattle). Avocations: skiing, scuba diving, music. Home: 1624 38th Ave E Seattle WA 98112-3134 Office: Phycom Corp 3380-146th Pl SE Bellevue WA 98007

PUCKETT, C. LIN, plastic surgeon, educator; b. Burlington, N.C., Oct. 19, 1940; s. Harry W. And Lula C. Puckett; m. Florence Elizabeth Loy, June 18, 1961 (div. 1976); children: Loy C., Lisa A., Leslie A.; m. Patricia Louise Wells, June 17, 1984 (div. 1994); 1 child, Henry James. MD, Bowman Gray Sch. Medicine, 1966. Assoc. in surgery Duke U. Med. Ctr., Durham, N.C., 1971-73; assoc. prof., head div. plastic surgery U. Mo. Med. Ctr., Columbia, 1976-81; prof., head attending plastic surgeon U. Mo. Med. Ctr., Truman VA Hosp., Columbia, 1982—. Contbr. numerous articles to profl. jours. Fellow ACS (gov. 1992); mem. AMA, Am. Assn. Hand Surgery (bd. dirs. 1982-84, chmn. nominating com., 1985, v.p. 1987, pres.-elect 1988, pres. 1988—), Am. Assn. Plastic Surgeons, Am. Cleft Palate Assn., Am. Soc. Plastic and Reconstructive Surgeons Inc. (bd. dirs. 1985—, asst. sec. 1988, trustee 1990, chmn. bd. trustees 1992), Am. Bd. Plastic Surgery (cert., bd. dirs. 1988-94, chmn. 1993-94), Am. Soc. Surgery of the Hand, Am. Trauma Soc., Internat. Microsurgical Soc., Mo. Chpt. ACS, Plastic Surgery Rsch. Coun., So. Med. Assn., Assn. Acad. Chmn. Plastic Surgery (bd. dirs. 1985—, pres. 1987-88), Sigma Xi, Alpha Omega Alpha. Republican. Avocation: breeding Quarter horses, angus cattle. Home: RR 1 Box 146 Ashland MO 65010-9801 Office: U Mo Med Ctr Dept Plastic Surgery 1 Hospital Dr #M349 Columbia MO 65201-5276

PUCKETT, ELIZABETH ANN, law librarian, law educator; b. Evansville, Ind., Nov. 10, 1943; d. Buell Charles and Lula Ruth (Gray) P.; m. Joel E. Hendricks, June 1, 1964 (div. June 1973); 1 child, Andrew Charles; m. Thomas A. Wilson, July 19, 1985. BS in Edn., Eastern Ill. U., 1964; JD, U. Ill., 1977, MS in L.S., 1977. Bar: Kans. 1978, Ill. 1979. Acquisitions/reader services librarian U. Kans. Law Library, Lawrence, 1978-79; asst. reader services librarian So. Ill. U. Law Library, Carbondale, 1979-81, reader services librarian, 1981-83; assoc. dir. Northwestern U. Law Library, Chgo., 1983-86, co-acting dir., 1986-87; dir./assoc. prof. South Tex. Coll. Law Library, Houston, 1987-89; dir./prof. South Tex. Coll. Law Libr., Houston, 1990-94, U. Ga. Law Libr., Athens, 1994—. Co-author: Evaluation of System-Provided Library Services to State Correctional Centers in Illinois, 1983; co-editor Uniform Commercial Code: Confidential Drafts, 1993. Mem. ABA, Am. Assn. Law Librs. (mem. exec. bd. 1993-96). Avocations: reading, antiques. Office: U Georgia Law Libr Athens GA 30602-6018

PUCKETT, FRANK, newspaper publisher; b. North Tazewell, Va., Oct. 24, 1946; s. Frank and Mayleen I. (Little) P.; m. Linda K. Cofer, Nov. 25, 1965; children: Frank Todd, James M. Student, Ind. U., 1964-67. Advt. dir. Daily Banner, Greencastle, Ind., 1964-68; gen. mgr. Jour. Review, Crawfordsville, Ind., 1968-75; publ. Register Mail, Galesburg, Ill., 1975-77; gen. mgr. Jour. News, Hamilton, Ohio, 1977; publ. Cloucester County Times, Woodbury, N.J., 1977-80, Jour. News, 1980-81; pres., publisher Abilene (Tex.) Reporter News, 1981—; corp. v.p. Harte Hanks Comms., Inc., San Antonio, 1985-95; chmn. Air Combat Command Adv. Group, Langley, Va., 1993—, Harte Hanks Quality Coun., 1991-94. Chmn. devel. commn. West Tex. Rehab. Ctr., Abilene, 1991—; pres. Downtown Redevel. Corp., Abilene, 1990. Named outstanding citizen Abilene C. of C., 1991, USAF Strategic Air Command, 1990. Mem. Tex. Daily Newspaper Assn. (pres. 1993). Methodist. Avocations: golf, jogging, hunting. Home: 75 Glen Abbey Abilene TX 79606 Office: Abilene Reporter News 100 Cypress Abilene TX 79604

PUCKETT, HOYLE BROOKS, agricultural engineer, research scientist, consultant; b. Jesup, Ga., Oct. 15, 1925; s. Lawrence Parham and Martha Elizabeth (Mizell) P.; m. Faye Eloise Bowden, June 22, 1945; children: Carol P. Keeley, Hoyle B. Jr., Kristina P. Berbaum. BS in Agrl. Engring., U. Ga., 1948; MS in Agrl. Engring. Mich. State U., 1949; student, Ga. Inst. Tech., 1964-65. reg. profl. engr. Ill. Rsch. engr. GS 7-9 USDA/ARS, Oxford, N.C., 1949-55; res. engr. GS 11-13 USDA/ARS, Urbana, Ill., 1955-68, res. ldr. GS 14-15, 1968-55; ret., 1968-85; engring. cons. pvt. practice, Champaign, Ill., 1985—. Fellow Am. Soc. Agrl. Engrs.; mem. Exchange Club of Urbana. Home: 407 W University Ave Apt 104 Champaign IL 61820-3944

PUCKETT, KIRBY, professional baseball player; b. Chgo., Mar. 14, 1961; s. Catherine Puckett; m. Tonya Hudson; children: Catherine, Kirby, Jr. Student, Bradley U., Ill., Triton Coll., Ill. Baseball player Minnesota Twins, Mpls., 1982—. Author: I Love This Game!, 1993, Be The Best You Can Be, 1993. Founder, benefactor Kirby Puckett Eight-Ball Invitational to benefit Children's Heart Fund, United Way. Recipient All-Star Most Valuable Player award, 1993, Gold Glove award, 1986-89, 1991-92, Silver Slugger award, 1986-89, 92, 94, All-Star team, 1986-94; named to Sporting News All-Star Team, 1986-89, 92, 94, Am. League All-Star team, 1986-89, Am. League Batting Champion, 1989, Minn. Twins Most Valuable Player 1985, 86, 88, 89, 92; named Calif. League Player of the Yr., 1983, Most Valuable Player, Am. League Championship Series, 1991, Best Hitter and Most Exciting Player, Baseball America, 1992; inducted Triton Coll. Hall of Fame, 1993. Mem. Alexis de Tocqueville Soc. Achievements include: led Major League in hits 1988-92, highest batting average among active batters 1988-92, seasons with 200 or more hits: 1986-89, 92. Office: Minnesota Twins Hubert H Humphrey Metrodome 501 Chicago Ave Minneapolis MN 55415-1596*

PUCKETT, ROBERT HUGH, political scientist, educator; b. Kansas City, Mo., July 16, 1935; s. John William and Marjorie (Shirlaw) P.; m. Barbara Ann Chandley, Dec. 23, 1964; 1 child, Sarah Anne. BA, De Pauw U., 1957; MA, U. Chgo., 1958, PhD, 1961. Asst. prof. polit. sci. Mary Washington Coll., Fredericksburg, Va., 1961-63; vis. scholar, postdoctoral fellow social sci. rsch. coun. MIT, Cambridge, 1963-64; asst. prof. govt. and fgn. affairs U. Va., Charlottesville, 1964-66; asst. prof. social sci. Mich. State U., East Lansing, 1966-68; prof. polit. sci. Ind. State U., Terre Haute, 1968—; cons. in field.; cons. Rand Corp., 1962, U.S. Army, 1985-89, U.S. Dept. Edn., 1987-88, USN, 1990-95; del. Ind. Gov.'s Conf. on Librs. and Info. Svcs., 1990. Author: America Faces the World: Isolationist Ideology in American Foreign Policy, 1972, (with Oscar H. Rechtschaffer) Reflections on Space, 1964, The United States and Northeast Asia, 1993; contbr. articles to polit. sci. jours. Bd. dirs. So. Ind. Health Systems Agy., 1978-81; adv. com. U.S. Army Command and Gen. Staff Coll., 1985-89; mem. Pres.'s Commn. on White House Fellowships, 1990-93; bd. advisors to pres. Naval War Coll., 1990-95; active Ind. Commn. for Higher Edn., 1993-94. Mem. DePauw U. Alumni Assn. (pres. chpt. 1973-74), Am. Polit. Sci. Assn., Indpls. Com. Fgn. Rels., Midwest Polit. Sci. Assn., Internat. Studies Assn., Ind. Consortium for Security Studies, Ind. Acad. Social Scis., Ind. Polit. Sci. Assn. (v.p. 1977-79), Coun. Fgn. Rels., Ind. Coun. on World Affairs, Inter-Univ. Seminar on Armed Forces and Soc., Japan-Am. Soc. Ind., Nat. Strategy Forum, Econ. Club Indpls., Columbia Club (Indpls.), MVP Club (Terre Haute), Phi Beta Kappa, Sigma Iota Rho, Phi Eta Sigma, Pi Sigma Alpha, Pi Kappa Alpha, Alpha Phi Omega. Home: 122 Marigold Dr Terre Haute IN 47803-1538 Office: Dept Polit Sci Ind State U Terre Haute IN 47809

PUCKETTE, STEPHEN ELLIOTT, mathematics educator, mathematician; b. Ridgewood, N.J., Oct. 18, 1927; s. Charles McDonald and Elizabeth Argyle (Gettys) P.; m. Upshur Smith, June 22, 1957; children: Robert B. E., Miller S., Emily E., Charles McD., Charlotte Elliott. BS, U. of the South, 1949; MS, Yale U., 1950, MA, 1951, PhD, 1957. Asst. prof. math. U. of the South, Sewanee, Tenn., 1956-64; vis. asst. prof. math. U. Ga., Athens, 1962-63; assoc. prof. math. U. Ky., Lexington, 1966-69; dean of arts and scis. prof. U. of the South, Sewanee, Tenn., 1969-79; prof. associé U. Nationale Côte d'Ivoire, Côté d'Ivoire, Ivory Coast, 1979-80; prof. math. U. of the South, Sewanee, Tenn., 1980-93, prof. emeritus, 1993—; vis. prof. U. N.C.,

Chapel Hill, 1986-87; vis. lectr. Math. Assn. Am., Washington DC, 1967-77. NSF faculty fellow, Yale U., 1964-65; Fulbright scholar (France), 1952-53; Fulbright lectr. (Ivory Coast), 1979-80. Mem. Am. Math. Soc., Societé Mathématique de France, Deutsche Matematiker-Vereiniging, London Math. Soc. Democrat. Episcopalian. Home: Morgan's Steep Sewanee TN 37375 Office: Univ of the South Sewanee TN 37375

PUCKO, DIANE BOWLES, public relations executive; b. Wyndotte, Mich., Aug. 15, 1940; d. Mervin Arthur and Bernice Letitia (Shelly) Bowles; m. Raymond J. Pucko, May 22, 1965; children: Todd Anthony, Gregory Bowles. BA in Sociology, Bucknell U., Lewisburg, Pa., 1962. Accredited in pub. rels. Asst. to pub. rels. dir. Edward C. Michener Assocs., Inc., Harrisburg, Pa., 1962-65; advt./pub. rels. coord. Superior Switchboard & Devices, Canton, Ohio, 1965-66; editorial dir. women's svc. Hutchins Advt. Co., Inc., Rochester, N.Y., 1966-71; pres. Editorial Communications, Rochester and Elyria, Ohio, 1971-77; mgr. advt. and sales promotion Tappan Air Conditioning, Elyria, 1977-80; mgr. pub. affairs Kaiser Permanente Med. Care Program, Cleve., 1980-85; corp. dir. pub. affairs Keystone Health Plans, Inc., Camp Hill, Pa., 1985-86; v.p., dir. client planning Young-Liggatt-Stashower, Cleve., 1986; v.p., dir. pub. rels. Marcus Pub. Rels., Cleve., 1987-91; sr. v.p. Proconsul, Cleve., 1991—, also bd. dirs.; mgr., role model Women in Mgmt. Field Placement program, Cleve. State U., 1983—; prof. advisor, pub. rels. adv. bd. Pub. Rels. Student Soc. Am., Kent State U., 1988—. Bd. trustees, mem. exec. com., chmn. pub. rels. adv. com. Ronald MacDonald House of Cleve., 1993—; bd. dirs., chmn. pub. rels. com. Assn. Retarded Citizens, Cleve., 1987-91. Recipient Woman Profl. Excellence award YMCA, 1984, MacEachern award Acad. Hosp. Pub. Rels., 1985, Bell Ringer award Cmty. Rels. Report, 1985, Bronze Quill Excellence award Internat. Assn. Bus. Communicators, 1992, 93, Cleve. Comms. award Women in Comms. Internat., 1993, 95, Tower award Bus./Profl. Advt. Assn., 1993, 95, Creativity in Pub. Rels. award, 1994, Silver Screen award U.S. Internat. Film & Video Festival, 1995. Fellow Pub. Rels. Soc. Am. (bd. dirs. 1983-85, 86-94, officer 1991-95, mem. counselors acad. 1986—, Silver Anvil award 1985, Mktg./Consumer Rels. award East Ctrl. dist. 1992, Lighthouse award 1995); mem. Press Club Cleve. (bd. dirs. 1989—, v.p. 1990—), Cleve. Advt. Club, Women's City Club Cleve. Republican. Methodist. Avocation: soccer. Home: 656 University Ave Elyria OH 44035-7239 Office: Proconsul 25825 Science Park Dr Cleveland OH 44122-7315

PUCKORIUS, THEODORE D., consulting company executive; b. Chgo., Apr. 7, 1930; s. Paul Joseph and Lucy (Idul) P.; m. Joyce Carlyn Bormuth, June 29, 1952 (div. 1975); m. Lana Campbell Spruel, Dec. 26, 1978; children: Philip, Thimothy, Mary. Student, DePaul U., 1949-51, Tampa U., 1951-52; grad. with honors, U. Ill., 1955; grad., Ohio State U., 1963. Cert. mgmt. cons. Mgr. bus. systems N.Am. Aviation, Columbus, Ohio, 1960-65; v.p. Booz Allen & Hamilton, Chgo., 1965-70, Lester B. Knight & Assocs., Chgo. and Washington, 1970-75; commr. ADTS Gen. Svcs. Adminstrn., Washington, 1975-77; dir. adminstrv. svcs. State of Ill., Springfield, 1977-79; dep. program mgr. Royal Commn. of Yanbu, Saudi Arabia, 1979-82; sr. div. v.p. The Austin Co. Cons. Div., Chgo., 1982-87; v.p. govt. svcs. The Austin Co., Chgo. and Washington, 1987-90, group v.p., 1990—. Contbr. 40 articles to profl. jours. Chmn. ad hoc govt. rels. ACME, Washington, 1985-86; mem. zoning bd. City of Fox Lake, Ill., 1984-86; mem. sch. bd. dist. 58, Downers Grove, Ill., 1971-73. Staff sgt. USAF, 1953-56. Republican. Episcopalian. Home: 15068 Holly St Onancock VA 23417-3000

PUDDINGTON, IRA EDWIN, chemist; b. Clifton, N.B., Can., Jan. 8, 1911; s. Charles Edwin and Elizabeth (Currie) P.; m. Hazel Jean Duncan, Aug. 27, 1936; 1 child, James Donald. B.S., Mt. Allison U., Sackville, N.B., Can., 1933, D.Sc. (hon.), 1967; M.S., McGill U., Montreal, Que., Can., 1936, Ph.D., 1938; D.Sc. (hon.), Carleton U., Ottawa, Ont., Can., 1975, Meml. U., St. John's, Nfld., Can., 1977. Chemist Nat. Research Council Can., Ottawa, 1938-52, dir. div. chemistry, 1952-75. Contbr. numerous articles to profl. jours.; patentee (over 50) in field. Fellow Am. Inst. Chemists (Pioneer award 1984), Royal Soc. Can., Chem. Inst. Can. (pres. 1967-68, Montreal medal 1971); mem. Am. Chem. Soc., Soc. Chem. Engring. (R.S. Jane award 1975). Mem. United Ch. of Can. Avocations: sailing; gardening. Home: 2324 Alta Vista Dr, Ottawa, ON Canada K1H 7M7 Office: Nat Research Council Can, Div Chemistry, Ottawa, ON Canada K1A 0R9

PUDNEY, GARY LAURENCE, television executive; b. Mpls., July 20, 1934; s. Lawrence D. and Agnes (Hansen) P. BA, UCLA, 1956. V.p. ABC, Inc., N.Y.C., 1968—; v.p., sr. exec. in charge of spls. and talent ABC Entertainment, 1979-89; pres. The Gary L. Pudney Co., Beverly Hills, Calif., 1988—; chief oper. officer Paradigm Entertainment, Beverly Hills, 1989-92; exec. producer World Music Awards, ABC-TV, 1993—, World's Greatest Magic, NBC-TV, 1994—, Grand Illusions, 1994, Caesar's World Entertainment, 1994-95, Lance Burton and Houdini, NBC-TV, 1995. Exec. producer for United Cerebral Palsy Aspen and Lake Tahoe Pro-Celebrity Tennis Festivals, 4 yrs., AIDS Project L.A. Dinner, 1985, The 25th Anniversary of the L.A. Music Ctr. Bd. dirs. nat. Cerebral Palsy Found., Ctr. Theatre Group Ahmanson Theatre, L.A., Ctr. Theatre Group of L.A. Music Ctr.; mem. bd. La Quinta Arts Found., 1991—. Recipient Helena T. Deveraux Meml. award, 1985, Humanitarian award Nat. Jewish Ctr. for Immunology and Respiratory Medicine, 1986, Gift of Love award Nat. Ctr. Hyperactive Children, 1988, Winner award Excellence The L.A. Film Adv. Bd. Mem. Hollywood Radio and TV Soc. (bd. dirs.), Acad. TV Arts and Scis. (exec. com.), Met. Mus. Art, Mus. Modern Art. Democrat. Lutheran.

PUENTE, TITO ANTHONY, orchestra leader, composer, arranger; b. N.Y.C., Apr. 20, 1923; s. Ernest Anthony and Ercilia (Ortiz) P.; m. Margaret Asencio, Oct. 19, 1963; children: Ronald, Audrey, Tito Anthony. Student, Julliard Conservatory Music, N.Y. Sch. Music, Schillinger System; MusD (hon.), SUNY, Albany, 1987. Orch. leader appearing in numerous night clubs and ballrooms, throughout U.S., 1949—; appeared in Woody Allen's Radio Days, John Candy's Armed & Dangerous, 1986-87; recorded 96 albums; appeared in concert Red Sea Jazz Festival, Israel, all major jazz festivals, including Montreaux, Monterey, Munich, North Sea, others, Tribute in P.R., 1986, Los Angeles Ford Theatre Tribute, 1987; composer Para Los Rumberos, 1960, Oye Como Va, 1962, numerous other works recorded with Dizzy Gillespie, Lionel Hampton, George Shearing, Woody Herman, other major jazz artists; sold out performance Radio City Music Hall & Apollo Theatre, 1986; appeared Madison Square Garden, N.Y.C., 1986, Los Angeles Amphitheatre, 1986, on Bill Cosby Show, 1987, Regis Philbin, Bill Boggs shows, 1987; guest artist with Bklyn. Philharmonic Symphony Orch., N.Y. and Phila., 1987. Founder T. Puente Scholarship fund, 1980. Served with USN, 1942-45. Recipient Bronze medallion City of N.Y., 1969, Key to City Los Angeles, 1976, Key to City of Chgo., 1985, Key to City of Miami, 1986; named Musician of Month on several occasions by Downbeat, Metronome, Playboy and trade mags., 1950's; named King of Latin Music, La Prensa newspaper, 1955; his band named Best Latin Am. Orch. New York Daily News, 1977; recipient 6 Grammy nominations, Grammy award, 1978, 83, 85, 90; N.Y. Music award, 1986. Office: Thomas Cassidy Inc 366 Horseshoe Dr Basalt CO 81621*

PUERNER, JOHN, newspaper publishing executive. V.p., dir. mktg. and devel. Chgo. Tribune; now pres., pub. The Orlando Sentinel, Fla. Office: The Orlando Sentinel 633 N Orange Ave Orlando FL 32801-1349*

PUFFER, RICHARD JUDSON, retired college chancellor; b. Chgo., Aug. 20, 1931; s. Noble Judson and Lillian Katherine (Olson) P.; m. Alison Foster Cope, June 28, 1952; children—Lynn, Mark, Andrew. Ph.B., Ill. Wesleyan U., 1953, M.S. in Edn, Ill. State U., 1962; PhD (Roy Clark Meml. scholar), Northwestern U., 1967. Asst. plant supt. J.A. Olson Co., Winona, Miss., 1957-59; tchr. Leroy Community Unit Dist. 1, 1959-60; tchr., prin. Community Unit, Dist. 7, Lexington, Ill., 1960-62; asst. county supt. schs. Cook County, Ill., 1962-65; dean arts and scis. Kirkwood Community Coll., Cedar Rapids, Iowa, 1967-69; v.p. Black Hawk Coll., Moline, Ill., 1969-77; pres. Black Hawk Coll., 1977-82, chancellor, 1982-87; pres. The Ark Computer Ctr., 1989-92; dir. W. Central Ill. Ednl. TV Corp., Springfield, Ill., 1977-87; cons. examiner North Central Assn., 1978-87. Editor: Cook County Ednl. Digest, 1962-65. Bd. dirs. Cedar Rapids Symphony, 1967-69, United Way of Rock Island and Scott Counties, Ill., 1978-80; sec., treas. Ill. Ednl. Retirement Cts. 1987-91; vice-chmn. Illini Hosp. Bd., 1988-93, chmn., 1993-95; bd. dirs. Illowa coun. Boy Scouts Am., 1979-83, v.p., 1981-83. With Supply Corps USNR, 1953-57. Mem. Rotary (pres. 1975-76, East

Moline, Ill.), Green Medallion, Blue Key, Phi Delta Kappa, Pi Gamma Mu. Home and Office: 1119 20th Ave East Moline IL 61244-2223

PUFFER, WINTHROP FREEMAN, JR., behavioral science company executive, clergyman; b. Concord, Mass.; s. Winthrop Freeman and Ester Alice (Robinson) P.; m. Geneva Woodruff, May 5, 1962 (div. 1976); m. Carolyn D. Puffer, Dec. 20, 1976; children: Alexandra Woolsey, Winthrop Freeman III. BA, Tufts U., 1956; STB, MDiv, Boston U., 1959, STM, 1968; EdD, U. Mass., 1974. Ordained to ministry Ch. of Christ, 1959. Minister 1st Ch. of Christ, Essex, Mass., 1962-64, 2d Ch. of Christ, Holyoke, Mass., 1965-66; asst. dean U. N.H., Durham, Mass. 1966-72; mgr. tng. Mind/APC, N.Y.C. and Palm Beach, Fla., 1973-79; pres. owner PKT Assocs., behavioral change cons., Durham, 1979—. Mem. Conf. Com. on Ecumenical Affairs, Boston, 1961-67; officer North Shore Com. on Alcoholism, Beverly, Mass., 1963; mem. Com. on Social Issues, Concord, N.H., 1986-88; moderator Com. Check, Durham, 1987. Mem. Internat. Registry OD Profls. (accredited). Democrat. Episcopalian. Avocation: raising sheep. Home: RR 1 Newmarket NH 03857 Office: The Round Table Group 172 Packers Falls Rd Durham NH 03824

PUGH, ARTHUR JAMES, retired department store executive, consultant; b. Glen Morrison, W.Va., Sept. 24, 1937; s. Arthur James and Mary (Hoff) P.; m. Sharon Hubacher, Sept. 26, 1961; children: James Gregory, Mary Elizabeth. BSBA, W.Va. U., 1959; Master of Retailing, U. Pitts., 1960. Mgmt. trainee, buyer Woodward & Lothrop, Washington, 1960-71, v.p., 1971-77, sr. v.p., 1977-80, exec. v.p., 1980-87; exec. v.p. Coun. of Better Bus. Bur., Arlington, Va., 1987-90; bd. dir. Coun. of Better Bus. Bur.; cons., bd. dir. Fairfax, Va., 1990—; trustee, chmn. audit com. Calvert Mut. Funds, Washington, 1983—; bd. dirs. Acacia Capital Corp., Washington; bd. dirs., exec. com. compensation com., chmn. investment com. Acacia Fed. Savs. Bank, Annadale, Va. Chmn. bd. dirs. Better Bus. Bur. Met. Washington, 1987. Mem. Rotary Found. of Washington (pres. 1990-91), Nat. Retail Mchts. Assn. (bd. dirs. 1986), W.Va. U. Alumni Assn. (bd. dirs. 1993-98), Fairfax Country Club (bd. dirs. 1990-92), Rotary Club of Washington (Rotarian of Yr. 1982, pres. 1984). Republican. Presbyterian. Avocations: tennis, running, skiing. Home and Office: 4823 Prestwick Dr Fairfax VA 22030-4533

PUGH, EDISON NEVILLE, metallurgist; b. Glamorgan, Wales, May 5, 1935; naturalized U.S. citizen; BSc, U. Wales, 1956, PhD in Metallurgy, 1959. Sci. officer def. stds. labs. NSW br. Australian Def. Supply, 1959-63; scientist rsch. inst. advanced studies Martin Marietta Corp., Md., 1963-65, staff scientist, 1965-66, sr. rsch. scientist, 1966-69; assoc. prof. engring. and applied sci. George Washington U., 1969-70; assoc. prof. metallurgy and mining engring. U. Ill., Urbana, 1970-73, prof., 1973-80; mem. staff Nat. Inst. Stds. & Tech., 1980-85, chief metallurgy divsn., 1985—. Fellow Am. Soc. Metals Internat., Nat. Assn. Corrosion Engrs. (Willis Rodney Whitney award 1984). Office: Nat Inst of Stds and Tech Materials Sci and Engring Lab Materials Bldg Rm B268 Gaithersburg MD 20899

PUGH, EMERSON WILLIAM, electrical engineer; b. Pasadena, Calif., May 1, 1929; s. Emerson Martindale and Ruth Hazel (Edgin) P.; m. Elizabeth Burnam Russell; children: William Russell, Sarah Elizabeth, David Emerson. BS in Physics, Carnegie Mellon U., 1951, PhD in Physics, 1956. Asst. prof. physics Carnegie Mellon U., Pitts., 1956-57; with IBM, 1957-93, rsch. staff mem. rsch. div., Poughkeepsie, N.Y., 1957-61, engring. mgr. components div., 1962-65, group dir. data processing group, Harrison, N.Y., 1965-66, dir. tech. planning rsch. div., Yorktown Heights, N.Y., 1966-68, asst. to v.p. IBM Corp., Armonk, N.Y., 1968-71, rsch. mgr. rsch. div., Yorktown Heights, 1971-85, mgr. tech. history, 1985-93; vis. scientist IBM Lab., Zurich, Switzerland, 1961-62; mem. United Engring. Trustees Bd., N.Y.C., 1986-92; mem. Engring. Soc. Libr. Bd., N.Y.C., 1986-89; trustee Chalres Babbage Found., 1990—. Author: Principles of Electricity and Magnetism, 1960, Memories That Shaped an Industry, 1984, IBM's Early Computers, 1986, IBM's 360 and Early 370 Systems, 1991, Building IBM, 1995; also articles; 10 patents. Fellow IEEE (v.p. 1986-87, pres. 1989, chmn. friends com. Ctr. for History Elec. Engring. 1991-94), AAAS, Am. Phys. Soc. Home: 40 Brandon Dr Mount Kisco NY 10549 Office: IBM T J Watson Rsch Ctr PO Box 218 Yorktown Heights NY 10598-0218

PUGH, GEORGE WILLARD, legal educator; b. Napoleonville, La., Aug. 17, 1925; s. William Whitmell and Evelyn (Foley) P.; m. Jean Earle Hemphill, Sept. 6, 1952; children: William Whitmell III, George Willard, David Nicholls, James Hemphill. B.A. La. State U., 1947, J.D., 1950; J.S.D., Yale U., 1952; Dr. h.c., U. Aix-Marseille III, France, 1984. Bar: La. 1950. Instr. La. State U. Law Sch., 1950, mem. faculty, 1952-94, prof. law, 1959-94, Julius B. Nachman prof. law, 1984-94; prof. law emeritus, 1994—; faculty summer session abroad U. Thessaloniki Greece summer 1974, Aix-en-Provence, France, 1985; mem. faculty summer program U. San Diego, Paris, 1977; part-time rsch. cons. La. State Law Inst., 1953-54; 1st jud. administr. Jud. Coun. Supreme Ct. La., 1954-56; vis. prof. U. Tex., summer 1961; vis. Doherty prof. law U. Va., 1966-67; mem. faculty orientation program in Am. law Assn. Am. Law Schs., 1968, law teaching clinic, summer 1969; vis. prof. U. Aix-Marseille III, France, 1983, fall 1987, U. Catholique de Louvain, Belgium, fall 1987; cons. La. State U.S. Vietnam Legal Adminstrn. Project, 1969. Author: Louisiana Evidence Law, 1974, supplement, 1978; co-author: Cases and Materials on the Administration of Criminal Justice, 2d edit., 1969, Handbook on Louisiana Evidence Law, 1989, 7th edit., 1995; coord., reporter Code of Evidence for La. Bd. dirs. Legal Aid Soc. Baton Rouge, 1965-89, chmn., 1963-64; adv. bd. St. Alban's Episcopal Student Ctr., La. State U., 1965-68, 70-72. Served with AUS, World War II. Fellow Comparative Study Adminstrn. Justice, 1962-65. Mem. Am., La. State bar assns., Order of Coif, Omicron Delta Kappa, Lambda Chi Alpha. Democrat. Episcopalian. Home: 167 Sunset Blvd Baton Rouge LA 70808-5073

PUGH, GRACE HUNTLEY, artist; b. Schenectady, N.Y., Sept. 25, 1912; d. Grant and Grace La Vallée (Lake) Huntley; m. Cresson Pugh, Sept. 21, 1940; 1 child, Gigi Grace Huntley Pugh Sundstrom. Student, Wellesley Coll., 1930-34; BA, Barnard Coll., 1934; postgrad., Nat. Acad. Design, 1934-36, Art Students League, 1938. Head art dept., artist in residence Briarcliff Jr. Coll., Briarcliff Manor, N.Y., 1936-40; mem. staff directions in Am. painting exhibit Carnegie Inst., Pitts., 1942-44; asst. art dir. Young & Rubicam Inc., N.Y.C., 1946-50; painting instr. Westchester County Workshop, White Plains, N.Y., 1961-63; chair fine arts and exhbn. Mamaroneck (N.Y.) Libr., 1950-88; co-chair Emelin Theatre Street Fair, Mamaroneck, 1975-81; fine arts advisor, artist in residence Village of Mamaroneck, 1977—. Exhibited oil and watercolor paintings in numerous group and one-woman shows including Nat. Acad. Design, N.Y.C., 1957, N.Y. State Painters, N.Y. State bldg. in World's Fair, 1965, Franklin & Marshall Colls., 1974, Carnegie Inst., 1950, Canton Art Inst., Ohio, 1995, Canton (Ohio) Art Inst., 1995, Kinderhook (N.Y.) Lib., 1971 many others; Editor Mamaroneck Historical Society Newsletter, 1980—. Charter pres. Mamaroneck Hist. Soc., 1980-82, trustee emerita, 1980—; 1st chair Landmarks Adv. Com. Village of Mamaroneck, 1982-92, co-chair cherry blossom festival centennial com., 1993—; trustee Friends of Wildlife Sanctuary, Rye, N.Y., 1990—; founding pres. Mamaroneck Artists Guild, 1953-55; founding sec. Westchester Soc. Archeol. Inst. of Am., 1976-78. Day named in her honor Village of Mamaroneck, 1982, 91. Mem. Am. Watercolor Soc., Rockport Art Assn. (Longfellow award 1944), Federated Conservationists of Westchester County (Cert. of Appreciation 1991), DAR (conservation chair 1982-88). Republican. Episcopalian. Avocations: swimming, gardening, community service, research, sailing. Home: 823 Stuart Ave Mamaroneck NY 10543

PUGH, KEITH E., JR., lawyer; b. L.A., Mar. 17, 1937; s. Keith Emerson and Serena (Reynolds) P.; m. Kathleen Perry, Aug. 28, 1958 (div. Mar. 1973); children—Linda, Lisa, Scott; m. Pamela Carolyn Winberry, May 20, 1973; children—Alexander, Caroline. Student, Principia Coll., 1955-58; J.D., U. So. Calif., 1962. Bar: Calif. 1962, D.C. 1969, U.S. Supreme Ct. 1976, U.S. Ct. Internat. Trade 1983, U.S. Ct. Appeals (fed. cir.) 1994. Dep. atty. gen. antitrust sect. Office Calif. Atty. Gen., San Francisco, 1962-65; assoc. Broad, Busterud & Khourie, San Francisco, 1965-66, Office Joseph Alioto, San Francisco, 1966-68, Howrey & Simon, Washington, 1968-69; ptnr. Howrey & Simon, 1970—; also mem. mgmt. com., 1980—. Mem. ABA, Fed. Cir. Bar Assn., State Bar Calif., D.C. Bar Assn., Anapolis Yacht Club, Capitol City Club, Phi Delta Phi. Avocation: boating. Home: 3939

Fordham Rd NW Washington DC 20016-1937 Office: Howrey & Simon 1299 Pennsylvania Ave NW Washington DC 20004-2402

PUGH, LAWRENCE R., apparel executive; b. 1933; (married). Grad., Colby Coll., 1956. Div. sales mgr. Borden Inc., 1958-66; product mgr., gen. mktg. mgr. Hamilton Beach Co., 1966-70; dir. mktg. Ampex Corp., 1970-72; group pres. Beatrice Foods Co., 1972-80; pres. V.F. Corp., Wyomissing, Pa., 1980-83, chmn., chief exec. officer, 1983—. Office: VF Corp 1047 N Park Rd Reading PA 19610*

PUGH, MARION STIRLING, archaeologist, author; b. Middletown, N.Y., May 12, 1911; d. Louis and Lena May (Randall) Illig; m. Matthew Williams Sirling, Dec. 11, 1933 (dec. 1975); children: Matthew Williams, Jr. (dec.), Ariana Stirling Withers; m. John Ramsey Pugh, Aug. 7, 1977 (dec. Mar. 1994). BS, Rider Coll., 1930; postgrad. George Washington U., 1931-33. Office sec. Bur. Am. Ethnology, Smithsonian Instn., Washington, 1931-33; archaeologist with Matthew W. Stirling, Fla., 1934-38, Smithsonian Instn.-Nat. Geog. Soc. archeol. expdn. Mex., 1939-46, Panama, 1948-53, Ecuador, 1957, Costa Rica, 1962. Author: (with Matthew Stirling) Tarqui, an Early Site in Manabi, Ecuador, 1962, El Limon, an Early Tomb Site in Cocle Province, Panama, 1963, Archaeological Notes on Almirante Bay, Bocas del Toro, Panama, 1963, The Archeology of Taboga, Uraba and Taboguilla Islands, Panama, 1963; contbr. articles to Nat. Geog. mag. and Ames. mag. Trustee The Textile Mus., Washington, 1968—, pres. 1984-87. Co-recipient Franklyn L. Burr award Nat. Geog. Soc., 1941, Disting. Svc. medal Peruvian Embassy, 1985. Fellow Am. Anthrop. Assn., Gen. Div. Anthropology; mem. Am. Ethnol. Soc., Soc. Latin Am. Anthropology, Washington Anthrop. Soc., Washington Acad. Sci., Soc. Woman Geographers (pres. 1960-63, 69-72, mem. exec. council 1954-74, Gold medal 1975). Avocations: swimming, textiles. Home: 20351 Airmont Rd Round Hill VA 22141

PUGH, RICHARD CRAWFORD, lawyer; b. Phila., Apr. 28, 1929; s. William and Myrtle P.; m. Nanette Bannen, Feb. 27, 1954; children: Richard Crawford, Andrew Lembert, Catherine Elizabeth. AB summa cum laude, Dartmouth Coll., 1951; BA in Jurisprudence, Oxford (Eng.) U., 1953; LLB, Columbia U., 1958. Bar: N.Y. 1958. Assoc. firm Cleary, Gottlieb, Steen & Hamilton, N.Y.C., 1958-61; ptnr. Cleary, Gottlieb, Steen & Hamilton, 1969-89, counsel, 1989—; disting. prof. law U. San Diego, 1989—; mem. faculty Law Sch. Columbia U., 1961-89, prof., 1964-69, adj. prof., 1969-89; lectr. Columbia-Amsterdam-Leyden (Netherlands) summer program Am. law, 1963, 79; dep. asst. atty. gen. tax div. U.S. Dept. Justice, 1966-68; Cons. fiscal and fin. br. UN Secretariat, 1962, 64. Editor: Columbia Law Rev., 1957-58; editor: (with W. Friedmann) Legal Aspects of Foreign Investment, 1959, (with others) International Law, 1993, Taxation of International Transactions, 1991, Taxation of Business Enterprises, 1995. Served with USNR, 1954-56. Rhodes scholar, 1953. Mem. ABA, Am. Law Inst., Am. Coll. Tax Counsel, Am. Soc. Internat. Law, Internat. Fiscal Assn. (pres. U.S. br. 1978-79). Home: 7335 Encelia Dr La Jolla CA 92037-5729 Office: Univ San Diego Sch Law Alcala Park San Diego CA 92110-2429

PUGH, ROBERT GAHAGAN, lawyer; b. Shreveport, La., Aug. 25, 1924; m. Jo Ann Powell; children: Robert G. Jr., Jean Anne Pugh Cottingham, Lamar Powell. BS, Centenary Coll., Shreveport; LLB, La. State U. Bar: La. 1949. Former lectr. St. John's High Sch., Shreveport; former prof. law and medicine La. State U. Med. Ctr., Shreveport. Author: Juvenile Laws of Louisiana, Their History and Developmment. La. commr. Nat. Conf. Commrs. on Uniform State Laws; bd. regents State of La., mem. Judiciary Commn.; coun. mem. Lat. State Law Inst.; del. La. Constl. Conv., 1973; chmn. La. Indigent Defender Bd. Navigator USAAF, World War II; intelligence and security officer USAF, Korea. Recipient Disting. Atty. award La. Bar Found., 1990; named to Hall of Fame La. State U. Law Ctr. Fellow at large Am. Bar Found; mem. ABA (La. ho. of dels., chmn. standing com. on membership 1977-84, mem. sect. on real property, probate and trust law, sect. taxation), Bar Assn. for 5th Fed. Cir. (pres. 1985-87), La. Bar Assn. (pres. 1975-76), Shreveport Bar Assn. (pres. 1971-72), Fed. Bar Assn., Can. Bar Assn., La. Bar Found., Nat. Conf. Bar Pres. (pres. 1981-82), Am. Judicature Soc., Am. Law Inst., Bartolus Soc., La. State U. Law Sch. Alumni Assn. (pres. 1977), The Shreveport Club, East Ridge Country Club (past pres.), Order of Coif (hon.). Roman Catholic. Office: Commercial National Tower 333 Texas St Ste 2100 Shreveport LA 71101-5386

PUGH, ROBERT KENNETH, textbook distributing company executive; b. Fayette, Mo., Jan. 17, 1940; s. William Edward and Thelma Francis (Cleeton) P.; m. Connie Grogger, Aug. 18, 1962; children: Douglas Fowler, Lesley Parmenter. BS in Acctg., U. Mo., 1963. Acct. Shelter Ins., Columbia, Mo., 1966; contr. Mo. Store Co., Columbia, 1967-81, CEO, 1981-85; CEO MBS Textbook Exch., Columbia, 1985—; dir. Commerce Bank Mid Mo., Columbia. Councilman City of Columbia, 1973-75, mayor, 1975-77; chmn. Land Clearance Redevel. Authority, Columbia, 1978-80; mem. Water & Light Bd., Columbia, 1979-82. Capt. U.S. Army, 1963-65. Office: MBS Textbook Exch 2711 W Ash St # 637 Columbia MO 65203-4613

PUGH, RODERICK WELLINGTON, psychologist, educator; b. Richmond, Ky., June 1, 1919; s. George Wilmer and Lena Bernetta (White) P.; m. Harriet Elizabeth Rogers, Aug. 29, 1953 (div. 1955). B.A., Fisk U., 1940; M.A., Ohio State U., 1941; Ph.D., U. Chgo., 1949. Diplomate: Am. Bd. Profl. Psychology. Instr. Albany (Ga.) State Coll., 1941-43; psychology trainee VA, Chgo., 1947-49; lectr. Roosevelt U., Chgo., 1951-54; staff clin. psychologist VA Hosp., Hines, Ill., 1950-54, asst. chief psychologist for psychotherapy, 1954-58, chief clin. psychology sect., 1958-60, supervising psychologist, coord. psychol. internship tng., 1960-66; pvt. practice clin. psychology Chgo., 1958—; assoc. prof. psychology Loyola U., Chgo., 1966-73, prof., 1973-88, emeritus prof. psychology, 1989—; Cons. St. Mary of the Lake Sem., Niles, Ill., 1965-66, Ill. Div. Vocational Rehab., 1965-82, Center for Inner City Studies, Northeastern State U., Chgo., 1966-67, VA Psychology Tng. Program, 1966—; Am. Psychol. Assn. and Nat. Inst. Mental Health Vis. Psychologists Program, 1966-89; juvenile problems research rev. com. NIMH, 1970-74; cons. Center for Minority Group Mental Health Programs, 1975-77, cons. psychology edn. br., 1978-82; lectr. U. Ibadan, Nigeria, 1978; Mem. profl. adv. com. Div. Mental Health, City of Chgo., 1979-82; mem. adv. com. U.S. Army Command and Gen. Staff Coll., 1981-83. Author: Psychology and the Black Experience, 1972; Contbr.: chpt. in Black Psychology, 1972; Cons. editor: Contemporary Psychology, 1975-79; contbr. articles to profl. jours. Served bd. trustees Fisk U., 1968-78. Served to 2d lt. AUS, 1943-46, ETO. Vis. scholar Fisk U., 1966. Fellow Am. Psychol. Soc., Am. Psychol. Assn. (nat. adv. panel to Civilian Health and Med. Program of Uniformed Services 1980-83, joint coun. on profl. edn. in psychology 1988-90); mem. Midwestern Psychol. Assn., Ill. Psychol. Assn. (chmn. legis. com. 1961, council mem. 1960-62, Disting. Psychologist award 1988), Soc. for Psychol. Study Social Issues, Assn. Behavior Analysis, AAUP, Sigma Xi, Alpha Phi Alpha, Psi Chi. Home: 5201 S Cornell Ave Chicago IL 60615 Office: 30 N Michigan Ave Chicago IL 60602-3402 also: Loyola U 6525 N Sheridan Rd Chicago IL 60626-5311

PUGH, THOMAS WILFRED, lawyer; b. St. Paul, Minn., Aug. 3, 1949; s. Thomas Leslie and Joann Marie (Tauer) P.; m. Susan Elizabeth Beattie, Sept. 12, 1971; children: Aimee Elizabeth, Douglas Thomas. AB cum laude, Dartmouth Coll., 1971; JD cum laude, U. Minn., 1976. Assoc. Thuet & Lynch, South St. Paul, 1976-79; ptnr. Thuet, Lynch & Pugh, South St. Paul, 1980-85; atty., pres. Thuet, Pugh & Rogosheske, Ltd., South St. Paul, 1986—; mem. Minn. Ho. of Reps., St. Paul, 1989—; mem. Supreme Ct. Task Force Conciliation Ct., St. Paul, 1992, Dakota County Tech. Coll. Adv. Bd., 1991—. Bd. dirs. Wakota Arena, South St. Paul, 1984-87; pres. Luther Meml. Ch., South St. Paul, 1983-84. Daniel Webster scholar Dartmouth Coll., 1970, Rufus Choate scholar, 1971. Mem. Minn. State Bar Assn., 1st Dist. Bar Assn., Ducks Unltd., Pheasants Forever, South St. Paul C. of C. (local issues chair 1982, Dedicated Svc. award 1983), South St. Paul Jaycees (pres. 1978-79, Key award 1979), Lions. Lutheran. Avocations: tennis, golf, hunting, fishing, reading. Office: Thuet Pugh & Rogosheske 833 Southview Blvd South Saint Paul MN 55075-2237

PUGLIESE, MARIA A., psychiatrist; b. Phila., Sept. 16, 1948; d. Peter Francis and Ida Agnes (Rosa) P.; m. J. Paul Hieble, Sept. 14, 1985; q child, Helen Elisa Hieble. BS, Chestnut Hill Coll., 1970; MD, U. Pa., 1974. Diplomate Am. Bd. Psychiatry and Neurology. Attending psychiatrist Inst.

Pa. Hosp., Phila., 1978—, Malvern (Pa.) Inst., 1982—. Office: 111 N 49th St Philadelphia PA 19139

PUGLIESE, ROBERT FRANCIS, lawyer, business executive; b. West Pittston, Pa., Jan. 15, 1933. BS, U. Scranton, 1954; LLB, Georgetown U., 1957, LLM, 1959; grad. advanced mgmt. program Harvard U., 1976. Bar: D.C. 1957, U.S. Dist. Ct. 1957, U.S. Ct. Claims 1958, U.S. Tax Ct. 1957, U.S. Ct. Appeals 1957. Assoc. Hedrick & Lane, Washington, 1957-60; tax counsel Westinghouse Electric Corp., Pitts., 1961-70, gen. tax counsel, 1970-75, v.p., gen. tax counsel, 1975-76, v.p., gen. counsel, sec., 1976-86, sr. v.p., 1987, exec. v.p., 1988-92; spl. counsel Eckert, Seamans, Cherin & Mellott, Pitts., 1993—. Mem. exec. com. U. Scranton; bd. dirs. St. Clair Meml. Hosp. Mem. Assn. Gen. Counsel. Office: Eckert Seamans Cherin & Mellott 600 Grant St 42nd fl Pittsburgh PA 15219

PUGLIESE, ROBERT J., lawyer; b. Charles City, Iowa, July 7, 1953. BA, Drake U., 1974; JD, U. Ill., 1978. Bar: Ill. 1978, U.S. Dist. Ct. (no. dist.) Ill. 1978. Ptnr. Lord, Bissell & Brook, Chgo. Mem. ABA. Office: Lord Bissell & Brook Harris Bank Bldg 115 S La Salle St # 36 Chicago IL 60603-3801

PUGLISI, PHILIP JAMES, electrical engineer; b. Paterson, N.J., Feb. 26, 1943; s. Philip James and Josephine Theresa (Guido) P.; children: Brent, Tara. BEE, Poly. U., 1971; MEE, Stanford U., 1972. Researcher, mem. staff Bell Telephone Labs., Whippanny, N.J., 1967-77; chief engr. Dionex Corp., Sunnyvale, Calif., 1977-80; engring. supr. AT&T Microelectronics, Lees Summit, Mo., 1980-83, with semiconductor design dept., 1983-86, mktg. mgr., 1986-91; dir. engring. PPG Biomed. Systems, Lenexa, Kans., 1991-93; product mgr.- optics AT&T, Lee's Summit, Mo., 1993—; mem. exec. com. Optical Data Link Forum, Murry Hill, N.J., 1987-91. Contbr. articles to profl. jours. Organizing parent Dist. and State Music Festival, Springfield & Columbia, Mo., 1984-88; bd. dirs. Dist. Water Com., Grovespring, Mo., 1987-88; scoutmaster Boy Scouts Am., Bonny Doon, Calif., 1976-79. With USN, 1960-64. Mem. Electronic Industries Assn. (mem. optical communication com. 1987-91). Avocations: pocket billiards, home computing, carpentry, country dancing. Home: 405 Cline St Pleasant Hill MO 64080-1805 Office: AT&T CS & CT 777 NW Blue Pky Lees Summit MO 64086-5712

PUGMIRE, ROBERT, wholesale distribution executive. V.p. Nat. Clothing Co., Inc., Kirkland, Wash. Office: National Clothing Co Inc 10809 120th Ave NE Kirkland WA 98033*

PUGSLEY, FRANK BURRUSS, lawyer; b. Kansas City, Mo., Apr. 3, 1920; s. Charles Silvey and Emma (Burruss) P.; m. Aline East, May 7, 1943; children—John, Susan Pugsley Patterson, Nancy Pugsley Young. B.S. in Mech. Engring. U. Tex., Austin, 1942; J.D., DePaul U., Chgo., 1950. Bar: Ill. 1950, Tex. 1953, U.S. Supreme Ct. 1960. Engr. Gen. Electric Co., Schenectady, 1946-50; patent atty. Gen. Electric Co., 1950-52; assoc. Baker & Botts, Houston, 1952-60; ptnr. Baker & Botts, 1960-84, sr. ptnr., 1974-84; lectr. Southwestern Legal Found., Practising Law Inst., Bur. Nat. Affairs Conf. Contbr. articles to legal jours. Trustee West Univ. Methodist Ch., Houston, 1959-65; bd. dirs. St. Stephens Episcopal Day Sch., 1960-62; adminstrv. bd. St. Luke's United Meth. Ch., 1981-83. Served to lt. USNR, 1942-46. Fellow Tex. Bar Found.; mem. ABA (chmn. intellectual property law sec. 1980-81), Am. Intellectual Property Law Assn. (pres. 1966-67), Tex. Bar Assn. (chmn. intellectual property law sect. 1960-61), Houston Bar Assn., Petroleum Club, Frisch Auf! Valley Country Club, Friars. Home: 3602 Nottingham St Houston TX 77005-2221 Office: 3000 One Shell Plz Houston TX 77002

PUGSLEY, JOHN EAST, financial executive, accountant; b. Schenectady, N.Y., Dec. 28, 1946; s. Frank Burruss and Aline (East) P.; m. Kathleen Ellen Partain, Aug. 24, 1974; children: Frank East, Paul Burruss. BSEE, U. Houston, 1971, MS in Acctg., 1977. CPA, profl. engr. Power cons. Houston Lighting & Power, 1971-77; CPA Deloitte & Touche, Houston, 1977-83; v.p. fin. Capital Excavation Co., Austin, Tex., 1983-94. Commr. Western Hills Youth Football, Austin, 1991-93. Mem. FEI, Tex. Soc. CPAs. Office: Capital Excavation Co PO Box 1301 Austin TX 78767

PUHALA, JAMES JOSEPH, lawyer; b. Pitts., Sept. 5, 1942; s. Leo Andrew and Agnes (Ruglovsky) P.; m. Linda Sue Lash, Oct. 1, 1977; children: Stephen, Susan, Matthew. BBA, U. Dayton, 1964; MBA, U. Pitts., 1965; JD, Duquesne U., 1974. Bar: Pa. 1974, U.S. Dist. Ct. (we. dist.) Pa. 1974. Mgr. internat. taxes Dravo Corp., Pitts., 1974-79, sr. counsel, 1979-86, group gen. counsel, 1986-87, v.p., gen. counsel, sec., 1987—. Decorated D.F.C., Bronze Star. Mem. Am. Corp. Counsel Assn., Allegheny County Bar Assn., Mobile Bar Assn. (assoc.). Home: 505 Cumberland Rd E Mobile AL 36608-3305 Office: Dravo Corp PO Box 1685 Mobile AL 36633-1685

PUHVEL, JAAN, philologist, educator; b. Tallinn, Estonia, Jan. 24, 1932; came to U.S., 1952, naturalized, 1962; s. Karl and Meta Elisabeth (Pärn) P.; m. Sirje Madli Hansen, June 4, 1960; children—Peter Jaan, Andres Jaak, Markus Jüri. B.A., McGill U., 1951, MA, 1952; PhD (Jr. fellow 1953-57), Harvard, 1959; Dr.Phil. (hon.), U. Tartu, Estonia, 1991. Lectr. McGill U., 1955-56; instr. U. Tex., 1957-58, vis. prof., 1960; mem. faculty UCLA, 1958—, prof. classics and Indo-European studies, 1964-92, prof. emeritus, 1993—; dir. Center Research Langs. and Linguistics, 1962-67, vice chmn. charge sect. Indo-European studies, 1964-68, chmn. dept. classics, 1968-75; Collitz prof. Indo-European comparative philology SUNY at Buffalo, 1971; prof. extraordinarius U. Tartu, Estonia, 1993—. Author, editor: Laryngeals and the Indo-European Verb, 1960, Ancient Indo-European Dialects, 1966, Substance and Structure of Language, 1969, Myth and Law among the Indo-Europeans, 1970, Analecta Indoeuropaea, 1981, Hittite Etymological Dictionary, Vols. 1-2, 1984, Vol. 3, 1991, Comparative Mythology, 1987. Recipient Gold medal Gov. Gen. Can., 1951; officer 1st class Order White Rose Finland, 1967; Moyse travelling fellow, 1952; fellow Am. Council Learned Socs., 1961-62, 75-76; Guggenheim fellow, 1968-69. Mem. Am. Oriental Soc., Assn. Advancement Baltic Studies (pres. 1971-72). Office: UCLA Dept Classics Los Angeles CA 90024

PULASKI, CHARLES ALEXANDER, JR., lawyer; b. Flushing, N.Y., Oct. 22, 1941; s. Charles Alexander and Mary Ann (Spencer) P.; m. Linda Shannon Holden, Aug. 16, 1965; 1 child, Alison. BA in Econs., Yale U., 1964, LLB, 1967. Bar: Conn. 1968, U.S. Dist. Ct. Conn. 1968, U.S. Ct. Appeals (2d cir.) 1968, Iowa 1974, U.S. Dist. Ct. (no. and so. dists.) Iowa 1975, U.S. Ct. Appeals (8th cir.) 1975, Ariz. 1986, U.S. Dist. Ct. Ariz. 1986, U.S. Supreme Ct. 1970. Prof. law U. Iowa, 1975-80, Ariz. State U., Tempe, 1980-88; assoc. Snell & Wilmer, Phoenix, 1986-87; ptnr. Snell & Wilmer, 1988—. Author: Criminal Procedure Case Book, 1982, also numerous articles in law revs. Recipient Kalven award, Law and Soc. Assn., 1987. Mem. ABA, Ariz. Bar Assn. Office: Snell & Wilmer 1 Arizona Ctr Phoenix AZ 85004

PULEO, FRANK CHARLES, lawyer; b. Montclair, N.J., Nov. 25, 1945; s. Frank and Kathren (Despenzerie) P.; m. Alice Kathren Leek, June 1, 1968; children—Charles F., Richard James. B.S.E., Princeton U., 1967; J.D., N.Y.U., 1970. Bar: N.Y. 1971. Ptnr., Milbank, Tweed, Hadley & McCloy, N.Y.C., 1970—. Mem. ABA (mem. com. on fed. regulation securities), N.Y. State Bar Assn. Office: Milbank Tweed Hadley & McCloy 1 Chase Manhattan Plz New York NY 10005-1401

PULGRAM, ERNST, linguist, philologist, Romance and classical linguistics educator, writer; b. Vienna, Austria, Sept. 18, 1915; came to U.S. 1939, naturalized 1943; s. Sigmund and Gisela (Bauer) P.; m. Frances McSparran, Nov. 29, 1985. Dr. Phil. in Romance and Classical Philology, U. Vienna, 1947, Dr. phil. honoris causa, 1990; PhD in Comparative Linguistics, Harvard U., 1944. Asst. prof. Union Coll., Schenectady, N.Y., 1946; asst. prof. U. Mich., Ann Arbor, 1948-51, assoc. prof., 1951-56, prof., 1956—, H. Keniston disting. prof. romance and classical linguistics, 1979-86, prof. emeritus, 1986—; vis. prof. U. Florence, Italy, 1956-57, U. Cologne, Germany, 1970, U. Heidelberg, Germany, 1972, U. Regensburg, Germany 1975, U. Vienna, 1977, Internat. Christian U., Tokyo, 1982, U. Innsbruck, Austria, 1983. U. Munich, Germany, 1987; lectr. numerous univs., internat. linguistic congresses; cons. Sch. Langs. and Linguistics, Georgetown U., Washington. Author: Theory of Names, 1951, The Tongues of Italy, 1958,

Introduction to Spectrography of Speech, 1959, Syllable, Word, Nexus, Cursus, 1970, Latin-Romance Phonology, Prosodics and Metrics, 1975, Italic, Latin, Italian: 600 B.C.-A.D. 1250, 1978, Practicing Linguist, Essays 1950-1985 (2 vols.), 1986; editor: Studies Presented to Joshua Whatmough, 1957, Romanitas: Studies in Romance Linguistics, 1984; contbr. articles to profl. jours.; author revs.; mem. editorial bd. Current Issues in Linguistic Theory (Amsterdam), Mich. Germanic Studies, Jour. Linguistics and Philology, Mediteranean Language Rev. Served to pvt. inf. U.S. Army, 1942-44; PTO. fellow Am. Council of Learned Socs., 1951-52, 59-60, Guggenheim Found., 1954-55, 62-63; recipient Henry Russell award U. Mich., 1951, Festschrift, Amsterdam, 1980. Mem. Linguistic Soc. Am. (exec. com., com. on appointment of hon. mems., program com.), Internat. Linguistic Assn., Internat. Phonetics Assn., Linguistic Assn. Can. and the U.S. (founding mem., pres. 1978-79). Avocations: collecting drawings and watercolors; hiking; swimming. Home: 1050 Wall St Ann Arbor MI 48105-1974

PULGRAM, WILLIAM LEOPOLD, architect, space designer; b. Vienna, Austria, Jan. 1, 1921; came to U.S., 1940; s. Sigmund and Gisela (Bauer) P.; married, Jan. 12, 1952; children: Deirdre, Laurence, Anthony, Christopher. BS, Ga. Inst. Tech., 1949, BArch, 1950; postgrad., Ecole des Beaux Arts, Fontainebleau, France, 1951. Archtl. designer various firms, Atlanta, 1951-58; assoc., chief interior design FABR&P, Atlanta, 1958-63; exec. v.p., gen. mgr. Associated Space Design Inc., Atlanta, 1963-70, pres., chief exec. officer, 1971-85, chmn., chief exec. officer, 1985-86, chmn. emeritus, 1986-88; architect, cons. Atlanta, 1988—; cons. UN, 1986; com. mem. NAS, 1980-84; lectr. at colls., univs., U.S. and abroad. Author: Designing the Automated Office, 1984, Japanese transl., 1985; contbr. articles to jours. in field. Mem., lectr. High Mus. Art, Atlanta, 1970—. With U.S. Army, 1943-46. Named to Hall of Fame, Interior Design mag., 1986. Fellow AIA (chmn. interiors 1978-84, archt. res. coun. AIA Found. 1983-85); mem. Architects, Designers and Planners for Social Responsibility (nat. bd. dirs. 1989—), Am. Soc. Interior Designers, Atlanta C. of C., Atlanta City Club, Lake Lanier Sailing Club. Mem. Unitarian Universalist Ch. Home and Office: W L Pulgram FAIA Cons 4317 E Conway Dr NW Atlanta GA 30327-3528

PULHAMUS, MARLENE LOUISE, elementary school educator; b. Paterson, N.J., Sept. 11, 1937; d. David Weeder and Elfrieda (Ehler) Wemmell; m. Aaron R. Pulhamus, Aug. 20, 1960; children: Steven, Thomas, Nancy. Student, Trenton State U., 1957; BS, William Paterson U., 1959; postgrad., Rutgers U., 1992. Cert. elem. tchr., N.J. Kindergarten tchr. Wayne (N.J.) Bd. Edn., 1959-63; kindergarten tchr. Paterson Bd. Edn., 1974-75, 2d grade tchr., 1975-81; basic skills instr. Paterson Pub. Schs., 1981—; tchr. accelerated program 1st grade, 1992—; trainer for insvc. groups of learning ctrs. and math. with manipulatives for local pub. schs., trainer for local pub. schs. Pres. Friends of Eisenhower Libr., Totowa, N.J., 1975-77; coord. ch. sch. Preakness Reformed Ch., Wayne, 1990—. Recipient Gov.'s award for tchg. excellence State of N.J. Commn. Edn., 1991, 4Mation program award, 1994. Mem. ASCD, NEA, Nat. Coun. Tchrs. Math., Nat. Assn. for Edn. Young Children, N.J. Edn. Assn., Passaic County Edn. Assn., Paterson Edn. Assn. (mem. exec. bd., 1985-89, legis. chmn. 1986-89). Home: 47 Easedale Rd Wayne NJ 07470 Office: Paterson Pub. Sch # 3 448 Main St Paterson NJ 07501-2418

PULITZER, EMILY S RAUH (MRS. JOSEPH PULITZER, JR.), art consultant; b. Cin., July 23, 1933; d. Frederick and Harriet (Frank) Rauh. AB, Bryn Mawr Coll., 1955; student, Ecole du Louvre, Paris, France, 1955-56; MA, Harvard U., 1963. Mem. staff Cin. Art Mus., 1956-57; asst. curator drawings Fogg Art Mus., Harvard, 1957-64, asst. to dir., 1962-63; curator City Art Mus., St. Louis, 1964-73; mem. painting and sculpture com. Mus. Modern Art, 1975—; chmn. visual arts com. Mo. Arts Council, 1976-81; co-chmn. fellows Fogg Art Mus., 1978—; mem. bd. dirs. Mus. Services, 1979-84; commr. St. Louis Art Mus., 1981-88, vice chmn., 1988; bd. dirs. Pulitzer Pub. Co. Bd. dirs. Forum, St. Louis, 1980—, pres. 1990-94; bd. dirs. Mark Rothko Found., 1976-88, Grand Ctr., 1993—; bd. dirs. arts in transit com. Bi-State Devel. Agy., vice chmn., 1987—; mem. overseers com. to visit Harvard Art Mus., 1990—; trustee Mus. Modern Art, 1994—. Mem. Am. Fedn. Arts (dir. 1976-89), St. Louis Mercantile Libr. Assn. (bd. dirs. 1987-93), Women's Forum of Mo. Home: 4903 Pershing Ave Saint Louis MO 63108-1201

PULITZER, MICHAEL EDGAR, publishing executive; b. St. Louis, Feb. 23, 1930; s. Joseph and Elizabeth (Edgar) P.; m. Cecille Stell Eisenbeis, Apr. 28, 1970; children: Michael Edgar, Elizabeth E. Voges, Robert S., Frederick D., Catherine D. Culver, Christina H. Eisenbeis, Mark C. Eisenbeis, William H. Eisenbeis. Grad., St. Mark's Sch., Southborough, Mass., 1947; AB, Harvard U., 1951, LLB, 1954. Bar: Mass. 1954. Assoc. Warner, Stackpole, Stetson & Bradlee, Boston, 1954-56; reporter Louisville Courier Jour., 1956-60; reporter, news editor, asst. mng. editor St. Louis Post-Dispatch, 1960-71, assoc. editor, 1978-79; pub. Ariz. Daily Star, Tucson, 1971—; pres. chief operating officer Pulitzer Pub. Co. (and subs.), 1979-84, vice chmn., 1984-86, pres., chmn., 1986—, also bd. dirs., chief exec. officer, 1988—. Trustee St. Louis U., 1989—. Clubs: St. Louis Country; Mountain Oyster (Tucson). Office: Pulitzer Pub Co 900 N Tucker Blvd Saint Louis MO 63101-1069

PULITZER, ROSLYN K., social worker, psychotherapist; b. Bronx, N.Y., Apr. 25, 1930; d. George and Laura Eleanor (Holtz) P. BS in Human Devel. and Life Cycle, SUNY, N.Y.C., 1983; MSW, Fordham U., 1987; postgrad., Masterson Inst., N.Y.C., 1992. Lic. clin. social worker, N.Y.; cert. in psychoanalytic psychotherapy of the personality disorders. Clinic dir. Resources Counseling and Psychotherapy Ctr., N.Y.C., 1985-89; social worker, clin. supr. methadone maintenance treatment program Beth Israel Med. Ctr., N.Y.C., 1989—; 1989-92; cons. therapist, clin. supr. Identity House, N.Y.C., 1980—, clin. dir., 1985, clin. dir., 1993-94. Mem. regional adv. coun. N.Y. State Div. Human Rights, N.Y.C., 1975-76; mem. Community Bd. 6, N.Y.C., 1978-81; founder, legis. chmn. N.Y. State Women's Polit. Caucus, 1978-80. Mem. NASW, Acad. Cert. Social Workers, Soc. Masterson Inst., N.Y. Milton Erickson Soc. for Psychotherapy and Hypnosis (cert.). Avocations: photography, snorkeling. Home: 110 Bank St Apt 5F New York NY 10014-2168

PULLEN, EDWIN WESLEY, anatomist, university dean; b. Flushing, N.Y., June 2, 1923; s. Edwin Leeson and Henrietta Esther (Treharne) P.; m. Ruthann Chambers, Sept. 7, 1946; children—Wayne, Jeffrey, Susan, Kimberly. A.B. (Pres.'s scholar) Colgate U., 1943; M.S., U. Mass., 1948; Ph.D. (DuPont fellow), U. Va., 1953. Instr. anatomy U. Va., 1951-53, asst. prof., 1953-57, asso. prof., 1957-73, prof., 1973-91; assoc. dean U. Va. (Sch. Medicine), 1974-91, ret., 1991—. Served with USNR, 1943-46. Mem. Am. Assn. Anatomists, AAAS, Sigma Xi. Home: 2700 Magnolia Dr Charlottesville VA 22901-2019

PULLEN, KEATS A., JR., electronics engineer; b. Onawa, Iowa, Nov. 12, 1916; s. Keats A. and Mabel Jeannette (Faus) P.; m. Phyllis Kouwenhoven, Jan. 6, 1945; children: Peter K., Paul V., Keats A. 3d, Andrew W., Victoria F. B.S. in Physics, Calif. Inst. Tech., 1939; Dr.Engring., Johns Hopkins U. Registered profl. engr.: Md. Electronic research engr. Ballistic Research Labs., Aberdeen Proving Ground, Md., 1946-78; electronic engr. Army Material Systems Analysis Activity, Aberdeen Proving Ground, 1978-90; cons. engr. Proving Ground, 1990—. Author 9 books; Contbr. articles to profl. jours. Recipient Marconi Meml. award Vet. Wireless Operator's Assn., 1982. Fellow IEEE (officer Balt. sect. 1962-66); mem. Am. Def. Preparedness Assn., Assn. U.S. Army, Armed Forces Communications and Electronics Assn. (ex-pres. Aberdeen chpt.), Am. Assn. of Concerned Engrs. (bd. dirs.), Sigma Xi. Episcopalian. Home: 2807 Jerusalem Rd Kingsville MD 21087-1098

PULLEN, PENNY LYNNE, non-profit administrator, former state legislator; b. Buffalo, Mar. 2, 1947; d. John William and Alice Nettie (McConkey) P.; BA in Speech, U. Ill., 1969. TV technician Office Instructional Resources, U. Ill., 1966-68; community newspaper reporter Des Plaines (Ill.) Pub. Co., 1967-72; legislative asst. to Ill. legislators, 1968-77; mem. Ill. Ho. of Reps., 1977-93, chmn. Ho. exec. com., 1981-82, minority whip, 1983-87, asst. minority leader, 1987-93; pres., founder Life Advocacy Resource Project, 1992—; exec. dir. Ill. Family Inst., 1993-94; dir. Legal Svcs. Corp., 1989-93; mem. Pres.'s Commn. on AIDS Epidemic, 1987-88; mem. Ill. Goodwill Del. to Republic of China, 1987. Del. Atlantic Alliance Young

Polit. Leaders, Brussels, 1977, Rep. Nat. Conv, 1984; mem. Republican Nat. Com., 1984-88; summit conf. observer as mem. adhoc Women for SDI, Geneva, 1985; former mem. Maine Twp. Mental Health Assn.; active Nat. Coun. Ednl. Rsch., 1983-88. Recipient George Washington Honor medal Freedoms Found., 1978, Dwight Eisenhower Freedom medal Chgo. Captive Nations Com., 1977, Outstanding Legislator awards Ill. Press Assn., Ill. Podiatry Soc., Ill. Coroners Assn., Ill. County Clks. Assn., Ill. Hosp. Assn., Ill. Health Care Assn.; named Ill. Young Republican, 1968, Outstanding Young Person, Park Ridge Jaycees, 1981, One of 10 Outstanding Young Persons, Ill. Jaycees, 1981. Mem. Am. Legis. Exchange Council (dir. 1977-91, exec. com. 1978-83, 2d vice chmn. 1980-83), DAR. Lodge: Kiwanis.

PULLER, LINDA TODD, state legislator; b. Cedar Rapids, Iowa, Jan. 19, 1945; d. Robert Grant and Margaret Jean (Threlkeld) Todd; m. Lewis Burwell Puller, Apr. 26, 1968; children: Lewis B. III, Margaret Todd. BA in Art History, Mary Washington Coll., 1967. With campaign Moore for Chmn., Fairfax, Va., 1987; adminstrv. aide Chair Bd. Suprs., Fairfax, 1988; polit. cons. Wilder for Gov., 1989; mem. Va. Ho. of Dels., 1992—. Democrat. Episcopalian. Office: VA House of Reps State Capitol Richmond VA 23219

PULLEYBLANK, EDWIN GEORGE, history educator emeritus, linguist; b. Calgary, Alta., Can., Aug. 7, 1922; s. W. George E. and Ruth Elizabeth (Willoughby) P.; m. Winona Ruth Relyea, July 17, 1945 (dec. Jan. 1978); children: David Edwin, Barbara Jill, Marcia Ruth. B.A., U. Alta., 1942; Ph.D., U. London, 1951. Research officer Nat. Research Council, Ottawa, 1943-46; lectr. Sch. Oriental and African studies U. London, 1948-53; prof. Chinese U. Cambridge, 1953-66; prof. Asian studies U. B.C., 1966-87, prof. emeritus, 1988—, head dept., 1966-75; editorial adviser Ency. Brit. Author: The Background of the Rebellion of An Lu-shan, 1955, Middle Chinese, 1984, Lexicon of Reconstructed Pronunciation in Early Middle Chinese, Late Middle Chinese and Early Mandarin, 1991; (with W.G. Beasley) Historians of China and Japan, 1961; contbr. articles to profl. jours. Fellow Royal Soc. Can.; mem. Royal Asiatic Soc. (council 1956-59), Philol. Soc. London (council 1961-66), Assn. Asian Studies (dir. 1969-73), Linguistic Soc. Am., Canadian Soc. Asian Studies (pres. 1971-74), Am. Oriental Soc. (pres. 1990-91). Office: U BC, Dept Asian Studies, Vancouver, BC Canada V6T 1Z1

PULLEYN, S(AMUEL) ROBERT, publishing company executive; b. Milford, Pa., Nov. 18, 1946; s. Samuel Robert and Jeanne (Phillips) P.; m. Kathryn Susan Mathews, June 20, 1971 (div. 1986); 1 child, Micah Marion. B.A., Lake Forest Coll., 1969; postgrad., U. N.Mex., 1971. Dir. New Directions Ctr., Albuquerque, 1971-72; pres. Mediaworks Film Co., Albuquerque, 1972-74; pub. Fiberarts, Albuquerque, 1974-79; pres., pub. Lark Communications Corp., Asheville, N.C., 1979-85, Nine Press, Inc., Asheville, 1985-90, Altamont Press, Asheville, 1988—; adj. instr. U. N.C., Asheville, 1985; lectr. in fields of pub., art and textiles; coord. Small Mags. Pubs. Group, 1983-88. Author: Everlasting Floral Gifts, 1989, Wreaths 'Round the Year, 1990; editor: Fiberarts Design Book, 1980, Fiberarts Design Book II, 1983, The Basketmaker's Art, 1985, The Wreath Book, 1988, Fiberarts Design Book IV, 1990; mem. editorial bd. The Arts Jour., 1985-88; contbr. articles to profl. jours. Bd. dirs. Children's Grammar Sch. Asheville, 1980-84, Beaucatcher Prodns., 1987-90, The Preservation Soc., 1989-92, Planned Parenthood, 1994—. Democrat. Home: Scotton Hills Craine Rd Marshall NC 28753 Office: Altamont Press Inc 50 College St Asheville NC 28801-2818

PULLIAM, BRENDA JANE, secondary school educator; b. Griffin, Ga., Jan. 28, 1941; d. Delmus Lawton and Eva Jane (Cobb) P. BA, Tift Coll., 1963; MA in Teaching, Converse Coll., 1972; EdD, Nova U., 1993; postgrad., U. Toulouse, France. Cert. secondary tchr., Ga. Tchr. French Jonesboro (Ga.) H.S., 1963—, chair fgn. lang. dept., 1970—; co-founder KPS Leadership Specialists, 1993—; correlator Harcourt Brace Jovanovich, 1989; speaker So. Conf. Lang. Teaching, 1993, adv. bd. Contbr. articles to profl. jours.; contbr. ednl. papers to ERIC. Chair citizen exchs. Atlanta-Toulouse Sister Cities, 1987—; tour leader, 1989, 94; interpreter Travelers Aid Met. Atlanta, 1989—. Grantee NDEA, 1963; recipient STAR Tchr. award, 1983. Mem. NEA, Am. Coun. Teaching Fgn. Langs., Am. Assn. Tchrs. French, Ga. Assn. Educators, Fgn. Lang. Assn. Ga., Clayton County Edn. Assn., So. Conf. Lang. Teaching. Baptist. Avocations: piano, traveling, writing, reading, gardening. Home: 9261 Brave Ct Jonesboro GA 30236-5110 Office: Jonesboro High Sch 7728 Mount Zion Blvd Jonesboro GA 30236-5110

PULLIAM, EUGENE SMITH, newspaper publisher; b. Atchison, Kans., Sept. 7, 1914; s. Eugene Collins and Myrta (Smith) P.; m. Jane Bleecker, May 29, 1943; children: Myrta, Russell, Deborah. A.B., DePauw U., 1935, LL.D., 1973. Reporter, UP, Chgo., Detroit, Buffalo, 1935-36; news editor Radio Sta. WIRE, Indpls., 1937-41; city editor Indpls. Star, 1947-48; mng. editor Indpls. News, 1948-62; asst. publisher Indpls. Star and News, 1962-76; pres. Phoenix Newspapers, 1979—; exec. v.p. Central Newspapers, Indpls., 1979—. Mem. Am. Soc. Newspaper Editors, Am. Newspaper Pubs. Assn. Found. (past pres.), Soc. Profl. Journalists, Delta Kappa Epsilon. Club: Crooked Stick Golf. Office: Indpls Star Indpls Newspapers Inc 307 N Pennsylvania St Indianapolis IN 46204-1899 also: Phoenix Newspapers Inc 120 E Van Buren St Phoenix AZ 85004

PULLIAM, FREDERICK CAMERON, educational administrator; b. Mesa, Ariz., Jan. 5, 1936; s. Fredrick Posy and Nathana Laura (Cameron) P.; AA., Hannibal LaGrange Coll., 1955; AB, Grand Canyon Coll., 1958; M.Ed., U. Mo., Columbia, 1966, Ed.S., 1976, EdD, 1981; m. Deborah Jean Botts, June 1, 1979; 1 child, Sarah Elizabeth; children by previous marriage: Cameron Dale, Joy Renee. tchr., Centerview (Mo.) Public Schs., 1958-59; ordained to ministry So. Baptist Conv., 1955; minister Bethel Bapt. Ch., Kansas City, Mo., 1959-61; adminstr. Fiti'uta, Manu'a sch., Am. Samoa, 1966-69; cons. in fin. Mo. State Tchrs. Assn., Columbia, 1969-79; supt. schs. Midway Heights C-VII, Columbia, 1979-83; dir. elem. edn. Brentwood Pub. Schs. (Mo.), 1983-90; founder, coordinator Mo. Computer-Using Educators Conf., 1982-84; contbg. writer St. Louis Computing News, 1984—; adj. asst. prof. ednl. studies U. Mo., St. Louis, 1986-90; assoc. prof. edn. Mo. So. State Coll., 1990—, dir. clinical and field experiences in tchr. edu., Mo. So. State Coll., 1994—; adj. assoc. prof. grad. studies Southwest Baptist Univ., 1991—; cons. sch. fin., curriculum improvement. Mem. Columbia Am. Revolution Bicentennial Commn. Inst. Devel. Ednl. Activity fellow, 1969, 78-84. Mem. Am. Assn. of Colls. for Tchr. Edn., Mo. Assn. Supervision and Curriculum Devel., Nat. Assn. Supervision and Curriculum Devel. (bd. dirs. 1984-90),Mo. Gov's. Transition Team (edn. adv. com. 1992-93), Phi Delta Kappa (chpt. pres.). Contbr. articles to profl. jours. Home: 2140 Kayla Lane Mount Vernon MO 65712-9801 Office: Mo So State Coll 224 Taylor Hall Joplin MO 64801-1595

PULLIAM, HOWARD RONALD, federal agency administrator; b. Miami Beach, Fla., Sept. 7, 1945; s. Joe J. Jr. and Rachel Elizabeth (Miller) P.; m. Janice L. Crowder, June 20, 1969; children: Juliet, Tomlin. BS, U. Ga., 1968; PhD, Duke U., 1969. Asst. prof. U. Ariz., Tucson, 1971-78; rsch. biologist H. S. Colton Rsch. Ctr., Flagstaff, Ariz., 1978-80; assoc. prof. SUNY, Albany, 1980-84; prof. U. Ga., Athens, 1984—, dir. Inst. Ecology, 1987-94; dir. Nat. Biol. Svc., Dept. of the Interior, Washington, 1994—. Author 2 books; contbr. over 60 articles to sci. jours. Bd. dirs. Ga. Conservancy, 1987—. Mem. Ecol. Soc. Am. (v.p. 1986-87, pres. 1991-92), Southeastern U. Rsch. Assn. (v.p. 1990-91). Office: Nat Biol Svc Dept of the Interior Mail Stop 3070 1849 C St NW Washington DC 20240

PULLIAM, RUSSELL BLEECKER, editor, elder; b. Indpls., Sept. 20, 1949; s. Eugene S. and Jane B. Pulliam; m. Ruth Eichling, Nov. 26, 1977; children: Christine, Daniel, John, Sarah, David, Anna. BA, Williams Coll., 1971. Reporter, editor AP, N.Y.C. and Albany, N.Y., 1971-76; editorial writer, columnist Indpls. News, 1978-92, editor, 1992—; deacon Second Reformed Presbyn. Ch., Indpls., 1983-89, elder, 1989—; mem., bd. dirs. Cen. Ind. Radio Reading Inc. Contbr. articles to religious jours. Bd. dirs. Community Outreach Ctr., Noble 'Ctrs. Marion County Assn. for the Mentally Retarded, Indpls., 1984—; participant Stanley K. Lacey Leadership Series, 1980—; mem. adv. bd. Youth as Resources. Recipient Casper award Community Svc. Coun., 1980, 81, 82, 86; 1st place editorial writing Hoosier State Press Assn., 1979, 80, 3d place editorial writing UPI, 1983, 2d and 3d place, 1986; named Sagamore of the Wabash Gov. of Ind., 1980. Mem.

Prison Fellowship, Ind. Assn. for Home Educators, Indpls. C. of C., Soc. Profl. Journalists (treas. Ind. chpt. 1982—, found. bd. 1991—, 2d place editorials and columns 1984, 85, hon. mention editorials 1988, 3d place columns 1989), Nat. Conf. Editorial Writers. Home: 1025 W 52nd St Indianapolis IN 46208-2463 Office: Indpls News 307 N Pennsylvania St Indianapolis IN 46204-1811

PULLING, RONALD WILSON, SR., aviation systems planner, civil engineer, consultant; b. L.A., Oct. 30, 1919; s. Albert Elmer and Mary (Porter) P.; m. Florence Dorothy Rooke, June 24, 1945 (dec.); children: Mary Anna, Ronald Jr. (dec.), William. BSCE, U. Calif., Berkeley, 1940; postgrad., Princeton U., 1963-64; PhD (hon.), Sierra Madre City Coll., 1981. Registered profl. engr., Calif., Fla., Hawaii, Md., Va. Civil engr. CAA, Honolulu, 1943-51; chief facility materials div. CAA, Oklahoma City, 1951-63; chief airport planning div. FAA, Washington, 1964-66, dep. dir. Office of Policy, 1966-68, dep. assoc. adminstr. for plans, 1968-73; sr. v.p. William L. Pereira Assoc., Washington, 1973-74; staff cons. TAMS Cons. Inc., Washington, 1975—; pres. Ronald W. Pulling Assoc., Alexandria, 1976—; v.p. United Global Airlines, Sierra Madre, Calif., 1984—. Author: (with others) Airport Economic Planning, 1971, Airport Planning, 1972; contbr. articles to profl. jours.; corr. Sierra Madro News, 1988-94. Recipient Meritorious Svc. award FAA, 1971, Disting. Career Svc. award, 1973. Fellow ASCE (James Laurie prize 1981); mem. NAE (elected), Transp. Rsch. Bd. (Disting. Svc. award 1984), Am. Planning Assn., Am. Inst. Cert. Planners (cert.), Springfield (Va.) Golf Club, Nat. Aviation Club. Episcopalian. Avocations: golf, creative writing, travel. Home: 4809 Polk Ave Alexandria VA 22304-2257 Office: R W Pulling Assoc PO Box 9526 Alexandria VA 22304-0526

PULLING, THOMAS LEFFINGWELL, investment advisor; b. N.Y.C., May 1, 1939; s. T.J. Edward and Lucy (Leffingwell) P.; m. Lisa Canby, Sept. 14, 1962 (div. 1968); children: Elizabeth, Edward L.; m. Sheila Sonne, Mar. 12, 1970 (div 1980);children: Victoria, Diana, Christopher; m. Eileen Kingsbury-Smith, Dec. 21, 1989. BA cum laude, Princeton U., 1961. Asst. treas. J.P. Morgan & Co. Inc., N.Y.C., 1962-68; v.p. N.Y. Securities Co., N.Y.C., 1968-71, L.M. Rosenthal & Co., N.Y.C., 1971-76; mng. dir. Smith Barney (formerly Shearson Lehman Hutton), N.Y.C., 1977—; CEO Smith Barney Investment ADvisors, 1985—; chmn., CEO Smith Barney Shearson Asset Mgmt., N.Y.C., 1985—. Bd. dirs. Henry Luce Found., 1988—, Met. Opera Assn., 1978—, Woodlawn Cemetery, 1980—, Police Athletic League, N.Y.C., 1985—; trustee South Street Seaport Mus., Long Island U., 1994—. With USMC, 1962-67. Mem. Century Assn., Pilgrims of the U.S. (N.Y.C.), Piping Rock Club (Locust Valley, N.Y.), Surf Club (Miami, Fla.), Univ. Club (N.Y.C.). Republican. Episcopalian. Home: 34 Yellow Cote Rd Oyster Bay NY 11771-4111 Office: Smith Barney 388 Greenwich St New York NY 10013

PULLMAN, BILL, actor; b. Hornell, N.Y., 1954; m. Tamara Pullman, 3 children. Attended, SUNY, Oneonta; MFA, U. Mass., Amherst. co-founder Jam Ctr., Los Angeles; theatre instr. Mo. State Univ., Bozeman. Actor: (theatre) The Rover, 1981, Ah, Wilderness!, 1983, The Old Flag, 1983, Dramathon '84, 1984, Curse of the Starving Class, 1985, All My Sons, 1986, Barabbas, 1986, Nanawatai, 1986, Demon Wine, 1988, (films) Ruthless People, 1986, Spaceballs, 1987, The Serpent and the Rainbow, 1988, Rocket Gibraltar, 1988, The Accidental Tourist, 1989, Cold Feet, 1989, Brain Dead, 1989, Sibling Rivalry, 1990, Going Under, 1991, Bright Angel, 1991, Newsies, 1992, A League of Their Own, 1992, Singles, 1992, Sommersby, 1993, Sleepless in Seattle, 1993, Malice, 1993, Mr. Jones, 1993, The Favor, 1994, Wyatt Earp, 1994, While You Were Sleeping, 1995, Casper, 1995, (TV movies) Home Fires Burning, 1989, Crazy in Love, 1992, The Last Seduction, 1994. Office: UTA 9560 Wilshire Blvd 5th Fl Beverly Hills CA 90212*

PULLMAN, MAYNARD EDWARD, biochemist; b. Chgo., Oct. 26, 1927; s. Harry and Gertrude (Atlas) P.; m. E. Phyllis Light, Sept. 12, 1948; children: H. Cydney, B. Valerie, Jacky Leigh. B.S., U. Ill., 1948, M.S., 1950; Ph.D. (NIH fellow), Johns Hopkins U., 1953. Fellow in pediatrics Johns Hopkins Hosp., 1953-54; asst. Pub. Health Rsch. Inst., City N.Y., 1954-56; assoc. Pub. Health Rsch. Inst., 1956-61, assoc. mem., 1961-65, mem., 1965-89, chief, 1973-87, assoc. dir., 1983-89; sr. rsch. scientist Coll. Physicians and Surgeons Columbia U., 1989-92; vis. prof. biochemistry U. São Paulo (Brazil) Sch. Medicine, 1963-64; research assoc. prof. biochemistry Sch. Medicine NYU, 1966-76, research prof., 1976-90; biochemistry study section mem. NIH, 1969-73. Editorial bd.: Jour. Biol. Chemistry, 1967-71, 78-80. NIH grantee, 1956-85; Shubert Found. grantee, 1972-74. Fellow N.Y. Acad. Scis.; mem. AAAS, Am. Soc. Biol. Chemistry and Molecular Biology, Brit. Biochem. Soc., Am. Chem. Soc. Home and Office: 338 Archer St Freeport NY 11520-4233

PULOS, ARTHUR JON, industrial design executive; b. Vandergrift, Pa., Feb. 3, 1917; s. John and Argyro (Tsakalos) Palukakos; m. Elizabeth Jane McQueen, Jan. 28, 1944; children—Cristofer, Maria, Demetra. B.F.A., Carnegie Inst. Tech., 1939; M.F.A., U. Oreg., 1943. Teaching asst. design and crafts U. Oreg. at Eugene, 1939-41; assoc. prof. design U. Ill., 1946-55; prof., chmn. dept. design Syracuse (N.Y.) U., 1955-82, prof. emeritus, 1982—; pres. Pulos Design Assos., Syracuse, 1958-87; Mem. planning council Expo 67, Montreal, Can., Fed. Design Assembly, 1974, Am. Design Bicentennial, 1974-75; mem. policy panel for architecture, planning and design Nat. Endowment for Arts, 1978—; cons. Colonial Williamsburg; lectr. in, USSR, Romania, Pakistan, Japan Ministry of Internat. Trade and Industry, others for UNESCO, USIA. Author: Careers in Industrial Design, 1978, Contact-Selling Design Services, 1975, American Design Ethic, 1983, The American Design Adventure, 1988; contbr. articles in design and design edn. to profl. jours. Bd. dirs. Everson Mus. Art, Syracuse, 1983—; mem. Budapest Cultural Forum, 1985. Served to 1st Lt. USAF, 1944-46. Ford Found. fellow; Nat Endowment Arts fellow, 1984; Graham Found. grantee, 1987; recipient Chancellor's citation Syracuse U., 1982; Bronze Apple award, N.Y.C., 1983, Worldesign award, N.Y.C., 1988, Misha Black Meml. medal for design edn. Royal Soc. Arts, London, 1993. Fellow Indsl. Design Soc. Am. (pres. 1973-74; Disting. Educator award 1988), Internat. Council Socs. Indsl. Design (pres. 1980-81, senator 1982—, keynote speaker ICSID Congress in Japan 1989), Am. Steel Inst. (juror, cons.), Design Inst. Australia (hon.), Mexican Acad. Design (hon.) Japan Design Fedn. Internat. Competition (chmn. Jury, Osaka 1983), Alpha Rho Chi, Alpha Zi Alpha. Unitarian. Home: 3 The Orch Fayetteville NY 13066

PUMERANTZ, PHILIP, medical school president; m. Harriet Krinsky; children: Andrew, Beth, Richard. BA in History and Edn., U. Conn., 1959, MA, 1963, PhD in Edn., 1967; postgrad., Wesleyan U.; LHD (hon.), Coll. of Osteo. Medicine. Prof. edn. U. Bridgeport, Conn., co-founder Coll. Continuing Edn.; pvt. mgmt. cons.; nat. dir. edn. Am. Osteopathic Assn., Chgo.; founding pres. Coll. of Osteo. Medicine of the Pacific, Pomona, Calif.; co-founder Caribbean U., P.R.; Andrew Taylor Still Meml. lectr. Am. Osteo. Assn. Ho. of Dels. 1989. Founder, editor ednl. jours.; co-author coll. textbooks in field of edn.; contbr. numerous articles to profl. jours. Mem. gov. bd. Unquowa Prep. Sch., Fairfield, Conn., Park Ave. Hosp., Pomona, Hollywood Comty. Hosp., L.A., Mt. Baldy coun. Boy Scouts Am., Pomona Red Cross, Pomona Econ. Devel. Corp., Nat. Coun. on Specialized Accrediting Agys., Nat. Def. U. Found., Washington; mem. corp. bd. Nu-Med Hosp. Corp., Encino, Calif.; past chmn. univs. and colls. divsn. Mt. Baldy region United Way. Recipient Proclamation by the City of Pomony, Eby Humnanitarian award Osteo. Physicians and Surgeons of Calif., Maimonides award State of Israel, Disting. Alumni award U. of Conn.; numerous commendations and recognitions Pomona City Coun.; named Humanitarian of Yr., Pomona Hispanic Youth Task Force. Mem. Am. Assn. of Colls. of Osteo. Medicine (chmn. bd. govs.), Pomona C. of C. (past pres., mem. gov. bd.), Rotary Club of Pomona, Univ. Club Claremont, Phi Delta Kappa, Kappa Delta Pi, Phi Alpha Theta. Office: Coll of Osteo Medicine Office of President 309 E College Plz Pomona CA 91766-1889

PUMPER, ROBERT WILLIAM, microbiologist; b. Clinton, Iowa, Sept. 12, 1921; s. William R. and Kathrine M. (Anderson) P.; m. Ruth J. Larkin, June 24, 1951; 1 son. Mark. B.A., U. Iowa, 1951, M.S., 1953, Ph.D., 1955. Diplomate: Am. Soc. Microbiology. Asst. prof. Hahnemann Med. Coll., Phila., 1955-57; prof. microbiology U. Ill. Med. Sch., Chgo., 1957—; Raymond B. Allen Med. lectr., 1970, 74, 76, 87. Co-author: Essentials of Medical Virology; contbr. articles to profl. jours. Served with USAAF, 1942-46. Recipient Chancellors' award U. Ill., Bombeck award for excellence in med. edns., 1992. Mem. Tissue Culture Assn., Sigma Xi, Phi Rho Sigma. Lutheran. Home: 18417 Argyle Ave Homewood IL 60430-3007 Office: U Ill Med Sch Dept Microbiology 808 S Wood St Chicago IL 60612-7300

PUOTINEN, ARTHUR EDWIN, college president, clergyman; b. Crystal Falls, Mich., Sept. 7, 1941; s. Kaleva Weikko and Ines Pauline (Maki) P.; m. Judith Cathleen Kapoun, Aug. 8, 1964; children: Anne, Marjetta, Sara. AA, Suomi Coll., 1961; BA, Augustana Coll., Rock Island, Ill., 1963; MDiv, Luth. Sch. Theology, Chgo., 1967; MA, U. Chgo., 1969, PhD, 1973; MBA, Wake Forest U., 1984. Pastor Trinity Luth. Ch., Chgo., 1968-70; asst. prof. religion Cen. Mich. U., Mt. Pleasant, 1971-74; dean faculty Suomi Coll., Hancock, Mich., 1974-78; v.p. acad. affairs Lenoir-Rhyne Coll., Hickory, N.C., 1978-83; assoc. dean acad. affairs Roanoke Coll., Salem, Va., 1983-84; exec. dir. Luth. Ednl. Conf. of N.Am., Washington, 1984-88; pres. Grand View Coll., Des Moines, 1988—; dir. Iowa Luth. Hosp., Des Moines, 1989—; pastor S.E. Iowa Synod, Evang.-Luth. Ch. Am. Author: Finnish Radicals..., 1979; contbr. articles to books and jours. Grantee NEH, U.S. Dept. Edn. Mem. Des Moines Club, Pioneer Club, Rotary. Democrat. Avocations: jogging, reading, travel. Home: 528 Valley West Ct West Des Moines IA 50265-4047 Office: Grand View Coll 1200 Grandview Ave Des Moines IA 50316-1599

PURAVS, JOHN ANDRIS, journalist; b. Ruckersdorf, Fed. Republic Germany, Feb. 23, 1945; s. Janis Alfreds and Alma Otilija (Grundulis) P.; m. Trudi Ann Tiedeman, July 2, 1966 (div. Feb. 1982). BA, U. Mich., 1966. Reporter Saginaw (Mich.) News, 1966-78, suburban editor, 1978-79, editorial editor, 1979—, chmn. editorial bd., 1981—; commentator Sta. WUCM-TV, Univ. Ctr., Mich. Contbr. articles to profl. jours. Mem. adv. bd. Saginaw State Valley State U. Coll. Edn., 1991—. 1st lt. U.S. Army, 1967-69, Vietnam. Fellow Northwestern U., 1970; Regents-Alumni scholar Chgo. House Coun. Mem. Soc. Profl. Journalists, Am. Coun. on Germany (fellow 1980, Haus Rissen fellow 1982), Saginaw Valley Press Club (pres. 1976), Nat. Conf. Editorial Writers (group chmn. 1991), Latvian Club Saginaw. Avocations: sports, history, politics. Home: 3925 Cabaret Trl W Apt 4 Saginaw MI 48603-2205 Office: Saginaw News 203 S Washington Ave Saginaw MI 48607-1283

PURCELL, ALEXANDER HOLMES, entomologist, educator; b. Summit, Miss., Oct. 12, 1942; s. Alexander H. and Dorothy (Adams) P.; m. Rita Hall, Oct. 14, 1946. BS, USAF Acad., 1964; PhD, U. Calif., Davis, 1974. Commd. capt. USAF, 1964, officer, pilot, 1964-70, resigned, 1970; grad. rsch. asst. U. Calif., Davis, 1971-74; prof. entomology U. Calif, Berkeley, 1974—, dept. chair, 1993, head div. entomology and plant and soil microbiology, 1994, head divsn. environ. biology dept. environ. sci., policy and mgmt.; cons. FAO (UN), 1981. Contbr. articles to profl. jours. Mem. AAAS, Entomological Soc. Am., Am. Phytopath. Soc., Soc. Invertebrate Pathology. Avocations: flying, camping. Office: U Calif Dept Environ Sci and Policy and Mgmt 201 Wellman Hall Berkeley CA 94720-3112

PURCELL, ANN RUSHING, state legislator, office manager medical business; b. Reidsville, Ga., May 12, 1945; d. William Robert and Katie (Dasher) Rushing; m. Dent Wiley Purcell, May 26, 1966; children: Edwin Wiley, Mieke Ann, Mikki Marie. BS in Edn., Ga. So. Coll., 1966. Cert. secondary tchr. Tchr. math. Evans (Ga.) High Sch., 1966-68; tchr. math., earth and sci. Beaumont Jr. High Sch., Lexington, Ky., 1969-70; substitute tchr. Tallahassee, Fla., 1970's; agt. Noblin Realty, Tallahassee, 1970's; office mgr. Radiation Therapy Assocs., PC, Savannah, Ga., 1979—; state legislator Ho. of Reps. Ga. Gen. Assembly, Atlanta, 1991—. Author: Purcells of South Georgia and Other Related Families, 1976. Bd. dirs. Med. Assn. Ga. Polit. Action Com., Atlanta, 1988-89, Girl Scout Coun. Savannah, 1991—, Ga. So. U. Found., 1992—; mem. adv. com. Effingham County Extension Svc., 1992—; fin. chmn. State YMCA, 1991—; bd. adv. Claxton Youth Detnetion Ctr. Recipient Friend of Medicine award Med. Assn. Ga., 1991, 93, 94, Guardian of Small Bus. award Nat. Fedn. Ind. Bus., 1992, 94, Commendation cert. Ga. Emergency Mgmt. Agy., 1995. Mem. Aux. to the Med. Assn. Ga. (pres. 1985), Aux. to the Ga. Med. Soc. (pres. 1981-82), Ga. Salzburger Soc., Effingham County Pub. Officials Assn., Rotary Internat. Democrat. Methodist. Avocations: painting, genealogy, fishing. Home: 410 Willowpeg Way Rincon GA 31326-1295 Office: State Capitol Ste 401 Atlanta GA 30334

PURCELL, ARTHUR HENRY, environmental engineering educator, consultant; b. Evanston, Ill., Aug. 11, 1944; s. Edward and Ethel (Lohman) P.; m. Deborah Ross Purcell, Feb. 2, 1973; 1 child:Christina Jean Ethel. B.S., Cornell U., 1966; M.S., Northwestern U., 1971, Ph.D., 1972. Environmentalist U.S. Army Environ. Office, 1971; assoc. dir. office of sci. and govt. AAAS, 1973-74; co-founder, dir. Resource Policy Inst., Washington, 1975—; assoc. professorial lectr. dept. civil, mech. and environ. engring. George Washington U., 1975-89; professorial lectr. Ctr. for Tech. and Adminstrn., Am. U., 1980-81; cons. engr., 1974—; staff prin. Pres.'s Commn. on Accident at Three Mile Island, 1979; chmn. D.C. Adv. Neighborhood Commn., 1981-84, 86—; spl. cons. Econ. Commn. for Europe, 1982—; lectr. USIA, Europe, 1982, 90; vis. scientist Hazardous Substances Control Rsch. Ctr. UCLA, 1989; assoc. prof., lectr. environ. mgmt. U. Soc. Calif., West Coast U.; chmn. First Internat. Conf. on Waste Minimization and Clean Tech., Geneva, 1989; keynote lectr. Envirotech '90, Vienna, Austria, 1990, EC/Finnish Rsch. Inst. series on setting priorities in environ. mgmt., Finland, 1992, Italy, 1993; sr. environ. engr. Jacobs Engring. Group, 1991; chmn. Pollution Prevention Tech. Conf., L.A., 1994; mem. environ. mgmt. faculty West Coast U., 1994—. Contbr. publs. and lectrs. on resource policy, materials research and sci. and tech. policy to popular and profl. jours.; author: The Waste Watchers, 1980; contbg. travel writer Washington Post and others; editorial bd. Resources Policy. Chmn. Scientist and Engrs. for Carter, 1976-77; mem. Jimmy Carter Sci. Policy Task Force, 1976, Pres.'s Commn. on Scholars, 1978—; sr. adviser sci. Mondale-Ferraro campaign, 1984; mem. Environmentalists for Pete Wilson, 1990. Recipient Environ. Program award Friends of UNEP, 1988; German Marshall Fund Travel award scholar, 1980, 82. Mem. World Coun. for Biosphere, Sigma Xi. Democrat. Office: 1745 Selby Ave No 11 Los Angeles CA 90024-5774 *We are all environmentalists. We have to be. So we are all part of the solution to solving the world's ecological dilemmas. Let's get on with the job.*

PURCELL, BRADFORD MOORE, publishing company executive; b. Garden City, N.Y., Oct. 1, 1929; s. William Lawrence and Margaret (Moore) P.; m. Louise Rauth, July 10, 1954; children: Margaret, Philip, Mark, Louisa, Christopher. B.A., Williams Coll., 1951; M.B.A., Columbia U., 1957. Sr. v.p. devel. McGraw Hill, Inc., 1976-79; sr. v.p., 1979-81, group v.p. tng. systems, 1981-83, sr. v.p. mktg., 1983-85; pres. W.H. Smith Pubs Inc., N.Y.C., 1985-91; Rsch. Books Inc., 1992. Served to 1st lt. USAF, 1951-53. Home: RR 3 128 Sarles St Bedford Corners NY 10549-9803 Office: Rsch Books Inc 38 Academy St Box 1507 Madison CT 06443

PURCELL, DALE, college administrator, consultant; b. Baxley, Ga., Oct. 20, 1919; s. John Groce and Agnes (Moody) P.; m. Edna Jean Rowell, Aug. 2, 1944; children: David Scott, Steven Dale, Pamela Jean; m. Mary Louise Gerlinger, Aug. 26, 1962; adopted children: Amelia Allerton, Jon Allerton. B.A., U. Redlands, 1948, M.A., 1949; postgrad., Northwestern U., 1951-52; LL.D., Lindenwood Colls., 1974. Topographer U.S. E.D., 1939; U.S. counter-intelligence agt., 1940-42; assoc. prof. Ottawa U., 1953-54, asst. to pres., 1954-58; gen. sec. Earlham Coll., 1958-61; dir. devel. U. So. Fla., 1961-63; pres. MITAC, Inc., Beverly Hills, Calif., 1961-72; exec. dir. Cancer Research Center, Columbia, Mo., 1963-65; pres. Dale Purcell Assocs., 1972-92, Westminster Coll., Fulton, Mo., 1973-76; founding dir. Am. Sports Medicine Inst., Birmingham, Ala., 1987-92; chmn. Corp. Health Solutions, Arlington, Tex., 1988—; cons. Hughston Sports Medicine Found. Columbus, Ga., Berry Coll., Mt. Berry, Ga., Hope Coll., Holland, Mich., William Woods Coll., Fulton, Mo., Eureka (Ill.) Coll., Brescia Coll., Owensboro, Ky., Cranbrook Insts., Bloomfield Hills, Mich., Penrose Hosp., Colorado Springs, Colo., Northwestern Coll., Orange City, Iowa, Centro Medico Docente, Caracas, Venezuela, Wayland Acad., Beaver Dam, Wis., Cen. Coll., Pella, Iowa, U. Stirling, Scotland, U. Ottawa, Ont., Can., Washington & Lee U., Lexington, Va., Taylor U., Upland, Ind., Menninger Found., Topeka, Kans., Ill. Wesleyan U., Bloomington, Cox Med. Ctr., Springfield, Mo., Nat. Council Family Rels. Mpls., Albert Schweitzer Ctr., Great Barrington, Mass., Stephens Coll., Columbia, Mo., Hist. Savannah

Found., Ga. Served to capt. USMCR, 1942-46, 52-53. Recipient Disting. Achievement award Berry Coll., 1974, medal Pres. of China, 1945, medal Pres. of Korea, 1953. Mem. Pi Kappa Delta (Alpha chpt.). Presbyn. (elder 1964—). Clubs: HousaTonics, (Salisbury, Conn.), St. Louis (Clayton), Univ. (St. Louis and N.Y.C.), Litchfield Country. Home: Woodlands 120 Belden St Falls Village CT 06031-1112

PURCELL, EDWARD MILLS, physics educator; b. Taylorville, Ill., Aug. 30, 1912; s. Edward A. and Mary Elizabeth (Mills) P.; m. Beth C. Busser, Jan. 22, 1937; children: Dennis W., Frank B. B.S. in Elec. Engring. Purdue U., 1933, D. Engring. (hon.), 1953; Internat. Exchange student, Technische Hochschule, Karlsruhe, Germany, 1933-34; A.M., Harvard U., 1935, Ph.D., 1938. Instr. physics Harvard U., 1938-40, asso. prof., 1946-49, prof. physics, 1949-58, Donner prof. sci., 1958-60, Gerhard Gade Univ. prof., 1960-80, emeritus, 1980—; sr. fellow Soc. of Fellows, 1949-71; group leader Radiation Lab., MIT, 1941-45. Contbg. author: Radiation Lab. series, 1949, Berkeley Physics Course, 1965; contbr. sci. papers on nuclear magnetism, radio astronomy, astrophysics, biophysics. Mem. Pres.'s Sci. Advisory Com., 1957-60, 62-65. Co-winner Nobel prize in Physics, 1952; recipient Oersted medal Am. Assn. Physics Tchrs., 1968, Nat. Medal of Sci., 1980, Harvard medal 1986. Mem. NAS, Am. Philos. Soc., Am. Phys. Soc., Am. Acad. Arts and Scis., Royal Soc. (fgn. mem.). Office: Harvard U Lyman Lab Cambridge MA 02138*

PURCELL, JAMES FRANCIS, consultant, former utility executive; b. Miles City, Mont., May 13, 1920; s. Robert E. and Mary A. (Hickey) P.; m. Dorothy Marie Abel, Nov. 4, 1944; children—Angela, Ann, Alicia, Anita, Alanna, James Francis, Andrea, Adria, Michael, Gregory, Amara. A.B. magna cum laude, U. Notre Dame, 1942; MBA, Harvard U., 1943. With McGraw-Hill Pub. Co., N.Y.C., 1946-48; dir. public relations Am. Maize Products Co., N.Y.C. 1948-51; public relations cons. Selvage & Lee, Chgo., 1951-53; with No. Ind. Public Service Co., Hammond, 1953—, v.p. public relations, 1961-75, sr. v.p., 1975-84, bd. dirs., chmn. environ. and consumer affairs com.; owner, pres. James F. Purcell and Assocs., 1984—. Chmn. bd. govs. Our Lady of Mercy Hosp., Dyer, Ind., 1979-83; past chmn. Hammond Community Chest drive; past mem. nat. president's council St. Mary's (Ind.) Coll.; bd. dirs. Catholic Charities, 1965-83; chmn. bd. dirs. Bishop Noll Found., 1988-90. Served to lt. USNR, 1943-46. Named Man of Year Notre Dame U., 1967. Mem. Pub. Rels. Soc. Am. (past pres. Hoosier chpt.), N.W. Ind. Assn. Commerce and Industry (v.p., dir. 1979-83), Newcomen Soc. N. Am., Briar Ridge Country Club (Schererville), Serra Club (past pres. Calumet region), Notre Dame Club, Harvard U. Bus. Sch. Club of Chgo. Office: 2842 45th Ave Highland IN 46322

PURCELL, JAMES LAWRENCE, lawyer; b. Wilkes-Barre, Pa., July 29, 1929; s. Joseph Ligouri and Mary Theresa (Walter) P.; m. Mary Louise Gallagher, Nov. 22, 1956 (dec. 1968); children: Joseph, Joan, James Lawrence, Catherine; m. Regina M. Bligh, May 31, 1971; 1 son, Daniel. Student, King's Coll., 1947-49; LL.B., St. John's U., 1952; LL.M., NYU, 1955. Bar: N.Y. 1953, U.S. Ct. Appeals (2d cir.) 1953, U.S. Tax Ct. 1954, U.S. Supreme Ct. 1956, U.S. Dist. Ct. (so. and ea. dists.) N.Y. 1957, D.C. 1970. Assoc. Dewey, Ballantine, Bushby, Palmer & Wood (and predecessor firms), N.Y.C., 1952-55, Crisona Bros., N.Y.C., 1955-58, Paul, Weiss, Rifkind, Wharton & Garrison, N.Y.C., 1958-64; ptnr. Paul, Weiss, Rifkind, Wharton & Garrison, 1964—; mem. bd. advs. Nat. Ctr. for Paralegal Tng., N.Y.C., 1978—. Bd. dirs. King's Coll., Wilkes-Barre, Pa., 1977—. Fellow Am. Bar Found.; mem. ABA, Assn. Bar City N.Y., Cath. Lawyers Guild Diocese N.Y., Nassau County Bar Assn. Roman Catholic. Office: Paul Weiss Rifkind Wharton & Garrison 1285 Ave Of The Americas New York NY 10019-6064

PURCELL, JAMES NELSON, JR., international organization administrator; b. Nashville, July 16, 1938; s. James Nelson and Mary Helen P.; m. Walda Jean Primm, July 16, 1961; children: Deirdre Ann, Carole Elizabeth. BA in Polit. Sci., Furman U., 1961; M.P.A. (Maxwell Grad. Sch. fellow), Syracuse U., 1962. Mgmt. intern U.S. AEC, N.Y.C., Washington, Oak Ridge, 1962; budget analyst U.S. AEC, Oak Ridge, Washington, 1962-66; mgmt. analyst AID, State Dept., Washington, 1966-68; budget preparation specialist Office Mgmt. and Budget/Exec. Office of the Pres., 1968-69, dept. chief budget preparation, 1969-72; sr. budget examiner Internat. Ednl. Exch. program Office of Pres., 1972-74; chief Justice-Treasury br. Office Mgmt. and Budget/Exec. Office of the Pres., 1974-76; chief resources programming and mgmt. div. Bur. Ednl. and Cultural Affairs, Dept. State, Washington, 1976-77; exec. dir. Bur. Adminstrn., Dept. State, Washington, 1978-79; dep. asst. sec. Bur. Refugee Programs, Dept. State, Washington, 1979-82, dir., 1982-87; dir. gen. Internat. Orgn. for Migration, Geneva, 1988—. Mem. Am. Soc. Pub. Adminstrn. Home: 6 Chateau-Banquet, CH-1202 Geneva Switzerland Office: IOM / Case postale 71, 17 Rt des Morillons, 1211 Geneva Switzerland

PURCELL, JOHN R., holding company executive. Sr. v.p. fin. Gannett Co. Inc., 1968-77; exec. v.p. CBS, 1977-81; chmn. bd., CEO SFN Cos., Inc., 1982-86; pres. DM Holdings, Stamford, Conn., 1991—. Office: DM Holdings Inc 70 Seaview Ave Stamford CT 06902*

PURCELL, KENNETH, psychology educator, university dean; b. N.Y.C., Oct. 21, 1928; s. Herman and Ann (Bulkin) P.; m. Claire Dickson Kepler, Dec. 17, 1949 (div. Dec. 1986); children: Kathleen Ann, Andrew Kepler; m. Marjorie Bayes, Jan. 17, 1987. B.A., Ph.D., U. Nebr. Asst. prof. U. Ky., 1956-58; dir. behavior sci. div. Children's Asthma Research Inst.; asst. prof. U. Colo. Med. Center, 1958-68; prof., dir. clin. tng. psychology U. Mass., 1968-69, chmn. dept. psychology, 1969-70; prof. psychology, chmn. dept. U. Denver, 1970—, dean Coll. Arts and Scis., 1976-84, prof. psychology, 1984—. Author papers in field. Served to 2d lt. AUS, 1953-56. Fellow Am. Psychol. Assn., Soc. Research Child Devel., AAAS, Colo. Psychol. Assn. (dir. 1962-64). Home: 3759 E Noble Rd Littleton CO 80122-2042 Office: Univ Denver Coll Arts And Scis Denver CO 80208

PURCELL, LEE, actress; b. N.C., June 15, 1953; m. Gary A. Lowe; 1 child, Gary; 1 stepchild. Student, Royal Acad. Dramatic Art; studies with Margot Lister, Milton Katselas, Jeff Corey, Robert F. Lyons. Appeared in (films) Adam at 6 A.M., 1970, The Toy Factory, 1971, Dirty Little Billy, 1972, Kid Blue, 1973, Mr. Majestyk, 1974, Almost Summer, 1978, Stir Crazy, 1980, Valley Girl, Eddie Macon's Run, 1983, Laura's Dream, 1986, (TV) Highjack, 1973, Stranger in Our House, 1978, Kenny Rogers as the Gambler, 1980, Killing at Hell's Gate, 1981, Magnum P.I., Murder, She Wrote, 1985, My Wicked Wicked Ways: The Legend of Errol Flynn, 1986, Secret Sins of the Father, 1994 (Emmy nomination, Supporting Actress - Special, 1994), (stage) Richard III, A Streetcar Named Desire, The Taming of the Shrew, A Midsummer Night's Dream. Recipient Bronze Halo Career Achievement award So. Calif. Motion Picture Council, 1985. Mem. Actors' Equity Assn., Screen Actors Guild, AFTRA, Acad. Motion Picture Arts and Scis., Acad. TV Arts And Scis. Avocations: writing, collecting antiques and music boxes. Office: The Artists Group 1930 Century Park W Suite 403 Los Angeles CA 90067*

PURCELL, NANCY LOU, alcohol/drug abuse services executive; b. Reading, Pa., Nov. 26, 1934; d. Russel Louis Button and Helen Geneve (Wichrowski) Shuker; m. John Joseph Crimmins, Dec. 19, 1953; (div. 1982) children: John B. Crimmins, Mark A. Crimmins, Cathy A. Crimmins; m. Grant S. Purcell, May 20, 1989. Sec. US Navy, NH Security Agy., Wash., 1952-55, Harvard U., Cambridge, Mass., 1956-58; personnel mgr. 3B's Corp., Columbia, S.C., 1972-75; mgr., buyer Card N Such, Columbia, S.C.; mgr., trainer Casual Corner, Columbia, 1979-82; dist. mgr. Casual Corner, 1982-85; co-owner, buyer Grant Purcell, Hilton Head, S.C., 1985-89; wardrobe cons., pvt. practice Charleston, S.C., 1981-89; v.p., co-owner Charleston (S.C.) Ctr. for Relapse Prevention, 1992—; dir. mktg. Fenwick Hall Hosp., 1990-91; cons. S. Bell Mktg. SCN Bank, Bankers Trust Bob Capes Realty, Christian Women's Assn, Profl. Women's Club, Columbia, 1981-89. Mem. Nat. Orgn. for Women, Christian Women, Bus. Profl. Women. Democrat. Protestant. Avocations: writing prose & poetry, water colors, travel. Office: Charleston Ctr Relapse Prevention 125G Wappoo Creek Dr Charleston SC 29412

PURCELL, PATRICK B., motion picture company executive; b. Dublin, Ireland, Mar. 16, 1943; s. James P. and Rita (Donohoe) P.; m. Simone Gros-Long, Feb. 1, 1968; children: Alexander J., Christopher P., Benjamin J. Student, Staffordshire Coll. Commerce, 1964-66; M.B.A., Fordham U., 1973. CPA. Various positions in pub. and pvt. acctg. Eng. and U.S., 1960-70; with Paramount Pictures Corp., N.Y.C., Los Angeles, 1970—, v.p. fin., 1980—83, exec. v.p. fin. and adminstrn., 1983-89, exec. v.p., chief fin. and adminstrv. officer, 1989—. Fellow AICPA, Calif. Soc. CPAs, Chartered Assn. Cert. Accts.; mem. Fin. Execs. Inst., Inst. Taxation. Roman Catholic. Club: Jonathan. Home: 1449 Capri Dr Pacific Palisades CA 90272-2706 Office: Paramount Pictures 5555 Melrose Ave Pacific Palisades CA 90272

PURCELL, PATRICK JOSEPH, newspaper publisher; b. N.Y.C., Nov. 9, 1947; s. Patrick Joseph and Sarah (Muller) P.; m. Maureen T. Shuart, Aug. 8, 1970; children: Erin, Patrick, Kerry. B.B.A., St. John's U., 1969; M.B.A., Hofstra U., 1977. Various supr. positions N.Y. Daily News, N.Y.C., 1969-80; assoc. Village Voice, N.Y.C., 1980-82; v.p. advt. N.Y. Post, N.Y.C., 1982-83; v.p. sales and mktg. Skyband Inc., N.Y.C., 1983; pres., pub. Boston Herald, 1984—; pub. The N.Y. Post, 1986-88; exec. v.p. News Am./Newspapers, 1986-90, pres., 1990-93, chief exec. officer, 1993-94; bd. dirs. BayBank Middlesex, The Genesis Fund. bd. dirs. NCCJ, Boston, 1984-86, Boy Scouts Am., Boston 1984-85 (v.p. communications), Cath. Charitable Bur., Boston, 1984-86, John F. Kennedy Found.; mem. Greater Boston Assn. Retarded Citizens, 1984-86; chmn. of Boston Against Drugs, 1988—, mem. White House Conf. for a Drug Free Am., 1987—. Mem. Boston Better Bus. Bur., Am. Newspaper Pub. Assn., New Eng. Newspaper Assn., Boston C. of C. (bd. dirs. 1984-86), Downtown Crossing Assn. (bd. dirs.). Roman Catholic. Clubs: Publicity, Ad (Boston). Avocations: jogging, skiing. Office: Boston Herald 1 Herald Sq Boston MA 02118-2297*

PURCELL, PHILIP JAMES, financial services company executive; b. Salt Lake City, Sept. 5, 1943; m. Anne Marie Mc Namara, Apr. 2, 1964. B.B.A., U. Notre Dame, 1964; M.sc. in Econs., London Sch. Econs. and Polit. Sci., U. London, 1966; M.B.A., U. Chgo., 1967. Mng. dir., cons. McKinsey & Co., Inc., Chgo., 1967-78; v.p. planning and adminstrn. Sears, Roebuck and Co., Chgo., 1978-82; from pres., CEO, to chmn., CEO Dean Witter Discover & Co., N.Y.C., 1982—; also bd. dirs. Dean Witter InterCapital Inc., N.Y.C.; bd. dirs. Dean Witter Realty Inc., Dean Witter Reynolds, Inc., N.Y. Stock Exchange, SPS Payment Systems Inc., Transaction Svcs. Inc.; mem. coun. Grad. Sch. Bus., Univ. Chgo.; chmn. Discover Card Svcs. Inc.; chmn., CEO Novus Credit Svcs. Inc. Bd. trustees U. Notre Dame Bus. Sch., Ind. Served with USNR. Roman Catholic. Clubs: Economic of Chgo., The Chgo. Office: Dean Witter Reynolds/Discover & Co Ste 9650 2921 N Leisure World Blvd Silver Spring MD 20906-1372*

PURCELL, RICHARD FICK, lawyer, food companies advisor and counsel; b. Washington, Apr. 19, 1924; s. Richard J. and Clara A. (Fick) P.; m. Judith Wyckoff, Nov. 28, 1964; children: Richard Wyckoff, Edward Thomas, Carolyn Elizabeth P. Reichenbach. B.A., George Washington U., 1948; M.A., Columbia U., 1949; cert., U. Fribourg (Switzerland), 1949; LL.B., Harvard U., 1952; grad., Command and Gen. Staff Coll., Ft. Leavenworth, Kans., 1970, Indsl. Coll. Armed Forces, 1971. Bar: D.C. 1953, Mass. 1953, Minn. 1953, N.Y. 1954, U.S. Ct. Appeals (D.C. and 2d cirs.) 1954, U.S. Dist. Ct. D.C. 1954, U.S. Dist. Ct. (so. and ea. dists.) N.Y. 1954, U.S. Ct. Mil. Appeals 1954, U.S. Supreme Ct. 1963. Assoc. Shearman & Sterling, N.Y.C., 1954-74; v.p., dep. gen. counsel 1st Nat. City Bank (now Citibank N.A.), N.Y.C., 1974-75; sr. v.p., gen. counsel The Connell Co. and related cos., Westfield, N.J., 1975-93; food co. cons. and counsel, 1993—; bd. dirs. Combined Life Ins. Co., N.Y. Author: Government Administration of Wage Incentives in Wartime, 1949, Church and State in Colonial Connecticut, 1953; contbr. to Cath. Ency., legal and banking jours.; law editor (Banking Law Jour.), 1965-67; mem. adv. bd. Letter of Credit Update, 1987—. Lt. col. F.A., U.S. Army, 1943-46, 52-53, PTO, ETO. Mem. ABA (task force on study and revision of UCC Article 5), D.C. Bar Assn., Minn. Territorial Pioneers, Mil. Order of World Wars, Army and Navy Club (Washington), Harvard Club (N.Y.C.). Republican. Roman Catholic. Office: Box 257 Oldwick NJ 08858

PURCELL, ROBERT HARRY, virologist; b. Keokuk, Iowa, Dec. 19, 1935; s. Edward Harold and Elsie Thelma (Melzl) P.; m. Carol Joan Moody, June 11, 1961; children: David Edward, John Leslie. BA in Chemistry, Okla. State U., 1957; MS Biochemistry, Baylor U., 1960; MD, Duke U., 1962. Intern in pediatrics Duke U. Hosp., Durham, N.C., 1962-63; officer USPHS, 1963, advanced through grades to med. dir. (O-6), 1974; with Epidemic Intelligence Svc., Communicable Disease Ctr. Atlanta; assigned to vaccine br. Nat. Inst. Allergy and Infectious Diseases, Bethesda, Md., 1963-65; sr. surgeon Lab. Infectious Diseases, NIH, Bethesda, Md., 1965-69, med. officer, 1969-72, med. dir., 1972-74, head hepatitis viruses sect., 1974—; organizer, invited participant, speaker numerous nat. and internat. symposia, confs., workshops, meetings; temporary advisor WHO, 1967—; expert cons. in hepatitis U.S.—China, U.S.—Taiwan, U.S.—Japan, U.S.—Russia, U.S.—India, U.S.—Pakistan Bilateral Sci. Agreements; lectr. various virology classes. Mem. editl. bd. and/or reviewer Am. Jour. Epidemiology, Gastroenterology, Hepatology, Infection and Immunity, Jour. Clin. Microbiology, Jour. Infectious Diseases, Jour. Med. Virology, Jour. Nat. Cancer Inst., Nature, Sci.; contbr. over 500 articles to profl. jours., chpts. to books; numerous patents in field. Decorated D.S.M.; recipient Superior Svc. award USPHS, 1972, Meritorious Svc. medal USPHS, 1974, Gorgas medal, 1977, Disting. Alumni award Duke U. Sch. Medicine, 1978, Eppinger prize 5th Internat. FALK Symposium on Virus and Liver, Switzerland, 1979, Medal of City of Turin, Italy, 1983, Gold medal Can. Liver Found., 1984, Inventor's Incentive award U.S. Commerce Dept., 1984; fellowships Baylor U., 1959-60, Duke U., 1960-62. Fellow Washington Acad. Scis.; mem. Am. Epidemiology Soc., Am. Soc. Microbiology, Am. Soc. Virology, Am. Acad. Microbiology, AAAS, Soc. Epidemiol. Rsch., Infectious Diseases Soc. Am. (Squibb award 1980), N.Y. Acad. Scis., Am. Soc. Clin. Investigation, Assn. Am. Physicians, Am. Coll. Epidemiology, Am. Assn. Study of Liver Diseases, Internat. Assn. Study and Prevention Virus Associated Cancers, Internat. Assn. Biol. Standardization, Internat. Assn. Study Liver, Soc. Exptl. Biology and Medicine (Disting. Scientist award 1986), Nat. Acad. Scis. Office: NIH Lab Infectious Diseases NIH Bldg 7 Rm 202 7 Center Dr MSC 0740 Bethesda MD 20892-0740

PURCELL, STEVEN RICHARD, international management consultant, engineer, economist. BS of Mech. and Indsl. Engring., NYU Coll. Engring. 1950; MS in Indsl. Engring., Columbia U., 1951; EdM, Harvard U. 1968. Registered profl. engr., Can. Lectr. engring. NYU Coll. Engring., N.Y.C., 1948-50; gen. mgr. Dapol Plastics Co., Inc., Boston, 1956-58; gen. div. mgr. Am. Cyanamid Co., Sanford, Maine, 1958-61; sr. prin., mgmt. cons. investment banking Purcell & Assocs., N.Y.C., 1961-66; prof., chmn. Bristol Coll., Fall River, Mass., 1966-68; assoc. dean grad. faculty adminstrv. studies York U., Toronto, Ont., Can., 1969-71; chief economist Dept. Manpower and Immigration, Ottawa, Ont., Can., 1970-71; cons. Treasury Bd., Ottawa, 1971-72; dir. urban and internat. environ. policy Ministry of State for Urban Affairs Internat. Activities, Ottawa, 1973-74; mem. com. on challenges of modern soc. NATO, Ottawa, 1973-74; mem. sci., econ. policy com. OECD UN, Ottawa, 1973-74; prof. Grad. Sch. Bus. Adminstrn. and Econs. Algonquin Coll., Ottawa, 1974-76; advisor, cons. House of Commons, 1976-77; sr. prin. Purcell & Assocs., Washington, 1977-80, chmn., Mgmt. Cons., Washington, 1977-80, chmn., CEO 1981—; chmn., CEO Phoenix Internat. Capital Assocs., Washington, 1981—; exec. dir. nat. coastal zone mgmt. adv. com. NOAA U.S. Dept. Commerce, Washington, 1980-81; profl. lectr. Northeastern U. Grad. Sch. Bus. Adminstrn., Boston, 1953-56, U. Toronto, 1968-69, George Washington U. Grad. Sch. Bus. Adminstrn., Washington, 1979; vis. prof. Rensselaer Poly. Inst. Advanced Mgmt. Program, 1967, U. Ottawa Grad. Sch. Bus. Adminstrn., 1971-74; lectr. Council for Internat. Progress in Mgmt., N.Y.C., 1960, Royal Bank Can. Mgmt. Assn., Toronto, Ont., 1970; corp. appointment cons. Harvard U., Cambridge, Mass., 1967-68; cons. Govt. Venezuela, 1967-68, Can. Inst. Bankers, Toronto, 1969-70; internat. sr. adviser NASA, 1985-86, mem. nat. adv. bd. Ctr. for Nat. Policy; dir. Rental Resource Corp., 1986-89. Contbr. articles on indsl. orgn., sci. policy and fin. to profl. jours. Lt. AC, USNR, 1943-46. Mem. UN Assn., Soc. for Advancement of Mgmt. (pres. 1949-50, leadership award 1950), Tau Beta Pi, Alpha Pi Mu (v.p. 1949-50), Columbia Univ. Club (Washington, trustee 1982-84, chmn., sr. trustee 1984-85), Harvard Univ. Club. Office: 12904 Old Chapel Pl Bowie MD 20720-3368

PURCELL, WILLIAM PAXSON, III, state representative; b. Phila., Oct. 25, 1953; s. William Paxson Jr. and Mary (Hamilton) P.; m. Deborah Lee Miller, Aug. 9, 1986; 1 child, Jesse Miller. AB, Hamilton Coll., 1976; JD, Vanderbilt U., 1979. Bar: Tenn. 1979, U.S. Ct. Appeals (6th cir.) 1985, U.S. Supreme Ct. 1986. Staff atty. West Tenn. Legal Svcs., Nashville, 1979-81; asst. pub. defender Metro Pub. Defender, Nashville, Tenn., 1981-84, sr. asst. pub. defender, 1984-85; assoc. Lionel R. Barrett, P.C., Nashville, 1985-86; ptnr. Farmer, Berry & Purcell, Nashville, 1986-90; majority leader Tenn. Ho. of Reps., Nashville, 1990—; chmn. select com. on children and youth Tenn. Ho. Reps., 1989-96; exec. dir. Vanderbilt Legal Aid Soc., 1978-79. Mem. exec. com. 6th dist. Dems., Nashville, 1986-88, Mem. Tenn. State Ho. of Reps., Nashville, 1986—, majority leader, 1990—, chmn. human svcs. com. Nat. Conf. State Legislatures, Washington, 1993. Toll fellow Coun. State Govts., 1988; named Legislator of Yr. Tenn. Conservation League, Dist. Attys. Gen. Conf. Mem. ABA, Tenn. Bar Assn., Nashville Bar Assn., Dem. Legis. Leaders Assn. (chmn. 1994-95). Methodist. Home: PO Box 60331 Nashville TN 37206 Office: 18 A Legislative Plz Nashville TN 37243

PURCIFULL, DAN ELWOOD, plant virologist, educator; b. Woodland, Calif., July 1, 1935; s. Ernest Lee and Virginia (Margaroli) P.; m. Marcia Ann Weatherby, Sept. 7, 1966; children: Scott, Douglas. B.S., U. Calif., Davis, 1957, M.S., 1959, Ph.D., 1964. Asst. prof. plant pathology U. Fla., Gainesville, 1964-69; assoc. prof. U. Fla., 1969-75, prof., 1975—; dept. grad. coord., 1988-91; mem. plant virus subcom. Internat. Com. for Taxonomy of Viruses, 1973-75, mem. potyvirus study group, 1987-90; mem. plant virology adv. com. Am. Type Culture Collection, 1993—; mem. Internat. Legume Virus Working Group. Assoc. editor Phytopathology, 1971-73, Plant Disease, 1987-89; contbr. articles to profl. jours. Mem. Morningside Nature Center Commn., City of Gainesville, 1978-81, treas., 1981. Served with U.S. Army, 1957. Fellow AAAS, Am. Phytopathol. Soc. (Lee Hutchins award 1981, Ruth Allen award 1992); mem. Fla. State Hort. Soc., N.Y. Acad. Sci., Am. Soc. Virology, Sigma Xi. Home: 3106 NW 1st Ave Gainesville FL 32607-2504

PURCIFULL, ROBERT OTIS, insurance company executive; b. Grinnell, Iowa, July 1, 1932; s. Chauncey O. and Mildred E. (Clendenen) P.; m. Mary G. White, Sept. 12, 1953; children: Jane, Robert Otis, Patricia, Elizabeth. B.A., Grinnell Coll., 1954. C.L.U. With Occidental Life Ins. Co., Calif., 1960-78; 1st. v.p. charge agys. Occidental Life Ins. Co., Los Angeles, 1966-71; exec. v.p. sales Occidental Life Ins. Co., 1971-76; pres., chief exec. officer Transmerica Ins. Mgmt., Inc., Los Angeles, 1972-78, Countrywide Life Ins. Co., Los Angeles, 1973-76; dir. Countrywide Life Ins. Co., 1973-78; chmn. bd., pres. Plaza Ins. Sales Inc., San Francisco; pres. Canadian div. Occidental Life Ins. Co., 1977-78; pres., chief exec. officer Occidental Life of Can., 1977-78; pres., chief operating officer, dir. Penn Mut. Life Ins. Co., Phila., 1979-80; sr. v.p. life divsn. Am. Gen. Corp., 1981-82; pres. Lincoln Am. Life Ins. Co., Am. Gen. Life Co. Del., Am. Gen. Life Ins. Co. Tex., Am. Amicable Life Ins. Co., Houston, 1982-84; vice chmn. Pioneer Security Life Ins. Co., 1982-84; pres., CEO Gulf Life Ins. Co., Interstate Fire Co., Jacksonville, Fla., 1984-88, also dir.; pres. Am. Gen. Group Ins. Co. Fla., 1986-89; vice chmn. Gulf Life Ins. Co., 1988-91; chmn., CEO ROP & Assocs. Past pres. Vols. of Am., L.A.; councilman City of Upper Arlington, Ohio, 1962-66; trustee Life Underwriters Tng. Coun., Washington, 1975-78; campaign chmn. Jacksonville United Way, 1988, 89, chmn., 1989-90; pres. Jacksonville Univ. Coun., 1992, 93; pres. Jacksonville Symphony Orch., 1993-94; chmn. bus. adv. coun. U. North Fla.; bd. dirs. Acordia Benefits Fla. Mem. Life Ins. Mktg. and Rsch. Assn. (bd. dirs. 1982-85), Rancho Las Palmas Club, San Jose Club, River Club. Home: 12940 Riverplace Ct Jacksonville FL 32223-1773

PURDES, ALICE MARIE, secondary education educator; b. St. Louis, Jan. 8, 1931; d. Joseph Louis and Angeline Cecilia (Mozier) P. AA, Belleville Area Coll., 1951; BS, Ill. State U., Normal, 1953, MS, 1954; PhD, Fla. State U., Tallahassee, 1976. Cert. in music edn., elem. edn., secondary edn., adult edn. Teaching/grad. asst. Ill. State U., 1953-54; music supr. Princeton (Ill.) Pub. Schs., 1954-55; music dir. Venice (Ill.) Pub. Schs., 1955-72, secondary vocal music dir., 1955-72; coord. literacy program Venice-Lincoln Tech. Ctr., 1983-86, chair lang. arts dept., 1983—. Mem. St. Louis chpt. World Affairs Coun., UN Assn.; charter mem. St. Louis Sci. Ctr., Harry S Truman Inst.; contbr. Old Six Mile Mus., 1981, Midland Repertory Players, Alton, Ill., 1991; chair Cystic Fibrosis Spring Bike-A-Thon, Madison, Ill., 1981, Granite City, Ill., 1985. Recipient gold medal Nat Senior Olympics, 1989, Senior World Games, 1992, several scholarships. Mem. AAUW, Music Educators Nat. Conf., Ill. Music Educators Assn., Am. Choral Dirs. Asns., Fla. State Alumni Assn., Ill. Adult and Continuing Educators Assn., Am. Fedn. Tchrs. (pres. 1957-58), Western Cath. Union, Croation Fraternal Union, Nat. Space Soc., Travelers Abroad (pres. 1966-68, 89—), Internat. Platform Assn., Archaeol. Inst. Am., Friends of St. Louis Art Mus., St. Louis Numis. Assn., Madison Rotary Club (internat. amb.), Slavic and East European Friends (life), Lovejoy Libr. Friends, Ill. State U. Alumni Assn. Roman Catholic. Avocations: bowling, travel. Home: PO Box 274 Madison IL 62060-0274 Office: Venice-Lincoln Tech Ctr S 4th St Venice IL 62090-1063

PURDOM, PAUL WALTON, JR., computer scientist; b. Atlanta, Apr. 5, 1940; s. Paul Walton and Bettie (Miller) P.; m. Donna Armstrong; children—Barbara, Linda, Paul. B.S., Calif. Inst. Tech., 1961, M.S., 1962, Ph.D., 1966. Asst. prof. computer sci. U. Wis.-Madison, 1965-70, asst. prof., 1971-82; mem. tech. staff Bell Telephone Labs., Naperville, Ill., 1970-71; assoc. prof., chmn. computer sci. dept. Ind. U., Bloomington, 1977-82, prof. computer sci., 1982—; grant researcher FAW, Ulm, Germany. Author: (with Cynthia Brown) The Analysis of Algorithms; assoc. editor: Computer Surveys; contbr. articles to profl. jours. NSF grantee, 1979, 81, 83, 92, 94. Mem. AAAS, Soc. for Indsl. and Applied Math., Assn. Computing Machinery, Sigma Xi. Democrat. Methodist. Home: 2212 S Belhaven Ct Bloomington IN 47401-6803 Office: Ind U 215 Lindley Hall Computer Sci Dept Bloomington IN 47405

PURDOM, THOMAS JAMES, lawyer; b. Seymour, Tex., Apr. 7, 1937; s. Thomas Exer and Juanita Florida (Kuykendall) P.; m. Betty Marie Shoemaker, May 31, 1969; 1 son, James Robert. Student, U. Syracuse, 1956-57, U. Md., 1958-59; BA, Tex. Tech. Coll., 1962; JD, Georgetown U., 1966. Bar: Tex. 1966, U.S. Supreme Ct. 1978, U.S. Ct. Appeals (5th cir.) 1983. Ptnr. Griffith & Purdom, Lubbock, Tex., 1966-67; asst. dist. atty. 72d Jud. Dist., Lubbock, 1967-68; county atty. Lubbock County, Tex., 1968-72; pres. Purdom Law Offices, P.C. and predecessor firms, Lubbock, Tex., 1972—; mem. com. for Vol. 5 pattern jury charges, 1988-94. Author: West's Texas Forms Vols. 16, 17, 18, 1984-94; (with others) Family Law, Texas Practice and Procedure,, 1981. Served with USAF, 1956-60. Fellow Tex. Bar Found.; mem ABA, Lubbock County Bar Assn. (bd. dirs. 1970), State Bar Assn. Tex. (sec. family law sect 1974-75, chmn. family law sect 1975-77, mem. examining commn. for family law specialization), Am. Acad. Matrimonial Lawyers (cert. family law, Tex. bd. legal specialization), Tex. Assn. Def. Counsel, Delta Theta Phi. Democrat. Baptist. Home: 3619 55th St Lubbock TX 79413-4713 Office: Purdom Law Offices PC 1801 Avenue Q Lubbock TX 79401-4891

PURDUM, ROBERT L., steel manufacturing company executive; b. Wilmington, Ohio, 1935; married. BS, Purdue U., 1956. With U.S. Navy and Ind. Toll Road commn., 1956-62; with Armco Inc., Middletown, Ohio, 1962—, dist. engr. metal product div., 1962-66, sales staff, 1966-72; dist. mgr. Columbus, Ohio, 1972-76; gen. mgr. adminstrn. Armco Inc., Columbus, Ohio, 1976-78; v.p. div. subs., pres. Midwestern Steel, Kansas City, Mo., 1978-80; area v.p. Midwestern Steel, Columbus, Ohio, 1980-82; group v.p., chief exec. officer steel svcs. group Middletown, Ohio, 1982-86; exec. v.p., chief operating officer Armco Inc., Middletown, Ohio; pres., chief operating officer Armco Inc., Parsippany, N.J., 1986-90, pres., COO, 1990—; also. bd. dirs., chmn. Capt. USNR. Recipient Disting. Engring. Alumnus award Purdue U., 1986. Office: Armco Inc 1 Oxford Ct Pittsburgh PA 15237*

PURDY, ALAN HARRIS, biomedical engineer; b. Mt. Clemens, Mich., Dec. 13, 1923; s. Harry Martin and Elinor (Harris) P.; m. Anna Elizabeth Sohn, Aug. 16, 1968; children: Catherine, Charles, Susan, Harry. BSME, U. Miami, 1954; MS in Physiology, UCLA, 1967; PhD in Engring., U. Mo. 1970. Cert. clin. engr., Washington. Project engr. in acoustics Arvin Industries, Columbus, Ind., 1954-56, AC Spark Plug Co., Flint, Mich., 1956-62; asst. prof. engring. Calif. Poly. U., Pomona, 1960-62; assoc. dir.

bioengineering U. Mo., Columbia, 1967-71; dep. assoc. dir. Nat. Inst. for Occupational Safety and Health, Rockville, Md., 1971-81; scientist, biomed. engr. Nat. Inst. for Occupational Safety and Health, Cin., 1983-86; asst. dir. Fla. Inst. Oceanography, St. Petersburg, 1981-83; pres. Alpha Beta R & D Corp., Cape Coral, Fla., 1986—; cons. Smithy Muffler Corp., L.A., 1961-62, Statham Instruments, L.A., 1966; cons. faculty, Tex. Tech. U., Lubbock, 1972-73; lectr. U. Cin., 1980. Patentee in diving, acoustical and occupational safety fields. Pilot CG Aux., Ft. Myers, Fla., 1989—; mem. Dem. Exec. Com., Lee County, 1989—. With USAF, 1942-43. Nat. Heart Inst. spl. fellow, 1963-67; Fulbright scholar, Yugoslavia, 1984. Mem. Acoustical Soc. Am., Biomed. Engring. Soc., Am. Inst. Physics, Internat. Oceanopgraphic Found., Exptl. Aircraft Assn., Aircraft Owners and Pilots Assn., DAV. Democrat. Home and Office: 5228 SW 5th Pl Cape Coral FL 33914-6504

PURDY, ALAN MACGREGOR, financial executive; b. Iowa City, Iowa, Apr. 23, 1940; s. Rob Roy MacGregor and Frances Norrine (Edwards) P.; m. Sarah Lane Robins, June 13, 1964; children—William Wallace, John Alan, Tammi Ann. A.B., Duke U., 1962; M.B.A., Wharton Sch. Fin. and Commerce, U. Pa., 1968. Bus. analyst Gen. Mills, Inc., Mpls., 1968-71; sr. fin. analyst Dayton Hudson Corp., Mpls., 1972-73, mgr. capital expenditure analysis, 1973, dir. corp. analysis, 1973-75, dir. planning and analysis, 1975-77; v.p., treas. Fleming Cos., Inc., Oklahoma City, 1977-81; v.p. fin., chief fin. officer John A. Brown Co. subs. Dayton Hudson Corp., Oklahoma City, 1981-83; sr. v.p., chief fin. officer B. Dalton Co. subs. Dayton Hudson Corp., Mpls., 1983-86, Robinson's of Fla. subs. May Co., St. Petersburg, 1986-87, Miller's Outpost (subs. Amcena Corp.), Ontario, Calif., 1988-92, Builders Emporium subs. Collins and Aikman Group, Irvine, Calif., 1993; Remedy Temp, San Juan Capistrano, Calif., 1994—. Served with USN, 1962-66. Home: 1980 San Remo Dr Laguna Beach CA 92651-2626 Office: Remedy Temp 32122 Camino Capistrano San Juan Capistrano CA 92675-3717

PURDY, CHARLES ROBERT, corporate executive; b. St. Louis, Oct. 2, 1937; s. Wilbur Charles and Myrtle (Baker) P.; m. Carolyn Joan Leppa, Aug. 29, 1959; children—Maureen Carol, Kelly Ann, Jeffrey Scott, Mark Edward. B.S.C., DePaul U., 1959. Jr. accountant Price Waterhouse & Co., Chgo., 1958-61, sr. accountant, 1961-62; asst. controller Scot Lad Foods, Inc., Chgo., 1962-64, adminstrv. v.p., 1964-66, exec. v.p., dir., 1966-69, pres., dir., 1969-71; vice-chmn., chief exec. officer, dir. Scot Lad Foods, Inc., Lansing, Ill., 1977-78; prin. Purdy Enterprises, Chgo., 1971-77, 78—; chmn. Computrition Inc, Chatsworth, Calif., 1989—. Recipient DePaul U. Alumni Assn. Achievement award, 1971-72. Mem. Delta Sigma Pi, Beta Gamma Sigma, Beta Alpha Psi. Club: Olympia Fields (Ill.) Country. Office: 20300 Western Ave Olympia Fields IL 60461

PURDY, JAMES, writer; b. 1923. Ed., Spain. Interpreter, editor, other positions Cuba, Mexico, Washington. Author: Don't Call Me by My Right Name, 1956; 63, Dream Palace, 1956, 1980, Color of Darkness, 1957, Malcolm, 1959, 1980, paperback, 1987, The Nephew, 1960, , 1980, paperback, 1987, (play) Children is All, 1962, Cabot Wright Begins, 1964, Eustace Chisholm and The Works, 1967, An Oyster is A Wealthy Beast, 1967, Mr. Evening, 1968, Jeremy's Version, 1970, On the Rebound, 1970, (poems) The Running Sun, 1971, Collected Poems, 1990, (novel) I am Elijah Thrush, 1971; Sunshine is an Only Child, 1973, Sleepers in Moon Crowned Valleys, The House of the Solitary Maggot, 1974, (selected stories) Color of Darkness, Children is All, The Candles of Your Eyes, 1991, (fairy tale) Kitty Blue, 1993 (Eng. edit. The Netherlands); (novel) In a Shallow Grave, 1976; (plays and stories) A Day After the Fair, 1977; (recordings) Eventide, 63; Dream Palace, 1968, 1980; (novel) Narrow Rooms, 1978; (poetry) I Will Arrest the Bird that has No Light, 1978, Lessons and Complaints, 1978; Sleep Tight, 1978, Proud Flesh, 4 short plays, 1980; (novel) Mourners Below, 1981, The Berry-Picker, 1981, Scrap of Paper, 1981, Dawn, 1985, (novel) On Glory's Course, 1983, (poems) Don't Let the Snow Fall, 1985, Are You in the Winter Tree?, 1987, (novel) In the Hollow of His Hand, 1986, (collected stories) The Candles of your Eyes, 1987, Garments the Living Wear, 1989, (play) Ruthanna Elder, 1989; subject of book: James Purdy (Stephen D. Adams), 1976, Collected Poems, 1990, (plays) In The Night of Time and Four Other Plays, 1992, A Day After the Fair, 1993, (novel) Out With The Stars, 1992, In the Night of Time and Four Other Plays, 1992, (plays) Foment, 1994, Brice, 1994, Where Quentin Goes, 1994; intro. to Weymouth Sands (by John Cowper Pwys); contbr. article to Life Mag., 1965. Recipient Morton Dauwen Zabel Fiction award Am. Acad. Arts and Letters, 1993; subject of The Not-Right House, Essays on the Books of James Purdy (Bettina Schwarzschild), 1969-70. Address: 236 Henry St Brooklyn NY 11201

PURDY, SHERRY MARIE, lawyer; b. Billings, Mont., Mar. 12, 1960. Student, U. Mont., 1978-80; BS, Mont. State U..., Billings, 1983; JD, Willamette U., 1987. Bar: Colo. 1987, U.S. Dist. Ct. Colo. 1987. Assoc. Holland & Hart, Denver, 1987-90; sr. atty. Atlantic Richfield Co., Denver, 1990—. Contbr. articles to profl. jours. Mem. ABA, Colo. Bar Assn., Colo. Women's Bar Assn., Colo. Hazardous Waste Mgmt Soc. (program com. chair 1989-90, v.p. 1990-91), Denver Bar Assn. Office: Atlantic Richfield Co Ste 1600 555 17th St Denver CO 80202-3916

PURDY, WILLIAM CROSSLEY, chemist, educator; b. Bklyn., Sept. 14, 1930; s. John Earl and Virginia (Clark) P.; m. Myrna Mae Moman, June 17, 1953; children—Robert Bruce (dec.), Richard Scott, Lisa Patrice, Diana Lori. B.A., Amherst Coll., 1951; Ph.D., MIT, 1955. Instr. U. Conn., Storrs, 1955-58; faculty U. Md., College Park, 1958-76, prof. chemistry, 1964-76, head div. analytical chemistry, 1968-76; prof. chemistry McGill U., 1976-86, assoc. in medicine, 1976—; Sir William Macdonald prof. chemistry, 1986—, assoc. vice prin. (acad.), 1986-91; vis. prof. Institut für Ernährungswissenschaft, Justus Liebig-Universität, Giessen, Germany, 1965-66; nat. lectr. Am. Assn. Clin. Chemistry, 1971; Fisher Sci. Lecture award Chem. Inst. Can., 1982; cons. Surg. Gen., U.S. Army, 1959-75; sci. adviser Balt. dist. FDA. Author: Electro-analytical Methods in Biochemistry, 1965, also numerous articles; mem. bd. editors Clin. Chemistry, 1971-80, Anal. Letters, 1979-95, Anal. Chim. Acta, 1979-84, Clin. Biochemistry, 1983-91, Pure and Applied Chemistry, 1983-91; adv. bd. editors Analytical Chemistry, 1971-73. Bd. govs. Trafalgar Sch. Girls, Montreal, 1980-90, chmn., 1983-87; bd. trustees Trafalgar-Ross Found., Montreal, 1983-90, chmn., 1983-87. Fellow Nat. Acad. Clin. Biochemistry, Royal Soc. Chemistry (London), Chem. Inst. Can., Can. Acad. Clin. Biochemistry; mem. Am. Chem. Soc., Am. Assn. Clin. Chemistry (Outstanding Contbns. to Clin. Chemistry award 1984), Can. Soc. Clin. Chemists (Outstanding Contbr. through Rsch award, 1990), Sigma Xi. Achievements include research in application of modern analytical methods to biochem. and clin. systems, separation sci., electroanalytical chemistry. Home: 1321 Sherbrooke St W C-40, Montreal, PQ Canada H3G 1J4 Office: McGill U, 801 Sherbrooke St W, Montreal, PQ Canada H3A 2K6

PURI, MADAN LAL, mathematics educator; b. Sialkot, Feb. 20, 1929; came to U.S., 1957, naturalized, 1973; s. Ganesh Das and S. V. P.; m. Uma Kapur, Aug. 24, 1962; 3 children. B.A., Punjab U., India, 1948, M.A., 1950, D.Sc., 1975; Ph.D., U. Calif. at Berkeley, 1962. Head dept. math. D.A.V. Coll., Punjab U., 1955-57; instr. U. Colo. 1957-58; teaching asst., research asst., jr. research statistician U. Calif. at Berkeley, 1958-62; asst. prof., asso. prof. math. Courant Inst., N.Y. U., 1962-68; vis. asso. prof. U. N.C., summers 1966-67; prof. math. Ind. U., Bloomington, 1968—; guest prof. statistics U. Gottingen, West Germany, 1972, Alexander von Humboldt guest prof., 1974-75; guest prof. U. Dortmund, West Germany, 1972, Technische Hochschule Aachen, West Germany, 1973, U. Goteborg, Chalmers U. Tech., both Sweden, 1974; vis. prof. U. Auckland, N.Z., 1977, U. Calif., Irvine, 1978, U. Wash., Seattle, 1978-79, U. Bern (Switzerland), 1982, Va. Poly. Inst., 1988; disting. visitor London Sch. Econs. and Polit. Sci., 1991; vis. prof. U. Göttingen, Fed. Republic Germany, 1991, June-July 92; rsch. fellow Katholieke U., Nijmegen, the Netherlands, 1992; vis. prof. U. des Scis. et Tech. de Lille, France, 1994. Co-author: Non Parametric Methods in Multivariate Analysis, 1971, Non Parametric Methods in General Linear Models, 1985. Editor Statochastic Process and Related Topics, 1975, Statistical Inference and Related Topics, 1975, Non Parametric Techniques in Statistical Inference, 1970; co-editor: Nonparametric Statistical Inference, Vols. I and II, 1982, New Perspectives in Theoretical and Applied Statistics, 1987, Mathematical Statistics and Probability Theory, Vol. A, 1987, Statistical Sciences and Data Analysis, 1993, Recent Advances in Statistics and Probability, 1994. Recipient Sr. U.S. Scientist award,

Humboldt Preis, 1974-75, 83. Fellow Royal Statis. Soc., Inst. Math. Statistics, Am. Statis. Assn.; mem. Math. Assn. Am., Internat. Statis. Inst., Bernoulli Soc. Math. Stats. and Probability. Office: Ind U Dept Math Rawles Hall Bloomington IN 47405

PURIS, MARTIN FORD, advertising agency executive; b. Chgo., Feb. 22, 1939; s. Martin and Virginia Lee (Farmer) P.; m. Mary M. Herrmann; children: Kimberly Mayo, Jason Patterson. Student, DePauw U., 1961. With Campbell-Ewald Co., N.Y.C., 1962-64, Young & Rubicam, Inc., N.Y.C., 1964-66; v.p. Carl Ally, Inc., N.Y.C., 1966-74; pres., CEO Ammirati & Puris, Inc., N.Y.C., 1974-94; chmn., CEO Lintas Worldwide, N.Y.C., 1995—; chmn. bd. The Upward Fund, Inc., N.Y.C.; media advisor Pres. George Bush. Vice-chmn., trustee Mystic Seaport Mus. Recipient awards Art Dir. Club, Copy Club, N.Y.C., Cannes Film Festival. Mem. Am. Assn. Advt. Agys. (gov.), N.Y. Yacht Club, Nantucket Yacht Club, Am. Yacht Club, Union Club. Republican. Roman Catholic. Avocations: sailing, tennis, riding, hunting. Office: Lintas Worldwide 100 5th Ave New York NY 10011-6903

PURL, O. THOMAS, retired electronics company executive; b. East St. Louis, Ill., June 5, 1924; s. Ruthford Keith and Muriel Agnes (Thompson) P.; m. Martha Elaine Smalley, Feb. 21, 1948; children—Thomas Keith, Jeanne Marie Purl Elder. B.S., U. Ill., 1948, U. Ill., 1951; M.S., U. Ill., 1952, Ph.D., 1955. Head high-power traveling wave tube sect., mem. tech. staff Hughes Research Lab., Culver City, Calif., 1955-58; sect. head, dept. mgr., group v.p., v.p. shareholder relations and planning coordination Watkins-Johnson Co., Palo Alto, Calif., 1958-86. Contbr. articles to profl. jours. Chmn. career guidance com. Santa Clara Valley Joint Engring. Council, 1971-73; bd. dirs. Jr. Achievement of Santa Clara County, 1975-79. Served to 1st lt. USAAF, 1943-46. Fellow IEEE (chmn. Santa Clara Valley subsect. 1972); mem. Sigma Xi, Eta Kappa Nu, Phi Kappa Phi, Sigma Tau. Club: Commonwealth of Calif. Patentee in field. Home: 466 La Mesa Portola Valley CA 94028

PURNELL, CAROLYN JEAN, lawyer; b. Memphis, Aug. 16, 1939; d. James Clarence and Mardine (Taylor) P.; B.A., U. Wash., Seattle, 1961, J.D., 1971; divorced; children—Mardine, Monica. Admitted to Wash. bar, 1972; dep. pros. atty. King County, Seattle, 1972-74; legal counsel to mayor of Seattle, 1974-77; atty. Weyerhaeuser Co., Tacoma, 1977—, dir. purchasing, 1981—; chief coun. Metro Legal Svcs divsn., 1990; dep. dir. Metro, 1993, dep. exec., metro exec. dir. King County, 1994. Legal officer Weyerhaeuser Found.; del. Am. Assembly Law, Palo Alto, Calif., 1981. Vice pres. Housing Devel. Corp., 1977—; loaned exec. Wash. Roundtable and Pacific Celebration '89, 1986—. Mem. Wash. Bar Assn., Seattle-King County Bar Assn., Delta Sigma Theta. Home: 3415 E Denny Way Seattle WA 98122-3347 Office: Weyerhaeuser Co Tacoma WA 98477

PURNELL, MAURICE EUGENE, JR., lawyer; b. Dallas, Feb. 17, 1940; s. Maurice Eugene Sr. and Marjorie (Maillot) P.; m. Diane Blake, Aug. 19, 1966; children: Maurice Eugene III, Blake Maillot. BA, Washington and Lee U., 1961; MBA, U. Pa., 1963; LLB, So. Meth. U., 1966. Bar: Tex. 1966. Ptnr. Locke, Purnell, Boren, Laney & Neely, Dallas, 1966-87; shareholder Locke Purnell Rain Harrell P.C., Dallas, 1987—; bd. dirs. Leggett & Platt, Inc. Bd. dirs. Dallas Summer Musicals. Mem. ABA, Tex. Bar Assn., Dallas Bar Assn. Am. Judicature Soc., Dallas C. of C. Clubs: Brook Hollow Golf, Koon Kreek Klub (Dallas). Home: 4409 Versailles Ave Dallas TX 75205-3012 Office: Locke Purnell Rain Harrell PC 2200 Ross Ave Ste 2200 Dallas TX 75201-6766

PURPURA, DOMINICK P., neuroscientist, university dean; b. N.Y.C., Apr. 2, 1927; m. Florence Williams, 1948; children—Craig, Kent, Keith, Allyson. A.B., Columbia U., 1949; M.D., Harvard U., 1953. Intern Presbyn Hosp., N.Y.C., 1953-54; asst. resident in neurology Neurol. Inst., N.Y.C., 1954-55; Prof., chmn. dept. anatomy Albert Einstein Coll. Medicine, Yeshiva U., N.Y.C., 1967-74, sci. dir. Kennedy Ctr., 1969-72, dir. Kennedy Ctr., 1972-82, prof., chmn. dept. neurosci., 1974-82, dean, 1984—; dean Stanford U., Calif., 1982-84; mem. neurophysiol. panel Internat. Brain Rsch. Orgn., pres. 1987—; v.p. med. affairs UNESCO, 1961—; chmn. internat. congress com. Internat. Brain Rsch. Orgn./World Found. Neuroscientists, 1983—. Mem. editorial bd. Brain Rsch., 1965—, editor-in-chief, 1975—; editor-in-chief Brain Rsch. Revs., 1975—, Developmental Brain Rsch., 1981—, Molecular Brain Rsch., 1985—, Cognitive Brain Rsch., 1991—. Served with USAAF, 1945-47. Fellow N.Y. Acad. Scis.; mem. Inst. Medicine of Nat. Acad. Scis., Nat. Acad. Scis., Am. Acad. Neurology, Am. Assn. Anatomists, Am. Assn. Neurol. Surgeons, Am. Epilepsy Soc., Am. Physiol. Soc., Assn. Research in Nervous and Mental Disease, Soc. Neurosci., Sigma Xi. Office: Yeshiva U Albert Einstein Coll Medicine 1300 Morris Park Ave Bronx NY 10461-1975

PURPURA, PETER JOSEPH, museum curator, exhibition designer; b. Bklyn., Nov. 29, 1939; s. Salvatore and Vincenza (Scozzari) P. B in Indsl. Design, Pratt Inst., 1962. Package designer Walter Dorwin Teague Assocs., N.Y.C., 1961-65; exhibit designer Will Burtin, Inc., N.Y.C., 1965-69; sr. exhibits designer Corning Glass Works, N.Y., 1969-71; assoc. exhibits dir. Met. Mus. Art, N.Y.C., 1971-72; exhibits dir. Mus. Sci., Boston, 1972-74; curator, dir. Explorers Hall, Nat. Geographic Soc., Washington, 1974-82; pres. Purpura & Kisner Inc., N.Y.C., 1983—; vis. design instr. Cornell U., 1971; lectr. Parsons Sch. Design, 1988, Phila. U. for Arts, 1992, 93, 94. Recipient Gold medal award Internat. Film and TV Festival of N.Y., 1973, Edison award for excellence GE, 1985. Mem. Indsl. Designers Soc. Am. (v.p. Mid Atlantic chpt. 1978); Am. Assn. Museums. Office: Purpura & Kisner 142 E Court St Doylestown PA 18901-4338

PURSE, CHARLES ROE, real estate company executive; b. Redhill, Surrey, Eng., May 19, 1960; came to U.S., 1960; s. James Nathanial II and Rolande Marie-Louise (Redon) P.; m. Carole Lynn Sadler, July 5, 1986; children: Hayley Elizabeth, Cameron James. BA, Dartmouth Coll., 1982; MBA, Northwestern U., 1985. Account officer Northern Trust Bank, Chgo., 1982-85; asst. v.p. Citicorp Real Estate, Inc., Chgo., 1985-88; v.p. Citibank, Ltd., Sydney, Australia, 1988-91, Citibank Realty Investment Advisors, N.Y.C., 1991-94; sr. v.p. The Yarmouth Group, N.Y.C., 1994—. V.p., bd. dirs. Perrot Meml. Libr., Old Greenwich, Conn., 1993. Mem. Nat. Assn. Comml. Real Estate Investment Fiduciaries, Pension Real Estate Assn., The Country Club (Cleve.), Cromer Golf Club (Sydney, Australia), The Hillsboro Club (Hillsboro Beach, Fla.). Republican. Episcopalian. Avocations: golf, photography, skiing, tennis. Office: The Yarmouth Group Inc 10 E 50th St New York NY 10022-6831

PURSELL, CARROLL WIRTH, history educator; b. Visalia, Calif., Sept. 4, 1932; s. Carroll Wirth and Ruth Irene (Crowell) P.; m. Joan Young, Jan. 28, 1956 (dec. 1985); children: Rebecca Elizabeth, Matthew Carroll; m. Angela Woollacott, Dec. 20, 1986. B.A. U. Calif., Berkeley, 1956, Ph.D., 1962; M.A., U. Del., 1958. Asst. prof. history Case Inst. Tech., Cleve., 1963-65; asst. prof. U. Calif., Santa Barbara, 1965-69; asso. prof. U. Calif., 1969-76, prof., 1976-88; Adeline Barry Davee Disting. prof. history Case Western Res. U., Cleve., 1988—; Mellon prof. Lehigh U., Bethlehem, Pa., 1974-76; vis. research scholar Smithsonian Instn., 1970. Author: Early Stationary Steam Engines in America, 1969, Military Industrial Complex, 1972, From Conservation to Ecology, 1973, White Heat, 1994, The Machine in America, 1995. Fellow AAAS; mem. Soc. History of Tech. (pres. 1990-92, Leonardo da Vinci medal 1991), History of Sci. Soc., Orgn. Am. Historians, Am. Hist. Assn., Phi Beta Kappa. Democrat. Office: Case Western Res U Dept History Cleveland OH 44106

PURSEY, DEREK LINDSAY, physics educator; b. Glasgow, Scotland, Oct. 22, 1927; came to U.S., 1964; s. Henry Edwin and Margaret Martin (Lindsay) P.; m. Barbara Ann Parker, Aug. 4, 1962; 1 child, John. BS, U. Glasgow, Scotland, 1948, PhD, 1952. Asst. lectr. theoretical physics King's Coll., London, 1951-54; lectr. math. physics U. Edinburgh, Scotland, 1954-59; vis. lectr. UCLA, 1959-60; mem. sch. math. Inst. for Advanced Studies Princeton U., 1960-61; lectr. in theoretical physics U. Glasgow, Scotland, 1961-64; vis. prof. Iowa State U., Ames, 1964-65, prof. physics, 1965-93, emeritus prof. physics, 1993—. Contbr. articles to profl. jours. Fellow Royal Soc. Edinburgh, Am. Phys. Soc.; mem. Am. Assn. Assn. Advancement Sci., Sigma Xi. Democrat. Presbyterian. Avocations: church-related activities, photography; music; reading; wilderness camping.

PURSLEY, MICHAEL BADER, electrical engineering educator, communications systems research and consulting; b. Winchester, Ind., Aug. 10, 1945; s. Bader E. and Evelyn L. (Bennett) P.; m. Lou Ann Hinchman, July 6, 1968; 1 child, Jessica Ann. B.S., Purdue U., 1967, M.S., 1968; Ph.D., U. So. Calif., 1974. Mem. tech. staff Hughes Aircraft Co., Los Angeles, 1967; engr. Northrop Co., Hawthorne, Calif., 1968; staff engr. Hughes Aircraft Co., Los Angeles, 1968-74; acting asst. prof. UCLA, 1974; asst. prof., then assoc. prof. elec. engring. U. Ill., Urbana, 1974-80, prof., 1980-93; Holcombe prof. elec. and computer engring. Clemson (S.C.) U., 1992—; assoc. Ctr. Advanced Study, 1980-81; vis. prof. UCLA, 1985; cons. U.S. Army, Huntsville, Ala., 1977, Ft. Monmouth, N.J., 1983-86, 91; cons. ITT, Ft. Wayne, Ind., 1979—; pres. SIGCOM, Inc., 1986-90; prin. scientist Techno-Scis. Inc., 1990—. Contbr. chpts. to books. Fellow IEEE (pres. info. theory group 1983, Centennial medal 1984); mem. Inst. Math. Stats. Office: Clemson U 102 Riggs Hall Box 340915 Clemson SC 29634-0915

PURSWELL, BEVERLY JEAN, veterinary medicine educator, theriogenologist; b. Atlanta; d. Henry D. and Frances (Martin) P.; m. C.M. Wall, Jan. 1, 1990. DVM, U. Ga., 1977, MS, 1981, PhD, 1985. Equine vet., 1977-79; theriogenology resident Medical Microbiology, 1979-85; assoc. prof. vet. medicine Va. Poly. Inst. and State U., Blacksburg, 1985—. Mem. AVMA, Soc. for Theriogenology (bd. dirs. 1989—, sec.-treas., v.p. 1992-93, pres. 1993-94), Va. Vet. Med. Assn. (bd. dirs. 1990-96). Avocations: dressage, livestock breeding. Office: Va Poly Inst and State U Coll Vet Medicine Duck Pond Rd Blacksburg VA 24061

PURTELL, LAWRENCE ROBERT, lawyer; b. Quincy, Mass., May 2, 1947; s. Lawrence Joseph and Louise Maria (Loria) P.; m. Cheryl Lynn Tymon, Aug. 3, 1968; children: Lisa Ann, Susan Elizabeth. AB, Villanova U., 1969; JD, Columbia U., 1972. Bar: N.Y. 1973, N.J. 1978, Conn. 1988. Assoc. White & Case, N.Y.C., 1972-73; judge advocate USMC, Washington, 1973-76; assoc. White & Case, N.Y.C., 1977-79; corp. counsel Great Atlantic & Pacific Tea Co., Montvale, N.J., 1979-81; asst. gen. counsel United Techs. Corp., Hartford, Conn., 1981-84, assoc. gen. counsel, 1984-92, sec., gen. counsel, 1989-92; v.p., gen. counsel and sec. Carrier Corp., 1992-93; sr. v.p., gen. counsel and corp. sec. Mc Dermott Internat., New Orleans, La., 1993—. Capt. USMC, 1973-76. Roman Catholic. Avocations: running. Home: 13 Rosedown Ct New Orleans LA 70131 Office: Mc Dermott Internat 1450 Poydras St New Orleans LA 70112

PURTLE, JOHN INGRAM, lawyer, former state supreme court justice; b. Enola, Ark., Sept. 7, 1923; s. John Wesley and Edna Gertrude (Ingram) P.; m. Marian Ruth White, Dec. 31, 1951; children: Jeffrey, Lisa K. Student, U. Central Ark., 1946-47; LLB, U. Ark., Fayetteville, 1950. Bar: Ark. 1950, U.S. Dist. Ct. (ea. dist.) Ark. 1950. Pvt. practice Conway, Ark., 1950-53, Little Rock, 1953-78; mem. Ark. State Legislature, 1951-52, 69-70; assoc. justice Ark. Supreme Ct., 1979-90; ret. N000, Little Rock, Ark., 1990; pvt. practice Little Rock, Ark., 1990—. Tchr. deacon Baptist Ch. Served with U.S. Army, 1940-45. Mem. ABA, Ark. Bar Assn., Am. Judicature Soc., Ark. Jud. Council. Democrat. Office: 300 S Spring St Apt 620 Little Rock AR 72201-2421

PURVES, ALAN CARROLL, English language educator, education educator; b. Phila., Dec. 14, 1931; s. Edmund Randolph and Mary Carroll (Spencer) P.; m. Anita Woodruff Parker, June 18, 1960 (dec. 1975); children: William Carroll, Theodore Rehn; m. Anne Hathaway Nesbitt, July 14, 1976. A.B., Harvard U., 1953; M.A., Columbia U., 1956, Ph.D., 1960. Lectr. Hofstra U., 1956-58; instr. Columbia U., 1958-61; asst. prof. English Barnard Coll., N.Y.C., 1961-65; examiner in humanities Ednl. Testing Service, 1965-68; assoc. prof. English U. Ill., Urbana, 1968-70, prof., 1970-73, prof. humanities, 1973-86; dir. U. Ill. (Curriculum Lab.), 1976-86; prof. edn. and humanities SUNY-Albany, 1986—, dir. Ctr. for Writing and Literacy, 1987—; staff assoc. Ctrl. Midwest Regional Ednl. Lab., St. Ann, Mo., 1968-70; cons. Coll. Entrance Exam Bd., 1987-90, Grad. Record Exam Bd., 1988-91, N.Y State Found. for Sci. and Tech., N.Y State Edn. Dept. Acad. Systems Inc.; pres. The Scribes, Inc. Edtl. Svcs. Author: The Essays of Theodore Spencer, 1968, The Elements of Writing about a Literary Work, 1968, Testing in Literature, 1971, How Porcupines Make Love, 1972, Literature and the Reader, 1972, Responding, 1973, Literature Education in Ten Countries, 1973, Educational Policy and International Assessment, 1975, Common Sense and Testing in English, 1975, Evaluation in English, 1976, Achievement in Reading and Literature: New Zealand in International Perspective, 1979, Evaluation of Learning in Literature, 1980, Achievement in Reading and Literature: The U.S. in International Perspective, 1981, The Implementation of Language and International Schools, 1981, An International Perspective on the Evaluation of Written Composition, 1982, Experiencing Children's Literature, 1984, How to Write Well in College, 1984, Contrastive Rhetoric, 1988, Cultural Literacy and General Education, 1988, International Study of Writing Achievement, 1988, The Scribal Society, 1989, International Research And Educational Reform, 1989, How Porcupines Make Love II, 1990, The Idea of Difficulty in Literature, 1991, Literate Systems and Individual Lives, 1991, Tapestry: A Multicultural Anthology, 1992, International Study of Writing Achievement 2, 1992, Encyclopaedia of English Studies and Language Arts, 2 vols., 1994, Creating the Writing Portfolio, 1995, How Porcupines Make Love III, 1995; editor: Research in the Teaching of English, 1971-77, IMEN Rev., 1986-92. Pres. Wonalancet (N.H.) Corp., 1967-69, 75-77; mem. vestry Episcopalian ch., 1970-73, 77-79, 88-91, 92-94, warden 1994—). With AUS, 1953-55. Fellow Internat. Assn. Evaluation Edn. Achievement Internat., 1971, Coolidge Colloquium, 1994; recipient Fulbright Hayes award, 1977, 86, Leppert award, 1980, noted lectr. award U. B.C., 1991, disting. rsch. award NCRE, 1994. Mem. MLA, Nat. Coun. Tchrs. English (trustee rsch. found. 1969-72, 83-86, mem. com. rsch. 1968-77, 82-85, v.p. 1977-78, pres. 1979-80), Newcomen Soc. (hon.), N.Y. State Coun., Nat. Conf. Rsch. English, Internat. Reading Assn., Am. Ednl. Rsch. Assn., Internat. Assn. for Evaluation of Ednl. Achievement (chmn. 1986-90), Farm Bur. (edn. com. 1991—), Wonalancet Outdoor Club (pres. 1965-69), Appalachian Mountain Club, Harvard Club. Home: RR 1 Box 344 Melrose NY 12121-9747 Office: SUNY Sch Edn Ctr for Writing and Literacy 1400 Washington Ave Albany NY 12222-0001

PURVES, WILLIAM KIRKWOOD, biologist, educator; b. Sacramento, Calif., Oct. 28, 1934; s. William Kirkwood and Dorothy (Brandenburger) P.; m. Jean McCauley, June 9, 1959; 1 son, David William. B.S., Calif. Inst. Tech., 1956; M.S., Yale U., 1957, Ph.D., 1959. NSF postdoctoral fellow U. Tubingen, Fed. Republic Germany, 1959-60; Nat. Cancer Inst. postdoctoral fellow UCLA, 1960-61; asst. prof. botany U. Calif., Santa Barbara, 1961-65; assoc. prof. biochemistry U. Calif., 1965-70, prof. biology, 1970-73, chmn. dept. biol. scis., 1972-73; prof. biology, head biol. sci. group U. Conn., Storrs, 1973-77; Stuart Mudd prof. biology Harvey Mudd Coll., Claremont, Calif., 1977—, chmn. dept. biol., 1985-95; chmn. dept. computer sci. Harvey Mudd Coll., 1985-90; adj. prof. plant physiology U. Calif., Riverside, 1979-85; vis. fellow computer sci. Yale U., 1983-84; vis. scholar Northwestern U., 1991. Author: Life, the Science of Biology, 1983, 4th edit., 1995. NSF sr. postdoctoral fellow U. London, 1967; NSF sr. postdoctoral fellow Harvard U., 1968; NSF rsch. grantee, 1962-83. Fellow AAAS; mem. Am. Soc. Plant Physiologists, Sigma Xi. Home: 2817 N Mountain Ave Claremont CA 91711-1550 Office: Harvey Mudd Coll 301 E 12th St Claremont CA 91711-5994

PURVINES, VERNE EWALD, JR., lawyer; b. St. Louis, Feb. 13, 1945; s. Verne Ewald and Gertrude (Griese) P.; m. Mary Garland Adams, Dec. 16, 1987. BS, U. Wash., 1966; JD, NYU, 1971. Bar: N.Y. 1973, D.C. 1979, U.S. Ct. Appeals (4th and D.C. cirs.) 1979, Mo. 1982, U.S. Supreme Ct. 1983, U.S. Ct. Appeals (8th cir.) 1983. Assoc. LeBoeuf, Lamb, Leiby & MacRae, N.Y.C., 1971-75; atty. Chesapeake & Potomac Telephone, Washington, 1975-76, Geico Corp., Washington, 1976-81; v.p., gen. counsel, sec. Navco Cos., St. Louis, 1981—; bd. dirs. Navco Corp., St. Louis, Nat. Gen. Ins. Co., St. Louis, Nat. Gen. Assurance Co., St. Louis, Nat. Gen. Mgt. Inc., St. Louis. Mem. Forest Park Forever, St. Louis, Mem. ABA, St. Louis Bar Assn., Mo. Bar Assn. Republican. Office: Navco Cos 1 National General Plz Hazelwood MO 63045-1313

PURVIS, GEORGE FRANK, JR., life insurance company executive; b. Rayville, La., Nov. 22, 1914; s. George Frank and Ann Mamie (Womble) P.; m. Virginia Winston Wendt, May 16, 1942; children: Virginia Reese (Mrs. William H. Freshwater), Winston Wendt, George Frank III. AA, Kemper

Mil. Sch., 1932; LLB, La. State U., 1935. Bar: La. bar 1935. Sole practice Rayville, 1935-37; atty. Office Sec. State State of La., Baton Rouge, 1937-41; also dep. ins. commr. State of La., 1945-49; atty. La. Ins. Dept., also spl. asst. to atty. gen., 1937-41; with Pan-Am. Life Ins. Co., New Orleans, 1949—, exec. v.p., 1962-64, pres., chief exec. officer, 1964—, chmn. bd., 1969—, also bd. dirs.; pres., bd. dirs. Compania de Seguros Panamericana, S.Am.; pres. Pan-Am. de Colombia Compania de Seguros de Vida, S.A.; chmn., bd. dirs. Internat. Reins. Co.; chmn. bd. govs. Internat. Ins. Seminars, Inc., 1984—; mem. Industry Sector Adv. Com. for Trade Policy Matters, 1986; lectr. ins. law Tulane U., New Orleans, 1949-56; bd. dirs. 1st Nat. Bank Commerce in New Orleans, Republic Airlines Inc., 1st Commerce Corp., So. Airlines-Republic Airlines, Pan-Am de Mex.Compania de Seguros Sobre la Vida, S.A., 1964-88. Compiler, author: Louisiana Insurance Code, 1948; contbr. articles to profl. jours. Chmn. big donors com. New Orleans Christmas Seal Campaign, 1961, gen. campaign chmn., 1962, chmn. profl. group VIII, 1963; vice chmn. New Orleans United Fund campaign, 1965, gen. chmn., 1967; pres. Tb Assn. Greater New Orleans, 1967, La. State U. Found., 1967, YMCA New Orleans, 1968—, Internat. House, 1977, Met. Area Com., 1979; geog. chmn. U.S. Savs. Bond Campaign, Greater New Orleans, 1971; mem. Bd. City Park Commrs., 1965-79, mem. bd. commrs. Port of New Orleans, 1979—, pres. bd. commrs., 1982; chmn. S.S. Huebner Found. Ins. Edn., 1977—; Bus. Task Force on Edn., Inc., 1980—; mem. adv. bd. Bapt. Hosp., 1985—, Salvation Army, 1986—; bd. dirs. Family Svc. Soc. New Orleans, Council for a Better La., New Orleans Philharm. Symphony Soc., Summer Pop Concerts, Bur. Govt. Rsch. New Orleans; mem. Govs. Cost Control Commn., 1981-89; trustee Greater New Orleans Found., 1987—, chmn. bd. trustees La. Ind. Coll. Fund Inc., 1987-88, mem. 1987—. Served with USNR, 1941-45. Named Distinguished Alumnus of Yr., La. State U., 1975, role model Young Leadership Coun., 1993; recipient award Inst. for Human Understanding, 1975, Weiss Meml. award, 1976, Vol. Activist award, 1978, award of excellence Greater New Orleans Fedn. Chs., 1983, Disting. Service award Navy League, 1983, Humanitarian award Nat. Jewish Hosp./Nat. Asthma Ctr., 1984, Internat. Ins. award Internat. Ins. Adv. Council, 1986, Order of Vasco Nunez de Balboa award Govt. Panama, 1986, 1st Am. award for outstanding efforts in promoting trade with Latin Am. Rotary Club, 1987, Hall of Fame award La. State U., 1987, Man of Yr. award Fedn. Ins. and Corp. Counsel, 1988, Integritas Vitae award Loyola U. of the South, 1991, Jr. Achievement Bus. Hall of Fame award, 1993; selected Role Model by Young Bus. Leadership Coun., 1993. Mem. ABA, La. Bar Assn., La. Law Inst., Am. Judicature Soc., Assn. Life Ins. Counsel, Am. Life Conv. (past chmn. legal sect., exec. com., v.p. La., chmn. 1972), Health Ins. Assn. Am. (dir., chmn. 1970), Ins. Econs. So. Am. (chmn 1980-81), La. Assn. Legal Res. Life Ins. Cos. (pres. 1963-68), New Orleans Assn. Life Underwriters (award for Loyal and Unselfish Service to the Ins. Industry 1987), Internat. Trade Adminstrn. (industry sector and functional adv. coms. for trade policy matters), C. of C. Greater New Orleans Area (dir., pres. 1970), Phi Delta Phi, Omicron Delta Kappa, Delta Kappa Epsilon. Episcopalian. Home: 5501 Dayna Ct New Orleans LA 70124-1042

PURVIS, GEORGE PORTER, III, health services company executive, consultant; b. Bryn Mawr, Pa., Aug. 31, 1942; s. George Porter Jr. and Virginia Moor (Smith) P.; m. Jacqueline Marie Pavone, Sept. 21, 1974. BA, BEng, Pa. State U., 1969, MBA, 1971. Ops. mgr. Western Electric Co., Phila., 1971-73; sr. mgmt. cons. N.J. Hosp. Assn., Princeton, 1973-76; sr. asst. dir. Hershey (Pa.) Med. Ctr., 1976-82; exec. v.p. Columbus, Cuneo, Cabrini Med. Ctr., Chgo., 1982-85; dir. gen. Aga Khan Health Svcs., Gouvieux, France, 1985—; bd. dirs. Aga Khan Health Svcs., Kenya, Tanzania, India, Pakistan. Contbr. articles to profl. jours. Sgt. USAF, 1962-66. Fellow Am. Coll. Healthcare Execs., Healthcare Fin. Mgmt. Assn., Alpha Pi Mu, Beta Gamma Sigma. Republican. Presbyterian. Avocations: skiing, trekking, sailing, antiquarian books. Home: 21 rue Henri Barbusse, 75005 Paris France Office: MSH 165 Allandale Rd Boston MA 02130

PURVIS, HOYT HUGHES, political scientist, academic administrator, educator; b. Jonesboro, Ark., Nov. 7, 1939; s. Hoyt Somervell and Jane (Hughes) P.; children: Pamela R., Camille C. BJ, U. Tex., 1961, MJ, 1963; postgrad., U. Nancy, France, 1962-63, Vanderbilt U., Nashville, 1963-64. Researcher/writer So. Edn. Reporting Svc., Nashville, 1963-64; reporter Houston Chronicle, 1964-65; press sec., spl. asst. Sen. J.W. Fulbright, Washington, 1967-74; dir. pubs. and lectr. LBJ Sch. Pub. Affairs, U. Tex., Austin, 1974-76; fgn./def. advisor and dep. staff dir. Sen. Majority Leader and Sen. Dem. Policy Com., Washington, 1977-80; sr. rsch. fellow LBJ Sch. Pub. Affairs, U. Tex., 1980-82; dir. and prof. Fulbright Inst. Internat. Rels., U. Ark., Fayetteville, 1982—. Author: Interdependence, 1992; co-author: Legistling Foreign Policy, 1984, Seoul & Washington, 1993; editor: The Presidency and the Press, 1976, The Press: Free and Responsible?, 1982; co-editor: Old Myths and New Realities in U.S.-Soviet Relations, 1990. Mem. adv. coun. Sci. Info. Liaison Office, Ark. Gen. Assembly, Little Rock, 1984—; chmn. Fayetteville City Cable Bd., 1991-93; apptd. J. Wm. Fulbright Fgn. Scholarship Bd., 1994—, vice chair, 1995. Rotary fellow, 1962-63, others; recipient Fulbright Coll. Master Tchr. award, Disting. Faculty Achievement award U. Ark. Alumni Assn. Mem. Internat. Studies Assn. (regional v.p. 1984-86), Am. Polit. Sci. Assn., Assn. for Edn. in Journalism and Mass Communication, Phi Beta Delta, Delta Phi Alpha. Methodist. Home: PO Box 1872 Fayetteville AR 72702-1872 Office: Fulbright Inst Internat Rels 722 W Maple St Fayetteville AR 72701-3229

PURVIS, RICHARD GEORGE, former superintendent of schools; b. Milw., Oct. 31, 1945; s. Robert E. and Violet (Roberts) P.; m. Janis Ann Borden, Jan. 27, 1966; children: Kelly Lyn, Cassie Ann. BS, Ea. N.Mex. U., 1967, MS, 1970; postgrad., Tex. Tech U., 1992—. Tchr. Jefferson County Schs., Arvada, Colo., 1967-68; tchr. Clovis (N.Mex.) Mcpl. Schs., 1968-71, asst. prin., 1971-72, jr. high prin., 1972-80, high sch. prin., 1980-85, supt., 1985-92; v.p. Ea. N.Mex. Research & Study Council, Portales, 1988—. Bd. dirs. Project Uplift, Albuquerque, 1988—. Named Adminstr. of Yr. N.Mex. Music Educators Assn., 1991, Nat. Superintendent of the Yr. awd., N.Mex., Am. Assn. of School Administrators, 1992. Mem. N.Mex. Supts. Assn. (bd. dirs. 1987—, pres. 1990, Supt. of Yr. 1992), Am. Assn. Sch. Adminstrs., N.Mex. Sch. Adminstrs., Assn. Supervision and Curriculum Devel., Rotary. Republican. Christian Ch. Avocations: hunting, fishing, travel.

PURYEAR, ALVIN NELSON, management educator; b. Fayetteville, N.C., Apr. 6, 1937; s. Byron Nelson and Gladys (Bizzell) P.; m. Catherine Paulette Wiggins, Aug. 30, 1962; children: Pamela, Susan, Karen. B.A., Yale U. 1960; M.B.A., Columbia U., 1962, Ph.D, 1966. Employee relations adviser Mobil Oil Corp., N.Y.C., 1965-66; fin. analyst Mobil Oil Corp., 1966-67; specialist computational systems Allied Chem. Corp., 1967-68; assoc. prof. mgmt. Grad. Sch. Bus. Adminstrn. Rutgers U., Newark, 1968-69; assoc. prof. mgmt. Bernard M. Baruch Coll., N.Y.C., 1970-72; prof. mgmt. Bernard M. Baruch Coll., 1972—, chmn. dept., 1978-79, dean coll., 1972-75, dir. Baruch/Cornell Indsl. and Labor Relations program, 1977-81; v.p. for orgn. and mgmt. Ford Found., 1980-82; 1st dep. comptroller City of N.Y., 1983-85; chmn. bd. Broadcast Capital Fund Inc., 1993-95; bd. dirs. G.P. Fin. Corp.; trustee Greenpoint Savs. Bank, 1992—. Co-author: Black Enterprise, Inc, 1973; also articles. Trustee Barber-Scotia Coll., 1977-82, Loyola coll., Balt., 1976-82, Riverdale Country Sch., Bronx, 1980-92, chmn. bd., 1987-89, Grad. Sch. Polit. Mgmt., 1987—, Pitts. Theol. Sem., 1989-92, Yale U., New Haven, 1994—; bd. dirs. Program Agy. United Presbyn. Ch., 1978-88, pres. 1983-86, Presbyn. Ch. U.S.A., 1987—, chmn. 1991-93, Yale Alumni Fund, 1977-82. John Hay Whitney fellow, 1960-61; Samuel Bronfman fellow, 1960-62. Mem. Acad. Mgmt., Assn. Yale Alumni (vice chmn. 1984-86, chmn. 1986-88), Am. Mgmt. Assn., Smithsonian Nat. Bd., Internat. Coun. Bus. Opportunity (bd. dirs.). Presbyn. (elder).

PURYEAR, JAMES BURTON, college administrator; b. Jackson, Miss., Sept. 2, 1938; s. Harry Henton and Doris (Smith) P.; m. Joan Copeland, June 13, 1965; children: John James, Jeffrey Burton, Joel Harry. BS, Miss. State U., 1960, MEd, 1961; PhD, Fla. State U., 1969. Lic. profl. counselor, Ga. Assoc. dir. YMCA, Starkville, Miss., 1962-64, dir., 1964-65; dir. fin. aid Fla. State U., Tallahassee, 1967-69; asst. dir. student affairs Med. Coll. of Ga., Augusta, 1969-70, dir. student affairs, 1970-86, v.p. student affairs, 1986—. Adv. bd. mem. Ga. Fed. Bank, Augusta, 1978-85; chmn. bd. First Bapt. Ch., Augusta, 1978-80; pres. Learning Disabilities Assn., Augusta, 1987, PTA, 1994; bd. dirs. Augusta Tng. Shop for Handicapped, 1994—; exec. bd. mem. Boy Scouts Am. Yearbook Dedication MCG Student Yearbook, 1975; scholar Med. Coll. Ga., 1988; recipient Svc. to Mankind award Sertoma, 1988. Mem. Nat. Assn. Student Pers. (S.E. regional bd.

1985), Am. Coll. Pers. Assn., So. Assn. Coll. Student Affairs, Rotary (pres. 1978, Paul Harris fellow 1985). Baptist. Avocations: golf, photography, scouting. Office: Med Coll Ga Augusta GA 30912

PURYEAR, JOAN COPELAND, English language educator; b. Columbus, Miss., May 10, 1944; d. John Thomas and Mamie (Cunningham) Copeland.; m. James Burton Puryear, June 13, 1965; children: John James, Jeffrey Burton, Joel Harry. BA summa cum laude, Miss. State U., Starkville, 1965; MA, Fla. State U., 1969; EdD, U. Ga., 1987. Cert. tchr., Ga. English instr. Fla. State U., Tallahassee, 1965-69, Augusta (Ga.) Coll., 1987-88; head English dept. Augusta Tech. Inst., 1989-93; chairperson gen. edn. and devel. studies, 1993—, mem. dean's coun., mgmt. team and grant proposal team, 1994—; chmn. State Bd. English, Ga., 1990-92, East Ctrl. Consortium English, Ga., 1990-92; mem. Augusta Tech. Inst. Tech. Com., 1990—; chmn. Capital Funds Raising Family Campaign, Augusta Tech. Inst., vice chmn. Capital Fund Raising Cmty. Campaign; mem. Continuous Improvement Coun. Augusta Tech. Inst., facilitator Total Quality Mgmt. Training; chmn. editing com. Augusta Tech. Inst. Self-Study, 1992-93, chmn. long range planning goals and objectives com., 1994. Co-pres. Davidson Fine Arts Sch. PTA; pres. Med. Coll. Spouse's Club, Augusta, 1972; dir. Womens' Missionary Orgn., First Bapt. Ch., Augusta, 1982; dir. Youth Sunday Sch., 1992, chmn. 175th Anniversary, 1992. Mem. Modern Lang. Assn., Nat. Coun. Tchrs., Am. Vocat. Assn., Ga. Vocat. Assn., So. Assn. Colls. (accreditation team 1994), Phi Theta Kappa (adv. 1992—). Baptist. Avocations: flower arranging, home decorating, reading. Office: Augusta Tech Inst 3116 Deans Bridge Rd Augusta GA 30906-3375

PURYEAR, MARTIN, artist; b. Washington, May 23, 1941; s. Reginald Thomas and Martina Alice (Morse) P. B.A., Cath. U., 1963; postgrad., Swedish Royal Acad., Stockholm, 1966-68; M.F.A., Yale U., 1971. Asst. prof. Fisk U., Nashville, 1971-73; U. Md., College Park, 1974-77; assoc. prof. art U. Ill., Chgo., 1978-86, prof., 1986-88; represented by Donald Young Gallery, Chgo. Exhibited in group shows at Whitney Biennial Exhbn., 1979, 81, 89, Whitney Mus. Am. Art, N.Y., Guggenheim Mus., N.Y.C., 1978, 85, 87, Mus. Modern Art, N.Y.C., 1984, St. Louis Art Mus., 1988, others; one-man shows include Corcoran Gallery Art, 1977, Joslyn Art Mus., 1980, Univ. Art Mus., 1985, Bklyn. Mus., 1988; commd. sculptures include Bodard Art, Nathan Manila Sculpture Pk., Govs. State U., University Park, Ill., Chevy Chase Garden Pla., Md.; traveling retrospective art Inst. Chgo., Hirshorn Museum, Washington, D.C., Museum of Contemporary Art, Los Angeles, 1991-92; Documenta IX, Kassel, Germany, 1992. Recipient Best Artist prize Sao Paulo Bienal, 1989, Creative Arts award for sculpture Brandeis U., 1989, medal for sculpture Skowhegan Sch. Painting & Sculpture, 1990; Louis Comfort Tiffany Found. grantee, 1981; Guggenheim fellow, 1982. Office: Nancy Drysdale Gallery 2103 O St NW Washington DC 20037

PUSATERI, JAMES ANTHONY, federal bankruptcy judge; b. Kansas City, Mo., May 20, 1938; s. James A. and Madeline (LaSalle) P.; m. Jacqueline D. Ashburne, Sept. 1, 1962; children—James A., Mark C., Danielle L. B.A., U. Kans., 1960, LL.B., 1963. Bar: Kans. 1963, U.S. Dist. Ct. Kans. 1963, U.S. Ct. Appeals (10th cir.) 1964. Assoc. Payne, Jones, Chartered, Olathe, Kans., 1963-65; assoc. James Cashin, Prairie Village, Kans., 1965-69; asst. U.S. atty. Dept. Justice, Kansas City, Kans., 1969-76; judge U.S. Bankruptcy Ct. Dist. Kans., Topeka, 1976—. Mem. Prairie Village City Council, 1967-69. Mem. Kans. Bar Assn., Topeka Bar Assn., Nat. Conf. Bankruptcy Judges, Am. Bankruptcy Inst. Office: US Dist Ct 215 Fed Bldg 444 SE Quincy St Topeka KS 66683-3501

PUSATERI, LAWRENCE XAVIER, lawyer; b. Oak Park, Ill., May 25, 1931; s. Lawrence E. and Josephine (Romano) P.; m. Eve M. Graf, July 9, 1956; children: Joanne, Lawrence F., Paul L., Mary Ann, Eva. JD summa cum laude, DePaul U., 1953. Bar: Ill. 1953. Asst. state's atty. Cook County, 1957-59; ptnr. Newton, Wilhelm, Pusateri & Naborowski, Chgo., 1959-77; justice Ill. appellate ct., Chgo., 1977-78; ptnr. Peterson, Ross, Schloerb & Seidel, Chgo., 1978-91, Peterson & Ross, 1991—; pres. Conf. Consumer Fin. Law, 1984-92, chmn. gov. com., 1993—; mem. Ill. Supreme Ct. Com. on Pattern Jury Instrns., 1981—; mem. U.S. Senate Jud. Nominations Commn. State Ill., 1993; exec. dir. State of Ill. Jud. Inquiry Bd., 1995—; mem. Merit Selection Panel for U.S. Magistrate; lectr. law DePaul U., Chgo., 1962, Columbia U., N.Y.C., 1965, Marquette U., Milw., 1962-82, Northwestern U. Law Sch., Def. Counsel Inst., 1969-70; apptd. by U.S. Senator Paul Simon to Merit Screening Com. Fed. Judges, U.S. Atty. and U.S. Marshal, 1993, others; mem. task force indigent appellate def. Cook County Jud. Adv. counsel, 1992—; mem. Ill. Gen. Assembly, 1964-68. Contbr. articles to profl. jours. Chmn. Ill. Crime Investigating Commn. 1967-68, chmn. Ill. Parole and Pardon Bd., 1969-70; bd. dirs. Ill. Law Enforcement Commn., 1970-72; chmn. Com. on Correctional Facilities and Services; exec. v.p. and gen. counsel Ill. Fin. Svcs. Assn., 1980—; chmn. law forum Am. Fin. Svcs. Assn., 1975-76; mem. spl. commn. on adminstrn. of justice in Cook County, Ill. (Greylord Com.) 1984-90, bd. dirs. Chgo. Crime Commn., 1986-91; mem. Ill. Supreme Ct. Spl. Commn. on the Adminstrn. of Justice, Ill. Supreme Ct. Appointment, 1991. Served to capt. JAGC, AUS, 1955-58. Named One of Ten Outstanding Young Men in Chgo., Chgo. Jr. Assn. Commerce and Industry, 1960, 65; recipient Outstanding Legislator award Ill. Gen. Assembly, 1966. Mem. ABA (com. consumer fin. svcs. 1975—, ho. dels. 1981-90, judicial adminstrn. divsn. 1980—, mem. exec. com. lawyer's conf. 1994—, mem. bench and bar rels. com. 1994—, mem. adv. com. to Ill. State Del., Jud. Adminstrn. Divsn. in Recognition of Leadership in Improvement of Adminstrn. of Justice award 1993), Ill. State Bar Assn. (pres. 1975-76, com. on fed. jud. and related appointments; Abraham Lincoln Legal Writing award 1959, mem. adv. com., state del., 1994—), Chgo. Bar Assn. (bd. mgrs. 1965-66), Mid-Am. Club Chgo. Republican. Roman Catholic.

PUSCH, WILLIAM GERARD, lawyer; b. La Porte, Ind., Jan. 29, 1935; s. William C. and Margaret (Elshout) P.; m. Mikellanne Peet, June 1, 1963; children: Jeffrey, Gregory, Anne. BA with honors, Mich., 1957; JD, Stanford U., 1960. Bar: Wash. 1961, U.S. Dist. Ct. (we. dist.) Wash. 1961. Ptnr. Davis Wright Tremaine (and predecessor firms), Seattle, 1961—. Editor: Wash. Partnership Law, 1981-84; bd. editors: Stanford Law Rev., 1959-60. Mem. ABA, Wash. State Bar Assn. (chair partnership law com., 1988—, exec. com. bus. law sect.), Seattle-King County Bar Assn., Order of Coif. Avocations: gardening, fishing, golf. Home: 8434 W Mercer Way Mercer Island WA 98040-4861 Office: Davis Wright Tremaine 2600 Century Sq 1501 4th Ave Seattle WA 98101-1662

PUSCHECK, HERBERT CHARLES, educator; b. Marshfield, Wis., July 14, 1936; s. Herbert and Ella (Sanger) P.; m. Elizabeth, Oct. 17, 1959; children: Elizabeth E. and Lisa Marie. BS in Gen. Engring., U.S. Mil. Acad., 1958; MS in Elec. Engring., Purdue U., 1964, PhD in Ops. Rsch., 1969. Officer U.S. Army, various cites, 1958-78; dir. spl. studies Office of Sec. Def., Washington, 1974-78, dep. asst. sec. def., 1987-94; prof. Nat. Def. U., Washington, 1979; assoc. dir. Selective Svc. System Hdqrs., Washington, 1980-82; asst. chief staff Army Materiel Command, Alexandria, Va., 1983-86; army chief Def. Systems Mgmt. Coll., Ft. Belvoir, Va., 1986-87; prof. pub. and internat. affairs George Mason Univ., Fairfax, 1994—; pres. H & BI (investments), Alexandria, 1985—. Contbr. articles to profl. jours. Co-chmn. Mt. Vernon Coun., Fairfax, Va., 1977-79. Recipient Meritorious Achievment award Pres., 1989. Mem. Mil. Ops. Rsch. Soc. (v.p. 1972-74, sponsor 1988—), Internat. Club. Avocations: sailing, hiking, fly fishing. Home: 8106 W Boulevard Dr Alexandria VA 22308-1711

PUSCHEL, PHILIP P., textiles executive. AB, Hamilton Coll., 1960; MBA, Stanford U., 1962. V.p. F Schumacher & Co., N.Y.C., 1971, pres., CEO, 1981, chmn. bd., CEO officer, 1989—. With USN, 1962-65. Office: F Schumacher & Co 79 Madison Ave New York NY 10016-7802*

PUSEY, WILLIAM ANDERSON, lawyer; b. Richmond, Va., Mar. 17, 1936; s. Paul H. and Vernelle (Barnes) P.; m. Patricia Powell, Sept. 3, 1960; children: Patricia Brent, William A. Jr. Margaret Glen. AB, Princeton U., 1958; JD, U. Va., 1962. Bar: Calif. 1963, Va. 1964, D.C. 1987. Assoc. McCutchen, Brown, et al, San Francisco, 1962-63; dep. dist. atty. Alameda County, Oakland, Calif., 1963-64; assoc., ptnr. Hunton & Williams, Washington, D.C., Fairfax and Richmond, Va., 1964—; trustee Ea. Mineral Law Found., Morgantown, W.Va., 1985—, pres. 1987-88. Chmn. bd. dirs. Presbyn. Sch. Christian Edn. Richmond, 1984-85. Mem. Order of Coif, Phi

Beta Kappa, Omicron Delta Kappa. Home: 3910 N Glebe Rd Arlington VA 22207-4221 Office: Hunton & Williams 2000 Pennsylvania Ave NW Washington DC 20006-1812

PUSEY, WILLIAM WEBB, III, retired dean, foreign language educator; b. Wilmington, Del., Nov. 16, 1910; s. William Webb, II and Edith White (Lobdell) P.; m. Mary Hope Smith, June 18, 1940 (dec. Sept. 1990); children: Mary Faith Pankin, Diana P. Pickral. B.S., Haverford Coll., 1932; A.M., Harvard U., 1933; Ph.D., Columbia U., 1939; Litt.D. (hon.), Washington and Lee U., 1983. Exchange scholar Bonn, Germany, 1934-35; asst. in German Columbia U., 1935-37, instr. German and humanities, 1937-39; assoc. prof., head German dept. Washington and Lee U., 1939-47, prof., head German dept., 1947-76, prof. German on Thomas Ball Found., 1956-60, S. Blount Mason, Jr. prof. German, 1974-81, dean coll., 1960-71, acting pres., 1967, dean emeritus, S. Blount Mason, Jr. prof. emeritus, 1981—. Author: Louis Sebastien Mercier in Germany, 1939, The Interrupted Dream, 1976, Elusive Aspirations, 1983; editor: (with A.G. Steer and B.Q. Morgan) Readings in Military German, 1943; contbr. articles and revs. to profl. jours. Served as lt. (j.g.), lt., lt. comdr. USNR, 1942-45, Washington, London, Berlin. Recipient Am. Council Learned Socs. faculty study fellowship, 1952-53. Mem. Phi Beta Kappa.

PUSHKAREV, BORIS S., research foundation director, writer; b. Prague, Czechoslovakia, Oct. 22, 1929; came to U.S., 1949, naturalized, 1954; s. Sergei G. and Julie T. (Popov) P.; B.Arch., Yale U., 1954, M.C.P., 1957; m. Iraida Vandellos Legky, Oct. 20, 1973; Instr. city planning Yale U., New Haven, 1957-61; chief planner Regional Plan Assn., N.Y.C., 1961-69, v.p. research, 1969-89, sr. v.p., 1989-90; adj. assoc. prof. N.Y.U., 1967-79; chmn. Russian Research Found. for Study of Alternatives to Soviet Policy, 1981—. Bd. dirs. Russian Solidarists; lectr. New Humanitarian U., Moscow, 1993—. Recipient Nat. Book award (with C. Tunnard), 1964. Mem. Am. Assn. for Advancement of Slavic Studies, editorial bd. POSSEV. Russian Orthodox. Author: (with Christopher Tunnard) Man-Made America, 1963; (with Jeffrey Zupan) Urban Space for Pedestrians, 1975, Public Transportation and Land Use Policy, 1977; Urban Rail in America, 1982; contbr. articles to profl. jours. Home: 300 Winston Dr Cliffside Park NJ 07010-3236

PUSKAR, MILAN, pharmaceuticals executive; b. 1935. Grad., Youngstown State U., 1961. V.p. Mylan Pharm. Inc., 1961-72; divsn. v.p. ICN Pharms., Inc., 1972-75; pres. Mylan Lab. Inc., 1976—. Office: Mylan Labs Inc 1030 Century Bldg Pittsburgh PA 15222*

PUSTILNIK, DAVID DANIEL, lawyer; b. N.Y.C., Mar. 10, 1931; s. Philip and Belle (Gerberholtz) P.; m. Helen Jean Todd, Aug. 15, 1959; children: Palma Elyse, Leslie Royce, Bradley Todd. BS, N.Y. U., 1952, JD, 1958, LLM, 1959; postgrad., Air War Coll., 1976. Bar: N.Y. 1959, U.S. Supreme Ct. 1962, Conn. 1964. Legis. tax atty. legis. and regulations div. Office Chief Counsel, IRS, Washington, 1959-63; atty. Travelers Ins. Co., Hartford, Conn., 1963-68; assoc. counsel Travelers Ins. Co., Hartford, 1968-73, counsel, 1973-75; assoc. gen. counsel, 1975-87, dep. gen. counsel, 1987-93; mem. adv. coun. Hartford Inst. on Ins. Taxation, 1978-93, vice chmn., 1991-92, chmn., 1992-93. Grad. editor NYU Tax Law Rev., 1958-59. Trustee Hartford Coll. for Women, 1985-91; life sponsor Am. Tax Policy Inst. Served to col. USAFR. Kenneson fellow NYU, 1958-59. Fellow Am. Coll. Tax Counsel; mem. ABA (chmn. ins. com. 1976-78), Am. Coun. Life Ins. (chmn. co. tax com. 1982-84), Am. Ins. Assn. (chmn. tax com. 1979-81), Assn. Life Ins. Counsel (chmn. tax sect. 1991-93), Twentieth Century Club, Sea Pines Country Club. Democrat. Jewish.

PUSTILNIK, JEAN TODD, elementary education educator; b. Ranger, Tex., Dec. 12, 1932; d. Lonnie Elvin and Frances Elvira (Lee) Todd; m. David Daniel Pustilnik, Aug. 15, 1959; children: Palma Elyse, Leslie Royce, Bradley Todd. BA, U. Okla., 1954; MA, St. Joseph Coll., West Hartford, Conn., 1983. Asst. buyer Foley's, Houston, 1954-58; buyer Kerr's, Oklahoma City, 1958-59; mgr. Woodward & Lothrup, Washington, 1959-61; instr. M. Webster Jr. Coll., Washington, 1961-63; tchr. West Hartford (Conn.) Bd. Edn., 1974-92; instr. St. Joseph Coll., 1976—; curriculum creator Conn. Home Econs. Dept., Middletown, 1985-88. Mem. Am.Home Econs. Assn., Hadassah (p[res. 1967-71), Sea Pines Country Club. Home: 60 N Sea Pines Dr Hilton Head Island SC 29928

PUSTOVAR, THOMAS M., manufacturing executive, heavy; b. 1957. V.p. Wheelbrator Engineered Sys., Saint Paul, Minn. Office: Wheelbrator Engineered Systems 1950 Old Hwy 8 Saint Paul MN 55112*

PUTH, JOHN WELLS, consulting company executive; b. Orange, N.J., Mar. 14, 1929; s. Leonard G. and Elizabeth R. (Wells) P.; m. Betsey Leeds Tait, Mar.1, 1952; children: David Wells, Jonathan Craig, Alison Leeds. BS cum laude, Lehigh U., 1952. Dir. mktg. Purolator Products, Rahway, N.J., 1955-61; pres., chief exec. officer Bridgeport (Conn.) Hardware Mfg. Co. subs. Purolator, 1962-65; group v.p. H.K. Porter Co., Pitts., 1965-72; pres., CEO Disston Inc., Pitts., 1972-75, Vapor Corp., Niles, Ill., 1975-83; chmn., pres., CEO Clevite Industries Inc., Glenview, Ill., 1983-89; pres. JW Puth Assocs., Skokie, Ill., 1989—; chmn. Am. Lantern, Newport, Ark.; bd. dirs. L.B. Foster, Pitts., A.M. Castle & Co., Franklin Park, Ill., Lindberg Corp., Chgo., V.J. Growers Inc., Apopka, Fla., Sys. Software Assocs., Chgo., Pierce Mfg., Appleton, Wis., TNT Freightways Inc., Rosemont, Ill., George W. Schmidt Inc., Niles, Ill, MSP Comm., Lansing, Mich., Golder, Thomas Cressy & Funds, Chgo., Brockway Std., Atlanta, Am. Acads., Cary, Ill., Allied Products Corp., Chgo. Chairman bd. trustees Hadley Sch. for Blind, Winnetka, Ill., 1982-84, trustee Lehigh U., Kenilworth Union Ch.; mem. adv. coun. Iaccoca Inst., Stuart Sch., Ill Inst. Tech. With U.S. Army, 1944-47, PTO. Mem. Chgo. Club, Econ. Club, Comml. Club, Indian Hill Country Club, Old Elm Club, Loblolly Pines Club. Republican. Presbyterian. Home: 180 De Windt Rd Winnetka IL 60093-3744

PUTKA, ANDREW CHARLES, lawyer; b. Cleve., Nov. 14, 1926; s. Andrew George and Lillian M. (Koryta) P. Student, John Carroll U., 1944, U.S. Naval Acad., 1945-46; A.B., Adelbert Coll., Western Res. U., 1949; J.D., Western Res. U., 1952. Bar: Ohio 1952. Practice law Cleve.; instr. govt. Notre Dame Coll.; v.p. Koryta Bros. Coal Co., Cleve., 1952-56; supt. div. bldg. and loan assns. Ohio Dept. Commerce, 1959-63; pres., chmn. bd., chief exec. officer Am. Nat. Bank, Parma, Ohio, 1963-69; dir. fin. City of Cleve., 1971-74; dir. port control, 1974-78; dir. Cleve. Hopkins Internat. Airport, 1974-78. Mem. Ohio Ho. of Reps., 1953-56, Ohio Senate, 1957-58; dep. auditor, acting sec. Cuyahoga County Bd. Revision, 1970-71; mem. exec. com. Cuyahoga County Democratic Com., 1973-81, Assn. Ind. Colls. and Univs. Ohio, 1983-89; bd. govs. Sch. Law, Western Res. U., 1953-56; mem. exec. com. World Service Student Fund, 1950-52; U.S. rep. Internat. Pax Romana Congress, Amsterdam, 1950, Toronto, 1952; mem. lay advisory bd. Notre Dame Coll., 1968-90, trustee, 1990-93, hon. trustee, 1993—; mem. adv. bd. St. Andrew's Abbey, 1976-88 ; trustee Case-Western Res. U., Newman Found. No. Ohio, 1980-93, hon. trustee, 1993—; 1st v.p. First Cath. Slovak Union of U.S., 1977-80; pres. USO Council of Cuyahoga County, 1980-83. Voted an outstanding legislator Ohio Press Corrs., 1953; named to All-Star Legislative team Ohio Newspaper Corrs., 1955; named one of Fabulous Clevelanders Cleve. Plain Dealer, John Henry Newman honor Soc. Mem. Cuyahoga County, Cleve. Bar Assn., Nat. Assn. State Savs. and Loan Suprs. (past. nat. pres.), U.S. Savs. and Loan League (mem. legis com, 1960-63), Am. Legion, Ohio Mcpl. League (bd. trustees 1973), Parma C. of C. (bd. dirs., treas. 1965-67), Newman Fedn. (past nat. pres.), NCCJ, Catholic Lawyers Guild (treas.), Am. Ohio Bankers Assn., Am. Inst. Banking, Adelbert Alumni Assn. (exec. com.), Cathedral Latin Alumni Assn. (trustee 1952—), Internat. Order of Alhambra (internat. parliamentarian 1971—, past grand comdr., supreme advocate 1973), Amvets, KC, Pi Kappa Alpha, Delta Theta Phi (past. pres. Cleve. alumni senate, master inspector 1975). Home: 28 Pond Dr Cleveland OH 44116-1062

PUTNAM, DALE CORNELIUS, management consultant, lawyer; b. Ponca, Nebr., Apr. 29, 1927; s. Merle H. and Catherine V. (Sheahan) P.; m. Alice Anselmi, Sept. 8, 1951; children: Mark, Lee, Neil, Bruce, Kirk, Nancy, Wendy. B.S., U. Nebr., 1949, LL.B., 1951. Bar: Nebr. 1951, Iowa 1951, Mo. 1977. Mgr. Interstate Assn. Credit Mgmt., Sioux City, Iowa, 1951-52; sec., legal counsel Metz Baking Co., Sioux City, 1953-66; v.p. Metz Baking Co., 1966-69, exec. v.p., 1969-72, pres., 1972-76; chief operating officer Interstate Brands Corp., Kansas City, Mo., 1976-77; pres., dir. Interstate

Brands Corp., 1977-80, pres., chief exec. officer, 1980-84; chmn., chief exec. officer, pres., dir. Interstate Bakeries (formerly DPF, Inc.), 1980-84; pvt. practice mgmt. cons., 1984—. Served with U.S. Army, 1945-46. Republican. Roman Catholic. Home: 8405 Reinhardt Ln Shawnee Mission KS 66206-1316

PUTMAN, ROBERT DEAN, golf course architect; b. Wallace, Idaho, Dec. 18, 1924; m. Sally Harmon, 1945; 3 children. Grad., Fresno State Coll. Art dir. Sta. KJEO-TV, Fresno, Calif. Prin. works include Arvin Mcpl. Golf Course, Wasco, Calif., Madera (Calif.) Mcpl. Golf Course, Rancho Canada Golf Course, Carmel Valley, Calif., La Manga Golf Couse, Costa Blanca, Spain, Monterey (Calif.) Country Club Shore Course, San Joaquin Country Club, Fresno, Visalia (Calif.) Mcpl. Golf Course, River Island Golf Course, Poterville, Calif., Kings River Country Club, Kingsburg, Calif. Office: Robert Dean Putnam GCA 5644 N Briarwood Ave Fresno CA 93711-2501

PUTNAM, CHARLES DUANE, manufacturing company executive; b. Northport, Mich., Apr. 21, 1928; s. Evits W. and Mabel Ruth (Lanham) P.; Gladys Louise Neiderhiser, July 23, 1955; children: Andrea, Charles Jr., Cynthia, Robert. BEE, Mich. Coll. Mining and Tech., 1950; MD, Cleveland-Marshall Law Sch., 1955. With Clark Controller Co., Cleve., 1950-63; patent atty. Whirlpool Corp., Benton Harbor, Mich., 1963-65, sr. patent atty., 1965-67, dir. labor relations, 1967-77, gen. mgr. personnel, 1977-78, v.p. personnel, 1978-83, sr. v.p. human resources, 1983-84, sr. v.p. adminstrn., 1984-85, exec. v.p. adminstrn., 1985—; also bd. dirs. Mem. ABA, Mich. Bar Assn., Ohio Bar Assn. Home: 411 Broadwater Cir Anderson SC 29624-9740 Office: Whirlpool Corp 2000 M-63 N Benton Harbor MI 49022

PUTNAM, FRANK WILLIAM, biochemistry and immunology educator; b. New Britain, Conn., Aug. 3, 1917; s. Frank and Henrietta (Holzmann) P.; m. Dorothy Alice Linder, Nov. 18, 1942; children—Frank William, Beverly Susan. B.A., Wesleyan U., Middletown, Conn., 1939, M.A., 1940; Ph.D., U. Minn., 1942; M.A. (hon.), Cambridge (Eng.) U., 1973. Instr., research asso. Duke U. Med. Sch., 1942-46; biochemist CWS, Camp Detrick, Md., 1946; asst. prof. U. Chgo., then assoc. prof. biochemistry, 1947-55; Lasdon research fellow Cambridge U., 1952-53; prof. biochemistry, head dept. U. Fla., 1955-65; prof. biology, dir. div. biol. scis Ind U., Bloomington, 1965-69; prof. molecular biology and zoology Ind. U., 1972-74, disting. prof. molecular biology and biochemistry, 1974-88, prof. emeritus, 1989—; bd. visitors Duke U. Med. Center, 1970-75; chmn. com. nomenclature of human immunoglobulins Internat. Union Immunol. Socs., 1971-76; chmn. basic sci. rev. bd. VA, 1972-76; chmn. cancer cause and prevention adv. com. Nat. Cancer Inst., 1974-75; sci. adv. com. Papanicolaou Cancer Research Inst., 1976-82; research rev. com. ARC, 1977-81, chmn. com. Brussels Colloquium on Protides of Biol. Fluids, 1970-90; chmn. virus cancer program adv. com. Nat. Cancer Inst., 1975-77; sr. med. adv. group VA, 1976-80; council div. biol. scis. and Pritzker Med. Sch., U. Chgo., 1977-87; chmn. Assembly Life Scis. Nat. Acad. Scis., 1977-81; mem. U.S. Nat. Com. Biochemistry, 1973-79; pres. sci. adv. com. G.E.R.M.I., Lyon, France, 1981-87. Co-author, editor: The Plasma Proteins, vol. 1, Isolation, Characterization and Function, 1960, vol. 2, Biosynthesis, Metabolism, Alterations in Disease, 1960, The Plasma Proteins, 2d edit., Structure, Function, and Genetic Control, Vol. 1, 1975, Vol. 2, 1975, Vol. 3, 1977, Vol. 4, 1984, Vol. 5, 1987; mem. editorial bd. Archives of Biochemistry and Biophysics, 1954-59, Science, 1968-82, Immunochemistry, 1972-75, Biomed. News, 1969-73, Fedn. Proc, 1958-63; Author numerous research papers. Trustee Argonne Univs. Assn., 1981-82; bd. govs. U. Chgo. Argonne Nat. Lab., 1983-89, chmn. Sci. ad tech. com., 1983-87; bd. dirs. Radiation Research Found., 1981-87. Markle scholar med. scis., 1950-56; Guggenheim fellow, 1970; fellow Churchill Coll., Cambridge U., 1973—; recipient Distinguished award teaching and research Wesleyan U., 1964, Distinguished Service award in medicine U. Chgo., 1968; Outstanding Achievement award U. Minn., 1974. Fellow AAAS, N.Y. Acad. Scis.; mem. Nat. Acad. Scis., Am. Acad. Arts and Scis. (Midwest council 1975-84), Pan-Am. Assn. Biomed. Scis. (sec.-gen. 1975-78), Japan Electrophoresis Soc. (hon.), Am. Inst. Biol. Scis. (life), Am. Soc. Biol. Chemists (sec. 1958-63), Soc. Exptl. Biology and Medicine, Am. Assn. Immunologists, Am. Chem. Soc. (chmn. div. biol. chemistry 1966-67), Soc. Peruana de Patologia (hon.), Fedn. Socs. Exptl. Biology (chmn. secs. com. 1958-63), Phi Beta Kappa, Sigma Xi, Phi Lambda Upsilon, Delta Sigma Rho. Club: Cosmos. Address: 5025 E Heritage Woods Rd Bloomington IN 47401-9314

PUTNAM, FREDERICK WARREN, JR., bishop; b. Red Wing, Minn., June 17, 1917; s. Frederick W. and Margaret (Bunting) P.; m. Helen Kathryn Prouse, Sept. 24, 1942; children—James Douglas, John Frederick, Andrew Warren. B.A., U. Minn., 1939; M.Div., Seabury-Western Theol. Sem., 1942, D.D., 1963; postgrad., State U. Iowa, 1946-47. Ordained to ministry Episcopal Ch. as deacon, priest, 1942. Pastor in Windom and Worthington, Minn., 1942-43, Iowa City, 1943-47, Evanston, Ill., 1947-59, Wichita, Kans., 1960-63; Episcopalian chaplain State U. Iowa, 1943-47; suffragan bishop Episcopal Diocese, Okla., 1963-79; bishop Episc. Ch. in, Navajoland, 1979-83; assisting bishop Diocese of Minn., 1983-89; acting rector St. George's, Pearl Harbor, Hawaii, 1984-85, St. Clement's, Honolulu, 1986, St. John's, Kula, Maui, Hawaii, 1988, St. Elizabeth's, Honolulu, 1990; interim rector St. Stephen's Episcopal Ch., Edina, Minn., 1991-92, Trinity Episcopal Ch., Pocatello, Idaho, 1994; vis. bishop Diocese of N.J., 1995; bd. dirs. Kiyosoto Ednl. Experiment Program, 1954-91, v.p., 1989-91; cons. Oklahoma City Community Relation Commn., 1966-70; Pres. Okla. Conf. Religion and Race, 1963-67; v.p. Greater Oklahoma City Council Chs., 1966-67; nat. chaplain Brotherhood of St. Andrew, 1967-79, mem. brotherhood legion, 1972—; priest assoc. Order Holy Cross, 1942—; exec. com. Conf. Diocesan Execs., 1969-76, pres., 1972-74; mem. Okla. Commn. United Ministries in Higher Edn., 1970-79, pres., 1973-75; mem. nat. com. on Indian work Episc. Ch., 1977-80; chaplain Okla. Assn. Alcoholism and Alcohol Abuse, 1974-78; hon. life mem. Oklahoma City and County Criminal Justice Council, 1978—. Editor: (pub.) Sharers Mag., 1957-63; contbr. articles to profl. publs. Founder, pres. Oklahoma City Met. Alliance for Safer City, 1971-78; Trustee Seabury-Western Theol. Sem., 1959-65, Episcopal Theol. Sem. Southwest, 1966-69, St. Simeon's Episcopal Home, 1963-79, St. Crispins Episcopal Conf. Center, 1963-79, Casady Sch., 1963-79, Holland Hall Sch., 1963-79, Episcopal Soc. Cultural and Racial Unity, 1967-70; trustee Neighborhood Services Orgn., treas., 1969; founder, 1st pres. Friends of Wichita Pub. Library, 1962; bd. dirs. Minn. Photographic Exbn.; chmn. Mpls.-St. Paul Internat. Photographic Exhbn., 1987, 89; State Bd. Minn. Common Cause, 1989—, state chmn., 1993—. Recipient Disting. Service award Evanston Jr. C. of C., 1952; Merit award Photog. Soc. Am. Fellow Coll. Preachers; mem. ACLU, Assoc. Parishes (pres. 1960-64), Mpls. Soc. Fine Arts (mem. photo coun.), Photog. Soc. Am., Am. Com. for KEEP (v.p. 1961-70, 90), Walker Art Ctr., Sierra Club, Met. Sr. Fedn., Audubon Club, Am. Assn. Ret. Persons, Minn. Hort. Soc., Hist. Soc. Episcopal Ch., Archaeol. Conservancy, Ancient Bibl. Manuscripts Ctr., Claremont, Calif., World Future Soc., Photographic Soc. Am. (assoc. 1989—, mem. v.p., 1995—), Twin Cities Assn. Camera Clubs (v.p. 1987), U. Minn. Alumni Assn., Minn. Hist. Soc., St. Paul Camera Club, N.Am. Rights Fund., People for the Am. Way, Episcopal Peace Fellowship, Amnesty Internat., Greenpeace, Liturgical Conf., Living Ch. Found., Worldwatch Inst., Clan Douglas Soc., Phi Kappa Psi. Clubs: Normandale Tennis and Swim. Home: 5229 Meadow Rdg Edina MN 55439-1412

PUTNAM, GEORGE W., JR., army officer; b. Ft. Fairfield, Maine, May 5, 1920; s. George W. and Rae B. (Merrithew) P.; m. Elaine Anderson (dec. 1973); m. Claudine Mahin; children: James M., J. Glenn; stepchildren: Philip Mahin, Leslie Mahin. Served as enlisted man U.S Army, 1941-42, commd. 2d lt., 1942, advanced through grades to maj. gen., 1970; comdg. gen. (1st Cavalry Div.), Vietnam, 1970-71; dir. Mil. Personnel Mgmt., Hdqrs. Dept. Army, Washington, 1971-75; comdg. gen. U.S. Army So. European Task Force, Vicenza, Italy, 1975-77, U.S. Army Phys. Disability Agy., Washington, 1977-81; ret. U.S. Army, 1981; dir. Army Coun. Rev. Bds., 1977-81; pres. Nat. Capital Retiree Coun., 1982-85. Internat. judge 5th and 6th World Helicopter Championships, 1986, 89, chief judge 7th World Championship, 1992; U.S. mem. Internat. Helicopter com. Fedn. Aeronautique Internationale, 1988-91, 93—; bd. dirs. Army Aviation Mus. Found., 1987—, pres., 1993—. Inducted Army Aviation Hall of Fame, 1980. Mem. Nat. Aero. Assn. (sr. v.p. 1991-95, v.p. FAI affairs 1995—), Army Aviation Assn. Am. (sr. v.p., pres. 1983-87, pres. scholarship found. 1991-93), Helicopter Club Am. (pres. 1988-90). Home: PO Box 343 Basye VA 22810-0343

PUTNAM, HOWARD DEAN, investor, former airline executive; b. Bedford, Iowa, Aug. 21, 1937; s. Virgil Glen and Mary Nancy (Livingston) P.; m. Krista Delight Moser, Oct. 20, 1957; children: Michael Dean, Susan Delight. M.B.A. in Mktg., U. Chgo., 1966; grad., Advanced Mgmt. Program, Harvard U., 1978. With Capital Airlines, Chgo., 1955-61; passenger service mgr. Capital Airlines, 1957-59, sales rep., 1959-61; with United Airlines, Chgo., 1961-78; regional v.p. United Airlines, San Francisco, 1971-74; group v.p. mktg. United Airlines, Chgo., 1974-78; pres., chief exec. officer S.W. Airlines, Dallas, 1978-81, also dir.; chmn., exec. v.p., chief exec. officer Braniff Internat. Corp., Dallas, 1981-83; chmn., co-owner Continental Steel Co., Dallas, Continental Builders Supply, Dallas, N.Am. Cabinet Corp., Marshall, Tex., The Diamond Mgmt. Group, Dallas; dir. Fidelity Nat. Bank, Dallas. Presbyterian. Club: Bohemian (San Francisco). Avocations: golf, flying, singing. Office: Diamond Mgmt Group 1701 N Greenville Ave Ste 101 Richardson TX 75081-1843

PUTNAM, HUGH DYER, environmental scientist, educator, consultant; b. Carrington, N.D., Feb. 12, 1928; s. Hugh Rodney and Blanche Putnam; m. Natalie Joy Knott, Dec. 23, 1950; children: Mark, Lynn, Charles. BA in Microbiology, U. Minn., 1953, MS in Microbiology, 1956, PhD in Pub. Health Biology/Environ. Health, 1963. Rsch. asst. U. Minn., 1952-54, teaching asst., 1954-55, instr., 1956-59, rsch. fellow, 1959-63, asst. prof. sanitary sci., asst. rsch. prof. U. Fla., Gainesville, 1963-66, assoc. prof. environ. sci., 1966-70, prof. environ. engring. studies, 1970-74, adj. prof. environ. engring. scis., 1974-85; founder, v.p. environ. scis. divsn. Environ. Sci. and Engring., Inc., Gainesville, 1965-74; v.p., prin. scientist Water and Air Rsch., Gainesville, 1974-94; vis. prof. U. Minn., 1974-75; mem. ad hoc com. on environ. rsch. and toxicology NAS; mem. environ. biology review panel EPA; vice chmn. sect. 1000 15th Edit. Standard Methods for Water and Wastewater, chmn. sect. 1000 16th and 17th Edits.; coord. water and wastewater biol. examination sect. 17th Edit. Standard Methods; mem. site selection bd. U.S. Army Med. Rsch. abd Devel. Command Effect of Munition Wastes on Aqatic Life; mem. site vis. team for evaluation NERQ Corvalis Ecol. programs Inst. Ecology, Madisin, Wis.; guest lectr. NASA, U. Minn, Duluth, USAF Acad.; cons. EPA, TVA, Muscle Shoals, Ala., Met. Waste Control Commn., St. Paul, Dept. Water and Power, L.A. Contbr. over 75 profl. reports and publs. to sci. jours. Mem. tech. awareness com. City of Tampa Water Reuse Com. Master sgt. U.S. Army, 1946-48, 50-52. Recipient Best Paper award TAPPI Environ. Conf. Planning Com., 1993. Mem. Am. Soc. Limnology and Oceanography, Water Environment Fedn., Internat. Soc. Theoretical and Applied Limnology, Sigma Xi. Office: Water & Air Rsch Inc 6821 SW Archer Rd Gainesville FL 32608-4748

PUTNAM, J. STEPHEN, financial executive; m. Pamela Schirmer; 3 children. BA, Bowdoin Coll., 1965. Pres. Robert Thomas Securities, Inc., St. Petersburg, Fla.; sr. v.p. Raymond James & Assocs., Inc.; bd. dirs. Raymond James Fin., Inc.; treas. Meerschaert Mut. Fund; v.p., bd. dirs. F.L. Putnam Securities. Bd. dirs., treas. Citizens Scholarship Found. Am., Inc.; pres. Palm Harbor (Fla.) Community Svc. Agy. Decorated Bronze Star, Army Commendation medal. Mem. NASD (by-laws and spl. com. to investigate investment adv. regulation, chmn. southeastern dist. nominating com.), Fla. Securities Dealers Assn. (bd. dirs.), Youth Soccer Assn. Office: Rober Thomas Securities Inc 880 Carillon Pky Saint Petersburg FL 33716-1102

PUTNAM, LINDA LEE, communication educator, researcher; b. Frederick, Okla., Aug. 10, 1945; d. Allard Warren and Etta Wanona (Tucker) Loutherback; m. Thomas Milton Putnam III, Mar. 28, 1970; 1 child, Ashley Ann. BA, Hardin-Simmons U., 1967; MA, U. Wis., 1968; PhD, U. Minn., 1977. Instr. U. Mass., Amherst, 1968-69; instr., chair dept. speech-theatre Normandale Community Coll., Bloomington, Minn., 1969-77; prof. communication Purdue U., West Lafayette, Ind., 1977-93; dept. head Tex. A & M Univ., 1993—; vis. scholar Stanford U., U. Calif.-Berkeley, San Francisco, 1984, Harvard U.-Harvard Negotiation Project, 1992. Editor: Communication and Organization, 1983(Best Publ. award 1985), Handbook of Organizational Communication, 1987 (Best Publ. award 1988), Communication and Negotiation, 1992. Del. Dem. State Conv., Mpls., 1972-74; treas. local dist. Dem. Farm Labor Party, Mpls., 1973-74, co-chairperson, 1974-75; block chair Am. Can. Soc. Fund Raiser, West Lafayette, 1986-87. Recipient AMOCO Teaching award Purdue U., 1986, Andersch award Ohio U., 1991, Disting. Alumni award Hardin-Simmons U., 1991, Charles H. Woolbert Rsch. award Speech Comm. Assn., 1993. Fellow Internat. Comm. Assn. (chair 1986-88); mem. Acad. Mgmt. (chair power negotiation, conflict mgmt. com. 1989-91), Speech Comm. Assn. (mem. at large 1984-87), Ctrl. States Speech Assn. (sec. comm. theory com. 1978-79, Scholar Showcase award 1989), Internat. Assn. for Conflict Mgmt. (bd. dirs. 1990-92, pres. 1994). Avocation: cooking. *In an age when change is inevitable, we often fear and try to avoid the unknown. In our drive for security, we forget that one of our richest blessings is change—the change that preserves diversity and the balance of power.*

PUTNAM, MICHAEL COURTNEY JENKINS, classics educator; b. Springfield, Mass., Sept. 20, 1933; s. Roger Lowell and Caroline (Jenkins) P. A.B., Harvard U., 1954, A.M., 1956, Ph.D., 1959; LL.D. (hon.), Lawrence U., 1985. Instr. classics Smith Coll., Northampton, Mass., 1959-60; faculty classics Brown U., Providence, 1960—; prof. Brown U., 1967—, chmn., 1968, 70-72, 77-78, 1994-95, prof. comparative lit., 1980—, MacMillan prof. of classics, 1985—; acting dir. Ctr. for Hellenic Studies, Harvard U., 1961-62, sr. fellow, 1971-86; Townsend prof. classics Cornell U., 1985; Mellon prof.-in-charge Am. Acad. at Rome, 1989-91; scholar in residence Am. Acad. in Rome, 1969-70, mem. classical jury, 1982-83, trustee, 1991—; assoc. univ. seminar on classical civilization Columbia U., N.Y.C., 1972—; mem. cath. Commn. on Intellectual and Cultural Affairs, 1969—; mem. adv. coun. dept. classics Princeton U., 1981-87, chmn., 1983-87; assoc. Am. Coun. Learned Socs., 1987—; mem. Inst. for Advanced Study, 1987-88; vis. scholar Phi Beta Kappa, 1994-95. Author: The Poetry of the Aeneid, 1965, Virgil's Pastoral Art, 1970, Tibullus: A Commentary, 1973, Virgil's Poem of the Earth, 1979, Essays on Latin Lyric, Elegy and Epic, 1982, Artifices of Eternity: Horace's Fourth Book of Odes, 1986, Virgil's Aeneid: Interpretation and Influence, 1995; contbr. articles to profl. jours. Sole trustee Lowell Obs., Flagstaff, Ariz., 1967-87, bd. advisors, 1987—; trustee Bay Chamber Concerts, Camden, Maine, 1972-88, incorporator, 1988-94; mem. bd. cons. Portsmouth Abbey Sch., 1985-89; hon. sec. Keats-Shelley Meml. Assn., 1994-97. Rome Prize fellow Am. Acad. in Rome, 1963-64; Guggenheim Meml. fellow, 1966-67; sr. fellow NEH, 1973-74, cons. 1974-78, 87—; Am. Council Learned Soc. fellow, 1983-84. Mem. Am. Philol. Assn. (bd. dirs. 1972-75, mem. com. on award of merit 1975-78, chmn. 1977-78, 1st v.p. 1981, pres. 1982, del. Am. Coun. Learned Socs. 1984-87, Charles J. Goodwin award of merit 1971), Archaeol. Inst. Am., Classical Assn. New Eng., Mediaeval Acad. Am., Vergilian Soc. Am. (trustee 1969-73, v.p. 1974-76), Accademia Nazionale Virgiliana, Acad. Lit. Studies. Club: Art (Providence). Office: Brown U Dept Classics Providence RI 02912

PUTNAM, PAUL ADIN, retired government agency official; b. Springfield, Vt., July 12, 1930; s. Horace Adin and Beatrice Nellie (Baldwin) P.; m. Elsie Mae (Ramseyer) June 12, 1956; children: Pamela Ann, Penelope Jayne, Adin Tyler II, Paula Anna. B.S., U. Vt., 1952; M.S., Wash. State U., 1954; Ph.D., Cornell U., 1957. Research animal scientist Agrl. Research Service, USDA, Beltsville, Md., 1957-66, investigation leader beef cattle nutrition, 1966-68, chief beef cattle research br., 1968-72; asst. dir. Beltsville Agrl. Research Ctr., 1972-80, dir., 1980-84; dir. cen. plains area Beltsville Agrl. Research Ctr., Ames, Iowa, 1984-87; assoc. dir. mid. south area Beltsville Agrl. Research Ctr., Stoneville, Miss., 1987-88, dir. mid. south area, 1988-94. Contbr. articles to profl. jours. Recipient Kidder medal U. Vt.; Outstanding Performance award USDA, also cert. merit; Danforth fellow; Borden fellow; Purina Research fellow. Fellow AAAS (rep. sect. O), Am. Soc. Animal Sci. (pres., North Atlantic sect., chmn. various coms., N.E. sect. Disting. Service award); mem. Am. Dairy Sci. Assn., Orgn. Profl. Employees USDA (pres. Beltsville chpt.), Council for Agrl. Sci. and Tech. Home: 36 Putnam Rd Springfield VT 05156

PUTNAM, PETER BROCK, author, lecturer; b. Georgia, June 11, 1920; s. Brock and Margaret (Faber) P.; m. Durinda Dobbins, Aug. 12, 1944; children: Brock II, Barbara Durinda, John Gerry. Grad., Hill Sch., 1938; B.A., Princeton, 1942, Ph.D., 1950. Lectr. history Princeton, 1950-55; v.p. Unitarian Universalist Assn., 1965-67. Author: Keep Your Head Up, Mr.

Putnam, 1952, Seven Britons in Imperial Russia, 1952, Cast off the Darkness, 1957, Triumph of the Seeing Eye, 1962, Peter, the Revolutionary Tsar, 1973, Love in the Lead, 1979; Translator: (Marc Bloch): Apologie Pour l'Histoire, 1953. Pres. Chapin Sch., 1961-63; exec. com. Princeton Alumni Coun., 1972-76; bd. dirs. Recording for Blind, 1975—, pres., 1976-80; bd. dirs. Mass. Assn. Blind, 1967-71, Star Island Corp.; pres. Unitarian Ch., 1954-57; bd. dirs. Lucerna Fund, 1976—; trustee Seeing Eye, 1981-90; trustee Continental Assn. Funeral and Meml. Socs., 1983-89; pres. Meml. Soc. Fund, 1983-87, Talking Books for Hosps., 1983-87. Mem. Author's League, Princeton Meml. Assn. (dir. 1954-56). Clubs: P.E.N., Cottage, Princeton Triangle (trustee 1962-87), Nassau Club. Home: 48 Roper Rd Princeton NJ 08540-4070 *The fear of uncertainty is the principal fear from which all others flow. It is always necessary to act on insufficient evidence. The acceptance of uncertainty is a major step on the road to maturity. A sense of humor is indispensable.*

PUTNAM, RICHARD JOHNSON, federal judge; b. Abbeville, La., Sept. 27, 1913; s. Robert Emmett and Mathilde (Young) P.; m. Dorethea Gooch, Jan. 27, 1940; children: Richard Johnson, Claude Robert, Mary Stacy, Cynthia Anne. BS cum laude, Springhill Coll., Mobile, 1934; LLB, Loyola U., New Orleans, 1937. Bar: La. 1937. Pvt. practice law Abbeville, 1937-54; dist. atty. 15th Jud. Dist., La., 1948-54; judge 15th Jud. Dist. Ct., La., 1954-61; dist. judge U.S. Dist. Ct. (we. dist.) La., La., 1961-75; sr. U.S. Dist. judge, 1975—; temporary judge U.S. Ct. Appeals for 5th cir., 1983; rep. fed. cts. Coun. La. Law Inst., 1976-89, sr. mem. inst. coun., 1989—; liaison judge for we. dist. 5th Cir. Archives - Hist. Com. , 1980; chmn. sr. judges adv. bd. Fed. Judges Assn., 1983—. Served from ensign to lt. USNR, 1942-45. Recipient Student Coun. Key Loyola U., 1937. Mem. Dist. Judges Assn., ABA, La. Bar Assn., Fifth Cir. Dist. Judges Assn., Am. Legion, VFW, St. Thomas Moore Soc. (Svc. award 1937), Delta Theta Phi. Lodge: KC. Office: US Dist Ct Fed Bldg 705 Jefferson St Rm 300 Lafayette LA 70501

PUTNAM, ROBERT E., writer, editor; b. Mt. Sterling, Ill., Sept. 13, 1933; s. John Harold and Florence Pauline (Curran) P.; m. Linda J. Wiant, Aug. 30, 1960; children: Justine, Robbie, Dylan. B.A., U. Ill., 1959; M.A., Roosevelt U., 1969. Assoc. engr. Western Electric Co., Chgo., 1960-62; with Am. Tech. Pubs., Inc., Chgo., 1964—; editor-in-chief Am. Tech. Pubs., Inc., 1973—, v.p. editorial, 1980-82. Author: Fundamentals of Carpentry, 1967, Concrete Block Construction, 3d edit, 1973, Bricklaying Skill and Practice, 3d edit, 1974, Architectural and Building Trades Dictionary, 3d edit, 1974, Fundamentals of Carpentry: Tools, Materials and Practices, 5th edit, 1977, Basic Blueprint Reading: Residential, 1980, Builder's Comprehensive Dictionary, 1984, 89, Construction Blueprint Reading, 1985, Building Trades Blueprint Reading, 1985; Welding Print Reading, 1986, Motorcycle Operation and Service, 1986, Masonry, 1988. Served with U.S. Army, 1953-55. Mem. Am. Welding Soc., Am. Soc. Tng. and Devel., Am. Soc. for Quality Control, Nat. Soc. Performance and Instrn. (Chgo. chpt.). Home: 256 Lester Rd Park Forest IL 60466-2039

PUTNAM, RUTH ANNA, philosopher, educator; b. Berlin, Germany, Sept. 20, 1927; d. Martin and Marie (Kohn) Hall; m. Hilary W. Putnam, Aug. 11, 1962; children: Samuel, Joshua, Polly Maxima. BS in Chemistry, UCLA, 1954, PhD in Philosophy, 1960. Instr. Philosophy UCLA, 1957-59; acting asst. prof. U. Oreg., 1959-62; from lectr. to prof. Wellesley (Mass.) Coll., 1963—, chair dept. Philosophy, 1979-82, 91-93; dir. summer seminar NEH, 1986, 89; mem. extramural grad. fellowships Wellesley Coll., faculty benefits com., com. budget, academic review bd., taskforce on affirmative action, bd. of admissions; presenter in field. Contbr. chpts. to books, articles to profl. jours., encyclopedias. Mem. Am. Philos. Assn. (program com. ea. divsn. 1977). Jewish. Office: Wellesley Coll 106 Central St Wellesley MA 02181

PUTNAM, TERRY MICHAEL, federal judge; b. Albany, Ga., June 7, 1954; s. Thomas Arnold and Betty Lavonia (Taylor) P.; m. Leigh Ann Smith, Aug. 20, 1983; 1 child, Thomas. Ala. U. Ala., 1976, JD, 1979. Bar: Ala. 1979, U.S. Dist. Ct. (no. dist.) Ala. 1980, U.S. Ct. Appeals (5th cir.) 1980, U.S. Ct. Appeals (11th cir.) 1981, U.S. Supreme Ct. 1985. Assoc. Potts, Young & Blasingame, Florence, Ala., 1979-83; ptnr. Potts, Young, Blasingame & Putnam, Florence, 1983-86; U.S. magistrate judge U.S. Dist. Ct. (no. dist.) Ala., Birmingham, 1987—; lectr. continuing legal edn. Ala. Bar Inst., 1985, 88, 90, 92, Cumberland Sch. Law, 1993. Mem. ABA, Fed. Magistrate Judges Assn., Order of Coif, Phi Beta Kappa. Democrat. Avocations: sailing, reading. Office: 268 US Courthouse 1729 5th Ave N Birmingham AL 35203

PUTNEY, JOHN ALDEN, JR., insurance company executive; b. Bklyn., Mar. 5, 1939; s. John Alden and Anne Marie (Davenport) P.; m. Theresa Rose DeFrisco, Feb. 9, 1964; children: Angela, Kathleen. B.S. cum laude in Math, St. John's U., 1960. Systems engr. IBM, N.Y.C., 1961-64; mktg. rep. IBM, 1964-66; cons. Topas Computer Corp., N.Y.C., 1966-67; dir., v.p. sec. Topas Computer Corp., 1967-70; with Tchrs. Ins. and Annuity Assn., N.Y.C., 1971—; v.p. Tchrs. Ins. and Annuity Assn., 1977-79, sr. v.p. 1979-80, exec. v.p., 1980—, office and info. systems area mgr., 1979-87, mgr. ops. support area, 1987—. Served with USMC, 1960. Home: 9 Concord Ave Larchmont NY 10538-3105 Office: Tchrs Ins & Annuity Assn 730 3rd Ave New York NY 10017-3206

PUTNEY, MARK WILLIAM, lawyer, utility executive; b. Marshalltown, Iowa, Jan. 25, 1929; s. Lawrence Charles and Geneva (Eldridge) P.; m. Ray Ann Bartnek, May 25, 1962; children: Andi Bartnek, William Bradford, Blake Reinhart. BA, U. Iowa, 1951, JD, 1957. Bar: Iowa 1957, U.S. Supreme Ct. 1960. Ptnr. Bradshaw, Fowler, Proctor & Fairgrave, Des Moines, 1961-72, of counsel, 1992-94; chmn., CEO. Bradford & Blake Ltd., Des Moines, 1992—; pres., chmn., chief exec. officer Iowa Resources, Inc., 1984-90; chmn., chief exec. officer Iowa Power & Light Co., 1984-90, Iowa Gas Co., 1984-85, Midwest Resources Inc., 1990-92; bd. dirs. Midwest Resources, Inc. Civilian aide to Sec. Army for Iowa, 1975-77; bd. dirs. Greater Des Moines YMCA, 1976-86, Boys' Home Iowa, 1982-86, Hoover Presdle. Libr. Assn., 1983—, U. Iowa Found., 1984—, Edison Electric Inst., 1986-89; bd. dirs. Greater Des Moines Com., 1984—, pres. 1988; bd. dirs. Assoc. Edison Illuminating Cos., 1988-93, pres., 1991-92; chmn. Iowa Com. Employer Support of Guard and Res., 1979-86; bd. dirs. Des Moines Devel. Corp., 1984-92, chmn., 1989-90. With USAF, 1951-53. Mem. Iowa Utility Assn. (chmn. 1989, dir.), Des Moines Club (pres. 1977), Desert Forest Golf Club (Carefree, Ariz.), Dakota Dunes Country Club, Masons, Shriners, Delta Chi, Phi Delta Phi. Republican. Episcopalian. Home: # 110 230 Courtyard Dr Dakota Dunes SD 57049 Office: # 101 600 Stevens Point Dr Dakota Dunes SD 57049

PUTNEY, PAUL WILLIAM, lawyer; b. Phila., Feb. 6, 1940; s. R. Emerson and Dorothea (Schulz) P.; m. Joan E. High, June 9, 1961; children: Joanna E., Andrew E. AB, Princeton U., 1962; JD, Harvard U., 1965. Bar P Pa. 1965, U.S. Dist. Ct. (ea. dist.) Pa. 1966, U.S. Supreme Ct. 1977, N.Y. 1988. Assoc. Dechert Price & Rhoads, Phila., 1965-73, ptnr., 1973-74, 77-87; mng. ptnr. Dechert Price & Rhoads, N.Y.C., 1987-94; chmn. trust and estates dept., 1994—; dep. chief broadcast bur. FCC, Washington, 1974-77; chmn. Phila. Presbytery Homes, Inc., 1987-93. Mem. ABA (past chair com. fin. planning for bus. owners, task force on legal fin. planning of real property, trust and probate sect.). Office: Dechert Price & Rhoads 4000 Bell Atlantic Tower 1717 Arch St Philadelphia PA 19103

PUTTER, IRVING, French language educator; b. N.Y.C., Dec. 3, 1917; s. Joseph and Anna (Schrank) P.; children—Paul Stephen, Candace Anne Putter. B.A., CCNY, 1938; M.A., State U. Iowa, 1941; Ph.D., Yale U., 1949. Mem. faculty U. Calif.-Berkeley, 1947-88; prof. French U. Calif. at Berkeley, 1961-83, chmn. dept., 1968-71, humanities research fellow, 1971-72, 78-79, 84-85. Author: Leconte de Lisle and His Contemporaries, 1951, The Pessimism of Leconte de Lisle: Sources and Evolution, 1954, The Pessimism of Leconte de Lisle: The Work and The Time, 1961, La Dernière Illusion de Leconte de Lisle: Lettres Inédites a Emilie Leforestier, 1968; also numerous articles; editor, translator: Chateaubriand: Atala, René, 1952. Guggenheim fellow, 1955-56; Fulbright fellow, 1955-56. Home: 115 St James Dr Piedmont CA 94611-3603

PUTTERMAN, FLORENCE GRACE, artist, printmaker; b. N.Y.C., Apr. 14, 1927; d. Nathan and Jean (Feldman) Hirsch; m. Saul Putterman, Dec. 19, 1947. BS, NYU, 1947; MFA, Pa. State U., 1973. Founder, pres. Arts

Unlimited, Selinsgrove, Pa., 1969—; curator Milton Shoe Collection, 1970—; artist in residence Title III Program Cultural Enrichment in Schs. Program, 1969-70; instr. Lycoming Coll., Williamsport, Pa., 1972-74, Susquehanna U. Selinsgrove, PA, 1984—. Exhibited one-woman shows, Everson Mus., Syracuse, N.Y., 1976, Hagerstown, Md., 1978, Stuhr Mus., Grand Island, N.B., 1979, Muhlenburg Ctr. for the Arts, Pa., 1985, Harmon Gallery, Fla., 1985, The State Mus. of Pa., 1985-86, Segal Gallery, N.Y., 1986, Canton Inst. Fine Arts, Ohio, 1986, Fla. Biennial Polk Mus., Lakeland, Fla., 1987, 89, Artists Choose Artists, Tampa Mus., 1987, Auburn Works on Paper, 1987, Ala., Ruth Volid Gallery, Chgo., 1989, Polk Mus. Art, Lakeland, Fla., 1989, Lowe Gallery, Atlanta, 1990, Mickelson Gallery, Washington, 1990, Palmer Mus., Pa. State U., 1990, Payne Gallery, Moravian Coll., 1991, Everhart Mus., Scranton, Pa., 1991, Lowe Gallery, L.A., 1992, Center Gallery, Bucknell U., Pa., 1993, Lore Degenstein Gallery, Susquehanna U., Selinsgrove, Pa., 1993, Lowe Gallery, Atlanta, 1993, Down Roll Gallery, Sarasota, Fla., Gallery 10, Washington; group shows, Library Congress, Soc. Am. Graphic Artists, Ball State Drawing Ann., Muncie, Ind., Arts Club N.Y., Colorprint, U.S.A., Smithsonian Traveling Exhbn., Boston Printmakers, N.C. Print & Drawing, Chautauqua Nat., U. Dallas Nat. Print Invitational, Segal Gallery, Rutgers Drawing, Polk Mus., Tampa Mus., Sichaun Fine Art Inst., Mickelson Gallery, Harmon Gallery, Mus. Art U. Ariz., 1988, U. Del., Newark, 1988 Mid Am. Biennial, Owensboro Mus. Art, VCCA Exhbn. Mcpl. Gallery, Regensburg, Federal Republic of Germany, 1989, Erie (Pa.) Art Mus., 1990, 1990 twenty year survey Palmer Mus., Pa. State U., Univ. Park, Payne Gallery Moravian Coll., Bethlehem, Pa., 1991, Everhart Mus., Scranton, Pa., 1991, U. Del. Biennial, Phila. Watercolor Soc., Noyes Mus., N.J., 1992, Erie (Pa.) Mus., 1991, Mus. Fine Arts, Hanoi, 1991, Spanish Embassy, Madrid, 1992, Anita Shapolsky Gallery, N.Y., 1990, American Women's Artists, Foster Harman Gallery Sarasota, Fla., 1993, Humphrey Gallery, N.Y., 1992, Anita Shapolsky Gallery, N.Y., 1993, Fla. Printmakers, Miami, 1993, Fla. Artists Ringling Mus., 1994. Recipient award Silvermine Guild Conn. Appalachian Corridors, Arena, 1976, Gold medal of honor Audubon Artists ann. competition, Whitehead award Boston Printmakers, 1985, Shellenberg award Artists Equity, 1985, award N.C. Print & Drawing, 1985, award Chautauqua Nat., 1985, Johnson & Johnson award 3rd Ann. Nat. Printmaking Council of N.J., 1985, Purchase award N.J. State Mus., 1987, Disting. Alumni award Pa. State U. Sch. Arts & Architecture, 1988, Ethel Klassen Meml. award Fla. Artists Group, 1992, Earl Horter award Phila. Water Color Club, 1992, Stella Drabkin Meml. award Color Print Soc.; Va. Ctr. for the Creative Arts fellow, 1983-84; Nat. Endowment Arts grantee. Mem. Soc. Am. Graphic Artists (v.p.), Nat. Assn. of Women Artists (Nat. Medal of Honor, Elizabeth Blake award). Home: 220 Morningside Dr Sarasota FL 34236 *I examine the world through painting. I consider the act of art a spiritual experience. My work is informed by nature and visually recalled and then made permanent on paper or canvas. Maintaining a feeling of being in harmony with the world allows for periods of quiet meditation and creativity.*

PUTTERMAN, LOUIS G., economics educator; b. N.Y.C., Apr. 27, 1952; s. Milton and Eileen L. (Goldstein) P.; (div.); 1 child, Laura Lee; m. Vivian Tseng, Apr. 5, 1981; children: Serena Rose, Mark Isaac. BA summa cum laude, Columbia U., 1976; MA in Internat. Relations, Yale U., 1978, PhD in Econs., 1980; MA (hon.), Brown U., 1983. From asst. prof. to prof. econs. Brown U., R.I., 1980—; rsch. assoc., Ctr. for East Asian Rsch. Harvard U., Cambridge, Mass., 1987-93. Author: Peasants, Collectives and Choice, 1986, Division of Labor and Welfare, 1990, Continuity and Change in China's Rural Development: Collective and Reform Eras in Perspective, 1993; co-author: Economics of Cooperation and the Labor-Managed Economy, 1987; editor: The Economic Nature of the Firm, 1986; State and Market in Development: Synergy or Rivalry, 1992; mem. editorial bd. Modern China, 1990—, Comparative Economic Studies, 1991—, Annals of Public and Cooperative Economics, 1992—, Jour. Comparative Econs., 1989-91. Recipient Sloan Rsch. fellowship, Alfred P. Sloan Found., 1983, Fellowship in Chinese Studies, Wang Inst., 1986. Mem. Am. Economic Assn., Assn. for Comparative Economic Studies, Phi Beta Kappa. Office: Brown U Dept Econs 64 Waterman St Providence RI 02912-9029

PUTTNAM, SIR DAVID TERENCE, film producer; b. London, Feb. 25, 1941; s. Leonard Arthur and Marie Beatrix P.; m. Patricia Mary Jones, 1961; two children. LLD (hon.) Bristol (Eng.) U., 1983; DLitt (hon.) Leicester U., 1986, Leeds U., 1992, U. Bradford, 1993. Knighted, 1995. With advt. firms, 1958-66; photographer's agt., 1966-68; film producer, 1968—. Chmn., Columbia Pictures, 1986-88. Producer films including That'll Be the Day, 1971, Mahler, 1973, Bugsy Malone, 1975, The Duellists (Spl. Jury prize Cannes 1977), 1977, Midnight Express, 1977 (2 Acad. awards), Chariots of Fire (4 Acad. awards and 3 BAFTA awards including Best Film award 1981, 4 Oscars including Best Picture), Local Hero, 1982, The Killing Fields, 1984 (3 Am. Acad. awards, 8 Brit. Acad. awards, BAFTA award for Best Picture), Cal, 1984, The Mission, 1986 (Palme d'Or 1986, Acad. award), Memphis Belle, 1990, Meeting Venus, 1991, Being Human, 1992, War of the Buttons, 1993, The Burning Season, 1994 (Golden Globe award best film for TV), Le Confessional, 1995. Chmn. Nat. Film and TV Sch., ITEL; vis. prof. films Bristol U.; dir. Anglia TV. Survival Anglia; trustee Nat. Energy Found.; hon. fellow The Chartered Soc. Designers; hon. fellow Manchester Polytechnic. Decorated Officier dans l'Ordre des Arts et des Lettres, 1986; comdr. of the Most Excellent Order of the Brit. Empire, 1982, Kt., 1995; recipient Michael Balcon award for Outstanding Contbn. Brit. Film Industry, BAFTA, 1982. Fellow Royal Soc. Arts, Royal Photographic Soc., Royal Geog. Soc. Address: 13/15 Queen's Gate Pl Mews, London SW7 5BG, England

PUTZEL, CONSTANCE KELLNER, lawyer; b. Balt., Sept. 5, 1922; d. William Stummer and Corinne (Strauss) Kellner; m. William L. Putzel, Aug. 28, 1945; 1 son, Arthur William. A.B., Goucher Coll., 1942; LL.B., U. Md., 1945, J.D., 1969. Bar: Md. 1945. Social worker Balt. Dept. Pub. Welfare, 1945-46; atty. New Amsterdam Casualty Co., Balt., 1947; staff atty. Legal Aid Bur., Balt., 1947-49; mem. Putzel & Putzel, P.A., Balt., 1950-89; pres. Constance K. Putzel, P.A., 1989—; instr. U. Balt. Sch. Law, 1975-77, Goucher Coll., 1976-77; chmn. character com. Ct. Appeals for 3d Cir., 1976—. Author: Divorce Organization System, 1984, 3d edit., 1993, Representing the Older Client in Divorce, 1992. Mem. Md. Com. on Status of Women, 1972-76; mem. Com. to Implement ERA, 1973-76; Pres. U. Md. Law Alumni Assn., 1978; bd. dirs. Legal Aid Bur., 1951-52, 71-73. Fellow Am. Acad. Matrimonial Lawyers, Internat. Acad. Matrimonial Lawyers; mem. ABA, Md. Bar Assn. (bd. govs. 1972-73, chmn. family law sect. 1978-79). Home: 8207 Spring Bottom Way Baltimore MD 21208-1859 Office: 29 W Susquehanna Ave Baltimore MD 21204-5201

PUTZEL, MICHAEL, journalist; b. Washington, Sept. 16, 1942; s. Max and Nell (Converse) P.; m. Ann Blackman, Feb. 23, 1974; children: Leila Elizabeth, Christof Blackman. BA, UNC in Polit. Sci., 1967. Reporter Charleston (W.va.) Gazette, 1963-66; newsman AP, Raleigh, N.C., 1967-68, N.Y.C., 1968-69; war corr. AP, Vietnam, 1969-72; reporter AP, Washington, 1972-79; asst. metro editor Washington Post, Washington, 1979; White House corr. AP, Washington, 1979-84; chief White House corr. AP, 1984-87; chief of bur. AP, Moscow, 1987-90; diplomatic corr. AP, Washington, 1990-91; Washington bureau chief Boston Globe, 1991-92; White House corr. Boston Globe, Washington, 1993-94; columnist "Plugged In", 1994—. With USAR, 1964-65. Recipient AP Mgn. Editors citation, 1975, 81, Merriman Smith Meml. award White House Corr. Assn., 1986. Home: 4938 Quebec St NW Washington DC 20016 Office: The Boston Globe 1130 Connecticut Ave NW Washington DC 20036

PUTZELL, EDWIN JOSEPH, JR., lawyer, mayor; b. Birmingham, Ala., Sept. 29, 1913; s. Edwin Joseph and Celeste (Joseph) P.; children: Cynthia Putzell Reidy, Edwin Joseph III; m. Dorothy Corcoran Waters, Aug. 5, 1967. AB, Tulane U., 1935; LLB, Harvard U., 1938. Bar: N.Y. 1939, Mo. 1947, U.S. Supreme Ct. 1945. Atty. Donovan, Leisure, Newton & Lumbard, N.Y.C. and Washington, 1937-42; asst. dir.-exec. officer Office of Strategic Svcs., 1942-45; asst. treas. Monsanto Co., St. Louis, 1945-46, asst. sec., atty., 1946-51, sec., 1951-77, dir. law dept., 1953-68, v.p., gen. counsel, 1963-77; ptnr. Coburn, Croft, Shepherd, Herzog & Putzell, St. Louis, 1977-79; of counsel Coburn, Croft & Putzell, St. Louis, 1979—; mayor City of Naples, Fla., 1986-90. Dir. St. Louis Symphony Soc., 1955-69; pres. The Conservancy, Inc., 1981-85, chmn. bd. dirs., 1984-85; vice chmn. St. Louis County Bd. Police Commrs., 1964-72, Big Cypress Basin Bd., South Fla. Water Mgmt. Dist., 1985-86; pres. Social Planning Coun., St. Louis, 1954-57;

chmn. Naples Airport Authority, 1979-83, 94—; vice chmn. Westminster Coll., 1976-79; chmn. Sta. KETC-TV, St. Louis, 1977-79; trustee St. Luke's Hosp., 1973-79; bd. dirs. Hospice of Naples, Cmty. Found. Collier County, The Moorings, Inc., Collier/Naplescape, Inc. Mem. ABA, Mo. Bar Assn., St. Louis Bar Assn., Am. Soc. Corp. Secs. (pres. 1968-69), Assn. Gen. Counsel, Bogey Club, Noonday Club, Port Royal Club, Hole in the Wall Golf Club, Naples Yacht Club, Phi Beta Kappa, Delta Sigma Phi. Episcopalian. Home: 1285 Gulf Shore Blvd N Naples FL 33940-4911

PUYAU, FRANCIS ALBERT, physician, radiology educator; b. New Orleans, Dec. 1, 1928; s. Frank Albert and Rose Sue (Jones) P.; m. Geraldine Sally diBenedetto, June 6, 1951; children: Michael, Stephen, Jeanne Marie, Julie, Melissa. B.S., Notre Dame U., 1948; M.D., La. State U., 1952. Diplomate Am. Bd. Pediatrics, Am. Bd. Pediatric Cardiology, Am. Bd. Radiology. Intern Charity Hosp., New Orleans, 1952-53; resident in pediatrics Charity Hosp., 1955-57; instr. pediatrics La. State U. Sch. Medicine, New Orleans, 1957-59; asst. prof. La. State U. Sch. Medicine, 1959-61, clin. asso. prof., 1968-71, prof. radiology and pediatrics, 1971-74, acting head dept. radiology, 1971-72, head dept., 1972-74; asst. prof. pediatrics Vanderbilt U., 1961-68; fellow dept. diagnostic radiology Charity Hosp., New Orleans, 1968-70; prof. radiology, pediatrics and medicine Tulane U. Sch. Medicine, New Orleans, 1974—; acting chmn. dept. pediatrics Tulane U. Sch. Medicine, 1976-78; cons. St. Tammany Hosps., Covington, La., 1968-81; dir. cardiac catherization lab. dept. cardiology Charity Hosp., New Orleans, 1970-85; staff radiologist Our Lady of the Lake Regional Med. Ctr., Baton Rouge, 1986-93; mem. staff Hotel Dieu, New Orleans, 1973-80; head x-ray dept. Children's Hosp. of New Orleans, 1976-82. Contbr. articles to med. jours. Served with USPHS, 1953-55. Fellow Am. Coll. Cardiology, Am. Coll. Radiology; mem. East Baton Rouge Med. Soc., So. Soc. Pediatric Research, Am. Coll. Radiology, La. Radiology Soc., New Orleans Radiology Soc. (pres. 1985), New Orleans Pediatric Soc., Soc. Chmn. Acad. Radiology Depts., Radiol. Soc. N.Am., Am. Roentgen Ray Soc., Assn. Univ. Radiologists, Southern Yacht Club (New Orleans), City Club New Orleans, Alpha Omega Alpha. Roman Catholic. Home: 458 Shady Lake Pky Baton Rouge LA 70810-4322 Office: Tulane U Med Ctr Dept Radiology 1415 Tulane Ave New Orleans LA 70112

PUZO, MARIO, author; b. N.Y.C., Oct. 15, 1920; s. Antonio and Maria (Le Conti) P.; m. Erika Lina Broske, 1946; children: Anthony, Joey, Dorothy, Virginia, Eugene. Student, New Sch. for Social Research, Columbia U. Lit. reviewer various mags.; former civil service employee; former editor Male Mag. Author: The Dark Arena, 1955, The Fortunate Pilgrim, 1964, The Runaway Summer of Dave Shaw, 1966, The Godfather, 1969, The Godfather Papers and Other Confessions, 1972, Inside Las Vegas, 1977, Fools Die, 1978, The Sicilian, 1984, The Fourth K, 1991; screenwriter: (with Francis Ford Coppola) The Godfather, 1972 (Academy award best adapted screenplay 1972, Screen award Writers Guild Am. West 1972, Golden Globe award best screenplay 1973), (with Coppola) The Godfather, Part II, 1974 (Academy award best adapted screenplay 1974, Screen award Writers Guild Am. West 1974), (with George Fox) Earthquake, 1974, (with Robert Benton, David Newman, and Leslie Newman) Superman, 1978, (with D. Newman and L. Newman) Superman II, 1981, (with Coppola and William Kennedy) The Cotton Club, 1984, (with Coppola) The Godfather, Part III, 1990 (Golden Globe award best screenplay 1990), (with John Briley and Cary Bates) Christopher Columbus: The Discovery, 1992. Office: Greenberg Glusker Fields Claman & Machtinger 1900 Avenue of Stars Los Angeles CA 90067*

PYATT, EVERETT ARNO, government official; b. Kansas City, Mo., July 22, 1939; s. Arno Doyne and Myrl Elizabeth (Osborn) P.; m. Susan Evelyn Kristal, Sept. 28, 1968; children: Jennifer, Laura, Jeffrey. B.E., B.S., Yale U., 1962; M.B.A., U. Pa., 1977. Staff engr. office dir. fed. research and devel. Office Asst. Sec. Def., Dept. Def., Washington, 1962-72; dir. acquisition planning Office Asst. Sec. Def. for Program Analysis and Evaluation, 1972-75; dir. logistics resources Office Asst. Sec. Def. for Installations and Logistics, 1975-77; prin. dep. asst. sec. for logistics Dept. Navy, Washington, 1977-79, prin. dep. asst. sec. for shipbldg. and logistics, 1981-84; asst. sec. for shipbldg. and logistics Dept. Navy, 1984-89; exec. advisor Coopers & Lybrand, 1989—; pres. EV Ventures; dep. chief fin. officer Dept. Energy, 1979-81; dir. Dept. Energy (Office of Alcohol Fuels), 1980. Recipient Disting. Civilian Svc. medal USN, 1980-81, 87, Superior Civilian Svc. medal, 1981, Outstanding Svc. medal Dept. Energy, 1981, Pres.'s award of meritorious excellence, 1983, Disting. Civilian Pub. Svc. award Dept. Def., 1989; Office of Sec. Def. fellow, 1975-77. Mem. IEEE. Club: Yale. Home: 4560 25th Rd N Arlington VA 22207-4147 Office: Coopers & Lybrand 1530 Wilson Blvd Arlington VA 22209-2411

PYATT, LEO ANTHONY, real estate broker; b. Key Port, N.J., Oct. 20, 1925; s. Ralph James and Anna Regina (Kussmaul) P.; m. Geraldine Genevive Gibb, May 31, 1947; children: Steven Lee, Rebecca Lynn. Student, Franklin U., 1947-49. Salesperson Standard Oil Co., Columbus, Ohio, 1947-49, Borden Dairy Co., Columbus, 1950-57, Frito-Lay, Inc., Columbus, 1958-74; sec., treas. Snack Time, Inc., Columbus, 1974-75; agt. N. NE Realty Co., Columbus, 1976-86; owner-broker Pyatt's Rose Realty Co., Columbus, 1986—. Presiding judge County Rep. Party, Franklin County, 1991. With USN, 1943-46, PTO. Decorated Air medal, Philippine Liberation award. Mem. Nat. Assn. Realtors, Ohio Bd. Realtors, Lions (treas. 1981-81). Republican. Roman Catholic. Avocations: writing, travel, hiking, reading. Home: 4400 Wanda Lane Rd Columbus OH 43224-1026 Office: Pyatts Rose Realty Co 4400 Wanda Lane Rd Columbus OH 43224-1026

PYE, GORDON BRUCE, economist; b. Oak Park, Ill., Oct. 30, 1933; s. Harold Charles and Florence Martha P. B.S. in Chem. Engring, M.I.T., 1955, Ph.D. in Econs, 1963. Asst. prof. bus. adminstrn. U. Calif., Berkeley, 1963-66; assoc. prof. U. Calif., 1966-69, prof., 1969-72; econ. cons. Standard Oil Co. Calif. (name changed to Chevron Corp.), San Francisco, 1972-74; v.p., sr. economist Irving Trust Co., N.Y.C., 1974-78, sr. v.p., mgr. econ. research and planning div., 1978-89; prin. Gordon B. Pye Assocs., N.Y.C., 1990—. Assoc. editor: Fin. Analysts Jour., 1972-89. Mem. Forecasters Club N.Y. (pres. 1980-81). Club: Univ. (San Francisco). Home: 230 E 50th St New York NY 10022-7702

PYE, LENWOOD DAVID, materials science educator, researcher, consultant; b. Little Falls, N.Y., May 16, 1937; s. Lenwood George and Elizabeth Marie (Murphy) P.; m. Constance Lee Lanphere, Sept. 6, 1958; children: DeAnn, Lorie, Lisa, Brien. BS, Alfred U., 1959, PhD, 1968. Rsch. engr. PPG Industries, Pitts., 1959-60; rsch. scientist Bausch & Lomb, Rochester, N.Y., 1960-61, 62-64; prof. glass sci. N.Y. State Coll. Ceramics, Alfred U., 1968-92. dir. Inst. Glass Sci. and Engring., 1984—; dir. Industry-Univ. Ctr. Glass Rsch., 1986—; mem. steering com. The Internat. Commn. on Glass; bd. dirs. Alfred Tech. Resources, Inc.; dir. Paul Vicker Gardner Glass Ctr. 1st lt. U.S. Army, 1960-62. Mem. Am. Ceramics Soc. (bd. trustees). Office: Alfred U NY State Coll Ceramics Ctr Glass Rsch New York NY 14802

PYE, LUCIAN WILMOT, political science educator; b. Shansi, China, Oct. 21, 1921; s. Watts Orson and Gertrude (Chaney) P.; m. Mary Toombs Waddill, Dec. 24, 1944; children: Evelyn, L. Christopher, Virginia. B.A. Carleton Coll., 1943; M.A., Yale U., 1949, Ph.D., 1951. Instr., then asst. prof. polit. sci. Washington U., St. Louis, 1949-52; research assoc. Yale U., 1951-52, Princeton, 1952-56; vis. lectr. Columbia U., 1956; mem. faculty Mass. Inst. Tech., 1956-92, prof. polit. sci., 1960-92, Ford prof., 1972-92, chmn. sect., 1961-63; sr. staff mem. Mass. Inst. Tech. (Center Internat. Studies), 1956—; vis. assoc. prof. Yale U., 1959-61; vis. prof. George Washington U., 1993, Ballial Coll., Oxford U., 1994, Fletcher Sch., Tufts U., 1994; chmn. com. comparative politics Social Sci. Rsch. Coun., 1963-73; mem. adv. com. adminstr. AID, 1961-68; cons. Dept. State, 1962-68, MSC, 1968—; trustee Asia Found., 1963—; gov. East-West Ctr., Honolulu, 1976-80; bd. dirs., v.p. Nat. Com. U.S.-China Rels. Author: Guerrilla Communism in Malaya, 1956, Politics, Personality and Nation Building, 1961, Aspects of Political Developments, 1966, Southeast Asia's Political Systems, 1967, The Spirit of Chinese Politics, 1968, Warlord Politics, 1971, China: An Introduction, 1972, Mao Tse-tung: The Man in The Leader, 1976, Dynamics of Chinese Politics, 1982, Asian Power and Politics, 1985; co-author: The Politics of the Developing Areas, 1960, The Emerging Nations, 1961; Editor:

Communications and Political Development, 1963, Political Culture and Political Development, 1965, Political Science and Area Studies, 1975. Served as 1st lt. USMCR, 1945-46. Fellow Center Advanced Study Behavioral Scis., 1963. Fellow Am. Acad. Arts and Scis., Am. Philos. Soc.; mem. Assn. Asian Studies (dir.) Am. Polit. Sci. Assn. (dir., pres. 1989), Council Fgn. Relations (dir.), Asia Soc. (dir.), Pilgrim Soc., Phi Beta Kappa. Unitarian. Club: Cosmos. Home: 72 Fletcher Rd Belmont MA 02178-2017 Office: Mass Inst Tech Dept Polit Sci Cambridge MA 02139

PYKE, JOHN SECREST, JR., lawyer, polymers company executive; b. Lakewood, Ohio, July 11, 1938; s. John S. and Elma B. P.; student Haverford Coll., 1956-58; BA, Columbia Coll., 1960, postgrad. Columbia Sch. Grad. Faculties, 1960-61; JD, Columbia Law Sch., 1964; m. Judith A., Dec. 26, 1970; 1 child, John Secrest, III. Bar: N.Y. 1965. Assoc. firm Townsend & Lewis (now Thacher, Proffit & Wood), N.Y.C., 1964-68; atty. M.A. Hanna Co., Cleve., 1968—, sec., 1973—, v.p., 1979—. Trustee, Western Res. Acad., Hudson, Ohio, 1976—. Mem. ABA, Assn. of Bar of City of N.Y., Am. Soc. Corp. Secs., Am. Corp. Counsel Assn., Union Club, Clifton Club, Cleve. Yachting Club. Author: Landmark Preservation, 1969, 2d edit., 1972. Office: MA Hanna Co 200 Public Square Ste 36-5000 Cleveland OH 44114-2304

PYKE, RONALD, mathematics educator; b. Hamilton, Ont., Can., Nov. 24, 1931; s. Harold and Grace Carter (Digby) P.; m. Gladys Mary Davey, Dec. 19, 1953; children: Darlene, Brian, Ronald, Gordon. BA (hon.), McMaster U., 1953; MS, U. Wash., 1955, PhD, 1956. Asst. prof. Stanford U., Calif. 1956-58; asst. prof. Columbia U., N.Y.C., 1958-60; prof. math. U. Wash., Seattle, 1960—; vis. prof. U. Cambridge, Eng., 1964-65, Imperial Coll., London, 1970-71, Colo. State U., Ft. Collins, 1979, Technion, Israel, 1988, 90, 92; pres. Inst. Math. Stats., 1986-87; mem. bd. math. scis. NRC/NAS, 1984-88, chmn. com. applications and theoretical stats., 1985-88. Editor Ann. Prob., 1972-75; contbr. articles to profl. jours. NSF grantee, 1961-91. Fellow Internat. Statis. Inst. (v.p. 1989-91), Am. Statis. Assn., Inst. Math. Stats. (pres. 1986-87); mem. Am. Math. Soc., Statis. Soc. of Can. Office: U Wasington Dept Math Box 354350 Seattle WA 98195-4350

PYKE, THOMAS NICHOLAS, JR., government science and engineering administrator; b. Washington, July 16, 1942; s. Thomas Nicholas and Pauline Marie (Pingitore) P.; m. Carol June Renville, June 22, 1968; children—Christopher Renville, Alexander Nicholas. B.S., Carnegie Inst. Tech., 1964; M.S. in Engring., U. Pa., 1965. Electronic engr. Nat. Bur. Standards, Gaithersburg, Md., 1964-69, chief computer networking sect., 1969-75, chief computer systems engring. div., 1975-79, dir. ctr. for computer systems engring., 1979-81, dir. ctr. programming sci. and tech., 1981-86; asst. administr. for satellite and info. services NOAA, Washington, 1986-92, dir. high performance computing and comm., 1992—; dir. The Globe Program The White House, Washington, 1994—; organizer profl. computer confs., 1970-86; mem. Presdl. Adv. Com. on Networking Structure and Function, 1980, Interagy. com. on Info. Resources Mgmt., 1983-84, bd. dirs., 1984-87, vice chmn. 1986-87 (Exec. Excellence award 1991), chmn. Interagy. Working Group on Data Mgmt. for Global Change, 1987-93; speaker in field. Editorial bd. Computer Networks Jour., 1976-86; contbr. articles to profl. jours. Bd. dirs. Glebe Commons Assn., Arlington, Va., 1976-79, v.p. 1977-79; chmn. Student Congress, Carnegie Inst. Tech., 1963-64; mem. Task Force on Computers in Schs., Arlington, 1982-85; pres. PTA, Arlington, 1983-84. Recipient Silver medal Dept. Commerce, 1973, award for exemplary achievement in pub. adminstrn. William A. Jump Found., 1975, 76, Presdl. Rank award of Meritorious Exec., 1988; Westinghouse scholar Carnegie Inst. Tech., Pitts., 1960-64; Ford Found. fellow U. Pa., Phila., 1964-66. Fellow Washington Acad. Scis. (Engring. Sci. award 1974); mem. Am. Fedn. Info. Processing Socs. (bd. dirs. 1974-76), IEEE (sr. mem.), Computer Soc. of IEEE (bd. govs. 1971-73, 75-77, vice chmn. tech. com. on personal computing 1982-86, chmn. 1986-87), AAAS, Assn. Computing Machinery, Sigma Xi, Eta Kappa Nu, Omicron Delta Kappa, Pi Kappa Alpha (chpt. v.p. 1963-64). Episcopalian. Office: The Globe Program 744 Jackson Pl Washington DC 20503

PYLE, ALAN JAMES, trust company executive; b. Toronto, Ont., Can., Aug. 27, 1946; s. Donald Graham and Mary Christine (Shaughnessy) P.; m. Mary Lou Pyle, May 9, 1975 (div. Nov. 1989); children: Ryan, Christopher, Andrew, Colin; m. Cora Alexandra Broadhurst. BA in Econs. with honors, U. Toronto, 1968; MBA, Stanford U., 1970. Systems analyst IBM Can., Toronto, 1970-71; fin. analyst Traders Group, Toronto, 1972-73; sr. v.p. Mercantile Bank Can., Toronto, 1973-86; exec. v.p. First City Trust, Toronto, 1986—; bd. dirs. Portland Lakes Devels., Halifax, N.S., Can. Mem. Can. water polo team Pan Am. Games, 1967, 71, Olympic Games, 1972. Avocations: triathalons, squash, reading. Home: 91 Walmsley Rd, Toronto, ON Canada M4V 1X7

PYLE, KENNETH BIRGER, historian, educator; b. Bellefonte, Pa., Apr. 20, 1936; s. Hugh Gillespie and Beatrice Ingeborg (Petterson) P.; m. Anne Hamilton Henszey, Dec. 22, 1960; children: William Henszey, Anne Hamilton. AB magna cum laude, Harvard U., 1958; PhD, Johns Hopkins U., 1965. Asst. prof. U. Wash., 1965-69, assoc. prof., 1969-75, prof. history and Asian studies, 1975—, dir. Henry M. Jackson Sch. Internat. Studies, 1978-88; pres. Nat. Bur. Asian Rsch., 1988—; vice chmn. Japan-U.S. Friendship Commn., 1990-92, chmn., 1992—; vis. lectr. in history Stanford U., 1964-65; vis. assoc. prof. history Yale U., 1969-70. Author: The New Generation in Meiji Japan, 1969, The Making of Modern Japan, 1978, rev. edit., 1995; editor: The Trade Crisis: How Will Japan Respond?, 1987, The Japanese Question: Power and Purpose in a New Era, 1992; founding editor: Jour. Japanese Studies, 1974-86, chmn. editorial bd., 1987-89. Bd. dirs. Maure and Mike Mansfield Found., 1979-88; mem. bd. govs. Henry M. Jackson Found., 1983—. Ford Found. fellow, 1961-64; Fulbright-Hays fellow, 1970-71; Social Sci. Research Council-Am. Council Learned Socs. fellow, 1970-73, 77, 83-84. Mem. Assn. Asian Studies, Am. Hist. Assn., Coun. Fgn. Rels. Presbyterian. Home: 8416 Midland Rd Bellevue WA 98004-5336 Office: Henry M Jackson Sch Internat Studies U Wash Seattle WA 98195

PYLE, ROBERT MILNER, JR., financial services company executive; b. Orange, N.J., Oct. 24, 1938; s. Robert M. and Dorothy (Collings) P.; m. C. Page Neville, May 31, 1969; children: Cynthia Neville, Laura Collings. BA, Williams Coll., 1960; LL.B., U. Va., 1963. Bar: N.Y. 1964. Assoc. Mudge Rose Guthrie & Alexander, N.Y.C., 1963-68; with Studebaker-Worthington, Inc., N.Y.C., 1968-77; sec. Studebaker-Worthington, Inc., 1972-76, assoc. gen. counsel, 1974-77; with Singer Co., N.Y.C., 1977-79; corp. counsel, asst. to sec. Singer Co., 1977-78, sr. corp. counsel, asst to sec., 1979; v.p., counsel Am. Soc. Corp. Secs., Inc., N.Y.C., 1979-89, v.p., sec., counsel, 1989-91; v.p., sr. asst. sec. Am. Express Co., N.Y.C., 1991—; Career counseling rep. for Williams Coll., 1977—. Trustee Pingry Sch., Martinsville, N.J., 1972-74; trustee Arts Coun. Suburban Essex Inc., 1979-84, chmn. bd., 1981-84; bd. govs. Colonial Dances, Ltd., N.Y.C., 1970-74; bd. dirs. Millburn-Short Hills Hist. Soc., 1985-90, v.p., 1985-87; trustee Suburban Cmty. Music Ctr., 1985-87. Mem. ABA, Assn. Bar City N.Y., Am. Soc. Corp. Secs. (hon.), Pingry Sch. Alumni Assn. (pres. 1972-74, bd. dirs. 1966-78, cert. of merit 1968), Pilgrims U.S., Met. Squash Racquets Assn. (past treas.), Racquet and Tennis Club, Bay Head Yacht Club (N.J.), Short Hills Club, Sigma Phi, Delta Theta Phi, Pi Delta Epsilon. Republican. Episcopalian. Office: Am Express Tower World Fin Ctr New York NY 10285-5000

PYLE, ROBERT NOBLE, public relations executive; b. Wilmington, Del., Oct. 23, 1926; s. Joseph Lybr and LaVerne Ruth (Noble) P.; m. Claire Thoron; children: Robert Noble Jr., Mark C., Nicholas A., Sarah L. BA, Dickinson Coll., 1948; postgrad., Wharton Sch., U. Pa., 1949, U. Minn. Pres. Robert N. Pyle, Inc., Wilmington, 1949-52; adminstrv. asst. to U.S. Congress, Washington, 1952-63; bus. and polit. cons. and lobbyist Robert N. Pyle & Assoc., Washington, 1970—; pres. Ind. Bakers Assn., 1981—; treas. Bulgarian Am. Bus. Ctr. Contbr. numerous articles to profl. jours.; reporter covering Nurnburg Trials, Paris Peace Conf. for, Stars & Stripes, Europe, 1946. Part-time field man Rep. Nat. Congl. Com., 1959-74; Selective Service Bd.; Served with U.S. Army, 1945-46, ETO. Mem. City Tavern Club, Nat. Press Club, Kenwood Golf & Country Club, Commodity Club. Presbyterian. Home: 1343 27th St NW Washington DC 20007-3103 Office: 1223 Potomac St NW Washington DC 20007-3212

PYLE, THOMAS ALTON, instructional television and motion picture executive; b. Phoenix, Sept. 8, 1933; s. Thomas Virgil and Evelyn B. (Redden) P.; m. Victoria K. Bileck, Apr. 21, 1957; children: Pamela V., Brett T. BA, Ariz. State U., 1956. Freelance unit mgr. theatrical motion picture industry, N.Y.C. and L.A., 1956-60; v.p. sales Depicto Films Corp., N.Y.C., 1960-65; prodr. John Sutherland Prodns., N.Y.C. and L.A., 1965-67; v.p. mktg. Audio Prodns. Ednl. Svcs., N.Y.C., 1967-71; exec. v.p. Data Plex Systems, N.Y.C., 1971-74; divsn. pres., exec. prodr. Sterling Inst. Video Prodns., Washington, 1974-80; pres. Applied Video Concepts, Inc., Washington, 1980-83; pres., CEO Nat. Sci. Ctr. Found., Burke, Va., 1983-85; CEO Network for Instrnl. TV, Inc., Reston, Va., 1987—; active in new bus. and project fundraising; bd. dirs. Cmty. Ednl. Svcs., So. Fla. Instrnl. TV, Delaware Valley (Del.) Ednl. Telecomms. Network, Inc., Instrnl. Opportunities/St. Louis, Inc.; cons. Wireless Cable Industry, 1993—. Writer, dir., producer film on Pres. John F. Kennedy, 1962; producer film biography on Pres. Lyndon B. Johnson, 1964. V.p. Dexter Park Assn., Spring Valley, N.Y., 1968-74, Solaridge Cluster Assn., Reston, Va., 1990. Recipient numerous awards from nat. and internat. film and video festivals, also 2 Commendation awards White House, 2 Acad. award nominations. Mem. Internat. Platform Assn., N.Y. Acad. of Scis. Republican. Methodist. Avocation: photography. Office: Network Instructional TV Ste 110 11490 Commerce Pk Dr Reston VA 22091

PYLE, WILLIAM CARMODY, human resource management educator, researcher; b. Indpls., Nov. 28, 1939; s. William Branham and Florence Evelyn (Carmody) P.; m. Barbara Bostian, Aug. 1978 (div. 1982); stepchildren: Lori Weaver, Jeffrey Bostian, Kyle Bostian; 1 foster child, Ramin Sobhian. BBA, U. Notre Dame, 1961; MBA, Butler U., 1962; PhD, U. Mich., 1971. Rsch. fellow U. Mich., Ann Arbor, 1967-69, rsch. assoc., 1969-72, dir. human resource acctg. program, 1972-74; assoc. prof. indsl. rels., dir. human resource rsch. program U. Minn., Mpls., 1974-78; dir. Human Resource Rsch. Ctr., U. Mass., Amherst, 1978-86; prof. mgmt. Eckerd Coll., St. Petersburg, Fla., 1986-90, Holder prof. mgmt. and internat. bus., 1990—, dir. Human Resource Inst., 1986—; cons. to over 100 Fortune 500 firms, 1970—. Contbr. articles to profl. jours. 1st lt. USAF, 1962-65. Recipient award for outstanding contbn. to field of human resource mgmt. Am. Soc. for Pers. Adminstrn., 1971. Mem. Bahai Faith. Achievements include director of research project to implement first human resource accounting system. Avocations: classical music, reading. Home: 6600 Sunset Way Unit 520-B St Petersburg Beach FL 33706 Office: Eckerd Coll Human Resource Inst 4200 54th Ave S Saint Petersburg FL 33711

PYLES, CAROL DELONG, dean, consultant, educator; b. Oil City, Pa., Apr. 6, 1948; d. William J. and Doris (Gresh) DeLong; m. Richard Pyles, Mar. 26, 1980; 1 child, Whitney Dawn. BS, Alderson-Broaddus Coll., Philippi, W.Va., 1966-70; MS in Nursing, Tex. Woman's U., 1982-85; MA, W. Va. U., 1972-73, EdD, 1974-80. RN, W.Va., Tex., Fla.; cert. health edn. specialist; lic. profl. counselor, Tex., Okla.; nat. cert. counselor. Instr. nursing Fairmont (W.Va.) State Coll., 1971-73, asst. prof. nursing edn., 1973-76, asst. dean Com. Coll., 1976-78, prof. nursing, chmn. divsn. health careers, 1978-81; cons., adj. faculty Salem Coll., Clarksburg, W.Va., 1978-81; officer Allied Health Houston Com. Coll. System, 1981-83, chmn. divsn. sales, mktg. & mgmt., 1983-85; dean Coll. Spl. Arts & Scis., prof. health edn. adminstrn. Cen. State U., Edmond, Okla., 1985-87; dean Coll. of Health, Phys. Edn. & Recreation Ea. Ill. U., Charleston, 1987-91, prof. health studies, 1987-91; dean, prof. allied health techs. Miami-Dade (Fla.) C.C., 1991—; bd. dirs. Dade County Area Health Edn. Ctr., Inc.; treas. bd. dirs. Nat. Network for Health Career Programs in Two Yr. Colls.; pres. cons. seminar devel., P & P Assoc., Inc., Houston; coun. pvt. practice for marriage, life crises, behavior & image problems. Author: articles for Issues in Higher Edn. Mem. South Fla. Health Planning Coun., Inpatient Health Care Task Force, Met. Dade County, Fla., Dade County Area Health Edn. Ctr., Inc.; chmn. Indsl. Commn., Charleston (Ill.) Recreation Ctr., 1989; bd. dirs. ARC, East Coles County chpt., Reg. United Way, Coalition Against Domestic Violence, Am. Cancer Soc. Named Personality of Am. 1986, Outstanding Young Leader in Allied Health, 1984, Most Outstanding Young Women of Am., 1983; recipient Svc. award Am. Cancer Soc., 1984. Mem. Am. Coun. Edn., Nat. Identification Program, Am. Cancer Soc., Am. Assn. Coll. for Tchrs. Edn. Inst. Reps., Assn. Schs. Allied Health Professions, Fla. Assn. Community Colls., Alliance of 100 (Fla. Hosp. Assn.), Rotary Internat., Sigma Theta Tau. Avocations: water & snow skiing, bridge, sailing, golf, tennis. Office: Miami Dade Community Coll Med Ctr Campus 950 NW 20th Med Ctr Miami FL 33127-4693

PYLES, RODNEY ALLEN, archivist, county official; b. Morgantown, W.va., June 23, 1945; s. Melford John and Luci L. (Scarcella) P.; m. Carol Louise Wrobleski, May 20, 1972; 1 child, Janessa Louise. B.A., M.A. (Benedum scholar 1966-67, grad. research asst. 1967-68, grad. teaching fellow 1968-69), W.Va. U., 1967, 69. Instr. polit. sci. Alderson-Broaddus Coll., Philippi, W.Va., 1969-71; asst. curator W.Va. U. Library, 1971-77; dir. archives and history div. W.Va. Dept. Culture and History, 1977-85; dep. chief Assessor's Office Monongalia County, 1985-88; assessor Monongalia County, 1989—. Mng. editor: W.Va. History quar., 1977-85. Mem. Morgantown (W.Va.) Dem. exec. com., 1966-69, Monongalia County (W.Va.) Dem. exec. com., 1972-74; mem. Morgantown Libr. Bd., 1988-91; pres. Morgantown Hist. Landmarks Commn., 1986—. Mem. Soc. Am. Archivists, Mid-Atlantic Regional Archives Conf., W.Va. Hist. Soc. (exec. sec. 1977-90), W.Va. Libr. Assn., Am. Assn. State and Local History (state awards chmn. 1980-85, state membership com. 1981-87), Monongalia Hist. Soc. (pres. 1986-88), W.Va. Polit. Sci. Assn. (treas. 1991—), W.Va. Assessors' Assn. (pres. 1992-93), KC, Sons of Italy (treas. 1995—). Roman Catholic. Home: 536 Harvard St Morgantown WV 26505-2157 Office: County Court House Rm 215 Morgantown WV 26505

PYLIPOW, STANLEY ROSS, retired manufacturing company executive; b. Coudersport, Pa., Apr. 4, 1936; s. Stanley Edward and Helen L. (Haskins) P.; m. Phyllis Beverly Moore, Dec. 1, 1956; children—David, James, Vicky, Kenneth, Sandra. B.B.A. in Acctg. cum laude, St. Bonaventure U., 1957. Various fin. positions Chicopee Mfg., New Brunswick, N.J., 1957-65; various positions to v.p., gen. mgr. Domestic Coatings div. Mobil Chem. Co., N.Y.C., 1965-73; asst. corp. controller Monsanto Co., St. Louis, 1974-76; controller, dir. planning Monsanto Comml. Products, St. Louis, 1976-79; sr. v.p., chief fin. officer Fisher Controls Internat., Inc., St. Louis, 1979-92; ret., 1992, now advisor to closely held businesses; mem. Acctg. Edn. Change Commn., 1985-89. Treas., City of Town and Country, Mo., 1980-84; bd. dirs. Ecumenical Housing Prodn. Corp., St. Louis, 1980-90; sr. warden St. Peter's Episcopal Ch., St. Louis, 1984-87. Served to 1st lt., U.S. Army, 1958. Named Exec. of Yr., Profl. Secs. Internat., 1982. Mem. Inst. Mgmt. Accts. (chmn. com. chpt. ops. 1984-86, rsch. com. 1986-87, v.p. 1983-84, exec. com. 1988-90, pres. 1990-91, chmn. 1991-92), Fin. Execs. Inst., Inst. Mgmt. Cons., Mfrs. Alliance for Productivity and Innovation (fin. coun. II), Bellerive Country Club. Republican. Avocations: golf, fitness, spectator sports. Home: 244 Carlyle Lake Dr Saint Louis MO 63141-7544

PYM, BRUCE MICHAEL, lawyer; b. Alameda, Calif., Sept. 29, 1942; s. Leonard A. and Willamay (Strandberg) P. B.B.A., U. Wash., 1964, J.D., 1967. Bar: Wash. 1967, U.S. Dist. Ct. (we. dist.) Wash. 1968, U.S. Ct. Appeals (9th cir.) 1968, U.S. Tax Ct. 1969, U.S. Supreme Ct. 1971. Law clk. Wash. State Supreme Ct., 1968-73; shareholder, 1973-92; ptnr. Heller, Ehrman, White & McAuliffe, Seattle, 1991—; mng. ptnr. Northwest Offices, 1994—. Bd. dirs. United Way of King County, 1986-92, chmn., 1990. Mem. ABA, Wash. State Bar Assn., Seattle-King County Bar Assn. (pres. 1984-85). Office: Heller Ehrman White & McAuliffe 701 5th Ave Ste 6100 Seattle WA 98104-7098

PYNCHON, THOMAS RUGGLES, JR., author; b. Glen Cove, N.Y., May 8, 1937; s. Thomas R. Pynchon. BA, Cornell U., 1958. Former editorial writer Boeing Aircraft Co., Seattle. Author: V, 1963 (William Faulkner novel award 1963), The Crying of Lot 49, 1966 (Rosenthal Found. award Nat. Inst. Arts and Letters 1967), Gravity's Rainbow, 1973 (Nat. Book award 1974), Slow Learner, 1984, Vineland, 1989; contbr. short stories to pubs. including N.Y. Times Mag., N.Y. Times Book Rev., Cornell Writer, Saturday Evening Post, Kenyon Rev. Served with USNR. Recipient Howells medal Nat. Inst. and Am. Acad. Arts and Letters, 1975. Office: Little Brown & Co 34 Beacon St Boston MA 02106*

PYNE, EBEN WRIGHT, banker; b. N.Y.C., June 14, 1917; s. Grafton H. and Leta Constance (Wright) P.; grad. Groton Sch., 1935; AB, Princeton, 1939; m. Hilda Holloway, Dec. 16, 1941; children: Constance Howland Pyne Ranges (dec.), Lillian Stokes (Mrs. Lillian Pyne-Corbin), Mary Alison (Mrs. M. Alison McNaughton). Clerk 1st Nat. City Trust Co. (formerly City Bank Farmers Trust Co., 1939, v.p., asst. to pres., 1952-56, exec. v.p., 1956, pres., dir., 1957-61; asst. cashier Nat. City Bank of N.Y., 1946-50, asst. v.p., 1950-52, v.p., 1952-53, sr. v.p., 1960-82; vice chmn., bd. dirs. The Home Group Inc.; bd. dirs. U.S. Life Ins. Co. City of N.Y., Home Ins. Co., U.S. Internat. Reins., Inc., Gen. Devel. Corp., Slattery Group, Inc., USLIFE Corp., L.I. Lighting Co., W.R. Grace and Co. Mem. N.Y. State Met. Transp. Authority, 1965-75; commr. N.Y.C. Transit Authority, Triborough Bridge and Tunnel Authority, Manhattan and Bronx Surface Transit Authority, Stewart Airport, S.I. Rapid Transit Operating Authority, all 1965-75; adv. bd. Nassau County council Boy Scouts Am.; bd. dirs. Winthrop U. Hosp.; trustee Juilliard Sch., St. Luke's Hosp., Grace Inst., Grace Found.; mem. exec. com. Pres.'s Pvt. Sector on Cost Control. Served as maj. AUS, 1940-46. Decorated Bronze Star. Mem. Pilgrims of U.S. (exec. com.), Bklyn. Inst. Arts and Scis. (trustee), N.Y. Zool. Soc. (trustee). Clubs: Piping Rock (Locust Valley, L.I.); Bond, Racquet and Tennis, River (N.Y.C.); Ivy (Princeton, N.J.). Home: 134 Willets Rd Box 195 Old Westbury NY 11568 Office: WR Grace & Co 1114 Ave Of The Americas New York NY 10036-7703

PYNE, FREDERICK WALLACE, genealogist, clergyman, retired civil engineer, retired mathematics educator; b. El Paso, Tex., Aug. 19, 1926; s. Frederick Cruger and Helen Louise (Wallace) P.; m. Jo Ann Rammes, July 18, 1952; children: Stephen VanRensselaer, Anne Wallace, Elizabeth Glover, Mary Clinton. BS in Civil Engring., Tri-State U., 1951; MS in Engring., Johns Hopkins U., 1966. Profl. engr., Md., Pa. Del., N.Y.; registered land surveyor; registered sanitarian; ordained priest Episcopal Ch., 1993; certified genealogist. Mcpl. engr., 1951-54; hwy. engr., pub. health engr., chief engr. State of Md., Balt., 1954-81; civil engr., biomedical engr. Dept. Def., Frederick, Md., 1981-88; adj. prof. math. Frederick C.C., 1988-94; priest Episcopal Ch. Author: The John Pyne Family in America, 1992. County surveyor Carroll County, Md., 1966-74; scout commr. Boy Scouts Am., Carroll and Frederick Counties, 1956—. Lt. inf. U.S. Army, 1944-51. Named Disting. Commr. Boy Scouts Am., 1993. Fellow ASCE; mem. Am. Acad. Environ. Engrs. (diplomate), Md. Soc. Surveyors (bd. dirs. 1972-78); life mem. SAR (Md. state registrar 1994), Descs. Signers Declaration Independence (pres.-gen. 1975-78), Soc. Colonial Wars, Mayflower Soc. Republican. Avocations: history, languages, stamp collecting. Home: 7997 Windsail Ct Frederick MD 21701

PYNN, ROGER, physicist; b. Maidstone, Kent, Eng., Feb. 15, 1945; s. Herbert John and Kathleen (Coleman) P. MA, Trinity Coll., Cambridge, Eng., 1966; PhD, U. Cambridge, 1969. Postdoctoral fellow AB Atomenergi, Studsvik, Sweden, 1970-71; rsch. fellow Inst. for Atomenergi, Kjeller, Norway, 1971-73; assoc. physicist Brookhaven Nat. Lab., Upton, N.Y., 1973-75; staff scientist Inst. Laue-Langevin, Grenoble, France, 1975-87; dir. Manuel Lujan Jr. Neutron Scatterin Ctr. Los Alamos (N.Mex.) Nat. Lab., 1987—. Mem. Norwegian Phys. Soc., Materials Rsch. Soc. Office: Los Alamos Nat Lab Manuel Lujan Neutron Scattering Ctr MS H805 Los Alamos NM 87545

PYTELL, ROBERT HENRY, lawyer, former judge; b. Detroit, Sept. 27, 1926; s. Henry Carl and Helen (Zielinski) P.; m. Laurie Mazur, June 2, 1956; children: Mary Beth, Mark Henry, Robert Michael. JD, U. Detroit, 1951. Bar: Mich. 1952. Prin. R.H. Pytell & Assocs., P.C., Detroit, 1952—; asst. U.S. atty. Ea. Dist. Mich., 1962-65; judge Mcpl. Ct., Grosse Pointe Farms, Mich., 1965-72. With USNR, 1945-46. Mem. Nat. Acad. Elder Law Attys., Am. Coll. Trust and Estate Coun., Comml. Law League Am., Crescent Sail Yacht Club (Grosse Pointe), Delta Theta Phi. Roman Catholic. Office: 18580 Mack Ave Grosse Pointe MI 48236-3251

PYTTE, AGNAR, university president; b. Kongsberg, Norway, Dec. 23, 1932; came to U.S., 1949, naturalized, 1965; s. Ole and Edith (Christiansen) P.; m. Anah Currie Loeb, June 18, 1955; children: Anders H., Anthony M., Alyson C. A.B., Princeton U., 1953; A.M., Harvard U., 1954, Ph.D., 1958. Mem. faculty Dartmouth Coll., 1958-87, prof. physics, 1967-87, chmn. dept. physics and astronomy, 1971-75, assoc. dean faculty, 1975-78, dean grad. studies, 1975-78, provost, 1982-87; pres. Case Western Res. U., Cleve., 1987—; researcher in plasma physics; mem. Project Matterhorn, Princeton, 1959-60, U. Brussels, 1966-67, Princeton U., 1978-79; bd. dirs. Goodyear Tire & Rubber Co.; A.O. Smith Corp. Bd. dirs. Sherman Fairchild Found. Inc., 1987—, Greater Cleve. Growth Assn., Cleve. United Way; bd. trustees Univs. Rsch. Assn., Ohio Aerospace Inst., Cleve. Inst. Music, Cleve. Orch. Mem. Am. Phys. Soc., Ohio Sci. and Tech. Coun., Cleve. Roundtable, Cleve. Tech. Leadership Coun., Phi Beta Kappa, Sigma Xi. Office: Case Western Res U Office of Pres Cleveland OH 44106

QASIM, SYED REAZUL, civil engineering educator, researcher; b. Allahabad, India, Dec. 1, 1938; came to U.S., 1960; s. Syed Zamir and Fakhira (Begum) Q.; m. Mujtaba Rizvi, Dec. 17, 1966; children: Zeba Saira, Saba Bano. BCE, Aligarh (India) Muslim U., 1957; MCE, W.Va. U., 1962, PhD in Environ. Engring., 1965. Registered profl. engr., Tex. Ohio. Sr. lectr. Allahabad Agrl. Inst., 1958-59; asst. dist. engr. Allahabad Mcpl. Corp., 1959-60; pool officer Indian Agrl. Rsch. Inst., New Delhi, 1965-66; design civil engr. Alden E. Stilson and Assocs., Columbus, Ohio, 1966-68; sr. civil engr. Battelle Meml. Inst., Columbus, 1968-70; assoc. prof. Poly. Inst. Bklyn., 1970-73; assoc. prof. U. Tex., Arlington, 1973-78, prof. civil engring., 1978—; cons. Chiang, Patel & Assocs., Dallas, 1981—, Butterrez, Smouse, Wilmut & Assocs., Dallas, 1984—, Kuwait Inst. for Sci. Rsch., 1992; TOKTEN (Transfer of Knowledge throuth Expatriate Nats.) cons. to UN Devel. Program, 1992. Author: Wastewater Treatment Plants: Planning, Design and Operation, 1985, Sanitary Landfill Leachate: Generation, Control and Treatment, 1994; contbr. articles to profl. jours. Recipient Halliburton award U. Tex. Arlington Coll. Engring., 1988-89, Disting. Rsch. award U. Tex. Arlington, 1990-91; Fulbright scholar India, 1986. Mem. ASCE, NSPE (chmn. awards com. 1969-70), Water Environ. Fedn., Am. Water Works Assn., Tech. Transfer Soc., Sigma Xi, Chi Epsilon, Tau Beta Pi. Home: 907 Leslie Dr Arlington TX 76012-4109 Office: U Tex at Arlington Dept Civil Engring Box 19308 Arlington TX 76019

QI, JIANG, dancer. Attended, Beijing Dancing Acad. of China. Dancer Ctrl. Dance Co., Beijing, 1978-86; dancer Ballet West, Salt Lake City, 1986-88, prin. artist, 1988—; instr. dance Ballet West Conservatory, U. Utah Dept. Ballet. Dance performances include Abdallah, Corsaire Pas de Deux, Grand Pas Classique, Coppelia, La Bayadere, Les Patineurs, The Nutcracker, Paquita, Romeo & Juliet, The Dream, others. Recipient Silver prize China Ballet Competition, 1980; named Premier Artist of China, Chinese Govt., 1980. Office: Ballet West 50 West 200 South Salt Lake City UT 84101*

QUAAL, WARD LOUIS, broadcast executive; b. Ishpeming, Mich., Apr. 7, 1919; s. Sigfred Emil and Alma Charlotte (Larson) Q.; m. Dorothy J. Graham, Mar. 9, 1944; children: Graham Ward, Jennifer Anne. A.B., U. Mich., 1941; LL.D. (hon.), Mundelein Coll., 1962, No. Mich. U., 1967, DePaul U., 1974. Announcer-writer Sta. WBEO (now sta. WDMJ), Marquette, Mich., 1936-37; announcer, writer, producer Sta. WJR, Detroit, 1937-41; spl. events announcer-producer WGN, Chgo., 1941-42, asst. to gen. mgr., 1945-49; exec. dir. Clear Channel Broadcasting Service, Washington, 1949-52, pres., chief exec. officer, 1964-74; v.p., asst. gen. mgr. Crosley Broadcasting Corp., Cin., 1952-56; v.p., gen. mgr., mem. bd. WGN Inc., Chgo., 1956; exec. v.p., then pres. WGN Continental Broadcasting Co. (now Tribune Broadcasting Co.), 1960-75; pres. Ward L. Quaal Co., 1975—; dir. Tribune Co., 1961-75; dir., mem. exec. com. U.S. Satellite Broadcasting Co., 1982—; bd. dirs. Christine Valmy Inc., Nat. Press Found., chmn. exec. com., dir. WLW Radio Inc., Cin., 1975-81; co-founder, dir. Universal Resources Inc., 1961-86; mem. FCC Adv. Com. on Advanced TV Systems, 1988—. Author: (with others) Broadcast Management, 1968, rev. edit., 1995; co-prodr. (Broadway play) Teddy and Alice, 1988. Mem., Hoover Commn. Exec. Br. Task Force, 1954-59; mem. U.S.-Japan Cultural Exchange Commn., 1960-70; mem. Pres.'s Council Phys. Fitness and Sports, 1983-93; bd. dirs. Farm Found., 1963-73; bd. trustees Hollywood (Calif.) Mus., 1964-78, MacCormac Jr. Coll., Chgo., 1974-80; chmn. exec. com. Council for TV Devel., 1969-72; mem. bus. adv. coun. Chgo. Urban League, 1964-74; bd.

dirs. Broadcasters Found., Internat. Radio and TV Found., Sears Roebuck Found., 1970-73; trustee Mundelein Coll., 1962-72, Hillsdale Coll., 1966-72. Served as lt. USNR, 1942-45. Recipient Disting. Bd. Gov's award Nat. Acad. TV Arts and Scis., 1966, 87, Freedoms Found. award, Valley Forge, 1966, 68, 70, Disting. Alumnus award U. Mich., 1967, Loyola U. Key, 1970, Advt. Man of Yr. Gold medallion, Chgo. Advt. Club, 1968, Disting. Svc. award Nat. Assn. Broadcasters, 1973, Ill. Broadcaster of Yr. award, 1973, Press Vet. of Yr. award, 1973, Comm.award of distinction Brandeis U., 1973 Founder & Leadership award Broadcast Pioneers Libr., 1991; first recipient Sterling Medal, Barren Found., 1985, Lifetime Achievement award in broadcasting Ill. Broadcasters Assn., 1989; 1st person named to Better Bus. Bur. Hall of Fame, Council of Better Bus. Burs. Inc., 1975; named Radio Man of Yr. Am. Coll. Radio, Arts, Crafts & Scis., 1961, Laureate in Order of Lincoln, Lincoln Acad. Ill., 1965, Communicator of Yr., Jewish United Fund, 1969, Advt. Club Man of Yr., 1973; named to Broadcasting mag. Hall Fame, 1991, Delta Tau Delta Disting. Svc. Chpt., 1970. Mem. NATAS (bd. govs. 1966-76, Silver Circle award 1993), Nat. Press Found. (bd. dirs. 1991—), Nat. Assn. Broadcasters (bd. dirs. 1952-56), Fed. Comm. Bar Assn., Broadcast Music Inc. (bd. dirs. 1953-70), Assn. Maximum Svc. Telecasters Inc. (bd. dirs. 1952-72), Broadcast Pioneers (pres., bd. dirs. 1962-73), Broadcast Pioneers Libr. (pres. 1981-84), Broadcast Pioneers Ednl. Fund Inc., Am. Advt. Fedn. (ethics com.), Delta Tau Delta (Alumni Achievement award 1990, disting. svc. chpt.), Internat. Club (Washington), Mid.-Am. Club, Exmoor Country Club (Chgo.), Kenwood Golf. Office: Ward L Quaal Co 401 N Michigan Ave Ste 3140 Chicago IL 60611-4207

QUACKENBUSH, JUSTIN LOWE, chief federal judge; b. Spokane, Wash., Oct. 3, 1929; s. Carl Clifford and Marian Huldah (Lowe) Q.; m. Marie McAtee; children: Karl Justin, Kathleen Marie, Robert Craig. BA, U. Idaho, 1951; LLB, Gonzaga U., Spokane, 1957. Bar: Wash. 1957. Dep. pros. atty. Spokane County, 1957-59; ptnr. Quackenbush, Dean, Bailey & Henderson, Spokane, 1959-80; dist. judge U.S. Dist. Ct. (ea. dist.) Wash., Spokane, 1980—, now chief judge; part-time instr. Gonzaga U. Law Sch., 1960-67. Chmn. Spokane County Planning Commn., 1969-73. Served with USN, 1951-54. Mem. ABA, Wash. Bar Assn., Spokane County Bar Assn. (trustee 1976-78), Internat. Footprint Assn. (nat. pres. 1967), Spokane C. of C. (trustee, exec. com. 1978-79). Episcopalian. Club: Spokane Country. Lodge: Shriners. Office: US Dist Ct PO Box 1432 Spokane WA 99210-1432

QUACKENBUSH, MARGERY CLOUSER, psychoanalyst, administrator; b. Reading, Pa., Apr. 30, 1938; d. Carl Brumbach and Katherine Elvina (Althouse) Clouser; m. Robert Mead Quackenbush, July 3, 1971; 1 child, Piet Robert. BA, Pratt Inst., 1960; MA, Calif. Grad. Inst., 1982. Cert. in psychoanalysis. Instr. Pratt Inst., Bklyn., 1978-79, Fash. Inst. of Tech., N.Y.C., 1980-81; counselor Wiltwyck, Bronx Ctr., 1981-82; administr. Nat. Assn. for Advancement of Psychoanalysis, N.Y.C., 1982—; pvt. practice in psychoanalysis N.Y.C., 1982—. Mem. Lenox Hill Dem. Club, N.Y.C., 1993-95; spkr. various community groups, 1991-95. Recipient Award Maison Blanche, 1959, Miriam Berkman Spotnitz, 1992. Mem. Nat. Assn. for Advancement of Psychoanalysis, Nat. Soc. DAR , Alumni Assn. of the Center for Modern Psych. Studies (sec. 1992-94, Alumni Assn. program dir., v.p. 1992-94). Democrat. Avocations: reading, writing, golf, horseback riding. Home: 460 E 79th St #14E New York NY 10021 Office: Nat Assn Advancement Psychoanalysis 80 8th Ave #1501 New York NY 10011

QUACKENBUSH, ROBERT MEAD, artist, author, psychoanalyst; b. Hollywood, Calif., July 23, 1929; s. Roy Maynard and Virginia (Arbogast) Q.; m. Margery Clouser, July 3, 1971; 1 child: Piet Robert. Bachelor Profl. Arts, Art Ctr. Coll. of Design, Pasadena, Calif., 1956; grad., Ctr. Modern Psychoanalytic Studies, N.Y.C., 1991; MSW, Fordham U., 1994. Art dir. Scandinavian Airlines System, N.Y.C. and Stockholm, 1956-61; pvt. practice N.Y.C., 1961—; educator Robert Quackenbush Studios, N.Y.C.; lectr. U.S., Europe, Middle East and South Am.; TV performer Ednl. TV; mem. faculty N.J. Ctr. for Modern Psychoanalysis. Author/artist over 160 books for young readers including Old MacDonald Had A Farm, 1972, Clementine, 1974, There'll Be a Hot Time in the Old Town Tonight, 1974, Pop! Goes the Weasel and Yankee Doodle, 1976, The Holiday Song Book, 1977, Along Came the Model T! How Henry Ford Put the World on Wheels, 1978, Who Threw That Pie?, The Birth of Comedy Movie, 1979, Piet Potter's First Case, 1980, The Boy Who Waited for Santa Claus, 1981, Detective Mole Mystery Series (winner Edgar Allen Poe Spl. Award 1982), Henry's Important Date, 1981, No Mouse for Me, 1981, Here a Plant, There a Plant, Everywhere a Plant, Plant! The Story of Luther Burbank, 1982, Henry Babysits, 1983, I Don't Want To Go, I Don't Know How to Act, 1983, Taxi to Intrigue, 1984, Who Said There's No Man on the Moon? The Story of Jules Verne, 1985, Who Let Muddy Boots into the House? The Story of Andrew Jackson, 1986, Mouse Feathers, 1988, Danger in Tibet, 1989, Robert Quackenbush's Treasury of Humor, 1990, Benjamin Franklin and His Friends, 1991, Evil Under the Sea, 1992, James Madison & Dolly Madison and Their Times, 1993, Arthur Ashe and His Match with History, 1994, Clara Barton and Her Victory Over Fear, 1994; producer: TV series Dear Mr. Quackenbush and The Great American Storybook for Educational Television; films include American Songfest, 1978. With U.S. Army 1951-53. Recipient 2 Citations for outstanding Troop Info. & Edn. instrn. from commdg. gen. 31st Inf. Divsn. 1953, 3 time winner Am. Flag Inst. award for outstanding contbn. to field of children's lit., 1976, 77, 81, Edgar Allen Poe Spl. award, 1982. Mem. Mystery Writers of Am., Authors' Guild, Authors' League of Am., Holland Soc. of N.Y., Nat. Assn. for Advancement of Psychoanalysis (bd. trustees), Soc. Modern Psychoanalysts (cert.). Avocations: travel, antique restoration. Home: 460 E 79th St Apt 14E New York NY 10021-1445 Office: Robert Quackenbush Studios 223 E 78th St New York NY 10021-1222

QUACKENBUSH, ROGER E., secondary education educator; b. Cooperstown, N.Y., Jan. 22, 1940; s. Eugene W. and Marion I. (Clark) Q.; m. Cathy E. Quackenbush, Mar. 31, 1973; children: Michele, Stacey, Thomas. BS, SUNY, Albany, 1961, MS, 1966; PhD, Columbia Pacific U., San Rafael, Calif., 1984; postgrad., numerous univs. Cert. permanent biology and gen. sci. tchr., N.Y. Tchr. gen. sci. and math Troy (N.Y.) Pub. Sch. System, 1961-64; tchr. earth sci. and biology Schuylerville (N.Y.) Cen. High Sch., 1964-66; tchr. biology Bethlehem Cen. High Sch., Delmar, N.Y., 1966—; instr. Tchr. Expectation Student Achievement program, 1985-91; lectr. on marine mammals SUNY, Albany, 1986; lectr. on whales; workshop leader on use microcomputers in classroom; mem. Mid. States Commn. on Evaluation Local High Schs.; past mem. adv. bd. Upstate N.Y. Jr. Sci. and Humanities Symposium; test writer Regents biology exams. N.Y. State Dept. Edn.; leader, naturalist for whale watch trips and Kenya safaris; workshop presenter for DNA-molecular biology lab. techniques; mem. Select Seminar on Evaluating Tchrs., 1985, Wells Conf. Regents Biology Syllabus Revision, 1991. Editor/writer of alternative assessments for N.Y. State Edn. Dept., 1993-94; contbr. numerous articles to profl. jours. Hon. admisssions liaison officer USAF Acad., 1988. Recipient Excellence in Teaching award, 1989, letter of commendation U. Chgo., 1978, MIT, 1985, U.S. Army, 1989, Tufts U., 1990, 94, Tchr. of Yr. award Tufts U., 1985, Golub Tchr.-Scholar award SUNY, 1991; Chpt. II grantee N.Y. State Dept. Edn., 1987, NSF grantee, 1965, 67, 68, 72, 87, 90, Future Directions, 1990, Greenwall Found., 1993, Tandy Tech. Scholar prize for excellence in sci. tchg., 1995; named Hon. Grad. Marshall, 1991, 94. Mem. NEA, NEA of N.Y., Biology and Life Sci. Assn., Nat. Assn. Biology Tchrs., Soc. for Marine Mammology, Am. Cetacean Soc., Conn. Cetacean Soc., Sci. Tchrs. Assn. N.Y. State (past sect. dir., past state bd. dirs.), Bethlehem Cen. Tchrs. Assn., Phi Delta Kappa. Home: 25 Robinhood Rd Albany NY 12203-5133 Office: Bethlehem Cen H S 700 Delaware Ave Delmar NY 12054-2499

QUADE, QUENTIN LON, political science educator; b. Ft. Dodge, Ia., Jan. 28, 1933; s. Louis Anton and Vera (Chrisman) Q.; m. Phyllis F. Fleskes, Jan. 2, 1954; children: Zachary, Christopher, Matthew, Stephanie, Leslie. BS, Creighton U., 1957; M.A., Notre Dame U., 1958, Ph.D., 1965. Instr. polit. sci. St. Louis U., 1959-61; faculty polit. sci. Marquette U., Milw., 1961—, prof., dean —1988, Raynor prof. polit. sci., 1991—, dean Grad. Sch., 1968, assoc. acad. v.p., grad. dean, 1970-72, acad. v.p., 1972-74, exec. v.p., 1974-90; dir. Ctr. for Parental Freedom in Edn., 1992—. Author: Paths to Parental Freedom and School Choice, 1995, Pope and Revolution, 1982, (with T.J. Bennett) American Politics: Responsible and Effective?, 1969, U.S. and Wars of National Liberation, 1966; contbr. articles to profl. jours. Served with USAF, 1950-53. Roman Catholic. Home: 7326 Maple Ter Milwaukee WI 53213-3153 Office: 615 N 11th St Milwaukee WI 53233-2305 *Love the truth. Know the good. Do it.*

QUADE, VICTORIA CATHERINE, editor, writer; b. Chgo., Aug. 15, 1953; d. Victor and Virginia (Uryasz) Q.; m. Charles J. White III, Feb. 15, 1986; children: Michael, David, Catherine. BS in Journalism, No. Ill. U., 1974. Staff reporter news divsn. The News-Tribune, LaSalle, Ill., 1975-77; staff writer news divsn. The News-Sun, Waukegan, Ill., 1977-81; staff writer ABA Jour., Chgo., 1981-85; mng. editor ABA Press, Chgo., 1985-90, editor, 1990—, sr. editor, 1994—. Author: Rain and Other Poems, 1976, Laughing Eyes, 1979, Two Under the Covers, 1981; co-author: (plays) (with Maripat Donovan) Late Nite Catechism: Saints, Sisters & Ejaculation, 1993, Room for Advancement, 1994; editor Human Rights mag.; contbr. to numerous anthologies and publs. Recipient numerous awards from Soc. Nat. Assn. Publs., AP, UPI. Mem. Am. Soc. Bus. Press Editors (award), Chgo. Newspaper Guild (award), Am. Soc. Assn. Execs. (Gold Circle award 1989, 90). Avocations: traveling, photography. Office: ABA 750 N Lake Shore Dr Chicago IL 60611-4403

QUADER, PATRICIA ANN, elementary education educator; b. Pitts., Sept. 9, 1941; d. Andrew and Julia (Gutilla) Supira; m. Walter Anthony Quader, Jan. 15, 1966. BA, Carlow Coll., 1963; MEd, U. Pitts., 1967. Cert. elem. tchr., supt., Pa. Tchr. Diocese of Pitts., 1963-64; tutor Pitts. Tchrs. Tutoring Svc., 1964-65; intern tchr. Burrell Sch. Dist., Lower Burrell, Pa., 1966; tchr. Kiski Area Sch. Dist., Vandergrift, Pa., 1966-91; computer, libr. skills tchr. Vandergrift Elem. Sch., 1991—; instr. Pa. State U., New Kensington, 1970-72; in-svc. instr. in computer literacy Kiski Area Sch. Dist., 1985-91, 95, edited K-3 computer skills curriculum. Co-author: 4th and 5th grade computer literacy curricula for Kiski Sch. Dist.; editor Kiski Area K-6 Computer Skills Curriculum, 1991—. Chmn. Bell-Avon PTA, Salina, Pa., 1988-91. Recipient scholarship Carlow Coll., 1959. Mem. NEA, ASCD, Pa. State Edn. Assn., Kiski Area Edn. Assn., Phi Delta Kappa. Democrat. Roman Catholic. Avocations: mystery novels, computer games. Office: Vandergrift Elem Sch 420 Franklin Ave Vandergrift PA 15690-1311

QUADRACCI, HARRY R., printing company executive. Chmn. bd. Quad Graphics Inc., Pewaukee, Wis. Office: Quad Graphics Inc W224N3322 Duplainville Rd Pewaukee WI 53072

QUADRACCI, HARRY V., printing company executive, lawyer; b. 1936. JD, Columbia U., 1959. Assoc. N.Y.C., Milw., 1961-71; corp. counsel W.A. Krueger Co., Brookfield, Wis., 1961-71; pres. Quad Graphics, Inc., Pewaukee, Wis., 1971—. Office: Quad Graphics Inc W224n3322 Duplainville Rd Pewaukee WI 53072-4137

QUADT, RAYMOND ADOLPH, metallurgist, cement company executive; b. Perth Amboy, N.J., Apr. 16, 1916; s. Adolph and Florence (MacCracken) Q.; 1 child, Brian. B.S., Rutgers U., 1939; M.A., Columbia U., 1943; M.S., Stevens Inst. Tech., 1948. Tchr. high sch. Plainfield, N.J., 1939-42; research metallurgist Am. Smelting & Refining Co., Barber, N.J., 1942-48; dir. aluminum devel. Am. Smelting & Refining Co., 1948-50; v.p. Hunter Douglas Corp., Riverside, Calif., 1950-57; v.p. spl. metals, 1962-63; v.p. Nat. Distillers and Chem. Corp., N.Y.C., 1963—; chmn. bd. Loud Co., Pomona, Calif., 1963—; pres., gen. mgr. Reactive Metals Inc., 1960-62; v.p., gen. mgr. Pascoe Steel Corp., Pomona, 1965-73; pres. Phoenix Cement Co., 1973-80, cons., 1980-83; chmn. bd. Trendex, Inc., Phoenix, 1983-87, Mesco Phoenix, 1983-88; vice chmn. Sunstate Bancshares Inc., Casa Grande, Ariz., 1982; bd. dirs. Republic Nat. Bank, Phoenix, 1982—; chmn. Express Delivery, Phoenix, 1991-94, Mariah Internat., Inc., Phoenix, 1992-93; v.p., sec. Ariz. Custom Motorcoaches, Mesa, Ariz., 1995—. Mem. Am. Soc. Metals, Pomona C. of C. (pres. 1970), Phi Beta Kappa. Home and Office: 6454 S Willow Dr Tempe AZ 85283-3968

QUAID, DENNIS, actor; b. Houston, Apr. 9, 1954; s. William Rudy and Juanita B. Q.; m. Meg Ryan, 1991; 1 child, Jack Henry. Student, U. Houston, 1972-75. Appearances include (film) I Never Promised You A Rosegarden, 1977, Sept. 30, 1955, 1978, Our Winning Season, 1978, The Seniors, 1978, Breaking Away, 1979, G.O.R.P., 1980, The Long Riders, 1980, Caveman, 1981, All Night Long, 1981, The Night the Lights Went Out in Georgia, 1981, Tough Enough, 1983, Jaws 3-D, 1983, The Right Stuff, 1983, Dreamscape, 1984, Enemy Mine, 1986, Innerspace, 1987, The BigEasy, 1987, Suspect, 1987, D.O.A., 1988, Everybody's All-American, 1988, Great Balls of Fire, 1989, Postcards from the Edge, 1990, Come See the Paradise, 1990, Undercover Blues, 1993, Wilder Napalm, 1993, Flesh and Bone, 1993, Wyatt Earp, 1994; (theatre) The Last of the Knucklemen, 1983, True West, 1984, (TV movies) Are You In the House Alone?, 1978, Amateur Night at the Dixie Bar and Grill, 1979, Bill, 1981, Johnny Belinda, 1982, Bill: On His Own, 1983, Wyatt Earp, 1994. *An artist must take chances in performing his craft. If he is to succeed he must be willing to fall flat on his face.*

QUAID, RANDY, actor; b. Houston, Oct. 1, 1950; s. William R. and Juanita B. Quaid; m. Ella Marie Jolly, May 11, 1980 (div.); 1 child. Student, Houston Baptist Coll., 1969-70, U. Houston, 1970-71. Film appearances include Targets, 1968, The Last Picture Show, 1971, What's Up Doc, 1972, Lolly Madonna XXX, 1972, The Last Detail, 1973 (Acad. award, Golden Globe nominations for best supporting actor), Paper Moon, 1973, Apprenticeship of Duddy Kravitz, 1974, Breakout, 1974, Missouri Breaks, 1975, Bound for Glory, 1976, The Choirboys, 1977, Three Warriors, 1978, Midnight Express, 1979, Foxes, 1980, Long Riders, 1980, Heart Beeps, 1981, National Lampoon's Vacation, 1983, The Wild Life, 1984, The Slugger's Wife, 1985, Fool for Love, 1986, The Wraith, 1986, Caddyshack II, 1988, Moving, 1988, Parents, 1989, Out Cold, 1989, Blood Hounds of Broadway, 1989, National Lampoon's Christmas Vacation, 1989, Quick Change, 1990, Martians Go Home, 1990, Days of Thunder, 1990, Quick Change, 1990, Texasville, 1990, Freaked, 1993, The Paper, 1994, Bye Bye, Love, 1995; appeared in TV films Getting Away From It All, 1972, The Great Niagara, 1974, The Last Ride of the Dalton Gang, 1979, To Race the Wind, 1980, Guayana Tragedy: The Story of Jim Jones, 1980, Of Mice and Men, 1981, Inside the Third Reich, 1982, Cowboy, 1983, A Street Car Named Desire, 1984, LBJ: The Early Years, 1986, Dead Solid Perfect, 1988, Evil in Clear River, 1988, Murder in the Heartland, 1993, Frankenstein, 1993, Next Door, 1994; TV series Saturday Night Live, 1985-87, Davis Rules, 1991-92; off-Broadway play True West, 1983. Mem. Acad. Motion Picture Arts and Scis. *

QUAIL, BEVERLY J., lawyer; b. Glendale, Calif., June 19, 1949; d. John Henry and Dorothy Marie (Gamblin) Q.; m. Timothy D. Roble; children: Benjamin W., Elizabeth L. BA magna cum laude, U. So. Calif., 1971; JD, U. Denver, 1974. Bar: Colo. 1974. Assoc., Conover, McClearn & Heppenstall, P.C., Denver, 1974-75; dir. Dufford & Brown, P.C., Denver, 1975—; broker Colo. Assn. Realtors, 1982-93; lectr. continuing legal edn. Colo.; v.p., bd. mem. Girls Club Denver, 1984-87; bd. dirs. Swedish Hosp. Found., Legal Aid of Colo. Found. Mem. ABA (chmn. real property litigation and dispute resolution com., coun. real property, probate & trust sect. 1990—), Am. Coll. Real Estate Lawyers (bd. govs.), Colo. Real Estate Council, Cen. City Opera House Assn., Phi Beta Kappa. Clubs: Univ., (coms.), Castle Pines Golf, Cherry Hills Country (Denver). Author Colo. Real Estate Forms-Practice, Real Property Practice & Litigation; editor newsletter The Colo. Lawyer, 1983-87; contbr. articles to profl. jours. Office: Dufford & Brown 1700 Broadway Ste 1700 Denver CO 80290-1701

QUAIN, MITCHELL L, investment executive; b. N.Y.C., Nov. 15, 1951; m. Cherie Quain; children: Sam, Rhonda, Jacob, Samuel, Michelle. BSEE, U. Pa., 1973; MBA, Harvard U., 1975. CFA. Mng. dir. Wertheim Schroder, N.Y.C., 1975—; bd. dirs. Allied Products Corp. Mem. bd. overseers Sch. Engring. & Applied Scis., U. Pa.; trustee St. Lukes Acad. Office: Wertheim Schroder & Co Inc 787 7th Ave New York NY 10019-6018

QUAINTANCE, ROBERT FORSYTH, JR., lawyer; b. Evanston, Ill., Apr. 22, 1950. BA, Amherst Coll., 1972; JD, NYU, 1977. Bar: Vt. 1977, N.Y. 1980. Clk. Vt. Supreme Ct., 1977-78; instr. NYU Sch. Law, 1978-80; assoc. Debevoise & Plimpton, N.Y.C., 1980-87; ptnr. Debevoise & Plimpton, 1987—; lectr. in field. Contbr. articles to profl. jours. Mem. Assn. of Bar of City of N.Y. Office: Debevoise & Plimpton 875 3rd Ave New York NY 10022

QUAINTON, ANTHONY CECIL EDEN, diplomat; b. Seattle, Apr. 4, 1934; s. Cecil Eden and Marjorie Josephine (Eates) Q.; m. Susan Long, Aug. 7, 1958; children: Katherine, Eden, Elizabeth. B.A., Princeton U., 1955; B.Litt., Oxford (Eng.) U., 1958. Research fellow St. Antony's Coll., Oxford, 1958-59; with Fgn. Service, State Dept., 1959—; vice consul Sydney, Australia, 1960-62; Urdu lang. trainee, 1962-63; 2d sec., econ. officer Am. embassy, Karachi, Pakistan, 1963-64, Rawalpindi, Pakistan, 1964-66; 2d sec., polit. officer Am. embassy, New Delhi, 1966-69; sr. polit. officer for India Dept. State, Washington, 1969-72; 1st sec. Am. embassy, Paris, 1972-73; counselor, dep. chief mission Am. embassy, Kathmandu, Nepal, 1973-76; ambassador to Central African Empire, Bangui, 1976-78, Nicaragua, Managua, 1982-84, Kuwait, 1984-87; dir. Office for Combatting Terrorism, Dept. State, Washington, 1978-81; dep. insp. gen. Dept. State, 1987-89; ambassador Peru, 1989-92; asst. sec. of state for diplomatic security Dept. State, Washington, 1992—. English Speaking Union fellow, 1951-52; Marshall scholar, 1955-58; recipient Rivkin award, 1972, Herter award, 1984. Mem. Am. Fgn. Svc. Assn., Lions Internat., Met. Club, Phi Beta Kappa. Home: 3424 Porter St NW Washington DC 20016-3126 Office: care Dept State 2201 C St NW Washington DC 20520

QUALE, ANDREW CHRISTOPHER, JR., lawyer; b. Boston, July 7, 1942; s. Andrew Christopher and Luella (Meland) Q.; m. Sally Sterling Ellis, Oct. 15, 1977; children: Andrew, Addison. BA magna cum laude, Harvard U., 1963, LLB cum laude, 1966; postgrad., Cambridge (Eng.) U., 1966-67. Bar: Mass. 1967, N.Y. 1971. Fellow Internat. Legal Ctr., Bogota, Colombia, 1967-68; cons. Republic of Colombia, Bogota, 1968-69; assoc. Cleary, Gottlieb, Steen and Hamilton, N.Y.C., 1969-75; ptnr. Coudert Brothers, N.Y.C., 1975-82, Sidley and Austin, N.Y.C., 1982—; bd. dirs. Den Danske Corp.; adj. prof. Sch. of Law U. Va., Charlottesville, 1976-88; cons. privatizations World Bank, UN, Harvard Inst. Internat. Devel., 1982—. Contbr. to profl. publs. Pres. Bronxville (N.Y.) Sch. Bd., 1991—; founder, bd. dirs. Bronxville Sch. Found., 1991—. Mem. ABA, Assn. Bar City N.Y., N.Y. State Bar Assn., N.Y.C. Bar Assn. (chmn. inter-Am. affairs com. 1982-85), Bronxville Field Club, Norfolk (Conn.) Country Club, Doolittle Club (Norfolk). Avocations: singing, skiing, fishing. Office: Sidley and Austin 875 3d Ave New York NY 10022

QUALE, JOHN CARTER, lawyer; b. Boston, Aug. 16, 1946; s. Andrew C. and Luella (Meland) Q.; m. Diane Zipursky, Jan. 19, 1992; children: Virginia Ann, Jane Harris, John Andrew. AB cum laude, Harvard Coll., 1968; JD cum laude, Harvard Law Sch., 1971. Bar: Mass. 1971, D.C. 1972. Assoc. Kirkland & Ellis, Washington, 1971-78, ptnr., 1978-83; ptnr. Wiley, Rein & Fielding, Washington, 1983—; Speaker mass media trade groups. Contbr. articles to profl. jours. Trustee Fed. Comm. Bar Assn. Found., 1992-93. Mem. ABA, Fed. Comm. Bar Assn. (treas. 1982-83, exec. com. 1993—), Mass. Bar Assn., Barristers, Met. Club. Office: Wiley Rein & Fielding 1776 K St NW Washington DC 20006-2304

QUALLEY, CHARLES ALBERT, fine arts educator; b. Creston, Iowa, Mar. 19, 1930; s. Albert Olaf and Cleora (Dietrick) Q.; m. Betty Jean Griffith, Nov. 26, 1954; children: Janet Lynn, John Stuart. B.F.A., Drake U., 1952; M.A., U. Iowa, 1956, M.F.A., 1958; Ed.D., Ill. State U., 1967. Art tchr. Des Moines Pub. Schs., 1952, 54-55; critic art tchr. U. Iowa, 1955-57; prof. fine arts U. Colo., Boulder, 1958-90, prof. emeritus, 1990—; chmn. dept. fine arts U. Colo., 1968-71, assoc. chmn., 1981-82; vis. prof. Inst. for Shipboard Edn., semester at sea, 1979, Ill. State U., 1983. Author: Safety in the Art Room, 1986; contbg. editor Sch. Arts, 1978-85, mem. editorial adv. bd., 1985-87; author column Safetypoint, 1981-85. Served with AUS, 1952-54, Korea. Mem. Nat. Art Edn. Assn. (v.p. 1980-82, pres. 1987-89, dir. conv. svcs. 1990—, fellow 1990—, trustee 1987—, art educator of yr. 1993), Colo. Art Edn. Assn. (editor 1965-67, 75, pres. 1976-78), Delta Phi Delta, Omicron Delta Kappa, Pi Kappa Delta. Home: 409 Fillmore Ct Louisville CO 80027-2273

QUALLS, ROBERT L, manufacturing executive, banker, former state official, educator; b. Burnsville, Miss., Nov. 6, 1933; s. Wes E. and Letha (Parker) Q.; m. Carolyn Morgan, Feb. 10, 1979; 1 dau., Stephanie Elizabeth. BS, Miss. State U., 1954, MS, 1958; PhD, La. State U., 1962; LLD, Whitworth Coll., 1974; DBA (hon.), U. of the Ozarks, 1984. Prof., chmn. div. econs. and bus. Belhaven Coll., Jackson, Miss., 1962-66; asst. to pres. Belhaven Coll., 1965-66; asst. prof. finance Miss. State U., State College, 1967-69, adj. prof., 1969-73; sr. v.p., chmn. venture com. Bank of Miss., Tupelo, 1969-73; v.p. Wesleyan Coll., Macon, Ga., 1974; pres. U. of the Ozarks, Clarksville, Ark., 1974-79; mem. cabinet Bill Clinton Gov. of Ark., 1979-80; exec. v.p. Worthen Nat. Bank, 1980-85; chmn., chief exec. officer, dir. Worthen Nat. Bank, Harrison, Ark., 1985-86; sr. v.p. 1st Ark. Bankstock Corp. (name changed to Worthen Nat. Bank), 1980-85; pres., dir. First Bank Fin. Services, Inc., 1980-85, Advt. Assocs., Inc., 1980-85; pres., chief oper. officer Baldor Electric Co., Ft. Smith, Ark., 1986—, CEO, 1992; mktg. cons. Ill. Central Industries, Chgo., 1964; mem. faculty, thesis examiner Stonier Grad. Sch. Banking, Rutgers U., 1973-86; mem. faculty Miss. Sch. Banking, U. Miss., 1973-78; course coordinator Sch. Banking of the South, La. State U., 1978-88, Banking Sch., Duke U., 1977; lectr. Southwestern Sch. Banking, So. Meth. U., 1983; adj. prof. bus. adminstrn. U. Central Ark., 1985-86. Author: Entrepreneurial Wit and Wisdom, 1986; co-author: Strategic Planning for Colleges and Universities: A Systems Approach to Planning and Resource Allocation, 1979; mem. editorial adv. bd.: Bank Mktg. Mag., 1984-86. Chmn. cmty. svc. and continuing edn. com. Tupelo Cmty. Devel. Found., 1972-73; mem. Miss. 4-H adv. coun., 1969; active Boy Scouts Am.; mem. Lee County Dem. Exec. Com., 1973-74; trustee Wal-Mart Found., 1975-79, Oklahoma City U., 1990—; trustee, mem. exec. com. U. Ozarks, 1982-88; mem. Pres.'s Roundtable U. Ctrl. Ark., 1982-87; mem. exec. com. Coll. Bus. Adv. Bd., U. Ark., Little Rock, 1980-85; bd. dirs. U. Ark. Med. Sch. Found., 1991—, Ark. Inst., 1991-94, Associated Industries Ark., treas., 1993-94, v.p., 1994-95. Lt. AUS, 1954-56. Found. for Econ. Edn. fellow, 1964; Ford Found. faculty research fellow Vanderbilt U., 1963-64; recipient Pillar of Progress award Johnson County, 1977. Mem. Am. Bankers Assn. (mktg. planning and rsch. com. 1972-73), Ark. Coun. Ind. Colls. and Univs. (chmn. 1978-79), Johnson County C. of C. (pres. 1977), Fort Smith C. of C. (dir. 1995—), Blue Key, Omicron Delta Kappa, Delta Sigma Pi, Sigma Phi Epsilon (citation 1977), Masons (32 deg.), Clarksville Rotary (pres. 1979). Presbyterian. Office: Baldor Electric Co 5711 S 7th St Fort Smith AR 72901-8394

QUALLS, ROXANNE, mayor of Cincinnati. Former exec. dir. Women Helping Women; former dir. No. Ky. Rape Crisis Ctr.; former dir. Cin. office Ohio Citizen Action; councilwoman City of Cin., 1991-93, mayor, 1993—; former chairperson Cin. City Council's Intergovtl. Affairs and Environment Com.; former vice chairperson Community Devel., Housing and Zoning Com.; 2d v.p. OKI Regional Coun. Govts.; mem. Gov.'s Commn. on Storage and Use of Toxic and Hazardous Materials, Solid Waste Adv. Com. of State of Ohio, Gov.'s Waste Minimization Task Force; former chair bd. commrs. Cin. Met. Housing Authority; bd. dirs. Shuttlesworth Housing Found. Hon. chair Friends of Women's Studies; mem. Jr. League Adv. Coun. Recipient Woman of Distinction award Girl Scouts U.S., 1992, Woman of Distinction award Soroptomists, 1993, Outstanding Achievement award Cin. Woman's Polit. Caucus, 1993. Office: City Hall 801 Plum St Rm 150 Cincinnati OH 45202*

QUALSET, CALVIN O., agronomy educator; b. Newman Grove, Nebr., Apr. 24, 1937; s. Herman Qualset and Adeline (Hanson) Vakoc; m. Kathleen Boehler; children: Douglas, Cheryl, Gary. BS, U. Nebr., 1958; MS, U. Calif., Davis, 1960, PhD, 1964. Asst. prof. U. Tenn., Knoxville, 1964-67; from asst. prof. to assoc. prof. U. Calif., Davis, 1967, prof., 1973-94, prof. emeritus, 1994—, chmn. dept. agronomy and range sci., 1975-81, 91-94, assoc. dean coll. agrl. and environ. sci., 1981-86; dir. Genetic Resources Conservation Program, Davis, 1985—; sci. liaison officer U.S. Agy. Internat. Devel., Washington, 1985-93, mem. rsch. adv. com., 1989-92; mem. nat. plant genetic resources bd. USDA, Washington, 1982-88. Contbr. over 180 articles to profl. jours. Fulbright fellow, Australia, 1976, Yugoslavia, 1984. Fellow AAAS (chmn. agr. sect. 1992), Am. Soc. Agronomy (pres. 1994); mem. Genetics Soc. Am., Crop Sci. Soc. Am. (pres. 1989). Achievements include development of 8 cultivars of wheat and triticale. Office: Genetic Res Conserv Prog Univ of Calif Davis CA 95616

QUALTER, TERENCE HALL, retired political science educator; b. Eltham, New Zealand, Apr. 15, 1925; emigrated to Can., 1957; s. Michael Frederick and Mary (Hall) Q.; m. Shirley Anne Card, May 19, 1951; children: Karen Anne, Matthew John, Paul Michael, Adam James. B.A., U. New Zealand, 1951; Ph.D., U. London-London Sch. Econs., 1956. Newscaster New Zealand Broadcasting Service, Wellington, 1948-51; various positions London, 1951-57; lectr. United Coll., Winnipeg, Man., Can., 1957-58; spl. lectr. U. Sask., 1958-60; lectr. polit. sci. U. Waterloo, Ont., Can., 1960-61; asst. prof. polit. sci. U. Waterloo, 1961-64, assoc. prof., 1964-67, prof. polit. sci., 1967—; chmn. dept. polit. sci., 1965-67, 70-73. Author: Propaganda and Psychological Warfare, 1962, The Election Process in Canada, 1970, Graham Wallas and the Great Society, 1980, Opinion Control in the Democracies, 1985, Conflicting Political Ideas in Liberal Democracies, 1986, Advertising and Democracy in the Mass Age, 1991. Served with Royal New Zealand Air Force, 1944-47. Grantee Can. Council, NRC Can., Social Sci. and Humanities Research Council Can. Home: 249 Stonybrook Dr, Kitchener, ON Canada

QUANDT, RICHARD EMERIC, economics educator; b. Budapest, Hungary, June 1, 1930; came to U.S., 1949, naturalized, 1954; s. Richard F. and Elisabeth (Toth) Q.; m. Jean H. Briggs, Aug. 6, 1955; 1 son, Stephen. BA, Princeton U., 1952; MA, Harvard U., 1955, PhD, 1957; Dr. Econs. (hon.), Budapest U. Econs. Scis., 1991, Kossuth Lajos U., Hungary, 1994. Mem. faculty Princeton U., 1956—, prof. econs., 1964-95, prof. emeritus, sr. rsch. economist, 1995—, Hughes-Rogers prof. econs., 1976-95, chmn. dept., 1968-71, 85-88; dir. Fin. Rsch. Ctr., 1982—; rsch. prof. Ford Found., 1967-68; prof. emeritus, sr. rsch. economist Princeton U., 1995—; cons. Alderson Assocs., 1959-61; sr. cons. Mathematica, Inc., 1961-67; cons. Internat. Air Transport Assn., 1974-75, N.Y. Stock Exch., 1976-77, N.Y. State Dept. Edn., 1978; adviser Am.-Hungarian Found., 1977-78; editorial advisor Holt, Rinehart & Winston, 1968-72; fin. adviser Inst. for Rsch. in History, 1986; sr. advisor Andrew W. Mellon Found., 1989—; mem. adv. coun. Budapest U. Econ. Scis., 1992-93; vis. prof. Birkbeck Coll., 1981, U. Leicester, 1989-92; mem. Census Adv. Com., 1983-86; mem. adv. com. Coll. Fin. and Acctg., Budapest, 1993-94. Author: (with J. M. Henderson) Microeconomic Theory: A Mathematical Approach, 1958, 2d edit., 1971, 3d edit., 1980, (with W.L. Thorp) The New Inflation, 1959, (with B.G. Malkiel) Strategies and Rational Decisions in the Securities Option Market, 1969; editor: The Demand for Travel: Theory and Measurement, 1970; (with S.M. Goldfeld) Nonlinear Methods in Econometrics, 1972, Studies in Nonlinear Estimation, 1976; (with P. Asch) Racetrack Betting: The Professor's Guide to Strategies, 1986, (with M. Peston) Prices, Competition and Equilibrium, 1986, The Econometrics of Disequilibrium, 1988, (with H.S. Rosen) The Conflict Between Equilibrium and Disequilibrium Theories, 1988; also numerous articles; editorial bd.: Applied Econs., Econs. of Planning, Rev. Econ. and Stats., 1980-91; assoc. editor: Econometrica, 1976-80, Jour. Am. Statis. Assn, 1974-80, Bell Jour. Econs., Jour. of Comparative Econs., 1988-91, Empirica, 1988-93. Trustee Corvina Found., 1992—. Recipient merit citation Jagiellonian U., Poland, 1991, gold medal Eötvös Lóránd U., Budapest, 1991; Guggenheim fellow, 1958-59; McCosh fellow, 1964; NSF sr. postdoctoral fellow, 1971-72. Fellow Am. Statis. Assn., Econometric Soc. (mem. coun. 1985-88), Am. Acad. Arts and Scis.; mem. Am. Econ. Assn., Math. Programming Soc., Am. Philos. Soc., Hungarian Librs. Assn. (hon.). Home: 162 Springdale Rd Princeton NJ 08540-4948 Office: Princeton U Fin Rsch Ctr Dept Econs Princeton NJ 08544

QUANDT, WILLIAM BAUER, political scientist; b. Los Angeles, Nov. 23, 1941; s. William Carl and Dorothy Elaine (Bauer) Q.; m. Anna Spitzer, June 21, 1964 (div. 1980); m. Helena Cobban, Apr. 21, 1984; 1 child, Lorna. B.A., Stanford U., 1963; Ph.D., MIT, 1968. Researcher Rand Corp., Santa Monica, Calif., 1968-72; staff mem. Nat. Security Council, Washington, 1972-74, sr. staff mem., 1977-79; assoc. prof. U. Pa., Phila. 1974-76; sr. fellow Brookings Instn., Washington, 1979-94; prof. govt. and fgn. affairs U. Va., Charlottesville, 1994—; sr. assoc., Cambridge Energy Research Assocs., Mass., 1983—. Author: Revolution and Political Leadership: Algeria, 1954-68, The Politics of Palestinian Nationalism, 1973, Decade of Decisions, 1977, Saudi Arabia in the 1980's, 1981, Camp David: Peacemaking and Politics, 1986, The United States and Egypt, 1990, Peace Process, 1993. Social Scis. Research Council fellow, 1966; Council Fgn. Relations fellow, 1972; NDEA fellow, 1963. Mem. Council Fgn. Relations, Middle East Inst., Middle East Studies Assn. (pres. 1987-88). Avocations: tennis; travel; photography. Home: 2318 44th St NW Washington DC 20007-1101 Office: U Va Dept Govt and Fgn Affairs Cabell Hall 255 Charlottesville VA 22901

QUANN, JOAN LOUISE, English language educator, real estate broker; b. Phila., Oct. 14, 1935; d. John Joseph and Pauline Cecelia (Karpink) Q. Diploma, U. Paris, 1963; BA in French, U. Pa., 1976; grad., Temple U. Real Estate Inst., 1988; MEd, Temple U, 1994. Lic. real estate broker. Exec. sec. to chief fgn. corr. Newsweek, Inc., Paris, 1964-70; internat. editorial asst. Newsweek, Inc., N.Y.C., 1971-73; exec. sec., adminstrv. asst. Richard I. Rubin & Co., Inc., Phila., 1977-91; tchr. French and English to speakers of other langs. The Sch. Dist. of Phila., Bd. Edn., 1991—. Judge of elections City of Phila., 1977-81. Mem. AAUW (2d v.p. membership 1985-87, bd. dirs., corr. sec. 1987-91, fin. com. 1993), Alliance Francaise, La Societe Francophone Arts et Loisirs (bd. dirs. 1988—), Pa. Acad. Fine Arts, MLA of Phila. and Vicinity. Republican. Roman Catholic. Avocations: art history, reading, swimming, travel. Office: Sch Dist of Phila Bd Edn 21st St S Of The Pky S Philadelphia PA 19103

QUARLES, CARROLL ADAIR, JR., physicist, educator; b. Abilene, Tex., Nov. 24, 1938; s. Carroll Adair and Marguerite Marie (Vollmers) Q.; m. Sonja Gale Bandy, May 14, 1971; children: Jennifer Anne, John Patrick. B.A., Tex. Christian U., 1960; Ph.D., Princeton, 1964. Research physicist Brookhaven Nat. Lab., Upton, N.Y., 1964-67; mem. faculty Tex. Christian U., 1967—, asso. prof. physics 1970-76, prof., 1976—, W.A. Moncrief Jr. prof. physics, 1986—, chmn. physics dept., 1978-84; asso. dean Tex. Christian U. (Coll. Arts and Scis.), 1974-78. Contbr. articles to profl. jours. Mem. AAAS, Am. Phys. Soc. (sec.-treas. Tex. sect. 1984), Am. Assn. Physics Tchrs. (pres. Tex. sect. 1984), Sigma Xi, Phi Beta Kappa (pres. Delta of Tex. chpt. 1982-84), Alpha Chi, Pi Mu Epsilon. Roman Catholic. Office: Tex Christian U Dept Physics Fort Worth TX 76129

QUARLES, JAMES CLIV, law educator; b. Charlottesville, Va., Mar. 18, 1921; s. James Cliv and Lucy (Sinclair) Q.; m. Prudence White, Sept. 1, 1944 (dec.); children: Rebecca Wayne (Mrs. Douglas S. McLeod), James Peyton, Christopher Sinclair.; m. Audrey Clark Keeter, June 10, 1983. B.A., U. Va., 1942, LL.B., 1945. Bar: Va. 1944, Ga. 1955. Law clk. U.S. circuit judge, 1945-47; instr. law Walter F. George Sch. Law, Mercer U., 1947-48, asst. prof., 1948-49, asso. prof., 1949-52, prof., 1952-69, acting dean, 1950-51, 56-58, dean, 1958-69; prof. law U Fla., Gainesville, 1969—; Exec. dir. Fla. Law Revision Commn., 1969-71; chmn. research group Ga. Criminal Law Study Com., 1961-66; mem. Gainesville Human Relations Adv. Bd., 1972-85, chmn., 1975-77, 81-83; bd. dirs. Macon Legal Aid Soc., 1956-60; mediator State Atty.'s Citizen Dispute Resolution Program, 1983—. Editor: Cases and Materials on Florida Constitutional Law, 1977; contbr. articles to legal publs. Mem. ABA; Ga. Bar Assn.; Macon Bar Assn.; Mem. Am. Law Inst., State U. System Law Faculty Assn. (pres. 1975—), Order Coif, Raven Soc., Pi Delta Epsilon. Democrat. Presbyn. Home: 9519 NW 27th Pl Gainesville FL 32606-5119

QUARLES, JAMES LINWOOD, III, lawyer; b. Huntington, W.Va., Oct. 12, 1946; s. James Linwood Jr. and Beatrice (Hardwick) Q.; m. Sharon Taft, Dec. 20, 1969; children: Jessica, Matthew. BS cum laude, Denison U., 1968; JD cum laude, Harvard U., 1974. Bar: Mass. 1974, U.S. Dist. Ct. Mass. 1975, U.S. Ct. Appeals (D.C. cir.) 1975, U.S. Ct. Appeals (6th cir.) 1979, U.S. Supreme Ct. 1980, D.C. 1981, U.S. Ct. Appeals (2d cir.) 1981, U.S. Ct. Appeals (1st and 4th cirs.) 1983, Md. 1985. Law clk. to presiding justice U.S. Dist. Ct. Md., Balt., 1972-73; with Watergate Spl. Pros. Force, Washington, 1973-75; from assoc. to sr. ptnr. Hale and Dorr, Boston and Washington, 1975—. Mem. Am. Law Inst. Democrat. Office: Hale & Dorr 1455 Pennsylvania Ave NW Washington DC 20004-1008

QUARTARARO, PHIL, recording industry executive. Pres., CEO, CHB Virgin Records Am. Inc. Office: Virgin Records Am Inc 338 N Foothill Rd Beverly Hills CA 90210*

QUARTON, WILLIAM BARLOW, broadcasting company executive; b. Algona, Iowa, Mar. 27, 1903; s. William B. and Ella B. (Reaser) Q.; m. Elnora Bierkamp, Aug. 24, 1935; 1 dau., Diane (Mrs. Waldo F. Geiger). Student, U. Iowa, 1921-22, George Washington U., 1923-25. Joined radio sta. KWCR, Cedar Rapids, Iowa, 1931; comml. mgr. radio sta. WMT, 1936, gen. mgr., 1943; v.p. Am. Broadcasting Stas., Inc., 1959-68, chmn., 1968-70; chmn. bd. KWMT Inc., Ft. Dodge, Iowa, 1968-88, Cable Communications Iowa, Inc., 1971-83; pres. WMT-TV, Inc., 1959-68; chmn. adv. bd. CBS-TV Affiliates, 1960; Mem. bd. Iowa Ednl. Broadcasting Network, 1967-77; bd. govs. Pub. Broadcasting Service, 1973-78. Trustee Coe Coll., 1946-78; trustee, mem. exec. com. Herbert Hoover Presdl. Library; bd. regents State Iowa, 1965-71. Mem. Cedar Rapids C. of C. (pres. 1944), Nat. Assn. Broadcasters (chmn. TV bd. 1962-63, chmn. joint bd. 1963-64). Clubs: Ft. Lauderdale Country (Fla.), Coral Ridge Yacht (Ft. Lauderdale); Cedar Rapids Country. Lodge: Rotary. Home: 134 Kyrie SE Cedar Rapids IA 52403-1712 Office: 1810 I E Tower Cedar Rapids IA 52401

QUASHA, ALAN G., oil and gas company executive; b. Manila, Philippines, 1950. JD, Harvard U., 1976, MBA, 1976. Assoc. Davis Polk & Wardwell, 1976-79; ptnr. Quasha Richter Schneider & Wessely, N.Y.C., 1980—; now chmn. bd. Harken Oil & Gas Inc.; dir. Crystal Oil Co.; chmn. Restructuring Assocs. Mem. ABA. Office: Harken Energy Corp 2505 N Highway 360 Dallas TX 75261

QUASHA, WILLIAM HOWARD, lawyer; b. N.Y.C., May 19, 1912; BS in Mech. Engring., NYU, 1933, MA, 1935; LLB, St. John's U., 1936; HHD honoris causa, Lyceum of the Philippines, 1995; 1 child: Angelina; m. Isabel Abad Santos, May 22, 1989. Bar: N.Y., 1936, Philippine, 1945, U.S. Supreme Ct., 1947. Pvt. Practice law, N.Y.C., 1936-42, Manila, 1946—; sr. ptnr. Quasha, Asperilla, Ancheta, Peña, and Nolasco; chmn., bd. dirs. Marcopper Mining Corp., Manila. Faculty, N.Y. U., 1933-35, Santo Tomas U., Manila, 1946-48; vis. assoc. prof. L.I. U., 1966; lectr. Harvard U. Law Sch., 1976, U. Philippines Coll. Law, 1979. Mem. nat. exec. bd. Boy Scouts Philippines, 1955-74, mem. exec. bd. Manila coun., 1949-74, v.p., treas., 1964-74, hon. life pres., 1970; v.p., legal counsel Acacia Mut. Aid Soc., Inc., Manila, 1963—; mem. exec. bd. Far East coun. Boy Scouts Am., 1973—; pres., chmn. bd. trustees St. Luke's Med. Ctr., Manila, 1975—, incorporator, cons. to bd. trustees St. Luke's Coll. Medicine; mem. coun. advisers Jose P. Laurel Meml. Found.; chmn. Reps. Abroad Com., Philippines, 1979-84, chmn. Asia-Pacific region, 1985-86, chmn. adv. com. 1987-90; founder bd. trustees Filipino Am. Meml. Endowment. With AUS, 1942-46, PTO; lt. col. Res. Decorated Bronze Star with oak leaf cluster, Philippine Legion of Honor (officer rank); recipient Silver Tamaraw, Boy Scouts Philippines, 1959, Silver Fir Tree Br., Boy Scouts Austria, 1960; Distinguished Eagle Scout award Boy Scouts Am., 1970, Silver Buffalo award, 1974. Named Outstanding Manilan City of Manila, 1970, 93; tribute of appreciation U.S. Dept. State, 1983; Conrado Benitez Heritage award Philippine Women's U., 1983. Mem. ABA, Integrated Bar of Philippines (Pioneer of Bar Integration award 1994), Law Asia, Interlaw, Am. Soc. Internat. Law, Am. Col. of C. of Philippines, USN League U.S. (judge adv., chartermem.), Am. Assn. Philippines, Propeller Club U.S. (past pres., charter mem. Manila chpt.), Philippine Constn. Assn. (life), Philippine Soc. Internat. Law, Ramon Magsaysay Meml. Soc., Knights of Rizal (knight comdr.), Nat. Sojourners (pres. 1959), Am. Legion (dept. comdr. 1954-55), Manila Jr. C. of C. (assoc., v.p. 1949), Internat. C. of C. (gov. Philippine coun. 1964-86). Episcopalian (sr. warden, chancellor). Lodge: Masons (33 deg., grand master 1962-63, Chevalier of Legion of Honor Supreme Coun. of Order De Molay 1986, dean of preceptory Philippines chpt. 1991—), regent, trustee Cathedral St. John the Divine, N.Y., 1988—; Shriner, Elk (bd. dirs. palsy project 1954-69, chmn. 1963-65), Rotarian (past bd. dir. Manila). Clubs: Nat. Lawyers' (Washington); Am. Nat. (Sydney, Australia); Univ. (N.Y.); Army and Navy, Manila Polo, others. Author: (with Rensis Likert) Revised Minnesota Paper Form Board Test. Home: 22 Molave Pl, Makati Metro Manila The Philippines Office: Don Pablo Bldg, 114 Amorsolo St, Legaspi Village Metro Manila The Philippines

QUATE, CALVIN FORREST, engineering educator; b. Baker, Nev., Dec. 7, 1923; s. Graham Shepard and Margie (Lake) Q.; m. Dorothy Marshall, June 28, 1945 (div. 1985); children: Robin, Claudia, Holly, Rhodalee; m. Arnice Streit, Jan., 1987. B.S. in Elec. Engring., U. Utah, 1944; Ph.D., Stanford U., 1950. Mem. tech. staff Bell Telephone Labs., Murray Hill, N.J., 1949-58; dir. research Sandia Corp., Albuquerque, 1959-60, v.p. research, 1960-61; prof. dept. applied physics and elec. engring. Stanford (Calif.) U., 1961—, chmn. applied physics, 1969-72, 78-81, Leland T. Edwards prof. engring., 1986—; assoc. dean Sch. Humanities and Scis., 1972-74, 82-83; sr. research fellow Xerox Research Ctr., Palo Alto, Calif., 1984—. Served as lt. (j.g.) USNR, 1944-46. Recipient Rank prize for Opto-electronics, 1982, Pres.'s Nat. medal of Sci. 1992. Fellow IEEE (medal of honor 1988), Am. Acad. Arts and Scis., Acoustical Soc.; mem. NAE, NAS, Am. Phys. Soc., Royal Microscop. Soc. (hon.), Sigma Xi, Tau Beta Pi. Office: Stanford University Dept Applied Physics Stanford CA 94305-4090*

QUATTLEBAUM, WALTER EMMETT, JR., telephone company executive; b. Midville, Ga., Dec. 22, 1922; s. Walter Emmett and Eva (Bagley) Q.; student Murrey Vocational Sch., Charleston, S.C., 1941, U. Hawaii, 1943; m. Dorothy Evelyn Clewis, Oct. 19, 1946; children: Walter Emmett III, Amalia Ann. Former owner Fla. Telephone Exchange, Sneads, Cottondale, Grand Ridge, Bonifay, Westville, and Seagrove Beach, Quattlebaum Telephone Supply Co., Quattlebaum Investments, also Spanish Trail Motel, Bonifay, Fla.; v.p., dir. Seminole Telephone Co., Donalsonville, Ga.; now investment analyst Quattlebaum Investments and others. Author: Journey of Intrigue and Success. City councilman, Sneads, 1950-52, pres. City Council, 1953. Served with AUS, 1944-46. Mem. Fla. Telephone Assn., Telephone Pioneers Am. Methodist. Office: Quattlebaum Investments PO Box 36 Bonifay FL 32425-0036

QUAY, THOMAS EMERY, lawyer; b. Cleve., Apr. 3, 1934; s. Harold Emery and Esther Ann (Thomas) Q.; divorced; children: Martha Wyndham, Glynis Cobb, Eliza Emery; m. Winnifred B. Cutler, May 13, 1989. A.B. in Humanities magna cum laude (Univ. scholar), Princeton U., 1956; LL.B. (Univ. scholar), U. Pa., 1963. Bar: Pa. 1964. Assoc. Pepper, Hamilton & Scheetz, Phila., 1963-65; with William H. Rorer, Inc., Ft. Washington, Pa., 1965—; sec., counsel William H. Rorer, Inc., 1974-79, v.p., gen. counsel, sec., 1979-88; v.p. legal planning and adminstrn. Rorer Group, 1988-90; counsel Reed Smith Shaw and McClay, Phila., 1991-93; pvt. practice, 1993—. Bd. dirs. Main Line YMCA, Ardmore, Pa., 1971-73, chmn. bd., 1972-73; editor 10th Reunion Book Princeton Class of 1956, 1966, 25th Reunion Book, 1981—, class sec., 1966-71, class v.p., 1971-81, pres., 1981-86. Lt. (j.g.) USNR, 1957-60. Recipient Svc. Commendation Main Line YMCA, 1973. Mem. ABA, Pa. Bar Assn., Phila. Bar Assn., Pharm. Mfrs. Assn. (chmn. law sect. 1983), Pa. Biotech. Assn. (chmn. legis. com., mem. exec. com. 1991-93), Phila. Drug Exch. (chmn. legis. com 1975-78), Cannon Club of Princeton U., Sharswood Law Club of U. Pa., Princeton Club of Phila. Democrat. Presbyterian. Home: 30 Coopertown Rd Haverford PA 19041-1013 Office: 9 Union Ave Ste 202 Bala Cynwyd PA 19004-3323

QUAYLE, J(AMES) DANFORTH, former vice president of United States, investment company executive; b. Indpls., Feb. 4, 1947; s. James C. and Corinne (Pulliam) Q.; m. Marilyn Tucker, Nov. 18, 1972; children: Tucker Danforth, Benjamin Eugene, Mary Corinne. BS in Polit. Sci., DePauw U., Greencastle, Ind., 1969; JD, Ind. U., 1974. Bar: Ind. 1974. Ct. reporter, pressman Huntington (Ind.) Herald-Press, 1965-69, assoc. pub., gen. mgr., 1974-76; mem. consumer protection div. Office Atty. Gen., State of Ind., 1970-71; adminstrv. asst. to gov. State of Ind., 1971-73; dir. Ind. Inheritance Tax Div., 1973-74; mem. 95th-96th Congresses from 4th Dist. Ind.; U.S. Senator from Ind., 1981-89, V.P. of U.S., 1989-93; with Circle Investors, Indpls., 1993—; tchr. bus. law Huntington Coll., 1975. Author: Standing Firm, 1994. Capt. Ind. Army N.G., 1970-76. Mem. Huntington Bar Assn. Hoosier State Press Assn., Huntington C. of C. Club: Rotary. Home: 10550 Hussey Ln Carmel IN 46032

QUAYLE, MARILYN TUCKER, lawyer, wife of former vice president of U.S.; b. 1949; d. Warren and Mary Alice Tucker; m. J. Danforth Quayle, Nov. 18, 1972; children: Tucker, Benjamin, Corinne. BA in Polit. Sci., Purdue U., 1971; JD, Ind. U., 1974. Pvt. practice atty. Huntington, Ind.,

1974-77; ptnr. Krieg, DeVault, Alexander & Capehart, Indpls., 1993—. Author: (with Nancy T. Northcott) Embrace the Serpent, 1992. Office: Krieg DeVault Alexander & Capehart 1 Indiana Sq Ste 2800 Indianapolis IN 46204-2017*

QUAYTMAN, HARVEY, painter; b. Far Rockaway, N.Y., 1937. Student, Syracuse U., 1955-57; BFA, Tufts U., 1959, Sch. of Mus. of Fine Arts, Boston, 1959; grad. cert., Tufts U. One-man shows include AIA Gallery, London, 1962, Ward-Nasse Gallery, Boston, 1964, Royal Marks Gallery, N.Y., 1966, Contemporary Arts Mus., Houston, 1967, 73, Paula Cooper Art Gallery, 1969, 71, Onnasch Galerie, Cologne, Germany, 1971, Galerie Ostergren, Malmo, Sweden, 1973, Henri 2, Washington, 1973, Cunningham Ward Gallery, 1974, David McKee Gallery, N.Y., 1975, 77, 78, 80, 82, 84, 86, 87, 91, 93, 94, Nina Nielsen Gallery, Boston, 1976, 78, 80, 83, 86, 89, 93, 94, 95, Galerie Arnesen, Copenhagen, Galerie Nordenhake, Malmo, 1982, 86, 87, Stockholm, 1990, Galerie Engstrom, Stockholm, 1982, Storrer Gallery, Zurich, 1983, Galleria Katarina, Helsinki, Finland, 1984, Dolan/Maxwell Gallery, Phila., 1987, Hoffman/Borman Gallery, L.A., 1988, Persons & Lindell Gallery, Helsinki, 1990, Gilbert Brownstone Gallery, Paris, 1990, Tony Oliver Gallery, Melbourne, Australia, 1990, Art Gallery New South Wales, Sydney, Australia, 1991, Haines Gallery, San Francisco, 1994; group exhbns. include Paula Cooper Gallery, 1968, 69, 70, 71, 73, The Jewish Mus., N.Y.C., 1969, Akron Art Inst., 1969, Art Inst. Chgo., 1972, Poindexter Gallery, N.Y.C., 1973, Phyllis Kind Gallery, N.Y.C., 1973, Power Gallery Contemporary Art, Sydney, 1973, Balt. Mus. Art, 1974, Albright-Knox Art Gallery, Buffalo, 1974, Inst. Contemporary Art, Boston, 1974, High Mus. Art, Atlanta, 1974, 76, PSI, Queens, N.Y., 1977, Mus. Contemporary Art, N.Y.C., 1978, 87-88, Nina Nielsen Gallery, Boston, 1979, 84, 90, Gallerie Schlegl, Zurich, 1979, Grand Palais, Paris, 1980, Axiom Gallery, Melbourne, 1981, Israel Mus., Jerusalem, 1982, Weatherspoon Art Gallery, Greensboro, N.C., 1982, Jersey City Mus., 1983, Galerie Norballe, Copenhagen, 1983, Harvard U., 1983, Hokkaido (Japan) Mus. Modern Art, 1984, Galerie Grafiart, Turku, Finland, 1984, Hill Gallery, Birmingham, Mich., 1985, Jay Gorney Modern Art, N.Y.C., 1985, Pamela Auchincloss Gallery, Santa Barbara, Calif., 1986, Asher/Faure Gallery, L.A., 1987, Corcoran Bienvale, Washington, 1987, Ateneum, Helsinki, Finland, 1987, Dart Gallery, Chgo., 1988, Germans Van Eck Gallery, N.Y.C., 1989, Ljubiana Bienale 18, Yugoslavia, 1989, Tony Oliver Gallery, 1992, Rose Art Mus., Waltham, Mass.; public collections include Mus. Modern Art, N.Y.C., Tate Gallery, London, Whitney Mus. Am. Art, N.Y.C., Corcoran Gallery Art, Washington, Mus. Fine Arts, Boston, Henie-Onstad Mus., Oslo, Israel Mus., Jerusalem, Kuntsthalle Malmo, Sweden, Mus. Contemporary Art, Helsinki, Allen Meml. Art Mus., Oberlin, Ohio, Del. Art Mus., Wilmington, Denver Mus. Art, Fogg Art Mus., Cambridge, Mass., High Art Mus., Atlanta, Houston Mus. Fine Arts, Lannan Mus., L.A., The Lousiana Mus., Humlebaeck, Denmark, Newberger Mus., Purchase, N.Y., Nat. Gallery Art, Canberra, Australia, Nat. Gallery Art, Wellington, New Zealand, Pasadena (Calif.) Art Mus., Pori Mus., Finland, Rose Art Mus., Waltham, Mass., Tel Aviv Mus., Va. Mus. Fine Arts, Richmond, Worcester (Mass.) Mus. Art., Henie-Onstad Art Ctr., Oslo, Queensland Art Gallery, Australia, Cleve. Ctr. for Contemporary Art, N.Y. Hill Gallery, Tony Oliver Gallery, Galerie Denis Cade, N.Y., Tel Aviv Mus. Art, Henie-Onstaad Ctr., Norway, The Painting Ctr., N.Y., Bill Maynes Contemporary Art, N.Y., Haines Gallery, San Francisco, Stephen Wirtz Gallery, Phillips Collection, Washington D.C. Grantee: CAPS, 1972, 75, Elizabeth Found. for the Arts, 1994; Guggenheim fellow, 1979, 85, Artist's fellow NEA, 1983. Mem. NAD. Avocation: early 20th century model airplane building. Home: 231 Bowery New York NY 10002

QUEBE, JERRY LEE, architect; b. Indpls., Nov. 7, 1942; s. Charlie Christopher and Katheryn Rosella (Hankins) Q.; m. Julie Ann Gordon (div.); 1 child, Dana Ann; m. Lisbeth Jane Gray, Mar. 16, 1968. BArch, Iowa State U., 1965. Registered architect, Ill., Calif. Mem. staff Hansen Lind Meyer, Iowa City, 1965-70, assoc., 1970-74, prin., 1975-77; prin., v.p. Hansen Lind Meyer, Chgo., 1977-86; prin., exec. v.p. VVKR, Inc., Alexandria, Va., 1986-88; prin., exec. v.p. Perkins & Will, Chgo., 1988-93, exec. v.p., 1994—, also bd. dirs.; chmn. Cedar Rapids/Iowa City Architects Council, 1974. Author: Drafting Practices Manual, 1978; contbr. articles to profl. jours. Pres. bd. dirs. Mental Health Assn. of Greater Chgo. 1990-95. Fellow AIA; mem. Am. Hosp. Assn., Chgo. Health Exec. Forum, Forum for Health Care Planning (bd. dirs. 1992—). Avocations: photography, scuba diving, sports car racing, reading. Home: 1908 N Sedgwick St Chicago IL 60614-5410 Office: Perkins & Will 330 N Wabash Ste 3600 Chicago IL 60611

QUEBEDEAUX, BRUNO, horticulture educator; b. Arnandville, La., June 8, 1941; s. Bruno Sr. and Iola (Guidry) Q.; m. Maureen Fahey, Aug. 13, 1966; children: Anette M., Michael J., Adele M. BS, La. State U., 1962, MS, 1963; PhD, Cornell U., 1968. Horticulturist Tex. A&M U., College Station, 1963-65; rsch. scientist E.I. du Pont de Nemours & Co., Wilmington, Del., 1968-80; team leader/COP U.S. AID Contract, Mauritania, 1980-83; chmn. dept. horticulture U. Md., College Park, 1983-90, prof., 1983—. Assoc. editor Crop Sci. Soc. Am., Madison, Wis., 1979-82; editor: Horticulture and Human Health, 1988; author: (publ.) Oxygen: New Factor Controlling Reproductive Growth, 1973. Bd. dirs. League of Internat. Food Edn., Washington, 1987-90; sch. bd. chmn. Internat. Sch. Nauakchott, Mauritania, 1980-82; asst. scout master Boy Scouts Am., Wilmington, 1978-80; bd. dirs. Chapelcroft Civic Assn., Wilmington, 1978-80, v.p., 1975-77. Recipient Merit award USDA/ARS Nat. Resources, 1989. Fellow Am. Soc. Hort. Sci. (v.p internat. merit 1988-89, L. Ware award 1962); mem. Am. Soc. Plant Physiology (pres. 1989-90, pres. Washington sect. 1990-91), Am. Soc. Agronomy (assoc. editor 1979-82), N.Y. Acad. Sci. Alpha Zeta. Achievements include patents for Method of Increasing Sugar Content in Crops, for Carbomoyl Phosphonate as Plant Growth Regulators, for Ureidotriazoles as Cytokinins and Yield Increasing Agents for Crop Plants, for Ureidotriazoles as Cytokinins and Plant Antisenescence Agents, for Selected Amidoxy Compounds as Flower Preservatives; research on oxygen regulation of plant growth. Home: 2417 Laurelwood Ter Silver Spring MD 20905-6419 Office: U Md Horticulture Dept College Park MD 20742-5611

QUEEN, EVELYN E. CRAWFORD, judge, law educator; b. Albany, N.Y., Apr. 6, 1945; d. Iris (Jackson) Crawford; m. Charles A. Queen, Mar. 6, 1971; children: Angela, George. BS, Howard U., 1968, JD, 1975. Bar: N.Y. 1976, U.S. Dist. Ct. (D.C. dist.) 1978, U.S. Ct. Appeals (D.C. cir.) 1977, U.S. Supreme Ct. 1980. Park ranger Nat. Park Svc., Washington, 1968-69; pers. specialist NIH, Bethesda, Md., 1969-75; staff atty. Met. Life Ins. Co., N.Y.C., 1975-76; atty. advisor Maritime Adminstrn.-U.S., Washington, 1976-78; att. U.S. atty.-D.C. Justice Dept., Washington, 1978-81; hearing commr. D.C. Superior Ct., Washington, 1981-86, judge, 1986—; adj. law prof. Howard U., 1988. Recipient Trifoil award Hudson Valley Girl Scout Coun., Albany, 1988, Spl. Achievement awards HEW, 1975, Appreciation certs. and plaques Dept. Justice, 1980. Mem. ABA, Nat. Bar Assn., Nat. Assn. Women Judges, Washington Bar Assn. Office: DC Superior Ct 500 Indiana Ave NW Washington DC 20001

QUEENAN, JAMES F., JR., judge; m. Helen E. Wood; 5 children. BA cum laude, Boston Coll., 1953, JD magna cum laude, 1958. Bar: Mass. 1958, U.S. Supreme Ct. 1966, U.S. Tax Ct. 1968, U.S. Dist. Ct. Mass. 1959. Law clk. Mass. Supreme Judicial Ct., Boston, 1958-59; ptnr. Bowditch & Dewey, Worcester, Mass.; judge U.S. Bankruptcy Ct. Dist. Mass. Worcester, 1986—; adjunct prof. bankruptcy law, Western New England Sch. of Law, Suffolk Univ. Law Sch.; mem. special com. on legal edn. Mass. Supreme Judicial Ct., Mass. Judicial Conduct Commn. Assoc. Editor: The Am. Bankruptcy Law Jour.; former editor in chief Mass. Law Review; contbr. to profl. jours. Chmn.task force Worcester Area C. of C., pres. Friends of the Worcester Public Libr. Mem. Mass. Bar Assn. (bd. of delegates, sec., chmn. bus. bankruptcy com.). Office: US Bankruptcy Ct Edwards Bldg 10 Mechanic St Worcester MA 01601-2000

QUEENAN, JOHN THOMAS, obstetrican, gynecologist, educator; b. Aurora, Ill., June 4, 1933; s. John William and Alice Margaret (Thomas) Q.; m. Carrie Ethel Neher, June 15, 1957; children: John Thomas Jr., Carrie Lynne. BS cum laude, U. Notre Dame, 1954; MD, Cornell U., 1958. Diplomate Am. Bd. Ob-Gyn., Am. Bd. Maternal-Fetal Medicine. Intern, Bellevue Hosp., N.Y.C., 1958-59; resident N.Y. Hosp., 1959-62; instr. Cornell U., 1962-65, clin. asst. prof. ob-gyn, 1965-70, assoc. prof., 1970-72;

prof. ob-gyn, chmn. dept. ob-gyn U. Louisville, 1972-80; chief ob-gyn Norton-Children's Hosps., Louisville Gen. Hosp., 1972-82; prof., chmn. dept. ob-gyn Georgetown U., 1980—, obstetrician and gynecologist-in-chief Georgetown U. Hosp., 1980—; spl. adv. ob-gyn devices panel FDA, 1978—. Bd. dirs. ARC, Greenwich, Conn., 1970-72. Fellow Am. Gynecol. and Obstet. Soc.; mem. Am. Coll. Obstetricians and Gynecologists, ACS, Am. Fertility Soc., Nat. Perinatal Assn. (pres. 1976-78), So. Perinatal Assn. (pres. 1975), Royal Soc. Medicine, Round Hill Club (Greenwich), Cosmos Club (Washington), Chevy Chase Club (Md.), Edgartown Yacht Club (Mass.), Alpha Omega Alpha. Author: Modern Management of the Rh Problem, 1977; Management of High Risk Pregnancy, 1980, 2d edit., 1985, 3d edit., 94; (with Carrie N. Queenan) A New Life, 1980, 2 edit., 1986, (with Kimberly K. Leslie) Preconceptions: Preparation for Pregnancy, 1989 edit.: (with John C. Hobbins) Protocols for High Risk Pregnancies, 1982, 3d edit., 1995; editor-in-chief Contemporary Ob-Gyn, 1973—. Home: 3257 N St NW Washington DC 20007-2845 Office: Georgetown U Hosp 3800 Reservoir Rd NW Washington DC 20007-2196

QUEENAN, JOSEPH MARTIN, JR., writer, magazine editor; b. Phila., Nov. 3, 1950; s. Joseph M. and Agnes Catherine (McNulty) Q.; m. Francesca Jane Spinner, Jan. 7, 1977; children: Bridget Noelle, Gordon Pasha. B.A., St. Joseph's U., 1972. Editor in chief Uncle Sam Mag., N.Y.C., 1981-82; mng. editor Moneysworth, Am. Bus., N.Y.C., 1982-83; editor in chief Am. Bus., Moneysworth, Better Living, N.Y.C., 1983-86; staffwriter Barron's, 1987-89; sr. editor Forbes Mag., N.Y.C., 1989; free-lance writer, 1989—. Author: Imperial Caddy, 1992, If You're Talking to Me Your Career Must Be in Trouble, 1994; dir. 12 Steps to Death, 1995. Democrat. Roman Catholic.

QUEENEY, JACK, public relations executive. Ptnr. Fin. Rels. Bd., Chgo. Office: Fin Rels Bd John Hancock Ctr 875 N Michigan Ave Chicago IL 60611*

QUEHL, GARY HOWARD, association executive, consultant; b. Green Bay, Wis., Mar. 25, 1938; s. Howard and Virginia Babcock (Dunning) Q.; children: Scott Boyer, Catherine Mary. BA, Carroll Coll., 1960; MS, Ind. U., 1962, EdD, 1965; LHD (hon.), Buena Vista Coll., 1977, Davis and Elkins Coll., 1979; EdD (hon.), Columbia Coll., S.C., 1987. Asst. dean students Wis. State U., 1962; asst. dean coll. Wittenberg U., 1965-76; v.p., dean coll. Lindenwood Colls., St. Charles, Mo., 1967-70; exec. dir. Coll. Center of the Finger Lakes, Corning, N.Y., 1970-74; pres. Council of Ind. Colls., Washington, 1974-86, Council for Advancement and Support of Edn., Washington, 1986-90, Quehl Assocs., Quehl Group, Lafayette, Calif., 1990—; cons. in field, 1990—. Editor, author books in field. Mem. secretariat Nat. Center for Higher Edn.; bd. dirs. Carroll Coll., Muskingum Coll., Elmira Coll., Nat. Assn. Ind. Colls. and Univs., ind. sector, Cornell Coll. Mem. Am. Council Edn., Am. Conf. Acad. Deans, Nat. Panel for Women in Higher Edn., North Central Assn. Acad. Deans (past pres.). Mem. United Ch. Christ.

QUELER, EVE, conductor; b. N.Y.C. Student, Mannes Coll. Music, CCNY. Music dir. Opera Orchestra of N.Y. Music staff, N.Y.C. Opera, 1958-70, assoc. condr., Ft. Wayne (Ind.) Philharm., 1970-71, founder, music dir., Opera Orch., N.Y., 1968, condr. Lake George Opera Festival, Glen Falls, N.Y., 1971-72, Queentle (Ohio) Music Festival, 1972, Romantic Festival, Indpls., 1972, Mostly Mozart Festival, Lincoln Center, 1972, New Philharmonia, London, 1974, Teatro Liceu, Barcelona, 1974, 77, San Antonio Symphony, 1975, guest condr., Paris Radio Orch., 1972, P.R. Symphony Orch., 1975, 77, Mich. Chamber Orch., 1975, Phila. Orch., 1976, Montreal Symphony, 1977, Cleve. Orch., 1977 (Recipient Martha Baird Rockefeller Fund for Music award 1968, named Musician of Month, Mus. Am. Mag. 1972), N.Y.C. Opera, 1978, Opera Las Palmas, 1978, Opera de Nice, 1979, Nat. Theatre of Prague, 1980, Opera Caracas, Venezuela, 1981, San Diego Opera, 1984, Australian Opera, Sydney, 1985, Kirov Opera, St. Petersburg, Russia, 1993, Hamburg Opera, Germany, 1994; recording CBS Masterworks, 1974, 76, Hungaroton Records, 1982-85. Office: care Robert J Lombardo 61 5th Ave New York NY 10003-4304 Office: Opera Orch NY 239 W 72nd St # 2R New York NY 10023-2734

QUELLE, FREDERICK WILLIAM, JR., physicist; b. Chgo., Sept. 4, 1934; s. Fred William and Viola Mildred (Miller) Q.; m. Claudia Jean Suba, June 18, 1961 (div. 1979); children: Frederick William, Geoffrey William. B.S., Ill. Inst. Tech., 1955; M.A., Harvard U., 1957, Ph.D., 1964. Staff mem. Lincoln Labs., Lexington, Mass., 1955-61; mem. solid state and molecular theory group M.I.T., Cambridge, 1958-63; physicist Office Naval Research, Boston, 1961—; pres. Tech. Engring. Devel. Co., Cohasset, Mass., 1978—; head ONR laser team, 1968-78, SHAD Space Navigation Team, 1979—; Navy mem. Adv. Group on Electronic Devices, 1975-80; mem. Exploritory Research and Devel. Com., 1980-89. Contbr. articles in field to profl. jours. Gen. Communication Co. fellow Harvard U., 1955. Mem. Am. Phys. Soc., Sigma Xi, Sigma Pi Sigma. Patentee in field. Home: 120 Nichols Rd Cohasset MA 02025-1146 Office: 495 Summer St Boston MA 02210-2109 *The name of the game is to cover as much unplowed ground and tread on as much snow where no man has ever walked as one can in his lifetime.*

QUELLER, DONALD EDWARD, historian, educator; b. St. Louis, Jan. 14, 1925; s. A.J. and Lee (Straub) Q.; m. Marilyn Lucille Johnson, June 12, 1949 (dec.); children: Kurt, David, Susan, Katherine, Sarah. AB, U. Mich., 1949; postgrad., Stanford Law Sch., 1949-50; MA, U. Mich., 1951; PhD, U. Wis., 1954. With Beloit Coll., 1955-56; faculty U. So. Cal., 1956-68; prof. medieval and renaissance history U. Ill., Urbana, 1968—. Author: Early Venetian Legislation on Ambassadors, 1966, The Office of the Ambassador in the Middle Ages, 1967, The Fourth Crusade, 1977, Two Studies on Venetian Government, 1977, Medieval Diplomacy and the Fourth Crusade, 1980, The Venetian Patriciate, 1986, Italian transl., 1987; editor: The Latin Conquest of Constantinople, 1971; co-editor: Post Scripta, Essays in Honor of Gaines Post. Chmn. South Pasadena Human Relations Council, 1964-65; chmn. Marilyn Queller Child Care Center. Served with AUS, 1943-46. Fulbright fellow Belgium, 1954-55; Fulbright research fellow Italy, 1962-63; Rockefeller Internat. Relations fellow, 1962-63, 64-65; Guggenheim fellow, 1972-73; Am. Council Learned Socs. grantee-in-aid, 1973; Gladys Krieble Delmas Found. grantee, 1978; Inst. Advanced Study fellow, 1979-80. Fellow Medieval Acad. Am.; mem. Am. Hist. Assn., Medieval Acad. Am., Renaissance Soc. Am. Home: 2406 S Prospect Ave Champaign IL 61820-7616 Office: U Ill 309 Gregory Hall 810 S Wright St Urbana IL 61801-3611 *My track coach at Indiana University, Billy Hayes, the best teacher I ever had, taught me and my teammates to prepare with discipline, to give our best efforts, and not to worry before or after the race about winning or losing, but only about performing up to the standards that he and we knew we could achieve. I hesitate to speak of "success," but this seems to me an excellent way to approach one's tasks.*

QUELLMALZ, HENRY, printing company executive; b. Balt., May 18, 1915; s. Frederick and Edith Margaret (Shaw) Q.; m. Marion Agar Lynch, Aug. 2, 1940; children: Lynn Quellmalz Johnson, Susan Quellmalz Mastan, Jane Quellmalz Carey. BA with high honors, Princeton U., 1937. Pres. Princeton Advt. Agy., 1936-37; dir. pres. Macy's Men's Store, 1938-40; asst. mgr. Fowlers Dept. Store, Glens Falls, N.Y., 1940-41; pers. dir. U.S. Army Post Exchs., Ft. Meade, Md., 1941-44; with Boyd Printing Co., Albany, N.Y., 1944—, pres., 1952-84, chmn. bd., 1984—; v.p. Q Corp. U.S.; agt. for WHO publs., 1965—. Campaign chmn. ARC, Albany, 1956, 57; bd. govs. Doane Stuart Sch., Albany, 1977-79, treas. bd., 1977-78; vice chmn. Family Svc. Assn. Am. Salute to Families, 1979—, Nat. UN Day com., 1980-82; mem. adv. bd. Ind. Coll. Fund of N.Y., 1971-91, corp. trustees, 1992—; bd. dirs. Am. Assn. World Health, 1977-82, Combined Health Appeal of Capitol Dist., Inc., 1984, Camelot Home for Boys, 1975; trustee St. Peter's Hosp. Found., Albany, 1982—, asst. sec., 1987-89, chmn. bd. dirs., 1989-91. With AUS, 1943. Recipient Pres.'s award Am. Assn. Mental Deficiency, 1976; 25 Yrs. Svc. award N.Y. State Bar Assn., 1983, 34 Yrs. Svc. Award Am. Sociol. Assn., 1985. Mem. Albany Area C. of C., Printing Industry Am. Assn. East Ctrl. N.Y. (pres. 1958), Ft. Orange Club. Democrat. Episcopalian. Home: 1 Park Hill Dr Apt 6 Albany NY 12204-2142 Office: 49 Sheridan Ave Albany NY 12210

QUELLO, JAMES HENRY, government official; b. Laurium, Mich., Apr. 21, 1914; s. Bartholomew and Mary Katherine (Cochis) Q.; m. Mary

---

Elizabeth Butler, Sept. 14, 1937; children: James Michael, Richard Butler. BA, Mich. State U., 1935, D of Humanities (hon.), 1977; D of Pub. Svc. (hon.), No. Mich. U., 1975. V.p., sta. mgr. Goodwill Stas., Inc., Detroit, 1947-72; v.p. Capital Cities Communications Corp., 1968; commr. FCC, Washington, 1974—; communications com., Detroit, 1972-74; commr. FCC, Washington, 1974—; commr. Detroit Housing and Urban Renewal Commn., 1951-72. Contbr. articles to mags., newspapers. Bd. dirs. Greater Detroit Hosp. Assn.; trustee Mich. Vet. Trust Fund; mem. Gov.'s Spl. Commn. on Urban Problems, Mich., Gov.'s Spl. Study Com. on Legis. Compensation, Mayor's Com. on Human Relations; bd. dirs. Am. Negro Emancipation Centennial; mem. exec. bd. Boy Scouts Am.; TV-radio chmn. United Found. Lt. col. AUS, 1940-45. Decorated Bronze Star with oak leaf cluster, Croix de Guerre (France); recipient Internat. Pres.'s award Nat. Assn. TV Program Execs., 1985, Silver Satellite award Am. Women in Radio and TV, 1988, 93, Sol Taishoff award Washington Area Broadcasters Assn., 1989, 93, Pub. Svc. award Fed. Comm. Bar Assn., 1993, Disting. Svc. award Media Inst., 1993, Golden Eagle Amb. award Pa. Assn. Broadcasters, 1993, Disting. Alumni award Mich. State U., Club Dir. award Detroit Adcraft Club, 1993, L.I. Coalition for Fair Broadcasting award, 1993, Nat. Disting. Svc. award Nat. Assn. Pub. TV, 1993, Obie award Ohio Ednl. TV Stas., 1993, Gold Eagle Leadership award Wireless Cable Assn. Internat., 1993, Pres. award Alaska Broadcasting Assn., 1994, Chmn. award Nat. Religious Broadcasters, 1994, Ga. Broadcasters award Broadcasters of Am., 1994, 1st Amendment award Radio & TV News Dirs. Found., 1994. Mem. Nat. Assn. Broadcasters (mem. gov. liaison com. 1964-72, Keystone award 1990, Disting. Svc. award 1994, Honor award for protecting the technical integrity of radio and TV 1994), Mich. Assn. Broadcasters (pres. 1958, legis. chmn. 1959-72, dir., Outstanding Mich. Citizen 1989, Pioneer award 1991, Lifetime Achievement award 1994), Greater Detroit Bd. Commerce, Sigma Alpha Epsilon. Clubs: Adcraft (Detroit); Detroit Athletic, Army and Navy Country; Nat. Press (Washington). Office: FCC 1919 M St NW Washington DC 20554-0002

QUENCER, ROBERT MOORE, neuroradiologist, researcher; b. Jersey City, Nov. 14, 1937; s. Arthur Bauer and Isabell (Moore) Q.; m. Christine F. Thomas, Sept. 16, 1972; children: Kevin, Keith. BS, Cornell U., 1959, MS, 1963; MD, SUNY, Syracuse, 1967. Diplomate Am. Bd. Radiology, Nat. Bd. Med. Examiners. Intern Jackson Meml. Hosp., Miami, Fla., 1967-68; resident in radiology Columbia U., N.Y.C., 1968-71, fellow in neuroradiology, 1971-72; assoc. prof. Downstate Med. Ctr., Bklyn., 1972-76; assoc. prof. U. Miami, 1976-79, prof., 1979-92, chmn., prof., 1992—, chief sect. neuroradiology, 1976-86, dir. divsn. magnetic resonance imaging, 1986-92; vis. prof. U. Tenn. Coll. Medicine, Memphis, 1982, Downstate Med. Ctr. Coll. Medicine, Bklyn., 1992, U. Vt. Coll. Medicine, Burlington, 1983, N.Y. Med. Coll., Valhalla, 1984, U. Va. Sch. Medicine, Charlottesville, 1984, U. Ky. Sch. Medicine, Lexington, 1985, Yale U. Sch. Medicine, New Haven, 1986, Columbia U. Sch. Medicine, N.Y.C., 1986, The Mayo Clinic & Found, Rochester, Minn., 1987, Med. Coll. Va., Richmond, 1988, U. Pa. Sch. Medicine, Phila., 1988, Harvard U. Sch. Medicine/Mass. Gen. Hosp., Boston, 1989, U. Conn., Farmington, 1990, U. Man., Can., 1992; dir. programs in dept. radiology U. Miami Sch. Medicine, 1984, 86, Med. Coll. Wis., Tucson, 1990, 92, Kauai, Hawaii, 1991, Whistler, British Columbia, 1990; adv. cons. NIH, 1987, 90; sci. merit reviewer V.A., 1987; presenter, lectr. in field. Author: Neurosonography, 1988; dep. editor Am. Jour. Neuroradiology, 1984—; assoc. editor for neuroimaging Yearbook of Neurology and Neurosurgery, 1991—; book reviewer Am. Jour. Neuroradiology, 1984—, Paraplegia, 1989—, Radiographics, 1991—, Pediatrics, 1993—; mem. editorial bd. Jour. Clin. Neuro-Ophthalmology, 1980—; contbr. articles to profl. jours. Pres. Am. Soc. Neuroradiology, 1994-95; prin. investigator NIH Grant on imaging/pathology of spinal cord injury. Lt. (j.g.) USN, 1959-61. Fellow Am. Coll. Radiology, Am. Soc. Neuroradiology (pres. 1994-95, program com. 1985-89, 92, editl. com. 1984—, publs. com. 1984—); mem. AMA, Radiol. Soc. N.Am. (program subcom. on neuroradiology 1990-94), Southeastern Neuroradiol. Soc. (founder, pres. 1980-81), Dade County Med. Assn., Soc. Chmn. Acad. Radiology Depts., Fla. Radiol. Soc. (magnetic resonance com. 1991-92), Alpha Omega Alpha. Avocations: golf, travel. Office: U Miami 1115 NW 14th St Miami FL 33136

QUENEAU, PAUL ETIENNE, metallurgical engineer, educator; b. Phila., Mar. 20, 1911; s. Augustin L. and Jean (Blaisdell) Q.; m. Jean Osgood Hodges, May 20, 1939; children: Paul Blaisdell, Josephine Downs (Mrs. George Stanley Patrick). B.A., Columbia U., 1931, B.Sc., 1932, E.M., 1933; postgrad. (Evans fellow), Cambridge (Eng.) U., 1934; D.Sc., Delft (Netherlands) U. Tech., 1971. With Corps of Engrs. USAR, 1937-62; With Internat. Nickel Co., 1934-69, dir. research, 1940-41, 46-48, v.p., 1958-69, tech. asst. to pres., 1960-66, asst. to chmn., 1967-69; vis. scientist Delft U. Tech., 1970-71; prof. engring. Dartmouth Coll., 1971-87, prof. emeritus, 1987—; cons. engr., 1972—; vis. prof. U. Minn., 1974-75, U. Utah, 1987-91; geographer Perry River Arctic Expdn., 1949; chmn. U.S. Navy Arctic Research Adv. Com., 1957; gov. Arctic Inst. N.Am., 1957-62; mem. engring. council Columbia U., 1965-70; mem. vis. com. MIT, 1967-70; mem. extractive metallurgy and mineral processing panels NAS; pres. Q-S Oxygen Processes Inc., 1974-79, dir., 1974—. Author: (with Hanson) Geography, Birds and Mammals of the Perry River Region, 1956; Cobalt and the Nickeliferous Limonites, 1971; editor: Extractive Metallurgy of Copper, Nickel and Cobalt, 1961; (with Anderson) Pyrometallurgical Processes in Nonferrous Metallurgy, 1965; The Winning of Nickel, 1967; contbr. articles to profl. jours. patentee 34 U.S. patents including processes and apparatus employed in the pyrometallurgy, hydrometallurgy and vapometallurgy of nickel, copper, cobalt, lead, zinc and iron, extractive metallurgy oxygen tech. including INCO oxygen flash smelting, oxygen top-blown rotary converter, lateritic ore matte smelting, nickel high pressure carbonyl and iron ore recovery processes; co-inventor Lurgi QSL direct lead-making, QSOP direct coppermaking and nickelmaking reactors, Lurgi direct steelmaking reactors, and Dravo oxygen sprinkle copper smelting furnaces. Bd. dirs. Engring. Found., Phila. chmn., 1973-75. Served with U.S. Army, World War II, ETO; col. C.E. (ret.). Decorated Bronze Star, ETO medal with 5 battlestars, Commendation medal; recipient Egleston medal Columbia U., 1965, Fletcher award Dartmouth Coll., 1991. Fellow Metall. Soc. of AIME (dir. 1964, 68-71, pres. 1969, Extractive Metallurgy Lecture award 1977, Paul E. Queneau Internat. Symposium on Extractive Metallurgy of Copper, Nickel and Cobalt 1993); mem. AIME (Douglas Gold medal 1968, v.p. 1970, dir. 1968-71, Henry Krumb lectr. 1984, keynote lectr. ann. meeting 1990), NAE, NSPE, Can. Inst. Mining and Metallurgy, Inst. Mining and Metallurgy U.K. (overseas mem. council 1970-80, Gold medal 1980), Sigma Xi, Tau Beta Pi. Office: Dartmouth Coll Thayer Sch Engring Hanover NH 03755

QUENNELL, NICHOLAS, landscape architect, educator; b. London, Sept. 30, 1935; s. Cecil William and Beatrice Irene Quennell; m. Grace Tankersley, Apr. 30, 1983. AA, Archtl. Assn., London, 1957; MLA, Harvard U., 1969. Registered architect, N.Y., Pa., N.J., Conn., U.K.; registered landscape architect, N.Y., N.J., Conn., Mass., N.C. Architect London County Coun., 1959-61, Jose Luis Sert, Cambridge, Mass., 1961-62, Lawrence Halprin & Assocs., San Francisco, 1962-65, Vollmer Assocs., N.Y.C., 1965-68; prin. Nicholas Quennell Assocs., N.Y.C., 1968-79, Quennell Rothschild Assocs., N.Y.C., 1979—; v.p. The Mcpl. Art Soc. (dir. 1978-85), N.Y.C., 1985-92, dir. The Archtl. League, N.Y.C., 1984-89. Bd. dirs. nat. Assn. for Olmsted Pks., Washington, 1988-90, chmn., 1990-93; mem. Art Commn. of City of N.Y., 1992—, pres., 1993—. Fellow Am. Soc. of Landscape Architects; mem. Century Assn. Office: Quennell Rothschild Assocs 118 W 22nd St New York NY 10011-2416

QUENON, ROBERT HAGERTY, mining consultant, retired holding company executive; b. Clarksburg, W.Va., Aug. 2, 1928; s. Ernest Leonard and Josephine (Hagerty) Q.; m. Jean Bowling, Aug. 8, 1953; children: Evan, Ann, Richard. B.S. in Mining Engring., W.Va. U., 1951; LL.B., George Washington U., 1964; PhD (hon.), U. Mo., 1979, Blackburn Coll., 1983, W.Va. U., 1988. Mine supt. Consol. Coal Co., Fairmont, W.Va., 1956-61; mgr. deep mines Pittston Co., Dante, Va., 1964-66; gen. mgr. Riverton Coal Co., Crown Hill, W.Va., 1966-67; mgr. ops. coal and shale oil dept. Exxon Co., Houston, 1967; pres. Monterey Coal Co., Houston, 1969-76; sr. v.p. Carter Oil Co., Houston, 1976-77; exec. v.p. Peabody Coal Co., St. Louis, 1977-78; pres., chief exec. officer Peabody Coal Co., 1978-83; pres., chief exec. officer Peabody Holding Co., Inc., St. Louis, 1983-90, chmn., 1990-91; bd. dirs. Newmont Gold Co., Denver, Union Electric Co., St. Louis, Laclede Steel Co., St. Louis; bd. dirs., chmn. Fed. Res. Bank St. Louis, 1993—, dep. chmn., 1990-92; mem. coal industry adv. bd. Internat. Energy Agy., 1980—,

---

bd. chmn., 1984-90; chmn. Bituminous Coal Operator's Assn., 1980-83, 89-91. Trustee Blackburn Coll., Carlinville, Ill., 1975-83, St. Louis U., 1981-91; pres. St. Louis Art Mus., 1985-88. Served with AUS, 1946-47. Mem. Am. Mining Congress (vice-chmn. 1980-91), Nat. Coal Assn. (chmn. bd. 1978-80), U.S. C. of C. (dir. 1982-88). Office: PO Box 11328 Saint Louis MO 63105-0128

QUENTEL, ALBERT DREW, lawyer; b. Miami, Fla., Nov. 27, 1934; s. Charles Edward Jr. and Alberta Amelia (Drew) Q.; m. Paula Staelin Hagar, Feb. 9, 1957; children: Albert D. Jr., Stephen C., Marshall Lee, Paul G., Peter E., Michael J. BA, U. Fla., 1956, JD with honors, 1959. Bar: Fla. 1959. Assoc. Mershon, Sawyer, Johnston, Dunwody & Cole, Miami, 1959-64, ptnr., 1965-71; princ. Greenberg, Traurig, Hoffman, Lipoff, Rosen & Quentel, P.A., Miami, 1971—. Editor-in-chief U. Fla. Law Rev., 1959; contbg. author: Florida Real Property Practice, 1965, Real Estate Partnerships Selected Problems and Solutions, 1991, Commercial Real Estate Finance, 1993. Mem. Gov.'s Growth Mgmt. Adv. Com., Tallahassee, 1985-87; bd. dirs. Nat. Parkinson Found., Miami, 1980—, v.p., 1985—. Mem. NRA (life 1989—), Am. Coll. Real Estate Lawyers, Urban Land Inst., Fla. Bar Assn. (chmn. pub. rels. com. 1970-72, chmn. editorial com. jour. 1972-73), Lions (pres. Key Biscayne, Fla. club 1973), Miami Club (pres. 1991-92), Bath Club, Blue Key, Beta Theta Pi (pres. local chpt. 1954-55), Phi Eta Sigma, Phi Kappa Phi. Republican. Congregationalist. Avocations: reading, shooting, photography. Home: 3410 Poinciana Ave Miami FL 33133-6525 Office: Greenberg Traurig Hoffman Lipoff Rosen & Quental PA 1221 Brickell Ave Miami FL 33131-3200

QUERSHEY, SAFI U., computer company executive; b. 1951. BS in Engring., U. Tex., 1975. Test specialist A M Internat., 1975-77; engr. Computer Automation Corp., Irvine, Calif., 1977-78, Telefile Computer Corp., Irvine, 1978-79; chmn bd., CEO AST Research%, 1979—. Office: AST Research Inc 16215 Alton Pkwy Irvine CA 92718*

QUERY, JOY MARVES NEALE, medical sociology educator; b. Worcestershire, Eng.; came to U.S., 1952; d. Samuel and Dorree (Oakley) Neale; children: Jonathan, Margo, Evan. A.B., Drake U., 1954, M.A., 1955; postgrad., U. Syracuse, 1955-56; Ph.D., U. Ky., 1960. Tchr. secondary schs. Staffordshire, Eng., 1947-52; dep. prin. Smethwick Hall Girls' Sch., Staffordshire, 1948-52; instr. U. Ky., 1956-57, asst. prof., 1960; assoc. prof. sociology Transylvania Coll., Lexington, Ky., 1961-66; assoc. prof. N.D. State U., Fargo, 1966-68; prof. sociology and psychology N.D. State U., 1969-75, also then sociology and psychology depts., 1969-70, chmn. sociology and anthropology dept., 1968-73; prof. div. psychiatry behavioral sci., dept. neurosci. U. N.D. Sch. Medicine, Fargo, 1975-89, prof. emeritus, 1989—; on sabbatical leave Yale U., 1974-75; coord. AIDS Edn. State Program NIMH, 1989-93. Mem. bd. adv. editors Sociological Inquiry jour., 1987-93; contbr. articles and papers to profl. jours. Field dir. Girl Scouts U.S.A., 1953-55; mem. Lexington Civil Rights Commn., 1960-66; bd. dirs. Fargo-Moorhead Family Service Agy., 1967-70; mem. Mayor's Coordinating Council for Youth, Fargo-Moorhead, 1976—; pres. Hospice of Red River Valley, 1986-87 (Svc. award 1987). Named Profl. Woman of Yr. Fargo-Moorhead YWCA, 1981, Disting. Lectr. of Yr., N.D. State U., 1991, Outstanding Educator U. N.D. Sch. Medicine Class of 1992; recipient Burlington No. award, 1987, Alumni award U. Ky., 1988, Disting. Svc. award Gt. Plains Sociol. Assn., 1988; Joy M. Query scholarship at N.D. State U., U. Md. Coll. Medicine created in her honor, 1987. Fellow Internat. Assn. Social Psychiatry; mem. AAUP, Am. Sociol. Assn., N.D. Mental Health Assn. (pres. Red River Valley chpt., Heritage award 1987), midwest Sociol. Soc. (dir. 1970-73, 75-78, mem. standards, tng. and employment com. 1988-89), Alpha Kappa Delta. Unitarian. Home: 1202 Oak St Fargo ND 58102-2707 Office: U ND Sch Medicine 1919 Elm St Fargo ND 58102-2416

QUESENBERRY, KENNETH HAYS, agronomy educator; b. Springfield, Tenn., Feb. 28, 1947; s. James William and Cora Geneva (Moore) Q.; m. Joyce Ann Kaze, July 28, 1947; children: James Kenneth, Kendra Joyce. BS, Western Ky. U., 1969; PhD U. Ky., 1975. D. F. Jones predoctoral fellow U. Ky., Lexington, 1972-75; asst. prof. U. Fla., Gainesville, 1975-80, assoc. prof. agronomy, 1980-86, prof. agronomy, 1986—; contbr. articles to profl. jours. Chair So. Pasture and Forage Crop Improvement Conf., 1991. Served with U.S. Army, 1969-71, Vietnam. Named Prof. of Yr., Coll. Agr., U. Fla., 1976. Mem. Am. Soc. Agronomy, Crop Sci. Soc. Am. (chair divsn. C-8 1993-94), Gamma Sigma Delta. (pres. 1984-85). Democrat. Avocations: sports, antique furniture refinishing. Achievements include rsch. in germplasm enhancement of forages with release of four cultivars of tropical grasses and one clover. Office: Univ Fla PO Box 110500 Gainesville FL 32611-0500

QUESNEL, GREGORY L., transportation company executive; b. Woodburn, Oreg., May 24, 1948. Sr. v.p., CFO Consol. Freightways, Inc., Palo Alto, Calif., 1991—.

QUEST, JAMES HOWARD, advertising executive; b. Johnstown, Pa., June 21, 1934; s. Norris R.D.O. and Edna Jane (Nichols) Q.; m. Sarah Jo Ames, June 11, 1960 (dec. 1973); m. Leslie Reiman; children: Daniel, Anna, Benjamin. BS in Hotel Adminstrn., Cornell U., 1956. Brand mgr. Procter & Gamble, Cin., 1956-60; v.p. SSC&B Advt., N.Y.C., 1961-64; group product dir. Pfizer Consumer Products, N.Y.C., 1964-67; v.p. Am. Home Products, N.Y.C., 1967-71, RS&L Advt., N.Y.C., 1971-75; sr. v.p., mem. bd. dirs. The Marschalk Co., Advt., N.Y.C., 1975-80; chmn., chief exec. officer Posey & Quest Advt., Greenwich, Conn., 1980-90; exec. v.p. TBWA Advt., N.Y.C., 1990-95; CEO Quest Assoc. LTD., Stamford, Conn., 1995—; speaker AAAA, N.Y.C., 1985-87, Assn. Nat. Advertisers, 1987-89; guest lectr. Cornell Sch. Hotel Adminstrn., 1985. Author: (with others) Developing New Products, 1980, Executive Chess, 1987. Bd. dirs., exec. com. Children of Alcoholics Found., N.Y.C., 1987—; mem. Cornell U. Coun.; v.p. Cornell Class of 1956. With U.S. Army, 1956-58. Mem. Cornell Soc. Hotelmen, Cornell Club (N.Y.C.), Friars Club N.Y., Woodway Country Club, Darien, Conn. Avocations: tennis, golf., travel, writing. Home: 14 Alfred Ln Stamford CT 06902-1238 Office: Quest Assocs Ltd PO Box 3005 Stamford CT 06905-0005

QUESTEL, MAE, actress; b. Bronx, N.Y., Sept. 13, 1908; d. Simon and Frieda (Glauberman) Q.; m. Leo Balkin, Dec. 22, 1930 (dec.); children: Robert (dec.), Richard; m. Jack E. Shelby, Nov. 19, 1970. Student in drama, J.G. Geiger, N.Y.C., 1916-24; scholar, Theatre Guild, N.Y.C., 1923, Columbia U., 1949, Theatre Wing, 1951. Appeared in vaudeville at Palace Theatre, 1930, on RKO theater circuit, 1931-38; radio shows include Betty Boops Frolics, NBC, 1932; cartoon voices Betty Boop, 1931—, Olive Oyl, 1933—, Mr. Bugs Goes to Town, 1934, Little Audrey, 1946; TV cartoon Winky Dink and You, 1956-60, Popeye (as Olive Oyl), 1981; stage appearances include Dr. Social, 1948, A Majority of One, 1959-61, Come Blow Your Horn, 1963, Enter Laughing, 1963, Bajour, 1964, The Warm Peninsula, 1966, Walk Like A Lion, 1969, Barrel Full of Pennies, 1970, Where Have You Been, Billy Boy, 1969, Betty Boop—60 Yrs., N.Y., 1990, Betty Boop (Olive Oyl), N.Y. Nebr., Lincoln, 1990; appeared: films A Majority of One, 1961, It's Only Money, 1962, Funny Girl, 1967, Move, 1969, Zelig, 1983, Hot Resorts, 1984, Who Framed Roger Rabbit?, 1988, New York Stories: A Trilogy, 1988-89, Christmas Vacation, 1989; TV spokeswoman for Scott Paper Co. as Aunt Bluebell films, 1971-78; other commls. include Playtex, 1970-72, Romilar, 1970-72, Folger's Coffee, 1972-79, Speidel Watch Bands, 1980, S.O.S, 1981, Parker Bros. video game Popeye, 1983-84; soap opera Somerset, 1976-77, All My Children, 1983; other TV appearances include Good Morning America, 1980, Good Day Show, 1980, Picture Pages, 1981, Entertainment Tonight, Joan Rivers and Her Friends; also numerous recs. including Good Ship Lollipop; (Troupers award for outstanding contbn. to entertainment 1979, Annie award Internat. Animated Film Soc. 1979). Named Living Legend NYU Sch. Social Work, 1979. Mem. Screen Actors Guild, AFTRA, Actors Equity Assn., Nat. Acad. TV Arts and Scis. (award 1978), Hadassah. Clubs: Troupers (award 1963), Variety. Mae Questel Day named by City of Indpls., 1968. Home: 27 E 65th St Apt 7C New York NY 10021-6556 *My mother was a singer and a mimic - took me to the theater when I was about 3 yrs. old - performed in school and for many charities - always wanted to entertain - at seventeen won a "Betty Boop" contest. I have never turned down anything - performed on radio, tv, soap, theater and movies - always acted - because I just love show business.*

QUESTER, GEORGE HERMAN, political science educator; b. Bklyn., July 14, 1936; s. Jacob George and Elizabeth (Mattern) Q.; m. Aline Marie Olson, June 20, 1964; children: Theodore, Amanda. A.B., Columbia U., 1958; M.A., Harvard U., 1964, Ph.D., 1965. Instr., then asst. prof. govt. Harvard U., 1965-70; assoc. prof. govt. Cornell U., 1970-73, prof., 1973-82; prof. polit. sci. U. Md., College Park, 1982—; vis. prof. U.S. Naval Acad., Annapolis, Md., 1991-93. Author: Deterrence Before Hiroshima, 1966, Nuclear Diplomacy, 1970, The Politics of Nuclear Proliferation, 1973, The Continuing Problem of International Relations, 1974, Offense and Defense in the International System, 1977, American Foreign Policy: The Lost Consensus, 1982, The Future of Nuclear Deterrence, 1986, The International Politics of Television, 1990. Served with USAF, 1958-61. Fellow Center Advanced Study Behavioral Sci., 1974-75. Mem. Council Fgn. Relations, Inst. Strategic Studies, Am. Polit. Sci. Assn. Home: 5124 37th St N Arlington VA 22207-1862 Office: Univ Md Lefrak # 2181 College Park MD 20742

QUESTROM, ALLEN I., retail executive; b. Newton, Mass., Apr. 13, 1941; s. Irving Allen and Natalie (Chadbourne) Q.; m. Carol Brummer, Sept. 9, 1967. BS, Boston U., 1964. From exec. trainee to div. mdse. mgr. Abraham & Straus, Bklyn., 1965-73; v.p., gen. mdse. mgr. home store Bullock's, L.A., 1973-74, sr. v.p., gen. mdse. mgr. all stores, 1974-77; exec. v.p. Bullock's div. Federated Dept. Stores, L.A., 1977-78; pres. Rich's div. Federated Dept. Stores, Atlanta, 1978-80, chmn. bd., chief exec. officer, 1980-84, chmn. bd., chief exec. officer Bullock's/Bullocks Wilshire div., 1984-88; corp. exec. v.p. Federated Dept. Stores, Cin., 1987-88, vice-chmn., 1988; pres., chief exec. officer Neiman Marcus Group Inc., Dallas, 1988-90; chmn., chief exec. officer Federated Dept. Stores Inc., Cin., 1990—; also chmn., chief exec. officer Allied Stores Corp., Cin., 1990—. Avocations: skiing; golf; travel. *

QUEVEDO, HECTOR ADOLF, operations research analyst, environmental scientist; b. Juarez, Mex., June 25, 1940; came to U.S., 1973; s. Robert and Margaret (Urias) Quevedo Endlich; m. Gloria Guijarro, June 2, 1971; children: Gloria, Hector. BA, U. Tex., El Paso, 1966; MS in Environ. Scis., U. Okla., 1972, PhD in Environ. Scis., 1977. Part-time instr. maths. U. Tex., El Paso, 1977-80; environ. engr. El Paso Natural Gas Co., 1978-79; systems analyst U.S. Army, White Sands, N.Mex., 1980-84, Ft. Bliss, Tex., 1985—. Democrat. Roman Catholic. Avocations: classical music, reading, outdoor recreation, writing books, playing dominoes. Home: 11148 Voyager Cove Dr El Paso TX 79936-3007

QUIAT, GERALD M., lawyer; b. Denver, Jan. 9, 1924; s. Ira L. and Esther (Greenblatt) Q.; m. Roberta M. Nicholson, Sept. 26, 1962; children: James M., Audrey A., Melinda A., Daniel P., Ilana L., Leonard E. A.A., U. Calif., Berkeley, 1942; A.B. and LL.B., U. Denver, 1948, changed to J.D., 1970. Bar: Colo. 1948, Fed. Ct. 1948. Dep. dist. atty. County of Denver, Colo., 1949-52; partner firm Quiat, Seeman & Quiat, Denver, 1952-67, Quiat & Quiat (later changed to Quiat, Bucholtz & Bull, P.C.), 1968; pres. firm Quiat, Bucholtz & Bull & Laff, P.C. (and predecessors), Denver, 1968-85; pvt. practice Denver, 1985—; bd. dirs., chmn. audit com. Guaranty Bank & Trust Co., Denver; past bd. dirs. and chmn. bd. ROMED, RMD, Inc. Trustee, mem. Holding Co., Rose Med. Ctr., Denver, pres., chmn. bd., 1976-79; mem. Colo. Civil Rights Commn., 1963-71, chmn., 1966-67, 69-70, chief hearing officer, 1963-71; bd. dirs., mem. exec. com. AMC Cancer Rsch. Ctr., Denver, chmn. bd., 1991-93; chmn. bd. Am. Med. Ctr., 1993—; mem. nat. civil rights com., hon. nat. exec. com., hon. nat. commr. Anti-Defamation League, B'nai B'rith, also bd. dirs., mem. exec. com., chmn. bd. dirs. Mountain States region, 1980-82. With inf. U.S. Army, 1942-45. Decorated Bronze Star. Mem. ABA, Colo. Bar Assn., Denver Bar Assn., Colo. Trial Lawyers Assn. (pres. 1970-71), Am. Legion (comdr. Leyden-Chiles-Wickersham Post 1, 1955-56, past judge adv. Colo. dept.), Rotary. Home: 8130 Lt Wm Clark Rd Parker CO 80134 Office: Penthouse Suite 1720 S Bellaire St Denver CO 80222-4304

QUIBAN, ESTELITA CABRERA, controller; b. Manila, Sept. 3, 1938; came to U.S., 1969; d. Apolonio and Regina (Lacasmana) Cabrera; m. Teodoro Quiban Jr., June 20, 1964; children: Erwin James, Theodelinde, Joyce Ann, Rina Francis. Assoc. Bus., Phillipine Coll. Commerce, Manila, 1956; BS in Acctg., Far Ea. U., Manila, 1958. Cost acct. Associated Pharms., Manila, 1959-65; chief acct. Allied Travels, Manila, 1965-69; acct. Allied Outlets, San Francisco, 1969-70, Chalet 21, San Francisco, 1970-75; head acct. Anna Millers Inc., San Francisco, 1976-81, contr., 1981—; v.p. Pacific Outlets Inc., San Francisco, 1985—; corp. sec. Anna Millers Inc., San Francisco, 1989—; trustee Anna Millers Pension Plan, San Francisco, 1990—. Treas. St. Augustine Chorale, 1990-92. Democrat. Roman Catholic. Avocations: reading, travel, camping, singing. Home: 2926 Dublin Dr South San Francisco CA 94080-5522 Office: Anna Millers Inc 86 Dorman Ave San Francisco CA 94124-1808

QUICK, ALBERT THOMAS, academic law administrator, educator; b. BattleCreek, Mich., June 28, 1939; s. Robert and Vera Quick; m. Brenda Jones; children: Lori, Traci, Becki, Breton, Regan, Leigh. BA, U. Ariz., 1962; MA, Cen. Mich. U., 1964; J.D, Wayne State U., 1967; LLM, Tulane U., 1974. Bar: Mich. 1968, Ky. 1987. Asst. prosecutor Calhoun County, Marshall, Mich., 1968-69; assoc. Hatch & Hatch, Marshall, 1969-70; asst. prof. U. Maine, Augusta, 1970-73; prof. law U. Louisville, 1974-87, spl. asst. to univ. provost, 1987-88; dean, prof. law Ohio No. U., Ada, 1987-95; dean prof. law U. Toledo, Ohio, 1995—. Co-author: Update Federal Rules of Criminal Procedure; contbr. articles to profl. jours. Mem. ABA, Assn. Am. Law Schs. (criminal justice sect.), Ky. State Bar Assn., Mich. State Bar Assns., Allen County Bar Assn., Hardin County Bar Assn., Willis Soc., Rotary, Phi Kappa Phi. Episcopalian. Avocations: racquetball, tennis, art, reading. Office: Univ Toledo Coll Law 2801 W Bancroft St Toledo OH 43606

QUICK, CAROLYN MAY, nurse administrator; b. Providence, June 20, 1938; d. Arland Reuben Merchant and Helen Veronica (Barbour) De Ve; m. Ronald. BS, St. Mary's Coll., 1978. Head nurse ICU, Roger Williams Gen. Hosp., Providence, 1960-63; pharmacology research asst. Shell Research & Devel., Salida, Calif., 1964-66; operating room nurse Dr. Med. Ctr., Modesto, Calif., 1965-66; staff nurse St. Joseph's Hosp., Eureka, Calif., 1966-67, Columbus (Ga.) Med. Ctr., 1967-68; nursing supr. Meml. Hosp. Assocs., Modesto, 1972-76, nurse educator, 1976-80, asst. v.p., dir. nursing, 1980-89; v.p. nursing Meml. Med. Ctr., Modesto, 1989—. Patron, Modesto Symphony Orchestra, 1973—; troop leader, Muir Trail Girl Scout Council, Modesto, 1975-77, mem. Mayor's Council, Pub. Relations. Mem. N. Cen. Calif. Nursing Council, Calif. Soc. Nursing Service Admistrn, Calif. Soc. Nursing Service Adminstr. Legis. Com. Democrat. Avocations: cooking, bicycling, travel, reading, painting.

QUICK, EDWARD RAYMOND, museum director; b. L.A., Mar. 22, 1943; s. Donald Russell Quick and Gertrude Ruth (Albin) Thornbrough; m. Ruth Ann Lessig; children: Jeannette Lee, Russell Raymond. BA, U. Calif., Santa Barbara, 1970, MA, 1977. Adminstr. supr. Civil Service, Santa Ana, Calif., 1971-75; sr. computer operator Santa Barbara Rsch. Ctr., 1975-77; asst. collections curator Santa Barbara Mus. Art, 1977-78; registrar Montgomery (Ala.) Mus. Fine Arts, 1978-80; head dept. registration and preparation Joslyn Art Mus., Omaha, 1980-85; dir. Sheldon Swope Art Mus., Terre Haute, Ind., 1985-95; advisor Ind. Arts Commn., Indpls., 1986-91; mem. Arts in Pub. Places Commn., Terre Haute, 1986-93; bd. dirs. Arts Illiana, Terre Haute, 1986-91; pres. Friends Vigo County Pub. Libr., 1988-90, treas., 1990-93. Co-author: Code of Practice for Couriering Museum Objects, 1985, Registrars on Record, 1987, Gilbert Brown Wilson and Herman Melville's "Moby Dick," 1993. Bd. dirs. Vol. Action Ctr., Terre Haute, 1987-90, Terre Haute Community Relief Effort for Environ. and Civic Spirit, 1989. With USAF, 1961-65, Air N.G., 1979—. Mem. Am. Assn. Mus., Assn. Ind. Mus., Am. Assn. for State and Local History, Internat. Coun. Mus., Wabash Valley Press Club, Alpha Gamma Sigma, Aero Club. Republican. Avocation: working on nat. and internat. couriering of art objects. Office: Berman Mus 304 11th St NE Jacksonville AL 36265

QUICK, LESLIE CHARLES, III, brokerage house executive; b. Bklyn., Mar. 15, 1953; s. Leslie C. Jr. and Regina A. (Clarkson) Q.; m. Eileen Manning, July 7, 1979; children: L. Christopher, Ryan F., Kelsey M., Maura G. BBA in Fin., St. Bonaventure U., 1975; postgrad., Stanford U., 1987. Prin., pres. Quick & Reilly Group, N.Y.C., 1975—. Trustee St. Bonaventure

U., N.Y., 1985—; bd. dirs. Mt. Iraneus-Franciscan Mountain Retreat, St. Bonaventure, N.Y., 1981—; Ireland/U.S. Coun. for Commerce and Industry, Inc., 1991—, St. Vincents Hosp., N.Y.C., 1992—. Mem. Securities Industry Assn. (bd. dirs. 1993), Nat. Assn. Securities Dealers (com. dist. 10 1989-91), Nat. Acad. Design (bd. advisors 1992—), Downtown Athletic Club, Plainfield Country Club (Edison, N.J.). Roman Catholic. Avocations: golf, family activities. Office: Quick & Reilly Group Inc 26 Broadway New York NY 10004-1700

QUICK, NORMAN, bishop. Bishop of R.I. Ch. of God in Christ, Bklyn.

QUICK, THOMAS CLARKSON, brokerage house executive; b. Westbury, N.Y., Feb. 26, 1955; s. Leslie Charles and Regina (Clarkson) Q. BS in Bus. Fairfield U., 1977. Br. mgr. Quick & Reilly Inc., Palm Beach, Fla., 1977-81; dir., v.p. The Quick & Reilly Group, Palm Beach, 1981—; v.p. Quick & Reilly Inc., Palm Beach, 1981-86; pres. Quick & Reilly Inc., N.Y.C., 1986—; also bd. dirs.; mem. Securities Industry Assn. Econ. Adn. Com., N.Y.C., 1986—; chmn. com. Wall St. Friends of St. Jude Children's Rsch. Hosp., 1979—, mem. endowment com.; trustee Security Industry Found. for Econ. Edn., Securities Industry Inst., United World Colls.; trustee, mem. adv. coun. Fairfield U.; bd. advisors Cath. Near East Welfare Assn.; trustee Nat. Corp. Theater Fund. Mem. investment adv. bd., endowment com. St. Jude Children's Research Hosp., Memphis, 1986—; chmn. com. Wall St. Friends of St. Jude Children's Research Hosp., 1979—, mem. endowment com.; trustee Sec. Industry Found. for Econ. Edn. Mem. The Investment Assn. N.Y., N.Y. Stock Exch., Securities and Industry Assn. (econ. edn. com.), Am. Assn. of Sovereign Mil., Order of Malta, Young Pres.'s Orgn., Univ. Club, Friendly Sons of St. Patrick, Apawamis Country Club (Rye, N.Y.), The Beach Club (Palm Beach, Fla.). Home: 25 E End Ave New York NY 10028-7052 Office: Quick & Reilly Group Inc 26 Broadway New York NY 10004-1700

QUICKEL, KENNETH ELWOOD, JR., physician, medical center executive; b. Harrisburg, Pa., Aug. 20, 1939; s. Kenneth E. and Carolyn (Chick) Q.; m. Mary Wickersham Jennings, July 1, 1961; children: Robert Reid, Mary Elizabeth, David Blake. BA, Dartmouth Coll., 1961, B in Med. Sci., 1962; MD, Johns Hopkins U., 1964. Med. resident Johns Hopkins Hosp., Balt., 1964-66; endocrine fellow Duke U., Durham, N.C., 1966-67, 69-71; staff endocrinologist Geisinger Med. Ctr., Danville, Pa., 1971-84, pres., 1982-84; asst. dean Milton S. Hershey Med. Ctr., Hershey, Pa., 1973-77; pres. Geisinger Med. Mgmt. Corp., Danville, 1978-82, NPW Med. Ctr., Wilkes Barre, Pa., 1979-82; exec. v.p. Geisinger Found., Danville, 1981-84; pres. Ramsey Clinic, St. Paul, 1984-87, Joslin Diabetes Ctr., Boston, 1987—; bd. dirs. Controlled Risk Ins. Co., Barbados, 1987—. Contbr. articles to sci. jours. Trustee Deaconess Hosp., Boston, 1987—. Surgeon USPHS, 1967-69. Fellow ACP, Am. Coll. Physician Execs. (disting.); mem. Am. Diabetes Assn., Endocrine Soc., Harvard Club. Republican. Home: 10 Hickory Dr Medfield MA 02052-1131 Office: Joslin Diabetes Ctr 1 Joslin Pl Boston MA 02215-5397

QUIE, PAUL GERHARDT, physician, educator; b. Dennison, Minn., Feb. 3, 1925; s. Albert Knute and Nettie Marie (Jacobson) Q.; m. Elizabeth Holmes, Aug. 10, 1951; children: Katie, Bill, Paul, David. B.A., St. Olaf Coll., 1949; M.D, Yale U., 1953; PhD (hon.), U. Lund, 1993. Diplomate Am. Bd. Pediatrics, Nat. Bd. Med. Examiners (mem.). Intern Hennepin County Hosp., 1953-54; pediatric resident U. Minn. Hosps., 1957-59; mem. faculty U. Minn. Med. Sch., 1959—, prof. pediatrics, 1968—, prof. microbiology, 1974—; assoc. dean of students, 1992—; Am. Legion meml. heart research prof. U. Minn. Med. Sch., 1974-91, Regents prof., 1991, interim dir. Ctr. for Biomed. Ethics, 1985-86; attending physician Hennepin County Hosp., 1959-91; cons. U. Minn. Nursery Sch., 1959-91; chief of staff U. Minn. Hosp., 1979-84; vis. physician Radcliffe Infirmary, Oxford, Eng., 1971-72; mem. Adv. Allergy and Infectious Disease Coun., 1976-80; mem. pediatric com. NRC, 1978; mem. bd. sci. counselors Gamble Inst., 1985-90; vis. prof. U. Bergen, 1991; hon. prof. U. Hong Kong Med. Sch., 1995. Mem. editorial bd. Pediatrics, 1970-76, Rev. Infectious Diseases, 1989-92. Served with USNR, 1954-57; med. officer. Recipient E. Mead-Johnson award Am. Acad. Pediatrics, 1971; Guggenheim fellow, 1971-72; John and Mary R. Markle scholar, 1960-65; Alexander Von Humbolt fellow, 1986. Mem. Inst. Medicine of NAS, N.W. Pediatrics Soc., Minn. Med. Found. (pres. 1986-88), Am. Fedn. Clin. Rsch., Am. Soc. Microbiology, Infectious Diseases Soc. Am. (coun. 1977-82, pres. 1985, Bristol award 1994), Soc. Pediatric Rsch. Am. Pediatric Soc. (coun. 1976-83, pres. 1987-88), Am. Soc. Clin. Investigation, Minn. Acad. Pediatrics, Am. Acad. Pediatrics, Assn. Am. Physicians, Minn. Acad. Medicine (pres. 1993-94). Research in function of human leukocytes. Home: 2154 Commonwealth Ave Saint Paul MN 55108-1717 Office: U Minn Hosp PO Box 483 Minneapolis MN 55455-0483

QUIGG, DONALD JAMES, lawyer; b. Kansas City, Mo., Apr. 28, 1916; s. James Smith and Lorna (Shields) Q.; m. Louise Marie Heinzelman, Feb. 14, 1942; children: Sandra Louise Quigg Porter, James Michael. Student, Bartlesville Jr. Coll., Okla., 1933-34; B.S. in Bus. Adminstrn., U. Okla., 1937; postgrad., Kansas City Sch. Law, 1937-38; J.D., Kansas City U., 1940. Bar: Mo. 1940, Okla. 1947, Va. 1990. Assoc. Hovey, Beals & Boley, Kansas City, 1937-42; patent atty. Phillips Petroleum Co., Bartlesville, 1945-81; dep. commr. U.S. Patent and Trademark Office, Arlington, Va., 1981-85, asst. sec., commr., 1985-89. Patentee in field. Served to 1st lt. F.A., AUS, 1942-46, PTO. Mem. ABA, Okla. Bar Assn., Mo. Bar Assn., Va. Bar Assn., Am. Intellectual Property Law Assn., Assn. Corp. Patent Counsel (emeritus). Republican. Presbyterian. Office: Roper & Quigg 2231 Crystal Dr Ste 410 Arlington VA 22202-3706

QUIGG, JEAN, principal. Prin. Frostwood Elem. Sch., Houston. Recipient Elem. Sch. Recognition award U.S. Dept. Edn., 1989-90. Office: Frostwood Elem Sch 12214 Memorial Dr Houston TX 77024-6299

QUIGLEY, AUSTIN EDMUND, literature and language educator; b. Newcastle-upon-Tyne, Eng., Dec. 31, 1942; came to U.S., 1969; s. Edmund and Marguerita Mary (Crilley) Q.; m. Patricia Doreen Denison, June 1, 1979. BA with honors, U. Nottingham, Eng., 1967; MA, U. Birmingham, Eng., 1969; PhD, U. Calif., Santa Cruz, 1971. Asst. prof. U. Mass., 1971-73; from asst. prof. to prof. U. Va., 1973-90, chmn. dept. English, 1986-90; H. Gordon Garbedian prof. English and comparative lit. Columbia U., N.Y.C., 1990—, chmn. PhD program theatre Hammerstein Ctr. Theatre Studies, 1990—; chmn. Lionel Trilling Seminars, 1993—; vis. prof. U. Konstanz, Germany, 1981, U. Geneva, 1982, U. Nottingham, Eng., 1983-84; lectr. at univs., convs. and theatres. Author: The Pinter Problem, 1975, The Modern Stage and Other Worlds, 1985; contbr. many articles on modern lit., drama, lit. theory to profl. jours.; mem. edit. bd. New Lit. History, Va., 1974—, Modern Drama, Toronto, 1978—, The Pinter Rev., Tampa, Fla., 1987—, Theater/Theory/Text Performance, Ann Arbor, Mich., 1988—. Danforth fellow U. Calif., 1970-71; fellow NEH, London, 1977-78. Mem. MLA (exec. com. drama div. 1987-92), Linguistics Assn. Gt. Britain, Samuel Beckett Soc., Harold Pinter Soc., Am. Soc. Theatre Rsch., Shakespeare Assn. Am., Phi Beta Kappa, Omicron Delta Kappa. Avocations: tennis, squash, soccer, hiking. Office: Columbia U Dept English Philosophy Hall New York NY 10027

QUIGLEY, JACK ALLEN, service company executive; b. Bloomington, Ill., Apr. 11, 1914; s. Thomas M. and Margaret (Brown) Q.; m. Eleanor T. Steen, Nov. 17, 1946; children: J. Timothy, J William, Margaret N., Richard A. B.S.; Northwestern U., 1935. With Means Services, Inc., 1935—, personnel dir., 1935-37, div. mgr., 1937-41, gen. mgr., 1946-48, v.p., dir., 1948-50, pres., dir., 1950-72, chmn. bd., chief exec. officer, 1972-81; cons., 1981—; Co-chmn. First and Second Internat. Linen Supply Congresses, 1959, 62; founder, chmn. Chgo. Pres.'s Orgn., 1966-68, Young Pres.'s Orgn., 1951-62. Served with USAF, World War II. Mem. Linen Supply Assn. Am. (pres. 1955-57, founder chmn. rsch. group 1957-60), Chief Execs. Forum, Royal Poinciana Golf Club (Naples Fla.). Home: 114 Moorings Park Dr Apt A-812 Naples FL 33942-2112

QUIGLEY, JOHN BERNARD, law educator; b. St. Louis, Oct. 1, 1940; s. John Bernard and Ruth Rosina (Schieber) Q. BA, Harvard U., 1962, MA, LLB, 1966. Bar: Ohio 1973, Mass. 1967. U.S. Dist. Ct. (so. dist) Ohio 1976, U.S. Ct. Appeals (6th cir.) 1986, U.S. Supreme Ct. 1989. Research assoc. Harvard U. Law Sch., Cambridge, Mass., 1967-69; prof. law Ohio State U.,

Columbus, 1969—. Author: Basic Laws on the Structure of the Soviet State, 1969, The Soviet Foreign Trade Monopoly, 1974, Palestine and Israel: A Challenge to Justice, 1990, The Ruses for War: American Interventionism since World War II, 1992. Mem. Nat. Lawyers Guild (v.p. 1977-79), Am. Soc. Internat. Law, AAUP. Avocations: tennis, speed skating, violin. Office: Ohio State U Coll. of Law Coll of Law 55 W 12th Ave Columbus OH 43210-1338

QUIGLEY, JOHN MICHAEL, economist, educator; b. N.Y.C., Feb. 12, 1942. B.S. with distinction, U.S. Air Force Acad., 1964; M.Sc. with honors, U. Stockholm, Sweden, 1965; A.M., Harvard U., 1971, Ph.D., 1972. Commd. 2d lt. USAF, 1964, advanced through grades to capt., 1968; asst. prof. econs. Yale U., 1972-74, assoc. prof., 1974-81; prof. pub. policy U. Calif., Berkeley, 1979—, prof. econs., 1981—, chmn. dept. econs., 1992—; vis. prof. econs. and stats. U. Gothenberg, 1978; cons. numerous govt. agys. and pvt. firms; econometrician Hdqrs. U.S. Air Force, Pentagon, 1965-68; research assoc. Nat. Bur. Econ. Research, N.Y.C., 1968-78; mem. com. on nat. urban policy Nat. Acad. Sci., 1985—. Author, editor, contbr. articles to profl. jours.; editor in chief Reg. Sci. and Urban Econs., 1987—; mem. editorial bd. Land Econs., 1974-81, Jour. Urban Econs., 1978—, Coun. on Pub. Policy and Mgmt., 1979—, AREUEA Jour., 1985—, Property Tax Jour., 1990—, Jour. Housing Econs., 1990—. Fulbright scholar, 1964-65; fellow NSF, 1968-69, Woodrow Wilson, 1968-71, Harvard IBM, 1969-71, NDEA, 1969-71, Thord-Gray Am. Scandinavian Found. 1971-72, Social Sci. Research Council, 1971-72. Mem. Am. Econ. Assn., Econometric Soc., Regional Sci. Assn. (bd. dirs. 1986—), Nat. Tax Assn., Assn. for Pub. Policy and Mgmt. (bd. dirs. 1986-89, v.p. 1987-89), AREUEA (bd. dirs. 1987—, v.p. 1995—). Home: 875 Hilldale Ave Berkeley CA 94708-1319 Office: U Calif 2607 Hearst Ave Berkeley CA 94720-0001

QUIGLEY, KEVIN WALSH, state legislator, lawyer; b. Everett, Wash., Feb. 23, 1961; s. David W. Quigley and Mary (Cernetig) Thoreson; m. Suzanne Marion Bakke. BA with spl. honors, George Washington U., 1983; JD cum laude, NYU, 1986; LLM, Harvard U., 1992. Bar: Wash. 1988. Jr. fellow ctr. internat. studies NYU Law Sch., N.Y.C., 1986; assoc. Perkins Coie, Seattle, 1987-94; of counsel Perkins Cole, Seattle, 1995—; mem. Wash. State Senate, Olympia, 1993—; chmn. health and long term care com., mem. ways and means com., law and justice com. Grad. fellow Harvard Law Sch., 1987. Mem. Rotary, Phi Beta Kappa. Democrat. Avocations: mountain climbing, biking, hiking. Home: 1029 Springbrook Rd Lake Stevens WA 98258-9425

QUIGLEY, LEONARD VINCENT, lawyer; b. Kansas City, Mo., June 21, 1933; s. Joseph Vincent and Rosemary (Cannon) Q.; m. Lynn Mathis Pfohl, May 23, 1964; children: Leonard Matthew, Cannon Louise, Daniel Pfohl, Megan Mathis. A.B., Coll. Holy Cross, 1953; LL.B. magna cum laude, Harvard U., 1959; LL.M. in Internat. Law, NYU, 1962. Bar: N.Y. 1960. Assoc. Cravath, Swaine & Moore, N.Y.C., 1959-67; ptnr. Paul, Weiss, Rifkind, Wharton & Garrison, N.Y.C., 1967—; gen. counsel Archaeol. Inst. Am., Boston. Served to lt. USN, 1953-56. Mem. ABA, Can. Bar Assn., Assn. Bar City N.Y. Clubs: Harvard (N.Y.C.); West Side Tennis (Forest Hills, N.Y.).

QUIGLEY, MARTIN SCHOFIELD, publishing company executive, educator; b. Chgo., Nov. 24, 1917; s. Martin Joseph and Gertrude Margaret (Schofield) Q.; m. Katherine J. Dunphy, July 2, 1946; children: Martin, Elin, William, Kevin, Karen, Patricia, John, Mary Katherine, Peter. AB magna cum laude, Georgetown U., 1939; MA, Columbia U., 1973, EdD, 1975. Reporter Motion Picture Herald, N.Y.C. and Hollywood, Calif., 1939-41; with overseas br. OWI, 1942; secret war work U.S. Govt., 1943-45; various editorial and mgmt. posts Quigley Pub. Inc., N.Y.C., 1946—; pres. Quigley Pub. Co. Inc., 1964—; staff, dept. higher and adult edn. Tchrs. Coll., 1974-75; prof. higher edn. grad. courses Baruch Coll. CUNY, 1977-89; prof. higher edn. grad. courses Tchrs. Coll. Columbia U., 1979-80, 1990-92; higher edn. grad. courses Seton Hall U., 1981-82; pres. QWS, Inc., 1975-80; ednl. cons.; cons. supt. schs. N.Y. Archdiocese, 1962-70. Author: Great Gaels, 1944, Roman Notes, 1946, Magic Shadows—the story of the origin of motion pictures, 1948, Government Relations of Five Universities in Washington, D.C., 1975, Peace Without Hiroshima-Secret Action at the Vatican in Spring of 1945, 1991, First Century of Film, 1995; co-author: Catholic Action in Practice, 1962, Films in America, 1969; editor: New Screen Techniques, 1953. Pres. N.Y. Christian Family Movement, 1960-62, mem. nat. exec. com., 1960-65; founder, chmn. N.Y. Inst. Schs. Opportunity Project, 1965-77; pres. Found. Internat. Coop., 1960-65; bd. dirs. Will Rogers Inst., Motion Picture Pioneers; treas. Religious Edn. Assn. U.S. and Can., 1975-81, chmn., 1981-84; trustee Village of Larchmont, N.Y., 1977-79, mayor, 1980-84; mem. Laymen's Nat. Bible Assn., 1981—; trustee Am. Bible Soc., 1984—; bd. dirs. William J. Donovan Meml. Found., 1994—. Roman Catholic. Club: Larchmont Yacht. Home: 8 Pheasant Run Larchmont NY 10538-3423 Office: 159 W 53d St New York NY 10019

QUIGLEY, PHILIP J., telecommunications industry executive; b. 1943. With Advanced Mobile Phone Svc. Inc., 1982-84, v.p., gen. mgr., Pacific region; with Pac Tel Mobile Access, 1984-86, pres., chief exec. officer; with Pac Tel Personal Communications, 1986-87, pres., chief exec. officer; exec. v.p., chief oper. officer Pac Tel Corp., 1987; with Pacific Bell, San Francisco, 1987—; now chmn., pres., chief exec. officer Pacific Bell Group, Pacific Telesis, San Francisco. Office: Pacific Bell 140 New Montgomery St San Francisco CA 94105-3705*

QUIGLEY, ROBERT LAWRENCE, cardiothoracic surgeon, educator; b. Halifax, N.S., Can., Dec. 16, 1957; came to U.S., 1988; s. John Howden and Gloria Lorraine (Monseur) Q.; m. Debra Kristine Crumb, Sept. 4, 1993. BS, Dalhousie U., Halifax, 1978; MD, U. Toronto, Ont., Can., 1982; DPhil, Oxford (Eng.) U., 1988. Diplomate Am. Bd. Surgery, Am. Bd. Critical Care, Am. Bd. Thoracic Surgery. Intern U. Toronto, 1982-83, resident in surgery, 1983-85; rsch. fellow Oxford U., 1985-88; resident in Surgery Duke U. Med. Ctr., Durham, N.C., 1988-90, fellow in cardiothoracic surgery, 1990-92; asst. prof. surgery Northwestern U.-Evanston (Ill.) Hosp., 1992—, dir. Surg. Rsch. Lab., 1994—. Recipient rsch. award Med. Rsch. Coun. Can., 1986-88, Golden Apple award med. students Duke U. Med. Ctr., 1990; faculty fellow ACS, 1994-96. Mem. Soc. Critical Care Medicine, Alpha Omega Alpha. Avocations: running, sailing, water and snow skiing, swimming. Home: 2730 Sheridan Rd Evanston IL 60201 Office: Evanston Hosp Dept Surgery 2650 Ridge Ave Evanston IL 60201

QUIGLEY, ROBERT MURVIN, engineering educator, research consultant; b. Toronto, Ont., Can., Jan. 22, 1934; s. Murvin John and Estelle Rosina (Nelles) Q.; m. Marian Margaret Flack, July 2, 1957; children: Steven, James, Peter. BASc, U. Toronto, 1955, MASc, 1956; PhD, MIT, 1961. Registered profl. engr., Ont. Sr. soils engr. Geocon Inc., Toronto and Montreal, Que., Can., 1956-63; asst. prof. U. Western Ont., London, 1963-66, assoc. prof., 1966-70, prof., 1970-94, prof. emeritus, 1994—, dir. Geotech. Rsch. Centre, 1985—; pres. R.M. Quigley Inc., London, 1974—. Editor: Can. Geotech. Jour., Ottawa, Ont., 1980-84; contbr. articles to profl. jours. Recipient excellence in rsch. award Ont. Ministry Environ., 1989, R.F. Legget award, 1991. Fellow Engring. Inst. Can., Can. Acad. Engring.; mem. ASTM, Can. Geotech. Soc. (R.F. Legget award), Clay Minerals Soc., Geol. Assn. Can. Avocation: water color and oil painting. Home: River Ridge Unit 18, 1331 Commissioners Rd W, London, ON Canada N6K 1E2 Office: U Western Ont, Faculty Engring, London, ON Canada N6A 5B9

QUIGLEY, THOMAS J., lawyer; b. Mt. Carmel, Pa., July 22, 1923; s. James S. and Helen C. (Laughlin) Q.; m. Joan R. Reifke, Aug. 11, 1956; children: Thomas J., Jr., Joan E., James S. AB, Bucknell U., 1947; LLB, Yale U., 1950. Bar: Ohio, U.S. Dist. Ct. Ohio, U.S. Ct. Appeals (6th and D.C. cirs.). With Squire, Sanders & Dempsey, 1950—; adminstr. labor dept., 1971-80, mng. ptnr., Washington, 1980-85; vice chmn., 1985-86; nat. chmn., 1986-90. Bd. dirs., exec. com. Fed. City Coun., Washington pres.; dir. exec. com. Nat. Symphony Orch., nat. trustee Musical Arts Assn. Cleve. 1st lt. USAAF, 1942-45. Decorated D.F.C., Air medal with oak leaf cluster, Belgium's Order of the Crown. Mem. ABA, Ohio Bar Assn., D.C. Bar Assn., Cleve. Bar Assn., Belgian-Am. C. of C. (bd. dirs.), Yale Law Sch. Alumni Assn. (bd. dirs.), Case-Western Res. Univ. Law Sch. (vis. com.). Roman Catholic. Clubs: Union (Cleve.); Yale (N.Y.C.); Edgartown Yacht (Mass.); Chevy Chase; Metropolitan (Wash.). Office: Squire Sanders & Dempsey 1201

Pennsylvania Ave NW PO Box 407 Washington DC 20004 also: Soc Ctr Bldg Cleveland OH 44114

QUILICO, LOUIS, baritone; b. Montreal, Que., Can., Jan. 14, 1931; s. Louis and Jeanne (Gravel) Q.; m. Lina Pezzolongo, Oct. 30, 1949 (dec. Sept. 1991); children: Donna Maria, Gino; m. Christina Petrowska, Nov. 30, 1993. Studied, Conservatoire de la Province de Que., Ont., Can., Mannes Coll. Music, N.Y.C., Conservatoir de Santa Cecilia, Rome. Prof. U. Toronto, Ont. Operatic debut in La Traviata, N.Y.C. Opera, 1956; performed with major opera cos. including Royal Opera, Covent Garden, Staatsoper, Opera Nat. de Belgique, L'Opera de Quebec, Canadian Opera Co., Bolshoi Opera, Opera Co. of Phila., San Francisco Opera, Seattle Opera, San Diego Opera, Opera Soc. of Washington (D.C.), many others; created numerous roles; resident mem., Met. Opera, (Winner Nos Futurs Étoi Les, Montreal 1953, Met. Opera Audition of the Air 1955). Named Esquire Montreal Expo, 1967; decorated companion Order of Can. Roman Catholic. Office: care Robert Lombardo Assocs One Harkness Plaza 61 W 62nd St Ste 6F New York NY 10023-7201 also: Ann Summers Int, Box 188 Station A, Toronto, ON Canada M5W 1B2

QUILL, LEONARD WALTER, banker; b. Wilmington, Del., Dec. 11, 1931; s. Timothy Joseph and Katherine (McCann) Q.; m. Martina Mary Quinn, July 12, 1958; children—Martina, Teresa, Katherine, Timothy, Leonard, James. B.S., U. Del., M.B.A. With Wilmington Trust Co., Wilmington, Del., 1957—, now mgr. comml. banking dept., sr. v.p., treas.; dir. Wilmington Econ. Devel. Corp. Bd. dirs. United Way Del., 1983—. Served to sgt. USAF, 1951-53. Mem. Del. Bankers Assn. (bd. dirs. 1985—). Roman Catholic. Home: 1104 Arundel Dr Wilmington DE 19808-2135 Office: Wilmington Trust Co 1100 N Market St Wilmington DE 19890

QUILLEN, CAROL E., historian, educator; b. St. Albans, N.Y., Jan. 9, 1961; d. William Tatem and Marcia Everhart (Stirling) Q.; m. Terry Michael Lohrenz, Oct. 10, 1987. AB History, U. Chgo., 1983; PhD History, Princeton U., 1991. Asst. prof. Rice U., Houston, 1989—. Recipient Brown Teaching award Brown Found., 1993; fellow Mellon Found., 1983; Whiting fellow MB Gilles Whiting Found., 1987. Mem. Am. Hist. Assn., Renaissance Soc. Am. Office: Rice U Dept History PO Box 1892 Houston TX 77251

QUILLEN, CECIL DYER, JR., lawyer, consultant; b. Kingsport, Tenn., Jan. 21, 1937; s. Cecil D. and Mary Louise (Carter) Q.; m. Vicey Ann Childress, Apr. 1, 1967; children: Cecil D., Ann C. BS, Va. Poly. Inst., 1958; LLB, U. Va., 1962. Bar: Va. 1962, N.Y. 1963, Tenn. 1974. Atty. patent dept., Eastman Kodak Co. Rochester, N.Y., 1962-65, atty. patent sect. Tenn. Eastman Co. (div. Eastman Kodak), Kingsport, Tenn., 1965-69, mgr., 1969-72, mgr. licensing, 1972-74, sec. and asst. chief counsel, 1974-76, dir. patent litigation, Eastman Kodak, 1976-82, dir. antitrust litigation, Eastman Kodak, 1978-82, v.p. and chief counsel, Tenn. Eastman, 1983-85, v.p.,and assoc. gen. counsel, Eastman Kodak, 1986, sr. v.p., gen. counsel, dir., 1986-92; sr. adv., Putnam, Hayes & Bartlett, Inc., Washington, 1992—. Mem. ABA, Va. State Bar, Am. Intellectual Property Law Assn., Va. Poly. Inst. Com. of 100, Assn. of Gen. Counsel.

QUILLEN, FORD CARTER, state legislator, lawyer; b. Gate City, Va., Sept. 21, 1938; s. Cecil Dyer and Mary Louise (Carter) Q.; m. Barbara Gail Burdette, Dec. 17, 1961; children—Madre, Carter, Lenoir. B.S., U. Tenn. 1961, J.D., 1966. Bar: Va. 1966. Ptnr. Quillen and Carter, Gate City, 1966-78; sole practice, Gate City, 1978—; mem. Va. Legislature, 1970—, mem. rules com., chmn. privileges and elections com., mines and minerals resources com., mem. appropriations com.; mem. Joint Legis. and Audit Rev. commn., Coal and Energy Commn. Served with U.S. Army, 1961-63. Recipient Outstanding Legislator award Eagleston Inst., 1975, Wildlife Legislator of Yr. award 1989, Educator of Yr. award, 1987, Va. Jefferson Cup, Assn. of Cts., 1993. Mem. ABA, Def. Lawyers Assn., Va. Bar Assn., Va. Trial Lawyers, Va. State Bar, Va. Def. Assn. Democrat. Baptist. Office: PO Box 339 Gate City VA 24251-0339

QUILLEN, JAMES HENRY (JIMMY QUILLEN), congressman; b. Wayland, Va., Jan. 11, 1916; s. John A. and Hannah (Chapman) Q.; m. Cecile Cox, Aug. 9, 1952. Ed. high sch.; LL.D. (hon.), Milligan Coll., Tenn., 1978. With Kingsport Press, 1934-35, Kingsport Times, 1935-36; founder newspaper Kingsport Mirror (semi-weekly), 1936, pub., 1936-39; founder Johnson City (Tenn.) Times, 1939, pub., 1939-44; pub. Johnson City (Tenn.) Times (converted to daily), 1940; Mem. Tenn. Ho. of Reps., 1954-62, minority leader, 1959-60, mem. legislative council, 1957, 59, 61, mem. rules com., subcom. legis. process, Rep. chmn. emeritus; mem. U.S. Congress from Tenn., 1963—. Served to lt. USNR, 1942-46. Mem. Am. Legion, VFW, C. of C. Republican. Methodist. Clubs: Lions, Ridgefields Country (Kingsport); Capitol Hill (Washington). Office: US Ho Reps 102 Cannon Ho Office Bldg Washington DC 20515*

QUILLEN, WILLIAM TATEM, state judge, lawyer, educator; b. Camden, N.J., Jan. 15, 1935; s. Robert James and Gladys Collings (Tatem) Q.; m. Marcia Everhart Stirling, June 27, 1959; children: Carol Everhart, Tracey Tatem. B.A., Williams Coll., 1956; LL.B., Harvard U., 1959; LL.M., U. Va., 1982. Bar: Del. 1959. Assoc. Richards, Layton & Finger, Wilmington, Del., 1963-64; adminstrv. asst. to Gov. of Del., 1965; assoc. judge Superior Ct. of Del., 1966-73; chancellor State of Del., 1973-76; sr. v.p. Wilmington Trust Co., 1976-78; justice Supreme Ct. of Del., 1978-83; ptnr. Potter Anderson & Corroon, Wilmington, 1983-86; gen. counsel, v.p. Howard Hughes Med. Inst., 1986-91; sec. of state State of Del., Dover, 1993-94; assoc. judge Superior Ct. Del., 1994—; mem. adj. faculty Widener U. Sch. Law, Wilmington, 1976-83, 95—, disting. vis. prof. law, 1992-94. Trustee Widener U., 1979-91; Democratic candidate for gov. Del., 1984. Served with JAGC, USAF, 1959-62. Mem. Am. Bar Assn., Del. State Bar Assn., Phi Beta Kappa. Democrat. Presbyterian. Club: Wilmington.

QUILLIAN, WARREN WILSON, II, pediatrician, educator; b. Miami, Fla., Jan. 21, 1936; s. Warren Wilson and Rosabel (Brown) Q.; m. Sallie Ruth Creel, July 26, 1958; children: Rutledge, Ruth, Warren C., Frances. MD, Emory U., 1961. Diplomate Am. Bd. Pediat. (examiner 1966—), bd. dirs. 1974-80, 1992—, treas. 1978, v.p. 1979, pres. 1980). Intern in pediatrics Vanderbilt U., Nashville, 1961-62; resident Children's Hosp. Med. Ctr., Harvard U., Boston, 1962-63; chief resident Grady Meml. Hosp., Emory U., Atlanta, 1963-64; pvt. practice, Coral Gables, Fla., 1966; instr., asst. clin. prof., assoc. clin. prof., now clin. prof. pediat. U. Miami Med. Sch., 1966—; active staff, bd. dirs. Miami Children's Hosp.; active staff Jackson Meml. Hosp.; chief pediat. Doctors' Hosp.; mem. courtesy staff Mercy Hosp., Bapt. Hosp., South Miami Hosp., Cedars of Lebanon Hosp.; chmn. health adv. com. Dade County Schs.; bd. dirs., v.p. Bd. Pediat. Found., 1991—; mem. adv. bd. McGlannon Sch.; cons. Fla. Div. Med. Svcs.; bd. dirs. Bank Coral Gables. Contbr. articles to med. jours. Hon. bd. dirs. Soc. for Abused Children of Children's Home Soc., Miami, 1980-84; mem. Coral Gables Code Enforcement Bd., 1986-88; team-sch. physician Coral Gables Sr. H.G., 1980-88; bd. dirs. Dade County March of Dimes, Miami, 1968-72; bd. advisors Dade County Assn. Retarded Children, 1968-76; trustee Emory U., 1991—; mem. coun. ministries, youth coord., mem. fin. com., Sunday sch. tchr. United Meth. Ch. Coral Gables, 1966—; mem. parrish rels. com.; mem. bd. advisors The Growing Place. Capt. M.C., U.S. Army, 1964-66. Recipient citation of merit Emory U., 1980, alumni commendation Miami Children's Hosp., 1983. Fellow Am. Acad. Pediat.; mem. AMA, Fla. Med. Assn. (sch. health com.), Fla. Pediatric Soc. (past chmn. sch. health com.), So. Med. Assn., Dade County Med. Assn. (sch. health com., continuing edn. com.), Empirical Soc. (past pres.), So. Soc. for Pediatric Rsch., So. Perinatal Soc., Greater Miami Pediatric Soc. (past pres., chmn. legis. and sch. health com.), Miami Med. Forum (past pres., Maxwell Cup 1985), Alpha Omega Alpha, Omicron Delta Kappa, Alpha Epsilon Upsilon, Phi Delta Theta. Democrat. Avocations: fishing, golf. Office: 305 Granello Ave Coral Gables FL 33146-1806

QUILLIAN, WILLIAM FLETCHER, JR., retired banker, former college president; b. Nashville, Apr. 13, 1913; s. William Fletcher and Nonie (Lane) Q.; m. Margaret Hannah Weigle, June 15, 1940; children—William Fletcher III, Anne Acree, Katherine, Robert. A.B., Emory U., 1935, Litt.D. (hon.), 1959; B.D., Yale, 1938, Ph.D., 1943; postgrad., U. Edinburgh, 1938-39, U. Basel, 1939; Day fellow from Yale, 1938-39; Rosenwald fellow, 1940-41;

LL.D., Ohio Wesleyan U., 1952, Hampden-Sydney Coll., 1978, Randolph-Macon Coll., 1967; D.H.L., Randolph-Macon Woman's Coll., 1978. Ordained to ministry Meth. Ch., 1942. Student asst. Stamford (Conn.) Presbyn Ch., 1936-38; del. Gen. Com. of World Student Christian Fedn., Bievres, France, 1938; discussion leader World Conf. Christian Youth, Amsterdam, Holland, 1939; pastor Clarendon (Vt.) Community Ch., summer 1940; asst. prof. philosophy Gettysburg Coll., 1941-43, prof., 1943-45; prof. philosophy Ohio Wesleyan U., 1945-52; pres. Randolph Macon Woman's Coll., 1952-78; pres. emeritus Randolph Macon Woman's Coll., 1978—; sr. v.p. Central Fidelity Bank, 1978-88; exec. dir. Greater Lynchburg (Va.) Community Trust, 1988—; v.p., bd. dirs Pride of Virginia Meats, Inc.; tchr. Garrett Biblical Inst., summer 1951. Author: The Moral Theory of Evolutionary Naturalism, 1945, Evolution and Moral Theory in America, Evolutionary Thought in America, 1950; Contbr. articles to philos. and religious jours. Pres. bd. dirs. United Way Cen. Va., campaign chmn., 1987; bd. dirs. Alpha Tau Omega Found., Lynchburg Gen. Hosp.; hon. life trustee Va. Found. Ind. Colls.; pres., 1958-61. Mem. Assn. Am. Colls. (past pres.), So. U. Conf. (pres. 1967-68), So. Assn. Colls. for Women (pres. 1956), Nat. Assn. United Methodist Colls. and Univs. (pres. 1973), Am. Philos. Assn., Soc. for Values in Higher Edn. (mem. central com. 1945-48, chmn. 1947-48), Nat. Assn. Bibl. Instrs., AAUP, Greater Lynchburg C. of C. (dir. pres. 1979-80), Phi Beta Kappa., Omicron Delta Kappa, Alpha Tau Omega (dir. found.). Home: 1407 Club Dr Lynchburg VA 24503-2503 Office: Cen Fidelity Bank Lynchburg VA 24505

QUILLIGAN, EDWARD JAMES, obstetrician/gynecologist, educator; b. Cleve., June 18, 1925; s. James Joseph and Maude Elvira (Ryan) Q.; m. Betty Jane Cleaton, Dec. 14, 1946; children—Bruce, Jay, Carol, Christopher, Linda, Ted. B.A., Ohio State U., 1951, M.D., 1951; M.A. (hon.), Yale, 1967. Intern Ohio State U. Hosp., 1951-52, resident, 1952-54; resident Western Res. U. Hosps., 1954-56; asst. prof. obstetrics and gynecology Western Res. U., 1957-63, prof., 1963-65; prof. obstetrics and gynecology UCLA, 1965-66; prof., chmn. dept. Ob-Gyn Yale U., 1966-69; prof., chmn. dept. Ob-Gyn U. So. Calif., 1969-78, assoc. v.p. med. affairs, 1978-79; prof. Ob-Gyn. U. Calif., Irvine, 1980-83, vice chancellor health affairs, dean Sch. Medicine, 1987-89; prof., chmn. ob.-gyn. dept. U. Wis., 1983-85; prof., chmn. Ob-Gyn Davis Med. Ctr. U. Calif., Sacramento, 1985-87; vice chancellor Health Scis., dean Coll. Med. U. Calif., Irvine, 1987-89, prof. ob-gyn, 1987-94, prof. emeritus, 1994—. Contbr. articles to med. jours.; co-editor-in-chief: Am. Jour. Obstetrics and Gynecology. Served to 2d lt. AUS, 1944-46. Recipient Centennial award Ohio State U., 1970. Mem. Soc. Gynecologic Investigation, Am. Gynecol. Soc., Am. Coll. Obstetrics and Gynecology, Sigma Xi. Home: 24 Urey Ct Irvine CA 92715-4045 Office: UC Irvine Med Ctr Dept Ob-Gyn Bldg 22 101 The City Dr S Orange CA 92668-3201

QUIMBY, GEORGE IRVING, anthropologist, former museum director; b. Grand Rapids, Mich., May 4, 1913; s. George Irving and Ethelwyn (Sweet) Q.; m. Helen M. Ziehm, Oct. 13, 1940; children: Sedna H., G. Edward, John E., Robert W. B.A., U. Mich., 1936, M.A., 1937, grad. fellow, 1937-38; postgrad., U. Chgo., 1938-39; LHD (hon.), Grand Valley State U., Mich., 1992. State supr. Fed. Archaeol. Project in La., 1939-41; dir. Muskegon (Mich.) Mus., 1941-42; asst. curator N.Am. archaeology and ethnology Field Mus. Natural History, 1942-43, curator exhibits, anthropology, 1943-54, curator N.Am. archeology and ethnology, 1954-65, research assoc. in N. Am. archaeology and ethnology, 1965—; curator anthropology Thomas Burke Meml. Wash. State Mus.; prof. anthropology U. Wash., 1965-83, emeritus prof., 1983—, mus. dir., 1968-83, emeritus dir., 1983—; lectr. U. Chgo., 1947-65, Northwestern U., 1949-53; Fulbright vis. prof., U. Oslo, Norway, 1952; archaeol. expdns. and field work, Mich., 1935, 37, 52, 56-63, Wis., 1936, Hudson's Bay, 1939, La., 1940-41, N.Mex., 1947, Lake Superior, 1956-61. Author: Aleutian Islanders, 1944, (with J. A. Ford) The Tchefuncte Culture, an Early Occupation of the Lower Mississippi Valley, 1945, (with P. S. Martin, D. Collier) Indians Before Columbus, 1947, Indian Life in the Upper Great Lakes, 1960, Indian Culture and European Trade Goods, 1966, A Thing of Sherds and Patches: The Autobiography of George Irving Quimby, American Antiquity, vol. 58, 1, 1993; prodr. documentary film (with Bill Holm) In the Land of the War Canoes, 1973, Edward S. Curtis in the Land of the War Canoes: A Pioneer Cinematographer in the Pacific Northwest, 1980; Contbr. articles to profl. jours. Honored by festschrift U. Mich. Mus. Anthropology, 1983. Fellow AAAS, Am. Anthrop. Assn.; mem. Soc. Am. Archaeology (pres. 1958, 50th Anniversary award 1983, Disting. Svc. award 1989), Am. Soc. Ethnohistory, Wis. Archeol. Soc., Soc. Historical Archeology (council 1971-74, 75-78, J.C. Harrington medal 1986), Assn. Sci. Mus. Dirs. (pres. 1973-74), Arctic Inst. N.Am., Am. Assn. Museums (council 1971-74), Sigma Xi, Phi Sigma, Chi Gamma Phi, Zeta Psi. Home: 6001 52nd Ave NE Seattle WA 98115-7711 Office: U Washington Thomas Burke Meml Wash State Mus Seattle WA 98195

QUIMBY, ROBERT SHERMAN, retired humanities educator; b. St. Albans, Vt., Feb. 20, 1916; s. Christopher Sherman and Lura Mae (Wills) Q.; m. Shirley Lenore Lay, Oct. 19, 1957. B.S. in Edn, U. Vt., 1937, M.A., 1938; Ph.D., Columbia U., 1952; postgrad., Am. Sch. Classical Studies, Athens, Greece, 1958. Teaching asst. in history U. Vt., Burlington, 1938-39, 41-42; instr. history U. Vt., 1942-44, Cornell U., Ithaca, N.Y., 1944-45; instr. history of civilization Mich. State U., East Lansing, 1945-52; asst. prof. humanities Mich. State U., 1952-59, asso. prof., 1959-68, prof., 1968-81, prof. emeritus of humanities, 1981—; Mem. Mich. Commn. of United Ministries in Higher Edn., 1970-87, sec., 1975-77. Author: The Background of Napoleonic Warfare; contbr. articles to profl. jours. and encys. George Ellis fellow Columbia U., 1939-41. Mem. Am. Inst. Archaeology, Mich. Hist. Soc., Am. Mil. Inst., U.S. Naval Inst., Rwy. and Locomotive Hist. Soc. Republican. Episcopalian. Club: University. Address: 145 Columbia Ave #207 Holland MI 49423-2983 Address (winter): 3400 S Ironwood Dr Lot 379 Apache Junction AZ 85220-7114

QUIN, LOUIS DUBOSE, chemist, educator; b. Charleston, S.C., Mar. 5, 1928; s. Louis DuBose and Olga vonOven (Jatho) Q.; children: Gordon, Howard, Carol. B.S., The Citadel, 1947; M.A., U.N.C., 1949, Ph.D., 1952. Research chemist Am. Cyanamid Co., Stamford, Conn., 1949-50; research project leader FMC Corp., South Charleston, W.Va., 1952-54, 56; mem. faculty dept. chemistry Duke U., Durham, N.C., 1956-86; prof. Duke U., 1967-81, James B. Duke prof. chemistry, 1981-86, chmn. dept., 1970-76; prof. chemistry U. Mass., Amherst, 1986—, head dept., 1986-94; Mem. Durham Human Relations Commn., 1978-81. Author: Heterocyclic Chemistry of Phosphorus, 1981; contbr. articles to profl. jours. Served to 1st lt. U.S. Army, 1954-56. Fellow AAAS; mem. Am. Chem. Soc., Chem. Soc. (London). Office: U Mass Dept Of Chemistry Amherst MA 01003

QUIMBY, CHARLES EDWARD, JR., manufacturing company executive; b. Passaic, N.J., Jan. 12, 1943; s. Charles Edward and Josephine (Smolak) Q.; married Kathleen Vogel Stankavish; children: Charles, Tammy, Robert Stankavish. B.S., Fairleigh Dickinson U., Rutherford, N.J., 1968. Various adminstrn. and accounting positions Becton Dickinson & Co., East Rutherford, N.J., 1964-68; corp. contr. Athlone Industries, Inc., Parsippany, N.J., 1973-78; v.p.—contr. Athlone Industries, Inc., 1978-89, v.p., treas., chief fin. officer, 1989-90; chief fin. officer, v.p. fin. Omnisource Corp., Fort Wayne, Ind., 1991—. Home: 10717 Lake Pointe Dr Fort Wayne IN 46845-6410 Office: 1610 N Calhoun St Fort Wayne IN 46808-2762

QUINBY, WILLIAM ALBERT, lawyer; b. Oakland, Calif., May 28, 1941; s. George W. and Marge (Diaz) Q.; m. Marion Bach, Nov. 27, 1964; 1 child, Michelle Kathleen. BA, U. Calif., 1963; JD, Hastings Coll. Law, San Francisco, 1967. Bar: Calif. 1967. V.p., dir., shareholder Crosby, Heafey, Roach & May, Oakland, Calif., 1967—; bd. dirs. Haws Drinking Faucet Co., Berkeley, Calif.; mem. faculty Hastings Coll. Advocacy, San Francisco, 1980; co-moderator Counsel Connect's Calif. ADR Discussion Group; lectr. current devels. in banking arbitration and mediation; mem. fellowship rev. com. HEW; mem. panel disting. neutrals Ctr. for Pub. Resources, Inc. Author: Six Reasons—Besides Time and Money—To Mediate Rather Than Litigate, Why Health Care Parties Should Mediate Rather Than Litigate; editor Calif. Continuing Edn. of Bar, California Discovery, 1980. Bd. dirs. Big Bros. East Bay, Oakland, 1983-87, Easter Seals Soc. East Bay, 1973, Oakland East Bay Symphony; chmn. bd. dirs. Bay Area Tumor Inst. Scholar Harvard U., 1962-63. Mem. ABA, Calif. Bar Assn., Alameda County Bar Assn., Assn. Trial Lawyers Am., Calif. Bus. Trial Lawyers Assn., Am. Arbitration Assn. (large, complex case panel), Oakland C. of C. (bd. dirs., exec. com.),

Alameda County Barristers Club (bd. dirs., pres. 1972), Harvard Club, San Francisco Calimari Club, Lakeview Club, Bohemian Club. Republican. Avocations: running, skiing, tennis, travel, gardening. Office: Crosby Heafey Roach & May 1999 Harrison St Oakland CA 94612-3515

QUINDLEN, ANNA, journalist, author; b. Phila., July 8, 1953; d. Robert V. and Prudence Quindlen; m. Gerald Krovatin; children: Quin, Christopher, Maria. BA, Barnard Coll., 1974. Reporter New York Post, N.Y.C., 1974-77; gen. assignment, city hall reporter New York Times, N.Y.C., 1977-81, columnist About New York, 1981-83, dep. met. editor, 1983-85, columnist Life in the 30's syndicated, 1986-89, columnist Public and Private, 1990-94. Author: Living Out Loud, 1988, (novel) Object Lessons, 1991, The Tree That Came to Stay, 1992, Thinking Out Loud, 1993, One True Thing, 1994. Recipient Mike Berger award for Disting. Reporting, 1983, Pulitzer Prize for commentary, 1992; named Woman of Yr., Glamour mag., 1991. •

QUINE, WILLARD VAN ORMAN, philosophy educator; b. Akron, Ohio, June 25, 1908; s. Cloyd Robert and Hattie Ellis (Van Orman) Q.; m. Naomi Ann Clayton, Sept. 19, 1930; children: Elizabeth Roberts, Norma; m. Marjorie Boynton, Sept. 2, 1948; children: Douglas Boynton, Margaret McGovern. AB in Math. summa cum laude, Oberlin Coll., 1930, LittD (hon.), 1955; AM in Philosophy, Harvard U., 1931, PhD, 1932, LLD (hon.), 1979; MA, Oxford U., 1953, LittD (hon.), 1970; LittD (hon.), Ohio State U., 1957; hon. doctorate, U. Lille, France, 1965, Uppsala U., Sweden, 1980, U. Berne, Switzerland, 1982, U. Granada, Spain, 1986; LittD (hon.), Akron U., 1965, Washington U., St. Louis, 1966, Temple U., 1970, Cambridge (Eng.) U., 1978, Syracuse U., 1981; LHD (hon.), U. Chgo., 1967, Ripon Coll., 1983, Adelphi U., 1989. Instr. tutor philosophy Harvard U., Cambridge, Mass., 1936-41, assoc. prof., 1941-48, prof., 1948—, Edgar Pierce prof. philosophy, 1955-78, chmn. dept. philosophy, 1952-53; vis. prof. U. Sao Paulo, Brazil, 1942, Rockefeller U., 1968, Coll. de France, 1969; George Eastman vis. prof. Oxford U., 1953-54, U. Tokyo, 1959; mem. Inst. Advanced Study, Princeton U., 1956-57; Gavin David Young lectr. in philosophy U. Adelaide, Australia, 1959; Paul Carus lectr. Am. Philos. Assn., 1971; Hagerstrom lectr. U. Uppsala, Sweden, 1973; Ferrater Mora lectr. Gerona, Spain, 1990. Author: A System of Logistic, 1934, Mathematical Logic, 1940, Elementary Logic, 1941, O Sentido da Nova Logica, 1944, Methods of Logic, 1950, From a Logical Point of View, 1953, Word and Object, 1960, Set Theory and Its Logic, 1963, The Ways of Paradox, 1966, Selected Logic Papers, 1966, Ontological Relativity, 1969, Philosophy of Logic, 1970, (with J.S. Ullian) The Web of Belief, 1970, The Roots of Reference, 1974, Theories and things, 1981, The Time of My Life, 1985, Quiddities, 1987, La Scienza e i Dati di Senso, 1987, Pursuit of Truth, 1989, The Logic of Sequences, 1990, From Stimulus to Science, 1995; co-author: Philosophical Essays for A.N. Whitehead, 1936; Philosophy of A.N. Whitehead, 1941; Philosophy of Rudolf Carnap, 1963; Words and Objections, 1969, Aspectos de la Filosofia de W.V. Quine, 1975, Philosophy of W.V. Quine, 1986, Symposio Quine, 1988, Perspectives on Quine, 1989; also articles. Served to lt. comdr. USNR, 1942-46. Recipient Nicholas Murray Butler Gold medal Columbia U., 1970, Frantisek Polacky gold medal, Czech Republic, 1991, Charles U. silver medal, Prague, 1993, Rolf Schock prize in philosophy, Sweden, 1993; Harvard U. Soc. Fellows jr. fellow, 1933-36, sr. fellow, 1948-78; univ. scholar Harvard U.; James Walker fellow Harvard U.; Sheldon traveling fellow, Europe, 1932-33; Rockefeller fellow, Bellagio, 1975; fellow Ctr. Advanced Study Behavioral Scis., 1958-59, Ctr. Advanced Studies, Wesleyan U., 1965; Sir Henry Savile fellow Merton Coll., Oxford, 1973-74. Fellow Am. Philos. Soc., Brit. Acad. (corr.); mem. Am. Philos. Assn. (pres. East div. 1957), Assn. Symbolic Logic (pres. 1953-56), Am. Acad. Arts and Scis., Nat. Acad. Scis., Institut de France (corr.), Norwegian Acad., National Internat. de Philosophie, Instituto Brasileiro de Filosofia (corr.), Academie Internationale de la Philosophie de Sci., Phi Beta Kappa. Office: Harvard U Dept Philosophy Emerson Hall Cambridge MA 02138

QUINLAN, GUY CHRISTIAN, lawyer; b. Cambridge, Mass., Oct. 28, 1939; s. Guy Thomas and Yvonne (Carver) Q.; m. Mary-Ella Holst, Apr. 18, 1987. AB, Harvard Coll., 1960, JD, Harvard U., 1963. Bar: N.Y.A. Mass, U.S. Dist. Ct. (so. and ea. dists.) N.Y. 1965, U.S. Ct. Appeals (2d cir.) 1967, U.S. Supreme Ct. 1969, U.S. Ct. Appeals (8th cir.) 1973, (10th cir.) 1977, (4th cir.) 1993, U.S. Tax Ct. 1977. Assoc. Rogers & Wells, N.Y.C., 1963-70, ptnr., 1970-90, of counsel, 1991—. Past pres. Unitarian Universalist Service Com., Yorkville Common Pantry; past pres. Unitarian Universalist Dist. of Met. N.Y.; mem. adv. council on ministerial studies Harvard U. Div. Sch. Mem. ABA, N.Y. State Bar Assn., Fed. Bar Council, Am. Judicature Soc., Am. Assn. Internat. Commn. Jurists, Lawyers Alliance for World Security. Democrat. Club: Harvard (N.Y.C.). Office: Rogers & Wells 200 Park Ave New York NY 10166-0153

QUINLAN, JOHN MICHAEL, insurance company executive; b. Worcester, Mass., Jan. 8, 1936; s. Edward Francis and Emma Elizabeth (Leahy) Q.; m. Loretta Lucile Messier, Nov. 11, 1957; children—Brenda, Michael, Kevin. B.S. in Bus. Adminstrn., Clark U., 1967. Mng. dir. Ins. Systems Am., Atlanta, 1971-73; 2d v.p. data processing State Mut. Am., Worcester, 1973-74, v.p. data processing, 1974-80, sr. v.p. ins. adminstrn., 1980-81, sr. v.p. ind. ins., 1981-86, exec. v.p. ind. ins., 1986—; pres., dir. SMA Life Assurance Co., Worcester; dir., chmn. bd. SMA Equities, Worcester. Mem. adv. bd. Mohegan council Boy Scouts Am., Worcester; trustee Clark U., Worcester. Mem. Life Ins. Mktg. Research Assn. (bd. dirs.), Worcester C. of C. (bd. dirs.). Club: Worcester Country. Home: 10 Pheasant Hill Ln Duxbury MA 02332-3635 Office: State Mut Life Assurance Co Am 440 Lincoln St Worcester MA 01653-0001

QUINLAN, J(OSEPH) MICHAEL, lawyer; b. Rockville Centre, N.Y., Nov. 2, 1941; s. Joseph Charles Quinlan and Harriet Veronica (Gorman) Greene; m. Agnes Mary Quinlan, May 5, 1973; children: Kara Ann, Kristen Mary. BS. in Social Sci., Fairfield U., 1963; JD, Fordham U., 1966; LLM, George Washington U., 1970. Bar: N.Y. 1966, D.C. 1967, Va. 1993, U.S. Ct. Mil. Appeals 1967, U.S. Supreme Ct. 1970. Exec. asst. to warden U.S. Penitentiary, Leavenworth, Kans., 1973-74; of counsel N.E. region U.S. Bur. Prisons, Phila., 1974-75, exec. asst. to dir., Washington, 1975-78; supt. Fed. Prison Camp, Eglin AFB, Fla., 1978-80; warden Fed. Correctional Inst., Otisville, N.Y., 1980-85; dep. asst. dir. U.S. Bur. Prisons, Washington, 1985-86, dep. dir., 1986-87; dir. U.S. Bur. Prisons, 1987-92; dir. strategic planning, Corrections Corp. Am., 1993—; dir., bd. dirs. United Kingdom Detention Svcs., London. 1st vice chmn. bd. dirs. Horton Meml. Hosp. Middletown, N.Y., 1982-85; criminal justice cons. Lt. Col. USAFR, 1966-93. Recipient SES Presdl. Disting. Rank award, 1988, SES Presdl. Meritorious Rank award, 1991, Exceptional Leadership award U.S. Atty. Gen., 1991, Nat. Pub. Svc. award Nat. Acad. Pub. Adminstrn./Am. Soc. Pub. Adminstrn., 1992, John Marshall award Dept. Justice, 1993. Fellow Nat. Acad. Pub. Adminstrn.; mem. ABA (corrections and sentencing com. 1985—, Am. Correctional Assn. (mem. legis. com.), Nat. Com. Comm. Corrections, N.Y. Bar Assn., D.C. Bar Assn., Va. Bar Assn. Roman Catholic. Avocations: reading, family activities.

QUINLAN, KATHLEEN, actress; b. Pasadena, Calif., Nov. 19, 1954. Actress: (theatre) Taken in Marriage, 1979 (Theatre World award 1979), Accent on Youth, 1983, Les Liaisons Dangereuses, 1988, (feature films) One is a Lonely Number, 1972, American Graffiti, 1973, Lifeguard, 1976, Airport '77, 1977, I Never Promised You a Rose Garden, 1977, The Promise, 1979, The Runner Stumbles, 1979, Sunday Lovers, 1981, Hanky Panky, 1982, Independence Day, 1982, Twilight Zone: The Movie, 1983, The Last Winter, 1983, Warning Sign, 1985, Wild Thing, 1987, Sunset, 1988, Clara's Heart, 1988, The Doors, 1991, Trial by Jury, 1994, Apollo 13, 1995, (TV movies) Can Ellen Be Saved?, 1974, Lucas Tanner, 1974, Where Have All the People Gone?, 1974, The Missing Are Deadly, 1975, The Turning Point of Jim Malloy, 1975, The Abduction of Saint Anne, 1975, Little Ladies of the Night, 1977, She's in the Army Now, 1981, When She Says No, 1984, Blackout, 1985, Children of the Night, 1985, Dreams Lost, Dreams Found, 1987, Trapped, 1989, The Operation, 1990, Strays, 1991, An American Story, 1992, Stolen Babies, 1993, Last Light, 1993, Perfect Alibi, 1994. Mem. Actors' Equity Assn., Screen Actors Guild. •

QUINLAN, MICHAEL ROBERT, fast food franchise company executive; b. Chgo., Dec. 9, 1944; s. Robert Joseph and Kathryn (Koerner) Q.; m. Marilyn DeLashmutt, Apr. 23, 1966; children: Kevin, Michael. BS, Loyola U., Chgo., 1967, MBA, 1970. With McDonald's Corp., Oak Brook, Ill.,

1966—, v.p., 1974-76, sr. v.p., 1976-78, exec. v.p., 1978-79, chief ops. officer, 1979-80, pres. McDonald's U.S.A. 1980-82, pres., 1982-89, chief oper. officer, 1982-87, chief exec. officer, 1987—, chmn., 1989—, also bd. dirs. Republican. Roman Catholic. Clubs: Butterfield Country, Oakbrook Handball-Racquetball. Office: McDonald's Corp 1 Kroc Dr Oak Brook IL 60521-2278*

QUINLAN, WILLIAM JOSEPH, JR., lawyer; b. Chgo., Nov. 4, 1939; s. William Joseph and Catherine E. (Bowman) Q.; m. Susan L. Collins, June 16, 1962; children—Kathleen, Michael, Julie, Jennifer. A.B. cum laude, Loyola, U., Chgo., 1961, J.D. cum laude, 1966. Bar: Ill. 1966, U.S. Dist. Ct. (no. dist.) Ill. 1966, U.S. Tax Ct. 1968, U.S. Ct. Appeals (7th cir.) 1972. Assoc. Wilson & McIlvaine, Chgo., 1966-73; ptnr. McDermott, Will & Emery, Chgo., 1973-78, sr. ptnr., 1978—; dir. Wickman Machine Tools, Elk Grove Village, Ill., 1978-81, Eiger Machinery, Inc., Bensenville, Ill., 1981—. Contbr. articles to profl. publs. Mem. St. Athanasius Bd. Edn., Evanston, Ill., 1976, pres., 1978. Mem. ABA (com. on fed. regulation of securities), Chgo. Bar Assn. (chmn. subcom. on securities law), Ill. Bar Assn., Blue Key, Phi Alpha Delta. Roman Catholic. Clubs: Union League, Wilmette Harbor Assn. Office: McDermott Will & Emery 227 W Monroe St Chicago IL 60606-5016

QUINN, AIDAN, actor; b. Chgo., Mar. 8, 1959. Actor: (films) Reckless, 1984, Desperately Seeking Susan, 1985, The Mission, 1986, Stakeout, 1987, Crusoe, 1989, The Handmaid's Tale, 1990, The Lemon Sisters, 1990, Avalon, 1990, At Play in the Fields of the Lord, 1991, The Playboys, 1992, Benny & Joon, 1993, Blink, 1994, Legends of the Fall, 1994, Mary Shelley's Frankenstein, 1994, The Stars Fell on Henrietta, 1994, Haunted, 1994; (plays) The Man in 605, Fool for Love, 1983, Hamlet, 1984, A Lie of the Mind, 1985, A Streetcar Named Desire, 1988 (Theatre World award 1988), Scheherazade, The Irish Hebrew Lesson, (TV) An Early Frost, 1985 (Emmy award nominee 1985), Perfect Witness, 1989, Lies of the Twins, 1991, A Private Matter, 1992. Office: Creative Artists Agy 9830 Wilshire Blvd Beverly Hills CA 90212-1825

QUINN, ANDREW PETER, JR., lawyer, insurance executive; b. Providence, Oct. 22, 1923; s. Andrew Peter and Margaret (Canning) Q.; m. Sara G. Bullard, May 30, 1952; 1 child, Emily H. AB, Brown U., 1945; LLB, Yale U., 1950. Bar: R.I. 1949, Mass. 1960, U.S. Tax Ct. 1960, U.S. Supreme Ct. 1986. Pvt. practice Providence, 1950-59, Springfield, Mass., 1959-88; ptnr. Letts & Quinn, 1950-59; with Mass. Mut. Life Ins. Co., 1959-88, exec. v.p., gen. counsel, 1971-88; of counsel Day, Berry & Howard, Hartford, Conn. and Boston, 1988—; pres., trustee MML Series Investment Fund, 1971-88; bd. dirs. Sargasso Mut. Inst. Co., Ltd., 1986—, pres., 1986-89, chmn. bd. dirs., 1989-93. Trustee, MacDuffie Sch., 1974-87, chmn. bd., 1978-85; trustee Baystate Med., Springfield, 1977-80. Lt. (j.g.) USNR, 1944-46. Mem. ABA (co-chmn. nat. conf. lawyers and life ins. cos. 1973), Assn. Life Ins. Counsel (pres. 1983-84), Am. Coun. Life Ins. (chmn. legal sect. 1971), Life Ins. Assn. Mass. (chmn. exec. com. 1975-77), Brown U. Alumni Assn. (bd. dirs. 1969-72), N.Y. Yacht club, Longmeadow Country Club, Dunes Club, Hillsboro Club, Conn. Valley Brown U. (past pres.). Home: 306 Ellington Rd Longmeadow MA 01106-1559 Office: Day Berry & Howard City Pl Hartford CT 06103-3499

QUINN, ANTHONY RUDOLPH OAXACA, actor, writer, artist; b. Chihuahua, Mexico, Apr. 21, 1915; naturalized, 1947; s. Frank and Nellie (Oaxaca) Q.; m. Katherine de Mille, Oct. 2, 1937 (div.); children: Christina, Kathleen, Duncan, Valentina; m. Iolanda Addolori, Jan. 1966; children: Francesco, Daniele, Lorenzo. Student pub. schs. Actor in plays including Clean Beds, 1936, Gentleman from Athens, 1947, Street Car Named Desire, Let Me Hear the Melody, Beckett, 1961, Tchin-Tchin, 1963, Zorba, 1983-86; has appeared in over 200 motion pictures including Guadalcanal Diary, 1943, Buffalo Bill, 1944, Irish Eyes are Smiling, 1944, China Sky, 1945, Back to Bataan, 1945, Where Do We Go From Here?, 1945, Tycoon, 1947, The Brave Bulls, 1951, Mask of the Avenger, 1951, World in his Arm, 1952, Against all Flags, 1952, Viva Zapata (Acad. award 1952), Ride Vaquero, 1953, City Beneath the Sea, 1953, Seminole, 1953, Blowing Wild, 1953, East of Sumatra, 1953, Long Wait, 1954, Magnificent Matador, 1955, Ulysses, 1955, Naked Street, 1955, Seven Cities of Gold, 1955, Lust for Life, (Acad. award best supporting actor 1956), La Strada, 1954, Man from Del Rio, 1956, Wild the Wind, 1957, Attila the Hun, 1958, The Wild Party, 1956, The Ride Back, 1957, The Hunchback of Notre Dame, 1957, The River's Edge, 1957, Hot Spell, 1958, Heller with a Gun, Savage Innocents, 1959, The Black Orchid, 1958, Last Train From Gun Hill, 1958, Warlock, 1959, Heller in Pink Tights, 1960, Portrait in Black, 1960, Guns of Navarrone, 1961, Becket, 1961, Barabbas, 1962, Lawrence of Arabia, 1962, Requiem for a Heavyweight, 1963, The Visit, 1963, Behold a Pale Horse, 1964, Zorba the Greek, 1964, High Wind in Jamaica, 1965, Guns for San Sebastian, 1968, The Shoes of the Fisherman, 1968, The Secret of Santa Vittoria, 1969, A Dream of Kings, 1969, Flap, 1970, A Walk in Spring Rain, 1970, R.P.M., 1970, The City, 1971, Jesus of Nazareth, 1971, Across 110th Street, 1972, Arruza, Deaf Smith and Johnny Ears, 1973, The Don Is Dead, 1973, Mohammed Messenger of God, 1977, Caravans, 1978, The Children of Sanchez, 1978, The Greek Tycoon, 1978, The Inheritance, 1978, The Passage, 1979, Lion of the Desert, 1981, High Roll, 1981, Valentina, 1984, The Salamander, 1984, Treasure Island, 1986, Stradivarius, 1987, Revenge, 1990, Ghosts Can't Do It, 1990, A Star for Two, 1990, Jungle Fever, 1990, Only the Lonely, 1991, Mobsters, 1991, The Last Action Hero, 1993, Somebody to Love, 1994, A Walk in the Clouds, 1995; appeared in TV prodns. of The Life of Christ, Onassis: The Richest Man in the World, 1988, Old Man and the Sea, 1990, This Can't Be Love, 1994; script writer: Metro-Goldwyn-Mayer prodn. The Farm; author: The Original Sin, 1972, Self-Portrait, 1995; artist 13 major exhbns. oil paintings, sculptures and serigraphs, Hawaii, 1982, 87, San Francisco, 1983, N.Y.C., 1984, 89, San Antonio, 1984, Houston, 1984, Washington, 1985, Beverly Hills, Calif., 1986, Mexico City, 1990, Paris, 1990, Zurich, Switzerland, 1990, Vienna, Austria, 1991, Buenos Aires, 1992, Las Vegas, 1993. Office: care Anthony Quinn Studios 241 E 86th St Apt 2A New York NY 10028-3623*

QUINN, ART JAY, veterinarian; b. Bennington, Kans., Aug. 2, 1936; s. Arthur Jess and Edith Mae (Reigle) Q. BS, Kans. State U., 1959, DVM, 1961. Diplomate Am. Coll. Vet. Ophthalmologists. Pvt. practice Albuquerque, 1961-75; field rep. Am. Animal Hosp. Assn., Denver, 1968-69; prof. medicine and surgery Coll. Vet. Medicine, Okla. State U., Stillwater, 1975—; adjunct asst. prof. ophthalmolgy Coll. Medicine-McGee Eye Inst., Oklahoma City. Contbr. articles to profl. jours. Capt. U.S. Army, 1962-64. Recipient Kans. Vet. Med. Assn. Small Animal Proficiency award, 1961, Upjohn award, 1961, AAHA Western Region Practitioner award, 1993; Sarkey Found. grantee, 1981. Mem. AVMA, Am. Animal Hosp. Assn., Am. Coll. Vet. Ophthalmologists, Am. Assn. Vet. Clinicians, North Cen. Okla. Vet. Med. Assn. Democrat. Home: 1528 S Shalamar Dr Stillwater OK 74074-1648 Office: Okla State U Coll Vet Medicine Stillwater OK 74078

QUINN, BETTY NYE, former classics educator; b. Buffalo, Mar. 22, 1921; d. Fritz Arthur and Alma (Svenson) Hedberg; A.B., Mt. Holyoke Coll., 1941; A.M., Bryn Mawr Coll., 1942, Ph.D., 1944; m. John F. Quinn, Sept. 21, 1950. Analyst, U.S. Army, 1944-46, CIA, 1947; instr., asst. prof. Vassar Coll., Poughkeepsie, N.Y., 1948-59, dir. pub. relations, 1952-59, assoc. prof., 1959-68; prof. classics Mt. Holyoke Coll., South Hadley, Mass., 1968-91, prof. emeritus, 1991—. Am. Acad. Rome fellow, 1942-43; Am. Philos. Soc. grantee, 1952. Mem. Am. Philos. Assn., Mediaeval Acad. Am., Classics Assn. New Eng. (pres. 1970-71) Vergilian Soc. Am. Republican. Lutheran. Home: 27 W Parkview Dr South Hadley MA 01075-2164

QUINN, C. JACK, mechanical engineering educator, consultant; b. Westbaden, Ind., June 4, 1929; s. C. Cleo and Lillian I. (Jones) Q.; m. B. Louise Stahl, Dec. 21, 1953; children: Bryan J., Myron R., Kelvin C., Sharla L. BSME, Ind. Inst. Tech., 1956; MA in Math., Ball State U., 1961. Registered profl. engr., Ind. Asst. prof. Ind. Inst. Tech., Ft. Wayne, 1956-64, assoc. prof., 1964-69; assoc. prof. Ind. U.-Purdue U., Ft. Wayne, 1969-77, prof., 1977—; chmn. dept. mech. engring., 1985—; chmn. dept. mfg. tech., 1985—; cons. Phelps Dodge, Ft. Wayne, 1972, Environ. Engring., Ft. Wayne, 1973-75, Petro & Assocs., Ft. Wayne, 1976-78, Bhar Inc., Ft. Wayne, 1978-82, Essex, Ft. Wayne, 1979, Kemtune, Inc., Ft. Wayne, 1980—. Cpl. U.S. Army, 1951-53; Korea. Recipient Citizen Engr. award Ind. Soc. Profl. Engrs., 1990; NSF grantee, 1962, 64. Mem. NSPE (chmn. 1981-84),

ASME (chmn. 1969-75), ASHRAE (chmn. 1975-81), Soc. Mfg. Engrs. (mem. exec. bd. 1989—). Avocations: golf, fishing, camping, hiking. Office: IPFW Mfg Dept Fort Wayne IN 46805

QUINN, CHARLES NICHOLAS, journalist; b. Utica, N.Y., July 28, 1930; s. Charles Dunaway and Elsa (Zarth) Q.; children—Diana David, Ben, Jane. B.A., Cornell U., 1951; M.S. Columbia U. Sch. Journalism, 1954. Reporter Providence Jour., 1954-56, N.Y. Herald Tribune, 1956-62; corr. NBC News, N.Y.C., 1962-66, Washington, 1966-71, Rome, 1971-74; mng. editor, chief corr. NBC Radio News, Washington, 1978-80; corr. Ind. Network News, Washington, 1980-81; electronic media rep. Am. Petroleum Inst., Washington, 1981-91. Reported on Huntley-Brinkley Report, (co-recipient Emmy 1969) Served with arty. U.S. Army, 1951-53. Mem. Nat. Press Club (bd. govs. 1990-91).

QUINN, DAVID W., building company executive; b. 1942. BA, Midwestern U. Ptnr. Arthur Andersen, Dallas, 1967-84; COO Alpert Cos., 1984-87; exec. v.p. Centex Corp., Dallas, 1987—, also bd. dirs. Office: Centex Corp 3333 Lee Pky Dallas TX 75219

QUINN, DENNIS B., English language and literature educator; b. Bklyn., Oct. 3, 1928; s. Herbert John and Thelma Leona (Warren) Q.; m. Eva M. Jensen, Aug. 13, 1952; children—Timothy, Monica, Alison. Student, Creighton U., 1948-50; B.A. in English, U. Wis., 1951, M.A. in English, 1952, Ph.D. in English, 1958. Instr. English U. Kans., Lawrence, 1956-60, asst. prof. English, 1960-64, assoc. prof. English, 1964-68, prof. English, 1968—, dir. Pearson Coll., 1968-75, dir. integrated humanities program, 1971-79. Contbr. articles on Medieval and Renaissance literature and children's literature to profl. jours. Served with U.S. Army, 1946-48; Japan. Recipient student Fulbright award, Leiden, The Netherlands, 1955-56, research Fulbright award, Salamanca, Spain, 1962-63; H. Bernard Fink Outstanding Tchr. award U. Kans., 1965, H.O.P.E. Teaching award, 1969; NEH grantee, 1971. Roman Catholic. Avocations: gardening, travel. Home: 1102 W 25th St Lawrence KS 66046-4441 Office: Univ Kansas Dept English Lawrence KS 66045

QUINN, EUGENE FREDERICK, government official, clergyman; b. Oil City, Pa., Sept. 16, 1935; s. Frederick Anthony and Wilma (Scott) Q.; m. Charlotte Alison Smith, Aug. 25, 1965; children: Christopher Edward Vermilye, Alison Moore. AB, Allegheny Coll., 1957; MA in African studies, UCLA, 1966, MA in History, 1969, PhD in History, 1970; diploma in theol. studies, Va. Theol. Sem., 1974. Ordained to ministry Episcopal Ch. U.S.A., 1975. Info. officer Am. Embassy, Rabat, Morocco, 1958-59; cultural affairs officer Am. Embassy, Port-au-Prince, Haiti, 1959-61; country pub. affairs officer Ouagadougou, Upper Volta, 1961-63; field rep. Joint U.S. Affairs Office, Saigon, Vietnam, 1964-66; country pub. affairs officer Am. embassy, Yaounde, Cameroun, 1966-68; counselor embassy for press and cultural affairs Am. embassy, Prague, Czechoslovakia, 1975-78; apptd. career mem. Sr. Fgn. Service with class of counselor, 1981, minister-counselor, 1986; dir. fgn. service personnel Voice of Am., Washington, 1981-83; dep. asst. sec. pub. affairs Dept. Transp., 1983-85; dir. Office Pub. Affairs Voice of Am., 1985-86; internat. coord. for Bicentennial U.S. Constn., dir.'s office U.S. Info. Agy., 1986-91; cons. internat. affairs, 1992—; dir. rule of law programs, conf. on security and cooperation in Europe, Office of Dem. Instns. and Human Rights, Warsaw, 1993-95. Author: Federalist Papers' Reader, 1992, To Heal the Earth, 1994; editor: Diplomacy for the Seventies, 1969; editorial bd. Fgn. Service Jour., 1972-75, Dept. State Open Forum Jour., 1982-83; contbr. articles to profl. jours., chpts. to books. Trustee N.J. Ednl. Consortium, 1970-72; coordinator USIA Yorktown Bicentennial Activities, 1981; assisting clergyman St. Columba Ch., Washington, 1973-75, 78-81, Nat. Cathedral, Washington, 1981-82, Grace Ch., Silver Spring, Md., 1981-82, Epiphany Ch., Washington, 1983, 86-92; chaplain Anglo-Am. Diplomatic Community, Prague, 1975-78; vicar St. James Ch., Bowie, Md., 1983-84; rector Christ Ch., Accokeek, Md., 1985, St. John's Ch., Pomonkey, Md.; assisting clergyman All Saints Ch., Chevy Chase, Md., 1981-82, 86-90; interim pastor Ch. of Holy Communion, Washington, 1992-93; chaplain Anglo-Am. Diplomatic Cmty., 1993-95; chair environ. com. Episcopal Diocese of Washington Peace Commn., 1991-92; mem. Environ. Stewardship Team, Episcopal Ch., 1992-95. Recipient Meritorious Honor award USIA, 1964, 66, 85; Merit medal Republic of Vietnam, 1965, medal of honor, 1966. Club: Cosmos (Washington). Home and Office: 5702 Kirkside Dr Chevy Chase MD 20815-7116

QUINN, FRANCIS A., bishop; b. L.A., Sept. 11, 1921. Ed., St. Joseph's Coll., Mountain View, Calif., St. Patrick's Sem., Menlo Park, Calif., Cath. U., Washington, U. Calif., Berkeley. Ordained priest Roman Cath. Ch., 1946; ordained titular bishop of Numana and aux. bishop of San Francisco 1978; bishop Diocese of Sacramento, 1979-94, bishop emeritus, 1994—. Office: 2110 Broadway Sacramento CA 95818

QUINN, FRANCIS XAVIER, arbitrator and mediator, author, lecturer; b. Dunmore, Pa., June 9, 1932; s. Frank T. and Alice B. (Maher) Q.; m. Marlene Stoker Quinn; children: Kimberly, Catherine, Cameron, Lindsay, Megan. AB, Fordham U., 1956, MA, 1958; STB, Woodstock Coll., 1964; MSIR, Loyola U., Chgo., 1966; PhD in Indsl. Rels., Calif. Western U., 1976. Assoc. dir. St. Joseph's Coll. Inst. Indsl. Rels., Phila., 1966-68; Manpower fellow Temple U., 1969-74, asst. to dean Sch. Bus. Adminstrn., 1972-78; arbitrator Fed. Mediation and Conciliation Svc., Nat. Mediation Bd., Am. Arbitration Assn., Nat. Assn. Railroad Referees, Dem. Nat. Steering Com.; chair, S.W. Region Nat. Acad. Arbitrators, 1995—; apptd. to Rail Emergency Bd., 1975, to Fgn. Service Grievance Bd., 1976, 78, 80—; chmn. Hall of Fame com. Internat. Police Assn., 1990—, Tulsa City-County Mayor's Task Force to Combat Homelessness, 1991-92; mem. exec. bd. Tulsa Met. Ministries, 1990-92, Labor-Religion Coun. Okla., 1990—. Named Tchr. of Yr., Freedom Found. 1959; recipient Human Rels. award City of Phila., others. Mem. Nat. Acad. Arbitrators, Indsl. Rels. Rsch. Assn., Assn. for Social Econs., Soc. for Dispute Resolution, Am. Arbitration Assn. (arbitrator), Internat. Soc. Labor Law and Social Security, Internat. Ombudsman Inst. Democrat. Author: The Ethical Aftermath of Automation, Ethics and Advertising, Population Ethics, The Evolving Role of Women in the World of Work, Developing Community Responsibility. Editor: The Ethical Aftermath Series, 1962—; contbr. articles to profl. jours. Home: 230 Hazel Blvd Tulsa OK 74114-3926

QUINN, JACK, congressman, English language educator, sports coach; b. South Buffalo, N.Y., 1951; s. Jack Sr. and Norma Ide Q.; m. Mary Beth McAndrews, 1974; children: Jack III, Kara. BA, Siena Coll.; MA in Edn., SUNY, Buffalo. English language tchr. Orchard Park (N.Y.) Schs.; town councilman City of Hamburg, N.Y.; also town supv. City of Hamburg; mem. 103d-104th Congresses from 30th N.Y. Dist., 1993—; mem. transp. and infrastructure com., mem. vet. affairs com., mem. congl. reform task force, mem. joint econ. com. Vice chmn. bd. dirs. St. Francis High Sch.; chmn. Hamburg Indsl. Devel. Agy.; bd. dirs. Greater Buffalo ARC, N.Y. State Adv. Coun. ARC, Bry-Lin Found.; active Southtowns Sewage Treatment Agy., United Way Western N.Y., St. Mary's of the Lake Roman Cath. Ch. Recipient Humanitarian award Erie County for the Disabled, Pub. Svc. award Niagara Frontier Parks and Recreation Soc., Disting. Grad. award Nat. Catholic Elementary Schs. Assn., Bronze Good Citizen medal Nat. Soc. Sons Am. Revolution, New Horizons award Drug Edn. of Internat. Assn. of Lions Club, Red, White and Blue award Am. Legion of N.Y., Honor medal Hilbert Coll., Fin. Reporting award Govt. Finance Officer's Assn. Mem. Hamburg C. of C., Greater Buffalo C. of C., Buffalo KC, Hamburg Kiwanis Club. Republican. Roman Catholic. Office: US Ho Reps 331 Cannon HOB Washington DC 20515-3230*

QUINN, JACK J., professional hockey team executive; b. Boston; s. John Quinn; m. Connie Quinn; children: Beth, Kay, Connie, John. Exec. v.p. St. Louis Blues, 1983-86, pres., 1986—. Office: St Louis Blues Kiel Ctr 1401 Clark Saint Louis MO 63103*

QUINN, JAMES W., lawyer; b. Bronxville, N.Y., Oct. 1, 1945; s. James Joseph Quinn and Marie Joan (Blossy) Tisi; m. Kathleen Manning, Kellianne, Christopher, Tierney, Kerrin. AB cum laude, U. Notre Dame, 1967; JD, Fordham U., 1971. Bar: N.Y. 1972, U.S. Dist. Ct. (so. and ea. dist.) 1973, U.S. Ct. Appeals (2d cir.) 1976, U.S. Supreme Ct. 1984, U.S. Ct. Appeals (3d, 7th and 9th cirs.) 1985. Assoc. Weil, Gotshal & Manges,

N.Y.C., 1971-77, 78-79, ptnr., 1979—; ptnr. Fleisher & Quinn, N.Y.C., 1977-78; adj. assoc. prof. law Fordham U., N.Y.C., 1985-87. Editor Fordham U. Law Rev., 1969-71; contbr. articles to legal jours. Mem. ABA (litigation sect., co-chmn. subcom. alternate means of dispute resolution of com. corp. counsel, program chmn. trial practice com., sports and entertainment forum), Assn. of Bar of City of N.Y. (com. of state jurisdiction, com. on entertainment sports, com. on anti-trust regulation, chmn. sports com.). Home: 1 Maple Way Armonk NY 10504-2602

QUINN, JANE BRYANT, journalist, writer; b. Niagara Falls, N.Y., Feb. 5, 1939; d. Frank Leonard and Ada (Laurie) Bryant; m. David Conrad Quinn, June 10, 1967; children—Matthew Alexander, Justin Bryant. B.A. magna cum laude, Middlebury Coll., 1960. Assoc. editor Insiders Newsletter, N.Y.C., 1962-65, co-editor, 1966-67; sr. editor Cowles Book Co. N.Y.C., 1968; editor-in-chief Bus. Week Letter, N.Y.C., 1969-73, gen. mgr., 1973-74; syndicated financial columnist Washington Post Writers Group, 1974—; contbr. fin. column to Women's Day mag., 1974—; contbr. NBC News and Info. Service, 1976-77; bus. corr. WCBS-TV, N.Y.C., 1979, CBS-TV News, 1980-87, ABC-TV Home Show, 1991-93; contbg. editor Newsweek mag., 1978—. Author: Everyone's Money Book, 1979, 2d edit., 1980, Making the Most of Your Money, 1991, A Hole in the Market, 1994. Mem. Phi Beta Kappa. Office: Newsweek Inc 251 W 57th St New York NY 10019-1802

QUINN, JARUS WILLIAM, physicist, former association executive; b. West Grove, Pa., Aug. 25, 1930; s. William G. and Ellen C. (DuRoss) Q.; m. Margaret M. McNerney, June 27, 1953; children: J. Kevin, Megan, Jennifer, Colin, Kristin. BS, St. Joseph's Coll., 1952; postgrad., Johns Hopkins U., 1952-55; PhD, Cath. U. Am., 1964. Rsch. assoc. physics Johns Hopkins U., 1954-55; staff scientist Rsch. Inst. Advanced Study, 1956-57; rsch. assoc. physics Cath. U. Am., 1958-60, instr., 1961-64, asst. prof., 1965-69; exec. dir. Optical Soc. Am., Washington, 1969-93; governing bd. Am. Inst. Physics, 1973-94; pres. Stellar Focus, Sunnyvale, Calif., 1994-95. Bd. govs. Am. Assn. Engring. Socs., 1990-93. Fellow Optical Soc. Am.; mem. Am. Phys. Soc., Am. Soc. Assn. Execs., Coun. Engring. and Sci. Soc. Execs. Home: 360 Fearrington Post Fearrington Village NC 27312-8502

QUINN, JOHN ALBERT, chemical engineering educator; b. Springfield, Ill., Sept. 3, 1932; s. Edward Joseph and Marie (Von De Bur) Q.; m. Frances Wilkie Daly, June 22, 1957; children: Sarah D., Rebecca V., John E. B-SChemE, U. Ill., 1954; PhDChemE, Princeton U., 1959. Mem. faculty chem. engring. U. Ill., Urbana, 1958-70; prof. U. Pa., Phila., 1971—, Robert D. Bent prof., 1978—, chmn. dept. chem. engring., 1980-85; vis. prof. Imperial Coll. U. London, 1965-66; vis. scientist MIT, 1980; vis. prof. U. Rome/La Sapienza, 1992; mem. sci. adv. bds. Sepracor, Inc., Marlborough, Mass., 1984—, Whitaker Found., Mechanicsburg, Pa., 1987—; Mason lectr. Stanford U., 1981; Katz lectr. U. Mich., 1985; Reilly lectr. U. Notre Dame, 1987. Contbr. articles to profl. publs.; editl. advisor Jour. Membrane Sci., 1975—, Indsl. and Chem. Engring. Rsch., 1987-88, Revs. in Chem. Engring., 1980—; pioneer rschr. on mass transfer and interfacial phenomena. Sr. postdoctoral fellow NSF, 1965-66; Sherman Fairchild scholar Calif. Inst. Tech., 1985. Fellow AAAS, Am. Inst. Med. and Biol. Engring.; mem. NAE, AIChE (Allan P. Colburn award 1966, Alpha Chi Sigma award 1978), Am. Acad. Arts and Scis., Am. Chem. Soc., Internat. Soc. Oxygen Transport to Tissue, Sigma X, Phi Lambda Upsilon, Tau Beta Pi. Home: 275 E Wynnewood Rd Merion Station PA 19066-1627 Office: Univ Pa Towne Bldg 220 S 33rd St Philadelphia PA 19104-6393

QUINN, JOHN COLLINS, publishing executive, newspaper editor; b. Providence, Oct. 24, 1925; s. John A. and Katheryn H. (Collins) Q.; m. Lois R. Richardson, June 20, 1953; children: John Collins, Lo-anne, Richard B., Christopher A. A.B., Providence Coll., 1945; M.S., Columbia U. Sch. Journalism, 1946. Successively copy boy, reporter, asst. city editor, Washington corr., asst. mng. editor, day mng. editor Providence Jour.-Bull., 1943-66; with Gannett Co. Inc., Rochester, N.Y., 1966-90; exec. editor Rochester Democrat & Chronicle, Times-Union, 1966-71; gen. mgr. Gannett News Service, 1967-80, pres., 1980-88, v.p. parent co., 1971-75, sr. v.p. news and info., 1975-80, sr. v.p., chief news exec. parent co., editor USA TODAY, 1983-89; exec. v.p. Gannett Co., Arlington, Va., 1983-90; trustee Gannett Found., Arlington, 1988-91; trustee, dep. chmn. Freedom Forum, Arlington, 1991—. Named to R.I. Hall of Fame, 1975, Editor of Yr. Nat. Press Found., 1986; recipient William Allen White citation, 1987, Women in Communications Headliner award, 1986; Paul Miller/Okla. State U. medallion, 1988. Mem. AP Mng. Editors (past dir., nat. pres. 1973-74), Am. Soc. Newspaper Editors (dir., chmn. editorial bd., chmn. conv. program, nat. pres. 1982-83). Roman Catholic. Home: 365 S Atlantic Ave Cocoa Beach FL 32931-2719 Office: Freedom Forum 1101 Wilson Blvd Arlington VA 22209-2248

QUINN, JOHN E., lawyer; b. Pitts., Oct. 28, 1950. BA, Duquesne U., 1972, JD, 1976. Bar: Pa. 1976, U.S. Dist. Ct. (we. dist.) Pa. 1976, U.S. Ct. Appeals (3d cir.) 1981. Ptnr. Evans, Portnoy & Quinn, Pitts. Mem. ABA, Pa. Bar Assn., Allegheny County Bar Assn. (vice chmn., chmn. lawyer referal com. 1983-87), Pa. Trial Lawyers Assn. (bd. govs. 1989-91), Assn. Trial Lawyers Am. Office: Evans Portnoy & Quinn One Oxford Ctr 36th fl Pittsburgh PA 15219

QUINN, JOHN JOSEPH, bank executive; b. Newark, Nov. 13, 1944; s. James Richard and Teresa Mary (Byrne) Q.; m. Mary Ann Kuchmas; children: Michelle, John, Sean, Kathleen, Ryan. BA in Econs., Seton Hall U., 1966, MBA in Fin., 1971. Asst. treas. The Howard Savs. Bank, Newark, 1972-75, asst. v.p., 1975-77, investment officer, 1976-77, v.p., 1977-80, sr. v.p., treas., 1980—. Mem. Bond Club N.J. (assoc.). Republican. Roman Catholic. Office: Howard Savs Bank PO Box 34 Newark NJ 07101-0034

QUINN, JOHN R., archbishop; b. Riverside, Calif., Mar. 28, 1929; s. Ralph J. and Elizabeth (Carroll) Q. Student, St. Francis Sem., Immaculate Heart Sem., San Diego, 1947-48; Ph.B., Gregorian U., Rome, 1950, Licentiate in Sacred Theology, 1954, S.T.L., 1954. Ordained priest Roman Cath. Ch., 1953, as bishop, 1967. Assoc. pastor St. George Ch., Ontario, Calif., 1954-55; prof. theology Immaculate Heart Sem., San Diego, 1955-62, vice rector, 1960-62; pres. St. Francis Coll. Sem., El Cajon, Calif., 1962-64; rector Immaculate Heart Sem., 1964-68; aux. bishop, vicar gen. San Diego, 1967-72; bishop Oklahoma City, 1972-73, archbishop, 1973-77; archbishop San Francisco, 1977—; provost U. San Diego, 1968-72; pastor St. Therese Parish, San Diego, 1969; apptd. consultor to Sacred Congregation for the Clergy in Rome, 1971; pres. Nat. Conf. Cath. Bishops, 1977-80, chmn. Com. of Liturgy; chmn. com. on Family Life U.S. Cath. Conf.; chmn. Bishops' Com. on Pastoral Rsch. and Practices, Bishops' Com. on Doctrine; mem. Bishops' Com. on Sems., Pontifical Commn., Seattle, 1987-88, Bishops' Com. for Pro-Life Activies, 1989—; apptd. pontifical del. for religious in U.S. 1983; pres. Calif. Cath. Conf., 1985; mem. Synod of Bishops, Rome, 1994; chmn. Nat. Conf. Cath. Bishops Com. on Doctrine, 1994—. Trustee U. San Diego, 1991-93. Mem. Cath. Theol. Soc. Am., Canon Law Soc. Am., Am. Cath. Hist. Soc. Address: 445 Church St San Francisco CA 94114-1720*

QUINN, JOSEPH MICHAEL, coatings industry executive; b. N.Y.C., Jan. 17, 1937; s. Joseph Michael and Madeline Lucile (Roche) Q.; m. Marilyn Anne Muller, Sept. 15, 1962; children: Christine, Michael, Timothy. BS, U.S. Merchant Marine Acad., Kings Point, N.Y., 1958; cert. mgmt. devel. program, Harvard U., 1969. Ships officer Am. Export Lines, Hoboken, N.J., 1958-62; sales rep. Devoe & Raynolds Co., Newark, 1962-65, sales mgr., 1965-69; pres. Devoe & Raynolds Co., Louisville, 1987—; sales mgr. Celanese Resins Co., Louisville, 1969-74; v.p. Celanese Coatings Co., Louisville, 1974-76; pres. Devoe Marine Coatings Co. (subs. Grow Group Inc.), Louisville, 1976—; group v.p. Grow Group Inc., Louisville, 1976—, exec. v.p. coatings and chems., 1989—, bd. of dirs., 1989—, exec. v.p., chief oper. officer, 1991—. Cons. Jr. Achievement, Louisville, 1982-83. Served to lt. (j.g.) USNR, 1954-68. Recipient Outstanding Profl. Achievement award U.S. Merchant Marine Acad., 1984. Mem. Soc. Naval Architects and Marine Engrs., Nat. Paint and Coatings Assn. (chmn. marine coatings com., chmn. indsl. coatings com. 1987-92, bd. dirs., mem. exec. com. 1989-94, treas., chmn. budget and fin. com.), Owl Creek Country Club. Roman Catholic. Avocations: golf, sailing, reading, carpentry. Office: Grow Group Inc 4000 Dupont Cir Louisville KY 40207-4802

QUINN, KENNETH MICHAEL, foreign service officer, international relations educator; b. N.Y.C., May 26, 1942; s. George Kenneth and Marie Teresa (Farrell) Q.; m. Le Son Nguyen, May 11, 1974; children: Davin, Shandon, Kelly. BA, Loras Coll., 1964, LLB (hon.), 1984; MA, Marquette U., 1965; PhD, U. Md., 1982. Advisor MACV/CORDS, Sadec, Vietnam, 1968-70; vice consul U.S. Consulate Gen., Chau Doc, Vietnam, 1971-74; mem. staff Nat. Security Coun., Washington, 1974-76; spl. asst. Asst. Sec. of State-East Asia, Washington, 1977-78; adminstrv. asst. Gov. of Iowa, Des Moines, 1978-82; counselor of mission U.S. Mission to UN, Vienna, Austria, 1982-84; dep. exec. sec. Dept. State, Washington, 1985-87; dep. chief of mission Am. Embassy, Manila, 1987-90; dep. asst. sec. East Asia Bur. Dept. State, 1990—. Contbr. articles to profl. jours. Mem. athletic bd. Thomas Jefferson H.S., Fairfax, Va., 1993—. Recipient Eagle award N.G. Bur., 1982, Disting. Honor award U.S. Dept. Def., 1982, Presdl. Disting. Svc. award The White House, 1994. Mem. Am. Fgn. Svc. Assn. (Christian Herter award 1993, William R. Rivkin award 1978). Home: 8131 Briar Creek Dr Annandale VA 22003

QUINN, MICHAEL DESMOND, diversified financial services executive; b. Balt., Sept. 4, 1936; s. Michael Joseph and Gladys (Baldwin) Q.; m. Mary Annette McHenry, Apr. 11, 1961; children: Cailin A., Maureen K., Patricia B., Marianne P. BA, U. Md., 1970. With Weaver Bros., Inc. of Md., Balt., 1960—, investment v.p., corporate dir. interim loan dept., 1978-86; chmn. bd. Wye Mortgage Co., L.P., 1977—, Christiana Capital Group, Inc.; chmn., chief exec. officer Alliance Recovery Group, Inc., 1990—, Estate Trust Co. Inc.; faculty evening coll. Johns Hopkins U., Essex Community Coll. 1967—. Mem. gov.'s task force Md. Housing Ins. Fund; mem. Md. Health Claims Arbitration Panel; bd. visitors U. Md.; dist. adv. coun. U.S. Small Bus. Adminstrn. With USN, 1956-58. Mem. Md. Mortgage Bankers Assn. (pres. bd. govs.), Real Estate Bd. Greater Balt. (bd. dirs.), Home Builders Assn. Md., Md. Bankers Assn., Balt. Econ. Soc., N.Am. Soc. Corp. Planning, Greater Balt. Com., Ancient Order Hibernians, Balt Jr. Assn. Commerce (Richard Troja Meml. award 1967, Outstanding Young Man of Balt. 1969), Balt. County C. of C. (bd. dirs.). Home: 8207 Robin Hood Ct Baltimore MD 21204-1900 Office: 7400 York Rd Ste 300 Baltimore MD 21204-7502

QUINN, PAT (JOHN BRIAN PATRICK QUINN), professional sports team manager; b. Hamilton, Ont., Can., Jan. 29, 1943; s. John Ernest and Jean (Ireland) Q.; m. Sandra Georgia Baker, May 1, 1963; children: Valerie, Kathleen. BA in Econs., York U., 1972; JD, Del. Law Sch., 1987. Player Toronto Maple Leafs, Ont., 1968-70, Vancouver Canucks, B.C., Can., 1970-72, Atlanta Flames, 1972-77; coach Phila. Flyers, 1977-82, L.A. Kings, 1984-86; head coach Team Canada, 1986; pres., gen. mgr. Vancouver Canucks, 1987—, head coach, 1990—; player rep. NHL, Atlanta, 1973-77, bd. govs., 1987—. Named Def. Man of Yr., Vancouver Canucks, 1971, Coach of Yr. NHL, 1979-80, Coach of Yr., Sporting News, 1980, 92, Coach of the Yr. Hockey News, 1980, 92, Coach of the Yr. Acad. Awards of Sports, named to the Longest Unbeaten Record in Profl. Sports of 35 Games, 1979-80, named to the Best Record in the History of the Canucks Franchise, 1991-92; recipient Jake Milford award, 1994, Jack Diamond award, 1994. Roman Catholic. Avocations: sports, reading. Office: care Vancouver Canucks, Pacific Coliseum, 100 N Renfrew St, Vancouver, BC Canada V5K 3N7

QUINN, PATRICK, tranportation executive. Pres., co-chmn, treas. U.S. Xpress Enterprises, Inc., Chattanooga, Tenn., 1985—. Office: US Xpress Enterprises Inc 3931 S Market St Chattanooga TN 37410*

QUINN, PATRICK MICHAEL, wholesale food executive; b. Grand Rapids, Mich., Mar. 5, 1934; s. Robert George and Albertine Frances (Kolzinski) Q.; m. Rita Lee Ronan, Aug 6, 1955; children: Suzanne, Brian, Karen, Timothy, Catherine, Patricia. BSBA, Aquinas Coll., 1958. Sales mgr. Nabisco, Inc., Grand Rapids, 1958-73; exec. v.p. D&W Food Ctrs., Grand Rapids, 1973-85; pres., chief exec. officer Spartan Stores, Inc., Grand Rapids, 1985—; bd. dirs. Aquinas Coll., Grand Rapids; adv. bd. N. Am. Wholesale Grocers Assn., Falls Church, Va. Chmn. United Way Appeal, Grand Rapids, 1988. With U.S. Army, 1953-55. Mem. Nat. Grocers Assn. (vice chmn., bd. dirs. 1983—, chmn. 1989). Roman Catholic. Avocations: reading, hunting, fishing, golf. Office: Spartan Stores Inc 850 76th St SW Grand Rapids MI 49518

QUINN, PHILIP LAWRENCE, philosophy educator; b. Long Branch, N.J., June 22, 1940; s. Joseph Lawrence and Gertrude (Brown) Q. AB, Georgetown U., 1962; MS, U. Del., 1967; MA, U. Pitts., 1968, PhD, 1970; MA (hon.), Brown U., 1972. Asst. prof. philosophy Brown U., Providence, R.I., 1969-72, assoc. prof. philosophy, 1972-78, prof. philosophy, 1978-85, William Herbert Perry Faunce prof. philosophy, 1982-85; John A. O'Brien prof. philosophy U. Notre Dame, South Bend, Ind., 1985—. Author: (book) Divine Command and Moral Requirements, 1978; editor Faith and Philosophy, 1990-95; contbr. articles to profl. jours. Fulbright fellow, 1962-63; Danforth fellow, 1967-69. Mem. Am. Philos. Assn. (sec., treas. ea. div. 1982-85, chmn. career opportunities com. 1985-90, exec. comm. cen. div. 1987-90, v.p. cntrl. div. 1993-94, pres. cen. div. 1994-95), Philosophy of Sci. Assn. (nominating com. 1984-86), Soc. Christian Philosophers (exec. com. 1981-84), N.Y. Acad. Scis. Roman Catholic. Avocations: reading, swimming, film, theatre. Home: 1645 W Turtle Creek Dr South Bend IN 46637-5660 Office: Univ Notre Dame Dept Philosophy Notre Dame IN 46556

QUINN, PHYLLIS, association executive; b. Chgo.; m. James Quinn; children: Bobby, Debby, Diane, Teddy. Graduated high sch., Chgo. Agt. Hollywood, Calif.; pres. Motion Picture Mothers, Hollywood. Co-Author: Cookbook of the Stars, Star Mothers. Pres. Screen Smart Set aux. of Motion Picture and TV Fund; active Variety Club Telethon; lectr. for Am. Heart Assn. Art Inst. Chgo. scholar. Home: 11755 Addison St North Hollywood CA 91607-3201

QUINN, ROBERT HENRY, surgeon, medical school administrator; b. Omaha, July 3, 1919; s. Henry Thomas and Esther Mary (Hecklin) Q.; m. Ruth Elizabeth Binder, Aug. 1, 1942; children: Karen, Terrence, Thomas, Lisa. B.S., Creighton U., 1941, M.D., 1943. Intern St. Joseph's Hosp., Denver, 1943; resident in ob-gyn Northwestern U., 1946-47, Luth. Deaconess Hosp., Chgo., 1948; gen. practice medicine Sioux Falls, S.D., 1946-54; surgery fellow Ochsner Clinic, New Orleans, 1954-58; practice medicine specializing in surgery Sioux Falls, S.D., 1958-75; asso. dean U. S.D. Sch. Medicine, Sioux Falls, 1974-81; prof., chmn. div. surgery U. S.D. Sch. Medicine, 1977-82, v.p., dean, 1982-87, acting chmn. dept. surgery, 1982-89, prof. surgery emeritus, 1989—; chief staff McKennan Hosp., Sioux Falls, 1966; assoc. dean West River Campus, 1987-89; mem. adv. bd. clin. fellowship Bush Found., 1983-88. Bd. dirs. Karl Mundt Found., 1970—, McCrossan Boys Ranch, 1985—, Rapid City Regional Eye Inst. Found., 1987. Served with M.C., USNR, 1943-46. Recipient Disting. Service award U. S.D., 1978, Alumni Merit award U.S. Medicine Creighton U., 1985. Mem. AMA (mem. council on continuing physician edn. 1978-81, cert. of appreciation ho. of dels. 1971-75), ACS, Assn. Surg. Chmn., Ochsner Surg. Soc., S.D. State Med. Assn. (pres. 1969-70), Alpha Omega Alpha. Republican. Roman Catholic. Club: Rotary. Home: 110 Fairway Dr Spearfish SD 57783-3109 Office: 3526 5th St Ste 200 Rapid City SD 57701-3530

QUINN, SALLY, journalist; b. Savannah, Ga., July 1, 1941; d. William Wilson and Bette (Williams) Q.; m. Benjamin Crowninshield Bradlee, Oct. 20, 1978; 1 child, Josiah Quinn Crowninshield Bradlee. Grad., Smith Coll. Reporter, Washington Post, 1969-73, 74-80; co-anchorperson CBS Morning News, N.Y.C., 1973-74. Author: We're Going to Make You a Star, 1975, (novels) Regrets Only, 1986, Happy Endings, 1991. Address: 3014 N St NW Washington DC 20007

QUINN, TOM, communications executive; b. Los Angeles, Mar. 14, 1944; s. Joseph Martin and Grace (Cooper) Q.; m. Amy Lynn Friedman, Nov. 24, 1982; children—Douglas, Lori. B.S., Northwestern U., 1965. Reporter, newswriter ABC Radio, Chgo. and Los Angeles, 1965; reporter, producer Sta. KXTV, Sacramento, 1966; day editor City News Service, Los Angeles, 1966-68, chmn., 1980-85; pres. Americom, Inc., Los Angeles, 1985—; pres. Radio News West, Los Angeles, 1968-70; campaign mgr. Jerry Brown for Sec. State, Los Angeles, 1970; dep. sec. state Calif., Sacramento, 1971-74; campaign mgr. Brown for Gov., Los Angeles, 1974; sec. Calif. Dept. Environ. Affairs, Sacramento, 1975-79; pres. Sta. KFSO Radio, Fresno,

1985—; pres. K-HITS Radio, Reno, Nev.; dir. Parallel Communications Co. Chmn. Tom Bradley Mayoral Campaign, 1985. Recipient Headliner of Yr. award Greater Los Angeles Press Club, 1978; Environ. Protection award Calif. Trial Lawyers Assn., 1979. Democrat. Office: 6255 W Sunset Blvd Bldg 1901 Los Angeles CA 90028-7420

QUINN, WILLIAM FRANCIS, lawyer; b. Rochester, N.Y., July 13, 1919; s. Charles Alvin and Elizabeth (Dorrity) Q.; m. Nancy Ellen Witbeck, July 11, 1942; children: William Francis, Stephen Desford, Timothy Charles, Christopher Thomas, Ann Cecily, Mary Kaiulani, Gregory Anthony. B.S. summa cum laude, St. Louis U., 1940; LL.B. cum laude, Harvard U., 1947. Bar: Hawaii 1948. Ptnr. Robertson, Castle & Anthony, Honolulu, 1947-57; gov. Ter. of Hawaii, 1957-59, state Hawaii, 1959-62; partner Quinn & Moore, Honolulu, 1962-64; exec. v.p. Dole Co., Honolulu., 1964-65; pres. Dole Co., 1965-72; ptnr. Jenks, Kidwell, Goodsill & Anderson, Honolulu, 1972-73, Goodsill Anderson & Quinn, 1973-82, Goodsill Anderson Quinn & Stifel, 1982-91; mem. sr. adv. bd. 9th Cir. Jud. Coun. Served with USNR, 1942-46. Decorated knight of Holy Sepulchre Order. Republican. Roman Catholic. Clubs: Waialae Country, Pacific (Honolulu). Home: 1365 Laukahi St Honolulu HI 96821-1407 Office: Alii Place 1099 Alakea St Ste 1800 Honolulu HI 96813

QUINN, WILLIAM WILSON, army officer, manufacturing executive; b. Crisfield, Md., Nov. 1, 1907; s. William Samuel and Alice (Wilson) Q.; m. Bette Williams, Dec. 16, 1939; children: Sally, Donna, William Wilson. Student, St. John's Coll., Annapolis, Md., 1927-29; B.S., U.S. Mil. Acad., 1933; postgrad., Inf. Sch., Ft. Benning, Ga., 1938-39, Command and Staff Sch., Ft. Leavenworth, Kans., 1941, Nat. War Coll., Washington, 1948-49. Commd. 2d lt. inf. U.S. Army, 1933, advanced through grades to lt. gen., 1961; co. comdr. inf., 1933-36; provost marshal city of Manila, 1937-38; assigned G-2 IV Corps, 1943-44, G-2 7th Army Invasion S. France, 1944-45; dir. Strategic Service Unit, 1946-47, G-2 X Corps, Inchon Landing, Inchon Landing, Korea, 1950; comdg. officer 7th Inf. Div. 17th Inf. Regt., Korea, 1951; office Chief of Staff U.S. Army, 1952; asst. divsn. comdr. 47th Inf. Div., 1953; chief Army sect. Joint U.S. Mil. Adv. Group to Greece, 1953-55; asst. divsn. comdr. 9th Inf. Div., Germany, 1955-56; comdg. gen. Ft. Carson, Colo., 1956; comdg. gen. 4th Inf. Div. Ft. Lewis, Washington, 1957; chief pub. info. Dept. Army, 1960-61; dep. dir. Def. Intelligence Agy., 1961-64; comdg. gen. 7th U.S. Army Germany, 1964-66; ret., 1966; v.p. Martin Marietta Corp., Washington, 1966-72; pres. Quinn Assos., Washington, 1972—. Vice chmn. Goldwater Edn. Found. Decorated D.S.M. with cluster, Silver Star, Legion of Merit with cluster, Air medal with clusters, Purple Heart U.S., Bronze star with V device, officer Legion of Honor (France); recipient Presdl. Unit Citation Korea, Das Grosse Verdienstkreuz mit Stern (Germany). Mem. SAR, Army Navy Club, Chevy Chase Club, Bohemian Club of San Francisco, Kappa Alpha. Episcopalian. Address: 9787 Unionville Rd Easton MD 21601

QUINN, YVONNE SUSAN, lawyer; b. Spring Valley, Ill., May 13, 1951; d. Robert Leslie and Shirley Eilene (Morse) Q.; m. Ronald S. Rolfe, Sept. 1, 1979. BA, U. Ill., 1973; JD, U. Mich., 1976, MA in Econs., 1977. Bar: N.Y., U.S. Dist. Ct. (ea. and so. dists.) N.Y., U.S. Ct. Appeals (2d, 3d, 4th, 10th and D.C. cirs.), U.S. Supreme Ct. Assoc. Cravath, Swaine & Moore, N.Y.C., 1977-80; assoc. Sullivan & Cromwell, N.Y.C., 1980-84, ptnr., 1984—. Mem. ABA, Assn. of Bar of City of N.Y., India House Club. Office: Sullivan & Cromwell 125 Broad St New York NY 10004

QUINNAN, EDWARD MICHAEL, management consultant; b. Scranton, Pa., Dec. 11, 1935; s. Francis Patrick and Mary Angela (Mannion) Q.; m. Hilarion Swift, Nov. 22, 1962; children: Edward, Hilarion Doyle, Maryanne. B.S., Georgetown U., 1957; M.B.A., NYU, 1959. With Chase Manhattan Bank, N.Y.C., 1957-65, U.S. Agy. Internat. Devel., Washington, 1965-67; with Kaiser Aluminum & Chem. Corp., Oakland, Calif., 1967-89, v.p., chief fin. officer, 1982-89; v.p., chief fin. officer Kaiser Tech., Ltd., 1987-89, cons., 1989—. Served to 1st lt. USAR, 1959-64. Republican.

QUINNAN, GERALD VINCENT, JR., medical educator; b. Boston, Sept. 7, 1947; s. Gerald Vincent and Mary (Lally) Q.; children: Kevin, Kylie, Kathleen, John; m. Leigh A. Sawyer. AB in Chemistry, Coll. Holy Cross, 1969; MD cum laude, St. Louis U., 1973. Diplomate Am. Bd. Internal Medicine. Intern, resident, fellow Boston U. Med. Ctr., 1973-77; med. officer Bur. Biologics, USPHS, Bethesda, Md., 1977; advanced through grades to asst. surgeon gen. USPHS, 1992; dir. herpes virus br., dep. dir. div. virology Bur. Biologics, Bethesda, 1980-81; dir. div. virology Ctr. for Drugs and Biologics, Bethesda, 1981-88; dep. dir. Ctr. Biologics Evaluation and Rsch., Bethesda, 1988-93, acting dir., 1990-92; dir. off-blood rsch. and rev. Ctr. Biologics Evaluation and Rsch., 1993; prof. uniformed svcs. U. Health Scis., Bethesda, 1993—; cons. World Health Orgn., Geneva, Switzerland, Pan Am. Health Orgn., liaison adv. coms. Contbr. chpts. to books, numerous articles to profl. jours. Fellow Infectious Diseases Soc. Am.; mem. AAAS, Am. Soc. for Microbiology, Am. Assn. Immunology, Am. Soc. for Clin. Investigation, Sigma Xi, Alpha Omega Alpha. Roman Catholic. Office: Uniformed Svcs U Hlth Scis Div Tropical PH 3401 Jones Bridge Rd Bethesda MD 20814

QUINNELL, BRUCE ANDREW, retail book chain executive; b. Washington, Jan. 6, 1949; s. Robert Kay and Marion Louise (Moseley) Q.; m. Aug. 31, 1972 (div. June 1986); children: Paul David, Andrea Carolyn; m. Marcia Melodie Mundie. BS in Acctg., Va. Poly. Inst. and State U., 1971, MA in Acctg., 1972. CPA, Ohio, Mo., Tex., Tenn. Sr. auditor Ernst & Whinney, Columbus, Ohio, 1972-75; treas., chief fin. officer Midway Ford Truck Ctr., Kansas City, Mo., 1975-82; sr. v.p., chief fin. officer Rsch. Health Svcs., Kansas City, 1982-85; sr. v.p. VHA Enterprises Inc., Irving, Tex., 1985-87; v.p., treas., chief fin. officer Dollar Gen. Corp., Nashville, 1987-92; exec. v.p., COO Walden Book Co., Stamford, Conn., 1993, pres., 1994—. Bd. dirs. Advs. Tenn. State U. Coll. Bus., Nashville, 1991-92, Jr. Achievement Mid. Tenn., 1992. Mem. Fin. Execs. Inst., Am. Inst. CPA'S, Nat. Investor Rels. Inst. Republican. Lutheran. Avocations: racquetball, golf, scuba diving. Office: Walden Book Co 201 High Ridge Rd Stamford CT 06905-3417

QUINN-JUDGE, PAUL MALACHY, journalist; b. London, Feb. 2, 1949; came to U.S., 1977; s. Charles and Marion Judge; m. Sophia Whitney Sears, May 1, 1971; children: Emma, Katharine. MA, Trinity Coll., Cambridge U., Eng., 1971. Saigon rep. Am. Friends' Svc. Com., Saigon, S. Vietnam, 1973-75; S.E. Asia rep. Am. Friends' Svc. Com., Singapore, 1976-80; freelance corr. Christian Sci. Monitor, Bangkok, 1992-94; Moscow corr. Christian Sci. Monitor, Moscow, Russia, 1986-89, The Boston Globe, Moscow, Russia, 1989-92; nat. security corr. The Boston Globe, Washington, 1992—; free-lance corr. Far Eastern Econ. Rev., Bangkok, 1980-86; diplomatic corres. The Boston Globe, 1994—; cons. BBC-The Second Russian Revolution (TV series), London, 1990-91. Avocations: running, wine. Home: 3401 Pauline Dr Chevy Chase MD 20815-3917 Office: The Boston Globe Washington Bur 1130 Connecticut Ave NW Washington DC 20036-3904

QUIÑONES, JOSE ANTONIO, structural engineer, consultant; b. Camuy, P.R., June 28, 1939; s. Antonio and Julia (Lopez) Q.; m. Dorisoraida Rivera Mathews, July 17, 1965; children: Antonio, Rafael, Doris Julia, Zoraida. BSCE magna cum laude, U. P.R., 1963; postgrad. in Marine Engring., UCLA, 1973-74. Registered profl. engr., P.R. Design engr. Barrett & Hale, Columbus, Ohio, 1963-65; assoc. design engr. R.A Bermudez & Assocs./P.R. Testing Svcs., San Juan, 1965-69; prin. ptnr. Jose A Quiñones, Jr. Assocs., San Juan, 1970—; v.p. Metro. Soils and Engring. Materials Lab., Inc. Contbr. articles to profl. jours. Mem. AAAS, ASCE (sec. P.R. chpt. 1969-70), NSPE, Am. Acad. Mechanics, Am. Concrete Inst., Am. Soc. Testing and Materials, Am. Welding Soc., Am. Water Works Soc., Am. Inst. Steel Constrn., Internat. Soc. Soil Mechanics and Foundations, Sociedad Española del Pretensado, Colegio de Ingenieros, Arquitectos y Agrimensores de P.R., Geotech. Soc. P.R. (sec. 1970-77), P.R. Soc. Profl. Engrs. P.R. Soc. Engrs., P.R. Planning Soc., P.R. Geotech. Soc., P.R. Inst. Architects, Prestressed Concrete Inst., Interam. Planning Soc., N.Y. Acad. Scis., London Concrete Soc., Inst. Eduardo Torroja, Calif. Alumni Assn. Roman Catholic. Achievements include construction of longest three hinges arech structure for Dorado Reef in the Caribbean, Sport Colosseum at Bayamon, largest prefabricated floating caisson structure, Palmas del Mar Marina, Humacao,

P.R., unique three story loading and unloading structure floating in a pontoon, San Juan Bay, P.R., tallest microwave communication structure in the Caribbean, La Punta Mountain, Jayuya, P.R., largest regional shopping mall in the Caribbean, Plaza las Americas, hato Rey, P.R. Home: PO Box 71387 San Juan PR 00936 Office: Jose Quiñones Jr Assocs 41 Calle Mayaguez San Juan PR 00917-4917

QUINOT, JEAN MICHEL, chemicals executive. Pres. Ruossel UCLAF Holdings Corp., Montvale, N.J., 1994—. Office: Ruossel UCLAF Holdings Corp 95 Chestnut Ridge Rd Montvale NJ 07645*

QUINSLER, WILLIAM THOMSON, retired investment advisor; b. Watertown, Mass., June 21, 1924; s. Phillips Brooks and Eleanor (Macurdy) Q.; m. Barbara Jean Faust, June 15, 1957; children: William Thomson, Jr., Harry Faust, Catharine Marten Quinsler Orn. B.S. in Elec. Engring., U. Ariz., 1950. Registered profl. engr., Ariz. Engr. Ariz. Pub. Service Co., Phoenix, 1950-53; staff cons. treasury dept. Ariz. Pub. Service Co., 1953, supr. treasury dept., 1954, mgr. fin. services, 1955-62, asst. treas., 1962-69, sec., asst. treas., 1969-83; founding dir. Utility Svcs. Ins. Co. Ltd., Hamilton, Bermuda, 1970-84; pres., chief oper. officer Utility Svcs. Ins. Co. Ltd., 1982-84; trustee Tax-Free Trust of Ariz., 1986—, chmn. audit com., 1992—. Mem. adv. bd. Apache Nat. Forest Service; mem. Phoenix Symphony Assn. Served with USAAF, 1943-46. Mem. IEEE, NSPE, Ariz. Soc. Profl. Engrs., Am., Pacific Coast gas assns., Am. Soc. Corp. Secs., Pacific Coast Electric Assn., C. of C., Ariz. Cattle Growers Assn., Greenlee County Cattle Growers Assn., Phoenix Soc. Fin. Analysts (past pres. and dir.). Home and Office: 5428 E Calle Del Medio Phoenix AZ 85018-4530

QUINSON, BRUNO ANDRE, publishing executive; b. Norwich, Conn., Jan. 1, 1938; s. Louis Jean and Suzanne Marie (Richard) Q.; m. Mary Ann Goodman, May 3, 1980; children by previous marriage: Timothy Bruno, Marc Albert (dec.), Christopher Louis; stepchildren: J. Geoffrey Taylor, Luke J. Taylor, Adam J. Taylor, Joshua P. Taylor. BA, Williams Coll., 1958; postgrad., NYU, 1960-61. Product mgr. Simon & Schuster, N.Y.C., 1960-65; pub., gen. mgr. Golden Press (div. Western Pub. Co., Inc.), 1965-70; pres. Larousse & Co., Inc., N.Y.C., 1970-82, also bd. dirs.; pres. trade and reference div. Macmillan Pub. Co., N.Y.C., 1982-88; pres., chief exec. officer Henry Holt & Co. Inc., N.Y.C., 1988—, also bd. dirs.; bd. dirs., chmn. Nat. Book Found., 1989—; bd. dirs. The Voyager Co., Columbia Univ. Press. Bd. dirs. Rye (N.Y.) Art Ctr., treas., 1973-74; bd. dirs. Lycee Francais de New York, 1994—. Mem. Am. Assn. Pubs. (bd. dirs. 1991-95), Century Assn., Manhattan Theater Club (bd. dirs. 1991—), Players Club, Norfolk Country Club, The River Club. Office: Henry Holt & Co Inc 115 W 18th St New York NY 10011-4113

QUINT, ARNOLD HARRIS, lawyer; b. Boston, Jan. 3, 1942; s. Milton and Esther (Kirshen) Q.; m. Susan Arenson, July 23, 1967; children: Edward, Michael. AB, Haverford (Pa.) Coll., 1963; LLB, Yale U., 1966. Bar: D.C. 1967. Supervisory atty. Fed. Power Commn., Washington, 1967-70; assoc. Hunton & Williams, Washington, 1970-74, ptnr., 1974—. Mem. ABA, Fed. Energy Bar Assn. (com. chmn. 1979-83, bd. dirs. 1989-92). Office: Hunton & Williams 2000 Pennsylvania Ave NW PO Box 19230 Washington DC 20036

QUINT, IRA, retail executive; b. N.Y.C., May 29, 1930; s. Theodore Issac and Rebecca (Ginandes) Q.; m. Ruth Adele Jones, June 1, 1955 (div. Feb. 1984); children—Susan Amy, Stephanie Ann. B.S., NYU, 1951; M.B.A., Harvard U., 1954. Group nat. mdse. mgr. Sears Roebuck & Co., Chgo., 1954-78; pres. Colonial Corp. Am., N.Y.C., 1978-79; pres., CEO Venture Stores, St. Louis, 1979-81; exec. v.p. Montgomery Ward, Chgo., 1981-84; pres. Lane Bryant Stores, N.Y.C., 1985-90; pres., chief exec. officer Conston Corp., Phila., 1990-92; pres. Quint Consultancy, N.Y.C., 1992—. Club: Harvard (N.Y.C.). Home: 130 E 67th St New York NY 10021-6136 Office: 130 E 67th St New York NY 10021

QUINTANA, JOSE BOOTH, health care executive; b. Coral Gables, Fla., July 13, 1946; s. Jose Luis and Carmen Elaine (Booth) Q.; m. Mary Jo Gregg, Sept. 7, 1968; children: Stephanie Elizabeth, Meredith Caroline. BSBA, U. Fla., 1968; MHA, Duke U., 1974; PhD, U. Ala., 1984. Commd. 2d lt. USAF, 1969, advanced through grades to lt. col., 1985, resigned, 1989; dir. pers. and adminstrv. svcs USAF Regional Hosp., March AFB, Calif., 1969-71, adminstrv. asst. hosp. svcs., 1971-72; adminstr. USAF Hosp., Ubon Royal Thai Air Base, Thailand, 1974, Kunsan Air Base, South Korea, 1974-75; dir. pers. and adminstrv. svcs. USAF Regional Hosp. Maxwell AFB, Ala., 1975, dir. patent info., 1975-76, dir. med. resource mgmt., 1976-78; chief med. readiness ops. divsn. Office of Surgeon, USAF in Europe, Ramstein AFB, West Germany, 1978-81; strategic planner, health affairs and plans divsn. Office Air Force Surgeon Gen., Bolling AFB, Washington, 1984-86, sr. health rsch. analyst, directorate med. plans and resources, 1986-89; health svcs. rsch. and devel. coord., rsch. svc. VA Med. Ctr., Birmingham, Ala., 1989—, exec. asst. to dir. (quality), 1991—; asst. prof. dept. health svcs. adminstrn. U. Ala., Birmingham, 1989—; lectr. in field. Contbr. articles to profl. jours. Fellow ACHE; mem. Am. Soc. Quality Control (mem. edn. com. 1993), Ala. Hosp. Assn. (mem. quality innovation com. 1992—), Assn. Health Svcs. Rsch., Assn. Univ. Programs in Health Adminstrn., Acad. Mgmt., Phi Kappa Phi, Beta Gamma Sigma. Republican. Southern Baptist. Avocations: computers, bridge, bible study. Office: U Ala Dept Health Svcs Adminstrn 1675 Univ Blvd 512 Webb Birmingham AL 35294-3361

QUINTANA, MACK, newspaper publishing executive. Former v.p. advt. The Miami Herald, Fla.; now dir. sales and mktg. The San Diego Union-Tribune, Calif. Office: The San Diego Union-Tribune PO Box 191 350 Camino de la Reina San Diego CA 92112-4106*

QUINTANA, SAMMY J., lawyer; b. Santa Fe, Mar. 15, 1949; s. Genaro and Mary (Sena) Q.; m. Patricia Lujan, June 5, 1971; children: Paul, Ana Maria. BA, U.N.Mex., 1971, JD, 1974. U.S. Dist. Ct. Asst. atty. gen. Atty. Gen. N.Mex., Santa Fe, 1978-80; asst. dist. atty. Dist. Atty. Santa Fe, 1980-84; dep. dist. atty. Dist. Atty. Taos, N.Mex., 1984-91; chief pub. defender Pub. Defender N.Mex., Santa Fe, 1991—; Bd. dirs. N.Mex. Bd. Bar Examiners, Santa Fe, 1987—. Mem. sch. bd. Pojoaque (N.Mex.) Valley Schs., 1977—; bd. dirs. Gov.'s Mental Health Planning Coun., Santa Fe, 1991—, Nat. Sch. Bds. Assn., Alexandria, Va., 1990—; sec./treas., 1993—; bd. dirs. exec. com. N.Mex. Sch. Bds. Assn., Santa Fe, 1986—. Recipient Outstanding Sch. Bd. Mem. award N.Mex. Sch. Bds. Assn., 1987, Outstanding Svc. award Nat. Sch. Bds. Assn., 1991. Mem. N.Mex. Bar Assn., Nat. Assn. Criminal Def. Laywers. Democrat. Roman Catholic. Avocations: golf, bowling, softball, hiking. Home: RR 11 Box 85 Santa Fe NM 87501-8301 Office: Pub Defender Dept 301 N Guadalupe St Santa Fe NM 87501-5502

QUINTERO, JOSE, theatrical director; b. Panama City, Panama, Oct. 15, 1924; s. Carlos Rivira and Consuelo (Palmerola) de Q. Student, Goodman Theater, Chgo., 1934-35, U. So. Calif. and L.A. State U., 1948. Producer, dir. Circle in the Square Theatre, N.Y.C., 1951-63; instr. Fla. State U., U. Houston. Producer, dir.; (plays) Desire Under the Elms, Cradle Song, La Ronde, The Iceman Cometh, The Girl on the Via Flaminia, Summer and Smoke, The King and the Duke, Burning Bright, Yerma, Dark of the Moon, The Balcony, Our Town, Plays for Bleecker Street, (Broadway plays) A Moon for the Misbegotten (Tony award), The Innkeepers, Portrait of a Lady, Gabrielle, In the Summer House, The Girl on the Via Flaminia, The Skin of Our Teeth, Long Days Journey into Night, A Touch of the Poet, Look We've Come Through, Great Day in the Morning, Strange Interlude, Diamond Orchid, Anna Christie, Faith Healer, Clothes for a Summer Hotel, Welded, 1981, Cat On A Hot Tin Roof, 1984, Long Days Journey Into Night, 1987, Private Lives, 1990, Our Town, 1993, others, (film) The Roman Spring of Mrs. Stone, 1961, (TV movies) Hughie, Medea, Our Town; dir. Eugene O'Neill play for Nat. Pub. Radio, 1988/93. Decorated Caballero de la Order de Vasco Nunez de Balboa; recipient spl. citation La Asamblea Nacional de Panama, Drama Desk award, Tony award, Page One award, Disting. Artist award, 1985, L.A. Drama Circle award, O'Neill Gold Medal award, 1988, South Ea. Theatre Conf. award for life achievement; named to Theatre Hall of Fame. Mem. Dirs. Guild Am., Soc. Stage Dirs. and Choreographers, Am. Fellows of Theatre. Address: The Lantz Office 888 7th Ave Ste 2500 New York NY 10106

QUINTERO, RONALD GARY, management consultant; b. Detroit, Jan. 5, 1954; s. John Urdiales and Jean Lorraine (Morton) Q.; m. Barbara Kay McDaniel, June 15, 1985; children: Jean Marie, Alexandra Lisa. AB, Lafayette Coll., 1975; MS, NYU, 1976, APC, 1978. CPA, CFA, CFP, cert. mgmt. acct., cert. fraud examiner, cert. insolvency and reorgn. acct., cert. turnaround profl. Sr. mgr. Peat, Marwick, Mitchell & Co., N.Y.C., 1975-85; workout cons. Zolfo, Cooper & Co., N.Y.C., 1985-87; assoc. Bear, Stearns & Co., Inc., N.Y.C., 1987-88; prin. R. G. Quintero & Co., N.Y.C., 1988—; mng. dir. Chartered Capital Advisers, Inc., N.Y.C., 1988—; adj. prof. New Sch. for Social Rsch., N.Y.C., 1983-85; adj. prof. N.Y. Inst. Fin., N.Y.C., 1988—; instr. Ctr. for Profl. Edn., Berwyn, Pa., 1991—. Author: (book and cassette) Mergers and Acquisitions, 1990; contbg. author several books; contbr. articles to profl. jours.; creator: Quintero Index of Bankrupt Stocks. Mem. AICPAs, Am. Bankruptcy Inst., N.Y. Soc. CPAs (chmn. com. 1990-91, Max Block Disting. Article award 1990, Outstanding Discussion Leader 1991), Turnaround Mgmt. Assn. (bd. dirs., exec. com.). Avocations: squash, softball, running, computers, reading. Office: R G Quintero & Co 145 4th Ave New York NY 10003-4906

QUINTIERE, GARY G., lawyer; b. Passaic, N.J., Nov. 26, 1944; s. Benjamin and Sadie (Riotto) Q.; m. Judy Rosenthal, Aug. 16, 1966; children: Karen, Geoffrey. AB in Govt., Lafayette Coll., 1966; JD, George Washington U., 1969. Law clk. to Judge Philip Nichols, Jr. U.S. Ct. Appeals (Fed. cir.), Washington, 1969-70; from assoc. to ptnr. Miller & Chevalier, Washington, 1970-85; ptnr. Morgan, Lewis & Bockius, Washington, 1985—. Mem. ABA, D.C. Bar Assn., Va. Bar Assn. Avocations: tennis, skiing, golf. Home: 14 Mercy Ct Potomac MD 20854-4540 Office: Morgan Lewis & Bockius 1800 M St NW Washington DC 20036-5802

QUINTON, PAUL MARQUIS, physiology educator, researcher; b. Houston, Tex., Sept. 17, 1944; s. Curtis Lincoln and Mercedes Genale (Danley) Q.; m. Liesbet Joris, Dec. 31, 1992; 1 child, Marquis. B.A., Univ. Tex., 1967; Ph.D., Rice U., 1971. Asst. prof. physiology and medicine UCLA Med. Sch., 1975-79; asst. prof. biomed. scis. U. Calif., Riverside, 1979-81, assoc. prof., 1981-84, prof., 1984—; assoc. prof. physiology UCLA, 1981-91. Assoc. ed. Am. Journal Physiology: Cell Biology (Bethesda), assoc. ed. Experimental Physiology (Cambridge). Recipient Paul di Sant'Agnese Disting. Sci. Achievement award Nat. Cystic Fibrosis Found., 1991, Joseph Levy Meml. award Internat. Cystic Fibrosis (Mucovisidosis) Assn., 1994. Office: U Calif Biomed Scis Weber Hall W Riverside CA 92521

QUIRICO, FRANCIS JOSEPH, retired state supreme court justice; b. Pittsfield, Mass., Feb. 18, 1911; s. Luigi and Lucia (Giovanetti) Q. LL.B., Northeastern U., 1932, LL.D., 1970; J.D. (hon.), Suffolk U., 1971; LL.D. (hon.), Am. Internat. U., 1974, New Eng. Sch. Law, 1975, Western New Eng. Coll., Springfield, Mass., 1981, North Adams (Mass.) State Coll., 1981. Bar: Mass. 1932, U.S. Ct. Appeals (1st cir.), U.S. Supreme Ct. 1939. Pvt. practice law Pittsfield, 1932-56, city solicitor, 1948-52; justice Superior Ct. Mass., 1956-69, Supreme Jud. Ct. Mass., 1969-81; recalled to active service with Superior Ct., 1981-86, Appeals Ct., 1986-87. Served with USAAF, 1942-46. Mem. Berkshire County Bar Assn., Am. Law Inst., Am. Legion. Roman Catholic.

QUIRK, BARBARA LONG, medical center executive, nurse; b. Kansas City, Mo., July 31, 1935; d. Anthony James and Nelle G. (Martin) Long; .m Patrick G. Quirk (div.); 1 child, Erin Christine. Diploma in nursing, St. Luke's Hosp., 1956; BSN, U. Kans., 1965, M in Nursing, 1972; PhD in Edn., U. Mo., 1984. RN, Kans., Mo. Staff nurse St. Luke's Hosp., Kansas City, 1958-65; sch. nurse Kansas City Bd. Edn., 1965-70; clin. nurse specialist Kans. U. Med. Ctr., 1972-75; adminstrv. asst. Truman Med. Ctr. West, 1975-78; dir. nursing Truman Med. Ctr. East, 1978-85, assoc. adminstr., 1985—; asst. prof. U. Mo. Sch. Medicine, Kansas City, 1976—, asst. prof. grad. studies, 1977—; mem. adj. faculty Avila Coll., Kansas City, 1986—; assoc. sci. med. and dental staff Truman Med. Ctr., Kansas City, 1980—. Contbg. author: Sexual Counseling & The Health Professional, 1978. Chmn. adv. bd. vocat. tech. program for LPN's Kansas City Bd. Edn., 1979—; mem., vice chmn. Joint Commn. Accreditation for Health Care Orgns., 1989—, PTAC com. for LTC, 1989—. Mem. Am. Hosp. Assn. (rep.), Mo. Orgn. Nurse Execs. (bd. dirs. 1981-83, 87-89, pres.-elect 1989-90, pres. 1990—), Greater Kansas City Area Nursing Adminstrs. (pres. 1982-83, sec.-treas. 1985-86), Acad. Health Professions (bd. dirs. 1980-88), Sigma Theta Tau. Roman Catholic. Avocations: oil painting, gardening. Office: Truman Med Ctr East 7900 Lees Summit Rd Kansas City MO 64139-1246

QUIRK, FRANK JOSEPH, management consulting company executive; b. N.Y.C., Feb. 27, 1941; s. Frank J. and Madeline B. Quirk; B.A., Cornell U., 1962, M.B.A., 1964; m. Betty Josephine Mauldin, Jan. 7, 1967; children—Laura Josephine, Katherine Elizabeth. Assoc., Booz, Allen & Hamilton, Inc., Chgo. and Washington, 1967-72; exec. v.p. Macro Internat., Inc., Silver Spring, Md., 1972-79, pres., chief exec. officer, 1980—. bd. dirs. Profl. Svcs. Coun. Served to capt. U.S. Army, 1964-66. Club: Belle Haven Country. Home: 2110 Foresthill Rd Alexandria VA 22307-1128 Office: Macro Internat Inc 11785 Beltsville Dr Beltsville MD 20705

QUIRK, JOHN JAMES, investment company executive; b. N.Y.C., July 10, 1943; s. Francis J. and Madeline A. (Meizinger) Q.; m. Kathryn Anne O'Brien, Mar. 21, 1963; children: John James, Ashlin Carter, Merritt Andrew. B.A., Georgetown U., 1965; M.B.A., U. Va., 1967. Asst. treas., mgr. corp. fin. dept. W.R. Grace & Co., N.Y.C., 1967-74; asst. v.p., asst. treas. City Investing Co., N.Y.C., 1974-77; v.p., treas. City Investing Co., 1978-81, sr. v.p., treas., 1982-85; chmn. bd. Quirk Carson Peppet Inc., 1985—; dir. Global Union Bank, N.Y.C., Entertainment Completions Inc., Haywood & Co. Clubs: Racquet and Tennis; Wee Burn (Conn.); John's Island (Fla.). Home: 445 Hollow Tree Ridge Rd Darien CT 06820-3226 Office: 99 Park Ave Ste 900 New York NY 10016-1503

QUIRK, PETER RICHARD, engineering company executive; b. New Orleans, Dec. 28, 1936; s. Andrew John and Elise (Richard) Q.; m. Marilyn Ann Montalban, Aug. 16, 1958; children: Karen, Cheryl, Brian, Kathleen, Aimee, Elizabeth. BS, La. State U., 1959. Registered profl. engr., La. Sr. staff engr. Continental Oil Co., Ponca City, Okla., 1959-64; pres. Walk, Haydel & Assocs. Inc., New Orleans, 1964—, now pres., COO; mem. Bur. Govtl. Rsch., Natural Gas Assn. of New Orleans, 1991—. Active World Trade Ctr., 1972—; bd. dirs. Closer Walk Ministries, 1984—, Covenant Ho. New Orleans, 1989—, Met. Area Com., 1989—, La. State U. Found., 1989—, Phi Kappa Theta Nat. Found., 1990—; bd. dirs. United Way of Greater New Orleans, 1990—, chmn. gen. campaign, 1991; bd. dirs. U. New Orleans Higher Edn. Coun., 1992—; mem. adv. bd. U. New Orleans Ctr. for Energy Resources Mgmt., 1992—; vice chair exec. com. Archbishop's Community Appeal, 1993—. Served as 2d lt. C.E., AUS, 1960. Recipient A.E. Wilder Jr. award Cons. Engr. Coun. L.A., 1989, Vol. Activist award, 1993, Man of Achievement award Phi Kappa Theta Nat. Found., 1991. Mem. Instrument Soc. Am., NSPE, Constrn. Mgmt. Assn. Am. (bd. dirs. 1987-90), La. Engring. Soc., Am. Cons. Engrs. Council (trustee polit. action com. 1984-90, fellow 1988), Cons. Engrs. Council La. (pres. 1982-83), New Orleans and River Region C. of C., La. Chem. Industry Alliance, Greater New Orleans Bus. Roundtable, Paper Industry Mgmt. Assn., Phi Kappa Theta. Republican. Roman Catholic. Clubs: Serra (New Orleans) (pres. 1986), Engineers (New Orleans) (pres. 1984-85). Lodge: K.C. Home: 1201 Beverly Gardens Dr Metairie LA 70002-1903 Office: Walk Haydel & Assocs Inc 600 Carondelet St New Orleans LA 70130-3511*

QUISGARD, LIZ WHITNEY, artist, sculptor; b. Phila., Oct. 23, 1929; d. Kenneth E. and Elizabeth (Warwick) Whitney; children: Kristin, Berit. Grad. night sch., Md. Inst. Coll. Art, 1947, grad. day sch., 1949; student, Johns Hopkins U., evenings 1952-58; pupil of Morris Louis, 1958-60; BFA in Painting, Md. Inst., 1966, MFA in Sculpture, 1966. Pvt. tchr. painting Balt., 1955-65; tchr. Balt. Hebrew Congregation, 1962-80; mem. faculty Md. Inst. Coll. Art, 1965-76, Goucher Coll., 1966-68, Balt. Jewish Community Ctr., 1974-78, Villa Julie Coll., Stevenson, Md., 1978-80; art critic Balt. Sun, 1969-71, Craft Horizons, 1969-72, The Paper, 1971-72; designer prodns. Center Stage, Goucher Coll., Johns Hopkins U.; lectr. in Md., Va., W.Va., Pa., Ark., Ohio, N.Y., N.J. One-woman exhbns. include Jefferson Pl. Gallery, Washington, 1960, Emmerich Gallery, N.Y.C., 1962, Goucher Coll., Balt., 1966, U. Md., 1969, Gallery, 707, Los Angeles, 1974, Arts and Sci. Center, Nashua, N.H., 1975, Mechanic Gallery, Balt., 1978, Marymount

Manhatten Coll., N.Y.C., 1983, Tiffany's windows, N.Y.C., 1984, Starkman Gallery, N.Y.C., 1984, Fordham U., N.Y.C., 1985, Henri Gallery, Washington, 1987, Artemisia Gallery, Chgo., 1987, Savannah (Ga.) Coll. Art and Design, 1987, Life of Maryland Gallery, Balt., 1988, Franz Bader Gallery, Washington, 1989, Fairleigh Dickinson U., N.J., 1990, Herr-Chambliss Gallery, Hot Springs, Ark., 1990, Huntington (Ind.) Coll., 1991, Bergdorf Goodman Windows, 1991, Coll. of New Rochelle, N.Y., 1992, Broadway windows, N.Y.C., 1992, Nexus Found., Phila., 1993, Carnegie Arts Ctr., Leavenworth, Kans., 1994, Asheville (N.C.) Mus., 1995; group exhbns. include, Balt. Mus., 1951-53, 58, Corcoran Gallery Area Show, 1956, 64, Corcoran Biennial Show, 1963, Peale Mus., Balt., 1947, 56, Butler Inst. Am. Art, Youngstown, Ohio, 1957, Provincetown (Mass.) Art Assn., 1955, Pa. Acad. Am. Art ann., 1964, Chgo. Art Inst., 1965, Gallery 707, 1973, S. Houston St. Gallery, N.Y.C., 1974, Balt. Mus. travelling show, 1978, Mus. of Hudson Highlands, Cornwall, N.Y., 1983; represented in permanent collections U. Ariz., U. Md., U. Balt., Johns Hopkins U., Lever House, N.Y.C., Center Club, Balt., Libyan Mission to UN, Englewood, N.J., Datalogix Corp., Valhalla, N.Y., Gt. Northern Nekoosa Corp., Norwalk, Conn., Quality Inns, Newark, Can. Imperial Bank of Commerce, N.Y.C., Rosenberg Diamond Co., N.Y.C., Marsh, Inc., Indpls., Kirkpatrick and Lockhart, Pitts., Fordham U., N.Y.C., Atlantic Realty, Atlanta, Miss. Mus. Art, Jackson, St. Joseph Health Ctr., Hot Springs, Ark., Dermatology Assocs., Pitts., Scudder, Stevens & Clark, Boston, also pvt. collections; executed mural William Fell Elem. Sch., Balt., 1980, Urban Wall, Atlanta, 1990, floor painting Vet.'s Stadium, Phila., 1992, mural Med. Coll. Va., Richmond, 1994. Recipient Best in Show award Loyola Coll. Invitational, Balt., 1966, Florsheim Purchase Grant, 1991; scholar Md. Inst., 1947-49; Rinehart fellow in sculpture, 1964-66. Address: 145 Reade St New York NY 10013

QUIST, BETH DOBSON, small business owner; b. Salt Lake City, July 4, 1953; d. Jay Leroy and Beverly (Bracken) Dobson; m. Robert Quist, Dec. 21, 1976; children: Rachel, Jacob. BSN, U. Utah, 1976; MPA, Brigham Young U., 1983. ICU staff nurse LDS Hosp., Salt Lake City, 1976; nursing supr. Alta View Hosp., Sandy, Utah, 1981; sr. mgmt. engr. Intermountain Health Care, Salt Lake City, 1983; sr. cons. Peat Marwick, L.A., Affiliated Svcs., Salt Lake City, 1985-87; dir. nusing Univ. Hosp., Salt Lake City, 1987-91; pres. Workflow Systems, Inc., Bountiful, Utah, 1991—. Coantbr. articles to profl. jours. Chair Gov.'s Commn. for Women and Families, Salt Lake City, 1991—, sec.-treas., 1989-91; chair Women's Bus. Devel. Coun., Salt Lake City, 1991—; sec., treas. Davis County LWV, 1989; mem. child care task force State of Utah, 1989-91. Mem. Nat. Assn. Commns. for Women (bd. dirs. 1990-92), UHA Himss, Utah Info. Tech. Assn. Democrat.

QUIST, GORDON JAY, federal judge; b. Grand Rapids, Mich., Nov. 12, 1937; s. George J. and Ida F. (Hoekstra) Q.; m. Jane Capito, Mar. 10, 1962; children: Scot D., George J., Susan E., Martha J., Peter K. BA, Mich. State U., 1959; JD with honors, George Washington U., 1962. Bar: D.C. 1962, Ill. 1964, U.S. Dist. Ct. (no. dist.) Ill. 1964, U.S. Supreme Ct. 1965, Mich. 1967, U.S. Dist. Ct. (we. dist.) Mich. 1967, U.S. Ct. Appeals (6th cir.) 1967. Assoc. Hollabaugh & Jacobs, Washington, 1962-64, Sonnenschein, Carlin, Nath & Rosenthal, Chgo., 1964-66; assoc. Miller, Johnson, Snell & Cummiskey, Grand Rapids, 1967-72, ptnr., 1972-92, mng. ptnr., 1986-92; judge U.S. Dist. Ct. (we. dist.) Mich., Grand Rapids, 1992—. Bd. dirs. Wedgewood Acres-Ch. Youth Home, 1968-74, Mary Free Bed Hosp., 1979-88, Christian Ref. Publs., 1968-78, 82-88, Opera Grand Rapids, 1986-92, Mary Free Bed Brace Shop, 1988-92, Better Bus. Bur., 1972-80, Calvin Theol. Sem., 1992-93; bd. dirs. Indian Trails Camp, 1970-78, 82-88, pres., 1978, 88. Mem. Am. Indicature Soc., Mich. State Bar Assn., Fed. Bar Assn., Univ. Club Grand Rapids, Order of Coif. Avocations: reading, travel. Office: 482 Ford Fed Courthouse 110 Michigan St NW Grand Rapids MI 49503

QUITTMEYER, CHARLES LOREAUX, business educator; b. Peekskill, N.Y., Dec. 23, 1917; s. Ernest Martin and Edith Grace (Loreaux) Q.; m. Maureen J. Rankin, June 2, 1956; children: Peter Charles, David Rankin, Andrew Robert, Jane Loreaux. A.B., Coll. William and Mary, 1940; M.B.A., Harvard U., 1947; Ph.D. (fellow), Columbia U., 1955. Bus. and govt. positions, 1941-42, 47-48; asst. prof. bus. adminstrn. Coll. William and Mary, Williamsburg, Va., 1948-54, prof., head dept., 1962-68, founding dean Sch. Bus. Adminstrn., 1968-83, Floyd Dewey Gottwald prof. bus. adminstrn., 1982-88, Floyd Dewey Gottwald prof. bus. adminstrn. emeritus, 1988—; lectr., asst. prof. mktg. U. Buffalo, 1954-57; rsch. assoc., assoc. prof. commerce U. Va., 1957-61; sr. scientist Tech. Ops., Inc., 1961-62; dir., adv. bd. First & Mchts. Nat. Bank, Peninsula, 1972-83; dir., treas., exec. com. Williamsburg Landing, Inc., 1983-89. Contbr. to Ency. Brit., also papers in field. Mem. adv. bd. supts. James City County, 1969-71, chmn., 1971; mem. Peninsula Airport Commn., 1971-81, sec., 1973-81; lifetime mem. Sch. Bus. Adminstrn. Bd. Sponsors, Inc. Coll. of William and Mary. Served to capt., F.A. and M.I. AUS, 1942-46. Recipient William and Mary Alumni medallion, 1976. Mem. Acad. Mgmt., Am. Econ. Assn., So. Bus. Adminstrn. Assn. (pres. 1976-77), Soc. of Alumni Coll. William and Mary (dir. 1984-90), Phi Beta Kappa, Beta Gamma Sigma. Episcopalian. Club: Harvard of Virginia. Home: 210 Kingswood Dr Williamsburg VA 23185-3223

QURAISHI, MARGHOOB A., management consultant; b. Jaipur, India, July 15, 1931; s. Nazir A. Quraishi and Khudija B. Khan; married; 4 children. B of Commerce, U. Karachi, Pakistan, 1955, postgrad., 1956; cert. in bus. fin., indsl. mgmt. & rels., McGill U., Montreal, Que., 1958; MBA, Stanford U., 1959. Rsch. economist Riches Rsch., Inc., 1960-61; acct., auditor Webb & Webb, CPAs, 1961-62; contr. adminstrv. asst. to pres. Capcom, 1963; v.p., sr. cons. CPM Internat., Inc., 1964-65; mgr., contr. Woodside Homes, 1965-66; founder, pres. Associated Mgmt. Systems, Palo Alto, Calif., 1966—; guest speaker, tchr. in field. Author numerous publs. in field. Mem. Inst. Mgmt. Cons., Am. Arbitration Assn., Am. Mgmt. Assn., Am. Mktg. Assn., Am. Soc. Appraisers. Office: Associated Mgmt Systems 974 Commercial St Ste A Palo Alto CA 94303

QURAISHI, MOHAMMED SAYEED, health scientist, administrator; b. Jodhpur, India, June 23, 1924; came to U.S., 1946, naturalized, 1973; s. Mohammed Latif and Akhtar Jahan Q.; m. Akhtar Imtiaz, Nov. 12, 1953; children: Rana, Naveed, Sabah. B.Sc., St. John's Coll., 1942; M.Sc., Aligarh Muslim U., 1944; Ph.D., U. Mass., 1948. Sr. mem. UN, WHO Team to Bangladesh, 1949-51; entomologist Malaria Inst. Pakistan, 1951-55; sr. rsch. officer Pakistan Council Sci. and Indsl. Rsch., 1955-60; sr. sci. officer Pakistan AEC, 1960-64; assoc. prof. entomology U. Man., 1964-66; assoc. prof. entomology N.D. State U., Fargo, 1966-70, prof., 1970-74; chief scientist biology N.Y. State Sci. Svc., Albany, 1974-75; entomologist, toxicologist, chief pest control and consultation sect. NIH, Bethesda, Md., 1976-84; health scientist adminstr., exec. sec. microbiology and infectious disease rsch. com. Nat. Inst. Allergy and Infectious Diseases, Bethesda, Md., 1984-88, sci. rev. adminstr. spl. revs., 1988—; sr. scientist Cen. Treaty Orgn., Inst. Nuclear Sci., Tehran, Iran, 1960-64; program mgr. interdepartmental contract Project THEMIS, Dept. Def., 1968-74. Author: Biochemical Insect Control: Its Impact on Economy, Environment and Natural Selection, 1977; mem. editorial bd. Jour. Environ. Toxicology and Chemistry, 1981-84; author numerous sci. papers. Chmn. NIH Asian-Am. Cultural Assn., 1980-81. Recipient Sustained High Quality Performance award, 1980, Merit Pay Performance awards, 1984, 86, 87, Recognition and Appreciation of Spl. Achievement award NIH, 1988, Spl. Recognition award for Svcs. to NIH, Asian Am. Cultural Com., 1989, Appreciation in Recognition of Outstanding Support for Combined Fed. Campaign, 1991. Mem. Am. Chem. Soc., Soc. Environ. Toxicology and Chemistry (mem. publs. com. in charge spl. publs. 1982-84), Sigma Xi, Phi Kappa Phi. Home: 19813 Cochrane Way Gaithersburg MD 20879-1637 Office: NIH Rm 4C22 Solar Bldg 6003 Executive Blvd Bethesda MD 20892

QURAISHI, NISAR ALI, internist; b. Rawalpindi, Punjab, Pakistan, May 15, 1946; came to U.S., 1970; s. Jehan Dad and Sahib Jan (Qureshi) Q.; m. Shahida Parveen, June 25, 1970; children—Abid, Zahid. M.B., B.S. Dacca (Pakistan) Med. Coll., 1969. Diplomate Am. Bd. Internal Medicine. House surgeon Dacca Med. Coll., 1969, sr. house physician, 1969; intern Beekman Downtown Hosp., N.Y.C., 1970-71, resident, 1971-74; asst. attending Cabrini Med. Ctr., N.Y.C., 1981—; assoc. attending N.Y. Infirmary-Beekman Downtown Hosp., N.Y.C., 1982—; physician in charge exercise EKG, Mobil Oil Corp., N.Y.C., 1977-86. Mem. N.Y. County Med. Soc., N.Y. State Med. Soc., AMA, ACP, Am. Soc. Internal Medicine. Office:

37812 Greenwich St New York NY 10013 Office: 1 Chopin Ct Jersey City NJ 07302-3240

QUREISHI, A. SALAM, computer software and services company executive; b. Aligarh, India, July 1, 1936; s. M.A. Jabbar and Saira (Sattar) Q.; m. Naheed Fatima; children: Lubna, Leila. BS in Physics and Math., Aligarth U., India, 1954; MS in Stats., Patna U., India, 1957. Mgr. applications IBM Corp., Palo Alto, Calif., 1961-67; founder, pres., chmn. bd. Optimum Sys., Inc., Palo Alto, Calif., 1967-71; chmn. bd. Sysorex Internat., Inc., Mountain View, Calif., 1972—. Republican. Home: 925 Mountain Home Rd Redwood City CA 94062 Office: Sysorex Internat Inc 225 E Middlefield Rd Mountain View CA 90000*

QURESHEY, SAFI U., electronics manufacturing company executive; b. Karachi, Pakistan, Feb. 15, 1951; s. Razi and Ishrat (Temuri) Q.; m. Anita Sue Savory, Sept. 19, 1976; children: Uns, Zeshan, Anisa. BS in Physics, U. Karachi, 1971; BSEE, U. Tex., 1975. Test specialist Documentor div. A.M. Internat., Santa Ana, Calif., 1975-77; test engr. Computer Automation, Irvine, Calif., 1977-78; design engr. Telefile Computer Products, Irvine, 1978-80; founder, pres. AST Research, Inc., Irvine, 1980—; CEO AST Research Inc., 1988—. Mem. So. Calif. Tech. Execs. Network (bd. dirs.). Islamic. Avocations: bicycling, golf. Office: AST Rsch Inc PO Box 19658 Irvine CA 92713-9658*

QUTUB, MUSA YACUB, hydrogeologist, educator, consultant; b. Jerusalem, June 2, 1940; came to U.S., 1960; s. Yacub and Sarah Q.; married, July 21, 1971; children: Hania, Jennan, Sarmad, Muntaser. B.A. in Geology, Simpson Coll., Indianola, Iowa, 1964; M.S. in Hydrogeology, Colo. State U., 1966; Ph.D in Water Resources, Iowa State U. Sci. and Tech., 1969. Instr. earth sci. Iowa State U., Ames, 1966-69; from asst. prof. to prof. Northeastern Ill., Chgo., 1969-80, prof. geography and environ. studies, 1980—; cons. hydrogeology, Des Plaines, Ill., 1970—; sr. adviser Saudi Arabian Ministry Planning, Riyadh, 1977-78; leader U.S. environ. sci. del. to People's Republic of China, 1984; pres., founder Islamic Info. Ctr. Am. Author: Secondarity Environmental Science Methods, 1973; contbr. numerous articles to profl. jours.; editor Environ. Resource, Directory Environ. Educators and Cons. World. NSF grantee, 1970-71, 71-72, 72-73, 75, 76, Hew grantee, 1974, grantee Ill. Dept. Edn., 1970. Mem. AAAS, NSF (cons.), Am. Waterworks Assn., Am. Men and Women Sci., Nat. Assn. Geology Tchrs. (pres. central sect. 1974), Environ. Sci. Inst. (edn. com.), Internat. Assn. Advancement of Earth and Environ Sci. (pres. 1975—, founder), Ill. Earth Sci. Edn. (pres. 1971-73, founder), Phi Delta Kappa. Muslim. Avocations: tennis, track, cross country, soccer.

RAAB, G. KIRK, biotechnology company executive; b. N.Y.C., Sept. 27, 1935; s. George Rufus and Ann Maria (Wood) R.; m. Mollie Elizabeth Painter, Dec. 6, 1986; children; Julia Woodson, Dean Kirk; children from previous marriage: Kristina Elizabeth, Alyson Ann, Michael George. B.A. with honors, Colgate U., 1959. With Pfizer Inc., 1959-65; gen. mgr. A.H. Robins Co., Mex., 1965-68; v.p. Latin Am. Beecham Group Ltd., 1968-75; v.p. Latin Am., then exec. v.p. internat. Abbott Labs., North Chicago, Ill., 1975-79, corp. group v.p., 1980-81, pres., COO, dir., 1981-85; pres., COO Genentech Inc., San Francisco, 1985—, now pres., CEO. Chmn. Bd. Calif. Healthcare Inst., Biotech. Inds. Orgn.; trustee U. Calif. San Francisco Found., Colgate U. San Francisco Ballet; bd. dirs. Planned Parenthood San Mateo County, Pharmaceutical Mfrs. Assn., Found. Nat. Sci. and Tech. medals, Cholestech Inc., Oclassen Pharmaceuticals Inc., Shaman Pharmaceuticals Inc. Office: Genentech Inc 460 Point San Bruno Blvd South San Francisco CA 94080-4990

RAAB, HARRY FREDERICK, JR., physicist; b. Johnstown, Pa., May 9, 1926; s. Harry Frederick and Marjorie Eleanor (Stiff) R.; m. Phebe Ann Duerr, June 16, 1951; children: Constance Diane, Harry Frederick, Cynthia Ann Raab Morgenthaler. Student Navy Electronics Tech. Sch., 1944-45; SB and SM E.E., MIT, 1951; postgrad. Oak Ridge Sch. Reactor Tech., 1954-55. Reactor control engr. Bettis Atomic Power Lab. Westinghouse Electric Corp., West Mifflin, 1951-54, mgr. surface ship physics, 1955-62, mgr. light water breeder reactor physics, 1962-72; chief physicist Navy Nuclear Propulsion Directorate, Washington, 1972—. Patentee light water breeder reactor. Lay reader Episc. Ch. of the Good Shepherd, Burke, Va., 1957—, Sunday Sch. tchr., 1957-72, dir. liturgy, 1987—, stewardship chmn., 1979-82, 84, 92—, chmn. presch. bd., 1994—, healing ministry, 1989—, sr. warden, 1983, 85; mem. stewardship com. Diocese of Va., 1983—, chmn. stewardship, 1995—; chaplain for mentally retarded No. Va. Tng. Ctr., 1983—; bd. dirs. Phoenix Cmty. Svcs., 1995—. With USNR, 1944-46, PTO. Fellow Am. Nuclear Soc.; mem. Internat. Platform Assn., Sigma Xi, Tau Beta Pi, Eta Kappa Nu. Republican. Lodge: Masons. Home: 8202 Ector Ct Annandale VA 22003-1342 Office: Naval Sea Systems Command Code 08A Washington DC 20362-5101

RAAB, HERBERT NORMAN, retail executive; b. N.Y.C., Nov. 7, 1925; s. Jacob and Pauline (Neuwirth) R.; m. Blanche Muriel Levin, Jan. 27, 1952 (dec. Mar. 1981); children: Nancy Renée, James Harris; m. Carmen Sandra Fernandez, Aug. 17, 1986. AB, Harvard U., 1947; postgrad., Harvard U. Bus. Sch., 1947-48, Seton Hall U. Law Sch., 1972-75. V.p. Bamberger Div. R.H. Macy Inc., N.Y.C., 1968-75, v.p., 1975-78; pres. and chief exec. officer W&J Sloane, N.Y.C., 1978-80; pvt. practice cons. N.Y.C., 1980-84; sr. v.p. Wayside Furniture Co., Milford, Conn., 1984-90; adj. prof. U. Bridgeport (Conn.), 1986-91. Jewish.

RAAB, IRA JERRY, lawyer; b. N.Y.C., June 20, 1935; s. Benjamin and Fannie (Kirschner) R.; divorced; children: Michael, Shelley; m. Katie Rachel McKeever, June 30, 1979 (div. 1991); children: Julie, Jennifer, Joseph. BBA, CCNY, 1955; JD, Bklyn. Law Sch., 1957; MPA, NYU, 1959, postgrad., 1961; MS in Pub. Adminstrn., L.I. U., 1961; MBA, Adelphi U., 1990. Bar: N.Y. 1958, U.S. Dist. Ct. (so. and ea. dists.) N.Y. 1960, U.S. Supreme Ct. 1967, U.S. Tax Ct. 1976, U.S. Ct. Appeals (2d cir.) 1977. Pvt. practice Woodmere, N.Y., 1958—; agt. Westchester County Soc. Prevention of Cruelty to Children, White Plains, N.Y., 1958; counsel Dept. Correction City of N.Y., 1959, trial commr. Dept. Correction, 1976, asst. corp. counsel Tort divsn., 1963-70; staff counsel SBA, N.Y.C., 1961-63; counsel Investigation Com. on Willowbrook State Sch., Boro Hall, S.I., N.Y., 1970; gen. counsel Richmond County Soc. Prevention of Cruelty to Children, Boro Hall, 1970-81; pro bono counsel N.Y.C. Patrolmen's Benevolent Assn., 1974-81; rep. to UN Internat. Criminal Ct., 1977-78; arbitrator Small Claims Ct., Day Cts., N.Y.C., 1970—, L.I. Better Bus. Bur., 1976-93, Nassau County Dist. Ct., 1978-93; hearing officer Nassau and Suffolk County Supreme Ct., 1982—; spl. master N.Y. County Supreme Ct., 1977—; judge N.Y.C. Parking Violations Bur., 1991-93; lectr. community and ednl. orgns.; instr. paralegal course Lawrence Sch. Dist., N.Y., 1982-84. Chmn. Businessmen's Luncheon Club, Wall Street Synagogue, 1968-79; sec Cmty. Mediation Ctr., Suffolk County, 1978-80, exec. v.p., 1980-81; vice chmn. Woodmere Inc. Com., 1980-81; mem. adv. bd. Nassau Expressway Com., 1979-80; bd. dirs. Woodmere Mchts. Assn., 1979-80, v.p., 1979-83, chmn. 1984-93; candidate for dist. ct. judge Nassau County, 1987, 88, 89, 91, 93, 94. Recipient Consumer Protection award FTC, 1974, 76, 79, Recognition award Pres. Ronald Reagan, 1986, Man of Yr. award L.I. Coun. of Chambers, 1987. Mem. Am. Judges Assn. (nat. treas. 1978-82, mem. exec. com. 1978—, gov. dist. II 1973-78, 82-83, 89—, chmn. civil ct. ops. com. 1975-79, chmn. ednl. film com. 1972-79, mem. editorial bd. Ct. Rev. mag. 1975-79, 82-86, chmn. speakers' bur. com. 1976-77, chmn. legis. com. 1983—, historian 1988—), William H. Burnett award 1983), Am. Judges Found. (pres. 1977-79, chmn. bd. trustees 1979-83, treas. 1974-75, 76-77, trustee 83—), Assn. Arbitrators of Civil Ct. City of N.Y. (past pres.), ABA (chmn. cts. and community com. 1988-93, mem. exec. com. jud. adminstrn. divsn. lawyers conf. 1989—), N.Y. State Bar Assn. (sec. dist., city town and villages cts. com.), Nassau County Bar Assn. (mem. criminal cts. com., matrimonial and family ct. com., mem. ct. com., mem. ethics com.), Profl. Group Legal Svc. Assn. (past pres.), Internat. Assn. Jewish Lawyers and Jurists (mem. com. to draft Internat. Bill of Rights of Privacy 1982, mem. coun. 1981—, bd. govs. 1984—), Am. Arbitration Assn. (1975—, mem. adv. bd. community dispute ctr. 1979-81), K.P. (past chancellor comdr.). Democrat. Home and Office: 375 Westwood Rd Woodmere NY 11598-1624

RAAB, LAWRENCE EDWARD, English educator; b. Pittsfield, Mass., May 8, 1946; s. Edward Louis and Marjorie (Young) R.; m. Judith Ann

Michaels, Dec. 29, 1968; 1 child, Jennifer Caroline. BA, Middlebury Coll., 1968; MA, Syracuse U., 1972. Lectr. Am. U., Washington, 1970-71; jr. fellow U. Mich. Soc. Fellows, Ann Arbor, 1973-76; prof. English Williams Coll., Williamstown, Mass., 1976—. Author: (poems) Mysteries of the Horizon, 1972, The Collector of Cold Weather, 1976, Other Children, 1987, What We Don't Know About Each Other, 1993 (National Book award nominee, 1993). Creative Writing fellow Nat. Endowment Arts, 1972, 84; recipient Bess Hokin prize Poetry mag., 1983; residencies at Yaddo, 1979-80, 82, 84, 86-90, 94, MacDowell Colony, 1993, 95. Office: Williams Coll English Dept Williamstown MA 01267

RAAB, SELWYN, journalist; b. N.Y.C., June 26, 1934; s. William and Berdie (Glantz) R.; m. Helene Lurie, Dec. 25, 1963; 1 dau., Marian. B.A. Coll. City N.Y., 1956. Reporter N.Y. World-Telegram and Sun, N.Y.C., 1960-66; producer, news editor NBC-TV News, N.Y.C., 1966-71; exec. producer WNET-News, N.Y.C., 1971-74; reporter New York Times, 1974—. Author: Justice in the Back Room, 1967; co-author: Mob Lawyer, 1994. Recipient award for best mag. consumer protection article U. Mo. Sch. Journalism, 1969, Deadline awards for excellence in television reporting Sigma Delta Chi, 1971, 73, 1st prize for excellence in television reporting N.Y. State A.P., 1973, Best Television Reporting award N.Y. Press Club, 1973, Heywood Broun Meml. award, 1974, Page One award Newspaper Guild of New York, 1975, Best Feature Story award N.Y. Press Club, 1984, N.Y.C. Patrolmen's Benevolent Assn. award, 1985. Office: NY Times 229 W 43d St New York NY 10036

RAAB, SHELDON, lawyer, Bklyn. Nov. 30, 1937; s. Morris and Eva (Shereshevsky) R.; m. Judith Deutsch, Dec. 15, 1963; children: Michael Kenneth, Elisabeth Louise, Andrew John. A.B., Columbia U., 1958; LL.B. cum laude, Harvard U., 1961. Bar: N.Y. 1961, U.S. Ct. Appeals (2d cir.) 1963, U.S. Dist. Ct. (so. and ea. dists.) 1967. Dep. asst. atty. gen. State of N.Y., 1961-63, asst. atty gen., 1963-64; assoc. Fried, Frank, Harris, Shriver & Jacobson and predecessor firm, N.Y.C., 1964-69, ptnr., 1970-81, inc. ptnr., 1981—. Mem. ABA, Am. Law Inst., N.Y. State Bar Assn. (trial lawyers sect. 1968—), Assn. of Bar of City of N.Y. (adminstrv. law com. 1968-71, spl. com. electric power and environment 1971-73, chmn. energy com. 1974-79, fed. cts. com. 1981-84, state superior cts. juris. com. 1985-88). Democrat. Office: Fried Frank Harris Shriver & Jacobson 1 New York Pla New York NY 10004

RAAB, WALTER FERDINAND, manufacturing company executive; b. Phila., Nov. 25, 1924; m. Bernice M. Jacobs, 1952; children: Laurie Ann Raab Kucher, Wendy Louise Raab Robbins, Mandy Margaret Raab Carson. BSE, U. Pa., 1945. With Coopers Lybrand Co., 1945-53; with AMP Inc., Harrisburg, Pa., 1953—, treas., 1968-71, v.p., treas., 1971-75, treas., pr., 1975-79, v.p., chief fin. officer, 1979-81, vice chmn., chief fin. officer, 1981, chmn. bd., chief exec. officer, 1982-90, ret., chmn. exec. com. of bd. dirs., 1990-92, bd. dirs., 1993—; bd. dir. The West Co., Harris Corp., Dauphin Deposit Trust Co., Air Products and Chems., Inc. Bd. dirs. Holy Spirit Hosp. Mem. Elec. Mfrs. Club. Office: AMP Inc PO Box 3608 Harrisburg PA 17105-3608

RAAD, VIRGINIA, pianist, lecturer; b. Salem, W.Va., Aug. 13, 1925; d. Joseph M. and Martha (Joseph) R. BA in Art History, Wellesley Coll., 1947; spl. student, New Eng. Conservatory Music, 1947-48; diplôme, Ecole Normale de Musique, Paris, 1950; Doctorate with honors (French Govt. grantee 1950-52, 54-55), U. Paris, 1955; student, Alfred Cortot, Jeanne Blancard, Berthe Bert, Jacques Chailley. Artist in residence Salem (W.Va.) Coll., 1957-70; in concert pianist, 1960—; musician in residence N.C. Arts Council, at community colls., 1971-72; adjudicator Nat. Guild Piano Tchrs., Nat. Fedn. Music Clubs; panelist, grant reviewer NEH, 1978-84, 92—; mem. com. Nat. Endowment Arts, 1978; Am. rep. Debussy Centennial Colloque, Paris, 1962. Performances, concerts, lectrs. master classes at Carleton Coll., U. Fla., Viterbo Coll., Portland State U., Notre Dame U., Mt. Mary Coll., Mundelein Coll., Trinity Coll., Washington, Phillips Gallery, Washington, Norton Gallery, Rollins Coll., Marietta Coll., Huntington (W.Va.) Galleries, W.Va. U., Coll. William and Mary, Channel 13 (Sta. WQED), Pitts., Channel 24 (WNPB, Morgantown, W.Va., Lincoln (Pa.) U., U. Pitts., U Mich., Dearborn, Fordham U., Piano Tchrs. Congress of N.Y., So. Conn. State U., Wellesley Coll., Middlebury Coll., Ladycliff Coll., numerous other colls. and univs.; contbg. author: Debussy et l'Evolution de la Musique au XX Siècle, 1965, The Piano Sononity of Claude Debussy, 1994; recording arts: EDUCO, 1995—; contbr. articles to profl. jours. Active Amnesty Internat. Urgent Action Network; regional rep. Wellesley Coll. Named Outstanding W.Va. Woman Educator Delta Kappa Gamma, 1965; included in Schlesinger Library on History of Women in Am. Radcliffe Coll., 1967; grantee Govt. France, Am. Coun. Learned Socs. Mem. Soc. Française de Musicologie, Am. Musicol. Soc. (regional officer 1960-65), Am. Soc. for Aesthetics (grant reviewer), Internat. Musicol. Soc., Music Tchrs. Nat. Assn. (adjudicator, musicology program chair 1983-87), W.Va. Music Tchrs. Assn., Coll. Music Soc., Alpha Delta Kappa (hon.). Republican. Avocations: hiking, gardening, birding. Address: 60 Terrace Ave Salem WV 26426-1116 Whether on the concert stage or in the classroom, I am a teacher with the desire to enlarge each person's vision in the arts.

RAAF, JOHN ELBERT, neurosurgeon, educator; b. Hailey, Idaho, Nov. 12, 1905; s. John J. and Madge (Hart) R.; m. Lorene Rardin, Oct. 26, 1938; children: John Hart, Jean Raaf Binnewies. A.B., Stanford U., 1926, M.D. 1930; M.S., U. Minn., 1935, Ph.D., 1941. Diplomate: Am. Bd. Neurol. Surgery (bd. dirs., 1956-62). Intern, asst. resident Strong Meml. Hosp., also Rochester Municipal Hosp., Rochester, N.Y., 1929-31; fellow gen. surgery and neurosurgery Mayo Clinic, Rochester, Minn., 1931-36; practice of neurosurgery Portland, Oreg., 1936—; assoc. clin. prof. surgery U. Oreg., 1946-57, clin. prof., 1957-80, prof., 1980-86, clin. prof. emeritus, 1986—; John Raaf prof. neurol. scis. Oreg. Health Scis. U., 1992; chief neurol. surgery Good Samaritan Hosp., 1947-80; spl. med. advisor VA, Washington, 1953-58. Editorial bd.: Western Jour. Surgery, Obstetrics and Gynecology, 1946-68, Jour. of Trauma, 1961-84; contbr. articles on med. subjects to profl. jours. Trustee Med. Rsch. Found., Oreg., 1950—, pres., 1951-56. Recipient Aubrey R. Watzek award Lewis and Clark Coll., 1993; established John Raaf Chair in Neuroscis., Oreg. Health Scis. U., 1992. Fellow A.C.S. (v.p. 1964); mem. Soc. Neurol. Surgery, Am. Trauma Soc. (bd. dirs. 1972), Neurol. Scis. Found. (pres. 1971—), Western Neurosurg. Assn. (founder, pres. 1956), AMA, No. Pacific Soc. Neurology and Psychiatry (pres. 1945-46), North Pacific Surg. Assn., Pacific Coast Surg. Assn. (pres. 1961-62), Western Surg. Assn., Am. Surg. Assn., Am. Assn. Surgery Trauma (pres. 1968-69), Am. Acad. Neurosurgery (pres. 1948-49), Am. Assn. Neurol. Surgeons, Phi Beta Kappa, Sigma Xi, Alpha Omega Alpha. Republican. Episcopalian. Clubs: Waverley Country (Portland), University (Portland), Arlington (Portland), Multnomah Athletic (Portland); Army and Navy (Washington); Bohemian (San Francisco). Home: 618 NW Westover Ter Portland OR 97210-3134 Office: 1120 NW 20th Ave Portland OR 97209-1539

RAAFLAUB, KURT A., classics educator; b. Buea, Cameroon, Feb. 15, 1941; s. Fritz and Heidi (Ninck) R.; m. Deborah Dickmann Boedeker, July 14, 1978. MA, U. Basel, Switzerland, 1967, PhD, 1970. Asst. prof. ancient history Free U. Berlin, Fed. Republic Germany, 1972-78; asst. prof. ancient history Brown U., Providence, 1978-80, assoc. prof. classics and history, 1980-83, prof., 1983—, John Rowe Workman Disting. prof. classics and humanistic tradition, 1989-92, chmn. dept. classics, 1984-89; co-dir. Ctr. for Hellenic Studies, Washington, 1992—. Author: Dignitatis Contentio, 1974, Die Entdeckung der Freiheit, 1985; co-author: Studien zum Attischen Seebund, 1984, Aspects of Athenian Democracy, 1990; editor: Social Struggles in Archaic Rome, 1986, Between Republic and Empire: Interpretations of Augustus and His Principate, 1990, Athens and Rome, Florence and Venice: City-States in Classical Antiquity and Medieval Italy, 1991, Anfänge politischen Denkens in der Antike: Die nahöstlichen Kulturen und die Griechen, 1993, Democracy 2500: Questions and Challenges, 1995; contbr. articles to profl. jours. Mem. Historisches Kolleg Munich, 1989-90. Am. Coun. Learned Socs. fellow 1983-84, Ctr. for Hellenic Studies fellow, 1976-77, NEH fellow, 1989. Mem. Philol. Assn., Assn. Ancient Historians, Am. Inst. Archaeology. Avocation: music. Home and Office: Ctr Hellenic Studies 3100 Whitehaven St N W Washington DC 20008

RAASCH, ERNEST MARTIN, company executive; b. Norfolk, Nebr., May 15, 1927; s. Ernest Carl and Esther Eleanor (Martin) R.; m. Helen Veronica Gillespie, Dec. 15, 1973. Student, NYU, Columbia U. Pres. Dixon Co. Ltd., Newmarket, Can., 1967-69; v.p. mktg. Joseph Dixon Crucible Co., Jersey City, 1962-69; dir. mktg./gen. mgr. Borden Chem., N.Y.C., 1969-71; pres., chief operating officer Swingline Co., div. SWL Inc., L.I.C., 1971-75; exec. v.p. Swingline Co., div. SWL Inc., 1975-78, pres., chief exec. officer, 1978-80; pres., chief exec. officer Gesistner Corp., Yonkers, N.Y, 1980-84; exec. v.p., chief operating officer Codenoll Tech. Corp., Yonkers, 1984-87; pres., chief exec. officer SRS/C-Tech Inc., N.Y.C., 1987—; bd. dirs. Exercycle Inc., Woonsocket, R.I., 1984—; SRS/C Tech., Acquivest Inc., Framingham, Mass., 1987—. Contbr. articles to profl. jours.; patentee in field. Trustee The Hudson River Mus., Yonkers, 1982-84. Named Man of the Yr., Office Product Mfrs. Assn., 1980. Mem. Soc. Mfg. Engrs., Nat. Indsl. Conf. Bd., Sales/Mktg. Execs. of N.Y. (bd. dirs. 1984—), N.Y. Athletic Club. Lutheran. Avocations: skiing, sailing, writing. Office: SRS/C Tech Inc 330 7th Ave New York NY 10001-5010

RABADJIJA, NEVEN, lawyer; b. Zagreb, Yugoslavia, June 2, 1954; came to U.S., 1965; s. Luka and Mirjana (Peradin) R.; m. Ruth Day, May 20, 1983. BA, Harvard U., 1977, MA, 1977; JD, Boston Coll., 1980. Bar: Ohio 1980, Mass. 1985. Assoc. Arter & Hadden, Cleve., 1980-84; assoc. Hale & Dorr, Boston, 1984-87, jr. ptnr., 1987—. Office: Hale & Dorr 60 State St Boston MA 02109-1803

RABASSA, GREGORY, Romance languages educator, translator; b. Yonkers, N.Y., Mar. 9, 1922; married 1966. A.B., Dartmouth Coll., 1945, Litt.D. hon., 1982; M.A., Columbia U., 1947, Ph.D. in Portuguese, 1954. Instr. Spanish Columbia U., 1947-52, assoc., 1952-58, asst. prof., 1958-63, assoc. prof. Spanish and Portuguese, 1963-68; prof. Romance langs. Queens Coll., CUNY Grad. Sch., Flushing, N.Y., 1968-86; Disting. prof. Queens Coll., CUNY Grad. Sch., 1986—; assoc. editor Odyssey Rev., 1961-64. Contbr. articles to profl. jours. Staff sgt. OSS, 1942-45. Decorated Croce al Merito di Guerra (Italy); Order of San Carlos (Colombia); recipient Nat. Book award for transl., 1967, transl. prize PEN Am. Ctr., 1977, Gode award Am. Transl. Assn., 1980, PEN transl. medal, 1982, arts award N.Y. Gov., 1985, transl. prize Wheatland Found., 1988, lit. award Am. Acad. and Inst. Arts and Letters, 1989, Presdl. medal Dartmouth Coll., 1991, Ivan Sandrof award The Nat. Book Critics Cir., 1993, Literary Lion award N.Y. Pub. Libr., 1993; Fulbright-Hays fellow, 1965-66, NEH fellow, 1979-80, Guggenheim fellow, 1988-89. Mem. Renaissance Soc. Am., MLA, Am. Assn. Tchrs. Spanish and Portuguese, Latin Am. Studies Assn., Am. Lit. Translators Assn., Hispanic Soc. Am., PEN Club, Phi Beta Kappa. Office: Dept of Romance Lang CUNY Queens College Flushing NY 11367

RABB, BERNARD PAUL, book publisher, consultant; b. N.Y.C., Sept. 23, 1939; s. Saul and Rachel S. (Cohen) R.; BA, Washington Sq. Coll., NYU, 1960. Asst. editor Music Jour. N.Y.C., 1960-62; mng. editor Mus. Am., N.Y.C., 1962-63; music editor Ednl. Audio-Visual, Hawthorne, N.Y., 1963-64; trade editor Chilton Book Co., Phila., 1964-65; mng. editor Grove Press, N.Y.C., 1965-70; pub., pres. Columbia Pub. Co., Inc., Balt., 1971—; editorial, prodn. and typography cons. Ford Found., Andrew W. Mellon Found., Whitney Mus. Am. Art, Art Mus. Princeton U., Met. Mus. Art, Nat. Gallery of Art, Sotheby's; instr. music N.Y.U. Sch. Continuing Edn. Commr. Hunterdon County (N.J.) Library Commn.; judge Lambda Literary Awards; typographic cons. Health Edn. and Resource Orgn., Balt. Author: (with others) Good Shelter, 1975. Pub., editor Tribe: An Am. Gay Jour., 1989-91. Editor works by Jean-Paul Sartre, Pablo Neruda, Alain Robbe-Grillet, William Herrick, Eric Berne, Clifford Irving, William Eastlake, Kay Boyle, Octavio Paz, John Lahr, Josef Skvorecky, others. Contbr. music criticism and articles on classical music to mus. publs. Bd. dirs. Gay and Lesbian Alliance Against Defamation, Balt.; co-chair Black and White Men Together, Balt. Office: 234 E 25th St Baltimore MD 21218-5218

RABB, BRUCE, lawyer; b. Cambridge, Mass., Oct. 4, 1941; s. Maxwell M. and Ruth (Cryden) R.; m. Harriet Rachel Schaffer, Jan. 4, 1970; children: Alexander Charles, Katherine Anne. AB, Harvard U., 1962; Cert. d'Etudes Politiques, Institut d'Etudes Politiques, Paris, 1963; LLB, Columbia U., 1966. Bar: N.Y. 1966. Law clk. to judge U.S. Ct. Appeals (5th cir.), 1966-67; assoc. Stroock & Stroock & Lavan, N.Y.C., 1967-68, 71-75, ptnr., 1976-91; ptnr. Kramer, Levin, Naftalis, Nessen, Kamin & Frankel, N.Y.C., 1991—; staff asst. to Pres. U.S., 1969-70; vice-chmn., bd. dirs. Lawyers Com. Human Rights, 1977—; mem. bd. dirs. Chiquita Italia, S.P.A., 1982—; supr. bd. dirs. Agora-Gazeta, Sp.zo.o., 1993—; pub. mem. Adminstrv. Conf. of U.S., 1982-86, 89-92, spl. counsel, 1986-88. Bd. dirs. Citizens Union of N.Y., 1981-87, 88-94, 95—; bd. dirs. Am. Friends of Alliance Israelite Universelle, 1987—, Human Rights Watch, 1987—; mem. Human Rights Watch/Ams., 1982—, Human Rights Watch/Helsinki, 1985—, Fund for Free Expression, 1987—, Human Rights Watch/Middle East, 1989—, vice chmn., 1990—; mem. internat. adv. com. Internat. Parliamentary Group for Human Rights in the Soviet Union, 1984-88, Prin. of the Coun. for Excellence in Govt., 1990—; sec. Lehrman Inst., 1978-88. Mem. ABA (adv. panel Internat. Human Rights Trial Observer Project 1987—), Am. Law Inst., Assn. of Bar of City of N.Y. (fed. legis., internat. human rights, civil rights, legal edn. and admission to bar coms., coun. on fgn. rels., chmn. com. on internat. law 1992—), Harvard Club N.Y.C., Met. Club of Washington. Office: Kramer Levin Naftalis et al 919 3d Ave New York NY 10022

RABB, CARLOS C., JR., petroleum company executive; b. 1924. With Ashland Oil Co., 1958-73; with Scurlock Oil Co. Inc., Houston, 1973—, formerly sr. v.p.; now pres., also bd. dirs. Office: Scurlock Oil Co PO Box 4648 Houston TX 77210-4648

RABB, GEORGE BERNARD, zoologist; b. Charleston, S.C., Jan. 2, 1930; s. Joseph and Teresa C. (Redmond) R.; m. Mary Sughrue, June 10, 1953. BS, Coll. Charleston, 1951; MA, U. Mich., 1952, PhD, 1957. Teaching fellow zoology U. Mich., 1954-56; curator, coord. rsch. Chgo. Zool. Park, Brookfield, Ill., 1956-64; assoc. dir. rsch. and edn. Chgo. Zool. Park, 1964-75, dep. dir., 1969-75, dir., 1976—; rsch. assoc. Field Mus. Natural History, 1965—; lectr. dept. biology U. Chgo., 1965-89; mem. Com. on Evolution Biology, 1969—; pres. Chgo. Zool. Soc., 1976—; mem. steering com. Species Survival Commn., Internat. Union Conservation of Nature, 1983—, vice chmn. for N.Am., 1986-88, dep. chmn., 1987-89, chmn., 1989—; chmn. policy adv. group Internat. Species Info. System, 1974-89, chmn. bd., 1989-92. Fellow AAAS; mem. Am. Soc. Ichthyologists and Herpetologists (pres. 1978), Herpetologists League, Soc. Systematic Zoology, Soc. Mammalogists, Soc. Study Evolution, Ecol. Soc. Am., Soc. Conservation Biology (council mem. 1986), Am. Soc. Zoologists, Soc. Study Animal Behavior, Am. Assn. Museums, Am. Soc. Naturalists, Am. Assn. Zool. Parks and Aquariums (dir. 1979-80), Internat. Union Dirs. Zool. Gardens, Am. Com. Internat. Conservation (chmn. 1987—), Chgo. Coun. Fgn. Relations (Chgo. com.), Sigma Xi. Club: Economic (Chgo.), Tavern. Office: Brookfield Zoo 3300 Golf Rd Brookfield IL 60513-1060*

RABB, HARRIET SCHAFFER, lawyer, educator; b. Houston, Sept. 12, 1941; d. Samuel S. and Helen G. Schaffer; m. Bruce Rabb, Jan. 4, 1970; children: Alexander, Katherine. BA in Govt., Barnard Coll., 1963; JD, Columbia U., 1966. Bar: N.Y. 1966, U.S. Supreme Ct. 1969, D.C. 1970. Instr. seminar on constl. litigation Rutgers Law Sch., 1966-67; staff atty. Center for Constl. Rights, 1966-69; spl. counsel to commr. consumer affairs N.Y.C. Dept. Consumer Affairs, 1969-70; sr. staff atty. Stern Community Law Firm, Washington, 1970-71; asst. dean urban affairs Law Sch., Columbia U., N.Y.C., 1971-84, prof. law, dir. clin. edn., 1984—; George M. Jaffen prof. law and social responsibility Law Sch., Columbia U., 1991—, vice dean, 1992—; gen. counsel Dept. Health and Human Svcs., Washington, 1993—; mem. faculty employment and tng. policy Harvard Summer Inst., Cambridge, Mass., 1975-79. Author: (with Agid, Cooper and Rubin) Fair Employment Litigation Manual, 1975, (with Cooper and Rubin) Fair Employment Litigation, 1975. Bd. dirs. Ford Found., 1977-89, N.Y. Civil Liberties Union, 1972-83, Lawyers Com. for Civil Rights Under Law, 1978-86, Legal Def. Fund NAACP, 1978-93, Am. Legal Def. and Edn. Fund, 1986-90, Legal Aid Soc., 1990-93; mem. exec. com. Human Rights Watch, 1991-93; trustee Trinity Episcopal Sch. Corp., 1991-93. Office: Dept Health and Human Svcs 200 Independence Ave SW Rm 722A Washington DC 20201

RABB, MAXWELL M., lawyer, former ambassador; b. Boston, Sept. 28, 1910; s. Solomon and Rose (Kostick) R.; m. Ruth Criedenberg, Nov. 2, 1939; children: Bruce, Sheila Rabb Weidenfeld, Emily Rabb Livingston, Priscilla Rabb Ayres. AB, Harvard U., 1932, LLB, 1935; LLD (hon.), Wilberforce U., 1957; DHL (hon.), Mt. St. Mary's Coll., 1983; LLB (hon.), Pepperdine U., 1985, St. Thomas U., 1986; DHL (hon.), Hebrew Union Coll., 1990. Bar: Mass. 1935, N.Y. 1958. Mem. firm Rabb & Rabb, Boston, 1935-37; adminstrv. asst. to U.S. Senator H.C. Lodge Jr., Mass., 1937-43; adminstrv. asst. U.S. Senator Sinclair Weeks, Mass., 1944; legal and legis. cons. Sec. Navy Forestal, 1946; practice law Boston, 1946-51; cons. U.S. Senate Rules Com., 1952; presdl. asst. to Pres. Eisenhower, sec. to Cabinet, 1953-58; partner Stroock & Stroock & Lavan, N.Y.C., 1958-81, of counsel, 1989-91; of counsel Kramer, Levin, Natalis, Nessen, Kamin & Frankel, N.Y.C., 1991—; amb. to Italy, 1981-89; bd. dirs. Sterling Nat. Bank, MIC Industries, Micro Health Systems Inc., Data Software Systems Inc., Alusit Internat. Corp., Liberty Cable Co., Inc., ComputTower, Inc. Exec. asst. campaign mgr. Eisenhower presdl. campaign, 1951-52; del. Republican Nat. Conv., 1952, 56, 76, 80; mem. exec. com. U.S. Commn. for UNESCO, 1959-60; chmn. U.S. del. UNESCO conf., Paris, 1958; Council on Fgn. Relations, 1978; pres. Congregation Emanu-El, N.Y.C., 1973-81; mem. bd. advisors John F. Kennedy Sch. Govt., Harvard U.; trustee Cardinals Cooke and O'Connor Inner City Scholarship Fund; bd. mgrs. Seamen's Ch. Inst.; mem. presdl. adv. panel on South Asian Relief assistance, 1971; mem. panel conciliators World Bank Internat. Centre for Settlement of Investment Disputes, 1967-73, U.S. rep., 1974-77; mem. Presdl. Commn. on Income Maintenance Programs, 1968-69; hon. chmn. bd. Am. Friends of Alliance Israelite Universelle; trustee N.Y. Med. Coll., Eisenhower Inst., Annenberg Inst., John Cabot U. (Italy), George Marshall Meml. Found.; vice chmn. United Cerebral Palsy, Inc., Nat. Com. on Am. Fgn. Policy, Coun. for U.S. and Italy; mem. adv. bd. Auburn U. Served as lt. amphibious corps USNR, 1944-46. Decorated Commendation Ribbon, commendatore Order of Merit, 1958, Grand Cross ofOrder of Merit (Italy), 1982; Grand Cross of Order of Malta, 1989. Mem. ABA, Am. Law Inst., Humanitarian of Am. C. of C., Inc. (bd. dirs.), Laymen's Nat. Bible Assn. (bd. dirs.), Amb.'s Club of Reps. Abroad (hon. chmn.), Harvard Club (N.Y.C.), Harmonie Club (N.Y.C.), Army and Navy Club (Washington), Met. Club (Washington). Home: 480 Park Ave New York NY 10022-1613 also: Wilson Hill Rd Colrain MA 01340 Office: Kramer Levin Natalis et al 919 3rd Ave New York NY 10022-3903

RABB, THEODORE K., historian, educator; b. Teplice-Sanov, Czechoslovakia, Mar. 5, 1937; came to U.S., 1956, naturalized, 1978; s. Oskar Kwasnik and Rose (Oliner) Rabinowicz; m. Tamar Miriam Janowsky, June 7, 1959; children: Susannah Rabb Bailin, Jonathan Richard, Jeremy David. BA, Queen's Coll. Oxford U., Eng., 1958; M.A., Queen's Coll. Oxford U., 1962, Princeton U., 1960; Ph.D., Princeton U., 1961. Instr. Stanford U., 1961-62; instr. Northwestern U., 1962-63; asst. prof. Harvard U., 1963-67; mem. faculty Princeton U., 1967—, prof. history, 1976—; vis. assoc. prof. Johns Hopkins U., 1969, SUNY-Binghamton, 1973-74; visitor Inst. Advanced Studies, Princeton, 1973, 82; mem. nat. bd. cons. NEH, Nat. Coun. History Edn. (chair); N.J. Com. for Humanities (chair); chief historian Renaissance Television Series; bd. dirs. Humanities West; cons. in field. Author: The Thirty Years War, 2d edit, 1972, Enterprise and Empire, 1967, The Struggle for Stability in Early Modern Europe, 1975, The Origins of Modern Nations, 1981, Renaissance Lives: Portraits of an Age, 1993, Origins of the Modern West, 1993; co-author: The Western Experience, 6th edit., 1994, Peoples and Nations, 1982; editor: Jour. Interdisciplinary History, 1970—; co-editor: Action and Conviction in Early Modern Europe, 1969, The Family in History, 1973, Marriage and Fertility, 1981, Industrialization and Urbanization, 1981, Climate and History, 1981, The New History, 1982, Hunger and History, 1985, Population and Economy, 1986, Art and History, 1988, La Fame nella storia, 1991, Origin and Prevention of Major Wars, 1988. Bd. govs. Hebrew U. Fellow and/or grantee Folger Shakespeare Library, Am. Philos. Soc., Social Sci. Research Council, Am. Council Learned Socs., Guggenheim Found., NEH. Mem. Am. Hist. Assn. (chmn. com. quantitative rsch. history, chmn. nominating com.), Social Sci. History Assn. (exec. com., treas.), Am. Assn. Advancement Humanities (dir., sec.-treas.), Nat. Coun. History Stds., C.C. Humanities Assn. (steering com.), Royal Hist. Soc., Internat. Commn. History Parliamentary and Rep. Instns., Renaissance Soc. Am., Hakluyt Soc., Nat. Coun. History Edn. (chair), Historians Early Modern Europe, Conf. Brit. Studies. Office: Princeton University History Dept Princeton NJ 08544

RABBAN, DAVID M., law educator; b. 1949. BA, Wesleyan U., 1971; JF, Stanford U., 1974. Bar: N.Y. 1975, D.C. 1980. Assoc. Murray A. Gordon, P.C., N.Y., 1974-76; assoc., counsel AAUP, D.C., 1976-80, counsel, 1980-82; asst. prof. U. Tex., Austin, 1983-86, prof. law, 1986—. Mem. Phi Beta Kappa. Office: U Tex Sch Law 727 E 26th St Austin TX 78705-3224

RABBITT, EDWARD THOMAS, singer, songwriter; b. Bklyn., Nov. 27, 1941; m. Janine Girardi; children: Demelza Anne, Timmy (dec.), Thomas Edward. Nightclub and concert singer, 1962—; founder Hare Trigger band, composer more than 300 songs, including Kentucky Rain, 1970, Pure Love, 1974, Drivin' My Life Away, 1980, I Love a Rainy Night; recs. of own compositions include: Two Dollars in the Jukebox, Forgive and Forget, Rocky Mountain Music, Drinkin' My Baby Off My Mind; recorded albums: Horizon, 1981 (2 Gold Album awards.), Best of Eddie Rabbitt, Step by Step, 1981, Rabbitt Trax, 1985, The Best Year of My Life, 1985, I Wanna Dance with You, 1987, Greatest Country Hits, 1991. Office: Moress Nanas Shea Entertainment 1209 16th Ave S Nashville TN 37212*

RABE, DAVID WILLIAM, playwright; b. Dubuque, Iowa, Mar. 10, 1940; s. William and Ruth (McCormick) R.; m. Elizabeth Pan, 1969 (div.); 1 child; m. Jill Clayburgh, Mar. 1979. BA in English, Loras Coll., 1962; MA, Villanova U., 1968. Feature writer Register, New Haven, 1969-70; asst. prof. Villanova U., 1970-72. Author: (plays) The Basic Training of Pavlo Hummel, 1971 (Obie award disting. playwriting 1971, Drama Desk award 1971, Drama Guild award 1971), Sticks and Bones, 1971 (Elizabeth Hull-Kate Warriner award Dramatists Guild 1971, Variety Poll award 1971, Outer Critics' Circle award 1972, Tony award best play 1972, N.Y. Drama Critics' Circle citation 1972), The Orphan, 1973, In the Boom Boom Room, 1974, Burning, 1974, Streamers, 1976 (N.Y. Drama Critics' Circle award best Am. play 1976), Goose and Tomtom, 1976, Hurlyburly, 1985, Those the River Keeps, 1990, Crossing Guard, 1994, (screenplays) I'm Dancing as Fast as I Can, 1982, Streamers, 1983, Casualties of War, 1989, State of Grace, 1990, The Firm, 1993, (novel) Recital of the Dog, 1992. With U.S. Army, 1965-67. Recipient AP award, 1970, Am. Acad. Arts and Letters award, 1974, Nat. Inst. and Am. Acad. award, 1976; Rockefeller Found. grantee, 1969; Guggenheim fellow, 1976. Address: care Ellen Neuwald Inc 902 N Ronda Sevilla Laguna Hills CA 92653*

RABEL, ED, news correspondent. BA in Political Sci., Morris Harvey Coll., 1963; LHD (Hon.), U. Charleston, 1985. Dir., anchor CBS Affiliate-WCHS-TV, 1962-66; chief so. correspondent CBS, 1967-70; war correspondent CBS News, Saigon, 1970-71; middle east correspondent CBS, Tel Aviv, 1971-73; roving correspondent CBS News, Atlanta, Ga., 1973-81; nat. correspondent CBS Evening News, N.Y., 1981-85; sr. correspondent NBC Nightly News, Wash., 1985-88; chief Latin Am. correspondent NBC Nightly News, Miami, 1988-89; sr. correspondent NBC Nightly News, Wash., 1989-93; Pentagon correspondent CBS Evening News, Wash., 1993—; trustee bd. dirs. U. Charleston. Recipient News and Documentary Emmy award, CBS Evening News, 1981, CBS Reports, 1981, George Polk award, 1982, three time Emmy nominee, CBS Sunday Morning, Communication award Nat. Easter Seal Soc., 1990. Home: 507 Scenic Way Great Falls VA 22066 Office: NBC News Washington Bur 4001 Nebraska Ave NW Washington DC 20016

RABENSTEIN, DALLAS LEROY, chemistry educator; b. Portland, Oreg., June 13, 1942; s. Melvin Leroy and Rose Marie (Nelson) R.; m. Gloria Carolyn Duncan, Aug. 30, 1964; children: Mark, Lisa. BS, U. Wash., 1964; PhD, U. Wis., 1968. Lectr. U. Wis., Madison, 1967-68; research chemist Chevron Research Co., Richmond, Calif., 1968-69; from asst. prof. to prof. chemistry U. Alta., Edmonton, Can., 1969-85; prof. U. Calif., Riverside, 1985—, chmn. chemistry dept., 1989-92, dean Coll. Natural and Agrl. Scis., 1993-94; McElvain lectr. U. Wis., 1981; Dow lectr. U. B.C., 1989; Eli Lilly lectr., Ind. U., 1993. Contbr. articles to profl. jours. NIH grantee. Fellow Chem. Inst. Can. (Fisher Sci. Lecture award 1984); mem. Am. Chem. Soc.

Avocations: reading, gardening, music. Home: 5162 Palisade Cir Riverside CA 92506-1521 Office: U Calif Dept Chemistry Riverside CA 92521

RABER, MARVIN, consultant, retired utility company executive; b. Bklyn., Aug. 3, 1937; s. Robert Abraham and Claire (Miller) R.; m. Miriam Lewin, Dec. 18, 1960; children: Steven, Suzanne Beth. BChemE, Poly. Inst. Bklyn., 1958; MChemE, NYU, 1963. Registered profl. engr., N.Y., Md. Engr. Nuclear Devel. Corp. Am./United Nuclear Corp., White Plains, N.Y., 1958-66; section chief, v.p. subs. Hittman Corp. (Hittman Nuclear & Devel. Corp.), Columbia, Md., 1966-70; sect. mgr. Combustion Engring., Inc., Windsor, Conn., 1970-78; v.p. strategic planning Gen. Pub. Utilities Corp., Parsippany, N.J., 1978-95; ret., 1995; founder Raber Cons., Randolph, N.J., 1995—. Co-patentee subcooled liquid inlet fog cooled nuclear reactor, 1965, reactor power reduction system and method, 1978. Mem. Am. Mgmt. Assn., The Planning Forum, Am. Nuclear Soc., NSPE. Jewish. Avocation: boating. Home: 5 Bayberry Ln Randolph NJ 07869-3801

RABETAFIKA, JOSEPH ALBERT BLAISE, UN representative; from Malagasy Republic; b. Tananarive, Madagascar, Feb. 3, 1932; L.esL, MA, MEd. Tchr. in U.K., France and Madagascar, 1953-59; joined Ministry Def., France, 1960; mem. Madagascar delegation to ind. negotiations with France, 1960; counsellor charge cultural affairs and info. Madagascar Diplomatic Mission to France, 1960-63; permanent del. UNESCO, Paris, 1961-63; head delegation to IBE confs., Geneva, 1961-63; mem. delegation to UN Gen. Assembly, 1963-69, counsel gen. NY, 1968—, amb. to Can., 1970-89, amb. to Cuba, 1974—, permanent rep. to UN, 1969—; vice chmn. UN polit. com., 1973; v.p. UN econ. and social com., 1973-74; pres. UN security coun., 1985 and 86; chmn. UN group of 77, 1975. Decorated Knight Grand Officer Malagasy Nat. Order, 1986, Knight Officer and/or Knight Commdr. from France, Germany, Japan, China, Liberia, Malawi, Senegal, Ethiopia, Philippines. Mem. Internat. Assn. Permanent Reps. to the UN (bd. dirs. 1990—). Avocations: reading, music, violin playing. Address: 801 2d Ave Suite 404 New York NY 10017

RABEY, T. W., JR., financial company executive. BA, Calif. State, 1976. With E.F. Hutton Co. Inc., Bakersfield, Calif., 1977-79; asst. treas. Contel Group, Atlanta, 1987-91; v.p. GTE Fin. Corp., Stamford, Conn., 1991—. Office: GTE Finance Corp 1 Stamford Forum Stamford CT 06901*

RABIDEAU, PETER WAYNE, university dean, chemistry educator; b. Johnstown, Pa., Mar. 4, 1940; s. Peter Nelson and Monica (Smalley) R.; m. Therese Charlene Newquist, Sept. 1, 1962 (div.); children—Steven, Michael, Christine, Susan; m. Jennifer Lee Mooney, Nov. 15, 1986; children: Mark, Leah. B.S., Loyola U., Chgo., 1964; M.S., Case Inst. Tech., Cleve., 1967; Ph.D., Case Western Res U, Cleve., 1968. Postdoctoral asst. U. Chgo., 1968-69, instr., 1969-70; asst. prof. Ind. U.-Purdue U., Indpls., 1970-73, assoc. prof., 1973-76, prof., 1976-90, chmn. dept. chemistry, 1985-90; dean Coll. Basic Scis. La. State U., Baton Rouge, 1990—; program officer NSF, 1988-89. Contbr. numerous articles to profl. jours. Recipient research award Purdue Sch. Sci. at Indpls., 1982. Mem. AAAS, Am. Chem. Soc. (chmn. Ind. sect. 1974, councilor 1981-90). Home: 15160 Old Oak Ave Baton Rouge LA 70810-5546 Office: La State U Office of the Dean 338 Choppin Baton Rouge LA 70803

RABIL, ALBERT, JR., humanities educator; b. Rocky Mount, N.C., May 8, 1934; s. Albert and Sophie Mae (Safy) R.; m. Janet Spain, Aug. 29, 1956; children—Albert, III, J. Alison. B.A., Duke U., 1957; M.Div., Union Theol. Sem., 1960; Ph.D., Columbia U., 1964. Instr. religion Trinity Coll., Hartford, Conn., 1964-65, asst. prof., 1965-68; asst. prof. hist. theology Chgo. Theol. Sem., 1969-71; assoc. prof. SUNY-Old Westbury, 1971-74, prof., 1974-77, disting. teaching prof. humanities, 1977—; program dir. NEH Summer Inst., 1992, 94, 95. Author: Merleau-Ponty, 1967 (Ansley award 1964), Erasmus and the New Testament, 1972, Laura Cereta, 1981, (with others) Her Immaculate Hand, 1983, Erasmus' Paraphrases of Romans and Galatians, 1983, Erasmus' Annotations on Romans, 1994; editor: Renaissance Humanism (3 vols.), 1988; editor, translator: Knowledge, Goodness, and Power, 1991; co-editor Renaissance Quarterly, 1992—; series co-editor The Other Voice in Early Modern Europe, 1993—; editorial bd. Soundings: An Interdisciplinary Jour., 1992-94. Travelling fellow Union Theol. Sem., 1960, Soc. for Values in Higher Edn., 1961; grantee. Fulbright Found., 1961, NEH, 1981. Mem. Erasmus Rotterdam Soc. (mem. editorial bd. 1980—), Soc. for Values in Higher Edn. (bd. dirs. 1981-90, 94—), Renaissance Soc. Am. (bd. dirs. 1991—). Democrat. Home: 324 Post Ave Apt 9H Westbury NY 11590-2249 Office: SUNY PO Box 210 Old Westbury NY 11568-0210

RABIL, MITCHELL JOSEPH, lawyer; b. Smithfield, N.C., Sept. 19, 1931; s. Albert G. and Eva (Nassif) R.; BS, Wake Forest Coll., 1953; LLB, Georgetown U., 1961; m. Antoinette M. Olivry, Nov. 25, 1956 (div. Oct. 1986); children: Elizabeth, Nathalie, Marcus, Gregory; m. Dolores E. Bleam, Jan. 21, 1989; children: Susan Starr Vermes, Scott Starr. Bar: N.C. 1961, N.J. 1967, D.C. 1980, Pa. 1981, U.S. Tax Ct. 1962, U.S. Supreme Ct. 1979. Supervisory acct. GAO, Washington, 1956-60; fin. analyst, staff acct. SEC, Washington, 1960-62; tax atty. Office Chief Counsel, IRS, Phila. and N.Y.C., 1962-66; assoc. Archer, Greiner, Hunter & Read, Camden, N.J., 1966-71; ptnr. Myers, Matteo, Rabil, Norcross & Landgraf, Cherry Hill, N.J., 1971-89; Montgomery, McCracken, Walker and Rhoads, Cherry Hill, 1989-95, Mitchell J. Rabil & Assocs., P.A., 1995—. Mcpl. chmn. Riverton (N.J.) Rep. Com., 1976-83; chmn. area 2 Burlington County Rep. Com., 1976-82; bd. dirs. Archway Programs, West Jersey Chamber Music Soc., 1990-91, Zurbrugg Meml. Hosp., 1991-93. Served with AUS, 1953-55. C.P.A., N.J. Soc. CPAs, N.C. Mem. Am. Bar Assn., AICPA, N.J. Bar Assn., Phila. Bar Assn., N.J. Soc. CPAs, Am. Assoc. Atty. CPAs, Cherry Hill C. of C. (bd. dirs. 1990-94), World Affairs Council Phila., Union League (Phila.), Riverton Country Club. Roman Catholic. Home: 107 Wayside Ct Delran NJ 08075-2000 Office: Montgomery McCracken et al 1010 Kings Hwy S Ste 2A Cherry Hill NJ 08034-2524

RABIN, BRUCE STUART, immunologist, physician, educator; b. Buffalo, Jan. 25, 1941; s. Eli and Dorothy R.; children: Andrew L., Alison J. B.A., Case Western Res. U., 1962; M.D., SUNY, Buffalo, 1966, Ph.D. (NIH predoctoral fellow, 1967), 1969. Diplomate Am. Bd. Med. Lab. Immunology. Asst. prof. pathology SUNY and Ctr. for Immunology, Buffalo, 1970-72; asst. prof. pathology Sch. Medicine, U. Pitts., 1972-76, assoc. prof. pathology, 1976-86, prof. pathology, 1986—, prof. psychiatry, 1987—, dir. Brain, Behavior and Immunity Ctr., 1989—; dir. div. clin. immunopathology Univ. Health Ctr. of Pitts., 1972—, med. dir. clin. lab. svcs., 1985—; interim chmn. dept. pathology, U. Pitts. Sch. Medicine, 1990-91; mem. merit rev. bd. for immunology VA Central Office, 1980-83; mem. study sect. NIMH, 1988-91. Assoc. editor Clin. Immunology Newsletter, 1980, Brain Behavior and Immunity, Clin. Immunology and Immunopathology; contbr. sci. papers in field to profl. publs. NIH research grantee, 1971—. Mem. AAAS, Pitts. Pathology Soc., Am. Assn. Pathologists, Acad. Clin. Lab. Physicians and Scientists, Am. Acad. Allergy, Am. Assn. Immunologists, Am. Assn. Clin. Histocompatibility Testing, Am. Soc. Clin. Pathologists (clin. immunopathology coun. 1978-84, editor Clin. Immunology Check Sample Program), Am. Acad. Microbiology (com. on postdoctoral edn. 1980), Assn. Med. Lab. Immunologists (pres. 1988), Psychoneuroimmunology Rsch. Soc. (pres. 1995). Home: 318 Schenley Rd Pittsburgh PA 15217-1173 Office: Presbyn-U Hosp Clin Immunopathology DeSoto & O'Hara Sts Pittsburgh PA 15213-2582

RABIN, HERBERT, physics educator, university official; b. Milw., Nov. 14, 1928; 2 children. B.S., U. Wis. 1950; M.S., U. Ill., 1951; Ph.D. in Physics, U. Md., 1959. Physicist elec. div. US Naval Research Lab., 1952-54, physicist solid state physics div., 1954-62, head radiation effects sect. optical materials br., 1962-67, head quantum optics sect., applied optics br., 1967-68, head quantum optics br., 1968-71, asso. dir. research for space sci. and tech., 1971-77, asso. dir. research for space and communication sci. and tech., 1977-79; dep. asst. sec. of Navy for research, applied and space tech. Office of Navy Secretariat, Washington, 1979-83; dir. engring. research ctr., prof. elec. engring., assoc. dean Coll. Engring., U. Md., College Park, 1983—; vis. scientist Technisch Hochschule, Stuttgart, Germany, 1960-61; mem. staff physics dept. George Washington U., 1955-73; cons. Sch. Engring. of Sao Carlos, U. Sao Paulo, Brazil, 1964, 70. Contbr. articles to tech. jours.; patentee in field. Recipient Meritorious Civilian Svc. award USN, 1969, Disting. Civilian Svc. award, 1976, 93; Disting. Civilian Svc. award

Dept. Def., 1979, cert. of commendation NASA, 1986, Centennial medal U. Md. Coll. Engring., 1994. Fellow Am. Phys. Soc., AAAS, Optical Soc. Am., AIAA; mem. IEEE (sr. mem.), Brazilian Acad. Scis. (corr.). Home: 7109 Radnor Rd Bethesda MD 20817-6332 Office: U Md Engring Rsch Ctr College Park MD 20742

RABIN, JACK, lawyer; b. Bklyn., Aug. 19, 1930; s. Leo and Bertha R.; m. Roberta Edith Libson, Oct. 25, 1953; children: Keith Warren, Michael Jay, Adam Douglas. Student Bklyn. Coll., 1948-50; LLB, Bklyn. Law Sch., 1953. Bar: N.Y. 1953, U.S. Ct. Mil. Appeals 1955, U.S. Dist. Ct. (so. and ea. dists.) N.Y. 1957, U.S. Tax Ct. 1960, U.S. Ct. Claims 1964, U.S. Supreme Ct. 1964, U.S. Ct. Appeals (2d cir.) 1968. Ptnr. Hoffberg, Rabin & Engler and predecessor firms, N.Y.C., 1968-82, Javits, Hinckley, Rabin & Engler, N.Y.C., 1982-84; Phillips, Nizer, Benjamin, Krim & Ballon, N.Y.C., 1984—; arbitrator gen. commi. and constrn. panel Am. Arbitration Assn., 1968—; instr. Real Estate Inst., NYU, 1976-78; ct. apptd. mediator U.S. Dist. Ct. (so. dist.), N.Y., 1994—. Assoc. editor Bklyn Law Rev., 1952, editor-in-chief, 1953, also author law rev. note. Served to 1st lt. JAGC, U.S. Army, 1953-57, col. Res. Mem. N.Y. State Bar Assn., Res. Officers Assn. U.S. (pres. Rockland County chpt. 1967-68), B'nai B'rith (pres. New City, N.Y. 1965-66). Jewish. Home: 10 W 66th St New York NY 10023 Office: Phillips Nizer Benjamin Krim & Ballon 31 W 52nd St New York NY 10019-6118

RABIN, KENNETH HARDY, public relations executive; b. Rochester, N.Y., Apr. 6, 1943; s. Martin and Ruby (Hardy) R.; m. Renee Efland, June 2, 1967; children: Max, Glennie. BA cum laude, Cornell U., 1965; MAT, Yale U., 1966; MA, U. N.C., 1968; PhD, Vanderbilt U., 1974. Accredited pub. relations practitioner. Fgn. svc. info. officer U.S Info. Agy., Uganda, Nigeria, 1967-70; news dir. U. Tenn., Chattanooga, 1970-72; communications specialist Meharry Med. Coll., Nashville, 1972-73; asst. editor Peabody Jour. of Edn. Vanderbilt U., Nashville, 1973-74; assoc. prof. pub. relations Am. Univ., Washington, 1974-80; dir. U.S. pub. affairs Squibb Corp., Princeton, N.J., 1980-83; exec. v.p., dir. health care commn. Hill and Knowlton, Washington, 1984-92; mng. dir. Interscience Comm. Ltd., Washington, 1992—. Co-editor: Regulating Change, 1990, Informing the People, 1981; mem. editorial bd. Pub. Rels. Rev., 1978—. Bd. dirs. Am. Soc. Hypertension, 1993—; mem. bus. adv. bd. Nat. Downs Syndrome Soc., N.Y.C., 1985—. Mem. Am. Med. Writers Assn. (assoc.), Nat. Assn. Sci. Writers (assoc.), Pub. Relations Soc. Am. (Silver Anvil award, 1986). Democrat. Jewish. Avocations: reading, tennis, video. Home: 3918 Ingomar St NW Washington DC 20015-1916 Office: Interscience Comm Ltd 1615 L St NW # 1150 Washington DC 20036-5610

RABIN, PAUL, insurance company executive; b. 1938. With U.S Gov., 1960-70; treas. Va. Surety Co. Inc., Chgo., 1970—. Office: Virginia Surety Co Inc 123 N Wacker Dr Fl 30 Chicago IL 60606*

RABIN, ROBERT L, lawyer, educator; b. 1939. B.S., Northwestern U., 1960, J.D., 1963, Ph.D., 1967. Bar: Ill. 1963. Asst. prof. U. Wis., Madison, 1966-69, assoc. prof., 1969-70; vis. assoc. prof. Stanford U., Calif., 1970-71, assoc. prof., 1971-73, prof., 1973-84, A. Calder Mackay prof., 1984—; reporter ABA Action Commn. to Improve Tort Liability System; cons. Am. Law Inst. Author: Perspective on the Administrative Process, 1979, Perspectives on Tort Law, 3d edit., 1990, Cases and Materials on Tort Law and Alternatives, 1983, 4th edit., 1987; mem. editorial adv. bd. Found. Press. Office: Stanford U Law Sch Nathan Abbott Way Stanford CA 94305

RABIN, STANLEY ARTHUR, metal products manufacturer; b. N.Y.C., 1938. B.A., B.S. in Metall. Engring., Columbia U., 1958; M.B.A., U. Santa Clara, 1969. With Comml. Metals Co., Inc., Dallas, 1970—, pres., 1978—, now also chief exec. officer, mem. exec. com., dir. Office: Comml Metals Co Inc PO Box 1046 7800 N Stemmons Fwy Dallas TX 75247-4217

RABIN, STEVE ARTHUR, public affairs executive; b. Chgo., Sept. 26, 1955; s. Seymour N. and Norma L. Rabin. BA, U. Ill., 1977; JD, George Washington U., 1980. Sr. assoc. Kamber Group, Washington, 1980-83; v.p. Ogilvy and Mather, Washington, 1983-86, sr. v.p., 1986-88, pres., 1988-91; gen. mgr. Porter/Novelli, Washington, 1992—; bd. dirs. Legal Aid Soc., Washington; vis. fellow Harvard Sch. Pub. Health, 1991; asst. prof. Columbia U. Bd. dirs. Epilepsy Found. Am., Washington, Nat. Leadership Coalition on AIDS, Washington. Office: Porter/Novelli 1120 Connecticut Ave NW Washington DC 20036

RABINER, LAWRENCE RICHARD, electrical engineer; b. Bklyn., Sept. 28, 1943; s. Nathan Marcus and Gloria Hannah (Bodinger) R.; m. Suzanne Login, June 23, 1968; children—Sheri Lynn, Wendi Beth, Joni Elizabeth. B.S., MIT, 1964, M.S., 1964, Ph.D., 1967. Mem. tech. staff AT&T Bell Labs., Murray Hill, N.J., 1967-70, supr. human machine voice communications group, 1971-85, head speech rsch. dept., 1985-90, dir. info. principles rsch. lab., 1990—. Author: Theory and Application of Digital Signal Processing, 1975, Digital Speech Processing, 1979, Multirate Digital Signal Processing, 1983, Fundamentals of Speech Recognition, 1993. Bd. dirs. Summit Jewish Community Ctr., N.J., 1985-90. Fellow NAE, NAS, IEEE (pres. ASSP Soc. 1974-75, Piori award 1980), Soc. award 1980, Centennial award 1984), Acoustical Soc. Am. (Biennial award 1974, v.p. 1994-95). Republican. Jewish. Avocations: stamp collecting, bridge, racquetball. Home: 58 Sherbrook Dr Berkeley Heights NJ 07922-2346

RABINER, SUSAN, editor; b. Bklyn., May 5, 1948; d. Nathan M. and Gloria (Bodinger) R.; m. Alfred G. Fortunato, Mar. 27, 1974; children: Anna, Matthew. B.A. cum laude, Goucher Coll., 1969. Asst. editor Random House, N.Y.C., 1969-72; editor Oxford U. Press, N.Y.C., 1973-79, sr. editor, 1980-86; sr. editor St. Martin's Press, N.Y.C., 1986-87, Pantheon Books, N.Y.C., 1987-90, Basic Books, Inc., N.Y.C., 1990—; vis. lectr. Yale U., New Haven, 1983, 84. Home: 1009 Brent Dr Wantagh NY 11793-1043 Office: Basic Books Inc 10 E 53rd St New York NY 10022-5244

RABINOVICH, RAQUEL, painter, sculptor; b. Buenos Aires, Argentina, Mar. 30, 1929, came to U.S., 1967, naturalized, 1973; d. Enrique Rabinovich and Julia Dinitz; m. Jose Luis Reissig, Feb. 14, 1956 (div. 1981); children—Celia Karen, Pedro Dario, Nora Vivian. Student U. Córdoba, Argentina, 1950-53, Sorbonne, Paris, 1957, U. Edinburgh, Scotland, 1958-59; lectr. Whitney Mus. 1983-86, Marymount Manhattan Coll., 1984-90. Exhbns. include Hecksher Mus., Huntington, N.Y., 1974, Susan Caldwell Gallery, N.Y.C., 1975, CUNY Grad. Ctr., 1978, The Jewish Mus. Sculpture Ct., N.Y.C., 1979, Ctr. Inter-Am. Rels., 1983, Bronx Mus. Arts, N.Y.C., 1987, Fordham U. Lincoln Ctr., N.Y.C., 1985, Ams. Soc., 1990, Erik Stark Gallery, 1991, Montgomery Ctr., 1992, Trans-Hudson Gallery, 1993, Noyes Mus., 1994, others; represented in collections World Bank Fine Art Collection, Washington, Univ. Art Mus., Austin, Cin. Art Mus., Walker Art Ctr., others. NEA fellow, 1991-92. Avocations: travel; music. Home and Studio: 141 Lamoree Rd Rhinebeck NY 12572

RABINOVICH, SERGIO, physician, educator; b. Lima, Peru, Apr. 8, 1928; m. Nelly; children—Gina, Sergio, Norca, Egla. M.D., San Fernando Med. Sch., U. San Marcos, Lima, Peru, 1953. Intern San Fernando Med. Sch., U. San Marcos, Lima, 1947-54; resident in medicine Grasslands Hosp., Valhalla, N.Y., 1954-57, Henry Ford Hosp., Detroit; prof. head dept. internal medicine U. Arequipa Med. Sch., 1960-61; asst. prof. dept. internal medicine U. Iowa, Iowa City, 1963-65; asst. prof. U. Iowa, 1965-69; attending physician and cons. VA Hosp., Iowa City, 1965-73; assoc. prof. U. Iowa, 1969-73; prof.; chief dept. medicine div. infectious disease So. Ill. U. Sch. Medicine, Springfield, 1973—; prof., chmn. dept. medicine So. Ill. U. Sch. Medicine, 1974-88, pres. Faculty Coun., 1992-93. Author: (with I.M. Smith, S.T. Donta) Antibiotics and Infection, 1974. Fellow ACP, Infectious Disease Soc. Am.; mem. AMA, Am. Soc. Microbiology, N.Y. Acad. Sci., Am. Fedn. Clin. Research, AAAS, Am. Thoracic Soc., Ill. Thoracic Soc. (pres. 1978-79), Central Soc. Clin. Research, Sigma Xi. Office: So Ill U Sch Medicine 800 N Rutledge St Springfield IL 62781-0002

RABINOVITCH, BENTON SEYMOUR, chemist, educator emeritus; b. Montreal, Que., Can., Feb. 19, 1919; came to U.S., 1946; s. Samuel and Rachel (Schachter) R.; m. Marilyn Werby, Sept. 18, 1949; children—Peter Samuel, Ruth Anne, Judith Nancy, Frank Benjamin; m. Flora Reitman, 1980. BSc, McGill U., 1939, PhD, 1942; DSc (hon.), Technion Inst., Haifa,

1991. Postdoctoral fellow Harvard, 1946-48; mem. faculty U. Wash., Seattle, 1948—, prof. chemistry, 1957—, prof. chemistry emeritus, 1985—; Cons. and/or mem. sci. adv. panels, coms. NSF, Nat. Acad. Scis.-NRC; adv. com. phys. chemistry Nat. Bur. Standards. Former editor: Ann. Rev. Phys. Chemistry; mem. editorial bd.: Internat. Jour. Chem. Kinetics, Rev. of Chem. Intermediates, Jour. Phys. Chemistry, J. Am. Chem. Soc. (assoc. editor). Served to capt. Canadian Army, 1942-46, ETO. Nat. Research Council Can. fellow, 1940-42; Royal Soc. Can. Research fellow, 1946-47; Milton Research fellow Harvard, 1948; Guggenheim fellow, 1961; vis. fellow Trinity Coll., Oxford, 1971; Recipient Sigma Xi award for original research, Debye award in phys. chemistry, 1984, Polanyi medal Royal Soc. Chemistry. Fellow Am. Phys. Soc., Am. Acad. Arts and Scis., Royal Soc. London; mem. Am. Chem. Soc. (past chmn. Puget Sound sect., past chmn. phys. chemistry div., editor jour.), Faraday Soc. Spl. research Unimolecular gas phase reaction. Home: 12530 42nd Ave NE Seattle WA 98125-4621

RABINOVITZ, JASON, film and television consultant; b. Boston, Aug. 17, 1921; s. Morris J. and Martha (Leavitt) R.; m. Frieda Pearlson, July 18, 1948; children: Abby, Judith, Daniel, Jonathan. B.A. magna cum laude, Harvard U., 1943, M.B.A. with distinction, 1948. dir. Pacific Rim Entertainment, 1993-95. With Chase Nat. Bank, N.Y.C., 1948-49; asst. to sec.-treas. United Paramount Theatres, Inc., N.Y.C., 1949-53; dir. Microwave Assocs., Burlington, Mass., 1952-54; asst. controller ABC, N.Y.C., 1953-56; adminstrv. v.p. ABC-TV Network, N.Y.C., 1956-57; with Metro-Goldwyn-Mayer, Inc., N.Y.C., 1957-69; treas., CFO Metro-Goldwyn-Mayer, Inc., 1963, financial v.p., 1967-69; dir., exec. v.p., gen. mgr. Ency. Brit. Ednl. Corp., Chgo., 1971-73; sr. v.p., gen. mgr. Am. Film Theatre, N.Y.C., 1974-75; v.p., asst. to pres. Metro-Goldwyn-Mayer, Inc., Culver City, Calif., 1976-79; v.p. fin. Metro-Goldwyn-Mayer, Inc., 1979-83; sr. v.p. fin. and corp. adminstrn. MGM/UA Entertainment Co., 1983-84; cons. motion picture and TV, 1984—; dir. Pacific Rim Entertainment, 1993—. Served to capt., parachutist AUS, 1942-46. Decorated Bronze Star. Mem. Phi Beta Kappa, Phi Eta Sigma. Home: 1675 Stone Canyon Rd Los Angeles CA 90077-1912

RABINOWITZ, JOEL, lawyer, educator; b. 1939. A.B., Cornell U., 1960; LL.B., Harvard U., 1963. Bar: N.Y. 1963, Calif. 1981. Asst. prof. U. Fla., Gainesville, 1966-68; vis. assoc. prof. UCLA, 1968-69, acting prof., 1969-72, prof., 1972-79; ptnr. with Irell & Manella, L.A., 1981—; vis. prof., NYU, 1976; with Dep. Internat. Tax Counsel, Dept. Treasury, 1980-81. Office: Irell & Manella 1800 Ave Of The Stars Ste 900 Los Angeles CA 90067

RABINOW, JACOB, electrical engineer, consultant; b. Kharkov, Russia, Jan. 8, 1910; came to U.S., 1921, naturalized, 1930; s. Aaron and Helen (Fleisher) Rabinovich; m. Gladys Lieder, Sept. 26, 1943; children: Jean Ellen, Clare Lynn. B.S. in Elec. Engring., Coll. City N.Y., 1933, E.E., 1934; D.H.L. (hon.), Towson State U., 1983. Radio serviceman N.Y.C., 1934-38; mech. engr. Nat. Bur. Standards, Washington, 1938-54; pres. Rabinow Engring. Co., Washington, 1954-64; v.p. Control Data Corp., Washington, 1964-72; research engr. Nat. Bur. Standards, 1972-89; cons. Inst. Standards and Tech., Gaithersburg, Md., 1989—; Regent's lectr. U. Calif.-Berkeley, 1972; lectr., cons. in field. Author. Recipient Pres.'s Certificate of Merit, 1948; certificate appreciation War Dept., 1949; Exceptional Service award Dept. Commerce, 1949; Edward Longstreth medal Franklin Inst., 1959; Jefferson medal N.J. Patent Law Assn., 1973; named Scientist of Yr. Indsl. R&D mag., 1980. Fellow IEEE (Harry Diamond award 1977), AAAS; mem. Nat. Acad. Engring., Philos. Soc. Washington, Audio Engring. Soc., Sigma Xi. Club: Cosmos (Washington). Patentee in field. Home: 6920 Selkirk Dr Bethesda MD 20817-4750 Office: Inst Standards and Tech Gaithersburg MD 20899 *I believe that inventions enrich both the material wealth and the cultural life of a nation and the world. Being a product of original thought, they are an art form and should be supported as such.*

RABINOWICZ, ERNEST, mechanical engineer, tribologist, educator; b. Berlin, Germany, Apr. 22, 1926; came to U.S., 1950, naturalized, 1963; s. Leo and Fanny (Bochner) R.; m. Ina Lee Feldman, Aug. 23, 1953; children: Deena P. Dugan, Judith R. Raymond, Laura A. B.A., Cambridge U., Eng., 1947, Ph.D., 1950. Research staff MIT, 1950-54, asst. prof. mech. engring., 1954-61, assoc. prof., 1961-67, prof., 1967—; vis. prof. Haifa Technion, 1969; Jacob Kurtz Meml. lectr. MIT and Technion, 1983. Author: (with N.H. Cook) Physical Measurement and Analysis, 1963, Friction and Wear of Materials, 1965, An Introduction to Experimentation, 1970, videotaped lecture series, 1972; Friction, Wear and Lubrication, 1974, Tribology, Part II, 1981. Recipient Ragner Holm sci. achievement award Holm Conf. on Elec. Contacts, 1983. Fellow Soc. Tribologists and Lubrication Engrs. (Walter D. Hodson award 1957, Nat. award 1988), ASME (Mayo D. Hersey award 1985); mem. Am. Phys. Soc. Home: 14 Exmoor Rd Newton MA 02159-1208 Office: MIT Rm 35-010 Cambridge MA 02139

RABINOWITCH, DAVID GEORGE, sculptor; b. Toronto, Ont., Can., Mar. 6, 1943; came to U.S., 1972; s. Joseph and Ruthe (Calverley) R.; m. Sheila Martin, June (div. 1981); m. Catrina Neiman, Mar. 14, 1983. BS, U. Western Ont., London, 1966. Instr. sculpture Yale U., New Haven, 1974-75; prof. sculpture Staatliche Kunstakademie Düsseldorf, Germany, 1984—; sculptor in residence Atelier Calder, Saché, France, 1994. Sculptures include Box Troughs, 1963, Fluid Sheet Pieces, 1964, Gravitational Vehicles, 1965, Tubers and Wood Constructions, 1966-67, Phantoms, 1967, Sectioned Mass Constructions, 1968, Metrical Constructions, 1973—, Tyndale Constructions, 1974—, Construction of Vision Drawings, 1969—, Ottonian Drawings, 1977—, Collinasca Cycle (Woodcuts), 1991-92. Recipient CAPS award N.Y. State Coun., 1974, Lynch-Staunton award of distinction Can. Coun., Ottawa, Ont., 1977; J.S. Guggenheim Meml. Found. fellow, N.Y.C., 1975, Nat. Endowment Arts fellow, Washington, 1986-87. Mem. Royal Can. Acad. Arts and Scis. Avocations: music. Studio: 49 E 1st St New York NY 10003-9324

RABINOWITZ, HOWARD K., physician, educator; b. Pitts., Sept. 25, 1946; s. Mac and Anne (Morgan) R.; m. Carol A. Gelles, Feb. 4, 1968; children: Elyse, Daniel J. Student, Rutgers Coll., 1964-67; MD, U. Pitts. 1971. Diplomate Am. Bd. Family Practice, Am. Bd. Pediatrics. From instr. to assoc. prof. Dept. Family Medicine Jefferson Med. Coll., Phila., 1976-90, vice chmn., 1990-95; prof., 1990—; bd. dirs. Am. Bd. Family Practice, Lexington, Ky., pres., 1992-93. Contbr. articles to profl. jours. With USPHS, 1972-74. RWJ Health Policy fellow, 1993-94. Fellow Phila. Coll. Physicians; mem. AMA, Soc. Tchrs. Family Medicine, Am. Acad. Family Physicians. Office: Jefferson Medical College Dept Family Medicine 1015 Walnut St Ste 401 Philadelphia PA 19107

RABINOWITZ, JACK GRANT, radiologist, educator; b. Monticello, N.Y., July 9, 1927; s. Abraham and Bessie (Sussman) R.; m. Rica Gedalia Arnon, Oct. 19, 1972; children—Antoine, Anne, Pierre, Yaron, Tal. B.A., UCLA, 1949; M.D., U. Berne, Switzerland, 1955. Diplomate: Am. Bd. Radiology. Intern Kings County Hosp., Bklyn., 1955-56; resident Kings County Hosp., 1956-59; instr. radiology Downstate Med. Center, Bklyn., 1960-61; asst. prof. radiology Downstate Med. Center, 1967-70, prof. radiology, 1970-73; asst. radiologist Mt. Sinai Sch. Medicine, N.Y.C., 1962-65; asst. prof. radiology Mt. Sinai Sch. Medicine, 1965-66, assoc. prof. radiology, 1966-67, prof., chmn. dept. radiology, 1978—; asso. attending radiologist Mt. Sinai Hosp., N.Y.C., 1965-67, dir. radiology, 1978—; radiologist-in-chief Bklyn.-Cumberland Med. Center, Bklyn. 1967-70; dir. diagnostic radiology Kings County Hosp. Center, Bklyn., 1970-73; chmn. dept. diagnostic radiology U. Tenn., Memphis, 1973-78; cons. in radiology VA Hosp., Bronx, N.Y. Author: Pediatric Radiology, 1978, Radiology for the Primary and Emergency Care of Physicians, 1981. Fellow Am. Coll. Radiology; mem. Radiol. Soc. N. Am., Am. Roentgen Ray Soc., Assn. Univ. Radiologists, AMA, Soc. Chmn. Acad. Radiology Depts., Tenn. Radiol. Soc., Tenn. Med. Soc., Memphis and Shelby County Med. Soc., Memphis Roentgen Soc. Office: Mt Sinai Hosp 1 Gustave L Levy Pl New York NY 10029-6504

RABINOWITZ, JAY ANDREW, state supreme court justice; b. Phila., Feb. 25, 1927; s. Milton and Rose (Rittenberg) R.; m. Anne Marie Nesbit, June 14, 1957; children: Judith, Mara, Max, Sara. B.A., Syracuse U., 1947; LL.B., Harvard, 1952. Bar: N.Y. 1952, Alaska 1958. Pvt. practice law N.Y.C., 1952-57; law clk. to presiding judge U.S. Dist. Ct., Fairbanks, Alaska, 1957-58; asst. U.S. atty. Fairbanks, 1958-59; dep. atty. gen., chief civil div. State of Alaska, 1959-60; judge Superior Ct. Alaska, 1960-65;

Column 1

justice Alaska Supreme Ct., 1965–; chief justice Alaska Supreme Ct., Juneau, 1972-75, 78-81, 1984-87, 90-92. Served with AUS, 1945-46. Mem. N.Y. Bar Assn., Alaska Bar Assn. (commr. on uniform laws 1971–). Office: Alaska Supreme Ct 303 K St Anchorage AK 99501-2084

RABINOWITZ, LEONARD, apparel executive. Grad., NYU, 1968. With Good Fellow, Inc., N.Y.C., 1968-72; dir. sales Baggs, Inc., L.A., 1972-74; v.p. Fashion Makers, L.A., 1974-75; chmn. bd. dirs. Calif. Fashion Industries, L.A., 1975–. Office: Calif Fashion Industries 102 E Martin Luther King Los Angeles CA 90011*

RABINOWITZ, MARK ALLAN, lawyer; b. Chgo., Feb. 9, 1954; s. Marvin Harold and Pauline Betty (Robins) R.; m. Linda Kay Beauseigneur, Feb. 7, 1982. BA summa cum laude, U. Ill., 1975; JD, Harvard U., 1978. Bar: Ill. 1978, U.S. Dist. Ct. (no. dist.) Ill. 1978, U.S. Ct. Appeals (7th cir.) 1979. Ptnr. Levy & Erens, Chgo., 1978-85, McDermott, Will & Emery, Chgo., 1985-93; Rudnick & Wolfe, Chgo., 1993–. Mem. Phi Beta Kappa. Avocations: history, polit. theory, philosophy.

RABINOWITZ, MAYER ELYA, librarian, educator; b. N.Y.C., Jan. 31, 1939; s. Simcha Rabinowitz and Dvora (Resnikoff) Masovetsky; m. Renah Lee Levine, June 16, 1965; children: Adi, Dalya, Ayelet. BA, B in Hebrew Lit., Yeshiva U., 1960, MA, 1961; M in Hebrew Lit., Jewish Theol. Sem., 1965, PhD, 1974. Ordained rabbi, 1967. Instr. Jewish Theol. Sem., N.Y.C., 1970-74, asst. prof., 1974-76, dean students Tchrs. Inst., 1974-76, assoc. prof., 1976–, assoc. dean grad sch., 1976-79, dean grad. sch., 1979-88, libr., 1988–; mem. com. on Jewish law and standards Rabbinical Assembly, N.Y.C., 1978–; chair Joint Bet Din Conservative Movement, N.Y.C., 1990–. Author: Sefer Hamordekhai Gittin, 1990; contbr. articles to profl. jours. Mem. Assn. Jewish Studies, Assn. Jewish Librs. Office: Jewish Theol Sem 3080 Broadway New York NY 10027

RABINOWITZ, MAYNARD, publishing executive; b. 1942. BA, Columbia U., 1963; LLB, Harvard U., 1966. Pvt. practice N.Y.C., 1966-75; ptnr. Townsend, Rabinowitz, Pantaleoni & Valente P.C., N.Y.C., 1975–; with Enquirer/Star Group Inc., 1990–; v.p.- sec. Enquirer/Star Inc., Lake Worth, Fla., 1989–; vice chmn. bd. dirs. Am. Media, Inc., Lake Worth, Am. Media Ops., Inc., Lake Worth. Office: Enquirer Star Inc 600 S East Coast Ave Lake Worth FL 33464*

RABINOWITZ, SAMUEL NATHAN, lawyer; b. Hazleton, Pa., Sept. 16, 1932; s. Morris M. and Bodia (Janowitz) R.; m. Barbara G. Cohen, Mar. 27, 1955; children—Fredric E., Mark I., Joshua A. BA, Pa. State U., 1955; JD, Temple U., 1959. Bar: D.C. 1959, Pa. 1960. Agt. IRS, Phila., 1956-60; sole practice Phila., 1960-61; ptnr. Blank, Rome, Comisky & McCauley, Phila., 1961–; mem. trust com. Continental Bank, Phila., 1983-91; faculty Temple U. Sch. Law. Contbr. articles to profl. jours. Active Phila. Friends Boys Town Jerusalem; bd. dirs. Jerusalem Soc. Boys Town, Phila. Friends of Ben Gurion U. the Negev, Jewish Nat. Fund Coun., Phila.; bd. dirs., pres. Jewish Cmty. Ctrs. Greater Phila.; past chmn. Albert Einstein Soc. Albert Einstein Med. Ctr., past trustee; trustee Jewish Fedn. Phila. (officer Fedn. Endowments Corp.). Member Am. Coll. Trust and Estate Counsel; mem. ABA, Pa. Bar Assn., Phila. Bar Assn. (chmn. probate and trust sect. 1985-86), Green Valley Country Club, Elkview Country Club, Vesper Club, Golden Slipper, B'nai B'rith, U.S. Com. Sports for Israel (exec. com., counsel). Home: 1161 Norsam Rd Gladwyne PA 19035-1419 Office: Blank Rome Comisky et al 1200 Four Penn Ctr Plz Philadelphia PA 19103

RABINOWITZ, STANLEY SAMUEL, rabbi; b. Duluth, Minn., June 8, 1917; S. Jacob Mier and Rose (Zeichik) R.; m. Anita Bryna Lifson, June 24, 1945; children: Nathaniel Herz, Sharon Deborah, Judith Leah. B.A., State U. Iowa, 1939; M.A., Yale U., 1950; M. Hebrew Lit., Jewish Theol. Sem., 1944, Doctor Hebrew Lit., 1971. Ordained rabbi, 1943; dir. United Synagogue, N.Y.C., 1943-46; rabbi B'nai Jacob Synagogue, New Haven, Conn., 1946-53, Adath Jeshurun Synagogue, Mpls., 1953-60; rabbi Adas Israel Synagogue, Washington, 1960-86, rabbi emeritus, 1986–; v.p. Rabbinical Assembly, N.Y.C., 1974-76, pres., 1976-78; vice chmn. B'nai B'rith Youth Commn., 1965-76; pres. Mercaz, 1977-83. Club: Cosmos (Washington). Home: 3115 Normanstone Ter NW Washington DC 20008-2732 Office: Adas Israel Synagogue 2850 Quebec St NW Washington DC 20008-5296

RABINS, MICHAEL JEROME, mechanical engineer, educator; b. N.Y.C., Feb. 24, 1932; s. Herman and Ida (Olinsky) R.; m. Joan Rose, Apr. 6, 1956; children: Andrew, Evan, Alexandra. BS, MIT, 1953; MS, Carnegie Inst. Tech., 1954; PhD, U. Wis., 1959. Lic. engr., Calif., Tex. Asst. prof. U. Wis., Madison, 1959-60; asst. prof. NYU, N.Y.C., 1960-64, assoc. prof., 1964-70; prof. Polytechnic Inst. N.Y., Bklyn., 1970-75; dir. Office Univ. Rsch., U.S. Dept. Transp., Washington, 1975-77; chmn. mech. engring. dept. Wayne State U., Detroit, 1977-85, assoc. dean, 1985-87; prof. mech. engring., head dept. Tex. A&M U., College Station, 1987-89; TEES rsch. prof., 1989-91; dir. engring. ethics & professionalism program Tex. A&M U., College Station, 1992–. Author: Controls and Dynamics Systems Response, 1970, Introducing Systems and Controls, 1974, Engineering Ethics: Concepts and Cases, 1995. Chmn. Detroit 3 Ctr. Transp. Conv., 1977-87. Recipient Superior Svc. award Dept. Transp., Washington, 1976, Cert. of Merit, Mayor of Detroit, 1980. Fellow ASME (exec. com., chmn., editor jour., v.p. 1985-87, bd. govs. 1989-90, com. on program rev. 1992–, Disting. Svc. award 1974); mem. Am. Soc. Engring. Edn. (projects bd. 1987-90), Am. Automatic Control Coun. (pres. 1984-86, Edn. award 1991). Avocations: reading, Chinese cooking, stained glass, classical music. Office: Tex A&M U Mech Engring Dept College Station TX 77843

RABITZ, HERSCHEL ALBERT, chemistry educator; b. Los Angeles, Apr. 10, 1944. B.S. in Chemistry, U. Calif.-Berkeley, 1966; Ph.D. in Chem. Physics, Harvard U., 1970. Faculty Princeton U., (N.J.), 1971–; prof. chemistry, 1977–. Alfred P. Sloan fellow, 1975; Camille and Henry Dreyfus fellow, 1976. Home: 13 Holly Ln Trenton NJ 08648-1053 Office: Princeton U Dept Chemistry Washington Rd Princeton NJ 08540-6431

RABJOHN, NORMAN, chemistry educator emeritus; b. Rochester, N.Y., May 1, 1915; s. Alfred Augustus and Elizabeth Mary (Hooper) R.; m. Dora I. Taylor, Sept. 9, 1943; 1 son, James Norman. B.S., U. Rochester, 1937; M.S., U. Ill., 1939, Ph.D., 1942. Instr. chemistry U. Ill., Champaign-Urbana, 1942-44; research Goodyear Tire, Akron, Ohio, 1944-48; from assoc. prof. to prof. chemistry U. Mo., Columbia, 1948-83; prof. emeritus, 1983–. Mem. editorial bd.: Organic Syntheses, 1960–; assoc. editor: Chem. Revs., 1965-67. Fellow AAAS; mem. Am. Chem. Soc. (chmn. council com. publs. 1970-71), Phi Beta Kappa, Sigma Xi, Phi Lambda Upsilon, Alpha Chi Sigma. Home: 100 E Ridgeley Rd Columbia MO 65203-3530

RABKIN, MITCHELL THORNTON, hospital administrator, educator; b. Boston, Nov. 27, 1930; s. Morris Aaron and Esther (Quint) R.; m. Adrienne M. Najarian, June 24, 1956; children: Julia Margaret, David Gregory. AB. magna cum laude, Harvard U., 1951, M.D. cum laude, 1955; D.Sc. (hon.), Brandeis U., 1983; D.Pharm. (hon.), Mass. Coll. Pharmacy, 1983; D.Sc. (hon.), Curry Coll., 1989, Northeastern U., 1994. Intern Mass. Gen. Hosp., Boston, 1955-56; resident in internal medicine Mass. Gen. Hosp., 1956-57, 59-60, chief resident, 1962, mem. staff, 1963-72, bd. consultation, 1972-80, hon. physician, 1981–; clin. fellow NIH, Bethesda, Md., 1957-59; gen. dir. Beth Israel Hosp., Boston, 1966-80; pres. Beth Israel Hosp., 1980–; asst. prof. medicine Harvard U., 1969-70, assoc. prof., 1971-83, prof., 1983–; mem. Health Care Adv. Coun. U.S. Gen. Acctg. Office, 1991–. Served with USPHS, 1957-59. Fellow ACP, AAAS; mem. Am. Fedn. Clin. Rsch., Mass. Med. Soc., Soc. Med. Adminstrs., Assn. Am. Med. Colls. (past chmn. coun. teaching hosps.), Conf. Boston Teaching Hosps. (past chmn.), Inst. Medicine, NAS, Century Assn. (N.Y.C.), Harvard Club of Boston. Jewish. Office: Beth Israel Hosp 330 Brookline Ave Boston MA 02215-5400

RABÓ, JULE ANTHONY, chemical research administrator, consultant; b. Budapest, Hungary; came to U.S., 1957; m. Sheelagh Ennis; children: Benedict, Sebastian. BSChemE, Poly. U., Budapest, 1946, DSc in Chemistry, 1949, D honoris causa, 1986. From asst. prof. to assoc. prof. Poly U., Budapest, 1946-54; assoc. dir. Hydrocarbon Rsch. Inst., Budapest,

Column 2

1951-56; rsch. assoc. Union Carbide Corp., Buffalo, 1957-60; rsch. mgr. Union Carbide Corp., Tarrytown, N.Y., 1960-72, corp. fellow, 1969-82, sr. corp. rsch. fellow, 1982–; sr. corp. rsch. fellow UOP, Tarrytown, 1988–; cons. in chemistry and catalysis, Armonk, N.Y.; former mem. adv. bd. Ctr. for Advanced Materials, Lawrence-Berkeley Lab.; mem. adv. bd. dept. chemistry Lehigh U. Author: Zeolite Chemisty and Catalysts; former mem. editorial bd. Jour. Catalysis, Applied Catalysis; contbr. articles to profl. jours.; patentee in field. Recipient Kossuth award Govt. of Hungary, 1953, Excellence in Catalysis award N.Y. Catalysis Soc., 1982, Humboldt award, Fed. Republic of Germany, 1990. Mem. Am. Chem. Soc. (E.V. Murphree award 1988), Am. Catalysis Soc. (Eugene J. Houdry award 1989), Hungarian Acad. Sci. (Varga medal 1991), Am. Inst. Chemists (Chem. Pioneer award 1993).

RABOLT, JOHN FRANCIS, optics scientist; b. N.Y.C., May 14, 1949; married, 1990; 1 child. BS, SUNY, Oneonta, 1970; PhD in Physics, Ill. U., Carbondale, 1974. Rsch. Coun., NAS assoc. Nat. Bur. Standards, 1976-77; scientist polymers rsch. staff rsch. lab IBM Corp., San Jose, Calif., 1978–. Recipient Coblentz award, 1985, Williams-Wright award, 1990, Ellis R. Lippincott award Optical Soc. Am., 1993. Achievements include research in the use of Fourier transform (FT) infrared and FT and Conventional Raman spectroscopy to investigate crystal and molecular structure of long chain molecules and polymers, integrated optical techniques in conjunction with Raman Spectoscopy to investigate submicron polymer films and polymer surfaces, FTIR studies of self assembled and Langmoir-Blodgett films on metals and dielectrics, and co-development of FT Raman spectroscopy. Office: IBM Almaden Research Center K95/801 650 Harry Rd San Jose CA 95120-6001

RABON, WILLIAM JAMES, JR., architect; b. Marion, S.C., Feb. 7, 1931; s. William James and Beatrice (Baker) R.; m. Martha Ann Hibbitts, Mar. 7, 1987. BS in Arch., Clemson (S.C.) Coll., 1951; BArch, N.C. State Coll., 1955; MArch, MIT, 1956. Registered architect, Calif., Ky., N.C., Ohio, Pa., Ga. Designer archtl. firms in N.Y.C. and Birmingham, Mich., 1958-61; designer, assoc. John Carl Warnecke and Assocs., San Francisco, 1961-63, 64-66, Keyes, Lethbridge and Condon, Washington, 1966-68; prin. archtl. ptnr. A.M. Kinney Assocs. and William J. Rabon, Cin., 1968-85; v.p., dir. archtl. design A.M. Kinney, Inc., Cin., 1977-85; v.p., dir. programming svcs. Design Art Corp., 1977-85; sr. architect John Portman & Assocs., Atlanta, 1985-88; dir. architectural design Robert and Co., Atlanta, 1988-89; studio dir., design prin. Carlson Assocs., Atlanta, 1990-93; prin. Rosser Internat., 1993–; lectr. U. Calif., Berkeley, 1963-65; asst. prof. archtl. design Cath. U. Am., 1967-68. Prin. works include Kaiser Tech. Ctr. Pleasanton, Calif. (Rsch. Devel. Lab. of Yr. award), 1970, Clermont Nat. Bank, Milford, Ohio, 1971, Pavilion bldg. Children's Hosp. Med. Ctr., Cin. (Cin. AIA design award), 1973, EG&G, Hydrospace, Inc., Rockville, Md. (Potomac Valley AIA design award), 1970, Mead Johnson Park, Evansville, Ind. (Rsch. Devel. Lab. of Yr. merit award), 1973, Hamilton County Vocat. Sch., Cin., 1972, hdqrs. lab. EPA, Cin., 1975, Arapahoe Chem. Co. Rsch. Ctr., Boulder, Colo. (Rsch. Devel. Lab. of Yr. award 1976, Concrete Reinforced Steel Inst. Nat. Design award, Regional AIA Design award), 1976, corp. hdqrs. Ohio River Co., Cin., 1977, Children's Hosp. Therapy Ctr., Cin. (Cin. AIA design award 1978, award of merit Am. Wood Council 1981), VA Hosp. addition, Cin. (Cin. ASHRAE Design award 1980), NALCO Chem. Co. Rsch. Ctr., Naperville, Ill. (Ohio and Cin. AIA design award 1980, 81), 1980, Proctor & Gamble-Winton Hill Tunnel, Cin. (Ohio AIA design award), 1978, Toyota Regional Ctr., Blue Ash, Ohio (Ohio AIA and Ohio Masonry Council combined design award 1981), planning cons. Nat. Bur. Standards, Republic of China, 1982, East and West fleet hdqrs. and Data Ctr. Librs. of Royal Saudi Arabian Navy, 1985, corp. hdqrs. The Drackett Co., Cin., 1983, corp. hdqrs. Brown & Williamson, Louisville, 1984, Inst. Paper Sci. and Tech., Atlanta, 1989, 93, Animal Sci. Complex, Athens, Ga., 1994. 1st lt. AUS, 1951-53, Korea. Decorated Silver Star, Bronze Star with V device, Bronze Star, Purple Heart with bronze cluster; MIT Grad. Sch. scholar, 1956; Fulbright scholar, Italy, 1957-58. Mem. AIA, Nat. Council Archtl. Registration Bds.

RABSON, ALAN SAUL, physician, educator; b. N.Y.C., July 1, 1926; s. Abraham and Florence (Shulman) R.; m. Ruth L. Kirschstein, June 11, 1950; 1 son, Arnold B. B.A., U. Rochester, N.Y., 1948; M.D., State U. N.Y. Downstate, 1950. Intern Mass. Meml. Hosp., Boston, 1951-52; resident in pathology N.Y. U. Hosp., 1952-54, USPHS Hosp., New Orleans, 1954-55; pathologist Nat. Cancer Inst., Bethesda, Md., 1955–; prof. pathology Georgetown U. Med. Sch., 1974–; Uniformed Services U. Health Scis., 1978–; professorial lectr. pathology George Washington U., 1978–. Asso. editor: Am. Jour. Pathology; Contbr. articles to med. jours. Mem. Am. Assn. Pathologists, Phi Beta Kappa, Sigma Xi, Alpha Omega Alpha. Address: NIH-National Cancer Institute Bldg 31-Cancer Biology 9000 Rockville Pike Bethesda MD 20892

RABSON, ROBERT, plant physiologist, administrator; b. Bklyn., Mar. 4, 1926; s. Samuel and Rose (Strauss) R.; m. Eileen K. Rabson, Aug. 27, 1950; children: Michael, Barbra, Laurel. BS, Cornell U., 1951, PhD, 1956. Rsch. assoc. biolog. div. Oak Ridge (Tenn.) Nat. Lab., 1956-58; asst. prof. U. Houston, 1958-62, assoc. prof., 1962-63; biochemist civ. biology and medicine AEC, Washington, 1963-67, asst. br. chief, 1967-73; first officer plant breeding and genetics sect. FAO/IAEA, Vienna, Austria, 1973-76; dir. div. energy bioscis. U.S. Dept. Energy, Washington, 1979–. Mem. plant scis. adv. bd. McKnight Found., Mpls., 1981–. With U.S. Army, 1944-45, PTO, ETO. Fellow AAAS; mem. Am. Soc. Plant Physiologists (chmn. publ. com. 1984-86, treas. 1988–, Adolph Gude award 1986). Office: US Dept Energy Basic Energy Scis Er # 17 Washington DC 20545

RABSON, THOMAS AVELYN, electrical engineering educator, researcher; b. Houston, July 31, 1923; s. Charles Avelyn and Sara Kathleen (Drake) R.; m. Sylvia Mary Jenny, Aug. 22, 1957; children: William, Tamara, Robert. BA, Rice Inst. (now U.), 1954, BSEE, 1955, MA, 1957, PhD, 1959. Registered profl. engr., Tex. Asst. prof. elec. engring. Rice U., Houston, 1959-63, assoc. prof., 1963-70, prof., 1970–; tech. advisor Energy Rsch. and Edn. Found., Houston, 1974-79. Contbr. numerous articles to profl. jours. Fellow NSF, Basel, Switzerland, 1965, Rice Quantum Inst., 1987. Mem. IEEE, Am. Phys. Soc., Optical Soc. Am. Methodist. Achievements include 7 patents, construction of memory transistor with lithium niobate gate. Home: 4521 Ivanhoe St Houston TX 77027-4807 Office: Rice U Dept Elec Engring PO Box 1892 6100 South Main St Houston TX 77251

RABSTEJNEK, GEORGE JOHN, management consultant; b. Queens, N.Y., June 14, 1932; s. George John and Anna (Krasa) R.; m. Patsy Kidd, July 17, 1964; 1 child, Marley Ann. B in Indsl. Engring., Ga. Inst. Tech., 1954; postgrad., U. Conn. Sch. Law, 1960, NYU Sch. Bus., 1965-69; advanced mgmt. program, Harvard U., 1975. Supr. purchasing Westinghouse Electric, Bridgeport, Conn., 1957-61; project mgr. systems div. IBM Corp., Poughkeepsie, N.Y., 1961-65; dir. material mgmt. services Div. Harbridge House, Inc., Boston, 1965-69; v.p. and head Harbridge House, Inc., Boston, 1969-75, exec. v.p., 1975-76, pres., 1976-83, chmn., chief exec. officer, 1983-92, chmn., 1992-93; retired, 1993. Contbr. articles to profl. jours. Vice chmn. World Affairs Coun. Boston, 1984-87, vice chmn. 1988); trustee Internat. Coord. Coun., Boston, 1984–; trustee Mass. Eye and Ear Infirmary, Boston, 1984–, vice chmn. bd. dirs.; mem. Draper Labs. Corp., 1994; mem. adv. bd. Town of Cohasset, Mass., 1975; chmn. nat. adv. bd. Ga. Inst. Tech., 1991-92; mem. exec. adv. bd. Ivan Allen Coll.; mem. bd. visitors Northea. U. Comdr. USNR, 1958-75. Mem. Am. Inst. Indsl. Engrs., Nat. Security Indsl. Assn. (v.p. 1987–), Nat. Def. Transp. Assn. (Def. Transp. award 1980), Assn. Naval Aviators, Navy League, Reynolds Soc. (chmn.), Nat. Security Industry Assn. (trustee 1990-93), Harvard Club, Algonquin Club (Boston), Cohasset Golf Club (Mass.), Cohasset Yacht Club, Cohasset Tennis and Squash Club, Mill Reef Club, Antigua, B.W.I., Comml. Club, F St. Club (Washington), Phi Kappa Sigma. Republican. Unitarian. Home: 181 Border St Cohasset MA 02025-2043

RABUN, JOHN BREWTON, JR., criminal justice agency administrator; b. Augusta, Ga. Nov. 16, 1946; s. John Brewton and Alsie Imor (Bateman) R.; m. Anna Betsy Park, Dec. 27, 1967; children: Kerry Kristin, John Candler. B.A., Mercer U., 1967; postgrad. So. Bapt. Theol. Sem., 1967-70; M.S. in Social Work, U. Louisville, 1971. Cert. social worker, Ky., D.C. Exec. dir. Ky. Civil Liberties Union, Louisville, 1971-72; dir. Community Residential Treatment Services, Louisville, 1973-78; program mgr. Field Services,

Column 3

Louisville, 1978-80; program mgr. Exploited and Missing Child Unit, Louisville, 1980-84; v.p., chief oper. officer Nat. Ctr. for Missing & Exploited Children, Washington, 1984–; mem. Alderman's Task Force on Social Svcs., Louisville, 1982, Mayor's City Youth Commn., Louisville, 1983-84; trainer and/or cons. to numerous agys. in U.S., U.K., Can. Contbr. articles to criminal justice and healthcare publs. and books. Recipient Key to City of Louisville, 1983, Disting. Alumnus award U. Louisville, 1985, Russell L. Colling lit. award Internat. Assn. for Healthcare Security and Safety, 1991, Russell Colling Lit. award Internat. Assn. for Healthcare Security and Safety, 1991; named hon. chief of police, City of Louisville, 1982. Mem. ACLU, Nat. Assn. Social Workers, Nat. Sheriff's Assn., Nat. Coun. Juvenile and Family Ct. Judges, Internat. Juvenile Officers Assn., Acad. Cert. Social Workers, Internat. Assn. Chiefs of Police. Baptist (deacon). Avocations: photography; hunting; fishing. Home: 13519 Oak Ivy Ln Fairfax VA 22033 Office: Nat Ctr for Missing and Exploited Children 2101 Wilson Blvd Ste 550 Arlington VA 22201-3062

RABURN, RANDALL K., school system administrator. Supt. Edmond (Okla.) Pub. Schs. Recipient Nat. Superintendent of the Yr. awd., Oklahoma, Am. Assn. of School Administrators, 1993. Office: Edmond Pub Schs 1216 S Rankin St Edmond OK 73034-4769

RABUZZI, DANIEL D., medical educator; b. Pitts., June 19, 1935; s. Daniel Ralph and Viioctoria (Bruni) R.; m. Kathryn Allen, June 11, 1958; children: Daniel, Matthew, Douglas. AB, Harvard Coll., 1957; MD, U. Pa., 1961. Diplomate Am. Bd. Otolaryngology. Instr. otolaryngology U. Md., Balt., 1967-68; asst. prof. SUNY, Syracuse, 1968-71, assoc. prof., 1971-77, prof., 1966-81, clin. prof. otolaryngology, 1984–; prof., chmn. N.Y. Med. Coll. and N.Y. Eye & Ear Infirmary, N.Y.C., 1981-84; pres. St. Joseph's Hops. Med. Staff, Syracuse, 1990-92. Contbr. 54 articles to profl. jours. and chpts. to books. Capt. U.S. Army, 1966-68. Fellow ACS; mem. Am. Soc. Head and Neck Surgery, Am. Acad. Otolaryngology, Am. Cancer Soc. (pres. County unit 1978-80), Onondaga County Med. Soc. (pres. 1987-88). Avocations: Roman archeology, European travel, golfing, historical readings. Office: Ctrl NY Ear Nose & Throat Cons 1100 E Genesee Syracuse NY 13210

RABY, WILLIAM LOUIS, author; b. Chgo., July 16, 1927; s. Gustave E. and Helen (Burgess) R.; m. Norma Claire Schreiner, Sept. 8, 1956; children: Burgess, Marianne, Marlene. BSBA, Northwestern U., 1949; MBA, U. Ariz., 1961, PhD, 1971. Ptnr. VAR CPA Firms, 1950-76, Touche Ross & Co., N.Y.C., 1977-87; pres. Ariz. State Bd. Accountancy, 1993-94; mem. Ariz. State Bd. Tax Appeals, 1994–; prof. acctg. emeritus Ariz. State U., 1994–; columnist Tax Notes mag., Arlington, Va., 1990–. Author: The Income Tax and Business Decisions, 1964, Building and Maintaining a Successful Tax Practice, 1964, The Reluctant Taxpayer, 1970, Tax Practice Management, 1974, Introduction to Federal Taxation, annually, 1980-91, Tax Practice Management: Client Servicing, 1986; editor: Raby Report on Tax Practice, 1986–, PPC Guide To Successful Tax Practice, 1991; mem. editorial adv. bd. Taxation for Accountants, The Tax Adviser; contbr. articles to profl. jours. Served with USN, 1942-45. Mem. AICPA (chmn. fed. tax divn. 1980-83, v.p. 1983-84, coun. 1983-90), Ariz. Tax Ct. Bar, Ariz. C. of C. (chmn. 1987), Beta Gamma Sigma (past pres. Ariz. alumni chpt.), Delta Mu Delta. Presbyterian (elder, chmn. adv. coun. on ch. and soc. 1979-81). Office: PO Box 26846 Tempe AZ 85285-6846

RACE, GEORGE JUSTICE, pathology educator; b. Everman, Tex., Mar. 2, 1926; s. Claude Ernest and Lila Eunice (Bunch) R.; m. Annette Isabelle Rinker, Dec. 21, 1946; children: George William Daryl, Jonathan Clark, Mark Christopher, Jennifer Anne (dec.), Elizabeth Margaret Rinker. M.D., U. Tex., Southwestern Med. Sch., 1947; M.S. in Pub. Health, U. N.C., 1953; Ph.D. in Ultrastructural Anatomy and Microbiology, Baylor U., 1969. Intern Duke Hosp., 1947-48, asst. resident pathology, 1951-53; intern Boston City Hosp., 1948-49; asst. pathologist Peter Bent Brigham Hosp., Boston, 1953-54; pathologist St. Anthony's Hosp., St. Petersburg, Fla., 1954-55; staff pathologist Children's Med. Center, Dallas, 1955-59; dir. labs. Baylor U. Med. Center, Dallas, 1959-86; chief dept. pathology Baylor U. Med. Center, 1959-86, vice chmn. exec. com. med. bd., 1970-72; emeritus assoc. dean VA Hosp., Dallas, 1955-71; adj. prof. anthropology and biology So. Meth. U., Dallas, 1969; instr. pathology Duke, 1951-53, Harvard Med. Sch., 1953-54; asst. prof. pathology U. Tex. Southwestern Med. Sch., 1955-58, clin. assoc. prof., 1958-64, clin. prof., 1964-72, 1973-94, prof. emeritus, 1994–; dir. Cancer Center, 1973-76, assoc. dean for continuing edn., 1973-94; emeritus prof., 1994–; pathologist-in-chief Baylor U. Med. Ctr., 1959-86, prof. biomed. studies Baylor Grad. Sch., 1989-94; chmn. Baylor Rsch. Found., 1986-89; prof. microbiology Baylor Coll. Dentistry, 1962-68, prof. pathology, 1964-68, prof., chmn. dept. pathology, 1979-83, dean A. Webb Roberts Continuing Edn., 1973-94; spl. advisor on human and animal diseases to gov. State of Tex., 1979-83. Editor: Laboratory Medicine (4 vols.), 1973, 10th edit., 1983; Contbr. articles to profl. jours., chpts. to textbooks. Pres., Tex. div. Am. Cancer Soc., 1970 (chmn. Gov.'s Task Force on Higher Edn. 1981. Served with AUS, 1944-46; flight surgeon USAF, 1948-51, Korea. Decorated Air medal. Fellow Coll. Am. Pathologists, Am. Soc. Clin. Pathologists, AAAS; mem. AMA (chmn. multiple discipline research forum 1969), Am. Assn. Pathologists, Internat. Acad. Pathology, Am. Assn. Med. Colls., Explorer's Club (dir., v.p. 1993–), Sigma Xi. Home: 3429 Beverly Dr Dallas TX 75205-2928

RACE, JOHN STEPHEN, electronics manufacturing and technology executive; b. Evansville, Ind., Sept. 19, 1942; s. John Edward and Mary Rosetta (Doran) R.; m. Lisa Kame; children: Kimberly Anne, John Kevin, Erin Nichole. BS in Physics, Ind. U., 1964. Adminstr. quality improvement RCA, Bloomington, Ind., 1964-70, mgr. quality control, 1971-72; mgr. prodn. engring. and quality assurance RCA, Juanez, Mexico, 1972-74, mgr. mfg. and prodn. engring., 1975-76; mgr. mfg. technology RCA, Indpls., 1976-80; pres. Hirata Corp. of Am., Indpls., 1980–, also bd. dirs. Contbr. articles to profl. jours. Appointed to Ind. dist. export council, Indpls., 1982–, vice chmn. 1988–; subcom. chair Peace Games, Indpls., 1977–. Mem. Soc. Mfg. Engrs., Machine Vision Assn., Robotics Inst. Am., Midwest Bdminton Assn., U.S. Badminton Assn. (dir.), Sigma Pi Sigma. Home: 5122 Jensen Rd Martinsville IN 46151-8401 Office: Hirata Corp of Am 3901 Industrial Blvd Indianapolis IN 46254-2509

RACHELEFSKY, GARY S., medical educator; b. N.Y.C., 1942. Intern Bellevue Hosp. Ctr., N.Y.C., 1967-68; resident in pediatrics Johns Hopkins Hosp., 1968-70, Ctr. Disease Control, 1970-72; fellow UCLA Med. Ctr., 1972-74; clin. prof., assoc. dir. A/I Tng. Program UCLA. Mem. Am. Acad. Allergy, Asthma and Immunology (bd. dirs., sec., treas.). Office: 11620 Wilshire Blvd Ste 200 Los Angeles CA 90025-1767

RACHIE, CYRUS, lawyer; b. Willmar, Minn., Sept. 5, 1908; s. Elias and Amanda (Lien) R.; m. Helen Evelyn Duncanson, Nov. 25, 1936; children: John Burton Rachie, Janice Carolyn MacKinnon, Elisabeth Dorthea Becker. Student, U. Minn., 1927-28; JD, George Washington U., 1932, William Mitchell Coll. Law, 1934. Bar: Minn. 1934, U.S. Supreme Ct. Atty. Minn. Hwy. Dept., 1934-43; spl. asst. atty. gen. Minn., 1946-50; counsel Luth. Brotherhood (fraternal life ins. co.), 1950-61; pvt. practice law Mpls., 1961-62; v.p., counsel Gamble-Skogmo, Inc., Mpls., 1962-64; v.p., gen. counsel Aid Assn. Lutherans, Appleton, Wis., 1964-70; sr. v.p., gen. counsel Aid Assn. Lutherans, 1970-73; with Rachie & Rachie, 1973-83; pvt. practice, 1983–. Councillor Nat. Luth. Coun., 1959-66, sec., 1962-64, mem. exec. com., 1965-66; United Luth. Ch. in Am. del. to 4th Assembly Luth. World Fedn., Helsinki, 1963; past pres. Luth. Welfare Soc. Minn.; past chmn. Mpls. Mayor's Coun. on Human Rels.; chmn. finance United Fund drive, 1967-68; past mem. bd. dirs. Mpls. YMCA; trustee emeritus William Mitchell Coll. Law Augsburg Coll. With USNR, 1943-46. Recipient Disting. Alumnus award William Mitchell Coll. Law, 1987. Mem. ABA Minn. Bar Assn., Am. Legion, Minn. Fraternal Congress (past pres.). Lutheran. Club: Rotarian. Home: 7500 York Ave S Apt 101 Minneapolis MN 55435-4736 *I always try to keep in mind that the Christian Cross consists of both vertical and horizontal lines. The vertical is the longest line and represents a direct line from all of us on the bottom to God on the top and we must commune with Him. The horizontal represents an encompassing line that takes in all of mankind. If my life activities do not include the implementation of both lines of the cross, I will not have a balanced and Christian life.*

RACHLEFF, OWEN SPENCER (OWEN SPENCER RACKLEFF), actor, author; b. N.Y.C., July 16, 1934; s. Harold Kirman and Theresa (Friedman) R. BFA, Columbia, 1956; MA, London U., 1959. Editor Harry N. Abrams, Inc., Am. Heritage Co.; asst. prof. humanities N.Y. U., 1962-74. Profl. actor: (theater prodns.) Catsplay, 1978, The Lesson, 1978, Arms and the Man, 1980, Escoffier: King of Chefs, 1981-92, A New Way to Pay Old Debts, Enter Laughing, 1984, The Imaginary Invalid, 1985, The Jew of Malta, 1987, Sunday Promenade, 1989, Variations Without Fugue, 1992(films) The Dain Curse, 1977, Night Flowers, 1979, Question of Honor, 1981, Murder of Mary Phagan, 1988, (TV shows) The Bloodhound Gang, Ryan's Hope, All My Children; author: Rembrandt's Life of Christ, 1968, Young Israel, 1969, Great Bible Stories and Master Paintings, 1970, The Occult Conceit, 1971, Sky Diamonds, 1973, Secrets of Superstitions, 1976, Exploring the Bible, 1981, The Occult in Art, 1990; (plays) Javelin 1966, Uncle Money, 1980, Escoffier: King of Chefs, 1982, Tosca '43, 1984, The Fabulous La Fontaine, 1990; (novels) Eric's Image, 1982, Enigma, 1988. MacDowell Colony fellow, 1970. Mem. Actors Equity Assn., Screen Actors Guild, AFTRA, Dramatists Guild. Home and Office: Omar Prodns 135 E 71st St New York NY 10021-4258 *It's a lucky man who has a goal and is not sidetracked. Personally, I was fooled into looking for comfort and security while in my twenties. As a result, a dream I'd cherished of a life in the theatre grew dim; dim, but not extinguished. At age 42 I opted for myself and pursued the dream.*

RACHLIN, HARVEY BRANT, author, music company executive; b. Phila., June 23, 1951; s. Philip and Mazie (Drucker) R.; m. Marla Sivak Goldwert, June 28, 1987; 1 child, Glenn. BA in Biology, Hofstra U., Hempstead, N.Y., 1973. With music pub. cos., 1973—; owner Western Hemisphere Music Co., Ellipsis Music Mgmt. Co., Manhasset Hills, N.Y., 1975—, pres. 1982—; faculty Five Towns Coll., Seaford, N.Y., 1978-84. Author: The Songwriter's Handbook, 1977 (N.Y. Pub. Libr. Book for Teen Age 1979-82); The Encyclopedia of the Music Business, 1981 (ASCAP-Deems Taylor award 1982); Love Grams, 1983; The Money Encyclopedia, 1984 (Encyclopedia Britannica Home Libr. selection); The Kennedys: A Chronological History 1823—, 1986; The Songwriter's and Musician's Guide to Making Great Demos, 1988 (N.Y. Pub. Libr. Book for Teen Age 1989); The Making of a Cop, 1991, The Songwriter's Workshop, 1991, The TV and Movie Business: An Encyclopedia of Careers, Technologies, and Practices, 1991, The Making of a Detective, 1995; free-lance music journalist; contbr. Law and Order Mag., 1992—, Songwriter's Market 1979, 80, 87, 92; guest on The Dinah Shore Show, 1978, The Sally Jessy Raphael Show, 1993; compositions performed L.I. Mandolin and Guitar Orch., 1988. Recipient Outstanding Reference Book Yr. Am. Libr. Assn., 1981, Outstanding Reference Book Yr. Libr. Jour., 1984. Mem. ASCAP, Am. Guild Authors and Composers, L.I. Songwriters Workshop (bd. dirs.). Home: 878 Warner Rd Valley Stream NY 11580-1526

RACHLIN, LAUREN DAVID, lawyer; b. Buffalo, Feb. 6, 1929; s. Harry A. and Thelma (Goldberg) R.; m. Jean K. Rachlin, June 27, 1954; children: Laura Gail, Ellen Joan, James N. BS, U. Buffalo, 1948; JD, Harvard U., 1951. Bar: N.Y. 1952, U.S. Dist. Ct. (no. and we. dists.) N.Y. 1952, U.S. Supreme Ct. 1958, U.S. Ct. Appeals (2nd cir.) 1967, U.S. Tax Ct. 1952, U.S. Ct. Internat. Trade 1978. Ptnr. Rachlin & Rachlin, Buffalo, 1952-81; sr. ptnr. Kavinoky & Cook, Buffalo, 1981—; lectr. in internat. law and trade; U.S. appointee to Bi-nat. Dispute Settlement Panel created under U.S.-Can. Free Trade Agreement, 1989-93; U.S. appointee N.Am. Free Trade Agreement Bi-nat. Dispute Settlement Panel, 1994—; arbitrator Internat. C. of C. Am. Arbitration Assn. U.S. del. to UN Human Rights Commn., 1970; cons. to temporary commn. N.Y. State Constl. Conv.; mem. Erie County Charter Rev. Commn.; mem.-at-large U.S. Nat. Commn. for UNESCO, 1972-76, chmn. human rights task force; mem. industry functional adv. com. Customs for Trade Policy Matters of U.S. Dept. Commerce, Office U.S. Trade Rep., 1987—. Mem. ABA (fgn. investment in U.S. real estate com., internat. bus. law com., subcom. on trade import), N.Y. State Bar Assn. (founding chmn. internat. sect. 1987-89, chmn. internat. divsn. 1989-94), World Arbitration Inst. (adv. bd., bd. dirs.), Am. Assn. Exporters & Importers (various coms.), Internat. Law Assn., Am. Soc. Internat. Law, Internat. Bar Assn., U.S. Inst. Human Rights (adv. coun.), Customs and Internat. Trade Bar Assn., Erie County Bar Assn., Union Internationale des Advocats. Office: Kavinoky & Cook 120 Delaware Ave Buffalo NY 14202-2704

RACHLIN, STEPHEN LEONARD, psychiatrist; b. N.Y.C., Mar. 6, 1939; s. Murray and Sophie (Rodnitsky) R.; m. Florence Einsidler, Nov. 22, 1962; children: Michael Ira, Robert Alan. BA, NYU, 1959; MD, Albert Einstein Coll. Medicine, 1963. Diplomate Nat. Bd. Med. Examiners, Am. Bd. Forensic Psychiatry, Am. Bd. Psychiatry and Neurology with added qualifications in forensic psychiatry. Internship UCLA, 1963-64; resident, chief resident in psychiatry Mt. Sinai Hosp., N.Y., 1964-67; staff psychiatrist Bronx Psychiat. Ctr., Bronx, N.Y., 1969-72; asst. chief svc. Bronx Psychiat. Ctr., 1970-72, chief svc., 1972-74; dep. dir. Meyer-Manhattan Psychiat. Ctr., N.Y.C., 1974-76; acting dir. Meyer-Manhattan Psychiat. Ctr., 1976-77; dep. dir. Manhattan Psychiat. Ctr., N.Y.C., 1977; clin. dir. dept. psychiatry & psychology Nassau County Med. Ctr., E. Meadow, N.Y., 1978-80; assoc. chmn. dept. psychiatry & psychology Nassau County Med. Ctr., 1979-80, chmn. dept. psychiatry & psychology, 1980-94; assoc. prof. clin. psychiatry sch. medicine SUNY, Stony Brook, 1978-87, prof. clin. psychiatry, 1987-94; spl. prof. law Hofstra U., Hempstead, N.Y., 1983—. Editor in chief Psychiat. Quar., 1990—; assoc. editor Bull. of the Am. Acad. os Psychiatry and the Law, 1990—; contbr. articles to profl. jours. Lt. comdr. USNR, 1967-69. Mem. Am. Psychiat. Assn. (chmn. com. adminstrv. psychiatry 1987-92, mem. assembly 1991-94, mem. com. confidentiality 1993—), N.Y. State Psychiat. Assn. (chmn. com. on pub. psychiatry 1986-94), Am. Assn. Psychiat. Adminstrs. (pres. 1989-90), Am. Acad. Psychiatry and Law (pres. tri-state chpt. 1988-90), Am. Assn. Gen. Hosp. Psychiatrists (pres. 1993-94), Am. Bd. Forensic Psychiatry (dir. 1990-94, treas. 1992-93), Am. Hosp. Assn. (gov. coun. sect. psychiat. and substance abuse 1991-92), Hosp. Assn. N.Y. State (chmn. mental health 1992, 93). Office: PO Box 117-H Scarsdale NY 10583

RACHOFSKY, DAVID J., lawyer; b. Oceanside, N.Y., Nov. 17, 1936; s. Lester M. and Marjorie A.; m. Faith Allen; children: Robert, Patricia, Edward. BSEE, MIT, 1958; JD, Temple U., 1968. Bar: Pa., U.S. Dist. Ct. (ea. dist.) Pa., U.S. Tax. Ct., U.S. Ct. Fed. Claims, Pa. Supreme Ct. 1968. Ptnr. Dechert Price & Rhoads, Phila., 1968—; lectr. law Temple U. Law Sch., 1976—. Contbr. articles to profl. jours. With USAF, 1969-72. Mem. ABA, Phila. Bar Assn., Internat. Fiscal Assn. (chmn. mid-Atlantic region 1985-87, mem. coun. 1986-92, v.p./sec. 1992—), Internat. Bus. Forum (tax sect. coun.). Office: Dechert Price & Rhoads 1717 Arch St Philadelphia PA 19103-2713

RACHOW, LOUIS A(UGUST), librarian; b. Shickley, Nebr., Jan. 21, 1927; s. John Louis and Mable (Dondlinger) R. B.S., York Coll., 1948; M.S. in L.S., Columbia U., 1959. Librarian York Coll., Nebr., 1949-54; instr. library asst. Queens Coll., N.Y.C., 1956-57; serials acquisition asst. Columbia U. Law Library, N.Y.C., 1957-58; asst. librarian Univ. Club, N.Y.C., 1958-62; librarian Hampden-Booth Theatre Library at the Players, N.Y.C., 1962-86, curator, 1986-88; library dir. Internat. Theatre Inst. U.S., N.Y.C., 1989—; cons. theatre sect. U. Calif., San Diego, new campuses program, 1964, Music Ctr. Operating Archives, Los Angeles, 1985; mem. library adv. bd. Eugene O'Neill Meml. Theatre Center, 1966—. Editor, compiler: Guide to Performing Arts, 1968; assoc. editor Am. Notes and Queries, 1971-74, asst. editor, 1967-71; mem. editorial adv. bd. Nat. Dir. for Performing Arts and Civic Ctrs.; editor Performing Arts series Gale Info. Guide, 1976-83, Theatre and Performing Arts Collections, 1981; contbr. articles and revs. to profl. jours. Mem. adv. bd. Am. Theatre Co., OKC Theatre Prodns. Served with AUS, 1954-56. Mem. Theatre Libr. Assn. (rec. sec. 1966-67, pres. 1967-72, 81-83, v.p. 1976-80, editor Broadside 1973-81), ALA, Spl. Librs. Assn. (sec.-treas. mus. group N.Y.C. chpt. 1964-66), N.Y. Libr. Club (pres. 1979-80), Am. Theatre Assn., New Drama Forum Assn. (pres. 1983-86), Am. Soc. Theatre Rsch., N.Y. Tech. Svcs. Librs., Archons of Colophon (convener 1982-83), Episcopal Actors Guild Am. (bd. dirs. 1976—), Broadway Theatre Inst. Outer Critics Circ., Players Club. Home: 528 W 114th St New York NY 10025-7841 Office: Internat Theatre Inst/US 47 Great Jones St New York NY 10012

RACHWALSKI, FRANK JOSEPH, JR., financial executive; b. Chgo., Mar. 26, 1945; s. Frank Joseph and Julia Alice (Cwikowski) R.; children: Mark, Karla, Brian. B.B.A., Loyola U., Chgo., 1967, M.B.A., 1969. Chartered fin. analyst. Systems analyst N. Am. Life/U.S. Life, Chgo., 1963-73; portfolio mgr. Kemper Fin., Chgo., 1973—; v.p. Kemper Fin. Services Inc., Chgo., 1979—; v.p. Kemper Investors Life Ins. Co., Chgo., and subs. cos., Cash Equivalent Fund Inc., Chgo. Mem. Investment Analyst Soc. Chgo. Roman Catholic. Club: Elmhurst Tennis (treas. 1979-81) (Ill.). Avocations: tennis, exercise, golf. Home: 380 S Kenilworth Elmhurst IL 60126-4112 Office: Kemper Fin Services Inc 120 S La Salle St 21st Fl Chicago IL 60603-3402

RACICOT, MARC F., governor; b. Thompson Falls, Mont., July 24, 1948; s. William E. and Patricia E. (Bentley) R.; m. Theresa J. Barber, July 25, 1970; children: Ann, Timothy, Mary Catherine, Theresa, Joseph. BA, Carroll Coll., Helena, Mont., 1970; JD, U. Mont., 1973; postgrad., U. Va., 1973, Cornell U., 1977. Bar: Mont. 1973. With U.S. Army, 1973-76; advanced through grades to capt., 1973; legal assistance officer U.S. Army, Ft. Lewis, Wash., 1973; chief trial counsel U.S. Army, Kaiserslautern, Fed. Republic of Germany, 1975-76; resigned, 1976; dep. county atty. Missoula (Mont.) County, 1976-77; bur. chief County Prosecutor Svcs. Bur., Helena, Mont., 1977-89; asst. atty. gen. State of Mont., Helena, 1977-89; spl. prosecutor for the Atty. Gen.'s Office State of Mont., atty. gen., 1989-93, gov., 1993—. Founder Missoula Drug Treatment Program, 1977; active United Way, Helena; bd. visitors U. Mont. Sch. Law. Inducted into Basketball Hall of Fame Carroll Coll., 1982. Mem. Mont. Bar Assn., Carroll Coll. Century Club. Republican. Roman Catholic. Office: State Capitol RM 204 Helena MT 59620*

RACITI, CHERIE, artist; b. Chgo., June 17, 1942; d. Russell J. and Jacque (Crimmins) R. Student, Memphis Coll. Art, 1963-65; B.A. in Art, San Francisco State U., 1968; M.F.A., Mills Coll., 1979. Assoc. prof. art San Francisco State U., 1984-89, prof., 1989—; lectr. Calif. State U., Hayward, 1974, San Francisco Art Inst., 1978; mem. artist com. San Francisco Art Inst., 1974-85, sec., 1980-81. One woman show U. Calif., Berkeley, 1972, Nicholas Wilder Gallery, Los Angeles, 1975, San Francisco Art Inst., 1977, Marianne Deson Gallery, Chgo., 1980, Site 375, San Francisco, 1989, Reese Bullen Gallery, Humboldt State U., Arcata, Calif., 1990; group shows include Whitney Mus. Art, 1975, San Francisco Sci. Fiction, The Clocktower, N.Y.C., Otis-Parsons Gallery, Los Angeles, 1984-85, San Francisco Art Inst., 1985, Artists Space, N.Y.C., 1988, Angles Gallery, Santa Monica, 1987, Terrain Gallery, San Francisco, 1992, Ctr. for the Arts, San Francisco, 1993. Bd. dirs. New Langton Arts, 1988-92. Recipient Adaline Kent award San Francisco Art Inst., 1976; Eureka fellow Fleishhacker Found., San Francisco, 1988; Djerassi resident, 1994. Home: 1995 Tyrone Guthrie Ctr, Annaghmakerrig Ireland Office: San Francisco State U Art Dept 1600 Holloway Ave San Francisco CA 94132-1722

RACKLEFF, OWEN SPENCER See RACHLEFF, OWEN SPENCER

RACKOW, JULIAN PAUL, lawyer; b. Phila., Dec. 16, 1941; s. Lawrence Lionel and Blanche (Wachman) R.; m. Paulette Schorr, June 23, 1963; children: Jeffrey A., Andrea B. AB, Cornell U., 1963; JD, Harvard U., 1966. Bar: Pa. 1966, U.S. Dist. Ct. (ea. dist.) Pa. 1966. Assoc. atty. Goodis, Greenfield, Narin & Mann, Phila., 1966-69; ptnr., co-chmn. dept. real estate Blank, Rome, Comisky & McCauley, Phila., 1970—. Sec., mem. exec. com., bd. dirs. Ctrl. Phila. Devel. Corp., 1990—. Mem. Pa. Bar Assn., Phila. Bar Assn., Harvard Law Sch. Assn. Phila. (v.p., exec. com. 1991—). Avocations: tennis, travel, piano. Office: Blank Rome Comisky & McCauley 4 Penn Center Plz Fl 1200 Philadelphia PA 19103-2512

RACLIN, ERNESTINE MORRIS, banker; b. South Bend, Ind., Oct. 25, 1927; d. Ernest M. and Ella L. Morris; m. O.C. Carmichael, Jr., Sept. 28, 1946; children: Carmen Carmichael Murphy, O.C., II, Ernestine Carmichael Nickle, Stanley Clark; m. Robert L. Raclin, July 22, 1977. Student, St. Mary's Coll., South Bend, 1947; LL.D. (hon.), U. Notre Dame, 1978, Ind. State U., 1981; L.H.D. (hon.), Converse Coll., 1974; D (hon.), Vincennes U., 1987, U. So. Ind., 1988; D in Tech. (hon.), Purdue U., 1992. Chmn. 1st Source Corp., 1976, South Bend, Ind.; Chmn. 1st Source Bank; former bd. dirs. First Chgo. Corp., First Nat. Bank Chgo.; bd. dirs. No. Ind. Pub. Service Co. Trustee U. Notre Dame, 1973—; bd. govs. United Way Am., 1973-80; adv. bd. Ind. U. South Bend; bd. dirs. Mich. Public Broadcasting, United Way of Ind.; bd. dirs., former chmn. Project Future, Ind. Acad. Bd. Regents; mem. nat. fin. com. George Bush for Pres., steering com., co-chair Ind. fin. com. Bush/Quayle, 1992. Recipient E.M. Morris Meml. award Ind. Acad., Community Service award St. Mary's Coll., Ivy Tech's Excellence in Edn. award, Edmund F. Ball award Ind. Pub. Broadcasting Soc., Castaldi award United Way Ind., Top Vol. award United Way Ind., 1987, Helping Hands award Hospice of St. Joseph County. Mem. St. Joseph County C of C. South Bend (dir. 1977— , chmn.-elect 1986, Woman of Yr. award 1970, Disting. Bus. Leader award, 1993), Ind. State C of C. (mem. edn. task force). Republican. Presbyterian. Clubs: Summit (South Bend); Ocean (Delray Beach, Fla.); Signal Point (Niles, Mich.), Audubon (Naples, Fla.). Office: 1st Source Corp PO Box 1602 South Bend IN 46634-1602

RACTLIFFE, ROBERT EDWARD GEORGE, management executive; b. Hertfordshire, Eng., July 25, 1943; came to U.S., 1985; s. Augustus David John and Veronica Phyllis (Jones) R.; m. Nancy Jane Brumbaugh, June 29, 1968; children: Richard Alban, Tiffany Elizabeth, Courtney Veronica. BS with honors, U. London, 1965; MSEE, U. Pitts., 1969, MBA with honors, 1972; PMD, Harvard U., 1975. Engr. Westinghouse Electric Corp., Pitts., 1965-69, sales mgr. LRA Div., 1969-73, mfg. engr. mgr. LRA Div., 1974-76, dept. mgr. Hydrogenerator Dept., 1976-78; mgr. product mktg. Steam Turbine Generator Div. Westinghouse Electric Corp., Phila., 1978-81; mgr. strategic planning Power Generation Bus. Unit, 1981-84; gen. mgr. Power Generation Comml. Div. Westinghouse Electric Corp., Orlando, Fla., 1984-86; pres., North Am. Ops. United Tech. Carrier Corp., Syracuse, N.Y., 1986-88; pres., chief exec. officer NORDYNE Inc., St. Louis, 1989—. Patentee in field; contbr. articles to profl. jours. Mem. AAIM (bd. dirs.), Gas Appliance Mfrs. Assn. (co. rep.), Manufactured Housing Inst. (co. rep.), Air Conditioning and Refrigeration Inst. (bd. dirs., v.p. exec. com., chmn., co. rep.). Republican. Episcopalian. Avocations: golf, tennis, skiing. Office: NORDYNE Inc 1801 Park 270 Dr Ste 600 Saint Louis MO 63146-4020

RACZKIEWICZ, MACIEJ A., engineering company executive; b. 1942. With Epstein Engring. Export Ltd., Chgo., 1961—, pres. Office: Epstein Engring Export Ltd 600 W Fulton St Chicago IL 60661*

RACZKIEWICZ, PAUL EDWARD, hospital administrator; b. Buffalo, N.Y., June 17, 1944; s. Edward Paul and Helen (Lentivech) R.; m. Rosemary Raczkiewicz, Jan. 16, 1971; children: Ann, Edward, Ellen. AA, Niagara County C.C., 1965; BS, SUNY, Brockport, 1968; Master in Hosp. and Health Care Adminstrn., St. Louis U., 1973. Dir. profl. svcs. Alton (Ill.) Meml. Hosp., 1973; v.p., corp. officer St. Elizabeth Hosp., Granite City (Ill.), 1973-86; exec. v.p. St. Elizabeth Med. Ctr., Granite City, 1986—; pres., chief exec. officer St. Elizabeth Captive Med. Ins. Co.; v.p. Providence Mgmt. and Mktg. Svcs., Provide Med. Equipment Supply Co.; pres.-elect HAMSTL, Hosp. Industry Data Inst., bd. dirs. HIDI Ill. State rep. for HAMSTL; mem. adv. com., adv. bd. regional incinerator project Shared Resource Enterprises (HAMSTL). Past pres. bd. Tri-Cities Area United Way; mem. quality measurement tech. com. St. Louis Bus. Coalition. With U.S. Army, 1969-71. Fellow Am. Coll. Healthcare Execs.; Ill. Hosp. Assn. (past pres. region 4, cost containment coun., coun. institutional regulation), Assn. Ind. Hosps., Southwestern Ill. Indsl. Assn. (govt. affairs com.). Office: St Elizabeth Medical Ct 2100 Madison Ave Granite City IL 62040-4799

RADAN, GEORGE TIVADAR, art history and archaeology educator; b. Budapest, Hungary, Dec. 31, 1923; came to U.S. 1959; s. Alfred Albert and Jolanda (Odescalchi) R.; m. Maryann Patricia Radan; children: Christopher Byron, Cornelius Alfred. MA, U. Budapest, 1946, PhD, 1948; AEM, Ecole Du Louvre, Paris, 1968. Asst. dir. Nat. Marit Mus. of Israel, Haifa, 1952-58; dir., sr. researcher Wayne State U., Ky. State U., Hist. Inst. Archeology Excavation, Siena, Italy, 1969-84; prof. Dept. Art History Villanova U., Pa., 1967—. Author: Sons of Zebulon, 1980, Archaeology of Roman Pannonic, 1982, The V.U. Art Collection, 1986; contbg. author: Lecceto, Eremi Augustiniani in Terra Siena, 1991. Recipient Ancien Eleve Museologie;

Rosemont Coll. Connely grantee, 1968; U. Pa. postdoctoral grant in archaeology, 1969; ACLS grantee to Hungarian Acad. Sci., 1972-73; Internat. Rsch. and Exch. grantee to Archaeol. Inst. Hungary, 1975; Friends of the Haifa, Maritime Mus. grantee to Israeli Nat. Maritime Mus., 1985; NEH grantee to Vatican Libr., 1988. Mem. AAUP. Office: Villanova U Dept Art History Villanova PA 19085

RADANDT, FRIEDHELM K., college president; b. Gross-Jestin, Germany, Oct. 23, 1932; came to U.S., 1960; married; 3 children. Diploma in Theology, Bapt. Theol. Sem., Germany, 1957; AM, U. Chgo., 1961, PhD in German, 1967. Instr. German Lake Forest Coll., 1961-64, assoc. prof., 1970-77, acting dean faculty, 1973-74, dean faculty, 1974-77; from instr. to asst. prof. U. Chgo., 1964-70; prof. humanities, v.p. acad. affairs Northwestern Coll., Iowa, from 1977, pres., 1979-85; pres. King's Coll., Briarcliff Manor, N.Y., 1985—. Author: Transitional Time in Keller's Zuricher Novellen, 1974, From Baroque to Storm and Stress, 1720-1775, 1977. Office: The King's Coll Office of Pres Briarcliff Manor NY 10510-9985

RADANOVICH, GEORGE P., congressman. BS in Agr. Bus. Mgmt., Calif. State Polytechnic U. Radanovich Wine, Mariposa, Calif., 1982—; County supr.; chair County Planning Comm.; mem. U.S. Ho. of Reps., 104th Congress, Washington, 1995—; mem. Budget Com., Resources Com., subcoms. Water & Power Resources, Nat. Parks, Forests & Lands. U.S. Ho. of Reps., 104th Congress, also mem. Resources Com. Task Force dealing with Endangered Species Act. Mem. Calif. Agrl. Leadership Program Class XXI, Rotary (Paul Harris Fellowship). Office: US House Reps Office House Mem Washington DC 20515*

RADCLIFF, WILLIAM FRANKLIN, lawyer; b. Fredericksburg, Ind., May 21, 1922; s. Samuel Pearl and Hester Susan (Sherwood) R.; m. Elizabeth Louise Doeller Haines, May 15, 1982; children—Forrest Lee, Stephanie Anne; foster children—Cheryl Lynn, Sandra Lee, Richard Alan, Lezlie Laverne; stepchildren—Mark David, Laura Louise, Pamela Lynn, Veronica Leigh. B.A., Yale U., 1948; J.D., Ind. U., 1951. Bar: Ind. 1951. With DeFur, Voran, Hanley, Radcliff & Reed and predecessors, Muncie, Ind., 1951—, ptnr., 1954—; dir., mem. exec. com. Am. Nat. Bank and Trust Co., Muncie . Pres. Delaware County Mental Health Assn., 1962-63; founding mem. Ind. Mental Health Meml. Found., 1962, sec., 1962-84; bd. dirs. Delaware County Cancer Soc.; trustee Acad. Community Leadership. Served with AUS, 1940-46, PTO. Mem. ABA, Ind. Bar Assn., Muncie Bar Assn., Muncie-Delaware County C. of C. (pres. 1972-73). Clubs: Muncie Tennis and Country (bd. dirs., sec.), Muncie, Delaware Country (pres. 1972-73), Exchange (pres. 1962) (Muncie). Lodge: Masons. Home: 1809 N Winthrop Rd Muncie IN 47304-2532 Office: 201 E Jackson St Muncie IN 47305-2832

RADCLIFFE, GEORGE GROVE, retired life insurance company executive; b. Balt., Nov. 12, 1924; s. George G. and Elsie (Winter) R.; m. Bettie Howell, Feb. 10, 1951 (div.); 1 child, Cynthia; m. Kathleen Moore Smith, 1991. B.A., Johns Hopkins U., 1947; grad. Advanced Mgmt. Program,, Harvard U. Grad. Sch. Bus. Adminstrn., 1962. With Balt. Life Ins. Co., 1947-89, v.p. treas., 1963-69, exec. v.p., 1969-72, pres., 1972-89, chief exec. officer, 1974-89, chmn. bd., 1980-89, pres., 1981-86, ret., 1989; dir., 1989—, EA Engring. Sci. and Tech., Inc. Chmn. bd. trustees Johns Hopkins U., 1984-90, trustee, 1975-93, trustee emeritus, 1993—. Mem. Delta Upsilon. Methodist. Clubs: Maryland (Balt.), Tred Avon Yacht Club. Home and Office: PO Box 166 Oxford MD 21654-0166

RADCLIFFE, REDONIA WHEELER (DONNIE RADCLIFFE), journalist, author; b. Republican City, Nebr.; d. Donnel F. and Lois (Woolman) Wheeler; m. Robert C. Radcliffe, 1957; 1 son, M. Donnel Nunes. B.A., San Jose (Calif.) State U., 1951. Reporter, women's editor, county editor The Salinas Californian, 1951-59; free-lance writer Europe, 1959-66; reporter Washington Star, 1967-72; reporter, columnist Washington Post, 1972-95. Author: Simply Barbara Bush: A Portrait of America's Candid First Lady, 1989, Hillary Rodham Clinton: A First Lady for Our Time, 1993; contbr.: The Fall of a President, 1974, Guide to Washington, 1989. Mem. White House Corr. Assn. Address: 2795 Spout Ln Lusby MD 20657

RADDER, BRUCE MILTON, business owner; b. Bloomington, Ind., Dec. 7, 1925; s. Norman John and Elsie (Fjelstad) R.; m. Shirley Ann Abeles, Nov. 25, 1948; children: Susan Beecher, Bruce Jr., Brian, Scott, Robin Matthews. BA, Lake Forest (Ill.) Coll., 1949. Account exec. Sta. WOBT, Rhinelander, Wis., 1953-55, Sta. WBBM, Chgo., 1956-57, Sta. WOTV-TV, Grand Rapids, Mich., 1953-58; pres. Indoor Mktg., Inc., Grand Rapids, Mich., 1961-63, Silver Jack Wanigan, Inc., Grand Rapids, Mich., 1963-65, Radder Advt., Inc., Grand Rapids, Mich., 1958-74, Main St., Inc., Grand Rapids, Mich., 1974-78; owner, mgr. Print Pros, Escondido, Calif., 1978-91. Served as ensign USMC, 1943-46. Recipient ADDY awards Advt. Fedn. Am., 1960, 61, 62. Mem. Agy. Group (founding dir., pres. 1969), Soc. for Preservation and Encouragement of Barber Shop Quartet Singing in Am. (pres. Palomar Pacific chpt. 1980-81). Republican. Congregationalist. Clubs: Advt. North County (Escondido) (chmn. bd. dirs. 1986-87); Advt. (Grand Rapids) (pres. 1960). Avocations: music, sailing, travel. Home: 1401 82 El Norte Pkwy San Marcos CA 92069

RADECKI, ANTHONY EUGENE, paper company executive; b. St. Paul, Aug. 8, 1939; s. Anthony Edmund and Agnes Jane R.; m. Patricia Ann Kelly, June 18, 1960; children: Robert Eugene, Linda Marie, Greg Anthony. B.A., B.S., St. Thomas Coll., 1961. C.P.A., Minn. Acct. Taylor McCaskill & Co., St. Paul, 1961-72; sr. v.p. fin and adminstrn. Blandin Paper Co., Grand Rapids, Minn., 1972—; also bd. dirs.; bd. dirs. Norwest Bank, Grand Rapids; pres. Itasca Growth Fund, Grand Rapids, 1984-90. Chmn., bd. dirs. Itasca Community Coll. Found., 1974-80; bd. dirs. Grand Rapids YMCA, 1982-91, Reif Ctr., Grand Rapids, 1981-83. Mem. Nat. Assn. Accts., Am. Inst. CPA's, Minn. Soc. CPA's. Office: Blandin Paper Co 115 SW 1st St Grand Rapids MN 55744-3699

RADEKA, VELJKO, electronics engineer; b. Zagreb, Yugoslavia, Nov. 21, 1930; came to U.S. 1962; s. Milan and Neda (Ilic) R.; m. Jelena Horvat, May 17, 1958; children: Dejan, Dina. Diploma Engr., U. Zagreb, 1955, D. Engring. Scis., 1961. Scientist Inst. Ruder Boskovic, Zagreb, 1955-62, 64-66; scientist Brookhaven Nat. Lab., Upton, N.Y., 1962-64, 66-72; sr. scientist, head instrumentation div. Brookhaven Nat. Lab., 1972—. Contbr. in field. Fellow IEEE; mem. Am. Phys. Soc., Nuclear and Plasma Physic Soc., South Bay Cruising Club, Bellport Bay Yacht Club. Home: 29 Academy Ln Bellport NY 11713-2742 Office: Brookhaven Nat Lab Upton NY 11973

RADELL, NICHOLAS JOHN, management consultant; b. South Range, Mich., Sept. 2, 1930; s. Nicholas and Anna (Pekkala) R.; m. Jennifer L. Beemer, May 19, 1989; childrenfrom previous marriage: Susan Diane, Sally Anne, Nicholas Steven; stepchildren: Andrew Justin Beemer, Shana Kristen Beemer. B.S. U. Mich., 1952, M.B.A., 1956. C.P.A., Mich. registered profl. engr., Mich. Application engr. Square D Co., Detroit, 1954-55; mem. firm Touche, Ross, Bailey & Smart (C.P.A.'s), Detroit, 1956-61; with Cresap, McCormick & Paget Inc., Chgo., 1961-83, ptnr., 1969-71, v.p., dir., 1969-82, region mgr., 1971-82; v.p., dir. Cresap, a Towers Perrin Co., 1983-90; chmn. Towers Perrin Australia, 1989-90; v.p. Mercer Mgmt. Consulting, Chgo., 1991—. Contbg. author: Handbook of Process Planning and Estimating, 1962, Scientific Inventory Management, 1963, Introduction to Manufacturing Management, 1969. Bd. dirs. Chgo. Conv. and Tourism Bur., 1983, U. Mich. Alumni Assn., 1989. 1st lt. USAF, 1952-54. Fellow Instn. Prodn. Engrs. (U.K., hon.); mem. Soc. Mfg. Engrs. (bd. dirs., nat'l v.p. 1971, pres. 1973), Am. Assn. Engring. Socs. (chmn. 1984), Inst. Indsl. Engrs., Chgo. Club, Mid-Day Club, Met. Club, Indian Hill Club, Phi Gamma Delta. Presbyterian. Home: 1230 Sunset Rd Winnetka IL 60093-3628 Office: 10 S Wacker Dr Fl 13 Chicago IL 60606-7407

RADEMACHER, RICHARD JOSEPH, librarian; b. Kaukauna, Wis., Aug. 20, 1937; s. Joseph Benjamin and Anna (Wyuts) R.; m. Mary Jane Liethen, Feb. 12, 1966; children: Alicia Mary, Ann Marie, Amy Rose. A.B., Ripon Coll., 1959; M.S. Library Sch. U. Wis., 1961. Dir. Kaukauna Public Library, 1964-66, Eau Claire (Wis.) Public Library, 1966-69; librarian Salt Lake City Public Library, 1969-76; dir. Wichita (Kans.) Public Library, 1976—. Bd. dirs. Salt Lake Art Center, Reading Room for the Blind.; mem.

Kans. Com. for the Humanities, 1977-82; mem. exec. bd. Wichita Girl Scouts, 1977—. Served with AUS, 1962-64. Mem. ALA; Mem. Mountain Plains Library Assn. (sect. chmn.); mem. Kans. Library Assn. (pres. 1982-83); Mem. Wichita Library Assn. Office: Wichita Pub Libr 223 S Main St Wichita KS 67202-3715

RADEMAKER, STEPHEN GEOFFREY, lawyer; b. Balt., July 18, 1959; s. Thomas Joseph and Ruth Virginia (Wentz) R.; m. Danielle Pletka; 1 child, Andrew. BA with Highest Distinction, U. Va., 1981, JD, 1984, MA in Fgn. Affairs, 1985. Bar: Va. 1984, D.C. 1985. Assoc. Covington & Burling, Washington, 1984-86; law clk. to Hon. James L. Buckley U.S. Ct. Appeals (D.C. cir.) Washington, 1986; counsel to vice chmn. U.S. Internat. Trade Commn., Washington, 1986-87; spl. asst. to asst. sec. for Inter-Am. affairs Dept. State, Washington, 1987-89; assoc. counsel to Pres. of U.S. and dep. legal advisor to NSC, Washington, 1989-92; gen. counsel Peace Corps, Washington, 1992-93; Rep. chief counsel Com. Fgn. Affairs U.S. Ho. of Reps., Washington, 1993-95, chief counsel Com. Internat. Rels., 1995—. Recipient Raven award U. Va.,1984; S. Philip Heiner scholar U. Va., 1983. Mem. Va. Bar Assn., D.C. Bar Assn., Coun. Fgn. Rels., Phi Beta Kappa, Omicron Delta Kappa. Republican. Lutheran. Avocations: skiing, cycling, scuba diving. Office: US House Reps Com Internat Rels Washington DC 20515

RADEN, LOUIS, tape and label corporation executive; b. Detroit, June 17, 1929; s. Harry M. and Joan (Morris) R.; m. Mary K. Knowlton, June 18, 1949; children: Louis III, Pamela (Mrs. T.W. Rea III), Jacqueline. BA, Trinity Coll., 1951; postgrad. NYU, 1952. With Time, Inc., 1951-52; with Quaker Chem. Corp., 1952-63, sales mgr., 1957-63; exec. v.p. Gen. Tape & Supply, Inc., Detroit, 1963-68, pres., chmn. bd., 1969—; pres. Mich. Gun Clubs, 1973-77. Fifth reunion chmn. Trinity Coll., 1956, pres. Mich. alumni, 1965-72, sec. Class of 1951, 81-86, pres. 1986-91, The McCook Fellow Soc.; trustee, v.p. Mich. Diocese Episcopal Ch., 1980-82, mem. urban evaluation com., 1975-78, chmn. urban evaluation com., 1978, chmn. urban affairs com., 1977-79; vice chmn., bd. dirs. Robert H. Whitaker Sch. Theology, 1983-85; vice chmn. Mich. Diocese Econ. Justice Commn., 1989—, bd. dirs. Poverty and Social Reform Inst., 1992—, Person of Yr. award, 1994; founding sponsor World Golf Hall of Fame; mem. Founders Soc. Detroit Inst. Arts; trustee Mich. Housing Trust Fund, 1993—. Mem. NRA (life), Nat. Skeet Shooting Assn. (life, nat. dir. 1977-79, 5 Man Team World Champion award 1977, pres. coun.), Mich. Skeet Assn. (all state team 1975-80, inductee Hall of Fame 1994), Greater Detroit Bd. Commerce, Automotive Industry Action Group, Detroit Sportsmen's Congress, Mich. C. of C., U.S. C. of C., Greater Hartford Jaycees (exec. v.p. 1955-57, Key Man award 1957), Theta Xi (life, Disting. Service award 1957, alumni pres. 1952-57, regional dir. 1954-57). Republican. Clubs: Detroit Golf, Detroit Gun, Katke-Cousins Golf, Midland Country, Black Hawk Indians, Pinehurst Country; Oakland U. Pres.'s, Round Table, Detroit Sportsmen'sCongress. Home: 1133 Ivyglen Cir Bloomfield Hills MI 48304-1236 Office: Gen Tape & Supply Inc 7451 W 8 Mile Rd Detroit MI 48221-1295

RADER, CHARLES GEORGE, chemical company executive; b. Niagara Falls, N.Y., Apr. 9, 1946; s. Carl Franklin and Eileen (Adler) R.; m. Sheila Ann Dunlop, Oct. 30, 1971; children: Carla Beth, Kevin Alexander. B-SChemE, Rensselaer Polytech. Inst., 1968; MS, U. Rochester, 1970; PhD, SUNY, Buffalo, 1974. Sr. research engr. Occidental Chem. Corp., Grand Island, N.Y., 1974-77, group leader, 1977-78; tech. mgr. Occidental Chem. Corp., Niagara Falls, N.Y., 1978-81; tech. dir. Occidental Chem. Corp., Grand Island, 1981-84, dir. tech., 1984—; now v.p., tech. & develop.; v.p D.S. Ventures, Dallas, 1987—; bd. dirs. TreaTek, Grand Island. Patentee in field; contbr. articles to profl. jours. Industrial adv. bd. dept. chem. engring. SUNY, Buffalo. Mem. Am. Inst. Chem. Engrs., Am. Chem. Soc. (Jacob F. Schoellkopf Medal, 1995), Electrochem. Soc., Regional Tech. Strategy Com., Niagara Frontier Assn. Research and Devel. Dirs., Tau Beta Pi, Phi Lambda Upsilon, Sigma Xi, Delta Tau Delta. Office: Occidental Chem Corp Tech Ctr 2801 Long Rd Grand Island NY 14072-1244

RADER, DOTSON CARLYLE, author, journalist; b. Evanston, Ill., July 25, 1942; s. Paul Carlyle and Lois (Schacht) R. Student, Columbia, 1962-68. Editor Defiance: A Radical Rev. (Warner Communications, Inc.), 1969-71; contbg. editor Evergreen Rev., 1969-73, Esquire, N.Y.C., 1973-77, N.Y. mag., 1977-80; cons. Nat. Com. for Lit. Arts at Lincoln Center, N.Y.C., 1980—; Mem. sponsoring bd. New Politics, 1972—; host Free Time Show, WNET-TV, N.Y.C., 1972-73. Author: I Ain't Marchin' Anymore!, 1969, Government Inspected Meat and Other Fun Summer Things, 1971, Blood Dues, 1973, Tennessee: Cry of the Heart; An Intimate Memoir of Tennessee Williams, 1985; screenplay The Bronze Lily, 1974, The Dream's on Me: A Love Story, 1976, Miracle, 1978; novel Beau Monde, 1981; play (with Mike Miller) Shattered Glass, 1990; contbg. editor Parade Mag., 1984—. Mem. Student Peace Union, 1961-63, Students for a Democratic Soc., 1964-69, War Resisters League, 1970—; pres. Humanitas, Columbia, 1963-67; vice chmn. Peoples Coalition for Peace and Justice, 1972. Named hon. ambassador State of W. Va., 1982; recipient award for nat. journalism Odyssey Inst., 1982, Spl. Olympics award for nat. journalism Joseph P. Kennedy Found., 1985. Mem. PEN, Overseas Press Club, The Dramatists Guild.

RADER, HANNELORE, library director, consultant; b. Berlin, Germany, Dec. 19, 1937; d. Henry H. and Talia E. (Tramontin) Busch; widowed; 1 child, Ingrid M. BA in Russian, U. Mich., 1960, MA in Libr. Sci., 1968, MA in German Lit., 1971; Degree in Ednl. Leadership, Eastern Mich. U., 1978. Children's librarian Washington D.C. Pub. Libr., 1960-62; asst. humanities librarian Eastern Mich. U., Ypsilanti, 1968-70, orientation librarian, 1970-76, coord. edn., psychology div., 1976-80; libr. dir. learning ctr. U. Wis.-Parkside, Kenosha, 1980-87; dir. univ. libr. Cleve. State U., 1987—; evaluator, libr. instr. Ball State U., Muncie, Ind., 1983; evaluator for self study Calif. State U.-L.A. Libr., 1989, CCNY Libr., 1989. Contbr. articles to numerous jours. Recipient Walter H. Kaiser award Mich. Libr. Assn., 1977, Disting. Alumnus award U. Mich. Libr. Sch., 1984; fellow Coun. Libr. Resources, 1975-76; USIA and West German Libr. grantee, 1987. Mem. ALA (mem. coun. 1980-84, 84-92, 92—), AAUW (pres. Cleve. chpt. 1993-95, Edn. Found. honoree 1994), Assn. Coll. and Rsch. Librs. (pres., bd. dirs. 1985-88, Miriam Dudley Libr. Instrn. award 1993), Spl. Librs. Assn., Ohio Libr. Assn., Rotary. Avocations: physical fitness, baking and gourmet cooking, music, theater, travel. Office: Cleve State U Libr 1860 E 22d St Cleveland OH 44115

RADER, LOUIS T., corporation executive, educator; b. Frank, Can., Aug. 24, 1911; came to U.S. 1934, naturalized, 1940; s. Italo and Louise (Bonamico) R.; m. Constance Wayland, Sept. 10, 1938; children—Louis Albert, John Newton. B.S., U. B.C., 1933; Ph.D. in Elec. Engring. Calif. Inst. Tech., 1938. Engr. Gen. Electric Co., 1937-45; prof., head dept. elec. engring. Ill. Inst. Tech., 1945-47; with Gen. Electric Co., 1947-59, gen. mgr. splty. control div., 1951-59; v.p., dir. ITT, N.Y.C., 1959-61; group v.p. U.S. Commercial, 1961—; pres. Univac div. Sperry Rand Corp., N.Y.C., 1962-64; v.p., gen. mgr. Indsl. Process Control div. Gen. Electric Co., N.Y.C., 1964-69; prof. elec. engring. U. Va., 1969-82, prof. emeritus, 1982—, prof., Grad. Sch. Bus., 1969-82; vis. com. div. engring. and applied sci. Calif. Inst. Tech., 1968-75. Recipient Alumni distinguished service award Calif. Inst. Tech.; 1966; Va. Engring. Found. award, 1982. Fellow IEEE; mem. Am. Soc. Engring. Edn., Nat. Acad. Engring., Sigma Xi, Tau Beta Pi, Beta Gamma Sigma, Eta Kappa Nu, Omicron Delta Kappa. Home: 250 Pantops Mt Rd Charlottesville VA 22901 Office: U Va Darden Grad Sch Bus PO Box 6550 Charlottesville VA 22906-6550

RADER, PAUL ALEXANDER, minister, administrator; b. N.Y.C., Mar. 4, 1934; s. Lyell M. and Gladys Mina (Damon) R.; m. Kay Fuller, May 29, 1956; children: Edith Jeanne, James Paul, Jennifer Kay. BA, Asbury Coll. Wilmore, Ky., 1956; BD, Asbury Theol. Sem. 1959; LLD (hon.), Asbury Coll., Wilmore, Ky., 1984; ThM, So. Bapt. Theol. Sem., Louisville, 1961; D Missiology, Fuller Theol. Sem., 1973. Ordained to ministry Salvation Army, 1961. Tng. prin. The Salvation Army, Seoul, 1973-74, edn. sec., 1974-77, chief sec., 1979-83; tng. prin. The Salvation Army, Suffern, N.Y., 1983-86; divisional commdr. for Ea. Pa. and Del. The Salvation Army, Phila., 1986-88; chief sec. ea. ter. The Salvation Army, N.Y.C., 1988; territorial commdr. U.S.A. western ter. The Salvation Army, Rancho Palos Verdes, Calif., 1989—; adj. prof. Seoul Theol. Sem., 1980-82; trustee Asian Ctr. for Theol. Studies and Mission, 1980-83, Asbury Coll., 1988—; pres. The Salvation

Army Calif. Corp., Rancho Palos Verdes, 1989—. Recipient Alumnus A award Asbury Coll., 1982, Disting. Alumni award Asbury Theol. Sem., 1989; Paul Harris fellow Rotary Internat., 1989. Mem. Am. Soc. Missiology, Internat. Assn. Mission Studies. Office: The Salvation Army 639 Sabrina Way Vista CA 92084-6264

RADER, PAUL MACFARLAND, healthcare administrator; b. Mpls., Feb. 12, 1939; s. Paul Carlyle and Lois Pauline (Schacht) R.; m. Linda Emmy Frances Tschaepe, Dec. 19, 1981; 1 child, James E. Bayles. BA, U. Minn., 1973, MHA, 1975; cert., Am. Grad. Sch. Instl. Mgmt., Phoenix, 1985; PhD, Knightsbridge U., Copenhagen, 1993. Dir. mktg. Reality, Inc., Alexandria, Va., 1962-71; assoc. dir. U. Minn. Hosps., Mpls., 1973-76; sr. cons. James Hamilton Assocs., Mpls., 1976-79; v.p. Roseville (Calif.) Community Hosp., 1979-81; exec. v.p. Whittaker Saudi Arabia, Ltd., Khamis Mushayt, Saudi Arabia, 1981-83; ops. dir. Commonwealth Health Ctr. Project, Saipan, Mariana Islands, 1983-85; exec. dir. Chinese Hosp., San Francisco, 1986-89; chief exec. officer Woodland Pk. Hosp., Portland, Oreg., 1989-91; sr. v.p. Healthcare Enterprise Internat., Washington, 1991-95; pres. Internat. Healthcare Devel. Group Ltd., Warsaw, Poland, 1995—; exec. cons. World Bank/ USAID, Washington, 1985. Mem. Chinese Am. Citizens' Alliance, San Francisco, 1986-90, Rep. Inner Circle, Washington, 1985, Chinatown Social Agcy. Consortium, San Francisco, 1986-89. Recipient Merit awd. Trust Territory/Pacific, Saipan, Mariana Islands, 1984. Fellow Am. Coll. Healthcare Execs.; mem. Am. Hosp. Assn., Am. Heart Assn., Soc. for Healthcare Planning, Healthcare Execs. of N. Calif., West Bay Hosp. Conf. (trustee 1987-88), Oreg. Assn. Hosps. Avocations: travel, reading, writing. Home: 729 Grapevine Hwy Ste 156 Hurst TX 76054 Office: Internat Healthcare Devel Group Ltd, ul Kaniowska 110, 01-529 Warsaw Poland

RADER, RALPH TERRANCE, lawyer; b. Clarksburg, W.Va., Dec. 5, 1947; s. Ralph Coolidge and Jeanne (Cover) R.; m. Rebecca Jo Vorderman, Mar. 22, 1969; children: Melissa Michelle, Allison Suzanne. BSME, Va. Poly. Inst., 1970; JD, Am. U., Washington, 1974. Bar: Va. 1975, U.S. Ct. Customs and Patent Appeals 1977, U.S. Dist. Ct. (ea. dist.) Mich. 1978, Mich. 1979, U.S. Ct. Appeals (6th cir.) 1979, U.S. Dist. Ct. (we. dist.) Mich. 1981, U.S. Ct. Appeals (fed. cir.) 1983. Supervisory patent examiner U.S. Patent Office, Washington, 1970-77; patent atty., ptnr. Cullen, Sloman, Cantor, Grauer, Scott & Rutherford, Detroit, 1977-88; ptnr. Dykema, Gossett, 1989—. Contbr. articles to profl. jours. Mem. adminstrv. bd. First United Methodist Ch., Birmingham, Mich., 1980—. With U.S. Army, 1970-76. Recipient Superior Performance award U.S. Patent Office, Washington, 1971-77. Mem. Am. Patent Law Assn., ABA, Mich. Patent Law Assn., Mich. Bar. (mem. governing council patent trademark and copyright law sect. 1981-84), Engring. Soc. Detroit, Masons, Tau Beta Pi, Pi Tau Sigma, Phi Kappa Phi. Methodist. Home: 4713 Riverchase Dr Troy MI 48098-4186 Office: Dykema Gossett 1577 N Woodward Ave Ste 300 Bloomfield Hills MI 48304-2967

RADER, RANDALL RAY, federal judge; b. 1949. BA magna cum laude, 1974; JD with honors, George Washington U., 1978. Bar: D.C., U.S. Ct. Appeals (fed. cir.) 1990, U.S. Claims Ct., U.S. Supreme Ct. Legis. asst. to Congresswoman Virginia Smith U.S. Ho. of Reps., 1975-78; mem. staff Ways and Means Com. U.S. Ho. Reps., 1978-81; chief counsel subcom. on Constn. U.S. Senate Judiciary Com., chief counsel, staff dir. subcom. on patents, copyrights and trademarks, 1981-87; counsel to Senator Orrin Hatch, 1981-87; judge U.S. Ct. Claims, Washington, 1988-90, U.S. Ct. Appeals (fed. cir.), Washington, 1990—; lectr. patent law U. Va. Sch. Law, trial advocacy George Washington U. Nat. Law Ctr. Contbr. articles to profl. jours.; co-editor: Criminal Justice Reform, 1983. Mem. Fed. Bar Assn. Office: US Ct Appeals Fed Cir 717 Madison Pl NW Ste 913 Washington DC 20439-0002

RADER, ROBERT MICHAEL, lawyer; b. Camden, N.J., Sept. 9, 1946; s. Raymond Cornelius and Martha Lou (Freas) R.; m. Eileen Charnesky, June 5, 1976; children: Brennan Matthew, Ashley Marie. BA cum laude, Lafayette Coll., 1968; JD, Cornell U., 1971. Bar: N.J. 1972, D.C. 1977. Law sec. to chief judge U.S. Dist. Ct. N.J., Newark, 1971-73; trial atty. U.S. Justice Dept., Washington, 1973-78; assoc. Conner & Wetterhahn P.C., Washington, 1978-79, ptnr., 1980—. Contbr. articles to profl. jours. Ward chmn. Falls Church Rep. com., Va., 1980-86. Mem. Phi Beta Kappa. Roman Catholic. Club: River Bend Country (Great Falls, Va.). Home: 812 Hickory Vale Ln Great Falls VA 22066-2810 Office: Winston & Strawn 1400 L St NW Washington DC 20005-3509

RADEST, HOWARD BERNARD, clergyman, educator; b. N.Y.C., June 29, 1928; s. Louis and Gussie (Permison) R.; m. Rita Stollman, Dec. 22, 1951; children: Robert, Michael. A.B., Columbia U., 1949, Ph.D. 1971; M.A. (Hillman fellow 1950), New Sch. Social Research, 1951. Dir. youth activities N.Y. Soc. Ethical Culture, 1955-56; leader Ethical Culture Soc. Bergen County, Teaneck, N.J., 1956-64, Ethical Culture Movement, 1956—; mem. Coun. Ethical Leaders, 1958—; exec. dir. Am. Ethical Union, N.Y.C., 1964-70; assoc. prof. philosophy Ramapo Coll., N.J., 1971-73; prof. Ramapo Coll., 1973-79; dir. Ethical Culture Schs., 1979-91; adj. prof. philosophy U. S.C., Beaufort, 1991—; co-chmn., sec. gen. Internat. Humanist and Ethical Union, 1970-86, bd. trustees, 1986—; assoc. Am. Civilization Seminar Columbia U., chmn. moral edn. seminar, 1983-91; adv. bd. NBC, 1988-94; dir. Camp Elliott, Jeffersonville, N.Y., 1963, 64; dean Humanist Inst., 1982-92; dean emeritus; cons. state based programs NEH, Beaufort Meml. Hosp., 1994—, Hilton Head Hosp., 1994—; mem. assessment com. Vols. in Medicine, 1994—. Author: Understanding Ethical Religion, 1958, On Life and Meaning, 1963, Toward Common Ground, 1969, To Seek a Humane World, 1971, Can We Teach Ethics, 1989, The Devil and Secular Humanism, 1990, Community Service Encounter with Strangers, 1993; also articles; editor: Ramapo Papers, 1976-79, International Humanism; editorial bd.: Religious Humanism, Free Inquiry, The Humanist. Mem. bd. Encampment for Citizenship, 1963-71, Mental Health Assn. Bergen County, Bergen Co. Mental Health Bd., 1964-67, Assn. Moral Edn., 1986-94; mem. bd. past treas., v.p. N.J. Welfare Conf., 1958-64; mem. bd., past pres. Health and Welfare Coun. Bergen County, 1956-64; bd. mgrs. Bergen Pines County Hosp., 1966-70; Bergen County (N.J.) Mem. Democratic Com., 1970-71. Served with AUS, 1953-55. Mem. AAUP (treas. N.J. coun. 1973-74), Com. Sane Nuclear Policy (sponsor N.J.), Am. Assn. UN, Am. Philos. Assn., Soc. Advancement Am. Philosophy, N.Am. Com. Humanism (trustee 1985—), S.C. Philos. Assn., Grad. Faculties Alumni Columbia U. (trustee 1989-91), Network Progressive Educators (steering com. 1988-91), Phi Beta Kappa. Home: 108 Devil's Elbow Ln Moss Creek Hilton Head Island SC 29926

RADEWAGEN, FRED, publisher, organization executive; b. Louisville, Mar. 20, 1944; s. Hobart Fred and Mildred Lillian (Carlsen) R.; m. Amata Catherine Coleman, Dec. 4, 1971; children—Erika Catherine, Mark Peter, Kirsten Alexandra. B.A., Northwestern U., 1966; M.S., Georgetown U., 1968. Rsch. asst. Republican Nat. Com., Washington, 1967-68; dir. mgmt. services Republican Presdl. Campaign and Inaugural Com., Washington, 1968-69; liaison officer Trust Terr. Washington, 1969-71; staff coordinator for territorial affairs Dept. Interior, Washington, 1971-75; assoc. dir. govtl. and polit. participation programs C. of C. U.S., 1975-76, dir., 1976-79; dir. resource devel. Rep. Govs. Assn., Washington, 1979-81; dir. state and fed. relations Rep. Govs. Assn., 1981-82; Washington rep. Govt. of Am. Samoa, 1982-85, 89-93; pub. Washington Pacific Report, 1982—; dir. Pacific Islands Washington office, 1984—; rep. Cook Islands, Washington, 1986-89; pres. Washington and Pacific Assocs., 1975-84; staff exec. Bus. Alliance for Congl. Action, 1974-77; lectr. Insts. for Orgn. Mgmt., 1977-79; exec. dir. Nat. Chamber Alliance for Politics, 1977-79; mem. U.S. del. UN Trusteeship Coun., 1972, advisor U.S. del. to Com. of Twenty-Four, 1982-83; mem. Am. Samoa dels. to South Pacific Conf., 1982-83, 89, 91, Post-Forum Dialogue, 1991, UN Conf. on Environment and Devel., 1992; del. Am. Coun. Young Polit. Leaders, 1982-83, mem. coun., 1984—; exec. dir. U.S.- New Zealand Coun., 1995—. Mem. Alexandria Rep. City Com., 1979-80; del. Va. Rep. State Conv., 1981, 89, 93, 94; participant Rep. Nat. Convs., 1968, 80, 84, 88, 92; past mem. Christian edn. com. Westminster Presbyn. Ch. Mem. Northwestern U. Alumni Assn. Club: Washington bd. govs.), Washington Roundtable for Asian/Pacific Press, Nat. Capital Interfrat. Forum (past pres.), Nat. Eagle Scout Assn. (life), Mensa, Delta Tau Delta (past pres. Washington alumni). Clubs: Ill. State Soc. (past v.p.), Capitol Hill (life), Circumnavigators. Home: 103 E Luray Ave Alexandria VA 22301-2027 also: 1245 N Taft Ave Berkeley IL 60163-1043 also: 1019 3rd St Rehoboth Beach DE 19971-1503 Office: PO Box 26142 Alexandria VA 22313-6142

RADEY, FRANK HERBERT, JR., architect; b. Camden, N.J., Nov. 8, 1931; s. F. Herbert and Estelle (Magnuson) R.; m. Patricia Hoops Lapp, June 24, 1960; children: Frank H. III, Cheryl Lynn. Degree in architecture, Ga. Inst. Tech., 1954. Registered architect, N.J. Ptnr. Radey & Radey, Camden, 1960-80, Radey & Fuller, Cherry Hill, N.J., 1980-91; commr. N.J. State Bd. Architects, 1986-91; chmn. N.J. Joint Bd. Architects and Engrs., 1989-91; arbitrator constrn. disputes Am. Arbitration Assn., 1975—; mem. Nat. Coun. Archtl. Registration Bds., Washington, 1987-91. Architect, designer over 300 pub. sch. projects, N.J. and Pa. Trustee Stratford (N.J.) Mil. Acad., 1965-80; commr. Moorestown (N.J.) Appearance Com., 1989—. Recipient award of merit for excellence in architecture AIA, 1980, Presdl. citation N.J. Soc. Architects. Lutheran. Avocations: flying, sports. Home: 781 Mcelwee Rd Moorestown NJ 08057-3935 Office: Radey & Fuller AIA 100 Haddontowne Ct Cherry Hill NJ 08034-3602

RADFORD, LINDA ROBERTSON, psychologist; b. Winnipeg, Man., Can., Nov. 6, 1944; came to U.S. 1954; d. William and Ruth Aileen (Wheatley) Robertson; 1 child, Drew Richard; m. Richard D. Polley, Sept. 21, 1991. BA, Seattle Pacific U., 1970; MEd, U. Wash., 1972, PhD, 1980. Lic. psychologist, Fla.; cert. hypnotherapist. Dir. support svcs. Highline-West Seattle Mental Health Clinic, 1973-75; rsch. asst. in human affairs Battelle, Seattle, 1976-80, rsch. scientist, 1982-87; sr. cons. Martin Simmonds Assoc., Seattle, 1980-82; pres., owner R.R. Assocs., Seattle and Miami, 1982—; pres. PGI Inc., Miami and London, 1989—; pvt. clin. psychologist Bay Harbor Island, Fla., 1991—, West Palm Beach, Fla., 1991—; chmn., chief exec. officer Swiver Corp., North Miami, Fla., 1994—; chair Swiver Corp., 1994—; vis. sr. assoc. Joint Ctr. for Environ. and Urban Problems, North Miami, Fla., 1986-88; cons. Health Ministry Govt. Thailand, Bangkok, 1989—. Contbr. articles to profl. jours. Community Mental Health Ctr fellow, Seattle, 1972-73. Mem. Am. Psychol. Assn., Am. Soc. Clin. Hypnosis, N.Y. Acad. of Sci. Avocations: tennis, music, snorkeling, racquetball, fishing. Home: 9264 Bay Dr Surfside FL 33154 Office: 1160 Kane Concourse Ste 401 Bal Harbour FL 33154 also: Ste 680 1645 Palm Beach Lakes Blvd West Palm Beach FL 33409

RADFORD, NORMAN DEPUE, JR., lawyer; b. Quantico, Va., Sept. 29, 1943; s. Norman D. Sr. and Mary A. (Boyer) R.; m. Dorothy Ann Posobiec; Apr. 25, 1975. BS in Civil Engring., Va. Milit. Inst., 1965; MS in Sanitary Engring., U. N.C., 1967; JD, U. Va., 1972. Bar: Tex. 1972, U.S. Ct. Appeals (10th cir.) 1973, U.S. Ct. Appeals (D.C. and 5th cirs.) 1974, U.S. Dist. Ct. (so. dist.) Tex. 1975, U.S. Supreme Ct. 1977, U.S. Ct. Appeals (4th cir.) 1980, U.S. Ct. Appeals (11th cir.) 1981, U.S. Dist. Ct. (ea. and we. dists.) 1983, U.S. Dist. Ct. (no. dist.) Tex. 1990; registered profl. engr., Pa., Va. Project engr. Roy F. Weston, Inc., West Chester, Pa., 1967-69; assoc. Vinson & Elkins, Houston, 1972-79, ptnr. 1979-89; ptnr. Vinson & Elkins, L.L.P., Dallas, 1989-93; of counsel Vinson & Elkins, Dallas, 1993—. Mem. Air and Waste Mgmt. Assn., Water Environ. Fedn., Am. Soc. Civil Engrs., State Bar Tex. (chairperson environ. and natural resources sect. 1984-85), Houston C. of C. (chair environ. com. 1979-81). Avocation: running. Office: Vinson & Elkins LLP 3700 Trammell Crow Ctr 2001 Ross Ave Dallas TX 75201-2975

RADICE, ANNE-IMELDA, museum director; b. Buffalo, Feb. 29, 1948; d. Lawrence and Anne (Marino) R. A.B., Wheaton Coll., Norton, Mass., 1969; M.A., Villa SchiFanoia, Florence, Italy, 1971; Ph.D., U. N.C., 1976; M.B.A., Am. U., 1984. Asst. curator Nat. Gallery of Art, Washington, 1972-76; archtl. historian U.S. Capitol, Washington, 1976-80, curator Office of Architect, 1980-85; dir. Nat. Mus. Women in the Arts, 1985-89; chief div. of creative arts USIA, 1989-91; sr. dep. chmn. Nat. Endowment for Arts, Washington, 1991-92; acting chmn., 1992-93; exec. v.p. Gray & Co. II, Miami, Fla., 1993; prodr. World Affairs TV Prodn., 1994; assoc. producer Think Tank, 1994; chief spl. projects, confidential adviser Courtney Sales Ross, 1994—; cons. in pub. rels. and TV, 1994—. Contbr. articles to profl. jours.

RADIGAN, FRANK XAVIER, pharmaceutical company executive; b. Paterson, N.J., Apr. 13, 1933; John Joseph and Susan Clair (Brett) R.; m. Julia Lou Smith, Aug. 27, 1960 (div. Nov. 1988); children: Francis Gregory, Patricia Louise, Brett Frasier; m. Carol E. Berkley, June 26, 1992. AB in Sociology, Seton Hall U., 1955; MBA Mktg., U. Hartford, 1968. Asst. mgr. Beneficial Fin. Co., Newark, 1955-57; hosp. rep. Becton-Dickinson Co., Rutherford, N.J., 1957-58; dist. mgr. Merck Sharp & Dohme, West Point, Pa., 1958—. Chmn. St. John the Baptist Social Justice, New Freedom, Pa., 1981-85; mem. Passaic County Dem. Com., 1985-86. Capt. USAR, 1956. Mem. Am. Mktg. Assn., Md. Pharmacists Assn. (chmn. indsl. rels. com.), W.Va. Pharm. Soc., Balt. Pharm. Assn. (hon. pres. 1989), Hopewell Fish and Game Assn., Bon Air Country Club, Elk, Lion (pres. Glen Rock 1975-76, 86-88). Roman Catholic. Avocation: horsebreeding. Home and Office: 2440 Bradenbaugh Rd White Hall MD 21161-9661

RADIGAN, JOSEPH RICHARD, human resources executive; b. N.Y.C., Apr. 9, 1939; s. Joseph Anthony and Mae Cecilia (Holden) R.; m. Margaret Mary Krug, Apr. 23, 1962; children—Kateri, Laureen, Kenneth. BA, Fordham Coll., 1961; MA, Fordham U., 1962; grad. advanced mgmt. program, Harvard U., 1982; grad., Air War Coll., 1982, Navy War Coll., 1989. Mgr. employee relations Gen. Electric Co., N.Y.C., 1965-79; cons. orgn. planning Gen. Electric Co., Fairfield, Conn., 1981-83; dir. orgn. and mgmt. Kennecott Co., Stamford, Conn., 1979-81; sr. v.p. human resources Donaldson, Lufkin & Jenrette Inc., N.Y.C., 1983-86, The Equitable, N.Y.C., 1986-90; sr. v.p., gen. mgr. Manchester Co., N.Y.C., 1991-92; pres. Cove Communications, 1991—; sr. v.p. human resource Blue Cross/Blue Shield Ga., 1993—. Mem. Cardinal's Com. of Laity. 1st lt. U.S. Army, 1962-65, col. USAR. Mem. Wall Street Pers. Mgrs. Assn. (sec. 1984-85), Knights of Malta. Republican. Roman Catholic. Home: 6 Cardinal Ln Westport CT 06880

RADIN, ALEX, former association executive, consultant; b. Chattanooga, June 14, 1921; s. Joseph and Mollie (Pernat) R.; m. Sara Leah Gordon, Sept. 6, 1943 (dec. Nov. 20, 1964); children—Jay Jacob, William Gordon m. Carol Nita Schuman, Sept. 21, 1979. B.A., U. Chattanooga, 1948. Reporter Chattanooga Times, Chattanooga, 1938-42; adminstrv. asst. Office of Price Adminstrn., Washington, 1942-43; adminstrv. analyst Dept. of State, Washington, 1945-48; asst. to gen. mgr. Am. Pub. Power Assn., Washington, 1948-51, exec. dir., 1951-86; pres. Radin & Assocs. Inc., 1986—; cons. U.S. Senate Com. on Interior and Insular Affairs, Washington, 1959; mem. exec. com. Am. Nuclear Energy Coun., Washington, 1973-88; v.p. Consumer Fedn. Am., Washington, 1978-86; mem. So. States Energy Bd.'s Adv. Com. on TVA, 1986-87; chmn. Monitored Retrievable Storage Rev. Commn., 1988-89; rep., sec. U.S. Dept. Energy, Independent Mgmt. and Fin. Rev. of Yucca Mt. (Nev.) Project, 1994-95; mem. adv. bd. Ford Found. Energy Policy Project, 1973-74. Columnist, Pub. Power Mag.; contbr. articles to newspapers. Mem. adv. bd. Dance Theatre of Harlem, N.Y.C., 1995—. Recipient Leland Olds award Western States Water and Power Consumers Conf., 1970, Philip Hart Disting. Consumer Svc. award Consumer Fedn. Am., 1985, Alex Radin Disting. Svc. award Am. Pub. Power Assn., 1986. Democrat. Jewish. Club: Nat. Press. Avocations: photography; music; art; hiking. Home: 2510 Virginia Ave NW Apt 610N Washington DC 20037-1904 Office: Radin & Assocs Inc 1200 New Hampshire Ave NW Washington DC 20036-6801

RADIN, JOHN WILLIAM, agriculturalist, physiologist; b. N.Y.C., Jan. 8, 1944; m. 1965; 2 children. BS, U. Calif., Davis, 1965, PhD in Plant Physiology, 1970. Assoc. agronomist U. Calif., Davis, 1970-71; plant physiologist Western Cotton Res. Lab Agrl. Res. Svc., USDA, 1971—. Mem. Am. Soc. Plant Physiologists (Dennis Robert Hoagland award 1991), Crop Sci. Soc. Am. Home: 4135 E Broadmor Dr Tempe AZ 85282 Office: Western Cotton Lab USDA Agr Res Svc 4135 E Broadway Rd Phoenix AZ 85040-8803*

RADIN, NORMAN SAMUEL, retired biochemistry educator; b. N.Y.C., July 20, 1920; s. Joseph and Bertha (Sherson) R.; m. Norma Levinson, Dec. 23, 1947; children: Lon, Laurie. B.A., Columbia U., 1941, Ph.D., 1949. Asst. research scientist Nat. Def. Research Com., Carnegie Inst. Tech., 1942-45; research chemist Biochem. Inst., U. Tex., Austin, 1950-52; prin. scientist Hines Hosp., Va, Maywood, Ill., 1952-54, VA Research Hosp., Chgo., 1954-57; mem. faculty dept. biochemistry Northwestern U. Med. Sch., Chgo., 1952-60; assoc. prof. Northwestern U. Med. Sch., 1957-60; research scientist Mental Health Research Inst., U. Mich., 1960-91, prof. biol.

chemistry, 1973-84, prof. neurochemistry, 1984-91; prof. emeritus in neurochemistry, 1992—. Editor book in field. NIH fellow, 1946-48; AEC fellow, 1949-50. Mem. Am. Soc. Biol. Chemists, Am. Soc. Neurochemistry, Internat. Soc. Neurochemistry. *In reviewing how best I might help humanity, I came to the conclusion that the greatest human need is higher intelligence. This feature is the characteristic which reflects the major product of the evolutionary process. Evolution has brought man to a point so high that he can destroy civilization, but not high enough to realize the foolishness of so many efforts. The best hope for higher intelligence seems to me to lie in neurochemical research. This analysis led me to devote my life to neurochemistry.*

RADKE, JAN RODGER, pulmonologist, hospital program administrator; b. Detroit, Nov. 16, 1942; s. Edward V. and Dorothy M. Radke; m. Judith Hogan, June 20, 1987; children: Jennifer, John, Colin, Cameron. BS, Mich. State U., 1965; MD, U. Wis., 1969. Diplomate Am. Bd. Internal Medicine, Am. Bd. Pulmonary. Intern Henry Food Hosp., 1969-70, resident internal medicine, 1970-71, resident, 1974-75, chief med. resident internal medicine, 1975-76, fellow pulmonary/critical care, 1977-78; v.p. satellite program Henry Ford Health Systems, Detroit, 1989; assoc. v.p. ambulatory program, assoc. prof. medicine Loyola U. Med. Ctr., Maywood, Ill., 1990-93, v.p. health care svcs., 1993—. Lt. comdr. USNR, 1971-73. Fellow ACP, Am. Coll. Chest Physicians; mem. Am. Thoracic Soc., Am. Coll. Physician Execs. Avocation: bird watching. Office: Loyola Univ Med Ctr 2160 S 1st Ave Maywood IL 60153

RADKE, RODNEY OWEN, agricultural research executive, consultant, research biologist; b. Ripon, Wis., Feb. 5, 1942; s. Edward Ludwig and Vera Ione (Phillips) R.; m. Jean Marie Rutsch, Sept. 1, 1963; children—Cheryl Lynn, Lisa Diane, Daniel E. B.S., U. Wis., 1963, M.S., 1965, Ph.D., 1967. Research sci. Monsanto Agrl. Co., St. Louis, 1969-75, sr. research group leader, 1975-79, research mgr. 1979-81, mgr. research, 1981-93; pvt. practice cons., 1993—. Contbr. articles to profl. jours. Served to capt. U.S. Army, 1967-69. Mem. Weed Sci. Soc. North Crtl. Weed Sci. Soc. Lutheran. Club: First Capitol Soccer (coach 1981-92) (St. Charles). Avocations: power boating; soccer; gardening; woodshop. Home and Office: 1119 Grand Prix Dr Saint Charles MO 63303-6313

RADLEY, VIRGINIA LOUISE, humanities educator; b. Marion, N.Y., Aug. 12, 1927; d. Howard James and Lula (Ferris) R.; B.A., Russell Sage Coll., 1949, L.H.D., 1981; M.A., U. Rochester, 1952; M.S., Syracuse U., 1957, Ph.D., 1958. Instr. English Chatham (Va.) Hall, 1952-55; asst. dean students, asst. prof. English Goucher Coll., 1957-59; dean freshmen, asst. prof. English Russell Sage Coll., 1959-60, assoc. dean, assoc. prof. English, 1960-61, prof. chmn. dept., 1961-69; dean coll., prof. English Nazareth Coll., Rochester, N.Y., 1969-73; provost for undergrad. edn., central adminstrn. SUNY, Albany, 1973-74; exec. v.p., provost Coll. Arts and Scis., SUNY, Oswego, 1974-76; acting pres. Coll. Arts and Scis., SUNY, 1976-78; pres. SUNY, Oswego, 1978-88; prof. English and Humanities SUNY, 1988-93; scholar-in-residence Russell Sage Coll., 1993—; vis. prof. Syracuse U., summer 1957-59, Nazareth Coll., summer 1965; cons. N.Y. State Dept. Edn.; chmn. commn. on women Am. Coun. on Edn., 1978-81, sr. assoc. Office of Women, 1990—; trustee Marymount Manhattan Coll., 1988-90; mem. commn. on higher edn. Middle States Assn., 1979-86; disting vis. prof. Russell Sage Coll., 1994-95. Author: Samuel Taylor Coleridge, 1966, Elizabeth Barrett Browning, 1972, also articles. Mem. MLA (chmn. regional sect. Romanticism 1969), English Inst., Pi Lambda Theta. Republican. Home: RR 1 Box 1697 Poestenkill NY 12140-1706

RADLOFF, ROBERT ALBERT, real estate executive; b. Chgo., Mar. 30, 1947; s. Henry O. and Virginia G. (Grothus) R.; m. Ann Macy Beha, June 21, 1975; children: Macy, Allison. BS in Fin., Boston U., 1969. V.p. Kuras & Co., Inc., Boston, 1971-76; sr. v.p. Boston Co. Real Estate Counsel, Inc., 1976-81, pres., 1981-89, chmn., 1989-91; real estate investments counselor Boston, 1991—; bd. dirs. Boston Pvt. Bank and Trust Co. Bd. dirs. First Night, Boston, 1990, Mass. Cultural Coun., 1992, Friends of Vieilles Maison Francais, 1992; chmn. bd. overseers Isabella Stewart Gardner, 1995; overseer Children's Hosp., WGBH Ednl. Found. Mem. Am. Soc. Real Estate Counselors (cert.), Somerset Club. Avocations: art, tennis, travel. Office: 33 Kingston St Boston MA 02111-2208

RADLOFF, WILLIAM HAMILTON, editor, writer; b. Milw., Mar. 5, 1914; s. Alfred Carl and Florence (Hamilton) R.; m. Mary Ellen Borgman, Nov. 10, 1940; children: Thomas M., Susan M. BA, Ripon Coll., 1936. Reporter, writer Milw. Sentinel, 1937-42; reporter, writer Milw. Jour., 1946-49, asst. city editor, 1949-60, asst. feature editor, 1960-61, feature editor, 1961-69; asst. story editor 20th Century Fox Film Corp., L.A., 1969-72; freelance writer, poet L.A., 1972—. Author, editor numerous news and feature articles. Lt. U.S. Army, Counter Intelligence, 1942-46, PTO. Recipient Letter of Commendation, Japanese Occupation. Home: 313 S Anita Ave Los Angeles CA 90049-3805

RADMER, MICHAEL JOHN, lawyer, educator; b. Wisconsin Rapids, Wis., Apr. 28, 1945; s. Donald Richard and Thelma Loretta (Donahue) R.; children from previous marriage: Christina Nicole, Ryan Michael; m. Laurie J. Anshus, Dec. 22, 1983; 1 child, Michael John. B.S., Northwestern U., Evanston, Ill., 1967; J.D., Harvard U., 1970. Bar: Minn. 1970. Assoc. Dorsey & Whitney, Mpls., 1970-75, ptnr., 1976—; lectr. law Hamline U. Law Sch., St. Paul, 1981-84; gen. counsel, rep., sec. over 170 federally registered investment cos., Mpls. and St. Paul, 1977—. Contbr. articles to legal jours. Active legal work Hennepin County Legal Advice Clinic, Mpls., 1971—. Mem. ABA, Minn. Bar Assn., Hennepin County Bar Assn. Club: Mpls. Athletic. Home: 4329 E Lake Harriet Pky Minneapolis MN 55409-1725 Office: Dorsey & Whitney Pillsbury Ctr S 220 S 6th St Minneapolis MN 55402-4500 *A key to a successful and happy life is achieving a balance. Intellectual, academic and vocational goals are important, but their pursuit should be balanced with ample time spent with family and friends, travel and enjoying reading, music, art and sports. Don't be afraid to try something new; realize that education should be a lifelong pursuit. Much frustration can be avoided by realizing that life is full of trade-offs. You can't experience the joy of raising children and have the complete freedom of the child-free. Finally, while you should strive for perfection, be content with less. We are only human, and live in an imperfect, yet wonderful, world.*

RADNAY, PAUL ANDREW, physician; b. Szolnok, Hungary, Aug. 6, 1913; came to U.S., 1949, naturalized, 1954; s. Ferenc and Ida (Varsa) R.; m. Eva Balazs, Aug. 6, 1939. MD, U. Szeged, 1937. Diplomate Hungarian Bd. Surgery, Hungarian Bd. Dentistry, Am. Bd. Anesthesiology. Intern Univ. Clinics, Budapest and Szeged, Hungary, 1936-37; chief head and neck surgery outpatient dept. Orszagos Tarsadalom Biztosito Intezet, Budapest, 1945-49; asst. Polyclinic Hosp., Budapest, 1945-49; resident in anesthesiology Queens Gen. Hosp., Jamaica, N.Y., 1953-54; dir. anesthesia sect. cardio-thoracic surgery Montefiore Hosp., Med. Ctr., Bronx, N.Y., 1970-79; cons. Montefiore Hosp., Med. Ctr., Bronx, 1979-83, emeritus attending anesthesiologist, 1983—; prof. anesthesiology Albert Einstein Coll. Medicine, Bronx, 1981-83, prof. emeritus, 1983—; cons. respiratory therapy program Manattee Community Coll., Bradenton, Fla. Editor: Anesthetic Considerations for Pediatric Cardiac Surgery, 1980, 2 English, 1 Spanish edits.; contbr. articles to profl. lit. Pres. Am.-Hungarian Med. Assn., 1966-67; vice chmn. bd. dirs. Am.-Hungarian Found., 1974-90; bd. dirs. Sarasota Opera Assn. Capt. M.C., Hungarian Army, intrmittantly, 1934-45. Decorated Cross Knighthood Order St. Martin, Austria; decorated Cross St. John of Jerusalem, Knights of Malta; recipient Disting. Svc. award Am. Hungarian Found., 1978, Incentive N.Y. County Med. Soc., 1983; recipient Goldzieher award Am.-Hungarian Med. Assn., 1976, also Disting. Svc. award. Fellow Am. Coll. Anesthesiologists, N.Y. Acad. Medicine, N.Y. Cardiological Soc., Internat. Coll. Surgeons; mem. Am. Soc. Anesthesiologists, N.Y. State Soc. Anesthesiologists, N.Y. County Med. Soc., N.Y. State Med. Soc., Soc. Cardiovascular Anesthesiologists, Hungarian Soc. Anesthesiologists and Intensive Therapists (hon.). Home and Office: 101 S Gulfstream Ave Sarasota FL 34236-8917 *A good physician has humility. He must give the patient consideration first as a human being, and secondly as a patient who requires treatment. One must never see the sick only as a source of financial reward. In academic life one should be a clinician, a teacher and a researcher. The contribution which appears to be insignificant may one day become the base of a major discovery.*

RADNER, ROY, economist, educator, researcher; b. Chgo., June 29, 1927; s. Samuel and Ella (Kulansky) R.; m. Virginia L. Honoski, July 26, 1949 (dec. Apr. 1976); children: Hilary A., Erica H. (dec.), Amy E., Ephraim L.; m. Charlotte Virginia Kuh, Jan. 22, 1978. PhB with honors, U. Chgo, 1945, BS in Math., 1950, MS in Math., 1951, PhD in Math. Stats., 1956. Rsch. asst. Cowles Commn. for Rsch. in Econs. U. Chgo., 1951, rsch. assoc., 1951-54, asst. prof., 1954-55; mem. Cowles Found. for Rsch. in Econs. Yale U., New Haven, 1955-57, asst. prof. econs., 1955-57; assoc. prof. econs. and stats. U. Calif., Berkeley, 1957-61, prof. econs. and stats., 1961-79, chmn. dept. econs., 1966-69; Taussig prof. econs. Harvard U., Cambridge, Mass., 1977-78, vis. prof. Kennedy Sch. Govt., 1978-79; mem. tech. staff AT&T Bell Labs, Murray Hill, N.J., 1979-84, disting. mem. tech. staff, 1985—; rsch. prof. econs. NYU, N.Y.C., 1983—; mem. com. on fundamental rsch. relevant to edn. NRC-NAS, 1976-77. mem. commn. on human resources, 1976-79; mem. assembly of behavioral and social scis. NRC, 1979-82, mem. com. on risk and decision making, 1980-81, mem. working group on basic rsch. in behavioral and social scis., 1985-86; mem. panel on contingent valuation methdlogy NOAA, U.S. Dept. Commerce, 1992-93; mem. steering com. Enjeux et Procedures de Decentralization Commisariat du Plan, Paris, 1992—; active Com. on Prevention of Nuclear War, also various other profl. coms., bds., panels. Author: (books, monographs) Notes on Theory of Economic Planning, 1963, (with D. Jorgenson and J.J. McCall) Optimal Replacement Policy, 1967, (with J. Marshack) Economic Theory of Teams, 1972, (with L.S. Miller) Demand and Supply in U.S. Higher Education, 1975, (with C.V. Kuh) Mathematicians in Academia, 1980; also articles on econ. theory, orgn. theory, econs. of edn.; co-editor: Decision and Organization, 1972, Education as an Industry, 1976, Information, Incentives and Economic Mechanisms, 1987, Perspectives on Deterrence, 1989, Bargaining with Incomplete Information, 1992; assoc. editor Mgmt. Sci., 1959-70, Econometrica, 1961-68, Jour. Econ. Theory, 1968—, Am. Econ. Rev., 1970-82, Games and Econ. Behavior, Econ. Theory, Econ. Design, Rev. Acctg. Studies. 2d lt. U.S. Army, 1945-48, PTO. William Cook scholar U. Chgo., 1944-45; fellow Ctr. Advanced Study in Behavioral Scis., Stanford, Calif., 1955-56, Guggenheim Found. fellow, 1961-62, 65-66, overseas fellow Churchill Coll., Cambridge U., Eng., 1969-70, 89. Fellow AAAS (disting. fellow), Econometric Soc. (v.p. 1970-72, pres. 1972-73), Am. Acad. Arts and Scis., Am. Econ. Assn. (disting. fellow); mem. NAS (chair econ. sect. 1994—), Inst. Math. Stats. Avocations: music, backpacking, cross-country skiing. Home: 1 Park Pl Short Hills NJ 07078-2825 Office: AT&T Bell Labs 600 Mountain Ave Murray Hill NJ 07974-0636

RADNER, SIDNEY HOLLIS, retired rug company executive; b. Holyoke, Mass., Dec. 8, 1919; s. William I. Radner; m. Helen Jane Cohen, Dec. 12, 1946; children: William Marc, Richard Scott. Student, Yale U., 1941. Ret. pres. Am. Rug Co., Holyoke; lectr., cons., investigator on crooked gambling, U.S. Armed Forces, FBI, Govt. of Can., state and mcpl. police squads; dir. Houdini Magical Hall of Fame, Niagara Falls, Ont., Can.; dir., organizer Annual Ofcl. Houdini Seance. Author: Radner on Poker, Radner on Dice, Radner on Roulette and Casino Games, How to Detect Card Sharks; contbr. articles to profl. jours.; appeared in First TVseries Turn of a Card, 1953, BBC Omnibus: Houdini, 1971, CNN, 1993, 94, Tonight Show, 1956, Today Show, Merv Griffin Show, CNBC, PBS, CBC, In Search Of..., First TV series exposing crooked gambling techniques, 1956; cons. to Houdini TV spl. A&E. Past pres. Holyoke C. of C.; co-founder Volleyball Hall of Fame; past bd. dirs. Greater Springfield (Mass.) Better Bus. Bur.; hon. curator, dir. Houdini Hist. Ctr., Appleton, Wis. Served with criminal investigation divsn. U S Army, 1942-46. Mem. Soc. Am. Magicians (occult investigation com.), Internat. Brotherhood Magicians, Magic Circle London (inner magic circle), Magicians Guild (charter), Magic Collector's Assn. (charter, Honor award 1992), Am. Platform Assn., Houdini Club Wis. (hon.), Inner Magic Cir., Nat. Assn. Bunco Investigators, China-Burma-India Vets. Assn. (life), Rotary, Masons, Shriners. Jewish. Home: 1050 Northampton St Holyoke MA 01040-1321 Office: 1594 Dwight St Holyoke MA 01040-2397

RADNOFSKY, BARBARA A., lawyer; b. Broomall, Pa., July 8, 1956; m. Daniel Edward Supkis Jr.; children: Danielle Esther, Max David, Michaela Sarah. BA magna cum laude, U. Houston, 1976; JD with honors, U. Tex., 1979. Bar: Tex. Assoc. Vinson & Elkins, L.L.P., Houston, 1979-87, ptnr., 1987—; mem. faculty intensive trial advocacy program U. Tex. Sch. Law, 1985-86; speaker in field. Contbr. articles to profl. jours. Albert Jones scholar U. Tex. Sch. Law; named Outstanding Young Lawyer Houston, Houston Young Lawyers Assn., 1988-89. Mem. ABA (chmn. Nat. Trial Competition 1983), Tex. Young Lawyers Assn. (Outstanding Young Lawyer Tex. 1988-89), Tex. Assn. Def. Counsel (mem. rules of evidence com. 1987-89, med. malpractice com. 1984-86), Nat. Health Lawyers Assn. Avocations: sailing, ballet, modern dance, basketball. Office: Vinson & Elkins 3300 First City Tower 1001 Fannin Houston TX 77002

RADNOR, ALAN T., lawyer; b. Cleve., Mar. 10, 1946; s. Robert Clark and Rose (Chester) R.; m. Carol Sue Hirsch, June 22, 1969; children: Melanie, Joshua, Joanna. B.A., Kenyon Coll., 1967; M.S. in Anatomy, Ohio State U., 1969, J.D., 1972. Bar: Ohio 1972. Ptnr., Vorys, Sater, Seymour & Pease, Columbus, Ohio, 1972—; adj. prof. law Ohio State U., Columbus, 1979—. Contbr. articles to profl. jours. Bd. dirs., trustee Congregation Tifereth Israel, Columbus, 1975—, 1st v.p. 1983-85, pres., 1985-87; trustee Columbus Mus. Art, 1995. Named Boss of Yr., Columbus Assn. Legal Secs., 1983. Mem. ABA, Ohio State Bar Assn., Columbus Bar Assn. (chmn. dr.-lawyer com. 1979-80), Columbus Def. Assn. (pres. 1980-81), Def. Research Inst., Internat. Assn. Def. Counsel, Ohio Hosp. Assn. Democrat. Jewish. Avocations: reading; sculpture. Home: 400 S Columbia Ave Columbus OH 43209-1629 Office: Vorys Sater Seymour & Pease 52 E Gay St PO Box 1008 Columbus OH 43216-1008

RADOCK, MICHAEL, foundation executive; b. Belle Vernon, Pa., July 17, 1917; s. Nicholas M. and Pauline (Radich) R.; m. Helen Adelaide Hower, Sept. 2, 1944; children: Robert Hower, William Michael. AB magna cum laude, Westminster Coll., New Wilmington, Pa., 1942, LittD (hon.), 1965; MS in Journalism, Northwestern U., 1946; postgrad., Case Western Res. U., 1950-52. Reporter Fayette City (Pa.) Jour., 1937-39; corr. for Pa. newspapers, 1937-39; reporter, sports editor Charleroi (Pa.) Daily Mail, 1942; dir. news bur., asst. prof. journalism Westminster Coll., 1942-45; dir. pub. relations, prof. journalism Kent (Ohio) State U., 1945-53; with corp. pub. relations Ford Motor Co., Dearborn, Mich., 1953-61; established Inst. for Pub. Rels. Kent (Ohio) State U., 1947; v.p. univ. relations, prof. journalism U. Mich., Ann Arbor, 1961-81; sr. v.p. devel. and univ. relations, prof. journalism U. So. Calif., Los Angeles, 1981-82; v.p. resource devel. Aspen Inst. Humanistic Studies, N.Y.C., 1982-83; advisor to pres. C.S. Mott Found., Flint, Mich., 1983-90, cons., 1990—; mem. faculty Harvard U. Inst. in Ednl. Mgmt., 1972, 73, Williamsburg Devel. Inst., 1979-81; vis. prof. journalism U. Wyo., Laramie, 1952, U. Kent, Canterbury, Eng., 1989; trustee Westminster Coll., 1972-82; mem. adv. bd. Pub. Rels. News; cons. NSF, 1972-73; mem. adv. bd. Chronicle of Non-Profit Enterprise, 1990—. Contbr. Handbook of Institutional Advancement, 1977, (books) Lesly's Public Relations Handbook, 1978, Public Relations Career Directory, 1987, 88, 89, 93, 95, Lesly's Handbook of Public Relations and Communications, 1990. Mem. Football Bd. Fgn. Scholarships, Washington, 1972-74; mem. exec. bd. U. Mich., 1979-81, mem. bd. in control of intracollegiate athletics, 1961-81; trustee Glacier Hills Retirement Ctr., Ann Arbor, 1988-93, Ann Arbor Area Cmty. Found., 1989-92, Mich. Hist. Ctr. Found., 1990—; chmn. White House Sci. and Tech. Adv. Com. on Black Colls., Washington, 1986-88. Recipient Disting. Service award Kent State U., 1965, Frank Ashmore award for disting. service to edn. Am. Coll. Pub. Relations Assn., 1968-69; Disting. Service award for leadership in institutional advancement for minority colls. and univs., 1980. Fellow Pub. Rels. Soc. Am. (accredited); mem. Inst. for Pub. Relation Rsch. and Edn. (bd. trustees 1980-84), Nat. Soc. Fund Raising Execs., Higher Edn. Roundtable. Jewish. Presbyterian. Home: 851 Green Hills Dr Ann Arbor MI 48105-2719

RADOFF, LEONARD IRVING, librarian, consultant; b. Houston, Jan. 9, 1927; s. Morris Aaron and Jenny (Goldberg) R.; m. Lisel Ruth Ephraim, July 25, 1953; 1 child, Lesley Radoff Rappaport. B.A., Rice U., Houston, 1949; M.L.S., U. Tex., Austin, 1965. Cert. secondary sch. tchr., Tex. Tchr. math Aldine Ind. Sch. Dist., Houston, 1959-61, sch. librarian, 1961-63; head pub. services Abilene Pub. Library, Tex., 1964-65; library dir. Pasadena Pub. Library, Tex., 1966-70; chief br. services Houston Pub. Library, 1971-92, ret., 1992; library bldg. cons. Houston, 1975—. Treas. Literacy Vol. Am., Houston, 1984-85; mem. Northside Interests, Houston, 1982-85. Served with

USN, 1945-46. Hoenthal scholar, 1948. Mem. Tex. Library Assn., ALA, Freedom to Read Found., Houston Great Books Council (leader trainer 1953-59, pres. 1967-69). Avocations: tutoring; listening to music; stamp collecting. Home: 4013 Gano St Houston TX 77009-4119

RADOJCSICS, ANNE PARSONS, librarian; b. Mansfield, Ohio, Mar. 23, 1929; d. Richard Walbridge Parsons and Iva Pearl (Ruth) Kemp; m. Joseph Michael Radojcsics, July 8, 1950; children: Kurt Joseph, Jo Anne Radojcsics Kent. Diploma, Bethel Woman's Coll., Hopkinsville, Ky., 1949; BS, Miss. State U., 1972, MEd, 1974. Cert. secondary tchr., Miss. Chemist Humphries Borg-Warner Co., Mansfield, 1950-53; asst. reference libr. Mansfield Pub. Libr., 1953-59; libr. media specialist Verona (Miss.) Sch., 1970-92, supr. Verona computer lab., 1985-92; libr. media specialist Pierce St. Elem. Sch., Miss., 1992—; supr. libr. Guntown (Miss.) Sch., 1988-90, Shannon (Miss.) Sch., 1988-92; chmn. assessment project Miss. Libr.-Miss. Dept. Edn. Jackson, 1986-92; coord. region I Miss. Conf. on Libr. and Info. Svc., 1990; mem. Miss. Edn. TV Adv. Coun., 1985—; cons. content instrnl. prodn.-libr. rsch. skills Miss. Ednl. Tv., 1995. Author: Clay Tablets to Media Centers: Library Development from Ancient to Modern Times, 1975. Bd. dirs., past pres. SAFE, Inc., Tupelo, Miss., 1978-92, bd. dirs. emeritus, 1992—; mem. Lee County Adult Lit. Task Force, Tupelo, 1987-90; schs. chmn. Target Tupelo, 1981-85. Recipient Ed Ransdell Instructional TV award, 1991. Mem. AECT, DSMS, AAUW (pres. Tupelo chpt. 1977-81, Miss. div. 1984-86), Miss. Profl. Educators, Mississippians for Ednl. Broadcasting, Miss. Ednl. Computer Assn., Miss. Libr. Assn. (project chmn. com. on sch. librs. 1989, awards chmn. 1987-88, Ednl. Comm. and Tech. Roundtable chair 1993), Miss. Profl. Educators Lee County (pres. 1989-92), Miss. Profl. Educators Tupelo/Lee County (treas. 1993—), Apple Computer User Group (co-organizer). Democrat. Episcopalian. Avocations: aerobics, reading, church music and liturgy, quilt making. Home: Carr Vista 3 Michael St Tupelo MS 38801-8608 Office: Pierce St Media Ctr 1008 Pierce St Tupelo MS 38801

RADOJEVIC, DANILO, ballet dancer; b. Sydney, Australia, Sept. 8, 1957. Mem. corps de ballet Australian Ballet Co., soloist, from 1977; soloist Am. Ballet Theatre, N.Y.C., 1978-81; prin. dancer Am. Ballet Theatre, 1981-1993; prin. guest artist with Basel Ballet, 1988, Royal Ballet of Flanders, 1988; mem. ballet faculty Univ. of California, Irvine, 1994—. Created role of Head Fakir, La Bayadere, also leading male role in Grand Pas Romantique; created ballet Sirens, Univ. of California, Irvine. Gold medalist Internat. Ballet Competition Moscow, 1977. Office: Univ of Calif Irvine Dance Dept HTC 101 Irvine CA 92717*

RADOMSKI, JACK LONDON, scientist; b. Milw., Dec. 10, 1920; s. Joseph Elwood and Evelyn (Hansen) R.; B.S., U. Wis., 1942; Ph.D., George Washington U., 1950; m. Teresa Pascual, Feb. 19, 1971; children—Mark, Linda, Eric, Janet, Mayte. Chemist, Gen. Aniline & Film Corp., Binghamton, N.Y. 1942-44; pharmacologist FDA, Washington, 1944-52, acting chief acute toxicity br., 1952-53; prof. pharmacology U. Miami, Coral Gables, Fla., 1953-82; pres. Covington Tech. Services, Andalusia, Ala., 1982-88; pvt. practice cons. in toxicology, Hudson, Fla., 1988—; cons. WHO, IARC, GAO, EPA, HEW, NIOSH. Contbr. articles to profl. jours. Recipient Sci. award Commr. FDA, 1952; diplomate in gen. toxicology Acad. Toxicol. Sci., 1982. Mem. Am. Soc. Pharmacology and Exptl. Therapeutics, Soc. Toxicology, Am. Assn. Cancer Research, N.Y. Acad. Scis., Am. Bd. Forensic Examiners. Home and Office: 6432 Driftwood Dr Port Richey FL 34667-1018 *The single most important thing in life is to make a continuous, intensive effort to comprehend things as they really are, as distinct from as we wish them to be. Failure to perceive the world and everything in it accurately and objectively, admittedly a difficult and frequently fearful task, causes untold misery and misfortune to individuals, organizations and nations. Success in all endeavors is in direct proportion to the degree we achieve this goal.*

RADY, ERNEST S., thrift and loan association executive; b. 1938. Chmn. bd. Western Thrift & Loan, Orange, Calif., 1973—; chmn. bd., CEO Westcorp, Irvine, Calif., 1975—. Office: Westcorp 23 Pasteur Irvine CA 92718-3816

RADYS, RAYMOND GEORGE, laser scientist; b. Kaunas, Lithuania, Aug. 30, 1940; came to U.S., 1949; s. Valerian Felix and Ella Lydia (Heinrich) R. BSEE, U. Ill., 1963. Engr. Hughes Aircraft, Culver City, Calif., 1963-76; scientist Hughes Aircraft, El Segundo, Calif., 1985—; sr. engr. Transaction Tech., Santa Monica, Calif., 1976-83; participant GM electric vehicle impact project, 1991-94. Recipient tech. award NASA, 1980, 89. Mem. U.S. Chess Found., Hughes Chess Club (champion 1971). Libertarian. Avocations: chess, computers, hiking, investments. Office: Hughes Aircraft Bldg E1 MS B131 PO Box 902 El Segundo CA 90245-0902

RADZINOWICZ, MARY ANN, language educator; b. Champaign, Ill., Apr. 18, 1925; d. Arthur Seymour and Ann (Stacy) Nevins; m. Leon Radzinowicz, June 16, 1958 (div. 1978); children: Ann Stacy Radzinowicz Prior, William Francis Henry. BA, Radcliffe Coll., 1945; MA, Columbia U., 1947, PhD, 1953; MA (hon.), U. Cambridge, Eng., 1960. Prof. Vassar Coll., Poughkeepsie, N.Y., 1947-50, 52-59, Girton Coll., Cambridge, Eng., 1960-80, U. Cambridge, 1973-80, Cornell U., Ithaca, N.Y., 1980-90; Jacob Gould Schurman prof. English emeritus Cornell U., Ithaca, 1990—; mem. adv. bd. 2d, 3d, 4th Internat. Milton Symposia, 1985—. Author: Toward Samson Agonistes, 1978 (Hanford prize 1979), Milton's Epics and Psalms, 1989; editor American Colonial Prose, 1984, Paradise Lost, Book VIII, 1974; mem. editorial bd. Milton Quarterly, 1981—, Christianity and Literature, 1989—. Mem. MLA, Renaissance Soc. Am., Milton Soc. Am. (honored scholar 1987), John Donne Soc. Home: Ballyconry House, Ballyvaughan County Clare Ireland Office: Cornell U Dept English Lit Ithaca NY 14850

RAE, BARBARA JOYCE, employee placement company executive; b. Prince George, B.C., Can., May 17, 1930; d. Alfred and Lottie Kathleen (Davis) Holmwood; m. George Suart, Feb. 14, 1984; children: Jamie, Glenn, John. MBA, Simon Fraser U., Burnaby, B.C., 1975. Chmn. Adia Can., Ltd., Vancouver, B.C., 1953—; bd. dirs. Can. Imperial Bank of Commerce, Grosvenor Internat. Ltd.; B.C. Telephone Co., B.C. Telecom, Noranda, Inc., Seaboard Life Ins. Co.; dir. Canadian Inst. Adv. Rsch., 1995—, B.C. Women's Hosp. & Health Ctr. Found., 1994—, KTCS Pub. Broadcasting; mem. bd. govs. Multiple Schlerosis Soc., 1995—. Chancellor Simon Fraser U., 1987-93; mem. Jud. Appts. Com., B.C., 1988-90; mem. adv. coun. Imagine Campaign, 1988; mem. Premier's Econ. Adv. Coun., B.C., 1987-91; mem. Price Minister's Com. on Sci. and Tech., B.C., 1989-94; gen. chmn. United Way Lower Mainland, 1987, Salvation Army Red Shield Vancouver Campaign, 1986; bd. dirs. Vancouver Bd. Trade, 1972-76; nat. co-chmn. Can. Coun. Christians and Jews. Decorated Order of Can., Order of B.C.; recipient Simon Fraser U. Outstanding Alumnae award, 1985, Vancouver YWCA Bus. Women of Yr. award, 1986, West Vancouver Achievers award, 1987, B.S. Entrepreneur of Yr. award, 1987, Nat. Vol. award, 1990, Can. Woman Entrepreneur B.C. award, 1992. Home: 2206 Folkestone Way #3, West Vancouver, BC Canada V7S 2X7 Office: Adia Can Ltd, 744-1055 Dunsmuir St POBox 49292, Vancouver, BC Canada V5A 1S6

RAE, MATTHEW SANDERSON, JR., lawyer; b. Pitts., Sept. 12, 1922; s. Matthew Sanderson and Olive (Waite) R.; m. Janet Hettman, May 2, 1953; children: Mary-Anna, Margaret Rae Mallory, Janet S. Rae Dupree. AB, Duke, 1946, LLB, 1947; postgrad., Stanford U., 1951. Bar: Md. 1948, Calif. 1951. Asst. to dean Duke Sch. Law, Durham, N.C., 1947-48; assoc. Karl F. Steinmann, Balt., 1948-49, Guthrie, Darling & Shattuck, L.A., 1953-54; nat. field rep. Phi Alpha Delta Law Frat., L.A., 1949-51; research atty. Calif. Supreme Ct., San Francisco, 1951-52; ptnr. Darling, Hall & Rae (and predecessor firms), L.A., 1955—; mem. Calif. Common. Uniform State Laws, 1985—, chmn., 1993-94; chmn. drafting com. for revision Uniform Prin. and Income Act of Nat. Conf., 1991—. V.p. L.A. County Rep. Assy., 1959-64; mem. L.A. County Rep. Ctrl. Com., 1960-64, 77-90, exec. com., 1977-90; vice chmn. 17th Congl. Dist., 1962-64, 28th Congl. Dist., 1962-64; chmn. 46th Assy. Dist., 1962-64, 27th Senatorial Dist., 1977-85, 29th Senatorial Dist., 1985-90; mem. Calif. Rep. State Ctrl. Com., 1966—, exec. com., 1966-67; pres. Calif. Rep. League, 1966-67; trustee Rep. Assocs., 1979-94, pres., 1983-85, chmn. bd. dirs., 1985-87. 2d lt. USAAF, WWII. Fellow Am. Coll. Trust and Estate Counsel; academician Internat. Acad. Estate and Trust Law (exec. coun. 1974-78); mem. ABA, Los Angeles County Bar Assn. (chmn. probate and trust law com. 1964-66, Arthur K. Marshall award probate and trust law sect. 1984, chmn. legislation com. 1980-86, chmn.

program com. 1981-82, chmn. membership retention com. 1982-83, trustee 1983-85, Shattuck-Price Meml. award 1990, dir. Bar Found. 1987-93), South Bay Bar Assn., State Bar Calif. (chmn. state bar jour. com. 1970-71, chmn. probate com. 1974-75, exec. com. estate planning trust and probate law sect. 1977-83, chmn. legislation com. 1977-89, co-chmn. 1991-92, probate law cons. group Calif. Bd. Legal Specialization 1977-88, chmn. conf. dels. resolutions com. 1987-90, com. conf. dels. 1987-90), Lawyers Club of Los Angeles (bd. govs. 1981-87, 1st v.p. 1982-83), Am. Legion (comdr. Allied post 1969-70), Legion Lex (dir. 1964—, pres. 1969-71), Air Force Assn., Aircraft Owners and Pilots Assn., Town Hall (gov. 1970-78, pres. 1975), World Affairs Coun., Internat. Platform Assn., Los Angeles Com. on Fgn. Rels., Breakfast Club (law, pres. 1989-90), Commonwealth Club, Chancery Club (treas. 1994—), Rotary, Phi Beta Kappa (councilor Alpha Assn. 1983—, v.p. 1984-86, 1994—), Omicron Delta Kappa, Phi Alpha Delta (supreme justice 1972-74, elected to Disting. Service chpt. 1978), Sigma Nu. Presbyterian. Home: 600 John St Manhattan Beach CA 90266-5837 Office: Darling Hall & Rae 777 S Figueroa St Fl 37 Los Angeles CA 90017-5800

RAE, ROBERT KEITH, Canadian premier of Ontario; b. Ottawa, Ont., Can., Aug. 2, 1948; s. Saul Forbes and Lois Esther (George) R.; m. Arlene Perly, Feb. 23, 1980; children: Judith Florence, Lisa Ruth, Eleanor Grace. BA, U. Toronto, Ont., 1969, LLB, 1977; BPhil, Oxford U., 1971. Bar: Ont. 1980. M.P. from Broadview-Greenwood dist. Ho. of Commons, 1978-82, fin. spokesman New Dem. Party, 1979-82; mem. for York South, provincial legislature Ont., 1982-90, leader official opposition, 1987-90; premier Province of Ont., Toronto, 1990—; spl. lectr. in indsl. rels. U. Toronto, 1976-77. Contbr. articles on law and politics to profl. jours. Mem. com. on univ. govt. U. Toronto, 1968-69; community worker London, Eng., 1973-74; extensive legal aid and community worker, Toronto, 1974—; asst. to Can. gen. counsel United Steelworkers Am., 1975-77; vice chmn. Can.-U.S. Interparliamentary Group, 1979-82. Rhodes scholar Balliol Coll., Oxford, 1969. Avocations: tennis, golf, skiing, fishing, music. Office: Office of Premier, 281 Legislative Bldg Queen's Pk 1, Toronto, ON Canada M7A 1A1

RAEBER, JOHN ARTHUR, architect, construction specifier consultant; b. St. Louis, Nov. 24, 1947; s. Arthur William and Marie (Laux) R.; m. Sandi Hartupee, Aug. 16, 1969. AA, Jefferson Coll., 1968; AB, Washington U., 1970, MArch, 1973. Registered architect, Calif., Mo.; cert. constrn. specifier; cert. Nat. Coun. Archtl. Registration Bds. Specification writer Hellmuth, Obata & Kassabaum, St. Louis, 1973-78, constrn. administr., 1978-79; mgr. of specifications Gensler & Assocs., San Francisco, 1979-82; ind. constrn. specifier San Francisco, 1982—; adj. prof. architecture Calif. Coll. Arts and Crafts, San Francisco, 1986—; access code advisor Constrn. Industry & Owners, 1982—; spkr., instr. seminars orgns., univs., 1982—; mem. Calif. State Bldg. Standards Commn. Accessibility Adv. Panel, Sacramento, 1981, Calif. Subcom. Rights of Disabled Adv. Panel, Sacramento, 1993. Author: CAL/ABL: Interpretative Manual to California's Access Barriers Laws, 1982; co-author: (with Peter S. Hopf) Access for the Handicapped, 1984; columnist Constrn. Specifier Mag., 1988-95. Vol. Calif. Office Emergency Svcs. Safety Assessment, Sacramento, 1991—. Fellow AIA (San Francisco chpt. codes com., Calif. coun. codes and standards com., nat. masterspec rev. com. 1982-84, nat. codes com. corr.), Contrns. Specifications Inst. (cert., columnist newsletter San Francisco chpt. 1984—, Ben John Small award for Outstanding Stature as practicing specifications writer 1994, pres. St. Louis chpt. 1978-79, pres. San Francisco chpt. 1990-92, nat. tech. com., edn. com., publs. com., Specifications Proficiency award San Francisco chpt. 1989, Tech. Commendation award 1987); mem. Specifications Cons. in Ind. Practice (nat. pres. 1990-92, nat. sec./treas. 1988-90), Am. Soc. Testing and Materials, Internat. Conf. Bldg. Officials, Phi Theta Kappa. Avocations: history, anthropology, sci. fiction. Home and Office: 519 Teresita Blvd San Francisco CA 94127

RAEBURN, ANDREW HARVEY, performing arts administrative, record producer; b. London, July 22, 1933; arrived in U.S., 1964, Can., 1993; s. Walter Augustus Leopold and Dora Adelaide Harvey (Williams) R. M.A. in History, King's Coll., Cambridge (Eng.) U., 1959. Mus. dir. Argo Record Co., London, 1959-64; asst. to music dir., program editor Boston Symphony Orch., 1964-73; dir. artists and repertory New World Records, N.Y.C., 1975-79; artistic adminstr. Detroit Symphony Orch., 1979-82; exec. dir. Van Cliburn Found. Inc., Ft. Worth, 1982-85; performing arts cons., 1985-93; exec. v.p. The Peter Pan Children's Fund, 1990-91; exec. dir. Esther Honens Internat. Piano Competition Found., 1993-95, pres., 1995—; cons. music; radio and TV commentator; mem. faculty Boston U., 1966-67; condr. New World String Orch., 1978. Author record liner notes, Argo, RCA, Time-Life records, 1960-79, program notes, Boston Symphony Orch., 1968-73. Served with Royal Army. Brit. Army, 1952-55. Home: Apt 406, 929 18th Ave SW, Calgary AB, AB Canada T2T 0H2 Office: 116 8th Ave SE 3rd Fl, Calgary, AB Canada T2G OK6

RAEBURN, JOHN HAY, English language educator; b. Indpls., July 18, 1941; s. Gordon Maurice and Katherine (Calwell) R.; m. Gillian Kimble, Aug. 18, 1963 (div. July 1979); children—Daniel Kennedy, Nicholas Kimble; m. Kathleen Kamerick, July 5, 1986. A.B. with honors, Ind. U., 1963; A.M., U. Pa., 1964, Ph.D., 1969. Asst. prof. U. Mich., Ann Arbor, 1967-74; vis. lectr. U. Iowa, Iowa City, 1974-75, assoc. prof., 1976-83, prof. English, 1983—; chmn. Am. Studies dept., 1983-85, 94—; chmn. English dept. U. Iowa, Iowa City, 1985-91; assoc. prof. U. Louisville, 1975-76. Author: Fame Became of Him: Hemingway as Public Writer, 1984; editor: (with others) Frank Capra: The Man and His Films, 1975. Mem. Am. Studies Assn. Democrat. Home: 321 Hutchinson Ave Iowa City IA 52246-2407 Office: U Iowa Dept Am Studies Dept English 202 Jefferson Bldg Iowa City IA 52242

RAEDER, MYRNA SHARON, lawyer, educator; b. N.Y.C., Feb. 4, 1947; d. Samuel and Estelle (Auslander) R.; m. Terry Oliver Kelly, July 13, 1975; children: Thomas Oliver, Michael Lawrence. BA, Hunter Coll., 1968; JD, NYU, 1971; LLM, Georgetown U., 1975. Bar: N.Y. 1972, D.C. 1972, Calif. 1972. Spl. asst. U.S. atty. U.S. Atty.'s Office, Washington, 1972-73; asst. prof. U. San Francisco Sch. Law, 1973-75; assoc. O'Melveny & Myers, L.A., 1975-79; assoc. prof. Southwestern U. Sch. Law, L.A., 1979-82, prof., 1983—, Irwin R. Buchalter prof. law, 1990. Mem. faculty Nat. Judicial Coll., 1993—. Prettyman fellow Georgetown Law Ctr., Washington, 1971-73. Author: Federal Pretrial Practice, 1987, ALI, 1989. Fellow Am. Bar Found.; mem. ABA (chmn. com. on fed. rules and criminal procedure criminal justice sect. 1987-93, vice-chair pubs. criminal justice sect. 1994—, trial evidence com. litigation sect. 1980—), Assn. Am. Law Schs. (com. on sects. 1984-87, chairperson women in legal edn. sect. 1982), Nat. Assn. Women Lawyers (bd. dirs. 1991—, pres.-elect 1993, pres. 1994-95), Women Lawyers Assn. L.A. (bd. dirs., coord. mothers support group 1987—), Order of Coif, Phi Beta Kappa. Office: Southwestern U Sch Law 675 S Westmoreland Ave Los Angeles CA 90005-3905

RAEL, HENRY SYLVESTER, health administrator; b. Pueblo, Colo., Oct. 2, 1928; s. Daniel and Grace (Abyeta) R.; m. Helen Warner Loring Brace, June 30, 1956 (dec. Aug. 1980); children: Henry Sylvester, Loring Victoria. AB, U. So. Colo., 1955; BA in Bus Adminstrn., U. Denver, 1957, MBA, 1958. Sr. boys counselor Denver Juvenile Hall, 1955-58; adminstrv. asst. to pres. Stanley Aviation Corp., Denver, 1958-61; Titan III budget and fin. control supr. Martin Marietta Corp., Denver, 1961-65; mgmt. adv. services officer U. Colo. Med. Center, Denver, 1965-72; v.p. fin., treas. Loretto Heights Coll., Denver, 1972-73; dir. fin. and adminstrn. Colo. Found. for Med. Care, 1973-86, Tri-County Health Dept., Denver, 1986—; instr. fin. mgmt., mem. fin. com. Am. Assn. Profl. Standards Rev. Orgn., 1980-85 ; speaker systems devel., design assns., univs., 1967-71. Mem. budget lay adv. com. Park Hill Elem. Sch. Denver, 1967-68, chmn., 1968-69; vol. worker Boy and Girl Scouts, 1967-73; bd. dirs. Community Arts Symphony, 1981-83, 85-87; controller St. John's Episcopal Cathedral, 1982-83; charter mem. Pueblo (Colo.) Coll. Young Democrats, 1954-55; block worker Republican party, Denver, 1965-68, precinct committeeman, 1978-84 ; trustee Van Nattan Scholarship Fund, 1974—; bd. dirs. Vis. Nurse Assn., 1977-84, treas., 1982-84. Served with USAAF, 1947-53; res. 1954-61. Recipient Disting. Service award Denver Astron. Soc., 1968, Citation Chamberlin Obs., 1985; Stanley Aviation masters scholar, 1957; Ballard scholar, 1956. Mem. Assn. Systems Mgmt. (pres. 1971-72), Hosp. Systems Mgmt. Soc., Budget Execs Inst. (v.p. chpt. 1964-65, sec. 1963-64), Colo. Pub. Employees Retirement Assn. (bd. dirs. 1993), Denver Astron. Soc. (pres. 1965-66, bd. dirs. 1982-

94), Am. Assn. Founds. for Med. Care (fin. com. 1981-82), Nat. Astronomers Assn. (exec. bd. 1965—). Episcopal. Home: 70 S Albion St Denver CO 80222-1002

RAEMER, HAROLD ROY, electrical engineering educator; b. Chgo., Apr. 26, 1924; s. Leo and Fannie (Marx) R.; m. Paulyne Barkin, Dec. 21, 1947; children: Daniel, Liane, Diane. B.S., Northwestern U., 1948, M.S., 1949, Ph.D., 1959. Teaching asst. Northwestern U., 1950-52; physicist Bendix Research Labs., Detroit, 1952-55; staff engr. Cook Research Labs., Chgo., 1955-60; sr. engring. specialist Sylvania Applied Research Lab., Waltham, Mass., 1960-63; assoc. prof. elec. engring. Northeastern U., Boston, 1963-65, prof., 1965—, chmn. dept., 1976-77, acting chmn., 1982-84, Snell prof. engring., 1986-93; prof. emeritus, 1994—; vis. lectr. Harvard U., 1962, hon. research assoc., 1972-73; vis. scientist MIT, 1984-85; cons. in field. Author: Statistical Communication: Theory and Application, 1969; contbr. articles to profl. jours. Served with USAAF, 1943-46. Mem. IEEE (sr.), AAAS, Am. Soc. for Engring. Edn., Sigma Xi, Pi Mu Epsilon, Eta Kappa Nu, Tau Beta Pi. Home: 120 Noanet Rd Needham MA 02194-2442 Office: Dept Elec and Computer Engring Northeastern U Boston MA 02115

RAFAEL, RUTH KELSON, archivist, librarian, consultant; b. Wilmington, N.C., Oct. 28, 1929; d. Benjamin and Jeanette (Spicer) Kelson; m. Richard Vernon Rafael, Aug. 26, 1951; children: Barbara Martinez Yates, Brenda Elaine. BA, San Francisco State U., 1953, MA, 1954; MLS, U. Calif.-Berkeley, 1968. Cert. archivist, 1989; life credential. Libr. Tchr. San Francisco Unified Sch. Dist., 1956-57; libr. Congregation Beth Sholom, San Francisco, 1965-83; archivist Western Jewish History Ctr. of Judah L. Magnes Mus., Berkeley, Calif., 1968, head archivist, libr., curator of exhibits, 1969—; cons. NEH, Washington, NHPRC, Congregation Sherith Israel, San Francisco, Mount Zion Hosp., San Francisco, Benjamin Swig archives project, San Francisco, Koret Found., Camp Swig, Saratoga, Calif.; project dir. Ethnicity in Calif. Agriculture, 1989, San Francisco Jews of European Origin, 1880-1940, an oral history project, 1976, curator exhibits Western U.S. Jewry. Author: Continuum, San Francisco Jews of Eastern European Origin, 1880-1940, 1976, rev. edit., 1977; (with Davies and Woogmaster) poetry book Relatively Speaking, 1981; Western Jewish History Center: Archival and Oral History Collections, Judah L. Magnes Meml. Mus., 1987; contbg. editor Western States Jewish History, 1979—. Mem. exec. bd. Bay Area Library Info. Network, 1986-88. Bur. Jewish Edn. scholar, San Francisco, 1983; NEH grantee, 1985. Mem. CLA, Soc. Am. Archivists, Soc. Calif. Archivists, Calif. Library Assn., No. Calif. Assn. Jewish Librarians (pres. 1975-76), Jewish Arts Council of the Bay (bd. dirs. 1981-83),

RAFAJKO, ROBERT RICHARD, medical research company executive; b. Chgo., Sept. 3, 1931; s. Edward Michael and Mildred Eleanor (Simo) R.; m. Mary Ann Filipi, June 24, 1954 (div. 1979); children: Rorie Rae, Ronald Raymond, Robin Rene, Rod Richard, Rebecca Rae.; m. Anne Thorne Sloan, Jan. 26, 1982; 1 son, Andrew Sloan. BA, Coe Coll., 1953; MS, U. Iowa, 1958, PhD, 1960. Research assoc. Merck Sharp and Dohme, West Point, Pa., 1960-61; research scientist Microbiol. Assos., Bethesda, Md., 1961-66; v.p., gen. mgr. Med. Research Cons., Rockville, Md., 1966-69; v.p. research and devel. M. Am. Biols., Rockville, 1969-74; pres. Biofluids, Inc., Rockville, 1974—; pres. Tysan Serum, Inc., Rockville, 1974—, Kytaron Inc, Rockville, 1987—; breeder thoroughbred horses, 1980—. Contbr. 23 articles to profl. jours. Chmn. PVAAU Swimming Program, Washington, Md. and Va., 1973-76; bd. dirs. Montgomery County Swim League, Montgomery County, Md., 1968-76. Served with USAF, 1954-55. Mem. AAAS, N.Y. Acad. Scis., Am. Soc. Microbiology, Tissue Culture Assn., Am. Horse Council, Horsemans Benevolent and Protective Assn. Republican. Presbyterian. Avocations: scuba diving, photography, collecting stamps, travel. Home: 12053 Wetherfield Ln Rockville MD 20854-1113 Office: Biofluids Inc 1146 Taft St Rockville MD 20850-1310

RAFANELLI, KENNETH ROBERT, physics educator; b. N.Y.C., Nov. 11, 1937; s. Robert and Anna (Bigini) R.; m. Marie Ann Gambetta, Dec. 2, 1961; 1 child, Lisa Marie. M in Engring., Stevens Inst. Tech., 1958, MA in Physics, 1960, PhD in Physics, 1964. Asst. prof. Queens Coll., N.Y.C., 1964-73, prof., 1973—; vis. prof. Clene State U. 1969-70, Istituto Nazionale Fisica Nucleare U. Florence, Italy 1979-80, Barcelona (Spain) U. 1981-83; cons. TRW Systems, Redondo Beach, Calif., 1965-68. Mem. Am. Phys. Soc., Profl. Staff Congress, Sigma Xi. Home: 56-09 187th St Flushing NY 11365 Office: Queens Coll Dept Physics Flushing NY 11367

RAFEEDIE, EDWARD, federal judge; b. Orange, N.J., Jan. 6, 1929; s. Fred and Nabeeha (Hishmeh) R.; m. Ruth Alice Horton, Oct. 8, 1961; children: Fredrick Alexander, Jennifer Ann. BS in Law, U. So. Calif., 1957, JD, 1959; LLD (hon.), Pepperdine U., 1978. Bar: Calif. 1960. Pvt. practice law Santa Monica, Calif., 1960-69; mcpl. ct. judge Santa Monica Jud. Dist., Santa Monica, 1969-71; judge Superior Ct. State of Calif., Los Angeles, 1971-82; dist. judge U.S. Dist. Court for (cen. dist.) Calif., Los Angeles, 1982—. Trustee Santa Monica Hosp. Med. Ctr., 1979—; bd. dirs. UniHealth, L.A., 1985. With U.S. Army, 1950-52, Korea. Office: US Dist Ct 312 N Spring St Los Angeles CA 90012-4701

RAFELSON, BOB, film director; b. N.Y.C., 1933. Dir.: (films) Head, 1968, Five Easy Pieces, 1970 (Acad. award nomination for best picture), The King of Marvin Gardens, 1972, Stay Hungry, 1976, The Postman Always Rings Twice, 1981, Black Widow, 1987, Mountains of the Moon, 1990, Man Trouble, 1992, (short film) Wet, 1993, (rock video - Lionel Richie) All Night Long, 1983; author: (TV series) Play of the Week; creator (TV series) The Monkees. Recipient N.Y. Film Critics award for Five Easy Pieces, 1970.

RAFELSON, MAX EMANUEL, JR., biochemist, medical school administrator; b. Detroit, June 17, 1921; s. Max Emanuel and Lillian (Kay) R.; m. Trudy Diane Hellem, Mar. 31, 1973; children—Mark Thomas, Anne Elizabeth. B.S., U. Mich., 1943; Ph.D., U. So. Calif., 1951. Postdoctoral rsch. fellow U Stockholm, Sweden, 1951-52; asst. prof. biol. chemistry U. Ill. Coll. Medicine, Chgo., 1953-55, assoc. prof., 1955-60, prof., 1961-70; assoc. dean biol. and behavioral scis. Rush Med. Coll., Rush-Presbyn.-St. Luke's Med. Center, 1970-71, v.p. info. scis., 1971-77, v.p., 1972—; prof. biochemistry Rush Med. Coll., 1972-90, prof. and chmn. emeritus, 1990—; John W. and Helen H. Watzek meml. chmn. biochemistry Presbyn.-St. Lukes Hosp., Chgo., 1967-70; vis. prof. U. Paris, France, 1960, 77-78, U. Ulm, Fed. Republic Germany, 1986; assoc. mem. commn. influenza Dept. Def., 1961—. Author: Basic Biochemistry, 1965, 68, 71, 80; contbr. articles on biochemistry, blood platelets, viruses, protein structure, endothelial cells and metabolism to profl. publs. Served with USNR, 1943-46. Mem. Am. Soc. Biol. Chemists, Biochem. Soc. (London), Am. Chem. Soc., AAAS, Nat. Acad. Clin. Biochemistry, Société de Chemie Biologique, Sigma Xi. Home: 2246 N Seminary Ave Chicago IL 60614-3507 Office: Rush-Presbyn-St Luke's Med Ctr 1653 W Congress Pky Chicago IL 60612-3833

RAFF, GILBERT, publishing company executive; b. Newark, May 7, 1928; s. Nathan and Rose (Silberstein) R.; m. Cynthia Rae Freedman, June 7, 1953; children—Hilary, Merritt, David. B.S., NYU, 1949, M.B.A., 1959. CPA, N.J., N.Y., Ill., Calif. Individual practice pub. acctg. Newark, 1954-55; ptnr. Kosson, Ruby & Raff, Passaic, N.J., 1955-60, W.C. Heaton & Co., N.Y.C., 1960-63, Raff, Kuzmiak & Metsky, East Orange, N.J., 1963-72; exec. v.p. Littlefield, Adams & Co., Totowa, N.J., 1963-69, pres., chief exec. officer, dir., 1969-88, resigned, chmn. bd., 1989—; chmn. bd. Berkeley Fed. Savs. & Loan Assn., Millburn, N.J., Irish Acad. Press, Dublin, Ireland; lectr. Pace U., 1955-59; instr. Fairleigh Dickinson U., 1959-60. Chmn. bd. trustees Pub. Industry Group Ins. Fund; bd. govs.Hyde Sch., Bath, Maine, past trustee, past vice chmn. Served with USAF, 1950-52. Mem. AICPA, N.J. Soc. CPAs, Calif. Soc. CPAs. Home: Claridge House I # 603 Claridge Dr Verona NJ 07044 also: 2214 Plaza Bonita Carlsbad CA 92009 Office: Berkeley Fed Savs & Loan 21 Bleeker St Millburn NJ 07041-1414 also: Investment Adv Cumberland Adv 7609 El Camino Dr Ste # 209 Carlsbad CA 92009

RAFF, JOSEPH ALLEN, publishing company executive, author; b. N.Y.C., Sept. 28, 1933; s. Bertram and Billie (Martin) R.; m. Judy Ann Oberfelder, Aug. 5, 1959. B.A., U. N.C., 1955, postgrad., 1956-57; postgrad., Harvard, Ind. U., Ohio U. Wire editor A.P., Charlotte, N.C., 1958; staff writer Burlington (N.C.) Times News, then Raleigh (N.C.) Times, Sports Illus., N.Y.C., 1958-61; editor Rome Daily Am., 1961; pres. Temple Fielding

Enterprises, Mallorca, Spain; cons. internat. pub. relations, internat. tour packaging. Author: Fielding's Europe, Fielding's Economy Europe, Fielding's Britain; host (film) Shopping London; contbr. numerous articles to mags., newspapers. Decorated chevalier Ordre de Couteaux (France). Mem. Soc. Am. Travel Writers. Clubs: Overseas Press, Nautico de Puerto de Pollensa. Home: PO Box 50, Pollensa Mallorca Spain Office: Edificio Xaloc, Placa Xaloc, Pto Pollensa, Mallorco Spain

RAFFAEL, JOSEPH, artist; b. Bklyn., Feb. 22, 1933; m. Lannis; children: Matthew, Robert, Rachel, Reuben. Student, Cooper Union Sch. Art and Architecture, 1953-54; B.F.A., Yale U., 1955; studies with Josef Albers. Instr. U. Calif., Davis, 1966; instr. Visual Arts, N.Y.C., 1967-69, U. Calif. at Berkeley, summer 1969; prof. Calif. State U. at Sacramento, 1969-74. One-man shows: Stable Gallery, N.Y.C., 1965, 66, 68, Reese Palley Gallery, San Francisco, 1970, N.Y., 1972, Nancy Hoffman Gallery, N.Y., 1972-74, 76, 79, 80-84, 86, 87, 89, 90, 92, 94, Hunter Mus. Art, Chattanooga, Butler Inst. Am. Art, Mus. Contemporary Art, Chgo., 1973, Wichita Art Mus., Kans., 1970, U. Calif. at San Diego Art Gallery, 1971, U. Calif. at Berkeley Art Mus., 1973, John Berggruen Gallery, San Francisco, 1978, 81, 82, 87, Barbara Fendrick Gallery, Washington, 1978, 81, Birmingham (Ala.) Mus. Art, Mint Mus. Art, N.C., 1980, Mus. Arts and Scis., Columbus, Ga., Miss. Mus. Art, 1981, Butler Inst. Am. Art, Youngstown, Ohio, 1991, Naples (Fla.) Philharm. Ctr., 1992, Jorgensen Gallery, U. Conn., Storrs, traveled to Nebr. Wesleyan U., Lincoln, U. N.D. Art Gallery, Grand Forks, Charles A. Wustum Mus. Fine Arts, Racine, Wis., Phyllis Rothman Gallery, Madison, N.J., 1991, Glenbow Mus., Calgary, Alta., Can., Boise Gallery Art, Idaho, N.Y. Acad. Scis., 1985, Univ. Austin, Tex., 1983, Jacksonville (Fla.) Mus., 1982, Elvehjem Art Ctr., Madison, Wis., 1981, travelled to Norton Gallery and Sch. Art, West Palm Beach, Fla., retrospective exhbn., San Francisco Mus. Modern Art, 1978-79; traveled to Des Moines Art Center, Joslyn Art Mus., Omaha, Newport Harbor Art Mus., Del. Art Mus., 1982, Denver Art Mus., Richard Gray Gallery, Chgo., 1983, 86, Gibbes Art Gallery, Charleston, S.C., 1985, Salt Lake Art Ctr., 1985-86, Yellowstone Art Ctr., Billings, Mont., 1986, Nicolaysen Art Mus., Casper, Wyo., 1986, Davenport (Iowa) Mus. Art, 1987; exhibited in group shows: Bklyn. Mus., Art Inst. Chgo., Woodson Art Mus., Wamsau Wis., Canton Art Inst., Ohio, Ft. Wayne Mus. Art, Ind., Minn. Mus. Art, St. Paul, Miyagi Mus. Art, Sogo Mus. Art, Tokushima Modern Art Mus., Mus. Modern Art, Shiba, Kochi Pref. Mus. Folk Art, Japan, Weatherspoon Art Gallery, U. N.C., Scottsdale (Ariz.) Art Ctr., Pa. State U., Valparaiso U. Mus. Art, Ind., Stamford (Conn.) Mus., Ctr. for Arts, Vero Beach, Fla., Guggenheim Mus., N.Y.C., Mus. Modern Art, Kent U., Corcoran Gallery Art, Washington, U. Ill., Champaign, Newport Harbor Mus., Calif., Whitney Mus. Am. Art, Los Angeles Municipal Art Gallery, DeCordova Mus., Lincoln, Mass., Worcester Art Mus., Mass., San Francisco Mus. Modern Art, Boise (Idaho) Art Gallery, Smithsonian Instn., Fla. Internat. Un., Miami, Pa. Acad. Fine Arts, Va. Mus. Fine Arts, Oakland (Calif.) Mus. Art, Gulbenkien Mus., Lisbon, Portugal, Las Salas Exposiciones Bella Artes, Madrid, Kunsthalle, Nuremberg, Germany, Mus. Fine Arts, Boston, San Antonio Mus. Art, Indpls. Mus. Art, Tucson Mus. Art, Carnegie Inst., Pitts., Cleve. Mus. Art, Univ. Art Mus., Berkeley, Calif., McNay Art Inst., Columbus (Ohio) Gallery Fine Arts, Australian Nat. Gallery, Western Australia Art Gallery, Queensland Art Gallery, Art Gallery NSW, Art Gallery South Australia, Nat. Gallery Victoria, Tasmanian Mus. and Art Gallery, Mus. Contemporary Art, Chgo., Galleria d'arte moderna, Milan, Flint (Mich.) Inst. Arts, Columbus (Ohio) Mus. Art, La. State U. Sch. Art Gallery, Baton Rouge, Oklahoma City Art Mus., Wichita Art Mus., Bergstrom-Mahler Mus., Neenah, Wis., 1993, Sewall Art Gallery, Rice U., Houston, 1993, Nassau County Mus. Art, Roslyn Harbor, N.Y. 1993, Bergstrom-Mahler Mus., Neenah, WIs., Oklahoma City Art Mus., Wichita Art Mus., Kans., Denver Art Mus., Flint (Mich.) Inst. Arts, others; represented in private and pub. collections: Allentown Mus. Art, Pa., Denver Art Mus., Smithsonian Inst., Met. Mus. Art, N.Y.C., Bklyn. Mus., Hirshhorn Mus. and Sculpture Garden, U. Calif. Berkeley Mus., Los Angeles County Mus. of Art, Long Beach Mus., Calif., Everson Mus., Syracuse, N.Y., Library of Congress, San Francisco Mus. Modern Art, Wichita Mus., Joslin Mus., Krannert Mus., Lowe Mus. U. Miami, Calif. Coll. Arts and Crafts, Oakland, Chgo. Art Inst., Des Moines Art Center, Jacksonville Art Mus., Mus. Contemporary Art, Mus. Fine Arts, St. Petersburg, Fla., Oakland Mus. Art, Phila. Mus. Art, Santa Barbara Mus., Toledo Mus. Art, Utah Mus. Fine Art, Va. Mus. Fine Arts, Washington County (Md.) Mus. Fine Art, Whitney Mus. Am. Art, Cleve. Mus. Art, Del. Art Mus., Ft. Worth Art Mus., Walker Art Ctr. Recipient 1st prize Tokyo Internat. Biennial, 1974; purchase prize Concours d'Antiques Oakland (Calif.) Mus., 1975; Fulbright fellow Florence, Rome, 1958-60; Tiffany Found. fellow, 1961. Address: Nancy Hoffman Gallery 429 W Broadway New York NY 10012

RAFFAY, STEPHEN JOSEPH, manufacturing company executive; b. McAdoo, Pa., Oct. 25, 1927; s. Stephen John and Stephanie (Severa) R.; m. Audree Eugenia Kuehne, Sept. 12, 1953; children: Andrea, Stephen, Leslie. B.A., Columbia, 1950, M.S., 1951. C.P.A., N.Y. Sr. accountant Arthur Andersen & Co., N.Y.C., 1951-56; asst. controller Emhart Corp., Farmington, Conn., 1956-61, asst. treas., 1961-63, treas., 1963-67, v.p. internat., 1967-72, v.p., group pres., 1972-79, exec. v.p., 1979-84, vice chmn., chief adminstrv. officer, 1984-87, dir. 1980-87; sr. v.p. Dexter Corp., Windsor Locks, Conn., 1987-90; bd. dirs. Reflexite Corp., Coating Scis., Inc., Fresnel Optics, Inc., Schaar Inds., Inc., United Plumbing Tech., Inc., Trust Co. Conn., Rossi Enterprises, Inc. Bd. dirs. Hartford Symphony Soc.; active Greater Hartford Arts Coun. With AUS, 1946-47. Mem. AICPA, Conn. Soc. CPAs. Office: 93 Westmont St West Hartford CT 06117-2929

RAFFEL, JEFFREY ALLEN, urban affairs educator; b. Bklyn., June 19, 1945; s. George A. and Renee (Lane) R.; m. Joanne Ruth Traum, Aug. 27, 1966; children: Allison, Lori, Kenneth. AB, U. Rochester, 1966; PhD, MIT, 1972. Asst. prof. U. Del., Newark, 1971-76, assoc. prof., 1976-82, dir. M Pub. Adminstrn. program, 1980-86, prof., 1982—, chair pub. mgmt. faculty, 1994—; acting assoc. dean Coll. Urban Affairs and Pub. Policy U. Del., 1989; chair pub. mgmt. faculty U. Del., Newark, 1994—; pub. svc. fellow, spl. asst. to gov. for intergovtl. rels. State of Del., 1979-80; chair urban ednl. policy group Nat. Assn. State Univs. and Land Grant Colls., 1987-93; mem. state supt.'s adv. com. on tchr. recruitment, Del., 1988-91. Author: Politics of School Desegregation, 1980; co-author: Systematic Analysis of University Libraries, 1969, Selling Cites: Attracting Homebuyers Through Schools and Housing Programs, 1995; mem. editl. bd. Pub. Productivity Rev., N.Y.C., 1984—; contbr. articles to urban affairs pubs. Treas. Nottingham Swim Club, Inc., Newark, 1985-88; co-chair Gov.'s Task Force on Enhancing Ednl. Dollar, 1986-87; chair long-range planning com. and membership com Delmarva coun. Boy Scouts Am., 1988-89; mem. Gov.'s Sch. Reform Partnership, Del, 1990—. Recipient cert. of recognition, NCCJ Greater Wilmington, 1980, numerous profl. and civic awards. Mem. ACLU (Del. chpt. sec. 1992—), Del. Assn. Pub. Adminstrn. (pres. 1981-82), Am. Soc. Pub. Adminstrn., Am. Edn. Rsch. Assn. Avocations: golf, reading. Home: 4 High Pond Dr Newark DE 19711-2597 Office: U Del Coll Urban Affairs Pub Policy Newark DE 19716

RAFFEL, LEROY B., real estate development company executive; b. Zanesville, Ohio, Mar. 13, 1927; s. Jacob E. and Anne M. (Oliker) R.; m. Shirley Balbot, Sept. 11, 1949; children: Kenneth, Janet, James, Nancy. B.S., U. Pa., 1949. Pres. Raffel Bros. Co., Youngstown, Ohio, 1949-78; ret., 1978; pres. York Mahoning Co., Youngstown, 1950-64, Arby's, Inc., Youngstown, 1964-70; chmn. bd. Arby's, Inc., 1971-79; ret., 1979; pres. Brom Equity Devel., Inc., Miami, Fla., 1979—. Served with USNR, 1945-46. Home: 2141 NE 190th Ter N Miami Bch FL 33179-4352 Office: Brom Equity Devel Inc # 100 1400 NE Miami Gardens Dr Miami FL 33179

RAFFEL, LOUIS B., association executive; b. Chgo., Mar. 17, 1933; s. Martin G. and Donnette (Rogers) R.; m. Trudi Weiner, Sept. 11, 1955; children: Lawrence, Sharon, Mark. B.S., U. Ill., 1955. Account exec. Glassner & Assos., Chgo., 1957-60, Buchen Pub. Rels., Chgo., 1960-62; asst. pub. rels. dir. Am. Meat Inst., Chgo., 1962-68; pub. rels. dir. Nat. Dairy Council, Chgo., 1960-70, Armour & Co., Chgo., 1970-72; v.p. for pub. rels. and advt. Greyhound Corp., Phoenix, 1972-76; pres. Am. Egg Bd., Chgo., 1976—. Served with U.S. Army, 1955-57. Mem. Am. Soc. Assn. Execs. (cert.). Pub. Relations Soc. Am. (accredited; pres. Phoenix chpt. 1975), Chgo. Soc. Assn. Execs. (bd. dirs. 1985-88), Publicity Club Chgo. (Pub-Clubber award 1964, pres. 1966-67). Home: 1724 Seton Rd Northbrook IL 60062-1341 Office: AEB 1460 Renaissance Dr Park Ridge IL 60068-1331

RAFFERTY, BRIAN JOSEPH, investor relations consultant; b. Washington, Sept. 1, 1957; s. James Francis and Betty Jane (Finney) R.; m. Helen Marie Glancy, Oct. 10, 1986. BA in Philosophy, Georgetown U., 1979. Clk. Corcoran, Youngman & Rowe, Washington, 1977-80; account exec. Ogilvie Talyor Assocs., Inc., N.Y.C., 1980-82; ptnr. Taylor, Rafferty Assoc. Inc., N.Y.C., 1983—. Mem. N.Y. Soc. Security Analysts, Nat. Investor Rels. Inst. Avocations: flying, martial arts. Office: Taylor Rafferty Assocs 11th Fl 145 E 32nd St Fl 11 New York NY 10016-6002

RAFFERTY, CRAIG ELLIOT, architect, educator; b. St. Paul, Apr. 11, 1946; s. George Elliot and Betty Jane (Kates) R.; m. Kathleen Anne Riley, Feb. 14, 1969; children: Erin Marie, Anne Terese, Lynn Maureen. BA, BArch, U. Minn., 1970; MArch, MIT, 1972. Registered architect, Minn. Archtl. designer Ralph Rapson, Mpls., 1969-70, Freeman & Liston, Boston, 1971-72; architect Hugh Stubbins, Cambridge, Mass., 1972-73, Brown Daltas, Rome, 1974; prin. Rafferty Rafferty Mikutowski, St. Paul, 1975—; lectr. Boston Archtl Ctr., 1971-73; asst. prof. U. Minn., Mpls., 1975—. Contbg. to author: Building Tomorrow: The Mobile Manufactured Housing Industry, Ice Castles, The Form of Housing; contbr. articles to architecture Mags. First vice chmn. dist 17 Downtown Community Devel. Council, St. Paul, 1988; chmn. dist 17 Downtown Long Range Plan Com., St. Paul, 1985; commr. St. Paul Heritage Preservation Commn., 1988; exec. com. Small Bus. Council, St. Paul, 1985; mem. Downtown Framework Com., St. Paul, 1985; chmn. art and environment bd. Archdiocese of St. Paul, 1977-81, advisor to bd. dirs. St. Paul Pub. Arts Com., 1988; past pres., bd. dirs. Park Square Community Theater, St. Paul, 1987. Rotch Archl. Found. scholar, 1974; recipient Fed. Design Achievement award NEA, 1984, Presidential Design award, 1985, Nat. Honor award Inter Faith Forum on Religion Art and Architecture, 1987. Mem. AIA, Minn. Soc. AIA (past pres., v.p., dir. 1987—, Corp. Report Archtl. Honor award 1986, 2 Interior Architecture awards, 1987, 3 Paper Architecture awards 1984, 86), Nat. Council Archtl. Registration Bds. Roman Catholic. Club: St. Paul Athletic. Avocations: photography, video, sketching. Home: 1884 Lincoln Ave Saint Paul MN 55105-1421 Office: Rafferty Rafferty Tollefson Architects 253 4th St E Saint Paul MN 55101-1632

RAFFERTY, JAMES PATRICK, violinist, violin educator; b. Toledo, Ohio, June 1, 1947; s. James A. and Eileene L. (Davis) R.; m. Barbara Elizabeth Janiec, Aug. 17, 1985; children: Erin Colleen, Sean Patrick. MusB in Performance, Bowling Green State U., 1970. Violinist St. Louis Symphony Orch., 1971-72, Cleve. Orch., 1972-74, Cin. Symphony Orch., 1974-78; concertmaster Cin. Symphony Chamber Orch., 1976-78; assoc. concertmaster Dallas Symphony Orch., 1978-86; acting concertmaster Seattle Symphony Orch., 1980, 81, San Diego Symphony Orch., 1981; assoc. concertmaster Dallas Chamber Orch., 1981-86; concertmaster Dallas Bach Orch., 1981-86, Milw. Symphony Orch., 1986-91; assoc. prof. violin U. Ala., Tuscaloosa, 1991—; instr. violin Wis. Conservatory Music, Milw., 1986-91; sr. lectr. U. Wis., Milw., 1987, 89-91. Soloist Milw. Symphony Orch., Dallas Bach Orch., Dallas Fine Arts Orch., Dallas Symphony Orch., Brevard Music Ctr. Orch., Cin. Symphony Orch., St. Louis Symphony Orch., others; music festivals include Interlochen Music Camp, 1965, Brevard Music Ctr., 1967, 69, 81, 93—, Berkshire Music Festival, 1968, Grand Teton Music Festival, 1979-80, Southeastern Music Festival, 1992; performed with New Marlboro Chamber Players, Am. Chamber Trio, Grand Teton Music Festival, Brevard Music Ctr., Fine Arts Chamber Players, Walden Chamber Players, Paganini Trio, Stradivari Trio, from 1971—, Cadek Trio, 1991—. Mem. Am. Violin Soc., Music Tchrs. Nat. Assn., String Tchrs. Assn. Office: U Ala Sch Music PO Box 870366 Tuscaloosa AL 35487-0366

RAFFERTY, MICHAEL ROBERT, editor, columnist; b. Williamsport, Pa., July 23, 1949; s. Daniel Willis and Kathleen Mary (Griffin) R.; m. Patricia Ann Roth, Dec. 18, 1971; children: Ryan C., Sharon B., Brennan J., Meghan M., Reagan D. AS, Williamsport Area Community Coll., 1971; BA, Mount St. Mary's Coll., Emmitsburg, Md., 1973. Reporter Grit, Williamsport, 1973-81, Sun-Gazette, Williamsport, 1981-82; editor The Sunday Grit, Williamsport, 1982-86; exec. editor Grit Pub. Group, Williamsport, 1986-92; editor Grit mag., 1986-92; freelance typographer and writer Hi-Rez Output, Williamsport, Pa., 1993—; cons. various writing orgns., 1985—. Mem. bd. govs. Lycoming County (Pa.) Hist. Soc., 1990; mem. Williamsport City Coun., 1992, v.p. 1994, pres., 1995. Recipient Keystone Press award Pa. Newspaper Pubs. Assn., 1986; named Outstanding Alumnus, Williamsport Area Community Coll., 1985. Mem. Rotary. Avocations: golf, baseball, American history 1860-1963. Home: 639 Campbell St Williamsport PA 17701-4831

RAFFERTY, NANCY SCHWARZ, anatomy educator; b. Jamaica, N.Y., June 11, 1930; d. Franklin and Louise (Barry) Schwarz; m. Keen Alexander Rafferty, Aug. 7, 1953; children: Burns Arthur, Katherine Louisa. B.S., Queens Coll., 1952; M.S., U. Ill., 1953, Ph.D., 1958. Instr. anatomy Johns Hopkins U., 1963-66, asst. prof., 1966-70; asst. prof. anatomy Northwestern U., Chgo., 1970-72; asso. prof. Northwestern U., 1972-76, prof., 1976-94, prof. emeritus, 1994—; corp. mem., gen. libr. reader Marine Biol. Lab., Woods Hole, Mass. Contbr. articles on cell biology of the crystalline lens to profl. jours. USPHS fellow, 1958-63; USPHS grantee. Mem. Assn. Research in Vision and Ophthalmology, Internat. Soc. for Eye Research, Am. Assn. Anatomists, AAAS, Am. Soc. Cell Biology, Visual Scis. (study sect. of NIH), Sigma Xi, Phi Sigma. Home: 59 Harbor Hill Rd Woods Hole MA 02543-1219 Office: Marine Biol Lab Woods Hole MA 02543

RAFFERTY, WILLIAM BERNARD, lawyer; b. Balt., May 15, 1912; s. John Patrick and Dorothy Amalye (Hartje) R.; m. Elizabeth Catherine Henkel, Dec. 26, 1938; children: Patricia Carol Buchan, Susan Elizabeth Magri, George Lee Schultz. AB with honors, U. Md., 1934, LLB with honors, 1936. Bar: Md. 1936, U.S. Supreme Ct. 1942. Assoc. Miles & Stockbridge (and predecessor firms), Balt., 1936-41, ptnr., 1941-92, of counsel, 1992-94, ret., 1994; bd. dirs. Fidelity Fed. Savs. and Loan Assn., Henkel-Harris Co. Inc., Rolling Road Realty Co., Balt., 1975—; lectr. pub. utility law U. Balt. Law Sch., 1951-56. Pres., Roland Park Civic League, 1954-57. Fellow Md. Bar Found.; mem. Wednesday Law Club (pres. 1953), Merchants. Democrat. Presbyterian. Home: 9 Midvale Rd Baltimore MD 21210-2113 Office: Miles & Stockbridge 10 Light St Baltimore MD 21202-1435

RAFFI (RAFFI CAVOUKIAN), folksinger, children's entertainer; b. Cairo, July 8, 1948. Attended, U. Toronto. Recordings include: Singable Songs for the Very Young, 1976, More SIngable Songs for the Very Young, 1977, Love Light, 1977, The Corner Grocery Store, 1979, Baby Beluga, 1980, Rise and Sun, 1982, Raffi's Christmas Album, 1983, One Light One Sun, 1985, Everything Grows, 1987, Raffi in Concert with the Rise and Shine Band, 1989, Evergreen, Everblue: An Ecology Album for the '90's, 1990; Broadway appearances: A Family Concert, 1993, Bananaphone, 1994; videos: A Young Children's Concert with Raffi, 1985, Raffi and the Rise and Shine Band, 1988; author: Down By the Bay, 1988, Shake My Sillies Out, 1988, Baby Beluga, 1990, (with Debi Pike) Like Me and You, 1994. Recipient Order of Can., 1983, Parents' Choice award Parents' Choice Mag.,. Office: Troubadour Records Ltd, 1075 Cambie St, Vancouver, BC Canada M2M 3W3*

RAFFIN, THOMAS A., physician; b. San Francisco, Jan. 25, 1947; s. Bennett L. and Carolyn M. Raffin; m. Michele Raffin, June 19, 1987; children: Elizabeth S., Ross Daniel, Jake Bennett, Nicholas Ethan. AB in Biol. Sci., Stanford Med. Sch., 1968, MD, 1973. Diplomate Am. Bd. Pulmonary Medicine, Am. Bd. Internal Medicine (also in Critical Care Medicine). Intern Peter Brent Brigham Hosp., 1973-75; fellow in respiratory medicine sch. medicine Stanford U., Stanford, Calif., 1975-78, med. fiberoptic bronchoscopy service dir. med. ctr., 1978—, acting asst. prof. sch. medicine, 1978-80, assoc. dir. med. ctr. intensive care units, med. dir. dept. respiratory therapy hosp., 1978—, assoc. prof. medicine sch. medicine, 1986-95, acting chief div. respiratory medicine, 1988—; chief div. pulmonary and critical care Stanford U., 1990—, prof. medicine sch. of medicine, 1995—; co-dir. Stanford U. Ctr. for Biomed. Ethics, 1989—; chmn. ethics com. Stanford U. Med. Ctr., 1987—. Author: Intensive Care: Facing the Critical Choices, 1988; contbr. articles to profl. jours. V.p. lung cancer com., No. Calif. Oncology Group, 1983-85; com. mem. NIH Workshop, 1984. Recipient Henry J. Kaiser Found. award, 1981, 84, 88, Arthur L. Bloomfield award, 1981. Fellow ACP (rep. coun. subspity. socs. 1986), Am. Coll. Chest Physicians (program

com. mem. 1985—); mem. AAAS, Am. Fedn. for Clin. Rsch., Am. Thoracic Soc., Santa Clara County Lung Assn. and Med. Soc., Calif. Med. Assn. (chmn. sect. chest diseases 1984-85), Soc. for Critical Care Medicine, Calif. Thoracic Soc. Jewish. Avocations: painting, gardening. Home: 13468 Three Forks Ln Los Altos CA 94022-2404 Office: Stanford U Med Ctr Dept Medicine Div Pulmonary & Critical Care Medicine Div Pulmonary Critical # H3151 Stanford CA 94306

RAFII, SHAHIN, medicine educator; b. Tehran, Iran, May 16, 1960; came to U.S., 1977; s. Daniel and Touran Rafii. BA cum laude in Chemistry, Cornell U., 1982; MD, Albert Einstein Coll. Medicine, 1986. Diplomate Am. Bd. Internal Medicine, Am. Bd. Oncology, Am. Bd. Hematology. Intern in internal medicine N.Y. Hosp., N.Y.C., 1986-87, resident, 1987-89; fellow in hematology and oncology N.Y. Hosp.-Cornell U. Med. Coll., 1989-92, chief fellow, 1991, instr. medicine, 1992-94, asst. prof., 1994—, cons. in hematology and oncology, 1992—. Contbr. articles to med. jours.; designer elec. circuit. Recipient Jack Friedman young investigator award N.Y. Hosp.-Cornell U. Med. Coll., 1993, trainee's award Soc. for Study Blood, 1993, scholar award Am. Soc. Hematology, 1994, clin. investigator award NIH, 1994, Tolly Vinik award, 1994; fellow NSF, 1981, rsch. fellow N.Y. Heart Assn., 1990-92. Mem. Phi Beta Kappa, Alpha Omega Alpha. Avocations: karate, swimming, weightlifting. Office: NY Hosp-Cornell U Med Ctr 525 E 70th St Rm C-606 New York NY 10021-4805

RAFKIN, ALAN, television and film director; b. N.Y.C., July 23, 1928; s. Victor and Til (Bernstein) R.; children—Dru, Leigh Ann. B.S., Syracuse U., 1950. guest lectr. Bowling Green State U., 1975. Actor Robert Q. Lewis TV Show, 1955, daytime shows, CBS-TV; dir. Verdict is Yours, 1960, Mary Tyler Moore Show, 1970-71, Sanford and Son, 1972, Bob Newhart Show, 1972-73, Rhoda, 1973, Let's Switch, 1975, MASH, 1976-77, Love, American Style, 1970-71, Laverne & Shirley, 1977-83; TV movie: One Day at a Time: Barbara's Crisis, 1981-82; films include Ski Party, 1965, The Ghost and Mr. Chicken, 1966, The Ride to Hangman's Tree, 1967, Nobody's Perfect, 1968, The Shakiest Gun in the West, 1968, Angel in my Pocket, 1969, How to Frame a Figg, 1971. Served with U.S. Army, 1950-52. Democrat. Jewish. Office: care Catherine Byrne Gelford Rennert & Feldman 1800 Century Park E Ste 900 Los Angeles CA 90067-1512 also: The Brillstein Co 9200 W Sunset Blvd Los Angeles CA 90069-3502

RAFSHOON, GERALD MONROE, communications executive; b. N.Y.C., Jan. 11, 1934; s. Jack and Helen (Goodman) R.; m. Eden White Donohue, Mar. 3, 1978; children by previous marriage: Susan, Patricia, Janet, Scott. B.J., U. Tex., 1955. Copywriter Rich's Dept. Store, Atlanta, 1959; Southeastern advt. and publicity mgr. 20th Century Fox Film Corp., Atlanta, 1959-62; nat. advt. mgr. 20th Century Fox, N.Y.C., 1962-63; pres. Gerald Rafshoon Advt., Inc., Atlanta, 1963-77; chmn. bd. Gerald Rafshoon Advt., Inc., 1977-78; asst. to pres. U.S. for communications White House Washington, 1978-79; media and communications dir. Carter Presdl. Campaign, 1976, Carter Re-election Campaign, 1980; pres. Rafshoon Communications, Washington, 1980-88, Rafshoon Prodns., Washington, 1981-88, Consol. Prodns., Inc., Washington, 1988-91; vice-chmn. Consol. Entertainment, Inc., L.A., 1988-91; pres. Gerald Rafshoon Prodn., 1991—; guest scholar Brookings Instn., Washington, 1991—. Exec. producer TV spls. and movies including: The Atlanta child Murders (CBS-TV), 1985 Circle of Violence (CBS-TV), 1986, The Nightmare Years (TNT), 1989, Bob Hope 75th Birthday Spl. (NBC-TV), 1977, Iran (TNT), 1990, Abraham (TNT), 1993, Jacob (TNT), 1994, Joseph (TNT), 1995, Moses (TNT) 1995, ind. film prodn., 1991—. Trustee Kennedy Center for Performing Arts. Served to lt. USN, 1955-58. Office: 1775 Massachusetts Ave NW Washington DC 20036-2188

RAGAINS, CHARLES C., public relations executive; b. Owensboro, Ky., July 24, 1943. BA in Sociology, Mich. State U., 1965, MA in Journalism, 1967. Pub. rels. rep. Burroughs, 1969-72, mgr. pub. rels. internat. group, 1972-74, mgr. corp. publs. and employee comm., 1974-82; dir. advt. and mktg. comm. Burroughs Corp., Detroit, 1982-88; v.p. Anthony M. Franco, Inc., Detroit, 1987-89, sr. v.p., 1989-91, exec. v.p., COO, 1991—. Mem. NIRI (sec. Detroit chpt. 1978-79). Office: Anthony M Franco Inc 400 Renaissance Ctr Ste 600 Detroit MI 48243-1509*

RAGALS, WILLIAM CHARLES, JR., lawyer, business executive; b. N.Y.C., Feb. 4, 1939; s. William Charles and Frances (Spiegel) R.; m. Jane Gottlieb, June 26, 1960; children: Jonathan William, David Charles. BA, Colgate U., 1960; LLB, NYU, 1963. Bar: N.Y. 1963, U.S. Dist. Ct. (so. and ea. dists.) N.Y. 1963. Assoc. Wikler Gottlieb Taylor & Howard, N.Y.C., 1963-66, 1970-71; corp. counsel Bermec Corp., N.Y.C., 1966-70; v.p., sec., corp. counsel Creative Capital Corp., N.Y.C., 1971-73; sec., corp. counsel Internat. Controls Corp., Thomaston, Conn., 1973-83, v.p., sec., corp. counsel, 1978-83; v.p., sec. gen. counsel Internat. Controls Corp., Somerset, N.J., 1983-88; v.p., sec., gen. counsel Vernitron Corp., N.Y.C., 1988-90; v.p., sec., gen. counsel Health-Chem Corp., N.Y.C., 1990—, also bd. dirs., 1991—. Mem. planning bd. Town of New Castle, Chappaqua, N.Y., 1980-89; adv. bd. local region Am. Youth Soccer Assn., 1980-86. Mem. ABA, N.Y. Bar Assn., N.Y. County Lawyers Assn., Am. Soc. Corp. Secs., Am. Corp. Counsel Assn. Office: Health-Chem Corp 3 Empire Blvd South Hackensack NJ 07606-1806

RAGAN, CHARLES RANSOM, lawyer; b. N.Y.C., Aug. 13, 1947; s. Charles Alexander Jr. and Josephine Forbes (Parker) R.; m. Barbara Thiel McMahon, Aug. 30, 1969; children: Alexandra Watson, Madeline McCue. AB, Princeton U., 1969; JD, Fordham U., 1974. Bar: N.Y. 1975, U.S. Ct. Appeals (3d cir.) 1975, Calif. 1976, U.S. Ct. Appeals (9th cir.) 1976, U.S. Dist. Ct. (no. dist.) Calif. 1976, U.S. Supreme Ct. 1981, U.S. Dist. Ct. (so. dist.) N.Y. 1982, U.S. Ct. Appeals (2d cir.) 1984. Law clk. to Hon. R.J. Aldisert U.S. Ct. Appeals (3rd cir.), 1974-76; assoc. Pillsbury, Madison & Sutro, San Francisco, 1976-81, ptnr., 1982—; mem. exec. com. 9th Cir. Judicial Conf., 1987-91. Contbr. articles to profl. jours. Mem. Inst. Transnational Arbitration (bd. dirs., advisor), San Francisco Bar Assn. (chair feds. cts. 1982-89), Chartered Inst. Arbitrators (assoc.). Avocations: biking, ballet, sports spectator. Office: Pillsbury Madison & Sutro 225 Bush St San Francisco CA 94104-4207

RAGAN, DAVID, publishing company executive; b. Jackson, Tenn., Aug. 26, 1925; s. Amos and Esther Lee (Tacker) R.; m. Violet Claire Sills, Dec. 27, 1948; children—David Nathaniel, Sarah Sills, Jennifer Leigh. B.A. in English, Union U., Jackson, 1947; M. Theatre Arts, Calif. Sch. Theatre, 1950. Radio writer Grand Central Sta., 1950; syndicated columnist Hollywood South Side, 1951; mng. editor Tele-Views mag., 1952; free-lance writer, 1952-57, 74-77, 82—; editor TV and Movie Screen Sterling Group, Inc., N.Y.C., 1957-61; mng. editor Motion Picture mag. Fawcett Pub. Co., N.Y.C., 1961-64; editor TV Radio Mirror, Macfadden-Bartell Pub. Co., N.Y.C., 1964-71; pub. editorial dir. Movie Digest, Words and Music, Planet mags. Nat. Periodical Publs. (Warner Communications), N.Y.C., 1971-74; editorial dir. Photoplay, Motion Picture, TV Mirror mags.; Macfadden Women's Group, N.Y.C., 1977-79; entertainment editor Globe Nat. Weekly, N.Y.C., 1979-82. Author: Who's Who in Hollywood 1900-1976, 1977, Movie Stars of the '30s, 1985, Movie Stars of the '40s, 1985, Mel Gibson: An Intimate Biography, 1985, Who's Who in Hollywood: The Largest Cast of Film Personalities Ever Assembled, rev., 1992; co-author: Richard Pryor: This Cat's Got Nine Lives, 1982; contbr. articles to profl. jours. Served with U.S. Army, 1952-54. Mem. Screen Actors Guild, TV Acad., Alpha Tau Omega, Tau Kappa Alpha. Republican. Presbyterian. Home: 1230 Park Ave New York NY 10128-1724

RAGAN, JAMES OTIS, engineer, consultant; b. Prineville, Oreg., Apr. 9, 1942; s. Robert Ray Ragan and Lois (Renfro) Williams. Student, Seattle U., 1961, Cerritos Coll., 1962-63. Profl. quality engr., cert. nondestrictive testing level III. Sr. engr. Combustion Engring., Inc., Chattanooga, 1973-78; quality control mgr. Brown & Root, Inc., Houston, 1978-84; nondestructive testing level III Texas Utilities Electric Co., Dallas, 1984—; cons. FMC Corp., Stephenville, Tex., 1990—; Bonded Inspection, Inc., Garland, Tex., 1992—. With U.S. Army, 1964-66. Recipient First Use award Electric Power Rsch. Inst. Comanche Peak Stream Electric Station, Glen Rose, Tex., 1991. Mem. ASME, Am. Soc. Nondestructive Testing. Republican. Avocation: computers. Home: RR 2 Box 184 Bluff Dale TX 76433-9749 Office: Tex Utilities Electric PO Box 1002 Glen Rose TX 76043-1002

RAGAN, JAMES THOMAS, communications executive; b. San Diego, Mar. 15, 1929; m. Susan Held, Nov. 9, 1957; children: James, Maria, Carey, Andrew. BA, Oxford U., Eng., 1951, MA, 1955. With Gen. Electric Co., 1954-69; pres., chief operating officer Athena Communications Corp. subs. Gulf & Western Industries, Inc., N.Y.C., 1969-74; v.p. broadcast services Western Union Telegraph Co., 1974-76, v.p. satellite services, 1976-82, pres. Western Union personal communications corp., v.p. communication systems group, 1982-85; pres. Associated Info. Services Corp., 1985-86, Bunting, Inc., 1986-88; ptnr. Pierce Kennedy Hearth, 1988-91; CEO Nat. Lang. Assocs., Guilford, Conn., 1990—. Patentee recreational sports equipment. Pres. Wilton (Conn.) Pop Warner Football League, 1972-73. Served with USMCR, 1952-54, maj. (ret.). Mem. Sachem's Head Assn. (v.p., treas.), Sachem's Head Yacht Club (Guilford, Conn.), Madison (Conn.) Winter Club (pres.). Clubs: Racquet and Tennis (N.Y.C.); Sachem's Head Yacht (Guilford, Conn.); Madison Winter (pres.). Home: 630 Colonial Rd Guilford CT 06437-3139 Office: Nat Lang Assocs PO Box 442 Guilford CT 06437

RAGAN, SAMUEL TALMADGE, newspaper editor, publisher, educator, poet laureate; b. Berea, N.C., Dec. 31, 1915; s. William Samuel and Emma Clare (Long) R.; m. Marjorie Usher, Aug. 19, 1939; children: Nancy, Ann Talmadge. A.B., Atlantic Christian Coll., 1936, Litt.D., 1972; Litt.D., U. N.C., 1987; D.Letters, Meth. Coll., 1980; D.Lit., St. Andrews Coll., 1987. Newspaperman in N.C. and Tex., 1936—; mng. editor, author column Southern Accent in Raleigh (N.C.) News and Observer, 1948-69; exec. editor Raleigh News and Observer, also Raleigh Times, 1957-69; editor, pub., author column The Pilot, Southern Pines, N.C., 1969—; sec. N.C. Dept. Arts, Culture and History, 1972-73; conductor program, commentator sta. WTVD, Durham, 1969—; spl. lectr. contemporary issues N.C. State U., 1959-68; dir. Writer's Workshop, 1963—; instr. creative writing St. Andrews Coll., 1970—, Sandhills Coll., 1969—; cons. editor St. Andrews Rev., Pembroke Mag. Author: (collected poems) The Tree in the Far Pasture, 1964, To the Water's Edge, 1971, Journey Into Morning, 1981, In the Beginning, 1985; The Democratic Party: Its Aims and Purposes, 1961, The New Day, 1964, Free Press and Fair Trial, 1967, (with Elizabeth S. Ives) Back to Beginnings, 1969, In the Beginning (with Thad Stem Jr.), 1984, A Walk Into April, 1986, Collected Poems, 1990; Editor: Weymouth Anthology, 1987; Contbg. editor: World Book Ency., 1964—; author articles, poems. Pres. Friends Coll., Inc., N.C. State, 1961-62; mem. N.C. Library Resources Com., N.C. Govt. Reorgn. Commn., 1970—; moderator N.C. Writers Forum of Charlotte, 1963—; Trustee N.C. Sch. Arts, 1963-72; mem. N.C. Adminstrn. of Justice Council, 1964—, chmn., 1980-83; bd. dirs. N.C. Symphony Soc., 1975-79. Served with AUS, 1943-46, PTO. Recipient N.C. Tercentenary Poetry award, 1963. Spl. Citation for Contbns. to Journalism Atlantic Christian Coll., North Caroliniana Soc. award, 1981, Disting. Svc. medal DAR, 1974, Edward Arnold Young award for Poetry, 1965, 72, 91, Morrison award for contbns. to arts N.C., 1976, N.C. award for achievements in arts, 1979, R. Hunt Parker award for contbns. to lit., 1987, N.C. Artists award United Arts Coun., 1990, Caldwell award for contbns. and achievements in humanities N.C. Humanities Coun., 1993; inducted into N.C. Journalism Hall of Fame, 1984; appointed Poet Laureate N.C. for life, 1982. Mem. N.C. Lit. Forum (moderator 1956—), N.C. Writers Conf. (chmn. 1962-63), Eastern N.C. Press Assn. (past pres.), N.C. Press Assn. (pres. 1973-74), Asso. Press Mng. Editors Assn. (dir. gen. chmn. continuing studies 1961, sec. 1962, v.p. 1963, pres. 1964), Am. Soc. Newspaper Editors (dir., chmn. freedom of info. com. 1968), Roanoke Island Hist. Soc. (dir.), N.C. News Council (past pres.), N.C. Arts Council (chmn. 1967-72), Am. Newspaper Pubs. Assn., N.C. Lit. and Hist. Assn. (pres. 1977), Friends of Weymouth (pres. 1979-84), Sigma Delta Chi. Democrat. Presbyterian. Club: Sandhills Kiwanis (Southern Pines); Builders Cup 1985. Home: 255 Hill Rd Southern Pines NC 28387-6633 Office: 145 W Pennsylvania Ave Southern Pines NC 28387-5428

RAGATZ, THOMAS GEORGE, lawyer; b. Madison, Wis., Feb. 18, 1934; s. Wilmer Leroy and Rosanna (Kindschi) R.; m. Karen Christensen, Dec. 19, 1965; children—Thomas Rolf, William Leslie, Erik Douglas. BBA, U. Wis.-Madison, 1957, LLB, 1961. Bar: Wis. 1961, U.S. Dist. Ct. (ea. and we. dists.) Wis. 1961, U.S. Tax Ct. 1963, U.S. Ct. Appeals (7th cir.) 1965, U.S. Supreme Ct. 1968; CPA, Wis. Staff acct. Peat, Marwick, Mitchell & Co., Mpls., 1958; instr. Sch. Bus., U. Wis.-Madison, 1958-60, formerly lectr. in acctg. and law U. Wis.; law clk. Wis. Supreme Ct. , 1961-62; assoc. Boardman Suhr Curry & Field, Madison, 1962-64, ptnr., 1965-78; ptnr. Foley & Lardner, Madison, 1978—, mgr. ptnr., 1984-93; dir. Sub-Zero Freezer Co., Inc., Wis. Tales & Trails, Inc., Acme Equipment Corp., Mortenson, Matzell & Meldrem, Inc., Norman Bassett Found.; dir., past pres. Wis. Amateur Sports Corp.; lectr. seminars on tax subjects. Editor in chief Wis. Law Rev., 1960-61; chmn. Nat. Conf. Law Revs., 1960-61; author: The Ragatz History, 1989; contbr. articles to profl. jours. Formerly active United Way, Meth. Hosp. Found.; chmn. site selection com. U. Wis. Hosp.; bd. regents U. Wis., panel provision of legal svcs.; former moderator 1st Congl. Ch.; past pres. First Congl. Ch. Found.; bd. dirs. Met. YMCA, Madison, 1983-90, YMCA Found.; pres. Bus. & Edn. Partnership, 1989, also bd. dirs. Fellow Am. Bar Found.; mem. ABA, Seventh Cir. Bar Assn., Wis. Bar Found., State Bar Wis. (sec. 1969-70, bd. govs. 1971-75, chmn. fin. com. 1975-80, chmn. tax sect., chmn. spl. com. on econs., chmn. svcs. for lawyers com.), Dane County Bar Assn. (pres. 1978-79, chmn. jud. qualification com., sect.), Am. Judicature Soc., Wis. Inst. CPAs, Madison Club (pres. 1980-81), Order of Coif, Beta Gamma Sigma, Sigma Chi, Order of Constantine. Republican. Home: 3334 Lake Mendota Dr Madison WI 53705-1469 Office: Foley & Lardner 1st Wisconsin Plaza 1 S Pinckney St PO Box 1497 Madison WI 53701-1497 also: Foley & Lardner 1st Wisconsin Ctr 777 E Wisconsin Ave Milwaukee WI 53202-5367

RAGENT, BORIS, physicist; b. Cleve., Mar. 2, 1924; s. Samuel and Bertha (Lev) R.; m. Dorothy Kohn, Sept. 11, 1949; children—David Stefan, Lawrence Stanton, Jesse Ron. Student, Ohio State U., 1941-44; B.S.E.E., Marquette U., 1944; Ph.D. in Physics, U. Calif., Berkeley, 1953. Registered profl. engr., Calif. Engr. Victoreen Instrument Co., Cleve., 1946-48; engr., physicist Radiation Lab., U. Calif., Berkeley, 1948-53; physicist Livermore, 1953-56, Broadview Research Corp., Burlingame, Calif., 1956-59, Vidya div. Itek Corp., Palo Alto, Calif., 1959-66, Ames Research Ctr., NASA, Moffett Field, Calif., 1966-87, San Jose (Calif.) State U. Found., 1987—; lectr. Stanford U., U. Calif. Extension. Served in USNR, 1944-46. Mem. AAAS, Am. Phys. Soc., Optical Soc. Am., Am. Geophys. Union, Sigma Xi. Office: Ames Research Ctr NASA Mail Stop 245-1 Moffett Field CA 94035

RAGGI, REENA, federal judge; b. Jersey City, May 11, 1951. BA, Wellesley Coll., 1973; JD, Harvard U., 1976. Bar: N.Y. 1977. U.S. atty. Dept. Justice, Bklyn., 1986; ptnr. Windels, Marx, Davies & Ives, N.Y.C., 1987; judge U.S. Dist. Ct. (ea. dist.) N.Y., Bklyn., 1987—. Office: US Courthouse 225 Cadman Plz E Brooklyn NY 11201

RAGGIO, KENNETH GAYLORD, lawyer; b. Dallas, Oct. 18, 1949; s. Grier H. and Louise (Ballerstedt) R.; m. Patricia Thornbury, June 28, 1980; children: Jeffrey, Michael. BA, U. Tex., Austin, 1971, JD, 1974. BarL Tex. 1974, U.S Dist Ct. (no. dist.) Tex. 1974. Pvt. practice Austin, 1974-76; shareholder Raggio & Raggio, Inc., Dallas, 1977—; speaker, lectr. in field of tracing and characterization of property, and applying tech. to clients cases. Contbr. to profl. publs. Recipient Cici Simon Meml. award Children's Rights Coun., 1990. Mem. ABA (chair family law sect. 1991-92, spl. com. on project 2000, 1991-94), Tex. Bar Found., Am. Acad. Matrimonial Lawyers, Internat. Acad. Matrimonial Lawyers, Tex. Acad. Family Law Specialists, State Bar Tex., Dallas Bar Assn. (chair family law sect. 1980-81, chair media rels. com. 1980-83, chair bar activities com. 1984). Office: Raggio & Raggio Inc 3316 Oak Grove Ave Dallas TX 75204-2331

RAGGIO, LOUISE BALLERSTEDT, lawyer; b. Austin, Tex., June 15, 1919; d. Louis F. and Hilma (Lindgren) Ballerstedt; m. Grier H. Raggio, Apr. 19, 1941; children: Grier, Thomas, Kenneth. B.A., U. Tex., 1939; student, Am. U. Washington, 1939-40; J.D., So. Methodist U. 1952. Bar: Tex. 1952, U.S. Dist. Ct. (no. dist.) Tex. 1958. Intern Nat. Inst. Pub. Affairs, Washington, 1939-40; asst. dist. atty. Dallas County, Tex., 1954-56; shareholder Raggio and Raggio, 1956—. Sec. Gov's Commn. on Status of Women, 1970-71; trustee Tex. Bar Found., 1982-86, chmn., 1984-85, chmn. fellows, 1993—, Dallas Women's Found., 1993—, Nat. Conf. Bar Founds., 1986-92. Recipient Zonta award, Bus. and Profl. Women's Club award, So. Meth. U. Alumni award, Woman of Yr. award Tex. Fedn. Bus. and Profl.

Women's Clubs, 1985, award Internat. Women's Forum, 1990, Disting. Law Alumni award So. Meth. U., 1992; Disting. Trial Lawyer award, 1993, Outstanding Trial Lawyer award Dallas Bar Assn., 1993, Pacemaker award Nat. Bus. Women Owners Assn., 1994; inducted into Tex. Women's Hall of Fame, 1985. Fellow Am. Bar Found.; mem. ABA (chmn. family sect. 1975-76), State Bar Tex. (chmn. family law sect. 1965-67, dir. 1979-82, citation for law reform 1967, Pres.'s award 1987, Sarah T. Hughes award 1993), Dallas Bar Found. (pres. fellows com. 1991), Am. Acad. Matrimonial Lawyers (gov. 1973-81, trustee found. 1992—), Bus. and Profl. Women's Club (pres. Town North 1958-59), LWV (pres. Austin 1945-46), Phi Beta Kappa (pres. Dallas chpt. 1970-71, 90-92). Unitarian. Home: 3561 Colgate Ave Dallas TX 75225-5010 Office: Raggio and Raggio 3316 Oak Grove Ave Dallas TX 75204-2331 *All things are possible in our expanding universe if we can tune in to the infinite power available to all of us. Our ancestors concentrated on the problems—let us be a part of the solutions so desperately needed in our complex and troubled world.*

RAGGIO, WILLIAM JOHN, state senator, lawyer; b. Reno, Oct. 30, 1926; s. William John and Clara M. (Cardelli) R.; student La. Poly. Inst., 1944-45, U. Okla., 1945-46; BA, U. Nev., 1948; JD, U. Cal. at Hastings, 1951; m. Dorothy Brigman, August 15, 1948; children: Leslie Ann, Tracy Lynn, Mark William. Bar: Nev. 1951, U.S. Supreme Ct. 1959. Atty., Reno and Las Vegas; asst. dist. atty. Washoe County, Nev., 1952-58, dist. atty., 1958-71; ptnr. firm Wiener, Goldwater, Galatz & Raggio, Ltd., 1971-72, Raggio Walker & Wooster Reno and Las Vegas, 1974-78, Raggio, Wooster & Lindell, 1978-92, sr. ptnr. Vargas & Bartlett, 1992—; mem. Nev. Senate, 1973—, minority floor leader, 1977-81, 82-87, 91, majority flr. leader, 1987—; mem. legis. commn., vice chmn. criminal law and adminstrn. com. Council State Govts., 1972-75; bd. dirs. Am. Savs. & Loan Assn.; v.p., dir. Sahara Resorts, Casino Properties, Inc., Sahara Las Vegas, Inc. Adv. bd. Salvation Army, Reno; mem. Nev. Am. Revolutionary Bicentennial Commn., 1975-81; mem. Republican State Cen. Com. Bd. dirs. YMCA, Reno chpt. NCCJ, Salvation Army; nat. chmn. Am. Legislative Exchange Council, dir. Sierra Health Svcs.; trustee Nat. Dist. Attys. Found. (vice chmn. 1962-65); trustee Community Action Program Washoe County. Republican candidate for U.S. Senate, 1970. Served with USNR, 1944-46; to 2d lt. USMCR, 1946-47. Named Young Man of Yr., Reno-Sparks Jr. C. of C., 1959; recipient Disting. Nevadan award, 1968, Fellows award The Salvation Army, Torch of Liberty award The Anti-Defamation League. Fellow Am. Bd. Criminal Lawyers (v.p. 1978—); mem. ABA (state chmn. jr. bar conf. 1957-60, ho. dels.) Am. Judicature Soc., Navy League, Air Force Assn., Nat. (nat. pres. 1967-68; named Outstanding Prosecutor 1965), Nev. State (sec. 1959, pres. 1960-63) Dist. Attys. Assns., NCCJ (Brotherhood award 1965), Nev. Peace Officers Assn., Internat. Assn. Chiefs Police, Am. Legion, Elks, Lion Club, Prospectors Club, Alpha Tau Omega, Phi Alpha Delta. Republican. Roman Catholic. Home: PO Box 281 Reno NV 89504-0281*

RAGINSKY, NINA, artist; b. Montreal, Quebec, Can., Apr. 14, 1941; d. Bernard Boris and Helen Theresa R.; 1 child, Sofia Katrina. BA, Rutgers U., 1962; studied painting with Roy Lichtenstein; studied sculpture with, George Segal; studied Art History with Allan Kaprow, Rutgers U. Freelance photographer Nat. Film Bd., Ottawa, Ont., Can., 1963-81; instr. metaphysics Emily Car Coll. Art, Vancouver, B.C., Can., 1973-81; painter Salt Spring Island, B.C., 1989—; sr. artist, jury Can. Coun.; selected Can. rep. in Sweden for Sweden Now Mag., 1979; tchr., lectr. in field, 1973—. One woman shows include Vancouver Art Gallery, Victoria Art Gallery, Edmonton Art Gallery, Art Gallery Ont., San Francisco Mus. Art, Acadia U., Nancy Hoffman Gallery, N.Y.C., Meml. U Newfoundland Art Gallery; exhibited in group shows at Rutgers U., 1962, Montreal Mus. Fine Arts, 1963, Nat. Film Bd., Ottawa, 1964, 65, 67, 70, 71, 76, 77, Internat. Salon Photography, Bordeaux, France, 1968, Nat. Gallery Ottawa, 1968, Eastman House Rochester, N.Y., 1969, Vancouver Art Gallery, 1973, 80, Mural for Conf. Ctr. Ottawa, 1973, Field Mus., Chgo., 1976, Edmonton Art Gallery, 1978, 79, Walter Philips Gallery, 1979, Glenbow Mus. Gallery, 1979, Harbour Front Community Gallery, 1980, Hamilton Art Gallery, 1980, Musée Maisil de St. Lambert, 1981, Mendel Art Gallery, 1981, Dunlop Art Gallery, Regina, Can., 1981; represented in permanent collections Nat. Film Bd. Stills divsn., Ottawa, Ont., Banff (Alta.) Sch. Fine Arts, Nat Gallery Ottawa, Can., George Eastman House, Wadsworth Atheneum, Edmonton Art Gallery, various pvt. collections. Bd. dirs. Island Watch, Salt Spring Island, B.C., 1993; founder, coord. Salt Spring Island Ecosys. Stewardship Project, 1993. Mem. Royal Can. Acad. Arts, Order Can. (officer 1985). Avocation: gardening. Subject of numerous publications. Home and Office: 272 Beddis Rd, Salt Spring Island, BC Canada V8K 2J1

RAGIR, JOHN ARTHUR, theatrical company executive; b. Chgo., May 10, 1950; s. Benjamin and Julia (Nathan) R.; m. Nancy Rosanoff, June 15, 1971 (div. 1980); m. Sharon Evans, July 14, 1985; 1 child, Tamar. BA, New Sch. for Social Rsch., N.Y.C., 1979; MBA, NYU, 1982; postgrad., U. Chgo., 1986-87. Project mgr. Selfix Inc., Chgo., 1983-85; cons. Brettschneider & Assoc., Deerfield, Ill., 1986-88; pres. Live Bait Inc., Chgo., 1988—. Author: (plays) Wally's Demon, 1987, La Svengali, 1990, What's This in My Coke, 1992. Bd. dirs. NAME Gallery, Chgo., 1983-87, League of Chgo. Theaters, 1989. Office: Live Bait Inc 3914 N Clark St Chicago IL 60613-2602

RAGLAND, ALWINE MULHEARN, judge; b. Monroe, La., July 28, 1913; m. LeRoy Smith, 1947 (dec.); children—LeRoy, Caroline Smith Christman; m. 2d., L. Percy Ragland (dec.). A.A., Principia Coll., St. Louis; J.D. Tulane U., 1935. Bar: La. 1935. Sole practice, Tallulah, 1935-74; mem. firm Mulhearn & Smith, 1972-74; judge 6th Jud. Dist. Ct., Lake Prvidence, La., 1974-90; atty. for inheritance tax collector Madison Parish, La., 1968-74; former city atty., Delta, La.; temporary judge La. Ct. Appeals (2d cir.), 1976; atty., Tallulah, La., 1991. Charter bd. dirs. Silver Waters council Girl Scouts U.S.A.; past pres. Band Boosters Assn. Tallulah High Sch., Tallulah High Sch. PTA; past dist. dir., past bd. dirs, lay reader 1st Ch. Christ Scientist, Vicksburg, Miss.; past bd. dirs. Delta Christian Sch. Mem. ABA, La. Bar Assn., 6th Jud. Bar Assn., La. Def. Counsel Assn. (jud. assoc. mem.), Am. Judges Assn., La. Judges Assn., Am. Judicature Soc., La. Council Juvenile and Family Ct. Ct. Judges (past pres.), Nat. Council Juvenile Ct. Judges, So. Juvenile Ct. Judges, Assn. Trial Lawyers Am., La. Trial Lawyers Assn., Family Conciliation Cts. and Services, Nat. Juvenile Ct. Service Assn., La. Conf. Social Welfare, Practicing Law Inst., Nat. Assn. Women Judges, La. Assn. Def. Counsel. Home and Office: PO Box 752 Tallulah LA 71282

RAGLAND, JACK WHITNEY, artist; b. El Monte, Calif., Feb. 25, 1938; s. Jack Rider and Dorsey (Whitney) R.; m. Marilee J. Weaver, July 31, 1969; children—Roxanne, Natasha. BA, Ariz. State U., 1960, M.A., 1964; postgrad., UCLA, 1961-64. Grad. asst. tchr. Ariz. State U., 1960-61; grad. teaching asst. UCLA, 1961-64; head art dept. Simpson Coll., Indianola, Iowa, 1964-76; demonstrator Nat. Art Materials Trade Assn., Denver, 1993, Pasadena Conv. Ctr., 1994. One-man shows include Kleine Gallery, Vienna, Austria, Billy Son Gallery, Coralville, Iowa, Tamarack Gallery, Stillwater, Minn., Percival Galleries, Des Moines, Simpson Coll., Pan Pacific Hotel, San Diego, Lakes Art Center, Okaboji, Iowa, Greenstone Ct. Collection, Fallbrook, Calif., Santa Barbara (Calif.) Art Co.; exhibited in group shows, Lyn Kottler Gallery, N.Y.C., Phoenix Art Mus., Tucson Festival Art, Talisman Gallery, Bartlesville, Okla., Exhibiting Artists Fedn., Poultney, Vt., Des Moines Art Center, Danskin Gallery, Palm Desert, Calif., Joslyn Mus. Art, Omaha, Lagerquist Gallery, Atlanta, Robert Wright Gallery, Escondido, Calif., Cabrillo Art Ctr., Point Loma, Calif., San Diego, NAMTA Art Show, San Francisco, 1995, Dennis Connors Gallery, San Diego, Internat. Art Svcs., San Diego, Arts Internat., ASID, Pasadena, Rancho Santa Fe, Calif., 1995; represented in permanent collections, Albertina Museum, Vienna, Kunsthaus, Basel, Switzerland, Bibliothèque National, Paris, Los Angeles County Mus., Simpson Coll., Phoenix Art Mus., Ariz. State collection, Graphische Bundes Versuchsanstalt, Vienna, Austria, also pvt. collections, works include stained glass windows, Meth. Ch., Perry, Iowa.; works reproduced Applause mag, 1971, New Woman mag, 1974, Artists of Cen. and No. Calif., Vol. II, San Diego Better Homes and Gardens Lifestyles mag., 1995, San Diego Decorating mag., 1995. Recipient award purchase prize Ariz. Ann. Art Show, 1961, 1st prize in prints Iowa State Fair, 1974, 1st prize So. Calif. Expn., Del Mar; featured in Am. Artist mag. Oct. 1993. Home: 5490 Rainbow Heights Rd Fallbrook CA 92028-9619 *To capture the spiritual essence of a subject through form and color is the goal of my art.*

RAGLE, JOHN LINN, chemistry educator; b. Colorado Springs, Colo., Feb. 4, 1933; s. Richard Charles and Jane Addams (Hulbert) R.; m. Roberta Ann Litzerman, July 26, 1990. BS, U. Calif., Berkeley, 1954; PhD, Wash. State U., 1957. Asst. prof. U. Mass., Amherst, 1957-60, assoc. prof., 1964-67, prof., 1968-75, 1976—; rsch. assoc. Cornell U., Ithaca, N.Y., 1960-62; scientist Northrop Space Labs., Hawthorne, Calif., 1962-64; vis. assoc. prof. U. B.C., Vancouver, Can., 1967-68; vis. prof. Technische Hochschule, Darmstadt, Fed. Republic Germany, 1975-76. Contbr. articles to profl. jours. Recipient Sr. U.S. Scientist award von Humboldt Stiftung, 1975. Mem. Am. Phys. Soc., Am. Chem. Soc. Republican. Avocations: music, computers, amateur radio, hiking, gardening. Office: U Mass Dept Chemistry Amherst MA 01003

RAGNO, NANCY NICKELL, educational writer; b. Phila., Sept. 2, 1938; d. Paul Eugene and Sara Jane (Mensch) Nickell; m. Joseph Diego Ragno, Aug. 25, 1961; 1 child, Michelle Angela. BA, Lebanon Valley Coll., 1960, MA, NYU, 1968. Cert. tchr., N.J. Tchr. N.J. pub. schs., 1961-68; project editor Prentice-Hall, Inc., Englewood Cliffs, N.J., 1968-70, Harcourt Brace Jovanovich, N.Y.C, 1970-72; sr. editor Silver Burdett Co., Morristown, N.J., 1972-76; editor, writer Houghton Mifflin Co., Boston, 1976-77; sr. editor J.B. Lippincott Co., Phila., 1977-79; sr. author Silver Burdett Ginn, Morristown, 1984—. Author: (textbook series) Silver Burdett English, 1984, World of Language, 1992, (sound filmstrip) The City and the Modern World, 1970, Buying on the Installment Plan, 1974. Bassoonist Harrisburg (Pa.) Symphony Orch., 1959, Plainfield (N.J.) Symphony Orch., 1976, Somerset (N.J.) County Orch., 1989, Princeton (N.J.) Community Orch., 1992. Mem. ASCD, Nat. Coun. Tchrs. English, Internat. Reading Assn., Am. Soc. Journalists and Authors, Textbook Authors Assn., Authors Guild, U.S. Power Squadron. Democrat. Mem. Ch. of United Methodist. Avocations: music, writing, boating. Home: 12 Hillcrest Terr Stuart FL 34996-6729

RAGO, ANN D'AMICO, public relations professional; b. Pitts., Aug. 24, 1957; d. Jack and Florence (Zappa) D'Amico; m. John Thomas Rago, Aug. 31, 1984; 1 child, Annie J. BA, Duquesne U., Pitts., 1979, MA, 1987. From communications assoc. to dir. pub. relations Duquesne U., 1979-89, coord. univ. relations, 1989-93, exec. dir. pub. affairs, 1993—. Editor University Record, 1989 (silver medal). Bd. dirs. Support, Pitts., 1989-91; sch. dir. Carlynton Sch. Bd., Pitts., 1989, pres. sch. bd., 1990. Mem. Pub. Relations Soc. Am., Internat. Assn. Bus. Communicators, Am. Mgmt. Assn., Press Club Western Pa., Sigma Delta Chi. Office: Duquesne U 405 Adminstrn Bldg Pittsburgh PA 15282

RAGON, ROBERT RONALD, clergyman; b. Flintstone, Ga., Sept. 10, 1939; s. Robert Emmett and Frances Cora (Stoner) R.; m. Judith Ann Ward, Apr. 27, 1962; children: Ronald Russell, Regina Renee. BS, U. Chattanooga, 1962; BDiv, MDiv, Columbia Theol. Sem., Decatur, Ga., 1967. Ordained to ministry Presbyn. Ch., 1967. Pastor Trion (Ga.) Presbyn. Ch., 1967-72; dir., pastor Chattooga County Presbyn. Ministries, Trion, 1971-72; pastor Brainerd Presbyn. Ch., Chattanooga, 1972—; moderator Knoxville Presbytery, 1979-80; founder An Order of Slaves of Christ, Chattanooga, 1970; stated clk. Presbytery of S.E., 1990-93. Author: Covenant Agreement: O.S.C., 1970, The Journey, 1990. Trustee King Coll., Bristol, Tenn., 1983-86. Mem. Masons (Ga. chaplain 1980), KT (sec. 1991), Shriners, Kiwanis (bd. dirs. Chattanooga 1986-90). Republican. Avocation: investments. Home: 4229 Happy Valley Rd Flintstone GA 30725 Office: Brainerd Presbyterian Church 7 N Tuxedo Chattanooga TN 37411

RAGONE, DAVID VINCENT, former university president; b. N.Y.C., May 16, 1930; s. Armando Frederick and Mary (Napier) R.; m. Katherine H. Spaulding, Dec. 18, 1954; children: Christine M., Peter V. S.B., MIT, 1951, S.M., 1952, Sc.D., 1953. Asst. prof. chem. and metall. engring. U. Mich., Ann Arbor, 1953-57, assoc. prof., 1957-61, prof., 1961-62; asst. dir. John J. Hopkins Lab for Pure and Applied Sci., also chmn. metallurgy dept. Gen. Atomic div. Gen Dynamics, La Jolla, 1962-67; Alcoa prof. metallurgy Carnegie-Mellon U., Pitts., 1967-69; assoc. dean Carnegie-Mellon U. (Sch. Urban and Pub. Affairs), 1969-70; dean Thayer Sch. of Engring., Dartmouth Coll., 1970-72, Coll. Engring., U. Mich., 1972-80; pres. Case Western Res. U., Cleve., 1980-87; vis. prof., dept. materials sci. and engring MIT, Cambridge, 1987-88, sr. lectr. dept. materials sci. and engring., 1988—; gen. ptnr. Ampersand Splty. Materials Ventures, 1988-92; ptnr. Ampersand Specialty Materials Ventures, 1992—; trustee Mitre Corp.; bd. dirs. Cabot Corp., Augat Inc., Sifco Inc. Mem. Nat. Sci. Bd., 1978-84; mem. tech adv. bd. U.S. Dept. Commerce, 1967-75; chmn. adv. com. advanced auto power systems Council on Environ. Quality, 1971-75; Trustee Henry Luce Found. Named Outstanding Young Engr., Engring. Soc. Detroit, 1957. Mem. Univ. Club (N.Y.C.), Longwood Cricket Club (Boston), Sigma Xi, Tau Beta Pi. Office: MIT Dept Materials Sci Eng Rm 8-301 Cambridge MA 02139

RAGSDALE, CARL VANDYKE, motion picture producer; b. Illmo, Mo., May 16, 1925; s. Vandyke and Iona Lee (Bledsoe) R.; m. Diane E. Ringrose, Sept. 18, 1976; children: John Sheldon, Susan Lee. Student, Wash. U., 1942-43; BA, Denison U., 1950. Commd. ensign USN, 1945, advanced through grades to capt., 1972; ops. officer on staff commdr. in-chief Pacific, 1945; officer-in-charge Western Pacific Fleet Camera Party, 1946-47; capt. Res., 1954-85; photo officer USS Eldorado, Korea, 1950-52; dir.-prodr. USN Photo Ctr., 1952-53; comdg. officer Naval Res. Combat Camera Group—Atlantic, 1972-74; comdg. officer Naval Res. Office Info., N.Y.C., 1975-76, Houston, 1977-83; v.p. Depicto Films Inc., N.Y.C., 1954-62; pres. Carl Ragsdale Assocs. Inc., Houston and N.Y.C., 1962—. Producer Films including A Year Towards Tomorrow, 1966, While I Run This Race, 1967. Vice-chmn. USS San Jacinto Com., 1987; chmn. USS Houston Com., 1983. Decorated Navy Commendation medal with Gold star, Navy Meritorious Service medal; recipient Oscar award Acad. Motion Picture Arts and Scis., 1966, nomination, Acad. Motion Picture Arts and Scis., 1967, Silver Anvil award Publ. Relation Soc. Am., 1983. Mem. Dirs. Guild Am., Naval Res. Assn., Naval Order of U.S. (founder Tex. commandery), Am. Legion, DAV, Naval Aviation Commandery, Navy League, Inst. Diving, Underwater Photog. Soc., Soc. Motion Picture and TV Engrs., Houston C. of C., Mil. Affairs Com., N.Y. Athletic Club, Riverbend Country Club, Masons, Shriners. Republican.

RAGSDALE, GEORGE ROBINSON, lawyer; b. Raleigh, N.C., Mar. 26, 1936; s. George Young and Susan (Jolly) R.; m. Adora Prevost, Oct. 20, 1962; children: John Robinson, George Young II, Adora P. AB, U. N.C., 1958, LLB, 1961. Asst. to chief counsel U.S. Senate Subcom. on Constnl. Rights, Washington, 1961-62; law ptnr. Bailey & Ragsdale, Raleigh, 1962-65; legal counsel to Dan K. Moore, Gov. of N.C., Raleigh, 1965-68; judge Superior Ct. of N.C., Raleigh, 1968-70; ptnr. Moore, Ragsdale, Liggett, Ray & Foley, Raleigh, 1970-86, LeBoeuf, Lamb, Leiby & MacRae, Raleigh, 1987-93, Ragsdale, Liggett & Foley, 1994—; lectr. N.C. Assn. Def. Counsel. Trustee U. N.C., Chapel Hill, 1979-87, vice-chmn. bd. trustees, 1983-84, chmn., 1984-85; trustee U. N.C. Endowment, 1980—, chmn., 1984-85; bd. dirs. U. N.C. Instnl. Devel. Found., Inc., 1985—, U. N.C.-Chapel Hill Found.; bd. visitors U. N.C., The Ednl. Found., Inc. Mem. ABA, N.C. Bar Assn., Wake County Bar Assn., Assn. Bar of City of N.Y., Def. Rsch. Inst., Raleigh C. of C., Kiwanis, Sphinx Club of Raleigh, Terpsichorean Club, Raleigh Execs. Club, Carolina Country Club, Laurel Ridge Country Club. Episcopalian. Office: Ragsdale Liggett & Foley 2840 Plaza Pl PO Box 31507 Raleigh NC 27622

RAGSDALE, KEITH ELLEN, nurse, educator; b. Austin, Tex., Dec. 27, 1949; d. Kenneth B. and Janet (Dittlinger) R. AAS, Del Mar Coll., 1971; BS, Purdue U., 1973; MS, U. Colo., 1974; EdD, Nova Southeastern U., 1994. Asst. prof. rsch. and mgmt. U. So. Miss., Hattiesburg, 1974-75; asst. prof. community health Tex. Christian U., Ft. Worth, 1975-78; assoc. prof., acting asst. dean U. N.D., Grand Forks, 1978-79; chair dir. nursing and allied health Austin Community Coll., 1982—. Contbr. articles to profl. publs. Mem. AAAS, Nat. League for Nursing (sec. Tex. chpt.), World Future Soc., Tex. Assn. ADN's (chmn. legis. com.), Tex. Deans & Dirs., Tex. Jr. Coll. Tchrs. Assn., Sigma Theta Tau. Home: Rte 1 1300 Cardinal Dr Paige TX 78659-9742 Office: Austin CC 1020 Grove Blvd Austin TX 78741

RAGSDALE, RICHARD ELLIOT, hospital management executive; b. St. Louis, Dec. 20, 1943; s. Billie Oscar and Isabelle (Roques) R.; m. Anne Elizabeth Ward, Aug. 20, 1968; children: Richard, Kevin, Bethany. B.B.A., Ohio U., 1965; M. in Internat. Commerce, Am. Grad. Sch. Internat. Mgmt.,

1968. Asst. treas. Chase Manhattan Bank, N.Y.C., 1968-73; v.p., treas. Hosp. Affiliates Internat., Nashville, 1973-80; v.p., treas., chief fin. officer INA Health Care Group, Dallas, 1980-81; sr. v.p., chief fin. officer, dir. Republic Health Corp., Dallas, 1981-83, sr. exec. v.p., dir., 1983-85; chmn. Community Health Systems Inc., Brentwood, Tenn., 1985—, Great No. Health Mgmt., Ltd. London, 1986-89; dir. RehabCare Corp., St. Louis, 1993—. Coach Spring Valley Athletic Assn., Dallas, 1985; trustee Watkins Inst., 1988—; trustee Benton Hall Sch., 1988—, chair, 1991—; trustee Maryville Coll., 1990—, chair, 1992—. Recipient Thunderbird Disting Alumni award Entrepreneurship, 1990, Jonas Meyer Disting. Alumni award, 1993. Mem. Fedn. Am. Hosps. (legis. commn 1984-95). Republican. Avocations: SCUBA diving, drag racing. Office: Community Health Systems Inc 155 Franklin Rd Ste 400 Brentwood TN 37027-4677

RAGUSA, OLGA MARIA, Italian language educator; b. Catania, Italy, Feb. 11, 1922; came to U.S., 1932; d. Andrea and Anna (von Weiskopf) R. BA summa cum laude, Hunter Coll., 1943; MA, Columbia U., 1947, PhD, 1954. Instr. French and German Rutgers U., Newark, 1946-47; instr. Italian Vassar Coll., Poughkeepsie, N.Y., 1949-52; asst. prof. Columbia U., N.Y.C., 1955-61, assoc. prof., 1961-65, prof., 1965-79, Da Ponte prof. Italian, 1979—, chmn. dept., 1973-92; co-owner, editor S.F. Vanni (book dealers), 1974—; mem. exec. coun. MLA, 1972-75; mem. selection com. Am. Coun. Learned Socs., 1976-80; mem. area adv. com. for Western Europe, Coun. Internat. Exchange Scholars, 1983-86. Author: Mallarmé in Italy: Literary Influence and Critical Response, 1957, Verga's Milanese Tales, 1964, Narrative and Drama: Essays in Modern Italian Literature from Verga to Pasolini, 1976, Pirandello: An Approach to His Theatre, 1980; editor: Romance Section: Italian, Columbia Dictionary of Modern European Literature, 1980; editor Italica jour., 1968-84; mem. editorial bd. European Womens Writers Series, U. Nebr. Press, 1984—; contbr. numerous articles, revs. to Am. and European publs. Recipient Disting. Svc. award Am. Assn. Tchrs. of Italian, 1990; Fulbright fellow U. Milan, Italy, 1958-59, Am. Coun. Learned Socs. fellow, 1971-72; decorated knight Order of Merit (Italy), 1982. Mem. Phi Beta Kappa. Roman Catholic. Home: 30 W 12th St New York NY 10011-8635 Office: Columbia U Dept Italian 601 Casa Italiana New York NY 10027

RAHALL, NICK JOE, II (NICK RAHALL), congressman; b. Beckley, W.Va., May 20, 1949; s. Joe and Alice Rahall; children: Rebecca Ashley, Nick Joe III, Suzanne Nicole. AB, Duke U., 1971. Staff asst. U.S. Senator Robert C. Byrd, 1971-74; sales rep. Sta. WWNR, Beckley, 1974; pres. Mountaineer Travel Co., Beckley, 1975-77, W.Va. Broadcasting, 1980—; mem. 95th-104th Congresses from 4th (now 3rd) W.Va. dist., Washington, 1977—; mem. pub. works and transp. com.with subcoms. surface transp., water resources and econ. devel.; del. Dem. Nat. Conv., 1972, 74, 78, 80, 84, 88, 92; bd. dirs. Rahall Comm. Corp. W. Va. state chmn. March of Dimes, 1979. Named Young Man of Year, Beckley Jaycees, 1972; Outstanding Young Man in W.Va., W.Va. Jaycees, 1977; recipient Achievement award Logan Cripple Children Soc., 1978; Citizenship award K.C., 1978, Disting. Svc. award Am. Fedn. Govt. Employees W.Va., 1984, Young Dem. of Yr. Dem. Nat. Conv., 1980, Outfitter of Yr. Profl. Outfitters, 1987, Seneca award Sierra Club 1988, River Conservation award Am. River 1988; named Coal Man of Yr. Coal Industry News, 1979. Mem. NAACP, NRA, Rotary, Elks, Moose, Eagles, Shriners, Masons (32 Degree). Presbyterian. Office: US Ho of Reps 2269 Rayburn HOB Washington DC 20515-4803*

RAHE, MARIBETH SEMBACH, bank executive; b. Evanston, Ill., Oct. 3, 1948; d. Daniel F. and Boysie (Beebe) Sembach; m. Martin E. Rahe, May 31, 1975. BA, Bowling Green State U., 1970; postgrad., Ohio State U., 1970-72; MA in Internat. Mgmt., Am. Grad. Sch. Internat. Mgmt., 1974. Internat. banking officer Harris Bank, Chgo., 1974-77; asst. v.p. Harris Bank, London, 1977-80; v.p. Morgan Guaranty Trust Co., London, 1980-83, N.Y.C., 1983-84; sr. rep. Sparebanken Oslo Akershus, N.Y.C., 1984-85; v.p. Morgan Guaranty Trust Co., N.Y.C., 1985-87, J.P. Morgan Investment Mgmt., N.Y.C., 1987-88; sr. v.p. Harris Bank, Chgo., 1988-91, dept. exec., 1991-94, sr. exec. v.p., 1994-95, vice chmn. bd., 1995—; bd. dirs. Harris Bankcorp., Trustmark Ins. Co. Bd. dirs. Children's Meml. Hosp., Landmarks Preservation Coun. of Ill.; trustee Ill. Inst. Tech. Recipient Outstanding Alumni award Am. Grad. Sch., 1991. Mem. Am. Bankers Assn. (vice chmn. 1991-92, chmn. 1992-93, exec. com. pvt. banking, banking advisor 1993—), Com. of 200, Econ. Club, Chgo. Women's Network, Chgo. Club. Republican. Lutheran. Office: Harris Trust & Savs Bank 111 W Monroe St Chicago IL 60603-4003

RAHILL, MARGARET FISH, retired museum curator; b. Milw., Feb. 21, 1919; d. Joseph Benedict and Margaret (Scherdan) Schmidt; m. William James Fish, Nov. 14, 1941 (dec. 1945); 1 child, Mary Fish Arcuri; m. Frank M. Rahill, Mar. 14, 1951 (dec. Oct. 1986); children: Marguerite, Laura Rahill Maramba. BA, U. Wis., 1958; student, Mt. Mary Coll., 1958. With pub. rels. Blackland Army Air Base, Waco, Tex., 1942-43; reporter, art critic Milw. Sentinel, 1945-62; with pub. rels. dept. Milw. Art Ctr., 1962-63, Layton Sch. Art, Milw., 1965-68, Bel Canto Chorus, Milw., 1965-68; curator in charge Charles Allis Art Mus., Milw., 1968-91; prin. Book Bay, Milw., 1962-72; vis. instr. journalism Marquette U., Milw., 1972-73; mem. organizing com. Florentine Opera Club, 1962, with pub. rels. dept. 1962-65; mem. organizing com. Wis. Chamber Orch., Milw., 1975-76; v.p. art, councillor-at-large Wis. Acad. Sci. Arts and Letters, Madison, 1981-85; juror numerous art competitions, Wis., 1962-91. Contbr. articles to profl. jours. Active City of Milw. Art Commn., 1982-90, pres., 1984-85. Recipient Gridirm award Milw. Press Club, 1955, 57, 59, 60, Community Svc. award Milw. Art Commn., 1976, Ann. Bookfellows award Milw. Pub. Libr., 1977, Devel. award Milw. County Hist. Soc., 1982, Promotion of Hispanic Culture award Centro de la Communidad Unida, 1988. Mem. AAUW, Wis. Painters and Sculptors (hon.), Wis. Crafts Coun. (hon.). Roman Catholic. Avocations: Oriental art research, child care, reading. Home: 4801 Connecticut Ave Apt 302 Washington DC 20008

RAHM, DAVID ALAN, lawyer; b. Passaic, N.J., Apr. 18, 1941; s. Hans Emil and Alicia Katherine (Onuf) R.; m. Susan Eileen Berkman, Nov. 23, 1972; children: Katherine Berkman, William David. AB, Princeton U., 1962; JD, Yale U., 1965. Bar: N.Y. 1966, D.C. 1986. Assoc. Paul, Weiss, Rifkind & Wharton, N.Y.C., 1965-66, 1968-69; asst. counsel N.Y. State Urban Devel. Corp., N.Y.C., 1969-72, assoc. counsel, 1972-75; counsel real estate div. Internat. Paper Co., N.Y.C., 1975-80; ptnr. Stroock & Stroock & Lavan, N.Y.C., 1980-83, sr. ptnr., 1984—; mem. legis. com. Real Estate Bd. N.Y., 1988-92; lectr. Old Dominion Coll., Norfolk, Va., 1967-68, NYU, 1986—; mem. editorial bd. Comml. Leasing Law and Strategy, 1988-95. Contbr. articles to profl. jours. Fund raiser corp. com. N.Y. Philharm., N.Y.C., 1980-84; trustee Manhattan Sch. Music, 1989—, treas., 1991-94, chmn., 1994—. Mem. ABA (comml. leasing com. 1987-88, 94—, pub./pvt. devel. com. 1989—, real property sect.), Assn. of Bar of City of N.Y. (housing and urban devel. com. 1977-80, 81-84, real property com. 1989-92), Princeton Club. Democrat. Presbyterian. Avocations: music, reading, theatre. Office: Stroock & Stroock & Lavan 7 Hanover Sq New York NY 10004-2616

RAHM, SUSAN BERKMAN, lawyer; b. Pitts., June 25, 1943; d. Allen Hugh and Selma (Wiener) Berkman; m. David Alan Rahm, Nov. 23, 1972; children: Katherine, William. BA with honors, Wellesley, 1965; postgrad., Harvard U., 1966-68; JD, NYU, 1973. Bar: N.Y. 1974, D.C. 1988. Assoc. Marshall, Bratter, Greene, Allison & Tucker, N.Y.C., 1973-81, ptnr., 1981-82; ptnr. Kaye, Scholer, Fierman, Hays & Handler, N.Y.C., 1982—; chair real estate dept., 1993—. Editor: New York Real Property Service, 1987. Bd. dirs. Girls Inc., 1989-93; mem. aux. bd. Mt. Sinai Hosp., N.Y.C., 1987—. Recipient cert. of outstanding svc. D.C. Redevel. Land Agy., 1969, She Knows Where She's Going award Girls' Clubs of Am., 1987. Mem. ABA, Assn. of Bar of City of N.Y., N.Y. Bar Assn. (real property law com., co-chmn. real-estate devel. 1987-91), Am. Coll. Real Estate Lawwyers, Comml. Real Estate Women N.Y. (bd. dirs. 1988-94), v.p. 1988-91, pres. 1991-93). Office: Kaye Scholer Fierman Hays & Handler 425 Park Ave New York NY 10022-3506

RAHMAN, MUHAMMAD ABDUR, mechanical engineer; b. Sylhet, Assam, India, Mar. 1, 1930; came to U.S., 1950; s. Haji Sajjad Ali Khan and Momotaj Khanom. BSME, U. Toledo, 1953, MSME, 1968; PhD in Engring., Calif. Coast U., 1985. Registered profl. engr., Calif. Mech. design engr.

various cons. firms, L.A., 1955-61; aerospace engr. Douglas Aircraft Co., Santa Monica, Calif., 1962-63, N.Am. Aviation, Inc., L.A., 1963-64, NASA Manned Spacecraft Ctr., Houston, 1964-70; safety engr. U.S. Dept. Labor, OSHA, Washington, 1975-86; invention researcher Arlington, Va., 1987—; Contbr. articles to profl. jours. Mem. N.Y. Acad. Scis. Democrat. Islam. Achievements include patent for solar energy collector, supersonic MHD generator system; copyrights for hypothesis on unified field theory and creation of the universe, on the mechanism of superconductivity, others. Home and Office: 1805 Crystal Dr # 1013-S Arlington VA 22202-4407

RAHMAN, YUEH-ERH, biologist; b. Kwangtung, China, June 10, 1928; came to U.S., 1960; d. Khon and Kwei-Phan (Chan) Li; m. Aneesur Rahman, Nov. 3, 1956; 1 dau., Aneesa. B.S., U. Paris, 1952; M.D. magna cum laude, U. Louvain, Belgium, 1956. Clin. and postdoctoral research fellow Louvain U., 1956-60; mem. staff Argonne (Ill.) Nat. Lab., 1960-72, biologist, 1972-81, sr. biologist, 1981-85; prof. pharmaceutics Coll. Pharmacy, U. Minn., Mpls., 1985—, dir. grad. studies, pharmaceutics, 1989-92, head dept. pharmaceutics, 1991—; vis. scientist State U. Utrecht, Netherlands, 1968-69; adj. prof. No. Ill. U., DeKalb, 1971-85; cons. NIH.; Mem. com. of rev. group, div. research grants NIH, 1979-83. Author. Recipient IR-100 award, 1976; grantee Nat. Cancer Inst., Nat. Inst. Arthritis, Metabolic and Digestive Diseases. Fellow Am. Assn. Pharm. Scientists; mem. AAAS, Am. Soc. Cell Biology, N.Y. Acad. Scis., Radiation Rsch. Soc., Assn. for Women in Sci. (1st pres. Chgo. area chpt. 1978-79). Unitarian. Patentee in field. Home: 902 Dartmouth Pl SE Minneapolis MN 55414-3158 Office: Coll Pharmacy U Minn Minneapolis MN 55455

RAHN, ALVIN ALBERT, former banker; b. St. Paul, Apr. 8, 1925; s. Albert and Manda (Lau) R.; m. Helen Lyngen, June 10, 1950; children: Jennifer, Karen, Paul. B.B.A., U. Minn., 1949; postgrad., Stonier Sch. Banking, 1968. C.P.A., Minn. With income tax div. Minn. Dept. Taxation, 1949-61, asst. dir., 1957-61; with 1st Bank System Inc., Mpls., 1961-85; treas. 1st Bank System Inc., 1969-85, chief fin. officer, 1973-74, sr. v.p., 1974-85. Served with USNR, 1943-46. Mem. Am. Inst. C.P.A.s, Minn. Soc. C.P.A.s, Fin. Execs. Inst. Home: 5601 Dewey Hill Rd Minneapolis MN 55439-1919

RAHN, RICHARD WILLIAM, economist, business executive; b. Rochester, N.Y., Jan. 9, 1942; s. William Fred and Evelyn Janet (Chapman) R.; children: Margie Lynn, Richard William Jr.; m. Anneli Heinonen. BA, U. South Fla., 1963; MBA, Fla. State U., 1964; PhD, Columbia U., 1972; LLD (hon.), Pepperdine U., 1993. Instr. Fla. State U., Tallahassee, 1964-66; mem. grad. faculty dept. mgmt. Poly. Inst. N.Y., 1964-72, assoc. prof., 1973, administrv. officer, 1970-72; head dept., 1972-73; mng. dir. Ripon Soc., Cambridge, Mass., Washington, 1973-74; pres. Richard W. Rahn & Assocs. (Managerial Economists), Washington, 1974-76; econ. cons. N.Y. Merc. Exch., 1974-80; exec. dir., 1976-80; bd. dirs. Am. Coun. for Capital Formation, Washington, 1976—; v.p., chief economist C of C. of U.S. Chamber, 1981-87; exec. v.p. Nat. Chamber Found., 1985-91; adj. prof. George Mason U., Fairfax, Va., 1974-80; adj. scholar Hudson Inst., 1987—; commentator on nat. radio and TV; bd. dirs. IRET. Editor-in-chief Jour. Econ. Growth, 1986-91; contbr. articles to profl. jours., newspapers and mags. Mem. N.Y. County Republican Com., 1973, Nat. Social Security Adv. Council, 1982-83. Mem. Nat. Assn. Bus. Econs. (pres. Washington chpt. 1980), Adj. Scholar Discovery Inst. (pres. 1992—, CEO Novecon Mgmt. and Novecon Ltd.), Bus. Leadership Coun. (chmn. bd. 1995—), Mont Pelerin Soc., Pvt. Sector Coun. (bd. advisors). Republican. Club: Internat. Home: 8917 Potomac Forest Dr Great Falls VA 22066-4111 Office: 1020 16th St NW Ste 200 Washington DC 20036

RAIBLE, PETER SPILMAN, minister; b. Peterborough, N.H., Nov. 22, 1929; s. Robert Jules and Mildred (Galt) R.; m. Dee Dee Rainbow, June 18, 1950 (div. 1968); children: Stephen M., Robin S., Robert R., Deborah R.; m. Marcia McClellan Barton, June 5, 1987. PhB, U. Chgo., 1949; BA, U. Calif., Berkeley, 1952; MDiv, Starr King Sch. Ministry, 1953, D in Sacred Theology (hon.), 1974. Ordained to ministry Unitarian Ch. Asst. minister First Unitarian Ch., Providence, 1953-55; minister Unitarian Ch., Lincoln, Nebr., 1955-61, Univ. Unitarian Ch., Seattle, 1961—; bd. pres. Starr King Sch., Berkeley, 1967-68; mem. exec. com. Coun. Chs., Seattle, 1982-88; adj. prof. Meadville Lombard, 1987-88, N.W. Theol. Union, 1989. Author: How to Case a Church, 1982, Manual for Ordination Installation Services, 1994; book editor: Jour. Liberal Ministry, 1965-71; editor: UU Policy Manual, 1992. Bd. dirs. Council Planning Affiliates, Seattle, 1969-73, Wash. State chpt. ACLU, Seattle, 1963-67; chmn. ministerial adv. com. Planned Parenthood Ctr., Seattle, 1963-68; pres. United Nations Assn., Lincoln, 1959-61. Served as cpl. USAF, 1948-49. Merrill fellow Harvard U., Cambridge, Mass., 1972. Mem. Unitarian Universalist Ministers Assn. (pres. 1973-75), Pacific N.W. dist. Unitarian Universalist Assn. (exec. 1962-64, pres. 1985-87, mem. commn. on appraisal 1977-81). Office: U Unitarian Ch 6556 35th Ave NE Seattle WA 98115-7393

RAICHLE, MARCUS EDWARD, radiology, neurology educator; b. Hoquiam, Wash., Mar. 15, 1937; m. Mary Elizabeth Rupert, 1964; children: Marcus Edward, Timothy Stephen, Sarah Elizabeth, Katherine Ann. BS, U. Wash., 1960, MD, 1964. Diplomate Am. Bd. Psychiatry and Neurology. Intern Balt. City Hosps., 1964-65, resident, 1965-66; asst. neurologist N.Y. Hosp. Cornell Med. Ctr., N.Y.C., 1966-68, neurologist chief resident, 1968-69; clin. instr. dept. medicine divsn. neurosci. U. Tex. Med. Sch., San Antonio, 1969-70; rsch. instr. Washington U. Sch. Med., St. Louis, 1971-72, from asst. prof. neurology to assoc. prof. neurology, 1972-78, from asst. prof. radiology (radiation scis.) to assoc. prof. radiology Edward Mallinckrodt Inst. Radiology, 1972-79, from asst. prof. to assoc. prof. biomedical engring., 1974-79, prof. neurology, 1978—, prof. radiology Edward Mallinckrodt Inst. Radiology, 1979—, prof. biomedical engring., 1979—; instr. dept. neurology Cornell U. Med. Coll., N.Y.C., 1968-69; asst. neurologist Barnes Hosp., St. Louis, 1971-75, assoc. neurologist, 1978-78, neurologist, 1978—; cons. neurologist St. Louis Children's Hosp., 1975—; neurologist Jewish Hosp., St. Louis, 1984—, St. Louis Regional Hosp., 1985—; mem. neurology study sect. A NIH, 1975-79; mem. com. cerebrovascular diseases Nat. Inst. Neurol. Diseases and Stroke, long range planning effort, 1978, basic sci. task force, 1978; mem ad hoc adv. panel, Nat. Inst. Neurol. Diseases and Stroke, 1983, chmn. PET grants spl. rev. com., 1983, chmn. brain imaging ctrs. spl. rev. com., 1985; mem. adv. bd. McDonnell-Pew Program cognitive neuroscience, 1989; other coms. Editorial bds. Stroke, 1974-82, Neurology, 1976-82, Annals of Neurology, 1979-86, Journal Cerebral Blood Flow and Metabolism, 1983-86, dep. chief editor, 1981-83, Brain, 1985-90, Human Neurobiology, 1985-87, Brain Research, 1985-90, Synapse, 1987-90, Journal Neuroscience, 1989—, Journal Cognitive Neuroscience, 1989—, Cerebral Cortex, 1990—, Journal Nuclear Medicine, 1990—, Biological Psychiatry, 1993—, Learning and Memory, 1993—; over 120 pub. papers; contbr. over 75 book chpts. revs. Major USAF, 1969-71. Recipient numerous awards, lectrs., fellows; sr. McDonnell fellow McDonnell Ctr. Studies Higher Brain Function, Washington U., St. Louis, 1982—. Mem. AAAS, Am. Heart Assn. (stroke coun. 1974—, cardiovascular D rsch. study com. 1975-78, Academia Rodinensis Pro Remediatione (acting), Am. Acad. Neurology, Am. Neurological Assn. (councillor 1986-88, nom. com. 1990-91), Am. Physiological Soc., Assn. Rsch. Nervous and Mental Disease, Birmingham Med. Rsch. Expeditionary Soc., Explorers Club (N.Y.), Internat. Soc. Cerebral Blood Flow and Metabolism (sec. 1985-89, pres. elect 1989-91, pres. 1991-93), Inst. Medicine/NAS, Internat. Double Reed Soc., Soc. Neuroscience (pub. rels. com. 1988—), St. Louis Soc. Neurological Scis., Soc. Nuclear Medicine.

RAICHLEN, FREDRIC, civil enginering educator, consultant; b. Balt., Oct. 12, 1932; s. Samuel Israel and Ethel Lee (Fribush) R.; m. Judith Raichlen, May 2, 1968; children: Robert, David. B of Engring., Johns Hopkins U., 1953; MSc, MIT, 1955, DSc, 1962. Profl. engr., Calif., N.J. From asst. to assoc. prof. Calif. Inst. Tech., Pasadena, 1962-72, prof. civil engring., 1972—; fellow, asst. prof. civil engring. MIT, 1962; consulting engr., Pasadena, 1962—. 1st Lt. USAF, 1956-59. Fellow ASCE (John C. Moffatt and Frank E. Nichol Harbor and Coastal Engring. award 1994); mem. Nat. Acad. Engring., Internat. Assn. Hydraulic Rschrs., Sigma Xi. Home: 2157 Hornet Rd San Marino CA 91108 Office: Calif Inst Tech Dept Civil Engineering 1201 E California Blvd Pasadena CA 91125*

RAIKES, CHARLES FITZGERALD, lawyer; b. Mpls., Oct. 6, 1930; s. Arthur FitzGerald and Margaret (Hawthorne) R.; m. Antonia Raikes, Dec. 20, 1969; children: Jennifer Catherine, Victoria Samantha. B.A., Washington

U., 1952; M.A., Harvard U., 1955, LL.B., 1958. Bar: N.Y. State 1959. Assoc. White & Case, N.Y.C., 1958-69; assoc. gen. counsel Dun & Bradstreet, Inc., N.Y.C., 1969-72; v.p., gen. counsel Dun & Bradstreet, Inc., 1972-73; v.p., gen. counsel The Dun & Bradstreet Corp., N.Y.C., 1973-76, sr. v.p., gen. counsel, 1976-94, of counsel, 1994—; cons. Bd. Govs. Fed. Reserve System, 1958—. Served with U.S. Army, 1952-54. Woodrow Wilson fellow, 1952. Mem. Assn. Bar City of N.Y., Harvard Club, Sky Club, Phi Beta Kappa. Home: 26 Crooked Trl Rowayton CT 06853-1106 Office: Dun & Bradstreet Corp 187 Danbury Rd Wilton CT 06897

RAILTON, WILLIAM SCOTT, lawyer; b. Newark, July 30, 1935; s. William Scott and Carolyn Elizabeth (Guiberson) R.; m. Karen Elizabeth Walsh, Mar. 31, 1979; 1 son, William James; children by previous marriage: William Scott, Anne Greenwood. BSEE, U. Wash., 1962; JD with honors, George Washington U., 1965. Bar: D.C. 1966, Md. 1966, Va. 1993; U.S. Patent Office 1966. Assoc., then ptnr. Kemon, Palmer & Estabrook, Washington, 1966-70; sr. trial atty. Dept. Labor, Washington, 1970-71, asst. counsel for trial litigation, 1971-72; chief counsel U.S. Occupational Safety and Health Rev. Commn., Washington, 1972-77; acting gen. counsel U.S. Occupational Safety and Health Rev. Commn., 1975-77; ptnr. Reed, Smith, Shaw & McClay, Pitts., 1977—; lectr. George Washington U. Law Sch., 1977-79, seminar chmn. Occupational Safety and Health Act, Govt. Inst., 1979—; lectr. Practicing Law Inst., 1976-79. Author: (legal handbooks) The Examination System and the Backlog, 1965, The OSHA General Duty Clause, 1977, The OSHA Health Standards, 1977; OSHA Compliance Handbook, 1992; contbg. author: Occupational Safety and Health Law, 1988, 93. Regional chmn. Montgomery County (Md.) Republican party, 1968-70; pres. Montgomery So. Citizens Assn., 1970-71; bd. dirs., pres. Foxvale Farms Homeowners Assn., 1979-82; pres. Orchards on the Potomac Homeowners Assn., 1990-92; dir. Great Falls Hist. Soc., 1991-94; scoutmaster Troop 55 Boy Scouts Am., 1993—. With USMC, 1953-58. Recipient Meritorious Achievement medal Dept. Labor, 1972, Outstanding Service award OSHA Rev. Commn., 1977. Mem. ABA, Md. Bar Assn., Va. Bar Assn., Bar Assn. D.C. (vice chmn. young lawyers sect. 1971), Order of Coif, Sigma Phi Epsilon, Phi Delta Phi. Home: 10102 Walker Lake Dr Great Falls VA 22066-3502 also: 1200 18th St NW Washington DC 20036-2506 *Lawsuits are won by pre-trial preparation. A litigator should be candid with his clients and honest in his dealings with associates, opponents and the courts; an attorney should also volunteer his service to the community of which he is a part.*

RAIMI, BURTON LOUIS, lawyer; b. Detroit, May 5, 1938; s. Irving and Rae (Abel) R.; m. Judith Morse, Mar. 31, 1963 (div. Mar. 1985); children: Diane L. and Matthew D. BA, Brandeis U., 1960; JD with honors, U. Mich., 1963; LLM, George Washington U., 1964. Bar: Mich. 1963, D.C. 1964, Fla. 1991; U.S. Ct. Appeals (4th, 7th, 8th, 9th, 10th and D.C. cirs.). Atty. NLRB, Washington, 1964-69; assoc. Morgan, Lewis & Bockius, Washington, 1969-71; dep. gen. counsel FDIC, Washington, 1971-78; ptnr. Rosenman and Colin, Washington, 1978-86, Dechert Price & Rhoads, Washington, 1986-93; shareholder McCaffrey & Raimi, P.A., Naples and Sarasota, Fla., 1994—; speaker various insts. Mem. ABA (chmn. bank receiverships subcom. of banking com.), FBA, D.C. Bar Assn. (past chmn. banking law com., com. on interest on lawyers trust accounts), Fla. Bar. Avocations: sailing, racketball, tennis, travel. Home: 4452 Staghorn Ln Sarasota FL 34238-5626 Office: McCaffrey & Raimi PA 2033 Main St Ste 406 Sarasota FL 34237

RAIMI, SAMUEL M., film director; b. Royal Oak, Mich., Oct. 23, 1959; s. Leonard Ronald and Celia Barbara (Abrams) R. Student in humanities study, Mich. State U., East Lansing, 1977-79. V.p. Renaissance Pictures, Ferndale, Mich., 1979—. Writer, dir. (film) Evil Dead, 1981, Crimewave, 1985 (Best Dir. award 1986), Evil Dead II, 1986, Darkman, 1990, Army of Darkness: Evil Dead 3, 1993; co-writer: (screenplay) The Hudsucker Proxy, 1994; prodr. Hard Target, 1993, Timecop, 1994; dir. film The Quick and the Dead, 1995; appeared in films Spies Like Us, 1985, Thou Shalt Not Kill...Except, 1987, Maniac Cop, 1988, Miller's Crossing, 1990, Innocent Blood, 1992, Intruder, 1994, Terminal Force, 1995; appeared on TV in Journey to the Center of the Earth, 1993, Body Bags, 1993, The Stand, 1994; prodr., writer Mantis, 1993; exec. prodr. syndicated TV series The Legendary Journeys of Hercules, 1994-95. Recipient Best Horror Film, Knokke'heist Film Festival Belgium, 1982, Best Horror Film and Best Spl. Effects, Sitges Film Festival, Spain, 1982, 1st Prize of the Critics, 1st Prize of the Pub., Paris Festival Sci. Fiction, Fantasy and Horror, 1983, Best Horror Film of Yr., Fangoria Mag., 1983. Mem. Mich. State U. Soc. for Creative Film Making (founder, pres. 1978, 79), Calif. Rare Fruit Growers. Office: ICM 8942 Wilshire Blvd Beverly Hills CA 90211-1908

RAIMO, BERNARD, JR. (BERNIE), lawyer; b. Kansas City, Mo., May 29, 1944; m. Sharon Marie Brady, Aug. 23, 1974; children: Sara Elizabeth, Peter Bernard. BA, U. Notre Dame, 1965; MA, U. Md., 1967; JD with honors, George Washington U., 1972. Bar: D.C. Staff asst. to Sen. Stuart Symington Mo., 1968-72; asst. corp. counsel Washington, 1972-76; legis. analyst Am. Petroleum Inst., 1976-78; counsel Permanent Select Com. Intelligence U.S. Ho. Reps., Washington, 1978-91, chief counsel Ho. Com. Standards of Official Conduct, 1991—. Office: Ho Com Standards of Official Conduct HT 2 The Capitol Washington DC 20515-6328

RAIMONDI, ALBERT ANTHONY, mechanical engineer; b. Plymouth, Mass., Mar. 29, 1925; s. William and Amelia (Taddia) R. B.S., Tufts U., 1945; M.S., U. Pitts., 1963, Ph.D. in Mech. Engring. 1968. Rsch. engr. Westinghouse Rsch. Labs., Pitts., 1945-68; mgr. lubrication mechanics Westinghouse Rsch. Labs., 1968-85, mgr. tribology and exptl. mechanics, 1978-90, cons. engr. mechanics and tribology dept., 1990—. Contbr.: Am. Soc. Lubrication Engr. Handbook, 1968, 84; editor: jours. Am. Soc. Lubrication Engrs, 1971-76; assoc. editor: Trans. Am. Soc. Lubrication Engrs., 1960-71; Contbr. articles to profl. jours. Fellow Soc. for Tribologists and Lubrication Engrs. (Hunt award 1959, nat. award 1968, Westinghouse Maj. Innovation award 1990). Home: 125 8th St Turtle Creek PA 15145-1805 Office: Westinghouse Sci & Tech Ctr 1310 Beulah Rd Pittsburgh PA 15235-5098

RAIMONDI, RUGGERO, opera singer; b. Bologna, Italy, Oct. 3, 1941; m. Isabel Maier, 1987. Studies with Teresa Pediconi, Rome; studies with Maestro Piervenanzi. Debut as opera singer in La Boheme, Spoleto, Italy, 1964; opera singer in major houses, Europe and U.S.; Met. debut in Ernani, N.Y.C., 1970; favorite roles include Don Giovanni, Philip II, Boris and Don Quichotte; recorded Verdi Requiem, Vespri Siciliani, La Boheme, Aida, Attila, Don Carlos, Macbeth, I Masnadieri, Simon Boccanegra, Don Giovanni, Boris Godunov, Il Pirata, Norma, Tosca, Turandot, Berbiere di Siviglia, Mosé, Nozze di Figaro; appeared in films Don Giovanni , 1978, Six Characters in Search of a Singer, 1983, Carmen (Francesco Rosi), 1986, others. Decorated Officier des Arts et Lettres, Chevalier del'Order de Malte, Commendatore della Repubblica Italiana. Office: care Michael Lewin/ Künstler- management/Wasagasse 12/1/3, A 1030 Vienna Austria also: care SA Gorlinsky Ltd, 35 Dover St, London WLX 4NJ, England•

RAINBOLT, DAVID EUGENE, banker; b. Norman, Okla., Jan. 7, 1956; s. Harry E. and Jeannine (T.) R.; m. Mary Stevenson, Dec. 15, 1979 (div. Aug. 1987); 1 child, Adam D.; m. Kim Phillips, Oct. 6, 1990. BBA, U. Okla., 1978; MBA, Tulane U., 1979. Sr. credit analyst Republic Bank, Dallas, 1980, comml. loan officer, 1980-82; pres. Trencor, Inc., Oklahoma City, 1982-84; chief fin. officer BancFirst, Oklahoma City, 1984—; bd. dirs. BancFirst, Oklahoma City, BancFirst Corp., Trend Venture Corp.; mng. ptnr. Aero-Meridian Ptnrs., Oklahoma City, 1987—; trustee Okla. Tchrs. Retirement System, Oklahoma City, 1988—. Bd. dirs. Okla. Arts Inst., Oklahoma City, 1988—, Jr. Achievement, Oklahoma City, 1988—; bd. dirs., treas. Leadership Okla., Inc., Oklahoma City, 1989—; trustee Okla. Med. Rsch. Found., Oklahoma City, 1988—, Big Bros. Oklahoma City, 1983-89; exec. bd. Last Frontier coun. Boy Scouts Am., 1990—. Mem. Bldg. Owners and Mgrs. of C. (treas. bd. dirs 1988—), Okla. Bankers Assn. (bd. dirs. 1987-88, named one of Oklahoma's Future Banking Leaders, 1989, Leadership Oklahoma City (adv. bd. 1988-89), Leadership Okla. (treas., bd. dirs. 1989—), Rotary, Okla. Meml. Union (trustee 1989—). Avocations: fly fishing, snow skiing, Little League coach, hunting. Office: BancFirst 101 N Broadway PO Box 26788 Oklahoma City OK 73126-0788

RAINEAR, ROBERT E., utilities executive; b. 1936. AA, Pa. State U., BS in Elec. Engring. With Delmarva Power and Light Co., Del., N.J., 1961-80; exec. v.p. engring. and ops. S.C. Pub. Svc. Authority, Moncks Corner, S.C., 1980—. Office: South Carolina Pub Svc Auth 1 Riverwood Dr Moncks Corner SC 29461

RAINER, JOHN DAVID, psychiatrist; b. N.Y.C., July 13, 1921; s. Louis W. and Daisy (Harris) Rosen; m. Barbara Antin, Dec. 23, 1944; children: Jeff, Peter. AB, Columbia Coll., N.Y.C., 1941; MA, Columbia U., 1944, MD, 1951; DLitt (hon.), Gallaudet U., 1968. Rotating intern Mt. Sinai Hosp., N.Y.C., 1951-52; resident psychiatry N.Y. State Psychiat. Inst., N.Y.C., 1952-55; rsch. assoc. in psychiatry Columbia U., N.Y.C., 1956-59; asst. clin. prof. psychiatry Columbia U., 1959-67; chief psychiat. rsch. (genetics) N.Y. State Psychiat. Inst., N.Y.C., 1965-91; assoc. clin. prof. psychiatry Columbia U., N.Y.C., 1967-70; assoc. prof. clin. psychiatry Columbia U., 1970-72, prof. clin. psychiatry, 1972—; tng. and supervising analyst Columbia Psychoanalytic Ctr., N.Y.C., 1972—; attending psychiatrist Presbyterian Hosp., N.Y.C., 1972—. Editorial bd. mem. Am. Annals of the Deaf, Neuropsychobiology, Jour. Preventive Psychiatry; contbr. over 150 articles to profl. jours. Pres. Lake Isle Civic Assn., Eastchester, N.Y., 1989-91. With U.S. Army, 1945-46. Recipient Samuelson award N.Y. League for Hard of Hearing, 1974. Fellow Am. Psychiat. Assn. (life), Am. Psychoanalytic Assn. (life), Am. Coll. Psychoanalysts; mem. Am. Soc. Human Genetics, Am. Psychopathol. Assn. (life), Eastern Psychiat. Rsch. Assn. (pres. 1971-73), Westchester Psychoanalytic Soc. (pres. 1975-76), Phi Beta Kappa, Alpha Omega Alpha. Achievements include establishment of first psychiatric program for deaf people. Home: 9 Innisfree Pl Eastchester NY 10707-1207 Office: NY State Psychiat Inst 722 W 168th St New York NY 10032-2603

RAINER, REX KELLY, civil engineer, educator; b. Montgomery, Ala., July 17, 1924; s. Kelly Kenyon and Pearl (Jones) R.; m. Betty Ann Page, Aug. 28, 1945; children: Rex Kelly, John Kenyon. B.S., Auburn (Ala.) U., 1944, M.S., 1946; Ph.D., Okla. State U., 1957. Asst. engr. L. & N.R.R. Co., Cin., 1944-45; design engr. Polglaze & Basenberg, Birmingham, Ala., 1945-51; pres., chmn. Rainer Co., Inc., Orlando, Fla., 1951-62; prof. civil engring. Auburn U., 1962-67, head civil engring. dept., 1967; exec. v.p., 1980; hwy. dir. State of Ala., 1979-80, fin. dir., 1981-82; spl. asst. to gov. of Ala., 1981-82; dir. Office for Advancement Devel. Industry U. Ala., Birmingham, 1982-86; pres., cons. engr. Rex K. Rainer, Inc., 1982—; cons. to ins. cos., constrn. engring. firms; mem. Ala. Bd. Registration Profl. Engrs. and Land Surveyors, 1977—. Contbr. articles to profl. jours. Mem. Municipal Planning Bd., 1963-65, Indsl. Park Devel. Bd., 1969-71, So. Regional Edn. Bd. 1982-86. Served with AUS, 1943. Fellow ASCE (sec. 1976-79, pres. Ala. chpt. 1976-77, chmn. Constrn. Rsch. Coun., chmn. hwy. div. publs. com.; Civil Govt. award 1981); mem. Assn. Gen. Contractors Am. (bd. dirs. 1955), Am. Soc. for Engring. Edn. (chmn. constrn. engring. com.), Am. Pub. Works Assn., Phi Kappa Phi, Tau Beta Pi, Chi Epsilon. Home: 901 Ogletree Rd Auburn AL 36801

RAINER, WILLIAM GERALD, cardiac surgeon; b. Gordo, Ala., Nov. 13, 1927; s. Jamie Flournoy and Lula (Davis) R.; m. Lois Sayre, Oct. 7, 1950; children: Vickie, Bill, Julia, Leslie. Student, Emory U., Atlanta, Ga., 1943-44, U. Ala., 1944-45; MD, U. Tenn., Memphis, 1948; MS in Surgery, U. Colo., Denver, 1958. Diplomate Am. Bd. Surgery, Am. Bd. Thoracic Surgery. Intern Wesley Hosp., Chgo., 1949; gen. practice medicine Blue Island, Ill., 1950-52; resident Denver VA Hosp., 1954-59; practice medicine specializing in cardiac surgery Denver, 1960—; bd. dirs. St. Joseph Hosp. Found., Denver. Contbr. articles to profl. jours. Lt. U.S. Army, 1952-54. Decorated Bronze Star; recipient Disting. Alumnus award U. Tenn. Health Sci. Ctr., 1992. Mem. Soc. Thoracic Surgeons (sec. 1980-85, pres. 1989), Colo. Med. Soc. (pres. 1984-85), Denver Med. Soc. (pres. 1984), Am. Coll. Chest Physicians (pres. 1984), Am. Bd. Thoracic Surgeons (bd. dirs. 1982-88), Am. Surg. Assn., Am. Assn. Thoracic Surgery, Société Internationale de Chirugie, Denver Athletic Club. Avocations: photography, traveling. Office: 2005 Franklin St Ste 700 Denver CO 80205-5401

RAINES, FRANKLIN DELANO, investment banker; b. Seattle, Jan. 14, 1949; s. Delno Thomas and Ida Mae (Fortson) R.; m. Wendy Farrow, Sept. 11, 1982; children: Laura Farrow, Andrea Landon. BA magna cum laude, Harvard U., 1971, JD cum laude, 1976; postgrad., Oxford U., 1971-73. Assoc. dir. Seattle Model Cities Program, 1972-73; assoc. Preston, Thorgrimson, Ellis, Holman & Fletcher, Seattle, 1976-77; asst. dir. White House Domestic Policy Staff, Washington, 1977-78; assoc. dir. U.S. Office of Mgmt. and Budget, Washington, 1978-79; v.p. Lazard, Freres & Co., N.Y.C., 1979-82, sr. v.p., 1983-84, gen. ptnr., 1985-90; ltd. ptnr., 1990-91; vice chmn. Fed. Nat. Mortgage Assn., Washington. Mem. bd. overseers Harvard U.; trustee U. Puget Sound, German Marshall Fund of U.S., French-Am. Found., Am. Mus. Natural History, Mitre Corp.; mem. Nat. Adv. Coun. Edn. Disadvantaged Children, N.Y.C. Commn. on Early Childhood Edn., White House Confs. on Children and Youth, N.Y. Gov.'s Task Force on Poverty and Welfare Reform, Commn. on Behavioral and Social Scis.; bd. dirs. Ctr. Law and Social Policy, Am. Inst. Rsch., Washington, Black Student Fund, Washington, Nat. Inst. Dispute Resolution. Rhodes scholar, 1971. Mem. Nat. Assn. Securities Profls., N.Y. Stock Exch. (allied), Washington State Bar Assn., D.C. Bar Assn. Avocations: running, tennis. Office: Fed Nat Mortgage Assn 3900 Wisconsin Ave NW Washington DC 20016

RAINES, HOWELL HIRAM, newspaper editor, journalist; b. Birmingham, Ala., Feb. 5, 1943; s. W.S. and Bertha Estelle (Walker) R.; m. Laure Susan Woodley, Mar. 22, 1969 (div.); children: Ben Hayes, Jeffrey Howell. BA, Birmingham So. Coll., 1964; MA, U. Ala., 1973. Reporter Birmingham Post-Herald, 1964-65, Sta. WBRC-TV, Birmingham, 1965-67, Tuscaloosa (Ala.) News, 1968-69, Birmingham News, 1970-71; polit. editor Atlanta Constitution, 1971-74, St. Petersburg (Fla.) Times, 1976-78; Atlanta bur. chief N.Y. Times, 1978-80, White Ho. corr., 1980-82, nat. polit. corr., 1982-84, dep. Washington editor, 1985-86, London bur. chief, 1987-88, Washington editor, 1988-92; editl. page editor N.Y. Times, 1993—. Author: Whiskey Man, 1977, My Soul is Rested, 1977, Fly Fishing Through the Midlife Crisis, 1993. With U.S. Army N.G., 1965-71. Recipient Pulitzer Prize for feature writing, 1992. Office: NY Times 229 W 43d St New York NY 10036

RAINES, JOAN BINDER, literary agent; b. N.Y.C., July 25, 1931; d. Samuel Lawrence and Shirley (Cooper) Binder; m. Theron Raines, July 29, 1971; 1 child, Keith B. Korman. Ptnr. Raines &g., N.Y.C., 1974—. Contbr. articles to N.Y. Daily News Sunday Mag., St. Anthony Messenger. Mem. Assn. Authors Reps. Office: 71 Park Ave New York NY 10016-2507

RAINES, MARY ELIZABETH, airline executive; b. Tifton, Ga., Nov. 28, 1951; d. Marvin D. and Lou E. (Collins) R. BBA, Coll. William and Mary, 1973; JD with distinction, Emory U., 1979. Bar: Ga. 1979. Atty. Delta Air Lines, Inc., Atlanta, 1980-84, sr. atty., 1984-85, asst. sec., 1985-90, corp. sec., 1990-94, gen. atty., 1994—. Mem. ABA, Am. Soc. Corp. Secs., State Bar Ga. Office: Delta Air Lines Inc Hartsfield Atlanta Internat Airport Atlanta GA 30320

RAINES, TIMOTHY, professional baseball player; b. Sanford, Fla., Sept. 16, 1959; m. Virginia Raines; children: Tim Jr., André Darrell. Baseball player Montreal Expos, 1977-90, Chgo. White Sox, 1990—; mem. Nat. League All-Star Team, 1981-87. Recipient Silver Slugger award 1986, Sporting News Gold Shoe award, 1984; named Minor League Player of the Yr. The Sporting News, 1980, Nat. League Batting Champion, 1986; named to Sporting News Nat. League Rookie of Yr., 1981, Sporting News All-Star Team, 1983, 86, Nat. League Stolen Base Leader, 1981-84, N.L. All-Star Game, 1981-87 (named MVP 1987). Office: Chgo White Sox Comiskey Park 333 W 35th St Chicago IL 60616*

RAINESS, ALAN EDWARD, psychiatrist; b. N.Y.C., Sept. 24, 1935; s. George W. and Ida Rainess; m. Alice Maree Haber, June 5, 1960; 1 child, Alice Jeanne Kules. AB, Columbia Coll., 1957; MD, U. Paris, 1965. Intern Meadowbrook Hosp., East Meadow, L.I., 1965-66; resident in psychiatry N.Y. VA Hosp., N.Y.C., 1966-67; teaching fellow in psychiatry Harvard Med. Sch., Boston, 1967; resident in psychiatry Walter Reed Med. Ctr., Washington, 1970-72; clin. instr. St. Elizabeth's Hosp., Washington, 1973-76; asst. chief psychiatry Andrews AFB Hosp., Camp Springs, Md., 1976-80, chief neurology, 1989-91; resident in neurology Wilford Hall USAF Med. Ctr., San Antonio, 1980-83; chief medicine and neuropsychiatry Air Univ. Hosp., Maxwell AFB, Ala., 1983-89, chief neurology, 1991-94; psychiatrist Manhattan Psychiat. Ctr., N.Y.C., 1994—; asst. clin. prof. psychiatry Georgetown U. Med. Sch., Washington, 1974-79, Uniformed Svcs. U. Health Scis., Bethesda, Md., 1989—, assoc. profl. clin. neurology, clin. asst. profl. psychiatry, 1989-94. Col. USAF, 1968-73, 76-94. Fellow Am. Psychiat. Assn.; mem. Am. Acad. Neurology (assoc., uniformed svcs. com. 1988-92), Uniformed Svcs. Soc. Neurologists (pres. 1987-88), Am. Acad. Psychoanalysis (psychiat. assoc.), Am. Soc. Psychoanalytic Physicians, Mason, Shriners, Scottish Rite, York Rite. Home: 345 E 93d St Apt 22H New York NY 10128 Office: Manhattan Psychiat Ctr New York NY 10035

RAINEY, ARTHUR H., lawyer; b. Harrisburg, Pa., Oct. 8, 1943; s. David Cotter and Helen Hambleton (Hull) R.; m. Nancy Jeanne Bowen, July 29, 1967; 1 child, Douglas H. AB cum laude, Dartmouth Coll., 1965; JD cum laude, U. Pa., 1968. Bar: Pa. 1968, U.S. Supreme Ct. 1972, U.S. Ct. Appeals (3d cir.) 1973, U.S. Dist. Ct. (ea. dist.) Pa. 1973, U.S. Dist. Ct. (mid. dist.) Pa. 1988. Assoc. Dechert, Price & Rhoads, Phila. 1968, 73-79, ptnr., 1979—. Lt. JAGC, USNR, 1968-72. Office: Dechert Price & Rhoads 4000 Bell Atlantic Tower 1717 Arch St Philadelphia PA 19103

RAINEY, CLAUDE GLADWIN, retired health care executive; b. Enloe, Tex., Apr. 21, 1923; s. Claude C. and Pauline (Whitlock) R.; m. Peggy Ballard, July 27, 1947; children—Kathy Suzanne, David Claude, Mark Jeffery, Joel Allen, Peggy Jan, Susan Elise. Student pub. health and adminstry. medicine, Columbia U., 1961-62. Med. adminstrv., officer dept. medicine and surgery VA, Temple, Tex., 1946-51; med. adminstrv., officer dept. medicine and surgery VA, Muskogee, Okla., 1951-56; med. adminstr. Fite Clinic, Lakeland Med. Ctr., Muskogee, Okla., 1956-59; hosp. adminstr. M.-K.-T. R.R. Employees Hosp. Assn., Denison, Tex., 1959-62, also sec., treas. trustee; hosp. adminstr., cons. Denison Hosp. Authority, Meml. Hosp. 1962-66; adminstr. Seton Hosp., Austin, Tex., 1966-74; exec. v.p. Fort Worth Osteo. Hosp., 1974-83; pres. Health Care of Tex., Inc., Fort Worth, 1983-88, ret. Pres. North Grayson County chpt. Am. Cancer Soc., 1960-66, bd. dirs., Tex., 1961—. Served with USNR, 1942-46. Fellow Am. Coll. Hosp. Adminstrs., Am. Hosp. Assn.; mem. Am. Coll. Osteo. Hosp. Adminstrs. (award of merit 1984); mem. Am. Hosp. Assn., Tex. Hosp. Assn., Am. Osteo. Hosp. Assn. (Disting. Service award 1985).

RAINEY, GORDON FRYER, JR., lawyer; b. Oklahoma City, Apr. 26, 1940; s. Gordon F. and Esther (Bliss) R.; m. Selina Norman, Aug. 3, 1968; children—Kate, Melissa, Gordon III. B.A. in English, U. Va., 1962, LL.B., 1967. Bar: Okla. 1967, Va. 1968. Assoc. Rainey, Flynn, Wallace, Ross & Cooper, Oklahoma City, 1967-68; assoc. Hunton & Williams, Richmond, Va., 1968-75, ptnr., 1975—; chmn. of the exec. com. Hinton & Williams, dir. Crestar Fin. Corp. and Crestar Bank; bd. dirs. Weidmuller, Inc., Bryan Bros., Inc., Health Corp. of Va., Meml. Regional Med. Ctr., Inc. Campaign chmn. United Way of Greater Richmond, 1982, trustee, 1981-84; bd. dirs., past pres. Sheltering Arms Hosp., 1984, now trustee; chmn. Gov.'s Econ. Devel. Adv. Coun. Dist. 12; mem. Gov.'s Blue Ribbon Strike Force Commn. on Govtl. Reform; past mem. bd. govs. St. Catherine's Sch.; trustee Ch. Schs. Diocese Va.; chmn. bd. dirs. Leadership Met. Richmond; mem. Mayor's Emergency Shelter Task Force, 1981; pres., bd. dirs. Met. Found.; exec. com., bd. mgrs. U. Va. Alumni Assn. Served to 1st lt. U.S. Army, 1962-64, Korea. Recipient Communication and Leadership award Toastmasters Internat., 1983. Mem. ABA (sect. on bus. law, banking law com.), mem. com. on devel. in investment services), Richmond Metro C. of C. (bd. dirs., past chmn.). Republican. Episcopalian. Clubs: Forum (Richmond, Va.). Office: Hunton & Williams Riverfront Plz East Tower 951 E Byrd St Richmond VA 23219-4040

RAINEY, JEAN OSGOOD, public relations executive; b. Lansing, Mich., Apr. 5, 1925; d. Earle Victor and Blanche Mae (Eberly) Osgood; m. John Larimer Rainey, Nov. 29, 1957 (dec. Oct. 1991); children: Cynthia, John Larimer, Ruth. Grad., Lansing Bus. U., 1942. Pub. rels. dir. Nat. Assn. Food Chains, Washington, 1954-59; v.p. pub. rels. Manchester Orgns., Washington, 1959-61; ptnr. Rainey, McEnroe & Manning, Washington, 1962-73; v.p. Manning, Selvage & Lee, Washington, 1973-79, pres. Washington div., 1979-84, sr. counsellor, 1985—; owner Jean Rainey Assocs., Washington, 1986-87; sr. v.p Daniel J. Edelman Inc., 1987—. Author: How to Shop for Food, 1972. Pres. Hyde Home and Sch. Assn., Washington, 1969-71; co-chmn. Nat. Com. for Reelection of the Pres., 1972. Mem. Pub. Rels. Soc. Am. (accredited), Am. Women in Radio and TV (pres. Washington chpt. 1962-63, mem. nat. bd. 1963-65), Am. News Women's Club (pres. 1973-75). Republican. Episcopalian. Clubs: City Tavern, International. Home: Apt 250B 4000 Cathedral Ave NW Washington DC 20016-5249 Office: Edelman Pub Rels 1420 K St NW Washington DC 20005-2500

RAINEY, JOHN DAVID, federal judge; b. Freeport, Tex., Feb. 10, 1945; s. Frank Anson and Jewel Lorene (Hortman) R.; m. Judy Davis, Aug. 17, 1968; children, John David Jr., Jacob Matthew, Craig Thomas. BBA, So. Meth. U., 1967, JD, 1972. Bar: Tex. 1972, U.S. Dist. Ct. (no. dist.) Tex. 1974, U.S. Tax Ct. 1974, U.S. Ct. Appeals (5th cir.) 1981, U.S. Supreme Ct. 1981, U.S. Dist. Ct. (so. dist.) Tex. 1986. Assoc. Taylor, Mizell, Price, Corrigan & Smith, Dallas, 1973-79; ptnr. Gilbert, Gilbert & Rainey, Angleton, Tex., 1979-82, Rainey & LeBoeuf, Angleton, 1982-86; judge 149th Dist. Ct., Brazoria County, Tex., 1987-90, U.S. Dist. Ct. (so. dist.) Tex., 1990—; bd. dirs. Angleton Bank of Commerce. Mem. City of Angleton Planning and Zoning Commn., 1981-84; mem. Angleton Charter Rev. Commn., 1984, chmn. 1982. Served with U.S. Army, 1969-70. Mem. ABA, State Bar Tex., Brazoria County Bar Assn. (pres. 1983-84). Republican. Methodist. Lodge: Lions (pres. Angleton 1986-87). Avocations: hunting, fishing, woodworking. Office: US Dist Ct 515 Rusk St Ste 8613 Houston TX 77002-2600

RAINEY, KENNETH TYLER, English language educator; b. Memphis, Feb. 27, 1936; s. Andrew Laughlin Jr. and Gracie Ruth (Mullins) R.; m. Elaine Fitts, Jan. 1, 1960; children: Kenneth Tyler Jr., Timothy Andrew, Kevin Laughlin. BA, Miss. Coll., Clinton, 1958; AM, U. Mich., 1959; ThD, New Orleans Bapt. Sem., 1966; PhD, Ohio State U., 1976. Asst. prof. Eng. Miss. Coll., Clinton, 1965-70, Ohio State U., Lima, 1977-83, Memphis State U., 1983-89; prof. English and tech. comm. So. Coll. Tech., Marietta, Ga., 1989—; cons. in field. Contbr. articles to profl. jours. Woodrow Wilson fellow, 1958-59; Nat. Endowment Humanities grantee, 1981-82. Mem. Soc. Tech. Comm. (sr., asst. to pres. for acad. and tech. programs), Nat. Coun. Tchrs. of English (conf. coll. composition and comm.), Soc. for Applied Learning Tech., Assn. Tchrs. Tech. Writing. Baptist. Avocation: gourmet cooking. Home: 1194 Robert Ln Marietta GA 30062 Office: So Coll Tech 1100 S Marietta Pky Marietta GA 30060-2896

RAINEY, WILLIAM JOEL, lawyer; b. Flint, Mich., Oct. 11, 1946; s. Ralph Jefferson and Elsie Matilda (Erickson) R.; m. Cynthia Hetsko, June 15, 1968; children: Joel Michael, Allison Elizabeth. A.B., Harvard U., 1968; J.D., U. Mich., 1971. Bar: N.Y. 1973, Wash. 1977, Ariz. 1987, Mass. 1992, U.S. Dist. Ct. (so. and ea. dists.) N.Y. 1973, U.S.Ct. Appeals (2nd cir.) N.Y. 1973, U.S. Dist. Ct. (we. dist.) Wash. 1977, U.S. Supreme Ct. 1976, U.S. Ct. Appeals (9th cir.) Wash. 1978, U.S. Dist. Ct. Ariz. 1987, U.S. Dist. Ct. Mass. 1992, U.S. Ct. Appeals (1st cir.) Mass. 1992. Assoc. atty. Curtis, Mallet-Prevost, Colt & Mosle, N.Y.C., 1971-76; atty. assoc. corp. sec. Weyerhaeuser Co., Tacoma, Wash., 1976-85; v.p., corp. sec., gen. counsel Southwest Forest Industries Inc., Phoenix, 1985-87; sr. v.p., corp. sec., gen. counsel Valley Nat. Corp. and Valley Nat. Bank, Phoenix, 1987-91; v.p., gen. counsel Cabot Corp., Boston, 1991-93; exec. v.p., gen. coun., corp. sec. Fourth Fin. Corp., Wichita, Kans., 1994—. Editor U. Mich. Jour. Law Reform, 1970-71. Bd. dirs. 1st Ave. Svc. Ctr., Seattle, 1977-85, Mcpl. League Seattle and King County, 1982-84, Phoenix Symphony Orch. Assns., 1988-91, Salvation Army, 1988-91; Bellevue (Wash.) Planning Commn., 1984. Maj. USAR, 1970-91. Mem. ABA (tech. task force 1984-91), Wash. State Bar Assn., State Bar of Ariz., Boston Bar Assn., Assn. Bank Holding Cos. (steering com. 1989-91, chmn. lawyers com. 1990-91), Harvard Club of Phoenix (bd. dirs. 1989-91). Avocations: backpacking, running, fishing. Home: 1441 Sport of Kings Ct Wichita KS 67230 Office: Fourth Fin Corp PO Box 4 Wichita KS 67201-0004

RAINIER, ROBERT PAUL, publisher; b. Adrian, Mich., Oct. 19, 1940; s. Paul Leslie and Mildred Sofia (Magdefrau) R.; m. Dorothy Krauss, May 28, 1966; children: Michele Carole, Kenneth Charles. BA, Northwestern U., 1962, MA, 1964. Various positions with mktg. and sales dept. Times Mirror/McGraw Hill Book Co., N.Y.C., 1964-70, sponsoring editor coll. div., 1970-74, editor in chief humanities, 1974-79; pub. engring. coll. dept. Holt-Rinehart and Winston, N.Y.C., 1979-80, editor in chief, sci. and engring., 1980-81, pub. humanities, 1981-83, v.p., editor in chief, 1983-84; v.p., editor in chief CBS Coll. Pub., N.Y.C., 1984-86; dir. publs. AICPA, N.Y.C., 1986—. Vestryman St. Johns Episcopal Ch., Larchmont, N.Y., 1987-90, fundraiser, 1988-89. Staff sgt. N.Y. N.G., 1964-70. Mem. The Dessoff Choirs (treas. 1993—), Soc. Nat. Assn. Publs. (bd. dirs. 1988—, pres. 1992-93). Democrat. Episcopalian. Avocations: music, sports. Home: 21 Summit Ave Larchmont NY 10538-2913 Office: Journal of Accountancy 1211 Ave of the Americas New York NY 10036

RAINIS, EUGENE CHARLES, brokerage house executive; b. N.Y.C., Sept. 24, 1940; s. Charles William and Louise Theresa (Nold) R.; m. Jane Margaret Micucci, Nov. 28, 1964; children—Ellen, David, Mark. B.S., Fordham U., 1962; M.B.A. U. Pa., 1964. Security analyst trainee Merrill, Lynch Pierce Fenner & Smith, N.Y.C., 1963-65; ptnr. Brown Bros. Harriman & Co., N.Y.C., 1965—, also bd. dirs.; bd. dirs. Jefferson Ins. Co. N.Y., Monticello Ins. Co. Trustee St. Vincents Hosp., N.Y.C., Fordham U., N.Y.C. Mem. Inst. Chartered Fin. Analysts, Down Town Assn. (N.Y.C.), Knights of Malta. Republican. Roman Catholic. Avocations: fishing; trap and skeet shooting. Office: Brown Bros Harriman & Co 59 Wall St New York NY 10005-2818

RAINONE, SALVATORE RAFFAELLO, vocalist; b. Bklyn., Nov. 27, 1931; s. Nicola and Immacolata Incepcione (Mascolo) R.; m. Celeste, Aug. 19, 1962 (div. Jan. 1976); children: Celeste, Laura; m. Gail Thompson, Feb. 19, 1990. BA in Music, N.Y. Coll. Music, 1958. Arranger, engr. Songwriters Workshop, N.Y.C., 1975—. Featured vocalist various resort hotels, Catskill Mt. area, N.Y. and "Red Devil Battery Sign", Shubert Theater, Boston, 1976; author/composer The Foorball Wedding, 1991—. 1st lt. USN, 1950-54. Mem. Psychic Rsch. Group. Roman Catholic. Avocation: cancer rsch. Home: 2344 New York Ave Huntington Station NY 11746-4255 Office: Songwriters Workshop 27 Main St New York NY 10044-0052

RAINS, HARRY HANO, lawyer, arbitrator, mediator; b. N.Y.C., Jan. 27, 1909; s. Jackson and Roller (Heller) R.; m. Muriel, May 17, 1942; 1 child, Peggy Jane Rains Goodman. LL.B., St. Lawrence U., 1932; M.P.A., NYU, 1947, LL.M. in Labor Law, 1954. Bar: N.Y. 1933, U.S. Supreme Ct. 1965, U.S. Dist. Ct. (so. and ea. dists.) N.Y. 1947. Referee N.Y. State Dept. Labor, 1933-38, unemployment ins. mgr., 1939-42; sole practice Mineola, N.Y., 1933-42; sr. ptnr. firm Rains & Pogrebin, N.Y.C., 1947-81, of counsel, cons., 1982—; labor arbitrator, mediator, lectr.; prof. labor law CCNY, 1935-37, 46-47; prof. labor law Hofstra U., 1947-54, Harry H. Rains Disting. prof. arbitration and alternative dispute settlement law, 1982—; mem. faculty L.I. U. 1953; dir. Sealectro Corp., John Hassall Co., Inc. Contbr. articles to profl. jours. Mem. Fed. Mediation and Conciliation Service, 1948—; mem. N.Y. State Pub. Employment Relations Bd. Panel Mediators and Fact Finders, 1968—. Served to capt. QMC, AUS, 1942-46. Mem. ABA, Fed. Bar Coun., N.Y. State Bar Assn., Nassau County Bar Assn., Nat. Acad. Arbitrators, Indsl. Rels. Rsch. Assn., Am. Arbitration Assn. (panel labor arbitrators), L.I. C. of C. (bd. dirs.), Univ. Club (Garden City, N.Y.). Home: 14871 David Dr Fort Myers FL 33908-1638 Office: Rains Bldg 210 Old Country Rd Mineola NY 11501

RAINS, HAZEL GRACE, curriculum director; b. Gainesville, Mar. 27, 1941; d. Clarence Lafayette and Bertie Lucille (Jones) Beeler; m. Alvin Ray Rains, Dec. 22, 1960; children: Shelby Ray, Bradley Myles. BS in Edn., U. N. Tex., 1967; MA in Polit. Sci., Midwestern State U., Wichita Falls, Tex., 1982. Cert. tchr., mid-mgmt. supt., Tex. Elem. tchr. Rad Ware/Callisburg Ind. Sch. Dist., Gainesville, 1967, Henrietta (Tex.) Ind. Sch. Dist., 1967-81; elem., mid. sch. tchr. Pilot Point (Tex.) Ind. Sch. Dist., 1981-86; mid. sch./high sch. tchr. Callisburg Ind. Sch. Dist., Gainesville, 1986-87, elem., mid. sch. and high sch. prin., 1987-92; curriculum dir. Krum (Tex.) Ind. Sch. Dist., 1992—; adv. com. sch. bd. Henrietta Ind. Sch. Dist., 1979. Mem. Delta Kappa Gamma, Alpha Phi Sigma, Phi Delta Kappa. Democrat. Baptist. Avocations: oil painting, ceramics, crossword puzzles.

RAINS, MERRITT NEAL, lawyer; b. Burlington, Iowa, July 26, 1943; s. Merritt and Lucille (Lepper) R.; m. Jean Baldwin, July 26, 1980 (div. 1995); children: Robert Baldwin, Kathleen Kellogg. B.A. in Polit. Sci. with honors, U. Iowa, 1965; J.D., Northwestern U., 1968. Bar: Ohio 1968. Assoc. Arter & Hadden, Cleve., 1968-76, ptnr., 1976—, mem. exec. com., 1981—, mem. mgmt. com., 1987-90, mng. ptnr., 1990-92; master bencher Inns of Ct., 1990—; lectr. on profl. topics including Alternative Dispute Resolution, Litigation Practice and Procedure, and Antitrust. Contbr. articles to profl. jours. Former trustee Legal Aid Soc. Cleve.; trustee Cleve. Play House, mem. adv. coun., 1988—; trustee Citizens League Greater Cleve., Cleve. Art Assn. With U.S. Army, 1968-70. Fellow Am. Bar Found.; mem. ABA, Ohio Bar Assn., Bar Assn. Greater Cleve. (chmn. young lawyers sect. 1975-76, recipient cert. merit 1975), Def. Rsch. Inst., Internat. Assn. Def. Counsel, Ohio Assn. Civil Trial Attys., Union Club, Cleve. Skating Club, Cleve. Playhouse Club, City Club, Print Club, Rowfant Club, Phi Beta Kappa, Omicron Delta Kappa, Phi Delta Phi. Home: 18414 Parkland Dr Cleveland OH 44122-3451 Office: Arter & Hadden 1100 Huntington Bldg Cleveland OH 44115

RAINSFORD, BETTIS C., textile company executive. Exec. v.p., chief fin. officer Delta Woodside Industries Inc., Greenville, S.C. Office: Delta Woodside Industries Inc 233 N Main St Greenville SC 29601-2142

RAINSON, RONALD LEE, engineering executive, consultant; b. N.Y.C., May 20, 1940; s. E. G. and E. (Burke) R.; B.S. in Elec. Engring., Lawrence Inst. Tech., 1966, B.S. in Indsl. Mgmt., 1969; m. Patricia J. Zugay, Aug. 29; children—Athena, Felicia, Erica. Project Chief, Bendix Corp., Southfield, Mich., 1970-72; gen. mgr. Holland PBW (Mich.), 1972-75; pres. E. Ky. Power, Lexington, 1975-80; v.p. Central Ill. Light Co., Peoria, 1980-88; pres., CEO Environ. Sci. & Engring., Peoria, 1988—, now chmn. bd. dirs.; dir. Breeder Reactor Corp., Ky. Center for Energy Research, NERC. Mem. Gov.'s Ill. Econ. Tech. Adv. Com., Gov.'s Task Force on Utility Regulation. Registered profl. engr., Mich., Ohio, Vt., Ill.; recipient Alumni Alumni award Lawrence Tech., 1977. Mem. IEEE (sr.), Tau Beta Pi. Republican. Clubs: Freemasons. Office: Environ Sci & Engring Inc 8901 N Industrial Rd Peoria IL 61615*

RAISBECK, GORDON, systems engineer; b. N.Y.C., May 4, 1925; s. Milton Joseph and Marcelle (Ellinger) R.; m. Barbara Wiener, Dec. 22, 1948; children: Michael Norbert, Lucy Margaret, Alison Jane, Timothy Gordon, James Gregory. Rhodes scholar, Oxford (Eng.) U., 1947-48; B.A., Stanford U., 1944; Ph.D., MIT, 1949. Registered profl. engr., Mass., Maine. Instr. M.I.T., Cambridge, 1948-49; mem. tech. staff Bell Telephone Labs., Inc., Murray Hill, N.J., 1949-61; dir. transmission line research Bell Telephone Labs., Inc., 1954-61; mem. profl. staff research and devel. Advanced Research Projects Agy., Washington, 1959-60; mem. profl. staff Arthur D. Little, Inc., Cambridge, 1961-86; dir. systems engring. Arthur D. Little, Inc. 1966-70, dir. phys. systems research, 1970-75, v.p. systems engring., 1973-86, part-time 1982-86; cons. mgmt. of technol. innovation, 1982—; instr. Drew U., Stanford U., MIT. Contbr. articles to profl. jours.; author: Information Theory: An Introduction for Engineers and Scientists, 1964. Served to lt. (j.g.) USNR, 1944-46, ATO, PTO. Rhodes scholar, 1947. Fellow IEEE, Acoustical Soc. Am.; mem. Oceanic Engring. Soc. IEEE (sec. 1988-92), Engring. Mgmt. Soc. IEEE, N.Y. Acad. Scis., New Coll. Soc., Math. Assn. Am., Oxford Soc., Maine Soc. Profl. Engrs., NSPE, Inst. Ops. Rsch. and the Mgmt. Scis., Assn. Am. Rhodes Scholars, Amateur Chamber Music Players, Chamber Music Am., Sigma Xi. Democrat. Episcopalian. Patentee in field (22). Home and Office: 40 Deering St Portland ME 04101-2212 also: RR # 1 Barrington, Blanche Rd Cape Negro, Nova Scotia, Canada

RAISBECK, JAMES DAVID, aircraft design executive; b. Milw., Sept. 29, 1936; s. Clifford Clinton and Minnie (Hommersand) R.; BS in Aero. Engring., Purdue U., 1961; m. Sherry Bylund; 1 child, Jennifer Lee Raisbeck Hunter. Aero. rsch. engr. Boeing Co., Seattle, 1961-69, rsch. aerodynamist,

1961-64, commercial aircraft preliminary design, 1965-66; liaison to U.S. Air Force, 1966-68, program mgr. comml. STOL programs, 1968-69; chmn., CEO Robertson Aircraft Corp., Renton, Wash., 1969-73; v.p. tech. Am. Jet Industries, L.A., 1973-74; founder, chmn. bd., CEO Raisbeck Engring., Inc., 1974—; cons. Served with SAC, USAF, 1955-58. Recipient Disting. Engring. Alumnus in Aeronautics, Purdue U. Fellow AIAA (assoc. fellow); mem. Soc. Automotive Engrs., Tau Beta Pi, Sigma Gamma Tau, Phi Eta Sigma. Patentee in field of wing design, propellors and aircraft systems; achievements include designing and building aerodynamic improvement systems for airline business and corp. turbine-powered airplanes. Address: 7536 Seward Park Ave S Seattle WA 98118

RAISH, DAVID LANGDON, lawyer; b. Cleve., Mar. 12, 1947; s. John E. Raish and Roslyn V. (Skeels) Pettibone; m. Roslyn Anne Dinnick, Sept. 12, 1969; children: David Jr., Anne, Julia. BA, Yale U., 1969; JD, Harvard U., 1973. Bar: Mass. 1975, D.C. 1981. Law clk. to hon. James R. Browning U.S. Ct. Appeals-9th Cir., San Francisco, 1973-74; assoc. Ropes & Gray, Boston, 1974-82, ptnr., 1982—; mem. Com. on U.S. Activities of Foreigners and Tax Treaties, ABA Tax sect. 1981—, chair, 1991-93. Author: Cafeteria Plans, 1985, Cash or Deferred Agreements, 1986, Compensation and Benefits for Key Employees of Tax-Exempt Organizations, 1995; editor Tax Highlights Boston Bar Assn., 1985-93. Tenor Tanglewood Festival Chorus. Office: Ropes & Gray One International Pl Boston MA 02110

RAISIAN, JOHN, public policy institute executive, economist; b. Conneaut, Ohio, July 30, 1949; s. Ernest James and Ruby Lee (Owens) R.; m. Joyce Ann Klak, Aug. 17, 1984; children: Alison Kathleen, Sarah Elizabeth. BA, Ohio U., 1971; PhD, UCLA, 1978. Rsch. assoc. Human Resources Rsch. Ctr., U. So. Calif., L.A., 1972-73; cons. Rand Corp., Santa Monica, Calif., 1974-75, 76; vis. asst. prof. econs. U. Wash., Seattle, 1975-76; asst. prof. econs. U. Houston, 1976-80; sr. economist Office Rsch. and Evaluation, U.S. Bur. Labor Stats., Washington, 1980-81; spl. asst. for econ. policy Office Asst. Sc. for Policy, U.S. Dept. Labor, Washington, 1981-83, dir. rsch. and tech. support, 1981-84; pres. Unicon Rsch. Corp., L.A., 1984-86; sr. fellow Hoover Instn., Stanford, Calif., 1986—, assoc. dir., dep. dir., 1986-90, dir., 1990—; exec. dir. Presdl. Task Force on Food Assistance, Washington, 1983-84. Mem. editorial bd. Jour. Labor Rsch., 1983—; contbr. articles to profl. jours. Advisor Nat. Coun. on Handicapped, Washington, 1985-86, Nat. Commn. on Employment Policy, Washington, 1987-88; chmn. minimum wage bd. Calif. Indsl. Welfare Commn., 1987; mem. nat. adv.com. Student Fin. Assistance, Washington, 1987-89; corp. mem. Blue Shield Calif. Recipient Best Publ. of Yr. award Econ. Inquiry, Western Econ. Assn., 1979, Disting. Teaching award U. Houston Coll. Social Scis., 1980, Disting. Svc. award U.S. Dept. Labor, 1983; predoctoral fellow Rand Corp., 1976. Mem. Am. Econs. Assn., Western Econ. Assn. (chmn. nominating com. 1992), Commonwealth Club of Calif., World Affairs Coun., Mont Pelerin Soc., Coun. on Fgn. Rels., Nat. Assn. Scholars, Phi Beta Kappa. Republican. Avocations: wine collecting, sports enthusiast. Office: Stanford U Hoover Hoover Inst War-Revolution Stanford CA 94305-6010

RAISIG, PAUL JONES, JR., lawyer; b. Jamestown, N.Y., June 21, 1932; s. Paul Jones and Marian Elizabeth (Christian) R.; m. Carolyn Virginia Sides, June 12, 1955; children: Dawn Virginia, Paul Christian, Anne Sibley. B.G.E., U. Nebr., 1961; M.B.A., U. Ala., 1965; JD, Campbell U., 1989. Bar: N.C., 1989, D.C. 1991, U.S. Supreme Ct. 1992. Commd. 2d lt. U.S. Army, 1953, advanced through grades to col., 1973, ret., 1977, served in Vietnam, 1963, btn. comdr., Vietnam, 1968; dep. dir. U.S. Army Reorganization, 1973; v.p. Armed Forces Relief and Benefit Assn., Washington, 1977-79; sr. cons. Dept. Def., Washington, 1979-80; exec. dir. Am. Fedn. Info. Processing Socs., Arlington, Va., 1980-84; v.p., dir. Designs, Ltd., Alexandria, Va., 1985-86; ptnr. Barrington, Herndon & Raisig, P.A., Fayetteville, N.C., 1989-92; adj. prof. bus. law Campbell U., 1992-95; cons. in field. Decorated Legion of Merit (4), Bronze Star medal (2), Air medal (7), Purple Heart (2), Meritorious Service medal, Army Commendation medal with V Device (3). Mem. U.S. Council for World Communications, Beta Gamma Sigma. Club: University. Home and Office: Buffalo Lake RR 6 Box 447 Sanford NC 27330-8444

RAISLER, KENNETH MARK, lawyer; b. New Rochelle, N.Y., May 15, 1951; s. Herbert A. and Norma (Glauback) R.; m. Sara Ann Kelsey, June 11, 1978; children: Caroline Elisabeth, Katharine Kelsey, David Mark. BSBA, Yale Coll., 1973; JD, NYU, 1976. Bar: N.Y. 1977, D.C. 1977, U.S. Dist. Ct. (so. dist.) N.Y. 1977, U.S. Dist. Ct. D.C. 1977, U.S. Ct. Appeals (2d cir.) 1977, U.S. Ct. Appeals (D.C. cir.) 1977, U.S. Ct. Appeals (7th cir.) 1982, U.S. Ct. Appeals (10th cir.) 1983, U.S. Supreme Ct. 1985. Law clk. U.S. Dist. Ct. (so. dist.) N.Y., N.Y.C., 1976-77; asst. U.S. atty., Washington, 1977-82; dep. gen. counsel Commodity Futures Trading Commn., Washington, 1982-83, gen. counsel 1983-87; ptnr. Rogers & Wells, N.Y.C., 1987-92, Sullivan & Cromwell, N.Y.C., 1992—. Mem. Assn. of Bar of City of N.Y. (chair futures regulation com. 1988-91). Office: Sullivan & Cromwell 125 Broad St New York NY 10004

RAISZ, LAWRENCE GIDEON, medical educator, consultant; b. N.Y.C., Nov. 13, 1925; s. Erwin Joseph and Marie Georgette (Patai) R.; s. Helen Martin, June 5, 1948; children: Stephen, Matthew, Jonathan, Katherine, Nicholas. Student, Harvard U., 1943, MD, 1947; DOdontology (hon.), U. Umea, Sweden, 1990. Diplomate Am. Bd. Internal Medicine, Nat. Bd. Med. Examiners. Intern Harvard Med. Svc., Boston City Hosp., 1947-48; resident in medicine Cushing VA Hosp., 1950, Boston VA Hosp., 1952-54; asst. and instr. in physiology NYU-Bellevue Med. Ctr., 1948-50; asst. and instr. in medicine sch. medicine Boston U., 1953-56; chief renal sect. Boston VA Hosp., 1954-56; asst. chief radioisotope svc. Syracuse VA Hosp., 1956-57; asst. prof. medicine Coll. Medicine SUNY, Syracuse, 1956-61; assoc. prof. pharmacology and medicine Sch. Medicine U. Rochester, 1961-66, assoc. prof. medicine Sch. Medicine, 1966-68, prof. pharmacology, toxicology, and medicine Sch. Medicine, 1966-74, chief div. of clin. pharmacology Sch. Medicine, 1961-74; prof. medicine, head div. of endocrinology and metabolism Sch. Medicine U. Conn., Farmington, 1974—; sr. assoc. physician Strong Meml. Hosp., Rochester, 1961-68, physician, 1968-74; acting chmn. dept. pharmacology Sch. Medicine U. Rochester, 1962-63, vis. prof. pharmacology, toxicology and medicine Sch. Medicine Stanford U., 1966; vis. prof. Coll. Medicine U. Lagos, Nigeria, 1973; mem. gen. B study sect. NIH, 1986-88; mem. subspecialty bd. on endocrinology and metabolism Am. Bd. Internal Medicine, 1990—; mem. U.S.-Japan Malnutrition Panel, 1980-91; clin. investigator Syracuse VA Hosp., 1957-60; William N. Creasy Vis. Prof. Clin. Pharmacology Med. Sch. Dartmouth Coll., 1977; chmn. Gordon Conf. on Bones and Teeth, 1980; Edwin B. Astwood lectr. Endocrine Soc., 1983. Mem. numerous editorial bds.; contbr. more than 300 articles to profl. jours. With USNR, 1943-45; capt. AUS, 1950-52. Spl. Rsch. fellow Nat. Inst. Arthritis and Metabolic Disease, Strangeways Rsch. Lab., 1960-61, Nat. Inst. Dental Rsch. NIH, 1971-72; Burroughs-Wellcome scholar in Clin. Pharmacology, 1963-68; recipient Pica Andre Lichtwitz, 1980, Class of 1947 Disting. Prof. award Med. Sch. U. Wis., 1988. Mem. AAAS, Am. Fedn. for Clin. Rsch., Am. Soc. for Clin. Investigation, Am. Soc. for Pharmacology and Exptl. Therapeutics, Endocrine Soc., Assn. Am. Physicians, Conn. Endocrine Soc. (pres. 1976), Am. Soc. for Bone and Mineral Rsch. (pres. 1980-81, William F. Neuman award 1986), Conn. Acad. Sci. and Engring., Sigma Xi. Avocations: travel, skiing, wind surfing. Home: 118 Waterville Rd Farmington CT 06032-1624 Office: U Conn Health Ctr 263 Farmington Ave Farmington CT 06030-0002

RAITT, BONNIE LYNN, blues singer, guitarist; b. Burbank, Calif., Nov. 8, 1949. Student, Radcliffe Coll. Performer blues clubs, East Coast; concert tours in Britain, 1976, 77; albums include Bonnie Raitt, 1971, Give It Up, 1972, Takin' My Time, 1973, Streetlights, 1974, Home Plate, 1975, Sweet Forgiveness, 1977, The Glow, 1979, Green Light, 1982, Nine Lives, 1986, Nick of Time, 1989 (Grammys 1990, Rock-Best Vocal Performance, Female, Pop-Best Vocal Performance, Female, Album of Yr.), I'm in the Mood (with John Lee Hooker) (Grammy 1990, Blues-Best Traditional Record), The Bonnie Raitt Collection, 1990, Luck of the Draw, 1991 (Grammy 1992, Rock-Best Vocal Performance, Female), Longing In Their Hearts, 1994 (Grammy award Best Pop Album); songs include Something to Talk About (Grammy 1992, Country-Best Vocal Performance, Female), Good Man, Good Woman (with Delbert McClinton) (Grammy 1992, Rock-Best Vocal by a Duo or Group). Recipient numerous Grammy nominations, four

Grammy awards 1990, three Grammy awards 1992. Office: PO Box 46037 Los Angeles CA 90046*

RAJAB, MOHAMMAD HASAN, biostatistician, educator; b. Oct. 8, 1955; married; 2 children. BS in Agrl. Scis., Damascus (Syria) U., 1976; MS in Quantitative Genetics, Tex. A&M U., 1983, MS in Stats., 1987, PhD in Quantitative Genetics, 1987. Instr. Coll. Agr., Damascus (Syria) U., 1976-80, asst. prof. quanitiative genetics, 1987-90; tchg. asst. dept. stats. Coll. Sci., Tex. A&M U., College Station, 1986-87; vis. asst. prof. Tex. A&M U., College Station, 1990; rsch. sci. dept. stats. Coll. Sci., Tex. A&M U., College Station, 1990-93, asst. prof. dept. psychiatry-behavioral scis. Coll. Medicine, 1993—; vis. asst. prof. Inst. für Tierenranhrung, U. Bonn, Bermany, 1990; co-investigator Coordinating Ctr. Partial Hospitalization of High-Rise Suicidal Youth Study, NIH, 1990-94, statistician ctrl. vein occlusion study, 1994—; epidemiologist biostats dept. Scott and White Hosp., Temple, Tex., 1993—; presenter in field. Contbr. articles to profl. jours. Acad. scholar USAID, 1980; recipient Govt. award Damascus U., 1976. Mem. Am. Statis. Assn., Soc. Clin. Trials, Biometrics Soc., Sigma Xi. Office: Texas A&M U Health Sci Ctr Coll Med Temple Campus 600 S 25th St Temple TX 76504 also: Scott and White Biostats Dept 2401 S 31st St Temple TX 76508

RAJADHYAKSHA, VIKRAM, civil engineering consulant, engineering company executive; b. 1946; came to U.S., 1967.; MS, U. Cin., 1968. CEO Dodson-Lindblom Assoc., Columbus, 1979—; pres., CEO, chmn. bd. dirs. DLZ Corp., Columbus. Office: DLZ Corp 1121 Huntley Rd Columbus OH 43229*

RAJAMANNAN, AMBROSE HARRY, agriculture products supplier; b. Jaffna, Sri Lanka, Feb. 27, 1931; came to U.S., 1959; s. Karthigesu and Alice (Solomon) Ambrose; m. Concie, Oct. 1958; children: Nalini, Lohini. DVM, Bengal Vet. Coll., Calcutta, 1955; MS, U. Minn., St. Paul, 1962, PhD, 1964. Rsch. assoc. U. Minn., St. Paul, 1968-69; pres. Internat. Genes, St. Paul, 1970-73, Internat. Cryo-Biol. Svcs., St. Paul, 1971-75, Agro-K Corp., Mpls., 1975—; chmn. Aqua Heat Tech Inc., 1992—. Patentee in field. Roman Catholic. Office: Agro-K Corp 36-37th Ave Fridley MN 55421

RAJAN, FRED E. N., clergy member, church administrator. Exec. dir. Commn. for Multicultural Ministries of the Evangelical Lutheran Church in America, Chicago, Ill. Office: Evangelical Lutheran Church Am 8765 W Higgins Rd Chicago IL 60631

RAJANI, PREM RAJARAM, transportation company financial executive; b. Bombay, Nov. 9, 1949; came to U.S., 1973; s. Rajaram N. and Devibai Rajani; m. Rekha Rohera, Apr. 21, 1977; children: Anand, Harshada. B Tech., Indian Inst. Tech., Bombay, 1973; MBA in Acctg. and Fin., Columbia U., 1975. Sr. ops. auditor Pfizer, Inc., N.Y.C., 1975-78; sr. projects fin. analyst Sea-Land Industries subs. RJR, Edison, N.J., 1978-80, fin. mgr. joint ventures, 1980-81, mgr. corp. planning and analysis, 1981-84; mgr. corp. fin. Sea-Land Corp., Edison, 1984-87; asst. treas.-internat. Sea-Land Svc. Inc. subs. CSX Corp., Edison, 1987-88, asst. treas.-domestic, 1988, staff v.p., treas., 1988-94, staff v.p. fin. and planning Americas, 1994—. Mem. Nat. Assn. Corp. Treas., Soc. Internat. Treas. Office: Sea-Land Svc Inc 150 Allen Rd Liberty Corner NJ 07938

RAJARAM, SANJAYA, agricultural scientist, plant breeder; b. Varanasi, India, Feb. 10, 1943; arrived in Mexico, 1969; s. Jaggu and Mangala (Devi) R.; children: Sheila, Jaiprakash, Arun. BS, Gorakhpur U., India, 1962; MSc, Indian Agrl. Rsch., India, 1964; PhD in Agrl. Sci., Sydney U., Australia, 1968. Postdoctoral fellow Rockefeller Found., New Delhi, India, 1968-69; postdoctoral fellow Centro Internacional de Mejoramiento Maiz y Trigo, Mexico City, 1969-70, geneticist/plant pathologist, 1971-72, head, wheat breeder, 1973-88, leader plant breeding dept., 1989—; cons. agrl. issues related to wheat to Brazil, Paraguay, Guatemala, Mexico, India, Pakistan, Nepal, Bangladesh, Thailand, Syria, Turkey, Algeria, Kenya, Ethiopia, Portugal, Spain, China. Contbr. numerous articles and papers to profl. publs.; cultivator over three hundred wheat varieties. Recipient Caballero del Orden de Quetzal award, Govt. of Guatemala, 1988, Mex. Inst. Agr. and Forestry award, 1988. Fellow Am. Soc. Agronomy, Am. Soc. Crop Sci. Office: CIMMYT, Lisboa 27, Apdo 6-641, 06600 Mexico City Mexico

RAJESHWAR, KRISHNAN, chemist, educator; b. Trivandrum, India, Apr. 15, 1949; m. Rohini Chidambaram, 1977; children: Reena, Rebecca. BSc, U. Col, India, 1969; postgrad., Indian Inst. Technol. Sci., 1971, PhD in Chemistry, 1974. From asst. to assoc. prof. chemistry U. Tex., Arlington, 1983-89, prof. chemistry, 1989—; rsch. chemist Prods Formulation Group Foseco Internat., India, 1974-75, rsch. fellow in chemistry St. Francis, Xavier U., Can., 1975-76; rsch. fellow Colo. State U., 1976-78, vis. assoc. prof., 1978-79, sr. rsch. assoc., 1979-83; cons. U. Wyo Rsch. Corp. & Forensic Labs., Edwards Aerospace Inc., Tex. Mem. Am. Chem. Soc. (Wilford T. Doherty award 1994), Electrochem. Soc. Achievements include research in charge storage and transport mechanisms in avariety of metals, semiconductors and polymers, environmental electrochemistry and photoelectrochemistry. Office: U Texas Dept Chemistry & Biochemistry PO Box 19065 Univ Of Texas At Arlington TX 76019*

RAJKI, WALTER ALBERT, manufacturing company executive; b. Cleve., Sept. 24, 1925; s. Stephen and Julia (Zajac) R.; m. Mary Elizabeth Koch, July 12, 1952; children: William, Carl, Joan. B.S., M.I.T., 1951; J.D., Cleve. State U., 1958. Bar: Ohio 1958. Engr. Chain Belt Co., Milw., 1951-53; plant mgr., pres. Adalet Mfg. Co., Cleve., 1953-72; group v.p. Scott & Fetzer Co., Cleve., 1972-78; sr. v.p. Scott & Fetzer Co., 1978-88; mng. ptnr. Commvest Co., Ft. Myers, Fla., 1988—; dir. Highland Farms Inc., Commonwealth Investment Co., Commvest Co. Mem. Ohio Bar Assn., Cleve. Bar Assn. Clubs: Cleve. Yachting, Union.

RAJLICH, VACLAV THOMAS, computer science educator, researcher, consultant; b. Prague, Czech Republic, May 3, 1939; came to U.S., 1980; s. Vaclav and Marie (Janovska) R.; m. Ivana m. Bartova, Aug. 6, 1968; children: Vasik, Paul, John, Luke. MS, Czech Tech. U., Prague, 1962; PhD, Case Western Res. U., 1971. Rsch engr. Rsch. Inst. for Math. Machines, Prague, 1963-67, scientist, 1971-75, mgr., 1975-79; vis. assoc. prof. computer sci. Calif. State U., Fullerton, 1980-81; assoc. prof. computer and communication sci. U. Mich., Ann Arbor, 1982-85; prof. Wayne State U., Detroit, 1985—, chair dept. computer sci., 1985-90; vis. scientist Carnegie-Mellon U., Pitts., 1987, Harvard U., Cambridge, Mass., 1988. Contbr. articles to profl. jours. Recipient Chrysler Challenge Fund, 1988. Mem. Computer Soc. of IEEE, Assn. for Computing Machinery. Roman Catholic. Achievements include development of tools for software maintenance, program comprehension, software design methods, and parallel grammars. Office: Wayne State U Dept Computer Sci Detroit MI 48202

RAJOTTE, RAY V., biomedical engineer, researcher; b. Wainwright, Alta., Can., Dec. 5, 1942; s. Sam and Bernadette (Tremblay) R.; m. Gloria A. Yackimetz, Aug. 20, 1966; children: Brian, Michael, Monique. RT, No. Alta. Inst. Tech., 1965; BSc in Elec. Engring., U. Alta., 1971, MSc in Elec. Engring., 1973, PhD in Biomed. Engring., 1975. Postdoctoral fellow U. Alta. Dept. Medicine, Edmonton, 1975-76, Oak Ridge (Tenn.) Nat. Lab., 1976-77, Washington U., St. Louis, 1977, UCLA, 1977; rsch. assoc. dept. medicine U. Alta., Edmonton, 1977-79, asst. prof. dept. medicine, 1979-82, asst. prof. dept. medicine & surgery, 1983-84, assoc. prof., 1984-88, prof., 1988—; dir. Islet Cel Transplant Lab. U. Alta., 1982—, Divsn. Exptl. Surgery U. Alta., 1988—; assoc. dir. Surg.-Med. Rsch. Inst. U. Alta., 1984-87, dir., 1987—; co-dir. Juvenile Diabetes Fund Diabetes Interdisciplinary Rsch. Program U. Alta.; 1992—. Co-editor The Immunology of Diabetes Mellitus, 1986; mem. adv. bd. Diabetologia jour., 1993—; author over 350 publs. in field; contbr. 18 chpts. to books. Mem. Cell Transplant Soc. (founding mem., councillor 1991—), Internat. Pancreas and Islet Transplant Assn. (founding mem., treas. 1991—), Can. Transplantation Soc. (Western councillor 1987—), European Assn. for Study of Diabetes, Assn. Profl. Engrs., Geologists & Geophysicists Alta., Soc. Cryobiology, Am. Diabetes Assn., Can. Soc. Clin. Investigation, N.Y. Acad. Sci., Transplantation Soc., Can. Diabetes Assn., Acad. Surg. Rsch., Internat. Diabetes Fedn. Achievements include patent for glucose sensor. Office: U Alta, Surgical-Med Rsch Inst, Edmonton, AB Canada T6G 2N8*

RAJSIC, ROBERT, secondary education educator. Tchr. River Forest High Sch., Hobart, Ind. Named Outstanding High Sch. Tchr. Inland Steel Ryerson Found., 1992. Office: River Forest High Sch Indiana St Huber Blvd Hobart IN 46342

RAJSKI, PEGGY, film director, film producer; b. Stevens Point, Wis.. Attended, U. Wis. Films include: (prodn. mgr.): Lianna, 1982, Almost You, 1984; (prodr., prodn. mgr.) The Brother From Another Planet, 1984, Matewan, 1987, Eight Men Out, 1988; (prodr.) The Grifters, 1990, Little Man Tate, 1991 (also 2nd. unit dir.), Used People, 1992; (prodr. video) Bruce Springstein's Glory Days; (dir.) Trevor, 1994 (Acad. award for Best Live Action Short Film). Office: 140 Riverside Dr Ste 5E New York NY 10024*

RAKAY, WILLIAM R., publishing company executive; b. San Antonio, Dec. 12, 1955; s. Charles J. and Aixa (Aceuedo) R.; m. Cynthia Joan Smith, July 12, 1980; children: Christopher William, Michael Charles. BA in Bus., Rutgers Coll., 1978. Salesman Gordon Publs. Inc., Morristown, N.J., 1978-79, nat. sales mgr., 1979-81, assoc. pub., 1981-82; pub. Gordon Publs. Inc., Randolph, N.J., 1982—, pub. Aerospace Products mag., Lab. Equipment mag., 1986—, pub. Pharm. Processing mag., 1987—; v.p., group pub., 1987-89, exec. v.p., 1989-91, pres., chief oper. officer, 1991-94; sr. v.p., gen. mgr. Boston divsn. Cahners Pub. Co., 1994—. Mem. AAAS, AIAA, Biomed. Marketers Assn., Fedn. of Am. Socs. for Exptl. Biology (mem. exhibit adv. com. 1983). Avocations: golfing, reading, raquetball, music, skiing. Office: Cahners Pub Co 275 Washington St Newton MA 02158

RAKEL, ROBERT EDWIN, physician, educator; b. Cin., July 13, 1932; s. Edwin J. and Elsie (Machino) R.; m. Peggy Klare; children—Barbara, Cindy, Linda, David. BS in Zoology, U. Cin., 1954, MD, 1958. Diplomate: Charter diplomate Am. Bd. Family Practice (v.p., dir.). Intern St. Mary's Hosp., Cin., 1958-59; resident in internal medicine USPHS Hosp., Seattle, 1959-61; resident in gen. practice Monterey County Hosp., Salinas, Calif. 1961-62; practice medicine Newport Beach, Calif., 1962-69; chmn. family practice program U. Calif., Irvine, 1969-71; prof., head dept. family practice U. Iowa, 1971-85; assoc. dean acad. and clin. affairs, Richard M. Kleberg, Sr. prof., chmn. dept. family medicine Baylor Coll. Medicine, Houston, 1985—; dir. family practice residency program Hoag Meml. Hosp., Newport Beach, 1969-71; med. staff Mercy Hosp., Iowa City, 1971-85; chief family practice service St. Luke's Episc. Hosp., The Meth. Hosp., Houston, 1985—; trustee The Hospice of Tex. Med. Ctr., 1986—, Inst. of Religion Tex. Author: Selected References in Family Medicine, 1973, (with H.F. Conn & T.W. Johnson) Family Practice, 1973, (with H.F. Conn.) Textbook of Family Practice, 1978, editor 3d edit., 1984, 5th edit., 1995, Principles of Family Medicine, 1977; author foreword Neurology for the Everyday Practice of Medicine, R.G. Feldman, 1984; contbr. Dictionary of Am. Med. Biography Vols. I and II, 1984; editor: Conn's Current Therapy, 1984—, Yearbook of Family Practice, 1977-90, (series) Procedures for Your Practice Patient Care, Vol. 18, Essentials of Family Practice, 1992; mem. 13 editorial bds. med. jours.; contbr. articles to med. jours. Served with USPHS, 1959-61. Recipient Mead-Johnson Scholar award in Gen. Practice, 1971. Fellow Am. Acad. Family Physicians (pres. Orange County chpt. Calif. 1969, commn. on edn. 1970-76, Thomas W. Johnson award 1973); mem. AMA (sect. on med. schs. 1985—, gov. council of sect. 1986-88), Tex. Med. Assn., Am. Bd. Family Practice (bd. dirs. 1973-79, v.p. 1977-79, chmn. exam. com. 1974-79, recert. com. 1973-79, others), Am. Bd. Med. Spltys. (com. spltys. evaluation 1978-81), Nat. Bd. Med. Examiners (bd. dirs. 1975-79), Soc. Tchrs. Family Medicine (dir. 1971-79, sec. 1971-73), Council Acad. Socs., Assn. Am. Med. Colls., History of Medicine Soc. (founder, chmn. U. Iowa 1978-85, founder, chmn. Baylor Coll. Medicine 1986—), Am. Osler Soc. (bd. dirs. 1989—, pres. 1994), Cosmos Club. Home: 2420 Underwood St Houston TX 77030-3506 Office: Baylor Coll Medicine 1 Baylor Pl Houston TX 77030

RAKES, GANAS KAYE, finance and banking educator; b. Floyd, Va., May 2, 1938; s. Samuel D. and Ocie J. (Peters) R.; m. Mary Ann Simmons, Oct. 1, 1961; 1 child, Sabrina Darrow. BS, Va. Tech., 1960, MS, 1964; D of Bus. Adminstrn., Washington U., St. Louis, 1971. Assoc. prof. commerce U. Va., Charlottesville, 1968-80; O'Bleness prof. fin. and banking Ohio U., Athens, 1980—; chmn. fin. dept. Coll. of Bus. Adminstrn., 1983—; bd. dirs. Caldwell Savs. and Loan Co.; pres. bd. dirs. Enterprise Devel. Corp. Contbr. articles to profl. jours. Served to 1st lt. U.S. Army, 1961-63. Mem. Fin. Mgmt. Assn., Midwestern Bus. Adminstrs. Assn., Eastern Fin. Assn., Rotary, Reynolds Nat. Club. Republican. Episcopalian. Avocation: sailing. Office: Ohio U Dept of Fin Athens OH 45701

RAKESTRAW, WARREN VINCENT, lawyer; b. Dayton, Ohio, July 6, 1940; s. David Warren and Lou Ann (Hobbs) R.; m. Susan M. Rich, 1993. B.S., Ohio U., 1963; J.D., Capital U., 1968. Bar: Ohio bar 1968. Asst. atty. gen. State of Ohio, Columbus, 1968; legis. dir. to U.S. Senator William B. Saxbe, Washington, 1969-74; asst. atty. gen. U.S. Dept. Justice, Washington, 1974-75; counsel to ambassador New Delhi, India, 1975-77; partner firm Chester Hoffman & Willcox, Columbus, 1977-86; sole practice Columbus, 1986—. Mem. ABA (Ohio, Fla., D.C. chpts.), Sigma Chi, The Athletic Club of Columbus. Home: 8403 Beeswing Ct Muilfield Village Dublin OH 43017 Office: 4930 Reed Rd Columbus OH 43220

RAKIC, PASKO, neuroscientist, educator; b. Ruma, Yugoslavia, May 15, 1933; came to U.S., 1969; m. Patricia Goldman, 1969. MD, U. Belgrade, Yugoslavia, 1959, ScD in Neuroembryology, 1969. With inst. path. physiology Med. Sch. U. Belgrade, 1959-61, resident in neurosurgery, 1961-62; NIH research fellow neuropathology Harvard Med. Sch., Boston, 1962-66; rsch. assoc. devel. biology Inst. Biol. Rsch., Belgrade, 1967-68; from asst. prof. to assoc. prof. neuropathology and neuroscience Harvard Med. Sch., 1969-77; prof. neurosci. Yale Med. Sch., New Haven, 1977-78, Dorys McConnell Duberg prof. neurosci., 1978—, also chmn. neurobiology sect. Author of 200 sci. papers and gen. books on brain orgn. and devel. Mem. NAS, Am. Acad. Arts & Sci. Office: Yale U Sch Medicine Sect Neurobiology 333 Cedar St New Haven CT 06510-3289*

RAKITA, LOUIS, cardiologist, educator; b. Montreal, Que., Can., July 2, 1922; came to U.S., 1951, naturalized, 1962; s. S. and Rose (Weinman) R.; m. G. Blanche Michlin, Dec. 4, 1945; 1 son, Robert M. B.A., Sir George Williams Coll., Montreal, 1942; M.D., C.M., McGill U., 1949. Diplomate: Am. Bd. Internal Medicine. Intern Montreal Gen. Hosp., 1949-50; resident in medicine Jewish Gen. Hosp., Montreal, 1950-51; fellow in medicine Alton Ochsner Med. Found., New Orleans, 1951-52; chief resident in medicine Cleve. City Hosp., 1952-53, Am. Heart Assn. fellow, 1954-55; Am. Heart Assn. fellow Inst. for Med. Research, Cedars of Lebanon Hosp., Los Angeles, 1953-54; practice medicine Western Res. U., Cleve., 1954-55; sr. instr. Western Res. U., 1955-57, asst. prof., 1957-61, asso. prof., 1961-71; asst. vis. physician Cleve. City Hosp., 1954-57, vis. physician, 1957—; advanced fellow Cleve. Met. Gen. Hosp., 1959-61, dir. cardiology, 1966-87, immediate past dir., div. cardiology, 1987—; asso. dir. of research in med. edn. Case Western Res. U., Cleve., 1969-75; prof. medicine Case Western Res. U., 1971-93, prof. emeritus medicine, 1993; chmn. Phase IIA Cardiovascular com. Case Western Res. U., 1965-70, Faculty Senate Subcom. for Devel. and Evaluation of Ednl. Methods, 1969, Univ. Com. on Ednl. Planning, 1971-73, Faculty Council Sch. Medicine, 1979-80, Faculty Council Steering Com. Sch. Medicine, 1979-80, mem. bd. trustees Com. on Univ. Plans, 1971-73; Faculty Senate, Exec. Council; cons. in cardiology Lutheran Med. Center, Cleve., 1970—, Crile VA Hosp., Cleve., 1969—; vis. cardiologist Sunny Acres Hosp., Cleve., 1973—; cardiologist rep. of del. to, USSR, 1973. Author: (with M. Broder) Cardiac Arrhythmias, 1970, (with M. Kaplan) Immunological Diseases, 1972; Contbr. (with M. Kaplan) articles on cardiovascular diseases to profl. publs. Served with RCAAF, 1942-45. Recipient Research Career Devel. award USPHS, 1962-69. Fellow Am. Heart Assn. (mem. exec. com. N.E. Ohio chpt. 1972—, trustee 1969—, pres. N.E. Ohio chpt 1972-74, council on clin. cardiology 1977—, chmn. regional subcom. on reaffiliation N. Cen. region 1982-85, chmn. nat. reaffiliation subcom. 1992, chmn. chpt. standards revision com. 1984-85, v.p. North Central region 1985-86, bd. dirs. 1985-86, hon. life trustee Northeast Ohio affiliate, vice chmn. task force on practice licensing feasibility 1987—, award of Merit 1987, Gold Heart award 1989), ACP (Laureate award Ohio chpt. 1992), Am. Coll. of Cardiology, Royal Coll. Physicians and Surgeons Can. (cert.); mem. Am. Fedn. Clin. Research, Central Soc. Clin. Research, Soc. Exptl. Biology and Medicine, AAUP, Cleve. Med. Library Assn. (trustee

1972—), Nat. Bd. Med. Examiners, The Press of Case Western Reserve U. (adv. com. 1970), Nat. Heart and Lung Inst., Nat. Insts. Health (left ventricular assist device clin. trial program div. extramural affairs, data rev. bd. 1981—, adv. com. med. devices applications program 1971-75), Sigma Xi, Alpha Omega Alpha. Home: 24151 S Woodland Rd Cleveland OH 44122-3315 Office: 2500 Metrohealth Dr Cleveland OH 44109-1900

RAKOFF, JED SAUL, lawyer, author; b. Phila., Aug. 1, 1943; s. Abraham Edward and Doris Tobiah (Michell) R.; m. Ann Rosenberg, Aug. 4, 1974; children: Jena Lynn, Elana Beth, Keira Jan. BA, Swarthmore Coll., 1964; MPhil, Balliol Coll., Oxford U., Eng., 1966; JD, Harvard U., 1969. Bar: N.Y. 1971, D.C. 1983, U.S. Supreme Ct. 1986. Law clk. U.S. Ct. Appeals (3rd cir.), Phila., 1969-70; assoc. Debevoise, Plimpton, Lyons & Gates, N.Y.C., 1970-73; asst. U.S. atty. So. Dist. N.Y., N.Y.C., 1973-80, chief bus. and securities fraud prosecutions U.S. Atty.'s Office, 1978-80; ptnr. Mudge Rose Guthrie Alexander & Ferdon, N.Y.C., 1980-90, Fried Frank Harris Shriver & Jacobson, N.Y.C., 1990—; lectr. in law Columbia Law Sch., 1988—. Author: (with S. Arkin et al) Business Crime, 6 vols., 1982, Criminal Defense Techniques, 6 vols., 1982, (with H. Goldstein) RICO: Civil and Criminal Law and Strategy, 1989, (with L. Blumkin and R. Sauber) Corporate Sentencing Guidelines: Compliance and Mitigation, 1993; editor-in-chief Bus. Crimes Bull., 1994—; columnist N.Y. Law Jour., 1985—; contbr. numerous articles to law revs. Mem. exec. bd. N.Y. chpt. Am. Jewish Com., 1971-80, 82—. Fellow Am. Coll. Trial Lawyers (chmn. N.Y. State 1993-94); mem. ABA, N.Y. State Bar Assn., Assn. of Bar of City of N.Y. (chmn. criminal law com. 1986-89), Fed. Bar Coun., N.Y. Coun. Def. Lawyers (dir. 1990-94). Democrat. Jewish. Home: 99 W Garden Rd Larchmont NY 10538-1726 Office: Fried Frank Harris Shriver & Jacobson 1 New York Plz New York NY 10004

RAKOFF, TODD D., law educator; b. 1946. BA, Harvard U., 1967, JD, 1975; PhB, Oxford U., Eng., 1969; MS in Edn., U. Pa., Phila., 1971. Assoc. Foley, Hong & Eliot, Boston, 1976-79; asst. prof. Harvard U., Cambridge, Mass., 1979-83, prof., 1983—. Office: Harvard U Law Sch Cambridge MA 02138

RAKOFF, VIVIAN MORRIS, psychiatrist, writer; b. Capetown, South Africa, Apr. 28, 1928; s. David Wilfred and Bertha Lillian (Woolf) R.; m. Gina Shochat, Nov. 27, 1959; children: Simon, Ruth, David. B.A., U. Capetown, 1947, M.A. with 1st class honors, 1949; M.B.B.S., U. London, 1957; diploma psychiat. medicine, McGill U., 1963. Intern St. Charles Hosp., London, 1957, Victoria Hosp., Capetown, 1958; resident Groote Schuur Hosp., Capetown, 1959-61, Jewish Gen. Hosp., Montreal, 1961-62, Verdun Protestant Hosp., Montreal, 1961-62; staff psychiatrist Jewish Gen. Hosp., Montreal, 1963-66, dir. research psychiatry, 1967-68; dir. postgrad. edn. dept. psychiatry U. Toronto, Ont, Can, 1968-75; prof. psychiat. edn. U. Toronto, Ont., Can., 1975-80, prof., chmn. dept. psychiatry, 1980-90; prof. emeritus U. Toronto, 1990—; head dept. psychiatry Sunnybrook Hosp., Toronto, 1978-80; dir., psychiatrist-in-chief Clarke Inst. Psychiatry, Toronto, 1980-90. Author: plays Nonquasi, 1967; Mandelstam's Witness, 1975; editor: Psychiatric Diagnosis, 1977, A Method of Psychiatry, 1979. Fellow Royal Coll. Physicians and Surgeons, Am. Psychiat. Assn., Am. Coll. Psychiatrists; mem. Sigma Xi. Jewish. Office: Clarke Inst Psychiatry, 250 College St, Toronto, ON Canada M5T 1R8

RAKOLTA, JOHN, construction company executive; b. 1923. Student, U. Detroit. With Walbridge Aldinger Co., Livonia, Mich., 1945—, sec., treas., 1955-70, pres., treas., 1970-78, pres., 1978-80, now chmn. bd. dirs., 1980—. Office: Walbridge Aldinger Co 613 Abbott St Detroit MI 48226-2521

RAKOV, BARBARA STREEM, marketing executive; b. Bklyn., Jan. 4, 1946; d. Harold B. and Claire (Colbert) Streem; m. Harris J. Rakov, Nov. 20, 1970 (div. Mar. 1972). BS, Boston U., 1967; postgrad. NYU, 1972-74. Market rsch. analyst, product mgr., mktg. mgr. J.B. Williams, N.Y.C., 1967-77; mktg. mgr. Del Labs., Farmingdale, N.Y., 1977-78; product mgr., sr. product mgr., asst. to office of pres., dir. mktg. and sales Benelux countries, v.p. group mktg., dir., dir. new products, v.p. bus. devel. Joseph E. Seagram & Sons, 1978-89; pres. BSR Assocs., N.Y.C., 1990-92; v.p. mktg. Del Labs., 1992-94; v.p. mktg. Tsumura Internat., Secaucus, N.J., 1994—. Mem. L'Ordre des Coteaux de Champagne, Les Gastronomes de la Mer, Am. Mgmt. Assn. Avocations: tennis, skiing, squash, reading, water skiing. Office: Tsumura Internat 300 Lighting Way Secaucus NJ 07096-1578

RALEIGH, CECIL BARING, geophysicist; b. Little Rock, Aug. 11, 1934; s. Cecil Baring and Lucile Nell (Stewart) R.; m. Diane Lauster, July 17, 1982; children: Alison, Marianne, Lawrence, David. B.A., Pomona (Calif.) Coll., 1956; M.A., Claremont (Calif.) Grad. Sch., 1958; Ph.D., UCLA, 1963. Fellow Research Sch. Phys. Sci., Australian Nat. U., Canberra, 1963-66; geophysicist U.S. Geol. Survey, Menlo Park, Calif., 1966-80; program mgr. for earthquake prediction research program U.S. Geol. Survey, 1980-81; dir. Lamont-Doherty Geol. Obs. and prof. geol. scis. Columbia U., Palisades, N.Y., 1981-89; dean Sch. Ocean and Earth Sci. and Tech. U. Hawaii, Honolulu, 1989—; chmn. bd. dirs. DOSECC, Inc., 1985-88; mem. NAS/NRC Ocean Studies Bd.; bd. dirs. JOI, Inc.; bd. dirs. Nat. Energy Lab. Hawaii Authority; chmn. NAS/NRC Yucca Mountain Panel. Author papers control earthquakes, rheology of the mantle, mechanics of faulting, crystal plasticity. Recipient Interdisciplinary award U.S. Nat. Com. Rock Mechanics, 1969, 74; Meritorious Service award Dept. Interior, 1974; Barrows Dist. Alumnus award Pomona Coll. Fellow Am. Geophys. Union, Geol. Soc. Am. Democrat. Inventor formation fracturing method. Office: U Hawaii Sch Ocean Earth Sci & Tech Honolulu HI 96822

RALES, STEVEN M., automotive parts company executive; b. Pitts., Mar. 31, 1951; married. BA, DePauw U., 1973; JD, America U., 1978. With Equity Group Holdings, Washington, 1979—; chmn. bd., chief exec. officer Danaher Corp., Washington, 1984—, now chmn. bd. Office: Danaher Corp 1250 24th St NW Washington DC 20037-1124

RALL, DAVID PLATT, pharmacologist, environmentalist; b. Aurora, Ill., Aug. 3, 1926; s. Edward Everett and Nell (Platt) R.; children: Jonathan D., Catharyn E.; m. Mary Gloria Monteiro, Apr. 22, 1989. BS, North Ctrl. Coll., Naperville, Ill., 1946; MS, Northwestern U., 1948, MD, PhD, 1951. Intern Bellevue Hosp., N.Y.C., 1952-53; officer USPHS, 1953-90, asst. surgeon gen., 1971-90; sr. investigator Lab. Chem. Pharmacology, Nat. Cancer Inst., NIH, Bethesda, Md., 1953-55, Clin. Pharmacology and Exptl. Therapeutics Service, 1956-58, head service, 1958-63; chief Clin. Pharmacology and Exptl. Therapeutics Service (Lab. Chem. Pharmacology), 1963-69; assoc. sci. dir. for exptl. therapeutics Nat. Cancer Inst., 1966-71; dir. Nat. Inst. Environ. Health Scis., 1971-90, dir. Nat. Toxicology Program, 1978-90; adj. prof. pharmacology U. N.C., Chapel Hill, 1972-90, Foreign Sociology NAS Inst. Medicine, 1994—. Trustee Environ. Def. Fund, 1991; treas. Ramazzini Soc., 1992. Fellow AAAS; mem. Am. Assn. Cancer Rsch., Am. Soc. Clin. Investigation, Am. Soc. Pharmacology and Exptl. Therapeutics, Inst. Medicine, Soc. Toxicology. Home and Office: 5302 Reno Rd NW Washington DC 20015

RALL, JOSEPH EDWARD, physician; b. Naperville, Ill., Feb. 3, 1920; s. Edward Everett and Nell (Platt) R.; m. Caroline Domm, Sept. 28, 1944 (dec. Apr. 1976); children: Priscilla, Edward Christian. B.A., North Central Coll., 1940, D.Sc. (hon.), 1966; M.S., Northwestern U., 1944, M.D., 1945; Ph.D., U. Minn., 1952; Dr. honoris causa, Faculty of Medicine, Free U. Brussels, Belgium, 1975; M.D. (hon.), U. Naples, 1985. Assoc. mem. Sloan Kettering Inst., N.Y.C., 1950-55; chief clin. endocrinology br. Nat. Inst. Arthritis, Metabolism and Digestive Diseases, NIH, 1955-62; dir. intramural research Nat. Inst. Arthritis, Diabetes, Digestive and Kidney Diseases, 1962-83; dep. dir. intramural research NIH, 1983-91; sr. investigator Nat. Inst. Diabetes and Digestive and Kidney Diseases, NIH, 1991; mem. NRC, 1960-65. Author numerous articles, chpts. in books on thyroid gland and radiation. Chmn. Coun. of Scientists for Internat. Human Frontier Sci. Program, 1989-93. Served to capt. M.C. AUS, 1946-48. Recipient Van Meter prize Am. Goiter Assn., 1950, Fleming award, 1959, Outstanding Achievement award Mayo Clinic and U. Minn., 1964; Disting. Service award Am. Thyroid Assn., 1967; Disting. Service award HEW, 1968, Disting. Exec. rank, sr. exec. service, 1980, R.H. Williams Disting. Leadership award in endocrinology, 1983, Disting. Achievement award N.Y. Hosp., Cornell Med. Ctr., 1987; named Outstanding Alumnus N. Central Coll., 1966. Mem. NAS, AAAS,

Am. Acad. Arts and Scis.; Am. Soc. Clin. Investigation; Am. Phys. Soc.; Endocrine Soc.; Assn. Am. Physicians; Societe de Biologie (France); Royal Acad. Medicine (Brussels). Home: 3947 Baltimore St Kensington MD 20895-3913 Office: NIH Bldg 10 Rm 8N307 Bethesda MD 20892

RALL, LLOYD LOUIS, civil engineer; b. Galesville, Wis., Dec. 7, 1916; s. Louis A. and Anna (Kienzle) R.; m. Mary Moller, July 12, 1952; children: Lauris, David, Christopher, Jonathan. BCE, U. Wis., 1940. Commd. 2d lt. U.S. Army, 1940, advanced through grades to col., 1972, engr. forward area strategic air force, 1944-45, ret., 1977; chief construct divsn. Far East forces U.S. Army, Tokyo, 1945-47; engr., mem. mil. survey mission U.S. Army, Turkey, 1947; with office joint chiefs of staff U.S. Army, Washington, 1947-49, exec. officer R&D office chief engrs., 1949-51; asst. dist. engr. U.S. Army, Seattle, 1952-54; dept. engr. Comm. Zone U.S. Army, France, 1954-56; commanding officer 540th combat engr. group U.S. Army, 1956-57, prof. mil. sci. and tactics Mo. Sch. Mines and Metallurgy, 1957-60; dep. dir. topography office chief engrs. U.S. Army, Washington, 1960-64; dir. geographic intelligence and mapping U.S. Army, Ft. Belvoir, Va., 1964-66, dep. asst. dir. defense intelligece mapping, 1966-69, asst. dir. defense intelligence agy. mapping and charting, 1969-72; dir. Washington ops. Itek Optical Systems, Washington, 1977-91; mem. nat. tech. adv. com. Antarctica Mapping, 1960-64. Decorated Legion of Merit with oak leaf cluster, Bronze star. Home: 301 Cloverway Alexandria VA 22314

RALLI, CONSTANTINE PANDIA, lawyer; b. Bronxville, N.Y., Apr. 6, 1948; s. Pandia C. and Mary (Motter) R.; m. Alison Rhoads, Aug. 11, 1973; children: Pandia C., Christopher A. BA, Middlebury Coll., 1970; JD, Fordham U., 1973; LLM in Taxation, NYU, 1986. Bar: N.Y. 1974, U.S. Ct. Appeals (2d cir.) 1974, U.S. Dist. Ct. (so. and ea. dists.) N.Y. 1975, U.S. Dist. Ct. Conn. 1987, U.S. Tax Ct. 1977, Fla. 1985, Conn. 1985. Assoc. Davis Polk & Wardwell, N.Y.C., 1973-81; ptnr. Hall, McNicol, Hamilton & Clark, N.Y.C., 1981-88, LeBoeuf, Lamb, Greene & MacRae, N.Y.C., 1988—; sec., bd. dirs. Fairfield-Maxwell Ltd., Campo Tankers SA, N.Y.C., 1987—. Bd. dirs. Samaritan Counseling Ctr., Rye, N.Y., 1987-90, Rye Free Reading Room, 1990-93. Mem. Union Club, Am. Yacht Club, Ekwanok Country Club (Manchester, Vt.). Republican. Presbyterian. Home: 11 Rockridge Rd Rye NY 10580-4130 Office: LeBoeuf Lamb Greene & MacRae 125 E 55th St New York NY 10022-3502 also: 3 Landmark Sq Stamford CT 06901-2501

RALLIS, JOHN, manufacturing holding company executive; b. 1937. Grad., Brown U. Active Foamex L.P. and Predecessor Co., Marcus Hook, Pa., 1952—; pres/CEO Foamex Internat. Co., Marcus Hook, Pa. Office: Foamex Internat Inc 1000 Columbia Ave Marcus Hook PA 19061*

RALLS, KATHERINE, zoologist; b. Oakland, Calif., Mar. 21, 1939; d. Alvin Wallingsford and Ruth (McQueen) Smith; m. Kenneth M. Ralls, June 1958 (div. Sept. 1968); children: Robin, Tamsen, Kristin. AB, Stanford U., 1960; MA, Radcliffe Coll., 1962; PhD, Harvard U., 1965. Guest investigator Rockefeller U., N.Y.C., 1968-70, adj. asst. prof. biology, 1970-76; asst. prof. Sarah Lawrence Coll., Bronxville, N.Y., 1970-73; rsch. zoologist Inst. Rsch. in Animal Behavior, N.Y. Zool. Soc., 1970-73; zoologist Nat. Zool. Park, Smithsonian Instn., 1976—; mem. psychobiology adv. panel NSF, 1982-83; mem. sea otter recovery team U.S. Fish and Wildlife Svc., 1989—, mem. Calif. condor recovery team, 1990—. Mem. editorial bd. Signs, 1975-78; contbr. articles to profl. jours. Radcliffe Inst. fellow, 1973-74, Smithsonian Instn. fellow, 1973-76. Fellow AAAS, Animal Behavior Soc.; mem. Am. Soc. Mammalogists (bd. dirs. 1984-87, 2d v.p 1990-91, 92), Internat. Union Conservation of Nature and Natural Resources (captive breeding specialist group 1979—, otter specialist group 1989—), Am. Assn. Zool. Pks. and Aquaria (species survival plan subcom. 1981-88), Soc. Marine Mammalogy (editorial bd., book rev. editor Marine Mammal Sci. 1983-89), Soc. Conservation Biology (bd. govs. 1985-90), Animal Behavior Soc., Assn. Women in Sci., Wildlife Soc. Achievements include research in relationship between mammalian social behavior and other aspects of mammalian biology; conservation biology; genetic problems of small populations; and threatened and endangered mammals. Office: Nat Zoo Smithsonian Instn Washington DC 20008

RALPH, DAVID CLINTON, communications educator; b. Muskogee, Okla., Jan. 12, 1922; s. Earl Clinton and Rea Jane (Potter) R.; m. Kathryn Juanita Wicklund, Nov. 29, 1947; children: David Randall, Steven Wicklund. AA, Muskogee Jr. Coll., 1941; BS in Theatre, Northwestern U., 1947, MA in Theatre, 1948, PhD in Speech, 1953. Lectr. Ind. U., Hammond, 1947-48; instr. speech U. Mo., Columbia, 1948-53; tchr. debateforensics summer program for high sch. students Northwestern U., Evanston, Ill., 1949-51; asst. prof. speech Mich. State U., East Lansing, 1953-57, assoc. prof., 1957-64, prof. speech and theatre, 1964-68, prof. communication, 1968—, dir. communication undergrad. program, 1968-88; cons. on pub. speaking, 1948—. Co-author: Group Discussion, 1954, 2d edit., 1956, Principles of Speaking, 1962, 3d edit., 1975; contbr. articles to profl. jours., chpts. to books. Coach Jr. League Boys' Baseball, Lansing, Mich., 1958-74; mem. civilian aux. to Lansing Fire Dept., 1987—. Lt. USNR, 1942-46, PTO, ETO. Named Hon. State Farmer, Future Farmers Am., 1965; recipient Community Svc. award Mich. State U. Sr. Class Coun., 1979, Outstanding Faculty award, 1987, 91; Teaching Excellence award State of Mich., 1990. Mem. AAUP, Speech Communication Assn., Internat. Communication Assn., Cen. States Communication Assn., Golden Key (hon., faculty advisor), Omicron Delta Kappa. Democrat. Methodist. Avocation: model trains and fire engines. Office: Mich State U Dept Communication East Lansing MI 48824

RALPH, ROGER PAUL, arbitrator; b. Hammond, Ind., May 19, 1953; s. Bobby Gene Ralph and Nora Gwynn (Cornell) Baldwin; m. LaDonna Susan McDonald, July 15, 1972; children: Jarrod Keith, Rebecca Ann, Elizabeth Susan. BS in History, U. So. Ind., 1984; JD, Ind. U., 1987. Bar: Ind. 1987. Mill worker Ozark-Mahoning Co., Rosiclare, Ill., 1977-78; constrn. laborer Laborer's Internat. Union North Am. Local No. 561, Evansville, Ill., 1978-86; labor atty. Fillenworth Dennerline Groth & Towe, Indpls., 1987-88; litigation atty. Ricos & Price, Indpls., 1989-92; pvt. practice labor arbitrator Indpls., 1989—; chmn. Ind. Edn. Employment Rels. Bd., Indpls., 1992—. Democrat. Avocation: bluegrass music. Home: 808 Serenity Way Greenwood IN 46142 Office: Ind Edn Employment Rels Bd 9247 N Meridian St Ste 300 Indianapolis IN 46260-1976

RALPH, THOMAS A., lawyer; b. Phila., Feb. 17, 1941; s. Thomas L. and Ruth A. R.; m. Margaret Walton; children: Weatherly H., William W., Elizabeth F. BA, Dartmouth Coll., 1963; LLB, U. Pa., 1968. Bar: Pa. 1968. Mng. ptnr. Dechert Price & Rhoads, Brussels, Belgium, 1978-80; ptnr. Dechert Price & Rhoads, Phila., 1976—. Trustee Shipley Sch., 1989—; bd. dirs. World Affairs Coun. Phila., 1991—. 1st lt. USAR, 1963-65. Office: Dechert Price & Rhoads 4000 Bell Atlantic Tower 1717 Arch St Philadelphia PA 19103-2793

RALPH, WILLIAM J., lawyer; b. Springfield, Ill., June 30, 1953. BS summa cum laude, Ohio State U., 1974; JD, Columbia U., 1978. Bar: Ill. 1978, U.S. Dist. Ct. (no. dist.) Ill. 1978. Ptnr. Winston & Strawn, Chgo. Office: Winston & Strawn 35 W Wacker Dr Chicago IL 60601-1614

RALSON, LESLEY LLOYD, insurance company executive; b. Rusk, Tex., Oct. 12, 1929; s. James Herbert and Virginia Mae (Sword) R.; m. Dorothy Ralson, Sept. 14, 1984; children: William Garrett, Dana Marie; children by previous marriage—Leslie Ann, Sylvia Simone, Stephanie Jean. B.B.A., U. Houston, 1952; grad., Am. Coll. Life Underwriters, Pa., 1963; postgrad. in bus. adminstrn., Columbia U., 1975. C.L.U. Mgmt. trainee Prudential Ins. Co. Am., Houston, 1957-59, group service rep., 1959-60; group sales rep. Prudential Ins. Co. Am., Tulsa, 1960-61, dist. group mgr., 1961-63, dist. group supr., 1963-64; regional group mgr. Prudential Ins. Co. Am., Milw., 1964-66; assoc. dir. group ins. Prudential Ins. Co. Am., Newark, 1966-67, dir. group sales and service, 1967; dir. group ins. Prudential Ins. Co. Am., Houston, 1968-71, v.p. group ins., 1971-73; v.p. Prudential Ins. Co. Am., Newark, 1973-77; sr. v.p. Prudential Ins. Co. Am., Newark and Roseland, N.J., 1977-87, group ops. 1987—; chmn. PruCare, Houston, PruCare of Okla., PruCo Life of Ill., Tesseract, Inc. Served to 1st lt. USMC, 1952-57. Office: The Prudential Ins Co Am 56 Livingston Ave Roseland NJ 07068-1733 also: The Prudential Ins Co Am Prudential Plz Newark NJ 07102

RALSTON, ANTHONY, computer scientist, mathematician, educator; b. N.Y.C., Dec. 24, 1930; s. Alfred Joseph and Ruth (Bien) R.; m. Jayne Madeleine Rosenthal, Feb. 14, 1958; children: Jonathan, Geoffrey, Steven, Elizabeth. BS, MIT, 1952, PhD, 1956. Mem. tech. staff Bell Tel. Labs., 1956-59; lectr. U. Leeds, 1959-60; mgr. tech computing Am. Cyanamid Co., 1960-61; assoc. prof. math. Stevens Inst. Tech., 1961-64, prof., 1964-65; dir. computer services SUNY, Buffalo, 1965-70; prof. SUNY, 1967—, chmn. dept. computer sci., 1967-80; bd. examiners Grad. Record Exam in Computer Sci., 1976-82; mem. computer bd. NRC, 1976-79, mem. math. sci. edn. bd., 1985-89. Author: A First Course in Numerical Analysis, 1965, 2d edit., 1978, Introduction to Programming and Computer Science, 1971, Discrete Algorithmic Mathematics, 1991; editor: Ency. of Computer Science, 1976, 2d edit., 1982, 3d edit., 1992, ABACUS, 1988; co-editor: Mathematical Methods for Digital Computers, Vol. 1, 1960, Vol. 2, 1967, Vol. 3, 1977, The Influence of Computers and Informatics in Mathematics and Its Teaching, 1993. 2d lt. U.S. Army, 1957. Fellow AAAS, Assn. Computing Machinery (pres. 1972-74, mem. coun. 1968-76, Disting. Svc. award 1982); mem. Math. Assn. Am. (bd. govs. 1984-87), Am. Fedn. Info. Processing Socs. (pres. 1975-76), Com. Concerned Scientists (bd. dir.). Home: Flat 4 Albert Court Lodge, 58 Prince Consort Rd, London SW7 2BA, England

RALSTON, HENRY JAMES, III, neurobiologist, anatomist, educator; b. Berkeley, Calif., Mar. 12, 1935; s. Henry James and Sue Harris (Mahnke) R.; m. Diane Cornelia Daly, Oct. 29, 1960; children: Rachel Anne, Amy Sue. BA, U. Calif., Berkeley, 1956, MD, 1959. Intern Mt. Sinai Hosp., N.Y.C., 1959-60; resident in medicine U. Calif., San Francisco, 1960-61, prof., 1973—, chmn. dept. anatomy, 1973—, chair acad. senate, 1986-88; asst. prof. anatomy Stanford (Calif.) U., 1965-69; assoc. prof. U. Wis., Madison, 1969-73; cons. NIH; mem. com. for future of anat. scis., Macy Found., 1977-80; vis. prof. French Med. Rsch. Inst.-INSERM, Paris, 1981-82; chair step I U.S. Med. Lic. Examination Com. Nat. Bd. Med. Examiners, 1992-96. With M.C. U.S. Army, 1961-63. Recipient Henry J. Kaiser award for excellence in teaching, 1978, Jacob Javits Neurosci. Investigator award NIH, 1988—; USPHS grantee, 1966—. Mem. AAAS, Soc. Neurosci., Soc. Study Pain, Am. Pain Soc., Am. Assn. Anatomists (pres. 1987-88, chair publs. com. 1989-91), Anat. Assn. Gt. Britain, Phi Beta Kappa, Anat. Assn. Gt. Britain, Phi Beta Kappa. Research in field of organization of mammalian nervous system studied by electron microscopy, mechanisms subserving pain in animals and humans. Office: U Calif Dept Anatomy PO Box 0452 San Francisco CA 94143

RALSTON, JAMES ALLEN, lawyer; b. Cin., Oct. 24, 1946; s. Edward John and Gladys Mae (Herrmann) Overman R.; m. Karen Lee Kilgore, Dec. 29, 1969; children—Matthew Allen, Emily Anne. B.A., U. Va., 1968; J.D., U. Cin., 1973. Bar: Ohio 1973, U.S. Dist. Ct. (so. dist.) Ohio 1973. Assoc. Frost & Jacobs, Cin., 1973-79; atty. Eagle-Pitcher Industries, Inc., Cin., 1979-82, asst. sec., 1982—, gen. counsel, 1982—, v.p., 1984—. Served with U.S. Army, 1969-71. Office: Eagle-Picher Industries Inc 580 Walnut St Cincinnati OH 45202-3108

RALSTON, JOANNE SMOOT, public relations counseling firm executive; b. Phoenix, May 13, 1939; d. A. Glen and Virginia (Lee) Smoot; m. W. Hamilton Weigelt, Aug. 15, 1991. B.A. in Journalism, Ariz. State U., 1960. Reporter, The Ariz. Republic, Phoenix, 1960-62; co-owner, pub. relations dir. The Patton Agy., Phoenix, 1962-71; founder, pres., owner Joanne Ralston & Assocs., Inc., Phoenix, 1971-87, 92—; pres. Nelson Ralston Robb Comm., Phoenix, 1987-91; pres. Joanne Ralston & Assocs., Inc., Scottsdale, Ariz., 1992—. Contbr. articles to profl. jours. Bd. dirs. Ariz. Parklands Found., 1984-86, Gov.'s Council on Health, Phys. Fitness and Sports, 1984-86; task force mem. Water and Natural Resources Council, Phoenix, 1984-86; mem. Ariz. Republican Caucus, 1984—, others. Recipient Lulu' awards (36) Los Angeles Advt. Women, 1964—, Gold Quill (2) Internat. Assn. Bus. Communicators, Excellence awards Fin. World mag., 1982-93, others; named to Walter Cronkite Sch. Journalism Hall of Fame, Coll. Pub. Programs Ariz. State U., 1987; name one of 25 Most Influential Arizonians, Phoenix Mag., 1991. Mem. Pub. Relations Soc. Am. (counselor sect.), Internat. Assn. Bus. Communicators, Phoenix Press Club (pres. bd.), Investor Rels. Inst., Phoenix Met. C. of C. (bd. dirs. 1977-84, 85-91), Phoenix Country Club. Republican. Avocations: horses, skiing.

RALSTON, KEN, graphics expert. Freelance comml. maker, 1971-77; cameraman Indsl. Light & Magic, San Rafael, Calif., 1977-83, visual effects supr., 1983—. Cameraman (films) Star Wars, 1977, The Empire Strikes Back, 1980; co-effects supr. (films) The Return of the Jedi, 1983 (Oscar award); visual effects supr. (films) Dragonslayer, 1981 (Oscar Award), Star Trek II: The Wrath of Khan, 1982, Star Trek III: The Search for Spock, 1984, Out of Africa, 1985, Back to the Future, 1985, Cocoon, 1985, Star Trek IV: The Voyage Home, 1986, The Golden Child, 1986, Who Framed Roger Rabbit?, 1988 (Oscar award), Back To The Future II, 1989 (Oscar award), Back To The Future III, 1990, The Rocketeer, 1991, Cocoon (Oscar award), Death Becomes Her, 1992 (Oscar Award). Office: Indsl Light & Magic PO Box 2459 San Rafael CA 94912-2459*

RALSTON, LUCY VIRGINIA GORDON, artist; b. Washington, Sept. 9, 1926; d. Byron Brown and Lucy (Virginia (Gordon) R. Grad., Finch Jr. Coll., 1942; student, Parsons Sch. Design; studied with, Leon Kroll. Freelance artist Tiffany and Co., 1947-48; designer U.S.S. Constution book Am. Bible Soc. and John Jay and Eliza Jane Watson Found. for presentation Bibles to grads. U.S. Naval Acad., USCG Acad., Marchant Marine Acad., 1953—; art tchr. Sr. Citizens of Pelham, 1948-50. One-woman show Pelham (N.Y.) Meml. High Sch., 1939; exhibited in group shows Westchester Fedn. Women's Clubs, Bronxville, N.Y., 1954, Mt. Vernon (N.Y.) Art Assn., 1955, Allied Artists Am., N.Y.C., 1955, others; represented in permanent collections Assn. Jr. Leagues Am., N.Y.C. and tour U.S. and Can., John Jay and Eliza Jane Watson Found., Elizabeth, N.J.; executed mural at Westchester Restaurant, Mamaroneck, N.Y.; commd. portraits of Princess Anne and Prince Charles of Eng., Brit. Am. Soc. Vol. numerous civic orgns., 1942-45. Recipient Popular prize Manor Club, 1947, 48, 2d prize, 1958, 1st prize for graphic art, 1957; Popular prize Westchester Assn. Women's Clubs, 1951, Mt. Vernon Art Assn., 1954, 2d prize Met. Mus., Pelham, 1969. Mem. DAR (registrar Knapp chpt. 1961-63, recording sec. Anne Hutchinson chpt. 1989—), Jr. League Pelham, Daus. of Cin. (registrar 1973-78), Nat. Soc. Colonial Dames State N.Y., Colonial Soc. Ams. Royal Descent, Nat. Soc. Magna Carta Dames, Colonial Soc. Descendants Knights of Garter, Colonial Order Crown, Huguenot Soc. Am., Welcome to Washington Internat. Club. Republican. Episcopalian. Avocations: raising purebred dogs, swimming, sailing. Home and Studio: 4784 Boston Post Rd Pelham NY 10803

RALSTON, MERRELL EDWARD, textiles executive. Pres. United Carpet Mills Inc., Chatsworth, Ga., 1973—. Office: United Carpet Mills Inc 2858 Highway 76 Chatsworth GA 30705*

RALSTON, PATRICK ROBERT, state government official; b. Terre Haute, Ind., Jan. 23, 1948; s. George Avery and Stephanie Catherine Ralston; m. Nancy Carol Price, July 31, 1971; children: Kellie Elizabeth, Ryan Patrick. BS, Ind. State U., 1972, MS, 1973. Dir. parks and recreation City of Butler, Ind., 1973-74; regional supr. Ind. State Parks, Indpls., 1974-79; supr. parks, recreation and cemeteries City of Terre Haute, 1979-89; dir. Ind. Dept. Natural Resources, 1989—; lectr. Ind. State U., Terre Haute, 1981-83; pres., bd. dirs. West Cen. Econ. Devel. Dist., Terre Haute, 1987—. Author: Policy Manual, 1986, Preventative Maintenance Book, 1986; contbr. articles to Outdoor Indiana mag. Bd. dirs. Alliance for Growth and Progress, Terre Haute, 1986—; exec. com. White River Park State Games, Indpls., 1986—; pres. Lost Creek PTA, Terre Haute, 1988—; v.p. fin. United Cerebral Palsy, Terre Haute, 1986-88; vice chmn. United Way Campaign, Terre Haute, 1988—. Recipient Heroism award Gov. Otis R. Bowen, Indpls., 1979, World Health Day award World Health Org., 1987, Hand Clasp award Kiwanis Internat., 1987; named one of Outstanding Young Men of Am. 1983. Mem. Nat. Recreation and Park Assn., Ind. Park and Recreation Assn., Ind. State U. Alumni Council (bd. dirs.), Ducks Unltd. (bd. dirs. Terre Haute chpt. 1988—), Humboldt #42, Elks, Rotary, Breakfast Optimist Club. Home: 207 Terre Vista Dr Terre Haute IN 47803-2445

RALSTON, ROBERT O., manufacturing executive; b. Cin., Oct. 8, 1938; s. Henry and Ethel (Williams) R.; m. Susann Rose Fels, July 27, 1963; children: Stephen R., Julia S. MBA, Xavier U. Mfg. mgr., then v.p. svc. parts dept. Milacron; pres. Rsch. Design and Devel. Corp., Erie, Pa., 1988-90; v.p. mfg. Mazak Corp., Florence, Ky., 1990—. Active ARC; mem. bd. govs. Cin. Shriners Burns Inst. With USMC. Recipient Hon. Legion of Honor, Internat. Supreme Coun. Order of DeMolay. Mem. Masons (sovereign grand comdr. No. Jurisdiction Scottish Rite, 33 degree, worshipful master 1967, trustee 1968-72, dist. dept. Grand Lodge of Ohio 1983-85, trustee Ohio Masonic Home at Springfield 1988-90, trustee Cin. Scottish Rite Bodies, chmn. 1979, 92, Hon. Mem. No. Jurisdiction, mem. Supreme Coun. 1992, bd. dirs.), Royal Order of Jesters, Royal Order of Scotland. Home: 8705 Tanager Woods Ln Cincinnati OH 45249

RAM, CHITTA VENKATA, physician; b. Machilipatnam, India, Oct. 24, 1948; s. Chitta M. Row and Chitta (Cheruvu) Sarojini; m. Ashalata Ram, Feb. 17, 1979; children: Gita, Radha. B.Sci, Marathwada U., Aurangabad, India, 1966; MD, Osmania U., Hyderabad, India, 1972. Diplomate Am. Bd. Internal Medicine. Resident in internal medicine Brown U., R.I. Hosp., Providence, 1974-76; fellow in hypertension Hosp. U. Pa., Phila., 1976-77; faculty assoc. U. Tex. Southwestern Med. Ctr., Dallas, 1977-78, asst. prof., 1978-83, assoc. prof., 1983-89; prof., 1989—; dir. hypertension clinic Parkland Meml. Hosp., Dallas, hypertension unit St. Paul Med. Ctr., Dallas. Contbr. numerous articles to profl. jours. and chpts. to textbooks; editl. cons., reviewer numerous nat. and internat. jours. and pubs. Pres. Tex. IndoAm. Physician Soc., Dallas, 1988; trustee Dallas/Ft. Worth Hindu Temple Soc., Dallas, 1988. Named Outstanding Tchr. St. Paul Med. Ctr., 1982; recipient Mother of India award, 1992. Fellow ACP, Am. Coll. Cardiology, Am. Coll. Chest Physicians (regent), Am. Coll. Clin. Pharmacology; mem. Am. Assn. Physicians from India (pres.-elect 1994-95), Tex. Indo-Am. Physicians Soc. also: St Paul Med Ctr # 600 5939 Harry Hines Blvd Dallas TX 75235

RAM, TRACY SCHAEFER, ballet company manager; b. San Francisco, June 4, 1960; d. Donald Worth and Leslie Lorraine Wells Schaefer; m. Michael Francis Ram, May 29, 1987. BA in Polit. Sci. and Mass Communications, U. Calif., Berkeley, 1982. Legal asst. Morrison & Foerster, San Francisco, 1982-84; asst. to gen. mgr. San Francisco Ballet, 1984-86, mgr. co., 1986—. Democrat. Home: 761 Noe St San Francisco CA 94114-2941 Office: San Francisco Ballet 455 Franklin St San Francisco CA 94102-4471

RAMACHANDRAN, VENKATANARAYANA DEEKSHIT, electrical engineering educator; b. Mysore, India, May 3, 1934; s. K.C. Venkatanarayana Deekshit and Subbamma Deekshit R.; m. Kamala Visweswaraiya, June 12, 1960; 1 child, Ravi P. BS, U. Mysore, 1953; B in Engring., Indian Inst. Sci. Bangalore, 1956, M in Electronics, 1958, PhD, 1965. Registered profl. engr. Sr. research asst. Indian Inst. Sci., 1958-59, lectr., 1959-66; asst. prof. N.S. Tech. Coll., Halifax, Can., 1966-69; prof. elec. engring. Concordia U. (formerly Sir George Williams Univ.), Halifax, Can., 1971—; acting chmn. dept. elec. and computer engring. Montreal, various times; grad. program dir. dept., 1969-84; adj. prof. U. Windsor, Ont., Can., 1983—, Ecole Tech. Superieure U. Quebec, Montreal, 1989—; mem. program com. Internat. Symposium on Operator Theory of Networks and Systems, 1975; vice chmn. Internat. Symposium on Circuits and Systems IEEE, Montreal, 1984, mem. tech. program com., 1987; internat. coordinator Internat. Conf. on Computers, Systems and Signal Processing, Indian Inst. Sci., 1984. Author papers in profl. jours., 120 papers presented to confs., others. Named to Order of Engrs. of Que.; recipient Merit award Concordia Council on Student Life, 1981-82. Fellow Inst. Electronics and Telecomms. India (edit. bd. jour. 1986), Inst. Engrs. India, Inst. Elec. Engrs. Eng., Engring. Inst. Can. (sec. Montreal chpt. 1979-80, centennial bd. 1983-84), IEEE; mem. Circuits and Systems IEEE (chmn. Montreal sect. 1978-84), Can. Soc. Elec. Engrs. (editor jour. 1983-85, editor bull. 1981-83), Am. Soc. Engring. Edn. (chmn. awards com. St. Lawrence chpt. 1987-88, Western Elec. Fund award 1983, Myril B. Reed Best Rsch. Paper award 1984, Outstanding Svc. 1993). Office: Concordia Univ, Faculty of Engring, 1455 de Maisonneuve Blvd W, Montreal, PQ Canada H3G 1M8

RAMADAN, SAR, design automation company executive; b. Ismaila, Egypt, Feb. 8, 1943; came to U.S., 1970; s. Hosny and Saadia (Awad) R.; m. Carol Mulcahy, Aug. 1, 1987; children: Samira, Janine, Celene, Ameer, Ramadan. BS, Ain Shams U., Cairo, 1965; MBA, U. New Haven, 1974; postgrad., Harvard U., 1986. Fin. administr. Suez Canal Authority, Ismailia, 1962-70; plant acct. Cities Services Corp., New Haven, 1971-73; corp. controller Home Care Services, New Haven, 1973-74; contract controller GTE Internat., Burlington, Mass., 1974-79; v.p. group controller Computervision Corp., Bedford, Mass., 1979-86; v.p. fin., controller CAD/CAM Resources, Inc., Waltham, Mass., 1986-87; corp. controller Mentor Graphics Corp., Portland, Oreg., 1987—; cons. Supercals Inc., Calif., 1986, TSI Internat., Mass., 1986. Mem. Harvard Alumni Assn. Republican. Avocations: tennis, wind surfing. Home: 2431 Palisades Crest Dr Lake Oswego OR 97034-7551 Office: Mentor Graphics Corp 8005 SW Boeckman Rd Wilsonville OR 97070-9733

RAMAKRISHNAN, VENKATASWAMY, civil engineer, educator; b. Coimbatore, India, Feb. 27, 1929; came to U.S., 1969, naturalized, 1981; s. Venkataswamy and Kondammal (Krishnaswamy) R.; m. Vijayalakshmi Unnava, Nov. 7, 1962; children: Aravind, Anand. B.Engring., U. Madras, 1952, D.S.S., 1953; D.I.C. in Hydropower and Concrete Tech, Imperial Coll., London, 1957; Ph.D, Univ. Coll., U. London, 1960. From lectr. to prof. civil engring., head dept. P.S.G. Coll. Tech., U. Madras, 1952-69; vis. prof. S.D. Sch. Mines and Tech., Rapid City, 1969-70; prof. civil engring. S.D. Sch. Mines and Tech., 1970—, dir. concrete tech. research, 1970-71, head grad. div. structural mechanic and concrete tech., 1971—, program coordinator materials engring. and sci. Ph.D program, 1985-86. Author: Ultimate Strength Design for Structural Concrete, 1969; also over 200 articles. Colombo Plan fellow, 1955-60; recipient Outstanding Prof. award S.D. Sch. Mines and Tech., 1980, 1st Rsch. award, 1994. Mem. Internat. Assn. Bridge and Structural Engring., ASCE (vice chmn. constrn. div. publs. com. 1974), Am. Concrete Inst. (chmn. subcom. gen. considerations for founds., chmn. com. 214 on evaluation of strength test results, sec.-treas. Dakota chpt. 1974-79, v.p. 1980, pres. 1981), Instn. Hwy. Engrs., Transp. Rsch. Bd. (chmn. com. on admixtures and curing, chmn. com. on mech. properties concrete), Am. Soc. Engring. Edn., NSPE, Internat. Coun. Gap-Graded Concrete Rsch. and Application, Sigma Xi. Address: 1809 Sheridan Lake Rd Rapid City SD 57702-4219 *To me, success is a coin with hard work on one side and perseverance with devotion on the other. No matter what—head or tails—the message is the same: keep on working. Goals in my life were pursuit of truth and beauty. The structures I have created, and my writings based on research have given me greater satisfaction than any wealth, position, or power.*

RAMALEY, JUDITH AITKEN, university president, endocrinologist; b. Vincennes, Ind., Jan. 11, 1941; d. Robert Henry and Mary Krebs (McCullough) Aitken; m. Robert Folk Ramaley, Mar. 1966 (div. 1976); children: Alan Aitken, Andrew Folk. BA, Swarthmore Coll., 1963; PhD, UCLA, 1966; postgrad., Ind. U., 1967-69. Rsch. assoc., lectr. Ind. U., Bloomington, 1967-68, assist. prof. dept. anatomy and physiology, 1969-72; asst. prof. dept. physiology and biophysics U. Nebr. Med. Ctr., Omaha, 1972-74, assoc. prof., 1974-78, prof., 1978-82, assoc. dean for rsch. and devel., 1978-82; asst. v.p. for acad. affairs U. Nebr., Lincoln, 1980-82, v.p. for biol. scis. SUNY, Albany, N.Y., 1982-87, v.p. for acad. affairs, 1982-85, acting pres., 1984, exec. v.p. for acad. affairs, 1985-87; exec. vice chancellor U. Kans., Lawrence, 1987-90; pres. Portland (Oreg.) State U., Oreg., 1990—; bd. dirs. Bank of Am.; mem. endocrinology study sect. NIH, 1981-84; cons.-evaluator North Cen. Assn. accreditation, 1978-82, 89-90; mem. regulatory panel NSF, 1979-82; mem. Ill. Commn. Scholars, 1980—. Co-author: Progesterone Function: Molecular and Biochemical Aspects, 1972; Essentials of Histology, 8th edit., 1979; editor: Covert Discrimination, Women in the Sciences, 1978; contbr. articles to profl. jours. Bd. dirs. Family Svc. of Omaha, 1979-82, Albany Symphony Orch., 1984-87, mem. exec. com., 1986-87, Urban League Albany, 1984-87, 2d v.p., mem. exec. com., 1986-87, Upper Hudson Planned Parenthood, 1984-87, Capital Repertory Co., 1986-89, Ass. Portland Progress, 1990—, City Club of Portland, 1991-92, Metro Family Svcs., 1993—, Campbell Inst. for Children; bd. dirs. NCAA Pres. Commn., 1991, chair divsn. II subcom., 1994, mem. joint policy bd., 1994; chmn. bd. dirs. Albany Water Fin. Authority, 1987; mem. exec. com. United Way Douglas County, 1989-90;

mem. adv. bd. Emily Taylor Women's Resource Ctr., U. Kans., 1988-90; mem. Silicon Prarie Tech. Assn., 1989-90, Portland Opera Bd., 1991-92, Portland Leaders Roundtable, 1991—; mem. bd. devel. com. United Way of Columbia-Williamette, 1991—; active Oreg. Women's Forum, 1991—, Portland Met. Sports Authority; progress bd. Portland-Multinomah County, 1993—. NSF grantee, 1969-71, 71-77, 75-82, 77-80, 80-83. Fellow AAAS; mem. Nat. Assn. State Univs. and Land Grant Colls. (exec. com., mem. senate 1986-88, vice chair comn. urban agenda 1992—), Assn. Am. Colls. and Univs., Endocrine Soc. (chmn. edn. com. 1980-85), Soc. Study Reprodn. (treas. 1983-85), Soc. for Neuroscis., Am. Physiol. Soc., Am. Coun. on Edn. (chmn. commn. on women in higher edn. 1987-88), Assn. Portland Progress (bd. dirs.), Portland C. of C. (bd. dirs. 1995), Western Assn. of Schs. and Colls. (commr. 1994). Office: Portland State U Office of the President PO Box 751 Portland OR 97207-0751

RAMAMOORTHY, CHITTOR V., computer science educator; b. Henzada, Burma. MS, U. Calif., 1953, ME, 1953; PhD, Harvard U., 1964. Design engr. Marchant Calculators Inc., Emeryville, Calif., 1953-56; sr. staff scientist Honeywell Inc., Waltham, Mass., 1956-71; prof. U. Tex., Austin, 1967-72, U. Calif., Berkeley, 1972—. Fellow IEEE (editor-in-chief Trans. on Knowledge and Data Engring. 1987—, Taylor Booth award Computer Soc. 1990). Home: 1117 Sierra Vista Way Lafayette CA 94549-3128 Office: Univ Calif Computer Sci Div 571 Evans Hall Berkeley CA 94720

RAMANARAYANAN, MADHAVA PRABHU, science administrator, researcher, educator; b. Varapuzha, Kerala, India, Feb. 5, 1945; came to U.S., 1972; s. Srinivasa Madhava and Priyothama (Shenoy) Prabhu; m. Leelavati Murthy, Sept. 2, 1972; children: Malini, Ananth. BS, American Coll., Madurai, India, 1964, MS, 1966; PhD, Indian Inst. Sci., Bangalore, India, 1972. Post-doctoral research worker dept. biochemistry Coll. Physicians and Surgeons of Columbia U., N.Y.C., 1972-75; staff assoc. Inst. Cancer Research, Columbia U., N.Y.C., 1975-81; dir. research & devel. Diagnostic Reagent Tech., Teaneck, N.J., 1981-85; v.p. research & devel. Visual Diagnostics, Inc., Teaneck, 1985-88; pres. Windsor Park Labs., Inc., Teaneck, 1988—; lectr., instr. postgrad. courses Am. Acad. Otolaryngic Allergy. Contbr. sci. articles to profl. jours. Fellow Am. Inst. Chemists, Nat. Acad. Clin. Biochemistry; mem. N.Y. Acad. Scis., Am. Chem. Soc., Internat. Union Pure and Applied Chemistry, Am. Assn. for Clin. Chemistry.

RAMANATHAN, KAVASSERI VAIDIANATHA, accounting educator, researcher, consultant; b. Trichur, Kerala, India, Nov. 26, 1932; came to U.S., 1966; s. Kavasseri Viswanatha and Saraswathy (Apathira) Vaidianathan; m. Rajalakshmi Ramanathan, Apr. 22, 1959; 1 dau., Saraswathy. B.Com., Calcutta U., India, 1954; M.B.A., Northwestern U., 1962, Ph.D., 1970. Systems mgr. Philips India Ltd., Calcutta, 1955-59; prof. acctg. Indian Inst. Mgmt., Ahmedabad, 1963-66; assoc. prof. acctg. U. Wash., Seattle, 1969-79, prof. acctg., 1979—, chmn. exec. M.B.A. program, 1982-86; dir. Russian programs, 1992—; vis. scientist Battelle Meml. Inst., Seattle, 1974-77; vis. prof. Harvard U., Cambridge, Mass., 1979-80; vis. fellow Australian Nat. U., Canberra, 1983, Monash U., Australia, 1983; vis. prof. NYU, N.Y.C., 1986-87, U. Auckland, 1992. Author: Management Control in Nonprofit Organizations, 1982; editor: Accounting for Managerial Decision Making, 1974, Readings in Management Control in Nonprofit Organizations, 1982. Adviser Sandeepany West, Piercy, Calif., 1981-82; bd. dirs. Arsha Vidya Pitam, Los Gatos, Calif., 1982—; pres. Ragamala, Seattle; founder, chmn. Hindu Temple & Community Ctr. Pacific N.W., Seattle, 1988—. Fulbright scholar Calcutta, 1960-63. Fellow Indian Inst. of Cost and Works Accts.; mem. Am. Acctg. Assn. , Fin. Execs. Inst., Inst. of Mgmt. Accts. Home: 13311 63rd Ave NE Seattle WA 98155-3331 Office: Univ Wash Dj 10 Dept Acctg # 10 Seattle WA 98195

RAMANATHAN, RAMA, foundation executive. CFO Annie E. Casey Found., Inc., Greenwich, Conn. Office: Annie E. Casey Found Inc 1 Lafayette Pl Greenwich CT 06830*

RAMANI, RAJA VENKAT, mining engineering educator; b. Madras, India, Aug. 4, 1938; came to U.S., 1966; s. Natesa and Meenakshi (Srinivasan) Rajaraman; m. Geetha V. Chalam, July 9, 1972; children: Deepak, Gautam. BSc. with honors, Indian Sch. Mines, Dhanbad, Bihar, 1962; MS, Pa. State U., 1968, PhD, 1970. Registered profl. engr., Pa., 1971; lic. first class mine mgr., 1965. Mining engr., mgr. Andrew Yule & Co., Asansol, West Bengal, India, 1962-66; grad. asst. Pa. State U., University Park, 1966-70, asst. prof., 1970-74, assoc. prof., 1974-78, prof. mining engring., 1978—, chmn. mineral engring. mgmt. sect., 1974—, head dept. mineral engring., 1987—; chmn. com. post-disaster survival/rescue NAS, Washington, 1979-81; cons. UN, UN Devel., N.Y.C., 1983-94; cons./expert panels U.S. Dept. Labor, 1979, 92, HHS, 1977, 92, U.S. Dept. State, 1986, 87, U.S. Dept. Interior, 1995, Dept. Environ. Resources, Commonwealth of Pa., 1990, 92; co-dir. Generic Mineral Rech. Ctr. on Respirable Dust, U.S. Bur. Mines, 1983—, Nat. Mines/Land Reclamation Tech., 1988—; Std. Oil Ctr. of Excellence on Longwall Tech., 1983-89. Sect. editor, author: Computer Methods for the Eighties, 1979, SME Mining Engineering Handbook, 1992; editor: State-of-the-Art in Longwall-Shortwall Mining, 1981, Proceedings: 19th International APCOM Symposium, 1986. Recipient Disting. Alumni award Indian Sch. Mines, Dhanbad, 1978, Ednl. Excellence award Pitts. Coal Mining Inst., 1986, Environ. Conservation award AIME, N.Y.C., 1990, Howard N. Eavenson award SME/AIME, N.Y.C., 1991, Percy H. Nicholls award AIME/ASME Joint Soc., 1992, Robert Stefanko Best Paper award SME/AIME, 1993, Coal Div. Disting. Svc. award SME/AIME, 1993; Henry Krumb lectr. AIME, 1994; Fulbright scholar to Soviet Union Coun. Internat. Exch. of Scholars, Washington, 1989-90. Mem. Internat. Coun. for Application of Computers in the Mineral Industry (Disting. Achievement award 1989), Soc. Mining, Metall. and Exploration (Disting. Mem. 1989, pres. 1995), Mine Ventilation Soc. South Africa, Inst. Mgmt. Scis. Achievements include research in health, safety, environmental and productivity aspects in underground and surface mining engineering. Home: 285 Oakley Dr State College PA 16803-1349 Office: Dept Mineral Engring Pa State U University Park PA 16802

RAMAT, CHARLES S., apparel executive. Chrm. bd., pres., ceo, asst. sec. Aris Industries Inc, N.Y.C. Office: Aris Industries Inc 675 3rd Ave Ste 3000 New York NY 10017-5704

RAMATY, REUVEN ROBERT, physicist, researcher; b. Timisoara, Rumania, Feb. 25, 1937; came to U.S., 1963; s. Nikolas and Elizabeth (Markowitz) Reiter; m. Vera Marie Klein, Aug. 8, 1961; children: Daphne, Deborah. BSc, Tel-Aviv (Israel) U., Israel, 1961; PhD, UCLA, 1966. Rsch. assoc. UCLA, 1966-67; rsch. assoc. NASA/Goddard Space Flight Ctr., Greenbelt, Md., 1967-69, astrophysicist, 1969-80, head Theory Office, 1980-93, sr. scientist, 1993—; adj. prof. U. Md., College Park, 1983—. Contbr. over 200 articles and papers to sci. jours. Fellow Am. Phys. Soc. (chmn. div. cosmic physics 1977-78, councilor div. astrophysics 1985-89); mem. Am. Astron. Soc. (chmn. div. high energy astrophysics 1984-85), Internat. Astron. Union. Avocations: linguistics, foreign languages, history, geography. Office: Goddard Space Flight Ctr Greenbelt MD 20771

RAMAZANI, ROUHOLLAH KAREGAR, government and foreign affairs educator; b. Tehran, Iran, Mar. 21, 1928; came to U.S., 1952, naturalized, 1961; s. Ali Karegar and Khadijeh (Sultani) R.; m. Nesta Shahrokh, Feb. 22, 1952; children: Vaheed, David, Jahan, Sima. LL.M., U. Tehran, 1951; postgrad., U. Ga., 1952; S.J.D., U. Va., 1954. Lectr. fgn. affairs U. Va., Charlottesville, 1954-57; research assoc. Soviet Fgn. Econ. Relations Project U. Va., 1956-59, asst. prof. fgn. affairs, 1957-60, assoc. prof., 1960-64, prof. govt. and fgn. affairs, 1964—, Edward R. Stettinius Jr. prof. govt. and fgn. affairs, 1972, Harry F. Byrd Jr. prof. govt. and fgn. affairs, 1983; Aga Khan vis. prof. Islamic studies Am. U., Beirut, 1967-68; vis. prof. Middle East studies Sch. Advanced Internat. Studies, Johns Hopkins, 1967, 70-71, 72-73, 75, 77, 79; vis. prof. Cambridge (Eng.) U., spring 1975; cons. internat. relations Rockefeller Found.; cons. Inst. Fgn. Policy Analysis, U.S. Dept. State, UN, White House.; Vice pres., trustee Am. Inst. Iranian Studies; cons. Pan Am. Internat. Oil Co., Research Analysis Corp.; bd. govs. Middle East Inst.; Am. participant USIA, 1974, 79, 80, 84, 86. Author: The Middle East and the European Common Market, 1964, The Northern Tier: Iran, Afghanistan and Turkey, 1966, The Foreign Policy of Iran, 1500-1941: A Developing Nation in World Affairs, 1966, The Persian Gulf: Iran's Role, 1972, Iran's Foreign Policy, 1941-1973: A Study of Foreign Policy in

Modernizing Nations, 1975, Beyond the Arab-Israeli Settlement: New Directions for U.S. Policy in the Middle East, 1977, The Persian Gulf and the Strait of Hormuz, 1979, Security of Access to Persian Gulf Oil Supplies in the 1980s, 1982, The United States and Iran: The Patterns of Influence, 1982, Revolutionary Iran: Challenge and Response in the Middle East, 1986, paperback edit. with new epilogue on Iranian-American Arms Deal, 1988, The Gulf Cooperation Council: Record and Analysis, 1988; editor, co-author Iran's Revolution: The Search for Consensus, 1990; assoc. editor: Jour. South Asian and Middle Eastern Studies; adv. editor: Middle East Jour., Fgn. Policy Report, Levant; contbr.: Soviet Foreign Relations and World Communism, 1965, The Search for World Order, 1971, Concise Ency. of the Middle East, 1973, The Anatomy of Communist Takeovers, 1975, Energy and World Politics, 1975, Iran: Past, Present, and Future, 1976 From June to October: The Middle East Between 1967 and 1973, 1978, Iran in the 1980's, 1978, The Middle East Contemporary Survey, 1967-77, The Middle East Contemporary Survey, 1977-78, World Politics and the Arab-Israeli Conflict, 1979, The Impact of the Iranian Events upon Persian Gulf and United States Security, 1979, The Revolution in Iran: Its Character and Political-Economic Complications, 1979, In Search of Peace, 1980, Comparative Regional Systems, 1980, The Indian Ocean in Global Politics, 1981, Middle East Perspectives, 1981, The Iran Crisis and International Law, 1981, Revolution in Iran: A Reappraisal, 1982, Islam in Foreign Policy, 1983, Arm Disarm for Peace, 1984, The Indian Ocean: Perspectives on A Strategic Arena, 1985, Shi'ism and Social Protest, 1986, The Middle East After the Invasion of Lebanon, 1986, Encyclopedia of World Biography: Twentieth Century Supplement "Khomeini", 1987, Yearbook of International Communist Affairs "Iran", 1987, 88, 89, Crosscurrents in the Gulf, 1988, Musaddiq, Iranian Nationalism and Oil, 1988. Mem. exec. com. Council on Fgn. Relations, Charlottesville, 1965-67; mem. Citizens for Albemarle, 1972—. Recipient prize for distinguished contbn. Am. Assn. Middle East Studies, 1964, Raven Soc. Svc. award, Disting. Prof. award; Social Sci. Research Council grantee, 1967; Fulbright research grantee, 1968. Fellow Middle East Studies Assn. N.Am.; mem. Am. Soc. Internat. Law, Am. So. polit. sci. assns., Middle East Inst., Shaybani Soc. Internat. Law (exec. officer), Raven Soc., Phi Beta Kappa. Home: 1140 Mountain Rd Charlottesville VA 22901-9245 *The three principles that have most often guided my professional conduct are integrity, innovation and persistent hard work. Without such a guiding trinity "success" in life may be attainable, but I believe it would be largely illusory.*

RAMBERG, CHRISTINA, artist, educator; b. Fort Campbell, Ky., Aug. 21, 1946; d. Vernon Charles and Norma Elizabeth (Boie) R. B.F.A., Art Inst. Chgo., 1968, M.F.A., 1973. Instr., chmn. dept. painting and drawing Sch. Art Inst., Chgo., vis. artist-instr. painting U. Colo., Boulder, 1972, vis. artist drawing and painting Northwestern U., Evanston, Ill., 1979-80. One woman shows, Phyllis Kind Gallery, Chgo., 1975, 81, N.Y.C., 1977, 82; group shows include, Whitney Biennials, 1972, 73, 79, Sao Paolo Biennial, Brazil, 1973, Sunderland Arts Center, Eng., 1980, Mid-career Retrospective, Renaissance Soc., Chgo., 1988; represented in permanent collections, Art Inst. Chgo., Whitney Mus. Modern Art, N.Y.C., Mus. Am. Art, Washington, Mus. Contemporary Art, Chgo., Mus. de 20 Jahrhunderts, Vienna. James Nelson Raymond fellow, 1973; NEH grantee, 1978, 83. Office: Phyllis Kind Gallery 313 W Superior St Chicago IL 60610-3515

RAMBERG, WALTER DODD, architect; b. Charlotte, N.C., Feb. 17, 1932; s. Walter Gustav Charles and Julia Elisabeth (Lineberger) R.; m. Lucinda Jenifer Ballard, Nov. 25, 1961 (dec. 1989); children: Lucinda E.G., Jenny S.F., Julia E.L. B.A., Yale U., 1953, M.Arch., 1956. Fulbright fellow Kyoto (Japan) U., 1956-58; apprentice architect Paul Rudolph, New Haven, 1958-61; project designer Meyer & Ayers, Balt., 1961-63; partner Howe & Ramberg, Washington, 1963-65; prin. Walter Dodd Ramberg (Architect), Washington, 1965—; prof. architecture Cath. U. Am., 1977—; mem. design adv. panel Balt. Dept. Housing and Community, 1973—; mem. bd. architecture rev. Baltimore County, 1986-89. Designer: N.W. Balt. High Sch, 1963 (P.A. Excellence in Design award); architect: Bridge for Washington Cathedral, 1965 (Excellence in Design award Washington Bd. Trade, AIA), Kidder Guest House, 1965 (1st Honor award Balt. AIA), Azrael House, 1969 (Honor award Balt. AIA), Cutts House, 1973 (Honor award Balt. AIA), Woody House, 1975 (Merit award Balt. AIA), Lineberger Meml. Library, 1976 (Merit award Nat. AIA, ALA); contbr. articles to profl. publs. Served to lt. USCGR, 1958-59. Mem. AIA (corp.), AAUP, Soc. Archtl. Historians. Episcopalian. Club: Met. (Washington). Home: 1651 Belfast Rd Sparks MD 21152 Office: 1830 T St NW Washington DC 20009-7138

RAMBO, A. TERRY, anthropologist, research program director; b. San Francisco, Apr. 3, 1940; s. Arthur Ira Rambo and Dorothy V. (Miller) Schlee; m. Dawn Jean Bowman, Jan. 24, 1971 (dec. July 1987); children: Charmaine Malia, Claire Norani. AB in Anthropology with distinction, U. Mich., 1963; MA in Anthropology, Am. U., 1969; PhD in Anthropology, U. Hawaii, 1972. Rsch. scientist Human Scis. Rsch., Inc., McLean, Va., 1964-69; acting asst. prof. anthropology U. Hawaii, 1971-72; asst. prof. anthropology Wash. State U., 1972-73; vis. prof. social sci. Grad. Sch. Politics and Econs., Dalat U., Saigon, Vietnam, 1973-75; lectr. dept. anthropology and sociology U. Malaya, 1975-80; sr. fellow, coord. program on renewable resources mgmt. East-West Ctr. Environ. and Policy Inst., Honolulu, 1980-92; dir. program on environ., coord. Indochina initiative East-West Ctr., Honolulu, 1992—; bd. dirs. S.E. Asian Univs. Agroecosystem Network; cons. in field. Author: Primitive Polluters, 1985, Comparison of Peasant Social Systems of Northern and Southern Viet-nam, 1973; editor: Profiles in Cultural Evolution, 1991; mem. editorial bd. Biodiversity Letters; assoc. Current Anthropology; co-editor: An Introduction to Human Ecology Research on Agricultural Systems in Southeast Asia, 1984, also reports, papers, monographs, procs. in field; contbr. articles and revs. to profl. publs., chpts. to books. Grantee Asia Soc./SEADAG, 1969-70, U. Malaya, 1976-79, Ford Found., 1978-79, 84, 85-87, 87-89, 91-93, 95—, U. Hawaii/East-West Ctr., 1981-82, 84-85, Rockefeller Bros. Fund, 1988-89, 90-92, 94-95, MacArthur Found., 1990-91, 91-93, 93—; Nat. Def. Fgn. Lang. fellow, 1970-71, Ford Found. S.E. Asia rsch. fellow, 1972, 73-74, 75-76. Avocations: gardening, backpacking, reading. Office: East-West Ctr Program on Environment 1777 East-West Rd Honolulu HI 96848

RAMBO, DAVID L., religious organization administrator. Pres. The christian and Missionary Alliance, Nyack, N.Y., 1988—. Office: Christian and Missionary Alliance PO Box 35000 Colorado Springs CO 80935-3500

RAMBO, SYLVIA H., federal judge; b. Royersford, Pa., Apr. 17, 1936; d. Granville A. and Hilda E. (Leonhardt) R.; m. George F. Douglas, Jr., Aug. 1, 1970. BA, Dickinson Coll., 1958; JD, Dickinson Sch. Law, 1962; LLD (hon.), Wilson Coll., 1980, Dickinson Sch. Law, 1993. Bar: Pa. 1962. Atty. trust dept. Bank of Del., Wilmington, 1962-63; pvt. practice Carlisle, 1963-76; public defender, then chief public defender Cumberland County, Pa., 1974-76; judge Ct. Common Pleas, Cumberland County, 1976-78, U.S. Dist. Ct. (mid. dist.) Pa., Harrisburg, 1979-92; chief judge Pa. & Md., 1992—; asst. prof., adj. prof. law Dickinson Sch. Law, 1974-76. Mem. Nat. Assn. Women Judges, Phi Alpha Delta. Democrat. Presbyterian. Office: US Dist Ct Federal Bldg PO Box 868 Harrisburg PA 17108-0868

RAMDAS, ANANT KRISHNA, physicist, optics scientist; b. Poona, India, May 19, 1930; married, 1956. BSc, U. Poona, India, 1950, MSc, 1953, PhD in Physics, 1956. Rsch. assoc. physics, 1956-60, from asst. prof. to assoc. prof., 1960-67; prof. physics Purdue U., Lafayette, Ind., 1967—; Alexander von Humboldt U.S. sr. scientist, 1977-78. Fellow Am. Physical Soc. (Frank Isakson prize 1994), Indian Acad. Sci. Research in spectroscopy; application of spectroscopic techniques to solid state physics; electronic and vibrational spectra of solids studied by absorption and emission spectra in the visible and the infrared and by laser Raman spectroscopy. Office: Purdue Univ Dept Of Physics West Lafayette IN 47907*

RAMDIN, R. H., mining executive. Pres. Suriname Aluminum Co., Pitts. Office: Suriname Aluminum Co 425 6th Ave Pittsburgh PA 15219*

RAMER, BRUCE M., lawyer; b. Teaneck, N.J., Aug. 2, 1933; s. Sidney and Anne S. (Strassman) R.; m. Ann Greenberg Ramer, Feb. 15, 1965; children: Gregg B., Marc K., Neal I. BA, Princeton U., 1955; LLB, Harvard U., 1958. Bar: Calif. 1963, N.J. 1958. Assoc. Morrison, Lloyd & Griggs, Hackensack, N.J., 1959-60; ptnr. Gang, Tyre, Ramer & Brown, Inc., L.A., 1963—. Exec. dir. Entertainment Law Inst., Law Ctr. of U. So. Calif.; bd. of

councilors Law Ctr. U. So. Calif.; past pres. L.A. chpt.; bd. govs., chmn. nat. exec. coun. Am. Jewish Com. (nat. v.p. 1982-88, pres. L.A. chpt. 1980-83, chair Western region 1984-86, community svc. award, 1987); chmn. Pacific Rim Inst.; trustee Loyola Marymount U. (mem. exec. com.); vice chair United Way, 1991-93, corp. bd. dirs., 1981-93, chair coun. pres. 1989-90, mem. community issues coun., 1989-90, chair discretionary fund distbn. com., 1987-89; bd. dirs. L.A. Urban League, 1987—, Jewish Fedn. Coun. of greater L.A. (mem. Community Rels. com.), Jewish TV Network, Sta. KCET-TV; mem., bd. dirs. Rebuild L.A.; vice chmn., bd. govs. Calif. Community Found.; recipient Ann. Brotherhood award Nat. Conf. of Christians and Jews, 1990; mem. Fellows of Am. Bar Found. Pvt. U.S. Army, 1958-59, 2d lt., 1961-62. Mem. ABA, L.A. County Bar Assn., Calif. Bar Assn., Beverly Hills Bar Assn. (exec. dirs. award 1988), L.A. Copyright Soc. (pres. 1974-75), Calif. Copyright Conf. (pres. 1973-74), Princeton Club (pres. 1975-78). Office: Gang Tyre Ramer & Brown Inc 132 S Rodeo Dr Beverly Hills CA 90212

RAMER, HAL REED, college president; b. Kenton, Tenn., June 8, 1923; s. Claude Orion and Dixie Clayton (Carroll) R. BS, George Peabody Coll., 1947; MSW, U. Tenn., 1952; PhD, Ohio State U., 1963. Asst. dean men Ohio State U., Columbus, 1953-58, dir. internat. house, 1958-60, staff asst. to pres., 1960-62; asst. commr. State Dept. Edn., Nashville, 1963-70; founding pres. Vol. State C.C., Gallatin, Tenn., 1970—; bd. dirs. Sumner Regional Health Sys., Inc. Mem. adv. bd. First Union Bank Mid. Tenn., Hendersonville, Tenn., com. March of Dimes, Gallatin; trustee Nashville United Way, 1970s; bd. govs. Aquinas Coll., Nashville, 1967—; bd. dirs. Y.M.C.A.; former chmn. Tenn. Fulbright-Hays Sch. Commn. With USAAF, 1943-45; col. Tenn. Def. Force. Recipient Distinctive Svc. award Devel. Coun. Peabody Coll., Nashville, 1960s, Distinguished Svc. award Tenn. Dept. Edn., 1970, Outstanding Leader award Vanderbilt U. chpt. Phi Delta Kappa, 1987, Gov.'s Svc. award State of Tenn., 1993; named Rotarian of the Yr., 1979; Paul Harris fellow Rotary Internat., 1981. Mem. Am. Legion, Coun. Pres. C.Cs. (chmn. state Tenn. 1988-89), Tenn. Coll. Assn. (pres. 1985-86), Nat. Alumni Assn. Peabody Coll. (pres. 1970-71, bd. trustees), Tenn. Acad. Sci., Tenn. and Sumner Co. Hist. Socs. (bd. dirs.), English Speaking Union Internat. (Nashville chpt.), So. Assn. Colls. and Schs., Univ. Club Nashville, Gallatin and Hendersonville C. of C., Torch Club Internat., Alpha Tau Omega, Kappa Phi Kappa, Alpha Phi Omega, Phi Delta Kappa. Methodist. Avocations: antiques, antique cars, photography. Home: 148 Kenner Ave Nashville TN 37205-2219 Office: Vol State CC Office of Pres Nashville Pike Gallatin TN 37066

RAMER, JAMES LEROY, civil engineer; b. Marshalltown, Iowa, Dec. 7, 1935; s. LeRoy Frederick and Irene (Wengert) R.; m. Jacqueline L. Orr, Dec. 15, 1957; children: Sarah T., Robert H., Eric A., Susan L. Student U. Iowa, 1953-57; MCE, Washington U. St. Louis, 1976, MA in Polit. Sci., 1978; postgrad. U. Mo., Columbia, 1984—. Registered profl. engr., land surveyor. Civil and constrn. engr. U.S. Army C.E., Tulsa, 1960-63; civil and relocations engr. U.S. State Dept., Del Rio, Tex., 1964; project engr. H. B. Zachry Co., San Antonio, 1965-66; civil and constrn. engr. U.S. Army C.E., St. Louis, 1967-76, tech. advisor for planning and nat. hydropower coordinator, 1976-78, project mgr. for EPA constrn. grants, Milw., 1978-80; chief architecture and engring. HUD, Indpls., 1980-81; civil design and pavements engr. Whiteman AFB, Mo., 1982-86, project mgr. maintenance, 1993—; soil and pavements engr. Hdqtrs. Mil. Airlift Command, Scott AFB, Ill., 1986-88; project manager AF-1 maintenance hangar; cattle and grain farmer, 1982—; pvt. practice civil-mech. engr., constrn. mgmt., estimating, cost analysis, cash flow, project scheduling, expert witness, Fortuna, Mo., 1988—; chief construction inspector divsn. Design and Construction, State of Mo., 1992-93; adj. faculty civil engring. Washington U., 1968-78, U. Wis., Milw., 1978-80. Ga. Mil. Coll., Whiteman AFB., Longview Coll., Kansas City; adj. research engr. U. Mo., Columbia, 1985—. Author tech. writing operation and maintenance manuals, fin. reports and environ. control plans; holder 25 U.S. patents in diverse art, 8 copyrights. Achievements include developer solar waterstill, deep shaft hydropower concept. Mem. ASCE, NSPE, AAUP, Am. Mil. Engrs. Lutheran. Club: Optimists Internat. Home: RR 1 Box 50-aa Fortuna MO 65034-9720

RAMER, LAWRENCE JEROME, corporation executive; b. Bayonne, N.J., July 29, 1928; s. Sidney and Anne (Strassman) R.; m. Ina Lee Brown, June 30, 1957; children: Stephanie Beryl, Susan Meredith, Douglas Strassman. B.A. in Econs, Lafayette Coll., 1950; M.B.A. Harvard U., 1957; LLD (hon.), Lafayette Coll., 1992. Sales rep., then v.p. United Sheet Metal Co., Bayonne, 1953-55; with Am. Cement Corp., 1957-64; v.p. mktg. div. Riverside Cement Co., 1960-62, v.p. mktg. parent co., 1962-64; vice chmn. bd., chief exec. officer Clavier Corp., N.Y.C., 1965-66; exec. v.p., vice chmn. bd. Pacific Western Industries, Los Angeles, 1966-70; pres., chief exec. officer Nat. Portland Cement Co. Fla., 1975-89; chmn. bd. Sutro Partners, Inc., Los Angeles, 1977-89, Somerset Mgmt. Group, 1975-92, Luminall Paints Inc., Los Angeles, 1972—; chmn. bd., chief exec. officer Bruning Paint Co., Balt., 1979—, Pacific Coast Cement Co., Los Angeles, 1979-90; pres., chief exec. officer Ramer Equities, Inc., 1990—; chmn. Lawrence J. Ramer Family Found., 1986—; bd. dirs. Project Orbis, N.Y.C., The Music Ctr., L.A., Music Ctr. Operating Co., L.A., Canyon Ranch, Tucson, Music Ctr. Found., L.A.; chmn. bd. dirs. Ctr. Theatre Group-Taper Ahmanson Theatres, L.A. Chmn. bd. trustees Lafayette Coll., Easton, Pa.; trustee, chmn.-elect Calif. Inst. Arts, Valencia, Calif.; bd. dirs. Non-Traditional Casting Project, N.Y.; nat. bd. govs. Am. Jewish Com., N.Y. Office: Ramer Equities Inc Ste 1090 1999 Avenue of Stars Los Angeles CA 90067

RAMETTE, RICHARD WALES, chemistry educator; b. Hartford, Conn., Oct. 9, 1927; s. Joel Edward and Grace Margaret (Wales) R.; m. Lenora Kathryn Kelleher, Aug., 21, 1949; children: Cheryl Lee, James Edward, John Richard, David Joel, William Michael. BA, Wesleyan U., Middletown, Conn., 1950; D. U. Minn., 1954. Prof. chemistry Carleton Coll., Northfield, Minn., 1954-90, Laurence M. Gould prof. chemistry, 1971-90, prof. emeritus, 1990—; sci. advisor FDA, Mpls., 1969-80. Author: Chemical Equilibrium and Analysis, 1981. Asst. scoutmaster Boy Scouts Am., Northfield, 1968-73; calligraphy instr. Northfield Arts Guild, 1974-80. Served with USN, 1946-48. Recipient Chemistry Teaching award Mfg. Chemists, 1966, Analytical Chemistry Teaching award Am. Chem. Soc., 1991. Avocations: fishing, computer programming. Home: 805 Highland Ave Northfield MN 55057-1327

RAMEY, CARL ROBERT, lawyer; b. Binghamton, N.Y., Feb. 15, 1941; s. Clinton W. and Hester May (Wisdom) R.; m. Maryan Sitzenkopf, Aug. 11, 1962 (div. Sept. 1987); children: Mark Alan, Christian David; m. Karen Reichard, Nov. 28, 1987. AB, Marietta Coll., 1962; MA, Mich. State U., 1964; JD, George Washington U., 1967. Bar: D.C. 1968, U.S. Dist. Ct. D.C. 1968, U.S. Ct. Appeals (2d, 3d, 4th, 5th, 7th and 9th cirs.), U.S. Supreme Ct. 1972. Assoc. McKenna, Wilkinson & Kittner, Washington, 1967-71, ptnr., 1971-86; ptnr. Wiley, Rein & Fielding, Washington, 1986—. Contbr. articles to profl. jours., chpt. to Copyright Law Symposium, 1969; editorial staff George Washington Law Rev., 1965-67. Recipient First Prize award Nat. Nathan Burkan Meml. Writing Competition, ASCAP, 1969. Mem. ABA, Fed. Communications Bar Assn. (treas. 1977-78), D.C. Bar Assn. Republican. Episcopalian. Avocations: skiing, tennis, boating, biking. Home: Pine Cove 5081 Reed Rd Oxford MD 21654 Office: Wiley Rein & Fielding 1776 K St NW Washington DC 20006-2304

RAMEY, CECIL EDWARD, JR., lawyer; b. Shreveport, La., Nov. 9, 1923; s. Cecil Edward and Blanche (Gwin) R.; m. Betty Loper, June 15, 1945; children—Martha L., L. Christine, Stephen E. BS summa cum laude, Centenary Coll., 1943; LLB, Yale U., 1949; postgrad., Tulane U., 1950-51. Bar: Wis. 1949, La. 1951. Assoc. Miller, Mack & Fairchild, Milw., 1949-50; mem. faculty Tulane U., 1950-54; assoc. Hargrove, Guyton, Van Hook and Hargrove, Shreveport, 1954-56, ptnr., 1956-63; ptnr. Hargrove, Guyton, Van Hook and Ramey, Shreveport, 1963-73; ptnr. Hargrove, Guyton, Ramey and Barlow, Shreveport, 1973-89, of counsel, 1989-94; of counsel Barlow and Hardtner, L.C., Shreveport, 1994—; adj. prof. Centenary Coll., 1992—. Former chmn. Citizens Capital Improvements com. City of Shreveport; former mem. governing bd. Shreveport YMCA; former chmn. bd. trustees Broadmoor Meth. Ch., Shreveport, chmn. bd. stewards; former bd. dirs., former chmn. Shreveport-Bossier Found.; former trustee Centenary Coll. With AC, U.S. Army, 1943-46. Named Shreveport's Outstanding Young Man of Yr., 1956, Mr. Shreveport, 1968; recipient Clyde E. Fant Meml.

award community service United Way, 1979. Fellow Am. Coll. Trust and Estate Counsel; mem. ABA, La. Bar Assn., Shreveport Bar Assn., La. Law Inst., Shreveport C. of C. (pres. 1974), Centenary Coll. Alumni Assn. (past pres.), Shreveport Club, Order of Coif, Phi Delta Phi, Kappa Sigma. Club: Shreveport. Home: PO Box 873-C RD 1 Karnack TX 75661-9708 Office: Barlow and Hardtner LC 401 Edwards St Shreveport LA 71101-3129

RAMEY, DENNY L., bar association executive director; b. Portsmouth, Ohio, Feb. 22, 1947; s. Howard Leroy and Norma Wylodine (Richards) R.; m. Jeannine Gayle Dunmyer, Sept. 24, 1971 (div. Nov. 1991); children: Elizabeth Michelle, Brian Michael. BBA, Ohio U., 1970; MBA, Capital U., 1976. Cert. assn. exec. Adminstrv. mgr. Transit Warehouse div. Elston Richards Storage Co., Columbus, Ohio, 1970-73; mgr. continuing profl. edn. Ohio Soc. CPA's, Columbus, 1973-79; exec. dir. Engrs. Found. of Ohio, Columbus, 1979-80; asst. exec. Ohio State Bar Assn., Columbus, 1980-86, exec. dir., sec., treas., 1986—; treas., exec. com., bd. dirs. Ohio Bar Liability Ins. Co., Columbus, 1986—; treas. Ohio State Bar Found., 1986—; treas. Ohio Legal Ctr. Ins., Columbus, 1988-91; sec. Ohio Printing Co., Ltd., 1991—. Mem. Nat. Assn. Bar Execs. (chmn. various coms.), Am. Soc. Assn. Execs., Ohio Soc. Assn. Execs., The Player's Club. Methodist. Avocations: tennis, golf, sports, wine appreciation. Office: Ohio State Bar Assn 1700 Lake Shore Dr PO Box 16562 Columbus OH 43216-6562

RAMEY, JAMES MELTON, chemist; b. Waco, Tex., Sept. 1, 1928; s. Ernest Sylvester and Audrey Lee (McCasland) R.; m. Frankie Jo Montomery, Aug. 23, 1952; children: Marlana Ramey Wylodine, James Monte Ramey, Douglas Dwain Ramey, Susan Elizabeth Ramey Attebery, Angela Dawn Ramey. BS, Southwestern U., 1949. Cert. product safety profl., profl. source for safety cons. Chemist Celanese Chem. Co., Bishop, Tex., 1954-57, group leader, spl. problems lab., 1957-60, dir. spl. problems lab., 1960-67; dir. quality assurance to dir. product standards Celanese Chem. Co., N.Y.C., 1967-76, dir. indsl. hygiene and toxicology, 1976-78; corp. dir. of product safety Celanese Corp., N.Y.C., 1978-83, dir. safety, 1983-85, dir. environ. health and safety audit program, 1985-87; dir. environ. health and safety audit programs Hoechst Celanese Corp., Somerville, N.J., 1987-88; cons. environ. health scis. Horseshoe Bay, Tex., 1988—; chmn. bd. Formaldehyde Inst., Washington, 1978-82, chmn. OSHA com. SOCMA, Washington, 1978-84; mem. environ. audit roundtable, Washington, 1985-88. Contbr. chpt. on quality control to Ency. Chem. Process and Design, 1980; contbr. articles to profl. jours.; patentee in field. Adv. Jesse Owens Found., N.Y., 1982-88; del. Tex. Dem. Conv., Tex., 1964-68; v.p. Internat. Amateur Athletic Assn., N.Y., 1982-88; bd. dirs Property Owners Assn., Horseshoe Bay, 1991-94; mem. Horseshoe Bay Chapel Choir, 1992-94; mem. PLAN. Fellow Am. Inst. Chemists; mem. Bishop C. of C. (pres. 1965-66). Methodist. Achievements include development of health surveillance and info. systems for Celanese Chem. Co., one of first comprehensive product safety programs in chemical industry and charter mem. of product safety forum, one of first comprehensive environ. health audit programs. Home and Office: PO Box 8634 Horseshoe Bay TX 78657

RAMEY, PETER M., holding company executive. Sec. Lou Fusz Motor Co., Inc., Saint Louis, 1987—. Office: Lou Fusz Motor Co Inc 925 N Lindbergh Blvd Saint Louis MO 63141*

RAMEY, SAMUEL EDWARD, bass soloist; b. Colby, Kans., Mar. 28, 1942; s. Robert Guy and Grace Irene (Mallory) R.; m. Carrie Tanate, Jan. 10, 1970. Student, Kans. State U., 1960-62; B.Mus., Wichita State U., 1968. Debut in Carmen, N.Y.C. Opera, 1973, leading bass, 1973—; European debut, Glyndebourne Festival, 1976, debut, Hamburg Staatsoper, 1978, Paris Opera, 1979, Houston Grand Opera, 1975, San Francisco Opera, 1978, Chgo. Lyric Opera, 1979, Festival International Aix-en-Provence, 1979, 80, Teatro della Scala, 1981, Vienna Staatsoper, 1981, in Rinaldo, Met. Opera, 1984; recording artist opera and oratorio, Philips, Angel, RCA, Deutsche Grammophone, London, CBS Records. Named Kansan of the Year Native Sons and Daughters of Kansas, 1994. Office: Columbia Artists Mgmt Inc Arbib Div 165 W 57th St New York NY 10019-2201*

RAMICONE, JOHN R., school system administrator; b. Manchester, Eng., Oct. 21, 1944; came to U.S., 1946; s. Ovie J. and Ann (Ryder) Ramicone; m. Jane E. Sockrider; children: Elizabeth, Michael. BS in Edn., Kent State U., 1967, MEd in Ednl. Administrn., 1975. Cert. supr., high sch. prin., health and phys. edn., polit. sci. and history, driver edn., Ohio. Tchr., coach John Adams High Sch., Cleve., 1967-71; tchr., coach Cuyahoga Heights Schs., Cleve., 1971-75, asst. prin. dir. high sch. athletics, 1975-80, prin. high sch., 1980-84, supt., 1984—. Bd. mem. Greater Cleve. Safety Coun., 1991—; mem. Cuyahoga Heights PTA, 1975—. Mem. Lakeshore N.E. Ohio Computer Assn., Cuyahoga Spl. Edn. Svc. Ctr., Greater Cleve. Sch. Coun. (gov. bd.), Greater Cleve. Supt. Assn. (treas. 1990—), Alliance for Adequate Sch. Funding (exec. com. 1990—), Buckeye Assn. Sch. Adminstrs. Office: Cuyahoga Hgts Local SD 4820 E 71st St Cleveland OH 44125-1043

RAMIG, ALEXANDER, JR., paint company executive, chemist; b. Scottsbluff, Nebr., Nov. 15, 1941; s. Alexander and Elizabeth (Reichel) R.; m. Janet L. Diemer. BS, U. Nebr., 1964; PhD, U. Louisville, 1970. Devel. chmn. Celanese Coatings Co., 1964-68; scientist The Glidden Co., Strongsville, Ohio, 1970-73; tech. mgr. The Glidden Co., Strongsville, 1973-76, asst. mgr., 1976-82, dir., 1982-87, v.p. rsch. and devel.; mem. awards com. Indsl. Rsch. Inst., 1990—, co. del. Contbr. numerous tech. and sci. papers to profl. jours.; patentee in field. Mem. Am. Chem. Soc., Fedn. Socs. for Coatings Tech. (Roon award 1977), Indsl. Rsch. Inst. (co. del.). Office: The Glidden Co 925 Euclid Ave Cleveland OH 44115-1401 Office: The Glidden Co 16651 Sprague Rd Strongsville OH 44136

RAMIREZ, ENRIQUE RENE, social sciences educator; b. Mayaguez, P.R., Feb. 10, 1930; s. Sergio Ramirez and Ofelia Rivera-Zapata; m. Lydia Gonzalez, Sept. 29, 1951; children: Enrique, Hector, Pierangeli, Roxanna. BA, Okla. State U., 1975, MA, 1976, PhD, 1979. Writer, rschr. U.S. Army, Fort Dix, N.J., 1963-66; pers. supr. U.S. Army, Vietnam, 1970-71; writer, rschr. White Sands Proving Grounds, Las Cruces, N.Mex., 1956-58; instr., ROTC Okla. State U., Stillwater, 1968-70, instr., 1976-79; prof., chmn. Tex. Coll., Tyler, 1979-92; dir. history and geography Tyler Jr. Coll., 1992—; Disting. panelist Nat. Grad Fellows program U.S. Dept. Edn., 1986—; coord. internat. studies Southwestern Internat. Consortium, 1984—; chmn. Cmty. Devel. Commn., Tyler, 1989—; lectr. in field. Author: Encounter of Two Worlds: The Mexican Experience, 1991; editor: Newspaper Voz Hispana, Tyler, 1987-89. Chmn. Community Devel. Comm., 1988—; Pres. East Tex. Coun. on World Affairs, Tyler, 1988-89, Hispanic Assn. East Tex., 1989—; commr. Clean Tyler Commn., 1984-85; rep. Conf. on Ergn. Policy/Dept. State, Washington, 1988; bd. dirs United Way of Greater Tyler, 1986—; Ct. Apptd. Advocates, 1990—, Parents Svc. Ctr., 1990—, Am. Cancer Soc., 1988—, ARC, 1987—, TV Prog. Mundo Hispano, 1990—; precinct chmn. Dem. party. Fulbright-Hays scholar Soviet Studies/U.S. Dept. Edn., 1989, Brazilian Studies, 1991; recipient award United Negro Coll. Fund/MacArthur Found., Spain, 1983, Sears-Roebuck Found. Prof. of Yr. award, Tyler, 1991, Okla. Regents for Higher Edn. Rsch. award, Stillwater, 1979; fellow Students in Free Enterprise, 1988. Mem. Southwestern Social Scis. Assn., Kiwanis. Roman Catholic. Avocations: writing, rsch., stamp collecting, Chess. Home: 2807 Apache Trl Tyler TX 75707-9317 Office: Tyler Jr Coll 510-2441 PO Box 9020 Tyler TX 75702

RAMIREZ, MARIA FIORINI, economist, investment advisor; b. Naples, Italy, Jan. 1, 1948; came to U.S., 1961; d. Fernando and Clelia Ambrosio Fiorini; m. George M. Ramirez, Apr. 28, 1973. BBA, Pace U., 1972, postgrad., 1974-76. Analyst Meinhard-CIT Comml. Fin., N.Y.C., 1967-68; credit analyst Am. Express Internat. Bank, N.Y.C., 1968-72; credit mgr. Banca Nazionale del Lavoro, N.Y.C., 1972-73; credit mgr., asst. v.p. Merrill Lynch G.S.I., 1973-74, economist 1974—, v.p., sr. money market economist Merrill Lynch Econs. Inc., 1981-84; sr. v.p., sr. money market economist Becker Paribas Inc., N.Y.C., 1984; corp. first v.p., money market economist Drexel Burnham Lambert Inc., N.Y.C., 1984-86, mng. dir., chief money market economist, 1986—; pres. Maria Ramirez Capital Cons. Inc. (subs. Hancock Freedom), N.Y.C., 1990—; pres. and CEO Maria Fiorini Ramirez, Inc., 1992—; bd. dirs. various orgns. Roman Catholic. Home: PO Box 992 Belcher Ln Far Hills NJ 07931 Office: 1 World Fin Ctr 200 Liberty St Fl 4 New York NY 10281-1003

RAMIREZ, MARIO EFRAIN, physician; b. Roma, Tex., Apr. 3, 1926; s. Efren M. and Carmen (Hinojosa) R.; m. Sarah B. Aycock, Nov. 25, 1949; children: Mario, Patricia Ann, Norman Michael, Jaime Eduardo, Roberto Luis. Student, U. Tex., 1942-45; M.D., U. Tenn., 1948. Diplomate: Am. Bd. Family Physicians. Intern Shreveport (La.) Charity Hosp., 1949; resident; practice medicine specializing in family practice Shreveport (La.) Charity Hosp., Roma, 1950-75, Rio Grande City, Tex., 1975-93; assoc. medical dir. Blue Cross, Blue Shield of Tex., Rio Grande City, 1993—; owner, adminstr. Ramirez Meml. Hosp., Roma, 1958-75; assoc. med. dir. South Tex. Blue Cross/Blue Shield of Tex., 1994—. County judge, Starr County, Rio Grande City, 1969-78; chmn. South Tex. Devel. Council, 1975-76; chmn. Tri-County Community Action Council, 1971-78; mem. coordinated bd. Tex. Colls. and Univs., 1979-85; mem. devel. bd. U. Tex., 1986—; presdl. appointee bd. regents Uniformed Services U. Health Scis., 1985-92; bd. regents U. Tex. System, 1989—, vice chmn. bd., 1991-92. Served to capt. USAF, 1955-57. Recipient Spl. citation Surgeon Gen., 1967, Disting. Alumnus award U. Tex., 1975, 78, Achievement award Lab World, 1978, Presdl. citation U. Tex., 1979, Outstanding Alumnus award U. Tenn., 1991; named Family Dr. of Yr., Good Housekeeping mag. and Am. Acad. Family Physicians, 1978; honoree Founder's Day for contbns. to higher edn. U. Tex. Pan Am., 1989. Fellow Am. Acad. Family Physicians; mem. AMA (vice chmn. com. health care of poor 1971-75, Benjamin Rush Bicentennial award 1976, Council of Med. Services 1985-94), Tex. Med. Assn. (chmn. com. health care of poor 1971, Disting. Service award 1972, pres. 1979-80), Tex. Acad. Family Physicians (v.p. 1973, pres. 1975, Distinguished Service award 1967, Outstanding Leadership award 1975-76, v.p. Valley chpt. 1960-61, pres. 1961-62), Hidalgo-Starr Counties Med. Soc. (pres. 1964). Clubs: Lions, K.C. Rotary, Alhambra. Address: 212 Pineridge Mcallen TX 78503

RAMIREZ, MICHAEL P., editorial cartoonist; b. Tokyo; s. Ireneo Edward and Fumiko Maria R. Syndicated cartoonist Copley News Svc., 1986-90; cartoonist The Comml. Appeal, Memphis, 1990—. Recipient Pulitzer Prize for editorial cartooning, 1994. Office: The Commercial Appeal 495 Union Ave Memphis TN 38103*

RAMIREZ, RAUL ANTHONY, lawyer, former federal judge; b. L.A., Mar. 8, 1944; s. Joseph M. and Jessie A. R.; m. Sharon Anne Bush, May 26, 1979; children: John, Suzanne, Joseph, Christina. BA, Los Angeles State Coll. 1967; LLB, JD (Am. Jurisprudence award criminal law 1970), U. Pacific, 1970. Bar: Calif. 1971. Law clk. to presiding judge Sacramento Superior Ct., 1970-71; pvt. practice law Sacramento, 1971-77; judge Sacramento Mcpl. Ct., 1977-80; U.S. dist. judge U.S. Dist. Ct. (ea. dist.) Calif., Sacramento, 1980-90; sr. ptnr. Orrick, Herrington & Sutcliffe, Sacramento, 1990—. Recipient various service awards, certs. commendation. Mem. Calif. Judges Assn. Office: Orrick Herrington & Sutcliffe 400 Capitol Mall Sacramento CA 95814-4407

RAMIREZ, RICARDO, bishop; b. Bay City, Tex., Sept. 12, 1936; s. Natividad and Maria (Espinosa) R. B.A., U. St. Thomas, Houston, 1959; M.A., U. Detroit, 1968; Diploma in Pastoral Studies, East Asian Pastoral Inst., Manila, 1973-74. Ordained priest Roman Catholic Ch., 1966; missionary Basilian Fathers, Mex., 1968-76; exec. v.p. Mexican Am. Cultural Ctr., San Antonio, 1976-81; aux. bishop Archdiocese of San Antonio, 1981-82; bishop Diocese of Las Cruces, N.M., 1982—; cons. U.S. Bishop's Com. on Liturgy, from 1981; advisor U.S. Bishop's Com. on Hispanic Affairs, from 1981. Author: Fiesta, Worship and Family, 1981. Mem. N.Am. Acad. on Liturgy, Hispanic Liturgical Inst., Padres Asociada Derechos Religiosos Educativos y Sociales. Lodges: K.C. Holy Order Knights of Holy Sepulcher. Office: Diocese of Las Cruces 1280 Med Park Dr Las Cruces NM 88005-3239*

RAMIREZ, TINA, artistic director; b. Caracas, Venezuela; d. Gloria Maria Cestero and Jose Ramirez Gaonita. Studied dance with Lola Bravo, Alexandra Danilova, Anna Sokolow. Toured with Federico Rey Dance Co.; founder, artistic dir. Ballet Hispanico, N.Y.C., 1970—; panelist NEA, N.Y. Sate Coun. on Arts; mem. advisory panel N.Y.C. Dept. Cultural Affairs; bd. dirs. Dance Theater Workshop. Appearances include (Broadway) Kismet, Lute Song, (TV) Man of La Mancha. Recipient Arts and Culture Honor award Mayor of N.Y.C., 1983, Ethnic New Yorker award N.Y.C., 1986, Gov.'s Arts award N.Y. State Gov. Mario Cuomo, 1987; honoree Nat. Puerto Rican Forum, Hispanic Inst. for Performing Arts. Office: Ballet Hispanico 167 W 89th St New York NY 10024*

RAMIREZ-RIVERA, JOSE, physician; b. Mayaguez, P.R., June 26, 1929; S. Jesus Ramirez and Nieves Rivera; m. Leila Suner, May 14, 1971; children: Federico, Steven, Sally, Juliette, Natasha, Leila. B.A., Johns Hopkins U., 1949; M.D., Yale U., 1953. Diplomate Am. Bd. Internal Medicine. Intern U. Md. Hosp., 1953-54; resident in medicine Univ. Hosp., Balt., 1954-55, fellow in hematology, 1958-59, resident, 1959; staff physician VA Hosp., Balt., 1960-67; assoc. chief of staff VA Hosp., 1962-68; asst. in medicine Johns Hopkins U., 1960-67, instr. in medicine, 1967-68; asst. prof. medicine U. Md., 1961-68; assoc. prof. Duke U., Durham, N.C., 1968-70; dir. med. edn. and clin. investigation Western Region P.R., 1970-80; chief medicine Mayaguez (P.R.) Med. Ctr., 1971-82; prof. medicine U. P.R., San Juan, 1974—, dir. univ. med. svcs. Med. Sci. Campus, 1982-86; dir. Rincon Rural Health Project, 1975-82, assoc. chief staff for edn. VA Med. Ctr., San Juan, 1990-92. Contbr. articles to med. jours. Bd. dirs. Soc. Edn. Suroeste. With USPHS, 1955-57. Fellow ACP (pres. P.R. chpt. 1986-88), Royal Soc. Medicine (London), Coll. Chest Physicians; mem. Am. Fedn. Clin. Rsch., P.R. Lung Assn. (bd. dirs 1975-80), Soc. Autores Puertorrigueños, PEN Club. Roman Catholic. Office: Dept Vets Affairs Med Ctr One Veterans Pla San Juan PR 00927-5800

RAMIS, HAROLD ALLEN, film director, screenwriter, actor; b. Chgo., Nov. 21, 1944; s. Nathan and Ruth (Cokee) R.; m. Erica Mann; children: Violet, Julian, Daniel. B.A., Washington U., St. Louis, 1966; ArtsD (hon.), Washington U., 1993. Assoc. editor Playboy mag., 1968-70; actor, writer Second City, Chgo., 1970-73, Nat. Lampoon Radio Hour, Lampoon Show, 1974-75; actor, head writer SCTV, 1977-78; producer, head writer Rodney Dangerfield Show, ABC-TV, 1982. Screenwriter (with Douglas Kenny and Chris Miller) National Lampoon's Animal House, 1978, (with Janice Allen, Len Blum and Dan Goldberg) Meatballs, 1979, (with Douglas Kenny, Brian Doyle-Murray) Caddyshack, 1980, (with Len Blum and Dan Goldberg) Stripes, 1981, (with Dan Aykroyd) Ghostbusters, 1984, (with Brian Doyle-Murray) Club Paradise, 1986; co-screenwriter (with Peter Torokvei) Armed and Dangerous, 1986; writer (with Dan Akroyd) Ghostbusters II, 1989; dir. feature films: Caddyshack, 1980, National Lampoon's Vacation, 1983, Club Paradise, 1986; exec. producer, co-screenwriter (with Rodney Dangerfield) Back to School, 1986; film appearances include: Stripes, 1981, Ghostbusters, 1984, Baby Boom, 1987, Stealing Home, 1988, Ghostbusters II, 1989; dir., exec. producer, co-writer Groundhog Day, 1993. Mem. AFTRA, Screen Actors Guild, Writers Guild Am., Dirs. Guild Am. Office: CAA 9830 Wilshire Blvd Beverly Hills CA 90212-1804 also: Ocean Pictures Inc 10202 Washington Blvd Culver City CA 90232-3119

RAMLER, SIEGFRIED, school administrator; b. Vienna, Austria, Oct. 30, 1924; s. Lazar and Eugenia Ramler; m. Piilani Andrietta Ahuna, Jan. 27, 1948; children: David K., Dita L., Laurence K., Malia R. Diplôme supérieur, U. Paris, 1958; MA, U. Hawaii, 1961. Interpreter Internat. Mil. Tribunal, Nuremberg, Germany, 1945-46, chief interpreting br., 1946-49; chair fgn. lang. dept. Punahou Sch., Honolulu, 1951-71, dir. instnl. svcs., 1971-91, dir. Wo Internat. Ctr., 1990—; exec. dir. Found. for Study in Hawaii and abroad, Honolulu, 1969-90. Contbr. articles to profl. publs. Sec., bd. dirs. crown Prince Akihito Scholarship Found., 1989—. Decorated medal Freedom Found., 1958, Order of the Palmes Académiques, French Govt., 1964, Order of the Sacred Treasure, Japanese Govt., 1992, Ordre National du Mérite, French Govt., 1993. Mem. ASCD, Internat./Global Edn. Com. (chair nat. adv. com. 1987-93), Japan-Am. Soc. Hawaii (pres. 1986-87, program chmn. 1975—, Alliance Française of Hawaii (pres. 1961, bd. dirs. 1992—). Avocations: running, travel, swimming. Home: 921 Maunawili Cir Kailua HI 96734 Office: Wo Internat Ctr Punahou Sch 1601 Punahou St Honolulu HI 96822

RAMM, RICHARD W., retail executive; b. Omaha, Oct. 12, 1949; s. Carl H. and Violet (Cartwright) R.; m. Colleen M. McGonical; children: Jessica, Jeffrey. BA in Bus., U. Nebr., 1972. CPA, Nebr. Exec. v.p. Pamida, Inc.,

Omaha. Home: 13416 Seward St Omaha NE 68154-3819 Office: Pamida Inc 8800 F St Omaha NE 68127-1507

RAMMING, MICHAEL ALEXANDER, school system administrator; b. St. Louis, Feb. 4, 1940; s. William Alexander and Emily Louise (Reingruber) R.; m. Susan Ray Oliver, July 9, 1962; children: Michael Murray, Todd Alexander. BS, Centenary Coll., 1963; MA, Washington U., St. Louis, 1968. Cert. adminstr. secondary schs. Mo. Teacher and coach Ladue Sch. Dist., St. Louis, 1963-88, adminstr., 1988—. Vol. Sr. Olympics, St. Louis, 1992, 93. Mem. Nat. Assn. Secondary Sch. Prins., Mo. Assn. Secondary Sch. Prins., Nat. Interscholastic Athletic Adminstrs. Assn., Mo. Interscholastic Athletic Adminstrs. Assn. (25 Yr. Svc. award). Avocations: tennis, walking, travel. Home: 13309 Kings Glen Dr. Town and Country MO 63131 Office: Ladue Horton Watkins High Sch 1201 S Warson Rd Saint Louis MO 63124

RAMO, ROBERTA COOPER, lawyer; b. Denver, Aug. 8, 1942; d. David D. and Martha L. (Rosenblum) Cooper; m. Barry W. Ramo, June 17, 1964. BA magna cum laude, U. Colo., 1964; JD, U. Chgo., 1967. Bar: N.Mex., 1967, Tex. 1971. With N.C. Fund, Durham, N.C., 1967-68; nat. teaching fellow Shaw U., Raleigh, N.C., 1968-70; mem. Sawtelle, Goode, Davidson & Troilo, San Antonio, 1970-72, Rodey, Dickason, Sloan, Akin & Robb, Albuquerque, 1972-74; sole practice law, Albuquerque, 1974-77; dir., shareholder Poole, Kelly & Ramo, Albuquerque, 1977-93; shareholder Modrall, Sperling, Roehl, Harris & Sisk, 1993—; bd. dirs. United N.Mex. Bank of Albuquerque, 1983-88. Bd. dirs., past pres. N.Mex. Symphony Orch., 1977-86; bd. dirs. Albuquerque Community Found., N.Mex. First, 1980-90; trustee Manzano Day Sch., 1975-77; bd. regents U. N.Mex., 1988-94, pres. 1990-93. Recipient Disting. Pub. Svc. award Gov. of N.Mex., 1993. Fellow Am. Bar Found.; mem. Albuquerque Bar Assn. (dir., pres. 1980-81), N.Mex. Bar Assn. (chmn. bus., banking sect. 1979-80, Outstanding Contbr. award 1981, 84), ABA (pres. elect 1994, bd. govs. 1994—, vice chmn. 1981-82, chmn. law practice sect. 1984, ALI/ABA com.), Am. Bar Retirement Assn. (bd. dirs. 1990-94), Am. Judicature Soc. (bd. dirs. 1988-91), Greater Albuquerque C. of C. (bd. dirs. exec. com. 1987-91). Contbr. articles to profl. jours. Address: Modrall Sperling Roehl Harris & Sisk PO Box 2168 Albuquerque NM 87103-2168

RAMO, SIMON, engineering executive; b. Salt Lake City, May 7, 1913; s. Benjamin and Clara (Trestman) R.; m. Virginia Smith, July 25, 1937; children: James Brian, Alan Martin. BS, U. Utah, 1933, DSc (hon.), 1961; PhD, Calif. Inst. Tech., 1936; DEng (hon.), Case Western Res. U., 1960, U. Mich., 1966, Poly. Inst. N.Y., 1971; DSc (hon.), Union Coll., 1963, Worcester Polytechnic Inst., 1968, U. Akron, 1969, Cleve. State U., 1976; LLD (hon.), Carnegie-Mellon U., 1970, U. So. Calif., 1972, Gonzaga U., 1983, Occidental Coll., 1984, Claremont U., 1985. With Gen. Electric Co., 1936-46; v.p. ops. Hughes Aircraft Co., 1946-53; with Ramo-Wooldridge Corp., 1953-58; dir. U.S. Intercontinental ballistic missile program, 1954-58; dir. TRW Inc., 1954-85, exec. v.p., 1958-61, vice chmn. bd., 1961-78, chmn. exec. com., 1969-78, cons., 1978—; pres. The Bunker-Ramo Corp., 1964-66; chmn. bd. TRW-Fujitsu Co., 1980-83; bd. dirs. Arco Power Techs.; vis. prof. mgmt. sci. Calif. Inst. Tech., 1978—; Regents lectr. UCLA, 1981-82, U. Calif. at Santa Cruz, 1978-79; chmn. Center for Study Am. Experience, U. So. Calif., 1978-80; Faculty fellow John F. Kennedy Sch. Govt., Harvard U., 1980-84; mem. White House Energy Research and Devel. Adv. Council, 1973-75; mem. adv. com. on sci. and fgn. affairs U.S. State Dept., 1973-75; chmn. Pres.'s Com. on Sci. and Tech., 1976-77; mem. adv. council to Sec. Commerce, 1976-77, Gen. Atomics Corp., 1988—, Aurora Capital Ptnrs., 1991—, Chartwell Investments, 1992—; co-chmn. Transition Task Force on Sci. and Tech. for Pres.-elect Reagan; mem. roster consultants to adminstr. ERDA, 1976-77; bd. advisors for sci. and tech. Republic of China, 1981-84; chmn. bd. Aetna, Jacobs & Ramo Venture Capital, 1987-90, Allenwood Ventures Inc., 1987—. Author: The Business of Science, 1988, other sci., engring. and mgmt. books. Bd. dirs. L.A. World Affairs Coun. 1973-85, Mus. Ctr. Found., L.A., L.A. Philharm. Assn., 1981-84; life trustee Calif. Inst. Tech., Nat. Symphony Orch. Assn., 1973-83; trustee emeritus Calif. State Univs.; bd. visitors UCLA Sch. Medicine, 1980—; bd. dirs. W.M. Keck Found., 1983—; bd. govs. Performing Arts Coun. Mus. Ctr. L.A., pres., 1976-77. Recipient award IAS, 1956; award Am. Inst. Elec. Engrs., 1959; award Arnold Air Soc., 1960; Am. Acad. Achievement award, 1964; award Am. Iron and Steel Inst., 1968; Disting. Svc. medal Armed Forces Communication and Electronics Assn., 1970; medal of achievement WEMA, 1970; awards U. So. Calif., 1971, 79; Kayan medal Columbia U., 1972; award Am. Cons. Engrs. Coun., 1974; medal Franklin Inst., 1978; award Harvard Bus. Sch. Assn., 1979; award Nat. Medal Sci., 1979; Disting. Alumnus award U. Utah, 1981; UCLA medal, 1982; Presdl. Medal of Freedom, 1983; named to Bus. Hall of Fame, 1984; recipient Aesculapian award UCLA, 1984, Durand medal AAIA, 1984, John Fritz medal, 1986, Henry Townley Heald award Ill. Inst. Tech., 1988, Nat. Engring. award Am. Assn. Engring. Socs., 1988, Franklin-Jefferson medal, 1988, Howard Hughes Meml. award, 1989. Fellow IEEE (Electronic Achievement award 1953, Golden Omega award 1975, Founders medal 1980, Centennial medal 1984), Am. Acad. Arts and Scis.; mem. N.Y. Acad. of Sci., Nat. Acad. Engring. (founder, coun. mem. Bueche award), Nat. Acad. Scis., Am. Phys. Soc., Am. Philos. Soc.; Instit. Advancement Engring., Internat. Acad. Astronautics, Eta Kappa Nu (eminent mem. award 1966), Theta Tau (Hall of Fame laureate). Office: 9200 W Sunset Blvd Ste 801 Los Angeles CA 90069-3603

RAMO, VIRGINIA M. SMITH, civic worker; b. Yonkers, N.Y.; d. Abraham Harold and Freda (Kasnetz) Smith; B.S. in Edn., U. So. Calif., DHL (hon.), 1978; m. Simon Ramo; children—James Brian, Alan Martin. Nat. co-chmn. ann. giving U. So. Calif., 1968-70, vice chmn., trustee, 1971—, co-chmn. bd. councilors Sch. Performing Arts, 1975-76, co-chmn. bd. councillors Schs. Med. and Engring.; vice-chmn. bd. overseers Hebrew Union Coll., 1972-75; bd. dirs. The Muses of Calif. Mus. Sci. and industry, UCLA Affiliates, Estelle Doheny Eye Found., U. So. Calif. Sch. Medicine; adv. council Los Angeles County Heart Assn., chmn. com. to endow Chair in cardiology at U. So. Calif.; vice-chmn., bd. dirs. Friends of Library U. So. Calif.; bd. dirs., nat. pres. Achievement Rewards for Coll. Scientists Found., 1975-77; bd. dirs. Les Dames Los Angeles, Community TV So. Calif.; bd. dirs., v.p. Founders Los Angeles Music Center; v.p. Los Angeles Music Center Opera Assn.; v.p. corp. bd. United Way; v.p. Blue Ribbon-400 Performing Arts Council; chmn. com. to endow chair in gerontology U. So. Calif.; vice chmn. campaign Doheny Eye Inst., 1986. Recipient Service award Friends of Libraries, 1974, Nat. Community Service award Alpha Epsilon Phi, 1975, Disting. Service award Am. Heart Assn. 1978, Service award U. So. Calif., Spl. award U. So. Calif. Music Alumni Assn., 1979, Life Achievement award Mannequins of Los Angeles Assistance League, 1979, Woman of Yr. award PanHellenic Assn., 1981, Disting. Service award U. So. Calif. Sch. Medicine, 1981, U. So. Calif. Town and Gown Recognition award, 1986, Asa V. Call Achievement award U. So. Calif., 1986, Phi Kappa Phi scholarship award U. So. Calif., 1986, Vision award Luminaires of Doheny Eye Inst., 1994. Mem. UCLA Med. Aux., U. So. Calif. Pres.'s Circle, Commerce Assos. U. So. Calif., Cedars of Lebanon Hosp. Women's Guild (dir. 1967-68), Blue Key, Skull and Dagger.

RAMON, DAVID A., consumer products company executive. V.p., chief exec. officer Gillette Holdings Inc., Denver. Office: Gillette Holdings Inc 555 17th St Ste 3300 Denver CO 80202-3933

RAMON, KOHNE K., federal official; b. Pinglap Atoll, Pohnpei, Federated States of Micronesia, Feb. 11, 1950; s. Konral and Melihser (Paul) R.; m. Elsyner Solomon, Aug. 25, 1974; 1 child, James K. BA in Bus. Adminstrn., U. Guam, 1972. Personnel specialist Trust Ter. Govt., Saipan, Northern Mariana Islands, 1972-78; personnel dir. Coll. Micronesia, Pohnpei, 1978-80; spl. svcs. coord. Embassy to U.S.A. Federated States of Micronesia, Washington, 1980-84; dir. dept. personnel Federated State of Micronesia Nat. Govt., Pohnpei, 1984-88, dir. adminstrv. svcs., 1988—. Pres. Pohnpei Pub. Libr., 1985-93; lay min. United Ch. of Christ, Pohnpei, 1988—; traditional title Traditional Hieroschy, Pohnpei, 1986—; chmn. SS Bd. Trustees, Pohnpei, 1986-92. Avocations: fishing, farming. Home: PO Box 1108 Ponape FM 96941 Office: Fed States Micronesia Nat Govt Box PS-35 Ponape FM 96941

RAMOS, J. MARIO, opera director, conductor; b. Volta Redonda, Brazil, June 23, 1956. MusB, Tex. Christian U., 1982; MA, MBA, So. Meth. U., Dallas, 1985. Assoc. producer Motion Graphics, Rio de Janeiro, 1972-74;

gen. dir. Teatro Poeira, Volta Redonda, 1975-77; dir. devel. Pub. Opera Dallas, 1985; gen. mgr. Ft. Worth Opera, 1985-86, gen. dir., 1986-91; gen. dir. Hawaii Opera Theatre, Honolulu, 1991—. Southwestern Petroleum Corp. scholar Tex. Christian U., 1977-78, Walsh scholar, 1977-82. Mem. Opera Am. Office: Hawaii Opera Theatre 987 Waimanu St Honolulu HI 96814-3319

RAMOS, MELVIN JOHN, artist, educator; b. Sacramento, July 24, 1935; s. Clifton John and Agnes (Enos) R.; m. Lolita Alice Helmers, Aug. 14, 1955; children: Bradley, Scot, Rochelle. B.A., Calif. State U.-Sacramento, 1957, M.A., 1958. Tchr. Elk Grove High Sch., (Calif.), 1957-60, Mira Loma High Sch., Sacramento, 1960-66; prof. art Calif. State U.-Hayward, 1966—. Exhibited one man shows, Louis Meisel Gallery, N.Y.C., 1974, 76, 81, 85, 89, Mus. Haus Lange, 1975, Oakland Mus., 1977, Rose Art Mus., 1980, group shows, Whitney Mus., N.Y.C., 1969, 78, 83, Bklyn Mus., 1970, Mus. Modern Art, N.Y.C., 1970; Ludwig Mus. Cologne, 1992, Mus. of Cont. Art La., 1993; represented in permanent collections, San Francisco Mus. Modern Art, Oakland Mus., Indpls. Mus., Mus. Modern Art, N.Y.C., Crystler Mus., Va., Smithsonian Instn., Washington, Guggenheim Mus., N.Y.C., Nat. Gallery, Washington, Kunsthaus, Darmstadt, W.Ger., Whitney Mus. Am. Art; author: Mel Ramos: Watercolors, 1979. Democrat. Roman Catholic. Home: 5941 Ocean View Dr Oakland CA 94618-1842 Office: 25800 Hillary St Hayward CA 94542

RAMOS, ROSE MARY, elementary education educator; b. San Antonio, Aug. 8, 1942; d. Henry Barbosa and Bertha Alice (Cuellar) Gonzalez; m. Jesus Ramos Jr., Sept. 11, 1965; children: Rebecca Anne, Veronica Anne. BS in Elem. Edn., Our Lady of Lake U., San Antonio, 1965; MA in Edn., U. Houston, 1992. Cert. elem. educator, kindergarten, reading specialist, bilingual and ESL. Tchr. San Antonio Ind. Sch. Dist., 1965-89, Ft. Bend County (Tex.) Ind. Sch. Dist., 1989—. Mem. Nat. Space Soc., Tex. State Reading Assn., Tex. Educators of Speakers of Other Langs., Greater Houston Area Reading Assn., San Antonio Conservation Soc., Internat. Reading Assn., Sci. Club (sponsor), Spanish Club (organizer), Ft. Bend I.S.D. Bilingual Advisory Coun. Democrat. Roman Catholic. Avocations: reading, life sciences, arts and crafts, writing, physical fitness. Home: 3614 Belle Grove Ln Sugar Land TX 77479-2257

RAMPEN, LEONARDUS EDUARD, broadcasting company executive; b. Surabaya, Indonesia, Mar. 29, 1928; came to Can., 1952; s. Wilhelmus Christiaan and Julie (Ramakers) R.; m. Sybil Salvin Calverley, Apr. 11, 1954; children—William, Edmund Leveson, Christopher, Hugo, Benjamin. B.A. in Art History, U. Toronto, 1953, M.A. in Art History, 1955. Graphic designer CBC, Toronto, Ont., 1953-61; TV producer current affairs CBC, Toronto, 1961-65, exec. producer TV current affairs, 1965-67, exec. producer TV religious program, 1967-80; dir. TV programming CBC, Montreal, Que., 1980-91; cons. Can. Intefaith Network, Toronto, 1983-85, Nat. Inst. on Mental Retardation, Toronto, 1979—; mem. documentary jury Prix Italia, Bologna, Italy, 1975; mem. bilingual jury Nat. Mag. Awards, Toronto, 1981-83; vice chmn. Prix Anik, Montreal, 1984-85. Recipient Gabriel award for Man Alive; grantee Can. Council, 1971, 81, Nat. Inst. for Mental Retardation, 1985. Mem. IATSE (stewart CBC Toronto, pres. 1957), Art Dirs. Club (exec. mem. 1959), Assn. TV Producers (exec. mem. 1967, pres. 1967). Roman Catholic.

RAMPERSAD, ARNOLD, writer, literature educator; b. Trinidad, W.I., Nov. 13, 1941. BA, Bowling Green State U., MA; MA, Harvard U., PhD. Prof. English Stanford (Calif.) U., 1974-83, Rutgers U., New Brunswick, N.J., 1983-88; Zora Neale Hurston prof. English Columbia U., N.Y.C., 1988-90; Woodrow Wilson prof. literature Princeton (N.J.) U., 1990—. Author: Melville's Israel Potter: A Pilgrimage and Progress, 1969, The Art and Imagination of W.E.B. DuBois, 1976, The Life of Langston Hughes, Vol. I: 1902-41: I, Too, Sing America, 1986 (Nat. Book Critics Cir. award nomination for biography 1986, Anisfield-Wolf Book award in race rels. Cleve. Found. 1987, Clarence L. Holte prize Phelps Stokes Fund 1988), The Life of Langston Hughes, Vol. II: 1941-67: I Dream a world, 1988 (Pulitzer Prize nomination in biography 1989, Am. Book award Before Columbus Found. 1990), (with Arthur Ashe) Days of Grace: A Memoir, 1993; co-editor: Slavery and the Literary Imagination, 1989, The Collected Poems of Langston Hughes, 1994; editor: Richard Wright's Works (2 vols.), 1991, Richard Wright: A Collection of Critical Essays, 1994. Recipient Literary Lion award N.Y. Pub. Libr., 1993. Office: Princeton Univ Dept of English McCosh Hall Princeton NJ 08544-1016*

RAMSAY, DONALD ALLAN, physical chemist; b. London, July 11, 1922; s. Norman and Thirza Elizabeth (Beckley) R.; m. Nancy Brayshaw, June 8, 1946; children: Shirley Margaret, Wendy Kathleen, Catharine Jean, Linda Mary. BA, Cambridge (Eng.) U., 1943, MA, 1947, PhD, 1947, ScD, 1976; D honoris causa, U. Reims, France, 1969; Filosofie hedersdoktor, U Stockholm, Sweden, 1982. With divs. chemistry Nat. Research Council Can., Ottawa, Ont., 1947-49; with divs. physics Nat. Research Council Can., 1949-75; with Herzberg Inst. Astrophysics, 1975-87, sr. research officer, 1961-68, prin. research officer, 1968-87; vis. prof. U. Minn., 1964, U. Orsay, 1966, U. Stockholm, 1967, 71, 74, U. Calif., Irvine, 1970, U. Sao Paulo, 1972, 78, U. Bologna, 1973, U. Western Australia, 1976, Australian Nat. U., 1976, Tex. Christian U., 1988, U. Wuppertal, Germany, 1988, U. Canterbury, Christchurch, New Zealand, 1991, U. Ulm, Germany, 1992; guest worker Steacie Inst. Molecular Scis. Editor: (with J. Hinze) Selected Works of Robert S. Mulliken, 1975; contbr. numerous articles on molecular spectra and molecular structure to profl. jours. Recipient commemorative medal for 125th anniversary Confederation Can., 1992, Alexander von Humboldt Rsch. award, 1993-95; decorated Queen Elizabeth Silver Jubilee medal. Fellow Royal Soc. London, Royal Soc. Can. (hon. treas. 1976-79, 88-91, Centennial medal 1982), Am. Phys. Soc., Chem. Inst. Can. (Chem. Inst. Can. medal 1992). Mem. United Ch. of Canada (organist 1954—). Club: Leander (Henley-on-Thames, Eng.). Home: 1578 Drake Ave, Ottawa, ON Canada K1G 0L8 Office: Nat Research Council, 100 Sussex Dr, Ottawa, ON Canada K1A 0R6

RAMSAY, ERNEST CANADAY, lawyer; b. Statesboro, Ga., Feb. 14, 1939; s. Ernest Francis and Miriam Carolyn (Canaday) R.; m. Barbara Ann Gazaway, Dec. 18, 1960; children: Elizabeth Kennerly, Lydia Katherine. Student, Ga. Tech., 1957; AB, Mercer U., Macon, Ga., 1961; JD, Mercer U., 1963. Bar: Ga. 1964. Assoc. Bryan, Carter, Ansley & Smith, Atlanta, 1963-65; ptnr. Carley & Ramsay, Decatur, Ga., 1965-69; assoc. Hansell & Post, Atlanta, 1969-74, mng. ptnr. 1974-89; mng. ptnr. Ramsay & Calloway, Atlanta, 1989—; bd. dirs. Attys.' Title Guaranty Fund, Inc., Cartersville, Ga. 1974-93. Mem. Atlanta Bar Assn. (real property law sect. 1979—), State Bar Ga. (real property law sect. chmn. 1971-72), Decatur-DeKalb Bar Assn. (real estate sect. chmn. 1973-74)., Ravinia Club (Atlanta), DeKalb Hist. Soc. (pres. 1973-75). Office: Ramsay & Calloway 56 Perimeter Ctr E Ste 400 Atlanta GA 30346

RAMSAY, GUSTAVUS REMAK, actor; b. Balt., Feb. 2, 1937; s. John Breckinridge and Caroline V. (Remak) R. BA, Princeton U., 1958. Appeared in plays Hang Down Your Head and Die, 1964, Half A Sixpence, 1965, Lovely Ladies, Kind Gentlemen, Sheep on the Runway, 1970, On the Town, 1971, The Real Inspector Hound, After Magritte, 1972, Jumpers, 1974, Private Lives, 1975, Landscape of the Body, Dirty Linen, 1977, The Rear Column, 1978, All's Well That Ends Well, 1978, Every Good Boy Deserves Favor, 1980, Save Grand Central, 1980, The Winslow Boy, 1980-81, The Dining Room, 1982, as St. John Quartermaine in Quartermaine's Terms, 1983— (Obie award), Woman in Mind, 1988, The Devil's Disciple, 1988, Love Letters, 1989, Prin, 1990, Nick & Nora, 1991, St. Joan, 1993, The Moliere Comedies, 1995; appeared in movies The Tiger Makes Out, The Stepford Wives, The Great Gatsby, The Front, Class, Simon, The House on Carroll Street, Mr. and Mrs. Bridge, Shadows and Fog, King of the Hill; TV movies The Dining Room, Heartbreak House, Kennedy, Liberty, Concealed Enemies, Dream House, Mellon, Lincoln and Seward, 1992, Dead Ahead: The Exxon Valdez Disaster. With U.S. Army, 1959-62. Democrat. Presbyterian. Home: 115 Central Park W New York NY 10023-4153

RAMSAY, LOUIS LAFAYETTE, JR., lawyer, banker; b. Fordyce, Ark., Oct. 11, 1918; s. Louis Lafayette and Carmile (Jones) R.; m. Joy Bond, Oct. 3, 1945; children—Joy Blankenship, Richard Louis. JD, U. Ark., 1947; LLD (hon.), U. Ark., Fayetteville, 1988, U. Ark., Pine Bluff, 1992. Bar:

Ark. 1947, U.S. Dist. Ct. Ark. 1947, U.S. Ct. Appeals (8th cir.) 1948, U.S. Supreme Ct. 1952. Ptnr. Ramsay, Bridgforth, Harrelson & Starling and predecessor firm Ramsay, Cox, Lile, Bridgforth, Gilbert, Harrelson & Starling, Pine Bluff, Ark., 1948—; pres. Simmons First Nat. Bank, Pine Bluff, Ark., 1970-78; chmn. bd., chief exec. officer Simmons First Nat. Bank, 1978-83; chmn. bd. dirs. Blue Cross-Blue Shield of Ark.; chmn. exec. com. Simmons First Nat. Corp., Pine Bluff. Chmn. Ark. Sesquicentennial Celebration Commn., Little Rock, 1985-86; mem. bd. Jefferson County Indsl. Found.; mem. official bd. First United Methodist Ch. With USAF, 1942-45, maj. Res., 1945-49. Recipient Disting. Alumnus award U. Ark., 1982, Outstanding Lawyer award Ark. Bar Found., 1966, 87. Mem. ABA (mem. spl. com. on presdl. inability and vice presdl. vacancy 1966), Ark. Bar Assn. (pres. 1963-64), Ark. Bar Found. (pres. 1960-61, Joint Bar Assn.-Bar Found. Outstanding Lawyer award 1966, Lawyer Citizen award 1987), Ark. Bankers Assn. (pres. 1980-81), Pine Bluff C. of C. (pres. 1968), Rotary (pres. Pine Bluff 1954-55). Methodist. Lodge: Rotary (Pine Bluff) (pres. 1956-57). Office: Ramsay Bridgforth Harrelson & Starling PO Box 8509 Pine Bluff AR 71611-8509

RAMSAY, WILLIAM CHARLES, writer; b. N.Y.C., Nov. 6, 1930; s. Claude Barnett and Myrtle Marie (Scott) R.; m. Charlotte Appleton Kidder, June 10, 1988; children from previous marriages: Alice, John, Carol Ramsay Serrano, David. BA in English Lit., U. Colo., 1952; MA in Physics, UCLA, 1957, PhD in Physics, 1962. NFS postdoctoral fellow U. Calif., San Diego, 1962-64; asst. prof. U. Calif., Santa Barbara, 1964-67; tech. mgr. Systems Assocs., Inc., Long Beach, Calif., 1967-72; sr. environ. economist U.S. AEC, Bethesda, Md., 1972-75; tech. adviser U.S. Nuclear Regulatory Agy., Washington, 1975-76; sr. fellow Resources for the Future, Washington, 1976-83, Ctr. for Strategic and Internat. Studies, Washington, 1985-86; sr. staff officer NAS, Washington, 1985-86; freelance writer, editor, publ. Washington, 1986—; cons. Vols. in Tech. Assistance, Arlington, Va., 1987-90, Internat. Resources Group, Washington, 1991. Author: Unpaid Costs of Electrical Energy, 1979, Bicenergy and Economic Development, 1985; co-author: Managing the Environment, 1972, Energy in America's Future, 1979; editor, pub. Fiction-Online (electronic lit. jour.). Buenos Aires Conventional fellow, 1952, NSF fellow, 1962; NATO scholar, 1960, 62. Mem. Am. Phys. Soc., Am. Astron. Soc., Internat. Assn. Energy Economists, Washington Ind. Writers, Writers' Ctr. (bd. dirs.). Avocations: piano, musical composition. Home and Office: 2930 Foxhall Rd NW Washington DC 20016-3429

RAMSBY, MARK DELIVAN, lighting designer and consultant; b. Portland, Oreg., Nov. 20, 1947; s. Marshall Delivan and Verna Pansy (Culver) R.; divorced; children: Aaron Delivan, Venessa Mercedes. Student, Portland (Oreg.) State U., 1966-67. With C.E.D., Portland, 1970-75; minority ptnr. The Light Source, Portland, 1975-78, pres., 1978-87; prin. Illume Lighting Design, Portland, 1987-90; ptnr. Ramsby, Dupuy & Seats, Inc., Portland, 1990-91; dir. lighting design PAE Cons. Engrs., Inc., Portland, 1991—; pvt. practice cons. Portland, 1979—. Recipient Top 10 Outstanding Achievement award Metalux Lighting, 1981-85, 100% award, 1985, Edwin F. Guth award of merit, 1990, Edison award of excellence, 1990, Edwin F. Guth award of excellence, 1993, 94. Mem. Illuminating Engring. Soc. Am. (sec.-treas. Oreg. sect. 1978-79, Oreg. Section and Regional award 1989, 90, 93, 94, Lighting Design awards), Internat. Assn. Lighting Designers. Republican. Lutheran. Avocations: lighting design, historical restoration, flyfishing, downhill skiing. Office: PAE Cons Engrs 808 SW 3rd Ave Ste 300 Portland OR 97204-2426

RAMSEIER, ROGER I., aerospace and defense products company executive; b. 1936. V.p. GenCorp., Fairlawn, Ohio; with Aerojet subs. GenCorp., La Jolla, Calif., 1959—, pres., 1988—. Office: Aerojet-Gen Corp 10300 N Torrey Pines Rd La Jolla CA 92037

RAMSEY, BILL (WILLIAM MCCREERY), singer, actor, composer-lyricist, television executive; b. Cin., Apr. 17, 1931; s. William McCreery II and Olivia (James) R.; m. Erica Moeckli, Dec. 14, 1962 (div. Feb. 1982); 1 son, Joachim.; m. Petra Bock, Aug. 3, 1983. Student, Yale U., 1949-51, Goethe U., Frankfurt/Main, Germany, 1955, 57, U. Cin., 1956-57. guest prof. vocal jazz and presentation in pop and jazz program Hamburg U. Music and Drama, Hamburg, 1983-86. Partime profl. singer, 1949; appeared on Horace Heidt show, Hollywood, Calif., 1951, Eddie Fisher tour, Europe, 1953, Raymond Burr tour, Europe and North Africa, 1954, series jazz concerts, Germany and Am., 1953-55; 1st American to appear at German Jazz Festival, 1955, 1st American jazz vocalist after war to tour Yugoslavia, 1955, 1st TV portrait, Frankfurt/Main, 1955, 1st films in Baden-Baden, Munich, Hamburg, 1955; full-time profl. jazz and pop vocalist, 1957—, numerous recs.; actor numerous films, TV shows; songwriting, disc jockey work with Radio Luxembourg, Europawelle Saar, Radio Salzburg; 1st American jazz singer to tour Poland after war, also appearances Polish Jazz Festival, 1957, 67, Czek Jazz Festival, 1966; 1st pop record hit German version of Purple People Eater, 1958; program dir. Televco AG, Zurich/Gockhausen, Swiss TV and Film Prodn. Co., 1968-72, rec. artist for Polydor, Electrolia, Columbia, Cornet, Warner Bros., Stockfish, Ariola, Dino, Bear Family; in addition to singing, TV moderator on all three German Programs as well as in Austria since 1970. With USAF, 1951-55. Recipient top positions in various jazz polls. Mem. German Authors and Composers Soc. Address: Elbchaussee 118, D-22763 Hamburg Germany

RAMSEY, CHARLES EUGENE, sociologist, educator; b. Paragon, Ind., Apr. 24, 1923; s. Sarcefield Dodson and Stella (Goss) R.; m. Alberta Mae Jordan, July 19, 1943; children—James D., Charles W., Jane E., Suzanne. B.S., Ind. State Tchrs. Coll., 1947; M.S., U. Wis., 1950, Ph.D., 1952. Faculty U. Wis., 1951-52, U. Minn., 1952-54, Cornell U., 1954-62, Colo. State U., 1962-65; prof. sociology U. Minn., Mpls., 1965-77; chmn. dept. sociology U. Tex., Arlington, 1977-83; vis. prof. Inter-Am. Instn. Agrl. Sci., Costa Rica, 1961, Exptl. Sta., U. P.R., 1961-62; research cons. to various univs., agys. Author: (with Lowry Nelson and Cooley Verner) Community Structure and Change, 1960, (with David Gottlieb) The American Adolescent, 1965, Understanding the Deprived Child, S.R.A, 1967, Problems of Youth, 1967, (with D.J. McCarty) The School Managers: Power and Conflict in American Public Education, 1971, (with William A. Stacey) Social Statistics, 1992; also articles. Mem. Am. Sociol. Assn., Rural Sociol. Soc., Sigma Xi. Developed and tested theory of variations in community power structure, types of sch. bds., and roles of sch. supt., developed method of comparative measurement of level of living for different countries. Home: 1102 De Pauw Dr Arlington TX 76012-5339 Office: U Tex Dept Sociology Arlington TX

RAMSEY, CLAUDE SWANSON, JR., former industrial executive; b. Asheville, N.C., Feb. 6, 1925; s. Claude Swanson and Nell Grace (Hendon) R.; m. Kay Kemp; children: Kay (Mrs. George Saenger), Scott, Steven. B.S. in Textiles, N.C. State U. at Raleigh, 1949; M.S. in Retailing, NYU, 1950. With Am. Enka Corp., N.C., 1950-70; v.p. Am. Enka Corp., 1962-65, exec. v.p., 1965-67, pres., chief exec. officer, 1967-70; also dir., chmn. exec. com.; pres., chief exec. officer, chmn. exec. com. Akzona Inc. (formerly Am. Enka Corp.), 1970-82, chmn. bd., 1972-82, chmn. adv. council, 1983-85; past dir. Wachovia Corp., Akzo N.V., Arnhem, Holland, Amstar Corp. Trustee U. N.C.-Asheville (formerly Asheville-Biltmore Coll.), 1964-69, N.C. Engring. Found., 1965-69, N.C. Textile Found., 1965-69, Rockefeller U. Council, 1973-84. Served to 1st lt. USAAF, 1943-46. Mem. Union League (N.Y.C.), Biltmore Forest Country Club.

RAMSEY, DAVID SELMER, hospital executive; b. Mpls., Feb. 19, 1931; s. Selmer A. and Esther D. (Dahl) R.; m. Elinor Corfield, Aug. 15, 1953; children—Scott, Stewart, Thomas. B.S., U. Mich., 1953, M.S. in Microbiology, 1954, M.H.A. 1962. Research asst. Detroit Inst. Cancer Research, 1954-60; asst. administr. Harper Hosp., Detroit, 1962-68; assoc. administr. Harper Hosp., 1968-72; exec. v.p. Iowa Meth. Med. Ctr., Des Moines, 1972-83; pres. Iowa Meth. Med. Ctr., 1983—. chmn. bd. Des Moines Pastoral Counseling, 1981-84; bd. dirs. Arts and Recreation Council Greater Des Moines, 1983-86; group chmn. United Way Campaign, Des Moines, 1984. Fellow Am. Coll. Hosp. Administrs.; mem. Am. Hosp. Assn. (ho. of dels. 1982—), Iowa Hosp. Assn. (bd. dirs. 1974—). Republican. Presbyterian. Clubs: Des Moines, Wakonda. Lodge: Rotary. Avocations: golf; tennis; photography. Home: 2825 Caulder Ave Des Moines IA 50321-2634 Office: Iowa Meth Med Ctr 1200 Pleasant St Des Moines IA 50309-1406

RAMSEY, DOUGLAS KENNETH, television anchor, journalist; b. Norman, Okla., June 15, 1951; s. Edwin P. and Madeline (Willoquet) R.; m. Ann Polya, Dec. 30, 1977 (div. 1985). BA in Polit. Sci., UCLA, 1970; MA in European Studies, Coll. Europe, Bruges, 1971; MA in Internat. Affairs, Johns Hopkins U., 1972. Freelance corr. Washington Post, Brussels, 1973-74; writer The Economist, London, 1975; corr. The Economist, Tokyo, 1976-79, NBC News, N.Y.C., 1985-87; bus. editor Newsweek, N.Y.C., 1979-82; exec. prodr. Bus. Times on ESPN, N.Y.C., 1982-85; mng. editor. Fin. News Network, N.Y.C., 1987-91; anchor CNBC, Ft. Lee, N.J., 1991-95; pres. Global Media Assocs., 1995—. Author: (non-fiction) The Corporate Warriors; contbr. columns to N.Y. Times, L.A. Times, Fin. Times. Mem. Authors Guild. Office: CNBC The Money Wheel 2200 Fletcher Ave Fort Lee NJ 07024

RAMSEY, FORREST G., computer company executive. BS, U.S. Naval Acad., 1952; MBA, U. Colo., Boulder, 1965. Chmn. Am. Sys. Corp., Chantilly, Va., 1976—. with USN, 1952-57. Office: Am Systems Corp 14200 Park Meadow Dr Chantilly VA 22021*

RAMSEY, FORREST GLADSTONE, JR., engineering company executive; b. Wichita, Kans., Oct. 25, 1930; s. Forrest Gladstone and Anastasia Ruth (Linot) R.; m. Gwendolyn Moreton, June 22, 1953 (div. Jan. 1982); children: Deborah Jenkins, Rebecca Johnson, Susan Klopp, Diane Hayes, Forrest G. III, Mark, Kenneth; m. Carmen Bergen, Apr. 30, 1988. BS in Engring., U.S. Naval Acad., 1952; postgrad., Wichita State U., 1957-58, U. Colo., 1958-64. Commd. ensign USN, 1952, res., 1957; planner, engr. Boeing Corp., Wichita, Kans., 1957-58; engr., logistician Martin-Marietta, Denver, 1959-65; div. dir. Computer Scis., Washington, 1965-73; program dir. Systems Cons., Washington, 1973-76; CEO Am. Systems Corp., Washington, 1976-92, also chmn., bd. dirs. Mem. Profl. Svcs. Coun. (vice chmn. 1990), Naval Submarine League (bd. dirs. 1982-90). Roman Catholic. Home: 8 Hidden Valleys Palmyra VA 22963

RAMSEY, FRANK ALLEN, veterinarian, retired army officer; b. Rocksprings, Tex., May 1, 1929; s. Reynolds Allen and June (Burdette) R.; m. Lucette C. Reboul, Jan. 1958; children: Randal R., Ramsay A.; m. 2d, Mary Lou Cain, June 1991. D.V.M., Tex. A & M U., 1954; grad., U.S. Army Command and Gen. Staff Coll., 1965, U.S. Army War Coll., 1972. Commd. 1st. lt. U.S. Army Vet. Corps, 1955, advanced through grades to brig. gen., 1980; chief vet. service Ft. Leonard Wood, Mo., 1958-61; acad. vet. U.S. Mil. Acad., West Point, N.Y., 1962-64; vet. staff officer U.S. Army Combat Devel. Command Med. Service, Ft. Sam Houston, Tex., 1965-67; asst. chief profl. programming and planning br. Office Surgeon Gen., Washington, 1967-68, chief profl. programming and planning br., 1968-71, chief food inspection policy office, 1972-73, sr. vet. staff officer, 1973-77; asst. chief of staff Vet. Service, 7th Med. Command, Army Europe and 7th Army, Heidelberg, W. Ger., 1977-80; asst. for vet. services to surgeon gen. and chief U.S. Army Vet. Corps, Hdqrs. Dept. Army, Washington, 1980-85; ret., 1985. Decorated Army Commendation medal, Legion of Merit with oak leaf cluster, D.S.M. Mem. AVMA, Assn. Fed. Veterinarians, Assn. Mil. Surgeons U.S., Assn. Equine Practitioners, Am. Assn. Food Hygiene Veterinarians, Conf. Pub. Health Veterinarians, Tex. Vet. Med. Assn. Presbyterian. Lodge: Masons (32 degree). Home: 8 El Norte Cir Uvalde TX 78801

RAMSEY, HENRY, JR., university dean-official, lawyer, retired judge; b. Florence, S.C., Jan. 22, 1934; s. Henry Ramsey and Mary Ann Brunson; reared by Chales Arthur and Nellie Tillman; m. Evelyn Yvonne Lewis, June 11, 1961 (div. Sept. 1967); children: Charles, Githaiga, Robert, Ismail; m. Eleanor Mason Ramsey, Sept. 7, 1969; children: Yetunde, Abeni. Student, Howard U.; BA, U. Calif., Riverside, 1960; LLB, U. Calif. 1963; student Inst. Edn. Mgmt., Harvard U., 1992. Bar: Calif., 1964, U.S. Supreme Ct., 1967. Dep. dist. atty. Contra Costa County, Calif., 1964-65; pvt. practice Ramsey & Rosenthal, Richmond, Calif., 1965-71; prof. law U. Calif., Berkeley, 1971-80; judge Superior Court County of Alameda State Calif., Oakland, 1980-90; dean Sch. Law, Howard U., Washington, 1990—, v.p. for legal affairs, acting gen. counsel, 1994—; vis. prof. law U. Tex., Austin, 1977, U. Colo., Boulder, 1977-78, Am. Indian Law Ctr. U. N.Mex., 1980; mem., pres. Coun. Legal Edn. Opportunity, Washington, 1987-93; chair Law Sch. Admission Coun.-Bar Passage Rate Study Group, 1990-93. Mem. City Coun. Berkeley, 1973-77, Criminal Justice Planning Bd., County of Alameda, 1973-76; trustee City of Berkeley Retire. Bd., 1973-74, Fibreboard Asbestos Compensation Trust, 1994—; bd. dirs. Redevel. Agy., Berkeley, 1971-73. With USAF, 1951-55. Recipient Jefferson Jurist award Calif. Assoc. Black Lawyers, 1986, Disting. Alumnus award U. Calif., 1987, Disting. Svc. award Wiley Manuel Law Found., 1987. Mem. ABA (mem. sect. legal edn. and admissions to bar 1982—, chair 1991-92, mem. standards com. 1992—), Nat. Bar Assn., Nat. Ctr. State Courts (mem. commn. trial court performance stds. 1987—, Dist. Svc. award 1990), Am. Law Inst., Am. Judicature Soc., Calif. Judges Assn., Cosmos Club, Federal City Club, Alpha Phi Alpha. Democrat. Avocations: cooking, reading, gardening, travel. Office: Howard U Sch of Law 2900 Van Ness St NW Washington DC 20008-1106

RAMSEY, IRA CLAYTON, pipeline company executive; b. Quitman, Ga., May 13, 1931; s. James Redding and Ruth Frances (Treadaway) R.; m. Marianne Vinzant, Dec. 23, 1962; children: Clayton Hamilton, Robin Leigh. BBA, U. Ga., Atlanta, 1954; LLB, Atlanta Law Sch., 1950; postgrad., U. Tex., 1968, U. Pitts., 1973. With Plantation Pipe Line Co., Atlanta, 1948—, asst. sec., 1967-70, treas., contr., 1970-90, v.p. fin., 1990—. Trustee Ga. Found. for Ind. Colls. With U.S. Army Res. 1954-56. Mem. Fin. Execs. Inst. Baptist. Home: 780 Wesley Oak Rd NW Atlanta GA 30328-4738 Office: Plantation Pipe Line Co 945 E Paces Ferry Rd NE Fl 20 Atlanta GA 30326-1125

RAMSEY, JACKSON EUGENE, management educator; b. Cin., Dec. 20, 1938; s. Leonard Pershing and Edna Willa (Blakeman) R.; m. Inez Mae Linn, Apr. 22, 1961; children: John Earl, James Leonard. BS in Metall. Engring., U. Cin., 1961; MBA, SUNY-Buffalo, 1969, PhD, 1975. Registered profl. engr., Va., Ohio. Welding engr. Gen. Electric Co., Cin., 1961-62, Westinghouse-Bettis Lab., Pitts., 1962-66; prodn. control mgr. Columbus-McKinnon Corp., Buffalo, 1966-71; asst. prof. mgmt. SUNY, Buffalo, 1971-73; prof. mgmt. James Madison U., Harrisonburg, Va., 1973—; provost; cons. in field. Chmn. Harrisonburg Reps., 1978-86, vice chmn., 1974-78; vice chmn. 6th Dist. Rep. Com., 1984-94. Served with USMCR, 1956-62. Named Outstanding Young Scholar, Xerox Corp., 1976. Mem. Acad. of Mgmt., Am. Inst. for Decision Scis., Inst. of Mgmt. Sci., Am. Soc. for Metals, Nat. Soc. Profl. Engrs. Republican. Baptist. Author: R D Strategic Decision Criteria, 1986; Handbook for Professional Managers, 1985; Budgeting Basics, 1985; Library Planning and Budgeting, 1986. Contbr. articles to profl. jours. Home: 282 Franklin St Harrisonburg VA 22801-4019 Office: James Madison U Coll Intergrated Sci & Tech Harrisonburg VA 22807

RAMSEY, JAMES P., marine engineering consultant, computer services company consultant; b. 1942. Pres., CEO Mar, Inc., Rockville, Md., 1971—. Office: Mar Inc 6110 Executive Blvd 410 Rockville MD 20852*

RAMSEY, JAROLD WILLIAM, English language educator, author; b. Bend, Oreg., Sept. 1, 1937; s. Augustus S. and Wilma E. (Mendenhall) R.; m. Dorothy Ann Quinn, Aug. 16, 1959; children: Kate, Sophia, John. B.A. with honors, U. Oreg., 1959; Ph. D., U. Wash., 1966. Acting instr. U. Wash., Seattle, 1963-65; asst. prof. English U. Rochester, (N.Y.), 1965-70, assoc. prof., 1970-81; prof. U. Rochester (N.Y.), 1981—, dir. undergrad. rsch., 1990—; vis. prof. English U. Victoria, B.C., Can., 1974, 75-76; dir. NEH summer seminars on Indian lit., 1985, 88. Author: The Space Between Us, 1970, Love in an Earthquake, 1973 (Lillian Fairchild award 1973), Demographia, 1982, Reading the Fire, 1983, Hand-shadows, 1989, (play) Coyote Goes Upriver, premier 1985, (cantata) (with Samuel Adler) The Lodge of Shadows, premiere 1988; editor: Coyote Was Going There, 1977, Nehalem Tillamook Tales, 1990, The Stories We Tell: Oregon Folk Literature (with Suzi Jones), 1994. Recipient Don Walker award Western Am. Lit., 1979, Borestone Mount Found. Best Poems award, 1972, 75, 76; Helen Bullis prize, 1984, Poetry prize Quar. Rev., 1989; Alumni Achievement award U. Oreg. Alumni Assn. 1990; Nat. Endowment Arts writing grantee, 1974, 76; Ingram Merrill Found. writing grantee, 1976. Mem. MLA (chair com. on lits. and langs. of Am. 1991-92), Assn. Study Am. Indian Lit. (pres. 1981), Am. Folklore Soc., Phi Beta Kappa. Democrat. Home: 519 Wellington Ave Rochester NY 14619-1828 Office: U Rochester English Dept Rochester NY 14619

RAMSEY, JERRY VIRGIL, radio broadcaster, educator, financial planner; b. Tacoma, July 24, 1940; s. Virgil Emory and Winifred Victoria (Carothers) R.; m. Elaine Sigrid Perdue, June 24, 1967; 1 child, Jason Perdue. BA in Elem. Edn., U. Puget Sound, 1967; MEd in Tchr. Tng. and Curriculum Devel., U. Wash., 1971; PhD in Econ. Geography, Columbia Pacific U., 1995. Tchr. Tacoma Pub. Schs., 1967-95; fin. planner Primerica Corp., Tacoma, 1986-90, Gig Harbor Fin. Svcs., 1986—; Waddell & Reed, Inc., Tacoma, 1990-93; N.Am. Mgmt., 1993—; real estate investor, CEO Ramsey Properties, Gig Harbor, Wash., 1970—; radio broadcaster KGHP/KJUN, The Country Gold Network/KMAS, 1990—; lectr. Pacific Luth. U., Tacoma, 1972-86. Precinct committeeman Pierce County Rep. Com., Tacoma, 1968-78; mem. steering com. Peninsula Neighborhood Assn., Gig Harbor, Wash., 1991-92. With USAF, 1959-62. Recipient Golden Acorn award PTA, 1975, Meritorious Teaching award Nat. Coun. Geog. Edn., 1978, achievement award Rep. Nat. Com., 1985; grantee U.S. Office Edn. 1971. Mem. NEA (life), Knife and Fork Club (pres. 1983), Kiwanis (pres. Tacoma 1976), Phi Delta Kappa. Methodist. Avocation: real estate investing, management and education. Office: Ramsey Properties Gig Harbor Fin Svcs PO Box 1311 Gig Harbor WA 98335-3311

RAMSEY, JOHN ARTHUR, lawyer; b. San Diego, Apr. 1, 1942; s. Wilbert Lewis and Lillian (Anderson) R.; m. Nikki Ann Ramsey, Feb. 9, 1943; children: John William, Bret Anderson, Heather Nichole. AB, San Diego State U., 1965; JD, Calif. Western Sch. Law, 1969. Bar: Colo. 1969, Tex. 1978. Assoc., Henry, Cockrell, Quinn & Creighton, 1969-72; atty. Texaco Inc., 1972-80, asst. to pres. Texaco U.S.A., 1980-81, asst. to div. v.p., Houston, 1981-82, div. atty., Denver, 1982-88; ptnr. Holland & Hart, 1989—. Bd. dirs. Selective Service, Englewood, Colo., 1972-76; chmn. council Bethany Lutheran Ch., Englewood, 1976. Mem. ABA (chmn. oil, natural gas exploration and prodn. com. sect. natural resource law 1983—). Republican. Editor-in-chief: Calif. Western Law Rev., 1969. Office: Holland & Hart 555 17th St, Ste 2900 Denver CO 80202-3941

RAMSEY, JOHN HANSBERRY, executive search firm executive, investment banker; b. Scranton, Pa., May 4, 1941; s. Robert Martin and Elizabeth Mary (Durrick) R.; children: Mark Joseph, Craig Andrew, Alison Dianne. B.S., Tufts U., 1963; M.B.A. with distinction, Harvard U., 1968. Commd. 2d lt. USAF, 1963, advanced through grades to maj., 1971, resigned, 1972; sr. v.p., treas., chief fin. officer Union Commerce Corp./Bank, Cleve., 1972-81; sr. v.p. devel. Am. Savs. and Loan Assn. of Fla., 1982-84; co-founder, pres. Mark Stanley & Co., Miami, Fla., 1983—; treas., dir. Union Commerce Leasing Corp., 1974-75; treas. Union Capital Mgmt. Corp., 1974-75. Participant Leadership Cleve., 1980-81; co-fin. chmn. Cuyahoga County George Bush for Pres. Campaign, 1980; trustee mem. Beacon Council. Decorated Bronze Star, AF Commendation Medal. Mem. Fin. Execs. Inst., Greater Miami C. of C. (trustee), Venture Coun. Forum, Planning Forum, Harvard Club of N.Y., Harvard Bus. Sch. So. Fla. Republican. Office: Mark Stanley & Co PO Box 149071 Coral Gables FL 33114

RAMSEY, LISTON BRYAN, state legislator; b. Marshall, N.C., Feb. 26, 1919; s. John Morgan and Della Lee (Bryan) R.; m. Florence McDevitt; 1 childm Martha Louise Ramsey Geouge. Student, Mar Hill Coll., 1936-38. Mem. N.C. Ho. of Reps., Raleigh, 1961—, speaker of House, 1981-88; exec. com. So. Legis. Conf., 1981-88; chmn. 11th congl. dist. Dem. Exec. Com., 1972, 74, 76, 80; del. Dem. Nat. Conv., 1968; mem. Govtl. Ops. Commn., 1973-76, co-chmn., 1981-88; co-chmn. Legis. Svcs. Commn., 1971, 73-74, 75-76, 81-88, Legis. Rsch. Commn., 1975-76, 81-88, Joint Com. on Separation Powers, 1982; mem. Adv. Budget Commn., 1973-80, 91-92, Blue Ribbon Study Commn. on Transp., 1979-80. County chmn. Dem. Exec. Com., 1958-60, 62; bd. alderman Town of Marshall, 1949-61. Served as sgt. U.S. Army, 1944-46. Recipient Roy A. Taylor Service award, 1978, N.C. Pub. Service award, 1985, Friend Edn. award N.C. Assn. Edn., 1985; Liston B. Ramsey Regional Activity Ctr., Western Carolina U. dedicated and named after him, 1986. Mem. Am. Legion, VFW, N.C. AFL-CIO (hon.). Baptist. Lodges: Elks, Masons. Office: NC Ho of Reps State Legislative Bldg Raleigh NC 27601-1096

RAMSEY, LLOYD BRINKLEY, retired savings and loan executive, retired army officer; b. Somerset, Ky., May 29, 1918; s. William Harold and Mary Ella (Barnett) R.; m. Glenda Burton, Feb. 22, 1941; children: Lloyd Ann (Mrs. Kyle D. Wallace), Larry Burton, Judi Carol (Mrs. David E. Derr). A.B., U.Ky., 1940; postgrad., Yale U., 1946, Command and Gen. Staff Coll., Ft. Leavenworth, Kans., 1949-50, U.S. Army War Coll., Carlisle Barracks, Pa., 1953-54, Harvard, 1961. Commd. 2d lt. U.S. Army, 1940, advanced through grades to maj. gen., 1968; bn. comdr. 7th Inf., 3d Inf. Div., 1944-45; instr. Inf. Sch., Ft. Benning, Ga., 1946-49; assigned Office G-2 Dept. Army Gen. Staff, 1950-53; sec. joint staff UN Far East Command, 1954-57; comdg. officer 1st Inf. Brigade, 1957-58; with Office Chief Legis. Liaison, Dept. Army Gen. Staff, 1960-63, Office Asst. Chief Staff Force Devel., 1963-64; dep. chief information, 1966-67; div. comdr. Am. 23d Div., Vietnam, 1969-70; provost marshall gen. Army, Washington, 1970-74; ret. Army, 1974; chmn. bd. McLean Savs. & Loan Assn., Va., 1974-88. Decorated D.S.M. with oak leaf cluster, Silver Star medal with two oak leaf clusters, Legion of Merit with oak leaf cluster, D.F.C., Bronze Star medal with three oak leaf clusters, Air medal with 16 oak leaf clusters, Army Commendation medal with oak leaf cluster, Purple Heart with four oak leaf clusters, Combat Inf. badge; mem. Order Brit. Empire; Croix de Guerre France; Vietnamese Nat. Order; Vietnamese Armed Forces Honor medal; Vietnamese Gallantry Cross with palm. Mem. Sigma Chi, Omicron Delta Kappa. Baptist. Home: 6451 Dryden Dr Mc Lean VA 22101-4625 *Accept a man for what he is, not for what you want him to be.*

RAMSEY, MARJORIE ELIZABETH, early childhood education educator; b. Kimball, Minn., May 25, 1921; d. William Emil and Emma Edith (Ryti) Leppa; children: Rebecca, Cynthia. B.S., St. Cloud State Coll., 1955, M.S., 1957; Ed.D. (Ford Found. fellow), George Peabody Coll., 1961. Tchr., prin., vis. lectr. Minn., 1940-57; asst. prof. St. Cloud State Coll., Minn., 1957-59; supr. edn. Montgomery County, Md., 1961-64; research assoc. George Peabody Coll., Nashville, 1964-68; supr. Vanderbilt U. Nashville, 1964-69; assoc. prof. early childhood edn. Kent (Ohio) State U., 1969-73, prof., 1973-79, dean student pers. Coll. Edn., 1973-79; head div. edn., dir. tchr. edn. Ga. Southwestern Coll., Americus, 1979-89, Ga. Adv. Coun. Edn. 1983-89. Author: Music: A Way of Life for the Young Child, 1978, 4th edit., 1991, Kindergarten: Programs and Practices, 1980; contbr. articles to profl. jours. Mem. AAUW, Nat. Assn. Edn. Young Children, Assn. Childhood Edn. Internat. (publs. com. 1980-86), Mid-South Writers Assn., Delta Kappa Gamma, Kappa Delta Pi, Phi Delta Kappa. Home: 242 S Reese St Memphis TN 38111-4517

RAMSEY, MARK, school system administrator. Supt. Osseo Area Schs. # 279, Maple Grove, Minn. State finalist Nat. Supt. of Yr., 1993. Office: Osseo Area Schs # 279 11200 93rd Ave N Osseo MN 55369-3669

RAMSEY, NORMAN F., physicist, educator; b. Washington, Aug. 27, 1915; s. Norman F. and Minna (Bauer) R.; m. Elinor Jameson, June 3, 1940 (dec. Dec. 1983); children: Margaret, Patricia, Janet, Winifred; m. Ellie Welch, May 11, 1985. AB, Columbia U., 1935; BA, Cambridge (Eng.) U., 1937, MA, 1941, DSc, 1954; PhD, Columbia U., 1940; MA (hon.), Harvard U., 1947; DSc (hon.), Case Western Res. U., 1968, Middlebury Coll., 1969, Oxford (Eng.) U., 1973; DCL (hon.), Oxford (Eng.) U., 1990; DSc (hon.), Rockefeller U., 1986, U. Chgo., 1989, U. Sussex, 1990, U. Houston, 1991, Carleton Coll., 1991, Lake Forest Coll., 1992, U. Mich., 1993, Phila. Coll. Pharmacy & Sci., 1995. Kellett fellow Columbia U., 1935-37, Tyndall fellow, 1938-39; Carnegie fellow Carnegie Inst. Washington, 1939-40; assoc. U. Ill., 1940-42; asst. prof. Columbia U., 1942-46; assoc. MIT Radiation Lab., 1940-43; cons. Nat. Def. Research Com., 1940-45; expert cons. sec. of war, 1942-45; group leader, asso. div. head Los Alamos Lab., 1943-45; assoc. prof. Columbia U., 1945-47; head physics dept. Brookhaven Nat. Lab. of AEC, 1946-47; assoc. prof. physics Harvard U., 1947-50, prof. physics, 1950-66, Higgins prof. physics, 1966—; sr. fellow Harvard Soc. of Fellows, 1970—; Eastman prof. Oxford U., 1973-74; Luce prof. cosmology Mt. Holyoke Coll., 1982-83; prof. U. Va., 1983-84; dir. Harvard Nuclear Lab.,

1948-50, 52-53, Varian Assos., 1963-66; mem. Air Forces Sci. Adv. Com., 1947-54; sci. adviser NATO, 1958-59; mem. Dept. Def. Panel Atomic Energy; exec. com. Cambridge Electron Accelerator and gen. adv. com. AEC. Author: Nuclear Moments and Statistics, 1953, Nuclear Two Body Problems, 1953, Molecular Beams, 1956, 85, Quick Calculus, 1965; contbr.: articles Phys. Rev.; other sci. jours. on nuclear physics, molecular beam experiments, radar, nuclear magnetic moments, radiofrequency spectroscopy, masers, nucleon scattering. Trustee Asso. Univs., Inc., Brookhaven Nat. Lab., Carnegie Endowment Internat. Peace, 1962-85, Rockefeller U., 1977-90; pres. Univs. Research Assocs., Inc., 1966-72, 73-81, pres. emeritus, 1981—. Recipient Presdl. Order of Merit for radar devel. work, 1947, E.O. Lawrence and AEC, 1960, Columbia award for excellence in sci., 1980, medal of honor IEEE, 1983, Rabi prize, 1985, Monte Ferst award, 1985, Compton medal, 1985, Rumford premium, 1985, Oersted medal, 1988, Nat. medal of Sci., 1988, Nobel prize for Physics, 1989, Pupin medal Columbia Engring. Sch. Alumni Assn., 1992, Sci. for Peace prize, 1992, Einstein medal, 1993, Vannevar Bush award, 1995; Guggenheim fellow Oxford U., 1954-55. Fellow Am. Acad. Sci., Am. Phys. Soc. (coun. 1956-60, pres. 1978-79, Davisson-Germer prize 1974); mem. NAS, French Acad. Sci., Am. Philos. Assn., AAAS (chmn. physics sect. 1977), Am. Inst. Physics (chmn. bd. govs. 1980-87), Phi Beta Kappa (senator 1979-88, v.p. 1982-85, pres. 1985-88), Sigma Xi. Home: 24 Monmouth Ct Brookline MA 02146-5634 Office: Harvard U Lyman Physics Lab Cambridge MA 02138

RAMSEY, PETER CHRISTIE, bank executive; b. N.Y.C., Oct. 1, 1942; s. Norman Carnegie and Rosalie Amelia (Christie) R.; m. Maryalice Ives, Nov. 15, 1969. BA, Brown U., 1964. Mgmt. trainee Irving Trust Co., N.Y.C., 1965-67; account exec. Hayden Stone, N.Y.C., 1967-72; regional sales mgr. Autex, Inc., Chgo., 1972-78; v.p. Chem. Bank, N.Y.C., 1978—. Mem. coun. of chairs YMCA Greater N.Y., N.Y.C., 1987-90; chmn. bd. mgrs. McBurney YMCA, N.Y.C., 1980-92. Mem. Brown U. Club. Home: 345 E 80th St New York NY 10021-0644

RAMSEY, ROBERT LEE, judge, lawyer; b. Glen Allen, Va., Jan. 9, 1929; s. Hubert Smith and Louise Estelle (Ennis) R.; m. Dorothea Catherine Cherubini, Mar. 28, 1958 (div. 1972); children: Craig John, Matthew Lee, Scott Garrett; m. Lynn Marie Giubbini, July 15, 1978. BA, Hofstra U., 1954; LLB, Union U., 1957, JD, 1968; MPA, SUNY-Albany, 1966; LLM, So. Meth. U., 1969. Bar: N.Y. 1958, Tex. 1970, Calif. 1991. Assoc. Kouray & Kouray, Schenectady, 1957-60; spl. agt. FBI, U.S. Dept. Justice, Washington, 1960-64; asst. atty. gen. State of N.Y., Albany, 1964-65; ptnr. Kalteux & Ramsey, Schenectady, 1965-68; chief asst. dist. atty. Schenectady County, N.Y., 1965-68; asst. gen. counsel Internat. Air Transport Assn., Montreal, Que., Can., 1969-70; sr. atty. Air Transport Assn. Am., Washington, 1970; sole practice Dallas, 1970-76; adminstrv. law judge U.S. Dept. Labor, San Francisco, 1976-77; adminstrv. law judge U.S. Dept. Labor, Washington, 1977-81, chmn., chief adminstrv. appeals judge Benefits Rev. Bd., 1981-88; adminstrv. law judge U.S. Dept. Labor, San Francisco, 1988-89; ptnr. Mullen & Filippi, San Francisco, 1989-91; adminstrv. law Judge Calif. Pub. Utilities Commn., San Francisco, 1991; mem. adj. faculty So. Meth. U. Sch. Law, 1970-75;. Served with USMC, 1946-48, 50-52. Mem. ABA, State Bar Tex., State Bar Calif., Fed. Adminstrv. Law Judges Conf. Republican. Presbyterian. Home: 4725 Fairway Dr Rohnert Park CA 94928-1304 Office: Calif Pub Utilities Commn 505 Van Ness Ave San Francisco CA 94102

RAMSEY, RUSSELL WILCOX, national security affairs educator; b. Sandusky, Ohio, May 29, 1935; s. Russell Archibald and Louise (Wilcox) R.; m. Linda Stevens, Apr. 12, 1958 (div. 1976); children: Lyndall Ellen, Sally Ramsey Price, Elizabeth Ramsey Brady; m. Roberta Smith, Sept. 4, 1977; 1 child, Russell Rober. BS, U.S. Mil. Acad., 1957; MA, U. So. Miss., 1963; PhD, U. Fla., 1970. Commd. 2d lt. U.S. Army, 1957, advance through grades to maj., resigned, 1969; rsch. assoc. U. Fla. Ctr. for Latin Am. Studies, Gainesville, 1969-70, adj. prof., 1974-79; prin. Mountain Top Sch., Gainesville, 1970-72, Lincoln Vocat. Ctr., Gainesville, 1972-74, Alternative Sch., Gainesville, 1974-79; dir. Gainesville Job Corps Ctr., Gainesville, 1979-81, Turner Job Corps Ctr., Albany, Ga., 1981-84; author, cons. Albany, 1984-87; prof. nat. security affairs Air command and Staff Coll., Maxwell AFB, Ala., 1987-92; disting. prof. Sch. of the Ams., Ft. Benning, Ga., 1992—; elected commr. City of Gainesville, 1973-76; adj. prof. U.S. Army Cen. Fla. Benning, Ga., 1964-65, Nova. U., Ft. Lauderdale, Fla., 1974-80, Cen. Fla. Community Coll., Ocala, 1976-78, Albany (Ga.) State Coll., 1985-87, Troy State U., 1988—, Auburn U., Montgomery, 1989-92, U. Ala., Maxwell AFB, 1990-92; cons. White House, 1970, Superior Ct. Dougherty County, Ga., 1986. Author: Peasant Revolution, 1967, Zarpazo, the Bandit, 1977, Civil Military Relations in Colombia, 1978, Soldiers and Guerrillas, 1982, A Lady, A Champion, 1985, A Lady, A Healer, 1986, God's Joyful Runner, The Biography of Eric H. Liddell, 1987, A Lady, A Peacemaker, 1988, Readings in Latin America Security Issues, 1989, 10 Soviet Sports Stars, 1990, On Law and Country, 1992; contbr. 300 articles and book revs. to profl. jours. Chmn. Action Conf., U. Fla., 1968, Citizen Adv. Bd. for Housing, Gainesville, 1970-73; founder, chmn. Alachua County Juvenile Coun., Gainesville, 1971-79; tenor soloist Montgomery Civic Chorale, 1991, Albany Chorale, 1992—; commd. lay preacher Presbyn. ch., 1994. Lt. col. USAR, 1980-88. Decorated Bronze Star, Air medal, 6 other medals; NEH fellow, 1978; Nat. Record Holder men's age group 55-59 U.S. Masters Swimming. Mem. Am. Assn. Sch. Adminstrs., Res. Officers Assn., Kiwanis, Jaycees (Nat. Fitness Leader award 1988), Phi Alpha Theta, Phi Delta Theta. Home: 1808 Dawson Rd Albany GA 31707-3304 Office: Sch of th Ams Fort Benning GA 31905

RAMSEY, STEPHEN DOUGLAS, lawyer; b. Oklahoma City, Okla., May 10, 1947; s. Oliver F. and Gladys O'Neil (Smith) R.; m. Abigail Havens, June 11, 1977 (div. 1983); 1 child, Andrew Havens; m. Ann Jones, Nov. 4, 1990. AB, Princeton U., 1969; JD, U. Tex., 1978. Assoc. Coffee, Goldston & Bradshaw, Austin, Tex., 1972-77; atty. U.S. Dept. Justice, Washington, 1978-79, asst. chief pollution control sect., land and nat. resourses div., 1979-80, chief environ. enforcement sect., 1980-85; ptnr. Sidley & Austin, 1985-90; v.p. corp. environ. programs GE, 1990—. Author: Superfund Handbook, 1985. Mem. com. to nominate alumni trustees Princeton U., (N.J.), 1977-80; pub. weigher Travis County, Austin, Tex., 1772-74; bd. dirs. Clean Sites, Inc., 1991—. Recipient Atty. Gen. Disting. Svc. award Dept. Justice, 1983. Mem. ABA (nat. resources and adminstrv. law sects., chmn. environ. values subcom.), Tex. Bar Assn., D.C. Bar Assn. Democrat. Baptist.

RAMSEY, V. BRUCE, electronics executive; b. 1933. With Teledyne, Lewisburg, Tenn., 1964-87; pres Avex Electronics, Inc., Huntsville, Ala., 1987—. Office: Avex Electronics Inc 4807 Bradford Blvd NW Huntsville AL 35805

RAMSEY, WILLIAM C., ambassador; b. Pontiac, Mich., Sept. 13, 1943; m. Lorna R. B.A., Mich. State Univ., M.A.; M.A., Stanford Univ. With Fgn. Svc., 1970—; asst. comml. charge d'affaires Kinshasa, Zaire, 1971-72; commerce attache Abidjan, Ivory Coast, 1973-75; with Office of Fuels & Energy, Bur. of Econ. & Bus. Affairs Dept. State, 1976; resources officer U.S. Mission to the Commn. of European Communities, Brussels, Belgium, 1982-83; dep. chief then chief econ. counselor U.S. Liaison Office & U.S. Embassy, Riyadh, Saudi Arabia, 1983-85; dir. office of energy-producing country affairs Bur. of Econ. and Bus. Affairs, 1986-88, dep. asst. sec. energy, resources and food policy; U.S. amb. to the Congo Brazzaville with USAR. Office: Am Embassy Brazzaville US Dept of State Washington DC 20521-2090

RAMSEY, WILLIAM EDWARD, retired naval officer, space systems executive; b. San Diego, Sept. 7, 1931; s. Paul Hubert and Isabelle (Turton) R.; m. Peggy Scott Booth, Oct. 23, 1954; children—Timothy Scott, William Blake, Christopher Booth. B.S., U.S. Naval Acad., 1953. Commd. ensign U.S. Navy, 1953, advanced through grades to vice adm., 1985; comdg. officer USS Pensacola, Little Creek, Va., 1972-73; instr. Naval War Coll., Newport, R.I., 1973-75; comdg. officer in USS Dwight D. Eisenhower, Norfolk, Va., 1975-79; comdr. Carrier Group One, Coronado, Calif., 1979-81; dir. Navy space systems div. Dept. Navy, Washington, 1981-85; deputy comdr.-in-chief U.S. Space Command, Peterson AFB, Colo., 1985-89; ret. U.S. Space Command, 1989; v.p. dir. corp. bus. devel. div. CTA, Inc., Rockville, Md., 1989—; also dir. corp. bus. devel. Decorated Bronze star, Air medal (11), Navy Commendation medal (3), Legion of Merit (2), Def. Disting. Svc. medal.

Fellow Assn. Naval Aviation (trustee), Daedelian Soc., Soc. Exptl. Test Pilots; mem. Am. Inst. Aeros. and Astronautics, Tailhook Soc., Nat. Sec. Indsl. Assn., Armed Forces Communications and Elect. Assn. Episcopalian. Club: Nat. Space (bd. govs. 1983—). Avocations: golf; tennis. Home: 7332 Pea Neck Rd Saint Michaels MD 21663-2712 Office: CTA Inc Space Systems Dv Rockville MD 20852

RAMSEY, WILLIAM RAY, association executive; b. Minerva, Ohio, Aug. 25, 1926; s. Carl Andrew and Alwilda Pauline (Foss) R.; m. Betty Jane Hawkins, Dec. 2, 1950 (dec. Dec. 1975); children: Thomas, Kevin (dec.), Mary Joanne, Robert, Matthew; m. Linda Rae Foss, May 14, 1977. B.S., Mt. Union Coll., 1948; postgrad., Kent State U., 1948; M.H.A., Washington U., St. Louis, 1950; postgrad. in health systems mgmt. Harvard Bus. Sch., 1974. Exec. sec. King County Med. Soc., Seattle, 1953-61; field rep. AMA, Chgo., 1961-64; asst. dir. div. field service AMA, 1964-68; exec. dir. Am. Soc. Internal Medicine, San Francisco, 1968-78; exec. v.p. Am. Soc. Internal Medicine, Washington, 1978-85; ret., 1985. Served with USAAF, 1944; with USAF, 1950-53. Mem. Am. Assn. Med. Soc. Execs. (dir. 1978-81). Home: 8294 Old Olympic Hwy Sequim WA 98382-8855

RAMSEYER, J. MARK, law educator; b. 1954. BA, Goshen Coll., 1976; AM, Mich. U., 1978; JD, Harvard U., 1982. Bar: Ill. 1983. Law clk. to Hon. S. Breyer U.S. Ct. Appeals (1st cir.), Boston, 1982-83; assoc. Sidley & Austin, Chgo., 1983-85; acting prof. UCLA, 1986-89, prof., 1989—. Fulbright fellow U. Tokyo, 1985-86, Japan Soc. Promotion Sci. fellow U. Tokyo, 1988. Mem. Am. Econ. Assn., Japan-Am. Soc. Legal Studies. Office: UCLA Sch Law 405 Hilgard Ave Los Angeles CA 90024-1722

RAMSEYER, LORETTA LYNNE, lawyer; b. L.A., Aug. 10, 1946; d. Dean Melvin and Doris Elaine (Crofoot) Krebs. Diplome, U. Dijon, France, 1965; BA, Grinnell Coll., 1967; JD, UCLA, L.A., 1977. Bar: Calif. 1977, U.S. Dist. Ct. (cen. dist.) Calif. 1977, U.S. Ct. Appeals (9th cir.) 1979, U.S. Dist. Ct. (ea. dist.) Calif. 1981, U.S. Dist. Ct. (so. dist.) Calif. 1982, U.S. Dist. Ct. (no. dists.) Calif. 1984. Law clk. to Robert L. Ordin, bankruptcy judge, 1976; assoc. Sulmeyer, Kupetz, Baumann & Rothman, L.A., 1977-79; sr. counsel, team leader Bank of Am. N.T. and S.A., L.A., 1979—; mem. editorial bd. San Joaquin Sch. Law, Fresno, Calif., 1990—. Recipient cert. of achievement YWCA, 1990. Mem. ABA (legis. subcom. bus. bankruptcy sect., judge negotiation competition nat. finals 1990), Calif. Bar Assn. (uniform comml. code com. environ. law sect.), Los Angeles County Bar Assn. (comml. law com. comml. law and bankruptcy sect.), Fin. Lawyers Conf. L.A.*. Office: Bank of Am NT-SA 555 S Flower St Bldg 800 Los Angeles CA 90071-2309

RAMSEY-GOLDMAN, ROSALIND, physician; b. N.Y.C., Mar. 22, 1954; d. Abraham L. and Miriam (Colen) Goldman; m. Glenn Ramsey, June 29, 1975; children: Ethan Ramsey, Caitlin Ramsey. BA, Case Western Res. U., 1975, MD, 1978; MPH, U. Pitts., 1988, DPH, 1992. Med. resident U. Rochester (N.Y.), 1978-81; chief resident Rochester Gen. Hosp., 1981-82; staff physician Univ. Health Svc., Rochester, 1982-83; rheumatology fellow U. Pitts. 1983-86, instr. medicine, 1986-87, asst. prof., 1987-91, co-dir. Lupus Treatment and Diagnostic Ctr., 1987-91; asst. prof. medicine Northwestern U., Chgo., 1991—; dir. Chgo. Lupus Registry, Northwestern U., Chgo., 1991—. Contbr. rsch. articles to profl. jours. Recipient Finkelstein award Hershey (Pa.) Med. Ctr., 1986. Fellow Am. Coll. Rheumatology; mem. Am. Coll. Physicians, Soc. for Epidemiologic Rsch., Ctrl. Soc. Clin. Rsch. Office: Northwestern U Ward 3-315 303 E Chicago Ave Chicago IL 60611

RAMSIER, PAUL, composer, psychotherapist; b. Louisville, Ky., Sept. 23, 1927; s. Paul and Lucie (Herrmann) R. PhD., N.Y.U., 1972; MSW, SUNY, Stony Brook, 1976. Composer N.Y.C., 1950—; psychotherapist in pvt. practice, 1977—; adj. prof. music N.Y.U., 1970—. Composer numerous musical compositions, including Divertimento Concertante on a Theme of Couperin, 1965, Road to Hamelin, 1978, Eusebius Revisited, 1980, Silent Movie, 1985, Zoo of Dreams, 1994. Huntington Hartford fellow, 1960, MacDowell fellow, 1963, Yaddo fellow, 1970; NEA grantee, 1975; recipient Disting. Alumnus award U. Louisville, 1983, Composer award Internat. Soc. Bassists, 1995. Mem. ASCAP. Home and Office: 210 Riverside Dr New York NY 10025-6802

RAMSTAD, JIM, congressman, lawyer; b. Jamestown, N.D., May 6, 1946; s. Marvin Joseph and Della Mae (Fode) R. BA, U. Minn., 1968; JD with honors, George Washington U., 1973. Bar: N.D. 1973, D.C. 1973, U.S. Supreme Ct. 1976, Minn., 1979. Adminstrv. asst. to speaker Minn. Ho. Reps., 1969; spl. asst. to Congressman Tom Kleppe, 1970; pvt. practice law, Jamestown, 1973, Washington, 1974-1978, Mpls., 1978-90; mem. Minn. Senate, 1981-90, asst. minority leader, 1983-87; mem. 102nd-103rd Congresses from 3rd Minn. dist., 1990—; adj. prof. Am. U., Washington, 1975-78. Bd. dirs. Children's Heart Fund, Lake Country Food Bank. Served as 1st lt. U.S. Army Res. 1968-74. Mem. Minn. Bar Assn., D.C. Bar Assn., N.D. Bar Assn., Hennepin County Bar Assn., U. Minn. Alumni Assn. (nat. dir.), Am. Legion, Wayzata C. of C., TwinWest C. of C., U. Minn. Alumni Club (past pres. Washington), Lions, Phi Beta Kappa, Phi Delta Theta. Republican. Office: 103 Cannon House Office Bldg Washington DC 20515

RAN, SHULAMIT, composer; b. Tel Aviv, Oct. 21, 1949; came to U.S., 1963; m. Abraham Lotan, 1986. Studied composition with, Paul Ben-Haim, Norman Dello, Joio, Ralph Shapey; student, Mannes Coll. Music, N.Y.C., 1963-67. With dept. music U. Chgo., 1973—; prof. music; composer-in-residence Chgo. Symphony Orch., 1990—, Lyric Opera of Chgo., 1994—. Compositions include 10 Children's Scenes, 1967, Structures, 1968, 7 Japanese Love Poems, 1968, Hatzvi Israel Eulogy, 1969, O the Chimneys, 1969, Concert Piece for piano and orchestra, 1970, 3 Fantasy Pieces for Cello and Piano, 1972, Ensembles for 17, 1975, Double Vision, 1976, Hyperbolae for Piano, 1976, For an Actor: Monologue for Clarinet, 1978, Apprehensions, 1979, Private Game, 1979, Fantasy-Variations for Cello, 1980, Excursions for violin, cello, piano, 1980, A Prayer, 1982, Verticals for piano, 1982, String Quartet No. 1, 1984, (for woodwind quintet) Concerto da Camera I, 1985, Amichai Songs, 1985, Concerto for Orchestra, 1986, (for clarinet, string quartet and piano) Concerto da Camera II, 1987, East Wind, 1987, String Quartet No. 2, 1988-89, Symphony, 1989-90, Mirage, 1990, Inscriptions for solo violin, 1991, Chicago Skyline for brass and percussion, 1991, Legends for Orch., 1992-93, Invocation, 1994; commd. pieces include for Am. Composers Orch., Phila. Orch., Chgo. Symphony, Chamber Soc. of Lincoln Ctr., Mendelssohn String Quartet, Da Capo Chamber Players, Sta. WFMT; composer, and soloist for 1st performances Capriccio, 1963, Symphonic Poem, 1967, Concert Piece, 1971. Recipient Acad. Inst. Arts and Letters award, 1989, Pulitzer prize for music, 1991, Friedheim award for orchestral music Kennedy Ctr., 1992; Guggenheim fellow, 1977, 90. Office: U Chgo Dept Music 1010 E 59th St Chicago IL 60637-1404

RANADIVE, PRAKASH KAMLAKANT, government official, diplomat; b. Bombay, India, Jan. 24, 1940; came to U.S., 1959; s. Kamalakant and Sumitra Ranadive; m. Ujwal Deshmukh, May 21, 1967; children: Rahul, Vrushali. BCE, NYU, 1965; MS in Ops. Rsch., Columbia U., 1969. Various sr. positions Internat. Civil Svc. Commn. UN, N.Y.C., 1959-88, exec. sec. Internat. Civil Svc. Commn., 1988—; liaison with reps. of mem. states to UN Gen. Assembly and sr. ofcls. of other internat. orgns. Avocations: reading, exercising. Office: Internat Civil Svc Commn UN 2 UN Plz Rm 1060 New York NY 10017

RANCOURT, JAMES DANIEL, optical engineer. BA in Physics, Bowdoin Coll., 1963; MS in Physics, Carnegie Tech., 1965; PhD in Optical Scis., U. Ariz., 1974. Engr. Itek Corp., Lexington, Mass., 1965-69; rsch. assoc. U. Ariz., Tucson, 1969-74; engr. OCLI, Santa Rosa, Calif., 1970—. Author: Optical Thin Films Users Handbook, 1987; 12 patents in field. Office: OCLI 2789 N Point Pkwy Santa Rosa CA 95407

RAND, ALBERT, computer systems company executive; b. 1927. BS, MIT, 1950. With Gen. Electric Co., Lynn, Mass., 1956-60; assoc. Dynamics Rsch. Corp., Wilmington, Mass., 1960—, now CEO. Office: Dynamics Research Corp 50-60 Concord St Wilmington MA 01887*

RAND, CALVIN GORDON, arts and education producer and consultant; b. Buffalo, May 15, 1929; s. George Franklin and Isabel (Williams) R.; m. Patricia Clemens Andrew, Aug. 18, 1951; children—Robin, Melissa, Jennifer, Lucinda, Elizabeth. B.A., Princeton U., 1951; M.A., Columbia U., 1954; Dr of Letters (hon.), York U., Can., 1984. Head history dept. Riverdale Sch., N.Y.C., 1955-60; lectr. philosophy SUNY-Buffalo, 1961-68, acting dir. cultural affairs, 1968-71; founder, pres. The Niagara Inst., Niagara-on-the-Lake, Can., 1971-79; pres. Am. Acad. in Rome, N.Y.C., 1980-84; intl. producer, theatre and film cons., N.Y.C., 1985-90; founding chmn., dir. Shaw Festival Theatre, Niagara-on-the-Lake, 1964-78,, bd. govs., 1979; trustee Playwrights Horizons Theatre, N.Y.C., 1982-92; bd. dirs. Niagara Inst.; pres. Arts in Edn. Inst.; mem. N.Y. State Coun. on Arts, 1978-82, Arts Coun. Western N.Y., 1987-93; chmn. World Ency. Contemporary Theater; chmn. arts coun. SUNY, Buffalo, 1987—, adj. prof. theater, 1988—. Contbr. articles to profl. jours. Bd. dirs. Burchfield Art Ctr., Buffalo, 1991—, Irish Classical Theater, 1993—; trustee Albright-Knox Gallery, Buffalo, 1976-80, 84-88, 90-94. Recipient spl. citation Ont. Arts Coun., 1976, Fellowship Fund award Niagara Inst., 1980, Centennial Arts award Nichols Sch., 1992; named Man of Yr., Coun. World Affairs, 1976, Buffalo Courier Express, 1976, Arts Patron of Yr., Western N.Y. Arts Coun. and C. of C., 1989; Vanier Coll. fellow York U. Mem. Players Club, Princeton Club, Saturn Club. Home and office: 930 Fifth Ave New York NY 10021-2651

RAND, DUNCAN D., librarian; b. Biggar, Sask., Can., Oct. 28, 1940; s. Dawson Ellis and Elizabeth Edna (Gabie) R.; m. Nancy Jean Daugherty, Sept. 7, 1963; children: Jacqueline Nancy, Duncan Dawson, Thomas Nelson, John David. B.A., Sask., 1963; B.L.S., McGill U., 1964. Young adult librarian Regina Pub. Library, Sask., 1964-65; coordinator library services Regina Separate Sch. Bd., 1965-68; asst. chief librarian Regina Pub. Library, 1968-71; dep. dir. London Pub. Library and Art Mus., 1971-73, acting dir., 1973-74; chief librarian Lethbridge Pub. Library, Alta., 1974—; dir. So. Alta. Art Gallery. Editor: Sask. Geneal. Soc. Bull, 1968-71. Vice pres. Alta. council Boy Scouts. Mem. Libr. Assn. Atlanta (dir., pres. 1986-87), Can. Libr. Assn. (dir.), Sask. Geneal. Soc. (pres.), Assn. Profl. Librs. of Lethbridge (chmn. 1982-84), Samaritans (bd. dirs. 1993—), Allied Arts Coun. (bd. dirs. 1993—), Rotary Internat., Ippallosh (archivist, sec. 1980-94). Office: 810 5th Ave S, Lethbridge, AB Canada T1J 4C4

RAND, HARRY ISRAEL, lawyer; b. N.Y.C., July 27, 1912; s. Samuel and Rose (Hirth) R.; m. Anna Tulman, Oct. 22, 1938; children: Steven, Deborah, Naomi. BS, CCNY, 1932; JD, NYU, 1936. Bar: N.Y. 1936, U.S. Supreme Ct. 1943, D.C. 1947, U.S. Dist. Cts. (so. and ea. dists.) N.Y. 1959, 60, U.S. Ct. Appeals (2d cir.) 1966. Atty. U.S. Pub. Works Adminstrn., 1938-39, U.S. Dept. Interior, 1939-43, U.S. Dept. Justice, 1943-48; pvt. practice Washington, 1948-58; mem. Weisman, Celler, Allan, Spett & Sheinberg, N.Y.C., 1959-67, Botein, Hays & Sklar, N.Y.C., 1967-89; counsel Herrick, Feinstein, N.Y.C., 1990—. Mem. Assn. of Bar of City of N.Y., Am. Law Inst. Home: 66 Hillandale Rd Westport CT 06880-5319 also: 320 W 86th St New York NY 10024 Office: Herrick Feinstein LLP Two Park Ave New York NY 10016

RAND, HARRY ZVI, art historian, poet; b. N.Y.C., Jan. 10, 1947; m. Jennifer Rand; 1 child, Leah Zoë. BA, CCNY, 1969; AM, Harvard U., 1971, PhD, 1974. Contbg. editor Arts mag., N.Y.C., 1975-91, 1975—; assoc. curator Nat. Mus. Am. Art, Washington, 1977-79, curator, 1979-93, chmn. dept., 1978-84, sr. curator, 1993—; adv. bd. mem. Awards in Visual Arts, Winston-Salem, N.C., 1982—, Austrian Internat. Art Inst., 1989—; arts advisor Virlane Found., New Orleans, 1980—; cons. NAS, 1983, Cosanti Found., 1989—, Exodus Found., 1992—, World Bank, 1994—. Co-author: The Genius of American Painting, 1973; author: Seymour Lipton, 1979, Arshile Gorky, 1981, 91, Recent Trends in Collecting, 1982, The Beginning of Things, 1983, Martha Jackson Meml. Collection, 1985, Der Maler Hundertwasser, 1986, Manet's Contemplation at the Gare Saint-Lazare, 1987, paperback edit. 1991, Paul Manship, 1989, Julian Stanczak, 1990, Hundertwasser, 1991, 92, Jochen Seidel, 1992, Color, 1993; hon. editor Leonardo mag., 1983—; patentee in field. Bd. dirs. Soc. to Prevent Trade in Stolen Art, 1995. N.Y. State Regents scholar, 1965-68; travelling fellow Harvard U., 1973, Andrew W. Mellon Found. fellow, 1976-77; Rockefeller Found. devel. grantee, 1982-83, Rsch. Opportunities grantee Smithsonian Instn., 1985, 86, 87, 88, 89, 90, 91, Spl. Scholarly Studies grantee, 1987—. Fellow Explorers Club; mem. World Art Coun. (steering com. Geneva 1992—). Home: 5511 Greystone St Chevy Chase MD 20815-5556 Office: Nat Mus Am Art MRC 210 8th and G Sts NW Washington DC 20560

RAND, JOELLA MAE, nursing educator; b. Akron, Ohio, July 9, 1932; d. Harry S. and Elizabeth May (Miller) Halberg; m. Martin Rand; children: Craig, Debbi Stark. BSN, U. Akron, 1961, MEd in Guidance, 1968; PhD in Higher Edn. Adminstrn., Syracuse U., 1981. Staff nurse Akron Gen. Hosp., 1953-54; staff-head nurse-instr. Summit County Receiving, Cuyahoga Falls, Ohio, 1954-56; head nurse psychiat. unit Akron Gen. Hosp., 1956-57; instr. psychiatric nursing Summit County Receiving, Cuyahoga Falls, 1957-61; head nurse, in-service instr. Willard (N.Y.) State Hosp., 1961-62; asst. prof. Alfred (N.Y.) U., 1962-76, assoc. prof., assoc. dean, 1976-78, acting dean, 1978-79, dean, 1979-90, dean coll. profl. studies, 1990-91, prof. counseling, 1991—; cons. N.Y. State Regents Program for Non-Collegiate Sponsored Instrn., 1984; cons. collegiate programs N.Y. State Dept. Edn., 1985, Elmira Coll., 1991, U. Rochester, 1992-93; accreditation visitor Nat. League for Nursing, 1984-92; ednl. cons. Willard Psychiat. Hosp., 1992-93; mem. profl. practice exam. subcom. Regents Coll., 1990-95. Recipient Teaching Excellence award Alfred U., 1977, Mary E. Gladwin Outstanding Alumni award Akron U. Coll. Nursing, 1983, Alfred Alumni Friends award, 1989, Grand Marshall commencement Alfred U., 1993. Mem. N.Y. State Coun. of Deans (treas. 1984-88), Genesee Regional Consortium (v.p.), Western N.Y. League Nursing (bd. dirs. 1991-93), Genesee Valley Edn. Com. (chair 1984-86), Sigma Theta Tau (treas. Alfred chpt. 1984-85). Avocations: boating, fishing, public speaking in areas of family and child abuse. Office: Alfred U 343 Myers Hall Alfred NY 14802

RAND, KATHY SUE, public relations executive; b. Miami Beach, Fla., Feb. 24, 1945; d. William R. and Rose (Lasser) R.; m. Peter C. Ritsos, Feb. 19, 1982. BA, Mich. State U., 1965; M in Mgmt., Northwestern U., 1980. Asst. editor Lyons & Carnahan, Chgo., 1967-68; mng. editor Cahners Pub. Co., Chgo., 1968-71; pub. rels. writer Super Market Inst., Chgo., 1972-73; account supr. Pub. Communications Inc., Chgo., 1973-77; divisional mgr. pub. rels. Quaker Oats Co., Chgo., 1977-82; exec. v.p., dep. gen. mgr. Golin/Harris Communications, Chgo., 1982-90; exec. v.p. Lesnik Pub. Rels., Northbrook, Ill., 1990-91; mng. dir. Manning, Selvage & Lee, Chgo., 1991—. Dir. midwest region NOW, 1972-74; mem. Kellogg Alumni Adv. Bd.; bd. dirs. Jr. Achievement of Chgo. Mem. Pub. Rels. Soc. Am. (Silver Anvil award 1986, 87), Pub. Club Chgo. (Golden Trumpet awards 1982-87, 90, 94), Northwestern Club Chgo., Kellogg Alumni Club, Beta Gamma Sigma. Home: 400 Riverwoods Rd Lake Forest IL 60045-2547

RAND, LAWRENCE ANTHONY, investor and financial relations executive; b. Bklyn., Nov. 19, 1942; s. Gerald M. and Elaine Shirley (Borenstein); m. Madelon L., July 4, 1942; children: Allan, Joshua, Emily. AB with honors, Brown U., 1964; MA, NYU, 1965, postgrad., 1966-67. Lectr. NYU, 1967, CUNY, 1968; analyst CIA, Langley, Va., 1966-67; account supr. Ruder & Finn Inc., N.Y.C., 1968-71; co-founder, sr. v.p. Kekst & Co., N.Y.C., 1971—, also bd. dirs.; chmn., bd. dirs. ALS Assn., L.A., 1987-92. Chmn. ethics com. Village of Rye Brook, N.Y. Mem. City Athletic Club, Brown U. Club, Bailiwick Club (Greenwich, Conn.). Office: Kekst & Co 437 Madison Ave New York NY 10022-7001

RAND, LEON, university administrator; b. Boston, Oct. 8, 1930; s. Max B. and Ricka (Muscanto) Rakisky; m. Marian L. Newton, Aug. 29, 1959; children: Debra Ruth, Paul Martin, Marta Leah. B.S., Northeastern U., 1953; M.A., U. Tex., 1956, Ph.D., 1958. Postdoctoral fellow Purdue U. 1958-59; asst. prof. to prof. U. Detroit, 1959-68; prof., chmn. dept. chemistry Youngstown (Ohio) State U., 1968-74, dean grad. studies and research, 1974-81, acting acad. v.p., 1980; vice chancellor acad. affairs Pembroke (N.C.) State U., 1981-85; chancellor Ind. U.-S.E., New Albany, 1986; bd. dirs. INB Banking Co., Jeffersonville, Ind, Jewish Hosp., Louisville, Ky., 1991—. Bd. dirs., mem. exec. com. Louisville (Ind.) Area chpt. ARC; bd. dirs. Floyd Meml. Hosp., New Albany, 1987-90. Mem. Am. Chem. Soc., Am. Inst. Chemists, Metroversity (bd. dirs.), Sigma Xi, Phi Kappa Phi. Home: 3119 Brazil Lake Pky Georgetown IN 47122-8605 Office: Ind U SE New Albany IN 47150

RAND, PAUL, graphic designer, educator; b. N.Y.C., Aug. 15, 1914. Student, Pratt Inst., 1929-32, Art Students League, 1934; DFA (hon.), Phila. Coll. Art, Parson Sch. Design, U. Hartford Sch. Visul Arts, Kutztown U.; MA, Yale U. Art dir. Esquire/Apparel Arts; creative dir. William H. Weintraub Advt. Agy., N.Y.; prof. graphic design Sch. Art Yale U., New Haven, 1956-91, prof. emeritus; cons. IBM, 1956-92, Cummins Engine Co., 1962—, Westinghouse Electric, 1960-81, numerous others; tchr. Yale Summer Sch. Program, Brissago, Switzerland. Author: Thoughts on Design, 1946, Design and the Play Instinct, 1965, The Trademarks of Paul Rand, 1960, A Paul Rand Miscellaney, 1984, Paul Rand: A Designer's Art, 1985, Design, Form and Chaos, 1993; contbr. numerous articles to profl. publs.; represented in permanent collections various museums, U.S., Europe and Japan. Fellow RISD; recipient Florence prize for Visual Comm., City of Florence, 1987. Home: 87 Good Hill Rd Weston CT 06883

RAND, PETER ANDERS, architect; b. Hibbing, Minn., Jan. 8, 1944; s. Sidney Anders and Dorothy Alice (Holm) R.; m. Nancy Ann Straus, Oct. 21, 1967; children—Amy, Dorothy. B.A., St. Olaf Coll., 1966; cert. Oslo Internat. Summer Sch., Norway, 1964; student U. Minn. Sch. Architecture, 1969-72. Registered architect, Minn. Designer, architect, dir. pub. relations Setter, Leach & Lindstrom, Inc., Mpls., 1972-78; dir. bus. devel. and head Eden Prairie Office, Archtl. Design Group, Inc., Minn., 1979-80; dir. mktg. and publs. Minn. Soc. AIA, 1981-82, exec. dir., 1982-85, exec. v.p./CEO, 1986—; pub. Architecture Minn. mag.; cons., archtl. designer. Bd. dirs. Project for Pride in Living, 1979-88, chmn. 1980-86; trustee Bethlehem Luth. Ch., 1980-86, chmn. bd. trustees, 1985, chmn. com. on worship, 1993—, mem. ch. coun., 1993—; mem. Minn. Ch. Ctr. Commn., 1981-89, chmn., 1985-88; sec. Council of Component Execs. of AIA, 1987, 92; bd. dirs. Minn. Council of Chs. 1985-89, sec. 1989, Mpls. Council of Chs., 1985-88, Arts Midwest, 1987—; treas. 1989, v.p. 1990-91, chmn., 1992-93; bd. dirs. Nordic Ctr., 1989—. Served with U.S. Army, 1966-69. Fellow AIA (jour. honor award 1981, Nat. Svc. award 1993); mem. MSAADA Architects & Engrs. (bd. dirs. 1994—), Minn. Soc. AIA, Nat. Trust Hist. Preservation, Torske Klubben. Home: 1728 Humboldt Ave S Minneapolis MN 55403-2809 Office: 275 Market St Ste 54 Minneapolis MN 55405-1621

RAND, PHILLIP GORDON, chemist; b. Meredith, N.H., Nov. 5, 1934; s. Roger Orville and Mary Isabel (Gordon) R.; m. Lela Joyce Magouirk, Aug. 14, 1955; children: Bruce Edward, Brenda Lea, Steven Alan. B.A., John Brown U., 1956; M.S., U. Wyo., 1958; Ph.D., Purdue U., 1963. With Miles Labs., Elkhart, Ind., 1963-89; prin. rsch. scientist Miles Labs., 1978-83, sr. devel. scientist, 1983-89; sales rep. Crain Industries, 1990-92; quality control technician Ross Labs., 1992-94; sr. scientist Environ. Test Systems, 1994—. Mem. Am. Chem. Soc. Republican. Methodist. Clubs: Toastmasters, Gideons. Patentee in field. Home: 1320 W Lexington Ave Elkhart IN 46514-2048

RAND, ROBERT WHEELER, neurosurgeon, educator; b. L.A., Jan. 28, 1923; s. Carl W. and Catherine (Humphrey) R.; m. Helen L. Pierce, Dec. 17, 1949; children: Carl W., Richard P. Student, Harvard U., 1940-42, UCLA, 1942-44; MD, U. So. Calif., 1947; MS, U. Mich., 1951, PhD in Anatomy, 1952; JD, U. West L.A., 1974. Intern, resident in neurosurgery U. Mich., Ann Arbor, 1947-52; from instr. to prof. neurol. surgery UCLA, 1953-89; expert witness malpractice cases Superior Ct. Author: Spinal Cord Tumors in Childhood, 1960, Microneurosurgery, 3d edit., 1985; contbr. articles to profl. jours.; inventor neuropledgets, thermomagnetic surgery coil system, microballoon for aneurysm occlusion, Malcolm-Rand graphite cranial frame, cobalt scalpel. Lt. comdr. USNR, 1943-46, 54-56. Recipient Profl. award UCLA, 1973. Fellow ACS; mem. AMA, Calif. Med. Assn., L.A. County Med. Assn., Am. Surg. Assn., Internat. Coll. Surgeons, Assn. Neurol. Surgeons, Soc. Neurol. Surgeons, Western Neurosurg. Soc., L.A. Country Club, Calif. Club L.A. Office: John Wayne Inst St John's Hosp 1328 22nd St Santa Monica CA 90404-2091

RAND, SIDNEY ANDERS, retired college administrator; b. Eldred, Minn., May 9, 1916; s. Charles William and Ida Alice (Pedersen) R.; m. Dorothy Alice Holm, Sept. 1, 1942 (dec. Jan. 1974); children: Peter Anders, Mary Alice; m. Lois Schiager Ekeren, Nov. 23, 1974. BA, Concordia Coll., Moorhead, Minn., 1938, DD (hon.), 1956; degree in theology, Luther Sem., St. Paul, 1943; LHD (hon.), Colo. Coll., 1976; LLD (hon.), Carleton Coll., 1980, St. Olaf Coll., 1980, Coll. of St. Scholastica, 1985; DTh (hon.), St. John's U., 1980; LHD (hon.), Augustana Coll., 1988. Faculty Concordia Coll., Moorhead, Minn., 1945-51; pres. Waldorf Coll., Forest City, Iowa, 1951-56; exec. dir. coll. edn. Am. Luth. Ch., Mpls., 1956-63; pres. St. Olaf Coll., Northfield, Minn., 1963-80; U.S. ambassador to Norway, Oslo, 1980-81; higher edn. cons. Mpls., 1981—; pres. Augustana Coll., Sioux Falls, S.D., 1986-87, 92-93, Suomi Coll., Hancock, Mich., 1990-91; sr. cons. Minn. Pvt. Coll. Council, St. Paul, 1981-87. Pastor Nashwauk (Minn.) Luth. Ch., 1943-45; pres. Fund for Theol. Edn., Princeton, N.J., 1984-87; mem. Gov.'s Tax Commn., Minn., 1984-85; chmn. Minn. Citizens for Ct. Reform, 1984-87. Decorated Comdr. Norwegian Order of Merit, 1986; named Knight 1st Class Order of St. Olaf Kingdom of Norway, 1974. Mem. Phi Beta Kappa. Club: Torske Klubben (Mpls.). Home: 19 S 1st St Apt 907B Minneapolis MN 55401-1808

RAND, TOM, costume designer. Costume designer: (films) The Duellists, 1978, The French Lieutenant's Woman, 1981 (Academy award nomination best costume design 1981), The Pirates of Penzance, 1983, The Shooting Party, 1984, Eleni, 1985, Young Toscanini, 1988, Strike It Rich, 1990, The Power of One, 1992, The Temp, 1993. Office: care Costume Designer's Guild 13949 Ventura Blvd Ste 309 Sherman Oaks CA 91423*

RAND, WILLIAM, lawyer, former state justice; b. N.Y.C., Oct. 11, 1926; s. William and Barbara (Burr) R.; married; children: Alicia, Carley Coudert, William Coudert, Paula Burr. AB, Harvard U., 1948; LLB, Columbia U., 1951. Bar: N.Y. 1951, U.S. Dist. Ct. N.Y. 1951, U.S. Supreme Ct., 1958, U.S. Ct. Appeals (2d cir.) 1961, U.S. Ct. Appeals (4th cir.) 1985. Asst. dist. atty. New York County, 1954-59; asst. counsel to gov. of State of N.Y., 1959-60; assoc. Coudert Bros., N.Y.C., 1961-62, ptnr., 1963—; justice N.Y. County Supreme Ct., 1962; justice Village of Cove Neck, Oyster Bay, N.Y., 1974—. Mem. exec. com. New York County Reps., 1968-72. Served with USN, 1944-46, PTO. Clubs: Piping Rock (Locust Valley, N.Y.); Seawanhaka Corinthian Yacht (Oyster Bay); Racquet and Tennis (N.Y.C.). Home: 73 Cove Neck Rd Oyster Bay NY 11771-1821 Office: Coudert Bros 1114 Avenue Of The Americas New York NY 10036-7701

RANDA, RUDOLPH THOMAS, federal judge; b. Milw., July 25, 1940; s. Rudolph Frank and Clara Paula (Kojis) R.; m. Melinda Nancy Matera, Jan. 15, 1977; children: Rudolph Daniel, Daniel Anthony. B.S., U. Wis.-Milw., 1963; J.D., U. Wis.-Madison, 1966. Bar: Wis. 1966, U.S. Dist. Ct. (ea. and we. dists.) Wis., 1966, U.S. Ct. Appeals (7th cir.) 1973, U.S. Supreme Ct. 1973. Sole practice, Milw., 1966-67; prin. city atty. Office Milw. City Atty., 1970-75; judge Milw. Mcpl. Ct., 1975, Milwaukee County Circuit Ct., 1979-81, 1982-92, Appellate Ct., Madison, Wis., 1981-82; federal judge U.S. Dist. Ct. (ea. dist.) Wis., 1992—; chmn. Wis. Impact, Milw., 1980—; lectr. Marquette U. Law Sch., Milw.—. Served to capt. U.S. Army, 1967-69, Vietnam. Decorated Bronze Star medal. Mem. Milw. Bar Assn., Wis. Bar Assn., Trial Judges Wis., Am. Legion (adjutant Milw. 1980), Thomas More Lawyers Soc. (former pres. Milw.), Milw. Hist. Soc., Phi Alpha Theta. Roman Catholic. Office: US Courthouse 517 E Wisconsin Ave Rm 247 Milwaukee WI 53202-4507

RANDALL, CLAIRE, church executive; b. Dallas, Oct. 15, 1919; d. Arthur Godfrey and Annie Laura (Fulton) R. A.A., Schreiner Coll., 1948; BA, Scarritt Coll., 1950; DD (hon.), Berkeley Sem., Yale U., 1974; LHD (hon.), Austin Coll., 1982; LLD, Notre Dame U., 1984. Assoc. missionary edn. Bd. World Missions Presbyterian Ch., U.S., Nashville, 1949-57; dir. at Gen. Council Presbyterian Ch., U.S., Atlanta, 1957-61; dir. Christian World Mission, program dir., assoc. dir. Ch. Women United, N.Y.C., 1962-73; gen. sec. Nat. Council Ch. of Christ in U.S.A., N.Y.C., 1974-84; nat. pres. Ch. Women United, N.Y.C., 1988-92; ret., 1992—. Mem. Nat. Commn. on Internat. Women's Yr., 1975-77, Martin Luther King Jr. Fed. Holiday Commn., 1985. Recipient Woman of Yr. in Religion award Heritage Soc.,

1977; Empire State Woman of Yr. in Religion award State of N.Y., 1984; medal Order of St. Vladimir, Russian Orthodox Ch., 1984. Democrat. Episcopalian. Avocations: golf, swimming; painting; reading; music. Home: 13427 W Countryside Dr Sun City West AZ 85375-4711

RANDALL, CLIFFORD WENDELL, civil engineer; b. Somerset, Ky., May 1, 1936; s. William Lesbert and Geneva (James) R.; m. Phyllis Amis, Aug. 15, 1959; children: Andrew Amis, William Otis. B.S. in Civil Engring., U. Ky., 1959, M.S. in San. Engring., 1963; Ph.D. (AEC trainee 1963-65), U. Tex., 1966. Assist. prof. civil engring. U. Tex., Arlington, 1965-68; mem. faculty Va. Poly. Inst. and State U., 1968—, prof. civil engring., 1972—, Charles Lunsford prof., 1981—; vis. prof. U. Cape Town, South Africa, 1983; chmn. environ. engring. and scis. program Va. Poly. Inst. and State U., 1979—; lectr. Shanghai Archtl. and Mcpl. Engring. Inst., Wuhan Tech. U., 1987; dir. Occoquan Watershed Monitoring Program, 1971—; mem. U.S. nat. com. Internat. Water Quality, 1976-88, chair 1986-88, mem. 1992 Biennial Conf. Com., chair conf. arrangements, Washington; tng. grant cons. EPA, 1970-71; cons. to industry, 1969—; WHO cons. to Nat. Environ. Engring. Rsch. Inst. India, 1983-84; gov. appointee sci. and tech. adv. com. EPA Chesapeake Bay Restoration Project, 1984—, chmn. 1993—. Author tech. papers in field: co-author: Biological Process Design for Wastewater Treatment, 1980, Stormwater Management in Urbanizing Areas, 1983, Design and Retrofit of Wastewater Treatment Plants for Biological Nutrient Removal, 1992. Troop com. chmn. local Boy Scouts Am., 1978-82, chmn. dist. Camporee com., 1977; camp pres. Gideons Internat., 1976-78, 80, 95—; state cabinet mem., 1985-88; vice moderator Highlands Bapt. Assn., 1980-81, moderator, 1982-83; mem. bd. deacons Blacksburg Bapt. Ch., 1971-74, 79-82, chmn., 1974. Lt. U.S. Coast and Godetic Survey, 1959-62. Ford Found. fellow, 1964-65; recipient citation Engring. News-Record, 1988, Disting. Svc. award U.S. nat. com. Internat. Assn. Water Quality, 1989, Salute to Excellence Gov. of Md., 1994; named Conservationist of Yr., Chesapeake Bay Found., 1986. Mem. ASCE (chmn. water resources mgmt. com. 1977, environ. engring. rsch. coun. 1989-90, svc. award 1978, 80, meritorious tech. paper award 1969), Am. Water Works Assn. (cert. of recognition 1980, 89), Watern Environ. Fedn. (bd. dirs. 1981-84, cert. of merit 1982, Bedell award 1983, svc. award 1984), Internat. Assn. Water Quality (mem. governing bd. 1986-88, USA rep. on sci. and tech. com. 1994—, mem. nutrient removal specialist group mgmt. com. 1980—, chmn. 1994—), Va. Water Pollution Control Assn. (pres. 1975-76), Assn. Environ. Engring. Profs. (sec.-treas. 1979-80, bd. dirs. 1978-80, 93—, v.p. 1994). Home: 1302 Crestview Dr Blacksburg VA 24060-5609 Office: Va Poly Inst & State U Dept Civil Engring 330 Norris Hall Blacksburg VA 24061

RANDALL, DAVID JOHN, physiologist, zoologist, educator; b. London, Sept. 15, 1938. BSc, U. Southampton, 1960, PhD, 1963, FRSC, 1981. From asst. to assoc. prof. U. B.C., 1963-73, prof. zoology, 1973—, assoc. dean grad. studies, 1990—; vis. lectr. Bristol U., 1968-69; vis. sci. Marine Labs U. Tex., 1970, Zool. Sta., Naples, Italy, 1973; NATO vis. sci. Acadia U., 1975, Marine Lab U. Tex., 1977; chief sci. Alpha Helix Amazon Expedition, 1976; mem. adv. bd. J. Comp Physiology, 1977-92, J. Exp. Biol., 1981-84; chmn. animal biol. com. Nat. Res. Coun., Can., 1974; vis. prof. U. Nairobi, 1988, George Washington U., 1988-89; concurrent prof. Nanjing U., China, 1993—; external examiner U. Singapore, 1990-91. Associate editor: Marine Behavior Physiology. Guggenheim Found. fellow, 1968-69. Fellow Royal Soc. Can.; mem. Can. Soc. Zoologists (Fry medal 1993), Soc. Exp. Biologists. Office: U BC, Dept Zoology 6270 Unv Blvd, Vancouver, BC Canada V6T 1Z4

RANDALL, DEAN BOWMAN, retired electronics manufacturing company executive; b. Mpls., May 4, 1920; s. Heman Ward and Elizabeth (Silver) R.; m. Ann Owen, Sept. 30, 1941; children: Ann Randall Godfrey, Dean B. Jr., David Stratton. B.B.A., U. Minn., 1942. Plant layout engr. McDonnell Aircraft, St. Louis, 1942-43; dir. schedules Northwest Airlines, St. Paul, 1943-51; asst. to sales mgr. Honeywell Inc., Mpls., 1951-53, advt. mgr., 1953-66, v.p. merchandising, 1966-74, v.p. communications, 1974-85; bd. dirs. Bus. Pub. Audit, N.Y.C., 1971-74, Nat. Advt. Rev. Bd., N.Y.C., 1973-76, Art Ctr. of Minn., 1986. Pres. Courage Ctr. Rehab. Orgn., Mpls., 1973, bd. dirs. 1970-94; pres. Community Health and Welfare Council, 1975; v.p. United Way Mpls., 1972; mem. Met. Health Planning Bd., 1984-90. Mem. Minn. Advt. Fedn. (bd. dirs. 1960-63), Assn. Nat. Advertisers (bd. dirs. 1970-73), Minn. State Hist. Soc. (bd. dirs. 1982-92), Sr. Resources (bd. dirs. 1986-92), Beta Gamma Sigma, Beta Theta Pi. Club: Minikahda. Home: 4717 Eastwood Cir Minnetonka MN 55345-2408

RANDALL, ELIZABETH ELLEN, personnel manager; b. Maple Hill, Kans., Mar. 21, 1915; d. Edwin and Ann (Scott) Sage; m. George Albert Randall, May 29, 1941; children: Cheryl Ann, Rebecca Lynn. Student, Kans. State U., 1932-34. Tchr. elem. sch Maple Hill, Kans., 1932-34, Dover, Kans., 1934-46; reader Luce Press Clippings, Topeka, 1959-63, supr., 1964, office mgr., 1964—. Tchr. Jr. High Ch. Sch., 1964-67; mem. pastoral com. Dover Federated Ch., 1991—. Mem. Dover 4-H Club (leader 1960-62), Dover Rebekah Lodge, Eastern Star, Am. Leg. Aux., Disabled Am. Vets. Aux., 14th Armored Divsn. Aux. Democrat. Avocations: collecting antiques, plates and dolls, needlework. Home: 6715 SW 22nd Ter Topeka KS 66614-1831 Office: Luce Press Clippings 912 S Kansas Ave Topeka KS 66612-1211

RANDALL, FRANCIS BALLARD, historian, educator, writer; b. N.Y.C., Dec. 17, 1931; s. John Herman, Jr. and Mercedes (Moritz) R.; m. Laura Regina Rosenbaum, June 11, 1957; children: David R., Ariane R. B.A., Amherst Coll., 1952; M.A., Columbia, 1954, Ph.D., 1960. Instr. history Amherst Coll., 1956-59; instr., asst. prof. history Columbia, 1959-61, vis. prof., 1967-68; mem. humanities faculty Sarah Lawrence Coll., Bronxville, N.Y., 1961—, chmn., 1985-89; trustee Sarah Lawrence Coll., 1971-76. Author: (with others) Essays in Russian and Soviet History, 1963, Stalin's Russia, an Historical Reconsideration, 1965, N.G. Chernyshevskii, 1967, Vissarion Belinskii, 1987. Freedom rider civil disobedience to racism, 1961, war draft resistance arrests, 1967, 70. Fulbright fellow for study in India, 1965; Wye fellow, 1986. Mem. Am. Hist. Assn., Am. Assn. for Advancement Slavic Studies, Am. Assn. U. Profs. (chpt. chmn. 1966-69), Phi Beta Kappa, Sigma Xi. Home: 425 Riverside Dr # 10I New York NY 10025-7730 Office: Sarah Lawrence Coll Bronxville NY 10708

RANDALL, GENE, news correspondent, anchor; b. Port Chester, N.Y., Jan. 10, 1942; m. Susan Biggs; children: Christopher, Gina. BA in English, Georgetown U., 1964. Anchor, corr. Sta. WLWT, Cin., 1966-71; anchor Sta. WTVC, Chattanooga, 1972-74; corr., anchor Sta. KTVI, St. Louis, 1974-76, Sta. WMAO-TV, Chgo., 1976-80; bur. chief/corr. NBC, Moscow, 1980-83; nat./nat. polit. corr. CNN, Washington, 1983—. Recipient Emmy awards for Best TV Talk Show, 1975, Best Spot News Story, 1976, U.S. Operation in Somalia, 1993, Ace award. Office: CNN Bldg Wash Bureau 820 1st St NE Washington DC 20002-4243

RANDALL, GERALD J., insurance company executive; b. Sparta, Wis., Mar. 6, 1931; s. Jean Oliver and Mabel E. (Olson) R.; m. Beverly J. Gehrig, Apr. 23, 1955; children: Robin Jean, Scott Gerald, Susan Kay. BBA, U. Wis., 1954, JD, 1957. Bar: Wis., U.S. Supreme Ct.; CLU, ChFC. With Conn. Mutual Life Ins. Co., Hartford, 1957-61, asst. counsel advanced sales, 1961-69, asst. v.p. advanced sales, 1969-70, 2d v.p. advanced sales, 1970-73, v.p. pension divsn., 1973-80, sr. v.p., 1980-81; pres. Diversified Ins. Svcs. Am., Inc. subs. Conn. Mutual Life Ins. Co., 1981-84; pres. Conn. Mutual Fin. Svcs., Inc. subs. Conn. Mutual Life Ins. Co., 1984-88, sr. v.p. advanced sales SBU, 1988—; instr. CLU pgm. courses U. Conn., 1957—; founder, charter mem., pres. Estate & Bus. Planning Coun. Hartford, 1969-70; mem. exec. program Dartmouth Coll., 1973, Columbia U., 1988; chmn. pension com. Am. Coun. Life Ins., 1976. Contbr. articles to profl. jours. Mem. Jaycees, 1960-65; bd. dirs. Hartford Better Bus. Bureau, 1981-84, greater Hartford YMCA, 1989—. 1st Lt. U.S. Army, 1955-56. Recipient CLU Inst. scholarship, 1971. Mem. ABA, Wis. Bar Assn., Hartford Life Underwriters Assn., Estate & Bus. Planning Coun. Hartford, Life Ins. Mgmt. Rsch. Assn. (chmn. advanced sales com. 1978-79), Gen. Agents and Mgrs. Assn., Assn. Advanced Life Underwriting, Hartford Club. Republican. Congregationalist. Avocations: antique cars, travel, jogging, antique watch collecting. Home: 178 Tall Timbers Rd Glastonbury CT 06033-3351 Office: Conn Mut Life Ins Co 140 Garden St Hartford CT 06154-0001

RANDALL, JAMES R., manufacturing company executive; b. 1924; married. BS in Chem. Engring., U. Wis., 1948. Tech. dir. Cargill Inc., 1948-68; v.p. prodn. and engring. Archer-Daniels-Midland Co., Decatur, Ill., 1968-69, exec. v.p., 1969-75, pres., 1975—, also dir. Served with AUS, 1943-46. Office: Archer-Daniels-Midland Co 4666 E Faries Pky Decatur IL 62526-5666

RANDALL, LILIAN MARIA CHARLOTTE, museum curator; b. Berlin, Feb. 1, 1931; came to U.S. 1938; d. Frederick Henry and Elizabeth Agnes (Ziegler) Cramer; m. Richard Harding Randall, Apr. 11, 1953; children: Christopher, Julia, Katharine. BA cum laude, Mount Holyoke Coll., 1950; MA, Radcliffe Coll., 1951, PhD, 1955; LHD (hon.), Towson State U., 1993. Asst. dir. Md. State Arts Coun., 1972-73; curator manuscripts and rare books Walters Art Gallery, Balt., 1974-85, rsch. curator manuscripts, 1985—; vis. lectr. dept. art history Johns Hopkins U., 1964-68; hon. vis. lectr. U. Mich., Ann Arbor; lectr. in field. Author: Images in the Margins of Gothic Manuscripts, 1966, Gatherings in Honor of Dorothy Miner, 1974, The Diary of George A. Lucas: An American Art Agent in Paris, 1959-1957, 1979, Illuminated Manuscripts: Masterpieces in Miniature, 1984, Medieval and Renaissance Manuscripts in the Walters Art Gallery, vol. I, France, 875-1420, 1989, vol. II, France, 1420-1540, 1992; contbr. numerous articles to profl. jours. Mem. Williston Libr. com., 1988-89; reviewer, panelist NEH, 1980—. Grantee AAUW, 1953-54, ACLS, 1960, 65, Bunting Inst., 1961-63, Ford Found., 1967-69, Am. Philosophical Soc., 1971, NEA, 1975, Samuel H. Kress Found., 1979, 81-84, NEH, 1977-80, 81-84, 89-92; grantee publ. subsidy Md. State Arts Coun., 1972, Mcpl. Art Soc. Balt., 1972, Andrew W. Mellon Found., 1988, Getty Grant Program, 1990-92, NEA Mus. Program, 1992-93; fellow Am. Numismatic Soc., 1955. Fellow Medieval Acad. Am. (libr. preservation com., various coms. 1985-87, 90-93); mem. Internat. Ctr. Medieval Art (bd. dirs. 1978-82), Coll. Art Assn. (Arthur Kingsley Porter prize 1957), Balt. Bibliophiles (bd. dirs. 1966-80, pres. 1980-83), Pyramid Atlantic (bd. dirs. 1985-88), Phi Beta Kappa, Grolier Club. Home: 301 Kendall Rd Baltimore MD 21210 Office: Walters Art Gallery 600 N Charles St Baltimore MD 21201-5185

RANDALL, LINDA LEA, biochemist, educator; b. Montclair, N.J., Aug. 7, 1946; d. Lowell Neal and Helen (Watts) R.; m. Gerald Lee Hazelbauer, Aug. 29, 1970. BS, Colo. State U., 1968; PhD, U. Wis., 1971. Postdoctoral fellow Inst. Pasteur, Paris, 1971-73; asst. prof. Uppsala (Sweden) U., 1975-81; assoc. prof. Washington State U., Pullman, 1981-83, prof. biochemistry, 1983—; guest scientist Wallenberg Lab., Uppsala U., 1973-75; study section NIH, 1984-88. Editorial bd. Jour. of Bacteriology, 1982—; co-editor: Virus Receptors Part I, 1980; contbr. articles to profl. jours. Recipient Eli Lilly Award in Microbiology and Immunology, Am. Soc. Microbiology, Am. Assn. Immunologists, Am. Soc. Exptl. Pathology, 1984, Faculty Excellence Award in Rsch., Washington State U., 1988, Disting. Faculty Address, 1990. Mem. Am. Microbiol. Soc., AAAS, Am. Soc. Biol. Chemists, Protein Soc. Avocation: dancing. Office: Washington State U. Biochemistry/Biophysic Dept Pullman WA 99164-4660

RANDALL, MALCOM, health care administrator; b. East St. Louis, Ill., Aug. 9, 1916; s. John Leeper and Barbara May R.; m. Christine Sheppard, Nov. 10, 1972. A.B., McKendree Coll., 1939; M.H.A., St. Louis U., 1955. Chief br. office VA, St. Louis, 1946-49, asst. area dir. area office, 1949-53; spl. asst. to dir. VA Hosp., St. Louis, 1953-56; hosp. adminstr. VA Hosp., Spokane, Wash., 1956-57, Chgo., 1957-58, Indpls., 1958-60, Wood, Wis., 1960-64; hosp. dir. VA Hosp., Miles City, Mont., 1964-66; med. ctr. dir. and med. dist. dir. VA, Gainesville, Fla., 1966—; regional rep. VA, Gainesville, 1991—; prof. health and hosp. adminstrn. U. Fla., Gainesville 1966—; pres. N. Cen. Fla. Health Planning Council; mem. Fla. State Health Planning Council; chmn. Gov.'s Commn. on Alzheimer's Disease; mem. Alachua County Emergency Med. Svcs. Coun.; bd. dirs. emeritus 1st Union Nat. Bank Fla., Regional Med. Programs; mem. editorial bd. Jour. Am. Coll. Health Care Execs.; cons. on health care Univ. Clin. Ctr., Ljubljana, Slovenia, 1982—, Ministry of Health, Hungary and Med. U. Debrecen, 1989—. Contbr. numerous articles to profl. jours. Bd. dirs. Civitan Regional Blood Ctr., Gainesville, 1970. Served to capt. USN, 1942-46. Recipient Presdl. Rank award Pres. U.S., 1983, Meritorious Svc. award U. Fla., 1984, Exceptional Svc. award, 1985, Exec. Performance award, 1986, all VA; named Citizen of Yr., Gainesville, 1977. Fellow Am. Coll. Health Care Execs. (council regents, VA liaison); mem. Inst. Medicine, Nat. Acad. Sci., Assn. Am. Med. Colls. (bd. dirs., council tchg. hosps.), Am. Health Planning Assn. (bd. dirs.), Am. Hosp. Assn. (governing council met. and fed. hosp. sect.). Club: Heritage. Lodge: Rotary. Home: 1617 NW 19th Cir Gainesville FL 32605-4092 Office: VA Med Ctr Archer Rd Gainesville FL 32608

RANDALL, RICHARD HARDING, JR., art gallery director; b. Balt., Jan. 31, 1926; s. Richard Harding and Mary Scott (Buzby) R.; m. Lilian M.C. Cramer, Apr. 11, 1953; children: Christopher, Julia, Katherine. AB, Princeton U., 1950; MA, Harvard U., 1951. Asst. and assoc. curator medieval art The Cloisters, N.Y.C., 1953-59; asst. curator decorative arts Mus. Fine Arts, Boston, 1959-64; asst. dir. Walters Art Gallery, Balt., 1964-65, dir., 1965-81, curator medieval art, 1981-85; vis. prof. medieval art Columbia U., 1955. Author: A Cloisters Bestiary, 1960, American Furniture, 1965, Masterpieces of Ivory, 1985, The Golden Age of Ivory, 1993. With armored divsn. AUS, 1944-46, ETO. Mem. Walpole Soc., Colonial Soc., Armor and Arms Club (N.Y.C.), South River Club (Annapolis, Md.).

RANDALL, RICHARD RAINIER, geographer; b. Toledo, July 21, 1925; s. Robert Henry and Maree (Gard) R.; m. Patricia Lee Spencer, June 9, 1962; children: Allison Maree, Susan Rebecca, Richard Rainier Jr. BA, George Washington U., 1949, MA, 1950; PhD, Clark U., 1955; postgrad., Graz U., Austria. Geog. analyst U.S. Govt., Washington, 1955-61; Washington rep. Rand McNally & Co., Washington, 1961-72; owner Randall Assocs., Washington, 1972-73; exec. sec. U.S. Bd. Geog. Names, Washington, 1973-93; geographer Def. Mapping Agy., Washington, 1973-93; ret., 1993, cons. on geog. names., 1993—; convenor UN Working Group on Undersea and Maritime Feature Names, 1975-84; mem., prin. U.S. tech. advisor U.S. and U.K. Conf. on Geog. Names, 1976, 79, 81, 84, 86, 88, 92; dep. head U.S. del. UN Conf. on Geog. Names, 1977, 87, head, 1982, 92; prin. U.S. expert UN Group Experts on Geog. Names, 1975, 77, 79, 82, 84, 86, 87, 89, 92; pres. com. on geog. terminology Pan Am. Inst. Geography and History, 1973-77, pres. working group on geog. names and gazetters, 1981-94. Contbr. articles to profl. jours.; inventor flexible fishhook. V.p. North Cleveland Park Citizens Assn., Washington, 1968. With U.S. Army, 1943-46, ETO. Fulbright scholar, NRC, Austria, 1953-54. Mem. Am. Congress on Surveying and Mapping (dir. cartography divsn. 1973-75, dir. press rels. 1961-72, program dir. cartography divsn. ann. meeting 1967), Am. Geog. Soc., Assn. Am. Geographers (chmn. Mid-Atlantic divsn. 1978, dir. press rels. ann. conf. 1968), Am. Names Soc., Am. Austrian Soc. (v.p. 1955-57), Explorers Club, Cosmos Club. Republican.

RANDALL, ROBERT L(EE), ecological economist; b. Aberdeen, S.D., Dec. 28, 1936; s. Harry Eugene and Juanita Alice (Barstow) R. MS in Phys. Chemistry, U. Chgo., 1960, MBA, 1963. Market devel. chemist E.I. du Pont de Nemours & Co., Inc., Wilmington, Del., 1963-65; chem. economist Battelle Meml. Inst., Columbus, Ohio, 1965-68; mgr. market and econ. rsch. Kennecott Copper Corp., N.Y.C., 1968-74, economist, 1974-79, dir. new bus. venture devel., 1979-81; pres., mng. dir. R.L. Randall Assocs., Inc., 1981—; economist U.S. Internat. Trade Commn., Washington, 1983—; founder, pres., exec. dir. The RainForest ReGeneration Inst., 1986—; indsl. panel policy rev. of effect of regulation on innovation and U.S.-internat. competetion U.S. Dept. Commerce, 1980-81; participant preparatory com. UN Conf. on Environ. and Devel., Rio de Janeiro, 1991; del. observer internat. negotiating com. Framework Conv. on Climate Change, 1991—. Contbr. articles to profl. jours.; contbg. author: Computer Methods for the '80's. Mem. AAAS (organizer ann. meeting Tropical Forest Regeneration Symposium), AIME (econs. coun. sec. mineral econ. subsect.), Am. Econ. Assn., Am. Statis. Assn., Am. Chem. Soc. Mining Engrs., Chemists Club of N.Y.C., Metall. Soc., N.Y. Acad. Scis., Nat. Econs. Club Washington (sec., reporter), Assn. Environ. and Resource Economists, Internat. Soc. Ecol. Economists, Wanderbirds Hiking Club (hike leader, treas. Washington), Capital Hiking Club (hike leader, Washington). Home: 1727 Massachusetts Ave NW Washington DC 20036-2153 Office: US Internat Trade Com 500 E St NW Washington DC 20436-0003

RANDALL, RONALD FISHER, grocery store chain executive; b. Sioux City, Iowa, June 25, 1934; s. F. Dwain and J. Gale (Fisher) R.; m. Lavonne E. Woltoff, Dec. 27, 1961 (dec. May 1966); children—DaLinda, Ronald; m. Charlys Fern Stewart, Mar. 7, 1969. B.S. in Engring., U.S. Naval Acad., 1958. Dir. ops. Randall Stores, Mitchell, S.D., 1958-72, pres., 1972-81, pres., chmn. bd., 1981—; pres. Coca-Cola Bottling Co. of Central S.D. Inc., Mitchell; dir. Comml. Bank, Mitchell, Dakota Mfg. Inc., Mitchell. Clubs: Interlachen Country (Mpls.); Minnehaha Country (Sioux Falls, S.D.). Office: Randall Stores Inc 1705 N Main St Mitchell SD 57301-1019

RANDALL, TONY (LEONARD ROSENBERG), actor; b. Tulsa, Feb. 26, 1920; m. Florence Gibbs. Student, Northwestern U., Columbia; studies, Neighborhood Playhouse Sch. of Theater, N.Y.C. Founder, artistic dir. Nat. Actors' Theatre, N.Y.C. Appearances include: (theatre) Circle of Chalk, 1941, Candida, 1941, The Corn is Green, 1942, The Barretts of Wimpole St., 1947, Antony and Cleopatra, 1948, Caesar and Cleopatra, 1950, Oh Men, Oh Women, 1944, Inherit the Wind, 1955-56, Oh Captain, 1958, UTBU, 1966, Two Into One, 1988, M. Butterfly, 1989, A Little Hotel on the Side, 1992, Three Men on a Horse, 1993, The Government Inspector, 1994, tour with Jack Klugman The Odd Couple, 1994; (tv) Mr. Peepers, 1952-55, Max Liebman Spectaculars, Tonight Show, 1956, The Odd Couple, 1970-75, also The Tony Randall Show, 1976-77, Love Sydney, 1981-83; (motion pictures) Oh Men, Oh Women, 1957, Will Success Spoil Rock Hunter, 1957, The Mating Game, 1959, Pillow Talk, 1959, Let's Make Love 1960, Lover Come Back, 1962, Bang, Bang, You're Dead, 1966, Huckleberry Finn, 1974, Scavenger Hunt, 1979, Foolin' Around, 1980, The King of Comedy, 1983, My Little Pony, 1986, That's Adequate, It Had to Be You; appeared in TV movies: Kate Bliss and the Ticker Tape Kid, 1978, Sidney Shorr: A Girl's Best Friend, 1981, Off Sides, 1984, The Man in the Brown Suit, 1989, The Odd Couple Returns, 1993; author: (with Michael Mindlin) Which Reminds Me, 1989. Served from pvt. to 1st lt. Signal Corps, AUS, 1942-46. Recipient Emmy award for The Odd Couple 1975. Office: care Nat Actors' Theatre 1560 Broadway Ste 409 New York NY 10036-1525

RANDALL, WILLIAM, bank executive. CEO, S.W. region 1st Howard Hughes Nev. Nat., Las Vegas. Office: 1st Interstate Bank Nev Na 3800 Howard Hughes Pkwy Las Vegas NV 89109*

RANDALL, WILLIAM SEYMOUR, leasing company executive; b. Champaign, Ill., July 5, 1933; s. Glenn S. and Audrey H. (Honnold) R.; m. Sharon Larsen; children: Steve, Cathy, Mike, Jennifer. B.S., Ind. State U., 1959. Controller Amana Refrigeration Co., Iowa, 1966-70; div. controller Trane Co., Clarksville, Tenn., 1970-74; corporate controller Trane Co., La Crosse, Wis., 1974-79; v.p., chief fin. officer Sta-Rite Industries, Milw., 1979-82; pres., owner Profl. Staff Resources, Inc., Milw., 1982—. Served with AUS, 1953-55. Mem. Financial Execs. Inst. Lodge: Rotary. Home: 13365 Tulane St Brookfield WI 53005-7141 Office: 2401 N Mayfair Rd # 202 Milwaukee WI 53226-1408

RANDALL, WILLIAM THEODORE, state official; b. Seattle, July 8, 1931; s. Heaton Henry Randall and Mabel Maud (Johnson) Landstrom; m. Barbara Ann Bouffard; children: Julie Randall Waybright, Linda A. Randall Wiggins, Mary Lee Randall Lane. BA in Far Ea. Studies, U. Wash., 1953, BA in Polit. Sci., 1959, MEd in Edn. Adminstrn., 1966; EdD in Edn. Adminstrn., Ariz. State U., 1969. Agt. Aetna Ins. Co., Seattle, 1957-59; tchr. Shoreline Pub. Schs., Seattle, 1959-61, prin., 1961-66, dir. rsch., 1969-70; asst. supt. Wash. Sch. Dist., Phoenix, 1970-73; supt. Scottsdale (Ariz.) Pub. Schs., 1973-80; pres. William Randall Assocs., Phoenix, 1980-83; supt. Creighton Sch. Dist., Phoenix, 1983-88; commr. edn. State of Colo., Denver, 1988—; cons. Edge Learning Corp., Tempe, Ariz., 1978-82; edn. advisor Gov. of Ariz., 1985; pres.-elect Ariz. Adminstrs., Inc., 1986-88. Author: Stress Management, 1978; co-author: Role of Teacher, 1979, Management Development, 1980. Chmn. Ariz. Child Care Coalition, Phoenix, 1986; bd. dirs. Colo. Childrens Trust, Denver, 1989—; mem. exec. bd. Communities for Drug Free Colo., Denver, 1988. Sgt. U.S. Army, 1955-57. Named Adminstr. of Yr. Shoreline Edn. Assn., Seattle, 1966, Ariz. Supt. of Yr. Ariz. Sch. Adminstrs., Phoenix, 1988. Avocations: hiking, skiing. Office: Colo Dept Edn 201 E Colfax Ave Denver CO 80203-1704

RANDAZZO, ANTHONY, dancer; b. Ann Arbor, Mich.. Student, Nat. Ballet Can. Mem. Nat. Ballet of Can.; soloist San Francisco Ballet, 1987-88, prin. dancer, 1988—. Ballets with the San Francisco Ballet include The Sleeping Beauty, Swan Lake, Handel-a Celebration, Ballet d' Isoline, Valses Poeticos, Intimate Voices, La Fille mal gardee, The Four Temperaments, Symphony in C, Theme and Variations, Ballo della Regina, Glinka Pas de Trois, Duo Concertant, Forgotten Land, The Comfort Zone, Dream of Harmony, Nutcracker, In the middle, somewhat elevated, Rodeo, Connotations, Rodin, La Sylphide, Variations of Ballet, Krazy Kat, Harvest Moon, The Wonder Fantasy, ballets with other cos. including Etudes, Nutcracker, Napoli, Don Juan, Don Quixote, The Merry Widow. Office: 133 W 71st St New York NY 10023-3834 Office: San Francisco Ballet 455 Franklin St San Francisco CA 94102-4471*

RANDEL, RONALD DEAN, physiologist, educator; b. Lewis, Kan., May 22, 1938; s. Emery Howard and Pauline (Mahan) R.; m. Colleen Kay O'Brien, Sept. 4, 1966; 1 child, Lowell Warren. BS in Animal Sci., Washington State U., 1965; PhD in Animal Physiology, Purdue U., 1971. Research fellow Purdue U., West Lafayette, Ind., 1965-71; visiting scientist U.S. Range Livestock Experiment Station, Miles City, Mont., 1971-72; research physiologist USDA, Agrl. Rsch. Svc., Miles City, 1972-74; assoc. prof. Texas A & M U., Overton, Tex., 1974-78, prof., 1978—; cooperating scientist USDA-Office Internat. Coop. and Devel./Taiwan Livestock Rsch. Inst., Ping Tung, 1987—. Mem. editl. bd. Jour. Animal Sci., 1990-93, 95—; Theriogeneology, 1994—; contbr. over 125 papers to profl. jours., 2 chpts. to books, over 315 paper presentations, over 175 misc. papers and over 40 symposia. Adult leader 4-H, Rusk County Riding Club Overton, 1981-90. With USN, 1958-62. Named Alpha Zeta agrl. hon. Wash. State U., 1964, Phi Kappa Phi scholastic hon. Wash. State U., 1964, Sigma Xi rsch. hon. Purdue U., 1970, Award in Excellence for Rsch. Tex. A&M U., 1987, 90, Svc. award Dept. Animal Sci., 1994; sr. Fulbright rsch. fellow James Cook U. of N. Queensland, Townsville, Australia, 1984; Donald Henry Barron lectr., 1995. Mem. Am. Soc. of Animal Sci., Soc. for the Study of Reproduction, Assn. Latino Americana de Prodn. Animal, Reproductive Performance of Domestic Ruminants (W-112Reg. Proj. Com.; pres. 1986). Protestant. Home: 604 W Patricia Dr Overton TX 75684-1526 Office: Tex A&M U Agrl Rsch & Extension Drawer E Overton TX 75684

RANDELL, JOSEPH DAVID, airline executive; b. Corner Brook, Newfoundland, Can., Feb. 20, 1954; s. Sterling A. and Mercedes O. (Locke) R.; m. Kathryn Janet Oxford, Sept. 3, 1977; children: David, Adam, Leah, Rebecca. B in Indsl. Engring., Tech. U. Nova Scotia, Halifax, 1976; MBA, Meml. U. Newfoundland, St. John's, 1985. Mgr. market devel. Ea. Provincial Airways, Gander, Newfoundland, 1976-77, asst. to v.p. mktg., 1977-78; dir. product planning Ea. Provincial Airways, Halifax, 1978-79; asst. mgr. Locke's Elec. Ltd., Corner Brook, 1979-80; v.p. Atlantis Corp. Ltd., St. John's 1981-86; trans. cons. Atlantis Cons. Ltd., St. John's, 1980-81; exec. v.p. Air Nova Inc., Halifax, 1986-88, pres., CEO, 1988—; Dir. Air Transp. Assn. Can., Ottawa, 1991, 92. Dir. Bedford (Can.) Econ. Devel. Commn., 1992; Izaak Walton Killam Hosp. Found.; mem. Tech. U. of Nova Scotia President's Adv. Program; mem. adv. bd. of the Frank H. Sobey Faculty of Commerce, Saint Mary's U. Sexton Scholar, Tech. U. Nova Scotia, 1976. Mem. Assn. Profl. Engrs. of Nova Scotia, Young President's Orgn. Anglican. Avocations: swimming, downhill and cross country skiing, tennis. Home: 110 Peregrine Crescent, Bedford, NS Canada B4A 3C1 Office: Air Nova, 310 Groudey Dr Halifax Int'l Airport, Enfield, NS Canada B2T 1E4

RANDHAVA, SERGE, electronics executive; b. 1941. With Air King Corp., Chgo., 1965-69; cons. in mfg., planning and control systems IIT Rsch. Inst., Chgo., 1969-74; supervisor in systems devel. Internat. Harvester, Hinsdale, Ill., 1974-75; with Xytel Corp., CEO. Office: Xytel Corp 801 E Business Center Dr Mount Prospect IL 60056*

RANDHAWA, BIKKAR SINGH, psychologist, educator; b. Jullundur, India, June 14, 1933; came to Can., 1961, naturalized, 1966; s. Pritam S. and Sawaran K. (Basakhi) R.; m. Leona Emily Bujnowski, Oct. 8, 1966; children—Jason, Lisa. B.A. in Math., Panjab U., 1954, B.T. in Edn., 1955, M.A. in History, 1959; B.Ed., U. Alta., Can., 1963; M.Ed. in Measurement and Evaluation, U. Toronto, Ont., Can., 1967, Ph.D., 1969. Registered psychologist. Tchr. secondary sch. math. Panjab, 1955-61; asst. headmaster, then headmaster, 1955-61; tchr. high sch. math. and sci. Beaver County, Riley, Alta., 1964-65, Camrose County, Alta., 1961-64; tchr. high sch. math. and sci. Edmonton (Alta.) Public Schs., 1965-67; tutor in math. for social sci. Ont. Inst. Studies in Edn., Toronto, 1968-69; mem. faculty U. Sask., Saskatoon, 1969-76, 77—; prof. ednl. psychology U. Sask., 1977—; asst. dean research and field services, 1982-87; prof., coord. Visual Scholars' Program, U. Iowa, 1976-77; cons. in field. Contbr. articles profl. jours. Fellow Am. Psychol. Assn., Am. Psychol. Soc. (charter), Can. Psychol. Assn., mem. Am. Ednl. Research Assn., Can. Soc. Study Edn., Nat. Coun. Measurement in Edn., Sask. Psychol. Assn., Phi Delta Kappa (pres. Saskatoon chpt. 1971, 85). Home: 510 Forsyth Crescent, Saskatoon, SK Canada S7N 4H8 Office: U Sask, 3117 Edn Bldg, Saskatoon, SK Canada S7N 0W0

RANDI, JAMES (RANDALL JAMES HAMILTON ZWINGE), magician, writer, educator; b. Toronto, Ont., Can., Aug. 7, 1928; naturalized U.S. citizen, 1987; s. George Randall and Marie Alice (Paradis) Zwinge. Student, Oakwood Collegiate Inst., Toronto, 1940-45; LittD (hon.), U. Indpls., 1995. Internationally known conjuror; regent's lectr. UCLA, 1984; skeptical lectr. on paranormal subjects. Author: The Magic of Uri Geller, 1975 (with Bert Sugar) Houdini, His Life and Art, 1978, Flim-Flam, 1982, Test Your ESP Potential, 1983, The Faith Healers, 1987, The Magic World of the Amazing Randi, 1989, The Mask of Nostradamus, 1990, James Randi: Psychic Investigator, 1991, Conjuring, 1992, An Encyclopedia of Claims, Frauds, and Hoaxes of the Occult and Supernatural, 1995; host TV spls. Recipient Blackstone award Internat. Platform Assn., 1983, 87, Forum award Am. Phys. Soc., 1988, Nat. Consumer Svc. award Nat. Coun. Against Health Fraud, 1988, Gold medal U. Ghent, Belgium, 1989, Humanist Disting. Svc. award Am. Humanist Assn., 1990, medal with golden wreath Hungarian Soc. for Dissemination Sci. Knowledge, 1992; MacArthur Found. fellow, 1986, Spl. fellow Acad. Magical Arts and Scis., 1987. Founding fellow Com. for Sci. Investigation of Claims of the Paranormal (exec. bd. dirs. 1973-91); mem. Am. Magicians (inducted into Hall of Fame 1988, named Internat. Amb. of Magic 1988). Performed at White House, 1974. Home and Office: 12000 NW 8th St Fort Lauderdale FL 33325-1406 *Irrationalism and the anti-science movement continue to grow, fed by the irresponsible media. Quack medicine, Creation "Science," TV psychics and other pseudo-scientific matters are heedlessly and increasingly embraced by the public. This flight into superstition must be checked; that can be done if legislators accept their responsiblity to look into the activities of those who publish wild claims with no foundation in fact. We are facing a crisis.*

RANDINELLI, TRACEY ANNE, magazine editor; b. Morristown, N.J., Apr. 6, 1963; d. Andrew R. and Patricia Ann (Brenner) R. BA in Comm., U. Del., 1985. Copywriter Macy's N.J., Newark, 1985-86; edit. asst. Globe Comms. Corp., N.Y.C., 1986-87; from asst. editor to assoc. editor Scholastic Math and DynaMath Mags. Scholastic, Inc., N.Y.C., 1987-89, editor Scholastic Math Mag., 1989—. Mem. Soc. Children's Book Writers, Ednl. Press Assn. Am. (Disting. Achievement award featrue article divsn. 1991, 95).

RANDLETT, GLORIA, clerk of the New Hampshire Senate; b. Concord, N.H., Aug. 9, 1946; d. Edwin Isreal and Edna Abby (Burley) Champagne; children: Darla Jean, David Damon, Daniel Webster. Mem. N.H. Ho. of Reps., Concord, 1979-80; asst. clk. N.H. Senate, Concord, 1980-89, clk., 1989—. Selectman, Town of Boscawen, N.H., 1983-85. Mem. Sons of Union Vets. of Civil War Aux. (sec. 1984-85), Patrons of Husbandry. Republican. Roman Catholic. Avocation: singing with folk music group. Home: 447 Buck St Suncook NH 03275-3053 Office: NH Senate Clerk State Hosue Rm 303 Concord NH 03301

RANDLETT, MARY WILLIS, photographer; b. Seattle, May 5, 1924; d. Cecil Durand and Elizabeth (Bayley) Willis; m. Herbert B. Randlett, Oct. 19, 1950 (div.); children—Robert, Mary Ann, Peter, Susan. B.A., Whitman Coll., Walla Walla, Wash., 1947. Freelance photographer, 1949—; one-person shows include Seattle Sci. Center, 1971, Western Wash. State U., 1971, Seattle Art Mus., 1971, Art Gallery of Greater Victoria, 1972, Alaska State Mus., 1972, State Capitol Mus., 1983, Whatcom Mus. History and Art, Bellingham, Wash., 1986, Janet Huston Gallery, LaConner, Wash., 1990, Gov.'s Office of Gov., Olympia, Wash., 1991, Stonington Gallery, Seattle, 1992, Valley Mus. Art, LaConner, 1992, others; group shows: Am. Soc. Mag. Photographers, 1970, Whatcom Mus., Bellingham, Wash., Henry Gallery, Seattle, 1971, 74, Royal Photog. Soc., 1979, Heard Mus., Phoenix, 1979, Gov.'s Invitational State Capital Mus., Olympia, Wash., 1983, Helmi Interpretations N.W. Indian Art State Capital Mus., 1984, The Small Show Santa Fe Ctr. for Photography, 1987, Wash. State Capital Mus., 1988, Wash. State Capital Mus., Olympia, 1988, 89, 93, Tacoma (Wash.) Art Mus., 1989, Helen Day Art Ctr., Stowe, Vt., 1989, Valley Mus. Northwest Art, LaConner, 1991, Allen Libr. U. Wash., Seattle, 1991, Wing Luke Asian Mus., Seattle, 1991, Cheney Cowles Mus., Spokane, 1991, Security Pacific Gallery, Seattle, 1992, Benham Gallery, Seattle, 1993, Stonington Gallery, 1993, Rainier Club, Seattle, 1994, Valley Mus. of Northwest Art, La Conner, Wash., 1994, Port Angeles Fine Arts Ctr., Port Angeles, Wash., 1994, Mus. History and Industry, Seattle, 1994, Whatcom Mus., Bellingham, Wash., 1994, others; works represented in permanent collections Met. Mus., Nat. Collection of Fine Arts, Nat. Portrait Gallery, Washington State Library, Manuscript div. U. Wash., Pacific Northwest Bell, Seattle, Swedish Med. Center, Seattle, Whatcom Mus., Bellingham, Henry Gallery, Seattle, Wash. State Capitol Mus., Olympia, Phillips Collection, Washington; works appeared in books: The Master and His Fish (Roderick Haig-Brown), 1982; Theodore Roethke: The Journey to I and Otherwide (Neal Bowers), 1982; Mountain in the Clouds (Bruce Brown), 1982; Masonry in Architecture (Louis Redstone), 1982; Writings and Reflections from the World of Roderick Haig-Brown, 1982; Pike Place Market (Alice Shorett and Murray Morgan), 1982; The Dancing Blanket, (Cheryl Samuel), 1982, Collected Poems of Theodore Roethke, 1982; Spires of Form (Victor Scheffer), 1983; Assault on Mount Helicon (Mary Barnard), 1983; New as a Wave (Eve Triem), 1983; Sketchbook: A Memoir of the '30's and the Northwest School (William Cumming), 1983; Good Intentions (Jane Adams), 1985; Blackbirds of the Americas (Gordon Orians and Tony Angell), 1985; Historic Preservation in Seattle (Larry Kreisman), 1985; Down Town Seattle Walking Tours (Mary Randlett and Carol Tobin), 1986; Seattle, the Seattle Book, 1986; When Orchids were Flowers (Kate Knap Johnson), 1986, Jacob Lawrence, American Painter, (Ellen Wheat), 1986, Manic Power: Robert Lowell and His Circle, (Jeffrey Meyers), 1987, The Isamu Noguchi Garden Museum, (Isamu Noguchi), 1987, Washington's Audacious State Capitol and its Builders, (Norman Johnston), 1988, The Bloedel Reserve: Gardens in the Forest, (Lawrence Kreisman), 1988, Washingtonians: A Biographical Portrait of the State on the Occasion of its Centennial, 1988, Directory of Literary Biography: Canadian Writers 1920-59, 2d series, 1989, Crafts of America, 1989, The Lone Tree Tragedy (Bruce Brown), 1989, Northwest Coast Handbook of North American Indians, 1990, Dancing on the Rim of the World, 1990, Openings, Original Essays by Contemporary Soviet and American Writers (eds. Robert Atwan, Valeri Vinokurov), 1990, George Tsutakawa (Martha Kingsbury), 1990, Contemporary American Poetry (ed. Al Polin Jr.), 1991, Natural History of Puget Sound Country (Arthur Kruckberg), 1991, Bones (Joyce Thompson), 1991, Cebu (Peter Basho), 1991, Catalogue of Historic Preservation Publications, 1992, Art in Seattle's Public Places (James Rupp), 1992, The Olympic Rainforest (Ruth Kirk with Jerry Franklin), 1992, Steelhead Fly Fishing, (Trey Combs), 1992, Illustrated Guidelines for Rehabilitation Historic Buildings, 1993, A History of African American Artists (Bearden and Henderson), 1994, Childrens Literature Review Vol. 1, 1994, Invisible Gardens: The Search for Modernism in the American Landscape (Walker and Simo), 1994, Seeing Seattle (Roger Sale), 1994, Reaching Home (Jay and Matson), 1994others; works also appeared in newspapers and mags. Nat. Endowment for Arts grantee, 1976; recipient Wash. State Gov.'s award for spl. commendation for contbns. in field of photography, 1983, Individual Artist award King County Arts Commn., 1989. Mem. Am. Soc. Mag. Photographers. Home: PO Box 10536 Bainbridge Island WA 98110

RANDOLPH, ALAN DEAN, chemical engineering educator; b. Muskogee, Okla., Mar. 25, 1934; married 1957, 3 children. BSChE, U. Colo., 1956; MSChE, Iowa State U., 1959, PhD in Crystallization, 1962. Asst. tech. Shell Chem. Corp., 1956-58; rsch. proj. engr. Am. Potash & Chem. Corp., Calif.,

1962-65; head crystallization sec. Res. Dept., 1965; assoc. prof. chem. engr. U. Fla., 1965-68; vis. prof. U. Colo. London, 1981, cons.Comt Nuclear Waste Immobilization, 1971-79, Los Alamos Sci. Lab, 1978-81, US Borax, 1978-82. Recipient Clarence Gerhold award Am. Inst. Chem. Engrs., 1993. Mathematical simulation description and control of particulate systems, especially crystallization processes, theoretical and experimental study of nucleation-growth rate kinetics and residence-time distribution of particulate systems. Home: 2131 Rainbow Vista Dr Tucson AZ 85712-2910*

RANDOLPH, ARTHUR RAYMOND, federal judge, lawyer; b. Riverside, N.J., Nov. 1, 1943; m. Eileen J. O'Connor, May 18, 1984; children from previous marriage: John Trevor, Cynthia Lee. BS, Drexel U., 1966; JD summa cum laude, U. Pa., 1969. Bar: Calif. 1970, D.C. 1973, U.S. Supreme Ct. 1973. Law clk. to hon. judge Henry J. Friendly U.S. Ct. Appeals, 2d Cir., N.Y.C., 1969-70; asst. to solicitor gen. U.S. Dept. Justice, Washington, 1970-73, dep. solicitor gen., 1975-77; ptnr. Sharp, Randolph & Green, Washington, 1977-83, Randolph & Truitt, Washington, 1983-87, Pepper, Hamilton & Scheetz, Washington, 1987-90; judge U.S. Ct. Appeals (D.C. cir.), Washington, 1990—; spl. asst. atty. gen. State of Mont., 1983-90, State of N.Mex., 1985-90, State of Utah, 1986-90; mem. adv. panel Fed. Cts. Study Com., 1989-90; spl. counsel Com. on Standards of Ofcl. Conduct, U.S. Ho. of Reps., 1979-80; adj. prof. law Georgetown U. Law Ctr., 1974-78; exec. sec. Atty. Gen.'s Com. on Reform of Fed. Jud. System, 1975-77; mem. com. on Fed. Rules of Evidence U.S. Justice Dept., 1972; chmn. Com. on Govtl. Structures, McLean, Va., 1973-74; adj. prof. law sch. George Mason U., 1992; mem. com. codes conduct Jud. Conf. U.S., 1993—. Recipient Spl. Achievement award U.S. Dept. Justice, 1971. Mem. Am. Law Inst., Calif. Bar Assn., D.C. Bar Assn., Order of Coif. Office: US Ct Appeals 3rd Constitution Ave NW Washington DC 20001

RANDOLPH, CARL LOWELL, chemical company executive; b. Pasadena, Calif., May 30, 1922; s. Carl L. and Lulu (McBride) R.; m. Jane Taber, June 25, 1943; children—Margaret, Stephen. B.A., Whittier Coll., 1943; M.S., U. So. Calif., 1947, Ph.D., 1949; LL.D. (hon.), Whittier Coll., 1982; D. Pub. Service (hon.), U. Alaska, 1983. Prin. chemist Aerojet-Gen. Corp., 1949-57; v.p. U.S. Borax Research Corp., Anaheim, Calif., 1957-63; asst. to pres. U.S. Borax & Chem. Corp., Los Angeles, 1963-66; v.p. U.S. Borax & Chem. Corp., 1966-68, exec. v.p., 1968-69, pres., 1969-86, vice chmn., 1983-87. Trustee, chmn. bd. Whittier Coll., emeritus 1969—; bd. dirs., chmn., Ind. Colls. So. Calif., 1982—. Served from ensign to lt. (j.g.) USNR, 1944-46. Mem. Phi Beta Kappa, Sigma Xi. Home: 1407 Seaview Way Anacortes WA 98221-9794

RANDOLPH, DAVID, conductor; b. N.Y.C., Dec. 21, 1914; s. Morris and Elsie (Goodman) R.; m. Mildred Greenberg, July 18, 1948. BS, CCNY, 1936; MA, Tchrs. Coll., Columbia U., 1941. Music specialist OWI, N.Y.C., 1943-47; adj. prof. music NYU, 1948-85, Mostly Mozart course, 1976-85; lectr. Town Hall, N.Y.C., 1955-60, Columbia U., 1957, Cosmopolitan Club, N.Y.C., 1962-63; pre-concert lectr. N.Y. Philharmonic, Avery Fisher Hall, 1964-86,Cleve. Orch., 1981, Vienna Symphony Orch., 1988; tchr. conducting Dalcroze Sch., 1948-49; music commentator Little Orch. Soc. Concerts and Broadcasts, 1950-62, Met. Opera Intermission Broadcasts; vis. prof. music SUNY-New Paltz, 1970-72, Fordham U., 1972-73; lectr. New Sch. for Social Rsch., 1973—, IBM, N.Y.C., 1978-86, Beethoven Soc., 1977, 83; prof. music Montclair State Coll., Upper Montclair, N.J., 1973-87; guest cond. Rockland County (N.Y.) Ann. Choral Festival, 1972, 73; adviser film Music to Live By, mem. N.J. Arts Council, 1967-70; mem. music com. Gov. N.J.'s Commn. to Study Arts, 1965; honored guest Handel Festival, Halle, Fed. Republic Germany, 1991. Cond. Randolph Singers, 1944-62 (appeared on NBC Today, and Tonight Shows), United Choral Soc., 1961-86, N.J. Ballet Orch., 1977, 83, Masterwork Chamber Orch., 1982, 83, The Philharmonia Orch. in Brahms' Requiem, London, 1988, Barge Concert, N.Y.C., 1987, 89; guest condr., Conn. Symphony Orch., 1961; condr. concert tour Spain with Am. choruses and Radio TV Orch. of Moscow, 1992; music annotator, CBS, N.Y.C., 1947-48; yearly choral seminar leader Mohonk Mountain House, 1986—; music dir., condr. Masterwork Chorus and Orch., 1955-93, St. Cecilia Chorus and Orch., N.Y.C., 1965—; numerous performances at Carnegie Hall including Brahms' Requiem, Mozart's Requiem, Mozart's C Minor Mass, Beethoven's Missa Solemnis, Bach's Mass in B Minor, St. John Passion, St. Matthew Passion, Christmas Oratorio, Vaughan Williams' A Sea Symphony, Hodie, Verdi's Requiem, Mendelssohn's Elijah, Die erste Walpurgisnacht, Poulenc's Gloria, Berlioz' Requiem, Avery Fisher Hall, Lincoln Ctr., N.Y.C. and Kennedy Ctr., Washington (including 166 complete performances of Handel's Messiah); broadcaster: David Randolph Concerts, WNYC and numerous radio stas. of Nat. Assn. Ednl. Broadcasters, 1946-79, Young Audience telecasts, CBS-TV, 1958-59, series of candid rehearsals of Bach's Mass in B minor, PBS, 1965; host: weekly broadcasts Lincoln Ctr. Spotlight, Sta. WQXR, N.Y.C., 1966-67; regular guest critic First Hearing program Sta. WQXR, N.Y.C., and 68 other stas., 1986—; author: This Is Music, 1964, numerous album jacket notes; editor: David Randolph Choral Series; writer, narrator: Instruments of the Orchestra, 1958, Stereo Review's Guide to Understanding Music, 1973; music critic, High Fidelity Mag., 1952-57; composer: A Song for Humanity, 1968, Andante for Strings, Edward; contbg. author: The N.Y. Times Guide to Listening Pleasure, 1968; Recs. for Columbia, Vanguard, Westminster, Concert Hall Soc., Esoteric records; analyzed Mendelssohn's Symphony No. 3 on records for Book of Month Club. Recipient 1st award for edn. by radio Ohio State Inst., 1948, 50, 51, Sylvania TV award, 1959, Disting. Alumni award Columbia U., 1982, cert. of appreciation Mayor of City of N.Y. at Carnegie Hall, 1991. Address: Apt 4-C 420 E 86th St New York NY 10028-6456

RANDOLPH, FRANCIS FITZ, JR., cable television executive; b. N.Y.C., July 13, 1927; s. Francis Fitz and Sarah Tod (Bulkley) R.; m. Catherine Ann Meyers, June 6, 1969. BA, Yale U., 1950; LLB, Columbia U., 1953. Bar: U.S. Ct. Appeals (2d cir.) 1954. Law clk. to presiding judge U.S. Ct. Appeals 2d cir., 1953-54; assoc. Cravath, Swaine & Moore, N.Y.C., 1954-61, ptnr., 1962-81; vice chmn. Cablevisions Systems Corp., Woodbury, N.Y., 1982-94; ret., chmn. Exec. com. NAACP Legal Def. Fund, N.Y., 1968-80; trustee Vassar Coll., 1980-92. With USN, 1946. Mem. N.Y. Bar Assn., Assn. of Bar of City of N.Y., Down Town Assn., Union Club; Silver Spring Country Club (Ridgefield, Conn.). Democrat. Office: Cablevision Systems Corp 1 Media Crossway Dr Woodbury NY 11797-2062

RANDOLPH, JACKSON HAROLD, utility company executive; b. Cin., Nov. 17, 1930; s. Dward Bradley and Cora Belle (Puckett) R.; m. Angelina Losito, June 20, 1958; children: Terri, Patti, Todd, Craig. B.B.A., U. Cin., 1958, M.B.A., 1968. C.P.A., Ohio. Acct. Arthur Andersen & Co., Cin., 1958-59; with Cin. Gas & Electric Co., 1959—, v.p. fin. and corp. affairs, 1981-85, exec. v.p./ 1985-86, chmn., pres., chief exec. officer, 1986—, also dir.; chmn., CEO CINergy Corp., 1994—; also pres. Union Light Heat and Power Co., Covington, Ky.; bd. dirs. Cen. Trust Bank, N.A., Cin. Fin. Corp., PNC Corp.; chmn., CEO CINergy Corp., 1994—. V.p., bd. dirs. Gen. Protestant Orphan Home, Cin., 1981-86; treas., bd. dirs. Cin. chpt. ARC, 1975—; mem. adv. com. Catherine Booth Home, 1980—, Dan Beard council Boy Scouts Am., 1985. Served with USN, 1951-55. Mem. Cin. Country Club, Queen City Club, Met. Club, Bankers Club, Delta Sigma Pi, Phi Eta Sigma, Beta Gamma Sigma. Home: 414 Bishopsbridge Dr Cincinnati OH 45255-3900 Office: CINergy Corp 139 E 4th St Cincinnati OH 45202-4034 also: Union Light Heat & Power Co 107 Brent Spence Sq Covington KY 41011

RANDOLPH, JAMES C., professor; b. Knox City, Tex., Mar. 26, 1944; s. James T. and Helen (Collier) R.; m. Mary C. Broihier, Aug. 24, 1985. BA, U. Tex., 1966, MA, 1968; PhD, Carleton U., 1972. Staff ecologist Environ. Sciences Div. Oak Ridge (Tenn.) Nat. Lab., 1972-74; asst. prof. Ind. U., Bloomington, 1974-77, assoc. prof., 1977-83, prof., 1983—; assoc. dean Sch. Pub. & Environ. Affairs, Bloomington, 1986—; chmn. Ind. Energy Devel. Bd., Indpls., 1988—. Mem. Ecol. Soc. Am. (sect. chmn. 1987—). Home: 3470 Pitkin Rd Martinsville IN 46151-9523 Office: Ind U Nat Inst Global Environ Change SPEA Rm 441 Bloomington IN 47405

RANDOLPH, JAMES HARRISON, SR., realty company executive; b. Springfield, Tenn., Feb. 17, 1917; s. Bayless Jones and Effie Lee (Cummings) R.; m. Millicent Roma Lincoln, Aug. 14, 1943; 1 child, James Har-

rison. BSBA, U. Tenn., 1940. Spl. agt., adminstrv. asst. to dir. FBI, Washington, 1942-52; personnel dir. Dallas Housing Authority, 1952-54; real estate broker Bolanz & Bolanz, Dallas, 1954-58; real estate broker, investor Jim Randolph & Co., Dallas, 1958—. Former bd. govs. U. Tenn. Mem. Soc. Former Spl. Agts. of FBI, Greater Dallas Assn. Realtors (life), Soc. Indsl. and Office Realtors, Dallas C. of C. (hon. life), Scarabbean, Brookhaven Country Club (Dallas), Phi Sigma Kappa. Baptist. Home and Office: 11433 Lamplighter Ln Dallas TX 75229-2900

RANDOLPH, JENNINGS, JR. (JAY RANDOLPH), sportscaster; b. Cumberland, Md., Sept. 19, 1934; s. Jennings and Mary Katherine (Babb) R.; m. Sue Henderson, May 28, 1966; children: Jennings, Brian Robert, Rebecca Sue. B.A., Salem (W.Va.) Coll., 1963. Sports and promotion dir. Sta. WHAR, Clarksburg, W.Va., 1958-61; sportscaster Sta. KLIF, Dallas, 1963-66; Sta. KMOX, St. Louis, 1966-68; with Sta. KSDK-TV, St. Louis, 1968—; sports dir. Sta. KSDK-TV, 1968-88, spl. sports corr., 1988—, also on nationally televised broadcasts for various sports events.; TV announcer Fla. Marlins Baseball Club, Ft. Lauderdale, 1993—; TV announcer St. Louis Cardinals, 1970-87, Cin. Reds., 1988; mem. NBC's broadcast staff for 1988 Olympics, Seoul, Korea and 1992 Summer Games, Barcelona, Spain; host nationally syndicated The Golf Show. Trustee Salem Coll., 1976-89. With U.S. Army, 1954-56. Inducted into Boys and Girls Clubs of Am. Hall of Fame, 1990. Mem. Nat. Assn. Sportscasters, Delta Tau Delta. Amateur golf champion. Office: The Fla Marlins 2267 NW 199th St Miami FL 33056

RANDOLPH, JOE WAYNE, machine manufacturing executive; b. Madisonville, Ky., Aug. 5, 1938; s. Albert Clay and Helen (Brown) R.; m. Mary Ann Rabenau, July 20, 1963; children: Ann E., Charles J. BS, Murray State U., 1962, MS, 1964; MBA, Washington U./Lindenwood Coll., 1978. High sch. tchr. Benton (Ky.) Sch. System, 1962-64, St. Charles (Mo.) Sch. System, 1964-65; mfg. mgr. Sunnen Products Co., St. Louis, 1967—. 1st lt. U.S. Army, 1965. Named Col., Hon. Order of Ky. Cols., 1990. Mem. AAIM Mgmt. Assn. (prodn. exec. round table, leader 1984—), Elks. Avocations: golf, fishing, travel, hunting. Home: 5700 Hwy T Augusta MO 63332 Office: Sunnen Products Co 7910 Manchester Rd Saint Louis MO 63143

RANDOLPH, JOHN, actor; b. Bronx, June 1, 1915; s. Louis and Dorothy (Shore) Cohen; Jan. 3, 1942; m. Sarah Cunningham Randolph; children—Martha Eoline, Harrison Henry. Student, CCNY, 1932-35, Columbia U., summer 1934. Artistic cons. Phila. Drama Guild. Appeared in Broadway plays Broadway Bound, 1986-87 (Tony award 1986-87), The Visit; films Serpico, Heaven Can Wait, Prizzi's Honor; numerous TV appearances including Lucas Tanner, Blind Ambition, M*A*S*H, Bob Newhart Show, Roseanne, Grand, A Foreign Field; adaptations include Portrait of an Artist (J. Joyce), 1961-62, Magic Mountain (T. Mann); 1963; TV drama Jew in Old Country, 1965, The Unknown Chekhov, 1965. V.p. U.S. Com. for Friendship with German Dem. Republic, 1978-90; chmn. Nat. Council for U.S. Soviet Friendship, 1987-90; bd. dirs. Theatricum Botanicum, Topanga, Calif., Access Theater of Santa Barbara; bd. dirs. Nat. Com. Against Racist and Polit. Repression; mem. adv. com. TransAfrica. With USAAF, 1942-46. Recipient Paul Robeson medal German Democratic Republic Soc., Berlin, 1980, Drama Desk award, 1986-87, Plaque award Abraham Lincoln Brigade. Mem. Actors Equity Assn. (council 1958-63, dir.), Acad. Motion Picture Arts and Scis., Nat. TV Acad., Screen Actors Guild (dir. 1972-93), AFTRA (bd. dirs. 1986-93), Actors Fund Am. (life). Office: Paradigm Agy 10100 Santa Monica Blvd Los Angeles CA 90067*

RANDOLPH, JUDSON GRAVES, pediatric surgeon; b. Macon, Ga., July 19, 1927; s. Milton Fitz and Abigail Theresa (Graves) R.; m. Susan Comfort Adams, June 14, 1952; children: Somers, Garrett, Judson, Adam, Comfort. BA, Vanderbilt U., 1950, MD, 1953. Intern in surgery U. Rochester, N.Y., 1953-54; asst. resident in pathology Vanderbilt U., 1954-55; asst. resident, then sr. resident in surgery Mass. Gen. Hosp., Boston, 1956-58; asst. resident in surgery Children's Hosp., Boston, 1955-56, sr. resident, then chief resident, 1958-61, asst. surgeon, 1961-63; teaching fellow to instr. surgery Med. Sch. Harvard U., 1960-63; jr. assoc. in surgery Peter Bent Brigham Hosp., Boston, 1961-63; surgeon-in-chief Children's Hosp., Washington, 1964-91; mem. faculty Med. Sch. George Washington U., 1964-91, prof. surgery and child health, 1968-91; prof. surgery Meharry Med. Coll., 1992—; cons. Naval Med. Ctr., NIH, Walter Reed Army Med. Ctr.; trustee Children's Hosp. Nat. Med. Ctr., 1972-84, Vanderbilt U., 1980—. Editor: Pediatric Surgery, 3d edit., 2 vols., 1979, 4th edit., 2 vols., 1985, The Injured Child, 1980; mem. editl. bd. Surgery, 1978-92; contbr. numerous articles to med. jours. With USNR, 1945-46, PTO. Mem. ACS (gov. 1969-75), AMA, Am. Acad. Pediats. (chmn. exec. com. surg. sect. 1974-75), Am. Assn. Thoracic Surgery, Am. Pediat. Surg. Assn. (gov. 1980—, pres. 1984), Washington Acad. Surgery (pres. 1989), Soc. U. Surgeons, Am. Surg. Assn., So. Surg. Assn., Am. Bd. Surgery (bd. dirs. 1973-79, diplomate), Alpha Omega Alpha (faculty), Cosmos Club (Washington). Methodist.

RANDOLPH, LILLIAN LARSON, medical association executive; b. Spokane, Wash., May 3, 1932; d. Charles P. and Juanita S. (Parrish) Larson; m. Philip L. Randolph, Nov. 12, 1952; children: Marcus, Andrew. BA, U. Wash., 1954, MA, 1956; PhD, U. Calif., Berkeley, 1966; EdD, N.Mex. State U., 1979. Researcher U. Wash., Seattle, 1954-59; asst. prof. Calif. State U. Hayward, 1964-68, U. Tex., El Paso, 1972-74; dir. S.W. Conservatory of Music, El Paso, 1972-74; adj. prof. Loyola U. and DePaul U., Chgo., 1974-78; asst. prof. DeVry Inst. Tech., Lombard, Ill., 1982-84; mgr. AMA, Chgo. 1985—; cons. Weber Co., Chgo., 1979-85. Author: Fundamentals of Government Organizations, 1971, Third Party Settlement of Disputes, 1973. Mem. AAUP, Phi Beta Kappa. Home: 408 W Wilshire Dr Wilmette IL 60091-3154

RANDOLPH, LINDA JANE, mathematics educator; b. Ypsilanti, Mich., Feb. 25, 1942; d. Roy Lawrence and Sarah (Jefferson) Robinson; m. Jerry F. Basler; children: Deborah L. Bolton, Sandra A. Randolph. BS in Teaching and Math., Ea. Mich. U., 1983, M in Math., 1989, postgrad., 1989—. Math. tutor Ea. Mich. U., Ypsilanti, 1980-82, supr. adult edn., tchr., 1983-94, instr. math.; substitute tchr. Tecumseh (Mich.) Pub. Sch., 1983-91; instr. math, program coord. UAW-FORD/EMU Milan Plastic Plant, 1991-94; peer-advisor Acad. Svcs. Ctr., Ea. Mich. U., 1979-83; lecturer computer sci. dept. Ea. Mich. U., 1986-89, equity program, 1990-91. Mem. Am. Math. Assn., Mich. Math. Assn., Bus. and Profl. Women (v.p. chpt. 1991-92, sec. 1994-95), Nat. Edn. Computing Conf., Mich. Assn. Computer Users in Learning, Ea. Mich. U. Alumni Assn. (bd. dirs.). Home: 1414 Collegewood Ypsilanti MI 48197-1672 Office: Ea Mich U 34 N Washington Ypsilanti MI 48197

RANDOLPH, ROBERT DEWITT, lawyer; b. Sligo, Pa., Mar. 6, 1929; s. DeWitt Lyman and Hazel Irene (McCall) R.; m. Betty Ann McElhattan, May 8, 1953 (dec. Aug. 1979); children: Douglas, Andrew; m. Susan Denise Hopkins, Oct. 15, 1988. BA, Westminster Coll., 1951; LLB, Harvard U., 1957. Bar: Ohio 1958, Pa. 1960, U.S. Supreme Ct. 1981. Assoc. Buckingham, Doolittle & Burroughs, Akron, Ohio, 1957-59, Rose, Houston, Cooper & Schmidt, Pitts., 1959-60, 61-65; fgn. svc. officer U.S. Dept. State, Washintgon, 1960-61; ptnr. Houston, Cooper, Spear & German, Pitts., 1965-70, Randolph & O'Connor, Pitts., 1970-74, Buchanan Ingersoll P.C., Pitts., 1974-93. Pres. Assn. Retarded Citizens Allegheny, Pitts., 1990-92. With U.S. Army, 1951-54. Mem. ABA, Pa. Bar Assn., Allegheny County Bar Assn., Indsl. Rels. Rsch. Assn. Western Pa. (pres. 1987-88), Duquesne Club, St. Clair Country Club. Democrat. Presbyterian. Avocations: golf, skiing. Home: 750 Washington Rd Pittsburgh PA 15228

RANDOLPH, ROBERT LEE, economist, educator; b. East St. Louis, Ill., Jan. 2, 1926; s. John Andrew and Willye (Smith) R.; m. Patricia Smith, June 13, 1954 (div. 1986); 1 dau., Heather Elizabeth. A.B., DePauw U., Greencastle, Ind., 1948; M.S., U. Ill., Urbana, 1954, Ph.D., 1958; postdoctoral student, Case Western Res. U., 1960, U. Mich., 1962. From instr. to assoc. prof. econs. Springfield (Mass.) Coll., 1958-65, chmn. dept., 1960-63, dir. eve. and summer schs., 1960-64; dep. exec. dir. Equal Employment Opportunity Commn., Washington, 1967-68; dep. assoc. dir. Job Corps, 1965-67; exec. v.p. Chgo. State U., 1969-73; pres. Westfield (Mass.) Coll., 1973-79; vice-chancellor Mass. State Coll. System, 1979-81; pres. Ala. State U., 1981-83; prof. econs. U. Montevallo, Ala., 1983-86; pres. Randolph Assocs., Birmingham, Ala., Boston, 1983-91, Hyannis, Mass., 1991—; pres. State C.C., East St. Louis, Ill., 1993-95; cons. to industry. Author articles, monographs. Vice pres. Springfield Urban League, 1962-66; Bd. dirs.

Wesson Hosp., Springfield, Holyoke (Mass.) Hosp., Sickle-Cell Anemia Found. Served to lt. (j.g.) USNR, 1943-45, 50-51. Decorated Bronze Star; recipient Danforth Found. award, 1943; Republic Steel Found. award, 1961; Vice Pres.'s award excellence pub. service U.S. Govt., 1967; Outstanding Alumni award Lincoln High Sch., E. St. Louis, 1973, Alumni Svc. award U. Ill., 1990, DePauw U., 1991; Navy V-12 scholar, 1943-45; State of Ill. scholar, 1952-56; Bailey fellow, 1957-58, Carnegie fellow, 1962. Mem. Am. Assn. State Colls. and Univs. (chmn. personnel com. 1974-75), Am. Assn. Polit. and Social Scis., Am. Econ. Assn., Phi Delta Kappa, Alpha Phi Omega, Kappa Alpha Psi. Clubs: Quandrangle (Chgo.); Internat. (Washington). Home: 101 John Joseph Rd Harwich MA 02645

RANDOLPH, ROBERT RAYMOND, lawyer; b. San Antonio, Mar. 19, 1937; s. Ellis C. and Evelyn (Baxter) R.; children: Robert Cean, Grayson Moore, Justin Ellis Beloff; m. Margaret N. Lloyd, May 29, 1989. BSEE, U. Tex., 1960, LLB, 1962. Bar: Tex. 1962. Assoc. Branscomb, Gary, Thomasson & Hall, Corpus Christi, Tex., 1962-63; atty. Tidewater Oil Co., Houston, 1963-64; asst. atty. Harris County, Houston, 1964-65; ptnr. Vinson & Elkins L.L.P., Houston, 1965—. Mem. ABA, Tex. Bar Assn., Houston Bar Assn., Greater Houston Partnership, South Main Ctr. Assn., Greater Houston Convention & Visitors Bur. Home: 1812 Albans St Houston TX 77005-1706 Office: Vinson & Elkins LLP 2701 First City Tower 1001 Fannin St Houston TX 77002-6760

RANDOM, IDA, production designer. Art dir.: (films) On Golden Pond, 1981, Partners, 1982, Frances, 1982; prodn. designer: (TV movies) The Kid from Nowhere, 1982, First Flight, 1989, (films) The Big Chill, 1983, Irreconcilable Differences, 1984, Body Double, 1984, Silverado, 1985, About Last Night..., 1986, Throw Momma from the Train, 1987, Who's That Girl?, 1987, Rainman, 1988 (Academy award nomination best art direction 1988), The War of the Roses, 1989, How I Got into College, 1989, Defending Your Life, 1991, Hoffa, 1992, Housesitter, 1992, Wyatt Earp, 1994. Office: care Spyros Skouras Sanford Skouras Gross & Assoc 1015 Gayley Ave 3rd Fl Los Angeles CA 90024*

RANDOUR, PAUL A(LFRED), lawyer; b. Bakersfield, Calif., Aug. 15, 1935; s. Alfred Edward and Shirley (Sutherland) R. A.B., Stanford U., 1957, LL.B., 1960; Jur.Drs., Leiden U., The Netherlands, 1961. Bar: Calif. 1962, N.Y. 1963. Assoc. Cahill, Gordon & Reindel, N.Y.C., 1962-65; atty. Gen. Electric Co., N.Y.C., 1965-66; assoc. Chadbourne, Parke, Whiteside & Wolff, N.Y.C., 1966-72, ptnr., 1972-85; sr. v.p., gen. counsel Am. Brands, Inc., N.Y.C., 1986-91; counsel Chadbourne & Parke, 1992-94, ptnr., 1994—. Mem. Assn. of Bar of City of N.Y., Internat. Bar Assn. Clubs: University, Explorers. Office: Chadbourne & Parke, 86 Jermyn St, London SW1 6JD, England

RANDS, BERNARD, composer, educator; b. Sheffield, Eng., Mar. 2, 1934. B.Music, U. Wales, 1956, M.Music, 1958; pvt. student composition, 1958-62. Former concert performer Europe, Australia and U.S.; co-founding artistic dir. Contemp Music. Fest, Calif. Inst. Arts; lectr. U. Wales, 1963-67; vis. fellow Princeton U., N.J., 1967-68; mem. faculty music, Granada fellow creative arts York U., 1968-75; composer in residence U. Ill, 1969-70; fellow creative arts Brasenose Coll., Oxford U., Eng., 1972-73; prof. music U. Calif.-San Diego, 1976-85, founder, conductor SONOR; prof. music Boston U., 1985-89, Harvard U., 1989—. Compositions include Actions for Six, 1963, Wildtrack 1, 2 & 3, 1969-75, Mésalliance, 1972, AUM, 1974, Madrigali, 1977, déjà, 1979, Obbligato, 1980, Canti Lunatici, 1980/81, Canti del Sole for tenor and orch., 1982/83 (Pulitzer prize 1984), Le Tambourin: Sts. #1 and 2, 1984, Hiraeth for cello and orch., 1987, Ceremonial II, 1988, "...in the receding mist...", 1988, "...among the voices...", 1988, "...body and shadow...", 1989, Bells, 1989, Canti dell' Eclisse for bass and orch., 1991, Canti d'Amor, 1991, "...where the murmurs die...", 1991-92, Symphony, 1994, Canzoni per Orch., 1995. Harkness Internat. fellow Commonwealth Fund N.Y., 1966; grantee Nat. Endowment Arts, 1977; recipient Calif. Arts Council award, 1978, Koussevitzky award, 1984, 94, Barlow award, 1994. Office: Harvard U Dept Music Cambridge MA 02138

RANDT, CLARK THORP, physician, educator; b. Lakewood, Ohio, Nov. 18, 1917; s. Herbert W. and Bessie (Thorp) R.; m. Mary-Louise Paull Mitchell, Jan. 15, 1944; children: Clark Thorp, Dana M., Thomas P. A.B., Colgate U., 1940; M.D. Western Res. U., 1943. Intern, Univ. Hosps., Cleve., 1943-45; resident Neurol. Inst. N.Y., 1947-50; practice medicine, specializing in neurology N.Y.C., 1962-87; asst. in neurology Coll. Physicians and Surgeons, Columbia U., 1949-50; asso. prof. neurology Sch. Medicine, Western Res. U., 1950-59; dir. life sci. NASA, Washington, 1959-61; prof. neurology Sch. Medicine, NYU, 1962-70, prof., chmn. dept. neurology, 1970-87, prof. neurology emeritus, 1988—; established NASA Ames Research Ctr., Life Sci. Lab., Calif., 1960; dir. Neurology Service, NYU-Bellevue Med. Center, also NYU Hosp.; cons. in neurology N.Y. VA Hosp., 1962-87; dir. life scis. NASA, Washington, 1959-61; chief neurology sect. U.S. Army Psychiat. Center, Mason Gen. Hosp., Brentwood, N.Y.; co-chmn. NASA-DOD bioastronautics coordinating com., Washington, 1960-61. Served to capt. M.C., AUS, 1945-47. Fellow Am. Acad. Neurology; mem. Am. Neurol. Assn., N.Y. Neurol. Soc. (pres. 1967-68), Aerospace Med. Assn. (v.p. 1961-62), Assn. for Research in Nervous and Mental Disease (chmn. bd. trustees 1972-73). Home: 59 Husted Ln Greenwich CT 06830-3907 Dreams are a prelude to accomplishment. The determining influence of self-fulfilling prophecy cannot be overestimated.

RANE, MICHAEL GREGORY, preservation company executive; b. Dothan, Ala., Sept. 30, 1952; s. Anthony J. and Elizabeth (Mills) R.; m. Kathleen Mace, 1984; children: Keith, Kylie, Tom, G.G. BS in Mktg., Auburn U., 1974. Exec. v.p. Great Southern Wood Preserving, Inc., Abbeville, Ala., 1971—. Office: Great Southern Wood Preserving US Hwy 431 N Abbeville AL 36310

RANEY, LEON A., librarian; b. Charleston, Ark., Jan. 14, 1939; s. J.D. Raney and Grace (Dunn) Pugh; m. Mary Lee Wilson, May 17, 1958; children: Joel, Jason. BSE, U. Cin. Ark., 1960; MS, La. State U., 1962; PhD, Ind. U., 1972. Libr. Grant Parish Libr., Colfax, La., 1962-64; catalog dept. head Ark. State U. Libr., Jonesboro, 1964-66; acquisitions libr. U. Okla. Libr., Norman, 1966-69; grad. teaching fellow Ind. U, Bloomington, 1969-72; dean librs. S.D. State U., Brookings, 1972—; cons. libr. Botswana Agrl. Coll., Gabrone, 1981, Northwestern Coll., Orange City, Iowa, 1983, U. Wis., River Falls, 1993; mem. exec. bd. S.D. Libr. Network, 1987—. Author libr. bldg. program S.D. State U., 1973; editor Index to S.D. Experiment Station Publications, 1978; contbr. articles to profl. jours. Mem. Pub. Libr. Bd., Brookings, 1985-88; chair adminstv. bd. Brookings United Meth. Ch., 1987; mem. S.D. Pub. Employees Retirement Bd., 1984-87. Grad. scholar La. State U., Baton Rouge, 1961-62; higher edn. fellow Ind. U., Bloomington, 1969-72. Mem. ALA (mem. coun. 1978-84), Mountain Plains Libr. Assn., S.D. Libr. Assn. (pres. 1991-92, Libr. of Yr. 1983), Brookings Masons (master 1979), Rotary, Elks. Home: 404 12th Ave Brookings SD 57006 Office: SD State U Briggs Libr Box 2115 Brookings SD 57007

RANGEL, CHARLES BERNARD, congressman; b. Harlem, N.Y., June 11, 1930; s. Ralph and Blanche (Wharton) R.; m. Alma Carter, July 26, 1964; children: Steven, Alicia. BS, NYU, 1957; JD, St. John's U. Sch. Law, 1960; LLD (hon.), Wagner Coll., 1982, Atlanta U., 1983, St. John's U., Mt. Sinai Sch. Medicine, NYU, Howard U., 1988, Hofstra U., 1989. Bar: N.Y. 1960. U.S. atty. So. Dist. N.Y., 1961-62; mem. N.Y. State Assembly, 1966-70, 92nd-103rd Congresses from 19th (now 15th) N.Y. dist., Washington, D.C., 1971—; mem. Ways and Means Com., subcom. on trade, subcom on human resources; mem. Joint Com. on Taxation. Served with AUS, 1948-52, Korea. Decorated Bronze Star, Purple Heart (U.S.); Korean presdl. citations. Home: 40 W 135th St New York NY 10037-2504 Office: US Ho of Reps 2354 Rayburn Ho Office Bldg Washington DC 20515

RANGELL, LEO, psychiatrist, psychoanalyst; b. N.Y.C., Oct. 1, 1913; s. Morris and Pauline (Kaiser) R.; m. Anita J. Buchwald, Feb. 22, 1939; children: Judith Ellen, Susan Roberta, Richard Neal, Paul Charles. AB, Columbia, 1933; MD, U. Chgo., 1937. Diplomate Am. Bd. Neurology and Psychiatry, 1943. Intern Bklyn. Jewish Hosp., 1937-39; resident neurology Montefiore Hosp., NYC, 1939; resident psychiatry Grasslands Hosp., Valhalla, N.Y., 1940, N.Y. State Psychiat. Inst. and Hosp., N.Y.C., 1941; pvt. practice neurology and psychiatry N.Y.C., 1942-43; instr. neurology

Columbia U. Coll. Physicians and Surgeons, 1942-46; Stroock rsch. fellow neuropsychiatry Montefiore Hosp., 1942-43; psychoanalytic tng. N.Y. Psychoanalytic Inst., later L.A. Psychoanalytic Inst., 1941-49; tng. analyst L.A. Psychoanalytic Inst., 1956—, dir. extension divsn., 1956-57, mem. bd. trustees, 1958—; pvt. practice psychoanalysis and neuropsychiatry Beverly Hills and L.A., 1946—; cons. Reiss-Davis Clinic Child Guidance, L.A., 1953-65; clin. prof. psychiatry Sch. Medicine UCLA, 1953—; clin. prof. psychiatry/psychoanalysis U. Calif., San Francisco, 1976—; fellow Ctr. Advanced Study Behavioral Scis., Stanford, 1962-63, Ctr. Advanced Psychoanalytic Studies, Princeton, N.J., 1962-70, Ctr. Advanced Psychoanalytic Studies, Aspen, Colo., 1970, 86; John B. Turner vis. prof. psychiatry Columbia U. Psychoanalytic Clinic for Tng. and Rsch., N.Y.C., 1971-72. Mem. editl. bd. Israel Annals Psychiatry and Related Disciplines, 1973—, Jour. Phila. Psychoanalytic Assn., Rev. Psychoanalytic Books, 1980—; contbr. numerous articles to profl. jours. Pres. bd. dirs. Westwood Hosp., L.A., 1959-60. Maj. M.C., USAAF, 1943-46. Guggenheim fellow, 1971-72; Recipient Internat. Clin. Essay prize Brit. Inst. Psychoanalysis, 1951, 53, Disting. Alumni award U. Chgo. Sch. Medicine, 1987, Sigourney Hon. award, 1991. Mem. Am. Psychoanalytic Assn. (pres. 1961-62, 66-67, mem. bd. editors 1956-60, 62-66, 76-79, cons. 1979-81, 82-84, Edn. award Phila. chpt. 1978, Jour. award 1981, Hartmann award N.Y. chpt. 1985), L.A. Psychoanalytic Soc. (hon., pres. 1956-58, 64-65), Internat. Psychoanalytic Assn. (v.p. 1967-69, pres. 1969-71, 71-73, hon. v.p. 1994—), Am. Psychiat. Assn., So. Calif. Psychiat. Assn. (pres. 1955-56), So. Calif. Psychoanalytic Soc. (hon.), Peruvian Psychoanalytic Soc. (hon.). Home and Office: 456 N Carmelina Ave Los Angeles CA 90049-2704 also: Spindrift Rd Carmel Hglds CA 93923

RANGOS, ALEXANDER W., waste management environmental services administrator. Student, U. Pitt.; pres., COO, Chambers Devel. Co., 1994—. Office: Chambers Devel Co 10700 Frankstown Rd Pittsburgh PA 15235*

RANGOS, JOHN G., SR., waste management company executive; b. Steubenville, Ohio, July 27, 1929; s. Gust and Anna (Svokas) R.; children: John G. Jr., Alexander William, Jenica Anne. Attended, Houston Bus. Coll., 1949-50; grad., U.S. Signal and Communications Sch., Ft. Gordon, Ga. Formerly gen. agt. Rockwell Mfg. Co., Pitts.; also formed several cos. and pioneered technol. advances in waste transp. and disposal resources recovery and recycling during 1960s; pres., chief exec. officer Chambers Devel. Co., Inc., Pitts., 1971—. Innovations include converting powerplant boiler ash into a useful product for cinder block material and anti-skid material for hwys.; contbd. to invention of techniques for recycling bituminous by-products, disposing of sewage sludge; co-developer of techniques for disposing liquid indsl. waste; developer of a resource recovery system which converts waste-generated methane into energy. Fundraising chmn. UNICEF; contbr. Children's Hosp., Pitts., United Cerebral Palsy, Muscular Dystrophy, Leukemia Soc.; bd. trustees Lukemia Soc. Am.; bd. dirs. The Pitts. Opera, Carnegie Mellon U., Duquesne U., Allegheny Conf., The Carnegie, Carnegie Sci. Ctr., U. Pitts., Boy Scouts Am., Children's Hosp., Presentation of Christ Diocese, Clergy Liturgy Council; nat. del. U.S. Olympic Conf.; active Truman Libr. Found. Served with U.S. Army, 1951-54, Korea. Decorated Nat. Def. medal, U.N. medal, Korean Campaign medal; named Pitts. Man of Yr. in bus. and labor Vector's Community Svc. Orgn., 1990, Man of Yr. in bus. Juvenile Diabetes Found., 1990, Outstanding Philathropist of Yr. Nat. Soc. Fundraising Execs., 1990; recipient Nat. Patriots award Congrl. Medal of Honor Soc., 1991, Ellis Island award Am. Hellenistic Edn. Progressive Assn., 1991, Environ. Recognition award Soc. Preservation Greek Heritage, 1991, Art Rooney award Cath. Youth Assn., 1992, B'Nai B'rith Internat. Corp. Leadership award, 1992, Aristotelian award Am. Hellenistic Edn. Progressive Assn., 1992, Man of Yr. award Hellenic-Am. C. of C., 1992, Handicapped Svc. award Boy Scouts of Am., 1992, Jr. Achievement award S.W. PA Corp., 1992, Acad. of Achievement award Am. Hellenistic Edn/ Progressive Assn., 1992; elected Archon of Ecumenical Patriarchate Order St. Andrew the Apostle, Greek Orthodox Ch., 1988. Mem. Nat. Dem. Club, Young Dems., Internat. Platform Assn. Clubs: The Allegheny, The Pitts. Press, U. Pitts. Golden Panther, Churchill Valley Country. Lodges: Masons (32nd degree), Shriners (Syria). Avocations: racquetball, golf, tennis, collecting art. Home: 1 Trimont Ln Apt 2200A Pittsburgh PA 15211-1255 Office: Chambers Devel Co Inc 10700 Frankstown Rd Pittsburgh PA 15235-3039

RANHEIM, DAVID A., lawyer; b. Tyler, Minn., 1942. BA summa cum laude, Macalester Coll., 1964; JD, NYU, 1967. Ptnr. Dorsey & Whitney, Mpls. Office: Dorsey & Whitney 220 S 6th St Minneapolis MN 55402-4500

RANIERI, LEWIS S., financial services company executive. Mem. exec. com. Salomon Bros. Inc., N.Y.C., vice-chmn., 1986-89; founder Hyperion Capital, N.Y.C., 1989—. Office: United Svgs Assn of Tex 2300 Southwest Fwy Houston TX 77027-7528 Office: Hyperion Capital Mgmt Inc 520 Madison Ave New York NY 10022-4213

RANIS, GUSTAV, economist, educator; b. Darmstadt, Germany, Oct. 24, 1929; s. Max and Bettina (Goldschmidt) R.; m. Ray Lee Finkelstein, June 15, 1958; children: Michael Bruce, Alan Jonathan, Bettina Suzanne. BA summa cum laude, Brandeis U., 1952, hon. degree, 1982; MA, Yale U., 1953, PhD, 1956. Asst. adminstr. program and policy AID/Dept. of State, 1965-67; dir. Econ. Growth Ctr. Yale U., New Haven, 1967-75, prof. econs. 1964—, Frank Altschul prof. internat. econs., 1981—; Ford Found. vis. prof. U. De Los Andes, Bogota, Colombia, 1976-77; Ford Found. faculty fellow Colegio de Mex., 1971-72; fellow Inst. for Advanced Study, Berlin, 1993-94; cons. World Bank, AID, Ford Found., ILO, FAO, Inter-Am. Devel. Bank. Author: (with John Fei) Development of the Labor Surplus Economy: Theory and Policy, 1964, (with Fei and Shirley Kuo) Growth with Equity: The Taiwan Case, 1979, (with Keijiro Otsuka and Gary Saxonhouse) Comparative Technology Choice in Development, 1988, (with F. Stewart and E. Angeles-Reyes) Linkages in Developing Economies: A Philippine Study, 1990, (with S.A. Mahmood) Political Economy of Development Policy Change, 1992; editor: Taiwan: From Developing to Mature Economy, 1992, En Route to Modern Economic Growth: Latin America in the 1990s, 1994; co-editor: The State of Development Economics, 1988, Science and Technology: Lessons for Development Policy, 1990. Trustee Brandeis U., 1967-93, chmn. acad. affairs com., 1986-93. Social Sci. Rsch. Coun. fellow, Japan, 1955-56. Mem. Am. Econ. Assn., Coun. Fgn. Rels., Overseas Develop. Coun. (mem. exec. com.). Home: 7 Mulberry Rd Woodbridge CT 06525-1716 Office: Yale U Econ Growth Ctr 27 Hillhouse Ave New Haven CT 06520-8269

RANK, EVERETT GEORGE, government official; b. Fresno, Calif., Dec. 1, 1921; s. Everett George and Evelyn Lydia (Dawson) R.; m. Evelyn Ingeborg Karschen, Apr. 30, 1948; children—Patricia, Judy, Ginny. Student pub. sch., Clovis, Calif. Farmer Fresno 1946-81; chmn. Fresno County Agrl. Stblzn. and Conservation Service, 1959-69, Calif. Agrl. Stblzn. and Conservation Service, Berkeley, 1969-73; western regional dir. Agrl. Stblzn. and Conservation Service, Dept. Agr., Washington, 1974-76, adminstr. 1981-86. Pres. Clovis Unified Sch. Bd., 1959-72; bd. govs. U. Calif.-Fresno, 1977-81. Served with USN, 1941-45, PTO. Mem. Masons (32 degreer), Shriners. Republican. Baptist. Avocation: golf. Home: 11868 Old Friant Rd Fresno CA 93720-9701

RANK, JOHN THOMAS, lawyer; b. Chgo., Aug. 22, 1947; s. Gerald T. and Estelle M. (Lawler) R.; m. Linda Ann Prasil, July 25, 1970; 1 child, Sean Patrick. BA, U. Notre Dame, 1969; JD, Stanford U., 1972. Bar: Ill. 1972, Calif. 1973, U.S. Ct. Mil. Appeals 1973, U.S. Supreme Ct. 1977, U.S. Dist. Ct. (no. dist.) Ill. 1979. Assoc. Baker & McKenzie, Chgo., 1977-84, ptnr., 1984—. Served as capt. U.S. Army, 1973-77. Mem. ABA, Am. Arbitration Assn. (arbitrator), Calif. Bar Assn., Ill. Bar Assn., Ill. Assn. Hosp. Attys., Chgo. Bar Assn., Chgo. Trial Lawyers Club. Roman Catholic. Avocation: tennis. Office: Baker & McKenzie 130 E Randolph St Chicago IL 60601

RANK, LARRY GENE, executive director; b. Auburn, Ind., July 14, 1935; s. Lloyd R. Rank and Elizabeth M. (Williamson) Jackson; m. Bette Whitehurst, May 2, 1959; children—Kevin, Karen. Grad., Am. Inst. Banking, 1962, U. Balt., 1969, Grad. Sch. Banking, Brown U., 1975, Nat. Council Savs. Instns., 1985. Asst. treas. Provident Savs. Bank, Balt., 1967-70, v.p., 1975-76, treas., v.p., 1976-79, sr. v.p., treas., 1979-82; exec. v.p.

Provident Bank Md., Balt., 1982-85, pres., chief operating officer, 1985-90; dir. Provident Bank Md., 1984-90; mng. dir. Jannotta, Bray & Assocs. Inc., Balt., 1991-92; exec. dir. Big Bros. and Big Sisters Ctrl. Md. Inc., 1993—. Bd. dirs. Children's Cancer Found., Inc., Balt., 1984-90, Balt. chpt. ARC, 1990-92, bd. dirs., 1984—; dir. chmn. United Way of Central Md. Balt., 1984-85, group chair, chair pub. sector mktg. com., Mktg. Task Force, bd. dirs., 1991-93; blood chmn. ARC, 1984-87, bd. dirs., first vice chair, 1988, 89 Balt. Regional chpt., mem. campaign cabinet, hon. chmn. 1988 ARC Humanitarian Award Dinner; chair Gov.'s Vol. Awards Selection com., 1989; chmn. Am. Heart Assn./Heart Ball, 1989, bd. dirs. Am. Heart Assn., 1989—, treas. 1992-94; mem. Vol. Council on Equal Opportunity; bd. trustees Md. Banking Sch.; chmn. bd. Neighborhood Hous ing Services, 1990; exec. com. Nat. Jewish Ctr. Immunology and Respiratory Medicine; mem. 1988 Com. for a Capital Affair; bd. dirs. Balt. Goodwill Industries, 1989—, 1st vice chmn., 1992; trustee Northwest Hosp. Ctr., 1988, exec. com., 1989—, chair capital campaign, 1990-91—, sec., 1992, 1st v.p., 1992—; chmn. bd. trustees Md. Banking Sch. Mem. Nat. Coun. Savs. Instns. (mem. ecn. com. 1984-85), Assn. Corp. Growth (pres. 1985-86), Assn. Balt. Area Grantmakers, Am. Inst. Banking (chmn. sr. exec. commn. 1989), Balt. Mentoring Inst. (bd. dirs.), Md. Hosp. Assn. (mem. PAC com.), Deacon Club, Wake Forest Wildcat Club, Villanova Club, Hunt Valley Golf Club, Camden Club. Lutheran. Avocations: golf, sports, books, travel. Office: 3600 Clipper Mill Rd # 250 Baltimore MD 21211

RANKAITIS, SUSAN, artist; b. Cambridge, Mass., Sept. 10, 1949; d. Alfred Edward and Isabel (Shimkus) Rankaitis; m. Robbert Flick, June 5, 1976. B.F.A. in Painting, U. Ill., 1971; M.F.A. in Visual Arts, U. So. Calif., 1977. Rsch. asst., art dir. Plato Lab., U. Ill., Urbana, 1971-75; art instr. Orange Coast Coll., Costa Mesa, Calif., 1977-83; chair dept. art Chapman Coll., Orange, Calif., 1983-90; Fletcher Jones chair in art Scripps Coll., Claremont, Calif., 1990—; represented by Ruth Bloom Gallery, Santa Monica, Calif.; represented by Ruth Bloom Gallery, Santa Monica, Calif., Robert Mann Gallery, N.Y.C.; overview panelist visual arts Nat. Endowment for Arts, 1983, 84. One-woman shows include Los Angeles County Mus. Art, 1983, Internat. Mus. Photography, George Eastman House, 1983, Gallery Min. Tokyo, 1988, Ruth Bloom Gallery, Santa Monica, 1989, 90, 92, 95, Schneider Mus., Portland, Ore., 1990; Ctr. for Creative Photography, 1991, Robert Mann Gallery, N.Y.C., 1994. Mus. Contemporary Photography, Chgo., 1994; represented in permanent collections U. N.Mex. Art, Santa Monica Coll., Ctr. for Creative Photography, Mus. Modern Art, Santa Barbara Mus. Art, Los Angeles County Mus. Art, Mpls. Inst. Arts, San Francisco Mus. Modern Art, Security Pacific Bank, Mus. Modern Art, Lodz, Poland, Princeton U. Art Mus., others. Active L.A. Ctr. for Photographic Studies, 1988—, mem. adv. bd. trustees. Nat. Endowment for Arts fellow, 1980, 88, U.S./France fellow, 1989, Agnes Bourne fellow in Painting and Photography, Djerassi Found., 1989; recipient Graves award in Humanities, 1985. Mem. Coll. Art Assn., L.A. Contemporary Exhbns. (adv. trustee L.A. Ctr. for Photographic Studies), L.A. County Mus. Art. Studio: Studio 5 1403 S Santa Fe Ave Los Angeles CA 90021-2531

RANKIN, ALFRED MARSHALL, JR., business executive; b. Cleve., Oct. 8, 1941; s. Alfred Marshall and Clara Louise (Taplin) R.; m. Victoire Conley Griffin, June 3, 1967; children: Helen P., Clara T. BA in Econs. magna cum laude, Yale U., 1963, JD, 1966. Mgmt. cons. McKinsey & Co., Inc., Cleve., 1970-73; with Eaton Corp., Cleve., 1974-81, pres. materials handling group, 1981-83, pres. indsl. group, 1984-86, exec. v.p., 1986, vice chmn., chief oper. officer, 1986-89; pres., COO NACCO Industries, Inc., Cleve., 1989-91, pres., CEO, 1991-94, also bd. dirs., chmn., pres., CEO, 1994—, chmn., 1994—; bd. dirs. B.F. Goodrich Co., The Std. Products Co., Vanguard Group. Former pres., trustee Hathaway Brown Sch.; trustee Univ. Hosps. Cleve., Mus. Arts Assn., Univ. Cir., Inc., Cleve. Mus. Art, Greater Cleve. Growth Assn., John Huntington Art and Poly. Inst., Cleve. Tomorrow; chmn. distbn. com. The Cleve. Found. Mem. Ohio Bar Assn. Republican. Clubs: Chagrin Valley Hunt, Union, Tavern, Pepper Pike, Kirtland Country (Cleve.); Rolling Rock (Ligonier, Pa.); Met. (Washington). Home: Old Mill Rd Gates Mills OH 44040-9658 Office: NACCO Industries Inc 5875 Landerbrook Dr Mayfield Heights OH 44124

RANKIN, ARTHUR DAVID, paper company executive; b. Bklyn., July 5, 1936; s. David Emerson and Elizabeth Howe (Smart) R.; m. Judith Ann Clark, Sept. 6, 1958; children: Debi Lynn Murlowski, Kristen Lori. B-SChemE, 5-Yr. Cert. Pulp and Paper, U. Maine, Orono, 1960, MS in Pulp and Paper, 1960. Tech. svc. engr. Mead Corp., Chillicothe, Ohio, 1960-65; product engr. Jones div. Beloit Corp., Dalton, Mass., 1965-69; tech. asst. paper supt. Crown Zellerbach St. Francisville, La., 1969-71; stock prep. supr. Crown Zellerbach, St. Francisville, La., 1971-74; paper machine supt. Appleton Papers, Inc., Combined Locks, Wis., 1974-84, steps project coord., 1984-85, sr. paper machine supt., 1986-88, sr. prodn. assoc., 1988-90, edn. and mill planning mgr., 1991—; instr. video U. Wis., Stevens Point, 1988, 89. Officer Jaycees, Waverly, Ohio, 1960-63, Chillicothe, Ohio, 1963-65, Pittsfield, Mass., 1965-69; bd. dirs. acad. adv. coun. U. Minn. Paper Sci. Sch., Mpls., 1988—; bd. dirs. U. Minn. Paper Sci. Sch. Mem. ASTM, TAPPI, Nat. Paper Indsl. Mgmt. Assn. (bd. dirs. 1988—, pres. 1993, treas. 1994—), North Ctrl. Paper Indsl. Mgmt. Assn. (bd. dirs. 1977—). Republican. Congregationalist. Avocations: reading, golf, YMCA fitness center, wine collecting and study. Home: 1408 S Lee St Appleton WI 54915-3824

RANKIN, CLYDE EVAN, III, lawyer; b. Phila., July 3, 1950; s. Clyde Evan, Jr. and Mary E. (Peluso) R. A.B., Princeton U., 1972; J.D., Columbia U., 1975; postgrad. Hague Acad. Internat. Law, 1975. Bar: N.Y., N.J., D.C., U.S. Supreme Ct. Law clk. to judge U.S. Dist. Ct. So. Dist. N.Y., 1975-77; assoc. Debevoise, Plimpton, Lyons & Gates, N.Y.C., 1977-79; assoc. Coudert Bros., N.Y.C., 1979-83, ptnr., 1984—. Trustee The Rensselaerville (N.Y.) Inst., 1989—. Stone scholar, 1974. Mem. ABA, Assn. of Bar of City of N.Y., N.Y. State Bar Assn., D.C. Bar Assn., N.J. Bar Assn. Roman Catholic. Club: Amateur Comedy (N.Y.C.). Contbr. article to legal jour. Office: Coudert Bros 1114 Avenue Of The Americas New York NY 10036-7701

RANKIN, HAYWOOD FORNEY, diplomat; b. Washington, July 31, 1946; s. Forney Anderson and Jean Smith (Cantrell) R.; m. Sabine Irmgard Schmid, Aug. 5, 1982; children: Johanna, Susanna. AB in Sociology, U. N.C., 1968, JD, 1971; BS in Geology, Oxford U., Eng., 1982. Bar: N.C. 1971. Law clk. to chief justice N.C. Supreme Ct., Raleigh, 1971-72; vice consul Am. Consulate Gen., Tangier, Morocco, 1973-75; consul Am. Consulate Gen., Port Said, Egypt, 1977-79; polit. analyst Bureau Intelligence and Rsch. Dept. State, Washington, 1982-84; polit. officer Am. Embassy, Damascus, Syria, 1984-86; chief polit. sect. Am. Embassy, Baghdad, Iraq, 1986-88; dep. chief mission Am. Embassy, Muscat, Oman, 1989-92, Algiers, Algeria, 1992-94; dep. dir. Office Near East South Asia Bur. Intelligence & Rsch., Washington, 1994—. Recipient Meritorious Honor award, 1986, Superior Honor award, 1992. Democrat. Presbyterian. Avocations: travel, photography. Home: 4948 Ashby St NW Washington DC 20007 Office: Dept State Rm 4634 Washington DC 20520

RANKIN, JAMES WINTON, lawyer; b. Norfolk, Va., Sept. 9, 1943; s. Winton Blair and Edith (Griffin) R.; m. Donna Lee Carpenter, June 25, 1966 (dec.); children—Thomas James, William Joseph, Elizabeth Jeanne; m. JoAnne Katherine Murray, Feb. 11, 1978. A.B. magna cum laude, Oberlin Coll., 1965; J.D. cum laude, U. Chgo., 1968. Bar: Ill. 1968, U.S. Dist. Ct. (no. dist.) Ill. 1969, U.S. Ct. Appeals (7th cir.) 1971, U.S. Ct. Appeals (5th cir.) 1979, U.S. Supreme Ct. 1975, Calif. 1986. Law clk. U.S. Dist. Ct. (no. dist.) Ill., 1968-69; assoc. Kirkland & Ellis, Chgo., 1969-73, ptnr., 1973—. Mem. ABA, Order of Coif, Mid-Am. Club, Univ. Club, Mich. Shores Club, Kenilworth Club, Ephriam Yacht Club. Presbyterian. Home: 633 Kenilworth Ave Kenilworth IL 60043-1070 Office: Kirkland & Ellis 200 E Randolph Dr Chicago IL 60601-6401

RANKIN, JIM, real estate developer. V.p. Forecast Corp., Rancho Cucamonga, Calif. Office: Forecast Corp 10670 Civic Ctr Dr Rancho Cucamonga CA 91730*

RANKIN, JOANNA MARIE, astronomy educator; b. Denver, Mar. 10, 1942; d. Robert McCurdy and Julia Bernice (Pelsor) R.; life ptnr. Mary Rose Fillmore. BS, So. Meth. U., 1965; MS, Tulane U., 1966; PhD in Astrophysics, U. Iowa, 1970. Asst. prof. astronomy dept. Cornell U., Ithaca,

N.Y., 1974-78; acting head computer dept. Arecibo (P.R.) Obs., 1976; sr. rsch. assoc. history dept. Ctr. for Radiophysics and Space Rsch., Cornell U., Ithaca, 1978-80; assoc. prof. physics dept. U. Vt., Burlington, 1980-88, prof. physics and astronomy physics dept., 1988—; organizer Internat. Astron. Union Colloquium 128, Lagow, Poland, 1990; organizer, participant in internat. astron. collaborations with astronomers, India, USSR, Poland, 1985-90; lectr. in field. Contbr. articles to profl. jours. Bd. dirs. Vt. Pro-Choice, 1987-90; activist Women's Internat. League for Peace and Freedom, Burlington, Vt., 1981-86; mem. War Resister's League, N.Y.C., 1982—; supporter Lesbian Herstory Archives, N.Y.C., 1987—; creator, collector polit. poster art show, 1983-85. Recipient NASA traineeship U. Iowa, 1966-70; named Van Allen/Link fellow astron. dept. U. Iowa, 1970, finalist Kellogg Nat. fellow Kellogg Found., 1984, U.S./India fellow Fulbright Found., 1990; rsch. grantee NSF, 1972, 73, 78, 89. Mem. Internat. Astron. Union, Am. Astron. Soc., Fedn. Am. Scientists, Am. Women in Sci., Sci. for the People, Nat. Women's Studies Assn. Avocations: hiking, camping, sailing. Office: U Vt Physics Dept Burlington VT 05405

RANKIN, M. DOUGLAS, electronics executive; b. 1938. V.p. sales and mkgt. Inmos Corp., Colo. Springs, 1980-86, Signetics Corp., Sunnyvale, Calif., 1983-86; sr. v.p. sales, mktg. Actel Corp., Sunnyvale, Calif., 1986—. Office: Actel Corp 955 E Arques Ave Sunnyvale CA 94086*

RANKIN, ROBERT, retired educational foundation executive; b. Des Moines, Sept. 14, 1915; s. Wiley Strange and Estelle Blanche (Renne) R.; m. Martha Jean Roberts, Sept. 7, 1940; children: Mary Renne (Mrs. Joseph L. Sturdevant Jr.), Margaret Lloyd, Wiley Robert, William Roberts. B.A., U. Iowa, 1937; B.D., Yale, 1940; M.A., 1942; D.D. (hon.), Lindenwood Coll., St. Charles, Mo., 1964, Northland Coll., Ashland, Wis., 1981; D.H.L. (hon.), U. So. Calif., 1967. Ordained to ministry Methodist Ch., 1944, United Ch. Christ, 1960; minister Sunnyvale, Calif., 1942-44; campus minister, lectr. religion, dir. YMCA Oberlin Coll. 1946-51; chaplain, assoc. prof. religion Claremont Colls., 1951-58; exec. dir. Rockefeller Bros. Theol. Fellowship Program, Princeton, N.J., 1954-55; assoc. dir. Danforth Found. St. Louis, 1958-66; v.p. Danforth Found., 1966-80, dir. programs campus ministry, 1958-80, assoc. program, 1958-75; cons. Fund Theol. Edn., Lilly Endowment, Pres.'s Commn. on Campus Unrest; chmn. St. Louis Met. Conf. Edn. Culturally Disadvantaged, 1962; cons. to bd. dirs. Nat. Inst. for Campus Ministry, 1974-83; mem. St. Louis region selection panel White House fellows, 1975, 77, chmn., 1978; mem. Nat. Commn. Higher Edn., United Meth. Ch., 1975-77; chmn. exec. com. Wingspread Conf., 1969-73. Author, editor: The Recovery of Spirit in Higher Education, 1980; author articles, chpts. in books; edit. adv. bd. Religion and Intellectual Life, 1984—. Trustee Sch. Theology at Claremont, 1955-59, advisor, 1985—, Am. Friends of Wilton Park, 1975, Healing Community St. Louis, 1976-81, Claremont, 1984-90, Nat. Task Force for Disability and the Art, 1978-81, Evangelicals for Social Action; mem. Com. on Disability City of Claremont; resident Pilgrim Place, Claremont, 1981; advisor Pilgrim Festival, 1983—, Pilgrim Aquatic Fitness Ctr., 1993—. Recipient E. Harris Harbison hon. award for gifted teaching, 1970; Fellow Wilton Park Conf., Sussex, Eng.; Fellow Soc. Values Higher Edn. Mem. Nat. Assn. Coll. and Univ. Chaplains, Assn. for Religion and Intellectual Life, Nat. Campus Ministry Assn., Am. Friends Svc. Com., Am. Assn. UN, Am. Acad. Religion, Am. Assn. for Higher Edn., ACLU, NAACP, Sigma Chi, Univ. Claremont Club. Mem. United Ch. of Christ. Home: 737 Alden Rd Claremont CA 91711-4221

RANKIN, ROBERT ARTHUR, journalist; b. Richmond, Va., May 31, 1949; s. Arthur Norton and Martha Louise (Rountree) R.; m. Janis Johnson, May 11, 1979; 1 child, Benjamin John. BA in Polit. Sci., Randolph Macon Coll., 1971; MA in Govt., U. Va., 1974. Reporter Richmond News Leader, Va., 1972-75; reporter Congl. Quar., Washington, 1975-78; editorial writer Miami Herald, Fla., 1980-85, Phila. Inquirer, 1985-87; nat. corr. Washington bur. Knight Ridder Newspapers, 1987—. V.p. Civic Assn. Hollin Hills, Alexandria, Va., 1991-92. Co-recipient Pulitzer prize for editorial writing 1983, Olive Branch award N.Y.U. Ctr. for War, Peace and The News Media, 1990; recipient 1st prize Va. Press Assn., 1974; best editorial award Phila. chpt. Sigma Delta Chi, 1987; Walter Bagehot fellow Columbia U., 1978-79. Mem. White House Corres. Assn., Nat. Press Club. Office: Knight Ridder Newspapers 700 Nat Press Bldg Washington DC 20045

RANKIN, THOMPSON L., utilities executive, agricultural executive. With Lykes Bros. Inc., Tampa, Fla., 1971—, chmn., pres.; chmn., CEO Lykes Energy Inc., Tampa; chmn., pres. Lykes Pasco, Inc., Dade City, Fla.; chmn., CEO People's Gas Sys., Tampa, 1993—; chmn., pres. Shore Mgmt. Inc., Tampa. Office: Peoples Gas Sys 111 E Madison St Tampa FL 33602*

RANNEY, (JOSEPH) AUSTIN, political science educator; b. Cortland, N.Y., Sept. 23, 1920; s. Frank Addison and Florence Edith (Ranney) R.; m. Elizabeth Mackay (div. Oct. 1975); m. Nancy Boland; children: Joseph, Douglas, Gordon, David. BS, Northwestern U., 1941, LLD (hon.), 1995; MA, U. Oreg., 1943; PhD, Yale U., 1948, DSS (hon.), 1985; LLD (hon.), SUNY, 1986. Statistician Douglas Aircraft Corp., Chgo., 1942-44; instr. Yale U., New Haven, 1945-47; from instr. to prof. U. Ill., Urbana, 1947-63; prof. U. Wis., Madison, 1963-76; resident scholar Am. Enterprise Inst., Washington, 1976-86; prof. U. Calif., Berkeley, 1986-91, prof. emeritus, 1991—, chmn. dept. polit. sci., 1987-90. Author: The Doctrine of Responsible Party Government, 1954, Governing, 1958, Curing the Mischiefs of Faction, 1975, Channels of Power, 1983. Mem. Presdl.-Congl. Commn. on Polit. Activity Govtl. Employers, Washington, 1967-68, Dem. Nat. Com. Commn. on Party Structure, Washington, 1969-72, Commn. on Presdl. Debates, Washington, 1980-88; chmn. Gov.'s Commn. on Registration and Voting Participation, Madison, Wis., 1964, social sci. rsch. coun. Com. on Govtl. Processes, 1964-71, coun. on social scis. policy Yale U., 1983-88. Recipient Wilbur Lucius Cross medal Yale U. Grad. Sch., 1977; sr. rsch. fellow NSF, 1970, John Simon Guggenheim fellow, 1974, fellow Ctr. for Advanced Study in Behavioral Scis., 1978. Mem. Am. Polit. Sci. Assn. (pres. 1975-76), Am. Acad. Arts and Scis. (v.p. 1981-84). Home: 990 Regal Rd Berkeley CA 94708-1430 Office: Univ Calif Dept Polit Sci Berkeley CA 94720

RANNEY, CARLETON DAVID, plant pathology researcher, administrator; b. Jackson, Minn., Jan. 23, 1928; s. Carleton Oran and Ada Elizabeth (Harriman) R.; m. Mary Kathryn Ransleben, July 16, 1949; children: David Clayton, Mary Elizabeth. AA, Chaffey Jr. Coll., Ontario, Calif., 1952; BS, Tex. A&M U., 1954, MS, 1955, PhD, 1959. Plant pathologist Crops Rsch. Div. Agrl. Rsch. Svc. USDA, College Station, Tex., 1955-58, Stoneville, Miss., 1958-70; investigations leader Crops Rsch. Div. Agrl. Rsch. Svc. USDA, Beltsville, Md., 1970-72; area dir. Ala. No. Miss. area Agrl. Rsch. Svc. USDA, Starkville, Miss., 1973-78; area dir. Delta States area Agrl. Rsch. Svc. USDA, Stoneville, Miss., 1978-84; area dir. Mid-South area Agrl. Rsch. Svc. USDA, Stoneville, Miss., 1984-87; asst. dir. Miss. and Forestry Exptl. Stas., Stoneville, 1987-94, head Delta br. sta., 1987-94, emeritus plant pathologist, 1994—; adj. prof. agronomy Miss. State U., 1970-94; sr. exec. svc. USDA, Stoneville, Miss., 1984-87; adv. bd. Belt Wide Meetings Nat. Cotton Coun., Memphis, Tenn., 1987—. Contbr. articles to profl. jours. Sect. advisor SE2 Order Arrow Boy Scouts Am., Miss. and W. Tenn., 1973-83; pres. Delta Area Coun. Boy Scouts Am., Clarksdale, Miss., 1990-91. Sgt. USAF, 1946-49. Recipient Silver Beaver Boy Scouts Am., Stoneville, 1981, Disting. Svc. Order of Arrow, Stoneville, 1983. Mem. Agron Soc. Am., Nat. Cotton Disease Coun. (sec. 1959-60, chmn. 1961-62), Lions Club, Sigma Xi, Alpha Zeta, Phi Kappa Phi. Methodist. Achievements include development of fungicide control seedling diseases; definition of relationship of microclimate to boll rot of cotton; development of non-mercurial seed treatments. Office: Delta Rsch & Ext Ctr PO Box 197 Stoneville MS 38776-0197

RANNEY, DAVID C., urban economics educator; b. Lakewood, Ohio, May 16, 1939; s. Omar Steele and Dorothy Mae (Phillips) R.; m. Patricia Wright, Dec. 31, 1991; 1 child, Christopher. BA, Dartmouth Coll., 1961; MA, Syracuse U., 1963, PhD, 1964. Asst. prof. So. Ill. U., 1966-67, U. Wis., 1967-70; assoc. prof. U. Iowa, 1970-76; rsch. assoc. prof. U. Ill., Chgo., 1982-87, assoc. prof., 1987-93, assoc. prof., acting dir. Ctr. Urban Econ. Devel., 1993—; cons. Calcutta Met. Planning Orgn., 1962-63, City of East St. Louis, Ill., 1966-67, Cleve. City Planning Commn., 1970; ptnr. Workers' Rights Ctr., 1976-81; mem. pub. policy analysis PhD curriculum com. U. Ill., Chgo., pub. policy analysis PhD admissions com., Sch. Urban Planning & Policy curriculum com., Art, Arch., Urban Planning and Performing Arts Coll. exec. com., Gt. Cities com. on new coll.; presenter in field. Contbr. book chpts., revs., monographs, and articles to profl. pubs. Office: U of Ill at Chgo Ctr for Urban Econ Devel 400 S Peoria Chicago IL 60607

RANNEY, GEORGE A., JR., lawyer; b. Chgo., Apr. 11, 1940. BA magna cum laude, Harvard U., 1962; JD, U. Chgo., 1966. Bar: Ill. 1966. Law clk. to hon. Carl McGowan U.S. Ct. Appeals, Washington, 1966-67; dep. dir. Bur. Budget, State of Ill., 1969-73; counsel, v.p. Inland Steel Co., 1973-86; ptnr. Mayer, Brown & Platt, Chgo.; mem. Commn. Uniform State Laws, 1969-73; chmn. State Task Force on Future Ill., 1978-80; lectr. U. Chgo., 1975-79. Editor-in-chief U. Chgo. Law Rev., 1966-67. Mem. ABA, Chgo. Bar Assn. Office: Mayer Brown & Platt 190 S La Salle St Chicago IL 60603-3441

RANNEY, GEORGE ALFRED, lawyer, former steel company executive; b. Chgo., May 30, 1912; s. George Alfred and Cornelia (Williams) R.; m. Nora Ryerson, June 18, 1938 (dec. Mar. 1987); children: George Alfred, Edward R., David M., Nancy R. (Mrs. David F. Levi). A.B., Yale, 1934, LL.B., 1939. Bar: Ill. 1939. Mem. firm Sidley, Austin, Burgess & Smith, Chgo., 1939-62; v.p., gen. counsel Inland Steel Co., Chgo., 62-68; sr. v.p. Inland Steel Co., 1968-71, vice chmn., 1971-77, also dir. Trustee U. Chgo. Served as 1st lt. AUS, 1942-45. Mem. Am., Ill., Chgo. bar assns. Episcopalian. Home: 17370 W Casey Rd Libertyville IL 60048-9748

RANNEY, HELEN MARGARET, physician, educator; b. Summer Hill, N.Y., Apr. 12, 1920; d. Arthur C. and Alesia (Toolan) R. AB, Barnard Coll., 1941; MD, Columbia U., 1947; ScD, U. S.C., 1979. Diplomate: Am. Bd. Internal Medicine. Intern Presbyn. Hosp., N.Y.C., 1947-48, resident, 1948-50, asst. physician, 1954-60; practice medicine specializing in internal medicine, hematology N.Y.C., 1954-70; instr. Coll. Phys. and Surg. Columbia, N.Y.C., 1954-60; assoc. prof. medicine Albert Einstein Coll. Medicine, N.Y.C., 1960-64, prof. medicine, 1965-70; prof. medicine SUNY, Buffalo, 1970-73; prof. medicine U. Calif., San Diego, 1973-90, chmn. dept. medicine, 1973-86, Disting. physician vet. adminstr., 1986-91; mem. staff Alliance Pharm. Corp., San Diego, 1991—. Master ACP; fellow AAAS; mem. NAS, Inst. Medicine, Am. Soc. for Clin. Investigation, Am. Soc. Hematology, Harvey Soc., Am. Assn. Physicians, Am. Acad. Arts and Scis., Phi Beta Kappa, Sigma Xi, Alpha Omega Alpha. Office: Alliance Pharm Corp 3040 Science Park Rd San Diego CA 92121-1102

RANNEY, MAURICE WILLIAM, chemical company executive; b. Buffalo, Jan. 13, 1934; s. Maurice Lynford and Helen Hart (Birdsall) R.; m. Theresa Ann Berthot, Oct. 24, 1953 (div. 1974); children: William, Linda, Laurel, James, Michael; m. Elisa Ramirez Villegas, Dec. 21, 1974; 1 stepchild, Elisa. BS in Chemistry, Niagara U., 1957, MS in Organic Chemistry, 1959; PhD in Phys. Organic Chemistry, Fordham U., 1967. Group leader, tech. mgr. Union Carbide Corp., Tarrytown, N.Y., 1957-75; gen. mgr. Union Carbide Japan KK, 1976-80; exec. v.p. Showa Union Gosei Co., Ltd., 1976-80; rep. dir. Union Carbide Svcs. Eastern Ltd., 1976-80; dir. Nippon Unicar Co., Ltd., 1976-80, Union Showa KK, 1976-80; pres. Union Carbide Formosa Co., Ltd., Hong Kong, Tokyo, 1980-82; bus. dir. Union Carbide Eastern, Inc., Tokyo, 1982-85; pres., rep. dir. Union Carbide Japan KK, 1986—; pres. Union Indsl. Gas Corp.; rep. dir. Oriental Union Chem. Corp., 1980-82; mng. dir. Nippon Unicar Co., Ltd., 1982-85; v.p. internat. Union Carbide Chems. and Plastics Co., 1986—; vice chmn., rep. dir. Nippon Unicar, 1986—; pres. Nihon Parylene, 1992; lectr. in field. Author: Flame Retardant Textiles, 1970, Power Coatings, 1971, Synthetic Lubricants, 1972, New Curing Techniques, 1976, Fuel Additives, 1976, Durable Press Fabrics, 1976, Silicones, Vols. I, II, 1977, Reinforced Plastics and Elastomers, 1978, Offshore Oil Technology, 1979, Oil Shale and Tar Sands, 1980, Primary Electrochemical Cell Technology, 1981; contbr. articles to profl. jours. Union Carbide fellow, Mellon Inst. Indsl. Rsch., 1958-60. Achievements include numerous patents in field. Home: PO Box 5363 Hilton Head Island SC 29938

RANONE, JOHN LOUIS, school board executive; b. N.Y.C., July 7, 1940; s. Michael Nicholas and Josephine Clara (Iannone) R.; m. Carolyn Margaret Smith, June 13, 1964; children: Michelle Mary, Margaret Anne. AA in data processing, Fairleigh Dickinson, 1960; BA in Elem. Edn., Jersey City State Coll., 1964; AA/Classroom Renaissance, Montclair State Coll., 1969; M in Adminstrn., Monmouth Coll., 1974. Cert. elem. tchr., adminstr., sex edn., classroom renaissance. Teaching prin. Hollie M. Davis Sch., River Edge, N.J., 1972-77; prin. Lincoln Sch., Ridgefield Park (N.J.) Bd. Edn., 1977-89; dir. curriculum and instruction Ridgefield Park Bd. Edn., 1989—; cons., lectr., N.J. State Dept. Edn., Trenton, 1974—; chmn. N.J. State Adv. Council, Trenton, 1976—; lectr. Jersey City State Coll., 1979—; rep. U.S. Council for Individually Guided Edn., Atlanta, 1979-87; bd. trustees for teacher edn. Felician Coll. Trustee River Edge Pub. Libr., 1978-85. Recipient Outstanding Svc. award, Cath. Youth Orgn., Newark, 1965, Bergen County Outstanding Tchr. award, PTA, 1971, Child Assault Prevention award, N.J. State Dept. Edn., 1988, Halls Motor Co. scholarship, Jersey City, N.J., 1958-59; named to Edn. at the Met., Met. Opera Co., N.Y.C., Workshop Series I, 1988. Mem. Assn. Supervision and Curriculum Devel., Prins. and Suprs. Assn., River Edge Edn. Assn. (pres. 1974-76, v.p. 1972-74), Ridgefield Park Adminstr. Assn. (treas. 1981—), River Edge Dem. Club, Friends of the Libr. Roman Catholic. Avocations: travel, reading, ceramic, collector. Home: 490 Windsor Rd River Edge NJ 07661-1834 Office: Ridgefield Park Bd Edn Ridgefield Park NJ 07660

RANSOHOFF, MARTIN, motion picture producer; b. New Orleans, 1927. Grad., Colgate U., 1949. Founder Filmways, Inc., N.Y.C., 1952, chmn. bd., pres., until 1972; pres. Martin Ransohoff Prodns., Inc., 1972—. Prodns. include Boy's Night Out, 1962, The Americanization of Emily, 1964, Topkapi, 1964, The Loved One, 1965, The Cincinnati Kid, 1965, The Sandpiper, 1965, Ice Station Zebra, 1969, Catch 22, 1970, See No Evil, 1971, Ten Rillington Place, 1971, Save the Tiger, 1972, Fuzz, 1972, The White Dawn, 1974, Nightwing, 1979, Silver Streak, 1976, The Wanderers, 1976, A Change of Seasons, 1980, American Pop, 1981, Hanky Panky, 1982, Class, 1983, Jagged Edge, 1985, Welcome Home, 1989; TV prodns. Mister Ed, The Beverly Hillbillies, Petticoat Junction, The Addams Family. Office: Martin Ransohoff Prodns Inc 9350 Wilshire Blvd Ste 219 Beverly Hills CA 90212-3204

RANSOM, BILL, author; b. Puyallup, Wash., June 6, 1945; s. Bert and LaVerne (Marcoe) R.; m. Kathy Ann Potocki, June 17, 1967 (div.); 1 child, Hali Kalae. Student, Wash. State U., 1963-65, U. Puget Sound, 1965-67; BA in English and Sociology Edn., U. Wash., 1970; postgrad., U. Nev., 1970-72. Nat. Endowment for Arts and Wash. State Arts Commn. poet-in-residence Tacoma and Port Townsend, Wash., 1972-75; Manpower Tng. Act master poet for Wash. and Colo., 1974; instr. writing So Utah U, Cedar City; dir. Port Townsend Writer's Conf., 1973-77; instr. So. Utah U. Author: Finding True North, 1974 (Nat. Book award and Pulitzer prize nominee 1974), Last Rites, 1978; author: (chapbook) Waving Arms At The Blind, 1975, (novel with Frank Herbert) The Jesus Incident, 1979, (chapbook) The Single Man Looks at Winter, 1983, Last Call, 1984, (novels with Frank Herbert) The Lazarus Effect, 1982, The Ascension Factor, 1988, (novels) Jaguar, 1990, Viravax, 1993, Learning the Ropes, 1995, Burn, 1995; author documentary of Artists-in-Schs. Program, Look: Listen, 1975; freelance journalist, Ctrl. Am., 1982-84; contbr. articles, stories, poems to mags., newspapers. Mem. PEN (selected stories for syndicated fiction project 1983, 85), AAUW, Sci. Fiction and Fantasy Writers Am., Poets & Writers, Inc., Associated Writing Programs. Office: S Utah U Box 9473 Cedar City UT 84720

RANSOM, DAVID MICHAEL, diplomat; b. St. Louis, Nov. 23, 1938; s. Clifford Fredic and Inez Natalie (Green) R.; m. Marjorie Ann (Marilley) Ransom; children: Elizabeth Inez, Katherine Hope, Sarah Grace. AB, Princeton U., 1960; MA, Johns Hopkins Sch. of Advanced Internat. Studies, 1962; student, The Nat. War Coll., 1982-83. With U.S. Dept. State, Yemen, Iran, Lebanon, Saudi Arabia, 1965-71; nat. security coun. staff White House U.S. Dept. State, Washington, 1971-73; dep. chief mission-Am. Embassy Sanaa U.S. Dept. State, Yemen Arab Rep., 1975-78; dir., dept. dir. near east divsn. internat. security affairs-office of Sec. of Defense U.S. Dept. State, Washington, 1978-82; dep. chief of mission-Am. Embassy Abu Dhabi U.S. Dept. State, United Arab Emirates, 1983-85; dep. chief of mission-Am.

Embassy Damascus U.S. Dept. State, Syria, 1985-88; country dir. Arabian Peninsula-Near East bureau U.S. Dept. State, Washington, 1988-90, country dir. Greece, Turkey, Cyprus-European bureau, 1990-93; Am. ambassador to State of Bahrain-Am. Embassy Manama U.S. Dept. State, 1994. 1st lt. inf. USMC, 1962-65. Mem. Met. Club (Washington). Episcopalian. Avocations: scuba diving, canoeing, skiing. Home: Am Embassy FPO AE 09834-5100

RANSOM, JEREMY, ballet dancer; b. St. Catharines, Ont.. Grad., Nat. Ballet Sch. With Nat. Ballet Canada, Toronto, Ont., 1980—, 2d soloist, 1984-85, 1st soloist, 1985-90, prin. dancer, 1990—; performed with Zurich Ballet, Switzerland, 1986-87, Australian Ballet. Created roles in David Allan's Occasion, Capriccio, Etc!; Glen Tetley's Alice; James Kudelka's The Actress, The Miraculous Mandarin; also L'Ile Inconnue, Oiseaux Exotiques. Office: National Ballet of Canada, 157 King St East, Toronto, ON Canada M5C 1G9*

RANSOM, MARGARET PALMQUIST, public relations executive; b. Davenport, Iowa, Aug. 13, 1935; d. Herman Philip and Margaret (Burchell) Palmquist; m. David Duane Ransom, July 16, 1960; 1 child, David Burke. BA in Speech and English, Augustana Coll., 1957. Tchr. speech and English Beloit (Wis.) High Sch., 1957-59; tchr. English Lake Forest (Ill.) High Sch., 1959-60, Warren High Sch., Gurnee, Ill., 1960-62, 64-66; asst. to dean Grad. Sch. Bowling Green (Ohio) State U., 1963; freelance writer Coll. Bd. Examinations, 1966; market rsch. analyst Kitchens of Sara Lee, Deerfield, Ill., 1972-74; pub. affairs mgr. Sara Lee Bakery, Deerfield, 1975-89; sr. cons. Ransom Pub. Svc. Cons., Libertyville, Ill., 1990-94; cons. Olsten Staffing Svcs., Chgo., 1994—; judge nat. competitions Pub. Rels. Soc. Am., 1986-89; speaker on motivation and orgn.; vice-chmn. Ill. Dept. Employment Security's Job Security Employers Com., 1995. Bd. dirs. Early Childhood Adv. Coun., Northeastern Ill. State U., 1989-91; mem. Main St. Libertyville com., 1990-92; vice chair Ill. Dept. Employment Security Job Svc. Employers Com., 1995. Recipient Ill. Citizens Svc. medal, 1993. Mem. AAUW, Bus. and Profl. Women Lake County, Mortar Bd. Avocations: computer science, reading, original art. Office: 1037 Mayfair Dr Libertyville IL 60048-3548

RANSOM, RICHARD EDWARD, state supreme court justice; b. Hampton, Iowa, Dec. 9, 1932. BA, U. N.Mex., 1954; LLB, Georgetown U., 1959. Bar: N.Mex. 1959, D.C. 1959. Trial lawyer Albuquerque, 1959-86; justice N.Mex. Supreme Ct., Santa Fe, 1987—; chief justice N. Mex. Supreme Ct., 1992-94. 1st lt. USMC, 1954-56. Fellow Am. Coll. Trial Lawyers, Internat. Soc. Barristers, Internat. Acad. Trial Lawyers. Office: N Mex Supreme Ct PO Box 848 237 Don Gaspar Ave Santa Fe NM 87504-0848

RANSOM, WILLIAM HARRISON, lawyer; b. Flint, Mich., Aug. 15, 1938; s. Earl Jarvis and Aileen (Halpin) R.; m. Marilyn Jean Novotny, Aug. 27, 1960; children: Nancy Aileen Maggard, Andrew William, Elizabeth Hope. BA in Econs., U. Mich., 1960, JD, 1963. Bar: Ohio, 1964. Assoc. Squire, Sanders & Dempsey, Cleve., 1964-74, ptnr., 1974-91, counsel, 1992—. Mem. ABA (tax sect. benefits com.), Ohio Bar Assn., Greater Cleve. Bar Assn., Midwest Pension Conf. Office: Squire Sanders & Dempsey 4900 Society Ctr 127 Public Sq Cleveland OH 44114-1304

RANSOME, ERNEST LESLIE, III, transportation and retail company executive; b. Riverton, N.J.; s. Percy A. and Clarice (Frishmuth) R.; m. Nancy Ellis Clark, Aug. 16, 1947 (div. Jan. 1984); children: Leslie Ransome Hudson, Elizabeth Ransome, Jane Ransome Bromley; m. Myradean Alcott, Feb. 12, 1984. AB in Econs., Princeton U., 1947. Ins. exec. Johnson & Higgins, Phila., 1947-48; asst. to dean Princeton (N.J.) U., 1948-50; asst. treas. Giles & Ransome, Bensalem, Pa., 1950-55; v.p. adminstrn. Giles & Ransome, Bensalem, 1955-69, exec. v.p., 1969-82, vice chmn., 1982-88, chmn. bd., 1988—; v.p. Ransome Airlines, Bensalem, Pa., 1966-86; bd. dirs. Mannington Mills, Salem, N.J., chmn., 1991-92, Midlantic Corp., Edison, N.J., Midlantic Nat. Bank, Edison, Sun Distbrs., Phila. Mem. Zoning Bd. Borough of Riverton, N.J., 1965-69; bd. trustees Riverton Library, 1959-79; campaign chmn. Zurbrugg Hosp., Riverside, N.J., 1971. 2d lt. USMC, 1944-46. Mem. Pine Valley Golf Club (pres. 1977-88, chmn. 1988—), Royal and Ancient Golf Club (St. Andrews, Scotland). Republican. Episcopalian. Avocation: golf.

RANSON, GUY HARVEY, clergyman, religion educator; b. Godley, Tex., Nov. 26, 1916; s. Jake Mincer and Willie Ann (Hardesty) R.; m. Rose Ellen Clark, May 24, 1949; children: Kenneth Clark, Kelly Maurice, Diana Louise. BA, Hardin-Simmons U., 1939; MA, U. Ky., 1944; postgrad., U. Cambridge, Eng., 1947-48; PhD, Yale U., 1956. Ordained to ministry Presbyn. Ch., 1961. Asst. prof. philosophy William Jewell Coll., Liberty, Mo., 1948-49, prof., chmn. dept. philosophy, 1949-52; asst. prof. ethics So. Bapt. Theol. Sem., Louisville, 1952-53, assoc. prof., 1953-58; assoc. prof. Div. Sch., Duke U., Durham, N.C., 1959-60, Princeton (N.J.) Theol. Sem., 1960-61; prof. religion Trinity U., San Antonio, 1961-82, prof. emeritus, 1982—, chmn. dept. religion, 1961-77, mem. curriculum council, 1961-77, chmn. curriculum council, 1967-68, mem. faculty senate, 1964-69, chmn. faculty senate, 1968-69; mem. ecumenical rels. Alamo Presbytery and Synod of Tex., 1967-70; mem. gen. coun. Alamo Presbytery, 1967-73, vice moderator, chmn. ministerial com., 1973. Author: F.D. Maurice's Theology of Society, 1956; mng. editor: Rev. and Expositer, 1957, 58; contbr. articles to profl. jours. Chmn. social action com. San Antonio Council Chs., 1968-70; mem. cen. priorities com. Community Welfare Council, San Antonio, 1968-69, Com. to Study San Antonio Sch. Dist., 1966-67; bd. dirs. Inman Christian Ctr., 1964-70, chmn. bd., 1969-70. Recipient research grant Trinity U. for archeol. excavation Hebron, Jordan, summer 1966. Mem. AAUP (chpt. pres. 1962-63), Am. Soc. Ch. History, Am. Philos. Assn., Am. Soc. Christian Ethics, Am. Acad. Religion, Am. Inst. Archaeology, Southwestern Philos. Soc. Club: South Tex. Yale U. (pres. 1977). Home: 115 Irvington Dr San Antonio TX 78209-4217

RANTA, RICHARD ROBERT, university dean; b. Virginia, Minn., Nov. 18, 1943; s. V. Robert and Bernice (Smith) R.; 1 child, Erick H. AS, Hibbing (Minn.) Community Coll., 1963; BS, U. Minn., 1965; MA, Cornell U., 1967; PhD, U. Iowa, 1974. Floor dir. Sta. KDAL-TV, Duluth, Minn., 1964-65; asst. prof. U. Va., Charlottesville, 1969-72; assoc. prof. U. Memphis, 1972-75, assoc. prof., 1975-91, prof., 1991—, interim dean Univ. Coll., 1975; asst. v.p. academic affairs Memphis State U., 1976-78, dean Coll. Comm. and Fine Arts, 1977—; gen. mgr. High Water Records, Memphis, 1980—; bd. dirs. Concerts Internat., Memphis, pres., 1988-90; TV cons. free-lance producer, 1973—. Assoc. producer: (tv program) Nat. Arthritis Telethon, 1985-90; Rec. Acad. graphics and prodn. coord. Grammy Awards TV program, 1983—; author articles in Communication Adminstrn. Bull., 1977—, editorial bd., 1977—. Chmn., v.p. Tenn. Humanities Coun., Nashville, 1980-82; v.p. Memphis Devel. Found., 1983-86; bd. dirs., chmn. mktg. com. Leadership Memphis, 1987-90, chmn. selection com., 1994-95; bd. dirs. Life Blood, Memphis, 1984-92; treas. Memphis-Shelby County Film, Tape and Music Commn., 1986—; chmn. adv. com. Tenn. Film, Entertainment and Music Commn., Nashville, 1987-93, chmn., 1993—; chmn. bd. dirs. Crime Stoppers Memphis Assn.; chmn. Memphis Arts Festival, 1992-94. Recipient Edn. Operational Models grant Ednl. Testing Svc., 1975, Communication Lab. grant HEW, 1976, Disting. Alumnus award Minn. Cmty. Coll. System, 1984; named to Recording Hall of Fame Selection panel, Nat. Rec. Acad., L.A., 1986—. Mem. NARAS (v.p. 1986-88, 92-93, chmn. com. 1983—, trustee 1982-86, 88-92, 93—, pres. Memphis chpt. 1984-86, bd. govs. 1978—), So. States Comm. Assn. (pres. 1987-88, fin. bd. 1985-87, 93—, exec. dir. 1995—), Tenn. Speech Comm. Assn. (pres. 1986-87), Speech Comm. Assn. (vice chmn., then chmn. exptl. learning com. 1979-83, mem. fin. and adminstrn. coms. 1989-93, chmn. fin. com. 1991-93)), So. Arts Fedn. (bd. dirs.), Delta Sailing Assn. Club (sec. 1984—). Avocations: sailing, farming, photography. Office: U Memphis Coll Communication & Fine Arts Memphis TN 38152

RANTS, CAROLYN JEAN, college official; b. Hastings, Nebr., Oct. 3, 1936; d. John Leon and Christine (Helzer) Halloran; m. Marvin L. Rants, June 1, 1957 (div. July 1984); children: Christopher Charles, Douglas John. Student, Hastings Coll., 1954-56; BS, U. Omaha, 1960, MEd, U. Nebr., 1968; EdD, U. S.D., 1982. Tchr. elem. Ogallala (Nebr.) Community Sch., 1956-58, Omaha Pub. Schs., 1958-60, Hastings Pub. Schs., 1960-64, Grosse Pointe (Mich.) Community Schs., 1964-67; asst. prof., instr. Morn-

ingside Coll., Sioux City, Iowa, 1974-82, dean for student devel., 1982-84, v.p. for student affairs, 1984-94, interim v.p. for acad. affairs, 1992-94; v.p. enrollment and student svcs., 1994—. Mem. new agy. com., chmn. fund distbn. and resource deployment com. United Way, Sioux City, 1987-94; mem. Iowa Civil Rights Commn., 1989—; bd. dirs. Leadership Sioux City, 1988-95, pres., 1992-93; bd. dirs. Girls, Inc., Siouxland Y, Sioux City, 1985-90, pres., 1988; mem. Vision 2020 Cmty. Planning Task Force, 1990-92. Mem. Iowa Women in Ednl. Leadership (pres. Sioux City chpt. 1986), Nat. Assn. Student Pers. Adminstrs.(region IV-E adv. bd.), Nat. Assn. for Women Deans, Adminstrs. and Counselors, Iowa Student Pers. Adminstr. (chmn. profl. devel. Iowa chpt. 1988-89, pres. 1991-92), AAUW (corp. rep., coll./univ. rep. 1994-95), P.E.O. (pres. Sioux City chpt. 1994—, Tri-State Women's Bus. Conf. (treas., planning com. Sioux City chpt. 1987-89), Quota Club (com. chmn. Sioux City 1987-89, v.p. 1992-94, pres. 199495, Siouxland Woman of Yr. award 1988), Sertoma (officer, bd. govs., regional dir.), Omicron Delta Kappa, Delta Kappa Gamma (state 1st v.p. 1993—), state pres. 1995—). Republican. Methodist. Avocations: handbells, cross-stitching. Home: 2904 S Cedar St # 4 Sioux City IA 51106-4246 Office: Morningside Coll 1501 Morningside Ave Sioux City IA 51106-1751

RANU, HARCHARAN SINGH, biomedical scientist, administrator, orthopaedic biomechanics educator; b. Lyallpur, India; came to U.S., 1976; s. Jodh Singh and Harnam Kaur R. BSc, Leicester Poly., Eng., 1963; MSc, U. Surrey, Guilford, Eng., 1967, Cambridge (Eng.) U., 1972; PhD, Middlesex Hosp. Med. Sch. and Poly. of Cen. London, 1975; diploma, MIT, 1984. Chartered engr., Eng. Med. scientist Nat. Inst. Med. Rsch. of the Med. Rsch. Coun., London, 1967-70; rsch. fellow Middlesex Hosp. Med. Sch. and Poly. of Cen. London, 1971-76; rsch. scientist Plastics Rsch. Assn. at Great Britain, Shawbury, Eng., 1977; asst. prof. Wayne State U., Detroit, 1977-81; prof. biomed. engring./orthopaedic biomechanics biomaterials La. Tech. U., Ruston, 1982—; prof., chmn. Dept. Biomechanics N.Y. Coll. Osteo. Medicine, Old Westbury, 1989-93; dir. tng. Rehab. Rsch. and Devel. Ctr., 1983-85; mem. La. Tech. U. Libr. Com., 1983-85; chmn. design competition Assn. Biomed. Engrs.; mem. steering com. So. Biomed. Engring. Confs., 1983—; chmn. tech. in health care conf. U. Cambridge, 1985; chmn. Internat. Symposium on Bioengring., Calcutta, India, 1985; dir. orthopaedic biomechanics rsch. labs.; staff Nassau County Med. Ctr., Long Island, 1989—; prof., asst. to pres., dir. doctoral program Life Coll., Marietta, Ga., 1993—; mem. biomed. engring. faculty com. La. Tech. U., faculty com., rsch. awards com., grad. studies com., grad. faculty, acad. bd. dirs; vis. scientist Dryburn Hosp., Durham, Eng., 1985-87, cons., 1988—; vis. prof. U. Istanbul, 1982, Lab. de Recherch Orthopediques, Paris, 1985—, Kings Coll. Med. Sch. U. London, 1989—, Indian Inst. Tech., New Delhi, Postgrad Inst. Med. Edn. and Rsch., Chandigarh, India, 1989—; Inst. Biol. Physics USSR Acad. Sci., Moscow, 1990, Polytech. Ctrl. London, 1991—; adj. prof. Coll. Physicians and Surgeons Columbia U., N.Y., 1988—, Inst. Biol. Physics USSR Acad. Sci., Moscow, 1990, N.Y. Coll. Podiatric Medicine, 1991—, CUNY, 1992—; cons. Lincoln Gen. Hosp., Ruston, La., 1982-85, La. State U. Med. Ctr., Shreveport, 1982—, St. Luke's and Roosevelt Hosp. Ctr., N.Y., 1988—, Foot Clinics N.Y., 1991—, Vets. Affairs Med. Ctr., N.Y., 1992—, various biomed. rsch. & legal corps., U.S., United Kingdom; mem. media resource svc. Inst. Pub. Info., N.Y., 1989—; med. scientist, cons. NATO, 1982—; presenter, lectr., dir. organizer numerous sci. orgns. and nat. & internat. confs. Author: Rheological Behavior of Articular Cartilage Under Tensile Loads, 1967, Effects of Ionizing Radiation on the Mechanical Properties of Skin, 1975, Effects of Fractionated Doses of X-irradiation on the Mechanical Properties of Skin--A Long Term Study, 1980, Effects of Ionizing Radiation on the Structure & Physical Properties of the Skin, 1983, 3-D Model of Vertebra for Spinal Surgery, 1985, Application of Carbon Fibers in Orthopaedic Surgery, 1985, Relation Between Metal Corrision & Electrical Polarization, 1989, The Distribution of Stresses in the Human Lumbar Spine, 1989, Medical Devices & Orthopaedic Implants in the United States, 1989, Spinal Surgery by Modeling, 1989, Multipoint Determination of Pressure-Volume Curves in Human Intervertebral Discs, 1993, Evaluation of Volume-Pressure Relationship in Lumbar Discs Using Model and Experimental Studies, 1994, A Mechanism of Laser Nuclectomy, 1994, Microminiaturization in Laser Surgery in Vivo Intradiscal Pressure Measurements in Lumbar Intervertebral Discs, 1994, An Experimental and Mathematical Simulation of Fracture of Human Bone Due to Jumping, 1994; editor The Lower Extremity, 1993—; guest editor IEEE Engring. in Medicine & Biology, 1991; mem. editorial bd. Med. Instrumentation, 1988—, Jour. Biomed. Instrumentation & Tech., 1988—, Jour. Med. Engring. & Tech., 1989—, Jour. Med. Design & Material, 1990—, Jour. Long-Term Effects Med. Implants, 1991—, Biomed. Sci. & Tech., 1991—; reviewer Jour. Biomechanics, 1981—, Clin. Biomechanics, 1984—, Jour. Biomed. Engring., 1981, Phys. Therapy, 1990—, IEEE Biomed.Engring. in Medicine, 1989—; contbr. articles to profl. jours. Faculty advisor India Students Assn. Wayne State U., 1980. Recipient Edwin Tate award U. Surrey, 1968, numerous rsch. grants. Fellow ASME (bioengring. com. 1990—, award L.I. chpt. 1991), Biol. Engring. Soc. (London) (President's prize 1984), Instn. Mech. Engrs. (chmn. revv. bd. for corp. memberships, James Clayton awards 1974-76); mem. Am. Soc. Biomechanics (edn. com. 1990—), Orthopaedic Rsch. Soc., Biomed. Engring. Soc., India Assn., India Assn. North La. Sikh. Office: Life Coll Sch Grad Studies Marietta GA 30060

RANUM, OREST ALLEN, historian, educator; b. Lyle, Minn., Feb. 18, 1933; s. Luther George and Nada (Chaffee) R.; m. Patricia McGroder, July 4, 1955; children--Kristin, Marcus. B.A., Macalester Coll., St. Paul, 1955; M.A., U. Minn., 1957, Ph.D., 1961. Asst. prof. U. So. Calif., 1960-61, Columbia U., N.Y.C., 1961-63; assoc. prof. Columbia U., 1963-69; prof. history Johns Hopkins U., Balt., 1969—; mem., chmn. GRE Ednl. Testing Service, Princeton, 1973-78. Author: Richelieu and Councilors, 1963; Paris, Age of Absolutism, 1968; Artisans of Glory, 1981, The Fronde, 1993. Recipient Bronze medal City of Tours, France, 1980. Mem. Am. Hist. Assn., Soc. French Hist. Studies, Inst. de France (corr.), Académie des Sciences Morales et Politiques (Paris; corr. 1989), Société de l'Histoire de France, Collège de France (internat. chair 1994-95). Home: 208 Ridgewood Rd Baltimore MD 21210-2539 Office: Johns Hopkins U Baltimore MD 21218

RANUS, ROBERT D., food marketing executive; b. 1940. BS in Acctg., U. Buffalo, 1961, MBA, 1962. CPA, N.Y. With Price Waterhouse & Co., 1963-78, Fox Industries, 1978-80; v.p. fin. and adminstrn. Pitts. divsn. Wetterau, Inc., 1980-86; 1st v.p. adminstrn. Roundy's Inc., 1986-87, v.p. CFO, bd. dirs., 1987—. Office: Roundys Inc 23000 Roundy Dr Pewaukee WI 53072-4001

RANZAHUER, GUILLERMO GONZALEZ, bishop; b. Huatusco, Veracruz, Mex., Mar. 12, 1928; s. Edmundo Ranzahuer Cárcamo and Lucia (Gónzalez) Lecuona. Ordained priest Roman Catholic Ch.; consecrated bishop of Diocese of San Andres Tuxtla. Office: Constitucion Y Morelos, San Andres Tuxtla, Veracruz CP 95700, Mexico

RAO, ATAMBIR SINGH, nuclear engineer. Principal engineer, BWR program GE Nuclear Energy, San Jose. Recipient George Westinghouse Silver Medal ASME, 1990. Office: GE Nuclear Energy 175 Curtner Ave # C754 San Jose CA 95125-1088*

RAO, DESIRAJU BHAVANARAYANA, meteorologist, oceanographer, educator; b. Visakhapatnam, India, Dec. 8, 1936; came to U.S., 1960, naturalized, 1974; s. Desiraju Sreeramulu and Desiraju Hanumayamma Adavikolanu; m. Padmavati Kavuru; children: Desiraju Pramila, Desiraju Kavitha. B.Sc., Andhra U., Waltair, India, 1956, M.Sc., 1959; M.S., U. Chgo., 1962, Ph.D., 1965. Rsch. scholar Indian Naval Phys. Labs., Cochin, 1959-60; postdoctoral fellow Nat. Center Atmospheric Rsch., Boulder, Colo., 1965-67; rsch. scientist marine scis. br. Can. Dept. Energy, Mines and Resources, Ottawa, Ont., 1967-68; asst. prof. atmospheric sci. Colo. State U., Ft. Collins 1968-71; assoc. prof. energetics, also Center Gt. Lakes Studies, U. Wis.-Milw. 1971-74, prof., 1974-76; head phys. limnology and meteorology group Gt. Lakes Environ. Rsch. Lab., NOAA, Ann Arbor, Mich., 1975-80; adj. prof. limnology and meteorology U. Mich., Ann Arbor, 1977-80; head oceans and ice br. Lab. for Atmospheric Sci., Goddard Space Flight Ctr., NASA, Greenbelt, Md., 1980-84; chief marine prediction br. Nat. Meteorol. Ctr., NOAA, Washington, 1984—; adj. prof. meteorology U. Md. College Park, 1981—; cons. in field. Contbr. articles on atmospheric, oceanic and lake dynamics to sci. jours. Fellow Am. Meteorol. Soc. (v.p. Denver chpt. 1969-70); Mem. Am. Soc. Limnology and Oceanography, AAAS, Internat. Water Resources Assn. (charter), Am. Geophys. Union, Internat. Assn. for Gt. Lakes Research, The Oceanography Soc. (charter), Sigma Xi. Home: 13101 Hugo Pl Silver Spring MD 20906-5916 Office: Nat Meteorol Ctr Rm 204 W/NMC 21 WWB Washington DC 20233

RAO, NANNAPANENI NARAYANA, electrical engineer; b. Kakumanu, Andhra Pradesh, India; m. Sarojini Jonnalagadda, June 10, 1955; children: Vanaja, Durgaprasad, Hariprasad. BSc in Physics, U. Madras, India, 1952; DMIT in Electronics, Madras Inst. Tech., 1955; MSEE, U. Wash., 1960, PhD in Elec. Engring, 1965. Acting instr. elec. engring. U. Wash., 1960-64, acting asst. prof., 1964-65; asst. prof. elec. engring. U. Ill., Urbana, 1965-69; asso. prof. U. Ill., 1969-75, prof., 1975—, assoc. head elec. and computer engring., 1987—; cons. Fakultas Teknik, Univ. Indonesia, Jakarta, 1985-86, 87. Author: Basic Electromagnetics with Applications, 1972, Elements of Engineering Electromagnetics, 4th edit., 1994; contbr. numerous articles to profl. jours. Recipient Engring. award Telugu Assn. N.Am., 1983, Fakultas Teknik award Universitatas Indonesia, 1986. Fellow IEEE (Undergrad. Teaching award 1994); mem. Am. Soc. Engring. Edn. (AT&T Found. award for excellence in instrn. engring. students 1991), Internat. Union Radio Sci. (U.S. Commn. G). Activities include rsch. carried out in the general area of ionospheric propagation. Home: 2509 S Lynn St Urbana IL 61801-6841 Office: U Ill Dept Elec & Computer Engring 1406 W Green St Urbana IL 61801-2918

RAO, SETHURAMIAH LAKSHMINARAYANA, United Nations official; b. Mysore, Karnataka, India, Apr. 28, 1942; came to U.S., 1967; s. Ramakrishnaih Sethuramiah and Bhageerathi; m. Sudha Bagur Viswanath, Aug. 1, 1971; children: Rekha, Kumar. MSc, U. Mysore, 1963; MPH, U. N.C., 1968; cert., U. Mich., 1969; PhD, U. Pa., 1971. Asst. prof. Brown U., Providence, 1971-73; UN adviser Govt. of Sri Lanka, Colombo, 1974-77; chief population and devel UN Population Fund, N.Y.C., 1978-82, chief policy br., 1982-90; country dir. UN Population Fund, Addis Ababa, Ethiopia, 1991-92; dep. dir. info. & extern rels. UN Population Fund, N.Y.C., 1992—; sec. exec. bd. UNDP/UNFPA; sec. UNFPA segment of UNDP/ UNFPA exec. bd. Author: Socio-Religious Factors in Fertility, 1973; co-author: Population Problems of Sri Lanka, 1977, Population Program Experience, 1991; contbr. articles to profl. jours. V.p Mysore Self Reliance Assn., Mangalore, 1963-65, Indo-Am. Forum for Polit. Edn., N.Y., 1989-90; founder, pres. New Eng. Kannada Koota, Providence, 1972-73. Mem. Delta Omega. Avocations: traveling, debate, bridge playing. Home: 143 Nelson Rd Scarsdale NY 10583 Office: UN Population Fund 220 E 42nd St New York NY 10017-5806

RAO, TANNIRU R., marketing educator, consultant; b. Guntur, A.P., India, Sept. 2, 1940; came to U.S., 1964; s. Krishna Murthy and Seeta (Seetamraju) Tanniru; m. Susan A. Czajkowski, June 29, 1969; 1 child, Maya S. MA, Andhra U., Waltair, India, 1959; MStat, Indian Stat. Inst., 1961; PhD, Mich. State U., 1967. Statis. quality control officer M/S Duncan Bros. Ltd., Calcutta, India, 1962-64; systems analyst Lear Siegler, Inc., Grand Rapids, Mich., 1966-68; asst. prof. U. Wis., Milw., 1967-73, assoc. dean, assoc. prof., 1978—; pres. Market Probe, Inc., Milw., 1984—, cons., 1976—. Contbr. articles to profl. jours. Mem. Wauwatosa (Wis.) Sch. Bd., 1982-86. Inst. Internat. Edn. fellow, 1965-66. Mem. Am. Mktg. Assn., Health Care Planning and Mktg. Soc. Wis. (chmn. edn. com. 1990—), Beta Gamma Sigma. Republican. Home: 1521 N 122d St Wauwatosa WI 53226 Office: Market Probe Inc 1233 N Mayfair Rd Ste 117 Milwaukee WI 53226-3277

RAO, VITTAL SRIRANGAM, electrical engineering educator; b. Inumpamula, India, June 8, 1944; came to U.S., 1981; s. Rangaiah Srirangam and Lakshmamma (Immadi) R.; m. Vijaya Morishetti, Feb. 28, 1965; children: Asha, Ajay. M of Tech., Indian Inst. Tech., 1972, PhD, 1975. Asst. prof. Indian Inst. of Tech., New Delhi, India, 1975-79; vis. prof. T.U., Halifax, N.S., Can., 1980-81; assoc. prof. U. Mo., Rolla, 1981-88, prof., 1988—; dir. Intelligent Systems Ctr., Rolla, 1991—; cons. Delco Remy, Anderson, Ind., 1985-87, Allison Gas Turbines, Indpls., 1986-87, U.S. Army Picatinny Arsenal, N.J., 1988-91. Contbr. articles to profl. jours. including Suboptimal/Near Optimal Control, Reduced Order Modeling Techniques, Robust Control, Large Space Structures, Smart Structures. Fellow AIAA (assoc.); mem. IEEE (sr., subsect. 1981-88, Centennial medal 1984). Achievements include devel. of reduced order modeling techniques for large space structures, interdisciplinary approach for control of smart structures. Home: 501 Oak Knoll Rd Rolla MO 65401-4727 Office: U Mo Intelligent Systems Ctr Rolla MO 65401

RAOS, JOHN G., manufacturing executive. Pres. Hanson Industries N. Am., Iselin, N.J. Office: Hanson Industries N Am 99 Wood Ave S Iselin NJ 08830-2715

RAPACCIOLI, MICHEL ANTOINE, financial executive; b. Paris, Apr. 1, 1934; came to U.S., 1977; m. Janette Rapaccioli, Sept. 5, 1959; children: François, Philippe. H.E.C., Ecole des Hautes Etudes Commerciales, Paris, 1957; MBA, U. Chgo., 1958; cert. advanced mgmt. program, Harvard U. 1975. Asst. treas. S.N. Elf Aquitaine, Paris, 1962-66, treas., contr., 1972-74; v.p. Aquitaine Co. Can., Calgary, Alta., Can., 1966-72, Le Nickel, Paris, 1974-77; pres. Elf Petroleum Corp., N.Y.C., 1977-83; sr. v.p., chief fin. officer Elf Aquitaine, Inc., N.Y.C., 1983—; chmn., CEO Elf Techs., N.Y.C., 1993—. Served to lt. French Navy, 1959-62.

RAPACZYNSKI, ANDRZEJ, law educator; b. 1947. PhD, Columbia U., 1974; JD, Yale U., 1982. Bar: N.Y. 1984. Asst. prof. philosohy Yale U. 1974-79; asst. prof. Columbia U., N.Y.C., 1982-86, prof. law, 1986—; vis. asst. prof. philosophy Princeton U., 1977-78. Mem. Am. Soc. Polit. and Legal Philosophy. Office: Columbia U Sch Law 435 W 116th St New York NY 10027-7201

RAPAPORT, DAVID ALAN, corporate legal executive; b. Bklyn., Nov. 12, 1942; s. Efred and Jacqueline (Victorson) R.; m. Sandra F. Jackson, June 30, 1963; children: Fredrik, Ian, Howard. Student, CUNY, 1960-63; LLB, St. John's U., 1966. Bar: N.Y. 1967, U.S. Dist. Ct. (so. and ea. dists.) N.Y. 1969. Asst. regional atty. HEW, N.Y.C., 1968-69; ptnr. Anderson & Allergaert, N.Y.C., 1970-71; assoc. Davis & Cox, N.Y.C., 1972-74; gen. counsel Nat. Patent Devel. Corp., N.Y.C., 1975-86, sr. v.p., 1984-90; sr. v.p., sec. Gen. Physics Corp., Columbia, Md., 1989-90; exec. v.p., gen. counsel, sec. Conversion Industries Inc., Pasadena, Calif., 1990—; pres. Sci. Testing Inc. New Brunswick, N.J., 1986-88; bd. dirs. Duratek, Greenbelt, Md., 1977-90, pres., CEO, 1988-90; bd. dirs. Joseph Land Group, Inc., Myriad Industries, Inc. Mem. ABA, Assn. of Bar of City of N.Y., N.Y. State Bar Assn. Jewish. Avocations: swimming, computer sci., photography, boating. Office: Conversion Industries Inc Mezzanine 230 E Colorado Blvd Pasadena CA 91101-2203

RAPAPORT, FELIX THEODOSIUS, surgeon, editor, researcher, educator; b. Munich, Germany, Sept. 27, 1929; s. Max W. and Adelaide (Rathaus) R.; m Margaret Birsner, Dec. 14, 1969; children: Max, Benjamin, Simon, Michel, Adelaide. A.B., NYU, 1951, M.D., 1954. Diplomate Am. Bd. Surgery. Intern Mt. Sinai Hosp., N.Y.C., 1955-56; resident, chief resident NYU Surg. Services, 1958-62, USPHS postdoctoral fellow in pathology, 1956; exec. officer Naval Med. Rsch. Unit No. 1, U. Calif., Berkeley, 1956-58; trainee in allergy and infectious diseases NYU, 1958-61; head, transplantation and immunology div NYU Surg. Svcs., 1965-77; dir. rsch. Inst. Reconstrn. and Plastic Surgery, NYU, 1965-77; assoc. prof. surgery NYU Med. Ctr., 1965-70, prof., 1970-77; prof. surgery, prof. pathology, dir. transplantation svc. SUNY, Stony Brook, 1977—, chmn. dept. surgery, 1989-91; guest investigator Hosp. St. Louis, Paris, 1963-79; Claude Bernard vis. prof. expel. medicine Coll. de France, Paris, 1985; sr. attendingsurgeon SUNY Hosp., 1980—, surgeon-in-chief, 1989-91; pres. bd. dirs. regional N.Y. Transplant Program, 1972-89; cons. VA Hosp., N.Y.C., 1963-77 Northport, N.Y., 1977—; adv. panei on medicine and dentistry U.S. Office of Naval Res., 1974-78; adv. com. NIAID, 1964-68; merit review bd. immunology V.A. Dept. of Medicine and Surgery, 1974-78. Editor in chief Transplantation Proc., 1968—; assoc. editor Am. Jour. Kidney Diseases, 1981-86, Am. Jour. Craniofacial Genetics and Developmental Biology, 1980-85, Cellular Immunology, 1980—; contbr. over 500 articles to profl. jours.; author, editor 20 books on transplantation. Bd. dirs. United Network for Organ Sharing, 1986-88. Served to lt. comdr. M.C. USNR, 1956-58. Decorated

comdr. Order Sci. Merit, chevalier Ordre National du Merite, France, 1970, officer Legion of Honor (France), 1990; recipient Gold medal Societe d'Encouragement au Bien, 1979, Gold medal City of Paris, France, 1980, Commandeur Ordre des Palmes Academiques, France, 1981, Samuel L. Kountz award Howard U., 1989, Lester Hoenig award Nat. Kidney Found., 1990, Sol Berson award NYU, 1990, Disting. Achievement in Med. Scis. award Touro Coll. B. Levine Sch. Health Scis., 1991, USPHS Res. Career Devel. award, NIAID, 1961-62, Career Scientist award Health Rsch. Coun., 1963-72, Maimonides Physician award, new Skwere Institutions, 1995. Mem. ACS, French Acad. Scis., Soc. Univ. Surgeons, N.Y. Surg. Soc., Am. Burn Assn., Am. Surg. Assn., Am. Assn. Immunologists, Soc. Exptl. Biology and Medicine, Harvey Soc., Am. Soc. Transplant Surgeons, Am. Soc. Transplant Physicians, Soc. for Organ Sharing (hon. pres.), Am. Assn. Clin. Histocompatibility Testing, Internat. Soc. Exptl. Hematology, Transplantation Soc. (founding sec., v.p., treas., councillor, historian, pres. 1986-88), Alpha Omega Alpha. Jewish. Current Work: induction of specific tolerance to major transplantable organs in man; research concerned with effects of irradiation and bone marrow transplantation in the production of host unresponsiveness to tissue allografts. Office: SUNY Stony Brook Dept Surgery Health Sc Ctr Stony Brook NY 11794

RAPAPORT, MARK SAMUEL, lawyer; b. N.Y.C., July 31, 1947; s. Joseph and Sadie (Schwartz) R.; m. Jennifer Munnell, Nov. 22, 1971. B.A. cum laude, U. Wis., 1968, J.D. cum laude, 1973. Bar: Wis. 1973, N.Y. 1974, Calif. 1981. Assoc. Dewey, Ballantine, Bushby, Palmer & Wood, N.Y.C., 1973-80; assoc. Hahn and Cazier, Los Angeles, 1980-82, ptnr. 1982—. Mem. donor fin. planning com. Greater Los Angeles affiliate Heart Fund, 1981—; mem. devel. com. The Dance Gallery, 1984—. Mem. State Bar Calif. (vice chmn. trust adminstrn. subcom. 1982—, probate com. 1985—), ABA (investments by fiduciaries com. 1979—), N.Y. State Bar Assn., State Bar of Wis. Note and comment editor Wis. Law Rev., 1972-73. Office: Morgan Lewis & Bockius 801 S Grand Ave Los Angeles CA 90017-4613

RAPAPORT, ROBERT M., financial executive; b. Vienna, Austria, July 12, 1931; came to U.S., 1940, naturalized, 1944; s. Gustav H. and Rose (Katz) R.; m. Annette Kohn, Aug. 2, 1953; children—Gary Michael, Steven Mark, Gail Ann, Amy Sue. B.S., U. Mo., 1952. Mgr. Breddo Food Products, Midland Labs., Kansas City, Mo., 1953-60, pres., 1960-67; v.p. Sucrest Corp., N.Y.C., 1967-74; pres., chief exec. officer Sucrest Corp., 1974-77; also dir.; internat. commodity exec. E.F. Hutton & Co., N.Y.C., 1977-78; sr. ptnr. Lamborn & Co., N.Y.C., 1978—; owner, pres. Foote & Jenks, Inc., Camden, N.J., 1981—; dir. Bestex Corp., Kansas City, Mo. Mem. Am. Soc. Bakery Engrs. and Food Technicians, Am. Soc. Cereal Chemists. Patentee in field. Home: 124 Centura Cherry Hill NJ 08003 Office: Foote & Jenks Inc 1420 Crestmont Ave Camden NJ 08103-3124

RAPER, CHARLES ALBERT, retired management consultant; b. Charleston, W.Va., Aug. 18, 1926; s. Kenneth B. and Louise (Williams) R.; m. Margaret Ann Weers, Dec. 26, 1947; children: Kathleen, Josephine, Charles. Student, Okla. State U., 1945; B.S., U. Ill., 1949. Sales mgr. Meyer Furnace Co., Peoria, Ill., 1949-54; v.p. mktg. Master Consol., Inc., Dayton, Ohio, 1954-61; mgmt. cons. McKinsey & Co., Inc., Chgo., 1961-67; v.p. mktg. Gen. Portland Inc., Dallas, 1967-69; pres. Gen. Portland Inc., 1969-75, also dir.; v.p., gen. mgr. Scholl Inc., Chgo., 1975-81; pres Oxford Group of Sara Lee, 1981-84; mgmt. cons. McKinsey & Co., 1984—. Vice chmn. devel. bd. U. Tex. at Dallas; exec. bd. Circle 10 council Boy Scouts Am. Served with USNR, 1944-46. Mem. Dallas C. of C. (chmn. bd. dirs. 1974—), Sales Execs. Club, Phi Gamma Delta. Methodist. Club: Cherokee Country. Home: 301 Townsend Pl NW Atlanta GA 30327-3035

RAPER, MARK IRVIN, public relations executive; b. Greensboro, N.C., Aug. 26, 1954; s. James Crawford and Jean Elizabeth (Willick) R.; m. Martha Jefferson Taylor, Sept. 17, 1977; children: Carter Jefferson, Martha Stuart, Lucy Colston. Student, U. Richmond, 1972-75; pharmacy cert., Baylor U., 1976; BS in Mass Communications, Va. Commonwealth U., 1981, postgrad., 1981. Cert. pharmacy specialist. Dir., pub. relations Stuart Circle Hosp., Richmond, Va., 1980-81, Leigh Meml. Hosp.- Alliance, Norfolk, Va., 1981-82; dir. mktg. Alliance Health Services Corp., Norfolk, 1982-84; mgr. advt., pub. relations Figgie Internat. Holding Co., Richmond, 1984-86; dir. pub. rels. Ford & Westbrook Agy., Richmond and Atlanta, 1986-88; pres. Earle Palmer Brown Pub. Rels., Richmond, 1988-94; mng. ptnr. Earle Palmer Brown Pub. Rels., 1994—; asst. editor Va. Family Physician (quarterly), Richmond, 1981; coordinator communications In-Vitro program Norfolk Gen. Hosp., 1982. Creator Legends Festival Program, 1987. Rep. Va. 1st Amendment Congress, 1981; dir. Children's Miracle Network, ctrl. Va., 1987; bd. dirs. Richmond Forum, 1987, Carpenter Ctr. for Performing Arts, Richmond, 1988. Recipient Top Student Scholarship Richmond Pub. Relations Assn., 1980, Gold Quill award Internat. Assn. Bus. Communicators, 1983; named one of Best in East Am. Soc. Hosp. Pub. Relations, 1983, Outstanding Young Men in Am., 1987. Mem. Pub. Rels. Soc. Am. (cert. of achievement 1983), L. Ginter Recreation Assn. Richmond (treas. 1987-90), Phi Kappa Phi, Kappa Tau Alpha. Avocations: tennis, golf, basketball, travel, music. Home: 3911 Seminary Ave Richmond VA 23227-4107 Office: Earle Palmer Brown 1 E Cary Richmond VA 23219

RAPER, WILLIAM BURKETTE, retired college president; b. nr. Wilson, N.C., Sept. 10, 1927; s. William Cecil and Beulah Maybelle (Davis) R.; m. Rose Mallard, Aug. 19, 1951; children: Olivia, Kristie, Burkette, Elizabeth, Stephen, Laura. AB, Duke U., 1947, MDiv, 1951; MS (Kellogg fellow), Fla. State U., 1962; LLD, Atlantic Christian Coll. (now Barton Coll.), 1960. Ordained to ministry Free Will Baptist Ch., 1946; pastor Hull Rd. Free Will Bapt. Ch., Snow Hill, N.C., 1951-55; pres. Mt. Olive (N.C.) Coll., 1954-95, ret., 1995; dir. Wachovia Bank and Trust Co.; promotional dir. Free Will Bapt. State Conv. N.C., 1953-54; pres. council Ch.-Related Colls. N.C., 1966-67; mem. N.C. Edn. Assistance Authority, 1972-76; sec. Ind. Coll. Fund of N.C., 1976-78; Mem. N.C. Gov.'s Com. on Hwy. Traffic Safety, 1968; regional coordinator U.S. Office Edn. Program with Developing Instns., 1968-70; dir. Edn. Professions Devel. Act Grant for Strengthening Devel. in Pvt. Two-Year Colls., 1970-72; trustee N.C. Coll. Found., 1977-94; adv. com. Ind. Coll. Presidents, U.N.C. Recipient Disting. Service award Mt. Olive Jr. C. of C., 1961; named N.C. Young Man of Year, 1961. Mem. Am. Assn. Community and Jr. Colls. (commn. on legislation 1963-66, cons. 1968-71, chmn. commn. on student personnel 1970-71), N.C. Assn. Ind. Colls. and Univs. (exec. com. 1967-70, 76-77, 83-85), N.C. Assn. Colls. and Univs. (pres. 1969-70), Masons. Democrat. Office: Mt Olive Coll Office of the Pres Mount Olive NC 28365

RAPER, WILLIAM CRANFORD, lawyer; b. Asheville, N.C., Aug. 17, 1946; s. James Sidney and Kathryn (Cranford) R.; m. Patricia Dotson, Sept. 28, 1974; children: Kimber-leigh, Heather, James. AB, U.N.C., 1968; JD, Vanderbilt U., 1972. Bar: N.C. 1972, U.S. Ct. Appeals (4th cir.) 1972, U.S. Supreme Ct. 1977, U.S. Ct. Appeals (fed. cir.) 1985. Law clk. to Senator Sam Ervin Jr. Washington, 1971; law clk. to presiding justice U.S. Ct. Appeals (4th cir.), Richmond, Va., 1972-73; ptnr. Womble, Carlyle, Sandridge & Rice, Winston-Salem, N.C., 1984—. Mem. ABA, N.C. Bar Assn., N.C. Assn. of Def. Attys. (charter). Office: Womble Carlyle Sandridge & Rice 3300 One First Union Ctr 301 S College St Charlotte NC 28202-6000

RAPHAEL, ALBERT ASH, JR., lawyer; b. N.Y.C., June 4, 1925; s. Albert Ash and Clare (Schindler) R.; m. Dorothy Buck, Oct. 7, 1960; 1 child, Bruce William. A.B., Yale U., 1947; LL.D., Harvard U., 1950. Bar: N.Y. 1950, Vt. 1972. Mem. firm Gallert, Hilborn & Raphael, N.Y.C., 1950-60, Alter, Lefevre, Raphael, Lowry, and Gould, N.Y.C., 1960-78; individual practice Waitsfield, Vt., 1972-86; ptnr. Raphael and Ware, Waitsfield, 1986—; Dir. various real estate cos. Mem. bd. zoning appeals, Waitsfield, 1974-83, selectman, 1976-82, chmn. bd. selectmen, 1981-82. Served with F.A., AUS, 1943-46. Mem. Vt. Bar Assn., Assn. of Bar of City of N.Y. Home: PO Box 1149 Waitsfield VT 05673-1149 Office: Raphael Rd Waitsfield VT 05673

RAPHAEL, BRETT, artistic director, choreographer; b. New Haven, Conn., Nov. 10, 1954; s. Howard Boone Jacobson and Dana Raphael. Artistic dir. L.I. Ballet, Huntington, 1979-80, Conn. Ballet, Stamford, 1980—; mem. faculty Harkness House, N.Y.C., 1978-79, Alvin Ailey Am. Dance Theatre, N.Y.C., 1990-92, divsn. continuing edn. SUNY, 1984-96. Choreographer 15 original ballets Conn. Ballet, Boston Ballet, Netherlands Dans Theatre, Joffrey II Dancers; restager Nutcracker, Giselle, Coppelia. Named Chore-

ographer of Yr. by Internat. Beaux Arts Soc., N.Y.C., 1979. Office: Conn Ballet 20 Acosta St Stamford CT 06902

RAPHAEL, COLEMAN, business school dean; b. N.Y.C., Sept. 16, 1925; s. Morris and Adella (Leav) R.; m. Sylvia Moskowitz, Feb. 28, 1948; children—Hollis, Gordon. B.Civil Engring., CCNY, 1945; M.C.E., Poly. Inst. Bklyn., 1951, Ph.D. in Applied Mechanics, 1965. Registered profl. engr., N.Y., Fla. Structural research engr., test research engr. Republic Aviation Corp., 1945-47; instr. mech. engring. Pratt Inst., Bklyn., 1947-51; from sr. research engr. to mgr. space systems div. Republic Aviation Corp., 1951-65; gen. mgr. space and electronics systems div., then v.p. Fairchild Hiller Corp., Germantown, Md., 1965-70; with Atlantic Rsch. Corp., Alexandria, Va., 1970-86, chmn. bd., 1980-86; chmn. bd. SJI Industries, 1968-70; dean bus. sch. George Mason U., Fairfax, Va., 1986-91; ret., 1991; bd. mem., prin. owner Applied Bus. Systems, Bethesda, Md., 1990—; bd. dirs. ENVIPCO (chmn. 1995), Fairfax, Va., Night Owl Security, Landover, Md., Geico, Chevy Chase, Md.; mem. engring. adv. com. Montgomery Coll., Md., 1968-69, George Washington U., 1977-82; mem. Gov. Va. Task Force Nuclear Power Plants, 1969; chmn. energy com. Gov. Md. Sci. Adv. Coun., 1974-76; bd. visitors U. Pitts., 1980-82. Author textbook, papers, reports in field. Chmn. U.S. Bond drive, Alexandria, 1975-76; chmn. adv. com. Montgomery County Bldg. Codes, 1976-77. Recipient Citizenship award Montgomery County Press Assn., 1967, Disting. Service award Montgomery County C. of C., 1969, Disting. Citizenship award State of Md., 1970. Mem. AIAA (chmn. mgmt. com. 1976), Aircraft Industries Assn., Nat. Space Club, disting Alumus, Poly. Inst. of Bklyn., 1982. Home: 508 Hermleigh Rd Silver Spring MD 20902-1608

RAPHAEL, FREDERIC MICHAEL, author; b. Chgo., Aug. 14, 1931; s. Cedric Michael and Irene (Mauser) R.; m. Sylvia Betty Glatt, Jan. 17, 1955; children: Paul Simon, Sarah Natasha, Stephen Matthew Joshua. M.A. (Major Open scholar), St. John's Coll., Cambridge (Eng.) U., 1954. Author: (novels) Obbligato, 1956, The Earlsdon Way, 1958, The Limits of Love, 1960, A Wild Surmise, 1961, The Graduate Wife, 1962, The Trouble with England, 1962, Lindmann, 1963, Darling, 1965, Two for the Road, 1966, Orchestra and Beginners, 1967, Like Men Betrayed, 1970, Who Were You With Last Night?, 1971, April, June and November, 1972, Richard's Things, 1973, California Time, 1975, The Glittering Prizes, 1976, Heaven and Earth, 1984, After the War, 1988, A Double Life, 1993, Old Scores, 1995; short stories Sleeps Six, 1979, Oxbridge Blues, 1980, Think of England, 1986, The Hidden I, 1990, The Latin Lover, 1994; screenplays Nothing But the Best, 1964, Darling, 1965, Two For the Road, 1967, Far From the Madding Crowd, 1967, A Severed Head, 1971, Daisy Miller, 1973, The Glittering Prizes, 1976, Rogue Male, 1976, Something's Wrong, 1978, Orestaia of Aeschylus, 1978, The Best of Friends, 1980, School Play, 1980, Richard's Things, 1981, Oxbridge Blues, 1984, After The War, 1989, The Man in the Brooks Brothers Shirt, 1990, Armed Response, 1995; (criticism) Somerset Maugham and His World, 1977, Byron, 1982, Euripides' Meden, 1995; also books revs. in other publs; translator (with Kenneth McLeish) book revs. The Poems of Catullus, 1978, The Oresteia of Aeschylus, 1979, Aeschylus Complete Plays, 1991, Of Gods and Men, 1993; editor: (with Kenneth McLeish) Essays Bookmarks, 1975, Cracks In The Ice (Views & Reviews), 1978, A List of Books, 1981; screenwriter, dir. The Man in the Brooks Brothers Shirt, 1990. Recipient Oscar award for original screen-play Darling, 1966, Ace awards 1987, 92; named Writer of Yr. Royal TV Soc. 1976. Fellow Royal Soc. Lit. Address: Lagardelle, St Laurent-la-Vallée, 24170 Belves France

RAPHAEL, LOUISE ARAKELIAN, mathematician, educator; b. N.Y.C., Oct. 24, 1937; d. Aristakes and Antionette (Sudbeaz) Arakelian; m. Robert Barnett Raphael, June 12, 1966 (div. 1985); children: Therese Denise, Marc Philippe. BS in Math., St. John's U., 1959; MS in Math., Cath. U., Washington, 1962; PhD in Math, Cath. U., 1967. Asst. prof. math. Howard U., Washington, 1966-70, vis. prof., 1981-82, assoc. prof., 1982-86, prof., 1986—; assoc. prof. Clark Coll., Atlanta, 1971-79, prof., 1979-82; vis. assoc. prof. MIT, Cambridge, 1977-78, vis. prof., 1989-90. Contbr. over 30 rsch. articles to profl. jours. Program dir. NSF, Washington, 1986-88; acting adminstrv. officer Conf. Bd. Math. Scis., 1985-86. Grantee NSF, 1975-76, 79-81, 89-91, Army Rsch. Office, 1981-89, Air Force Sci. Rsch., 1981-82, 91-95, Nat. Security Agy., 1994—. Mem. AAAS, Am. Math. Soc. (com. mem.), Math. Assn. Am. (chmn. minorities in math. task force 1988), Soc. Indsl. and Applied Math., Sigma Xi. Democrat. Roman Catholic. Office: Howard U Dept Math Washington DC 20059

RAPHAEL, SALLY JESSY, talk-show host; b. Easton, Pa., Feb. 25, 1943; children: Allison (dec.), Andrea; m. Karl Soderlund; 2 step-daughters, 1 adopted son, also foster children. BFA, Columbia U. Anchored radio program Jr. High Sch. News Sta. WFAS-AM, White Plains, N.Y., 1955; host of cooking program WAPA-TV, San Juan, P.R., 1965-67; radio and television broadcaster Miami and Ft. Lauderdale, Fla., 1969-74; host Sta. WMCA-Radio, N.Y.C., 1976-81; talk show host NBC Talk-net, N.Y.C., 1982-88, ABC Talkradio, N.Y.C., 1988-91; syndicated TV talk-show host N.Y.C., 1983—; part-time owner of a perfume factory, 1964-68; owner of an art gallery, 1964-69; owner, The Wine Press, N.Y.C., 1979-83; ind. producer TV films, 1991;. Author: (with M.J. Boyer) Finding Love, 1984, (with Pam Proctor) Sally: Unconventional Success, 1990; film appearances include: Resident Alien, 1990, The Addams Family, 1991; TV appearances include: Murphy Brown, Dave's World, The Nanny, The Tonight Show, Nightline. Recipient Bronze medal, Internat. Film & Television Festival of NY, 1985; Emmy award as outstanding talk-show host, daytime, 1988, 89. Office: Multimedia Entertainment 515 W 57th St New York NY 10019-2902*

RAPHAEL-HOWELL, FRANCES JAYNE, clinical psychologist; b. Alexandria, Va., Apr. 26, 1945; d. Robert Arthur and Isabelle Georgiana (Francis) Raphael; m. Frederick Alfred Howell, June 14, 1977; children: Robert, Carolyn, Cheryl. BS in Psychology, Howard U., 1971; MA in Clin. Psychology, Clark U., 1976, PhD, 1992; pre-doctoral intern, Children's Hosp. Med. Ctr., Boston, 1974-75. Cert. clin. psychologist; play therapist and supr. Assn. for Play Therapy. Spl. edn. tchr. Boston U. Mini Sch., 1975-76; instr. psychopathology U. Mass., Boston, 1976; psychologist Boston U. Med. Ctr., 1976-77; psychologist cons. Head Start, Boston, 1977; psychologist Montgomery County Pub. Schs., 1978; clin. psychologist D.C. Pub. Schs., Washington, 1978-91, supr. psychol. svcs., 1991-93, dir. Chpt. I Pupil Pers. Svcs., 1993—; presentations at confs. and workshops. Harvard U. fellow, 1974-75. Mem. APA (div. Clin. Psychology), Assn. for Play Therapy, Inc., D.C. Assn. for Sch. Psychologists. Democrat. Methodist. Home: 3010 W St SE Washington DC 20020 Office: DC Pub Schs Winston Ednl Ctr 31st and Erie Sts SE Washington DC 20020

RAPHAELSON, JOEL, retired advertising agency executive; b. N.Y.C., Sept. 27, 1928; s. Samson and Dorothy (Wegman) R.; m. Mary Kathryn Hartigan, Aug. 20, 1960; children: Matthew, Katherine, Paul. B.A., Harvard U., 1949. Copywriter Macy's, N.Y.C., 1950-51, BBDO, N.Y.C., 1953-58; with Ogilvy & Mather, Inc., N.Y.C., 1958-60, v.p., joint copy chief, 1964-66, prin. 1968-75, mem. exec. com., 1970-75; creative cons. Ogilvy & Mather, Inc., Europe, 1975-76; exec. creative dir. Ogilvy & Mather, Inc., Chgo., 1976-82; sr. v.p. internat. creative svcs. Ogilvy & Mather Worldwide, 1982-92, spl. assignments as editor, writer, speechwriter, cons., 1993-94, ret. 1994; lectr. bus. writing for Am. Assn. Advt. Agencies, other bus. orgns. Author: (with Kenneth Roman) How To Write Better, 1978, Writing That Works, 1981, rev. expanded edit., 1992; editor: The Unpublished David Ogilvy, 1986, Viewpoint (co. jour.), 1983-94. Cons. Lyric Opera Chgo., Snake River Inst. With AUS, 1951-53. Home: 20 E Cedar St Chicago IL 60611

RAPHAEL, ROBIN, federal official; b. Vancouver, Wash., Sept. 16, 1947; m. Leonard Arthur Ashton; 2 children. BA, U. Wash.; Diploma in Hist. Studies, Cambridge U., Eng.; MA, U. Md. Econ. analyst CIA; lectr. history Damavand Coll., Tehran, Iran; with Fgn. Svc., 1977, Islamabad, Pakistan, 1977-78; with office investment affairs bur. econs. Dept. of State, 1978-80, staff asst. to asst. sec. Near East and South Asian affairs, 1980-81, econ. officer Israel desk, 1981-82, spl. asst. to under sec. polit. affairs, 1982-84; 1st sec. polit. affairs London, 1984-88; polit. counselor Pretoria, South Africa, 1988-91, New Delhi, 1991-93; asst. sec. South Asian affairs Dept. of State, Washington, 1993—. Mem. Am. Econ. Assn., Am. Fgn. Svc. Assn., Pres.'s

Estate Polo Club (New Delhi), Phi Beta Kappa. Office: S Asian Affairs 2201 C St NW Washington DC 20520-6243

RAPIN, ISABELLE, physician; b. Lausanne, Switzerland, Dec. 4, 1927; d. Rene and Mary Coe (Reeves) R.; m. Harold Oaklander, Apr. 5, 1959; children: Anne Louise, Christine, Stephen, Peter. Physician's Diploma. Faculte de Medicine, U. Lausanne, 1952, Doctorate in Medicine. 1955. Diplomate Am. Bd. Psychiatry and Neurology. Intern in pediatrics N.Y. U. Bellevue Med. Center, 1953-54; resident in neurology Neurol. Inst. of N.Y. Columbia-Presbyn. Med. Center, 1954-57, fellow in child neurology, 1957-58; mem. faculty Albert Einstein Coll. Medicine, Bronx, N.Y., 1958—; prof. neurology and pediatrics Albert Einstein Coll. Medicine, 1972—; attending neurologist and child neurologist Einstein Affiliated Hosps., Bronx.; Mem. Nat. Adv. Neurol. and Communicative Disorders and Stroke Coun., NIH. 1984-88. Contbr. chpts. to books, articles to med. jours. Recipient award Conf. Ednl. Adminstrs. Serving the Deaf, 1988. Fellow Am. Acad. Neurology; mem. Internat. Child Neurology Assn. (sec.-gen. 1979-82, v.p. 1982-86, Frank R. Ford lectr. 1990), Am. Neurol. Assn. (v.p. 1982-83), Child Neurology Soc. (Hower award 1987), Internat. Neuropsychology Soc., AAAS, N.Y. Acad. Scis., Assn. Research in Nervous and Mental Diseases (v.p. 1986). Office: Albert Einstein Coll Medicine 1410 Pelham Pky S Bronx NY 10461-1101

RAPKE, JACK, agent. Co-head of motion picture divsn. Creative Artists Agy., Beverly Hills, Calif. Office: Creative Artists Agy 9830 Wilshire Blvd Beverly Hills CA 90212-1825

RAPOPORT, ANATOL, peace studies educator, mathematical biologist; b. Lozovaya, Russia, May 22, 1911; emigrated to U.S., 1922, naturalized, 1928; s. Boris and Adel (Rapoport) R.; m. Gwen Goodrich, Jan. 29, 1949; children: Anya, Alexander, Charles Anthony. Ph.D., U. Chgo., 1941; D.H.L., U. Western Mich., 1971; LL.D., U. Toronto, 1986. Faculty dept. math. Ill. Inst. Tech., 1946-47; com. math. biology U. Chgo., 1947-54; fellow Ctr. Advanced Study Behavioral Scis., Stanford, 1954-55; assoc. prof. Mental Health Research Inst., prof. math. biology U. Mich., 1955-70; prof. psychology and math. U. Toronto, 1970-80; dir. Inst. for Advanced Studies, Vienna, 1980-83; prof. peace studies U. Toronto, 1984—. Author: Science and the Goals of Man, 1950, Operational Philosophy, 1953, Fights, Games, and Debates, 1960, Strategy and Conscience, 1964, Prisoner's Dilemma, 1965, Two-Person Game Theory, 1966, N Person Game Theory, 1970, The Big Two, 1971, Conflict in Man Made Environment, 1974, Semantics, 1975, The 2 x 2 Game, 1976, Mathematische Methoden in den Sozialwissenschaften, 1980, Mathematical Models in the Social and Behavioral Sciences, 1983, General System Theory, 1986, The Origins of Violence, 1989, Decision Theory and Decision Behavior, 1989, Canada and the World, 1992, Peace: An Idea Whose Time Has Come, 1992, Gewissheiten und Zweifel, 1994; editor General Systems, 1956-77. Served to capt. USAAF, 1942-46. Fellow Am. Acad. Arts and Scis.; mem. Am. Math. Soc., Internat. Soc. Gen. Semantics (pres. 1953-55), Canadian Peace Research and Edn. Assn. (pres. 1972-75), Soc. for Gen. Systems Research (pres. 1965-66), Sci. for Peace (pres. 1984-86). Home: 38 Wychwood Park, Toronto, ON Canada M6G 2V5

RAPOPORT, BERNARD, life insurance company executive; b. San Antonio, July 17, 1917; s. David and Riva (Feldman) R.; m. Audre Jean Newman, Feb. 15, 1942; 1 child, Ronald B. B.A., U. Tex.-Austin, 1939. Chmn. bd., chief exec. officer Am. Income Life Ins. Co., Waco, Tex., 1951—; chmn. bd. regents U. Tex., 1991; apptd. by pres. adv. com. for trade policy and negotiations, 1994—. Mem. Nat. Council on Crime and Delinquency, San Francisco, 1979—, Jerusalem Found., N.Y.C., 1979—, Hebrew Union Coll., Cin., 1980—, Union Am. Hebrew Congregations, 1981—; Nat. Hispanic Ctr. for Advanced Studies and Policy Analysis, Oakland, Calif. 1981—; assoc. mem. U. Cancer Found., Houston, 1976—, Jt. Ctr. Polit. and Econ. Studies, 1987—; appointed mem. Adv. Com. for Trade Policy and Negotiation; chmn. United Negro Coll. Fund, Waco, 1979-80, United Way of Waco, 1982-83; trustee Paul Quinn Coll., Waco, 1963-90, Boy's Club, Waco, 1990—. Fellow City of Jerusalem, 1994. Democrat. Jewish. Club: Brazos. Avocations: tennis; politics; reading. Home: 2332 Wendy Ln Waco TX 76710-2011 Office: Am Income Life Ins Co PO Box 2608 Waco TX 76797

RAPOPORT, BERNARD ROBERT, lawyer; b. N.Y.C., Jan. 18, 1919; s. Max and Rose (Gerard) R.; m. Robyrta Wechter, May 31, 1959; 1 son: Michael. AB, Cornell U., 1939, JD, 1941. Bar: N.Y. 1941, Fed. Ct. (so. dist.) 1946. Assoc. firm Proskauer, Rose, Goetz, Mendelsohn, N.Y.C., 1941-50; gen. counsel M. Lowenstein Corp., N.Y.C., 1950-86, bd. dirs., 1961-86, treas., 1975-86, sec., 1970-86; dir., treas., sec. Leon Lowenstein Found. Served to capt. Signal Corps, U.S. Army, 1942-45. Mem. ABA, Assn. of Bar of City of N.Y. Address: 910 5th Ave New York NY 10021-4155

RAPOPORT, DAVID E., lawyer; b. Chgo., May 27, 1956; s. Morris H. and Ruth (Tecktiel) R.; m. Andrea Gail Albun; children: Alyson Faith, Steven Andrew. BS in Fin., No. Ill. U., 1978; JD with high honors, Ill. Inst. Tech., 1981; cert. in trial work Lawyers Postgrad. Inst., Chgo., 1984; cert. civil trial specialist Nat. Bd. Trial Adv., 1991. Bar: Ill. 1981, U.S. Dist. Ct. (no. dist.) Ill. 1981, U.S. Dist. Ct. (trial bar) Ill. 1983, U.S. Dist. Ct. (so. and cent. dists.), U.S. Ct. Appeals (7th cir.) 1981. Litigation clk. Steinberg, Polacek & Goodman, Chgo., 1979-81; assoc. Katz, Friedman, Schur and Eagle, Chgo., 1981-90, of counsel, 1993; ptnr. Katz, Friedman, Schur and Eagle, 1990, Baizer & Rapoport, Chgo., Highland Park, Ill., 1990—; arbitrator Cir. Ct. Cook County, Ill.; instr. legal writing Ill. Inst. Tech.-Kent Coll. Law, Chgo., 1981, guest lectr., 1985—; arbitrator Cir. Ct. Cook County, Ill., Million Dollar Advocates Forum, 1995—. Fellow Roscoe Pound Found.; mem. ABA, Am. Trial Lawyers Assn., Ill. Bar Assn., Ill. Trial Lawyers Assn., Chgo. Bar Assn. (mem. workers compensation com. 1981—, tort litigation com. 1982—), Ill. Inst. for Continuing Legal Edn., Trial Lawyers for Pub. Justice, Trial Lawyers for Civil Justice, Lake County Bar Assn. Office: Baizer & Rapoport 77 W Washington St Fl 20 Chicago IL 60602-2801 also: 513 Central Ave Fl 5 Highland Park IL 60035-2660

RAPOPORT, JUDITH, psychiatrist; b. N.Y.C., July 12, 1933; d. Louis and Minna (Enteen) Livant; m. Stanley Rapoport, June 25, 1961; children: Stuart, Erik. BA, Swarthmore Coll., 1955; MD, Harvard U., 1959. Lic. psychiatrist. Cons., child psychiatrist NIMH/St. Elizabeth's Hosp., Washington, 1969-72; clin. asst. prof. Georgetown U. Med. Sch., Washington, 1972-82, clin. assoc. prof., 1982-85, clin. prof. psychiat., 1985—; med. officer biol. psychiatry br. NIMH, Bethesda, Md., 1976-78, chief, child mental illness unit, biol. psychiat. br., 1979-82, chief, child psychiatry lab. of clin. scis., 1982-84, chief, child psychiatry div. intramural rsch. programs, 1984—; prof. psychiatry George Washington U. Sch. Med., Washington, 1979—; prof. pediatrics Georgetown U., Washington, 1985—; cons. in field. Author: (non-fiction) The Boy Who Couldn't Stop Washing, 1989 (best seller literary guild selection 1989), Childhood Obsessive Compulsive Disorder, 1989. Fellow Am. Psychiat. Assn., Am. Acad. Child Psychiat.; mem. D.C. Psychiat. Assn., Inst. Medicine. Home: 3010 44th Pl NW Washington DC 20016-3557 Office: NIMH Bldg 10 Rm 6N240 Bethesda MD 20892

RAPOPORT, MILES S., state official; m. Sandra Luciano; children: Jeff, Ross. BA in Polit. Sci., NYU, 1971. Exec. dir. Conn. Citizen Action Group, 1979-84; mem. Conn. Ho. of Reps., asst. majority leader, 1987-92, house chmn. govt. adminstrn. and elections com., mem. fin., revenue and bonding com.; sec. of state State of Conn., 1994—. Address: 30 Montclair Dr West Hartford CT 06107 Office: State Capitol # 104 Hartford CT 06106*

RAPOPORT, RONALD JON, journalist; b. Detroit, Aug. 14, 1940; s. Daniel B. and Shirley G.; m. Joan Zucker, Sept. 2, 1968; children—Rebecca, Julie. B.A., Stanford U., 1962; M.S., Columbia U., 1963. Reporter Mpls. Star, 1963-65; assoc editor Sport mag., Macmillan; sports reporter AP, N.Y.C., San Francisco, 1966-70, Los Angeles Times, 1970-77; sports columnist Chgo. Sun-Times, 1977-88, Los Angeles Daily News, 1988—; sports commentatorWeekend Edit. Nat. Pub. Radio, 1986—. Author: (with Chip Oliver) High for the Game, 1971, (with Stan Love) Love in the NBA, 1975, (with Jim McGregor) Called for Travelling, 1978; editor: A Kind of Grace: A Treasury of Sportswriting by Women, 1994. Served with U.S. Army Res.,

1963. Office: Los Angeles Daily News 21221 Oxnard St Woodland Hills CA 91367-5015

RAPOPORT, SONYA, artist; b. Boston; d. Louis Aaron and Ida Tina (Axelrod) Goldberg; m. Henry Rapoport; children—Hava Rapoport de Fereres, David, Robert. Student Mass. Coll. Art., 1941-42; B.A., NYU, 1945; M.A., U. Calif.-Berkeley, 1949. One woman shows N.Y.C. Pub. Library, 1979, New Sch. Social Research, N.Y.C., 1981, NYU Grad. Sch. Bus. Adminstrn., 1982, Sarah Lawrence Coll., Bronxville, N.Y., 1984, Kuopio Mus., Finland, 1992; group shows include Union Gallery San Jose State U., Calif., 1979, Ctr. for Visual Arts, Oakland, Calif., 1979, Walker Art Ctr., Mpls., 1981, Nat. Library, Madrid, 1982, SUNY Library, Purchase, 1983, Otis Art Inst. of Parsons Sch. of Design, Los Angeles, 1984, Cleve. Inst. Art, 1984, FISEA93 4th Internat. Symposium on Electronic Art, Mpls.also others; represented in permanent collections Stedelijk Mus., Amsterdam, Indpls. Mus. Art, Grey Art Gallery, NYU, San Francisco Mus. Modern Art, San Jose State U. Found.-Union Gallery, Crocker Art Mus., Sacramento, Hall of Justice, Hayward, Calif.; book artist Shoe-Field, Chinese Connections, About Me, Objects on My Dresser, (interactive books) Gateway to Your Ka, Your Fate is in Your Feet, Digital Mudra2; producer A Shoe-In, Biorhythm, Coping with Sexual Jealousy, (computer assisted interactive installations) The Animated Soul, Digital Mudra, Transgenic Bagel; contbr. to profl. publs. Home: 6 Hillcrest Ct Berkeley CA 94705-2805

RAPP, FRED, virologist; b. Fulda, Germany, Mar. 13, 1929; came to U.S., 1936, naturalized, 1945; s. Albert and Rita (Hain) R.; children: Stanley I., Richard J., Kenneth A.; m. Pamela A. Miles, Aug. 28, 1988. BS, Bklyn. Coll., 1951; MS, Albany Med. Coll., Union U., 1956; PhD, U. So. Calif., 1958. Jr. bacteriologist to bacteriologist divsn. labs. and rsch. N.Y. State Dept. Health, 1952-55; from teaching asst. to instr. dept. med. microbiology Sch. Medicine U. So. Calif., 1956-59; asst. virologist div. pathology Philip D. Wilson Research Found., N.Y.C.; asst. prof. microbiology and immunology Cornell U. Med. Coll., N.Y.C.; assoc. prof. Baylor U. Sch. Medicine, Houston, 1962-66, prof., 1966-69; prof., chmn. dept. microbiology and immunology Pa. State U. Coll. Medicine, Hershey, Pa., 1969-90; Evan Pugh prof. microbiology Pa. State U. Coll. Medicine, University Park, 1978-90, prof. emeritus, 1990—, assoc. provost, dean health affairs, 1973-80, sr. mem. grad. faculty, assoc. dean acad. affairs, research and grad. studies, 1987-90, professor emeritus, 1990—; research career prof. of virology Am. Cancer Soc., 1966-69, prof. virology, 1977-90; dir. Coll. Med. Pa. State U. (Specialized Cancer Research Ctr.), 1973-84; mem. del. on viral oncology, U.S./USSR Joint Com. Health Cooperation; chmn., Gordon Rsch. Conf. in Cancer, 1975; virology Task Force, 1976-79; chmn. Atlantic Coast Tumor Virology Group, Nat. Cancer Insts. Health, 1971-77; mem. council for projection and analysis Am. Cancer Soc., 1976-80; chmn. standards and exam. com. on virology Am. Bd. Med. Microbiology, 1977, 80; chmn. subsect. on virology program com. Am. Assn. Cancer Research, 1978-79; mem. adv. council virology div. Internat. Union Microbiol. Socs., 1978-84; referee Macy Faculty Scholar Award Program, 1979-81; mem. programme com. Fifth Internat. Congress for Virology, Strasbourg, France, 1981; mem. basic cancer rsch. group U.S.-France Agreement for Cooperation in Cancer Research, 1980-84; mem. organizing com. Internat. Workshop on Herpes viruses, Bologna, Italy, 1980-81, NATO Internat. Advanced Study Inst. Corfu Island, Greece, 1981; mem. Herpes viruses Study Group, 1981-84; mem. sci. adv. com. Wilmot Fellowship Program, U. Rochester Med. Ctr., 1981-90 ; mem. scientific rev. com. Hubert H. Humphrey Cancer Research Ctr., Boston U., 1981; mem. fin. com. Am. Soc. Virology, 1982-89, mem. council, 1984-88; mem. adv. com. on persistent virus-host interactions research program R.J. Reynolds Scientific Bd./Wistar Inst., 1983-90; mem. med. adv. bd. Herpes Resource Ctr., Am. Social Health Assn., 1983-90; bd. dirs. U.S.-Japan Found. Biomedicine, 1983-90; mem. council Soc. Exptl. Biology and Medicine, 1983-87; mem. scientific adv. com. Internat. Assn. Study and Prevention of Virus-Associated Cancers, 1983-90; mem. Basil O'Connor Starter Research Adv. Com., 1984-90; mem. council for research and clin. investigation awards Am. Cancer Soc., 1984-90; mem. recombinant DNA adv. com. NIH, 1984-87; mem. outstanding investigator grant rev. com. Nat. Cancer Inst., 1984-90; mem. organizing com. Fourth Symposium Sapporo Cancer Seminar, Japan, 1984, Second Internat. Conf. Immunobiology and Prophylaxis of Human Herpes virus Infections, Ft. Lauderdale, Fl., 1984-85, Internat. Congress of Virology, Sendai, Japan, 1984; mem. internat. sci. com. Internat. Meeting on Adv. in Virology, Catania, Italy, 1984-85; mem. adv. bd. Cancer Info., Dissemination and Analysis Ctr. Carcinogenesis and Cancer Biology, 1984-89; mem. internat. programme com. 7th Internat. Congress of Virology, Edmonton, Can., 1985-87; councilor div. DNA viruses Am. Soc. Microbiology, 1985-87; mem. adv. com. rsch. on etiology, diagnosis, natural history, prevention and therapy of multiple sclerosis Nat. Multiple Sclerosis Soc., 1985-89; mem. sci. adv. bd. Tampa Bay Rsch. Inst., 1985-91; mem. sci. adv. coun. Pitts. Ctr. AIDS Rsch. U. Pitts., 1988; mem. recombinant DNAdv. com. Working Group on Transgenic Animals. NIH, 1988; mem. adv. com. 15th Internat. Herpes Virus Workshop, Washington, 1989-90. Editor on oncology: Intervirology, 1972-84, assoc. editor, 1978-84, editor-in-chief, 1985-90; adv. bd. Archives Virology, 1976-81; editorial bd. Jour. Immunology, 1966-73, Jour. Virology, 1968-88; assoc. editor Cancer Research, 1972-79; editorial bd. Virology, 1979-83, editor, 1983-90; mem. adv. bd. Ency. Americana, 1992—. Recipient 1st CIBA-Geigy Drew award for biomed. research, 1977. Nat. award for teaching excellence in microbiology, U. Medicine and Dentistry N.J. Med. Sch., 1988; Wellcome vis. professorship in microbiology, 1989-90; Disting. fellow Inst. Advanced Biotech., 1991. Mem. AAAS, AAUP, Am. Acad. Microbiology (fellow, diplomate), Soc. Microbiology (mem. com. med. microbiology and immunology, bd. pub. sci. affairs 1979-88, chmn. DNA viruses div. 1981-82, divsn. councilor DNA viruses), Am. Soc. Virology (chmn. fin. com. 1987-88, emeritus 1991), Am. Assn. Immunologists, The Harvey Soc., Soc. Exptl. Biology and Medicine (emeritus 1993), Am. Assn. Cancer Rsch. (emeritus 1991), Assn. Med. Sch. Microbiology Chmn. (pres. 1980-81), Sigma Xi (Monie A. Ferst award 1990, nat. lectr. 1977-79), Alpha Omega Alpha. Home: 68 Azalea Dr Hershey PA 17033-2602

RAPP, GEORGE ROBERT, JR. (RIP), geology and archeology educator; b. Toledo, Sept. 19, 1930; s. George Robert and Gladys Mae (Warner) R.; m. Jeannette Messner, June 15, 1956; children: Kathryn, Karen. BA, U. Minn., 1952; PhD, Pa. State U., 1960. Asst. then assoc. prof. S.D. Sch. Mines, Rapid City, 1957-65; assoc. prof. U. Minn., Mpls., 1965-75; prof. geology and archeology U. Minn., Duluth, 1975—; dean Coll. Letters and Sci., 1975-84, dean Coll. Sci. and Engring., 1984-89; prof. Ctr. for Ancient Studies, U. Minn., Mpls., 1990-93, prof. interdisciplinary archaeol. studies, 1993—; dir. Archeometry Lab., U. Minn., Duluth, 1975—; cons USIA, Westinghouse Corp., Exxon Corp., Ford Found. Author and editor: Excavations at Nichoria, 1978, Troy: Archeological Geology, 1982, Archeological Geology, 1985, Excavations at Tel Michal, 1989, Encyclopedia of Minerals, 1989; mem. editorial bd. Jour. Field Archeology, 1976-85, Jour. Archeol. Sci., 1977-79, Geoarcheology Jour., 1984—, Am. Jour. Archeology, 1985-92. NSF postdoctoral fellow, 1963-64, Fulbright-Hayes sr. rsch. fellow, 1972-73. Fellow AAAS. (chmn. sect. E 1987-88, nat. coun. 1992—), Geol. Soc. Am. (Archeol. Geology award 1993), Mineral. Soc. Am.; mem. Nat. Assn. Geology Tchrs. (pres. 1968-69), Soc. for Archeol. Sci. (pres. 1983-84), Assn. Field Archeology (pres. 1979-81), Sigma Xi (bd. dirs. 1990—). Avocation: classical music, archaeological excavations in Greece, Turkey, Cyprus, Israel. Office: U Minn-Duluth Archaeometry Lab Duluth MN 55812

RAPP, GERALD DUANE, lawyer, manufacturing company executive; b. Berwyn, Ill., July 19, 1933; s. Kenneth F. and Mildred (Price) R.; m. Jane Carol Thomas, Aug. 14, 1954; children—Gerald Duane Jr., Gregory T., Amy Frances. B.S., U. Mo., 1955; J.D., U. Mich., 1958. Bar: Ohio bar 1959. Practice in Dayton, 1960—; ptnr. Smith & Schnacke, 1963-70; asst. gen. counsel Mead Corp., Dayton, 1970, v.p. human resources and legal affairs, 1973, v.p., corp. sec., 1975, v.p., gen. counsel, corp. sec., 1976, v.p., gen. counsel, 1979, sr. v.p., gen. counsel, 1981-91, counsel to bd. dirs., 1991-92; of counsel Bieser, Greer & Landis, 1992—; pres. R-J Holding Co., Weber Canyon Ranch, Inc. Sr. editor U. Mich. Law Rev., 1957-58. Past chmn. Oakwood Youth Commn.; past v.p., bd. dirs. Big Bros. Greater Dayton; mem. pres.'s visitors com. U. Mich. Law Sch.; past trustee Urbana Coll.; past chmn., trustee Ohio Ctr. Leadership Studies, Robert K. Greenleaf Ctr., Indpls.; past pres. bd. trustees Dayton and Montgomery County Pub. Libr.; past mem. bd. visitors law schs. of Dayton. 1st Lt. U.S. Army, 1968-60. Mem. ABA, Ohio Bar Assn., Dayton Bar Assn., Moraine Country Club,

Dayton RacquetClub, Dayton Lawyers Club, Met. Club of Washington, Phi Kappa Psi, Phi Delta Phi, Beta Gamma Sigma. Presbyterian. Office: Bieser Greer & Landis 400 National City Ctr Dayton OH 45402-1908

RAPP, RICHARD TILDEN, economist, consultant; b. Miami, Fla., Nov. 30, 1944; s. Melville Benjamin and Rachel (Mayer) R.; m. Wilma J. Levin, Aug. 20, 1967; children: Ethan, Sandra. BA cum laude, Bklyn. Coll., 1965; MA, U. Pa., 1966, PhD, 1970. Asst. prof. SUNY, Stony Brook, 1970-75, assoc. prof. econ. history, 1976-77; pres., chief exec. officer Nat. Econ. Research Assocs., Inc., White Plains, N.Y., 1977—; cons. on internat. trade and competition econs. Author: Industry and Economic Decline in Seventeenth-Century Venice, 1976, Trade Warfare and the New Protectionism, 1986; co-author: European Economic History, 1975. Nat. adv. bd. Santa Fe Opera, 1989—. Kent fellow Danforth found., 1968-70; Fulbright fellow, 1968-69. Mem. Am. Econ. Assn., Inst. for Advanced Study. Home: 52 Whippoorwill Lake Rd Chappaqua NY 10514-3622 Office: Nat Econ Rsch Assocs Inc 50 Main St White Plains NY 10606-1920

RAPP, ROBERT ANTHONY, metallurgical engineering educator, consultant; b. Lafayette, Ind., Feb. 21, 1934; s. Frank J. and Goldie M. (Royer) R.; m. Heidi B. Sartorius, June 3, 1960; children: Kathleen Rapp Raynaud, Thomas, Stephen, Stephanie Rapp Surface. BSMetE, Purdue U., 1956; MSMetE, Carnegie Inst. Tech., 1959, PhDMetE, 1960. Asst. prof. metall. engring. Ohio State U., Columbus, 1963-66, assoc. prof., 1966-69, prof., 1969—, M.G. Fontana prof., 1988—, Univ. prof., 1989—; cons. DuPont, Lanxide, KB Alloys, IGT; vis. prof. Ecole Nat. Superior d'Electrochimie, Grenoble, France, 1972-73, U. Paris-Sud, Orsay, 1985-86, Ecole Nat. Superior de Chimie, Toulouse, France, 1985-86, U. New South Wales, Australia, 1987; Acta/Scripta Metallurgica lectr., 1991; rsch. metallurgist WPAFB, Ohio, 1960-63. Editor: Techniques of Metals Research, vol. IV, 1982, High Temperature Corrosion, 1984; translator Metallic Corrosion (Kaesche), 1986; bd. rev. jour. Oxid. Metals; contbr. numerous articles to profl. jours. Recipient W.R. Whitney award Nat. Assn. Corrosion Engring., 1986, NAE award, 1988, Disting. Engring. Alumnus award Purdue U., 1988, B.F. Goodrich Collegiate Inventor's award, 1991, 92, Ulrick Evans award Brit. Inst. Corrosion, 1992; Guggenheim fellow, 1972; Fulbright scholar Max Planck Inst. Phys. Chem., 1959-60. Fellow ASME, Electrochem. Soc. (assoc. editor jour.), Nat. Assn. Corrosion Engrs., French Soc. Metals and Materials (hon., Chevalier des Palmes Acad. 1994); mem. NAE. Lutheran. Home: 1379 Southport Dr Columbus OH 43235-7649

RAPP, ROBERT NEIL, lawyer; b. Erie, Pa., Sept. 10, 1947; m. Sally K. Meder; 1 child: Jeffrey David. BA, Case Western Res. U., 1969, JD, 1972; MBA, Cleve. State U., 1989. Bar: Ohio 1972, U.S. dist. Ct. (no. dist.) Ohio 1973, U.S. Ct. Appeals (6th cir.) 1981, U.S. Supreme Ct. 1980. Assoc. Metzenbaum, Gaines & Stern, Co., L.P.A., Cleve., 1972-75; ptnr. Calfee, Halter & Griswold, Cleve., 1975—; adj. prof. law Case Western Res. U., 1975-78, 94—, Cleve. Marshall Coll. Law, Cleve. State U., 1976-82; disting. lawyer-in-residence Cornell U. Law Sch., 1993; mem. legal adv. bd. Nat. Assn. Securities Dealers; U.S. commentator Can.-U.S. Comparative Corp. Law Conf., 1984; arbitrator Nat. Futures Assn., Nat. Assn. Securities Dealers, Inc.; ind. arbitrator securities and future law matters. Contbr. numerous articles to law jours. Mem. ABA (sect. bus. law: mem. com. fed. regulation of securities, subcom. broker-dealer regulation, sect. litigation: mem. com. securities litigation), Am. Arbitration Assn. (securities arbitrator, mem. comml. adv. coun. Cleve. region), Ohio State Bar Assn. (elected mem. coun. dels. 1976-82, corp. law com. 1980—), Cleve. Bar Assn. (chmn. young lawyers sect. 1976-77), assoc. mem. cert. grievance com., sect. securities law: exec. coun. 1980-85, chmn. govt. liaison com. 1980-81). Office: Calfee Halter & Griswold Ste 1800 800 Superior Ave Cleveland OH 44114-2688

RAPPAPORT, CHARLES OWEN, lawyer; b. N.Y.C., May 15, 1950; s. Edward and Edith (Novick) R.; m. Valerie B. Ackerman, Oct. 11, 1987; children: Emily Randle, Sarah Elisabeth. BA, Columbia U., 1970; JD, NYU, 1975. Bar: N.Y. 1976. Assoc. Simpson, Thacher & Bartlett, N.Y.C., 1975-82, ptnr., 1982—. Home: 26 N Moore St Apt 4W New York NY 10013-2461 Office: Simpson Thacher & Bartlett 425 Lexington Ave New York NY 10017-3903

RAPPAPORT, GARY BURTON, defense equipment and computer company executive; b. Mpls., Apr. 27, 1937; s. Max and Beatrice (Berkinsky) R.; m. Susan Heller, Nov. 26, 1961; children: Debra Lynn, Melissa Ellen. B.S., U. Pa., 1959. Asst. to pres. Napco Industries, Inc., Hopkins, Minn., 1959-61, v.p., 1961-65, exec. v.p., 1964-65, pres., 1965-74, chmn. bd., chief exec. officer, 1974-84; chmn. bd., chief exec. officer Venturian Corp., Hopkins, 1984—; dir. La Maur, Inc., Mpls., 1980-87. Chmn. bd. govs. Mt. Sinai Hosp., Mpls., 1979-81. Served with Air N.G., 1960-64. Jewish. Office: 1600 2nd St S Hopkins MN 55343-7464

RAPPAPORT, LAWRENCE, plant physiology and horticulture educator; b. N.Y.C., May 28, 1928; s. Aaron and Elsie R.; m. Norma, Nov. 21, 1953; children: Meryl, Debra Kramer, Craig. BS in Horticulture, U. Idaho, 1950; MS in Horticulture, Mich. State Coll., 1951; PhD in Horticulture, Mich. State U., 1956. Lectr. U. Calif., Davis, 1956-67, jr. olericulturist dept. vegetable crops, 1956-58, asst. olericulturist, 1958-63, assoc. olericulturist, 1963-67, prof., 1968-91, prof. emeritus, 1991—, dir. plant growth lab., 1975-78, chairperson dept. vegetable crops, 1978-84; vis. scientist Calif. Inst. Tech., 1958; co-dir. Hurriculture Subproject, Calif./Egypt project, 1978-82. Contbr. articles to profl. jours. 1st pres. Davis Human Rels. Coun., 1964-66; v.p. Jewish Fedn. Sacramento, 1969; pres. Jewish Fellowship, Davis, 1985-89. Sgt. maj. U.S. Army, 1952-53, Korea. Decorated Bronze star; Guggenheim Found. fellow, 1963, Fulbright fellow, 1964, USPHS Spl. fellow, 1970, Am. Soc. Horticulture Sci. fellow, 1987, Sir Frederick McMaster fellow, 1991. Achievements include discovery of evidence for gibberellin-binding protein in plants; evidence for the signal hypothesis operating in plants, positive evidence for phytochrome-mediated gibberellin metabolism and stem growth; isolation of somaclonal variants of celery bearing stable resistance to Fusarium oxysporum f. sp. apii. Home: 637 Elmwood Dr Davis CA 95616-3514 Office: dept Vegetable Crops Asmundson Hall Rm 210 U Calif Davis CA 95616

RAPPAPORT, MARTIN PAUL, internist, nephrologist, educator; b. Bronx, N.Y., Apr. 25, 1935; s. Joseph and Anne (Kramer) R.; BS, Tulane U., 1957, MD, 1960; m. Bethany Ann Mitchell; children: Karen, Steven. Intern, Charity Hosp. of La., New Orleans, 1960-61, resident in internal medicine, 1961-64; pvt. practice medicine specializing in internal medicine and nephrology, Seabrook, Tex., 1968-72, Webster, Tex., 1972—; mem. courtesy staff Mainland Ctr. Hosp. (formerly Galveston County Meml. Hosp.), Houston, 1968—, Bapt. Meml. System, 1969-72, 88—; mem. staff Clear Lake Regional Med. Ctr., 1972—; cons. staff St. Mary's Hosp., 1973-79; cons. nephrology St. John's Hosp., Nassau Bay, Tex.; fellow in nephrology Northwestern U. Med. Sch., Chgo., 1968; clin. asst. prof. in medicine and nephrology U. Tex., Galveston, 1969—; lectr. emergency med. technician course, 1974-76; adviser on respiratory therapy program Alvin (Tex.) Jr. Coll., 1976-82; cons. nephrology USPHS, 1979-80. Served to capt. M.C., U.S. Army, 1961-67. Diplomate Am. Bd. Internal Medicine, Nat. Bd. Med. Examiners. Fellow ACP, Am. Coll. Chest Physicians; mem. Internat., Am. Socs. Nephrology, So. Med. Assn., Tex. Med. Assn., Tex. Soc. Internal Medicine (bd. govs. 1994—), Am. Soc. Artificial Internal Organs, Tex. Acad. Internal Medicine, Am. Geriatrics Soc., Am. Heart Assn., Bay Area Heart Assn. (bd. govs. 1969-75), Clear Lake C. of C., Phi Delta Epsilon, Alpha Epsilon Pi, Tulane Alumni Assn. Lodge: Rotary. Home: 1818 Linfield Way Houston TX 77058-2324 Office: PO Box 57609 Webster TX 77598-7609

RAPPAPORT, STEVEN N., financial information services executive; b. N.Y.C., July 10, 1948; s. Abraham and Frances (Schwartz) R.; m. Judith A. Garson, Dec. 20, 1970; children: Peter Benjamin Garson-Rappaport. BA, Northeastern U., 1971; JD, Washington U., 1974; LLM, NYU, 1980. Ptnr. Hartman & Craven, N.Y.C., 1974-87; exec. v.p. Telerate, Inc., N.Y.C., 1987—, also mem. ABA, N.Y. State Bar Assn., Assn. of Bar of City of N.Y. (com. on fgn. and comparative law). Clubs: City Athletic; Sedgewood (Carmel, N.Y.). Home: 325 W End Ave New York NY 10023-8135 Office: Telerate Inc 1 World Financial Ctr 200 Liberty St New York NY 10281-1003

RAPPAPORT, STUART R., lawyer; b. Detroit, Apr. 13, 1935; s. Reuben and Zella (Golechen) R.; m. Anne M. Plotnick; children: Douglas, Erica Rappaport Witt. BA in History, U. Mich., 1956; JD, Harvard U., 1959. Bar: Calif. 1962. Trial lawyer, chief trials, bur. chief, chief. asst. pub. defender L.A. County Pub. Defender's Office, L.A., 1962-87; pub. defender Santa Clara County Pub. Defender's Office, San Jose, Calif., 1987—; mem. standing adv. com. on criminal law Judicial Coun. Calif., San Francisco, 1993—. Contbr. articles to profl. jours. Mem. Calif. Pub. Defender's Assn. (pres. 1982-83), L.A. County Pub. Defender's Assn. (pres.). Democrat. Jewish. Office: Santa Clara County Pub Defender County Govt Ctr W Wing 70 W Hedding St San Jose CA 95110-1768

RAPPAPORT, THEODORE SCOTT, electrical engineering educator; b. Bklyn., Nov. 26, 1960; s. Eugene and Carol Ann (Cooper) R.; m. Brenda Marie Velasquez, May 30, 1981; children: Matthew B., Natalie M., Jennifer L. BSEE, Purdue U., 1982, MSEE, 1984, PhD, 1987. Registered profl. engr., Va. Engring. coop. Magnavox Govt./Ind. Elec. Co., Fort Wayne, Ind., 1980-81; engr. Harris Corp., Melbourne, Fla., 1983, systems engr.; 1986; rsch., teaching asst. Purdue U., West Lafayette, Ind., 1982-87; prof. Va. Poly. Inst. and State U., Blacksburg, 1992—; founding dir. Mobile & Portable Radio Rsch. Corp.; cons. Ralph M. Parsons Co., Pansonic, Inc., Ericsson/GE Mobile Comm. Co-author, co-editor 6 books on wireless personal comm. including Wireless Communications, Cellular Raido and Personal Communications; contbr. articles to profl. jours. V.p. Gilbert Linkous Elem. Sch. PTA, Blacksburg, 1990-91; exec. com., asst. den leader Boy Scouts of Am., Blacksburg, 1992. Named Marconi Young scientist IEEE, 1990, one of Young Men of Am., 1988, Pres. Faculty fellow NSF, 1992. Fellow Radio Club Am. (dir.); mem. NSPE, IEEE (sr. mem., developer first wireless textbook and learning program 1995), Am. Radio Relay League, Am. Soc. Engring. Edn. Achievements include patents in Tunable Discone Antenna, computer-based bit error simulation for digital wireless communications, real-time DSP receivers.

RAPPEPORT, IRA J., lawyer; b. Phila., Jan. 13, 1954. BA with honors, Washington U., 1975; JD with honors, Villanova U., 1978. Bar: Calif. 1978. Assoc. Pillstory Madison & Sutro, 1978-83; assoc. Memel, Jacobs, Pietro & Gersh, 1983-85, ptnr., 1985-87; ptnr. McDermott, Will & Emory, L.A., 1987—. Mng. editor Villanova Law Rev., 1977-78. Recipient Scribes award Villanova Sch. Law, 1978. Mem. Am. Acad. Hosp. Attys., L.A. County Bar Assn. (mem. healthcare law sect.), Beverly Hills Bar Assn. (mem. healthcare law sect.), Century City Bar Assn. (mem. healthcare law sect.), Nat. Health Lawyers Assn., Calif. Soc. Healthcare Attys. Office: McDermott Will & Emery 2049 Century Park E Ste 3400 Los Angeles CA 90067-3208

RAPPLEYE, RICHARD KENT, financial executive, consultant, educator; b. Oswego, N.Y., Aug. 10, 1940; s. Robert Edward and Evelyn Margaret (Hammond) R.; m. Karen Tobe Greenberg, Sept. 7, 1963; children: Matthew Walker, Elizabeth Marion. AB, Miami U., Oxford, Ohio, 1962; postgrad. in theology Boston U., 1962-63; MBA, U. Pa., 1964; postgrad. in law DePaul U., 1965-66. CPA, Ill. Auditor DeLoitte Haskins & Sells, Chgo., 1962-67, mgmt. cons., 1967-71; controller, United Dairy Industry Assn., Rosemont, Ill., 1971, dir. fin. and adminstrn., 1971-73, exec. v.p., 1973-74; asst. to exec. v.p. Florists' Transworld Delivery, Southfield, Mich., 1974-75, group dir. fin. and adminstrn., 1975-80; asst. treas. Erb Lumber Co., Birmingham, Mich., 1980, v.p. fin., chief fin. officer, 1981-83; v.p., sec.-treas. CS Mott Found., Flint, Mich., 1983—; lectr. U. Mich., Flint, 1987-91; cons. in field; instr. Oakland U., Rochester, Mich., 1981-83; bd. dirs. Mich. Nat. Bank, Treas. Council Mich. Founds. 1986-92. Mem. AICPAs, Mich. Assn. CPAs. Unitarian. Lodge: Masons, Rotary. Home: 503 Arlington St Birmingham MI 48009-1639 Office: CS Mott Found 503 S Saginaw St Flint MI 48502-1807

RAPPOLT, WILLIAM CARL, banker; b. N.Y.C., Oct. 17, 1945; s. William Herbert and Loretta (Risk) R.; m. Pamela Hodgkins, June 7, 1969; children: Gabrille, Sarah, William. BS, Lafayette Coll., 1967; MBA, Columbia U., 1969. Fgn. exch. dealer Brown Bros. Harriman & Co., N.Y.C., 1970-72; v.p., mgr. trading 1st Nat. State Bank of N.J., Newark, 1972-74; v.p. fgn. exch. trading United Calif. Bank, N.Y.C., 1974-76; sr. v.p., mgr. trading Fidelity Bank Phila., 1976-84; exec. v.p., treas. M&T Bank, Buffalo, 1984—. Trustee Delta Upsilon, 1978—. Lt. USNR, 1969-71. Mem. Forex USA (pres. 1988—). Methodist. Avocation: horseback riding. Office: M&T Bank 1 Montana Ave Buffalo NY 14211-1638

RAPSON, RALPH, architect, educator; b. Alma, Mich., Sept. 13, 1914; s. Frank Thomas and Mable (Nickols) R.; m. Mary Dolan; children—Richard, Thomas. B.Arch., U. Mich.; M.Arch., Cranbrook Inst. Art. Dir. archtl. dept. Inst. Design, Chgo., 1942-46; assoc. prof. Sch. Architecture, Mass. Inst. Tech., 1946-54; prof. architecture, head Sch. Architecture and Landscape Architecture, U. Minn., Mpls., 1954—; now propr. Ralph Rapson & Assocs., Inc., Mpls.; lectr., hon. prof. Tienjin (China) U., 1981; cons. architect-planner U. Man., Can.; adv. bd. Sch. Architecture, U. Kans.; mem. Mpls. Planning Commn., Mpls. Housing Forum, Mpls. Com. Urban Design; Thomas Jefferson vis. prof. U. Va.; mem. Thomas Jefferson selection com. U. Va. Contbr. articles to profl. jours.; latest works include Hope Lutheran Ch, Mpls., 1970, Butwin residence, Mendota Heights, Minn., 1970, Internat. Studies Bldg, U. Chgo., 1971, Performing Arts Center, U. Calif., Santa Cruz, 1971, Performing Arts Center, U. Minn., Mpls., 1972. Bd. dirs. Walker Art Center, Mpls. Recipient Peabody award design State of Mass.; also four honors awards design; 34 honor awards for outstanding design pub. and pvt. bldgs. Fellow AIA (Honor award); mem. Internat. Housing Forum (charter), Minn. Soc. Architects. Democrat. Office: Ralph Rapson & Assocs Inc 409 Cedar Ave S Minneapolis MN 55454-1032

RAPSON, RICHARD L., history educator; b. N.Y.C., Mar. 8, 1937; s. Louis and Grace Lillian (Levenkind) R.; m. Susan Burns, Feb. 22, 1975 (div. June 1981); m. Elaine Catherine Hatfield, June 15, 1982; 1 child, Kim Elizabeth. BA, Amherst Coll., 1958; PhD, Columbia U., 1966. Asst. prof. Amherst (Mass.) Coll., 1960-61, Stanford (Calif.) U., 1961-65; from assoc. prof. to prof. history U. Hawaii, Honolulu, 1965—, founder, dir. New Coll., 1968-73; bd. dirs. Semester at Sea, U. Pittsburgh, 1979—; psychotherapist, Honolulu, 1982—. Author: Individualism and Conformity in the American Character, 1967, Britons View America, 1971, The Cult of Youth, 1972, Major Interpretations of the American Past, 1978, Denials of Doubt, 1980, Cultural Pluralism in Hawaii, 1981, American Yearnings, 1989; co-author: (with Elaine Hatfield) Love, Sex and Intimacy: Their Psychology, Biology and History, 1993, Emotional Contagion, 1994, A World of Passion: Cross-Cultural Perspectives on Love and Sex, 1995; mem. editorial bd. Univ. Press Am., 1981—. Woodrow Wilson fellow, Wilson Found., Princeton, 1960; Edward Perkins scholar, Columbia U., 1961; Danforth fellow, Danforth Found., St. Louis, 1965; recipient E. Harris Harbison for Gifted Teaching award, Danforth Found., 1973, Outstanding Tchr. award Stanford U. 25th Reunion Class, 1992. Mem. Am. Hist. Assn., Orgn. Am. Hist., Nat. Womens Hist. Project, Phi Beta Kappa, Outrigger Canoe Club, Honolulu Club. Avocations: squash, travel, classical music. Office: U Hawaii Dept History 2530 Dole St Honolulu HI 96822-2310

RAPSON, WILLIAM HOWARD, chemical engineering educator; b. Toronto, Ont., Can., Sept. 15, 1912; s. Alfred Ernest and Lillian Jane (Cannicott) R.; m. Mary Margaret Campbell, Jan. 29, 1937 (dec. 1989); children—Margaret (Mrs. Brian A. Fox), Linda (Mrs. Morris Manning), Lorna (Mrs. John A. Ferguson), William Howard II. B.A.Sc., U. Toronto, 1934, M.A.Sc., 1935, Ph.D., 1941; D.Eng., U. Waterloo, 1976; D.Sc. (hon.), McGill, 1980, U. Guelph, 1990. Demonstrator chem. engring. U. Toronto, 1934-40, instr., 1940, prof., 1953—, Univ. prof., 1976-81, Univ. prof. emeritus, 1981—; with research dept. Canadian Internat. Paper Co., 1940-42, head pioneering research, 1942-53; cons. in field, 1953—; v.p. Chem. Engring. Research Cons., Ltd., 1962-70, pres., 1970-81; pres. W.H. Rapson Ltd., 1964-77, chmn. bd., 1977—; chmn. bd. Rapson Farms Ltd., 1974-81. Author, editor: The Bleaching of Pulp, 1963; patentee in field; pioneer use of chlorine dioxide for pulp bleaching. Trustee Hawkesbury (Ont.) Pub. Sch. Bd., 1947-52, chmn., 1949-52; Bd. govs. Ont. Inst. Studies in Edn., 1971-77. Recipient Weldon medal, 1954; R.S. Jane Meml. award, 1965; McCharles prize, 1966; Canadian Centennial medal, 1967; Brazilian Pulp and Paper Assn. medal, 1974; Shalimar Gold Medal Indian Pulp and Paper Assn., 1976; Forest Products Div. award Am. Inst. Chem. Engrs., 1976; Anselme Payen award Am. Chem. Soc., 1978; Can. medal Soc. Chem. Industry, 1978; named

to Engring. Hall of Distinction U. Toronto, 1979; Engring. Alumni medal, 1979; Palladium medal Chem. Inst. Can., 1980; Izaak Walton Killam Meml. prize Can. Council, 1986, John S. Bates Meml. Gold medal Can. Pulp and Paper Assn., 1993. Fellow Royal Soc. Can. (Eadie medal 1981), Chem. Inst. Can. (hon., Palladium medal 1980, pres. 1985-86), TAPPI (hon. life; Mfg. Div. award 1967, Gold medal 1976, bd. dirs. 1972-75), Can. Pulp and Paper Assn. (tech. sect.)(sr., hon. life mem.; chmn. 1970-71), Canadian Soc. Chem. Engring. (dir. 1966-68), Assn. Profl. Engrs. Province Ont. (Gold medal 1975), Royal Swedish Acad. Engring. Sci. (fgn.). Club: Faculty (U. Toronto). Home: Ste 100, 110 Bloor St W, Toronto, ON Canada M5S 2W7 Office: U Toronto, Dept Chem Engineering, Toronto, ON Canada M5S 1A4*

RARIDON, RICHARD JAY, computer specialist; b. Newton, Iowa, Oct. 25, 1931; s. Jack Allison and Letha Helen (Woods) R.; m. Mona Marie Herndon, May 28, 1956; children—Susan Gayle, Ann Chaney. B.A., Grinnell Coll., 1953; M.A., Vanderbilt U., 1955, Ph.D., 1959. Assoc. prof. phys. sci. Memphis State U., 1958-62; research scientist Oak Ridge Nat. Lab., 1962-92; cons. ORNL, fusion energy divsn., 1992—; environ. specialist Coop. Sci. Edn. Center, Oak Ridge, 1971-72. Contbr. articles to profl. jours. Radiol. Physics fellow AEC, 1953-55. Fellow AAAS, Tenn. Acad. Sci. (pres. 1971); mem. Assn. Acads. Sci. (sec.-treas. 1972-76, pres. 1977), Sigma Xi. Home: 111 Columbia Dr Oak Ridge TN 37830 Office: Oak Ridge Nat Lab Oak Ridge TN 37831-8071

RASCH, ELLEN MYRBERG, cell biology educator; b. Chicago Heights, Ill., Jan. 31, 1927; d. Arthur August and Helen Catherine (Stelle) Myrberg; m. Robert W. E. Rasch, June 17, 1950; 1 son, Martin Karl. PhB with honors, U. Chgo., 1945, BS in Biol. Sci., 1947, MS in Botany, 1948, PhD, 1950. Asst. histologist Am. Meat Inst. Found., Chgo., 1950-51; USPHS postdoctoral fellow U. Chgo., 1951-53, rsch. assoc. dept. zoology, 1954-59; rsch. assoc. Marquette U., Milw., 1962-65, assoc. prof. biology, 1965-68, prof. biology, 1968-75, Wehr Disting. prof. biophysics, 1975-78; rsch. prof. biophysics East Tenn. State U., James H. Quillen Coll. Medicine, Johnson City, 1978-94, interim chmn. dept. cellular biophysics, 1986-94, prof. anatomy and cell biology, 1994—. Mem. Wis. Bd. Basic Sci. Examiners, 1971-75, sec. bd., 1973-75. Recipient Post-doctoral fellowship USPHS, 1951-53, Research Career Devel. award, 1967-72; Teaching Excellence and Disting. award Marquette U., 1975; Kreeger-Wolf vis. disting. prof. in biol. sci. Northwestern U., 1979. Mem. Royal Microscopic Soc., Am. Soc. Cell Biology, Am. Soc. Zoologists, Am. Soc. Ichthyologists and Herpetologists, The Histochem. Soc., Phi Beta Kappa, Sigma Xi. Contbr. articles to various publs. Home: 1504 Chickees St Johnson City TN 37604-7103 Office: East Tenn State U Dept Anatomy & Cell Biology PO Box 70, 421 Johnson City TN 37614-0421

RASCHE, ROBERT HAROLD, economics educator; b. New Haven, June 29, 1941; s. Harold A. and Elsa (Bloomquist) R.; m. Dorothy Anita Bensen, Dec. 28, 1963; children: Jeanette Dorothy, Karl Robert. B.A., Yale U., 1963; A.M., U. Mich., 1965, Ph.D., 1966. Asst. prof. U. Pa., Phila., 1966-72; assoc. prof. econs. Mich. State U., East Lansing, 1972-75, prof., 1975—; vis. scholar St. Louis Fed. REs., 1971-72, 76-77, San Francisco Fed. Res., 1985, Bank of Japan, Tokyo, 1990; vis. scholar Fed. Res. Bank of St. Louis, 1994-95; disting. vis. prof. econs. Ariz. State U., Tempe, 1986; rsch. assoc. Nat. Bur. Econ. rsch., Cambridge, Mass., 1982-91; mem. Mich. Gov. Coun. Econ. Advisers, 1992—. Mem. Am. Econs. Assn. Lutheran. Home: 1736 Hitching Post Rd East Lansing MI 48823-2144 Office: Mich State U Dept Econs East Lansing MI 48824-1038

RASCO, CAROL HAMPTON, federal official; b. Columbia, S.C., Jan. 13, 1948; d. Frank Barnes and Mary Ruby (Dallas) Hampton; children: Howard Hampton, Mary-Margaret. Student, Hendrix Coll., 1965-66; BSE. U. Ark., 1969; MS, U. Ctrl. Ark., 1972. Elem. sch. tchr. Springdale and Fayetteville (Ark.) Pub. Schs., 1969-71; counselor Bryant (Ark.) Middle Sch., 1972-73; liaison to human svcs. and health agys. Gov. Bill Clinton, Little Rock, Ark., 1983-85; exec. asst. for govtl. ops. Gov. Bill Clinton, Little Rock, 1985-91, sr. exec. asst., 1991-92; liaison to Nat. Govs. Assn., 1985-92; asst. to President U.S. for domestic policy White House, Washington, 1993—. V.p., pres. Ark. Symphony Orch. Soc. Guild Bd., 1975-78, mem. exec. com., 1976-78; pres. Fulbright Elem. Sch. PTA, 1982-83; child advocate coord. Little Rock Conf. United Meth. Women's Bd., 1979-80; family life coord. Little Rock Conf. United Meth. Ch. Coun. Ministries, 1980-82; active Friends of Ark. Repertory Theatre Bd., 1977-79, First United Meth. Ch., 1973—, chmn. bd. stewards, 1981, chmn.coun. on ministries, 1980, lay leader, 1982, chmn. child devel. ctr. bd., 1982, bd. trustees, 1988-90, Ark. Devel. Disabilities Svcs. Bd., 1979-82; vol. Ark. Coalition for Handicapped, 1977-84, Little Rock Mcpl. Ct. Vols. in Probation, 1975-78, Gov. Task Force on Coordination of Svcs. Sch.-Aged Children, 1979, Little Rock Pub. Sch. Spl. Edn. Adv. Com., 1981-91, Pulaski County Coord. for Bill Clinton for Gov., 1982. Recipient Germaine Menteil Vol. Activist award, 1976, Community Svc. award Channel 4-GOVCP, 1979. Spl. Friend of Children award Ark. Advocates for Children and Families, 1985. Democrat. Avocations: reading, travel, cooking. Office: The White House 1600 Pennsylvania Ave NW Washington DC 20500-0001

RASCOE, PAUL STEPHEN, librarian, researcher; b. Corpus Christi, Tex., July 7, 1954; s. Stephen Thomas and Barbara Jean (Butler) R. BA, U. Tex., Arlington, 1975, U. Tex., Austin, 1976; M Libr. Info. Sci., U. Tex., Austin, 1983; MA, U. London, 1977. Govt. documents and electronic info. svcs. libr. U. Tex., Austin, 1985—, libr., 1978-85; dir. rsch. Weissmann Travel Reports, Austin, 1990—. Avocation: travel. Office: U Tex Austin Documents Collection Gen Libr PCL 2.400 Austin TX 78713-7330

RASDAL, WILLIAM D., electronics executive; b. 1933. Gen. mgr. TRW, 1960-72, v.p., 1972-80; pres., COO Granger Assoc., Santa Clara, Calif., 1980-85; chb, CEO Symmetricom Inc., San Jose, Calif., 1986—. Office: Symmetricom Inc 85 W Tasman Dr San Jose CA 95134*

RASHAD, AHMAD (BOBBY MOORE), sports broadcaster, former professional football player; b. Portland, Oreg., Nov. 19, 1949; m. Phylicia Allen; 1 child, Condola Phylea. Student, U. Oreg. With St. Louis Cardinals, 1972-73, Buffalo Bills, 1974-76, Seattle Seahawks, 1976, Minn. Vikings, 1976-82; sports broadcaster NBC, N.Y.C., 1982—; played in Pro Bowl (Nat. Football League All-Star Game), 1979. Author: Vikes, Mikes and Something on the Backside, 1988. Named to Nat. Football Conf. All-Star Team Sporting News, 1978, 79. Office: care NBC Sports 30 Rockefeller Plz New York NY 10112-0002

RASHID, KAMAL A., biotechnology training program director, educator; b. Sulaimania, Kurdistan, Iraq, Sept. 11, 1944; came to U.S., 1972; s. Ahmad Rashid and Habiba M. Muhiedin; m. Afifa B. Sabir, May 23, 1970; children: Niaz K., Neian K., Suzanne K. BS, U. Baghdad, Iraq, 1965; MS, Pa. State U., 1974, PhD, 1978. Lab. instr. U. Baghdad, Iraq, 1966-72; mem. faculty U. Basrah, Iraq, 1978-80, U. Sulaimania, Iraq, 1980-83; sr. rsch. assoc., vis. prof. Pa. State U., University Park, 1983—, rsch. assoc. prof., 1992—; dir. Biotech. Short Course program Pa. State U., 1989—, dir. summer symposium molecular biology, 1991—; v.p. Cogenic Inc., State College, Pa., 1989-90; cons. in field; spkr. in field; developer workshops in field. Contbr. articles to profl. jours. Iraqi Ministry Higher Edn. scholar. Mem. Am. Chem. Soc., Environ. Mutagen Soc., Pa. Biotech. Assn. (mem. edn. com.), Rotary. Avocations: travel, swimming, reading. Home: 100 Berwick Dr Boalsburg PA 16827 Office: Pa State U 519 Wartik Lab University Park PA 16802

RASHKOW, RONALD, home improvement company executive; b. Chgo., Oct. 25, 1940; s. Joseph and Esther (Goran) R.; m. Linda Merle Karlov, Dec. 14, 1963; children: Andrew, Mark, Amy. BS in Mktg., Ill. Inst. Tech., 1963. V.p. Arrow Lumber, Chgo., 1962-68, pres., 1968-80; pres. Handy Andy Home Improvement Ctrs., Chgo., 1973—; chmn. bd. dirs. Handy Andy Home Improvement Ctrs., Schaumburg, Ill., 1975—, AOK, 1985—; mem. adv. leadership coun. Nat. Home Ctr.; chmn. adv. bd. Homecenter Industry Pres.' Coun.; nat. bd. dirs. Home Ctrs.; bd. dirs. Home Ctr. Inst. Pres. Nat. Hardware/Home Improvement Council for City of Hope, 1984-85, chmn., 1986-87; bd. dirs., pres. Jewish United Fund of Chgo. Served as sgt. USAR, 1960-66. Recipient Spirit of Life award City of Hope, 1988; named Retailer of Yr., Bldg. Supply and Home ctrs., 1977, 84, 90. Jewish.

Club: Twin Orchard (Long Grove, Ill.). Lodge: B'nai B'rith. Avocations: racquetball, jogging, golf. Office: Handy Andy Home Improvement 905 E Golf Rd Schaumburg IL 60173-4503

RASI, HUMBERTO MARIO, educational administrator, editor, minister; b. Buenos Aires, Argentina, Mar. 23, 1935; came to U.S., 1962, naturalized, 1968; s. Mario and Gertrudis Frida (Heyde) R.; m. Julia Cuchma, Feb. 28, 1957; children—Leroy Mario, Sylvia Beatrice. B.A., Instituto Superior del Profesorado, Buenos Aires, 1960; M.A., San Jose State U., 1966; Ph.D., Stanford U., 1971. Ordained to ministry Seventh-day Adventist U., 1980. Mem. faculty Instituto Florida, Buenos Aires, 1957-61; asst. editor Pacific Press Publ. Assn., Mountain View, Calif., 1962-66; asst. prof., assoc. prof. modern langs. Andrews U., 1969-76, prof., dean Sch. Grad. Studies, 1976-78; chief editor internat. publs. Pacific Press Publ. Assn., 1978-83, v.p. editorial devel., 1984-86; assoc. world dir. edn. Gen. Conf. Seventh-day Adventists, Silver Spring, Md., 1987-90, world dir. edn., 1990—; exec. dir. Inst. for Christian Teaching, 1987—. Author: The Life of Jesus, 3 vols., 1984-85; contbg. editor Handbook of L.Am. Studies, Libr. of Congress, 1972-82; gen. editor Comentario Biblico Adventista, 7 vols., 1978-90; co-editor: Meeting the Secular Mind, 1985; editor Coll. and Univ. Dialogue, 1988—; compiler Christ in the Classroom, 15 vols., 1991—; also articles on modern Hispanic lit., current events and religious trends; bd. dirs. Andrews U., Loma Linda U. NEH postdoctoral fellow Johns Hopkins U., 1975-76. Mem. MLA, Instituto Internacional de Literatura Iberoamericana. Office: 12501 Old Columbia Pike Silver Spring MD 20904-6601

RASIN, RUDOLPH STEPHEN, corporate executive; b. Newark, July 5, 1930; s. Simon Walter and Anna (Sinovc) R.; m. Joy Kennedy Peterkin, Apr. 11, 1959; children: Rudolph Stephen, James Stenning, Jennifer Shaw Denniston. B.A., Rutgers Coll., 1953; postgrad., Columbia, 1958-59. Mgr. Miles Labs., Inc., 1959-61; devel. mgr. Gen. Foods Corp., White Plains, N.Y., 1961-62; asst. to pres., chmn. Morton Internat. Inc., Chgo., 1962-72; pres. Rasin Corp., Chgo., 1971—, GRG Interest, Chgo.; bd. dirs. GRG Interests Inc., Federated Foods Inc. Bd. dirs. Ctr. for Def. Info., 1972—, English Speaking Union, Ct. Theatre. Served with USAF, 1954-56. Mem. Hinsdale Golf Club, Mid America Club (Chgo.), Lake Geneva Country Club, Williams Coll. Club (N.Y.C.). Republican. Mem. United Ch. of Christ. Home: 328 E 8th St Hinsdale IL 60521 Office: One First Nat Plz Ste 2690 Chicago IL 60603

RASKIN, EDWIN BERNER, real estate executive; b. Savannah, Ga., Mar. 19, 1919; s. Isacc and Hannah (Berner) R.; m. Rebecca Kornman, Nov. 13, 1946; children: Susan, Joan. B.B.A., Tulane U., 1940. Cert., Inst. Real Estate Mgmt. Pres., Superior Shoe Co. and Nat. Shoe Co., Savannah, Ga., 1946-50; pres. A.L. Kornman Co., Nashville, 1947-54; from pres. to sr. chmn. Edwin B. Raskin Cos., Nashville, 1954—. Served to capt. USAAF, 1942-46. Mem. Nashville Bd. Realtors, Tenn. Assn. Realtors, Nat. Assn. Real Estate Bds., Inst. Real Estate Mgmt. (past pres. middle Tenn. chpt.). Club: Woodmont (Nashville). Lodge: Rotary. Home: 419 Ellendale Ave Nashville TN 37205-3401 Office: Edwin B Raskin Co 110 Westwood Pl Brentwood TN 37027-5015

RASKIN, FRED CHARLES, transportation and utility holding company executive; b. N.Y.C., Sept. 11, 1948; s. Harry and Isabel (Wexler) R.; m. Lorraine Mary Sabourin, Apr. 25, 1974; children: Elizabeth Harris, Alexander Eastwood. B.S., Syracuse U., 1970; J.D., NYU, 1973. Bar: R.I. 1973, Mass. 1974; CPA, Ohio. Assoc. counsel Fleet Nat. Bank, Providence, 1973-75, Bank of Boston, 1975-78; asst. gen. counsel Eastern Enterprises, Boston, 1978-79, treas., 1979-81, v.p., treas., 1981-84; sr. v.p. fin. Eastern Assoc. Coal Co., Pitts., 1984-87; exec. v.p. Midland Enterprises, Inc., Cin., 1987-90, pres., 1991—; Dept. of Energy Nat. Coal coun. Mem. Fin. Execs. Inst., Treas.' Home: 9866 Bennington Dr Cincinnati OH 45241-3617 Office: Midland Enterprises Inc 580 Walnut St Cincinnati OH 45202-3108

RASKIN, MARCUS GOODMAN, writer, educator; b. Milw., Apr. 30, 1934; s. Benjamin Samuel and Anna (Goodman) R.; m. Barbara Raskin (div.); m. Lynn Randels, May 4, 1985; children: Erika Raskin Littlewood, Jamin Ben, Noah Annin, Eden McArtor. B.A., U. Chgo., 1954, J.D., 1957. Advisor to Congressional Liberal Project Group, 1959-61; mem. spl. staff NSC, 1961-63; advisor Bur. Budget, Washington, 1963; co-founder, co-dir. Inst. Policy Studies, 1963-77, disting. fellow, 1978—; prof. govt. and pub. policy George Washington U., Washington, 1993—; mem. Presdl. Commn. on Edn. Research and Devel., 1963-65, U.S. Disarmament del. 18 Nation Geneva Conf., 1962; cons. Office of Sci. and Tech., 1963-65. Author and co-author: The Limits of Defense, 1962, After Twenty Years, 1965, The Vietnam Reader, 1965, An American Manifesto, 1970, Washington Plans an Aggressive War, 1971, Being and Doing, 1971, Notes on the Old System, 1975, The Problem of the Federal Budget, 1976, The Federal Budget and Social Reconstruction, 1978, The Politics of National Security, 1978, The Common Good, 1986, New Ways of Knowing, 1987, Winning America, 1988, Essays of a Citizen, 1991, Abolishing the War System, 1993, Visions and Revisions, 1995; mem. editorial bd. The Nation, 1979—; editor: Paths for the 21st Century; contbr. articles on public policy, polit. philosophy and edn. to major jours. Bd. dirs. Inst. So. Studies, 1977-87; trustee Antioch Coll., 1965-71; chmn. SANE Edn. Fund. Recipient U. Chgo. Alumni award, 1971; Johns Hopkins Centennial fellow, 1976; citation award for disting. educator Pa. State Legislature, 1980. Office: Inst Policy Studies 1601 Connecticut Ave NW Washington DC 20009-1035 *The first question to open in nature is the secret of humankind. Then we will be in a position to live with each other - ourselves - and make sense of the self-inflicted problems that now beset humanity. We will be able to initiate a social reconstruction in our institutions that better fit with people as liberated and critically thinking human beings. This is the intellectual and political project in which I am engaged.*

RASKIN, MICHAEL A., retail company executive; b. N.J., Feb. 26, 1925; s. Harry and Elizabeth Rose (Furstenberg) R.; m. Mary Bonetta Whalen, June 12, 1948; children: Robin Raskin Crowell, Hillary Raskin Maass, Mary Allison Sullivan. A.B., Pa. State Coll., 1947; M.B.A., Columbia U., 1948. With Abraham & Straus, 1949-65; successively mdse. v.p., dir. stores, sr. v.p. Abercrombie & Fitch, N.Y.C., 1966-68; exec. v.p. Dayton's div. Dayton Hudson Corp.; pres. Jos. Magnin Co., San Francisco, 1978—; chmn., CEO, bd. dirs. Inmar Corp., San Francisco, Info. Please; chmn. exec. com. Acajoe Internat.; bd. dirs. Fortune Almac, Canterbury Cuisine, Cultural Devel. Assocs., HELP Inc., Express Yourself Through Art Inc., Munsingwear Inc., HigginsNatural. Served to lt. USNR, 1942-46.

RASKIN, PAUL D., resource management and environmental research administrator. Pres. Tellus Inst., Boston, Mass. Office: Tellus Institute 11 Arlington St Boston MA 02116*

RASKIND, LEO JOSEPH, law educator; b. Newark, Nov. 2, 1919; s. Isaac and Fannie (Michelson) R.; m. Mollie Gordon, June 14, 1948; children—Carol Inge, John Richard. A.B., UCLA, 1942; M.A., U. Wash., 1949; Ph.D. (Fulbright fellow), London Sch. Econs., 1952; LL.B., Yale, 1955. Faculty Stanford Law Sch., 1955-56; lectr., research asso. Yale Law Sch., 1956-58; faculty Vanderbilt Law Sch., 1958-64, Ohio State U. Coll. of Law, 1964-70; vis. prof. Bklyn. Law Sch., 1993-94, U. Calif., Davis, 1995—; vis. tchr. NYU, 1964, 83, U. Tex., 1964, U. Utah, 1967, So. Meth. U., 1973, U. N.C., 1978, Lyon III, 1984, Kiel U., 1988; vis. prof. Bklyn. Law Sch., 1991-94, Coll. Law U. Tenn., Knoxville, 1994, Law Sch., U. Calif.-Davis, 1995. Co-author: Casebook Corporate Taxation, 1978, Casebook Antitrust Law, 1983; mem. adv. bd. BNA jour. Served to capt. AUS, 1942-46. Mem. Am. Law Inst. Office: Bklyn Law Sch 250 Joralemon St Brooklyn NY 11201-3798

RASKY, HARRY, producer, director, writer; b. Toronto, Ont., Can., May 9, 1928; emigrated to U.S., 1955; s. Louis Leib and Pearl (Krazner) R.; m. Ruth Arlene Werkhoven, Mar. 21, 1965; children: Holly Laura, Adam Louis. BA, U. Toronto, 1949, LLD, 1984. Reporter No. Daily News, Kirkland Lake, Ont., 1949; news editor-producer Sta. CHUM, Toronto, 1950, Sta. CKEY, 1951-52; co-founder new documentary dept. CBC, 1952-55; assoc. editor Saturday Night Mag., 1955; producer-dir-writer Columbia Broadcasting Corp., 1955-60, NBC-TV, N.Y.C., 1960-61, ABC-TV, N.Y.C. 1963-69, CBC-TV, Toronto, 1971-78; pres. Harry Rasky Prodns., N.Y.C. and Toronto, 1971—, Maragall Prodns., Toronto, 1978—; guest lectr. film and TV at various univs., colls. Creator: Raskymentary (recipient numerous awards, including Emmy award 1978, 86, San Francisco Film Festival award 1978, Grand prize N.Y. TV-Film Festival 1978, Jerusalem medal 1975); numerous films include Travels Through Life with Leacock, 1976, The Peking Man Mystery, 1978, Arthur Miller on Home Ground, 1979, (TV film) Hall of Kings (Emmy award, 1965); producer, dir., writer: numerous films including Next Year in Jerusalem, 1973, The Wit and World of G. Bernard Shaw, 1974, Tennessee Williams South, 1975, Homage to Chagall-The Colours of Love, 1977 (200 internat. prizes including Oscar nomination, Emmy 1986), Stratasphere, The Mystery of Henry Moore, Karsh: The Searching Eye; play Tiger Tale, 1978, The War Against The Indians, 1992 (Humanities Prize, Great Plains Film Festival, Lincoln, Nebr., Golden Hugo award Chgo. Film Festival), Prophecy, 1994 (Golden Angel award, honored by Smithsonian, Jerusalem Found.); author: memoirs Nobody Swings on Sunday-The Many Lives of Harry Rasky, 1980, Tennessee Williams a Portrait in Laughter and Lamentation, 1986, Karsh: The Searching Eye, 1986, To Mend the World, 1987, Stratas: An affectionate tribute, 1988, Degas co-prodn. Met. Mus. of N.Y., 1988, The Great Teacher, 1989, Robertson Davies-The Magic Season, 1989; 19 hour retrospective of his films on Rasky's Gallery: Poets, Painters, Singers and Saints, CBC, 1988, The War Against the Indians, 1993 (12 Internat. awards, adopted Huron Nation title Keeper of teh Flame. Mem. YMCA; mem. adv. coun. Univ. Coll./U. Toronto. Recipient honors City of Venice, Italy, 1970, Golden Eagle, Grand prize N.Y. Intenat. TV and Film Festival of N.Y., 1977, Cert. of Merit, Acad. Motion Picture Arts and Scis., 1984, Red Ribbon, Am. Assn. Film and Video, N.Y.C., 1988, Blue Ribbon, Am. Film Festival, Emmy award, 1990, Moscow award for cultural contbn. to 20th Century USSR, 1991, Retrospective of Films, 1990, Golden Hugo award Chgo. Film Festival, 1993; named Best Non-Fiction Dir., Dirs. Guild Am., N.Y.C. and L.A., 1988, hon. Mayor N.Y.C., 1977, City of Toronto, 1979; Harry Rasky Day named in his honor, City of Toronto, 1988; Moscow Film Festival honoree, 1991; adopted by Huron Indians, named Keeper of the Spirit, adopted by Ojibway Tribe, named Mountain Eagle. Mem. Writers Guild Am. (best non-fiction dir. 1986), Dirs. Guild Am., Writers Union Can., Am., Acad. TV Arts and Scis., Assn. Can. TV and Radio Artists, Producers Assn. Can., Acad. Motion Picture Arts and Scis., Overseas Press Club, Acad. of Can. TV and Film Can. (lifetime achievement award 1992), PEN (Toronto). Nat. Arts Club. Jewish. Avocations: swimming, lecturing. Home: 15 Gregory Ave, Toronto, ON Canada M4W 2X7 Office: care CBC, Box 500 Terminal A, Toronto, ON Canada M5W 1E6 I have tried to find the positive forces in life and out of them create works of art of a lasting nature with the idea of improving the lives of others. This, plus the adventure of passing on the tradition of my father and his, is my life.

RASMUS, JOHN A., magazine executive; b. St. Louis, Mar. 20, 1954; s. Robert Nelson and Annette (Avery) R.; m. Sue A. Alexander; 1 child, Grace Alexander. B.S., Boston U., 1975. Assoc. editor Chgo. Mag., 1975-78, editorial dir., 1978; mng. editor Outside mag., Chgo., 1979-84, editor, 1984-90; exec. editor Outside Business mag., Chgo., 1986-90; columnist Universal Press Syndicate, 1987-90; editor Men's Jour. mag. Wenner Media, Inc., N.Y.C., 1990—; instr. Medill Sch. Journalism, Northwestern U., Evanston, Ill., 1985-86. Mem. Am. Soc. Mag. Editors (Nat. Mag. award 1984). Office: Wenner Media Inc 1290 Avenue Of The Americas New York NY 10104-0012

RASMUSON, ELMER EDWIN, banker, former mayor; b. Yakutat, Alaska, Feb. 15, 1909; s. Edward Anton and Jenny (Olson) R.; m. Lile Vivian Bernard, Oct. 27, 1939 (dec. 1960); children: Edward Bernard, Lile Muchmore (Mrs. John Gibbons, Jr.), Judy Ann; m. Col. Mary Louise Milligan, Nov. 4, 1961. BS magna cum laude, Harvard U., 1930, AM, 1935; student, U. Grenoble, 1930; LLD, U. Alaska, 1970, Alaska Pacific U., 1993. C.P.A., N.Y., Tex., Alaska. Chief accountant Nat. Investors Corp., N.Y.C., 1933-35; prin. Arthur Andersen & Co., N.Y.C., 1935-43; pres. Nat. Bank of Alaska, 1943-65, chmn. bd., 1966-74, chmn. exec. com., 1975-82, now chmn. emeritus; mayor City of Anchorage, 1964-67, dir., emeritus and cons., 1989; civilian aide from Alaska to sec. army, 1959-67; Swedish consul Alaska, 1955-77; Chmn. Rasmuson Found.; Rep. nominee U.S. Senate from Alaska, 1968; U.S. commr. Internat. N. Pacific Fisheries Commn., 1969-84; mem. Nat. Marine Fisheries Adv. Com., 1974-77, North Pacific Fishery Mgmt. Council, 1976-77, U.S. Arctic Research Commn., 1984-92. Mem. City Coun. Anchorage, 1945, chmn. city planning commn., 1950-53; pres. Alaska coun. Boy Scouts Am., 1953; regent U. Alaska, 1950-69; trustee King's Lake Camp, Inc., 1944—, Alaska Permanent Fund Corp., 1980-82; bd. dirs. Nat. Mus. Natural History Smithsonian Inst. 1994—. Decorated knight first class Order of Vasa, comdr. Sweden; recipient silver Antelope award Boy Scouts Am., Japanese citation Order of the Sacred Treasure, Gold and Silver Star, 1988; outstanding civilian service medal U.S. Army; Alaskan of Year award, 1976. Mem. Pioneers Alaska, Alaska Bankers Assn. (past pres.), Defense Orientation Conf. Assn., NAACP, Alaska Native Brotherhood, Explorers Club, Phi Beta Kappa. Republican. Presbyn. Clubs: Masons, Elks, Anchorage Rotary (past pres.); Harvard (N.Y.C.; Boston); Wash. Athletic (Seattle), Seattle Yacht (Seattle), Rainier (Seattle); Thunderbird Country (Palm Desert, Calif.); Bohemian (San Francisco); Eldorado Country (Indian Wells, Calif.); Boone & Crockett. Home: PO Box 100600 Anchorage AK 99510-0600

RASMUSSEN, ALICE CALL, nursing educator; b. Grand Rapids, Mich., Dec. 16, 1947; d. Amon Burton and Jessie Pearl (Dann) Call; m. Charles P. Rasmussen, Apr. 16, 1972. BSN, Andrews U., 1971; MSN, Med. Coll. Ga., 1977; postgrad., Ferris State U., 1990. Staff nurse Lockwood-MacDonald Hosp., Petoskey, Mich.; instr. Lake Michigan Coll., Benton Harbor, Mich.; nursing coord. Lake Mich. Coll., Benton Harbor, Mich.; Mem. Mich. Bd. Nursing. Mem. NAFE, Mich. League for Nursing, Mich. Coun. Nursing Edn. Adminstrs., Nat. Ordn. ADN, Mich. Assn. Women in Edn., Sigma Theta Tau. Home: Lake Michigan Coll 9088-1 4th St Berrien Springs MI 49103-1600 Office: Lake Mich Coll 2755 E Napier Benton Harbor MI 49022

RASMUSSEN, DAVID GEORGE, lawyer; b. Mpls., Mar. 6, 1943; s. Ivan Raymond and Helen Ann (Wojcichowski) R.; m. Patricia Ann Howell, July 12, 1969; children: Andrea, Christopher, Mary Patricia. BSEE, U. Minn., 1967; JD, Wayne State U., 1972. Bar: Pa. 1972, U.S. Patent Office 1973, D.C. 1982, Mass. 1987. Elec. engr. Univac, Phila., 1967-69; patent atty. Howson & Howson, Phila., 1972-73, Dupont Co., Wilmington, Del., 1973-75, U.S. Dept. Navy, Washington, 1975-79; div. patent counsel Burroughs Corp., Washington, 1979-84; corp. patent counsel Analog Devices Inc., Boston, 1984—. Served as staff sgt. USAF, 1963-69. Mem. ABA, Am. Intellectual Property Assn., Boston Patent Law Assn., Fed. Bar Assn., Am. Corp. Counsels Assn. Democrat. Roman Catholic. Avocation: outdoor sports. Home: 8 Hazel St Hopedale MA 01747-1035 Office: Analog Devices Inc 3 Technology Way Norwood MA 02062-2634

RASMUSSEN, DAVID TAB, physical anthropology educator; b. Salt Lake City, June 17, 1958; s. David Irvin and Deon (Robison) R.; m. Asenath Marian Bernhardt, May 23, 1987. BA, Colo. Coll., 1980; PhD, Duke U., 1986. Rsch. assoc Duke Primate Ctr., Durham, N.C., 1986-87; vis. asst. prof. Rice U., Houston, 1987-88; asst. prof. UCLA, 1988-91; asst. prof. phys. anthropology Washington U., St. Louis, 1991-93, assoc. prof., grad. coord. dept. anthropology, 1993—; rsch. assoc Los Angeles County Mus., L.A., 1989—, Carnegie Mus., Pitts.; condr. paleontol. fieldwork in Africa and N.Am. Editor: Origin and Evolution of Humans and Humanness, 1993; contbr. numerous articles to sci. jours. Achievements include finding fossils of early primates from 30 to 50 million years old; research on anthropoid origins, on mammal and bird evolution. Avocations: birding, mountain climbing, canoeing. Office: Washington U Dept Anthropology Saint Louis MO 63130-4862

RASMUSSEN, FRANK MORRIS, lawyer; b. Modesto, Calif., Sept. 21, 1934; s. Elmer Christian and Mary Evelyn (Bonham) R.; m. Carolyn Anne Humbert, Aug. 22, 1959; children—Kathryn Anne, James Russell, Peter Bonham. A.B., Wabash Coll., 1956; LL.B., Harvard U., 1960. Bar: Ohio 1960, U.S. Dist. Ct. (no. dist.) Ohio, U.S. Mil. Ct. Appeals 1962. Assoc. Squire, Sanders & Dempsey and predecessor firms, Cleve., 1960-70, ptnr., 1970—; sec. United Screw & Bolt Co., Cleve.; sec., bd. dirs Ohio Aerospace Inst., Cleve.; A.E. Ehrke & Co., Cleve.; bd. dirs. Nat. Machinery Corp., Tiffin, Ohio, Hartzell Propellor, Inc., Piqua Ohio, Weatherhead Industries, Inc., Ohio, Health-Mor, Inc., Cleve. Trustee, past pres. Interchurch Coun. of

Greater Cleve.; trustee, chmn. Cleve. Coun. on World Affairs, 1970—; trustee, past pres. Greater Cleve. Neighborhood Ctrs. Assn., 1975-90; trustee Wabash Coll. Alumni Assn., 1970-83. Mem. ABA, Ohio Bar Assn., Bar Assn. Greater Cleve. Union. Home: 15289 Russell Rd Chagrin Falls OH 44022-2660 Office: Squire Sanders & Dempsey 4900 Society Ctr 127 Public Sq Cleveland OH 44114

RASMUSSEN, GERALD ELMER, museum director; b. Janesville, Wis., June 14, 1935; s. Elmer Henry and Esther Adelaide (Holliday) R.; m. Joan Mary Bassaro (div. Jan. 1984); children: Gideon Thomas, Aaron Michael. Student, Milton Coll., 1953-54; BS, U. Wis., 1958, MS, 1960; postgrad., Columbia U., 1960-62. Teaching instr. Hunter Coll., N.Y.C., 1961-62, 62-63; mus. apprentice Newark Mus., 1963-64; curator sci. Stamford (Conn.) Mus. and Nature Ctr., 1964-68, dir. edn., 1968-70, exec. dir., 1970—. Singer, songwriter: (albums) Get Down Home, 1981, Secret Life of Jerry Rasmussen, 1984, Handful of Songs, 1989; songwriter: New Folk Favorites, 1987. NSF grantee, 1963. Lutheran. Avocations: part-time profl. folk singer, instrument maker. Home: 35 Scofieldtown Rd Stamford CT 06903-4023 Office: Stamford Museum & Nature Ctr 39 Scofieldtown Rd Stamford CT 06903-4096

RASMUSSEN, GERALDINE DOROTHY, composer, artist, musician, author; b. Beaverton, Mich., May 12, 1925; d. Edwin Ludwig and Hazel Helen (Colbeck) R.; m. Vance Hatcher, 1950 (div. 1950); m. Henry L. Oppenborn Jr., June 30, 1953 (div.). B in Music Edn., U. Miami, 1947. Music instr. U. Miami, Coral Gables, Fla., 1948-49; stewardess Nat. Airlines, Miami, 1949-51; substitute tchr. U. Miami Sch. Music, 1948; tchr. Our Lady Queen of Martyrs, Ft. Lauderdale, Fla., 1961-62; pvt. piano instr., 1961-65; music tchr. Broward County Schs., Ft. Lauderdale, 1962-63; tchr. St. Anthony's Sch., Ft. Lauderdale, 1963-64; landlord Ft. Lauderdale, 1964-89; freelance portrait artist Miami, Ft. Lauderdale, 1947—; violist U. Miami Symphony, Coral Gables, 1943-47; mezzo-contralto First Congl. Ch. Choir, Coral Gables, 1944-47, Miami (Fla.) Opera Guild, 1944-47; violinist, violist Ft. Lauderdale (Fla.) Symphony, Hollywood (Fla.) Phil., 1956-64. Author: The Invisible Force, 1981, Toronita: Land of Sunshine and Good Will, 1995; composer: (opera) Julius Caesar, 1983, Christopher Columbus, (for piano and mandolin obligato) The Bataan Death March, 1989, (for tenor, piano and flute) Columbus Quincentennial; composer songs for voice, piano and flute obligato, La Florida, 1995, La Pieta, 1995; exhibited in group shows at Ft. Lauderdale Libr. and Ft. Lauderdale City Hall; also pvt. collections. Founder, dir. Citizens Against Radioactive Pollution, Ft. Lauderdale, 1976-79; interviewer USA Poll, Ft. Lauderdale, 1989-90; rec. sec. Morning Musicale Ft. Lauderdale, 1990-91, pres., 1992-94. Mem. Fla. Fedn. Music Clubs (pres. Royal Poinciana dist. 1994-96), Internat. Assn. Hydrogen Energy (hon.), Mortar Bd., Sigma Alpha Iota. Republican. Avocations: gardening, dress designing, writing, research in radiation, health and nutrition. Home: 1609 SE 4th St Fort Lauderdale FL 33301

RASMUSSEN, HOWARD, medical educator, medical institute executive; b. Harrisburg, Pa., Mar. 1, 1925; s. Frederick and Faith (Elliott) R.; m. Jane Claire Spence, June 10, 1950; children: Gail, Paul, Jane, Craig. AB in Chemistry and Physics, Gettysburg Coll., 1948; MD, Harvard U., 1952; PhD in Biochemistry and Physiology, Rockefeller U., 1959. Asst. prof. physiology Rockefeller U., N.Y.C., 1959-61; assoc. prof. biochemistry U. Wis., Madison, 1961-64; prof. sch. medicine U. Pa., Phila., 1964-75, Benjamin Rush prof. biochemistry, 1964-75, prof. biochemistry and biophysics, 1964-76, chmn. dept. biochemistry, 1964-70, prof. pediatrics, 1975-76; prof. medicine and cell biology sch. medicine Yale U., New Haven, 1976-93; prof. medicine, surgery, cell biology, anatomy Med. Coll. Ga., Augusta, 1993—; dir. SCOT Urolithiasis Ctr., Sch. Medicine, Yale U., 1977-82, chief divsn. endocrinology, 1980-86, dir. med. scientist trng. program, 1983-91; dir. Inst. for Molecular Medicine and Genetics, Med. Coll. Ga., 1993—; Wellcome vis. prof. U. Va., Richmond, 1988; Klenk lectr. U. Koln, West Germany, 1989; Lily lectr. XI Internat. Conf. Calcium Regulation, Florence, Italy, 1992. Author: Calcium and c Amp as Synarchic Messengers, 1981, The Physiological and Cellular Basis of Metabolic Bone Disease, 1984. Staff sgt. U.S. Army, 1942-44. Recipient Cotlove award Acad. Clin. Lab. Physicians and Scientists, 1993. Avocations: opera, hiking. Office: Med Coll Ga 1120 15th St CB-2803 Augusta GA 30912

RASMUSSEN, JOHN OSCAR, chemist, scientist; b. St. Petersburg, Fla., Aug. 8, 1926; s. John Oscar and Hazel (Ormsby) R.; m. Louise Brooks, Aug. 27, 1950; children—Nancy, Jane, David, Stephen. B.S., Calif. Inst. Tech., 1948; Ph.D., U. Calif. at Berkeley, 1952; M.A. (hon.), Yale U., 1969. Mem. faculty dept. chemistry U. Calif., Berkeley, 1952-68, 73-91, prof. chemistry, 1971-91, ret., 1991, mem. research staff, 1952-68; sr. rsch. assoc. Lawrence Berkeley Lab., 1972—; prof. chemistry Yale U. 1969-73; asso. dir. Yale Heavy Ion Accelerator Lab., 1970-73; vis. research prof. Nobel Inst. Physics, Stockholm, 1953; vis. prof. Inst. Nuclear Sci. U. Tokyo, 1974, Fudan U., Shanghai, 1979, hon. prof., 1984. Contbr. articles on radioactivity, nuclear models, heavy ion reactions. Served with USN, 1944-46. Recipient E.O. Lawrence Meml. award AEC, 1967; NSF sr. postdoctoral fellow Niels Bohr Inst., Copenhagen, 1961-62, NORDITA fellow, 1979, Guggenheim Meml. fellow, 1973, Alexander von Humboldt sr. rsch. fellow Tech. U. Munich, 1991. Fellow Am. Phys. Soc., AAAS; mem. Am. Chem. Soc. (Nuclear Applications in Chemistry award 1976), Fedn. Am. Scientists (chmn. 1969). Office: Lawrence Berkeley Lab Ms 70A # 3307 Berkeley CA 94720

RASMUSSEN, LYNN C., fashion accessories company executive; b. Neosho, Mo., July 16, 1942; s. Murlin Albert and Trudy E. (Hart) R.; m. Holly S. Gruher, Nov. 23, 1987 (div. Jan. 1992); children: Derek, Renae, Aleigha. BA, U. Santa Clara, 1965. Acct. Coca Cola, San Jose, 1967-69; contr. Micropoint Imaging., Sunnyvale, Calif., 1969-71; sr. acct. NBC, San Francisco, 1972-73; contr. Hatch/Helco, Palo Alto, Calif., 1973-76, Good Samaritan, San Jose, 1976-81, P.A.T. Inc., Burlingame, Calif., 1981-85; CFO Home Computing Ctr., San Francisco, 1985-89, Hygolet Inc., Deerfield Park, Fla., 1989-93; CFO, AGI Inc., Delray Beach, Fla., 1993—. Author: (manual) Calif. RCHA, 1986. Mem. adv. bd. Tough Love, San Francisco, 1985-87; assoc. mem. Greenpeace. Mem. Am. Assn. Ret. Persons, Swiss Am. C. of C. Republican. Avocation: golf. Home: 6205 Balboa Cir # 104 Boca Raton FL 33433

RASMUSSEN, NEIL WOODLAND, insurance agent; b. Portland, Oreg., Sept. 14, 1926; s. Ernest Roy and Lulu Mildred (Woodland) R.; m. Mary Ann Cannon, Aug. 10, 1957; children: Kirk, Sally, P. Cannon, Eric (dec.). BA, Stanford U., 1949. Registered mut. funds rep. Warehouseman Consol. Supply Co., Portland, Oreg., 1949-50, sales rep., 1955-56; sales rep. Consol. Supply Co., Eugene, Oreg., 1950-52; sales rep. Consol. Supply Co., Salem, Oreg., 1956-64, br. mgr., 1964-82; agt. life and health ins. N.Y. Life Ins. Co., Salem, 1982—. Lt. Cmdr. USN, 1952-55, Res. ret. Recipient Nat. Quality award Nat. Assn. Life Underwriters, 1986-88. Mem. Salem Assn. Life Underwriters, Res. Officers Assn. (bd. dirs. 1988-91, v.p. 1988-91), Rotary (bd. dirs. East Salem 1980-83, sr. active mem. 1990-92, Paul Harris fellow). Republican. Episcopalian. Avocations: golf, fishing, camping. Office: NY Life Ins Co 530 Center St NE Salem OR 97301

RASMUSSEN, NORMAN CARL, nuclear engineer; b. Harrisburg, Pa., Nov. 12, 1927; s. Frederick and Faith (Elliott) R.; m. Thalia Tichenor, Aug. 23, 1952; children: Neil, Arlene. BA, Gettysburg (Pa.) Coll., 1950, ScD (hon.), 1968; PhD, MIT, 1956; Dr honoris causa, Cath. U. Leuven, Belgium, 1980. Mem. faculty MIT, 1956—, prof. nuclear engring., 1965—, McAfee prof. engring., 1983—, head dept., 1975-81; dir. reactor safety study AEC, 1972-75; mem. Def. Sci. Bd., 1974-78, sr. cons., 1978-84; mem. nat. sci bd NSF, 1982-88; prof. emeritus MIT, 1993—; mem. Presdl. Adv. Group on Contbns. Tech. to Econs. Strength, 1975; dir. Bedford Engring. Corp.; adv. com. components tech. div. Argonne Univs. Assn., 1977-80; chmn. sci. rev. com. Idaho Nat. Engring. Lab. 1977-86; mem. adv. council Princeton Plasma Physics Lab., 1983-91; mem. safety adv. bd. Three Mile Island Unit-2 Program, 1980-90; trustee N.E. Utilities, 1977—. Co-author: Modern Physics for Engineers, 1966; contbr. articles to profl. jours. Chmn. Lincoln-Sudbury Sch. Com., 1971-72; bd. dirs. Atomic Indsl. Forum, 1980-84; mem. Utility Sci. Review Council for Nuclear Safety Analysis Center. Served with USNR, 1945-46. Recipient Disting. Achievement award Health Physics Soc., 1976; Disting. Service award NRC, 1976; Disting. Alumni award Gettysburg Coll., 1983; Enrico Fermi award Dept. Energy, 1985. Fellow Am. Nuclear Soc. (spl. award nuclear power reactor safety 1976, Theos J.

Thompson award nuclear reactor safety div. 1981, bd. dirs. 1976-80, Ahlstrom prize 1990); mem. Am. Acad. Arts and Scis., Nat. Acad. Engring., Nat. Acad. Sci., Soc. Risk Analysis, Health Physics Soc. Home: 80 Windsor Rd Sudbury MA 01776-2371 Office: MIT 77 Massachusetts Ave Cambridge MA 02139

RASMUSSEN, ROBERT, museum director. Dir. National Museum of Naval Aviation, Pensacola, Fla. Office: National Mus Naval Aviation 1750 Radford Blvd Ste C Pensacola FL 32508

RASMUSSON, GARY HENRY, medicinal chemist; b. Clark, S.D., Aug. 2, 1936; s. Rudolf M. and Alice Ernestine (Henry) R.; m. Nancy Elaine Torkelson, June 7, 1958; children: Randall, Korise, Tamara, Todd. BA, St. Olaf Coll., 1958; PhD, MIT, 1962. Postdoctoral fellow Stanford U., Palo Alto, Calif., 1962-64; sr. chemist Merck, Sharp & Dohme Rsch. Labs., Rahway, N.J., 1964-72, rsch. fellow, 1972-77, sr. rsch. fellow, 1977-85, sr. investigator, 1985-1994. Medicinal discovery new type drug 5alpha reductase inhibitors, 1986. Named Inventor of Yr. Intellectual Property Owners, Washington, 1993. Mem. AAAS, Am. Chem. Soc. Lutheran. Office: Merck Rsch Labs Box 2000 Rahway NJ 07065

RASOR, DINA LYNN, investigator, journalist; b. Downey, Calif., Mar. 21, 1956; d. Ned Shaurer and Genevieve Mercia (Eads) R.; m. Thomas Taylor Lawson, Oct. 4, 1980. BA in Polit. Sci., U. Calif., Berkeley, 1978. Editorial asst. ABC News, Washington, 1978-79; researcher Pres.'s Commn. on Coal, Washington, 1979; legis. asst. Nat. Taxpayers Union, Washington, 1979-81; founder, dir. Project on Mil. Procurement, Washington, 1981-89; investigative reporter Lawson-Rasor Assocs., El Cerrito, Calif., 1990-92; pres., CEO, investigator Bauman & Rasor Group, El Cerrito, Calif., 1993—. Author: The Pentagon Underground, 1985; editor: More Bucks, Less Bang, 1983; contbr. articles to profl. jours. Recipient Sigma Delta Chi Outstanding Leadership award Soc. Profl. Journalists, 1986; named to register Esquire Mag., 1986, Nat. Jour., 1986. Mem. United Ch. Christ.

RASOR, ROBERT D., lawyer; b. Bloomington, Ind., Aug. 3, 1948. BA, DePaul U., 1970; JD, Northwestern U., 1973. Bar: Ill. 1973, U.S. Dist. Ct. (no. dist.) Ill. 1973. Ptnr. Lord, Bissell & Brook, Chgo. Mem. ABA, Ill. State Bar Assn., Chgo. Bar Assn. Office: Lord Bissell & Brook Harris Bank Bldg 115 S La Salle St Stes 2600-3600 Chicago IL 60603-3801

RASPBERRY, WILLIAM JAMES, journalist; b. Okolona, Miss., Oct. 12, 1935; s. James Lee and Willie Mae (Tucker) R.; m. Sondra Patricia Dodson, Nov. 12, 1966; children—Patricia D., Angela D., Mark J. BS in History, Ind. Central Coll., 1958, L.H.D., 1973. Reporter-editor Indpls. Recorder, 1956-60; reporter-editor Washington Post, 1962-65, urban affairs columnist, 1966—; Instr. journalism Howard U., 1971-73; lectr. on race relations and pub. edn. Mem. Pulitzer Prize Bd., 1979-86. TV commentator, Sta. WTTG, Washington, 1973-75, TV discussion panelist, Sta. WRC-TV, Washington, 1974-75; Contbr. articles on race relations and pub. edn. to popular mags. Bd. visitors U. Md. Sch. Journalism, 1985—; bd. advisors Poynter Inst. for Media Studies, 1984-94. With AUS, 1960-62. Recipient Pulitzer Prize for commentary, 1994. Mem. Capital Press Club, Kappa Alpha Psi. Club: Gridiron. Home: 1301 Iris St NW Washington DC 20012-1434 Office: Washington Post Co 1150 15th St NW Washington DC 20071-0002

RASPORICH, ANTHONY WALTER, university dean; b. Port Arthur, Ont., Can., Jan. 9, 1940; s. Milan and Sophia (Grgurich) R.; m. Beverly Jean Matson. BA, Queen's U., Kingston, Ontario, 1962, MA, 1965; PhD, U. Man., Winnipeg, 1970. Tchr. Kingston Bd. Edn., 1962-63; prof. history U. of Calgary, Alta., 1966—, dean social scis. faculty, 1986-94. Author: For a Better Life, 1982, Oil and Gas in Western Canada 1900-80, 1985; editor: The Making of the Modern West, 1984; co-editor: Canadian Ethnic Studies, 1980-95, Sports in the West, 1990. C.D. Howe postdoctoral fellow, fellow Assn. Univs. Colls. Can., Thunder Bay, Ontario, 1970. Vis. Can. Studies, Sussex, Eng., 1979, Killam Found., Calgary, 1979, Social Scis. Human Rsch. Coun., Ottawa, Can., 1981. Mem. Canada Ethnic Studies Assn., Can. Hist. Assn., Ont. Hist. Soc. Office: U of Calgary, Faculty of Social Scis, Calgary, AB Canada T2N 1N4

RASSBACH, HERBERT DAVID, marketing executive; b. Glen Ridge, N.J., Mar. 23, 1944; s. Merrill Augustus and Ruth Bruce (Sims) R.; m. Sherry Miriam Reichel, July 14, 1974. BS, Del. State Coll. 1971; MBA, Drexel U., 1979. Prodn. planning mgr. Standard Brands Chem. Industries, Edison, N.J., 1971-74; order fulfillment mgr. P Q Corp., Valley Forge, Pa., 1974-77, mkt. devel. project mgr., 1977-82; market mgr. Willson Safety Products, Reading, Pa., 1983-85; pres. HDR Group, mktg. and mgmt. cons., Wayne, Pa., 1986—; guest speaker Wharton Sch. U. Pa., 1988, Temple U., Phila., 1989, Wharton Club, 1995. Committeeman Upper Merion Twp., Pa., 1977; Media Comms. bd., Upper Merion Twp., 1989, vice chmn., 1990, 92-95, chmn., 1991. Mem. Drexel U. Alumni Assn. (v.p. Montgomery County chpt. 1988-91), Alpha Kappa Mu, Delta Mu Delta. Democrat. Avocations: golf, tennis, racquetball, travel, American History, arts. Home: 635 Mallard Rd Wayne PA 19087-2346 Office: HDR Group PO Box 904 Valley Forge PA 19482

RASSEL, RICHARD EDWARD, lawyer; b. Toledo, Jan. 10, 1942; s. Richard Edward and Madonna Mary (Tuohy) R.; m. Elizabeth Ann Frederick, Dec. 5, 1967 (wid. June 1977); children: Richard III, Elizabeth; m. Dawn Ann Lynch, Sept. 17, 1983; children: Lauren, Brian. BA, U. Notre Dame, 1964; JD, U. Mich., 1966. Bar: Mich. 1966, U.S. Dist. Ct. (ea. dist.) Mich. 1969, U.S. Ct. Appeals (6th cir.) 1971, U.S. Supreme Ct. 1980. Law clk. to presiding judge Mich. Ct. Appeals, Detroit, 1966; shareholder, chmn. CEO Butzel & Long, Detroit, 1970—; bd. dirs. Lex Mundi Law Firm Alliance, Rochester-Jamieson Corp. Contbr. articles to profl. jours.; lectr. in field. Past pres., bd. dirs. Birmingham Cmty. House; bd. advisors U. Detroit Grad. Sch. Bus.; mem. steering com. Friends of Legal Aid; pres. Rosa Parks Scholarship Found., Detroit, Detroit Police Athletic League, S.E.E.D. Found.; bd. dirs. Met. Affairs Corp. Fellow Am. Coll. Trial Lawyers, Mich. Bar Found.; mem. ABA (forum com., vice chmn. law & media com. tort and ins. practice sect.), Am. Arbitration Assn., Fed. Bar Assn., State Bar Mich. (past chmn. media and the law com., chmn. TV in the cts. com.), Detroit Bar Assn. (exec. com., U.S. dist. cts. com.), Libel Def. Resource Ctr. (vice chmn. def. counsel sect.), Detroit C. of C. (bus. attraction and expansion coun. southeast Mich.), Leadership Detroit Alumni Assn., U.S. Navy League, Detroit Athletic Club, Birmingham Athletic Club, Otsego Ski Club, Village Club. Roman Catholic. Home: 700 Browning Ct Bloomfield Hills MI 48304-3715 Office: Butzel Long 150 W Jefferson Ste 900 Franklin MI 48025

RASSMAN, JOEL H., real estate company executive, accountant; b. N.Y.C., May 16, 1945. BBA, CUNY, 1967. CPA, N.Y. Acct. Ernst & Young, N.Y.C., 1967-73; ptnr. Kenneth Leventhal & Co., N.Y.C., 1973-84; sr. v.p. Toll Bros., Inc., Horsham, Pa., 1984—. Mem. AICPA, N.Y. State Soc. CPA's.

RAST, WALTER, JR., hydrologist, water quality management; b. San Antonio, Jan. 14, 1944; s. Walter and Jane Irene (Tudyk) R.; m. Claudia Leigh Jones, July 16, 1971; children: Margaret Amanda, Elizabeth Miranda. BA in Zoology, U. Tex., Austin, 1970; MS in Molecular Biology, U. Tex., Richardson, 1974, MS in Environ. Sci., 1976, PhD in Environ. Sci., 1978. Limnologist Gt. Lakes Regional Office, Internat. Joint Commn., Windsor, Ont., Can., 1977-79; environ. advisor U.S. Hdqrs. sect. Internat. Joint Commn., Washington, 1979-82; rsch. hydrologist U.S. Geol. Survey, Sacramento, 1982-86, Austin, 1986-92; chief freshwater unit UNEP, Nairobi, Kenya, 1993—; adj. prof. dept. biology Wayne State U., Detroit, 1978-79; adj. prof. dept. aquatic biology S.W. Tex. State U., San Marcos, 1992—; mem. core editorial group program on man and biosphere UNESCO, 1982-89, chmn. sci. adv. com., 1988—; instr. Austin Community Coll., 1989—; reviewer sci. books and films AAAS, Washington, 1989-92. Co-author: Control of Eutrophication of Lakes and Reservoirs, 1989; co-author: Phosphorus Management Strategies for Lakes, 1979; mem. editorial bd. Internat. Jour. Devel., 1993—; contbr. articles to sci. jours. Mem. secondary edn. adv. com. Austin Ind. Sch. Dist., 1989-92. Scholar Richardson Environ. Action League, 1976-77. Mem. N.Am. Lake Mgmt. Soc. (co-chmn. scholarship com. 1988—, mem. internat. com. and lake cert. com. 1988—, tech. chmn. 9th internat. symposium 1989), Am. Soc. Limnology and Oceanography, Internat. Soc. Applied and Theoretical Limnology. Roman Catholic. Avocations: jogging, model railroads, piano, reading, amateur politics. *One of the most difficult things for a person to do is undertake necessary and even unpleasant tasks, at the same time others are content to offer excuses as to why they cannot be done. Fortunately, a sufficient number of people display this virtue to make it all worthwhile.*

RASTOGI, ANIL KUMAR, medical device manufacturer executive; b. India, July 13, 1942; came to U.S., 1969, naturalized, 1978; s. R.S. and K.V. Rastogi; m. Anjali Capur, Mar. 18, 1970; children: Priya, Sonya. B.S. with honors, Lucknow U., 1963, M.S., 1964; Ph.D. in Polymer Sci., McGill U., 1969. Mem. staff Owens-Corning Tech. Ctr., Granville, Ohio, 1969-87; lab. supr. Owens-Corning Tech. Ctr., 1975-76; lab. mgr. materials tech. labs Owens-Corning Tech. Ctr., Granville, Ohio, 1976-79; lab. mgr. product devel. labs. Owens-Corning Tech. Ctr., Granville, Ohio, 1979-80, research dir., 1980-83, dir. corp. diversification portfolio, 1983-87; v.p. Mead Imaging, Miamisburg, Ohio, 1987-89; pres. Mead Cycolor Div., Dayton, Ohio, 1989-92; v.p., gen. mgr.infusion systems div. Pharmacia Deltec, Inc., St. Paul, 1992-93; exec. v.p. Pharmacia Deltec, Inc., 1993-94; COO SIMS Deltec, Inc., St. Paul, 1994—; mem. adv. bd. Central Ohio Tech. Coll.; lectr., cons. in field. Author of 11 bus. and tech. publs.; patentee in field. Bd. dirs. Licking County Family Services Assn.; bd. dirs. Tech. Alliance of Central Ohio; v.p. local United Way; bd. dirs. and treas. Columbus Bus. Tech. Ctr.; mem. Overview Adv. Com. Strategic Hwy. Research Program. Fellow NRC Can., 1966-69. Mem. AAAS, Am. Mgmt. Assn., Am. Chem. Soc., Soc. Plastics Engrs., Comml. Devel. Assn., Med. Alley (bd. dirs.), Health Ind. Mfrs. Assn., Sigma Xi. Club: Toastmasters (past pres.). Lodge: Rotary. Home: 4445 Foothill Trl Saint Paul MN 55127-6002 Office: SIMS Deltec Inc 1265 Grey Fox Rd Saint Paul MN 55112-6967

RATAJ, EDWARD WILLIAM, lawyer; b. St. Louis, Oct. 14, 1947; m. Elizabeth Spalding, July 4, 1970; children: Edward, Suzanne, Anne, Thomas, Charles. BS in Acctg., St. Louis U., 1969, JD, 1972. Assoc. Bryan, Cave, McPheeters & McRoberts, St. Louis, 1972-82, ptnr., 1983—. Office: Bryan Cave McPheeters & McRoberts 1 Metropolitan Sq Saint Louis MO 63102-2750

RATCLIFF, JAMES LEWIS, administrator; b. Indpls., Mar. 3, 1946; s. Perry Albert and Viola Ruth (Hall) R.; m. Carol Rocklin Kay, Dec. 24, 1984 (dec.). Student, Raymond Coll.; B of History, Polit. Sci., Utah State U., 1968; MA in History, Wash. State U., 1972, PhD, 1976. Dir. Ctr. for the Study of Higher Edn.; dir. Nat. Ctr. Postsecondary Teaching/Learning/ Assessment Pa. State U., University Park; prof., leader higher edn. section Iowa State U., Ames; assoc. prof. Fla. Atlantic U., Boca Raton; asst. prof. Wash. State U., Pullman. U.S. Dept. Edn. grantee. Mem. Am. Assn. Community Jr. Colls., Assn. Study Higher Edn. (bd. dirs.), Coun. Universities Colls. (past pres., bd. dirs.), European Assn. for Inst. Rsch.,Consortium Higher Edn. Rschs., Phi Delta Kappa, Phi Kappa Phi, Phi Alpha Theta.

RATCLIFF, SARA BONEY, federal agency administrator; b. Burlington, N.C., Jan. 11, 1957; d. Thomas Evans and Jean (Sandifer) Boney; m. Blake Dale Ratcliff, Aug. 26, 1990; 1 child, Virginia Blake. BS in Sci. Teaching, U. N.C., 1980. Legis. aide to Rep. Don Clausen Washington, 1980-82, sr. legis. asst. to Rep. Frank R. Wolf, 1982-85; assoc. staff appropriations com. U.S. Ho. of Reps., Washington, 1988-89; chief of staff to Rep. Ernie Konnyu Washington, 1988-89; pers., legis. specialist USAF, Washington, 1989; dep. dir. Office of Policy U.S. Office of Pers. Mgmt., Washington, 1989-90; dep. asst. sec. def. for civilian pers. policy/equal opportunity Dept. Def., Washington, 1990—. Vol. Reagan for Pres., Chapel Hill, N.C., 1976, Reagan/ Bush presdl. campaign, Washington, 1980, 84; counselor Barcroft Bible Ch. Youth Group, Arlington, Va., 1985-86; policy advisor Bush/Quayle, Washington, 1988. Mem. Sr. Exec. Assn. (Disting Svc. award 1988). Republican. Presbyterian. Avocations: tennis, snow skiing, scuba diving, water sports.

RATCLIFFE, GEORGE JACKSON, JR., business executive, lawyer; b. Charleston, W.Va., Mar. 22, 1936; s. George Jackson and Dorothy (Ward) R.; m. Nancy Lenhardt, Oct. 5, 1963; children: George Jackson III, Dorothy Margaret. AB, Duke U., 1958; JD, U. Va., 1961. Bar: N.Y. 1964, Ohio 1962. Assoc. Taft, Stettinius & Hollister, Cin., 1961-63; lawyer IBM Corp., 1963-65; assoc. Perkins, Daniels & McCormack, N.Y.C., 1965-70, ptnr., 1970; v.p., sec., gen. counsel Helme Products Inc., N.Y.C., 1970, exec. v.p., 1971-74, pres., 1974; v.p., sec., gen. counsel Hubbell Inc., Orange, Conn., 1975-80, sr. v.p. fin. and law, 1980-83, exec. v.p. adminstrn., 1983-87, chmn. bd., 1987—, pres., chief exec. officer, 1987—; bd. dirs. Aquarian Co., Bridgeport, Conn., Olin Corp., Stamford, Conn., Praxair Inc., Danbury, Conn.; mem. listed co. adv. com. N.Y. Stock Exch. Mem. Conn. Bus. and Industry Assn. (bd. dirs.), Nat. Elec. Mfrs. Assn. (bd. govs.), Brooklawn Country Club (Fairfield, Conn.), Aspetuck Fish and Game Club (Bridgeport), Clove Valley Rod and Gun Club (LaGrangeville, N.Y.), Loblolly Pines Club (Hobe Sound, Fla.), Merion Golf Club (Ardmore, Pa.), Blind Brook Country Club (Purchase, N.Y.), Links Club (N.Y.). Home: 278 Sherwood Dr Southport CT 06490-1049 Office: Hubbell Inc PO Box 549 584 Derby Milford Rd Orange CT 06477-2204*

RATH, ALAN T., sculptor; b. Cin., Nov. 25, 1959; s. George and Carolyn R. BSEE, MIT, 1982. One-man exhbns. include San Jose (Calif.) Art Mus., 1990, Dorothy Goldeen Gallery, Santa Monica, Calif., 1990, 92, Walker Art Ctr., Mpls., 1991, Mus. Contemporary Art, Chgo., 1991, Carl Solway Gallery, Cin., 1991, Inst. Contemporary Art, Phila., 1992, The Contemporary Mus., Honolulu, 1992, Ctr. Fine Art, Miami, Fla., 1992, Galerie Hans Mayer, Dusseldorf, Germany, 1992, Hiroshima (Japan) City Mus. Contemporary Art, 1994, Worcester (Mass.) Art Mus., 1994, John Weber Gallery, N.Y.C., 1994, Haines Gallery, San Francisco, 1995; group exhbns. include Visiona, Zurich, 1989, Ars Electronica, Linz, Austria, 1989, L.A. Contemporary Exhbns., 1989, Mus. Folkwang, Essen, Germany, 1989, Cite des Arts et des Nouvelles Technologies, Montreal, 1990, Stadtmuseum Siegburg, Siegburg, Germany, 1990, San Francisco Mus. Modern Art, 1990, Denver Art Mus., 1991, Whitney Mus. Am. Art, N.Y.C., 1991, Alvar Alto Mus., Jyvaskyla, Finland, 1992, Internat. Ctr. Photography, N.Y.C., 1992, Padiglione d'Arte Contemporanea, Ferrara, Italy, 1992, John Weber Gallery, N.Y.C., 1993, Spiral Art Ctr. Tokyo, 1994. Grantee NEA, 1988; Guggenheim fellow, 1994. Office: IKON 830 E 15th St Oakland CA 94606-3631

RATH, BERNARD EMIL, trade association executive; b. Arnstein, Fed. Republic of Germany, Oct. 9, 1949; arrived in Can., 1952; U.S. resident, 1985; s. Rudolph and Elfriede (Kraft) R.; m. Susan Elaine Garner, July 8, 1972; children: Vanessa, Andrew, Lauren. BA in Polit. Sci., McMaster U., Can., 1972, BA in Phys. Edn., 1972; Diploma Edn., U. Western Ont., Can., 1973. Sales rep. Doubleday Pubs., Toronto, Ont., Can., 1973-75; sales mgr. Macmillan Pubs., Toronto, Ont., Can., 1975-77; nat. sales mgr., 1977-79; exec. dir. Can. Booksellers, Toronto, 1979-83, Am. Booksellers Assn., N.Y.C., 1984—; pres. Booksellers Order Service, N.Y.C., 1984—. Pub. Booksellers Publishing, N.Y.C., 1984—; contbr. articles to profl. jours. Am. Soc. Assn. Execs. Home: 33 Chester Ct Cortlandt Mnr NY 10566-6361 Office: Am Booksellers Assn 560 White Plains Rd Tarrytown NY 10591-5112

RATH, FRANK E., SR., electronics executive; b. 1915. Grad., Carnegie Inst. of Tech., Pitt., 1937. Chief engr. U.S. Steel Corp., Pitts, 1937-49; chmn, CEO Spang & Co., Butler, Pa., 1958—. Office: Spang & Co Brugh Ave Butler PA 16001*

RATH, FRANK E., JR., electronics executive; b. 1946. BS, Carnegie Mellon U., 1968. With Ernst & Ernst CPAs, Pitts., 1968-70; with Spang & Co., Butler, Pa., 1974—, pres., 1977—. Office: Spang & Co Brugh Ave Butler PA 16001-6428*

RATH, GEORGE EDWARD, bishop; b. Buffalo, Mar. 29, 1913; s. Edward F. and Eudora Pearl (Chadderdon) R.; m. Margaret Webber, Apr. 7, 1934; children: Peter F. (dec.), Gail (Mrs. Richard M. Sherk). A.B., Harvard U., 1933; B.D., Union Theol. Sem., 1936; S.T.D., Gen. Theol. Sem., 1964. Ordained deacon Episcopal Ch., 1938, priest, 1939; asst. to chaplain Columbia, 1939-36; asst. chaplain, 1939-41; vicar All Saints' Ch., Millburn, N.J., 1941-49; rector All Saints' Ch., 1949-64; suffragan bishop Episcopal Diocese Newark, 1964-70; bishop coadjutor, 1970-73, bishop, 1974-78, ret.,

1978; archdeacon Morris County, 1959-64; assisting bishop Episcopal Diocese of Mass., 1982-94. Chmn. bd. trustees Christ Hosp. Jersey City, 1966-79; trustee Cape Cod Mus. Natural History, 1980-85; bd. dirs. Nauset Inc., 1981-86, 88-93. Mem. Cape Cod (Mass.) Bird Club, Harvard Club of Cape Cod, Montclair (N.J.) Bird Club. Home: PO Box 996 2 Cedar Land Rd East Orleans MA 02643-0996

RATH, GUSTAVE J(OSEPH), industrial engineering educator, psychologist; b. N.Y.C., May 19, 1929; s. Gustave Julian and Margaret Rose (Payor) R.; m. Clovia Poock, Sept. 1, 1953 (div. 1976); 1 child, G. Alexander; m. Karen Sue Braatz Stoyanoff, Oct. 15, 1977. BS, MIT, 1952; MS, Ohio State U., 1955, PhD, 1957. Psychologist IBM, Peekskill, N.Y., 1957-59; mgr. ops. rsch. Admiral Co., Chgo., 1959-60; mgr. behavioral tech. Raytheon Co., Lexington, Mass., 1960-63; prof. indsl. engring. and mgmt. sci. Northwestern U., Evanston, Ill., 1963—; pres. Fundamental Systems, Inc., Evanston, 1967-70; Cassell, Rath & Stoyanoff, Ltd., Evanston, 1979-84; v.p. Resource Profls., Inc., Evanston, 1990—. Author: Punch Card Data Processing, 1966; co-author: Marketing for Congregations, 1992, Benchmarks of Quality in the Church, 1994; author, co-author chpts. in books. 1st lt. USAF, 1952-54. Danforth fellow, 1983; Sloan Found. grantee, 1970. Fellow AAAS, APA. Am. Psychol. Soc., Sigma Xi, Tau Beta Pi. Achievements include invention of computer-assisted instrn. Office: Northwestern U Dept Indsl Engring 2145 Sheridan Rd Evanston IL 60208-0834

RATH, HOWARD GRANT, JR., lawyer; b. L.A., Sept. 2, 1931; s. Howard Grant and Helen (Cowell) R.; m. Peyton McComb, Sept. 13, 1958 (dec. Apr. 1984); children: Parthenia Peyton, Francis Cowell; m. Dorothy Moser, Aug. 29, 1986. BS, U. Calif., 1953; JD, U. So. Calif., 1958. Bar: Calif. 1959, U.S. Dist. Ct. (cen. dist.) Calif., 1959, U.S. Ct. Claims 1974, U.S. Tax Ct. 1960. Assoc. O'Melveny & Myers, L.A., 1959-66; tax counsel, dir. tax adminstrn., asst. treas. Northrop Corp. L.A., 1966-74; sr. tax ptnr. Macdonald, Halsted & Laybourne, L.A., 1974-86, Hill & Weiss, L.A., 1986-90; ptnr. Lewis, D'Amato, Brisbois & Bisgaard, L.A., 1990—; dir. Rath Packing Co., Waterloo, Iowa, 1966-81. 1st lt. U.S. Army, 1953-55. Mem. ABA, State Bar Calif., L.A. County Bar Assn., Order of Coif, Phi Beta Kappa. Republican. Episcopalian. Club: Valley Hunt (pres. 1981-82). Office: Lewis D'Amato Brisbois & Bisgaard 221 N Figueroa St Ste 1200 Los Angeles CA 90012-2601

RATH, R. JOHN, historian, educator; b. St. Francis, Kans., Dec. 12, 1910; s. John and Barbara (Schauer) R.; m. Isabel Jones, June 26, 1937; children: Laurens John (dec.), Donald (dec.), Isabel Ferguson. A.B., U. Kans., 1932; A.M., U. Calif., Berkeley, 1934; Ph.D., Columbia U., 1941. Instr. history U. Ark., 1936-37, summer vis. prof., 1947; pre-doctoral field fellow Social Sci. Research Council in Austria and Italy, 1937-38; instr. history Coll. Puget Sound, Tacoma, Wash., 1938-39; head dept. history and polit. sci. Lindenwood Coll., St. Charles, Mo., 1939-41; assoc. prof. history Miss. State Coll. for Women, 1941-43; chief bur. documentary evidence UNRRA Bur. Documents and Tracing, U.S. Zone of Ger., 1945-46; asst. prof. history U. Ga., 1946-47; assoc. prof. history, assoc. editor Jour. Central European Affairs, U. Colo. 1947-51, vis. prof., summer 1958; prof. history U. Tex., Austin, 1951-63; prof. history, chmn. dept. history and polit. sci. Rice U., 1963-68, Mary Gibbs Jones prof., 1968-80, prof. emeritus, 1980—; prof. history U. Minn., Mpls., 1980-85; vis. prof. U. Wis., 1955, Duke U., 1963; Guggenheim fellow in Italy, 1956-57; mem. hist. commn. Theodor Körner Found., also Leopold Kunschak prize com., Vienna, 1971—. Author: The Fall of the Napoleonic Kingdom of Italy, 1941, The Viennese Revolution of 1948, 1957, L'amministrazione austriaca nel Lombardo Veneto, 1814-21, 1959, The Austrian Provisional Regime in Lombardy Venetia, 1969; contbg. author: The Fate of East Central Europe (edited Stephen Kertesz), 1956, East Central Europe and the World (edited S. Kertesz), 1962; also Ency. Americana; founder, editor: Austrian History Newsletter, 1960-63, Austrian History Yearbook, 1965-82; contbr.: Die Aufloesung des Habsburgerreiches, 1970, Native Fascism in the Successor States, 1971, Beitraege zur Zeitgeschichte, 1976, The Austrian Socialist Experiment, 1985, The Mirror of History, 1988. Mem. Twin Cities Coun. Fgn. Relations. Served in AUS, 1943-45. Recipient 1st class Austrian Cross of Honor in arts and scis., 1963. Mem. Am. Hist. Soc. (com. internat. activities 1960-66, exec. com. modern European history sect. 1963-66), So. Hist. Soc. (chmn. European sect. 1961-62, mem. exec. council 1965-68), Soc. Italian Hist. Studies (Sr. Scholar Citation, 1984), Conf. Central European History (mem. nat. exec. bd. 1959-61, vice chmn. 1969, chmn. 1970, mem. com. on Austrian history 1957-68, 70-81, exec. sec. 1957-68), Am. Assn. Study of Hungarian History (chmn. 1978), Southwestern Social Sci. Assn. (pres. 1976-77), Austrian Acad. Sci. (corr.). Deputazione di Storia Patria per le Venezie (corr.), Phi Beta Kappa. Home: 5015 35th Ave S Apt 130 Minneapolis MN 55417-1562

RATH, THOMAS DAVID, lawyer, former state attorney general; b. East Orange, N.J., June 1, 1945; s. Harvey and Helen R.; m. Christine Casey, Dec. 18, 1971; children—Erin, Timothy. A.B., Dartmouth Coll., 1967; J.D., Georgetown U., 1971. Bar: N.J. 1971, N.H. 1972, U.S. Supreme Ct. 1978. Law clk. Judge Clarkson Fisher, U.S. Dist. Ct. N.J., 1971-72; atty. criminal div. Office of Atty. Gen., State of N.H., 1972-73; asst. atty. gen. Office of Atty. Gen., 1973-76, dep. atty. gen., 1976-78, atty. gen., 1978-80; ptnr. Orr & Reno, P.A., Concord, 1980-87, Rath & Young, P.A., Concord, 1987-91; founding ptnr. Rath, Young, Pignatelli & Oyer, P.A., Concord, 1991—; polit. analyst WHDH-TV, Boston, WGBH Pub. TV, Boston, WENH, N.H. Pub. TV, WBUR-Boston Radio. Host State of the State, Yankee Cable Network; co-host Close-Up, WMUR-TV. chmn. campaign Warren B. Rudman for U.S. Senate, 1980, 86; bd. overseers Aquinas House, Dartmouth Coll.; nat. dir. Baker Exploratory Com., 1986-87; sec. bd. trustees Concord Hosp.; treas. N.H. Rep. party, 1981-93; trustee DWC, 1981-87, chmn., 1982-86; mem. Baker Exploratory Com., 1986-87; trustee Concord Hosp., 1980-86; sr. nat. cons. Dole for Pres.; del. Rep. Nat. Conv., 1984, 88, 92, rules com., 1988, 92. Mem. Nat. Assn. Attys. Gen. (vice-chmn. Eastern region, vice chmn. standing com. on energy), N.H. Bar Assn. (Spl. Pres. award 1992). Roman Catholic. Club: Dartmouth (N.Y. or Merrimack County). Office: R Young Pignatelli & Oyer PA 2 Capital Pla PO Box 854 Concord NH 03302-0854

RATHBONE, PERRY TOWNSEND, art museum director; b. Germantown, Pa., July 3, 1911; s. Howard Betts and Beatrice (Connely) R.; m. Euretta de Cosson, Feb. 10, 1945; children: Peter Betts, Eliza, Belinda. A.B., Harvard U., 1933, postgrad., 1933-34; Arts D., Washington U. St. Louis, 1958; L.H.D., Northeastern U., 1960, Suffolk U., Williams Coll., 1970; A.F.D., Bates Coll., 1964, Boston Coll., 1970, R.I. Sch. Design, 1982. Co-dir. Harvard Soc. Contemporary Art, 1931-33; ednl. asst. Detroit Inst. Arts, 1934-36; instr. fine arts Wayne U., Detroit; curator Alger House (suburban br. Detroit Inst. Arts) and gen. rsch. asst. to Dir. Valentiner, 1936-39; asst. to Dir. Valentiner (dir. gen. masterpieces of art), N.Y. World's Fair; later dir.); dir. City Art Mus., St. Louis, 1940-55; dir. Mus. Fine Arts, Boston, 1954-72; dir. Mus. Fine Arts, 1955-72, dir. emeritus, cons., 1972—; dir. Christie's USA, 1973-77; sr. v.p., dir. Christie's Internat., 1977-86; cons. to Christie's Internat., 1987—; Pres. St. Louis Art Commn., 1940-55, St. Louis Little Symphony, 1950-55; adviser council Harvard Found. for Advanced Study and Research, 1953-58; mem. vis. com. Fogg Art Mus., Harvard, 1955-66; mem. U.S. nat. commn. Internat. Council of Museums; adviser program for humanities Ford Found., 1957-73; adviser art com. Chase Manhattan Bank, 1958-76; pres. Met. Boston Arts Center, Inc., 1958-61, chmn. bd., 1961-72; mem. Rockefeller Panel on Performing Arts, 1963-64, Skowhegan Sch. Painting and Sculpture, 1965-77; fine arts vis. com. R.I. Sch. Design, 1966-68, trustee, 1968-74; adviser Urasenke Found., Kyoto, Japan, 1974—; vice chmn. Mass. Art Commn.; v.p. Cosmopolitan Art Found., 1974-13; mem. Cambridge Arts Council, 1978-79, 79—. Author: (with Peter Selz) Great Drawings of All Times, 1962 The Arts and Public Policy in the U.S., chpt. 3, 1984. Mem. bd. overseers Brandeis U., Strawbery Banke, Inc.; trustee Am. Fedn. Arts, 1959-79, New Eng. Conservatory of Music, 1960-80, Boston Arts Festival, Cape Cod Art Assn., Internat. Exhbns. Found., 1965-81, Royal Oak Found., 1974-92, Opera Co. of Boston, 1976-90. Lt. comdr. USNR, 1942-45, PTO. Decorated chevalier Légion d'Honneur; Benjamin Franklin fellow Royal Soc. Art; fellow R.I. Sch. Design, 1981. Mem. Am. Assn. Mus. (v.p. 1960—, coun.), St. Louis

Round Table, Mass. Hist. Soc., Colonial Soc. Mass., Assn. Art Mus. Dirs. (pres. 1959-60, 69-70, trustee 1969-72), Am. Acad. Arts and Scis., Royal Art Soc. London, Phi Beta Kappa (hon. Harvard chpt.), Century Club (N.Y.C.), Tavern Club (Boston), Odd Volumes Club (Boston), Harvard Club (Boston). Episcopalian. Home: Univ Green 130 Mt Auburn St Apt 506 Cambridge MA 02138

RATHBUN, JOHN WILBERT, American studies educator; b. Sioux City, Iowa, Oct. 24, 1924; s. Wilbert W. and Paulina Amanda (Baldes) R.; m. Mary Regina Walsh, Aug. 2, 1947 (div. Sept. 19, 1985); children: Mary Walsh, John Philip. Ph.B., Marquette U., Milw., 1951, M.A., 1952; Ph.D., U. Wis., 1956. Mem. faculty Calif. State U., Los Angeles, 1956—; prof. English/Am. studies Calif. State U., 1959—, chmn. dept. Am. studies, 1969-75, prof. emeritus, 1991—. Author: American Literary Criticism, 1800-1860, vol. 1, 1979, (with Harry Hayden Clark) American Literary Criticism, 1860-1905, vol. 2, 1979, Literature and Literary Analysis, 1983; (with Monica Grecu) American Literary Critics and Scholars, 1800-1850, vol. 1, 1987, 1850-1880, vol. 2, 1880-1900, 1988, vol. 3, 1988; contbr. articles to profl. jours. Served with AUS, 1943-46. Recipient Service citation Calif. State U., Los Angeles, 1977, Univ. Meritorious Achievement award, 1986; Fulbright fellow Romania, 1979-81. Mem. Am. Studies Assn. (council 1974), So. Calif. Am. Studies Assn. (pres. 1973), Coll. English Assn. So. Calif. (pres. 1966-67), MLA. Democrat. Office: 5151 State University Dr Los Angeles CA 90032-4221

RATHER, DAN, broadcast journalist; b. Wharton, Tex., Oct. 31, 1931; m. Jean Goebel; children: Dawn Robin, Danjack. B.A. in Journalism, Sam Houston State Coll., Huntsville, Tex., 1953; student, U. Houston, South Tex. Sch. Law. Instr. journalism Sam Houston State Coll., for 1 year; later worked for U.P.I. and Houston Chronicle; with CBS; joined staff of radio Sta. KTRH (CBS affiliate), Houston; staying about 4 years as news writer, reporter, and later, as news dir.; became dir. news and pub. affairs with CBS Houston TV affiliate KHOU-TV, in the late 1950's; became White House corr., 1964; and then transferred to overseas burs., including chief of London bur., 1965-66, then worked in Vietnam, returned to White House position in fall of 1966; appearing nightly on segments of CBS Evening News; became anchorman-corr. for CBS Reports, 1974-75; co-editor 60 Minutes, CBS-TV, 1975-81; anchorman Dan Rather Reporting, CBS Radio Network, 1977—; Midwest desk CBS news coverage of nat. election night returns, 1972-88; mem. CBS news team nat. polit. convs., 1964—; anchorman, mng. editor CBS Evening News with Dan Rather, 1981—; Writer, sportscaster KSAM-TV; co-editor show Who's Who, CBS-TV, 1977; Anchored numerous CBS News spl. programs including: (with Charles Kuralt) co-anchor, The Moon Above, The Earth Below, 1989; as White House corr. accompanied Pres. on numerous travels, including visits to the Mideast, USSR, People's Republic of China. Author: (with Gary Gates) The Palace Guard, 1974, (with Mickey Herskowitz) The Camera Never Blinks, 1977, The Camera Never Blinks Twice: The Further Adventures of a Television Journalist, 1994, (with Peter Wyden) Memoirs, I Remember, 1991. Recipient numerous Emmy awards; honors include dedication of Dan Rather Comm. Bldg., classroom facility Sam Houston State U., Huntsville, Tex. Office: CBS News 524 W 57th St New York NY 10019-2902

RATHER, LUCIA PORCHER JOHNSON, library administrator; b. Durham, N.C., Sept. 12, 1934; d. Cecil Slayton and Lucia Lockwood (Porcher) Johnson; m. John Carson Rather, July 11, 1964; children: Susan Wright, Bruce Carson. Student, Westhampton Coll., 1951-53; A.B. in History, U. N.C., 1955, M.S. in Library Sci., 1957; PhD in History, George Washington U., 1994. Cataloger Library of Congress, Washington, 1957-64; bibliographer Library of Congress, 1964-66, systems analyst, 1966-70; group head MARC Devel. Office, 1970-73, asst. chief, 1973-76, acting chief, 1976-77, dir. for cataloging, 1976-91; Chmn. standing com. on cataloguing Internat. Fedn. Library Assns., 1976-81; sec. Working Group on Content Designators, 1972-77; chmn. Working Group on Corp. Headings, 1978-79, Internat. ISBD Rev. Com., 1981-87. Co-author: the MARC II Format, 1968. Recipient Libr. Congress Disting. Svc. award, 1991, Disting. Alumnus award U. N.C. Sch. Libr. and Info. Sci., 1992. Mem. ALA (Margaret Mann award 1985, Melvil Dewey award 1991), Phi Beta Kappa. Democrat. Presbyterian. Home: 10308 Montgomery Ave Kensington MD 20895-3327

RATHI, MANOHAR LAL, pediatrician, neonatologist; b. Beawar, Rajasthan, India, Dec. 25, 1933; came to U.S. 1969; s. Bagtawarmal and Sitadevi (Laddha) R.; m. Kamla Jajoo, Feb. 21, 1960; children: Sanjeev A., Rajeev. M.B.B.S., Rajasthan U., 1961. Diplomate Am. Bd. Pediats., sub-bd. Neonatal Perinatal Medicine; lic. physician, N.Y., Ill., Calif. Resident house physician internal medicine Meml. Hosp., Darlington, U.K., 1963-64; resident sr. house physician pediatrics Gen. Hosp., Oldham, U.K., 1964-65; dir. perinatal medicine, attending pediatrician Christ Hosp. Perinatal Ctr., Oak Lawn, Ill., 1974—; assoc. prof. pediatrics Rush Med. Coll., Chgo., 1979—; cons. obstetrician Christ Hosp., Oak Lawn, 1976—; cons. neonatologist Little Co. of Mary Hosp., Evergreen Park, Ill., 1972—, Palos Community Hosp., Palos Heights, Ill., 1978—, Silver Cross Hosp., Joliet, Ill., 1989—; cons./lectr. in field. Contbr. articles to profl. jours.; editor: Clinical Aspects of Perinatal Medicine, 1984, Vol. I, 1985, Vol. II, 1986, Current Perinatology, 1989, Vol. II, 1990; editor with others: Perinatal Medicine Vol. I, 1978, Vol. I, 1980, Vol. II, 1982. Hummell Found. grantee, 1976-77, WyethLab grantee, 1977-78; recipient Physicians Recognition award AMA, 1971-74, 91-92, Outstanding New Citizen's award State of Ill., 1978, Asian Human Svcs. of Chgo., 1988, Nitric Oxide Study by Ohmeda, 1994-95. Fellow Am. Acad. Pediatrics (perinatal sect., treas. Ill. chpt. 1994—); mem. AMA, Chgo. Med. Soc., Ill. Med. Soc., Chgo. Pediatric Soc., Med. Soc. of County of Kings Bklyn., N.Y. Acad. Scis., Am. Thoracic Soc., Soc. Critical Care Medicine. Republican. Hindu. Office: Christ Hosp & Med Ctr Ste N232 4440 W 95th St Oak Lawn IL 60453

RATHJENS, GEORGE WILLIAM, political scientist, educator; b. Fairbanks, Alaska, June 28, 1925; s. George William and Jennie (Hansen) R.; m. Lucy van Buttingha Wichers, Apr. 5, 1950; children: Jacqueline, Leslie, Peter. B.S., Yale U., 1946; Ph.D., U. Calif., Berkeley, 1951. Instr. chemistry Columbia U., 1950-53; staff weapons systems evaluation group Dept. Def., 1953-58; research fellow Harvard U., 1958-59; staff spl. asst. to Pres. U.S. for sci. and tech., 1959-60; chief scientist Advanced Research Projects Agy., Dept. Def., 1961, dep. dir., 1961-62; dep. asst. dir. U.S. ACDA, 1962-64, spl. asst. to dir., 1964-65; dir. weapons systems evaluation div. Inst. Def. Analyses, 1965-68; prof. dept. polit. sci. MIT, 1968—. Fellow Am. Acad. Arts and Scis.; mem. Coun. for Livable World (bd. dirs.), Fedn. Am. Scientists (councilor), Fedn. Am. Scientists Fund (chmn.), Coun. Fgn. Rels., Inst. Strategic Studies. Office: Mass Inst Tech 77 Massachusetts Ave Cambridge MA 02139-4307

RATHKE, SHEILA WELLS, advertising and public relations executive; b. Columbia, S.C., Aug. 9, 1943; d. Walter John and Betty Marie (McLaughlin) Wells; m. David Bray Rathke, Sept. 1966 (div. Apr. 1977); 1 child, Erinn Michele. BA summa cum laude, U. Pitts., 1976, postgrad., 1976-77. Loan coord. Equibank, Pitts., 1961-65; office mgr. US Steel Corp., Pitts., 1966-70; various account and mgmt. positions Burson-Marsteller, Pitts., 1977-87, exec. v.p., gen. mgr., 1987-94; CEO Can. ops. Burson-Marsteller, Toronto, Montreal, Ottawa, Vancouver, 1994—; also bd. dirs. Burson-Marsteller Americas; bd. dirs. Y & R Group of Cos., Can.; instr. Slippery Rock Coll., Pitts., 1984-85; adviser Exec. Report Mag., Pitts., 1986-88. Trustee U. Pitts., 1976-80; mem. alumni bd. dirs., trustee Robert Morris Coll., 1992—; bd. dirs. Vocat. Rehab. Ctr., 1987-93, Freewheeelers, 1989-92, Pitts. Hist. Soc., River City Brass Band. Named Disting. Alumnus, U. Pitts., 1992. Mem. Female Execs. Am., Am. Assn. Advt. Agys. (chair ea. region 1994-95), Pitts. Advt. Club (bd. dirs. 1988-91, pres. 1990), Alpha Sigma Lambda (charter). Avocations: skiing, reading, gardening, traveling, music. Home: 15 Marquette Rd Pittsburgh PA 15229-1766 Office: Burson-Marsteller, 80 Bloor St W, Toronto, ON Canada M5S 2V1 office: Burson-Marsteller One Gateway Center #2000 Pittsburgh PA 15222

RATHMAN, WILLIAM ERNEST, lawyer, minister; b. Middletown, Ohio, Jan. 10, 1927; s. Ernest Daniel and Marguerite (Sebald) R.; m. Constance Schedler, Nov. 28, 1958; children: Marchie, William E. Jr. Grad., Phillips Exeter Acad., 1944; BA, Kenyon Coll., 1948; postgrad., Harvard U., 1950, Ohio State U. Coll. of Law, 1951, United Theol. Seminary, Dayton, Ohio, 1975. Bar: Ohio 1952; ordained to ministry Episc. Ch., 1975. Pvt. practice law Middletown, Ohio, 1952-78; sr. ptnr. Rathman, Elliott & Boyd, Middletown, 1979-84, Rathman, Combs, Schaefer, Valen & Kaup, Middletown, 1985-88, Rathman, Combs, Schaefer & Kaup, Middletown, 1989—; spl. counsel to County of Butler, 1956-64, City of Middletown, 1965-66, Ohio Atty. Gen., 1967-69; acting judge Middletown Mcpl. Ct., 1969-74. Pres. Middletown Community Found., 1972-76, Middletown Chamber Found., 1977-80, Butler County Park Commn., 1986-90; trustee-at-large Ohio Found. of Ind. Colls., Columbus, 1972-90; trustee, mem. exec. com. Middletown United Way, 1983-90; trustee Middleton Req. Hosp. Found., 1986-90; adv. bd. Middletown campus Miami U., 1984-90. With USN, 1944-46, capt. USAF, 1959, comdr. Am. Legion, 1965. Named Exec. Yr., Middletown chpt. Nat. Secs. Assn., 1969; recipient Outstanding Community Svc. award Middletown post Am. Legion, 1975, Outstanding Svc. award Parstoral Counselling Svc., 1983, Vol. of Yr. award Middletown Area United Way, 1986. Fellow Am. Coll. Trust and Estate Counsel; mem. ABA (estate tax com. 1966-69), Ohio Bar Assn. (coun. dels. 1980-93), Butler County Bar Assn. (pres. 1980), Middletown Bar Assn. (pres. 1967), Fed. Bar Assn. (pres. Cin. chpt. 1975), Ohio State Bar Found. (trustee 1992—), City Club (Hamilton, Ohio), Moraine Country Club (Dayton), Jefferson Lodge, Browns Run Country Club, Masons (master 1959-60), Scottish Rite Valley of Cin. (treas. 1986, 33rd degree mason 1988—, chmn. bd. 1990), Bankers Club. Republican. Episcopalian. Home: 501 Thornhill Ln Middletown OH 45042-3750 Office: Rathman Combs Schaefer & Kaup 2 N Main St Middletown OH 45042-1918

RATHMANN, GEORGE BLATZ, genetic engineering company executive; b. Milw., Dec. 25, 1927; s. Louis and Edna Lorle (Blatz) R.; m. Frances Joy Anderson, June 24, 1950; children: James, Margaret, Laura, Sally, Richard. BS with honors, Northwestern U., 1948; MS, Princeton U., 1950, PhD in Phys. Chemistry, 1952. With 3M Co., St. Paul, 1951-72, various positions including rsch. chemist, rsch. dir., group tech. dir., mgr. X-ray products; with Litton Med. Systems, Des Plaines, Ill., 1972-75; v.p. R & D diagnostics div. Abbott Labs., North Chicago, Ill., 1975-80; pres., chief exec. officer Amgen Inc., Thousand Oaks, Calif., 1980-88; chmn. Amgen Inc., Newbury Park, Calif., 1988—; chmn. ICUS Corp., 1990—. Mem. AAAS, Am. Chem. Soc., Indsl. Biotech. Assn. (bd. dirs.), Phi Beta Kappa, Sigma Xi. Office: Amgen Ctr Thousand Oaks CA 91320*

RATHORE, NAEEM GUL, United Nations official, retired; b. Lahore, Punjab, Pakistan, Nov. 21, 1931; arrived in country, 1950; s. Jalaluddin and Zohra (Butt) R.; m. Carol Salima, Sept. 19, 1951; 1 child, Amna Elona. BS, Mich. U., 1952; MA in Polit. Sci., Columbia U., 1955, PhD in Internat. Affairs, 1965. Dir. personnel and adminstrn. UNRWA, Beirut, 1975-76; exec. sec. Internat. Civil Svc. Commn. UN, N.Y.C., 1980-81; sec. First Com., 1980-84, asst. dir. Office Under-Sec. Gen./Dept. Polit. Affairs, 1984-87, chief Div. of Palestinian Rights, 1987-89, acting dir. Dept. Polit. Affairs, 1983—; coord. Pakistan Expatriates in UN Systems, 1992—; adviser to the Pakistan amb., and permanent rep. of Pakistan, 1994—; advisor to speaker Punjab Assembly, Lahore, Pakistan, 1994—; lectr. Pakistan studies Near and Mid. E. Inst., Columbia U., N.Y., 1954-55; prof., head dept. internat. affairs U. Islamabad, 1974; active numerous coms., panels and task forces with Office of Human Resources Mgmt., UN, field including chmn. N.Y. Gen. Svc. Classification Appeals and Rev. Com., 1986-92; pres. FICSA, 1971-74; chmn. UN staff com. 1971-74; active External Exam. in Polit. Affairs (France, Japan, others.). Author: In Defense of the International Civil Service: Statements and Submission, 1974, United Nations Secretariat: Problems and Prospects, 1974, other publs. in field; contbr. articles to profl. jours. Mem. Fedn. of Nat. Civil Svcs. (pres. 1971-74). Muslim. Avocations: reading, writing newspaper columns, horseback riding, scuba diving, swimming. Home: 1305 Elm St Concord MA 01742

RATHWELL, PETER JOHN, lawyer; b. Windsor, Ont., Can., Aug. 20, 1943; came to U.S., 1947; s. Harold Wilfred and Jean Isabel (Lucas) R.; m. Ann Wickstrom Williams, Sept. 10, 1977; 1 child, James Michael. BA, U. Ariz., 1965, JD, 1968. Bar: Ariz. 1968. Assoc. Boettcher, Crowder & Schoolitz, Scottsdale, Ariz., 1972-73; ptnr. Snell & Wilmer, Phoenix, 1973—; seminar lectr. Nat. Bus. Inst. Inc., 1987-90. Mem. exec. com. Jr. Achievement Ctrl. Ariz., Phoenix, 1980-92; chmn. scholarship fund St. Mary H.S., 1982-91; mem., chmn. Phoenix Parks Bd., 1982-87; trustee Orme Sch., 1991—. Capt. JAGC, USAF, 1969-72. Fellow State Bar Ariz. Found. (founding mem.), Maricopa County Bar Found. (founding mem.); mem. Am. Bankruptcy Inst., Ariz. Bar Assn. (chmn. discipline hearing com. 1987-93, mem. bankruptcy sect.), Maricopa County Bar Assn. (seminar lectr. 1987), Comml. Law League, Am. Phoenix Zoo Wildlest Club in Town (founding mem. 1972). Republican. Avocations: fishing, raising cattle, riding, stamp collecting. Home: 4523 E Mountain View Rd Phoenix AZ 85028-5213 Office: Snell & Wilmer 1 Arizona Ctr Phoenix AZ 85004

RATKOWSKI, DONALD J., mechanical engineer, consultant; b. Cleve., July 29, 1938; m. Joyce Ellen Kotlarczyk, July 15, 1961; children: Rhonda, Tamyra, Cheryl, Randall. Student, Ariz. State U.; AAS, Alliance Coll. 1959, DSc (hon.), 1986. Sr. project engr. semiconductor products div. Motorola, 1960-70, 75-77; v.p. engring. Danker & Wohlk, 1970-75; founder, pres. Paragon Optical Inc., 1976-90; exec. v.p. Pilkinton Vision Care, 1987-90, cons., 1990-91; pres. DJR Resources Inc., Chandler, Ariz., 1990—; mem. adv. bd. Am. Soc. Coun., 1988-89; mem. steering com. Optometry Coll., Marcinkowski Acad. Medicine, Poland, 1989-91; founder Rigid Gas Permeable Lens Inst., 1985; speaker Nat. Contact Lens Examiners, 1984-91. Contbr. articles to profl. jours.; patentee in field. Sustaining mem. Rep. Nat. Com., 1983-90; mem. U.S. Congl. Adv. Bd., 1990. Recipient Alumnus of Yr. award Alliance Coll., 1985. Mem. Opticians Assn. Am. (assoc. mem. adv. coun. 1987-88), Contact Lens Soc. Am. (bd. dirs. 1986-88, founder scholarship program 1988, hon. chmn. steering com. edn. fund 1989-91), Contact Lens Mfrs. Assn. (chmn. external communication com. 1981-90, bd. dirs. 1982-84, Trailblazer award 1987, program chmn. 1989-90, Leonardo DaVinci award 1990), Ariz. Soc. Plastic Engrs. bd. dirs. 1976-78, 83, v.p. 1980-81, pres. 1981-82), Sigma Tau Gamma (Outstanding Alumni award 1985). Home: 31 E Oakwood Hills Dr Chandler AZ 85248-6200 Office: DJR Resources Inc 574 E Alamo Dr Ste 60 Chandler AZ 85225

RATLIFF, CHARLES EDWARD, JR., economics educator; b. Morven, N.C., Oct. 13, 1926; s. Charles Edward and Mary Katherine (Liles) R.; m. Mary Virginia Heilig, Dec. 8, 1945; children: Alice Ann, Katherine Virginia, John Charles. B.S., Davidson Coll., 1947; A.M., Duke U., 1951, Ph.D., 1955; postgrad., U. N.C., Harvard, Columbia. Instr. econs. and bus. Davidson Coll., 1947-48, asst. prof. 1948-49; scholar econs. Duke, 1949-51; mem. faculty Davidson (N.C.) Coll., 1951—, prof., 1960—, chmn. dept. econs., 1966-83, Charles A. Dana prof., 1967-77, William R. Kenan prof., 1977-92, prof. emeritus, 1992—; prof. econs. Forman Christian Coll., Lahore, Pakistan, 1963-66, 69-70; summer vis. prof. U. N.C. at Charlotte, 1958, 60, Appalachian State U., 1962, Punjab, Pakistan, 1963-64, Kinnaird Coll., Pakistan, 1965, Fin. Svcs. Acad., Pakistan, 1966, NDEA Inst. in Asian History, 1968; lectr. U.S. Cultural Affairs Office, East and West Pakistan, 1969-70. Author: Interstate Apportionment of Business Income for State Income Tax Purposes, 1962, A World Development Fund, 1987, Economics at Davidson: A Sesquicentennial History, 1987; co-author textbooks and monographs; contbg. author: Dictionary of the Social Sciences, Distinguished Teachers on Effective Teaching, 1986, Those Who Teach, 1988, Britain-USA: A Survey in Key Words, 1991; mem. editorial bd. Growth and Change: A Journal of Urban and Regional Policy, 1993—; contbr. articles to profl. jours. Mem. Mayor's Com. Cmty. Rels., Davidson, 1973-80, chmn., 1973-78; mem. Mecklenburg County Housing and Devel. Commn., 1975-81; mem. exec. com. Mecklenburg Dem. Com., 1967-69, precinct com., 1967-69, 72-74, 89—, issues com. 1979—, nat. bd. dirs. Rural Advancement Fund Nat. Sharecroppers Fund, Inc., 1978-94, exec. com., 1990-94, treas., 1981-94; mem. Mecklenburg County Cmty. and Rural Devel. Exec. Com., 1981—; bd. dirs. Bread for the World, Inc., 1983-84, Pines Retirement Cmty., 1990—, Crisis Assistance Ministry, 1992—, Davidson Coll. Devel. Corp., 1992-95; bd. advisors Mecklenburg Ministries, 1992—. Ford Found. rsch. grantee, 1969-70, Fulbright-Hays grantee, 1973; rsch. fellow Inter-Univ. Com. Econ. Rsch. on South, 1960-61; recipient Thomas Jefferson award Davidson Coll., 1972, Gold medalist Prof. of Yr. award Coun. Advancement and Support of Edn., 1985, Teaching Excellence and Campus Leadership award Sears Roebuk Found., 1991, Hunter-Hamilton Love of Teaching award, 1992. Mem. AAUP, So. Econ. Assn. (exec. com. 1961-63, v.p. 1975-76, N.C. curr. So. Econ. Jour.), Am. Econ. Assn., So. Fin. Assn. (exec. com. 1966-68), Nat. Tax Assn. (chmn. interstate allocation and apportionment of bus. income

com. 1972-74), Assn. Asian Studies, Fulbright Alumni Assn., Old Catawba Soc., Phi Beta Kappa, Omicron Delta Kappa (Teaching award 1991). Home: 301 Pinecrest St PO Box 597 Davidson NC 28036-0597

RATLIFF, FLOYD, biophysics educator, scientist; b. La Junta, Colo., May 1, 1919; s. Charles Frederick and Alice (Hubbard) R.; m. Orma Vernon Priddy, June 10, 1942; 1 child, Merry Alice. BA magna cum laude, Colo. Coll., 1947, DSc (hon.), 1975; MS, Brown U., 1949, PhD, 1950; NRC postdoctoral fellow, Johns Hopkins, 1950-51. Instr., then asst. prof. Harvard U., 1951-54; assoc. Rockefeller Inst., 1954-58; mem. faculty Rockefeller U., 1958-89, prof. biophysics and physiol. psychology, 1966-89, prof. emeritus, 1989—, head lab. biophysics, 1974-86; pres. Harry Frank Guggenheim Found., N.Y.C., 1983-89, bd. dirs., 1983—; rsch. assoc. Sch. Am. Rsch., Santa Fe, N.Mex., 1989—; cons. to govt., 1957-89, to John D. and Catherine T. MacArthur Found., 1986. Author: Mach Bands: Quantitative Studies on Neural Networks in the Retina, 1965, Paul Signac and Color in Neo-Impressionism, 1992, also articles; editor: Studies on Excitation and Inhibition in the Retina, 1974; editorial bd.: Jour. Gen. Physiology, 1969-86. Bd. dirs. Esperanza, Santa Fe, 1990-93, pres., 1992-93. Served to 1st lt. AUS, 1941-45, ETO. Decorated Bronze Star; recipient Howard Crosby Warren medal Soc. Exptl. Psychologists, 1966; Edgar D. Tillyer medal Optical Soc. Am., 1976; medal for disting. service Brown U., 1980; Pisart Vision award N.Y. Assn. for Blind, 1983. Fellow AAAS; mem. NAS, Am. Inst. Physics, Am. Psychol. Assn. (disting. sci. contbn. award 1984), Am. Psychol. Soc. (William James fellow 1989), Manhattan Philos. Soc., Internat. Brain Rsch. Orgh., Am. Philos. Soc., China Inst. Am., Oriental Ceramic Soc. (London), Oriental Ceramic Soc. (Hong Kong), 20th Century Chinese Ceramic Soc., Asia Soc., Japan Soc., Phi Beta Kappa, Sigma Xi. Home: 2215 Calle Cacique Santa Fe NM 87505-4944

RATLIFF, GERALD LEE, dean, speech and theatre educator; b. Middletown, Ohio, Oct. 23, 1944; s. Ray and Peggy (Donisi) R. BA magna cum laude, Georgetown (Ky.) Coll., 1967; MA, U. Cin., 1970; PhD, Bowling Green (Ohio) State U., 1975. Area head English theatre Glenville State Coll., 1970-72; prof., chair theatre Montclair State Coll., Upper Montclair, N.J., 1975-92; dean Sch. Fine and Performing Arts Ind.-Purdue U., Ft. Wayne, Ind., 1993-95; dean Coll. Arts and Architect Mont. State U., Bozeman, Mont., 1995—; feature writer Lexington (Ky.) Herald-News, 1967-68. Author: Beginning Scene Study: Aristophanes to Albee, 1980, Speech and Drama Club Activities, 1982, Oedipus Trilogy, 1984, Combating Stagefright, 1985, Playscript Interpretation and Production, 1985, (Machiavelli's) The Prince, 1986, (with Suzanne Trauth) Introduction to Musical Theatre, 1986, Playing Scenes: A Sourcebook for Performance, 1993; contbr. articles and revs. to profl. jours. Fulbright scholar, 1989; recipient Nat. Medallion of Honor award Theta Alpha Phi, 1989; Alumni Assn. faculty rsch. grantee, 1980, 83, 86. Mem. Speech Communication Assn. (legis. coun. 1987-88, chair theatre div. 1986-87), Am. Assn. Theatre in Secondary Edn. (nat. bd. dirs. 1986-87), Secondary Sch. Theatre Assn. (nat. bd. dirs. 1983-86), Internat. Arts Assn. (v.p. 1975-76), Eastern Communication Assn. (exec. sec. 1986-89, 1st v.p. elect 1989, exec. com. 1986—, pres. 1991, Disting. Svc. award 1993), Theta Alpha Phi (nat. pres. 1984-87, nat. coun. 1979-82, 84-87). Avocations: writing, softball. Office: Coll Arts & Architect Mont State U Cheever Hall Bozeman MT 59715

RATLIFF, JACK, law educator; b. 1934. LLB, U. Tex., 1962. Bar: Tex. 1962, N.Mex. 1983. Atty. Kemp, Smith, et al, El Paso, Tex., 1962-71; pres. Equity Control Corp., El Paso, 1971-73; atty. Ratliff, Haynes & Stading, El Paso, 1973-79; pvt. practice law El Paso, 1979-83; from vis. prof. to prof. law U. Tex., Austin, 1983—, Sewall Chair in Law, 1992—. Robert W. Calvert faculty fellow in law, 1990—. Office: U Tex Sch Law 727 E 26th St Austin TX 78705-3224

RATLIFF, LOUIS JACKSON, JR., mathematics educator; b. Cedar Rapids, Iowa, Sept. 1, 1931; s. Louis Jackson and Ruth Sara (Sidlinger) R. BA, State U. Iowa, 1953, MA, 1958, PhD, 1961. Lectr. Ind. U., Bloomington, 1961-63, U. Calif., Riverside, 1963-64; asst. prof. math. U. Calif., 1964-67, assoc. prof., 1967-69, prof., 1969—. Author: Chain Conjectures in Ring Theory, 1978; assoc. editor Procs. of AMS, 1987-92, Comm. in Algebra, 1990-95; contbr. articles to profl. jours. 1st lt. USAF, 1953-57. NSF fellow, 1960-62, grantee, 1965-69, 71-88; recipient Disting. Teaching award, U. Calif.-Riverside, 1983. Mem. Am. Math. Soc., Phi Beta Kappa. Democrat. Seventh Day Adventist. Home: 3139 Newell Dr Riverside CA 92507-3147 Office: U Calif Dept Math Riverside CA 92521

RATLIFF, WILLIAM D., III, lawyer; b. Ft. Worth, Aug. 25, 1949; s. William D. and Barbara (Warner) R.; m. Julie Martin, Oct. 4, 1980; children: William D., Emily Martin. B.B.A., U. Tex., 1971, J.D., 1974; LL.M., So. Meth. U., 1975. Law clk. U.S. Tax Ct., Washington, 1975-77; mem. Cantey, Hanger, Gooch, Munn & Collins, Ft. Worth, 1977-84, Haynes and Boone, Ft. Worth, 1984—. Fellow Am. Coll. Trust and Estate Counsel, Tex. Bd. Legal Specialization (cert.), Tex. Bar Found.; mem. ABA, State Bar Tex. Republican. Clubs: Ft. Worth, Rivercrest Country. Office: Haynes and Boone 1300 Burnett Plz Fort Worth TX 76102

RATLIFF, WILLIAM DURRAH, JR., lawyer; b. Gainesville, Tex., Nov. 17, 1921; s. William Durrah and Fay (Tippit) R.; m. Barbara Warner, June 20, 1947; children: William Durrah III, Robert Warner, Bryan Prichard, Barbara Louise, Edwin Brent, Dorothy Jeanne. B.B.A., U. Tex., 1943, LL.B., 1948. Bar: Tex. 1948; cert. in estate planning and probate law, Tex. Ptnr. Shannon, Gracey, Ratliff & Miller, 1968-90, of counsel, 1991—; bd. dirs. Aztec Mfg. Co. Bd. dirs. Southwestern Expn. and Livestock Show. Fellow Tex. Bar Found. (sustaining life). Am. Coll. Trust and Estate Counsel. Clubs: River Crest Country, Fort Worth. Home: 5820 El Campo Ave Fort Worth TX 76107-4640 Office: Ste 1600 500 Throck Morton Fort Worth TX 76102

RATMANSKY, ALEXEI, dancer; b. St. Petersburg, Russia. Studied with A. Markeyeva, Pyotr Pestov, Moscow Bolshoi Ballet Sch.; grad. choreographer's divsn., Moscow State Inst. Theatrical Arts, 1992. Dancer Kiev Ballet, 1986-88, prin. dancer, 1988-92; soloist Royal Winnipeg (Man., Can.) Ballet, 1992—; guest artist Ballet Nat. du Québec. Dance performances include Tarantella (George Ballanchine), Spectre de la Rose (Michel Fokine), Giselle (Peter Wright), La Sylphide, Cinderella, Square Dance (Ballanchine), Tchaikovsky Pas de Deux (Ballanchine), Lilac Garden (Antony Tudor), La Bayadere Act II (Petipa), Nutcracker (John Neumeier), Romeo and Juliet (Rudi van Dantzig), Don Quixote, Pas de Dix (Ballanchine). Recipient First prize Second Nat. Ballet Competition, Donietsk, Russia, 1987, Vaslav Nijinsky prize First Internat. Diaghilev Ballet Competition, Moscow, 1992, 2nd prize for choreography Serge Lifar Ballet Competition, 1994; named Honored Artist of Ukraine, 1992. Office: Royal Winnipeg Ballet, 380 Graham Ave, Winnipeg, MB Canada R3C 4K2*

RATNER, ALBERT B., building products company executive, land developer; b. Cleve., 1927. Grad., Mich. State U., 1951. With Forest City Enterprises, Inc., Cleve., 1964—, sec., 1960-68, exec. v.p., from 1968, now pres., chief exec. officer, dir.; mem. exec. com., dir. Univ. Circle Devel. Corp.; dir. Am. Greetings Corp. Mem. Internat. Council Shopping Ctrs. Office: Forest City Enterprises Inc 10800 Brookpark Rd Cleveland OH 44130-1199

RATNER, BUDDY DENNIS, bioengineer, educator; b. Bklyn., Jan. 19, 1947; s. Philip and Ruth Ratner; m. Teri Ruth Stoller, July 7, 1968; 1 child, Daniel Martin. BS in Chemistry, Bklyn. Coll., 1967; PhD in Polymer Chemistry, Polytech. Inst. Bklyn., 1972. Postdoctoral fellow U. Wash., Seattle, 1972-73, from rsch. assoc. to assoc. prof., 1973-86, prof., 1986—; dir. Nat. ESCA and Surface Analysis Ctr., Seattle, 1984—. Editor: Surface Characterization of Biomaterials, 1989, Plasmas and Polymers, 1994—; mem. editl. bds. 8 jours. and book series; contbr. more than 200 articles to profl. jours. Recipient faculty achievement/outstanding rsch. award Burlington Resources Found., 1990, Perkin Elmer Phys. Electronics award for excellence in surface sci.; grantee NIH. Fellow Am. Inst. Med. Biol. Engring. (founder), Am. Vacuum Soc., Soc. for Biomaterials (pres. 1991, 92, Clemson award 1989); mem. AAAS, AIChE, Adhesion Soc., Am. Chem. Soc., Internat. Soc. Contact Lens Rsch. (coun. mem.), Materials Rsch. Soc. Achievements include 10 patents in field. Office: U Wash Dept Chem Engring Box 351750 Seattle WA 98195

RATNER, DAVID LOUIS, legal educator; b. London, Sept. 2, 1931. AB magna cum laude, Harvard U., 1952, LLB magna cum laude, 1955. Bar: N.Y. 1955. Assoc. Sullivan & Cromwell, N.Y.C., 1955-64; assoc. prof. Cornell Law Sch., Ithaca, N.Y., 1964-68, prof., 1968-82; prof. law U. San Francisco Law Sch., 1982—, dean, 1982-89; exec. asst. to chmn. SEC, Washington, 1966-68; chief counsel Securities Industry Study, Senate Banking Com., Washington, 1971-73; vis. prof. Stanford (Calif.) U., 1974, Ariz. State U., Tempe, 1974, U. San Francisco, 1980, Georgetown U., Washington, 1989-90, U. Calif., Hastings, San Francisco, 1992; mem. Larkspur (Calif.) Planning Commn., 1992—. Fulbright scholar Monash U., Australia, 1981. Author: Securities Regulation; Cases and Materials, 4th edit., 1991, Securities Regulation in a Nutshell, 4th edit., 1992, Institutional Investors: Teaching Materials, 1978. Fellow Royal Soc. Arts (London); mem. Am. Law Inst., Cosmos Club (Washington), Phi Beta Kappa. Home: 84 Polhemus Way Larkspur CA 94939-1928 Office: U San Francisco Law Sch 2130 Fulton St San Francisco CA 94117-1080

RATNER, ELLEN FAITH, radio talk show host, writer; b. Cleve., Aug. 28, 1951; d. Harry Ramer and Anne Spott. BA, Goddard Coll., 1974; EdM, Harvard U., 1978. Coord. women's svcs. Homophile Comty. Health Svc., Boston, 1971-73; co-dir., co-founder Boundaries Therapy Ctr., Acton, Mass., 1973-86; dir. psychiat. day treatment program South Shore Mental Health Ctr., Quincy, Mass., 1974-81; v.p. rsch., devel. and svc., dir. ARC Rsch. Found. Addiction Recovery Corp., Rockville, Mass., 1986-90; health care cons., dir. Found. for Addiction Rsch., 1990-94; pres. Talk Radio News Svc., White House corr. Good Day USA "The Washington Reality Check", Washington, 1991—; tchr. dept. psychiatry Tufts U. Med. Sch., 1973; tchr. Curry Coll., Milton, Mass., 1979-80; cons. program devel. Addiction Recovery Corp., 1984-86; developer, planner The Art's in Mileau Treatment of Psychiatric Outpatients, Quincy, 1980, New Eng.'s first conf. on Chem. Dependency and AIDS, 1988. Author: The Other Side of the Family: A Book for Recovery from Abuse, Incest and Neglect, 1990; appeared on nat. TV and radio shows including C-SPAN, The Oprah Winfrey Show, CNN, Nat. Empowerment TV, others; mem. adv. bd. The Counselor Mag., 1987-90. Bd. trustees, mem. exec. com., vis. com. presdl. search com. Goddard Coll., Plainfield, Vt., 1977-81; adv. com. minority women and AIDS Ctr. for Constitutional Rights, N.Y.C., 1988-89; bd. trustees Samaritan Coll., L.A., 1988-90; bd. dirs. Nat. Lesbian and Gay Health Found., Washington, 1985-92, pres., exec. com., program com., program chair; v.p. Harry Ratner Human Svcs. Fund, Cleve., 1991—; mem. adv. bd. Women of Washington, Inc., 1992—; bd. dirs. Theater Chamber Players, Kennedy Ctr., Washington, 1988-92, An Uncommon Legacy Found., N.Y.C., 1993—, The Ctr. for Spiritual Enlightenment, Falls Church, Va., 1994—. Recipient Comty. Svc. award Lesbian and Gay Counseling Svc., Boston, 1985, The Addams-Brown award Nat. Lesbian and Gay Health Found., 1993. Mem. Nat. Assn. Radio Talk Show Hosts, Mass. Assn. Day Treatment Adminstrs. (chair regulations and standards com. 1979-81), Lily Dale Assembly. Democrat. Spiritualist. Avocation: writing works on spiritualism. Office: Talk Radio News Svc 2514 Mill Rd NW Washington DC 20007

RATNER, GERALD, lawyer; b. Chgo., Dec. 17, 1913; s. Peter I. and Sarah (Soreson) R.; m. Eunice Payton, June 18, 1948. PhB, U. Chgo., 1935, JD cum laude, 1937. Bar: Ill. 1937. Since practiced in Chgo.; sr. ptnr. Gould & Ratner and predecessor firm, 1949—; officer Henry Crown & Co., CC Industries, Inc., Material Svc. Corp., Freeman United Coal Mining Co., Mineral and Land Resources Corp.; lectr., writer on real estate law; mem. vis. com. for Law Sch., U. Chgo. Capt. AUS, 1942-46. Mem. ABA, Ill. Bar Assn., Chgo. Bar Assn., Order of Coif, Phi Beta Kappa. Home: 900 N Lake Shore Dr Apt 2902 Chicago IL 60611-1525 Office: 222 N La Salle St Chicago IL 60601

RATNER, HARVEY, professional basketball team owner; m. Barbara Ratner; children: Mark, Edward, David, Rachel. Co-founder Northwest Racquet, Swim and Health Clubs, Minn., 1963—; co-owner Minn. Timberwolves (NBA), Mpls., 1989—. Supporter numerous Mpls.-St. Paul charities including Crisis Nursery Ctr., Groves Learning Ctr., Mpls. Children's Med. Ctr., Intervarsity Christian Fellowship, Mpls. Fedn., also arts orgns. Office: Minn Timberwolves Target Ctr 600 1st Ave N Minneapolis MN 55403

RATNER, MARINA, mathematician, educator, researcher; b. Moscow, Oct. 30. MA, Moscow State U., PhD. Asst. High Tech. Engring. Sch. Moscow, 1969-71; lectr. Hebrew U., Jerusalem, 1971-74; sr. tchr. pre-acad. sch., 1974-75; from acting asst. prof. to assoc. prof. U. Calif., Berkeley, 1975-82, prof., 1982—. Alfred P. Sloan rsch. fellow, 1977-79, Miller rsch. prof., 1985-86, John Simon Guggenheim fellow, 1987-88. Mem. NAS (John J. Carty Medal for the Advancement of Science, 1994), AAAS. Office: Univ California Ctr Pure & Applied Math Berkeley CA 94720

RATNER, MARK ALAN, chemistry educator; b. Cleve., Dec. 8, 1942; s. Max and Betty (Wohlvert) R.; m. Nancy Ball, June 19, 1969; children—Stacy, Daniel. A.B., Harvard U., 1964; Ph.D., Northwestern U., 1969; Amanuensis (hon.), Aarhus U., Denmark, 1970; Akad Rat (hon.), Tech. U., Munich, W. Ger., 1971. Asst. prof. NYU, 1971-75; prof. chemistry Northwestern U., Evanston, Ill., 1975—, Dow rsch. prof., 1988-90; cons. U.S. Army, Huntsville, Ala., 1973-75; lectr. IBM, Yorktown Heights, N.Y., 1973; dir. Electrochem. Industries, Israel, 1980—; assoc. dean arts and scis. Northwestern U., Evanston, 1980-84; vis. prof. Rush Presbyn. Sch. Medicine, 1990—. Contbr. numerous articles and manuscripts to profl. jours. Bd. dirs. Hillel Found., Evanston, 1984—. Fellow A.P. Sloan Found., 1973-76, Inst. Advanced Study, Israel, 1979. Fellow AAAS, Am. Phys. Soc.; mem. Am. Chem. Soc., Rumplestiltskin Soc., Sigma Xi. Jewish. Avocations: scientific education; canoeing; conservation. Home: 615 Greenleaf Ave Glencoe IL 60022-1745 Office: Northwestern U Chemistry Dept 2145 Sheridan Rd Evanston IL 60208-0002

RATNER, MAX, building products company executive, land developer; b. Bialystok, Poland, 1907; m. Betty Ratner; children—Charles, Mark, James, Ronald. J.D., Cleve. Marshall Law Sch. With Forest City Enterprises, Inc., Cleve., 1928—, chmn. bd., 1974—, dir.; pres., bd. dirs. Am. Electrochem. Industries (Frutarom), Ltd., Israel; bd. dirs. Banc One, Cleve. Trustee, past v.p. Jewish Community Fedn.; bd. dirs. Am. Friends Hebrew U., Jewish Theol. Sem., Greater Cleve. Growth Assn., Technion U., Theol. Sem.; trustee Mt. Sinai Hosp.; founder, past bd. dirs. Suburban Hosp.; chmn. bd., past pres. Am.-Israel C. of C. Recipient Scopus award, Eisenman award Am. Friends Hebrew U.; Ohio Gov.'s award, 1980. Office: Forest City Enterprises Inc 10800 Brookpark Rd Cleveland OH 44130-1199

RATNER, RHODA SUE, librarian; b. Bklyn., Apr. 25, 1935; d. Leon Elias and Anne Ella (Nissenbaum) Mitteldorf; m. Fredric Beryl Ratner, Dec. 25, 1954 (div. 1983); children—Jessica, Deborah, Judith. A.A., Montgomery Coll., 1974; B.A., U. Md., 1976; M.L.S., 1978. Chief librarian mus. reference ctr. Smithsonian Instn., Washington, 1978-82, chief librarian Nat. Mus. Am. History, 1982—. Editor proceedings panels on libraries in mus.', 1980-83. Leader Montgomery County council Girl Scouts Am., 1968-72. Mem. Am. Libraries Assn., Am. Assn. Mus.' (chmn. ad hoc com. 1979—). Democrat. Jewish. Clubs: NAAMAT U.S.A. (council pres.), Jewish Community Council (exec. bd.). (Washington). Office: Smithsonian Instn Nat Museum Am History 10th and Constitution Ave NW Washington DC 20560

RATNOFF, OSCAR DAVIS, physician, educator; b. N.Y.C., Aug. 23, 1916; s. Hyman L. and Ethel (Davis) R.; m. Marian Foreman, Mar. 31, 1945; children: William Davis, Martha. A.B., Columbia U., 1936, M.D., 1939; LL.D. (hon.), U. Aberdeen, 1981. Intern Johns Hopkins Hosp., Balt., 1939-40; Austin fellow in physiology Harvard Med. Sch., Boston, 1940-41; asst. resident Montefiore Hosp., N.Y.C., 1942; resident Goldwater Meml. Hosp., N.Y.C., 1942-43; asst. in medicine Columbia Coll. Physicians and Surgeons, N.Y.C., 1942-46; fellow in medicine Johns Hopkins, 1946-48, instr. medicine, 1948-50, instr. bacteriology, 1949-50; asst. prof. medicine Western Res. U., Cleve., 1950-56; assoc. prof. Case Western Res. U., 1956-61, prof., 1961—; asst. physician (Univ. Hosp.), Cleve., 1952-56; assoc. physician (Univ. Hosp.), 1956-67, physician, 1967—. Author: Bleeding Syndromes, 1960; mem. editorial bd. Jour. Lab. Clin. Medicine, 1956-62, assoc. editor, 1986-91; editor: Treatment of Hemorrhagic Disorders, 1968, (with C. D. Forbes) Disorders of Hemostasis, 1984, 2d edit., 1991; mem. editorial bd. Circulation, 1961-65, Blood, 1963-69, 78-81, Am. Jour. Physiology, 1966-72, Jour.

Applied Physiology, 1966-72, Jour. Lipid Rsch., 1967-69, Jour. Clin. Investigation, 1969-71, Circulation Rsch., 1970-75, Annals Internal Medicine, 1973-76, Perspectives in Biology and Medicine, 1974—, Thrombosis Rsch., 1981-84, Jour. Urology, 1981-88, Internat. Jour. Hematology, 1991—; contbr. articles to med. jours. Career investigator Am. Heart Assn., 1960-86. Served to maj. M.C., 1943-46, Ind. Recipient Henry Moses award Montefiore Hosp., 1949, Disting. Achievement award Modern Medicine, 1967, James F. Mitchell award 1971, Murray Thelin award Nat. Hemophilia Found., 1971, H.P. Smith award Am. Soc. Clin. Pathology, 1975, Joseph Mather Smith prize Columbia Coll. Physicians and Surgeons, 1976, Disting. Achievemtn in Med. Sci. award U. Hosps. of Cleve, 1992, Saltzman award Mt. Sinai Hosp. of Cleve., 1994; named to Heart Hall of Fame, N.E. Ohio Heart Assn., 1989. Master ACP (John Phillips award 1974); fellow AAAS; mem. NAS (Kovalenko award 1985), AMA, Am. Fedn. Clin. Rsch., Soc. Scholars Johns Hopkins U., Am. Soc. Clin. Investigation, Ctrl. Soc. Clin. Rsch. (Disting. Svc. award 1992), Assn. Am. Physicians (Kober lectr. 1985, Kober medal 1988), Am. Soc. Hematology (Dameshek award 1972), Internat. Soc. Hematology, Internat. Soc. Thrombosis (Grant award 1981, spl. award 1993), Am. Physiol. Soc., Am. Soc. Biol. Chemists. Home: 2916 Sedgewick Rd Cleveland OH 44120-1840 Office: Univ Hosps of Cleve Cleveland OH 44106

RATNY, RUTH LUCILLE, publishing company executive, writer; b. Chgo., Dec. 8, 1935; d. Herman Joseph and Bertha (Levy) R. Student, De Paul U., 1950-54. Creative v.p. Niles Communications Ctrs., Chgo., 1954-64; prin. Ruth L. Ratny Mktg. Communications, Chgo., 1964-69; owner Screen mag., Chgo., 1979—; bd. dirs. Ind. Feature Project/Midwest. Bd. dirs. Chgo. Coalition, 1979-85. Named Advt. Women of Yr., 1979, Midwest Advt. Person of Yr., 1979; recipient Recognition award Chgo. Coalition, 1983, Clio awards, 1960-61, Women in Film's Recognition award, 1993. Mem. Women in Film, Chgo. Advt. Club, Women's Advt. Club, Acad. TV Arts and Scis., Pearl S. Buck Found. (bd. dirs. Perkasie, Pa. chpt. 1986—), Sigma Delta Chi. Mem. Christian Sci. Ch. Office: Screen Mag 720 N Wabash Ave Chicago IL 60611-2516

RATTAZZI, SERENA, art museum and association administrator; b. Taranto, Italy, Aug. 20, 1935; came to U.S., 1969; d. Umberto and Ligetta (Maresca) Bardelli; m. Mario Cristiano Rattazzi, Jan. 15, 1962; 1 child, Claudia. BA, Liceo Umberto I, Naples. Italy, 1953; MSW, U. Naples, 1958; postgrad. in legal problems of mus. adminstrn., Am. Legal Inst., ABA, 1985, 86, 87, 89. Pub. rels., publs. asst. Albright-Knox Art Gallery, Buffalo, 1974-76, coord. pub. rels., 1976-82, asst. dir. for adminstrn., 1982-84; asst. dir. for adminstrn. The Bklyn. Mus., 1984-85, vice dir. for adminstrn., 1985-89, assoc. dir., 1989-90; dir. Am. Fedn. Arts, N.Y.C., 1990—; adv. bd. The Pitts. Ctr. for Arts, 1989-92, A.I.R. Gallery, N.Y.C., 1990-93; field reviewer Inst. Mus. Svcs., Washington, 1990; adv. coun. dept. art history and archaeology Columbia Univ., 1992—. Mem. ArtTable Inc. (bd. dirs. 1986-88, pres. 1986-88), Am. Assn. Museums (standing profl. com. on pub. rels. mgmt. 1978-82, bd. 1990—). Avocation: reading. Office: Am Fedn Arts 41 E 65th St New York NY 10021-6594

RATTERMAN, DAVID BURGER, lawyer; b. Louisville, Sept. 8, 1946; s. Joseph A. and Esther M. (Burger) R.; m. Mary Miles Sledd, May 31, 1969; children—Andrew August, Sara Chandler. B.S.M.E., U. Ky., 1968; J.D., U. Louisville, 1975, M.B.A., 1980. Bar: Ky. 1976, U.S. Dist. Ct. (we. dist.) Ky. 1976, U.S. Dist. Ct. (so. dist.) Ga. 1979, U.S. Ct. Claims 1990, U.S. Ct. Appeals (6th cir.) 1986, U.S. Ct. Appeals (5th cir.) 1987, U.S. Ct. Appeals (Fed. cir.) 1991, U.S. Supreme Ct. 1981. Design engr. Square D Co., Lexington, Ky., 1968-70; ptnr. Goldberg & Simpson, Louisville, 1975—; tchr. seminars in constrn. law; legal counsel Ky. Council for the Blind, 1975-85. Contbr. articles to profl. jours. Mem. sch. bd. St. Leonard Sch., 1981-84, pres. 1983-84; counsel County Govt. Handicapped Compliance Commn. 1980-85; bd. dirs. United Crescent Hill Ministries, 1974-81, Clifton Neighborhood Devel. Corp., 1974-81. Served with USN, 1970-73, to comdr. Res. Decorated Naval Commendation medal. Fellow Am. Bar Found. (sustaining life fellow), Am. Inst. Steel Constrn. (sec., gen. counsel 1989—), Am. Coll. Constrn. Lawyers; mem. ABA, Am. Arbitration Assn., Ky. Bar Assn. (ho. of dels. 1986-92, founding chmn. sect. constrn. and pub. contract law), Louisville Bar Assn., Constrn. Specifications Inst., Rotary Club Louisville (bd. dirs. 1991-93). Roman Catholic. Home: Unit 209 2525 George Rogers Clark Pl Louisville KY 40206-2578 Office: Goldberg & Simpson 2800 First National Tower Louisville KY 40202

RATTHAHAO, SISOUPHANH, minister. Dir. Lao Ministry Dist. of the Christian and Missionary Alliance. Office: 1687 Maple Ln # 3 Elgin IL 60123-5071

RATTI, RONALD ANDREW, economics educator; b. Neath, West Glamorgan, Wales, Oct. 10, 1948; came to U.S., 1970; s. Ronald Rudolph and Janet (Marshall) R. BA, U. Lancaster, 1970; MA, Case Western Res. U., 1972; PhD, So. Meth. U., 1975. Asst. prof. to assoc. prof. U. Mo., Columbia, 1975-85, prof. econs., 1985—, chmn. dept., 1982-89; vis. scholar Fed. Res. Bank Kansas City, Mo., 1978, Fed. Res. Bank St. Louis., 1984-85; acad. visitor London Sch. Econs., 1985. Contbr. articles to profl. jours. Office: U Mo Dept Econs 118 Profl Bldg Columbia MO 65211

RATTLE, SIMON, conductor; b. Liverpool, Eng., 1955. Studied conducting and piano, Royal Acad. Music; PhD (hon.), Birmingham U., 1985. At age 15 occasional percussion player Royal Liverpool Philharm. Orch.; prin. condr., artistic adviser City of Birmingham Symphony Orch., 1980-91, mus. dir., 1990—; prin. guest condr. L.A. Philharm. Orch., 1981-93, princ. guest condr. of the Orch. of the Age of Enlightenment, 1992—, Rotterdam Philharm. Orch., 1981-84; prin. condr. London Choral Soc., 1979-84; assoc. condr. Royal Liverpool Philharm. Orch., 1977-80, BBC Scottish Symphony Orch., 1977-80; artistic dir. South Bank Summer Music, 1981-83; asst. condr. Bournemouth Symphony Orch. and Bournemouth Sinfonietta, 1974-76; debut at Glyndebourne Festival Opera, 1977, appeared regularly since; debuts at English Nat. Opera, 1985, Berlin Philharmonic, 1987, Los Angeles Opera, 1988, Royal Opera House, 1990, Vienna Philharmonic, 1993, Philadelphia Orchestra, 1993. Decorated comdr. Brit. Empire, knight Brit. Empire; chevalier des Arts et Lettres (France); recipient 1st prize John Player Internat. Condrs. Competition, 1974, Edison award, 1987, Gramophone Record of Yr., 1988, Gramophone Opera award, 1989, Internat. Record Critics award, 1990, Grand Prix in Honorem de l'Academie Charles Cros, 1990, Artist of Yr. Gramophone award, 1993, Montblanc de la Culture prize, Paris, 1993. Office: care Harold Holt Ltd, 31 Sinclair Rd, London W14 ONS, England also: Frank Salomon Assoc 201 W 54th St Ste 4C New York NY 10019

RATTNER, JUSTIN, supercomputer research manager. With Intel Corp., Beaverton, Oreg. named 1989 Scientist of the Yr., R&D mag. mem. IEEE. Office: Intel Corp 15201 NW Greenbrier Pky Beaverton OR 97006-5771

RATTNER, STEVEN LAWRENCE, investment banker; b. N.Y.C., July 5, 1952; s. George Seymour and Selma Ann (Silberman) R.; m. P. Maureen White, June 22, 1986; children: Rebecca White, Daniel Irvin, David William, James Brennan. AB in Econ. honors, Brown U., 1974. Asst. to James Reston, corr. N.Y. Times, Washington, N.Y.C., London, 1974-82; assoc., v.p. Lehman Bros. Kuhn Loeb, N.Y.C., 1982-84; assoc., v.p., prin., mng. dir., head communications group Morgan Stanley & Co., N.Y.C., 1984-89; gen. ptnr., head communications group Lazard Frères & Co., N.Y.C., 1989—; dir. Falcon Cable Holding Group, 1993—. Contbr. articles to various publs. including N.Y. Times, Wall St. Jour., Newsweek. Trustee Brown U., 1987-93, 94—, Ednl. Broadcasting Corp., 1990—, vice chmn., 1994—; dir. N.Y.C. Outward Bound Ctr., 1990—; bd. advisors Russian-Am. Press and Info. Ctr., 1993—; mem. print acquisition com. Whitney Mus., 1994—; mem. chmn.'s coun. and bus. com. Met. Mus. of Art, 1994—. Harvey Baker fellow Brown U. 1974, Poynter fellow Yale, 1979. Mem. Coun. Fgn. Rels., Royal Inst. for Internat. Affairs (assoc.). Home: 998 Fifth Ave New York NY 10028

RATTNER, WILLIAM EDWARD, lawyer; b. Chgo., Sept. 26, 1936; s. Herbert and Ethel (Weiss) R.; m. Gale Golovan, Nov. 27, 1963; 1 child, David Herbert. BS in Econ., U. Pa., 1958; JD, Harvard U., 1961. Bar: Ill. 1962, U.S. Dist. Ct (no. dist.) Ill. 1962, U.S. Ct. Appeals (7th cir.) 1963, U.S. Tax Ct. 1969, U.S. Dist. Ct. (no. dist.) Tex. 1989. Atty. Peterson, Lowry,

Rall, Barber & Ross, Chgo., 1962-67, Schwartz & Freeman, Chgo., 1967-72; ptnr. Levy & Erens, Chgo., 1972-86, Hopkins & Sutter, Chgo., 1986—. Vice chmn. Am. Jewish Com. With U.S. Army, 1961-67. Mem. ABA, Chgo. Bar Assn. (vice chmn. urban affairs com. 1970-72), 7th Cir. Bar Assn., Chgo. Coun. Lawyers, Mid-Day Club. Home: 1046 Michigan Ave Evanston IL 60202-1436 Office: Hopkins & Sutter 3 First National Plz Chicago IL 60602

RATZENBERGER, JOHN DESZO, actor, writer, director; b. Bridgeport, Conn., Apr. 6, 1947; s. Dezso Alexander and Bertha (Grohowski) R.; m. Elizabeth Georgia Stiny, Sept. 9, 1984; children: James John, Nina Katherine. Grad. high sch., Bridgeport, Conn.; Doctorate, Sacred Heart U., 1992. Actor, writer, dir. own theater troupe Sal's Meat Market, 1971-75; touring actor Europe, 1971-81; pres., founder Eco-Pack Industries, Kent, Wash. Appeared in plays Curse of the Starving Class, The Connection; films include The Ritz (film debut), 1974, Yanks, Ragtime, Motel Hell, Superman I, II, A Bridge Too Far, Firefox, The Empire Strikes Back, Protocol, Gandhi, Outland; TV performances include Songs of a Sourdough, The Good Soldier, (series) Cheers, 1982-1993; co-author TV plays: Friends in Space, 1978, Scalped, 1979. Recipient cash award Arts Council of Great Britain. Mem. AFTRA, SAG, Writers Guild Am., Dirs. Guild, Am. Farmland Trust, Brit. Actors Equity Assn., Greenpeace, Wilderness Soc., Nat. Resources Def. Coun., Sierra Club (San Francisco). Avocations: sailing, reading, woodworking. Office: c/o The Agency 10351 Santamonica Blvd Los Angeles CA 90025*

RATZER, MARY BOYD, secondary education educator, librarian; b. Troy, N.Y., Sept. 6, 1945; d. John Leo and Katherine M. (Van Derpool) Boyd; m. Philip J. Ratzer, July 30, 1972; children: Joseph, David. BA cum laude, Coll. of St. Rose, Albany, N.Y., 1967; MA, SUNY, Albany, 1968, MLS, 1981. Cert. secondary tchr., sch. libr. media specialist, N.Y. Secondary tchr. English, Shenendehowa Cen. Sch., Clifton Park, N.Y., 1968-85; sch. libr. media specialist Shendehowa Cen. Sch., Clifton Park, N.Y., 1985—; coord., mentor tchr. intern program; lectr. SUNY Grad. Sch. Info. Sci. and Policy, Albany; frequent speaker at state-level confs., 1986—. Contbr. articles to profl. jours. Recipient grants. Mem. ALA, N.Y. Libr. Assn., Nat. Coun. Tchrs. English, N.Y. Assn. for Supervision and Curriculum Devel., BIRT, LUERT (past pres.). Home: 433 County Rd 68 Saratoga Springs NY 12866

RATZLAFF, JAMES W., investment company executive. BS, U. Kans., 1958; JD, George Washington U., 1968. Vice chmn. Capital Rsch. and Mgmt Co., San Francisco, 1988—; pres. bd. dirs. Fundamental Investors; sr. ptnr. The Capital Group Ptnrs., L.P., 1991—; chmn. Am. Balanced Fund, AMCAP Fund, Am. Funds Svc. Co., The Growth Fund of Am., The Income Fund of Am.; vice chmn., bd. dirs. Am. Mut. Fund; exec. v.p., bd. dirs. The Investment Co. of Am.; bd. dirs. New Perspective Fund; bd. trustees EuroPacific Growth Fund. Office: Capital Rsch & Mgmt Co PO Box 7650 4 Embarcadero Ctr San Francisco CA 94111-4106

RATZLAFF, JUDITH L., secondary school educator; b. Oakland, Calif., May 2, 1937; d. Jack J. Bayard and Billie (Hart) Mills; m. Rulan R. Ratzlaff, Aug. 3, 1957 (dec. May 1991); children: Guy A., Scott A., Elizabeth A. Ratzlaff Perkins. Student, Southwestern Jr. Coll., San Diego, 1964-65, U. Md., Rota, Spain, 1968-70; BA in History, Spanish, U. Jacksonville, 1971-74. Cert. secondary tchr. history, Spanish, social studies, state trainer ethics, Fla. Tchr. social studies Clay County Sch. Bd., Orange Park, Fla., 1974—; dept. head Clay County Sch. Bd., 1974-77, grade level chairperson, 1977-80, sch. improvement com., 1994-95; mem. Edn. Practicel Commn., State of Fla., 1985-93, chairperson, 1991-93; participant First China-Am. Edn. Conf., 1992; co-originator Ethics Workshops for New Tchrs.; ethics trainer State of Fla., 1993. Regional dir. Tchrs. Adv. Com., Rep. party State of Fla., 1985—; sec. Clay County Rep. Exec. Com., 1986-93; candidate Fla. State Senate, 1986; sponsor Students Against Drunk Driving, 1982-85; active Rep. Exec. Com. Taft fellow Taft Inst. Polit. Studies Cath. U. Am., 1978, 80, 93. Mem. NEA (del. convs. Mpls., 1995, San Francisco 1993, Washington, 1992, Miami 1991, chairperson legis. com. on Fla. tchg. profession 1985-86), Nat. Coun. Edn. Standards and Practices Commns. (charter), Clay County Edn. Assn. (pres. 1981-83), Northeast Fla. Uniserve Coun. (vice chair 1990, sec. 1991, chair FTP-NEA 1993-95). Baptist. Avocations: scuba diving, swimming, running, knitting. Home: 3211 Doctors Lake Dr Orange Park FL 32073-6927 Office: Orange Park High Sch 2300 Kingsley Ave Orange Park FL 32073

RAU, ALAN SCOTT, law educator; b. 1942. BA, Harvard U., 1963, LLB, 1967. Bar: N.Y. 1968. Assoc. Coudert Freres, Paris, 1968-71; asst. prof. U. Tex., 1971-74, Robert F. Windfohr and Anne Burnett Windfohr prof., 1974—; vis. prof. U. Toronto, 1974-75; vis. prof., Fulbright grantee China U. Law and Polit. Sci., Beijing, 1985-86, vis. prof., Fred Paulus chair in Pub. Policy Willamette U., Salem, Oreg. Co-author: (with Hamilton and Weintraub) Cases and Materials on Contracts, 2d edit. 1991, (with Murray and Sherman) Dispute Resolution: The Role of Lawyers, 1989. Frank Knox Meml. fellow Harvard Sch. Econs., 1967-68. Office: U Tex Sch Law 727 E 26th St Austin TX 78705-3224

RAU, DAVID EDWARD, real estate company executive; b. Lincoln, Nebr., Sept. 27, 1956; s. Leo George and Anne Marie (Pavel) R.; m. Kayle Georgette Wilcox, May 17, 1980; children: Andrew David, Peter Nicholas, Victoria Anne. BBA, U. Ariz., 1978. CPA, Ariz., N.Mex. Sr. Peat Marwick Main, Albuquerque, 1978-82; supervising sr. Peat Marwick Main, Phoenix, 1982-83; asst. treas. Kroy Inc., Scottsdale, Ariz., 1983-85; acct. Zolondek & Blumenthal, Phoenix, 1985; v.p., controller Del Webb Corp., Phoenix, 1985—; bd. dirs. Ariz. Tax Rsch. Assn. Chmn. Phoenix chpt. walk Juvenile Diabetes Found., 1993—; mem. 1992, 93, 94; mem. Ariz. Town Hall; advisor Phoenix Sky Harbour Ctr. Tech. Adv. Panel, 1987; treas. Drugs Don's Work in Ariz., 1994—. Mem. Ariz. Soc. CPAs, Albuquerque Jaycees (treas. 1981-82), Nat. Assn. Real Estate Cos. (tax com.), Ariz. C-of C. (bd. dirs.), Beta Alpha Psi. Republican. Roman Catholic. Avocations: skiing, fishing, family. Office: Del E Webb Corp 2231 E Camelback Rd Phoenix AZ 85016-3453

RAU, LEE ARTHUR, lawyer; b. Mpls., July 22, 1940; s. Arthur W. and Selma A. (Lund) R.; m. Janice R. Childress, June 27, 1964; children—Brendan D., Patrick C., Brian T. BSB, U. Minn., 1962; JD, UCLA, 1965. Bar: Calif. 1966, D.C. 1972, Va. 1986, U.S. Dist. Ct. D.C. 1973, U.S. Dist. Ct. (ea. dist.) Va. 1988, U.S. Ct. Mil. Appeals 1966, U.S. Ct. Appeals (D.C. cir.) 1972, U.S. Ct. Appeals (3d cir.) 1975, U.S. Ct. Appeals (6th cir.) 1980, U.S. Ct. Appeals (4th cir.) 1988, U.S. Supreme Ct. 1971. Trial atty. evaluation sect. antitrust div. U.S. Dept. Justice, Washington, 1965-66, appellate sect., 1970-72; assoc. Reed Smith Shaw & McClay, Washington, 1972-74, ptnr., 1975—; former mem. constl. and adminstrv. law adv. com. Nat. Chamber Litigation Ctr. Inc.; sec., bd. dirs. Old Dominion Land Co., Inc. Contbr. articles to profl. jours. Sec. bd. dirs. Reston Found., 1982-93; bd. dirs. Reston Interfaith Inc., 1973-89, pres., 1984-88; bd. dirs. Greater Reston Arts Ctr., 1988—, pres., 1989-91, sec., 1991—; mem. Washington Dulles Task Force, 1982-91; mem. exec. com., ops. com. Fairfax-Falls Church United Way, mem. regional coun., 1988-92. Capt. JAGC, U.S. Army, 1966-70. Named Restonian of Yr., 1990; decorated Commendation medal with oak leaf cluster. Mem. ABA (antitrust, adminstrv. law, corp. banking and bus., sci. and tech. sects.), D.C. Bar Assn. (past chmn. energy study group), Calif. Bar Assn., U.S. C. of C. (antitrust policy com.). Democrat. Lutheran. Home: 1930 Upper Lakes Dr Reston VA 22091-3620 Office: Reed Smith Shaw & McClay 8251 Greensboro Dr Ste 1100 Mc Lean VA 22102-3844

RAU, RALPH RONALD, physicist; b. Tacoma, Sept. 1, 1920; s. Ralph Campbell and Ida (Montgall) R.; m. Maryjane Uhrlaub, June 2, 1944; children: Whitney Leslie, Littie Elise. B.S in Physics, Coll. Puget Sound, 1941; M.S. in Physics, Calif. Inst. Tech., 1943, Ph.D. in Physics, 1948. Asst. prof. physics Princeton U., 1947-56; Fulbright research prof. physics Ecole Polytechnique, Paris, 1954-55; physicist Brookhaven Nat. Lab., Upton, N.Y., 1956-66; chmn. dept. physics Brookhaven Nat. Lab., 1966-70, assoc. dir. for high energy physics, 1970-81; adj. prof. U. Wyo.; vis. prof. MIT, 1984-88; staff scientist Desy Lab., Hamburg, Fed. Republic Germany, 1984-85. Trustee U. Puget Sound, 1978-84. Named Alumnus Cum Laude U. Puget Sound, 1968; recipient Alexander von Humboldt U.S. Sr. Scientist award 1988. Mem. Am. Phys. Soc., N.Y. Acad. Sci. Office: Brookhaven Nat Lab Upton NY 11973

RAU, ROBERT NICHOLAS, pipe distribution executive; b. Phila., Oct. 14, 1927; s. Nicholas A. and Mary A. (McCandless) R.; m. Alice Marie Farrington, May 21, 1949; children: Robert N., Donna-Marie Murphy, Karen Gamble, Patricia A. Pinkston. Student, Drexel U., 1947-48. Clk. to inside sales Hajoca Corp., Phila., Lansdale, Pa., 1951-54; inside sales to v.p. Standard Pipe and Supply, Bala Cynwyd, Pa., 1954-71; pres. BBL Co., Kulpsville, Pa., 1971-94, CEO, 1994—. Contbr. articles to profl. jours. Coach Spl. Olympics, 1982—; active Boy Scouts of Am. With USN, 1945-46, PTO. Named Vol. of Yr. Spl. Olympics, 1991. Mem. ASTM (sec. 1975—), Nat. Assn. Steel Pipe Dist. (dir. 1977—, v.p. 1988-89, pres. 1989-92, Pres.' award 1992). Republican. Roman Catholic. Avocations: cross country skiing, spl. olympics, grandchildren, travel.

RAU, SHIRLEY A., secondary school educator; b. Morrison, Ill., Dec. 30, 1955; d. Harold A. and Audrey A. (Moore) R. BA, Idaho State U., 1978; MA, Middlebury (Vt.) Coll., 1985; postgrad., Boise (Idaho) State U., 1978-87, Winona (Minn.) State U. 1984-87. Tchr. English, South Jr. High Sch., Nampa, Idaho; instr. freshman composition Boise State U.; tchr. English, Nampa High Sch., cheerleading coach, 1984—; participant Rockefeller Conf., 1984; workshop presenter. Contbr. articles to profl. jours. Named Nampa Tchr. of Yr., 1981, 89, Idaho State Tchr. of Yr., 1990-91 (finalist Nat. Tchr. of Yr. 1991); Cheerleading Coach of Yr. Internat. Cheerleading Found., 1989; fellow Treasure Valley Writing Project, 1979; Mina Shaughnessy scholar, 1985. Mem. NEA, Nat. Assn. Secondary Sch. Prins. (advisor activities program 1979—), Nat. Coun. Tchrs. English, (women's com.), Idaho Edn. Assn., Nampa Edn. Assn., Idaho Coun. Tchrs. English. Home: 6490 Plantation Ln Boise ID 83703-2642 Office: Nampa High Sch 203 Lake Lowell Ave Nampa ID 83686-6697

RAU, WILLIAM ARTHUR, health care company financial executive; b. Portsmouth, Ohio, May 29, 1939; s. Arthur Henry and Ruth (Carson) R.; m. Carolyn Jackson, Oct. 21, 1972; children: Sarah Ruth, Anne Forest, Katherine Carson, Arthur Henry II. BS in Arts and Scis., Ohio U., 1963, MS in Accountancy, 1967, MBA in Gen. Bus., 1981. Acct. Peat, Marwick, Mitchell & Co., Columbus, 1966-68; v.p. fin., chief fin. officer The Williams Mfg. Co., Portsmouth, 1968-76, Mercy Hosp. Corp., Portsmouth, 1976-87, U.S. Health Corp. So. Ohio, Portsmouth, 1987—; bd. dirs. Bank One, Portsmouth, The Martings Bros. Co., Portsmouth; mem. exec. adv. bd. Coll. Bus., Ohio U., Athens, 1983—. Bd. dirs. YMCA, Portsmouth, 1971-81, Gt. Lakes regional bd. dirs., 1980-81. Fellow Am. Coll. Healthcare Execs.; mem. Fin. Execs. Inst., Nat. Assn. Accts., Healthcare Fin. Mgmt. Assn. Avocation: golf. Office: Southern Ohio Med Ctr 1248 Kinneys Ln Portsmouth OH 45662-2913

RAUB, DONALD WILMER, minister, author; b. Quakertown, Pa., Dec. 24, 1931; s. Harvey Wilmer and Estella Martha (Bleam) R.; m. Dolores Jean Kern, Oct. 20, 1951; children: Diane, Donald, Deborah, Devlyn. DRE, Evang. Bible Sem., Lake Worth, Fla., 1987. Ordained minister Evang. Ch. Alliance, 1951. Evangelist Evang. Ch. Alliance, Bradley, Ill., 1951-58; pastor Troy (Ohio) Gospel Tabernacle, 1959-60; writer and photographer Quakertown (Pa.) Free Press, 1963-73; pastor East Rockhill Chapel, 1965—; with Merck & Co., West Point, Pa., 1968-94; ret., 1994; advisor Lebanon (Pa.) Gospel Assn., 1992-94; lectr. in field. Author: I, Being of Sound Mind, 1988, 2d edit., 1989, Unusual Experiences and Special Moments, 1990, The Value of Christian Holiness, 1992; inventor fin. game: Independence, 1976; patentee in field; contbr. articles to profl. jours. Bd. dirs. Transylvania Bible Sch., Freeport, Pa., 1957—, North Penn Symphony Orch. Soc., Lansdale, Pa., 1980-90; v.p. Transylvania, Inc., 1994—. Mem. Songwriters of N.Am. (founder). Republican. Avocation: horticulture. Home: 422 Thousand Acre Rd Sellersville PA 18960

RAUCH, ARTHUR IRVING, management consultant; b. N.Y.C., Sept. 18, 1933; s. David and Miriam (Frankel) R.; m. Roxane M. Spiller, Aug. 19, 1962 (div. 1977); children: David S., Janine B.; m. Lynn R Saidenberg, Oct. 11, 1987. BA magna cum laude Dartmouth Coll., 1954, MS, 1955. Chartered fin. analyst. Security analyst Lionel D. Edie & Co., N.Y.C., 1959-64; group dir. rsch. Eastman Dillon, Union Securities & Co., N.Y.C., 1964-68; v.p., sr. analyst Laird, Inc., N.Y.C., 1968-69, dir. rsch., v.p., sr., 1970-73; ptnr. Oppenheimer & Co., N.Y.C., 1973-77; v.p. corp. devel. Rorer Group Inc., Ft. Washington, Pa., 1977-84; v.p. corp. fin. Arnhold & S. Bleichroeder, Inc., 1984-88; cons. corp. devel. ICN Pharms. Inc., N.Y.C., 1988-89; mem. investment com. Becker Fund, 1969-73; bd. dirs. Sonomed Tech., Inc., 1983—; exec. com. Dartmouth Class of 1954, 1968-79. Lt. (j.g.) USNR, 1956-59. Rufus Choate scholar Dartmouth Coll. Mem. N.Y. Soc. Security Analysts, Assn. Corp. Growth. Fin. Analysts Fedn. (corp. info. com.), Phi Beta Kappa. Home and Office: 250 E 73d St Apt 19C New York NY 10021

RAUCH, CHARLES FREDERICK, JR., academic official; b. Lancaster, Ohio, Oct. 24, 1925; s. Charles Frederick and Mary Catherine (Getz) R.; m. Diane Matilda Wilcox, Jan. 1, 1951 (div. July 1974); 1 child, Frederick Whitman; m. Esther Eleze Nettles, Apr. 25, 1975. BS, U.S. Naval Acad., 1947; MSME, U.S. Naval Postgrad. Sch., Monterey, Calif., 1957; MBA, Ohio State U., 1980, PhD, 1981. Commd. ensign USN, 1947, advanced through grades to rear adm., 1972; comdg. officer nuclear submarines, New London, Conn., 1962-66; systems analyst, sr. naval advisor, spl. asst. Office Chief Naval Ops., Washington and Saigon, Vietnam, 1967-71; dir. human resource mgmt. programs Office Chief Naval Ops., Washington, 1971-76; ret., 1976; asst. prof. U. Maine, Orono, 1981-84, dir. fin. mgmt., 1984-92, v.p. bus. and fin., 1992—; acting pres. Am. Univ. Bulgaria, 1992; cons. to dep. asst. sec. def., Washington, 1976; cons. Maine Maritime Acad., Castine, 1982-84, dir. Maritime Career Devel. Inst., 1984. Contbg. author: Leaders and Managers: International Perspectives on Managerial Behavior and Leaderships, 1984. Decorated D.S.M. with gold star. Mem. Acad. Mgmt., Inst. Mgmt. Scis., Greater Bangor C. of C. (chmn. com. on univ.-community rels. 1986-89, bd. dirs. 1988-92), Navy League, Maine Audubon Soc., Phi Kappa Phi, Beta Gamma Sigma. Episcopalian. Avocations: wildlife photography, woodcarving. Home: 102 Stillwater Ave Orono ME 04473-1016 Office: U Maine 118 Alumni Hall Orono ME 04469

RAUCH, GEORGE WASHINGTON, lawyer; b. Marion, Ind., July 18, 1919; s. George W. and Emma Asenath (Nolen) R.; m. Audrey M. Cranfield, Feb. 28, 1943 (div.); children: George Washington III, Nancy Lynn, Jane Nolen; m. Dorothy D. Farlow, June 26, 1970. B.S., Ind. U., 1941; LL.B., U. Va., 1947. Bar: Ind. 1948, Ill. 1957, Mass. and Fla. 1972. Practice law Batton, Harker and Rauch (and predecessor firms), Marion, Ind., 1948-57; v.p., gen. counsel The Greyhound Corp., Chgo., 1957-61; mem. firm Hubachek & Kelly Ltd. and predecessor firms, Chgo., 1961-82; pres. Hubachek & Kelly Ltd., 1972-80; of counsel firm Chapman and Cutler, Chgo., 1982—; gen. counsel Household Finance Corp., 1967-78, dir., 1967-92, mem. fin. com., 1969-92, exec. com., 1972-92; dir. Edwards Engring. Corp., Constrn. Materials Co., Indsl. Air & Hydraulics Co., 1976-90; dir. Burch Co., 1977-92, pres., 1975—; dir. 1242 Lake Shore Dr. Corp., 1971-83, pres., 1973-74; bd. dirs. Gen. Propeller Co.; mem. Nat. Conf. Commrs. on Uniform Laws, 1955-57. Served as aviator USNR, 1941-45; lt. comdr. Mem. Fla. Bar Assn., Raven Soc., Univ. Club, Racquet Club (Chgo.), Sankaty Head Golf Club (Nantucket), Masons, Casino Club (Nantucket), Beach Club (Palm Beach., Fla.), Masons, Shriners, Phi Delta Phi, Delta Tau Delta. Home: 455 Australian Ave Palm Beach FL 33480-4532 also: 83 Baxter Rd PO Box 149 Siasconset MA 02564-0149 Office: 111 W Monroe St Chicago IL 60603-4003

RAUCH, IRMENGARD, linguist, educator; b. Dayton, Ohio, Apr. 17, 1933; d. Konrad and Elsa (Knott); m. Gerald F. Carr, June 12, 1965; children: Christopher, Gregory. Student, Nat. U. Mex., summer 1954; B.S. with honors, U. Dayton, 1955; M.A., Ohio State U., 1957; postgrad. (Fulbright fellow), U. Munich, Fed. Republic Germany, 1957-58; Ph.D., U. Mich., 1962. Instr.: German and linguistics U. Wis., Madison, 1962-63, asst. prof., 1963-66; assoc. prof. German U. Pitts., 1966-68; assoc. prof. German and linguistics U. Ill., Urbana, 1968-72, prof. 1972-79; prof. U. Calif., Berkeley, 1979—. Author: The Old High German Diphthongization: A Description of a Phonemic Change, 1967, The Old Saxon Language: Grammar, Epic Narrative, Linguistic Interference, 1992; editor: (with others) Approaches in Linguistic Methodology, 1967, Spanish edit., 1974, Der Heliand, 1974, Linguistic Method: Essays in Honor of Herbert Penzl, 1979, The Signifying Animal: The Grammar of Language and Experience, 1980,

Language Change, 1983, The Semiotic Bridge: Trends from California, 1989, On Germanic Linguistics: Issues and Methods, 1992, editor of two series: Berkeley Insights in Linguistics and Semiotics, Berkeley Models of Grammars; contbr. articles to profl. jours. Named outstanding woman on campus U. Ill. Sta. WILL, 1975; recipient Disting. Alumnus award U. Dayton, 1985; research grantee U. Wis., summer 1966, U. Ill., 1975-79, Eastern Ill. U., 1976, Nat. Endowment Humanities, 1978, U. Calif., Berkeley, 1979—; travel grantee NSF, Linguistics Soc. Am., 1972; Guggenheim fellow, 1982-83; IBM Distributed Acad. Computing Environment, 1986; NEH grantee, 1988. Mem. Linguistics Soc. Am., MLA, Am. Assn. Tchrs. German, Society for Germanic Philogy, Philogical Assn. of the West Coast, Phonetics Assn., Semiotic Soc. Am. (pres. 1982-83), Semiotic Circle of Calif. (founder), Internat. Assn. for Semiotic Studies (pres., dir. 5th congress 1994), Alpha Sigma Tau, Delta Phi Alpha. Home: 862 Camden Ct Benicia CA 94510-3633 Office: U Calif Dept German Berkeley CA 94720

RAUCH, JOHN KEISER, JR., architect; b. Phila., Oct. 23, 1930; s. John Keiser and Marjorie (Gretz) R.; m. Carol Pfaff, Mar. 11, 1953 (div. June 1978); children: John David, Charles Daniel, Kathryn Mari, Peter, Carol Anne; m. Carol A. McConochie, Jan. 10, 1981. Student, Wesleyan U., Middletown, Conn., 1948-51; B.Arch., U. Pa., 1957. Draftsman Cope & Lippincott, Phila., 1957-60; architect Venturi and Short, Phila., 1960-64; partner Venturi and Rauch (Architects and Planners), Phila., 1964-79; partner Venturi, Rauch and Scott Brown, 1980-82, v.p., mng. prin., 1982-87, mgmt. cons., mediator, arbitrator, 1988—; instr. U. Pa. Grad. Sch. Fine Arts, 1969-70, 89; lectr. dept. architecture Princeton (N.J.) U., 1990-94. Trustee Found. for Architecture, 1977-84, mem. adv. com., 1994—; treas. Phila. Rehab., Inc., 1984-94; pres. Reading Terminal Market Pres. Fund, 1988-93, bd. dirs., 1994—; bd. dirs. United Cerebral Palsy Assn., 1988-91. Recipient Good Neighbor award Mellon/PSFS Bank, 1992. Fellow AIA (Firm award 1983, John Harbeson Disting Svc. Phila. Chpt. award 1992); mem. Pa. Soc. Architects. Democrat. Home and Office: 620 Gate House Ln Philadelphia PA 19118-4303

RAUCH, LAWRENCE LEE, aerospace and electrical engineer, educator; b. L.A., May 1, 1919; s. James Lee and Mabel (Thompson) R.; m. Norma Ruth Cable, Dec. 15, 1961; children: Lauren, Mary Rauch. A.B., U. So. Calif., 1941; postgrad., Cornell U., 1941; A.M., Princeton U., 1948, Ph.D., 1949. Instr. math. Princeton U., 1943- 49; faculty U. Mich., 1949—, prof. aerospace engring., 1953-79, emeritus, 1979, chmn. instrumentation engring. program, 1952-63, chmn. computer, info. and control engring. program, 1971-76, asso. chmn. dept. elec. and computer engring., 1972-75; chief technologist telecommunication sci. and engring. div. NASA/Calif. Inst. Tech. Jet Propulsion Lab., 1979-85; vis. prof. Ecole Nationale Supérieure de L'Aéronautique et de l'Espace, Toulouse, France, 1970, Calif. Inst. Tech., Pasadena, 1977-85, U. Tokyo, 1978; cons. govt. and industry, 1946—; chmn. telemetering working group, panel test range instrumentation Research and Devel. Bd. Dept. Def., 1952-53; mem. exec. com. (Nat. Telemetering Conf.), 1959-64; Western Hemisphere program chmn. (1st Internat. Telemetering Conf.), London, 1963, program chmn., U.S.A., 1967; supr. air blast telemetering, Bikini, 1946; mem. project non-linear differential equations Office Naval Research, 1947-49; mem. research adv. com. on communications, instrumentation and data processing NASA, 1963-68. Author: Radio Telemetry, 1956; also numerous sci. articles and papers on radio telemetry. Recipient award for outstanding contbn. to WWII Army and Navy, 1947, award for outstanding contbn. to telemetering field Nat. Telemetering Conf., 1960; Donald P. Eckman award for disting. achievement in edn. Instrument Soc. Am., 1966; Pioneer award Internat. Telemetering Conf./USA, 1985. Fellow IEEE (spl. award contbns. radio telemetry 1957, adminstrv. com. profl. group space electronics and telemetry 1958-64), AAAS, Explorers Club; mem. Am. Math. Soc., AIAA, U. Mich. Research Club, Phi Beta Kappa, Sigma Xi, Phi Eta Sigma, Phi Kappa Phi. Achievements include patent in field; development of first electronic time-division multiplex radio telemetering system, of pre-detection recording; radio telemetry of first U.S. jet aircraft, of air blast over pressure for Operation Crossroads at Bikini Atoll; analysis of optimum demodulation of frequency-modulated signals. Address: 759 N Citrus Ave Los Angeles CA 90038-3401

RAUCH, RUDOLPH STEWART, III, periodical editor, arts education executive; b. Bryn Mawr, Pa., July 5, 1943; s. Rudolph Stewart and Frances (Brewster) R.; m. Sheila Prentice, Oct. 31, 1972; children: Edward Prentice, Michael Brewster. BA, Princeton U., 1965. Corr. Time mag., N.Y.C., 1969-70, Bonn, W. Ger., 1970-71, Saigon, Vietnam, 1971-72, Rio De Janeiro, Brazil, 1972-74, Buenos Aires, Argentina, 1974-76, Atlanta, 1976-79; dep. chief of corrs. Time mag., N.Y.C., 1979-80; asst. to chmn. bd. Time Inc., N.Y.C., 1981-84; internat. dir. mag. devel. Time Inc., 1984-85; exec. editor N.Y. N.J. Conn. Real Estate, 1986-87; mng. editor Constitution, 1989-94; mng. editor, mng. dir. Met. Opera Guild, Inc., N.Y.C., 1994—. Edward R. Murrow Press fellow Council on Fgn. Relations, 1980-81. Mem. Coun. Fgn. Rels., Knickerbocker Club, Century Assn. Club. Office: Time-Life Bldg Met Opera Guild 70 Lincoln Center Plaza New York NY 10023

RAUCHER, HERMAN, novelist, screenwriter; b. Bklyn., Apr. 13, 1928; s. Benjamin Brooks and Sophie (Weinshank) R.; m. Mary Kathryn Martinet, Apr. 20, 1960; children: Jacquelene Leigh, Jennifer Brooke. BS, NYU, 1949. Asst. trade ad mgr. 20th Century Fox Films, N.Y.C. and Los Angeles, 1950-54; copy dir. Walt Disney Studios, N.Y.C., 1954-55; copy supr. Calkins & Holden Advt., N.Y.C., 1955-57; copy dir., v.p. dir. Reach McClinton Advt., N.Y.C., 1957-63; v.p., creative dir. Maxon Advt., N.Y.C., 1963-64; creative supr. Gardner Advt., N.Y.C., 1964-65; v.p. advt., cons. Benton & Bowles Advt., N.Y.C., 1965-67; freelance novelist, screenwriter, 1967—; pres. Bearfilm Prodns., 1971-76. Author: (novels and screenplays) Watermelon Man, 1970, Summer of '42 (nominated Acad. award for best original screenplay 1971, Writers Guild award nomination, Photoplay award), Ode to Billy Joe, 1975, A Glimpse of Tiger, 1972, (novels) Sweet November, 1968, Maynard's House, 1979, (screenplays) The Other Side of Midnight, 1977, Class of 44, 1972, Hieronymus Merkin (Best Original Screenplay award Writers Guild of Great Britain 1969), There Should Have Been Castles, 1978, also various dramas appearing on TV in Alcoa Hour, Studio One, Matinee Theatre, Goodyear Playhouse, (TV mini-series under pseudonym) Master of the Game, 1984, (TV pilot) Remember When, 1974; playwright: Harold, 1962, Two Weeks Somewhere Else, 1967; contbg. editor: Greenwich Time; contbr. to book revs. to N.Y. Times. Served with U.S. Army, 1950-52. Mem. Writers Guild Am., Authors League Am., Am. Film Inst., Dramatists Guild, Acad. of Motion Picture Arts and Scis.

RAUDENBUSH, MICHAEL H., nuclear energy industry executive; b. 1943. Pres. The S M Stoller, Corp., Boulder, 1974—. With USN, 1966-71. Office: The S M Stoller Corp 5700 Flatiron Pky Boulder CO 80301*

RAUE, JORG EMIL, electrical engineer; b. Stettin, Germany, June 13, 1936; came to U.S., 1952; s. Ludwig and Liselotte (Barth) R.; m. Anke Volkmann, June 29, 1957; children: Monika Kay, Jennifer Faye. BSEE, Milw. Sch. Engring., 1961; MSEE, Marquette U., 1965, PhDEE, 1968. Mem. faculty Milw. Sch. Engring., 1961-68, chmn. dept., 1968-69; research engr. TRW Systems, Redondo Beach, Calif., 1969-76; mgr. dept. TRW Systems, Redondo Beach, 1976-79; sr. research scientist TRW Electronic Systems, Redondo Beach, Calif., advanced systems mgr., 1980-93; tech. cons. Calif., 1993—; chmn. dept. elec. engring. Calif. Polytech State U., San Luis Opispo, 1979-80; mem. faculty Marquette U., Milw., 1968-69, Loyola U., Los Angeles, 1970-72, U. So. Calif., Los Angeles, 1983—. Contbr. articles to profl. jours. Served with U.S. Army, 1955-58. Recipient Disting. Tchr. award Milw. Sch. Engring., 1968; named Outstanding Alumnus Milw. Sch. Engring., 1985. Fellow IEEE; mem. Microwave Soc. of IEEE (sec. adminstrn. com. 1985—), Sigma Xi. Avocations: tennis, bicycling, flying. Home and Office: 28813 Rothrock Dr Palos Verdes Peninsula CA 90274

RAUENHORST, GERALD, architectural, construction and development executive; b. Mpls., Dec. 8, 1927; s. Henry and Margaret (Keltgen) R.; m. Henrietta Schmoll, Sept. 2, 1950; children: Judith, Mark, Neil, Joseph, Michael, Susan, Amy. BA, U. St. Thomas, 1948, Dr. Laws (hon.), 1971; B.S.C.E., Marquette U., 1951. Instr. in civil engring. Marquette U., 1950-51; engr. Peter Rasmussen & Son, Oshkosh, Wis., 1951-52, Viking Constrn., Mpls., 1952-53; pres., founder. Rauenhorst Corp., Mpls. 1953— (name changed to Opus Corp. chrm. bd., ceo, 1982—); deputy chrm. 1991-93, chmn. bd. dirs. Fed. Res. Bank, Mpls., 93—; dir., chmn. human resources com. ConAgra, Omaha; bd. dirs. Arico, N.Y. Chmn. bd. trustees Marquette U., 1985-87. Recipient Disting. Engring. award Marquette U., 1974; named Alumnus of Yr., Marquette U., 1969, Coll. St. Thomas, 1978, Minn. Exec. of Yr., Corp. Report Mag., 1983, Devel. of Yr., NAIOP, 1992; named to Minn. Bus. Hall of Fame, 1980. Mem. ASCE, Am. Soc. Profl. Engrs., World Press Orgn., Minn. Soc. Profl. Engrs, Mpls. Club, Interlachen Club. Roman Catholic. Avocations: fishing, golf, pottery. Office: Opus Corp PO Box 150 Minneapolis MN 55440-0150

RAUH, CARL STEPHEN, lawyer; b. Washington, Dec. 14, 1940; s. Joseph L. and Olie (Westheimer) R. A.B., Columbia U., 1962; LL.B., U. Pa., 1965; LL.M., Georgetown U., 1968. Bar: D.C. 1966, U.S. Supreme Ct. 1969. Asst. U.S. atty. for D.C., 1966-69; atty. Dep. Atty Gen.'s Office Dept. Justice, Washington, 1969-71; 1st asst. atty. gen. U.S. V.I., 1971-73; prin. asst. U.S. atty. for D.C., 1974-79, U.S. atty. for D.C., 1979; ptnr. Dunnells, Duvall, Bennett & Porter, Washington, 1980-90, Skadden, Arps, Slate, Meagher & Flom, Washington, 1990—. Mem. D.C. Jud. Nomination Commn., 1985-90. Recipient Dir.'s award Dept. Justice, 1976; Atty. Gen.'s Disting. Service award, 1980. Fellow Am. Coll. Trial Lawyers; mem. ABA, D.C. Bar Assn., Nat. Assn. Former U.S. Attys., Asst. U.S. Attys. Assn. (Harold J. Sullivan award 1980). Office: 1440 New York Ave NW Washington DC 20005-2111

RAUH, JOHN DAVID, manufacturing company executive; b. Cin., May 28, 1932; s. Carl J. and Grace (Stix) R.; m. Elizabeth Gibbons, June 19, 1954; children: Carol Miller, Daniel Gibbons; m. Mary Stoner, Dec. 23, 1984; children: Brooks Tomb, Howard Tomb. AB, Harvard U., 1954, MBA, 1956. Gen. mgr. Rauh Shirt Co., Cin., 1959-61, Clopay Corp., Cin., 1961-85; pres. Clopay Corp., 1972-75, chmn., chief exec. officer, 1975-85, also chmn.; adj. faculty mktg. Colby-Sawyer Coll., New London, N.H., 1989—; fellow Kennedy Sch., Harvard, 1989. Pres. Charter Com. Greater Cin., 1969-76; canidate U.S. Senate, N.H., 1990, 92. 1st lt. Finance Corps. AUS, 1956-59. Home: 11 Clearwater Dr Box 729 Sunapee NH 03782

RAUHALA, ANN ELAINE, reporter; b. Sudbury, Ont., Can., Dec. 7, 1954; d. Esko Alexander and Iona Anna (Tormala) R.; m. Lorne Franklin Slotnick, Feb. 27, 1990; 1 child, Sam Aleksander Nathan. BA in Arts, U. Toronto, 1977; B in Applied Arts, Ryerson U., 1979. Copy editor Globe and Mail, Toronto, Ont., 1979-83, asst. fgn. editor, 1983-86, reporter, 1986-89, fgn. editor, 1989-95, columnist, 1993-95; TV reporter Can. Broadcasting Corp., Toronto, 1995—; panelist, organizer Can. Assn. Journalists of Toronto, 1990, Ottawa, Ont., 1992, Winnipeg, Man., 1993. Bd. dirs. YMCA, Toronto, 1989-92, Montrose Child Care, Inc., Toronto, 1992—. Recipient Robertine Berry award Can. Rsch. Inst. for Advancement of Women, Ottawa, 1987. Avocations: film, travel, literature. Office: Can Broadcasting Corp, PO Box 500 Sta A, Toronto, ON Canada M5W 1E6

RAUL, ALAN CHARLES, lawyer; b. Bronx, N.Y., Sept. 9, 1954; s. Eugene and Eduarda (Müller-Mañas) R.; m. Mary Tinsley, Jan. 30, 1988; children: Caroline Tinsley, William Eduardo Tinsley. AB magna cum laude, Harvard U., 1975, MPA, 1977; JD, Yale U., 1980. Bar: N.Y. 1982, D.C. 1982, U.S. Ct. Appeals (D.C. cir.) 1982, U.S. Dist. Ct. D.C. 1986, U.S. Ct. Internat. Trade 1988, U.S. Claims Ct. 1988, U.S. Ct. Appeals (fed. cir.) 1988, U.S. Ct. Appeals (9th cir.) 1991, U.S. Supreme Ct. 1988. Law clk. to judge U.S. Ct. Appeals (D.C. cir.), Washington, 1980-81; assoc. Debevoise & Plimpton, N.Y.C., 1981-86; White House assoc. counsel Pres. Reagan, Washington, 1986-88; gen. counsel Office Mgmt. and Budget, Washington, 1988-89, USDA, Washington, 1989-93; prin. Beveridge & Diamond P.C., Washington, 1993—; cons. Reagan-Bush campaign, N.Y.C., 1984; com. mem. Food and Drug Law Inst. Co-chairperson, co-founder Lawyers Have Heart; chmn. bd. USDA Grad. Sch., 1991-93; bd. dirs. Am. Heart Assn., Nations Capital Affiliate, 1993—; treas. Citizens Assn. Georgetown; mem. Nat. Policy Forum's Environ. Policy Coun. Recipient Disting. Achievement award Am. Heart Assn., 1991, Vol. of Yr. award, 1993. Mem. ABA (coun. sect. Internat. Law and Practice, 1992—, chmn. com. on nat. security and internat law, 1990-92), Assn. of Bar of City of N.Y. (chmn. subcom. on Cen. Am. issues 1985, mem. com. on inter-Am. affairs 1983—), Am. Soc. Internat. Law, Federalist Soc., Coun. on Fgn. Rels. Office: Beveridge & Diamond PC 1350 I St NW Ste 700 Washington DC 20005

RAULINAITIS, PRANAS ALGIS, electronics executive; b. Kaunas, Lithuania, May 13, 1927; came to U.S., 1954, naturalized, 1960; s. Pranas Viktoras and Paulina (Gervaite) R.; m. Angele Staugaityte, Oct. 4, 1952; 1 son, Pranas Darius. With Commonwealth Rys. of Australia, Melbourne, 1949-53; asst. to fin. acct. Kitchen & Sons, Pty. Ltd., Melbourne, 1953-54; v.p. Photo div. Interphoto Corp., Los Angeles, 1954-71; sr. v.p., sec. Craig Corp., Los Angeles, 1971-87; pres. PAR Enterprises, Burbank, Calif., 1987—; adviser Ministry Fgn. Affairs Republic of Lithuania, 1992. Former pres. Lithuanian Am. Coun., Inc. of Calif.; bd. dirs. Lithuanian-Am. assns.; founder, treas. Baltic Am. Freedom League; former mem. Am. Soc. Internat. Law. Home and Office: Par Enterprises 1501 W Riverside Dr Burbank CA 91506-3027

RAULLERSON, CALVIN HENRY, political scientist, consultant; b. Utica, N.Y., Dec. 18, 1920; s. Calvin Thomas and Cora (White) R.; m. Olive Lewis, Dec. 1, 1956; children: Kevin Greer, Cheryl Harp, Earl Henry. A.B., Lincoln (Pa.) U., 1943; M.P.A., NYU, 1949; postgrad., Harvard, 1947, Harvard Bus. Sch., 1979. Instr. polit. sci. Lincoln U., 1946, 49; editor, dir. research Christian E. Burckell Assocs., Yonkers, N.Y., 1950-52; asst. to exec. dir. United Negro Coll. Fund, 1952-57, dir. ednl. services, 1957-61; dir. African programs Am. Soc. African Culture, Lagos, Nigeria, 1961-64; exec. dir. Am. Soc. African Culture, N.Y.C., 1964-66; chief Peace Corps, East and So. Africa, 1966-69; dir. Kenya, 1969-71, Africa regional dir., 1971-73; exec. asst. to dean Sch. Medicine, spl. asst. to pres. for internat. programs, spl. cons. research and devel., exec. dir. Internat. Ctr. for Arid and Semi-Arid Lands, Tex. Tech U., 1973-78; asst. prof. health orgn. mgmt., Health Svcs. Ctr. Tex. Tech U., 1973-78; asst. adminstr. Bur. Pvt. Devel. Cooperation, AID, 1978-81; v.p. African Am. Inst., 1981-84; assoc. Keene, Monk Assocs., Middleburg, Va., 1985-86; dir. internat. programs One Am., Inc., 1987-88; pres. internat. group LABAT Anderson, 1988-94; v.p. internat. group Gardner Kamya Inc., Washington, 1994—; mgmt. cons. Mgmt. Devel. Consortium, Phelps Stokes Fund, 1973-75; Mem. information resources com. group on bus. affairs Assn. Am. Med. Colls.; mem. adv. com. on desertification AAAS, 1976-78; mem. Career Ministers Selection Bd., Dept. State, 1980; U.S. del. U.N. Conf. Desertification Nairobi, 1977; chmn. U.S. del. Com. on Food Aid and Policy, World Food Program, Rome, 1980; research analyst Pres.'s Com. on Fair Employment Practices, 1944; treas. U.S. planning com. 1st World Festival Negro Art, Dakar, 1965-66; del. Internat. Conf. on African History, U. Ibadan (Nigeria), 1962, Internat. Conf. on African Affairs, U. Ghana, 1963. Assoc. editor: Who's Who in the United Nations, 1952; Contbr. to: Negro Yearbook, 1952. Mem. nat. adv. com. Peace Corps, 1986-89; trustee African Wildlife Found., 1992—, chmn. strategic planning com., 1993—. Rockefeller travel grantee East and Central Africa, 1960; Woodrow Wilson scholar, 1978-79. Clubs: Harvard (Washington). Home: 5823 Bradley Blvd Bethesda MD 20814-1104

RAUM, ARNOLD, federal judge; b. Lynn, Mass., Oct. 27, 1908; s. Isaac and Ida (Ross) R.; m. Muriel Leidner Slaff, Jan. 26, 1944 (div.); m. Violet Gang Kopp, Apr. 26, 1957; stepchildren—Robert E., Elizabeth A., Katherine F. AB summa cum laude, Harvard, 1929, LLB magna cum laude, 1932. Bar: Mass. 1932, U.S. Supreme Ct. 1935, D.C. 1935, bars of various other fed. cts 1935. Sheldon fellow Cambridge U., Eng. 1932; atty. for RFC, 1932-34; spl. asst. to atty. gen. U.S., 1934-50; spl. prosecutor in connection with fed. grand jury investigation of corruption La., 1939; 1st dep. solicitor gen. U.S., also occasional acting, 1939-1950; directed litigation of all Fed. tax cases as well as other types of cases in U.S. Supreme Court, 1939-1950; made arguments in numerous Supreme Ct. cases, including Calif. Tidelands case; judge U.S. Tax Ct., Washington, 1950—; lectr. on taxation Yale Law Sch., 1937-38; mem. faculty Harvard Law Sch., 1947. Editor Harvard Law Rev. 1930-32. Served as lt. comdr. USCGR, World War II. Hon. mem. D.C. Bar Assn., Fed. Bar Assn.; mem. Am. Law Inst., Phi Beta Kappa. Club: Cosmos (Washington). Home: 2622 31st St NW Washington DC 20008-3519 also: 1121 Crandon Blvd Apt F 1106 Key Biscayne FL 33149 Office: US Tax Ct 400 2nd St NW Washington DC 20217-0002

RAUNER, MARY ELLEN, nursing administrator, critical care nurse; b. Dover, N.J., Oct. 22, 1947; d. Vincent A. and Elizabeth H. (Ryan) Grogan; m. James F. Rauner, Sept. 6, 1969; children: Megan Marie, Frederick Vincent. AA, Feterox Coll., 1967; BSN, SUNY, Albany, 1987; MA, Columbia U., 1989. RN, N.J. Clin. instr. Riverside Hosp., Boonton, N.J., patient care mgr. ambulatory svcs.; clin. coord. CCU Gen. Hosp. Ctr. Passaic, N.J., dir. nursing CCU. Passaic Heart Found. grantee. Mem. ANA, AACCN, Am. Orgn. Nurse Execs. Home: 530 Essex Ave Orange NJ 07050-3499

RAUP, DAVID MALCOLM, paleontology educator; b. Boston, Apr. 24, 1933; s. Hugh Miller and Lucy (Bland) R.; m. Susan Creer Shepard, Aug. 25, 1956; 1 son, Mitchell D.; m. Judith T. Yamamoto, May 30, 1987. B.S., U. Chgo., 1953; M.A., Harvard U., 1955, Ph.D., 1957. Instr. Calif. Inst. Tech., 1956-57; mem. faculty Johns Hopkins U., 1957-65, assoc. prof., 1963-65; mem. faculty U. Rochester, 1965-78, prof. geology, 1966-78, chmn. dept. geol. scis., 1968-71, dir. Center for Evolution and Paleobiology, 1977-78; curator geology, chmn. dept. geology Field Mus. Natural History, Chgo., 1978-80; dean of sci. Field Mus. Natural History, 1980-82; prof. geophys. sci. U. Chgo., 1980—, chmn. dept., 1982-85, Sewell L. Avery disting. service prof., 1984—; geologist U.S. Geol. Survey, part-time, 1959-77; vis. prof. U. Tubingen, Germany, 1965, 72. Author: (with S. Stanley) Principles of Paleontology, 1971, 78, The Nemesis Affair, 1986, Extinction: Bad Genes of Bad Luck?, 1991; editor: (with B. Kummel) Handbook of Paleontological Techniques, 1965; contbr. articles to profl. jours. Recipient Best Paper award Jour. Paleontology, 1966; Schuchert award Paleontol. Soc., 1973; Calif. Research Corp. grantee, 1955-56; Am. Assn. Petroleum Geologists grantee, 1957; Am. Philos. Soc. grantee, 1957; NSF grantee, 1960-66, 75-81; Chem. Soc. grantee, 1965-71; NASA grantee, 1983—. Fellow Geol. Soc. Am.; mem. Nat. Acad. Sci., Paleontol. Soc. (pres. 1976-77), Am. Soc. Naturalists (v.p. 1983), Soc. for Study Evolution, AAAS, Sigma Xi. Home: RR 1 Box 168-y Washington Island WI 54246-9753 Office: U Chgo Dept Geophys Scis Chicago IL 60637

RAUP, RONALD B., electronics executive; b. 1949. Computer operator Nat. Cash Register, Rowling Meadows, Ill., 1970-71; store mgr. Weavers Hammond Organ Studio, Elgin, Ill., 1971-75; mgr. Hammond Organ Showcase, Tulsa, Okla., 1975-77; dist. mgr. Wurlitzer Piano Co., Dekalb, Ill., 1977; sr. v.p. Yamaha Internat. Corp., Buena Park, Calif., 1977—. Office: Yamaha Internat Corp 6600 Orangethorpe Ave Buena Park CA 90620

RAUSCH, HOWARD, information service executive; b. N.Y.C., June 29, 1928; s. Sol and Helen (Kartiganer) R.; m. Sidra Cohn, Apr. 22, 1979. A.B., Syracuse U., 1950. Reporter Phila. Bull., N.Y.; copy editor Wall St. Jour., 1961-63, N.Y. Times, 1963-64; editor, fgn. corr. McGraw-Hill, N.Y.C. and Moscow, 1964-68; pres. Advanced Tech. Publs., Inc., Newton, Mass., 1968-80; editor, pub. Laser Focus mag., 1968-80; editor, founder Energy Research, 1975-80; editor Electronic Business, 1980-82; founder, pub. Lightwave Jour., 1983-90; tech. dir. Optical Soc. Am., Washington, 1991-93; pres. Capitol Gains, Info. and Cons. Svcs., Washington, 1993—. Home and Office: 2541 Waterside Dr Washington DC 20008

RAUSCH, JOAN MARY, art historian; b. Calmar, Iowa, Dec. 25, 1937; d. Bernard Joseph and Irene Sophia (Wieling) Menne; m. Gerald William Rausch, Sept. 3, 1960; children: John Thomas, Jennifer Nicole Rausch Goodhart. BS, Coll. St. Teresa, Winona, Minn., 1959; postgrad., U. Wis., LaCrosse, 1974-79; MA, U. Wis., Milw., 1982. Instr. nursing Mercy Hosp., Iowa City, Iowa, 1960-63, St. Francis Hosp./Viterbo Coll., LaCrosse, 1966-71; rsch. asst. dept. art U. Wis., LaCrosse, 1977-79; asst. dept. art history U. Wis., Milw., 1979-81; historic planner Southwest Regional Planning Commn., Platteville, Wis., 1982-83; pres. Archtl. Researches, Inc., LaCrosse, 1983—; cons. historic preservation divsn. State Hist. Soc. Wis., 1983—, Wis. Dept. of Transp., Dist. 5, 1991—. Author: A Catalog of the Oyen Collection, 1979, Historic LaCrosse Architectural and Historic Record, 1984, Chippewa Falls, 1985, Watertown, A Guide to Its Historic Architecture, 1987; (with Joyce McKay) Richland Center Wiconsin, Architectural and Historical Survey Report, 1988; (with Carol Cartwright) City of Mineral Point, Architectural and Historical Survey Report, 1992. Pres. Women's Polit. Caucus, LaCrosse, 1972-73, coord., 1974-75. Recipient Scholarship award Victorian Soc. in Am., 1981, Workshop award Ctr. for Art Criticism, Mpls., 1986. Recipienc Scholarship award Victorian Soc. in am., 1981, Workshop award Ctr. for Art Criticism, Mpls., 1986. Mem. Soc. Archtl. Historians (pres. Wis. chpt. 1982-84), Nat. Trust Hist. Preservation (Preservation Forum(, Wis. Trust Hist. Preservation (charter, task force mem. 1986), Preservation Alliance of LaCrosse (bd. dirs. 1982-88, Heritage award 1989), LaCrosse County Hist. Soc. (hist. preservation com. 1992—, bd. dirs. 1994—). Avocations: painting, ceramics, landscape gardening, travel, swimming. Home and Office: Archtl Researches Inc 5722 W Sherwood Dr La Crosse WI 54601

RAUSCHENBERG, BRADFORD LEE, museum research director; b. Atlanta, Sept. 11, 1940. BS in Archaeology and Biology, Ga. State Coll., 1963; MA in History, Wake Forest U., 1995. Archaeologist Ga. Hist. Commn., 1963-64; site supr., asst. Stanley South, State Archaeologist of N.C., 1964-66; antiquarian, asst. Dir. Restoration Old Salem, Inc., Winston-Salem, N.C., 1966-73; asst. to dir. Mus. Early So. Decorative Arts, Winston-Salem, 1973-76, rsch. fellow, 1976-87, dir. rsch., 1987-93; dir. rsch. Mus. Early So. Decorative Arts and Old Salem, Inc., Winston-Salem, 1993—; cons., lectr. in field. Author: British Regional Carving (1600-1640) and Furniture (1600-1800), 1984; contbr. articles to profl. jours. With USCG, 1964-72. Recipient Halifax Resolves award, 1986; grantee NEH, 1972-81, Kaufman Americana Found., 1981-82. Mem. Am. Ceramic Circle (grantee), Orgn. Am. Historians, No. Ceramic Soc., So. Hist. Assn., Friends of Swiss Ceramic Circle, Regioanl Furniture Soc., Furniture History Soc., Soc. Hist. Archaeology, Soc. Post-Medieval Archaeology, Soc. Historians Early Am. Republic. Address: 221 Harmon Ct Winston Salem NC 27106 Office: Mus Early So Decorative Arts PO Box 10310 Winston Salem NC 27108-0310

RAUSCHENBERG, ROBERT, artist; b. Port Arthur, Tex., Oct. 22, 1925; m. Sue Weil, 1950 (div. 1952); 1 child, Christopher. Student, U. Tex., Kansas City Art Inst., Academie Julian, Paris, Black Mountain Coll., N.C., Art Students League, N.Y.C.; LHD (hon.), Grinnell Coll., 1967; DFA (hon.), U. So. Fla., 1976. One man shows include Parsons Gallery, N.Y.C., 1951, Stable Gallery, N.Y.C., 1953, White Chapel Art Gallery, London, 1964, Leo Castelli Gallery, 1972, 73, Galerie Ileana Sonnabend, Paris, 1971, 72, 73, Ace Gallery, Los Angeles, 1973, Vancouver Art Gallery, 1978, Tate Gallery, London, 1981, Phoenix Art Mus., 1982, G.H. Dalsheimer Gallery, Balt., 1983, Castelli Graphics, 1984, others; exhbn. art constructions Rome and Florence Italy, 1953, Leo Castelli Gallery, N.Y.C., 1957—; rep. internat. art festivals, Carnegie Inst. Internat. exhbns., Sao Paulo Biennial, 1959, Exposition Internat. du Surrealisme, Paris, 1959-60, Amsterdam, others; group shows include Mus. Modern Art, 1959, Guggenheim Mus., 1961, 92, N.Y. Collection in Stockholm, 1972, Whitney Mus., N.Y.C., 1972, 73, Garage Show, Rome, 1973, Autumne Festival d'Artes, Paris, 1973, Mus. South Tex., Corpus Christi, 1974, N.Y. Cultural Center, 1973, retrospective exhbn., Nat. Collection Fine Arts, Smithsonian Inst., Washington, 1976, Mus. Modern Art, N.Y.C., 1977, Albright Knox Gallery, 1977, San Francisco Mus. Modern Art, 1977, Art Inst. Chgo., 1977, Staatliche Kunsthalle, Berlin, 1980, Kunsthalle, Düsseldorf, 1980, Louisiana Mus., Copenhagen, 1980, Stadelsches Kunstinstitut, Frankfurt, 1981, Städtische Galerie im Lembachhaus, Munich, 1981, Tate Gallery, London, 1981, Galerie Beyeler, Basle, 1984, Juan March, Madrid, 1985, Inst. Contemporary Art, London, 1987, L.A. County Mus. Art, 1987, Galerie Alfred Kren, Cologne, Germany, 1988-89, Tretyakov Gallery, Moscow, 1989, Nat. Art Gallery, Kuala Lampur, Malaysia, 1990; permanent collections include Albright-Knox Art Gallery, Whitney Mus. Am. Art, Wadsworth Atheneum, Tate Gallery, Mus. Modern Art, Neue Galerie Aachen, Fed. Republic Germany, Hirshhorn Mus., Moderna Museet, Stockholm, others; reprodn. photographs by silk screen stenciling technique to allow change in scale; set and costume designer, lighting expert, stage mgr. Merce Cunningham Dance Co., 1964; choreographer: dance Pelican; others; works include electronic sculpture Soundings; paintings Tut-Scape; originator Overseas Culture Interchange traveling exhbns., 1985—. Served with USNR, World War II; neuropsychiat. tech. Calif. Naval Hosps. Recipient 1st prize Internat. Exbn. Prints Gallery Modern Art, Ljubljana, Yugoslavia, 1963, 1st prize Venice Biennale, 1964, 1st prize Corcoran Biennial Contemporary Am. Painters,

1965, Skowhegan Sch. Painting and Sculpture medal, 1982, NAD assoc., 1983, Grammy award, 1984. Mem. Am. Acad. and Inst. Arts and Letters. Gallery: Knoedler & Co 19 E 70th St New York NY 10021

RAUSCHER, TOMLINSON GENE, electronics company executive; b. Oneida, N.Y., May 27, 1946; s. Grant Koster and Rosalind Rebecca (Smith) R.; B.S., Yale U., 1968; M.S., U. N.C., Chapel Hill, 1971; Ph.D., U. Md., 1975; M.B.A., U. Rochester, 1984; children—David Grant, Tasha Candice, April Abigail, Nathan Tomlinson. Computer specialist Naval Research Lab., Washington, 1972-75; mgr. software tech. applications NCR Corp., Cambridge, Ohio, 1975-76; sr. computer architect Amdahl Corp., Sunnyvale, Calif., 1976-77; mgr. software systems GTE Labs., Waltham, Mass., 1977-78; mgr. product devel. and software systems design Xerox Corp., Rochester, N.Y., 1978—; vis. asst. prof. Ohio U., 1976; adj. prof. Rochester Inst. Tech., 1991—. Cert. computer programmer, data processor. Winner Masters Pole Vault—Empire State Games Championship, Eastern Region Masters Championship, Can. Nat. Masters Championship, U.S. Nat. Championship, N.Am. Masters Championship; named All-Am. champion. Mem. IEEE (sr.), Assn. Computing Machinery, Greater Rochester Track Club. Author: (with A. Agrawala) Foundations of Microprogramming—Architecture, Software and Applications, 1976, Software Development and Management for Microprocessor-Based Systems, 1987; contbr. articles on time to market, orgn., mgmt., software engring., computer architecture, microprogramming to profl. jours.; patentee computer systems design. Home: 85 Sunset Blvd Pittsford NY 14534-2142 Office: Xerox Corp 300 Main St East Rochester NY 14445

RAUSHENBUSH, WALTER BRANDEIS, law educator; b. Madison, Wis., June 13, 1928; s. Paul A. and Elizabeth (Brandeis) R.; m. Marylu de Watteville, May 3, 1956; children: Lorraine Elizabeth, Richard Walter, Carla de Watteville, Paul Brandeis. AB magna cum laude in Govt., Harvard U., 1950; JD with high honors, U. Wis., 1953. Bar: Wis. 1953. Ptnr. LaFollette, Sinykin & Doyle, Madison, 1956-58; mem. faculty U. Wis.-Madison, 1958—, prof. law, 1966—; vis. prof. law U. San Diego, 1992-94; project dir. real estate transfer study Am. Bar Found., 1967-72; trustee nat. Law Sch. Admission Coun., 1968-70, 72-95, chmn. pre-law com., 1970-74, chmn. svcs. com., 1976-78, pres. 1980-82; legal advisor Madison Citizens Fair Housing, 1961-63, Wis. Citizens Family Planning, 1965-73; mem. real property drafting com. Multistate Bar Exam., 1986—. Author: Wisconsin Construction Lien Law, 1974, (with others) Wisconsin Real Estate Law, 1984, 4th edit., 1994, Brown on Personal Property, 3d edit., 1975, Real Estate Transactions Cases and Materials, 1994. Served with USAF, 1953-56, col. Res. ret. Mem. ABA, State Bar Wis., Dane County Bar Assn., AAUP, Order of Coif, Phi Beta Kappa, Phi Delta Phi (province pres. 1963-75). Presbyterian (elder). Club: Stage Harbor Yacht (Chatham, Mass.). Home: 3942 Plymouth Cir Madison WI 53705-5212 Office: U Wis Law Sch Madison WI 53706-1399

RAUSSER, GORDON C(LYDE), agricultural and resource economics educator; b. Lodi, Calif., July 21, 1943; s. Elmer A. and Doyve Ester (Meyers) R.; children: Sloan, Stephanie, Paige. BS summa cum laude, Calif. State U., 1965; MS with highest honors, U. Calif., Davis, 1968, PhD with highest honors, 1971. Prof. econs. and agrl. econs. U. Calif., Davis, 1969-74; vis. prof. U. Chgo., 1972-74; prof. econs. and stats. Iowa State U., 1974-75; prof. bus. adminstrn. Harvard U., 1975-78; prof., chmn. dept. agrl. and resource econs. U. Calif., Berkeley, 1979-85, 93-94, Robert Gordon Sproul disting. prof., 1985—; dir. Giannini Found., Berkeley, 1984-86; dean nat. resources U. Calif., 1994—; vis. prof. Hebrew U. and Ben-Gurion U., Israel, 1978; Ford Found. vis. prof., Argentina, 1972; spl. cons. and sr. economist Council Econ. Advisors, 1986-87; chief economist Agy. for Internat. Devel., 1988-90; advisor econ. research U.S. Dept. Agriculture, 1988-90, 86-88, Agriculture Can., 1977-79, Bur. Agrl. Econs., Australia, 1987, U.S. Office Mgmt. and Budget, 1986; mem., chmn. planning com. Sch. Bus. Adminstrn. U. Calif., Berkeley, 1986-87, mem. adv. com. Agrl. Issues Ctr., 1984-85, mem. planning com. Agrl. and Natural Resources Program, 1986, mem. econs. programs evaluation com., 1987-88; mem. Citrus Planning Commn., Brazil, 1984; pres. Inst. for Policy Reform, Washington, 1989—; prin. Law & Econ. Cons. Group, Berkeley, Calif., Washington, Chgo., N.Y.C., 1988—. Author numerous books including Macroeconomic Environment for U.S. Agricultural Policy, Alternative Agricultural and Food Policies and the 1985 Farm Bill, The Emergence of Market Economies in Eastern Europe, New Directions in Econometric Modeling and Forecasting in U.S. Agriculture, Dynamics of Agricultural Systems: Economic Prediction and Control, Quantitative Methods in Agricultural Economics, GATT Negotiations and the Political Economy of Policy Reform; editor: Decision-Making in Business and Economics, 1977-79, Am. Jour. Agrl. Econs., 1983-86. Mem. western nutrition ctr. coordinating com. U.S. Dept. Agr., 1980-83; mem. Arab-Am. Council for Cultural and Econ. Exchange, 1979-81; bd. dirs. Giannini Found. Agrl. Econs., 1979-84, mem. exec. com., 1979-84 ; mem. planning com. Berkeley Food Coop., 1980-83, planning com. for agrl. and food policy Resources for the Future, 1984-85; mem. adv. com. Calif. State Dept. Agriculture, 1982-84; bd. dirs. Am. Agrl. Econs. Awards. Grantee U.S. Dept. Agr., NSF, World Bank, Chgo. Merc. Exch., U.S. Bur. Mines; Fulbright scholar, Australia, 1987; sr. fellow Resources for Future, 1984-85, Outstanding tchr. award Harvard U., 1978. Fellow AAAS, Am. Statis. Assn., Am. Agrl. Econs. Assn. (agrl. policy planning com. 1984-86, outstanding enduring rsch. contbn. com. 1982-84, outstanding PhD dissertation com. 1974-76, chmn. outstanding article com. 1983-86, Pub. Enduring Quality award 1993, Disting. Policy Contbn. award 1993, award of merit 1976, 78, 80, 82, 86, 89, 92); mem. Am. Econ. Assn., Am. Acad. Polit. and Social Sci., Econometric Soc., Math. Assn. Am., Ops. Rsch. Soc., Western Agrl. Econ. Assn. (Best Pub. Rsch. award 1978, Outstanding Pub. Rsch. award 1994), Alpha Gamma Rho, Alpha Zeta, Phi Beta Kappa. Club: Commonwealth (dir. agriculture study group 1983-84). Home: 649 Creston Rd Berkeley CA 94708-1239 Office: U Calif Dept Agr & Resource Econs Berkeley CA 94720-3310

RAUTENBERG, ROBERT FRANK, consulting statistician; b. Milw., Sept. 14, 1943; s. Raymond Clarence and Anna Josephine (Winter) R.; m. Meredith Taylor, June 2, 1965 (div. Feb. 1975); 1 child, Matthew Carl. PhD in Bus. Adminstrn., Pacific Western U., 1983; post doctorate rsch., Sorbonne U., Paris. Pvt. practice acctg. Kansas City, Mo., 1975-76; pres. Seven Diamond Enterprises, San Francisco, 1976-78; chief exec. officer Assurance Systems, San Francisco, 1984—. Author: The Analytical Management Handbook, 1989, Supplement to the Analytical Management Handbook, 1991; contbr. articles to profl. jours. and conf. proceedings. Fellow Royal Statis. Soc.; mem. Internat. Soc. Bayesian Analysis (charter). Episcopalian. Avocations: swimming, skiing, traveling. Home: 711 Leavenworth St San Francisco CA 94109-6084 Office: Assurance Systems 588 Sutter St Ste 434 San Francisco CA 94102-1102 *Personal philosophy: I am always surprised at the willingness of the human spirit to face new challenges.*

RAVE, JAMES A., bishop. Bishop of Northwestern Ohio, Evang. Luth. Ch. in Am., Toledo. Office: Evang Luth Ch Am 621 Bright Rd Findlay OH 45840-6987

RAVECHÉ, HAROLD JOSEPH, university administrator, physical chemist; b. N.Y.C., Mar. 18, 1943; s. Harold Edward Raveche and Helen Patricia (DeVincent) Gravino; m. Elizabeth Marie Scott, Jan. 26, 1974; children—John Vincent, Justin Blaise, Bernice Helen, Elizabeth Ann. B.A. in Chemistry, Hofstra U., 1963; Ph.D. in Phys. Chemistry, U. Calif.-San Diego, 1968. NRC postdoctoral assoc. Nat. Bur. Standards, Gaithersburg, Md., 1968-70, research chemist, 1970-78, chief thermophysics div., 1978-85; dean Sch. of Sci., prof. chemistry Rensselaer Poly. Inst., Troy, N.Y., 1985-88; pres. Stevens Inst. Tech., Hoboken, N.J., 1988—; bd. dirs. Nat. West N.J. and Bancorp, Atlantic Energy Inc.; commr. of sci. and tech., N.J. Editor: Perspectives in Statistical Physics, 1980; contbr. articles to profl. jours. Pres. Potomac Highlands Citizens Assn., Md., 1978-80. Recipient Disting. Young Scientist of Yr. award Md. Acad. Scis., 1975, U.S. Sr. Exec. Service award Nat. Bur. Standards, 1983, Equal Employment Opportunity award Nat. Bur. Standards, 1984. Mem. AAAS (commn. on sci. edn. 1972-75), Am. Phys. Soc. (adv. council 1975-78), Soc. for Indsl. and Applied Math. (adv. bd. conf. on large-scale computational problems 1984-88), Am. Chem. Soc., Sigma Xi. Roman Catholic. Avocations: hiking, swimming, skiing, music, theater. Office: Stevens Inst Tech Office of Pres Castle Point On Hudson Hoboken NJ 07030

RAVEL, DILIP N., pharmaceutical executive; b. 1933. BS in Physics and Chemistry, U. Bombay, India, 1953, MS in Clin. Biochemistry, 1955; PhD in Physics and Chemistry, U. Oregon, 1962. Mgr. Varian Arrowgraph, Calif., 1955-68; dir. U. Calif. Med. Ctr., San Francisco, 1968-70; dir. rsch. Alcon Labs., Inc., Fort Worth, 1970-72, gen. mgr. science and tech., 1972-75, v.p. rsch. and devel., 1975-88, sr. v.p. rsch. and devel., 1988—. Office: Alcon Laboratories Inc 6201 South Fwy Fort Worth TX 76134

RAVEN, BERTRAM H(ERBERT), psychology educator; b. Youngstown, Ohio, Sept. 26, 1926; s. Morris and Lillian (Greenfeld) R.; m. Celia Cutler, Jan. 21, 1961; children: Michelle G., Jonathan H. BA, Ohio State U., 1948, MA, 1949; PhD, U. Mich., 1953. Research assoc. Research Ctr. for Group Dynamics, Ann Arbor, Mich., 1952-54; lectr. psychology U. Mich., Ann Arbor, 1953-54; vis. prof. U. Nijmegen, U. Utrecht, Netherlands, 1954-55; psychologist RAND Corp., Santa Monica, Calif., 1955-56; prof. UCLA, 1956—, chair dept. psychology, 1983-88; vis. prof Hebrew U., Jerusalem, 1962-63, U. Wash., Seattle, U. Hawaii, Honolulu, 1968, London Sch. Econs. and Polit. Sci., London, 1969-70; external examiner U. of the W.I., Trinidad and Jamaica, 1980—; rsch. assoc. Psychol. Rsch. Ctr., 1993—; participant Internat. Expert Conf. on Health Psychology, Tilburg, The Netherlands, 1986; cons., expert witness in field, 1979—. co-dir. Tng. Program in Health Psychology, UCLA, 1979-88; cons. World Health Orgn., Manila, 1985-86; cons., expert witness various Calif. cts., 1978—. Author: (with others) People in Groups, 1976, Discovering Psychology, 1977, Social Psychology, 1983, Social Psychology: People in Groups (Chinese edition), 1994; editor: (with others) Contemporary Health Services, 1982, Policy Studies Rev. Ann., 1980; editor: Jour. Social Issues, 1969-74; contbr. articles to profl. jours. Guggenheim fellow, Israel, 1962-63; Fulbright scholar The Netherlands, 1954-55, Israel, 1962-63, Britain, 1969-70; Citation from Los Angeles City Council, 1966, Rsch. on Soc. power by Calif. Sch. of profl. psychology, L.A., 1991; NATO sr. fellow, Italy, 1989. Fellow Am. Psychol. Assn. (chair bd. social and ethical responsibility 1978-82), Am. Psychol. Soc., Soc. for Psychol. Study of Social Issues (pres. 1973-74); mem. AAAS, Am. Sociol. Assn., Internat. Assn. Applied Psychology, Soc. Exptl. Social Psychology, Assn. Advancement of Psychology (founding, bd. dirs. 1974-81), Internat. Soc. Polit. Psychology, Interam. Psychol. Soc., Am. Psychology-Law Soc. Avocations: guitar, travel, international studies. Home: 2212 Camden Ave Los Angeles CA 90064-1906 Office: UCLA Dept Psychology Los Angeles CA 90095-1563

RAVEN, CORINNE, principal. Prin. Mother McAuley Liberal Arts High Sch., Chgo. Recipient Blue Ribbon Sch. award U.S. Dept. Edn., 1990-91. Office: Mother McAuley Liberal Arts High Sch 3737 W 99th St Chicago IL 60642-3321

RAVEN, GREGORY KURT, retail executive; b. Elmhurst, Ill., Sept. 14, 1949; s. Eugene Alexander and Eloise Irene (McGhee) R.; m. Margot Clesta Theis, Feb. 2, 1974; children: Scott, Bryan, Ashley, Michael. B.B.A., Bucknell U., 1971. Second v.p. Chase Manhattan Bank, N.Y.C., 1973-76; corp. fin. specialist, dir. corp. fin. Gt. Atlantic and Pacific Tea Co., Inc., Montvale, N.J., 1977-80, asst. treas., 1980-82, treas., asst. chief fin. officer, 1982-87; v.p., treas. Revco Drug Stores, Twinsburg, Ohio, 1987-88, exec. v.p. fin. and chief fin. officer, 1988—. Republican. Office: Revco Drug Stores Inc 1925 Enterprise Pky Twinsburg OH 44087-2207

RAVEN, PETER HAMILTON, botanical garden director, botany educator; b. Shanghai, China, June 13, 1936; s. Walter Francis and Isabelle Marion (Breen) R.; children—Alice Catherine, Elizabeth Marie, Francis Clark, Kathryn Amelia. AB with highest honors, U. Calif.-Berkeley, 1957; PhD, UCLA, 1960; DSc (hon.), St. Louis U., 1982, Knox Coll., 1983, So. Ill. U., 1983, Miami U., 1986, U. Goteborg, 1987, Rutgers U., 1988, U. Mass., 1988, Leiden U., The Netherlands, 1990; HHD (hon.), Webster U., 1989; D.Sc. (hon.), Universidad Nacional de La Plata, Argentina, 1991, Westminster Coll., 1992, U. Mo., 1992, Washington U., 1993, U. Conn., 1993; DSc (hon.), U. Cordoba, Argentina, 1993. Taxonomist, curator Rancho Santa Ana Botanic Garden, Claremont, Calif., 1961-62; asst. prof., then assoc. prof. biol. scis. Stanford U., Calif., 1962-71; dir. Mo. Bot. Garden, St. Louis, 1971—; adj. prof. biology St. Louis U., 1973—; Engelmann prof. botany Washington U., St. Louis, 1976—; adj. prof. biology U. Mo., St. Louis, 1976—; sr. rsch. fellow New Zealand Dept. Sci. and Indsl. Rsch., 1969-70; v.p. XIII Internat. Bot. Congress, Sydney, 1981; home sec. Nat. Acad. Scis., 1987—; chmn. report rev. com. NRC, 1989—; mem. pres. com. Adv. on Sci. and Tech., 1994—; hon. vice-chair 27th Internat. Geographical Cong., 1992; hon. v.p. XV Internt. Bot. Cong., Tokyo, 1993; mem. Nat. Sci. Bd., 1990-94; mem. jury Internat. St. Francis Prize for Environment, 1990-93; mem. exec. com. Joint Appeal by Religion and Sci. for Environment, 1991—; mem. external adv. bd. Com. on Peabody Mus., Yale U., 1992-94; mem. coun. World Resources Inst., 1992—; mem. adv. com. Africa Ctr. for Resources and Environment, 1992—; Third World Found. N.Am., 1993; mem. adv. com. to biodiversity com. Chinese Acad. Scis., 1993—; mem. Exec. Com. Round Table, St. Louis, 1993—; mem. hon. fgn. adv. bd. Botanical Garden Orgn. Thailand, 1993—. Author: Native Shrubs of Southern California, 1966, (with P.R. Ehrlich, R.W. Holm) Papers on Evolution, 1969, (with H. Curtis) Biology of Plants, 1971, 4th edit., 1986, (with R.F. Evert and S.E. Eichhorn) 5th edit., 1992, (with B. Berlin and D. Breedlove) Principles of Tzeltal Plant Classification, 1974, (with G.B. Johnson) Biology, 1986, 3d edit., 1992, Understanding Biology, 1988, 3d edit., 1995; editor: (with L.E. Gilbert) Coevolution of Animals and Plants, 1981, (with F.J. Radovsky & S.H. Sohmer) Biogeography of the Tropical Pacific, 1984, (with others) Topics in Plant Population Biology, 1979, (with K. Iwatsuki and W.J. Bock) Modern Aspects of Species, 1986; editor-in-chief Brittonia, 1963-66; mme. editorial bd. Flora Neotropica, 1965-84; editor (with D.E. Osterbrock) Origins and Extinctions, 1988, paperback, 1992, (with R.M. Polhill) Advances in Legume Systematics, 1981 (with L. Berg and G.B. Johnson) Environment, 1995; mem. editorial bd. Evolution, 1965-63, 76-79, Memoirs of N.Y. Botanical Garden, 1966-84, N.Am. Flora, 1966-84, Am. Naturalist, 1967-70, Annual Rev. Ecology and Systematics, 1971-75, Flora of Ecuador, 1974—, Evolutionary Theory, 1975—, Adansonia, 1976—, Jour. Biogeography, 1978—, Science, 1979-82, Proceedings of U.S. Nat. Acad. Scis., 1980-87, World Book, Inc., 1982-86, Diversity, 1985-90, Bothalia, 1985—, Serie Botánica of the Anales del Instituto de Biología UNAM, 1989, Ecol. Applications, 1989-92, others; mem. adv. bd. Applied Botany Abstracts, 1981—, Tropical Plant Sci. Research, 1982—, Darwiniana, 1985—; mem. internat. edit. com. Acta Botánica Mexicana, 1987—; mem. editorial bd. Botanical Bulletin Academia Sinica, 1988—, Botanical Mag., 1988-92; co-chmn. editorial com. Flora of China, 1988—; advisor Plants Today, 1988-89; contbr. over 400 articles to profl. jours. bd. curators U. Mo., 1985-90; commr. Tower Grove Park, St. Louis, 1971—; mem. Arnold Arboretum Vis. Com., 1974-81, chmn. 1976-81; bd. overseers Morris Arboretum, 1977-81; mem. sci. adv. bd. Nat. Tropical Botanical Garden, 1975—; mem. Smithsonian Council, 1985-90; chmn. St. Louisollaborative, 1985-91, Commn. for Flora Neotropica, 1985—; mem. Commn. on Mus. for New Century, 1981-84; mem. sci. and engring. panel Com. on Scholarly Communication with People's Republic China, 1981-85; chmn. com. to visit dept. organismic and evolutionary biology Harvard U., 1982-84, mem. 84-85; ednl. adv. bd. John Simon Guggenheim Meml. Found., 1986—; research assoc. botany Bernice P. Bishop Mus., 1985—; hon. trustee Acad. of St. Louis, 1986—; chmn. Internat. Union for the Conservation of Nature, World Wildlife Fund, 1984-87, hon. chmn. 1987-90; mem. adv. and tech. bd. Fundación de Parques Nacionales and Fundación Neotrópica, Costa Rica, 1988—; mem. Nat. Coun. World Wildlife Fund and Conservation Foun., 1989—, U.S. bd. dirs. 1983-88, bd. dirs. Conservation Found., 1985-88, sci. adv. com. Conservation Internat., 1988—, chmn's. coun., 1989, World Wildlife Fund, 1987-90, Conservation Found., 1989—, Found. Flora Malesianna, 1992—, Sci. Svc., 1993—; hon. scientific adv. com. XVII Pacific Sci. Congress, 1990-91; adv. bd. The Winslow Found., 1993—, The Internat. Sci. Camp The Earth We Share, 1993—; exec. bd. Internat. Sci. Found. for the Former Soviet Union, 1992—; internat. adv. bd. Fifth ICSEB Congress, Hungary, 1994—; mem. editl. bd. Chinese Jour. of Botany, 1991—, Edinburgh Jour. Botany, 1994—; mem. internat. editl. adv. bd. Caldasia, 1995—. Commn. mem. U.S. MAB, 1994-95. Recipient A.P. DeCandolle prize, Geneva, 1970; Disting. Service award Japan Am. Soc. So. Calif., 1977; award of Merit, Bot. Soc. Am., 1977; Achievement medal Garden Club Am., 1978; Willdenow medal Berlin Bot. Garden, 1979; Disting. Service award Am. Inst. Biol. Scis., 1981; Joseph Priestly medal, Dickinson Coll., 1982; Gold Seal medal Nat. Council of State Garden Clubs, 1982; Internat. Environ. Leadership medal UN Environ. Program, 1982; Spl. citiation Doña Doris Yankelewitz de Monge, 1985,

Internat. Prize for Biology, Govt. Japan, 1986, Hutchinson medal Chgo. Hort. Soc., 1986, Archie F. Carr medal, 1987, Global 500 Honor Roll UN Environ. Program, 1987, Am. Fuchsia Soc. Achievement Medal, 1987, George Robert White Medal of Honor Mass. Horticultural Soc., 1987, Robert Allerton Medal Nat. Tropical Bot. Garden, 1988, Nat. Conservation Achievement award Nat. Wildlife Fedn., 1989, Delmer S. Fahrney medal Franklin Inst., Phila., 1989, (with E.O. Wilson) Environ. prize Institut de la Vie (Paris), 1990, Order of Golden Ark (officer), The Netherlands, 1990, award for Support of Sci. Coun. Sci. Soc. Pres., 1990, (with Norman Myers) Volvo Environ. prize, 1992, Pres.'s Conservation Achievement Awd., 1993, Nature Conservacyvement award TNC, 1993, Internat. award Internat. Inst. of St. Louis, 1994, Founder's Coun. Centennial Merit award The Field Mus. of Natural History, 1994, Sword of St. Ignatius Loyola award St. Louis U., 1994, Tyler Environ. Achievement prize, 1994, and numerous other botanical awards and honors; Guggenheim fellow, 1969-70; John D. and Catherine T. MacArthur Found. fellow, 1985-90, NSF postdoctoral fellow, Brit. Mus. London, 1960-61. Fellow Am. Acad. Arts and Scis. (com. on membership 1980-82), Linnean Soc. London (fgn. mem.), Calif. Acad. Scis. (CAS Fellow, Fellows' medal 1988), AAAS, Indian Nat. Sci. Acad., Third World Acad. Scis., World Acad. Art & Sci.; mem. NSF (systematic biology panel 1973-76, chmn. adv. com. for biol. behavioral and social scis. 1984-90), NAS (com. on human rights 1984-87, home sec. 1987—), Royal Danish Acad. Scis. and Letters (fgn. hon.), Royal Swedish Acad. Scis. (fgn.), Royal Soc. New Zealand (hon.), NRC (gov. bd. 1983-86, 87-88, chmn. com. on research priorities in tropical biology 1977-79, assembly life scis. 1979-81, com. on selected research problems in humid tropics 1980-82, commn. internat. relations 1981-82), Calif. Bot. Soc. (v.p. 1968-69), Am. Soc. Plant Taxonomists (pres. 1972), Assn. Systematics Collections (pres. 1980-82, Fed. Council Arts and Humanities, Nat. Geographic Soc. (com. onsearch and exploration 1982-), Internat. Orgn. Plant Biosystematists (v.p. 1989-92, pres. 92-95), Internat. Assn. for Plant Taxonomy (council 1981—), Orgn. Tropical Studies (treas. 1981-84, v.p. devel. 1984-85, pres. 1985-88, past pres. 1988-90, bd. dirs. 1981-91), Am. Soc. Naturalists (pres. 1983), Miller Inst. Basic Research in Sci. (adv. bd. 1983-89), Am. Inst. Biol. Scis. (pres. 1983-84), Am. Acad. Scis., Geol. Soc. Am., Bot. Soc. Am. (pres. 1975, chmn. com. on sci. exchange with People's Republic China 1978-84), Assn. Tropical Biology (bd. dirs. 1981-85), Am. Assn. Mus. (exec. com. 1980-83), Assn. Sci. Mus. Dirs., Assn. Pacific Systematists, Sociedad Argentina de Botanica (socio honorario), Fundación Miguel Lillo (hon.), Soc. Systematic Zool., Sociedad Botánica de México (life), Assn. pour l'Etude Taxonomique de la Flore d'Afrique Tropicale, Orgn. for Phyto-Taxonomic Investigation of Mediterranean Area (council 1975-89), All-Union Botanical Soc. USSR (hon. fgn. mem.), Accademia Nazionale delle Scienze detta dei XL (fgn.), Am. Philosophical Soc, Russian Acad. Scis. (fgn. mem.), Nat. Acad. Scis. India (fgn. fellow 1990—), Academia de Ciencias Exactas, Físicas y Naturales, Austrian Acad. Scis., Academia Chilena de Ciencias, Academia Nacional de Ciencias, Academy Scis. Ukraine, Chinese Acad. Scis., Nature Conservancy (Pres. Conservation Achievement Awd., 1993), Phi Beta Kappa, Sigma Xi. Office: Mo Bot Garden PO Box 299 Saint Louis MO 63166-0299

RAVEN, ROBERT DUNBAR, lawyer; b. Cadillac, Mich., Sept. 26, 1923; s. Christian and Gladys L. (Dunbar) R.; m. Leslie Kay Erickson, June 21, 1947; children: Marta Ellen, Matt Robert, Brett Lincoln. AB with honors, Mich. State U., 1949; LLB, U. Calif., Berkeley, 1952. Bar: Calif. 1953. Assoc. Morrison & Foerster and predecessor, San Francisco, 1952-56, ptnr., 1956-94, sr. of counsel, 1994—; chmn. Morrison & Foerster (and predecessor), San Francisco, 1974-82; mem. Jud. Coun. of Calif., 1983-87. Bd. dirs. Bay Area USO, 1964-73, pres., 1968-70; mem. San Francisco Mayor's Criminal Justice Coun., 1971-72; co-chmn. San Francisco Lawyer's Com. for Urban Affairs, 1976-78; bd. dirs. Lawyers Com. for Civil Rights Under Law, 1976—. With USAAF, 1942-45. Decorated Air medal with oak leaf cluster. Mem. ABA (pres. 1988-89, mem. standing com. on fed. judiciary 1975-80, chmn. 1978-80, chmn. standing com. on legal aid and indigent defendents 1981-83, chair standing com. dispute resolution 1991-93, chair sect. dispute resolution 1993-94), State Bar Calif. (gov. 1978-81, pres. 1981), Fed. Bar Assn., Bar Assn. San Francisco (pres. 1971), Am. Law Inst., Am. Coll. Trial Lawyers, Am. Bar Found., Am. Judicature Soc., Boalt Hall Alumni Assn. (pres. 1972-73), Order of Coif., World Trade Club (San Francisco), Bankers Club of San Francisco, Am. Arbitration Assn. (bd. dirs. 1988—), Internat. Acad. Trial Lawyers, CPR Inst. for Dispute Resolution (exec. com.). Democrat. Home: 1064 Via Alta Lafayette CA 94549-2916 Office: Morrison & Foerster 345 California St Fl 35 San Francisco CA 94104

RAVENAL, EARL CEDRIC, international relations educator, author; b. N.Y.C., Mar. 29, 1931; s. Alan M. and Mildred S. (Sherman) R.; m. Carol Bird Myers, May 26, 1956; children: Cornelia Jane, John Brodhead, Rebecca Eliza. B.A., Harvard U., 1952; postgrad., U. Cambridge, Eng., 1952-53; M.M.P. diploma, Harvard Bus. Sch., 1958; M.A., Johns Hopkins U., 1971; Ph.D., John Hopkins U., 1975. Treas. Elbe File & Binder Co., Inc., Fall River, Mass., 1955-64, pres., 1965-67; dir. Asian div. systems analysis Office Sec. Def., Washington, 1967-69; prof. internat. relations Johns Hopkins U. Sch. Advanced Internat. Studies, Washington, 1973-78, Georgetown U. Sch. Fgn. Service, Washington, 1976—; mem. bd. advisors Ctr. for Def. Info., Washington, 1971—; Inst. for Study of Diplomacy, 1983—, The Ind. Inst., Calif., 1989—. Author: (with others) Peace with China?, 1971, (with James Chace) Atlantis Lost, 1976, Never Again, 1979, Toward World Security, 1978, Strategic Disengagement and World Peace, 1979, NATO's Unremarked Demise, 1979, Defining Def., 1984, NATO: The Tides of Discontent, 1985, Large-Scale Foreign Policy Change, 1989, Designing Defense, 1991; contbg. editor Inquiry Mag., 1976-85, Critical Rev., 1987—; contbr. articles in field to profl. jours. Advisor Democratic Presdl. Campaign, 1972; advisor Jerry Brown Presdl. Campaign, 1976, Libertarian Presdl. Campaign, 1980; shadow def. sec. Libertarian Party, 1993—. Served with JAGC U.S. Army, 1953-55. Henry fellow U. Cambridge, 1952-53; mem. faculty Salzburg Seminar in Am. Studies, 1977; fellow Bellagio Ctr. Rockefeller Found., 1975, Woodrow Wilson Internat. Ctr. for Scholars, 1973, Washington Ctr. for Fgn. Policy Research, 1974, Inst. Policy Studies, 1977-80; sr. fellow Cato Inst., 1985-91. Mem. Council Fgn. Relations, Am. Polit. Sci. Assn., Internat. Inst. Strategic Studies, Fed. Am. Scientists, Internat. Studies Assn. Libertarian. Clubs: Cosmos (Washington); Fed. City (Washington); Harvard (N.Y.C.); Signet (Cambridge, Mass.); Tred Avon Yacht (Oxford, Md.). Home: 4439 Cathedral Ave NW Washington DC 20016-3562

RAVENHALL, COLIN, chemicals executive. CEO Courtaulds Aerospace, Inc., Glendale, Calif. Office: Courtaulds Aerospace Inc 5430 San Fernando Rd Glendale CA 91203*

RAVENHILL, PHILIP LEONARD, curator, art historian; b. Bath, U.K., June 2, 1945; s. Leonard and Martha (Wilson) R.; m. Judith Timyam, 1968; children: Geoffrey, Brendan, Amanda. BA in Philosophy, Nyack Coll., 1968; MA in Anthropology, New Sch. for Social Rsch., 1970, PhD, 1976. Lectr. in anthropology Richmond Coll., CUNY, 1970-71, 72, Bard Coll., 1971, Finch Coll., 1972; rsch. assoc. Inst. d'Ethno-Sociologie Univ. d'Abidjan, 1972-74, rsch. assoc. Inst. d'Histoire, d'Art et d'Archéologie Africains, 1975-77, attaché de recherche, 1978-79, chargé de recherche, 1979-82; sr. rsch. fellow Internat. African Inst., London, 1982-87; project dir. West African Mus. Project, Abidjan, Ivory Coast, 1982-87; chief curator Nat. Mus. African Art, Smithsonian Inst., Washington, 1987—; cons. in econ. anthropology Compagnie Ivoirienne pour le Développement des Textiles, 1977-78; cons. on cultural preservation and edn. The Ford Found., West Africa, 1982, 84-87; mem. steering com. Smithsonian Inst. Forum on Material Culture, 1988-91, West African Mus. Project Internat. African Inst., 1987-92; dir. joint Nat. Mus. African Art-Musée National du Mali film team, 1989; co-chair Eighth Triennial Symposium on African Art, 1989; bd. dirs. West African Mus. Programme; N.Am. coord. ICOM Conf., 1991; cons. in field; participant numerous confs. Author: (book) The Art of the Personal Object, 1991; author, field coord. video films for exhbns.; contbr. articles to profl. jours. Office: Smithsonian Inst Nat Mus African Art 950 Independence Ave SW Washington DC 20560

RAVENHOLT, REIMERT THOROLF, epidemiologist; b. Milltown, Wis., Mar. 9, 1925; s. Ansgar Benedikt and Kristine Henriette (Petersen) R.; divorced; children: Janna, Mark, Lisa, Dane; m. Betty Butler Howell, Sept. 26, 1981. B.S., U. Minn., 1948, M.B., 1951, M.D., 1952; M.P.H., U. Calif.-Berkeley, 1956. Intern USPHS Hosp., San Francisco, 1951-52; epidemic intelligence service officer USPHS Communicable Disease Ctr., Atlanta, 1952-54; dir. epidemiology and communicable disease div. Seattle-King

County Health Dept., 1954-61; epidemiology cons. European area USPHS, Paris, 1961-63; assoc. prof. preventive medicine U. Wash. Med. Sch., Seattle, 1963-66; dir. Office of Population, AID, Washington, 1966-79, World Health Surveys, Ctrs. for Disease Control, 1980-82; asst. dir. epidemiology and research Nat. Inst. Drug Abuse, Rockville, Md., 1982-84; chief epidemiology br. FDA, Rockville, Md., 1984-87; dir. World Health Surveys, Inc., Seattle, 1987-93; pres. Population Health Imperatives, Seattle, 1993—. Contbr. articles to profl. publs. Served with USPHS, 1951-54, 61-63. Recipient Disting Honor award AID, 1973, Hugh Moore Meml. award IPPF and Population Crisis Com., 1974. Fellow Am. Coll. Epidemiology, APHA (Carl Schultz award 1978); mem. Am. Coun. on Sci. and Health (bd. dirs.), N.W. Danish Found. (bd. dirs.), Cosmos Club (Washington). Independent. Home: 3156 E Laurelhurst Dr NE Seattle WA 98105-5333

RAVENTOS, ANTOLIN, radiology educator; b. Wilmette, Ill., June 3, 1925; s. Enrique Antolin and Juanita (Gillespie) R.; m. Anne Patricia Gray, 1976. Student, Northwestern U., 1941-44; S.B., U. Chgo., 1945, M.D., 1947; M.Sc., U. Pa., 1954. From instr. to prof. radiology Sch. Medicine U. Pa., Phila., 1950-70; prof. radiology Sch. Medicine, U. Calif.-Davis, 1970-91, chmn. dept., 1970-77, prof. emeritus, 1991—. Assoc. editor: Cancer, 1964-91. Served with AUS, 1944-46, 52-54. Fellow Am. Coll. Radiology (chancellor 1964-70), Am. Radium Soc. (pres. 1972-73). Home: PO Box 3136 El Macero CA 95618-0736 Office: 44434 Country Club Dr El Macero CA 95618-1043

RAVETCH, IRVING, screenwriter; b. Newark, Nov. 14, 1920; s. I. Shalom and Sylvia (Shapiro) R.; m. Harriet Frank Jr., Nov. 24, 1946. BA, UCLA, 1941. Screenwriter: (films) (with La Cava) Living in a Big Way, 1947, The Outriders, 1950, Vengeance Valley, 1951; (with Harriet Frank, Jr.) The Long, Hot Summer, 1958, The Sound and the Fury, 1959, Home from the Hill, 1959, The Dark at the Top of the Stairs, 1960, House of Cards, 1969, The Cowboys, 1972, Conrak, 1974, The Spikes Gang, 1974, Norma Rae, 1979 (Academy award nomination best adapted screenplay 1979), Murphy's Romance, 1985, Stanley and Iris, 1990; writer, prodr.: (with Frank) Hud, 1963 (Academy award nomination best adapted screenplay 1963, N.Y. Film Critics Circle award best screenplay 1963), Hombre, 1967, The Reivers, 1969; story: (with Frank) Ten Wanted Men, 1955. Recipient N.Y. Film Critics award, 1963, Writers' Guild Am. award, 1988; Oscar nomination for Hud, Acad. Motion Picture Arts and Scis., 1963, Norma Rae, 1979. Office: care William Morris Agy Inc 151 S El Camino Beverly Hills CA 90212*

RAVIS, HOWARD SHEPARD, conference planner and publishing consultant; b. Waterbury, Conn., Mar. 3, 1934; s. Paul Morton and Ida Ruth (Levin) R.; m. Sophie G. Simons, Nov. 1, 1959; 1 dau., Heidi. B.S. in Journalism, Boston U., 1959. Sports editor Milford (Conn.) Citizen, 1959-60; editor Stratford (Conn.) News, 1960-61; news editor Wallingford (Conn.) Post, 1961-62; editor Needham (Mass.) Chronicle, 1962-66; reunion coordinator Boston U. Alumni Assn., 1966; copy desk man, writer Boston Globe, 1966; news editor Scholastic Tchr. mag., 1966-67; mgmt. and careers editor Electronic Design mag., 1967-68; mng. editor Teacher mag., 1968-74; editor, assoc. pub. Folio: The Magazine for Mag. Mgmt., New Canaan, Conn., 1977-80; speaker; bd. dirs. Ossining (N.Y.) Open Door Med. Assocs., 1973-77; chmn. United Ossining Party, 1973, Ossining Citizens Com. Edn., 1972-73; treas., bd. dirs. Ossining Interfaith Council for Action, 1970-73. Editor: Magazine Publishing Management, 1976, the Handbook of Magazine Publishing, 2d edit., 1983. Rep. Town Meeting, Needham, 1966; mem. nat. alumni coun. Boston U., 1977-91; trustee Ossining Pub. Libr., 1986—, v.p., 1988-89, pres., 1989-91. Served with AUS, 1956-58. Recipient Jesse H. Neal Editorial Achievement award Am. Bus. Press, 1976; Top News Writing award New Eng. Press Assn., 1962. Mem. Boston U. Alumni Assn. (chmn. Westchester County 1972-83). Democrat. Home: 5 Amawalk Ct Ossining NY 10562-4509

RAVITCH, BEVERLY, lawyer; b. N.Y.C.. AB, Antioch Coll., 1958; JD, N.Y.U., 1979. Bar: N.Y. 1980, U.S. Dist. Ct. (so. and ea. dists.) N.Y. 1980. Prin. atty. N.Y. Power Authority, 1980—. Office: NY Power Authority 1633 Broadway New York NY 10019-6708

RAVITCH, DIANE SILVERS, historian, educator, author, government official; b. Houston, July 1, 1938; d. Walter Cracker and Ann Celia (Katz) Silvers; m. Richard Ravitch, June 26, 1960 (div. 1986); children: Joseph, Steven (dec.), Michael. BA, Wellesley Coll., 1960; PhD, Columbia U., 1975; LHD (hon.), Williams Coll., 1984, Reed Coll., 1985, Amherst Coll., 1986, SUNY, 1988, Ramapo Coll., 1990, St. Joseph's Coll., N.Y., 1991. Adj. asst. prof. Tchrs. Coll., Columbia U., N.Y.C., 1975-78, assoc. prof., 1978-83, adj. prof., 1983-91; asst. sec. edn. ednl. rsch. and improvement U.S. Dept. Edn., Washington, 1991-93, counselor to the sec. edn., 1991-93; vis. fellow Brookings Instn., Washington, 1993-94; sr. rsch. scholar NYU, 1994—; bd. dirs. Ency. Britannica. Author: The Great School Wars, 1974, The Revisionists Revised, 1977, The Troubled Crusade, 1983, The Schools We Deserve, 1985, National Standards in American Education, A Citizens Guide, 1995, (with others) Educating an Urban People, 1981, The School and the City, 1983, Against Mediocrity, 1984, Challenges to the Humanities, 1985, What Do Our 17 Year Olds Know?, 1987, The American Reader, 1990; co-editor: The Democracy Reader, 1992; editor: Learning from the Past, 1995. Chair Ednl. Excellence Network, 1988-91, 94—; trustee N.Y. Pub. Libr., N.Y.C., 1981-87, hon. life trustee, 1988—; bd. dirs. Woodrow Wilson Nat. Fellowship Found., 1987-91, Coun. Basic Edn., 1989-91. Recipient Award for Disting. Svc., N.Y. Acad. Pub. Edn., 1994; Guggenheim fellow, 1977-78; Phi Beta Kappa vis. scholar. Mem. Nat. Acad. Edn., Am. Acad. Arts and Scis., Soc. Am. Historians, N.Y. Hist. Soc. (trustee 1995—). Office: NYU 32 Press Bldg Washington Place New York NY 10003-6644

RAVITCH, NORMAN, history educator; b. N.Y.C., Nov. 22, 1936; s. Louis and Sylvia (Schwey) R.; m. Helen Lee Thornton, Dec. 16, 1989; children: Michael Joseph, Nicholas Louis (dec.). BA, Queens Coll., 1957; MA, Princeton U., 1959, PhD, 1962. Instr. Phila. Mus. Coll. Art, 1961-62 from asst. prof. to prof. U. Calif., Riverside, 1962—. Author: Sword and Mitre, 1966, Catholic Church and French Nation, 1990; editor: Images of Western Man, 3 vols., 1973. Fulbright scholar, 1960-61. Mem. Am. Hist. Assn., Western Soc. for French History (editor proceedings 1991). Roman Catholic. Office: U Calif Dept History Riverside CA 92521

RAVITZ, LEONARD J., JR., physician, scientist, consultant; b. Cuyahoga County, Ohio, Apr. 17; s. Leonard Robert and Esther Evelyn (Skerball) R. BS, Case Western Res. U., 1944; MD, Wayne State U., 1946; MS, Yale U., 1950. Diplomate Am. Bd. Psychiatry and Neurology, 1952. Rsch. asst. EEG to A.J. Derbyshire, PhD Harper Hosp., Detroit, 1943-46; spl. trainee in hypnosis to Milton H. Erickson, MD Wayne County Gen. Hosp., Eloise, Mich., 1945-46, 46-80; rotating intern St. Elizabeth's Hosp., Washington, 1946-47; jr./sr. asst. resident in psychiatry Yale-New Haven Hosp.; asst. in psychiatry and mental hygiene Yale Med. Sch., 1947-48, assoc. in psychiatry and mental hygiene, 1948-49, rsch. fellow to Harold S. Burr, PhD, sect. neuro-anatomy, 1949-50; sr. resident in neuropsychiatry Richard S. Lyman svc. Duke Hosp., Durham, N.C., 1950-51; instr. Duke U. Med. Sch., Durham, 1950-51; assoc. to R. Burke Suitt, MD Pvt. Diagnostic Clinic, Duke Hosp., Durham, 1951-53; assoc. Duke U. Med. Sch., 1951-53; vis. asst. prof. neuropsychiatry and asst. to vis. prof. Richard S. Lyman, MD Meharry Med. Ctr., Nashville, 1953; asst. dir. profl. edn. in charge tng. U. Wyo. Nursing Sch. affiliates; chief rsch. rehab. bldg. Downey VA Hosp. (now called VA Hosp.), N. Chicago, Ill., 1953-54; assoc. psychiatry Sch. Medicine and Hosp., U. Pa., Phila., 1955-58; dep. asst. sec. def. in charge of health and med., 3E772 E. H. Cushing, MD Electromagnetic Field Measurement Project, Pentagon, 1958; dir. tng. and rsch. Ea. State Hosp., Williamsburg, Va., 1958-60; pvt. practice neuropsychiatry specializing in hypnosis Norfolk, Va., 1961—; psychiatrist, cons. Div. Alcohol Studies and Rehab., Va. Dept. Health (later Va. Dept. Mental Health and Mental Retardation), 1961-81; psychiatrist Greenpoint Clinic, Bklyn., 1983-87, 17th St. Clinic, N.Y.C., 1987-92; sec.-treas. Euclid-97th St. Clinic, Inc., Cleve., 1957-63, pres., 1963-69; spl. tng. in epistemology F.S.C. Northrop, PhD, 1973-92; electrodynamic field rsch. with Harold S. Burr, PhD, Yale Med. Sch., New Haven, 1948-73; consulted on hypnosis with Milton H. Erickson, MD, 1945-80; clin. asst. prof. psychiatry, SUNY Health Sci. Ctr. Med. Sch., 1983—; psychiatrist Downstate Mental Hygiene Assocs., Bklyn., 1983—; pvt. cons., Cleve., 1961-

69, Upper Montclair, N.J., 1982—; lectr. sociology Old Dominion U., Norfolk, 1961-62, cons. nutrition rsch. project, Old Dominion U. Research Found., 1978-90; spl. med. cons. Frederick Mil. Acad., Portsmouth, Va., 1963-71; cons. Tidewater Epilepsy Found., Chesapeake, Va., 1962-68, USPH Hosp. Alcohol Unit, Norfolk, 1980-81, Nat. Inst. Rehab. Therapy, Butler, N.J., 1982-83; participant 5th Internat. Congress for Hypnosis and Psychosomatic Medicine, Gutenborg U., Mainz, Fed. Republic Germany, 1970; organizer symposia on hypnosis in psychiatry and medicine, field theory as an integrator of knowledge, hypnosis in office practice, history of certain forensic and psychotherapeutic aspects of the study of man, Eastern State Hosp., Coll. William and Mary, James City County Med. Soc., Va. Soc. Clin. Hypnosis, Williamsburg, Va., 1959-60; founding pres. Va. Soc. Clin. Hypnosis, 1959-60, Found. for Study Electrodynamic Theory of Life, 1989—. Asst. editor Jour. Am. Soc. Psychosomatic Dentistry and Medicine, 1980-83; mem. editorial bd. Internat. Jour. Psychosomatics, 1984—; contbr. sects. to books, articles, book revs., abstracts to profl. publs. Sr. v.p. Willoughby Civic League, 1971-75. 1st lt. AUS, 1943-46. Lyman Rsch. Fund grantee, 1950-53. Fellow AAAS (life), Am. Psychiat. Assn., N.Y. Acad. Scis., Am. Soc. Clin. Hypnosis (charter, cons. cert. program), Royal Soc. Health (London); mem. Va. Soc. Clin. Hypnosis (founding pres. 1959-60), Norfolk Acad. Medicine, Soc. for Investigation Recurring Events, Va. Med. Soc., Sigma Xi, Nu Sigma Nu. Achievements include discovery of electromagnetic field correlates of hypnosis, emotions, psychiatric/medical disorders, aging, and electrocyclic phenomena in humans which parallel thosthier life forms, earth and atmosphere underwriting beginning short- and long-range predictions, such seemingly disparate phenomena united under a single regulating principle defined in terms of measurable field intensity and polarity. Office: SUNY Med Sch Health Sci Ctr Dept Psychiatry Box 1203 450 Clarkson Ave Brooklyn NY 11203-2098 Office: PO Box 9409 Norfolk VA 23505-0409

RAVITZ, ROBERT ALLAN, advertising agency executive; b. Omaha, May 26, 1938; s. Ben and Frances (Cooper) R.; m. Muriel Strickler, May 12, 1977; 1 dau. by previous marriage, Anne Cooper (dec.); stepchildren: Matthew and Todd Wilson. B.S., Northwestern U., 1960. Trainee/account exec. Edward H. Weiss Advt., Chgo., 1962-65; account exec. Tatham-Laird & Kudner Advt., Chgo., 1965-68; v.p., account supr. Stern, Walters & Simmons Advt., Chgo., 1968-72; sr. v.p., mgmt. rep. McCann-Erickson Inc., Chgo., 1972-77, N.Y.C., 1977-85; exec. v.p. Grey Advt., 1985—; mem. Svcs. Policy Adv. Com. U.S. Trade Rep.; guest lectr. Adv. Edn. Found.; bd. dirs. Meridian Coun.; trustee Naval Inst.; adj. prof. NYU. Rear Adm. USNR, ret. Mem. Naval Res. Assn., Navy League U.S. Jewish. Clubs: Rotan Point (Rowayton, Conn.), Wings (N.Y.C.), Army-Navy (Washington). Home: 15 Westview Ln Norwalk CT 06854-2413 Office: Grey Advt Inc 777 3d Ave New York NY 10017

RAVIV, SHEILA, public relations executive. Degree, Ind. U., U. Wis. Faculty mem. Sch. Medicine and Health Sci. George Washington U.; dir. rsch. Ministry Social Welfare, Israel; dir. Nat. Vol. Orgns. for Ind. Living for the Aging; asst. dir. Nat. Coun. on the Aging; sr. v.p., dir. of constituency rels. Burson-Marsteller, 1988-91, mem. Am. bd. dirs., 1993, exec. v.p., dir. constituency rels., 1991-94; pres., CEO Burson-Marsteller/Washington, 1994—. Office: Burson-Marsteller 1850 M St NW Washington DC 20036*

RAWITCH, ROBERT JOE, newspaper editor; b. L.A., Oct. 11, 1945; s. Sam and Jean (Reifman) R.; m. Cynthia Z. Knee, Oct. 27, 1968; children—Dana Leigh, Jeremy Aaron, Joshua Eric. BA in Journalism, Calif. State U.-Northridge, 1967; MS in Journalism, Northwestern U., 1968. Reporter L.A. Times, 1968-80, asst. met. editor, 1980-82, editor Valley sect., 1982-83, suburban editor, 1983-89, exec. editor Valley and Ventura County edits., 1989-93; dir. editorial ops. Valley and Ventura County edits., 1993—; lectr. Calif. State U.-Northridge, 1971-83. Co-author: Adat Ari El, The First Fifty Years, 1988. Chmn. Calif. Freedom of Info. Com., 1978-79; pres. Calif. First Amendment Coalition, 1991-93; bd. dirs. Temple Adat Ari El, 1987-92; pres. Calif. Soc. Newspaper Editors, 1995-96. Recipient Greater L.A. Press Club award, 1973, 75, 79, L.A. Jewish Youth of Yr. award United Jewish Fund, 1963, Clarence Darrow Found. award, 1979. Mem. Soc. Profl. Journalists (nat. bd. dirs. 1979-82). Avocation: tennis. Office: L A Times 20000 Prairie St Chatsworth CA 91311-6595

RAWL, ARTHUR JULIAN, retail executive, accountant, consultant, author; b. Boston, July 6, 1942; s. Philip and Evelyn (Rosoff) R.; m. Karen Lee Werby, June 4, 1967; 1 child, Kristen Alexandra. BBA, Boston U., 1967, postgrad, 1972-74. CPA, Mass., N.Y., La. Audit mgr. Touche Ross & Co., Boston, 1967-77; audit mgr. Touche Ross & Co., N.Y.C., 1977-79, ptnr., 1979; ptnr. Touche Ross & Co., Newark, 1980-88, N.Y.C., 1988-89; ptnr. Deloite & Touche, N.Y.C., 1989; exec. v.p., chief fin. officer Hanlin Group, Inc., Linden, N.J., 1990-94, United Auto Group, Inc., N.Y.C., 1994—; bd. dirs. BiakaInterPlast (USSR), Kuperwood Enterprises, Hanlin Group, Inc.; mem. adj. faculty Boston U., 1971-75. Contbr. articles to profl. journals, mags. and trade pubs. Mem. Newton Upper Falls (Mass.) Hist. Commn., 1977; bd. dirs Sherburne Scholarship Fund Boston U., 1977-80; mem. Englewood (N.J.) Planning Bd., 1981-83; trustee Englewood Bd. Edn., 1983-85, 89-93, pres., 1991-92; trustee, treas. exec. com. Englewood Econ. Devel. Corp., 1986-89; fin. and compensation com. Dwight Englewood Sch., 1985-90; mem. parent devel. com. Mt. Holyoke Coll., 1991-94. Served to 2d class petty officer USN, 1960-63. Fellow AICPA, Mass. Soc. CPAs, N.Y. Soc. CPAs; mem. Am. Legion, Navy League U.S., N.J. Hist. Soc. (bd. govs., exec. com., nominating com., treas. 1987—), St. George's Soc. N.Y., Univ. Club, Essex Club, Sloane Club (London). Home: 72 Booth Ave Englewood NJ 07631-1907 Office: United Auto Group Inc 375 Park Ave New York NY 10152

RAWLES, LEWIS GENE, manufacturing executive; b. Kendallville, Ind., Aug. 26, 1948; s. Lewis G. and Virginia E. (Franks) R.; m. Linda Lou Wright, Sept. 20, 1975; children: Lara Lin, Lesli Ann. Student, Indiana U., 1966-68, 72-73. Gen. mgr. parkway dist. Holiday Rambler Corp., Sweetwater, Tex., 1976-77, v.p Sweetwater div., 1977-80; pres. formtec plastics and harborcraft marine div.s Holiday Rambler Corp., Wakarusa, Ind., 1980-83; pres. HRO Inc., Wolcottville, Ind., 1983-84; sr. v.p. Coachmen Industries Inc., Elkhart, Ind., 1984, exec. v.p., 1985-90, mem. fin. com., 1986-90; v.p. bd. dirs. So. Ambulance Builders, La Grange, Ga., 1986—. Served in USAF, 1968-72. Mem. Soc. Plastics Engrs., Elkhart C. of C. Republican. Methodist. Avocations: golf, boating. Home: 8326 N 86th St Scottsdale AZ 85258-2505

RAWLEY, ANN KEYSER, small business owner, picture framer; b. N.Y.C., July 11, 1923; d. Ernest Wise and Beatrice (Oberndorf) Keyser; m. James Albert Rawley, Apr. 7, 1945; children: John Franklin, James Albert. BA, Smith Coll., 1944. Owner Ann Rawley Custom Framing, Lincoln, Nebr., 1969—. Pres. Friends of Fairview, Lincoln, 1976, Lincoln City Ballet Co., 1983-84; bd. dirs. Lincoln Community Playhouse; mem. adv. bd. Nebr. Repertory Theatre. Mem. Nebr. Art Assn. (sec. 1976-77, life trustee). Republican. Episcopalian. Avocations: foreign travel, tennis, needle work. Home and Office: 2300 Bretigne Dr Lincoln NE 68512-1910

RAWLEY, JAMES ALBERT, history educator; b. Terre Haute, Ind., Nov. 9, 1916; s. Frank S. and Annie B. (Vanes) R.; m. Ann F. Keyser, Apr. 7, 1945; children: John Franklin, James Albert. A.B., U. Mich., 1938, A.M., 1939; Ph.D., Columbia U., 1949. Instr., Columbia U., 1946-48; Instr. N.Y. U., 1945-51, Hunter Coll., 1951-53; asso. prof. to prof. Sweet Briar Coll., 1953-64, chmn. history dept., 1953-57, chmn. div. social studies, 1962-64; prof. U. Nebr., 1964-87, prof. emeritus 1987—, chmn. history dept., 1966-67, 73-82, acting dean univ. libraries, 1984-85, honors MASUA lectr., 1984-85, Carl Happold Disting. prof., 1986-87; resident scholar Rockefeller Study and Conf. Center, Italy, 1977; vis. prof. U. Hanover, 1990; mem. adv. bd. Salmon P. Chase Papers and Abraham Lincoln Prize. Author: Edwin D. Morgan: Merchant in Politics, 1811-1883, 1955, Turning Points of the Civil War, 1966, Race and Politics, 1969, The Politics of Union, 1974, The Transatlantic Slave Trade, 1981, Secession: The Disruption of the American Republic, 1844-1861, 1989; editor: The American Civil War: An English View, 1964; editor: Lincoln and Civil War Politics, 1969; contbr.: Essays in American Historiography, 1960. Served to 1st lt. AUS, 1942-46. Recipient Outstanding Research and Creativity award U. Nebr., 1983, George Howard-Louise Pound Disting. Career award U. Nebr., 1987; NEH fellow Huntington Library, 1979. Fellow Royal Hist. Soc.; mem. Am. Hist. Assn.,

So. Hist. Assn., Nebr. State Hist. Soc. (past pres.), Orgn. Am. Historians, Soc. Am. Historians, Civil War Round Table Nebr. (charter pres. 1989-90), Lincoln U. Club, Lincoln Country Club, Phi Beta Kappa. Home: 2300 Bretigne Dr Lincoln NE 68512-1910

RAWLINGS, BOYNTON MOTT, lawyer; b. El Paso, Tex., Dec. 6, 1935; s. Junius Mott and Laura Bassett (Boynton) R.; m. Nancy Mary Peay, Aug. 24, 1962 (div. 1973); children: Laura Bassett, James Mott; m. Judith Reed, Dec. 10, 1977; 1 child, William Reed. A.B. Princeton U., 1958; LLB, Stanford U., 1961; Diploma, U. Strasbourg (France), 1963. Bar: Calif., 1962, D.C., 1980, Conseil Juridique Paris, 1973, Avocat Paris, 1992. Assoc. Broad, Busterud & Khourie, San Francisco, 1963-65, Homer G. Angelo, Brussels, 1966; assoc., ptnr. S.G. Archibald, Paris, 1967-74; ptnr. Boynton M. Rawlings, Paris, Los Angeles, 1974-84, Kevorkian & Rawlings, Paris, 1984-90; ptnr. Oppenheimer, Wolff and Donnelly, Paris, 1990—; bd. dirs. Isomat S.A., Cherbourg, France, I.T.S. Fabry, Inc., Charleston, S.C. Contbr. articles to profl. jours. Mem. Los Angeles Bar Assn. (bd. dirs. sect. internat. law 1975-82), French Am. C. of C. L.A. (bd. dirs., v.p. 1985—). Republican. Episcopalian. Avocations: music; tennis; skiing; hiking. Office: Oppenheimer Wolff Donnelly, 53 Ave Montaigne, 75008 Paris France

RAWLINGS, HUNTER RIPLEY, III, university administrator; b. Norfolk, Va., Dec. 14, 1944; married; 4 children. BA, Haverford Coll., 1966; PhD in Classics, Princeton U., 1970. Asst. prof. U. Colo., Boulder, 1970-74, assoc. prof., 1975-80, prof. classics, from 1980, v.p. acad. affairs, rsch., dean System Grad. Sch., 1984-88; pres. U. Iowa, Iowa City, 1988-95, Cornell U., Ithaca, NY, 1995—; chair Iowa Commn. on Fgn. Lang. Studies and Internat. Edn., 1988-91. Author: The Structure of Thucydides' History, 1981; editor-in-chief: Classical Jour., 1977-83; contbr. articles to jours. Jr. fellow Ctr. Hellenic Studies, 1975-76. Fellow Am. Acad. of Arts and Scis.; mem. Am. Philol. Assn., Classical Assn. Midwest and South, Am. Inst. Archaeology, Assn. Ancient Historians, Am. Assn. Univs. (exec. com. 1990-92); bd. dirs. Am. Coun. on Edn.; adv. bd. Nat. Fgn. Lang. Ctr. Office: Cornell University Office of President Ithaca NY 14853

RAWLINGS, JAMES SCOTT, architect; b. Richmond, Va., June 26, 1922; s. Byrd Lundy and Finetta Ann (Gardner) R. BS in Architecture, U. Va., 1947; MFA in Architecture, Princeton U., 1949. Registered architect, Va., Ind., N.C., S.C. Instr. architecture U. Va., Charlottesville, 1947; draftsman, staff architect Marcellus, Wright & Son, Architects, Richmond, 1949-53; founder, ptnr. Rawlings & Wilson, Architects, Richmond, 1955-80, pres., chmn., 1980-93, chmn. emeritus, cons., 1993—. Author: Virginia's Colonial Churches, 1963, Virginia's Ante-Bellum Churches, 1978, Colonial Churches of Virginia, Maryland, North Carolina, 1985. Past pres., trustee Va. Found. for Archtl. Edn.; chmn. Com. for Architecture Rev., Richmond, 1967-77; bd. dirs. St. Peter's Parish Ch. Restoration Assn., New Kent, Va., 1985—. Lt. (j.g.) USNR, 1942-46, PTO. Fellow AIA; mem. Va. Assn. Professions, Raven Soc. U. Va., Country Club of Va., Pi Kappa Alpha. Episcopalian. Home: 103 Canterbury Rd Richmond VA 23221-3211 Office: Rawlings Wilson & Assocs PC 1100 N Thompson St Richmond VA 23230-4913

RAWLINGS, JOHN OREN, statistician, researcher; b. Archer, Nebr., July 26, 1932; s. Cecil Curtis and Mildred Louise (Suck) R.; m. Mary Jane Reichardt, Aug. 17, 1952; children: Gweneth Marie, Bradley John, Kalen Louise. BSc, U. Nebr., 1953, MSc, 1957; PhD, N.C. State U., 1960. Geneticist USDA/Agrl. Rsch. Svc., Raleigh, N.C., 1959-60; asst. statis. N.C. State U., Raleigh, 1960-61, asst. prof., 1961-63, assoc. prof., 1963-68, prof., 1968-94; prof. emeritus, 1994—. Author: Applied Regression Analysis: A Research Tool, 1988; contbr. over 75 articles to profl. jours. Lt. U.S. Army, 1953-55. U. Reading (Eng.) fellow, 1967-68. Fellow Am. Soc. Agronomy, Am. Stats. Assn.; mem. Crop Sci. Soc. Am., Biometrics Soc., Gamma Sigma Delta (Cert. merit 1979), Sigma Xi (Rsch. award 1964), Phi Kappa Phi. Home: 6216 Splitrock Trl Apex NC 27502-9778 Office: NC State U PO Box 8203 Raleigh NC 27695

RAWLINGS, PAUL C., retired government official; b. Cave City, Ark., June 21, 1928; s. Otha A. and Leona (King) R.; m. Catherine Terral, 1951 (div. 1970); children: William A., Rebecca, Neal; m. Erma Martin, June 20, 1971. Grad., Little Rock Jr. Coll.; LL.B. Ark. Law Sch., 1950. Bar: Ark. 1950. Practiced in Little Rock, 1950, 52-73; adminstrv. law judge Office Hearings and Appeals, Social Security Adminstrn., HEW, Hattiesburg, Miss., 1973-92; ret. adminstrv. law judge sr. status, 1992; partner firm Terral, Rawlings, Matthews & Purtle, until 1973; asst. atty. gen., Ark., 1955-56. Bd. dirs. Ark. Enterprises for Blind, 1964-67. Served with AUS, 1950-52. Mem. Ark. Bar Assn., Law Sci. Acad. Methodist (past chmn. bd. adminstrn., trustee). Club: Lion (past pres.). Home: 3002 Navajo Cir Hattiesburg MS 39402-2446

RAWLINGS, ROBERT HOAG, newspaper publisher; b. Pueblo, Colo., Aug. 3, 1924; s. John W. and Dorothy (Hoag) R. Student Colo. U., 1943-44; BA, Colo. Coll., 1947; m. Mary Alexandra Graham, Oct. 18, 1947; children: Jane Louise, John Graham, Carolyn Anne, Robert Hoag II. Reporter Pueblo Chieftain and Pueblo Star-Jour., 1947-51, advt. rep. 1951-62, gen. mgr., 1962-79, pub. and editor, 1980—; sec. Star-Jour. Pub. Corp., 1962-84, pres., 1984—; Chmn. bd. dir. Colo. Nat. Bank-Pueblo; bd. dir. U.S. Air Force Acad. Found., U. So. Colo. Found., Colo. Water Edn. Found.; pres. Robert Hoag Rawlings Found. Served with USNR, 1942-46. Named Colo. Newspaper Person of 1989, Disting. Univ. Fellow Pres. Club U. So. Colo., 1993, Outstanding Citizen of Yr. Pueblo C. of C., 1993, Colo. Bus. Leader of the Yr. Colo. Assn. of Commerce and Industry, 1994; recipient Outstanding Svc. to Univ. award U. So. Colo. Alumni Assn., 1993, Colo. Corp. Philanthropy award Nat. Philanthropy Assoc., 1993. Mem. Colo. Press Assn., (dir. 1963-66, 76-78, pres. 1985, chmn. bd. dirs. 1986), Rocky Mountain Ad Mgrs. (past pres.), Colo. AP (past pres.), Elks, Rotary. Presbyterian. Office: Star-Jour Pub Corp PO Box 4040 Pueblo CO 81003-0040

RAWLINS, BENJAMIN W., JR., bank holding company executive; b. 1938; married. BA, Vanderbilt U., 1961; MBA, Ga. State U., 1969. With Union Planters Nat. Bank, Memphis, 1974—, v.p., 1974-84, pres., chief exec. officer, 1984-86, chmn., pres., 1986—; pres., chief exec. officer Union Planters Corp., Memphis, 1984—, also dir. Office: Union Planters Corp 67 Madison Ave Memphis TN 38103-2147

RAWLINSON, HELEN ANN, librarian; b. Columbia, S.C., Mar. 30, 1948; d. Alfred Harris and Mary Taylor (Moon) R. BA, U. S.C., 1970; MLS, Emory U., 1972. Asst. children's librarian Greenville (S.C.) County Library, 1972-74, br. supr., 1974-76, asst. head extension div., 1976-78; children's room librarian Richland County Pub. Library, Columbia, 1978-81; sr. adult services librarian Richland County Pub. Library, 1981-82, chief adult services, 1982-85, dep. dir., 1985—; mem. adv. com. S.C. Pre-White House Conf. on Libr. and Info. Svcs., chmn. program com. Mem. ALA, S.E. Libr. Assn., S.C. Libr. Assn. (2d v.p.1987-88, 88-93, editorial com., chmn. pub. libr. sect. 1995). Baptist. Home: 1316 Guignard Ave West Columbia SC 29169-6137 Office: Richland County Pub Libr 1431 Assembly St Columbia SC 29201-3101

RAWLS, EUGENIA, actress; b. Macon, Ga.; d. Hubert Fields and Louise (Roberts) R.; m. Donald Ray Seawell, Apr. 5, 1941; children: Brook Ashley, Donald Brockman. Grad., Wesleyan Conservatory, Macon, 1932; student, U.N.C., 1933; L.H.D., U. No. Colo., Greeley, 1978; D.F.A., Wesleyan Coll., Macon, Ga., 1982. Participant 25th Anniversary of Lillian Smith Book Awards, Atlanta, 1993. Author: Tallulah—A Memory, 1979; Broadway appearances include The Children's Hour, 1934, Pride and Prejudice, 1936, The Little Foxes, 1939, 41, Guest in the House, 1942, Rebecca, 1945, The Second Mrs. Tanqueray, 1947, The Shrike, 1952, Private Lives, 1949, The Great Sebastians, 1956, First Love, 1961, The Glass Menagerie, 1964, 67, Our Town, 1967, Tallulah: A Memory; appeared at Lincoln Ctr., 1971, London, 1974, U.S. tour, 1979, Denver Ctr. Performing Arts, 1980, Theatre of Mus., N.Y.C., 1980, Four Arts Soc., Palm Beach, Fla., 1981, Herbst Theater, San Francisco, 1981, Kennedy Ctr. (cable TV), 1981, Nat. Theatre Great Britain, 1984, Queen Elizabeth II, 1984-86; one-woman show Affectionately Yours Fanny Kemble, London, 1974, U.S. tour, 1979, Nat. Portrait Gallery, Washington, 1983, Grolier Club Exhbn., N.Y.C., 1988; appeared in The Enchanted, 1973, Sweet Bird of Youth, 1975, 76, Daughter of the Regiment, 1978, Just the Immediate Family, 1978, Women of the West, U.S.

tour, 1979, Am. Mus. in Britain, Bath, Eng., 1981, Kennedy Ctr. and Denver Ctr. Performing Arts, 1980; one-woman show Fanny Kemble, Arts Theatre, London, 1969, Queen's Hall, Edinburgh, 1980, St. Peter's Ch., N.Y.C., 1980, Internat. Theater Festival, Denver, 1982, also Kennedy Center; appeared as Emily, Denver, 1976; with Abbey Theatre, Dublin, Ireland, 1972; one-woman show tour of Europe, 1972; appeared as: Fanny Kemble, Shakespeare World Congress, Washington, 1976; TV appearances, U.S. Steel Hour, Love of Life, Women of the West; (for ednl. TV) Tallulah: A Memory (performed for presdl. inauguration), 1977; Memory of a Large Christmas, Folger Shakespeare Library, 1977; mem., Sarah Caldwell Opera Co., Boston, 1978; rec. talking books for blind; mem. com.: Plays for Living, 1964-67; Rockefeller Found. artist-in-residence, Denver U., 1967, 68, U. Tampa, Fla., 1970, artist-in-residence, U. No. Colo., 1971, 72, 73; artist Annenberg Theatre, Desert Art Mus., Palm Springs, Calif., 1988, 89, "Our Town" Pitts. Pub. Theatre, 1990; author: (poems) A Moment Ago, 1984; participant Edwin Forrest Day Celebrating Shakespeare's 427th Birthday The Actors' Fund of Am.'s Nursing and Retirement Home Lucille Lortel Theatre, 1991; appeared in Our Town, Pitts. Pub. Theater, 1990-91, Three Sisters, 1991—. Mem. Internat. Women's Forum, Vail, Colo., 1989. Recipient Alumna award U. N.C., 1969; Disting. Achievement award Wesleyan Coll., 1969; Gold Chair award Central City (Colo.) Opera House Assn., 1973; (with husband) Frederick H. Koch Drama award U. N.C., 1974; citation Smithsonian Instn., 1977. Address: care Donald Seawell 1050 13th St Denver CO 80204

RAWLS, L(OYD) NEAL, communications executive; b. Hollywood, Fla., July 8, 1946; s. Dallis Loyd and Katherine Elizabeth (Neal) R.; m. Linda Rae Robinson, Dec. 8, 1978 (div. Nov. 1986); 1 child, Joseph Neal. BS, Fla. State U., 1973; MS, Nova U., 1979. Mgr. Floridel Farms, Delray Beach, Fla., 1965-69; restaurant mgr. M.H. and G. Enterprises, Sarasota, Fla., 1969-70; city law enforcement/police sgt. Delray Beach Police Dept., 1972-81; instr. Palm Beach Police Acad. Palm Beach C.C., Lake Worth, Fla., 1976-81; dir. security Nat. Enquirer, Lantana, Fla., 1981-90, dir. quality control, 1983-90; gen. mgr. Enquirer/Star Group Inc., Lantana, 1990-94, Am. Media Inc., Lantana, 1994—; bd. dirs. K.L.V. Distbn. Inc., Lake Worth. Recipient 13 Police Commendations. Democrat. Avocations: sailing, water sports. Home: 1204 S Lake Dr Apt 12 Lantana FL 33462 Office: American Media Inc 600 S Eastcoast Ave Lantana FL 33462

RAWLS, S(OL) WAITE, III, business executive; b. Norfolk, Va., July 15, 1948; s. Sol Waite Jr. and Ann Arendel (Peace) R.; m. Margaret Louise Thorn, Sept. 26, 1970. BA, Va. Mil. Inst., 1970; MBA, U. Va., 1975, JD, 1975. Mng. dir. Chem. Bank, N.Y.C., 1975-88, with retail banking dept., 1975-77, with comml. lending dept., 1977-79, with securities trading and sales dept., 1980-88; vice chmn. Continental Bank Corp., Chgo., 1988-91; now exec. v.p. of Fixed Income Chgo. Corp., Chgo.; bd. dirs. Liberty Brokerage, Inc., N.Y.C.; vice chmn., bd. dirs. Alpha Ctr. for Pub. and Pvt. Initiatives, Inc.; bd. dirs. Nevander Asset Mgmt., Inc.; mem. fin.instruments adv. com. Chgo. Merc. Exch.; vis. prof. Darden Sch., U. Va., 1991-92; mem., former chmn. com. Chgo. Risk Mgmt. Ctr. Bd. dirs. Chgo. Urban League Devel. Corp., Camp Found.; trustee Mus. Sci. and Industry, The Civil War Trust, 1994—, Va. Mil. Inst. Found., 1993—, Darden Found. of the Darden Sch., U. Va., 1991—; chmn. nat. adv. coun. The Seeing Eye, Inc.; mem. Chgo. Com. Mem. Japan-Am. Soc. Chgo., Chgo. Coun. Fgn. Rels., Econ. Club Chgo., Chgo. Club, Chgo. Golf Club, Farmington Country Club, Torrington Country Club. Baptist. Avocations: golf, quail hunting, art, antiques.

RAWN, WILLIAM LEETE, III, architect; b. Berkeley, Calif., Aug. 8, 1943; s. William Leete Jr. and Betsy (Blanckenburg) R. BA, Yale U., 1965; JD, Harvard U., 1969; MArch, MIT, 1979. Bar: D.C., 1969. Assoc. Arent, Fox, Kintner, Plotkin & Kahn, Washington, 1969-71; asst. to pres. U. Mass., Boston, 1971-73, asst. chancellor phys. planning, 1973-75; architect Davis Brody & Assocs., N.Y.C., 1979-83, William Rawn Assocs., Boston, 1983—. Designer serigraphs, 1971-79; contbr. articles to profl. jours., newspapers. Mem. Boston Civic Design Com., 1990; trustee 1000 Friends of Mass., Boston, 1990, Bennington Coll. Recipient Urban Design Citation, Progressive Architecture, Cultural Ctr. Commn., Rochester, N.Y., 1987. Mem. AIA (nat. Honor award in architecture 1994, nat. Award of Excellence in urban design 1993), Boston Soc. Architects (regional and local AIA design awards 1985-93, selected Fabla 1994), D.C. Bar Assn., Yale Club of N.Y.C., Harvard Club of Boston. Office: William Rawn Assocs Archs Inc 101 Tremont St Ste 204 Boston MA 02108-5004

RAWNSLEY, HOWARD MELODY, physician, educator; b. Long Branch, N.J., Nov. 20, 1925; s. Walter A. and Elizabeth (Melody) R.; m. B. Eileen Fiddes, Sept. 5, 1967; children—Virgilia Ingram, Elizabeth Sue. A.B., Haverford Coll., 1949; M.D., U. Pa., 1952. Diplomate Am. Bd. Pathology (trustee 1988—). Intern Hosp. U. Pa., 1952-53, resident, 1953-57; practice medicine, specializing in pathology Phila., 1957-75; mem. Wm. Pepper Lab., U. Pa., 1957-75, asst. dir., 1960-68, dir., 1968-75; assoc. dir. Clin. Research Ctr., 1962-67, acting dir., 1969—70, asst. prof. pathology and medicine, 1960-65, assoc. prof., 1965-69, prof., 1969-75; prof. pathology Dartmouth Hitchcock Med. Ctr., Hanover, N.H., 1975-95, chmn. dept., 1980-87, sr. v.p. med. affairs, 1987-94, emeritus, 1995—; cons. VA Hosp. Served with AUS, 1944-46. Woodward fellow in chemistry, 1953-55. Mem. AMA, ARC (biomed. svcs. com. 1990-92), Pathology Soc. Phila. (pres.), Coll. Am. Pathologists (bd. govs. 1985-93), Am. Soc. Clin. Pathologists. Home: 7 Haskins Rd Hanover NH 03755-2204

RAWSKI, CONRAD H(ENRY), humanities educator, medievalist; b. Vienna, Austria, May 25, 1914; came to U.S., 1939, naturalized, 1944; s. Stanislaus and Johanna (Buberl-Maffei) R.; m. Helen Orr, July 5, 1957; children: Thomas George, Judith Ellen Rawski Kleen. M.A., U. Vienna, 1936, Ph.D., 1937; postgrad., Péter Pázmány Egyetem, Budapest, 1938-39, Harvard U., 1939-40; M.S. in LS, Western Res. U., 1957. Lectr. in music U. Louisville, 1940; asst. prof., assoc. prof., prof. music Ithaca (N.Y.) Coll., 1940-56; dir. grad. studies, dean Ithaca (N.Y.) Coll. (Sch. Music), 1951-56; head fine arts dept. Cleve. Public Library, 1957-62; assoc. prof., prof. library sci., coordinator Ph.D. program in info. sci. M.A. Baxter Sch. Info. and Libr. Sci., Case Western Res. U., 1957-80; prof., sr. research scholar M.A. Baxter Sch. Info. and Libr. Sci., Case Western Res. U., 1980-85, prof. emeritus for life, dean emeritus, 1985; music columnist Boston Evening Transcript, 1939-40, Ithaca Jour., 1943-50; lectr. in musicology, medieval studies, info. sci. Fellow Fund for the Advancement of Edn., Ford Found., 1952-53, Nat. Endowment for Humanities, 1979. Author: Petrarch: Four Dialogues for Scholars, 1967, Toward a Theory of Librarianship, 1973, Petrarch's Latin Prose Works and the Modern Translator, 1977, Introduction to Research in Information Science, 1982; translator and editor: Petrarch's Remedies for Fortune Fair and Foul, 5 vols., 1991, Petrarch to Boccaccio: The Griseldis Letters, 1994; contbr. papers on Petrarch's Latin prose works, Petrarch's Latinity, medieval music, info. sci. and theory to profl. publs. and encys. Mem. Renaissance Soc. Am., Medieval Acad. Am., Soc. for Medieval Latin, ALA (nat. Beta Phi Mu award 1979), Am. Musicol. Soc. Club: Rowfant of Cleve. Address: 17877 Lost Trl Chagrin Falls OH 44023-5835

RAWSKI, EVELYN SAKAKIDA, history educator; b. Honolulu, Feb. 2, 1939; d. Evan T. and Teruko (Watase) Sakakida; m. Thomas G. Rawski, Dec. 16, 1967. B.A., Cornell U., 1961; M.A., Radcliffe Coll., 1962; Ph.D., Harvard U., 1968. Asst. prof. history U. Pitts., 1967-72, assoc. prof., 1973-79, prof. history, 1980—. Author: Agricultural Change and the Peasant Economy of South China, 1972, Education and Popular Literacy in Ch'ing China, 1979; co-author: Chinese Society in the Eighteenth Century, 1987; co-editor: Popular Culture in Late Imperial China, 1985; Death Ritual in Late Imperial and Modern China, 1988. Am. Coun. Learned Soc. grantee, 1973-74; NEH fellow, 1979-80, Chinese Studies fellow Am. Coun. Learned Soc./ Sci. Rsch. Coun., 1989, Guggenheim Meml. Found. fellow, 1990, Woodrow Wilson Internat. Ctr. fellow 1992-93. Mem. Assn. Asian Studies (China-Inner Asia coun., bd. dirs. 1976-79, v.p. 1994-95, pres. 1995-96). Home: 5317 Westminster Pl Pittsburgh PA 15232-2120 Office: U Pitts Dept History Pittsburgh PA 15260

RAWSON, CLAUDE JULIEN, English educator; b. Shanghai, Feb. 8, 1935; came to U.S., 1985; s. Bernard and Helen (Sapiro) R.; m. Judith Ann Hammond, July 14, 1959; children: Hugh, Tim, Mark, Harriet, Annabel. BA, Oxford (Eng.) U., 1955, MA, BLitt, 1959. English lectr. U. Newcastle, Eng., 1957-65; from lectr. to prof., chmn. dept. U. Warwick,

Coventry, Eng., 1965-85, hon. prof., 1986—; George Sherburn prof. English U. Ill., Urbana, 1985-86; George M. Bodman prof. English Yale U., New Haven, Conn., 1986—; vis. prof. U. Pa., Phila., 1973, U. Calif., Berkeley, 1980. Author: Henry Fielding and the Augustan Ideal, 1972, 2d edit., 1991, Gulliver and the Gentle Reader, 1973, 2d edit., 1991, Order from Confusion Sprung, 1985, 2d edit., 1992, Satire and Sentiment 1660-1830, 1994; editor: Modern Lang. Rev. and Yearbook of English Studies, London, 1974-78; gen. editor: Cambridge (Eng.) History of Literary Criticism, 1983—, Unwin Critical Libr., London, 1974—, Blackwell Critical Biographies, 1985—; intro. gen. editor: Yale Boswell Papers, 1990—. Recipient Cert. of Merit for Disting. Svc. Conf. of Editors of Learned Jours., 1988; Andrew Mellon fellow Clark and Huntington Libr., 1980, 90, Guggenheim fellow, 1991-92, Sr. Faculty fellow Yale U., 1991-92; NEH grantee, 1991. Mem. Modern Humanities Rsch. Assn. (life mem., com. mem. 1974-88), Internat. Soc. 18th Century Studies, Am. Soc. for 18th Century Studies, Brit. Soc. for 18th Century Studies (pres. 1973-74). Office: Yale U Dept English PO Box 208302 New Haven CT 06520-8302

RAWSON, DAVID P., ambassador; b. Addison, Mich., Sept. 10, 1941; m. Sandra Miller; 2 children. BA, Malone Coll.; MA, PhD, Am. U. Joined Fgn. Svc., 1971; asst. for Zaire, desk officer for Rwanda and Burundi Dept. State, 1971-72; polit. officer Dept. State, Kigali, Rwanda, 1973-75, Bamako, Mali, 1975-78; chief polit. sect. Dakar, Senegal, 1978; spl. asst. for trade and devel. Pearson Fellowship Program Trumbull County Commrs., Warren, Ohio; dep. chief of mission Antananarivo, Madagascar, 1983-85, Mogadishu, Somalia, 1986-88; fellow Woodrow Wilson Sch. Pub. Affairs Princeton U.; dir. Office West African Affairs Dept. State, 1989-90; sr. fellow Ctr. for Study Fgn. Affairs, 1991-92; advisor Coun. on Fgn. Diplomacy's Exec. Exchange Program Mobil South, Inc., 1993; amb. to Rwanda Kigali, 1993—. Recipient 2 Superior Honor awards, Sr. Performance Pay award, Alumnus of Yr. award Malone Coll. Mem. Mande Studies Assn., Trumbull County Farm Bureau, Am. Fgn. Svc. Assn. Office: Am Embassy Kigali Dept State Washington DC 20521-2210

RAWSON, ELEANOR S., publishing company executive; m. Kennett Longley Rawson (dec.); children—Linda, Kennett Longley. V.p., exec. editor David McKay Co.; exec. v.p., editor-in-chief Rawson, Wade Publishers, Inc.; v.p. Scribner Book Cos.; pub. Rawson Assocs. divsn. Macmillan; v.p., chmn. Rawson Assocs./Simon & Schuster) lectr. NYU, New Sch., N.Y.; organizer, panelist various writers' confs.; mem. exec. coun., nominating chair Am. Assn. Pubs., 1970-74. Former editorial staff writer Am. mag.; free-lance writer radio and mags., newspaper syndicates; fiction editor Collier's mag., Today's Woman. Trustee, past v.p. Museums at Stony Brook. Mem. Assn. Women's Nat. Book Assn., P.E.N., Am. Assn. Museums, Yale Club, Cosmopolitan Club, Old Field Club, Women's Forum, Women In Media, Women in Comms. Office: 866 3rd Ave New York NY 10022-6221

RAWSON, RAYMOND D., dentist; b. Sandy, Utah, Nov. 2, 1940; s. James D. and Mable (Beckstead) R.; m. Linda Downey, July 23, 1959: children: Raymond Blaine, Mark Daniel, Pamela Ann, David James, Kristi Lynn, Kenneth Glenn, Richard Allen. B.S., U. Nev. at Las Vegas, 1964; D.D.S., Loma Linda U., 1968; M.A., U. Nev., 1978; m. Linda Downey, July 23, 1959; children: Raymond Blaine, Mark Daniel, Pamela Ann, David James, Kristi Lynn, Kenneth Glenn, Richard Allen. Diplomate Am. Bd. Forensic Odontology (pres. 1984), Am. Bd. Oral Medicine. Gen. practice dentistry, Las Vegas, 1968—; instr. dental hygiene, dental dir. Clark County Community Coll., 1977—; dep. coroner, chief dental examiner, 1977—; adj. prof. U. Nev., 1977—; adj. assoc. prof. oral diagnosis and forensic dentistry Northwestern U., Chgo., 1985—. Contbr. articles to profl. jours. Active Boy Scouts Am., 1968—; imen. youth and family health comm. assembly on fed. issues, Nat. Conf. State Legislators, mem. steering comm. Reforming States Group, council of State Govts.; recipient Community Heroes award, Nat. Conf. Christians and Jews, Las Vegas, 1994; pres. Red Rock Stake; bishop Ch. Jesus Christ Latter-day Saints, 1978-84; asst. majority leader Nev. State senator. Fellow Am. Acad. Forensic Scis. (pres., chmn.), ADA (editorial rev. bd. jour.), Federation Dentaire International, Omicron Kappa Upsilon (commr. edn. commn. of the states). Republican. Office: 6375 W Charleston Blvd Las Vegas NV 89102-1139

RAWSON, ROBERT H., JR., lawyer; b. Washington, Oct. 18, 1944. M.A. Princeton U., 1966; MA, Oxford U., Eng., 1968; JD, Harvard U., 1971. Bar: Ohio 1971, D.C. 1972. Ptnr. Jones, Day, Reavis & Pogue, Cleve. Rhodes scholar. Mem. Phi Beta Kappa. Office: Jones Day Reavis & Pogue North Point 901 Lakeside Ave E Cleveland OH 44114-1190

RAWSON, ROBERT ORRIN, physiologist; b. East St. Louis, Apr. 25, 1917; s. Orrin Garfield and Mabel Estelle (Casteel) R.; m. Barbara Ellis, Nov. 19, 1966; children—David Garfield, Mary Ellen, Judith Ann. Student, Ill. State Normal U., 1935-37; B.S. in Physiology, U. Ill., 1940; Ph.D. in Physiology, Loyola U., 1961. Broadcaster radio and TV St. Louis and Chgo., 1941-56; instr. biology U. Ill., Chgo., 1956-58; instr. physiology Yale U. Sch. Medicine, 1961-68, asst. prof., 1968-75, sr. research assoc., lectr., 1975-82; asst., then asso. fellow John B. Pierce Found. of Conn., New Haven, 1961-69, fellow, 1969-83, fellow emeritus, 1982. Contbr. articles to profl. jours. Mem. Inland Wetlands Commn., Guilford, Conn., 1980-86; mem. Mcpl. Preservation Bd., Guilford, 1980-86;sec. Madison Planning and Zoning Commn., 1987—. NIH grantee. Mem. Am. Physiol. Soc. Republican. Episcopalian. Home: 273 Legend Hill Rd Madison CT 06443-1864 Office: 290 Congress Ave New Haven CT 06519-1403

RAWSON, WILLIAM ROBERT, lawyer, retired manufacturing company executive; b. Montclair, N.J., Mar. 14, 1925; s. William Howard and Maude Elizabeth (Wheeler) R.; m. Elizabeth S. Crandall, Sept. 30, 1949; children—Shirley, Jean, Elizabeth. A.B., Brown U., 1947; LL.B., N.Y. U., 1950. Bar: N.J. 1950, Ill. 1974. Practice of law Bloomfield, N.J., 1950-52; legal asst. Thomas A. Edison Industries, West Orange, N.J., 1952-57; asst. counsel T.A. Edison div. McGraw-Edison Co., Elgin, Ill., 1957-67; v.p. adminstrn., div. T.A. Edison div. McGraw-Edison Co., 1967-72, asst. gen. counsel, 1972-77, corp. v.p. adminstrn., 1977-80, v.p. law, adminstrn. also corporate sec., 1980-85; corp. counsel L. Kaiser/Estech div. Vigoro Industries, Inc., Savannah, Ga., 1985-89; dir. Chgo. Econ. Devel. Corp. Chmn. Millburn (N.J.) Planning Bd. and Bd. Adjustment, 1962-70, Millburn Red Cross, 1969-70; mem. twp. coun., dep. mayor Twp. of Millburn, 1970-72; v.p. Elgin (Ill.) United Way, 1978-79; bd. dirs. United Way Suburban Chgo., 1981-85; pres. Regional Adult Literacy Partnership, Savannah, 1990-91; pres., bd. dirs. The Landings Homeowners Assn., 1992-94, pres., 1992-93. Lt. (j.g.) USN, 1943-46. Mem. ABA, Ill. State Bar Assn., Am. Arbitration Assn. (arbitrator constrn. industry panel 1985—), Elgin C. of C. (v.p. 1978-79). Republican. Episcopalian. Home: 4 Sandsfield Way Savannah GA 31411-2511

RAY, BENJAMIN CALEB, African studies and religion educator; b. Portland, Maine, May 5, 1940; s. Roger Bray and Helen (Winslow) R.; Maruta Lietins, June 25, 1965; children: Indra Elizabeth, Alexandra Winslow. BA, Bowdoin Coll., 1962; MA in Philosophy, U. Chgo., 1964, MA in Divinity, 1967, PhD, 1971. Asst. prof. Princeton U., 1969-77; assoc. prof. U. Va., 1978-90, prof., 1991—; vis. prof. Makerere U., Kampala, Uganda, 1972; vis. assoc. prof. Barnard Coll., 1976, Dartmouth Coll., 1987. Author: African Religions, 1976, Myth, Ritual & Kingship in Buganda, 1991 (recipient Outstanding Academic Book award Choice, 1991); curator African Art: Aesthetics & Meaning Exhibit Bayly Mus., 1993. Recipient Study fellowship Am. Coun. of Learned Societies, 1972-73, Ind. Study award Nat. Endowment for the Humanities, 1977-78, Sesquicentennial Associateship U. Va., 1985. Mem. Am. Acad. Religion, Am. Soc. Study Religion, African Studies Assn., Internat. African Inst. Office: Dept of Religious Studies University of Virginia B-10 Cocke Hall Charlottesville VA 22903-3281

RAY, BRADLEY STEPHEN, petroleum geologist; b. Ada, Okla., Feb. 15, 1957; s. Walter Lloyd and Betty Louise (McCurley) R. BS in Geology, Baylor U., 1980; MS in Geology, U. Tex., 1985. Cert. geologist. Asst. geologist Hunt Oil Co., Dallas, 1978, geologist, 1979-81; intl. oil and gas producer Dallas, 1981—; chmn. adv. bd. Geol. Info. Libr. Dallas, 1988—; bd. dirs. Global Mapping Internat. Trustee Dallas Bapt. U., 1988—, Criswell Coll., 1990-92; chmn. The Habitats Project, 1993—; co-chmn. Peoples

and Habitats Project, 1994—. Mem. Am. Assn. Petroleum Geologists, Ind. Petroleum Assn. Am., Soc. Ind. Profl. Earth Scientists, Dallas Geol. Soc., Tex. Ind. Producers and Royalty Owners, Okla. Ind. Petroleum Assn., Geol. Soc. Am., Computer Oriented Geol. Soc., Nat. Stripper Well Assn., Energy Club, Oklahoma City Geol. Soc., Colbert-Tracht Club. Republican. Baptist. Home: 3333 Rankin St Dallas TX 75205-1420 Office: 1348 One Energy Sq Dallas TX 75206

RAY, BRUCE DAVID, lawyer; b. Denver, Dec. 19, 1955; s. John Denver Ray and Jane (Guiney) Mitchell; m. Faith Theofanus, Aug. 20, 1978; children: Ellena, Constance, Christian. BA magna cum laude, U. Colo., 1978; JD, Union U., Albany, N.Y., 1981. Bar: Colo. 1981. Spl. environ. counsel URS-Berger, San Bernardino, Calif., 1982-84; asst. regional counsel EPA, Denver, 1984-90; spl. asst. U.S. atty. U.S. Dept. Justice, Denver, 1987-90; environ. counsel Manville Corp., Denver, 1990—. Asst. editor Natural Resources and Environment, 1989—; contbr. articles to legal jours. First v.p. St. Catherine Greek Orthodox Ch. of S.E. Denver. Recipient bronze medal EPA, 1986, 91, gold medal, 1989, Environ. Excellence award, 1987, Best Article award, 1988, Roasch prize Albany Law Sch., 1981. Mem. ABA (sect. on natural resources, energy and environ. law), Colo. Bar Assn. (environ. law coun. 1987—), Aurora Bar Assn., Environ. Law Inst., Air and Waste Mgmt. Assn., Phi Beta Kappa. Avocation: German language and literature, modern Greek. Office: Manville Corp 717 17th St Denver CO 80202-3330

RAY, C. EUGENE, chemicals executive; b. 1932. Sr. adv. Ernst & Whinney, 1987-88; exec. v.p. finance Signode Industries, Inc., 1987; dir. Am. Colloid Co., Arlington Heights, Ill., 1981—. Office: Am Colloid Co 1500 W Shure Dr Arlington Heights IL 60004-1443*

RAY, CHARLES AARON, foreign service officer; b. Center, Tex., July 5, 1945; m. Deborah Lott, Dec. 18, 1966 (div. 1973); children: Gayle Denene, Jason Andre; m. Myung Wook Soe, Nov. 3, 1973; children: David Edward, Denise Ellen. BSBA, Benedictine Coll., 1972; MS in Sys. Mgmt., U. So. Calif., 1981. Commd. 2d lt. U.S. Army, 1965, advanced through grades to maj., ret., 1982; consular officer U.S. Consulate Gen., Guangzhou, China, 1983-84; chief consular sect. U.S. Consulate Gen., Shenyang, China, 1985-87; chief adminstrv. sect. U.S. Consulate Gen., Chiangmai, Thailand, 1988-91; spl. asst. to dir. Office Def. Trade Controls, Washington, 1991-93; dep. chief of mission Am. Embassy, Freetown, Sierra Leone, 1993—. Editl. cartoonist Spring Lake News, 1975-79; contbr. articles to Asia Mag., 1974-79; editor mag. Psyop Digest, 1976-78; exec. editor Def. Trade News, 1992-93. Mem. Heritage Found., Washington, 1991. Avocations: taekwondo, softball, tennis, painting, poetry. Office: Am Embassy, Walpole & Siaka Stevens St, Freetown Sierra Leone

RAY, CHARLES KENDALL, retired university dean; b. Boise City, Okla., Mar. 15, 1928; s. Volney Holt and Mamie (Burton) R.; m. Doris Derby, Aug. 26, 1951. B.A., U. Colo., 1951; M.A., Columbia, 1955, Ed.D., 1959. Teaching prin. Bur. Indian Affairs, Savoonga, Alaska, 1951-54; mem. faculty U. Alaska, 1957-93, prof. edn., 1960-93, dean Sch. Edn., 1961-80, dir. summer sessions, 1980-93. Author: A Program of Education for Alaska Natives, 1959, Alaskan Native Secondary School Dropouts, 1961. Mem. N.E.A., Am. Assn. Sch. Adminstrs., Am. Assn. U. Profs., Am. Assn. Colls. Tchr. Edn. (state liaison officer), Phi Delta Kappa. Home: 1209 10th Ave Fairbanks AK 99701-4112

RAY, CREAD L., JR., retired state supreme court justice; b. Waskom, Tex., Mar. 10, 1931; s. Cread L. and Antonia (Hardesty) R.; m. Janet Watson Keller, Aug. 12, 1977; children: Sue Ann (dec.), Robert E., Glenn L., David B., Marcie Lynn, Anne Marie. B.B.A., Tex. A&M U., 1952; J.D., U. Tex., 1957; L.H.D. (hon.), Wiley Coll., Marshall, Tex., 1980. Bar: Tex. 1957. Practiced in Marshall, 1957-59; judge Harrison County, 1959-61; justice 6th dist. Ct. Civil Appeals, Texarkana, 1970-80, Supreme Ct. Tex., 1980-90; ret. Supreme Ct. Tex., Austin, 1990; prin. C.L Ray, Austin, 1991—. Past pres. Marshall Jaycees, Marshall C. of C.; mem. Tex. Ho. of Reps., 1966-70; active local, regional, nat. Boy Scouts Am.; trustee Wiley Coll. Lt. col. USAF, 1952-54, Korea; ret. Recipient various Boy Scouts awards. Mem. State Bar Tex., N.E. Tex. Bar Assn. (past pres.), Harrison County Bar Assn. (past pres.), VFW, Am. Legion. Democrat. Methodist. Clubs: Rotary, Elks, Tex. Aggies. Home: 604 Beardsley Ln Austin TX 78746 Office: 400 W 15th St Ste 600 Austin TX 78701-1647

RAY, DAVID SCOTT, mathematics educator; b. New Haven, Oct. 5, 1930; s. Wilbert Scott and Dorothy Philips (Clark) R.; m. Leslie Ann Mason, Sept. 8, 1956 (dec. Mar. 1985); children: Susan Elizabeth, Jennifer Ray Simonton, Alison Ray Dillman, Bethany Carolyn Rudloff; m. Jane Altmeyer, June 18, 1988. A.B., Washington and Jefferson Coll., 1952; M.A., U. Mich., 1956; Ph.D., U. Tenn., 1964. Teaching asst. U. Mich., 1956-58; instr. U. Tenn., 1958-64; assoc. prof. math. Bucknell U., 1964-71, prof., 1971—, chmn. dept. math., 1970-90, coord. grad. studies, 1966-71, dir. January program, 1977-90, chmn. faculty, 1980—. Served with USNR, 1952-55. Recipient Lindback award for distinguished teaching Bucknell U., 1970; NSF Sci. Faculty fellow, 1962-63. Mem. Math. Assn. Am., Am. Math. Soc., AAUP, AAAS, Sigma Xi. Home: 91 Anlyn Dr Lewisburg PA 17837-8810

RAY, DEE, television executive; b. Canton, N.C., Dec. 16, 1944; d. William O.K. and Edith Frances (Sellers) King; m. Eugene Andrew Birke, Feb. 20, 1967 (div. Feb. 1974); m. William Eric (Rick) Ray, Feb. 2, 1980; children: William Douglas, Deanna Melanie. V.p. Interstate Outdoor Advt., Charlotte, N.C., 1969-73; account exec. Naegele Outdoor Advt., Charlotte, 1973-75; pres. Birke Advt., Charlotte, 1975-79, Raycom, Inc., Charlotte, 1979—. Campaign supporter John Belk Mayor, Charlotte, 1971, Liz Hair County Commr., Charlotte, 1971. Mem. Nat. Assn. Programming TV Execs. Avocations: reading, cooking, gardening. Home and Office: Raycom Inc PO Box 33367 Charlotte NC 28233-3367

RAY, DENNIS JAY, regulatory policy educator, researcher; b. Hobbs, N.Mex., Jan. 29, 1950; s. J.W. and Beatrice Doris (Smith) R.; m. Mary Barnard, June 7, 1973; children: Mark Wilson, Kathryn Barnard, William Eric. BSEE, U. N.Mex., 1972; MBA in Finance, U. Wis., 1983, PhD in Bus., 1987. Rsch. analyst Pub. Svcs. Commn. Wis., Madison, 1977-79; rsch. asst. U. Wis., Madison, 1979-82; program mgr. Wis. Pub. Utility Inst., Madison, 1982-87, dir, 1987—; asst. prof. sch. bus. U. Wis., Madison, 1992—; mem. rsch. adv. com. Wis. Ctr. for Demand-Side Rsch., Madison, 1992—. Contbr. articles to profl. jours. Chmn. pastoral rels. com. First Bapt. Ch., Madison, 1988-89, chmn. budget com., 1993-94; bd. dirs. Capital City United Youth Soccer, Madison, 1990-91, Wayland Found., Madison, 1992—. Mem. IEEE, Am. Econ. Assn., Transp. and Pub. Utilities Group (vice chmn. 1994, chmn. 1995). Avocations: travel, camping, computers, softball. Office: Wis Pub Utility Inst U Wis Madison Sch Bus 975 University Ave Madison WI 53706-1323

RAY, DONALD HENSLEY, biologist; b. Hamilton AFB, Calif., Sept. 23, 1952; s. Cecil C. and Harriet Ellen (Graham) R.; m. Joni Lynn Rogers, June 26, 1976. AA, Okaloosa Walton Jr. Coll., 1972; BS in Biology, U. West Fla., 1974. Range technician Vitro Services, Eglin AFB, Fla., 1972; survey asst. Lowe Engrs., Fort Walton Beach, Fla., 1972; research asst. Hennison, Durham, Richardson Engrs., Pensacola, Fla., 1973-74, U. West Fla., Pensacola, 1974; v.p. Theta Analysis, Inc., Pensacola, 1974-75, pres., 1975; biologist Fla. Dept. Environ. Regulation, Gulf Breeze, Fla., 1976—, biol. scientist supr., 1989—, environ. specialist, 1990, environ. supr., 1992; charter affiliate Jour. Freshwater Invertebrate Biology, Port Washington, Wis., 1982; staff mem. Gov.'s Fla. Rivers Study com., Tallahassee, Fla., 1985; research subcom. Bayou Area Foresight com., Pensacola, 1987—; mem. Fla. Dept. Environ. Regulations Biocriteria Com. Tallahassee, 1991; mem. environ. adv. com. Pensacola Jr. Coll., Milton, Fla., 1991. Contbr. articles to profl. jours. Mem. North Am. Benthological Soc., Southeastern Pollution Biologist Assn. (exec. com., moderator 1985—), Sigma Xi. Discovered hydroperla phormidia species U.S. Nat. Mus. Natural History at Smithsonian Inst. Washington, 1981. Avocations: sports, natural history. Office: Fla Dept Environ Protection 160 Governmental Ctr Pensacola FL 32501

RAY, DOUGLAS, newspaper editor. Now editor, v.p. Daily Herald/Sunday Herald, Arlington Heights, Ill. Office: Daily Herald/Sunday Herald Paddock Publs PO Box 280 Arlington Heights IL 60006-0280°

RAY, EDWARD JOHN, economics educator, administrator; b. Jackson Heights, N.Y., Sept. 10, 1944; s. Thomas Paul and Cecelia Francis (Hiney) R.; m. Virginia Beth Phelps, June 14, 1969; children: Stephanie Elizabeth, Katherine Rebecca, Michael Edward. B.A., Queens Coll., CUNY, 1966; M.A., Stanford U., 1969, Ph.D., 1971. Asst. prof. econs. Ohio State U., Columbus, 1970-74, assoc. prof., 1974-77, prof., 1977—, chmn. dept. econs., 1976-92, assoc. provost acad. affairs Office Acad. Affairs, 1992-93; sr. vice provost, chief info. officer Office Acad. Affairs, 1993—; cons. Dept. Labor, 1974-76, Dept. Commerce, 1977; cons. AID, Office Tech. Assessment, winter 1982. Contbr. numerous articles on econs. to profl. jours. Active Upper Arlington Civic Assn., Columbus, 1983—. Mem. Am. Econs. Assn., Western Econ. Assn., Econ. History Assn., Phi Beta Kappa. Home: 1977 Rosebery Dr Columbus OH 43220-3044 Office: Ohio State U Acad Affairs 203 Bricker Hall 190 N Oval Mall Columbus OH 43210-1321

RAY, FRANK DAVID, government agency official; b. Mt. Vernon, Ohio, Dec. 1, 1940; s. John Paul and Lola Mae (Miller) R.; children: Susan M., Frank D. II; BS in Edn., Ohio State U., 1964, JD, 1967. Bar: Ohio 1967, U.S. Dist. Ct. 1969, U.S. Cir. Ct. Appeals (6th cir.) 1970, U.S. Supreme Ct. 1971. Legal aide to atty. gen. Ohio, 1965-66; bailiff probate ct., Franklin County, Ohio, 1966-67, gen. referee, 1967-68; with firm Stouffer, Wait and Ashbrook, Columbus, Ohio, 1967-71; jour. clk. Ohio Ho. of Reps., 1969-71; dist. dir. SBA, 1971—; mem. Ohio Pub. Defender Commn., 1983-91; mem. U.S. Dept. Commerce So. Ohio Dist. Export Council, 1988—; mem. Ohio Export Promotion and Trade Coun., 1992—, Ohio Rural Devel. Coun., 1993—; mem. vocat. edn. adv. com. Columbus Pub. Schs., 1993—; mem. Columbus Mayor's Econ. Devel. Council, 1983-84; mem. Small Bus. and High Tech. adv. com. Ohio Div. Securities, 1983-84; mem. tech. alliance Central Ohio Adv. Bd., 1983-89; mem. Ohio Small Bus. and Entrepreneurship Coun., 1994—. Mem. Upper Arlington (Ohio) Bd. Health, 1970-75; pres. Buckeye Republican Club, 1970, Franklin County Forum, 1970; chmn. Central Ohio chpt. Nat. Found.-March of Dimes, 1974-77; trustee Columbus Acad. Contemporary Art, 1976. Recipient Service award Nat. Found.-March of Dimes, 1974, 75, 76, 77; Am. Jurisprudence award for Excellence, 1967, In Search of Excellence award SBA, 1985; named Ohio Commodore, 1973. Mem. Leadership Columbus (grad. 1976), Delta Upsilon, Alpha Epsilon Delta. Clubs: Ohio Press, Ohio State U. Pres. Home: 4200 Dublin Rd Columbus OH 43221-5005

RAY, GARY J., food products executive. Chmn bd. dirs. Rochelle (Ill.) Foods Inc. Office: Rochelle Foods Inc 1001 S Main St Rochelle IL 61068°

RAY, GAYLE ELROD, sheriff; b. Murfreesboro, Tenn., Oct. 22, 1945; d. Jesse Smith and Jennie Hare (McElroy) Elrod; m. Roy Norman Ray, Dec. 27, 1970; children: Molly Elizabeth, Austin Elrod. BA, Mid. Tenn. State U., 1967; MA, U. Ark., 1969; MBA, Belmont U., 1989. Instr. English La. State U., Baton Rouge, 1969-72, Tenn. State U. Nashville, 1972-76; program coord. Vanderbilt U., Nashville, 1992-94; sheriff Davidson County, Nashville, 1994—. Pres. LWV, Nashville, 1987-89; mem. Women's Polit. Caucus, Nashville, 1987—; mem. alumni bd. Leadership Nashville, 1993. Recipient Polit. Star award Davidson County Dem. Women, 1993. Avocations: reading, hiking.

RAY, GENE WELLS, industrial executive; b. Murray, Ky., Apr. 23, 1938; s. Terry Lee and Loreen (Lovett) R.; m. Becky Huie, Mar. 5, 1956 (dec. 1976); children: Don Dickerson, Kathy Pratt, Nancy Dickerson. BS in Math., Physics and Chemistry, Murray State U., 1956; MS in Physics, U. Tenn., 1962, PhD in Theoretical Physics, 1965. With tech. staff Aerospace Corp., San Bernardino, Calif., 1965-68; mgr. strategic div. USAF (OA), Washington, 1968-70; scientist, sr. v.p., systems group mgr. Sci. Applications Inc., La Jolla, Calif., 1970-81, also bd. dirs.; pres., chief exec. officer Titan Systems Inc., San Diego, 1981-85, Titan corp., 1985—; assoc. prof. Carson Newman Coll., Tenn., 1964-65. Inventor mass flow meter. 1st lt. USAR, 1963-68. Republican. Avocations: tennis, wine collecting. Home: PO Box 2464 Rancho Santa Fe CA 92067-2464 Office: Titan Corp 3033 Science Park Rd San Diego CA 92121-1101

RAY, GEORGE EINAR, lawyer; b. Gloucester, Mass., Apr. 23, 1910; s. Matti and Sandra Sofia (Kujala) R.; m. Mary Lee Osborne, Sept. 7, 1940 (dec.); children: Mary Danforth White, Priscilla Ray Sartwelle, Elizabeth Ray Haenchen, George Einar Jr., Clifford Osborne, Michael Gritton (dec.). AB, Harvard U., 1932, JD, 1935. Bar: Mass. 1935. Practiced in N.Y.C., 1936-38, Boston, 1942-44; lawyer Ray, Trotti, Hemphill, Finfrock & Needham, P.C., Dallas, 1946-94, Hemphill, Needham & Garner, Dallas, 1994—; faculty assoc. Columbia Law Sch., 1935-36; atty. U.S. Bd. Tax Appeals, Washington, 1938-41; spl. asst. to atty. gen. U.S., tax div. Dept. Justice, 1941; prin. atty. Office Tax Legis. Counsel, U.S. Treasury Dept., 1941-42; adj. prof. So. Meth. U. Law Sch., N.Y.U. Tax Inst., Practicing Law Inst.; attended Sch. Mil Govt., Columbia, 1944; head dept. internat. law Naval Sch. Mil. Govt., Princeton, 1944-45; chief counsel Office Army-Navy Liquidation Commr., M.T.O. 1945; dep. exec. dir. Office Fgn. Liquidation Commr., State Dept., 1946. Author: Incorporating the Professional Practice, 1972, 3d edit., 1984; also articles in legal publs. Lt. comdr. USNR, World War II. Mem. Am., Tex., Dallas County bar assns., Tex. Bar, Tex. Bar Found., Southwestern Legal Found., Harvard Law Sch. Assn. Tex. (ex-pres.), Dallas Estate Council (pres. 1949-50). Baptist (deacon). Clubs: Northwood, Harvard (pres. 1950-51), Salesmanship, Dallas Knife and Fork (pres. 1967-68). Home: 12615 Breckenridge Dr Dallas TX 75230-2001 Office: Hemphill Needham Garner & Needham PC 1401 Elm St Ste 3404 Dallas TX 75202-2983

RAY, GEORGE WASHINGTON, III, English language educator; b. Binghamton, N.Y., Dec. 4, 1932; s. George Washington and Margaret (Nicholson) R.; m. Elizabeth DuPree Osborn, Dec. 29, 1956; children—Virginia, George, Melissa, Grace Elizabeth. A.B., Wesleyan U., 1954; postgrad., Colgate U., 1957-59; Ph.D., U. Rochester, 1966. Instr. English U. Rochester, N.Y., 1961-62, U. Va., Charlottesville, 1962-64; instr. English Washington and Lee U., Lexington, Va., 1964-66; asst. prof. Washington and Lee U., 1966-69, assoc. prof., 1969-74, prof., 1974—, acting chmn. dept., 1985, 91-92; vis. fellow Univ. Coll., Oxford (Eng.) U., 1980. Editor: Duke of Byron, 1979, The Chi Psi Story, 1995. Bd. dirs. Rockbridge Concert-Theater Series, 1966-83, Lime Kiln Arts Inc., 1983-86, Rockbridge Area Mental Health Assn., 1975-78 . Served as 1st lt. USMC, 1954-57. Recipient various fellowships. Mem. Va. Humanities Conf., Southeastern Renaissance Conf., Renaissance Soc. Am., Chi Psi (nat. Distinctive Service award 1985, trustee ednl. trust 1989—), Am. Soc. Theatre Rsch. Democrat. Presbyterian (elder 1979-85, 89-91). Home: 13 Sellers Ave Lexington VA 24450-1930 Office: Dept English Washington and Lee U Lexington VA 24450

RAY, GILBERT T., lawyer; b. Mansfield, Ohio, Sept. 18, 1944; s. Robert Lee Ray and Renatha (Goldie) Washington; m. Valerie J. Reynolds, June 14, 1969; children: Tanika, Tarlin. BA, Ashland Coll., 1966; MBA, U. Toledo, 1968; JD, Howard U., 1972. Bar: Ohio 1972. Assoc. O'Melveny & Myers, Los Angeles, 1972-79, ptnr., 1980—. Bd. dirs. L.A. area C. of C., NAACP Legal Def. Fund, Haynes Found., 2000 Partnership, L.A. Conv. and Visitor Bur. Mem. Riviera Club (L.A.), The Calif. Club. Democrat. Office: O'Melveny & Myers 400 S Hope St Los Angeles CA 90071-2801

RAY, GORDON THOMPSON, communications executive; b. N.Y.C., Jan. 31, 1928; s. John Henry and Hama Thompson (Potter) R. m. Ingrid Ray; children: Stuart, John, Lawrence, Carl. BEE, Rensselaer Poly. Inst., 1954; PhD, Midwest Coll. Engring., 1983. With The Bell System, various locations, 1954-83; successively engr., chief engr. N.Y. Tel., Albany, Utica, Jamaica, White Plains, N.Y., Bklyn., 1983; asst. v.p. long range planning N.Y. Tel., N.Y.C.; former mem. tech. staff Bell Tel. Labs., N.Y.C., Murray Hill and Holmdel, N.J.; engr. AT&T, N.Y.C.; dir. Bell System Computer Seminar; del. CCITT, Body Planning Internat. Direct Distance Dialing; v.p. planning NYNEX Materiel Enterprises Co. subs. NYNEX Corp., 1983-84, sr. v.p. NEC Am Inc., Melville, N.Y., 1985-91, exec. v.p., 1992—; mem. bus. and industry ctr. SUNY, adv. bd. Marine Scis. Rsch. Ctr., Harriman Coll., Stonybrook, sci. & bus. coun. L.I. Rsch. Inst.; bd. dirs. NEC Am Inc., NEC Rsch. Inst., Tel. Industry Assn., Electronic Indsl. Assn., L.I.

Assn., Summa Four Corp., L.I. Forum for Tech.; exec. com. Computer and Communications Industry Assn., Nat. Comm. Forum. Trustee U.S. Coun. for Internat. Bus., N.Y. Hall of Sci.; mem. exec. com. Akron Golf Charities. With U.S. Army, 1946-49. Fellow Royal Soc. of Arts; mem. AAAS, NSPE (sr. mem.), IEEE (sr. mem.), IEEE Communications Soc. (past chmn. quality assurance mgmt. com., internat. communications field award com.), N.Y. Acad. Scis., Am. Mgmt. Assn., Internet Soc., Cedarbrook Country Club, Firestone Country Club (bd. govs.). Office: NEC Am Inc 8 Old Sod Farm Rd Melville NY 11747-3148

RAY, H. M., lawyer; b. Rienzi, Miss., Aug. 9, 1924; s. Thomas Henry and Isabelle (Dunlap) R.; m. Merle Burt, Nov. 28, 1953 (dec. Dec. 1993); children: Howard Manfred, Mark Andrew. J.D., U. Miss., 1949. Bar: Miss. 1949. U.S. atty. No. Dist. Miss. Oxford, 1961-81; pvt. practice law Corinth, Miss., 1949-61, Jackson, Miss., 1981-85, 90—; asst. atty. gen. State of Miss., Jackson, 1986-90; treas., bd. dirs. Am. Sawmill Machinery Co., 1956-57; mem. Atty. Gen.'s Adv. Com. of U.S. Attys., 1973-78, chmn., 1976; vis. lectr. UN, Asia and Far East, UN (Ist. for Prevention Crime and Treatment of Offenders), Tokyo, 1977; pros. atty. Alcorn County, Miss., 1956-57, 58-61; mem. Miss. Ho. of Reps., 1948-51; mem. Miss. Gov.'s Com. To Study Laws Regarding Use of Deadly Force on Fleeing Felons, 1982-83, Miss. Gov.'s Constl. Study Commn., 1985-86. Co-author: Miss. Workmens' Compensation Act, 1948. Chmn. Corinth-Alcorn County Airport Bd., 1959-61; trustee Alcorn County Public Library, 1959-62. Served with USAAC, 1943-45, ETO; with USAF, 1951-53. Recipient Corinth's Young Man of Yr. award, 1958. Presbyterian (elder). Clubs: Kiwanis (lt. gov. 1955-56, dist. chmn. 1956-57, pres. Corinth 1943-53). Home: 12 Windy Ridge Cv Jackson MS 39211-2904 Office: PO Box 2449 Jackson MS 39225-2449

RAY, HAROLD BYRD, utilities executive; b. Lynwood, Calif., Aug. 30, 1940; s. Chester Bennett and Essie (Byrd) R.; m. Penny Lee Headding, Mar. 30, 1963; children: Claire, Jill. BS in Engring. with honors, UCLA, 1963; MS in Engring, Calif. Inst. Tech., 1970; MA in Mgmt., Claremont Grad Sch., 1979. Registered profl. nuclear and mech. engr., Calif. Systems engr. AEC, Washington, 1964-69; supervising engr. So. Calif. Edison Co., Rosemead, 1970-75, quality assurance mgr., 1975-79, San Onofre project mgr., 1979-81, San Onofre sta. mgr., 1981-83, v.p., 1983—. Served to lt. USN, 1963-69. Oak Ridge fellow, 1969. Mem. ASME, Sigma Xi. Republican. Presbyterian. Avocations: snow skiing. Office: So Calif Edison Co 2244 Walnut Grove Ave Rosemead CA 91770-3714

RAY, HUGH MASSEY, JR., lawyer; b. Vicksburg, Miss., Feb. 1, 1943; s. Hugh Massey and Lollie Landon (Powell) R.; m. Florence Hargrove, Sept. 3, 1966; children—Hugh, Hallie. B.A., Vanderbilt U., 1965, J.D., 1967. Bar: Tex. 1967, U.S. Dist. Ct. (so. dist.) Tex. 1967, U.S. Dist.Ct. (we. dist.) La. 1979, U.S. Dist. Ct. (we. dist.) Tex. 1979, U.S. Dist Ct. (no. dist.) Tex. 1980, U.S. Ct. Appeals (11th cir.) 1982, U.S. Dist. Ct. (no. dist) Calif. 1989, D.C. 1991, N.Y. 1992. Assoc. Andrews & Kurth, Houston, 1968-77, ptnr., 1977—. Co-author: Bankruptcy Investing, 1992; editor-in-chief Creditor's Rights in Texas, 1975; contbr. articles to law revs. Mem. ABA (chmn. real property practice com. 1975-77, chmn. continuing legal edn. com. young lawyers divsn. 1976-78, vice chmn. 1979, chmn. oil and gas subcom. bus. bankruptcy com. 1985-89, chmn. executory contracts subcom. 1989-93, chmn. bus. bankruptcy com. 1993—), Fed. Bar Assn., Houston Bar Assn., Tex. Bar Assn. (chmn. bankruptcy com. 1985-88), Am. Law Inst., Tex. Bd. Legal Specialization (cert.), Houston Country Club, Tex. Club, Houston Club. Episcopalian. Home: 5785 Indian Cir Houston TX 77057-1302 Office: Andrews & Kurth 4200 Tex Commerce Tower Houston TX 77002

RAY, JOHN WALKER, otolaryngologist, educator, broadcast commentator; b. Columbus, Ohio, Jan. 12, 1936; s. Kenneth Clark and Hope (Walker) Ray; m. Susanne Gettings, July 15, 1961; children: Nancy Ann, Susan Christy. AB magna cum laude, Marietta Coll., 1956; MD cum laude, Ohio State U., 1960; postgrad. Temple U., 1964, Mt. Sinai Hosp. and Columbia U., 1964, 66, Northwestern U., 1967, 71, U. Ill., 1968, U. Ind., 1969, Tulane U., 1969. Intern, Ohio State U. Hosps., Columbus, 1960-61, clin. rsch. trainee NIH, 1963-65, resident dept. otolaryngology, 1963-65, 1966-67, resident dept. surgery 1965-66, instr. dept. otolaryngology, 1966-67, 70-75, clin. asst. prof., 1975-82, clin. assoc. prof., 1982-92, clin. prof., 1992—; active staff, past chief of staff Bethesda Hosp.; active staff, past chief of staff Good Samaritan Hosp., Zanesville, Ohio, 1967—; courtesy staff Ohio State U. Hosps., Columbus, 1970—, Meml. Hosp., Marietta, Ohio, 1992—; radio-TV health commentator, 1982—. Past pres. Muskingum chpt. Am. Cancer Soc.; trustee Ohio Med. Polit. Action Com. Capt. USAF, 1961-63. Recipient Barraquer Meml. award, 1965; named to Order of Ky. Col., 1966, Muskingum County Country Music Hall of Fame. Diplomate Am. Bd. Otolaryngology. Fellow ACS, Am. Soc. Otolaryn. Allergy, Am. Acad. Otolaryngology-Head and Neck Surgery (gov.), Am. Acad. Facial Plastic and Reconstructive Surgery; mem. Nat. Assn. Physician Broadcasters, Muskingum County Acad. Medicine (past pres.), AMA (del. hosp. med. Staff sect.), Ohio Med. Assn. (del.), Columbus Ophthalmol. and Otolaryngol. Soc. (past pres.), Ohio Soc. Otolaryngology (past pres.), Pan-Am. Assn. Otolaryngology and Bronchoesophagology, Pan-Am. Allergy Soc., Am. Acad. Invitro Allergy, Am. Auditory Soc., Am. Soc. Contemporary Medicine and Surgery, Acad. Radio and TV Health Communicators, Fraternal Order Police Assocs., Phi Beta Kappa, Alpha Tau Omega, Alpha Kappa Kappa, Alpha Omega Alpha, Beta Beta Beta. Presbyterian. Contbr. articles to sci., med. jours; collaborator with surg. motion picture: Laryngectomy and Neck Dissection, 1964. Office: 2945 Maple Ave Zanesville OH 43701-1733

RAY, KELLEY, production company technical director. MA in Animation, Photography and Graphic Design, Ill. Inst. Tech. Tech. dir. MetroLight Studios, L.A. Office: MetroLight Studios Ste 400 5724 W 3rd St Los Angeles CA 90036-3043

RAY, MARY-ANN, architect, educator; b. Seattle, July 19, 1958; d. Norman Gene and Barbara Ann (Wechsler) R. BFA, U. Wash., 1981; MArch, Princeton U., 1987. Designer Michael Graves, Architect, Princeton, N.J., 1984, Richard Meier and Ptnrs., L.A. and N.Y.C., 1987-88; prin., designer Studio Works, L.A., 1985—; grad. designer So. Calif. Inst. Architecture, L.A., 1988—; mem. adv. bd. L.A. Mcpl. Art Gallery, 1992—. Prin. works include (master plans) Progressive Architecture, 1990-91 (Urban Design award 1992), Inland Architect, 1990-91, Lotus Internat., 1990-91. Recipient Lili Auchincloss fellowship Am. Acad. Rome, 1987-88, Norton prize Princeton U., 1987, Max Beckmann Meml. fellowship Bklyn. Mus., 1981-82, Ford Found. grant in fine arts U. Wash. and Ford Found., 1978, 80, 81. Home and Office: Studio Works Bldg # 3 6775 S Centinela Ave Culver City CA 90230-6303

RAY, MICHAEL EDWIN, lawyer; b. Charlotte, N.C., Dec. 13, 1949; s. Daniel Shaw Ray and Jane (Horne) Keziah; m. Janet Langston Jones, July 14, 1973; children: John Daniel, Jennifer Marjory. BA, Furman U., 1972; JD, U. S.C., 1978. Bar: N.C. 1978, U.S. Dist. Ct. (ea., mid. and we. dists.) N.C. 1978, U.S. Ct. Appeals (4th cir.) 1981, U.S. Ct. Appeals (Fed. cir.) 1989. Legal administr. Wyche Burgess Freeman & Parham, Greenville, S.C., 1973-75; assoc. Womble Carlyle Sandridge & Rice, Winston-Salem, N.C., 1978-85, ptnr., 1985—. Mem. S.C. Manpower Planning Coun., Columbia, S.C., 1971-72. T. B. Clarkson scholar Furman U. 1971-72. Mem. ABA, N.C. Bar Assn., S.C. Bar Assn., Fed. Cir. Bar Assn. (bd. govs. 1994—), Am. Intellectual Property Law Assn., N.C. Assn. Def. Attys., Forsyth County Bar Assn., Furman U. Alumni Assn. (bd. govs. 1995—), Lex Mundi, Ltd. (dir. 1995—). Democrat. Presbyterian. Avocations: sailing, woodworking, guitar. Home: 4269 Stonehenge Ln Winston Salem NC 27106-3535 Office: Womble Carlyle Sandridge & Rice PO Box 84 Winston Salem NC 27102-0084

RAY, NORMAN WILSON, career officer; b. Hillsboro, Ill., June 26, 1942; s. Glen B. and Genevieve (Sandifer) R.; m. Priscilla Songer, Dec. 27, 1964; children: Melinda Caron, Molly Ellen. BS, US. Naval Acad., 1964. Commd. ensign USN, 1964, advanced through grades to vice adm., 1992, pilot Patrol Squadron 50, 1965; with Test Pilot Sch., 1969; project test pilot Naval Air Test Ctr. USN, 1970-72; advanced VP systems project officer Naval Air Systems USN, Washington, 1972-75; pilot Patrol Squadron 16 USN, Jacksonville, Fla., 1975-78; comdr. Patrol Squadron 56 USN, 1978-81; air readiness officer ASW Systems Project Office USN, Washington, 1981-82;

naval armaments officer, dep. nat. armaments rep. U.S. Mission to NATO, Brussels, 1982-84; air ASW br. head, dep. div. dir. for force level plans and warfare appraisal Dir. Naval Warfare, Washington, 1984-87; exec. asst., naval aide Under Sec. Navy, Washington, 1987-88; comdr. Naval Air Sta., Jacksonville, 1988-89; exec. asst. Sec. Navy, Washington, 1989-90; dir. Office of Program Appraisal USN, 1990-92; dep. chmn. NATO Mil. Com., Brussels, 1992—. Decorated Disting. Svc. medal, Legion of Merit with 2 gold stars, Def. Meritorious Svc. medal, Meritorious Svc. medal with 1 gold star, Navy Commendation medal, Navy Achievement medal. Mem. Army and Navy Club (Washington and Arlington, Va.). Avocation: golf. Office: NATO Mil Com IMS/DEL PSC 80 Box 300 APO AE 09724

RAY, NORRETTA, clinical social worker, administrator, psychotherapist, educator, consultant; b. Inwood, N.Y., June 5, 1937. AA, Voorhees Jr. Coll., Denmark, S.C., 1957; BA in Sociology, St. Augustine Coll., 1959; MSW, Atlanta U., 1963; postgrad., Columbia U., 1976—. Diplomate Am. Bd. Examiners in Clin. Social Work. Psychiat. social worker Creedmoor Psychiat. Ctr., Queens Village, N.Y., 1963-66; fellow Psychoanalysis Postgrad. Ctr. Mental Health, N.Y., 1968-70; clinical supr. edn. Creedmoor Psychiat. Ctr., Queens Village, N.Y., 1970-74, coord. for field work, 1974-77, dir. social work, 1981-86, clin. social work supr., 1986—; psychiat. social worker North Shore Child Guidance Ctr., Manhasset, N.Y., 1966; social work supr. Soc. Prevention Cruelty to Children, Jamaica, N.Y., 1967-68; counselor coll. adv. com. Harlem Teams for Self Help, N.Y.C., 1968-71; clinic dir. Jamaica (N.Y.) Outpatient Clinic, 1978-79; active Nat. Com. to Preserve Social Security & Medicare. Recipient Disting. Cmty. Svc. Alumni award St. Augustine's Coll., 1990. Mem. NASW, APHA, NABSW, Nat. Assn. Black Psychologists, Nat. Action Network (life, Outstanding Alumni award 1995), Soc. for Hosp. S.W. Dirs., Vogue Club (founder), Delta Sigma Theta. Home and Office: 683 Midwood St Uniondale NY 11553-1903

RAY, PAUL RICHARD, JR., executive search consultant; b. Columbus, Ga., Nov. 6, 1943; s. Paul R. and Sarah (Campbell) R.; m. Elizabeth Richards, June 29, 1968; children: Paul Ray III, John Ray, Alice Ray. BSBA, U. Ark., 1966; JD, U. Tex., 1969. Bar: Tex. 1970. Dir. mktg., various mktg. positions tobacco div. R.J. Reynolds Tobacco Co., Winston-Salem, N.C., 1969-78; cons. Paul R. Ray & Co., Ft. Worth, 1978, v.p., 1978-79, sr. v.p., 1979-83, exec. v.p., 1983-84, pres., COO, 1984-86, pres., CEO, 1986—. Bd. dirs. Cook-FortWorth Children's Med. Ctr., United Way of Met. Tarrant County, Ft. Worth Mus. Sci. & History; mem. liberal arts adv. bd. U. Tex.; mem. dean's exec. adv. bd. U. Ark. Mem. ABA, Tex. Bar Assn., Young Pres.' Orgn., River Crest Country Club, City Club. Office: Paul Ray Berndtson Inc 301 Commerce St Ste 2300 Fort Worth TX 76102-4123

RAY, RICHARD T., manufacturing executive, heavy; b. 1957. BBA, U. North Fla., MBA. With Peat, Marwick, Mitchell and Co.; sr. v.p., CFO The Charter Co., 1983-92; exec. v.p., CFO Continental Emsco Co., Garland, Tex., 1993—. With USN, 1975-79. Office: Continental Emsco Co 2441 Forest Ln Garland TX 75042°

RAY, ROBERT D., health insurance company executive; b. Des Moines, Sept. 26, 1928; s. Clark A. and Mildred (Dolph) R.; m. Billie Lee Hornbuerger, Dec. 21, 1951; children: Randi Sue, Lu Ann, Vicki Jo. BA in Bus. Admin., Drake U., 1952, JD, 1954. Bar: Iowa 1954. Ptnr. Lawyer, Lawyer & Ray, Des Moines; gov. State of Iowa, 1969-83; pres., chief exec. officer Life Investors Inc. subs. Aegon NV, Cedar Rapids, Iowa, 1983-89; also chmn., bd. dirs. Life Investors Devel. Co. subs. Life Investors Inc., Cedar Rapids; pres., chief exec. officer IASD Health Svcs. Corp. dba in Iowa as Blue Cross & Blue Shield of Iowa and in S.D. as Blue Cross of S.D., Des Moines, 1989—; chmn., pres., bd. dirs. Bankers United Life Assurance Co. subs. Life Investors Devel. Co., Cedar Rapids. Office: Blue Cross and Blue Shield Iowa 636 Grand Ave Des Moines IA 50309-2502

RAY, ROBERT FRANKLIN, banker; b. Lynchburg, Va., Feb. 8, 1949; s. Homer M. and Jewel Ray; children: Meredith, David, Kevin. BS in Econs., Hampden-Sydney Coll., 1971; MBA in Fin., George Washington U., 1976. Sr. v.p. investments 1st Nat. Bank Md., Balt., 1976—. Mem. Mcpl. Bond Club Balt. Office: 1st Nat Bank Md 25 S Charles St Baltimore MD 21201-3330

RAY, ROGER BUCHANAN, retired communications executive, lawyer; b. Tampa, Fla., Aug. 12, 1935; s. Ralph Jackson and Virginia Marie (Stewart) R.; m. Mary Frye Gaillard, Dec. 27, 1957; children: Mary Katherine, Roger Buchanan Jr. BA in Acctg., U. South Fla., 1967; MBA with honors, U. Notre Dame, 1980, JD, Stetson U., 1991. Bar: Fla. 1992. Acct. Gen. Telephone Co. Fla., Tampa, 1959-67; internal audit mgr. GTE Service Co., N.Y.C., 1967-69; budget dir. Gen. Telephone Co. of S.E., Durham, N.C., 1969-74; v.p., controller Gen. Telephone Co. Mich., Muskegon, 1974-78; regional v.p. fin. GTE Service Corp., Westfield, Ind., 1978-82; v.p. fin. Gen. Telephone Co. Wis., 1982-84, Gen. Telephone Co. Ohio, 1982-84, Gen. Telephone Co. Pa., 1982-84, Gen. Telephone Co. Ill., 1982-84; v.p. fin., bd. dirs. Gen. Telephone Co. Mich., 1982-84, Gen. Telephone Co. Ind., 1982-84; v.p. fin., mem. exec. com., bd. dirs. GTE Communications Systems, Phoenix, 1985-87; asst. state's atty. 13th jud. cir. Tampa, Fla. bar, 1992; asst. state atty. 6th Jud. Cir., Pinellas County, Fla., 1992—. Lay eucharistic min., vestry mem., jr. warden Ch. of Ascension, Clearwater, Fla. Mem. Fin. Execs. Inst., Clearwater Bar Assn., Notre Dame Alumni Assn., Kappa Alpha. Republican. Episcopalian. Avocations: jogging, golf, reading, church work. Home: 2337 Kings Point Dr Largo FL 34644-1010

RAY, THOMAS KREIDER, clergyman. Bishop No. Mich. region Episcopal Ch., 1982—. Office: Diocese of No Mich 131 E Ridge St Marquette MI 49855-4298

RAY, W. HARMON, chemical engineering educator, consultant, author; b. Washington, Apr. 4, 1940; s. Willis Henry and Dorothy Rebecca (Smith) R.; m. Nell Freda Rose, Aug. 25, 1962; children: Gregory, Steven, Jonathan. BA, Rice U., 1962, BS, 1963; PhD, U. Minn., 1966. Cert. profl. engr., Ont. Postdoctoral research fellow U. Minn., 1966; asst. prof. chem. engring. U. Waterloo, Ont., Can., 1966-69; assoc. prof. U. Waterloo, 1969-70; assoc. prof. SUNY, Buffalo, 1970-73, prof., 1974-76; prof. chem. engring. U. Wis.-Madison, 1976—. Steenbock prof. engring., 1986—, Vilas prof. chem. engring., 1995; indsl. cons. Author: (with Szekely) Process Optimization, 1973; (with Lainiotis) Distributed Parameter Systems, 1978; (with Stewart and Conley) Dynamics and Modelling of Reactive Systems, 1980; Advanced Process Control, 1981; (with Ogunnaike) Process Dynamics, Modeling, and Control, 1994; contbr. articles to profl. publs. Recipient Donald P. Eckman award Am. Automatic Control Council, 1969, Control Edn. award, 1989, Automatica Prize Paper award Internat. Fedn. Automatic Control, 1981, John Simon Guggenheim Meml. fellow, 1973-74, Reilly Lectureship award U. Notre Dame, 1984, Byron Bird award U. Wis., 1987, Lacey lectr. award Calif. Inst. Tech., 1988. Fellow Am. Inst. Chem. Engrs. (profl. progress award 1982); mem. NAE, Am. Chem. Soc. (organic coatings, plastics div., Arthur K. Doolittle award 1981), Am. Soc. Engring. Edn., Assn. Profl. Engrs., Ont., Can. Soc. Chem. Engrs., Chem. Inst. Can., Soc. Indsl. and Applied Math., Sigma Xi. Office: U Wis Dept Chem Engring Madison WI 53706

RAY, WILLIAM F., banker; b. Cin., Sept. 17, 1915; s. William F. and Adele (Daller) R.; m. Helen Payne, 1939; children: Katharine Ray Sturgis, Barbara Ray Stevens, Mary Ray Struthers, Margaret Ray Gilbert, Whitney Ray Dawson, William F. III, Susan. A.B., U. Cin., 1935; M.B.A., Harvard, 1937. With Brown Bros. Harriman & Co., 1937—, asst. mgr., 1944-49; mgr. Brown Bros. Harriman & Co., Boston, 1950-67; ptnr. Brown Bros. Harriman & Co., N.Y.C., 1968-94, Boston, 1994—; trustee emeritus Atlantic Mut. Ins. Co., N.Y.C.; mem. internat. bd. advisors Australia and New Zealand Banking Group, Ltd., 1987-91; bd. dirs. U.S.-New Zealand Bus. Coun. Bd. dirs. Robert Brunner Found., 1957-94, Downtown-Lower Manhattan Assn., Inc., 1978-89; bd. dirs. trustee Am. Friends of the Australian Nat. Gallery. Mem. Bankers Assn. for Fgn. Trade (pres. 1966-67), Harvard Bus. Sch. Assn. (pres. 1963-64, exec. coun.), Robert Morris Assocs. (pres. N.E. 1962-63), Pilgrims U.S., Am. Australian Assn. (hon. dir.), U.S.-New Zealand Bus. Coun., S.R. (life), Asia Soc. (Ann. award 1988), Skating Club (Boston)(pres. 1956-58), Brookline (Mass.) Country Club, Union Club (N.Y.C.), India House (N.Y.C.), Fishers Island (N.Y.) Club, Mountain Lake Club (Lake

Wales, Fla.), Order of Australia (hon., officer), Order of Malta, Somerset Club (Boston), Phi Beta Kappa Assocs. (hon. bd. dirs.). Republican. Home: 10 Longwood Dr Apt 468 Westwood MA 02090-1146 Office: Brown Bros Harriman & Co 40 Water St Boston MA 02109-3661

RAY, WILLIAM JACKSON, psychologist; b. Birmingham, Ala., Sept. 3, 1945; s. Norman M. and Mary K. Agnew; m. Judith Mebane, Aug. 22, 1987; children from previous marriage: Adam, Lauren. BA, Eckerd Coll., 1967; MA, Vanderbilt U., 1969, PhD, 1971; Fellow in med. psychology, Langley Porter Neuropsychiat. Inst., U. Calif. Med. Center, San Francisco, 1971-72. Prof., dir. clin. psychology tng. program Pa. State U., 1972—; dir. clin. trng. 1991—. Author: (with R. M. Stern) Biofeedback, 1977, (with others) Evaluation of Clinical Biofeedback, 1979, (with R.M. Stern and C.M. Davis) Psychophysiological Recording, 1980, Methods toward a Science of Behavior and Experience, 1981, 4th edit., 1992; series editor: Plenum Series in Behavioral Psychophysiology and Medicine. Recipient Nat. Media award Am. Psychol. Found., 1976, 78. Mem. AAAS, APA, Soc. Psychophysiol. Rsch. Office: Dept Psychology Pa State U University Park PA 16802

RAYAN, GHAZI M., surgeon; b. Haifa, Palestine, Dec. 6, 1949; s. Moh H. and Kay K. (Harti) R.; m. Hoda Khatib, Feb. 15, 1962; children: Nadine, Basil. PNS, Alexandria U., Egypt, 1968, MBBCh, 1973. Dipomate Am. Bd. Orthpaedic Surgery; lic. MD, N.C., Md., Okla. Internship Alexandria U., Egypt, 1974-75; physician ARAMCO, Saudi Arabia, 1975; fellow radiology Johns Hopkins Hosp., Balt., 1975; intern, resident gen. surgery South Balt. Gen. Hosp./U.Md., 1976-77; resident orthopedic surgery Union Meml.-Johns Hopkins Hosp., Balt., 1977-80; fellow in hand/microsurgery Raymond Curtis Hand Ctr., Balt., 1980-81; chief hand surgery dept. U. Okla., Oklahoma City, 1981-87; asst. prof. Health Scis. Ctr., Oklahoma City, 1981-86; assoc. prof. U. Okla., Oklahoma City, 1986-91, clin. prof., 1992—; med. dir. hand rehab. Bapt. Med. Ctr., Oklahoma City, 1987-92, dir. hand surgery fellowship program, 1992—. Mem. editorial adv. bd. Orthopaedics Today, 1982—; editor-in-chief Eastern Mediterranean Hand Bull., 1985—; contbr. chpts. to books, numerous articles to profl. jours. Recipient Am. Physician's Recognition award AMA, 1982-84, 84-87, Best Paper award, 1983, 86, 90, Outstanding Tchrs. award U. Okla. Health Scis. Ctr., 1992-93; Harris fellow, 1986. Fellow ACS, Am. Acad. Orthopaedic Surgeons; mem. AMA, Johns Hopkins Med. and Surgery Assn., Oklahoma County Med. Soc., Okla. State Med. Soc., Ctrl. Okla. Orthopaedic Ctrl., Arthritis Found., Am. Soc. Surgery of Hand, Ea. Mediterranean Hand Soc., Am. Assn. for Hand Surgery, Orthopaedic Rsch. Soc., Am. Soc. for Reconstructive Microsurgery, So. Med. Assn., Am. Soc. for Peripheral Nerve Surgery, Am. Med. Writers Assn. Avocations: tennis, swimming, painting. Office: Upper Extremity Hand & Microsurgery Ctr 3366 NW Expressway Ste 700 Oklahoma City OK 73112

RAYBALL, SHARON A., medical/surgical nurse, administrator; b. West Palm Beach, Fla., Mar. 27, 1955; d. Leo B. and Murielle (Kennedy) R. BSN, Barry Coll., 1977; MS in Nursing Administrn., Boston U., 1985. Cert. nurse administr. Nurse mgr. Brookline (Mass.) Hosp.; asst. DON Mary Imogene Bassett Hosp., Cooperstown, N.Y., acting DON. Mem. Am. Orgn. Nurse Execs., N.E. N.Y. Orgn. Nurse Execs.

RAYBORN, WILLIAM LEE, state senator; b. McComb, Miss., May 15, 1936; student Am. Sch., Chgo.; m. Doris Nettles; 5 children. Mem. Miss. Senate; dental technician, denturist. Mem. Am. Acad. Denturists, Nat. Denturists Assn. Democrat. Baptist. Lodges: Civitan, Moose, Masons, Shriners, Order Eastern Star. Home: 3404 Harmony Dr SE Brookhaven MS 39601 Office: Miss Senate Jackson MS 39205

RAYBOULD, BARRY JOHN, computer software company executive; b. Stourbridge, Eng., Jan. 14, 1956; came to U.S., 1984; s. Arthur Wesley and Edna (Tromans) R.; m. Jacqueline Seddon, June 19, 1981. Grad. with honors, U. Cambridge, Eng., 1977, BA and MA in Engineering, 1978. Supt. prodn. Delta Metal Group, Manchester, U.K., 1980-81, mgr. overseas mfg., 1981-82; sr. engr. Prime Computer Inc., Stevenage, U.K., 1982-85; product mgr. Prime Computer Inc., Natick, Mass., 1985-88; pres. Ariel PSS Corp., Mountain View, Calif., 1989—, pres., CEO, 1991—. Editor: International Directory of Peformance Support Authoring Systems, 1991. Mem. Nat. Soc. for Performance and Instrn. (bd. dirs. 1990-91), Applied Learning Tech., Internat. Interactive Communications Soc., Soc. for Tech. Communication (highest award of distinction 1990, 92). Avocations: watercolor painting, skiing, reading, travel, art. Office: Ariel PSS Corp 100 View St Ste 114 Mountain View CA 94041-1366

RAYBURN, B. B., state senator,farmer, cattleman; b. Aug. 11, 1916; student Sullivan Trade Sch., Bogalusa, La.; hon. doctorate Loyola U., New Orleans, 1959; m. Hazel Eugene Blanchard. Pipefitter, Crown-Zellerback Corp., 30 yrs.; mem. La. Ho. of Reps., 1948-51; mem. La. Senate, 1951—, currently chmn. Senate Fin. Com., Joint Legis. Com. on Budget, former mem. numerous coms. including conservation, edn., transp., pub. works, indsl. relations, labor, others; del. 1973 Constl. Conv., chmn. com. on revenue, fin. and taxation. Mem. Washington County Police Jury, 1944-48. Rayburn Sch. Vet. Sci., La. State U., named in his honor, 1978. Mem. La. Vet. Med. Assn. (hon.). Democrat. Baptist. Clubs: Masons, Shriners, Lions. Office: PO Box 94183 Baton Rouge LA 70804-9183

RAYBURN, BILLY J., Church administrator. Dir. of cross cultural ministries Ch. of God. Office: Ch of God PO Box 2430 Cleveland TN 37320

RAYBURN, CAROLE (MARY AIDA) ANN, psychologist, researcher, writer; b. Washington, Feb. 14, 1938; d. Carl Frederick and Mary Helen (Milkie) Miller; m. Ronald Allen Rayburn (dec. Apr. 1970). BA in Psychology, Am. U., 1961; MA in Clin. Psychology, George Washington U., 1965; PhD in Edni. Psychology, Cath. U. Am., 1969; MDiv in Ministry, Andrews U., 1980. Lic. psychologist, Md., Mich. Psychometrician Columbian Prep. Sch., Washington, 1963; clin. psychologist Spring Grove State Hosp., Catonsville, Md., 1966-68; pvt. practice, 1969, 71—; staff clin. psychologist Instl. Care Svcs. Div. D.C. Children's Ctr., Laurel, Md., 1970-78; psychologist Md. Dept. Vocat. Rehab., 1973-74; psychometrician Montgomery County Pub. Schs., 1985-88; lectr. Strayer Coll., Washington, 1969-70; forensic psychology expert witness, 1973—; guest lectr. Andrews U., Berrien Springs, Mich., 1979, Hood. Coll, Frederick, Md., 1986-88; instr. Johns Hopkins U., 1986, 88-89; adj. faculty Profl. Sch. Psychol. Studies, San Diego, 1987; adj. asst. prof. Loyola Coll., 1987; cons. Julia Brown Montessori Schs., 1972, 78, 82—, Va. Ctr., 1978, 91-93. Editor: (with M.J. Meadow) A Time to Weep and a Time to Sing, 1985; contbg. author: Montessori: Her Method and the Movement (What You Need to Know), 1973, Drugs, Alcohol, and Women: A National Forum Source Book, 1975, The Other Side of the Couch: Faith of the Psychotherapist, 1981, Clinical Handbook of Pastoral Counseling, 1985, An Encyclopedic Dictionary of Pastoral Care and Counseling, 1990, Religion, Personality, and Mental Health, 1993; author copyrighted inventories Religious Occupations and Stress Questionnaire, 1986, Religion and Stress Questionnaire, 1986, Organizational Relationships Survey, 1987, Attitudes Toward Children Inventory, 1987, State-Trait Marital Inventory, 1987, Body Awareness and Sexual Intimacy Comfort Scale (Basics), 1993; cons. editor Profl. Psychology, 1980-83; assoc. editor Jour. Pastoral Counseling, 1985-90, guest editor, 1988; contbr. numerous articles to profl. jours. Recipient Svc. award Coun. for Advancement Psychol. Professions and Scis., 1975, cert. D.C. Dept. Human Resources, 1975, 76, cert. recognition D.C. Psychol. Assn., 1976, 1985; AAUW rsch. grantee, 1983. Fellow Am. Orthopsychiat. Assn., Md. Psychol. Assn. (editor newsletter 1975-76, cert. recognition 1978, chair ins. com. 1981-83, pres. 1984-85, exec. adv. com. 1985—). Am. Assn. of Applied & Preventive Psychology (sec. 1992-93, chair fellows com. 1992-93), APA (chair equal opportunity affirmative action div. clin. psychology 1980-82, mem. editorial bd. Jour. Child Clin. Psychology 1978-82, pres. clin. psychology women sect. 1984-86, program chair 1991-94, div. psychology women chair task force on women and religion 1980-81, div. psychology of religion 1980-81, div. psychology 1978-80, 92—, mem. task force on religious issiues in grad. edn. and clin. tng. 1988—, pres. 1995-96); mem. Assn. Practicing Psychologists Montgomery-Prince George's Counties (pres. 1986-88, editor newsletter 1990—), Balt. Assn. Cons. Psychologists (pres. 1976-78), Internat. Torch (pres. 1991-92), Psi Chi (hon.). Achievements include research on stress in religious profls., women and stress, women and religion,

pastoral counseling, psychotherapy, children. Address: 1200 Morningside Dr Silver Spring MD 20904

RAYBURN, GEORGE MARVIN, business executive, investment executive; b. Cape Girardeau, Mo., Jan. 30, 1920; s. Walter Marvin and Alma Fay (McBride) R.; m. Louise (Taylor) R.; m. Kimberly Ann Pearce, June 4, 1983; 1 child from previous marriage, George Marvin. Student, Central Coll. Fayette, Mo., 1937-39; B.S. in Bus. Adminstrn, Washington U., St. Louis, 1941, M.S. in Bus. Adminstrn, 1947. Auditor Internat. Harvester Co., 1941-45; accountant Tallman Co., 1946-47; asst. prof. U. Omaha, 1947-49; assoc. prof. Millikin U., 1949-52; pvt. practice as George M. Rayburn (C.P.A.), 1948-52; regional internal auditor Olin-Mathieson Chem. Corp., 1952-55; comptroller Orchard Paper Co., 1955-56; asst. controller St. L.S.F Ry., St. Louis, 1956-62; sec., treas. St. L.S.F. Ry., 1963-69, v.p., 1969-72; pres., dir. N.M. & Ariz. Land Co., 1966-81; chmn., dir. G.M. Resources, Inc., 1982—. Author: Standard Costs Applied to Distribution Costs, 1947, Budgets Bewitched or Bewildered, 1960. Served to capt. AUS, 1942-45, 51-52. Mem. AICPA, Am. Accounting Assn., Financial Execs. Inst., Planning Forum Inc., Delta Sigma Pi, Phi Sigma Phi, Phi Kappa Delta. Methodist. Home and Office: 12410 W 82d Pl Lenexa KS 66215-2738

RAYBURN, TED RYE, newspaper editor; b. Manchester, Tenn., Dec. 16, 1956; s. Ted and Thelma (Taylor) R.; m. Kimberly Ann Pearce, June 4, 1983. BS in Mass Comm., Mid. Tenn. State U., 1986. State corr. Nashville Banner, Murfreesboro, Tenn., 1978-79; reporter, photographer, sports editor Murfreesboro Press, 1978-80; state corr. The Tennessean, Murfreesboro, 1979-80; copy editor Jackson (Tenn.) Sun, 1980-82, asst. copy desk chief, 1982-85; copy editor Tennessean, Nashville, 1985-90, page one editor, 1990—, asst. copy desk chief, 1990—. Avocations: film, literature, jazz music. Office: The Tennessean 1100 Broadway Nashville TN 37203

RAYBURN, WENDELL GILBERT, college president; b. Detroit, May 20, 1929; s. Charles Jefferson and Grace Victoria (Winston) R.; m. Gloria Ann Myers, Aug. 19; children: Rhonda Renee, Wendell Gilbert; 1 stepson, Mark K. Williams. B.A., Eastern Mich. U., 1951; M.A., U. Mich., 1952; Ed.D., Wayne State U., Detroit, 1972. Tchr., adminstr. Detroit public schs., 1954-68; from asst. dir. to dir. spl. projects U. Detroit, 1968-72, asso. dean acad. support programs, 1972-74; dean Univ. Coll., U. Louisville, 1974-80; pres. Savannah (Ga.) State Coll., 1980-88, Lincoln U., Jefferson City, Mo., 1988—; chair adv. com. Office for Advancement of Pub. Black Colls., 1989—. Trustee Candler Gen. Hosp., 1982-85, Telfair Acad. Arts, 1980-87; bd. dirs. Candler Health Svcs., 1985-88, YMCA Blue Ridge Assembly, 1986-88, Internat. Food and Agrl. Devel. and Econ. Cooperation, 1988-94, Meml. Cmty. Hosp., Jefferson City, 1988-94, United Way Mo., 1989—, Mo. Capital Punishment Resource Ctr., 1990—, Stephens Coll., Columbia, Mo., 1993—, Capital Regional Med. Ctr., 1994—; campaign chair Jefferson City Area United Way, 1994-95. With AUS, 1952-59. Decorated Commendation medal with oak leaf cluster; recipient Wayne State U. Disting. Alumni award, 1993, Whitney M. Young Jr. award Lincoln Found., 1980, Disting. Citizens award City of Louisville, 1980. Mem. Mo. Bar Assn. (foresight com.), Am. Assn. Higher Edn., Am. Assn. State Colls. and Univs. (bd. dirs. 1988—, chmn. 1992-93), Nat. Assns. State Univs. and Land Grant Colls., Nat. Assn. for Equal Opportunity in Higher Edn., Coun. on Pub. Higher Edn. for Mo. (chmn. 1991-93), Coun. of 1890 Colls. and Univs., Jefferson City C. of C. (bd. dirs. 1988—), Rotary (bd. dirs. Jefferson City 1989—, pres. 1994—), Kappa Alpha Psi, Sigma Pi Phi. Episcopalian. Office: Lincoln U Office of Pres Jefferson City MO 65101

RAYDON, MAX E., consumer products company executive. With Safeway Inc., Okla. City, 1962-87; pres. Homeland Stores, Okla. City, 1987—. Office: Homeland Stores 400 NE 36th St Oklahoma City OK 73105-2598

RAYEN, JAMES WILSON, art educator, artist; b. Youngstown, Ohio, Apr. 9, 1935; s. James Wendell and Marjorie (Wilson) R. BA, Yale U., 1957, BFA, 1959, MFA, 1961. Instr. Wellesley (Mass.) Coll., 1961-67, asst. prof., 1967-69, assoc. prof., 1969-76, prof., 1976-80, Elizabeth Christy Kopf prof., 1980—. One-man shows include Durlacher Bros., N.Y.C., 1966, Eleanor Rigelhaupt Gallery, Boston, 1968, Brockton (Mass.) Mus., 1973, Chapel Gallery, West Newton, Mass., 1984, Gallery on the Green, Lexington, Mass, 1990; paintings commd. by New Eng. Med. Ctr., Boston, Mariott Hotel Corp., Cambridge, Mass., Hyatt Hotel Corp., Washington. Trustee Boston Concert Opera, 1984-86, bd. dirs., 1986-90; pres. Boston Concert League, 1988-90; bd. dirs. Boston Acad. Music, 1991—. Grantee Italian govt., 1959-60, Ford Found., 1969; recipient Mass. Artists Found. award in printmaking, 1989. Democrat. Episcopalian. Avocation: garden design. Home: 108 Fox Hill St Westwood MA 02090-1120 Office: Wellesley Coll 106 Central St Wellesley MA 02181-8203

RAYFIEL, DAVID, screenwriter; b. N.Y.C., Sept. 9, 1923; s. Leo F. and Flora (Marks) R.; m. Lila Paris, 1950 (div. 1953); 1 child, Eliza; m. Maureen Stapleton, 1963 (div. 1969); m. Lynne Schwarzenbek, 1988. Scripts include (with Daniel Taradash) Castle Keep, 1968, (with Roland Kibbee) Valdez Is Coming, 1970, (with Lorenzo Semple, Jr.) Three Days of the Condor, 1975 (Edgar Allan Poe award best screenplay Mystery Writers of Am. 1975), Lipstick, 1976, (with Bertrand Tavernier) Death Wish, 1982, (with Tavernier) Round Midnight, 1986, (with Judith Rascoe) Havana, 1990, The Firm, 1993, (with Marshall Brickman) Intersection, 1994; plays include P.S. 193, 1962, Nathan Weinstein, Mystic, Connecticut, 1966. Office: care George Diskant Diskant & Assocs 1033 Gayley Ave Ste 202 Los Angeles CA 90024*

RAYFIELD, ALLAN LAVERNE, electronics company executive; b. Mobile, Ala., May 11, 1935; s. Allan Edger and Clara Louise (Dalee) R.; m. Joan Pilgrim Boucher, July 5, 1958; children: Michael Jon, Mark Allan. BSCE, Pa. State U., 1959; MBA, Rensselaer Poly. Inst., 1965; grad. Advanced Mgmt. Program, Harvard U. Bus. Sch., 1976. Various positons medium A.C. motors GE, Schenectady, 1964-72; gen. mgr. armament systems dept. GE, Burlington, Vt., 1972-77; gen. mgr. transp. equipment dept. GE, Erie, Pa., 1977-80; chmn. bd., chief exec. officer Gen. Electric do Brasil, Sao Paulo, 1980; pres. GTE Communications Products Corp., Stamford, Conn., 1980-83, GTE Diversified Products, Stamford, 1983-87; pres. GTE Products and Systems, Stamford, 1987-89, also bd. dirs., sr. v.p. joint venture ops., 1989; with Forstmann-Rayfield, Southport, Conn., 1989-90; chmn. Internat. Telecharge, Inc., Dallas, 1990-91; pres., CEO M/A-Com. Inc., Lowell, Mass., 1991—, also bd. dirs.; corporator Burlington Savs. Bank, 1978-79; bd. dirs. Parker Hannifin Corp., Cleve. Trustee Com. for Econ. Devel., 1985-89, 94—; mem. bd. overseers Rensselaer Poly. Inst.; pres. Greater Burlington Indsl. Devel. Coun., 1975-77; bd. dirs. YMCA, Burlington, 1976-79, Erie, 1978-79; pres. Family Y, Erie, 1975-77. Recipient Clarence E. Davies award Rensselaer Poly. Inst., 1981, Disting. Alumni award Pa. State U., 1988; named Alumni Fellow, Pa. State U., 1985. Mem. Nat. Assn. Mfrs. (bd. dirs. 1988-89, 92—), Nat. Action Coun. for Minorities in Engring. (trustee 1984-89), Peugot Yacht Club, Eastern Yacht Club, Tau Beta Pi, Chi Epsilon. Republican. Methodist. Office: M/A-Com Inc 100 Chelmsford St Lowell MA 01853-3294

RAYFIELD, GORDON ELLIOTT, playwright, political risk consultant; b. Newark, Sept. 1, 1950; s. Bernard George and Rhoda Gertrude (Glucklisch) R.; m. Jean Metzger, July 12, 1981; children—Michael Evan, Jillian Amy. B.A., The American U., 1972; Ph.D., CUNY, 1980. Adj. lectr. Hunter Coll., CUNY, 1977-79, Bklyn Coll., Bklyn., 1977-79; research assoc. Ralph Bunche Inst., UN, N.Y.C., 1978-79; dir. Assn. Polit. Risk Analysts, N.Y.C., 1980-84, 87-90; polit. risk analyst Gen. Motors Corp., N.Y.C., 1979-86; prin. Rayfield Assocs., N.Y.C., 1986—; writing instr. Rutgers U., 1993. Editor newsletter Polit Risk Rev., 1983-87; columnist World Wide Projects, 1985-87; author: (plays) Fever of Unknown Origin, 1988, Bitter Friends, 1989, Living Proof, 1995, ABC-TV afterschool spl. It's Only Rock and Roll, 1991 (nominated Writers Guild award, nominated Daytime Emmy award), PBS dramatic spl. In the Shadow of Love, 1991 (nominated Emmy award), Fox TV Pilot Skin-to-Skin, 1992, HBO life stories: Portrait of a Bulimic (nominated Cable Ace award); episodes of Law & Order, CBS Schoolbreak Spl. Stand Up, 1995, also co-producer. Mem. Dramatists Guild, Writers Guild of Am. East, Assn. Polit. Risk Analysts (co-founder 1980, pres. 1981-83). Home and Office: 47 Nance Rd West Orange NJ 07052-1630

RAYLESBERG, ALAN IRA, lawyer; b. N.Y.C., Dec. 6, 1950; s. Daniel David and Sally Doris (Mantell) R.; m. Caren Thea Coven, Nov. 20, 1983;

children: Lisa Maris, Jason Todd. BA, NYU, 1972; JD cum laude, Boston U., 1975. Bar: N.Y. 1976, U.S. Dist. Ct. (so. dist.) N.Y. 1976, U.S. Dist. Ct. (ea. dist.) N.Y. 1978, U.S. Tax Ct. 1981, U.S. Ct. Appeals (2d and 5th cirs.) 1982, U.S. Ct. Appeals (1st cir.) 1986. Assoc. Orans, Elsen & Polstein, N.Y.C., 1975-77; assoc. Guggenheimer & Untermyer, N.Y.C., 1977-83, ptnr., 1983-85; ptnr. Rosenman & Colin, N.Y.C., 1985—; adj. instr. N.Y. Law Sch., 1980-83; instr. Nat. Inst. of Trial Advocacy. Mem. Town Club of New Castle (exec. bd.). Mem. ABA, Fed. Bar Coun., Assn. of Bar of City of N.Y., N.Y. County Lawyers Assn. (bd. dirs. 1995—, fed. ct. com. 1988—, co-chmn. appellate ct. com. 1992-93, chair appellate ct. com. 1993—), Securities Industry Assn. (legal and compliance divsn.), N.Y. Coun. of Def. Lawyers, Fund for Modern Cts. (bd. dirs.). Democrat. Jewish. Office: Rosenman & Colin 575 Madison Ave New York NY 10022-2511

RAYMAN, RUSSELL B., physician; b. Toledo, Ohio, Jan. 13, 1936; m. Ludy Rayman; children: Joseph, David, Ariel. MD, U. Mich., 1961. Commd. 2d lt. USAF, 1962, advanced through grades to col., 1989; mgr. operational medicine Lockheed, Washington, 1989-92; exec. dir. Aerospace Med. Assn., Alecandria, Va., 1992—. Author: Clinical Aviation Medicine, 1990. Decorated numerous mil. awards. Home: 8710 Linton Ln Alexandria VA 22308-2433

RAYMER, DONALD GEORGE, utility company executive; b. Jackson, Mich., July 16, 1924; s. Donald Rector and Vivian Alverda (Wolfinger) R.; m. Joan Elizabeth Steck, Oct. 16, 1948; children: Mary Margaret Dorward, Dorothy Elizabeth, Charles George. B.S.E.E., U. Mich., 1948; M.S. (Sloan fellow), M.I.T., 1960. Relay engr. Central Ill. Public Service Co., Springfield, 1948-56; mgr. system ops. Central Ill. Public Service Co., 1956-65; div. mgr. Central Ill. Public Service Co., Mattoon, Ill., 1965-68; v.p. Central Ill. Public Service Co., Springfield, 1968-78; exec. v.p. Cen. Ill. Pub. Svc. Co., 1978-80, pres., chief exec. officer, 1980-89, also bd. dirs.; bd. dirs. Bank One Springfield, CIPSCO Inc. Vice chmn. Springfield United Fund Campaign, 1964, asso. chmn., 1974; vice chmn. Mattoon United Welfare Fund, 1967; bd. dirs. Meml. Med. Center; chmn. Meml. Med. Ctr., 1987-89. Served to lt. (j.g.) USNR, 1943-46. Mem. IEEE, Am. Mgmt. Assn., Ill. State C. of C. (dir. 1982-88, vice chmn. 1985-87), Greater Springfield C. of C. (dir. 1968-71, 85-88, vice chmn. 1985-88), Chi Phi, Illini Country Club, Sangamo Club. Republican. Episcopalian.

RAYMOND, ARTHUR EMMONS, aerospace engineer; b. Boston, Mar. 24, 1899. BS, Harvard U., 1920; MS, MIT, 1921; DSc (hon.), Poly. Inst. Bklyn., 1947. Engr. Douglass Aircraft Co., 1925-34, v.p. engring., 1934-60; cons. Rand Corp., 1960-85; ret., 1985; mem. Nat. Adv. Com. Aero., 1946-56; cons. NASA, 1962-68. Trustee Aerospace Corp., 1960-71, Rsch. Analysis Corp., 1965-71. Recipient Nat. Air and Space Mus. Trophy/Lifetime Achievement award Smithsonian Instn., 1991. Fellow AIAA (hon.); mem. NAS, Nat. Acad. Engring. Achievements include research in aeronautics and astronautics. Home: 65 Oakmont Dr Los Angeles CA 90049-1901*

RAYMOND, GENE, actor, producer, director; b. N.Y.C., Aug. 13, 1908; s. LeRoy D. and Mary (Smith) Guion; m. Jeanette MacDonald, June 16, 1937 (dec. Jan. 14, 1965); m. former Mrs. Nel Bentley Hees, Sept. 8, 1974. Student, Profl. Children's Sch., N.Y.C. Broadway debut in: The Piper, 1920; other Broadway appearances include Eyvind of the Hills, 1921, Why Not?, 1922, The Potters, 1923, Cradle Snatchers, 1925, Take My Advice, 1927, Mirrors, 1928, Sherlock Holmes, 1928, Say When, 1928, The War Song, 1928, Jonesy, 1929, Young Sinners, 1929, A Shadow of My Enemy, 1957; other theater appearances include The Man in Possession, Dennis, Mass., 1946; appeared in The Guardsman, 1951, The Voice of the Turtle, 1952, Angel Street, Richmond, Va., 1952, Petrified Forest, 1952, Call Me Madam, 1952, Private Lives, 1953, The Moon is Blue, 1953, Be Quiet, My Love, 1953, Detective Story, 1954, The Devil's Disciple, 1954, The Fifth Season, 1955, Will Success Spoil Rock Hunter, Los Angeles, San Francisco, 1956, Romeo and Juliet, 1956, The Seven Year Itch, 1958, Holiday for Lovers, Chgo., 1959; appeared as Joseph Cantwell in nat. touring co.: The Best Man, 1960; other theater appearances include Majority of One, 1962, Write Me A Murder, 1962, Mr. Roberts, 1962, Kiss Me Kate, 1962; other roles include Candida, 1961, The Moon is Blue, 1963, Madly in Love, 1963; film appearances include Personal Maid, 1931, Stolen Heaven, 1931, Ladies of the Big House, 1932, The Night of June 13th, 1932, Forgotten Commandments, 1932, If I Had a Million, 1932, Red Dust, 1932, Ex-Lady, 1933, The House on 56th Street, 1933, Zoo in Budapest, 1933, Brief Moment, 1933, Ann Carver's Profession, 1933, Flying Down to Rio, 1933, Sadie McKee, 1934, I Am Suzanne, 1934, Coming Out Party, 1934, Transatlantic Merry-Go-Round, 1934, Behold My Wife, 1935, The Woman in Red, 1935, Seven Keys to Baldpate, 1935, Hooray for Love, 1935, Love on a Bet, 1936, Walking on Air, 1936, The Bride Walks Out, 1936, The Smartest Girl in Town, Transient Lady, 1936, There Goes My Girl, 1937, Life of the Party, 1937, That Girl From Paris, 1939, Mr. and Mrs. Smith, 1939; film appearances include: Cross-Country Romance, 1940, Smilin' Thru', 1941, The Locket, 1946, Assigned to Danger, 1948, Million-Dollar Weekend, 1948, Sofia, 1948, Hit the Deck, 1955, Plunder Road, 1957, The Best Man, 1964, I'd Rather Be Rich, 1964; TV appearances include: U.S. Steel Hour, The Defenders, Playhouse 90, Ironside, Name of the Game, Judd for the Defense, Bold Ones, Mannix, others; author: teleplay Prima Donna; composer: songs Release, Will You?, Let Me Always Sing. Past v.p. Arthritis Found. So. Calif.; pres. Motion Picture and TV Fund, 1980; trustee Falcon Found., USAF Acad. Served with USAAF, 1942-45, ETO; served to col. USAFR, 1945-68. Decorated Legion of Merit and others.; Recipient Disting. Service award Arthritis Found.; Humanitarian award Air Force Assn.; Better World award VFW; Bronze Halo award So. Calif. Motion Picture Council. Mem. Screen Actors Guild (dir.), Acad. TV Arts and Scis. (bd. dirs.), Air Force Assn. (pres. Los Angeles chpt.). Clubs: Players (N.Y.C.); N.Y. Athletic; Bel Air Country (Los Angeles); Army and Navy (Washington); Order of Daedalians. Address: 9350 Wilshire Blvd Beverly Hills CA 90212

RAYMOND, GEORGE GAMBLE, JR., material handling equipment company executive; b. Bklyn., Nov. 29, 1921; s. George Gamble and Madeleine (Crombie) R.; m. Cynthia Spencer, June 27, 1942 (dec. June 1977); children: George Gamble III, Stephen Spencer, Jean Crombie; m. Ellen Robinson, Oct. 14, 1978. Student, Cornell U., 1939-42; LLD (hon.), Alfred U., 1983. With Raymond Corp., Greene, N.Y., 1942—; sales mgr. Raymond Corp., 1942-43, 47-49, adminstrv. asst. to pres., 1946-47, v.p. incharge sales, 1949-51, exec. v.p., 1951-55, pres., 1955-87, chief exec. officer, 1959-87. Pres. Greene Central Sch. Bd. Edn., 1955-71; trustee Raymond Found. Alfred U., 1973—, chmn. bd. trustees, 1977-83, chmn. emeritus, 1983—; pres. dir. Grand Bay Condo Assn., Inc. Served with inf. AUS, 1943-46. Recipient Mgr. of Year award Soc. Advancement Mgmt., Binghamton, N.Y., 1970. Mem. Material Handling Inst. (past pres.), Assn. Lift Truck (past pres.), Indsl. Truck Assn. (pres. 1986-87), Assn. Lift Truck and Portable Elevator Mfrs. (past pres.), Young Presidents Orgn. (past v.p. N.E. area, past chmn. Empire chpt.), Broome County C. of C. Republican. Episcopalian. Clubs: Masons (Greene, N.Y.), Rotarian (past pres. Greene), The Club at Pelican Bay (Naples, Fla.), Sankaty Head Golf and Beach Club (Nantucket, Mass.). Office: Raymond Corporation South Canal St Greene NY 13778

RAYMOND, GEORGE MARC, city planner, educator; b. Odessa, Russia, Jan. 1, 1919; came to U.S., 1937, naturalized, 1942; s. Mark J. and Rachelle (Schneiderman) R.; m. Kathleen E. Waid, Oct. 3, 1942 (div. Mar. 1978); 1 dau., Valerie M.; m. Lois Jean Gainsboro, Mar. 26, 1979. BArch, Columbia, 1946. Planning dir. Harrison, Ballard & Allen, Inc., N.Y.C., 1952-54; founder, pres. Raymond, Parish, Pine & Weiner, Inc., 1954-83; pres. George M. Raymond Assocs., 1983—; prof. planning, chmn. dept. city and regional planning Pratt Inst., Bklyn., 1959-75; founder, dir. Pratt Ctr. for Community Improvement, Bklyn., 1963-70; lectr. planning Columbia U., 1955-58; lectr. planning and urban renewal New Sch. Social Rsch., 1967-72; pres. Assn. Collegiate Sch. Planning, 1968-69; chmn. Westchester County Housing Implementation Commn., 1992-93. Editor: Pratt Planning Papers, 1963-73, (with Astrid Monson) Pratt Guide to Housing, Planning and Urban Renewal for New Yorkers, 1965. V.p. Citizens Housing and Planning Coun. N.Y.C., 1967-86, N.Y. Assn. Environ. Profls., 1977-79; pres. Westchester Citizens Housing Coun., 1964-66, Mem. Com. on Planning, 1950-51; founder, pres. Friends of Music Concerts, 1954-57, Spoken Arts Soc., 1966-67; bd. dirs. Nat. Housing Conf.; past 1st v.p. Federated Conservationists Westchester County; past dir. Phipps Houses, Wave Hill, Settlement Housing Fund;

chmn. Westchester County Housing Opportunity Commn., 1994—; land use adv. com. N.Y. State Legis. Commn. on Rural Resources, 1992—. Mem. Am. Soc. Cons. Planners (pres. 1968-70), Am. Inst. Cert. Planners, Am. Planning Assn. (pres. N.Y. met. chpt. 1983-85), Nat. Assn. Housing and Redevel. Ofcls. (N.Y. met. chpt.). Home: 192 Locust Ln Irvington NY 10533-2315 Office: 560 White Plains Rd Tarrytown NY 10591-5109

RAYMOND, JACK, journalist, public relations executive, foundation executive; b. Sulejow, Poland, Oct. 6, 1918; s. Harry and Anna (Lange) R.; m. Gertrude Silverman, Oct. 6, 1946; children: David Alan, Judith. Student, CCNY, 1939. Sports writer N.Y. World-Telegram, 1934-38; ct. reporter, city editor, columnist N.Y. Daily North Side News, 1938-40; Corr. N.Y. Times, 1940-66, Berlin, 1946-47, Frankfurt, 1947-49, Bonn, 1949-52, Balkans, Belgrade, 1952-56, Moscow, 1956; Pentagon corr. N.Y. Times, Washington, 1956-66; pub. relations exec., pres. Thomas J. Deegan Co., Washington and N.Y.C., 1966-70; v.p. Bryan Publs., N.Y.C., 1970-74; founding pres. Internat. Inst. Environ. Affairs, 1970; pres. Dialog div. J. Walter Thompson Co., 1973-75; pres. Jack Raymond & Co., Inc., N.Y.C., 1975-87; chmn. Jack Raymond & Co., Inc., 1987-92; pres. JR Cons. Svc., Inc., 1987—; acting communications dir. Commonwealth Fund, 1987; book reviewer The Villager, N.Y.C., 1970-74; cons. UN Conf. on Human Environment, 1972, Aspen Inst. Humanistic Studies, HABITAT, UN Conf. Human Settlements; adv. com. Ctr. for Environ. Info. UN Assn. U.S., 1975-78; mem. Rumanian-U.S. econ. coun. U.S. C. of C., 1973-75; project dir. 1987 Workshop Internat. Environ. Bur. Internat. C. of C.; cons. INFORM, 1989, The Rene Dubos Ctr. for Human Environments, 1989—; mem. adv. bd. Volvo Journalists Retreat Duke U., 1992; internat. adv. bd. Ctr. for Social Policy in Mid-East, 1983-91; mem. exec. bd. Ency. of Environment. Author: Power at Pentagon, 1964, Your Military Obligations and Opportunities, 1963, Robert O. Anderson: Oil Man/Environmentalist, 1988; co-author: This is Germany, 1950; editor Upton Nooz, 1942-43; combat correspondant Stars and Stripes, news editor Naples and Rome edits., mng. editor Marseilles edit.; combat correspondant, war editor, editor Stars and Stripes mag. Paris edit.; combat correspondant, news editor Frankfurt edit., 1943-45; also author articles. Trustee N.Y. Urban League, 1969-72; bd. dirs. Internat. Inst. Environ. Affairs, N.Y.C., 1970-74, pres., 1970-73; bd. dirs. Internat. Inst. Environment and Devel., London, 1974-89, mem. adv. coun., 1978-82, mem. exec. com., 1982-89; bd. dirs. Epoch B. Found., La Jolla, Calif., acting pres., 1977-85; trustee Moroccan-Am. Found., 1982-88; bd. overseers Heller Grad. Sch., Brandeis U., 1981-88; founding assoc. John J. McCloy Internat. Ctr., N.Y.C.,1986, bd. dirs., 1987—; mem. adv. bd. Ctr. for East-West Dynamics, 1992—, Volvo JNLSTS Retreat, Williamsburg, Va., 1992. Decorated 5 Battle Stars, Bronze Star, Purple Heart. Mem. Council on Fgn. Relations. Clubs: Overseas Press Am. (N.Y.C.) (pres. 1972-76), Century Assn. (N.Y.C.), Nat. Press (Washington). Home: 340 E 57th St New York NY 10022-2901 also: J R Cons Svcs 6 Flintlock Ridge Rd Katonah NY 10536-2508

RAYMOND, JOHN CHARLES, physicist; b. Edgerton, Wis., Nov. 28, 1948; s. John Sayre and Marjorie (Price) R.; m. Bonnie Ecklund, May 30, 1975; children: Jennifer, Aaron. BS, U. Wis., 1970, PhD, 1976. Rsch. assoc. Harvard Coll. Observatory, Cambridge, Mass., 1976-80; physicist Smithsonian Instn., Cambridge, 1980—. Mem. Am. Astron. Soc. Office: Ctr for Astrophysics 60 Garden St Cambridge MA 02138-1596

RAYMOND, KENNETH NORMAN, chemistry educator, research chemist; b. Astoria, Oreg., Jan. 7, 1942; s. George Norman and Helen May (Dunn) R.; m. Jane Galbraith Shell, June 19, 1965 (div. 1976); children: Mary Katherine, Alan Norman; m. Barbara Gabriele Sternitzke, June 17, 1977; children: Gabriella Petra, Christopher Norman. B.A., Reed Coll., 1964; Ph.D., Northwestern U., 1968. Asst. prof. chemistry U. Calif.-Berkeley, 1968-74, assoc. prof., 1974-78, prof., 1978—; vice chmn. dept. U. Calif. Berkeley, 1982-84, chmn., 1993—; mem. study sect. NIH, 1983; mem. chemistry adv. com. NSF, 1985-87. Editor: Bioinorganic Chemistry II, 1977; assoc. editor Biology of Metals, 1987-91; mem. bd. editors Topics in Current Chemistry, 1981—; mem. editorial bd. Inorganic Chemistry, 1979-86, Accounts Chem. Rsch., 1982-90, Inorganica Chimica Acta f-Block Elements, 1984-90, Jour. Coordination Chemistry, 1981—, Jour. Inorganic and Nuclear Chemistry, 1974-81, Jour. Am. Chem. Soc., 1983—, Metallobiochemistry, 1992-93, Metals in Biology, 1993—; U.S. editorial advisor Springer-Verlag in Chemistry, 1972-91; contbr. over 240 articles to profl. jours.; 8 patents in field. Alfred P. Sloan rsch. fellow, 1971-73; Miller rsch. prof., 1977-78; Guggenheim fellow, 1980-81; recipient E.O. Lawrence award, Dept. Energy, 1984, Humboldt Rsch. award for U.S. Scientists, 1982. Mem. Am. Chem. Soc. (Alfred Bader award in Bioorganic Chemistry 1994), Am. Crystallographic Soc., Sigma Xi. Democrat. Office: U Calif Berkeley Dept Chemistry Berkeley CA 94720

RAYMOND, LEE R., oil company executive; b. Watertown, S.D., Aug. 13, 1938; m. Charlene Raymond. BSChemE, U. Wis., 1960; PhDChemE, U. Minn., 1963. Various engrng. positions Exxon Corp., Tulsa, Houston, N.Y.C. and Caracas, Venezuela, 1963-72; mgr. planning Internat. Co. div. Exxon Corp., N.Y.C., 1972-75; pres. Exxon Nuclear Co. div. Exxon Corp., 1979-81, exec. v.p. Exxon Enterprises Inc. div., 1981-83; sr. v.p., dir. Exxon Corp., N.Y.C., 1984-86, pres., dir., 1987-93, chmn., CEO, 1993—; v.p. Lago Oil, Netherlands Antilles, 1975-76, pres., dir., 1976-79; pres., dir. Esso Inter-Am. Inc., Coral Gables, Fla., 1983-84, sr. v.p., dir., 1984—; bd. dirs. J.P. Morgan & Co, Inc., N.Y.C., Morgan Guaranty Trust Co. of N.Y., N.Y.C., Am. Petroleum Inst. Bd. dirs. United Negro Coll. Fund, New Am. Schs. Devel. Corp., 1991—; Project Shelter PRO-AM, 1991—, Dallas Citizens Coun.; trustee Wis. Alumni Rsch. Found., 1987—, Bus. Coun. Internat. Understanding, Inc., 1988—; trustee So. Meth. U.; mem. Tri Lateral Commn., U. Wis. Found.; mem. emergency com. Am. trade; ptnr. emeritus N.Y.C. Partnership; mem. bd. govs. United Way Am.; active Am. Coun. on Germany, Dallas Com. Fgn. Rels., Dallas Wildcat Com., 1993. Mem. Am. Soc. Engring (mem. nat. adv. coun.), Am. Soc. Royal Bot. Garden (founder), Bus. Coun., Bus. Roundtable (mem. policy taxation task force 1993), Nat. Petroleum Coun., Coun. Fgn. Rels.

RAYMOND, MAURICE A., corporate director research; b. New Bedford, Mass., Jan. 8, 1938; s. J. Donat and Marie Anne (Begin) R.; m. E. Beatty Elliott, Jan. 12, 1963; children: Catherine S., Elizabeth B. BS in Chemistry, Providence Coll., 1958; PhD in Chemistry, U. Fla., Gainesville, 1962; postgrad., U. New Haven, 1968-70. R & D mgr. Olin Corp., New Haven, 1962-74; mktg. mgr. Olin Corp., Stamford, Conn., 1974-75, bus. mgr., 1975-82, venture mgr., 1982-85; corp. dir. R & D Tremco Inc., Div. of B.F. Goodrich Co., Beachwood, Ohio, 1985-89; dir. rsch. Rhone-Poulenc, Inc., Princeton, N.J., 1990—; lectr. on polymer sci. St. Joseph's Coll., West Hartford, Conn., 1968. Author nine papers published in profl. jours.; patentee in field. Mem. Planning and Zoning Bd., North Branford, Conn., 1976. Recipient Petroleum Rsch. Fund fellowship, 1960. Mem. Am. Chem. Soc., Indsl. Rsch. Inst., Comml. Devel. Assn., Sierra Club, Raritan Yacht Club, Delta Epsilon Sigma. Republican. Roman Catholic. Avocations: sailing, fishing, hiking, travel. Home: 107 Sayre Dr Princeton NJ 08540-5814 Office: Rhone Poulenc Inc # Cn7500 Cranbury NJ 08512

RAYMOND, SPENCER HENRY, lawyer; b. Omaha, Jan. 19, 1926; s. Anan and Florence (Hostetler) R.; m. Priscilla Falley, Dec. 28, 1950 (div. Dec. 1973); children: Margaret Raymond Stickel, Anan, Elizabeth Raymond Hybel, Daniel; m. Joan R. Strouse, Jan. 28, 1993. BS, Princeton U., 1950; JD, Harvard U., 1953. Bar: Ill. 1953. Assoc. Jenner & Block, Chgo., 1953-62, ptnr., 1962—. Trustee Rush North Shore Med. Ctr., Skokie, Ill., 1959-90, Glencoe (Ill.) Union Ch., 1976-82. With USN, 1944-46. Mem. ABA, Ill. State Bar Assn. (mem. estate planning, probate and trust law sect.coun. 1989-93), Chgo. Bar Assn. (chmn. probate com. 1976-77, chmn. real property sect. 1979-80), Am. Acad. Hosp. Attys., Am. Coll. Trust and Estate Counsel, Chgo. Co. of Lawyers, Law Club, Legal Club Chgo., Harvard Law Soc. Ill. (pres. 1985), Sheridan Investment Co. (pres. 1973, 93, Chgo.). Home: 183 Lake St Glencoe IL 60022-2108 Office: Jenner & Block 1 E Ibm Plz Chicago IL 60611-3608

RAYMONDA, JAMES EARL, retired banker; b. Piseco, N.Y., Feb. 20, 1933; s. Floyd E. and Bertha (Kramer) R.; m. Marie A. Countryman, Aug. 18, 1956; children—David J., Diane J., Daniel J. B.S. magna cum laude, Syracuse U., 1955. With Fleet Bank (formerly Oneida Nat. Bank & Trust Co. Cen. N.Y.), Utica, 1957—; v.p., comptroller Norstar Bank (formerly Oneida Nat. Bank & Trust Co. Central N.Y.), 1968—, adminstrv. v.p., until 1973, exec. v.p., 1973—, regional pres., 1987-90; chmn. reg. bd. Fleet Bank, 1990-94. Treas. Oneida County chpt. Nat. Found.; pres. Whitestown Jaycees, 1964; adv. com., sec. Whitestown Sr. Ctr., 1965-87; trustee St. Elizabeth Hosp., Utica, N.Y.; gen. chmn. campaign Greater Utica United Way, 1977, pres., 1979-80, 95; mem. Utica Found. bd., Oneida County Hist. Soc. bd. Recipient Len Wilbur award Utica Kiwanis, 1980, Indsl. Man Yr. award, 1981, Humanitarian of Yr. award St. Elizabeth Hosp., 1989, Business Man of Year award Utica Observer Dispatch, 1990. Mem. KC (Utica), Nat. Assn. Accts., C. of C. of Greater Utica Area (v.p. adminstrn., Person of Yr. 1991), Rotary (pres. Fort Schuyler 1985-86, dist. gov. 1993-94). Home: 35 Chateau Dr Whitesboro NY 13492-2528

RAYMUND, STEVEN A., computer company executive; b. 1955. BS, U. Oreg.; Georgetown U. Sch. Fgn. Svc. Pres., CEO, chmn. bd., dir. Tech Data Corp., 1981—. Office: Tech Data Corp 5350 Tech Data Dr Clearwater FL 34620-3134*

RAYNAULD, ANDRE, economist, educator; b. Quebec, Que., Can., Oct. 20, 1927; s. Léopold and Blanche (Gauthier) R.; m. Michelle Nolin, Oct. 15, 1951; children: Francoy, Olivier, Dominique, Isabelle. BA cum laude, U. Montreal, 1948, MA in Indsl. Rels. magna cum laude, 1951; D. in Econs., U. Paris, 1954; D. in Econs. (hon.), U. Ottawa, 1976, U. Sherbrooke, 1976. Mem. faculty U. Montreal, 1954-71, founder, dir. Ctr. Econ. Research and Devel., 1970-72; vis. prof. U. Toronto, 1962-63; chmn. Economic Council Can., Ottawa, 1971-76; mem. Que. Nat. Assembly, Montreal, 1976-80; prof. U. Montreal, 1980-93, prof. emeritus, 1993—; exec. com. Can. Social Sci. Rsch. Coun., 1961-63, 64-65; pres. Inst. Canadien Affaires Publiques, 1961-62; bd. govs. Can. Labour Coll., 1962-66; dir., exec. com. CBC, 1964-67; trustee CBC Pension Fund, 1967-70; pres. Soc. Canadienne de Sci. Economique, 1967-69; mem. Royal Commn. Bilingualism and Biculturalism, 1969-70, Can. Coun. Urban and Regional Rsch., 1971, Quebec Coun. Planning and Devel., 1971; chmn. com. inquiry French-lang. tchr.-rng. Western provinces Dept. Sec. State, 1971; mem. interfutures study group OECD, Paris, 1976-78; mem. bd. Inst. Rsch. Pub. Policy, 1980—; rsch. fellow Devel. Ctr. OECD, Paris, 1986-94; invited prof. College de France, Paris, 1987. Author: Economic Growth in Quebec, 1961, The Canadian Economic System, 1967, La propriete des entreprises au Quebec, 1974, Institutions Economiques Canadiennes, 2d edition, 1977, Le financement des exportations, 1979, Government Assistance to Export Financing, 1984, The External Financing of Tunisia's Imports, OECD, 1988, Financing Exports to Developing Countries, OECD, 1992; co-editor: Economic Integration in Europe and North America, 1992, Can. Jour. Econs., 1965-70. Recipient ann. award des Diplomes de l'U. de Montreal, 1974; apptd. Officer of Order of Can., 1986; fellow Walter Levy Coun. on Fgn. Rels., Boston, 1977. Fellow Royal Soc. Can.; mem. Can. Econs. Assn. (pres. 1983-84), Am. Econs. Assn., Atlantic Econ. Soc. (disting. assoc.). Liberal. Roman Catholic. Home: 4820 Roslyn St, Montreal, PQ Canada H3W 2L2

RAYNER, JOHN NORMAN, science educator; b. Worstead, Norfolk, Eng., Mar. 12, 1936; came to U.S., 1966; s. William Norman Rayner; m. Valerie Gilmore, Dec. 21, 1957; children: Caroline Anne, Alexander Charles, Jonathan Robert. BA with honors, U. Birmingham, Eng., 1958; MSc, McGill U., Montreal, Que., Can., 1961; PhD, U. Canterbury, Christchurch, New Zealand, 1965. Lectr. U. Canterbury, 1961-65; asst. prof. Ohio State U., Columbus, 1966-67, assoc. prof., 1967-71, prof. geography, 1971—, chair geography dept., 1975-95, dir. atmospheric scis., 1986-95, rsch. scientist Inst. Polar Studies, 1966; Ohio State mem. rep. Univ. Corp. for Atmospheric Rsch., Boulder, Colo., 1986—; state climatologist NOAA, U.S. Dept. Commerce, Columbus, 1977-87. Author: An Introduction to Spectral Analysis, 1971; editor: Proximity and Preference, 1982; contbr. articles to profl. jours. Arctic Carnegie scholar, 1958-59, Norfolk County Major scholar, 1955-58. Fellow Royal Meteorol. Soc.; mem. Am. Meteorol. Soc., Assn. Am. Geographers (Honors award 1990). Office: Ohio State U Dept Geography Derby Hall 154 N Oval Mall Columbus OH 43210-1361

RAYNER, ROBERT MARTIN, financial executive; b. London, Sept. 21, 1946; s. Henry John and Kathleen Mary (Edwards) R.; m. Mindy S. Miller, May 28, 1979. BSc with honors in Eng., Bristol (Eng.) U., 1968; MBA, London Bus. Sch., 1976. Sr. engr. Halcrow and Ptnrs., London, 1968-74; fin. dir. Pepsico Inc., Purchase, N.Y., 1976-88; pres. constrn. materials group, sr. v.p., CFO ESSROC Corp., Murray Hill, N.J., 1988-94, COO, 1994—; bd. dirs. ESSROC Materials Inc., Murray Hill, San Juan Cement Co., P.R., Ciment Quebec Inc., St. Basile. Mem. Inst. Civil Engrs. Avocations: running, golf, theatre, music. Office: ESSROC 430 Mountain Ave Mountain Heights Center Murray Hill NJ 07974-2732

RAYNER, WILLIAM ALEXANDER, retired newspaper editor; b. Winnipeg, Man., Can., Nov. 7, 1929; s. William and Annie Mitchell (McDonald) R.; divorced; 1 child, Robert William. Student Can. schs. Sports editor Trail Times, B.C., 1954-55; sportswriter Victoria (B.C.) Times, 1955-57, Vancouver (B.C.) Herald, 1957; copy editor, reporter Montreal (Que.) Star, 1957-58; asst. sports editor Vancouver Sun, 1958-62, copy editor, then slotman, 1962-74, news editor, 1974-83, systems mgr., 1983-88, ret., 1988; copy editor Toronto Globe & Mail, 1962. Author: Vancouver Sun Style Guide, 1976. Dir. Vancouver Press Club Found. With Can. Navy, 1947-52, Korea. Mem. Vancouver Press Club.

RAYNOLDS, HAROLD, JR., retired state education commissioner; b. Chgo., Feb. 7, 1925; s. Harold and Dorothy (Smith) R.; m. Ann Richards Ellis, June 1950 (div. 1968); children—Christopher, Timothy, Madeline, Dorothy, m. Patricia Adele Miller, Jan. 20, 1973. BS, Cornell U., 1948, MA, 1953; postgrad., NYU, 1968-69. Cert. supt. schs., N.Y., Maine, Alaska. Supt. schs. Cape Elizabeth Sch. Dist., Maine, 1969-74; supt. schs. Portland Sch. Dist., Maine, 1974-79; commr. edn. State of Maine, Augusta, 1979-83, State of Alaska, Juneau, 1983-86, Commonwealth of Mass., 1986-91; interim supt. Windsor Ctrl. Supervisory Union Sch. Dist., Woodstock, Vt., 1991-92; vice chair Windsor Ctrl. Supervisory Union Sch. Dist., Woodstock, 1993—; supt. Springfield (Vt.) Sch. Dist., 1994—; mem. Pomfret (Vt.) Sch. Com., Woodstock (Vt.) Union High Sch. Bd. Contbr. articles to ednl. jours. Mem. sch. com., Pomfret, Vt., 1993—; mem. Woodstock Union High Sch. Bd. Edn., 1993—; vice chair Windsor Ctrl. Supervisory Union Bd., 1993—; mem. Vt. Senate, 1965-66; chmn. Vt. Bd. Edn., Montpelier, 1963-68; trustee U. Maine, Orono, 1979-83; Dem. candidate for U.S. Congress, Vt., 1962. Staff sgt. U.S. Army, 1943-45, ETO. Mem. Am. Assn. Sch. Adminstrs., Chief State Sch. Officers, Phi Delta Kappa. Unitarian-Universalist. Avocations: reading; gardening; cross-country skiing; theater; music.

RAYNOLDS, JOHN F., III, executive search consultant. Chmn., CEO Ward Howell Internat., N.Y.C., 1993—. Office: Ward Howell Internat 99 Park Ave New York NY 10016

RAYNOR, DENNIS L., architect, firm executive. BS in Architecture, U. Nebr., 1976. Registered arch., Nebr., Mo., Iowa, Colo.; cert. Nat. Coun. Archtl. Registration Bd. Joined Keeler Raynor Hinz Archs., P.C., Bellevue, Nebr., 1976—, now prin. Prin. works include Chambers Protestant Chapel, Boys Town, Nebr. (Environ. Integration Honor award Landmarks Inc., Innovative Excellence in Masonry Honor award Nebr. Masonry Inst., Internat. Archtl. Design award for excellence in design Interfaith Forum on Religion, Art and Architecture, 1992), Elkhorn (Nebr.) Hills United Meth. Ch. (Excellence in Architecture award AIA Ctrl. States Region), Immanuel Luth. Ch., Bellevue, Nebr. (Disting. Accomplishment in Architecture Honor award Nebr. Soc. Archs.), Farmers Bank, Nebraska City, Nebr. (Disting. Accomplishment in Architecture award Nebr. Soc. Archs.), Fuchs Machinery, Omaha (Bldg. of Yr., Sys. Builders Assn., 1991, Nat. Preservation Honor award Nat. Trust Hist. Preservation, Pres. Hist. Preservation award Adv. Coun. Hist. Preservation-White House). Chmn. Bellevue (Nebr.) Bd. Appeals; pres. bd. dirs. United Cath. Social Svcs.; active Cathedral Arts Project Bd., Boys Town Booster Club. Mem. AIA, Nebr. Soc. Archs. Office: Keeler/Raynor & Associates 101 West Mission Ave Bellevue NE 68005

RAYNOR, JOHN PATRICK, university administrator; b. Omaha, Oct. 1, 1923; s. Walter V. and Mary Clare (May) R. AB, St. Louis U., 1947, MA, 1948, Licentiate in Philosophy, 1949, Licentiate in Theology, 1956; PhD, U. Chgo., 1959. Ordained priest Roman Cath. Ch., 1954. Joined Soc. of Jesus, 1941; instr. St. Louis U. High Sch., 1948-51, asst. prin., 1951; asst. to dean Coll. Liberal Arts, Marquette U., 1960, asst. to v.p. acad. affairs, 1961-62, v.p. acad. affairs, 1962-65, pres., 1965-90, ret., 1990; now, chancellor Marquette Univ., Milwaukee, Wis.; dir. Kimberly-Clark Corp. Mem. Greater Milw. Com.; Pub. Policy Forum; corp. mem. United Community Services Greater Milw.; hon. bd. dirs. Goethe House; mem. Froedtert Meml. Luth. Hosp. Corp.; hon. com. mem. Endowment Fund Metro Milw. Luth. Campus Ministry; trustee Milw. Heart Research Found., Inc.; bd. dirs. Greater Milw. Edn. Trust, Mus. Sci., Econs. & Tech., Inc. Discovery World. Recipient Disting. Service award Edn. Commn. of States, 1977. Mem. Nat. Cath. Edn. Assn., North Central Assn. (examiner, cons.), Am. Council Edn., Wis. Assn. Ind. Colls. and Univs. (past pres., exec. com.), Wis. Found. Ind. Colls. (past pres.), Assn. Jesuit Colls. and Univs. (past chmn., dir., mem. exec. com.), Internat. Fedn. Cath. Colls. and Univs., Met. Milw. Assn. Commerce, Phi Beta Kappa, Phi Delta Kappa, Alpha Sigma Nu. Office: Marquette U 615 N 11th St Milwaukee WI 53233-2305

RAYNOR, RICHARD BENJAMIN, neurosurgeon, educator; b. N.Y.C., Aug. 16, 1928; s. Murray and Mildred (Pitt) R.; m. Barbara Golob; children: Geoffrey, Michele. BSME, U. Mich., 1950; MD, U. Vt., 1955. Diplomate Am. Bd. Neurol. Surgery. Intern Mt. Sinai, N.Y.C., 1955-56; residency Neurol. Inst. Presbyn. Hosp., N.Y.C., 1956-57, Nat. Hosp., London, 1957; residency neurosurgery Neurol. Inst. Presbyn. Hosp., 1958-62; assoc. in neurosurgery Coll. Physicians and Surgeons Columbia U., N.Y.C., 1965-77; clin. assoc. prof. NYU, N.Y.C., 1977-84, clin. prof., 1984—; pvt. practice neurosurgery, N.Y.C., 1965—. Consulting editor Spine; contbr. more than 40 articles to profl. jours., chpts. to books. Served as capt. U.S. Army, 1962-64. Fellow Am. Coll. Surgeons; mem. Cervical Spine Research Soc. (pres. 1986-87), Am. Assn. Neurol. Surgeons, Congress Neurol. Surgeons. Club: University (N.Y.C.). Avocations: skiing, squash. Office: 112 E 74th St New York NY 10021-3562

RAYNOR, WANDRA ADAMS, middle school educator; b. Angier, N.C., Oct. 29, 1942; d. Lacoma Eldridge and Edna (Mangum) Adams; m. Donald David Stewart, June 16, 1964 (dec. Dec. 1965); 1 child, Dona Jean Stewart Raynor; m. Ira Kent Raynor, June 28, 1969; children: Richard Kent, Ira Adam. BS in Edn., Campbell Coll., 1971; MA in Early Childhood Edn., Campbell U., 1979; EdS in Adminstrn. Supervision, East Carolina U., 1983. Cert. tchr., advanced adminstr., supr., N.C. Clk. Am. Guaranty Ins. Co., Fayetteville, N.C., 1960-62; sec. Am. Defender Life, Fayetteville, 1962-64; tchr. Gentry Primary Sch., Erwin, N.C., 1971-73; tchr., asst. prin. North Harnett Primary Sch., Angier, 1973-85; tchr. Angier Mid. Sch., 1986—, Harnett Cen. Middle Sch., 1993—, Inst. Children's Lit., 1994—. Mem. Internat. Reading Assn. (pres. Lillington, N.C. 1983-84, treas. Harnett coun. 1992-93, participant state conf. seminars 1992—), N.C. Assn. Educators, Math. Tchrs. Assn., Environ. Educators, N.C. Writers Network, Crepe Myrtle Investors (pres. 1995), Angier C. of C. (Disting. Educator award 1983), Order Ea. Star (worthy matron 1973-75, dist. dep. grand matron 1976-77), Delta Kappa Gamma, Epsilon Phi Beta. Democrat. Baptist. Avocations: golf, reading, snow skiing, writing. Home: 203 Pleasant St Angier NC 27501 Office: Harnett Cen Middle Rt 4 PO Box 293-B Angier NC 27501

RAYSON, EDWIN HOPE, lawyer; b. Earlville, Ill., Jan. 13, 1923; s. Edwin H. and Lillian (Astley) R.; m. Evelyn Sherry Kirkland, Oct. 1, 1983; children: Jane Rayson Young, Edwin Hope III, G. Scott. A.B., U. Tenn., 1944, LL.B., 1948. Bar: Tenn. 1948. Pvt. practice Knoxville, 1948—; ptnr. Kramer, Rayson, Leake, Rodgers & Morgan, 1949—; lectr. labor law U. Tenn. Coll. Law, 1951-71. Served to lt. (j.g.) USNR, 1944-46. Mem. Order of Coif, Sigma Chi, Omicron Delta Kappa. Home: 501 River Rd Loudon TN 37774-5555 Office: Plaza Towers Knoxville TN 37901

RAYSON, GLENDON ENNES, internist, preventive medicine specialist, writer; b. Oak Park, Ill., Dec. 2, 1915; s. Ennes Charles and Beatrice Margaret (Rowland) R. AB, U. Rochester, 1939; MD, U. Ill., Chgo., 1948; MPH, Johns Hopkins U., 1965; MA, Northwestern U., 1965. Diplomate Am. Bd. Internal Medicine, Am. Bd. Preventive Medicine. Resident in internal medicine Presbyn.-St. Luke's Hosp., Chgo., 1953-56; physician-in-charge Contagious Disease Hosp., Chgo., 1956-58, asst. med. supt., 1958-64; rsch. assoc. Sch. Hygiene and Pub. Health Johns Hopkins U., Balt., 1966-71; internist Johns Hopkins Hosp., 1971-82, Columbia Free State Health Plan, Balt., 1984-91; pvt. practice Balt., 1984—; with Neurodiagnostics Assocs., 1990—; attending internist emergency rm. South Balt. Gen. Hosp., 1982-84; asst. prof. health sci. U. Ill., Chgo., 1958-64; fellow in gastroenterology and endocrinology Presbyn.-St. Luke's Hosp., 1956-58. Contbr. articles to med. jours., chpt. to book. Vol. physician, Vietnam, 1968, 71, 72, 73; mem. Citizens Amb. Program Delegation to Vietnam, 1993. Capt. M.C., USAF, 1951-53. Fellow Am. Coll. Preventive Medicine, Am Geriatrics Soc.; mem. AMA, Am. Pub. Health Assn. Avocations: writing poetry, short stories, composing songs. Home: 337 Poplar Point Rd Perryville MD 21903-1803 Office: 218 N Charles St Apt 1407 Baltimore MD 21201-4027

RAYSON, JACK HENRY, dentist, educator, retired; b. Gonzales, Tex., July 22, 1931; s. Jack Henry and Florence (Zint) R.; m. Donna Thornton, Oct. 19, 1957; children—Susan, Scott, David. D.D.S., U. Tex., 1957; M.A., U. New Orleans, 1976. Gen. practice dentistry San Antonio, 1961-62; asst. prof. Baylor Coll. Dentistry, 1962-66, U. Ky. Coll. Dentistry, 1967-69; prof., dean Sch. Dentistry, La. State U., New Orleans, 1969-93; ret., 1993; cons. VA hosps., New Orleans, Biloxi. Author: Synopsis of Complete Dentures, 1977. Served to capt. USAF, 1956-61. Fellow Am. Coll. Dentists; mem. Am., La., New Orleans dental assns., Southeastern Acad. Prosthodontics, Xi Psi Phi, Omicron Kappa Upsilon. Office: La State U Sch Dentistry 1100 Florida Ave New Orleans LA 70119-2714

RAYWARD, WARDEN BOYD, librarian, educator; b. Inverell, New South Wales, Australia, June 24, 1939; s. Warden and Ellie Rayward. B.A., U. Sydney, 1960; diploma in libr., U. NSW, 1964; M.S. in L.S., U. Ill., 1965; Ph.D., U. Chgo., 1973. Asst. state library NSW, 1961-64, research librarian planning and devel., 1970; lectr. Sch. Librarianship U. NSW, 1971-72, prof., head sch. INfo., Libr. and Archive Studies, 1986-92, prof., 1992—, dean Faculty of Profl. Studies, 1993—; asst. prof. U. Western Ont., 1973-74; asst. prof. Grad. Library Sch. U. Chgo., 1975-77, assoc. prof., 1978-80, prof., 1980-86; dean U. Chgo. Grad. Library Sch., 1980-86; cons. Nat. Endowment Humanities, 1976-79, U.S. Dept. Edn., 1981; mem. bd. govs. Charles Stuart U., 1994—. Author: The Universe of Information: The Work of Paul Otlet for Documentation and International Organization, 1975 (also transl. Russian and Spanish); editor: The Variety of Librarianship: Essays in Honour of John Wallace Metcalfe, 1976, The Public Library: Circumstances and Prospects, 1978, Library Quar., 1975-79, Library History in Context, 1988, Libraries and Life in a Changing World: the Metcalfe Years 1920-1970, 1993; editor, translator: International Organization and the Dissemination of Knowledge: Selected Papers of Paul Otlet, 1990; editor Confronting the Future, University Libraries in the Next Decade, 1992; mem. internat. editorial adv. bd. World Book of Encyclopedia, 1990—; contbr. articles to profl. jours. Coun. on Library Resources fellow, 1978; vis. fellow U. Coll. London, 1986, 90, Mortenson fellow U. Ill., 1992-93. Mem. ALA, Australian Library and Info. Assn., Bibliog. Soc. Australia and New Zealand, Am. Soc. for Info. Sci. Office: U New South Wales, PO Box 1, Kensington NSW 2033, Australia

RAZ, HILDA, editor-in-chief periodical, educator; b. Rochester, N.Y., May 4, 1938; d. Franklyn Emmanuel and Dolly (Horwich) R.; m. Frederick M. Link, June 9, 1957 (div. 1976); children: John Franklin Link, Sarah Link; m. Dale Nordyke, Oct. 4, 1980. BA, Boston U., 1960. Assoc. dir. Planned Parenthood League of Mass., Boston, 1960-62; edit. asst. Prairie Schooner, Lincoln, Nebr., 1970-74; contbg. editor Prairie Schooner, 1974-77, assoc. editor, 1977-87, acting editor, 1981-83, 85, poetry editor, 1980-87, editor-in-chief, 1987—; assoc. prof. dept Eng. U. Nebr., Lincoln, 1990—; lectr., reader, panelist in field; participant many workshops, symposia, confs.; panelist arts com. NEA, 1994; judge Kenyon Rev., 1990, Soc. Midland Authors Best Book of 1987 award, 1988, Ill. Art Coun./NEA fellowships, 1987; bd. govs. Ctr. for Great Plains Studies, U. Nebr. 1989-95. Author numerour poems, essays; editor Nebr. Humanist, 1990. Pres. Assoc. Writing Programs, bd. dirs., 1988-89, ex-officio pres., 1989-90, v.p., 1987-88; mem. program com. Friends of Libr's. U. Nebr., 1989-90; bd. dirs. Nebr. Libr. Heritage Assn., 1988-91; mem. Mayor's Blue Ribbon Com. on Arts, 1985-88; bd. dirs. Planned Parenthood League Nebr. 1978-83, sec. bd. dirs., 1979-80, chairperson long-term planning com., 1980-81, 81-82. Recipient Literary Heritage award Mayor's Art Awards, Lincoln, 1988; Bread Loaf scholar editors, 1974, poetry, 1985; Robert Frost fellow, 1988, 89, Mag. Panel fellow, 1993, 94. Avocations: gardening. Home: 960 S Cotner Blvd Lincoln NE 68510 Office: Univ of Nebraska Lincoln Prairie Schooner 201 Andrews Hall Lincoln NE 68588-0334

RAZ, ROBERT EUGENE, librarian; b. Michigan City, Ind., Mar. 15, 1942; s. Eugene and Claradelle (Perham) R.; m. Elizabeth Alden, June 18, 1965 (div. Feb. 1978); children: Richard, Philip; m. Susan Margaret Spiers, June 10, 1978; 1 child, Katherine. BA, Andrews U., 1964; MA, Western Mich. U., 1965. Librarian Library for the Blind, Mich. State Library, Lansing, 1965-67; library cons. Mich. State Library, 1967-71; dir. Willard Library, Battle Creek, Mich., 1971-79, Grand Rapids (Mich.) Pub. Library, 1979—; Trustee Libr. of Mich., 1982-88. Mem. Grand Rapids Coun. for Humanities, 1980—, v.p., 1981, pres., 1983, 84; mem., treas. Kent County Literacy Coun., 1987—. Mem. Mich Library Assn. (pres. 1979, Mich. Librarian of Yr. 1980), ALA (council 1982-86). Home: 2750 7th St NW Grand Rapids MI 49504-4614 Office: Grand Rapids Pub Libr 60 Library Plz NE Grand Rapids MI 49503-3219

RAZNOFF, BEVERLY SHULTZ, education educator; b. Ft. Myers, Fla., Apr. 24, 1946; d. John William and Dora Lucille (Galloway) S.; m. Gregory Michael Raznoff, June 8, 1968; children: John Gregory, James William. BA, Fla. So. Coll., 1968; MEd, Fla. Atlantic U., 1974. Elem. educator Pine Grove Elem. Sch., Delray Beach, Fla., 1968-69; secondary educator Pompano Beach (Fla.) High Sch., 1969-70, Deerfield Beach (Fla.) High Sch., 1970-71; prof. Broward C.C., Ft. Lauderdale, 1974-82, Palm Beach C.C., Boca Raton, Fla., 1977-93, Fla. Atlantic U., Boca Raton, Fla., 1984, Truett-McConnell Coll., Cleveland, Ga., 1994—; dir. instr. Toccoa Regional Campus, Cleveland, Ga., 1994—; advisor Phi Theta Kappa, South campus Palm Beach C.C., 1983-93, Toccoa Regional Campus-TMC, 1994—. Contbr. articles to profl. jours. Recipient Fred Baker Nat. award Phi Theta Kappa, Outstanding Advisor, Fla. region, 1992. Mem. Fla. Comm. Assn. (pres. 1990-91, Tchr. of Yr. 1990), Internat. Listening Assn., So. States Comm. Assn., Assn. of Leadership Educators. Avocations: reading, needlework, cooking, mountain living. Home: 307 Old Deer Path Way Cleveland GA 30528

RAZZANO, FRANK CHARLES, lawyer; b. Bklyn., Feb. 25, 1948; s. Pasquale Anthony and Agnes Mary (Borgia) R.; m. Stephanie Anne Lucas, Jan. 10, 1970; children: Joseph, Francis, Catherine. BA, St. Louis U., 1969; JD, Georgetown U., 1972. Bar: N.Y. 1973, U.S. Dist. Ct. (so. dist.) N.Y. 1973, U.S. Dist. Ct. (es. dist.) N.Y. 1973, N.J. 1976, D.C. 1981, Va. 1984, U.S. Dist. Ct. N.J. 1976, U.S. Dist. Ct. Md. 1977, U.S. Dist. Ct. (no. dist.) Calif. 1981, U.S. Dist. Ct. D.C. 1982, U.S. Dist. Ct. (ea. dist.) Va. 1989, U.S. Dist. Ct. (we. dist.) Va. 1990, U.S. Ct. Appeals (2d cir.) 1973, U.S. Ct. Appeals (3d cir.) 1975, U.S. Ct. Appeals (D.C. and 5th cirs.) 1983, U.S. Ct. Appeals (4th cir.) 1984, U.S. Ct. Appeals (6th cir.) 1990, U.S. Supreme Ct. 1976. Assoc. Shea & Gould, N.Y.C., 1972-75; asst. U.S. atty. Dist. of N.J., Newark, 1975-78; asst. chief trial atty. SEC, Washington, 1978-82; ptnr. Shea & Gould, Washington, 1982-94, mng. ptnr., 1991-92; ptnr. Camhy Karlinsky Stein Razzano & Rubin, Washington, 1994—; lectr. in field. Civil law editor Rico Law Reporter; mem. adv. bd. Corp. Confidentiality and Disclosure Letter; hon. adv. com. Jour. Internat. Law and Practice, Detroit Coll. Law; contbr. articles to legal jours. Scoutmaster Vienna coun. Boy Scouts Am., 1984. Recipient spl. achievement award Justice Dept., 1977, spl. commendation, 1978. Mem. ABA, Va. Bar, D.C. Bar (chmn. litigation sect. 1987-89, vice-chmn. coun. sects. 1988-89), Assn. Securities & Exch. Commn. Alumni (pres. 1993—), Phi Beta Kappa, Eta Sigma Phi. Roman Catholic. Home: 1713 Paisley Blue Ct Vienna VA 22182-2326

RE, EDWARD DOMENIC, law educator, retired federal judge; b. Santa Marina, Italy, Oct. 14, 1920; s. Anthony and Marina (Maetta) R.; m. Margaret A. Corcoran, June 3, 1950; children: Mary Ann, Anthony John, Marina, Edward, Victor, Margaret, Matthew, Joseph, Mary Elizabeth, Mary Joan, Mary Ellen, Nancy Madeleine. BS cum laude, St. John's U., 1941, LLB summa cum laude, 1943, LLD (hon.), 1968; JSD, NYU, 1950; PhD (hon.), Aquila, Italy, 1960; LL.D. (hon.), St. Mary's Coll., Notre Dame, Ind., 1968, Maryville Coll., St. Louis, 1969, N.Y. Law Sch., 1976, Bklyn. Coll., CUNY, 1978, Nova U., 1980, Roger Williams Coll., 1982, Dickinson Sch. Law, Carlisle, Pa., 1983, Seton Hall U., 1984, Stetson U., 1990, William Mitchell Coll. Law, 1992, St. Francis Coll., Bklyn., 1993; L.H.D. (hon.), DePaul U., 1980, Coll. S.I., CUNY, 1981, Pace U., 1985, Am. U. of Rome, 1995; D.C.S. (hon.), U. Verona, Italy, 1987; J.D. (hon.), U. Bologna, Italy, 1988, U. Urbino, Italy, 1994. Bar: N.Y. 1943. Appointed faculty St. John's U., N.Y., 1947, prof. law, 1951-69, adj. prof. law, 1969-80, Disting. prof., from 1980; vis. prof. Georgetown U. Sch. Law, 1962-67; adj. prof. law N.Y. Law Sch., 1972-82, Martin disting. vis. prof., from 1982; spl. hearing officer U.S. Dept. Justice, 1956-61; chmn. CUNY, 1961-68; asst. sec. ednl. and cultural affairs U.S. Dept. State, 1968-69; judge U.S. Customs Ct. (now U.S. Ct. Internat. Trade), N.Y.C., 1969-91, chief judge, 1977-91, chief judge emeritus, 1991—; CUNY, U. Urbino, Italy, 1994; mem. Jud. Conf. U.S., 1986-91, adv. com. on appellate rules, 1976-88, com. on internat. jud. rels. 1994—; chmn. adv. com. on experimentation in the law Fed. Jud. Ctr., 1978-81; mem. bd. higher edn. City of N.Y., 1958-69, emeritus, 1969—; Jackson lectr. Nat. Coll. State Trial Judges, U. Nev., 1970. Author: Foreign Confiscations in Anglo-American Law, 1951, (with Lester B. Orfield) Cases and Materials on International Law, rev. edit, 1965, Selected Essays on Equity, 1955, Brief Writing and Oral Argument, 6th edit, 1987, (with Joseph R. Re) 7th edit., 1993, (with Zechariah Chafee, Jr.) Cases and Materials on Equity, 1967, Cases and Materials on Equity and Equitable Remedies, 1975; (with Joseph R. Re) Law Students' Manual on Legal Writing and Oral Argument, 1991; chpt., freedom in internat. soc. Concept of Freedom (edited Rev. Carl W. Grindel), 1955; Cases and Materials on Remedies, 1982, 3rd edit., 1992; contbr. articles to Legal jours. Served with USAAF, 1943-47; col. JAGC, ret. Decorated Grand Cross Order of Merit Italy; recipient Am. Bill of Rights citation; Morgenstern Found. Interfaith award; USAF commendation medal; Distinguished service award Bklyn. Jr. C. of C., 1956. Mem. ABA (ho. of dels. 1976-78, chmn. sect. internat. and comparative law 1965-67), Am. Fgn. Law Assn. (pres. 1971-73), Am. Law Inst., Fed. Bar Coun. (pres. 1973-74), Am. Soc. Comparative Law (pres. 1969-91), Am. Justinian Soc. Jurists (pres. 1974-76), Internat. Assn. Jurists: Italy-USA (pres. 1991—), Internat. Assn. Judges (prin. rep. to UN 1993—), Scribes Am. Soc. Writers on Legal Subjects (pres. 1978). Office: St Johns U Sch Law Jamaica NY 11439

RE, RICHARD N., endocrinologist; b. Sept. 4, 1944; marrried; 3 children. AB summa cum laude, Harvard U., 1965, MD cum laude, 1969. Diplomate Am. Bd. Internal Medicine, Am. Bd. Endocrinology and Metabolism. Med. intern Mass. Gen. Hosp., Boston, 1969-70, med. resident, 1970-71, clin. and rsch. fellow in endocrinology, 1971-74, clin. asst. in medicine, 1974-76, chief Hypertension Clinic, 1975-79, asst. in medicine, 1976-79; rsch. fellow Harvard Med. Sch., Boston, 1971-74, instr. in medicine, 1975-76, asst. prof. medicine, 1977-79; mem. staff Ochsner Med. Instns., New Orleans, 1979—; assoc. clin. prof. medicine Tulane U. Sch. Medicine, New Orleans, 1980—; head sect. on hypertensive diseases Ochsner Clinic, New Orleans, 1981—; v.p., dir. rsch. Alton Ochsner Med. Found., New Orleans, 1985—; adj. prof. biology New Orleans, 1984—; chmn. clin. investigations com. Alton Ochsner Med. Found., 1980-86; mem. sci. rev. panel VA, 1988—; chmn. sci. resources com. Blood Rsch. Ctr., New Orleans, 1989—, trustee, 1989—; mem. adv. bd. Internat. Consortium for the Study of Tissue Renin Angiotensin Systems, 1990—; mem. rsch. com. Am. Heart Assn.-La., 1990-91, mem. sci. peer rev. com., 1990-91; mem. rsch. adv. com. Medicare Clinics Pilot Project, 1990-92. Author: Bioburst: The Impact of Modern Biology on the Affairs of Man, 1986; author: (with others) Clinical Pharmacy and Clinical Pharmacology, 1976, Biological Handbook II, 1977, Methods in Immunodiagnosis, 1981, Prostaglandins, Platelets, and Salicylates: Basic and Clinical Aspects, 1982, Systemic Disease in Dental Treatment, 1982, Kidney in Essential Hypertension, 1984, Current Clinical Practice, 1987, Current Advances in ACE Inhibition, 1989, Advances in Vascular Pathology, 1990; contbr. numerous articles to profl. jours. including Am. Jour. Hypertension, New Eng. Jour. Medicine, Jour. Inorganic Biochemistry, Current Opinion in Cardiology, Contemporary Internal Medicine, Lancet, Modern Medicine, Am. Jour. Cardiology. Fellow coun. on high blood pressure rsch. Am. Heart Assn. Grantee Nat. Heart and Lung Inst. NIH, 1981-85, La. Heart Assn., 1981-83, Indsl. Support, 1981-91.

Fellow Am. Coll. Physicians; mem. AAAS, Am. Fedn. for Clin. Rsch., Assn. Am. Med. Colls. Group on Med. Edn., N.Y. Acad. Scis., Cen. Soc. for Clin. Investigation, So. Soc. for Clin. Investigation, So. Med. Assn., Internat. Soc. Hypertension, Endocrine Soc., Soc. for Exptl. Biology and Medicine, Phi Beta Kappa. Achievements include research on growth factors and cardiovascular structure, on angiotensin and regulation of cellular growth, and on hypertension. Office: Alton Ochsner Med Found 1516 Jefferson Hwy New Orleans LA 70121-2484

REA, AMADEO MICHAEL, ethnobiologist, ornithologist; b. Oakland, Calif., Oct. 15, 1939. BA, San Luis Rey Coll., 1963; MS, Ariz. State U., 1969; PhD, U. Ariz., 1977. Curator birds and mammals San Diego Natural History Mus., 1977-91, rsch. assoc., 1991—. Author: Once a River, Bird Life and Habitat Changes on the Middle Gila, 1983. Mem. Soc. Ethnobiology (pres. 1987-89). Democrat. Roman Catholic. Home: 1455 49th St San Diego CA 92102-2625

REA, ANN W., librarian; b. Jefferson City, Mo., Aug. 3, 1944; d. William H. and Ruby (Fogleman) Webb; m. Glen N. Rea, Sept. 28, 1974; children: Sarah, Rebecca. BA, U. Mo., 1966; MLS, U. So. Calif., 1968. Libr. St. Charles (Mo.) County Libr., 1967-71; libr. adult svcs. Paterson (N.J.) Free Pub. Libr., 1971-74; libr. Beal Coll. Libr., Bangor, Maine, 1983—. Mem. Am. Libr. Assn., Maine Libr. Assn. Office: Beal Coll Libr 629 Main St Bangor ME 04401-6896

REA, DAVID K., geology and oceanography educator; b. Pitts., June 2, 1942; m. Donna M. Harshbarger, Feb. 11, 1967; children: Gregory, Margaret. AB, Princeton U., 1964; MS, U. Ariz., 1967; PhD, Oreg. State U., 1974. Prof. geology & oceanography U. Mich., Ann Arbor, 1975—; assoc. dir. NSF Climate Dynamics Program, Washington, 1986-87; interim dir. Ctr. for Great Lakes and Aquatic Scis., 1988-89, chmn. dept. geol. scis., 1995—. Contbr. more than 300 articles, reports to profl. publs. Recipient numerous NSF rsch. grants, 1976—. Office: U Mich Dept Geological Sci Ann Arbor MI 48109-1063

REA, STEPHEN, actor; b. Belfast, Ireland, 1949; m. Dolours Price, 1983; children: Oscar, Danny. Student, Queens Univ., Belfast. Formed (with Brian Friel) Field Day Theatre Co., 1980. Stage appearances include (London) The Shadow of a Gunman, The Cherry Orchard, Miss Julie, High Society; (Royal Court Theatre) Endgame, The Freedom of the City; (Field Day Theatre Co.) Translations, Communication Card, St. Oscar, Boesman and Lena, Hightime and Riot Act, Double Cross, Pentecost, Making History, Three Sisters (dir. only), The Cure at Troy (dir. only); (Broadway) Someone Who'll Watch Over Me, 1992 (Tony award nominee 1993), Uncle Vanya, 1995; films include Angel, 1982, Danny Boy, 1984, Company of Wolves, 1985, The Doctor and the Devils, 1985, Loose Connections, 1988, Life Is Sweet, 1991, The Crying Game, 1992 (Acad. award nominee best actor 1993), Bad Behavior, 1993, Princess Caraboo, 1993, Angie, 1994, Interview with the Vampire, 1994, Ready to Wear (Prêt-a-Porter), 1994, All Men Are Mortal, 1994, Citizen X, 1994, The Devil and the Deep Blue Sea, 1994; TV appearances include Four Days in July, Lost Belongings, Scout, St. Oscar, Not with a Bang, Hedda Gabler. Office: Peters Fraser & Dunlop Ltd, 503 The Chambers Lots Rd, Chelsea Harbor London SW10 OXF, England*

REA, WILLIAM, oil industry executive. With Arthur Young, Jacksonville, Fla., 1977-80, Charter Co., Jacksonville, Fla., 1980-83, Haskell Co., Jacksonville, Fla., 1983-88; v.p., cfo TR Trading Inc., Long Beach, Calif., 1989—. Office: TR Trading Inc 1 World Trade Ctr Long Beach CA 90831-0001

REA, WILLIAM J., district judge; b. 1950; BA, Loyola U., 1942, LLB, U. Colo., 1949. With U.S. Census Bur., Denver, 1949-50; adjuster Farmers Ins. Group, L.A., 1950; pvt. practice law, L.A., 1950-64, Santa Ana, Calif., 1964-68; judge Superior Ct., L.A., 1968-84; judge U.S. Dist. Ct. (cen. dist.) Calif., L.A., 1984—. Past pres. L.A. chpt. Nat. Exec. Com.; chmn. Constn. and By-Laws Com. With USN, WWII. Mem. L.A. County Bar Assn. (Outstanding Jurist award 1985), So. Calif. Def. Counsel Assn. Disting. Svc. award 1982), Internat. Acad. Trial Lawyers (Trial Judge of Yr. 1982), L.A. Trial Lawyers Assn., Am. Bd. Trial Advs. (nat. pres.). Office: US Dist Ct 312 N Spring St Los Angeles CA 90012-4701

READ, ALLAN ALEXANDER, minister; b. Toronto, Ont., Can., Sept. 19, 1923; s. Alec P. and Lillice (Matthews) R.; m. Mary Beverly Roberts, Sept. 28, 1949; children—John Allan, Elizabeth Anne, Peter Michael, Martha Ruth. B.A., U. Toronto, Can., 1946; Licentiate in Theology, Trinity Coll., Toronto, 1947, D.D., 1972; D.D., Wycliffe Coll., Toronto, 1972; D.S.T. (hon.), Thornloe Coll., Sudbury, Ont., 1982. Ordained diaconate, 1948, priest, 1949, Anglican Ch. of Canada. Rector 7 chs. Diocese Toronto-Anglican Ch., Parish of East and West Mono, Ont., Can., 1947-54; rector Diocese of Toronto-Trinity Anglican Ch., Christ Ch. Vespra, Barrie, Ont., Can., 1954-72; founder Barrie East End Mission, Parish of St. Giles, 1954; chaplain Simcoe County Gaol, 1954-72; Suffragan bishop Diocese of Toronto-Anglican Ch., Toronto, Ont., Can., 1972-81; bishop Diocese of Ont., Kingston, Ont., Can., 1981-92; canon St. James Cathedral, Toronto 1957-61; mem., chmn. provincial synod rural chm. com., 1953-63, Diocese of Toronto Exec. Com., 1959-71, Diocesan Com. Prayer and Evang., 1950-70, Diocesan Com. Corrections, 1950-72, Gen. Synod Com. Music and Hymn Book, 1965-71, chmn. Boy Scout Com., Barrie # 1, 1954-71, provincial synod, 1955-91, rural ch. unit gen. synod Anglican Ch. Can., 1959-89; archdeacon of Simcoe, 1961-72, Can. churchman. bd. trustees; participant World Anglican Congress, Toronto, 1963; mem. Anglican World Wide Lambeth Conf., 1978, 88; dir. Anglican Found.; Toronto; priest-in-charge St. Patrick's Cathedral, Trim, Ireland, 1992, Parish of Dunster Diocese of Bath and Wells, Eng., 1993, Parish of St. Ippolyts, Diocese St. Alban's, Eng., 1994, Parish of St. Mary the Virgin Westerham, Diocese of Rochester Eng., 1995. Author: Unto The Hills, 1951; Shepherds in Green Pastures, 1953. Patron Grenville Christian Coll., Brockville, Ont., 1981—; mem. hon. pres. Can. Coll. Organists, Simcoe Br., 1954-71; hon. Reeve, Black Creek Pioneer Village, 1981-82; mem. Barrie and Dist. High Sch. Bd., 1961-70; exec. com. Alcohol and Drug Concerns, 1971-83. Recipient Rural Workers Fellowship award Episc. Ch. U.S., 1952, Citizenship awards Gov. of Ontario, 1980, 85; named Citizen of Yr. City of Barrie, 1967. Mem. Rural Workers Fellowship (hon. pres. 1967—), Barrie Ministerial Assn. (sec. 1954-81). Home: 39 Riverside Dr, RR 1, Kingston, ON Canada K7L 4V1

READ, BEVERLY MONEY, military officer; b. Lexington, Va., Dec. 17, 1919; s. Hernando Money and Ann Katherine (Bosworth) R.; m. Jane Elizabeth Read (dec. 1958); children: B.C. John, James Money, Cynthia E. Read Kendig; m. Suzanne Legg, Jan. 1971; children: Reid Scott Perry, Brooke Nelson Perry, Meade Kirkpatrick. BA, Va. Mil. Inst., 1941; postgrad, Armed Forces Staff Coll., Norfolk, Va., 1954, Commd. & Gen. Staff Coll., 1954-59; postgrad., The Army War Coll., Carlisle, Pa., 1959. With intelligence staff, guerilla liaison officer U.S. Army, Philippines, 1944-45; exec. officer airborne bn. U.S. Army, 1947; with 11th airborne div. U.S. Army, Leavenworth, Kans., Japan, 1948-49; comdr. 2d Bn., 20th inf. U.S. Army, Calif., 1950-52; commdr. 1st bn. 17th inf., Korea, 1953-54; faculty U.S. Army, 1955-58; comdr. 2d bn. 19th inf. 24th div. 2d battle group, 1959-62; comdr. 1st brigade 24th inf. div. U.S. Army, 1962-64, chief of staff 24th inf. div., 1964—; G-3 U.S. Army, Vietnam, 1969-70. Editor Historian 1971-86, contbr. articles to mags., books, and jours. Chmn. Lexington Hwy. Safety Commn., 1973—; mem. adv. bd. trustees Mary Baldwin Coll., 1983-88. Decorated Bronze Star, Legion of Merit with 3d oak leaf cluster, Disting. Service Cross, Armed Forces Honor medal 1st class. Mem. Kiwanis (v.p. Lexington chpt. 1985-87). Methodist. Avocation: jogging. Home: 305 S Jefferson St Lexington VA 24450-2030

READ, CHARLES RAYMOND, SR., business executive; b. Clovis, N.Mex., Apr. 21, 1915; s. Charles Edward and Mary Ellen (Elder) R.; m. Elenore Littlefield, Oct. 10, 1936 (dec. July 1985); children: Charles Raymond Jr., Nancy Ann Walsh; m. Debra Rae Stutzman, Mar. 30, 1989. Baker, candymaker Peter-Paul's Candy, Clovis, 1932-34; baker Holsum Bakery, Boise, Idaho, 1934-35, Elsner's Bakery, Everett, Wash., 1935-37; head baker United Bakery, Ellensburg, Wash., 1937-40; owner, baker Read's Royal Bakery, Ellensburg, 1940-42; mgr., baker Clark's Bakery, Seattle, 1945-57; owner, baker Read's Bakery, Seattle, 1957-62; pres.

Read Products, Inc., Seattle, 1962—; ptnr. Peasley-Read, Seattle, 1968—; guest TV programs KING-5, Seattle, 1950-62; distbr. Richlite, 1962—. With USN, 1942-45. Seattle Pacific U. fellow; recipient trophies, plaques for cake decorating Pacific N.W. Clinary Arts Exhibit, 1950-62. Mem. United Comml. Travelers, Smithsonian Inst., Masons (3d degree). Avocations: collecting coins, Persian art, gems, jewelry, antiques, international travel. Office: Read Products Inc 3615 15th Ave W Seattle WA 98119

READ, DAVID HAXTON CARSWELL, clergyman; b. Cupar, Fife, Scotland, Jan. 2, 1910; came to U.S., 1956; s. John Alexander and Catherine Haxton (Carswell) R.; m. Dorothy Florence Patricia Gilbert, 1936; 1 son, Rory David Gilbert. Student, Daniel Stewart's Coll., Edinburgh, 1927; M.A. summa cum laude, U. Edinburgh, 1932, D.D., 1957; student, Montpelier, Strasbourg, Paris, 1932-33, Marburg, 1934; B.D., New Coll., Edinburgh, Scotland, 1936; D.D., Yale U., 1959, Lafayette Coll., 1965, Hope Coll., 1969; Litt.D., Coll. Wooster, 1966; L.H.D., Trinity U., 1972, Hobart Coll., 1972, Knox Coll., 1979; D.H.L., Japan Internat. Christian U., 1979, Rockford Coll., 1982. Ordained to ministry Ch. Scotland, 1936; min. Colstdream West, 1936-39; minister Greenbank Ch., Edinburgh, 1939-49; chaplain U. Edinburgh, 1949-55; chaplain to Her Majesty the Queen, Scotland, 1952-56; minister Madison Ave. Presbyn. Ch., 1956-89, minister emeritus, 1989—. Author: The Spirit of Life, 1939, Prisoners' Quest, 1944, The Communication of the Gospel, 1952, The Christian Faith, 1956, I Am Persuaded, 1962, Sons of Anak, 1964, God's Mobile Family, 1966, Whose God is Dead?, 1966, The Pattern of Christ, 1967, Holy Common Sense, 1966, The Presence of Christ, 1968, Christian Ethics, 1968, Virginia Woolf Meets Charlie Brown, 1968, Religion without Wrappings, 1970, Overheard, 1971, Curious Christians, 1972, An Expanding Faith, 1973, Sent from God, 1974, Good News in the Letters of Paul, 1976, Go . . . And Make Disciples, 1978, Unfinished Easter, 1978, The Faith is Still There, 1980, This Grace Given, 1984, Grace Thus Far, 1986, Preaching About the Needs of Real People, 1988, Christmas Tales for All Ages, 1989; translator (from German): The Church to Come, 1939; editor-in-chief The Living Pulpit, 1992; contbr. articles religious jours., periodicals, U.S. and Eng., The Living Pulpit, 1992. Chaplain Brit. Army, 1939-45. Mem. Century Assn. (N.Y.C.), Pilgrims Club. Prisoner of war, 1940-45. Home: 258 Riverside Dr Apt 9A New York NY 10025

READ, FRANK THOMPSON, lawyer, legal association consultant; b. Ogden, Utah, July 16, 1938; s. Frank Archie and Fay Melrose (Thompson) R.; m. Lenet Hadley; 5 children. BS with high honors, Brigham Young U., 1960; JD, Duke U., 1963. Bar: Minn. 1963, Mo. 1966, N.Y. 1968, Okla. 1975. Pvt. practice Mpls., St. Paul, 1963-65; atty. AT&T, Kansas City, Mo., and N.Y.C., 1965-68; asst. prof. law, asst. dean Law Sch., Duke U., 1968-70, assoc. prof., asst. dean, 1970-72, prof., assoc. dean, 1972-73, prof., 1973-74; dean, prof. law U. Tulsa Coll. Law, 1974-79, Ind. U. Sch Law., Indpls., 1979-81, U. Fla. Coll. Law, 1981-88; dean, chief exec. officer Hastings Coll. Law, U. Calif., San Francisco, 1988-93; dep. cons. sect. on legal edn. ABA, Indpls., 1993—; trustee Law Sch. Admission Coun., 1976-88, pres., 1984-85; chmn. Okla. Jud. Coun., 1976-78, pres., 1984-85; vis. prof. U. N.C., So. Meth. U., Brigham Young U. Author: Let Them Be Judged: The Judicial Integration of the Deep South, 1978, The Oklahoma Evidence Handbook, 1979, Read's Florida Evidence, 2 vols., 1987; contbr. articles to profl. jours. Mem. ABA (sect. legal edn.), Am. Law Inst., Assn. Am. Law Schs., Order of Coif, Phi Kappa Phi. Home: 281 Arbor Dr Carmel IN 46032 Office: ABA 550 W North St Indianapolis IN 46202

READ, FREDERICK WILSON, JR., lawyer, educator; b. Providence, July 30, 1908; s. Frederick Wilson and Araminta Rowena (Briggs) R.; m. Evelyn Elaine Avery, Feb. 21, 1942; children: Frederick Wilson III, Cynthia Avery. Student, Trinity Coll., 1925-26; AB, Columbia U., 1930, LLB, 1932. Bar: N.Y. 1933, Mass. 1939, U.S. Supreme Ct. 1955. Assoc. Hervey, Barber & McKee, N.Y.C., 1932-35, Menken, Ferguson & Idler, N.Y.C., 1937-39; atty. legal dept. Nat. Realty Mgmt. Co., N.Y.C., 1935-37, French Air Commn., N.Y.C., 1939-40; mem. legal and contracts depts. Brit. Purchasing Commn., Brit. Air Commn., N.Y.C. and Washington, 1940-41; atty. Glenn L. Martin Co., Middle River, Md., 1941-42; with Home Life Ins. Co., N.Y.C., 1945-73; atty. Home Life Ins. Co., 1945-47, asst. counsel, 1947-54, counsel, 1954-64, gen. counsel, 1964-71, v.p., gen. counsel, 1971-73; counsel Daiker, D'Elia, Turtletaub & Cantino, Port Washington, N.Y., 1973-77, D'Elia, Turtletaub & Cantino, 1977-80, Capobianco, D'Elia, Turtletaub, Cantino & Aitken (P.C.), 1980-83, D'Elia & Turtletaub, 1983—; prof. Coll. Ins., 1974-84, N.Y. Law Sch., 1974-76; counsel N.Y.C. Life Underwriters Assn., 1974-83, hon. mem., 1984—. Mem. Bd. Edn., Port Washington, 1949-52, 59-66, pres., 1950-52, v.p., 1962-66; trustee McAuley Water St. Mission, 1970-81, trustee emeritus, 1981—; dir. John Philip Sousa Meml. Band Shell, Inc., 1990—; mem. sr. adv. coun. Port Washington Pub. Libr., 1991—. Capt. USNR, 1942-45; mem. Res. (ret.). Recipient Bishops Cross, 1988. Fellow Am. Bar Found. (life); mem. ABA (rep. ho. dels. 1969-77, sr. lawyer div. com. liaison with state and local bar sr. lawyers 1986—), N.Y. State Bar Assn. (assn. ins. program com. 1973-84, vice-chmn. 1974-77, chmn. 1977-84), Nassau County Bar Assn. (chmn. assn. ins. plans com. 1973-83, dir. 1977-80), Assn. of Bar of City of N.Y. (ins. law com. 1946-49, 61-64, mil. justice and mil. affairs com. 1951-68, chmn. 1965-68), Assn. Life Ins. Counsel (sec.-treas. 1960-63, v.p. 1965-66, pres. 1967-68), Judge Advs. Assn. (life), Am. Council Life Ins., Health Ins. Assn. Am., Am. Soc. CLUs, Ins. Soc. of N.Y. (1974-84), Cow Neck Peninsula Hist. Soc. (trustee, 3d v.p.-legal 1974-83, trustee emeritus 1983—), U.S. Naval Inst. (life), Naval Res. Assn. (life), Ret. Officers Assn., Nat. Maritime Hist. Soc., Acad. Political Sci., Alpha Delta Phi. Episcopalian. Clubs: Lions (Port Washington) (bd. dirs. 1980-82, 87—); Masons. Home: 2 Lynn Rd Port Washington NY 11050-4447 Office: 927 Port Washington Blvd Port Washington NY 11050-2910

READ, GREGORY CHARLES, lawyer; b. St. Louis, Jan. 21, 1942; s. Charles Hadley and Margaret Olive (Kumlien) R.; m. Mary Beth Bartulis, Aug. 28, 1965; children: Laura Elizabeth, Andrew Nathan. BA, U. Ill., 1964, JD, 1967. Bar: Ill. 1967, Calif. 1971, U.S. Dist. Ct. (no., ea. and cen. dists.) Calif., U.S. Ct. Claims, U.S. Ct. Appeals (9th cir.), U.S. Ct. Appeals (fed. cir.), U.S. Supreme Ct. Law clk. to Hon. Henry Wise U.S. Dist. Ct. Ill., Danville, 1967; assoc. Sedgwick, Detert, Moran & Arnold, San Francisco, 1971-76, ptnr., 1976—. Contbr. articles to profl. jours. Lt. JAGC, USN, 1968-70. Mem. ABA, Am. Bd. Trial Advocates, Ill. Bar Assn., Calif. Bar Assn., Internat. Assn. Def. Counsel, Def. Rsch. Inst. Home: 66 La Cuesta Rd Orinda CA 94563-2326 Office: Sedgwick Detert Moran & Arnold 16th Fl 1 Embarcadero Ctr Fl 16 San Francisco CA 94111-3600

READ, SISTER JOEL, college administrator. BS in Edn., Alverno Coll., 1948; MA in History, Fordham U., 1951; hon. degrees, Lakeland Coll., 1972, Wittenburg U., 1976, Marymount Manhattan Coll., 1978, DePaul U., 1985, Northland Coll., 1986, SUNY, 1986. Former prof., dept. chmn. history dept. Alverno Coll., Milw., pres., 1968—; pres. Am. Assn. for Higher Edn., 1976-77; mem. coun. NEH, 1977-83; bd. dirs. Ednl. Testing Svc., 1987-93, Neylan Commn., 1985-90; past pres. Wis. Assn. Ind. Colls. and Univs.; mem. Commn. on Status of Edn. for Women, 1971-76, Am. Assn. Colls., 1971-77; mem. exec. com. Greater Milw. com. GMC Edn. Trust. Mem. exec. bd. Milw. YMCA. First recipient Anne Roe award Harvard U. Grad. Sch. Edn., 1980. Fellow Am. Acad. Arts and Scis.; mem. Found. for Higher Edn. Office: Alverno Coll Office of the President PO Box 343922 Milwaukee WI 53234-3922

READ, JOHN CONYERS, management consultant; b. N.Y.C., May 21, 1947; s. Edward Cameron Kirk and Louise (Geary) R.; m. Alexandra Gould, Mar. 30, 1968; children: Cameron Kirk, Trevor Conyers, Alexandra. AB, Harvard, 1969, MBA, 1971. Ops. rsch. analyst HEW, Washington, 1971-72; exec. asst. to dir. Cost of Living Council, Washington, 1973; chief econ. adviser to Gov. Mass., 1974; exec. asst., counselor to sec. labor Washington, 1975; asst. sec. labor for employment standards, 1976-77; dir. corp. employee rels., pers. Cummins Engine Co., Columbus, Ind., 1977-80, plant mgr., 1980-85; v.p. Midrange Engines, 1986-90; v.p., gen. mgr. engine group Donaldson Co., Inc., Mpls., 1990-92; exec. v.p., 1992-94; cons. nat. productivity and energy policies; chmn. NAM Task Force on Wage and Price Policies, 1978-80. Author Ford Found. monograph on occupational disease and workers' compensation; contbr. articles to newspapers and mags. Trustee Nat. Ctr. Occupational Readjustment, 1984-87; chmn. Charleston Pvt. Industry Coun., 1985; mem. plant closing task force U.S. Dept. Labor, 1986, mfg. task force NRC, 1989, critical industries task force Def. Dept., 1989; bd. of advisors

N.C. Outward Bound Sch. Mem. Nat. Assn. Mfrs. (dir., chair employee rels. com. 1993——). Home: 2697 E Lake Of The Isles Pky Minneapolis MN 55408-1051

READ, MICHAEL OSCAR, editor, consultant; b. Amarillo, Tex., July 11, 1942; s. Harold Eugene and Madeline (Welch) R.; m. Jill Kay Vanderby, July 6, 1963 (div. Apr. 1967); 1 child, Rebecca Anne; m. Fawn Dale Barby, Apr. 10, 1977; 1 child, Nathan Michael. AA in Chemistry, Amarillo Coll., 1962; BA in Journalism, Tex. Tech. U., 1965. News editor Olton (Tex.) Enterprise, 1966-64; reporter, photographer Lubbock (Tex.) Avalanche-Jour., 1964-67, copy editor, 1967-70, city editor, 1970-72; copy editor Houston Post, 1972-74, systems editor, 1974-89, dir. news tech., 1989-95; electronic media content coord. Houston Chronicle, 1995——; bd. dirs. News Media Credit Union, Houston, Meadows (Tex.) Econ. Devel. Corp.; tchr. Let's Compute!, Stafford, Tex., 1985——; cons. Newspaper Pub. Sys., Stafford, 1989——; mem. joint Newspaper Assn. Am.-Internat. Press. Telecomm. Coun. Com. Wire Svc. Standards. Author weekly newspaper column, 1977——. Vol. United Way, Houston, 1973——; bd. dirs. Meadows Community Improvement Assn., 1985-91, Meadows Utility Dist., 1988-93. Eldon Durrett scholar, 1961-65. Mem. Am. MENSA, Am. Philatelic Soc., Am. 1st Day Cov. Soc. (life), U.S. Chess Fedn. (life), Soc. Profl. Journalists (conv. com. 1989-90). Avocations: philately, photography, gardening. Home: 12023 Alston Dr Stafford TX 77477-1505 Office: Houston Chronicle 801 Texas Ave Houston TX 77002

READ, PAUL E., horticulture educator; b. Canandaigua, N.Y., July 13, 1937; s. Irwin Austin and Mildred Emma (Moore) R.; m. Ann Shirley Langlitz, June 2, 1957 (div. 1976); children: Sharon Ann, Nancy Beth, Norman Allen; m. Christine Ann Streed, Aug. 13, 1989; 1 child, Emma Jane. BS, Cornell U. Ithaca, N.Y., 1959, MS, 1964; PhD, U. Del. 1967. 4-H agt. Fulton County, Gloversville, N.Y., 1959-62; teaching asst. Cornell U., Ithaca, 1962-64; rsch. assoc. U. Del., Newark, 1964-67; asst. prof. U. Minn., St. Paul, 1967-72, assoc. prof., 1972-78, prof., 1978-87; prof., head dept. horticulture U. Nebr., Lincoln, 1987——; cons. Internat. Atomic Energy Agy., Vienna, Austria, 1985, 86, 88, Internat. Exec. Svc. Corps, Greenwich, Conn., 1988. Author: Plant Propagation Lab Manual, 1977, 79, The Biology of Horticulture, 1993; editor jour. Plant Growth Regulator Bull., 1975-88; contbr. book chpts. and articles to profl. jours. Fellow Am. Soc. Hort. Sci. (v.p. edn. 1986); mem. Plant Growth Regulator Soc. Am. (charter, v.p. 1990, pres. 1992-93), Internat. Assn. Plant Tissue Culture (U.S. corres. 1991-94), Am. Chestnut Found. (charter, v.p. 1991-92, pres. 1992-94).

READ, PETER KIP, health care administrator; b. Chgo., Nov. 28, 1941; s. Edwin Lewis and Virginia Beaupre (Miller) R.; m. Lucy Plerson Wilson, June 4, 1966; children: Dana Dominick, Peter Kip, Jodi Marie. BS, U. Ariz., 1971; MS, Trinity U., 1973. Corw. coord. Hilton Hotels, Palmer House, Chgo., 1963-67; exec. dir. Dental Found. Colo., Denver, 1967-69; assoc. dir. St. Luke's Hosp., Cleve., 1973-76, exec. v.p., chief ops. officer, 1976-85; exec. v.p., chief ops. officer Bayfront Med. Ctr., St. Petersburg, Fla., 1985-87; pres. Indsl. Med. Supply Co., Tampa, 1988——; vice-chmn. Cancer Data Systems, Cleve., 1983-85. Served with ANG, 1962-68. Fellow Am. Coll. Health Care Execs.; mem. Health Care Adminstrn. N.E. Ohio (pres. 1983), Am. Hosp. Assn., Bay Area Hosp. Assn., Feather Sound Country Club, Rotary. Republican. Episcopalian. Avocations: golf, tennis, fishing, outdoor activities. Home: 2966 Teal Ln Clearwater FL 34622-3065 Office: Indsl Med Supply Co 8410 Sunstate St Tampa FL 33634-1310

READ, PHILIP LLOYD, computer design and manufacturing executive; b. Flint, Mich., Jan. 9, 1932; s. Harry Samuel and Maude Elizabeth (Jones) R.; m. Ann Elizabeth Goodall, June 23, 1956; children: Thomas, Elizabeth, Jane. AB, Oberlin Coll., 1953; MS in Physics, U. Mich., 1954, PhD in Physics, 1961. Physicist GE, Schenectady, N.Y., 1960-67; mgr. GE, Milw., 1967-70, gen. mgr., 1970-75; corp. v.p., divsn. gen. mgr. Computervision Corp., Bedford, Mass., 1975-81, sr. v.p., COO, 1981-83, sr. v.p., 1983-88, also bd. dirs. Contbr. articles to profl. jours.; patentee in field. Mem. Am. Phys. Soc. Avocations: photography, tennis. Home and Office: 80 Witherell Dr Sudbury MA 01776-1248

READ, PIERS PAUL, author; b. Beaconsfield, Eng., Mar. 7, 1941; s. Herbert Edward and Margaret (Ludwig) R.; m. Emily Albertine Boothby, July 29, 1967; children: Albert Nathaniel, Martha Marianna, William Edward, Beatrice Mary. B.A., St. John's Coll., Cambridge U., 1962, M.A., 1963. Sub-editor Times Lit. Supplement, 1963-64; adj. prof. writing Columbia U., 1980; lit. panel mem. Arts Coun. Gt. Britain, 1974-76; gov. Cardinal Manning Boys Sch., 1985; chmn. Cath. Writers Guild, 1993. Author: novels Game in Heaven with Tussy Marx, 1966, The Junkers, 1968 (Sir Geoffrey Faber Meml. prize, 1969), Monk Dawson, 1970 (Somerset Maugham award, Hawthornden prize, 1970), The Professor's Daughter, 1971, The Upstart, 1973, Polonaise, 1976, A Married Man, 1980, The Villa Golitsyn, 1982, The Free Frenchman, 1986, A Season in the West, 1988 (James Tait Black Meml. prize), On the Third Day, 1990; non-fiction Alive: The Story of the Andes Survivors, 1974 (Thomas More medal), The Train Robbers, 1978, Ablaze: The Heros and Victims of Chernobyl, 1993; (television playes) Coincidence, The Family Firm, The House on Highbury Hill. Mem. Brit. bd. of Aid to Church in Need, 1988. Ford Found. fellow, 1963-64; Harkness fellow, 1967-68. Fellow Royal Soc. Lit.; mem. Soc. Authors (com. mgmt. 1972-74), Inst. Contemporary Arts (com. mgmt. 1972-74). Roman Catholic. Address: 50 Portland Rd, London England W11 4LG

READ, WILLIAM LAWRENCE, business executive, former naval officer; b. Bklyn., July 8, 1926; s. Reginald A. and Martha (Bedell) R.; m. Martha Miller, Nov. 25, 1950; children: Allison, William Lawrence, John Alexander. B.S., U.S. Naval Acad., 1949; M.S., George Washington U., 1979. Commd. ensign U.S. Navy, 1949, advanced through grades to vice adm., 1977; comdr. U.S.S. Van Voorhis, 1961-63, U.S.S. King, 1966-68, Escort Squadron Ten, 1968-69, Cruiser-Destroyer Flotilla Three, 1972-73; sr. aide to SACEUR, 1970-72, mil. asst. to sec. Def., 1963-66, asst. chief Navy Personnel for officer devel. and distbn., 1973-74, dir. Ship Acquisition Div., Office Chief Naval Ops., 1974-77, comdr. Naval Surface Force, U.S. Atlantic Fleet, 1977-79; v.p. constrn. mgmt. Lone Star Industries, Greenwich, Conn., 1979-83; bd. dirs. Olin Corp., Meml. Health Sys. Decorated D.S.M., Legion of Merit, Navy Commendation medal with combat V, Navy Disting. Service Order 2d class (Republic of Vietnam). Mem. Surface Navy Assn. (bd. dirs.). Episcopalian. Home: 8117 Leehaven Rd Easton MD 21601-9706

READ, WILLIAM MCCLAIN, retired oil company executive; b. Phila., July 30, 1918; s. William Tucker and Grace (McNeal) R.; m. Esther Donahoo, Sept. 15, 1945; children: Deborah Read Yoder, Suzanne Read DiFulvio, William W. B.A., Washington and Lee U., 1940; postgrad., U. Pa., 1941-42. Personal asst. Atlantic Refining Co., Phila., 1943-50, dir. tng., 1950-72; v.p. employee relations Atlantic Richfield Co., Los Angeles, 1972-78, sr. v.p. employee relations, 1978-83; now ret. Author: Now You Are a Supervisor, 1962; contbr. articles to profl. jours. Chmn. Verdugo Hills Hosp., Glendale, Calif., 1980-81, 85-86; dir. Hosp. Coun. So. Calif., L.A., 1982-84, chmn. trustees com., 1983-84; chmn. bd. dirs. Pacific Clinics, 1993. Recipient Algernon Sydney Sullivan award Washington and Lee U., 1940. Mem. Annandale Golf Club, Phi Beta Kappa, Omicron Delta Kappa. Home: 4141 Cambridge Rd La Canada Flintridge CA 91011-4003

READE, CLAIRE ELIZABETH, lawyer; b. Waltham, Mass., June 2, 1952; d. Kemp Brownell and Suzanne Helen (Dorntge) R.; m. Earl Phillip Steinberg, Nov. 22, 1980; children: Evan Samuel, Emma Miriam. BA, Conn. Wesleyan U., 1973; JD, Harvard U., 1979; MA in Law and Diplomacy, Tufts U., 1979. Bar: Mass. 1980, D.C. 1983. Sheldon fellow Harvard U., Cambridge, Mass. and. Republic of China, 1979-80; assoc. Ropes & Gray, Boston, 1980-82; assoc. Arnold & Porter, Washington, 1982-86, ptnr., 1987——. Exec. editor: International Trade Policy: The Lawyer's Perspective, 1985; contbr. articles to profl. jours. Mem. ABA (co-chair internat. trade com.), D.C. Bar Assn., Fed. Bar Assn., Am. Soc. Internat. Law, Washington Coun. Lawyers, Women in Internat. Trade. Office: Arnold & Porter 555 12th St NW Washington DC 20004-1202

READE, LEWIS POLLOCK, diplomat, engineer; b. N.Y.C., Nov. 1, 1932; s. Herman Ross and Dorothy Stella (Pollock) R.; m. Anne Carol Kulka, July 3, 1953 (div. Feb. 1968); children: Steven Gordon, Nicholas Edward; m. Margaret Ann Kilpatrick, Mar. 30, 1968; 1 child, Jonathan Collins. BS in

Mech. Engrin., U. Miami, 1953; postgrad., Hofstra U., 1953-54, U. Balt., 1957-59. Product engr. Sperry Gyroscope, Lake Success, N.Y., 1953-54; project engr. ARMA, Garden City, N.Y., 1954-55; field engr. Westinghouse Electric Corp., Balt. & Rome, 1957-66; v.p. Westinghouse Learning Corp., Washington & Pitts., 1966-70; v.p. corp. planning & devel. Tyco Labs., Waltham, Mass., 1970-71; chmn., chief exec. officer, treas. Kellett Corp., Willow Grove, Pa., 1971-72; exec. v.p. Big Bros./Big Sisters of Am., Phila. 1973-80; mission dir. U.S. Agency Internat. Devel., Kingston, Jamaica, Amman, Jordan, & Jakarta, Indonesia, 1980-92; dir. gen. U.S.-Asia Environ. Ptnrship., Washington, 1992——. Sgt. US Army, 1955-57. Mem. Athenaeum of Phila., Soc. Internat. Devel., Am. Fgn. Svc. Assn., Vesper (Phila.), Soc. Hill (Phila.), Internat. (Washington), Jamaica Club (Kingston), Royal Jordanian Automobile Club, Am. Club (Jakarta, Indonesia). Home: 827 F St NE Washington DC 20002 Office: US-AEP Dept State 321 21st St NW Ste 3208 Washington DC 20523

READE, RICHARD SILL, manufacturing executive; b. Romeo, Mich., Oct. 11, 1913; s. Richard Sill and Ella (Van de Car) R.; m. Arlyne Alice Conger, Apr. 9, 1938; children: William Kent, Todd Conger. B.S. in Mech. Engring., U. Mich., 1934. Mgr. F & B div. Am. Blower Co., Detroit, 1946-51; dir. purchasing Am.-Standard Corp., N.Y.C., 1951-55; pres. Ross Heater Corp., Buffalo, 1955-60; v.p. mfg. (Am.-Standard indsl. div.), Detroit, 1960-64; pres. Crane Can., Ltd., Montreal, Que., Can., 1964-76, Transcar Industries, Inc., Clover, S.C., 1977-92; ret. Mem. Newcomen Soc., Can. Inst. Plumbing and Heating (pres. 1971-72), Chi Phi. Home: 465 Village Pl Longwood FL 32779

READE, ROBERT MELLOR, advertising consultant, retired convenience store executive; b. Elmhurst, Ill., Jan. 9, 1940; s. M.G. and Virginia A. (Mellor) R.; m. Carol Jean Coon, May 26, 1962; children: Christopher, Gregory. BA in Liberal Arts, U. Ariz., 1962. Charting mgr. Eller Outdoor Advt., Phoenix, 1964-69; sales mgr. Mullins Neon, Denver, 1969-70; pres. Gannett Outdoor Co. Ariz., Phoenix, 1970-84; sr. v.p. Gannett Outdoor Group, N.Y.C., 1984-85; sr. v.p. real estate and devel. Circle K Corp., Phoenix, 1985-86; pres., chief operating officer Circle K Internat., Phoenix, 1986-90; ret., 1990; cons. Outdoor Sys. Co., Phoenix, 1992——; bd. dirs. Western Savs. and Loan. Chmn. Phoenix chpt. Am. Humanics, 1983, Valley Youth Coalition, 1981, Phoenix City Bond Election, 1984; active Thunderbirds, 1978-83, Theodore council Boy Scouts Am., Community Council, Phoenix United Way, Camelback Mental Health Found. With USAR, 1963-69. Recipient U. Ariz. Alumni Appreciation award, 1975, 77, Slouaker award, 1977; Anti Defamation League Torch of Liberty award, 1981. Mem. Ariz. Safety Assn. (pres. 1981), Young Pres. Orgn., Outdoor Assn. Am., Inst. Outdoor Advt., Phoenix Advt. Club (pres. 1974), Rotary (pres. 1982).

READER, GEORGE GORDON, physician, educator; b. Bklyn., Feb. 8, 1919; s. Houston Parker and Marion J. (Payne) R.; m. Helen C. Brown, May 23, 1942; children: Jonathan, David, Mark, Peter. BA, Cornell U., 1940, MD, 1943; DSc (hon.), Drew U., 1988. Diplomate Am. Bd. Internal Medicine. Intern N.Y. Hosp., N.Y.C., 1944; resident N.Y. Hosp., 1947-49, attending physician, 1962-92; hon. staff, 1992——; dir. comprehensive care and teaching program N.Y. Hosp., 1952-66, chief med. clinic, 1952-72; practice medicine specializing in internal medicine N.Y.C., 1949-93; chief div. ambulatory and community medicine N.Y. Hosp.-Cornell Med. Center, N.Y.C., 1969-72; prof. medicine Cornell U. Med. Coll., 1957-89, Livingston Farrand prof. pub. health, 1972-89, prof. emeritus pub. health and medicine, 1989——, chmn. dept. pub. health, 1972-92; Chmn. human ecology study sect. NIH, 1961-65; chmn. med. adv. com. Vis. Nurse Service N.Y., 1963——; mem. med. control bd. Health Ins. Plan Greater N.Y., 1964——; mem. Gov.'s Health Adv. Council, 1974-79. Author: (with R. Merton, P. Kendall) The Student Physician, 1957, (with Goss) Comprehensive Medical Care and Teaching, 1967, (with Goodrich and Olendzki) Welfare Medical Care: An Experiment, 1969; mem. editorial bd. Medical Care, 1969-70, Jour. Med. Edn, 1975-79; editor-in-chief Milbank Meml. Fund Quar.: Health and Society, 1972-76. Bd. dirs. N.Y.C. Vis. Nurse Svc., The Osborn Retirement Community, Health Ins. Plan Greater N.Y., 1983-93, Helen Keller Internat.; trustee Cornell U., 1982-87. Lt. USNR, 1944-46, PTO. Fellow ACP, Am. Coll. Preventive Medicine, Am. Public Health Assn. (governing council 1968-69); mem. AAAS, AMA, N.Y. Acad. Medicine (chmn. com. med. edn. 1968-71, v.p. 1978-80), Am. Sociol. Assn., Harvey Soc., Internat. Sociol. Assn., Internat. Epidemiological Assn., N.Y.C. Pub. Health Assn. (pres. 1956), Inst. Medicine Nat. Acad. Scis. (sr. mem.), Sigma Xi, Alpha Omega Alpha. Home: 155 Stuyvesant Ave Rye NY 10580-3112

READER, JOSEPH, physicist; b. Chgo., Dec. 1, 1934. BS, Purdue U., 1956, MS, 1957; PhD in Physics, U. Calif., 1962. Rsch. assoc. physics Argonne Nat. Lab., 1962-63; staff physicist Nat. Inst. Standards and Tech., Gaithersburg, Md., 1963——. Recipient Gold Medal Dept. Commerce, William F. Meggars Awd., 1992, Optical Soc. Am. Fellow Am. Phys. Soc., Optical Soc. Am. (William F. Meggers award 1992). Achievements includes research in experimental atomic physics, optical spectroscopy, hyperfine structure, electronic structure of highly ionized atoms, wave length standards, and ionization energies of atoms and ions. Office: Natl Inst Of Standards & Tech Gaithersburg MD 20899

READING, ANTHONY JOHN, physician; b. Sydney, Australia, Sept. 10, 1933; s. Abe Stanley and Esma Daisy R.; m. Elisabeth Ann Hoffman, July 27, 1975; children:—Wendy Virginia Elisabeth, Sarah Alexandra Jane. M.B., B.S., U. Sydney, 1956; M.P.H, Johns Hopkins U., 1961, Sc.D., 1964. Intern Sydney Hosp., 1957-58; resident in psychiatry Johns Hopkins Hosp., Balt., 1965-68; assoc. prof. psychiatry and medicine Johns Hopkins U. Sch. Medicine, Balt., 1968-73, assoc. prof. psychiatry, 1973-75, dir. psychiat. liaison service, 1974-75; dir. comprehensive alcoholism program Johns Hopkins Hosp., 1972-75; prof., chmn. dept. psychiatry and behavioral medicine U. South Fla. Coll. Medicine, 1975——, assoc. dean, 1993——. Mem. AMA, AAAS, Am. Psychosomatic Soc., Am. Psychiat. Assn. Home: 1171 Shipwatch Cir Tampa FL 33602-5787 Office: 3515 E Fletcher Ave Tampa FL 33613-4706

READING, JAMES EDWARD, transportation executive; b. Milw., June 26, 1924; s. James Edwards and Helen Marie (Boehm) R.; m. Ada Irene Kelly, May 24, 1944; children—Wendy Irene, James David, Christopher Kelly, Mary Katherine, Kevin Sinclair. Student, San Diego State U., 1942, Ga. Inst. Tech., 1944. With Union-Tribune Pub. Co., San Diego, 1942-59, dist. mgr., 1953-58; circulation promotion mgr. Union-Tribune Pub. Co., 1958-59; adminstrv. asst. to v.p. Copley Newspapers, La Jolla, Calif., 1959-60; dir. advt. and public relations San Diego Transit System, 1960-67; dir. mktg. Calif. Motor Express, 1967-68; asst. to exec. v.p. Am. Transit Assn., Washington, 1968; v.p. Nat. City Mgmt. Co.; resident mgr. Regional Transit Service, Rochester, N.Y., 1968-74; asst. gen. mgr. cons. Regional Transit Dist., Denver, 1974-77; gen. mgr. Central Ohio Transit Authority, Columbus, 1977-85; dir. Santa Clara County Transp. Agy., San Jose, Calif., 1985-90; ind. cons. San Diego, 1990—; guest lectr. numerous univs. Served with U.S. Army, 1943-46, ETO. Named Public Relations Man of Yr. Public Relations Club, San Diego, 1962; recipient Urban Mass Transp. Adminstrs. award for outstanding pub. service, 1980, 82. Mem. Pub. Rels. Soc. Am. (past pres. 4 chpts.), Am. Pub. Transit Assn. (bd. dirs.) Transp. Rsch. Bd., Am. Soc. Pub. Adminstrs., Am. Pub. Works Assn., Am. Legion, Rotary, Tau Kappa Epsilon. Republican. Roman Catholic. Home: 11728 Caminito Corriente San Diego CA 92128-4548

READMOND, RONALD WARREN, investment banking firm executive; b. Balt., Jan. 17, 1943; s. George Melvin and Dorothy Louise (Phillips) R.; m. Beth Blades, June 6, 1965 (div.); children: Robert, David; m. Janet Marie Adams, Dec. 20, 1974; children: Jefferson, Lorin, Carey. BA, Western Md. Coll., 1965. Mng. dir. Alexander Brown & Sons, Inc., Balt., 1970—, also bd. dirs.; bd. dirs. Nat. Securities Clearance Corp., N.Y.C., Govt. Securities Clearance Corp., N.Y.C.; trustee Securities Industry Inst., 1986—; adv. com. New York Stock Exchange Ops., 1987——. Capt. U.S. Army, 1965-70, Vietnam. Mem. Fin. Industry Securities Council (co-chair 1984-86). Republican. Roman Catholic. Avocations: fishing, hunting. Home: 1501 Phoenix Rd W Phoenix MD 21131-1021 Office: Schwab & Co 101 Montgomery St San Francisco CA 94104-4122

READY, ROBERT JAMES, financial company executive; b. Bridgeport, Conn., June 26, 1952; s. John Edward and Anne (Salata) R.; m. Margaret S. Neale, Aug. 23, 1975; children: Carolyn, Christopher and Steven (twins). AS, Housatonic Community Coll., 1972; BS, Babson Coll., 1974. CLU; chartered fin. cons.; cert. ins. cons. Agt. John Hancock Mut. Life Ins. Co., Hamden, Conn., 1975-77; broker Beardsley, Brown & Bassett Inc., Bridgeport, Conn., 1977-80; agt. Aetna Life and Casualty Ins. Co., Trumbull, Conn., 1980-83; v.p. Crestview Fin. Services Inc., Westport, Conn., 1983—, Crestview Securities Inc., Westport, Conn., 1983—, Crestview Investment Advisors Inc., Westport, Conn., 1983——. Mem. Nat. Assn. Life Underwriters, Conn. Assn. Life Underwriters, Bridgeport Life Underwriters (bd. dirs. 1977), Nat. Assn. Health Underwriters, Conn. Assn. Health Underwriters, Am. Soc. CLU and Chartered Fin. Cons., New Haven County CLU and Chartered Fin. Cons., Bridgeport Jaycees. Roman Catholic. Avocations: golf, tennis. Office: The Crestview Fin Group 431 Post Rd E Ste 1 Westport CT 06880-4403

READY, WILLIAM ANDREW, mergers/acquisitions and management consultant; b. Oakland, Calif., May 30, 1943; s. Thomas James and Cathrynn Maryann (Reinheimer) R.; m. Carroll Ann Beilke, Feb. 5, 1944; children: Robyn, Patrick. BA, Stanford U., 1965, MBA, 1968. Group v.p. Church's Fried Chicken, San Antonio, Tex., 1973-76; gen. mgr. Foster Farms Restaurants Inc., Modesto, Calif., 1976-79; pres., chief ops. officer Ky. Fried Chicken U.S.A., Louisville, 1979-83, Hickory Farms, Toledo, 1983-85; chief exec. officer, dir. Profitwatch Systems Inc., Indpls., 1985—; also bd. dirs. MBA Internat., Indpls.; pres., chief exec. officer Markets USA, Louisville, 1987—, Investment Finders USA, Louisville, 1988-90; bd. dirs. Steward & Loyd, Indpls.; trustee Heidelberg Coll., Tiffin, Ohio, 1983—; chmn., pres. The Phoenix Group, 1991—; mem. bd. adv. Water Polo Found. Mem. IBBA, IBC, MWBBA, Am. Mgmt. Assn. Republican. Presbyterian. Avocations: reading, gardening, stock market/investments, travel. Address: 255 W Broadway Louisville KY 40202

REAGAN, BARBARA BENTON, economics educator. B.S. with honors, U. Tex., 1941; M.A. in Stats., Am. U., 1947; M.A. in Econs., Harvard U., 1949, Ph.D. in Econs., 1952. Econ. researcher Dept. Agr., 1942-47; sr. project leader Agrl. Research Service, Washington, 1949-55; prof. econs. Tex. Woman's U., Denton, 1959-67; prof. econs. So. Meth. U., Dallas, 1967-90, prof. emeritus, 1990—, chmn. dept., 1984-90; dir. interdisciplinary research project So. Meth. U., 1969-70, dir. undergrad. studies econs. dept., 1972-75, assoc. dean Univ. Coll., 1975, asst. to pres. for student acad. services, 1975-76, pres. faculty senate, 1981-82; mem. exec. com., 1981-84; dir. Region IX Fed. Home Loan Bank, 1981-85; mem. Dallas Morning News Bd. Economists, 1982-88; dir. Agrl. Rsch. Svc. Project, Dallas, 1970-71; mem. adv. bd. econs. USA Wharton Econometric Forecasting Assocs., 1983-85; reviewer NSF; disting. vis. prof. econs. Kenyon Coll., spring, 1979; bd. dirs. 1st Am. Savs. Bank, 1990—, North Tex. Mesbic, 1991-93, Tex. Guaranteed Student Loan Corp., 1991—, sec., exec. com., chmn. policy com., 1992-93, chmn. bd., 1993—. Author: Economic Foundations of Labor Supply of Women, 1981; co-editor, contbg. author: Women in the Workplace: Implications of Occupational Segregation, 1976; editor, contbg. author: Issues in Federal Statistical Needs Relating to Women, 1979; bd. editors: Jour. Econ. Lit., 1977-79, Jour. Econ. Edn., 1984-92; referee profl. jours. contbr. articles to profl. publs. Mem. Nat. Adv. Food and Drug Coun., 1968-71; mem. adv. com. Nat. Rsch. Inst. on Family, 1973-76; nat. coordinator on issues in fed. statis. needs for women Census Bur. Conf., 1978; mem. Tex. adv. bd. Tex. Coastal Mgmt. Program, 1977-78; mem. adv. com. White House Conf. on Balance Nat. Growth and Econ. Devel., 1977-78; bd. dirs. League for Ednl. Advancement in Dallas, 1972-75; trustee, mem. instrnl. TV com. Pub. Communciation Found. North Tex., 1973-76; mem. N. Tex. Coun. Govts.' Manpower Coun., 1972-74; mem. adv. bd. Women's Ctr. Dallas, 1975-79, 82-85, pres. 1981, bd. dirs. 1990-92; bd. dirs. Dallas Urban League, 1975-79, co-chmn. com. on skills bank, 1977-79; Leadership Am., 1989-90. Ferguson fellow Harvard U., 1947-49; named Outstanding Tchr., So. Meth. U. 1972; recipient Women's Ctr. Dallas award as one of Dallas Outstanding Women, 1980, So. Meth. U. M award 1972, Willis M. Tate award as outstanding faculty mem., 1982, Laurel award AAUW, 1983, Headliner award Dallas Press Club, 1985, 86, Disting. Alumna award Mary Baldwin Coll., 1986. Mem. Am. Econ. Assn. (chmn. sessions 1977, 80, chmn. com. on status of women in econs. profession 1974-78), Southwestern Social Sci. Assn. (exec. com. 1977-80, pres. 1978-79), Assn. Am. Colls. (faculty rep. 1984), Dallas Economists Club, Dallas C. of C. (com. on urban affairs 1975), Phi Beta Kappa (pres. So. Meth. U. chpt. 1975-76), Town and Gown Club (pres. 1986-87), The Dallas Summit (exec. com. 1990-92). Home: 10 Duncannon Ct Dallas TX 75225-1809 Office: So Meth U Dept Econs Dept Econs Dallas TX 75275 *America's productivity can be improved greatly by making better use of its human resources. Equality of opportunity needs to become a reality.*

REAGAN, GARY DON, state legislator, lawyer; b. Amarillo, Tex., Aug. 23, 1941; s. Hester and Lois Irene (Marcum) R.; m. Nedra Ann Nash, Sept. 12, 1964; children: Marc, Kristi, Kari, Brent. AB, Stanford U., 1963, JD, 1965. Bar: N.Mex. 1965, U.S. Dist. Ct. N.Mex., 1965, U.S. Supreme Ct. 1986. Assoc. Smith & Ransom, Albuquerque, 1965-67; ptnr. Smith, Ransom, Deaton & Reagan, Albuquerque, 1967-68, Williams, Johnson, Houston, Reagan & Porter, Hobbs, N.Mex., 1968-77, Williams, Johnson, Reagan, Porter & Love, Hobbs, 1977-82; sole practice, Hobbs, 1982—; city atty. City of Hobbs, 1978-80; City of Eunice, N.M., 1980—; mem. N.Mex. State Senate, 1993—; instr. N.Mex. Jr. Coll. and Coll. of S.W., Hobbs, 1978-84; N.Mex. commr. Nat. Conf. Commrs. Uniform State Laws, 1993—; mem. adv. mem. N.Mex. Constl. Revision Commn., 1993—. Mayor, City of Hobbs, 1972-73, 76-77, city commr., 1970-78; pres., dir. Jr. Achievement of Hobbs, 1974-85; pres., trustee Landsun Homes, Inc., Carlsbad, N.Mex., 1972-84; trustee Lydia Patterson Inst., El Paso, Tex., 1972-84, N.Mex. Conf. United Meth. Ch., 1988—, Coll. of S.W., Hobbs, 1989—; chmn. County Democratic Conv., 1983-85. Mem. ABA, State Bar N.Mex. (coms. 1989—, v.p. 1992-93, pres. 1994—), Lea County Bar Assn. (pres. 1976-77), Hobbs C. of C. (pres. 1989-90), Rotary (pres. Hobbs 1985-86), Hobbs Tennis (pres. 1974-75). Home: 200 E Eagle Dr Hobbs NM 88240-5323 Office: 501 N Linam St Hobbs NM 88240-5715

REAGAN, HARRY EDWIN, III, lawyer; b. Wichita, Kans., Sept. 9, 1940; s. Harry E. II and Mary Elizabeth (O'Steen) R.; m. Marvene R. Rogers, June 17, 1965; children: Kathleen, Leigh, Mairen. BS, U. Pa., 1962, JD, 1965. Bar: Pa. 1965, U.S. Dist. Ct. (ea. dist.) Pa. 1965, U.S.Ct. Appeals (3d cir.) 1965. From assoc. to ptnr. Morgan, Lewis & Bockius, Phila., 1965—; Chmn. Northampton Twp. Planning Commn., Bucks County, Pa., 1974-79; mem. Warwick Twp. Plannig Commn., 1980—, chmn., 1994—. Mem. ABA (labor sect.), Pa. Bar Assn. (labor sect.), Phila. Bar Assn. (labor sect.), Indsl. Rels. Assn. (pres. Phila. chpt. 1990-91). Republican. Presbyterian. Avocations: coaching rugby, skiing, raising horses, bicycling. Home: 2930 Wilkinson Rd Rushland PA 18956 Office: Morgan Lewis & Bockius 2000 One Logan Sq Philadelphia PA 19103

REAGAN, JOSEPH BERNARD, aerospace executive; b. Somerville, Mass., Nov. 26, 1934; s. Joseph B. and Helen Lowry R.; m. Dorothy Hughes; children: Patrick, Michael, Kevin, Kathleen, Brian, John, Maureen. BS in Physics, Boston Coll., 1956, MS in Physics, 1959; PhD in Space Sci. Stanford U., 1975; postgrad. exec. mgmt., Pa. State U., State College, 1981. Staff scientist, rsch. scientist, sr. scientist, scientist Lockheed Rsch. & Devel. Div., Palo Alto, Calif., 1959-75, mgr., 1975-84, dir., 1984-86, dep. gen. mgr., 1986-88, v.p., asst. gen. mgr., 1988-90, v.p. gen. mgr., 1991—; bd. dirs. Southwall Technologies Inc., Palo Alto. Contbr. articles to profl. jours. Bd. dirs. Tech. Mus., San Jose. Capt. U.S. Army, 1956-64. Recipient Career Achievement in Sci. award Boston Coll. Alumni Assn., 1993. Fellow AIAA (outstanding engr. San Francisco chpt. 1988); mem. Am. Geophys. Union. Republican. Roman Catholic. Avocations: computer and woodworking hobbies. Home: 13554 Mandarin Way Saratoga CA 95070-4847 Office: Lockheed Rsch & Devel Orgn 90-01 3251 Hanover St Palo Alto CA 94304-1121

REAGAN, NANCY DAVIS (ANNE FRANCIS ROBBINS), volunteer, wife of former President of United States; b. N.Y.C., July 6, 1923; d. Kenneth and Edith (Luckett) Robbins; step dau. Loyal Davis; m. Ronald Reagan, Mar. 4, 1952; children: Patricia Ann, Ronald Prescott; stepchildren: Maureen, Michael. BA, Smith Coll.; LLD (hon.), Pepperdine U., 1983;

LHD (hon.), Georgetown U., 1987. Contract actress, MGM, 1949-56; films include The Next Voice You Hear, 1950, Donovan's Brain, 1953, Hellcats of the Navy, 1957; Author: Nancy, 1980; formerly author syndicated column on prisoner-of-war and missing-in-action soldiers and their families; author: (with Jane Wilkie) To Love a Child, (with William Novak) My Turn: The Memoirs of Nancy Reagan, 1989. Civic worker, visited wounded Viet Nam vets., sr. citizens, hosps. and schs. for physically and emotionally handicapped children, active in furthering foster grandparents for handicapped children program; hon. nat. chmn. Aid to Adoption of Spl. Kids, 1977; spl. interest in fighting alcohol and drug abuse among youth: hosted first ladies from around the world for 2d Internat. Drug Conf., 1985; hon. chmn. Just Say No Found., Nat. Fedn. of Parents for Drug-Free Youth, Nat. Child Watch Campaign, President's Com. on the Arts and Humanities, Wolf Trap Found. bd. of trustees, Nat. Trust for Historic Preservation, Cystic Fibrosis Found., Nat. Republican Women's Club; hon. pres. Girl Scouts of Am. Named one of Ten Most Admired Am. Women, Good Housekeeping mag., ranking #1 in poll, 1984, 85, 86; Woman of Yr. Los Angeles Times, 1977; permanent mem. Hall of Fame of Ten Best Dressed Women in U.S.; recipient humanitarian awards from Am. Camping Assn., Nat. Council on Alcoholism, United Cerebral Palsy Assn., Internat. Ctr. for Disabled; Boys Town Father Flanagan award; 1986 Kiwanis World Service medal; Variety Clubs Internat. Lifeline award; numerous awards for her role in fight against drug abuse. Address: Century City Fox Plaza Tower 34th Fl Los Angeles CA 90024*

REAGAN, RONALD WILSON, former President of United States; b. Tampico, Ill., Feb. 6, 1911; s. John Edward and Nelle (Wilson) R.; m. Jane Wyman, Jan. 25, 1940 (div. 1948); children: Maureen E., Michael E.; m. Nancy Davis, Mar. 4, 1952; children: Patricia, Ronald. AB, Eureka Coll., 1932. Gov. State of Calif., 1967-74; businessman, rancher, commentator on public policy, 1975-80, Pres. of U.S., 1981-89. Sports announcer, motion picture and TV actor, 1932-66. Author: Where's The Rest of Me?, Speaking My Mind: Selected Speeches, 1989, An American Life: The Autobiography, 1990. Served as capt. USAAF, 1942-45. Mem. Screen Actors Guild (pres. 1947-52, 59), Tau Kappa Epsilon. Republican. Address: Fox Plaza 2121 Ave Of The Stars Fl 34 Los Angeles CA 90067*

REAL, JACK GARRET, helicopter company executive; b. Baraga, Mich., May 31, 1916; s. Edward Ignatius and Elizabeth Irene (Leary) R.; m. Janeth May Paden, Nov. 20, 1941; children: Daniel, Patricia. BSME, Mich. Tech. U., 1937, D in Engring. (hon.), 1968; D in Engring. (hon.), Selma Coll., 1984, Northrop U., 1985. Registered profl. engr., Calif. Jr. engr. to chief devel. engr. Lockheed Aircraft, Burbank, Calif., 1939-65, v.p. rotary wing, 1965-71; v.p. aviation Hughes Tool Co., Encino, Calif., 1971-76; sr. v.p. aviation Summa Corp., Las Vegas, 1977-79; pres. Hughes Helicopter Co., Culver City, Calif., 1979-84; pres., dir. McDonnell Douglas Helicopter Co., Culver City, Calif., 1984—; bd. dirs. Midway Airline, Chgo., Evergreen Internat., McMinnville, Oreg., Davey Industries, Cin. Contbr. articles to profl. jours. Bd. dirs. Great Western council Boy Scouts Am., Los Angeles, 1965—; bd. overseers U. Pa. Sch. Engring. and Applied Sci., Phila., 1975-81. Served to 1st lt. C.E., U.S. Army, 1937-42. Recipient Americanism award Boy Scouts Am., 1983. Fellow AIAA; mem. Am. Helicopter Soc., Am. Assn. Army Aviation, Aero Club So. Calif. (bd. dirs.). Democrat. Roman Catholic. Office: McDonnell Douglas Helicopter Co Centinela & Teale Sts Culver City CA 90230

REAL, MANUEL LAWRENCE, federal judge; b. San Pedro, Calif., Jan. 27, 1924; s. Francisco Jose and Maria (Mansano) R.; m. Stella Emilia Michalik, Oct. 15, 1955; children: Michael, Melanie Marie, Timothy, John Robert. B.S., U. So. Calif., 1944, student fgn. trade, 1946-48; LL.B., Loyola Sch. Law, Los Angeles, 1951. Bar: Calif. 1952. Asst. U.S. Atty.'s Office, Los Angeles, 1952-55; pvt. practice law San Pedro, Calif., 1955-64; U.S. atty. So. Dist. Calif., 1964-66; U.S. Dist. Ct. (cen. dist.) Calif., L.A., 1966—. Served to ensign USNR, 1943-46. Mem. Am., Fed. Los Angeles County bar assns., State Bar Calif., Am. Judicature Soc., Chief Spl. Agts. Assn., Phi Delta Phi, Sigma Chi. Roman Catholic. Club: Anchor (Los Angeles). Office: US Dist Ct 312 N Spring St Los Angeles CA 90012-4701

REALE, WILLIAM A., lawyer; b. Mansfield, Ohio, May 13, 1933. BA, U. Notre Dame, 1955; JD, Ohio State U., 1961. Bar: Ohio 1961. Ptnr. Jones, Day, Reavis & Pogue, Cleve. Office: Jones Day Reavis & Pogue North Point 901 Lakeside Ave Cleveland OH 44114

REALS, WILLIAM JOSEPH, pathologist, academic administrator, educator; b. Hot Springs, S.D., June 22, 1920; s. Reuben Joseph and Gertrude Cecilia (Harrigan) R.;.m. Norma Rosalie Monahan, May 6, 1944; children: William J. Jr., John F., Elaine A., Mary C., Thomas C. BS, Creighton U., 1944, MD, MS in Medicine, 1945. Diplomate Am. Bd. Pathology (trustee 1973-80). Intern Creighton Meml./St. Joseph Hosp., Omaha, 1945-46; resident Creighton Meml./St. Joseph Hosp.; resident Creighton U. Sch. Medicine, Omaha, 1946-49, instr. in pathology, 1949-50; dir. labs. St. Joseph Med. Ctr., Wichita, Kans., 1953-80; prof. pathology, dean U. Kans. Med. Ctr., Wichita, 1980-91, vice chancellor, 1988—; cons. Office Pathology, VA, Washington, 1963-79, Under-sec. Def., Rsch. and Engring., Washington, 1975-79, Office Surgeon Gen., USAF, Washington, 1980—. Author: Aerospace Pathology, 1973; editor: Poems of Alice Henry Boone, 1980; contbr. numerous articles to profl. jours. Trustee Inst. Logopedics, Wichita, 1986, Kans. Newman Coll., Wichita, 1988, Kans. region NCCJ, 1988—. Brig. gen. USAF, 1950-80. Recipient Alumni Achievement citation Creighton U., 1986. Fellow ACP, Coll. Am. Pathologists (pres. 1970-73), Royal Coll. Pathologists Australia, Aerospace Med. Assn.; mem. Can. Assn. Pathologists (hon.), Most Venerable Order Hosp. of St. John of Jerusalem, Cosmos Club (Washington), Army-Navy Club (Washington), Alpha Omega Alpha. Home: 706 N Stratford St Wichita KS 67206-1455 Office: U Kans Sch Medicine 1010 N Kansas St Wichita KS 67214-3199

REAM, JAMES TERRILL, architect, sculptor; b. Summit, N.J., Sept. 8, 1929; s. Merrill Jay and Catherine Ada (Terrill) R.; m. Joyce Kimball Johnson, June 9, 1953 (div. Dec. 1976); children—Claudia, Sarah, Benjamin, m. Nancy Ann Buford, Jan. 1, 1980; stepchildren—Kathleen, Ann Maguire. BArch, Cornell U., 1953; postgrad., Pratt Inst., 1953-54, U. Rome, 1956-57. Registered architect. Assoc. W. C. Muchow Assocs., Denver, 1959-62; prin. Ream, Quinn & Assocs., Denver, 1962-66; v.p. design John Carl Warnecke & Assocs., San Francisco, 1966-69; prin., pres. James Ream & Assocs., Inc., San Francisco, 1969-78, Robbins and Ream Inc., San Francisco, 1978-83; prin. James Ream Architect, San Francisco, 1983—. Prin. archtl. works include Denver Convention Ctr., Currigan Hall, Pasadena Conf. Ctr., Stapleton Plaza Hotel, Vail Transp. Ctr. Bd. dirs. San Francisco Planning and Urban Rsch. Assn., 1977—; chmn. bd. dirs. San Francisco Heritage, 1984-91, pres., 1983-84. Served to 1st lt. USAF, 1954-56. Recipient citation for design in steel Am. Iron and Steel Inst., 1975; Honor award Am. Concrete Inst., 1975; Nat. Design award Prestressed Concrete Inst., 1983; Honor award for design in steel Am. Inst. Steel Constrn., 1970. Fellow AIA (honor award western region 1969, fellowship in design 1979, honor award for design excellence 1983, design cons. San Jose Arena). Democrat. Avocations: opera, theater, hiking, tennis. Office: James Ream/Architect 1 Market Plz 400 San Francisco CA 94105

REAM, JOHN K., banker; b. 1934. Student, U. Mo. With Acceptance Fin. Corp., St. Louis, 1956-84; pres., chief operating officer Citicorp Savs. of Ill., Chgo., 1984—. Served with USMC, 1951-54. Office: Citibank 8750 Doral Blvd Miami FL 33178-2419

REAMES, TIMOTHY PAUL, lawyer, toy company executive; b. Dallas, Jan. 24, 1935; s. Phillip B. and Grace A. (Plauche) R.; m. Ann Semmes, Nov. 7, 1959; children: Timothy, Peter, Jennifer. BBA, So. Methodist U., 1957, JD, 1961. Bar: Tex. bar 1961, Calif. bar 1962, N.Y. bar 1971. Atty. Union Oil Co. Calif., 1961-64, Litton Industries, Inc., 1964-68, City Investing Co., 1968-78; v.p., gen. counsel Home Ins. Co., N.Y.C., 1978-81; sr. v.p., gen. counsel Mattel, Inc., El Segundo, Calif., 1981—. Mem. Am. Bar Assn., N.Y. Bar Assn., Calif. Bar Assn., Tex. Bar Assn. Roman Catholic. Home: 1535 Hillcrest Ave Glendale CA 91202-1237 Office: Mattel Inc 333 Continental Blvd El Segundo CA 90245-5032

REAMS, BERNARD DINSMORE, JR., lawyer, educator; b. Lynchburg, Va., Aug. 17, 1943; s. Bernard Dinsmore and Martha Eloise (Hickman) R.;

m. Rosemarie Bridget Boyle, Oct. 26, 1968; children: Andrew Dennet, Adriane Bevin. BA, Lynchburg Coll., 1965; MS, Drexel U., 1966; JD, U. Kans., 1972; PhD, St. Louis U., 1983. Bar: Kans. 1973, Mo. 1986. Instr. asst. librarian Rutgers U., 1966-69; asst. prof. law, librarian U. Kans. Lawrence, 1969-74; mem. faculty law sch. Washington U., St. Louis, 1974-95, prof. law, 1976-95, prof. tech. mgmt., 1990-95, librarian, 1974-76, acting dean univ. libraries, 1987-88; prof. law, assoc. dean, dir. Law Libr. St. John's U., Jamaica, N.Y., 1995—. Author: Law For The Businessman, 1974, Reader in Law Librarianship, 1976, Federal Price and Wage Control Programs 1917-1979: Legis. Histories and Laws, 1980, Education of the Handicapped: Laws, Legislative Histories, and Administrative Documents, 1982, Housing and Transportation of the Handicapped: Laws and Legislative Histories, 1983, Internal Revenue Acts of the United States: The Revenue Act of 1954 with Legislative Histories and Congressional Documents, 1983 Congress and the Courts: A Legislative History 1978-1984, 1984, University-Industry Research Partnerships: The Major Issues in Research and Development Agreements, 1986, Deficit Control and the Gramm-Rudman-Hollings Act, 1986, The Semiconductor Chip and the Law: A Legislative History of the Semiconductor Chip Protection Act of 1984, 1986, American International Law Cases, 2d series, 1986, Technology Transfer Law: The Export Administration Acts of the U.S., 1987, Insider Trading and the Law: A Legislative History of the Insider Trading Sanctions Act, 1989, Insider Trading and Seourities Fraud, 1989, The Health Care Quality Improvement Act of 1989: A Legislative History of P.L. No. 99-660, 1990; The National Organ Transplant Act of 1984: A Legislative History of P.L. No. 98-507, 1990, United States and International Aviation Law Reports, 1993, A Legislative History of Individuals with Disabilities Education Act, 1994, Federal Legislative Histories: An Annotated Bibliography and Index to Officially Published Sources, 1994; co-author: Segregation and the Fourteenth Amendment in the States, 1975, Historic Preservation Law: An Annotated Bibliography, 1976, Congress and the Courts: A Legislative History 1787-1977, 1978, Federal Consumer Protection Laws, Rules and Regulations, 1979, A Guide and Analytical Index to the Internal Revenue Acts of the U.S., 1909-1950, 1979, The Numerical Lists and Schedule of Volumes of the U.S. Congressional Serial Set: 73d Congress through the 96th Congress, 1984, Human Experimentation: Federal Laws, Legislative Histories, Regulations and Related Documents, 1985, American Legal Literature: A Guide to Selected Legal Resources, 1985, The Constitution of the United States: A Guide and Bibliography, 1987, The Congressional Impeachment Process and the Judiciary, 1987, Tax Reform 1986: A Legislative History of the Tax Refrom Act of 1986, 1988, The Constitutions of the States: A State by State Guide and Bibliography, 1988, Executive and Professional Employment Contracts, 1988, The Legislative History of the Export Trading Company Act of 1982 Including the Foreign Trade Antitrust Improvements Act, 1989, Federal Deficit Control, 1989, The Legislative History of the Export Trading Company Act of 1982 Including the Foreign Trade Antitrust Improvements Act, 1989, United States-Canada Free Trade Act: A Legislative History, 1990, Electronic Contracting Law, 1991, Trade Reform Legislation 1988: A Legislative History of the Omnibus Trade and Competitiveness Act of 1988, 1992, Disability Law in the United States, 1992, Bankruptcy Reform Amendments, 1992, The Law of Hospital and Health Care Administration: Case and Materials, 1993, The Civil Rights Act of 1991: A Legislative History, 1994, The North American Free Trade Agreement, 1994. Recipient Thornton award for excellence Lynchburg Coll., 1986; named to Hon. Order of Ky.Cols., 1992. Mem. ABA, Am. Law Inst., ALA, Am. Soc. Law and Medicine, Nat. Health Lawyers Assn., Am. Law Libr. Edn., Spl. Librs. Assn., Internt. Assn. Law Librs., Am. Assn. Law Librs., Southwestern Assn. Law Librs. (pres. 1977-78), Nat. Assn. Coll. and Univ. Attys., Order of Coif, Phi Beta Kappa, Sigma Xi, Beta Phi Mu, Phi Delta Phi, Phi Delta Epsilon, Kappa Delta Pi, Pi Lambda Theta. Office: St John's U Sch Law 8000 Utopia Pkwy Jamaica NY 11439

REANEY, GILBERT, musician, educator; b. Sheffield, Eng., Jan. 11, 1924; came to U.S., 1960; s. Lawrence and Mabel (Crookes) R. BA with honors, Sheffield U., 1948, BMus, 1950, MA, 1951; postgrad., U. Paris, 1950-52. Researcher, tchr. Reading (Eng.) U., 1953-56, Birmingham (Eng.) U., 1956-59; vis. prof. musicology U. Hamburg, Fed. Republic Germany, 1960; assoc. prof. music dept. UCLA, 1960-62, prof., 1963—; founder, dir. London Medieval Group, 1958—; cons. panel BBC, 1958-60. Editor: Eng., Germany, U.S. Author: Early 15th Century Music, 7 vols., 1955-83, (with A. Gilles and J. Maillard) Philippe de Vitry, Ars Nova, 1964, International Inventory of Musical Sources, 2 vols., 1966-69, Machaut, 1971, (with Gilles) Franconis de Colonia Ars Cantus mensurabilis, 1974; gen. editor: Corpus Scriptorum de Musica, 1966—, Johannes Hothby, Opera Omnia de Musica Mensurabili, 1983, (with H. History) Johannes dictus Balloce, Abreviatio Magistri Franconis, etc., 1987; asst. editor: Musica Disciplina, 1956-76, co-editor: (with F. D'Accone), 1989—. With Brit. Army, 1943-46. Guggenheim fellow, 1964-65, Nat. Humanities Found. sr. fellow, 1967-68. Mem. Am. Musicol. Soc., Internat. Musicol. Soc., Royal Mus. Assn. (Dent medal 1961), Plainsong & Medieval Music Soc. Office: UCLA Musicology Dept Los Angeles CA 90025-1623

REANEY, JAMES CRERAR, dramatist, poet, educator; b. South Easthope, Ont., Can., Sept. 1, 1926; s. James Nesbitt and Elizabeth Henrietta (Crerar) R.; m. Colleen Thibaudeau, Dec. 29, 1951; children: James Stewart, Susan Alice. B.A., U. Toronto, 1948, M.A., 1949, Ph.D., 1957; D.Litt., Carleton U., 1975. Asst. prof. English U. Man., 1949-60; prof. English U. Western Ont., London, 1960—. (Recipient Massey award for the Killdeer 1960, Chalmers award for best Can. play The St. Nicholas Hotel 1975) Author: Poems, 1972, Colours in the Dark, 1969, Masks of Childhood, 1972, Listen to the Wind, 1972, Apple Butter and Other Plays for Children, 1973; plays include Sticks and Stones: The Donnellys Part I, 1975; The St. Nicholas Hotel: The Donnellys Part II, 1976, Handcuffs: The Donnellys Part III, 1977, 14 Barrels from Sea to Sea, 1977, The Dismissal, 1978, Wacousta, 1980, King Whistle, 1982, I the Parade, 1983, The House by the Churchyard, 1985, Alice Through the Looking-Glass, 1994, Serinette (opera libretto), 1986, Crazy to Kill (opera libretto), Performance Poems, 1991; novels for children include: The Boy with an R on his Hand, 1965, Take the Big Picture, 1986; editor, pub.: Alphabet, 1960-70; contbr. articles to profl. jours. Decorated Order of Can. Fellow Royal Soc. Can.; mem. Playwrights Union Can., Can. Poetry League. Mem. New Democratic Party. Home: 276 Huron St, London, ON Canada Office: U We Ont, Dept English, London, ON Canada N6A 3K7 also: John Miller Lit Agt, 14 Earl St, Toronto, ON Canada M4Y 1M3

REAP, SISTER MARY MARGARET, college administrator; b. Carbondale, Pa., Sept. 8, 1941; d. Charles Vincent and Anna Rose (Ahern) R. BA, Marywood Coll., Scranton, Pa., 1965; MA, Assumption Coll., Worcester, Mass., 1972; PhD, Pa. State U., 1979. Elem. tchr. St. Ephrem's, Bklyn., 1966-67; secondary tchr. South Catholic High, Scranton, Pa., 1967-69, Maria Regina High Sch., Uniondale, N.Y., 1969-72; mem. faculty Marywood Coll., Scranton, Pa., 1972-86, dean, 1986-88, pres., 1988—; dir. Mainland China, Wuhan, 1982, Marygrove Coll., Detroit, 1979; bd. dirs. Moses Taylor Hops., Scranton Prep. Sch.; bd. dirs., exec. com. Lourdesmont Sch. Contbr. articles to profl. jours. Recipient bilingual fellowship Pa. State U., 1976-79, Local Chpt. Svc. award UN, 1984, Woman of Yr. awrd Boy Scouts Am., 1993; named Northeast Woman, Scranton Times, 1986, Outstanding Alumna, Pa. State Coll. Edn., 1989. Mem. Pa. Assn. for Colls. and Univs. (exec. com.), Coun. for Ind. Colls. and Univs., Am. Assn. Cath. Colls., Phi Delta Kappa (Educator of Yr. award 1990). Office: Marywood Coll Office of the President Scranton PA 18509-1598

REARDON, PEARL RANCE, real estate executive, writer; b. Savanna La Mar, Westmoreland, Jamaica, Apr. 17, 1941; came to U.S., 1968; d. Hugh Lawrence Rance and Ada Louise (Mullings) Watson; m. Michael I. Phillips, June 9, 1962 (div. Sept. 1977); children: Karim Irving, Felitia Alessandra; m. Michael John Reardon, May 24, 1980. Student, Howard Community Coll., 1974-77, Am. U., 1993—. Cert. real estate broker Grad. Real Estate Inst. Sr. sec. Nat. Coun. Cath. Men, Washington, 1968-69; exec. sec. Nat. Acad. Sci, Washington. 1969-71; sr. sec. Pres.'s Commnn. on Population, Washington, 1971-72; exec. sec. Westinghouse Health System, Columbia, Md., 1972-76; adminstrv. group mgr. Price, Williams & Assocs., Silver Spring, Md., 1976-78; assoc. broker Merrill Lynch Realty, Silver Spring, 1977-81; pres. and CEO Pearl Properties, Silver Spring, 1982-93; v.p. Croton Mgmt. Svcs., Washington, D.C., 1994—. Organizer Peoples Nat. Party, Linstead, Jamaica, 1966; founding mem. Jamaica Nat. Assn., Washington, 1969, sec. 1969-73. Mem. Nat. Assn. Realtors, D.C. Bd. Realtors, Authors Guild,

Dramatists Guild. Avocations: writing, music, piano, reading, dancing, crafts. Office: Croton Mgmt Svcs 110 Gallatin St NW B 1 Washington DC 20011

REARICK, J. ARDEN, lawyer; b. Gary, Ind., Feb. 15, 1921; s. Charles and Helen (Parrott) R.; m. Jeanette Clara Schultz, Oct. 24, 1920; children: Charlotte Ann, Pamela Arden. A.B., Ind. U., 1942, LL.B., 1947. Bar: Ind. 1947, Ill. 1953. Asst. gen. atty. Monon R.R., Lafayette, Ind., 1947-48, gen. atty., 1948-50, gen. solicitor, 1950-51, gen. solicitor and sec., 1951-53; assoc. Winston & Strawn, Chgo., 1953-59; ptnr. Winston & Strawn, Chgo., Ill., 1959—; dir. Nat. Realty and Investment, Northbrook. Contbr. articles to profl. jours. Capt. U.S. Army, 1942-46. Decorated Purple Heart with 2 oak leaf clusters; decorated Bronze Star. Fellow Am. Coll. Real Estate Lawyers; mem. ABA, Ind. State Bar Assn., Chgo. Bar Assn. Republican. Presbyterian. Clubs: Michigan Shores (Wilmette); Law (Chgo.), Mid-Day (Chgo.), Plaza (Chgo.). Office: Winston & Strawn 35 W Wacker Dr Chicago IL 60601-1614

REASON, JOSEPH PAUL, naval officer; b. Washington, Mar. 22, 1941; s. Joseph Henry and Bernice (Chism) R.; m. Dianne Lillian Fowler, June 12, 1965; children: Rebecca, Joseph. BS, U.S. Naval Acad., 1965; MS, USN Postgrad. Sch., 1970. Cert. nuclear propulsion engr. Commd. ens. USN, 1965, advanced through grades to vice adm., 1986; naval aide to pres. The White Ho., Washington, 1976-79; exec. officer USS Miss., 1979-81; comdg. officer USS Coontz, 1981-83, USS Bainbridge, 1983-86; comdr. Naval Base, Seattle, 1986-88, Cruiser-Destroyer Group 1, 1988-90, Naval Surface Force Atlantic, 1991-94; dep. chief naval ops. plans, policy and ops. Dept. Navy, Washington, 1994—. Decorated Legion of Merit, other mil. awards. Avocations: fishing, tennis. Office: Dept Navy Plans Policy and Ops Washington DC 20350-2000

REASONER, HARRY MAX, lawyer; b. San Marcos, Tex., July 15, 1939; s. Harry Edward and Joyce Majorie (Barrett) R.; m. Elizabeth Macey Hodges, Apr. 15,1963; children: Barrett Hodges, Elizabeth Macey. B.A. summa cum laude, Rice U., 1960; J.D. with highest honors, U. Tex., 1962; postgrad., U. London, 1962-63. Bar: Tex., D.C., N.Y. Law clk. U.S. Ct. Appeals (2d cir.), 1963-64; assoc. Vinson & Elkins, Houston, 1964-69, ptnr., 1970—, mng.ptnr., 1992—; vis. prof. U. Tex. Sch. Law, 1971, Rice U., 1976, U. Houston Sch. Law, 1977; chair adv. group U.S. Dist Ct. (so. dist.) Tex.; mem. adv. com. Supreme Ct. Tex. Author: (with Charles Alan Wright) Procedure: The Handmaid of Justice, 1965; author: (with others) American Economic Policy in the 1980's, 1994. Life trustee U. Tex. Law Sch. Found.; trustee Southwestern Legal Found., 1990—, Baylor Coll. Medicine, 1992—; chair Tex. Higher Edn. Coordinating Bd., 1991; bd. govs. Rice U., 1994—; exec. bd. dirs. Greater Houston Partnership, 1992—; mem. exec. coun. Ex-Student's Assn. U. Tex., 1992—; gov. Houston Forum, 1992—; bd. dirs. Central Houston, Inc., 1993—. Rotary Found. fellow, 1962-63. Fellow Am. Coll. Trial Lawyers, Internat. Acad. Trial Lawyers, Internat. Soc. Barristers, ABA Found., Tex. Bar Found.; mem. ABA (chmn. antitrust sect. 1989-90), Houston Bar Assn., Assn. Bar City N.Y., Am. Law Inst., Chancellors, Houston Com. Fgn. Rels., Houston Philos. Soc., Philos Soc. Tex., Am. Bd. Trial Advocates, Century Assn. N.Y.C., Houston Country Club, Rotary Club, Ramada Tex. Club, Eldorado Country Club (Calif.), Cosmos Club of Washington, Galveston Artillery Club, Phi Beta Kappa, Phi Delta Alpha, Phi Delta Phi. Democrat. Baptist. Office: Vinson & Elkins 2800 First City Tower 1001 Fannin St Houston TX 77002-6760

REASONER, STEPHEN M., federal judge; b. 1944. BA in Econs., U. Ark., 1966, JD, 1969. Mem. firm Barret, Wheatley, Smith & Deacon, Jonesboro, Ark., 1969-88; from judge to chief judge U.S. Dist. Ct. (ea. dist.) Ark., Little Rock, 1988—; bd. dirs. U. Ark. Law Rev.; mem. judicial coun. 8th cir., 1990-93. Trustee Craighead-Jonesboro Pub. Libr., 1972—, chmn. 1984-88; bd. dirs. Jonesboro C. of C., 1981-84, Ark. IOLTA, 1987—, Abilities Unltd., 1974-81; mem. St. Marks Episcopal Ch. Vestry, 1976-79, sr. warden, 1979. With USAR, 1969-73. Mem. ABA, Am. Counsel Assn., Am. Judicature Soc., Ark. Bar Assn. (exec. com., ho. of dels. 1984-87), Craighead County Bar Assn. (pres. 1983-84). Avocation: flying. Office: US PO & Courthouse PO Box 1540 Little Rock AR 72203-1540

REASONER, WILLIS IRL III, lawyer; b. Hamilton, Ohio, Dec. 24, 1951; s. W. Irl Jr. and Nancy Jane (Mitchell) R.; m. Lana Jean Mayes, Apr. 19, 1975 (div. Sept. 1985); 1 child, Erick; m. Joan Marie Mogil, Dec. 30, 1986; children: Scott, Sally. BA in History, Ind. U., 1974; JD cum laude, U.S.C. 1978. Bar: Ohio 1978, U.S. Dist. Ct. (so. dist.) Ohio 1978, U.S. Dist. Ct. (no. dist.) Ohio 1979, U.S. Ct. Appeals (6th cir.) 1988, U.S. Ct. Appeals (1st cir.) 1991. Assoc. Porter, Wright, Morris & Arthur, Columbus, Ohio, 1978-83; ptnr. Baker & Hostetler, Columbus, 1983—. Mem. ABA, Ohio Bar Assn., Columbus Bar Assn. Home: 1101 Riva Ridge Blvd Columbus OH 43230-3808 Office: Baker & Hostetler 65 E State St Ste 2100 Columbus OH 43215-4260

REATH, GEORGE, JR., lawyer; b. Phila., Mar. 14, 1939; s. George and Isabel Duer (West) R.; children from a previous marriage: Eric, Amanda; m. Ann B. Rowland, 1990. BA, Williams Coll., 1961; LLB, Harvard U., 1964. Bar: Pa. 1965, U.S. Dist. Ct. (ea. dist.) Pa. 1965. Assoc. Dechert Price & Rhoads, Phila., 1964-70, Brussels, 1971-74; atty. Pennwalt Corp., Phila., 1974-78, mgr. legal dept., asst. sec., 1978-87, sr. v.p.-law, sec., 1987-89; sr. v.p., gen. counsel, sec. Elf Atochem N.Am., Inc. (formerly Pennwalt Corp.), Phila., 1990-92; sr. v.p. Legal Triage Svcs., Inc., Phila., 1993—; bd. dirs. Internat. Bus. Forum, Inc. 1978-91. Trustee Children's Hosp., Phila., 1974—, sec., 1980-81, vice chmn., 1984—; bd. mgrs. Phila. City Inst. Libr., 1974—, treas., 1981-88, pres., 1989—; bd. dirs. Phila. Festival Theatre for New Plays, 1983-94, Ctrl. Phila. Devel. Corp., 1987-93, Bach Festival Phila., 1990—, v.p., 1992-93; bd. dirs. Crime Commn. Del. Valley, 1st vice chmn., 1992-94, chmn., 1994—. Mem. ABA, Pa. Bar Assn., Am. Soc. Corp. Secs., Phila. Bar Assn., Penllyn Club, Winter Harbor Yacht Club, Phi Beta Kappa.

REAVES, BENJAMIN F., academic administrator. BA, Oakwood Coll., 1955; MDiv, Andrews U., 1966, MA, 1972; DMin, Chgo. Theol. Sem., 1974; diploma inst. for ednl. mgmt., Harvard U., 1987. Ordained to ministry. Pastor, evangelist various chs., Ill., Ind. and Ohio, 1956-68; tchr. adult edn. programs Chgo. Bd. Edn., 1968-72; pastor for Coll. Youth Pioneer Meml. Ch. Andrews U., 1972-73, assoc. prof. preaching and urban ministry, 1973-77; chmn. dept. religion and theology, prof. preaching Oakwood Coll., 1977-85, pres., 1985—; case worker dept. pub. aid Cook County, 1968-72; vis. prof. Chgo. cluster Theol. Sems., 1973-77; conductor workshops homiletics and liturgics U.S. Army Bd. Chaplains, 1977-85; speaker, lectr. in field. Contbr. articles to profl. jours. Counselor Vietnam vets. drug abuse case VA Westside Hosp., Chgo., 1968-72; coordinator convocation on black music and grad. programs Urban Ministry, 1973-77; adv. bd. Andrews U., Loma Linda U.; exec. com. south cen. conf., so. union conf. 7th Day Adventist; mem. United Negro Coll. Fund, Council for the Advancement Pvt. Colls. Ala.; developer various community programs. Mem. Acad. Homiletics, Nat. Assn. for Equal Opportunity in Higher Edn. Lodge: Rotary. Office: Oakwood Coll Office of Pres Huntsville AL 35896

REAVES, CHARLES WILLIAM, insurance company executive, writer, educator, investment advisor; b. Huron, S.D., Apr. 14, 1923; s. Charles Everet and Sophie France (Blume) R.; m. Yvonne Joan Ericson, July 6, 1946; children: Craig C., Shawn Marie. Student, Augustana Coll., 1946-47. CLU, ChFC; registered financial planner; registered rep. NASD; lic. ins. agt.; comml. pilot. Automobile dealer Wagner, S.D., 1947-56; gen. agt. John Hancock Ins. Co., Sioux Falls, S.D., 1957-64; field v.p. John Hancock Mut. Life Ins., Sioux Falls, 1964-70; gen. agt. John Hancock Mut. Life Ins., Kansas City, Mo., 1970-79; pres. Creative Fin. Cons., Inc., Overland Park, Kans., 1979—; mem. adv. bd. Kans. Ins. Dept., Topeka, 1989—; speaker in field. Author, publisher 17 seminars for use by ins. agts. to renew their licenses. Arbitrator, Better Bus. Bur., Kansas City, Mo., 1990—; fin. chmn. Fellowship of Christian Athletes, Sioux Falls, 1965-70, Kansas City, Mo., 1971-72; mem., organizer, moderator Crestwood Commun. Ch., 1972-75. Capt. USAFR, 1942-63. Mem. Sioux Falls Life Underwriters (pres. 1968-69), Kansas City Gen. Agts. Assn. (pres. 1979-80), Million Dollar Round Table (life), Masons, Shriners. Republican. Presbyterian. Home: 4803 W 96th Terr Overland Park KS 66207 Office: Creative Fin Cons Inc 4400 Madison Ave Kansas City MO 64111

REAVES, JOHN DANIEL, lawyer, playwright, actor; b. Camp Hill, Ala., Mar. 14, 1939; s. William Newell and Katherine (Rawlinson) R.; m. Wendy Wick; children: Paul Newell, Caroline Rawlinson. BS, Auburn U., 1961; LLB, U. Va., 1964. Bar: Ala. 1965, D.C. 1972, U.S. Supreme Ct. 1977. Law clk. to Hon. Richard T. Rives U.S. Ct. Appeals (5th cir.), 1964-65; asst. prof. law U. Ga., 1965-71; fellow Fed. Jud. Ctr., Washington, 1971-72; atty. Bur. Competition, FTC, Washington, 1972-73; legal advisor to Hon. Elizabeth Dole, commr. FTC, Washington, 1973-77; ptnr. Baker & Hostetler, Washington; vis. prof. law George Washington U., Washington, 1975. mem. editorial bd. Va. Law Rev.; founder Ga. Law Rev., 1966; writer, performer H.L. Mencken: Reveries of an Iconoclast, 1981; appeared in The Kingfish, 1979. Bd. dirs. Woolly Mammoth Theatre Co., 1992—. Mem. D.C. Bar, Ala. State Bar Assn., Cosmos Club (Washington). Office: Baker & Hostetler Washington Sq 1050 Connecticut Ave NW Ste 11 Washington DC 20036-5303

REAVES, RAY DONALD, civil engineer; b. Jacksonville, Ala., Aug. 6, 1935; s. William Ozzie and Josephine (Jackson) R.; m. Annette Baird, Dec. 18, 1959; children: Tanya Ann Walker, Ronald Ray. BS in Civil Engring., Auburn (Ala.) U., 1960; MBA, U. Utah, 1976; postgrad., U. Mo., Kansas City. Registered profl. engr., Okla.; diplomate Am. Acad. Environ. Engrs. Commd. 2d lt. USAF, 1961, advanced through grades to col., 1981; comdt. Airlift Ops. Sch., Scott AFB, Ill., 1980-82; dep. base comdr. Little Rock AFB, 1982-83; base comdr. Kunsan Air Base, Korea, 1983-84, Tinker AFB, Oklahoma City, 1984-85; dir. environ. mgr. Oklahoma City Air Logistics Ctr., Tinker AFB, 1985-89; ret. USAF, 1989; mgr. environ. engring. Oklahoma County, Oklahoma City, 1989-95, county engr., 1995—; bus. Tech. Delegation Citizen to Citizen ambassador to Russia and Ukraine, 1992. Mem. ASCE, NSPE, Okla. Soc. Profl. Engrs. (citizen ambassador to Russia and Ukraine 1992), Midwest City C. of C., Rotary, Masons, Shriners. Avocations: golf, boating, tinkering.

REAVES, WENDY WICK, museum curator; b. Youngstown, Ohio, July 25, 1950; d. Paul Myron and Christine (Gawne) Wick; m. John Daniel Reaves, Jan. 15, 1983; children: Paul Newell, Caroline Rawlinson. BA, U. Pa., 1972; MA, U. Del., 1977. Curator of prints Nat. Portrait Gallery, Washington, 1974-85, curatorof prints and drawings, 1985—; mem. coun. Am. Mus. in Britain, Bath, Eng., 1979—. Author: George Washington: An American Icon, 1982, Oliphant's Presidents: Twenty-five Years of Caricature, 1990; editor: American Portrait Prints, 1985. Mem. Print Coun. Am., Coll. Art Assn. Office: Nat Portrait Gallery F St at 8th NW Washington DC 20560

REAVEY, WILLIAM ANTHONY, III, lawyer; b. Springfield, Mass., Dec. 27, 1944; s. William A. Jr. and Deborah M. (Clancy) R.; Jacqueline R. Beauvais, Sept. 2, 1967; children: Patrick, Kevin, Brian, Michael. BS, USAF Acad., 1966; MA, Yale U., 1968, JD, 1976. Bar: Calif. 1976. Assoc. Latham & Watkins, Newport Beach, Calif., 1976-81; ptnr. Aylward, Kintz & Stiska, San Diego, 1981-87, Lillick & McHose, San Diego, 1987-90, Pillsbury, Madison & Sutro, San Diego, 1991—. Bd. dirs. Am. Liver Found., San Diego, 1991, Kind Found., San Diego, 1992, San Diego Comml. Indsl. Coun. Bldg. Industry Assn., 1992. Capt. USAF, 1966-73, Vietnam. Decorated Bronze Star. Mem. ABA. Roman Catholic. Avocations: fishing, back-packing, biking. Home: 10515 Linwood Rd San Diego CA 92131-2203 Office: Pillsbury Madison & Sutro 101 W Broadway Ste 1800 San Diego CA 92101-8298

REAVLEY, THOMAS MORROW, federal judge; b. Quitman, Tex., June 21, 1921; s. Thomas Mark and Mattie (Morrow) R.; m. Florence Montgomery Wilson, July 24, 1943; children—Thomas Wilson, Marian, Paul Stuart, Margaret. B.A., U. Tex., 1942; J.D., Harvard, 1948; LL.D., Austin Coll., 1974, Southwestern U., 1977, Tex. Wesleyan, 1982; LL.M., U. Va., 1983; LLD, Pepperdine U., 1993. Bar: Tex. 1948. Asst. dist. atty. Dallas, 1948-49; mem. firm Bell & Reavley, Nacogdoches, Tex., 1949-51; county atty. Nacogdoches, 1951; with Collins, Garrison, Renfro & Zeleskey, 1951-52; mem. firm Fisher, Tonahill & Reavley, Jasper, Tex., 1952-55; sec. state Tex., 1955-57; mem. firm Powell, Rauhut, McGinnis & Reavley, Austin, Tex., 1957-64; dist. judge Austin, 1964-68; justice Supreme Ct., Tex., 1968-77; counsel Scott & Douglass, 1977-79; judge U.S. Ct. Appeals (5th cir.), Austin, 1979—; now sr. judge U.S. Ct. Appeals (5th cir.), Austin, TX; lectr. Baylor U. Law Sch., 1976-94; adj. prof. U. Tex. Law Sch., 1958-59, 78-79, 88-95. Chancellor S.W. Tex. conf. United Meth. Ch., 1972-93, chancellor emeritus, 1993—. Lt. USNR, 1943-45. Club: Mason (33 deg.). Home: 24 Woodstone Sq Austin TX 78703-1159 Office: US Ct Appeals 903 San Jacinto Blvd # 434 Austin TX 78701-2450

REBACK, JOYCE ELLEN, lawyer; b. Phila., July 11, 1948; d. William and Sue (Goldstein) R.; m. Itzhak Brook, Aug. 2, 1981; children: Jonathan Zev, Sara Jennie. BA magna cum laude, Brown U., 1970; JD with honors, George Washington U., 1976. Bar: D.C. 1976, U.S. Dist. Ct. D.C. 1976, U.S. Ct. Appeals (D.C. cir.) 1976, U.S. Ct. Appeals (3d cir.) 1983, U.S. Ct. Appeals (Fed. cir.) 1985. Assoc. Fulbright & Jaworski, Washington, 1976-84, ptnr., 1984-87; legal cons. IMF, Washington, 1987—. Contbr. articles to profl. jours. Mem. ABA, D.C. Bar Assn., Phi Beta Kappa. Jewish. Office: Internat Monetary Fund 700 19th St NW Washington DC 20431-0001

REBAGAY, TEOFILA VELASCO, chemist, chemical engineer; b. Pangasinan, Philippines, Feb. 5, 1928; came to U.S., 1965; d. Dionisio Opiniano and Antonia (Flora) Velasco; m. Guillermo Rabadam Rebagay, Apr. 4, 1956; children: Guillermo V., Teofilo V. BS in Chemistry, U. Philippines, Quezon City, 1951; BS in Chem. Engring., Nat. U., Manila, 1954; PhD in Chemistry, U. Ky., 1969. Postdoctoral fellow U. Ky., Lexington, 1969-71, U. Va., Charlottesville, 1971-72; rsch. assoc. U. Ky., Lexington, 1973-76; sr. chemist Ky. Ctr. Energy Rsch., Lexington, 1976-78; radiochemist Allied-Gen. Nuclear Svcs., Barnwell, S.C., 1978-83; sr. chemist Rockwell Hanford Ops., Richland, Wash., 1983-87; prin. scientist Westinghouse Hanford Co., Richland, 1987—. Contbr. articles to profl. publs. IAEA fellow UN, Tokyo, 1963; grantee Rockefeller Found., 1965. Mem. ASTM, Soc. Applied Spectroscopy. Office: Westinghouse Hanford Co Richland WA 99352

REBANE, JOHN T., lawyer; b. Bamberg, Germany, Oct. 29, 1946; s. Henn and Anna (Inna) R.; m. Linda Kay Morgan, Sept. 22, 1972; children: Alexis Morgan, Morgan James. BA, U. Minn., 1970, JD, 1973. Bar: Minn. 1973. Atty. Land O'Lakes, Inc., Arden Hills, Minn., 1973-80, assoc. gen counsel, 1983, v.p., gen. counsel, 1984—; sec. Cenex Land O'Lakes Agronomy Co.; sec., dir. Land O' Lakes Internat. Devel. Corp. Mem. ABA, Minn. Bar Assn., Hennepin County Bar Assn., Nat. Coun. Farm Coop. (exec. com vice chmn.). Office: Land O'Lakes Inc PO Box 116 Minneapolis MN 55440

REBAR, ROBERT WILLIAM, obstetrician, gynecologist, educator; b. Stillwater, Okla., Apr. 22, 1947; s. John and Blanche (Fried) R.; m. Margo Storm Freeborn, July 7, 1969; children: Bryan Matthew, Jeannette Heather, Darren Wade. BS, U. Mich., 1969, MD, 1972. Diplomate Am. Bd. Ob-Gyn, cert. spl. competence in reproductive endocrinology. Intern Parkland Meml. Hosp., Dallas, 1972-73, resident in ob-gyn, 1973=74; sr. resident in ob-gyn U. Calif. San Diego Med. Ctr., 1976-78; asst. prof. dept. reproductive medicine U. Calif., San Diego, 1978-82, assoc. prof. div. reproductive endocrinology, dept. reproductive medicine, 1982-84; prof., head sect. reproductive endocrinology and infertility, dept. ob-gyn Northwestern U., Chgo., 1984-88; George B. Riley prof. dept. ob-gyn U. Cin., 1988—, chmn. dept., 1988—; clin. assoc. physician, NIH, 1974-76, mem. reproductive endocrinology study sect., 1986-89; mem. NIH population rsch. com., 1992—. Co-editor: Principles and Practice of Endocrinology and Metabolism, 1990, Gynecology and Obstetrics: A Longitudinal Approach, 1992; co-editor: Infertility, Evaluation and Treatment, 1995; mem. editorial bd. Jour. Clin. Endocrinology and Metabolism, 1985-88, Obstetrics and Gynecology, 1993—. Asst. surgeon USPHS, 1974-76. Fellow Am. Coll. Obstetrics and Gynecology; mem. Endocrine Soc., Am. Soc. Reprodn. Medicine (program com. 1989-91), Am. Gynecol. Obstetric Soc., Soc. Gynecol. Investigation, Pacific Coast Fertility Soc. (Wyeth award 1972, 82), Phi Beta Kappa, Alpha Omega Alpha. Home: 195 Sunny Acres Dr Cincinnati OH 45255-3902 Office: U Cin Coll of Medicine Dept Ob-Gyn PO Box 670526 Cincinnati OH 45267-0526

REBAY, LUCIANO, Italian literature educator, literary critic; b. Milan, Italy, Apr. 23, 1928; came to U.S., 1955; s. Angelo and Pierina (Doniselli) R.; m. Martha Virginia Krauss, Aug. 2, 1952; children: Alexandra, Ilari-

a. Maturita classica Liceo Manzoni, Milan, 1946; Licence es lettres, U. Aix-en-Provence, France, 1951; Ph.D., Columbia U., 1960. Instr. Italian Columbia U., N.Y.C., 1957-60, asst. prof., 1960-63, assoc. prof., 1963-65, prof., 1965-73, Giuseppe Ungaretti prof. Italian lit., 1973—; chmn. Italian Dept. Columbia U., 1970-73; dir. Ctr. Italian Studies, 1985-88; cons. to scholarly jours.; mem. Nat. Bd. Translators, Columbia U. Transl. Ctr. Author: Le origini della poesia di Giuseppe Ungaretti, 1962, Invitation to Italian Poetry, 1969, Alberto Moravia, 1970, Giuseppe Ungaretti, Gli scritti egiziani, 1909-1912, 1980, Montale, Clizia e l'America, 1982; editor: Giuseppe Ungaretti, Saggi e interventi, 1974, Jean Paulhan-Giuseppe Ungaretti, Correspondance, 1921-68, 1989, Montale per amico, 1994. Guggenheim fellow, 1966-67; Am. Council Learned Socs. fellow, 1970-71; NEH fellow, 1980-81; Am. Philos. Soc. research grantee, 1970, 75. Mem. MLA, Am. Assn. Tchrs. of Italian, Associazione Internazionale per gli Studi di Lingua e Letteratura Italiana. Office: Columbia U Dept Italian New York NY 10027

REBEC, GEORGE VINCENT, neuroscience researcher, educator, administrator; b. Harrisburg, Pa. Apr. 6, 1949; s. George Martin and Nadine (Bosko) R. AB, Villanova U., 1971; MA, U. Colo., 1974, PhD, 1975. Postdoctoral fellow U. Calif., San Diego, 1975-77; asst. prof. Ind. U., Bloomington, 1977-81, assoc. prof., 1981-85, prof. psychology, 1985—, dir. program in neural sci., 1985—; mem. rsch. rev. com. NIMH. Author: (with P.M. Groves) Introduction to Biological Psychology, 1988, 92; contbr. articles to profl. jours. Recipient Eli Lilly Teaching award, 1978, Pres.' award Ind. U., 1990; grantee NIDA, 1979—, NSF, 1985—. Fellow AAAS; mem. Soc. for Neurosci. (chmn. Ind. U. chpt.), Internat. Brain Rsch. Orgn., Am. Psychol. Soc., Assn. Neurosci. Depts. and Programs (treas.). Roman Catholic. Avocation: sports. Office: Ind U Program in Neural Sci Dept Psychology Bloomington IN 47405

REBEIZ, CONSTANTIN ANIS, plant physiology educator; b. Beirut, July 11, 1936; came to U.S., 1969, naturalized, 1975; s. Anis C. and Valentine A. (Choueyri) R.; m. Carole Louise Connelly, Aug. 18, 1962; children: Paul A., Natalie, Mark J. B.S., Am. U., Beirut, 1959; M.S., U. Calif. - Davis, 1960, Ph.D., 1965. Dir. dept. biol. scis. Agrl. Research Inst., Beirut, 1965-69; research assoc. biology U. Calif - Davis, 1969-71; assoc. prof. plant physiology U. Ill., Urbana-Champaign, 1972-76, prof., 1976—. Contbr. articles to sci. publs. plant physiology and biochemistry. Recipient Beckman research awards, 1982, 85, Funk award, 1985, John P. Trebellas Research Endowment, 1986, Sr. Rsch. award Univ. Ill., 1994; named One of 100 Outstanding Innovators, Sci. Digest, 1984-85. Mem. Am. Soc. Plant Physiologists, Comite Internat. de Photobiologie, Am. Soc. Photobiology, AAAS, Lebanese Assn. Advancement Scis. (exec. com. 1967-69), Sigma Xi. Achievements include research on pathway of chlorophyll biosynthesis, chloroplast devel., bioengring. of photosynthetic reactors; pioneered biosynthesis of chlorophyll in vitro; duplication of greening process of plants in test tube, demonstration of operation of multibranched chlorophyll biosynthetic pathway in nature; formulation and design of laser herbicides, insecticides and cancer chemotherapeutic agents. Home: 301 W Pennsylvania Ave Urbana IL 61801-4918 Office: U Ill 240A Pabl Urbana IL 61801 *Meaningful scientific discoveries are those that help humans achieve a better understanding of themselves, of their environment or of the universe at large, as well as those that contribute to the betterment of the human spiritual, psychological and physical condition.*

REBEK, JULIUS, JR., chemistry educator, consultant; b. Beregszasz, Hungary, Apr. 11, 1944; came to U.S. 1949; s. Julius and Eva (Racz) R.; divorced; children: Eva Louise, Anna Elizabeth. BA, U. Kans., 1966; PhD MIT, 1970. Asst. prof. chemistry UCLA, 1970-76; assoc. prof. U. Pitts., 1976-80, prof., 1980-89; prof. MIT, Cambridge, 1989—; cons. Cubist, Inc., Cambridge, Mass., Darwin, Seattle. Contbr. over 150 articles to rsch. publs. NSF fellow 1967-70, A. P. Sloane fellow, 1977, A. V. Humboldt fellow, 1981, Guggenheim fellow, 1986. Fellow Am. Acad. Arts and Sci.; mem. Am. Chem. Soc. (A.C. Cope scholar 1991), Nat. Acad. Sci. Achievements include discoveries in reaction mechanisms, molecular recognition and a self-replicating system. Home: 100 Memorial Dr Apt 53A Cambridge MA 02142-1327 Office: MIT Chemistry Dept 77 Massachusetts Ave Cambridge MA 02139-4307

REBENACK, JOHN HENRY, retired librarian; b. Wilkinsburg, Pa., Feb. 10, 1918; s. Charles Lewis and Carrie (Fielding) R.; m. Dorothy Merle Treat, Oct. 31, 1942 (dec. Apr. 1971); children: Charles Edwin, Christine (Mrs. Clair N. Hayes III); m. Frances Strabley Krieger, May 6, 1972. A.B., U. Pitts., 1942; B.S. in L.S, Carnegie Library Sch., 1947. Reference asst. Carnegie Library, Pitts., 1947-50; librarian Salem (Ohio) Pub. Library, 1950-53, Elyria (Ohio) Library, 1953-57; asst. librarian Akron (Ohio) Public Library, 1957-65, assoc. librarian, 1965-67, librarian-dir., 1967-80; dir. U.S. Book Exchange, Inc., 1972. Mem. United Community Council, Citizens' Com. Pub. Welfare, 1965-66, chmn. group work and recreation div., 1963-66, v.p., 1967-68, pres. conf. of execs., 1975-76; mem. steering com., planning div. United Way; mem. Akron Mayor's Task Force on Human Relations, 1962; mem. library com. President's Com. on Employment of Handicapped, 1967-80, chmn., 1973-80, mem. sch. library manpower adv. com., 1967-73; mem. coll. adv. com. U. Akron, 1972-85; mem. adv. council on fed. programs State Library of Ohio, 1975-79; bd. visitors Grad. Sch. Library and Info. Sci., U. Pitts., 1968-74; mem. exec. bd. Gt. Trail council Boy Scouts Am., 1977-80; bd. dirs. Summit County unit Am. Cancer Soc., 1976—, pres., 1979-81; bd. dirs. Ohio div., 1981-91, chmn. pub. info. com., 1989-90, exec. com. 1988-91. With AUS, 1942-45. Recipient Newton D. Baker citation, 1968. Mem. ALA (chmn. personnel adminstrv. sect. 1966-67, chmn. bldgs. and equipment sect. 1971-73, chmn. legislation assembly 1976-77), Ohio Library Assn. (exec. bd. 1957-60, chmn. adult edn. round table 1963, chmn. legis. com. 1965-66, 70-72, 76-80, pres. 1966-67, Librarian of Year 1979, named to Hall of Fame 1989), Ohio Library Found. (privileged mem. 1980, privileged dir. 1988—), Carnegie Library Sch. Assn. (pres. 1961-63), U. Pitts. Grad. Sch. Library and Info. Sci. Alumni Assn. (exec. com. 1978-79, Disting. Alumnus award 1980), Am. Assn. UN (v.p. Akron chpt. 1960), Beta Phi Mu. Congregationalist. Clubs: Torch (pres. 1968-69), Kiwanis (pres. Akron 1978-79). Home: 2095 Brookshire Rd Akron OH 44313-5323

REBENFELD, LUDWIG, chemist; b. Prague, Czechoslovakia, July 10, 1928; came to U.S., 1939, naturalized, 1946; s. Carl and Martha (Scheib) R.; m. Ellen Vogel, July 27, 1956. BS, Lowell Tech. Inst., 1951; MA, Princeton, 1954, PhD, 1955; D Textile Sci. (hon.), Phila. Coll. Textiles and Sci., 1980, Liberec Tech U., Czech Republic, 1993. Rsch. fellow, sr. scientist Textile Rsch. Inst., Princeton, N.J., 1951-59, assoc. rsch. dir., also edn. program dir., 1960-66, v.p. edn. and rsch., 1966-70, pres., 1971-92, pres. emeritus and rsch. assoc., 1993—; vis. lectr., assos. prof., prof. chem. engring. Princeton, 1964—; mem. governing council, sec.-treas. Fiber Soc., 1962-84; mem. Nat. Council Textile Edn.; trustee Phila. College Textiles and Sci. (life). Recipient Distinguished Achievement award Fiber Soc., Harold DeWitt Smith Meml. medal ASTM. Fellow Am. Inst. Chemists, Brit. Textile Inst. (Inst. medal), Inst. Textile Sci. Can.; mem. Am. Chem. Soc., Am. Assn. Textile Chemists and Colorists (Olney medal 1987), AAAS, Sigma Xi, Phi Psi. Home: 49 Pardoe Rd Princeton NJ 08540-2617 Office: Textile Rsch Inst PO Box 625 601 Prospect Ave Princeton NJ 08540-4034

REBER, RAYMOND ANDREW, chemical engineer; b. Bklyn., Apr. 16, 1942; s. Herbert and Dorothy Agnes (Schmidt) R.; m. Anita Jean Roe, June 22, 1963; children: Laura Jean Bucci, Paul Raymond, Jill Anita. BChemE, NYU, 1963, MChemE, 1966. Design engr. M.W. Kellogg, N.Y.C., 1964-66, process devel. engr., 1967-69; devel. engr., supr. Union Carbide, Tarrytown, N.Y., 1970-74, lic. bus. mgr., 1975-81; new bus. devel. mgr. Union Carbide, Danbury, Conn., 1982-84; tech. mgr. Union Carbide, Tarrytown, 1985-87; dir. of tech. UOP, Tarrytown, 1988-93; exec. v.p., COO Balchem Corp., Slate Hill, N.Y., 1994—. Patentee in field. Commr. Montrose (N.Y.) Improvement Dist. 1970—; soccer referee, 1977-93. Recipient Kirkpatrick award McGraw-Hill, 1967, 87. Mem. AIChE, NSPE, Comml. Devel. Assn. Episcopalian. Avocations: soccer, boating, table games, philatelist. Home: 10 Bonnie Hollow Ln Montrose NY 10548-1314 Office: Box 175 Slate Hill NY 10973

REBER, STANLEY ROY, insurance company executive; b. Phila., Dec. 28, 1943; s. Louis A. and Rose (Dubin) R.; m. Rose Marie J. Apostolico, June 21, 1970; children: Douglas, Matthew, Jessica. BA in Econs., U. Pa., 1965,

MA in Econs., 1967; PhD in Econs., U. Chgo., 1970; postgrad., Harvard U., 1989. V.p. Chase Econometrics Assocs., Inc., N.Y.C., 1971-73; dir. bus. analysis The Conf. Bd., N.Y.C., 1974-75; exec. v.p. Tex. Am. Bank, Ft. Worth, 1975-85; sr. v.p. Provident Mut. Life Ins., Phila., 1985-88, exec. v.p., 1988—; pres. Market St. Fund, Phila., 1986—, Provident Mut. Family of Funds, 1990—; bd. dirs. Cortland Trust, Newbold's Asset Mgmt., Inc., Sigma Am. Corp. Overseer U. Pa. Sch. Nursing, 1987—; exec. com. Pa. Economy League, Phila., 1987—; bd. dirs. Presbyn. Med. Ctr. Phila., 1989—, YMCA of Phila., 1990—. Mem. Nat. Assn. Bus. Economists (bd. dirs. 1987-88), Union League Club. Republican. Jewish. Avocations: jogging, skiing, tennis, bicycling, reading. Home: 926 Black Rock Rd Gladwyne PA 19035-1405 Office: Provident Mut Life Ins Co 1600 Market St Philadelphia PA 19103-7240

REBOZO, CHARLES GREGORY, banker; b. Tampa, Fla., Nov. 17, 1912; s. Francisco M. and Carmen (Sarmiento) R. Pres., chmn. Key Biscayne (Fla.) Bank, 1964-90; pres. Key Land Co., 1983—. Pres. Boys Clubs of Miami, 1956-60, Jr. Achievement, 1959-60. Recipient Pop Warner award, 1960, Man and Boy award Boys Clubs Am., 1956. Mem. Key Biscayne C. of C. (pres. 1976-77). Clubs: Kiwanis (past club pres.), Key Biscayne Yacht (past commodore). Office: 524 Fernwood Rd Miami FL 33149-1842

RECANATI, RAPHAEL, shipping and banking executive; b. Salonique, Greece, Feb. 12, 1924; s. Leon and Mathilde (Saporta) R.; m. Diane Hettena, Oct. 8, 1946; children: Yehuda, Michael. Student Israel and Eng. Chmn. El-Yam Ships Ltd., 1953—; chmn. Discount Bank & Trust Co., Geneva, Switzerland, 1970; chmn., mng. dir. IDB Bankholding Ltd., 1970—. Home: 944 5th Ave New York NY 10021-2656 Office: 511 5th Ave New York NY 10017-4903 also: Overseas Shipholding Group Inc 1114 Ave of the Americas New York NY 10036

RECCHIA, RICHARD D., automotive sales executive; b. 1939. MBA, Wayne State U. Gen. sales mgr. Chrysler Corp., Detroit, 1953-78; pres. Fiat Motors of N. Am., Inc., Newark, N.J., 1978-81, R.D.R. Svcs., Inc., L.A., 1981-82; exec. v.p., COO Mitsubishi Motor Sales of Am., Cypress, Calif., 1982—. Office: Mitsubishi Motor Sales of Amer 6400 Katella Ave Cypress CA 90630

RECCHIA, SUSAN MARGARET, artist, author; b. Hyde Park, N.Y., July 11, 1955; d. Gerard and Grace (Spaulding) R. Sculptress Blackbird Mold Co., Trenton, N.J., 1976; portrait artist Great Adventure Park, Trenton, N.J., 1976; photographer/bus. cons. Olan Mills, Inc., various locations, 1977-79; photographer I.B.M., Fishkill, N.Y., 1982; art tchr. Hyde Park (N.Y.) Sch. Dist., 1983-86, Dutchess County Sr. Citizens of United Way, Poughkeepsie, N.Y., 1992—; dir. Masque Gallery, Hyde Park, 1992—; creator Masque Gallery of Entertainers; works included with the Libr. of Congress, Washington, Fla., Dutchess County Arts Coun. Ref. File, Poughkeepsie, N.Y. Portrait artist, Kaydeross Park, Saratoga, N.Y., 1983; muralist, scenic designer Bardavon Theatre, Poughkeepsie, 1977, Children's Community Theatre, 1985, Dutchess Tourism, Dutchess County Fair, Rhineback, N.Y., 1993; one woman exhbn. Northbound Ent., 1980-87; exhbn. artist Fasia Tipton Yearling Sales, 1980-82; author: Our Western Worlds Greatest Poems, 1983, Who's Who in Poetry, 1986, Bible Series, from the Book of Revelation, Endangered Wildlife, 1976—, The Fantasy Collection, 1974—, Bicentennial Tribute, 1976, others; cover artist Albany Dist Directory, 1994. Recipient Freddy award for sculpture, Mid-Hudson Ceramic League of N.Y., 1974, Peggy award for best of show, 1975, Golden Poet award World of Poetry, Calif., 1982, Silver Poet award, 1983, Grand Marshall award Town of Hyde Park, N.Y., 1986. Mem. Hyde Park C. of C., Dutchess County Arts Coun., Nat. Mus. of Women in the Arts. Roman Catholic. Avocations: thoroughbred racing, swimming. Office: Masque Gallery 9350 Yellow Lake Dr New Port Richey FL 34654-4236

RECHARD, OTTIS WILLIAM, mathematics and computer science educator; b. Laramie, Wyo., Nov. 13, 1924; s. Ottis H. and Mary (Bird) R.; m. Dorothy Lee Duble, Nov. 19, 1943; children—Katherine L. (Mrs. Larry V. Baxter), Carol G. (Mrs. David P. Reiter), Nancy L. (Mrs. William Moore), Elizabeth A. B.A., U. Wyo., 1943; postgrad., U. Calif., Los Angeles, 1943; M.A., U. Wis., 1946, Ph.D., 1948. Instr. U. Wis., 1948; instr., asst. prof. Ohio State U., 1948-51; staff mem. Los Alamos (N.Mex.) Nat. Lab., 1951-56; prof., dir. computing ctr. Wash. State U., Pullman, 1956-68; prof., chmn. dept. computer sci. Wash. State U., 1963-76, prof., dir. systems and computing, 1968-70; prof. math. and computer scis. U. Denver, 1976—, dir. computing services, 1976-79; vis. prof., chmn. dept. computer sci. U. Wyo., 1986-87; cons. NSF, Idaho Nuclear Corp., Los Alamos Nat. Lab.; program dir. computer sci. program NSF, 1964-65, chmn. adv. panel on instl. computing facilities, 1969-70. Mem. Los Alamos Sch. Bd., 1954-56; mem. Pullman Sch. Bd., 1967-74; Trustee, past pres. Westminster Found., Synod Wash.-Alaska. Served to 1st lt. USAAF, 1943-45. Decorated Order of Leopold II Belgium). Fellow AAAS; mem. Assn. for Computing Machinery, Am. Math. Soc., Math. Assn. Am., IEEE Computer Soc., Soc. Indsl. and Applied Math., AAUP, Phi Beta Kappa, Sigma Xi, Phi Kappa Phi. Presbyn. (elder). Club: Rotarian. Home: RR 3 Box 369 Calder ID 83808 also: 6980 E Girard Ave Apt 405 Denver CO 80224-2915

RECHARD, PAUL ALBERT, consulting civil engineering company executive; b. Laramie, Wyo., June 4, 1927; s. Ottis H. and Mary R. (Bird) R.; m. Mary Lou Roper, June 26, 1949; children: Robert Paul, Karen Ann. BS, U. Wyo., 1948, MS, 1949, CE, 1955. Registered land surveyor, Wyo.; registered profl. engr., Wyo., Utah, Mont., Colo., Calif., Nebr., S.D., N.Mex.; cert. profl. hydrologist Am. Inst. Hydrology; diplomate Am. Acad. Environ. Engrs. Hydraulic engr. U.S. Bur. Reclamation, Cody, Wyo. and Billings, Mont., 1949-54; dir. water resources Natural Resource Bd., Cheyenne, Wyo., 1954-58; prin. hydraulic engr. Upper Colorado River Commn., Salt Lake City, 1958-64; dir. Water Resources Research Inst., U. Wyo., Laramie, 1964-81, mem. faculty dept. civil engring., 1964-82, prof., Emeritus; pres. Western Water Cons., Laramie, 1980—; Hydrology Assocs., Laramie, 1978-80; owner Paul A. Rechard, P.E., Laramie, 1964-78. Editor: Compacts, Treaties and Court Decrees Affecting Wyoming Water, 1956. Contbr. articles to tech. publs. Pres., Thayer Sch. PTA, Laramie, 1965; mem. Laramie City Planning Commn., 1974-80. Served with USNR, 1945-46. Recipient Wyo. Eminent Engr. award Tau Beta Pi, 1993. Fellow ASCE (life mem., pres. Wyo. sect. 1968); mem. Am. Soc. Testing Materials, NSPE, Am. Geophys. Union, Nat. Water Well Assn., Wyo. Engring. Soc. (pres. 1976, hon.), Am. Water Works Assn., Am. Water Resources Assn., U.S. Com. on Irrigation and Drainage, U.S. Com. on Large Dams, Sigma Xi (pres. Wyo. chpt 1973), Phi Kappa Phi (pres. Wyo. chpt. 1969), Gamma Sigma Delta, Sigma Tau (pres. Wyo. chpt. 1948, selected Wyo. Eminent Engr. 1993). Republican. Presbyterian. Lodges: Lions (pres. Laramie 1968), Masons. Home: 316 Stuart St Laramie WY 82070-4866 Office: Western Water Cons Inc 611 Skyline Rd Laramie WY 82070-8909

RECHCIGL, JACK EDWARD, soil and environmental sciences educator; b. Washington, Feb. 27, 1960; s. Miloslav and Eva (Edwards) R.; m. Nancy Ann Palko, Sept. 30, 1983; children: Gregory John, Kevin Thomas, Lindsey Nicole. BS, U. Del., 1982; MS, Va. Poly. Inst. and State U., 1983, PhD, 1986. Asst. prof. soil sci. U. Fla. Agrl. Rsch. and Edn. Ctr., Ona, 1986-91, assoc. prof. soil and environ. scis., 1991—. Editor: Soil Amendments and Environmental Quality, 1994, Soil Amendments: Impact on Biotic Systems, 1994; assoc. editor: Jour. Environ. Quality, 1994—; editor-in-chief: (book series) Agriculture and Environment; contbr. chpts. to books, articles to Environ. Quality, Soil Sci., Soil Fertility, Water Quality. Recipient rsch. achievement award U. Fla., 1991; rsch grantee TVA, 1984-86, Allied Signal, 1987—, So. Fla. Water Mgmt. Dist., 1994. Fla. Inst. Phosphate Rsch., 1990—, USDA, 1992—. Mem. Am. Soc. Agronomy, Soil Sci. Soc. Am., Sigma Xi, Gamma Beta Phi, Gamma Sigma Delta, Phi Sigma. Achievements include research leading to the reduction of fertilizer recommendations in Florida, thereby helping to improve water quality. Home: 13511 4th Plz E Bradenton FL 34202-9682 Office: Fla Agrl Rsch and Edn Ctr RR 1 Box 62 Ona FL 33865-9706

RECHCIGL, MILOSLAV, JR., government official; b. Mlada Boleslav, Czechoslovakia, July 30, 1930; s. Miloslav and Marie (Rajtrova) R.; came to U.S., 1950, naturalized, 1955; m. Eva Marie Edwards, Aug. 29, 1953; children: John Edward, Karen Marie. BS, Cornell U., 1954, M of Nutrition Sci., 1955, PhD, 1958. Teaching asst. Cornell U., Ithaca, N.Y., 1953-57, grad. rsch. asst., 1957-58, rsch. assoc., 1958; USPHS rsch. fellow Nat. Cancer Inst., 1958-60, chemist enzymes and metabolism sect., 1960-61, rsch. biochemist, tumor host rels. sect., 1962-64, sr. investigator, 1964-68; grants assoc. program NIH, 1968-69; spl. asst. for nutrition and health to dir. Regional Med. Programs Svc., Health Svcs. and Mental Health Adminstrn., HEW, 1969-70, exec. sec. nutrition program adv. com. Health Svcs. and Mental Health Adminstrn., 1969-70; nutrition adviser AID, Dept. State, Washington, 1970—, chief Rsch. and Instl. Grants div., 1970-73, exec. sec. rsch. and instl. grants coun., 1970-74, exec. sec. AID rsch. adv. com., 1971-83, AID rep. USC/FAR com., 1972-82, asst. dir. Office Rsch. and Instl. Grants, 1973-74, acting dir., 1974-75, dir. interregional rsch. staff, 1975-78, devel. studies program, 1978, chief rsch. and methodology div., 1979-82, rsch. mgmt. and rev. dir. Office of the Sci. Advisor, 1982-91, Office of Rsch., 1992-94, rsch. and methodology specialist, Bur. for Program and Policy Coordination, 1994—; del. White House Conf. on Food, Nutrition and Health, 1969, Agrl. Rsch. Policy Adv. Com. Conf. on Rsch. to Meet U.S. and World Food Needs, 1975; cons. Office Sec. Agr., 1969-70, Dept. Treasury, 1973, Office Technol. Assessment, 1977, FDA, 1979, NAS, NRC, 1985-93. Author: The Czechoslovak Contribution to World Culture, 1964, Czechoslovakia Past and Present, 1968, (with Z. Hruban) Microbodies and Related Particles: Morphology, Biochemistry and Physiology, 1969, Russian edit., 1972, Enzyme Synthesis and Degradation in Mammalian Systems, 1971, (with Eva Rechcigl) Biographical Directory of the Members of the Czechoslovak Society of Arts and Sciences in America, 3d edit., 1972, 4th edit., 1978, 5th edit., 1983, 6th edit., 1988, 7th edit., 1992, Food, Nutrition and Health: A Multidisciplinary Treatise Addressed to the Major Nutrition Problems from a World Wide Perspective, 1973, Man, Food and Nutrition: Strategies and Technological Measures for Alleviating the World Food Problem, 1973, World Food Problem: A Selective Bibliography of Reviews, 1975, Carbohydrates, Lipids and Accessory Growth Factors, 1976, Nutrient Elements and Toxicants, 1977, Nitrogen, Electrolytes, Water and Energy Metabolism, 1979, Nutrition and the World Food Problem, 1979, Educators with Czechoslovak Roots: A U.S. and Canadian Faculty Roster, 1980, Physiology of Growth and Nutrition, 1981, Nutritional Requirements, 1977, Diet, Culture Media and Food Supplements, 4 vols., 1977, Nutritional Disorders, 3 vols., 1978, Handbook of Nutritional Requirements in a Functional Context, 2 vols., 1981, Handbook of Agricultural Productivity, 2 vols., 1981, Handbook of Nutritive Value of Processed Food, 2 vols., 1982, Handbook of Foodborne Diseases of Biological Origin, 1983, Handbook of Naturally Occurring Food Toxicants, 1983, Handbook of Nutritional Supplements, 2 vols, 1983, U.S. Legislators with Czechoslovak Roots from Colonial Times to Present, 1987, others; co-editor: Internat. Jour. of Cycle Research, 1969-74, Jour. Applied Nutrition, 1970-82; series editor: Comparative Animal Nutrition, 1976-81; editor-in-chief: (series) Nutrition and Food, 1977—; mem. editorial bd.: Nutrition Reports Internat., 1977-80; translator: Chemical Abstracts, 1959-61; contbr. articles to sci. jours. Organizer, mem. council Montrose Civic Assn., Rockville, Md.; mem. ethnic affairs com., Montgomery County, Md., 1990-92, vice chair, 1991-92. Recipient Josef Hlavka Commemorative medal Czechoslovak Acad. Scis., 1991; NAS grantee, 1962. Fellow AAAS, Am. Inst. Chemists (councilor 1972-74, program chmn. 1974 ann. meeting, mem. pram com. 1980 meeting), Internat. Coll. Applied Nutrition, Intercontinental Biog. Assn.. Washington Acad. Scis. (del. 1972—); mem. Am. Inst. Nutrition (com. Western Hemisphere Nutrition Congress 1971, 74, program com. 1979-82), Am. Soc. Biol. Chemists, Am. Chem. Soc. (joint bd.-council com. on internat. activities 1975-76), D.C. Inst. Chemists (pres. 1972-74, councilor 1974-80), Am. Inst. Biol. Scis., Soc. for Exptl. Biology and Medicine, Am. Soc. Animal Sci., Internat., Am. socs. cell biology, Soc. for Developmental Biology, Am. Assn. for Cancer Research, Soc. for Biol. Rhythm, Am. Pub. Health Assn., N.Y. Acad. Scis., Chem. Soc. Washington (symposium com. 1970, 71), Internat. Coll. Applied Nutrition, Internat. Soc. for Research on Civilization Diseases and Vital Substances, Soc. for Geochemistry and Health, Soc. for Internat. Devel., Internat. Platform Assn., Am. Assn. for Advancement Slavic Studies, Czechoslovak Soc. Arts and Scis. in Am. (hon., dir.-at-large 1962—, dir. publs. 1962-68, 70-74, v.p. 1968-74, pres. 1974-78, pres. collegium 1978—), History of Sci. Soc., Soc. Research Adminstrs., Sigma Xi, Phi Kappa Phi, Delta Tau Kappa (hon.). Clubs: Cosmos, Cornell (Washington). Home: 1703 Mark Ln Rockville MD 20852-4106 Office: AID-Bur for Program & Policy Coord Washington DC 20523

RECHTIN, EBERHARDT, retired aerospace educator; b. East Orange, N.J., Jan. 16, 1926; s. Eberhardt Carl and Ida H. (Pfarrer) R.; m. Dorothy Diane Denebrink, June 10, 1951; children: Andrea C., Nina, Julie Anne, Erica, Mark. B.S., Calif. Inst. Tech., 1946, Ph.D. cum laude, 1950. Dir. Deep Space Network, 1949-67; asst. dir. Calif. Inst. Tech. Jet Propulsion Lab., 1949-67; dir. Advanced Rsch. Projects Agy., Dept. Def., 1967-70, prin. dep. dir. def. rsch. and engring., 1970-71, asst. sec. def. for telecom., 1972-73; chief engr. Hewlett-Packard Co., Palo Alto, Calif., 1973-77; pres., CEO Aerospace Corp., El Segundo, Calif., 1977-87; prof. U. So. Calif., 1988-94, emeritus prof. elec. engring. systems, 1994—. Served to lt. USNR, 1943-56. Recipient maj. awards NASA, Dept. Def., USN, Disting. Alumni award Calif. Inst. Tech., 1984, NEC C&C prize, Japan, 1992. Fellow AAAS, AIAA (Robert H. Goddard Astronautics award 1991), IEEE (Alexander Graham Bell award 1977); mem. NAE, Tau Beta Pi. Home: 1665 Cataluna Pl Palos Verdes Estates CA 90274-2162

RECHTSTEINER, STEVEN ALLEN, import/export company executive; b. Cin., June 25, 1945; s. Carl Joseph and Ruth Francis (Hucke) R.; m. Barbara A. Behrns, Dec. 14, 1968; children: Christopher, Gregory, Stephany. BS in Architecture, U. Notre Dame, 1968; postgrad., U. cin., 1969. V.p., gen. mgr. Fran Rica, Stockton, Calif., 1979-82, pres., 1982-85; chmn., CEO Prodo Pak Corp., Garfield, N.J., 1983-87; chmn., COO FR Mfg., Stockton, 1985-87; v.p. internat. CTI Inc., Barrington, Ill., 1987—; chmn., CEO C.G.S. Ltd., Barrington, 1990—, exec. v.p., 1992—; founder, COO Am. Internat. Homes, Ltd., 1993-95; bd. dirs. A.P.T. Engring., Inc.; cons. Vandor Corp., Richmond, Ind., 1990-93, Spartanburg (S.C.) Steel, 1990-93, A.P.T. Engring., Cin., 1989-94. Inventor, patentee in field; contbr. articles to profl. jours. Bd. dirs. St. Thomas More's Ch., Stockton, 1982-84, PTO, 220th Dist., Barrington, 1988-90. Recipient "E" award export Pres. of U.S., 1987. Mem. Inst. Food Technologists (Indsl. Achievement award 1973), Food Processing Machinery and Suppliers Assn., Dairy Food Industry Suppliers Assn., Packaging Machinery Mfrs. Inst., Instrument Soc. Am., Structural Panel Inst. Am. Republican. Roman Catholic. Home: 656 Golf Ln Barrington IL 60010 Office: CGS Ltd 656 Golf Ln Barrington IL 60010

RECHY, JOHN FRANCISCO, author; b. El Paso, Tex.; s. Roberto Sixto and Guadalupe (Flores) R.. B.A., U. Tex., El Paso; student, New Sch. Social Research. Instr. creative writing UCLA, Occidental Coll., U. So. Calif. Author: City of Night, 1963, Numbers, 1967, This Day's Death, 1969, The Vampires, 1971, The Fourth Angel, 1973, The Sexual Outlaw, 1977, Rushes, 1979, Bodies and Souls, 1983, Marilyn's Daughter, 1988, The Miraculous Day of Amalia Gómez, 1991; (plays) Momma As She Became—Not As She Was, 1968, Rushes, 1978, Tigers Wild, 1986; contbr.: short stories and articles to Tex. Observer, The Nation, Village Voice, London mag., Saturday Rev., N.Y. Times Book Rev., L.A. Times, Washington Post Book World, Phila. Inquirer, Contemporary Fiction, Big Table, others; also anthologies Chicano Voices, Black Humor, Urban Reader, Evergreen Rev. Reader, New Am. Story, The Moderns, Rediscoveries, Men on Men, others; trans.: stories and articles for Tex. Quar., Evergreen Rev. Served with AUS. Recipient Longview Found. award for short story The Fabulous Wedding of Miss Destiny; Nat. Endowment for Arts grantee, 1976. Mem. Authors Guild, Tex. Inst. Letters, PEN, Nat. Writers Union. Office: care Georges Borchardt Inc 136 E 57th St New York NY 10022-2707

RECK, ANDREW JOSEPH, philosophy educator; b. New Orleans, Oct. 29, 1927; s. Andrew Gervais and Katie (Mangiaracina) R.; m. Elizabeth Lassiter Torre, June 17, 1987. B.A., Tulane U., 1947, M.A., 1949; Ph.D., Yale U., 1954; student, U. St. Andrews, Scotland, 1952-53, U. Paris, summers 1962, 64. Instr. English U. Conn., 1949-50; instr. philosophy Yale, 1951-52, 55-58; mem. faculty Tulane U., 1958—, prof. philosophy, 1964—, chmn. dept., 1969-89, dir. Master Liberal Arts program, 1984—; Thomasfest lectr. Xavier U., Cin., 1970; Suarez Lectr. Spring Hill Coll., 1971; Niebuhr lectr. Elmhurst (Ill.) Coll., 1976; vis. prof. Fordham U., 1979; vis. scholar Hastings Ctr. (N.Y.), 1981; Woodruff lectr. Emory U., 1982; Fairchild lectr. U. So. Miss., 1982, 87; Matchette Found. lectr. Cath. U. Am., 1991; Sr. Scholar Inst. Humane Studies, Menlo Park, Calif., 1982; vis. scholar Poynter Ctr., Ind. U.,

Bloomington, 1983; Tulane U. faculty rep. to bd. adminstrs. Tulane Ednl. Fund, 1988-91. Author: Recent American Philosophy, 1964, Introduction to William James, 1967, New American Philosophers, 1968, Speculative Philosophy, 1972; editor: George Herbert Mead Selected Writings, 1964, 2d edit., 1981, Knowledge and Value, 1972, (with T. Horvath, T. Krittek and S. Grean) American Philosophers' Ideas of Ultimate Reality and Meaning, 1993; co-editor Ultimate Reality and Meaning, Interdisciplinary Studies in the Philosophy of Understanding, 1990—; mem. adv. editl. bd. Internat. Jour. World Peace, Trans. Charles Peirce Soc., Santayana edit. So. Jour. Philosophy; editor History of Philosophy Quar., 1993—. Served with AUS, 1953-55. Howard fellow, 1962-63, Liberty Fund grantee, 1982, Newcomb fellow, 1991-93; Fulbright scholar, 1952-53; Am. Coun. Learned Socs. grantee, 1961-62, Am. Philos. Soc. grantee, 1972, Huntington Libr. grantee, 1973, La. Ednl. Quality State Found. grantee, 1994—, U.S. Info. Agy. grantee, Brazil, 1993. Mem. Am. Philos. Assn. (program com. eastern divsn. 1969, nominating com. western divsn. 1975-76, 81-82, mem. ad hoc com. on history 1992—), Southwestern Philos. Soc. (exec. com. 1965-69, v.p 1971-72, pres. 1972-73), So. Soc. Philosophy and Psychology (treas. 1968-71, pres 1976-77), Am. Coun. Learned Socs. (Am. studies adv. com. 1972-76), Coun. for Internat. Exch. Scholars (philosophy screening com. 1974-77), Metaphys. Soc. Am. (councillor 1971-75, pres. 1977-78, program com. 1989-90, chair program com. 1995-96), Soc. Advancement Am. Philosophy (exec. com. 1980-83), Charles S. Peirce Soc. (sec.-treasurer 1985-86, v.p. 1986-87, pres 1987-88), Internat. Soc. for Study of Human Ideas of Ultimate Reality and Meaning (bd. dirs. 1989—), La. Endowment for Humanities (bd. dirs 1990—), Phi Beta Kappa (pres. Alpha of La. 1966-67), Alpha Sigma Lambda (hon. Theta chpt. of La.). Home: 6125 Patton St New Orleans LA 70118-5832 Office: Tulane U Dept Philosophy New Orleans LA 70118

RECK, GREGORY MILTON, aerospace engineer; b. Greenville, Ohio, Dec. 5, 1946; s. Ronald and Marie (Supak) R.; m. Barbara K. Petroff, Apr. 17, 1971; 1 child, Chelsea Marie. BS in Aerospace Engring., U. Cin., 1969; postgrad., Harvard U., 1985. Various positions NASA, 1964-90; acting assoc. adminstr. for advanced concepts and tech. NASA, Washington, 1990—. Recipient Disting. Alumni award U. Cin., 1992, Meritorious Presdl. Rank award U.S. Office Pers. Mgmt., 1992. Mem. AIAA, Phi Eta Sigma. Republican. Avocations: tennis, photography. Home: 2003 Gervais Dr Falls Church VA 22043-1676 Office: NASA 4th St at E St SW Washington DC 20546

RECK, JOEL M(ARVIN), lawyer; b. Worcester, Mass., Sept. 27, 1941; s. Saul I. and Sylvia (Levine) R.; m. Rachel E. Feinsilver, June 9, 1963; children: Daniel C., Deborah R. BA cum laude, Bowdoin Coll., 1963; JD, Harvard U., 1966. Bar: Mass. 1967. Assoc. Hoffman and Hoffman, Boston, 1966-68; ptnr., chmn. real estate dept. Brown, Rudnick, Freed & Gesmer, Boston, 1968—; chmn. Wayland (Mass.) Zoning Bd., 1979-82; trustee Mass. Continuing Legal Edn., Inc., Boston, 1988—. Mem. exec. com. Combined Jewish Philanthropies, Boston, 1982—; sec. Nat. Jewish Commn. on Rels. Adv. Coun., N.Y.C., 1992-93; pres. Jewish Community Rels. Coun., Boston, 1987-90; mem. Mass. Gov.'s Entrepreneurial Adv. Coun., Boston, 1986-90. Mem. ABA, Mass. Bar Assn., Boston Bar Assn. (chmn. real estate sect. 1985-87, exec. com. 1987-89, sec. 1991, treas. 1992-93, v.p. 1994—), Mass. Conveyancers Assn. (exec. com. Boston chpt. 1986), Abstract Club (exec. com. Boston chpt. 1990), Lawyers Alliance for World Security (exec. com. Mass. law), Real Estate Fin. Assn. (clk. 1992-93). Avocations: sailing, skiing, jogging. Office: Brown Rudnick Freed Gesmer One Financial Center Boston MA 02111-1000

RECK, W(ALDO) EMERSON, retired university administrator, public relations consultant, writer; b. Gettysburg, Ohio, Dec. 28, 1903; s. Samuel Harvey and Effie D. (Arnett) R.; m. Hazel Winifred January, Sept. 7, 1926; children: Phyllis (Mrs. Louis E. Welch, Jr.), Elizabeth Ann (Mrs. Gabriel J. Lada). A.B., Wittenberg U., 1926; A.M., U. Iowa, 1946; LL.D., Midland Coll., 1949. Reporter Springfield (Ohio) News, 1922-26; publicity dir. Midland Coll., Fremont, Nebr., 1926-28; dir. pub. rels., asst. prof. journalism Midland Coll., 1928-40; dir. pub. relations Colgate U., 1940-48; v.p. Wittenberg U., Springfield, Ohio, 1948-70; v.p. emeritus Wittenberg U., 1970—; pub. relations specialist Cumerford Corp., 1970-78; vis. lectr. pub. columnist Springfield Sun, 1973-81; spl. corr. AP, 1928-38; mng. editor Fremont Morning Guide, 1939; vis. lectr. pub. rels. State U. Iowa, summers 1941, 42, U. Wyo., summer 1948; co-dir. Seminar on Pub. Rels. for High Edn., Syracuse U., summers 1944, 45, 46; mem. commn. on ch. papers United Luth. Ch., 1951-62, cons. com. dept. of press, radio and TV, 1955-60; mem. commn. on ch. papers Luth Ch. in Am., 1962-64, 70-72, mem. exec. com., also chmn. com. periodicals of bd. publs., 1962-72; mem. mgmt com. Office of Communications, 1972-76; chmn. pub. relations com. Council Protestant Colls. and Univs., 1961-65. Author: Public Relations: a Program for Colleges and Universities, 1946, The Changing World of College Relations, 1976, Father Can't Forget, 1982, A. Lincoln: His Last 24 Hours, 1987, 93, When the Nation Said Farewell to Lincoln, 1989, (with others) The American College, 1949; contbg. author: Public Relations Handbook, 1950, 62, 67; editor: Publicity Problems, 1939, College Publicity Manual, 1948; contbr. hist. and pub. rels. articles to gen. edml., profl. mags. Cons. Gov. Mario Cuomo's Lincoln on Democracy Project, 1989. Recipient award Am. Coll. Pub. Rels. Assn. for Disting. Svc., 1942, Outstanding Achievement award, 1944, 47, Coun. for Advancement and Support of Edn. award, 1977, Medal of Honor, Wittenberg U., 1982, Diploma of Honor, Lincoln Meml. U., 1989, Distinction in Journalism award Midlands, 1991. Mem. Am. Coll. Pub. Relations Assn. (pres. 1940-41, historian 1966-76), Luth. Coll. Pub. Relations Assn. (pres. 1951-53), Pub. Relations Soc. Am. (nat. jud. council 1952), Assn. Am. Colls. (mem. com. on pub. relations 1945-48), AAUP, Nat. Luth. Ednl. Conf. (chmn. com. pub. relations 1949-50), Ohio Coll. Pub. Relations Officers (pres. 1954-55), Clark County Hist. Soc. (pres. 1985-86), Nat. Trust for Hist. Preservation, Archives Assocs., Nat. Hist. Soc. (founding asso.), Abraham Lincoln Assn., Blue Key, Sigma Delta Chi, Pi Delta Epsilon, Delta Sigma Phi, Omicron Delta Kappa. Home: # 231 1500 Villa Rd Springfield OH 45503

RECKARD, CRAIG REGINALD, physician; b. Phila., Dec. 21, 1940; s. C. John and Mary E. (Craig) R.; m. Jean M. Santoro, Nov. 9, 1968 (div. Dec. 1983); children—Jonathan, Justin. B.S., Ursinus Coll., 1962; M.D., U. Pa., 1967. Diplomate Am. Bd. Surgeons. Intern U. Pa., Phila., 1967-68, resident in surgery, 1968-74, transplantation fellow, 1970-72; assoc. prof. surgery U. Chgo., 1976-83; prof. surgery Loyola U., Maywood, Ill., 1983—. Served to maj. U.S. Army, 1974-76. Recipient Clin. Investigator award NIH 1977. Fellow ACS; mem. Am. Soc. Transplant Surgeons, Internat. Transplantation Soc., Chgo. Surg. Soc. Avocations: photography, skiing, tennis, racquetball. Office: Lehigh Valley Hosp PO Box 169 Allentown PA 18105

RECORD, JOHN F., public relations executive; b. 1942. Sr. officer Canadian Imperial Bank of Commerce, 1962-69; asst. corp. comptroller Four Seasons/Inn Park Internat. Hotel, 1969-71; v.p., treas. Media Buying Svcs., 1971-79; with Internat. Comm. Group, L.A., 1979—, now sr. v.p., treas. Office: Internat Communication Group 1925 Century Park E Los Angeles CA 90067-1739*

RECORD, LINCOLN FREDRICK, speech communications educator, communications consultant; b. Kokomo, Ind., Nov. 12, 1939; s. Fred William Record and Mary Louise (Greene) Pingleton; m. Marlene Jeanette Welly, June 22, 1963; children: Eric, Erin. BA, Ball State U., Muncie, Ind., 1963; MA, St. Francis Coll., Ft. Wayne, Ind., 1973; student, U. Aberdeen, Scotland, 1970. Tchr. Maconaquah Schs., Bunker Hill, Ind., 1963-67; English chairperson Dekalb Schs., Auburn, Ind., 1967-75; speech coord. Ft. Wayne (Ind.) Community Schs., 1975—; assoc. faculty Purdue U., Ft. Wayne, Ind., 1974—. Editor: Dekalb Educator, 1970-74, Educator, 1986-91; author: The Need for Communication in Education. Chmn. Educators for Dick Lugar, Ind., 1977; pres. Parish Coun., Auburn, 1970-72; mem. Auburn Port Authority, 1985-87; councilman Auburn City Coun., 1980-84. Recipient Polit. Action award, Ind. State Tchrs., Indpls., 1988; named to Ind. Hall of Fame, 1994. Mem. NEA (local pres. 1966, 68-69), Ind. Forensic Assn., Nat. Forensic League (dist. coun. 1988—, triple diamond award 1989, 93), Ind. Speech Assn., Ind. State Tchrs. Assn. (bd. dirs. 1974-77), KC, Kiwanis. Democrat. Roman Catholic. Avocations: commercial radio announcing, speech coach, volunteer counselor. Home: 908 N Main St Auburn IN 46706-1228

RECORD, PHILLIP JULIUS, newspaper executive; b. Fort Worth, Jan. 12, 1929; s. Phillip Cross and Frances Virginia (McElwee) R.; m. Patricia Ann Edwards, Sept. 29, 1954; children: Christopher Phillip, Gregory Edwards, Timothy James. B.A. in Journalism, U. Notre Dame, 1950. Gen. reporter Lubbock Avalanche-Jour., Tex., 1950-54; copy editor, reporter Fort Worth Star-Telegram, 1954-67, asst. city editor, 1967-68, city editor evening edit., 1968-76, mng. editor, 1976-80, assoc. exec. editor, 1980-91, spl. asst. to pub., ombudsman, 1991—; dir. Freedom Info. Found. Tex., 1987-93; mem. mass comms. com. Tex. Tech. U., chmn., 1990-92. Mem. conciliation/arbitration bd. Cath. Diocese of Ft. Worth, 1994—, publs. adv. com., 1982—; founding mem. Ft. Worth Theatre; mem. Friends of Ft. Worth Pub. Libr.; bd. dirs. Tarrant County Mental Health Assn. With U.S. Army, 1950-52. Recipient 3d ann. Ethics award Tex. Christian U., 1991, numerous other awards for reporting, photography and headline writing; named to Tex. Tech U. Mass Comms. Hall of Fame. Mem. ABA (nat. commn. on pub. understanding about law 1984-90, commn. on partnership programs 1990-93), Investigative Reporters and Editors Inc., Soc. Profl. Journalists (pres. 1983-84, bd. dirs. Found. 1980—, v.p. Found. 1991-94, bd. chair 1994—, Wells Key 1991), Creative Thinking Assn., Orgn. News Ombudsmen (dir. 1994—), Petroleum Club. Avocation: tennis. Home: 6144 Walla Ave Fort Worth TX 76133-3557 Office: Fort Worth Star-Telegram 400 W 7th St Fort Worth TX 76102-4701

RECTOR, JOHN MICHAEL, lawyer, association executive; b. Seattle, Aug. 15, 1943; s. Michael Robert and Bernice Jane (Allison) R.; m. Mary Kaaren Sueta Jolly, Feb. 8, 1977 (div. 1995). BA, U. Calif., Berkeley, 1966; JD, U. Calif., Hastings, 1969; PharmD (hon.), Ark. State Bd. Pharmacy, 1991. Bar: Calif. 1970, U.S. Supreme Ct. 1974. Trial atty. civil rights div. Dept. Justice, 1969-71; dep. chief counsel judiciary com. U.S. Senate, 1971-73, counsel to Sen. Birch Bayh, 1971-77, chief counsel, staff dir., 1973-77; confirmed by U.S. Senate as assoc. adminstr. to Law Enforcement Assistance Adminstn. and adminstr. of Office Juvenile Justice Dept. Justice, 1977-79; spl. counsel to U.S. Atty. Gen., 1979-80; dir. govt. affairs Nat. Assn. Retail Druggists, Washington, 1980-85; sr. v.p. govt. affairs, gen. counsel Nat. Assn. Retail Druggists, 1986—; chmn. adv. bd. Nat. Juvenile Law Center, 1973-77; mem. Hew panel Drug Use and Criminal Behavior, 1974-77; mem. cons. panel Nat. Commn. Protection Human Subjects of Biomed. and Behavioral Research, 1975-76; mem. bd. Nat. Inst. Corrections, 1977-79; chmn. U.S. Interdepartmental Council Juvenile Justice, 1977-79; mem. bd. com. civil rights and liberties Am. Democratic Action, 1976-80, Pres.'s Com. Mental Health-Justice Group, 1978; com. youth citizenship ABA, 1978-84; mem. Pharm. Industry Adv. Com.; exec. dir., treas. polit. action com. Nat. Pharmacists Assn., 1981—; exec. dir. Retail Druggist Legal Legis. Def. Fund, 1985—, founder, chmn. Washington Pharmacy Industry Forum; mem. numerous fed. narcotic and crime panels and coms.; owner Second Genesis, an antique and furniture restoration co. Contbr. articles to profl. jours.; editl. bd. Managed Care News. Exec. com. small bus. and fin. couns. Dem. Nat. Com.; dir. Dem. Leadership Coun.'s Network, 1989—, bd. advisers, 1992—; bd. dirs. Small Bus. Legis. Coun., 1987—; bd. dirs. Nat. Bus. Coalition for Fair Competition, 1984—. Perry E. Towne scholar, 1966-67; mem. U.S. Atty. Gen.'s Honors Program, 1968-71; recipient Children's Express Juvenile Justice award, 1981. Mem. Calif. Bar Assn., Nat. Health Lawyers Assn., Am. Soc. Assn. Execs. (govt. affirs sect.), Washington Coun. Lawyers, Assn. of Former Senior Senate Aides, Vinifera Wine Growers Assn. Va. (life), Health R Us, Am. League of Lobbyists, Theta Chi. Democrat. Avocation: collecting antique furniture, books and documents. Home: 7811 Carters Run Dr Marshall VA 22115-2123 Office: Nat Assn Retail Druggists 205 Daingerfield Rd Alexandria VA 22314-2885

RECTOR, MILTON GAGE, social work educator, former association executive; b. Fallon, Nev., Jan. 3, 1918; s. William L. and Virginia E. (Renfro) R.; m. Harriet Louise Phibbs, Aug. 1, 1940; children: Brian Eugene (dec.), Barbara Elaine (dec.), Dianne Eileen, Bruce Alan. B.A., U. So. Calif., 1940; postgrad., U. Calif.-Berkeley, Columbia U. With Los Angeles County Probation Dept., 1940-46, probation officer charge forestry camp for delinquent boys, 1943-46; with Nat. Council Crime and Delinquency, 1946-82, cons. Western region, 1946-52, dir. parole services, 1952-55, asst. exec. dir., 1955-59, exec. dir., 1959-82, pres., 1972-82; vis. prof. Grad. Sch. Social Work U. Utah, 1982-84; Mem. President's Adv. Com. on Delinquency and Youth Crime, 1960-66; Cons. to U.S. Senate subcom. investigation delinquency, 1953; organized Nat. Conf. Parole, 1956; bd. dirs. Am. Correctional Assn., 1959-73, Osborne Assn., 1960-75, Nat. Study Service, 1960-76, U. Md. Inst. Criminal Justice, 1972-78, Center for Correctional Justice, 1972-78, SUNY-Albany Criminal Justice Inst., Acad. Jud. Edn., 1970-75, Law in Am. Society Found.; chmn. bd. dirs. Joint Commn. Correctional Manpower and Tng., 1965-70; cons. Pres.'s Crime Commn., 1965-68; U.S. rep. on UN Social Def. Sect., 1965-75; U.S. del. UN World Congress on Crime and Delinquency, Stockholm, 1965, Kyoto, Japan, 1970; mem. Nat. Commn. on Reform Fed. Criminal Laws, 1969-70, N.Y.C. Criminal Justice Coordinating Council, 1967-73, Nat. Commn. on Criminal Justice Standards and Goals, 1971-73, Inst. on Jud. Adminstrn.-Am. Bar Assn. Commn. on Juvenile Justice Standards, 1973-76; mem. adv. com. on correctional edn. Edn. Commn. of States, 1975-77. Contbr. numerous articles profl. jours., procs., Nat. Council Crime and Delinquency; syndicated columnist: Of Crime and Punishment. Served to lt. (j.g.) USNR, 1944-46; comdr. Res. Recipient August Volmer award Am. Criminological Soc., 1971; Meritorious Service award Nat. Council Juvenile and Family Ct. Judges, 1962; John Howard award John Howard Assn., 1974; award John Jay Coll. Criminal Justice, 1977; Karl Menninger award Fortune Soc., 1979; Harold DeWolf award Offender Aid and Restoration U.S.A. Inc., 1980; award Nat. Forum on Criminal Justice, 1981; Margaret Mead award Internat. Halfway House Assn., 1982; award for enhancement profl. edn. U. Utah Grad. Sch. Social Work, 1983. Home: 27 James Buchanan Dr Cranbury NJ 08512-4847 *My life work in the field of juvenile and criminal justice and its insights into the depths of man's inhumanity to man have enabled me to serve in a ministry for the reform of a system which at times seems impervious to reform, and thus continues to deny the attainment of social justice in my country.*

RECTOR, ROBERT WAYMAN, mathematics and engineering educator, former association executive; b. San Jose, Calif., Jan. 28, 1916; s. Joseph Jones and Eva (Hembree) R.; m. Margaret Eileen Hayden, Aug. 25, 1940; children: Cleone Rector Black, Robin Rector Krupp, Bruce Hayden. B.A., San Jose State U., 1937; M.A., Stanford U., 1939; Ph.D., U. Md., 1956. Instr. Compton (Calif.) Coll., 1939-42; asso. prof. math. U.S. Naval Acad., 1946-56; staff mathematician Space Tech. Labs., Los Angeles, 1956-61; asso. dir. computation center Aerospace Corp., El Segundo, Calif., 1961-65; v.p. Informatics, Inc., Van Nuys, Calif., 1965-70, Cognitive Systems, Inc., Beverly Hills, Calif., 1970-71; asso. dir. continuing edn. engring. and math. UCLA, 1971-73, 81-92; dean Coll. Engring. and Computer Sci. West Cost U., L.A., 1992—; Exec. dir. Am. Fedn. Info. Processing Socs., Montvale, N.J., 1973-79; spl. asst. White House Conf. Library and Info. Services, 1979; v.p. Conf. and Meeting Assistance Corp., East Greenwich, R.I., 1980—. Bd. govs.: Pacific Jour. Math, 1957-92. Mem. Los Angeles Mayor's Space Adv. Com., 1964-73, Calif. Mus. Found. (aviation and space hist. research com. 1984—). Served with USNR, 1942-46. Mem. Math. Assn. Am., Assn. Computing Machinery, Naval Res. Assn., Res. Officers Assn., Ret. Officers Assn. Home: 10700 Stradella Ct Los Angeles CA 90077-2604

REDBONE, LEON, singer, musician. Albums include: On the Track, 1975, Double Time, 1976, Champagne Charlie, 1977, From Branch to Branch, 1981, Red to Blue, 1985, Christmas Island, 1988, No Regrets, 1988, Sugar, 1990, Up a Lazy River, 1992, Whistling in the Wind, 1994.

REDDA, KINFE KEN, chemist, educator; b. Senafe, Eritrea (Africa), Mar. 21, 1948; arrived in Can. 1973; came to U.S., 1979; s. Guangul and Demekech (Zewde) R.; m. Abeda Hindeya, 1978 (div. 1983); 1 child, Fre; m. Lul Haile, 1989; children: Aman, Aaron. BS in Pharmacy, Haile Selassie U., Addis Ababa, Ethiopia, 1970; PhD in Medicinal Chemistry, U. Alberta, Edmonton, Can., 1978. Lic. pharmacist, Ethiopia. Postdoctoral fellow U. Alberta, Edmonton, Can., 1977-78, Dalhousie U., Halifax, Can. 1978-79; asst. prof. U. Puerto Rico, San Juan, 1980-85; assoc. prof. Fla. A&M U. Tallahassee, 1985-89, prof., 1989—; nat. grant reviewer Nat. Inst. on Drug Abuse, Rockville, Md., 1985-88; dir. space life scis. tng. program NASA, Kennedy Space Ctr., Tallahassee, 1987—; dir. NIH's minority biomed. rsch. support program, Fla. A&M U., Tallahassee, 1988—. Chief editor: Cocaine, Marijuana and Designer Drugs Chemistry, Pharamacology and Behavior, 1989; contbr. articles to profl. jours; patentee synthesis of new biologically active compounds Tetrahydropyridines, 1979—. Mem. NAACP (Tallahassee chpt.), Tallahassee Urban League, Harambe Festival, Tallahassee. Recipient Inventor's medal, Canadian Patents & Developments, Ottawa, Can., 1978, grant Nat. Inst. Health, Bethesda, Md., 1985—, NASA, Washington, 1987—. Mem. numerous nat. and internat. profl. orgns. Democrat. Mem. Coptic Christian Ch. Avocations: jogging, swimming, reading, travel, spectator sports. *Sincere and voluntary service to others is the deepest form of human kindness.*

REDDAN, HAROLD JEROME, sociologist, educator; b. N.Y.C., Dec. 4, 1926; s. Harold B. and Catherine G. (Kelly) R.; m. Margaret M. Byrne, Oct. 11, 1952; children: Harold James, Patricia Anne, James Joseph, Kathleen Mary. B.A., St. Francis Coll., 1950; M.S., St. Johns U., 1957, Ph.D., 1961. Social investigator N.Y.C. Dept. Welfare, 1950-58; assoc. prof. sociology St. Johns U., 1958-69; lectr. sociology Kings County Hosp. Center Sch. of Nursing, N.Y.C., 1961-66; family counselor, 1961—; adj. assoc. prof. Manhattan Coll., 1968-69, prof. sociology, head dept. managerial scis., 1969-73; adj. sociology faculty Nassau Community Coll., 1971—, Mercy Coll.; adj. prof. L.I. corr. facility, 1980-84; administrv. cons. Molloy Coll., 1973-74; adj. prof. sociology and bus. adminstrn. C.W. Post Coll., 1974-80; mem. behavioral scis. faculty, police sci. program N.Y. Inst. Tech., 1974-75; adj. prof. sociology SUNY, Farmingdale; provost Molloy Coll., 1975-78, v.p. for planning and spl. programs, 1978-79; ednl. cons., 1979—. Author: Sociology, 1971, Arco GRE Tests, 1985. Dir. Jamaica VI Peace Corps Tng. Program, 1965; Coordinator New Hyde Park Citizens for Kennedy, 1960, campaign mgr. 1st Assembly Dist., 1962-64. Served with AUS, 1945-46. Mem. Am. Sociol. Assn., Am. Acad. Polit. and Social Sci., Am. Acad. Mgmt., Assn. Psychiat. Treatment Offenders, VFW, Garden City Park Hist. Soc. (pres. 1960-63), Delta Mu Delta, Delta Sigma Pi, Zeta Sigma Pi, Alpha Kappa Delta. Democrat. Home: 96 5th St New Hyde Park NY 11040-4108

REDDELL, DONALD LEE, agricultural engineer; b. Tulia, Tex., Sept. 28, 1937; s. Kimball Tuscola and Winonah (Claiborne) R.; m. Minnie Ellen Cox, Jan. 27, 1957; children: Revis Diane, Cheryl Reneé, Stephen Patrick. BS, Tex. Tech U., 1960; MS, Colo. State U., 1967, PhD, 1969. Registered profl. engr., Tex. Jr. engr. High Plains Underground Water Conservation Dist. No. 1, Lubbock, Tex., 1960-61, agrl. engr., 1961-63, engr., 1963-65; NSF trainee civil and agrl. engring. dept. Colo. State U., Ft. Collins, 1965-69; asst. prof. agrl. engring. dept. Tex. A&M U., College Station, 1969-72, assoc. prof. agrl. engring. dept., 1972-77, prof. agrl. engring. dept., 1977-89, prof. and head agrl. engring. dept., 1989-93, prof., 1993—. Author: Numerical Simulation of Dispersion in Groundwater Aquifers, 1970; assoc. editor: Jour. Environ. Quality, 1979-85, Energy in Agr. (The Netherlands), 1981-85; contbr. articles to profl. jours. Recipient Outstanding Jour. Paper award ASCE Jour. Irrigation and Drainage, 1989. Fellow Am. Soc. Agrl. Engrs. (pres. Tex. sect. 1979-80, ASAE Paper award 1977, 82, Agrl. Engr. of Yr. award Tex. sect. 1975, Disting. Young Agrl. Engr. of Yr. award SW region chpt. 1977); mem. Am. Geophys. Union, NSPE. Achievements include co-development of the Laplace Transform Finite Difference, Laplace Transform Finite Element, Laplace Transform Boundary Element, Laplace Transform Solute Transport techniques for modeling groundwater flow, eliminating the need for discretizing time in numerical simulations; development of Method of Characteristics used to describe solute transport in ground water, of automatic advance rate feedback furrow irrigation system. Home: 3808 Courtney Cir Bryan TX 77802-3407 Office: Tex A&M U Agrl Engring Dept College Station TX 77843

REDDEN, JAMES ANTHONY, federal judge; b. Springfield, Mass., Mar. 13, 1929; s. James A. and Alma (Cheek) R.; m. Joan Ida Johnson, July 13, 1950; children: James A., William F. Student, Boston U., 1951; LL.B., Boston Coll., 1954. Bar: Mass., 1954, Oreg., 1955. Pvt. practice Mass., 1954-55; title examiner Title & Trust Ins. Co., Oreg., 1955; claims adjuster Allstate Ins. Co., 1956; mem. firm Collins, Redden, Ferris & Velure, Medford, Oreg., 1957-73; treas. State of Oreg., 1973-77; atty. gen., 1977-80; U.S. dist. judge, now sr. judge U.S. Dist. Ct. Oreg., Portland, 1980—. Chmn. Oreg. Pub. Employee Relations Bd.; mem. Oreg. Ho. of Reps., 1963-69, minority leader, 1967-69. With AUS, 1946-48. Mem. ABA, Mass. Bar Assn., Oreg. State Bar. Office: US Dist Ct 612 US Courthouse 620 SW Main St Portland OR 97205-3023

REDDEN, LAWRENCE DREW, lawyer; b. Tallassee, Ala., Dec. 16, 1922; s. A. Drew and Berta (Baker) R.; m. Christine U. Cunningham, Dec. 20, 1943. A.B., U. Ala., 1943, LL.B., 1949. Bar: Ala. bar 1949. Since practiced in Birmingham; asst. U.S. atty. No. Dist. Ala., 1949-52; partner firm Rogers, Howard, Redden & Mills, 1952-79, Redden, Mills & Clark, 1979—; Civilian aide for Ala. to sec. army, 1965-69; Mem. Ala. Democratic Exec. Com., 1966-74. Editor-in-chief: Ala. Law Rev., 1948. Trustee Ala. Law Sch. Found.; adv. council Cumberland Law Sch. Served with AUS, 1943-46; maj. gen. Res. ret. Decorated D.S.M.; recipient Outstanding Civilian Service medal Dept. Army, 1970. Fellow Am. Coll. Trial Lawyers, Internat. Soc. Barristers; mem. ABA, Am. Judicature Soc., Ala. Bar Assn. (pres. 1972-73), Birmingham Bar Assn. (past pres.), Ala. Law Inst. (mem. coun.), U. Ala. Law Sch. Alumni Assn. (past pres.), Phi Beta Kappa, Alpha Tau Omega, Omicron Delta Kappa. Baptist. Home: 2513 Beaumont Cir Birmingham AL 35216-1301

REDDEN, NIGEL A., performing company executive; b. Nicosia, Cyprus, Nov. 12, 1950; s. Normand William and Annabel (Austin) R. B.A. in Art History, Yale U., 1972. Asst. dir. Italo-American Med. Edn. Found., Rome, 1975-76; press rep. Am. Dance Festival, New London, Conn., 1976; dir. performing arts Walker Art Ctr., Mpls., 1976-82; dir. dance programs Nat. Endowment for the Arts, Washington, 1982-86; gen. mgr. Spoleto Festival USA, Charleston, S.C., 1986-91; exec. dir. Santa Fe (N.Mex.) Opera, 1992-95; exec. prodr. Lincoln Ctr. Festival, N.Y.C., 1995—; cons., panelist Visual Arts program Nat. Endowment for the Arts, 1978, Inter-Arts program, 1979-82, N.W. Area Found., Mpls., 1981-82, MacArthur Found., Chgo., 1983-84; pres. New Music Alliance, Mpls., 1979-80, Am. Music Theater Festival, 1992-94; cons. Tenn. Bicentennial Commn., 1991—, Lincoln Ctr. for the Performing Arts. Mem. Century Club. Office: Lincoln Ctr Performing Arts 70 Lincoln Ctr Plz New York NY 10023

REDDEN, ROGER DUFFEY, lawyer; b. Washington, Dec. 19, 1932; s. Layman J. and Elizabeth (Duffey) R.; m. Gretchen Sause, July 14, 1962. A.B., Yale Coll., 1954; LL.B., U. Md., 1957. Bar: Md. 1958, U.S. Dist. Ct. Md. 1958, U.S. Ct. Appeals (4th cir.) 1958, U.S. Supreme Ct. 1965. Law clk. to judge U.S. Ct. Appeals (4th cir.), 1957-58; assoc. Smith, Somerville & Case, Balt., 1959-63, ptnr., 1965-68; asst. atty. gen. State of Md., 1964-65; ptnr. Piper & Marbury, Balt., 1969—; bd. dirs. Peoples Water Svc. Co.; draftsman Md. State Dept. Legis. Reference, 1958; counsel Md. Savs. and Loan Study Commn., 1960-61; mem. Gov.'s Commn. to revise testamentary laws of Md., 1965-70; mem. standing com. on rules of practice and procedure Md. Ct. Appeals, 1969-73, 88-91, Md. code revision com., 1970—, Appellate Jud. Nominating Commn., 1975-79, Commn. to study Md. Tax Ct., 1978-79, Gov.'s Task Force on Energy, 1991-95; chmn. Task Force on Permits Simplification, 1979-81. Editor in chief Md. Law Rev., 1956-57; contbr. articles to legal jours. Served with U.S. Army, 1958-59, 61-62. Fellow Am. Bar Found., Md. Bar Found.; mem. Md. State Bar Assn. (chmn. probate and estate law sect. 1966-68, chmn. long range planning com. 1972-73, chmn. com. on laws 1988-89, council sect. adminstrv. law 1980-82, council sect. bus. law 1978-81), Balt. City Bar Assn. (chmn. com. on continuing legal edn. 1976-77, chmn. com. on judiciary 1978-79, chmn. com. on by-laws 1981-82), ABA, Jud. Conf. U.S. Ct. Appeals for 4th Cir. (conf. study com. 1982-83). Democrat. Episcopalian. Office: Piper & Marbury 36 S Charles St Baltimore MD 21201-3020

REDDER, THOMAS H., newspaper publishing executive; b. Detroit, 1948. Student, U. Mich. Mich. State U. V.p. info. systems Newsday, Inc., Melville, N.Y. Mem. Data Processing Mgrs. Assn., Newspaper Systems Group. Office: Newsday Inc 235 Pinelawn Rd Melville NY 11747-4226*

REDDIN, GEORGE, religious organization administrator. Dir. Lifeword Broadcast Ministries, Conway, Ark. Office: Lifeword Broadcast Ministries PO Box 6 Conway AR 72033

REDDING, BARBARA J., nursing administrator, occupational health nurse; b. Youngstown, Ohio, Jan. 5, 1938; d. Richard Howard and Helen N.

(Price) Sterling; m. Philip L. Redding, Nov. 7, 1957; children: Cheryl J., Jeffrey A., Scott P. Diploma in nursing, Miami Valley Hosp., Dayton, Ohio, 1959; AA in Sociology, Miami U., Oxford, Ohio, 1984; postgrad., U. Cin. RN, Ohio; cert. EMT, CPR, BLS. Office nurse Dr. Stewart Adam, Dayton; primary nurse Miami Valley Hosp; adminstr. employee health Armco Steel Co., L.P., Middletown, Ohio; v.p. Redding Ins. Agy., Inc., Middletown, Ohio, 1993—. Instr. CPR, ARC. Mem. NAFE, Am. Assn. Occupational Health Nurses, Ind. Ins. Agts. Am., Inc. Home: 4501 Riverview Ave Middletown OH 45042-2938

REDDING, EVELYN A., dean, nursing educator; b. Gulfport, Miss., Mar. 13, 1945; d. Arthur Edward and Rebecca (Morris) R. BSN, U. Ala., 1967; MS, Fla. State U., 1971; EdD, Okla. State U., 1974; cert. PNP, Tex. Women's U., 1974; MSN, Wichita State U., 1980. Psychiat. nurse Camp Ponderosa, Mentone, Ala., 1967; dir. health svcs. Community Action Agy., Head Start, Dadeville, Ala., 1967-68; pediatric nurse All Children's Hosp., St. Petersburg, Fla., 1968-69; instr. Sch. Nursing A&M U., Tallahassee, 1969-71; coord. mater and child health Western Ky. U., Bowling Green, 1971-72; dir. grad. program U. Tex. Health Sci. Ctr., Houston, 1974-78; prof., assoc. dean Coll. Nursing U. Tulsa, 1978-81; dean; prof. Coll. Nursing U. Southwestern La., Lafayette, 1981—; presenter in field. Contbr. articles to profl. jours. Mem. policy adv. bd. Northwest Fla. Family Planning Project, 1969-71, Nurses Coalition for Action in Politics; mem. exec. com. Hospice of Acadiana, 1982-85, pres., bd. dirs., 1984; cons. big Bend Comprehensive Svcs. Clinic, Tallahassee, 1970-71; cons. family planning nurse practitioner program Planned Parenthood Ctr., Houston, 1975-78; cons. grad. edn., nurse clinician program Madigan Army Med. Ctr., Washington, 1975; pres. Dirs. Nursing Edn. and Nursing Svc. Acadiana, 1982-83; docent intern Gilcrease Mus.; chairperson Tulsa Area Dirs. Nursing Svc. and Nursing Edn. Mem. AAUW (cultural affairs and community com.), ANA, Nat. League for Nursing, ANA Coun. Nurse Researchers, Soc. for Rsch. Nursing Edn., La. State Nurses Assn. (program com. dist. IV 1986), Okla. Nurses Assn. (nurse edn. com. dist. 2 1978-79, by-laws com. 1978-80), Tex. Nurses Assn. (chairperson task force for profl. self-determination 1976-78), Coun. Adminstrs. Nursing Edn. La. (presenter 1987-88), Sigma Theta Tau, Omicron Nu. Avocations: bike riding, reading, fishing, yard work. Home: 125 Alyene Dr Lafayette LA 70506-6811 Office: U Southwestern La Coll Nursing PO Box 42490 Lafayette LA 70504-2490

REDDING, PETER STODDARD, manufacturing company executive; b. Bklyn., June 27, 1938; s. Kenneth Benckert and Frances Elizabeth (Hasselman) R.; m. Mary Lorelei LeBrun, Feb. 4, 1961; children: Shelagh, Mark, Todd, Jill. BA, U. Md., 1960; M in Decision Scis., Ga. State U., 1974. Dept. mgr. trainee J.C. Penney Co., 1960-62; sales rep. Standard Register Co., Washington, 1962-66, asst. dist. sales mgr., Washington, 1966-68, Atlanta, 1968-69, dist. sales mgr., Atlanta, 1969-76, regional sales mgr. Pacific region, Orinda, Calif., 1976-79, asst. to pres., Dayton, Ohio, 1979-81, v.p. mktg., 1981-87, v.p. CPG-90, exec. v.p. adminstrn., 1990, exec. v.p., gen. mgr. Forms Div., 1990-94, exec. v.p., COO, 1994, pres., CEO, 1994—; trustee The Children's Med. Ctr., Dayton, Human Race Theatre, Vitoria Theater Assn., Dayton Country Club, Country Club of the North, Orinda Country Club, Racquet Club, Rotary; bd. mem. standard register Soc. Bank, So. Ohio Divsn. Republican. Roman Catholic. Home: 4966 Ashwyck Pl Dayton OH 45429-1902 Office: Standard Register Co 600 Albany St Dayton OH 45408-1442

REDDING, ROGERS WALKER, physics educator; b. Louisville, July 15, 1942; s. George Walker and Carolyn Lorraine (Rogers) R.; m. Jennie Ruth Fincher, Sept. 6, 1966 (div.); children: Jeffrey Walker, Jonathan Hull; m. Shirley Rubrecht, Aug. 24, 1991. BS, Georgia Tech., 1965; PhD, Vanderbilt U., 1969. Research assoc. Nat. Bur. Standards, Washington, 1969-70; from asst. prof. to assoc. prof. North Tex. State U. (name now U. North Tex.), Denton, 1970-78, prof. physics, 1978-84, prof. chmn., 1980-87, dir. Tex. Acad. Math. and Sci., 1987-89, assoc. dean arts and scis., 1990-94; former prof. physics, dean Coll. Arts and Scis. No. Ky. U., Highland Heights; disting. vis. prof. USAF Acad., 1989-90. Author: Exploring Physics, 1984; contbr. articles to profl. jours. Mem. Am. Phys. Soc., Am. Assn. Physics Tchrs., AAAS, Optical Soc. Am. Democrat. Lodge: Kiwanis. Avocations: handball; jogging; referee high school and college football; little league coach. Home: 825 Woodmoor Dr Coppell TX 75019-3093 Office: No Ky U Coll Arts & Scis Highland Heights KY 41099*

REDDY, HELEN MAXINE, singer; b. Melbourne, Australia, Oct. 25, 1941; came to U.S., 1966; d. Max David and Stella Campbell (Lamond) R.; m. Jeff Wald, Nov. 1, 1966 (div.); children: Traci Donat, Jordan; m. Milton Robert Ruth. Student, UCLA Extension. Ind. entertainer, rec. artist, actress, 1966—; pres. entertainment prodn. co. Helen Reddy, Inc., 1983—. Rec. artist, composer I Am Woman, 1973 (Grammy award 1973); rec. artist: Delta Dawn, 1978, Crazy Love, I Don't Know How To Love Him, Peaceful, Keep on Singing, You and Me Against the World, Angie Baby, 1978, Leave Me Alone, 1978; star NBC Summer Show, 1973, permanent host Midnight Special; actress: (films) Pete's Dragon, 1977, Airport, 1975; (theatre) Blood Brothers, 1994-95; entertainer numerous concerts on 6 continents. Active Nat. Women's Polit. Caucus, Women's Ctr., Alliance for Women in Prison; commr. Calif. Dept. Parks and Recreation. Recipient Image award NAACP, 1974, Humanitarian award B'nai B'rith, N.Y., 1975, Maggie award People Helping People, L.A., 1976, numerous Gold and Platinum Album awards Rec. Industry Assn. Am.; named Woman of Yr., L.A. Times, 1975; honoree for her advocacy for women's health issues and AIDS, Weizmann Inst. of Sci. Founders Event, 1993. Mem. NOW.

REDDY, J. NARASIMHA, mechanical engineering educator. Formerly prof. mech. engring. Va. Poly. Inst. and State U., Blacksburg, Va.; prof. mech. engring Tex. A&M U., College Station, 1994—. Recipient Worcester Reed Warner medal ASME, 1992. Office: Texas A&M Univ Dept Mech Engring College Station TX 77843-3123

REDDY, KAMBHAM RAJA, plant physiology educator; b. Ambuvari Palli, India, July 1, 1953; came to U.S., 1988; s. Kambi Kambham and Ammamnamma (Reddy) R.; m. Anasuya Kambham, Feb. 9, 1982; 1 child, Sasank. BSc, S.V. U., Tirupati, India, 1975, MSc in Botany, 1977, PhD in Botany, 1984. Curator in botany S.V. U., 1977-88; asst. prof. plant physiology Miss. State U., 1988—; vis. scientist Govt. of India, 1988. Contbg. author: Climate Change and Agriculture: Analysis of Potential International Impacts, 1995. Mem. Agronomy Soc. Am., Crop Sci. Soc. Am., Biol. Sys. Simulation Work Group, Gamma Sigma Delta (Rsch. Merit award 1995). Achievements include development of new theories and concepts in plant growth regulation and incorporated into a cotton model GOSSYM/COMAX, used by cotton producers, consultants and researchers across the cotton belt. Home: PO Box 3648 Mississippi State MS 39762 Office: Mississippi State U PO Box 5367 Mississippi State MS 39762

REDDY, KRISHNA NARAYANA, artist, educator; b. Chittoor, India, July 15, 1925; s. Narayana B. and Laksmamma R.; m. Judith Blum, June 30, 1967; 1 child, Aparna. Diploma in Fine Arts, Internat. U. Santiniketan, India, 1947; cert. in Fine Arts, Slade Sch. Fine Arts, U. London, 1952; student of Zadkine in sculpture, Academie Grande Chaumière, Paris, 1952-55; student of Marino Marini in sculpture, Academia di Belle Arti di Brera, Milan, 1956-57; specialist in Gravure, Internat. Ctr. for Graphics, Atelier 17, Paris, 1952-55; D.Litt. (hon.), S.V. Univ., India, 1984. Asst. dir. Internat. Ctr. for Graphics, Atelier 17, Paris, 1957-64, prof., co-dir., 1964-76; prof. art, dir. graphics and printmaking program, dept. art and art edn. N.Y. U., N.Y.C., 1977—; lectr. art Arundale Montessori Tchrs. Tng. Center, 1948-49; dir. art dept. Coll. Fine Arts, Kalakshetra, Madras, India, 1947-49; vis. prof. Yale U. Summer Sch. Music and Art, 1978, Am. U., 1964, Kala Inst. Graphics, Berkeley, Calif., 1979, U. Calif., Santa Cruz, 1979, Andrew Mellon vis. prof. Cooper Union Sch. Art and Architecture, 1977; prof. U. Wis., Madison, 1973, U. Calif., Davis, 1970-71; guest prof. Nashik Sch. Music and Art, 1973. Retrospective exhbns., Bronx Mus. Arts, 1981-82, Indian Council for Cultual Relations, Ministry of Culture and India Nat. Acad. Fine Arts, 1984-85, Museo del Palacio de Bellas Artes, Mexico City, 1988-89. Recipient Gagan-Abani Puraskar Nat. award Viswa-Bharati, 1983; named Featured Guest Artist Printmaker of Yr., Northwest Print Council Ann. Meeting, 1985. Title of Padma Shree awarded by Pres. of India, 1972. Home: 80 Wooster St New York NY 10012-4347 Office: NYU Dept Art and Art Edn New York NY 10003

REDDY, NAGENDRANATH K., biochemist, researcher; b. Bangalore, India, Nov. 18, 1937; came to U.S., 1968; s. K. Rami and K. (Gnanamma) R.; m. Saraswati K., May 11, 1967; children: Kalpana, Sandip. BS, SRI Venkateswara U., Madras, 1957; MS, U. Saugor, Madhya Pradesh, India, 1959; PhD, Indian Inst. Sci., Bangalore, 1971. Jr. research asst. Nat. Dairy Research Inst., Bangalore, 1959-60; sr. research asst. Indian Inst. Sci., Bangalore, 1965-68; research assoc. Roswell Park Meml. Inst., Buffalo, 1968-73; asst. prof. U. Cin., 1975-80; asst. prof. research biochemistry U. So. Calif., L.A., 1980-90; biochemist Sci. Svcs. Bur., L.A., 1990—. Editor: Fibrinolysis, 1980; patentee fibrinolytic enzyme from snake venom; contbr. articles to profl. jours. Recipient Research Career Devel. award NIH, 1978. Mem. AAAS, Am. Soc. Biol. Chemists. Avocation: stamp collecting. Home: 3402 S Punta Del Este Dr La Puente CA 91745-6634

REDDY, PRATAP CHANDUPATLA, cardiologist, educator, researcher; b. Laxmipur, Andhra Pradesh, India, Apr. 12, 1944; came to U.S., 1969; s. Chandra C. and Butchamma (Kota) R.; m. Shobha Katangur, May 15, 1971; children: Ashutosh, Kirthi. MBBS, Osmania U., Hyderabad, India, 1968. Diplomate Am. Bd. Internal Medicine, Am. Bd. Cardiovascular Diseases. Resident in internal medicine St. Vincent Med. Ctr., S.I., N.Y., 1969-73; fellow in cardiology Maimonide Med. Ctr., Bklyn., 1973-74; rsch. assoc. USPHS Hosp., S.I., 1974-76; asst. prof. medicine U. Ky., Lexington, 1976-81, dir. cardiac electrophysiology, 1976-84, assoc. prof., 1981-84; prof. medicine La. State U. Med. Ctr., Shreveport, 1984—, assoc. dir. cardiology, 1984—, dir. cardiac electrophysiology program, 1984—; attending cardiologist VA Med. Ctr., Shreveport, La. Editor: Tachycardia, 1984; contbr. articles to profl. jours. Named Kentucky Colonel Gov. Ky., 1983. Fellow ACP, Am. Coll. Cardiology; mem. AMA, Am. Heart Assn. (v.p. La. affiliate 1988-89, pres. 1991-92, mem. coun. clin. cardiology), Cen. Soc. for Clin. Rsch., N.Am. Soc. Pacing and Electrophysiology. Office: La State U Med Sch 1530 Kings Hwy Shreveport LA 71103-4229

REDDY, YENAMALA RAMACHANDRA, metal processing executive; b. Polavaram, Andhra, India, Feb. 12, 1939; came to U.S., 1974; s. Y. Venkata and Y. Lakshamamma Reddy; m. Y. Uma Reddy, May 30, 1965; children: Y. Sharath, Y. Jay. BME, S.V. U., Andhra, 1961; M in Tech., IIT, Bombay, 1966, PhD, 1970. Lic. profl. engr., Wis. Asst. prof. IIT, Bombay, 1966-69; research and devel. mgr. Jyoti Pumps, Baroda, 1973-74; chief engr. Patterson Pumps, Toccoa, Ga., 1974-80; pres. R.B. Pump Co., Baxley, 1980—, U.B. Cons., Ga., 1980—. Contbr. articles to tech. jours. Postdoctoral fellow U. of Tech., Loughborough, Eng., 1970-73. Mem. Am. Soc. of Mech. Engrs. Office: R B Pump Co 1 Dixie Dr # 557 Baxley GA 31513

REDEKER, ALLAN GRANT, physician, medical educator; b. Lincoln, Nebr., Sept. 10, 1924; s. Fred Julius and Fern Frances (Grant) R.; m. Andrea K. Siedschlag, June 16, 1979; children by previous marriage—Martha, James, Thomas. B.S., Northwestern U., Chgo., 1949, M.D., 1952. Intern Hollywood Presbyn. Hosp., Los Angeles, 1952-53; resident in internal medicine Hollywood Presbyn. Hosp., 1953-54; asst. prof. medicine U. So. Calif., 1959-62, assoc. prof., 1962-69, prof., 1969—; mem. Nat. Digestive Diseases Adv. Bd., 1985-88; mem. U.S.-Japan Med. Sci. Program, U.S. Dept. State, 1978—; bd. dirs. Am. Liver Found. Contbr. numerous articles to research jours. Served with AUS, 1943-46. Recipient Research Career Devel. award NIH, 1962-69; research fellow Giannini Found., 1956-58. Mem. Assn. Am. Physicians, Am. Soc. Clin. Investigation, Am. Gastroent. Assn. Home: 9323 Samoline Ave Downey CA 90240-2716 Office: 7601 Imperial Hwy Downey CA 90242-3456

REDEKER, JAMES RUSSELL, lawyer; b. Primghar, Iowa, May 28, 1941; s. Russell James and Alice (Englesmann) R.; m. Nancy Vargish; children: Rebecca Hope, Eric James, Tricia Marie. BA, Cen. U. Iowa, 1963; MA, U. Ark., 1964; JD, U. Pa., 1968. Bar: Pa. 1968. From assoc. to ptnr. Cohen, Shapiro, Polisher, Shiekman & Cohen, Phila., 1971-78; ptnr. Saul, Ewing, Remick & Saul, Phila., 1978-86; ptnr., chmn. labor law dept., mem. exec. com. Wolf, Block, Schorr & Solis-Cohen, Phila., 1986—; bd. dirs. Pers. Mag., Human Resource Profl. Mag. Author: Employee Discipline, 1983, Redeker on Discipline, 1985, Employee Discipline: Policies and Practices, 1989; contbr. numerous articles to pers. mags. and legal jours. Founder, exec. bd. mem. Support Ctr. for Child Advocates, Phila., 1975; mem. Child Welfare Adv. Bd., Phila., 1983-88; mem. Commn. on Youth in Detention, Phila., 1985; mem. Mayor's Blue Ribbon Adv. Bd. for Youth Detention Ctr., Phila., 1985. Recipient Fidelity Bank award Phila. Bar, 1976; named Vol. of Yr., Dept. Health and Welfare, Region III, Phila., 1983, One of Phila. 100 Leaders to Watch, Phila. Bus. Mag., 1994. Mem. ABA, Pa. Bar Assn., Phila. Bar Assn. (Fidelity award 1976), Am. Soc. Human Resources Mgmt., Indsl. Rels. Assn. Greater Phila., Pa. Chamber Bus. and Industry (indsl. rels. com. 1978—, Human Resources Profl. of Yr. 1991), Internat. Assn. Pers. Women. Republican. Presbyterian. Office: Wolf Block Schorr & Solis-Cohen 111 S 15th St Philadelphia PA 19102-2625

REDENBACH, SANDRA IRENE, educational consultant; b. Boston, Nov. 18, 1940; d. David and Celia (Wish) Goldstein; m. Gunter L. Redenbach, Mar. 16, 1963 (div. 1980); 1 child, Cori-Lin; m. Kenneth L. Gelatt, June 25, 1989. BA, U. Calif., Davis, 1972; postgrad. in Ednl. Leadership, St. Mary's Coll., Moraga, Calif., 1988, 93-95. Cert. tchr., Calif. Tchr. Solano County Juvenile Hall, Fairfield, Calif., 1968-70, St. Basil's Sch., Vallejo, Calif., 1970-73, St. Philomenes Sch., Sacramento, 1973; tchr., assoc. dean Vet.'s Spl. Edn. Program, U. Calif., Davis, 1973-75, Woodland (Calif.) Jr. High Sch., 1973-76, Lee Jr. High Sch., Woodland, 1976-79, Woodland High Sch., 1979-89; founder, coord., tchr. Ind. Learning Ctr., Woodland, 1989-94; dir. curriculum and instrn. Dixon (Calif.) Unified Sch. Dist., 1994—; teaching asst., lectr. U. Calif., Davis, 1985-86; pres., cons. Esteem Seminar Programs and Pubs., Davis, 1983—; cons., leader workshop. Author: Self-Esteem: The Necessary Ingredient for Success, 1991; author tng. manual: Self-Esteem: A Training Manual, 1990-91, Innovative Discipline: Managing Your Own Flight Plan, 1994. Active Dem. Club of Davis, 1976-79; human rights chair Capitol Svc. Ctr., Sacramento, 1987-92. Martin Luther King scholar, 1986; Nat. Found. for Improvement of Edn. grantee, 1987-88. Mem. Assn. Calif. Sch. Adminstrs., Woodland Edn. Assn. (pres. 1980-83, Outstanding Educator 1992, 93), Phi Delta Kappa (pres. 1992-93). Jewish. Avocations: singing, acting, dancing, travel, politics. Home: 313 Del Oro Ave Davis CA 95616-0416 Office: Esteem Seminar Programs & Publs 313 Del Oro Ave Davis CA 95616-0416

REDFERN, JOHN D., manufacturing company executive; b. 1935. Grad. Queen's U., Kingston, Ont., 1958, DEng (honoris causa), Carleton U., 1992. With Lafarge Can. Inc. (formerly Can. Cement Lafarge Ltd.), Montreal, 1977—, pres., chief exec. officer, 1977-84, chmn., 1985—; chmn. bd. parent co. Lafarge Corp., Reston, Va., 1985-88, vice-chmn., 1989— Office: Lafarge Can Inc, 606 Cathcart Ste 800, Montreal, PQ Canada H3B 1L7

REDFORD, DONALD BRUCE, historian, archaeologist; b. Toronto, Ont., Can., Sept. 2, 1934; s. Cyril Fitzjames and Kathleen Beryl (Coe) R.; m. Susan Pirritano, Jan. 30, 1982; children: Alexander, Aksel; children by previous marriage: Christopher, Philip. B.A., U. Toronto, 1957, M.A., 1958; Ph.D., Brown U., 1965. Lectr. Brown U., 1960-61; lectr. U. Toronto, 1961-64, asst. prof. Egyptian history and language, 1965-67, asso. prof., 1967-69, prof., 1969—; site supr. Brit. Sch. Archaeol. Excavations, Jerusalem, 1964-67; dir. Soc. Study Egyptian Antiquities Expdn. to, Karnak, Egypt, 1970-72, Akhenaten Temple Project, Luxor, Egypt, 1972—; research asso. Univ. Museum, U. Pa., Royal Ont. Mus. Author: History and Chronology of the Egyptian 18th Dynasty, 1967, A Study of the Biblical Joseph Story, 1970, Papyrus and Tablet, 1973, The Akhenaten Temple Project, vol. I, 1975, Akhenaten, the Heretic King, 1984; Annals, King-Lists and Daybooks, 1986, The Akhenaten Temple Project, vol. II, 1988, Egypt, Canaan and Israel in Ancient Times, 1992. Killam grantee, 1975-79; Smithsonian Fgn. Currency grantee, 1973-76, 1979, Social Scis. Humanities Research Council Can. grantee, 1980—. Fellow Royal Soc. Can. Discovered Temple of Akhenaten at Luxor, 1976. Office: U Toronto, Dept Near Eastern Studies, Toronto, ON Canada M5S 1A1

REDFORD, ROBERT (CHARLES ROBERT REDFORD), actor, director; b. Santa Monica, Calif., Aug. 18, 1937; m. Lola Van Wegenen (div.); children: Shauna, Jamie, Amy. Student, U. Colo., Pratt Inst. Design, Am. Acad. Dramatic Arts; LHD (hon.), U. Colo., 1987; D (hon.), U. Mass., 1990. Owner ski resort Sundance, Provo, Utah. Stage appearances include:

Tall Story, The Highest Tree, Sunday in New York, Barefoot in the Park; Films include: (actor) War Hunt, 1961, Situation Hopeless But Not Serious, 1965, Inside Daisy Clover, 1965, The Chase, 1966, This Property Is Condemned, 1966, Barefoot in the Park, 1967, Butch Cassidy and the Sundance Kid, 1969, Tell Them Willie Boy is Here, 1969, Little Fauss and Big Halsey, 1970, The Hot Rock, 1972, Jeremiah Johnson, 1972, The Way We Were, 1973, The Sting, 1973 (Academy award nominee), The Great Gatsby, 1974, The Great Waldo Pepper, 1975, Three Days of the Condor, 1975, A Bridge Too Far, 1977, The Electric Horseman, 1979, Brubaker, 1980, The Natural, 1984, Out of Africa, 1985, Legal Eagles, 1986, Havana, 1990, Sneakers, 1992, Indecent Proposal, 1993; (actor, exec. prodr.) Downhill Racer, 1969, The Candidate, 1972, All The President's Men, 1976; (exec. prodr.) Promised Land, 1988, Some Girls, 1988, The Dark Wind; (exec. prodr., narrator) Yosemite: The Fate of Heaven, 1989, Incident at Ogala, 1992; (dir.) Ordinary People, 1980 (Academy and Golden Globe Awards, Best Director); (dir., prodr.) The Milagro Beanfield War, 1988, Quiz Show, 1994; (dir., prodr., narrator) A River Runs Through It, 1993. Recipient Audubon medal, 1989, Dartmouth Film Soc. award, 1990; Cecil B. Demille Golden Globe Award for Lifetime Achievement, 1994. *

REDGRAVE, LYNN, actress; b. London, Eng., Mar. 8, 1943; d. Michael Scudemore and Rachel (Kempson) R.; m. John Clark, Apr. 2, 1967; children: Benjamin, Kelly, Annabel. Ed.; Queensgate Sch., London, Central Sch. Speech and Drama, London. Stage debut as Helena in Midsummer Night's Dream, 1962; theatrical appearances include The Tulip Tree, Andorra, Hayfever, Much Ado About Nothing, Mother Courage, Love for Love, Zoo, Zoo, Widdershins Zoo, Edinburgh Festival, 1969, The Two of Us, London, 1970, Slag, London, 1971, A Better Place, Dublin, 1972, Born Yesterday, Greenwich, 1973, Hellzapoppin, N.Y., 1976, California Suite, 1977, Twelfth Night, Stratford Conn. Shakespeare Festival, 1978, The King and I, St. Louis, 1983, Les Liaisons Dangereuses, L.A., 1989, The Cherry Orchard, L.A., 1990, Three Sisters, London, 1990; Broadway appearances include Black Comedy, 1967, My Fat Friend, 1974, Mrs. Warren's Profession (Tony award nomination), 1975, Knock, Knock, 1976, St. Joan, 1977, Sister Mary Ignatius Explains It All, 1985, Aren't We All?, 1985, Sweet Sue, 1987, A Little Hotel on the Side, 1992, The Masterbuilder, 1992, Shakespeare For My Father (Tony and Drama Desk nominations, Elliot award 1993), 1993, also nat. tour, 1993; film appearances include Tom Jones, Girl With Green Eyes, Georgy Girl (Recipient N.Y. Film Critics award, Golden Globe award, Oscar nomination for best actress 1967), The Deadly Affair, Smashing Time, The Virgin Soldiers, Last of the Mobile Hotshots, Don't Turn the Other Cheek, Every Little Crook and Nanny, Everything You Always Wanted to Know About Sex, The National Health, The Happy Hooker, The Big Bus, Sunday Lovers, Morgan Stuart's Coming Home, Getting It Right; TV appearances include: The Turn of the Screw, Centennial, 1978, The Muppets, Gauguin the Savage, Beggarman Thief, The Seduction of Miss Leona, Rehearsal for Murder, 1982, Walking On Air, The Fainthearted Feminist (BBC-TV), 1984, My Two Loves, 1986, The Old Reliable, 1988, Jury Duty 1989, Whatever Happened to Baby Jane, 1990, Fighting Back (BBC-TV), 1992, Calling the Shots (Masterpiece Theatre), 1993; guest appearances include Carol Burnett Show, Evening at the Improv and Steve Martin's Best show Ever, Circus of the Stars; co-host nat. TV syndication Not for Women Only, 1977—; nat., TV spokesperson Weightwatchers, 1984-92; TV series include House Calls, 1981, Teachers Only, 1982, Chicken Soup, 1989; albums: Make Mine Manhattan, 1978, Cole Porter Revisited, 1979; video: (for children) Meet Your Animal Friends, Off We Go, Off We Go Again; audio book readings include, Pride and Prejudice, The Shell Seekers, The Blue Bedroom, The Anastasia Syndrome, The Women in His Life, Snow In April, Gone With The Wind, 1994; author: This is Living, 1990. Named Runner-up Actress, All Am. Favorites, Box Office Barometer 1975; recipient Sarah Siddons award as Chgo.'s best stage actress of 1976, 94. Mem. The Players (pres. 1994). Office: care John Clark PO Box 1207 Topanga CA 90290-1207

REDGRAVE, VANESSA, actress; b. London, Jan. 30, 1937; d. Michael and Rachel (Kempson) R.; m. Tony Richardson, Apr. 28, 1962 (div.); children: Natasha Jane, Joely Kim, Carlo. Student, Central Sch. Speech and Drama, London, 1955-57. Prin. theatrical roles include Helena in Midsummer Night's Dream, 1959, Stella in Tiger and the Horse, 1960, Katerina in The Taming of the Shrew, 1961, Rosalind in As You Like It, 1961, Imogene in Cymbeline, 1962, Nina in The Seagull, 1964, Miss Brodie in The Prime of Miss Jean Brodie, 1966; other plays include Cato Street, 1971, Threepenny Opera, 1972, Twelfth Night, 1972, Antony and Cleopatra, 1973, Design for Living, 1973, Macbeth, 1975, Lady from the Sea, 1976, 78, 79, The Aspern Papers, 1984, The Seagull, 1985, Chekhov's Women, 1985, The Taming of the Shrew, Ghosts, 1986, Touch of the Poet, 1988, Orpheus Descending, 1989, A Madhouse in Goa, 1989, Three Sisters, 1990, When She Danced, 1991, Heartbreak House, 1991, Maybe, 1993, Brecht in Hollywood, 1994, Vita and Virginia, 1994—; film roles include Leonie in Morgan-A Suitable Case for Treatment, 1965 (Best Actress award Cannes Film Festival 1966), Sheila in Sailor from Gibraltar, 1965, Anne-Marie in La Musica, 1965, Jane in Blow-Up, 1967, Guinevere in Camelot, 1967, Isadora in Isadora Duncan, 1968 (Best Actress award Cannes Film Festival); other films include The Charge of the Light Brigade, 1968, The Seagull, 1968, A Quiet Place in the Country, 1968, Daniel Deronda, 1969, Dropout, 1969, The Trojan Women, 1970, The Devils, 1970, The Holiday, 1971, Mary, Queen of Scots, 1971, Murder on the Orient Express, 1974, Winter Rates, 1974, 7 per cent solution, 1975, Julia, 1977 (Academy award Best Supporting Actress, Golden Globe award), Agatha, 1978, Yanks, 1978, Bear Island, 1979, Playing for Time, 1980, My Body My Child, 1981, Wagner, 1982, The Bostonians, 1984 (Oscar nomination Best Actress, Golden Globe nomination), Wetherby, 1985, Steaming, 1985, Prick Up Your Ears, 1987, Comrades, 1987, Consuming Passions, 1988, Diceria dell'Untore, 1989, The Ballad of the Sad Café, 1990, Howard's End, 1992 (Oscar nomination Best Supporting Actress), Great Moments in Aviation, 1993, Crime and Punishment, 1993, The House of the Spirits, 1994, Mother's Boys, 1994, A Month by the Lake, 1995, Little Odessa, 1995; TV film and miniseries appearances include Snow White and the Seven Dwarfs, 1985, Three Sovereigns for Sarah, 1985, Peter the Great, 1986, Second Serve, 1986 (Emmy award, Golden Globe award), A Man for All Seasons, 1988, Young Catherine, 1990, Whatever Happened to Baby Jane, 1990, Playing for Time (Emmy award), The Wall, 1992, Down Came A Blackbird, 1994; Author: Pussies and Tigers, 1964, (autobiography) Vanessa, 1991, Vanessa Redgrave: An Autobiography, 1994. Bd. govs. Central Sch. Speech and Drama, 1963—. Decorated comdr. Order Brit. Empire; recipient 4 times Drama award Evening Standard, 1961-91, Best Actress award Variety Club Gt. Brit., 1961, 66, Best Actress award Brit. Guild TV Producers and Dirs., 1966, Laurence Olivier award Best Actress for The Aspern Papers, 1984, London Standard Drama award Best Actress for The Seagull, 1985, New York Film Critics Circle award Best Supporting Actress for Prick Up Your Ears, 1988, Evening Standard award Best Actress for When She Danced, 1991, Ace award Best Supporting Actress movie/mini-series for Young Catherine, 1992, Variety Club of Great Britain award, 1992, Best Actress Nat. Film Critics (USA) New Delhi Internat. Film Festival for The Bostonians, Laurence Olivier award Actress of the Yr. in a Revival for A Touch of the Poet; fellow Brit. Film Inst., 1988. *

REDHEAD, PAUL AVELING, physicist; b. Brighton, Eng., May 25, 1924; m. Doris Packman, 1948; children: Janet, Patricia. BA with honors in Physics, Cambridge (Eng.) U., 1944, MA, 1948, PhD, 1969. Sci. officer dept. naval ordnance Brit. Admiralty, 1944-45, svcs. electronics rsch. lab., 1945-47; rsch. officer NRC Can., Ottawa, Ont., 1947-69; dir. planning group NRC Can., 1970-72, dir.-gen. planning, 1972-73, dir. div. physics, 1973-86, chmn. com. of lab. dirs., 1981-86, sec. sci. and tech. policy com., 1986-89, researcher emeritus, 1989—. Author: Physical Basis of Ultrahigh Vacuum, 1968, 2d edit., 1993; editor: Jour. Vacuum Scis. and Tech., 1969-74; contbr. numerous articles to profl. jours. Fellow IEEE, Royal Soc. Can., Am. Phys. Soc., Am. Vacuum Soc. (past pres., Medard W. Welch award 1975); mem. Can. Assn. Physicists (medal for achievement in physics 1989). Patentee in field. Home: 1958 Norway Crescent, Ottawa, ON Canada K1H 5N7 Office: Nat Rsch Coun Can, Inst Microstructural Scis, Ottawa, ON Canada K1A OR6

REDHEFFER, RAYMOND MOOS, mathematician, educator; b. Chgo., Apr. 17, 1921; s. Raymond L. and Elizabeth (Moos) R.; m. Heddy Gross Stiefel, Aug. 25, 1951; 1 son, Peter Bernard. S.B., MIT, 1943, S.M., 1946, Ph.D., 1948; DSc (hon.), Karlruhe, 1991. Rsch. assoc. MIT Radiation Lab., 1942-45, Rsch. Lab. of Electronics, 1946-48; instr. Harvard U., Rad-

cliffe Coll., 1948-50; mem. faculty UCLA, 1950—, prof. math., 1960—; guest prof. Tech. U. Berlin, 1962, Inst. for Angewandte Math., Hamburg, 1966, Math. Inst. U. Karlsruhe, 1971-72, 81, 88, 91, 95; U.S. sr. scientist Alexander von Humboldt Found., Karlsruhe, 1976, 85. Author: (with Ivan Sokolnikoff) Mathematics of Physics and Modern Engineering, 1958, (with Charles Eames) Men of Modern Mathematics, 1966, (with Norman Levinson) Complex Variables, 1970, Differential Equations, Theory and Applications, 1991, Introduction to Differential Equations, 1992; film author, animator, 1972-74; contbr. articles to profl. jours. Pierce fellow Harvard U., 1948-50; sr. postdoctoral fellow NSF, Göttingen, Germany, 1956; Fulbright rsch. scholar Vienna, 1957, Hamburg, 1961-62; recipient Disting. Teaching award UCLA Alumni Assn., 1969. Mem. Deutsche Akademie der Naturforscher (Leopoldina), Sigma Xi. Home: 176 N Kenter Ave Los Angeles CA 90049-2730 Office: UCLA Dept Mathematics 6224 Math Sci Bldg Los Angeles CA 90024

REDIG, DALE FRANCIS, dentist, association executive; b. Arcadia, Iowa, Mar. 24, 1929; s. Philip F. and Clara (Bohnenkamp) R.; m. Diane Marie Murphy, June 13, 1953; children: Mary Catherine, John Francis, Ann Bennett. Student, U. Iowa, 1949-51, DDS, 1955, MS, 1965. Pvt. practice specializing in pediatric dentistry Des Moines, 1955-61; mem. faculty U. Iowa Coll. Dentistry, Iowa City, 1961-69; assoc. prof. pedodontics U. Iowa Coll. Dentistry, 1968-69, head dept., 1964-69; Fulbright lectr. U. Baghdad, 1963-64; dean Sch. Dentistry U. Pacific, San Francisco, 1969-78; exec. dir. Calif. Dental Assn., Sacramento, 1978—; bd. dirs. CDA Holding Co., chmn., 1993—; mem. dental health rsch. and edn. adv. com. USPHS, 1972-74; UN devel. program cons. to Quatar Ministry of Health, 1991. Dir dental div. Des Moines United Campaign, 1958; bd. dirs Des Moines Health Ctr., 1956-61, pres., 1961; bd. dirs. Am. Fund for Dental Health, 1976-84, pres., 1980-83; regent U. Pacific, 1986—, chmn. bd. dirs. 1994; mem. adv. bd. Golden Gate U., 1992—; bd. dirs. Sacramento Theater Co., 1994—; mem. corp. cabinet Sacramento AIDS Found., 1994—. With USAAF, 1946-49. Mem. ADA (ednl. cons. Vietnam 1968, mem. coun. on dental edn. 1974-78), Am. Soc. Dentistry for Children, Am. Acad. Pediatric Dentistry (bd. dirs 1972-75), Am. Coll. Dentists, Internat. Coll. Dentists, Am. Soc. Constituent Dental Execs. (pres. 1989-90). Office: Calif Dental Assn PO Box 13749 Sacramento CA 95853-4749

REDIKER, ROBERT HARMON, physicist; b. Bklyn., June 7, 1924; s. Moe J. and Estelle (Rosenwasser) R.; m. Barbara June Zenn, May 26, 1980; children by previous marriage: Richard J., Donald E. SB, MIT, 1947, PhD, 1950. Research asso. physics MIT, 1950-51; staff Lincoln Lab., Lexington, Mass., 1951-52, 53-57; asst. group leader semi-conductor physics Lincoln Lab., 1957-59, group leader applied physics, 1959-66; prof. dept. elec. engring. MIT, 1966-76, adj. prof., 1976-82, sr. research scientist, 1982—; asso. head optics div. Lincoln Lab., 1970-72, head optics div., 1972-80, sr. staff, 1980-91; sr. v.p. advanced R&D Cynosure Inc., 1992—; research assoc. physics Ind. U., 1952-53; Vice pres. Newton Lower Falls Improvement Assn., 1968-71; Mem. spl. group optical masers Def. Dept., 1966-73, working group D (lasers), 1973-76, working group C (electro-optics), 1979-92, mem. adv. group on electron devices, high energy laser rev. group, 1973-75; mem. ad hoc com. on materials and processes for electron devices Nat. Acad. Scis., 1970-72; mem. evaluation panel Nat. Bur. Standards, 1975-78; mem. panel on Office of Naval Research Opportunities in Physics, 1988, 91. Author. Served with Signal Corps AUS, 1943-46. Fellow IEEE (mem. com. solid state devices 1961-63, sec. treas. group electron devices 1965-66, vice chmn. 1967, awards bd. 1976-79, chmn. Liebmann awards com. 1977-78, David Sarnoff award 1969), Am. Phys. Soc., Optical Soc. Am.; mem. Nat. Acad. Engring., Sigma Xi, Alpha Epsilon Pi. Jewish. Patentee in field. Home: 151 Coolidge Ave Watertown MA 02172 Office: MIT Rm 36-487 Cambridge MA 02139

REDING, NICHOLAS LEE, chemical company executive; b. Algona, Iowa, Nov. 7, 1934; s. Louis Clair and Alice Rosanne (Steil) R.; m. Patricia Jane Finnegan, Aug. 2, 1958; children: Nancy Allison, Scott Nicholas. B-SchemE, Iowa State U., 1956; grad. exec. program, Stanford U., 1975. With Monsanto Co., 1956—; v.p. mng. dir. Monsanto Agrl. Products Co., St. Louis, 1976-78; group v.p., mng. dir. Monsanto Agrl. Products Co., 1978-81, exec. v.p., 1981—; pres. Monsanto Agrl. Co., St. Louis, 1986-90; exec. v.p environ., safety, health and mfg. Monsanto Co., St. Louis, 1990—; mem. mgmt. com. parent co., bd. dirs. Internat. Multifoods Corp., 1986—; bd. dirs. NutraSweet Co., G.D. Searle & Co., Internat. Environ. Bur., The Keystone Ctr. Bd. dirs., exec. com. United Way greater St. Louis, 1982—, St. Louis Country Day Sch., 1986-90; bd. dirs. St. Louis Children's Hosp., 1986-91, St. Louis Mcpl. Theatre Assn., 1989—, St. Louis Zoo, 1990—; chancellor's coun. U. Mo., St. Louis, 1988—; mem. Conf. bd. coun. on Environ. Affairs. Recipient award for excellence in agrl. mktg. Nat. Agri-Mktg. Assn., 1982. Mem. Nat. Agrl. Chem. Assn. (chmn. exec. com. 1980-81, bd. dirs. 1986-91), Alpha Zeta (hon.), St. Louis Club, Bellerive Country Club, Bogey Club. Methodist. Office: Monsanto Co 800 N Lindbergh Blvd Saint Louis MO 63167

REDINGER, JAMES COLLINS, investment banker, financial consultant; b. Canonsburg, Pa., Mar. 21, 1937; s. Ruel Otis and Catherine (Collins) R.; m. Elizabeth Anne Gustason, Sept. 9, 1961; children: Michael, Jill Anne, Andrew, Patrick, Susan. BS, Purdue U., 1959; postgrad., N.Y. Sch. Fin., 1960-61. Stockbroker William J. Mericka & Co., Cleve., 1960-63, Hayden Miller & Co., Cleve., 1963-69; v.p. Saunders Stiver & Co., Cleve., 1969-71, J.N. Russell, Cleve., 1971-74; mng. dir. McDonald & Co., Cleve., 1974—; bd. dirs., pres. MCD Real Estate Inc., McDonald Money Market Funds; bd. dirs. Cleve., MCD Oil & Gas, Cleve, McDonald Capital Mgmt., Cleve. Mem. pres.'s coun. Purdue U., West Lafayette, Ind., 1988-89; trustee Johnson Island Trust, Marblehead, Ohio, 1988—. With USAAF, 1959-60. Mem. Nat. Assn. Securities Dealers (chmn. midwest region 1983-86), Securities Industry Assn., Cleve. Bond Club, Purdue U. Alumni Assn., Commerce Club, Westwood Country Club, Catawba Island Club, Society Club. Republican. Roman Catholic. Avocations: golf, football, basketball, boating. Home: 520 Kimerly Ct Cleveland OH 44140-1541 Office: McDonald & Co Securities Inc 800 Superior Ave Ste 2100 Cleveland OH 44114

REDINGTON, ROWLAND WELLS, physicist, researcher; b. Otego, N.Y., Sept. 26, 1924; s. Raymond Edgar and Sara Jane (Trask) R.; m. Shirley Alice Bennett, June 27, 1947; children: John Bennett, Philip Edgar. ME, Stevens Inst. Tech., 1945; PhD, Cornell U., 1951. Sr. aerodynamicist research div Curtiss-Wright, Buffalo, 1945; sr. aerodynamicist Cornell U. Aero. Lab., Buffalo, 1946; physicist Gen. Electric Research Lab., Schenectady, N.Y., 1951-66, program mgr., 1966-75, CT program mgr., 1975-79, NMR program mgr., 1979-81, br. mgr., 1981-89, physicist, 1989-91, ret., 1991; adj. prof. Rensselaer Polytech. Inst., Troy, N.Y., 1964-67, U. Calif., San Francisco, 1978-79; mem. grad. clin. faculty U. Calif., San Francisco, 1979-91; cons. adv. group electron devices Dept. of Def., N.Y.C., 1971-77. Contbr. articles to profl. jours.; patentee in field. Commr. Niskayuna Vol. Fire Dept. Coolidge fellow Gen. Electric Corp. Research and Devel., 1985; named Engr. of Yr., Design News, 1989; recipient Indsl. Applications of Physics prize Am. Inst. of Physics, 1989. Fellow Am. Phys. Soc.; mem. Nat. Acad. Engring., Sigma Xi. Avocations: sailing, gardening, photography. Home: 1169 Mohawk Rd Niskayuna NY 12309-1607 Office: Gen Elec R & D Ctr Med Diagnostics Sys Br PO Box 8 Schenectady NY 12301-0008*

REDISH, MARTIN HARRIS, legal educator; b. Lynbrook, N.Y., Aug. 16, 1945; m. Caren Beverly Redish, June 22, 1969; 1 dau., Jessica. A.B., U. Pa., 1967; J.D. magna cum laude, Harvard U., 1970. Bar: N.Y. 1971, U.S. Dist. Ct. (so. dist.) N.Y. 1971, U.S. Ct. Appeals (2d cir.) 1971, U.S. Ct. Appeals (7th cir.) 1973. Law clk. to presiding justice U.S. Ct. Appeals (2d cir.), 1970-71; assoc. Proskauer, Rose, Goetz & Mendelsohn, N.Y.C., 1971-73; prof. law Northwestern U. Sch. Law, Chgo., 1973—; vis. assoc. prof. law Cornell U., 1977, Stanford U., 1977, Mich. 1987-88; mem. 7th Cir. Rules Adv. Com.; cons. U.S. Senate Jud. Com. Mem. Am. Law Inst., Am. Coll. Trial Lawyers (reporter Project on Complex Civil Litigation). Author: Federal Jurisdiction: Tensions in the Allocation of Judicial Power, 1980; Federal Courts: Cases, Comments and Questions, 1983 2d edit.; Freedom of Expression: A Critical Analysis, 1984, (with others) Constitutional Law: Principles and Policy, 1987, (with others) Civil Procedure: A Modern Approach, 1989; contbr. articles to profl. jours. Office: Northwestern U Sch Law 357 E Chicago Ave Chicago IL 60611-3008

REDLICH, NORMAN, lawyer, educator; b. N.Y.C., Nov. 12, 1925; s. Milton and Pauline (Durst) R.; m. Evelyn Jane Grobow, June 3, 1951; children: Margaret Bonny-Claire, Carrie Ann, Edward Grobow. AB, Williams Coll., 1947, LLD (hon.), 1976; LLB, Yale U., 1950; LLM, NYU, 1955; LLD (hon.), John Marshall Law Sch., 1990. Bar: N.Y. 1951. Practiced in N.Y.C., 1951-59; assoc. prof. law NYU, 1960-62, prof. law, 1962-74, assoc. dean Sch. Law, 1974-75, dean Sch. Law, 1975-88, dean emeritus, 1992—, Judge Edward Weinfeld prof. law, 1982—; counsel Wachtell, Lipton, Rosen & Katz, N.Y.C., 1988—; editor-in-chief Tax Law Rev., 1960-66; mem. adv. com. Inst. Fed. Taxation, 1963-68; exec. asst. corp. counsel, N.Y.C., 1966-68, 1st asst. corp. counsel 1970-72, corp. counsel, 1972-74; asst. counsel Pres. Commn. on Assassination Pres. Kennedy, 1963-64; mem. com. on admissions and grievances U.S. 2d Circuit Ct. Appeals, 1978—, chmn., 1978-87. Author: Professional Responsibility: A Problem Approach, 1976, Constitutional Law, Cases and Materials, 1983, rev. edit., 1989; contbr. articles in field. Chmn. commn. on law and social action Am. Jewish Congress, 1978—; mem. Borough Pres.'s Planning Bd. Number 2, 1959-70, counsel N.Y. Com. to Abolish Capital Punishment, 1958-77; mem. N.Y.C. Bd. Edn., 1969; mem. bd. overseers Jewish Theol. Sem., 1973—; trustee Law Ctr. Found. of NYU, 1975—, Freedom House, 1976-86, Vt. Law Sch., 1977—, Practising Law Inst., 1980—; trustee Lawyers Com. for Civil Rights Under Law, 1976—, co-chmn., 1979-81; bd. dirs. Legal Aid Soc., 1983-88, NAACP Legal Def. Fund, 1985—; Greenwich House, 1987—. Served with AUS, 1943-45. Decorated Combat Infantryman's Badge. Mem. ABA (coun. legal edn. and admissions to bar 1981—, vice chmn. 1987-88, chmn. 1989-90, equal opportunities in legal profession 1986-92, ho. of dels. 1991—), Assn. of Bar of City of N.Y. (exec. com. 1975-79, professionalism com. 1988-92). Office: 51 W 52nd St 30th fl New York NY 10019-6150

REDMAN, BARBARA KLUG, nursing educator; b. Mitchell, S.D.; d. Harlan Lyle and Darlien Grace (Bock) Klug; m. Robert S. Redman, Sept. 14, 1958; 1 child, Melissa Darlien. BS, S.D. State U., 1958; MEd, U. Minn., 1959, PhD, 1964; LHD (hon.), Georgetown U., 1988; DSc (hon.), U. Colo., 1991. RN. Asst. prof. U. Wash., Seattle, 1964-69; assoc. dean U. Minn., Mpls., 1969-75; dean Sch. Nursing U. Colo., Denver, 1975-78; VA scholar VA Cen. Office, Washington, 1978-81; postdoctoral fellow Johns Hopkins U., Balt., 1982-83; exec. dir. Am. Assn. Colls. Nursing, Washington, 1983-89, ANA, Washington, 1989-93; prof. nursing Johns Hopkins U., Balt., 1993—; vis. fellow Kennedy Inst. Ethics, Georgetown U., 1993-94; fellow in med. ethics Harvard Med. Sch., 1994-95. Author: Process of Patient Education, 1968-93; contbr. articles to profl. jours. Bd. dirs. Friends of Nat. Libr. of Medicine, Washington, 1987—. Recipient Disting. Alumnus award S.D. State U., 1975, Outstanding Achievement award U. Minn., 1989. Fellow Am. Acad. Nursing; mem. Am. Ednl. Rsch. Assn., Internat. Patient Edn. Coun. (pres. 1988-89). Home: 12425 Bobbink Ct Potomac MD 20854 Office: Johns Hopkins U 1830 E Monument St Baltimore MD 21205

REDMAN, CHARLES EDGAR, diplomat; b. Waukegan, Ill., Dec. 24, 1943; s. Edgar Bell and Helen Louise (Baker) R.; m. Eileen Kowal, July 31, 1971; children: Melissa, Vanessa, Christina. BS, USAF Acad., 1966; MA, Harvard U., 1968. Commd. 2d lt. USAF, 1966, advanced through grades to capt., 1969; spl. asst. to asst. chief staff intelligence USAF, Washington, 1974, resigned; joined Fgn. Svc., Dept. State; staff asst. Ops. Ctr., Bur. European Affairs, Dept. State, 1974-76; polit. officer Am. Embassy, Paris, 1976-79; dep. dir. Office Sec. Gen., NATO Internat. Staff, Brussels, 1979-82; polit. officer Am. Embassy, Algiers, 1982-84; dep. dir. Office European Security and Polit. Affairs, NATO, Washington, 1984-85; dep. spokesman Bur. Pub. Affairs, Washington, 1985-87, spokesman, 1986-89; asst. sec. pub. affairs Bur. Pub. Affairs, 1987-89; U.S. amb. to Sweden, 1989-93, U.S. amb. to Germany, 1994—. Office: Am Embassy, Deichmanns Aue 29 Unit 21701, 53170 Bonn Germany*

REDMAN, DALE E., diversified financial services company executive, title company executive; b. 1947. B in Acctg., La. State U., 1968. CPA. With Ernst & Whinney CPA's, Baton Rouge, La., 1968-80; exec. v.p., cfo United Co. Fin. Corp., Baton Rouge, La., 1980—; mem. sec., treas. United Gen. Title Ins. Co., v. chmn. United Co. Lending corp. Office: United Co Lending Corp 4041 Essen Ln Baton Rouge LA 70809*

REDMAN, ERIC, lawyer; b. Palo Alto, Calif., June 3, 1948; s. M. Chandler and Marjorie Jane (Sachs) R.; children: Ian Michael, Graham James. AB, Harvard U., 1970, JD, 1975; BA, Oxford U., 1972, MA, 1980. Bar: Wash. 1975, U.S. Dist. Ct. (we. dist.) Wash. 1975, D.C. 1979, U.S. Ct. Appeals (9th cir.) 1981, U.S. Supreme Ct. 1983. Asst. U.S. senator W.G. Magnuson, Washington and Seattle, 1968-71, 74-75; assoc. Preston, Thorgrimson et al, Seattle, 1975-78, ptnr., 1979-82; ptnr. Heller, Ehrman, White & McAuliffe, Seattle, 1983—. Author: Dance of Legislation, 1973; also book revs., articles. Office: Heller Ehrman White & McAuliffe 6100 Columbia Ctr 701 5th Ave Seattle WA 98104-7098

REDMAN, MONTE N., bank executive. Sr. v.p., CFO, dir. Astoria Fin. Corp., New Hyde Park, N.Y. Office: Astoria Fin Corp 1 Astoria Federal Plz New Hyde Park NY 11040*

REDMAN, PETER, finance company executive; b. Phila., Feb. 9, 1935; s. Hamilton Matthew and Martha (Lawson) R.; m. Julie Anne Burr, June 9, 1984; children: Kirsten, Heidi, Gretchen, Britt. B.A. in Econs., Middlebury Coll., 1958. Sr. group ins. rep. Conn. Gen. Life Ins. Co., Hartford, 1962-65; v.p. Conn. Bank & Trust Co., Hartford, 1965-73; v.p. Midlantic Nat. Bank, Newark, 1973-75, 4th Nat. Bank, Wichita, Kans., 1975-78; v.p., gen. mgr. Cessna Internat. Fin. Corp. (subs. Cessna Aircraft Co.), Wichita, 1978-82, now pres., dir.; pres., gen. mgr., Cessna Fin. Corp., Wichita, 1982—, also dir. Served to 1st lt. U.S. Army, 1958-62. Republican. Episcopalian. Home: 721 Preston Trl Wichita KS 67230-1504 Office: Cessna Fin Corp PO Box 308 Wichita KS 67201-0308

REDMAN, TIMOTHY PAUL, English language educator, author, chess federation administrator; b. Elmhurst, Ill., June 26, 1950; s. William Charles and Eileen Marie (Keenan) R. B.A., Loyola U., Chgo., 1973; M.A., U. Chgo., 1974, Ph.D., 1987. Instr. Loyola U., Rome, 1977, Ill. Inst. Tech., Chgo., 1980-84; lectr. English dept. Loyola U., Chgo., 1982-84; lectr. U. Wis., Parkside, 1984-85; instr. Ohio State U., Lima, 1985-87, asst. prof., 1987-89; asst. prof. U. Tex., Dallas, 1989-91, assoc. dean, coll. master, 1991-92, assoc. prof., 1991—. Author: Ezra Pound and Italian Fascism, 1991; editor: Official Rules of Chess, 3d edit., 1987. Whiting fellow, 1981-82, NEH fellow, 1992-93. Mem. MLA, U.S. Chess Fedn. (past pres.), Nat. Coun. Tchrs. English, PEN U.S.A. West. Roman Catholic. Home: 3034 Brookshire Dr Plano TX 75075-7644 Office: U Tex at Dallas Sch Arts & Humanities JO31 PO Box 830688 Richardson TX 75083-0688 also: US Chess Fedn 186 US Highway 9W New Windsor NY 12553-7624

REDMON, HARRY SMITH, JR., lawyer; b. New Orleans, Mar. 24, 1934; s. Harry Smith Sr. and Mary Florance (Browne) R.; m. Mary Jane McAlister, Aug. 29, 1959 (div. Dec. 1984); children: Harry Smith III, Marshall McAlister; m. Jane Clement Cheney, July 15, 1989. BS, La. State U., 1957, JD, 1959. Bar: La. 1959, U.S. Dist. Ct. (ea. and mid. dists.) La. 1962, U.S. Dist. Ct. (we. dist.) La. 1963, U.S. Supreme Ct. 1972, U.S.Ct. Appeals (5th cir.) 1981. From assoc. to mng. ptnr. Phelps Dunbar, New Orleans, 1962-94. Capt. USAF, 1959-62. Avocations: golf, reading, motor racing, aviation. Office: Phelps Dunbar 400 Poydras St Fl 30 New Orleans LA 70130-3245

REDMOND, DONALD EUGENE, JR., neuroscientist, educator; b. San Antonio, June 17, 1939; s. Donald Eugene and Viola (Kellum) R.; m. Patricia Welder Robinson, Dec. 22, 1972 (div.). BA, So. Meth. U., 1961; MD, Baylor U., 1968; MAH, Yale U., 1987. Diplomate Am. Bd. Psychiatry and Neurology. With Lab. of Clin. Sci., NIMH, Bethesda, Md., 1973-74; assoc. chief clin. neurosci. unit Conn. Mental Health Ctr., New Haven, 1974-87; asst. prof. psychiatry Yale U., New Haven, 1974-77; assoc. prof. psychiatry Yale U., 1978-87, prof. psychiatry, dir. neurobehavior lab., 1987—; dir. neural transplant program for neurol. diseases, 1987—; pres. St. Kitts Biomed. Rsch. Found., St. Kitts, W.I., 1983—, Axion Rsch. Found., Hamden, Conn., 1985—; prof. neurosurgery, 1993—. Contbr. articles to profl. jours.; patentee in field. With USPHS, 1972-74. Recipient Rsch. Scientist award NIMH, 1980— Founds. Fund prize, 1981; grantee NIMH 1974-91, Nat. Inst. Neurol. Diseases and Stroke, 1986—, others. Mem. Am. Psychiat. Assn., Am. Coll. Neuropsychopharmacology, Am. Soc. Neural Transplantation (coun. mem. 1994—), Internat. Med. Soc. Motor Disturbances. Office: Neurobehavior Lab PO Box 3333 New Haven CT 06510-3289

REDMOND, JAMES MELVIN, medical association administrator; b. Syracuse, N.Y., June 14, 1947; s. James William and Shirleyanne (Crawford) R.; m. Candis Ann Jillson, Aug. 30, 1969; children: Amy, Carrie. BS in Pharmacy, U. Conn., 1970; MBA in Health and Hosp. Adminstrn., U. Fla., 1972. Unit adminstr. Milton S. Hershey Med. Ctr. of Pa. State U., Hershey, Pa., 1971-72, mgr. outpatient svcs., 1972-74, asst. hosp. dir., 1974-75; dir. ambulatory svcs. Hosp. Assn. Pa., Harrisburg, 1975-77, v.p. hosp. svcs., 1977-83, sr. v.p. hosp. svcs., 1983-86, exec. v.p., chief oper. officer, 1986-89, sr. v.p. legis. svcs., 1991—; cons. Heidrick and Struggles, Inc., Washington, 1989-91. Contbr. articles to profl. jours. Fellow Am. Coll. Healthcare Execs. (mem. specialist panel self-assessment program 1983-85); mem. Am. Hosp. Assn. (ad hoc com. tax exemption 1988-89, ad hoc com. hosp. facilities and standards 1987-88, steering com. state issues forum 1987-88, HAS adv. com. 1978-80), Pa. Profl. Liability Joint Underwriting Assn. (bd. dirs. 1977-80). Presbyterian. Avocations: golf, skiing, travel. Home: 1016 Chippenham Rd Mechanicsburg PA 17055 Office: Hosp Assoc of PA 4750 Lindle Rd Harrisburg PA 17111

REDMOND, JAMES RONALD, zoology educator, researcher; b. Cin., July 14, 1928; s. Matthew J. and Elizabeth (True) R.; m. Eleanor Hausfeld, Aug. 13, 1949; children: Cleve R., Jill A. BS, U. Cin., 1949; PhD, UCLA, 1954. Asst. prof. biology U. Fla., Gainesville, 1956-62; assoc. prof. zoology Iowa State U., Ames, 1962-67, prof., 1967-93, acting chmn. dept., 1983-84; prof. emeritus, 1993—; vis. asst. prof. U. Wash., Seattle, 1960; chief scientist Alpha Helix Nautilus Expdn., NSF, Philippines, 1975. Contbr. numerous articles to sci. jours., chpts. to books; contbr. zoology revs. Ency. Brit., 1986-89. With U.S. Army, 1954-56. NIH grantee, 1957-72. Fellow AAAS; mem. Am. Soc. Zoologists, Western Soc. Naturalists, Bermuda Biol. Sta. for Rsch. (corp.), Phi Beta Kappa, Sigma Xi, Phi Eta Sigma, Phi Kappa Phi. Avocations: travel, photography, electronics. Office: Dept Zoology and Genetics Iowa State U Ames IA 50011

REDMOND, PAUL ANTHONY, utility executive; b. Lakeview, Oreg., 1937. BSEE, Gonzaga U., 1965. Asst. elec. engr. Wash. Water Power Co., Spokane, 1965-67, maintenance engr., 1967-69, supt. contract constrn., 1969-73, constrn. and maintenance supt., 1973-75, mgr. constrn. and maintenance, 1975-77, asst. to pres., 1977-78, v.p., asst. to pres., 1978-79, sr. v.p. ops., 1979-80, exec. v.p., 1980-82, pres., 1982-88, chief oper. officer, 1982-84, chief exec. officer, 1984—, chmn. bd., 1985—, also bd. dirs.; former pres. Wash. Irrigation & Devel. subs. Wash. Water Power Co., Spokane, now chmn., pres., chief exec. officer, 1985—; bd. dirs Security Pacific Bank Washington, Spokane Indsl. Park Inc., Limestone Co. Inc., Devel. Assocs. Inc., Pentzer Corp., Water Power Improvement Co., Wash. Irrigation and Devel. Co., Itron Inc. Lt. col. USNG. Office: Wash Water Power Co PO Box 3727 Spokane WA 99220-3727

REDMOND, ROBERT FRANCIS, nuclear engineering educator; b. Indpls., July 15, 1927; s. John Felix and Marguerite Catherine (Breinig) R.; m. Mary Catherine Cangany, Oct. 18, 1952 (dec. May 1988); children: Catherine, Robert, Kevin, Thomas, John. B.S. in Chem. Engring. Purdue U., 1950; M.S. in Math, U. Tenn., 1955; Ph.D. in Physics, Ohio State U., 1961. Engr. Oak Ridge Nat. Lab., 1950-53; scientist, adviser-cons. Battelle Meml. Inst., Columbus, Ohio, 1953-70; prof. nuclear engring. Ohio State U., Columbus, 1970-92; assoc. dean Coll. Engring. Ohio State U., dir. Engring. Experiment Sta., 1977-92, acting dean, 1990—. Contbr. articles to profl. jours. V.p. Argonne Univs. Assn., 1976-77, trustee, 1972-80; mem. Ohio Power Siting Commn., 1978-82; trustee Edison Welding Inst., 1988-92. With AUS, 1945-46. Mem. Am. Nuclear Soc. (chmn. Southwestern Ohio sect.), AAAS, Nat. Regulatory Rsch. Inst. (bd. dirs. 1988-92), Trans. Rsch. Ctr., Am. Soc. Engring. Edn., Sigma Xi, Tau Beta Pi. Home: 1532 Trentwood Rd Columbus OH 43221-2252

REDMONT, BERNARD SIDNEY, university dean, journalism educator; b. N.Y.C., Nov. 8, 1918; s. Morris Abraham and Bessie (Kamerman) R.; m. Joan Rothenberg, Mar. 12, 1940; children: Dennis Foster, Jane Carol. B.A., CCNY, 1938; M.J., Columbia U., 1939; D.H.L., Fla. Internat. U., 1980. Reporter, book reviewer Bklyn. Daily Eagle, 1936-38; free lance corr. Europe, 1939, Mexico City, 1939-40; telegraph editor, editorial writer Herkimer (N.Y.) Evening Telegram, 1941-42; newswriter U.S. Office of Inter-Am. Affairs (Washington shortwave radio newscasts to Latin Am.), 1942-43, dir. News div., 1944-46; staff corr., bur. chief U.S. News & World Report, Buenos Aires and Paris, 1946-51; columnist Continental Daily Mail, Paris, 1951-53; chief corr. English Lang. World News Service Agence France-Presse, Paris, 1953-65; European corr. Paris news bur. chief Westinghouse Broadcasting Co., Paris, 1961-76; corr., bur. chief CBS News, Moscow, 1976-79; corr. CBS News, Paris, 1979-81; prof. journalism, dir. broadcast journalism program, dean Boston U. Coll. Communication, 1982-86, dean emeritus, prof. journalism, 1986—, mem. adv. bd. Latin Am. journalism program, 1989—; cons. Exec. Svc. Corps. of New Eng., 1991—, Internat. Exec. Svc. Corps, 1992—. Author: Risks Worth Taking: The Odyssey of a Foreign Correspondent, Univ. Press of Am., 1992. Served with USMCR, 1943-44. Decorated Purple Heart, chevalier Legion of Honor France; Pulitzer Traveling fellow; recipient Columbia Journalism award for advancement of journalism, 1986, Townsend Harris medal for life achievement, 1991. Mem. Overseas Press Club (award best radio reporting from abroad 1968, 73), Soc. Profl. Journalists, Nat. Press Club, Anglo-American Press Assn. of Paris (pres. 1961, treas. 1970-73, sec. 1974-76). Unitarian. *Life has more meaning when it affirms, with grace, the Yang and the Yin, reconciling opposites—independence, yet cooperative effort and community caring; courage and hard work, yet moderation and generosity; hatred of injustice, yet kindness,fairness and compassion.*

REDNER, EARL W., retail executive; b. 1925. With Washington divsn. Grand Union Co., 1946-70; with Redners Markets Inc., Reading, Pa., 1970—, now chmn. bd. dirs. Office: Redners Markets Inc 237 Buttonwood St Reading PA 19601*

REDNER, RICHARD, food products executive. Pres., CEO Redners Markets, Inc., Reading, Pa., 1970—. Office: Redners Markets Inc 237 Buttonwood St Reading PA 19601*

REDO, DAVID LUCIEN, investment company executive; b. Lakewood, Ohio, Sept. 1, 1937; s. Joseph L. and Florence M. (Morse) R.; m. Judy L. Ijams, Aug. 4, 1962; children: Jenny, Mark. BSEE, U. Calif., Berkeley, 1961; MBA, U. Santa Clara, 1967. Registered investment advisor. Asst. engring. mgr. AT&T, N.Y.C., 1961-71; pension fund mgr. Pacific Telephone, San Francisco, 1971-77; mng. dir. The Fremont Group (formerly Bechtel Investments Inc.), San Francisco, 1977—; pres., CEO Fremont Investment Advisors, Inc., San Francisco, 1986—; bd. dirs. The Fremont Group (formerly Bechtel Investments, Inc.) San Francisco, J.P. Morgan Securities Asia, Singapore, Sequoia Ventures Inc., San Francisco, Fremont Investment Advisors, Sit/Kim Internat. Investments. Bd. trustees U. Calif., Berkeley, 1988—; chmn. investment com. U. Calif. Found., 1988—. Mem. Sentinel Pension Inst. (bd. advisors), Fin. Execs. Inst., Treas. Club of San Francisco, Internat. Assn. of Fin. Planners. Avocations: golf, traveling, reading, walking. Office: Fremont Investment Advisors 50 Beale St Ste 100 San Francisco CA 94105-1819

REDO, S(AVERIO) FRANK, surgeon; b. Bklyn., Dec. 28, 1920; s. Frank and Maria (Guida) R.; m. Maria Lappano, June 27, 1948; children—Philip, Martha. B.S., Queens Coll., 1942; M.D., Cornell U., 1950. Diplomate: Am. Bd. Thoracic Surgery, Am. Bd. Surgery (pediatric surgery). Intern in surgery N.Y. Hosp., N.Y.C., 1950-51; asst. resident surgeon N.Y. Hosp., 1951-56, resident surgeon, 1956-57, asst. attending surgeon, 1958-60, assoc. attending surgeon, 1960-66, surgeon in charge pediatric surgery, 1960, attending surgeon, 1966—; practice medicine specializing in surgery; clin. asso. prof. surgery Cornell U. Med. Coll., 1963-72, prof., 1972—. Author: Surgery in the Ambulatory Child, 1961, Principles of Surgery in the First Six Months of Life, 1976, Atlas of Surgery in the First Six Months of Life, 1977; contbr. articles to profl. jours. Served to capt. USAAF, 1942-46. Fellow A.C.S., Am. Coll. Chest Physicians; mem. Harvey Soc., Pan Am. Med. Assn., Soc. Univ. Surgeons, Am. Acad. Pediatrics, Am. Fedn. for Clin. Research, Internat. Cardiovascular Soc., Am. Surg. Assn., Am. Assn. Thoracic Surgery,

Soc. for Surgery Alimentary Tract, Am. Soc. Artificial Internat. Organs, Am. Acad. Pediatrics, Assn. Advancement Med. Instrumentation, Soc. Thoracic Surgeons, Internat. Soc. Surgery, N.Y. Gastroent. Soc., N.Y. Acad. Sci., N.Y. Cardiovascular Soc., N.Y. Acad. Medicine, N.Y. Soc. Thoracic Surgery, N.Y. Pediatric Soc., Med. Soc. County N.Y., Queens Coll. Alumni Assn. (gov.), Sigma Xi. Patentee in field. Home: 435 E 70th St New York NY 10021-5342 Office: 525 E 68th St New York NY 10021-4873 *My life is based on the principles of doing as much for others as possible and doing no harm; to offer advice only when asked; to apply myself unstintingly, but not selfishly, to my work; to learn from my mistakes; to strive for perfection; and to always have a project and a dream.*

REDSTONE, DANIEL AARON, architect; b. Detroit, Apr. 24, 1942; s. Louis Gordon and Ruth Roslyn (Rosenbaum) R.; m. Barbara Osten, June 29, 1980; children—Adam, Carly. B.S., U. Mich., 1965, M.B.A., 1967. Registered architect, Mich. Architect., pres. Redstone Architects, 1986—; mem. bd. dirs. AIA-Mich., 1988-94, Nat. Coun. Archtl. Reg. Bds., Mich. Bd. Architects, 1994—, Mich. Bd. Engrs., 1994—, NCCJ Interfaith Roundtable (Detroit chpt.). Jewish. Avocations: raquet sports. Home: 3347 Bloomfield Shore West Bloomfield MI 48323-3303 Office: 29201 Telegraph Rd Ste 400 Southfield MI 48034-7647

REDSTONE, LOUIS GORDON, architect; b. Poland, Mar. 16, 1903; came to U.S., 1923; s. Abraham Aaron and Anna (Gordon) Routenstein; m. Ruth R. Rosenbaum, June 25, 1939; children: Daniel Aaron, Eliel Gordon. BS in Architecture, U. Mich., 1929; MArch, Cranbrook Acad. Arts, 1948. Pvt. practice architecture Israel, 1933-37; founder Louis G. Redstone Assocs. Inc. (architects/engrs./planners), Detroit, 1937-85; pres., chmn. Redstone Assocs. Inc. (architects/engrs./planners), 1985—; Del. internat. congresses, Caracas, Tokyo, Moscow and, Buenos Aires; exec. com. Pan Am. Fedn. Architects, 1955-70; juror archtl. and artists exhbns., profl. adviser archtl. competitions sponsored by Dow Chem. Co.; mem. Mich. Commn. on Art in State Bldgs., 1975-82; moderator Internat. Sculpture Conf., Washington, 1990. Author: Art in Architecture, 1968, New Dimensions in Shopping Centers and Stores, 1973, The New Downtown-Rebuilding Business Districts, 1976, Hospitals and Health Care Facilities, 1978, Institutional Buildings, 1980, Public Art-New Directions, 1981, Masonry in Architecture, 1984, From Israeli Pioneer to American Architect, 1989; contbr. articles to profl. mags. and newspapers; one-man watercolor exhibits include: Macomb County Art Ctr., Mt. Clemens, Mich., 1992, T'Marra Gallery, Ann Arbor, 1991, 93, Livonia (Mich.) Art Ctr., 1993, Cranbrook Acad. Arts, 1994; represented in permanent collections Long Beach (Calif.) Mus. Art, Detroit Inst. Art., Cranbrook Acad. Art. Trustee Mich. Found. for Arts; co-chmn. Bus. Consortium for Arts Sculpture Exhbns., Southfield, Mich. Recipient Patron award Mich. Found. for Arts, 1977, Detroit's Disting. Recognition award City Coun., 1993, Disting. Vol. Svc. award City of Southfield, 1993, Mich. Gov.'s Civic Leader award, 1993. Fellow AIA (pres. Detroit 1965, Gold medal outstanding contbn. to profession, Significant Lifetime Achievement award Detroit chpt. 1993), Mich. Soc. Architects (Robert F. Hastings award for outstanding achievement 1983), Engring. Soc. Detroit, Royal Acad. Fine Arts Netherlands (hon.); mem. Royal Acad. Fine Arts, San Fernando, Spain (corr. academician). Home: 19303 Appoline St Detroit MI 48235-1216 Office: Redstone Assocs Inc 29201 Telegraph Rd Ste 400 Southfield MI 48034-7647 *The architect must be a positive force in creating surroundings that enhance and fulfill all human needs, in which the arts become an integral part of man's daily environment. He must implement this approach by studying the specific needs and requirements of those who will use the building. These needs must then be satisfied within an aesthetically designed and functional enclosure that is in harmony with its surroundings. This basic concept must not be limited in application to individual buildings; it must be extended to the wider horizon of the total urban environment.*

REDSTONE, SUMNER MURRAY, entertainment company executive; b. Boston, May 27, 1923; s. Michael and Belle (Ostrovsky) R.; m. Phyllis Gloria Raphael, July 6, 1947; children: Brent Dale, Shari Ellin. B.A., Harvard U., 1944, LL.B., 1947; LLD (hon.), Boston U., 1994. Bar: Mass. 1947, U.S. Ct. Appeals (1st cir.) 1948, U.S. Ct. Appeals (8th cir.) 1950, U.S. Ct. Appeals (9th cir.) 1948, D.C. 1951, U.S. Supreme Ct. 1952. Law sec. U.S. Ct. Appeals for 9th Circuit, San Francisco, 1947-48; instr. law and labor mgmt. U. San Francisco, 1947; spl. asst. to U.S. Atty. Gen., Washington, 1948-51; ptnr. Ford, Bergson, Adams, Borkland & Redstone, Washington, 1951-54; pres., CEO Nat. Amusements Inc., Dedham, Mass., 1967—, chmn. bd., 1986-87; chmn. bd. Viacom Internat. Inc., N.Y.C., 1987—; prof. Boston U. Law Sch., 1982, 85-86; bd. dirs. TV Acad. Arts and Scis. Found.; vis. prof. Brandeis U., Waltham, Mass.; lectr. Harvard Law Sch., Cambridge, Mass.; Judge on Kennedy Libr. Found., (sel. comm. John F. Kennedy Profile in Courage award). Chmn. met. divsn. NE Combined Jewish Philanthropies, Boston, 1963; mem. exec. bd. Combined Jewish Philanthropies of Greater Boston; mem. corp. New Eng. Med. Ctr., 1967—, Mass. Gen. Hosp. Corp.; trustee Children's Cancer Rsch. Found.; founding trustee Am. Cancer Soc.; chmn. Am. Cancer Crusade, State of Mass., 1984-86; Art Lending Libr.; sponsor Boston Mus. Sci.; chmn. Jimmy Fund Found., 1960; v.p., mem. exec. com. Will Rogers Meml. Fund; bd. dirs. Boston Arts Festival; bd. overseers Dana Farber Cancer Ctr., Boston Mus. Fine Arts; mem. presdl. adv. com. on arts John F. Kennedy Libr. Found., also judge ann. John F. Kennedy Profile in Courage Award com. 1st lt. AUS, 1943-45. Decorated Army Commendation medal; recipient William J. German Human Rels. award Am. Jewish Com. Entertainment/Comm. Divsn., 1977, Silver Shingle award Boston U. Law Sch., 1985, Variety New Eng. Humanitarian award, 1989, Golden Plate award Am. Acad. Achievement 32d Ann. Salute to Excellence Program, Bus. Excellence award U. S.C., 1994, Bus. Excellence award U. So. Calif. Sch. Bus. Adminstrn., 1994, The Stephen S. Wise award U., 1995, Allan K. Jones Lifetime Achievement award Am. Cancer Soc., 1995, Man of Yr. award MIPCOM, the Internat. Film and Programme Market for TV, Video, Cable and Satellite, 1995, Humanitarian award Variety Club Internat., 1995; named Communicator of Yr., B'nai B'rith Comm./Cinema Lodge, 1980, Man of Yr., Enterntainment Industries Divsn. of UJA Fedn., 1988, Pioneer of Yr., Motion Picture Pioneers, 1991, Grad. of Yr., Boston Latin Sch., 1989. Mem. ABA, Nat. Assn. Theatre Owners (chmn. bd. dirs. 1965-66, exec. comm. 1995—), Theatre Owners Am. (asst. pres. 1960-63, pres. 1964-65), Motion Picture Pioneers (bd. dirs.), Boston Bar Assn., Mass. Bar Assn., Harvard Law Sch. Assn., Am. Judicature Soc., Masons, Univ. Club, Harvard Club. Home: 98 Baldpate Hill Rd Newton MA 02159-2825 Office: Nat Amusements Inc PO Box 9126 Dedham MA 02027-9126

REDWAY, ALAN ARTHUR SYDNEY, Canadian legislator, lawyer; b. Toronto, Ont., Can., Mar. 11, 1935; s. Alan Edwin Sydney and Phyllis May (Turner) R.; m. Mary Louise Harvey, Apr. 21, 1962; children: Kimberley Ann, Andrea Elizabeth. B. Commerce, U. Toronto, 1958; LLB, Osgoode Hall, Toronto, 1961; Diploma of Applied Arts and Scis. (hon.), Centennial Coll., Toronto, 1985. Bar: Ont. 1963; apptd. Queen's Counsel, 1977. Ptnr. Frost & Redway, Toronto, 1966-84, Redway Cooney & Roherty, Toronto, 1984-87, Redway & Butler, Toronto, 1987-89, 92—; M.P. Ho. of Commons, Ottawa, Ont., 1984-93, min. state for housing, 1989-91, chmn. spl. rev. com. on Employment Equity Act, 1991-92; vice chmn. Aboriginal affairs com., 1992-93. Recipient Hon. Diploma of Applied Arts and Tech., Centennial Coll., Toronto, 1985. Mem. Leaside Lions Club (pres. 1971-72). Progressive Conservative. Avocations: cross country skiing, gardening. Office: Ste 4086, 3080 Yonge St, Toronto, ON Canada M4N 3N1

REDWINE, RICHARD H., manufacturing executive, light; b. 1938. V.p. Kimble Glass, Inc., Vineland, N.J., 1968—. Office: Kimble Glass Inc 537 Crystal Ave Vineland NJ 08360-3239*

REDWINE, ROBERT PAGE, physicist, educator; b. Raleigh, N.C., Dec. 3, 1947; s. Robert Word and Hazel Virginia (Green) R.; m. Jacqueline Nina Hewitt, Nov. 22, 1986; children: Keith Hewitt, Jonathan Hewitt. AB, Cornell U., 1969; PhD, Northwestern U., 1974. Assoc. Los Alamos (N.Mex.) Nat. Lab., 1973-77, staff sci., 1977-79; rsch. assoc. U. Berne, Switzerland, 1974-75; asst. prof. physics MIT, Cambridge, Mass., 1979-82, assoc. prof., 1982-89, prof., 1989—; dir. lab. nuclear sci., 1992—; cons. Los Alamos Nat. Lab., 1980—. Contbr. articles to profl. jours. Fellow AAAS, Am. Phys. Soc. Office: MIT Lab Nuclear Sci Bldg 26-505 Cambridge MA 02139

REEB, PATRICIA A., nursing educator, administrator; b. Springfield, Ohio. BSN, Edgecliff Coll., 1958; MSN, Case Western Res. U., 1971; EdD, U. Cin., 1981. RN/BSN coord. Coll. Mt. St. Joseph (Ohio); cons. Sacred Heart Coll., Belmont, N.C.; asst. prof. U. Cin.; chairperson dept. nursing Coll. Mt. St. Joseph; dir. edn., aging svcs. Mercy Health System, Cin.; dir. mission svcs. Mercy St. Theresa Ctr., Cin. Mem. Ohio League Nursing (pres. 1982-84), SWONA (program chair 1988-89), OCLN (bd. dirs. southwestern Ohio action group). Home: 3107 Epworth Ave Cincinnati OH 45211-7008 Office: Mercy St Theresa Ctr 7010 Rowan Hill Dr Cincinnati OH 45227-3313

REECE, JOE WILSON, engineering company executive; b. Elkin, N.C., Mar. 1, 1935; s. Thad Marshall and Anita (Hobson) R.; m. Nancy Lee Fletcher, Aug. 25, 1955; children: Joe Wilson Jr. B in Nuclear Engring., N.C. State U., 1957, MS, 1961, PhD; U. Fla., 1963. Registered profl. engr., Ala. Instr. engring. mechanics N.C. State U., Raleigh, 1958-61; asst. prof. mech. engring. Auburn (Ala.) U., 1963-67, assoc. prof., 1967-76, prof., 1976-85; dep. dir. operating reactors div. U.S. Nuclear Regulatory Commn., 1976-78; pres. Reece Engring. Assocs., 1985—; cons. U.S Army Missile Command, Combustion Engring. Co., Westinghouse, others. Campus drive chmn. Auburn United Fund, 1969, chmn. bd., 1971. Named Disting. Classroom Tchr. N.C. State U. Sch. Engring., 1961, Outstanding Faculty mem. Auburn U. Sch. Engring., 1965, 73. Mem. Am. Soc. Engring. Edn. (pres. SE sect. 1977), ASME, Ala. Acad. Sci., Scabbard and Blade, Sigma Xi, Phi Kappa Phi, Tau Beta Pi, Phi Eta Sigma, Sigma Pi Sigma, Theta Tau, Pi Tau Sigma. Methodist (lay leader 1967, chmn. trustees 1972). Club: Civitan (Auburn) (pres. 1968). Home: RR 1 Box 1F Boonville NC 27011-9701

REECE, MAYNARD FRED, artist, author; b. Arnolds Park, Iowa, Apr. 26, 1920; s. Waldo H. and Inez V. (Latson) R.; m. June Carman, Apr. 7, 1946; children: Mark A., Brad D. Privately educated. Artist Meredith Pub. Co., Des Moines, 1938-40; artist, asst., mus. dir. Iowa Dept. History and Archives, Des Moines, 1940-50. Artist: Fish and Fishing, 1963, Waterfowl of Iowa, 1943; watercolor Trout, Saturday Evening Post (award of Distinctive Merit 1962); watercolors 73 Fish, Life mag. (cert. of merit 1955); print of Water's Edge Canada Geese for Am. Artist Collection, Am. Artist Mag., 1985; author, artist: The Waterfowl Art of Maynard Reece, 1985. Chmn. Gov.'s Com. Conservation of Outdoor Resource, 1963-64; trustee Iowa Natural Heritage Found., Des Moines, 1979—; hon. trustee Ducks Unltd. Inc., 1983—; trustee J.N. "Ding" Darling Conservation Found., Inc., Des Moines, 1962—. Served with AUS, 1943-45. Recipient awards for duck stamps and others Dept. Interior, 1948, 51, 59, 69, 71; recipient award Govt. Bermuda, 1963, award Iowa Conservation Commn., 1972, 77, 80, 81, award Fish and Game Commn., Little Rock, 1982, 88, award Tex. Parks and Wild Life Dept., 1983, award Nat. Fish & Wildlife Found., 1988, award Wash. State Dept. Wildlife, 1989; named Artist of Yr. Ducks Unltd. Inc., 1973; chosen Master Artist 1989, Leigh Yawkey Woodson Art Mus., Wausau, Wis., 1989. Mem. Nat. Audubon Soc., Nat. Wildlife Fedn., Izaak Walton League Am. (hon. pres. 1974-75). Home and Office: 5315 Robertson Dr Des Moines IA 50312-2133

REECE, ROBERT WILLIAM, zoological park administrator; b. Saginaw, Mich., Jan. 21, 1942; s. William Andrews and Mary Barbara (Murphy) R.; m. Jill Whetstone, Aug. 21, 1965; children: William Clayton, Gregory Scott, Mark Andrews. B.S., Mich. State U., 1964; postgrad., U. West Fla., 1969-71, U. South Fla., 1974-76. Dir. Northwest Fla. Zool. Gardens, Pensacola, Fla., 1970-72; zool. dir. Lion Country Ga., Stockbridge, 1972-73; asst. dir. Salisbury Zoo, Md., 1976-77; dir. zoology Wild Animal Habitat, Kings Island, Ohio, 1977-92; exec. dir. The Wilds Internat. Ctr. for Preservation of Wild Animals, Columbus, Ohio, 1992—. Assoc. editor: Sci. Jour. Zoo Biology, 1982—. Lt. USN, 1964-69, Korea. Profl. fellow Am. Assn. Zool. Parks and Aqariums; mem. Cin. Wildlife Rsch. Fedn., Am. Soc. Mammalogists, Animal Behavior Soc., Captive Breeding Specialist Group, Species Survival Commn., Internat. Union for Conservation of Nature and Natural Resources. Republican. Episcopalian. Home: 5359 Chimney Rock Westerville OH 43081 Office: The Wilds 85 E Gay St Ste 603 Columbus OH 43215*

REED, ADAM VICTOR, psychologist, engineer; b. Torun, Poland, Jan. 11, 1946; came to U.S., 1959, naturalized, 1965; s. Henry Kenneth and Eva (Tenenbaum) R.; B.S. in E.E., M.I.T., 1967, M.S. in Biology and M.S. in E.E., 1970; Ph.D, U. Oreg., 1974; m. Barbara Irene Birnbaum, Dec. 26, 1982; 1 child, Halina Brooke. Research programmer Artificial Intelligence Lab., M.I.T., Cambridge, 1965; research engr. Hewlett Packard Co., Palo Alto, Calif., 1966-67; mem. research staff Riverside Research Inst., N.Y.C., 1970-71; postdoctoral fellow, adj. asst. prof. Rockefeller U., N.Y.C., 1974-78; asst. prof., vis. lectr. psychology Grad. Faculty Social and Polit. Sci., New Sch. Social Research, N.Y.C., 1977-82; mem. tech. staff AT&T Bell Labs., 1981—; peer rev. referee NSF, others. Sci. and tech. adv. Libertarian Party v.p. candidate Tonie Nathan, 1972; mem. Marlboro Twp. Bd. Edn., N.J., 1994—. NDEA Title IV fellow, 1967-70; NSF fellow, 1970-73; NIMH Research Service fellow, 1974-77. Mem. N.Y. Acad. Sci., IEEE, Am. Psychol. Assn., Soc. Engring. Psychologists, Assn. Computing Machinery, Am. Soc. Cybernetics, AAAS, Sigma Xi, Tau Beta Pi, Eta Kappa Nu. Libertarian. Achievements include patents in field; first implementation of steepest descent, first statistically adaptive user interface, first switch-based facsimile server; research on experimental psychology-response signals method; contbr. articles to profl. jours.

REED, ALAN L., lawyer; b. Dec. 8, 1933. BA, Williams Coll., 1955; LLB, Harvard U., 1961. Bar: Pa. 1962. Ptnr. Morgan, Lewis & Bockius, Phila. Mem. ABA (chmn. sect. pub. utility, comm. and transp. law 1987-88). Office: Morgan Lewis & Bockius 2000 One Logan Sq Philadelphia PA 19103

REED, ALFRED, retired composer, conductor; b. N.Y.C., Jan. 25, 1921; s. Carl Mark and Elizabeth (Starsher) Friedman; m. Marjorie Beth Deley, June 20, 1941; children: Michael Carlson, Richard Judson. Student, Juilliard Sch. Music, 1946-48; MusB, Baylor U., 1955, MusM, 1956; MusD, Internat. Conservatory of Music, Lima, Peru, 1968. Exec. editor Hansen Publs., N.Y.C., 1955-66; prof. music U. Miami (Fla.) Sch. Music, 1966-93. Composer, arranger, N.Y.C., 1941-60; condr. Tri-State Music Festival, Okla., 1956-57, 60-66, 70, 73, Midwest Nat. Band Clinic, 1960-91, Bemidji (Minn.) Summer Music Camp, 1970-71, 75, Mid-East Instrumental Music Conf., Pitts., 1957-60, Can. Music Educators Assn., Edmonton, Alta., 1975; composer: Russian Christmas Music, 1944, Symphony for Brass and Percussion, 1952, Rhapsody for Viola and Orch., 1956, Choric Song, 1966, Titania's Nocturne, 1967, A Festival Prelude, 1962, Passacaglia, 1968, Music for Hamlet, 1973, Armenian Dances, 1974-75, Punchinello, Overture to a Romantic Comedy, 1974, Testament of an American, 1974, First Suite for Band, 1975, Othello, A Symphonic Portrait in Five Scenes, 1976, Prelude and Capriccio, 1977, Second Symphony, 1978, Siciliana Notturno, 1978, Second Suite for Band, 1978, The Enchanted Island, 1979, The Hounds of Spring, 1980, Third Suite for Band, 1981, Queenston Overture, 1982, Viva Musica!, 1983, A Little Concert Suite, 1983, El Camino Real, 1985, Centennial!, 1985, Three Revelations from the Lotus Sutra, 1985, Golden Jubilee, 1986, A Christmas Celebration, 1986, Praise Jerusalem!, 1987, Third Symphony, 1988, Eventide, 1988, Golden Eagle, 1989, Curtain Up!, 1990, A Springtime Celebration, Hymn Variants, 1991, With Trumpets and Drums, 1991, Concertino for Marimba and Winds, 1991, 4th Symphony, 1992, Fourth Suite for Band, 1993, Evolutions, A Concert Overture, 1993, also others. Served with AUS, 1942-46. Mem. ASCAP, Am. Bandmasters Assn., Am. Fedn. Musicians, Nat. Band Assn., Music Educators Nat. Conv. Home: 1405 Ancona Ave Miami FL 33146-1903 *As a composer, my desire has always been to achieve both a depth and intensity of communication between myself, my music and my audiences that would enable me to express something of value as regards myself and my time that, hopefully, would give rise to a deeply felt response on the part of my fellow human beings. I suppose this is true of the arts in general, and all artists, regardless of their medium of expression, but music, for me at least, has been the supreme expression of all time, for all men.*

REED, A(LFRED) BYRON, retired apparel and textile manufacturing company; b. Indpls., June 30, 1916; s. Alfred Lumpkin and Myrtle (Wood) R.; m. Mary Ellen Myers, Sept. 1, 1950; 1 child, Charles W. B.S., Butler U., 1939; postgrad., U. Chgo., 1946-47. Asst. brokerage mgr. Conn. Gen. Life Ins. Co., Chgo., 1939-41; sales mgr., mktg. mgr., asst. gen. mgr. Vassar Co.,

Chgo., 1946-57; gen. mgr. women's div. Munsingwear, Inc., Mpls., 1958-66; pres., chief exec. officer Munsingwear, Inc., 1966-79, chmn., 1979-81, also dir.; dir., trust com., exec. com. 1st Nat. Bank Mpls., Hoerner Waldorf Co., St. Paul, 1973-77, Murphy Motor Freight; mem. mgmt.-labor textile adv. com. U.S. Dept. Commerce. Chmn. Nat. Alliance Businessmen, Mpls., l41972; mem. Adv. Council U.S.-Japan Econ. Relations, Washington, also exec. com.; adviser Council Fin. Aid to Edn.; chmn. U.S. Savs. Bond Drive, 1975-76; bd. dirs. Better Bus. Bur. Mpls., 1973-74, Minn. Pvt. Coll. Fund, Mpls. YMCA; trustee Butler U. Served to lt. USNR, 1942-46. Mem. Am. Apparel Mfrs. Assn. (chmn. bd. dirs., exec com.), U.S. C. of C. (internat. policy com., internat. trade subcom.), Mpls. C. of C. (dir.), Minneapolis Club, Minikahda Club, Mission Viejo Country Club, Indian Wells Country Club, Phi Delta Theta. Republican. Episcopalian. Home: 76-750 Iroquois Dr Indian Wells CA 92210

REED, ALFRED DOUGLAS, university administrator; b. Bristol, Tenn., July 18, 1928; s. Roy Theodore and Elizabeth Brown (Tuft) R.; m. Emily Joyce Freeman, Mar. 18, 1950; children: Roy Frederick, Robert Douglas, David Clark, Timothy Wayne, Joseph William. AB, Erskine Coll., Due West, S.C., 1949. Reporter Citizen-Times, Asheville, N.C., 1949-51, city editor, 1953-60, mng. editor, 1962-63, assoc. editor, 1963-66, capital corr., 1959-66; asst. editor The Presbyn. Jour., Weaverville, N.C., 1951-52; assoc. editor Shelby (N.C.) Daily Star, 1961-62; dir. pub. info. Western Carolina U., Cullowhee, N.C., 1966—; cons. Devel. Office, East Carolina U., Greenville, 1980; bd. dirs. Wachovia Bank and Trust Co., Sylva, N.C., 1969—. Author: Prologue, 1968, Decade of Development, 1984, Our Second Century, 1992, Fulfillment of Promise, 1994; exec. editor: Western, The Mag. of Western Carolina University, 1991—. Mem. Asheville City Bd. Edn., 1958-62; vice chmn. bd. dirs. Sta. WCQS FM, Western N.C. Pub. Radio Inc., Asheville, 1978-88; bd. dirs. Cherokee Hist. Assn., 1985—, Western N.C. Assn. Comtys., 1985—, Jackson County Fund of N.C. Comty. Found., 1991-93; mem. Hunter Libr. Adv. Bd., 1991—, Pack Place Adv. Coun., Asheville, 1991—. Recipient Paul A. Reid Disting. Svc. award Western Carolina U., 1980. Mem. Coun. for Advancement and Support Edn., Pub. Rels. Assn. Western N.C. (bd. dirs., treas.), Coll. News Assn. Carolinas (bd. dirs. 1968-71, 80-82), N.C. Press Assn. (assoc.), Smoky Mountain Host Assn. (bd. dirs., 1st v.p. 1988—). Democrat. Presbyterian. Avocations: travel, stamps, gardening. Home: 310 University Hts Cullowhee NC 28723-9691 Office: Western Carolina U 420 Robinson Cullowhee NC 28723

REED, ANDRE DARNELL, professional football player; b. Allentown, Pa., Jan. 29, 1964. Grad., Kutztown State. Wide receiver Buffalo Bills, N.Y., 1985—. Pro Bowl Selection, 1988-93, Played in Super Bowl XXV, 1990, XXVI, 1991, XXVII, 1992, XXVIII, 1993. Office: Buffalo Bills 1 Bills Dr Orchard Park NY 14127*

REED, BILL, purchasing agent. Pres. Consol Purchasing Group, Atlanta, Ga. Office: Consol Purchasing Group 2849 Paces Ferry Rd NW Atlanta GA 30339*

REED, CHARLES ALLEN, anthropologist; b. Portland, Oreg., June 6, 1912; s. C. Allen and Gladys (Donohoe) R.; m. Lois Wells, Aug. 18, 1951; children: C. Allen, Robin M., Brian W. Student, Whitman Coll., 1929-30; B.S., U. Oreg., 1937; Ph.D., U. Calif. at Berkeley, 1943. Instr. biology U. Oreg., 1936-37; lectr. anatomy U. Calif. Med. Sch. at Berkeley, 1943; instr. biology Reed Coll., 1943-46; asst. prof. zoology U. Ariz., 1946-49; asst. prof., assoc. prof. zoology U. Ill. Sch. Pharmacy, 1949-54, 55-61; research assoc. anthropology U. Chgo., 1954-55; assoc. prof. biology Yale U., 1961-66; prof. biology and anthropology U. Ill., Chgo., 1966-67; prof. anthropology U. Ill., 1967—, acting head dept., 1967-70; Mem. Catlow Caves archeol. expdn. U. Oreg., 1937; Iraq-Jarmo archeol. expdn. Oriental Inst. U. Chgo., 1954-55; Iranian prehistoric project Oriental Inst., 1960; U. Istanbul-Chgo. Prehistoric project, Turkey, 1970; U. Ill. archeol. expedition to Sinai, 1986; curator mammals and reptiles Peabody Mus., Yale, 1961-66; dir. Yale prehistoric expdn. to Nubia, 1962-65; research asso. vertebrate anatomy Field Mus. Natural History, Chgo., 1966—; mem. U.S. com. Nat. Acad. Scis. for Internat. Union for Quaternary Research, 1967-74. Editor: Origins of Agriculture, 1977; Contbr. articles to profl. jours. Recipient Pomerance award for sci. excellence in archaeology Archaeol. Inst. Am. Fellow Am. Assn. Anthropologists (life), Asso. Current Anthropology, AAAS (life); mem. Am. Soc. Mammalogists (life), Am. Soc. Ichthyologists and Herpetologists (life), Am. Assn. Phys. Anthropology, Am. Soc. Zoologists, Am. Soc. Anatomists, Soc. Study Evolution, Soc. Vertebrate Paleontology, Am. Assn. Quaternary Research, Explorers Club, Chgo. Acad. Scis. (bd. dirs., govs.), Chgo. Anthrop. Soc. (pres. 1979-81), Phi Beta Kappa, Sigma Xi (life). Home: 151 N Kenilworth Ave Oak Park IL 60301 Office: U Ill Chgo Dept Anthropology Chicago IL 60607

REED, CHARLES BASS, university system chancellor; b. Harrisburg, Pa., Sept. 29, 1941; s. Samuel Ross and Elizabeth (Johnson) R.; m. Catherine A. Sayers, Aug. 22, 1964; children: Charles B. Jr., Susan Allison. BS, George Washington U., 1963, MA, 1964, EdD, 1970; postgrad. Summer Inst. for Chief State Sch. Officers, Harvard U. Grad Sch. Edn., 1977; D of Pub. Svc. (hon.), George Washington U., 1987; LLD (hon.), Stetson U., 1987; LittD (hon.), Waynesburg Coll., 1988; LHD (hon.), St. Thomas U., 1988. From asst. prof. to assoc. prof. George Washington U., Washington, 1963-70; asst. dir. Nat. Performance-Based Tchr. Edn. Project, Am. Assn. Colls. for Tchr. Edn., Washington, 1970-71; assoc. for planning and coordination Fla. Dept. Edn., Tallahassee, 1971-75, dir. Office Ednl. Planning, Budgeting, and Evaluation, 1975-79; edn. policy coord. Exec. Office of Gov., Tallahassee, 1979-80, dir. legis. affairs, 1980-81, dep. chief of staff, 1981-84, chief of staff, 1984-85; chancellor State Univ. System Fla., Tallahassee, 1985—; bd. dirs. Fla. Progress Corp., Capital Health Plan; chmn. bd. dirs. Regional Tech. Strategies, Inc. Mem. Coun. for Advancement and Support of Edn., Coun. on Fgn. Rels., Bus.-Higher Edn. Forum, Coun. of 100. Recipient Disting. Alumni award George Washington U., 1987. Mem. Am. Assn. State Colls. and Univs., Am. Assn. for Higher Edn., Am. Coun. on Edn., Fla. Assn. Colls. and Univs., Edn. Commn. on States (mem. exec. com. 1984-87, mem. exec. com. for campus compact project, Disting. Svc. award 1982), So. Regional Ednl. Bd. (vice-chmn. 1988-90, mem. exec. com.), Assn. Governing Bds. of Univs. and Colls., Nat. Assn. Sys. Heads, Golden Key. Democrat. Roman Catholic. Office: State U System Fla Office of Chancellor 325 W Gaines St Tallahassee FL 32399-6557

REED, CLARENCE RAYMOND, association executive; b. Shamokin, Pa., Sept. 23, 1932; s. Benton Howard and Gerda Maude (Hoover) R.; m. Joan Ann Engle, June 25, 1955; children: Ann Elizabeth, Susan Engle. B.A., U. Pa., 1954, M.B.A. with distinction, 1958; grad., Stonier Grad. Sch. Banking, 1969. With Prudential Ins. Co. Am., 1954; with Robert Morris Assos. Phila., 1958—; asst. sec. Robert Morris Assos., 1959-60, sec.-treas., 1960-74, exec. mgr., 1961-74, exec. v.p., 1974—, mem. exec. com., 1980—, also dir.; mem. faculty loan mgmt. seminar Ind. U., 1971-72; Chmn. Shares in Edn., 1968. Pres. Council Springfield (Pa.) Twp. Home and Sch. Assns., 1969-70. Served with AUS, 1954-56. Mem. Credit Mgmt. Assn. Delaware Valley, Am. Soc. Assn. Execs., Am. Mgmt. Assn., Central Home and Sch. Assn. (pres. 1966-67), Wharton M.B.A. Alumni Assn. Presbyterian (fin. sec. 1970, 79, ruling elder 1972-74, 83-85, chmn. 50th anniversary com. 1974, trustee 1977-79). Clubs: Union League (Phila.); Exchequer (chancellor 1984-85) (Washington); Rotary. Home: 15 Long Rd Berwyn PA 19312-1211 Office: Robert Morris Assocs 1 Liberty Pl Philadelphia PA 19103

REED, CORDELL, utility company executive; b. Chgo. Mar. 26, 1938; s. Clevon and Carrie Bell (Lacy) R.; m. Ora Lee McClelland, Sept. 17, 1961; children: Derrick Brazely, Brian, Steven, Michael. BSME, U. Ill., 1960. Registered profl. engr., Ill. Sr. v.p. nuclear ops. Commonwealth Edison Co., Chgo., 1960—; bd. dirs. Talman Home Fed. Savs. & Loan Assn. Pres. bd. trustees Abraham Lincoln Ctr., Chgo. Named Disting. Alumnus Coll. Engring. U. Ill., Urbana, 1983. Mem. Nat. Tech. Assn., Am. Nuclear Soc. Office: Commonwealth Edison Co PO Box 767 Chicago IL 60690-0767

REED, DARWIN CRAMER, health care consultant; b. Artesia, N.Mex., July 24, 1915; s. Darwin W. and Candace (Cramer) R.; m. Martha Gene Thalmann, Aug. 15, 1940; children—Geney Catherine Reed Fuller, Darwin Kim. A.B., Wichita U., 1937; M.D., Washington U., St. Louis, 1941; M.S., U. Pa., 1954. Diplomate: Am. Bd. Urology. Intern St. Francis Hosp., Wichita, Kans., 1941-42; resident St. Francis Hosp., 1946-48, U. Pa. Hosp.,

Phila., 1952-54, Med. Coll. Va. Hosp., 1954-55; practice medicine Wichita, 1948-52; partner Wichita Urology Group, Kans., 1955-70; dean Coll. Health Related Professions, Wichita State U., 1970-73, v.p. for health edn., 1973-77; prof. surgery, vice chancellor U. Kans. Sch. Medicine, Wichita, 1975-78; sr. v.p. Wesley Med. Center, Wichita, 1978-86; pres. Health Strategies, Inc., 1980-86; exec. dir. Greater Wichita Community Found., 1986-88; program cons. Kans. Health Found., 1989-93; pres. Cramer Reed & Assocs., 1993—; mem. Kans. Bd. Healing Arts, 1964-67; chmn. dean's com. Wichita VA Hosp., 1975-78. Chmn. bd. trustees Wichita State U., 1966-68. Lt. col. M.C., USAAF, 1942-46. Fellow A.C.S.; mem. AMA, Pan Am. Med. Assn., Am. Urologic Assn., Am. Cancer Soc. (pres. Kans. div. 1960-61, 65-66). Methodist. Home: 7520 E 21st St N Apt 22 Wichita KS 67206-1086

REED, DAVID ANDREW, foundation executive; b. Butler, Pa., Feb. 24, 1933; s. Sherman W. and Caroline (Janner) R.; m. Virginia Rogers, Dec. 1, 1956; children: Kristine Lynn, Katherine Louise, Elizabeth Anne, Amy Janner. A.B., Allegheny Coll., 1955; M.S., U. Pitts., 1961. Diplomate: Sch. Pub. Health, Columbia U. Adminstrv. resident Titusville (Pa.) Hosp., 1959, Cin. Gen. Hosp., 1960-61; asst. adminstr. Warren (Pa.) Gen. Hosp., 1961-62, Western Pa. Gen. Hosp., Pitts., 1962-63; with Cin. Gen. Hosp., 1963-69, adminstr., 1964-69; asso. prof. hosp. adminstrn. U. Cin. Coll. Medicine, 1966-69; preceptor program med. and hosp. adminstrn. U. Pitts. Grad. Sch. Pub. Health, 1966-69; pres. Lenox Hill Hosp., N.Y.C., 1969-78; v.p., chief exec. officer Good Samaritan Hosp., Phoenix, 1978-82; pres. SamCor/ Samaritan Health Service, Phoenix, 1982-89; pres., chief exec. officer The Samaritan Found., Phoenix, 1989, St. Joseph Health System, Orange, Calif. 1990—; instr.; past pres. Greater Cin. Hosp. Council, Phoenix Regional Hosp. Council; bd. govs. Greater N.Y. Hosp. Assn.; chmn. Am. Hosp. Assn., also trustee; cons. Hosp. Devel. and Research Inst. Contbr. articles to profl. jours. Bd. dirs. Urban League Cin. Served with AUS, 1955-57. Fellow Am. Coll. Hosp. Adminstrs.; mem. Hosp. Adminstrs. Club N.Y.C. (pres.), Hosp. Assn. N.Y., Phi Gamma Delta. Presbyterian. Clubs: Paradise Valley Country, Pacific Golf, Marbella Country, Center. Office: St Joseph Health System 440 S Batavia St Orange CA 92668-3907

REED, DAVID BENSON, bishop; b. Tulsa, Feb. 16, 1927; s. Paul Spencer and Bonnie Frances (Taylor) R.; m. Susan Henry Riggs, Oct. 30, 1954 (div.); children: Mary, Jennifer, David, Sarah, Catherine; m. Catherine Camp Luckett, Apr. 15, 1984. A.B., Harvard U., 1948; M.Div., Va. Theol. Sem., 1951, D.D., 1964; D.D., U. of South, 1972, Episc. Theol. Sem., Ky., 1985. Ordained priest Episcopal Ch., 1952; missionary priest in Panama and Colombia, 1951-58; with Nat. Ch. Exec. Office, 1958-61; mission priest S.D., 1961-63; bishop of Colombia, 1964-72, Ecuador, 1964-70; bishop coadjutor Diocese of Ky., Louisville, 1972-74; bishop of Ky. Diocese of Ky., 1974-94; asst. bishop of Conn. Episcopal Diocese of Conn., Hartford, 1994—; 1st pres. Anglican Council Latin Am., 1969-72; chmn. standing commn. on ecumenical relations Episcopal Ch., 1979-82; pres. Ky. Coun. Chs., 1988-91; mem. governing bd. Nat. Coun. of Chs. of Christ in U.S.A., 1982-91, mem. exec. com., 1989-91, sec., 1988-91; Anglican co-chmn. Anglican Orthodox Theol. Cons., 1984-94. Bd. dirs. Alliant Health Systems (formerly Norton Kosair Children's Hosp.), Louisville, 1979-94; trustee U. of the South, 1972—, regent, 1979-82; chmn. Louisville United Against Hunger, 1980-84, 86-87; chmn. Presiding Bishop's Com. on Interfaith Rels., 1991—. Mem. Harvard Club of Western Ky. (pres. 1992-94). Democrat. Home: 5226 Moccasin Trl Louisville KY 40207-1634 Office: Episcopal Diocese of Conn 1335 Asylum Ave Hartford CT 06105

REED, DAVID FREDRICK, artist; b. San Diego, Jan. 20, 1946; s. David Fredrick II and Beverly (Behl) R.; m. Lillian Ball, June 28, 1986; 1 child previous marriage, John. Student, Skowhegan (Maine) Sch. Painting and Sculpture, 1966, N.Y. Studio Sch., 1966-67; BA, Reed Coll., 1968. One-man shows include Max Protetch Gallery, N.Y.C., 1977, 79, 83, 85, 86, 88, 89, 91, 92, 95, Asher/Faure Gallery, L.A., 1988, Galerie Rolf Ricke, Cologne, Germany, 1991, 93, San Francisco Art Inst., 1992, Kölnischer Kunstverein, Cologne, Germany, 1995. Rockefeller Found. fellow, 1966, John Simon Guggenheim Meml. Found. fellow, 1988, Nat. Endowment Arts Visual Arts fellow, 1991; grantee Roswell (N.Mex.) Mus. and Art Ctr., 1969.

REED, DAVID GEORGE, entrepreneur; b. Alameda, Calif., July 19, 1945; s. David Francis and Anna Amelia Vangeline (Paulson) R.; m. Marianne Louise Watson, Apr. 7, 1971 (div. June 1975); m. Michele Ann Hock, June 28, 1989; 1 child, Casey Christine Michele. AA in Bus. Adminstrn., Diablo Valley Coll., Pleasant Hill, Calif., 1965; BA in Design and Industry, San Francisco State U., 1967, MBA in Mktg., 1969; cert. res. police officer, Los Medanos Coll., Pittsburg, Calif., 1977. Owner Western Furs, Ltd., Walnut Creek, Calif., 1963-72; mgmt. cons. Controlled Interval Scheduling, Rolling Hills Estates, Calif., 1972-73; owner Dave Reed's Texaco, Concord, Calif., 1973-76; mgmt. cons. Mgmt. Scheduling Systems, Houston, 1974-76, Thomas-Ross Assocs., Mercer Island, Wash., 1972-82; plant mgr. Bonner Packing, Morgan Hill, Calif., 1981; mfg. engr. Systron Donner, Concord, 1982-84, Beckman Instruments, San Ramon, Calif., 1984-90; owner Dave Reed & Co. Water Ski Sch., White Water Rafting, Chiloquin, Oreg., 1987—, Dave Reed & Co., design, market, mfg. Contender boats, Chiloquin, Oreg., 1976—; lectr. wildlife mgmt. Dave Reed & Co., Chiloquin, 1965—, lectr. mgmt. seminars, 1982—; coach Japanese Water Ski Team, Bluff Water Ski Club, Tokyo, 1984; fin. mgr. Japanese investors Dave Reed & Co., Chiloquin, 1986—, design and supply solar electric power sys., 1994—. Res. dep. sheriff Contra Costa County Sheriff's Dept., Martinez, Calif., 1977-80. With U.S. Army, 1969-71, Vietnam. Recipient Gold medal internat. freestyle wrestling Sr. Olympics, Fullerton, Calif., 1983. Mem. Am. Water Ski Assn. (Calif. state water ski champion 1977, 86, western region water ski champion 1977, silver medal nat. water ski championships 1977), Bay Area Tournament Assn. (chmn. 1968—), Diablo Water Ski Club (bd. dirs. 1968—). Republican. Avocations: water skiing, snow skiing, surfing, camping, fly fishing. Home: PO Box 336 Chiloquin OR 97624-0336

REED, DONALD ANTHONY, executive; b. New Orleans, Nov. 22, 1935; s. Roscoe and Mildred (Fauria) R. BS, Loyola U., 1957; MSLS, U. So. Calif., 1958, JD, 1968. Instr. U. Beverly Hills, L.A.; libr. Woodburg U., L.A.; instr. L.A. Valley Coll., Calif. Inst. of Arts, L.A.; founder, pres. Coun. Film Orgns., L.A., 1980—; Acad. of Family Films, L.A., 1980—; The Count Dracula Soc., L.A., 1962—; Acad. Sci. Fiction Fantacy & Horror Films, L.A., 1972—; cons. in field. Author: The Vampire on the Screen, 1964, The Outlawry of War in Outer Space, 1966, Admiral Leahy at Vichy France, 1968, Robert Redford, 1975, Science Fiction Film Awards, 1981. Recipient The Saturn award, 1978, Count Dracula Soc. award, 1964. Mem. Acad. Magical Arts, Sons of the Desert, Beta Phi Mu (pres. 1958-60), Phi Alpha Theta, Phi Kappa Alpha. Democrat. Roman Catholic. Avocations: comic operas of Gilbert and Sullivan, Count Dracula books and films, Calvin Coolidge, Abbott and Costello, dir. Bryan Singer. Office: Acad Sci Fiction Fantasy & Horror 334 W 54th St Los Angeles CA 90037

REED, DONALD JAMES, biochemistry educator; b. Montrose, Kans., Sept. 26, 1930; married, 1949; 6 children. BS, Coll. of Idaho, 1953; MS, Oreg. State U., 1955, PhD in Chemistry, 1957. Asst. Oreg. State U., Corvallis, 1953-55, asst., then assoc. prof., 1962-72, prof. biochemistry, 1972-90, prof. toxicology program, dist. prof. biochemistry, 1990, dir. environ. health sci. ctr., 1981—; acting chair dept. biochemistry, 1994-95; assoc. biochemist cereal investigations western regional rsch. lab., agr. rsch. svc. USDA, Calif., 1957-58; asst. prof. chemistry Mont. State U., Bozeman, 1958-62; mem. toxicology study sect. NIH, 1971-75, ad hoc rev. com. Nat. Cancer Inst., 1975-87, sabbatical scientist, 1984-85; mem. environ. sci. rev. panel health rsch. EPA, 1981, environ. health sci. rev. com. Nat. Inst. Environ. Health Sci., 1982-85; mem. Burroughs Wellcome Toxicology Scholar Award Selection Com., 1984-87; vis. prof. MRC Toxicology Unit, Carshalton, Eng., 1984; mem. task group health criteria, internat. program chem. safety WHO, 1986,biochem. & carcinogenesis rev. com. Am. Cancer Soc., 1984—; cons. U. Calif., San Francisco, 1985-90; mem. nat. adv. environ. health scis. coun. NIH, 1992—; mem. health review com. Health Effects Inst., 1993—; assoc. editor Jour. Toxicology & Environ. Health, 1980-84, Toxicology & Applied Pharmacology, 1981-84, Cancer Rsch., 1987—; editor Cell Biology & Toxicology. USPHS Spl. Rsch. fellow NIH, 1969-70, Eleanor Roosevelt Am. Cancer Soc. Internat. Cancer fellow Karolinska Inst., 1976-77; Burroughs Wellcome Travel grantee, 1984, 92; MERIT award NIH, 1984, Discovery award Med. Rsch. Found., 1988, Burroughs Wellcome Vis. Prof. in the Basic Med. Scis. award U. Ariz., 1988-89, Sam Kuna Lectr. award Rutgers U.,

1989, F.A. Gilfillan Meml. award for Dist. Scholarship in Sci., 1990. Mem. Am. Soc. Biol. Chemistry, Am. Soc. Pharmacology and Exptl. Therapeutics, Am. Assn. Cancer Rsch., Internat. Union of Toxicology (dir. 1992—), Soc. Toxicology, (pres. 1991-93), Phi Kappa Phi, Sigma Xi (rsch. award). Achievements include research in biological oxidations, environmental toxicology, biochemical anticancer drugs, protective mechanisms of glutathione functions, vitamin E status. Office: Oreg State U Environ Health Scis Ctr Agrl and Life Scis Bldg Rm 1011 Corvallis OR 97331-7302

REED, EDWARD CORNELIUS, JR., federal judge; b. Mason, Nev., July 8, 1924; s. Edward Cornelius Sr. and Evelyn (Walker) R.; m. Sally Torrance, July 14, 1952; children: Edward T., William W., John A., Mary E. BA, U. Nev., 1949; JD, Harvard U., 1952. Bar: Nev. 1952, U.S. Dist Ct. Nev. 1957, U.S. Supreme Ct. 1974. Atty. Arthur Andersen & Co., 1952-53; spl. dep. atty. gen. State of Nev., 1967-69; judge U.S. Dist. Ct. Nev., Reno, 1979—, chief judge, now sr. judge. Former vol. atty. Girl Scouts Am., Sierra Nevada Council, U. Nev., Nev. Agrl. Found., Nev. State Sch. Adminstrs. Assn., Nev. Congress of Parents and Teachers; mem. Washoe County Sch. Bd., 1956-72, pres. 1959, 63, 69; chmn. Gov.'s Sch. Survey Com., 1958-61; mem. Washoe County Bd. Tax Equalization, 1957-58, Washoe County Annexation Commn., 1968-72, Washoe County Personnel Com., 1973-77, chmn. 1973; mem. citizens adv. com. Washoe County Sch. Bond Issue, 1977-78, Sun Valley, Nev., Swimming Pool Com., 1978, Washoe County Blue Ribbon Task Force Com. on Growth, Nev. PTA (life); chmn. profl. div. United Way, 1978; bd. dirs. Reno Siver Sox, 1962-65. Served as staff sgt. U.S. Army, 1943-46, ETO, PTO. Mem. ABA (jud. adminstrn. sect.), Nev. State Bar Assn. (adminstrv. com. dist. 5, 1967-79, lien law com. 1965-78, chmn. 1965-72, probate law com. 1963-66, tax law com. 1962-65), Am. Judicature Soc. Democrat. Baptist. Office: US Dist Ct 5147 US Courthouse 300 Booth St Reno NV 89509-1316

REED, FRANK ENGELHART, banker; b. Orange, N.J., Mar. 15, 1935; s. Harvey E. and Ruth (Eaglesfield) R.; m. Ann Livingston, Nov. 30, 1957; children: Jeffrey L., Timothy G. B.A., Amherst Coll., 1957. Sr. v.p./group exec. Morgan Guaranty Trust Co., N.Y.C., 1968-84; pres., COO First Pa. Bank N.A., Phila., 1984-90; pres., CEO Phila. Nat. Bank, a CoreStates Bank, Phila., 1990—; dir. Centel Corp., Harleysville Group Inc., Harleysville Mutual Ins. Co., Hamilton Bank, Lancaster, Pa. Office: Phila Nat Bank Broad & Chestnut Sts FC-1-1-2-2 Philadelphia PA 19101-7618

REED, GEORGE FRANCIS, architect; b. Miami, Fla., Sept. 25, 1928; s. George Francis and Lillian Lucille (Hellerman) R. B.S. in Architecture, Ga. Inst. Tech., 1951, B.Arch., 1953. Draftsman-designer Rufus Nims Architect, Miami, 1954-56; assoc. architect Robert B. Browne Architect, Miami, 1957-60; pvt. practice architecture Miami, 1961—; chmn. Miami Design Rev. Bd., 1967. Dade County (Fla.) Housing and Urban Devel. Adv. Bd., 1968—; pres. South Fla. Inter-Profl. Council, 1970-71; mem. Dade County Art In Public Bldgs. Adv. Bd., 1974-77, Dade County Community Devel. Adv. Bd., 1975—, Dade County Housing Planning Adv. Bd., 1977—; Pres. Coconut Grove Assn., Miami, 1972-73. Served to ensign USCGR, 1952. Recipient various awards for archtl. design and public service Soc. Am. Foresters, 1967, 70, 73, 81, 84, Red Cedar Shingle, 1983, various awards for archtl. design and public service South Fla. Inter-Profl. Council, 1968, 69, 70, various awards for archtl. design and public service Met. Dade County, 1968, 77, 78, 88, various awards for archtl. design and public service Coconut Grove Corp. Am., 1971. Fellow AIA (Fla. Assn. awards 1964, 67, 68, 69, 73, 78, 82, 83, Test of Time awards 1993, Fla. South chpt. awards 1964, 66, 67, 68, 75, 77, 78, 81, pres. Fla. South chpt. 1967, Silver medal Miami chpt. 1991). Office: 11729 SW 119 Ter Miami FL 33186

REED, GLEN ALFRED, lawyer; b. Memphis, Sept. 24, 1951; s. Thomas Henry and Evelyn Merle (Roddy) R.; m. Edith Jean Renick, June 17, 1972; children: Adam Christopher, Alec Benjamin. BA, U. Tenn., 1972; JD, Yale U., 1976. Bar: Ga. 1976. Project dir. Tenn. Research Coordinating Unit, Knoxville, 1972-73; assoc. Alston Miller & Gaines, Atlanta, 1976-77; assoc. Bordurant Miller Hishon & Stephenson, Atlanta, 1978-81, ptnr., 1981-85; ptnr., King & Spalding, Atlanta, 1985—. Author: Practical Hospital Law, 1979. legal adv. Ga. Gov.'s Commn. on Healthcare, 1994; Gen. counsel Assn. Retarded Citizens-Atlanta, 1979—, pres., 1982—; vice-chmn. CARE Atlanta adv. bd., 1992-94, pres., 1994—; v.p. Ga. Network for People with Developmental Disabilities, 1991-92; bd. dirs. Ctrl. Health Ctr., 1989—, Vis. Nurse Health System, 1991—, Sch. Pub. Health Emory U., Atlanta, 1993—. Mem. ABA, Ga. Bar Assn., Acad. Hosp. Attys. (bd. dirs. 1991—), Ga. Acad. Hosp. Attys. (pres. 1991-92), Nat. Health Lawyers Assn., Phi Beta Kappa. Methodist. Office: King & Spalding 191 Peachtree St NE Atlanta GA 30303-1740

REED, GREGORY WILLIAM, broadcasting executive; b. Oakland, Calif., Mar. 6, 1943; s. William Andker and Guinevere Kathleen (Klint) R.; children: Stephen Gregory, Christian Andker; m. Leann Chambers. B.S., U. Oreg., 1966, M.S., 1969. Asst. dean men U. Oreg., 1966-69; trainee Procter & Gamble Co., 1969-70; rep. Radio 1, Pacific & So. Broadcasting Co., Los Angeles, 1970-71; account exec. Sta. KABC, Los Angeles, 1971-72; with Golden West Broadcasting, 1974—; gen. sales mgr. Sta. KSFO, San Francisco, 1978-79; corp. v.p., gen. mgr. Sta. KEX-AM, Portland, Oreg., 1979-82, Sta. KSFC San Francisco, 1982-83; pres., chief exec. officer Media Sports Inc., San Francisco, 1983—; exec. v.p. Focus Mgmt. Co., San Francisco, 1982-83, Henry Broadcasting Co., San Francisco, 1986—. Bd. dirs. Portland Goodwill Industries, Portland Jr. Achievement, Portland Urban League. Recipient various public service awards. Mem. Nat. Assn. Broadcasters, Oreg. Assn. Broadcasters, Greater Portland Radio Broadcasters Assn. (v.p. 1981-82), No. Calif. Broadcast Assn. (bd. dirs. 1982-83), Portland Advt. Fedn., Sigma Alpha Epsilon, Kappa Tau Alpha. Methodist. Office: KYTE 2040 SW 1st Ave Portland OR 97201-5302

REED, H(ORACE) CURTIS, insurance company executive, management consultant; b. Oneida, N.Y., May 6, 1917; s. Murry Eugene and Gertrude E. (Hicks) R.; m. Loraine McVicar, Dec. 20, 1941; children—Janice Louise (Mrs. C.J. McNeill), Allan Curtis, Donald McVicar. Student, Hamilton Coll., Clinton, N.Y., 1934; BSBA, Clarkson U., 1938. With Travelers Ins. Co., 1946-59, dir. tng., sales research and promotion, 1950-54; sec., dir. group sales Travelers Nat. and Canadian Orgn., 1955-59; exec. v.p. Fed. Life and Casualty Co., Battle Creek, Mich., 1959-68; also dir.; pres., gen. mgr., dir. West Coast Life Ins. Co., San Francisco, 1968-73; pres., dir. First Farwest Corp., Portland, Oreg., 1974-75; chmn. bd., dir. First Farwest Life Ins. Co.; pres. Farwest Ins. Group, 1976-77; v.p. Hutton Life Ins. Co., La Jolla, 1978-84; pres., dir. La Jolla Assos. Ltd., Calif., 1978—; bd. dirs. N.W. Life Assurance Co. Am. Trustee San Francisco Theol. Sem., 1972-75. Served from pvt. to maj. Fin. Corps, AUS, 1941-45. Named Man of Year Hartford (Conn.) Jr. C. of C., 1952, Outstanding Industrialist of Year Mich., 1967; recipient Golden Knight award Clarkson Coll., 1973. Home: 1229 Las Vistillas Ln San Marcos CA 92069 Office: La Jolla Assocs Ltd 1229 Las Vistillas San Marcos CA 92069

REED, HOWARD ALEXANDER, historian, educator; b. Izmir, Turkey, Feb. 26, 1920; s. Cass Arthur and Rosalind Christine (MacLachlan) R.; m. Shafiga Daulet, May 25, 1985; children from previous marriage: Seth Olcott, Heather MacLachlan, Deborah Lamont; stepchildren: Aylin, Sibel. Ed., Phillips Acad., Andover, Mass., 1933-37, Wellington Coll., Berkshire, Eng., 1937-38; B.A. with high orations, Yale, 1942; M.A., Princeton, 1949, Ph.D. 1951. Instr. history Princeton U., 1949-50; Instr. history Yale U., also dir. Internat. Student Ctr., 1950-52; co-founder, asst. dir., prof. Inst. Islamic Studies, McGill U., 1952-55; dir. Inst. Internat. and Intercultural Studies, U. Conn., 1967-71, prof. history, 1967-89, prof. emeritus, cons., 1989—; del. UNRRA and World Student Svc., Greece, 1946-47; program specialist internat. tng. and resch. Ford Found., 1955-57; dir. coll. and youth programs Am. Friends Svc. Com., 1958-60; assoc. dir. Danforth Found., St. Louis, 1960-64; exec. assoc. Edn. World Affairs, N.Y.C., 1964-67; dir. Nat. Survey Non-Western Studies in Liberal Arts Colls. Dept. Edn., Assn. Am. Colls., 1963-64; participant internat. confs.; cons. Dept. State, U.S. A.I.D., World Bank, India, Oman, Turkey, various unvis., lectr. Author: Non-Western Studies in the Liberal Arts College, 1964; contbr. author to: Ency. Islam, 2d edit., 1954—, Foreign Affairs Bibliography, 1942-52, 55, Islam and the West, 1957, A Guide to Historical Literature, 1961, Ency. Americana, 1964—, General Education, Current Ideas and Concerns, 1964, The Emergence of the Modern Middle East, 1970, Expanding Dimensions of World Education,

1976, Internat. Ency. Higher Edn., 1977, Social and Economic History of Turkey (1071-1920), 1980, Islam in the Contemporary World, 1981, 2d edit. 1986, Contributions à l'histoire économique et Sociale de l'Empire Ottoman, 1980, 83, Issues and Opportunities in Turkish Education, 1991; adv. editor: Muslim World, 1970—; bd. adv. editors: The Middle East Jour, 1977—; contbr. articles to profl. jours. Bd. dirs. Assn. Princeton Grad. Alumni, 1961-63, Lisle Fellowship, 1948-52, 58-60, 65-70, Pendle Hill, Wallingford, Pa., 1958-73, 75-86, Campus Christian Found., 1969-73, Univ. Senate, 1969-72, Am. Research Inst. Turkey, 1969-74, 77-79, Middle East Studies Assn., 1977-80; trustee Friends World Coll., 1976-87; bd. overseers Moses Brown Sch., 1975-77; mem. exec. council Conf. Peace Research in History, 1972-75. Served to lt. (s.g.) USNR, 1942-46. Decorated Legion of Merit; D.S.C. (Gt. Britain); fellow Internat. Scholboy, 1937-38, Mid. East Inst., 1948-49, Rockefeller Found., 1949-50, 52, Ford Found., 1954, Fulbright fellow, 1970, 81, fellow Am. Coun. Learned Socs.-Social Sci. Rsch. Coun., 1977. Fellow Mid. East Studies Assn. (charter), Soc. Values in Higher Edn., Turkish Studies Assn. (co-founder, sec.), Inst. Turkish Studies (hon.), AHEPA (hon.); mem. Am. Hist. Assn., Conf. on Peace Rsch. in History, Mid. East Inst., Internat. Soc. Oriental Rsch., Brit.-Am. Alumni, Turkish Hist. Soc. (hon.), Am.-Turkish Friendship Coun. (nat. adv. bd., Chmn.'s award in edn. 1991), Am.-Turkish Coun., Phi Beta Kappa, Phi Kappa Phi. Mem. Soc. of Friends. Office: U Conn Dept History U-103 241 Glenbrook Rd Storrs Mansfield CT 06268

REED, ISHMAEL SCOTT (EMMETT COLEMAN), writer; b. Chattanooga, Feb. 22, 1938; s. Bennie Stephen (stepfather) and Thelma (Coleman) R.; m. Priscilla Rose, 1960 (div. 1970); children: Timothy, Brett; m. Carla Blank; 1 child, Tennessee Maria. Co-founder Yardbird Pub. Co. Inc., Berkeley, 1971, editorial dir., 1971-75; editor Yardbird Reader, 1972-76; cofounder Reed, Cannon & Johnson Comm. Co., Berkeley, 1973—, Before Columbus Found., Berkeley, 1976—; editor-in-chief Y'Bird mag., 1978-80; co-founder Ishmael Reed and Al Young's Quilt, Berkeley, 1980—; co-editor Quilt mag., 1981—; co-founder East Village Other, 1965, Advance, 1965; tchr. St. Mark's in the Bowery prose workshop, 1966; guest lectr. U. Calif., Berkeley, 1968—, U. Wash., 1969-70, SUNY, Buffalo, 1975, 79, Yale U., 1979, Dartmouth Coll., 1980-81, Sitka Cmty. Assn., 1982, U. Ark., Fayetteville, 1982, Columbia U., 1983, Harvard U., 1987; assoc. fellow Calhoun Coll., Yale U., 1982—; Harvard Signet Soc., 1987—; regents lectr. U. Calif. Santa Barbara, 1988; mem. usage panel Am. Heritage Dictionary. Author: (novels) The Free-Lance Pallbearers, 1967, Yellow Back Radio Broke-Down, 1969, Mumbo Jumbo, 1972 (Nat. Book award nomination 1973), The Last Days of Louisiana Red, 1974 (Richard and Hinda Rosenthal Found. award Nat. Inst. Arts and Letters 1975), Flight to Canada, 1976, The Terrible Twos, 1982, Reckless Eyeballing, 1986, Cab Calloway Stands In for The Moon, 1986, The Terrible Threes, 1989, Japanese By Spring, 1993; (poetry) Catechism of a neoamerican hoodoo church, 1970, Conjure: Selected Poems 1963-70, 1972 (Nat. Book award nomination 1973, Pulitzer prize nomination 1973), Chattanooga, 1973, A Secretary to the Spirits, 1978, Ishmael Reed: New and Collected Poems, 1989; (essays) Shrovetide in Old New Orleans, 1978, God Made Alaska for the Indians, 1981, Airing Dirty Laundry, 1993; (play) (with Carla Blank and Suzushi Hanayagi) The Lost State of Franklin, 1976; editor: The Rise, Fall, and...? of Adam Clayton Powell, 1967, 19 Necromancers from Now, 1970 (Calif. Assn. Eng. Tchrs. certificate of merit 1972), Yardbird Lives!, 1978, Calafia: The California Poetry, 1979, Writin' Is Fightin': Thirty-seven Years of Boxing on Paper, 1988; exec. prodr.: (TV pilot) Personal Problems. Chmn. Berkeley Arts Commn., 1980, 81; bd. dirs. chmn. Coordinating Council Lit. Mags., 1975-79, adv. bd. chmn., 1977-79. Recipient John Simon Guggenheim Meml. Found. award for fiction, 1974, Lewis Michaux award, 1978, ACLU award, 1978, Pushcart prize, 1979; Wis. Arts Bd. fellow, 1982; Nat. Endowment for Arts writing fellow, 1974; Guggenheim fellow, 1975. Mem. Author's Guild am., PEN, Celtic Found. Address: 2140 Shattuck Ave Rm 311 Berkeley CA 94704 Office: care Avon Books div Hearst Corp 1790 Broadway New York NY 10019-1412*

REED, JAMES ALEXANDER, JR., lawyer; b. Rochester, N.Y., Feb. 7, 1930; s. James Alexander and Rose Winifred (Nellist) R.; m. Dora Anne DeVries, Feb. 17, 1972 (div. Mar. 1983); children: Geoffrey M., Diane E. BA cum laude, Amherst Coll., 1952; JD, Harvard U., 1955. Bar: N.Y. 1958, U.S. Dist. Ct. (we. dist.) N.Y. 1959, U.S. Dist. Ct. (no. dist.) N.Y. 1960. Assoc. Osborn, Reed, Burke & Tobin and predecessor firms, Rochester, 1958-63, ptnr., 1964—; dep. atty. Town of Pittsford, N.Y., 1976-77, atty. 1977—. Served to lt. USNR, 1955-58. Mem. ABA, N.Y. State Bar Assn., Monroe County Bar Assn., Am. Judicature Assn. Republican. Episcopalian. Home: 8 Greenwood Park Pittsford NY 14534-1911 Office: Osborn Reed Burke & Tobin 1 Exchange St Rochester NY 14614-2206

REED, JAMES DONALD, journalist, author; b. Jackson, Mich., Oct. 7, 1940; s. Clair and Esther (Bryden) R.; m. Christine Flowers, June 14, 1969; children: Phoebe C., Alicia M., Gabrielle A. Student, Albion Coll., 1958-60; BA, Mich. State U., 1962; postgrad., SUNY-Stony Brook, 1967-69; MFA, U. Mont., 1970. Mem. faculty dept. creative writing U. Mass., 1970-75; dir. M.F.A. program, 1974; staff writer Sports Illustrated, N.Y., 1975-80; assoc. editor Time mag., 1980-90; sr. writer People mag., N.Y.C., 1990-91, sr. editor, 1991-93; sr. assoc. editor spl. tissues, 1993—. Author: (poetry) Expressways, 1970, Fatback Odes, 1973; (fiction) Free Fall, 1980; (with Christine Reed) Exposure, 1987. Guggenheim fellow, 1971. Office: People Mag Time Life Bldg Rockefeller Ctr New York NY 10020

REED, JAMES WESLEY, social historian, educator; b. New Orleans, Oct. 17, 1944; married. BA, U. New Orleans, 1967; AM, Harvard U., 1968, PhD, 1974. Research fellow in history Schlesinger Library, 1973-75; prof. history Rutgers U., New Brunswick, N.J., 1975—; dean Rutgers Coll., Rutgers U., New Brunswick, 1985-94. Author: From Private Vice to Public Virtue: The Birth Control Movement and American Society Since 1930, 1978. Office: Rutgers U dept of History Van Dyke Hall New Brunswick NJ 08903-5059

REED, JAMES WHITFIELD, physician, educator; b. Pahokee, Fla., Nov. 1, 1935; s. Thomas Reed and Chineater (Grey) Whitfield; married; children: David M., Robert A., Mary I., Katherine E. BS, W.Va. State Coll., 1954; MD, Howard U., 1963. Diplomate Am. Bd. Internal Medicine, Am. Bd. Endocrinology and Metabolism. Commd. U.S. Army, 1963; advanced through grades to col., 1981; resident in internal medicine Madigan Army Med. Ctr., Tacoma, Wash., 1966-69, chief endocrinology and metabolism, 1971-76, chief dept. clin. rsch., 1976-78; chief dept. medicine Eisenhower Army Med. Ctr., Augusta, Ga., 1978-81; assoc. prof. internal medicine edn. for FP program U. Tex. at Dallas, 1981-84; prof. medicine Morehouse Sch. Medicine, Atlanta, 1985—, chmn. dept., 1985-92, chmn. grad. med. edn., 1992—, activity chmn., 1986-88; postdoctoral fellow in endocrinology and metabolism U. Calif. Med. Ctr., San Francisco, 1969-71; dir. endocrinology, fellow Madigan Army Med. Ctr., 1976-78; dir. internal medicine residency program Eisenhower Army Med. Ctr., 1978-81, chmn. directorate of clin. investigation, 1978-81, dir. endocrinology fellowship program; med. cons. Tuskgee (Ala.) VA Hosp., 1985—; mem. nat. high blood pressure edn. com. NHLBI/NIH, Nat. Diabetes Mellitus Adv. Coun., Nat. Diabetes Adv. Bd., NHLBI working Com. on Hypertension and Diabetes; chmn. Sub Com. Special Population and Situations, chmn. subcom., mem. exec. com. Joint Nat. Commn. for Detection Evaluation and Treatment of High Blood Pressure. Author: Black Man's Guide to Good Health, 1994; contbr. articles to profl. publs. Med. advisor, chmn. March of Dimes, Pierce County, Tacoma, 1976-78; pres. Charles Drew Sickle Cell and Health Bd., Tacoma, 1976-78. Decorated Legion of Merit; recipient Disting. Alumni award Nat. Assn. for Equal Opportunity in Higher Edn., 1988, Nat. Alumnus of Yr. award W.Va. State Coll., 1987; inducted into ROTC Hall of Fame, W.Va. State Coll., 1987. Fellow ACP; mem. Assn. Profs. Medicine, Endocrine Soc., Internat. Soc. Hypertension in Blacks (v.p. 1986, pres. 1992—), Assn. of Program Dirs. in Internal Medicine, Alpha Phi Alpha. Democrat. Avocations: bowling, skiing. Home: 380 Mcgill Pl NE Atlanta GA 30312-1069 Office: Morehouse Sch Medicine 720 Westview Dr SW Atlanta GA 30310-1495

REED, JANET LYNN, lawyer; b. South Bend, Ind., Jan. 20, 1951. BMus with high honors, Mich. State U., 1972; JD with honors, Loyola U., 1978. Bar: Ill. 1978, U.S. Dist. Ct. (no. dist. trial bar) Ill. 1978. Law clk. to Hon. Frank J. McGarr U.S. Dist. Ct. (no. dist.) Ill., 1977-78; ptnr. Mayer, Brown & Platt, Chgo. Mem. ABA (mem. litigation, corp., banking and bus. law

sects.), Chgo. Bar Assn. Office: Mayer Brown & Platt 190 S La Salle St Chicago IL 60603-3410*

REED, JOEL LESTON, diversified manufacturing company executive; b. Enid, Okla., Jan. 21, 1951; s. Arrel Leston and Velma Jo (Kesner) R.; m. Alicia Kay Biller, Nov. 28, 1970 (dec.); m. Ann Denise Timmersman, June 6, 1981; children: Benjamin Joel, Elizabeth Ann, Peter David. BS in Acctg., Okla. State U., 1972, MS in Acctg., 1973. CPA, Okla, Colo. Successively staff acct., sr. acct., mgr. Deloitte Haskins & Sells, Denver, 1973-81; contr., treas. Ensource Inc., Englewood, Colo., 1981-82, v.p., CFO, 1983-84; CFP Wagner & Brown, Midland, Tex., 1984-89, pres., CEO, 1993-94; ptnr. Batchelder & Ptnrs., Inc., La Jolla, Calif., 1994—; pres., CEO Insilco Corp., 1989-93. Contbr. articles to profl. jours. Mem. AICPA (oil and gas com., Elijah Watt Sells award 1973), Colo. Soc. CPAs, Am. Petroleum Inst., Ind. Petroleum Assn. Am., Porsche Car Club Am., Beta Alpha Psi. Home: 1608 Stanolind Ave Midland TX 79705-8651

REED, JOHN ALTON, lawyer; b. Washington, June 29, 1931; s. John Alton and Emma Powers (Ball) R.; m. Louisa Wardman, June 6, 1953; children: Donna, Joanne, Deborah. AB, Duke U., 1954, LLB, 1956. Bar: Fla. 1956. Assoc. firm Fowler-White, Tampa, Fla., 1956-57; partner firm Rush, Reed & Marshall, Orlando, Fla., 1957-67; judge Fla. 4th Dist. Ct. Appeal, 1967-73, chief judge, 1971-73; judge U.S. Dist. Ct. for Middle Dist. Fla., Orlando, 1973-84; ptnr., chmn. dept. litigation Lowndes, Drosdick, Doster, Kantor & Reed, Orlando, 1985—; mem. com. on standard civil jury instructions Fla. Supreme Ct. Bd. visitors Duke U. Law Sch., 1983—. Mem. Am., Orange County, Fla. bar assns., Am. Judicature Soc. Republican. Episcopalian. Home: 1020 Mayfield Ave Winter Park FL 32789-2613 Office: PO Box 2809 215 N Eola Dr Orlando FL 32802

REED, JOHN E., manufacturing executive; b. 1915. AB, Yale U., 1937; LLB, Northeastern U. Bar: Mass. Founder, pres., CEO Reed Nat. Corp., 1946-86; pres., CEO Mestek Inc., Westfield, Mass., 1986—, chmn. bd. dirs., 1989—. Office: Mestek Inc 260 N Elm St Westfield MA 01085-1614*

REED, JOHN FRANCIS (JACK REED), congressman, lawyer; b. Providence, Nov. 12, 1949; s. Joseph Anthony and Mary Louise (Monahan) R. BS, U.S. Mil. Acad., 1971; M in Pub. Policy, Harvard U., 1973, JD cum laude, 1982. Bar: D.C. 1982, R.I. 1983. Commd. 2d lt. U.S. Army, 1971, served with 82d Airborne Div., 1973-77; asst. prof. U.S. Mil. Acad., West Point, N.Y., 1977-79; resigned U.S. Army, 1979; assoc. Sutherland, Asbill & Brennan, Washington, 1982-83, Edwards & Angell, Providence, 1983-89; mem. R.I. Senate, 1984-90, 102nd-104th Congresses from 2d R.I. dist., 1990—; mem. judiciary com., mem. econ. and ednl. opportunity com., regional whip for New Eng. Dem. del.; vice chair N.E.-Midwest Congl. Coalition. Author: (with others) American National Security, 1981. Recipient Disting. Svc. award AARP, 1989, John Fogarty award, 1990, Disting. Legislator award United Way Southeastern New Eng., 1988. Mem. ABA, R.I. Bar Assn., D.C. Bar Assn., Environ. and Energy Study Inst., Phi Kappa Phi. Democrat. Roman Catholic. Avocations: reading, hiking. Office: US Ho of Reps 1510 Longworth HOB Washington DC 20515 also: Dist Office 100 Midway Rd Ste 5 Cranston RI 02920-5707*

REED, JOHN FRANKLIN, instrument manufacturing company executive; b. Winfield, Mo., Aug. 10, 1917; s. Claudé F. and Inez (Crenshaw) R.; m. Ann M. Walter, Aug. 31, 1940; children: John Franklin, James D., Thomas W., William C., Robert D. B.S. in Mining Engring. Mo. Sch. Mines and Metallurgy, 1940. Indsl. engr. Tenn. Coal Iron R.R. Co., 1940-42; time study methods engr. McDonnell Aircraft Corp., 1943; prodn. planner, chief estimator Fairchild Aircraft Co., 1944; joined Manning, Maxwell & Moore, Inc., Stratford, Conn., 1944; works mgr. Manning, Maxwell & Moore, Inc., Tulsa, Shaw Box, Crane and Hoist div., Muskegon, Mich., 1951-57; gen. mgr. Instrument and Gauge div., 1957-59, v.p., gen. mgr., 1959, exec. v.p. 1959-62, pres., chief exec. officer, dir., 1962-65; pres., dir. Manning, Maxwell and Moore of Can., Ltd., Galt, Ont., 1962-65; pres., chief oper. officer Hupp Corp., Cleve., 1965-67, pres., dir., 1967-68; pres., chief exec. officer, dir. Hercules Galion Products, Inc., Ohio, 1968-69; pres., chief exec. dir. Conrad Inc., Newark, 1969—; chmn. Conrad Inc., 1976-86; mem. exec. com. Conrad-Hanovia Inc., 1984-89, also bd. dirs., 1984-89; bd. dirs. Rhein Med, Tampa, Fla., Am. Health Capital, Irving, Tex. Mem. Royal Poinciana Golf. Presbyterian. Home: 745 Willowhead Dr Naples FL 33940-3543

REED, JOHN G., lawyer; b. Peterborough, Ont., Can., Apr. 5, 1929; s. John Theron Sproul and Lilian (Grady) R.; m. Miriam Wilkes Bell, May 14, 1954; children: Christine, Roberta, Karen, Laura, Margaret, Abigail, Elisabeth. A.B., Harvard U., 1951, LL.B. 1957. Bar: N.Y. 1954, D.C. 1957. Assoc. White & Case, N.Y.C., 1957-66; ptnr. White & Case, Washington, 1967-90, Singapore, 1990—; cons. U.S. Synthetic Fuels Corp., Washington, 1981; dir. Arrangements Abroad, Inc., N.Y.C. Served to lt. (j.g.) USNR, 1951-54; served to capt. Res., 1951-79. Mem. ABA, N.Y. State Bar Assn., Assn. Bar City N.Y., D.C. Bar Assn., Am. Law Inst., Fed. Energy Bar Assn., Harvard Law Sch. Assn. D.C. (pres. 1982-83, adv. com.), Singapore Acad. of Law, Met. Club, Chevy Chase Club (Md.), Cricket Club (Singapore). Roman Catholic. Office: White & Case, 50 Raffles Pl # 22-01, Shell Tower, Singapore 0104, Singapore also: White & Case 1155 Avenue Of The Americas New York NY 10036-2711

REED, JOHN HATHAWAY, former ambassador; b. Fort Fairfield, Maine, Jan. 5, 1921; s. Walter and Eva Ruth (Seeley) R.; m. Cora Mitchell Davison, Mar. 24, 1944; children:--Cheryl, Ruth. B.S., U. Maine, 1942, LL.D. (hon.), 1960; LL.D. (hon.), Ricker Coll.; grad. Harvard Naval Supply Sch., 1944. Officer Reed Farms, Inc., Fort Fairfield, Maine, 1948—; pres. Aroostook Raceway, Inc., 1958-59; adv. com. Fort Fairfield br. No. Nat. Bank of Presque Isle; mem. Nat. Transp. Safety Bd., Washington, 1967-75, chmn., 1969-75; ambassador to Sri Lanka Colombo, 1975-77; dir. govt. rels. assoc. Builders & Contractors, Inc., Washington, 1981; ambassador to Sri Lanka and Republic of Maldives, 1982-85; cons. Dept. State, 1985-90; pvt. practice cons. Washington, 1990—; chmn. Nat. Govs. Conf. Rep., 1966; rep. Fort Fairfield to Maine Legislature, 1954-56; mem. Senate, 1957-59, pres., 1959-60; gov. State of Maine, 1960-67. Pres. bd. Community Gen. Hosp., Fort Fairfield, 1952-54, No. Maine Fair, 1953-59; trustee Ricker Coll., 1953-60, Oak Grove Sch., Vassalboro, Maine; bd. advisors Coll. of Democracy, 1986—, chmn., 1991—. Served to lt. (j.g.) USNR, 1942-46. Mem. Am. Fgn. Svc. Assn., Coun. Am. Abassadors, Soc. Sr. Aerospace Execs. Inc. (bd. dirs. 1987—, pres. 1988-91), Nat. Inst. Former Govs. (bd. dirs. 1992—), Am. Legion, VFW, Grange, Maine Assn. Agrl. Fairs (pres. 1956), Mil. Order of Carabao, Capitol Hill Club, Driving Club (Ft. Fairfield) (pres. 1950-53), Rotary, Masons, KP. Republican. Congregationalist. Office: 410 O St SW Washington DC 20024-2239

REED, JOHN HOWARD, school administrator; b. Bloomfield, Mo., July 14, 1934; s. Floyd John and Lena Joyce (Howard) R.; m. Weymuth Heuiser; children: Cathy, David. BS cum laude, SE Mo. State U., 1956; M., U. Mo. 1959; edn. specialist, SE Mo. State U., 1977, PhD, So. Ill. U., 1983. Cert. supt., prin., tchr. Tchr., coach Scott County R-6 Schs., Sikeston, Mo., 1956-63; supt. student tchr. SE Mo. State U., Cape Girardeau, 1963-75; prin. Scott County R-3 Schs., Oran, Mo., 1975-76; supt. schs. Scott County R-2 Schs., Chaffee, Mo., 1976-79; bus. mgr. SE Mo. State U., Cape Girardeau, 1979-80; dean, pres. Sikeston (Colo.) C.C., 1980-83; planner exec. dir. (U.S. Govt.) So. Ill. U., Carbondale, 1980-83; dean, pres. Sikeston C.C., 1983-86; supt. Marion County Sch. Dist. 1, Centralia, Ill., 1986-88; head New Life Montessori Sch., Shreveport, La., 1989-90; Belleview Schs., Westminster, Colo., 1990—. Editor: History of Missouri National Guard, 1963. Bd. dirs., sec. Scott County Bd. Edn., Benton, Mo., 1970-79. Lt. col. U.S. Army, 1960-63. Mem. Rotary (sec. 1976-78), Phi Alpha Theta (pres. 1976-78). Baptist. Avocation: history. Home: 8175 Green Ct Westminster CO 80030-4101 Office: Belleview Schs 3455 W 83rd Ave Westminster CO 80030-4005

REED, JOHN SHEDD, former railway executive; b. Chgo., June 9, 1917; s. Kersey Coates and Helen May (Shedd) R.; m. Marjorie Lindsay, May 4, 1946; children: Ginevra, Keith, Helen, Peter, John Shedd. Student, Chgo. Latin Sch., Hotchkiss Sch.; B.S. in Indsl. Adminstrn, Yale U., 1939; grad. Advanced Mgmt. Program, Harvard U., 1955. With A.T. & S.F. Ry., 1939-83; test dept. asst., successively spl. rep. to gen. supt. transp. Chgo.; transp. insp. Amarillo, Tex.; trainmaster Slaton, Tex., Pueblo, Colo.; supt. Mo. div., Marceline, Mo.; asst. to v.p. Chgo., 1957-59, exec. asst. to pres., 1957-59,

v.p. finance, 1959-64, v.p. exec. dept., 1964-67, pres., 1967-78, chief exec. officer, 1968-82, chmn. bd., 1973-83; pres. Santa Fe Industries, Inc., 1968-78, chmn. bd. dirs., CEO Santa Fe So. Pacific Corp., 1987, chmn., 1987-88. Chmn. Nat. Merit Scholarship Corp.; past pres., now trustee Shedd Aquarium, Chgo. With USMF, 1940-45. Clubs: Chicago; Old Elm, Shoreacres, Onwentsia (Lake Forest). Home: 301 W Laurel Ave # 112 Lake Forest IL 60045-1180 Office: 224 S Michigan Ave Rm 200 Chicago IL 60604-2507

REED, JOHN SHEPARD, banker; b. Chgo., Feb. 7, 1939; divorced; 4 children; m. Cindy McCarthy, 1994. BA and BS, Washington and Jefferson Coll., MIT, 1961; MS, Sloan Sch. MIT, 1965. With Citicorp/Citibank, 1965—, chmn., chief exec. officer, 1984—; bd. dirs Philip Morris Inc., Monsanto Co.; mem. Bus. Coun.; mem. policy com., Bus. Roundtable; chmn. Coalition of Svc. Inds., svcs. policy adv. com. to the U.S. Trade Rep. Mem. bd. MIT, Meml. Sloan-Kettering Cancer Ctr., Rand Corp., Spencer Found., Am. Mus. NAt. History. Served with C.E. U.S. Army, Korea, 1962-64. Office: Citicorp 399 Park Ave New York NY 10043*

REED, JOHN THEODORE, publisher, writer; b. Camden, N.J., July 5, 1946; s. Theodore and Marion Theresa (Simonsick) R.; m. Margaret Ogden Tunnell, May 31, 1975; children: Daniel Tunnell, Steven Tunnell, Michael Tunnell. BS in Mil. Sci., U.S. Mil. Acad., West Point, N.Y., 1968; MBA, Harvard U., 1977. Salesman Pritchett & Co., Pine Hill and Collingswood, N.J., 1972-74; property mgr. Fox & Lazo Inc., Cherry Hill, N.J., 1974-75; writer Harcourt Brace Jovanovich, Boston, 1976-86; bank exec. Crocker Nat. Bank, San Francisco, 1977-78; writer, pub. Danville, Calif., 1977—. Author, pub.: Apartment Investing Check Lists, 1978, Aggressive Tax Avoidance for Real Estate Investors, 1981, 14th edit., 1995, How to Manage Residential Property for Maximum Cash Flow and Resale Value, 1995, 4th edit., 1991, How to Use Leverage to Maximize Your Real Estate Investment Return, 1984, 86, How to Increase the Value of Real Estate, 1986, Office Building Acquisition Handbook, 1982, 85, 87, Residential Property Acquisition Handbook, 1991, How To Buy Real Estate for at Least 20% Below Market Value, 1993, Coaching Youth Football Defense, 1994, John T. Reed's Real Estate Investor's Monthly Newsletter, 1984—. Served to 1st lt. U.S. Army, 1968-72, Vietnam. Mem. Nat. Assn. Real Estate Editors. Avocations: reading, baseball, youth and high sch. coaching, activities with family. Home: 342 Bryan Dr Danville CA 94526-1258 Office: John T, Reed Pub 342 Bryan Dr Danville CA 94526-1258

REED, JOHN W., religious organization administrator. Pres. Min. and Missionaries Benefit Bd. of the ABC inthe USA. Office: Min & Miss Benefit Board 475 Riverside Dr New York NY 10115

REED, JOHN WESLEY, lawyer, educator; b. Independence, Mo., Dec. 11, 1918; s. Novus H. and Lilian (Houchens) R.; m. Dorothy Elaine Floyd, Mar. 5, 1961; children: Alison A., John M. (dec.), Mary V., Randolph F., Suzanne M. AB, William Jewell Coll., 1939; LLB, Cornell U., 1942; LLM, Columbia U., 1949, JSD, 1957. Bar: Mo. 1942, Mich. 1953. Assoc. Stinson, Mag, Thomson, McEvers & Fizzell, Kansas City, Mo., 1942-46; assoc. prof. law U. Okla., 1946-49; assoc. prof. U. Mich., 1949-53, prof., 1953-64, 68-85, Thomas M. Cooley prof., 1985-87, Thomas M. Cooley prof. emeritus, 1987—; dean, prof. U. Colo., 1964-68; dean, prof. Wayne State U., Detroit, 1987-92, prof. emeritus, 1992—; vis. prof. NYU, 1949, U. Chgo., 1960, Yale U., 1963-64, Harvard U., 1982, U. San Diego, 1993; dir. Inst. Continuing Legal Edn., 1968-73; reporter Mich. Rules of Evidence Com., 1975-78, 83-84. Author: (with W.W. Blume) Pleading and Joinder, 1952; (with others) Introduction to Law and Equity, 1953, Advocacy Course Handbook series, 1963-81; editor in chief Cornell Law Quar., 1941-42; contbr. articles to profl. jours. Pres. bd. mgrs. of mins. and missionaries benefit bd. Am. Bapt. Chs. U.S.A., 1967-74, 82-85, 88-94; mem. com. visitors JAG Sch.; trustee Kalamazoo Coll., 1954-64, 68-70. Recipient Harrison Tweed award Assn. Continuing Legal Edn. Adminstrs., 1983, Samuel E. Gates award Am. Coll. Trial Lawyers, 1985, Roberts P. Hudson award State Bar Mich., 1989. Fellow Internat. Soc. Barristers (editor jour. 1980—); mem. ABA (coun. litigation sect.), Colo. Bar Assn. (bd. govs. 1964-68), Assn. Am. Law Schs. (exec. com. 1965-67), Am. Acad. Jud. Edn. (v.p. 1978-80), Mich. Supreme Ct. Hist. Soc. (bd. dirs. 1991—), Sci. Club U. Mich., Order of Coif. Office: U Mich Sch Law Ann Arbor MI 48109-1215

REED, JOSEPH RAYMOND, civil engineering educator, academic administrator; b. Pitts., Aug. 15, 1930; s. David Raymond and Mary (O'Neil) R.; m. Mary Morris Leggett, Mar. 19, 1960; children: Michelle Edwards, Stephanie Anne Reed Wilkinson, David Shepard Reed. BS in Civil Engring., Pa. State U., 1952, MS in Civil Engring., 1955; PhD in Civil Engring., Cornell U., 1971. Registered profl. engr., Tex. Asst. engr. George H. McGinness Assocs., Pitts., 1953-55; constrn. liaison officer USAF, Dallas, 1956-59; civil engring. faculty Pa. State U., University Park, 1959-64; rsch. asst. Cornell U., Ithaca, N.Y., 1964-67; prof. civil engring. Pa. State U., 1967—; cons. Westvaco, Tyrone, Pa., 1981, Ketron, Inc., Phila., 1982-83, McGraw-Hill Book Co., N.Y.C., 1984-91, MacMillan Pub. Co., N.Y.C., 1987, others; acad. officer dept. civil engring. Pa. State U., 1989—. Chmn. Stormwater Authority, State College, Pa., 1974-78; coach State Little League, Teener League (All-Star team state championship 1986) and Am. Legion Baseball, State College, 1978-89. Capt. USAF, 1956-59, USAFR, 1959-71. Sci.-Faculty fellow NSF, 1966-67; recipient Adviser Leadership award Tau Beta Pi Assn., 1986. Mem. ASCE, Internat. Assn. Hydraulic Rsch., Elks, Scottish Rite, Sigma Xi, Tau Beta Pi, Chi Epsilon, Phi Sigma Kappa (v.p. 1952). Presbyterian. Avocations: golf, youth baseball. Home: 1394 Penfield Rd State College PA 16801 Office: Pa State U Dept Civil Engring 212 Sackett Bldg University Park PA 16802

REED, JOSEPH VERNER, JR., diplomat; b. N.Y.C., Dec. 17, 1937; s. Joseph V. and Permelia (Pryor) R; m Marie Maude Byers, Dec. 19, 1959; children: Serena, Electra. BA, Yale U., 1961. With office of pres., The World Bank, Washington, 1959-62; asst. to pres. Internat. Bank for Reconstrn. and Devel., 1961-63; asst. to dir. Chase Manhattan Bank, 1963-68, v.p., exec. asst. to chmn., 1969-81; U.S. amb. to Morocco, 1981-85; amb. to ECOSOC of UN, N.Y.C., 1985-87; undersec. gen. UN, 1987-89; U.S. chief of protocol, The White Ho., Washington, 1989-91; U.S. rep. to UN Gen. Assembly, 1992—. Mem. Coun. on Fgn. Rels., Met. Club, Links club, River Club. Republican. Episcopalian. Home: 591 Riversville Rd Greenwich CT 06831 Office: Under-Sec-Gen UN Ste 3161A New York NY 10017

REED, JOSEPH WAYNE, American studies educator; b. St. Petersburg, Fla., May 31, 1932; s. Joseph Wayne and Gertrude (Cain) R.; m. Lillian Craig (Kit), Dec. 10, 1955; children: Joseph McKean, John Craig, Katherine Hyde. BA, Yale U., 1954, MA, 1958, PhD, 1961. Rsch. asst. Yale Libr., 1956-57; instr. English Wesleyan U., Middletown, Conn., 1960-61, asst. prof., 1961-67, assoc. prof., 1967-71, prof., 1971—, chmn. dept., 1971-73, 75-76, 85-86, prof. English and Am. studies, 1987; vis. lectr. Yale U., New Haven, 1974; lectr. U.S. dept. State and USIS, Can., India, Nepal, 1974; coord. cultural exch., New Delhi, Bombay, 1992; coord. music and writing workshop U.S. Van, Georgetown U., others. One man shows include Portal Gallery, London, 1971, USIS Library, New Delhi, 1974, 92, Addison/Ripley Gallery, Washington, 1987, 92, 95; author: English Biography in the Early Nineteenth Century, 1801-38, 1966, Faulkner's Narrative, 1973, Three American Originals: John Ford, William Faulkner, Charles Ives, 1984, American Scenarios, 1989, rev. edit., 1990; editor: Barbara Bodichon's American Diary, 1972, (with W.S. Lewis) Horace Walpole's Family Correspondence, 1975, (with F.A. Pottle) Boswell, Laird of Auchinleck, 1977. Chmn. Wesleyan Sesquicentennial, 1982; chmn. bd. trustees Yale Libr. Assocs. Lt. (j.g.) USNR, 1954-56. Mem. Elizabethan Club, The Johnsonians (chmn. 1988, mem. com. 1990-92). Democrat. Episcopalian. Home: 45 Lawn Ave Middletown CT 06457-3135

REED, KATHLYN LOUISE, occupational therapist, educator; b. Detroit, June 2, 1940; d. Herbert C. and Jessie R. (Krehbiel) R. BS in Occupational Therapy, U. Kans., 1964; MA, Western Mich. U., 1966; PhD, U. Wash., 1973; MLS U. Okla., 1988. Occupational therapist in psychiatry Kans. U. Med. Center, Kansas City, 1964-65; instr. occupational therapy U. Wash., Seattle, 1967-70; assoc. prof. dept. occupational therapy U. Okla. Health Scis. Ctr., Oklahoma City, 1973-77, prof., 1978-85; chmn. dept. occupational therapy U. Okla. Health Scis. Ctr., 1973-85; librarian edn. info. servicesHouston Acad. of Medicine Tex. Med. Ctr. Libr., 1988—; cons. to

Okla. State Dept. Health, 1976-77, Children's Convalescent Ctr., Oklahoma City, 1977-80, Oklahoma City pub. schs., 1980-81; vis. scholars program Tex. Woman's U., 1991—, adj. prof., 1992—. Author: (with Sharon Sanderson) Concepts of Occupational Therapy, 1980, 2d edit., 1983, 3rd edit., 1992, Models of Practice in Occupational Therapy, 1983, Quick Reference to Occupational Therapy, 1991. Vol. crisis counselor Open Door Clinic, Seattle, 1968-72; mem. exec. bd. Seattle Mental Health Inst., 1971-72; Mem. Citizen Participation Liaison Council, Seattle, 1970-72. Recipient Award of Merit, Can. Assn. Occupational Therapists, 1988. Fellow Am. Occupational Therapy Assn. (Merit award 1983, Slagle lecture award 1985, Svc. award 1985); mem. ALA, World Fedn. Occupational Therapists, Coun. Exceptional Children, Okla. Occupational Therapy Assn. (pres. 1974-76), Tex. Occupational Therapy Assn., Med. Libr. Assn. (Rittenhouse award 1987, Acad. Health Info. Professions), Spl. Libr. Assn., Nat. Rehab. Assn., Am. Occupational Therapy Found., Assn. Advancement Rehab. Tech., Sensory Integration Internat., Sigma Kappa (Colby award 1994). Democrat. Home: 6699 De Moss Dr Houston TX 77074-5003

REED, KEITH ALLEN, lawyer; b. Anamosa, Iowa, Mar. 5, 1939; s. John Ivan and Florence Lorine (Larson) R.; m. Beth Illana Kesterson, June 22, 1963; children: Melissa Beth, Matthew Keith. BBA, U. Iowa, 1960, JD, 1963. Bar: Ill. and Iowa 1963. Ptnr. Seyfarth, Shaw, Fairweather & Geraldson, Chgo., 1963—. Co-author: Labor Arbitration in Healthcare, 1981; co-editor: Federal Employment Law and Regulations, 1989; co-contbr. articles to Am. Hosp. Assn. publs., 1986-89. Trustee Meth. Hosp. Chgo., 1985—, Trinity Ch. North Shore, Wilmette, Ill., 1983—; mem. ad hoc labor adv. com. Am. Hosp. Assn., Chgo., 1980—; bd. dirs. Lyric Opera Chgo. Ctr. for Am. Artists, pres. 1983-86. Mem. ABA (dir. health law forum 1979-82), Chgo. Bar Assn. (labor and employment law com. 1978—), Union League Club Chgo. (bd. dirs. 1985-88), Sunset Ridge Country Club (Northbrook, Ill.). Republican. Methodist. Avocations: music, community theater, tennis, golf. Office: Seyfarth Shaw Fairweather & Geraldson 55 E Monroe St Ste 4200 Chicago IL 60603-5803

REED, KENNETH G., petroleum company executive; b. 1917; married. Ed., U. Tex. With Amerada Petroleum Corp., Tulsa, 1948-70; sr. v.p. Amerada Petroleum Corp., 1967-70; exec. v.p. internat. operations Amerada Hess Corp., N.Y.C., 1970; pres., chief exec. officer APEXCO, Inc., Tulsa, 1971-77; pres., chief exec. officer Natomas Internat. Corp., 1977, also dir.; exec. v.p. energy, dir. Natomas Co., San Francisco, 1977-83, vice chmn., pres., 1983—; pres., dir. Natomas Energy Co., 1979—; chmn., chief exec. officer Overseas Petroleum Ltd., San Francisco, 1984—; dir. Natomas N.Am. Inc., 1st Nat. Bank & Trust Co., Tulsa, Oneok Inc., Tulsa. Home: 7 BC Rocky Pl Condominium 1400 Poly Dr Billings MT 59102-1737 Office: 100 N 27th St Ste 440 Billings MT 59101-2054

REED, LESTER JAMES, biochemist, educator; b. New Orleans, Jan. 3, 1925; s. John T. and Sophie (Pastor) R.; m. Janet Louise Gruschow, Aug. 7, 1948; children—Pamela, Sharon, Richard, Robert. B.S., Tulane U., 1943; D.Sc. (hon.), 1977; Ph.D., U. Ill., 1946. Rsch. asst. NDRC, Urbana, Ill., 1944-46; rsch. assoc. biochemistry Cornell U. Med. Coll., 1946-48; faculty U. Tex., Austin, 1948—; prof. chemistry U. Tex., 1958—, Ashbel Smith prof., 1984—; rsch. sci. Clayton Found. Biochem. Inst., 1949—, assoc. dir., 1962-63, dir., 1963—. Contbr. articles profl. jours. Mem. NAS, Am. Acad. Arts and Scis., Am. Soc. for Biochemistry and Molecular Biology (Merck award 1994), Am. Chem. Soc. (Eli Lilly & Co. award in biol. chemistry 1958), Phi Beta Kappa, Sigma Xi. Home: 3502 Balcones Dr Austin TX 78731-5802 Office: U Tex Biochem Inst Experimental Sci Bldg 442 Austin TX 78712

REED, LOWELL A., JR., federal judge; b. Westchester, Pa., June 21, 1930; s. Lowell A. Sr. and Catherine Elizabeth (Pauly) R.; m. Diane Benson, Jan. 23, 1954; children: Jeffrey Barton, Lowell Andrew, Diane R. BBA, U. Wis., 1952; JD, Temple U., 1958. Bar: Pa. 1959, U.S. Dist. Ct. (ea. dist.) Pa. 1961, U.S. Ct. Appeals (3d cir.) 1962, U.S. Supreme Ct. 1970. Corp. trial counsel PMA Group, Phila., 1958-63; assoc. Rawle & Henderson, Phila. 1963-65, gen. ptnr., 1966-88; judge U.S. Dist Ct., Phila., 1988—; lectr. law Temple U. 1965-81, faculty Acad. Advocacy, 1988—, Pa. Bar Inst., 1972—. Contbr. articles to profl. jours. Elder Abington (Pa.) Presbyn. Ch.; past mem. Pa. Senate Select Com. Med. Malpractice; past pres., bd. dirs Rydal Meadowbrook Civic Assn.; bd. dirs. Abington Sch. Bd., 1971, World Affairs Coun. Phila., 1983-88; trustee Abington Meml. Hosp., 1983-88, 90-93. Lt. comdr. USNR, 1952-57. Recipient Alumni Achievement award Temple U. 1988. Mem. ABA, Pa. Bar Assn., Phila. Bar Assn. (chmn. medico legal com. 1975, constl. bicentennial com. 1986-87, commn. on jud. selection and retention 1983-87), Temple Am. Inn of Ct. (pres. 1990-93, master of bench), Am. Judicature Soc., Temple U. Law Alumni Assn. (exec. com. 1987-90), Hist. Soc. U.S. Supreme Ct., Hist. Soc. U.S. Dist. Ct. Ea. Dist. Pa. Republican. Office: US Dist Ct 11614 US Courthouse Independence Mall W Philadelphia PA 19106

REED, MICHAEL A., agricultural products supplier; b. 1947. Grad., U. Mo., 1969, JD, 1976. With Poole, Reed and Croessmann, Springfield, Mo., 1977-80, Tindle Mills, Springfield, 1980-83, Vigortone Ag Products, Inc., Cedar Rapids, Iowa, 1983-85; with PM AG Products Inc., Homewood, Ill., 1985—, now pres. With USAF, 1970-74. Office: PM AG Products Inc 1055 175th St Homewood IL 60430*

REED, MICHAEL HAYWOOD, lawyer; b. Phila., Jan. 17, 1949; s. Soloman Taylor and Vivian (Haywood) Reed; m. Yalta Gilmore, Aug. 12, 1978; children: Alexandra Haywood, Michael Haywood Jr. BA in Polit. Sci., Temple U., 1969; JD, Yale U., 1972. Bar: Pa. 1972, U.S. Dist. Ct. (ea. dist.) Pa. 1972, U.S. Dist. Ct. (ea. dist.) Mich. 1982, U.S. Supreme Ct. 1982. Assoc. Pepper, Hamilton & Scheetz, Phila., 1972-80, ptnr., 1980—; co-adj. prof. law Rutgers U., Camden, N.J., 1983, 85; adj. prof. sch. law Temple U. Phila., 1989; mem. Pa. Judicial Inquiry and Rev. Bd., 1990-93; mem. steering com. Ea. Dist. Pa. Bankruptcy Conf., 1992-93. Contbr. articles to profl. jours. Advisor Post 913 Law Explorers, Phila., 1974-84; trustee Acad. Natural Scis., Phila., 1988—, Episcopal Hosp., Phila., 1986—; bd. advisors Pub. Interest Law Ctr., Phila., 1992—; exec. bd. Com. of Seventy, Phila., 1985—. Fellow Am. Coll. Bankruptcy; mem. ABA (chmn. subcom. mass and massive torts, bus. bankruptcy com. 1991—, bus. bankruptcy com. sect. bus. law), Nat. Bar Assn., Pa. Bar Assn. (ho. of dels. 1985—, chmn. minority bar com. 1988—, bd. govs. 1993—, co-chair 1994 ann. meeting, Spl. Achievement award 1989, Cert. of Honor award 1995), Barristers Assn. Phila. (1st v.p. 1974-76), Alpha Phi Alpha. Democrat. Baptist. Club: Yale (Phila.). Avocations: racquetball, film, theatre, biking, piano. Home: 225 N 23rd St Philadelphia PA 19103-1005 Office: Pepper Hamilton & Scheetz 3000 Two Logan Sq 18th Arch St Philadelphia PA 19103

REED, MICHAEL ROBERT, agricultural economist; b. Lawrence, Kans., July 11, 1953; s. Robert Stanley and Marian Lucille (Karr) R.; m. Patricia Gail Gurtler, Mar. 16, 1973; children: Laura Gail, Brian Michael. BS, Kans. State U., 1974; MS, Iowa State U., 1976, PhD, 1979. Asst. prof. U. Ky., Lexington, 1978-83, assoc. prof., 1983-89; prof., 1989—, exec. dir. Ctr. for Export Devel., 1988—; dir. office of internat. affairs U. Ky., Lexington, 1994—; cons. USDA, 1994, U.S. Agy. for Internat. Devel., Washington, 1993-86. Editorial council So. Jour. of Agrl. Econs., 1983-86; contbr. articles to profl. jours. Recipient Outstanding Jour. Article award Soc. Farm Mgrs. and Rural Appraisers, 1986; grantee Farmer Coop. Svcs., 1982-84, 87-88, TVA, 1982-85, Fed. Crop Ins. Corp., 1985-87, USDA, 1986—. Mem. Am. Agrl. Econs. Assn., So. Agrl. Econs. Assn., Gamma Sigma Delta, Omicron Delta Epsilon. Home: 2216 Bonhaven Rd Lexington KY 40515-1150 Office: U Ky Dept Agrl Econs 300 Bradley Hall Lexington KY 40546-0215

REED, PAMELA, actress; b. Tacoma, Wash., Apr. 2, 1949; d. Vernie Reed; m. Sandy Smolar. BA in Drama, U. Wash. Prin. stage roles include Getting Through the Night, Ensemble Studio Theatre, N.Y.C., 1976, Curse of the Starving Class, N.Y. Shakespeare Festival, Pub. Theatre, 1978, The November People (Broadway debut), Billy Rose Theatre, 1978, All's Well That Ends Well, N.Y. Shakespeare Festival, Delacorte Theatre, 1978, Getting Out, Phoenix Theatre, Marymount Manhattan Theatre, N.Y.C., 1978, Seduced, Am. Place Theatre, N.Y.C., 1979, Sorrows of Stephen, N.Y. Shakespeare Festival, Pub. Theatre, 1979, Fools, Eugene O'Neill Theatre, N.Y.C., 1981, Criminal Minds, Theatre Guinevere, N.Y.C., 1984, Fen, N.Y. Shakespeare Festival, Pub. Theatre, 1984, Aunt Dan and Lemon, N.Y. Shakespeare Festival, Pub. Theatre, 1985, Mrs. Warren's Profession,

Roundabout Theatre, N.Y.C., 1985, Haft Theatre, 1986; film appearances include The Long Riders, 1980, Melvin and Howard, 1980, Eyewitness, 1981, Young Doctors in Love, 1982, The Right Stuff, 1983, The Goodbye People, 1984, The Best of Times, 1986, The Clan of the Cave Bear, 1986, Rachel River, 1989, Chattahoochee, 1990, Cadillac Man, 1990, Kindergarten Cop, 1990, Passed Away, 1992, Junior, 1994; TV series appearances include The Andros Targets, 1977, Tanner, 1988, The Dark Horse (HBO), 1988, Grand, 1990, The Home Court, 1995—; TV films include Inmates: A Love Story, 1981, I Want to Live, 1983, Heart of Steel, 1983, Scandal Sheet, 1985, Born Too Soon, 1993, Mary Hemingway miniseries, 1988, Caroline? (Hallmark Hall of Fame), 1989. Office: ICM 8942 Wilshire Blvd Beverly Hills CA 90211*

REED, PATSY BOSTICK, university administrator, nutrition educator; b. Holland, Tex., Dec. 1, 1936; d. William T. and Evelyn R. (Smith) Bostick; m. F. Dewitt Reed, Sept. 6, 1958. BS, U. Tex., 1959, MS, 1967, PhD, 1969. Tchr. pub. schs., Austin and Port Arthur, Tex., 1959-65; postdoctoral fellow U. Va., Charlottesville, 1969-70; research chemist U. Heidelberg, W.Ger., 1970-72; assoc. prof. nutrition Idaho State U., Pocatello, 1973-79; prof. nutrition, adminstr. No. Ariz. U., Flagstaff, 1979-94, dean Coll. Design and Tech., 1981-85; asst. v.p. acad. affairs U. N.C., Asheville, 1985-87, v.p. acad. affairs, 1987-94, chancellor, 1994—, UNC-Asheville. Author: Nutrition: An Applied Science, 1980. Mem. Ariz.-Mex. Commn. Named Outstanding Faculty Mem., Idaho State U., 1978, Outstanding Woman Faculty Mem., No. Ariz. U., 1983. Mem. AAAS, Am. Chem. Soc., Am. Dietetic Assn., Phi Kappa Phi, Sigma Xi. Office: U NC 1 University Heights Asheville NC 28804

REED, PAUL ALLEN, artist; b. Washington, Mar. 28, 1919; s. Charles Miler and Lula Rachael (Annadale) R.; m. Esther Kishter, July 10, 1939; children—Jean Reed Roberts, Thomas, Robert. Student, San Diego State Coll., 1936, Corcoran Sch. Art, 1937. Asst. art dir. USAF mag., N.Y.C., 1942-44; artist B.D. Adams Advt. Agy., Montclair, N.J., 1944-48; asst. art dir. M.F. Dreher Advt. Agy., N.Y.C., 1948-50; free lance graphics designer Washington, 1950-62; graphics dir. U.S. Peace Corps, Washington, 1962-71; asst. prof. Corcoran Sch. Art, Washington, 1971-81. Exhibited in one man shows at, Corcoran Gallery Art, 1966, Washington U., 1967, Ariz. State U., 1971, Phoenix Art Mus., 1977; represented in more than 50 permanent collections at Hirshhorn Mus., Nat. Mus. Am. Art, N.C. Mus. Art, Corcoran Gallery, San Francisco Mus. Art, Detroit Dist. Art, others; artist in residence, Phoenix Art Mus., 1976; vis. artist Ariz. State U., Tempe, 1980. Home: 3541 N Utah St Arlington VA 22207-4444

REED, RAYMOND DERYL, architect; b. Alturas, Calif., Mar. 29, 1930; s. Russell Jacob and Nita Ferne (Wilcox) R.; m. Patricia Reinerth, Apr. 30, 1954; children—Kathryn, Russell, Ann, Andrea. B.Arch., Tulane U., 1953; M.Arch., Harvard U., 1958. Chmn. architecture and interior design dept. U. Southwestern La., 1958-64; head dept. architecture Iowa State U., 1964-70, dir. grad. research in architecture, 1970-73; mem. faculty Tex. A&M U., 1973—, prof. architecture, 1973—; dean Tex. A&M U. (Coll. Architecture and Environ. Design), 1973-80; dir. Internat. Ctr. for Cybernetics and Informatics, 1990. Author: Sustainable Architecture, 1988, rev. edit, 1990; contbr. numerous articles on energy conservation and post petroleum architecture to research publs. Served with USNR, 1953-58. Mem. AIA, Nat. Council Archtl. Registration Bds., Am. Collegiate Schs. Architecture, Tex. Soc. Architects, La. Architects Soc. Home: 1601 Wolf Pen Ct College Station TX 77840-3169 Office: Tex A&M U Dept Architecture College Station TX 77843

REED, REX, author, critic; b. Ft. Worth, Oct. 2, 1938; s. Jimmy M. and Jewell (Smith) R. BA, La. State U., 1960. Film critic Holiday mag., Women's Wear Daily, 1968-71; music critic Stereo Rev., 1968-75; syndicated columnist Chgo. Tribune-N.Y. Daily News Syndicate, 1971—; film critic N.Y. Daily News, 1971-75; now columnist N.Y. Observer, N.Y.C.; critic At the Movies, public TV series, 1986. Appeared in film Myra Breckenridge, 1970, Superman, 1978; author: Do You Sleep in the Nude?, 1968, Conversations in the Raw, 1969, Big Screen, Little Screen, 1971, People Are Crazy Here, 1974, Valentines and Vitriol, 1977, Travolta to Keaton, 1979; author: (novel) Personal Effects, 1986. Office: NY Observer 54 E 64th St New York NY 10021-7326

REED, REX RAYMOND, retired telephone company executive; b. Peterson, Iowa, Mar. 19, 1922; s. Charles Bernard and Dagmar Helen (Heick) R.; m. Rita Compton, Dec. 3, 1944; children: Julie, Nancy, Linda. Student, Morningside Coll., 1940-41, Iowa State U. 1941-43, 46-47, U. Notre Dame, 1943-44; B.S. in Gen. Engring, Iowa State U., 1947. With Northwestern Bell Telephone Co. (various locations), 1947-60, 61-66; employee info. mgr., pub. relations dept. Northwestern Bell Telephone Co. (various locations), Omaha, 1957-58; gen. comml. mgr., comml. dept. Northwestern Bell Telephone Co. (various locations), Fargo, N.D., 1958-60; asst. v.p. personnel and employment Northwestern Bell Telephone Co. (various locations), 1961-62; asst. v.p. personnel Northwestern Bell Telephone Co. (various locations), Nebr. area, 1962-64; asst. v.p. personnel and labor relations Northwestern Bell Telephone Co. (various locations), 1964-66; with AT&T Corp., N.Y.C., 1960-61, 66-84; dir. labor relations, personnel dept. AT&T Corp., 1966-71, v.p. labor relations, 1971-83, sr. v.p. labor relations, 1984; ret., 1984; dir. Ind. Bell Telephone Co., Ill. Bell Telephone Co., First Investors Corp N.Y.C. Mem. Madison (N.J.) Bd. Edn. 1969-70, pres., 1971-75; Trustee Menninger Found, Topeka, 1979—, Morristown (N.J.) Meml. Hosp., 1977—; bd. dirs. Nat. Urban Coalition, 1981-84. Served with USMC, 1943-46; to capt. 1951-53. Mem. Bus. Roundtable (chmn. labor-mgmt. com. 1976-77), Labor Policy Assn. (chmn. 1979-83), Inst. Collective Bargaining (bd. dirs. 1976-84), Orgn. Resources Counselors, Morris County Golf Club (Morristown, N.J., pres. bd. govs. 1991-92). Home: 76 Keats Way Morristown NJ 07960

REED, RICHARD JOHN, retired meteorology educator; b. Braintree, Mass., June 18, 1922; s. William Amber and Gertrude Helen (Volk) R.; m. Joan Murray, June 10, 1950; children: Ralph Murray, Richard Cobden, Elizabeth Ann. Student, Boston Coll., 1940-41, Dartmouth Coll., 1943-44; BS, Calif. Inst. Tech., 1945; ScD, MIT, 1949. Research staff mem. MIT, Cambridge, 1950-54; asst. prof. atmospheric scis. U. Wash., Seattle, 1954-58, assoc. prof., 1958-63, prof., 1963-91, prof. emeritus, 1991—; cons. U.S. Weather Service, Suitland, Md., 1961-62, European Ctr. for Medium Range Weather Forecasts, Reading, Eng., 1985-86; exec. scientist NRC, Washington, 1968-69; trustee Univ. Corp. for Atmospheric Research, Boulder, Colo., 1987-92. Served to lt. (j.g.) USN, 1942-46. Fellow AAAS, Am. Meteorol. Soc. (pres. 1972, Meisinger award 1964, Second Half Century award 1972, Charles Franklin Brooks award 1983, Carl-Gustaf Rossby Rsch. medal 1989), Am. Geophys. Union; mem. NAS. Democrat. Unitarian. Office: U Wash Dept Atmospheric Scis Box 351640 Seattle WA 98195-1640

REED, ROBERT DANIEL, publisher; b. Pottsville, Pa., May 24, 1941; s. Robert Daniel R.; children: Robert Duane, Alan Andrija, Tanya. Purchasing mgr. Ogden Tech. Labs., Sunnyvale, Calif., 1962-69; mktg. mgr. Plaza Press, Sunnyvale, 1969-94; pub. R & E Pubs., Saratoga, Calif. 1966-94; founder Bob Reed Studios; ptnr. Reed's Mktg. Svcs.; co-founder Ceasefire USA; founder, pres. Green PR Internat. Mktg. Cons.; pres. Robert D. Reed Pubs. Author: We Care Cookbook, 1974; pub. over 1150 books on human rights, ethnic history edn., criminology, AIDS, Alzheimers disease, teen suicide, also how-to, trade, and humor books; co-author 50 books on poverty, hunger, homelessness, abuse, sexual assault. With U.S. Army, 1959-61. Mem. Ctr. for Dem. Instns., Nat. Fedn. Ind. Bus., Calif. Inventors Coun., Smithsonian Instn., Soc. for Scholarly Pub., World Future Soc. Inventor elec-tronics and web.-electronics devices, creative humor products. Home: 750 La Playa #647 San Francisco CA 94121 Spend your life doing what you like to do, by putting all your efforts into it. Don't be afraid to take a chance. Remember, if life gets dull-Risk it a bit.

REED, ROBERT GEORGE, III, petroleum company executive; b. Cambridge, Mass., Aug. 9, 1927; s. Robert George and Marjorie B. Reed; m. Maggie L. Fisher, Mar. 22, 1974; children: Sandra McNickle, Valerie Sloan, Jonathan J., John-Paul. BA in Econs., Dartmouth Coll., 1949; AMP, Harvard U., 1970. Mktg. mgr. Tidewater Oil subs. Getty Oil Co., L.A., 1957-64; v.p. mktg. Cities Svc. Oil Co., Tulsa, 1964-72; exec. v.p. Tesoro Petroleum Corp., San Antonio, 1972-79; chmn. bd., chief exec. officer Clark

Oil & Refining Corp., Milw., 1979-81, pres., chief exec. officer div. Apex Oil Co., St. Louis, 1981-85; chmn., pres., chief exec. officer Pacific Resources, Inc., Honolulu, 1985-92; bd. dirs. Alexander and Baldwin, Inc., Honolulu, BHP Petroleum Pty. Ltd., First Hawaiian Bank. With USN, 1945-46. Clubs: Cadillac, Plaza, Waialae Country. Office: BHP Petroleum Americas Inc 733 Bishop St Honolulu HI 96813-4020

REED, ROBERT MONROE, publishing executive b. Sheldon, Iowa, Feb. 18, 1932; s. Carl A. and Hazel A. (Dockendorf) R.; m. Maxine Kathryn Gordon, June 7, 1954; children—Robert G., Richard K., Deri L. B.A., U. Iowa, 1956; M.A., U. Mich., 1958. Prodn. mgr. Sta. WETV, Atlanta, 1958-60; program mgr. Sta. WHA-TV, Madison, Wis., 1960-62; founder, gen. mgr. Sta. KHET-TV, Honolulu, 1962-69; exec. dir. PBS Video, Washington, 1969-76; gen. mgr. Sta. KUED-TV, Salt Lake City, 1976-78; exec. v.p. Nat. Video Clearinghouse, Inc., Syosset, N.Y., 1978-88; pres. Reed-Gordon Books Inc., 1988—; asst. prof. U. Wis.-Madison, 1960-62; assoc. prof. U. Hawaii, 1962-69; cons HEW, Dept. Army, Toronto Bd. Edn., NSF, others. Author: American Telecommunications Market, 1982; Career Opportunities: TV/Video, 1982, 86, 90, Ency. of TV, Cable and Video, 1992, Dictionary of TV, Cable and Video, 1994; pub.: The Video Source Book, ann. 1978-89; Video Tape/Disc Guides, ann. 1978-88; contbr. articles to profl. jours. Chmn., Honolulu Council Chs., 1965; troop leader Boy Scouts Am., Honolulu, 1966. With USN, 1949-52; Korea. Mem. Nat. Assn. Ednl. Broadcasters, Assn. Ednl. Communications Tech., Rocky Mountain Corp. Pub. Broadcasting (dir. 1977-79), Pacific Mountain Network (dir. 1976-79), Pub. Broadcasting Service (dir. 1978-79). Presbyterian. Lodge: Masons. Home: 285 Burr Rd East Northport NY 11731-5201

REED, SHERMAN KENNEDY, chemical consultant; b. Chgo., Apr. 11, 1919; s. Frank Hynes and Helen Louise (Kennedy) R.; m. Octavia Bailey, Oct. 11, 1943; children: Martin Bailey, Holly Anne, Julie Marie Reed. B.S. with honors, U. Ill., 1940; Ph.D., Cornell U., 1949. Asst. instr. chemistry Cornell U., 1940-43; asst. research scientist Manhattan Project, N.Y.C., 1942-46; asst. prof. Bucknell U., Lewisburg, Pa., 1946-50; with FMC Corp., 1950—, mgr., asst. dir. research, 1950-60, divisional dir. research and devel., central research dir., 1960-76, v.p., 1976-82; cons. FMC Corp., Chgo., 1983—; dir. Avicon, Inc., 1970-82; pres., dir. FMC Gold Corp.; mng. dir. COGAS Devel. Co., 1975—; dir. Indsl. Research Inst., N.Y.C., Franklin Inst., Phila., 1976-83; chmn. bd. Franklin Research Corp., Phila., 1976-83. Fellow Am. Inst. Chemists; mem. Am. Chem. Soc., AAAS, Assn. Research Dirs. (pres. 1973). Republican. Clubs: Union League (Phila.); Nassau (Princeton, N.J.). Home and Office: 14 Sailfish Rd Vero Beach FL 32960-5279

REED, STANLEY FOSTER, editor, writer, publisher, lecturer; b. Bogota, N.J., Sept. 28, 1917; s. Morton H. and Beryl (Turner) R.; m. Stella Swingle, Sept. 28, 1940 (div. 1978); children: Nancie, Beryl Ann, Alexandra; m. Shirley Weihman, Sept. 28, 1985 (dec. Feb. 1988); m. Catherine Case Commander, Dec. 16, 1989 (div. 1991). Student, George Washington U., 1939-40, Johns Hopkins, 1940-41; MBA, Loyola U., Md., 1981. Registered profl. engr., D.C. With Bethlehem Steel Corp., Balt., 1940-41; cons. engr., 1942-44; founder, pres. Reed Research, Inc., Washington, 1945-62; pres. Reed Research Inst. Creative Studies, Washington, from 1951; founder, chmn. LogEtronics, Inc., 1955; founder, ptnr., chmn. Tech. Audit Corp., 1962; assoc. Mgmt. Analysis Corp., 1978-81; sr. cons. Hay Assocs., Phila., 1980-83; entrepreneur in residence Coll. Charleston; co-chmn. semi-ann. Merger Week Northwestern U.; lectr. numerous U.S. and fgn. groups and instns. including Union Theol. Sem., U. Pa., Pa. State U., U. Colo., Georgetown U., Rensselaer Poly. Inst., Am. U., Claremont Coll., So. Meth. U., Pace U., Wayne State U., U. Oreg., U. Conn., St. John's U., Pepperdine U., Loyola Coll. of Md., San Francisco State U., U. Pitts., U. R.I., Marquette U., Vanderbilt U., Boston U., U. Cin., Gustavus Adolphus Coll., U. Mo., Mich. State U., Lehigh U., Calif. Inst. Tech., Denver U., George Washington U., Elmhurst Coll.; vis. fellow Wilton Pk. Conf., Eng., 1968. Author: The Art of M&A: A Merger/Aquisition/Buyout Guide, 1989, The Toxic Executive, 1993; editor: The International Deals Dictionary, 1994; founder, editor, pub.: Mergers and Acquisitions mag., 1965—, Dirs. and Bds. mag., 1976—; founder, editor, pub.: Campaigns and Elections mag., 1979—; founder, pub. Export Today mag., 1985; contbr. articles to leading jours., chpts. to books; patentee. Bd. dirs. Nat. Patent Coun., 1970—; founder, chmn. ann Merger Week, Washington, 1973-77, Northwestern U., 1977-87. Mem. Soc. Naval Architects and Marine Engrs. (life), Am. Econ. Assn., Dictionary Soc. of N.Am., Am. Student Action Partnership (chmn. adv. bd.), N.Y. Yacht Club, Internat. Club (Washington). Home: 330 Concord St Charleston SC 29401 Office: 9 Liberty St Charleston SC 29424-0001

REED, STEWART B., manufacturing executive; b. 1947. Exec. v.p. Reed Nat. Corp., 1970-86, Mestek Inc., Westfield, Mass., 1986—. Office: Mestek Inc 260 N Elm St Westfield MA 01085-1614*

REED, SUELLEN KINDER, state education administrator. BA in History, Polit. Sci.and Secondary Edn., Hanover Coll.; MA in Elem. Edn. and History, Ball State U., PhD in Adminstrn. and Supervision; postgrad., Fla. Atlantic U., U. Scranton, Purdue U., Earlham Coll., Ind. U.; Ind. State U. Cert. secondary elem. tchr., elem. tchr., gifted and talented tchr., administr., supr., Fla., Ind., supt., Ind. Tchr. 5th and 6th grades Rushville (Ind.) Consol. Sch. Corp., 1967-70, asst. supt., 1987-91, supt., 1991-93; tchr. Shelbyville (Ind.) High Sch., 1970-71; tchr. 6th, 7th and 8th grade social studies, curriculum Broward County (Fla.) Sch. Corp., 1971-76; tchr. Rushville Jr. High Sch., 1976-77; asst. prin. Rushville Elem. Sch., 1977-79; prin. Frazee Elem. Sch., Connersville, Ind., 1979-87; asst. supt. Rushville Consolidated Schs., 1987-90, supt., 1991-93; supt. pub. instrn., chairperson bd. edn., CEO dept. edn. State of Indiana, Indpls., 1993—. Mem. ASCD (nat. and Ind. chpts.), Internat. Reading Assn., Nat. Assn. Elem. Sch. Prins. (assoc.), Ind. Assn. Pub. Sch. Supts., Ind. Assn. Elem. and Mid. Sch. Prins. (assoc.), Ind. Assn., Network Woman Adminstrs., Indpls. Zoo, Indpls. Art Mus., Bus. and Profl. Women of Rushville, Altrusa Club Connersville (chmn. internat. rels. 1979-87), Connersville Area Reading Coun., Smithsonian, Rushville County Players, Rushville (Ind.), Monday Cir., Delta Kappa Gamma (past pres., Phi Lambda Theta, Phi Delta Kappa (Conner Prairie). Office: Superintendent Edn Dept 229 State Office Bldg Indianapolis IN 46204-2212

REED, THOMAS CARE, business executive; b. N.Y.C., Mar. 1, 1934; s. Gordon W. and Naomi (Bradley) R. BSME, Cornell U., Ithaca, N.Y., 1956; MSEE, U. So. Calif., 1959. Engaged in weapons physics Law Radiation Lab., U. Calif. at Livermore, 1959-62; cons., 1962-66, 88—; founder, mng. partner Supercon, Ltd., Houston, 1962-65; chmn., chief exec. officer River Oaks Agricorp, Healdsburg, Calif., 1982-88, Quaker Hill Devel. Corp., Healdsburg, Calif., 1965—; dir. telecommunications and command and control systems Dept. Def., 1974-75; Sec. of the Air Force, 1976-77; mem. Def Sci. Bd., 1977-83; mem. sci. adv. group U.S Strategic Command, 1981-83, 89-94; asst. asst. for nat. security policy to Pres. of U.S., 1982-83. Del. Rep. Nat. Conv., 1968, 72; mem. Rep. Nat. Com. for Calif., 1968-72. Served to 1st lt. USAF, 1956-61. Mem. Alpha Delta Phi, Tau Beta Pi. Clubs: Pacific Union (San Francisco); Metropolitan (Washington). Office: Quaker Hill Devel Corp PO Box 2240 Healdsburg CA 95448-2240

REED, THOMAS H., livestock exchange executive. BS in Animal Husbandry, Mich. State U., 1968, postgrad. in bus. mgmt., 1975. Coop. extension agt. Mich. State U., E. Lansing, 1970-75; livestock commodities mktg. specialist Mich. Farm Bur., Lansing, 1975-77; owner/operator Comml. Beef-Cow Ops., Gratiot County, Mich., 1970-79; prog. coordinator Mich. Live Stock Exchange, E. Lansing, 1968-70; chief exec. officer Mich. Live Stock Exchange, 1977—; cons. in field; developer Payment Plus prog. Mich.; creator/mgr. Mich. Products Spl. Export, Inc.; mem. Mich. Agrl. Policy Devel. Com.; developer livestock feeding prog. credited with saving Mich.'s cattle feeding industry; lectr. in field; bd. dirs. Nat. Live Stock Producers Svc. Co.; founder, pres. Gratiot Diversified Investor, 1975; bd. dirs. Mfrs. Bank of Lansing. Bd. dirs. Mich. State U., 1980—, vice chmn. bd., 1985-87, vice chmn. fin. com., 1987—; bd. dirs. Mich. State U. Found., U.S. Asean Ctr. for Tech. Exchange, Inc.; mem. Mich. Task Force on Internat. Trade; steering com. Revitalization of Animal Agr.; bd. dirs. Nat. Live Stock Conservation Inst.; mem. Hannah Soc. Scholarship Fund; trustee Livestock Industry Inst.; founding mem., bd. dirs. Mich. Festival, Inc.; mem. Mich. Livestock Expansion Com.; past chmn. Mich. Spl. Olympics Ceremony. Named Agribusinessman of the Yr., Mich. Farmer Mag., 1988. Mem. Am.

Farm Bur. Assn., Mich. Farm Bur. Assn., Nat. Cattlemen's Assn., Mich. Cattlemen's Assn., Mich. Agrl. Edn. and Exhbn. Ctr. Devel. Assn., Rotary, Republican 300 Club. Home: 1011 E Geneva Dr Dewitt MI 48820-9579 Office: Michigan Livestock Exchange 806 Coolidge Rd East Lansing MI 48823-2413

REED, TONY NORMAN, aviation company executive; b. Odessa, Tex., Apr. 12, 1951; s. Norman W. and Naoma N. (Johnson) R.; m. Gwen Stanphill, Mar. 29, 1973; 3 children. Pres. Trinity Aviation, Trinity Communication, Tyler, Tex., 1986-90; v.p. internat. mktg. Cardinal Aerospace, Inc., Independence, Mo., 1990-92; v.p. comml. programs Multinat. Enterprises, Inc., N.Y.C., 1992—; internat. sales profl. Puritan-Bennett Aero Systems, Inc., Lenexa, Kans., 1993—; bd. dirs. Missionary Aviation Svcs., Tyler. Mem. Aircraft Owners and Pilots Assn. Home: PO Box 1085 Blue Springs MO 64013-1085

REED, TRAVIS DEAN, public relations consultant; b. Trinity, Tex., Sept. 27, 1930; s. Travis and Alma (Rains) R.; m. Caroline M. McDonald, June 15, 1957; children: Anne Reed Adams, Lisa Reed Lettau. Student, Tex. A&M U., 1948-51, U. Houston, 1951-53. Reporter Houston Post, 1951-53; Washington Bur. corr. McGraw-Hill Pub. Co., 1955-61, Boston Herald-Traveler, 1961-62; with Newhouse News Svc., Washington, 1962-79, chief corr., 1964-67, editor, 1967-79; pub. rels. cons. Washington, 1979—. 1st lt. U.S. Army, 1953-55. Mem. Nat. Press Club, Federal City Club, Gridiron Club. Home: RR 1 Box 417 Purcellville VA 22132-9801 Office: Madison Office Bldg 1155 15th St NW Ste 1003 Washington DC 20005

REED, V. KEITH, pension fund administrator; b. 1944. Profit and loss analyst Sears Roebuck & Co., Kansas City, Mo., 1963-73; adminstr. Mt. of David Crippled Children's Hosp., Bethlehem, Israel, 1973-78, Indian Creek Nursing Ctr. Mo., Kansas City, 1978-81; with Boilermakers Blksm Nat. Pension Tr., Kansas City, Kans., 1981—, exec. adminstr., 1986—. Office: Boilermakers Blksm Natl Pns Tr 754 Minnesota Ave Ste 522 Kansas City KS 66101*

REED, VINCENT EMORY, federal education official; b. St. Louis, Mar. 1, 1928; s. Artie David and Velma Veander (Body) R.; m. Frances Bullitt, Sept. 20, 1952. B.S. in Edn., W.Va. State Coll., 1956, H.L.D. (hon.), 1977; M.A., Howard U., Washington, 1965; D.P.A. (hon.), Southeastern U., Washington, 1976; postgrad., Wharton Sch., U. Pa., 1969; Ph.D. (hon.), Georgetown U., 1977; L.H.D. (hon.), Strayer Coll., Harris-Stowe U., 1983, Slippery Rock U., 1990; LLD (hon.), U. D.C., 1984. Football coach W.va. State Coll., 1955; mem. staff D.C. Pub. Schs., 1962—, asst. supt. secondary schs., 1971-74, assoc. supt. state office, 1974-75, supt. schs., 1975-80; asst. sec. for elem. and secondary edn. U.S. Dept. Edn., 1981—. Author articles, book revs. Dir. Home Fed. Savs. and Loan Assn.; bd. dirs. D.C. Goodwill Industries, Washington YMCA, 12 Neediest Kids; vol. worker S.E. Boys' Club, S.E. Youth Football Assn. Served as 1st lt. AUS, 1953-55, Korea. Named All-Am. Football Player Pitts. Courier, 1951, to W.Va. ROTC Hall of Fame, 1981; recipient Superior Service award D.C. Bicentennial Assembly, 1976; Outstanding Achievement award W.va. State Coll., 1976; Alumnus of Yr., 1976; named to Athletic Hall of Fame, 1983; Outstanding Community Service award NAACP, 1977; Scouter of Yr. award Washington, 1981; Human Relations award NCCJ, 1981; Man of Yr. award YMCA, 1984; Excellent Role Models for Edn. award Colgate-Palmolive; Martin Luther King, Jr. Civil Rights for Edn. award Com. Civil Rights and Urban Affairs; many others. Mem. Nat. Secondary Sch. Prins., Am. Assn. Sch. Personnel Adminstrs., Nat. Assn. Sch. Security Officers, Am. Soc. Bus. Ofcls., NAACP, NEA., D.C. PTA, Washington Sch., Club, Phi Delta Kappa, Kappa Alpha Psi. Baptist. Clubs: Pigskin, Kiwanis. Home: 7115 16th St NW Washington DC 20012-1537 Office: Washington Post Company 1150 15th St NW Washington DC 20071-0002

REED, W. FRANKLIN, lawyer; b. Louisville, Dec. 30, 1946; s. William Ferguson and Stella Elizabeth (Richardson) R.; m. Sharon Ann Coss, June 16, 1973; children: Jonathan Franklin, William Brian, Carrie Ann. BA, Williams Coll., 1968; JD, Columbia U., 1971. Bar: N.Y. 1972, U.S. Dist. Ct. (so. dist.) N.Y. 1975, U.S. Ct. Appeals (2d cir.) 1975, Pa. 1982, U.S. Dist. Ct. (we. dist.) 1983. Assoc. Milbank, Tweed, Hadley & McCloy, N.Y.C., 1971-82; assoc. Reed, Smith, Shaw & McClay, Pitts., 1982-83, ptnr., 1984—. Mem. ABA, Pa. Bar Assn., Allegheny Bar Assn., Carnegie 100, Williams Coll. Alumni Soc. W. Pa. (sec. 1983—), Rivers Club (Pitts.), St. Clair Country Club (Upper St. Clair, Pa.), Duquesne Club (Pitts.), Phi Beta Kappa. Democrat. Presbyterian. Avocations: fishing, golf. Home: 525 Miranda Dr Pittsburgh PA 15241-2039 Office: Reed Smith Shaw & McClay 435 6th Ave Pittsburgh PA 15219-1809

REED, WALLACE ALLISON, physician; b. Covina, Calif., May 19, 1916; s. Wallace Allison and Mary Julia (Birdsall) R.; m. Maria Eva Wiemers, Jan. 20, 1938; children: Ellen E., Barbara R. (Mrs. David Maurice Knize), Wallace J., Michael E., Kathryn L., Vicki T. A.B., UCLA, Los Angeles, 1937; postgrad., U. Cologne, 1937-38; U. Freiburg, Breisgau, 1938-39; M.D., U. So. Calif., 1944. Diplomate: Am. Bd. Anesthesiology. Intern Santa Fe Coast Lines Hosp., Los Angeles, 1943-44; resident Los Angeles County Gen. Hosp., 1946-47, asst. to head dept. anesthesiology, 1946-47; clin. instr. surgery U. So. Calif. Sch. Medicine, 1946-47; practice medicine, specializing in anesthesiology Phoenix, 1948-89; hon. staff mem. Good Samaritan Hosp., St. Joseph Hosp., Maricopa County Gen. Hosp.; mem. hon. staff Children's Hosp.; co-founder John L. Ford, M.D., Surgicenter, 1970; vice pres. Maricopa Found. for Med. Care, 1970-74, pres., 1975-76; mem. House Ways and Means Adv. Com.; adv. council Nat. Health Inst., 1975-76; mem. accreditation council for ambulatory health care Joint Commn. on Accreditation of Hosps., 1975-79; vice-chmn. Accreditation Assn. for Ambulatory Health Care, 1979-81, pres., 1981-83; mem. panel for study Nat. Health Ins., Congl. GAO; chmn. bd. Alterna Care Corp., 1984-87, now dormant; bd. emeritus; mem. adv. bd. Kind Inst., 1994—. Bd. dirs. South Phoenix Montessori Sch., pres. bd., 1971-75; bd. dirs. Ctrl. Ariz. Health Systems Agy., 1975-78; exec. dir. Surgicenter of Phoenix 1987—. Capt. M.C. AUS, 1944-46. Recipient Pinal award Ariz. Psychiat. Soc., 1967-68, Gerard B. Lambert Merit award for innovative ideas that improve patient care; John L. Ford M.D., 1972. Fellow Am. Coll. Anesthesiologists; mem. Am. Soc. Anesthesiologists, Ariz., Maricopa County socs. anesthesiologists, AMA, Acad. Anesthesiology (pres. 1969, dir. 1966-72), Soc. for Advancement Free-Standing Ambulatory Surg. Care (pres. 1974-75, dir.), Soc. for Ambulatory Anesthesia (bd. dirs. 1985-87), Ariz. Med. Assn. (dir. 1972-78), Maricopa County Med. Soc. (pres. 1964, dir.), Salsbury medal 1967, 71, Thomas Dooley medal 1970), Central Ariz. Physicians Service Assn. (pres. 1982-83), Am. Assn. Founds. for Med. Care (dir. 1970-74), Guedel Assn. (pres. 1972), Seed Money for Growth Found. (pres. 1984—). Methodist. Home: 4716 N Dromedary Rd Phoenix AZ 85018-2939 Office: 1040 E Mcdowell Rd Phoenix AZ 85006-2622

REED, WALTER GEORGE, JR., osteopath; b. Ardmore, Okla., Sept. 10, 1928; s. Walter George and Lillian Dorene (Gee) R.; m. Elaine Carol Collum; children: Jay Walter, David George, Kimberly Sue. BA, Phillips U., 1955; DO, Kansas City Coll. Osteopathy, 1959. Pvt. practice Oklahoma City, 1963-63, Atoka, Okla., 1963-80; flight surgeon USAF, Omaha, 1980-84, Lubbock, Tex., 1984-86; chief med. officer Army Health Clinic, McAlester, Okla., 1986—. Mayor City of Atoka, 1970s; v.p. Atoka Bd. Edn., 1980s. Lt. col. USAF, 1980-86. Mem. Assn. Mil. Osteo. Physicians and Surgeons, Assn. Mil. Surgeons U.S., Masons (32d degree). Mem. First Christian Ch. Avocations: flying, hunting, computing, auto mechanics, plate collecting. Home: Rt 3 Box F McAlester OK 74501 Office: Army Health Clinic Mcalester OK 74501

REED, WALTER GURNEE DYER, lawyer; b. N.Y.C., July 11, 1952; s. Stanley Forman and Harriet Tailer (Dyer) R.; m. Cynthia Ann Stewart, Sept. 6,1986. BA magna cum laude, Harvard Coll., 1974; JD, Columbia U., 1977. Bar: N.Y. 1978, R.I. 1983. Assoc. Milbank, Tweed, Hadley & McCloy, N.Y.C., 1977-81; assoc. Edwards & Angell, Providence, 1981-83, ptnr., 1983—. Bd. dirs. Children's Mus. R.I., Pawtucket, 1984-91, Providence Athenaeum, 1991-94. Scholar Columbia U., Stone scholar. Mem. ABA, R.I. Bar Assn. (chmn. com. on corp. law 1991-93), N.Y.C. Lawyers Assn., Spouting Rock Beach Assn., Hope Club, Agawam Hunt Club. Democrat. Congregationalist. Home: 14 Cooke St Providence RI 02906-2006 Office: Edwards & Angell 2700 Hospital Trust Towers Providence RI 02903

REED, WILLIAM EDWARD, government official, educator; b. Columbia, La., July 15, 1914; s. William Reed and Virginia (Barnes) R.; m. Mattye Marie Scott, Aug. 27, 1942; children: Edwarda Marie (Mrs. Lucien L. Johnson), Carol Ann, Beverlyn Bernetiae. B.S., So. U., 1937; M.S., Iowa State U., 1941; Ph.D., Cornell U., 1946. County agrl. agt. Agr. and Home Econs. Extension Service, La. State U., 1937-41; lectr. soil sci. and chemistry So. U., 1942-47; agrl. research specialist U.S. Econ. Mission to Liberia, 1947-49; dean agr. Agrl. and Tech. Coll. N.C., 1949-61; mem. U.S. del. Russia; rep. ICA in Togo, 1961; asst. dir. AID Mission to Nigeria, 1961-68; mem. U.S. del. to UN Conf. on Application Sci. and Tech., 1963; dep. dir. AID Mission to Ethiopia, 1968-72; fgn. service officer in residence N.C. A. & T. State U., Greensboro, 1972-74; spl. asst. to chancellor for internat. programs N.C. A. & T. State U., 1974-76, assoc. dean research and spl. projects, 1976-78, dir. internat. programs, 1978-84; cons. in field, 1984—. State rep. Sisters Cities Internat. Mem. Nat. Planning Assn., Am. Fgn. Svc. Assn., Sigma Xi, Phi Kappa Phi, Beta Kappa Chi, Sigma Pi Phi, Gamma Sigma Delta, Beta Epsilon (trustee Boulé Found. 1964—). Episcopalian. Home: 2711 Mcconnell Rd Greensboro NC 27401-4534

REED, WILLIAM G., JR., paper company executive; b. 1939. Grad., Duke U.; MBA, Harvard U., 1969. Mgmt. trainee Simpson Investment, Seattle, 1963-66, gen. mgr. engineered wood products divsn., 1966, vice chmn., 1970-71, chmn., 1971, now CEO; mgmt. trainee Weyerhaeuser Co., Federal Way, Wash., 1967-69; exec. v.p. Simpson Timber Co. (subs. Simpson Investment), 1969. Served USMC, 1961-63. Office: Simpson Investment Ste 4900 1201 3rd Ave Seattle WA 98101

REED, WILLIS, professional basketball team executive, former head coach; b. Hico, La., June 25, 1942; s. Willis and Inell R.; m. Geraldine Oliver (div.); children: Carl, Veronica. Student, Grambling Coll., 1960-64. Center, forward N.Y. Knickerbockers, NBA, 1964-74; coach N.Y. Knickerbockers, NBA, 1977-79, Creighton U., Omaha, 1981-85; asst. coach Atlanta Hawks, NBA, 1985-88, Sacramento Kings, NBA, 1988; head coach New Jersey Nets, NBA, 1988-89, v.p. basketball and bus. dev., 1989-90, sr. v.p., 1990—, now exec. v.p. basketball, gen mgr. Author: (with Phil Pepe) The View from the Rim, 1971. Mem. Nat. Basketball Assn. All-Star team, 1965-71, 73; mem. World Championship team, 1970, 73; recipient Most Valuable Player awards for playoffs and all-star games, 1970; named Nat. Basketball Assn. Rookie of Yr., 1965, NBA Playoffs Most Valuable Player, 1970, 73; named to Naismith Meml. Hall of Fame, 1981. Office: NJ Nets 405 Murray Hill Pky East Rutherford NJ 07073*

REEDER, CECELIA PAINTER, English educator; b. Tampa, Fla., Oct. 9, 1936; d. William Painter and Cecelia (Bachman) Hendry; children: Susan Reeder Shipp, William J. BEd, U. Miami, 1958; MA in Gifted Edn., U. South Fla., 1983. Cert. elem./gifted-talented tchr., K-12, English 7-9, Fla. Elem. tchr. Dade County Bd. Pub. Inst., Miami, Fla., 1958-70, 83-86, tchr., English, 1986-89; tchr. gifted English and Social Studies 7th and 8th grades Richmond Heights Mid. Sch., Miami, Fla., 1989-94. Recipient Assoc. Master Tchr. award State of Fla., 1986. Home: 1520 NW 10th St Homestead FL 33030-3824

REEDER, CHARLES BENTON, economic consultant; b. Columbus, Ohio, Oct. 31, 1922; s. Charles Wells and Lydia (Morrow) R.; m. Carol Lincoln, June 25, 1949 (div. June 1972); 1 son. Charles; m. Beverly Lawrence, Nov. 11, 1972; adopted children: Keith, Sue. BS, Ohio State U., 1945, PhD, 1951; MBA, Harvard U., 1947. Econ. analyst Cleve. Elec. Illuminating Co., 1947-48; instr. Ohio State U., Columbus, 1948-51; econ. analyst, asst. economist Armstrong Cork. Co., Lancaster, Pa., 1951-55; assoc. economist E. I. DuPont de Nemours & Co., Inc., Wilmington, Del., 1955-70; chief economist E.I. DuPont de Nemours & Co., Inc., Wilmington, Del., 1970-85; pres. Charles Reeder Assocs., 1986—; bd. dirs. Sentinel Group Mut. Funds, Montpelier, Vt. Author: The Sobering Seventies, 1981. Bd. dirs. Greater Wilmington Devel. Coun., 1963-84; treas. Del. Coun. on Econ. Edn., 1958-85, Bank of Del., Wilmington, 1975-92. 1st lt. Q.M.C., AUS, 1943-46. Recipient Silbert award Sterling Nat. Bank of N.Y., 1982. Fellow Nat. Assn. Bus. Economists (pres. 1966-67); mem. Nat. Bur. Econ. Research (past bd. dirs.). Methodist. Clubs: Wilmington, Greenville Country. Home: 16 Brendle Ln Wilmington DE 19807-1300 Office: Ste 4 16 Brendle Ln Wilmington DE 19807

REEDER, ELLEN DRYDEN, museum curator; b. Balt., Apr. 11, 1947; d. Oliver Howard and Nancy Hardcastle (Fisher) R. BA, Wellesley U., 1969; MA, Princeton U., 1972, PhD, 1974. Curator archaeological collection John Hopkins U., Balt., 1974-78; asst. prof. art George Washington U., Washington, 1978-84; assoc. curator ancient art Walters Art Gallery, Balt., 1984-86, curator ancient art, 1986—; mem. at large mng. com. Am. Sch. Classical Studies, Athens, Greece, 1987—; adv. bd. U.S. Ctr. Lexicon Iconographicum Mythologiae Classicae, New Brunswick, N.J., 1986—. Author: The Archaeological Collection of the John Hopkins University, 1984; author, editor: Hellenistic Art in the Walters Art Gallery, 1988, mem. editorial bd. 1985—; contbr. articles to profl. jours. Trustee Calvert Sch., Balt., 1990—. Woodrow Wilson fellow, 1969, Princeton Nat. U. fellow, 1969-74. Mem. Archaeol. Inst. Am., Coll. Art Assn., Phi Beta Kappa Assocs. (bd. dirs. 1993—, sec.-treas. 1994—), Phi Beta Kappa. Office: Walters Art Gallery 600 N Charles St Baltimore MD 21201-5185

REEDER, JAMES ARTHUR, lawyer; b. Baton Rouge, June 29, 1933; s. James Brown and Grace (Britt) R.; m. Mary Leone Guthrie, Dec. 30, 1958; children: Mary Virginia, James Jr., Elizabeth Colby. BA, Washington and Lee U., Lexington, Va., 1955; LLB, U. Tex., 1960; JD, La. State U., 1961. Ptnr. Booth, Lockard, Jack et al, Shreveport, La., 1961-72; pres. and mgng. ptnr. Shreveport Broadcasting Co., 1972-86; Chief exec. officer and mgng. gen. ptnr. Radio USA Limited, Houston, 1986-89; pres. SW subsidiaries Sun Group, Inc., Houston, 1990-92; atty. Patton, Boggs & Blow, Washington, 1991-94, ptnr., 1994—; dir. ABC Radio Sta. Affiliates adv. bd., N.Y.C., 1978-84. Dir. Boys Country, Houston, 1986-90; pres. Holiday in Dixie, Shreveport, 1968; chmn. Ambassadors Club, Shreveport, 1979. 1st Lt. U.S. Army, 1955-57. Named La. Outstanding Young Man, La. Jaycees, 1969. Mem. ABA (bd. dirs. young lawyers sect. 1967-68, Gavel awards com. 1980), La. Bar Assn. (pres. young lawyers sect. 1966, La. Outstanding Young Lawyer award 1968), D.C. Bar Assn., Tex. Bar Assn., Nat. Assn. Broadcasters, Houston Country Club, Demoiselle Club (Shreveport), Allegro Club (Houston). Roman Catholic.

REEDER, JEFFREY K., retail executive; b. 1952. BS in Econs., Purdue U., 1974. With Marsh Super Market, Yorktown, Ind., 1967-75, Fleming Foods, Houston, 1975-77; with Gerlands Food Fair Inc., Houston, 1977—, now v.p.-treas. Office: Gerlands Food Fair Inc 3131 Pawnee St Houston TX 77054*

REEDER, JOE ROBERT, federal official; b. Tacoma, Nov. 28, 1947; s. William Thomas and Marilyn Ruth (Parker) R.; m. Katharine Randolph Boyce, Jan 1, 1983; children: Rachael Anne, Aubrilyn, Julia, Kelsey. BS, U.S. Mil. Acad., West Point, N.Y., 1970; JD, U. Tex., 1975; LLM, Georgetown U., 1981. Bar: Tex. 1975, D.C. 1979, U.S. Dist. Ct. (so. dist.) Tex 1975, U.S. Ct. Appeals (5th cir.) 1989, U.S. Ct. Claims 1979, U.S. Dist. Ct. D.C. 1982, U.S. Ct. Appeals (Fed. cir.) 1984, U.S. Supreme Ct. 1988, U.S. Ct. Appeals (4th cir.) 1988, Md. 1989, U.S. Dist. Ct. (Md. dist) 1989, U.S. Dist. Ct. (no. dist.) Tex. 1991, U.S. Ct. Appeals (so. dist.) Tex. 1991. Commd. 2d lt. U.S. Army, 1970, advanced through grades to maj., 1985; law clk. to presiding justice U.S. Dist. Ct. (so. dist.) Tex., 1976; trial atty. litigation div. U.S. Army, Pentagon, D.C., 1976-78; trial atty. contract appeals div. U.S. Army, Pentagon, 1978-79; assoc. Patton, Boggs & Blow, Washington, 1979-82, ptnr. 1983-93; under sec. of U.S. Army U.S. Dept. Def., Washington, 1993—; chmn. bd. Panama Canal Commn., 1994—. Mem. ABA (assoc. editor pub. contract law jour. 1985-93), ATLA, Am. Law Inst., Fed. Bar Assn., D.C. Bar Assn., Tex. Bar Assn., Bar Assn. 5th Fed. Circuit, Bd. Contract Appeals Bar Assn., Rotary. Episcopalian. Home: 2301 Ft Scott Dr Arlington VA 22202-2262 Office: Under Sec of Army 102 Army Pentagon Washington DC 20310

REEDER, JOHN P., JR., religious studies educator; b. Charlotte, N.C., July 11, 1937; s. John Pickens and Vestal (Hawkins) R.; m. Jane Clark, June 26, 1965; children—Nicholas Clark, Katherine Whitworth. B.A., Yale U., New Haven, 1960, B.D., 1964, Ph.D., 1968. Instr. dept. religion Princeton

U., N.J., 1967-68, asst. prof. dept. religion, 1968-71; asst. prof. dept. religious studies Brown U., Providence, 1971-72, assoc. prof. dept. religious studies, 1973-79, prof. dept. religious studies, 1979—, chmn. dept. religious studies, 82-84, 85-92. Author: Source Sanction and Salvation; co-editor (with Gene Outka) Religion and Morality, Prospects for Common Morality; contbr. articles to profl. jours. Home: 51 Barnes St Providence RI 02906-1501 Office: Brown U Dept Religious Studies Providence RI 02912

REEDER, MICHAEL S., consulting firm executive. BSBA, U. Fla.; MBA, U. Tampa (Fla.). Mgr., employment svcs. Fla. Power Corp.; v.p. (exec. search div.) MSL Internat. Cons., Atlanta. Office: Lamalie Assocs Tower Pla 3340 Peachtree Rd NE Atlanta GA 30326-1000

REEDER, OLIVER HOWARD, paint products manufacturing executive; b. Balt., Sept. 19, 1916; s. Charles Howard and Nannie Dryden (Kensett) R.; m. Nancy Hardcastle Fisher, Apr. 18, 1942; children: Nancy Fisher, Ellen Dryden. A.B., Princeton U., 1939. With Balt. Copper Paint Co., Balt., 1939—; tech. dir., treas. Balt. Copper Paint Co., 1939-47, pres., 1947—, chmn., 1959—; v.p. Balt. Copper Paint div. Glidden-Durkee Div. SCM Corp., 1969—; pres. Jotun-Balt. Copper Paint Co., Inc., 1974-76, v.p., 1976-81. Pres. Hosp. for Consumptives of Md., 1968-84, trustee, 1951-95, trustee emeritus, 1995—; trustee Gilman Sch., Balt., 1948-65, Walters Art Gallery, 1978-83, U.S. Frigate Constellation Found., 1976-89; trustee Johns Hopkins Hosp., 1957-87, trustee emeritus, 1987—, vice chmn. bd., 1986-87; trustee Md. Hosp. Laundry, 1970-89, pres., 1975-84. Fellow Am. Inst. Chemists; mem. Am. Chem. Soc., Soc. Naval Architects and Marine Engrs., Phi Beta Kappa, Sigma Xi. Home: 1300 Dulaney Valley Rd Baltimore MD 21286

REEDER, ROBERT HARRY, retired lawyer; b. Topeka, Dec. 3, 1930; s. William Harry and Florence Mae (Cochran) R. AB Washburn U., 1952, JD, 1960. Bar: U.S. Dist. Ct. Kans. 1960, Kans. 1960, U.S. Supreme Ct. 1968. Rsch. asst. Kans. Legis. Council Rsch. Dept., Topeka, 1955-60; asst. counsel Traffic Inst., Northwestern U., Evanston, Ill., 1960-67, gen. counsel, 1967-92; exec. dir. Nat. Com. on Uniform Traffic Laws and Ordinances, Evanston, 1982-90. Co-author: Vehicle Traffic Law, 1974; The Evidence Handbook, 1980. Author: Interpretation of Implied Consent by the Courts, 1972. Served with U.S. Army, 1952-54. Mem. Com. Alcohol and Other Drugs (chmn. 1973-75). Republican. Methodist.

REEDS, ROGER, church administrator. Dir. Sunday School and Church Training Dept. of the Nat. Assn. of Free WillBaptists, Antioch, Tenn. Office: Natl Assn of Free Will Baptists PO Box 5002 Antioch TN 37011-5002

REEDY, EDWARD K., system engineer administrator. Dir. Georgia Inst. of Tech. Radar and Instrumentation Dev. Lab, Atlanta, Ga. Office: Ga Inst Tech Radar Instrumentation Lab Ga Tech Rsch Inst Atlanta GA 30332

REEDY, GEORGE EDWARD, educator, author, lecturer; b. East Chicago, Ind., Aug. 5, 1917; s. George Edward and Mary (Mulvaney) R.; m. Lillian Greenwald, Mar. 22, 1948 (dec.); children: Michael Andrew, William James; m. Ruth Brial Wissman, May 7, 1988. B.A. in Sociology, U. Chgo., 1938; D.J.C., Nashota Sem., 1981; LHD, Lycoming Coll., 1991. Reporter Phila. Inquirer, summer 1937; Congl. corr. U.P., 1938-41, 46-51; staff cons. armed services preparedness subcom. U.S. Senate, 1951-52, staff dir. minority policy com., 1953-54, staff dir. majority policy com., 1955-60; spl. asst. to Vice Pres. Lyndon B. Johnson, 1961-63; press sec. to Pres. Johnson, 1964-65; pres. Struthers Research and Devel. Corp., Washington, 1966-68; v.p. planning Struthers Wells Corp., N.Y.C., 1966-68; spl. cons. to President Lyndon B. Johnson, 1968-69; writer, lectr., cons., 1969—; dean, Nieman prof. Coll. Journalism, Marquette U., Milw., 1972-77, Nieman prof., 1977-90, prof. emeritus, 1991—; mem. Pres.'s Commn. on White House Fellowships, 1993; former fellow Woodrow Wilson Internat. Ctr. for Scholars, Smithsonian Instn., Washington; fellow in communication Duke U., 1973-74; lectr. S.Am., Cen. Am., Asia, India, 1975-84. Author: Who Will Do Our Fighting for Us?, 1969, The Twilight of the Presidency, 1970, The Presidency in Flux, 1973, Lyndon B. Johnson, A Memoir, 1982; The U.S. Senate: Paralysis or Search for Consensus, 1986, The Twilight of the Presidency, Johnson to Reagan, 1987, From the Ward to the White House, The Irish in American Politics, 1991; numerous articles on govt. and politics in mags. and newspapers. Mem. Pres.'s Nat. Adv. Commn. Selective Svc., 1966-67, Marine Sci., Engring. Resources, 1967-68, Pres.'s Commn. on White House Fellowships, 1993; mem. diocesan coun. Washington Diocese, Episcopal Ch. With USAAF, 1942-45. Office: Marquette U Coll Communications Milwaukee WI 53233

REEDY, JERRY EDWARD, editor, writer; b. Aberdeen, S.D., Feb. 4, 1936; s. Robert Emmett and Helen Mary (Issenhuth) R.; m. Susan Mary Rogers, June 22, 1968; children: Megan Marie, Erin Elizabeth, Matthew Robert-Emmett, Thomas Walter. A.B., U. Notre Dame, 1958; M.A., U. S.D., 1961. Area editor Red Wing (Minn.) Daily Republican Eagle, 1959-60; with Better Homes & Gardens mag. Meredith Pub. Co., Des Moines, 1961-69; assoc. editor Better Homes & Gardens mag. Meredith Pub. Co., 1966-67, spl. assignments editor, 1967-69; editor in chief, contbg. author Odyssey Mag., Chgo., 1969-78; free-lance editor, writer and photographer for nat. mags. and maj. met. daily newspapers, 1978—; travel editor Better Homes and Gardens Brides Book, 1983-84; instr. in English U., S.D., 1960-61, in mag. writing; Drake U., 1966-68, Barat Coll., 1976-77. Author: Great American Indian Leaders, Notable Quotables, Family Adventure Guide and Road Atlas, God, Country, Notre Dame: The Autobiography of Theodore M. Hesburgh, 1990, (with Rev. Theodore Hesbough); editor: Travels with Ted and Ned, 1992; contbr. to Ency. Brit., 1980, World Book, 1984, Family Vacation Atlas, 1986 and various nat. mags. Pres. Com. on Community Life, Chgo., 1976-78; chmn. bd. The Shelter, 1980-85. Recipient certificates of excellence Chgo. Communications Collaboration, 1976; Addy Gold 1st place award for mags. Am. Advt. Fedn., 1976; 1st pl. awards of excellence for overall quality and for photojournalism Chgo. Assn. Bus. Communicators, 1977. Mem. Midwest Writers, Am. Soc. Journalists and Authors. Roman Catholic. Home and Office: 3542 N Pine Grove Ave Chicago IL 60657-1877

REEF, ARTHUR, industry business consultant; b. N.Y.C., Sept. 21, 1916; s. Herman and Eva (Van Panich) R.; m. Barbara Blasser, May, 1958; children: Jennifer, Nancy. B.A., CCNY, 1937; postgrad., U. Pa., 1937-38, Am. U., 1941-42, Sorbonne, U. Paris, 1949. With Ruder & Finn. Internat., N.Y.C., 1955-57, Barnet & Reef, N.Y.C., 1957-64; with AMAX, Inc., Greenwich, Conn., 1964-81, sr. v.p. and dir. office communications and pub. affairs; sr. cons. to exec. office AMAX, Inc., Greenwich and N.Y.C., 1981-87; dir. AMAX Australia Ltd.; trustee, chmn. U.S. com. Internat. Inst. Communications, 1979-81; bd. mem. World Environ. Ctr. N.Y., 1974-79, Ctr. for the Study of the Presidency; trustee Am. Coun. of Young Polit. Leaders; councillor Am.-Australian Bi-Centennial Commn. Fellow Inst. Mining and Metallurgy London, Acad. Internat. Bus.; mem. French Am. C. of C. (former councillor), Fgn. Policy Assn. (assoc.), Overseas Press Club Am. (chmn. fgn. journalism com. 1958-63). Home: 2000 S Ocean Blvd Apt 608 Delray Beach FL 33483-6413

REELING, PATRICIA GLUECK, library educator, educational consultant; b. Cin., June 6, 1939; d. Arthur William and Bertha Louise Glueck; m. Glenn Eugene Reeling, Aug. 18, 1962; children: Craig Patrick, Aimee Reeling Berger. BA, Edgecliff Coll., Cin., 1960; MA, Ind. U., 1963; DLS, Columbia U., 1969. Reference libr. Ohio State U., Columbus, 1961-62; asst. to dir. Boston Coll. Librs., 1962-63; assoc. prof. Sch. Comm., Info. and Libr. Studies Rutgers U., New Brunswick, N.J., 1970—, chmn. dept. libr. and info. studies, 1984-89; ednl. cons. Reeling Assocs., Somerset, N.J., 1969—; evaluator Mid. States Assn. Commn. on Higher Edn., Phila., 1975—; vis. prof. Emporia State U., Denver, 1991—. Editor: Education for the Library/ Information Profession: Strategies for the Mid-90s, 1993; editor column Govt. Info., RQ, 1983-85; contbr. articles to profl. jours. Mem. depository libr. coun. to pub. printer U.S. Govt. Printing Office, Washington, 1982-85; mem. network rev. bd. N.J. State Libr., Trenton, 1989-90. Recipient 1st Leadership award N.J. State Libr. 1987; grantee Rutgers U. 1983. Mem. ALA (life, mem. or chmn. numerous coms. 1964—), James Bennett Childs award 1988, Libr. Edn. Centennial Honor Role award 1988), AAUP (officer Rutgers coun. chpts. 1967—), Assn. for Libr. and Info. Sci. Edn. (mem. or chmn. various coms. 1964—), Documents Assn. N.J. (pres. 1981-82, archivist 1983—), N.J. Libr. Assn. (various coms. 1964—, Disting. Svc.

award coll. and univ. sect. 1984), Beta Phi Mu (officer Omicron chpt. 1961—). Home: 131 Drake Rd Somerset NJ 08873 Office: Rutgers U Sch Comm Info-Libr Studies New Brunswick NJ 08901-1071

REEMTSMA, KEITH, surgeon, educator; b. Madera, Calif., Dec. 5, 1925; children: Lance Brewster, Dirk Van Horn. BS, Idaho State Coll., 1948; MD, U. Pa., 1949; D in Med.Sc., Columbia U., 1958. Diplomate Am. Bd. Med. Examiners, Am. Bd. Surgery (planning com. 1968-70, nominating com. 1970, com. on certification for spl. competence 1971), Am. Bd. Thoracic Surgery. Intern Presbyn. Hosp., N.Y.C., 1950-51, asst. resident in surgery, 1951-55, resident in surgery, 1956, chief resident in surgery, 1957; asst. surgery Columbia Coll. Physicians and Surgeons, N.Y.C., 1957; mem. faculty Tulane U. Sch. Medicine, New Orleans, 1957-66, prof. surgery, 1966—; head dept. surgery U. Utah Coll. Medicine, Salt Lake City, 1966-71; chmn. dept. surgery, Valentine Mott prof. surgery, Johnson and Johnson disting. prof. surgery Columbia U., N.Y.C., 1971-94; dir. surg. svc. U. Utah, 1966-71, Presbyn. Hosp., 1971-94. Contbr. articles to profl. jours. Lt. (j.g.) USNR, 1951-53; lt. MC USN, 1953. Mem. AMA, ACS, Soc. Clin. Surgery, Am. Surg. Assn., Soc. U. Surgeons (treas. 1962-75), So. Soc. for Clin. Rsch., Am. Fedn. for Clin. Rsch., Am. Assn. for Thoracic Surgery, Soc. for Vascular Surgery, Internat. Cardiovascular Soc., So. Thoracic Surg. Assn., New Orleans Surg. Soc., Surg. Assn. La., La. Med. Soc., Orleans Parish Med. Soc., Surg. Biology Club II, Western Surg. Assn., Alpha Omega Alpha. Office: Columbia University Dept Surgery 630 W 168th St New York NY 10032-3702

REEP, EDWARD ARNOLD, artist; b. Bklyn., May 10, 1918; s. Joseph and Elsie (Abramson) R.; m. Karen Patricia Stevens, Dec. 9, 1942; children—Susan Kay, Cristine Elyse, Janine J., Mitchell Jules. Student, Art Center Coll. Design, 1936-41. Instr. painting and drawing Art Center Coll. Design, Los Angeles, 1946-50, Chouinard Art Inst., Los Angeles, 1950-69; prof. painting, chmn. dept., artist in residence E. Carolina U., 1970-85, prof. emeritus, 1985—; cons. editor Van Nostrand Reinhold Pub. Co.; ofcl. war artist-corr. WWII, Africa and Italy. Author: The Content of Watercolor, 1968, A Combat Artist in World War II, 1987; shows include Whitney Mus. Am. Art Ann., N.Y.C., 1946-48, Los Angeles County Mus. Ann., 1946-60, Corcoran Gallery Art Biennial, Washington, 1949, Nat. Gallery Art, Washington, 1945, Mus. Modern Art, N.Y.C.; represented in permanent collections Los Angeles County Mus., U.S. War Dept., Grunwald Graphic Arts Collection, UCLA, Nat. Mus. Am. Art, Washington, Lytton Collection, Los Angeles, State of Calif. Collection, Sacramento. Guggenheim fellow, 1945-46; Nat. Endowment for Arts grantee, 1975. Mem. AAUP, Nat. Watercolor Soc. (past pres.), Watercolor USA Honor Soc. Democrat. Home: 9021 Crowningshield Dr Bakersfield CA 93311-1901 *I once was consumed by the desire to become an artist. I feel no differently today. There is work ahead. If I had set goals for myself I no longer can recall what they may have been; I go along painting as well or as inventively as I can. Never have I sacrificed living life as I feel I must for my art. My work is a reflection of my life—experiences real and imagined.*

REES, CHARLES H. G., retired financial officer, investor, consultant; b. Trenton, N.J., Mar. 6, 1922; s. Albert H. and Helen (Gallagher) R.; m. Nancy Thomas, Oct. 30, 1954; children: Liberty, Camilla, Nancy, Hilleary. BA, Princeton U., 1948. Salesman John A. Roebling's Sons Co., Trenton, 1948-50; staff officer CIA, Washington, 1951-54; assoc. J.H. Whitney & Co., N.Y.C., 1954-59; gen. ptnr. Whitcom Investment Co., N.Y.C., 1967-85; with Whitney Comm. Corp., N.Y.C., 1960-85, pres., 1982-85. Trustee Riverside Rsch. Inst., N.Y.C. Capt. U.S. Army, 1942-46, 50-51. Decorated Bronze Star. Mem. Brook Club, Pilgrims of N.Y.C., Ivy Club, Nassau Club (Princeton, N.J.), Misquamicut Club, Watch Hill (R.I.) Yacht Club. Republican. Home: 35 Ocean View Hwy Watch Hill RI 02891

REES, CLIFFORD HARCOURT, JR. (TED REES), association executive, retired air force officer; b. Newport News, Va., Dec. 11, 1936; s. Clifford Harcourt Sr. and Mary Evelyn (Brooks) R.; m. Joan Elizabeth Mittong, July 26, 1958; children—Clifford Harcourt III, Steven M., Daniel B., William B. BS in Fgn. Svc., Georgetown U., 1958; MS in Polit. Sci., Auburn U., 1969; grad., Air War Coll., Montgomery, Ala., 1978. Commd. 2d lt. U.S. Air Force, 1958; advanced through grades to lt. gen., 1988; later comdr. 421st Tactical Fighter Squadron, Udorn Royal Thai AFB, 1974-75; chief, house liaison office U.S. Ho. Reps., Washington, 1978-80; asst. col. assignments Randolph AFB, 1980-82; vice-comdr. Air Force Manpower and Personnel Ctr., 1982; dep. dir. legis. liaison Office Sec. Air Force, 1982-84, dir. legis. liaison, 1984-86; comdr. USAF Air Defense Weapons Ctr., Tyndall AFB, Fla., 1986-88; vice comdr. in chief USAF in Europe, Ramstein AB, Federal Republic of Germany, 1988-92; ret. USAF in Europe, 1992; founder, pres. Rees Group Cons.; pres. Air Conditioning and Refrigeration Inst., Arlington, Va., 1993—; U.S. rep. to v.p. Internat. Coun. Mil. Sports, Brussels, 1982-94. Decorated D.S.M. with one oak leaf cluster, DFC with one oak leaf cluster, Legion of Merit with one oak leaf cluster, Meritorious Svc. medal with one oak leaf cluster, Air medal with 11 oak leaf clusters USAF, Das Grosse Verdienstkreuz Mit Stern, Pres. Fed. Republic Germany, 1993; named Commander Order of Meritorious Svc. Mil. Sports Coun., 1993. Mem. Delta Phi Epsilon (v.p. membership 1957-58, nat. pres. 1984-86). Methodist. Home: 2487 Oakton Hills Dr Oakton VA 22124 Office: Air Conditioning & Refrigeration Inst 4301 N Fairfax Dr Ste 425 Arlington VA 22203

REES, FRANK WILLIAM, JR., architect; b. Rochester, N.Y., June 5, 1943; s. Frank William and Elizabeth R. (Miller) R.; m. Joan Mary Keevers, Apr. 1, 1967; children: Michelle, Christopher. BS in Architecture, U. Okla., 1970; postgrad., Harvard U., Boston, 1979, 90; OPM, Harvard U., 1990. Registered architect, 36 states; cert. Nat. Coun. Archtl. Registration Bds. Sales mgr. Sta. KFOM, Oklahoma City, 1967-70; project architect Benham-Blair & Affiliates, Oklahoma City, 1970-75; pres., founder Rees Assocs., Inc., Oklahoma City, 1975—; pres., chmn. bd. Weatherscan Radio Network, Oklahoma City, 1973-78; chmn. bd. Weatherscan Internat., Oklahoma City, 1972-78; pres. Frontier Communications, Oklahoma City, 1980-84; chmn. architecture bd. U. Okla., Norman, 1988-91. Past pres. Lake Hefner Trails, Oklahoma City, Hosp. Hospitality House, Oklahoma City, Oklahoma City Beautiful; mem. Leadership Oklahoma City. Mem. AIA, Am. Assn. Hosp. Architects, Am. Healthcare Assn., Tex. Hosp. Assn., World Pres. Orgn., Nat. Assn. Sr. Living Industries. Home: 1104 Stone Gate Irving TX 75063 Office: 511 Carpenter Fwy # 222 Irving TX 75062

REES, JAMES CONWAY, IV, historic site administrator; b. Richmond, Va., May 5, 1952. BA, Coll. William & Mary, 1974; MPA, George Washington U., 1978. Reporter, photographer Newport News Daily-Press, 1974; coord. radio and television programming The Coll. William & Mary, 1974-78; mng. editor The William & Mary Mag., 1978-82; promotions dir. Va. Shakespeare Festival, 1980; dir. annual giving and pub. info. The Coll. William & Mary, 1978-80, dir. annual support and corp. rels., 1980-81, dir. capital support, 1981-82; asst. dir. devel. Nat. Trust Historic Preservation, 1982-83, assoc. dir. devel., 1983; dir. devel. and comms. Historic Mount Vernon, 1983-85, assoc. dir., 1985-94, resident dir. 1994—; exec. v.p. Mount Vernon Inn, Inc., 1994—; Mem. bd. dirs. Va. Shakespeare Festival, Washington Area Chpt. Wllliam and Mary Alumni Soc. Mem. Nat. Trust for Historic Preservation, Friends of the Nat. Symphony, WETA Pub. Television. Mem. Am. Film Inst., Va. Assn. Mus. (pres. 1991—). Methodist. Home: 710 A St NE Washington DC 20002 Office: Mount Vernon Ladies Assn Mount Vernon VA 22121

REES, JOHN ROBERT, physicist; b. Peru, Ind., Feb. 17, 1930; s. Alton Edwin and Mary Katherine (Morse) R.; m. Marian Janet Heimert, Jan. 28, 1956; children: Carol Ellen, John Alton. AB, Ind. U., 1951, MS, 1953, PhD, 1956. Rsch. fellow Harvard U., Cambridge, Mass., 1956-65; chief accelerator br. high energy physics program AEC, Washington, 1967-69; mem. staff Stanford Linear Accelerator Ctr., Palo Alto, Calif., 1965-75; dir. Positron-Electron Project, Palo Alto, 1975-80; prof. Stanford U., Palo Alto, 1980—; assoc. dir. Stanford Linear Accelerator Ctr., Palo Alto, 1980-93; project mgr., assoc. dir. Superconducting Super Collider, Dallas, 1991-93. Fellow Am. Phys. Soc. Office: Stanford Linear Accelerator Ctr PO Box 4349 Stanford CA 94305

REES, MORGAN ROWLANDS, engineering educator; b. Kingston, Pa., Jan. 17, 1940; s. William Arthur and Anna Fae (Mericle) R.; m. Janet

Marsello, May 15, 1965; 1 child, Bradley Alan. BS in Civil Engring., Worcester Poly. Inst., 1961, MS in Civil Engring., 1969; M Pub. Adminstrn., U. So. Calif., Washington, 1988, D Pub. Adminstrn., 1993. Registered profl. engr., Mass. Mgmt. trainee Bell Telephone of Pa., Scranton, 1961-62; appraisal engr. Am. Appraisal Co., N.Y.C., 1964-67; hydraulic rsch. engr. Worcester (Mass.) Poly. Inst., 1967-69; coastal engr. New Eng. Corps Engrs., Waltham, Mass., 1969-73, chief regulatory br., 1973-81; chief regulatory policy sect. Hqrs. Army C.E., Washington, 1981-82; asst. regulatory affairs U.S. Army Civil Works, Washington, 1982-86, dep. asst. sec., 1986-95; prin. Rees Engring. and Environ. Svcs., Alexandria, Va., 1995—; civil engring. dept. adv. com. Worcester Poly. Inst., 1988—. Jr. warden St. Luke's Ch., Worcester, 1974-79; v.p. Collingwood Citizen's Assn., Alexandria, Va., 1983-84. 1st lt. U.S. Army, 1962-64. Named to Athletic Hall of Fame Worcester Poly. Inst., 1984. Mem. ASCE, Soc. Am. Mil. Engrs. Avocations: jogging, reading, home remodeling. Office: Rees Engring & Envrion Svcs Civil Works 2625 Childs Ln Alexandria VA 22308

REES, NORMA S., university president, educator; b. N.Y.C., Dec. 27, 1929; d. Benjamin and Lottie (Schwartz) D.; m. Raymond R. Rees, Mar. 19, 1960; children—Evan Lloyd, Raymond Arthur. B.A., Queens Coll., 1952; M.A., Bklyn. Coll., 1954; Ph.D., NYU, 1959. Cert. speech-language pathology, audiology. Prof. communicative disorders Hunter Coll., N.Y.C., 1967-72; exec. officer, speech and hearing scis. grad. sch. CUNY, N.Y.C., 1972-74, assoc. dean for grad. studies, 1974-76, dean grad. studies, 1976-82; vice chancellor for acad. affairs U. Wis., Milw., 1982-85, from 1986, acting chancellor, 1985-86; vice chancellor for acad. policy and planning Mass. Bd. Regent for Higher Edn., Boston, 1987-90; pres. Calif. State U., Hayward, 1990—; bd. dirs. Coun. of Postsecondary Accreditation, Washington, 1985-94; chmn. Comm. Recognition of Postsecondary Accreditation, 1994—. Contbr. articles to profl. jours. Trustee Citizens Govtl. Rsch. Bur., Milw., 1985-87; active Task Force on Wis. World Trade Ctr., 1985-87; bd. dirs. Greater Boston YWCA, 1987-90; mem. Mayor's Cabinet Ednl. Excellence, Oakland, Calif.; mem. steering com. Econ. Devel. Adv. Bd. Alameda County, 1995—. Fellow Am. Speech-Lang-Hearing Assn. (honors); mem. Am. Coun. Edn. (com. internat. edn. 1991-93), Am. Assn. Colls. and Univs. (chair task force on quality assessment 1991-92, mem. steering com. of coun. of urban met. colls. & univs. 1992—), Nat. Assn. State Univs. and Land Grant Colls. (exec. com. divsn. urban affairs 1985-87, com. accreditation 1987-90). Office: Calif State Univ 25800 Carlos Bee Blvd Hayward CA 94542

REES, RAYMOND F., military officer; b. Pendleton, Oreg., Sept. 29, 1944; s. Raymond Emmett and Lorna Doone (Gemmell) R.; m. Karen Kristine Young, Nov. 1966 (div. Mar. 1974); children: Raymond Gordon, Christian Frederick; m. Mary Len Middleton, Dec. 30, 1977; 1 child, Carrie Evelyn. BS, U.S. Mil. Acad., 1966; JD, U. Oreg., 1976. Commd. 2d lt. U.S. Army, 1966; platoon leader, troop exec. officer, co. comdr. 3d Armored Cavalry Regiment, Bamberg, Fed. Republic Germany; resigned U.S. Army, 1973; with Oreg. Army Nat. Guard, 1973—; advanced through grades to maj. gen., 1990; asst. ops. officer Infantry Brigade; co. comdr. 2d Battalion, 162d Infantry, Corvallis, Oreg.; with 116th Armored Calvary Regiment, 1976-87; adjutant gen. Oreg. Army Nat. Guard, 1987-91; dir. Army N.G., 1991-92; vice chief N.G. Bur., Washington, 1992—. State rep. Hometown Heroes Project for Congl. Medal of Honor Soc.; bd. dirs. Oreg. Hist. Soc. Decorated Bronze Star. Mem. Adjutant Gen. Assn. U.S., Nat. Guard Assn. U.S., Assn. of U.S. Army, Oreg. Nat. Guard Assn., U.S. Armor Assn., Oreg. Bar Assn., Am. Legion, Rotary, Mil. Order World Wars, West Point Soc. Oreg., 101st Airborne Div. Assn., 116th Armored Cavalry Assn., 41st Infantry Div. Assn., Elks. Office: Chief N G Bur Attn NGB-ZB 2500 Army Pentagon Washington DC 20310-2500

REES, ROGER, actor, educator; b. Aberystwyth, Wales, May 5, 1944; s. William John and Doris Louise (Smith) R. Educated, Camberwell Sch. Art, Slade Sch. Fine Art. Instr. theatre Columbia U., N.Y.C., 1981-82; Hoffman chair prof. Fla. State U., Tallahassee, 1986; assoc. dir. Bristol Old Vic Theatre Co., 1986—. Made theatre debut in Hindle Wakes, Wimbledon, Eng., 1964; other theatre appearances include The Cherry Orchard, Pitlochry, Scotland, 1965, The Merchant of Venice, Aldwych Theatre, London, also The Island of the Mighty, 1971-72; Candida, Neptune Theatre, Halifax, N.S., 1973; Paradise, Theatre Upstairs, London, also Moving Clocks Go Slow, 1975, The Alchemist, London, 1977, Macbeth, Warehouse Theatre, London, also Factory Birds, 1977, The Way of the World, Aldwych Theatre, 1978, The Suicide, various theatres, London, 1980, The Adventures of Nicholas Nickleby, Aldwych Theatre, London and Plymouth Theatre, N.Y.C., 1981 (Tony award for Best Actor 1982), The Real Thing, Strand Theatre, London, 1983, Cries from the Mammoth House, Royal Court Theatre, London, 1983, Double-Double, Watford Palace and Fortune Theatres, London, 1986, Archangels Don't Play Pinball, Bristol Old Vic Theatre Co., Theatre Royal, London, 1986, Hapgood, Aldwych Theatre, 1988; appeared with Royal Shakespeare Co. in The Taming of the Shrew, 1967, As You Like It, 1967, Julius Caesar, 1968, The Merry Wives of Windsor, 1968, Pericles, 1969, Twelfth Night, 1969, 70, 76, Henry VIII, 1969, The Winter's Tale, 1969, 70, The Plebeians Rehearse the Uprising, 1970, Major Barbara, 1970, Much Ado About Nothing, 1971, Othello, 1971, Romeo and Juliet, 1976, Macbeth, 1976, The Comedy of Errors, 1976, Cymbeline, 1979, Hamlet, 1984, Love's Labours Lost, 1984, Indiscretions, 1995 (Tony nominee - Lead Actor in a Play) tour London Assurance, various U.S. cities, 1974-75, tour Is There Honey Still For Tea?, The Three Sisters, Twelfth Night, various U.K. cities, 1978; toured U.K. cities with Cambridge Theatre Co., 1973-74, in Twelfth Night, Aunt Sally or the Triumph of Death, She Stoops to Conquer, Fear and Misery in the Third Reich, Jack and the Beanstalk, 1975, in The Importance of Being Earnest, The Birthday Party; appeared in film Star 80, 1983; appeared in TV film A Christmas Carol, 1984, The Ebony Tower, Great Performances, PBS, 1987, Charles and Diana: Unhappily Ever After, 1992; recurring role as Robin Colcord on TV series Cheers, NBC. Office: Charles Burrows Charles Prodns 5555 Melrose Ave Los Angeles CA 90038-3149*

REESE, ALFERD GEORGE, retired army civilian logistics specialist; b. Granville, N.D., Apr. 5, 1934; s. Ferdinand Emil and Iola May (Boulds) R.; m. Donna Mae Berger, 1955 (div. 1972); children: Rick, Denise, Roxanna; m. Nelda Cecilia Pena, May 31, 1985; children: Nancy, Joyce, Alfred, Jeffrey, Jessica, James, Alicia. AS, Humphreys Coll., 1963; BS, U. State of N.Y., Albany, 1983; MPA, U. Colo., Colorado Springs, 1985; postgrad., Ga. State U., 1987-88; PhD, Columbia Pacific U., 1994. Inspector, mechanic Sharp Army Depot, Lathrop, Calif., 1958-66; equipment specialist various stations U.S. Army Aviation Systems Command, 1966-84; supervisory equipment specialist U.S. Army Aviation Systems Command, Atlanta, 1984-88; supervisory logistics specialist U.S. Army Aviation Systems Command, St. Louis, 1988-93. Mem. com. Boy Scouts Am., Fed. Republic Germany, 1979-81. With USAF, 1953-57. Mem. Army Aviation Assn. Assn. (USAEUR Dept. Army Civilian of Yr. 1980, 81), Ctr. for the Study of the Presidency, Acad. Polit. Sci., Am. Soc. for Pub. Adminstrn., Nat. Rifle Assn. Avocations: golf, skiing, photography, painting. Home: 1590 Fairmount Dr Florissant MO 63033-2645

REESE, ANN N., financial executive. Formerly tres. Mobil Europe; asst. treas. ITT Corp., 1987-89, v.p., 1989-92, sr. v.p., treas., 1992—. Office: ITT Corp 1330 Avenue Of The Americas New York NY 10019-5422

REESE, CHARLES EDGAR, columnist; b. Washington, Ga., Jan. 29, 1937; s. Edgar Ernest and Neoma (Moody) R.; m. Gretchen Elise Krughoff, May 16, 1965 (div. July 1984); children: Benjamin, Alice, Theodore. PhD (hon.), Webber Coll., 1989. Caption writer Planet Newspictures Ltd., London, 1956-57; reporter Pensacola (Fla.) News-Jour., 1957-67; account exec. Dodson, Craddock & Born, Pensacola, 1967-69, Fry, Hammond & Born, Pensacola, 1971-72; chief bur. media svcs. State of Fla. Dept. of Commerce, Tallahassee, 1969-71; asst. metro editor Orlando Sentinel, 1972-75, asst. to pub., 1975-78, columnist, mem. editorial bd., 1978—. Author: Great Gods of the Potomac, Common Sense for the 80s. Active Hist. Commn., Pensacola, 1968; bd. dirs. Holocaust Meml., Orlando, 1985-90. With USAR, 1959-65. Named Best Columnist, Fla. Press Club, 1984, Fla. Soc. Newspaper Editors. Mem. SCV. Democrat. Avocations: pistol shooting, hunting, sketching. Office: Orlando Sentinel 633 N Orange Ave Orlando FL 32801

REESE, ERROL LYNN, university administrator, dentist; b. Fairmont, W.Va., May 3, 1939; s. Edgar B. and Elizabeth (Carpenter) R.; m. Julia Hinebaugh, June 8, 1963; children: Daniel, Elizabeth. BS, Fairmont State Coll., 1960; DDS, W.Va. U., 1963; cert. of tng., U. Detroit, 1968, MS, 1968. Grad. asst. Sch. Dentistry U. Detroit, 1966-68; asst. prof. Sch. Dentistry U. Md., Balt., 1968-73, assoc. prof. Sch. Dentistry, 1978, prof. Sch. Dentistry, 1978—, from assoc. dean to dean Sch. Dentistry, 1973-90, pres., 1990—. Capt. U.S. Army, 1963-66. Mem. ADA, Am. Assn. Dental Schs. (pres. 1989-90), Am. Acad. History of Dentistry, Nat. Found. Dentistry for Handicapped, Acad. Gen. Dentistry Found. Office: U Md 520 W Lombard St Baltimore MD 21201-1627

REESE, FRANCIS EDWARD, retired chemical company executive, consultant; b. Monaca, Pa., Nov. 3, 1919; s. Francis Edward and Vivian Iris (Hancuff) R.; m. Katherine Anne McBrien, June 29, 1946; 1 son, Francis Edward III. B.S. in Chem. Engring., Purdue U., 1941. Registered profl. engr., Pa. With Monsanto Co., St. Louis, 1941; research engr. plastics div. Monsanto Co., 1941-48, chief devel. engring. plastics div., 1948-53, asst. engr. plastics div., 1953-56, dir. engring. plastics div., 1956-59, asst. gen. mgr. plastics div., 1959-61, asst. gen. mgr. hydrocarbons div., 1961-65, asst. gen. mgr., hydrocarbons and polymers div., 1965-66, gen. mgr. internat. div., 1966-68, corp. v.p., 1968-74, gen. mgr., hydrocarbons and polymers div., 1968-71, gen. mgr. polymers and petrochems. div., 1971-73, gen. mgr. internat. div., 1973-74, dir., 1973-84, group v.p., 1974-79, sr. v.p., 1979-84; pres. FTR Assocs., Inc.; mem. engring. found. adv. coun. U. Tex. Fellow AAAS, Am. Inst. Chem. Engrs.; mem. Am. Chem. Soc., Nat. Soc. Profl. Engrs., Soc. Chem. Industry, Tau Beta Pi, Phi Lambda Upsilon. Home: Rydal Park 271W 1515 The Fairway Rydal PA 19046 Office: 100 Old York Rd Ste 1202A Jenkintown PA 19046-3249

REESE, HARRY BROWNE, lawyer, educator; b. Feb. 11, 1926. s. Harry Benson and Dorothy (Browne) R.; student Ohio Wesleyan U., 1943-44, B.A. summa cum laude, Ohio State U., 1947; LL.B. magna cum laude, Harvard U., 1950; m. Nancy Lea Wonders, Sept. 6, 1947; children: Ellyn Browne, David Wonders, Susan Elisabeth, Gwendolyn Alma, John Benson. Bar: Ohio 1950, Ill. 1954. Law clk. to judge, U.S. Ct. Appeals (2d cir.) 1950-51; asst. prof. law, Ohio State U., Columbus, 1951-53; asst. prof. Northwestern U., Chgo., 1953-55, assoc. prof., 1955-57, prof., 1957-75, William Wirt Gurley prof. law, 1975-91; cons. Pres.'s Commn. Gov. Security, 1957-58. Trustee Law Sch. Admission Coun., 1961-78, pres., 1969-72; Ill. commr. Nat. Conf. Commrs. on Uniform State Laws, from 1973; one of six law profs. to appear in film series Great Law Teachers to demonstrate teaching techs., 1967. Served with USNR, 1943-45. Mem. Assn. Am. Law Schs. (exec. com. 1976-80), Siot and Cynwydd Soc. (pres. 1964), Phi Beta Kappa, Phi Delta Theta, Phi Delta Phi. Republican. Episcopalian. Died Sept. 5, 1991; buried Ridgewood Cemetery, Wellston, Ohio.

REESE, HARRY EDWIN, JR., electronics executive; b. Balt., Oct. 27, 1928; s. Harry Edwin and Margery Lee (Stroud) R.; m. Elizabeth Syra Pfeiffer, Oct. 15, 1955; children: Clifford Owen, Susan Syra, Peter Eyre. BSEE, Tufts U., 1950; MS in Stats., Villanova U., 1960. Engr. Philco Corp., Phila., 1950-54; project engr. Burroughs Corp., Paoli, Pa., 1956-59, dept. mgr., 1959-65; dept. mgr. GE Co., King of Prussia, Pa., 1965-69; group staff mgr. Burroughs Corp., Paoli, Pa., 1969-75; gen. mgr. Burroughs Corp., Plainfield, N.J., 1975-82; corp. staff dir. Burroughs Corp., Detroit, 1982-83; v.p. quality assurance Am. Electronic Labs., Inc., Lansdale, Pa., 1984-90, ret., 1990. Chmn. Charlestown Twp. Planning Commn., Pa., 1973-75. With U.S. Army, 1954-56. Fellow IEEE (life, pres. Reliability Soc. 1969-70, gen. chmn. Rams symposium 1968, chmn. bd. 1969, Centennial medal 1984); mem. Nat. Mgmt. Assn. (life, chmn. formation com. Am. Electronics Labs. chpt. 1985, Leadership award 1973, 86), Lake Hopatcong Yacht Club (treas.), Masons, Rotary (Paul Harris fellow, treas.). Republican. Episcopalian. Avocations: carpentry, architecture, boating, antiques, travel. Home: 17 Bass Rock Rd Hopatcong NJ 07843-1901

REESE, HAYNE WARING, psychologist; b. Comanche, Tex., Jan. 14, 1931; s. Tom F. and Marion (Waring) R.; m. Patsy Atwood, Aug. 24, 1957 (div. Apr. 1967); children: Anne, William, Margaret; m. Nancy Mann, Dec. 16, 1967; 1 child, Bradley. Student, So. Meth. U., 1949-50; B.A., U. Tex., 1953, M.A., 1955; Ph.D., U. Iowa, 1958. Asst. prof. U. Buffalo, 1958-62; assoc. prof. SUNY-Buffalo, 1962-66, prof., 1966-67; prof. U. Kans., Lawrence, 1967-70; Centennial prof. psychology W.Va. U., Morgantown, 1970—, dir. grad. tng. in life-span devel. psychology, 1973—; mem. initial rev. groups div. research grants NIH, Washington, 1974-78, 79-84. Author: Perception of Stimulus Relations, 1968; co-author: Life-Span Developmental Psychology, 1977, Child Development, 1979; editor: Advances in Child Development and Behavior, 22 vols., 1969-94; co-editor: Life-Span Developmental Psychology, 7 vols., 1973-94; assoc. editor: Jour. Exptl. Child Psychology, 1975-83, editor, 1983—. Served with U.S. Army, 1954. Fellow AAAS, Am. Psychol. Soc.; mem. AAUP, Soc. for Rsch. in Child Devel., Psychonomic Soc., Assn. for Behavior Analysis, Phi Beta Kappa. Avocation: Internat. Soc. for Study Behavioral Devel. Office: W Va U Dept Psychology PO Box 6040 Morgantown WV 26506-6040

REESE, JOHN ROBERT, lawyer; b. Salt Lake City, Nov. 3, 1939; s. Robert McCann and Glade (Stauffer) R.; m. Francesca Marroquin Gardner, Sept. 5, 1964 (div.); children—Jennifer Marie Gardner, Justine Francesca; m. Robin Ann Gunsul, June 18, 1988. AB cum laude, Harvard U., 1962; LLB, Stanford U., 1965. Bar: Calif. 1966, U.S. Dist. Ct. (no. dist.) Calif. 1966, U.S. Ct. Appeals (9th cir.) 1966, U.S. Dist. Ct. (cen. dist.) Calif. 1974, U.S. Supreme Ct. 1976, U.S. Dist. Ct. (ea. dist.) Calif. 1977, U.S. Ct. Appeals (6th cir.) 1982, U.S. Ct. Appeals (8th cir.) 1985, U.S. Ct. Appeals (10th cir.) 1992, U.S. Ct. Appeals (Fed. cir.) 1994. Assoc. McCutchen, Doyle, Brown & Enersen, San Francisco, 1965-74, ptnr., 1974—; adj. assoc. prof. law Hastings Coll. of Law, 1991; lectr. U. Calif., Berkeley, 1987, 92. Mem. editorial, adv. bds. Antitrust Bull., Jour. Reprints for Antitrust Law and Econs. Bd. dirs. Friends of San Francisco Pub. Libr., 1981-87; bd. vis. Stanford U., 1983-86. Capt. U.S. Army, 1966-68. Decorated Bronze Star. Mem. ABA, State Bar Calif., San Francisco Bar Assn., U.S. Supreme Ct. Hist. Soc., Ninth Jud. Cir. Hist. Soc., Calif. Acad. Appellate Lawyers, Order of the Coif. Avocations: aviculture, gardening. Home: 9 Morning Sun Drive Petaluma CA 94952 Office: McCutchen Doyle Brown & Enersen 3 Embarcadero Ctr San Francisco CA 94111-4003

REESE, LOWELL D., editor, publisher; b. Pikeville, Ky., Mar. 12, 1940; s. Palmer R. and Ollie (Rose) R.; m. Carol Rowe, Dec. 26, 1970; 1 stepson, Tracy Lee Huffman. B.A., Berea Coll., 1963. Mktg. rep. Mobil Oil Corp., East Orange, N.J., 1967-68; chief Ky. Bur. Child Devel., Frankfort, 1969-70; exec. dir. Our Common Heritage, Lexington, Ky., 1970-71; v.p. govtl. affair Ky. C. of C., Frankfort, 1972-79; exec. v.p. S.C. C. of C., Columbia, 1979-86; pres. Ariz. C. of C., Phoenix, 1987-89. Exec. dir. Pres. Ford election campaign, Ky., 1976. Served to 1st lt. U.S. Army, 1963-67, Vietnam. Decorated Purple Heart, Bronze Star, Air medal, others. Mem. Ariz. C. of C. (exec. assns.), Ariz. Econ. Forum, Cen. Ariz. Water Project Assn. Home: 418 Shelby St Frankfort KY 40601-2822 Office: 420 Capitol Ave Frankfort KY 40601

REESE, MONTE NELSON, agricultural association executive; b. Mooreland, Okla., Mar. 31, 1947; s. James Nelson and Ruby Edith (Bond) R.; m. Treisa Lou Bartow, May 25, 1968; children: Bartow Allan, Monica Lynnelle. BS in Agrl. Econs., Okla. State U., 1969. Staff asst. Wilson Cert. Foods, Oklahoma City, 1969-71; assoc. farm dir. WKY Radio and TV, Oklahoma City, 1971-73; radio-TV specialist Tex. A&M U., College Station, 1973; dir. agrl. devel. Oklahoma City C. of C., 1973-76; asst. dir. Am. Morgan Horse Assn., Westmoreland, N.Y., 1976-77; v.p. pub. affairs Farm Credit Banks of Wichita, Kans., 1977-87; exec. dir. Coffey County Econ. Devel., Burlington, Kans., 1987-88; farm dir. Mid-Am. Ag Network, Wichita, 1988-89; CEO Cattlemen's Beef Promotion and Rsch. Bd., Englewood, Colo., 1989—. Lt. comdr. USAR, 1969—. Home: 982 S Dearborn Way #2 Aurora CO 80012 Office: Cattlemen's Beef Promotion and Rsch Bd PO Box 3316 Englewood CO 80155

REESE, PAUL WESLEY, JR., retail executive; b. Atlanta, Oct. 2, 1949; s. Paul Wesley and Elizabeth Irene (Currington) R.; m. Dianne Hassen Drescher, Sept. 4, 1971; children: Eric Adam, Adrienne Elaine, Lauren Leigh, Meredith Erin. BA, U. Fla., 1971; MBA, Mich. State U., 1984.

Mgmt. cons. Behavioral Systems, Inc., Atlanta, 1974-75; indsl. engr. Michelin Tire Corp., Greenville, S.C., 1975-78; cons. engr. Kurt Salmon Assocs., Atlanta, 1978-81; dir. distbn., leased ops. J.L. Hudson Co., Detroit, 1981-86; v.p. distbn. Emporium-Capwell Co., San Francisco, 1986-87; sr. v.p. distbn. and transp. Ames Dept. Stores, Inc., Rocky Hill, Conn., 1987—. Mem. Inst. of Indsl. Engrs., Council of Logistic Mgmt., Beta Gamma Sigma. Republican. Congregationalist. Office: Ames Dept Stores Inc 2418 Main St Rocky Hill CT 06067-2598

REESE, THOMAS SARGENT, neurobiology educator and researcher; b. Cleve., May 20, 1935; s. Thomas Sargent Reese and Jane Andrews; children: Andrea Coonley, Devin Andrews. BA magna cum laude, Harvard U., 1957; MD, Columbia U., 1962. Rsch. asst. psycho-acoustic lab. Harvard U., Cambridge, Mass., 1957-58; intern Boston City Hosp., 1962-63; rsch. assoc. NINDB NIH, Bethesda, Md., 1963-65, rsch. med. officer Lab. Neuropathology and Neuroanat. Scis. NINCDS, 1966-70, head sect. on functional neuroanatomy, Lab. Neuropathology and Neuroanat. Scis., NINCCS, 1970-83, chief neurobiology lab., 1983—; rsch. fellow in anatomy Harvard Med. Sch., Boston, 1965-66; instr. neurobiology course Marine Biol. Lab. Woods Hole, 1972—, co-instr. in chief, 1980-84, trustee, exec. com. 1984; assoc. neurosci. rsch. program Rockefeller U., 1986—. Mem. editorial bd. Anat. Record, 1977—, Jour. Neurocytology, 1976-78, Neurosci., 1978—, Jour. Cell Biology, 1976-79, Cryoletters, 1979-83, Jour. Neurosci., 1980—, Jour. Cellular and Molecular Neurobiology, 1980—, Neuron, 1986-88, Jour. Electron Microscopy Technique, 1984—, Cell Regulation, 1989—; contbr. over 120 articles to profl. jours. With USPHS, 1964-66. Recipient Superior Svc.award USPHS, 1976, 1989, Mathilde Solowey award Found. for Advanced Edn. in the Scis., 1977, W. Alden Spencer award Columbia U., 1981, Joseph Mather Smith prize Coll. Physicians and Surgeons Columbia U., 1985, Grass Found. award Soc. for Neurosci., 1987, Fidia Neurosci. Found. Neurosci. award, 1988. Mem. NAS, Am. Soc. Cell Biology, Neurosci. Soc., Soc. Gen. Physiologists, Am. Assn. Anatomists (C. Judson Herrick award 1966). Avocations: tennis, bicycling, backpacking. Home: 3009 P St NW Washington DC 20007 Office: NIH Bldg 36 Rm 2A-29 Bethesda MD 20892

REESE, WILLIAM LEWIS, philosophy educator; b. Jefferson City, Mo., Feb. 15, 1921; s. William Lewis and Lillian Amelia (Fisher) R.; m. Louise Weeks, June 11, 1945; children: Claudia, Patricia, William Lewis III. A.B., Drury Coll., 1942; B.D., U. Chgo., 1945, Ph.D., 1947; postdoctoral, Yale U., 1955-56. Asst. prof. philosophy Drake U., 1947-49, asso. prof. philosophy, 1949-57, head dept., 1954-57; asso. prof. philosophy Grinnell Coll., 1957-60; vis. prof. philosophy Iowa State U., 1958; prof. philosophy, chmn. dept. U. Del., Newark, 1960-67; H. Rodney Sharp prof. philosophy U. Del., 1965-67; prof. philosophy SUNY-Albany, 1967—, chmn. dept., 1968-74, 84; Tully Cleon Knoles lectr. U. Pacific, 1962; Del. U.S. Nat. Commn. for UNESCO, 1963; gen. mem. 4th East-West Philosophers Conf., 1964. Author, contbr.: Studies in C.S. Peirce, 1952, (with Charles Hartshorne) Philosophers Speak of God, 1953, The Ascent from Below, 1959, 2d edit., 1987, (with Eugene Freeman) Process and Divinity, 1964, Dictionary of Philosophy and Religion: Eastern and Western Thought, 1980; gen. editor: Philosophy of Science, The Delaware Seminar, vols. 1, 2, 1963, vol. 3, 1967; editor: Philosophy and World Religions: The Reader's Adviser, vol. 4, 1988; contbg. editor: Philosophical Interrogations, 1964, co-editor: Metaphilosophy, 1967-75; editorial bd.: State U. N.Y. Press, 1968-78; contbr. articles to profl. jours. Recipient Ford Found. Study award Argentina, 1967; Fulbright lectr. Argentina, summer 1971; Inst. Humanistic Studies fellow, 1977—. Mem. AAUP, Am. Philos. Assn., Metaphysical Soc. Am. (sec.-treas. 1962-65). Mem. Christian Ch. (Disciples of Christ). Home: Font Grove Rd Slingerlands NY 12159 Office: SUNY Dept Philosophy Albany NY 12222 *To have before one always the realistic sense that if one has been successful in one way one has failed in others, and that one's failures surely outnumber one's successes.*

REETZ, GARY, medical facility administrator; b. 1947. Grad., Mich. State U., 1970. With Deloitte & Touche CPA's, Detroit, 1970-78, St. John Hosp., Detroit, 1978-83, Peat Marwick & Mitchell CPA's, Detroit, 1983-85, The Healthsource Group Inc., Flint, Mich., 1985-88; with Genesys Regional Med. Ctr., Flint, 1988—, now v.p. fin. Office: Genesys Reg Med Ctr 302 Kensington Ave Flint MI 48503*

REETZ, HAROLD FRANK, JR., industrial agronomist; b. Wat., Ill.; s. Harold Frank and Evelyn Evedeen (Russell) R.; m. Christine Lee Kaiser, Aug. 25, 1973; children: Carrie, Wesley, Anthony. BS in Agrl. Sci., U. Ill., 1970; MS in Agronomy, Purdue U., 1972, PhD in Agronomy, 1976. Rsch. specialist Purdue U., West Lafayette, Ind., 1974-82; regional dir. Potash & Phosphate Inst., Monticello, Ill, 1982—; cons. Control Data Corp., Mpls., 1978-82, Internat. Harvester Co., Chgo., 1979-82, Monsanto Agrl. Chem. Co., St. Louis, 1981-82. Author: Crop Simulation Model, CORNCROPS, 1976, several crops mgmt. computer programs; contbr. articles to profl. jours. Chmn. Ill. Com. for Agrl. Edn., 1987-89; mem. Ill. Groundwater Adv. Coun., 1988—; mem. Ill. Fertilizer Rsch. and Edn. Coun., Ill. Dept. Agr., 1989—; chmn. Ill. Cert. Crop Adviser State Bd., 1992—; mem. Monticello Unit 25 Bd. Edn., 1989—. Recipient Hon. mem. Hon. State Farmer Ill. Assn. FFA, Urbana, 1987; IFCA Spl. Recognition award Ill. Fertilizer and Chem. Assn., 1988. Fellow Crop Sci. Soc. Am., Am. Soc. Agronomy; mem. Soil Sci. Soc. Am. (div. chmn. editorial bd.), Ill. Assn. Vocat. Agrl. Tchrs. (hon. life 1989—), Nabor House Alumni Assn. Methodist. Avocations: photography, travel, computers.

REEVE, CHRISTOPHER, actor; b. N.Y.C., Sept. 25, 1952; s. Franklin D. and Barbara (Johnson) R.; children: Matthew, Alexandra; m. Dana Morosini, 1 son, Will. BA, Cornell U., 1974; student, Juilliard Sch., N.Y.C.; studies with, Austin Pendleton, Sandra Seacat. Performed in theaters including Boothbay (Maine) Playhouse, The Williamstown (Mass.) Theatre, San Diego Shakespeare Festival, The Loeb Drama Center; appeared on Broadway with Katherine Hepburn, A Matter of Gravity, 1976, Fifth of July, 1980, The Winter's Tale, 1989; films include Gray Lady Down, 1978, Superman, 1978, Somewhere in Time, 1980, Superman II, 1980, Deathtrap, 1982, Monsignor, 1982, Superman III, 1983, The Bostonians, 1984, The Aviator, 1984, Street Smart, 1987, Superman IV, 1987, Switching Channels, 1988, Noises Off, 1992, The Remains of the Day, 1993, Morning Glory, 1993, Speechless, 1994, The Rhinehart Theory, 1994, Village of the Damned, 1995; appeared in over 110 plays including My Life, 1977, The Greeks, Williamstown Theatre Festival prodn., 1981, The Aspern Papers, London prodn., 1984, Marriage of Figaro, 1985, Summer and Smoke, Los Angeles prodn., 1988, also The Royal Family, Holiday, Richard Corey, Mesmer, Cherry Orchard; appeared in John Brown's Body (Stephen Vincent Benet), Williamstown Theatre Festival, 1989; TV appearances include: (series) Love of Life, 1968-76; (movies) Anna Karenina, 1985, The Great Escape II: The Untold Story, 1988, The Rose and the Jackal, 1990, Bump in the Night, 1991, Death Dreams, 1991, Mortal Sins, 1992, Nightmare in the Daylight, 1992, The Sea Wolf, 1993, Above Suspicion, 1995, The Black Fox, 1995. Address: 29 E 22nd St # 12 N New York NY 10010*

REEVE, FRANKLIN D., literature educator, writer; b. Phila., Sept. 18, 1928; m. Ellen Swift. AB, Princeton U., 1950; PhD, Columbia U., 1958; AM (hon.), Wesleyan, 1964. Instr., asst. prof. Columbia U., N.Y.C., 1952-61; assoc. prof., prof. Wesleyan U., Middletown, Conn., 1962-66, adj. prof., 1970-87, prof., 1988—; bd. dirs., sec. Poets House, N.Y.C., Translation Ctr., N.Y.C.; vis. scholar, Moscow, 1961; vis. prof. Oxford (Eng.) U., 1964, Columbia U., 1988; vis. lectr. Yale U. New Haven, 1972-84; cons. in field. Author: Aleksandr Blok: Between Image and Idea, 1962, Robert Frost in Russia, 1964, The Russian Novel, 1966, The Red Machines, 1968, In the Silent Stones, 1968, Just Over the Border, 1969, The Brother, 1971, The Blue Cat, 1972, White Colors, 1974, The White Monk, 1989, (edited with Jay Meek) After the Storm, 1991, Concrete Music, 1992, A Few Rounds of Old Maid and Other Stories, 1995. Recipient lit. award Am. Acad.-Nat. Inst., 1970. Mem. New Eng. Poetry Soc. Office: Wesleyan U Wesleyan Sta Middletown CT 06459

REEVE, JOHN NEWTON, molecular biology and microbiology educator; b. Wakefield, W. Yorkshire, Eng., June 21, 1947; came to U.S., 1979; s. Arthur Newton and Lilian Elsworth (Tallant) R.; m. Patricia Margaret Watson, Sept. 21, 1967; children: Simon Arthur, Daniel John. BS with 1st class honors, U. Birmingham, Eng., 1968; PhD, U. B.C., Vancouver, Can.,

1971. Rsch. scientist U. Ariz., Tucson, 1971-73, Nat. Inst. Med. Rsch., Mill Hill, London, 1973-74; rsch. dir. Max-Planck Inst., Berlin, 1974-79; prof. Ohio State U., Columbus, 1979—, chair dept. microbiology, 1985—; cons. Battelle Rsch. Lab., Columbus, 1982-87, Govt. of Bulgaria, Sofia, 1987, Promega Corp., Madison, Wis., 1990, Procter and Gamble Co., Cin., 1990; mem. sci. adv. bd. BioTrol. Inc., Chaska, Minn., 1986-90; Disting. vis. prof. U. Adelaide, Australia, 1984, U. Wyo., Laramie, 1988, U. Calcutta, India, 1989, Frei U., Berlin, 1991, U. Karachi, Pakistan, 1995, U. Concepcion, Chile, 1995. Named Disting. Rsch. Scholar Ohio State U., 1989. Mem. Am. Soc. for Microbiology (lectr. Found. for Microbiology 1987-88, 94—). Office: Ohio State U Dept of Microbiology 484 W 12th Ave Columbus OH 43210-1292

REEVE, RONALD CROPPER, JR., manufacturing executive; b. Logan, Utah, Jan. 29, 1943; s. Ronald Cropper and Aldus (Moser) R.; m. Susan Leticia Gardner, July 4, 1966 (div. June 1975); children: Heather Renee, Michael Scott; m. Deborah Lynn Crooks, Dec. 31, 1976 (div. Apr. 1986); 1 child, Thomas Adam; m. Barbara Ruttan Avery, June 20, 1992; 2 stepchildren: Bryan Keith Avery, Allison Kathleen Avery. BS in Physics, Ohio State U., 1967; MBA in Mktg., Xavier U., 1972. Successively devel. engr., research engr., product planner Specialty Materials dept. Gen. Electric Co., Worthington, Ohio, 1969-73; successively product mgr., mktg. mgr., gen. mgr. Air Products & Chems., Inc., Lancaster, Ohio, 1974-79; founder, pres., chmn. Advanced Robotics Corp., Columbus, Ohio, 1979-84; founder, pres. R.C. Reeve, Inc., Westerville, Ohio, 1983—; founder, chief exec. officer Edison Welding Inst., Columbus, 1984-87; chief exec. officer Control Systems and Equipment Co., Inc., Columbus, 1987-90, CYBO Robots, Inc., 1988—, Check Guarantee Inc., Columbus, 1989-92, Indpls., 1991-92. Tech. adv. bd. Franklin U. Served with USAF, 1968-69. Named Small Businessman of Year, SBA, 1981. Mem. Am. Welding Soc., Am. Soc. Metals, Soc. Mfg. Engrs., Robot Inst. Am., Internat. Inst. Welding, Welding Inst., Robotics Internat., Hoover Yacht Club, Worthington Hill Country Club. Patentee diamond crystal structure. Home: 1460 Briarcliffe Dr Powell OH 43065-9060 Office: CYBO Robots Inc Indianapolis IN 46241

REEVE, THOMAS GILMOUR, physical education educator; b. Memphis, Sept. 23, 1946; s. Paul Goodwin and Dorothy (Bourke) R.; m. Sandra Weidner Reeve, Mar. 26, 1992; children: Bourke, Spencer. BS in Phys. Edn., Tex. Tech. U., 1969, MEd, 1972; PhD, Tex. A&M U., 1976. Asst. prof. Auburn (Ala.) U., 1977-82, assoc. prof., 1982-87, prof., 1987-91, asst. v.p. for acad. affairs, 1992-93, alumni prof., 1991—; vis. asst. prof. Tex. A&M U., College Station, 1976-77. Co-editor: Stimulus-Response Compatibility, 1990; sect. editor Rsch. Quar. for Exercise and Sport, 1990-92; associate editor Jour. Sport Behavior, 1987—, contbr. articles to profl. jours. Fellow AAHPERD, Rsch. Consortium, Am. Acad. Kinesiology and Phys. Edn.; mem. N.Am. Soc. Psychology of Sport and Phys. Activity (publ. dir. 1985-87, pres. 1991-92). Avocation: masters swimming. Office: Auburn U Dept Health and Human Performance Auburn AL 36849-5323

REEVES, ALEXIS SCOTT, journalist; b. Atlanta, Feb. 4, 1949; d. William Alexander and Marian (Willis) Scott; m. Marc Anthony Lewis, Sept. 14, 1968 (div. 1973); m. David Leslie Reeves, Mar. 16, 1974; children: Cinque Scott, David Leslie, Jr. Student Barnard Coll., 1966-68; student Spelman Coll., 1989-90, Regional Leadership Inst., 1992. Reporter, asst. city editor, cable TV editor, mng. video edit., v.p. community affairs Atlanta Jour. & Constn., Atlanta, 1974-93; dir. Diversity and Community Rels. for Cox Enterprises Inc., 1993—; vis. instr. summer program for minority journalists, Berkeley, Calif., 1980, 81, 84, 85, 87 Grady High Sch., Atlanta, 1982-83; journalist-in-residence Clark Coll., Atlanta, 1983. Researcher, writer: The History of Atlanta NAACP, 1983 (NAACP award, 1984). Recipient Disting. Urban Journalism award Nat. Urban Coalition, 1980. Michele Clark fellow Columbia U. Sch. Journalism, 1974. Named one of 100 Top Black Bus. & Profl. Women, 1986; recipient Acad. Achievement award YWCA, 1989. Mem. Nat. Assn. Media Women (Media Woman of Yr. award, 1983, Media Woman of Yr. nat. award 1983, pres. Atlanta chpt. 1985-87), Atlanta Assn. Black Journalists (Commentary Print award 1983), Nat. Assn. Black Journalists, Sigma Delta Chi (bd. dirs. 1980-84, treas. 1985-88). Moderator, First Congl. Ch., 1982-92. Office: Cox Enterprises Inc PO Box 105357 1400 Lake Hearne Dr NE Atlanta GA 30348

REEVES, BARBARA ANN, lawyer; b. Buffalo, Mar. 29, 1949; d. Prentice W. and Doris Reeves; m. Richard C. Neal; children: Timothy R. Neal, Stephen S. Neal (dec.), Robert S. Neal, Richard R. Neal. Student, Wellesley Coll., 1967-68; B.A. (NSF fellow, Lehman fellow), New Coll., Sarasota, Fla., 1970; J.D. cum laude, Harvard U., 1973. Bar: Calif. 1973, D.C. 1977. Law clk. U.S. Ct. Appeals, 9th Circuit, Portland, Oreg., 1973-74; assoc. firm Munger, Tolles and Rickershauser, L.A., 1977-78; trial atty. spl. trial sect. Dept. Justice (Antitrust div.), 1974-75; spl. asst. to asst. atty. gen. Antitrust div. Dept. Justice, Washington, 1976-77; chief antitrust div. L.A. field office, 1978-81; ptnr. Morrison & Foerster, L.A., 1981-94, Fried, Frank, Harris, Shriver & Jacobson, L.A., 1995—; mem. exec. com. state bar conf. of dels. L.A. Delegation, 1982-91; del. 9th Cir. Jud. Conf., 1984-88; mem. Fed. Ct. Magistrate Selection Com., 1989; bd. dirs. Pub. Counsel, 1988-92, Western Ctr. Law and Poverty, 1992—; lectr. in field. Editor: Federal Criminal Litigation, 1994; contbr. articles to profl. jours. Mem. ABA (litigation sect., antitrust sect.), Am. Arbitration Assn. (arbitrator, mediator, mem. adv. panel large complex case program), L.A. County Bar Assn. (antitrust sect. officer 1980-81, litigation sect. officer 1988-93 trustee 1990-92, chair alternative dispute resolution sec. 1992—, L.A. County Ct. ADR com.). Home: 1410 Hillcrest Ave Pasadena CA 91106-4503 Office: Fried Frank Harris Shriver & Jacobson 725 S Figueroa St # 3890 Los Angeles CA 90017

REEVES, BARRY LUCAS, aerophysics research engineer; b. St. Louis, Jan. 11, 1935; s. Raymond O. and Frances M. (Lucas) R.; m. Marilyn Alva Riester, May 8, 1954; children: Katherine, Michael, Janet. BS, Washington U., St. Louis, 1956, MS, 1958, PhD, 1960. Rsch. assoc. McDonnell Aircraft Corp., St. Louis, 1959-60; postdoctoral rsch. fellow Calif. Inst. Tech., Pasadena, 1960-64; staff scientist Avco Corp., Wilmington, Mass., 1964-68, sr. staff scientist, 1968-74, sr. cons. scientist, 1974-86; prin. scientist Textron Corp., Wilmington, Mass., 1986—; cons. Space Gen. Corp., L.A., 1962-63, Nat. Engring. & Sci. Co., Pasadena, 1963-64, Aerojet Corp., Azusa Calif., 1964; contbr. engring. symposia; reviewer Jour. Fluid Mechanics, Physics of Fluids, Jour. Applied Mech., Internat. Jour. Heat and Mass Transfer, Jour. Spacecraft & Rockets, AIAA Jour. Contbr. over 30 articles to profl. jours. Mem. Snow Mountain Farms Assn., Vt., 1982—. Fellowship Convair Aircraft Corp., 1958, NSF, 1959, 60; postdoctoral rsch. fellow Air Force Office Sci. Rsch., 1960, 61; rsch. grantee Guggenheim Aero. Lab., Calif. Inst. Tech., Pasadena, 1962-63. Mem. Am. Inst. Physics, Smithsonian Assocs. (assoc.), Sigma Xi, Tau Beta Pi, Pi Tau Sigma (former v.p., treas.). Home: 10 Hillcrest Pky Winchester MA 01890-1427 Office: Textron Corp 201 Lowell St Wilmington MA 01887-4113

REEVES, BILLY DEAN, obstetrics/gynecology educator emeritus; b. Franklin Park, Ill., Jan. 17, 1927; s. Barney William and Martha Dorcus (Benbrook) R.; m. Phyllis Joan Faber, Aug. 25, 1951; children: Philip, Pamela, Tina, Brian, Timothy. BA, Elmhurst (Ill.) Coll., 1953; BS, U. Ill., Chgo., 1958, MD, 1960; post grad., UCLA, N.Mex. State U., 1953-54, 75-76. Diplomate Am. Bd. Ob-Gyn. Intern Evanston (Ill.) Hosp., 1960-61, resident ob-gyn., 1961-64; NIH fellow in reproductive endocrinology Karolinska Hosp. and Inst., Stockholm, 1968-69; pvt. practice Evanston, 1964-71, Las Cruces, N.Mex., 1972-77; from instr. to asst. prof. Dept. Obgyn. Northwestern U. Med. Sch., 1964-71; assoc. prof. Dept. Ob-gyn. Rush Med. Coll., Chgo., 1971-72; clin. assoc. in ob-gyn. U. N.Mex. Med. Sch., Albuquerque, 1972-77; clin. assoc. U. Ariz. Sch. Medicine, Tucson, 1975-78; from clin. prof. to prof. emeritus Tex. Tech. Med. Sch., El Paso, 1976-91. Contbr. 70 articles and chpts. to med., profl. jours., 1958-93. Adv. bd. Associated Home Health Svcs., Inc., Las Cruces; adv. com. N.Mex. State U. Nursing Sch.; community adv. com. Meml. Gen. Hosp., Las Cruces; tech. advisor on health edn. N.Mex. Health Systems Agy.; mem. N.Mex. State U. Task Force 88; bd. dirs. Meml. Med. Ctr, Los Cruces, 1989-91, Parenthood Edn. Assn. of El Paso, Inc., Planned Parenthood of South Ctrl. N.Mex. (chmn. med. adv. com.). With USNR, 1945-46, 82-88, U.S. Army, 1946-47. Recipient Elmhurst Coll. Alumni Merit award, 1990, William W. Fry award for profl. excellence Tex. Tech. U. Sch. Medicine, 1979. Mem. AMA, ACS, AAAS, ACOG, Am. Coll. Physician Execs., Am. Assn. Advancement Humanities, Am. Fertility Soc., Assn. Profs. Ob-Gyn., North Am. Ob-Gyn.

Soc., Ctrl. Assn. Ob-Gyn., Chgo. Gyn. Soc., Com. for Philosophy in Medicine, Dona Ana County Med. Soc. (assoc.), El Paso County Med. Soc., El Paso Surg. Soc., Endocrinve Soc., Inst. Medicine in Chgo., Hasting Ctr., N.Mex. Med. Soc. (assoc.), N.Mex. Ob-Gyn. Soc., Soc. for Health and Human Values, Tex. Med. Assn., Tex. Assn. Ob-Gyn., U.S.-Mexico Border Health Assn. Home: 1620 Altura Ave Las Cruces NM 88001-1532

REEVES, CHARLES HOWELL, classics educator; b. Schenectady, Nov. 23, 1915; s. Howell H. and Justina (Smith) R.; m. Lucille Jane Pritchard, Dec. 22, 1945; children—Jane L. Reeves McGee, Frances E. Reeves Herring, Helen Ann Reeves Hanks, Ruth M. Reeves Connell, Justina P., Charles Howell. A.B., Union Coll., Schenectady, 1937; Ph.D. in Classics, U. Cin., 1947. Instr. classics Ind. U., 1946-49; asst. prof. classics Johns Hopkins, 1949-52; asso. prof., then prof. classics U. Okla., 1952-66; prof. classics Case Western Res. U., 1966-83, prof. emeritus, 1986—, chmn. dept., 1966-77. Author articles on Greek tragedy. Served to It. USNR, 1942-45. Mem. Am. Philol. Assn., Am. Inst. Archaeology, Classical Assn. Middle West and South, Soc. Ancient Greek Philosophy, Virgilian Soc., N. Am. Patristics Soc., Phi Beta Kappa. Home: 1791 Cadwell Ave Cleveland OH 44118-1606 Office: Case Western Res U Dept Classics Cleveland OH 44106

REEVES, DANIEL EDWARD, professional football coach; b. Rome, Ga., Jan. 19, 1944; m. Pam Reeves; children: Dana, Laura, Lee. Grad., U. S.C. Running back Dallas Cowboys, NFL, 1965-72, player-coach, 1970-71, asst. coach, 1972, 74-80; head coach Denver Broncos, NFL, 1981-92, also v.p.; head coach N.Y. Giants, 1993—. Player NFL Championship Game, 1966, 67, 70, 71; recipient NFL Coach of the Year award, 1993; named to S.C. Hall Fame. Office: care New York Giants Giants Stadium East Rutherford NJ 07073 also: Denver Broncos 13665 E Davies Pl Englewood CO 80112-4004*

REEVES, DANIEL MCDONOUGH, video artist; b. Washington, Aug. 1, 1948; s. Suzanne Sticha Reeves; m. Delra Schweitzer, 1979 (div. 1986); m. Linda Garwood, Apr. 20, 1987; 1 child, Adele Grace. AS, Ithaca Coll., BA, 1979. Exec. prodr. Shakti Prodns., N.Y.C., 1980—. Artist Eingang/The Way In, 1990-94; exec. prodr. Obsessive Becoming, 1995. With USMC, 1966-68, Vietnam. Rockefeller fellow, 1995; recipient Blue ribbon Am. Film Inst., 1983. Buddhist. Avocations: computer graphics programs, poetry, writing, music, hiking. Home and Office: 799 Greenwich St # 6S New York NY 10014

REEVES, DONNA ANDREWS, golfer; b. Boston, Apr. 12, 1967; d. James Barclay and Helen Louise (Munsey) Andrews; m. John A. Reeves, Nov. 13, 1993. BBA, U. N.C., 1989. Qualified golfer LPGA Tour, 1990; winner Ping-Cellular One Golf Tournament, Portland, Oreg., 1993, Ping-Welch's Golf Tournament, Tucson, Ariz., 1994, Dinah Shore Major Golf Tournament, Palm Springs, Calif., 1994. Office: LPGA 2570 Volusia Ave Daytona Beach FL 32114-1119

REEVES, FRANK BLAIR, architect, educator; b. Beaumont, Tex., June 5, 1922; s. William Garland and Hazel Ann (Blackburn) R.; m. Mary Nell Gibson, Aug. 3, 1948; 1 son, William Gibson. B.Arch., U. Tex., 1948; postgrad., Archtl. Assn., London, 1945; M.Arch., U. Fla., 1953. Assoc. architect Stone and Pitts (Architects), Beaumont, Tex., 1946-49; mem. faculty dept. architecture U. Fla., 1949-87, now prof. emeritus, dir. grad. program in archtl. preservation, 1970-87; supervising architect Hist. Am. Bldgs. Survey, 1958-71; cons. archtl. preservation, 1960—; co-founder Preservation Inst., Nantucket; mem. adv. bd. Nat. Ctr. Preservation Tech. and Tng., 1993—. Contbr. articles to Jour. AIA. Mem. Fla. Bicentennial Commn., 1972-76. Served with U.S. Army, 1943-46. Fellow AIA (Fla. Assn. spl. citation for preservation 1976, AIA Found. Octagon com. 1991—); mem. Nat. Trust Hist. Preservation (trustee emeritus, Louise DuPont Crowninshield award 1987), Fla. Trust Hist. Preservation (trustee emeritus), Delta Tau Delta. Democrat. Methodist.

REEVES, GARLAND PHILLIP, newspaper editor; b. Birmingham, Ala., Mar. 16, 1944; s. Garland Dowdle and Rose Matilsa (Metzler) R.; m. Sylvia Lynnette Edge, Nov. 28, 1970; children: Roxanna August Lynlee, Garland Everett. BA, U. Ala., Birmingham, 1975. From gen. assignment reporter to travel editor The Birmingham News, 1966—. Named for Excellence in Journalism, Sigma Delta Chi, Ala., 1972, 73, 76; recipient AP Newswriting award, Ala., 1976. Roman Catholic. Home: 5240 Beacon Cir Birmingham AL 35210-2856 Office: The Birmingham News 2200 4th Ave N Birmingham AL 35203-3840

REEVES, GEORGE MCMILLAN, JR., comparative literature educator, educational administrator; b. Spartanburg, S.C., Oct. 18, 1921; s. George McMillan and Bina Fay (Garvey) R.; m. Francine Helene Wickman, Jan. 27, 1950 (div. 1962); m. 2d Mary Carolyn Honeycutt, Apr. 14, 1964; children: George McMillan III, Marianne Elizabeth, Miriam Katherine, Alison Adams. B.S., Wofford Coll., 1942; M.A., U. Ala., 1948; Doctorat D'Universite, Sorbonne U. Paris, 1953; cert. in meteorology, NYU, 1943; DLitt (hon.), Wofford Coll., 1992. Asst. prof. English Presbyn. Coll., Clinton, S.C., 1948-50; from instr. to prof. English and comparative lit. U. S.C., Columbia, 1953-68, chmn comparative lit. program, 1966-72, assoc. dean Grad. Sch., 1968-72, head dept. fgn. langs., 1972-74, dean Grad. Sch., 1974-94, interim provost, 1990-92, asst. to pres., 1992-93, dep. provost, 1993-94, dean emeritus, cons. to office of provost, 1994—; cons. lit. The Explicator, Columbia, 1957-65; mem. vis. teams So. Assn. Colls. and Schs., Atlanta, 1970—, SREB Small Grants program, Atlanta, 1980—; mem. exec. bd. Conf. So. Grad. Schs., 1983-86; mem. awards com. Drug Sci. Found., 1985-88; chmn. bd. Greenville, S.C. Higher Edn. Ctr., 1990-92. Author: Thomas Wolfe et L'Europe, 1955; editor: Gustave Flaubert: Poesies de Jeunesse Inedites, 1968; editor and translator: The Time of William Faulkner, 1971 (MLA Scholars Libarary award 1971). Mem. Columbia Mus. Art and Sci., 1957—. Served to capt. USAAF, 1946-42, ETO. Fulbright scholar Sorbonne, Paris, 1951-52. Mem. MLA, S. Atlantic MLA (chmn. comparative lit. sect. 1970-71), AAUP, Phi Beta Kappa. Democrat. Lutheran. Club: Quail Hollow Swim and Racquet (pres.) (1979-80). Home: 1436 Mohawk Dr West Columbia SC 29169-6201 Office: U SC Office of Provost Columbia SC 29208-0001

REEVES, JOHN EDWIN, JR., manufacturing company executive; b. Woodruff, S.C., Aug. 19, 1939; s. John Edwin and Jeneil Carolyn (Beason) R.; m. Katherine Richards Feighner, Nov. 27, 1965; children: John Edwin III, Katherine Mercer. B.B.A., NYU, 1962. Asst. collection mgr. controller's div. Reeves Bros., Inc., N.Y.C., 1964-65, trainee, 1965-67, adminstrv. asst. textile mfg., 1967, area group mgr., 1967-69, asst. to div. pres. spinning and weaving div., 1969-70, corp. v.p., ins. liaison officer, 1970-71, pres. Comfy Home Furnishings div., 1971-72, pres. Finished Goods div., 1972-73, pres., chief administrv. officer, mem. exec. com., 1975—, chief exec. officer, 1985—, also dir. Bd. dirs., mem. exec. com. Scouting for Handicapped, Greater N.Y. council Boy Scouts Am.; trustee United Methodist Ch. Summit, N.J., Wofford Coll., Spartanburg, S.C. Served with U.S. Army, 1962-64. Mem. Am. Textile Mfg. Inst. (bd. dirs., budget fin. and membership com. 1980-83), S.C. Textile Mfg. Assn. (bd. dirs. 1983—). Republican. Clubs: Beacon Hill Country (Summit); Hemisphere (N.Y.C.). Avocations: tennis; hunting; boating. Office: Reeves Bros Inc 1271 Ave Of The Americas New York NY 10020-1300

REEVES, KEANU, actor; b. Beirut, Sept. 2, 1964. Stage appearances: Wolf Boy (debut), For Adults Only, Romeo and Juliet; films: Flying, 1986, Youngblood, 1986, River's Edge, 1987, Permanent Record, 1988, The Night Before, 1988, The Prince of Pennsylvania, 1988, Dangerous Liaisons, 1988, BIll and Ted's Excellent Adventure, 1989, Parenthood, 1989, I Love You to Death, 1990, Tune in Tomorrow, 1990, Bill and Ted's Bogus Journey, 1991, Point Break, 1991, My Own Private Idaho, 1991, Bram Stoker's Dracula, 1992, Much Ado About Nothing, 1993, Little Buddha, 1994, Even Cowgirls Get the Blues, 1994, Speed, 1994, Johnny Mnemonic, 1995, A Walk in the Clouds, 1995; TV films: Letting Go, 1985, Act of Vengeance, 1986, Young Again, 1986, Babes in Toyland, 1986, Under the Influence, 1986, Brotherhood of Justice, 1986; TV special: Save the Planet, 1990. *

REEVES, MICHAEL STANLEY, public utility executive; b. Memphis, Oct. 2, 1935; m. Patricia Ann Board, June 27, 1959; children: Michael,

Michelle. Student Iowa State U., 1954-56; B.A., Roosevelt U., 1964; M.B.A., Northwestern U., 1972. With People Gas Light and Coke Co., Chgo., 1956—, supr., 1967-69, asst. supt., 1969-72, supt., 1972-75, gen. supt., 1975-77, v.p. mktg. and customer relations, 1977-87, exec. v.p., 1987—. Bd. dirs. chmn. Better Bus. Bur., Chgo., No. Ill.; mem. Local Initiatives Support Corp. Chgo. Adv. Com.; trustee Shedd Aquarium, Abraham Lincoln Centre; bd. dirs. Peoples Energy Corp., 1991, Children's Meml. Hosp. Served with U.S. Army. Mem. Chgo. Assn. Commerce and Industry, Am. Gas Assn., Am. Assn. Blacks in Energy, Am. Heart Assn. (Met. Chgo. bd. govs.), Chgo. Econ. Club. Club: University (Chgo., mem. bd. dirs.). Office: Peoples Energy Corp 122 S Michigan Ave 2nd fl Chicago IL 60603

REEVES, RALPH B., III, publisher, editor; b. Raleigh, N.C., Apr. 2, 1947; s. Ralph Bernard Reeves Jr. and Frances Rhoda (Campbell) M.; m. Caroline Holton Green, Apr. 24, 1971 (div. 1986); children: Ralph B. IV, Daniel MacQuarrie. AB in History, U. N.C., 1970. Field coord. FMI Mgmt. Group, Raleigh, N.C., 1972-76; gen. mgr., v.p. The Leader Newspaper, Rsch. Triangle Pk., N.C., 1976-78; pres., pub., founder Spectator Pubs. Inc., Raleigh, N.C., 1978—, Triad Bus., Greensboro, N.C., 1986-88, Triangle Bus., Raleigh, 1985-91, Spectator Pub., N.C. Architect, 1981-84. Editor: Mr. Spectator, 1978—. 1st v.p. Mordecai Square Hist. Soc., Raleigh, 1980-83; pres. Hilltop Home, 1982-84; chmn. Downtown Adv. Com., 1983-85; mem. Bus. Adv. Com. for N.C. Sec. of State, Raleigh, 1992—; bd. dirs. N.C. State U. Friends of Libr., Nike Carolina Classic Golf Tournament. Gov's. Bus. award in the Arts and Humanities, 1986, Benjamin Fine award, 1991, AABP award Triangle Bus., 1st place award Feature Writing, 1991. Mem. Fifty Group, U. N.C. Dean's Club, English Speaking Union (past pres. RTP br. 1988—), Carolina Co. Club, Sphinx Club. Democrat. Episcopalian. Avocations: golf, history, travel. Home: 1707 McDonald Lane Raleigh NC 27608 Office: Spectator Pubs Inc 1318 Dale St S 200 Raleigh NC 27605

REEVES, RICHARD, writer, historian; b. N.Y.C., Nov. 28, 1936; s. Furman W. and Dorothy (Forshay) R.; m. Carol A. Wiegand, June 1, 1959 (div. 1971); m. Catherine E. O'Neill, July 28, 1979; children: Cynthia Ann, Jeffrey Richard. ME, Stevens Inst. Tech., 1960. Engr. Ingersoll-Rand Co., Phillipsburg, N.J., 1960-61; editor Phillipsburg Free Press, 1961-63; reporter Newark News, 1963-65, N.Y. Herald Tribune, 1965-66; chief polit. corr. N.Y. Times, 1966-71; editor N.Y. Times Mag., 1971-77; lectr. Hunter Coll. 1969-70, Columbia U., 1971-72; nat. editor Esquire, 1977-79; syndicated columnist, 1979—; chief polit. corr. PBS-TV, 1984—; cons. Ford Found., 1972—; host "Sunday" NBC-TV, 1973-75, "American Journey" PBS-TV, 1983. Author: A Ford, Not a Lincoln, 1975, Old Faces of 1976, 1976, Convention, 1977, Jet Lag: The Running Commentary of a Bi-coastal Reporter, 1981, American Journey: Travelling with Tocqueuille in Search of Democracy in America, 1982, The Reagan Detour: Conservative Revolution, 1985, A Passage to Peshawar: Pakistan Between the Hindu Kush and the Arabian Sea, 1985, President Kennedy, 1993, President Kennedy: Profile of Power, 1994; columnist; article writer. Recipient Emmy award, 1980, Christopher Book award, 1983. Office: Lynn Nesbit, Agent ICM 40 W 57th St New York NY 10019*

REEVES, RICHARD ALLEN, government aerospace program executive, lawyer; b. Chgo., July 10, 1944; s. Harry Mathew and Hazel Louise (Parker) R.; m. Patricia Dean McKenney, Dec. 30, 1967 (div. 1977); children: Garth Kirkman, Blakely Catherine, Janice Emily; m. Elizabeth Marie Litkowski, Nov. 22, 1980. BBA, Ga. State U., 1970; JD, U. Tenn., 1973. Bar: Tenn. 1974. Atty. NASA Marshall Space Flight Ctr., Huntsville, Ala., 1974-77, NASA Hdqrs., Washington, 1977-80; dep. chief counsel NASA Goddard Space Flight Ctr., Greenbelt, Md., 1980-82, dep. dir. mgmt., 1982-85; assoc. dir. NASA Ames Rsch. Ctr., Mountain View, Calif., 1985-88; dir. planning NASA Hdqrs., 1988-90; asst. dir. NASA Hdqrs. Space Exploration, Washington, 1990-91; dir. for instns. NASA Hdqrs., Washington, 1991—. Capt. U.S. Army, 1967-71, Vietnam. Mem. AIAA, Tenn. Bar Assn., Nat. Space Club, Women in Aerospace. Republican. Baptist. Avocations: genealogical research, photography, old house restoration. Home: 7811 Custer Rd Bethesda MD 20814

REEVES, ROBERT GRIER LEFEVRE, geology educator, scientist; b. York, Pa., May 30, 1920; s. Edward LeGrande and Helen (Baker) R.; m. Elizabeth Bodette Simmons, June 11, 1942; children: Dale Ann, Edward Boyd. Student, Yuba Coll., 1938-40; B.S., U. Nev., 1949; M.S., Stanford U., 1950, Ph.D., 1965. Registered profl. engr., Tex. Geophysicist, geologist U.S. Geol. Survey, 1949-69; with assignments as project chief iron ore deposits of Nev., tech. adviser Fgn. Aid Program; vis. prof. econ. geology U. Rio Grande do Sul, Brazil; staff geologist for research contracts and grants and profl. staffing Washington; prof. geology Colo. Sch. Mines, Golden, 1969-73; staff scientist Earth Resources Observation Systems Data Center, U.S. Geol. Survey, Sioux Falls, S.D., 1973-78; prof. geology U. Tex.-Permian Basin, Odessa, 1978-85, chmn. earth scis., 1978-82; dean Coll. Sci. and Engring. U. Tex. Permian Basin, 1979-84; cons. geologist, engr. Orion, Ltd., Midland, Tex., 1984-87, cons. engr., geologist, 1987—; leader People to People Econ. Geology Trip to Brazil and Peru, 1985; co-leader Am. Geol. Inst. Internat. Field Trip to Brazil, 1966; vis. geol. scientist Boston Coll., Boston U., 1967; sr. Fulbright lectr. U. Adelaide, Australia, 1969. Contbr. articles profl. jours. Served to maj. Signal Corps AUS, 1941-46, ETO. Recipient Outstanding Service award U.S. Geol. Survey, 1965. Fellow Geol. Soc. Am., Soc. Econ. Geologists; mem. Am. Inst. Mining, Metall. and Petroleum Engrs. (sec. Washington 1964), Am. Soc. Photogrammetry (editor-in-chief Manual of Remote Sensing), Soc. Ind. Profl. Earth Scientists. Home and Office: 4025 Lakeside Dr Odessa TX 79762-7203

REEVES, ROSSER SCOTT, III, retired investment company executive; b. N.Y.C., Aug. 20, 1936; s. Rosser and Elizabeth (Street) R.; m. Colin McRae Squibb, Dec. 14, 1963; 1 dau., Elizabeth Robinson. Acad. degree with honors, Westminster Sch., 1954; postgrad., Yale, 1954-55; BS with honors in architecture, U. Va., 1961. Assoc. real estate firm Douglas L. Elliman & Co., N.Y.C., 1961-62; investment banker Lazard Freres & Co., N.Y.C., 1962-67; founder, mng. partner R.S. Reeves & Co., N.Y.C., 1967-68; sr. mng. partner Bacon, Stevenson & Reeves, N.Y.C., 1968-70; chmn. bd. Quantum Corp., N.Y.C., 1970-75; pres. Rosser Reeves Holdings, Ltd., N.Y.C., 1975—; pres., chief exec. officer dir. Rosser Reeves, Inc., N.Y.C., 1976—; pres. Charlie O Co., 1980-82; pres., chief exec. officer Tiderock Corp., Little Rock, Ark., 1990—; founder, CEO The Recovery Found., 1992—; mem. N.Y. Stock Exch., 1967-69; mng. ptnr. Wall St. Leasing Assn., 1968-70; chmn. bd. Internat. Subsea Devel. Corp., N.Y.C., 1969-75, Mil. Armament Corp., N.Y.C., 1969-75. Trustee Youth Consultation Service, N.Y.C., 1968-72; bd. dirs. Ark. Symphony Orch., 1982-85. Mem. Scarab. Clubs: Union League (N.Y.C.), Racquet and Tennis (N.Y.C.), N.Y. Stock Exchange Lunch (N.Y.C.); Little Rock (Ark.). Home: 1412 Pickering Dr Little Rock AR 72211-1618

REEVES, SAM T., agricultural products company executive. With T. J. White Co., Memphis, Tenn., 1948-71; pres. Dunavant Enterprises Inc., Memphis, Tenn., 1971—. Office: Dunavant Enterprises Inc 3797 New Getwell Rd Memphis TN 38118

REFF, THEODORE, art historian; b. N.Y.C., Aug. 18, 1930. BA, Columbia Coll., 1952; MA, Harvard U., 1953, PhD, 1958. prof. art history and modern art Columbia U., 1957; vis. prof. U. Mich., Princeton U., NYU; Slade prof. Johns Hopkins U., Cambridge U., others. Author Notebooks Edgar Degas, 1976, Degas: the Artist's Mind, 1976, Manet: Olympia, 1976, Manet and Modern Paris, 1983; arranged collections at M. Knoedler & Co., N.Y.C., 1963, Met. Mus. Art, N.Y.C., 1977, Mus. Modern Art, N.Y.C., 1977, Nat. Gallery, Washington, 1983; editor catalogue M. Knoedler & Co. Unpublished Correspondence of Toulouse-Lautrec, 1969, Modern Art in Paris, 1850-1900, 1981. Mem. Col. Art Assn. Am. (dir. 1977-81), Internat. Found. Art Res. (dir. 1980—), Swann Found. Caricature (dir. 1982-89), Psychoanalytic Perspectives Art (dir. 1984—), Ordre des Palmes Academiques (chevalier 1987). Office: Columbia Univ Dept Art Hist 420 Lewisohn Hall Broadway 116th St New York NY 10027

REFIOR, EVERETT LEE, labor economist, educator; b. Donnellson, Iowa, Jan. 23, 1919; s. Fred C. and Daisy E. (Gardner) R.; m. Marie Emma Culp, Sept. 12, 1943; children: Gene A., Wendell F., Paul D., Donna M.; m. Betty Pottenger Phelps, Nov. 27, 1993. BA, Iowa Wesleyan Coll., 1942; postgrad., U. Glasgow, 1945; MA, U. Chgo., 1955; PhD, U. Iowa, 1962. Instr. econs.

and bus. Iowa Wesleyan Coll., 1947-50; teaching asst. U. Iowa, 1950-51; research asst. Bur. of Labor and Mgmt., 1951-52, instr. mgmt. and social sci., 1954-55; assoc. prof. econs. Simpson Coll., 1952-54; asst. prof. econs. U. Wis. at Whitewater, 1955-62, assoc. prof., 1962-64, prof., 1964-83, prof. emeritus, 1983—, chmn., 1966-75. Lyricist (hymns) Eternal Love, 1980, Divine Order, 1980, If We But Dare, 1984, Humanity, 1989, others. Founder, pres. Whitewater chpt. World Federalists Assn., 1960-68, 76-78, 86-92, midwest regional pres., 1969-71, 75-87, nat. bd., 1968-89, 92—; del. World Congress, Ottawa, 1970, Brussels, 1972, Paris, 1977, Tokyo, 1980, Phila., 1987; mem. exec. com. Assn. World Citizens, 1980—; sec. World Govt. Orgns. Coalition, 1987—; mem. Gov's. Commn. on UN, 1971-89, state coord. Campaign for UN Reform, 1984—; mem. Wis. Conf. Bd. Social Concerns, Meth. Ch., 1961-68, 70-76; Dem. precinct committeeman, Whitewater, 1966—; chmn. Walworth County Dem. Party, 1968-72; vice chmn. 1st Congl. Dist. Dem. Party, 1975-78, Wis. Dem. Platform Com., 1978—; bd. dirs. Alcohol Problems Council Wis., 1976—. With AUS, 1943-46. Mem. Indsl. Rels. Rsch. Assn. (adv. bd. Wis. chpt. 1964-78, acad. v.p. 1978-83), Peace Action, Population Inst., Fedn. Am. Scientists, Walworth County UN Assn. (pres. 1979-80), Kiwanis (pres. local club 1987-88). Methodist (lay speaker). Home: 205 N Fremont St Whitewater WI 53190-1322 *Life is too precious to be spent on ourselves. We show love for our Creator by what we do for others. Happiness is a by-product.*

REFO, PATRICIA LEE, lawyer; b. Alexandria, Va., Dec. 31, 1958. BA with high honors and high distinction, U. Mich., 1980, JD cum laude, 1983. Bar: Ill. 1983, U.S. Dist. Ct. (no. dist.) Ill. 1988, U.S. Ct. Appeals (7th cir.) 1989, U.S. Ct. Appeals (11th cir.) 1990, U.S. Ct. Appeals (5th cir.) 1992, Fed. Trial Bar (no. dist.) Ill. 1993. Ptnr. Jenner & Block, Chgo., 1991—; mem. faculty Nat. Inst. Trial Advocacy, 1989—; bd. advisors Lender Liability News, Chgo. Legal Club, Chgo. Lincoln Inn Ct.; lectr. ALI/ABA and Practicing Law Inst. on various subjects including trial advocacy and lender liability. Co-author: Class Action Controversies, 1989, Notice to Members of the Class, IICLE Class Actions Handbook, 1986. Dir. Legal Clinic for the Disabled, 1994—, Chgo. Lawyers' Com. Civil Rights Under Law, 1987-91, Cabrini Green Legal Aid Clinic, 1987-91. Mem. ABA (chair sect. litigation 1990 annual meeting, co-chair sect. litigation Pro Bono com. 1990-93, dir. divsns. sect. litigation 1993—). Office: Jenner & Block 1 E IBM Plz Fl 47 Chicago IL 60611-3608

REFSLAND, GARY ARLAN, retired sociology educator; b. Big Timber, Mont., May 5, 1944; s. William Anton and Agnes Eline (Freeberg) R.; m. Judith Estelle Hall, Aug. 20, 1969 (div. Aug. 1974); m. Marjorie Gillette Shaw, Dec. 12, 1977. BS in Sociology, Mont. State U., 1970, MS in Sociology, 1971; postgrad. Internat. Grad. Sch., Stockholm, 1970; AA in funeral directing, Calif. Coll. Mortuary Sci., 1973. Cert. funeral dir., mortician. Instr. sociology Mont. State U., Bozeman, 1971-72, lectr., 1976-93, coord. aging svcs., 1976-77, acting dir. Ctr. Gerontology, 1977-79, dir. Mont. Ctr. Gerontology, 1979-93; mortician Dokken Nelson Funeral Service, Bozeman, 1974-76; ret., 1993; program coord. Mont. Area Health Edn. Ctr./Office Rural Health, 1987-93; mem. adv. bd. Sr. Cmty. Svcs. Employment program, Mont., 1983—, Regional Edn. and Tng. program Fed. Region VIII, 1980-82, Mont. State U., 1986-93, Mont. Area Health Edn. Ctr., 1987; mem. planning com. Gov's. Adv. Coun., Mont. Aging Policy Perspectives: 1990, 1987-93; mem. Gov's Third Priorities for People, 1988; state coord. White Ho. Conf. on Aging 1981-82. Writer, producer (TV show) Mont.'s Priorities for Aging, 1981; producer The Mental health Problems of Older Adults, 1988; writer, exec. producer (videotape) Senior Centers.: Opportunities for Older Montanans. Pres. Gallatin County Housing Authority Bd., Bozeman, 1981-82, sec. 1978-81; pres. Sourdough Ridge Property Owners Assn., Bozeman, 1982-84, Gallatin County Council on Aging, 1978-80. With USN, 1962-66. Recipient Armed Forces Community award San Diego C. of C., 1966, Cert. Appreciation U.S. Dept. HHS, 1982, Community Achievement award, 1989; named one of Outstanding Young Men Am. U.S. Jaycees, 1981. Mem. Am. Soc. Aging, Mont. Gerontology Soc. (charter officer 1982-83), Nat. Council on Aging (del. council 1982-83), Am. Legion, Alpha Kappa Delta. Avocations: hunting, carpentry, fishing. Home: 212 Ridge Trl Bozeman MT 59715-9253

REFUERZO, BEN J., architectural educator, architectural firm executive. BA, U. California, Berkeley, MArch; Ph.D., architecture, U. Michigan, Ann Arbor. Assoc. prof., architecture U. California, Los Angeles; principal R-2ARCH; Jury member P/A awards. Office: Univ California Grad School Arch/Urban Planning 405 Hilgard Ave Los Angeles CA 90024-1301*

REGALADO, RAUL L., airport parking executive; b. L.A., Jan. 31, 1945; s. Raul and Antonia (Estavillo) R.; m. Helen Sutcliffe; children: Stephanie, Jennifer. BS, Embry-Riddle Aero. U., 1972. Mgr. airport City of Klamath Falls, Oreg., 1972-74, City of Fresno, Calif., 1974-79, Orange County, Santa Ana, Calif., 1979-80; dir. aviation San Jose (Calif.) Airport, 1980-89; aviation cons. Raul Regalado & Assocs., Huntington Beach, Calif., 1989-91; dep. dir. aviation Houston Dept. Aviation, 1991-95; pres. airport properties West Airport Parking Co. Am., Houston, 1995—. Capt. U.S. Army, 1966-71, col. USAR (retired). Decorated Bronze Star, DFC, Air medal with 49 oak leaf clusters, Meritorious Svc. medal, Army Commendation medal with 3 oak cleaf clusters. Mem. Am. Assn. Airport Execs., Calif. Assn. Airport Execs. (pres. 1980-81), Res. Officers Assn., Assn. U.S. Army, Airport Operators Coun. Internat. (bd. dirs. 1986-88), Vietnam Helicopter Pilots Assn., Army Aviation Assn. Am., Aero. Club No. Calif. (bd. dirs. 1982-91, pres. 1987-89), Quiet Birdmen.

REGAN, DAVID, brain researcher, educator; b. Scarborough, Eng., May 5, 1935; arrived in Can., 1976; s. Randolph and Muriel Frances (Varley) R.; m. Marian Pauline Marsh, Aug. 15, 1959; children: Douglas Lawrence, Howard Michael. BSc, London U., 1957, MSc, 1958, PhD, 1964, DSc, 1974. Lectr. physics London U., 1960-65; reader neurosci. Keele U., Eng., 1965-75; prof. psychology Dalhousie U., Can., 1976-80, prof. physiology, 1980-84, assoc. prof. medicine, 1978-84, prof. medicine, 1984-87, prof. ophthalmology, 1980-87, prof. otolaryngology, 1980-84, Killam rsch. prof., 1978-82; prof. engring. Rutgers U., 1985-86; prof. psychology York U., Can., 1987—, prof. biology; prof. ophthalmology U. Toronto, Ont., Can., 1987—; retained inventor Wilkinson-Graviner Group, Eng., 1970-75; cons. Westinghouse, Pitts., 1980-86; co-dir. human performance in space lab. Inst. for Space and Terrestrial Sci., York U., 1989—, disting. rsch. prof., 1991—; indsl. rsch. chair aviation vision Natural Sci. and Engring. Rsch. Coun. Can./Can. Aviation Electronics, 1993. Author: Human Evoked Potentials, 1972, Human Brain Electrophysiology, 1989; editor: Spatial Vision, 1989, Binocular Vision, 1989, Vision Research, 1992; contbr. over 200 articles to profl. jours.; holder 8 patents. Recipient Forman prize for med. rsch. Dalhousie U., 1983; rsch. grantee NIH, NRC, Air Force Office Sci. Rsch., Nat. Scis. and Engring. Rsch. Coun. Can., Med. Rsch. Coun.; Killam fellow, 1990. Fellow Royal Soc. Can., Optical Soc. Am.; mem. Exptl. Psychology Soc., Soc. Clin. Electroretinography, Assn. Rsch. in Vision and Ophthalmology, Royal Coll. Sci. (London, assoc.), Am. Acad. Optometry (Prentice medal 1990). Avocations: cricket, walking, modern European history. Office: York U Dept Psychology, 4700 Keele St, North York, ON Canada M3J 1P3

REGAN, DONALD THOMAS, financier, writer, lecturer; b. Cambridge, Mass., Dec. 21, 1918; m. Ann G. Buchanan, July 11, 1942. BA, Harvard U., 1940; LLD (hon.), Hahnemann Med. Coll. Hosp., 1968, U. Pa., 1972, Pace U., 1973; DHL (hon.), Colgate U. With Merrill Lynch, Pierce, Fenner & Smith Inc. (and predecessor), 1946-81, sec., dir. adminstrv. div., 1960-64, exec. v.p., 1964-68, pres., 1968-70, chmn., chief exec. officer, 1971-80; chmn. bd., chief exec. officer Merrill Lynch & Co. Inc., 1973-81; sec. Dept. of Treasury, Washington, 1981-85; White House chief of staff Washington, 1985-87; vice chmn., dir. N.Y. Stock Exchange, 1972-75. Author: A View from the Street, 1972, For the Record, 1988. Trustee Charles E. Merrill Trust, 1961-80; chmn. bd. trustees U. Pa., 1974-78, life trustee, 1978-80; mem. policy com. Bus. Roundtable, 1978-80; trustee Com. for Econ. Devel., 1978-80. Served to lt. col. USMCR, World War II. Laureat Bus. Hall of Fame, 1974. Clubs: Army-Navy, Burning Tree. Office: Marketplace Ctr Ste 142 240 McLaws Cir Williamsburg VA 23185

REGAN, JOHN BERNARD (JACK REGAN), community relations executive, assemblyman; b. Chgo., Feb. 2, 1934; s. Andrew J. and Frances (O'Born) R.; m. Rosemary E. Seger, Aug. 17, 1980. BA, So. Ill. U., 1960. V.p. Collins Bros., Las Vegas, Nev., 1971-76; pres. Terra, Inc., Las Vegas,

1973-80; owner Jack's Place, Las Vegas, 1980-95; govt. and mil. affairs liaison C.C. So. Nev., North Las Vegas, 1984-95; dist. dir. Nat. Coun. for Community Rels., 1984-86; nat. treas. Nat. Coun. Mktg. and Pub. Rels., 1986-88; state dir. Internat. Coun. of Shopping Ctrs., Nev., 1976. State assemblyman Nev. State Legis., Carson City, 1988-90, 92-93, state senator 1994—; chmn. Am. Legis. Exch. Coun., 1990-93; trade, travel and tourism com. mem. Nat. Coun. of State Legis., 1990-93, com. on Devel. Disabilities; active Las Vegas Habitat for Humanity. With USN, 1951-55. Recipient Lion of Yr. award Las Vegas Lions Club, 1978, Paragon award Nat. Coun. for Community Rels., 1985. Mem. Thunderbird Chpt. Air Force Assn. (pres. 1989-90, named hon. Thunderbird, Nighthawk, stealth fighter), North Las Vegas C. of C. (v.p. 1986). Democrat. Jewish. Avocations: reading, community service, coin collecting. Home: 1650 Cookson Ct Las Vegas NV 89115-6948 Office: CC S Nev 3200 E Cheyenne Ave #N2A N North Las Vegas NV 89030-4228

REGAN, JOHN J., law educator; b. N.Y.C., July 1, 1929; s. John Joseph and Catherine (Marshall) R.; m. Mary O'Connell, Feb. 20, 1971; 1 child, Alycia Cathryn. B.A., Mary Immaculate Coll., 1951; M.A., St. John's U., N.Y., 1963; J.D., Columbia U., 1960, LL.M. Ford Urban Law Fellow, 1970-71), 1971, J.S.D., 1977. Bar: N.Y. 1961, D.C. 1979. Assoc. dean of men, lectr. in law St. John's U., N.Y.C., 1960-62; dean Colls. Liberal Arts and Scis., 1962-68, assoc. prof. law, 1968-70; prof. law Sch. of Law, U. Md., Balt., 1971-78; prof. of law Hofstra U., Hempstead, N.Y., 1978—, dean Sch. of Law, 1978-82; dir. Inst. Health Law and Policy Hofstra Law Sch., 1995—. Author: Law and the Dependent Elderly, 1977, Tax Estate and Financial Planning for the Elderly, 1985, 95, Your Legal Rights in Later Life, 1989, The Aged Client and the Law, 1990 (with M. Gilfix) Tax, Estate and Financial Planning for the Elderly: Forms and Practice, 1991, 95, Entitlements, 1994. Mem. ABA. Roman Catholic. Office: Hofstra U Sch Law 121 Hofstra U Hempstead NY 11550

REGAN, JUDITH THERESA, publishing executive; b. Leominster, Mass. Aug. 17, 1953; d. Leo James and Rita Ann (Imprescia) R.; children: Patrick, Lara. BA, Vassar Coll., 1975. Sr. editor, v.p. Simon & Schuster, N.Y.C., 1989-94; pres., pub. Regan Books, N.Y.C., 1994—; TV prodr. Entertainment Tonight, N.Y.C., Geraldo, N.Y.C.; prodr. 20th Century Fox Films, Fox TV; corr. Full Disclosure, Fox TV; pub. Regan Books, Harper Collins. Author: The Art of War for Women; editor numerous books including And the Beat Goes On (Sonny Bono), 1991, The Way Things Ought to Be (Rush Limbaugh), 1992, Shampoo Planet and Life After God (Douglas Coupland), 1992, She's Come Undone (Wally Lamb), 1992, Rogue Warrior (Richard Marcinko), 1992, Feminine Force: Release the Power Within You to Create the Life You Deserve (Georgette Mosbacher), 1993, Private Parts (Howard Stern), 1993, I Can't Believe I Said That (Kathie Lee Gifford), 1994. Office: Regan Books 1211 Ave of the Americas New York NY 10036

REGAN, MURIEL, small business owner; b. N.Y.C., July 15, 1930; d. William and Matilda (Riebel) Blome; m. Robert Regan, 1966 (div. 1976); 1 child, Jeanne Booth. BA, Hunter Coll., N.Y.C., 1952; MLS, Columbia U., 1952; MBA, Pace U., N.Y., 1982. Post libr. US Army, Okinawa, 1952-53; researcher P.F. Collier, N.Y.C., 1953-57; asst. libr. to libr. Rockefeller Found., N.Y.C., 1957-67; dep. chief libr. Manhattan Community Coll., N.Y.C., 1967-68; libr. Booz Allen & Hamilton, N.Y.C., 1968-69, Rockefeller Found., N.Y.C., 1969-82; prin. Gossage Regan Assocs., Inc., N.Y.C., 1980—; dir. NY Met. Reference and Rsch. Libr. Agy., 1988—, Coun. of Nat. Libr. and Info. Assns., 1991—; cons. Librs., info. ctrs. Mem. SLA (pres. 1989-90), Archons of Colophon, N.Y. Libr. Club. Avocations: cats, reading, playing piano, traveling. Home: 792 Columbus Ave New York NY 10025-5150 Office: Gossage Regan Assocs Inc 25 W 43rd St New York NY 10036-7406

REGAN, PETER FRANCIS, III, physician, psychiatry educator; b. Bklyn., Nov. 11, 1924; s. Peter Francis Jr. and Veronica (Tierney) R.; m. Laurette Patricia O'Connor, June 18, 1949; children: Peter, Stephen, William, Elizabeth, John, Carol. MD, Cornell U., Ithaca, N.Y., 1949. Diplomate Am. Bd. Psychiatry and Neurology, Nat. Bd. Med. Examiners. Intern in medicine N.Y. Hosp., 1949-50; asst. resident psychiatry Payne Whitney Psychiat. Clinic, 1950, 53-54, resident, 1954-56; asst. prof. psychiatry Cornell U. Med. Coll., 1956-58; prof., head dept. psychiatry U. Fla. Coll. Medicine, chief psychiat. svc. Univ. Teaching Hosp., 1958-64; prof. psychiatry SUNY, Buffalo, 1964-84, v.p. health affairs, 1964-67, exec. v.p. univ., 1967-69, exec. v.p., acting pres. univ., 1969-70, vice chancellor acad. programs, 1970-71; assoc. chief staff for edn. Buffalo VA Med. Ctr., 1979-84; prof. psychiatry U. Tex. Health Sci. Ctr., San Antonio, 1984—, assoc. dean Sch. Medicine, 1986-87; assoc. chief staff for edn. San Antonio VA Med. Ctr., 1984-86, chief.staff, 1986-87; dep. assoc. chief med. dir. for acad. affairs VA Cen. Office, Washington, 1987-88, assoc. chief med. dir. for acad. affairs, 1988-92; prof. emeritus / sen. cons. dept. psychiatry SUNY, Buffalo, N.Y., 1992—; project dir. Ctr. for Ednl. Rsch. and Innovation, OECD, 1972-74. Author: (with F. Flach) Chemotherapy in Emotional Disorders, 1960, (With E. Pattishall) Behavioral Science Contributions to Psychiatry; contbr. articles to profl. jours. Capt. M.C. AUS, 1951-52. Fellow Am. Psychiat. Assn., Am. Coll. Psychiatrists (bd. regents 1986-95, 2d v.p. 1988, 1st v.p. 1989, pres.-elect 1990, pres. 1991); mem. AMA, Alpha Omega Alpha. Home: 900 Delaware Ave # 504 Buffalo NY 14209-2012 Office: SUNY Dept Psychiatry 462 Grider St Buffalo NY 14215

REGAN, PETER JOHN, banker; b. Lawrence, Mass., Oct. 10, 1942; s. Walter A. and Mary (Murphy) R.; m. Julie R. Potter; children—John Peter, Katey Mary, James Peter, Kim Mary. B.S.B.A., Boston U., 1965. Acct. Deloitte, Haskins & Sells, C.P.A.s, Boston, 1965-66; account exec. James Talcott Inc., Boston, 1966-69; exec. v.p. dir. Market Masters Industries, Greenwich, Conn., 1969-71; comml. v.p. Ford Motor Co., Dearborn, Mich., 1971-73; sr. v.p. Shawmut Bank Boston, 1973—; dir. Fidelity Fin.; Boston; cons. Argus Mgmt., Newton, Mass. Contbr. articles to Sports Illus. mag. Mem. Am. Mgmt. Assns., Mktg. Assn. Am. (bd. dirs.), Mfg. Assn. Am. (bd. dirs.). Roman Catholic. Office: Shawmut Bank of Boston 1 Federal St 30th Fl Boston MA 01810

REGAN, PHILIP RAYMOND, professional baseball coach; b. Otsego, Mich., Apr. 6, 1937. Student, Western Mich. U. Baseball player Detroit Tigers, 1956-65, L.A. Dodgers, 1965-68, Chgo. Cubs, 1968-72, Chgo. White Sox, 1972-73; head coach Grand Valley State Coll., Mich., 1973-82; scout, minor league pitching instr. Seattle Mariners, 1983-84, pitching coach, 1984-86; pitching coach Cleve. Indians, 1994; scout L.A. Dodgers, 1987-93; head baseball mgr. Balt. Orioles, 1995—. Office: Oriole Park at Camden Yards 333 W Camden St Baltimore MD 21201*

REGAN, ROBERT CHARLES, English language educator; b. Indpls., Mar. 13, 1930; s. Francis Bernard and Alma Ophelia (McBride) R.; m. Katherine Jeanclos, Aug. 11, 1989; children by previous marriage: Christopher, Alison, Amelia. B.A., Centenary Coll., 1951; M.A., Harvard U., 1952; Ph.D., U. Calif., Berkeley, 1965. Instr. English, Centenary Coll., 1956-57; asst. prof. English, U. Va., 1963-67; Fulbright-Hays lectr. Am. civilization U. Montpellier, France, 1967-68; assoc. prof. English, U. Pa., Phila., 1968-82, prof., 1982—; undergrad. chmn. dept. English 1978-80, 81-83, 89-90, dir. Penn-in-London program; lectr. Internat. Communications Agy., Morocco, Algeria, Jordan, 1980; vis. prof. King's Coll., London, 1983-84. Author: Unpromising Heroes; Mark Twain and His Characters, 1966, Poe: A Collection of Critical Essays, 1967; mng. editor: Am. Quar., 1969-72; contbr. articles to lit. jours. Served with USNR, 1952-56, 61-62. Woodrow Wilson fellow, 1962-63; Am. Philos. Soc. research grantee, 1970. Democrat. Episcopalian. Office: U Pa Dept English Philadelphia PA 19104

REGAN, SYLVIA, playwright; b. N.Y.C., Apr. 15, 1908; d. Louis and Esther (Albert) Hoffenberg; m. James J. Regan, Feb. 11, 1931 (div. June 1936); m. 2d Abraham Ellstein, Nov. 7, 1940 (dec. Mar. 1963). Student pub. schs. Broadway actress N.Y.C., 1927-31; with pub. relations and promotion dept. Theatre Union and Orson Welles Mercury Theatre, N.Y.C., 1932-39; playwright, 1940—. Author: Morning Star, 1940, The Golden Door, 1951; musical Great to be Alive, 1951; The Fifth Season, 1953; libretto for grand opera The Golem, N.Y.C., 1962; Zelda, 1969. Sec. Sydney Epstein Meml. Fund for Strang Cancer Clinic, N.Y.C., 1948-68. Recipient cititation Fedn. Women Zionists of Gt. Britain and Ireland, 1953. Mem. Dramatists Guild, Authors League of Am., Am. Jewish Hist. Soc., Nat.

Council Jewish Women (citation of merit 1953). Democrat. Home: 55 E 9th St New York NY 10003

REGAN, TIMOTHY JAMES, grain company executive; b. Atchison, Kans., July 31, 1956; s. Vincent James and Phyllis (Brull) R.; m. Veronica Sue Kasten, June 25, 1977; children: Katrina Sue, Brian James. BS, Kans. State U., 1978. Corp. acct. Lincoln Grain Co., Atchison, 1978-80; acctg. supr. Pillsbury Co., St. Joseph, Mo., 1980; br. account mgr. Pillsbury Co., St. Joseph, 1980-82, Omaha, 1982; internal auditor Pillsbury Co., Mpls., 1983; regional account mgr. Pillsbury Co., Huron, Ohio, 1983-84; regional account mgr. Scoular Grain Co., Omaha, 1984-87, controller, 1987-91, v.p., mem. exec. com., 1990—, CFO, 1991—; Fin. advisor Grace Abbott Sch. PTO, Omaha, 1987, treas., 1990-91. Fin. adviser Grace Abbott Sch. PTO, Omaha, 1987, treas., 1990-91; coach Little League Baseball and Soccer. Mem. KC, Elks. Republican. Roman Catholic. Avocations: jogging, basketball, coaching little league baseball and soccer. Home: 2009 S 182d Cir Omaha NE 68130-2748 Office: Scoular Co 2027 Dodge St Omaha NE 68102-1234

REGAN, WILLIAM JOSEPH, JR., energy company executive; b. Bronx, N.Y., Mar. 7, 1946; s. William Joseph and Eleanor F. (Malone) R.; m. Mary Lee Wynn; children—Katrina Lee, Thomas Wynn, James William. B.S., U.S. Air Force Acad., 1967; M.B.A., U. Wis.-Madison, 1969, Ph.D., 1972. Asst. prof. Wayne State U., Detroit, 1971-75; with Nat. Bank Detroit, 1975-77; sr. bus. planner Am. Natural Resources Co., Detroit, 1977-78, dir. fin. planning, 1978-82, v.p., treas., 1982-85; v.p. corp. fin. United Svcs. Automobile Assn., San Antonio, 1986-88, sr. v.p., treas., 1988-95; v.p., treas. Entergy Corp., New Orleans, 1995—. Mem. The Club at Sonterra. Republican. Roman Catholic.

REGAZZI, JOHN HENRY, retired corporate executive; b. N.Y.C., Jan. 4, 1921; s. Caesar B. and Jennie (Moruzzi) R.; m. Doris Marry Litzau, Feb. 16, 1946; children: Mark, Dale. B.B.A., Pace Coll., 1951. C.P.A., N.Y. Mgr. Price Waterhouse, N.Y.C., 1946-62; comptroller ABC, N.Y.C., 1962-70; sr. v.p., CFO Avnet, Inc., N.Y.C., 1970-93; retired, 1993. Contbr. articles to profl. jours. Pres. bd. River Dell Regional High Sch., Oradell, N.J., 1962-65; trustee, treas. Oradell Pub. Library, 1970-79; councilman Borough of Oradell, 1979-88. Served as staff sgt. USAF, 1942-45. Mem. Fin. Execs. Inst., Am. Inst. CPA's. Nat. Assn. Accts., Nat. Assn. Corp. Treas. Republican. Roman Catholic. Lodge: Lions. Home: 637 Park Ave Oradell NJ 07649-2007

REGAZZI, JOHN JAMES, III, publishing executive; b. Bklyn., June 8, 1948; s. John James Jr. and Theresa Cecil (Fiore) R.; m. Marie Louise Ford, May 30, 1971; children: John James IV, Thomas Paul, Michael Rees. BS, St. John's U., Queens, N.Y., 1970; MA, U. Iowa, 1972; MS, Columbia U., 1974; PhD, Rutgers U., 1983. Systems mgr. No. Ill. U., De Kalb, Ill., 1974-76; dir. pub. Found. Ctr., N.Y.C., 1976-79; assoc. prof. Rutgers U., New Brunswick, N.J., 1979-81; v.p. The H.W. Wilson Co., N.Y.C., 1981-88; pres., chief exec. officer Engring. Info., Inc., N.Y.C., 1988—; chmn. FID/IPI Com.; bd. dirs. ICSTI; adj. prof. SUNY, Albany, Columbia U., Rutgers U. Author: Guide to Periodicals in Religion, 1974. Mem. AAAS, IEEE, ALA, Am. Assn. Pubs. (bd. dirs. N.Y.C. chpt. 1987-88), Nat. Info. Standards Orgn. (vice chmn. 1989-90), Nat. Fedn. of Abstracting and Info. Svcs. (bd. dirs. 1980-81, 88), Assn. Computing Machinery, N.Y. Acad. Sci. Avocation: tennis. Office: Engring Info Inc Castle Point On The Hudson Hoboken NJ 07030

REGEIMBAL, NEIL ROBERT, SR., retired journalist; b. Mpls., Mar. 16, 1929; s. Louis Odlin and Marie Elizabeth (O'Neill) R.; m. Mary Elizabeth Sutton, Aug. 18, 1950; children—Neil Robert, James Michael, Claire Marie, Stephen Louis, Mary Suzanne, Elizabeth Anne. B.S. in Journalism, U. Md., 1951. With AP, Washington, 1949-50; asso. editor Takoma (Md.) Jour., 1950-51; reporter Washington Times-Herald, 1951-54, Washington Post, 1954; Washington corr. Chilton Publs., 1954-71, Wash. bur. chief, v.p., 1975-91; dir. publ. relations Motor Vehicle Mfrs. Assn., Detroit, 1971-74; Washington editor Chilton Oil and Gas Jour., Washington, 1975-91; ret., 1991. Recipient Tom Campbell Editorial Achievement award, 1968, 69, 71, 78, Jesse H. Neal Editorial Achievement award, 1982, 84. Mem. White House Corrs. Assn., Sigma Delta Chi. Republican. Roman Catholic. Club: Nat. Press. Home and Office: 13811 Marianna Dr Rockville MD 20853-2737

REGELBRUGGE, ROGER RAFAEL, steel company executive; b. Eeklo, Belgium, May 22, 1930; came to U.S., 1953, naturalized, 1961; s. Victor and Rachel (Roesbeke) R.; m. Dorcas Merchant; children: Anita, Marc, Laurie, Jon, Craig, Kurt, Christiane, Lauren, Roger Rafael Jr. B.Sc. in Mech. Engring, State Tech. Coll., Ghent, 1951; B.Sc. in Indsl. Engring, Gen. Motors Inst., Flint, Mich., 1955; M.Sc. in Mech. Engring, Mich. State U., 1964. Supr. product engring. dept. Gen. Motors Corp., Antwerp, 1955-58; chief devel. engr., then gen. mgr. Airmaster div. Hayes Industries Inc., Jackson, Mich., 1958-66; with Koehring Co., 1966-74; group v.p. internat. ops. Koehring Co., Milw., 1969-74; exec. v.p. Korf Industries, Inc., Charlotte, N.C., 1974-77; chmn., pres., CEO, Georgetown Industries, Inc. (formerly Korf Industries, Inc.), 1977—; chmn. bd. Georgetown Steel Corp., Georgetown Investment Corp., Georgetown Fin. Corp., Georgetown Wire Co., Western Lumber Co., Tree Island Industries; chmn. Waccamaw Corp.; bd. dirs. Steel Mfrs. Assn., Am. Iron and Steel Inst.; chmn., CEO Fla. Wire and Cable, Inc. N.C. adv. bd. Fuqua Sch. Bus. Duke U.; mem. Charlotte Chamber Bd. Advisors; mem. adv. coun. Coll. Engring. U. Notre Dame; trustee Belmont (N.C.) Abbey Coll. Mem. ASME, Am. Soc. Automotive Engrs., Charlotte Athletic Club, Carmel Country Club, Tower Club (Charlotte), Georgetown Club (Washington). Roman Catholic. Office: Georgetown Industries Inc 1901 Roxborough Rd Ste 200 Charlotte NC 28211-0407

REGENSTEIN, LEWIS GRAHAM, conservationist, author, lecturer, speech writer; b. Washington, Feb. 21, 1943; s. Louis and Helen Lucile (Moses) R.; divorced; children: Ana Lucile, Daniel Louis. Cert. of European studies, Inst. Am. Univs., Aix-en-Provence, France, 1964; B.A. in Polit. Sci., U. Pa., 1965; M.A. in Polit. Sci., Emory U., 1975. Intelligence officer, analyst C.I.A., Washington, 1966-71; wildlife editor Environ. Quality mag., 1973; real estate agt., 1984—; v.p. Help Our Planet Earth; bd. dirs. The Monitor Consortium, 1977—, pres., 1979-81; bd. dirs. Washington Humane Soc., 1978-84, Interfaith Coun. for Protection Animals and Nature, 1982-88, Atlanta Outdoor Activities Coun., Ctr. for Respect of Life and Environment, 1989—, Earth Save Found., 1989—. Author: The Politics of Extinction: the Story of the World's Endangered Wildlife, 1975, America the Poisoned: How Deadly Chemicals are Destroying Our Environment, Our Wildlife— And Ourselves, 1982, paperback edit., 1983, How to Survive in America the Poisoned, 1987, Replenish the Earth: The Teachings of Religion on Protecting Animals and Nature, 1991, Cleaning Up America the Poisoned: How to Survive Our Polluted Society, 1993; co-author: (jokebook) Sex, Wealth, and Power: How to Live Without Them, 1990; contbr. Environmental Encyclopedia, 1993; mem. editorial bd. the Westminster Schs., 1991—; contbr. numerous articles and book revs. on environ. and nat. security to maj. newspapers; author text of comml. record album; writes speeches and humor for corp. execs. and polit. leaders. Alumni exec. bd. The Lovett Sch. 1986—; co-chmn. Mayor's Environ. Task Force City of Atlanta, 1994—; dir. Piedmont Park Conservancy, Atlanta. Mem. Am. Lung. Assn. Atlanta (coun. 1989—), Global Forum Ga. (steering com. 1991). Home and Office: 3691 Tuxedo Rd NW Atlanta GA 30305-9999

REGENSTEINER, ELSE FRIEDSAM (MRS. BERTOLD REGENSTEINER), textile designer, educator; b. Munich, Apr. 21, 1906; came to U.S., 1936, naturalized, 1942; d. Ludwig and Hilda (Nelson-Bachhofer) Friedsam; m. Bertold Regensteiner, Oct. 3, 1926; 1 dau., Helga Regensteiner Sinaiko-Botts. Tchrs. degree, Deutsche Frauenschule, Munich, 1925; student, U. Munich, Inst. Design, Chgo. Instr. Hull House, Chgo., 1941-45, Inst. Design, Chgo., 1942-46; asst. prof. Sch. Art Inst. Chgo., 1945-57, prof., 1957-71, prof. emeritus, 1971—; textile designer for industry; partner Reg Wick Studios, 1945-80; also lectr.; Cons. Am. Farm Sch., Thessaloniki, Greece, 1972-78. Exhibited one man shows throughout U.S., 1946—; represented in permanent collection, Art Inst. Chgo., Cooper-Hewitt Mus., N.Y.C.; Author: The Art of Weaving, 2d edit, 1981, 3d edit., 1986, German edit., 1987, Program for a Weaving Study Group, 1974, Weaver's Study Course- Sourcebook for Ideas and Techniques, 1982, 2d edit., 1987, Geometric Design in Weaving, 1986; contbr. articles to profl. mags. Recipient 1st prize for drapery and upholstery Internat. Textile Exhbn., 1946; five citations merit Am. Inst. Decorators, 1947, 48, 50; Regensteiner award Midwest Weavers Assn., 1980; Award of Merit in Textiles, The Textile Arts Ctr., Chgo., 1994. Fellow Collegium Craftsmen of Am. Crafts Coun.; mem. Am. Crafts Coun., Handweavers Guild Am. (bd. dirs. 1970-78). Address: 1416 E 55th St Chicago IL 60615-5409

REGENSTREIF, S(AMUEL) PETER, political scientist, educator; b. Montreal, Que., Can., Sept. 9, 1936; s. Albert Benjamin and Miriam Lillian (Issenman) R.; children: Anne Erica, Mitchell Chester, Jeffrey Gershon, Gail Aviva. B.A., McGill U., 1957; Ph.D., Cornell U., 1963. Mem. faculty U. Rochester, 1961—, prof. polit. sci., 1971—; coordinator Can. studies program, 1967—; editorial cons. Toronto Star, 1968-82, Chgo. Sun-Times, 1988-89; polit. cons. Bunting Warburg, Toronto, 1973-90, Coopers & Lybrand, Ltd., 1981-89, Loewen, Ondaatje, McCutcheon, 1991—; pres. Policy Concepts Inc., pub. affairs co., Toronto; broadcaster CKO Radio Network, 1983-89; pvt. polit. cons. Author: The Diefenbaker Interlude: Parties and Voting in Canada, 1965; syndicated columnist: Toronto Star, 1963-82; contbr. articles to profl. jours. Served to lt. Canadian Army, 1957. Ford. Found. fellow, 1960; Can. Council fellow, 1960, 65; Canadian Royal Commn. on Bilingualism and Biculturalism grantee, 1964-66; recipient Edward Peck Curtis award U. Rochester, 1979. Mem. AAAS, Am. Polit. Sci. Assn., Can. Polit. Sci. Assn., Assn. Can. Studies in U.S., Phi Beta Kappa. Jewish. Clubs: Faculty, Tennis. Home: 30 Glen Ellyn Way Rochester NY 14618-5346 Office: Univ Rochester Dept Polit Sci Rochester NY 14627

REGER, LAWRENCE LEE, association executive; b. Lincoln, Nebr., June 23, 1939; s. Lawrence John and Bertha (Hergenrader) R. Student, U. Nebr., 1961; LL.B., Vanderbilt U., 1964. Bar: Nebr 1964. Asso. firm Crosby, Guenzel & Binning, Lincoln, 1964-70; gen. counsel Nat. Endowment Arts, 1970-72, dir. program devel. and coordination, 1972-78; dir. Am. Assn. Mus., Washington, 1978-86; pres. Nat. Instn. for Conservation of Cultural Property, Washington, 1988—. Chmn. Nat. Humanities Alliance, 1982-86; bd. dirs. Nat. Musical Arts, 1990—. Home: 1937 39th St NW Washington DC 20007 Office: Inst Conserv Cultural Prop Ste 602 3299 K St NW Washington DC 20007-4445

REGES, MARIANNA ALICE, marketing executive; b. Budapest, Hungary, Mar. 23, 1947; came to U.S., 1956, naturalized, 1963; d. Otto H. and Alice M. R.; m. Charles P. Green, Feb. 15, 1975; children: Rebecca, Charles III. AAS with honors, Fashion Inst. Tech., N.Y.C., 1967; BBA magna cum laude, Baruch Coll., 1971, MBA in Stats., 1978. Media rsch. analyst Doyle, Dane, Bernbach Advt., N.Y.C., 1967-70; rsch. supr. Sta. WCBS-TV, N.Y.C., 1970-71; rsch. mgr. Woman's Day mag., N.Y.C., 1971-72; asst. media dir. Benton & Bowles Advt., N.Y.C., 1972-75; mgr. rsch. and sales devel. NBC Radio, N.Y.C., 1975-77; sr. rsch. mgr. Ziff-Davis Pub. Co., N.Y.C., 1977-84; media mgr. Bristol-Myers Squibb Co., 1984—; mem. Spanish Radio Adv. Coun., N.Y.C., 1986-88; mem. Pan-European TV Audience Rsch. Mgmt. Com., 1988—. Mem. Vt. Natural Resources Council, 1977—; advisor Baruch Coll. Adult Soc., 1975—. Mem. Am. Mktg. Assn., Am. Advt. Fedn., Media Rsch. Dirs. Assn., Radio and TV Rsch. Coun., Advt. Rsch. Found., Nature Conservancy, Vt. Natural Resources Coun., World Future Soc., Beta Gamma Sigma. Home: 626 E 20th St New York NY 10009 Office: Bristol-Myers Squibb Co 345 Park Ave New York NY 10154-0004

REGGIA, FRANK, electrical engineer; b. Northumberland, Pa., Oct. 30, 1921; s. Nicola and Rachela (DiPhillips) R.; m. Betty Jo Patterson, Jan. 14, 1945; children: James Allen, Daniel Lee. BSEE cum laude, Bucknell U., 1970, MSEE, 1972. Electronic engring. aide rsch. and devel. program microwaves Nat. Bur. Standards, Washington, 1945-48, radio engr., 1949-53; electronic engr. Harry Diamond Labs., Dept. Army, Washington, 1954-59, electronic scientist, 1960-65; elec. engr. Harry Diamond Labs., Dept. Army, Washington and Adelphi, Md., 1966-75, mgr. electronic fuze program, Adelphi, 1976-78; pvt. govt. and industry cons. microwaves Roanoke, Va., 1979—; speaker NATO Microwave Conf. Paris, 1962, Internat. Conf. Microwave Circuitry, Tokyo, 1964, Internat. Conf. Magnetics, Stuttgart, Fed. Republic Germany, 1966, others. Editor Proc. 1971 Internat. Microwave Conf., Washington; author, co-author over 50 articles to profl. jours. 22 patents microwave systems components. Pres. Chevy Chase (Md.) Civic League, 1960-61; scoutmaster, com. chmn. Chevy Chase Coun. Boy Scouts Am. 1962-68; bd. dirs. Post #105 Am. Legion, Bethesda, 1972-75; bd. dirs., trustee, pres. Men's Club St. Andrew Meth. Ch., Bethesda, 1973-78; bus. mgr. Cardinal Chorus, Roanoke, Va., 1982-89. With USN, 1940-45. Decorated Purple Heart. Fellow IEEE (life, editorial bd. Trans on MTT 9 yrs., citation award), AAAS, Wash. Acad. Sci.; mem. Washington Soc. Engrs. (Engr. of Yr. 1952), Washington chpt. MTT Soc. of IEEE (cofounder, life, chmn. 1961), Antenna and Propagation Soc. IEEE, Electron Devices Soc. IEEE, Nat. Assn. Ret. Fed. Employees (Fed. Employee of Yr. award 1978, pres., 1981, officer exec. com. 1978—, v.p. S.W. Va. Area VI 1993-94), Am. Radio Relay League, Tau Beta Pi, NRA, DAV. Democrat. Methodist. Avocations: choral singing, amateur radio, riflery. Address: 3343 Preston Ave NW Roanoke VA 24012-2860

REGGIO, VITO ANTHONY, management consultant; b. Rochester, N.Y., Dec. 17, 1929; s. Salvatore and Carrie Angela (LoRe) R.; m. Mary Ann Dolores Pippie, Sept. 28, 1957; children: Salvatore, Angela. BS, Purdue U., 1952; postgrad. sch. modern langs., Middlebury Coll., 1948; postgrad. fellowship, U. Ky., U. Tenn. and U. Ala., 1952-53. Jr. engr. Rochester (N.Y.) Gas and Electric Co., 1950; designer/drafter Globe Constrn. Co., Rochester, 1951; rsch. analyst Commonwealth of Ky., Frankfort, 1952; orgn. & methods analyst, then wage adminstrn. specialist USN Dept. Indsl. Rels., Indpls., 1955-56; cons. mgmt. to project mgr. to account exec. Bus. Rsch. Corp., Chgo., 1956-60; sr. cons. econ. feasibilities Ebasco Svcs., Inc., Chgo., 1960-63, dir. pers. mgmt. cons. dept., 1970-77; regional mgr., orgn. and pers. mgmt. svcs. EBS Mgmt. Cons., Chgo., 1963-65, nat. dir. orgn. and pers. mgmt. svcs., 1965-70; pres., bd. dirs. Reggio and Assocs., Inc., Chgo., 1977—; mng. dir. Pay Data Svc., 1977—; bd. dirs. Pay Data Svcs., Chgo. Contbr. papers to profl. publs. With U.S. Army, 1953-55. Named Solco Cultural Soc. fellow, Rochester, N.Y., 1948. Mem. Am. Compensation Assn., Am. Mgmt. Assn., Chgo. Compensation Assn., Soc. Human Resources Profls., Soc. Human Resources Mgmt., Human Resources Mgmt. Assn. Chgo., Western Soc. Engrs. Office: Reggio and Assocs Inc 550 W Jackson Blvd Chicago IL 60661-5716

REGINATO, ROBERT JOSEPH, soil scientist; b. Palo Alto, Calif., Apr. 13, 1935; s. Guiseppe Primo and Carolina Theresa (Boccignone) R.; m. Donna Marie LeStum, Aug. 26, 1956; children: Richard Lynn, David Lewis, Christopher Michael, Michael Jeffrey. B.S., U. Calif., Davis, 1957; M.S., U. Ill., 1959; Ph.D., U. Calif., Riverside, 1973. Rsch. asst. U. Calif., Davis, 1956-57, U. Ill., Urbana, 1957-59; soil scientist U.S. Water Conservation Lab., USDA-Agrl. Rsch. Svc., Phoenix, 1959-89 , rsch. leader, 1980-89; assoc. dir. Pacific W. Area USDA Agrl. Rsch. Svc., Albany, Calif., 1989-91, dir., 1991—; vis. scientist U. Calif., Davis, 1977-78; USDA collaborator U. Ariz., Tucson, 1959-89. Contbr. over 180 articles to tech. jours. Active Roosevelt coun. Boy Scouts Am., 1960-76. Fellow Am. Soc. Agronomy, Soil Sci. Soc. Am.; mem. Am. Geophys. Union, Internat. Soil Sci. Soc., Western Soil Sci. Soc., Sigma Xi, Alpha Zeta, Kappa Sigma. Roman Catholic. Home: 1494 London Cir Benicia CA 94510-1353 Office: Pacific West Area 800 Buchanan St Berkeley CA 94710-1100

REGIS, NINA, librarian, educator; b. Corinth, Miss., Oct. 19, 1928; d. W.C. and Mary Isabelle (Rushing) Hanner; m. George Regis, Sept. 5, 1949 (dec. Jan. 6, 1990); 1 child, Simonne Marie. BA, Bridgewater (Mass.) State U., 1971, MEd, 1975; MALS, U. South Fla., 1981. Cert. libr., tchr. Genealogical libr., asst. researcher to curator New Bedford (Mass.) Pub. Libr., 1963-71; assoc. libr. New Eng. Hist. Geneal. Soc., Boston, 1972-73; media specialist, libr. Brevard County Schs., Port Malabar Elem. Sch., Palm Bay, Fla., 1978-90; libr., faculty Brevard Community Coll., Palm Bay, 1990—. Developed and organized libraries, 1968, 80, 91—. Mem. ALA, Fla. Assn. C.Cs, Libr. Assn. of Brevard County, Phi Kappa Phi, Beta Phi Mu. Avocations: creative writing, genealogical research. Office: Brevard Community Coll Fla Advanced Tech Ctr 250 Grassland Rd Palm Bay FL 32909

REGISTER, ULMA DOYLE, nutrition educator; b. West Monroe, La., Feb. 4, 1920; s. John William and Lillian (Reagan) R.; m. Helen Louise Hite, June 15, 1942; children: Rebecca, Dorothy, Deborah. BS, Madison Coll.,

1942; MS, Vanderbilt U., 1944; PhD, U. Wis., 1950. Postdoctoral fellow Tulane Sch. Med., New Orleans, 1950-51; instr. biochemistry Loma Linda (Calif.) U., 1951-53, asst. prof., 1953-58, assoc. prof., 1959-67, prof. nutrition, 1967—, chmn. dept. nutrition, 1967-84; ret., 1985; part time prof., 1985-95; pres. Calif. Nutrition Coun., 1973. Co-author: Food for Us All, 1981, It's Your World Cookbook, 1981; contbr. numerous articles to sci. jours. Served to 1st lt. U.S. Army, 1944-47. Mem. Am. Inst. Nutrition, Am. Dietetic Assn., Calif. Nutrition Council (pres. 1973), Am. Soc. Clin. Nutrition. Republican. Adventist. Home: 11448 Benton St Loma Linda CA 92354-3679 Office: Loma Linda U Nutrition Sch Public Health Loma Linda CA 92350

REGNERY, HENRY, publisher; b. Hinsdale, Ill., Jan. 5, 1912; s. William Henry and Frances Susan (Thrasher) R.; m. Eleanor Scattergood, Nov. 12, 1938; children: Susan, Alfred S., Henry F. (dec.), Margaret. BS, MIT, 1934; student, U. Bonn., Germany, 1934-36; MA, Harvard U., 1938; LLD (hon.), Mt. Mary Coll., Milw. Staff Am. Friends Service Com., 1938-41; officer Joanna Western Mills Co., 1941-47, past chmn. bd.; founder Henry Regnery Co., 1947, pres., 1947-66, chmn. bd., 1967-1977; founded Gateway Editions, Ltd. (Book publishers), 1977; pres. Regnery Pub., 1977-83, also chmn. bd., 1977-83.

RÉGNIER, MARC CHARLES, lawyer, corporate executive; b. Rockland, Ont., Can., Apr. 24, 1939; s. Lucien and Joséphine (Mattar) R.; m. Claudette Picard, July 29, 1989; 1 child, Mathieu. BA, U. Ottawa, Ont., 1960, LLB, 1964. Bar: Que. 1969. Spl. asst. combines br. Dept. Justice, Ottawa, 1960-66; sollicitor, sec. Celanese Can. Ltd., Montréal, Que., Can., 1966-72; sec., legal counsel Microsystems Internat., Montréal, 1972-75; sr. group counsel No. Telecom Ltd., Montréal, 1974-75; sr. v.p., gen. counsel Avenor Inc. (formerly Can. Pacific Forest Products Ltd.), Montréal, 1976—; bd. dirs. NBIP Forest Products Inc., Dalhousie, N.B., Can., Pacific Forest Products Ltd., Vancouver, B.C., Can. Bd. dirs. Montréal Internat. Music Competition, Montréal Symphony Orch., Festival de Theatre des Ameriques, Fondation Hôpital St.-Luc, Montréal, Vie des Arts. Mem. Can. Bar Assn., Que. Bar Assn., Law Soc. Upper Can., Assn. Can. Gen. Counsel (pres. 1987-88), Club St.-Denis. Avocations: music, travel, fishing. Office: Avenor Inc, 1250 Réné-Lévesque Blvd West, Montreal, PQ Canada H3B 4Y3

REGO, ANTHONY C., food products executive; b. 1940. Officer Rego West, Cleve., 1964-88; mem. exec. com. Rini Rego Warehouse Co., Inc., 1980—; now chmn., CEO, dir. Riser Foods (merged with Rego West), Cleve. Office: Riser Foods Inc 5300 Richmond Rd Cleveland OH 44146*

REGULA, RALPH, congressman, lawyer; b. Beach City, Ohio, Dec. 3, 1924; s. O.F. and Orpha (Walter) R.; m. Mary Rogusky, Aug. 5, 1950; children: Martha, David, Richard. B.A., Mt. Union Coll., 1948, LL.D., 1981; LL.B., William McKinley Sch. Law, 1952; LL.D., Malone U., 1976. Bar: Ohio 1952. Sch. administr. Stark County Bd. Edn., 1948-55; practiced law Navarre, from 1952; mem. Ohio Ho. of Reps., 1965-66, Ohio Senate, 1967-72, 93rd-104th Congresses from 16th Ohio dist., 1973—; chmn. appropriations subcom. on the interior; ptnr. Regula Bros.; Mem. Pres.'s Commn. on Fin. Structures and Regulation, 1970-71. Mem. Ohio Bd. Edn., 1960-64; hon. mem. adv. bd. Walsh Coll., Canton, Ohio; Trustee Mt. Union Coll., Alliance, Ohio, Stark County Hist. Soc., Stark County Wilderness Soc. Served with USNR, 1944-46. Recipient Community Service award Navarre Kiwanis Club, 1963; Meritorious Service in Conservation award Canton Audubon Soc., 1965; Ohio Conservation award Gov. James Rhodes, 1969; named Outstanding Young Man of Yr. Canton Jr. C. of C., 1957, Legis. Conservationist of Yr. Ohio League Sportsmen, 1969. Republican. Episcopalian. Office: US Ho of Reps 2309 Rayburn HOB Washington DC 20515*

REHART, BURTON SCHYLER, journalism educator, freelance writer; b. Pacific Grove, Calif., July 24, 1934; s. Burton Schyler Sr. and Ruth Evelyn (Whitaker) R.; m. Catherine Loverne Morison, Apr. 14, 1962 (div. Aug. 1983); children: William, Anne Marie, Catherine Evelyn; m. Felicia Rose Cousart, June 30, 1984. BA in Journalism, Fresno (Calif.) State Coll., 1957; MA in History, Calif. State U., Fresno, 1966; cert., Coro found., 1961, Stanford U., summer 1975. Cert. adult edn. tchr., Calif. Reporter Bakersfield Californian, 1955; reporter, photographer Fresno Bee, 1957, Madera (Calif.) Daily Tribune, 1960-61, Ventura (Calif.) Free Press, 1961-62; from instr. to prof. journalism Calif. State U., Fresno, 1963—, prof. journalism, 1979—, chmn. dept. journalism, 1992-94. Author: M. Theo. Kearney-Prince of Fresno, 1988, (with others) Fresno in the 20th Century, 1986; editor, chmn. editorial bd. Fresno City, County Hist. Soc. Jour.; contbr. articles to profl. jours. Asst. foreman Fresno County Grand Jury, 1969. With U.S. Army, 1958-60. Mem. Soc. Profl. Journalists (pres. 1987-89), World Future Soc. (writer), Phi Kappa Phi (pres. 1977-78, Calif. State U. Fresno chpt.). Democrat. Episcopalian. Avocations: model ship building, photography, writing local history. Home: 1557 E Roberts Ave Fresno CA 93710-6433 Office: Calif State U Dept Journalism Shaw and Cedar Avenues Fresno CA 93740-0010

REHBERG, DENNIS R., state official; b. Billings, Mont., Oct. 5, 1955; m. Janice; 1 child. Student. Mont. State U., Wash. State U. Rancher and businessman, legis. aide, 1977, fin. dir. Congl. Campaigns, 1980-82; Mont. state rep. Dist. 88, 1985-89; lt. gov. Mont., from 1991. Home: 4235 Lombardy Dr Helena MT 59601-9603

REHERMAN, RONALD GILBERT, gas and electric company executive; b. Evansville, Ind., Aug. 14, 1935; s. Gilbert and Anna (Lawrence) R.; m. Rosalynn Reherman, Oct. 25, 1959; children: Robin, Chris, David. BS, U. Evansville, 1958; MBA, Ind. State U., 1971. Registered profl. engr., Ind. With So. Ind. Gas and Electric Co., Evansville, 1960—, v.p., dir. gas ops., 1982-84, exec. v.p., gen. mgr. ops., 1985-88; pres., COO So. Ind. Gas and Elec. Co., Evansville, 1988-90, pres., CEO, 1990-92, pres., chmn., CEO, 1992—. Bd. dirs. Evansville Indsl. Found., Evansville Coun. Boy Scouts Am., Vision 2000, Deaconess Hosp., Evansville United Way, campaign chmn. 1986-87; bd. trustees Evansville Mus. With U.S. Army, 1958-60. Mem. Met. Evansville C. of C. (bd. dirs. 1987), Ind. C. of C. (exec. com.)/. Avocations: camping, reading, golf, skiing. Office: So Ind Gas & Electric Co 20 NW 4th St Evansville IN 47741-0001

REHFELDT, DAVID JOHN, savings and loan executive; b. Appleton, Wis., May 21, 1955; s. Ewald and Lorraine E. (Schmidt) R.; m. Katherine Ann Kleinhuizen, May 24, 1975; children: Norah, Brittany, Charles. BBA in Acctg., U. Alaska, Anchorage, 1979. CPA, Alaska. Sr. acct. Touche Ross and Co., Anchorage, 1979-83; sr. v.p., chief fin. officer Home Savs. Bank, Anchorage, 1983—; bd. dirs. ARS Inc., Anchorage, Western Ins. Svcs. Inc., Anchorage. Mem. AICPA, Alaska Soc. CPA's, Fin. Mgrs. Soc., Anchorage Rebounders Boosters (pres. 1984—), Anchorage Seawolf Boosters (v.p. 1987—). Republican. Office: Home Savs Bank PO Box 6220 Newport Beach CA 92658-6220

REHG, KENNETH LEE, linguistics educator; b. East St. Louis, Ill., Nov. 21, 1939; s. Theophil Albert and Kathryn Louise (George) R.; 1 child, Laura Le'olani. BA, U. Ill., 1962; MA, So. Ill. U., 1965; PhD, U. Hawaii, 1986. Tng. officer Internat. Ctr. for Lang. Studies, Washington, 1966-67; lang. officer U.S. Peace Corp, Saipan, Micronesia, 1967-70; asst. rschr. social sci. rsch. inst. U. Hawaii, Honolulu, 1974-83, asst. prof., 1984—; cons. Micronesian govt., 1973-76, Samoa Dept. Edn., Pago Pago, 1978, U.S. Geol. Survey, Menlo Park, Calif., 1979-81, Japan Nat. Mus. Ethnology, Osaka, 1986; participant Fulbright-Hays Study Group, Ea. Indonesia, 1991. Author: Ponapean Reference Grammar, 1981; co-author: Kitail Lokaiahn Pohnpei, 1969, Ponapean-English Dictionary, 1979; mng. editor Oceanic Linguistics; contbr. articles to profl. jours. Rsch. fellow U. Hawaii, 1981-82; recipient Excellence in Teaching award Hawaii Tchrs. ESL, 1984, Mortar Bd., 1990. Mem. Linguistic Soc. Am., Linguistic Soc. Hawaii. Office: U Hawaii Dept Linguistics Moore Hall 569 1890 East-West Rd Honolulu HI 96822

REHKUGLER, GERALD EDWIN, agricultural engineering educator, consultant; b. Lyons, N.Y., Apr. 11, 1935; s. Charles James and Minnie Sophie (Tange) R.; m. Nancy Carolyn Poole, Sept. 11, 1982. B.S., Cornell U., 1957, M.S., 1958; Ph.D., Iowa State U., 1966. Registered profl. engr., N.Y. Grad.

asst. Cornell U., 1957-58, asst. prof. agrl. engring., 1958-64, assoc. prof., 1964-77, prof., 1977—, chmn. dept. agrl. and biol. engring., 1984-90, assoc. dean undergrad. programs, Coll. Engring., 1990—; vis. prof. Mich. State U., East Lansing, 1974; cons. in field. Patentee high capacity harvesting apparatus. Mem. Dryden Bd. Edn., N.Y., 1977-82, v.p., 1979-81, pres., 1981-82; mem. Bd. Coop. Ednl. Services, Ithaca, 1982-88. NSF sci faculty fellow, 1964-66. Fellow Am. Soc. Agrl. Engrs. (chmn. various coms. rsch. paper), Am. Inst. for Med. Biological Engring.; mem. Am. Soc. for Engring. Edn. Methodist. Home: 30 Rochester St Dryden NY 13053-9536 Office: Cornell U 223 Carpenter Hall Ithaca NY 14853-2201

REHM, JACK DANIEL, publishing executive; b. Yonkers, N.Y., Oct. 10, 1932; s. Jack and Ann (McCarthy) R.; m. Cynthia Fenning, Oct. 18, 1958; children: Lisabeth R., Ann M., Cynthia A., Jack D. Jr. BSBA, Coll. of the Holy Cross, 1954. Advt. sales trainee, asst. account exec. Batten, Barton, Durstine & Osborne, N.Y.C., 1954-59; mgr. Suburbia Today, N.Y.C., 1959-62; with advt. sales dept. Better Homes and Gardens Meredith Corp., N.Y.C., 1962-66; mgr. advt. sales Meredith Corp., Phila., 1966-67; mgr. advt. sales Meredith Corp. N.Y.C., 1967-69, advt. sales dir. Better Homes and Garden mag., 1969-73, v.p., pub. dir. mag. div., 1973-75, v.p., pub. Better Homes and Gardens, pub. dir. mag. div., 1975-76, v.p. pub. group, gen. mgr. mag. pub., 1976-80; pres. pub. group Meredith Corp., Des Moines, 1980-86, exec. v.p. corp. svcs., 1986-88, pres., chief oper. officer, 1988—, pres., chief exec. officer, 1989—, chmn., pres., chief exec. officer, 1992—, also bd. dirs.; bd. dirs. Norwest Bank Iowa, N.A., Vernon Co., Newton, Iowa, Internat. Multifoods, Mpls., Equitable of Iowa Cos.. Am. Coun. for Capital Formation. Bd. govs. Drake U., 1988—; trustee Coll. Holy Cross, Worcester, Mass.; mem. bus. com. Mus. Modern Art, N.Y.C., Greater Des Moines Com., Inc.; chmn. Des Moines Devel. Corp., 1993-94; active Iowa Bus. Coun.; mem. mag. and print com. USIA. With U.S. Army, 1956-57. Mem. Mag. Pubs. Am. (bd. dirs. 1981—, chmn. 1983-85, Publisher of Yr. 1988), Pine Valley Golf Club, Scarsdale Golf Club, Wakonda Golf Club. Roman Catholic. Avocation: golf. Home: 2913 Druid Hill Dr Des Moines IA 50315-2118 Office: Meredith Corp 1718 Locust St Des Moines IA 50309-3038*

REHM, JOHN BARTRAM, lawyer; b. Paris, Nov. 23, 1930; s. George and Mary (Torr) R.; m. Diana Mary Aed, Dec. 19, 1959; children: David Bartram, Jennifer Aed. AB, Harvard U., 1952; LLB, Columbia U., 1955; M.T.S., Wesley Sem., 1990. Bar: N.Y. 1955, D.C. 1969, U.S. Dist. Ct. D.C. 1971, U.S. Ct. Internat. Trade 1980, U.S. Supreme Ct. 1988. Assoc. Willkie, Owen, Farr, Gallagher & Walton, N.Y.C., 1955-56; atty.-advisor U.S. Dept. State, Washington, 1956-62, asst. legal advisor for econ. affairs, 1962-63; gen. counsel Office of Spl. Trade Rep., Washington, 1963-69; ptnr. Busby, Rivkin, Sherman, Levy & Rehm, Washington, 1969-77, Busby, Rehm and Leonard, Washington, 1977-87, Dorsey & Whitney, Washington, 1988—. Democrat. Episcopalian. Home: 5005 Worthington Dr Bethesda MD 20816-2748 Office: Dorsey & Whitney 1330 Connecticut Ave NW Washington DC 20036-1704

REHM, LEO FRANK, civil engineer; b. Milw., Jan. 8, 1916; s. Joseph V. and Theresa (Binder) R.; m. Irene R. Kegel, Aug. 24, 1940; children: Judith Ann LeDoux, Cecelia C. Nelson. B.C.E., Marquette U., 1938. Civil engr. Consoer, Townsend & Quinlan, Chgo., 1938-43; assoc. Consoer Townsend & Assocs. (Cons. Engrs.), Chgo., 1946-53; gen. partner Consoer Townsend & Assocs. (Cons. Engrs.), 1953-74, mng. partner, 1974-76; pres. PRC Consoer Townsend, Chgo., 1976-83, pres. emeritus, 1983-85; v.p. PRC Engring., Inc., Chgo., 1976-85; chmn. bd. Environ. Engring., Inc., 1976-83, Consoer Townsend Harris Internat., Inc., 1976-83; dir., v.p. Planning Research Corp., 1976-80; Mem. planning and adv. bd. Village of River Forest (Ill.), 1964-76; mem. exec. senate Marquette U., Milw., 1978—; mem. chmn. adv. council Marquette U. (Coll. Engring.), 1976-89. Mem. bldg. bd. appeals Village of River Forest, Ill., 1977-87, pres.'s adv. council Rosary Coll., River Forest, 1986-91, Exec. Svc. Corps Chgo. With U.S. Army, 1943-46. Recipient Disting. Engring. Alumnus award Marquette U. Coll. Engring., 1975; Alumnus of Yr. award Marquette U., 1983. Mem. Am. Public Works Assn., Am. Water Resources Assn., Am. Water Works Assn., Water Pollution Control Assn., Inter-Am. Assn. San. Engring., Nat. Soc. Profl. Engrs., Western Soc. Engrs., Ill. State C. of C. (bd. dirs. 1981-85), VFW. Roman Catholic. Clubs: Oak Park Country, KC, River Forest Service, Quail Creek Country.

REHME, ROBERT G., film company executive; b. Cin., May 5, 1935; s. Gordon W. and Helen H. (Henkel) R.; m. Kay Yazell, Jan. 9, 1964; children: Robin, Tracy. Ed., U. Cin. Theatre mgr. RKO Theatres, Cin.; advt. mgr. Cin. Theatre Co., 1961; publicist United Artists Pictures; dir. advt. and publicity United Artists Pictures and Paramount Pictures, 1969; pres. Avco Embassy Pictures Corp., Los Angeles, 1979; pres. distbn. and mktg. Universal Pictures Corp., 1981-82; pres. motion picture group MCA Universal, 1982-83; chief exec. officer New World Pictures, Los Angeles, 1983-89; prin. Neufeld/Rehme Prodns., 1989—; pres. Acad. Motion Picture Arts and Scis., 1992-93. Mem. Am. Film Inst. (trustee), Acad. Motion Picture Arts and Scis. Democrat. Presbyterian. Club: Variety. Office: Paramount Pictures 5555 Melrose Ave Los Angeles CA 90038-3197

REHMUS, CHARLES MARTIN, law educator, arbitrator; b. Ann Arbor, Mich., June 27, 1926; s. Paul A. and Amy D. (Martin) R.; m. Carolyn Brown, Dec. 21, 1948 (div. July 1982); children—Paul, James, Jon, David; m. Laura Carlson, Sept. 4, 1982. A.B., Kenyon Coll., 1947; M.A., Stanford U., 1951, Ph.D., 1955. Commr. Fed. Mediation and Conciliation Service, San Francisco, 1952-58; staff dir. Presdl. R.R. Commn., Washington, 1959-61; prof. polit. sci. U. Mich., Ann Arbor, 1962-80, dir. Inst. Labor and Indsl. Relations, 1962-76; chmn. Mich. Employment Relations Commn., Detroit, 1976-80; dean N.Y. State Sch. Indsl. and Labor Relations, Cornell U., Ithaca, 1980-86; prof. law U. San Diego, 1988—; bd. govs. Internat. Labor Orgn., 1986-92. Author: Final-Offer Arbitration, 1975, The Railway Labor Act at Fifty, 1977, Labor and American Politics, 1967, rev. edit., 1978, The National Mediation Board, 1984, Emergency Strikes Revisited, 1990. Chmn. 4 Presdl. emergency bds. at various times. Served to lt. USNR, 1943-45; PTO. Mem. Internat. Inst. Labor Studies (bd. govs. 1984-92), Indsl. Rels. Rsch. Assn. (exec. bd. 1984-88), Nat. Acad. Arbitrators (bd. govs. 1979-82, v.p. 1993—).

REHNQUIST, WILLIAM HUBBS, U.S. supreme court chief justice; b. Milw., Oct. 1, 1924; s. William Benjamin and Margery (Peck) R.; m. Natalie Cornell, Aug. 29, 1953; children: James, Janet, Nancy. BA, MA, Stanford U., 1948; MA, Harvard U., 1949; LLB, Stanford U., 1952. Bar: Ariz. Law clk. to former justice Robert H. Jackson, U.S. Supreme Ct., 1952-53; with Evans, Kitchel & Jenckes, Phoenix, 1953-55; mem. Ragan & Rehnquist, Phoenix, 1956-57; ptnr. Cunningham, Carson & Messenger, Phoenix, 1957-60, Powers & Rehnquist, Phoenix, 1960-69; asst. atty.-gen. office of legal counsel Dept. of Justice, Washington, 1969-71; assoc. justice U.S. Supreme Ct., 1971-1986, chief justice, 1986—; mem. Nat. Conf. Commrs. Uniform State Laws, 1963-69. Author: Grand Inquests: The Historic Impeachments of Justice Samuel Chase and President Andrew Johnson, 1992; contbr. articles to law jours., nat. mags. Served with USAAF, 1943-46, NATOUSA. Mem. Fed., Am. Maricopa (Ariz.) County bar assns., State Bar Ariz., Nat. Conf. Lawyers and Realtors, Phi Beta Kappa, Order of Coif, Phi Delta Phi. Lutheran. Office: Supreme Ct US 1 1st St NE Washington DC 20543

REHORN, LOIS MARIE SMITH, nursing administrator; b. Larned, Kans., Apr. 15, 1919; d. Charles and Ethel L. (Canaday) Williamson; m. C. Howard Smith, Feb. 15, 1946 (dec. Aug. 1980); 1 child, Cynthia A. Huddleston; m. Harlan W. Rehorn, Aug. 25, 1981. RN, Bethany Hosp. Sch. Nursing, Kansas City, Kans., 1943; BS, Ft. Hays Kans. State U., Hays, 1968, MS, 1970. RN, N.Mex. Office nurse, surg. asst. Dr. John H. Luke, Kansas City, Kans., 1943-47; supr. nursing unit Larned (Kans.) State Hosp., 1949-68, dir. nursing edn., 1968-71; dir. nursing 1972-81, ret., 1981. Named Nurse of Yr. DNA-4, 1986. Mem. Am. Nurses Assn., Kans. Nurses Assn. (dist. treas.), N.Mex. Nurses Assn. (dist. pres. 1982-86, dist. bd. dirs. 1992-94). Home: 1436 Brentwood Dr Clovis NM 88101-4602

REIBEL, KURT, physicist, educator; b. Vienna, Austria, May 23, 1926; came to U.S. 1938; s. Michael and Regina (Pak) R.; m. Eleanor Elvira Mannino, June 10, 1954; children—Leah, Michael, David. B.A., Temple U., Phila., 1954; M.S., U. Pa., Phila., 1956, Ph.D., 1959. Jr. research assoc. in

physics Brookhaven Nat. Lab., 1957-59; research assoc. U. Pa., Phila., 1959-61; asst. prof. Ohio State U., Columbus, 1961-64, assoc. prof., 1964-70, prof. physics, 1970-92, prof. emeritus, 1992—; vis. scientist CERN, Geneva, Switzerland, 1968-69, 75-76. Author research papers on nuclear and elementary particle physics. NSF fellow, 1954-56. Mem. Am. Phys. Soc., AAUP, Fedn. Am. Scientists, Union Concerned Scientists, Sigma Xi. Jewish. Office: Ohio State U Dept Physics 174 W 18th Ave Columbus OH 43210-1106

REIBMAN, JEANETTE FICHMAN, retired state senator; b. Ft. Wayne, Ind., Aug. 18, 1915; d. Meir and Pearl (Schwartz) Fichman; m. Nathan L. Reibman, June 20, 1943; children: Joseph M. Edward D., James E. AB, Hunter Coll., 1937; LLB, U. Ind., 1940; LLD, Lafayette Coll., 1969; hon. degree, Lehigh U., 1986, Wilson Coll., 1974, Cedar Crest Coll., 1977, Moravian Coll., 1990. Bar: Ind., 1940, U.S. Supreme Ct. 1944. Pvt. practice law Ft. Wayne, 1940; atty. U.S. War Dept., Washington, 1940-42, U.S. War Prodn. Bd., Washington, 1942-44; mem. Pa. Ho. of Reps., 1956-66, Pa. State Senate, Harrisburg, 1966-94; chmn. com. on edn. Pa. State Senate, 1971-81, minority chmn., 1981-90, majority caucus administr., 1992-94; mem. Edn. Commn. of the States. Trustee emeritus Lafayette Coll.; bd. mem. Pa. Higher Edn. Assistance Agy., Pa. Coun. on Arts, Camphill Schs. Recipient Disting. Dau. of Pa. award and medal Gov. Pa., 1968, citation on naming of Jeanette F. Reibman Adminstrn. Bldg., East Stroudsburg State Coll., 1972, Early Childhood Learning Ctr. Northampton Community Coll., 1992, Pub. Svc. award Pa. Psychol. Assn., 1977, Jerusalem City of Peace award Govt. Israel, 1977; named to Hunter Coll. Alumni Hall of Fame, 1974; U. Ind. Law Alumni fellow, 1993. Mem. Hadassah (Myrtle Wreath award 1976), Sigma Delta Tau, Delta Kappa Gamma, Phi Delta Kappa, Order Ea. Star. Democrat. Jewish. Office: 711 Lehigh St Easton PA 18042-4325

REIBSTEIN, RICHARD JAY, lawyer; b. Phila., Mar. 12, 1951; s. Albert Simon and Alma (Wilf) R.; m. Susan Barbara Fisch, May 18, 1975. BA with distinction, U. Rochester, 1973; JD with honors, George Washington U., 1976. Bar: Pa. 1976, N.Y. 1979, N.J. 1979, U.S. Dist. Ct. (so. dist.) N.Y. 1979, U.S. Dist. Ct. (ea. dist.) N.Y. 1979, N.J. 1979, U.S. Ct. Appeals (3d cir.) 1980, U.S. Ct. Appeals (2d cir.) 1982, U.S. Supreme Ct. 1983. Staff atty. Dept. Labor, Washington, 1976; counsel NLRB, Washington, 1976-78; assoc. Seham, Klein & Zelman (formerly Surrey, Karasik, Morse & Seham), N.Y.C., 1978-81; assoc. Epstein Becker & Green, P.C., N.Y.C., 1981-86, ptnr., 1986-91; ptnr. McDermott, Will & Emery, N.Y.C., 1992—. Co-author: Negligent Hiring, Fraud, Defamation, and Other Emerging Areas of Employer Liability, 1988, Employer's Guide to Workplace Torts, 1992; contbr. articles to legal jours. Mem. ABA (devel. of law under NLRA com., sect. labor and employment law 1976—), N.Y. State Bar Assn. Democrat. Office: McDermott Will & Emery 1211 Avenue Of The Americas New York NY 10036-8701

REICE, CHARLES THOMAS, department store, food service and lodging executive; b. Phila., June 3, 1926; s. Charles B. and Frances Elizabeth (Thompson) R.; m. Regina Frances Brown, Aug. 25, 1951; children: Linda Reice Dieter, Regina Reice Rogers, Charlene Reice Piereth, Sharon A., Charles Thomas. B.S., Rider Coll., Trenton, N.J., 1955. Accountant Price Waterhouse & Co. C.P.A.s, Phila., 1955-58; acctg. positions with Campbell Soup Co., 1958-65; v.p., treas. Bunker Ramo Corp., 1965-76; v.p. fin. Chamberlain Mfg. Corp., 1976-80; v.p. fin., treas. Carson, Pirie Scott & Co., Chgo., 1980—. Served with AUS, 1944-46. Mem. Fin. Execs. Inst. (past chmn. membership com.), Econ. Club Chgo. Club: Chgo. Athletic. Office: Carson Pirie Scott & Co 1 S State St Chicago IL 60603-2802 also: Carson Pirie Scott & Co 36 S Wabash Ave Chicago IL 60603

REICH, ABRAHAM CHARLES, lawyer; b. Waterbury, Conn., Apr. 17, 1949; s. Samuel and Esther (Gurvitz) R.; m. Sherri Engelman, Aug. 15, 1971; children: Spencer, Alexander. BA, U. Conn., 1971; JD, Temple U., 1974. Bar: Pa. 1974, U.S. Supreme Ct. 1979. Assoc. Fox, Rothschild, O'Brien & Frankel, Phila., 1974-81, ptnr., 1981—. Mem. Phila. Bar Assn. (chairperson profl. responsibility com. 1983-84, chairperson bench-bar com. 1985, chairperson profl. guidance com. 1987-88, bd. govs. 1987-89, chair bd. govs. 1989, vice chancellor 1993, chancellor-elect 1994, chancellor 1995). Home: 2224 Mt Vernon St Philadelphia PA 19130-3115 Office: Fox Rothschild O'Brien Frankel 2000 Market St Fl 10 Philadelphia PA 19103-3231

REICH, ALAN ANDERSON, association executive; b. Pearl River, N.Y., Jan. 1, 1930; s. Oswald David and Alma Carolyn (Anderson) R.; m. Gay Ann Forsythe, Dec. 19, 1954; children: James, Jeffrey, Andrew, Elizabeth. B.A., Dartmouth Coll., 1952; diploma in Slavic Studies, Oxford U., 1953; M.A., Russian Inst., Middlebury Coll., 1953; M.B.A., Harvard U., 1959; LLD (hon.), Gallaudet Coll., 1981, Dartmouth Coll., 1992. Exec. Polaroid Corp., Cambridge, Mass., 1960-70; dep. asst. sec. ednl. and cultural affairs Dept. State, Washington, 1970-75; spl. asst. to sec. HEW, 1976-77; dep. asst. sec. commerce, dir. Bur. East-West Trade, Dept. Commerce, 1977-78; pres. U.S. Council for Internat. Yr. of Disabled Persons, Washington, 1978-81, Nat. Orgn. Disability, Washington, 1982—, Bimillennium Found., 1982—, Disability 2000 CEO coun., 1991—. Chmn. Sudbury (Mass.) Community United Fund, 1962, 66; mem. U.S. del. WHO Gen. Assembly, 1970; pres. Nat. Paraplegia Found.; chmn. bd. dirs. Paralysis Cure Research Found., bd. dirs. of the Healing Community, chmn. People-to-people Com. for Handicapped; Impact Found., 1986—; chmn. World Com. on Disability, 1985—. Served to 1st lt. inf. AUS, 1953-57. Named to U.S. Army Inf. OCS Hall of Fame, 1994; recipient Sevier award for svc. to handicapped, 1994. Mem. Paralyzed Vets. Am., Cosmos Club, Achilles Club (London), Beta Theta Pi. Republican. Methodist. Home: 6017 Copely Ln Mc Lean VA 22101-2507 Office: Nat Orgn on Disability 910 16th St NW Ste 600 Washington DC 20006-2988

REICH, ALLAN J., lawyer; b. Chgo., July 9, 1948; s. H. Robert and Sonya (Minsky) R.; m. Lynne Susan Roth, May 23, 1971; children: Allison, Marissa, Scott. BA, Cornell U., 1970; JD cum laude, U. Mich. 1973. Bar: Ill. 1973, U.S. Dist. Ct. (no. dist.) Ill. 1973. Ptnr. McDermott, Will & Emery, Chgo., 1973-93; ptnr., chairperson corp./securities group D'Ancona & Pflaum, Chgo., 1993—. Bd. dirs., pres. Young Men's Jewish Council, Chgo., 1974-84, Coun. for Jewish Elderly, 1986—, v.p., mem. exec. com., 1989—; mem. men's council Mus. Contemporary Art, Chgo., 1983-90, pres. 1988-89; trustee Mus. of Contemporary Art, Chgo., 1988-89; v.p., mem. Chgo. exec. bd. Am. Jewish Com., 1989—; mem. adv. bd. Columbia Dance Ctr., 1992—. Mem. ABA, Chgo. Bar Assn. Clubs: Standard Club, Northmoor Country (Highland Park, Ill.). Home: 936 Skokie Ridge Dr Glencoe IL 60022-1434 Office: D'Ancona & Pflaum 30 N LaSalle St Chicago IL 60602

REICH, BERNARD, political science educator; b. Bklyn., Dec. 5, 1941; s. Moe and Rosalyn (Hartglass) R.; m. Madelyn Sue Ingber, June 16, 1963; children—Barry, Norman, Michael, Jennifer. BA cum laude with high honors, CCNY, 1961; MA, U. Va., 1963, PhD, 1964. Asst. prof. polit. sci. and internat. affairs George Washington U., Washington, 1964-70, assoc. prof., 1970-76, prof., 1976—, chmn. dept. polit. sci., 1976-82, 88-91; vis. prof. U. Va., 1969, 94, Sch. Advanced Internat. Studies Johns Hopkins U., 1978-80; vis. rsch. assoc. Tel Aviv U., 1971-72. Author: Quest for Peace: United States-Israel Relations and the Arab-Israeli Conflict, 1977, The U.S. and Israel: Influence in the Special Relationship, 1984, Israel: Land of Tradition and Conflict, 1985, 93, Historical Dictionary of Israel, 1992, Securing the Covenant: United States - Israel Relations After the Cold War, 1995; editor, co-author: Government and Politics of the Middle East and North Africa, 1980, 86, 95; editor, co-author: Israel Faces The Future, 1986, The Powers in the Middle East, 1987, Israeli National Security Policy: Political Actors and Perspectives, 1988, Political Leaders of the Contemporary Middle East and North Africa: A Biographical Dictionary, 1990, Israeli Politics in the 1990's Key Domestic and Foreign Policy Factors, 1991; co-author: United States Foreign Policy and the Middle East/North Africa: A Bibliography of Twentieth-Century Research, 1990, Asian States' Relations with the Middle East and North Africa: A Bibliography, 1950-93, 1994, U.S. Foreign Relations with the Middle East and North Africa: A Bibliography, 1994; mem. bd. adv. editors Middle East Jour., 1977—, Jour. Israel Affairs, 1994—, Terrorism, 1993, Fgn. Svc. Jour., 1987-90; contbr. articles to profl. jours. Bd. govs. Middle East Inst. Fulbright research scholar, UAR, 1965; NSF postdoctoral fellow, 1971-72. Mem. Internat. Inst. Strategic Studies, Middle East Studies Assn., Phi Beta Kappa. Home: 13800

Turnmore Rd Silver Spring MD 20906-2134 Office: George Washington U Dept Polit Sci Washington DC 20052

REICH, BERNARD, telecommunications engineer; b. N.Y.C., Jan. 7, 1926; s. Adolph and Rose (Gluck) R.; m. Sylvia Greenberg, June 15, 1947; children: Robin Reich Murphy, Richard. BS in Physics, CCNY, 1948; postgrad., Rutgers U., 1954. Electronic engr., supervisory electronic engr. U.S. Army Electronics R & D Command, Ft. Monmouth, N.J., 1948-81; unit mgr. Semcor, Farmingdale, N.J., 1981-88; telecommunications engr. Telos Corp., Shrewsbury, N.J., 1988—; mem. spl. working group on semicondts. and microelectronics NATO, Brussels, 1959-80, chmn. group experts on electronic parts, 1972-80; adv. editor Microelectronics and Reliability, 1970—. Contbr. over 100 articles to tech. jours.; patentee in field. Mem. Juvenile Conf. Com., Ocean Twp., N.J.; mem. Manor at Wayside Condominium Assn., Ocean Twp., 1990-91. Sgt. U.S. Army, 1945-46, ETO. Recipient decoration for meritorious civilian svc. U.S. Army Electronics R & D Command, 1981. Fellow IEEE (chartered), IEE (Eng.). Avocations: walking, grandparenting. Home: 45 Gimbel Pl Ocean NJ 07712-2565 Office: Telos Corp 656 Shrewsbury Ave Shrewsbury NJ 07701-4915

REICH, CHARLES WILLIAM, nuclear physicist; b. Oklahoma City, Sept. 12, 1930; s. Fred William And Gertrude Evelyn (Veal) R.; m. Juana Sue Woods, June 8, 1952; children: Paul William, Jane Kristen, Donna Karen. BS in Physics, U. Okla., 1952; MA in Physics, Rice U., 1954, PhD in Physics, 1956. Physicist, group leader Atomic Energy Div. Phillips Petroleum Co., Idaho Falls, Idaho, 1956-66; group leader, sect. chief Idaho Nuclear Corp., Idaho Falls, 1966-71; sect. chief Aerojet Nuclear Corp., Idaho Falls, 1971-76; prin. scientist, sect. chief EG&G Idaho, Inc., Idaho Falls, 1976-82, sci., engring. fellow, 1982-92, fellow emeritus, 1992—; guest scientist Niels Bohr Inst., Copenhagen, 1964-65; U.S. rep., coord. coordinated rsch. program IAEA, 1977-86; mem. transplutonium program com. U.S. Dept. Energy, 1978—; chmn. decay data subcom. Cross Sects. Evaluation Working Group, 1974-86; mem. task force on decay heat predictions nuclear data com. Nuclear Energy Agy., 1988-90; mem. sci. framework writing com. State of Idaho Dept. Edn., 1994. Contbr. articles to profl. jours. Recipient H.A. Wilson rsch. award Rice Inst., 1956; predoctoral fellow NSF, 1954-55. Fellow Am. Phys. Soc. (editorial bd. Phys. Rev. C); mem. N.Y. Acad. Scis., Sigma Xi, Phi Beta Kappa. Mem. Ch. Nazarene. Office: EG&G Idaho Inc Idaho Nat Engring Lab PO Box 1625 Idaho Falls ID 83415-2114

REICH, DANIEL H., physics educator. Asst. prof. dept. physics Johns Hopkins U., Baltimore, Md. Recipient Packard Fellowship David & Lucile Packard Found., 1993. Office: Johns Hopkins U Dept of Physics 3400 W Charles St Baltimore MD 21218-2608*

REICH, DAVID LEE, library director; b. Orlando, Fla., Nov. 25, 1930; s. P.F. and Opal Katherine (Wood) Reichelderfer; m. Kathleen Johanna Weichel, Aug. 2, 1954 (div. Sept. 1964); 1 son, Robert Weichel. Ph.B. magna cum laude, U. Detroit, 1961; A.M. in L.S. (Carnegie Library Sci. Endowment scholar), U. Mich., 1963. Tchr. English Jefferson Davis Jr. Sch., San Antonio, 1961-62; dir. emerging library Radiation Inc., Melbourne, Fla., 1963-64; asst. to dir. libraries Miami-Dade Jr. Coll., Miami, Fla., 1964-65; dir. learning resources Monroe County Community Coll., Monroe, Mich., 1965-68; dep. dir. Dallas Pub. Library, 1968-73; dep. chief librarian The Chgo. Pub. Library, 1973-74, commr., 1975-78; dir. Bd. Library Commrs., Commonwealth of Mass., Boston, 1978-80; exec. sec. New Eng. Library Bd., Augusta, Maine, 1980-82; dir. Lakeland Pub. Library, Lakeland, Fla., 1983—; vice chmn. New Eng. Library Bd., 1979-80; libr. cons. Macomb County C.C., Warren, Mich., 1967; chmn. adv. com. to libr. tech. asst. program El Centro Coll., Dallas, 1969-71; mem. inter-task working group Goals for Dallas, 1968-70, mem. Dallas Area Libr. planning coun., 1970-73; mem. adv. coun. dept. libr. sci. No. Ill. U., 1975-78; pres.-elect Tampa Bay Libr. Consortium, 1985-86, pres., 1986-87. Co-author: The Public Library in Non-traditional Education, 1974; Contbr. articles to library jours. Bd. dirs. The Villas II Homeowners Assn., 1994-95. Sgt. U.S. Army, 1952-55. Recipient Disting. Alumnus award U. Mich., 1978; William B. Calkins Found. scholar Orlando, 1963. Mem. ALA (coun.-at-large 1968-72, 75-79), S.E. Libr. Assn., Fla. Libr. Assn. (sec.-treas. coll. and spl. librs. div. 1965, steering com. mcpl. librs. caucus 1983-84, chmn. 1984-85, exec. bd. 1984-87), Soc. Fla. Archivists (exec. bd. 1994-95), Fla. Pub. Libr. Assn. (pres. 1987-88, exec. bd. 1988-89, 94-95, editor newsletter 1992-93, chmn. libr. adminstrn. div. 1992, friends and trustees div. 1993, 95), Alumni Assn. U. Mich. (pres. Libr. Sch. alumni 1973). Home: 3929 Old Road 37 Apt 134 Lakeland FL 33813-1058 Office: Lakeland Pub Libr 100 Lake Morton Dr Lakeland FL 33801-5347

REICH, HERB, editor; b. N.Y.C.; s. Herman S. and Hattie (Davis) R.; m. Gerri Toog, Aug. 7, 1960; children: Amanda Suri, Elizabeth Jo. B.A., Bklyn. Coll., 1950; M.A., Bklyn. Coll. and Kings County Hosp., 1951; postgrad., Columbia U., 1951-54. Author sketches and lyrics Tamiment Revues (Pa.), 1951; staff writer NBC-TV, N.Y.C. and Los Angeles, 1955-57; research coordinator Inst. for Motivational Research, Croton-on-Hudson, N.Y., 1958-59; research dir. Scientist and Engr. Technol. Inst., N.Y.C., 1960-64; mng. editor SETI Pubs. Inc., N.Y.C., 1961-64; sr. editor Odyssey Press, N.Y.C., 1964-65; editorial dir. Profl. and Tech. Programs Inc., N.Y.C., 1966-72; dir. Behavioral Sci. Book Service, N.Y.C., 1966-72; dir. behavioral scis. program Basic Books Inc., N.Y.C., 1973-79; editor intersci. div. John Wiley & Sons. Inc., N.Y.C., 1979-87, sr. editor profl. and trade div., 1987—; pres. H&G Reich, rsch., advt. & polit. cons., 1980—; researcher, statistician, rsch. cons. Am. Found. for Blind, Pepsi Cola Co., Nowland and Co., Communications and Media Rsch. Svcs.; freelance TV writer. Mng. editor: Odyssey Sci. Library Encyclopedia of Engineering, Signs and Symbols, 1965, Dictionary of Physics and Mathematics Abbreviations, Signs and Symbols, 1965, Dictionary of Electronics Abbreviations, Signs and Symbols, 1965; contbr.: Random House Dictionary of the English Language, 1967, revised edit., 1987, The Greatest Revue Sketches, 1982, Encyclopedia of Psychology, 2nd edit., 1994; TV writer: Broadway Open House, 1951, Milton Berle Texaco Star Theatre, 1952, All-Star Revue, 1952, Red Buttons Show, 1954, Tonight Show, 1956. Co-founder, vice chmn. Mt. Vernon United for Better Edn., N.Y., 1970-73; mem. Westchester County Democratic Com., 1972-76; exec. com. Mt. Vernon Dem. City Com., 1973-76; mem. supt.'s adv. com. Hastings Schs., Hastings-on-Hudson, N.Y., 1981-82. Recipient Gold award of excellence for radio advt. Advt. Club of Westchester, 1980; recipient Gold and Bronze awards of excellence for radio advt. Advt. Club of Westchester, 1981. Mem. AAAS, APA, N.Y. Acad. Scis., Internat. Platform Assn., Alpha Phi Omega.

REICH, JACK EGAN, insurance company executive; b. Chgo., June 17, 1910; s. Henry Carl and Rose (Egan) B.; m. Jean Grady, Apr. 30, 1935; children: Rosemary (Mrs. Jerry Semler), Judith (Mrs. Dan Hoyt). Student, Purdue U., 1928-31; LLD (hon.), Butler U., 1973; PhD (hon.), Marian Coll., 1983; LLD (hon.), Ind. U., 1986; PhD (hon.), Purdue U., 1993. With Inland Steel Co., East Chicago, Ind., 1925-31; field dir. gross income tax and employment security divs. State of Ind., 1933-40; field dir. Ind. C. of C., 1940-52, exec. v.p., 1952-62; pres., chmn. bd. Indpls. Water Co., 1962-67; chmn. bd. emeritus Am. United Life Ins. Co.; mem., past pres. Assn. Ind. Life Ins. Cos.; mem. exec. com.m bd. dirs. Indpls. Water Resources. Bd. dirs., past pres. Greater Indpls. Progress Com.; mem. exec. com., past chmn. Ind. Legal Found.; bd. dirs. Ind. Found., Wishard Meml. Found., Indpls. Downtown Inc.; bd. dirs., past campaign chmn., past pres. United Way Cen. Ind.; past mem. bd. lay trustees St. Mary-of-Woods Colls.; mem. adv. bd. St. Vincent Hosp.; bd. regents, past pres. Nat. Acad.; past local and state pres., nat. v.p. Jaycees. Mem. Ind. C. of C. (bd. dir., past chmn. and exec. v.p.), Econ. Club (past pres.), Columbia Club, Indpls. Athletic Club, Indpls. Press Club, Meridian Hills Country Club, Skyline Club (chmn.), Ind. Soc. Club (Chgo.), Pi Kappa Alpha. Home: 7404 N Pennsylvania St Indianapolis IN 46240-3067 Office: Am United Life Ins Co 1 American Sq PO Box 368 Indianapolis IN 46206

REICH, KENNETH IRVIN, journalist; b. Los Angeles, Mar. 7, 1938; s. Herman and Ruth Alberta (Nussbaum) R.; m. Nov. 14, 1970; children: Kathleen, David. B.A., Dartmouth Coll., 1960; M.A. (Woodrow Wilson fellow), U. Calif., Berkeley, 1962. With UPI, Sacramento, 1962-63, Life mag., 1963-65; with Los Angeles Times, 1965—, polit. writer, 1972-77, 1984 Olympics writer, 1977-84, investigative reporter ins. law, ins. politics & fin.

sports, 1985-92; lectr. in field. Author: Making it Happen, Peter Ueberroth and the 1984 Olympics, 1985, Covering Earthquakes, Volcanos and Other Issues Relating to Geology, 1992—; contbr. articles to mags. Daniel Webster Nat. Honor scholar Dartmouth Coll., 1956-60. Mem. Dartmouth Alumni Club (chpt. officer 1991—, dist. enrollment dir. 1992—, meml. chmn. Dartmouth Class of 1960, 1993—). Office: Times-Mirror Sq Los Angeles CA 90053

REICH, LARRY SAM, lawyer; b. Bklyn., Sept. 24, 1946; s. Sidney and Regina (Brown) R.; m. Patricia S. Neustein, Aug. 18, 1968; children: Ilysa Jill, Shari Beth. BA, Hofstra U., 1969; JD, Bklyn. Law Sch., 1973. Bar: N.Y. 1974, U.S. Dist. Ct. (so. and ea. dists.) N.Y. 1974, U.S. Ct. Appeals (2d cir.) 1974, U.S. Supreme Ct. 1980. Assoc. S. Edward Orenstein PC, N.Y.C., 1973-78; ptnr. Herzfeld & Rubin PC, N.Y.C., 1978—; arbitrator U.S. Dist. Ct. for Ea. Dist. N.Y., Bklyn., 1986—. Mem. ABA, N.Y. State Bar Assn. (chmn. com. on supreme cts. 1986-89, chmn. com. on jud. adminstrn. 1989-92, mem. com. jud. adminstrn. 1989—), N.Y. County Bar Assn., Nassau County Bar Assn., Assn. Trial Lawyers Am., N.Y. State Trial Lawyers Assn. Avocations: running, rowing, biking, reading. Office: Herzfeld & Rubin PC 40 Wall St New York NY 10005-1303

REICH, MERRILL DRURY, intelligence consultant, writer; b. Washington, Aug. 28, 1930; s. Merrill Dale Reich and Evelyn Merle (Wright) Menk; m. Georgia Ann Ewing, Aug. 28, 1953; 1 child, Alexandra Therese. BA in History, Govt., Rollins Coll., 1954; postgrad., U. Vienna, 1954-55, Naval War Coll., 1973-74; MA in Mgmt., Cen. Mich. U., 1981. Commd. ensign USN, 1955, advanced through grades to capt., ret., 1982; dir. systems mgmt. BDM Corp., Columbia, Md., 1982-92; cons. Crytec, Inc., 1992—. Fulbright scholar, 1954-55. Mem. U.S. Naval Inst., Naval War Coll. Found., Assn. Former Intelligence Officers, Navy Cryptologic Vets. Assn., Fulbright Assn., New Eng. Hist. Genealogical Soc., Omicron Delta Kappa, Pi Gamma Mu, Phi Kappa Tau. Republican. Avocations: genealogy, lapidary, antiques, swimming, sailing. Home: 1731 Tarleton Way Crofton MD 21114-2503

REICH, MICHAEL, economics educator; b. Poland, Oct. 18, 1945; came to U.S., 1949; s. Melvin and Betty (Mandelbaum) R.; m. Nancy J. Chodorow, 1977; children: Rachel, Gabriel. BA, Swarthmore Coll., 1966; PhD, Harvard U., 1974. Asst. prof. Boston U., 1971-74; asst. prof. U. Calif., Berkeley, 1974-81, acting assoc. prof., 1981-82, assoc. prof., 1982-89, prof., 1989—; rsch. dir. Nat. Ctr. for the Workplace, 1993—. Author: Segmented Work, Divided Workers, 1982, Racial Inequality, 1981, The Capitalist System, 1986, Social Structurs of Accumulation, 1994; editor: Indsl. Rels. Jour., 1986—; contbr. articles to profl. jours. Mem. Am. Econ. Assn., Indsl. Rels. Rsch. Assn., Phi Beta Kappa, Sigma Xi. Office: Dept of Econs U Calif 611 Evans Hall Berkeley CA 94720

REICH, MORTON MELVYN, marketing communications company executive; b. Phila., Aug. 11, 1939; s. Morris and Lillian (Rabinowitz) R.; m. Geraldine Joan Krassan, May 31, 1964; children: Hope, Marla. Student, Charles Morris Price Sch. Advt. and Journalism, 1961-62, Temple U., 1963-68. Asst. dir. pub. relations Goodwill Industries, Phila., 1962-63; dir. promotion and information services Yellow Cab Co., Phila., 1963-66; dir. corp. employee communications Philco-Ford Co., Phila., 1966-68; exec. dir. J.M. Korn & Son Inc., Phila., 1968-75; pres. Richard Yeager Assos., Moorestown, 1975—; Reich, Robinson, Inc., Phila., 1975-76; sr. v.p. Kalish & Rice, Phila., 1976-79; exec. dir. owner Mktg. Communications Mgmt., Phila., from 1979; now pres. The Reich Group (formerly Mktg. Communications mgmt.), Phila.; tchr. Charles Morris Price Sch.; lectr. in field. Contbr. articles to profl. jours. Served with USN, 1957-60. Recipient Disting. Alumni award Charles Morris Price Sch., 1973, Creative Marketing award Readers Digest, 1974, Nat. Jr. C. of C. award, 1972. Mem. Phila. Jr. C. of C. (dir. 1962-65), Advt. Chairmen Phila. Fellowship Commn., others. Home: 6N Woodleigh Dr Cherry Hill NJ 08003 Office: Reich Group 1635 Market St Fl 200 Philadelphia PA 19103-2202

REICH, NATHANIEL EDWIN, physician, poet, author, artist, educator; b. N.Y.C., May 19, 1907; s. Alexander and Betty (Feigenbaum) R.; m. Joan Finkel, May 22, 1943; children: Andrew, Matthew. B.S., NYU, 1927; student, Marquette U. Coll. Medicine, 1927-29; M.D., Rush Med. Coll., 1932. Diplomate Am. Bd. Internal Medicine. Intern, resident pathologist City Hosp., N.Y.C., 1931-33; emeritus attending physician Kingsbrook Jewish Med. Center Hosp.; vis. physician Kings County Hosp., Bklyn.; attending physician State U. Hosp.; faculty SUNY Downstate Med. Center, 1938—, asso. clin. prof. medicine, 1952-74, clin. prof., 1974-77, emeritus prof., 1977—; vis. prof. San Marcos U. Coll. Medicine, Lima, Peru, 1968, U. Afghanistan, 1970, U. Indonesia, 1972, U. Sri Lanka, 1975; asst. attending physician N.Y. Postgrad. Hosp., Columbia U., 1940; cons. Dept H and HS; cardiac cons. U.S. R.R. Retirement Bd., 1965—; program cons. Acad. Family Physicians, 1973, N.Y. State Disability Determinations; lectr. univs., Rome, Moscow, Rijeka, Haiti, Jerusalem, Cairo, Athens, Bangkok, Bucharest, Manila, Lisbon, Beijing, Shanghai, Witwatersrand, Capetown, Natal, Lima, Buenos Aires, Rio de Janeiro, Quito; lectr. univs. U. Madras (India), 1969, Spain, 1971, Auckland, N.Z., Sydney, Australia, also; lectr. univs. Japan Med. Assn., Philippine Heart Assn., Royal Thai Air Force Med. Service, China Med. Assn., Shanghai, 1978, Nat. Taiwan U., Taipei, 1978, Beijing Cardiac Inst., 1986; chmn. internat. cardiology sect. Congress Chest Diseases, Cologne, Germany, 1956; impartial specialist U.S. Fed. Employees; cons. N.Y. State Bur. Disability Determinations, N.Y.C.; Office Vocat. Rehab., Dept. Health and Human Services, 1965—; chief med. examiner SSS, 1942-44 (Presdl. commendation). Exhibited one-man show, L.I. U., 1961, NYU Loeb Ctr., 1962, 72, 74, Greer Gallery, 1962, 64, St. Charles, La., 1964, Nyack, N.Y., 1986, Prospect Park Ctrl. Art Show, 1966, Art Inst. Boston, 1970, 76, George Wiener Gallery, 1972; group shows Little Studio, 1952, Mus. Modern Art, Paris, 1970, Bodley Gallery, 1965, 69, Nyack, N.Y., 1987, others; represented permanent collections, Huntington Hartford collection N.Y. Cultural Ctr., 1969, Washington County Mus. of Fine Arts, Hagerstown, Md. Served from 1st lt. to maj. M.C., AUS, 1944-47. Recipient St. Gaudens award, 1923, 1st prize Art Assn. AMA, 1948, 1st prize Art Assn. Literary Soc., 1949, Disting. Achievement award Boys' H.S. Alumni Assn., 1988, Am. Poetry Assn. Hon. mention World of Poetry, 1990; named Best New Poets of 1989, 94, 95. Fellow ACP, Royal Soc. Medicine, Am. Coll. Cardiology, Am. Coll. Angiology (med. honor award 1956, 59), Am. Coll. Legal Medicine (founder), Am. Coll. Chest Physicians (chmn. exhibits com. 1961, cardiovascular rehab. com. 1965, coronary disease com. 1968, pres. N.Y. state chpt. 1970); mem. N.Y. State Med. Soc. (vice chmn. space med. sect. 1967, 75, chmn. chest sect. 1972), Internat. Soc. Internal Medicine, World Med. Assn., Am. Heart Assn. (coun. on thrombosis), N.Y. Heart Assn., Explorers Club, Temple Club (v.p.), Doctors Club Bklyn. (vice chmn. bd. govs.), Circumnavigators. Home: 1620 Avenue I Brooklyn NY 11230-3050

REICH, OTTO JUAN, political analyst, business consultant; b. Havana, Cuba, Oct. 16, 1945; came to U.S., 1960; s. Walter and Graciela Maria (Fleites) R.; m. Connie Lynn Dillinger, Apr. 19, 1975; children: Adrienne Michelle, Natalie Lauren. BA, U. N.C., Chapel Hill, 1966; MA, Georgetown U., 1973; grad., Officers Candidate Sch., U.S. Army, 1967. Civil affairs officer U.S. Army, Panama, 1967-69; staff asst. U.S. Ho. Reps., Washington, 1970-71; v.p. Cormorant Enterprises, Miami, Fla., 1972-73; internat. rep. Fla. Dept. Commerce, Coral Gables, 1973-75; community devel. coordinator City of Miami, 1975-76; dir. Washington ops. Council of the Americas, 1976-81; asst. adminstr. U.S. AID, Washington, 1981-83; spl. adv. for pub. diplomacy to sec. state with rank of ambassador U.S. Dept. State, Washington, 1983-86; ambassador to Venezuela, Caracas, 1986-89; sr. assoc. Ctr. for Strategic and Internat. Studies, Washington, 1989—; ptnr. Brock Group, 1990—; mem. alt. U.S. rep. UN Human Rights Commn., Geneva, 1991-92. 1st lt. U.S. Army, 1966-69. Decorated Order of Liberator grand cordon class (Venezuela); recipient Superior Honor award U.S. State Dept., 1986-89, 91, Exemplary Svc. award U.S. State Dept., 1988. Mem. Coun. Am. Ambs., Nat. Leadership Coun. (vice chmn.), Ctr. for Strategic and Internat. Studies. Office: Ctr for Strategic & Intl Studies 1800 K St NW Ste 400 Washington DC 20006-2200

REICH, PAULINE CAROLE, international business consultant, educator, author; b. Kew Gardens, N.Y., Nov. 13, 1946; d. Stanley Garfield and Elsa Olga (Doctor) R. Cert. in critical langs. program, Princeton U., 1967; BA,

---

CCNY, 1968; MA, CUNY, 1972; JD, N.Y. Law Sch., 1985; grad., Coro Found. Pub. Affairs Leadership Program, 1981. Bar: N.J., U.S. Ct. Internat. Trade, U.S. Ct. Appeals (Fed. cir.). Cons. Pan Pacific, Inc., Bayside, N.Y., 1988-90, Japan Pacific Group, N.Y.C., 1990-93, Asia Pacific Group, Great Neck, N.Y., 1994—; prof. Waseda U. Sch. Law, Tokyo, 1995—. Contbr. book chpts. and articles to profl. jours. Japan Found. fellow, 1973, Princeton Found. fellow, 1966-67, Carnegie Found. fellow, 1966-67, Nat. Def. Edn. Act. fellow, 1966; elected East Coast Dir. Ind. Scholars Asia, 1981-86. Mem. ABA (sect. of internat. law and practice, labor and employment law, dispute resolution sect., Asia-Pacific law com.), Japan Soc., Assn. for Asian Studies (exec. com. on Asian law). Avocations: international travel, underwater photography, genealogy. Office: Waseda U Sch Law, 1-6-1 Nishi-Waseda, Shinjuku-Ku, Tokyo Japan

REICH, ROBERT BERNARD, U.S. secretary of labor, political economics educator; b. Scranton, Pa., June 24, 1946; s. Edwin Saul and Mildred Dorf (Freshman) R.; m. Clare Dalton, July 7, 1973. BA, Dartmouth Coll., 1968, MA (hon.), 1988; MA, Oxford (Eng.) U., 1970; JD, Yale U., 1973. Asst. solicitor gen. U.S. Dept. Justice, Washington, 1974-76; dir. policy planning FTC, Washington, 1976-81; mem. faculty John F. Kennedy Sch. Govt. Harvard U., Cambridge, Mass., 1981—; Sec. Dept. of Labor, Washington, 1993—; chmn. biotech. sect. U.S. Office Tech. Assessment, Washington, 1990-91. Author: The Next American Frontier, 1983, Tales of a New America, 1987, The Work of Nations, 1991; co-author: The Power of Public Ideas, 1987; contbg. editor The New Republic, Washington, 1982-93; chmn. editorial bd. The Am. Prospect, 1990-93. Mem. governing bd. Common Cause, Washington, 1981-85; bd. dirs. Bus. Enterprise Trust, Palo Alto, Calif., 1989-93; trustee Dartmouth Coll., Hanover, N.H., 1989-93. Rhodes scholar, 1968; recipient Louis Brownlow award ASPA, 1983.

REICH, ROBERT SIGMUND, retired landscape architect; b. N.Y.C., Mar. 22, 1913; s. Ulysses S. and Adele G. R.; m. Helen Elizabeth Adams, May, 1945; children—Barbara, Betsy, Bob, Bill. B.S., Cornell U., 1934, Ph.D., 1941; postgrad., U. So. Calif., 1951. Instr. landscape design Cornell U., 1936-39, 40-41; instr. landscape design U. Conn., 1939-40; Inst. Land Design La. State U., 1941-46, asst. prof. landscape architecture, 1946-49, assoc. prof. 1949-60, prof., 1960—, Alumni prof., 1967—, head dept. landscape architecture, 1964-79, dir. Sch.Landscape Architecture, 1979-83; prof. Landscape Architecture, 1992—; instr. Shrivenham (Eng.) Am. U., 1946, Biarritz (France) Am. U., 1947; vis. lectr. Tulane U., 1958-67; judge, instr. Nat. Council Garden Clubs, 1956—; mem. task force on parks, recreation and tourism Goals for La. Program; mem. com. to establish Chicot State Park Arboretum, Ville Plate, La., 1964, mem. steering com., 1964-75; examiner La. Bd. Examination for Landscape Architects, 1957-77. Co-author: Landscape and You, 1953. Mem. com. to establish City/Parish Beautification Commn., 1961-82; mem. area and facilities com. Baton Rouge Recreation and Parks Commn., 1957-83; bd. dirs. Hubbard Edn. Trust, Weston, Mass., 1967—; adv. com. Friends of Frederick Law Olmsted Papers, 1983—. With U.S. Army, 1942-45; in charge alter arrangements U. United Meth. Ch. 1945—. Recipient Teaching award of merit Gamma Sigma Delta, 1963. Fellow Am. Soc. Landscape Architects (trustee 1968-71, 83-86, 3d v.p. 1971-73, Medal 1992); mem. S.W. Park and Recreation Tng. Inst. (dir. 1975-77, award of merit 1968), Phi Kappa Phi, Pi Alpha xi, Omicron Delta Kappa, Sigma Lambda Alpha. Home: 333 E Boyd Dr Baton Rouge LA 70808-4507 Office: La State U Sch Landscape Architecture Coll Design Bldg Baton Rouge LA 70803

REICH, ROSE MARIE, retired art educator; b. Milw., Dec. 24, 1937; d. Valentine John and Mary Jane (Grochowski) Kosmatka; m. Kenneth Pierce Reich, July 13, 1968; 1 stepson, Lance Pierce. BA, Milw. Downer Coll., 1959; MA, U. Wyo., 1967. Art tchr. Oconomowoc (Wis.) Area Schs., 1959-93, ret., 1993. Mem. Oconomowoc Edn. Assn., NEA (life), Wis. Edn. Assn., AAUW (v.p. membership 1989—), Delta Kappa Gamma (past pres.). Roman Catholic. Avocations: Newfoundland dogs, needlework, designing stationery, Polish paper cutting, restoring old church statues and mannequins. Home: 3717 N Golden Lake Rd Oconomowoc WI 53066-4104

REICH, SEYMOUR DAVID, lawyer, former fraternal organization executive; b. Bklyn., Apr. 23, 1933; s. James and Esther (Reich) R.; m. Helyn Brenner; children: Keith E., Leslie B., Jaime Reich Amiram. BA, U. Pa., 1954; LLB, Harvard U., 1957. Sr. ptnr. Dreyer and Traub, N.Y.C. Pres. B'nai Brith Internat., 1986-90; chmn. Conf. of Pres.'s Major Am. Jewish Orgns., 1989-90. Mem. Phi Beta Kappa. Office: Dreyer and Traub 101 Park Ave New York NY 10178-0001

REICH, STEVE, composer; b. N.Y.C., Oct. 3, 1936; m. Beryl Korot; children: Ezra, Michael. Studies in percussion with Roland Kohloff, 1950-53; BA in Philosophy with honors, Cornell U., 1957; studies in composition with Hall Overton, 1957-58; studies with Bergsma and Persichetti, Julliard Sch. Music, 1958-61; MA in Music, Mills Coll., 1963; studies in composition with Darius Milhaud and Luciano Berio; studies in drumming, Inst. for African Studies, U. Ghana, 1971; student, Am. Soc. for Ea. Arts, Seattle and Berkeley, 1973, 74, Cantillation of Hebrew Scriptures, N.Y.C. and Jerusalem, 1976-77. Organized ensemble Steve Reich and Musicians, 1966; performed throughout the world, 1971—; recs. with various cos. including Columbia Records, Disques Shandar, Hungaraton, Angel, ECM, Deutsche Grammophon, Nonesuch, Phillips, Virgin Classics, Argo. Composer, performer: (albums) Come Out, 1967, It's Gonna Rain, 1969, Violin Phase, 1969, Four Organs, 1970, Phase Patterns, 1970, Drumming, 1971, Four Organs, 1973, Six Pianos, 1973, Music for Mallet Instruments, Voices, and Organ, 1973, Music for Eighteen Musicians, 1978, Octet, 1980, Music for a Large Ensemble, 1980,Violin Phase, 1980, Tehillim, 1982, The Desert Music, 1984, Sextet, 1986, Six Marimbas, 1986, Electric Counterpoint, 1987, Different Trains, 1988 (Grammy award 1989), The Four Sections, 1987, others; composer: Vermont Counterpoint, Variations for Winds, Strings and Keyboards, Eight Lines for Chamber Orchestra, Piano Phase, Clapping Music, Pendulum Music, Music for Pieces of Wood, other works performed by major orchs. and ensembles; commd. to compose for Holland Festival, 1978, Radio Frankfurt, 1979, San Francisco Symphony, 1980, Rothko Chapel, 1981, West German Radio, Cologne, 1984, Frumm Music Found., 1985, Richard Stoltzman, 1985, Bklyn. Acad. Music, 1987, Kronos Quartet, 1988, St. Louis Sympnony, 1987, The Cave commd. by Vienna Festival, Holland Festival, Festival d'Automne à Paris, Theatre de la Monnaie, Brussels, Hebbel Theatre, Berlin, South Bank Centre/Serious Speakout, London and the Brooklyn Acad. Music, Next Wave Festival, 1993. Recipient Koussevitzky Found. award, 1981; Rockefeller Found. grantee 1975, 78, 81, 90, Nat. Endowment for the Arts grantee, 1974, 76, 91, N.Y. State Council on the Arts grantee, 1974; Guggenheim fellow, 1978. Office: care IMG Artists 22 E 71st St New York NY 10021*

REICH, WILLIAM MICHAEL, advertising executive; b. N.Y.C., July 28, 1943; s. William Adolph and Mildred Joan (Chestaro) R.; m. Carmela Louise Ezzone; children: Concetta M., John M., Russell D. Student, N.Y.C. Community Coll., 1961-62, Sch. Visual Arts, N.Y.C., 1962-65. Tech. illustrator Grumman Aerospace Corp., Bethpage, N.Y., 1965-67; tech. illustrator Dayton T. Brown, Inc., Bohemia, N.Y., 1967-68, art dir., 1968-69, art dir., prodn. mgr., 1969-71, sales and estimating mgr., 1971-74; art dir. Volt Info. Scis., Garden City, N.Y., 1974-75, salesman, 1975-78, directories mgr., 1978-80; corp. publs. mgr. Loral Microwave Group, Hauppauge, N.Y., 1980-93, mgr. sales adminstrn., 1993—. Recipient Bronze award Gold Book, 1980, Cert. of Merit award, Printing Industries of Metro N.Y., 1983. Mem. Bus. Mktg. Assn. (Bus. to Bus. Best award for product brochure 1993, Cert. Merit full line catalogs 1994), L.I. Advt. Club (Cert. of Merit award 1980-82, 85). Republican. Clubs: L.I. Studebaker (editor, Massapequa, N.Y.). Office: Loral Microwave Narda 435 Moreland Rd Hauppauge NY 11788-3926

REICH, YARON Z., lawyer; b. Bklyn., June 1, 1950. BA, Columbia U., 1975, JD, 1978; LLM in Taxation, NYU, 1984. Bar: Pa. 1978, N.Y. 1979. Law clk. to Hon. Arlin M. Adams U.S. Ct. Appeals (3d cir.), 1978-79; ptnr. Cleary, Gottlieb, Steen & Hamilton, N.Y.C. Spl. issue editor Columbia Law Review, 1977-78. Mem. Assn. Bar City of N.Y. (taxation of corps. com.) N.Y. State Bar Assn. (exec. com. tax sect. 1992-97). Office: Cleary Gottlieb Steen & Hamilton 1 Liberty Plz New York NY 10006-1401

REICHARD, HUGO MANLEY, English literature educator; b. South Plainfield, N.J., Jan. 21, 1918; s. Bernard and Emma (Klein) R.; m. Virginia

---

Evelyn Kougias, Aug. 28, 1943; children—Enid Evelyn Reichard Satariano, Claude Manley, Eric George. B.A., U. Mich., 1939; M.A., Harvard U., 1948, Ph.D., 1951. Instr. English lit. Duke U., 1951-56; mem. faculty Purdue U., 1956-88, prof. English lit., 1970-88, prof. emeritus, 1988—. Author articles in field. Served with AUS, 1941-46. Decorated Bronze Star. Mem. MLA, Johnson Soc. Central Region (pres. 1979-80). Office: Purdue U Heavilon Hall English Dept West Lafayette IN 47907

REICHARD, JOHN FRANCIS, educational consultant; b. Abington, Pa., June 2, 1924; s. Francis Radcliffe and Katharine (Butler) R.; m. Ruth Naomi Nachod, Aug. 5, 1950; children: Scot, John Nicholas. BA, Wesleyan U., 1949, postgrad., 1949-50; postgrad., Glasgow U., Scotland, 1950-51. Instr. English/humanities Wesleyan U., Middletown, Conn., 1951-52, Ohio Wesleyan U., Delaware, 1952-54; internat. campus adminstr. U.S. Nat. Student Assn., Cambridge, Mass., 1954; exec. dir. Internat. Student Assn. Greater Boston, 1955-60; pres. Phila. Coun. for Internat. Visitors, 1960-73; internat. coord. Phila. 76, 1973-75; exec. dir. Global Interdependence Ctr., 1975-79; exec. v.p. NAFSA: Assn. of Internat. Educators, Washington, 1980-92; internat. edn. cons., Bethesda, Md., 1992—. Bd. Internat. Devel. Conf.; mem. internat. program com. USDA Grad. Sch. Counselor Meridian House Internat.; travel adv. com. U.S. Travel Svc., 1963-64; pres. Nat. Coun. Internat. Visitors, 1963-65; organizer, co-chmn. Internat. Yr. of Child, UNICEF, Phila., 1977-78; internat. adv. bd. Bryn Mawr Coll., 1975-79; chmn. schools com. Phila. steering com. on alumni affairs Wesleyan U., 1968-76; adv. bd. Hariri Found.; mem. Nat. Liaison Com. on Fgn. Student Admissions. Contbr. articles to profl. jours. Served with USAAF, 1943-46. Winchester fellow Wesleyan U., 1949; Fulbright scholar Glasgow U., 1950-51; recipient Tribute of Appreciation, U.S. Dept. State, 1973, 92, Svc. award Coun. on Internat. Ednl. Exch., 1991. Mem. Am. Coun. on Edn. (secretariat, commn. on internat. edn. 1980-92), Internat. Ednl. Exch. Liaison Group (chmn. 1982-84), Test of English as a Fgn. Lang. (policy coun.), Fulbright Alumni Assn. (v.p. 1978-80), Cosmos Club, Phi Beta Kappa. Democrat. Home: 4974 Sentinel Dr Apt 301 Bethesda MD 20816-3571

REICHARDT, DELBERT DALE, financial executive; b. Chgo., Mar. 2, 1927; s. Arthur Christian and Kristine Neoline (Fulsaas) R.; children: Leslie Kirsten, Delbert Dale. B.A., Carroll Coll., Waukesha, Wis., 1949; M.B.A., Harvard U., 1956. Vice pres. Kidder, Peabody & Co., Inc., Boston and N.Y.C., 1956-68; v.p. fin. GAC Corp., Allentown, Pa. and Miami, Fla., 1968-72; exec. v.p. fin. and adminstrn. Gt. Am. Mgmt. & Investment Co., Atlanta, 1972-79; dir., sec. Gt. Am. Mgmt. and Investment Inc., Atlanta, 1979-81; regional mgr. J.P. Cleaver Co. div. Hay Group, 1981-83; exec. v.p. Am. Carbons Inc., 1983-85; regional investment banking officer Bank of Am., 1986-87; mng. dir. Baseline Capital Corp., Atlanta, 1988-90, Argent Fin. Svcs., Atlanta, 1990-93; pres., mng. dir., prin. Raven Capital Group, Atlanta, 1993—. Contbg. author: Chief Executive's Handbook, 1976. Bd. dirs. Productivity Ctr., Ga. State U.; pres., bd. dirs St. Anne's Terrace Inc. Served to 1st lt. USAF, 1950-54. Mem. Fin. Execs. Inst. (pres. 1985-86), Capital City Club, Harvard U. Bus. Sch. Club, Masons. Home: 2482 Brookhaven Pl NE Atlanta GA 30319-3018

REICHARDT, GLENN RICHARD, lawyer; b. Passaic, N.J., Sept. 22, 1951; s. Werner Richard and Angelina (Meli) R.; m. JoAnn Leigh Zuercher, Mar. 8, 1986; children: Joseph Zuercher, Joanna Zuercher, Alyssa Reichardt, Andrew Reichardt. AB, Duke U., 1973; M in Pub. Policy, Harvard U., 1977, JD, 1977. Bar: D.C. 1977, U.S. Ct. Internat. Trade 1973. Assoc. Warner, Norcross & Judd, Washington, 1977-79; assoc. Peabody, Lambert & Meyers, Washington, 1979-83, ptnr., 1983-84; ptnr. Kirkpatrick & Lockhart, Washington, 1984—. Mem. editl. adv. bd. N.Am. Trade Guide, 1993—; contbr. articles to Global Trade mag., 1988-89. Mem. ABA. Home: 6864 Tulip Hill Ter Bethesda MD 20816-1031 Office: Kirkpatrick & Lockhart 1800 M St NW Washington DC 20036-5891

REICHARDT, PAUL BERNARD, dean, chemistry educator; b. St. Louis, Aug. 15, 1943; s. Bernard George and Elaine Charlotte (Schmudde) R.; m. Cordelia Morris Hufnagel, Apr. 27, 1968; children: Laura, Rebecca, Daniel. BS, Davidson Coll., 1965; PhD in Organic Chemistry, U. Wis., 1969. Post-doctoral rsch. assoc. Yale U., New Haven, 1969-71, instr., 1971; asst. prof. Ohio State U., Columbus, 1971-72; asst. prof. chemistry U. Alaska, Fairbanks, 1972-75, assoc. prof. chemistry, 1975-81, prof. chemistry, 1981—, dean coll. natural scis., 1991—; head dept. chemistry U. Alaska, Fairbanks, 1978-82, 88-90, interim dean coll. natural scis., 1990-91, interim provost, 1993-94; interim dir. U. Alaska Mus., 1992-93; mem. Gov.'s Sci. & Engring. Adv. Com., 1986-90, Alaska 2000 Sci. Standards Com., 1992-93. Contbr. articles to profl. jours., chpts. to books and monographs. Named one of Outstanding Young Men of Am. Jaycees, 1980; recipient Inspirational Tchr. award U. Alaska at Fairbanks Alumni Assn., 1982. Mem. AAAS, Am. Chem. Soc., Internat. Soc. Chem. Ecology, Phi Beta Kappa, Sigma Xi (pres. local chpt. 1994-95), Phi Kappa Phi. Presbyterian. Avocations: fishing, camping, hiking. Office: University of Alaska Coll Natural Scis 465 Duckering Bldg Fairbanks AK 99775-1240

REICHART, STUART RICHARD, lawyer; b. N.Y.C., Nov. 18, 1924; s. Stanley and Rae (Wein) R.; m. Joan Feirtag, Mar. 28, 1981. LLB, Bklyn. Law Sch., 1948; LLM, NYU, 1951. Bar: N.Y. 1949, D.C. 1971, U.S. Supreme Ct. Adminstrv. judge Armed Services Bd. Contract Appeals, Washington, 1966-72; asst. gen. counsel for procurement USAF, Washington, 1972-75, dep. gen. counsel, 1975-78, gen. counsel, 1978-81; of counsel Fried, Frank, Harris, Shriver & Jacobson, Washington, 1982-90; ind. cons., 1991—; instr. govt. procurement Ohio State U., U. Dayton, U. Md., 1960-70. Contbr. legal articles on govt. procurement to profl. jours. Served with AUS, 1942-45; served to col. USAF, 1951-71. Decorated Legion of Merit, D.F.C., Air medal with silver oak leaf cluster, Purple Heart; recipient Disting. Civilian Service medals Dept. Air Force, 1979, Dept. Def., 1982, Stuart R. Reichart award USAF, 1982. Mem. ABA, Fed. Bar Assn. Lodge: Masons. Avocations: bridge, tennis, golf. Home and Office: 8000 Grand Teton Dr Potomac MD 20854-4074 also: 16873C Isle of Palm Dr Delray Beach FL 33484-6941

REICHARTZ, W. DAN, hotel executive; b. 1946. Exec. Hilton Hotels Corp., N.Y.C., 1965-76, 85-86; pres., treas. Va. Hot Springs Inc., Hot Springs Telephone Co. & Devel. Co., 1976-85; pres., CEO Caesars Palace, Las Vegas, 1987—. Office: Caesars Palace 3570 Las Vegas Blvd S Las Vegas NV 89109-8933

REICHE, FRANK PERLEY, lawyer, former federal commissioner; b. Hartford, Conn., May 8, 1929; s. Karl Augustus and LaFetra (Perley) R.; m. Janet Taylor, Sept. 26, 1953; children: Cynthia Reiche Schumacker, Dean S. AB, Williams Coll., 1951; LLB, Columbia U., 1959; MA, George Washington U., 1959; LLM in Taxation, NYU, 1966. Bar: N.J. 1960, D.C. 1981. Assoc. Stryker, Tams & Dill, Newark, 1959-61; assoc. Smith, Stratton, Wise & Heher, Princeton, N.J., 1962-64, ptnr., 1964-79; commr. Fed. Election Commn., Washington, 1979-85; chmn. Fed. Election Commn., 1982; ptnr. Katzenbach, Gildea & Rudner, Lawrenceville, N.J., 1986-93; pvt. practice law Princeton, N.J., 1993—. Trustee Westminster Choir Coll., Princeton, 1974-86, Ctr. Theol. Inquiry, Princeton, 1991—; Wells Coll., Aurora, N.Y., 1994—; mem. planned giving com. Williams Coll., Williamstown, Mass., 1973-87, nat. chmn. planned giving, 1983-87. Lt. USN, 1952-56. Mem. ABA, D.C. Bar Assn., N.J. Bar Assn. (N.J. state chair 1995—), Am. Coll. Trust and Estate Counsel. Republican. Presbyterian. Clubs: Washington Golf and Country, Capitol Hill.

REICHEK, JESSE, artist; b. Bklyn., Aug. 16, 1916; s. Morris and Celia (Bernstein) R.; m. Laure Guyot, May 16, 1950; children—Jonathan, Joshua. Student, Inst. Design, Chgo., 1941-42; diploma, Academie Julian, Paris, 1951. Instr. design architecture U. Mich., Ann Arbor, 1946-47; prof. Inst. Design Ill. Inst. Tech., Chgo., 1951-53; prof. dept. architecture U. Calif., Berkeley, 1953-87, prof. emeritus, 1987—; cons. Nat. Design Inst. Ford Found. project, Ahmedabad, India, 1963, San Francisco Redevel. Agy. Embarcadero Center, 1966—; lectr. Nat. Inst. Architects, Rome, 1960, U. Florence, 1960, U. Naples, 1960, Israel Inst. Tech., 1960, Greek Architects Soc., Athens, 1960, U. Belgrade, 1960, MIT, 1965, U. N.Mex., 1964, Am. Cultural Center, Paris, 1960, 64, Gujarat Inst. Engrs. and Architects, 1963, U. Colo., 1961, Harvard, 1962, U. Minn., 1962, U. Coll. London, 1967, Inst. Contemporary Arts, London, 1967, Ecole Nationale des Beaux-Arts, 1967; artist in residence Tamarind Lithography Workshop, 1966, Am. Acad. in

Rome, 1971-72; research prof. Creative Arts Inst. U. Calif., 1966-67; artist in residence IBM Los Angeles Sci. Center, 1970-71. Exhibited one man shows at, Galerie Cahiers d'Art Paris, 1951, 59, 68, U. Calif. at Berkeley, 1954, Betty Parsons Gallery, N.Y.C., 1958, 59, 63, 65, 67, 69, 70, Molton Gallery, London, 1962, Am. Culture Center, Florence, Italy, 1962, Bennington Coll., 1963, U. N.Mex., 1966, U. So. Calif., 1967, Axiom Gallery, London, 1968, Yoseido Gallery, Tokyo, 1968, Los Angeles County Mus. Art, 1971; exhibited in group shows, Bklyn. Mus., 1959, Mus. Modern Art, N.Y.C., 1962, 65, 69, Knox-Albright Art Gallery, 1962, and Can. Chgo., 1963, Cin. Art Mus., 1966, Balt. Art Mus., 1966, Yale Art Gallery, 1967, Grand Palais, Paris, 1970, Nat. Mus. Art, Santiago, Chile, 1970, art and tech. exhibit, Los Angeles County Mus. Art, 1971, Maeght Found., St. Paul de Vence, France, 1971, Mus. Modern Art, Paris, 1971; represented in permanent collections, Mus. Modern Art, Art Inst. Chgo., Bibliotheque Nationale, Paris, Victoria & Albert Mus., London, Los Angeles County Art Mus., Grunwald Graphic Arts Found., U. Calif. at Los Angeles, San Diego Mus. Art, Amon Carter Mus., Fort Worth; Author: Jesse Reichek-Dessins, 1960, La Monte de la Nuit, 1961, Fontis, 1961, Etcetera, 1965, Le Bulletin Des Baux, 1972; e.g., 1976. Served to capt. C.E. AUS, 1942-46. Home: 5925 Red Hill Rd Petaluma CA 94952-9437

REICHEK, MORTON ARTHUR, retired magazine editor, writer; b. N.Y.C., Nov. 2, 1924; s. Meyer and Katherine (Rabinowitz) R.; m. Sybil Green, June 13, 1953; children: Amy, Marjorie (dec.), James. BS, NYU, 1948; postgrad., Am. U., 1948-50. Press officer, editor U.S. Fish & Wildlife Svc., Washington, 1948-49, U.S. Br. Labor Statistics, Washington, 1949-51, U.S. Nat. Prodn. Authority, Washington, 1951-52; Washington corr. McGraw-Hill Mags., 1952-63, Newhouse Newspapers, 1963-65; assoc. editor Forbes, N.Y.C., 1965-66; assoc. editor Bus. WeeK, N.Y.C., 1966-76, sr. editor, writer, 1978-88; dir. editorial svcs. Gulf & Western. Industries, Inc., N.Y.C., 1976-78; U.S. rep. NATO journalist program U.S. Dept. State, France, 1957; adj. lectr. Columbia U. Graduate Sch. Journalism, N.Y.C., 1981. Contbr. articles to N.Y. Times Mag., New Republic, others. Staff sgt. U.S. Army, 1943-46. Journalist fellow Carnegie-Mellon U. Grad. Sch. Indsl. Adminstrn., 1979; grantee NEH, 1980. Mem. Nat. Press. Club, Nat. Soc. Journalists and Authors, Am. Book Critics Circle. Jewish. Avocations: tennis, computers, music. Home: 1 Worchester Dr Concordia Cranbury NJ 08512 Home (winter): 14388 Emerald Lake Dr Apt 1 Delray Beach FL 33446-3382

REICHEL, WALTER EMIL, advertising executive; b. Irvington, N.J., Dec. 12, 1935; s. Walter Edwin and Flora Maria (Pfister) R.; m. Priscilla Tedesco, Feb. 1, 1969; 1 son, Bradley Joseph. B.A., Columbia, 1959; M.A., N.Y. U., 1971, M. Philosophy, 1989, postgrad., 1989—. With Benton & Bowles, N.Y.C., 1959-67; v.p. Benton & Bowles, 1967-67, assoc. media dir., 1965-67; with Ted Bates & Co. Inc. N.Y.C., 1967-87; sr. v.p. Ted Bates & Co., Inc., N.Y.C., 1973-82; exec. dir. media and programs Ted Bates & Co., Inc., 1974-82, exec. v.p., 1982-87; cons., 1987-91; mng. ptnr. A.S. Link Inc., N.Y.C., 1991—. Mem. Advt. Rsch. Found. Home: 449 1/2 Henry St Brooklyn NY 11231 Office: 805 Third Ave New York NY 10022-5403

REICHERT, BRUCE ROBERT, travel industry executive; b. Chgo., Dec. 7, 1942; s. Walter Frederick and Helen (Wellman) R.; m. Marcia Pion-Bobadilla. BSC in Acctg., DePaul U., 1973; MBA, Roosevelt U., 1976. Fin. dir. Milton Bradley Ltd., London, 1974-76; mgr. cost devel. Rockwell Corp., Pitts., 1976-77; controller, plastics div. ITT Corp., Madison Heights, Mich., 1978-80; mgr. fin. control ITT Corp., N.Y.C., 1980-82, mgr. cost control, 1982-84; controller Summagraphics, Fairfield, Conn., 1984-86; pres. Mgmt. Controls Corp., Fairfield, 1986-91, Leisure Group Ltd., Milford, Conn., 1991—; bd. dirs. Malberg Enterprises, Inc., Bus. Connections, Inc., Royal Travel Network, Inc., Leisure Group Ltd., URW, Inc. Author: U.S. Lady, 1966, One-Up Production, 1986, Autofact '87, 1987, Flow Dynamics, 1987; editor Spotlight on Cost newsletter, 1985; columnist Paper Age MAg. Served with U.S. Army, 1966-69. Home: 15C Heritage Sound Milford CT 06460 Office: Leisure Group Ltd 344 W Main St Milford CT 06460-2524

REICHERT, DAVID, lawyer; b. Cin., Nov. 23, 1929; s. Victor E. and Louise F. (Feibel) R.; m. Marilyn Frankel, May 31, 1959; children—James G., Steven F., William M. B.A., Bowling Green State U., 1951; J.D., U. Cin., 1954. Bar: Ohio 1954, U.S. Supreme Ct. 1963. Ptnr. firm Porter, Wright, Morris & Arthur, formerly sr. ptnr. Reichert, Strauss & Reed and predecessors, Cin.; dir. numerous corps. Monthly columnist: Scrap Age mag, 1966-74; bd. editors: U. Cin. Law Rev, 1953-54. Pres. brotherhood Rockdale Temple, Cin., 1960-61, temple treas., 1973-75, v.p., 1975-79, pres., 1979-81; mem. Amberley Village Planning Commn. & Zoning Bd. Appeals, 1972-79, Ohio Solid Waste Adv. Group, 1974; treas. Contemporary Arts Ctr., Cin., 1973-75, pres., 1976-77, trustee, 1982-88; trustee Cin. Art Mus., 1978-93, v.p., 1992-93, chmn. vis. com. for contemporary art, 1990-92; trustee Jewish Publ. Soc., 1980-86, Cin. Sculpture Coun., 1984-87; mem. acquisitions com. Miami U. Art Mus., 1982-85. Mem. Cin. Print and Drawing Cir. (pres. 1974-76), The Literary Club (sec. 1988-91, v.p. 1991-92, pres. 1992-93), Losantiville Country Club (bd. govs. 1985-92, sec. 1986-90, pres. 1990-92), Omicron Delta Kappa, Sigma Tau Delta, Phi Delta Phi, Zeta Beta Tau. Office: Porter Wright Morris & Arthur 250 E 5th St Ste 2200 Cincinnati OH 45202-4103

REICHERT, JACK FRANK, manufacturing company executive; b. West Allis, Wis., Sept. 27, 1930; s. Arthur Andrew and Emily Bertha (Wallinger) R.; m. Corrine Violet Helf, Apr. 5, 1952; children: Susan Marie, John Arthur. Cert. mktg., U. Wis.-Milw., 1957; AMP, Harvard U., 1970; LLD (hon.), Marian Coll., 1994. Various mktg. positions GE, 1948-57; with Brunswick Corp., Lake Forest, Ill., 1957—; pres. Mercury Marine div. Brunswick Corp., 1972-77; corp. v.p. Brunswick Corp., Lake Forest, 1974-77, group v.p. Marine Power Group, 1974-77, pres., COO, 1977-93; CEO Brunswick Corp., 1982-95, chmn. bd., 1983—, dir., 1977—; bd. dirs. The Dial Corp, Phoenix, First Chgo. Corp. Trustee Carroll Coll., Waukesha, Wis., 1972; indsl. chmn. Fond du Lac United Fund, 1977. With C.E. U.S. Army, 1951-53. Named Disting. Alumnus of the Yr., U. Wis., Milw. 1979, Top Chief Exec. Officer in Multi-Industry Group, Fin. World Mag., 1984; recipient Gold award in leisure industry Wall St. Transcript, 1983, 86, Bronze award in multi-industry category Wall St. Transcript, 1985, Leisure Industry Silver award, 1988. Mem. Am. Mgmt. Assn., U. Wis.-Milw. Alumni Assn., Econ. Club of Chgo., Comml. Club of Chgo., Knollwood Club, Harvard Club, Mid-Am. Club, Met. Club, Beta Gamma Sigma (hon.). Presbyterian. Avocations: golf, reading. Home: 580 Douglas Dr Lake Forest IL 60045-3342 Office: Brunswick Corp 1 N Field Ct Lake Forest IL 60045-4810 To meet with any success, one must have a sense of urgency to get things done.

REICHERT, LEO EDMUND, JR., biochemist, endocrinologist; b. N.Y.C., Jan. 9, 1932; s. Leo and Anne (Holsten) R.; m. Gerda Sihler, July 20, 1957; children: Leo, Christine, Linda, Andrew. B.S., Manhattan Coll., N.Y.C., 1955; Ph.D., Loyola U., Chgo., 1960. Asst. prof. biochemistry Emory U. Med. Sch., Atlanta, 1960-66; assoc. prof. Emory U. Med. Sch., 1966-72, prof., 1972-79; prof. chmn. dept. biochemistry Albany (N.Y.) Med. Coll., 1979-88, prof. biochemistry, 1988—; dir. human and animal hormone isolation and distbn. program (NIH), Emory U. Med. Sch., 1960-75; mem. med. adv. bd. Nat. Pituitary Agy., 1971-74; com. on glycoprotein hormones Nat. Hormone and Pituitary Program, 1968-86; mem. reproductive biology study sect. NIH, 1971-75; mem. adv. panel on cellular physiology NSF, 1983-86, div. of integrative and neuro biology, 1992; mem. WHO Expert Adv. Panel on Biol. Standardization, 1984—, Nat. Bd. Med. Examiners, Part I, 1989-91. Mem. editl. bd. Endocrinology, 1967-75, Molecular and Cellular Endocrinology, 1977-83, 90-94, Biology of Reproduction, 1968-70, 86-90, Andrology, 1983-86, Molecular Andrology, 1989—; contbr. more than 250 articles to profl. jours.; patentee in field. Served with USMC, 1950-52. List among 75 endocrinologists, 1000 scientists most cited, 1965-78. Mem. AAAS, Am. Soc. Biol. Chemists, Endocrine Soc. (Ayerst award 1970), Andrology Soc. (coun. 1983-87), Soc. for Study of Reprodn. Home: 10 Laurel Dr Albany NY 12211-1618 Office: Albany Med Coll Dept Biochemistry Albany NY 12208

REICHERT, NORMAN VERNON, financial services consultant; b. Berwyn, Ill., Apr. 17, 1921; s. John G. and Valeria (Hoffman) R.; m. Wilma Eleanor Catey, Feb. 5, 1944; children: Susan, Norman Vernon. BS, Northwestern U., 1943; MBA, Harvard Bus. Sch., 1944. CPA, Ill. Acct.

Arthur Young & Co., Chgo., 1946-50; central fin. staff, controller styling div. Ford Motor Co., Dearborn, Mich., 1950-61; treas. Philco Ford Corp., Phila., 1961-69; asst. treas. United Air Lines, Inc., Chgo., 1969-72; v.p. fin. Trailer Train Co., Railbox Co., Railgon Co., Chgo., 1972-83; v.p. fin., treas. U.S. Windpower, Inc., San Francisco, 1983-86; pres. Blackhawk Fin., 1986—. Served to lt. USNR, 1943-46. Mem. AICPA, Fin. Execs. Inst., Navy League U.S., Exptl. Aircraft Assn., Union League Chgo., Knollwood Club (Lake Forest), Olympic Club San Francisco, Beta Alpha Psi, Sigma Alpha Epsilon. Home and Office: 921 Grandview Ln Lake Forest IL 60045-3913 Each day we must start over. One cannot live on yesterday's accomplishments, but instead, must establish new goals. Last year's champion is soon forgotten as we focus on the current achiever. This is the way I try to approach each new day. And, at the end of each day, I evaluate my performance against my goals for that day.

REICHERT, PATRICIA, mortgage company executive; b. 1936. With Park Fed. Savs. & Loan, Columbus, Ohio, 1975-79, Bancohio, Columbus, 1979-83; with Metmor Fin. Inc., Shawnee Mission, Kans., 1984—, now pres. Office: Metmor Fin Inc 9225 Indian Cr Pky 300 Shawnee Mission KS 66210*

REICHGOTT JUNGE, EMBER D., state legislator, lawyer; b. Detroit, Aug. 22, 1953; d. Norbert Arnold and Diane (Pincich) R.; m. Michael Junge. BA summa cum laude, St. Olaf Coll., Minn., 1974; JD, Duke U., 1977; MBA, U. of St. Thomas, 1991. Bar: Minn. 1977, D.C. 1978. Assoc., Larkin, Hoffman, Daly & Lindgren, Bloomington, Minn., 1977-84; counsel Control Data Corp., Bloomington, Minn., 1984-86; atty. The Gen. Counsel, Ltd., 1987—; mem. Minn. State Senate, 1983—, chmn. legis. com. on econ. status of women, 1984-86, vice chmn. senate edn. com., 1987-88, senate majority whip, 1990-94, chmn. property tax div. senate tax com., 1991-92, chmn. senate judiciary com., 1993-94; senate asst. majority leader, 1995—; instr. polit. sci. St. Olaf Coll., Northfield, Minn., 1993; dir. Citizens Ind. Bank, St. Louis Park, Minn., 1993—. Host (cable TV monthly series) Legis. Report, 1985-92. Trustee. bd. dirs. N.W. YMCA, New Hope, Minn., 1983-88; Greater Mpls. Red Cross, 1988—, United Way Mpls., 1989—. Youngest woman ever elected to Minn. State Senate, 1983; recipient Woman of Yr. award North Hennepin Bus. and Prof. Women, 1983, Award for Contbn. to Human Svcs., Minn. Social Svcs. Assn., 1983, Clean Air award Minn. Lung Assn., 1988, Disting. Svc. award Mpls. Jaycees, 1984, Minn. Dept. Human Rights award, 1989, Myra Bradwell award Minn. Women Lawyers, 1993, Disting. Alumnae award Lake Conf. Schs., 1993; named One of Ten Outstanding Young Minnesotans, Minn. Jaycees, 1984, Policy Advocate of Yr. NAWBO, 1988, Woman of Achievement Twin West C. of C., 1989, Marvelous Minn. Woman, 1993. Mem. Minn. Bar Assn. (bd. govs. 1992—, Pro Bono Publico Atty. award 1990), Hennepin County Bar Assn., Corporate Counsel Assn. (v.p. 1989—), Minn. Dem. Farmer-Labor Party (state co-chair Clinton/Gore Presdl. Campaign 1992, del. nat. Dem. conv. 1984, 92, state exec. com. 1980-82). Home: 7701 48th Ave N Minneapolis MN 55428-4515

REICHL, RUTH MOLLY, restaurant critic; b. N.Y.C., Jan. 16, 1948; d. Ernst and Miriam and (Brudno) R.; m. Douglas Wilder Hollis, Sept. 5, 1970 (div. 1985); married. BA, U. Mich., 1968, MA in History of Art, 1970. Chef, owner The Swallow Restaurant, Berkeley, Calif., 1973-77; food writer, editor New West mag., San Francisco, 1978-84; editor restaurant column L.A. Times, 1984-93, food editor, 1990-93; restaurant critic N.Y. Times, 1993—. Author: Mmmm: A Feastiary, 1972, The Contest Book, 1977; contbr. articles to profl. jours. Office: NY Times 229 W 43 St New York NY 10036

REICHLIN, SEYMOUR, physician, educator; b. N.Y.C., May 31, 1924; s. Henry and Celia (Rosen) R.; m. Elinor Thurman Dameshek, June 24, 1951; children: Seth David, Douglas James, Ann Elise. Student, CCNY, 1940-41; AB, Antioch Coll., 1945; MD, Washington U., St. Louis, 1948; PhD, U. London, 1954. Intern N.Y. Hosp., 1948-49; asst. resident Barnes Hosp., St. Louis, 1949-50, N.Y. Hosp., 1950-51; chief resident Barnes Hosp., 1951-52; research fellow physiology dept. Maudsley Hosp., London, Eng., 1952-54; instr. psychiatry Washington U., 1954-55, asst. prof. psychiatry and medicine, 1955-60; pvt. practice clin. endocrinology, St. Louis, 1955-60, instructor U. Rochester, 1960-66, prof., head dept. med. and pediatric spltys. Sch. Medicine U. Conn., 1969-71, prof., head dept. physiology, 1971-72; prof. medicine Tufts U., 1972—; rsch. prof. U. Ariz., 1994—; sr. physician New Eng. Med. Ctr., 1972-93, sr. endocrinologist, 1993—; cons. Genesee and Rochester Gen. Hosp., 1960-69, Hartford Hosp., 1970—, New Britain (Conn.) Gen. Hosp., 1970-72; mem. endocrinology study sect. HIH, 1966-70; mem. adv. panel FDA, 1977-79; mem. coun. Nat. Inst. Kidney, Diabetes, Digestive Diseases, 1987-90. Mem. editl. bd. Endocrinology, 1969-74, New Eng. Jour. Medicine, 1976-79, Jour. Psychoneuroendocrinology, 1979—, Brain, Brhavior and Immunity, 1990—; contbr. articles to profl. jours., also monographs. Bd. dirs. Founds. Fund, New Haven, 1968-70; med. adv. bd. Med. Found., Boston, adv. bd. MacArthur Found., 1988. Served with AUS, 1943-44. Commonwealth Fund fellow, 1952-54, Lowell M. Palmer fellow, 1954-56. Master ACP; fellow AAAS, Am. Acad. Arts and Scis.; mem. Ctrl. Soc. Clin. Rsch., Am. Soc. Clin. Investigation, Assn. Am. Physicians, Am. Physiol. Soc., Endocrine Soc. (Eli Lilly award 1972, pres. 1975-76), Brit. Soc. Endocrinology, Am. Psychosomatic Soc., Am. Thyroid Assn., Internat. Brain Orgn., Assn. for Rsch. in Nervous and Mental Disease (pres. 1976), Pituitary Soc. (pres. 1994-95), Alpha Omega Alpha. Home: X-9 Ranch Vail AZ 85641 also: U Ariz Coll Medicine Tucson AZ 85724

REICHMAN, FREDRICK THOMAS, artist; b. Bellingham, Wash., Jan. 28, 1925; s. Frederick and Ilma Lucia (Yearing) R.; m. Michela Madelene Robbins, Sept. 24, 1955; children: Alexandra Ilma, Matthew Nathaniel. BA cum laude, U. Calif., Berkeley, 1950, MA in Art, 1952; postgrad., San Francisco Art Inst., 1946-47. Instr. art San Francisco Art Inst., 1952, U. Calif., Davis, 1963-66, Dominican Coll., San Rafael, Calif., summer 1974, Calif. Coll. Arts and Crafts, Oakland, 1976, U. Calif. extension, San Francisco, 1966—; lectr. U. Calif., Berkeley, 1953; dir. children's art classes Jr. Center Art and Sci., Oakland, 1953-64, exib. 70—. One-man exhbns. include Rose Rabow Galleries, San Francisco, 1958, 61, 63, 69, 73, 75, San Francisco Mus. Modern Art, 1969, Benson Gallery, Bridgehampton, N.Y., 1966-72, Silvan Simone Gallery, L.A., 1971-73, Santa Barbara (Calif.) Mus. Art, 1974, Rose Rabow Galleries-James Willis Gallery, San Francisco, 1976, Gallery Paule Anglim, San Francisco, 1979-81, Chikyudo Gallery, Tokyo, 1980, Espace Doyoo, Tokyo, 1982, Ki-Do-Ai-Raku, Tokyo, 1982, Maeitetsu-Marukoshi, Kanazawa, Japan, 1982, The New Gallery, Taos, N.Mex., 1982, Charles Campbell Gallery, San Francisco, 1984, 86, David Barnett Gallery, Milw., 1985, 89, Artform Gallery, 1985, The New Gallery, Houston, 1985, Mekler Gallery Inc., L.A., 1988, Ruth Siegel Gallery, N.Y., 1991, U. Calif., Santa Cruz, Ann Porter Sesnon Art Gallery, 1991, Galerie B. Haasner, Germany, 1990, 92, 94, Harcourts Contemporary, San Francisco, 1992, 95, Louis Newman Galleries, Beverly Hills, Calif., 1992, 93, 94; 2-man show, Iannetti-Lanzone Gallery, San Francisco, 1989, Miyagi Mus. Art, Sendai, Japan, 1982, R.B. Stevenson Gallery, La Jolla, 1995; 3-man show, Milw. Art Mus., 1982, group exhbns. include, Esther Robles Gallery, L.A., 1961, Whitney Mus. Am. Art traveling exhbn., 1962-63, Expo '70, Osaka, Japan, 1970, Oakland Mus., 1971, Joslyn Art Mus. traveling exhbn., 1973-74, San Francisco Mus. Modern Art, 1974, Martha Jackson Gallery, N.Y.C., 1978, New Gallery, 1981, Forum Gallery, N.Y.C., 1984, Smith Andersen Gallery, Palo Alto, 1986, Ruth Siegel Gallery, N.Y.C., 1986, Kultorvert Galerie, Copenhagen, 1986, Richmond (Calif.) Art Ctr., 1987, Nat. Mus. Am. Art, Washington, 1989, Arte 7, San Francisco, 1990, Harcourts Contemporary, San Francisco, 1991, Kouros Gallery, N.Y.C., 1993, Berkeley Art Ctr., 1993, Estudio Moyo Coyatzin, San Jose, Costa Rica; represented in permanent collections throughout U.S., including Nat. Mus. Am. Art, San Francisco Mus. Modern Art, Oakland Mus., Univ. Art Mus., Berkeley, Santa Barbara Mus. Art, Milw. Art Mus., Ulrich Mus. Art, Wichita, Fine Arts Museums San Francisco, Okla. Art Center, Oklahoma City, Bank Am. World Hdqrs., San Francisco, Achenbach Found., San Francisco, Mills Coll. Art Gallery, Oakland, U. Calif., San Francisco; works rep. art publs.; commns. include stage set for, San Francisco Mime Troupe, The Exception to the Rule, 1965; mural, Boche Pediatrics Outpatient Clinic, Stanford U. Med. Ctr., 1961, San Francisco Civic Center, 1968. Served with USNR, 1943-45. Recipient Purchase prize San Francisco Art Festival, 1964, One-Man Show award, 1968; Irving prize Am. Wit and Humor U. Calif., Berkeley, 1951; Taussig traveling fellow U. Calif., Berkeley, 1952; profiled in 50 West Coast Artists

by Henry Hopkins, 1981, Art in the San Francisco Bay Area 1945-80 by Thomas Albright, 1985. There is a unique energy that exists on the Pacific Coast. It is different from our eastern seaboard, different from Europe and the Orient—yet it comes out of all these sources to create inspiration and fresh insights. The light and the land, the atmosphere that exist here, have their own particular ambience. I feel a part of this energy.

REICHMAN, JEROME H., law educator; b. 1936. BA, U. Chgo., 1955; JD, Yale U., 1979. From asst. prof. to prof. law Ohio State U, 1979-86; prof. law Vanderbilt U., Nashville, 1986—; vis. prof. curriculum enrichment program U. Fla., spring 1986; fellow German Marshall Fund U.S., fall 1986. editor; co-author: The Oil-Exporting Developing Countries: New Market Opportunities for Other Developing Countries, 1976-78, A Guide to the World's Foreign Trade Statistics, 1977; editor: Egypt and the United States: The Formative Years, 1980. Fulbright scholar Madras (India) U., 1958-59. Mem. Assn. Litteraire et Artistique Internat., Copyright Soc. of the South, Internat. Assn. Advancement of Teaching and Rsch. in Intellectual Property. Office: Vanderbilt U Sch Law 21st Ave S Nashville TN 37240

REICHMAN, JOEL H., retail executive. With The GAP, San Francisco, 1971-76; active CA and Slak Shak Inc., Boston, 1976—; exec. v.p. CA and Slak Shak Inc., 1987-93, dir., 1993; pres., COO Designs, Inc., Chestnut Hill, Mass., 1993—. Office: Designs Inc 1244 Boylston St Chestnut Hill MA 02167-2115*

REICHMAN, LEE BRODERSOHN, physician; b. N.Y.C., June 25, 1938; s. Theodore and Elinore (Brodersohn) R.; m. Rose Ehrinpreis, Oct. 9, 1965; children: Daniel Mark, Deborah Gar. AB, Oberlin Coll., 1960; MD, NYU, 1964; MPH, Johns Hopkins U., 1971. Intern Bellevue Hosp., I Med. Div., N.Y.C., 1964-65, resident, 1967-68; resident Harlem Hosp. Ctr. N.Y.C., 1968-69; fellow in pulmonary medicine Harlem Hosp. Ctr., 1969-70; dir. Bur. Tb, Bur. Chronic Disease, N.Y.C. Health Dept., 1971-73, asst. commr. health, 1973-74; assoc. prof. medicine N.J. Med. Sch., Newark, 1974-78, prof. medicine, 1978—; dir. pulmonary div. U. Medicine and Dentistry N.J.-N.J. Med. Sch. Univ. Hosp., 1974-92; exec. dir. N.J. Med. Sch. Nat. Tuberculosis Ctr., 1993—; cons. CDC, Atlanta, 1970—; prin. investigator pulmonary complications of HIV Infection, Nat. Heart Lung Blood Inst., 1987-95, Model TB Ctr. for Disease Control and Prevention, 1993—, Nat. Rsch. Consortium (CDC), 1994—. Contbr. articles to profl. jours. Bd. dirs. Art Ctr. No. N.J., 1979-86; chmn. N.J. Commn. on Smoking or Health, 1986-87; mem. N.J. TB Adv. Coun., 1976—, chmn., 1991-93; mem. N.J. Clean Air Council, 1987. Served with USPHS, 1965-67. Recipient Nat. Heart Lung and Blood Inst., Pulmonary Acad. career award, 1975-80, Preventive Pulmonary Acad. career award, 1987-92, Tb Acad. career award, 1993—. Fellow ACP, Am. Coll. Chest Physicians (gov. 1984-90, pres. N.J. chpt. 1982-84), Acad. Medicine of N.J.; mem. Am. Thoracic Soc., Internat. Union Against Tb and Lung Disease (exec. com. 1982-92, sec. 1982-84), Am. Lung Assn. (nat. bd. dirs. 1980-94, pres. elect 1991-92, pres. 1992-93, past pres. 1993-94), N.J. Thoracic Soc. (pres. 1982-84), Am. Lung Assn. N.J. (bd. dirs. 1976—, pres. 1984-86). Office: 65 Bergen St Ste GB1 Newark NJ 07107-3001

REICHSTETTER, ARTHUR CHARLES, banker; b. Providence, June 14, 1946; s. Edward Arthur and Joyce Marie (Scull) R.; children: Daniella Lynn, Hans Francis and Karl Arthur (twins). B.S., U. R.I., 1972; M.B.A., Dartmouth Coll., 1974. Assoc. 1st Boston Corp., N.Y.C., 1974-76, asst. v.p., 1976-78, v.p., 1978-82; mng. dir. The First Boston Corp., N.Y.C., 1982-93, Merrill Lynch & Co., N.Y.C., Md., 1993—. Served to 1st lt. U.S. Army, 1967-69.

REICIN, RONALD IAN, lawyer; b. Chgo., Dec. 11, 1942; s. Frank Edward and Abranita (Rome) R.; m. Alyta Friedland, May 23, 1965; children—Eric, Kael. B.B.A., U. Mich., 1964, M.B.A., 1967, J.D. cum laude, 1967. Bar: Ill. 1967, U.S. Tax Ct. 1967; CPA, Ill. Mem. staff Price Waterhouse & Co., Chgo., 1966; ptnr. Jenner & Block, Chgo., 1967—. Bd. dirs. Nat. Kidney Found., Ill., 1978—, v.p., 1992—; bd. dirs. Ruth Page Found., 1985—, v.p., 1990—; bd. dirs. Scoliosis Assn. Chgo., 1981—, Kohl Children's Mus., 1991—. Mem. Chgo. Bar Assn., Internat. Conf. Shopping Ctrs., ABA, Ill. Bar Assn., Chgo. Mortgage Attys. Assn., Phi Kappa Phi, Beta Gamma Sigma, Beta Alpha Psi. Clubs: Executive, Legal (Chgo.). Home: 1916 Berkeley Rd Highland Park IL 60035-2725 Office: Jenner & Block 41st Fl 1 E Ibm Plz Fl 41 Chicago IL 60611-3608

REICKERT, ERICK ARTHUR, automotive executive; b. Newport, Tenn., Aug. 30, 1935; s. Frederick Arthur and Reva M. (Irish) R.; m. Diane Lois Comens, June 10, 1961 (div. Jan. 1979); children: Craig A., Laura L.; m. Heather Kathleen Ross, Sept. 1, 1982. BSEE, Northwestern U., 1958; MBA, Harvard U., 1965. Various positions Ford Motor Co., Dearborn, Mich., 1965-73, exec. dir. small car planning, 1979-84; v.p. export ops. Ford Motor Co., Brentwood, Eng., 1973-79; v.p. advance product devel. Chrysler Motors, Detroit, 1984-86, v.p. program mgmt., 1986-87; chmn., mng. dir. Chrysler Mexico, 1987-89; pres., CEO New Venture Gear Inc., Troy, Mich., 1992—; v.p. power train ops. Chrysler Corp., Warren, Mich., 1991-92; bd. dirs. Truck Components Inc., Rockford, Ill., 1994—. Bd. dirs. Jr. Achievement of S.E. Mich., Detroit, 1992—, Children's Ctr., Detroit, 1993—; regent for S.E. Mich., Northwestern U., Evanston, Ill., 1994—. Mem. Soc. Automotive Engrs., Engring. Soc. Detroit, Harvard Bus. Sch. Club of Detroit. Avocations: photography, travel, sailing, skiing. Office: New Venture Gear Inc 1650 Research Dr Ste 300 Troy MI 48043

REID, ANTONIO (L. A. REID), musician, songwriter. With musical group The Deele; songwriter with Kenny Edmonds, also occasionally with Darryl Simmons. Songs include Girlfriend, 1987, Rock Steady, 1987, Two Occasions, 1987, Don't Be Cruel, 1988, Love Saw It, 1988, Lover In Me, 1988, Every Little Step, 1988 (Grammy award nomination for R&B Song of Yr. 1989), Dial My Heart, 1988, Way You Love Me, 1988, Secret Rendezvous, 1988, Superwoman, 1988, Roses Are Red, 1988, Can't Stop, 1989, My Kinda Girl, 1989, It's No Crime, 1989, On Our Own, 1989, Ready or Not, 1989, Tender Lover, 1989, Giving You the Benefit, 1990, I'm Your Baby Tonight, 1990. Office: Kear Music care Carter Turner & Co 9229 W Sunset Blvd West Hollywood CA 90069-3402

REID, CHARLES ADAMS, III, lawyer; b. Plainfield, N.J., Apr. 21, 1947; s. Charles Adams Jr. and Gertrude C. (Egan) R.; m. Teresa Keenan, May 11, 1974. BA, Colgate U., 1969; JD, Columbia U., 1974. Bar: N.Y. 1974, U.S. Dist. Ct. (ea. and so. dists.) N.Y. 1975, U.S. Dist. Ct. N.J. 1976, U.S. Ct. Appeals (3d cir.) 1983, U.S. Ct. Appeals (fed. cir.) 1989, U.S. Ct. Appeals (2d cir.) 1991. Law clk. to hon. John R. Bartels U.S. Dist. Ct. (ea. dist.) N.Y., Bklyn., 1974-75; assoc. Coudert Bros., N.Y.C., 1975-77, Shanley & Fisher, Newark, 1977-82; ptnr. Shanley & Fisher, Newark and Morris-town, N.J., 1983—. Mem. planning bd. Peapack-Gladstone, N.J., 1984-88, chmn., 1987-88; bd. dirs. Morris Ctr. YMCA, Cedar Knolls, N.J., 1986-93. Served with U.S. Army, 1970-72, Vietnam. Mem. ABA (litigation sect.), N.J. Bar Assn., Morris County Bar Assn., Essex County Bar Assn., Morris-town Club, Park Avenue Club (Florham Park). Home: PO Box 398 Gladstone NJ 07934-0398 Office: Shanley & Fisher PC 131 Madison Ave Morris-town NJ 07960-6097

REID, CHARLES MURRY, insurance company executive. CEO, pres. United Guaranty Corp., Greensboro, N.C., 1991—. Office: United Guaranty Corp 230 N Elm St Greensboro NC 27401-2436*

REID, CHARLES PHILLIP PATRICK, academic administrator, researcher, professor; b. Columbia, Mo., Jan. 8, 1940; s. Charles Henry and Fern Elnora (Chorlton) R.; m. Miriam Davis, July 17, 1961; children: Clayton Patrick, Miriam. BSF, U. Mo., 1961; MF, Duke U., 1966, PhD, 1968. Asst. prof. dept. forest and wood scis. Colo. State U., Ft. Collins, 1969-73, assoc. prof. dept. forest and wood scis., 1973-77, prof. dept. forest and wood scis., 1977-86; prof., chmn. dept. forestry U. Fla., Gainesville, 1986-92, interim dir. Sch. Forest Resources and Conservation, 1991-92; prof., dir. Sch. Renewable Natural Resources U. Ariz., Tucson, 1992—; vis. faculty mem. dept. botany Sheffield (Eng.) U., fall 1973; vis. scientist div. of soils Commonwealth Sci. and Indsl. Rsch. Orgn., Glen Osmond, South Australia, 1976-77; sr. Fulbright fellow dept. microbiology U. Innsbruck, Austria, 1985-86; chmn. working group on root physiology and symbiosis Internat.

Union Forestry Rsch. Orgns., 1984-88. Contbr. articles to profl. jours. Co-pres. Barton Elem. Parent Tchr. Orgn., Ft. Collins, 1979-80; bd. dirs. Vol. Clearing House, Ft. Collins, 1974-76, Fla. 4-H Found., Gainesville, 1988-89. Lt. (j.g.) USNR, 1961-64, comdr. USNR, ret. Mem. AAAS, Ecol. Soc. Am., Soc. Am. Foresters, Nat. Assn. Profl. Forestry Schs. and Colls. (exec. com. 1994-95), Sertoma (treas., bd. dirs. Ft. Collins chpt. 1972-75), Rotary. Republican. Episcopalian. Office: U Ariz Sch Renewable Natural Resources Bioscience East Tucson AZ 85721

REID, CLARICE DELORES, physician; b. Birmingham, Ala., Nov. 21, 1931; d. Noah Edgar, Sr., and Willie Mae (Brown) Wills; m. Arthur Joseph Reid, Jr., June 11, 1955; children—Kevin, Sheila, Jill, Clarice A. B.S., Talladega Coll., 1952; cert. and Degree Med. Tech., Meharry Med. Coll., 1954; M.D., U. Cin., 1959. Med. technologist Jewish Hosp., Cin., 1954-55, 57-59; intern, Jewish Hosp., Cin., 1959-60; resident, Jewish Hosp. and Children's Hosp., Cin., 1960-62; practice medicine specializing in pediatrice, Cin., 1962-68; dir. pediatric ents. Jewish Hosp., Cin., 1968-69, chmn. dept. pediatrics, 1969-70; dep. dir. sickle cell disease, USPHS, Rockville, Md., 1973-76; chief sickle cell disease NIH, Bethesda, Md., 1976—, nat. coordinator sickle cell disease program, 1976—; med. cons. USPHS, Rockville, 1971-73. Contbr. chpts. to books; editor proceedings, 1977. Named Outstanding Student, Meharry Med. Coll., 1954, Pres.' award, 1980; recipient NIH Dir.'s award, 1979; charter mem. sr. Exec. Service, 1979. Mem. Acad. Pediatrics, Nat. Med. Assn., Am. Soc. Hematology. Roman Catholic. Clubs: Altrusa, Links. Home: 9715 Fernwood Rd Bethesda MD 20817-1554 Office: Dept Heal & Hum Svcs/Nat Heart Lung & Blood Inst/Blood Diseases & Resources/7550 Wisconsin Ave Bethesda MD 20892

REID, DANIEL JAMES, public relations executive; b. Grand Rapids, Mich., Sept. 7, 1960; s. Robert Alexander and Janette Helen (Hickey) R.; m. Meredith Christine Ryan, Apr. 30, 1994. BA, Mich. State U., 1983. Sr. account exec. Burson-Marsteller, Chgo., 1983-88; group dir. Ogilvy & Mather, Chgo., 1988-90; ptnr., adv. dir. Fin. Rels. Bd., Inc., Chgo., 1990—; prodr. Stas. WLAV-WTWN, Grand Rapids, 1980-81; bd. dirs. Exch. Capital Mgmt., Auburn Hills, Mich. Contbr. articles to profl. publs. and newspapers. Recipient Bronze Anvil award Pub. Rels. Soc. Am., 1984, creative excellence award U.S. Film Festival, 1984, 87, gold award Fin. World mag., 1990-94, numerous others. Mem. Nat. Investor Rels. Inst., Union League Club Chgo. Republican. Roman Catholic. Office: Fin Rels Bd Inc 875 N Michigan Ave Chicago IL 60611

REID, DAVID EVANS, pipeline company executive; b. St. Thomas, Ont., Can., Jan. 10, 1943; s. Murray Reid and Betty Evans; m. Nancy Blake, Dec. 6, 1969; children: Lindsay, Graeme. BSc with honors, Queen's U., Kingston, Ont., 1965; MASc, Toronto (Ont.) U., 1967. Registered profl. engr. Ont., Alta. Various positions in head and field offices TransCanada PipeLines, Toronto and Winnipeg, Man., 1967-89; v.p. ops. TransCanada PipeLines, Toronto, 1989-90; v.p. for engring. TransCanada PipeLines, Calgary, Alta., 1990—. Mem. Assn. Profl. Engrs. in Province Ont., Assn. Profl. Engrs., Geologists and Geophysicists Alta., Glencoe Golf and Country Club, Glencoe Club. Office: TransCanada PipeLines Ltd, 111 5th Ave SW, Calgary, AB Canada T2P 4K5

REID, EDWARD SNOVER, III, lawyer; b. Detroit, Mar. 24, 1930; s. Edward S. Jr. and Margaret (Overington) R.; m. Carroll Grylls, Dec. 30, 1953; children: Carroll Reid Highet, Richard Gerveys, Jane Reid McTique, Margaret Reid Boyer. B.A., Yale U., 1951; LL.B. magna cum laude (Sheldon fellow), Harvard U., 1956. Bar: Mich. 1957, N.Y. 1958, D.C. 1982, Gaikokuho jimu-bengoshi, Tokyo 1991. Assoc. Davis, Polk & Wardwell, N.Y.C., 1957-64; partner Davis, Polk & Wardwell, 1964—; dir. Gen. Mills, Inc., 1974-89. Mem. N.Y.C. Bd. Higher Edn., 1971-73; trustee Bklyn. Inst. Arts and Scis., 1966-93, chmn., 1974-79; trustee Bklyn. Mus., 1973-93, 94—; bd. dirs. Bklyn. Bot. Garden Corp., 1977-92, Bargemusic Ltd., 1990-93. Lt. USMC, 1951-53. Mem. ABA, N.Y. State Bar Assn., Assn. of Bar of City of of N.Y., Am. Law Inst.,Internat. Bar Assn., Inter-Pacific Bar Assn., Union Club, Fgn. Corrs. Club, Tokyo Am. Club, Tokyo Lawn Tennis Club, Heights Casino Club, Rembrandt Club, Century Assn. Club, Yale Club, L.I. Wyandanch Club, Quoque Beach Club, Quoque Field Club, Shinnecock Yacht Club. Home: 5-14 Minami Azabu 5-chome Minato-ku, Tokyo 106 Japan also: 1 Pierrepont St Apt 5-A Brooklyn NY 11201 Office: Davis Polk & Wardwell, 2-1 Marunouchi, 1-chome Chiyoda-ku, Tokyo 100, Japan

REID, GEORGE BERNARD, JR., lawyer; b. Washington, May 14, 1948; s. George Bernard and Joyce Grace (Stitely) R.; m. Jeanne Fallon, Aug. 29, 1970; children: Elizabeth, Caroline. BA, Yale U., 1970; JD, MBA, Harvard U., 1974. Bar: D.C. 1975, U.S. Dist. Ct. (D.C. dist.) 1975, U.S. Ct. Appeals (D.C. cir.) 1975, U.S. Ct. Appeals (5th cir.) 1977, U.S. Supreme Ct. 1979. Assoc. Covington & Burling, Washington, 1974-82, ptnr., 1982—. Nat. adv. bd. Jour. Law and Politics, 1984-92. Bd. dirs. U.S. Assn. for Internat. Migration, Washington, 1988—; bd. dirs., sec. Inst. for Advanced Studies in Immunology and Aging, 1986—; treas., trustee Potomac Sch., 1991—; dep. gen. counsel Rep. Nat. Com., 1984-89; gen. counsel Com. on Rules and Order of Bus., Rep. Conv., New Orleans, 1988. Mem. ABA. Avocations: tennis, racquetball. Home: 8007 Greenwich Woods Dr Mc Lean VA 22102-1332 Office: Covington & Burling PO Box 7566 1201 Pennsylvania Ave NW Washington DC 20044

REID, GEORGE KELL, biology educator, researcher, author; b. Fitzgerald, Ga., Mar. 23, 1918; s. George Kell and Pauline (Bowles) R.; m. Eugénie Louise Chazal, July 23, 1949 (div. Dec. 1978); children: George Philip (dec.), Deborah Louise. BS, Presbyn. Coll., Clinton, S.C., 1940; MS, U. Fla., 1949, PhD, 1952. Instr. U. Fla., Gainesville, 1949-52; asst. prof. Coll. William and Mary, Williamsburg, Va., 1952-53, Tex. A&M U., College Station, 1953-56, Rutgers U., New Brunswick, N.J., 1956-60; prof. Eckerd Coll., St. Petersburg, Fla., 1960-83, prof. emeritus 1983—; pvt. practice cons., writer Boca Raton, Fla., 1988—; rsch. scientist Va. Inst. Marine Sci., Gloucester, 1953; rsch. biologist Tex. Game and Fish. Commn., Rockport, 1954-56; cons. in field, 1955—. Author: Ecology of Cedar Key Fishes, 1954, Ecology of Inland Waters and Estuaries, 1961, (co-author) rev. edit., 1976, Pond Life, 1967, rev. edit., 1992, Ecology of Intertidal Zones, 1967; co-author: Bioscience, 1967; contbr. articles to profl. jours. and popular periodicals. Mem. City Environ. Com., St. Petersburg, 1975. 1st lt. U.S. Army, 1942-46. Recipient numerous grants NIH, NSF, Explorers Club, others, 1953—. Fellow AAAS; mem. Am. Soc. Limnology and Oceanography, Am. Inst. Biol. Scis., Fla. Acad. Sci. (pres. 1963-64), Ecol. Soc. Am. (chmn. aquatic ecology sec. 1964-66), Sigma Xi, Phi Sigma, Chi Beta Phi, Sigma Chi. Presbyterian. Achievements include pioneering in fish community ecology research in Gulf of Mexico localities; research in population dynamics in mangrove ecosystems, Wetland utilization, early literature on natural history of Florida. Home: 6079 Town Colony Dr Apt 1022 Boca Raton FL 33433-1911

REID, HARRY, senator; b. Searchlight, Nev., Dec. 2, 1939; s. Harry and Inez Reid; m. Landra Joy Gould; children—Lana, Rory, Leif, Josh, Key. AS, Southern Utah State U., 1959; LLD (hon.), U. So. Utah, 1984; BA, Utah State U., 1961; JD, George Washington U., 1964.

REID, HOCH, lawyer; b. Chanute, Kans., Dec. 27, 1909; s. James W. and Anna (Hoch) R.; m. Mona McMillan, July 3, 1937; children: Wallis H., Luanna Reid. A.B., Amherst Coll., 1931; LL.B., Columbia U., 1934. Bar: N.Y. 1935. Practiced in N.Y.C., 1935—; ptnr. Valicenti, Leighton, Reid & Pine, 1942-75, Burke & Burke, Daniels, Leighton & Reid, 1976-78; ptnr. Townley & Updike, 1978-86, of counsel, 1986—; mem. staff Navy Price Adjustment Bd., 1944-46. Author: How to Use Investment Company Shares in Estate Planning, 1972, Paying Up for Services, 1976. Trustee Village of Pleasantville, N.Y., 1961-63; chmn. Pleasantville Library Bd., 1955-61; mem. Mt. Pleasant Pub. libr. bd., 1982-86; mem. social policy com., planning com. on aging Fedn. Protestant Welfare Agys., N.Y.C., 1970-86; mem. com. agri. missions Nat. Council Chs., 1962-91, chmn., 1962-76; bd. dirs. Bethel Methodist Homes, Ossining, N.Y., 1948-82, pres., 1975-76, hon. dir., 1982—; bd. dirs. Agrl. Missions, Inc., 1950-91, pres., 1962-76; bd. dirs., mem. exec. com. Japan Internat. Christian U. Found., 1965-91; pres., trustee Open Space Inst., 1969-72; trustee Natural Area Council, 1975-85. Mem. ABA, Assn. Bar City N.Y., New Eng. Soc. N.Y., Sawmill River Audubon Soc. (pres. 1984-86), Nature Conservancy, World Affairs Coun. (Hartford), Mark Twain

Meml. Congregationalist. Home: Duncaster 60 Loeffler Rd Bloomfield CT 06002-2275

REID, HUBERT M., computer software company executive, electronics executive; b. 1953. BBA in acctg., Howard U., Washington, 1975. Audit, tax mgr. Touche Ross & Co., Washington, 1979-80; with Ward Corp., Rockville, Md., 1980-84; sr. v.p., fin., sec., treas. OAO Corp, Greenbelt, Md., 1984—. Office: OAO Corp 7500 Greenway Ctr Dr Greenbelt MD 20770*

REID, INEZ SMITH, lawyer, educator; b. New Orleans, Apr. 7, 1937; d. Sidney Randall Dickerson and Beatrice Virginia (Bundy) Smith. BA, Tufts U., 1959; LLB, Yale U., 1962; MA, UCLA, 1963; PhD, Columbia U., 1968. Bar: Calif. 1963, N.Y. 1972, D.C. 1980. Assoc. prof. Barnard Coll. Columbia U., N.Y.C., 1972-76; gen. counsel youth div. State of N.Y., 1976-77; dep. gen. counsel HEW, Washington, 1977-79; inspector gen. EPA, Washington, 1979-81; chief legis. and opinions, dep. corp. counsel Office of Corp. Counsel, Washington, 1981-83; corp. counsel D.C., 1983-85; counsel Laxalt, Washington, Perito & Dubuc, Washington, 1986-90, ptnr., 1990-91; counsel Graham & James, 1991-93, Lewis, White & Clay, P.C., 1994-95; assoc. judge D.C. Ct. Appeals, 1995—. William J. Maier, Jr. vis. prof. law W.Va. U. Coll. Law, Morgantown, 1985-86. Author: Together Black Women, 1972; contbr. articles to profl. jours. and publs. Bd. dirs. Homeland Ministries Bd. United Ch. of Christ, N.Y.C., 1978-83, vice chmn., 1981-83; chmn. bd. govs. Antioch Law Sch., Washington, 1979-81; chmn. bd. trustees Antioch U., Yellow Springs, Ohio, 1981-82; bd. trustees Tufts U., Medford, Mass., 1988—, Lancaster (Pa.) Sem., 1988—; bd. govs. D.C. Sch. Law, 1990—, chmn., 1991—. Recipient Emily Gregory award Barnard Coll., 1976, Arthur Morgan award Antioch U., 1982, Service award United Ch. of Christ, 1983, Disting. Service (Profl. Life) award Tufts U. Alumni Assn., 1988. Office: DC Ct Appeals 500 Indiana Ave NW 6th Fl Washington DC 20001-2131

REID, IRVIN D., academic official. Dean bus. adminstrn. U. Tenn., Chattanooga, until 1989; pres. Montclair State Coll., Upper Montclair, N.J., 1989—. Office: Montclair State Coll Office of Pres Upper Montclair NJ 07043

REID, JACK POWELL, oil company executive; b. Sublette, Kans., Sept. 1, 1936; s. Eldon Gene and Leona M. (Powell) R.; m. Jane B. Logan, June 7, 1958; children: Willie Donald, Tonilou Michelle. BSChemE, U. Kans., 1958. Chief process engr. Refineria Panama, Republic of Panama, 1961-66; process supt. Conoco, Artesia, N.Mex., 1966-67; refinery mgr. Conoco-Navajo, Artesia, 1967-74; gen. mgr. Navajo Refining Co., Artesia, 1974-76, chief operating officer, 1976-82, pres., 1982—; bd.d irs. Holly Corp., Dallas. Avocation: golfing. Office: Holly Corp 100 Crescent Ct Ste 1600 Dallas TX 75201

REID, JACKSON BROCK, psychologist, educator; b. Honea Path, S.C., Sept. 18, 1921; s. Alexander Mack and Ann Orr (Brock) R.; m. Avis Boykin Long, Jan. 12, 1947; step-children: Jules Heywood Long, Barbara Banning Long. B.S., The Citadel, 1942; postgrad., Ariz. State Coll., Flagstaff, 1948; Ph.D., UCLA, 1951, postgrad., summer 1951. Cert., lic. psychologist, Tex. Asst. prof. ednl. psychology U. Tex., Austin, 1951-55; assoc. prof. U. Tex., 1955-59, prof., 1959-93, prof. emeritus 1993—, assoc. dean for grad. studies in edn., 1965-73; coordinator ESEA programs U.S. Office Edn., 1969—, chmn. dept. ednl. psychology, 1972-84; cons. in field. Served to capt. U.S. Army, 1942-47. Office Edn. grantee, 1966-73. Fellow Am. Psychol. Assn. (exptl. and ednl. divs.); mem. AAAS, Am. Ednl. Research Assn., Interam. Soc. Psychology, AAUP, Southwestern Psychol. Assn. (sec.-treas. 1965-66, pres. 1967-68), Tex. Psychol. Assn., Ret. Officers Assn., Nat. Psoriasis Found., ACLU, Common Cause, Fund for Peace, Planned Parenthood of Am., Sigma Xi. Clubs: U. Tex. Faculty Center; Lighthouse Resort and Club (Sanibel Island, Fla.). Research, publs. in learning theory, behavioral effects of radiation and drugs, child and adolescent behavior, programmed instn., computer-assisted instrn., 1951. Office: U Tex Dept Ednl Psychology Austin TX 78712 *The principal goal in my career has been to preserve psychology as an academic discipline devoted to objective inquiry into the etiology of behavior on the basis of logically directed empirical investigation as opposed to rationalistic - mystical - doctrinaire approaches.*

REID, JAMES DOLAN, mathematics educator, researcher; b. Augusta, Ga., June 24, 1930; s. Richard and Katherine (O'Leary) R.; m. Anne Carmody Donohue, Jan. 7, 1959; children: James Jr., Margaret, Gerald. BS, Fordham Coll., 1952, MA, 1954; PhD, U. Wash., 1960; MA (hon.), Wesleyan U., 1972. Asst. prof. Syracuse (N.Y.) U., 1960-61, 1963-65, assoc. prof., 1965-69; research assoc. Yale U., New Haven, 1961-62; asst. prof. Amherst (Mass.) Coll., 1962-63; assoc. prof. math. Wesleyan U., Middletown, Conn., 1969-70, prof., 1970—, chmn. math. dept., 1970-73, 85-88, cons. ednl. studies program, 1980—; vis. prof. U. Würzburg, Fed. Republic Germany, 1989. Contbr. numerous articles on algebra (Abelian groups) to profl. jours. Mem. Bd. Edn., Regional Sch. Dist. #17, 1983-87. With USN, 1954-56. Mem. Am. Math. Soc., Irish Math. Soc., Math. Assn. of Am. Home: 159 Green Hill Rd Killingworth CT 06419-2218 Office: Wesleyan U Dept Math Middletown CT 06459

REID, JAMES SIMS, JR., automobile parts manufacturer; b. Cleve., Jan. 15, 1926; s. James Sims and Felice (Crowl) R.; m. Donna Smith, Sept. 2, 1950; children: Sally, Susan, Anne (dec.), Jeanne. AB cum laude, Harvard U., 1948, JD, 1951. Bar: Mich., Ohio 1951. Pvt. practice law Detroit, 1951-52, Cleve., 1953-56; with Standard Products Co., Cleve., 1956—, dir., 1959, pres., 1962-89, chmn., chief exec. officer, 1989—. Trustee John Carroll U., 1967—, chmn., 1987-91, Musical Arts Assn. of Cleve. Orch., 1973—. Office: Standard Products Co 2130 W 110th St Cleveland OH 44102-3510

REID, JOHN MITCHELL, biomedical engineer; b. Mpls., June 8, 1926; s. Robert Sherman and Meryl (Mitchell) R.; m. Virginia Montgomery, Dec. 31, 1949 (div.); children: Donald, Kathryn, Richard; m. Shadi Wang, June 30, 1983. BS, U. Minn., 1950, MS, 1957; PhD, U. Pa., 1965. Engring. assoc. U. Minn., Mpls., 1950-54; rsch. engr. St. Barnabas Hosp., Mpls., 1954-57; assoc. U. Pa., Phila., 1957-66; rsch. asst. prof. U. Wash., Seattle, 1966-72; rsch. engr. Providence Hosp., 1972-74; dir. bioengring. Inst. of Applied Physiology & Medicine, 1973-81; Calhoun prof. emeritus Drexel U., Phila., 1981—; adj. prof. radiology Thomas Jefferson Med. Sch., Phila., 1982—; affiliate prof. U. Wash., 1995—; cons. Inst. Applied Physiology and Medicine, Seattle. Contbr. over 100 articles to profl. jours.; 5 U.S. patents. Scoutmaster Boy Scouts Am., Mpls., 1955-57, Phila., 1960-65, cub and scoutmaster, Seattle, 1965-70. With USN, 1950-52, World War II. Grantee NIH. Fellow IEEE, Am. Inst. Ultrasound in Medicine (bd. govs., Pioneer award), Acoustical Soc. Am., Engring. in Medicine and Biology Soc. (Lifetime Achievement award 1993), Am. Inst. Med. and Biol. Engrs. Home: Apt B 102 3062 231 Ln SE Issaquah WA 98027 Office: Drexel U Inst Biomed Engring & Sci 32D Chestnut Philadelphia PA 19104 also: IAPM 701 16th Ave Seattle WA 98122

REID, JOHN PHILLIP, law educator; b. Weehawken, N.J., May 17, 1930; s. Thomas Francis and Teresa Elizabeth (Murphy) R. B.S.S., Georgetown U., 1952; LL.B., Harvard U., 1955; M.A., U. N.H., 1957; J.S.D., NYU, 1962. Bar: N.H. 1955. Law clk. U.S. Dist. Ct. N.H., 1956; instr. NYU, N.Y.C., 1960-62, asst. prof. law, 1962-64, assoc. prof., 1964-65, prof. Sch. Law, 1966—. Author: Chief Justice: The Judicial World of Charles Doe, 1967, A Law of Blood: The Primitive Law of the Cherokee Nation, 1970, In a Defiant Stance, 1977, In a Rebellious Spirit, 1979, Law for the Elephant: Property and Social Behavior on the Overland Trail, 1980, In Defiance of the Law, 1981, Constitutional History of the American Revolution: The Authority of Rights, 1986, Constitutional History of the American Revolution: The Authority to Tax, 1987, The Concept of Liberty in the Age of the American Revolution, 1988, The Concept of Representation in the Age of the American Revolution, 1989, Constitutional History of the American Revolution: The Authority to Legislate, 1991, Constitutional History of the American Revolution: The Authority of Law, 1993. Fellow Guggenheim Found., 1980, Huntington Library-NEH, 1980, 84; hon. fellow Am. Soc. Legal History, 1986. Republican. Roman Catholic. Office: NYU Law Sch 40 Washington Sq S New York NY 10012-1099

REID, JOSEPH BROWNING, architect; b. Flint Hill, Va., June 24, 1924; s. Charles Garrison and Grace Pearl (Bradley) R.; m. Maria Aida Amadounian, July 5, 1957; children: Charles, Avedis, Robert. Student, U. Va., 1948; BS in Forestry with highest honors, N.C. State U., 1952; postgrad., Columbia U., 1955; cert. in architecture, Cooper Union, 1960. Registered architect, N.Y., Va., Md., Pa., D.C.; cert. Nat. Coun. Archtl. Registration Bds.; lic. interior designer, D.C. Staff architect Charles Luckman & Assocs., N.Y.C., 1956-63; sr. architect Clive Entwistle & Assocs., N.Y.C., 1963-64; sr. assoc. Perkins & Will, Washington, 1964-74; v.p. John Carl Warnecke FAIA, Washington, 1974-82; founding ptnr. Kemnitzer Reid & Haffler, Washington, 1982-89; prin. Einhorn Yaffee Prescott, Washington, 1989—; advisOr interior design program Marymount Coll., 1982-85; profl. coord. off-campus work program for architecture students Va. Poly. Inst., 1975-81; lectr. No. Va. C.C.; a juror for residential awards Washingtonian mag., 1986; advisor, organizer archtl. awards program Washington Mayor's Award Program. With Mcht. Marine, 1942-47. Recipient Disting. Svc. cert. USO, Washington, 1976, Presdl. Design award Nat. Endowment for Arts, 1987, Hist. Preservation Honor award, 1988, Design award Washington Metro chpt. Am. Soc. Interior Designers, 1989, 2 awards GSA, 1992; Hilda Johnson Cox scholar N.C. State U., 1950. Mem. AIA (sr. dir. Washington Met. chpt. 1979-80, treas. 1981-82, sec. 1982-83, v.p. 1983-84, pres. 1984-85, cert. of deep appreciation 1984, cert. of appreciation 1984), Constrn. Specifications Inst. (bd. dirs. 1979-81, 91-92, citation for disting. svc. 1982, nat. honor awards 1992), Soc. Archtl. Adminstrs. (co-founder Washington chpt.), Phi Eta Sigma, Alpha Zeta, Xi Sigma Pi, Alpha Sigma Pi. Democrat. Methodist. Avocations: surf fishing, Greek history, travel in Greece. Home: 6926 Tyndale St Mc Lean VA 22101-5070 Office: Einhorn Yaffee Prescott Arch 1000 Potomac St NW # 1 Washington DC 20007-3501

REID, JOSEPH LEE, physical oceanographer, educator; b. Franklin, Tex., Feb. 7, 1923; s. Joseph Lee and Ruby (Cranford) R.; m. Freda Mary Hunt, Apr. 7, 1953; children: Ian Joseph, Julian Richard. BA in Math., U. Tex., 1942; MS, Scripps Instn. Oceanography, 1950. Rsch. staff Scripps Instn. Oceanography, La Jolla, Calif., 1957-74; prof. oceanography Scripps Instn. Oceanography, La Jolla, 1974-91, ret., 1991; dir. Marine Life Rsch. Group, 1974-87; assoc. dir. Inst. Marine Resources, 1975-82; cons. Sandia Nat. Labs., Albuquerque, 1980-86. Author: On the Total Geostrophic Circulation of the South Pacific Ocean: Flow Patterns, Tracers and Transports, 1986, On the Total Geostrophic Circulation of the South Atlantic Ocean: Flow Patterns, Tracers and Transports, 1989; contbr. articles to profl. jours. Lt. USNR, 1942-46, ETO, PTO. Recipient award Nat. Oceanographic Data Ctr., Washington, 1984, Albatross award Am. Miscellaneous Soc., 1988, Alexander Agassiz medal NAS, 1992. Fellow AAAS, Am. Geophys. Union (pres. Ocean Scis. sect. 1972-74, 84-86); mem. Am. Meteorol. Soc., Oceanography Soc. Home: 1105 Cuchara Dr Del Mar CA 92014-2623

REID, LANGHORNE, III, merchant banker; b. Dallas, Apr. 3, 1950; s. Langhorne Jr. and Mary Anne (Beasley) R.; m. Sally Wolf, Dec. 26, 1972 (div. Aug. 1977); m. Eve Catherine Murphy, Sept. 6, 1986; 1 child, Claire Hart Reid. BA in Psychology, U. Tex., Austin, 1972, JD, 1975; MBA, U. Pa., 1977. Bar: Tex. 1975. V.p. Dillon, Read & Co., Inc., N.Y.C., 1977-82; mng. dir. Drexel Burnham Lambert Inc., N.Y.C., 1982-87; co-dir. mergers and acquisitions Paine Webber Group, N.Y.C., 1987-89; ptnr. Gordon Investment Inc., N.Y.C., 1989-93; pres. Beacon Advisors, Inc., Dallas, 1993—; bd. dirs. Windmill Holdings, pres. Partnership Svcs., 1992-93. Trustee, treas. Animal Med. Ctr., N.Y.C., 1981—. Mem. Tex. Bar Assn., River Club N.Y. Home: 4441 Belfort Pl Dallas TX 75205-3616 Office: Beacon Advisors Inc 4311 Oak Lawn Ave Ste 270 Dallas TX 75219-2311

REID, LOREN DUDLEY, speech educator; b. Gilman City, Mo., Aug. 26, 1905; s. Dudley Alver and Josephine (Tarwater) R.; m. Mary Augusta Towner, Aug. 28, 1930; children: Jane Ellen, John Christopher, Stephen Dudley Towner, Don Anthony. A.B., Grinnell Coll., 1927; A.M., State U. Iowa, 1930, Ph.D., 1932. Tchr. Vermillion (S.D.) High Sch., 1927-29; instr. State U. Iowa, 1931-33; tchr. Westport High Sch., Kansas City, Mo., 1933-35; English instr. U. Mo., 1935-37, asst. prof., 1937-39; asst. prof. and later assoc. prof. of speech Syracuse U., 1939-44; prof. of speech U. Mo., 1944—, sesquicentennial prof., 1990, chmn. dept. speech, 1947-52; vis. prof. speech U. So. Calif., summer, 1947; summer lectr. La. State U., 1949, Mich., 1950, 56; summer lectr. State U. Iowa, 1952, Denver, 1960, Oklahoma, 1962; vis. prof. U. Utah, summer 1952, San Diego State Coll., summer 1954, U. So. Calif., summer 1954; European staff U. Md., 1952-53, summer, 1955, 1961-62, London; European staff U. Mich., summer 1957, State U. Iowa, summer 1958; Carnegie vis. prof. U. Hawaii, 1957, La. State U., 1985; vis. lectr. Kyoto (Japan) Sangyo U., 1987. Author: Charles James Fox: An Eighteenth Century Parliamentary Speaker, 1932, Course Book in Public Speaking, (with Gilman and Aly) Speech Preparation, 1946, Fundamentals of Speaking, (with Gilman and Aly), 1951, Teaching Speech in High School, 1952, Teaching Speech, rev. edit., 1960, 4th edit., 1971, First Principles of Public Speaking, 1960, rev. edit., published in 1962, Studies in American Public Address, 1961, Speaking Well, 4th edit., 1982, Hurry Home Wednesday (Mo. Writers Guild award), Finally It's Friday, 1981, Professor on the Loose, 1987. Recipient Alumni Achievement award Grinnell Coll., 1962. Fellow Royal Hist. Soc.; mem. Speech Assn. Am. (exec. sec. 1945-51, pres. 1957, Disting. Svc. award 1981), N.Y. State Speech Assn., pres. 1942-44, Spl. award for outstanding svc. 1967), Cen. States Speech Assn. (exec. sec. 1937-39, Disting. Svc. award 1979), Speech and Theatre Assn. Mo. (Disting. Svc. award 1982), AAUP, Conf. on Brit. Studies. U. Mo. Club (pres. 1947). Democrat. Episcopalian. Home: 200 E Brandon Rd Columbia MO 65203-3566

REID, LYLE, judge; b. Brownsville, Tenn., June 17, 1930; m. Elizabeth W.; children: Betsy, Martha Lyle. BSBA, U. Tenn., JD, 1956. Asst. state atty. gen. State of Tenn., Nashville, 1961-63; county atty. Haywood County, Brownsville, Tenn., 1964-86; atty. Reid & Banks, Brownsville, Tenn., 1963-66; assoc. judge Tenn. Ct. Criminal Appeals, Tenn., 1987-90; chief justice Tenn. Supreme Ct., Nashville, 1990-94; deputy commr. Dept. Commerce & Ins., Tenn. With USAF, Korea. Mem. ABA, Am. Bar Found., Tenn. Bar Assn. Democrat. Methodist. Office: Tenn Supreme Ct 321 Supreme Ct Bldg Nashville TN 37219-1407

REID, LYNNE MCARTHUR, pathologist; b. Melbourne, Australia, Nov. 12, 1923; d. Robert Muir and Violet Annie (McArthur) R. M.D., U. Melbourne, 1946; M.D. (hon.), Harvard U., 1976. Reader in exptl. pathology London U., 1964-67, prof. exptl. pathology, 1967-76; dean Cardiothoracic Inst., 1973-76; pathologist-in-chief Children's Hosp., Boston, 1976-89, pathologist-in-chief emeritus, 1990—; S. Burt Wolbach prof. pathology Harvard Med. Sch., Boston, 1976—. Fellow Royal Coll. Physicians (U.K.), Royal Australian Coll. Physicians, Royal Coll. Pathologists, Royal Soc. Medicine, Royal Inst. Gt. Britain, Pathol. Soc. Gt. Britain and Ireland, Thoracic Soc., Assn. Clin. Pathologists, Brit. Thoracic/Soc., Fleischner Soc., Can. Thoracic Soc., Neonatal Soc., Am. Thoracic Soc., Am. Soc. Pathologists, Fleischner Soc., Am. Soc. Exptl. Biology. Office: 300 Longwood Ave Boston MA 02115-5737

REID, MARILYN JOANNE, state legislator, lawyer; b. Chgo., Aug. 14, 1941; d. Kermit and Newell Azile (Hahn) N.; m. M. David Reid. Nov. 26, 1966 (div. Mar. 1983); children: David, Nelson. Student, Miami U., 1959-61; BA, U. Ill, 1963; JD, Ohio No. U., 1966. Bar: Ohio 1966, Ark. 1967, U.S. Dist. Ct. 1967. Trust adminstr. First Nat. Bank, Dayton, Ohio, 1966-67; assoc. Sloan & Ragsdale, Little Rock, Ohio, 1967-69; ptnr. Reid and Reid, Dayton, 1969-76, Reid & Buckwalter, Dayton, 1975—; mem. Ohio Ho. of Reps., 1993—; mem. Judiciary and Criminal Justice com., vice chmn. ins. com., Vets. com., Pub. utilities com. Mem. Ohio adv. bd. U.S. Commn. Civil Rights; chmn., treas. various polit. campaigns, 1975—; trustee Friends Libr. Beavercreek (Ohio); bd. dirs. Beavercreek YMCA, 1985-88; active Mt. Zion United Ch. of Christ. Mem. ABA, Ohio Bar Assn., Greene County Bar Assn., Beavercreek C. of C. (pres. 1986-87), Dayton Panhellenic Assn. (pres. 1982), Altrusa (v.p. Greene County 1979-79, pres. 1979-80), Lioness (pres. Beavercreek 1975), Rotary, Kappa Beta Pi, Gamma Phi Beta (v.p. 1974-75). Republican. Mem. Ch. Christ. Avocations: tennis, skiing, boating, bridge. Office: Reid & Buckwalter 3866 Indian Ripple Rd Dayton OH 45440-3448

REID, MARION L., lieutenant governor, educator; b. North Rustico, P.E.I., Can., Jan. 4, 1929; d. Michael Doyle and Loretta Whelan; m. Lea P. Reid, June 29, 1949; children: Maureen and Colleen (twins), Kevin, Bethany, Marylea, David, Andrew, Tracy. Tchr.'s lic., Prince Wales Coll., P.E.I.,

1947. Tchr. elem. schs. P.E.I. from 1947; prin. St. Ann's Elem. Sch., Hope River, 1964-68; mem., dep. speaker Legis. Assembly of P.E.I., Charlottetown, 1974-84, speaker, 1984-86, opposition house leader; lt. gov. P.E.I., Charlottetown, 1990—; past bd. govs., sec. mem. various coms. P.E.I. Tchrs. Fedn. Pres. Sterling Women's Inst.; charter mem. Queen Elizabeth Hosp. Found. Named Dame of Grace, Order of Hosp. of St. John of Jerusalem, 1990. Mem. Cath. Women's League, Zonta Club. Address: Govt House, PO Box 846, Charlottetown, PE Canada C1A 7L9

REID, MARTIN J., electronics executive. BSEE, Northeastern U., 1964, MSEE, 1970. V.p. Alpha Industries, Inc., Woburn, Mass., 1975-81, sr. v.p., 1981-85, pres., COO, 1985-91, pres., CEO, 1991—. Office: Alpha Industries Inc 20 Sylvan Rd Woburn MA 01801-1845*

REID, MICHAEL J., international management consultant and educator; b. Chgo., Aug. 13, 1938; s. Robert and Dorothy (Wolfson) R.; m. Arlene Elaine Tufano, June 2, 1963; children: Cameron, Krista, Eaton. Student advt. design, U. Ill. Coll. Fine Art, 1956-58; Student med. illustration, U. Ill. Coll. Medicine, 1958-60; student, Ill. Inst. Tech., 1960-62, BS, 1962. Pres. Michael Reid Design Inc., Chgo., 1964-79; program designer, productivity seminar leader, 1979-85; exec. v.p. TTI Inc., Greenbrae, Calif., 1985-88; nat. tng. dir. Ctr. for Mgmt. Design, Greenbrae, 1988-90; chief exec. officer The Reid Cons. Partnership, San Francisco, 1990—; bd. dirs., designer-developer courses for mgmt. edn., strategic planning, team bldg., process reengring. and project implementation; mgmt. cons. USA and internationally; instr. visual design Art Inst. Chgo. Contbr. designs to profl. jours. Mem. Am. Inst. Graphic Arts, Soc. Typographic Arts, 27 Chgo. Designers.

REID, PAUL S., nortgage company executive; b. 1948. MA, U. Va., 1971. cert. mortgage broker. With Wachovia Mortgage Co., Winston-Salem, N.C., 1971-75, Mortgage Corp. of South, Winston-Salem, N.C., 1975-78, Mortgage Guaranty Ins. Corp., Richmond, Va., 1978-81; pres. Investors Home Mortgage Corp., Richmond, Va., 1981-88; exec. v.p. Investors Savings Bank, Richmond, Va., 1988-95; pres. Am. Home Funding Inc., Richmond, Va., 1995—. Office: Am Home Funding Inc 2812 Emerywood Pky Richmond VA 23294-3718*

REID, R(ALPH) BENJAMINE, lawyer; b. Concord, N.C., Jan. 11, 1950; s. Fred Herndon and Frances (Barnhardt) R.; m. Jennie Lou Divine, Dec. 19, 1970; children: Elisabeth Divine, Margaret Hethcox, Benjamine Joseph. AB, U. N.C., 1971; JD cum laude, U. Va., 1974. Bar: Ga. 1974, Fla. 1974, U.S. Dist. Ct. (so. dist.) Fla. 1974, U.S. Supreme Ct. 1981, U.S. Ct. Appeals (5th cir.) 1974, (11th cir.) 1981. Assoc. Kimbrell & Hamann, P.A., Miami, Fla., 1974-79, mem., 1980-90; shareholder Popham, Haik, Schnobrich & Kaufman, Ltd., Miami, 1990—; lectr. Atlanta Bar Product Liability Seminar, Emory U., 1983, U. Miami Law Sch., 1983, NBI Damage Seminar, 1989, Com. on Corp. Counsel, 1989, Product Liability Com., 1989, ABA Nat. Insts., 1990-92, Dispute Resolution in Pacific Rim, Hong Kong, 1995; mem. products liability com. Def. Research Inst., Chgo., 1986—; bd. dirs. Product Liability Adv. Coun. Vestryman, sr. warden St. Philip's Episcopal Ch., Coral Gables, Fla., 1982-85; mem. exec. bd. Episc. Diocese S.E. Fla., Miami, 1982-85, standing com., 1985-86, sec., 1986-87, mem. diocesan obligations and appeals com., 1985; trustee Trinity Episc. Sch., Miami, 1984-90; bd. dirs. Dade Pub. Edn. Fund, 1987—, v.p., 1988-89, pres., 1989-91; treas. Dade Heritage Trust, Miami, 1985, 1st v.p., 1986, mem. adv. bd., bd. dirs. Leadership Miami, 1984—, exec. com., 1986-91, chmn., 1989-91; mem. steering com. Fla. Internat. U. Coun. 100, 1990—, chmn., 1991—; chair Dade County selection com., John Motley Movehead Found., U. N.C., Chapel Hill, 1990—; bd. dirs. Environ. Edn. Found. Fla., 1995— Fellow Hist. Assn. So. Fla. (bd. trustees 1989-92); mem. ABA (mem. litigation sect., chair product liability com. 1986-89, divsn. dir. 1989-90, chair membership com. 1991-94, co-chair ann. meeting 1996), FBA, Dade County Bar Assn. (bd. dirs. 1982-85), Dade County Def. Bar Assn. (bd. dirs. 1983), Assn. for the Advancement of Automotive Medicine, Greater Miami C. of C. (bd. govs. 1988-90, vice chair exec. com. 1990-92), Phi Kappa Phi. Democrat. Home: 905 University Dr Miami FL 33134-6462 Office: Popham Haik Schnobrich & Kaufman Ltd 4000 International Pl 100 SE 2nd St Miami FL 33131-2100

REID, ROBERT CLARK, chemical engineering educator; b. Denver, June 11, 1924; s. Frank B. and Florence (Seerley) R.; m. Anna Marie Murphy, Aug. 26, 1950; children: Donald M., Ann Christine. Student, Colo. Sch. Mines, 1946-48; B.S. Purdue U., 1950, M.S., 1951; Sc.D., M.I.T., 1954. Prof. chem. engring. M.I.T., Cambridge, from 1954; now prof. emeritus chem. engring. M.I.T.; Olaf A. Hougen prof. chem. engring. U. Wis., 1980-81; cons. Nestle Corp., 1978—, Cabot Corp., 1982—. Author: (with J.M. Prausnitz and B.E. Poling) Properties of Gases and Liquids, 1966, 4th edit., 1987, (with M. Ohara) Modeling Crystal Growth Rates from Solution, 1973, (with M. Modell) Thermodynamics and Its Applications, 1974, 2d edit., 1983; Contbr. articles to profl. jours. Recipient Warren K. Lewis award, 1976; Chem. Engring. award Am. Soc. Engring. Edn., 1977; research fellow Harvard U., 1963-64. Mem. Am. Inst. Chem. Engrs. (Ann. lectr. 1967, council 1969-71, editor jour. 1970-76, Founders award 1984). Nat. Acad. Engring., Blue Key, Sigma Alpha Epsilon, Tau Beta Pi. Home: 22 Burroughs Rd Lexington MA 02173-1908 Office: MIT 66 540 Cambridge MA 02139

REID, ROBERT LELON, college dean, mechanical engineer; b. Detroit, May 20, 1942; s. Lelon Reid and Verna Beulah (Custer) Cook; m. Judy Elaine Nestell, July 21, 1962; children: Robert James, Bonnie Kay, Matthew Lelon. ASE, Mott Community Coll., Flint, Mich., 1961; BChemE, U. Mich., 1963; MME, So. Meth. U., 1966, PhDME, 1969. Registered profl. engr., Tenn., Tex., Wis. Asst. rsch. engr. Atlantic Richfield Co., Dallas, 1964-65; assoc. staff engr. Linde Div., Union Carbide Corp., Tonawanda, N.Y., 1966-68; from asst. to assoc. prof. U. Tenn., Knoxville, 1969-75; assoc. prof. Cleve. State U., 1975-77; from assoc. to full prof. U. Tenn., Knoxville, 1977-82; prof., chmn. U. Tex., El Paso 1982-87; dean Coll. Engring. Marquette U., Milw., 1987—; summer prof. NASA Marshall Space Ctr., Huntsville, Ala., 1970, EXXON Prodn. Rsch., Houston, 1972, 73, NASA Lewis Space Ctr., Cleve., 1986; cons. Oak Ridge Nat. Lab., 1974-75, TVA, 1978, 79, State of Calif., Sacramento, 1985, Tex. Higher Edn. Coordinating Bd., Austin, 1987. Contbr. 80 articles on heat transfer and solar energy to books, jours. and procs. Grantee NSF, DOE, TVA, NASA, DOI, 1976-87; named Engr. of Yr. Engring. Socs. El Paso, 1986. Fellow ASME (Centennial medallion 1980, chmn. cryogenics com. 1977-81, chmn. solar energy divsn. 1983-84, chmn. Rio Grande sect. 1985-87); mem. ASHRAE, Engrs. and Scientists Milw. (bd. dirs. 1988-93, v.p. 1989-90, pres. 1991-92). Lutheran. Avocations: travel, classic car restoration. Office: Marquette U Coll Engring PO Box 1881 Milwaukee WI 53201-1881

REID, ROBERT NEWTON, lawyer, mortgage and financial consultant; b. Ottawa, Ill., Mar. 28, 1906; s. Robert Joseph and Mae (Newton) R. Ph.B., U. Chgo., 1929, J.D., 1930. Bar: Ill. 1930, U.S. Supreme Ct. 1949, Md. 1961, D.C. 1961. Practiced in Chgo., 1930-39; with Follansbee, Shorey & Schupp, 1933-39; govt. atty. FCA, Washington, 1939-42; atty. counsel RFC, Fed. Nat. Mortgage Assn., 1942-49; asst. gen. counsel Fed. Nat. Mortgage Assn., 1949-50, gen. counsel, 1950-70, spl. counsel, 1970-73, v.p., 1950-59, 68-73, dir., 1954-59, cons., 1973—. Mem. bd. advisors Washington Studio Sch., 1985—. Served from 2d lt. to lt. col. Judge Adv. Gen. Corps USAR, 1942-46. Decorated Legion of Merit. Mem. ABA (life), Fed. Bar Assn. D.C. Bar Assn. (life), Am. Judicature Soc., Supreme Ct. Hist. Soc., Res. Officers Assn. (life), Am. Legion (life), SAR (life), Ret. Officers Assn. (life), Mil. Order of World Wars (life), Nat. Assn., Uniformed Svcs., English Speaking Union, Delta Sigma Phi (life), Phi Alpha Delta. Clubs: Nat. Lawyers (life), University (life) (Washington). Lodge: Masons (life). Home: University Club 1135 16th St NW Washington DC 20036-4801 Office: 3900 Wisconsin Ave NW Washington DC 20016-2892

REID, RUST ENDICOTT, lawyer; b. N.Y.C., Dec. 31, 1931; s. Thorburn and Mary (Newhall) R.; m., Jeanne Inge, Aug. 5, 1955; children: Dorothy, Elizabeth, Margaret, Mary. BA, U. Va., 1954, LLB, 1960. Bar: Tex. 1960, Va. 1960. Bd. cert. in estate planning, probate. Assoc. Thompson & Knight, Dallas, 1960-65, ptnr., 1965—; lectr. SW Grad. Sch. Banking, Dallas, 1978-88; adj. prof. So. Meth. U., Dallas, 1980-86. Contbg. author: Texas Estate Administration, 1975. Trustee Child Care, Dallas, 1968-72, pres. 1970-72, Hockaday Sch., Dallas, 1972-82 (chmn. 1976-78), Texas coun. Girl Scouts

U.S., 1982-83; trustee Vis. Nurse Assn., Dallas, 1984—, treas. 1986-89, v.p. 1989-91, pres., 1991-93; pres. Dallas Estate Planning Coun., 1988-89; trustee Dallas Children's Advocacy Center (v.p. 1993—). Lt. (j.g.) USNR, 1954-57. Fellow Am. Trust and Estate Counsel; mem. Tex. Bar Found. Presbyterian. Home: 7010 Tokalon Dr Dallas TX 75214-3830 Office: Thompson & Knight 1700 Pacific 3300 First City Ctr Dallas TX 75201

REID, SARAH LAYFIELD, lawyer; b. Kansas City, Mo., Sept. 22, 1952; d. Jim Tom and Sarah Pauline (Clark) R.; m. David Harris Gikow, June 12, 1983; children: Stephen Nathaniel, Emily Pauline. AB, Bryn Mawr Coll., 1974; JD, Harvard U. 1977. Bar: N.Y. 1978, U.S. Dist. Ct. (so. and ea. dists.) N.Y. 1978, U.S. Ct. Appeals (11th cir.) 1981, U.S. Ct. Appeals (2d cir.) 1982, U.S. Supreme Ct. 1988, U.S. Ct. Appeals (3d cir.) 1990. Assoc. Kelley Drye & Warren, N.Y.C., 1977-85, ptnr., 1986—. Mem. ABA, N.Y. State Bar Assn., Fed. Bar Coun., Assn. Of Bar of City of N.Y. (mem. task force Women in the Profession). Office: Kelley Drye & Warren 101 Park Ave New York NY 10178-0062

REID, SIDNEY WEBB, English educator; b. Neptune, N.J., Nov. 24, 1943; s. Sidney Webb and Mary Cook (Bennett) R.; m. Judith Wright, Aug. 22, 1969; 1 child, Laura. BA, Duke U., 1965; MA, U. Va., 1966, PhD, 1972. Grad. tchg. fellow U. Va., Charlottesville, 1968-70; asst. prof. English, Kent (Ohio) State U., 1970-75, assoc. prof., 1975-84, prof., 1984—, dir. Inst. Bibliography and Editing, 1985—; vis. fellow Clare Hall, Cambridge (Eng.) U., 1992-93, life mem., 1993—. Textual editor Bicentennial Edition of Charles Brockden Brown, 6 vols., 1977-87; editor-in-chief: (Cambridge edits. of Joseph Conrad) The Secret Agent, 1990, Almayer's Folly, 1994. NDEA fellow U.Va., 1965-68; Rsch. grantee NEH, 1977-84. Office: Kent State University Inst Bibliography-Editing 1118 Library Kent OH 44242

REID, STEPHEN ROBERT, power generation engineer, consultant; b. N.Y.C., July 2, 1957; s. Stephen and Marilyn Louise (Ruzicka) R.; m. Shari Joann Mariotti, Apr. 27, 1985; children: Stephen Thomas, Thomas Robert, Timothy Michael. AS, CUNY, 1978; BSME cum laude, Manhattan Coll., 1980. Registered profl. engr., Del. Assoc. engr. Westinghouse Electric Corp., Lester, Pa., 1981-82; engr. Westinghouse Electric Corp., Lester and Orlando, Fla., 1982-85; advanced engr. Westinghouse Electric Corp., Orlando, 1985-88; project engr. Delmarva Power & Light Co., Newark, Del., 1988-91, sr. engr., 1991—; cons. U.S. utilities, 1991—; lectr. short course Electric Power Rsch. Inst., Palo Alto, Calif., 1991—; presenter in field. Editor: Recent Innovations and Experience with Plant Monitoring and Utility Operations, 1991; contbr. articles to profl. jours.; patentee on solutions to cycling induced stress cracking of generators and method to correct turbine blade vibration induced failures. Recipient Engring. Excellence award S.E. Electric Exch., 1994. Mem. ASME, sec. Phila. sect. 1982, chmn. utility ops. tech. sessions Joint Power Generation Conf. with IEEE 1989, 91, lectr. short course N.Y.C. 1993—, paper rev. coord. utility ops. com. 1994-95, George Westinghouse silver medal 1993), Vibration Inst. Republican. Roman Catholic. Avocations: woodworking, golf. Home: 5 Forge Rd Newark DE 19711 Office: Delmarva Power & Light Co PO Box 6066 252 Chapman Rd Newark DE 19714-6066

REID, SUE TITUS, law educator; b. Bryan, Tex., Nov. 13, 1939; d. Andrew Jackson Jr. and Loraine (Wylie) Titus. BS with honors, Tex. Woman's U., 1960; MA, U. Mo., 1962, PhD, 1965; JD, U. Iowa, 1972. Bar: Iowa 1972, U.S. Ct. Appeals (D.C. cir.) 1978, U.S. Supreme Ct. 1978. From instr. to assoc. prof. sociology Cornell Coll., Mt. Vernon, Iowa, 1965-72; assoc. prof., chmn. dept. sociology Coe Coll., Cedar Rapids, Iowa, 1972-74; assoc. prof. law U. Wash., Seattle, 1974-76; exec. assoc. Am. Sociol. Assn., Washington, 1976-77; prof. law U. Tulsa, 1978-88; dean, prof. Sch. Criminology, Fla. State U., Tallahassee, 1988-90; prof. pub. adminstrn. Fla. State U., 1990—; acting chmn. dept. sociology Cornell Coll., 1965-66; vis. assoc. prof. sociology U. Nebr., Lincoln, 1970; vis. disting. prof. law and sociology U. Tulsa, 1977-78, assoc. dean 1979-81; vis. prof. law U. San Diego, 1981-82; mem. People-to-People Crime Prevention Del. to People's Republic of China, 1982; George Beto Vis. Prof. criminal justice Sam Houston U., Huntsville, Tex., 1984-85; lecture/study tour of Criminal Justice systems of 10 European countries, 1985; cons. Evaluation Policy Rsch. Assocs., Inc., Milw., 1976-77, Nat. Inst. Corrections, Idaho Dept. Corrections, 1984, Am. Correctional Inst., Price-Waterhouse. Author: (with others) Bibliographies on Role Methodology and Propositions Volume D - Studies in the Role of the Public School Teacher, 1962, the Correctional System: An Introduction, 1981, Crime and Criminology, 7th edit., 1994, Criminal Justice, 1987, 3d edit., 1993, Criminal Law, 1989, 3d edit., 1995; editor: (with David Lyon) Population Crisis: An Interdisciplinary Perspective, 1972; contbr. articles to profl. jours. Recipient Disting. Alumni award Tex. Woman's U., 1979; named One of Okla. Young Leaders of 80's Oklahoma Monthly, 1980. Mem. Am. Correctional Assn., Am. Soc. Criminology, Acad. Criminal Justice Scis. Avocations: walking, swimming, reading, sewing, cooking. Office: Fla State Univ Dept Pub Adminstrn Tallahassee FL 32306

REID, TERENCE C. W., corporation executive; b. Johannesburg, Republic of South Africa, Oct. 28, 1941; arrived in Canada, 1964; s. Edward Harold and Constance Mary (Jenner) R.; m. Carole Julie Davies; children: Alison, Michael, Christopher. Diploma in law, Witwatersrand U., Johannesburg, 1962; MBA, Toronto U., 1966. Articled clk. Bowen's Co., Johannesburg, 1959-64; various positions to vice chmn. Wood Gundy Inc., Toronto and Montreal, 1966—; Dir. Kinross Gold Corp. Office: Wood Gundy Inc, BCE Pl/PO Box 500, Toronto, ON Canada M5J 2S8

REID, THOMAS FENTON, minister; b. Buffalo, Sept. 9, 1932; s. Albert E. and Helen Gertrude (Rice) R.; m. Wanda Darlene Bousum, July 7, 1968; 1 child, Aimee Linette. Diploma, Cen. Bible Coll., Springfield, Mo., 1953; DD (hon.), Calif. Grad. Sch. Theology, 1981; LHD (hon.), Oral Roberts U., 1987. Ordained to ministry Assemblies of God, 1956. Missionary, evangelist Assemblies of God, Springfield, 1953-63; pastor Bethel Temple, Manila, 1959-60; st. pastor Full Gospel Tabernacle, Orchard Park, N.Y., 1963—; pres. Buffalo Sch. Bible, 1976—; pres. Nat. Ch. Growth Conf., Washington, 1984; sec., bd. dirs. Ch. Growth Inc., Seoul, Republic of Korea, 1979—. Author: The Exploding Church, 1979, Kingdom Now But Not Yet, 1988, Ethics, Excellence and Economics, 1989. Mem. Nat. Assn. Evangelicals (bd. dirs. 1979—), Nat. Religious Broadcasters, Friends of Anwar Sadat, Christians for Friends in Middle East. Republican. Home: 701 Willardshire Rd Orchard Park NY 14127-2038 Office: Full Gospel Tabernacle 3210 Southwestern Blvd Orchard Park NY 14127-1293 *The very center of my belief system is that God made man in His own image. Man has great value, dignity and purpose. It is my responsibility to lead men to God, and help them find their true purpose and potential through Jesus Christ.*

REID, TIMOTHY, business organization executive; b. Toronto, Ont., Can., Feb. 21, 1936; s. Escott and Ruth (Herriot) R.; m. Julyan Fancott, Oct. 11, 1962; children: Dylan, Vanessa. BA with honors. U. Toronto, 1959; MA, Yale U., 1960; MLitt, Oxford U., Eng., 1965; grad. Advanced Mgmt. Program, Harvard U., 1983. Half back Hamilton (Ont., Can.) Tiger Cats Football Club, 1962; asst. to pres. York U., Toronto, 1963-67; mem. provincial parliament Ont. Legislature, 1967-71; prin. adminstr. OECD, Paris, 1971-74; asst. dep. minister Govt. of Can., Ottawa, 1974-85; dean faculty of bus. Ryerson Poly. Inst., Toronto, 1985-89; commr. Ont. Securities Commn., 1987-89; pres. Can. C. of C., Ottawa, 1989—; bd. dirs., co-chair bus. Can. Labor Market and Productivity Ctr., 1989—. Rhodes scholar, 1960. Mem. Can. Exec. Svc. Orgn. (bd. dirs. 1992—). Office: Can Chamber of Commerce, 55 Metcalfe St # 1160, Ottawa, ON Canada K1P 6N4

REID, WILLIAM HILL, mathematics educator; b. Oakland, Calif., Sept. 10, 1926; s. William Macdonald and Edna Caroline (Hill) R.; m. Elizabeth Mary Kidner, May 26, 1962; 1 child, Margaret Frances. BS, U. Calif., Berkeley, 1949, MS, 1951; PhD, Cambridge U., Eng.; 1955, ScD (hon.) 1968; AM (hon.), Brown U., 1961. Lectr. Johns Hopkins U., Balt., 1955-56; NSF fellow Yerkes Observatory, Williams Bay, Wis., 1957-58; asst. prof. Brown U., Providence, 1958-61, assoc. prof., 1961-63; assoc. prof. U. Chgo., 1963-65, prof., 1965-89, prof. emeritus, 1989—; prof. Ind. U.-Purdue U., Indianapolis, 1989—; cons. research labs. Gen. Motors Corp., Warren, Mich., 1960-73. Author: (with P.G. Drazin) Hydrodynamic Stability, 1981; contbr. articles to profl. jours. Served with U.S. Mcht. Marine, 1945-47, with AUS, 1954-56. Fulbright research scholar Australian Nat. U., 1964-65. Fellow Am. Phys. Soc., Cambridge Philos. Soc.; mem. Am. Math. Soc., Am.

Meteorol. Soc., Sigma Xi. Home: 7554 Ballinshire N Dr Indianapolis IN 46254 Office: Ind U-Purdue U Dept Math Scis 402 N Blackford St Indianapolis IN 46202-3216

REID, WILLIAM JAMES, social work educator; b. Detroit, Nov. 14, 1928; s. James Macknight and Sophie Amelia (Schneider) R.; m. Anne E. Fortune, May 22, 1988; children by previous marriage—Valerie, Steven. B.A., U. Mich., 1950, M.S.W., 1952; D.S.W., Columbia U., 1963. Caseworker-in-charge Family Service of Westchester, Mt. Kisco, N.Y., 1956-59; asst. prof. social work U. Chgo., 1962-65, prof., 1968-75, George Herbert Jones prof., 1975-80; prof. Sch. Social Welfare, SUNY, Albany, 1980—; dir. Center for Social Casework Research, Community Service Soc., N.Y.C., 1965-68. Author: Brief and Extended Casework, 1969, Task-Centered Casework, 1972, Task-Centered Practice, 1977, The Task-Centered System, 1978, Models of Family Treatment, 1981, Research in Social Work, 1981, 2d edit., 1989, Family Problem Solving, 1985, The Role-Sharing Marriage, 1986, Advances in Clinical Social Work Research, 1990, Task Strategies, 1992, Qualitative Research in Social Work, 1994, Generalist Practice: A Task-Centered Approach, 1994. Served with U.S. Army, 1952-56. Recipient excellence in rsch. award Nat. Assn. Social Workers, 1990. Mem. Phi Beta Kappa. Office: 135 Western Ave Albany NY 12203-1011

REID, WILLIAM JAMES, retired physicist, educator; b. Abbeville, S.C., Nov. 2, 1927; s. William James and Mary Lelia (Shelley) R.; m. Nancy Louise Edwards, Nov. 25, 1964; children: Laura Louise, William James III, Sandra Shelley. AB in Chemistry, Erskine Coll., 1949; MS in Chemistry, Duke U., 1958; PhD in Physics, Clemson U., 1967. Instr. Erskine Coll., Due West, S.C., 1949-51, field rep., 1951-52; svc. mgr. Reid Motor Co., Abbeville, S.C., 1954-57; asst. prof. Erskine Coll., Due West, 1957-62, assoc. prof., 1966-68; prof., head physics dept. Jacksonville (Ala.) State U., 1968-91, head dept. phys. scis. and engring., 1991-94; pres. faculty senate Jacksonville State U., 1971-72, 76-77, 88-89. Contbr. various articles to profl. jours. With U.S. Army, 1945-46, 1st lt. S.C. NG, 1948-56. Recipient Disting. Svc. award Jr. C. of C. Abbeville, S.C., 1960; named Kiwanian of Yr., Jacksonville, 1975. Mem. Am. Phys. Soc., Am. Assn. Physics Tchrs., Ala. Acad. Sci., Exch. Club of Jacksonville, Sigma Xi, Phi Lambda Upsilon, Sigma Pi Sigma, Omicron Delta Kappa, Alpha Mu Gamma, Pi Kappa Phi. Methodist. Home: 905 5th Ave NE Jacksonville AL 36265-1355 Office: Jacksonville State U 700 Pelham Rd N Jacksonville AL 36265-1602

REID-CRISP, WENDY, publishing executive; m. Ewing Walker; 1 child, Max Crisp. BA in Eng., Whitman Coll., 1965. Editor-in-chief Savvy Mag.; founder, pub. New Chapter Press, N.Y.C.; editor-in-chief Small Press; nat. dir. Nat. Assn. Female Execs., founder, editor Profl. Libr. bus. books for women, liaison other women's orgns.; lectr. profl. women's issues, 1988—. Author: Give Me One Good Reason: Why Living Takes Up So Much Of Our Time, 1992. Bd. dirs. United Meth. Comms., 1984—. Office: National Assoc for Female Exec 127 W 24th St New York NY 10011-1914

REIDENBAUGH, LOWELL HENRY, retired sports editor; b. Lititz, Pa., Sept. 7, 1919; s. Harry Martin and Marian Marie (Nies) R.; m. Ruth Elizabeth Cameron, Nov. 23, 1944; children: Karen Lee (Mrs. William Rogers), Kathy Jean (Mrs. William J. Schuchman). A.B., Elizabethtown (Pa.) Coll., 1941. Gen. reporter Lancaster (Pa.) Intelligencer Jour., 1941-42; sports writer Phila. Inquirer, 1944-47; mem. staff The Sporting News, St. Louis, 1947-89; mng. editor The Sporting News, 1962-79, sr. editor, 1980-83, corp. editor, 1983-89. Author: National League History, 1976, The Super Bowl Book, 1981, Cooperstown, Where Baseball's Legends Live, 1983, Take Me Out to the Ballpark, 1983, The Sporting News, First 100 Years, 1985, The 50 Greatest Games, 1986, History 33d Va. Infantry Regiment, CSA, 1987, 25 Greatest Pennant Races, 1987, 25 Greatest Teams, 1988, History 27th Va. Infantry Regiment, CSA, 1993. Served with AUS, 1942-43.

REIDENBERG, MARCUS MILTON, physician, educator; b. Phila., Jan. 3, 1934; s. Leon and Adeline Reidenberg; m. June Wilson, July 14, 1957; children: Bruce, Joel, Julie. Student, Cornell U., 1951-54; MD, Temple U., 1958. Diplomate Am. Bd. Internal Medicine. Intern Community Gen. Hosp., Reading, Pa., 1958-59; resident Temple U. Hosp., Phila., 1962-65; from instr. to assoc. prof. Temple U. Med. Sch., Phila., 1962-75; assoc. prof. Cornell U. Med. Coll., N.Y.C., 1975-76, prof. pharmacology, head div. clin. pharmacology, 1976—, prof. medicine, 1980—, acting assoc. dean, 1981-82, asst. dean, 1988—; attending physician N.Y. Hosp., 1980—; vis. physician Rockefeller U. Hosp., N.Y.C., 1980—; mem. project adv. group FDA, Rockville, Md., 1977-82; vice chmn. Joint Commn. on Prescription Drug Use, Washington, 1977-80; mem. study sect. NIH, Bethesda, Md., 1980-86; del. U.S. Pharmacopeal Conv., 1975-80. Author: Renal Function and Drug Action, 1971; editor various books; editor Clin. Pharmacology and Therapeutics, 1985—; contbr. articles to profl. jours. Served to lt. M.C., USNR, 1960-62. Recipient Research Career Devel. award NIH, 1970, Julius Sturmer award Phila. Coll. Pharmacy and Sci., 1982. Fellow ACP; mem. Am. Soc. Clin. Investigations, Assn. Am. Physicians, Am. Soc. Clin. Pharmacology and Therapeutics (pres. 1984-85, Rawls Palmer award 1981), Am. Soc. Pharmacology and Exptl. Therapeutics (award 1983), Internat. Union Pharmacology (vice chmn. sect. clin. pharmacology 1984-87, chmn. 1987-89). Office: Cornell U Med Coll Dept Clin Pharmacology 1300 York Ave New York NY 10021-4805

REIDINGER, RUSSELL FREDERICK, JR., fish and wildlife scientist; b. Reading, Pa., June 19, 1945. BS, Albright Coll., 1967; PhD in Zoology, U. Ariz., 1972. Asst. prof. biology Augustana Coll., 1971-74; rsch. physiologist The Philippines, 1974-78; asst. mem., wildlife biologist Monell Chem. Senses Ctr., 1978-86; dir. Denver wildlife rsch. ctr. U.S. Fish & Wildlife Svc., Phila., 1987-93; dir. ctr. Excellence Nat. Rsch. Mgmt. Lincoln U., Jefferson City, Mo., 1993—; vis. rsch. dept. zoology U. Philippines, 1975-78; cons. Bangladesh Agr. Rsch. Coun., USAID, 1977, Ministry Agrl. Devel. & Agrarian Reform, Nicaragua, 1981. Mem. Am. Soc. Mammalogists, Wildlife Soc., Nat. Animal Damage Control Assn. Office: Lincoln U Dept Ag Nat & Home Econ Jefferson City MO 65102-0029*

REID-PETTY, JANE, artistic director, actor, playwright; b. Meridan, Miss., June 12, 1927; d. Samuel Butler and Mary Lessie (McDonald) Reid; m. Ford F. Petty, Dec. 12, 1948 (div. 1980); 1 child, Mary Daine. BA, U. Ala., 1948; postgrad., Mexico City Coll., 1950-51. Founder, dir. New Stage Theatre, Jackson, Miss., 1965; producer off Broadway, N.Y.C., 1970; actor Regional Theatres, N.Y.C., 1972-92; artistic dir. various plays, Jackson, 1984-92. Actor one-woman show based on Welty's The Ponder-Heart, 1988-92; playwrite A Season of Dreams, 1984, Edna Earle, 1987; author: Almost as Fairly, 1975; contbr. articles to profl. pubs. Bd. dirs. Inst. Arts and Letters, Jackson, 1974-75 (Performing Arts award 1992), Miss. Symphony, Jackson, 1960-65, New STages Theatre, 1965-92. Recipient Miss. Inst. Arts and Letters, 1992; named Artists Achievement State of Miss., 1992. Office: New Stage Theatre 7 Eastbrooke Jackson MS 39216

REIDY, CAROLYN KROLL, publisher; b. Washington, May 2, 1949; d. Henry August and Mildred Josephine (Mencke) Kroll; m. Stephen Kroll Reidy, Dec. 28, 1974. BA, Middlebury Coll., 1971; MA, Ind. U., 1974, PhD, 1982. Various positions to mgr. subs. rights Random House, Inc., N.Y.C., 1975-83, assoc. pub., 1987-88; dir. subs. rights William Morrow & Co., N.Y.C., 1983-85; v.p., assoc. pub. Vintage Books, N.Y.C., 1985-87, pub., 1987-88; pub. Anchor Books, Doubleday & Co., N.Y.C., 1988; pres., pub. Avon Books, N.Y.C., 1992—; pub. trade div. Simon & Schuster, N.Y.C., 1992—. Mem. Women's Media Group, Pubs. Lunch Club. Office: Simon & Schuster 1230 Ave of Americas New York NY 10022

REIDY, EDWARD, JR., state official. Dep. commr. learning results svcs. Edn., Arts and Humanities Cabinet, Frankfort, Ky. Office: Learning Results Svcs Capital Plaza Tower Rm 1924 500 Mero St Frankfort KY 40601-1957

REIDY, GERALD PATRICK, federal organization executive, arbitrator, mediator, fact-finder; b. N.Y.C., Apr. 25, 1929; s. Patrick Joseph and Kathleen Theresa (Holohan) R.; m. Patricia Hope Johnston, Nov. 28, 1953; children: Anne Marie Reidy Borenstein, James M., Susan P., Patricia Reidy Conrad, Daniel E., Thomas J., John G. BS, Fordham Coll., 1949, JD, 1952; LLM in Labor Law, Georgetown U., NYU, 1958; MBA, Iona Coll., 1969. Spl. agent FBI, Phila., Washington, N.Y.C., 1954-65; mgr. indsl. rels., asst.

dir. pers. Canada Dry Corp., N.Y.C., 1965-68; dir., administr. pers. Bunker Ramo Corp., Trumbull, Conn., 1968-71; dir. pers. The Roosevelt Hosp., N.Y.C., 1971-73; regional dir. U.S. Dept. Labor, Boston, 1973-77, factfinder, mediator, arbitrator, 1977-78; asst. dir. labor rels. Boston Pub. Libr., 1978-83; regional adminstr. OSHA U.S. Dept. Labor, N.Y.C., 1983-87; dir. Office of Constrn. and Maritime Compliance Assistance OSHA U.S. Dept. Labor, Washington, 1987-91, dir. Office of Constrn. and Civil Engring. Safety Standards OSHA, 1991—. Lt. USAF, 1952-54. Mem. Internat. Soc. for Fall Protection, Soc. of Former Spl. Agents FBI, Design Loads on Structures During Constrn. Standards Com. Republican. Roman Catholic. Avocations: fishing, walking seashore, reading, gourmet cooking. Office: OSHA US Dept Labor #13621 200 Constitution Ave NW Washington DC 20210-0002

REIDY, THOMAS ANTHONY, lawyer; b. Bronx, N.Y., Sept. 30, 1952; s. John Alexander and Elinor Ann (Tracey) R.; m. Victoria Mary Moxham, Mar. 12, 1977; children: J. Benjamin, Jacob T., Thomas A. II. BA with honors, Lehigh U., 1974; JD, U. Va., 1978. Bar: Ohio 1978, U.S. Dist. Ct. (so. dist.) Ohio 1980. Assoc. Moritz, McClure, Hughes, Kerscher & Price, Columbus, Ohio, 1978-80; assoc. Porter, Wright, Morris & Arthur, Columbus, 1980-87, ptnr., 1987-92; v.p. human resources and employment counsel The Longaberger Co., Dresden, Ohio, 1993-94, gen. counsel, 1994—; First v.p. Easter Seals Soc. Ctrl. Ohio, Columbus, 1990-92. Office: Longaberger Co PO Box 73 Dresden OH 43821-0073

REIF, (FRANK) DAVID, artist, educator; b. Cin., Dec. 14, 1941; s. Carl A. and Rachel L. (Clifton) R.; m. Ilona Jekabsons, July 30, 1966; 1 child, Megan Elizabeth. BFA, Art Inst. Chgo., 1968; MFA, Yale U., 1970. Asst. prof. art U. Wyo., Laramie, 1970-74, assoc. prof., 1974-81, prof., 1981—; assoc. prof. U. Mich., Ann Arbor, 1980-81; acting head dept. art U. Wyo., Laramie, 1986-87; selection coms. Ucross Found. Residency Program, Wyo., 1983—; exhibit juror Artwest Nat., Jackson, Wyo., 1986; panelist Colo. State U., Ft. Collins, 1981; lectr. U. Mich., 1980; apptd. Wyo. Arts Coun., 1993—. One-man shows include U. Wyo. Art Mus., 1993, Dorsky Galleries, N.Y.C., 1980, No. Ariz. U., 1977, 87, U. Mich., 1980, 81, One West Ctr. Contemporary Art, Ft. Collins, 1991; exhibited in group shows at First, Second and Third Who. Biennial Tour, 1984-88, U.S. Olympics Art Exhbn., L.A., 1984, Miss. Mus. Art and NEA Tour, 1981-83, L.A. Invitational Sculpture Tour Exhbn., 1991-92, Nicolaysen Art Mus., Casper, Wyo., 1994. With USAR, 1963-69. Recipient F.D. Pardee award Yale U., 1970; Best Sculpture award Joslyn Art Mus. Omaha, 1978; Nat. Endowment Arts grantee, 1978-79, Wyo. Basic Rsch. grantee, 1983-84, 86-87. Mem. Coll. Art Assn., Internat. Sculpture Ctr., Wyo. Arts Coun. (gubanitorial appointment). Democrat. Home: 3340 Aspen Ln Laramie WY 82070-5702 Office: U Wyo Dept Art PO Box 3138 Laramie WY 82071-3138

REIF, ERIC PETER, lawyer; b. Pitts., Nov. 2, 1942; s. Ernest Carl and Bernice Elizabeth (Thompson) R.; m. Donna Deeter, June 13, 1970; children: Roger Michael, Brian Peter. BA, U. Mich., 1963, JD, 1967. Bar: Mich. 1968, Pa. 1969, U.S. Dist. Ct. (ea., we. and mid. dists.) Pa. 1969. Law clk. to presiding justice Mich. Ct. Appeals, Lansing, 1967-68; trial lawyer Reed, Smith, Shaw & McClay, Pitts., 1968—, ptnr. litigation, 1979—. Mem. ABA, Pa. Bar Assn., Allegheny County Bar Assn., Acad. Trial Lawyers Allegheny County. Democrat. Presbyterian. Club: Longue Vue (Verona, Pa.). Avocations: running, skiing, boating, travel. Home: 14 Windsor Rd Pittsburgh PA 15215-1813 Office: Reed Smith Shaw & McClay 435 6th Ave Pittsburgh PA 15219-1886

REIF, LOUIS RAYMOND, lawyer, utilities executive; b. Buffalo, July 4, 1923; s. John Dennis and Sadie (Wilkenson) R.; m. Nancy C. Heuer, Apr. 12, 1958; children: Tracey Lynn, Christopher Louis. Student, Mich. State U., 1941-42, The Citadel, 1943; A.B. U. Buffalo, 1948; J.D., U. Mich., 1951. Bar: N.Y. 1953. Pvt. practice Chgo., 1951-52, Buffalo, 1953—; atty. Continental Ill. Nat. Bank, Chgo., 1951-52, Iroquois Gas Corp., Buffalo, 1952-53; asst. sec. Iroquois Gas Corp., 1953-58, v.p., 1958-63, sr. v.p., 1963-71, pres., 1971—; also bd. dirs.; v.p. Nat. Fuel Gas Co., N.Y.C., 1960-74, pres., 1974, pres., chief exec. officer, 1975-87, chmn., chief exec. officer, 1988—; asst. to chmn. Del. North Cos., Buffalo, 1988, chief oper. officer, 1989—, also bd. dirs.; bd. dirs. Goldome Bank; chmn. N.Y. Gas Group, 1973—; chmn. 17th World Gas Conf., Internat. Gas Union, 1986-88. Pres., dir. Buffalo Better Bus. Bur., 1970; trustee SUNY-Buffalo Found. Served with C.E. AUS, 1943-46, ETO. Mem. ABA, N.Y. Bar Assn., Fed. Power Bar Assn., Erie County Bar Assn., Barrister Soc., Am. Gas Assn. (chmn. dir. 1984-85, Disting. Svc. award 1986), Nat. Alliance Businessmen (dir., chmn. 1967-68), Buffalo C.C. (dir. 1973—), chmn. nat. affairs com. 1969—), Buffalo Club (bd. dirs. 1988, pres. 1991-92), Phi Alpha Delta. Office: Nat Fuel Gas Distbn Corp 10 Lafayette Sq Buffalo NY 14203-1824

REIFF, PATRICIA HOFER, space physicist, educator; b. Oklahoma City, Mar. 14, 1950; d. William Henry and Maxine Ruth (Hoffer) R.; m. Thomas Westfall Hill, July 4, 1976; children: Andrea Hofer Hill, Adam Reiff Hill, Amelia Reiff Hill. Student, Wellesley Coll., 1967-68; BS, Okla. State U., 1971; MS, Rice U., 1974, PhD, 1975. Cert. secondary tchr., Okla., Tex. Rsch. assoc. space physics and astronomy dept. Rice U., Houston, 1975, asst. prof. space physics and astronomy dept., 1978-81, asst. chmn. space physics and astronomy dept., 1979-85, assoc. rsch. sci., 1981-87, sr. rsch. scientist, 1987-90; resident rsch. assoc. Marshall Space Flight Ctr., Huntsville, Ala., 1975-76; adj. asst. prof. Rice U., 1976-78, disting. faculty fellow, 1990-92, prof. 1992—; mem. sci. team Atmosphere Explorer Mission, Dynamics Explorer Mission, Global Geospace Sci. Mission, ESA/Cluster Mission; prin. investigator The Public Connection NASA; cons. Houston Mus. Natural Sci., 1986—; adv. com. on atmospheric scis. NSF, Washington, 1988-92; mem. stategic implementation study panel NASA, Washington, 1989-91; mem. space sci. adv. com. NASA, 1993—; univ. rep. U. Space Rsch. Assn., Washington, 1993— (mem. nom. com.); exec. com. George Observatory, Houston, 1989-92, others. Designer Cockrell Sundial/Solar Telescope, 1989; editor EOS (U.S. newspaper), 1986-89; contbr. articles to profl. jours. Trustee, Citizens' Environ. Coalition, Houston, 1978—, pres. 1980-85; mem. air quality com. Houston/Galveston Area Coun., 1980-83, Green Ribbon Com., City of Houston, 1981-83; active coms. Macedonia United Meth. Ch., 1988—. Named rsch. fellow NAS/NRC, 1975, an Outstanding Young Woman Am., 1977, '80, to Houston's Women on the Move, 1990; recipient grant NSF, Houston, 1990-92, NASA, 1993, 94. Mem. Am. Geophys. Union (fin. com. 1980-82, editor search com. 1992, awards com.), Am. Meteorol. Soc. (coun. 1985-88), Cosmos Club, Wellesley Club, Internat. Union of Geodesy and Geophysics (del. 1975, 81, 83, 89, 91, 93, 95, chair working group 2F, 1991-95). Avocations: organic gardening, beef ranching. Office: Rice U Dept Space Physics 6100 S Main St Houston TX 77251-1892

REIFFEL, LEONARD, physicist, scientific consultant; b. Chgo., Sept. 30, 1927; s. Carl and Sophie (Miller) R.; m. Judith Eve Blumenthal, 1952 (div. 1962); children—Evan Carl, David Lee; m. Nancy L. Jeffers, 1971. B.Sc., Ill. Inst. Tech., 1947, M.Sc., 1948, Ph.D., 1953. Physicist Perkin-Elmer Corp., Conn., 1948; engring. physicist U. Chgo. Inst. Nuclear Studies, 1948-49; with Ill. Inst. Tech. Research Inst., Chgo., 1949-65, dir. physics research, 1956-63, v.p., 1963-65; cons. to Apollo program NASA Hdqrs., 1965-70, pvt. practice cons., 1970—; tech. dir. manned space flight expts. bd. NASA, 1966-68; chmn. bd. Instructional Dynamics, Inc., Franklin 81, Interand Corp., 1969-91, Telestrator Industries, Inc., 1970-73; sci. editor Sta. WBBM-CBS radio, Chgo.; sci. cons./commentator WBBM-TV, 1971-72; host Backyard Safari, 1971-73; sci. feature broadcaster WEEI-CBS radio, Boston, 1965-75; syndicated newspaper columnist World Book Ency. Sci. Service, Inc. (later Universal Sci. News, Inc.), 1966-72, Los Angeles Times Syndicate, 1972-76; sci. cons. CBS Network, 1967-71; chmn. Exelar Corp., Chgo., 1991—; chmn. bd., pres., CEO Ameraine Corp., Chgo., 1992-95; mem. bd of overseers Armour Coll. Ill. Inst. Tech., 1995—; cons. Korean Govt. on establishment atomic energy rsch. program; mem. adv. com. isotope and radiation devel. AEC; com. rsch. reactors NAS, 1958-64; cons. U.S. Army 1976—. Author: The Contaminant, 1979; author numerous sci. papers. Bd. dirs. Student Competitions on Relevant Engring. Named Outstanding Young Man of Year Chgo. Jr. C. of C., 1954, 61; recipient Merit award Chgo. Tech. Socs., 1968; Peabody award for radio edn., 1968; IR-100 award for inventing Telestrator CBS Chalkboard, 1970; award for coverage space events Aviation Writers Assn., 1971; IR-100 award for invention underwater diver communications system, 1972, IR-100 award for DISCON video teleconferencing

systems, 1985, Third Annual High Tech Entrepreneur award, 1986; also for invention Audiografix, 1973; Disting. Alumni Achievement award Ill. Inst. Tech., 1974, named to Hall of Fame, 1984. Fellow Am. Phys. Soc.; mem. AAAS, Sigma Xi, Tau Beta Pi, Eta Kappa Nu. Responsible for world's 1st indsl. nuclear reactor, 1956. Home: 602 W Deming Pl Chicago IL 60614-2618

REIFLER, CLIFFORD BRUCE, psychiatrist, educator; b. Chgo., Dec. 28, 1931; s. Eugene Alan and Harriet (Offer) R.; m. Barbara Karnuth, Sept. 11, 1954; children: Margery Sue, Cynthia Jean, Angela Harriet. A.B., U. Chgo., 1951; B.S., Northwestern U., 1953; M.D., Yale U., 1957; M.P.H., U. N.C., 1967. Intern Univ. Hosps., Ann Arbor, Mich., 1957-58; resident in psychiatry Strong Meml. Hosp., Rochester, N.Y., 1958-61; mem. faculty U. N.C. Med. Sch., 1963-70, assoc. prof. psychiatry, 1969-70, assoc. prof. mental health Sch. Pub. Health, 1969-70, sr. psychiatrist, chief mental health sect., student health svc., 1963-70; prof. health svcs., psychiatry and community and preventive medicine U. Rochester Med. Sch., 1970-94, dir. univ. health svc., 1970-80, 81-94, prof. emeritus of health svcs. and psychiatry, 1994—, interim v.p. student affairs, 1980-81, sr. assoc. dean for clin. affairs Sch. Medicine and Dentistry, acting chmn. dept. health svcs., 1983-85; med. dir. Strong Meml. Hosp., 1983-85; bd. dirs. Genesee Valley Group Health Assn., 1972-82; cons. in field; vis. prof. of psychiatry, Harvard U. Med. Sch., 1987; Dana L. Farnsworth hon. cons. Harvard U. Health Service, 1987. Coauthor: Mental Health on the Campus-A Field Study, 1973; co-author: The Alternative Services: Their Role in Mental Health, 1975, Old Folks at Home-A Field Study of Nursing and Board-and-Care Homes, 1976; exec. editor Jour. Am. Coll. Health, 1983—; mem. editorial bd. Jour. of Coll. Student Psychotherapy, 1986—; contbr. profl. jours. Mem. membership com. Rochester Philharm. Orch. Inc,. 1981-83; mem. med. adv. com., bd. dirs. Planned Parenthood Rochester and Monroe County, 1973-74; bd. dirs. Rochester Meml. Soc., 1971-74; mem. devel. com. Seneca Zool. Soc., 1990—, trustee, 1991—; bd. dirs. Am. Coll. Health Found., 1994—. Served with M.C. USAF, 1961-63. Fellow Am. Coll. Health Assn. (pres. 1976-77, Edward Hitchcock award 1981, Ruth C. Boynton award 1988), Am. Psychiat. Assn. (life), Am. Coll. Physician Execs. (disting.); mem. N.Y. State Coll. Health Assn. Home: 143 Palmerston Rd Rochester NY 14618-1247 Office: U Health Svc 250 Crittenden Blvd Box 617 Rochester NY 14642

REIFSNIDER, KENNETH LEONARD, metallurgist, educator; b. Balt., Feb. 19, 1940; s. David Leonard and Daisy Pearl (Hess) R.; m. Loretta Lieb, June 15, 1963; children—Eric Scott, Jason Miles. BA, Western Md. Coll., 1963; BS in Engring., Johns Hopkins U., 1963, MS in Engring., 1965, PhD, 1968. Jr. instr. John Hopkins U., Balt., 1966-67; asst. prof. Va. Poly. Inst. and State U., Blacksburg, 1968-72, assoc. prof., 1972-75, prof., 1975-83, Reynolds Metals prof. engring. sci. and mechanics, 1983-90, Alexander Giacco prof., 1990—, also chmn. materials engring. sci. Ph.D. program, 1974-92, chmn. adminstrn. bd. Ctr. Composite Materials and Structures, 1984, 1994—; dir. Va. Inst. for Material Systems, 1988—; engr. Lawrence Livermore Nat. Lab., 1981; cons. in materials sci. NATO, 1969, 75. Mem. troop 44 com. Boy Scouts Am., Blacksburg, Va. Recipient Va. Acad. Sci. J. Shelton Horsley award, 1978, Va. Poly. Inst. Alumni award, 1982, Disting. Rsch. award Am. Soc. Composites, 1992. Fellow ASTM (founder Jour. of Composites Tech. and Rsch., vice chmn. standing com. on pubs., award of merit 1982); mem. ASME, Council on Engring. Editor, co-editor, author books, book chpts., articles for profl. publs.

REIFSNYDER, WILLIAM EDWARD, meteorologist; b. Ridgway, Pa., Mar. 29, 1924; s. Howard William and Madolin (Boyer) R.; m. Marylou Bishop, Dec. 19, 1954 (dec. July 1990); children: Rita, Cheryl, Gawain. B.S. in Meteorology, NYU, 1944; M.F., U. Calif., Berkeley, 1949; Ph.D., Yale U., 1954. Cert. cons. meteorologist. Meteorologist Pacific S.W. Forest and Range Expt. Sta., 1952-55; mem. faculty Yale U., 1955-90, prof. emeritus, 1990—, prof. forest meteorology and biometeorology, 1967-90; cons. World Meteorol. Orgn., UN Univ., Internat. Coun. Rsch. in Agroforestry. Author: Hut Hopping in the Austrian Alps, Footloose in the Swiss Alps, The High Huts of the White Mountains, Radiant Energy in Relation to Forests, Weathering the Wilderness, Adventuring in the Alps; editor-in-chief Agrl. and Forest Meteorology; editor: Meteorology and Agroforestry. Bd. dirs. Am. Youth Hostels. Service with USAAF, 1943-47. Fellow AAAS; mem. Conn. Acad. Sci. and Engring. (corr.), Am. Meteorol. Soc. (Outstanding Achievement in Biometeorology award), Soc. Am. Foresters, Internat. Soc. Biometeorology (v.p.). Home: Lama Star Rte Box 3 Questa NM 87556 Office: Sch Forestry and Environ Studies Yale U New Haven CT 06511

REIG, JUNE WILSON, writer, director, producer; b. Schenectady, N.Y., June 1, 1933; d. Wallace John and Lillian Lucy (Gay) Wilson; m. Robert Maxwell, Nov. 26, 1969. BA summa cum laude, N.Y. State U., 1954; MA in Dramatic Arts, NYU, 1962. Instr. NYU, 1962-67; producer NYU Theater, 1963-67; writer, producer, dir. NBC, N.Y.C., 1963-73; writer-dir. NBC TV News & Public Affairs, 1966; pres. Bunny/Chord Prodns., N.Y.C., 1972—. Author: Diary of the Boy King Tut-Ankh-Amen, 1978; writer, dir. (TV film spl.) Stuart Little, 1966 (Peabody award Prix Jeunesse); writer (TV spl.) The Reluctant Dragon, 1968 (Brotherhood award), (music spls.) The Heart of Christmas, 1965, An Afternoon at Tanglewood (Peabody award); writer, dir., producer (TV spls.) Rabbit Hill, 1966 (ALA award) Bill Cosby As I See It, 1970 (Ohio State award) A Day With Bill Cosby, 1971, Jennifer & Me, 1972; (TV daily series) Watch Your Child - The Me Too Show, 1973 (Action for Children's TV Achievement award); prodr., writer (TV spl.) Little Women, the ballet, 1976, Tut, the Boy King, 1978 (Peabody award); films in permanent collection of Mus. Broadcasting, N.Y.C. Recipient Prix Jeunesse, 1966, Christopher award, 1970, Emmy award nomination, 1966, 76. Mem. Writers Guild Am., Dirs. Guild Am., Nat. Acad. TV Arts and Scis., NYU Alumni Assn., Internat. Soc. Animal Rights, Friends of Animals, Audubon Soc. Club: Alan Devoe Bird (Old Chatham, N.Y.) Avocations: photography, music, animals. Office: Bunny/Chord Prodns Inc Ste 1405 119 W 57th St New York NY 10019-2301 *Whether I am working on a teleplay or book, I write about things I believe children are interested in: feelings, aspirations, caring, animals, loving. As I see it, too much of the fare for young people gives them a distorted view of how much violence there is in the world, and I want to counteract that impression. I want to write about things that create a sense of worth, warm security, and an absence of unnecessary anxiety. When I do write about the darker things that happen in life, it is to help the young person understand himself and the world a little better.*

REIGHARD, HOMER LEROY, physician; b. Martinsburg, Pa., Dec. 1, 1924; s. David F. and Cora E. (Steele) R.; m. Barbara Jane Suttell, Dec. 14, 1951; children: Carol, Janet, Paul. B.S., Franklin and Marshall Coll., 1945; M.D., Temple U., 1948; M.P.H., Harvard U., 1961. Intern Temple U. Hosp., Phila., 1948-49; physician-in-charge accidents dispensary Temple U. Hosp., 1949-50; med. officer CAA, Washington, 1953-59; practice medicine Bethesda, Md., 1953-60; chief med. standards div. FAA, 1959-61, spl. asst. to civil air surgeon, 1962-63, dep. fed. air surgeon, 1963-75, fed. air surgeon, 1975-84; cons. in aviation medicine, 1984—; workplace anti-drug programs 1987—. Bd.dirs. Aviation Rsch. & Edn. Found., 1985-92. Served with M.C. USAF, 1950-53. Recipient Meritorious Service award FAA, 1970, Disting. Career Service award, FAA, 1984. Fellow Aerospace Med. Assn. (Harry G. Moseley flight safety award 1977); mem. Phi Beta Kappa. Developer passenger screening system to identify potential hijackers. Home: 10215 Hatherleigh Dr Bethesda MD 20814-2223

REIGLE, JAMES D., manufacturing executive; b. 1926. BS in Commerce, Ohio U., 1949. With Regal Ware Inc., 1949—, asst. gen. mgr., 1955-62, v.p. sales and mgmt., 1965-, pres., 1965—. Office: Regal Ware Inc 1675 Reigle Dr Kewaskum WI 53040*

REIGROD, ROBERT HULL, manufacturing executive; b. N.Y.C., Mar. 26, 1941; s. David and Beatrice (Simon) R.; divorced; children: Sandra, Donald. BA in Anthropology, Calif. State U. Long Beach, 1973. Account exec. Ira Haupt & Co., N.Y.C., 1961-64; regional adminstrv. mgr. Brother Internat. Corp., Los Angeles, 1964-70; regional sales mgr. Brother Internat. Corp., Irvine, Calif., 1970-77, gen. mgr. west region, 1977-82; v.p. Brother Internat. Corp., 1982-86; dir., sr. v.p. Brother Internat. Corp., Somerset, N.J., 1986—; pres. Brother Internat. de Mexico, S.A. de C.V., 1992—. Trustee Leukemia Soc. Am., 1982-84; bd. dirs. Irvine Children's Fund, 1988-

90. Office: Brother Internat Corp 3333 W Comml Blvd Fort Lauderdale FL 33309

REILAND, LOWELL KEITH, sculptor; b. Wahpeton, N.D., May 11, 1948; s. Peter Paul And Evelyn Ruth (Huss) R. Student, N.D. State U., 1966-68; BA, BS, Moorhead State U., 1971; MFA, Cornell U., 1974. Intern teaching Anglo-Am. Sch., Stockholm, 1971; artist-in-residence Pulpit Rock Artist's Community, Woodstock, Conn., 1974-76; asst. to Richard Lippold, Archtl. Sculptor, N.Y.C., 1970, 75, 77; artist-in-residence Moorhead (Minn.) State U., 1978; artist N.Y.C., 1976-92; lectr.-at-large N.D. State U., Fargo, 1988; lectr. art Conn. Assn. Psychiatrists Ann. Meeting, New Haven, 1985, New Sch., N.Y.C., 1986, Plains Art Mus., Moorhead, 1988, philosophy N.D. State U., Fargo, 1988, Westchester C.C., Westerly Pub. Libr., 1992, Lyman Allyn Art Mus., 1993; participant bronze casting invitational U. Conn., Storrs, 1982. Exhibited at Sarah Y. Rentschler Gallery, N.Y.C., 1979-83, Soho Ctr. for Visual Artists, N.Y.C., 1987, DiLaurenti Gallery, N.Y.C., 1987, Aldrich Mus. Contemporary Art, Ridgefield, Conn., 1988, Plains Art Mus., Moorhead, 1988, Bayly Art Mus. of U. Va., Charlottesville, Travel: Studio Sch., N.Y.C., 1990, Wichita (Kans.) Art Mus., 1990, Lyman Allyn Art Mus., 1993-94, Virginia Lynch Gallery, R.I., 1994; prin. works include City of Fargo, 1978, Moorhead State U., 1978, collection Clara M. Eagle Mus., Murray, Ky., 1984, collection Palace of the Sultan of Brunei, 1985; contbr. articles to profl. jours. Recipient Art award/prize Am. Acad. and Inst. Arts and Letters, N.Y.C., 1986; artist's grantee Pollock/Krasner Found., N.Y.C., 1987-88, Change, Inc., 1989, grantee Artist's Space, N.Y.C., 1985; grantee, resident Art League Schleswig-Holsteinisches Kunstlerhaus, Selk, Fed. Republic Germany, 1990. Avocations: studies Cen., S.Am. and Asian primative arts, studies Italian Renaissance art. Home and Studio: Lowell Reiland Sculpture Indsl Trust Co Bldg 14 High St Westerly RI 02891-1854

REILING, HENRY BERNARD, business educator; b. Richmond, Ky., Feb. 5, 1938; s. Henry Bernard and Lucille Frances (Fowler) R.; m. Carol-Lina Maria Schuetz, June 4, 1962; children: Christina Lucille, Maria Hays, Carol-Lena Alexis. B.A., Northwestern U., 1960; M.B.A., Harvard U., 1962; J.D., Columbia U., 1965. Bar: N.Y. 1965. Mem. faculty Columbia U. Bus. Sch., 1965-76, prof., 1974-76; vis. asso. prof. Harvard U. Bus. Sch., 1972-73, prof., 1976—, Eli Goldston prof. bus. adminstrn., 1978—; vis. prof. Stanford U. Bus. Sch., 1974-75; bd. dirs. Levitz Furniture Inc. Contbr. bus. and law jours. Trustee Riverside Ch. N.Y.C., 1976-77; mem. vis. com. Northwestern U. Coll. Arts and Scis., 1989—. Mem. Am. N.Y. bar assns., Bar Assn. City N.Y., Am. Finance Assn., Financial Mgmt. Assn., Nat. Tax Assn., Tax Inst. Am., Beta Gamma Sigma. Club: Union (N.Y.C.). Home: 28 Meriam St Lexington MA 02173-3600 Office: Harvard U Bus Sch Boston MA 02163

REILLY, DANIEL PATRICK, bishop; b. Providence, May 12, 1928; s. Francis E. and Mary (Burns) R. Student, Our Lady of Providence Sem., 1943-48, Grand Seminaire, St. Brieuc, France, 1948-53, Harvard U., 1954-55, Boston Coll., 1955-56; D. (hon.), Providence Coll., St. Michael's Coll., Holy Apostles Coll. and Sem., Salve Regina Coll., Our Lady of Providence Coll., Sacred Heart U. Ordained priest Roman Catholic Ch., 1953; asst. pastor Cathedral Saints Peter and Paul, Providence, 1953-54; asst. chancellor Diocese of Providence, 1954-56, sec. to bishop, 1956-64, chancellor, 1964-72, adminstr., 1971-72, vicar gen., 1972-75; became monsignor, 1965, consecrated bishop, 1975; bishop of Norwich, Conn., 1975-94; installed bishop of Worcester, Mass., 1994—; Conn. state chaplain K.C., 1976—; Episcopal moderator Nat. Cath. Cemetery Corp., 1977-87; ad hoc com. mem. to aid ch. in Ea. Europe NCCB/U.S. Cath. Conf., adminstrv. com. mem., 1976-86, 92—; pro-life com. mem. NCCB, 1989—, chmn. 10th anniversary peace pastoral com., 1992—, chmn. internat. policy com., 1993—; mem. Priestly Life and Ministry Commn., 1991—; past pres. New Eng. Consultation Ch. Leaders; drafting com. mem. U.S. Cath. Conf. Pastoral Letter, mem. com. on coms.; active Holy See Pontifical Coun.-Cor Unum, 1984-89. Trustee Cath. Mut. Relief Soc. Omaha, 1979—, St. John's Sem., Brighton, Mass., 1987—, Am. Coll., Louvain, Belgium; bd. dirs. United Way Southeastern Conn., 1976—, Conn. Drug and Adv. Coun., 1978-80; chmn. bd. Cath. Relief Svcs., 1978-86; mem. fin. and budget com. U.S. Cath. Conf., 1985-87; chancellor Holy Apostles Coll. and Sem., Cromwell, Conn.; mem. Conn. Cath. Conf., Christian Conf. Conn.; pres. Conn. Interfaith Housing. Mem. Rotary. Home: 2 High Ridge Rd Worcester MA 01602 *If you would make a true success of your life for time and for eternity, never forget that it will be achieved by your willingness to make countless efforts that will be known only to God.*

REILLY, DAVID HENRY, university dean; b. Paterson, N.J., Nov. 7, 1936; s. David Henry and Ethel Taylor (Alt) R.; m. Jean Lockwood, July 2, 1960; children—David Scott, Chris Robert, Sandra Jean. B.A., U. Vt., 1959; Ed.M., Rutgers U., 1962, Ed.D., 1965. Diplomate: Am. Bd. Profl. Psychology. Remedial reading instr. Drake Sch. of N.J. Neuro-Psychiat. Inst., Princeton, 1959-62; jr. fellow psychol. services at inst. Drake Sch. of N.J. Neuro-Psychiat. Inst., summer 1962-63; research asst. N.J. Bur. Research Neurology and Psychiatry; also sch. psychologist Woodbridge (N.J.) sch. system, 1962-63; clin. psychologist, then research asso. N.J. Bur. Research Neurology and Psychiatry, 1963-64, 65; sch. and research psychologist Woodbridge sch. system, 1964-65; post doctoral fellow clin. child psychology Devereux Found., Devon, Pa., 1965-66; mem. faculty U. N.C., Chapel Hill, 1966-74; prof. psychology U. N.C., 1974—, chmn. dept. sch. psychology program, 1966-74; dean U. N.C. (Sch. Edn.), Greensboro, 1974-86; dean Coll. of Grad. and Profl. Studies The Citadel, Charleston, 1992—; Mem. N.C. Bd. Examiners Practicing Psychologists, 1973—, treas., 1975, chmn., 1976. Contbr. articles to profl. jours. Research grantee NIMH, 1963; Fulbright Vis. scholar Republic of Cyprus, 1986-87, USSR, 1990. Fellow Am. Psychol. Assn.; mem. Southeastern Psychol. Assn., N.C. Psychol. Assn. (pres. 1980-81), N.C. Assn. Coll. Tchr. Edn. (pres. 1981), N.C. Sch. Psychology Assn. (pres. 1976-77). Home: 306 Mimms Ave Charleston SC 29409

REILLY, EDWARD ARTHUR, lawyer; b. N.Y.C., Dec. 17, 1943; s. Edward Arthur and Anna Marguerite (Sautter) R.; children: M. Teresa, Edward A. A.B., Princeton U., 1965; J.D., Duke U., 1968. Bar: N.Y. 1969, N.C. 1971, Fla. 1979, Conn. 1983. Asst. dean law sch. Duke U., 1970-72; assoc. Shearman & Sterling, N.Y.C., 1972-80, ptnr., 1980-87; ptnr. Harlow, Reilly, Derr & Stark, Research Triangle Park, N.C., 1988-90; counsel Morris & McVeigh, N.Y.C., 1991-93, ptnr., 1993—. Served to lt. USNR, 1968-70. Decorated Chevalier de l'Ordre des Arts et des Lettres, French Govt.-Ministry of Culture and Commn., 1992. Fellow Am. Coll. Trust & Estate Counsel; mem. N.Y. State Bar Assn., Fla. Bar Assn., Conn. Bar Assn. Episcopalian. Office: Morris & McVeigh 767 3rd Ave New York NY 10017-2023

REILLY, EDWARD FRANCIS, JR., former state senator, federal agency administrator; b. Leavenworth, Kans., Mar. 24, 1937; s. Edward F. and Marian C. (Sullivan) R.; BA, U. Kans., 1961. V.p. Reilly & Sons, Inc., Leavenworth, 1967-92; pres. Yllier Lake Estates, Inc., Easton, Kans., 1965-89; mem. Kans. Ho. of Reps., 1963-64; mem. Kans. State Senate, 1964-92, asst. majority leader, 1977-80, vice-chmn. govtl. orgn., chmn. ins. subcom., chmn. fed. and state affairs com. Mem. Nat. Commn. on Accreditation of Law Enforcement Agys.; chmn. U.S. Parole Commission Dept. of Justice, Md., 1992—; commr. ex officio U.S. Sentencing Commn., Washington; del. to Republican Nat. Conv., Miami Beach, Fla., 1968; chmn. Leavenworth County Radio Free Europe Fund, 1972; bd. dirs. St. John's Hosp., Leavenworth, 1970-79, sec.; bd. dirs. Leavenworth Assn. for Handicapped, 1968-69, ARC, Leavenworth chpt., Kans. Blue Cross/Blue Shield, 1969-72; apptd. by Pres. Reagan Nat. Hwy. Safety Adv. Com. Recipient. Community Leaders of Am., 1971, 85, 86, Hallpac Pub. Svc. award, 1988, Am. Police Hall of Fame award, 1990, Good Samaritan award Order of Michael the Arch Angel Police Legion, 1990, Commendation award mayor and city commn. of Leavenworth, Kans., 1990, Carnegie Hero Fund Commn. award and medallion, 1991, Silver Angel award Kans. Cath. Conf., 1992; named Outstanding Young Men Am., 1965-76. Mem. Leavenworth C. of C. (hon. dir. 1970-73), Assn. U.S. Army (Henry Leavenworth award 1960), Kansas City (Kans.) C. of C., Leavenworth Hist. Soc. (dir. 1968-73), John Carroll Soc., Native Sons of Kansas City, Ancient Order of Hibernians, Kiwanis (dir. 1969-70, Connelly award 1991), K.C., Elks, Eagles, Knights of Malta. Republican. Roman Catholic.

REILLY, EDWARD J., public relations executive. Ptnr. Robinson Lake Lerer & Montgomery Sawyer Miller Group, N.Y.C. Office: Robinson Lake Lerer & Montgomer Sawyer Miller Group 75 Rockefeller Plz New York NY 10019*

REILLY, EDWARD T., JR., publisher; b. N.Y.C., Oct. 21, 1946; s. Edward Thomas and Dorothy (Comba) R.; m. Susan M. Brooke, June 28, 1969; children: Kristen, Greg. B.B.A., St. Francis Coll., N.Y.C., 1968. Editor-in-chief Gregg div. McGraw Hill Book Co., N.Y.C., 1974-76; controller CTB, Monterey, Calif., 1976-78; gen. mgr. Instructo, Palli, Pa., 1978-79; group v.p. for Europe, Africa, Mideast McGraw Hill U.K. Ltd., Maidenhead, U.K., 1980-83; exec. v.p. McGraw-Hill Internat. Book Co., N.Y.C., 1983-84; sr. v.p. fin., planning and adminstrn. McGraw-Hill Broadcasting Co., N.Y.C., 1985-86; exec. v.p., chief operating officer McGraw-Hill Broadcasting Co., 1986-87; pres., 1987—; mem. corp. adv. council Nat. Council La Raza; mem. local carriage task force McGraw Broadcasting; bd. dirs. Internat. Radio and TV Found., Nat. Assoc. of Broadcasters, 1990-94, TV Bur. of Advt., 1988-95, chmn. 1990-93, assoc. of Max Svc. TV, 1987—, chmn. 1994—; Gov.- ABC TV network affiliates assoc., chmn. gov. rel., 1993-95. Chmn. Monterey County Overall Econ. Devel. Com., Monterey, Calif., 1977; bd. govs. Carmel Unified Sch. Dist. (Calif.), 1977. Fellow Inst. Dirs. Great Britain. Office: McGraw-Hill Broadcasting Co 1221 Ave of the Americas 20th Fl New York NY 10020

REILLY, FRANK KELLY, business educator; b. Chgo., Dec. 30, 1935; s. Clarence Raymond and Mary Josephine (Ruckrigel) R.; m. Therese Adele Bourke, Aug. 2, 1958; children: Frank Kelly III, Clarence Raymond II, Therese B., Edgar B. B.B.A., U. Notre Dame, 1957; M.B.A. Northwestern U., 1961, U. Chgo., 1964; Ph.D., U. Chgo., 1968; LLD (hon.), St. Michael's Coll., 1991. Chartered fin. analyst. Trader Goldman Sachs & Co., Chgo., 1958-59; security analyst Tech. Fund, Chgo., 1959-62; asst. prof. U. Kans., Lawrence, 1965-68, assoc. prof., 1968-72; prof. bus., assoc. dir. div. bus. and econ. research U. Wyo., Laramie, 1972-75; prof. fin. U. Ill., Champaign-Urbana, 1975-81; Bernard J. Hank prof. U. Notre Dame, Ind., 1981—, dean Coll. Bus. Adminstrn., 1981-87; bd. dirs. First Interstate Bank Northern Ind., First Interstate of Wis., Brinson Global Fund Inc. (also chmn.), Assn. Investment, Mgmt. & Rsch., NIBCO Corp., Internat. Bd. CFPs, Greenwood Trust Corp., Ft. Dearborn Income Securities. Author: Investment Analysis and Portfolio Management, 1979, 4th edit., 1994, Investments, 1982, 4th edit., 1995; co-editor: Ethics and the Investment Industry, 1989; editor: Readings and Issues in Investments, 1975, High Yield Bonds: Analysis and Risk Assessment, 1990; assoc. editor Fin. Mgmt., 1977-82, Quar. Rev. Econs. and Bus, 1979-87, Fin. Rev., 1979-87, 92—, Jour. Fin. Edn., 1981—, Jour. Applied Bus. Rsch., 1986—, Fin. Svcs. Rev., 1989—, Internat. Rev. Econs. and Fin., 1992—, European Jour. Fin., 1994—. Arthur J. Schmidt Found. fellow, 1962-65; U. Chgo. fellow, 1963-65. Mem. Midwest Bus. Adminstrn. Assn. (pres. 1974-75), Am. Fin. Assn., Western Fin. Assn. (exec. com. 1973-75), Eastern Fin. Assn. (exec. com. 1979-84, pres. 1982-83), Midwest Fin. Assn. (pres. 1993-94), Fin. Analysts Fedn., Fin. Mgmt. Assn. (pres. 1983-84, chmn. 1985-91, bd. dirs.), Acad. Fin. Svcs. (pres. 1990-91), Inst. Chartered Fin. Analysts (coun. of examiners, rsch. and edn. com. edn. steering com., C. Stewart Shepard award 1991), Internat. Assoc. Fin. Planners (ednl. resource com., bd. dirs.), Nat. Bur. Econ. Rsch., Assn. of Investment Mgt. and Rsch., Investments Analysts Soc. Chgo. (bd. dirs. 1988-89), Beta Gamma Sigma. Roman Catholic. Office: U Notre Dame Coll Bus Adminstrn Notre Dame IN 46556 *Any success I have enjoyed is due to the talents God has given me and my belief that I have an obligation to maximize the output from those talents by hard work, while never forgetting that my family comes first because they have always provided me with the love and support necessary for success and happiness.*

REILLY, GEORGE, lawyer; b. Waukegan, Ill., Nov. 29, 1934; s. James M. and Hilda Clara (Van Heirseele) R.; m. Dadee Bruce, Dec. 23, 1957; children: Laurene Beth, Theresa Ann. B.A. Ill. Coll., 1956; MS, S.D. State U., 1958; JD, U. Minn., 1964. Bar: Minn. 1964, U.S. Dist. Ct. Minn. 1964, U.S. Ct. Appeals (8th cir.) 1965. Assoc. Leonard, Street and Deinard, Mpls., 1964-70, ptnr., 1973-82, mng. ptnr., 1983-91, ptnr., chair of bus. divsn., 1991—; chief dep. atty. gen. State of Minn., St. Paul, 1971-72; chief counsel Minn. Housing and Fin. Agy., St. Paul, 1972-80. Campaign chair Spannaus for Atty. Gen. com., 1974, 78, Spannaus for Gov., 1982. Mem. ABA, Minn. State Bar Assn., Citizens League, Variety Children's Assn. Democrat. Avocations: travel, sports. Office: Leonard Street and Deinard 150 S 5th St Ste 2300 Minneapolis MN 55402

REILLY, GEORGE LOVE ANTHONY, history educator; b. Montclair, N.J., Oct. 17, 1918; s. James Joseph and Anna F. (Love) R.; m. Ethel M. Ehrlich, Aug. 29, 1953; children—Mary Anne, Elizabeth Ruthe, Georgette Louise. A.B. cum laude, Seton Hall U., 1940; A.M., Harvard U., 1942; Ph.D., Columbia U., 1951. Instr. Caldwell (N.J.) Coll., 1946-48, Rutgers U., New Brunswick, N.J., 1948-51; mem. faculty Seton Hall U., South Orange, N.J., 1951—; prof. history Seton Hall U., 1960—, chmn. dept., 1961—; faculty Irish Studies seminar Columbia U., 1974—. Author: Camden and Amboy Railroad in New Jersey Politics, 1951, Sacred Heart in Bloomfield, 1953, A Century of Catholicism, 1956, Neighbors in New Jersey, 1963, History of Seton Hall University, 1980; co-author: Shepherds of Newark, 1978, also articles; Adv. editor: Cath. Hist. Rev, 1957-61; mem. editorial bd. Avocate, Newark, 1968—. Served to capt. F.A. AUS, 1942-45. Mem. Nat. Geog. Soc., Am. Cath. hist. assns., Conf. on Brit. Studies, Victorian Studies Assn., N.J. Hist. Soc. Democrat. Roman Catholic. Club: Harvard (N.J.). Home: 273 Scotland Rd South Orange NJ 07079-2040

REILLY, GERARD DENIS, judge; b. Boston, Sept. 27, 1906; s. Thomas F. and Anne C. (O'Reilly) R.; m. Eleanor Fahey, July 15, 1939 (dec.); children: Gerard Denis (dec.), John Fahey, Margaret Anne Reilly Heffern.; m. Dorothy K. Owens, Jan. 1982. A.B., Harvard, 1927, LL.B., 1933. Bar: Mass. 1933, D.C. 1946. State House corr. for the Pawtucket Times, Providence Jour., 1927-29; night copy editor Boston Traveler, 1929-30; asso. firm Goodwin, Procter & Hoar, Boston, 1933-34; reviewing atty. Home Owner's Loan Corp., 1934; became atty. U.S. Dept. of Labor, 1934, asst. solicitor, 1935; adminstr. U.S. Dept. of Labor (Pub. Contracts Div.), 1936-37, solicitor, 1937-41; mem. NLRB, 1941-46; mem. firm Reilly, Johns & Zimmerman (and predecessor firms), 1946-70; asso. judge D.C. Ct. Appeals, 1970-72, chief judge, 1972-76, sr. judge, 1977—; Lectr. constl. law Cath. U., 1946-47; counsel Senate com. on labor and pub. welfare, 1947; dir. Reed & Prince Mfg. Co., Worcester, Mass., 1963-70. Fellow Am. Bar Found.; mem. Am., D.C., Boston bar assns. Roman Catholic. Clubs: Nat. Lawyers (Washington), Cosmos (Washington) (pres. 1976-77), Palaver (Washington), Harvard (Washington); Bass River Yacht. Home: 3515 Lowell St NW Washington DC 20016-5026 Office: DC Court House 500 Indiana Ave NW Washington DC 20001-2131

REILLY, JOHN E., automotive executive. Exec. v.p. Mid Altantic Motors, Balt., 1963-80; chmn. bd. American Isuzu Motors Inc., La Puente, Calif., 1980—. Office: American Isuzu Motors Inc 13181 Crossroads Pky N La Puente CA 91746-3419

REILLY, JOHN LAWRENCE, banker; b. N.Y.C., Jan. 16, 1940; s. John Joseph and Johanna M. (Bernhardt) R.; m. Lois M. Kessel, Aug. 29, 1964; children—John Joseph, Scott Lawrence. Cert., Am. Inst. Banking, 1965; grad., Grad. Sch. Savs. Banking, Brown U., 1972; Grad., Exec. Devel. Sch., U. Mass., 1975. Teller Am. Savs. Bank, N.Y.C., 1958-68, asst. sec. ops., 1968-71, investment officer, 1971-82, 1st sr. v.p., 1982-83, 1st sr. v.p., treas., 1983-87, exec. v.p., chief retail banking officer, 1987—; mem. faculty Nat. Sch. Fin., Fairfield U., 1978-89; vice chmn., chief fin. officer Greater N.Y. Am. Inst. Banking, 1978-80. Pres., bd. dirs. St. Thomas Cath. Ch. Manalapan Twp., N.J., 1981-82; vice chmn. Manalapan Twp. Planning Bd., 1985-87; mem. Lewisboro (N.Y.) Planning Bd., 1988—, chmn. 1990—; mem. adv. bd. Salvation Army Westchester County, N.Y. With M.I., U.S. Army, 1968-71. Mem. Am. Inst. Banking, Nat. Coun. Savs. Insts. (exec. com. 1989-90). Republican. Lutheran. Avocations: soccer coach, referee, gardening. Office: Am Savs Bank 99 Church St White Plains NY 10601-1579

REILLY, JOHN PAUL, manufacturing company executive; b. Phila., Aug. 18, 1943; m. Lynda J. Shepley; children: John P., Colleen K., Timothy S. BS, Xavier U., 1965; MBA, U. Detroit, 1967. Mfg. mgr. Chrysler Corp., 1965-79; pres. Mark div. Core Industries, 1979-80; sr. v.p. Internat. Harvester, 1980-83; sr. v.p., gen. mgr. Walker Mfg. Co. div. Tenneco Automotive, Racine, Wis., 1984-87; pres., chief exec. officer Tenneco Automotive, Lincolnshire, Ill., 1987—. Dir. Arden Shore Home for Boys, Lake Forest, Ill.; Racine Area Mfrs. and Commerce, 1984—. Mem. Motor and Equipment Mfrs. Assn. (bd. dirs.). Avocations: jogging, golf. Office: Tenneco Automotive Ste 300 100 Tri Stste International Lincolnshire IL 60061

REILLY, LAURA J., lawyer; b. Ames, Iowa; d. Lawrence J. and Dorothy J. (Waller) R.; m. James L. Abrams, 1975; children: Reilly Katherine, Merrill Elizabeth, Jacqueline Lee. BS, U. Iowa, 1969; MS, U. Calif., San Francisco 1970; JD, Rutgers U., 1975; LLM, U. Denver, 1983. Bar: Colo. 1975, Tex. 1978. Rsch. asst. Baker, Baker & Wilson, Oklahoma City, 1975-77; atty. Office of Gen. Counsel, U. Tex., Austin, 1977-79; asst. atty. gen. Colo., Denver, 1979-81; atty. U.S. West Communications, Denver, 1981-89; chief counsel U.S. West Svc. Link, 1989-91; sr. atty. U.S. West Inc., 1992—; bd. dirs. Vis. Nurses Support Svcs., Inc., 1985—, chmn. 1987-91. Mem. ABA, Colo. Bar Assn., Colo. Women's Bar Assn. Roman Catholic. Office: U S West Inc 7800 East Orchard Rd Englewood CO 80111

REILLY, MICHAEL K., mining executive; b. 1933. With Zeigler Coal Holding Co., Fairview Heights, Ill., 1963—; now CEO Zeigler Coal Holding Co., East Saint Louis, Ill. Office: Zeigler Coal Holding 50 Jerome Ln East Saint Louis IL 62208

REILLY, PHILIP RAYMOND, medical research administrator; b. Albany, N.Y., Oct. 3, 1947. MD, Yale U., New Haven, 1981. Diplomate Am. Bd. Clin. Genetics. Intern Boston City Hosp., 1983-85, resident, 1983-85; staff Mass. Gen. Hosp., Boston; dir. Eunice Kennedy Shriver Ctr. for Mental Retardation, Waltham, Mass. Mem. Am. Assn. for the Advancement of Sci., Am. Soc. of Human Genetics. Office: Eunice Kennedy Shriver Ctn 200 Trapelo Rd Waltham MA 02154*

REILLY, ROBERT FREDERICK, valuation consultant; b. N.Y.C., Oct. 3, 1952; s. James J. and Marie (Griebel) R.; m. Janet H. Steiner, Apr. 16, 1975; children: Ashley Lauren, Brandon Christopher, Cameron Courtney. BA in Econs., Columbia U., 1974, MBA in Fin., 1975. CPA, Ohio, Ill.; cert. mgmt. acct., cert. fin. analyst, cert. real estate appraiser; cert. gen. appraiser Ill.; accredited sr. appraiser. Sr. cons. Booz, Allen & Hamilton, Cin., 1975-76; dir. corp. planning Huffy Corp., Dayton, Ohio, 1976-81; v.p. Arthur D. Little Valuation, Inc., Chgo., 1981-85; ptnr., nat. dir. of valution svcs. Deloitte & Touche, Chgo., 1985-91; mng. dir. Willamette Mgmt. Assocs., Chgo., 1991—; adj. prof. accounting U. Dayton Grad. Sch. Bus., 1977-81; adj. prof. fin. econs., Elmhurst (Ill.) Coll., 1982-87; adj. prof. fin. Ill. Inst. Tech. Grad. Sch. Bus., Chgo., 1985—; adj. prof. taxation U. Chgo. Grad. Sch. Bus., 1985-87. Co-author: Valuing Small Businesses and Professional Practices, 1993, Business Valuation Video Course, 1993, Valuing a Business, 1995; editor, columnist Small Bus. Taxation, 1989-90, Bus. Valuation Rev., 1989-90, Jour. of Real Estate Acctg. and Taxation, 1991-93, Ohio CPA Jour., 1984-86, 91—, Jour. Property Taxation Mgmt., 1993—, Jour. Am. Bankruptcy Inst., 1993—; contbr. more than 200 articles to profl. jours. Mem. AICPA, Nat. Assn. Real Estate Appraisers (cert.), Am. Soc. Appraisers (bd. examiners 1985-89), Nat. Assn. Accts. (chpt. dir. 1976), Inst. Property Taxation, Soc. Mfg. Engrs., Ill. Soc. CPAs, Ohio Soc. CPAs (chpt. dir. 1978-81), Accreditation Coun. Accountancy (accreditation in fed. income), Bus. Valuation Assn., Chgo. Soc. Investment Analysts, Inst. Chartered Fin. Analysts, Am. Econ. Assn., Nat. Assn. Bus. Economists. Home: 310 Algonquin Rd Barrington Hills IL 60010 Office: 8600 W Bryn Mawr Ave Chicago IL 60631

REILLY, ROBERT JOSEPH, counselor; b. Spokane, Wash., Mar. 7, 1936; s. John Francis and Vivian Helen (White) R.; m. Joan Steiner, June 20, 1960; children: Sean Michael, Patrick Joseph, Bridget Colleen. BA in Psychology, Seattle U., 1985; postgrad., Infantry Officer Candidate Sch, Ft. Benning, 1960, EOAC, Ft. Belvoir, 1968, Leadership Inst. Seattle/City U., 1991-92. Ordained Congl. Ch. Practical Theology. Enlisted U.S. Army, 1953, advanced through grades to maj., 1981, ret., 1981; with U.S. Army, Korea, 1961-62, Vietnam, 1966-67, 68-69; counselor Schick Shadel Hosp., Seattle, 1984-89; dir. Canyon Counseling, Puyallup, Wash., 1987-92; counselor Wash. State Employee Adv. Svc., Olympia, 1992—; mem. Nat. Bd. for Hypnotherapy and Hypnotic Anaesthesiology, v.p. 1991—, pres. Wash Chpt., 1991-94; exec. v.p. Coll. Therapeutic Hypnosis, Puyallup, 1989-94; mem. adj. faculty Pierce Coll., Tacoma, 1991-92. Pres. Irich Cultural Club, Tacoma, 1983-85, 93-94; sec. Tacoma chpt. Ret. Officers Assn., 1983-87, pres., 1993-95. Decorated Vietnamese Cross of Gallentry with silver star, Bronze Star with oak leaf cluster, Meritorious Svc. medal, Army Commendation medal with 2 oak leaf clusters; named Prof. of Yr. Chem. Dependency Profls. Wash., 1994. Mem. Nat. Bd. Hypnotherapy and Hypnotic Anesthesiology (v.p. 1991—, Mem. of Yr. 1994, pres. Wash. chpt. 1991-94), Internat. Med. and Dental Hypnotherapy Assn., Nat. Assn. Alcohol and Drug Abuse Counselors, Am. Congress Hypnotist Examiners, Army Engr. Assn., Nat. 4th Inf. Divsn. Assn. (sec.-treas. N.W. chpt. 1993—), Employee Assistance Profls. Assn. Avocations: volksmarching, symphony music, theater. Office: Wash State Employee Adv Svc PO Box 47540 Olympia WA 98504-7540

REILLY, THOMAS, humanities educator; b. Hollymount, Mayo, Ireland, Dec. 16, 1941; arrived in Eng., 1967; s. Patrick and Josephine (Sheridan) R.; m. Feb. 22, 1977; children: Anna, Siobhán. BA, U. Coll. Dublin, Ireland, 1967; MSc, Royal Free Hosp., London, 1971; PhD, Liverpool (U.K.) Poly., 1975; M.I. Biology, Inst. Biology, London, 1977. Clerical officer Dublin Corp., 1960-65; tchr., athletic coach Govt. of Cameroun, 1968-70; technician Med. Rsch. Coun., London, 1971; rsch. asst. Liverpool Poly., 1972-75, lectr., then prin. lectr., reader, 1975-88, prof. sports sci., 1988—; dir. of sch. Liverpool John Moores U., 1991—; vis. prof. Tsukuba (Japan) U., 1977; vis. coach Nigerian Sports Coun., 1976; vis. rsch. assoc. U. Calif., Berkeley, 1980; invited spkr. 2d World Congress on Sci. and Football, Netherlands, 1991; contbd. consensus statement on nutrition for soccer F.I.F.A., Zürich, 1994. Editor: Sports Fitness and Sports Issues, 1981, Physiology of Sports, 1990, Science and Football, 1988; editor Jour. Sports Sci., 1983—. Organizer Hollymount Internat. Rd. Race, Mayo, Ireland, 1976—; coord. acclimation strategy Brit. Olympic Assn., London, 1993—, chair exercise physiology steering group, 1992—. Mem. Brit. Assn. Sport and Exercise Sci. (chair 1994—), Internat. Steering Group on Sci. and Football (chair 1987—). Roman Catholic. Avocations: soccer, Gaelic football, running, squash, orienteering. Office: Sch of Human Sciences, Mountford Building Byrom St, Liverpool L3 3AF, United Kingdom

REILLY, WILLIAM FRANCIS, publishing company executive; b. N.Y.C., June 8, 1938; s. William F. and Genevieve Reilly; m. Ellen Chapman, Nov. 19, 1966; children: Anthony Chapman and Jane Wasey (twins). AB cum laude, U. Notre Dame, 1959; MBA, Harvard U., 1964. Mgr. fin. analysis W.R. Grace & Co., N.Y.C., 1964-67, asst. to pres., 1969-71, CEO Bekaert Textile Divsn., 1971-74; pres., CEO Herman's World of Sporting Goods, Carteret, N.J., 1974-77; v.p., pres. W.R. Grace and Co., 1978; pres., CEO Home Ctr. Div., 1979-80; pres. Macmillan, Inc., N.Y.C., 1980-90; chmn., CEO K-III Comm. Corp., N.Y.C., 1990—. 1st lt. U.S. Army, 1959-61. Home: 8 E 96th St New York NY 10128-0820 Office: K-III Comm Corp 745 5th Ave New York NY 10151-2298

REILLY, WILLIAM KANE, former government official, educator, lawyer, conservationist; b. Decatur, Ill., Jan. 26, 1940; s. George P. and Margaret (Kane) R.; m. Elizabeth Buxton; children: Katherine, Megan. B.A. in History, Yale U., 1962; J.D., Harvard U., 1965; M.S. in Urban Planning, Columbia U., 1971. Bar: Ill., Mass. 1965. Atty. firm Ross & Hardies, Chgo., 1965; asso. dir. Urban Policy Center, Urban Am., N.Y.C.; also Nat. Urban Coalition, Washington, 1969-70; sr. staff mem. Pres.'s Council Environ. Quality, 1970-72; exec. dir. Task Force Land Use and Urban Growth, 1972-73; pres. Conservation Found., Washington, 1973-89, World Wildlife Fund, Washington, 1985-89; adminstr. U.S. EPA, Washington, 1989-93; chmn. Natural Resources Coun. Am., 1982-83; head U.S. del. Earth Summit, 1992; head U.S. del. to negotiate Amendments to Montreal Protocol on the Ozone Layer, 1990, 92; Payne vis. prof. Stanford U., 1993—; assoc. Tex. Pacific Group, San Francisco, 1994—; chmn. bd. dirs. Clean Sites, Inc.; bd. dirs. Am. Farmland Trust, E.I. DuPont de Nemours and Co., Evergreen Holdings, Inc., Nat. Geog. Soc., Ptnrs. for Livable Communities, World Wildlife Fund, Yale U.; mem. sci. adv. bd. The Nature Conservancy. Editor: The Use of Land, 1973, Environment Strategy America, 1994; author articles in field, chpts. in books. Served to capt., CIC U.S. Army, 1966-67. Clubs: University (Washington), Univ. (N.Y.C.). Office: c/o World Wildlife Fund 1250 24th St NW Washington DC 20037-1175

REILLY, WILLIAM THOMAS, lawyer; b. Passaic, N.J., Feb. 25, 1949; s. Thomas Edwin and Edna May (Dorritie) R.; m. Sheila Mary Brogan, Aug. 1, 1981; children: Kathleen Anne, Brendan Thomas, Timothy John. BS, Boston Coll., 1971; JD, Harvard U., 1974. Bar: N.J. 1974, U.S. Dist. Ct. N.J. 1974, U.S. Supreme Ct. 1979, U.S. Ct. Appeals (3rd cir.) 1984. Assoc. McCarter & English, Newark, 1974-81, ptnr., 1982—. Trustee United Hosps. Med. Ctr., Newark, 1983-89, One-to-One(N.J.), 1990—, chmn., 1993—. Mem. ABA, N.J. State Bar Assn., Harvard Law Sch. Assn., Eastward Ho Country Club. Avocation: golf. Home: 302 Kensington Dr Ridgewood NJ 07450-1822 Office: McCarter & English Four Gateway Ctr 100 Mulberry St Newark NJ 07102-4004

REIMAN, DONALD HENRY, English language educator; b. Erie, Pa., May 17, 1934; s. Henry Ward and Mildred Abbie (Pearce) R.; m. Mary Warner, 1958 (div. 1974); 1 child, Laurel Elizabeth Reiman Henneman; m. Hélène Liberman Dworzan, Oct. 3, 1975. A.B., Coll. of Wooster, 1956, Litt.D., 1981; M.A., U. Ill., 1957, Ph.D., 1960. Instr. English, Duke U., Durham, N.C., 1960-62, asst. prof., 1962-64; assoc. prof. U. Wis., Milw., 1964-65; adj. assoc. prof. grad. program in English CUNY, 1967-68; adj. prof. Columbia U., N.Y.C., 1969-70, sr. rsch. assoc. in English, 1970-73; vis. prof. St. John's U., Jamaica, N.Y., 1974-75; editor Shelley and His Circle, Carl H. Pforzheimer Library, N.Y.C., 1965-86, N.Y. Pub. Libr., 1986-92; with Carl & Lily Pforzheimer Found., 1992—; vis. lectr. U. Ill., 1963; vis. prof. U. Wash., Seattle, 1981, NYU, 1992; Lyell reader in bibliography Oxford U., 1988-89; adj. prof. English U. Del., 1992—, NYU, 1992; cons. Harvard U. Press, Yale U. Press, Princeton U. Press, Johns Hopkins U. Press, Garland Pub. Inc., W.W. Norton, Oxford U. Press, others. Author: Shelley's The Triumph of Life, A Critical Study, 1965, 2d edit., 1979, Percy Bysshe Shelley, 1969, 2d edit., 1990, (with D.D. Fischer) Byron on the Continent, 1974; English Romantic Poetry, 1800-1835, 1979, Romantic Texts and Contexts, 1987, Intervals of Inspiration: The Skeptical Tradition and the Psychology of Romanticism, 1988, The Study of Modern Manuscripts, 1993; editor: Shelley and His Circle, Vols. V-VI, 1973, Vols. VII-VIII, 1986, The Romantics Reviewed: Contemporary Reviews of English Romantic Writers, 9 vols., 1972; (with S.B. Powers) Shelley's Poetry and Prose: A Norton Critical Edition, 1977; The Romantic Context: Poetry, 128 vols., 1976-79; (with M.C. Jaye and B.T. Bennett) The Evidence of the Imagination, 1978; gen. editor: Manuscripts of the Younger Romantics; I The Esdaile Notebook: A Facsimile, 1985, II The Mask of Anarchy: Facsimiles, 1985, III Hellas, 1985, V The Harvard Shelley Poetic Manuscripts, 1991; editor in chief: The Bodleian Shelley Manuscripts, 1984—; I Peter Bell The Third and the Triumph of Life, 1986, VII Shelley's Last Notebook and Other MSS, 1990, (with M.J. Neth) The Hellas Notebook, XVI, 1994; mem. edit. com. adv. bd. Keats-Shelley Jour., 1968-73, Milton and the Romantics, 1975-80, Studies in Romanticism, 1977—, Romanticism Past and Present, 1980-86, Text, 1981—, Nineteenth-Century Literature, 1986—, Nineteenth-Century Contexts, 1987-90; contbr. articles to encyclopedias, books and profl. jours. Active Common Cause. Am. Coun. Learned Socs. fellow, 1963-64, Wesleyan Ctr. Advanced Studies fellow, 1963-64, NEH fellow, 1978; grantee Am. Coun. Learned Socs., 1961, NEH, 1983—. Mem. AAUP, MLA (life), Modern Humanities Rsch. Assn. (life), Wordsworth-Coleridge Assn. Am. (founder), Byron Soc. (Am. com. 1973—), Keats-Shelley Assn. Am. (bd. dirs., trans. 1973-91, v.p. 1991—, Disting. Scholar award 1987), Bibliog. Soc. Am., Soc. Textual Scholarship (exec. com. 1981-93), Coleridge in Somerset Assn., Charles Lamb Soc., Assn. Documentary Editing, N.Am. Soc. Study of Romanticism, Assn. Literary Scholars and Critics. Democrat. Presbyterian. Home: 907 Aster Ave Newark DE 19711-2631 Office: NY Pub Libr Fifth Ave at 42nd St Rm 226 New York NY 10018

REIMAN, JOEY, advertising executive; b. Mar. 31, 1953; s. Henry Rudolf and Phylliss Joy (Wilner) R. BA, Brandeis U., 1975. Writer Grey Advt., N.Y.C., 1979-81; assoc. creative dir. Benton & Bowles, N.Y.C., 1981-83; creative dir. DMB&B, Atlanta, 1983-84; chief creative officer Babbit & Reiman Advt., Atlanta, 1984—, also chmn. bd. dirs.; speaker in field, 1986—. Author: (ballet) Le Grande Jete, 1989; contbg. author How To Get The Right Job in Advertising, 1989. Media dir. Atlantans for Maynard Jackson, 1989; bd. dirs. Alliance Theater, 1985—. Named Best Big Idea Person Atlanta Bus. Chronicle, 1987, 88, 89, Writer of Yr. Adweek mag., 1987; recipient Best of Show 1985 award Atlanta Advt. Club, Best of Show award 1988. Avocation: magic. Office: The Joey Reiman Agency 3060 Peachtree Rd NW Ste 1 Atlanta GA 30305-2228

REIMANN, WILLIAM PAGE, artist, educator; b. Mpls., Nov. 29, 1935; s. Hobart and Dorothy (Sampson) R.; m. Helen Vera Sadowy, June 3, 1961; children: Christopher, Katherine. BA, Yale U., 1957, BFA, 1959, MFA in Sculpture, 1961. Instr. Old Dominion U., Norfolk, Va., 1961-62; asst. prof. Old Dominion U., 1962-64; asst. prof. design Harvard U., 1964-67, lectr., 1969-75, sr. preceptor in visual studies, 1975—, head tutor dept. visual studies, 1986-94. Recent major commns. include Tropicana Corp., Bradenton, Fla., Southwest Bell Telephone Co., Houston, Gen. Mills Corp., Mpls., Shell Oil Co., Houston, 1st Ch. of Christ, Scientist, Boston; designated artist Radnor (Pa.) Twp. Gateway Enhancement Project, Boston Redsox Baseball Club; represented in permanent collections, Mus. Modern Art, N.Y.C., Nat. Gallery Art, Washington, Whitney Mus. Am. Art, Boston Mus. Fine Art, Rockefeller U., Yale U., Harvard U., also numerous pvt. collections. Recipient 2 Gold medals U.S. Master's Rowing Nat. Championships, 1994. Mem. Cambridge Boat Club. Home: 1 Gerrys Landing Cambridge MA 02138-5511 Office: Carpenter Ctr Visual Arts 24 Quincy St Cambridge MA 02138-3804

REIMER, BENNETT, music educator, writer; b. N.Y.C., June 19, 1932; s. George and Sarah (Talkofsky) R.; children: Jan Ellen, Terry. BM, State Tchr.'s Coll. (now SUNY-Fredonia), 1954; MM, U. Ill., 1955, EdD, 1963. Asst. prof. music edn. U. Ill., Urbana, 1960-65; Kulas prof., chmn. dept. music edn. Case Western Res. U., Cleve., 1965-78; John W. Beattie prof., chmn. dept. Northwestern U., Evanston, Ill., 1978—. Author: A Philosophy of Music Education, 1970, 2d edit., 1989, Developing the Experience of Music, 1985; editor: Toward an Aesthetic Education, 1971, The Arts, Education and Aesthetic Knowing, 1992, On the Nature of Musical Experience, 1992; co-author: The Experience of Music, 1972, Silver Burdett Music Grades 1-8, 1974, 4th edit., 1985; contbr. over 100 articles on music and arts edn. to profl. jours. Mem. Music Educators Nat. Conf., Music Edn. Research Council, Edn. Aesthetic Awareness (bd. dirs.). Office: Northwestern U Sch Music Evanston IL 60208*

REIMER, BORGE R., motor vehicle parts manufacturer; b. 1931; married. Mech. engr. Odense Maskin Teknikum, Denmark, 1953-56; pres. Dana, Ltd., 1956-73; with Dana Corp., Toledo, 1973—; group v.p., 1973-76, sr. group v.p., 1976-78, pres. Indsl. div., 1978-81, exec. v.p., 1981—. Office: Dana Corp PO Box 1000 Toledo OH 43697-1000

REIMER, DENNIS J., career military officer. Gen. USA, Ft. McPherson, Ga. Office: General USA Comdr Forces Command Fort McPherson GA 30330-6000

REIN, BERT WALTER, lawyer; b. Bklyn., Feb. 7, 1941; s. Moe and Florence (Fishman) R.; m. Jennifer Christine Bulson July 11, 1966 (dec. Mar. 1989); children: Joanna, Benjamin, Samantha; m. Barbara Jean Kahn, Oct. 18, 1992. BA, Amherst Coll., 1961; LLB, Harvard U., 1964. Bar: D.C. 1965, U.S. Dist. Ct. D.C. 1965, U.S. Supreme Ct. (D.C. cir.) 1968, U.S Appeals (2nd cir.) 1973, U.S. Ct. Appeals (8th cir.) 1974, U.S.C. Appeals (4ht cir.) 1976, U.S. Ct. Appeals (11th cir.) 1982, U.S. Supreme Ct. 1982. Law ck. to Justice John M. Harlan U.S. Supreme Ct., Washington, 1966-67; assoc. Kirkland & Ellis, Washington, 1967-69, ptnr., 1973-83; spl. asst. U.S. Dept. State, Washington, 1969-70, dep. asst. sec., 1970-73; ptnr. Wiley, Rein & Fielding, Washington, 1983—; bd. dirs., chmn. govt. and regulation affairs com. U.S. C. of C., 1986-90; bd. dirs. Nat. Chamber Litigation Ctr.; advisor Reagan Dept. Justice Transition, Washington, 1980; mem. adv. com. U.S. Sentencing Commn., 1988-89; edn. gen. counsel Comty. Learning and Info. Network, 1992—. Contbr. articles to profl. publs. Capt. USAR, 1964-68. Mem. ABA, Am. Law Inst., Internat. Trade Commn. Trial Lawyers Assn. (pres. 1990-91), Internat. Aviation Club. Republican. Jewish. Home: 6423 Shadow Rd Chevy Chase MD 20815 Office: Wiley Rein & Fielding 1776 K St NW Washington DC 20006-2304

REIN, CATHERINE AMELIA, financial services executive, lawyer; b. Lebanon, Pa., Feb. 7, 1943; d. John and Esther (Scott) Shultz. BA summa cum laude, Pa. State U., 1965; JD magna cum laude, NYU., 1968. Bar: N.Y. 1968, U.S. Supreme Ct. 1971. Assoc. Dewey, Ballantine, Bushby, Palmer & Wood, N.Y.C., 1968-74; with Continental Group, Stamford, Conn., 1974-85, sec., sr. atty., 1976-77, v.p., gen. counsel, 1980-85; sec., asst. gen. counsel Continental Diversified Ops., 1978-80; v.p. human resources Met. Life Ins. Co., N.Y.C., 1985-88, sr. v.p. human resources, 1988-89, exec. v.p. corp. and profl. svcs. dept., 1989—; bd. dirs Bank of NY., Gen. Pub. Utilities, Corning Inc., Nat. Urban League, Inroads, N.Y.C. Trustee Nat. Urban League, NYU Sch. Law Found. Mem. ABA, Assn. of Bar of City of N.Y. Episcopalian. Avocations: decorating, restoration, cooking. Home: 21 E 22nd St Apt 8B New York NY 10010-5335 Office: Met Life Ins Co 1 Madison Ave New York NY 10010

REIN, MARTIN, educator, social worker; b. N.Y.C., Apr. 17, 1928; s. Max and Esther (Strenger) R.; m. Mildred Steinberg, Dec. 5, 1947; children: Glen, Lisa. B.A., Bklyn. Coll., 1950; M.S., Columbia U., 1954; Ph.D., Brandeis U., 1961. Program dir. Brownsville Boys Club, 1950-52; supr. Teen Age Gang Project, James Weldon Johnson Community Center, N.Y.C., 1954-56; br. dir. East Tremont YM-YWHA, 1956-59; lectr. sociology Clark U., 1960-62; prof. social work and social research Bryn Mawr Coll., 1962-70; prof. urban studies and planning M.I.T., 1970—; Downing prof. social econs. U. Melbourne, Australia, 1980; cons. President's Com. on Juvenile Delinquency and Youth Crime, 1962-64, President's Manpower Report, 1967, President's Commn. on Income Maintenance, 1968; research asso. Center for Environmental Studies, London, 1969-70, summer 1971; Mem. rev. com. on met. mental health programs NIMH, 1968; mem. Social Services Task Force, HEW, 1966; research scientist early retirement in regimes WZB-Sci. Ctr., Berlin, summers 1988-90; co-prin. investigator labor markets and welfare state regimes study WZB-Sci. Ctr., Berlin, 1986-87; co-prin. investigator "Social Service Labor Market" Russell Sage Found. Grant, 1988; co-prin. investigator Luxembourg income study Luxembourg Govt. & Ford Found., 1983—. Author: An Organizational Analysis of Planned Parenthood and its Local Affiliates, 1961, The Network of Agencies Providing Child Protective Services in Massachusetts, 1964, (with R. Morris and R. Binstock) Social Planning: A Feasible Approach, 1966, (with Peter Marris) Dilemmas of Social Reform, 1967, 2d edit., 1972, 2d edit. with new preface, 1982, Social Policy: Issues of Choice and Change, 1970, 2d edit., 1983, (with Sar Levitan and David Marwick) Work and Welfare Go Together, 1972, 2d edit., 1974, Social Science and Public Policy, 1976, From Policy to Practice, 1983, (with Lisa Peattie) Womens Claims, 1983, Income Packaging in the Welfare State, 1985, (with Lee Rainwater, et al, editors) The Public/Private Interplay in Social Production: A Comparative Study, 1987, Stagnation & Renewal in the Welfare State, 1987, (with Martin Kohli et al, editors) Time for Retirement: Comparative Studies of the Decreasing Age of Exit from the Labor Force; co-editor series: Comparative Studies in Social Policy, 1986. NIMH research fellow, 1959-61; sr. research Fulbright fellow London Sch. Econs., 1966-67; Ford Found. research grantee, 1969-70. Mem. Nat. Assn. Social Workers, Nat. Conf. Social Welfare, Am. Sociol. Soc. Home: 40 Crafts Rd Chestnut Hill MA 02167-1824 Office: MIT Dept Urban Studies and Planning Cambridge MA 02139

REIN, STANLEY MICHAEL, lawyer; b. St. Paul, Apr. 15, 1946; s. Clayton George Rein and Rose Gertrude (Mintz) Brown; m. Linda R. Arnold; children: Gabriel Todd, Leah Suzanne. BA, U. Minn., 1968; JD cum laude, Harvard U., 1973. Bar: Minn. 1973, U.S. Tax Ct. 1973. Assoc. Dorsey & Whitney, P.L.L.P., Mpls., 1973-78; ptnr. Dorsey & Whitney PLLP, Mpls., 1979—. Mem. planned giving adv. coun. ARC Mpls. chpt., 1986, 88, planned giving adv. com. Minn. Pub. Radio, 1988-89; bd. dirs. South Metro Airport Action Council, Mpls., 1986, 87. With U.S. Army, 1968-70, Vietnam. Fellow Am. Coll. of Trust and Estate Counsel; mem. Minn. Bar Assn. (probate and trust law sect.), Hennepin County Bar Assn. (probate and trust law sect.), Phi Beta Kappa. Jewish. Avocations: tennis, reading, travel. Office: Dorsey & Whitney PLLP 220 S 6th St Minneapolis MN 55402

REINECKE, MANFRED G., chemistry educator; b. Milw., May 19, 1935; s. Fritz Wilhelm and Erna (Rittmeyer) R.; m. Marlene Zwisler, June 15, 1957; children: Kurt, Kryn, Claire. BS in Chemistry, U. Wis., 1956; PhD in Organic Chemistry, U. Calif., 1960. Asst. prof. U. Calif., Riverside, 1959-64; asst. prof. Tex. Christian U., Ft. Worth, 1964-68, assoc. prof., 1968-73; vis. prof. U. Tubingen, Fed. Republic of Germany, 1971-72; prof. Tex. Christian U., Ft. Worth, 1973—; vis. prof. U. British Columbia, Vancouver, Can., 1987; chmn. health professions adv. com. Tex. Christian U., 1974-91; cons. in field. Contbr. more than 70 articles on natural product, organic chemistry and chem. edn. to profl. jours. Recipient W.T. Doherty award Ft. Worth, Dallas sect. Am. Chem. Soc., 1984; Nat. Sci. Found. Teaching fellow, 1971-72, NAS fellow, 1979, 90. Mem. Am. Chem. Soc. (chmn. Ft. Worth, Dallas sect. 1976), So. Assn. Advisors Health Professions (bd. dirs. 1986-89), Alpha Epsilon Delta (dir. SW region 1985—). Office: Tex Christian Univ Dept Of Chemistry Fort Worth TX 76129

REINECKE, ROBERT DALE, ophthalmologist; b. Ft. Scott, Kans., Mar. 26, 1929; s. George Alfred and Bessie Irene (Newell) R.; m. Mary Jeannetta Portwood, Oct. 5, 1952; 1 child, Karen Denise. O.D., Ill. Coll. Optometry, 1951; A.B., U. Kans., 1955, M.D., 1959. Diplomate: Am. Bd. Ophthalmology. Research fellow ophthalmology Harvard U. Med. Sch., 1957, 58; intern U. Kans. Med. Center, 1959-60; resident in ophthalmology Mass. Eye and Ear Infirmary, Boston, 1961-63; asst. in ophthalmology Mass. Eye and Ear Infirmary, 1963-69; asst. prof. ophthalmology Harvard U. Med. Sch., 1967-69; mem. faculty Albany (N.Y.) Med. Sch., 1970-81, prof. ophthalmology, 1970-81, chmn. dept., 1970-81; prof. ophthalmology Jefferson Med. Coll., Phila., 1981—; chmn. dept. Jefferson Med. Coll., 1981-85; ophthalmologist-in-chief Wills Eye Hosp., 1981-85, dir. Foerderer Eye Movement Ctr., 1985—; bd. dirs. Conrad Berens Internat. Eye Film Library, 1970-80; exec. com. N.Y. State Bd. Medicine, 1978-80, chmn., 1980-81; com. vision NRC, 1976-81, chmn., 1979-80; Alumni lectr. Georgetown U. Med. Sch., 1970; Proctor lectr. U. Calif. Med. Sch., San Francisco, 1977; Schoenberg lectr. N.Y. Acad. Medicine, 1979; Spaeth lectr. Coll. Physicians, 1982; Bajandas lectr., 1989. Contbr. numerous articles to med. jours. USPHS summer fellow, 1956, 58; Fight for Sight fellow, summers 1957, 60; recipient Senior Honor award Am. Acad. Ophthalmology, 1986. Fellow Am. Acad. Ophthalmology (sec. govt. relations 1980-86, pres. 1989); mem. Am. Bd. Ophthalmology (bd. dirs. 1984-87); Assn. Research Vision and Ophthalmology (trustee sect. on eye movements, strabismus and amblyopia, 1986-91), AMA, Am. Assn. Ophthalmology (sec. for program 1986-87), Pa. Med. Soc., N.Y. State Ophthal. Assn., Am. Assn. Pediatric Ophthalmology (pres. 1975-76), Phila. County Med. Soc. (chmn. med. econ. com 1994—), Pa. Acad. Ophthalmology (pres. 1991), Pa. Med. Soc., Coll. of Physicians, Am. Coll. of Surgeons, Ophthalmic Club of Phila. Office: Wills Eye Hosp 9th And Walnut St Philadelphia PA 19107

REINEMUND, STEVEN S., restaurant chain executive; b. Queens, N.Y., Apr. 6, 1948; s. Ott and Dora (Kramer) R.; m. Gail Timbers, Dec. 14, 1974; children: Steven S. Jr., Jonathan Craig. BS in Naval Sci., U.S. Naval Acad., 1970; MBA, U. Va., 1978. Commd. 2d lt. USMC, 1970, advanced through grades to capt., 1974, resigned, 1975; mktg. rep. IBM Corp., 1975-76; v.p. gen. mgr. Marriott-Roy Rogers, 1978-84; sr. v.p., field operator Pizza Hut Inc., Wichita, Kans., 1984-86, exec. v.p., 1986, pres., chief exec. officer, 1986—; bd. dirs. Bank IV, Wichita. Sec., treas. bd. dirs. U. Va., Darden Sch. Alumni Assn. Named one of Outstanding Young Men Am. Mem. Wichita Area C. of C. (bd. dirs.). Republican. Presbyterian. Avocations: tennis, running. Home: 3709 Potomac Ave Dallas TX 75205-2112 Office: Pizza Hut Inc 9111 E Douglas Ave Wichita KS 67207-1205

REINER, BERT LEO, consumer product engineering/manufacturing consultant; b. Dresden, Germany, May 30, 1937; came to U.S., 1949; s. Horace W. and Gertrude (Katz) R.; m. Sandra J. Winkler, June 25, 1960; children: Helaine, Eric, Dana. BME, Resselaer Poly. Inst., 1960. Design engr. Sikorsky Aircraft Div., Stratford, Conn., 1960-62; project engr. Soundscriber Corp., New Haven, Conn., 1962-63; chief engr. A.C. Gilbert Co., New Haven, 1963-66; dir.Far East Mfg. Ideal Toy Co., Jamaica, N.Y., 1967-69; v.p. engring. Coleco IndustriesInc., Hartford, Conn., 1964-88; sr. v.p. Coleco Industries Inc., West Hartford, Conn., 1985-88; pres. Reiner Assocs. Inc., Wallingford, Conn., 1988—. Patentee in field. Mem. ASME, IEEE, Am. Assn. Profl. Cons., Soc. Plastics Engrs. (sr.). Avocations: bonsai, stamp and coin collecting, skiing, racquetball. Office: Reiner Assocs Inc 21 Blakeslee Rd Wallingford CT 06492-5212

REINER, CARL, actor, writer, director; b. Bronx, N.Y., Mar. 20, 1922; s. Irving and Bessie (Mathias) R.; m. Estelle Lebost, Dec. 24, 1943; children: Robert, Sylvia A., Lucas. Student, Sch. Fgn. Service, Georgetown U., 1943. Appeared on Broadway and with road co.: Call Me Mister, 1947-48; on Broadway in: Inside U.S.A, 1948-49, Alive and Kicking, 1950; TV actor, 1950—; appeared: Your Show of Shows, 1950-54, Caesar's Hour, 1954-58 (Emmy award 1956, 57); master ceremonies: Keep Talking, 1958-59; writer-actor: Dinah Shore Show, 1960; producer, writer: The Dick Van Dyke Show (Emmy awards as writer 1962, 63, 64, as producer 1965, 66), The New Dick Van Dyke Show, Enter Laughing, written 1958, directed 1967, The Comics, 1968; dir.: (films) Enter Laughing, 1967, The Comic, 1969, Where's Poppa, 1970, Oh, God!, 1977, The One and Only, 1978, The Jerk, 1979, Dead Men Don't Wear Plaid, 1982, The Man With Two Brains, 1983, All of Me, 1984, Summer Rental, 1985, Summer School, 1987, Bert Rigby, You're a Fool, 1989, Sibling Rivalry, 1990, Fatal Instinct, 1993; appeared in: movie Happy Anniversary, 1959, The Gazebo, 1960, Gidget Goes Hawaiian, 1961, It's a Mad, Mad, Mad, Mad World, 1963, The Russians Are Coming, 1966, The End, 1978, Dead Men Don't Wear Plaid, 1982; writer, dir.: Something Different, 1967; writer: Sid Caesar, Imogene Coca, Carl Reiner, Howard Morris Special (Emmy award, 1967); producer: TV series Good Heavens, 1976 (recipient Emmy award 1957, 58, 62, 63); Author: (novel) All Kinds of Love, 1993; author short stories; screenplay The Thrill of It All; (with Mel Brooks) albums The 2000 Year Old Man, The 2001 Year Old Man, The 2013 Year Old Man; exec. producer: film Heaven Help Us, 1976; dir. The Man with Two Brains, 1983. Served with AUS, 1942-46. Recipient greatest number of Emmys (11) of any individual. Office: care George Shapiro Shapiro-West 141 S El Camino Dr Beverly Hills CA 90212-2731

REINER, IRA, lawyer; b. L.A., 1936; m. Diane Wayne; children: Annie, Tommy. BS in Finance, USC; JD, Southwestern U. Former trial lawyer Office of L.A. City Atty.; contr. City of L.A., 1977, former city atty.; dist. atty. County of L.A., 1984—; named to L.A. City Fire Commn., 1973, elected to L.A. Community Coll.'s Bd. Trustees, 1975. Office: LA County Dist Atty's Office Rm 18-709 210 W Temple St Los Angeles CA 90012

REINER, ROB, actor, writer, director; b. N.Y.C., Mar. 6, 1947; s. Carl and Estelle (Lebost) R.; m. Penny Marshall, 1971 (div.), m. Michele Singer, May 19, 1989. Student, UCLA. Co-founder Castle Rock Entertainment, Beverly Hills, Calif. Actor: (TV series) All In The Family, 1971-78 (Emmy award 1974, 78), (TV movie) Thursday's Game, 1974, (films) Throw Momma From The Train, 1987, Postcards From The Edge, 1990, The Spirit of '76, 1990, Sleepless in Seattle, 1993, Bullets Over Broadway, 1994, Mixed Nuts, 1994, Bye Bye, Love, 1995, (theatre) The Roast, 1980; actor, writer (films): Halls of Anger, 1970, Where's Pappa?, 1970, Summertree, 1971, Fire Sale, 1971; actor, co-writer (films) Enter Laughing, 1967; actor, co-writer, prodr. (TV): More Than Friends, 1978, Million Dollar Infield, 1982; actor, co-writer, dir. This Is Spinal Tap, 1984; dir. The Sure Thing, 1985, Stand By Me, 1986; dir. prodr. The Princess Bride, 1987, When Harry Met Sally, 1989, Misery, 1990, A Few Good Men, 1992, North, 1994; co-creator: The Super, 1972. Mem. SAG, AFTRA, Dir. Guild Am., Writers Guild Am. Office: Castle Rock Entertainment 335 N Maple Dr Ste 135 Beverly Hills CA 90210-3867

REINERT, JAMES A., entomologist, educator; b. Enid, Okla., Jan. 26, 1944; s. Andrew J. and Emma Reinert; m. Anita Irwin; children: Travis J., Gina N., Mindy K., Melanie B., Gregory W., Teresa J. BS, Okla. State U., 1966; MS, Clemson U., 1968, PhD, 1970. Asst. state entomologist U. Md., College Park, 1970; asst. prof. entomology to prof. entomology Ft. Lauderdale Rsch. and Edn. Ctr., U. Fla., 1970-84; resident dir. and prof. entomology Rsch. and Ext. Ctr., Tex. A&M Univ. System, Dallas, 1984—. Contbr. over 275 articles to profl. jours. NDEA fellow, 1968; recipient Porter Henegar Meml. award., So. Nurserymen's Assn., 1982. Mem. Inter-Turfgrass Soc., Entomol. Soc. Am., Fla. Entomol. Soc. (v.p. 1983, pres. 1984, Entomologist of Yr. 1985), Fla. State Hort. Soc. (v.p. 1982), S.C. Entomol. Soc., Rsch. Ctr. Adminstrs. Soc. (v.p. 1994, state rep. 1991-92, sec. 1993), Dallas Agr. Club (bd. dirs. 1989, v.p. 1990, pres. 1991). Roman Catholic. Home: 3805 Covinton La Plano TX 75023-7731 Office: Tex A&M Univ Rsch and Ext Ctr 17360 Coit Rd Dallas TX 75252-6502

REINERT, NORBERT FREDERICK, patent lawyer, retired chemical company executive; b. Hamilton, Ohio, Apr. 12, 1928; s. Fred F. and Jennie A. R.; m. Ida Elizabeth Barickman, Jan. 26, 1956; children: Matthew W., Paul H. B.Ch.E., Ohio State U., 1951; LL.B., Cleve.-Marshall Law Sch., 1959. Bar: Ohio 1959, D.C. 1961. Patent agt. Standard of Ohio, Cleve., 1957-59; patent lawyer Standard of Ohio, 1959-60, E.I. duPont de Nemours & Co., Wilmington, Del., 1960-71; dir. investor relations E.I. duPont de Nemours & Co., 1981-84, mng. counsel, 1985-91; v.p., gen. counsel Endo Labs, Inc. subs. DuPont, Garden City, N.Y., 1971-73; exec. v.p. Endo Labs, Inc. subs. DuPont, 1973-77, pres., 1977-81; pvt. practice patent law, 1991—. Served with Chem. Corps AUS, 1955-56. Mem. Am. Patent Law Assn., Tau Beta Pi. Republican. Roman Catholic. Home: PO Box 311 Mendenhall PA 19357-0311

REINERT, PAUL CLARE, university chancellor emeritus; b. Boulder, Colo., Aug. 12, 1910; s. Francis John and Emma (Voegtle) R. A.B., St. Louis U., 1933, A.M., 1934; Ph.D., U. Chgo., 1944; LL.D. (hon.), St. Ambrose Coll., 1951, Xavier U., 1954, Washington U., 1955, Colo. Coll., 1956, Loyola U., 1957, U. Mo., 1957, John Carroll U., 1961, U. Notre Dame, 1964, St. Joseph's Coll., 1964; Ped.D. (hon.), Bradley U., 1956; L.H.D. (hon.), Manhattan Coll., 1963; Litt.D. (hon.), McKendree Coll., 1966, St. Norbert Coll., 1975; LL.D. (hon.), St. Anselm's Coll., 1967, Coll. Mt. St. Joseph of Ohio, 1970, Loyola U., New Orleans, 1973, So. Ill. U., 1973, Creighton U., 1976; L.H.D. (hon.), Lindenwood Colls., 1972, DePaul U., 1973, Carroll Coll., 1974, St. Francis Coll., 1974, Canisius Coll., 1975, Brandeis U., 1975, Wittenberg U., 1976, Ursuline Coll., 1976, U. Portland, 1977, Tarkio Coll., 1977; P.C.S. (hon.), Regis Coll., 1977; Ed.Adm.D. (hon.), Drury Coll., 1973, numerous others. Entered Soc. of Jesus, 1927, ordained priest, 1940; instr. classical langs. and English Creighton U. High Sch., Omaha, Nebr., 1934-37; instr. edn. and registrar St. Mary's Coll., St. Marys, Kan., 1938-41; prof. edn. St. Louis U., 1950—; dean St. Louis U. (Coll. Arts and Scis.), 1944-48, dir. summer sessions, 1944-48, v.p., 1948, pres., 1949-74, chancellor, 1974-90, chancellor emeritus, 1990—; chmn. St. Louis Edn. TV Commn., 1955-77; Mem. President's Com. Beyond High Sch., 1956-57; co-chmn. Mayor's Commn. Equal Employment Opportunities, 1963-65; mem. Pres. Nixon's Task Force on Edn., 1968-69; bd. dirs. St. Louis Civic Alliance for Housing, 1969-71. Author: The Urban Catholic University, 1970, To Turn the Tide, 1972. Bd. dirs. Assn. Am. Colls., 1970—, chmn., 1972; trustee Ednl. Testing Service, 1969—; bd. dirs. Midwest Research Inst., 1962—; pres. Midtown, Inc., 1972—; mem. Mo. Commn. for Humanities, 1975—; trustee Regis Coll.; bd. overseers St. Meinrad Coll. Mem. N. Central Assn. Colls. and Secondary Schs. (pres. 1956-57), Nat. Cath. Ednl. Assn. (pres. coll. and univ. dept. 1956-58, v.p. 1964-65, pres. 1968-70, exec. bd. 1956-65), Am. Council Edn. (dir. 1965-68), Assn. Urban Univs. (pres. 1950-51), Nat. Council Ind. Colls. and Univs. (pres. 1973), Cath. Commn. on Intellectual and Cultural Affairs, NEA, Assn. for Higher Edn., Ind. Colls. and Univs Mo. (pres. 1974), Jesuit Edn. Assn. (pres. 1960-70), Phi Beta Kappa, Phi Delta Kappa. Address: Saint Louis U 221 N Grand Blvd Saint Louis MO 63103

REINERTSEN, NORMAN, retired aircraft systems company executive; b. Bklyn., Mar. 27, 1934; s. Berthin and Malene Katherine (Dahl) R.; m. Elizabeth T. O'Shea, Aug. 30, 1958; children: Michael, Christopher, Katherine. BEE, CCNY, 1960; postgrad., Harvard U., 1982. Registered profl.

engr., Calif. Various positions Grumman Aerospace Corp., 1960-75; gen. mgr. Grumman Aerospace Corp. (Great River ops.), 1975-77; v.p. automotive Grumman Allied Industries, Melville, N.Y., 1977-83; sr. v.p. vehicle div. Grumman Allied Industries, 1983-94; sr. v.p. Olson Bodies, Inc., 1977-79; exec. v.p. Grumman Flexible, Delaware, Ohio, 1979-82; pres. Grumman Olson, Mellville, 1983-85; sr. v.p. Vehicle div. Grumman Allied, 1985-87; v.p. quality ops. Northrop Grumman, 1987-94; ret., 1994. With U.S. Army, 1955-57. Mem. Air Force Assn., Northport Yacht Club. Home: 7 Oleander Dr Northport NY 11768-3438

REINES, FREDERICK, physicist, educator; b. Paterson, N.J., Mar. 16, 1918; s. Israel and Gussie (Cohen) R.; m. Sylvia Samuels, Aug. 30, 1940; children: Robert G., Alisa K. M.E., Stevens Inst. Tech., 1939, M.S., 1941; Ph.D., NYU, 1944; D.Sc. (hon.), U. Witwatersrand, 1966; D. Engring. (hon.), Stevens Inst. Tech., 1984. Mem. staff Los Alamos Sci. Lab., 1944-59; group leader Los Alamos Sci. Lab. (Theoretical div.), 1945-59; dir. (AEC expts. on Eniwetok Atoll), 1951; prof. physics, head dept. Case Inst. Tech., 1959-66; prof. physics U. Calif., Irvine, 1966-88, dean phys. scis., 1966-74, Disting. prof. physics, 1987-88, prof. emeritus, 1988—; Centennial lectr. U. Md., 1956; Disting. Faculty lectr. U. Calif., Irvine, 1979; L.I. Schiff Meml. lectr. Stanford U., 1988; Albert Einstein Meml. lectr. Israel Acad. Scis. and Humanities, Jerusalem, 1988; Goudschmidt Meml. lectr., 1990; co-discoverer elementary nuclear particles, free antineutrino, 1956. Contbr. numerous articles to profl. jours.; contbg. author: Effects of Atomic Weapons, 1950. Mem. Cleve. Symphony Chorus, 1959-62. Recipient J. Robert Oppenheimer Meml. prize, 1981, Nat. Medal Sci., 1983, medal U. Calif., Irvine, 1987, Michelson Morley award, 1990; co-recipient Rossi prize Am. Astron. Soc., 1990; Guggenheim fellow, 1958-59, Sloan fellow, 1959-63, Franklin medal Franklin Inst., 1992. Fellow Am. Phys. Soc. (W.K.H. Panofsky prize 1992), AAAS; mem. NAS, Am. Assn. Physics Tchrs., Argonne U. Assn. (trustee 1965-66), Am. Acad. Arts and Scis., Russian Acad. Sci. (fgn. mem.), Phi Beta Kappa, Sigma Xi, Tau Beta Pi. Office: U Calif Dept Physics Campus Dr Irvine CA 92717

REINFELDS, JURIS, computer science educator; b. Riga, Latvia, Apr. 1, 1936; came to U.S., 1989; s. Nikolais Janis and Irma (Kaulins) R.; m. Lauma Petersons, Sept. 15, 1962; children: Peteris Maris, Ivars Valdis, Martins Nikolais. BSc, U. Adelaide, Australia, 1959; PhD, U. Adelaide, 1963. Postdoctoral fellow U. Edinburgh, Scotland, 1961-64; postdoctoral rsch. fellow U. Adelaide, Australia, 1964-65; NSF postdoctoral rsch. assoc. NASA, Huntsville, Ala., 1965-66; asst. prof. computer sci. U. Ga., Athens, 1966-72; vis. scientist CERN, Geneva, 1972-75; found. prof. computer sci. U. Wollongong NSW, Australia, 1975-89; prof. computer sci. N.Mex. State U., Las Cruces, 1989—; cons. Australian Internat. Devel. Program, Hat Yai, Thailand, 1983-91, Los Banos, Philippines, 1983-90. Mem. IEEE Computer Soc., Assn. for Computer Machinery, Australian Computer Soc., Las Cruces Rotary Club. Avocations: skiing, hiking. Office: N Mex State U Computer Sci Dept PO Box 30001 Las Cruces NM 88003-8001

REINGOLD, HAIM, mathematics educator; b. Lodz, Poland, Mar. 16, 1910; came to U.S., 1930, naturalized, 1942; s. Shmaryahu and Esther (Rudnianski) R.; m. Laah Jacobson, Apr. 16, 1942 (dec. Mar. 1964); children—Edward M., Arthur L.; m. Badonna Levinson, Nov. 16, 1966; 1 son, David A. Student, NYU, 1931; A.B., U. Cin., 1933, M.A., 1934, Ph.D. in Math, 1938. Teaching asst. U. Cin., 1936-38; head dept. math. Our Lady of Cin. Coll., 1938-42; supr. math. Ill. Inst. Tech., 1942-43, asst. prof., 1943-47, assoc. prof., 1947-56, prof., 1956-75, prof. emeritus, 1975—, chmn. dept. math., 1951-75; adj. prof. math. Ind. U. Northwest, 1975-82; vis. prof. Purdue U.-Calumet (Ind.), 1982-84; prof., chmn. dept. math. Mundelein Coll., 1984-91; sr. prof. Loyola U., Chgo., 1991. Author: (with Andres, Miser) Basic Mathematics for Engineers, 1944, Basic Mathematics for Science and Engineering, 1955. Mem. Am. Math. Soc., Math. Assn. Am., Am. Soc. Engring. Edn. (chmn. math. div. 1955-56, mem. council 1957-59), AAAS, Soc. Engring. Sci., Sigma Xi (chpt. pres. 1966-67). Jewish. Home: 1329 E 55th St Chicago IL 60615-5301

REINGOLD, NATHAN, historian; b. N.Y.C., Mar. 23, 1927; s. Benjamin and Fanny R.; m. Ida Hornstein, Jan. 1, 1955 (dec. 1988); children: Matthew H., Nicholas F.; m. Ellen Miles, Nov. 28, 1992. B.A., NYU, 1947, M.A., 1948; Ph.D., U. Pa., 1951. Staff mem. Nat. Archives, Washington, 1951-59; history of sci. specialist Library of Congress, Washington, 1959-66; editor Papers of Joseph Henry, Smithsonian Instn., Washington, 1966-85; sr. historian Nat. Mus. Am. History, 1985—, historian emeritus, 1993; vis. prof. Johns Hopkins U., 1993-95; adj. fellow Woodrow Wilson Internat. Ctr. for Scholars, 1975; planning com. program on knowledge in Am. soc. Am. Acad. Arts and Scis., 1970-83; com. on history applied math. in World War II, Math. Assn. Am., 1979; adv. bd. archives History Am. Psychology, 1970; mem. oversight com. for history and philosophy sci. program NSF, 1981; Allen lectr. history of math. Rensselaer Poly. Inst., 1981. Contbr. sects. to books, numerous articles to profl. jours. Editorial bd. Hist. Studies of Phys. Scis., 1968-79, N.Y. History, 1973-77; editorial adv. bd. Social Studies of Sci., 1974-80, Isis, 1971-75. Council mem. Rockefeller Archive Ctr., Rockefeller U., 1973-82, 85-91, spl. com. governing council, 1983-84; pres. commn. on documentation Internat. Union History and Philosophy of Sci., 1981; panel for history and philosophy sci. NSF, 1976-78. Recipient Centennial medal Nat. Acad. Scis., 1963. Sesquicentennial medal Coast and Geodetic Survey, 1956; scholar: N.Y. State Regents, 1945-47, NYU, 1945-48; sr. fellow Yale, 1960-61; research grantee Am. Philos. Soc., 1962-63, NSF, 1965-66, 67-72, NEH, 1973-78, Lounsbery Found., 1982-83. Mem. Society for Documentary Editing (dir. publs. 1980-81), Soc. for History Tech. (adv. council 1962-65), History Sci. Soc. (council 1964-67), Phi Beta Kappa (selection com. sci. book award 1966-69). Jewish. Club: Cosmos (Washington). Office: Nat Mus Am History Smithsonian Instn Washington DC 20560

REINHARD, CHRISTOPHER JOHN, merchant banking company executive; b. Bridgeport, Conn., Nov. 11, 1953; s. Warren John and Marian Louise (Dutter) R.; m. Maureen Francis, Sept. 24, 1977; 1 child, Griffin John. BS, Babson Coll., 1976, MBA, 1977. Sr. fin. analyst Gen. Motors Corp., Detroit and N.Y.C., 1977-81; asst. sec. Wheelabrator-Frye Inc., N.H., 1981-83; asst. sec., asst. treas. The Signal Cos., Inc., La Jolla, Calif., 1983-86; mng. dir., v.p. The Henley Group, Inc., La Jolla, 1986-90; mng. dir. Fisher Sci. Group, Inc., La Jolla, 1986-90; mng. dir., v.p. Wheelabrator Tech. Inc., Henley Mfg. Corp., 1987-90; founder, pres. Colony Group Inc., Rancho Santa Fe, 1990—, Reinhard Assocs., Rancho Santa Fe, 1991—; pres. Direct Feedback, Inc., 1990—, Dairy Queen Ventures, 1990—, Winsor Sport Fencing, 1993—; v.p., CFO Collateral Therapeutics Inc., 1995—; gen. ptnr. Cabrillo Ventures, 1995—. Mem. Boston Athenaeum, N.Y. Athletic Club, San Diego Polo Club, Rancho Santa Fe Polo Club, Duquesne Club. Office: 5414 Oberlin Dr Ste 251 San Diego CA 92121-4745

REINHARD, JAMES RICHARD, judge; b. Pollock, Mo., July 7, 1929; s. Virgil and Meltha (Anspach) R.; m. Shari L. Horton, Dec. 30, 1958; 1 child, James K. Student, N.E. Mo. State U., 1947-50; AB, U. Mo., 1951, JD, 1953. Bar: Mo. 1953. Prosecuting atty. Sullivan County (Mo.), 1955-57; prosecuting atty. Monroe County (Mo.), 1959-65; spl. asst. atty. gen. State of Mo., 1967-68; judge 10th Jud. Circuit, 1967-83; judge Mo. Ct. Appeals (ea. dist.), St. Louis, 1977—, chief judge, 1984-85; pvt. practice Milan, Mo., 1955-57, Paris, Mo., 1957-73. Bd. regents N.E. Mo. State U., Kirksville, 1965-73, pres., 1967-73. Sgt. U.S. Army, 1953-55. Mem. ABA, 10th Jud. Bar Assn. (pres. 1972), Mo. Bar Assn. (bd. govs. 1965-69), Met. Bar Assn. St. Louis, Lawyers Assn. St. Louis, Mo. Bd. Cert. Ct. Reporter Examiner (vice chmn. 1988-90), Mo. Press-Bar Commn. (chmn. 1990-94). Judicial Fin. Commn. (chmn. 1990-94). Home: 5 Hamlin Heights Dr Hannibal MO 63401-1903 Office: Mo Ct Appeals Ea Dist 111N N 7th St Saint Louis MO 63101-2133

REINHARD, KEITH LEON, advertising executive; b. Berne, Ind., Jan. 20, 1935; s. Herman L. and Agnes V. R.; m. Rose-Lee Simons, Nov. 7, 1976; children: Rachel, Elizabeth; children by previous marriage: Christopher, Timothy, Matthew, Geoffrey, Jacqueline. Student public schs., Berne. Comml. artist Kling Studios, Chgo., 1954-56; mgr. tech. communications dept. Magnavox Co., Ft. Wayne, Ind., 1957-60; creative/account exec. Biddle Co., Bloomington, Ill., 1961-63; exec. v.p., dir. creative services, pres. Needham, Harper & Steers, Inc., Chgo., from 1964; then chmn., chief exec. officer Needham, Harper & Steers/USA, Chgo.; also dir. Needham, Harper & Steers, Inc.; chmn., chief exec. officer DDB Needham Worldwide Inc.,

N.Y.C., 1986—, chmn. exec. com., 1989—. Episcopalian. Office: DDB Needham Worldwide Inc 437 Madison Ave New York NY 10022-7099

REINHARD, SISTER MARY MARTHE, educational organization administrator; b. McKeesport, Pa., Aug. 29, 1929; d. Regis C. and Leona (Reese) R. AB, Notre Dame Coll.; MA, U. Notre Dame. Asst. prin. Regina High Sch., Cleve., 1960-62, prin., 1963-64; prin. Notre Dame Acad., Chardon, Ohio, 1965-72; pres. Notre Dame Coll. of Ohio, Cleve., 1973-88; dir. devel. Sisters of Notre Dame Ednl. Ctr., Chardon, 1989—. Trustee, mem. exec. com. NCCJ, Cleve., 1987; bd. dirs. Centerior Energy; mem. coun. Geauga United Way Svcs., 1990—, vice chair fund raising, 1991; mem. adv. bd. Kent State U., Geauga campus, 1991-94. Recipient Fidelia award Notre Dame Coll., 1989, Woman of Yr. award 1990; Humanitarian award Cleve. chpt. NCCJ, 1990; named one of 100 most influential women in Cleve. Women's City Club, 1983, one of 79 most interesting people in Cleve. The Cleve. mag., 1979. Roman Catholic. Home and Office: 13000 Auburn Rd Chardon OH 44024-9331

REINHARD, PHILIP G., federal judge; b. LaSalle, Ill., Jan. 12, 1941; s. Godfrey and Ruth R.; married Virginia Reinhard; children: Bruce, Brian, David, Philip. BA, U. Ill., Champaign, 1962, JD, 1964. Asst. state atty. Winnebago County, 1964-67; atty. Hyer, Gill & Brown, 1967-68; state atty. Winnebago County, 1968-76; judge 17th Jud. Cir., 1976-80, Appellate Ct., 1980-92, U.S. Dist. Ct. (no. dist.) Ill., 1992—. Mem. Ill. Bar Assn., Winnebago County Bar Assn., Am. Acad. Judicial Edn. Office: US Courthouse 211 South Court St Rm 260 Rockford IL 61101

REINHARDT, DANIEL SARGENT, lawyer; b. Orange, N.J., Jan. 27, 1949; s. Warren Irwin and Winifred Ruth (Sargent) R.; m. Elizabeth Ann Johnson, June 11, 1982; 1 child, Meredith Alexandra. BA, Duke U., 1971; JD, Georgetown U., 1974. Bar: Ga. 1975, U.S. Dist. Ct. (no. dist.) Ga. 1975, U.S. Ct. Appeals (5th and 11th cirs.) 1981, U.S. Dist. Ct. (so. dist.) Ga. 1984, U.S. Dist. Ct. (mid. dist.) Ga. 1985, U.S. Ct. Appeals (4th cir.) 1985. From assoc. to ptnr. Troutman Sanders (and predecessor firms), Atlanta, 1974—; dep. asst. atty. gen. State of Ga., 1975-79; instr. trial techniques seminar Emory U., Atlanta, 1984-86, civil practice and procedure seminar Ga. State U., 1986—; arbitrator Fulton County (Ga.) Superior Ct. Mem. ABA, Ga. Bar Assn., Atlanta Bar Assn., Lawyers Club. Avocation: sports. Office: Troutman Sanders 5200 NationsBank Plz 600 Peachtree St Atlanta GA 30308-2216

REINHARDT, JAMES ALEC, rubber industry executive; b. Birmingham, Ala., Jan. 4, 1942; s. Jefferson C. and Marene D. (Edmondson) R.; m. Sandra Mary Jackson, June 8, 1968; children: Jeffrey Alec, David Lee. BSEE, U. Cin., 1965; JD, Ohio State U., 1968, MBA, 1979. Bar: Ohio 1968, U.S. Supreme Ct. 1975. Assoc. law firm A.D. Cennamo, Columbus, Ohio, 1967-69; sec., asst. gen. counsel White Motor Corp., Cleve., 1969-76; gen. counsel Cooper Tire & Rubber Co., Findlay, Ohio, 1976-83, sec., 1977-86, v.p., 1982-91, chief fin. officer, 1983—, exec. v.p., 1991—, also bd. dirs.; bd. dirs. Fifth Third Bank Northwestern Ohio, N.A., Toledo. Bd. dirs. Blanchard Valley Health Assn., Findlay. Mem. Ohio Bar Assn., Fin. Execs. Inst., Rotary (pres. Findlay club 1986-87). Avocations: racquetball, golf, sailing. Office: Cooper Tire & Rubber Co Lima And Western Ave Findlay OH 45840

REINHARDT, JOHN EDWARD, former international affairs specialist; b. Glade Spring, Va., Mar. 8, 1920; s. Edward Vinton and Alice (Miller) R.; m. Carolyn Lillian Daves, Sept. 2, 1947; children: Sharman W. Reinhardt Lancefield, Alice N. Reinhardt Jeffers, Carolyn C. Reinhardt Fenstermaker. A.B., Knoxville Coll., 1939; M.S., U. Wis., 1947, Ph.D., 1950. Prof. English Va. State Coll., Petersburg, 1950-56; cultural affairs officer USIS, Manila, 1956-58; dir. Am. Cultural Ctr., Kyoto, Japan, 1958-61; cultural attache USIS, Tehran, Iran, 1963-66; dep. asst. dir. Office East Asia and Pacific, USIA, Washington, 1966-68, 70-71, asst. dir. Office for Africa, 1968-70; ambassador to Nigeria, 1971-75, asst. sec. state for pub. affairs, 1975-77; dir. USIA, Washington, 1977-78, U.S. Internat. Communication Agy., Washington, 1978-81; acting dir. Smithsonian Mus. African Art, Washington, 1981-83; asst. sec. for history and art Smithsonian Instn., Washington, 1983-84; dir. directorate internat. activities Smithsonian Instn., 1984-87; prof. polit. sci. U. Vt., Burlington, 1987-90, prof. emeritus, 1990—. Served as officer AUS, 1942-46. Mem. MLA, Am. Fgn. Svc. Assn. (v.p. 1969-71). Methodist. Clubs: Cosmos, International (Washington).

REINHARDT, STEPHEN ROY, federal judge; b. N.Y.C., Mar. 27, 1931; s. Gottfried and Silvia (Hanlon) R.; children: Mark, Justin, Dana. B.A. cum laude, Pomona Coll., 1951; LL.B., Yale, 1954. Bar: Calif. 1958. Law clk. to U.S. Dist. Judge Luther W. Youngdahl, Washington, 1956-57; atty. O'Melveny & Myers, L.A., 1957-59; partner Fogel Julber Reinhardt Rothschild & Feldman (L.C.), L.A., 1980—; Mem. exec. com. Dem. Nat. Com., 1969-72, nat. Dem. committeeman for Calif., 1976-80; pres. L.A. Recreation an dParks Commn., 1974-75; mem. Coliseum Commn., 1974-75; mem. L.A. Police Commn., 1974-78, pres., 1978-80; sec., mem. exec. com. L.A. Olympic Organizing com., 1980-84; bd. dirs. Amateur Athletic Found. of L.A., 1984-92; adj. prof. Loyola Law Sch., L.A., 1988-90. Served to 1st lt. USAF, 1954-56. Mem. ABA (labor law coun. 1975-77).

REINHARDT, UWE ERNST, economist, educator; b. Osnabrueck, Germany, Sept. 24, 1937; came to U.S., 1964; s. Wilhelm and Edeltraut (Kehne) R.; m. Tsung-mei Cheng, May 25, 1968; children—Dirk, Kara, Mark. B.Comm. in Econs. with honors, U. Sask., Saskatoon, Can., 1964; M.A. in Econs., Yale U., 1965, M.Ph. in Econs., 1967, Ph.D., 1970; DSc (hon.), Med. Coll. of Pa., 1987, CUNY, 1994. Asst. prof. econs. and pub. affairs Princeton (N.J.) U., 1968-74, assoc. prof., 1974-79, prof., 1979—; James Madison prof. polit. economy, prof. econs., 1984—; bd. dirs. McAllister Holdings; trustee Tchrs. Ins. and Annuity Assn., 1978-93, H&Q Health Fund; cons. Urban Inst., Washington, 1971-75, HEW, 1974—, HHS, Math., Inc., Princeton, 1970-80, AT&T, Basking Ridge, N.J., 1976-82, Nat. Westminster Bank USA, N.Y.C., 1979—; mem. Nat. Leadership Commn. Health Care, 1986—; mem. U.S. Physicians' Payment Rev. Commn., U.S. Congress, 1986—; pres. Assn. for Health Svcs. Rsch., 1989-90, Found. Health Svcs. Rsch., 1990-91,. Author: Physician Productivity and the Demand for Health Manpower, 1975; mem. editorial bd. Health Affairs, 1982—, New Eng. Jour. Medicine, 1989-92, Health Mgmt. Quar., Health Policy and Edn., Jour. AMA, 1991—; assoc. editor Jour. Health Econs., 1980-85, mem. editorial bd., 1981-83; contbr. articles to profl. jours. bd. dirs. Nat. Acad. Aging, 1993—. Mem. Nat. Inst. Health Care Mgmt., Inst. Medicine Nat. Acad. Scis. (gov. council 1979-82). Office: Princeton U Princeton NJ 08540

REINHARDT, WILLIAM PARKER, chemical physicist, educator; b. San Francisco, May 22, 1942; s. William Oscar and Elizabeth Ellen (Parker) R.; m. Katrina Hawley Currens, Mar. 14, 1979; children: James William, Alexander Hawley. BS in Basic Chemistry, U. Calif., Berkeley, 1964; AM in Chemistry, Harvard U., 1966, PhD in Chem. Physics, 1968; MA (hon.), U. Pa., 1985. Instr. chemistry Harvard U., 1967-69, asst. prof. chemistry, 1969-72, assoc. prof., 1972-74; prof. U. Colo., Boulder, 1974-84, chmn. dept. chemistry, 1977-80; prof. chemistry U. Pa., Phila., 1984-91, chmn. dept., 1985-88, D. Michael Crow prof., 1987-91; prof. chemistry U.Wash., Seattle, 1991—, assoc. chmn. undergrad. program, 1993—; vis. fellow Joint Inst. for Lab. Astrophysics of Nat. Bur. Stds. and U. Colo., 1972, 74, fellow, 1974-84; dir. Telluride Summer Rsch. Ctr., 1986-89, treas., 1989—; mem. com. on atomic, molecular and optical scis. NRC, 1988-90; vis. scientist Nat. Inst. Stds. and Tech., summers 1993, 94. Editorial bd. Phys. Rev. A., 1979-81, Chem. Physics, 1985—, Jour. Chem. Physics, 1987-89, Jour. Physics B. (U.K.), 1992—, Internat. Jour. Quantum Chemistry, 1994—; researcher theoretical chem. physics, theoretical atomic and molecular physics for numerous publs. Recipient Camille and Henry Dreyfus Tchr. Scholar award, 1972; Alfred P. Sloan fellow, 1972; J.S. Guggenheim Meml. fellow, 1978; Coun. on Rsch. and Creative Work faculty fellow, 1984. Fellow AAAS, Am. Phys. Soc.; mem. Am. Chem. Soc., Phi Beta Kappa, Sigma Xi (nat. lectr. 1980-82), Phi Lambda Upsilon (Fresenius award 1977). Office: U Wash Dept Chemistry BG-10 Seattle WA 98195

REINHART, DIETRICH THOMAS, university president, history educator; b. Mpls., May 17, 1949; s. Donald Irving and Eleanor Therese (Noonan)

R. BA in History, St. John's U., Collegeville, Minn., 1971; AM in History, Brown U., 1976, PhD in History, 1984. Benedictine monk St. John's Abbey, 1971—; assoc. prof. history St. John's U., 1981—, dean of the coll., 1988-91, pres., 1991—; dir. liturgy St. John's Abbey, 1983-88. Bd. dirs. Minn. Pvt. Coll. Coun., 1991—; George A. MacPherson Fund, 1991—, Hill Monastic Manuscript Library, 1991—, Inst. for Ecumenical and Cultural Rsch., 1991—, First Am. Nat. Bank St. Cloud, 1992—; bd. overseers St. John's Prep. Sch., 1990—. Home: St John's Abbey Collegeville MN 56321 Office: St John's U Office of Pres Collegeville MN 56321

REINHART, KELLEE CONNELY, journalist; b. Kearney, Nebr., Dec. 15, 1951; d. Vaughn Eugene and Mary Jo (Mullen) Connely; m. Stephen Wayne Reinhart, June 15, 1974; children: Keegan Connely, Channing Mullen. B.A., U. Ala., 1972, M.S., 1974. Advt. copywriter Stas. WTBC-AM, WUOA-FM, 1970-72; asst. mgr. Ala. Press Assn., 1972-74; asst. to the editor Antique Monthly mag., 1974-75, mng. editor, 1975-77; editorial dir. Antique Monthly and Horizons mags., 1977-89; dir. univ. rels. U. Ala. System, Tuscaloosa, 1989—. Editor: Wild Birds of America: The Art of Basil Ede, 1991. Bd. dirs. Ala. Humanities Found. Recipient Druids Arts award, 1995. Mem. Soc. Profl. Journalists, Am. Soc. Mag. Editors, Newcomen Soc. U.S., Art Table. Office: 401 Queen City Ave Tuscaloosa AL 35401-1569

REINHART, MARY ANN, medical book executive; b. Jackson, Mich. Aug. 14, 1942; d. Herbert Martin and Josephine Marie (Keyes) Conway; m. David Lee Reinhart, Dec. 28, 1963; children: Stephen Paul, Michael David. MA, Mich. State U., 1983, PhD, 1985. Rsch. asst. Mich. State U., East Lansing, 1979-82, 85, teaching asst. dept psychology, 1982-84, asst. prof. Office Med. Edn. R&D, Coll. Human Medicine, 1985-88; assoc. exec. dir. Am. Bd. Emergency Medicine, East Lansing, 1988—; cons. Am. Bd. Emergency Medicine, 1985-88; chairperson collegewide evaluation com. Coll. Human Medicine, Mich. State U., East Lansing, 1985-88; adj. assoc. prof. Office Med. Edn. Rsch. and Devel., Coll. Human Medicine, 1988—. Reviewer Annals of Emergency Medicine, 1987—. Bd. dirs. Neahtawanta Rsch. and Edn. Ctr., Traverse City, Mich., 1991—. Mem. APA (divsn. indsl./orgnl. psychology, health psychology), AAAS, Phi Kappa Phi. Achievements include application of chart stimulated recall method of assessment in a national medical recertification examination; development and implementation of national longitudinal study of emergency physicians. Office: Am Bd Emergency Medicine 3000 Coolidge Rd East Lansing MI 48823-6319

REINHART, PETER SARGENT, corporate executive, lawyer; b. Mineola, N.Y., May 17, 1950; s. Charles Woodham and Martha Way (Sargent) R.; m. Susan Stockwell, Aug. 29, 1970 (div. Jan. 1976); 1 child, Amy Lynn; m. Gale McElroy, Oct. 16, 1976 (div. May 1985); 1 child, James Gharrett; m. Carol O. Gaffney, Jan. 4, 1992. BA, Franklin and Marshall Coll., 1971; JD, Rutgers U., 1975. Bar: N.J. 1975. Atty. Pillsbury and Russell, Atlantic Highlands, N.J., 1975-78; corp. counsel K. Hovnanian Enterprises, Inc., Red Bank, N.J., 1978-81, sr. v.p., gen. counsel, 1981—; also bd. dirs.; pres. Inst. Multi-Family Housing, Plainsboro, N.J., 1989—. Trustee, mem. editorial bd. Housing N.J. mag., 1991—. Trustee Community Assns. Inst., Arlington, Va., 1986-91; chpt., 1988; trustee Assn. for Children of N.J., Newark, 1988-93, Keep Middlesex Moving, New Brunswick, 1990-93, Bayshore Community Hosp., Holmdel, N.J., 1992—, v.p., 1995; pres. Greater Red Bank Jaycees, 1978-79; v.p. Monmouth coun. Boy Scouts Am., Oakhurst, N.J., 1987-94, pres., 1994—; v.p. Garden State Games, Edison, N.J., 1991-94; mem. Coun. Affordable Housing, Trenton, N.J., 1993—. Named to community Assns. Inst. Hall of Fame, 1988; named Jaycee of Yr. Greater Red Bank Jaycees, 1977. Mem. N.J. State Bar Assn., N.J. Shore Builders Assn. (pres. 1989-90), Ea. Monmouth C. of C. (trustee 1992—), Nat. Assn. Indsl. and Office Parks (bd. dirs. 1990-92, Builder of Yr. 1987, Hall of Fame 1991), N.J. Builders Assn. (v.p. 1992-94, pres. 1995—), Atlantic Highlands Rep. Club (pres. 1978), Shore Athletic Club (Oakhurst, N.J.). Avocations: road racing, marathon running. Home: 2 Bayhill Rd Leonardo NJ 07737-1801 Office: Hovnanian Enterprises Inc 10 Hwy 35 PO Box 500 Red Bank NJ 07701

REINHART, ROBERT ROUNTREE, JR., lawyer; b. Chgo., Oct. 21, 1947; s. Robert Rountree and Ruth (Duncan) R.; m. Elizabeth Aileen Plews, July 26, 1969; children: Andrea Jean, Jessica Elizabeth, Rebecca Jill. BA, Northwestern U., 1968; JD, U. Mich., 1971. Bar: Ill. 1971, Mich. 1972, Minn. 1973, U.S. Supreme Ct. 1976. Law clk. to judge U.S. Dist. Ct. (we. dist.) Mich., Grand Rapids, 1971-73; assoc. Oppenheimer Wolff & Donnelly, Mpls., 1973-77, ptnr., 1978—, chair labor and employment bus. group, 1985-92; co-chair Upper Midwest Employment Law Inst., Mpls., 1984—. Mem. ABA (labor and employment, civil litigation sects.), Minn. Bar Assn. Office: Oppenheimer Wolff & Donnelly 3400 Plz VII 45 S 7th St Minneapolis MN 55402-1609

REINHARZ, JEHUDA, university president, history educator; b. Haifa, Israel, Aug. 1, 1944; came to U.S., 1961; s. Fred and Anita (Weigler) R.; m. Shulamit Rothschild, Nov. 26, 1967; children—Yael, Naomi. B.S., Columbia U., 1967; B.R.E., Jewish Theol. Sem., 1967; M.A., Harvard U., 1968; Ph.D., Brandeis U., 1972; LHD, Hebrew Union Coll., 1995. Prof. modern Jewish history U. Mich., Ann Arbor, 1972-82; Richard Koret prof. modern Jewish history Brandeis U., Waltham, Mass., 1982—; dir. Tauber Inst. Study of European Jewry, 1984-94; provost, sr. v.p. for acad. affairs Brandeis U., Waltham, Mass., 1992-94; pres. Brandeis U., Waltham, Mass., 1994—; mem. internat. acad. bd. Annenberg Rsch. Inst., 1986-90; bd. dirs. Yad Chaim Weizmann, 1990—; pres. Israel Prize, 1990. Author: Fatherland or Promised Land: The Dilemma of the German Jew 1893-1914, 1975, Chaim Weizmann: The Making of a Zionist Leader, 1985 (Present Tense Literary award 1985, Kenneth B. Smilen Literary award 1985, Nat. Jewish Book award 1986, Shazar prize in history Israel, 1988), (in Hebrew) Hashomer Hazair in Germany, 1931-39, 1989, Chaim Weizmann: The Making of a Statesman, 1993 (Nat. Jewish Book award, 1994); also numerous articles in French, German, Hebrew and English; gen. editor: Studies in Jewish History, 1984, European Jewish History, 1985; co-editor: The Jew in the Modern World, 1980, 2d edit. 1995, Mystics Philosophers and Politicians, 1982, Israel in the Middle East 1948-83, 1984, The Jewish Response to German Culture, 1985, The Jews of Poland Between Two World Wars, 1989, The Impact of Western Nationalisms, 1992, Zionism and Religion, Hebrew edit., 1994; editor: The Letters and Papers of Chaim Weizmann, 1918-20, 1977, Dokumente zur Geschichte des deutschen Zionismus, 1882-1933, 1981, Living with Antisemitism, 1987. Bd. govs. United Israel Appeal/Jewish Agy., 1994; mem. bd. dir., exec. com. Am. Joint Distbn. Com., 1994; mem. acad. com. U.S. Holocaust Mus., 1990—. Fellow Leo Baeck Inst., Royal Hist. Soc., Am. Acad. Jewish Rsch., Am. Acad. of Arts and Scis.; mem. Yad Vashem Soc. (adv. bd. 1983), Nat. Coun. Shazar Ctr., Assn. for Jewish Studies (sec. 1986-88, treas./sec. 1988-94). Home: 36 Westfield Rd Newton MA 02165-2563 Office: Brandeis U Waltham MA 02254

REINHERZ, HELEN ZARSKY, social services educator; b. Boston, Aug. 4, 1923; d. Zachary and Anna (Cohen) Zarsky; m. Samuel E. Reinherz, Aug. 29, 1943; 1 son, Ellis. A.B. magna cum laude, Wheaton Coll., 1944; M.S., Simmons Coll., 1946; S.M., Harvard U., 1962, Sc.D., 1965. Social worker Newton Family Service, Mass., 1946-49, Mass. Gen. Hosp., Boston, 1949-51; supr. psychiat. social work State Hosp., Waltham, Mass., 1958-61; faculty mem. Simmons coll., Boston, 1965—; prof. methods research, 1972—; dir. research Sch. Social Work, 1968—; dir. PhD program, 1993—; prin. investigator Identifying Children at Risk, 1976-84, Adaption in Adolescence, 1987-93, Early Adulthood Rsch. Project, 1993—; rsch. cons. Dept. Mental Health, 1970-80; prin. investigator Study Adolescent Drug Abuse, 1971-73; chmn. Gov.'s Adv. Coun. on Mental Health and Retardation, 1972; mem. adv. com. Mental Health Manpower to Fed. Govt., 1980-82. Author: (with H. Wechler, D. Dobbins) Social Work Research in the Human Services, 1976, (with M. Heywood, J. Camp) A Community Response to Drug Abuse, 1976; cons., assoc. editor: Jour. Prevention, 1980-91; mem. fed. adv. com. Rsch. in Prevention Rev., 1984-87; editorial bd. Jour. Early Adolescence; contbr. 55 articles to profl. jours. Recipient Maida H. Solomon award Simmons Coll. Alumni, 1961; NIH tng. fellow, 1961-65; Grant Found. grantee, 1963; Med. Found. grantee, 1967-69; NIMH grantee, 1975-84, 87—. Fellow Am. Orthopsychiat. Assn.; mem. Acad. Cert. Social Workers, Am. Pub. Health Assn., Council Social Work Edn., Harvard Sch. Pub. Health Alumni Assn. (sec.-treas. 1965-68), Phi Beta Kappa, Delta Omega. Home:

17 Corey Rd Malden MA 02148-1116 Office: Simmons Sch Social Work 51 Commonwealth Ave Boston MA 02116-2307 *As a teacher and researcher my efforts have been directed towards encouraging students to formulate the right questions about human problems as a first step to understanding and change.*

REINHOLD, JUDGE (EDWARD ERNEST REINHOLD, JR.), actor; b. Wilmington, Del.. Student, Mary Washington Coll., N.C. Sch. of the Arts. Actor: (feature films) Running Scared, 1979, Stripes, 1981, Thursday the Twelfth, 1982, Pandemonium, 1982, Fast Times at Ridgemont High, 1982, Gremlins, 1984, Beverly Hills Cop, 1984, Roadhouse, 1985, Ruthless People, 1986, Head Office, 1986, Off Beat, 1986, Beverly Hills Cop II, 1987, Vice-Versa, 1988, Rosalee Goes Shopping, 1990, Daddy's Dyin'...Who's Got the Will, 1990, Zandalee, 1991, Beverly Hills Cop III, 1994, The Santa Clause, 1994; (TV episodes) Wonder Woman, Magnum P.I., Seinfeld, 1993 (Emmy nomination, Guest Actor - Comedy Series, 1994); (TV movies) The Survival of Dana, 1979, Brothers and Sisters, A Step Too Slow, The Wilmar Eight, Booker, Promised a Miracle. Mem. Screen Actors Guild, AFTRA. Office: care ICM 8942 Wilshire Blvd Beverly Hills CA 90211*

REINHOLD, RICHARD LAWRENCE, lawyer; b. Buffalo, Feb. 24, 1951; s. Richard J. and Ann J. R.; m. Beth Stacey Grossman, May 11, 1991; 1 child: Elizabeth Jane. AB, Cornell U., 1973; JD, SUNY, Buffalo, 1976. Bar: N.Y. 1977, Fla. 1977. Assoc. Hodgson, Russ, Andrews, Woods & Goodyear, Buffalo, 1976-81; with office of tax legis. counsel U.S. Dept. Treasury, Washington, 1982-84; ptnr. Cahill Gordon & Reindel, N.Y.C., 1985—. Contbr. articles to profl. jours. Mem. N.Y. State Bar Assn. (1st vice chair, mem. exec. com. tax sect. 1987—), Internat. Fiscal Assn., Tax Club. Office: Cahill Gordon & Reindel 80 Pine St New York NY 10005-1701

REINHORN, ANDREI M., civil engineering educator, consultant; b. Bucharest, Romania, Oct. 23, 1945; s. Moritz A. and Dina (Rosenfeld) R.; m. Tova A. Waldman, Oct. 15, 1968; children: Michael, Gad. BSc, Technion - Israel Inst. Tech., Haifa, 1968, DSc, 1978. Registered profl. engr., N.Y., Israel. Structural engr. Milstein & Singer, Cons. Engrs., Tel Aviv, 1972-73; structural engr. Haifa, 1973-79, Buffalo, 1980-85; vis. asst. prof. SUNY, Buffalo, 1979-81, asst. prof., 1981-86, assoc. prof., 1986-90, prof., 1990—; cons. Niagara Machine & Tolls, Buffalo, 1982—, WSF Industries, Buffalo, 1983—, Walt Disney World, Lake Buenavista, Fla., 1986, Westinghouse, 1987-89, West Valley Nuclear Site, 1989, Princeton U., 1992, LeMessurier Cons., 1992, Dames & Moore, 1990-92, County of Los Angeles, 1993; investigator at Nat. Ctr. Earthquake Engring. Rsch. Inventor, patentee press brake deflection compensation structure, automatic diagnostic sys. for elec. cir. breakers; contbr. over 250 articles to profl. jours., chpts. to books and conf. procs. Pres. W.E.S.T. Age Group Swim Club, Buffalo, 1985. Served to capt. Israel Def. Force, 1968-72. Rsch. grantee NSF, 1983—, 86—, Nalge/Snyder Industries, 1987. Fellow ASCE (faculty advisor 1981-83, bd. dirs. 1986—, pres. Buffalo sect. 1993-94, Outstanding Svc. award 1982, 83); mem. N.Y. State Profl. Engring. Assn. (Engring. Educator of Yr. award 1991, Hist. Achievement award, 1995), Am. Concrete Inst., Earthquake Engring. Rsch. Inst., NCEER. Avocations: photography, skiing, bicycling. Home: 12 Troy View Ln Buffalo NY 14221-3522 Office: SUNY Buffalo Dept Civil Engring 231 Ketter Hall Amherst NY 14260

REINING, BETH LAVERNE (BETTY REINING), public relations consultant, journalist; b. Fargo, N.D.; d. George and Grace (Twiford) Reimche; student N.D. State Coll., U. Minn., Glendale Community Coll., Calif. State Coll., Carson; 1 dau., Carolyn Ray Toohey Hiett; m. Jack Warren Reining, Oct. 3, 1976 (div. 1984). Originated self-worth seminars in Phoenix, 1970-76; owner Janzik Pub. Relations, 1971-76; talk show reporter-hostess What's Happening in Ariz., Sta. KPAZ-TV, 1970-73; writer syndicated column People Want to Know, Today newspaper, Phoenix, 1973; owner JB Communications, Phoenix, 1976-84; owner, pres. Media Communications, 1984—; freelance writer; tchr. How to Weigh Your Self-Worth courses Phoenix Coll., Rio Solado Community Coll., Phoenix, 1976-84; instr. pub. rels. Scottsdale (Ariz.) Community Coll., 1987; muralist, works include 25 figures in med. office. Founder Ariz. Call-A-Teen Youth Resources, Inc., pres., 1975-76, v.p., 1976-77, now bd. dirs. Recipient awards including 1st pl. in TV writing Nat. Fedn. Press Women, 1971-88, numerous state awards in journalism Ariz. Press Women, 1971-76, Good Citizen award Builders of Greater Ariz., 1961. Mem. Ariz. Press Women (1st place award 1988), No. Ariz. Press Women (pres. 1983), Nat. Fedn. Am. Press Women, Pub. Relations Soc. Am., Phoenix Pub. Relations Soc., Nat. Acad. TV Arts and Scis., Phoenix Valley of Sun Convention Bur., Verde Valley C. of C. (bd. dirs., tourism chmn. 1986-87, Best Chair of Yr. award 1986), Phoenix Metro C. of C. Cottonwood C. of C. (chmn. of Yr. award, 1986). Inventor stocking-tension twist footlet, 1962. Club: Phoenix Press. Office: PO Box 10509 Phoenix AZ 85064-0509

REINING, PRISCILLA COPELAND, anthropologist; b. Chgo., Mar. 11, 1923; d. Kenneth Bayard and Mary Elsie (Weser) Copeland; m. Conrad Copeland Reining, June 26, 1944 (dec. Oct. 1984); children: Robert Cushman, Anne Elizabeth, Conrad Copeland Schilling. AB, U. Chgo., 1945, AM, 1949, PhD, 1967. Lectr. U. Minn., Mpls., 1956-60, Howard U., Washington, 1960-65; rsch. assoc. Cath. U. Am., Washington, 1966-68; assoc. Smithsonian Instn., Washington, 1966, 68, 70; cons. The World Bank, 1972, USAID, 1973; cons. AAAS, Washington, 1971-73, project dir., 1974-81, program dir., 1982-90; vis. prof. African Studies U. Fla., Gainesville, 1994—; mem. bd. on sci. and tech. for internat. devel. NAS, Washington, 1976-80; mem. arid ecosys. interation Internat. Geosphere/Biosphere Program, Boulder, 1989—; mem. adv. bd. Population and Environ., N.Y.C., 1990—; bd. dirs. Renewable Natural Resources Found., Bethesda, Md., 1991—; mem. U.S. del. UN Conf. on Desertification, Nairobi, Kenya, 1977. Author: Challenging Desertification, 1980; author, editor: Village Women, 1977; editor: Village Viability, 1980, Resource Inventory, 1984. Mem. Peace Commn. Washington Cathedral, 1986-91. Grantee NIMH, 1966, NSF, 1967, Nat. Geographic Soc. Com. for Rsch. and Exploration, 1994. Fellow AAAS (sec. 1978-89), Am. Anthrop. Assn. (task force on AIDS, task force on environ., Disting. Svc. award 1990), African Studies Assn. (bd. dirs. 1978-80); mem. Anthrop. Soc. Washington (pres. 1976-77), Soc. Women Geographers. Home: 3601 Rittenhouse St NW Washington DC 20015-2413

REININGHAUS, RUTH, artist; b. N.Y.C., Oct. 4, 1922; d. Emil William and Pauline Rosa (Lazarik) R.; m. George H. Morales, Feb. 20, 1944; children: George James, Robert Charles; m. Allan Joseph Smith, May 28, 1960. Student, Hunter Coll., NYU, Nat. Acad. Sch. of Design, 1960-61, Frank Reilly Sch. of Art, 1963, Art Students League, 1968. Instr. art Banker's Trust, N.Y.C., 1971-77, 79—, Kittredge Club for Women, N.Y.C. Exhibited in group shows at Berkshire Art Mus., 1970s, Hammer Galleries, Inc., N.Y.C., 1974, Far Gallery, N.Y.C., 1974, Mufalli Gallery, N.Y. and Fla., 1983-90, Pen and Brush Club, 1985—, Petrucci Gallery, Saugerties, N.Y., 1984-90, Pastel Soc. Am., 1988—, John Lane Gallery, Rhinebeck, N.Y., 1992—, Regianni Gallery, N.Y.C., 1994, Catherine Lorillard Wolfe Club, Salmagundi Club, Allied Arts Am., Heidi Nehwoff Gallery, N.Y.C., Hudson Valley Art Assn., Knickerbocker Artists, N.Y.C., others. Recipient Robert Lehman award, 1960s, 3d prize in oils Murray Hill Art Show, 1968, Coun. Am. Artists award, 1985, Internat. award Oil Pastel Assn., 1987; scholar Nat. Acad., 1962, Frank Reilly Sch. Art, 1963, NYU, 1968; subject NBC TV show You Are an Artist, 1950s. Fellow Am. Artists Profl. League (Claude Parsons Meml. award 1974), Hudson Valley Art Assn.; mem. Pastel Soc. Am. (bd. dirs. 1988-90, J. Giffuni purchase award 1988, Flora B. Giffuni pres.' award 1990), Allied Artists Am. (assoc.), Soc. Illustrators (hon. 1983-87), Nat. Arts Club, Reciprocal, Artists Fellowship, Washington Sq. Outdoor Art Assn. (bd. dirs. 1983-90, Talens award 1963, Richtone Artists award 1968), Salmagundi Club N.Y. (pres. 1983-87, curator 1989—, Baker Brush award 1969, scholar 1969, Philip Isenberg award 1974, 89, 90, 92, 95, hon. mention 1983, 84, Salmagundi Club prize 1985, Franklin B. Williams Fund prize 1987, Tom Picard award 1987, Mortimer E. Freehof award 1988, John N. Lewis award 1988, Salmagundi Club medal of honor 1989, John N. Lewis award 1989, Samuel T. Shaw award 1990, Thomas Moran award 1990, Helen S. Coes award 1990, hon. mention 1991, Alice B. McReynolds award 1991, Salmagundi award 1991, Alphaeus Cole Meml. award 1991), Catharine Lorillard Wolfe Art Club (bd. dirs. 1987—, Anna Hyatt Huntington award 1978), Coun. Am. Artists (award 1985, hon. mention 1991, Catharine Lorillard Wolfe award for pastel 1992, cash award

1993), Pen and Brush Club (Helen Slotman award 1986, OPA Internat. award 1987, Gene Alden Walker award 1988, Pen and Brush Solo award 1992, hon. mention 1991), Knickerbocker Artists (Flora B. Giffuni PSA Pres.' award 1990), Oil Pastel Assn. (Pen and Brush award 1987, Strathmore award 1989, Salmagundi Club award 1991), Am. Artists Profl. League (Claude Parson's Meml. award 1974, 2nd prize in oils 1992, 3d prize oils 1993, Pres. award 1994), Alpha Delta Pi. Lutheran. Avocations: travel, tech. illustration, oil and pastel painting, collecting antique music boxes and watches. Home: 222 E 93d St Apt 26A New York NY 10128

REINISCH, BODO WALTER, electrical engineering educator; b. Beuthen, Germany, Nov. 26, 1936; came to U.S., 1965; s. Kurt and Alice Ada (Walleiser) R.; m. Gerda Seidenschwand, June 1, 1963; children: Karin, Ulrike. MS, U. Freiburg, Germany, 1963; PhD, Lowell Tech. Inst., 1970. Rsch. asst. Ionosphären Inst., Breisach, Germany, 1961-63, physicist, 1963-65; physicist Lowell (Mass.) Tech. Inst., 1965-75; dir. Ctr. for Atmospheric Rsch. U. Mass., Lowell, 1975—, assoc. prof. elec. engring., 1980-83, prof., 1983—, dept. head, 1988—; cons. Royal Meteorol. Inst., Brussels, 1970-71; guest prof. physics U. Linz Austria, 1978-79. Contbr. over 100 articles to Radio Sci., Jour. Geophys. Rsch., Advances of Space Rsch., others. Mem. sch. com. German Saturday Sch., Boston, 1977—. Grantee USAF, NASA, NSF, others; awarded Bundesverdienstkreuz by Pres. of Germany, 1987; Univ. Prof. U. Mass., Lowell, 1987-90; recipient Outstanding Achievement award U. Mass., Lowell, 1986, 87, 88. Sr. mem. IEEE; mem. Am. Geophys. Union, Internat. Union Radio Sci. (chmn. working group G3 on ionospheric informatics, exec. com. commn. G, mem. COSPAR/URSI Task Force on Internat. Reference Ionosphere), Sigma Pi Sigma. Achievements include development of global network of "digisonde" sounders; established HF Doppler observations for ionospheric drift studies; 2 patents. Office: U Mass Lowell Ctr Atmosphere Rsch 450 Aiken St Lowell MA 01854-3602

REINISCH, JUNE MACHOVER, psychologist, educator; b. N.Y.C., Feb. 2, 1943; d. Mann Barnett and Lillian (Machover) R. BS cum laude, NYU, 1966; MA, Columbia U., 1970, PhD with distinction, 1976. Assoc. prof. psychology Rutgers U., New Brunswick, N.J., 1980-82, adj. assoc. prof., 1981-82; prof. psychology Ind. U., Bloomington, 1982-93, dir. Kinsey Inst. Rsch. in Sex, Gender, and Reprodn., 1982-93; prof. clin. psychology Sch. Medicine, Bloomington, 1983-93; treas., dir. emeritus Kinsey Inst., 1993—; dir., prin. investigator Prenatal Devel. Projects, Copenhagen, 1976—, sr. rsch. fellow, trustee The Kinsey Inst., 1993—; pres. R2 Sci. Comms., Inc., Ind., N.Y., 1985—; vis. sr. researcher Inst. for Preventative Medicine, Copenhagen Health Svcs., Kommunehospitalet, Copenhagen, 1994—, com. SUNY. Author: The Kinsey Institute New Report on Sex, 1990, 94, pub. 8 fgn. edits.; editor books Kinsey Inst. series; syndicated newspaper columnist: The Kinsey Report; contbr. rsch. reports, revs., articles to profl. jours.; appeared on TV shows including PBS, Discovery, Oprah Winfrey, Sally Jessy Rafael, Good Morning Am., Today Show, CBS This Morning; guest host TV shows including CNBC Real Personal, Talk Live, also fgn. appearances. Founders Day scholar NYU, 1966; NIMH trainee, 1971-74; grantee NIMH, 1978-80, Ford Found., 1973-75, Nat. Inst.- Drug, 1973-74, Nat. Inst. Child Health and Human Devel., 1981-88, Nat. Inst. on Drug Abuse, 1989-95; recipient Morton Prince award Am. Psychopath. Assn., 1976, Silver medal for 9th Dr. S.T. Huang-Chan Meml. Lectr., Hong Kong U., Dr. Richard J. Cross award Robert Wood Johnson Med. Sch., 1991, award First Internat. Conf. on Orgasm, New Delhi, 1991, Disting. Alumnae award Teachers Coll. Columbia U., 1992. Fellow AAAS, APA, Am. Psychol. Soc., Soc. for Sci. Study Sex; mem. Internat. Acad. Sex Rsch. (charter), Internat. Soc. Psychoneuroendocrinology, Internat. Soc. Rsch. Aggression, Internat. Soc. Devel. Psychobiology, Am. Assn. Sex. Educators, Counselors and Therapists, Sigma Xi. Office: SUNY-HSCB PB2 PBL Box 120 450 Clarkson Ave Brooklyn NY 11203-2012 also: The Kinsey Inst Prenatal Devel Project Ind U Bloomington IN 47405

REINKE, DORIS MARIE, retired elementary education educator; b. Racine, Wis., Jan. 12, 1922; d. Otto William Reinke and Louise Amelia Goehring. BS, U. Wis., Milw., 1943; MS, U. Wis., Whitewater, 1967. Tchr. kindergarten Elkhorn (Wis.) Area Sch. System, 1943-69, bldg. prin., 1968-70, summer sch. dir., 1974-75, grade 2 tchr., 1970-84, primary dept. chmn., 1971-84, administrv. asst., supervising tchr., 1957-83, student tchr., 1984, ret., 1984; oriented experience tchr. Program Area Sch. System, Elkhorn, 1966; pres. Elkhorn Edn. Assn., 1949-50; rep. dist. State Kindergarten Conf., Oshkosh, Wis., 1966; participant early edn. conf. State Early Edn. Conf., Eagle River, Wis., 1968. Columnist Mature Life Styles newspaper; monthly columnist Beacon, 1994—; contbr. weekly newspaper column Webster Notes, 1989; Walworth County Diary Monthly column in The Week, 1991—; author Doris' Corner newsletter Walworth County Geneal. Soc., 1992—. Bd. dirs. Food Pantry, Elkhorn, 1985-88, RSVP Vol. Food Pantry, Elkhorn, 1985-95; del. dist. constn. conv. Evang. Luth. Ch. Am., Beloit, Wis., 1987; com. mem. Luth. Ch., Elkhorn, 1987; chm. sch. centennial, Elkhorn, 1987; mem. Elkhorn Hist. Preservation Com., 1991—; archivist Sugar Creek Luth. Ch., 1992—. Recipient Wis. Edn. Research, West Bend, Wis., 1966, Outstanding Elem. Tchrs., Wash., 1973, Wis. Dept. Edn., Madison, 1980, Local History award State Hist. Soc. Wis., 1993. Mem. Nat. Ret. Tchrs. Assn., Walworth County Ret. Tchrs. Assn. (v.p. 1988, pres. 1991), Walworth County Hist. Soc. (treas. 1985-89, v.p. 1990-91, pres. 1991-95), Walworth County Geneal Soc. (bd. dirs. 1991-92), Alpha Delta Kappa (state pres. 1968-70, 76-78). Avocations: reading, baseball, bird watching, traveling. Home: 516 N Wisconsin St Elkhorn WI 53121-1119

REINKE, JOHN HENRY, clergyman, educational administrator; b. Covington, Ky., Sept. 14, 1915; s. Henry Tilden and Helena (Ungeheuer) R. B.A., Loyola U. 1937, M.A., 1942, postgrad., 1947-54; postgrad., UCLA, 1948-49. Ordained priest Roman Cath. Ch., 1945; instr. psychology Loyola U., Chgo., 1947-54, vice chancellor, 1975-76, chancellor, 1976—; instr. psychology Xavier U., Cin., 1954-56, asst. prof., 1956-59; dir. guidance Loyola Acad., Wilmette, Ill., 1959-60, headmaster, 1960-65, pres. 1965-75; instr. music therapy Ind. U., Bloomington, summers 1958-60; trustee Regis Coll., Denver, 1973—, Xavier U., 1973—, Hadley Sch. for Blind, Winnetka, 1971—; chancellor emeritus Loyola U. of Chgo., 1993—. Mem. Nat. Cath. Ednl. Assn., Nat. Sch. Public Relations Assn., Conf. Religious Dirs. Edn., Chgo. Art Inst., Field Mus., Nat. Assn. Ind. Schs., Jesuit Adminstrs. Assn., Nat. Cath. Guidance Conf. Clubs: Mid-Am, Internat, Plaza. Lodge: K.C. 1st U.S. priest to appear as soloist with maj. symphony orch., Cin., 1956, 57, 60. Office: Loyola U 820 N Michigan Ave Chicago IL 60611-2103

REINKE, LEONARD HERMAN, architect; b. Oshkosh, Wis., June 25, 1918; s. Leonard and Helen (Diestler) R.; m. Lucille Francis Fenn, Nov. 14, 1942; children—Ann Elizabeth, Mary Ellen, Joan Elaine. Student, U. Wis.-Oshkosh, 1936; B. in Architecture, Ill. Inst. Tech., 1941. Registered architect, Wis. Analyst Nat. Def. Research Commn., Princeton, N.J., 1943; architect designer Auler Irion Wertsch, Inc., Oshkosh, 1945-51; ptnr. T.H. Irion, AIA, L.H. Reinke, AIA, Oshkosh, 1951-69; sec., pres. Irion, Reinke & Assocs., Inc., Oshkosh, 1969-77; pres. Reinke, Hansche, Last, Inc., Oshkosh, 1978-89; pres. Nicolet Anchorage, Inc., Oshkosh, 1962-89. Architect: (library) Albertson Ctr., 1971 (Wis. AIA honor award), Polk Library, 1970; architectural designer Dartford Motor Inn, 1957(Wis. AIA honor award). Meml. Indsl. Devel. Com., Oshkosh, 1965-68, Riverfront Beautification Com., 1969-71, Parks Adv. Coun., 1972-76; bd. dirs. Paine Art Ctr. and Arboretum, Oshkosh, 1976-84, Oshkosh chpt. 2000 Assocs., 1988—; chmn. Oshkosh chpt. Svc. Corps Ret. Execs., 1992, 93, 94. Served with USAAF, 1944-45, ETO. Fellow AIA; mem. Wis. Soc. Architects (dir. 1959-63, 71-72, pres. 1964, Golden award 1991), Wis. Architects Found. (dir. 1978-84, pres. 1983-84). Republican. Presbyterian. Lodge: Rotary (dir. 1962-65). Avocations: cross county skiing, woodworking, travel, tree farming. Home: 937 Windward Ct Oshkosh WI 54901-2061

REINKE, RALPH LOUIS, retired academic administrator; b. Elmhurst, Ill., June 22, 1927; s. Louis Fred and Malinda Marie (Beckmann) R.; m. Lois Hermine Borneman, Aug. 28, 1948 (dec. Mar. 1984); children: Janice Reinke Eisenloeffell, Stephan, Sharon Reinke Holaway; m. Carole Louise Rediehs, June 14, 1986. Student, U. Ill. 1945-46; BS, Concordia Tchrs. Coll., River Forest, Ill., 1949; MA, Northwestern U., 1952; postgrad., U. Chgo., 1956-63; LittD, Concordia Sem., 1972. Prin. St. John Elem. Sch., Houston, 1949-56; assoc. prof. psychology and edn. Concordia U., River Forest, 1956-68; pres., chief exec. officer Concordia Pub. House, St. Louis, 1968-86; pres. Concordia Coll., Seward, Nebr., 1986-90; ret., 1990. Author: Christian Spelling Series,

2d edit, 1971. Mem. sch. bd. selecting com., Oak Park, Ill., 1965-67, chmn. lit. commn. Mo. Synod Luth. Ch., 1967-69. with USNR, 1944-46. Mem. Am. Assn. Ednl. Researchers, Am. Mgmt. Assn., Protestant Ch. Owned Pubs. Assn. (dir. 1969-84, pres. 1982-84), St. Louis Printing Assn. (bd. dirs. 1975-77), Am. Assn. Indsl. Mgmt. (bd. dirs. 1981-85), Assn. Ind. Colls. and Univs. of Nebr. (pres. 1988-89), Concordia Univ. (bd. dirs. 1992—), Rotary, Phi Delta Kappa. Lutheran. *Life is a most precious and finite gift of God to man. Those who would lead must make a commitment to devote their full energies and intellects to the improvement of the quality of life of their fellowmen. In the highest sense, leadership is the integrity to heed the quiet voice of conscience from within in the quest of that quality.*

REINKE, WILLIAM JOHN, lawyer; b. South Bend, Ind., Aug. 7, 1930; s. William August and Eva Marie (Hein) R.; m. Sue Carol Colvin, 1951 (div. 1988); children: Sally Sue Taelman, William A., Andrew J.; m. Elizabeth Beck Lockwood, 1991. A.B. cum laude, Wabash Coll., 1952; J.D., U. Chgo., 1955. Bar: Ind. 1955. Assoc. Barnes & Thornburg and predecessors, South Bend, Ind., 1957-61, ptnr., 1961—; former chmn. compensation com., former mem. mgmt. com. chmn. Construction Law Practice Group; trustee Stanley Clark Sch., 1969-80, pres. 1977-80; mem. adv. bd. Salvation Army, 1973—, pres., 1990-92; bd. dirs. NABE Mich. chpt., 1990-94, pres 1993-94, Isaac Walton League, 1970-81, United Way 1978-81; pres. South Bend Round Table, 1963-65; trustee First Meth. Ch., 1967-70. Served with U.S. Army, 1955-57. Recipient Outstanding Local Pres. award Ind. Jaycees, 1960-61, Boss of Yr. award , 1969, South Bend Outstanding Young Man award, 1961. Mem. ABA, Ind. State Bar Assn., St. Joseph County Bar Assn., Ind. Bar Found. (patron fellow), Am. Judicature Soc., Def. Rsch. Inst., Ind. Soc. Chgo., Summit Club (past gov., founders com.), Rotary (bd. dirs. 1970-73, 94—). Home: 51795 Waterton Square Cir Granger IN 46530-8317 Office: Barnes & Thornburg 600 1st Source Bank Ctr 100 N Michigan South Bend IN 46601

REINMUTH, JAMES E., college dean. Dean Coll. Bus. Adminstrn. U Oreg., Eugene. Office: Dean Business Administration U Oregon Eugene OR 97403

REINMUTH, OSCAR MACNAUGHTON, physician, educator; b. Lincoln, Nebr., Oct. 23, 1927; s. Oscar William and Catharine Anne (MacNaughton) R.; m. Patricia Dixon, June 19, 1951 (div. Jan. 1977); children—David Dixon, Diane MacNaughton, Douglas Stewart; m. Audrey Longridge Holland, June 26, 1980. B.S., U. Tex., Austin, 1948; M.D. (F.B. Hanes research fellow 1950-51), Duke U., 1952. Intern Duke Hosp., 1952-53; asst. resident in medicine Yale U. Med. Ctr., 1953-54, NIH research trainee, 1954-55; asst. resident in neurology Boston City Hosp., 1955-56, chief resident, teaching fellow in neurology Harvard U. Neurol. unit, 1956-57; NIH spl. trainee, clin. asst. Nat. Hosp., London, 1957-58; from asst. prof. to prof. neurology U. Miami (Fla.) Med. Sch., 1958-77; prof. neurology and behavioral neuroscience, chmn. dept. U. Pitts. Med. Sch., 1977-93, prof. emeritus, 1993—; prof. neurology U. Ariz. Med. Sch., Tucson, 1993—; mem. research tng. com. A and C NIH, 1966-73. Served with AUS, 1946-47. Recipient Mosby award, 1952. Fellow ACP, Am. Acad. Neurology (1st v.p. 1973-76), Am. Neurol. Assn. (1st v.p. 1977-78, 2d v.p. 1976-77), Am. Heart Assn. (fellow stroke coun., vice chmn. 1978-79, chmn. 1980-82, editor publs. 1975-78, editor-in-chief Stroke jour. 1987-91, Award of Merit 1992). Home: 5545 N Entrada Quince Tucson AZ 85718-4709 Office: U Med Ctr Dept Neurology 1501 N Campbell Ave Tucson AZ 85724-0001

REINOEHL, RICHARD LOUIS, writer, artist, consultant; b. Omaha, Oct. 11, 1944; s. Louis Lawrence and Frances Margaret (Robinson) R.; m. Linda Dale Iroff, Feb. 28, 1982; 1 child, Joy Margaret Iroff-Reinoehl. BS in Sociology, Portland State U., 1970; MSW, U. Minn., Duluth, 1977; postgrad., Cornell U., 1984-88. Acting dir. Vanguard Group Homes, Virginia, Minn., 1976-77; dir. Minn. Chippewa Tribe Group Home, Duluth, 1978, Human Devel. Consortium, Minn., N.Y., Ohio, 1978—; faculty Social Work Program U. Wis., Superior, 1981-84; adv. bd. Computers in Social Svcs. Network, 1982-85; mem. Com. on Internat. Social Welfare Edn., 1982-86, Am. Evaluation Assn., 1986-89; affiliate scholar Oberlin Coll., 1991—. Editor: Computer Literacy in Human Services Education, 1990, Computer Literacy in Human Services, 1990, Men of Achievement, 16th edit., 1993; mem. editorial bd. Computers in Human Svcs., 1983—; contbr. numerous articles to profl. jours. Mem. Legis. Task Force Regional Alcoholism Bd., 1972-73, Assn. Drug Abuse, Prevention and Treatment, 1973-74, Minn. Pub. Health Assn., 1976-78, Minn. Social Svc. Assn., 1976-83, Wis. Coun. Social Work Edn., 1983-84, N.Y. State Coun. Family Rels., 1986-89, Nat. Coun. Family Rels., 1986-89; exec. bd. Duluth Community Action Program, 1982-83; Dem. precinct chair, Portland, Oreg., 1972-74; precinct vice-chair Dem. Farmer-Labor Party, Duluth, 1979-81, chair, 1981-83, 2d vice-chair exec. bd., 1981-83. Mem. NASW (exec. com., chair program com. Arrowhead Region Minn. chpt., 1980-81, co-chair task force on computers in social work, 1981-82), Acad. Cert. Social Workers, Cornell U. Sailing Club (pres. 1990). Avocations: canoeing, sailing. Office: Human Devel Consortium Inc 46180 Butternut Ridge Rd Oberlin OH 44074-9735 *It's noteworthy that the most sought-after items in a society cannot be bought or sold. Included are wisdom, respect, generosity, truthfulness, and the love of family and friends.*

REINS, RALPH ERICH, automated service company executive; b. Detroit, Sept. 18, 1940; s. Erich John and Florence (Franz) R.; m. Victoria Louise Kolts, Sept. 14, 1963; children—Ann Marie, Christine Louise. B.S.I.E., U. Mich., 1963. Asst. supt. Chevrolet Motor div., Gen. Motors Corp., Detroit, 1963-72; v.p.; pres. hwy. product ops. Rockwell Internat., Troy, Mich., 1972-85; sr. v.p. ITT Corp., Bloomfield Hills, Mich., 1985-89; chmn. of the bd., pres., chief exec. officer Mack Trucks, Inc., Allentown, Pa., 1989-90; pres. United Tech. Automotive, Dearborn, Mich., 1990-91; exec. v.p., pres. automotive sector Allied Signal Corp., 1991-94; pres., CEO Envirotest Sys. Corp., Phoenix, 1995—. Mem. Roeper Sch. Bd. Trustees; mem. found. bd. Oakland U. Mem. Soc. Automotive Engrs., Bloomfield Hills Country Club. Republican. Avocations: golf; hunting; fishing. Home: 261 Indian Harbor Rd Vero Beach FL 32963 Office: Envirotest Sys Corp # 700 2525 E Camelback Rd Phoenix AZ 85016

REINSCH, HARRY ORVILLE, power company executive; b. Los Angeles, Feb. 12, 1922; s. Harry Orville and Olive Gladys (Cooper) R.; m. Helen Marsh, Oct. 19, 1942; children: E. James, John H.(dec.), Richard M., Linda Reinsch Marshall. Student engring., U. Calif.-Davis, 1940-42. Asst. supt. Bechtel Power Corp., San Francisco, 1950-55; gen. supt. to mgr. bus. devel. Bechtel Power Corp., San Francisco and Washington, 1955-68; v.p. Bechtel Power Corp., San Francisco, 1968-72, v.p., dir., 1972-73, exec. v.p., dir., 1973-75, pres., 1975-86, vice chmn., 1986-87, dir., 1973-87; dir. Wells Fargo & Co., Wells Fargo Bank; hon. chmn. Korean-Am. Bus. Inst. Dir. No. Calif. Soc. to Prevent Blindness, 1983; dir. That Man May See, 1982; com. Republic of China Econ. Council, U.S.; trustee U. Mont. Found., 1981-85; pres. Korean-Am. Ch. of Calif., 1982-83; dir. Calif. Council Environ. and Econ. Balance. Mem. ASCE, ASME, Council for Energy Awareness (dir., vice chmn., exec. com.). Clubs: World Trade, Bankers, Pacific Union (San Francisco). Home: 1940 Broadway St Apt 10 San Francisco CA 94109-2299 Office: Bechtel Energy Corp 50 Beale St San Francisco CA 94105-1813

REINSCH, WILLIAM ALAN, government executive, educator; b. Evanston, Ill., Jan. 15, 1946; s. Bert and Kathleen (Penn) R.; m. Susan Polley Reinsch, Jan. 3, 1970; children: Andrew, Christian. BA, Johns Hopkins U., 1968; MA in Internat. Studies, Johns Hopkins U.-Sch. Advanced Internat. Studies, 1969. Legis. asst. Congressman Gilbert Gude, Washington, 1973-76, Congressman Richard Ottinger, Washington, 1976; chief legis. asst. Senator John Heinz, Washington, 1977-91; legis. asst. Senator John D. Rockefeller IV, Washington, 1991-93; cons., under sec. for export administrn. Dept. Commerce, Washington, 1994—; tchr. Landon Sch., Bethesda, Md., 1968-73; adj. assoc. prof. U. Md. U. Coll. Grad. Sch. Mgmt. and Tech., College Park, Md., 1990—; acting staff dir. Environmental Study Conf. U.S. Ho. Reps., 1976. Contbr. articles to profl. jours. Pres. St. Mark Elderly Housing Corp., Rockville, Md. Mem. Phi Beta Kappa, Omicron Delta Kappa, Alpha Delta Phi. Democrat. Presbyterian. Office: Dept Commerce Rm 3898B Washington DC 20230

REINSCHMIDT, KENNETH FRANK, engineering and construction executive; b. Cin., Mar. 26, 1938; s. Christian Edward and Martha Marie (Kellerman) R.; m. Marlene Faye Taub, Dec. 16, 1967. BSCE, MIT, 1960,

MSCE, 1962, PhD in Engring., 1965. Assoc. prof. civil engring. MIT, Cambridge, 1965-75; sr. v.p. Stone & Webster Engring. Corp., Boston, 1975-93, also bd. dirs.; pres. Stone & Webster Advanced Systems Devel. Svcs., Boston, 1988—; bd. dirs. Stone & Webster Advanced Tech. Applications Inc., N.Y.C., 1990-94; sr. v.p. Stone & Webster, Inc.; chmn. com. on oversight of Ctr. for Bldg. Tech., Nat. Inst. Standards and Tech., Gaithersburg, Md., 1986-89. Author: Stress: A User's Manual, 1963; editor: Systems Building, 1974; contbr. numerous articles to profl. jours. Capt. U.S. Army, 1966-67. Decorated Legion of Merit; NSF fellow, 1962. Fellow AAAS; mem. NAE, ASCE, Soc. Mfg. Engrs., Mgmt. Scis., Ops. Rsch. Soc. Am. (assoc.). Office: Stone & Webster Inc 245 Summer St Boston MA 02210-1116

REINSDORF, JERRY MICHAEL, professional sports teams executive, real estate executive, lawyer, accountant; b. Bklyn., Feb. 25, 1936; s. Max and Marion (Smith) R.; m. Martyl F. Rifkin, Dec. 29, 1956; children: David Jason, Susan Janeen, Michael Andrew, Jonathan Milton. BA, George Washington U., 1957; JD, Northwestern U., 1960. Bar: D.C., Ill. 1960, CPA, Ill.; cert. specialist real estate securities, rev. appraiser; registered mortgage underwriter. Atty. staff regional counsel IRS, Chgo., 1960-64; assoc. law firm Chapman & Cutler, 1964-68; ptnr. Altman, Kurlander & Weiss, 1968-74; of counsel firm Katten, Muchin, Gitles, Zavis, Pearl & Galler, 1974-79; gen. ptnr. Carlyle Real Estate Ltd. Partnerships, 1971, 72; chmn. bd. Balcor Co., 1973-87; mng. ptnr. TBC Films, 1975-83; chmn. Chgo. White Sox, 1981—, Chgo. Bulls Basketball Team, 1985—; ptnr. Bojer Fin., 1987—; lectr. John Marshall Law Sch., 1966-68; former bd. dirs. Shearson Lehman Bros., Inc., Project Academus of DePaul U., Chgo., Sports Immortals Mus., 1987-89, Com. Commemorate U.S. Constn., 1987; lectr. in real estate, sports, and taxation. Author: (with I. Herbert Schneider) Uses of Life Insurance in Qualified Employee Benefit Plans, 1970. Co-chmn. Ill. Profls. for Sen. Ralph Smith, 1970; mem. Chgo. Region Bd. Anti-Defamation League, 1986—; trustee Ill. Inst. Tech., 1991—; mem. Ill. Commn. on African-Am. Males, 1992—; bd. dirs. Chgo. Youth Success Found., 1992—; nat. trustee Northwestern U., 1993—; bd. govs. Hugh O'Brian Youth Found. Recipient Hallmark award Chgo. Baseball Cancer Charities, 1986, Corp. Superstar award Ill. chpg. Cystic Fibrosis Found., 1988, Chicagoan of Yr. award Chgo. Park Dist., 1990, Kellogg Excellence award, 1991, Cmty. Hero award Interfaith Organizing Project, 1991, Operation Push Bridgebuilder award, 1992, Alumni Merit award Northwestern U., 1992, Ellis Island Medal of Honor award Nat. Ethnic Coalition of Orgns., 1993, Lifetime Achievement award March of Dimes, 1994, Hallmark Hall of Fame Civic award Ind. Sports Charities, 1994, Sportsman of Yr. award Cystic Fibrosis Found., 1994, Am. Spirit award USAF, 1995; inductee B'nai B'rith Nat. Jewish Am. Sports Hall of Fame, 1994. Mem. ABA, Ill. Bar Assn., Chgo. Bar Assn., Fed. Bar Assn., Nat. Sports Lawyers Assn., Nat. Assn. Rev. Appraisers and Mortgage Underwriters, Northwestern U. Law Sch. Alumni Assn. (bd. dirs.), Order of Coif, Omega Tau Rho. Office: Bojer Fin Ltd 980 N Michigan Ave Ste 1011 Chicago IL 60611-4501

REINSTEIN, JOEL, lawyer; b. N.Y.C., July 23, 1946; s. Louis and Ruth Shukovsky; children: Lesli, Louis, Mindy. B.S.E., U. Pa., 1968; J.D. cum laude, U. Fla., 1971; LL.M. in Taxation, NYU, 1974. Bar: Fla. 1971, U.S. Tax Ct. 1973, U.S. Dist. Ct. (so. dist.) Fla. 1976. Atty., office of chief counsel IRS, 1971-74; ptnr. Capp, Reinsein, Kopelowitz and Atlas, P.A., Ft. Lauderdale, Fla., 1975-85; dir., ptnr. Greenberg, Traurig, Hoffman, Lipoff, Rosen & Quentel, P.A., Ft. Lauderdale, 1985-92; gen. counsel Internat. Magnetic Imaging, Inc., Boca Raton, Fla., 1992-94; prin. Law Offices of Joel Reinstein, Boca Raton, 1993—; lectr. Advanced Pension Planning, Am. Soc. C.L.U.s; lectr. in field. Mem. Fla. Bar Assn. (tax sect.), ABA (tax sect, adj. mem. com. employee benefits), Order of Coif, Phi Kappa Phi, Phi Delta Phi. Mem. editorial bd. U. Fla. Law Rev., 1970-71; contbr. articles to profl. jours. Office: The Plaza 5355 Town Center Rd Ste 801 Boca Raton FL 33486-1069

REINSTEIN, PAUL MICHAEL, lawyer; b. N.Y.C., Jan. 19, 1952; s. Joseph and Edith (Ambaras) R.; m. Gila Ann Moldoff, Apr. 16, 1978; children: Meira, Rachel, Aryeh, Joseph. BA, Yeshiva Coll., 1973; JD, Yale U., 1976. Bar: N.Y. 1977. Assoc. Fried Frank Harris Shriver & Jacobson, N.Y.C., 1976-83, ptnr., 1983—. Mem. ABA, N.Y. State Bar Assn. Home: 282 Maple St West Hempstead NY 11552-3206 Office: Fried Frank Harris et al 1 New York Pla New York NY 10004

REINSTEIN, ROBERT J., dean, law educator; b. Balt., Mar. 17, 1945; m. Mary Taylor Aspinwall; children: Ellen, Thomas. BS in Engring. Physics with distinction, Cornell U., 1965; JD cum laude, Harvard U., 1968. Bar: Md. 1969, Pa. 1982, U.S. Supreme Ct. 1971. Law clk. to Hon. Frank A. Kaufman U.S. Dist. Ct. Md., 1968-69; from asst. prof. to assoc. prof. Sch. Law Temple U., Phila., 1969-73, prof. Sch. Law, 1973—; sr. atty. appellate sect. Civil Rights Divsn., U.S. Dept. Justice, 1977-78, chief litigation sect., 1979-80; chief legal officer Temple U., 1982-89, dean Sch. Law, 1989—; vis. prof. law Hastings Coll. Law, San Francisco, 1975, Georgetown U., 1978-79; cons. atty. NAACP Spl. Contbn. Fund, 1970-77. Contbr. articles to profl. jours. Chair civil rights com. B'nai Brith Anti-Defamation League, Phila. Mem. ABA, Pa. Bar Assn. Office: Temple U Sch Law 1719 N Broad St Philadelphia PA 19122-2504

REINTHALER, RICHARD WALTER, lawyer; b. N.Y.C., Feb. 27, 1949; s. Walter F. and Maureen C. (Tully) R.; m. Mary E. Maloney, Aug. 8, 1970; children: Brian, Scott, Amy. BA in Govt. magna cum laude, U. Notre Dame, 1970, JD summa cum laude, 1974. Bar: N.Y. 1974, U.S. Dist. Ct. (so. and ea. dists.) N.Y. 1974, U.S. Ct. Appeals (2d cir.) 1974, U.S. Ct. Appeals (9th cir.) 1976, U.S. Ct. Appeals (5th cir.) 1978, U.S. Ct. Appeals (11th cir.) 1981, U.S. Supreme Ct. 1977. Assoc. White & Case, N.Y.C., 1973-81, ptnr., 1981—; mem. adv. group U.S. Dist. Ct. (ea. dist.) N.Y., 1992—, chairperson subgroup on ethics, 1993—. Contbr. articles to profl. jours. Served to 1st lt. U.S. Army, 1974. Mem. ABA (2d cir. chmn. discovery com. 1982-87, program coord. 1986, ann. meeting litigation sect., vice chmn. com. on fed. procedure 1988-89, co-chmn. com. on profl. responsibility 1989-92, vice chmn. securities litigation com. 1993-94, vice chair Hong Kong meeting 1995). N.Y. State Bar Assn., Assn. of Bar of City of N.Y. (mem. com. to enhance profl. responsibility for minorities 1990—), mem. Orison S. Marden Meml. Lectrs com., 1994—; Scarsdale Golf Club (Hartsdale, N.Y., bd. govs. 1994—), Capital Hill Club (Washington). Republican. Roman Catholic. Avocations: golf, tennis. Office: Dewey Ballantine 1301 Ave of Americas New York NY 10019-6092

REIS, ARTHUR ROBERT, JR., men's furnishings manufacturer; b. N.Y.C., Dec. 8, 1916; s. Arthur M. and Claire (Raphael) R.; m. Muriel Henle, Sept. 25, 1953; children: Arthur, Diane, Pamela. B.A., Princeton U., 1939. Joined Pan. Am. Airways, 1940, asst. to v.p. 1943; joined Robert Reis & Co., N.Y.C., 1946, pres. 1947-79; ptnr. Energy Applications Assocs., 1980-82; mem. departmental disciplinary com. Appellate Ct. N.Y., 1994; supr. cons. Nat. Exec. Svcs. Corps. Mem. N.Y. State Com. on Refugee Relief Act of 1953; trustee, mem. exec. com. Storm King Sch., Cornwall-on-Hudson, N.Y. Served from pvt. to capt. Air Transport Command USAAF, 1943-46; asst. chief of staff Central Pacific Wing. Decorated B.S.M. Mem. Young Pres.' Orgn. (co-founder), N.Y.C. of C. (exec. com.), Princeton Club of N.Y. (bd. govs.). Home: 1136 5th Ave New York NY 10128-0122

REIS, DON, publishing executive; b. N.Y.C., Nov. 19, 1927; m. Barbara Weinberg, 1947; children: Robert, Richard. AB, Princeton U., 1947; MA, NYU, 1955. Rsch. editor Bantam Books, 1952-55, edn. editor, 1955-66; editor-in-chief Washington Square Press Divsn. Simon & Schuster, 1966-68; v.p., editorial dir. Ednl. Directions Inc., Westport, Conn., 1968-85; mng. editor Barron's Ednl. Series, 1985-87; gen. and ednl. editor Barron's, 1987-93; sr. cons. editor Barron's, Hauppauge, N.Y., 1993—; editorial dir. Reis Assocs., Forest Hills, N.Y., 1993—. Author: (with A. Butman and D. Sohn) Paperback Books in the Schools, 1962; editor The Collected Essays of Aldous Huxley, 1958. Home: 57 Summer St Forest Hills NY 11375 Office: Barron's Edn Series Inc 250 Wireless Blvd Hauppauge NY 11788

REIS, DONALD JEFFERY, neurologist, neurobiologist, educator; b. N.Y.C., Sept. 9, 1931; s. Samuel H. and Alice (Kiesler) R.; m. Cornelia Langer Noland, Apr. 13, 1985. A.B., Cornell U., 1953, M.D., 1956. Intern N.Y. Hosp., N.Y.C., 1956; resident in neurology Boston City Hosp.-Harvard Med. Sch., 1957-59; Fulbright fellow, United Cerebral Palsy Found. fellow

London and Stockholm, 1959-60; rsch. assoc. NIMH, Bethesda, Md., 1960-62; spl. fellow NIH, Nobel Neurophysiology Inst., Stockholm, 1962-63; asst. prof. neurology Cornell U. Med. Sch., N.Y.C., 1963-67; assoc. prof. neurology and psychiatry Cornell U. Med. Sch., 1967-71, prof., 1971—, First George C. Cotzias Disting. prof. neurology, 1982—; mem. U.S.-Soviet Exch. Program; mem. adv. coun. NIH; bd. sci. advisers Merck, Sharpe & Dohm, Sterling Rsch. Group; cons. Eli Lilly, Servier Pharms.; bd. dirs. China Seas, Inc., Charles masterson Burke Rsch. Found. Contbr. articles to profl. jours.; mem. editorial bd. various profl. jours. Recipient CIBA Prize award Am. Heart Assn. Fellow AAAS, ACP; mem. Am. Physiol. Soc., Am. Neurol. Assn., Am. Pharmacol. Soc., Am. Assn. Physicians, Telluride Assn., Am. Soc. Clin. Investigation, Century Assn., Ellis Island Yacht Club (commadore), Phi Beta Kappa, Sigma Xi, Alpha Omega Alpha. Home: 190 E 72d St New York NY 10021 also: 73 Water St Stonington CT 06378 Office: 1300 York Ave New York NY 10021-4896

REIS, JUDSON PATTERSON, investment banker; b. Bryn Mawr, Pa., July 31, 1942; s. Maurice J. and Wiley W. (Patterson) R.; m. Judith Morse (div.); children: Judson P. Jr., C. Parker; m. Kathryn Ann Fortuin, June 16, 1972; children: Mark B., Nicholas D., A. Curtis. BA cum laude, Washington and Lee U., 1964; MBA with distinction, Harvard U., 1966. Assoc. Morgan Stanley & Co., Inc., N.Y.C., 1966-72, v.p., 1973, prin., 1974, mng. dir., 1975-88; exec. v.p., mng. dir. Kleinwort Benson N.A., N.Y.C., 1988-91; pres. Sire Mgmt. Corp., N.Y.C., 1991—; mng. gen. ptnr. Sire Ptnrs., L.P., 1991—; bd. dirs. Kleinwort Benson Ltd., London; Morris vis. prof. bus. adminstrn. Colgate Darden Grad. Sch. Bus. U. Va., 1987-88, 989—. Treas. Caputo for Congress com., N.Y.C., 1977; treas. Caputo for Lt. Gov. com., 1978; bd. dirs. Pilobolus Dance Co.; pres. bd. trustees Showhegan Sch. Painting and Sculpture. Republican. Clubs: University (N.Y.C.), Farmington Country, Charlottesville, Va., Bond, Links (N.Y.C.); Bridgehampton (N.Y.). Home: 1035 5th Ave New York NY 10028-0135 Office: Sire Ptnrs LP 630 Fifth Ave New York NY 10111

REIS, MURIEL HENLE, lawyer, broadcast executive; b. N.Y.C.; d. Frederick S. and Mary (Meyers) Henle; m. Arthur Reis Jr., Sept. 25, 1953; children: Arthur Henle, Diane Mary, Pamela Robin. BA, Vassar Coll., 1946; LLB, Columbia U., 1949. Asst. gen. counsel ABC, N.Y.C., 1950-52; from asst. gen. counsel to assoc. gen. counsel Metromedia Inc., N.Y.C., 1956-86; v.p. WNEW, N.Y.C., 1974-86; v.p., legal affairs Fox TV Sta. Inc., N.Y.C., 1986—. Mem. Assn. of Bar of City of N.Y., Internat. Soc. Radio and TV Execs. Home: 1136 5th Ave New York NY 10128-0122 Office: Fox TV Sta Inc 205 E 67th St New York NY 10021-6048

REIS, VICTOR H., mechanical engineer, government official. PhD in Mech. Engring., Princeton U. Formerly sr. v.p. for strategic planning Sci. Applications Internat. Corp.; security adviser Office Sci. and Tech. Policy, Washington; spl. asst. to dir. Lincoln Labs MIT; dep. dir. Def. Advanced Rsch. Projects Agy., Arlington, Va., 1989-90, dir., 1990-93; asst. sec. Dept. Energy Def. Programs, Washington, 1993—. Office: Dept Energy Def Programs 1000 Independence Ave SW Washington DC 20585

REISBERG, BARRY, geropsychiatrist, neuropsychopharmacologist; b. Bklyn., Dec. 3, 1947; s. Harry and Claire (Cohen) R.; m. Rosalie DePaola, Feb. 23, 1974 (dec. Oct. 1975); m. Nancy A. Minich, May 7, 1988. BA, CUNY, Bklyn., 1968; MD, N.Y. Med. Coll., 1972. Diplomate Am. Bd. Psychiatry and Neurology, Am. Bd. Geriatric Psychiatry. Intern N.Y. Med. Coll./Met. Hosp., N.Y.C., 1972-75, resident in psychiatry, 1972-75; fellow dept. psychiatry Middlesex Hosp. Med. Sch. U. London, 1975; staff psychiatrist Franklin D. Roosevelt VA Hosp., Montrose, N.Y., 1975-78; staff psychiatrist Neuropsychopharmacology Rsch. Unit NYU Med. Ctr., N.Y.C., 1978-80, clin. dir. Aging and Dementia Rsch. Ctr., 1978—; adj. prof. Ctr. for Studies in Aging, McGill U., Montreal, Que., Can., 1993—; clin. instr. dept. psychiatry N.Y. Med. Coll., Valhalla, 1975-78; asst. prof. NYU Sch. Medicine, N.Y.C., 1978-84, assoc. prof., 1984-90, prof., 1990—; rsch. collaborator, vis. clinician Brookhaven Natl. Labs., Upton, N.Y., 1979-80; dir. clin. core NIMH Clin. Rsch. Ctr., 1989—, Natl. Inst. Aging Alzheimer's Disease Ctr., 1990—; med. and sci. adv. bd. Alzheimer's Assn., Chgo., 1993—; cons. psychiatrist N.Y. VA Hosp., 1980-89; chmn. work group WHO, Copenhagen, 1984; mem. aging sect. NIH, 1986-90; vis. prof. Palmerston North Postgrad. Med. Soc., New Zealand, 1991. Author: Brain Failure, 1981; editor: Alzheimer's Disease, 1983; (with others) Diagnosis and Treatment of Senile Dementia, 1989; mem. editl. bd. Jour. Am. Aging Assn., 1985—, Alzheimer's Disease and Associated Disorders, 1985—, Jour. Geriat. Psychiatry and Neurology, 1986—, Am. Jour. Alzheimer's Care, 1986—, Internat. Psychogeriat., 1989—, Am. Jour. Geriat. Psychiatry, 1992—, Integrative Psychiatry, 1994—; contbr. over 150 articles to med. and sci. jours. Fellow NSF, 1963, Coun. on Internat. Ednl. Exch.-Japan Soc., Tokyo, 1968; grantee NIH, 1979-81, 82-85, 87, 90, 92—, NIMH, 1983-85. Mem. Internat. Psychogeriat. Assn. (bd. dirs. 1985-93, treas. 1993-95, pres.-elect 1995—), Am. Aging Assn. (bd. dirs. 1990—), Alzheimer's and Related Disorders Soc. India (hon.), Am. Assn. Geriat. Psychiatry (sec. 1991-92, bd. dirs. 1992—), Am. Coll. Neuropsychopharmacology. Office: NYU Med Ctr Aging and Dementia Rsch Ctr 550 1st Ave New York NY 10016-6497

REISCH, MICHAEL STEWART, social work educator; b. N.Y.C., Mar. 4, 1948; s. Joseph and Charlotte (Rosenberg) R.; m. Amy Jane Lewis, May 21, 1972; children: Jennifer, Nikki. BA in History with highest honors, NYU, 1968; PhD in History, SUNY, Binghamton, 1975; MSW, CUNY, 1979. Youth worker Washington-Heights-Inwood YM-YWHA, N.Y.C., 1965-66; editor, columnist Heights Daily News, Bronx, N.Y., 1966-68; rsch./teaching asst. SUNY, Binghamton, 1970-72; unit dir., program cons. Child Study Assn.-Wel Met, Inc., N.Y.C., 1970-72; asst. dir. youth div. Mosholu-Montefiore Community Ctr., Bronx, 1972-73; project dir. Silberman Found./N.Y. Assn. Deans, N.Y.C., 1973-74; asst. dean Sch. Social Welfare, asst. prof. SUNY, Stony Brook, 1974-79; asst. prof., then assoc. prof. Sch. Social Work U. Md., Balt., 1979-86; dir. Sch. Social Work, prof. social work/pub. adminstrn. San Francisco State U., 1986-95; prof. social welfare U. Pa., Phila., 1995—; cons. and spkr. in field. Co-author: From Charity to Enterprise, 1989 (Social Sci. Book of Month); editor, author various books in field; contbr. articles to profl. publs., chpts. to books. Cons. to numerous local, state and fed. polit. campaigns, 1971—; mem. Gov.'s Adv. Coun. Human Resources, Md., 1983-86; pres. Welfare Advs., Md., 1983-86; campaign mgr. Rep. Barbara Mikulski, Balt., 1982; bd. dirs. Coleman Advs. for Children and Youth, 1986-95, San Francisco Internat. Program, 1987-95, Calif. Social Work Edn. Ctr., 1991-95, Ctr. for South East Asian Refugee Resettlement, 1992-95, Am. Jewish Congress, N.C., 1994-95; chair Children's Budget Task Force City of San Francisco, 1989-92; mem. Mayor's Adv. Coun. on Drug Abuse, San Francisco, 1988-91; steering com. Poverty Action Alliance, 1993-95. Woodrow Wilson Found. fellow, 1972-73. Mem. NASW (del. 1990-92, 94-96, chair peace and justice com. 1992—), Coun. on Social Work Edn. (com. on status of women 1989-92, bd. dirs. 1993—, chair commn. on ednl. policy and planning 1994—), Am. Hist. Assn., Nat. Assn. Deans/Dirs. of Schs. and Social Work (sec. 1993-95), Calif. Assn. Deans/Dirs. of Schs. of Social Work (pres. 1992-94). Avocations: travel, hiking, cooking, swimming, creative writing.

REISER, CHARLES EDWARD, JR., hospital software company executive; b. Louisville, Nov. 2, 1939; s. Charles Edward Sr. and Margaret Christina (Hoffmann) R.; m. Antonia Marie Dominick, Feb. 10, 1944; children: Michelle, Lynette, Jeffery. BA, Ky. Wesleyan Coll., 1963; MBA, U. Mich., 1967. Fin. analyst Ford Motor Co., Dearborn, Mich., 1963-67; v.p. fin. Aluminum div. Atlantic Richfield, Chgo., 1967-85; sr. v.p., chief fin. officer Cardinal Distbn. Inc., Dublin, Ohio, 1985-89, Health Systems Group, Am. Express Co., Charlotte, N.C., 1989—. Office: Am Express 10101 Claude Freeman Dr Charlotte NC 28262-2337

REISER, MORTON FRANCIS, psychiatrist, educator; b. Cin., Aug. 22, 1919; s. Sigmund and Mary (Roth) R.; m. Lynn B. Whisnant, Dec. 19, 1976; children: David E., Barbara, Linda. B.S., U. Cin., 1940, M.D., 1943; grad., N.Y. Psychoanalytic Inst., 1960. Diplomate Am. Bd. Psychiatry and Neurology. Intern King's County Hosp., Bklyn., 1944; resident Cin. Gen. Hosp., 1944-49; practice medicine, specializing in psychiatry Cin., 1947-52, Washington, 1954-55, N.Y.C., 1955-69; mem. faculty Cin. Gen. Hosp., also U. Cin. Coll. Medicine, 1949-52, Washington Sch. Psychiatry, 1953-55; faculty Albert Einstein Coll. Medicine, Yeshiva U., N.Y.C., 1955-69; prof. psychiatry Albert Einstein Coll. Medicine, Yeshiva U., 1958-69, dir. research

dept. psychiatry, 1958-65; chief div. psychiatry Montefiore Hosp. and Med. Center, N.Y.C., 1965-69; chmn. dept. psychiatry Yale Med. Sch., 1969—, prof., 1969-78, chmn. dept., 1969-86, Charles B.G. Murphy prof., 1978-86, Albert E. Kent prof., 1986-90, Albert E. Kent prof. emeritus, 1990—; cons. Walter Reed Army Inst. Research, 1957-58, High Point Hosp., Port Chester, N.Y., 1957-69; cons. WHO, 1963; mem. profl. adv. com. Jerusalem Mental Health Center, 1972—; mem. clin. program projects rev. com. NIMH, 1970—, chmn., 1973-74. Author: (with H. Leigh) The Patient: Biological, Psychological, and Social Dimensions of Medical Practice, 1980, Mind, Brain, Body: Toward a Convergence of Psychoanalysis and Neurobiology, 1984; (with H. Leigh) The Patient, 3d edit., 1992; Memory in Mind and Brain: What Dream Imagery Reveals, 1990; editor: American Handbook of Psychiatry, vol. IV, 1975; editor in chief Psychosomatic Medicine, 1962-72; mem. editorial bd. AMA Archives of Gen. Psychiatry, 1961-71, (with H. Leigh) Psychiatry Medicine and Primary Care, 1978; contbr. articles to profl. jours. and books. Fellow Am. Coll. Psychiatrists, Am. Psychiat. Assn. (Seymour Vestermark award 1986); mem. Am. Soc. Clin. Investigation, Am. Psychosomatic Soc. (pres. 1960-61), Am. Fedn. Clin. Research, Am. Assn. Chairmen Depts. Psychiatry (exec. com. 1971—, pres. 1975-76), Acad. Behavioral Medicine Research (exec. council 1978), Am. Psychoanalytic Assn. (pres.-elect 1980-82, pres. 1982-84), Internat. Psycho-Analytical Assn., Assn. Psychophysiol. Study of Sleep, Internat. Coll. Psychosomatic Medicine (pres. 1975), Psychiat. Research Soc., A. Graeme Mitchell Undergrad. Pediatric Soc., Benjamin Rush Soc., Rapaport-Klein Study Group, World Psychiat. Assn. (organizing com. sect. psychosomatic medicine 1967), Sigma Xi, Phi Eta Sigma, Pi Kappa Epsilon, Alpha Omega Alpha. Home: 200 Todd St Mount Carmel CT 06518 Office: 255 Bradley St New Haven CT 06510-1105

REISER, PAUL, actor, comedian; b. N.Y.C., Mar. 30, 1957; m. Paula Reiser. BFA in Music, SUNY, Binghamton, 1977. comedian various nightclubs and venues including Catch a Rising Star, N.Y.C., The Comic Strip, N.Y.C., The Improv, N.Y.C., 1979—. Performances include (feature films) Diner, 1982, Beverly Hills Cop, 1984, Aliens, 1986, Beverly Hills Cop II, 1987, Cross My Heart, 1987, Crazy People, 1990, The Marrying Man, 1991, Bye Bye, Love, 1995, (TV series) The Investigator, HBO, The Comedy Zone, (TV spls.) Paul Reiser: Out on a Whim, HBO, 1987, (TV pilots) Diner, CBS, Just Married, ABC, (TV movies) Sunset Limousine, 1987, You Ruined My Life, 1987, The Tower, 1993; regular (TV series) My Two Dads, NBC, 1987-1991, Mad About You, NBC, 1992— (Emmy nomination, Lead Actor - Comedy Series, 1994); guest star various talk shows including The Tonight Show, Late Night with David Letterman; author: Couplehood, 1994. Office: UTA 9560 Wilshire Blvd 5th fl Beverly Hills CA 90212*

REISERT, CHARLES EDWARD, JR., real estate executive; b. New Albany, Ind., Apr. 5, 1941; s. Charles Edward Sr. and Jane. W. (Willcox) R.; m. Mary Lynn Nunemacher, Nov. 9, 1963; children: Perry G., Heidi L. BS in Edn., Ind. U., 1963, MA, 1968. Cert. residential specialist, residential broker. Tchr. Ind. Pub. Schs., 1963-67; mgr. Indpl. Bell Tel. Co., Indpls., 1967-70; trust officer Ind. Nat. Bank, Indpls., 1970-72; ptnr. R.F.R. Prodns. Inc., Zionsville; dir. Wichita (Kans.) Art Assn., 1972-73; realtor Century 21 Reisert, Baker, Harrison, Jeffersonville, Ind., 1973—. Mem. Ind. Real Estate Commn., 1982-90, chmn., 1990; pres. bd. dirs. Clark County Youth Shelter, 1987—; bd. dirs., past pres. United Way Clark County; bd. dirs. New Hope, Inc., Sagamore of Wabash; mem. Leadership So. Ind., Leadership Louisville; trustee Jeffersonville Twp. Pub. Libr. Mem. So. Ind. Realtors Assn., (past pres. Realtor of Yr.) Nat. Assn. Realtors, Ind. Assn. Realtor (bd. dirs.), Realtors Nat. Mktg. Inst., So. Ind. C. of C. (past bd. dirs., Profl. of Yr.) Rotary (past pres., Paul Harris fellow). Roman Catholic. Home: 2005 Utica Pike Jeffersonville IN 47130-5003 Office: Century 21 Reisert Baker Harrison 1302 E 10th St Jeffersonville IN 47130-4299

REISIN, EFRAIN, nephrologist, researcher, educator; b. Cordoba, Argentina, Feb. 25, 1943; came to U.S., 1979; s. Maximo and Elisa Reisin; m. Ilana Hershkovitz, Sept. 6, 1971; children: Eyal, Thalia Alexis. MD, Nat. U., Cordoba, 1966. Intern internal medicine Nat. U. Cordoba-Clinicas Hosp., 1966; resident Jimenes Diaz Found., Madrid, 1966-68; resident Chaim Sheba Med. Ctr., Tel Hashomer, Israel, 1968-71, fellow in nephrology, 1971-74, staff physician nephrology, 1974-77; rsch. fellow in hypertension Health Sci. Ctr., Winnipeg, Man., Can., 1977-78; vis. scientist in hypertension Nat. Health Welfare Can., Winnipeg, Man., 1978-79; Ochsner vis. scientist in hypertension Ochsner Found. Hosp., New Orleans, 1979-82; from asst. prof. to assoc. prof. medicine La. State U., New Orleans, 1982-89, prof. medicine, 1989—; dir. nephrology dept. Med. Ctr. Charity Hosp., New Orleans, 1985—; panelist Consensus Conf., NIH, Bethesda, Md., 1991. Contbr. numerous articles to med. jours., chpts. to books on hypertension and nephrology; conducted 1st rsch. study documenting positive effects of weight reduction in treatment of hypertension, 1978 (citation classic Inst. Sci. Info. 1988). 1st lt. Israel Army, 1971-72. Grantee Nat. Health and Welfare Can., 1978-79, Am. Heart Assn., 1980-81, also several pharm. cos., 1984—. Fellow ACP, Am. Coun. High Blood Pressure Rsch., Am. Heart Fund, Am. Coll. Clin. Pharmacology (counselor south ctrl. regional chpt. 1991-92), Am. Fedn. Clin. Rsch., So. Soc. for Clin. Investigation; mem. Internat. Soc. Nephrology, Internat. Soc. Hypertension, Am. Soc. Nephrology, Am. Soc. Hypertension, Coun. Nephrology, Am. Heart Assn., Inter-Am. Soc. Hypertension, Orleans Parish Med. Soc. Avocations: tennis, reading, movies. Office: La State U Sch Medicine 1542 Tulane Ave New Orleans LA 70112-2825

REISINGER, GEORGE LAMBERT, management consultant; b. Pitts., Aug. 28, 1930; s. Eugene Merle and Pauline Jane (Lambert) R.; m. Judith Ann Brush, Nov. 24, 1967; children—Douglas Lambert, Christine Elizabeth. B.S. in Bus. Adminstrn., Central Coll., 1953; postgrad., Cleveland-Marshall Law Sch., 1962-67. Asst. personnel mgr. Continental Can Co., Houston, 1958-60; mgr. labor relations The Glidden Co., Cleve., 1960-67; dir. employee relations Mobil Oil Corp., N.Y.C., Caracas, Dallas, Denver, 1967-78; sr. v.p. Minton & Assocs., Denver, 1978-82; v.p., ptnr. Korn-Ferry Internat., Denver, 1982-86; pres. The Sigma Group, Inc., Denver, 1986—. Bd. dirs. Ponderosa Hills Civic Assn., 1977-80, Arapahoe County Youth League, Parker Action Team for Drug Free Colo.; pres. Douglas County Youth League; bd. dirs., steering com. Rocky Mountain Lions Eye Inst. With USAF, 1953-58. Mem. Am. Soc. Personnel Adminstrs., N.Y. Personnel Mgmt. Soc., Colo. Soc. Personnel Adminstrn., Am. Soc. Profl. Cons., Rocky Mountain Inst. Fgn. Trade and Fin., Employment Mgmt. Assn., Denver Den, Lions Internat. (bd. dirs.). Republican. Methodist. Clubs: Denver Petroleum, Pinery Country, Republican 1200. Lodge: Lions (bd. dirs. Denver den). Home: 7924 Deertrail Dr Parker CO 80134-8262 Office: The Sigma Group Inc 717 17th St Ste 1440 Denver CO 80202-3314

REISINGER, SANDRA SUE, journalist, lawyer; b. Washington Court House, Ohio, Feb. 27, 1946; d. Dale E. and Elinor Jean (McMurray) R. BS, Ohio State U., 1968, MA, 1969; JD, U. Dayton (Ohio), 1980. Bar: Ohio 1980. Teaching asst. Ohio State U., 1968-69; with Dayton Daily News, 1969-81, asst. mng. editor, 1976-81; mng. editor The Miami (Fla.) News, 1981-89, Broward Miami (Fla.) Herald, 1989-93, dep. mng. editor, 1994—; adj. prof. Sinclair (Ohio) C.C., 1971-74, U. Dayton, Ohio, 1980-81. Mem. ABA, AP Mng. Editors Assn. (bd. dirs. 1982-87, exec. com. 1987-94, pres. 1992). Office: The Miami Herald Pub Co One Herald Plz Miami FL 33132-1693*

REISMAN, ARNOLD, retired management science educator; b. Lodz, Poland, Aug. 2, 1934; came to U.S., 1946, naturalized, 1955; s. Isadore and Rose (Joskowitz) R.; m. Mar. 12, 1955 (div. 1978); children—Miriam Jennie, Ada Jo, Deborah Fawn, Nina Michelle; m. Ellen Kronheim, Aug. 3, 1980. B.S., UCLA, 1955, M.S., 1957, Ph.D., 1963. Registered profl. engr., Calif., Wis., Ohio. Design engr. Los Angeles Dept. Water and Power, 1955-57; assoc. prof. Calif. State U., Los Angeles, 1957-66; prof. U. Wis., Milw., 1966-68; prof. ops. research Case-Western Res. U., Cleve., 1968-95; chmn. dept., 1982-87, ret., 1995; vis. prof. Hebrew U., Jerusalem, 1975; affiliate faculty Japan-Am. Inst. Mgmt. Sci., Honolulu, 1975—; vis. prof. U. Hawaii, Honolulu, 1971; asso. research engr. Western Mgmt. Sci. Inst., UCLA, 1964-65; coordinator programs between inst. Mgmt. Scis. and AAAS, 1971—; examiner N. Central Assn. Colls., Univs. and Secondary Schs., 1971; v.p. Univ. Assocs., Inc. Cleve., 1968-75; expert witness solicitor gen. Dept. Labor, 1969-70, U.S. Equal Opportunities Commn., 1976-79, Office of Atty. Gen., State of Ohio, 1981; cons. to asst. sec. HEW, 1971-72, Office Program

Planning and Evaln., U.S. Office Edn., 1972-73; cons. Project Hope, 1981-82, Pan Am. Health Orgn., 1981—, Minister of Health, Barbados, 1989—, IRS Div. Research, 1985, UN Devel. Programme, 1988; cons. in gen. field systems analysis to numerous corps. and instns.; invited lectr. USSR Acad. Scis., 1989, Hungarian Acad. Sci.s, 1989. Author: Managerial and Engineering Economics, 1971, Systems Approach and The City, 1972, Industrial Inventory Control, 1972, Health Care Delivery Planning, 1973, Systems Analysis in Health Care Delivery, 1979, Materials Management for Health Services, 1980, Computer System Selection, 1981, Management Science Knowledge: Its Creation, Generalization and Consolidation, 1992; co-author: Welcome Tomorrow, 1982; series editor: Operations Management; assoc. editor: Socio Economic Planning Sciences; contbr. numerous articles to profl. jours. U.S. del. to Internat. Fedn. Ops. Research Socs., Conv., Dublin, Ireland, 1972; Review Bd. mem. Lake Erie Regional Transp. Authority, 1974-75; mem. del. assembly Jewish Community Fedn. Cleve., 1974-76; mem. Shaker Heights (Ohio) Citizens adv. com., 1972-84; bd. dirs., founder Greater Cleve. Coalition on Health Care Cost Effectiveness; Trustee Hillel Found. Named Cleve. Engr. of Yr., 1973; NSF fellow, 1963. Fellow AAAS (council), Soc. Advanced Med. Systems; mem. Ops. Rsch. Soc. Am., Inst. Mgmt. Scis., ASME, Pan Am. Health Orgn., Am. Soc. Engring. Edn., AAUP, Am. Inst. Indsl. Engrs., N.Y. Acad. Scis., Nat. Soc. Profl. Engrs., Sigma Xi, Phi Delta Kappa. Home: 18428 Parkland Dr Cleveland OH 44122-3451

REISMAN, BERNARD, theology educator; b. N.Y.C., July 15, 1926; s. Herman and Esther Sarah (Kavesh) R.; m. Elaine Betty Sokol, Aug. 26, 1951; children: Joel Ira, Sharon Fay, Eric K., Robin Sue. B in Social Sci, CCNY, 1949; M in Social Sci. and Adminstrn., Western Res. U., 1951; PhD, Brandeis U., 1970; LHD (hon.), Hebrew Coll., Boston, 1995; DHL (hon.), Gratz Coll., Phila., 1995. Agy. dir. Jewish Community Ctr., Chgo., 1951-67; prof. Brandeis U., Waltham, Mass., 1969—, dir. Hornstein program in Jewish communal svc., 1971-93; Klutznick prof. Contemporary Jewish Studies, 1993—; lectr. in field; vis. prof. Baerwald Sch. Social Work, Hebrew U., Jerusalem, 1978, Ctr. Jewish Edn. in Diaspora, 1978; sr. cons. Josephtal Found., Jerusalem, 1978; cons. European coun. Am. Joint Distbn. Com., 1978, Inst. for Jewish Life, N.Y.C., 1972-76; rsch. assoc. on future of religion Nat. Coun. Chs., 1972-73; Arnulf Pins meml. lectr. Hebrew U., Jerusalem, 1983, 84. Author: Reform Is a Verb, 1972, The Jewish Experiential Book: Quest for Jewish Identity, 1978, The Chavurah: A Contemporary Jewish Experience, 1977; contbr. articles to profl. jours. With AUS, 1944-46, ETO. Recipient Farfel Jewish Family Svc. award, 1984; Whiting Found. grantee, 1977. Mem. Conf. Jewish Communal Svc. (chmn. publs. com. 1980—), Nat. Jewish Family Ctr., Am. Jewish Com. (1st chmn. acad. adv. com. 1979-82, 75th Anniversary award 1981), Am. Jewish Hist. Soc. (acad. coun. 1979—), Assn. for Jewish Studies. Home: 28 Fairway Dr Newton MA 02165-1713 Office: Brandeis Univ Hornstein Prog in Jewish Communal Svc Waltham MA 02254

REISMAN, FREDRICKA KAUFFMAN, education educator; b. Rochester, N.Y., Sept. 22, 1930; d. Samuel Hopkins and Rosalind (Lessen) Kauffman; 1 dau., Lisa Reisman Halterman. Student, Barnard Coll., 1951; B.A., Syracuse U., 1952, M.S., 1963, Ph.D., 1968. Lectr. Syracuse U., 1967-69; adj. assoc. prof. ednl. psychology Maria Regina Coll., Syracuse, N.Y., 1968; asst. prof. elem. edn. U. Ga., Athens, 1969-74; assoc. prof. U. Ga., 1974-79, prof. and chair early childhood middle sch. and elem. edn., prof. math. edn. and spl. edn., 1979-83; vis. prof., dept. human behavior and devel.; coordinator tchr.-scholar program Drexel U., Phila., 1984-85, dir. Div. of Instrn. and Program/head tchr. preparation, 1991—; prof., dir. tchr. preparation, certification officer Drexel U., 1986—; vis. prof. U. Calif., Riverside, Marianne Frostig Center Ednl. Therapy, Los Angeles; cons. diagnostic teaching math.; mem. program approval com. Pa. State Dept. Edn., 1984—, tchr. cert. com., 1984—. Author: Guide to the Diagnostic Teaching of Arithmetic, 1972, 3d edit., 1982, Diagnostic Teaching of Elementary School Mathematics: Methods and Content, 1977, 2d edit., 1981, (with S. H. Kaufman) Teaching Mathematics to Children with Special Needs, 1980, Sequential Assessment in Mathematics, 1985, Elementary Education: A Basic Text, 1987; contbr. articles to profl. jours. Recipient outstanding faculty citizen recognition Am. Assn. Higher Edn., 1994. Mem. Nat. Coun. Tchrs. Math., Am. Psychol. Assn., Internat. Assn. Applied Psychology, Soc. for Rsch. in Child Devel., Sch. Sci. and Math. Assn., ASCD, Assn. for Tchr. Educators, Am. Edn. Rsch. Assn., Sigma Xi, Pi Lambda Theta, Phi Delta Kappa.

REISMAN, ROBERT E., physician, educator; b. Buffalo, Nov. 1, 1932; s. Harry S. and Jessie (Goldberg) R.; m. Rena Estry, Sept. 5, 1954; children: Jeanne, Linda, Nancy, David. M.D., SUNY-Buffalo, 1956; Dr.h.c., U. Montpellier (France), 1982. Diplomate Am. Bd. Internal Medicine (bd. dirs. 1984-86), Am. Bd. Allergy and Clin. Immunology (bd. dirs. 1981-86, chmn. 1985, mem. residency rev. com. for allergy and immunology, 1988-93, chmn. 1990-91). Intern Buffalo Gen. Hosp., 1956-57, resident in medicine, 1957-59; practice medicine specializing in allergy and clin. immunology Buffalo, 1961—; clin. prof. pediatrics and medicine SUNY, Buffalo, 1979—; co-dir. Allergy Research Lab., Buffalo Gen. Hosp., 1970-90 ; mem. panel on allergenic extracts Bur. Biologics, FDA. Served with U.S. Army, 1968-69. Master ACP; fellow Am. Acad. Allergy (pres. 1980-81). Home: 113 Carriage Cir Buffalo NY 14221-2163 Office: 295 Essjay Rd Williamsville NY 14221-8216 also: 85 High St Buffalo NY 14203-1194

REISMAN, WILLIAM M., lawyer, educator; b. 1939. LL.B., Hebrew U., 1963; LL.M., Yale U., 1964, J.S.D., 1965. Bar: Conn. 1964. Assoc. prof. Yale U. Law Sch., New Haven, 1969-72, prof., 1972-82, Hohfeld prof. jurisprudence, 1982—. Author: Nullity and Revision, 1971, Art of the Possible: Diplomatic Alternatives in Middle East, 1970, Puerto Rico and the International Process, 1974, Folded Lies: Bribery, Crusades and Reforms, 1979, (with Weston) Toward World Order and Human Dignity, 1976, (with McDougal) International Law in Contemporary Perspective, 1981, (with McDougal) International Law Essays, 1981, (with McDougal) Power and Policy in Quest of Law: Essays in Honor of Eugene V. Rostow, 1985, (with Schreiber) Jurisprudence: Understanding and Shaping Law, 1986, (with Willard) International Incidents: The Law that Counts in World Politics, 1988, (with James E. Baker) Regulating Covert Action: Practices, Contexts and Policies of Covert Coercion Abroad in International and American Law, 1991, Systems of Control in International Adjudication and Arbitration: Breakdown and Repair, 1992, (with Westerman) Straight Baselines in International Maritime Boundary Delimitation, 1992. Fulbright grantee, 1966-67. Office: Yale U Law Sch PO Box 401 New Haven CT 06520-0401

REISMANN, HERBERT, engineer, educator; b. Vienna, Austria, Jan. 26, 1926; s. Henrik and Olga (Pokorny) R.; m. Edith Falber, Aug. 14, 1952; children—Sandra Jean, Barbara Anne. BS in Aero. Engring., Ill. Inst. Tech., 1947, MS, 1949; PhD in Engring., U. Colo., 1962. Project engr. Convair, Ft. Worth, 1951-53; prin. structures engr. Republic Aviation Corp., Hicksville, N.Y., 1954-56; chief engr. systems analysis, chief solid mechanics Martin Marietta Corp., 1957-64; prof., dir. aerospace engring. SUNY, Buffalo, 1964—; Cons. NASA, Bell Aero Systems Corp. Co-author: Elastokinetics, 1974, Elasticity, 1980; author: Elastic Plates, 1988; contbr. articles to profl. jours. Assoc. fellow AIAA award best tech. paper 1962, oustanding aerospace achievement award 1987); mem. ASME, Internat. Assn. Bridge and Structural Engring., AAUP, Sigma Xi, Tau Beta Pi. Home: 71 Chaumont Dr Buffalo NY 14221-3511 Office: SUNY-Buffalo 605 Furnas Hall Buffalo NY 14260

REISNER, HOWARD MICHAEL, immunologist, educator; b. N.Y.C., June 24, 1946; s. Joe and Mildred (Belman) R.; m. Emily Ann Grothaus, Dec. 22, 1971; 1 child, Walter William. BS, CCNY, 1967; PhD, Case Western Reserve, 1972. Instr. U. N.C., Chapel Hill, 1975-80; asst. prof. U. N.C., 1980-85, assoc. prof., 1985—; bd. dirs. Lympholyte Tech. Ctr., Rsch. Triangle Park, N.C., 1987-90. Contbr. articles to profl. jours. NIH grantee, 1989—; postdoctoral fellow N.C., 1972-75. Mem. Am. Soc. Hematology, Am. Assn. Pathologists, Internat. Soc. Thrombosis Haemostasis, Triangle Area Rsch. Dirs. Club (sec. 1991—). Achievements include research in immunogenetics of hemophilia. Home: 2834 Stuart Dr Durham NC 27707-2860 Office: U NC Pathology Clb # 27525 Chapel Hill NC 27599

REISNER, MILTON, psychiatrist, psychoanalyst; b. N.Y.C., Jan. 30, 1934; s. Maximillian and Dora Reisner; m. Linda Ellis, Mar. 3, 1959 (div. 1975); children: Margaret Ann, Amanda Lee. BA, NYU, 1954; MD, Downstate

Med. Ctr., 1958. Diplomate Nat. Bd. Med. Examiners, N.Y. State Bd. Psychiat. Examiners. Resident in psychiatry Kings County Hosp., Bklyn., 1959-62; sr. psychiatrist Manhattan VA Hosp., N.Y.C., 1962-66; assoc. dir. psychiatry Westchester Community Mental Health Bd., White Plains, N.Y., 1966-69; dir. psychiatry Westchester Mental Health Bd., White Plains, 1969-74; pvt. practice N.Y.C., 1976—; cons. Cath. Charities, N.Y.C., 1965-66, H.I.P., N.Y.C., 1973-74, NYU Med. Ctr., 1963-68. Contbr. articles to profl. jours. Lt. j.g. USPHS, 1958-59. Fellow Am. Soc. Psychoanalytic Physicians; mem. Am. Assn. Psychoanalytic Physicians (pres. 1985-86, 87-88, Plaque 1988), Nat. Arts Club, Phi Beta Kappa. Achievements include research in mirroring as a technique for treating delusions. Office: 200 E 84th St New York NY 10028-2906

REISS, ALBERT JOHN, JR., sociology educator; b. Cascade, Wis., Dec. 9, 1922; s. Albert John and Erma Amanda (Schueler) R.; children: Peter C., Paul Wetherington, Amy. Student, Mission House Coll., 1939-42; Ph.B., Marquette U., 1944; M.A., U. Chgo., 1948, Ph.D., 1949; LL.D. (hon.), CUNY, 1980; Docteur (honoris causa), U. Montreal, 1985. Instr. sociology U. Chgo., 1947-49, asst. prof., 1949-52; asso. dir. Chgo. Community Inventory (U. Chgo.), 1948-51, acting dir., 1951-52; asso. prof. sociology Vanderbilt U., 1952-58, prof., 1954-58, chmn. dept., 1952-58; prof. sociology and dir. Iowa Urban Community Research Center, State U. Iowa, 1958-60; prof. sociology, dir. survey research labs. U. Wis., 1960-61; prof. sociology, dir. U. Mich. Center for Research on Social Orgn., Ann Arbor, 1961-70, chmn. dept., 1970; prof. sociology Yale U., 1970—, prof. social sci. Inst. Social and Polit. Sci., 1970-87, chmn. dept., 1972-80, 85-89; chmn. Census Com. on Enumeration Areas, Chgo., 1950-52, Nashville, 1952-58; mem. tech. adv. com. Chgo. Plan Commn., 1951-52; cons. USAF Human Resources Research Inst., 1952-54. Author: A Survey of Probation Needs and Services in Illinois, 1947, (with Paul K. Hatt) Reader in Urban Sociology, 1951, (with Evelyn R. Kitagawa) Mobility of Chicago Workers, 1951, Social Characteristics of Rural and Urban Communities, 1950 (with Otis Dudley Duncan), 1956, Cities and Society, 1958, Occupational and Social Status, 1960, The Police and the Public, 1971, (with J. Roth) Understanding and Preventing Violence, 1993. Served as pvt., meteorology program A.C., AUS, 1943-44. Recipient Disting. Alumnus award Lakeland Coll., 1990, Beccaria Gold medal, 1990. Fellow Am. Sociol. Assn. (chmn. methodology sect. 1960, coun. and exec. com. 1962-65), Sociol. Rsch. Assn. (pres. 1969), Am. Statis. Assn.; mem. NAS (chmn.), Ohio Valley Sociol. Soc. (pres. 1966), Am. Soc. Criminology (pres. 1983-84), Soc. for Study Social Problems (pres. 1968), Social Rsch. (pres. 1949), Internat. Soc. Criminology (sci. commn. 1982-89, pres. sci. commn. 1985-89, pres. 1990-95). Home: 600 Prospect St Apt 7A New Haven CT 06511-2116 Office: Yale U Dept Sociology PO Box 208265 New Haven CT 06520-8265

REISS, ALVIN, writer; b. Ft. Sill, Okla., Oct. 31, 1932; s. Clarence Gustav Alvin and Mabel Alma (Craig) R.; m. Audrey Spencer, Sept. 1, 1951 (div. 1974); children—Belinda, Karen. Student, U. Oreg., 1950-51, So. Oreg. Coll., 1969. With Union Pacific and Denver & Rio Grande, 1951-61, chief clk., 1955-61; with KBOY-FM, Medford, Oreg., 1961-68; FM program dir. KBOY-FM, 1966-68; news dir. KYJC, Medford, 1969-73; staff writer Medford Mail Tribune, 1969—; dir. Rogue Valley Writers Conf. So. Oreg. State Coll., 1992, 93, 94. Screenwriter, Larry Lansburgh Films, Inc., 1972 (Recipient John Masefield Meml. award Poetry Soc. Am. 1970, regional award for playwriting, Chgo., 1965, Ala. 1963); author (plays) The Smallest Giant, 1963, River Children, 1983, Nines and Lunch, 1986, also stories, poetry; contbg. writer: Matinee at the Bijou, 1984-85. Recipient Fiction prize West Wind Review, 1986, 2d prize Oreg. State Poetry Assn., 1987, 1st prize Oreg. State Poetry Assn., 1988. Mem. Am. Theater Critics Assn. (exec. com. 1983-86, adv. council 1986), Internat. Assn. Theatre Critics, Poetry Soc. Am., Jacksonville Art Alliance (poetry instr., dir. 1983), Mensa, Dramatists Guild, Authors League Am., Sigma Delta Chi (pres. So. Oreg. chpt. 1977-78). Home: PO Box 597 115 F St Jacksonville OR 97530 Office: c/o Archer King Ltd 10 Columbus Cir New York NY 10019

REISS, DALE ANNE, investment company executive, accounting executive; b. Chgo., Sept. 3, 1947; d. Max and Nan (Hart) R.; m. Jerome L. King, Mar. 5, 1978; 3 children: Matthew Reiss, Mitchell, Stacey King. BS, Ill. Inst. Tech., 1967; MBA, U. Chgo., 1970. CPA, Ill. Cost acct. First Nat. Bank, Chgo., 1967; asst. controller City Colls. of Chgo., 1967-71; dir. fin. Chgo. Dept. Pub. Works, 1971-73; prin. Arthur Young & Co., Chgo., 1973-80; sr. v.p., controller Urban Investment & Devel. Co., Chgo., 1980-85, mng. ptnr. Kenneth Leventhal & Co., Chgo., 1985—; bd. dirs., treas. Latin Sch. Chgo., Ill. Inst. Tech., Urban Land Inst., The Chgo. Network; adv. bd. Kellogg Real Estate. Mem. Fin. Execs. Inst., AICPA, Chgo. Network. Clubs: Econ. of Chgo., Metropolitan, Chgo. Yacht. Office: Kenneth Leventhal & Co 1 N Franklin St Ste 2100 Chicago IL 60606-3401

REISS, HOWARD, chemistry educator; b. N.Y.C., Apr. 5, 1922; s. Isidor and Jean (Goldstein) R.; m. Phyllis Kohn, July 25, 1945; children: Gloria, Steven. A.B. in Chemistry, NYU, 1943; Ph.D. in Chemistry, Columbia U., 1949. With Manhattan Project, 1944-46; instr., then asst. prof. chemistry Boston U., 1949-51; with Central Research Lab., Celanese Corp. Am., 1951-52, Edgar C. Bain Lab. Fundamental Research, U.S. Steel Corp., 1957, Bell Telephone Labs., 1952-60; asso. dir., then dir. research div. Atomics Internat., div. N.Am. Aviation, Inc., 1960-62; dir. N.Am. Aviation Sci. Center, 1962-67, v.p. co., 1963-67; v.p. research aerospace systems group N.Am. Rockwell Corp., 1967-68; vis. lectr. chemistry U. Calif. at Berkeley, summer 1957; vis. prof. chemistry UCLA, 1961, 62, 64, 67, prof., 1968-91, prof. emeritus, 1991—; vis. prof. U. Louis Pasteur, Strasbourg, France, 1986, U. Pa., 1989; vis. fellow Victoria U., Wellington, New Zealand, 1989; cons. to chem.-physics program Air Force Cambridge Rsch. Cambridge Rsch. Labs., 1950-52; chmn. editor proc. Internat. Conf. Nucleation and Interfacial Phenomena, Boston; mem. Air Force Office Sci. Rsch. Physics and Chemistry Rsch. Evaluation Groups, 1966—; Oak Ridge Nat. Lab. Reactor Chemistry Adv. Com., 1966-68; adv. com. math. and phys. scis. NSF, 1970-72, ARPA Materials Rsch. Coun., 1968—; chmn. site rev. com. NRC Associateships Program, Naval Rsch. Lab., 1989. Author: The Methods of Thermodynamics, 1965; author articles; editor in field.; editor: Progress in Solid State Chemistry, 1962-71, Jour. Statis. Physics, 1968-75, Jour. Colloid Interface Sci; mem. editorial adv. bd. Internat. Jour. Physics and Chemistry of Solids, 1955, Progress in Solid State Chemistry, 1962-73, Jour. Solid State Chemistry, 1969, Jour. Phys. Chemistry, 1970-73, Ency. of Solid State, 1970, Jour. Nonmetals, 1971—, Jour. Colloid and Interface Sci., 1976-79, Langmuir, 1985—. Guggenheim Meml. fellow, 1978. Fellow AAAS, Am. Phys. Soc. (exec. com. div. chem. physics 1966-69); mem. NAS, Am. Chem. Soc. (chmn. phys. chemistry sect. N.J. sect. 1957, Richard C. Tolman medal 1973, Kendall award in colloid and surface chemistry 1980, J.H. Hildebrand award in theoretical and exptl. phys. chemistry of liquids 1991, Van Arkel hon. chair in chemistry U. Leiden, The Netherlands, 1994), Phi Beta Kappa, Sigma Xi, Phi Lambda Upsilon. Office: U Calif Dept Chemistry Los Angeles CA 90024

REISS, IRA LEONARD, sociology educator, writer; b. N.Y.C., Dec. 8, 1925; s. Philip and Dorothy (Jacobs) R.; m. Harriet Marilyn Eisman, Sept. 4, 1955; children: David, Pamela, Joel. BS cum laude, Syracuse U., 1949; MA, Pa. State U., 1951, PhD, 1953. Instr. in sociology Bowdoin Coll., Brunswick, Maine, 1953-55; asst. prof. sociology Coll. William and Mary, Williamsburg, Va., 1955-59; asst. prof. Bard Coll., Annandale-On-Hudson, N.Y., 1959-61; assoc. to full prof. U. Iowa, Iowa City, 1961-69; prof. U. Minn., Mpls., 1969—; rsch. evaluator U.S. Dept. Edn. and Nat. Inst. Child Health and Human Devel., Washington, 1966-78; rsch. dir. Family Study Ctr., U. Minn., 1969-74; ednl. advisor Kimberly-Clark corp., Neenah, Wis., 1971-75; chair planning com. and bd. dirs. Inst. for Child, Adolescent Sexual Health, 1992-93; lectr. at 200 univs., 150 profl. mtgs., 100 civic groups, 1953—; vis. prof. Uppsala Univ., Sweden, 1975-76. Author: Premarital Sexual Standards in America, 1960, The Social Context of Premarital Sexual Permissiveness, 1967, Family Systems in America (4 edits.), 1971, 76, 80, 88, Journey into Sexuality: An Exploratory Voyage, 1986, An End to Shame: Shaping Our Next Sexual Revolution, 1990; editor 3 textbooks; contbr. over 100 articles to jours. and chpts. to textbooks in field. Mem. ACLU, 1948—, Planned Parenthood, 1960—, Nat. Abortion Rights Action League 1975—, Amnesty Internat., 1984—.With U.S. Army, 1944-46, ETO. Mem. Midwest Sociol. Soc. (pres. 1971-72), Am. Sociol. Assn. (chair family sect. 1975-76), Nat. Coun. on Family Rels. (pres. 1979-80, Reuben Hill award 1980, E.W. Burgess award 1984), Polish Acad. Sexual Sci. (hon., Internat. Sexual Sci. award 1989), Soc. for Sci. Study Sex (pres. 1980-81, Disting. Sci. Achieve-

ment award 1982, Alfred Kinsey award 1990), Internat. Acad. Sex Rsch. (pres. 1984-85), Am. Assn. Sex Educators, Counselors and Therapists (leadership award 1993). Democrat. Jewish. Avocations: good conversations with family and friends. Home: 5932 Medicine Lake Rd Minneapolis MN 55422-3328 Office: U Minn Dept Sociology 1031 Social Scis 267 19th Ave S Minneapolis MN 55455-0499

REISS, JEFFREY CHARLES, television executive; b. Bklyn., Apr. 14, 1942; s. Samuel and Hilda (Caplan) R.; m. Ellen Breckir Lear, Oct. 19, 1969. A.B., Washington U., St. Louis, 1963. Lectr. biology and sci. Bklyn. Coll., 1964-65; asst. lit. dept. Gen. Artists Corp. (name now Internat. Creative Mgmt.), N.Y.C., 1964-65; spl. instr. Project Apex, NYU, 1965-66; tchr. high sch. Commack and Freeport, N.Y., 1966-68; story editor Tandem Prodns., N.Y.C., 1968-69; ptnr. Kleiman-Reiss Prodns., producers off-Broadway plays, 1969-70; dir. programming Cartridge TV Inc., N.Y.C., 1970-73; founder, pres. Showtime Entertainment, pay TV network, N.Y.C., 1976-80; exec. v.p Viacom entertainment group Viacom Internat. Inc., N.Y.C., 1980-81; pres. Reiss Video Devel. Corp., cons., N.Y.C., 1981—; pres., chief exec. officer Cable Health Network, Inc., N.Y.C., 1981-83, vice chmn., chief exec. officer, 1983-84; chmn., chief exec. officer Reiss Media Enterprises Inc., 1984—; founder Request T.V. (parent co. Reiss Media Enterprises Inc.), 1985—; cons. in field. Contbg. author: Broadcasting Programming: Strategies for Winning Television and Radio Audiences, 1981, 2d edit., 1984. Recipient Effie award, 1978. Mem. Nat. Acad. TV Arts and Scis., Internat. Radio and TV Soc., Nat. Cable TV Assn. (award for excellence 1979), Cable TV Adminstrn. and Mktg. Soc., Cabletelevision Advt. Bur., Women in Cable. Office: Group W Satellite Communications 685 3rd Ave 20th FL New York NY 10017-3144

REISS, JEROME, lawyer; b. Bklyn., Dec. 7, 1924; s. William and Eva (Marenstein) R.; m. Naomi Betty Plutzik, June 15, 1947 (div.); children: Robert Scott, Harlan Morgan, Andrea Ellen, Samantha Glynis. BA, Bklyn. Coll., 1948; JD, Harvard U., 1951. Bar: N.Y. 1951, D.C. 1967. Staff atty. civil br. Legal Aid Soc., 1951-54; asst. corp. counsel City of N.Y., 1954-58; assoc. Max E. Greenberg, 1958-67; sr. ptnr. Max E. Greenberg, Trayman, Cantor, Reiss & Blasky, 1967-80, Max E. Greenberg, Cantor & Reiss, N.Y.C., 1980-88, Thelen, Marrin, Johnson & Bridges, N.Y.C., 1989—; lectr. on constrn. law; Small Claims Ct. arbitrator, 1960-88; bd. advisors Fed. Pub., Inc. Gen. counsel Artist Fellowship, Inc. Cpl. USAAF, 1943-46. Mem. ABA, Am. Judges Assn., Am. Coll. Constrn. Lawyers, Internat. Bar Assn., Mcpl. Assist. Corp. of City of N.Y. (bd. dirs.), Jacob K. Javits Convention Ctr. Oper. Corp. (bd. dirs.). Contbr. articles to profl. jours., chpts. in books.

REISS, JOHN BARLOW, lawyer; b. London, Aug. 29, 1939; came to U.S., 1963; s. James Martin and Margaret Joan (Ping) R.; m. Mary Jean Maudsley, Aug. 6, 1967 (div. 1978); m. Kathleen Strouse, Aug. 2, 1979; 1 child, Juliette Blanche. BA with honors, Exeter U., Devon, Eng., 1961; AM, Washington U., St. Louis, 1966, PhD, 1971; JD, Temple U., 1977. Bar: Pa. 1977, N.J. 1977, U.S. Dist. Ct. N.J. 1977, D.C. 1980, U.S. Supreme Ct. 1981, U.S. Dist. Ct. D.C. 1982. Economist Commonwealth Econ. Com., London, 1962-63; asst. prof. Allegheny Coll., Meadville, Pa., 1967-71; assoc. prof. Stockton State Coll., Pomona, N.J., 1971-75; asst. health commr. State of N.J., Trenton, 1975-79; dir. office of health regulation U.S. Dept. HHS, Washington, 1979-81; assoc. Baker & Hostetler, Washington, 1981-82; assoc. Dechert Price & Rhoads, Phila., 1982-86, ptnr., 1986-93, asst. chair health law group, 1984-91, chmn. health law group, 1991-93; ptnr. Saul, Ewing, Remick & Saul, Phila., 1993—, chmn. health law dept., 1995—. Mem. editl. bd. Topics in Hosp. Law, 1985-86, Hosp. Legal Forms Manual, 1985—, Jour. Health Care Tech., 1984-86; contbr. Hosp. Contracts Manual, 1983—; contbr. articles to profl. jours., chpts. to books. Bd. dirs. Gateway Sch. Little Children, Phila., 1986—, ECRI, Plymouth Meeting, Pa., 1994—; mem. vestry All Saints Ch., Wynnewood, Pa., 1993. Pub. Health Svc. fellow, 1979-81, English Speaking Union fellow, 1963-66, Econ. Devel. Adminstr. fellow Washington U., 1966-67. Mem. Nat. Health Lawyers Assn., N.J. Soc. Hosp. Attys., Phila. Bar Assn., Am. Hosp. Assn., N.J. Hosp. Assn., Brit. Am. C. of C. of Greater Phila. (bd. dirs. 1991). Avocations: gardening, house restoring, reading, philately. Home: 415 Wister Rd Wynnewood PA 19096-1808 Office: Saul Ewing Remick & Saul 3800 Centre Sq W Philadelphia PA 19102

REISS, JOHN C., bishop; b. Red Bank, N.J., May 13, 1922; s. Alfred and Sophia (Telljohan) R. Student, Immaculate Conception Sem., 1941-46; B.A., Steon Hall U., 1947; S.T.L., Catholic U., 1947, J.C.D., 1953. Ordained Priest Roman Catholic Ch., 1947. Asst. chancellor Diocese of Trenton, 1954, sec., master ceremonies, 1953-62, vice chancellor, 1956-62, officials, 1962-80, aux. bishop, 1967-80, bishop, 1982—. Mem. Trenton Mayor's Adv. Commn. on Civil Rights, 1962-68. Home: 901 W State St Trenton NJ 08618-5327 Office: 901 W State St Trenton NJ 08618*

REISS, MARTIN HAROLD, engineering executive; b. Long Beach, N.Y., Aug. 16, 1935; s. Arthur and Mary (Schreckinger) R.; m. Rhea Cohen, June 24, 1956; children—Mitchell, Randi, Robyn. B.S., MIT, 1956; M.S., Ohio State U., 1959; M.S., MIT, 1961. Staff member MIT Inst. Lab., Cambridge, 1959-61; tech. dir. Raytheon Co., Sudbury, Mass., 1961-65; pres. Alarmtronics Engring., Newton, Mass., 1965-73, Gamewell Corp., Medway, Mass., 1973-83, chmn. bd., 1983-90; dir. Cerberus Techs., Inc., Waltham, Mass., 1990-93, pres., Rolf, Jensen & Assoc., 1993—; sustaining fellow MIT, 1981—; bd. overseers WPI Fire Scis., Worchester, Mass., 1985—, chmn., 1989—; dir. Practicorp, Newton 1984-88; dir., treas. Nat. Fire Protection Research Found., Quincy, Mass., 1982—; dir. Nat. Fire Protection Assn., Quincy, 1991—. Patentee in field. Trustee Mass. Bay Community Coll., Wellesley, 1980-90, chmn. bd., 1985-86. Served to capt. USAF, 1956-59. Mem. Nat. Elec. Mfg. Assn. (sect. chmn. 1983-85, Man of Yr. award 1985), Automatic Fire Alarm Assn. (pres. 1978-80, Man of Yr. award 1985, bd. dirs. 1980-93), Soc. Fire Protection Engrs. (bd. dirs. 1988-94). Office: Rolf Jensen & Assoc 55 William St Wellesley MA 02181-4002

REISS, MICHAEL, medical oncologist, researcher; b. Addis Ababa, Ethiopia, Sept. 22, 1950; came to U.S., 1982; s. Willy and Lea (Gerzon) R.; m. Elisabeth Meta Souget, Mar. 15, 1977; children: Kim, Daniel J. Student, U. Amsterdam Med. Sch., The Netherlands, 1968-73; MD, U. Amsterdam, 1976. Cert. Bd. Internal Medicine, The Netherlands; fed. licensing exam.; lic. physician Conn. Clk., subintern U. Amsterdam Hosps. and Affiliated Hosps., 1974-76; rsch. assoc. Cen. Lab. Netherlands Red Cross Blood Trans. Lab. for Immunology, U. Amsterdam, 1976-77; intern in internal medicine Med. Coll. Ohio, Toledo, 1977-78; resident in internal medicine U. Hosp. Binnengasthuis, Amsterdam, 1978-82; rotation in med. oncology Netherlands Cancer Inst., Amsterdam, 1980; postdoctoral fellow in med. oncology Yale U. Sch. Medicine, 1982-85, instr. in med. oncology, 1985-87, asst. prof. dept. internal medicine Yale Comp. Cancer Ctr., 1987-91, assoc. prof. dept. internal medicine Yale Comp. Cancer Ctr., 1991—; attending physician Yale New Haven Hosp., 1985—; med. oncologist Yale Comprehensive Breast Care Ctr., 1989—, co-dir., 1992—; dir. breast cancer rsch. program Yale Cancer Ctr., 1994—; chmn. rsch. com. sect. med. oncology Yale U. Sch. Medicine, 1986—; fellowship com. sect. med. oncology, 1986—, cancer edn. com. Yale Comprehensive Cancer Ctr., 1989—, funds and fellowships com., 1991-95; mem. instnl. grant rev. com. Am. Cancer Soc., 1988-94; invited mem. Sec.'s Spl. Conf. on Breast Cancer, NIH, 1993; reviewer Netherlands Cancer Found. Rsch. Grants. Reviewer: Cancer Rsch., Blood, Jour. Cell Physiology, Cancer Comms., European Jour. Cancer Clin. Oncology; contbr. articles to profl. jours. 2d lt. Dutch Army, 1975-77. Recipient Swebilius Cancer Rsch. award, 1985-86; clin. fellow Queen Wilhelmina Cancer Found., Amsterdam, 1982-84; rsch. grantee numerous orgns. Mem. AAAS, Am. Assn. for Cancer Rsch., Am. Soc. Clin. Oncology, Am. Soc. Cell Biology, Am. Fedn. for Clin. Rsch. Avocations: complexity theory, computers, fishing, cycling, music. Office: Yale U Sch of Medicine 333 Cedar St New Haven CT 06510

REISS, PAUL JACOB, college president; b. Lake Placid, N.Y., Aug. 10, 1930; s. Julian J. and Margaret M. (Smith) R.; m. Rosemary A. Donohue, June 25, 1955; children: Catherine, Paul, Gregory, Mark, Julia, David, Steven, Martha, John. B.S., Holy Cross Coll., 1952; M.A., Fordham U., 1954; Ph.D., Harvard U., 1960. Tutor Harvard U., 1954-57; instr., asst. prof. Marquette U., 1957-63, chmn. dept. sociology, 1961-63; asso. prof. sociology Fordham U., Bronx, N.Y., 1963-75, prof., 1976-85, chmn. dept. sociology

and anthropology, 1964-68; dean Fordham U. (Liberal Arts Coll.), 1968-69, v.p. acad. affairs, 1969-75, exec. v.p., 1975-85; pres. St. Michael's Coll., Colchester, Vt., 1985—. Editor: Sociological Analysis: A Journal in the Sociology of Religion, 1961-68; contbr. articles to profl. jours. Exec. dir. Julian Reiss Found., Lake Placid, N.Y.; trustee Wadhams Hall Sem. Coll.; bd. dirs. Lake Placid Sinfonietta, Fanny Allen Hosp., Greater Burlington Indsl. Commn., Nat. Assn. Ind. Colls. and Univs., Assn. Cath. Colls. and Univs. Fellow Am. Sociol. Assn.; mem. Assn. for Sociology of Religion (pres.), Assn. Vt. Ind. Colls. (pres.), Vt. Higher Edn. Coun. (pres.), Vt. Bus. Roundtable. Democrat. Roman Catholic. Home: St Michael's Coll Colchester VT 05439

REISS, SIDNEY H., judge, lawyer; b. Passaic, N.J., Nov. 2, 1926; s. Theodore and Mollie (Holder) R.; m. Anester Feld, Apr. 3, 1955; children: Theodore F., Marci. BS, U.S. Mcht. Marine Acad., 1949; JD, Rutgers U., Newark, 1955; BA (hon.), Passaic County Coll., Paterson, N.J. 1976. Bar: N.J. 1956, U.S. Dist. Ct. N.J. 1956, U.S. Supreme Ct. 1957. Pvt. practice, Passaic, 1956-65; sr. ptnr. Reiss & Scancarella, Passaic, 1965-76; judge Superior Ct., State of N.J., Paterson, 1976—; criminal assignment judge, 1983—. Counsel Passaic County Bd. Social Svcs.; councilman City of Passaic, 1967-71; freeholder Passaic County, 1971-76, freeholder dir., 1974-75. Lt. USN, 1945-51, PTO, Korea. Recipient Disting. Svc. award Passaic C. of C., 1970, trustees outstanding achievement citation Passaic County Children's Shelter, 1973, outstanding svc. citation as criminal assigment judge Assn. Criminal Def. Lawyers of N.J., 1990. Mem. ABA, N.J. Bar Assn., Passaic County Bar Assn., Am. Legon, Masons, Lions (pres. Passaic 1964-65). Home: 85 Elmwood Ave Passaic NJ 07055-2408 Office: Passaic County Ct House Paterson NJ 07505

REISS, STEVEN ALAN, lawyer, law educator; b. N.Y.C., Dec. 18, 1951; s. Louis and Ruth (Harrow) R.; m. Mary A. Mattingly; children: Alexandra Mattingly Reiss, Tyler Brennan Reiss. BA, Vassar Coll., 1973; JD, Stanford (Calif.) U., 1976. Bar: N.Y., D.C., Calif. Law clk. to John Minor Wisdom U.S. Ct. Appeals for 5th Cir., New Orleans, 1976-77; law clk. to justice William J. Brennan U.S Supreme Ct., Washington, 1977-78; assoc. Miller, Cassidy, Larroca & Lewin, Washington, 1978-80; vis. prof. Georgetown U. Law Ctr., Washington, 1981; asst. prof. Law Sch., NYU, 1981-83, assoc. prof., 1984-87, prof., 1987-91; ptnr. Weil, Gotshal & Manges, N.Y.C., 1990—. Editor-in-chief White Collar Crime Reporter, 1987—. Trustee Vassar Coll., Poughkeepsie, N.Y., 1978-82; bd. dirs. NYU Cmty. Fund, 1984-87, Concert Artists Guild, 1991-94. Mem. N.Y. State Bar Assn., D.C. Bar Assn., Calif. Bar Assn., Assn. of Bar of City of N.Y. (fed. legis. com. 1981-87), 2d Jud. Conf. (reporter 1984—). Home: 25 E 86th St New York NY 10028 Office: Weil Gotshal & Manges 767 5th Ave New York NY 10153-0001

REISS, TIMOTHY JAMES, comparative literature educator, writer; b. Stanmore, Eng., May 14, 1942; came to U.S., 1964, 84; s. James Martin and Margaret Joan (Ping) R.; m. Patricia J. Penn Hilden, 1988; children from previous marriage: Matthew James, Suzanna Jean, Justin Timothy. B.A. hons., Manchester U., Eng., 1964; M.A., U. Ill., 1965, Ph.D., 1968. Instr. French U. Ill., Urbana, 1967-68; instr., then asst. prof. Yale U., New Haven, 1968-73; assoc. prof., then prof. comparative lit. U. Montreal, Can., 1973-84, dir. comparative lit., 1976-81; prof. comparative lit., French and philosophy Emory U., Atlanta, 1983-86, Samuel Candler Dobbs prof. French and comparative lit., 1986-87; prof. comparative lit. NYU, 1987—, chmn., 1987-94; vis. prof. U. Toronto, 1976-77, U. B.C., Vancouver, 1979, NYU, N.Y.C., 1982, U. Montreal, 1984-87, Grad. Ctr. CUNY, 1985, SUNY, Binghamton, 1988-89. Author: Toward Dramatic Illusion, 1971, Tragedy and Truth, 1980, Discourse of Modernism, 1982, 85, The Uncertainty of Analysis, 1988, The Meaning of Literature, 1992 (Morris D. Forkosch Intellectual History prize); editor: Science, Language and the Perspective Mind, 1973; (with others) Opening Up the Disciplines, 1982, Tragedy and the Tragic, 1983. Morse fellow, 1971-72; Am. Counc. Learned Socs. travel grantee, 1976, fellow, 1986-87; Can. Council fellow Oxford, Eng., 1977-78; rsch. fellow U. Montreal, 1979-80; Social Scis. and Humanities Rsch. Coun. of Can.; sr. fellow Oxford, Eng., 1983-84; Emory U. faculty fellow, 1986-87; Guggenheim fellow, 1990-91. Fellow Royal Soc. Can., Acad. Literary Studies; mem. MLA, Am. Comparative Lit. Assn., Renaissance Soc. Am., C. S. Peirce Soc., Can. Assn. Comparative Lit. (v.p. 1981-83), Internat. Comparative Lit. Assn., Can. Soc. Research in Semiotics. Office: NYU Dept Comparative Lit 19 University Pl New York NY 10003-4501

REISSMAN, MAURICE L., bank executive. Former chief operating officer Crossland Savs., FSB, Bklyn., now pres., chief exec. officer, also chmn. bd. dirs. Office: Crossland Savs FSB 211 Montague St Brooklyn NY 11201-3674

REISSNER, ERIC (MAX ERICH REISSNER), applied mechanics researcher; b. Aachen, Germany, Jan. 5, 1913; came to U.S., 1936, naturalized, 1945; s. Hans and Josephine (Reichenberger) R.; m. Johanna Siegel, Apr. 19, 1938; children: John E., Eva M. Dipl. Ing., Technische Hochschule, Berlin, 1935, Dr. Ing., 1936; Ph.D., MIT, 1938; Dr. Ing. (hon.), U. Hannover, Germany, 1964. Mem. faculty MIT, Cambridge, 1939-69, prof. math., 1949-66; prof. applied math. MIT, 1966-69; prof. applied mechanics U. Calif., San Diego, 1970-78, prof. emeritus, 1978—; aero. research scientist NACA, Langley Field, 1948, 51; vis. prof. U. Mich., Ann Arbor, 1949. Cons. editor Addison-Wesley Pub. Co., 1949-60; mng. editor Jour. Math. and Physics, 1945-67; assoc. editor Quar. Applied Math., 1946—, Studies Applied Math., 1970—, Internat. Jour. Solids and Structures, 1983—; contbr. chpts. to books, articles to profl. jours. Recipient Clemens Herschel award Boston Soc. Civil Engrs., 1956, Theodore von Karman medal ASCE, 1964; Guggenheim fellow, 1962. Fellow ASME (hon. mem. 1991; Timoshenko medal 1973, ASME medal 1988), AIAA (structure and materials award 1984), Am. Acad. Arts and Scis., Am. Acad. Mechanics; mem. NAE, Internat. Acad. Astronautics, Am. Math. Soc., Gesellschaft für Angewandte Mathematik und Mechanik (hon.). Office: U Calif San Diego Dept Applied Mechs Eng S La Jolla CA 92093-0411

REISTER, RAYMOND ALEX, lawyer; b. Sioux City, Iowa, Dec. 22, 1929; s. Harold William and Anne (Eberhardt) R.; m. Ruth Elizabeth Alkema, Oct. 7, 1967. AB, Harvard U., 1952, LLB, 1955. Bar: N.Y. 1956, Minn. 1960. Assoc. Paul, Weiss, Rifkind, Wharton & Garrison, N.Y.C., 1955-56; ptnr. Dorsey & Whitney, Mpls., 1956-92, of counsel, 1993—; instr. U. Minn. Extension Div., 1964-66. Editor (with Larry W. Johnson): Minnesota Probate Administration, 1968. Trustee Mpls. Soc. Fine Arts, 1981-87; treas. Minn. State Hist. Soc., 1986—. Served as 1st U.S. Army, 1956-59. Mem. Am. Coll. Trust and Estate Counsel (regent 1980-86), ABA, Minn. Bar Assn., Hennepin County Bar Assn., Mpls. Club, Harvard Club Minn. (pres. 1969-70). Home: 93 Groveland Ter Minneapolis MN 55403-1142 Office: Dorsey & Whitney 220 S 6th St Minneapolis MN 55402-1498

REISTER, RUTH ALKEMA, lawyer, business executive; b. Grand Rapids, Mich., May 30, 1936; d. Henry and Lena (Land) Alkema; m. Raymond A. Reister, Oct. 7, 1967. B.A., U. Mich., 1958, J.D., 1964; grad. Program in Bus. Adminstrn., Harvard U., 1959, postgrad. Program in Mgmt. Devel., 1976. Bar: Minn., Mich. 1964, U.S. Supreme Ct. 1976. Trust officer Northwestern Nat. Bank, Mpls., 1964-70; asst. counsel, asst. v.p., sec. Fed. Res. Bank, Mpls., 1970-81; asst. sec., bd. govs. Fed. Res. System, 1977; dep. under sec. U.S. Dept. Agr., Washington, 1981-83; pres. First Bank Systems Agrl. Credit Corp., Mpls., 1983-84; pres. Groveland Corp, Mpls., 1986—; dir. Herman Miller, Inc., Zealand, Mich., 1984—. Bd. dirs. United Way, ARC, Jones Harrison Home, Mpls.; chmn. Jones-Harrison Found. Mem. Harvard Bus. Sch. Club Minn., Minn. Women's Econ. Round Table (pres. 1980-81). Republican.

REISTLE, CARL ERNEST, JR., petroleum engineer; b. Denver, June 26, 1901; s. Carl E. and Leonora I. (McMaster) R.; m. Mattie A Muldrow, June 23, 1922; children: Bette Jean (Mrs. George F. Pierce), Mattie Ann (Mrs. James Tracy Clark), Nancy L. (Mrs. Travis Parker), Carl Ernest III. B.S. U. Okla., 1922; postgrad., Harvard Sch. Bus. Adminstrn., 1948. Petroleum chemist U.S Bur. Mines, 1922-29, petroleum engr. 1929-33; chmn. East Tex. Engring. Assn., 1933-36; engr. in charge Humble Oil & Refining Co. 1936-40, chief petroleum engr., 1940-45; gen. supt. prodn. 1945-46, mgr. prodn. dept., 1946-51, dir., 1948-51, dir. in charge prodn. dept., 1951-55, v.p., 1955-57, exec. v.p., 1957-61, pres., 1961-63, chmn. bd., chief exec. officer, 1963-66, ret., 1966, cons., 1966-69; dir. Eltra Corp.; dir., chmn. exec. com. Olinkraft,

Inc., 1967-78. Contbr. numerous articles to profl. jours. Bd. dirs. Tex. Tech Coll., Lubbock, 1966-69, U. Okla. Research Inst., Norman. Recipient Anthony F. Lucas Gold medal Am. Inst. Mining, Metall. and Petroleum Engrs., 1958. Mem. Am. Petroleum Inst., Am. Inst. Mining, Metall. and Petroleum Engrs. (pres. 1956), Sigma Xi, Tau Beta Pi, Sigma Tau, Alpha Chi Sigma. Club: River Oaks Country. Home: 3196 Chevy Chase Dr Houston TX 77019-3208 Office: 601 Jefferson St Ste 975 Houston TX 77002-7907

REITAN, DANIEL KINSETH, electrical and computer engineering educator; b. Duluth, Minn., Aug. 13, 1921; s. Conrad Ulfred and Joy Elizabeth R.; m. Marian Anne Stemme, July 18, 1946; children: Debra Leah, Danielle Karen. BSEE, N.D. State U., 1946; MSEE, U. Wis., 1949, PhD, 1952. Registered profl. engr., Wis. Control engr. Gen. Electric Co., Schenectady, N.Y., 1946-48; transmission line engr. Gen. Telephone Co., Madison, Wis., 1949-50; mem. faculty Coll. Engring. U. Wis., Madison, 1952-85; prof. elec. and computer engring. Coll. Engring. U. Wis., 1962-85; cons. Energy Industries, 1985-95; dir. power systems simulation lab. Coll. Engring. U. Wis., 1968-84, also dir. wind power research Energy Ctr.; cons. Nat. Inst. Sci. and Tech. (formerly U.S. Nat. Bur. Standards). Contbr. articles to profl. jours.; patentee in field. Served with U.S. Army, World War II. Recipient Outstanding Tchr. award Polygon Engring. Council., Gov.'s citation for service to State of Wis. Qellow IEEE (Centennial medal and cert. for outstanding achievement 1984, Centennial medal and cert. dept. ECE U. Wis. 1991, pub. book on Special Relativity 1995, IEEE Power Engring., Computer Control, Indsl. Applications, and Edn. Socs.), Conf. Internat. des Grands Reseaux Electriques a Haute Tension, Am. Soc. Engring. Edn., Wis. Acad. Scis., Am. Wind Energy Assn., Sigma Xi, Tau Delta Pi, Tau Beta Pi, Eta Kappa Nu, Kappa Eta Kappa. Lutheran. *I believe that in one's career professionalism and perseverance are key factors in success. In one's personal life, the family should be the center, but not the circumference, about which all activities revolve.*

REITAN, PAUL HARTMAN, geologist, educator; b. Kanawha, Iowa, Aug. 18, 1928; s. John Olsen and Anna (Meldahl) R.; m. Reidun Engebretsen, Sept. 28, 1962; children: Kirsten Berit, Eric Hartmann. A.B. (Salisbury fellow), U. Chgo., 1953; Ph.D. (Fulbright fellow), U. Oslo, Norway, 1959. Instr. U. Ill., Chgo., 1955; geologist U.S. Geol. Survey, 1953-56; state geologist Geol. Survey of Norway, 1956-60; asst. prof. mineralogy Stanford U., 1960-66; mem. faculty SUNY, Buffalo, 1966—; now rodf. dept. geology SUNY, dean, 1975-79; cons. U. Calif.-Davis. Am. Geol. Inst.; guest scientist Centre for Geol. Sci., Acad. Sci., Warsaw, Poland, Geol. Survey Prague, Czechoslovakia., Geol. Survey, Norway, Nat. Geophys. Rsch. Inst. and Geol. Survey, India. Author: (with Davis and Pestrong) Geology, 1976; contbr. articles to profl. jours. Served with U.S. Army, 1944-49. NATO sr. fellow in sci., 1972; G. Unger Vetlesen fellow, 1973; Fulbright sr. lectr., India, 1986; Norwegian Marshall Fund grantee, 1986, 93. Fellow Geol. Soc. Am., Mineral. Soc. Am., Soc. Econ. Geology, Geol. Soc. of India; mem. AAAS, Internat. Assn. Geochem. and Cosmochem., Norsk Geologisk Forening (life), Sigma Xi. Home: 120 Walton Dr Buffalo NY 14226-4556 Office: SUNY Buffalo NY 14260-3050

REITEMEIER, RICHARD JOSEPH, physician; b. Pueblo, Colo., Jan. 2, 1923; s. Paul John and Ethel Regina (McCarthy) R.; m. Patricia Claire Mulligan, July 21, 1951; children: Mary Louise, Paul, Joseph, Susan, Robert, Patrick, Daniel. A.B., U. Denver, 1944; M.D., U. Colo., 1946; M.S. in Internal Medicine, U. Minn., 1954. Diplomate: Am. Bd. Internal Medicine (gov. 1971-79, chmn. 1978-79, rep. to Federated Council Internal Medicine 1977-80, 83-84, accreditation council grad. med. edn. 1979-85, chmn. 1982-83). Intern Corwin Hosp., Pueblo, 1946-47; resident Henry Ford Hosp., Detroit, 1949-50, Mayo Found., Rochester, Minn., 1950-53; cons. internal medicine and gastroenterology Mayo Clinic, Rochester, 1954-87; chmn. dept. internal medicine Mayo Clinic (Mayo Clinic and Mayo Med. Sch.), 1967-74, prof., 1971—; bd. govs. Mayo Clinic, 1970-74; bd. dirs. Sisters of Mercy Health System, St. Louis, 1986-92; mem. governing bd. Am. Bd. Med. Specialties, 1983-86; sci. and med. dir. Ludwig Inst. Cancer Rsch., 1987-88; cons. Kaiser Family Med. Found., 1989-90; med. dir. Phoenix Alliance Inc., 1990-93. Author: (with C. G. Moertel) Advanced Gastrointestinal Cancer, Clinical Management and Chemotherapy, 1969; contbr. numerous articles to med. jours. Trustee Mayo Found., 1970-74; trustee St. Mary's Hosp., Rochester, 1976-82. Served with U.S. Army, 1947-49. Recipient Alumni award U. Colo. Sch. Medicine; Irving Cutter award Phi Rho Sigma, 1986. Master ACP (regent 1979-82, gov. for Minn. 1975-79, pres. 1983-84, Alfred Stengel Meml. award 1990); fellow Am. Gastroenterol. Assn., AMA, Am. Clin. and Climatol. Assn., Am. Fedn. Clin. Rsch., Am. Soc. Clin. Oncology, Coun. Med. Splty. Socs., Inst. Medicine, Am. Assn. Cancer Rsch., Am. Assn. Study Liver Disease, Nat. Bd. Med. Examiners (trans. 1987-89), Alpha Omega Alpha. Republican. Roman Catholic. Home: 707 12th Ave SW Rochester MN 55902-2027 Office: 200 1st Ave SW Rochester MN 55902-3129

REITEN, RICHARD G., electric power industry executive; b. 1939. BA, U. Wash., 1962. With Simpson Timber Co., Seattle, 1962-64, St. Regis Paper Co., Tacoma, 1964-66, Hearin Products, Inc., Portland, Oreg., 1966-71; with Di Giorgio Corp., San Francisco, 1971-79, pres. bldg. material group; with Nicoli Co., Portland, 1979-87; dir. Oreg. Econ. Devel. Dept., Salem, 1987-89; pres. Portland Gen. Corp., 1989-92 now Portland Gen. Electric Co., 1992—. Office: Portland Gen Electric 121 SW Salmon St Portland OR 97204

REITER, DAISY K., elementary education educator; b. Lewisburg, Pa., Aug. 25, 1936; d. Clark B. and Maude E. (Beninger) Zimmerman; m. Edward P. Reiter, June 3, 1978; children: Edward, Amy, Russ, Elizabeth Sieber White, Katheryn Sieber Ellis, Ann Sieber Myers. BS in Elem. Edn., Pa. State U., 1957; postgrad., U. No. Colo., Greeley, Pa. State U. Cert. permanent elem. tchr., Pa.; lic. real estate agt. Tchr. grade 4 Hershey (Pa.) Sch. Dist., 1957-58; tchr. grades 4 and 5 Red Land Sch. Dist., New Cumberland, Pa., 1959-61; kindergarten tchr. Topeka City Schs., 1958-59; tchr. grade 5 Wallaceton-Boggs Elem. Sch. Philipsburg (Pa.)-Osceola Area Sch. Dist., 1975—; inservice leader transactional analysis and arts in edn.; researcher Civil War, newspapers, animals and habitats, body systems. Mem. choir lst Luth Ch. Recipient Arts in Edn. grants (4 yrs.). Mem. NEA, Pa. State Edn. Assn., Philipsburg-Osceola Edn. Assn, Toughlove Chpt. (founder). Home: PO Box 704 Philipsburg PA 16866-0704

REITER, GLENN MITCHELL, lawyer; b. N.Y.C., Feb. 1, 1951; s. Bernard Leon and Helene (Edson) R.; m. Marilyn Beckhorn, Sept. 5, 1976; children: Benjamin, Diana, Julie. BA, Yale U., 1973, JD, 1976. Bar: N.J. 1976, Pa. 1977, D.C. 1978, N.Y. 1979. Law clk. to judge U.S. Ct. Appeals, Phila., 1976-77; assoc. Schnader, Harrison, Segal & Lewis, Phila., 1977-78; assoc. Simpson, Thacher & Bartlett, N.Y.C., 1978-84, ptnr., 1984—; resident ptnr. Simpson, Thacher & Bartlett, London, 1986-90. Mem. Phi Beta Kappa.

REITER, JOSEPH HENRY, judge; b. Phila., Mar. 21, 1929; s. Nicholas and Barbara (Hollman) R.; m. Beverlee A. Bearman, Nov. 8, 1993. AB, Temple U., 1950, LLB, 1953. Bar: D.C. 1953, Pa. 1954. Atty. advisor U.S. Army, 1955-61; asst. U.S. atty. Ea. Dist. Pa., 1961-63, asst. U.S. atty. in charge of civil div., 1963-69; chief organized crime and racketeering strike force Western N.Y. State, U.S. Dept. Justice, 1969-70, sr. trial atty. tax div. 1970-72, regional dir. office of drug abuse law enforcement, 1972-73; dep. atty. gen., dir. Drug Law Enforcement Office of Pa., 1973-77; ptnr. Stassen, Kostos and Mason, Phila. 1978-85, Kostos Reiter & Lamer, 1985-89; judge Armed Svcs. Bd. of Contract Appeals, Falls Church, Va., 1989—; mem. adv. com. Joint State Commn. on Procurement; lectr. in field. Contbr. articles to profl. jours. Mem. Citizens Crime Commn. Pa. With U.S. Army, 1953-55. Recipient Meritorious Svc. award U.S. Atty. Gen. Commn., St. Clark, 1967, Spl. Commendation Asst. U.S. Atty. Gen. Tax Div., 1969, Outstanding Performance award U.S. Atty. Gen. Richardson, 1973. Mem. ABA, Fed. Bar Assn., D.C. Bar Assn., Pa. Bar Assn., Phila. Bar Assn., Am. Legion, Vesper Club. Downtown Club. Office: Armed Svcs Bd Contract Appeals 5109 Leesburg Pike 7th Fl Falls Church VA 22041

REITER, MICHAEL A., lawyer; b. Pitts., Nov. 15, 1941. BS, U. Wis., 1963, MS, 1964, JD, 1967, PhD, 1969. Bar: Wis. 1967, Ill. 1975, U.S. Supreme Ct. 1975. Ptnr. Holleb & Coff, Chgo.; adj. prof. law Northwestern U., Chgo., 1977—; mem. faculty Nat. Inst. Trial Advocacy, 1980—. Office: Holleb & Coff 55 E Monroe St Ste 4100 Chicago IL 60603-5803

REITER, RICHARD RONALD, healthcare executive; b. Dubuque, Iowa, Nov. 2, 1938; m. Carol Kueter, Sept. 18, 1964; children: Pamela, Paula, Stephanie. BS, U. Iowa, Iowa City, 1962; MBA, U. Iowa, 1980, MHA, 1984. With Hoelscher's Apothecary, Dubuque, Iowa, 1953-68, Mercy Health Ctr., Dubuque, 1968—; exec. dir. ops. Mercy Health Ctr., 1983-85, v.p. ops., 1985-87, v.p. gen. and profl. svcs., 1987—; pres., chief exec. officer Amicare Home Health Services/Tri-State, Inc., Dubuque, 1986—; bd. dirs. Pharmacy Enterprises, Inc., Des Moines, 1987—, Amicare Home Health Services/Tri-State, Inc., 1986—; dir. United Clin. Labs., Inc., 1987—. Contbr. articles to profl. jours. Mem. MBA adv. council U. Dubuque, 1986—; mem. Planning and Zoning Commn., Dubuque, 1983-87. Iowa Pharmacy Found. trustee/scholar, 1958-59. Fellow Am. Acad. Med. Adminstrs.; mem. Am. Coll. Healthcare Execs., Iowa Pharmacists Assn., Iowa Hosp. Assn. (mem. council on patient svcs. 1987—). Avocations: fishing, skiing, photography. Home: 1055 Arrowhead Dr Dubuque IA 52003-8530 Office: Rapid City Reg Hosp PO Box 6000 353 Fairmont Blvd Rapid City SD 57701-7375

REITER, ROBERT EDWARD, banker; b. Kansas City, Mo., Dec. 27, 1943; s. Robert Vincent and Helen Margaret (Petrus) R.; m. Mary J. Darby, June 20, 1964; children: Mollie K., Jennifer M., Ellen R., Robert E. Jr. BA, Rockhurst Coll., 1964; JD, St. Louis U., 1967; LLM, U. Mo., Kansas City, 1969. Bar: Mo. 1967. Assoc. atty. Burke, Jackson & Millin, Kansas City, 1967-69; personal trust adminstr. City Nat. Bank and Trust Co., Kansas City, 1969-71; estate planning officer United Mo. Bank of Kansas City, 1971-73, v.p., 1973-80, sr. v.p., 1980-85, exec. v.p., 1985—; pres., corp. bd. Seton Ctr., Kansas City, 1992-95. Contbr. articles to profl. jours. Bd. of Counselors St. Joseph Health Ctr., Kansas City, 1977-85; pres. St. Joseph Health Ctr. Adv. Coun., Kansas City, 1985-86; sec. United Mo. Pub. Action Com., Kansas City, 1987-88. Grantee St. Louis U. Sch. of Law, 1964-67. Mem. Mo. Bar Assn., Kansas City Bar Assn. (chmn. employee benefits com. 1989-90), Employee Benefit Inst. (adv. bd. 1986—, chmn. 1989), Estate Planning Soc. Kansas City (pres. 1985-86), Lawyers Assn. Kansas City, Serra Club of Kansas City (v.p. 1987-89). Avocation: coaching youth soccer. Home: 1024 W 70th St Kansas City MO 64113 Office: UMB Bank NA 1010 Grand Ave PO Box 419692 Kansas City MO 64141-6692

REITER, STANLEY, economist, educator; b. N.Y.C., Apr. 26, 1925; s. Frank and Fanny (Rosenberg) R.; m. Nina Sarah Breger, June 13, 1944; children: Carla Frances, Frank Joseph. A.B., Queens Coll., 1947; M.A., U. Chgo., 1950, Ph.D., 1955. Rsch. assoc. Cowles Commn., U. Chgo., 1949-50; mem. faculty Stanford U., 1950-54, Purdue U., 1954-67; prof. econs. and math. Northwestern U., 1967—; now Morrison prof. econs. and math. Coll. Arts and Scis., Morrison prof. managerial econs. and decision scis. Kellogg Grad. Sch. Mgmt.; cons. in field. Trustee Roycemore Sch., Evanston, Ill., 1969-71, treas., 1970-71. Served with inf. AUS, 1943-45. Decorated Purple Heart. Fellow Econometric Soc., AAAS; mem. Soc. Indsl. and Applied Math., Inst. Mgmt. Scis., Ops. Research Soc. Am., Am. Math. Soc., Math. Assn. Am. Home: 2138 Orrington Ave Evanston IL 60201-2914 Office: Northwestern U Ctr for Math Studies 2001 Sheridan Rd Evanston IL 60201-2962

REITH, CARL JOSEPH, apparel industry executive; b. Peoria, Ill., Jan. 11, 1914; s. Joseph and May (Kolb) R.; m. Jennie S. Habbinga, Apr. 3, 1936; 1 child, Joyce Elaine. Grad. high sch. Office staff sales Peoria Creamery Co., Ill., 1932; with Kroger Co., 1934-60; successively asst. br. acct., office mgr., acct. Kroger Co., Terre Haute, Ind., Atlanta; adminstr., coord. tng. and mgmt. devel. programing Kroger Co. (Gen. Offices), Cin.; gen. merchandising mgr. Kroger Co. (St. Louis br.), 1946-50; br. mgr. Kroger Co., Indpls., 1950-55; div. v.p. Kroger Co., Cin., 1955-57; regional v.p. Kroger Co., 1957-60; pres., chief exec. officer Colonial Stores, Inc., 1960-67; bd. dir., pres. Oxford Industries, 1967-78, now dir.; bd. dir. Ga. Internat. Ins. Co., Bank South Atlanta, Atlanta and West Point R.R. Adv. bd. Salvation Army, Atlanta; bd. dirs. Atlanta Coll. Art; trustee Robert Woodruff Art Ctr. Mem. Mo. Chain Store Council, Indiana Chain Store Council (pres., v.p. 1951-55), Ind. C of C (bd. 1954-55), Indpls. C. of C. (bd. 1950), Ga. C of C. (indsl. devel. council), Atlanta C. of C. (v.p., bd. dir. 1964-67), Augusta (Ga.) Nat. Golf Club, Piedmont Driving Club, Capital City Club, Peachtree Golf Club, Masons, Shriners, Rotary. Home: 3747 Peachtree Rd NE Apt 1708 Atlanta GA 30319-1366 Office: Oxford Industries Inc 222 Piedmont Ave NE Atlanta GA 30308-3306

REITINGER, THOMAS ANTHONY, hospital administrator; b. Freeport, Ill., Aug. 12, 1944; married. BA, U. Wis., 1967; MA, Washington U., 1971. Adm. resident Jewish Hosp. St. Louis, 1970-71; asst. admin. St. John's Regional Health Ctr., Springfield, Mo., 1971-73, assoc. dir., 1973-75; exec. dir. Waupun (Wis.) Meml. Hosp., 1975-77, Fort Atkinson (Wis.) Meml. Hosp., 1977-83; v.p. St. Joseph's Hosp., Milw., 1983-84, sr. v.p., 1984-86, exec. v.p., COO, 1986-90, pres., 1990—. Home: 5554 Beechwood Ter West Des Moines IA 50266-6620 Office: Mercy Hosp Med Ctr 6th University Des Moines IA 50313

REITMAN, IVAN, film director, producer; b. Komarno, Czechoslovakia, Oct. 27, 1946; came to Can., 1951; s. Leslie and Clara R.; m. Genevieve Robert, Sept. 12, 1976; children: Jason, Catherine, Caroline. MusB, McMaster U., 1969. Judge FOCUS Nissan-Datsun, N.Y.C., 1981-83. Theatrical prodr.: The Magic show, 1974, The National Lampoon Show, 1975, Merlin, 1983 (also dir.); Films include: (dir., exec. prodr.) Cannibal Girls, 1973; (prodr.) They Came From Within (aka Shivers), 1975, Death Weekend (aka The House by the Lake), 1977, Blackout, 1978, National Lampoon's Animal House, 1978, Heavy Metal, 1981, Stop! Or My Mom Will Shoot, 1992; (prodr., dir.) Foxy Lady, 1971, Meatballs, 1979, Stripes, 1981, Ghostbusters, 1984, Legal Eagles, 1986, Twins, 1988, Ghostbusters II, 1989, Kindergarten Cop, 1990, Dave, 1993, Junior, 1994; (exec. prodr.) Rabid, 1976, Spacehunter: Adventures in the Forbidden Zone, 1983, Big Shots, 1987, Casual Sex?, 1988, Feds, 1988, Beethoven, 1992, Beethoven's 2nd, 1993; TV Series: (prodr., dir.) Delta House, 1978. Mem. Dirs. Guild Am. Office: CAA 9830 Wilshire Blvd Beverly Hills CA 90212-1804

REITMAN, JERRY IRVING, advertising agency executive; b. Phila., Jan. 9, 1938; s. Benjamin and Ruth (Eisenberg) R.; m. Monica Birgitta Hall, Oct. 27, 1968; children—Jennifer Sharon, Sarah Beth. B.S. in Fin., Pa. State U., 1961. Exec. v.p., chief exec. officer Brit. Pubs., N.Y.C. and London, 1965-69; pres., pub. Acad. Media, Sherman Oaks, Calif., 1969-73; v.p. Pubs. Clearing House, Port Washington, N.Y., 1973-78; exec. v.p. Ogilvy & Mather, N.Y.C., 1978-81; with Scali, McCabe, Sloves, Inc., N.Y.C., 1981-86; pres. Scali, McCabe, Sloves Direct, N.Y.C.; chmn. bd. The Reitman Group, 1986-87; exec. v.p. The Leo Burnett Co., Chgo., 1987—; dir. Scandinavian Airlines System Pub./Distbn. Svcs.; mem. adv. bd. Ill. Dept. Trade and Tourism, 1988—; internat. awards chmn., bd. dirs. John Caples Internat., 1989—; mem. Internat. Direct Mktg. Symposium, Zurich, Switzerland. Author: A Common Sense Approach to Small Business, 1968, Beyond 2000: The Future of Direct Marketing, 1994; contbr. articles to profl. jours. Trustee Locust Valley Libr. Assn., N.Y., 1982—; exec. com. Pub. Hall of Fame, 1987—; bd. govs. Children's Miracle Network, 1992—; bd. dirs. The Direct Mktg. Ednl. Found., 1993—. Recipient Key to City, New Orleans, 1959, Silver Apple award N.Y. Direct Mktg. Club, 1989; Anderson scholar, 1961. Fellow Psychiat. Re-Edn. Assn.; mem. Direct Mktg. Assn. (bd. mem. ethics com. 1984), Creative Guild (dir. 1984), Internat. Direct Mktg. Assn. (bd. dirs. 1981-82), Publ. Hall of Fame (exec. com. 1988—), Direct Mktg. Club N.Y. (pres. 1983-84), Beta Gamma Sigma, Delta Sigma Pi. Avocations: tennis; old car restoration; classical woodworking. Home: 2204 N Leavitt Chicago IL 60647 Office: Leo Burnett Co 35 W Wacker Dr Chicago IL 60601

REITMAN, ROBERT STANLEY, manufacturing and marketing executive; b. Fairmont, W.Va., Nov. 18, 1933; s. Isadore and Freda A. (Layman) R.; m. Sylvia K. Golden, Dec. 24, 1955; children: Scott Alan, Alayne Louise. BS in Acctg., W.Va. U., 1955; JD, Case Western Res. U., 1958. Bar: Ohio 1958. Mem. firm Burke, Haber & Berick, Cleve., 1958-60; ptnr. Burke, Haber & Berick, 1960-68; exec. v.p., vice-chmn. Tranzonic Cos. (formerly AAV Cos.), Pepper Pike, Ohio, 1968-70; pres., vice-chmn. Tranzonic Cos. (formerly AAV Cos.), 1970-73, chief exec. officer, pres., vice chmn., 1973-82, now chmn., chief exec. officer, 1982—; bd. dirs. Soc. Nat. Bank, Weirton Steel Corp., mem. Bus. adv.Com. Mandel Ctr. for non-profit Organ. Case Western Reserve U., 1995, vis. com. Weatherhead Sch. of Bus.

Case Western Reserve U., 1995. Mem. Republican fin. com., Cuyahoga County, 1968-78; mem. Com. for Econ. Growth for Israel, Cleve., 1977-80, pres., 1978-80; mem. adv. coun. Cleve. Mus. Nat. History, 1982-85, Cleve. Opera, 1977—; del. Coun. of Jewish Fedns., N.Y.C., 1981—; gen. co-chmn. Jewish Welfare Fund, Cleve., 1975-78, 81-85, gen. vice chmn., 1985-89, gen. chmn. 1989-91; sect. and div. chmn., team capt. United Way Svcs., 1974—, mem. del. assembly, 1976-85, trustee, 1977-83, 84-90, 91—, v.p. 1985-88, chmn. nominating. com., 1988-90, campaign chmn., 1993, chair fund raising planning com., 1994—; mem. employment com. Jewish Vocat. Svc., Cleve., 1974-83; bd. dirs. Capital for Israel, Inc., N.Y.C., 1986-87; nat. vice chmn. United Jewish Appeal, 1987-92, nat. allocations chmn., 1987-90, trustee, 1988-94, chair retirement fund com., 1994—; trustee B'nai B'rith Hillel Found., 1975-81, Cleve. Jewish News, 1976-79, Ednl. TV Sta. WVIZ, Cleve., 1976—, vice chmn. 1986-90, chmn. bd., 1990—; trustee, pres. Bus. Volunteerism Coun., 1994—; trustee Jewish Community Fedn. Cleve., 1983—, treas., 1991-94, v.p., 1995, Jewish Edn. Ctr. of Cleve., 1993—, Cleve. Zool. Soc., 1972—, pres., 1979-87, chmn., 1987-92, chmn. emeritus, 1992—, chmn. JDC-Brookdale Inst. of Gerontology and Human Devel., 1995; trustee Am. Jewish Joint Distbn. Com., 1988—, United Israel Appeal, 1987-94, Mt. Sinai Med. Ctr., Cleve., 1976—, chmn., 1982-85; trustee Cleve. State U. Devel. Found., 1986-89, Greater Cleve. Roundtable, 1991—; pres., trustee The Wilds, 1995. Mem. ABA, Cleve. Growth Assn., The 50 Club Cleve., Case Western Res. Univ. Sch. of Law Soc. Benchers, Am. Kennel Club (regional del. 1960-75), Western Res. Kennel Club (officer, trustee 1959-75), Beechmont Club (fin. com. 1972-80, house com. 1974), Pepper Pike Club, Union Club, Masons, B'nai Brith, Zeta Beta Tau, Tau Epsilon Rho. Avocations: golf, swimming, pure-bred dogs. Office: Tranzonic Cos 30195 Chagrin Blvd # 224E Cleveland OH 44124-5703

REITSEMA, HAROLD JAMES, aerospace engineer; b. Kalamazoo, Jan. 19, 1948; s. Robert Harold and Bernice Jean (Hoogsteen) R.; m. Mary Jo Gunnink, Aug. 6, 1970; children: Ellen Celeste, Laurie Jean. BA, Calvin Coll., 1972; PhD, N.Mex. State U., 1977. Rsch. assoc. U. Ariz., Tucson, 1977-79, sr. rsch. assoc., 1979-82, vis. scientist, 1987—; sr. mem. tech. staff Ball Aerospace, Boulder, Colo., 1982-85, prin. systems engr., 1985-88, program mgr., 1988-89, staff cons., 1989—; cons. Aerospace Tech., 1987—. Contbr. articles to Astrophys. Jour., Aston. Jour., Nature, Sci., Icarus. Bd. dirs. EE Barnard Obs., Golden, Colo., 1984-91. Fellow AIAA (assoc., tech. com. chair 1991, Engr. of Yr. 1990); mem. Am. Astron. Soc. (planetary sci. com. 1991-94), Internat. Astron. Union. Achievements include discovery of Larissa, fifth satellite of Neptune; co-discovery of Telesto, seventeenth satellite of Saturn; patents for Optically-coupled Shaft Angle Encoder. Home: 4795 Hancock Driver Boulder CO 80303 Office: Ball Aerospace 1600 Commerce Boulder CO 80302

REITTER, CHARLES ANDREW, personal financial planner; b. Chgo., Oct. 28, 1956; s. LeRoy Maurice and Carolyn Ruth (Nelson) R.; m. Kimberly Ann Uthoff, June 2, 1979; children: April Suzanne, Andrew Christopher. BJ, U. Mo., Columbia, 1978; MA in Mgmt., Webster U., Webster Groves, Mo., 1989. Sports editor Jefferson County Newspapers, Festus, Mo., 1978-79, Cleburne (Tex.) Times Rev., 1979-80; sports editor Jefferson County Newspapers, Festus, 1980, reporter, editor, 1980-81; asst. editor Am. Paint Jour. Co., St. Louis, 1981, editor, 1981-87, editor, v.p., 1987-91, pres., chief operating officer, 1991-94; personal fin. planner IDS/Am. Express, 1994—. Contbr. articles to profl. jours. Mem. Webster U. Presdl. Search Com., 1989-90; mem. pastorial search com. St. Lucas United Ch. of Christ, 1993. Recipient Outstanding Grad. award Webster U. Alumni Assn., 1989. Mem. Fedn. Socs. for Coatings Tech., St. Louis Soc. Coatings Tech. (pres.). Mem. United Ch. of Christ. Avocations: old cars, music, bus., family. Office: IDS Fin Svcs Inc 9052 Watson Rd Crestwood MO 63126-2234

REITZ, BRUCE ARNOLD, cardiac surgeon, educator; b. Seattle, Sept. 14, 1944; s. Arnold B. and Ruth (Stillings) R.; m. Nan N. Norton, Oct. 3, 1970; children: Megan, Jay. B.S., Stanford U., 1966; M.D., Yale U., 1970. Diplomate: Am. Bd. Surgery, Am. Bd. Thoracic Surgery. Intern Johns Hopkins Hosp., Balt., 1970-71, cardiac surgeon-in-charge, 1982-92; resident Stanford U. Hosp., (Calif.), 1971-72, 74-78; clin. assoc. Nat. Heart Lung Blood Inst., NIH, Bethesda, Md., 1972-74; asst. prof. Stanford U. Sch. Medicine, 1977-81, assoc. prof., 1981-82; prof. surgery Johns Hopkins U. Sch. Medicine, Balt., 1982-92; prof., chmn. Sch Medicine Stanford (Calif.) U., 1992—. Developer heart-lung transplant technique, 1981. Office: Stanford U Sch Medicine Dept Cardiothoracic Surgery Stanford CA 94305

REITZ, CURTIS RANDALL, lawyer, educator; b. Reading, Pa.; s. Lester S. and Magdalene A. (Crouse) R.; m. Virginia R. Patterson, Dec. 19, 1953 (div.); children—Kevin R., Joanne E., Whitney A.; m. Judith N. Renzulli, Sept. 18, 1983. B.A., U. Pa., 1951, LL.B. 1956. Bar: Pa. 1957, U.S. Supreme Ct. 1959. Law clk. to Chief Justice Earl Warren U.S. Supreme Ct., 1956-57; mem. faculty law U. Pa., Phila., 1957—; asst. prof. law U. Pa., 1957-60, assoc. prof., 1960-63, prof., 1963—; provost, v.p., 1970-71, Algernon Sydney Biddle prof. law, 1985—. Trustee Internat. House Phila.; bd. mgrs. Glen Mills Schs., Pa. Served to 1st lt. U.S. Army, 1951-53. Mem. Am. Law Inst., Nat. Conf. Commrs. on Uniform State Laws, Order of Coif. Office: U Pa Law Sch 3400 Chestnut St Philadelphia PA 19104-6204

REITZ, ELMER A., manufacturing company executive; b. 1909; married. With Greif Bros. Corp., Delaware, Ohio, 1934—, comptroller, 1951-53, sec., then v.p., sec., 1953-69, v.p., 1969-70, exec. v.p., from 1970, now chmn. fin. com., also bd. dirs. Office: Greif Bros Corp 621 Pennsylvania Ave Delaware OH 43015-1566

REITZ, WILLIAM, supermarket company executive; b. 1933. With Scott's Foodlane Inc., Ft. Wayne, Ind., 1954-70, Reitz #1, Ft. Wayne, 1970-78, SV Ventures, Ft. Wayne, 1978—; now pres., owner SV Ventures. Office: SV Ventures 4118 N Clinton St Fort Wayne IN 46805*

REJAI, MOSTAFA, political science educator; b. Tehran, Iran, Mar. 11, 1931; came to U.S., 1954; s. Taghi and Forough (Lashgari) R. AA, Pasadena City Coll., 1957; BA, Calif. State U., L.A., 1959, MS, 1961; PhD, UCLA, 1964. Teaching fellow UCLA, 1963-64; asst. prof. polit. sci. Miami U., Oxford, Ohio, 1964-67, assoc. prof., 1967-70, prof., 1970-83, Disting. prof., 1983—; vis. scholar Ctr. for Internat. Affairs, Harvard U., 1972, Hoover Instn. on War, Revolution and Peace, Stanford U., 1973, Inst. Internat. Studies, Iran, 1974-75; vis. prof. Western Coll., Oxford, 1971, 72. Author: The Strategy of Political Revolution, 1973, The Comparative Study of Revolutionary Strategy, 1977, Comparative Political Ideologies, 1984; (with Kay Phillips) Leaders of Revolution, 1979, World Revolutionary Leaders, 1983, Loyalists and Revolutionaries: Political Leaders Compared, 1988, Demythologizing an Elite: American Presidents in Empirical, Comparative, and Historical Perspectives, 1993; Political Ideologies: A Comparative Approach, 1991, 2d edit., 1995; editor: Democracy: The Contemporary Theories, 1967, Decline of Ideology?, 1971; editor: Mao Tse-Tung on Revolution and War, 1969, rev. edit., 1970; assoc. editor Jour. Polit. and Mil. Sociology, 1973—; contbr. articles to profl. jours., book chpts. Recipient Outstanding Teaching award Miami U., 1970. Mem. Am. Polit. Sci. Assn. (polit. psychology sect.), Am. Sociol. Assn. (polit. soc. sect.), Internat. Polit. Sci. Assn., Internat. Soc. Polit. Psychology, Internat Studies Assn., Inter-Univ. Seminar on Armed Forces and Soc., Conf. for Study Polit. Thought, Midwest Polit. Sci. Assn., So. Polit. Sci. Assn., Western Polit. Sci. Assn., Pi Gamma Mu, Pi Sigma Alpha. Office: Miami U Dept of Political Science Oxford OH 45056

REJEANGE, JACQUES F., pharmaceutical executive. With Sandoz Pharms Corp., East Hanover, N.J., 1966—, pres., ceo, 1989—. Office: Sandoz Pharms Corp 59 State Route 10 East Hanover NJ 07936-1011

REKATE, ALBERT C., physician; b. Buffalo, June 12, 1916; s. Gustave E. and Fannie (Hummell) R.; m. Elizabeth Foster, June 12 1943 (dec. 1985); 1 child, Suzanne (Mrs. R. Willis Post); m. Linda Ann Holt, Aug. 1, 1992. M.D., U. Buffalo, 1940. Diplomate Am. Bd. Internal Medicine. Intern E.J. Meyer Meml. Hosp., 1940-41, med. resident, 1941-44; asst. prof. medicine SUNY-Buffalo, 1954-61, assoc. prof., 1961-65, prof., 1965-86, prof. emeritus, 1986—; dir. rehab. medicine, 1965-72, acting dean Sch. Health Related Professions, 1965-66; assoc. dean SUNY-Buffalo (Sch. Health Related Professions), 1966-74; acting chmn. dept. rehab. medicine SUNY-Buffalo, 1972-75; assoc. dir. medicine E.J. Meyer Meml. Hosp., 1957-63, head dept. rehab. medicine, 1964-69, dir. primary rehab. center, 1965-69, acting head cardiology, 1966-69, dir., 1970-72; bd. dirs. Buffalo Hearing and Speech Center, 1973—; mem. adv. bd. Coastal Empire Mental Health Center, S.C., 1980-81, bd. dirs., 1981-93. Contbr. articles to profl. jours. Served with M.C. AUS, World War II. Mem. Am. Heart Assn., Western N.Y. Heart Assn. (pres. 1954-55), Assn. Am. Med. Colls., N.Y. State Heart Assembly, N.Y. Acad. Scis., Med. Union (pres. 1974-75), Buffalo Acad. Medicine (pres. 1969-70), Erie County Med. Soc., Med. Alumni Assn. U. Buffalo (pres. 1960-61), Beaufort-Jasper Mental Health Assn. (dir. 1980-86). Home: PO Box 3164 Hilton Head Island SC 29928-0164 Office: 462 Grider St Buffalo NY 14215-3021

REKSTIS, WALTER J., III, lawyer; b. San Diego, 1945. BBA, U. Cin., 1968, JD, 1972. Bar: Ohio 1972. Ptnr. Squire, Sanders & Dempsey, Cleve. Office: Squire Sanders & Dempsey 4900 Society Ct 127 Public Sq Cleveland OH 44114

RELIAS, JOHN ALEXIS, lawyer; b. Chgo., Apr. 2, 1946; s. Alexis John and Marie Helen (Metos) R.; m. Linda Ann Pontious, Nov. 27, 1971; children: Anne, Alexandra. BA, Northwestern U., Evanston, 1968; LLB, Northwestern U., Chgo., 1972. Bar: Ill., 1972, U.S. Dist. Ct. (no. dist.) Ill. 1972, U.S. Ct. Appeals (9th cir.) 1981, U.S. Ct. Appeals (7th cir.) 1983. Assoc. Vedder, Price, Kaufman & Kammholz, Chgo., 1972-78; ptnr. Vedder, Price, Kaufman & Kammholz, 1979-94, Franczek, Sullivan, Mann, Crement, Hein & Relias, Chgo., 1994—. Bd. edn. Wilmette (Ill.) Sch. Dist. # 39, 1989—, pres. 1992-93. Mem. Nat. Assn. Sch. Attys., Ill. Assn. Sch. Attys., Chgo. Bar Assn., Order of the Coif, Phi Beta Kappa. Greek Orthodox. Home: 2500 Kenilworth Ave Wilmette IL 60091-1337 Office: Franczek Sulian Mann Crement Hein & Relias 300 S Walker Dr Chicago IL 60606

RELIC, PETER, academic administrator; b. Cleve., May 22, 1936; s. Peter and Mary (Makar) R.; m. Mary Jo Mehl, Oct. 22, 1966; children: Rebecca, Matthew, Peter. BA, Bowdoin Coll., 1961; MA, CAS, Western Res. U., 1971; EdD, Harvard U., 1973; HHD, Belmont Abbey Coll., 1991. Tchr. English and polit. philosophy grades 4-12, coach Hawken Sch., Cleve., 1959-70; prin. Hawken Upper Sch., Cleve., 1963-68; curriculum coord. Middlesex County House of Corrections, Billerica, Mass., 1970-71; dir. edn. Middlesex County House of Corrections, Billerica, 1971-72; asst. supt. curriculum and instr. Pearl River (N.Y.) Sch. Dist., 1972-75; supt. schs. Hamilton (Ohio) City Sch. Dist., 1975-77; dep. asst. sec. for edn. Dept. Health, Edn. and Welfare, Washington, 1977-80, acting asst. sec. for edn., 1980; supt. of schs. West Hartford, Conn., 1980-87, Charlotte, N.C., 1990-91; pres. Nat. Assn. Ind. Schs., Washington, 1991—; tchr. basic skills, coord. athletic, med. and constrn. programs, Turkey, West Germany, Peru, P.R., summers 1961-66; prin. Greater Cleve. (Ohio) Summer Inst., 1965, Kyoto (Japan) Internat. Sch., 1968-70; English instr. Middlesex C.C., Bedford, Mass., 1971-72; tchg. fellow in edn. Harvard Grad. Sch., Cambridge, 1971-72; adj. prof. U. Hartford, Conn., 1981-87, St. Joseph Coll., West Hartford, 1986-87, Lenoir-Rayne Coll., Hickory, N.C., 1991—; bd. dirs. Nat. Assn. for Industry-Edn. Cooperation; ednl. cons. Ohio Civil Rights Commn., 1966-68, Jasper County (S.C.) Pub. Schs., 1970-72, Jennings Found., 1971-72, Lehigh U., Cleve. Indians Am. Baseball League, 1973-74, Birmingham (Ala.) Pub. Schs., 1975-77, Aetna Found., Hartford, 1980-84, Arlington (N.Y.) Sch. Dist., 1990-91, S.C. Ctr. for Tchg., Winthrop Coll., Rock Hill, 1990—, Worldwide Ednl. Svcs., Clifton, N.J., 1990—, Donruss Co.-Divsn. Leaf, Inc., Bannockburn, Ill., 1990—. Contbr. articles to profl. jours. I.O.N.A., House-Social Svcs., Washington; bd. visitors Mortensen Libr., U. Hartford, Conn., 1984-87, Charlotte (N.C.) Country Day Sch., 1987-91, John C. Smith U., 1987-91, U. N.C., Charlotte, 1987-91; mem. grad. tchr. and adminstr. programs Conn. State Bd. Edn. Vis. Com. to Sacred Heart U., 1986; bd. overseers Bowdoin Coll., 1987-93; bd. dirs. Tchrs.' Ctr., Greenwich, Conn., 1974, U. Regional Broadcasting, Dayton, Ohio, 1975-77, Safety Coun., Hamilton, Ohio, 1975-77, Hamilton (Ohio) YMCA, 1975-77, Noah Webster Hist. Assn., 1980-87, Hartford (Conn.) YMCA, 1980-87, Kodalyical Tng. Inst., Hartt Sch. Mus., U. Hartford, Conn., 1980-87; YMCA, Charlotte and Mecklenburg, 1988-91, United Way Ctrl. Carolinas Inc., 1988-91, Jr. Achievement Charlotte, Inc., 1989-90; internat. bus. ctr. adv. com. Ctrl. Piedmont C.C., 1988-90; adv. bd. mem. Mecklenburg County Coun., Boy Scouts Am., 1988-91; mem. adv. com. Charlotte (N.C.)-Mecklenburg Cmty. Rels., 1989-91; mem. alumni coun. Harvard U. Grad. Sch. Edn., Cambridge, 1990-91. Fulbright scholar Fulbright Commn., India, 1985, Paul Harris fellow Rotary Club Internat., Charlotte, N.C., 1989. Mem. Coun. for Am. Pvt. Edn. (treas. bd.), Edn. Leaders Consortium (pres.-elect). Office: Nat Assn Ind Schs 1620 L St NW Washington DC 20036-5605

RELIHAN, WALTER J., JR., lawyer; b. Binghamton, N.Y., Oct. 17, 1930; s. Walter J. Sr. and Marjorie Winifred (Allen) R.; m. Joan Marie; children: Elizabeth, Walter J. III, Susan. BA, Cornell U., 1952, JD, 1959. Bar: N.Y. 1959, U.S. Dist. Ct. (north dist.) N.Y. 1959, U.S. Supreme Ct. 1964. Ptnr. Night, Keller & Relihan, Binghamton, 1960-67; gen. counsel N.Y. State Office Gen. Svc., 1967-71; univ. counsel, vice chancellor legal affairs SUNY, 1971-78; univ. counsel Cornell U., 1979—, sec. of the corp., 1980—, dir. Nat. Assn. Coll. and Univ. Attys., 1982-85. Lt. (j.g.) USNR, 1952-56. Mem. ABA, Tompkins County Bar (bd. dirs.), N.Y. State Bar Assn. Office: Cornell U 500 Day Hall Ithaca NY 14850

RELKIN, ALLEN, commodities executive; b. 1944. With Philipp Bros., N.Y.C., 1966-88, group v.p.; with Centrotrade Mineral Metals Inc., N.Y.C., 1988—, now pres., CEO. Office: Centrotrade Mineral Metals Inc 330 Madison Ave Fl 25 New York NY 10017*

RELL, M. JODI, state official; b. Norfolk, Va.. Grad., Old Dominion U., Conn. State U. Mem., dep. minority leader Conn. Ho. Reps., 1984-94; lt. gov. State of Conn., 1995—. Past vice chmn. Brookfield Rep. Town Com.; trustee YMCA Western Conn. Mem. Nat. Order Women Legislators (immed. past nat. pres., former v.p., treas., corr. sec.), Brookfield Polit. Women's Club (past pres.), Brookfield Bus. and Profl. Womens Club. Address: 125 Long Meadow Hill Rd Brookfield CT 06804 Office: Lt Governor State Capitol Rm 304 Hartford CT 06106

RELLE, FERENC MATYAS, chemist; b. Gyor, Hungary, June 13, 1922; came to U.S., 1951, naturalized, 1956; s. Ferenc and Elizabeth (Netratics) R.; m. Gertrud B. Tubach, Oct. 9, 1946; children: Ferenc, Ava, Attila. B-SChemE, Jozsef Nador Poly. U., Budapest, 1944, MS, 1944. Lab. mgr. Karl Kohn Ltd. Co., Landshut, W.Ger., 1947-48; resettlement officer IRO, Munich, 1948-51; chemist Farm Bur. Coop. Assn., Columbus, Ohio, 1951-56; indsl. engr. N.Am. Aviation, Inc., Columbus, 1956-57; rsch. chemist Keever Starch Co., Columbus, 1957-65; rsch. chemist Ross Labs. div. Abbott Labs., Columbus, 1965-70, rsch. scientist, 1970-89; cons. in field. Chmn. Columbus and Central Ohio UN Week, 1963; pres. Berwick Manor Civic Assn., 1968; trustee Stelios Stelson Found., 1968-69; deacon Brookwood Presbyn. Ch., 1963-65, 92—, trustee, 1990-91. Mem. Am. Chem. Soc. (alt. councilor 1973, chmn. long range planning com. Columbus sect. 1972-76, 78-80), Am. Assn. Cereal Chemists (chmn. Cin. sect. 1974-75), Ohio Acad. Sci., Arpad Acad., Internat. Tech. Inst. (adv. dir. 1977-82), Nat. Intercollegiate Soccer Ofcls. Assn., Am. Hungarian Assn., Hungarian Cultural Assn. (pres. 1978-81), Ohio Soccer Ofcls. Assn., Columbus Männerchor, Germania Singing and Sport Soc., Civitan (gov. Ohio dist. 1970-71, dist. treas. 1982-83, pres. Eastern Columbus 1963-64, 72-73, gen. sec. for Hungary 1991-92, Eastern European Growth Mgr., 1993-94, amb. at large, 1994—, established 1st Civitan club in Hungary 1991, Ukraine 1992, Slovakia 1994, Internat. Gov. of Yr. award 1971, Internat. Honor Key 1992, master club builder award 1992, various other awards), World Fedn. of Hungarian Engrs. Home and Office: 3487 Roswell Dr Columbus OH 43227-3560

RELMAN, ARNOLD SEYMOUR, physician, educator, editor; b. N.Y.C., June 17, 1923; s. Simon and Rose (Mallach) R.; m. Harriet Morse Vitkin, June 26, 1953; children: David Arnold, John Peter, Margaret Rose. A.B., Cornell U., 1943; M.D., Columbia U., 1946; LLD (hon.), U. Pa.; ScD (hon.), Med. Coll. Wis., Union U., Med. Coll. Ohio, CUNY; DMSc (hon.), Brown U.; DLH (hon.), SUNY; LittD (hon.), Temple U. Diplomate Am. Bd. Internal Medicine. House officer New Haven Hosp., Yale, 1946-49; NRC fellow Evans Meml., Mass. Meml. hosps., 1949-50; practice medicine, specializing in internal medicine Boston, 1950-68, Phila., 1968-77; asst. prof.

prof. medicine Boston U. Sch. Medicine, 1950-68; dir. Boston U. Med. Services, Boston City Hosp., 1967-68; prof. medicine, chmn. dept. medicine U. Pa.; chief med. services Hosp. of U. Pa., 1968-77; editor New Eng. Jour. Medicine, Boston, 1977-91, editor emeritus, 1991—; sr. physician Brigham and Women's Hosp., Boston, 1977—; prof. medicine and social medicine Harvard Med. Sch., 1977-93, prof. medicine and social medicine emeritus, 1993—; cons. NIH, USPHS.; mem. bd. registration in medicine Commonwealth of Mass., 1995—. Editor: Jour. Clin. Investigation, 1962-67, (with F.J. Ingelfinger and M. Finland) Controversy in Internal Medicine, Vol. 1, 1966, Vol. 2, 1974; contbr. articles to profl. jours. Trustee Columbia U., 1990—; bd. dirs. Hastings Ctr., 1981-83. Recipient Columbia Alumni Gold medal, 1980, Disting. Svc. award Am. Coll. Cardiology, 1987, McGovern award Cosmos Club Washington, 1991, John Peters award Am. Soc. Nephrology, 1992. Fellow ACP (master, John Phillips medal 1985), Am. Acad. Arts and Scis.; mem. AMA, Assn. Am. Physicians (coun., pres. 1983-84, Kober medal 1993), Am. Physiol. Soc., Mass. Med. Soc., Inst. Medicine of NAS (coun. 1979-82), Am. Soc. Clin. Investigation (past pres.), Am. Fedn. Clin. Rsch. (past pres.), Phi Beta Kappa (senator 1991—), Alpha Omega Alpha. Office: Brigham and Women's Hosp Dept of Medicine 75 Francis St Boston MA 02115-6195

RELSON, MORRIS, patent lawyer; b. N.Y.C., Apr. 14, 1915; s. Benjamin and Minnie R.; m. Rita L. Rubenstein, Apr. 5, 1941; children—Katherine D., David M., Peter J. BSEE, CCNY, 1935; MA in Math, George Washington U., 1940; JD, NYU, 1945. Bar: N.Y. 1945, U.S. Supreme Ct. 1950. Elec. engr. Nat. Park Svc., Washington, 1936-37; patent examiner U.S. Patent Office, 1937-41; patent agt. and atty. Sperry Gyroscope Co., Gt. Neck, N.Y., 1941-48; ptnr. Darby & Darby P.C., and predecessor, N.Y.C., 1948—; vol. spl. master U.S. Dist. Ct. for So. Dist N.Y., 1979-80. Contbr. articles to legal jours. Mem. ABA (patent, trademark and copyright sect.), IEEE, Am. Patent Law Assn., N.Y. Patent Law Assn. (pres. 1976-77, bd. dirs. 1970-78), N.Y. Acad. Sci., Phi Beta Kappa, Sigma Xi., Sigma Pi Sigma. Patentee in field. Home: 27 Tain Dr Great Neck NY 11021-4422 Office: Darby & Darby 805 Third Ave New York NY 10022-7513

REMAK, HENRY H.H., foreign language educator; b. Berlin, July 27, 1916; came to U.S., 1936; s. Hans Ismar and Hedwig (Salz) R.; m. Ingrid Miriam Grünfeld, Aug. 3, 1946; children: Roy Andrew, Steven Bruce, Renée June, Ronald Frank. Licencié-ès-Lettres, U. Montpellier, France, 1936; MA, Ind. U., 1937; PhD, U. Chgo., 1947; D-ès-Lettres (hon.), U. Lille, France, 1973. From instr. to prof. Germanic studies and comparative lit. Ind. U., Bloomington, 1938—, also prof. West. European studies, dir. Inst. for Advanced Study, 1988-94, vice chancellor, dean of the faculties, 1969-74; dir. Middlebury (Vt.) German Summer Sch., 1967-71; dir. Nat. Endowment for Humanities Summer and Year-Long Seminar, Bloomington, 1977-79; vis. prof. U. Hamburg, U. Lille, Middlebury U., U. Pa., U. Wis.; bd. dirs. Ind. Humanities Coun., 1984-90; pres., mem. editorial policy bd. Comparative History of Literatures in European Langs., 1977-83. Author: Novellistische Struktur, 1983, German Novella, 1995; co-editor: Oeuvres de Charles-Michel Campion, 1945; contbr. chpts. to books, numerous articles to profl. jours. Bd. dirs. United Fund, Bloomington, 1970-74; mem. Hosp. Bd., Bloomington, 1971-77. Ensign, U.S. Mcht. Marine, 1944-46. Fulbright vis. prof., 1962-63, 67; Fulbright travel grantee, 1987, 88; Guggenheim fellow, 1967-68. Jewish. Avocations: running, tennis, outdoor swimming, reading, hiking. Home: 1212 E Maxwell Ln Bloomington IN 47401-5074 Office: Inst for Advanced Study Ind U 400 E 7th St Bloomington IN 47405-3085

REMBAR, CHARLES (ISAIAH), lawyer, writer; b. Oceanport, N.J., Mar. 12, 1915; s. Louis S. and Rebecca (Schneider) Zaremba; m. Billie Ann Olsson, Feb. 23, 1944; children: Lance Richard, James Carlson. A.B., Harvard U., 1935; LL.B., Columbia U., 1938. Bar: N.Y. 1938. Atty. govt. agencies, 1938-42, 45; law sec. N.Y. Supreme Ct., 1946; practice law N.Y.C., 1947—. Author: The End of Obscenity, 1968, Perspective, 1975, The Law of the Land, 1980; Editor: Columbia Law Rev, 1936-38; Contbr. articles to various periodicals. With USAAF, 1942-45. Recipient George Polk Meml. award for outstanding book of 1968, 1969. Mem. Assn. Bar City N.Y. (chmn. spl. com. on communications 1972-78), Authors League, P.E.N. Clubs: Century Assn. (N.Y.C.), Harvard (N.Y.C.). Office: Rembar & Curtis 19 W 44th St New York NY 10036-5903

REMBE, TONI, lawyer; b. Seattle, Apr. 23, 1936; d. Armin and Doris (McVay) R.; m. Arthur Rock, July 19, 1975. Cert. in French Studies, U. Geneva, 1956; LL.B., U. Wash., 1960; LLM in Taxation, NYU, 1961. Bar: N.Y., Wash., Calif. Assoc. Chadbourne, Parke, Whiteside & Wolff, N.Y.C., 1961-63; assoc. Pillsbury, Madison & Sutro, San Francisco, 1964-71, ptnr., 1971—; dir. Potlatch Corp., San Francisco, Pacific Telesis, San Francisco, Am. Pres. Cos., Ltd., Oakland, Calif., Transamerica Corp., San Francisco. Pres. Van Loben Sels Charitable Found., San Francisco; trustee Am. Conservatory Theatre, San Francisco. Fellow Am. Bar Found.; mem. ABA, Am. Judicature Soc., State Bar Calif., Bar Assn. San Francisco, Commonwealth Club of Calif. (govs. of the club). Office: Pillsbury Madison & Sutro 225 Bush St San Francisco CA 94104-4207

REMENICK, SEYMOUR, artist, educator; b. Detroit, Apr. 3, 1923; s. Oscar and Luba (Shackman) R.; m. Diane Kathryn Thommen, Aug. 30, 1950; children: Richard Vincent, Catherine Ann. Student, Tyles Sch. Fine Arts, Phila., 1940-42, 46, Hans Hofmann Sch., N.Y.C., 1946-48, Pa. Acad. Fine Arts, 1948. Instr. Pa. Acad. Fine Arts, Phila., 1977—. Exhibited one-man shows: Davis Gallery, N.Y.C., annually, 1954-62, Peridot Gallery, N.Y.C., annually, 1967-71, Pearl Fox Gallery, Pa., 1969, 73, 76, Gross McCleaf Gallery, Phila., 1981, Gallery K, Washington, 1983, (retrospective) Rosemont Coll., Pa., 1983; group shows: 3d Biennial Exhbn., Italy, 1955, Am. Painting, Rome, 1955, Paris exhbn., 1956, 57, Pa. Acad. Fine Arts 1957, 59, 64, 68, Festival of Arts, Spoleto, 1959, Nat. Acad., 1960, 63, 66, Phila. Mus. Art. Served with U.S. Army, 1942-45, ETO. Recipient Tiffany Found. award NAD, N.Y.C., 1955; recipient Altman Landscape Prize, 1960, Hallmark Purchase award Hallmark Co., 1960. Mem. NAD (academician 1983). Home: 812 Catharine St Philadelphia PA 19147-3902

REMER, DONALD SHERWOOD, chemical engineer, engineering economist, educator, administrator; b. Detroit, Mich., Feb. 16, 1943; s. Nathan and Harriet R.; m. Louise Collen, Dec. 21, 1969; children: Tanya, Candace, Miles. B.S., U. Mich., 1965; M.S., Calif. Inst. Tech., 1966, Ph.D., 1970. Registered profl. engr., Calif., Mich., La. Tech. service engr., chem. raw materials div. coordinator, sr. running plan coordinator, task team mgr. Exxon, Baton Rouge, 1970-75; assoc. prof. engring. Harvey Mudd Coll., Claremont, Calif., 1975-79, prof., 1980—, Oliver C. Field prof. engring., dir. Energy Inst., 1981-83; cons., mem. tech. staff, mgr. planning analysis Jet Propulsion Lab., Calif. Inst. Tech., 1976—; co-founder, ptnr. Claremont Cons. Group, 1979—; mem. adv. council Nat. Energy Found., N.Y.C., 1981-85; mem. Inst. Mgmt. Cons., 1988-89. Case study editor Am. Soc. Engring. Edn., Inst. Indsl. Engrs., Engring. Economist, 1977-89; mem. editorial bd. Jour. Engring. Costs and Prodn. Econs., 1985-91, Internat. Jour. Prodn. Econs., 1992—; contbr. articles to profl. jours. Shelter mgr. ARC, Baton Rouge, 1965-70. Recipient Outstanding Chem. Engr. award U. Mich., 1965, First Place Pub. Relations award Am. Inst. Chem. Engring., 1975, Outstanding Alumni Fund Achievement award Calif. Inst. Tech., 1976, Outstanding Young Man of Am. award, 1976, NASA award, 1983, Best Paper of the Year in Jour. Parametrics, Internat. Soc. Parametric Analysts, 1991-92, Centennial award certificate Am. Soc. Engring. Edn., 1993; named Outstanding Research Seminar Speaker Occidental Research Corp., 1976. Mem. Am. Soc. Engring. Mgmt. (bd. dirs. 1981-83), Toastmasters Club (pres. Claremont-Pomona chpt. 1978).

REMER, VERNON RALPH, travel consultant; b. Urbana, Iowa, July 14, 1918; s. Ralph William and Kittie (Weisbard) R.; m. Jane V. Bush, Sept. 19, 1941; children—Richard Charles, Linda Jane (Mrs. A.D. Bleiberg). B.S., U. Iowa, 1939. With Central Life Assurance Co., Des Moines, Iowa, 1939-78; sr. v.p. Central Life Assurance Co., 1972-77; travel cons., 1977—; pres. Urbana Savs. Bank, 1944-64, dir., 1944-67. Precinct committeeman Republican party, 1952-60; mem. Polk County Rep. Central Com., 1953-56. Fellow Life Office Mgmt. Assn.; mem. Life Ins. Mktg. and Research Assn. (dir. 1971-74, chmn. agy. mgmt. conf. com. 1971—), Am. Soc. Travel Agts. (diploma), Sigma Nu. Congregationalist. Clubs: Masons, Des Moines. Home: 13018 Pomard Way Poway CA 92064-1108

REMICK, FORREST JEROME, JR., former university official; b. Lock Haven, Pa., Mar. 16, 1931; s. Forrest Jerome Sr. and Ruth Betsy (Saiers) R.; m. Grace Louise Grove, June 7, 1953; children: Beth Ann Remick Gillio, Eric Forrest. BSME, Pa. State U., 1955, MSME, 1958, PhD in ME, 1963; diploma, Oak Ridge (Tenn.) Sch. Reactor Tech., 1956. Engr. Bell Telephone Labs., Whippany, N.J., 1955-56; dir. nuclear reactor facility Pa. State U., University Park, 1959-65, dir. Inst. Sci. Engring., 1967-79, acting dir. Ctr. Air Environ. Studies, 1976-78, dir. intercoll. research programs, 1979-85, asst. v.p. research, grad. studies, 1979-84, assoc. v.p. research, 1985-89; dir. Curtiss Wright Nuclear Research Lab., Quehanna, Pa., 1960-65; chief tng. sect. dept. tech. assistance IAEA, Vienna, Austria, 1965-67; mem. Nat. Nuclear Accrediting Bd., Inst. Nuclear Power Ops., Atlanta, 1982-88, Sci. Adv. Com. Idaho Nat. Engring. Lab., Idaho Falls, 1984-89, Reactor Safety Adv. Com., Savannah River Lab., Aiken, S.C., 1986-89, chmn., 1989; mem. Adv. Com. on Reactor Safeguards, Washington, 1982, vice chmn., 1987-88, chmn., 1989; commr. U.S. Nuclear Regulatory Commn., 1989-94, cons., 1994—. Served to sgt. U.S. Army, 1951-52. Named Outstanding Engring. Alumnus, Pa. State U., 1993; recipient Thomas P. Hamrick award for contbns. to tng. of nuclear facility pers., 1995. Fellow Am. Nuclear Soc. (meml. lectr. award 1971, disting. speaker award 1983); Nuclear Accrediting Bd., ASME, Am. Soc. Engring. Edn. Republican. Lutheran. Home and Office: 305 E Hamilton Ave State College PA 16801-5413

REMICK, OSCAR EUGENE, college president; b. Ellsworth, Maine, Aug. 24, 1932; s. Horace and Blanche (Rich) R.; m. Emma L. Lorance, Dec. 18, 1959; children: Mark Stephen, John Andrew, Paul Thomas. A.B., Ea. Coll., 1954; B.D. magna cum laude, Ea. Bapt. Theol. Sem., 1957; M.A., U.Pa., 1957; Ph.D., Boston U., 1966; student, Columbia U., 1959-61, Andover Newton Theol. Sem., 1957-58, Heidelberg (Germany) U., 1958-59; postdoctoral study, India, 1967; D.D., Assumption Coll., 1971, Allegheny Coll., 1974, Ea. Bapt. Theol. Sem., 1993; LL.D. (hon.), Alma Coll., 1987, Davis and Elkins Coll., 1991; HHD (hon.), Carroll Coll., 1991. Ordained to ministry Presbyn. Ch. (U.S.A.), 1957. Ordained minister United Presbyn. Ch. U.S.A.; minister United Baptist Ch., Topsham, Maine, 1961-63; part-time instr. philosophy Bates Coll., 1962-63; minister First Congregational Ch., Paxton, Mass., 1963-66; asst. prof. philosophy and theology Assumption Coll., 1966-67, assoc. prof., 1967-71, prof. religious studies, 1969-71, v.p., acad. dean, coordinator acad. affairs, 1968-71; co-dir. ecumenical Inst. Religious Studies, 1967-71; Minister theol. studies First Baptist Ch., Worcester, Mass., 1966-71; pres. Chautauqua (N.Y.) Instn., 1971-77; lectr. State U. N.Y., 1972-77, prof. philosophy, dean for arts and humanities, dir. internat. edn., 1977-80; theologian-in-residence First Presbyn. Ch., Jamestown, N.Y., 1974-80; pres. Alma (Mich.) Coll., 1980-87, prof. philosophy and religion, 1980-87; pres., prof. philosophy Westminster Coll., New Wilmington, Pa., 1987—; bd. dirs. Integra North Bank, Titusville, Pa. Author: Value in the Thought of Paul Tillich; Christianity and Other Major Religions, 1968, India and Hinduism, 1968, Responding to God's Call, 1970, The Hidden Crisis in Education, 1971. Pres. Worcester Area Coun. Chs., 1970-71; mem., chmn. Mich. Coun. for the Arts, 1981-87; mem. N.Y. State Coun. on Arts, 1983-87; mem., vice-chmn. Pa. Coun. on Arts, 1990—; mem. Hoyt Inst. for Arts; bd. dirs. Found. for Ind. Colls. Inc., Jameson Hosp.; bd. dirs., chmn. Pa. Assn. Colls. and Univs.; mem. exec. com., chmn. Pa. Commn. for Ind. Colls. and Univs.; mem. exec. com., chmn. Assn. Presbyn. Colls. and Univs., 1992—. Mem. Am. Philos. Assn., Soc. Advancement Continuing Edn. for Ministry, Am. Assn. for Advancement of Humanities, Paul Tillich Soc. N.Am., Deutsche Paul-Tillich-Gesellschaft, Am. Assn. Higher Edn., Am. Soc. Study Religion, Am. Acad. Religion, N.Am. Acad. Ecumenists, Soc. for Arts, Religion and Contemporary Culture, Assn. Presbyn. Colls. and Univs. (exec. com., vice chmn.), Nat. Assn. Ind. Colls. and Univs. (commn. on fins., higher edn.), Lawrence County C. of C. (past pres.). Home: 521 S New Castle St New Wilmington PA 16142-1426 Office: Westminster Coll South Market St New Wilmington PA 16172-0001 *The striving for excellence cannot be limited to a single discipline, task, or job. It involves a commitment of such intensity that the quest for excellence must be regarded as a way of life. I have taken a great deal of inspiration from both great artists and athletes whose achievements tell us that even if excellence cannot be readily defined, there is no way it can be approximated or achieved without self-discipline, dedication and commitment.*

REMINE, WILLIAM HERVEY, JR., surgeon; b. Richmond, Va., Oct. 11, 1918; s. William Hervey and Mabel Inez (Walthall) ReM.; m. Doris Irene Grumbacher, June 9, 1943; children—William H., Stephen Gordon, Walter James, Gary Craig. B.S. in Biology, U. Richmond, 1940, D.Sc. (hon.), 1965; M.D., Med. Coll. Va., Richmond, 1943; M.S. in Surgery, U. Minn., Mpls., 1952. Diplomate Am. Bd. Surgery. Intern Doctor's Hosp., Washington, 1944; fellow in surgery Mayo Clinic, Rochester, Minn., 1944-45, 47-52; instr. surgery Mayo Grad. Sch. Medicine, Rochester, Minn., 1954-59, asst. prof. surgery, 1959-65, assoc. prof. surgery, 1965-70, prof. surgery, 1970-83, prof. surgery emeritus, 1983—; surg. cons. to surgeon gen. U.S. Army, 1965-75; surg. lectr., USSR, 1987, 89, Japan, 1988, 90, Egypt, 1990; lectr. Soviet-Am. seminars, USSR, 1987, 89. Sr. author: Cancer of the Stomach, 1964, Manual of Upper Gastro-intestinal Surgery, 1985; editor: Problems in General Surgery, Surgery of the Biliary Tract, 1986; mem. editorial bd. Rev. Surgery, 1965-75, Jour. Lancet, 1968-77; contbr. 200 articles to profl. jours. Served to capt. U.S. Army, 1945-47. Recipient St. Francis surg. award St. Francis Hosp., Pitts., 1976, disting. service award Alumni Council, U. Richmond, 1976. Mem. ACS, AAAS, Am. Assn. History of Medicine, AMA, Am. Med. Writers Assn., Am. Soc. Colon and Rectal Surgeons, Soc. Surgery Alimentary Tract (v.p. 1983-84), Am. Surg. Assn., Assn. Mil. Surgeons U.S., Internat. Soc. Surgery, Digestive Disease Found., Priestley Soc. (pres. 1968-69), Central Assn. Physicians and Dentists (pres. 1972-73), Central Surg. Assn., Soc. Med. Cons. Armed Forces, Mayo Clinic Surg. Soc. (chmn. 1964-66), Soc. Head and Neck Surgeons, Soc. Surg. Oncology, Soc. Surg. Assn., Western Surg. Assn. (pres. 1979-80), Minn. State Med. Assn., Minn. Surg. Soc. (pres. 1966-67), Zumbro Valley Med. Soc., Sigma Xi; hon. mem. Colombian Coll. Surgeons, St. Paul Surg. Soc., Flint Surg. Soc., Venezuelan Surg. Soc., Colombian Soc. Gastroenterology, Dallas So. Clin. Soc., Ga. Surg. Soc., Postgrad. Surgeons Los Angeles County, Japanese Surg. Soc., Argentine Surg. Digestive Soc., Bassanese Surg. Assn. (Italy), Tex. Surg. Soc., Omicron Delta Kappa, Alpha Omega Alpha, Beta Beta Beta, Kappa Sigma. Methodist. Avocations: hunting, fishing, golf, photography, boating, music. Home: Sawgrass Players Club 8212 Seven Mile Dr Ponte Vedra Beach FL 32082-3639

REMINGER, RICHARD THOMAS, lawyer; b. Cleve., Apr. 3, 1931; s. Edwin Carl and Theresa Henrietta (Bookmyer) R.; m. Billie Carmen Greer, June 26, 1954; children: Susan Greer, Patricia Allison, Richard Thomas. AB, Case-Western Res. U., 1953; J.D., Cleve.-Marshall Law Sch., 1957. Bar: Ohio 1957, Pa. 1978, U.S. Supreme Ct. 1961. Personnel and safety dir. Motor Express, Inc., Cleve., 1954-58; mng. ptnr. Reminger & Reminger Co., L.P.A., Cleve., 1958-90; mem. nat. claims coun. adv. bd. Comml. Union Assurance Co., 1980—; lectr. transp. law Fenn Coll., 1960-62; lectr. bus. law Case Western Res. U., 1962-64; lectr. products liability U. Wirtschaft at Schloss Gracht, Erfstadt-Liblar, Germany, 1990-91, Bar Assn. City of Hamburg, Germany, 1990; mem. faculty Nat. Inst. for Trial Advocacy, 1992. Mem. joint com. Cleve. Acad. Medicine-Greater Cleve. Bar Assn.; trustee Cleve Zool. Soc., exec. com., 1984-89, v.p. 1987-89; trustee Andrew Sch., Hudson Rd. Hosp., Cleve., Cleve. Sch. for Blind, 1987-88, Cerebral Palsy Assn., 1984-87, Good Samaritan Hosp., Palm Beach, Fla., 1992—, bd. govs., 1992—. With AC, USNR, 1950-58. Named Man of Yr. Cleve.-Marshall Law Sch., 1989. Mem. Fedn. Ins. and Corp. Counsel, Trial Attys. Am. (mem. sect. litigation, also tort and ins. practice), Fed. Bar Assn., ABA (com. on law and medicine, profl. responsibility com. 1977—), Internat. Ins. Law Soc., Internat. Bar Assn., Ohio Bar Assn. (coun. dels. 1987—, internat. law com. 1990—), Pa. Bar Assn., Cleve. Bar Assn. (chmn. med. legal com. 1978-79, profl. liability com. 1977—), Transp. Lawyers Assn., Cleve. Assn. Civil Trial Attys., Am. Soc. Hosp. Attys., Soc. Ohio State Attys., Ohio Assn. Civil Trial Attys., Am. Judicature Soc., Def. Rsch. Inst., Maritime Law Assn. U.S., Am. Coll. Law and Medicine, 8th Jud. Bar Assn. (life Ohio dist.), Internat. Ins. Law Soc., Oil Painters Am. (assoc.), Mayfield Country Club (pres. 1980-82), Union Club, Cleve. Playhouse Club, Hermit Club (pres. 1973-75), Lost Tree Club (bd. govs.), Everglades (Fla.) Club, Kirtland Country Club, Rolling Rock (Pa.) Club.

REMINGTON, CHARLES BRADFORD, professional services firm executive; b. Highland Park, Ill., Nov. 12, 1935; m. JoAnn Gussie Little, June 10, 1978. BA, Mich. State U., 1957, MBA, 1961. Mktg. exec. Ernst & Young

LLP (formerly Ernst & Whinney and Ernst & Ernst), Cleve., 1962-72; ptnr. Ernst & Young (formerly Ernst & Whinney and Ernst & Ernst), Cleve., 1972—, regional dir. mktg. ctrl. region, 1982—. Office: Ernst & Young 1300 Huntington Bldg 925 Euclid Ave Cleveland OH 44115

REMINGTON, DEBORAH WILLIAMS, artist; b. Haddonfield, N.J., June 25, 1935; d. Malcolm Van Dyke and Hazel Irwin (Stewart) R. B.F.A.; San Francisco Art Inst., 1957. Adj. prof. art Cooper Union, N.Y.C., 1973—, NYU, 1994—. Exhibited one-woman show, Dilexi Gallery, San Francisco, 1962, 63, 65, Bykert Gallery, N.Y.C., 1967, 69, 72, 74, Galerie Darthea Speyer, Paris, 1968, 71, 73, 92, Hamilton Gallery, N.Y.C., 1977, Newport Harbor Art Mus., 1983, Oakland Mus., 1984, Jack Shainman Gallery, N.Y.C., 1987, Shoshana Wayne Gallery, Los Angeles, 1988; group show, Whitney Mus. Am. Art, N.Y.C., 1965, 67, 72, San Francisco Mus. Art, 1956, 60, 61, 63, 64, 65, Art. Inst., Chgo., 1974, Toledo Mus. Art, 1975, The 6 Gallery, 1954-57, Natsoulas Noveloso Gallery, Davis, Calif., 1990, Nat. Gallery Modern Art, Lisbon, 1981, 1st Trienalle des Ameriques Maubeuge, France, 1993; represented: permanent collections Whitney Mus. Am. Art, Nat. Mus. Am. Art, Washington, Art Inst., Chgo., Centre d'Art et de Culture Georges Pompidou, Paris,Carnegie Mus., Pitts. Recipient Hassam and Speicher Purchase award Am. Acad. and Inst. Arts and Letters, 1988; NEA fellow, 1979-80; Tamarind Inst. fellow, 1973; Guggenheim fellow, 1984. Home and Office: 309 W Broadway New York NY 10013-5325

REMINGTON, JACK SAMUEL, physician; b. Chgo., Jan. 19, 1931; s. Nathan and Sylvia R.; children: David Nathan, Lynne Denise. BS, U. Ill., Chgo., 1954, MD, 1956; honoris causa, U. Paul Sabatier, Toulouse, France, 1992. Diplomate Am. Bd. Internal Medicine. Intern U. Calif. Service, San Francisco County Hosp., 1956; research assoc. NIH, Bethesda, Md., 1957-59; resident in medicine U. Calif. Med. Center, San Francisco, 1959-60; sr. postdoctoral fellow Harvard U. Sch. Medicine, Thorndike Meml. Lab., Boston City Hosp., 1960-62; mem. faculty dept. medicine, div. infectious diseases Stanford (Calif.) U. Sch. Medicine, 1962—, prof., 1974—; chmn. dept. Immunology and Infectious Diseases, Research Inst. Palo Alto (Calif.) Med. Found., 1962—, Marcus A. Krupp Research Chair, 1987—; chief cons. in infectious diseases Palo Alto Med. Clinic, 1962—; cons. VA Hosp., Palo Alto, 1962—; cons. in infectious diseases WHO, 1967—, Pan Am. Health Orgn., 1967—, Dept. Army, 1971—; cons. Letterman Gen. Hosp., 1975—; sci. cons. Merit Rev. Bd. in Infectious Diseases VA, 1972-76; mem. adv. sci. bd. Gorgas Meml. Inst. of Tropical and Preventive Medicine, 1972—; mem. com. on infectious diseases Am. Bd. Internal Medicine, 1973-78; mem. adv. panel Am. Bd. Med. Lab. Immunology, 1978—, Sci. Adv. Com. Am. Found. for AIDS Research, 1985—. Editor: (with J.O. Klein) Infectious Diseases of the Fetus and Newborn Infant, 1976-94, (with M.N. Swartz) Current Clinical Topics in Infectious Diseases, 1980—; mem. editorial bd.: Antimicrobial Agts. and Chemotherapy, 1973-76, Jour. Clin. Investigation, 1975—, Am. Rev. Respiratory Disease, 1978—, Jour. Immunopharmacology, 1978-81, European Jour. Clin. Microbiology, 1981, Transplant Management, 1987, Jour. of Clinical Microbiology, 1987—, Laboratory Immunology, 1988—, Host, 1990—. Served with USPHS, 1957-59. Recipient Maxwell Finland award, Alexander von Humboldt award, 1988. Fellow A.C.P.; mem. Infectious Diseases Soc. Am. (bd. dirs. 1974-77, pres. 1988), Western Soc. Clin. Research (pres. 1975, mem. council 1975-77), Immunocompromised Host Soc. (pres. 1988-90), Western Assn. Physicians (councillor 1980), AAAS, Am. Assn. Immunologists, Am. Fedn. Clin. Research, AMA, Am. Soc. Clin. Investigation, Am. Soc. Microbiology, Am. Soc. Parasitologists, Am. Soc. Tropical Medicine and Hygiene, Assn. Am. Physicians, Internat. Coll. Tropical Medicine, Am. Soc. Protozoologists, Reticuloendothelial Soc., Assn. Am. Physicians, Alpha Omega Alpha, European Congress Clin. Microbiology (mem. european and internat. adv. bds.). Office: 860 Bryant St Palo Alto CA 94301-2707 also: Stanford U Sch Medicine Stanford CA 94305

REMLEY, AUDREY WRIGHT, educational administrator, psychologist; b. Warrenton, Mo., Dec. 26, 1931; d. Leslie Frank and Irene Lesetta (Graue) Wright; m. Alvin Remley, Mar. 25, 1951 (dec. Mar. 1986); children: Steven Leslie, David Mark. AA, Hannibal-LaGrange Coll., 1951; BS in Edn. cum laude, U. Mo., 1963, MA, 1969, PhD, 1974. Lic. psychologist, Mo; cert. health svc. provider, Mo. Asst. prof. psychology Westminster Coll., Fulton, Mo., 1969-74, assoc. prof., 1975-88, prof., 1988—, assoc. dean faculty, 1989—, chmn. dept. psychology, 1975-78, dir. counseling svcs., 1975-79, dir. student devel., 1979-80, dir. acad. advising and counseling svcs., 1980-88; cons. OVID Bell Press, 1988-89; mem. adv. bd. Callaway Cmty. Hosp., 1988-95, pres. 1992-95; bd. dirs. Serve, Inc., Fulton 1989-95, pres. 1991-93; mem. adv. bd. social learning program Fulton State Hosp., chair, 1992-94, mng. county govt. task force fin. mgmt. chair. Recipient Outstanding Young Woman of Am. award Jaycettes, 1965, Athena award, 1991; NDEA fellow, 1968. Mem. APA, AACD, Am. Coll. Pers. Assn. (exec. council 1982-85, co-editor ACPA Developments, 1984-87, v.p. state divs., 1987-89, treas.-elect 1990-91, treas., 1991-93, treas. ednl. found. bd., 1994—, Outstanding State Div. Leader 1982, profl. svc. award 1991), Annuit Coeptis awrd 1994), Mo. Coll. Pers. Assn. (pres. 1981-82, profl. svc. award 1987), Mo. Psychol. Assn. (lic.), Kiwanis (exec. bd. 1989-92, v.p. 1992, pres.-elect 1992-93, pres. 1993-94). Presbyterian. Avocations: singing; antique collecting; knitting. Office: Westminster Coll 501 Westminster Ave Fulton MO 65251-1299

REMLEY, THEODORE PHANT, JR., counselor, educator and lawyer; b. Eustis, Fla., Feb. 7, 1947; s. Theodore Phant Sr. and Era Annie (Forehand) R. BA, U. Fla., 1969, EdS, 1971, PhD, 1980; JD, Catholic U. 1980. Bar: Va. 1981, Fla. 1982; lic. profl. counselor, Va., Miss., La. Exec. dir. Am. Counseling Assn., Alexandria, Va., 1990-94; profl. counseling U. New Orleans, 1994—. Contbr. articles to profl. jours., chpts. to books. Mem. ABA, Am. Counseling Assn., Am. Sch. Counselor Assn., Am. Assn. State Counseling Bds. Democrat. Roman Catholic. Home: 3800 Camp St New Orleans LA 70115-2629 Office: Dept Edn Leadership Counseling & Founds U New Orleans New Orleans LA 70148

REMMEL, JERRY G., utilities executive; b. 1931. BS, Marquette U., 1955, MBA, 1959. With Wis. Electric Power Co., 1955—, staff asst., 1955-62, asst. treas. ext. sys., 1962-68, asst. treas., 1968-73, treas., 1973—; asst. sec., asst. treas. Wis. Natural Gas Co., treas., v.p., 1974—. Office: Wis Nat Gas Co 233 Lake Ave Racine WI 53403*

REMNICK, DAVID J., journalist; b. Hackensack, N.J., Oct. 29, 1958; s. Edward C. and Barbara (Seigel) R.; m. Esther B. Fein; children: Alexander, Noah. AB, Princeton U., 1981. Reporter The Washington Post, 1982-91; staff writer The New Yorker, N.Y.C., 1992—; vis. fellow Coun. Fgn. Rels., N.Y.C., 1992-94. Author: Lenin's Tomb: The Last Days of the Soviet Empire, 1993 (Pulitzer Prize for gen. non-fiction 1994, George Polk award 1994). Recipient Livingston award, 1991, Helen Bernstein award N.Y. Pub. Libr., 1994. Home: 322 W 72d St New York NY 10023 Office: The New Yorker 20 W 43d St New York NY 10036

REMONDI, JOHN F., student aid administrator. Treas. Nellie Mae, Inc., Braintree, Mass. Office: Nellie Mae Inc 50 Braintree Hill Park Braintree MA 02184*

REMPEL, GARRY LLEWELLYN, chemical engineering educator, consultant; b. Regina, Sask., Can., Aug. 20, 1944; s. Henry Jacob and Grace Violet (Pullman) R.; m. Flora Tak Tak Ng, Sept. 20, 1975. BSc with 1st class honours, U. B.C., Vancouver, Can., 1965, PhD in Catalysis, 1968. Nat. Rsch. Coun. Can. postdoctoral fellow Imperial Coll. Sci. and Tech., London, 1968-69; asst. prof. chem. engring. U. Waterloo, 1969-73, assoc. prof., 1973-80, prof., 1980—, chmn. dept., 1988—, mem. faculty dept. chemistry, 1976—, cons. Inst. for Polymer Rsch., 1984—, bd. dirs. Waterloo Ctr. for Process Devel., 1988-90; vis. scientist Inst. for Catalysis Rsch., Nat. Ctr. Sci. Rsch., Lyon, France, 19 78; vis. rsch. fellow dept. chemistry U. Chgo., 1978-79; mem. grant selection comm. in chem. and metall. engring. Natural Scis. and Engring. Rsch. Coun., 1992—; mem. sci. program com. Ont. Ctr. for Materials Rsch., 1991—, acad. leader polymers and plastic program mgmt. com., 1992—; cons. Polysar Rubber Corp., Sarnia, Ont., 1981—, Rempel Rsch. Inc., Waterloo, 1981—, Ortho McNeil Inc., Toronto, Ont., 1992—. Contbr. over 120 articles to profl. jours.; patentee for novel catalyst sys. and methods of preparation, polymer hydrogenation processes, oxidation of polythionates, gas consumption measuring sys., amine modified hydrogenation of nitrile rubber, nitrile rubber hydrogenation, hydrogenation of nitrile rubber, catalytic hydrogenation of nitrile rubber, catalytic solution hydrogenation of nitrile rubber. Grantee Nat. Scis. and Engring. Rsch. Coun., 1987-88, 90, 92-95, Polysar Ltd., 1987-88, Province of Ont. URIF, 1987-88, 90-92, 93, Nova Husky, 1989-91, Polysar Rubber Corp., 1989-92, 95, Ortho McNeil Inc., 1992-93; Recipient of Thomas W. Eadie Medal, 1993, Royal Soc. Canada. Recipient best rsch. paper award dept. chem. engring. U. Waterloo, 1988, 93; scholar Province of B.C., 1962, grad. scholar Nat. Rsch. Coun. Can., 1965-68, post doc. fellow, 1968-69; fellow Royal Soc. Can. (Thomas W. Eadie medal 1993), Chem. Inst. Can.; mem. AIChE, Can. Soc. for Chem. Engring. (award in indsl. practice 1994), Am. Chem. Soc., Soc. Chem. Industry. Office: U Waterloo, Dept Chem Engring, Waterloo, ON Canada N2L 3G1

REMSEN, CHARLES CORNELL, III, microbiologist, research administrator, educator; b. Newark, N.J., May 16, 1937; s. Charles Cornell Jr. and Elizabeth Havens (Atwood) Remsen; children: David Pratt, Linda Remsen Brandenburg, Stephen Dwyer, Andrew Walker; m. Margaret Ellis Fairchild, June 19, 1976; stepchildren: Elizabeth Hoffman Herzog, Jennifer Hoffman Jonas. BS in Food Chemistry and Microbiology, Delaware Valley Coll. Sci. and Agr., 1960; MS in Microbiology, Syracuse U., 1963, PhD in Microbiology, 1965. Rsch. asst. Schering Pharm., Bloomfield, N.J., 1959-60; rsch. asst. dept. preventive medicine Upstate Med. Ctr., Syracuse, N.Y., 1961-63; grad. teaching asst. Syracuse U., 1962-63, grad. rsch. asst., 1963-65; NIH post-doctoral fellow dept. gen. biology Swiss Fed. Inst. Tech., Zurich, Switzerland, 1965-67; asst. scientist Woods Hole (Mass.) Oceanographic Inst., 1967-71, assoc. scientist, 1971-75; rsch. assoc. in microbial ecology Marine Biol. Labs., Woods Hole, 1973-74; assoc. prof. dept. zoology/microbiology, assoc. scientist Ctr. Great Lakes Studies U. Wis., Milw., 1975-83, prof., sr. scientist, 1983—, coord. zoology/microbiology, 1976-84, acting dir. Ctr. Great Lakes Studies, Great Lakes Rsch. Facility, 1987-89, interim dir., 1989-92, dir., 1992—; mem. editorial bd. Jour. of Bacteriology, 1969-77; external examiner McGill U. Grad. Sch., 1971-73; chmn. joint com. for biol. oceanography MIT-WHOI PhD Program, 1971-74; mem. internat. adv. bd. ScienceQuest. Author: (with others) The Encyclopedia of Microscopy and Microtechnique, 1973, Effect of the Ocean Environment on Microbial Activities, 1974, The Phytosynthetic Bacteria, 1978, Responses of Marine Organisms to Pollutants, 1984, Structure of Photosynthetic Prokaryotes, 1991; contbr. articles to profl. jours. Del. Coun. on Ocean Affairs. Recipient NIH Foreign Postdoctoral fellowship, 1965-67, Disting. Svc. award Jour. of Bacteriology, 1977. Mem. Nat. Assn. Marine Labs. (exec. com.), Am. Geophys. Union, Am. Soc. for Microbiology, Internat. Assn. for Great Lakes Rsch., Coun. Great Lakes Rsch. Mgrs. (internat. joint commn.), N.E. Assn. Marine Labs. (co-v.p.), N.E. Assn. Marine and Great Lakes Labs., Nature Conservancy (bd. trustees Wis. chpt. 1987, exec. com. 1989—, sec. 1989—), Sigma Xi. Achievements include research in relating the structure of chemolithotrophs to their ecological niche, and to their response to the environment, methane-oxidizing bacteria and how these microorganisms fit into the overall carbon cycle in the Great Lakes, the study of sediment samples from Lakes Superior, Michigan and Huron in order to determine the extent and rate of organic matter diagenesis in sediments, the exchange of gases (CO_2, CH_4, O_2) with overlying waters and ultimately the atmosphere, the ecological role and significance of chemosynthesis and photosynthesis in sublacustrine hydrothermal vents and gas fumaroles. Office: University of Wisconsin Mil Ctr for Great Lakes Studies Milwaukee WI 53201*

REMSEN, JAMES VANDERBEEK, JR., biologist, museum curator; b. Newark, Sept. 21, 1949; s. James V. and Elizabeth (Willox) R.; m. Catherine Cummins, Nov. 12, 1988; 1 child, Kenneth William. BA, Stanford U., 1971, MA, 1971; PhD, U. Calif., Berkeley, 1978. Dir., curator birds, prof. La. State U. Mus. Natural Sci., Baton Rouge, 1978—. Author: Annotated List of the Birds of Bolivia, 1989, (monograph) Community Ecology of Neotropical Kingfishers, 1990; contbr. numerous articles to sci. jours. Fellow Am. Ornithologists Union; mem. AAAS, Am. Soc. Naturalists, Ecol. Soc. Am. Home: 545 Pecan Dr Saint Gabriel LA 70776-5513 Office: La State U Mus Natural Sci Baton Rouge LA 70803

REMSON, IRWIN, retired hydrogeology educator; b. N.Y.C., Jan. 23, 1923; s. Nathan and Julia Z. (Gottlieb) R.; m. Edna D. Miller, Jan. 25, 1948; children: Cathy J., Kenneth A. A.B., Columbia U., 1946, M.A., 1949, Ph.D., 1954. Cert. engring. geologist, Calif. registered geologist, Calif. Geologist, engr. U.S. Geol. Survey, Seabrook, N.J., 1949-60; prof. civil engring. Drexel Inst. Tech., Phila., 1960-68, chief marshall of faculty, 1965; prof. applied earth sci. and geology Stanford U., Stanford, Calif., 1968-93; Barney & Estelle Morris prof. earth scis. Stanford U., 1980-93, prof. emeritus, 1993—; cons. in field. Author: (with Hornberger and Molz) Numerical Methods in Subsurface Hydrology, 1971, (with Howard) Geology in Environmental Planning, 1978; contbr. articles to profl. jours. Served with USAF, 1943-46. Recipient Lindback award for Disting. Teaching Drexel Inst. Tech., 1966. Fellow Geol. Soc. Am. (Birdsall Disting. lectr. in hydrology 1980-81); mem. Am. Geophys. Union, Assn. Engring. Geologists, Sigma Xi. Home: 1016 Cathcart Way Palo Alto CA 94305-1047 Office: Stanford U Dept Applied Earth Sci Stanford CA 94305

REMY, RAY, chamber of commerce official; b. San Francisco. B in Polit. Sci., Claremont Men's Coll. (now Claremont McKenna Coll.); M in Pub. Adminstrn., U. Calif., Berkeley. Adminstrv. intern City of Berkeley, 1962-63; with So. Office League of Calif. Cities, 1963, then asst. to exec. dir. and mgr., to 1969; exec. dir. So. Calif. Assn. Govt., 1969-76; appointed dep. mayor City of L.A., 1976-84; pres. L.A. Area C. of C., 1984—; also prin. spokesman Los Angeles Area C. of C. Bd. dirs. Mus. Sci. and Industry; past chmn. bd. councilors U. So. Calif. Sch. Pub. Adminstrn., L.A.; vice chmn. bd. dirs. Rose Inst. for State and Local Govt.; vice chmn. bd. trustees Claremont (Calif.) McKenna Coll., Calif. Trust for Environ., Bay Delta Oversight Coun.; pres. Inst. for Local Self Govt.; bd. dirs. RLA, chmn. Calif. Trade and Goods Movement Study; mem. bus. adv. coun. U.S. Dept. Transp. Recipient numerous awards including Fletcher Bowron award, Donald Stone award, Mus. of Sci. and Industry Fellowship award, others. Mem. Nat. Acad. Pub. Adminstrn., Jr. Statesmen Found., Am. Soc. Pub. Adminstrn. (past pres.). Office: LA Area C of C PO Box 3693 350 S Bixel St Los Angeles CA 90051-1696

REN, CHUNG-LI, engineer; b. Chefoo, China, June 1, 1931; came to U.S., 1955; s. Shantsai and Fooching (Wang) R.; m. Rosalie Fen Lo, Aug. 4, 1962; children: Eric W., Caroline W. BSEE, Taiwan Coll. Engring., 1953; MSEE, U. Notre Dame, 1957; PhD in Electro Physics, Polytech Inst. Bklyn., 1964. Teaching asst. U. Notre Dame, South Bend, Ind., 1956-57; grad. asst., sr. lectr. Polytech Inst. Bklyn., Microwave Rsch. Inst., 1959-65; disting. mem. tech. staff AT&T Bell Labs., North Andover, Mass., 1965-90; lead engr. Mitre Corp., Advanced Satellite Terminals and Tech., Bedford, Mass., 1990—; chmn. tech. session Asia-Pacific Microwave Conf., Taiwan, 1993; spkr. and panelist in field. Patentee in field; contbr. articles to profl. jours. Rsch. fellow Polytech Inst. Bklyn., 1957-59. Mem. IEEE (sr., mem. review bd. 1982—), Sigma Xi. Avocations: tennis, soccer, classical music, landscape design. Office: The Mitre Corp Burlington Rd Bedford MA 01730

RENARD, KENNETH GEORGE, civil engineer; b. Sturgeon Bay, Wis., May 5, 1934; s. Harry Henry and Margaret (Buechner) R.; m. Virginia Rae Heibel, Sept 8, 1956; children: Kenlynn T., Craig G., Andrew T. BCE, U. Wis., 1957, MCE, 1959; PhD in Civil Engring., U. Ariz., 1972. Registered profl. civil engr., Ariz. Hydraulic engr. Agrl. Rsch. Svc., USDA, Madison, Wis., 1957-59; resident engr. Agrl. Rsch. Svc., USDA, Tombstone, Ariz., 1959-64; rsch. hydraulic engr. Agrl. Rsch. Svc., USDA, Tucson, 1964-72, rsch. leader, 1972-87, rsch. hydraulic engr., 1987—. Contbr. articles to profl. jours. Recipient Superior Service award USDA, 1984, 90. Fellow ASCE (pres. Ariz. sect. 1981, exec. com. irrigation and drainage div. 1987—, chair 1990, mgmt. group D 1991—, editor Jour. Irrigation and Drainage Engring. 1983-85, John C Park award 1987, Arid Lands Hydraulic Engr. award 1992), Soil Conservations Soc. Am. (pres. Ariz. sect. 1975, Conservationist of Yr. 1983), Am. Geophys. Union; mem. Lions (pres. Tombstone chpt. 1963). Roman Catholic. Home: 4822 E Paseo Del Bac Tucson AZ 85718-6708 Office: USDA Agrl Rsch Svc 2000 E Allen Rd Tucson AZ 85719-1520

RENAUD, BERNADETTE MARIE ELISE, author; b. Ascot Corner, Que., Can., Apr. 18, 1945; d. Albert and Aline (Audet) R.; m. Pierre La Brosse, 1973. Diploma, Présentation de Marie, Granby, Que., 1962-64. Librarian asst. Schs. of Waterloo, Que., 1964-67; tchr. primary schs. Schs. of Waterloo, 1967-70; adminstrv. sec. Assn. Medi-Tech-Sci., Montreal, Que., 1972-76.

Author: Emilie La Baignoire A Pattes, 1976 (Can. Council Children's Lit. prize 1976, Assn. Advancement of Scis. and Technics of Documentation award 1976); adaptations of 8 children's classics, 1977; 20 Short Stories for Young Children, 1978, 79, 80, Le Chat de l'Oratoire, 1978, Emilie la baignoire à pattes album, 1978, La maison tête de pioche, 1979, La révolte de la courte pointe, 1979; mem. adminstrv. bd.: Communication-Jeunesse, 1977-82, Conseil culturel de la Montérégie, 1987-90; author: La dépression de l'ordinateur, 1981, Une boîte Magique Trés Embétante, 1981, The Cat in the Cathedral, 1983, La grande question de Tomatelle, 1982, The Computer Revolts, 1984, Comment on fait un livre?, 1983; author (book and movie) Bach et Bottine, 1986 (awards for movie, 16 awards across the world, transl. into 5 langs., and subtitled into 3 langs.); (novel) Un Homme Comme Tant d'Autres, tome I 1992, tome II, 1993, tome III, 1994; (short movie for Nat. Film Bd. of Can.) Quand l'accent devient grave, 1989; dir., coord. Écriré pour la jeunesse project, 1990.

RENBARGER, LARRY D., prefabricated housing manufacturing executive. Pres., CEO Shelter Components Corp., Elkhart, Ind. Office: Shelter Components Corp 27217 County Rd 6 Elkhart IN 46514*

RENDA, DOMINIC PHILLIP, airline executive; b. Steubenville, Ohio, Dec. 25, 1913; s. Joseph J. and Catherine (Roberta) R.; m. Delores E. Noland, July 12, 1980; children: Dominique Patricia, Dominic Phillip, Patrick Blake. B.S. in Bus. Adminstrn; J.D., Ohio State U., 1938. Bar: Ohio 1938. Practice law Steubenville, 1938-41; adminstrv. asst. to mem. Congress, 1941-42; with Western Air Lines, Inc., Los Angeles, 1946-68; asst. sec. Western Air Lines, Inc., 1947, v.p. legal, 1954-65, sr. v.p. legal, corp. sec., 1958-68; pres. Air Micronesia, Inc., Los Angeles, 1968-73; sr. v.p. internat. and pub. affairs Continental Air Lines, Inc., 1968-73; exec. v.p., dir., mem. exec. com. Western Air Lines, 1973-76, pres., mem. exec. and nominating coms., 1976-81, chief exec. officer, mem. mgmt. resources and compensation com., 1979-81, chmn. bd., 1981, emeritus chmn., 1982-85; dir. Bank of Montreal, Calif.; Mem. bus. adminstrn. adv. council Coll. Adminstrv. Sci., Ohio State U., 1974-82; bd. councilors Sch. Internat. Relations, U. So. Calif., 1967-82. Trustee Peace Found., Ponape, Caroline Islands, 1976-84; chmn. devel. com. Marymount High Sch., 1977-82. Served to lt. comdr. USNR, 1942-46. Mem. Calif., Ohio state bars, ABA, Los Angeles County Bar Assn. (past trustee), Calif. C. of C. (dir.), Phi Alpha Delta (pres. Los Angeles 1965-66). Clubs: Los Angeles Chancery (pres. 1966-67), Bel-Air Country, Calif.

RENDA, RANDOLPH BRUCE, university dean; b. Tokat, Turkey, Mar. 31, 1926; came to U.S., 1945, naturalized, 1956; s. Abdurrahman and Adviye (Adams) R.; m. Martha McDowell Hill, Aug. 30, 1948; children: William, Susan, Bennett, Lyle, Bruce. B.S., Purdue U., 1952, M.S., 1957, Ph.D. (Proctor and Gamble fellow), 1959. Project engr. Nat. Castings Co., Indpls., 1951-53; instr. mfg. processes Purdue U., Lafayette, Ind., 1953-55; instr. mech. engring. Purdue U., 1955-59; asst. prof. U. Ky., 1959-60, Swarthmore (Pa.) Coll., 1960-61; assoc. prof. U. Ky., 1961-65; prof., chmn. mech. engring. U. Louisville, 1966-72; assoc. dean, dir. U. Louisville (Inst. Indsl. Research), 1972-74; dean Sch. Engring. and Tech., Purdue U. at Indpls., 1974-94; dean, prof. emeritus, 1994—; Cons. Spindletop Research, Inc., Lexington, Ky., Besmar Assos., Knoxville, Pratt & Whitney Co., West Hartford, Conn., Glove Valve Co., Delphi, Ind. Trustee St. Francis Sch., Louisville, 1968-70. Mass. Inst. Tech. summer fellow, 1960; NSF fellow, 1961; NASA/Case Inst. summer fellow, 1964, 65. Mem. ASME (pres. 1969), Louisville Engring. Socs. Coun., Am. Soc. Engring. Edn., Nat. Soc. Profl. Engrs., Ky. Soc. Profl. Engrs., Soc. Engring. Sci., Sigma Xi, Sigma Tau, Pi Tau Sigma. Clubs: Rotarian, Columbia. Home: 8639 Bay Colony Dr Indianapolis IN 46234-2912 Office: Purdue U Sch Engring & Tech 723 W Michigan St Indianapolis IN 46202-5191

RENDALL, STEVEN FINLAY, language educator, editor, translator, critic; b. Geneva, Ill., May 2, 1939; s. Harvard John and Jessie Evangeline (Galbraith) R.; children from previous marriage: Matthew, Ruby Larisch; m. Lisa Dow Neal, May, 1992; 1 child, Josephine Dow Neal. BA summa cum laude in Philosophy, U. Colo., 1961; postgrad., Université de Lille, 1961-62, Johns Hopkins U., 1962-67; PhD, Johns Hopkins U., 1967. From asst. prof. romance langs. to assoc. prof. romance langs. U. Oreg., Eugene, 1967-79, prof. romance langs., 1979—; guest prof. Universität Konstanz, 1981; leader NEH summer seminar, 1987. Author: Distinguo: Reading Montaigne Differently, 1992; editor: Montaigne, 1984, Of History, 1994; translator: The Practice of Everyday Life, 1984, History and Memory, 1992, Astrea, 1995; co-editor: Comparative Literature, 1990—, assoc. editor 1978—, asst. editor, 1972-78, acting editor, 1980, 85-86; mem. editl. bd., adv. com. Montaigne Studies, 1989—; contbr. 35 articles to profl. jours., 37 book revs. NEH fellow Ctr. Rsch. on Translation SUNY, Binghamton, 1993, Camargo Found. fellow, 1988, Alexander von Humboldt-Stiftung Rsch. fellow, 1980-82, 94, NEH fellow, 1977, Danforth fellow, 1962-67; Gilman fellow, 1964-67, Woodrow Wilson fellow, 1962-63; Fulbright scholar, 1961-62. Mem. Modern Lang. Assn., Phi Beta Kappa. Home: 3217 N 25th St Tacoma WA 98406-6115 Office: U Oregon 223 Friendly Hall Eugene OR 97403

RENDELL, EDWARD GENE, mayor, lawyer; b. N.Y.C., Jan. 5, 1944; s. Jesse T. and Emma (Sloat) R.; B.A. in Polit. Sci., U. Pa., 1965; J.D., Villanova (Pa.) U., 1968; m. Marjorie Osterlund, July 10, 1971; 1 son, Jesse Thompson. Admitted to Pa. bar, 1968, U.S. Supreme Ct., 1981; asst. dist. atty., chief homicide unit Office Dist. Atty. Phila., 1968-74; dep. spl. prosecutor Phila., 1976; dist. atty. Phila., 1978-86; mayor City of Phila., 1992—. Served as 2d lt. USAR, 1968-74. Recipient Man of Year award VFW, 1980, Am. Cancer League, 1981; Disting. Public Service award Pa. County Detectives Assn., 1981. Mem. Am. Bar Assn., Pa. Dist. Attys. Assn. (legis. chmn. 1979—), Phila. Bar Assn., United Jewish Orgns., Jewish War Vets, Democrat. Club: B'nai B'rith. Office: Office of the Mayor 215 City Hall Philadelphia PA 19107-3202

RENDELL, ROBERT SLOAT, lawyer; b. N.Y.C., Nov. 9, 1940; s. Jesse T. and Emma S. R.; m. Mardi M. Rendell, July 10, 1967; children: Meredith, Lauren. A.B., Princeton U., 1962, LL.B., Harvard U. 1965, LL.M., 1966. Bar: N.Y. 1965. Atty., advisor Office of Internat. Tax Counsel, U.S. Treasury Dept., 1970-72; dep. gen. counsel U.S. Export-Import Bank, 1973-77; ptnr. Rogers & Wells, N.Y.C., 1980—; dir. UMB Bank & Trust Co. Mem. ABA, Bar Assn. City N.Y. Club: Harvard N.Y. Editor: Internat. Fin. Law, 1980. Office: 900 Jackson St Dallas TX 75202-4404

RENDELL-BAKER, LESLIE, anesthesiologist, educator; b. St. Helens, Eng., Mar. 27, 1917; came to U.S., 1957, naturalized, 1963; s. Frank Nelder and Ada (Gill) Rendell-B.; m. Rosemary Carr Hogg, Aug. 17, 1946; children: Sheila Diane, Helen Rosemary, Frances Nelda. BS, MB, Guy's Hosp. Med. Sch., London, 1941. Diplomate: Am. Bd. Anesthesiology. Resident anesthesia Brit. Army of Rhine Hosps., 1945-46, Guy's Hosp., London, 1946-48; sr. asst. (assoc. prof.) anesthesiology Welsh Nat. Sch. Medicine, Cardiff, 1948-57; Fulbright asst. prof. anesthesiology U. Pitts., 1955-56; from asst. prof. to assoc. prof. Sch. Medicine Case Western Res. U., Cleve., 1957-62; dir. dept. anesthesiology Mt. Sinai Hosp., N.Y.C., 1962-79; prof., chmn. dept. anesthesiology Mt. Sinai Sch. Medicine, CUNY, 1966-79; prof. dept. anesthesiology Sch. Medicine Loma Linda (Calif.) U., 1979—; chmn. sect. com. Z79 standards for anesthesia and respiratory equipment Am. Nat. Standards Instn., 1962-69, 1969-81, mem. exec. com. med. devices standards mgmt. bd., 1973-79, bd. dirs., 1976-79; chmn. classification panel on anesthesiology devices FDA, 1972-76. Author: (with W.W. Mushin) Principles of Thoracic Anesthesia, 1953, (with W.W. Mushin and Thompson) Automatic Ventilation of the Lungs, 3d edit., 1980; editor: Problems with Anesthetic and Respiratory Therapy Equipment, 1982, Maintenance, Cleaning and Sterilization of Anesthetic Equipment, 1993, Future Directions in Anesthesia Apparatus, 1993, The History and Evolution of Pediatric Anesthesia Equipment, 1992; author (with others) The Care of Anesthesia Equipment, 1992. Served to capt. Royal Army Med. Corps, 1942-46. Fellow Royal Coll. Anaesthetists; fellow Royal Soc. Medicine, Assn. Anaesthetists Gt. Britain and Ireland; mem. Am. Soc. Anesthesiologists (chmn. com. equipment and standardization 1962-68), Am. Soc. for Testing and Materials (chmn. subcom. D10-34 1981-91), Assn. Advancement Med. Instrumentation, AAAS. Inventor baby endotracheal connector, pediatric face masks and equipment. Home: 630 Beauregard Cres Redlands CA 92373-5602 Office: Loma Linda U Sch Medicine Dept Anesthesiology 11234 Anderson St Loma Linda CA 92354-2870

RENDER, ARLENE, ambassador. Joined Fgn. Svc., Dept. State, 1970; consular officer Fgn. Svc., Dept. State, Abidjan, Cote D'Ivoire, 1971-73, Tehran, Iran, 1973-76, Genoa, Italy, 1976-78; polit. officer Fgn. Svc., Dept. State, 1978-79, internat. rels. officer AF/C, 1979-81; dep. chief of mission Fgn. Svc., Dept. State, Brazzaville, Republic of the Congo, 1981-84; consul-gen. Fgn. Svc., Dept. State, Kingston, Jamaica, 1984-86; dep. chief of mission Fgn. Svc., Dept. State, Accra, Ghana, 1986-89; mem. sr. seminar Fgn. Svc., Dept. State, 1989-90, amb. to The Gambia, 1990-93; dir. Office of Ctrl. African Affairs Fgn. Svc., Dept. State, Washington, 1993—. Office: State Dept Office Ctrl African Affairs Washington DC 20520

RENDINO, ANTHONY, trust company executive; b. Bklyn., June 5, 1926; s. William and Marion (DeMartino) R.; m. Anita F. Prince, Oct. 28, 1950; children: Claire Rendino Ryan, Lynn Rendino Schiro, Luann, Caren, Tracie. B.Elec. Engring., Pratt Inst., 1950; M.B.A., Fairleigh Dickinson U., 1966. With IBM, 1950-70, dir. real estate operations Western area, 1965-68, dir. field real estate, 1968-70; v.p. real estate mgmt. Irving Trust Co., N.Y.C., 1970-72; sr. v.p. adminstrv. services Irving Trust Co., 1972-73, sr. v.p. operational services div., 1973-76, exec. v.p. ops. group, 1976-80, exec. v.p. gen. services group, 1980-87, exec. v.p. gen. services group, 1987—; pres. One Wall Street Corp., Irving Life Ins. Co. Mem. Borough of Manhattan Community Coll. Fund, Inc. Served with USNR, 1944-46. Mem. N.Y. Chamber Commerce and Industry, Downtown Lower Manhattan Assn., Regional Plan Assn. Home: 15 Bramley Ln Dobbs Ferry NY 10522-3202 Office: Irving Trust Co 1 Wall St New York NY 10005-2501

RENDL-MARCUS, MILDRED, artist, economist; b. N.Y.C., May 30, 1928; d. Julius and Agnes (Hokr) Rendl. BS, NYU, 1948, MBA, 1950; PhD (Dean Bernice Brown Cronkhite fellow 1950-51), Radcliffe Coll., 1954; m. Edward Marcus, Aug. 10, 1956. Economist, GE, 1953-56, Bigelow-Sanford Carpet Co., Inc., 1956-58; lectr. econs. evening sessions CCNY, 1953-58; rsch. investment problems in tropical Africa, 1958-59; instr. econs. Hunter Coll. CUNY, 1959-60; lectr. econs. Columbia U., 1960-61; rsch. econ. devel. Nigeria, West Africa, 1961-63; sr. economist Internat. div. Nat. Indsl. Conf. Bd., 1963-66; asst. prof. Grad. Sch. Bus. Adminstrn., Pace Coll., 1964-66; assoc. prof. Borough of Manhattan Community Coll., CUNY, 1966-71, prof., 1972-85; vis. prof. Fla. Internat. U., 1986; prin. MRM Assocs., Rendl Fine Art; corp. art econ. and contemporary art cons.; fine arts appraiser; artist Allied Social Sci. Assn. Conf., Boston, 1994; participant Internat. Econ. Meeting, Amsterdam, 1968, Prague, Czech Republic, 1993, Brussels, 1994, Econs. of Fine Arts in Age of Tech., 1984, Internat. Economic Assn. N.Am., Laredo, Tex., 1987-88, London, 1994, Soc. Southwestern Economists, San Antonio, 1988, New Orleans, 1989, Dallas, 1989, Houston, 1991, Dallas, 1994, S.W. Soc. Economists, San Antonio, 1992, Dallas, 1994, San Diego, 1990, 92, Reno, 1991, Western Econ. Assn. Internat., 1990, Ind. U. Pa., 1990, London, 1992, 93. Exhibited New Canaan Art Show, 1982, 83, 84, 85, New Canaan Soc. for Arts Ann., 1983, 85, New Canaan Arts, 1985, Silvermine Galleries, 1986, Stamford Art Assn., 1987, Women in the Arts at Phoenix Gallery, Group Show, N.Y.C., 1988, Parkview Point Gallery, Miami Beach, Fla., 1982-89, Art Complex, New Canaan, 1988-89; group shows include Lever House, N.Y.C., 1990, Cork Gallery, Lincoln Ctr., N.Y.C., 1990, Women's Caucus for Art, San Antonio, 1990, Artist's Equity, Broome St. Gallery, N.Y.C., 1991, Greater Hartford Architecture Conservancy, 1991; symposium participant Sienna, Italy, 1988, South Fla. Art Ctr., Miami Beach, 1990, 92, 93, Wadsworth Atheneum, Hartford, Conn., 1994-95; contbr. articles to Women in the Arts newsletter, 1986-87, Coalition Womens Art Orgns., 1986-87. Bd. dirs. N.Y.C. Coun. on Econ. Edn., 1970—; mem. program planning com. Women's Econ. Roundtable, N.Y.C.; participant Eastern Econ. Assn., Boston, 1988, Art and Personal Property Appraisal, NYU, 1986-88. Recipient Disting. Svc. award CUNY, 1985. Fellow Gerontol. Assn.; mem. Internat. Schumpeter Econs. Soc. (founding), Am. (vice chmn. ann. meeting 1973), Met. (sec. 1954-56) econ. assns., Indsl. Rels. Rsch. Assn., Audubon Artists and Nat. Soc. Painters in Casein (assoc. 1987-88) Allied Social Sci. Assn. (vice chmn. conv. 1973, artist Boston nat. conv. 1994), AAUW, N.Y.C. Women in Arts, Allied Social Sci. Assn. (artist 1994), Women's Econ. Roundtable, Greater Hartford Architecture Conservancy, NYU Grad. Sch. Bus. Adminstrn. Alumni (sec. 1956-58), Radcliffe Club, Women's City Club (art and landmarks com.). Author: (with husband) Investment and Development of Tropical Africa, 1959, International Trade and Finance, 1965, Monetary and Banking Theory, 1965; Economics, 1969; (with husband) Principles of Economics, 1969; Economic Progress and the Developing World, 1970; Economics, 1978, Fine Art with Many Equilibrium Prices, 1995; also monographs and articles in field. Econ. and internat. rsch. on industrialization less developed areas, internat. debtor nations and workability of buffer stock schemes, pricing fine art; columnist economics of art, Art As An Investment, Money Substitute, or Consumer Durable Good Art Valuation; Fine Art With Many Equilibrium Prices, Prices and Varied Appraisals, Women in the Arts Found. Newsletter, other profl. publs. Home: PO Box 814 New Canaan CT 06840-0814 Office: Art Complex PO Box 814 New Canaan CT 06840-0814 also: 7441 Wayne Ave Miami Beach FL 33141

RENDU, JEAN-MICHEL MARIE, mining executive; b. Tunis, Tunisia, Feb. 25, 1944; s. Paul C. and Solange M. (Krebs) R.; m. Karla M. Meyer, Aug. 18, 1973; children: Yannick P., Mikaël P. Ingénieur des Mines, Ecole des Mines St. Etienne, France, 1966; MS, Columbia U., 1968, D. Engring. Sci., 1971. Mgr. ops. rsch. Anglovaal, Johannesburg, Republic of South Africa, 1972-76; assoc. prof. U. Wis., Madison, 1976-79; assoc. Golder Assocs., Denver, 1979-84; dir. tech. and sci. systems Newmont Mining Corp., Danbury, Conn., 1984-89; v.p. Newmont Gold Co., Denver, 1989—, Newmont Mining Corp., Denver, 1993-94. Author: An Introduction to Geostatistical Methods of Mineral Evaluation, 1978, 81; contbr. tech. papers to profl. jours. Fellow South African Inst. of Mining and Metallurgy (corr. mem. of coun.); mem. N.Y. Acad. Sci., Internat. Assn. for Math. Geology, Soc. Mining Engrs., Sigma Xi. Roman Catholic. Office: Newmont Gold Co 1700 Lincoln St Denver CO 80203-1014

RENEAU, DANIEL D., university administrator. Prof., head dept. biomed. engring. La. Tech. U., Ruston, 1973-80, v.p. acad. affairs, 1980-87, pres., 1987—. Office: La Tech U Tech Station RR 6 Ruston LA 71270

RENEBERG, RICHARD (RICHEY RENEBERG), professional tennis player; b. Phoenix, Oct. 5, 1965; m. Marget Reneberg, Nov. 16, 1991. Student, SMU, 1985-87. Ranked 10th U.S. Tennis Assn., 1991, ranked 8th U.S. Tennis Assn., 1993. Named All-American NCAA, 1985, 86, 87; winner of U.S. Open Men's Double Title (with Jim Grabb), 1992; mem. U.S. Davis Cup Team, 1993, (with Jared Palmer) Australian Open Men's Doubles Title, 1995, 8 U.S. Junior Titles, 2 Profl. Singles Titles. Office: US Tennis Assn 1212 Avenue Of The Americas New York NY 10036-1601*

RENEHAN, ROBERT FRANCIS XAVIER, Greek and Latin educator; b. Boston, Apr. 25, 1935; s. Francis Xavier and Ethel Mary (Sullivan) R.; m. Joan Lee Axtell-Damerow, Sept. 9, 1966; children—Martin, Sharon, Stephen, Judith, John. A.B., Boston Coll., Chestnut Hill, Mass., 1956; A.M., Harvard, 1958, Ph.D., 1963. Instr. Greek and Latin U. Calif. at Berkeley, 1963-64; instr. Harvard U., 1964-65; asst. prof. Boston Coll., 1966-69, assoc. prof., 1969-71, prof., 1971-77, chmn. dept. classical studies, 1969-77; prof. Greek and Latin U. Calif. at Santa Barbara, 1977—, chmn. dept., 1984-88, 93—. Author: Greek Textual Criticism, 1969, Leo Medicus, 1969, Greek Lexicographical Notes, 1975, 2d series, 1982, Studies in Greek Texts, 1975; assoc. editor Classical Philology, 1976—; Am. Jour. Philology, 1987-95; sr. mem. editl. bd. Classical Antiquity, 1980-87; contbr. articles to profl. jours. Nat. Endowment for Humanities Sr. fellow, 1972-73. Mem. Am. Philol. Assn., Soc. for Ancient Medicine. Office: Dept of Classics Univ of Calif Santa Barbara CA 93106

RENEKER, MAXINE HOHMAN, librarian; b. Chgo., Dec. 2, 1942; d. Roy Max and Helen Anna Christina (Anacker) Hohman; m. David Lee Reneker, June 20, 1964 (dec. Dec. 1979); children: Sarah Roeder, Amy Johannah, Benjamin Congdon. BA, Carleton Coll., 1964; MA, U. Chgo., 1970; DLS, Columbia U., 1992. Asst. reference libr. U. Chgo. Libraries, 1965-66; classics libr. U. Chgo. Libr., 1967-70, asst. head acquisitions, 1970-71, personnel libr., 1971-73; personnel/bus. libr. U. Colo. Libr., Boulder, 1978-80; asst. dir. sci. and engring. div. Columbia U., N.Y.C., 1981-85; assoc. dean of univ. librs. for pub. svcs. Ariz. State U. Libr., Tempe, 1985-89; dir. instrnl. and rsch. svcs. Stanford (Calif.) Univ. Librs., 1989-90; dir. info.

svcs., dir. Dudley Knox Libr. Naval Postgrad. Sch., Monterey, Calif., 1993—; acad. libr. mgmt. intern Coun. on Libr. Resources, 1980-81; chmn. univ. librs. sect. Assn. Coll. and Rsch. Librs., 1989-90. Contbr. articles to profl. jours. Rsch. grantee Coun. on Library Resources, Columbia U., 1970-71, fellow, 1990-92. Mem. ALA, Am. Soc. Info. Sci., Sherlockian Scion Soc., Phi Beta Kappa, Beta Phi Mu. Home: 437 College Ave Palo Alto CA 94306-1525 Office: Naval Postgrad Sch Dudley Knox Libr 411 Dyer Rd Monterey CA 93943

RENFORD, EDWARD J., hospital administrator; b. July 16, 1943; married. AA, L.A. City Coll., 1969; BA, Calif. State U., 1971; MA, Pepperdine U., 1983. Asst. fiscal officer Martin Luther King Jr., Drew Med. Ctr., L.A., 1974-75, assoc. adminstr. fin. svcs., 1984-86, hosp. adminstr., 1990—; dir. fiscal svcs. LAC Harbor UCLA Med. Ctr., Torrance, Calif., 1975-77, asst. adminstr. fin., 1977-79, assoc. adminstr., 1979-82; asst. adminstr. Centinela Hosp. Med. Ctr., Inglewood, Calif., 1982-84; assoc. exec. dir. LAC Rancho Los Amigos Med. Ctr., Downey, Calif., 1986-89; chief staff Hosp. Adminstrn./ Dept. Health Svcs., L.A., 1989-90. Recipient numerous awards. Home: PO Box 1149 Artesia CA 90702-1149 Office: LAC-King-Drew Med Ctr 12021 Wilmington Ave Los Angeles CA 90059-3019

RENFREW, CHARLES BYRON, oil company executive, lawyer; b. Detroit, Oct. 31, 1928; s. Charles Warren and Louise (McGuire) R.; m. Susan Wheelock, June 28, 1952 (div. June 1984); children: Taylor Allison Ingham, Charles Robin, Todd Wheelock, James Bartlett; m. Barbara Jones Orser, Oct. 6, 1984; 5 stepchildren. AB, Princeton U., 1952; JD, U. Mich., 1956. Bar: Calif. 1956. Assoc. Pillsbury, Madison & Sutro, San Francisco, 1956-65, ptnr., 1965-72, 81-82; U.S. dist. judge No. Dist. Calif., San Francisco, 1972-80; dep. atty. gen. U.S. Washington, 1980-81; instr. U. Calif. Boalt Hall Sch. Law, 1977-80; v.p. law Chevron Corp. (formerly Standard Oil Co. Calif.), San Francisco, 1983-93, also bd. dirs.; ptnr. LeBoeuf, Lamb, Greene & McRae, San Francisco, 1994—; mem. exec. com. 9th Cir. Jud. Conf., 1976-78, congl. liaison com. 9th Cir. Jud. Council, 1976-79, spl. com. to propose standards for admission to practice in fed. cts. U.S. Jud. Conf., 1976-79; chmn. spl. com. to study problems of discovery Fed. Jud. Ctr., 1978-79; mem. council on role of cts. U.S. Dept. Justice, 1978-83; mem. jud. panel Ctr. for Pub. Resources, 1981—; head U.S. del. to 6th UN Congress on Prevention of Crime and Treatment of Offenders, 1980; co-chmn. San Francisco Lawyers Com. for Urban Affairs, 1971-72, mem., 1983—; bd. dirs. Internat. Hospitality Ctr., 1961-74, pres., 1967-70; mem. adv. bd. Internat. Comparative Law Ctr., Southwestern Legal Found., 1983-93; trustee World Affairs Council No. Calif., 1984-87, 94—, Nat. Jud. Coll., 1985-91, Grace Cathedral, 1986-89. Contbr. articles to profl. jours. Bd. fellow Claremont U., 1986—; bd. dirs. San Francisco Symphony Found., 1964-80, pres., 1971-72; bd. dirs. Council for Civic Unity, 1968-72, pres., 1971-72; bd. dirs. Opportunity Through Ownership, 1969-72, Marin Country Day Sch., 1972-74, No. Calif. Service League, 1975-76, Am. Petroleum Inst., 1984—, Nat. Crime Prevention Council, 1982—; alumni trustee Princeton U., 1976-80; mem. vis. com. U. Chgo. Law Sch., 1977-79, U. Mich. Law Sch., 1977-81; bd. visitors J. Reuben Clark Law Sch., Brigham Young U., 1981-83, Stanford Law Sch., 1983-86; trustee Town Sch. for Boys, 1972-80, pres., 1975-80; gov. San Francisco Symphony Assn., 1974—; mem. nat. adv. bd. Ctr. for Nat. Policy, 1982—; bd. dirs. Nat. Council on Crime and Delinquency, 1981-82, NAACP Legal Def. and Edn. Fund, 1982—; parish chancellor St. Luke's Episcopal Ch., 1968-71, sr. warden, 1974-76; mem. exec. council San Francisco Deanery, 1969-70; mem. diocesan council Episcopal Diocese of Calif., 1970; mem. adv. council Episcopal Ch. Found., 1974—; chmn. Diocesan Conv., 1977, 78, 79. Served with USNR, 1946-48, to 1st lt. U.S. Army, 1952-53. Fellow Am. Bar Found.; mem. ABA (council mem. sect. antitrust law 1978-82, vice chmn. sect. antitrust law 1982-83), San Francisco Bar Assn. (past bd. dirs.), Assn. Gen. Counsel, State Bar Calif., Am. Judicature Soc., Am. Coll. Trial Lawyers, Am. Law Inst., Council on Fgn. Relations, Order of Coif, Phi Beta Kappa, Phi Delta Phi. Office: LeBoeuf Lamb Greene MacRae 4th Fl One Embarcadero Ctr San Francisco CA 94111

RENFREW, MALCOLM MACKENZIE, chemist, educator; b. Spokane, Wash., Oct. 12, 1910; s. Earl Edgar and Elsie Pauline (MacKenzie) R.; m. Carol Joy Campbell, June 26, 1938. B.S., U. Idaho, 1932, M.S., 1934, D.Sc., 1976; Ph.D., U. Minn., 1938. Asst. physics U. Idaho, 1932-33, Asst. chemistry, 1933-35; asst. chemistry U. Minn., 1935-37, duPont fellow, 1937-38; research chemist plastics dept. duPont Co., 1938-44, supr. process devel., 1944-46, supr. product devel., 1946-49; head chem. research dept., research labs. Gen. Mills, Inc., 1949-52, dir. chem. research, 1952-53, dir. chem. research and devel., 1953-54; dir. research and devel. Spencer Kellogg & Sons, Inc., 1954-58; phys. sci. div. head, prof. chemistry U. Idaho, 1959-73, prof., 1973-76, emeritus, 1976—; dir. U. Idaho (Coll. Chem. Cons. Service), 1969-76; on leave as sr. staff assoc. Adv. Council Coll. Chemistry, Stanford, 1967-68; mem. materials adv. bd. Nat. Acad. Scis.; exec. v.p. Idaho Research Found., 1977-78, patent dir., 1978-88. Editor: Safety in the Chemical Laboratory, Vol. IV, 1981, (with Peter Ashbrook), Safe Laboratories: Principles and Practices for Design and Remodeling, 1991; safety editor: Jour. Chem. Edn., 1977-91; Contbr. to tech. and trade publs. on plastics, coatings, safety, chem. edn. Recipient Excellence in Teaching award Chem. Mfrs. Assn., 1977, Outstanding Achievement award U. Minn., 1977; named to U. Idaho Hall of Fame, 1977. Fellow AAAS, Am. Inst. Chemists; mem. Am. Chem. Soc. (councilor 1948, 59, 67-89 , chmn. paint varnish and plastics div. 1949, chmn. chem. mktg. and econs. div. 1958-59, chmn. chem. health and safety div. 1982, James Flack Norris award 1976, Chem. Health and Safety award 1985, Roebuck award 1986), Am. Inst. Chem. Engrs., Soc. Chem. Industry, Phi Beta Kappa, Sigma Xi, Phi Kappa Phi, Sigma Pi Sigma, Phi Gamma Delta (disting. Fiji 1986). Presbyterian. Home: 1271 Walenta Dr Moscow ID 83843-2426

RENICK, KYLE, artistic director; b. St. Louis, Apr. 24, 1948; s. Mark Allen and Annabelle (Myers) R. B.A. magna cum laude, Tufts U., 1970. Sr. fund acct. New Eng. Mchts. Nat. Bank, Boston, 1970-73; fund acct. Fidelity Mgmt. and Research Corp., Boston, 1973; bus. mgr. American Place Theatre, N.Y.C., 1973-78; producing dir. WPA Theatre, N.Y.C., 1977-82, artistic dir., 1982—; pres. WPA Prodns., Inc., N.Y.C., 1987—; trustee Alliance of Resident Theatres-N.Y., 1982-92; cons. N.Y. State Council on Arts, 1982-85, Nat. Endowment for Arts, 1986. Producer Steel Magnolias, 1987, The Lady In Question, 1989; contbr. articles to profl. publs. Recipient spl. award for outstanding achievement Drama Desk Assn., 1983. Mem. N.Y. Zool. Soc., Soc. Preservation Film Music, Phi Beta Kappa. Club: The Players (N.Y.C.), The Packard Club. Avocations: early music; record collecting. Home: 2 Bethune St Apt 4B New York NY 10014-1860 Office: WPA Theatre 519 W 23rd St New York NY 10011-1102

RENIER, JAMES J., diversified electronic equipment manufacturing company executive; b. 1930. BS in Chemistry, Coll. St. Thomas; PhD in Phys. Chemistry, Iowa State U. With U.S. AEC, to 1956; with Honeywell, Inc., Mpls., 1956—, corp. v.p. gen. mgr. data systems ops., 1970-74, v.p. aerospace and def. group, 1974-76, group v.p., 1976-78, corp. exec. v.p., 1978-79, pres. control systems, 1979-82, vice chmn., 1982-87, also pres. info. systems div., corp. pres., chief operating officer, from 1987, chmn., pres., chief exec. officer, 1988-93, chmn. exec. com., 1993—, also dir. Chmn. Success By Six program United Way, 1988. Office: Honeywell Inc Honeywell Plz Minneapolis MN 55408

RENKA, ROBERT JOSEPH, computer science educator, consultant; b. Summit, N.J., Dec. 28, 1947; s. John and Elizabeth (Pierce) R. BA in Computer Sci., BS in Math., U. Tex., 1976, MA in Math., 1979, PhD in Computer Sci., 1981. Numerical analyst Oak Ridge (Tenn.) Nat. Lab., 1981-84; asst. prof. computer sci. U. North Tex., Denton, 1984-89, assoc. prof. computer sci., 1989—; cons. in scientific computing. Contbr. articles to profl. jours. With USN, 1967-69, Vietnam. Rsch. grantee U. North Tex., 1984-89, NSF, 1990-93. Mem. Assn. for Computing Machinery (algorithms editor 1984-94, editor-in-chief 1989-94), Soc. Indsl. and Applied Math. Avocations: racquetball, rock climbing. Home: 1700 Kendolph Dr Denton TX 76205-6940 Office: U North Tex PO Box 13886 Dept Computer Scis Denton TX 76203

RENKIEWICZ, MARY ANTOINETTE, hospital administrator; b. Sioux City, Iowa, May 15, 1933; d. Dominic and Rose (David) Tierno; m. Richard Renkiewicz, June 27, 1959; children: Teresa, Garbacz, Ann Kay, Joseph,

Nanette, David. Diploma, St. Francis Hosp. Sch. Nursing, Charleston, W.Va., 1954; BS, Mercy Coll. Detroit, 1982; MS, U. Detroit, 1986. Staff nurse St. Vincent's Hosp., Sioux City, 1955-57; staff nurse Children's Hosp., Detroit, 1957-69, adminstrv. nurse mgr., 1969-85, dir. clin. nursing, 1985—. Bd. dirs. Ronald McDonald House; trustee Hamtramck Bd. Edn., 1990, sec., 1992. Mem. Am. Orgn. Nurse Execs., Mich. Orgn. Nurse Execs., Greater Detroit Orgn. Nurse Execs. (membership com. chair 1989-91, sec. 1992), Assn. for Care Children's Health, Mich. League Nursing.

RENN, ERIN MCCAWLEY, museum administrator; b. Fort Sheridan, Ill., Oct. 23, 1934; d. John Clifford and Frances (Lenfestey) McCawley; divorced; children: Cecilia Frances Renn, Tracy Renn Mattox. BS in History and Art, Fla. State U., 1956, MA in European History and Humanities, 1967, PhD in Early 19th Century European History, 1970; post-doctoral study, Brown U., 1974. Adj. asst. prof. Wheeling (W.Va.) Coll., 1970-77, Bethany (W.Va.) Coll., 1970-77; staff asst. LeMoyne Art Found., Tallahassee, Fla., 1977-78; asst. prof. Valdosta (Ga.) State Coll., 1978-79; lectr. U. Md., Japan, Okinawa, the Azores, Spain, Germany, England, 1979-84; coord. grad. program in East Anglia U. Md., 1982-84; site adminstr. Deutschheim State Historic Site, Mo., 1984—; cons. 1840's Korthauer House and Mus. Project Bensenville (Ill.) Hist. Commn., 1990—, German Inn and Garden, Conner Prairie, Fishers, Inc., Naperville Settlement, Ill., Zoar Cmty., Ohio, travelling exhibit Cole Camp, 1992. Author: (books) The Breads, Cakes, Cookies, Sweets and Special Foods of a Missouri German Christmas, 1991, Weihnachtsgebäck, -konfect, und -speisen—The Breads, Cakes, Cookies, Sweets and Special Foods of a Midwest German Christmas, 1994; contbr. chpts. to books and articles to jours. in field. Mem. bd. dirs. Mo. Folklore Soc., 1988-91, 92—, pres. 1991-92, Mo. Mus. Assocs., 1988092, Mo. Alliance for Historic Preservation, 1989—, Hermann Area C. of C., 1985-86, Hermann Fine Arts Coun., 1987—; chair street entertainment Hermann Maifest Coun., 1988, 89; program chair Gasconade County Hist. Soc., 1992-93. Recipient Ford Found. Asian Studies grantee Fla. State U., 1964, Rsch. grantee Mil. Hist. Inst. Valdosta State Coll., Carlisle Barracks. Pa., 1979, Mil. Hist. Inst., 1979; U. Rsch. fellow Fla. State U., 1967-68, Dissertation fellow Coll. of Arts and Scis., 1968-69. Mem. Am. Assn. Mus., Am. Assn. State and Local History, Am. Livestock Breeds Conservancy, German Am. Heritage Soc., German Am. Soc., Carondelet Hist. Soc., Soc. German Am. Studies, German Studies Assn., Midwest Mus. Conf., Midwest Open Air Mus. Coord. Coun., Midwest Registrars Com., Assn. for Living Historical Farms and Agrl. Mus., Vernacular Architecture Forum. Avocations: reading, music, travel. Office: Deutscheim State Hist Site 109 W 2nd St Hermann MO 65041-1045

RENNE, LOUISE HORNBECK, lawyer; b. Pitts., Aug. 26, 1937; d. Lewis Alvin and Anne (Bartrem) Hornbeck; m. Paul A. Renne, July 11, 1959; Christine, Anne. BA, Mich. State U., 1958; postgrad. law, Harvard U., 1958-59, U. Pa., 1959-60; JD, Columbia U., 1961. Bar: Calif. 1964, D.C. 1961, U.S. Supreme Ct. 1969. With broadcast bur., office gen. counsel FCC, 1961-64; assoc. Peterson & Barr, San Francisco, 1964-66; dep. atty. gen. State of Calif., San Francisco, 1966-77; pres. Calif. Women Lawyers, San Francisco, 1977-78; mem. Bd. Suprs., San Francisco, 1978-86; city atty. San Francisco, 1986—. Office: Office of City Atty 1390 Market St 5th Fl San Francisco CA 94102

RENNEKER, FREDERICK WEYMAN, III, insurance executive; b. Birmingham, Ala., Nov. 2, 1939; s. Frederick Weyman Jr. and Jean Battle (Walker) R.; m. Elizabeth McCauley, Dec. 16, 1967; children: Elizabeth and Frederick IV (twins), Charlotte, Emilie. BS in Bus., Auburn U., 1961. CPCU. Underwriter Boykin & Co., Inc., Birmingham, 1961-65; pres. Renneker & Co., Inc., Birmingham, 1965-90; vice chmn. Hilb, Rogal & Hamilton, Inc., Birmingham, 1990—. Pres. Birmingham Jaycees, 1966-67, All Am. Bowl, Birmingham, 1989, Children's Hosp. Ala., Birmingham, 1992-93; chmn. region III Ala. Sesquicentennial, Montgomery Ala., 1969; chmn. bd. Birmingham area ARC, 1978-79, Mountain Brook (Ala.) Bd. Edn., 1990—; mem. Leadership Birmingham, 1985; vice chmn. Crippled Children's Found., Birmingham, 1990-92, chmn., 1993-94. Recipient Outstanding Young Man of Yr. award Birmingham Jaycees, 1967; named one of Four Outstanding Young Men in Ala., Ala. Jaycees, 1967. Mem. Monday Morning Quaterback Club (capt. 1980), Country Club Birmingham (pres. 1979-80), Kiwanis (pres. Birmingham club 1981-82), Delta Sigma Pi, Kappa Alpha. Avocations: tennis, fishing, hunting. Home: 76 Country Club Blvd Birmingham AL 35213 Office: Hilb Rogal & Hamilton Inc 600 Luckie Dr Ste 300 Birmingham AL 35223

RENNELS, MARSHALL LEIGH, neuroanatomist, biomedical scientist, educator; b. Marshall, Mo., Sept. 2, 1939; s. Ivory P. and Alfrieda S. Rennels; m. Margaret Ann Baker, Dec. 28, 1971. B.S., Eastern Ill. U., 1961; M.A., U. Tex.-Galveston, 1964, Ph.D., 1966. Asst. prof. anatomy U. Md., Balt., 1966-71; assoc. prof., 1971-79, prof., 1979—; dir. MD/PhD Program, 1989—. Contbr. articles to sci. jours. Mem. AAAS, Am. Assn. Anatomists, Soc. Neurosci., Soc. Cerebral Blood Flow and Metabolism. Office: U Md Sch Medicine Dept Anatomy Baltimore MD 21201

RENNER, GERALD ANTHONY, journalist; b. Phila., June 5, 1932; s. Walter C. and Marie (Watson) R.; m. Jacquelyn Breen, Sept. 7, 1957; children: Margaret, Anne Victoria, Mary X., Andrea, John. BS, Georgetown U., 1959. Reporter UPI, Washington, 1956, Reading (Pa.) Eagle, 1959-65; assoc. info. dir. Nat. Conf. Cath. Bishops, Washington, 1965-67; dir. pub. rels. NCCJ, N.Y.C., 1967-69; exec. dir. regional NCCJ, Ill., Md., 1969-76; mng. editor Religious News Svc., N.Y.C., 1976-79, editor, dir., 1979-84; religion writer Hartford (Conn.) Courant, 1985—. With USN, 1951-55. Office: Hartford Courant Co 285 Broad St Hartford CT 06155-2510

RENNER, ROBERT GEORGE, federal judge; b. Nevis, Minn., Apr. 2, 1923; s. Henry J. and Beatrice M. (Fuller) R.; m. Catherine L. Clark, Nov. 12, 1949; children: Robert, Anne, Richard, David. BS, St. John's U., Collegeville, Minn., 1947; JD, Georgetown U., 1949. Bar: Minn. 1949. Pvt. practice Walker, 1949-69; U.S. atty. Dist. of Minn., 1969-77, U.S. magistrate, 1977-80, U.S. dist. judge, 1980—. Mem. Minn. Ho. of Reps., 1957-69. Served with AUS, 1943-46. Mem. ABA, Fed. Bar Assn. Roman Catholic. Office: US Dist Ct 748 US Courthouse 316 Robert St N Saint Paul MN 55101-1423

RENNER, SIMON EDWARD, steel company executive; b. Florence, S.C., Feb. 5, 1934; s. Simon Samson and Ruby (Pickett) R.; m. Katherine May Schneider, May 10, 1958; children: Katherine Leah, J. Eric, Philip E., S. Todd. BS, Yale U., 1956; diploma, Carnegie Mellon U., 1972. Gen. mgr. specialty steel Jones & Laughlin Steel Corp., Pitts., 1973-74; gen. mgr. basic steel Jones & Laughlin Steel Corp., Pitts., 1974-75, v.p. prodn., 1975-77, pres. eastern div., 1977-79, corp. v.p., Pitts., 1979-86; pres. LTV R.R.'s, 1986-94; v.p. LTV Steel, 1994—; pres. LTV R.R.s, 1994—. Vice pres. Allegheny Trails council, Boy Scouts Am.; pres. Quigley High Sch. Bd. Edn. Baden. Pa., 1982. Capt. USMC, 1956-59. Mem. Am. Iron and Steel Inst. (chmn. mfg. com. 1980-82), Assn. Iron and Steel Engrs., Am. Short Line RR Assn. (bd. dirs.). Republican. Clubs: Duquesne (Pitts.); Allegheny Country (Sewickley, Pa.); Harvard-Yale-Princeton. Home: 104 Willow Rd Sewickley PA 15143 Office: LTV RRs 3600 2d Ave 25 W Prospect Ave Cleveland OH 44115

RENNERFELDT, EARL RONALD, farmer, rancher; b. Epping, N.D., July 10, 1938; s. Carl John and Margaret E. (Long) R.; m. Lois Ann Thune, Sept. 12, 1959; children: Charysse Renee, Carter Ryan. Student, NDSSS, Wahpeton, N.D., 1958. Farmer/rancher Williston, N.D. Mem. N.D. Ho. of Reps., Bismarck, 1991—; mem. Lake Sacajawea Planning Bd., Williston, N.D., 1992; mem. Am. Legis. Exch. Coun., 1991-92; adv. bd. N.D. State U. Exptl. Sta.; bd. dirs. Mercy Med. Found. With U.S. Army, 1962-64. Recipient Harvest Bowl award N.D. State U., 1988; named Outstanding Young Farmer C. of C., 1972. Mem. Am. Legion, N.D. Grain growers, N.D. Durum Growers, Williston C. of C., N.D. Stockmen's Assn., Elks. Republican. Evangelical Free Ch. Avocations: antiques, golf. Home and Office: 1704 Rose Ln Williston ND 58801-4362

RENNERT, IRA LEON, heavy manufacturing executive; b. 1934. BA, Bklyn. Coll., 1954; MBA, NYU, 1956. Credit analyst M. Lowenstein Corp., N.Y.C., 1956-57; salesman Underwood Corp., N.Y.C., 1957-58; registered rep. Francis I. Dupont & Co., N.Y.C., 1958-60; established I.L. Rennert &

Co., Inc. (formerly Rubin, Rennert & Co., Inc.), N.Y.C., 1960-64; cons. N.Y.C., 1964-75; pres. Consolidated Sewing Machine Corp., N.Y.C., 1975—; pres., ceo Renco Group, Inc., N.Y.C., 1980; ceo WCI Steel Inc., Warren, Ohio, 1988—; chmn. bd. Am. Gen. Corp., South Bend, Ind., 1992. Office: WCI Steel Inc 1040 Pine Ave SE Warren OH 44483-6528*

RENNIE, JOHN COYNE, aerospace company executive; b. Boston, May 30, 1937; s. John Christopher and Mary Elizabeth (Coyne) R.; m. Carol Jane Hornbeck, July 12, 1958; children: John P., Kathleen M., Carol L., Steven M., Michele H. BS in Engring., U.S. Naval Acad., 1958; MS in Engring. Mgmt., Northeastern U., Boston, 1971; diploma, Harvard Bus. Sch., 1975. Cert. exptl. test pilot. Sr. systems engr. Raytheon Co., Bedford, Mass., 1967-68; chmn., CEO, bd. dirs. Pacer Systems, Inc., Billerica, Mass., 1968—; bd. dirs. Laser Engring., Inc., Milford, Mass., Colorgen, Inc., Billerica, Mass., Prospect Assocs., Inc., Rockville, Md. Author, editor: Expertise, 1983, 4th edit., 1993; patentee in field. Pres. Smaller Bus. Assn. New Eng., Waltham, Mass., 1982-84; chmn. Profl. Svcs. Coun., Washington, 1987-88, Mass. Bus. Alliance for Edn., 1989—; pres. Small Bus. Found. Am., Boston, 1985—. Named Small Bus. Person of Yr. New Eng., SBA, 1983, Small Bus. Exporter of Yr. Mass. 1985. Mem. Nat. Small Bus. United (dir., pres. 1992-93), Nat. Security Indsl. Assn. (v.p. 1985—), U.S. Naval Acad. Alumni Assn. (trustee 1983—), Mass. Industry-Edn. Partnership Com. (chmn. 1987-88), U.S. C. of C. (dir. 1984-89), City Club. Democrat. Roman Catholic. Avocations: stamp collecting, golf, reading. Home: 18 Harvard Dr Bedford MA 01730-1020 Office: Pacer Systems Inc 900 Technology Park Dr Billerica MA 01821-4125*

RENNIE, PAUL STEVEN, science administrator, biochemist, surgeon; b. Toronto, Ont., Can., Feb. 9, 1946; m. Carol Andrews, 1968; 1 child, Jan. BSc, U. Western Ont., 1969; PhD in Biochemistry, U. Alta., 1973. Rsch. assoc. U. Alta., 1975-76, asst. prof. medicine, 1976-79, assoc. prof., 1979; rsch. scientist B.C. Cancer Agy., 1979-92, dir. rsch., 1992—; prof. surgery U. B.C., 1986—. Med. Rsch. Coun. rsch. fellow Imperial Cancer Rsch. Fund, 1973-75; rsch. scholar Nat. Cancer Inst. Can., 1976-79. Mem. Can. Soc. Clin. Investigation, Biochem. Soc., Endocrine Soc. Achievements include research on biochemical control of growth in androgen responsive organs and neoplasms; genetic markers in breast cancer. Office: B C Cancer Agy, 600 W 10th Ave, Vancouver, BC Canada V5Z 4E6*

RENNINGER, MARY KAREN, librarian; b. Pitts., Apr. 30, 1945; d. Jack Burnell and Jane (Hammerly) Gunderman; m. Norman Christian Renninger, Sept. 3, 1965 (div. 1980); 1 child, David Christian. B.A., U. Md., 1969, M.A., 1972, M.L.S., 1975. Tchr. English West Carteret High Sch., Morehead City, N.C., 1969-70; instr. in English U. Md., College Park, 1970-72; head network services Nat. Libr. Svc., Libr. of Congress, Washington, 1974-78, asst. for network support, 1978-80; mem. fed. women's program com. Libr. of Congress, Washington, 1978-80; chief libr. divsn. Dept. Vets. Affairs, Washington, 1980-90; chief serial and govt. publs. divsn. Libr. of Congress, Washington, 1991—, mem. fed. libr. com., 1980-90, mem. exec. adv. bd., 1985-90; mem. USBE pers. subcom., 1982-84; bd. regents Nat. Libr. of Medicine, 1986-90, mem. outreach panel, 1988-89; fed. libr. task force for 1990 White House Conf. on Librs., 1986-90; liaison to The White House Conf. Med. Libr. Assn., 1989-90. Recipient Meritorious Svc. award Libr. of Congress, 1974, Spl. Achievement award, 1976, Performance award VA, ann. 1982-89, Administr.'s Commendation, 1985, Spl. Contbn. award, 1986. Mem. ALA (Govt. Documents Roundtable), Libr. Tech. Assn., Med. Libr. Assn. (govt. rels. com. 1985—), D.C. Libr. Assn., Soc. Applied Learning Tech., Med. Interactive Videodisc Consortium, Govt. Documents Roundtable, Knowledge Utilization Soc., Nat. Multimedia Assn. Am., U.S. Tennis Assn., Phi Beta Kappa, Alpha Lambda Delta, Beta Phi Mu. Home: 840 College Pky Rockville MD 20850-1931 Office: Libr of Congress Ser and Govt Pub Divsn LM 133 Washington DC 20540

RENO, JANET, U.S. attorney general; b. Miami, Fla., July 21, 1938; d. Henry and Jane (Wood) R. A.B. in Chemistry, Cornell U., 1960; LL.B., Harvard U., 1963. Bar: Fla. 1963. Assoc. Brigham & Brigham, 1963-67; ptnr. Lewis & Reno, 1967-71; staff dir. judiciary com. Fla. Ho. of Reps., Tallahassee, 1971-72; cons. Fla. Senate Criminal Justice Com. for Revision Fla.'s Criminal Code, spring 1973; adminstrv. asst. state atty. 11th Jud. Circuit Fla., Miami, 1973-76, state atty., 1978-93; ptnr. Steel Hector and Davis, Miami, 1976-78; atty. gen. Dept. Justice, Washington, 1993—; mem. jud. nominating commn. 11th Jud. Circuit Fla., 1976-78; chmn. Fla. Gov.'s Council for Prosecution Organized Crime, 1979-80. Recipient Women First award YWCA, 1993. Mem. ABA (Inst. Jud. Adminstrn. Juvenile Justice Standards Commn. 1973-76), Am. Law Inst., Am. Judicature Soc. (Herbert Harley award 1981), Dade County Bar Assn., Fla. Pros. Atty.'s Assn. (pres. 1984-86). Democrat. Office: Dept Justice 10th & Constitution Ave NW Washington DC 20530

RENO, JENNIFER, principal. Prin. Western Hills Elem. Sch., Lawton, Okla. Recipient Elem. Sch. Recognition award U.S. Dept. Edn., 1989-90. Office: Western Hills Elem Sch 5402 NW Kinyon Ave Lawton OK 73505-4653

RENO, JOHN F., communications equipment company executive; b. Peoria, Ill., June 15, 1939; s. John Henkle and Alice Hanna (Findley) R.; m. Suzanne McKnight, Apr. 18, 1964; children: David, Anne. AB, Dartmouth Coll., 1961; MBA, Northwestern U., 1963. Ptnr. G.H. Walker & Co., Boston, 1968-74; divsn. pres. Dynatech Cryomedical Co., Burlington, Mass., 1974-79; corporate v.p. Dynatech Corp., Burlington, 1979-82, group v.p., 1982-87, pres., COO, 1987-93, pres., CEO, 1993—; bd. dirs. Millipre Corp., Bedford, Mass. Chmn. exec. com. Boston Masterminding, 1989—; trustee Boston Mus. of Sci., 1992—; bd. dirs. Boston Ptnrs. in Edn., CEO's for Fundamental Change in Edn., Cambridge, Mass. Named Entrepreneur of Yr., Inc. mag., 1995. Avocation: oil painting. Office: Dynatech Corp 3 N.E. Executive Park Burlington MA 01803

RENO, JOHN FINDLEY, corporate executive; b. Peoria, Ill., June 15, 1939; m. Suzanne McKnight, Apr. 18, 1964; children: David, Anne. BA, Dartmouth Coll., 1961; MBA, Northwestern U., 1963. V.p. G.H. Walker & Co., Boston, 1964-74; pres. Dynatech Cryomed. Co., Burlington, Mass., 1974-77; group v.p., CO, Dynatech Corp., Burlington, 1981-91, pres., COO, 1991-93, pres., CEO, 1993—, also bd. dirs.; bd. dirs. Utah Sci., Salt Lake City, Telecom Techniques. Germantown, Md., Millipore Corp.; corporator Winchester (Mass.) Savs. Bank. Trustee Boston Mus. Sci.; bd. dirs. Boston Ptnrs. in Edn. Home: 31 Prospect St Winchester MA 01890-3161 Office: Dynatech Corp 3 New England Executive Park Burlington MA 01803-5006

RENO, ROGER, lawyer; b. Rockford, Ill., May 16, 1924; s. Guy B. and Hazel (Kinnear) R.; m. Janice Marie Odelius, May 17, 1952; children: Susan Marie, Sheri Jan Reno-Rudolph, Michael Guy. Student, Kenyon Coll., 1943-44, Yale U., 1944, U. Wis., 1946; A.B., Carleton Coll., 1947; LL.B., Yale U., 1950. Bar: Ill. 1950. Practiced in Rockford, 1950; assoc. firm Reno, Zahm, Folgate, Lindberg & Powell, 1950-56, partner, 1956-84, of counsel, 1984—; chmn. Amcore Fin. Inc., 1982-95; atty. Rockford Bd. Edn., 1955-64. Past pres., bd. dirs. Childrens Home Rockford; trustee Swedish-Am. Hosp. Assn., 1967-77, Keith Country Day Sch. Served to 1st lt. USAAF, 1943-46. Mem. ABA, Ill. Bar Assn., Winnebago County Bar Assn. (pres. 1979-80). Republican. Methodist. Club: Forest Hills Country (Rockford). Home: 2515 Chickadee Trl Rockford IL 61107 Office: Reno Zahm Folgate Lindberg & Powell Amcore Fin Plaza Rockford IL 61104

RENO, RUSSELL RONALD, JR., lawyer; b. Gary, Ind., Nov. 28, 1933; s. Russell Ronald Sr. and Katherine Narcissus (White) R.; m. Mary Ellen Klock, Jan. 30, 1956; children: Mary Hall, Russell III, William, Elizabeth. AB, Haverford Coll., 1954; JD, U. Pa., 1957. Bar: Md. 1957, D.C. 1983. Assoc. Venable, Baetjer & Howard, Balt., 1958-66, ptnr., 1966—; asst. atty. gen. State of Md., Balt., 1962-64. Author: Maryland Real Estate Law-Practice, 1983. Bd. dirs. Balt. Choral Arts Soc., 1966—; trustee Goucher Coll., Balt., 1978—; chancellor Episcopal Diocese of Md., Balt., 1985—; bd. mgrs. Haverford Coll., 1990—. Fellow Am. Bar Found., Md. Bar Found.; mem. ABA, Md. State Bar Assn., Am. Coll. Real Estate Lawyers, Hamilton St. Club, Wednesday Law Club. Home: 706 W Joppa Rd Baltimore MD 21204-3810 Office: Venable Baetjer & Howard 2 Hopkins Plz Baltimore MD 21201-2930

RENOUF, EDDA, artist; b. Mexico City, June 17, 1943; d. Edward and Catharine (Smith) R.; m. Alain Middleton, Sept. 20, 1977; 1 child, Mélisande. B.A., Sarah Lawrence Coll., 1965; M.F.A., Columbia U., 1971. One-woman exhbns. include Yvon Lambert Gallery, Paris, 1972, 74, 76, 78, 80, 82, 84, 93, Konrad Fischer Gallery, Düsseldorf, Fed. Republic Germany, 1974, 79, Blum-Helman Gallery, N.Y.C., 1978, 80, 82, 85, 87-89; group exhbns. include 8th Paris Biennale, 1973, Mus. Modern Art, N.Y.C., 1973, 90, Stedelijk Mus., Amsterdam, 1974, Whitney Mus. Am. Art, N.Y.C., 1979, 85, Centre Georges Pompidou, Paris, 1979, Met. Mus. Art, N.Y.C., 1982, 87, Serpentine Gallery, 1984, Galerie Denise René, Paris, 1985, The Tel Aviv Mus., 1986, Mus. Fridericianum, Kassel, Fed. Republic of Germany, 1988, Mus. d'Art Moderne de Lille, France, 1992, Bibliothèque Nationale, Paris, 1992, Nat. Gallery Art, Washington, 1993, 94; represented in permanent collections, Mus. Modern Art, Whitney Mus. Am. Art, Met. Mus. Art, Centre Georges Pompidou, Chgo. Art Inst., Phila. Art Mus., Yale U. Art Gallery, Met. Mus. Art, Neuberger Mus., Australian Nat. Gallery, Cin. Mus. Art, St. Louis Art Mus., Tel Aviv Mus., La. Mus., Denmark, Walker Art Ctr., Nat. Gallery Art, Washington, Biblioteque Nationale Paris; subject of articles in art pubs. Nat. Endowment Arts grantee, 1978-79, Pollock-Krasner Found. Inc. grantee, 1990-91. Address: 37 Rue Volta, 75003 Paris France

RENOUF, HAROLD AUGUSTUS, business consultant; b. Sandy Point, St. George's Bay, Nfld., Can., June 15, 1917; s. John Robert and Louisa Maud R.; m. Dorothy Munro, June 16, 1942; children: Janet, Ann Petley-Jones, Robert, Susan. B.Commerce, Dalhousie U., 1938, LL.D. (hon.), 1981. N.S.C.A., Halifax, 1942 C.M.A., 1950. With H.R. Doane and Co., Halifax, N.S., Can., 1938-75, ptnr., 1942-75; ptnr. in charge H.R. Doane and Co., New Glasgow, N.S., Can., 1947-62; ptnr. in charge mgmt. services H.R. Doane and Co., Halifax, 1963-67, chmn., 1967-75; dir. Associated Acctg. Firms Internat., N.Y.C., 1967-75; commr. Anti-Inflation Bd., Ottawa, Ont., 1975-77, chmn., 1977-79; chmn. Petroleum Monitoring Agy., Ottawa, 1980-82, VIA Rail Can. Inc., Montreal, Que., 1982-85; ret., 1993; bd. dirs. N.S. Mcpl. Fin. Corp.; pres. Can. Inst. Chartered Accts., 1974-75. Contbr. articles to profl. publs. Chmn. adv. commn. Dalhousie U. Grad. Sch. Bus. Adminstrn., 1978-86. Decorated Queen's medal, 1977, officer Order of Can., 1979; recipient Commemorative medal for 125th anniversary of Can. Confederation, 1992; named to Acctg. Hall of Fame St. Mary's Univ., N.S., 1993. Fellow Inst. Chartered Accts. N.S.; mem. Soc. Mgmt. Accts., Dalhousie U. Alumni Assn. (hon. chmn. 1987-89), Halifax Club, Saraguay Club (treas. 1972-75), Waegwaltic Club. Liberal. Mem. United Ch. Can. Home: 6369 Coburg Rd Apt 1605, Halifax, NS Canada B3H 4J7

RENQUEST, RICHARD A., religious organization executive. Pres. Am. Baptist Men, Valley Forge, Pa. Office: Am Baptist Men PO Box 851 Valley Forge PA 19482-0851

RENSCH, JOSEPH ROMAINE, public utility holding company executive; b. San Bernardino, Calif., Jan. 1, 1923; s. Joseph R. and Lucille (Ham) R.; m. June Elizabeth Burley, Mar. 25, 1946; children: Steven R., Jeffrey P. BS, Stanford U., 1947; JD, Golden Gate U., 1955. Bar: Calif. 1955; registered profl. engr., Calif. Successively sales engr., regional gas engr., regional gas supt., asst. mgr. gas supply and control Coast Counties Gas & Electric Co., San Francisco, 1947-54; sr. pipeline operations engr. Pacific Gas & Electric Co., 1954-56; prodn. control supt. Western div. Dow Chem. Co., Pittsburg, Calif., 1956; asst. counsel So. Counties Gas Co. of Calif., L.A., 1957-58; asst. v.p., spl. counsel Pacific Lighting Gas Supply Co., L.A., 1958-61, v.p., bd. dirs., 1962-65; sr. v.p. Pacific Lighting Svc. Co., L.A., 1965-67, exec. v.p., 1967-69, pres., 1969-71, chmn. bd., 1971-73; exec. v.p., dir. Pacific Enterprises, L.A., 1967-72, pres., 1972-86, vice chmn., 1986-88. With USNR, 1942-46. Mem. Pacific Coast Gas Assn. (pres. 1966-67), Am. Gas Assn., Tau Beta Pi, Alpha Tau Omega. Office: Pacific Enterprises 555 W 5th St Los Angeles CA 90013-1010

RENSE, PAIGE, editor, publishing company executive; b. Iowa, May 4, 1929; m. Kenneth Noland, Apr. 10, 1994. Student, Calif. State U., Los Angeles. Editor-in-chief Architectural Digest, Los Angeles, 1970—; sr. v.p., also bd. dirs. Knapp Communications Corp. Recipient Nat. Headliner Women in Communications award, 1983, Pacifica award So. Calif. Resources Coun., 1978, Editorial award Dallas Mkt. Ctr., 1978, Golden award Chgo. Design Resources Svc., 1982, Agora award, 1982, Outstanding Profls. in Communications award, 1982, Trailblazers award, 1983, ; named Woman of Yr. Los Angeles Times, 1976, Woman of Yr. Muses, 1986; named to Interior Design Hall of Fame. Office: Architectural Digest 6300 Wilshire Blvd 11th Fl Los Angeles CA 90048

RENSHAW, AMANDA FRANCES, physicist, nuclear engineer; b. Wheelwright, Ky., Dec. 10, 1934; d. Taft and Mamie Nell (Russell) Wilson; divorced; children: Linda, Michael, Billy. BS in Physics, Antioch Coll., 1972; MS in Physics, U. Tenn., 1982, MS in Nuclear Engring., 1991. Rsch. asst. U. Mich., Ann Arbor, 1970-71; teaching asst. Antioch Coll., Yellow Springs, Ohio, 1971-72; physicist GE Schenectady, N.Y., 1972-74, Union Carbide Corp., Oak Ridge, Tenn., 1974-79; rsch. assoc. Oak Ridge Nat. Lab., 1979-91, mgr. strategic planning, 1991-92, liaison for environ. scis., 1993—; asst. to counselor for sci. and tech. Am. Embassy, Moscow, 1990; asst. to dir. nat. acid precipitation assessment program Office of Pres. U.S. 1993-94. Contbr. articles to profl. jours. Mem. AAUW, Am. Assn. Artificial Intelligence, Am. Nuclear Soc. (Oak Ridge chpt.), Soc. Black Physicists. Avocations: reading, travelling. Home: 1850 Cherokee Bluff Dr Knoxville TN 37920-2215 Office: Oak Ridge Nat Lab Bldg 1505 PO Box 2008 Oak Ridge TN 37831-6038

RENSHAW, CHARLES CLARK, JR., retired publishing executive; b. Chgo., Aug. 22, 1920; s. Charles Clark and Nanna Lou (Nysewander) R.; m. Elizabeth Campbell Fly, Apr. 11, 1953 (div. Jan. 1960); 1 child, Nina (Mrs. Daniel C. Baker III). Student, Hill Sch., Pottstown, Pa., 1934-39, Trinity Coll., Hartford, Conn., 1939-41. Reporter, feature writer, book critic Chgo. Herald-Am., 1943-46; assoc. editor Fin. mag., Chgo., 1947; writer, articles editor Hearst's Am. Weekly, N.Y.C., 1948-61; sr. editor, asst. mng. editor, mng. editor World Book Ency. Year Book, Chgo., 1962-67; free-lance writer N.Y.C., 1968-70; sr. editor Nat. Wildlife mag., Milw., 1970-72; editor Prism (the Socio-econ. Mag. of AMA), 1972-75; editor in chief Socioecon. Publs. AMA, Chgo., 1975-78, v.p., editl. dir. non-sci. publs., 1978-81, v.p., editl. dir. Consumer Books divsn., 1981-85, cons. Office Internat. Medicine, 1988, cons. group on health policy, 1989-90, cons. group on electronic media and consumer affairs, 1990-93; cons. to direct mktg. group World Book Ency., Evanston, Ill., 1993-94; cons. Consumer Books divsn. AMA, Chgo., Ill., 1994—. Home: 33 E Cedar St Chicago IL 60611-1158

RENSHAW, JOHN HUBERT, secondary education educator; b. Hazleton, Pa., July 9, 1936; s. Charles William and Mary (Drobeck) R.; m. Dorothy Sharon Montgomery, June 20, 1964; children: John Michael, Rebecca Lynn. BS in Edn., East Stroudsburg State U., 1961; MA in History, U. Del., 1965. Cert. tchr., Del. 10th and 12th grade social studies tchr. Pocomoke City (Md.) High Sch., 1961-64; 7th and 8th grade social studies tchr. Forwood Jr. High Sch., Wilmington, Del., 1965-78; 8th grade U.S. govt. and U.S. history tchr. Springer Jr. High Sch., Wilmington, 1978-81; 8th grade U.S. history tchr. Hanby Jr. High Sch., Wilmington, 1981—; audiovisual dir., equipment maintenance Hanby Jr. High Sch. and Brandywine Sch. Dist., 1981-94; curriculum leader social studies dept. Hanby Jr. High Sch., 1988—, chmn. social studies dept., 1994—; coach baseball, girl's softball teams Forwood Jr. High Sch., 1973-78, Springer Jr. High Sch., 1979-81, Hanby High Sch., 1982-86. Cpl. USMC, 1954-57. Mem. Nat. Coun. Social Studies, Del. Edn. Assn., Brandywine and New Castle County Edn. Assn. (rep. 1978-81). Republican. Methodist. Avocations: jogging, reading, mind-body readings and projects, baseball card collecting, sports watching and participation. Home: 2506 Bona Rd Wilmington DE 19810-2220 Office: Hanby Jr High Sch Brandywine Sch Dist 2523 Berwyn Rd Wilmington DE 19810-3599

RENSI, EDWARD HENRY, restaurant chain executive; b. Hopedale, Ohio, Aug. 15, 1944; s. Ernest Henry and Virginia Marie (Gill) R.; m. F. Anne Bossick, Oct. 9, 1965. Student, Ohio State U., 1962-66. Ind. paint contractor, 1963; salesman Hillcrest Dairy, Steubenville, Ohio, 1964, Borden's Dairy, Columbus, Ohio, 1965, Shoe Corp. Am., Columbus, 1966; with McDonald's Corp., Oak Brook, Ill., 1966—; v.p. McDonald's Corp., 1976-

78, sr. v.p. ops., tng. and product devel., 1978-80, sr. exec. v.p., chief operating officer, 1980-84; pres. McDonald's U.S.A., 1984—. Mem. nat. adv. bd. dirs. Children's Oncology Services, Oak Brook; chmn. Ronald McDonald's Children's Charities, 1985. Office: McDonald's Corp 1 Kroc Dr Oak Brook IL 60521

RENSON, JEAN FELIX, psychiatry educator; b. Liège, Belgium, Nov. 9, 1930; came to U.S., 1960; s. Louis and Laurence (Crahai) R.; m. Gisèle Bouillenne, Sept. 8, 1956; children: Marc, Dominique, Jean-Luc. MD, U. Liège, 1959; PhD in Biochemistry, George Washington U., 1971. Diplomate Am. Bd. Psychiatry. Asst. prof. U. Liège, 1957-60; rsch. fellow U. Liège, 1966-72; clin. assoc. prof. dept. psychiatry U. Calif., San Francisco, 1978—; vis. asst. prof. Stanford U. Palo Alto, Calif., 1972-77. Assoc. editor: Fundamentals of Biochemical Pharmacology, 1971. NIH fellow, 1960-66. Democrat. Avocations: neurosciences, music.

RENT, CLYDA STOKES, university president; b. Jacksonville, Fla., Mar. 1, 1942; d. Clyde Parker Stokes Sr. and Edna Mae (Edwards) Shuemake; m. George Seymour Rent, Aug. 12, 1966; 1 child, Cason Lynley Rent Helms. BA, Fla. State U., 1964, MA, 1966, PhD, 1968; LHD (hon.), Judson Coll., 1993. Asst. prof. Western Carolina U. Cullowhee, N.C., 1968-70; asst. prof. Queens Coll., Charlotte, N.C., 1972-74, dept. chair, 1974-78, dean Grad. Sch. and New Coll., 1979-84, v.p. for Grad. Sch. and New Coll., 1984-85, v.p. acad. affairs, 1985-87, v.p. community affairs, 1987-89; pres. Miss. U. for Women, Columbus, 1989—; bd. dirs. Trustmark Nat. Bank, Trustmark Corp.; cons. Colls. Bd. N.Y.C., 1983-89; sci. cons. N.C. Alcohol Rsch. Authority, Chapel Hill, 1976-89; bd. mem. So. Growth Policies Bd., 1992-94; mem. adv. bd. Nat. Women's Hall of Fame; rotating chair Miss. Instns. Higher Learning Pres.' Coun., 1990-91; commn. govtl. rels. Am. Coun. Edn., 1990-93; adv. bd. Miss. Power and Light, 1994—. Author rsch. articles in acad. jours.; speeches pub. in Vital Speeches; mem. editorial bds. acad. jours. Trustee N.C. Performing Arts Ctr., Charlotte, 1988-89, Charlotte County Day Sch., 1987-89; bd. visitors Johnson C. Smith U., Charlotte, 1985-89; exec. com. bd. dirs. United Way Allocations and Rev., Charlotte, 1982-88; bd. advisors Charlotte Mecklenburg Hosp. Authority, 1985-89; bd. dirs. Jr. Achievement, Charlotte, 1983-89, Miss. Humanities Coun., Miss. Inst. Arts and Letters, Miss. Symphony, Miss. Econ. Coun.; chair Leadership Miss. and Collegiate Miss.; chmn. bd. dirs. Charlotte/Mecklenburg Arts and Sci. Coun., 1987-88; Danforth assoc. Danforth Found., St. Louis, 1976-88, Leadership Am., 1989; golden triangle adv. bd. Bapt. Meml. Hosp.; pres. So. Univs. Conf., 1994-95; mem. commn. govt. rels. Am. Coun. Edn., 1990-93. Recipient Grad. Made Good award Fla. State U., 1990, Excellence medal Miss. U. for Women, 1995; named Prof. of Yr., Queens Coll., 1979, One of 10 Most Admired Women Mgrs. in Am., Working Women mag., 1993, one of 1000 Women of the 90's, Mirabella mag., 1994; grantee Ford Found., 1981; Paul Harris fellow, 1992. Mem. Am. Assn. State Colls. and Univs. (bd. dirs. 1994-96), Sociol. Soc., N.C. Assn. Colls. and Univs. (exec. com. 1988-89), N.C. Assn. Acad. Officers (sec.-treas. 1987-88), Soc. Internat. Bus. Fellows, Miss. Assn. Colls. (pres. 1992), Newcomen Soc. U.S., Internat. Women's Forum, Univ. Club, Rotary. 1st female pres. of Miss. U. for Women (1st pub. coll. for women in Am.). Office: Miss U Women Presidents Office Box W 1600 Columbus MS 39701

RENTFRO, LARRY DEAN, hospital administrator; b. Independence, Kans., Mar. 14, 1941; s. Floyd Raymond and Helen Louise (Merritt) R.; m. Clariece VanValkenburgh, Jan. 25, 1964; children: Donald R., Sheri R. BS, Okla. State U., 1964; MHA, Washington U., 1972. Tchr.-coach Thomas Edison High Sch., Tulsa, 1966-70; asst. administr. St. John's Hosp., Tulsa, 1972-76; asst. v.p. St. John's Med. Ctr., Joplin, Mo., 1976-78; v.p. Wadley Med. Ctr., Texarkana, Tex., 1978-80, sr. v.p., 1980-86; CEO Glenwood Regional Med. Ctr., West Monroe, La., 1986—. Past pres. N.E. La. U. Athletic Scholarship Found., Monroe, La.; bd. dirs. North La. Healthcare Alliance, Monroe, 1993, Boy Scouts Am., Better Bus. Bur. With U.S Army, 1964-66. Fellow Am. Coll. Healthcare Execs. (mem. regional adv. com., regent for state of La.); mem. La. Hosp. Assn. (bd. dirs., past chmn.). Republican. United Methodist. Avocations: fishing, gardening. Home: 143 Comanche Trl West Monroe LA 71291-8105 Office: Glenwood Reg Med Ctr PO Box 35805 503 Mcmillan Rd West Monroe LA 71291-5327

RENTMEESTER, LAWRENCE RAYMOND, insurance company executive; b. 1939. Exec. v.p. adminstrn. The Old Line Life Ins. of Am., Milw., 1961—. Office: The Old Line Life Ins of Am 707 N 11th St Milwaukee WI 53233*

RENTZEPIS, PETER M., chemistry educator; b. Kalamata, Greece, Dec. 11, 1934; m. Alma Elizabeth Keenan; children—Michael, John. B.S., Denison U., 1957, D.Sc. (hon.), 1981; M.S., Syracuse U., 1959, Ph.D. (hon.), 1980; Ph.D., Cambridge U., 1963; D.Sc. (hon.), Carnegie-Mellon U., 1983. Mem. tech. staff, rsch. labs. Gen. Electric Co., Schenectady, 1960-62; mem. tech. staff AT&T Bell Labs., Murray Hill, N.J., 1963-73, head phys. and inorganic chemistry rsch. dept., 1973-85; Presdl. prof. chemistry U. Calif., Irvine, 1986—, Presdl. chair, 1985—, regent lectr., 1984; vis. prof. Rockefeller U., N.Y.C., 1971, MIT, Cambridge, to 1975; vis. prof. chemistry U. Tel Aviv; adj. prof. U. Pa., Phila.; with Ctr. Biol. Studies, SUNY-Albany, 1979—; adj. prof. chemistry and biophysics Yale U., New Haven, 1980—; mem. numerous adv. bodies; lectr. Robert A. Welch Found., 1975; faculty lectr. Rensselaer Poly. Inst., Troy, N.Y., 1978; IBM lectr. Williams Coll., 1979; lectr. disting. lecture series U. Utah, 1980; Xerox lectr. N.C. State U., 1980; Frank C. Whitmore lectr. in chemistry Pa. State U., 1981; Dreyfus disting. scholar lectr., 1982; regent lectr. U. Calif., 1982, UCLA, 1985; Harry S. Ganning disting. lectr. U. Alta., Can., 1984; mem. IUPAC Commn. on Molecular Structure and Spectroscopy; chmn. 1981 Internat. Conf. on Photochemistry and Photobiology; bd. dirs. KRIKOS Sci. and Tech. Resources for Greece; mem. com. on kinetics Nat. Acad. Scis., NRC; chmn. fast reaction chemistry U.S. Fgn. Applied Sci. Assessment Ctr.; with NATO Advanced Study Insts., 1984—; dir. Quanex Corp. Assoc. editor Chem. Physics, Jour. Lasers and Chemistry, Jour. Biochem. and Biophys. Methods; editorial bd. Biophys. Jour., Jour. Chem. Intermediates; contbr. articles, papers to profl. publs.; patentee in field. Recipient Scientist of Yr. award, 1977, award for significant contbns. to field of biochem. instrumentation ISCO, 1979, award for leadership in sci. and edn. AHEPA, Disting. Alumni award SUNY, 1982, H.S. Ganning award U. Alta., 1984; Camille and Henry Dreyfus disting. scholar Williams Coll., 1982; AAAS fellow, 1985; alumni scholar Denison U., 1978. Fellow N.Y. Acad. Scis. (A Cressy Morrison award 1978), Am. Phys. Soc. (chmn. chem. physics divsn. 1979-80, exec. com. 1980-82, chmn. nominating com. 1981, Irving Langmuir award 1973); mem. NAS, Nat. Acad. Greece, Am. Chem. Soc. (exec. com. phys. chemistry to 1978, Peter Debye award phys. chemistry 1982), Inter-Am. Photochem. Soc. (nominating coun., chmn. phys. divsn. Laser Conf. prize 1989), Sigma Xi. Office: U Calif Dept Chemistry Irvine CA 92717

RENVALL, JOHAN, ballet dancer; b. Stockholm. Dancer Royal Swedish Ballet; with Am. Ballet Theater, N.Y.C., 1978—, soloist, 1980-87, prin. dancer, 1987—. Appeared in numerous ballet co-prodns. including La Bayadere, Coppelia, Etudes, The Rite of Spring, Romeo and Juliet, SinFonietta, The Sleeping Beauty, La Sylphide, Undertow; guest appearances with Royal Swedish Ballet; created role of the Young Fighter in The Informer (Agnes de Mille); appeared in film Dance; choreographer Persnickety, 1987, Tango, Jacob's Pillow Dance Festival, 1990, Romeo and Juliet, 1992. Recipient Silver medal Varna Internat. Ballet Competition, 1978. Office: Am Ballet Theatre 890 Broadway New York NY 10003-1211*

RENZAGLIA, KAREN SUE, botany educator. Prof. biol. scis. East Tenn. State U., Johnson City, Tenn. Recipient Edgar T. Wherry award Bot. Soc. Am., 1993. Office: Dept Biol Sci East Tenn State U Box 70 703 Johnson City TN 37614*

RENZETTI, ATTILIO DAVID, physician; b. N.Y.C., Nov. 11, 1920; s. Attilio and Anna (Accardi) R.; m. Mabel Lucille Woodruff, May 24, 1947; children: Patricia Ann, Laurence, Pamela Sorensen, David. AB, Columbia Coll., 1941, MD, 1944. Diplomate: Am. Bd. Internal Medicine (chmn. subsplty. bd. pulmonary disease 1970-72). Intern, resident Bellevue Hosp., N.Y.C., 1944-45, 47-49, 51-52; fellow cardiopulmonary physiology Bellevue Hosp., 1949-51; asst. prof. medicine U. Utah, 1952-53, State U. N.Y., Syracuse, 1953-57; assoc. prof. SUNY, 1957-60; asst. prof. Johns Hopkins U., 1960-61; assoc. prof. U. Md., 1960-61, U. Utah, Salt Lake City, 1961-67;

prof. U. Utah, 1967-90, emeritus, 1990—. Editorial bd.: Am. Rev. Respiratory Disease, 1964-67; Contbr. articles to med. jours. Pres. Utah TB and Health Assn., 1965-66; bd. dirs. Am. Lung Assn., 1965-74, 78-81. With M.C. AUS, 1945-47. Mem. Am. Thoracic Soc. (pres. 1975-76). Home and Office: 1801 London Plane Rd Salt Lake City UT 84124-3531

RENZI, PAUL, flutist; b. N.Y.C., Feb. 25, 1926; married; six children. Studied under, John Wummer; student, Julliard Sch. Music. Prof. emeritus San Francisco State U.; Prin. flute NBC Symphony, Symphony of the Air, San Francisco Symphony, 1957—. Office: San Francisco Symphony Orch Davies Symphony Hall 201 Van Ness Ave San Francisco CA 94102-4595

REOCK, ERNEST C., JR., retired government services educator and academic director; b. Belleville, N.J., Oct. 13, 1924; s. Ernest C. and Helen Rutan (Evans) R.; m. Jeanne Elizabeth Thomason, Jan. 25, 1953; children: Michael, Thomas, Kathleen. BS, Swarthmore Coll., 1948; MA, 1950, PhD, 1959. Rsch. assoc. bur. govt. rsch. Rutgers U., New Brunswick, N.J., 1950-59, asst. prof., dir., 1960-63, assoc. prof., dir., 1963-68, prof., dir., 1968-92; cons. N.J. Constl. Conv., New Brunswick, 1966, N.J. State and Local Revenue and Expenditure Comsns., 1986-88. Author: Handbook for New Jersey Assessors, 1962, School Budget Caps in New Jersey, 1981 (Govtl. Rsch. Assn. award 1983); editor: New Jersey Legislative District Data Book, 1976-92. Chmn. Middlesex County Charter Study Commn., New Brunswick, 1973-74; cons. various mcpl. charter commns., 1965-93. Lt. USN, 1943-46, 51-53. Mem. Am. Soc. Pub. Adminstrn. (Pub. Adminstr. of Yr. 1982), Am. Ednl. Fin. Assn. Avocations: sailing, swimming. Home: 7 Kendall Rd Kendall Park NJ 08824 Office: Rutgers U Dept Govt Svcs Bur Govt Rsch PO Box 5079 New Brunswick NJ 08903

REPHAN, JACK, lawyer; b. Little Rock, Mar. 16, 1932; s. Henry and Mildred (Frank) R.; m. Arlene Clark, June 23, 1957; children: Amy Carol, James Clark. BS in Commerce, 1954; LLB, U. Va., 1959. Bar: Va. 1959, D.C. 1961. Assoc. Kanter & Kanter, Norfolk, Va., 1959-60; law clk. to Judge Sam E. Whitaker, U.S. Ct. Claims, Washington, 1960-62; assoc. Pierson, Ball & Dowd, Washington, 1962-64; ptnr. Danzansky, Dickey, Tydings, Quint & Gordon, Washington, 1964-77; mem. Braude, Margulies, Sacks & Rephan, Washington, 1977-87; ptnr. Porter, Wright, Morris & Arthur, Washington, 1987-88, Sadur, Pelland & Rubinstein, Washington, 1988-93; counsel Hofheimer, Nusbaum, McPhaul & Samuels, Norfolk, Va., 1993—; mem. nat. panel arbitrators Am. Arbitration Assn.; lectr. joint com. continuing legal edn. State Bar Va. Contbr. articles to legal jours. Pres. Patrick Henry PTA, Alexandria, Va., 1968-69; treas. John Adams Mid. Sch. PTA, Alexandria, 1970-71; pres. Seminary Ridge Citizens Assn., 1976-77; Dem. candidate for Alexandria City Com., 1969. 1st Lt. AUS, 1955-57. Mem. ABA (chmn. subcom. on procurement of jud. remedies pub. contract sect. 1973-74), Va. Bar Assn. (govt. sect. constrn. law 1979—, vice chmn. 1980-81, chmn. 1981-82), D.C. Bar Assn., Kiwanis (pres. Landmark Club 1969), Westwood Country Club (v.p. 1977-78), Belle Haven Country Club, Cavalier Golf and Yacht Club. Jewish. Home: 3978 Ocean Hills Ct Virginia Beach VA 23415 Office: 1700 Dominion Towers PO Box 3460 Norfolk VA 23514-3460

REPINE, JOHN E., internist, educator; b. Rock Island, Ill., Dec. 26, 1944; married, 1969, 88; 6 children. BS, U. Wis., 1967; MD, U. Minn., 1971. Instr., then assoc. prof. internal medicine U. Minn., Mpls., 1974-79; asst. dir divsn. exptl. medicine Webb-Waring Lung Inst., Denver, 1979-89, prof. medicine, pres. and dir., 1989—; assoc. prof. medicine U. Colo., Denver, 1979—, assoc. prof. pediatrics, 1981—; mem. rsch. com., co-chmn. steering com. Aspen Lung Conf., 1980, chmn., 1981; assoc. dean for student advocacy Nat. Heart and Lung Inst., 1990—. Young Pulmonary Investigator grantee Nat. Heart & Lung Inst., 1974-75; recipient Basil O'Connor Starter Rsch. award Nat. Found. March of Dimes, 1975-77. Mem. AAAS, Am. Assn. Immunologists, Am. Fedn. Clin. Rsch., Am. Heart Assn. (established investigator award 1976-81), Am. Thoracic Soc., Am. Soc. Clin. Investigators, Assn. Am. Physicians. Achievements include research in role of phagocytes and oxygen radicals in lung injury and host defense. Office: Webb-Waring Lung Inst 4200 E 9th Ave Denver CO 80262-0001

REPKO, WILLIAM CLARKE, banker; b. New Haven, June 25, 1949; s. John Edward Jr. and Beatrice Jane (Martin) R.; m. Susan Sillcox, Oct. 29, 1983; children: John Edward III, Meaghan Ann, Andrew Spotswood, Parker Yates, Thomas Strong, Nathaniel Russell. Student, Lehigh U., 1973. Rep. Mfrs. Hanover Trust Co., N.Y.C., 1975, asst. sec., 1976-77, v.p., 1980-85, sr. v.p., 1985-89, mng. dir., 1989—; v.p. European Am. Bank, N.Y.C., 1980; mng. dir. Chem. Banking Corp., N.Y.C., 1990—; dir. Turnaround Mgmt. Assn. Dir. The Stanwick Club. Republican. Office: Chem Banking Corp 270 Park Ave New York NY 10017-2014

REPLINGER, JOHN GORDON, architect; b. Chgo., Nov. 9, 1923; s. Roy Lodawick and Dorothy Caroline (Thornstrom) R.; m. Dorothy Thiele, June 26, 1945; children: John Gordon Jr., Robert Louis, James Alan. B.S. in Architecture with highest honors, U. Ill., Urbana, 1949, M.S. in Architecture, 1952. Registered architect, Ill. Designer-draftsman I. Morgan Yost (Architect), Kenilworth, Ill., 1949-50; instr. U. Ill., 1951-53, asst. prof. architecture, 1953-57, assoc. prof. architecture, 1957-61, prof. architecture, 1961-85, prof. housing research and devel., 1972-85, prof. emeritus, 1985—, assoc. head dept. for acad. affairs, 1970-71; practice architecture Urbana, 1951—. Served with USAAF, 1943-45. Decorated Air medal with oak leaf clusters; recipient Sch. medal AIA, 1949, List of Tchrs. Ranked as Excellent by Their Students award U. Ill., 1976, 77, 78, 82, 83; Allerton Am. travelling scholar, 1948. Mem. Nat. Trust Hist. Preservation. Home and Office: 403 Yankee Ridge Ln Urbana IL 61801-7113

REPLOGLE, DAVID ROBERT, publishing company executive; b. Chgo., Feb. 24, 1931; s. Homer Mock and Helen (Fluke) R.; m. Jeanne Lonnquist, Nov. 4, 1954; children: William T., Bruce R., Stewart D., James M., John B. A.B., Dartmouth Coll., 1953; postgrad., Princeton U., 1957-58. V.p., gen. mgr. Doubleday & Co., Inc., N.Y.C., 1958-70; pres., chmn. bd. G. & C. Merriam Co., Springfield, Mass., 1970-75; pres. Praeger Publishers, N.Y.C., 1982—. Served to lt. USNR, 1953-57. Mem. Cohasset Golf Club. Home: 84 Gammons Rd Cohasset MA 02025-1406 Office: DR&A Inc 75 Terry Dr Ste 223 Hingham MA 02043

REPLOGLE, WILLIAM H(ENRY), II, lawyer; b. LaPorte, Ind., Mar. 19, 1946; s. William Henry and Lucille Jeanette (Schoettler) R.; m. Joyce Ann Pankonin, Jan. 8, 1977; children: Katherine Ann, Michael Scott, Patrick William. BS, Indiana U., 1968, JD, 1971. Bar: Oreg. 1971, U.S. Dist. Ct. Oreg. 1971. Law clerk Oreg. Tax Court, Salem, 1971-72; assoc. Joss, Bosch & Burns, Portland, Oreg., 1973-74, Pattulo, Gleason & Scarborough, Portland, 1974-76; house counsel Pacific N.W. Bell, Portland, 1976-79; assoc. Schwabe, Williamson & Wyatt, Portland, 1979-84, ptnr., 1984-94; ptnr. Meyers, Radler, Replogle & Bohy, Tigard, Oreg., 1994—. Chmn. Halfway House City Club of Portland, 1980-81, rsch. bd., 1982-83; divsn. chmn. United Way, Portland, 1984; bd. dirs. Vol. Bur. of Portland, 1987-89, Quadriplegics United Against Dependency, 1990—. Mem. ABA, Oreg. State Bar (mem. discipline rules com. 1976-79, mem. pub. svc. and info. com. 1973-76), Multnomah Bar Assn. (mem. professionalism com. 1989-92), Blue Goose Internat., Oswego Lake Country Club (bd. dirs.). Avocations: basketball, bicycling, golf, running, swimming. Office: Meyers Radler Replogle & Bohy Pacific Four Bldg Ste 200 6745 SW Hampton Tigard OR 97223

REPP, RONALD STEWART, insurance company executive; b. Phila., Dec. 12, 1944; s. Carl George Jr. and Pauline Francis (Hunley) R.; m. Nancy Elaine Hannigan, Sept. 16, 1967; children: Christopher Robert, Justin Ronald. Grad. high sch., Pitts.; cert., Am. Coll., Bryn Mawr, Pa., 1973, Am. Inst., Malvern, Pa., 1977. CLU, CPCU, assoc. in risk mgmt. Admistr. Liberty Mut. Ins. Group, Pitts., 1963-65, sales rep., 1967-70, sales supr., 1970-72, sales mgr., 1972-78; spl. agt. The Prudential, Pitts., 1966-67; account exec. Ind. Ins. Svc. Corp., Canton, Ohio, 1978-83, v.p., 1983-90, sr.v.p., 1990—. Contbr. articles to profl. jours. Staff sgt. U.S. Army, 1964-65. Mem. Soc. CPCUs, Soc. CLUs, Ind. Ins. Agts. Assn., Akron City Club (chmn. mem. com. 1992-94), Bay Point Yacht Club, Akron Cruising Club (bd. trustees), Silver Lake Country Club. Lutheran. Avocation: sailing.

Home: 3103 Silver Lake Blvd Silver Lake OH 44224-3130 Office: Ind Ins Svc Corp 236 Third St SW Canton OH 44702

REPPEN, NORBJORN DAG, electrical engineer, consultant; b. Hadsel, Norway, May 10, 1940; came to U.S., 1966; s. Harald and Bergit (Bakke) R.; m. Grete Elisabeth Holm, July 25, 1964; children: Dag, Anne, Erik Harald. Degree in elec. engring., Norwegian Inst. Tech., 1965. Registered profl. engr., N.Y. Application engr. GE, Schenectady, N.Y., 1966-69; application engr. Power Techs., Inc., Schenectady, 1969-73, sr. engr., 1973-84, sr. cons., 1984-91, unit mgr., 1991—; bd. dirs. Hydro Techs., Inc., Schenectady, Power Techs., Inc., Schenectady. Bd. dirs. 1st Unitarian Soc. Schenectady, 1984-87, 93. Fellow IEEE. Avocations: sailing, cross country skiing.

REPPERT, JOSEPH R., title company executive; b. 1943. Chief of staff Bob Dole; pres. Amerifirst Mortgage Corp., Miami, Fla., 1982-90; nat. accounts mgr. PMI, San Francisco, 1990-93; with Strategic Mortgage Svcs., Costa Mesa, Calif., 1993—, now CEO, chmn. bd. dirs. Office: Strategic Mortgage Svcs 3160 Airway Ave Costa Mesa CA 92626*

REPPERT, RICHARD LEVI, lawyer; b. Phila., Nov. 6, 1948; s. William Downing and Angela R. (Schmid) R.; m. Faith Simpson, Dec. 30, 1972 (div. Aug. 1992); 1 child, Richard Jacob; m. Jeanette T. deHaven, Apr. 10, 1994. BA, Lehigh U., 1970; JD, Villanova U., 1974. Bar: Ohio 1974, U.S. Dist. Ct. (no. dist.) Ohio 1974, Pa. 1993. Assoc. Thompson, Hine and Flory, Cleve., 1974-82, ptnr., 1982-89; ptnr. Jones, Day, Reavis & Pogue, Cleve., 1989—. Mem. ABA, Am. Coll. Real Estate Lawyers, Nat. Assn. Office and Indsl. Pks., Ohio State Bar Assn., Cleve. Bar Assn., Mortgage Bankers Assn. Greater Cleve. Office: Jones Day Reavis & Pogue 901 Lakeside Ave Cleveland OH 44114

REPPERT, STEVEN MARION, pediatrician, scientist, educator; b. Sioux City, Iowa, Sept. 4, 1946; s. Ray Fred and Norma Grace (Coppock) R.; m. Mary Alice Herman, Dec. 28, 1968; children—Jason Steven, Katherine Mary, Christina Marie. BS, U. Nebr., Lincoln, 1973; MD with distinction, U. Nebr.-Omaha, 1973, MA (hon.), Harvard U., 1993. Diplomate Nat. Bd. Med. Examiners. Intern, Mass. Gen. Hosp., Boston, 1973-74, resident in pediatrics, 1974-76, asst. in pediatrics, 1979-80, asst. pediatrician, 1980-85, dir. lab. devel. chronobiology, 1983—, assoc. pediatrician, 1985—; pvt. practice medicine specializing in pediatrics, Boston, 1973-88; clin. assoc. NIH, Bethesda, Md., 1976-79; instr. pediatrics Harvard Med. Sch., Boston, 1979-81, asst. prof., 1981-85, assoc. prof., 1985-93, prof. 1993—; vis. scientist Lab. Molecular Neurobiology Mass. Gen. Hosp., 1989-90. Mem. adv. com. Charles H. Hood Found., 1993—. Editor: Development of Circadian Rhythmicity and Photoperiodism in Mammals, 1989; co-editor: Suprachiasmatic Nucleus: The Mind's Clock, 1991; contbr. articles to sci. jours, chpts. to books. Regents scholar U. Nebr., 1971; Pfizer Labs. Med. scholar, 1971; Charles King Trust research fellow, 1981-83; Grantee NIH, 1981—, Nat. Found/March of Dimes, 1981-88; recipient E. Mead Johnson award, 1989, NIH Merit award, 1992. Mem. Am. Physiol. Soc., Am. Soc. for Clin. Investigation, Endocrine Soc., Soc. for Pediatric Research, Soc. for Neurosci., Soc. for Research on Biol. Rhythms (adv. com.), Am. Heart Assn. (established investigator 1985-90), Lepidopterists Soc., Cambridge Entomol. Club, Alpha Omega Alpha. Democrat. Avocation: natural history of saturniid moths. Office: Mass Gen Hosp 32 Fruit St Boston MA 02114-2698

REPPOND, JIM D., communications executive; b. 1941. Installer to mgr. Century Svc. Group, Inc., Monroe, La., 1960-70, dir. engring., 1970-81, v.p., sr. v.p. telecommunications ops., 1981—. Office: Century Svc Group Inc 100 Century Park Dr Monroe LA 71203*

REPPUCCI, NICHOLAS DICKON, psychologist, educator; b. Boston, May 1, 1941; s. Nicholas Ralph and Bertha Elizabeth (Williams) R.; m. Christine Marlow Onufrock, Sept. 10, 1967; children: Nicholas Jason, Jonathan Dickon, Anna Jin Marlow. BA with honors, U. N.C., 1962; MA, Harvard U., 1964, PhD, 1968. Lectr., rsch. assoc. Harvard U., Cambridge, Mass., 1967-68; asst. prof. Yale U., New Haven, 1968-73, assoc. prof., 1973-76; prof. psychology U. Va., Charlottesville, 1976—, dir. grad. studies in psychology, 1984-95; originator biennial conf. on community rsch. and action, 1986. Assoc. editor Law and Human Behavior, 1986—; mem. editorial bd. Am. Jour. Community Psychology, 1974-88, 88-91; author: (with J. Haugaard) Sexual Abuse of Children, 1988; editor: (with J. Haugaard) Prevention in Community Mental Health Practice, (with E. Mulvey, L. Weithorn and J. Monahan) Mental Health, Law and Children, 1984; contbr. over 100 articles to profl. jours, chpts. in books. Adv. bd. on prevention Va. Dept. Mental Health, Mental Retardation and Substance Abuse Svcs., Richmond, 1986-92. Disting. scholar in psychology Va. Assn. Social Sci., 1991. Fellow APA (chair task force on pub. policy 1980-84), Am. Psychol. Soc., Soc. for Community Rsch. and Action (pres. 1986), Phi Beta Kappa. Office: Univ Va Dept Psychology Charlottesville VA 22903

REPPY, WILLIAM ARNEILL, JR., law educator; b. Oxnard, Calif., Mar. 14, 1941; s. William Arneill and Margot Louise Reppy; m. Susan Westerberg, Sept. 30, 1967 (div. 1973); m. Juliann Tenney, Nov. 28, 1975. B.A. with great distinction, Stanford U., 1963, J.D. with great distinction, 1966. Bar: Calif. 1966, N.C. 1971, U.S. Supreme Ct. 1971. Law clk. to Justice William Douglas, U.S. Supreme Ct., Washington, 1967-68; assoc. Tuttle & Taylor, Los Angeles, 1968-71; prof. law Duke U., Durham, N.C. 1971—; cons. Calif. Law Revision Com., Palo Alto, 1979-83; mem. Condominium Statutes Commn., Raleigh, N.C., 1980—. Author: Community Property in California, 1980; Community Property-Gilbert Law Summaries, 1983; co-author: Community Property in U.S., 2d edit., 1982, Texas Matrimonial Property Law, 1983. Mem. editorial bd. Community Property Jour., 1973—. Recipient Nathan Abbot award Stanford U., 1966. Mem. Am. Law Inst., Order of Coif, Phi Beta Kappa. Republican. Office: Sch Law Duke U Durham NC 27706

REPS, DAVID NATHAN, finance educator; b. N.Y.C., July 30, 1926; s. Samuel and Fannie (Ginsberg) R.; m. Helene Shifrin, Aug. 10, 1958; children: Tamara, Aaron, Steven, Jennifer. BSEE, Columbia U., 1948; MSEE, U. Pitts., 1953, PhD, 1966. Elec. utility systems engr. Westinghouse Elec. Corp., Pitts., 1950-63, corp. planner, 1963-67; prin. mgmt. svcs. Ernst & Young, N.Y.C., 1967-75; prof., chmn. bus. econs., fin., pub. policy LI. Univ., N.Y.C., 1975-78; prof. fin. Pace U., Pleasantville, N.Y., 1978—; v.p. Video Frame Store, Inc., N.Y.C., 1983—, The Photoboard Group, N.Y.C., 1989-92; v.p. and treas. Digital Video Photo Imaging, Inc., N.Y.C., 1992—; bd. dirs. The Storyboard Group, Inc., N.Y.C.; exec. v.p. Video Frame Imaging, Inc., N.Y.C., 1994—. Contbr. articles to profl. jours. With USN, 1944-46. Home: 98 Soundview Ave White Plains NY 10606-3617 Office: Pace U Bedford Rd Pleasantville NY 10570

REQUARTH, WILLIAM HENRY, surgeon; b. Charlotte, N.C., Jan. 23, 1913; s. Charles William and Amelia (George) R.; m. Nancy Charlton, 1948 (div. 1966); children—Kurt, Betsy, Jeff, Jan, Tim, Suzanna; m. Connie Harper, 1977. A.B., Millikin U., 1934; M.D., U. Ill., 1938, M.S., 1939. Diplomate: Am. Bd. Surgery. Intern St. Luke's Hosp., Chgo., 1938-39; resident Cook County Hosp., Chgo., 1940-42, 46-48; pvt. practice medicine, specializing in surgery Decatur, Ill., 1950—; clin. prof. surgery U. Ill. Med. Sch., from 1962, now emeritus; Mem. Chgo. Bd. Trade. Author: Diagnosis of Abdominal Pain, 1953, The Acute Abdomen, 1958; also contbg. author chpts. books. Chmn. trustees Millikin U.; chmn. James Millikin Found.; bd. dirs. Decatur Meml. Hosp. Served to comdr. USNR, 1941-46. Mem. ACS, Cen. Surg. Assn., Western Surg. Assn., Chgo. Surg. Soc., Ill. Surg. Soc. (pres. 1970-71), Am. Soc. Surgery Hand (founder), Am. Soc. Surgery Trauma, Soc. Surgery Alimentary Tract, Warren Cole Soc., Societe Internationale Chirurgie, Nat. Pilots Assn. (pres. 1960-61), Soaring Soc. Am., Sportsman Pilot Assn. (pres. 1966-67), Aerobatic Club Am., Internat. Aerobatic Club. Home: 1860 S Spitler Dr Decatur IL 62521-4417 Office: 158 W Prairie Ave Decatur IL 62523-1230

RERES, MARY EPIPHANY, health care and administration consultant; b. Kansas City, Mo., Jan. 31, 1941; d. Mathew and Mary Ellen (Connelly) R. B.S. in Nursing, Creighton U., Omaha, 1963; M.Psychiat. Nursing, U. Nebr., 1965; Ed.D in Adminstrn., Columbia U., 1970. Staff nurse Nebr. Psychiat. Inst., 1963-65; clin. specialist Norfolk (Nebr.) State Hosp., 1965-66;

---

instr. Creighton U. Sch. Nursing, 1966-68; prof. nursing, medicine and edn. U. Va., 1970-77; prof., dean Sch. Nursing, UCLA, 1977-85, prof.-at-large Med. Sch., 1977-85; pres. Human Services Tng. and Research Corp., 1974-85; co-chmn. Gov.'s Mental Health and Mental Retardation Adv. Bd., 1973-76; rsch. review com. VA, 1992—; cons. in field. Co-author: Your Future in Nursing Careers, 1972; editor Am. Psychiat. Nurses Assn. Newsletter, 1989; mem. editorial bd. JAPNA, 1994—; book rev. editor: Jour. Psychosocial Nursing, 1980-94. Bd. dirs. Kaiser Permanente Health Plan and Hosps., 1980—, Med. Media Group, 1989—; mem. adv. bd. hosp. adminstrn. program Charles A. Drew Med. Ctr., 1992—. Recipient Outstanding Alumni award Creighton U. Sch. Nursing, 1972; named Disting. Vis. Scholar U. Tex., Arlington, 1986. Mem. Am. Acad. Nursing (pres. 1974), Am. Nurses Assn., Am. Assn. Colls. Nursing, Western Interstat Am. Hosp Higher Edn., Am. Psychosocial Nursing Assn. (bd. dirs., sec. 1986-90), Am. Hosp. Assn. (alt. Calif. del. 1992, trustee rep. regional policy bd. 1993—, regional policy bd. 1994—), Calif. Assn. Hosps. and Health Systems (Gov.'s Forum 1989—, nominating com. 1992. pub. affairs com. 1991—, vice chmn. program com. 1992), Governance Forum (chmn. 1993—, CAHHS trustee 1993—, trustee 1993-94), Am. Psychiat. Nurses Assn. (Disting. Leadership and Meritorious Svc. award 1989, vice chmn. progs. 1991-93, mem. pub. policy com. 1991—), Delta Sigma Rho, Alpha Sigma Nu, Sigma Theta Tau. Democrat. Roman Catholic. Office: Human Resource Assocs 6410 Surfside Way Malibu CA 90265-3628

RESCH, JOSEPH ANTHONY, neurologist; b. Milw., Apr. 29, 1914; s. Frank and Elizabeth (Zetsch) R.; m. Rose Catherine Ritz, May 25, 1939; children—Rose, Frank, Catherine. Student, Milw. State Tchrs. Coll., 1931-34; B.S., U. Wis., Madison, 1936, M.D., 1938. Intern St. Francisco Hosp., LaCrosse, Wis., 1938-39; gen. practice medicine Holmen, Wis., 1939-40; med. fellow in neurology U. Minn., 1946-48, clin. instr. neurology, 1948-51, clin. asst. prof., 1951-55, clin. assoc. prof., 1955-62, assoc. prof., 1962-65, prof., 1965-84, prof. emeritus, 1984—, head dept. neurology, 1976-82, asst. v.p. health sci., 1970-79, prof. lab. medicine and pathology, 1979-84; practice medicine specializing in neurology Mpls., 1948-62. Contbr. articles and abstracts to profl. jours., chpts. in books. Served to lt. col. M.C. U.S. Army, 1940-46; col. Med. Res. 1946-53. Mem. Hennepin County Med. Soc., Minn. Med. Assn., AMA, Minn. Soc. Neurol. Scis., Central Assn. Electroencephalographers, Am. Acad. Neurology, Am. Neurol. Assn., Am. Assn. Neuropathologists, Am. EEG Soc., Sonoma County Med. Assn., Am. Epilepsy Soc. Home: 900 River Beach Rd The Sea Ranch CA 95497

RESCH, RICHARD J., furniture manufacturing executive; b. 1938. Grad., MIT, Milw.; MBA, Harvard U. With Hudson Pulp & Paper, N.Y.C., 1959-64; with Krueger Internat. Inc., Green Bay, Wis., 1964—, now pres./CEO. Office: Krueger Internat Inc 1330 Bellevue St Green Bay WI 54302*

RESCHER, NICHOLAS, philosophy educator; b. Hagen, Westphalia, Germany, July 15, 1928; came to U.S. 1938, naturalized 1944; s. Erwin Hans and Meta Anna (Landau) R.; m. Dorothy Henle, Feb. 10, 1968; children: Mark, Owen, Catherine; 1 child from a previous marriage, Elizabeth. BS in Math., Queens Coll., 1949; PhD, Princeton U., 1951; LHD (hon.), Loyola U.-Chgo., 1970, Lehigh U., 1993; Dr. honoris causa U. Córdoba, Argentina, 1992, U. Konstanz, Germany, 1995. Instr. philosophy Princeton U., N.J., 1951-52; assoc. prof. philosophy Lehigh U., Bethlehem, Pa., 1957-61; Univ. prof. philosophy U. Pitts., 1961—, vice chmn. Ctr. for Philosophy of Sci., 1988—; trustee St. Edmunds Acad., Pitts., 1980-85; nonresident mem. Corpus Christi Coll., Oxford. Author: The Coherence Theory of Truth, 1973, Scientific Progress, 1978, The Limits of Science, 1985, others. Sec. gen. Internat. Union of History and Philosophy of Sci. (UNESCO), 1969-75. Served with USMC, 1952-54. Recipient Alexander von Humboldt Humanities prize 1983. Mem. Am. Philos. Assn. (past pres.), Royal Asiatic Soc., G.W. Leibniz Soc. Am. (past pres.), Institut International de Philosophie, Academie Internationale de Philosophie des Sciences. Roman Catholic. Avocation: reading history and biography. Home: 5818 Aylesboro Ave Pittsburgh PA 15217-1446 Office: Univ of Pitts Dept Philosophy 1012 Cathedral Pittsburgh PA 15260

RESCHKE, MICHAEL W., real estate executive; b. Chgo., Nov. 29, 1955; s. Don J. and Vera R. (Helmer) R.; m. Kim P. Shaw, July 17, 1977; children: Michael W. Jr., Tiffanie G. BS summa cum laude with univ. honors, No. Ill. U., 1977; JD summa cum laude, U. Ill., 1980. Bar: Ill. 1980; CPA, Ill. Assoc. Winston & Strawn, Chgo., 1980-82; pres., CEO The Prime Group, Inc., Chgo., 1982—, also chmn. bd. dirs.; chmn. bd. dirs. Prime Retail, Inc., NASDAQ: PRME and PRMEP; bd. dirs. Prime Residential, Inc., NASDAQ: PRES. Mem. Chgo. Devel. Coun., 1987. Mem. ABA, Ill. Bar Assn., Urban Land Inst., Chgo. Club, Econ. Club Chgo., Nat. Realty Com. (mem. chmn.'s roundtable 1992—), Nat. Assn. Real Estate Investment Trusts, Order of Coif, Phi Delta Phi, Beta Alpha Psi. Office: The Prime Group 77 W Wacker Dr Ste 3900 Chicago IL 60601-1690

RESCIGNO, NICOLA, conductor, administrator. Co-founder, dir. Chgo. Lyric Opera, 1954-56; co-founder, dir. music Dallas Opera, 1957-75, gen. mgr., 1974-77, artistic dir., prin. condr., 1977—; condr. major opera cos. in U.S., Can., Eng., Europe and South Am. Office: Dallas Opera 1925 Elm St Dallas TX 75201-4510

RESCORLA, ROBERT ARTHUR, psychology educator; b. Pitts, May 9, 1940; s. Arthur R. and Mildred J. (Jenkins) R.; m. Shirley Steele; children: Eric, Michael. BA, Swarthmore Coll., 1962; PhD, U. Pa., 1966; MA, Yale U., 1974. Successively asst. prof., assoc. prof., prof. Yale U., New Haven, 1966-80; prof. psychology U. Pa., Phila., 1981—; James Skinner prof. sci., 1986—, dean of coll. Sch. of Arts and Scis., 1994—. Author: Pavlovian Second-Order Conditioning, 1980; editor: Animal Learning and Behavior, 1995—; contbr. articles to profl. jours. Mem. APA (fellow, div. 3 1985, Disting. Sci. Contbn. award 1986), Am. Psychol. Soc. (William James fellow 1988), NAS, AAAS (pres. sect. J., psychology 1988-89), Soc. Exptl. Psychologists (Warren medal 1991), Psychonomic Soc. (mem. governing bd. 1979-85, chmn. publ. bd. 1985-86), Ea. Psychol. Assn. (bd. dirs. 1983-86, pres. 1986-87). Office: U Pa Dept Psychology 3815 Walnut St Philadelphia PA 19104-3604

RESDEN, RONALD EVERETTE, medical devices product development engineer; b. Littleton, N.H., Oct. 27, 1944; s. Lawerence A. and Rita Mae (Bowen) R.; m. Dee Kronenberg, Apr. 20, 1974 (div.); children: Philip, Alison; m. Louise Simons, June 18, 1994. Cons. Franklin Mfg. Co., Norwood, Mass., 1984—, Boston Sci. Co., Watertown, Mass., 1985—, Via Med, Easton, Mass., 1986—, White Marsh Labs., Balt., 1989—, Spectraphos Malmo Sweden, 1991—, Vision Scis. Inc., Natick, Mass., 1991—; Cordis Corp., Miami, Fla., 1993—; Active MIT Enterprise Forum. Author: Hologram Control Transfer, 1984; inventor, patentee in field. Mem. NRA (life), Soc. Plastics Engrs., Soc. Mfg. Engrs., Nat. Geographic Soc. Mass. Chiefs of Police Assn., Citizens for Ltd. Taxation. Home and Office: Resden Rsch Inc 44 Arrowhead Rd Weston MA 02193-1707

RESEK, ROBERT WILLIAM, university administrator; b. Berwyn, Ill., July 2, 1935; s. Ephraim Frederick and Ruth Elizabeth (Rummele) R.; m. Lois Doll, July 9, 1960; 1 child, Richard Alden. BA, U. Ill., 1957; AM, Harvard U., 1960, PhD, 1961. Vis. scholar MIT, Cambridge, 1967-68; asst. prof. econs. U. Ill., Urbana, 1961-65, assoc. prof., 1965-70, prof., 1970—; dir. Bur. Econ. and Bus. Rsch., 1977-89, acting v.p. for acad. affairs, 1987-89, v.p. for acad. affairs, 1989-94; vis. prof. U. Colo., 1967, 74, 75, 76, 82, Kyoto (Japan) U., 1976; cons. GM, 1964-66, U.S. Congress Joint Econ. Com., 1978-80, ABA, 1980-82; vis. scholar UCLA, 1994-95; co-dir. Midwest Economy: Issues and Policy, Midwest Govs. Conf., 1981; bd. dirs. Midwest U. Consortium Internat. Activities, v.p., 1991-94. Co-author: Environmental Contamination by Lead and Other Heavy Metals—Synthesis and Modeling, 1978, Special Topics in Mathematics for Economists, 1976, A Comparative Cost Study of Staff Panel and Participating Attorney Panel Prepaid Legal Service Plans, 1981; editor: Illinois Economic Outlook, 1982-87, Illinois Economic Statistics, 1981; co-editor: The Midwest Economy: Issues and Policy, 1982, Frontiers of Business and Economic Research Management, 1983, Illinois Statistical Abstract, 1987. Woodrow Wilson fellow, 1957; Social Sci. Rsch. Coun. grantee, 1964; NSF fellow, 1967-69, grantee, 1974-77; U.S. Dept. State scholar, Japan, 1976. Mem. Assn. Univ. Bus. and Econ. Rsch. (mem. exec. com. 1977-89, v.p. 1978-82, pres. 1982-83), Econometric Soc., Beta Gamma Sigma, Phi Kappa Phi. Home: 201 E Holmes St Urbana

IL 61801-6612 Office: Univ Ill 211 IGPA 1007 W Nevada Urbana IL 61801-3620

RESHOTKO, ELI, aerospace engineer, educator; b. N.Y.C., Nov. 18, 1930; s. Max and Sarah (Kalisky) R.; m. Adina Venit, June 7, 1953; children: Deborah, Naomi, Miriam Ruth. B.S., Cooper Union, 1950; M.S., Cornell U., 1951; Ph.D., Calif. Inst. Tech., 1960. Aero. research engr. NASA-Lewis Flight Propulsion Lab., Cleve., 1951-56; head fluid mechanics sect. NASA-Lewis Flight Propulsion Lab., 1956-57; head high temperature plasma sect. NASA-Lewis Research Center, 1960-61, chief plasma physics br., 1961-64; asso. prof. engring. Case Inst. Tech., Cleve., 1964-66, dean, 1986-87; prof. engring. Case Western Res. U., 1966-88, chmn. dept. fluid thermal and aerospace scis., 1970-76, chmn. dept. mech. and aerospace engring., 1976-79, Kent H. Smith prof. engring., 1989—; Susman vis. prof. dept. aero. engring. Technion-Israel Inst. Tech., Haifa, Israel, 1969-70; cons. United Technologies Research Ctr., United Research Corp., Dynamics Tech. Inc., Micro Craft Tech., Martin-Marietta Corp., Rockwell Internat.; mem. adv. com. fluid dynamics NASA, 1961-64; mem. aero. adv. com. NASA, 1980-87, chmn. adv. subcom. on aerodynamics, 1983-85; chmn. U.S. Boundary Layer Transition Study Group, NASA/USAF, 1970—; U.S. mem. fluid dynamics panel AGARD-NATO, 1981-88; chmn. steering com. Symposium on Engring. Aspects Magneto-hydro-dynamics, 1966, Case-NASA Inst. for Computational Mechanics in Propulsion, 1985-92, USRA/NASA ICASE Sci. Coun., 1992; Joseph Wunsch lectr. Technion-Israel Inst. Tech., 1990. Contbr. articles to tech. jours. Chmn. bd. govs. Cleve. Coll. Jewish Studies, 1981-84. Guggenheim fellow Calif. Inst. Tech., 1957-59. Fellow ASME, AAAS, AIAA (Fluid and Plasma Dynamics award 1980, Dryden Lectureship in Rsch. 1994), Am. Phys. Soc., Am. Acad. Mechanics (pres. 1986-87); mem. NAE, AAUP, Ohio Sci. and Engring. Roundtable, Sigma Xi, Tau Beta Pi, Pi Tau Sigma. Office: Case Western Res Univ University Cir Cleveland OH 44106

RESIKA, PAUL, artist; b. N.Y.C., Aug. 15, 1928. Student, Sol Wilson, N.Y.C., 1940-44, Hans Hofmann Sch., 1945-47, Venice, Italy, 1950-53. adj. prof. art Cooper Union, 1966-78; instr. Art Students League, 1968-69; faculty Skowhagen Sch. Painting and Sculpture, 1973, 76; chmn. M.F.A. program Parsons Sch. Design, 1978-89. Artist-in-residence, Dartmouth Coll., 1972; one-man shows include, George Dix Gallery, N.Y.C., 1948, Peridot Gallery, N.Y.C., 1964, 65, 67, 68, 69, 70, Washburn Gallery, N.Y.C., 1971, 73, Hopkins Center, Dartmouth Coll., 1972, Graham Gallery, N.Y.C., 1976, 77, 79, 81, 83, 85, Longpoint Gallery, Provincetown, Mass., 1979, 81, 85, 88, 92, 25-year survey Artists Choice Mus., 1985, Merideth Long Gallery, Houston, 1986, Kornbluth Gallery, Fairlawn, N.J., 1986, Crane Kalman Gallery, London, 1986, Graham/Modern Gallery, 1987-88, 90, Salander-O'Reilly Galleries, N.Y.C., 1990, Mead Art Mus., Amherst (Mass.) Coll., 1991, Salander-O'Reilly Galleries, N.Y.C., 1993, 94, Am. Acad. Arts and Letters, 1994, Walker-Kornbluth Gallery, Fairlawn, N.J., 1995; represented in permanent collections U. Nebr. Art Gallery, Indpls. Mus. Art, Chase Manhattan Bank, N.Y.C., Neuberger Mus., SUNY, Purchase, N.Y., U. Wyo., Laramie, Met. Mus. Art, Colby Coll., NAD, Owensboro (Ky.) Mus. Art, U. Ariz., William Benton Mus. Art, U. Conn., Crakow Mus. Art, Poland, NAD, N.Y.C., Parish Art Mus., Southampton, N.Y., Heckscher Mus., Huntington, N.Y., Hood Mus., Dartmouth Coll., Hanover, N.H., Mills Coll. Mus., Oakland, Calif., pvt. collections. Recipient award Am. Acad. Arts and Letters, 1977, Altman prize NAD, 1982, 91; Louis Comfort Tiffany grantee, 1959; Ingram Merrill grantee, 1969; Guggenheim fellow, 1984. Mem. NAD, Am. Acad. Arts and Letters. Office: care Salander-O'Reilly Galleries 20 E 79th St New York NY 10021-0106

RESNICK, ALAN HOWARD, health care and optics executive; b. Boston, Nov. 1, 1943; s. Max Lawrence and Natalie (Levine) R.; m. Janice M. Mark, Jan. 26, 1948; children: Stephen Seth, Helaine Elise, Eilleen Michelle. BS, Tufts U., 1965; MBA, Columbia U., 1967. Fin. analyst E.I. DuPont de Nemours & Co., Wilmington, Del., 1967-73; various positions Bausch & Lomb Inc., Rochester, N.Y., 1973—, treas., 1986—; mem. adv. bd. Allendale Ins. Co., Johnston, R.I., 1987. Bd. dirs. Vis. Nurse Service Rochester and Monroe County, 1977—, Rochester Monroe County chpt. ARC, 1988—, Park Ridge Hosp., 1990—. Jewish. Avocation: stamp collecting. Office: Bausch & Lomb Inc 1 Lincoln First Sq Rochester NY 14604

RESNICK, ALICE ROBIE, state supreme court justice; b. Erie, Pa., Aug. 21, 1939; d. Adam Joseph and Alice Suzanne (Spizarny) Robie; m. Melvin L. Resnick, Mar. 20, 1970. PhB, Siena Heights Coll., 1961; JD, U. Detroit, 1964. Bar: Ohio 1964, Mich. 1965, U.S. Supreme Ct. 1970. Asst. county prosecutor Lucas County Prosecutor's Office, Toledo, 1964-75, trial atty., 1965-75; judge Toledo Mcpl. Ct., 1976-83, 6th Dist. Ct. Appeals, State of Ohio, Toledo, 1983-88; instr. U. Toledo, 1968-69; justice Ohio Supreme Ct., 1989—; co-chairperson Ohio State Gender Fairness Task Force. Trustee Siena Heights Coll., Adrian, Mich., 1982—; organizer Crime Stopper Inc., Toledo, 1981—; mem. Mayor's Drug Coun.; bd. dirs. Guest House Inc. Mem. ABA, Toledo Bar Assn., Lucas County Bar Assn., Nat. Assn. Women Judges, Am. Judicature Soc., Toledo Women's Bar Assn., Ohio State Women's Bar Assn. (organizer), Toledo Mus. Art, Internat. Inst. Toledo. Roman Catholic. Home: 2407 Edgehill Rd Toledo OH 43615-2321 Office: Supreme Ct Office 30 E Broad St 3rd Fl Columbus OH 43266-0419

RESNICK, DONALD IRA, lawyer; b. Chgo., July 19, 1950; s. Roland S. and Marilyn B. (Weiss) R.; m. Jill Allison White, July 3, 1977; children: Daniel, Allison. BS with high honors, U. Ill., 1972; JD, Harvard U., 1975. Bar: Ill. 1975, U.S. Dist. Ct. (no. dist.) Ill. 1975. Assoc. Arvey, Hodes, Costello & Burman, Chgo., 1975-80, ptnr., 1981-83; sr. ptnr. Nagelberg & Resnick, Chgo., 1983-89, Levenstein & Resnick, Chgo., 1989-91; co-chmn. real estate dept. Jenner & Block, Chgo., 1992—; gen. counsel Real Estate Consortium. Bd. dirs. Ill. chpt. Real Estate/Investment Assn., Chgo., 1986—. Mem. ABA. Club: Birchwood (Highland Park, Ill.). Office: Jenner & Block 1 IBM Plz Chicago IL 60611

RESNICK, IDRIAN NAVARRE, foundation administrator; b. Wichita, Kans., Apr. 24, 1936; s. Herbert and Virginiae Miriam (Goldsmith) Speer; m. Jane Letham Riley (div. 1980); children: Michael Mosi, David Shaka; m. Kathleen Margaret Pelich (div. 1993); stepchildren: Robert Andrew, Kathleen Mary, Janice Margaret. BA, Clark U., 1958; PhD, New School U., 1961, PhD, 1966. Lectr. dept. econs. Columbia U., 1962-63; asst. prof. econs. Howard U., Washington, 1963-64; lectr. econs. U. Dar es Salaam, Tanzania, 1964-67; vis. prof. econs. Princeton (N.J.) U., 1967-68; asst. prof. econs. Columbia U., N.Y.C., 1968-70; sr. economist Ministry Econ. Planning, Dar es Salaam, 1970-72; exec. dir. Econ. Devel. Bur., New Haven, 1974-81; pres. Resnick Devel. Services, New Haven, 1982—; exec. dir. Am. Indian Affairs, N.Y.C., 1985-89, Action for Corp. Accountability, New Haven, 1991-94; prof. Cornell U., Ithaca, N.Y., 1982-84; cons. Govt. of Nicaragua, Managua, 1979-81, Govt. of the Netherlands, The Hague, 1977, Govt. of Somalia, Mogodishu, 1985. Author: The Long Transition: Building Socialism in Tanzania, 1981, Controlling Consulting, 1989; editor: Tanzania: Revolution by Education, 1968; video producer (in the Lakota lang.) AIDS, 1989; contbr. articles to profl. jours. Organizer Namibia Com., New Haven, 1977-79, Conn. Task Force on Cen. Am., 1985; mem. Pledge of Resistance, U.S., 1985—; vol. adviser AIDS Interfaith Network, New Haven, 1990. Nat. Edn. scholar U.S. Govt., 1959-62; Albert Schweitzer Resh fellow Columbia U., 1969-70. Avocations: chess, theatre, travel, tennis, golf, photography, woodworking, classical music. Home: 10 Collins St Hamden CT 06514

RESNICK, JEFFREY LANCE, federal judge; b. Bklyn., Mar. 5, 1943; s. Bernard and Selma (Monheit) R.; m. Margery O'Connor, May 27, 1990. BA, U. Conn., 1964; LLB, U. Conn., West Hartford, 1967. Bar: Conn. 1967, N.Y. 1968, U.S. V.I. 1968, D.C. 1979, U.S. Ct. Appeals (3d cir.) 1979. Assoc. Office of J.D. Marsh, Christiansted, St. Croix, V.I., 1967-69; asst. atty. gen. Dept. Law, Christiansted, 1969-73; ptnr. James & Resnick, Christiansted, 1973-89; magistrate judge U.S. Dist. Ct. V.I., Christiansted, 1989—. Active V.I. Bridge Team, 1971—. Jewish. Avocations: writing poetry and palindromes. Office: US District Court 3013 Est Golden Rock Christiansted VI 00820-4256

RESNICK, LAUREN B., psychology educator. EdD in Rsch. in Instrn., Harvard U., 1962; doctorate (hon.), U. Geneva, 1991. With dept. psychology U. Pitts., 1966—; dir. Learning Rsch. & Devel. Ctr., U. Pitts.,

1977—. Author, editor chpts. to books; contbr. articles to profl. jours. Trustee Nat. Ctn. Edn. and the Economy, Harvard U. Bd. of Overseers, Ednl. Testing Svc., Carnegie Found. for the Advancement of Teaching. Recipient Disting. Svc. medal Teacher's Coll., Columbia U.; fellow Ctr. Advanced Study in the Behavioral Scis., 1976-77; vis. fellow Nat. Inst. Edn., 1974-75. Fellow AAAS, Am. Psychol. Assn. (divsn. exptl. psychology, devel. psychology, ednl. psychology, exptl. analysis of behavior, past pres. divsn. ednl. psychology); mem. Am. Ednl. Rsch. Assn. (past v.p. divsn. learning and instrn., pres. 1986—; Disting. Contbns. in Edn. award). Nat. Acad. Edn. Office: U Pitts Learning Rsch Devel Ctr 3939 O'Hara St Pittsburgh PA 15260*

RESNICK, MARCIA AYLENE, photographic artist, educator; b. Bklyn., Nov. 21, 1950; d. Herbert Leonard and Sonia Martha (Panich) R. BFA, Cooper Union, 1972; MFA, Calif. Inst. Arts, 1973. Adj. instr. photography Queens Coll., CUNY, 1973-79, NYU, 1974-76, Cooper Union, N.Y.C., 1976, Internat. Ctr. Photography, N.Y.C., 1979-82, Pratt Inst., Manhattanville (N.Y.) Coll., 1987-88, La Guardia Comml. Coll., CUNY, 1988, Staten Island Coll., CUNY, 1988. One-woman shows include Gallery 115, Santa Cruz, Calif., 1974, Galerie Ricke, Cologne, Fed. Republic Germany, 1976, 78, Suzan Penzner, N.Y.C, 1976, Photoworks Gallery, The Fine Arts Bldg., N.Y.C., 1977, Lightworks Gallery, Syracuse, N.Y., 1977, Gotham Book Mart, N.Y.C., 1978, Night Gallery, N.Y.C., 1984, Ideé Gallery, Toronto, Ont., Can., 1985, U. Dallas, 1987; exhibited in group shows at Harvard Fogg Mus., Boston, 1974, Sidney Janis Gallery, N.Y.C., 1975, Tex. Ctr. for Photographic Studies, 1975, Rene Block Gallery, N.Y.C., 1975, Light Gallery, N.Y.C., 1975, San Francisco Mus. Modern Art, 1975, 85, Hallwalls, Buffalo, 1976, Visual Studies Workshop, Rochester, N.Y., 1977, L.A. Inst. Contemporary Art, 1978, Art Inst. Chgo., 1978, George Eastman House, Rochester, 1978, Friends of Photography, Carmel, Calif., 1980, The Kitchen, N.Y.C., 1980, U. Guelph, Ont., 1981, Gray Art Gallery, N.Y.C., 1981, P.S.I., N.Y.C., 1981, Mus. Fine Arts, Houston, 1983, Queens Mus., 1986, Wadsworth Athenaeum, Hartford, Conn., 1991, NYU, 1994; author: Tahitian Eve, 1975, See, 1975, Landscape, 1975, Re-visions, 1978. Nat. Endowment for Arts grantee, 1975, 78, Creative Artists Pub. Svc. Program grantee, 1977. Mem. Soc. for Photographic Edn., Coll. Art Assn., Nat. Art Edn. Assn., Visual Studies Workshop (Rochester). Home: 2 Grove St New York NY 10014-5315

RESNICK, MILTON, artist; b. Bratslav, Russia, Jan. 7, 1917. Student, Pratt Inst., 1932, Am. Artists Sch., 1933-37. Tchr. Pratt Inst., NYU, U. Wis., R.I. Sch. Design, N.Y. Studio Sch., Barnard Coll., Va. Commonwealth U., U. Calif., Berkeley, 1954—. One man shows include M.H. de Young Mus., San Francisco, 1955, Poindexter Gallery, N.Y., 1955, 57, 59, 75, Ellison Gallery, Fort Worth, 1959, Holland-Goldowsky Gallery, Chgo., 1959, Howard Wise Gallery, Cleve., N.Y., 1960, 61, 64, Feiner Gallery, N.Y., 1962, 63, 64, Zabriskie Gallery, Provincetown, Mass., 1963, Madison Art Ctr., Wis., 1967, Reed Coll., Portland, Oreg., 1968, Arden Anderson Gallery, Edgartown, Mass., 1969, Roswell Mus. and Art Ctr., N. Mex., 1971, Fort Worth Art Ctr., 1971, Max Hutchinson Gallery, N.Y., 1972, 77, 79, 80, 82, Kent State U., Ohio, 1973, Robert Miller Gallery, N.Y., 1979, 85, 86, 88, 91, 92, Gruenebaum Gallery, N.Y., 1983, San Jose State U., Calif., 1983, Mus. Contemporary Art, Houston, 1985, Hand in Hand Galleries, N.Y., 1985, Galerie Biedermann, Munich, 1986, Galerie Urban, Nagoya, 1986, Galerie Montenay, Delsol, Paris, 1987, Meredith Long Gallery, Houston, 1985, 87, Compassrose Gallery, Chgo., 1987, Daniel Weinberg Gallery, 1988, d.p. Fong and Spratt Galleries, San Jose, Calif., 1992; exhibited in numerous group shows, N.Y.C., Tex., Pa., Ill., Ohio, Minn., N.C., Mich., Conn., Washington, Calif.; represented in permanent collections Met. Mus. Art, N.Y., Guggenheim Mus., N.Y., Milw. Art Mus., Nat. Mus. Am. Art at the Smithsonian, Akron Art Inst., Australian Nat. Gallery, Mus. Modern Art N.Y., Nat. Gallery Art, Washington, Nat. Collection Fine Arts, Washington, Calif. Mus. Fine Arts, Mil. Art Ctr., Bundy Art Gallery, N.Y.U., Whitney Mus. Am. Arts, N.Y., U. Calif. Art Gallery, Reed Coll., Oreg., Weatherspoon Gallery, Cleve. Mus. Art, Roswell Mus. and Art Ctr., N. Mex., Honolulu Acad. Arts, Nat. Gallery Can., Fort Worth Art Mus. Office: 87 Eldridge St New York NY 10002-5201

RESNICK, MYRON J., insurance company executive, lawyer; b. Louisville, July 13, 1931; s. Harry C. and Sybil G. (Glick) R.; m. Alicia M. Ward, Dec. 16, 1967; children—Hugh, Clay, David. Bs in Econs., U. Pa., 1953; J.D., U. Mich., 1956. Various positions Allstate Ins. Co., Northbrook, Ill., 1959-88, sr. v.p., treas. bd. dirs., 1989-95; chmn. bd. Federated Ins. Co. Ltd. (U.K.), Sale, Cheshire, Eng., 1979-81; dir. Allstate Ins. Co. Ltd. (U.K.), Sale; pres. Allstate Investment Mgmt. Co. Mem. Chgo. exec. com. Anti-Defamation League, 1975—; bd. dirs. Chgo. Urban League, 1987—, St. Scholastica High Sch., Chgo., 1977-79; trustee George Williams Coll., Downers Grove, Ill., 1981-93, chmn. bd. trustees, 1991-93; trustee Aurora U., 1993—; bd. advisors Inst. Law and Econs. U. Pa., 1994—. With U.S. Army, 1956-58. Mem. ABA (resource devel. coun.), Chgo. Bar Assn., Ill. Bar Assn., Assn. Life Ins. Counsel, Chgo. Mortgage Attys. Assn. (bd. dirs. 1965-75), Reform Club (London).

RESNICK, PAUL R., research chemist; b. N.Y.C., Apr. 7, 1934; married, 1966; 1 child. BA, Swarthmore Coll., 1955; PhD in Organic Chemistry, Cornell U., 1961. Fellow U. Calif., Berkeley, 1960-62; from chemist to sr. rsch. chemist E.I. DuPont De Nemours & Co., Inc., 1962-74, rsch. assoc., 1974-85, rsch. fellow, 1985-88, sr. rsch. fellow, 1988—. Mem. Am. Chem. Soc. (Award for Creative Work in Fluorine Chemistry 1995). Office: Dupont Polymers PO Box 80293 Wilmington DE 19880-0293*

RESNICK, ROBERT, physicist, educator; b. Balt., Jan. 11, 1923; s. Abraham and Anna (Dubin) R.; m. Mildred Saltzman, Oct. 14, 1945; children—Trudy, Abby, Regina. A.B., Johns Hopkins U., 1943, Ph.D. (Pres.'s Fund scholar 1946-49), 1949. Physicist NACA, Cleve., 1944-46; asst. prof., assoc. prof. physics U. Pitts., 1949-56; assoc. prof., prof. physics Rensselaer Poly. Inst., Troy, N.Y., 1956-93; prof. emeritus, 1993—; chmn. interdisciplinary sci. curriculum Rensselaer Poly. Inst., Troy, N.Y., 1973-88, Edward P. Hamilton Disting. prof. sci., 1975-93; hon. research fellow Harvard U., 1964-65; Fulbright prof. Peru, 1971; hon. vis. prof. Peoples Republic of China, 1981, 85; mem. Commn. on Coll. Physics, 1960-68; commencement speaker Rensselaer Poly. Inst., 1993. Author: A Manual for Laboratory Physics, 1954, (with D. Halliday) Physics, 1960, 3d edit., 1978, 4th edit., 1991, extended version, 1986, 2d edit. extended version, 1991, Introduction to Special Relativity, 1968, (with R. Eisberg) Notes on Quantum Theory, 1968, Notes on Modern Physics, 1969, Quantum Physics of Atoms, Molecules, Solids, Nuclei and Particles, 1974, 2d edit., 1985, (with D. Halliday) Fundamentals of Physics, 1970, 4th edit., 1993, extended version, 1988, 2d edit., 1993, (with others) Student Study Guide for Physics, 1970, 5th edit., 1993, Basic Concepts in Relativity and Early Quantum Theory, 1972, 2d edit., 1985, Basic Concepts in Relativity, 1991; author: (with others) Sourcebook for Programmable Calculators, 1978, (with E. Derringh) Solutions to Physics Problems, 1980, 4th edit., 1992, (with K. Brownstein) Tests for Physics, 1987; books translated into numerous fgn. langs; mem. adv. bd., project staff: Physical Science for Non-Scientists, 1964-678, pub., 1968; co-dir.: Project Physics Demonstration Experiments, 1962-70; pub. project, 1970, Workshop on Apparatus for College Physics, 1964-65, 66, Videotapes in Physics Instruction, 1975-78, 1978; dir. project Physics Demonstration and Laboratory Apparatus Workshop, 1960-61; pub. project, 1961; adv editor: John Wiley & Sons, Inc., 1967-89, Macmillan Pubs., 1990-94; mem. U.S. adv. bd. Quantum joint USSR/USA sci. mag., 1989-93. Recipient Disting. Svc. citation Am. Assn. Physics Tchrs., 1967, Hans Christian Oersted medal, 1974, Esso award for outstanding teaching, 1953, Disting. Faculty award Rensselaer Poly. Inst., 1971; named to Hall of Fame, Balt. City Coll., 1989; Robert Resnick Ctr. for Physics established at Rensselaer Poly. Inst., 1993, Robert Resnick Ann. Sci. Lectr. series endowed, 1993. Fellow AAAS, Am. Phys. Soc.; mem. AAUP, Am. Assn. Physics Tchrs. (v.p. 1986, pres.-elect 1987, pres. 1988), Am. Soc. Engring. Edn., Am. Inst. Physics (governing bd. 1987-90), Textbook Author Assn. (coun. 1990-93), Phi Beta Kappa, Sigma Xi. Rsch. pubis. in aerodynamics, nuclear physics, atomic physics, upper atmosphere physics, history of physics, physics edn. Home: 13 Oxford Rd Troy NY 12180-7053

RESNICK, STEWART ALLEN, diversified company executive; b. Jersey City, Dec. 24, 1936; s. David and Yetta (Goldmaker) R.; children from previous marriage: Jeffrey Brian, Ilene Sue, William Jay; m. Lynda Rae

Harris, Nov. 26, 1972; children: Jonathon Charles Sinay, Jason Daniel Sinay. BS, UCLA, 1959, LLB, 1962. Chmn. Roll Internat. Corp., L.A., 1958—, The Franklin Mint, Franklin Center, Pa., 1985—; chmn. Teleflora, L.A. Bd. trustees Bard Coll., N.Y.C.; acquistions com. Nat. Gallery, Washington; co-chmn. mktg. dept.; adv. bd., mem. Mgmt. Edn. Coun., The Wharton Sch., U. Pa.; exec. com. mem. Mayor's Alliance for a Safer L.A. Mem. Young Pres.'s Orgn. Avocations: health and fitness related activities. Office: The Franklin Mint US Rt 1 Media PA 19091

RESNIK, FRANK EDWARD, tobacco company executive; b. Pleasant Unity, Pa., Oct. 14, 1928; s. Vincent and Augusta (Mauser) R.; m. Elizabeth Patterson, June 21, 1952; children—David A, Mary Ann, Anne Margaret. BS in Chemistry, St. Vincent Coll., Latrobe, Pa., 1952; MS, U. Richmond, Va., 1955; DSc (hon.), St. Vincent Coll., 1985. With Philip Morris Inc., 1952-91; v.p. ops. adminstrn., then v.p. tobacco ops. Philip Morris Inc., N.Y.C., 1976-80; corp. v.p., exec. v.p. tobacco tech. group Philip Morris Inc., 1980-81, pres. tobacco tech. group, 1981-84; pres., chief exec. officer Philip Morris U.S.A., 1984-89, chmn., 1989-91; ret. Philip Morris Inc., N.Y.C., 1991; bd. dirs. Philip Morris Inc., Philip Morris Cos., Horatio Alger Assoc., Nat. Tobacco Edn. Inst., 1985-90; bd. dirs., chmn. exec. com. Tobacco Inst., 1985-90. Contbr. 30 sci. articles to profl. jours. Bd. dirs. Benedictine High Sch., Richmond, Va., 1965-67, St. Vincent Coll., 1988—, Horatio Alger Assn., 1989—; mem. St. Edwards Sch. Bd., Richmond, 1972-75; bd. assocs. U. Richmond, 1986-90; bd. dirs. Found. for State Legislatures, 1986-90, With AUS, 1946-48, 51. Recipient Horatio Alger award, 1988, Nat. Assn. Intercollegiate Athletics award, 1992; named Letterman of Distinction St. Vincent Coll., 1974, 92. Mem. AAAS, NAM (bd. dirs. 1988-91), Am. Chem. Soc., N.Y. Acad. Scis., Am. Inst. Chemists, Internat. Tobacco Info. Ctr. (London, chmn. 1988-90), Innis Arden Country Club (Greenwich, Conn.), Jonathan's Landing Country Club (Jupiter, Fla.). Roman Catholic. Achievements include 7 patents. Home: 3327 Southern Cay Dr Jupiter FL 33477-1376 Office: Philip Morris USA 120 Park Ave New York NY 10017-5523

RESNIK, HARVEY LEWIS PAUL, psychiatrist; b. Buffalo, Apr. 6, 1930; s. Samuel and Celia (Greenberg) R.; m. Audrey Ruth Frey, Aug. 30, 1964 (dec. 1993); children: Rebecca Gabrielle, Henry Seth Maccabee, Jessica Ruth. B.A. magna cum laude, U. Buffalo, 1951; M.D., Columbia, 1955; grad., Phila. Psychoanalytic Inst., 1967. Diplomate: Am. Bd. Psychiatry and Neurology. Intern Phila. Gen. Hosp., 1955-56, resident in surgery, 1956-57; resident in psychiatry Jackson Meml. Hosp., Miami, Fla., 1959-61; fellow U. Pa. Hosp., 1961-62, mem. staff, 1962-67; instr. Sch. Medicine, U. Pa., 1962-66; instr. med. hypnosis Sch. Medicine, U. Pa. (Grad. Sch. Medicine), 1963-66; clin. dir. psychiatry E. J. Meyer Meml. Hosp., Buffalo, 1967; dir. psychiatry E. J. Meyer Meml. Hosp., 1968; assoc. prof. psychiatry Sch. Medicine, SUNY at Buffalo, 1967, prof., 1968-70, dep. chmn. dept. psychiatry, 1968-69; chief Nat. Center for Studies of Suicide Prevention, NIMH, 1969-74, chief mental health emergencies sect., 1974-76; with Reproductive Biology Research Found., St. Louis, 1971; clin. prof. psychiatry Sch. Medicine, George Washington U., 1969—; dir. Human Behavior Found., 1975—; lectr. Sch. Medicine, Johns Hopkins, 1969-74; adj. prof. Johns Hopkins U. Sch. Pub. Health, 1981-82; prof. community health Fed. City Coll., 1971-75; med. dir. Human Behavior Found., 1975—, Johns Hopkins U. Compulsive Gambling Ctr. (now Wash. Ctr. for Path. Gambling); med. dir. U. Alcohol and Substance Abuse Program, 1986—; instr. Del. Valley Group Therapy Inst.; vis. prof. Katholieke U., Leuven, Belgium, 1986—; cons. to Sec.-Gen. Ministry of Health, Belgium, 1986—; NATO, 1986-87, also fellow, Ten Kerselaere Psycho-Geriatric Hosp.; bd. dirs. Internat. Health Ctr., Belgium, Human Behavior Found.; cons. various hosps. and orgns. Author: Suicidal Behaviors: Diagnosis and Management, 1968, 2d edit., 1994, (with M. E. Wolfgang) Treatment of the Sexual Offender, 1971, Sexual Behaviors: Social, Clinical and Legal Aspects, 1972, (with B. Hathrone) Suicide Prevention in the Seventies, 1973, (with H.L. Ruben) Emergency Psychiatric Care, 1974, (with others) The Prediction of Suicide, 1974, Emergency and Disaster Management, 1976; (with J.T. Mitchell) Emergency Response to Crisis, 1981; Editor: Bull. Suicidology, 1969-74; Contbr. (with others) articles on hypnosis, sexual offenders, marriage and sexual dysfunction treatment, suicide, death and dying, emergency psychiatric care. Mem. Addictions Adv. Bd. Prince Georges County, 1980-85. Served to capt. USAF, 1957-59, ETO-Middle East; capt. USNR; ret. Decorated officer in the Order King Leopold, Belgium, 1990. Fellow Am. Coll. Psychiatrists, Am. Psychiat. Assn. (life); mem. Med-Chi of Md., Prince Georges County Med. Assn., Phila. Psychoanalytic Soc., Columbia Med. Alumni Assn. (bd. dirs.), Phi Beta Kappa, Beta Sigma Rho (grand vice warden 1963), Cosmos club (Washington). Jewish. Office: Air Rights Ctr # 1300W 7315 Wisconsin Ave Bethesda MD 20814-3202 also: Univ Med Center 4700 Berwyn House Rd # 201 College Park MD 20740-2474

RESNIK, LINDA ILENE, marketing and information executive, consultant; b. Dallas, Oct. 26, 1950; d. Harold and Reatha (Gordon) R. BJ in Broadcast Journalism, U. Mo., 1971; MA in Journalism, U. North Tex., 1977, MBA in Mktg., 1980. News and documentary producer Sta. KDFW-TV, Dallas, 1971-73; mktg.-info. officer Dallas County Community Coll. Dist., 1973-79; dir. mktg. The Learning Channel, Washington, 1980-82; dir. Nat. Narrowcast Service, Pub. Broadcasting Service, Washington, 1982-85; exec. dir. Am. Soc. Info. Sci., Washington, 1985-89, White House Conf. on Libr. and Info. Svcs., Washington, 1990—; mem. adv. com. ALA Library/Book Fellows Project; fellow Ctr. for Info. and Communication Scis., Ball State U.; mem. U.S. exec. com. U. of the World; mktg., tng. and telecommunications cons. to ednl. assns., others. Writer and editor college-level study guides; scriptwriter college credit TV courses. Youth activities coordinator YMCA, Dallas, 1975-78; spl. event organizer Am. Cancer Soc., Dallas, 1976-77; com. leader Goals for Dallas, 1978-80. Recipient Best TV Feature Story award AP, Tex., 1973. Mem. Am. Soc. Assn. Execs., Am. Soc. Info. Sci. (pub. bull. 1985-89), Women in Cable, Info. Inst., Am. Mktg. Assn., Washington Met. Cable Club. Avocations: travel, racquet sports, reading, theater. Office: 3533 Piedmont Dr Plano TX 75075-6254

RESNIK, PETER L., lawyer; b. New Britain, Conn., Feb. 4, 1945; m. Kathleen Ann Murphy; children: Rebecca, Elizabeth, Benjamin. BA, Yale U., 1967; JD cum laude, Boston U., 1970. Bar: Mass. 1970. Ptnr. McDermott, Will & Emory, Boston. Editor: Boston U. Law Rev., 1968-70. Mem. ABA, Mass. Bar Assn. Office: McDermott Will & Emery 75 State St Ste 1700 Boston MA 02109-1812

RESNIK, REGINA, operatic singer; b. N.Y.C., Aug. 30, 1924; d. Sam and Ruth R.; m. Harry W. Davis, July 18, 1946; 1 son, Michael Philip; m. Arbit Blatas, 1975. B.A., Hunter Coll., 1942. condr. seminars on opera New Sch. for Social Research. Debut as Lady Macbeth, 1942; soprano debut Met. Opera Co., N.Y.C., 1944; mezzo-soprano debut, Met. Opera Co., N.Y.C., 1946; regular guest, Vienna Staatsoper, La Scala, Milan, Covent Garden, Salzburg, Deutsche Oper, Berlin, Teatro Colon, Buenos Aires, Bayreuth Festival, Germany, Munich Staatsoper, Chgo., Phila., San Francisco, others; co-dir., starred in: Carmen, Hamburg Opera, 1971, Electra, 1971, Falstaff at Nat. Opera Poland, 1975; starred in broadway prodn. Cabaret, 1987-88 (nominated for Tony award), prize-winning documentary Ghetto of Venice, PBS, 1983-87; has recorded extensively. Decorated comdr. French Acad. Arts, Scis. and Letters; recipient awards including U.S. Pres.'s medal, 40th Anniversary medal San Francisco Opera, 1982; named Kammersänger in Austria. Office: Am Guild Musical Artists 1727 Broadway New York NY 10019-5214*

RESNIK, ROBERT, medical educator; b. New Haven, Dec. 7, 1938; s. Nathan Alfred and Elsie (Hershman) R.; m. Lauren Brahms, Oct. 29, 1966; children: Andrew Scott, Jamie Layne. BA, Yale U., 1960; MD, Case Western Res. U., 1965. Intern in internal medicine Mt. Sinai Hosp., Cleve., 1965-66; resident in ob-gyn. Yale U. Sch. Medicine, 1966-70; asst. prof. Sch. Medicine U. Calif., San Diego, 1974-78, assoc. prof., 1978-82, prof. reproductive medicine, 1982—, chmn. dept., 1982-95, dean clin. affairs, 1988-90, dean admissions, 1995—; cons. Nat. Heart, Lung and Blood Inst. NIH, Washington, 1987; mem. exec. com. Coun. Residency Edn. Ob-Gyn, Washington, 1988-94, residency rev. com., 1988-94. Editor: (textbook) Maternal-Fetal Medicine: Principles and Practice, 1984, 3d edit., 1994; contbr. numerous articles to profl. jours. Major U.S. Army, 1970-72. Rsch. grantee Nat. Found., NIH. Fellow Am. Coll. Obstetrics and Gynecology, Pacific Coast Obstet. and Gynecol. Soc.; mem. Soc. Gynecologic Investigation (coun. 1983-88), Perinatal Rsch. Soc. (pres. 1985), Am. Gynecologic and Obstet. Soc., San Diego Gynecol. Soc. (pres. 1982), Yale Club. Office: U Calif San Diego Med Ctr # 8433 200 W Arbor Dr Bldg 8433 San Diego CA 92103-1911

RESNIKOFF, GEORGE JOSEPH, university dean, mathematics and statistics educator emeritus; b. N.Y.C., Mar. 25, 1915; s. Isador and Jenny (Rapaport) R.; m. Florence Lisa Herman, Apr. 4, 1943; 1 son, David. B.S., U. Chgo., 1950; M.S., Stanford U., 1952, Ph.D., 1955. Assoc. prof. Ill. Inst. Tech., 1957-61, prof., 1961-64; prof. math. and statistics Calif. State U. at Hayward, from 1964, now prof. emeritus, dean of sci., 1969-72, dean grad. studies, 1972-80. Contbr. articles to profl. jours. Served with AUS, 1942-46. Fellow AAAS, Am. Statis. Assn., Inst. Math. Statistics. Office: 25800 Carlos Bee Blvd Hayward CA 94542-3000

RESO, ANTHONY, geologist, earth resources economist; b. London, Eng., Aug. 10, 1934; s. Harry and Marion (Gerth) R.; came to U.S., 1940, naturalized, 1952. AB, Columbia Coll., N.Y.C., 1954; MA, Columbia U., 1955; postgrad. U. Cin., 1956-57; PhD (fellow) Rice U., 1960; postgrad. Grad. Sch. Bus. U. Houston, 1964-68. Instr. geology Queens Coll., Flushing, N.Y., 1954; geologist Atlantic Richfield Corp., Midland, Tex., 1955-56; asst. prof. geology and curator invertebrate paleontology Pratt Mus., Amherst (Mass.) Coll., 1959-62; staff research geologist Tenneco Oil Co., Houston, 1962-86; geol. mgr. Peak Prodn. Co., Houston, 1986—, v.p., 1988—. Cons. in geol. research Tenn. Gas and Oil Co., 1960-61; lectr. U. Houston, 1962-65; vis. prof. Rice U., 1980; mem. bd. advisers Gulf Univs. Research Corp., Galveston, Tex., 1967-75, chmn., 1968-69; dir. Stewardship Properties, Houston, 1968—. Recipient research grants Am. Assn. Petroleum Geologists, 1958, 59, Geol. Soc. Am., 1958, Eastman Fund, 1962; NSF fellow, 1959. Fellow Geol. Soc. Am. (com. investments 1984—, chmn. 1985-92, budget com. 1993—), AAAS; mem. Am. Assn. Petroleum Geologists (life, com. convs. 1977-83, chmn. 1980-83, gen. chmn. nat. conv. 1979, com. on investments 1982-88, chmn. com. group on investments 1986-88, treas. 1986-88; Disting. service award 1985, found. trustee assoc. 1991), Paleontol. Soc., SEPM Soc. for Sedimentary Geology (com. on investments 1990—, chmn. 1992-95), Paleontol. Rsch. Instn., Tex. Acad. Sci., Houston Geol. Soc. (v.p. 1973-75, pres. 1975-76, chmn. constn. revision com. 1981; Disting. service award 1985), English-Speaking Union U.S. (dir. Houston chpt. 1978—, v.p. 1982-88, 94—, mem. scholarship com. 1988—, chmn. 1991—), Varsity C Club, Sigma Xi, Sigma Gamma Epsilon, Beta Theta Pi. Episcopalian. Contbr. profl. jours. Home: 1801 Huldy St Houston TX 77019-5754 Office: care Peak Prodn Co PO Box 130785 Houston TX 77219-0785

RESOR, STANLEY ROGERS, lawyer; b. N.Y.C., Dec. 5, 1917; s. Stanley Burnet and Helen (Lansdowne) R.; m. Jane Lawler Pillsbury, Apr. 4, 1942 (dec. 1995); children: Stanley R., Charles P., John L., Edmund L., William B., Thomas S., James P. B.A., Yale U., 1939, LL.B., 1946. Bar: N.Y. 1947. Assoc., then ptnr. firm Debevoise & Plimpton, N.Y.C., 1946-65, 71-73, 79-87, of counsel, 1988-90; undersec. Dept. Army, 1965, sec., 1965-71, ambassador negotiations for Mut. and Balanced Force Reductions in Central Europe, 1973-78; undersec. for policy Dept. Def., 1978-79. Fellow Yale Corp., 1979-86. Served to maj. AUS, 1942-45. Decorated Silver Star, Bronze Star, Purple Heart; recipient George C. Marshall award Assn. U.S. Army, 1974, Sylvanus Thayer award Assn. Graduates of U.S. Mil. Acad., 1984. Mem. ABA, Assn. of Bar of City of N.Y. (chmn. com. internat. arms control and security affairs 1983-86), Atlantic Coun. (bd. dirs.), Arms Control Assn. (chmn. bd.), UN Assn. U.S.A. (nat. coun.), Coun. Fgn. Rels., Lawyers Alliance for World Security (bd. dirs.), Internat. Inst. Strategic Studies. Republican. Episcopalian. Home: 809 Weed St New Canaan CT 06840-4023 Office: Debevoise & Plimpton 875 3rd Ave New York NY 10022-6225

RESTANI, JANE A., federal judge; b. San Francisco, Feb. 27, 1948; d. Roy J. and Emilia C. Restani. BA, U. Calif., Berkeley, 1969; JD, U. Calif., Davis, 1973. Bar: Calif., 1973. Trial atty. U.S. Dept. Justice, Washington, 1973-76, asst. chief comml. litigation sect., 1976-80, dir. comml. litigation sect., 1980-83; judge U.S. Ct. Internat. Trade, N.Y.C., 1983—. Mem. Order of Coif. Office: US Ct Internat Trade 1 Federal Plz New York NY 10278-0001

RESTER, ALFRED CARL, JR., physicist; b. New Orleans, July 11, 1940; s. Alfred Carl and Willietta (Voth) R.; m. Blanche Sue Bing, June 20, 1964 (div. Jan. 20, 1985); children: Andrea Dawn, Karen Alane; m. Sherry Alice Warren, Dec. 12, 1985. BS, Miss. Coll., 1962; MS, U. N.Mex., 1964; PhD, Vanderbilt U., 1969. Postdoctoral fellow U. Delft, Netherlands, 1969-70, scientist first class, 1970-71; guest prof. U. Bonn (Germany) Dept. Physics, 1972-74; asst. prof. Emory U., Dept. Physics, Atlanta, 1975-76; assoc. prof. Tenn. Tech. U., Dept. Physics, Cookeville, Tenn., 1976-77; vis. assoc. prof. U. Fla., Dept. Physics, Gainesville, 1978-81; assoc. rsch. scientist U. Fla. Space Astronomy Lab., Gainesville, 1981-88; U. Fla. Inst. for Astrophysics and Planetary Exploration, Alachua, 1988-93; pres., CEO Constellation Tech. Corp., St. Petersburg, Fla., 1992—; cons. Lockheed Ga., Marietta, 1976, Oak Ridge (Tenn.) Nat. Lab., 1976-77. Editor: High Energy Radiation Background in Space, 1989; contbr. articles to profl. jours. Recipient Antarctica Svc. medal NSF-USN, 1988; grantee various fed. agys. Mem. AAAS, Am. Phys. Soc., Am. Astron. Soc., Sigma Xi Sci. Rsch. Soc. Avocations: writing fiction, fishing, nature walks. Office: Constellation Tech Corp 9887 4th St N Ste 100 Saint Petersburg FL 33702

RESTIVO, JAMES JOHN, JR., lawyer; b. Pitts., Aug. 15, 1946; s. James J. and Dorothy (Ardolino) R.; m. Gail Sharon Hackenburg, July 11, 1970; 4 children. BA in History, U. Pa., 1968; JD, Georgetown U., 1971. Bar: Pa. 1971, U.S. Dist. Ct. (we. and ea. dists.) Pa. 1971, U.S. Ct. Appeals (3d cir.) 1971, U.S. Supreme Ct. 1979. Ptnr. Reed, Smith, Shaw & McClay, Pitts., 1979—, head litigation group, 1986—. Mem. editl. staff Georgetown Law Rev., 1970-71. Mem. ABA, Acad. Trial Lawyers Allegheny County, Allegheny County Bar Assn., Pa. Economy League (Western divsn.). Home: 209 Deer Meadow Dr Pittsburgh PA 15241-2253 Office: Reed Smith Shaw & McClay 435 6th Ave Pittsburgh PA 15219-1886

RESTON, JAMES BARRETT, retired newspaper publishing executive, author; b. Clydebank, Scotland, Nov. 3, 1909; s. James and Johanna (Irving) R.; came to U.S., 1910; m. Sarah Jane Fulton, Dec. 24, 1935; children: Richard Fulton, James Barrett, Thomas Busey. Student Vale of Leven Acad., Alexandria, Scotland, 1914-20; BS, U. Ill., 1932, LLD (hon.), 1962; LittD, Colgate U., 1951, Oberlin Coll., 1955, Rutgers U., 1957; LLD (hon.), Dartmouth, 1959, N.Y. U., 1961, Boston Coll., 1963, Brandeis U., 1964; LHD, Kenyon Coll., 1962, Columbia, 1963, U. Mich., 1965; LittD, U. N.C., 1968, Williams Coll., 1968; LHD,Harvard, 1970, Stanford, 1972, U. Utah, 1973, Kent State U., 1974, Colby Coll., 1975, Yale U., 1977, Miami U., Oxford, Ohio; hon. degrees U. Md., Northeastern U., 1976, U. Glasgow, 1983. With Springfield (Ohio) Daily News, 1932-33; with publicity dept. Ohio State U., 1933; publicity dir. Cin. Baseball Club, 1934; reporter A.P., N.Y.C., 1934-37, London, 1937-39; reporter London bur. N.Y. Times, 1939-41, Washington bur., 1941-89, chief Washington corr., bur. chief, 1953-64, assoc. editor, 1964-68, exec. editor, 1968-69, v.p., 1969-74, columnist, cons., 1974-89, also dir. N.Y. Times Co., ret., 1989; co-chmn. bd. The Vineyard Gazette, 1968—. Author: The Artillery of the Press, 1967, Sketches in the Sand, 1967, Washington, 1986, Deadline, 1991. Recipient Pulitzer prize for nat. corr., 1945, nat. reporting, 1957, Overseas Press Club award for interpretation internat. news, 1949, 51, 53, George Polk Meml. award for nat. reporting, 1954; U. Mo. medal, 1961, J.P. Zenger award, 1964, Elijah Parrish Lovejoy award, 1974, fourth Estate award Nat Press Club, 1974; Presdl. Medal of Liberty award, 1986; Helen B. Bernstein Excellence in Journalism award, 1988, Franklin D. Roosevelt Freedom of Speech medal, 1991; decorated Legion d'Honneur (France); ordre National du Mérite (France); Order St. Olav (Norway), Order of Merit (Chile); comdr. Order Brit. Empire. Clubs: Century (N.Y.C.); Chevy Chase (Md.).•

RESWICK, JAMES BIGELOW, former government official, rehabilitation engineer, educator; b. Ellwood City, Pa., Apr. 16, 1922; s. Maurice and Katherine (Parker) R.; children: James Bigelow, David Parker (dec.), Pamela Reswick; m. Irmtraud Orthlies Hoelzerkopf, Dec., 27, 1973. SBME, MIT, 1943; SM, Mass. Inst. Tech., 1948, ScD, 1952; DEng (hon.), Rose Poly. Inst., 1968. Asst. prof., then assoc. prof., head machine design and graphics div. MIT, 1948-59; Leonard Case prof. engring., dir. Engring. Design Ctr., Case Western Res. U., 1959-70; prof. biomed. engring. and orthopaedics U.

So. Calif., also dir. of rsch. dept. orthopaedics, 1970-80; assoc. dir. tech. Nat. Inst. Handicapped Rsch., U.S. Dept. Edn.; dir. VA Rehab. R & D Evaluation Unit VA Med. Ctr., Washington, 1984-88; dir. rsch. scis. Nat. Inst. on Disability and Rehab. Rsch. U.S. Dept. Edn., Washington, 1989-94; engring. cons. on automatic control, product devel., automation and bio-med. engring. Mem. com. prosthetics R & D Nat. Acad. Scis., 1962—; chmn. design and devel. com.; mem. bd. rev. Army R & D Office, 1965—; mem. applied physiology and biomed. engring. study sect. NIH, 1972—. Author: (with C.K. Taft) Introduction to Dynamic Systems, 1967; also articles.; Editor: (with F.T. Hambrecht) Functional Electrical Stimulation, 1977; series on engring. design, 1963—. Chmn. Mayor's Commn. for Urban Transp., Cleve., 1969. Served to lt. (j.g.) USNR, 1943-46, PTO. Decorated officer Yugoslav Flag with golden wreath medal (Yugoslavia), 1990; recipient Product Engring. Master Designer award, 1969, Isabelle and Leonard H. Goldenson award United Cerebral Palsy Assn., 1973; NSR sr. postdoctoral fellow Imperial Coll., London, 1957. Fellow IEEE, Am. Inst. Med. and Biological Engring. (founder); mem. ASME (honor award for best paper 1956, sr. mem.), Am. Soc. Engring. Edn., Instrument Soc. Am., Biomed. Engring. Soc. (sr. mem., pres. 1973, dir.), Am. Acad. Orthopedic Surgeons (asso.), Inst. Medicine of Nat. Acad. Scis., Nat. Acad. Engring., Internat. Soc. Orthotics and Prosthetics, Orthopaedics Research Soc., Rehab. Engring. Soc. N.Am. (founding pres.), Sigma XI. Patentee in field. Home: 1003 Dead Run Dr Mc Lean VA 22101-2120

RESZKA, ALFONS, computer systems architect; b. Imielin, Poland, Dec. 17, 1924; s. Alfons and Maria (Galazka) R.; m. Betty Reszka; children: Ann, Elizabeth, Alfred, Catherine. B.S., U. London, 1954; M.S.E.E., Northwestern U., 1960, Ph.D., 1976. Engr. Brit. Jeffrey Diamond, Wakefield, Eng., 1954-55; lectr. Bradford Tech. Coll., Eng., 1955-56; engr. A.C. Nielson, Chgo., 1956-59; with Teletype Corp., Skokie, Ill., 1959-80, project dir., 1969-75, sr. staff engr., 1975-80; cons. computer architecture, computer networks and data base mgmt. systems Bell Labbs., Naperville, Ill., 1980-85; prof. info. sci. North Central Coll., Naperville, 1983-86; computer systems cons. ARC, Wheaton, Ill., 1986—. Patentee in electronics. Mem. IEEE, Computer Soc., Inst. of Computer Architecture. Home: 1090 Creekside Dr Wheaton IL 60187-6173 Office: ARC 1090 Creekside Dr Wheaton IL 60187-6173

RETALLACK, GREGORY JOHN, geologist, educator; b. Hobart, Australia, Nov. 8, 1951; came to U.S., 1977; s. Kenneth John Retallack and Moira Wynn (Dean) Gollan; m. Diane Alice Johnson, May 21, 1981; children: Nicholas John, Jeremy Douglas. B.A., Macquarie U., Sydney, 1973; B.Sc. with honors, U. New Eng., 1974, Ph.D., 1978. Vis. asst. prof. Northern Ill. U., Dekalb, 1977-78; vis. scholar Ind. U., Bloomington, 1978-81; asst. prof. U. Oreg., Eugene, 1981-86, assoc. prof., 1986-92, prof., 1992—. Author: Geological Excursion Guide to the Sea Cliffs North of Sydney, 1978, Late Eocene and Oligocene Paleosols from Badlands National Park, South Dakota, 1983, Soils of the Past, 1990, Miocene Paleosols and Ape Habitats in Pakistan and Kenya, 1991; contbr. numerous articles in field to profl. jours. Grantee NSF, 1979—, Wenner-Gren Found., 1983. Mem. Geol. Soc. Am., Geol. Soc. Australia, Bot. Soc. Am., Paleontol. Soc. (pres. Pacific sect. 1986), Oreg. Acad. Sci. (pres. 1986), Soc. Econ. Paleontologists and Mineralogists, Sigma Xi (pres. U. Oreg. chpt. 1983-84). Home: 2715 Elinor St Eugene OR 97403-2513

RETHMEIER, KENNETH WAYNE, JR., publishing company executive; b. Lincoln, Nebr., Sept. 27, 1954; s. Kenneth Wayne and Patricia (Thompson) R.; m. Joyce Ellen Henning, Aug. 9, 1975; children: Elliott Henning, Claire Rose. BSBA, U. Nebr., 1975. Sales rep. Harcourt Brace Coll., Lincoln and Raleigh, N.C., 1977-83; mktg. dir. Harcourt Brace Coll., San Diego, 1983, acquisitions editor, 1984-87, exec. editor, 1987-91; pres. Harcourt Brace Profl. Pub., San Diego, 1991—. Office: Harcourt Brace Profl Pub 525 B St Ste 1900 San Diego CA 92101

RETHORE, BERNARD GABRIEL, diversified company executive; b. Bklyn., May 22, 1941; s. Francis Joseph and Katharine Eunice (MacDwyer) R.; BA, Yale U., 1962; MBA, U. Pa., 1967; m. Marilyn Irene Watt, Dec. 1, 1962; children: Bernard Michael, Tara Jean, Kevin Watt, Alexandra Marie, Rebecca Ann, Christopher Philip, Abigail Lyn. Assoc., McKinsey & Co., Inc., Washington, 1967, then sr. assoc., 1973; v.p./gen. mgr. Greer div. Microdot, Inc., Darien, Conn., 1973-77, v.p. ops. connector group, 1977-78, pres. bus. devel. group, 1978-82, pres. fastening systems and sealing devices groups, 1982-84, pres. Microdot Industries 1984-87, pres., chief exec. officer, 1988; pres. Microdot Europe Ltd., 1984-88; sr. v.p. Phelps Dodge Corp., Phoenix, 1989—; group exec. Phelps Dodge Industries, 1989-90, pres., 1990—; bd. dirs. Blue Cross/Blue Shield of Conn., 1989-90, Maytag Corp., 1994—; cons. U.S. Govt., UN; mem. Global Adv. Coun., Am. Grad. Sch. Internat. Mgmt., 1990—, chmn., 1991-94. Mem. dean's adv. bd. Wharton Sch. Bus., U. Pa., 1972-80; chmn. Emmaus adv. bd. Fairfield Prep. Sch.-Lauralton Hall Acad., 1981-85; elected mem. bd. fin. Town of Westport, Conn., 1986-90; trustee Ballet Arizona, 1989—, vice chmn. 1991—; bd. dirs. Boys Hope of Phoenix, 1989—; trustee Phoenix Country Day Sch., 1992—; trustee Am. Grad. Sch. Internat. Mgmt., 1994—. Served to capt., inf., AUS, 1962-65. Decorated Bronze Star. Mem. Nat. Assn. Mfrs. (bd. dirs. 1994—), Yale Club (N.Y.C.), Union League (Chgo.), Plaza Club (Phoenix), Elec. Mfrs. Club. Home: 6533 E Maverick Rd Paradise Vly AZ 85253-2632 Office: Phelps Dodge Corp 2600 N Central Ave 15th Fl Phoenix AZ 85004-3050

RETSINAS, NICOLAS P., federal official. BA in Economics, NYU; M in City Planning, Harvard U. Exec. dir. Housing and Mortgage Corp., R.I., 1987-93; asst. sec. for Housing-Fed. Housing Commr., Washington, 1993—; dir. policy for Gov. R.I., 1991; adj. assoc. prof. urban studies Brown U. Mem. Nat. Coun. State Housing Authorities (past sec.), Nat. Community Devel. Assn. (past pres.). Office: HUD Office of Housing 451 7th St SW Washington DC 20410-0001

RETTERER, BERNARD LEE, electronic engineering consultant; b. Waldo, Ohio, Sept. 23, 1930; s. Calvin C. and Gertrude S. (Kries) R.; m. Mary Susan Gaster, Dec. 22, 1951; children: John, Jeffrey, Laura. BSEE, Ohio No. U., 1952; MS in System Mgmt., George Washington U., 1972. Registered profl. engr., Ohio. Program mgr. RCA, Cherry Hill, N.J., 1953-65; v.p. engring. ARINC Rsch., Annapolis, Md., 1965-90; Del. to Internat. Electrotechnical Commn., 1975-85; cons. Inst. for Def. Analyses, Alexandria, Va., 1990—. Contbr. 39 tech. articles on maintainability to profl. jours. Mem. adv. bd. Embry-Riddle U., Daytona Beach, Fla., 1988-90, Anne Arundel Coll., Arnold, Md., 1987-90. Mem. IEEE (v.p. tech-ops. 1982), Operation Rsch. Soc., Armed Forces Prep. Assn., Armed Forces Comms. Assn. Achievements include development (with others) of maintainability prediction technique for electronic equipment; research into the use of information content of failure symptoms as a predictor of diagnostic time. Home: 37 Whittier Pkwy Severna Park MD 21146

RETTIG, RICHARD ALLEN, social sciences educator, policy analyst, administrator; b. Seattle, Sept. 14, 1936; s. Roy Edward and Mildred Januara (Hegdahl) Rettig; m. Angie L. Magnusson, Aug. 10, 1968; children: Kirsten, Mark, Jerry. U.S. Bur. Budget, Washington, 1967-68, N.J. Dept. Higher Edn., Trenton, N.J., 1968-69; Asst. prof. Cornell U., Ithaca, N.Y., 1969-71; assoc. prof. Ohio State U. 1971-75; sr. social scientist RAND Corp., Washington, 1975-81; prof. social sci. Ill. Inst. Tech., Chgo., 1981-86, chmn. dept., 1981-85, dir. M.P.A. program, 1981-86; Inst. Med. of NAS, Washington, 1987-95; sr. social scientist RAND corp., 1995—. Author: Cancer Crusade: The Story of the National Cancer Act, 1977; editor: (with Norman G. Levinsky) Kidney Failure and the Federal Government, 1991, (with Laurence E. Earley and Richard A. Merrill) Food and Drug Administration Advisory Committees, 1992, (with Adam Yarmolinsky) Federal Regulation of Methadone Treatment, 1995; mem. editorial bd. Am. Jour. Kidney Diseases; contbr. articles to profl. jours. Fellow AAAS; mem. AAAS, The Hastings Ctr. (assoc.). Home: 5411 42d St NW Washington DC 20015 Office: The RAND Corp 2100 M St NW Washington DC 20037

RETZ, WILLIAM ANDREW, naval officer; b. Blauvelt, N.Y., June 3, 1940; s. Andrew Macmillan and Katherine (Deyoe) R.; m. Julia Irene Patterson, Sept. 23, 1989; children: Andrew, Gregory, Mark. Student, Tex. A&M U., 1957; BS in Mech. Engring., U. N.Mex., 1963; MS, George Washington U., 1970; grad., Naval War Coll., 1972. Commd. ensign USN, 1963, advanced through grades to rear adm., 1991; patrol officer river div. 511 USN,

Vietnam, 1968-69; flag sec. to comdr. Amphibious Group Two USN, Norfolk, Va., 1972-74, exec. officer USS Ainsworth, 1974-76, commanding officer USS Stump, 1980-82, commodore Destroyer Squadron 22, 1985-87; placement officer Bur. Naval Pers. USN, Washington, 1976-78, dep. dir. policy, 1982-85, asst. chief naval pers., 1990—, exec. asst. surface warfare to chief naval warfare, 1978-80; dep. for ops. U.S. Cen. Command USN, Tampa, Fla., 1987-90; faculty, co. officer U.S. Naval Acad., Annapolis, Md., 1969-71. Active Episcopal Ch., Honolulu. Decorated Legion of Merit, Def. Disting. Svc. medal, Meritorious Svc. medal, Bronze Star. Mem. U.S. Naval Inst. Avocations: running, sailing.

RETZER, KENNETH ALBERT, mathematics educator; b. Jacksonville, Ill., Nov. 6, 1933; s. Samuel Stark and Cora Edith (Martin) R.; m. Dorcas Anne Schroeder, Apr. 18, 1953 (dec. Aug. 1990); children: Martin Wayne, Kent Arnold, Sheryl Kaye; m. Wei Dong, Feb. 14, 1991; 1 child, Roger Dong Retzer. AB, Ill. Coll., 1954; MEd, U. Ill., 1957, PhD, 1969. Cert. tchr., Ill., 1954-57; cert. sch. adminstrn., Ill., 1957—. Tchr. Saunemin (Ill.) Twp. High Sch., 1954-58, asst. supt., 1955-58; prof. math. Ill. State U., Normal, 1959-89, Abilene (Tex.) Christian U., 1989—; asst. chmn. math. dept. Ill. State U., Normal, 1969-71; vis. prof. U. Ga., Athens, 1973, Tex. A&M U., College Station, 1984, U. Hawaii-Maui, Kahului, 1990, 91; cons. Arabian Am. Oil Co., Dhahran, Saudi Arabia, 1984, Ill. State Bd. Edn., Springfield, 1983-88; rsch. fellow U. Western Sydney, Australia, 1993; lectr. Zhejiang U., Hangzhou, China, Northwest Normal U., Lanzhou, China, Gansu Edn. U., Lanzhou, Lanzhou Normal U., Zhangye Normal U., China, summer 1994. Contbr. articles to profl. jours. in the U.S., Can., China. Mem. NEA, AAUP, Nat. Coun. Tchrs. Math., Sch. Sci. and Math. Assn., Math. Assn. Am., Rsch. Coun. on Diagnostic and Prescriptive Math., Ill. Coun. Tchrs. Math. (Max Beberman award 1988), Tex. Coun. Tchrs. Math., Big County Coun. Tchrs. Math., Ill. Assn. Higher Edn., Pi Mu Epsilon, Phi Delta Kappa. Mem. Church of Christ. Avocations: travel, photography, hiking, reading, Christian studies. Home: 58 Bay Shore Ct Abilene TX 79602-4202 Office: Abilene Christian Univ Math Dept ACU Box 8012 1600 Campus Ct Abilene TX 79699-8012

RETZLER, KURT EGON, diversified management company executive, hospitality, travel and marketing company executive; b. Bechkerek, Mar. 31, 1927; came to U.S., 1950, naturalized, 1954; s. Joseph J. and Melinda (Beno) R.; m. Rali Tjotis, Aug. 3, 1957; children: Jo Elaine, Kurt Steven. B.B.A. with distinction, U. Mich., 1955, M.B.A. with distinction, 1956. C.P.A., Mich., Minn. C.P.A. Arthur Andersen & Co., Detroit, 1956-63; asst. controller Carlson Cos., Inc., Mpls., 1963-65; v.p., controller Carlson Cos., Inc., 1965-74, v.p., 1974—, v.p. corp. acquisitions and devel., 1974—, mem. fin. com., 1974—; bd. dirs. TGI Fridays, Inc., Dallas, Carlson Travel Network, Radisson Hotel Corp., Carlson Properties, Inc., Country Kitchen Internat., Inc. Treas. PTA, Golden Valley, Minn., 1967. Served with AUS, 1951-53. Mem. Financial Execs. Inst. (dir. Twin Cities chpt. 1969-70, treas. 1971-72), Nat. Assn. Accountants, Am. Inst. C.P.A.'s, Minn. Assn. C.P.A.'s, Am. Accounting Assn., Assn. for Corp. Growth, Beta Gamma Sigma, Phi Kappa Phi, Beta Alpha Psi. Home: 1100 Heritage Ln Wayzata MN 55391-9133 Office: Carlson Cos Inc Carlson Pkwy PO Box 59159 Minneapolis MN 55459-8214

REUBEN, ALVIN BERNARD, entertainment executive; b. Harrisburg, Pa., Aug. 11, 1940; s. Maurice and Lillian (Katzef) R.; m. Barbara Ann Harrison, Mar. 18, 1967; 1 dau., Mindee Jill. B.S. in Commerce, Rider U., 1962. Buyer Pomeroy's div. Allied Stores Corp., Harrisburg, 1962-67; sales rep. Random House, Inc., N.Y.C., 1967-74; dir. mktg. Ballantine Books, Inc. (div. Random House), N.Y.C., 1974-76; v.p. sales Simon & Schuster, N.Y.C., 1976-79, sr. v.p. sales Pocket Books div., 1979-81, sr. v.p. mktg., 1981-82, pres. promotional pub. group, 1982-83, exec. v.p. electronic pub. div., 1983-85; exec. v.p. Prentice Hall div. Simon & Schuster, 1985-86; sr. v.p. mktg., sales and distbn. Vestron, Inc., 1986-89; sr. v.p. St. Martin's Press, N.Y.C., 1989-91; sr. v.p. sales, mktg. Sony Music Video, N.Y.C., 1991-92; sr. v.p. spl. markets Sony Music, N.Y.C., 1992—; instr. edn. in pub. program, grad. program SUNY; active problem solving seminar Pubs. Weekly, N.Y.C., 1980. With USAFR, 1963-69. Mem. Tau Kappa Epsilon. Home: 54 High Point Rd Westport CT 06880-3911 Office: 550 Madison Ave New York NY 10022-3211

REUBEN, DON HAROLD, lawyer; b. Chgo., Sept. 1, 1928; s. Michael B. and Sally (Chapman) R.; m. Evelyn Long, Aug. 27, 1948 (div.); children: Hope Reuben Paul, Michael Barrett, Timothy Don, Jeffrey Long, Howard Ellis; m. Jeannette Hurley Haywood, Dec. 13, 1971; stepchildren: Harris Hurley Haywood, Edward Gregory Haywood. B.S., Northwestern U., 1949, J.D., 1952. Bar: Ill. 1952. With firm Kirkland & Ellis, Chgo., 1952-78, sr. ptnr., until 1978; sr. ptnr. Reuben & Proctor, Chgo. 1978-86, Isham, Lincoln & Beale, Chgo., 1986-88; sr. counsel Winston & Strawn, 1988-94; of counsel Altheimer & Gray, Chgo., 1994—; spl. asst. atty. gen. State of Ill., 1963-64, 69, 84; counsel spl. session Ill. Ho. of Reps., 1964, for Ill. treas. for congl., state legis. and jud. reapportionment, 1963; spl. fed. ct. master, 1968-70; dir. Lake Shore Nat. Bank, 1973-93, Heitman Fin.; mem. citizens adv. bd. to sheriff County of Cook, 1962-66, mem. jury instrns. com., 1963-68; rules com. Ill. Supreme Ct., 1963-73; mem. pub. rels. com. Nat. Conf. State Trial Judges; mem. com. study caseflow mgmt. in law div. Cook County Cir. Ct., 1979-88; mem. adv. implementation com. U.S. Dist. Ct. for No. Dist. Ill., 1981-82; mem. Chgo. Better Schs. Com., 1968-69, Chgo. Crime Commn., 1970-80; mem. supervisory panel Fed. Defender Program.; lectr. on libel, slander, privacy and freedom of press. Bd. dirs. Lincoln Park Zool. Soc., 1972-84; trustee Northwestern U., 1977—; mem. vis. com. U. Chgo. Law Sch., 1976-79. Mem. Ill. Bar Assn., Chgo. Bar Assn. (chmn. subcom. on propriety and regulation of contingent fees com. devel. law 1966-69, subcom. on media liaison 1980-82, mem. com. on profl. info. 1980-82), ABA (standing com. on fed. judiciary 1973-79, standing com. on jud. selection, tenure and compensation 1982-85), Am. Law Inst., Am. Judicature Soc., Fellows Am. Bar Found., Am. Coll. Trial Lawyers (Rule 23 com. 1975-82, judiciary com. 1987-91), Am. Arbitration Assn. (nat. panel arbitrators), Internat. Acad. Trial Lawyers, Union League Club (Chgo.), Tavern Club, Mid-Am. Club, Law Club, Casino Club, The Springs Club, Desert Riders of Palm Springs, Phi Eta Sigma, Beta Alpha Psi, Beta Gamma Sigma, Order of Coif. Home: 20 Jill Ter Rancho Mirage CA 92270-2635 Office: Altheimer & Gray 40th Fl 10 S Wacker Dr Chicago IL 60606

REUBER, GRANT LOUIS, banking insurance company executive; b. Mildmay, Ont., Can., Nov. 23, 1927; s. Jacob Daniel and Gertrude Catherine (Wahl) R.; m. Margaret Louise Julia Summerhayes, Oct. 21, 1951; children: Rebecca, Barbara, Mary. BA, U. Western Ont., 1950, LLD, 1985; AM, Harvard U., 1954, PhD, 1957; LLD (hon.), Wilfred Laurier U., 1983, Simon Fraser U., 1985, McMaster U., 1994; postgrad., Cambridge U., 1954-55. Mem. research dept. Bank Can., Ottawa, 1950-52; mem. Can. Dept. Finance, Ottawa, 1955-57; asst. prof. econ. U. Western Ont., London, 1957-59, assoc. prof., 1959-62, prof., 1962—, head dept., 1963-69, dean faculty Social Sci., 1969-74, mem. bd. govs., 1974-78, acad. v.p.; provost, 1975-78, chancellor, 1988-92; sr. v.p., chief economist Bank of Montreal, Que., Can., 1978-79; exec. v.p. Bank of Montreal, 1980-81, dep. chmn. chief exec. officer, 1981-83, dir., mem. exec. com., 1981-89 pres., chief operating officer, 1983-87, dep. chmn., 1987-89; dep. minister fin. Can., 1979-80; chmn. Can. Deposit Ins. Corp., 1992—; mem. Royal Commn. Banking and Fin., Toronto, 1962-63; chmn. Ont. Econ. Coun., 1973-78; cons. Can. Internat. Devel. Agy., 1968-69; hon. rsch. assoc. in econs. Harvard U., 1968-69; cons. devel. ctr. OECD, 1969-72; bd. dirs. Opinac Energy Corp., Genstar Capital Corp.; mem. adv. com. U. Western Ont. Sch. Bus.; lectr. U. Chgo. Sch. Bus., 1992-93; econ. advisor to prime min. of Lithuania, 1991-92. Author: Private Foreign Investment in Development, 1973, Canada's Political Economy, 1980; contbr. articles to profl. jours. Pres. Can. Ditchley Found., 1991—; vice chmn. Can. Merit Scholarship Found., 1994—. Decorated officer Order of Can. Fellow Royal Soc. Can.

REUDINK, DOUGLAS OTTO JOHN, communications company executive, researcher; b. West Point, Nebr., May 6, 1939; s. Raymond A. and Pearl Marie (Stolzman) R.; m. Jamie Karin Allinger, Aug. 27 1961; children: Mark, Michael, Matthew. B.A., Linfield Coll., 1961; Ph.D., Oreg. State U., 1965. Mem. tech. staff Bell Labs., Holmdel, N.J., 1965-72, head satellite research, 1972-78; dir. radio research, 1978-84; dir. computer and robotics research AT&T Bell Labs, Holmdel, N.J., 1984-86; dir. labs. Boeing Electronics Co., Seattle, 1986-89; dir. electronics techs. Boeing Aerospace and

Electronics, 1989-91; dir. wireless planning U.S. West NewVector Group, Bellevue, Wash., 1991—; advisor Voice of Am., Washington, 1983—. NASA, Washington, 1980-86. Mem. editorial bd. Jour. Space Communication and Broadcasting, Netherlands, 1982-86; contbr. chpts. to books, numerous articles to tech. jours.; patentee in field. Vice pres. Sea Girt Bd. Edn., N.J., 1980-86. NDEA fellow, 1961-64. Fellow IEEE (best paper award 1972); mem. AIAA, Internat. Sci. Radio Union. Lutheran. Home: 13916 SE 47th St Bellevue WA 98006-3048 Office: U.S. West NewVector Group 3350 161st Ave SE Mail Stop 572 Bellevue WA 98008

REUHL, GEORGE, retail executive; b. 1926. Factory mgr. Honeywell Inc., Morton Grove, Ill., 1946-68; v.p. ops. Unitek Corp., Monrovia, Calif., 1968-72; v.p. Symbolic Displays Inc., Irvine, Calif., 1972-73; with Am. TV & Appliance Madison, Wis., 1973—, now vice-chmn. bd. dirs. Office: Am TV & Appliance Madison 2404 W Beltline Hwy Madison WI 53713-2387*

REULECKE, HEIMO, pharmaceutical executive; b. 1947. With Fisons Cos., Germany; with Fisons Corp., Rochester, N.Y., 1992—, now pres., CEO, also chmn. bd. dirs. Office: Fisons Corp 755 Jefferson Rd Rochester NY 14623*

REULING, MICHAEL FREDERICK, supermarket company, real estate executive; b. Peoria, Ill., May 11, 1946; s. F.H. and Doris (Salzenstein) R.; m. Susan Ruth Morgan, Aug. 10, 1968; children—Jessica Sue, Jeremy Michael. B.A. in Econs., Carleton Coll.; J.D., U. Mich. Bar: Utah, Idaho. Tex., Fla. Assoc. Van Cott, Bagley, Cornwall & McCarthy, Salt Lake City, 1971-73; assoc. real estate Skaggs-Albertson's, Richardson, Tex., 1974-78; assoc. contracts Albertson's, Inc., Boise, Idaho, 1973-74, sr. v.p., gen. counsel, 1978-81, sr. v.p. real estate, 1981-86; exec. v.p. store devel. Albertson's, Inc., Boise, 1986—. Mem. Idaho State Bar Assn., Utah State Bar Assn., Fla. State Bar Assn., Tex. State Bar Assn. Office: Albertson's Inc 250 Parkcenter Blvd PO Box 20 Boise ID 83706

REUM, JAMES MICHAEL, lawyer; b. Oak Park, Ill., Nov. 1, 1946; s. Walter John and Lucy (Bellegay) R. BA cum laude, Harvard U., 1968, JD cum laude, 1972. Bar: N.Y. 1973, D.C. 1974, U.S. Dist. Ct. (so. dist.) N.Y. 1974, Ill. 1979, U.S. Dist. Ct. (no. dist.) Ill. 1982. Assoc. Davis Polk & Wardwell, N.Y.C., 1973-78; assoc. Minority Counsel Com. on Judiciary U.S. Ho. of Reps., Washington, 1974; ptnr. Hopkins & Sutter, Chgo., 1979-93, Winston & Strawn, Chgo., 1994—. Midwest advance rep. Nat. Reagan Bush Com., 1980; nominee commr. Securities and Exchange Comm., Pres. Bush, 1992. Served to SP4 USAR, 1969-75. Recipient Harvard U. Honorary Nat. Scholarship, 1964-72. Mem. ABA, Monte Carlo Country Club (Monaco), Chgo. Club, Univ. Club (N.Y.C.), Lawrence Beach Club (Atlantic Beach, N.Y.). Republican. Home: 3100 N Sheridan Rd # 3D Chicago IL 60657-4954 Office: Winston & Strawn 35 W Wacker Dr Chicago IL 60601

REUM, W. ROBERT, manufacturing executive; b. Oak Park, Ill., July 22, 1942; m. Sharon Milliken. BA, Yale U., 1964; JD, U. Mich., 1967; MBA, Harvard U., 1969. Dir. investment analysis City Investing Co., N.Y.C., 1969-72; v.p. corp fin. Mich. Nat. Corp., Bloomfield Hills, Mich., 1972-78; v.p., treas. White Motor Corp., Cleve., 1978-79; v.p. fin., chief fin. officer Lamson & Sessions, Cleve., 1980-82; v.p. fin., chief fin. officer The Interlake Corp., Oak Brook, Ill., 1982-88, exec. v.p., 1988-90, chmn., pres., chief exec. officer, 1991—; dir. Amsted Industries, Inc., Chgo., Duplex Products, Inc., Sycamore, Ill.; mem. nat. adv. bd. Chem. Bank, N.Y.C. Contbr. articles to Harvard Bus. Rev. Bd. trustees Mfrs. Alliance, Washington. Mem. Chgo. Golf Club, Chgo. Club, Dunham Woods Riding Club (Wayne, Ill.), Rolling Rock Club (Ligonier, Pa.). Office: Interlake Corp 550 Warrenville Rd Lisle IL 60532-4308

REUMAN, ROBERT EVERETT, philosophy educator; b. Foochow, China, Feb. 16, 1923; s. Otto G. and Martha Lydia (Bourne) R.; m. Dorothy Ann Swan, Sept. 2, 1949; children: Martha Claire, David Alan, Jonathan Robert, Ann Evalyn, Elizabeth Linda. A.B., Middlebury Coll., 1945; M.A., U. Pa., 1946, Ph.D., 1949. Asst. instr. U. Pa., 1946-48; instr. Temple U., 1947-49; mem. Friends' Ambulance Service Unit, China, 1949-51, chmn., 1950-51; dir. Quaker Student House, Freiburg im Breisgau, Fed. Republic Germany, 1951-53; instr. Lafayette Coll., 1953-54, asst. prof., 1954-56; mem. faculty Colby Coll., Waterville, Maine, 1956—, prof. philosophy, 1969—, chmn. social sci. div., 1975-78, chmn. dept. philosophy and religion, 1975-78; Dana prof. philosophy Colby Coll., 1986-91, ret., 1991. Author: Mauern, 1965, (with others) Anatomy of Anti-Communism, 1969; pamphlet Walls, 1966; contbr. articles to profl. jours. New Eng. regional chmn. Danforth Assocs., 1963-64; Quaker internat. affairs rep., Germany, 1964-66; bd. dirs. Am. Friends of Le College Cevenol, 1973-85; mem. Maine Humanities Coun., 1980-85, mem. exec. com., 1981-84. With Civilian Pub. Svc., 1943-46. Harrison fellow, 1945-46; Colby Coll. grantee, 1972, 79, 82. Mem. Am. Philos. Assn., AAUP, Soc. for Values in Higher Edn. Democrat. Unitarian-Quaker.

REUSCHLEIN, HAROLD GILL, university dean; b. Burlington, Wis., Dec. 2, 1904; s. Joseph Felix and Frances (Gill) R.; m. Marcella Christien, Apr. 24, 1930; 1 dau., Mary Frances. A.B., U. Iowa, 1927; LL.B., Yale, 1933; J.S.D., Cornell, 1934; LL.D., Dominican Coll., 1955, Dickinson Sch. Law, 1970, LaSalle Coll., 1971, Creighton U., 1975, St. Mary's U., 1984; L.H.D., Villanova U., 1972. Bar: Wis. 1936, U.S. Supreme Ct. 1944. Ph.B. 1955. Instr. history N.Y. U., 1930-32; asst. gen. counsel Fidelity Mut. Life Ins. Co., 1934; prof. law Georgetown U., 1934-46, U. Notre Dame, 1946-47, Syracuse U., 1947-48, U. Pitts., 1948-53; dean Sch. Law, Villanova U., 1953-72, dean emeritus, 1984; Ryan Distinguished prof. law St. Mary's U., 1972-84; vis. prof. Case Western Res. U., 1967-68. Author: The Schools of Corporate Reform, 1950, Jurisprudence-Its American Prophets, 1951, Cases on Unincorporated Business, 1952, Cases on Agency and Partnership, 1962, Handbook of Law of Agency and Partnership, 1990. Choirmaster, organist First Meth. Episcopal Ch., New Haven, 1927-33, Ch. St. Bernard of Clarivaux, Pitts., 1948-53; dir. Pub. Health Law Project, U. Pittsburgh. Served as col. Judge Adv. Gen. Dept., World War II; chief Office Legislative Service Hdqrs. AAF. Awarded Legion of Merit; Decorated Papal Knight of the Holy Sepulchre, Knight St. Gregory the Great. Mem. ABA, Wis. Bar Assn., Pa. Bar Assn., Cosmos Club (Washington), Order of Coif, Pi Kappa Alpha, Pi Gamma Mu. Roman Catholic. Home: Riddle Village Williamsburgh Bldg # 106 Media PA 19063

REUSCHLING, THOMAS LYNN, academic administrator, consultant; b. Conneaut, Ohio, Dec. 28, 1942; s. Fred Leonard and Florice Lucille (Corlew) R.; m. Dorothy Ellen Ford, Sept. 8, 1962; children: Renee, Tracy. BA, Hiram (Ohio) Coll., 1964; MBA, Kent State U., 1966; D. Bus. Adminstrn., U. Colo., 1970. Asst. prof. Kent State U., 1969-73; dir. Sch. Bus. U. No. Iowa, Cedar Falls, 1973-78; dean Sch. Bus. U. Richmond, Va., 1978-88; pres. St. Andrews Presbn. Coll., Lauringburg, N.C., 1988—. Pres. Jr. Achievement of Richmond, 1985-86, Carolina Intercollegiate Athletic Conf., 1993—; bd. dirs. United Way of Richmond, 1987-88; deacon, elder River Rd. Presbyn. Ch., Richmond; treas. Ind. Coll. Fund N.C. NDEA fellow U. Colo., 1966-69. Avocations: basketball, traveling, reading. Home: 612 S Main St Laurinburg NC 28352-4536 Office: St Andrews Presbyn Coll Dogwood Mile Laurinburg NC 28352

REUSS, LLOYD EDWIN ARMIN, automobile manufacturing company executive; b. Belleville, Ill., Sept. 22, 1936; s. Lawrence Phillip and Dorthea B. (Juenger) R.; m. Maurcine Kaye Bilderback, Aug. 10, 1957; children: Charlene Faye, Mark Lyle. BSME, U. Mo., Rolla, 1957; grad. sr. exec. course, M.I.T., 1971. With GM Corp., Detroit, 1959—, chief engr., Buick Motor div., 1975-78, dir. engring., Chevrolet div., 1978-80, v.p., gen. mgr., Buick Motor div., 1980-84, v.p., group exec., Chevrolet, Pontiac, GM of Can., 1984-86, exec. v.p. N.Am. passenger cars, 1986-90; exec. v.p. N.Am. automotive ops. GM Corp., 1987-90; pres. GM Corp., Detroit, Mich., 1990—. Trustee Lawrence Technol. U., Southfield, Mich., 1977—, Louisville Presbyn. Theol. Sem. Ky., 1985—, Vanderbilt U., Nashville, 1987—. Served with C.E. AUS, 1957-59. Mem. Soc. Automotive Engrs., Pi Tau Sigma, Tau Beta Pi. Presbyterian (elder). Office: GM Gen Motors Bldg 3044 W Grand Blvd Detroit MI 48202-3091

REUSS, ROBERT PERSHING, telecommunications executive, consultant; b. Aurora, Ill., Mar. 23, 1918; s. George John and Mary Belle (Gorrie) R.; m. Mildred Louise Daly, Dec. 22, 1940 (dec. May 1985); children: Lynn Ann

(Mrs. David Bohmer), Robert Cameron; m. Grace K. Brady, Aug. 28, 1986. BS, U. Ill., 1939; postgrad., Harvard U. 1943; MBA, U. Chgo., 1950; D Bus. Adminstrn., Blackburn Coll., 1976. Staff AT&T, 1955-58, asst. compt.. 1958-59; v.p. Ill. Bell Tel. Co., 1959-72, dir., 1970-72; pres., chief exec. officer, dir. Centel Corp., Chgo., 1972-76, chmn., 1977-88; cons. Chgo., 1988-93, Sprint Corp., 1993—; bd. govs. Midwest Stock Exch., 1978-82; bd. dirs. Tellabs, Inc. Trustee Rush-Presbyn.-St. Luke's Med. Ctr., Chgo., 1984-89, Aurora U., 1986—, Lyric Opera, 1987—; bd. dirs. U. Ill. Found., 1979—. Lt. (s.g.) USNR, 1943-46, PTO. Mem. Chgo. Assn. Commerce & Industry (bd. dirs. 1971-78), Comml. Club, Chgo. Club, Chgo. Golf Club, Ocean Club, Country Club of Fla., Phi Kappa Phi. Presbyterian (deacon, trustee). Office: 40 Shuman Blvd Ste 240 Naperville IL 60563-8465

REUTER, CAROL JOAN, insurance company executive; b. Bklyn., June 1, 1941; d. Michael John and Elizabeth Lucille (Garner) R. BA, St. John's U., 1962. Exec. dir. N.Y. Life Found., N.Y.C., 1979-89, sec., 1989-90, pres., 1990—, bd. dirs., 1992—; asst. v.p. N.Y. Life Ins. Co., N.Y.C., 1984-89, corp. v.p., 1990-95, v.p., 1995—. Mem., former chmn. contbns. coun. Conf. Bd., N.Y. Contbns. Adv. Group; mem. corp. adv. coun. ARC; chmn. nat. corp. adv. com. Found. Ind. Higher Edn.; mem. corp. adv. com. United Negro Coll Fund; mem. corp. assocs. United Way of Am. Named Acad. of Women's Achievers, YWCA, 1987. Republican. Roman Catholic. Office: NY Life Ins Co 51 Madison Ave New York NY 10010-1603

REUTER, FRANK THEODORE, history educator; b. Kankakee, Ill., Mar. 18, 1926; s. Frank Theodore and Evelyn Marie (Scott) R.; m. Kathleen Ann Pester, June 16, 1951; children: Mark, Stephen, Christopher, Ann, Katherine. B.S., U. Ill., 1950, M.A., 1959, Ph.D., 1960. Instr. West Liberty (W. Va.) State Coll., 1960-62; asst. prof. Texas Christian U., Fort Worth, 1962-66; assoc. prof. Texas Christian U., 1966-71; prof. history Tex. Christian U., 1971-92; dean Texas Christian U. (Grad. Sch.), 1970-75, chmn. dept. history, 1980-83; prof. emeritus Tex. Christian U., 1992—. Author: West Liberty State College: The First 125 Years, 1963, Catholic Influence on American Colonial Policies, 1898-1904, 1967, Trials and Triumphs: George Washington's Foreign Policy, 1983. Served with USNR, 1944-46. U. Durham Rsch. fellow, 1991. Mem. Orgn. Am. Historians, Am. Hist. Assn., Soc. Historians Early Republic, Soc. Historians Am. Fgn. Relations, Phi Beta Kappa, Phi Alpha Theta. Roman Catholic. Home: 3617 Winifred Dr Fort Worth TX 76133-2126 Office: Tex Christian U History Dept Fort Worth TX 76129

REUTER, JAMES D., aeronautical engineering manager. Project mgr. Pioneer Parachute Co., Manchester, Conn. Mem. AIAA (Aerodynamic Decelerator Sys. award 1992). Office: Pioneer Parachute Co 95 Lakewood Circle S Manchester CT 06040-7018*

REUTER, JAMES WILLIAM, lawyer; b. Bemidji, Minn., Sept. 30, 1948; s. John Renee and Monica (Dugas) R.; m. Patricia Carol Creelman, Mar. 30, 1968; children: Kristine, Suzanne, Natalee. B.A., St. John's U., 1970; J.D., William Mitchell Coll. of Law, 1974. Bar: Minn. 1974, U.S. Dist. Ct. Minn. 1975, U.S. Ct. Appeals (8th cir.) 1985; cert. civil trial specialist. Editor, West Pub. Co., St. Paul, 1970-73; assoc. Terpstra & Merrill, Mpls., 1974-77; ptnr. Barna, Guzy, Merrill, Hynes & Giancola, Ltd., Mpls., 1977-89, ptnr. Lindquist & Vennum, Mpls., 1989—. Recipient Cert. award Nat. Inst. Trial Advocacy, 1978. Mem. ABA (TIPS and civil litigation sects.), Assn. Trial Lawyers Am., Minn. Bar Assn. (civil litigation and computer sects.), Hennepin County Bar Assn. (ethics com.), Anoka County Bar Assn. (pres. 1981-82). Avocations: skiing; golf; camping; reading. Office: Lindquist & Vennum 4200 IDS Ctr 80 S 8th St Minneapolis MN 55402

REUTER, STEWART RALSTON, radiologist, lawyer, educator; b. Detroit, Feb. 14, 1934; s. Carl H. and Grace M. R.; m. Marianne Ahfeldt, June 6, 1966. B.A., Ohio Wesleyan U., 1955; M.D., Case Western Res. U., 1959; J.D., U. San Francisco, 1980. Diplomate: Am. Bd. Radiology. Bar: Tex. 1981. Intern U. Calif., San Francisco, 1959-60, resident in radiology, 1960-63; instr. radiology Stanford (Calif.) U., 1963-64; asst. prof. U. Mich., Ann Arbor, 1966-69, prof., 1972-76; assoc. prof. U. Calif., San Diego, 1969-72; prof. U. Calif., San Francisco and Davis, 1976-80; prof., chmn. dept. radiology Health Scis. Ctr., U. Tex., San Antonio, 1980—. Co-author: Gastrointestinal Radiology, 3d edit., 1986; mem. editorial bd. Am. Jour. Roentgenology, 1975-91, Iatrogenics, 1990-93; contbr. articles to profl. jours. Picker fellow, 1964-66. Fellow Am. Coll. Radiology, Am. Coll. Legal Medicine (bd. govs. 1985-91, 92-94, sec. 1994, pres.-elect 1995, pres. 1996); mem. AMA, Assn. Univ. Radiologists, Am. Roentgen Ray Soc., Tex. Radiol. Assn. (trustee 1989-92, pres. 1994), Soc. Cardiovascular and Interventional Radiologists (pres. 1979), Soc. Gastrointestinal Radiologists, Tex. Bar Assn. Home: 3923 Morgans Crk San Antonio TX 78230-1945 Office: U Tex Health Sci Ctr Dept Radiology 7703 Floyd Curl Dr San Antonio TX 78284-7700

REUTHER, DAVID LOUIS, children's book publisher, writer; b. Detroit, Nov. 2, 1946; s. Roy Louis and Fania (Sonkin) R.; m. Margaret Alexander Miller, July 21, 1973; children: Katherine Anna, Jacob Alexander. BA with honors, U. Mich., 1968. Tchr. Lewis-Wadhams Sch., Westport, N.Y., 1969-71; asst. dir. Children's Book Council, N.Y.C., 1971-73; editor children's books Macmillan Publishing Co., N.Y.C., 1973-76; sr. editor Four Winds Press-Scholastic Inc., N.Y.C., 1976-82; sr. v.p., editor-in-chief Morrow Jr. Books, N.Y.C., 1982—; co-founder Baseball Ink, Inc., 1986-90; co-founder Baseball Ink, Inc., 1986-90; mem. Nat. Sci. Tchrs. Assn.-Children's Book Coun. Joint Com., 1982-85; joint com. mem. Am. Bookseller Assn., 1990-93; treas. Childrens Book Coun., 1986, chmn., 1993-94. Author: with Roy Doty) Fun To Go, A Take-Along Activity Book, 1982, Save-the-Animals Activity Book, 1982, (with John Thorn and Pete Palmer) The Hidden Game of Baseball, 1984, Total Baseball, 1989, The Whole Baseball Catalog, 1990, Total Baseball II, 1991; editor: (with John Thorn) The Armchair Quarterback, 1982, The Armchair Aviator, 1983, The Armchair Mountaineer, 1984, The Armchair Book of Baseball, 1985, The Armchair Angler, 1986, The Armchair Book of Basesball II, 1987, The Armchair Traveler, 1988. Mem. ALA, Authors Guild, Soc. Children's Book Writers. Home: 271 Central Park W New York NY 10024-3020 Office: William Morrow & Co 1350 Avenue of the Americas New York NY 10019

REUTHER, WALTER, horticulture educator; b. Manganoui County, North Is., New Zealand, Sept. 21, 1911; came to U.S., 1919; s. Arthur W.G. and Martha (Kruger) R.; m. Flora Astbury Nelson, Aug. 4, 1935; children: David Walter, Charles Arthur. BS in Chemistry, U. Fla., 1933; PhD in Plant Physiology, Cornell U., 1940. Asst. horticulturist Agrl. Experiment Sta., U. Fla., Gainesville, 1933-37; rsch. asst. in pomology Cornell U., Ithaca, N.Y., 1937-40; asst. prof. pomology Cornell U., Ithaca, 1940; assoc. horticulturist, then prin. horticulturist USDA, Orlando, Fla., 1941-55; head dept. horticulture U. Fla., Gainesville, 1955-56; prof., chmn. dept. horticulture, researcher Citrus Ctr., U. Calif., Riverside, 1956-66, prof., horticulturist, 1966-72, 74-79; coord. regional rsch. Inst. Nat. Investigations in Agriculture, Valencia, Spain, 1972-74; prof. emeritus U. Calif., Riverside, 1979—; cons. Del Monte Corp., 1962-72, Govt. of Greece, 1963, 64, Rockefeller Found., 1965, 66-67, 69, UN, 1970, 75, 77, Govt. of Spain, 1972-74, Govt. of Brazil, 1975, 81, Govt. of Indonesia, 1977-78, 84, Govt. of Republic of China, 1979, Govt. of Honduras, 1980, Govt. of Mex., 1982, Govt. of Colombia, 1982. Editor: The Citrus Industry, 1967-90; contbr. 130 articles to profl. jours. Fellow Am. Soc. Hort. Sci. (pres. 1962-63, chmn. bd. dirs. 1963-64). Democrat. Avocations: reading, gradening, walking. Home: Apt # 322 12751 Gateway Park Rd Poway CA 92064 Office: U Calif Dept Botany and Plant Sci Riverside CA 92521

REUTIMAN, ROBERT WILLIAM, JR., lawyer; b. Mpls., June 4, 1944; s. Robert William and Elsbeth Bertha (Doering) R.; m. Virginia Lee Traxler, June 25, 1983; children: Robert James, Jospeh Lee. BA magna cum laude, U. Minn., 1966, JD, 1969. Bar: Minn. 1969, U.S. Ct. Mil. Appeals 1969, U.S. Dist. Ct. Minn. 1973, U.S. Ct. Appeals (8th cir.) 1976, U.S. Tax. Ct. 1979. Mem. Armstrong, Phleger, Reutiman & Vinokour, Ltd., Wayzata, Minn., 1973-76; ptnr. Phleger & Reutiman, Wayzata, Minn., 1976-81; pvt. practice Wayzata, 1981—. Chmn. Spring Pk. Planning Commn., 1978. Capt. U.S. Army, 1969-73. Decorated Army Commendation medal. Mem. ABA, Minn. Bar Assn., Hennepin County Bar Assn., Am. Arbitration Assn. (panel of arbitrators), Phi Beta Kappa. Lutheran. Avocations: fishing, rose growing. Home: 11610 3rd Ave N Plymouth MN 55441-5919 Office: 305 Rice St E Wayzata MN 55391-1615

REUTTER, EBERHARD EDMUND, JR., education and law educator; b. Balt., May 28, 1924; s. Eberhard Edmund and Irene Louise (Loewer) R.; m. Bettie Marie Lytle, Aug. 16, 1947; 1 son, Mark Douglas. B.A., Johns Hopkins U., 1944; M.A., Columbia U., 1948, Ph.D., 1950. Dir., Tokyo Army Edn. Program Sch., 1945-47; head math. dept. Barnard Sch., N.Y.C., 1947-49; mem. faculty Tchrs. Coll., Columbia U., 1950—, prof., 1957—; vis. prof. U. Alaska, 1960, 66, U. P.R., 1954, U. So. Calif., 1960; speaker, cons. Coordinator spl. edn. projects NAACP Legal Def. Fund, 1965-68. Author: The School Administrator and Subversive Activities, 1951, Schools and the Law, 5th edit., 1981, (with W.S. Elsbree) Staff Personnel in the Public Schools, 1954, (with R.R. Hamilton) Legal Aspects of School Board Operation, 1958, (with W.S. Elsbree) Principles of Staff Personnel Administration in Public Schools, 1959, (with L.O. Garber) The Yearbook of School Law, 1967, 68, 69, 70, Legal Aspects of Control of Student Activities by Public School Authorities, 1970, The Law of Public Education, 4th edit., 1994, The Courts and Student Conduct, 1975, The Supreme Court's Impact on Public Education, 1982; also articles, chpts. in books. Chmn. citizens adv. com. Emerson (N.J.) Bd. Edn., 1954-57. Served from pvt. to 1st lt. inf. AUS, 1943-46. Recipient Marion A. McGehey award for outstanding service in field edn. law, 1986. Mem. Nat. Orgn. Legal Problems of Edn. (pres. 1967), AAUP, Am. Assn. Sch. Adminstrs., NEA, Am. Assn. Sch. Personnel Adminstrs., Internat. Personnel Mgmt. Assn., Phi Beta Kappa, Kappa Delta Pi, Phi Delta Kappa. Home: 316 Grand Blvd Emerson NJ 07630-1157 Office: Columbia Univ Teachers Coll New York NY 10027

REVAK, JOANN, special education educator; b. Tucson, Jan. 21, 1943; d. Jack Charles and Irene Ruby (Zumwalt) Stubblefield; m. John James Revak, May 8, 1965; children: Elizabeth L., Elson L. BA in Edn., U. Ariz., 1965; MA in Edn., Ariz. State U., 1969. Cert. tchr. elem. and spl. edn., Ariz. Tchr. 1st grade Murphy Sch. Dist., Phoenix, 1965-67; spl. edn. resource tchr. Sierra Vista (Ariz.) Pub. Schs., 1980-81, tchr. spl. edn., 1981—. Leader Girl Scouts Am., Sierra Vista, 1976-78; coach Spl. Olympics, Sierra Vista, 1981-84; den mother Boy Scouts Am. 1981; v.p. Coun. for Exceptional Children, 1993—. Mem. NEA, Coun. for Exceptional Children (chair libr. com. 1990-93), Autism Soc. Am. Democrat. Eastern Orthodox. Avocations: hiking, reading, camping, traveling, gardening with house plants. Home: 2064 Sonoita Dr Sierra Vista AZ 85635 Office: Sierra Vista Pub Schs 3555 E Fry Blvd Sierra Vista AZ 85635

REVEAL, ERNEST IRA, food company executive; b. Huntington, W.Va., Oct. 27, 1915; s. Ernest I. and Edna Virginia (Wiltrout) R.; m. Hazel V. Holt, Apr. 30, 1945; children—Ernest I., Charles H. B.A., Northwestern U., 1937. Mng. editor Domestic Engring. Publ., Chgo., 1945-49; sales devel. mgr. Uarco Bus. Forms, Chgo., 1949-54; gen. mgr. Todd Co., Rochester, N.Y., 1954-60; chmn. R.T. French Co., Rochester, 1975—; chmn., chief exec. officer Schlegel Corp., Rochester, 1986-88; dir. Lincoln 1st Bank of Rochester, Schlegel Mfg. Co., Rochester, Gleason Works, Rochester, Sykes Datatronics, Rochester, Welch Foods, Inc., Westfield, N.H., Rochester Telephone Co., Reckitt & Colman, Ltd. of London. Chmn. United Community Chest Campaign, 1977; bd. dirs. Rochester Philharmonic Orch.; bd. trustees U. Rochester, Rochester Inst. Tech. Mem. Grocery Mfrs. Am. Republican. Presbyterian. Office: 890 Clinton Sq Rochester NY 14604-1730

REVEAL, ERNEST IRA, III, lawyer; b. Chgo., Oct. 19, 1948; s. Ernest Ira Jr. and Hazel (Holt) R.; m. Katherine Trennerry, Nov. 24, 1979; children: Genevieve, Adrienne, Danielle. BA, Cornell U., 1970; JD, U. Mich., 1973. Bar: Minn. 1973, U.S. Dist. Ct. Minn. 1973, U.S. Ct. Appeals (8th cir.) 1974, U.S. Dist. Ct. S.D. 1976, U.S. Ct. Claims 1976, U.S. Ct. Appeals (7th cir.) 1984, U.S. Dist. Ct. (so. dist.) Calif. 1991, U.S. Ct. Appeals (9th cir.) 1991, U.S. Supreme Ct., 1991. Assoc. Robins, Kaplan, Miller & Ciresi, Mpls., 1973-79, ptnr., 1979—. Author: Public Sector Labor Law, 1983. Mem. Civil Svc. Commn., St. Paul, Minn., 1976. Mem. ABA, Minn. Bar Assn. (past chair law and employment law sect.), Cornell Club of Minn. (past pres.), Assn. Trial Lawyers Am. Democrat. Presbyterian. Avocations: sports, reading. Office: Robins Kaplan Miller & Ciresi 600 Anton Blvd Ste 1600 Costa Mesa CA 92626-7147

REVEL, JEAN-PAUL, biology educator; b. Strasbourg, France, Dec. 7, 1930; came to U.S., 1953; s. Gaston Benjamin and Suzanne (Neher) R.; m. Helen Ruth Bowser, July 27, 1957 (div. 1986); children: David, Daniel Neher, Steven Robert; m. Galina Avdeeva Moller, Dec. 24, 1986; 1 stepchild, Karen. BS, U. Strasbourg, 1949; PhD, Harvard U., 1957. Rsch. fellow Cornell U. Med. Sch., N.Y.C., 1958-59; from instr. to prof. Harvard Med. Sch., Boston, 1959-71; prof. Calif. Inst. Tech., Pasadena, 1971—; AB Ruddock chair in biology Calif. Inst. Tech., 1978—; mem. sch. advisors bd. Nat. Insts. Aging, Balt., 1977-80; mem. ad hoc adv. biology NSF, Washington, 1982-83; mem. Nat. High Voltage Microscopy Adv. Group, Bethesda, Md., 1983, Nat. Rsch. Resources Adv. Coun., 1986-90. Author: (with E.D. Hay) Fine Structure of Developing Avian Cornea, 1969; editor: Cell Shape and Surface Architecture, 1977, Science of Biological Specimen Preparation, 1986; mem. editorial bd. Jour. Cell Biology, 1969-72, Internat. Rev. Cytology, 1970—, Cell and Tissue Rsch., 1979—, Molecular and Cell Biology, 1985-91. Fellow AAAS (leader biol. scis. sect. 1991—; Gordon conf. cell adhesion); mem. Am. Soc. Cell Biology (pres. 1972-73), Electron Micros. Soc. Am. (pres. 1988), Am. Soc. Devel. Biology. Avocations: watercolors, photography. Office: Calif Inst Tech # 156-29 Pasadena CA 91125

REVELEY, WALTER TAYLOR, III, lawyer; b. Churchville, Va., Jan. 6, 1943; s. Walter Taylor and Marie (Eason) R.; m. Helen Bond, Dec. 18, 1971; children: Walter Taylor, George Everett Bond, Nelson Martin Eason, Helen Lanier. A.B., Princeton U., 1965; J.D., U. Va., 1968. Bar: Va. 1970, D.C. 1976. Asst. prof. law U. Va., 1968-69; law clk. to Justice Brennan U.S. Supreme Ct., Washington, 1969-70; fellow Woodrow Wilson Internat. Ctr. for Scholars, 1972-73; internat. affairs fellow Coun. on Fgn. Rels., N.Y.C., 1972-73; assoc. Hunton & Williams, Richmond, Va., 1970-76, ptnr., 1976—; mng. ptnr., 1982-91; lectr. Coll. William and Mary Law Sch., 1978-80. Author: War Powers of the President and Congress: Who Holds the Arrows and Olive Branch, 1981; mem. editorial & mng. bds. Va. Law Rev., 1966-68; contbr. articles to profl. jours. Trustee Princeton U., 1986—, Presbyn. Ch. (U.S.A.) Found., 1991—, Va. Hist. Soc., 1991—, Union Theol. Sem., 1992—, Andrew W. Mellon Found., 1994—; bd. dirs. Fan Dist. Assn., Richmond, Inc., 1976-80, pres., 1979-80; bd. dirs. Richmond Symphony, 1980-92, pres., 1988-90, pres. symphony coun., 1994—; bd. dirs. Va. Mus. Found., 1990—; elder Grace Covenant Presbyn. Ch. Mem. ABA, Va. Bar Assn., D.C. Bar Assn., Richmond Bar Assn., Am. Soc. Internat. Law, Am. Judicature Soc., Am. Bar Found., Princeton Assn. Va. (bd. dirs. 1981—, pres. 1983-85), Edn. Lawyers (chmn. Va. State Bar sect. 1992—), Raven Soc., Order of Coif, Phi Beta Kappa, Omicron Delta Kappa, Knickerbocker Club (N.Y.C.), County Club of Va., Downtown Club (Richmond). Home: 2314 Monument Ave Richmond VA 23220-2604 Office: Hunton & Williams Riverfront Pla East Tower 951 E Byrd St Richmond VA 23219

REVELL, GRAEME, composer. Film scores include Dead Calm, 1989, Spontaneous Combustion, 1990, Child's Play 2, 1990, Until the End of the World, 1991, The Hand That Rocks the Cradle, 1991, Love Crimes, 1992, Traces of Red, 1992, Body of Evidence, 1993, Hear No Evil, 1993, The Crush, 1993, Hard Target, 1993, Boxing Helena, 1993, The Crow, 1994, Ghost in the Machine, 1994, The Basketball Diaries, 1995. Office: The Kraft Benjamin Agency 8491 Sunset Blvd Ste 492 West Hollywood CA 90069*

REVELLE, CHARLES S., environmental engineer, geophysicist, systems analysis and economics educator; b. Mar. 26, 1938; m. Penelope ReVelle; 2 children. BChemE, Cornell U., 1961, PhD, 1967. Chemist Nat. Starch and Chem. Co., Plainfield, N.J., 1961; rsch. engr., instr. dept. sanitary engring. Cornell U., 1962, environ. systems engring. fellow, 1963-67, asst. prof. dept. environ. systems engring., 1967-71; on leave to Johns Hopkins U. 1968-69; asst. prof. Johns Hopkins U., Balt., 1971, assoc. prof., 1971-75, prof. program in systems analysis and econs. for pub. decision making, dept. geography and environ. engring., 1975—; part-time vis. scholar Inst. Water Resources, U.S. Army Corps of Engrs. Ft. Belvoir, Va., 1993—; vis. prof. dept. geography U. Iowa, 1976; invited lectr. Oxford U., Eng., 1974, U. Genoa, 1975, 82, U. Bristol, U.K., 1975, U. Stirling, Scotland, 1975, Internat. Inst. for Applied Systems Analysis, Vienna, Austria, 1980, U. N.C., Chapel Hill, 1984, Ohio State U., 1987, others; del. Univ. Coun. on Water Resources, 1984—; mem. com. on water resources of water scis. and tech.

bd. NAE/NAS, 1985-87, subcom. on instl. rsch., 1986; advisor water resources rsch. com. ASCE, 1989; cons. in field; presenter papers at numerous profl. meetings. Co-author: (with Penelope ReVelle) Sourcebook on the Environment: The Scientific Perspective, 1974, The Environment: Issues and Choices for Society, 1981, 3d edit., 1988 (with Penelope ReVelle) The Global Environment: Securing a Sustainable Future, 1992; mem. edtl. bd. Geog. Analysis, 1987-91, European Jour. Ops. Rsch., 1991—; assoc. editor Mgmt. Sci.; contbr. over 130 articles to profl. jours. Recipient Robert B. Pond Sr. Excellence in Teaching award Johns Hopkins U., 1990; Fulbright-Hays fellow Erasmus U., The Netherlands, 1975; rsch. grantee City of Balt., 1975-76, 81-82, Nat. Bur. Standards, 1977, Office of Water Rsch. and Tech., 1977-81, U.S. Dept. Energy, 1980-82, N.J. Dept. Energy, 1980-81, Dept. Navy, 1985-87. Mem. Am. Geophys. Union, Arms Control Assn. Inst. Mgmt. Scis., Ops. Rsch. Soc. Am., Internat. Regional Sci. Assn., Phi Kappa Phi, Sigma Xi. Research in: (1) siting of emergency and other public sector facilities; (2) water quality and water resources systems; (3) arms control strategy development. Office: Johns Hopkins U Dept Geography & Environ Engring Ames Hall Baltimore MD 21218 *"Our challenge is to begin to erect the structure that preserves the earth we inherited."*

REVELLE, DONALD GENE, manufacturing and health care company executive, consultant; b. Cape Girardeau, Mo., July 16, 1930; s. Lewis W. and Dorothy R.; m. Jo M. Revelle, Aug. 1, 1954; children—Douglas, David, Daniel, Dianne. BA, U. Mo., 1952; JD, U. Colo., 1957; grad., Harvard U. Bus. Sch., 1971. Dir. employee relations Westinghouse Corp., Pitts., 1957-65; asst. to v.p. Diebold Corp., 1966; v.p. human resources TRW Corp., Cleve., 1967-84; sr. v.p. human resources Black and Decker Co., Towson, Md., 1984-86; exec. v.p. corp. rels. Montefiore Acad. Med. Ctr., Bronx, 1987—; univ. lectr.; cons. Duerba Ship, Blue Cross N.Y., Windsor Hosp., Salvation Army. Contbr. articles to profl. jours. Mem. sch. bd. State of N.Y. Lt. USNR, 1952-54. Mem. ABA (labor law com.), Colo. Bar Assn., Fed. Bar Assn., Human Resource Planning Soc., MBA Assn. Methodist. Home: 1004 Chestnut Ridge Dr Lutherville Timonium MD 21093-1703 Office: Montefiore Acad Med Ctr 111 E 210th St Bronx NY 10467-2490

RE VELLE, JACK B(OYER), statistician, consultant; b. Rochester, N.Y., Aug. 2, 1935; s. Mark A. and Myril (Bubes) Re V.; m. Brenda Lorraine Newcombe, Aug. 2, 1968; 1 child, Karen Alyssa. BS in Chem. Engring., Purdue U., 1957; MS in Indsl. Engring. and Mgmt., Okla. State U., 1965, PhD in Indsl. Engring. and Mgmt., 1970. Commd. 2d lt. USAF, 1957, advanced through grades to major, 1968, resigned, 1968; adminstrv. asst. Gen. Dynamics, Ft. Worth, 1970-71; cons. engr. Denver, 1971-72; chmn. decision scis. U. Nebr., Omaha, 1972-77; dean Sch. Bus. and Mgmt. Chapman U., Orange, Calif., 1977-79; sr. staff engr. McDonnell Douglas Space Systems, Huntington Beach, Calif., 1979-81; head mfg. tng. and devel. Hughes Aircraft Co., Fullerton, Calif., 1981-82; sr. statistician, 1982-86; corp. mgr. R & D Hughes Aircraft Co., L.A., 1986-88; corp. chief statistician, 1988-93; leader continuous improvement Hughes Missile Systems Co., Tucson, Ariz., 1994—; mem. bd. examiners Malcolm Baldrige Nat. Quality Award Nat. Inst. for Stds. and Tech., U.S. Dept. Commerce, Washington, 1990, 93; judge Ariz. Gov.'s Award for Quality, Ariz. Quality Alliance, Phoenix, 1994—, Rochester Inst. Tech.-USA Today Quality Cup Competition, 1994—; cons. to various pub. and pvt. orgns.; presenter in field; lectr. at seminars. Author: Safety Training Methods, 1980, The Two-Day Statistician, 1986, The New Quality Technology, 1988, Policy Deployment, 1993, (with others) Quest for Quality, 1986, Mechanical Engineers Handbook, 1986, Production Handbook, 1987, Handbook of Occupational Safety and Health, 1987, A Quality Revolution in Manufacturing, 1989, Quality Engineering Handbook, 1991; co-author: Quantitative Methods for Managerial Decisions, 1978, The Executive's Handbook on Quality Function Deployment, 1994, From Concept to Customer, 1995. Bd. dirs. Assn. for Quality and Participation, Cin., 1985-86. Fellow Inst. for the Advancement Engring., 1986; recipient Disting. Econs. Devel. award Soc. Mfg. Engrs., 1990. Fellow Am. Soc. for Quality Control (co-chair total quality mgmt. com. 1990-92), Am. Soc. Safety Engrs. (nat. accreditation project dir. 1978-80), Inst. Indsl. Engrs. (regional v.p 1982-84, treas. 1992-93, sr. v.p. 1993-94). Office: Hughes Missile Systems Co Old Nogales Hwy Tucson AZ 85734

REVELLE, WILLIAM ROGER, psychology educator; b. Washington, Nov. 22, 1944; s. Roger Randall and Ellen Virginia (Clark) R.; m. Eleanor McNown, June 20, 1965; children: Daniel James, David Robert. BA, Pomona Coll., 1965; PhD, U. Mich., 1973. Vol. U.S. Peace Corps Sarawak, Malaysia, 1965-67; rsch. asst. U. Mich., Ann Arbor, 1968-73; asst. prof. psychology Northwestern U., Evanston, Ill., 1973-79, assoc. prof., 1979-84, prof. psychology, 1984—, chmn. dept. psychology, 1987-93; mem. Cognitive Emotion Personality com. NIMH-IRG, 1986-90. Contbr. articles to profl. jours. NIH Fogarty Sr. Internat. fellow, Oxford U., 1981-82. Mem. APA, Am. Psychol. Soc., Internat. Soc. for Study of Individual Differences (dir. 1989-93), Soc. of Multivariate Exptl. Psychology (pres. 1984-85). Home: 2302 Orrington Ave Evanston IL 60201-2820 Office: Northwestern Univ Dept Psychology 2029 Sheridan Rd Evanston IL 60208-0828

REVENS, JOHN COSGROVE, JR., state senator, lawyer; b. Providence, Jan. 29, 1947; s. John C. and Rita M. (Williams) R.; AA, C.C. of R.I., 1966; BA, Providence Coll., 1969; JD, Suffolk U., 1973; m. Susan L. Shaw, Aug. 31, 1974; children: Leigh Elizabeth, Marcie Greene, Emily May. Mem. R.I. Ho. of Reps., 1968-74, sec. house steering com., 1971-74, mem. edn. and welfare com., 1968-70; admitted to R.I. bar, 1973; pres. firm Revens, Lanni, Revens & St. Pierre, Warwick, R.I., 1977—; mem. R.I. Senate, 1974-89, 1991—, mem. jud. and labor coms., 1974, chmn. jud. com., 1980-83, majority whip, 1977-80, Senate majority leader, 1983-89; Senate pres., pro tempore, 1993-95; dir. Abington Mut. Fire Ins. Co., Abington Casualty Ins. Co., Patrons Fire Ins. Co. R.I., New Eng. Bd. Higher Edn., 1975-83, chmn., 1977-81; chmn. R.I. Children's Code Commn., 1979-83; bd. dirs. C.C. of R.I. Found., Vols. of Warwick Schs., R.I. Acad. Decathlon Assn.; mem. Commn. on Jud. Tenure and Discipline, 1982-84, Family Ct. Bench Bar Com., 1980-82, Women and Infants Hosp. Corp., 1983—; commr. Uniform State Laws, 1982-84. Mem. ABA, R.I. Bar Assn., Kent County Bar Assn., Am. Arbitration Assn. (panel of arbitrators 1980—), KC Democrat. Roman Catholic. Office: 946 Centerville Rd Warwick RI 02886

REVER, GEORGE WRIGHT, psychiatrist, health facility administrator; b. Balt., May 18, 1928; s. William Benjamin and Amy Blanche (Wright) R.; m. Bridget Valerie Hanley, 1961 (dec. 1988); children: Kurt, Maeve Rever Raedle; m. Ann Roe, Feb. 4, 1994. BS, U. Md., 1950; MD, U. Md., Balt., 1957. Rotating intern Mercy Hosp., Balt., 1957-58; resident psychiatry VA Hosp., Boston, 1958-60; fellow Harvard Med. Sch., Cambridge, Mass., 1960-64, clin. instr. psychiatry, 1964—; pvt. practice Cohasset, Mass., 1963-90, Easton, Md., 1990-93; psychiatric cons. Travelers Aid Soc., Boston, 1966-74; psychiatrist Eunice Kennedy Shriver Ctr., Waltham, Mass., 1967-90; fellow child psychiatry Mass. Gen. Hosp., Boston, 1960-61, 62-63, fellow community mental health, 1963-64, staff psychiatrist, 1964-90, dir. child psychiatry tng. program neuropsychiatry devel. disabilities sect., 1967-90, asst. pediatrician, 1969-71, psychiat. cons. social svc. dept., 1970-74, psychiatrist Chelsea Health Ctr., 1974-77, hon. psychiatrist, 1991—; med. dir. Brockton (Mass.) Family and Community Rsch., 1979-90; child and adolescent psychiatrist Wicomico County Health Dept., Salisbury, Md., 1990-91, Queen Anne County Mental Health, Centreville, Md., 1990-92; child and adolescent psychiatrist Talbot County Mental Health, Easton, 1990-92, med. dir., 1992—; psychiatric cons. Benedictine Sch., Ridgely, Md., 1990—; part-time fellow child psychiatry Mass. Gen. Hosp., Boston, 1961-62, James Jackson Putnam Children's Ctr., Roxbury, Mass., 1961-62; cons. Am. Heritage Dictionaries, 1992. Sgt. U.S. Army, 1950-52, Korea. Decorated Bronze Star medal; Recipient Talbot County Assn. Retarded Citizens award, 1993. Mem. AMA, Am. Acad. Child and Adolescent Psychiatry, Am. Psychiatric Assn., Md. Psychiatric Soc., Med. and Chirurg. Faculty Md., Talbot County Med. Soc. Home: 104 W Chestnut St PO Box D Saint Michaels MD 21663-2980

REVERDIN, BERNARD J., lawyer; b. Baden, Switzerland, June 21, 1919; came to U.S., 1948, naturalized, 1954; s. Jean and Germaine Reverdin; children: Caroline Reverdin Flanagan, Brigitte Reverdin Sarasin, Nathalie. LLB, U. Geneva, 1942; postgrad., Harvard Law Sch., 1949. Bar: Switzerland 1945, N.Y. 1955. Atty., legal asst. Geneva Govt., 1945-48; assoc. Sullivan & Cromwell, N.Y.C., 1949-51; assoc., ptnr. Lovejoy, Wasson, Lundgren & Ashton, N.Y.C., 1951-84; ptnr., counsel Hunton & Williams,

N.Y.C., 19846-88; ptnr. Eaton & Van Winkle, N.Y.C., 1988—; dir. subs. of European corps. Contbr. articles to profl. jours.; lectr. in field. V. p., treas., bd. dirs. Friends of Cuttington Coll., Liberia; v.p. LCM Found. on European Affairs Inc. Mem. N.Y. State Bar Assn. (chair com. internat. trust and estate 1988-90), Am. Fgn. Law Assn. (past pres.), Consular Law Soc. (past pres.), Internat. Law Assn., Swiss Soc. N.Y., German Am. Law Assn. Home: 11 Beech Hill Rd Huntington NY 11743 Office: Eaton & Van Winkle 600 3rd Ave Fl 39 New York NY 10016-2001

REVESZ, RICHARD LUIS, law educator; b. Buenos Aires, Argentina, May 9, 1958. BSE in Civil Engring. summa cum laude, Princeton U., 1979; MS, Mass. Inst. Tech., 1980; JD, Yale U., 1983. Bar: N.Y. 1986, D.C. 1986, U.S. Supreme Ct. 1989, U.S. Ct. Appeals (D.C. cir.) 1986, U.S. Dist. Ct. (so. dist.) N.Y. 1986. Jud. clerk for Chief Judge Wilfred Feinberg U.S. Ct. Appeals (2d cir.) N.Y., 1983-84; jud. clerk for Justice Thurgood Marshall U.S. Supreme Ct., 1984-85; asst. prof. NYU Law Sch., 1985-88, assoc. prof., 1988-90, prof., 1990—; cons. superfund settlements Adminstrv. Conf. U.S., 1991-92, cons. nonacquiescence by agys., 1986-89; term mem. Coun. Fgn. Rels., 1989—; pro-bono rep. Natural Resources Def. Coun., 1987; cons. dept. tech. coop. for devel. UN, 1980-81. Contbr. articles to profl. jours. Cons. Carnegie Commn. Sci., Tech. and Govt., 1989-90. Recipient Exploratory Rsch. grant EPA, 1991—. Mem. ABA (vice chmn. com. jud. review sect. adminstrv. law 1988—), Am. Law Inst. (mem.'s consultative group 1993—), N.Y. State Bar Assn. (chmn. com. adminstrv. law 1988-91, sec. com. second century 1986-88, mem. com. environ. law 1986-88), Phi Beta Kappa, Sigma Xi, Tau Beta Pi (prize winner). Home: 32 Washington Square W Apt 5E New York NY 10011 Office: NYU Sch Law 40 Washington Square S New York NY 10012

REVOILE, CHARLES PATRICK, lawyer; b. Newark, Jan. 15, 1934; s. Charles Patrick and Olga Lydia (Zecca) R.; m. Sally Cole Gates, Nov. 8, 1963. B.A., U. Md., 1957, LL.B., 1960. Bar: Md. 1962, U.S. Dist. Ct. Md. 1962, U.S. Supreme Ct. 1970, U.S. Ct. Claims 1976, U.S. Ct. Appeals (fed. cir.) 1982. Legis. counsel Nat. Canners Assn., Washington, 1960-64; asst. counsel Deco Electronics Inc., Washington, 1964-67; div. counsel Westinghouse Electric, Leesburg, Va., 1967-71; v.p., gen. counsel Stanwick Corp., Arlington, Va., 1971-85, sr. v.p., gen. counsel, sec. CACI Internat. Inc., 1985-92, bd. dirs., 1992—; ret. lawyer and cons., 1993—; mem. regional adv. coun. NASD, 1989-92; lectr., panelist, advisor. Active in Md. Ednl. Found., College Park, 1974—; assoc. Nat. Symphony Orchestra, Washington, 1972-93, Smithsonian Instn., 1980-93, M Club Found., 1985—; lawyer, lobbyist various non profit orgns., Washington, 1984—; mem. exec. com. ann. bus. campaign Gallaudet U., 1989-91; chmh. various coms. Kemeer Open Championships, 1980-86; exec. com. 1995 USGA Sr. Open, 1997 USGA Open Championships; gen. counsel, mem. exec. com. 1995 Kemper Open Championship. Mem. Md. Bar Assn., Wash. Corp. Counsels Assn., Am. Corp. Counsels Assn., U.S. Golf Assn., Mid. Atlantic Golf Assn. (exec. com. 1989—). Republican. Roman Catholic. Club: Congl. Country (com. chmn. 1966-92, bd. govs. 1987-93, Bethesda, Md.). Avondale Golf (Pymble, Australia). Home: 4112 Culver St Kensington MD 20895-3624

REVSINE, LAWRENCE, accounting educator, consultant; b. Chgo., May 29, 1942; s. Victor and Pauline (Berger) R.; m. Barbara Sue Epstein, 1963; children: Pamela, David. B.S., Northwestern U., 1963, M.B.A., 1965, Ph.D., 1968. C.P.A., Ill. Staff acct. Peat, Marwick, Mitchell & Co., Chgo., 1963-64; asst. prof. U. Ill., Urbana, 1968-70, assoc. prof., 1970-71; assoc. prof. acctg. Northwestern U., 1971-74, prof., 1975-79, Eric L. Kohler prof. acctg., 1979-86, John and Norma Darling disting. prof. fin. acctg., 1986—, chmn. dept. acctg. and info. systems, 1985-93; vis. prof. U. Wis., Madison, 1974-75; cons. in field. Author: Replacement Cost Accounting, 1973, Accounting in An Inflationary Enviroment, 1977, (with others) Statement on Accounting Theory and Theory Acceptance, 1977; contbr. articles to profl. jours.; editorial cons.: Acctg. Rev., 1977-80, mem. editorial bd., 1971-74, Jour. Acctg. and Pub. Policy, 1982—, Jour. Acctg. and Bus., 1986—. Recipient commendation for teaching excellence Northwestern U. Grad. Mgmt. Assn., 1981, 82, 86, 91; recipient Tchr. of Yr. award Northwestern U. Grad. Mgmt. Assn., 1983; Ford Found. doctoral fellow, 1966-68; Peat, Marwick, Mitchell Found. grantee, 1978. Mem. AICPA, Am. Acctg. Assn. (chmn. com. on concepts and standards-external fin reports 1974-76, disting. overseas lectr. 1991, outstanding educator 1992), chmn. Fin. Reporting Issues Conf. Com., 1994, Ill. CPA Soc. (outstanding educator 1993), Fin. Acctg. Standards Adv. Coun., Beta Alpha Psi, Beta Gamma Sigma. Office: Northwestern U Kellogg Grad Sch Mgmt Evanston IL 60208

REVUELTA, RENÉ SERGIO, marine scientist, educator; b. La Habana, Cuba, Sept. 9, 1956; s. René Juan and Yolanda Paula (López) R.; m. Maria Soledad Tosteson, June 17, 1984 (div. 1993); children: Zinfandel, Luna. BA, U. Miami, 1978; PhD in Marine Scis., U. P.R., 1986. Grad. rsch. assoc. dept. marine scis. U. P.R., Mayaguez, 1978-86; postdoctoral fellow dept. biology and McCollum-Pratt Inst. Johns Hopkins U., Balt., 1986-88; postdoctoral assoc. divsn. marine and atmospheric chemistry U. Miami, Fla., 1988-89; asst. prof. dept. natural scis. Miami-Dade C.C., 1989-92, assoc. prof., 1992—. Editor: Physical Geography, 5th edit., 1993; contbr. articles to profl. jours. Mem. AAAS, Nat. Geog. Soc., Am. Mus. Nat. History (assoc.), Geol. Soc. Am. Avocations: reading, anthropology, history, fiction, music. Home: P O Box 902020 Homestead FL 33090 Office: Miami-Dade CC Dept Natural Scis 500 College Ter Homestead FL 33030-6009

REVZEN, JOEL, conductor. BS, MS, The Juilliard Sch. Music; studies with Jorge Master, Jean Martinon, Margaret Hillis, Abraham Kaplan. Music dir., condr. Prince William Symphony Orch., Lake Ridge, Va.; mem. faculty Aspen Music Festival; music dir. Orch. & Chorus of St. Louis, The Minn. Chorale; former faculty mem. SUNY, Fredonia; former dean St. Louis Conservatory Music. Office: Fargo Moorhead Symphony Orch 810 4th Ave S Moorhead MN 56560-2800

REWAK, WILLIAM JOHN, university president, clergyman; b. Syracuse, N.Y., Dec. 22, 1933; s. William Alexander and Eldora Venetia (Carroll) R. BA, Gonzaga U., 1957, MA in English, 1958; MA in Theology, Regis Coll., Toronto, Ont., Can., 1965; PhD in English, U. Minn., 1970. Joined S.J., 1951, ordained priest Roman Cath. Ch., 1964. Tchr. English Bellarmine Coll. Prep. Sch., 1958-61; asst. prof. English Santa Clara (Calif.) U., 1970-71, pres., 1976-88; rector Jesuit Community, 1971-76; pres. Spring Hill Coll., Mobile, Ala., 1989—; bd. dirs. Gulf Coast Broadcasting Inc., Badger-Stonewall Ins. Co., Marine Environ. Scis. Consortium. Contbr. articles to theol. and critical jours., poetry, short stories to lit. jours. Bd. dirs. Mobile Bay Area Partnership for Youth, Mercy Med. Ctr.; mem. Ala. Ind. Colls., Coun. for Advancement Pvt. Colls. in Ala.; bd. trustees Loyola U. New Orleans. Mem. MLA, Coll. English Assn., Bienville Club. Democrat. Home and Office: Spring Hill Coll Office of Pres 4000 Dauphin St Mobile AL 36608-1791

REWCASTLE, NEILL BARRY, neuropathology educator; b. Sunderland, Eng., Dec. 12, 1931; arrived in Can., 1955; s. William Alexander and Eva (Coapes) R.; m. Eleanor Elizabeth Barton Boyd, Sept. 27, 1958; 4 children. MB, ChB in Medicine cum laude, U. St. Andrews, Scotland, 1955; M.A., U. Toronto, 1962, FRCPC in gen. pathology, 1962, FRCPC in neuropathology, 1968. Rotating intern U. Vancouver, 1955-56; resident in pathology Shaughnessy Hosp., Vancouver, 1956-57, U. Toronto, Ont., Can., 1957-60; fellow Med. Rsch. Coun. Can., 1960-64; demonstrator dept. pathology U. Toronto, Ont., Can., 1964-65, lectr., acting head neuropathology, 1965-69, assoc. prof., 1969-70, prof. div. neuropathology, 1970-81, head div. neuropathology, 1969-81; prof., head dept. pathology U. Calgary, Alta., Can., 1981-91, prof., 1981—; dir. dept. histopathology Foothills Hosp., Calgary, 1981-91, pathologist, 1981—; cons. neuropathology, 1981—. Recipient Queen Elizabeth Silver Jubilee medal, 1977. Fellow: Royal Coll. Physicians (cert.); mem. Can. Assn. Neuropathologists (sec. 1965-69, pres. 1976-79). Office: Foothills Hosp Dept Histopathology, 1403 29th St NW, Calgary, AB Canada T2N 2T9

REX, CHRISTOPHER DAVIS, classical musician; b. Orlando, Fla., Feb. 1, 1951; s. Charles Gordon Rex and Betty Helen (MacCauslin) Soubricas; m. Martha Anne Wilkins, Nov. 30, 1985; 1 child, Caroline Bethea. MusB, Curtis Inst. of Music, Phila., 1972; postgrad., The Juilliard Sch., 1972-73. Cellist Lyric Opera and Grand Opera, Phila., 1970-75, Phila. Orchestra, 1972-79, Georgian Chamber Players, Atlanta, 1984—; cello tchr. Gettsburg

(Pa.) Coll., 1972-73, New Sch. of Music, Phila., 1969-74, Ga. State U., 1980-83; cellist, tchr. Eastern Music Festival, Greensboro, N.C., 1969-74; prin. cello Atlanta Symphony Orchestra, 1979—; concert soloist Hillyer Internat. Inc., N.Y.C., 1984—; bd. dirs. Ga. Cello Soc., Inc., Atlanta, Georgian Chamber Players, Atlanta; acting prin. during Europe Tour Cello of N.Y. Philharm., 1988; premiered Double Concerto for Violin, Cello, and Orch. N.Y. Philharm., 1994. Editor: (mus. transcription) Pictures at an Exhibition (Moussorgsky), 1987. Recipient First prize Young Artist Competition Am. Fedn. of Music Clubs, 1979. Mem. Phila. Musical Soc., Atlanta Fedn. of Music. Presbyterian. Avocations: art, watercolor painting. Home: 1237 Woods Cir NE Atlanta GA 30324-2725 Office: Atlanta Symphony Orch Woodruff Arts Ctr Atlanta GA 30309

REX, LONNIE ROYCE, religious organization administrator; b. Caddo, Okla., May 11, 1928; s. Robert Lavern and Lennie Cordy (Gilcrease) R.; m. Betty Louise Sorrells, Apr. 8, 1949; children: Royce DeWayne, Patricia Louise, Debra Kaye. MusB, Oklahoma City U., 1950; DD (hon.), Am. Bible Inst., 1970. Advt. mgr. Oral Roberts Evang. Assn., Tulsa, 1955-57; bus. mgr. T.L. Osborn Found., Tulsa, 1957-69; gen. mgr. Christian Crusade, Tulsa, 1969-80; sec.-treas. David Livingstone Missionary Found., Tulsa, 1970-80, pres., 1980—; dep. dir. gen. Internat. Biog. Assn.; bd. dirs. Intra-Ch. Pension Fund, Bethany, Okla.; speaker internat. confs. Eng., Hungary, Korea, Singapore, Spain, N.Y.C. Author: Never a Child, 1989. Mem. Internat. PHC Loan Fund; bd. dirs. Armand Hammer United World Coll. of Am. West, 1993—. Recipient Merit award Korea, 1975, Moran medal Republic of Korea, Humanitarian award Senator Hugh Scott, 1983, Svc. to Mankind award Internat. Biog. Congress, Spain, 1987, Internat. Lions Club award; named Outstanding Humanitarian of Yr., Am. Biog. Inst., 1987, Man of Yr., 1990, 1993; knighted in Moscow, 1993. Mem. Phi Beta Kappa. Home: 6919 S Columbia Ave Tulsa OK 74136-4328 Office: David Livingstone Missionary Found 6555 S Lewis Ave Tulsa OK 74136-1038 *In my work among the starving in Ethiopia, I walked into a tent of over 100 mothers, lying on mats, who had given birth during the last three days. It was silent! Morbid silence! That haunting silence lives with me since that moment. I asked why? I was informed the babies did not have the strength to cry. I'm thankful my children could cry.*

REXINGER, DANIEL MICHAEL, retail company executive; b. Buffalo, Apr. 12, 1938; s. John Frank and Mary Cecil (Madigan) R.; m. Joan Elisabeth Fraser, Nov. 26, 1961; children: Robin Ann, Daniel Fraser. AS, U. Buffalo, 1957. V.p. Wards Co., Richmond, Va., 1966-71; sr. v.p. Circuit City, Richmond, 1971-80, exec. v.p., 1980—, also bd. dirs. Bd. dirs. Stony Point Sch., Richmond, 1980, Family & Children's Services. Served with U.S. Army, 1959-61. Republican. Episcopalian. Avocations: tennis, fishing. Home: 3365 Cedar Grove Rd Richmond VA 23233-1845 Office: Cir City Stores Inc 2040 Thalbro St Richmond VA 23230-3224

REXROTH, NANCY LOUISE, photographer; b. Washington, June 27, 1946; d. John Augustus and Florence Bertha (Young) R. B.F.A., Am. U., 1969; M.F.A. in Photography, Ohio U., Athens, 1971. Asst. prof. photography Antioch Coll., Yellow Springs, Ohio, 1977-79, Wright State U., Dayton, Ohio, 1979-82. Author: Iowa, 1976, The Platinotype, 1977, 1976. Nat. Endowment Arts grantee, 1973; Ohio Arts Council, 1981. Mem. Am. Massage Therapy Assn. Democrat. Home and Office: 2631 Cleinview Ave Cincinnati OH 45206-1810

REY, MARGRET ELIZABETH, writer; b. Hamburg, Germany, May 16, 1906; came to U.S., 1940; d. Felix and Gertrude (Rosenfeld) Waldstein; m. Hans A. Rey (dec. 1977). Art degree, Art Acad., Hamburg, Germany, 1929, Bauhaus, Dessau, Germany, 1931, Acad. Art, Dusseldorf, Germany, 1932. Children's author Houghton Mifflin Co., Boston, 1941—, Harper & Row, N.Y.C., 1945—; script cons. Curgeo, Montreal, Quebec, Can., 1977-83; adj. prof. Brandeis U., Waltham, Mass., 1978-84. Author: Pretzel, 1944, Spotty, 1945, Billy's Picture, 1948; co-author: Curious George, 1941, Curious George Takes a Job, 1947, Curious George Rides a Bike, 1952, Curious George Gets a Medal, 1957, Curious George Flies a Kite, 1958, Curious George Learns the Alphabet, 1963, Curious George Goes to the Hospital, 1966. Founder, trustee The Curious George Found., Cambridge, Mass., 1991—; bd. dirs. Phillips Brooks House, Harvard U., Cambridge, Mass., 1989—. Mem. World Wildlife, Smithsonian, Mus. Fine Arts, Audobon Soc., Defenders of Wildlife. Democrat. Avocations: reading, gardening. Home: 14 Hilliard St Cambridge MA 02138-4922

REY, NICHOLAS ANDREW, ambassador; b. Warsaw, Poland, Jan. 23, 1938; m. Louisa Machado; 3 children. BA, Princeton U.; MA, Johns Hopkins U. From economist to dir. exec. secretariat, staff asst. to sec. Dept. Treasury, 1963-66; v.p. Drexel, Harriman, Ripley, Inc., 1968-70; staff mem. Pres.'s Commn. Internat. Trade and Investment Policy, 1970-71; mng. dir. Merrill Lynch Capital Markets, 1971-87, Bear, Stearns & Co., Inc., 1987-92; vice chair Polish-Am. Fund, 1990-92; with Productivity Consulting Firm, 1992-93; U.S. amb. to Poland, 1993—; Bd. dirs. Resource Found.; mem. Coun. Fgn. Rels., 1972—; N.Y. Stock Exchange; chmn. adv. com. Internat. Capital Markets; mem. internat. com. Security Industry Assn., 1987-92; participant sem. on fin. markets Soviet-N.Y. Stock Exchange, Moscow, 1990; mem. econ. devel. com., transitional corp. and Third World devel. subcom., 1980; mem. internat. Montary Fund study on access to capital markets Internat. Bank for Reconstrn. and Devel., 1978-79; mem. dept. treasury Clinton-Gore Transition Team; mem. fgn. portfolio investment adv. com. Dept. Treasury, 1979-80. Mem. Human Rights Commn., Larchmont, N.Y., 1984-92. With USAR, 1962-68. Office: Am Embassy Warsaw Unit 1340 APO AE 09213-1340

REYCRAFT, GEORGE DEWEY, lawyer; b. New Haven, May 2, 1924; s. George Dewey and Katherine Vivien R.; children: George C., Thomas C., Thaddeus J., Ann K., Nancy J., Pamela C., Sheilah M. B.A. with honors and distinction, Wesleyan U., 1947; LL.B., Harvard U., 1950; postgrad., Georgetown U., 1952, Wayne U., 1953. Bar: D.C. 1951, N.Y. 1964. Ptnr. Cadwalader, Wickersham & Taft, N.Y.C., 1963—; vis. prof. George Washington Law Sch., Washington, 1967; atty. Office Gen. Counsel, Dept. Navy, Washington, 1952; trial atty. U.S. Dept. Justice, Washington, 1952; asst. chief gen. litigation sect. U.S. Dept. Justice, 1957-58, chief spl. trial sect., 1958-60, chief sect. ops., 1960-63; vice chmn. M.A. Schapiro & Co. Inc., 1993—. Served to maj. USAF, 1943-45, 50-52. Mem. Am. Bar Assn., Fed. Bar Assn., Fed. Bar Council, Am. Bar Found., Am. Coll. Trial Lawyers, N.Y. State Bar Assn. (past chmn. antitrust sect.), Assn. Bar City N.Y. (past chmn. com. on trade regulation). Clubs: Harvard (N.Y.C.); Univ. (Washington); Ocean Reef, Shelter Island Yacht.

REYES, ANDRE, ballet dancer; b. San Francisco; s. Benjamin and Josefa Reyes. Student, Santa Clara Ballet Sch.; Sch. Am. Ballet, Am. Ballet Theatre Sch., San Francisco Ballet Sch. With San Francisco Ballet, 1981-95; prin. dancer Pacific Northwest Ballet, 1995—. Appeared in televised performances of Cinderella, 1985 (Dance in Am. Series), To the Beatles, 1984 (Smuin), Stravinsky Piano Pieces, 1984 (Smuin), Symphony in 3 Movements (Gladstein); guest artist Ballet Philippine 20th Anniversary Gala also San Francisco Opera. Office: 252 W 76th St Apt 6E New York NY 10023-8230 Office: Pacific Northwest Ballet 301 Mercer St Seattle WA 98109*

REYES, GREG, electronics executive; b. 1941. V.p., gen. mgr. Fairchild Camera & Instrument Corp., Mountainview, Calif., 1968-69, Eaton Corp., Cleve., 1978-81; pres. Nat. Micronetics, Inc., San Diego, 1981-84; with Sunward Tech. Inc., San Diego, 1985—, now CEO, chmn. bd. dirs. Address: Sunward Tech Inc 5828 Pacific Center Blvd San Diego CA 92121-4204*

REYES, JOSE ANTONIO, SR., minister; b. Canovanas, P.R., May 24, 1940; s. Dionisio Reyes and Antonia (Rodriguez) R.; m. Olfa R. Martinez, May 30, 1964; 1 child, Jose A. BA in Edn., U. P.R., 1962; MA, Sch. Theology, Cleveland, Tenn., 1984; D Ministry, Logos Sch., 1983. Ordained to ministry Ch. of God of Prophecy, 1969. Youth dir. Ch. of God of Prophecy, Rio Piedras, P.R., 1956-58, pastor, 1963-68; mission rep. for Latin Am. Ch. of God of Prophecy, Cleveland, Tenn., 1969-75, internat. radio speaker, 1969—, internat. assist. gen. overseer, 1991—; pres. Hispanic Nat. Religious Broadcasting, Parsippany, 1985-88; v.p. Nat. Orgn. Advancement of Hispanic, 1983-86; com. mem. Hispanic Task Force of Am. Bible Soc., 1985-87; mem. Hispanic Commn., Nat. Assn. Evangelicals, Carol Stream, Ill., 1988—; exec. com. Nat. Religious Broadcasters, 1990—. Author: The

Hispanics in USA - A Challenge, An Opportunity for the Church, 1984; author 10 Bible Study Guides on books of the Bible, 1985-90. Recipient Excellence in Hispanic Program Producer award Nat. Religious Broadcasters, 1988, Excellence in Ministry award Internat. Ministry Com., 1990. Mem. Spanish Voice of Salvation Sponsorship Club (pres.). Republican. Home: 3816 Northwood Dr NW Cleveland TN 37312-3805 *Equalling our Lord is an impossible task, but imitating Him is our supreme duty.*

REYNIK, ROBERT J., materials engineer; b. Bayonne, N.J., Dec. 25, 1932; s. Mary Reynik; m. Georgiana M. Walker, Apr. 12, 1959; children: Michael, Christopher, Jonathan, Katherine, Steven, Kevin. BS in Math. and Physics, U. Detroit, 1956; MS in Elec. Engring., U. Cin., 1960, PhD in Phys. Chemistry, 1963. Rsch. assoc. Sch. Metallurgical Engring. U. Pa., Phila., 1963-64, asst. prof., 1964-67; assoc. prof. Drexel U., Phila., 1967-70; assoc. dir. engring. materials program engring. divsn. NSF, Washington, 1970—; dir. engring. materials program Divsn. Materials Rsch., 1971—; dir. metallurgy program Divsn. Materials Rsch., 1974—; acting head metallurgy, polymers, ceramics and electronic material sect. Divsn. Materials Rsch., 1985-90, head metallurgy, polymers, ceramics and electronic materials sect. Divsn. Materials Rsch., 1985-90, head office spl. programs in materials Divsn. Materials Rsch., 1990—; vis. prof. dept. materials sci. and engring. U. Pa., 1982-83; official cognizant program US-USSR internat. agreement sci. and tech., 1974-90; mem. First U.S. Metallurgical Del. People's Republic China, 1978; liaison rep. Nat. Materials Adv. Bd., 1985—; co-chair FCCSET joint com. edn. and tng. Office of Sci. and Tech. Plicy, 1992-93; task group edn. and tng. Aeronautics Materials and Mfg. Techs. Working Groups Material Sci. and Tech. Coun. Office of Vice President of U.S., 1994; mgr. Sci. and Tech. Ctrs., 1990-94. Rsch. grantee tech. reinvestment project Fed. Govt., 1994—; recipient Univ. scholarships and Rsch. fellowships U. Cin., 1958-63, Post Doctoral fellowship U. Pa., 1963, ASM fellowship, 1993. Fellow Am. Soc. Materials (mem. at large materials sci. coun. 1990—, gold medal selection com.); mem. AAAS, AIME (chair govt. pub. affairs com. 1994—, rep. engrs. pub. policy coun. AAES), Am. Chem. Soc., Am. Phys. Soc., N.Y. Acad. Scis., Internat. Metals, Minerals and Materials Soc., Minerals Metals and Materials Soc. (mem., chmn. various coms.), EEPC task groups, Sigma Xi (past chpt. pres., exec. coord.), Tau Beta Pi. Office: Nat Sci Found Divsn Materials Rsch 4201 Wilson Blvd Arlington VA 22203

REYNOLDS, A. WILLIAM, manufacturing company executive; b. Columbus, Ohio, June 21, 1933; s. William Morgan and Helen Hibbard (McCray) R.; m. Joanne D. McCormick, June 12, 1953; children: Timothy M., Morgan Reynolds Brigham, Mary Reynolds Miller. AB in Econs., Harvard U., 1955; MBA, Stanford U., 1957. Pres. Crawford Door Co., Detroit, 1959-66; staff asst. to treas TRW Inc., Cleve., 1957-59, asst. to exec. v.p. automotive group, 1966-67, v.p. automotive aftermarket group, 1967-70, exec. v.p. indsl. and replacement sector, 1971-81, exec. v.p. automotive worldwide sector, 1981-84; pres. GenCorp, Akron, Ohio, 1984-85, pres., chief exec. officer, 1985-87, chmn., chief exec. officer, 1987—; also bd. dirs.; bd. dirs. Eaton Corp., Cleve., Boise (Idaho) Cascade Corp., Fed. Res. Bank Cleve., now chmn.; mem. dean's adv. coun. Standford (Calif.) U. Grad. Sch. Bus., 1981-88. Chmn. United Way-Red Cross of Summit County, Ohio, 1987; trustee Univ. Hosps. of Cleve., 1984—, chmn., 1987-94. Mem. SAE, Bus. Roundtable (policy com.), Coun. on Fgn. Rels., Kirtland Country Club, Union Club, Rolling Rock Club, John's Island Club, Pepper Pike Club. Episcopalian. Avocations: hunting, fly fishing, skiing, golf. Office: GenCorp Inc 175 Ghent Rd Akron OH 44333-3330*

REYNOLDS, ALAN ANTHONY, economist, writer, consultant; b. Abilene, Tex., Apr. 11, 1942; s. Alan DeForrest and Rosine (McDougall) R.; m. Karen Kane, Feb. 27, 1965; children: John Alan, Melissa Maurine. BA, UCLA, 1965; postgrad., Sacramento State Coll., 1967-71. Dept. mgr. J.C. Penny Co., Sacramento, 1965-71; assoc. editor Nat. Review, N.Y.C., 1972-75; sr. economist Argus Rsch. Corp., N.Y.C., 1976; v.p., economist First Nat. Bank, Chgo., 1977-80; v.p., chief economist Polyconomics Inc., Morristown, N.J., 1981-89; dir. econ. rsch. Hudson Inst., Indpls., 1994—; sr. v.p. H.C. Wainright & Co. Econs., Boston; cons. Leading Authorities, Washington. Contbr. Wall Street Jour., Washington Times, Forbes, Nat. Rev. Internat. Economy, Investment Profiles. Mem. Mont Pelerin Soc. Office: Hudson Inst PO Box 26-919 5395 Emerson Way Indianapolis IN 46226-1475

REYNOLDS, ALBERT BARNETT, nuclear engineer, educator; b. Lebanon, Tenn., Feb. 1, 1931; s. George Lazenby and Marion (Barnett) R.; m. Helen Buck, Sept. 6, 1954; children—Albert Jr., Charlotte, Marion. Student, U. of South, 1948-51; S.B. in Physics, MIT, 1953, S.M. in Nuclear Engring., 1955, Sc.D. in Chem. Engring., 1959. Physicist-mgr. Gen. Electric Co., San Jose, Calif., 1959-68; prof. nuclear engring. U. Va., Charlottesville, 1968—, chmn. dept. nuclear engring. and engring. physics, 1991-92; cons. NRC, Washington, 1970-84, U.S. Dept. Energy, 1987-89; fields of rsch. include liquid metal reactor safety, electric cable aging, boron neutron capture therapy, radiation detection for nuclear test ban treaty. Co-author: Fast Breeder Reactors, 1981; contbr. numerous articles to profl. jours. Fellow Am. Nuclear Soc. (past exec. com. div. nuclear reactor safety 1980-83, chair Va. sect. 1986-87); mem. ASME, IEEE, Am. Soc. Engring. Edn., Sigma Xi, Tau Beta Pi. Home: 1502 Holly Rd Charlottesville VA 22901-3132 Office: U Va Dept Mech Aerospace & Nuclear Engring Charlottesville VA 22903

REYNOLDS, BENEDICT MICHAEL, surgeon; b. N.Y.C., Sept. 12, 1925; s. Benedict and Delia (Coan) R.; m. Alice Marie Hodnett, May 3, 1952; children: Benedict, John, Ann Marie, Mary Alice, Daniel. Student, Columbia U., 1942-43, U. Rochester, 1943-44; MD, NYU, 1948. Diplomate: Am. Bd. Surgery, Pan Am. Med. Assn. Intern Bellevue Med. Center, N.Y.C., 1948-49; surg. resident Bellevue Med. Center, 1951-55; asst. in surgery N.Y. U., N.Y.C., 1953-55; instr. surgery Albert Einstein Coll. Medicine, Bronx, N.Y., 1955-56; asst. prof. surgery Albert Einstein Coll. Medicine, 1956-58, clin. asst. prof., 1958-71, vis. prof. surgery, 1977; prof. surgery N.Y. Med. Coll., N.Y.C., 1971—; practice medicine specializing in surgery Bronx, 1955—; dir. surgery Misericordia Hosp. Med. Center, Bronx, 1962-83, Fordham Hosp., 1964-76; chmn. dept. surgery Lincoln Hosp., Bronx, 1976-82; attending surgeon Met. Hosp., N.Y.C., 1972—; cons. Community Gen. Hosp. of Sullivan County, 1972—. Contbr. articles in field to med. jours. Served with USN, 1943-45, 49-51. Fellow N.Y. Acad. Medicine, A.C.S.; mem. AMA, N.Y. State Med. Soc., N.Y. Acad. Sci., Soc. Surgery Alimentary Tract, N.Y. and Bklyn. Regional Chpt. on Trauma, Internat. Soc. Lymphology, N.Y. Cancer Soc. Am. Gastroent. Assn. Roman Catholic. Home: 150 Overhill Rd Bronxville NY 10708-5136 Office: 1578 Williams Bridge Rd Bronx NY 10461-3000

REYNOLDS, BILL See ARCHER, WILLIAM REYNOLDS, JR.

REYNOLDS, BRETT W., managing director, playwright; b. Trenton, Mich., Apr. 21, 1963; s. John William and Carol B. (Arndt) R. Artistic dir. Vanguard Prodns., Detroit, 1983-86; resident playwright Gt. Am. Children's Theatre, Milw., 1989—; mng. dir. Young Playwrights Inc., N.Y.C., 1993—; also bd. dirs. Author: (play adaptations) The Secret Garden, 1990, The Wind in the Willows, 1991, Journey to the Center of the Earth, 1992, The Velveteen Rabbit, 1994. Mem. Dramatists Guild. Office: Young Playwrights Inc 321 W 44th St # 906 New York NY 10036

REYNOLDS, BURT, actor, director; b. Waycross, Ga., Feb. 11, 1936; s. Burt R.; m. Judy Carne (div. 1965); m. Loni Anderson, Apr. 29, 1988 (div. 1994). Ed., Fla. State U., Palm Beach Jr. Coll. Owner ranch, Jupiter, Fla. Actor numerous stage prodns. including The Rainmaker; movie appearances include: Angel Baby, 1961, Armored Command, 1961, Operation CIA, 1965, Navajo Joe, 1967, Impasse, 1969, 100 Rifles, 1969, Sam Whiskey, 1969, Skullduggery, 1970, Shark, 1970, Deliverance, 1972, Fuzz, 1972, Everything You've Always Wanted to Know about Sex But Were Afraid to Ask, 1972, Shamus, 1973, The Man Who Loved Cat Dancing, 1973, White Lightning, 1973, The Longest Yard, 1974, At Long Last Love, 1975, W.W. and the Dixie Dance Kings, 1975, Hustle, 1975, Lucky Lady, 1975, Silent Movie, 1976, Nickelodeon, 1976, Smokey and the Bandit, 1977, Semi-Tough, 1977, Hooper, 1978, Starting Over, 1979, Rough Cut, 1980, Smokey and the Bandit II, 1980, Cannonball Run, 1981, Paternity, 1981, The Best Little Whorehouse in Texas, 1982, Best Friends, 1982, Stroker Ace, 1983, The Man Who Loved Women, 1983, City Heat, 1984, Cannonball Run II, 1984, Stick,

1985, Uphill All The Way, 1986, Rent A Cop, 1987, Heat, 1987, Malone, 1987, Switching Channels, 1988, Physical Evidence, 1989, Breaking In, 1989, Modern Love, 1990, Cop and a Half, 1993, also voice in All Dogs Go To Heaven, 1989; dir., actor: Gator, 1976, The End, 1978, Sharkey's Machine, 1981; TV appearances include: Branded, 1964; regular appearances on Gunsmoke, 1962-65; star series Hawk, 1966, Dan August, 1970-71, B.L. Stryker, 1989, ABC Saturday Mystery Movie, 1988, Evening Shade, 1990-94. Recipient Emmy award as Outstanding Lead Actor in a Comedy Series ("Evening Shade") Nat. Acad. TV Arts and Scis., 1991. Mem. Dirs. Guild Am. Office: William Morris Agency 151 El Camino Beverly Hills CA 90212*

REYNOLDS, CALVIN, management consultant, business educator; b. N.Y.C., Oct. 2, 1928; s. Charles Edward and Edna (Klockgeter) R.; m. E. Juana Jaynes, Aug. 22, 1955 (div. 1984); m. Mary Virginia Gregg, May 4, 1985; children: Dwight, Neal J. BS in Bus., Columbia U., 1952, MS in Bus., 1959. Dir. ops. Europe Uniroyal Internat., Geneva, 1956-67; v.p. Nat. Fgn. Trade Coun., N.Y.C., 1967-74; sr. v.p. Orgn. Resources Counselors, N.Y.C., 1975-92; sr. counselor Orgn. Resources Counselors, Ossining, N.Y., 1993—; pres. Calvin Reynolds and Assocs., Inc., Ossining, N.Y., 1993—; dir. Yokogawa-ORC, Tokyo, Am. Compensation Assn.; pres. Indsl. Rels. Counselors. Adv. bd. ACA Jour., 1993—; contbr. articles to profl. jours. Wharton Sch. U. Pa. sr. fellow, 1993-94. Mem. Inst. for Internat. Human Resource Mgmt. Republican. Congregationalist. Avocations: golf, music, reading. Home and Office: Calvin Reynolds & Assocs Inc 52 Underhill Rd Ossining NY 10562-5118

REYNOLDS, CARL CHRISTIANSEN, government official; b. Wellsville, Utah, Sept. 8, 1934; s. Joseph William and Theresa (Christiansen) R.; m. Sharon Zollinger, Feb. 15, 1963; children: Rose Marie, Jeffrey Wayne. BS, Utah State U., 1957. Lab. technician Thiokol Chem. Corp., Brigham City, Utah, 1960-62; investigator FDA, Denver, 1962-66; resident investigator FDA, Albuquerque, 1966-72; supervisory investigator FDA, Dallas, 1972-77; dir. investigations FDA, Orlando, Fla., 1977-89; dist. dir. FDA, Detroit, 1989-95; dir. office field programs FDA, Washington, 1995—. Mem. council exec. bd. Boy Scouts Am., Albuquerque, 1967-72, mem. nat. com. Dallas, 1982-86, dist. com., Orlando and Dallas, 1972-87. Served with U.S. Army, 1957-59. Recipient Award of Merit Boy Scouts Am., 1975, Silver Beaver award, 1986. Mem. Assn. Food and Drug Officials. Republican. Mormons. Avocations: camping, computer programming, electronics.

REYNOLDS, CAROLYN MARY, elementary educator; b. Bklyn., May 17, 1936; d. Wesley and Christine (Cardieri) Russo; m. Richard Martin Reynolds, Apr. 12, 1958; children: Donna Marie Reynolds Dewey, Richard Edward. BS, Adelphi U., 1968; MA, SUNY, Stony Brook, 1971. Cert. tchr., N.Y. Tchr. Rocky Point (N.Y.) Sch., 1956-57, Little Flower Sch., Wading River, N.Y., 1957-59, Shoreham (N.Y.)-Wading River Sch. Dist., 1969—; supervising tchr. St. Joseph Coll., 1991, Dowling Coll., Oakdale, N.Y., 1992, S.W. Post Coll., Southampton, N.Y.; coord. constructivist course, Shoreham, N.Y., 1990—; active Sch. Consolidation Task Force, 1992-93. Editor tchr. union publ. VOX, 1989-90 (award 1990). Leader Girl Scouts U.S.A., Rocky Point, N.Y., 1956; mem. Sch. Consolidation Task Force, 1993-94. Noyes Found. fellow; NSF grantee. Mem. ASCD, Nat. Coun. Tchrs. English, N.Y. State United Tchrs., Shoreham-Wading River Tchrs. Assn. (co-pres., sec., negotiator tchrs. contract), United Fedn. Tchrs. (10 Yr. pin for leadership), Internat. Reading Assn. (coun. pres. 1980—). Home: 50 Highland Down Shoreham NY 11786

REYNOLDS, CLARK WINTON, principal investigator, program director, educator; b. Chgo., Mar. 13, 1934; m. Nydia O'Connor Viales. AB, Claremont (Calif.) Men's Coll., 1956; student, MIT, 1956-57, 58; student divinity sch., Harvard U., 1957-58; MA, U. Calif., Berkeley, 1961, PhD, 1962. Asst. prof. Occidental Coll., L.A., 1961-62; from asst. to assoc. prof. dept. edn. and econ. growth Yale U., New Haven, 1962-67; sr. fellow The Brookings Inst., Washington, 1975-76; prin. investigator, founding dir. Americas program, prof. Stanford (Calif.) U., 1967—; vis. prof. Nat. U. Mex., Chapingo, 1966, El Colegio de Mex., Mexico City, 1964, 65, 79; vis. lectr. in econs. Stockholm U. Econs., 1968; vis. rsch. scholar Internat. Inst. for Applied Systems Analysis, Laxenburg, Austria, 1978; advisor N.Am. forum Stanford U., 1990—. Author: The Mexican Economy, 1970; co-editor: Essays on The Chilean Economy, 1965, (with C. Tello) U.S.-Mexican Relations: Economic & Social Aspects, Las Relaciones Mexico Estados Unidos, 1983, Dynamics of North American Trade, 1991, North American Labor Market Interdependence, 1992, Open Regionalism in the Andes, 1995. Dir. Monticello West Found., 1980. Woodrow Wilson Found. fellow, 1956-57, Rockefeller Found. fellow, 1957-58, Doherty Found. fellow, 1960-61, Inst. Internat. Studies fellow Stanford U., 1990—; grantee Social Sci. Rsch. Coun., Ford Found., Hewlett Found., Rockefeller Found., Mellon Found., MacArthur Found., Tinker Found. Office: Stanford U Food Rsch Inst Encina Hall W Rm 305/306 Stanford CA 94305-6084

REYNOLDS, CLAYTON S., lawyer; b. White Plains, N.Y., June 18, 1955; s. Charles Wesley and Ota (Thomas) R. BA, Trinity Coll. Camgridge U., Eng., 1976, MA, 1982; JD, Harvard U., 1979; LLM, NYU, 1987. Assoc. Sullivan & Cromwell, N.Y.C., 1979-84; assoc. then ptnr. Bachner, Tally, Polevoy, Misher & Brinberg, N.Y.C., 1984-86; ptnr. Mudge, Rose, Guthrie, Alexander & Ferdon, N.Y.C., 1987—. Roman Catholic. Office: Mudge Rose Guthrie Alexander & Ferdon 180 Maiden Ln New York NY 10038-4925

REYNOLDS, COLLINS JAMES, III, association administrator; b. N.Y.C., Feb. 28, 1937; s. Collins James and Alta Roberta (Carr) R.; m. Harriet Virginia Blackburn (div. 1965); children: Collins James IV, Quentin Scott; m. Carol Ann Miller, June 24, 1967; children: Justin Blake, Carson Jonathan. Student govt. and econs., Harvard U., George Washington U. Data processing supr. missile and space vehicle div. Gen. Electric, Phila., 1961; contract adminstr. Allison div. Gen. Motors, Indpls., 1962-65; country dir. Peace Corps, Mauritania, 1966-67; dir. Peace Corps, Sierra Leone, 1971-74; dir. div. ops. Gen. Learning Corp., Time Inc., Washington, 1968-71; trustee, sec., treas., exec. dir. Center for Research and Edn., Denver, 1974-79; Carter Presdl. appointee, assoc. dir. Internat. Devel. Coop. Agy., AID, 1980; dir. mktg. Am. TV & Communications Corp., Time Inc., Denver, 1980-81; founder, chmn. bd., pres. Omnicom, Inc., Denver, 1981-87; Bush Presdl. appointee, sr. exec. svc., assoc. dir. mgmt. Peace Corps, 1989-92; dir. comms. divsn. Am. Water Works Assn., 1994—; cons., UN Secretariat, Econ. Devel. Adminstrn., OECD, USAID, USDA; project dir. Model Cities Edn. Plan, HUD, Gen. Learning, Balt.; Dept. Labor/HEW Remedial Edn. and Job Placement Program, Transcentury Corp., Washington; program mgr. Ft. Lincoln New Town Sch. Program, Washington; supervising dir. VISTA, Boston, N.Y.C., Atlanta; dir. adminstrn. Job Corps, Kansas City. Founder, editor, pub.: The Bridge; patentee in field. Served as aviator USMCR, 1956-60. Home: 1615 Krameria St Denver CO 80220-1552

REYNOLDS, DAVID G(EORGE), physiologist, educator; b. South Chicago Heights, Ill., Nov. 25, 1933; s. Gilbert J. and Louise C. (Roescheisen) R.; m. Carol J. Adams, Aug. 26, 1987. BA, Knox Coll., 1955; MS, U. Ill., 1957; PhD, U. Iowa, 1963. Commd. 2d lt. M.C., U.S. Army, 1957, advanced through grades to lt. col., 1971; chief basic scis. Med. Field Sci. Sch., Fort Sam Houston, Tex., 1957-60, 1963-65; chief gastroenterology Walter Reed Army Inst. Research, Washington, 1965-72, dir. surgery, 1972-77; ret., 1977; prof. surgery, dir. surg. research U. Iowa Hosp., Iowa City, 1977-87, U. South Fla., Tampa, 1987-90; prof. surgery, dir. exptl. surgery, dir. divsn. surg. scis. U. Minn., Mpls., 1991—. Co-editor: Advances in Shock Research, 1983; others; contbr. numerous articles, chpts., abstracts to profl. publs. Active youth athletics, Iowa City. Mem. AAAS, Am. Physiol. Soc., Assn. Acad. Surgery, Shock Soc. (pres. 1986-87), Soc. Exptl. Biology and Medicine. Home: 110 Bank St SE Apt 504 Minneapolis MN 55414-3902 Office: U Minn Dept Surgery Minneapolis MN 55455

REYNOLDS, DAVID PARHAM, metals company executive; b. Bristol, Tenn., June 16, 1915; s. Richard S. and Julia L. (Parham) R.; m. Margaret Harrison, Mar. 25, 1944 (dec. 1992); children: Margaret A., Julia P., Dorothy H. Student, Princeton U. With Reynolds Metals Co., Louisville, 1937—, salesman, 1937-41, asst. mgr. aircraft parts div., 1941-44, asst. v.p., 1944-46, v.p., 1946-58, exec. v.p., 1958-69, exec. v.p., gen. mgr., 1969-75, vice

chmn., chmn. exec. com., 1975-76, chief exec. officer, 1976-86, chmn. bd., 1986-88, chmn. emeritus, 1988—; former chmn. bd. dirs. Eskimo Pie Corp. Trustee emeritus Lawrenceville (N.J.) Sch., U. Richmond. Mem. AIA (hon.), Primary Aluminum Inst., Aluminum Assn. (past chmn.). Office: Reynolds Metals Co 6601 W Broad St Richmond VA 23230-1701

REYNOLDS, DEBBIE (MARY FRANCES REYNOLDS), actress; b. El Paso, Tex., Apr. 1, 1932; m. Eddie Fisher, Sept. 26, 1955 (div. 1959); children—Carrie, Todd; m. Harry Karl, Nov., 1960 (div. 1973); m. Richard Hamlett (separated). Active high sch. plays; screen debut Daughter of Rosie O'Grady; motion pictures include: June Bride, 1948, The Daughter of Rosie O'Grady, 1950, Three Little Words, 1950, Two Weeks With Love, 1950, Mr. Imperium, 1951, Singin' in the Rain, 1952, Skirts Ahoy!, 1952, I Love Melvin, 1953, The Affairs of Dobie Gillis, 1953, Give a Girl a Break, 1953, Susan Slept Here, 1954, Athena, 1954, Hit the Deck, 1955, The Tender Trap, 1955, The Catered Affair, 1956, Bundle of Joy, 1956, Tammy and the Bachelor, 1957, This Happy Feeling, 1958, The Mating Game, 1959, Say One for Me, 1959, It Started With a Kiss, 1959, The Gazebo, 1959, The Rat Race, 1960, Pepe, 1960, The Pleasure of His Company, 1961, The Second Time Around, 1961, How the West Was Won, 1962, My Six Loves, 1963, Mary, Mary, 1963, The Unsinkable Molly Brown, 1964, Goodbye Charlie, 1964, The Singing Nun, 1966, Divorce American Style, 1967, How Sweet It Is!, 1968, What's the Matter with Helen?, 1971, Charlotte's Web, (voice only) 1973, That's Entertainment!, 1974, The Bodyguard, 1992, Heaven and Earth, 1993; star TV program The Debbie Reynolds Show, 1969; star Broadway show Irene, 1973-74, Annie Get Your Gun, Los Angeles, San Francisco, 1977, Woman of the Year, 1984, The Unsinkable Molly Brown, 1989-90 (nat. tour); author: If I Knew Then, 1963, Debbie-My Life, 1988; creator exercise video Do It Debbie's Way, 1984. Prin. Debbie Reynolds's Hotel/Casino and Hollywood Motion Picture Mus., Las Vegas, 1993—. Named Miss Burbank, 1948. Office: Debbie Reynolds Studios care Margie Duncan 6514 Lankershim Blvd North Hollywood CA 91606-2496

REYNOLDS, DONALD MARTIN, art historian, foundation administrator, educator; b. Kansas City, Mo., Jan. 11, 1931; s. James Martin and Mary Helen (Hughes) R.; m. Nancy Zlobik, June 5, 1970. Student, Amarillo Coll., 1949-51; BA, Assumption Sem., San Antonio, 1955, Columbia U., 1968; MA, Columbia U., 1970, PhD, 1975. Announcer KGNC Radio/TV, Amarillo, Tex., 1949-51; account exec. Monte Rosenwald & Assocs., Amarillo, Tex., 1957-59; copy writer, account rep., account supr. J. Walter Thompson, N.Y.C., C.Am., 1959-61; mgr. Ctrl. Am., Young & Rubicam Advt., N.Y.C., Panama, 1961-62; advt. mgr., mktg. dir. Colgate-Palmolive Co. Western Hemisphere Divsn., 1962-64; founder, dir. Image, Internat. Mktg. Agy., N.Y.C., 1964-66; mus. educator in charge Dept. Pub. Edn. Met. Mus. of Art, 1977-79; curator of parks Dept. Parks and Recreation, N.Y.C., 1986-88; founder, coord. Ann. Symposium on Pub. Monuments, N.Y.C., 1991—; founder, dir. The Monuments Conservancy, Inc., N.Y.C., 1992—; adj. prof. art history Columbia U., N.Y.C., 1973—; adj. prof. art history Fairfield (Conn.) U., 1981—; adj. asst. prof. art history Hunter Coll., 1972-81; asst. prof. art history Coll. Mt. St. Vincent and Manhattan Coll., 1973-77. Author: The Ideal Sculpture of Hiram Powers, 1977, Manhattan Architecture, 1988, Eng., French edits., The Architecture of New York City: Histories and Views of Important Structures, Sites, and Symbols, 1984, paper, 1988, rev. edit., 1994, Monuments and Masterpieces: Histories and Views of Public Sculpture in New York City, 1988, Nineteenth Century Architecture, 1987, also fgn. langs. edits., Nineteenth Century Architecture, 1992, Masters of American Sculpture, the Figurative Tradition from the American Renaissance to the Millennium, 1993; editor, compiler: The Impact of Non-European Civilizations on the Art of the West: Selected Lectures of Rudolf Wittkower, 1989; contbg. author The Macmillan Ency. of Architects, 1982. Trustee Brookgreen Gardens, S.C., Brookgreen Gardens Mus., S.C. With U.S. Army, 1955-61. Mem. Nat. Sculpture Soc., Coll. Art Assn., Authors Guild. Office: PO Box 608 Cooper Sta New York NY 10003

REYNOLDS, EDWARD, book publisher; b. N.Y.C., Apr. 25, 1926; s. Edward and Dorothea Curtis (Jordan) R.; m. Joan Gale, Sept. 13, 1953; children—Edward, Peter Winsor, James Lyman, Joseph Warren. A.B., Harvard U., 1950, M.B.A., 1953. With United Aircraft Can. Ltd., Montreal, 1953-60; v.p. fin. and adminstn. Mitre Corp., Bedford, Mass., 1960-66; sr. v.p. fin. and adminstrn. Houghton Mifflin Co., Boston, 1967-76; dir. fin. New England Med. Ctr. Hosp., Boston, 1978-79; v.p. fin. and adminstrn. John Wiley & Sons, Inc., N.Y.C., 1980-83; v.p. fin. and adminstrn., 1983-86; pres., chief exec. officer Innovative Scis., Inc., Stamford, Conn., 1987-90, treas., 1991—; also bd. dirs. With USNR, 1944-46. Clubs: Union League, Cruising of Am. Office: Innovative Scis Inc 975 Walnut St Cary NC 27511-4216

REYNOLDS, ERNEST WEST, physician, educator; b. Bristow, Okla., May 11, 1920; s. Ernest West and Florence (Brown) R. B.S., U. Okla., 1942, M.D., 1946, M.S., 1952. Diplomate: Am. Bd. Internal Medicine. Intern Boston City Hosp., 1946-47; resident Grady Meml. Hosp., Atlanta, 1949-50; practice medicine Tulsa, Okla., 1953-54; prof. medicine U Mich., 1965-72; prof. medicine, dir. cardiology U.Wis., 1972—; dir. Kellogg Found. Comprehensive Coronary Care Project, 1967-72; chmn. NIH Cardiovascular Study Sect. A, 1972-73. Mem. editorial bd.: Am. Heart Jour; Contbr. articles to profl. jours. Served to capt. AUS, 1947-49. Mem. Am. Heart Assn. (fellow council clin. cardiology); mem. Central Soc. Clin. Research. Home: 17 Red Maple Trl Madison WI 53717-1515 Office: U Wis 600 Highland Ave Madison WI 53792-0001 *In the academic environment, research oriented toward the solution of human problems is more productive in career advancement than the pursuit of applications of new technology. In the private sector applied research which solves real problems rather than copies or improves existing technology is met with surprising sales success and few failures.*

REYNOLDS, FRANK EVERETT, religious studies educator; b. Hartford, Conn., Nov. 13, 1930; s. Howard Wesley and Caroline Mills Roys R.; m. Mani Bloch, Mar. 28, 1959 (dec. 1993); children: Roy Howard, Andrew Everett, Roger Frank. Student, Princeton U., 1948-51; B.A., Oberlin U., 1952; B.D., Yale Div. Sch., 1955; M.A., U. Chgo., 1963, Ph.D., 1971. Ordained to ministry Am. Baptist Ch., 1955. Program dir. Student Christian Ctr., Bangkok, Thailand, 1956-59; minister to fgn. students U. Chgo. Ecumenical Ministries, 1961-64; instr. U. Chgo., 1967-69, asst. prof. then assoc. prof., 1969-79, prof. history of religions and Buddhist studies, 1979—; program dir. Inst. for the Advanced Study of Religions, 1992—; co-dir. Liberal Arts and Study of Religions Project, 1985-90, NEH Sangitiyavasama Transl. Porject, 1991-93. Author: Guide to Buddhist Religion, 1981; (with others) Two Wheels of Dhamma, 1971, Religions of the World, 3d edit., 1993; editor, co-translator: 3 Worlds According to King Ruang, 1981; co-editor: Anthropology and the Study of Religion, 1984, Cosmology and Ethical Order, 1985, Myth and Philosophy, 1990, Beyond the Classics: Religious Studies and Liberal Education, 1990, Discourse and Practice, 1992, Religion and Practical Reason, 1994; co-editor History of Religion Jour., 1977—; assoc. editor Jour. Religion, 1976—, Jour. Religious Ethics, 1981—. Jacob Fox Found. fellow, 1952, Danforth Found. fellow, 1960, 64; sr. rsch. grantee Fulbright Commn., 1973-74, NEH, 1978-79. Mem. Am. Coun. Learned Socs. (com. on history of religions 1985-94), Am. Soc. Study Religion, Am. Acad. Religion (chmn. com. on history of religions 1994—), Assn. Asian Studies (co-editor monograph series 1978-86), Internat. Congress of History of Religions, Internat. Assn. Buddhist Studies, Law and Society. Home: 5433 S Blackstone Ave Chicago IL 60615-5406 Office: U Chgo Swift Hall 1025 E 58th St Chicago IL 60637-1509

REYNOLDS, FRANK MILLER, retired government administrator; b. Tulsa, Jan. 8, 1917; s. Frank Miller and Grace (Shields) R.; m. Barbara G. MacWilliams, Dec. 7, 1946; children: Susan G., Ellen M. Frank M. A.B. LL.B., U. Okla., 1939; LL.M., George Washington U., 1942; B.S., Georgetown Sch. Fgn. Service, 1941. Bar: Okla. 1940. Mem. firm Flippo & Reynolds, Tulsa, 1940; elec. engr. Bur. Ships, Dept. of Navy, 1942-43; with office Gen. Counsel Dept. of Navy, 1946; chief negotiator, dep. dir. contract div. Office Naval Research, 1947-54; dep. dir., dir. resources div. Office Asst. Sec. Def., 1954-57; asst. sec. Inst. for Defense Analyses, 1957-61; sec., treas. Logistics Management Inst., Washington, 1961-65; v.p. Logistics Management Inst., 1966-76; dir. adminstrv. affairs Uniformed Services U. Health Scis., Bethesda, Md., 1976-78; dir. resource mgmt. Uniformed Services U. Health Scis., 1978-82, exec. sec. bd. regents, 1978-83; dir. patient relations

Sibley Meml. Hosp., 1983-84, cons., 1984-87; professorial lectr. mgmt. research George Washington U. Sch. Engring., 1956—; cons. Nat. Exec. Service Corps., United Srs. Health Coop., 1984—. Served with radio div. Naval Research Lab., 1944-46. Mem. Okla. Bar Assn., Congl. Country Club, Delta Upsilon. Home: 9107 River Rd Potomac MD 20854-4627

REYNOLDS, GARY KEMP, librarian; b. Phila., June 2, 1944; s. Thomas Clifford and Lillian Olive (Thompson) R.; m. Regina Romano, May 16, 1970; 1 child, Elizabeth Alexandra Marie. BA in History with honors, Pa. State U., 1973, BA in East Asian Studies magna cum laude, 1973; MA in E.Asian Studies, U. Mich., 1975, MA in East Asian Studies, 1976. Reference libr. George Washington U., Washington, 1977-80; info. rsch. specialist congl. rsch. svc. Libr. of Congress, Washington, 1980—. Reviewer manuscripts for profl. jours.; contbr. articles to profl. publs. Sgt. USAF, 1962-66. Mem. Phi Beta Kappa, Phi Kappa Phi, Phi Alpha Theta, Mensa. Republican. Episcopalian. Avocations: painting, Oriental arts and antiques, science fiction. Home: 7603 Marian Ct Falls Church VA 22042-3515 Office: Libr of Congress Washington DC 20540

REYNOLDS, GENE, television producer, director; b. Cleve., Apr. 4, 1925; m. Bonnie Jones. Actor motion pictures including Thank You, Jeeves, 1936, In Old Chicago, 1937, Boys Town, 1938, They Shall Have Music, 1939, Edison the Man, 1940, Eagle Squadron, 1942, The Country Girl, 1954, The Bridges at Toko-Ri, 1955, Diane, 1955; exec. producer TV series Room 222, 1969-74, Anna and the King, 1972, Karen, 1975; producer TV pilot The Ghost and Mrs. Muir, 1968-70, Roll Out!, 1973-74; exec. producer Lou Grant, 1977-82 (Emmy award 1979, 80); producer TV series M*A*S*H, 1972-76, exec. producer from 1976; producer, dir. TV movie People Like Us, 1976; dir. In Defense of Kids, 1983, Doing Life, 1986. Recipient Emmy award Nat. Acad. TV Arts and Scis. 1970, 74, 75, 76; Dirs. Guild award for TV comedy (2); (with others) Peabody award for M*A*S*H. Mem. Dirs. Guild Am. Office: care Broder Kurland Webb Agy 9242 Beverly Blvd # 200 Beverly Hills CA 90210-3710

REYNOLDS, GEORGE THOMAS, physics educator, researcher, consultant; b. Trenton, May 27, 1917. B.Sc. in Physics and Math., Rutgers U., 1939; M.A. in Physics, Princeton U., 1942, Ph.D. in Physics, 1943. Research physicist Princeton (N.J.) U., 1943-44, asst. prof., 1946-51, assoc. prof., 1951-59, prof., 1959-78, Class of 1909 prof. physics, 1978-87, emeritus, 1987—, dir. high energy physics program, 1948-70, dir. sci. in human affairs program, 1963-67, dir. Ctr. Environ. Studies, 1970-73, mem. council on environ. studies, 1970-73, 80-87, prin. investigator biophysics program, 1964-87; mem. univ. research bd. Princeton (N.J.), 1980-86; physicist Manhattan Project, 1944-46; mem. NSF Adv. Com. for Planning and Instl. Relations, 1971-74; mem. vis. adv. com. dept. applied sci. Brookhaven Nat. Lab., 1971-74; mem. corp. Marine Biol. Lab., Woods Hole, Mass., 1968—, chmn. radiation com., 1973-77; mem. ad hoc adv. panel for environ. problems Dept. Energy Div. Biomed. and Environ Research; vis. prof. Imperial Coll.-U. London, 1955-56, Open U. (U.K.), 1981-82; cons. in field; mem. adv. panel for radiation physics Nat. Bur. Standards, 1962-64; seminar assoc. Columbia U. Sem. on Tech. and Social Change, 1966-85; mem. study panel on physics edn. Nat. Acad. Scis., 1970-72; cons. NSF div. Policy Research and Analysis, 1985-88. Bd. editors: Rev. Sci. Instruments, 1955-58; contbr. chpts. to books, numerous jour. articles. Chmn. adv. council for research and grad. edn. Rutgers U., New Brunswick, N.J., 1969-72, trustee, 1974-86, 89—. Served to lt. (j.g.) USNR, 1944-46. Recipient cert. appreciation Army-Navy, 1948; Guggenheim fellow U. London, 1955-56; Churchill fellow Cambridge (Eng.) U., 1973-74; vis. sr. research fellow Oxford (Eng.), 1981-82; Royal Soc. guest research fellow, 1985. Fellow AAAS, Am. Phys. Soc.; mem. Biophys. Soc., Am. Geophys. Union, IEEE, Am. Soc. Photobiology, Phi Beta Kappa, Sigma Xi (local pres. 1962-63). Office: Princeton U Dept Physics Joseph Henry Labs Jadwin Hall PO Box 708 Princeton NJ 08544

REYNOLDS, GLENN FRANKLIN, medicinal research scientist; b. Rahway, N.J., July 16, 1944; s. Frank Vanderbilt and Estell (Ohlott) R.; m. Marianne DelliSanti, Nov. 25, 1967; children: William Mathew, David Glenn, Wendy Joy. Student, Rutgers U., 1962-63, Union Coll., 1963-65; BS in Chemistry, Phila. Coll. Pharmacy and Sci., 1967. Rsch. scientist Merck & Co., Rahway, 1967-70, staff chemist, 1970-77, rsch. chemist, 1977-86, sr. rsch. assoc., 1991—; Merck recruiter Fairleigh Dickinson U., 1980, Howard U., 1980, U. N.C., 1981, Rutgers U., 1985. Inventor Proscar; contbr. articles to profl. jours.; patentee in field. Named Inventor of Yr. Intellectual Property Owners, 1993. Mem. Am. Chem. Soc., Masons (Lafayette lodge #27). Presbyterian. Avocations: computer science, hiking, skiing, reading. Home: 252 Edgewood Ave Westfield NJ 07090 Office: Merck & Co Inc PO Box 2000 126 E Lincoln Ave 50G/130 Rahway NJ 07065

REYNOLDS, GLENN HARLAN, law educator; b. Birmingham, Ala., Aug. 27, 1960; s. Charles Harlan Reynolds and Glenda Lorraine (Teal) Childress. BA, U. Tenn., 1982; JD, Yale U., 1985. Bar: Tenn. 1985, D.C. 1986. Law clk. U.S. Ct. Appeals, Nashville, 1985-86; assoc. Dewey, Ballantine, Bushby, Palmer & Wood, Washington, 1986-89; assoc. prof. law U. Tenn., Knoxville, 1989—; sr. assoc. Space Studies Inst., Princeton, N.J., 1990—. Author: Outer Space: Problems of Law and Policy, 1989. Recipient Outstanding Svc. award Space Cause, Washington, 1990. Mem. AAAS, Nat. Space Soc. (chair legis. com. 1989—). Office: U Tenn 1505 Cumberland Ave Knoxville TN 37916-3199

REYNOLDS, HARRY LINCOLN, physicist; b. Port Chester, N.Y., Mar. 31, 1925; s. Harry Benson and Lydia (Wilde) R.; m. Katherine Haile, 1950; children: Patricia Reynolds Cabral, Margaret Benson. B.S., Rensselaer Poly. Inst., 1947; Ph.D., U. Rochester, 1951. Sr. scientist Oak Ridge Nat. Lab., 1951-55; physicist Lawrence Livermore Nat. Lab., 1955-65; asst. program mgr. NASA Manned Spacecraft Center, Houston, 1965; asso. dir. nuclear test, nuclear design and nuclear explosives programs Lawrence Livermore Nat. Lab., Calif., 1965-80, spl. asst. to dir., 1980-81; dep. assoc. dir. advanced concepts Los Alamos Nat. Lab., 1981-85; dir. advanced concepts Rockwell Internat. Corp., Seal Beach, Calif., 1985-94; cons. in field. Contbr. articles to profl. jours. Trustee Valley Meml. Hosp., Livermore, 1980-81; mem. Army Sci. Bd., 1982-88. Served with U.S. Navy, 1944-46. AEC fellow, 1947-49. Fellow Am. Phys. Soc. Home: 801 Via Somonte Palos Verdes Peninsula CA 90274-1631

REYNOLDS, HERBERT YOUNG, physician, internist; b. Richmond, Va., Aug. 20, 1939; s. George Audney and Pearle Maupin (Young) R.; m. Anne Browning Leavell, July 11, 1964; children: Nancy, George, William Stuart. BA in English, U. Va., 1961, MD, 1965; MA (hon.), Yale U., 1979. Diplomate Am. Bd. Internal Medicine, Am. Bd. Allergy and Immunology. Intern in medicine The N.Y. Hosp., Cornell Med. Ctr., N.Y.C., 1965-66, asst. physician, fellow in medicine, 1966-67; clin. assoc., lab clin. investigator Nat. Inst. Allergy and Infectious Diseases, NIH, Bethesda, Md., 1967-70, chief clin. assoc. lab. clin. investigation, 1968-69; sr. investigator lab. of clin. investigation Nat. Inst. Allergy and Infectious Diseases, NIH, 1971-76; chief resident, instr. medicine U. Hosp. U. Wash., Seattle, 1970-71; assoc. prof. internal medicine, head pulmonary div. Sch. Medicine Yale U., New Haven, 1976-79, prof., 1979-88; J. Lloyd Huck prof. medicine, chmn. dept. Pa. State U.-Milton S. Hershey Med. Ctr., 1988—; mem. exec. com. Coll. Medicine Pa. State U.-Hershey Med. Ctr., 1988—, mem. bd. acad. enrichment fun, 1988-95, mem. dean's adv. com., 1988—, others; cons. in infectious diseases Nat. Naval Med. Ctr. NIH, Bethesda, 1971-76, clin. rsch. com. 1971-76, chmn., 1974, med. bd. mem., 1974-76, pulmonary disease adv. com. div. of lung diseases Nat. Heart, Lung and Blood Inst., 1978-82, mem. sci. counselors bd., 1984-88, mem. data and safety monitoring bd. registry of patients with deficiency of Alpha-1 Antitrypsin, 1989—. Assoc. editor or mem. editorial bd. Lung, 1978-95, Am. Jour. Medicine, 1979-86, Jour. Clin. Investigation, 1980-86, Am. Rev. Respiratory Disease, 1980-87, Jour. Applied Physiology, 1981-89, Resident Physician, 1981—; contbr. over 250 articles and revs. to profl. jours. Mem. parent com. Troop 1 Boy Scouts Am., Madison, 1979-82; bd. dirs. Neighborhood Music Sch., Guilford, Conn. 1978-87, Music at Gretna, 1994—; active All Saints Episc. Ch, Hershey; mem. pulmonary infections com. Cystic Fibrosis Found., Bethesda, 1980-86; mem. coun. sci. advisors Parker B. Francis Found., Kansas City, Kan., 1983-87; mem. internat. com. World Orgn. for Sarcoidosis and other Granulomatous Disorders, 1987—; bd. dirs., mem. coun. Am. Lung Assn., 1989-93, bd. govs. 1990-93, various com. positions, 1990—; coach Guilford Soccer League, 1985-88. Surgeon,

USPHS, 1967-70, 75-76. John Edward Nobel fellow, 1961-65; named Outstanding Med. Specialist in USA, Town and Country Mag., 1989, The Best Med. Specialists, 1995, One of 400 Best Drs. in U.S. Good Housekeeping Mag., 1991, named in The Best Doctors in America, 1st edit. 1992-93, 2d edit. 1994-95. Fellow ACP (coun. subspecialty socs. 1989—), Am. Coll. Chest Physicians (program com. 1978-84), Infectious Disease Soc. Am., Coll. of Physicians of Phila.; mem. Am. Thoracic Soc. (sec.-treas. 1987-88, bd. dirs. 1989-93, v.p. 1988-89, pres.-elect 1990-91, pres. 1992-93, various com. positions 1980—), Am. Soc. Clin. Investigation, Assn. Am. Physicians, Am. Assn. Immunologists, Am. Fedn. Clin. Rsch., Am. Clin. and Climatological Soc., Interurban Clin. Club (emeritus 1989), Assn. Profs. Medicine, Hershey Country Club, Farmington Country Club, Raven Soc., Alpha Omega Alpha, Phi Beta Kappa. Republican. Avocations: tennis, violin. Home: 226 E Caracas Ave Hershey PA 17033-1309 Office: Pa State U Milton S Hershey Med Ctr 850 University Dr Hershey PA 17033

REYNOLDS, JACK MASON, manufacturing company executive; b. East Orange, N.J., Jan. 27, 1927; s. Frederick Lynn and Bernice (Mason) R.; m. Rhea Evans, June 14, 1949; children: Jeff, Jennifer Reynolds Brickley, Mark. B.S., U.S. Mcht. Marine Acad., 1948. With Bendix Corp., Southfield, Mich., 1948-83, exec. v.p automotive group, 1979-80, pres. automotive group, 1980-83; pres. automotive sector, exec. v.p. Allied-Signal Inc., Morristown, N.J., 1983-89; dir. NBD Bancorp Inc. Bd. dirs. Detroit Renaissance, 1983-89, Citizens Rsch. Coun. of Mich., 1983-89, Detroit Econ. Growth Corp., 1983-89, Detroit Symphony Orch., 1983-89. With USNR, 1944-48. Mem. Soc. Automotive Engrs., Renaissance (Detroit) Club. Home: PO Box 744 Cooperstown NY 13326-0744

REYNOLDS, JACK W., retired utility company executive; b. Magazine, Ark., Feb. 28, 1923; s. Robert H. and Effie (Files) R.; m. Alberta Barkett, Nov. 13, 1949; children: John, David, Steven, Thomas, Laurie. B.S. in Phys. Sci., Okla. State U., 1943, B.S. in Indsl. Engring., 1947. Registered profl. engr., Wis. With B.F. Goodrich Co., Akron, Ohio, 1947-75, dir. union relations, 1969-70, dir. indsl. rels., 1970-75; v.p. pers. Consumers Power Co., Jackson, Mich., 1975-78, sr. v.p. pers. and pub. affairs, 1978-81, exec. v.p. energy supply, 1981-88; pres. Mich. Gas Storage Co., Jackson, 1981-88, Plateau Resources, Ltd., Jackson, 1988; now ret. Served to 1st lt. C.E. U.S. Army, 1943-46, CBI. Republican. Methodist. Clubs: Jackson Country.

REYNOLDS, JAMES, management consultant; b. Detroit, Mar. 22, 1941; s. Richard James and Esther (Nikander) R.; m. Joanne M.J. B.A. in Econs., NYU, 1965, postgrad., 1965-66. Cons. to pres. Rothrock, Reynolds & Reynolds Inc., N.Y.C., 1966-70; sr. v.p. health, med. div. Booz, Allen & Hamilton, N.Y.C., 1970-80; pres. Reynolds & Co. (mgmt. cons.), San Francisco, N.Y.C., Washington, 1981—; developer 1978, orgn. concepts for multihosp. systems, 1983, managed care contracting strategies, 1988, value chain analysis in the health field, 1994, leading the transition to Integrated Healthcare Sycs.; bd. dirs. Booz, Allen & Hamilton, 1977-79; chmn. bd. J.X. Reynolds Fine Arts, Ltd., 1979—; bd. dirs. Health Center Mgmt. Inst.; lectr. Harvard Sch. Pub. Health; faculty mem. Am. Coll. of Healthcare Execs.; bd. dirs. Health Center Mgmt. Inst., Richmond, Va., 1977; mem. health adv. bd. Hunter Coll., 1980—. Editorial bd. Physicians Fin. News. Recipient NYU Founders award, 1965. Mem. Am. Pub. Health Assn., Am. Mgmt. Assn., Assn. Am. Med. Colls., Am. Hosp. Assn., Hosp. Mgmt. Systems Soc., Hosp. Fin. Mgmt. Assn., Asia Soc., Phi Beta Kappa, Mus. Modern Art, Met. Mus. Art, Met. Opera Guild (N.Y.C.). Episcopalian. Home and Office: Reynolds Co 333 E 51st St New York NY 10022-6702 also: 2500 Three Mile Run Rd Perkasie PA 18944

REYNOLDS, JAMES E., lawyer; b. N.Y.C., 1943. BA, U. Notre Dame, 1965; LLB, U. Va., 1968. Bar: Mo. 1969. Ptnr. Bryan Cave, St. Louis. Office: Bryan Cave 1 Met Sq 211 N Broadway Saint Louis MO 63102

REYNOLDS, JEAN EDWARDS, publishing executive; b. Saginaw, Mich., Dec. 11, 1941; d. F. Perry and Kathrine (Edwards) R.; m. Cary Wellington, Sept. 10, 1975 (div. 1982); children, Bradley, Abigail, Benjamin. BA, Wells Coll., 1963; postgrad., CCNY, 1965-67. Asst. editor, sr. editor trade book div. Prentice-Hall, Englewood Cliffs, N.J., 1963-66; dir. children's books Prentice-Hall, Englewood Cliffs, 1966-69, McCall Pub. Co., N.Y.C., 1969-71; sr. v.p., editorial dir. Franklin Watts Inc., N.Y.C., 1971-75; pres. Pet Projects Inc., Ridgefield, Conn., 1975-81; editor in chief young people's publs. Grolier Inc., Danbury, Conn., 1981-89; pres. The Millbrook Press, Brookfield, Conn., 1989—; bd. dirs. Wellington Leisure Products, Atlanta, Kiper Enterprises, Oswego, N.Y.; chairperson Conn. Ctr. for the Book, 1991-94. Bd. dirs. Jewish Home for the Elderly, Fairfield, Conn., 1989-90, Book Industry Study Group, 1991—, The Wooster Sch., Danbury, Conn., 1992—; pres. Jewish Fedn. Greater Danbury, 1991-93. Mem. ALA, Children's Book Coun., Mensa, Assn. for Sch. Librs. Internat. (bd. dirs. 1993-94). Jewish. Avocations: skiing, tennis, sailing, needlework, SCUBA. Home: 33 Corntassle Rd Danbury CT 06811-3208 Office: The Millbrook Press Inc 2 Old New Milford Rd Brookfield CT 06804-2426

REYNOLDS, JOHN CHARLES, communications company executive, management consultant; b. Bklyn., May 12, 1933; s. Patrick J. and Mary (Keicher) R.; m. Theresa Ellen Donahue, July 6, 1957; children: Thomas, Brian, Catherine, Maureen, Patricia, Kevin. B.B.A., St. John's U., 1954; M.B.A., N.Y. U., 1961. Mgmt. trainee W.R. Grace Co., 1956-57; with Grace Line, N.Y.C., 1957-61, mgr. budgetary controls, 1958-61; with ITT Corp., 1961-85; gen. mgr. Caribbean div. P.R., 1967-76; gen. mgr. voice communications cos. N.Y.C., 1977-78, corp. v.p., pres. and group mgr. communications gp. group, 1979-83, corp. v.p., dir. offset and countertrade, 1984-85; pres., chief exec. officer Technicom Systems Inc., Whippany, N.J., 1986-87; exec. v.p. Votrax Inc., Troy, Mich., 1987-88; assoc. turn around and workout specialist R. Quintero & Co., 1989—. Adv. com. trustees Dartmouth Inst., Hanover, N.H.; mem. organizing com. Pan Am. Games; trustee Presbyn. Hosp., San Juan, 1972-76, Daytop Village, 1981—; 1st v.p. Jr. Achievement P.R., 1974-76; mem. Cardinal's Com. of Laity, N.Y.C., 1981; bd. trustees St. Leo Coll., St. Leo Fla., 1991—. Served with AUS, 1954-56. Recipient medal of honor Colegio San Ignacio de Loyola, P.R. 1976; named Hon. Citizen City of New Orleans, 1980, Hon. Citizen City of San Juan, 1975. Mem. Am. Mgmt. Assn., Armed Forces Communications and Electronics Assn., AIM, Nat. Edn. Council, Sovereign Mil. Order of Malta. Roman Catholic. Club: Ridgewood Country.

REYNOLDS, JOHN FRANCIS, insurance company executive; b. Escanaba, Mich., Mar. 29, 1921; s. Edward Peter and Lillian (Harris) R.; m. Dorothy Gustafson, May 1, 1946; children—Lois, Margaret, Michael. B.S., Mich. State U., 1942. Claims and assoc. surety mgr. Hartford Ins. Co., Battle Creek, Mich., 1955-64, v.p. underwriting, 1964-69; Midwest zone underwriting mgr. Transamerica Ins. Co. (Wolverine Ins. Co.), Battle Creek, Mich., 1969-74; pres., gen. mgr. Can. Surety Co. subs. Transamerica Ins. Co., Toronto, Ont., Canada, 1974-75; v.p. midwestern zone mgr. Transamerica Ins. Group, Battle Creek, Mich., 1975-83; pres., chief operating officer Transamerica Ins. Group, Los Angeles, 1983-84, chmn., chief exec. officer, 1984-85; apptd. spl. dep. ins. commr., dep. conservator Cadillac Inc. Co., 1989; pres. Underwriting Exec. Council Midwest, 1967; dir. Underwriters Adjustment Bur., Toronto, 1974, Underwriters Labs. of Canada, Montreal, 1974; chmn. Mich. Assn. Ins. Cos., Lansing, 1976, Mich. Basic Property Ins. Assn., Detroit, 1973. Commr. City of Battle Creek, 1967-69; dir. Urban League, Battle Creek, 1969, 70, dir. Mich. Ins. Fedn., Lansing, 1975-83. Served to sgt. U.S. Army, 1942-45; New Guinea. Roman Catholic. Avocations: golf; fishing.

REYNOLDS, JOHN HAMILTON, physicist, educator; b. Cambridge, Mass., Apr. 3, 1923; s. Horace Mason and Catharine (Coffeen) R.; m. Ann Burchard Arnold, July 19, 1975; children from previous marriages: Amy, Horace Marshall, Brian Marshall, Karen Leigh, Petra Catharine. AB. Harvard U., 1943; MS, U. Chgo., 1948, PhD, 1950; D. honoris causa, U. Coimbra, Portugal, 1987. Rsch. asst. Electroacoustic Lab., Harvard U. 1941-43; assoc. physicist Argonne Nat. Lab., 1950; physicist U. Calif. at Berkeley, 1950—, prof. physics, 1961-88; chmn. dept. physics U. Calif., Berkeley, 1984-86, faculty rsch. lectr., 1974; prof. emeritus U. Calif.-Berkeley, Berkeley, 1989—. Contbr. articles to profl. jours. Lt. USNR 1943-46. Recipient Wetherill medal Franklin Inst., 1965, Golden Plate award Am. Acad. Achievement, 1968, Exceptional Sci. Achievement award NASA,

1973; Guggenheim fellow U. Bristol, Eng., 1956-57, Los Alamos Nat. Lab., 1987, NSF fellow U. São Paulo, Brazil, 1963-64; Fulbright-Hays rsch. grantee U. Coimbra, Portugal, 1971-72; U.S.-Australia Coop. Sci. Program awardee U. Western Australia, 1978-79, Berkeley citation, 1988. Fellow AAAS, Am. Acad. Arts and Scis., Am. Phys. Soc., Am. Geophys. Union, Geochem Soc., Meteoritical Soc. (Leonard medal 1973); mem. NAS (J. Lawrence Smith medal 1967), Faculty Club (Berkeley), Phi Beta Kappa. Democrat. Office: U Calif Dept Physics Berkeley CA 94720

REYNOLDS, JOHN TERRENCE, oil industry executive; b. Madison, Wis., Oct. 2, 1944; s. John Francis and Evelyn Ruth (Straus) R.; m. Diane Marie Princl-Reynolds, Sept. 3, 1966; 1 child, Channing. BSME, U. Wis., 1967, MS in Metallurgical Engring., 1968. Engr. Shell Chem. Co., Denver, 1968-70, Royal Dutch/Shell, The Hague, The Netherlands, 1970-72; sr. engr. Shell Devel. Co., Houston, 1972-75, Shell Oil Co., Houston, 1975-78; staff engr. Shell Oil Co., Deer Park, Tex., 1978-81; engring. mgr. Shell Oil Co., Anacortes, Wash., 1981-87; sr. staff engr. Shell Oil Co., Houston, 1987—; chmn. inspection codes com., 1989—, inspection subcommittee, 1993—, Am. Petroleum Inst., Washington. Author: Mechanical Integrity of Refinery Equipment, 1993, The New In-Service Piping Inspection Code, 1993. Recipient of numerous certificates of appreciation. Mem. ASME, Am. Soc. for Metals, Nat. Assn. Corrosion Engrs., Am. Petroleum Inst., Nat. Petroleum Refiners Assn. Avocations: mountain climbing, backpacking, kayaking, rafting, fishing. Office: Shell Oil Co 3333 Highway 6 S Houston TX 77082

REYNOLDS, JOHN W., federal judge; b. Green Bay, Wis., Apr. 4, 1921; s. John W. and Madge (Flatley) R.; m. Patricia Ann Brody, May 26, 1947 (dec. Dec. 1967); children: Kate M. Reynolds Lindquist, Molly A., James B.; m. Jane Conway, July 31, 1971; children: Jacob F., Thomas J., Frances P., John W. III. PhB, U. Wis., 1946, LLB, 1949. Bar: Wis. 1949. Since practiced in Green Bay, dist. dir. price stblzn., 1951-53, U.S. commr., 1953-58, atty. gen. of Wis., 1958-62; gov. State of Wis., 1963-65; U.S. dist. judge Ea. Dist. Wis., Milwa., 1965-71, chief judge, 1971-86, sr. judge, 1986—. Served with U.S. Army, 1942-46. Mem. State Bar Wis., Am. Law Inst. Office: US Dist Ct 296 US Courthouse 517 E Wisconsin Ave Milwaukee WI 53202-4506

REYNOLDS, JOSEPH HURLEY, lawyer; b. Wilmington, Del., July 22, 1946; s. Peter G. and Elizabeth (Yorks) R.; m. Margaret Jack, Sept. 29, 1969; children: Joseph B., Alicia K., Charles Y. BA, Lehigh U., 1968, MA, 1972; JD, Union U., 1976. Bar: N.Y. 1976, D.C. 1985. Law clk. to hon. judge Dominick Gabrielli N.Y. Ct. of Appeals, Albany, 1976-78; assoc. Nixon, Hargrave, Devans & Doyle, Rochester, N.Y., 1978-85; ptnr. Nixon, Hargrave, Devans & Doyle, Washington, 1985—. Office: Nixon Hargrave Devans Doyle One Thomas Circle Washington DC 10005

REYNOLDS, JOSEPH P., publishing executive, educational consultant; b. Mt. Vernon, N.Y., July 7, 1949; s. Joseph A. and Patricia A. (Garvey) R.; m. Phyllis A. Becka, Jan. 11, 1974 (dec. June 1989); children: Alex, Mary; m. Elizabeth A. Jillings, May 16, 1993; stepchildren: Jacob, Alex, Timothy, Mary, Thomas. BA in Philosophy, Cath. U. Am., 1973. Sales rep. Prentice-Hall, Inc., Atlanta, 1973-75, sales mgr., 1975-81, mktg. mgr., 1981-82; cons. Bank Bldg. Corp., Atlanta, 1982; sales mgr. Delmar Pubs., Inc., Atlanta, 1982-84; v.p. sales & mktg. Delmar Pubs., Inc., Albany, N.Y., 1984-91, pres., CEO, 1991—. Bd. dirs. Coalition for Safer and Cleaner Vehicles, Washington, 1993—. Mem. Am. Vocat. Assn., Internat. Tech. Edn. Assn. Office: Delmar Publishers Inc 3 Columbia Cir Albany NY 12203

REYNOLDS, LEWIS DAYTON, administrator; b. Charleston, W.Va., July 26, 1937; s. James Shelby and Sybil Catherine (Lanham) R.; m. Ann Kathryn Combs, Aug. 25, 1962; children: John Mark, Daniel Adam. BBA, Marshall U., 1959; BTh, Aurora U., 1961; MDiv, Evang. Theol. Sem., Naperville, Ill., 1962. Ordained to ministry Advent Christian Ch., 1962. Pastor Mendota (Ill.) Advent Christian Ch., Mendota, Ill., 1961-64, Clendenin (W.Va.) Advent Christian Ch., Clendenin, W.Va., 1964-72, New Covenant Fellowship, Penfield, N.Y., 1972-89; gen. overseer Elim Fellowship, Lima, N.Y., 1989—; bd. adminstrn. Nat. Assn. Evang., Wheaton, Ill., 1989—, Pentecostal Fellowship N.Am. (now named Pentecostal/Charismatic Chs. N.Am.), Oklahoma City, 1989—, Virginia Beach; bd. dirs. Elim Bible Inst., Lima; mem. steering com. N.Am. Renewal Svcs., Oklahoma City, 1990—. Editor Elim Herald mag. Mem. Phi Eta Sigma. Republican. Home: 1701 Dalton Rd Apt 503 Lima NY 14485-9542 Office: Elim Fellowship Inc 7245 College St Lima NY 14485-9704

REYNOLDS, LLOYD GEORGE, economist, educator; b. Wainwright, Alberta, Can., Dec. 22, 1910; came to U.S., 1934, naturalized, 1940; s. George F. and Dorothy (Carl) R.; m. Mary F. Trackett, June 12, 1937; children: Anne Reynolds Skinner, Priscilla Reynolds Roosevelt, Bruce Lloyd. A.B., U. Alberta, 1931, LL.D., 1958; A.M., McGill U., 1933; Ph.D., Harvard, 1936. Instr. econs. Harvard, 1936-39; asso. polit. economy Johns Hopkins, 1939-41, asso. prof., 1941-45; asso. prof. econs. Yale, 1945-47, prof. econs., 1947-52, Sterling prof. econs., 1952-81, chmn. dept. econs., 1951-59; prof. emeritus, 1981—; dir. Econ. Growth Center, 1961-67; vis. fellow All Souls Coll., Oxford, 1967-68; Mem. adv. bd. Pakistan Inst. Devel. Econs., 1965-73; cons. to Social Sci. Research Center, U. P.R., 1951-65; dir. Nat. Bureau Econ. Research, 1958-81; Research dir. labor studies 20th Century Fund, 1940-43; research sec., com. on employment Social Sci. Research Council, 1941-42; co-chmn. appeals com. N.W.L.B., 1943-45; cons. Bur. of Budget, 1945-47; Guggenheim fellow, 1954-55, 1966-67; dir. program in econs. and bus. adminstrn. Ford Found., 1955-57. Author: The British Immigrant in Canada, 1935, Control of Competition in Canada, 1940, Labor and National Defense, 1941, An Index to Trade Union Publications, 1945, Labor Economics and Labor Relations, 1949, The Structure of Labor Markets, 1951, The Evolution of Wage Structure, 1956, Economics: A General Introduction, 1963, Wages, Productivity and Industrialization in Puerto Rico, 1965, The Three Worlds of Economics, 1971, Agriculture in Development Theory, 1975, Image and Reality in Economic Development, 1977, The American Economy in Perspective, 1981, Economic Growth in the Third World, 1850-1980, 1985; contbr. articles to profl. jours. Fellow Am. Acad. Arts and Scis.; mem. Indsl. Rls. Rsch. Assn. (pres. 1955), Am. Econ. Assn. (v.p. 1959, exec. com. 1952-54), Am. Acad. Polit. Sci., Am. Statis. Assn., Phi Beta Kappa. Clubs: Graduates (New Haven) (pres. 1961-64); Harvard (Boston); Century (N.Y.C.); Cosmos (Washington); Mill Reef (Antigua). Home: 4000 Cathedral Ave NW Washington DC 20016-5249 Office: Yale University Economics Dept New Haven CT 06520

REYNOLDS, LYNNE WARREN, special education educator, speech pathologist; b. Richmond, Va., June 6, 1940; d. Edward Paul Jr. and Margie (Meads) Warren; m. Thomas Grover Reynolds III, June 23, 1962; children: Thomas G. IV, Marguerite Agee. BS, U. Va., 1962, postgrad., 1963-65; MEd, R.I. Coll., 1973; EdD, Heed U., 1985. Cert. tchr., spl. edn. tchr., N.Y., Mass., R.I., Va.; lic. speech and lang. pathologist, N.Y. Tchr. spl. edn. Nelson County Pub. Schs., Lovingston, Va., 1962-63, Albemarle County Pub. Schs., Charlottesville, Va., 1963-66; tchr. spl. edn., program coord. Plainville (Mass.) Pub. Schs., 1967-73; pvt. practice speech-lang. pathology, edn. cons. Kingston, N.Y., 1973-85; edn. cons. Edn. for Relocation, Neunen and Eindhoven, Netherlands, 1986-91; tchr. spl. edn. W.S. Hart Union High Sch. Dist., Santa Clara, Calif. 1991-92; ind. edn. cons. Smyrna, Ga., 1992—; sec., chmn. mental health and mental retardation com. Ulster County Community Svcs. Bd., Kingston, 1978-85; mem. N.Y. State com. UN Yr. of Child, 1983-84; mem. community svcs. adv. bd. Spl. Edn. Svcs. Santa Clarita, Calif. 1991-92; mem. People to People citizen amb. del. on learning disabilities to Russia & Estonia; presenter seminars to parent, educator and profl. groups; presenter tng. workshops. Author classroom tchrs.' handbook: HELP, 1969. Mem. Chaminade Singers, Reynolds; mem. chmn. Indsl. Devel. Commn., Town of Plainville, 1969-73, mental health svcs. coord., 1970-73; dir., nautographer ann. synchronized swimming show Zena Recreation Park, N.Y., 1975-84; mem. learnint disabilities delegation to Russia and Estonia: People to People Citizen Amb. Program, 1993; active Internat. Women's Club Eindhoven, 1985-90. Recipient Profl. Svc. Recognition award Girl Scouts U.S., Plainville, 1971, Recognition of Svc. award Ulster County Mental Health Assn., 1983, 84, Award for Svc. Ulster County Community Svcs. Bd., 1985. Mem. Coun. Exceptional Children (div. communication disorders, div. learning disabilities, coun. ednl. diagnostic svcs., coun. behavioral disorders), Orton Dyslexia Soc., Assn. for Citizens with Learning Disabilities (chpt. bd. dirs. 1976-85, state bd. dirs.

1978-84, chair memberships com.), N.Y. Speech, Lang. and Hearing Assn., Assn. Ednl. and Psychol. Cons., Assn. Ednl. Therapists, Zeta Tau Alpha. Avocations: music, theater, reading, quilting, needlework.

REYNOLDS, MARSHALL T., bank executive, holding company executive, investor. Printer Chapman Printing Co. Inc., Huntington, W. Va., 1958-64; chmn. bd. dirs. The Harrah and Reynolds Corp., Huntington, W. Va., 1964—; prin. Banc One W. Va. Corp., Huntington, W. Va., 1993—. Office: Banc One West Va Corp 1000 5th Ave Huntington WV 25701*

REYNOLDS, MARY TRACKETT, political scientist; b. Milw., Jan. 11, 1913; d. James P. and Mary (Nachtwey) Trackett; m. Lloyd G. Reynolds, June 12, 1937; children: Anne Reynolds Skinner, Priscilla Reynolds Roosevelt, Bruce; m. Yoke San Lee. BA, U. Wis., 1935, MA, 1935; postgrad. (Rebecca Green fellow), Radcliffe Coll., 1935-36; PhD (U. fellow, Barnard fellow), Columbia U., 1939. Rsch. asst. Littauer Sch. Harvard U., 1938-39; instr. Queens Coll., 1939-40; instr. Hunter Coll., 1941-42, lectr.; 1945-47; assoc. in polit. sci. Johns Hopkins U., 1942-43; lectr. Conn. Coll., 1947-48, asst. prof., 1948-50; rsch. assoc. in econs. Yale U., 1961-67, vis. lectr. in English, 1973-82; meml. lectr. Joyce Centennial, 1982; assoc. fellow Berkeley Coll., 1982—. Author: Interdepartmental Committees in the National Administration, 1940, Joyce and Nora, 1964, Source Documents in Economic Development, 1966, Joyce and D'Annunzio, 1976, Joyce and Dante: The Shaping Imagination, 1982, Mr. Bloom and the Lost Vermeer, 1989, James Joyce: New Century Views, 1993; bd. editors James Joyce Quar., 1985—, James Joyce Studies Ann., 1990—. Rsch. asst. Pres.'s Com. Adminstrn. Mgmt., 1936; sr. economist Nat. Econ. Com., 1940; adminstrn. asst. Glenn L. Martin Aircraft Co., Balt., 1942-43; editorial asst. pub. adminstrn. com. Social Sci. Rsch. Coun., 1944-45; cons. Nat. Def. Adv. Commn., 1949, Nat. Mcpl. Assn., 1956, Orgn. Econ. Cooperation and Devel., Paris, 1964, U.S. State Dept.-AID 1965. Mem. MLA, AAUP, LWV, Am. Polit. Sci. Assn., Dante Soc. Am., Internat. James Joyce Found. (bd. trustees 1995—), Conn. Acad. Arts and Scis. (coun. 1988-89), Elizabethan Club (sec.-treas. 1984-89, bd. incorporators 1986-89), Sylvance Club (Washington), Grolier Club, Appalachian Mountain Club, Phi Beta Kappa. Home: 4000 Cathedral Ave NW Apt 147B Washington DC 20016-5249 Office: Yale Sta PO Box 604 New Haven CT 06520

REYNOLDS, MELVIN J. (MEL REYNOLDS), congressman; b. Mound Bayou, Mo., 1952; m. Marisol Reynolds; 1 child, Corean. Grad., U. Ill., Champaign; JD, Oxford U., England. Talk show host Sta. WLS-Radio, Chgo.; asst. prof. Roosevelt U., Chgo.; mem. 103rd-104th Congresses from 2d Ill. dist., 1993—; mem. econ. and ednl. opportunity com. Exec. dir. Community Econ. Devel. and Edn. Found.; founder, pres. Am. Scholars Against World Hunger. Rhodes scholar. Mem. NAACP (exec. com. Chgo. chpt.). Democrat. Office: US Ho of Reps 312 Cannon HOB Washington DC 20515*

REYNOLDS, MICHAEL JOSEPH, consulting company executive; b. N.Y.C., July 23, 1938; s. Thomas and Kathleen (Barry) R.; m. Anne Marie Reidy, June 27, 1964; children: Amy, Kathleen, Michael T. BBA, Manhattan Coll., 1959. Research asst. N.Y. Life Ins. Co., N.Y.C., 1960-65; asst. v.p. Frank B. Hall & Co. Inc., N.Y.C., 1965-71; v.p. Bayly Martin & Fay Inc., N.Y.C., 1971-77; sr. v.p. Frank B. Hall Cons. Co., N.Y.C., 1977-86; pres. Goodwins, Inc., N.Y.C., 1986—; bd. dirs. Employee Benefit Research Inst., Washington, Assn. Pvt. Pensions and Welfare Plans, Washington. Served with N.Y. NG, 1959-60. Club: Union League (N.Y.C.). Home: 51 Thunder Mountain Rd Greenwich CT 06831-3233 Office: Godwins Inc 549 Pleasantville Rd, N Bldg Briarcliff Manor NY 10510-1954

REYNOLDS, NANCY BRADFORD DUPONT (MRS. WILLIAM GLASGOW REYNOLDS), sculptor; b. Greenville, Del., Dec. 28, 1919; d. Eugene Eleuthere and Catherine Dulcinea (Moxham) duPont; m. William Glasgow Reynolds, May 18, 1940; children: Kathrine Glasgow Reynolds, William Bradford, Mary Parminter Reynolds Savage, Cynthia duPont Reynolds Farris. Student, Goldey-Beacom Coll., Wilmington, Del., 1938. One-woman shows include Rehoboth (Del.) Art League, 1963, Del. Art Mus., Wilmington, Caldwell, Inc., 1975, Wilmington Art Mus., 1976; exhibited group shows Corcoran Gallery, Washington, 1943, Soc. Fine Arts, Wilmington, 1937, 38, 40, 41, 48, 50, 62, 65, NAD, N.Y.C., 1964, Pa. Mil. Coll., Chester, 1966, Del. Art Ctr., 1967, Mem. Mus. Art, N.Y.C., 1977, Lever House, N.Y.C., 1979; sculpture work Brookgreen Gardens, S.C.; represented in permanent collections Wilmington Trust Co., E.I. duPont de Nemours & Co., Children's Home, Inc., Claymont, Del., Children's Bur., Wilmington, Stephenson Sci. Ctr., Nashville, Lutheran Towers Bldg., Travelers Aid and Family Soc. Bldg., Wilmington, bronze fountain head Longwood Gardens, Kennett Square, Pa., bronze statue Brookgreen Gardens, Murrells Inlet, S.C.; contbr. articles to profl. jours. Organizer vol. svc. Del. chpt. ARC, 1938-39; chmn. Com. for Revision Del. Child Adoption Law, 1950-52; pres. bd. dirs. Children Bur. Del.; pres., trustee Children's Home, Inc.; del. regent Gunston Hall Plantation, Lorton, Va.; mem. adv. com. Longwood Gardens, Kennett Sq., Pa.; garden and grounds com. Winterthur (Del.) Mus.; mem. rsch. staff Henry Francis DuPont Winterthur Mus., 1955-63. Recipient Confrerie des Chevaliers du Tastevin Clos de Vougeot-Bourgogne France, 1960; Hort. award Garden Club Am., 1964, medal of Merit, 1976; Dorothy Platt award Garden Club of Phila., 1980; Alumni medal of merit Westover Sch., Middlebury, Conn. Mem. Pa. Hort. Soc., Wilmington Soc. Fine Arts, Mayflower Descs., Del. Hist. Soc., Colonial Dames, League Am. Pen Women, Nat. Trust Hist. Preservation. Garden Club of Wilmington (past pres.), Garden Club of Am. (past asst. zone 4 chmn.), Vicmead Hunt Club, Greenville Country Club, Chevy Chase Club (Washington), Colony Club (N.Y.C.). Episcopalian. Address: PO Box 3919 Greenville DE 19807

REYNOLDS, NANCY REMICK, editor, writer; b. San Antonio, July 15, 1938; d. Donald Worthington and Edith (Remick) R.; m. Brian Rushton, June 25, 1983; 1 child, Ehren T. Park. Student, Sch. Am. Ballet, 1951, 53-61, Juilliard Sch. Music, 1957, Martha Graham Sch. Contemporary Dance, N.Y.C., 1959, U. Sorbonne, Paris, 1962; BA in Art History, Columbia U., 1965; postgrad., Goethe Inst., Prien, 1972, U. Chgo. and Sarah Lawrence Coll., 1974-77. Dancer N.Y.C. Ballet, 1956-61; editor Praeger Pubs., N.Y.C., 1965-71; dir. rsch. book Choreography by George Balanchine: A Catalogue of Works, N.Y., 1979-82 (pub. 1983); dir. rsch. pub. TV spl. Balanchine, N.Y., 1983-84; assoc. editor Internat. Ency. of Dance, 1991—; dir. rsch. The George Balanchine Found., N.Y.C., 1994—; co-pub. Twentieth-Century Dance in Slides, 1978—. Author: Repertory in Review: Forty Years of the New York City Ballet, 1978 (la Torre Bueno prize 1977), The Dance Catalog: A Complete Guide to Today's World of Dance, 1979, co-author: In Performance,1980, Dance Classics, 1991 (rec. for teen age N.Y. Pub Libr.); editor: Movement and Metaphor: Four Centuries of Ballet (Lincoln Kirstein), 1970, Dance as a Theatre Art: Source Readings in Dance History from 1581 to the Present (Selma Jeanne Cohen), 1974, School of Classical Dance (V. Kostrovitskaya and A. Pisarev), 1978; contbr. (book) Ballet: Bias and Belief, "Three Pamphlets Collected" and Other Dance Writings of Lincoln Kirstein, 1983, also numerous articles and revs. to Dancing Times, Ballet News, Playbill, ArtsLine, Dancemag., Town & Country, Connoisseur, N.Y. Times, Ency. Britannica, others. Ford Found. Travel and Study grantee, 1974; Mary Duke Biddle Found. grantee, 1990. Mem. Dance Critics Assn. (pres. 1986-87), Soc. Dance History Scholars, Soc. for Dance Rsch., Am. Soc. for Theatre Rsch., European Assn. Dance Historians, Internat. Fedn. for Theatre Rsch. in affiliation with Societe Internat. des Bibliotheques et Musees des Arts du Spectacle. Home: 9 Prospect Park W Brooklyn NY 11215-5902

REYNOLDS, NICHOLAS S., lawyer; b. Grosse Point, Mich., June 16, 1944. BS, Wilkes Coll., 1968; JD with honors, George Washington U., 1971. Bar: Va. 1971, D.C. 1973. Ptnr. Winston & Strawn, Washington. Mem. ABA (chmn. atomic energy com. sect. pub. utility, comm. and transp. law 1980—). Office: Winston & Strawn 1400 L St NW Washington DC 20005-3509

REYNOLDS, NORMAN, production designer, art director. Prodn. designer: (films) The Little Prince, 1974, Mr. Quilp, 1975, (with Leslie Dilley and John Barry) Star Wars, 1977 (Academy award best art direction 1977), (with Dilley, Harry Lange, and Alan Tomkins) The Empire Strikes Back, 1980 (Academy award nomination best art direction 1980), (with Dilley) Raiders of the Lost Ark, 1981 (Academy award best art direction 1981),

(with Fred Hole and James Schoppe) Return of the Jedi, 1983 (Academy award nomination best art direction 1983), Return to Oz, 1985, Young Sherlock Holmes, 1985, Empire of the Sun, 1987 (Academy award nomination best art direction 1987), Avalon, 1990, Mountains of the Moon, 1990, Alien 3, 1992, Alive, 1993; art dir.: (films) The Incredible Sarah, 1976 (Academy award nomination best art direction 1976). Office: care Spyros Skouras Sanford Skouras Gross & Assocs 1015 Gayley Ave 3rd Fl Los Angeles CA 90024*

REYNOLDS, NORMAN EBEN, lawyer; b. Muskogee, Okla., Dec. 1, 1919; s. Norman Eben and Elizabeth (Boyd) R.; m. Margaret Maxey Cooper, Nov. 21, 1953; children: Norman Eben III, Margaret Boyd, Nancy Elizabeth, Robert Cooper. A.B., U. Okla., 1941, LL.B., 1947. Bar: Okla. 1942, U.S. Supreme Ct. 1961. Ptnr. Reynolds, Ridings, Vogt & Morgan, Oklahoma City, 1947-89, of counsel, 1989—; dir. Oharco Corp.; mem. Okla. Ho. of Reps., 1949-55; spl. legal cons. Gov. Okla., 1959-63; spl. justice Okla. Supreme Ct., 1961. Pres. trustees Heritage Hall, 1970. Served to capt. AUS, 1942-46. Named Outstanding Young Man in Oklahoma City, 1951. Mem. Comml. Law League Am. (past nat. sec., Pres.'s Cup for disting. svc. 1980), ABA (co-chmn. nat. conf. lawyers and collection agys. 1979), Okla. Bar Assn., Okla. County Bar Assn. (most Outstanding Voluntary Pub. Svc. ann. award 1989), Am. Judicature Soc., Mil. Order World Wars, Phi Beta Kappa (past pres. alumni assn., Phi Beta Kappa of Yr. 1993), Sigma Alpha Epsilon (past pres. alumni assn.), Sooner Dinner Club (Oklahoma City) (pres. 1969), Kiwanis (Oklahoma City), Men's Dinner Club. Episcopalian (sr. warden 1971, chmn. com. to build Canterbury Living Ctr., pres. Episc. Retirement Community, Inc. 1981-94). Club: Sooner Dinner (Oklahoma City) (pres. 1969). Lodge: Kiwanis (Oklahoma City) (pres. 1968). Home: 2212 NW 56th St Oklahoma City OK 73112-7702 Office: Reynolds Ridings Vogt & Morgan 2200 First Nat Ctr Oklahoma City OK 73102

REYNOLDS, PHILIP REEVES, insurance company executive; b. Norwalk, Conn., June 28, 1927; s. Carlton Mortimer and Frances (Collings) R.; m. Catherine Greenway Cox, July 20, 1957; children: Mary, Frances, Philip. BA, Yale U., 1948. With investment dept. Traveler's Corp., Hartford, Conn., 1955-70, sr. v.p.b. fin., 1970-84; exec. v.p. Phoenix Mut. Life, Hartford, 1984-89; bd. dirs. Vestaur Securities, Phila. Chmn. Hartford Coll. for Women, 1977-81, Child and Family Services, Hartford, 1978-80; trustee Wadsworth Atheneum, Hartford, 1983—, Miss Porters Sch., Farmington, Conn., 1983—. Served to cpl. U.S. Army, 1950-52, Korea. Democrat. Episcopalian. Clubs: Hartford (pres. 1977), Twilight (Hartford). Avocations: woodworking, violin playing. Home: 43 Montclair Dr West Hartford CT 06107-1247

REYNOLDS, R. JOHN, university administrator; b. Milw., Dec. 3, 1936; s. Edward R. and Elizabeth (Wickenhauser) R.; m. Carol G. Lucas, Dec. 15, 1956; children: John D., Katherine A. BEd, U. Wis., Whitewater, 1961; MA, No. Mich. U., 1967; PhD, So. Ill. U., 1971. Bus. instr. Green Bay (Wis.) Tech. Inst., 1964-65; dir. vocat. tng. No. Mich. U., Marquette, 1965-68; v.p. Tech. Edn. Corp., St. Louis, 1968-69, prof., 1969-71; acting dean, chmn dept. So. Ill. U., Carbondale, 1969-71, 74-80, 81-82; assoc. acad. dean N.H. Coll., Manchester, 1971-74; head. bus. and econs. dept. Lake Superior State U., Sault Ste. Marie, Mich., 1981-82; pres. Nat. Coll., Rapid City, S.D., 1982-84, Huron (S.D.) U., 1984—; cons. various colls. and schs. Contbr. articles to profl. jours. Pres. Dakotaland Mus., Huron, 1986—. Named Researcher of Yr. Ill. Bus. Edn. Assn., 1971. Office: Huron U Office of Pres 8th And Ohio Huron SD 57350

REYNOLDS, RANDOLPH NICKLAS, aluminum company executive; b. Louisville, Nov. 22, 1941; s. William Gray and Mary (Nicklas) R.; m. Susan Van Reypen, Aug. 6, 1964; children: Randolph Nicklas, Ralph Seymour, Robert Gray. BA in Bus., Bellarmine Coll., 1966; postgrad., U. Louisville, 1967-68. With Reynolds Metals Co. Richmond, Va., 1969—; market dir. chems., 1975-77, gen. mgr. chems., 1977-78, pres. Reynolds Aluminum Internat. Svcs. divsn., 1978-85, v.p., exec. v.p. info., 1985-94, vice chmn., 1994—; v.p. Reynolds Internat., Inc., Richmond, 1978-79, pres., 1979—; pres. Reynolds Internat. Svc. Co., Southfield, Mich., 1987—; pres. Malakoff (Tex.) Industries, 1981—; bd. dirs. Reynolds Metals Co. and 36 subs. Bd. sponsors coll. William and Mary. Democrat. Episcopalian. Home: 8605 River Rd Richmond VA 23229-8301 Office: Reynolds Metals Co 6601 W Broad St Richmond VA 23230

REYNOLDS, RICHARD CLYDE, physician, foundation administrator; b. Saugerties, N.Y., Sept. 2, 1929; s. Thomas Watson and Myrtle Edith (Myer) R.; m. Mary Jane Beck, July 7, 1954; children—Karen Sue, Stephanie Ann, Wayne Thomas. B.Sc., Rutgers U., 1949; M.D., Johns Hopkins U., 1953; D.Sc. (hon.), Hahnemann U., 1988, N.Y. Med. Coll., 1992. Diplomate Am. Bd. Internal Medicine. Intern Johns Hopkins Hosp., Balt., 1953-54; asst. resident Johns Hopkins Hosp., 1954-55, 57-58, fellow in infectious disease, 1958-59; practice medicine specializing in internal medicine Frederick, Md., 1959-68; mem. faculty U. Fla. Coll. Medicine, 1968-78, prof. medicine, prof. chmn. dept. community health and family medicine, 1970-78; prof. medicine, prof. environ. and community medicine, dean U. Medicine and Dentistry N.J., Robert Wood Johnson Med. Sch., 1978-87; sr. v.p. acad. affairs U. Medicine and Dentistry N.J., 1984-87; exec. v.p. Robert Wood Johnson Found., 1987—; mem. Liaison Com. on Med. Edn., 1982-87. Co-author: The Health of a Rural County: Perspectives and Problems, 1976, Patient Wishes and Physician Obligations, 1978; co-editor: On Doctoring: Stories, Poems, Essays, 1991; contbr. articles to med. publns. Sr. asst. surgeon USPHS, 1955-57. Mem. ACP, AMA. Office: Robert Wood Johnson Found PO Box 2316 Princeton NJ 08543-2316

REYNOLDS, ROBERT EDGAR, academic administrator, physician; b. Pontiac, Mich., June 3, 1938; s. Arthur James and Jean Lucille (Thompson) R.; m. Barbara Fisher, June 11, 1961 (div. May 1980); children: Jennifer Robin, Lisa Anne; m. Erika Renate Forte, July 25, 1981; children: Timothy Williams, Julia Renate. BA, Yale U., 1960; MD, Harvard U., 1964; MPH, Johns Hopkins U., 1967, DrPH, 1970. Med. dir. Chonic Disease Hosp., Balt. City Hosps., 1968-70; assoc. prof. medicine and community medicine, assoc. dean Med. Coll. Ga., Augusta, 1970-73; assoc. prof. internal medicine, prof. preventive medicine, 1973-81, med. dir., 1975-81; assoc. dean, assoc. prof. medicine Johns Hopkins U. Sch. Medicine, Balt., 1981-88; sr. assoc. v.p. for health scis., prof. medicine U. Va. Health Sci. Ctr., Charlottesville, 1988—; sec.-treas. Med. Adminstrs. Conf., 1979-80, pres., 1981. Served to capt. USAF, 1965-73. Fellow ACP, Am. Coll. Preventive Medicine; mem. AMA, Assn. Am. Med. Colls. (assoc., chmn. group on instln. planning 1988-89), Found. for Health Svcs. Rsch. (nat. adv. com.), Assn for Health Svc. Rsch., Nat. Libr. Medicine (biomedical rev. com. 1992—), Computer-based Patient Record Inst. (bd. dirs. 1992—). Office: U Va Med Ctr Charlottesville VA 22908

REYNOLDS, ROBERT HUGH, lawyer; b. St. Louis, Jan. 3, 1937; s. Leslie A. and Rebecca (McWaters) R.; m. Carol Jemison, Apr. 8, 1961; children: Stephen H., Cynthia C., Laura M. BA, Yale U., 1958; JD, Harvard U., 1964. Assoc. Barnes & Thornburg, Indpls., 1964-70, ptnr., 1970—, chmn. bus. dept., 1983-91; chmn. internat. practice group, 1992—; bd. dirs. Capital Industries, Inc., Indpls. Co-chmn., editor Comml. Real Estate Financing for Ind. Attys., 1968; vice-chmn., co-editor Advising Ind. Businesses, 1974; chmn., editor Counseling Ind. Businesses, 1981, The Purchase and Sale of a Business, 1987. Bd. dirs. Crossroads Am. Coun. Boy Scouts Am., 1970—, v.p., 1971-75, pres., 1987-89; v.p. Area 4 Ctrl. Region Boy Scouts Am. 1989-92, pres., 1992-93, pres. Ctrl. Region 1993—; bd. dirs. Family Svc. Assn. Indpls., 1974-81, pres., 1978-80; bd. dirs. Family Svc. Am., 1979-88, Greater Indpls. Fgn. Trade Zone, 1987—, Indpls. Conv. and Visitors Assn. 1989—, Indpls. Econ. Devel. Corp., 1993—, exec. com., sec., Greater Indpls. Progress Com., 1986—, exec. com., vice chmn.; trustee Childrens Mus. Indpls., 1988—, chmn. 1992-94; Indpls. Downtown Inc., vice chmn. 1993—; bd. govt. Legacy Fund 1992—; bd. dirs Noyes Mem. Found., 1986—, Japan-Am. Soc. Ind., 1988—, pres. Fellow Ind. Bar Found., Indpls. Bar Found.; mem. ABA, Indpls. Bar Assn., Ind. Bar Assn., Internat. Bar Assn., Greater Indpls. C. of C. (bd. dirs. 1987—). Republican. Clubs: Univ., Skyline (Indpls.). Lodge: Kiwanis. Office: Barnes & Thornburg 1313 Merchants Bank Bldg 11 S Meridian St Indianapolis IN 46204-3506

REYNOLDS, ROBERT JOEL, economist, consultant; b. Indpls., May 13, 1944; s. Joel Burr and Betty (Schimpf) R.; m. Lucinda Margaret Lewis, May 27, 1979; children: Joel, Sarah. BSBA in Fin., Northwestern U., 1965, PhD in Econs., 1970. Asst. prof. econs. U. Idaho, Moscow, 1969-73, assoc. prof., 1973-75; asst. dir., sr. economist econ. policy office Dept. Justice, Washington, 1973-81; sr. economist, v.p. ICF Inc., Washington, 1981-87, sr. v.p., 1987-91; exec. v.p., prin. Econsult Corp., Washington, 1991—; vis. assoc. prof. U. Calif., Berkeley, 1976-77, Cornell U., Ithaca, N.Y., 1981. Reviewer: NSF, Rand Jour. of Econs., Internat. Econ. Rev., Internat. Jour. Indsl. Orgn., Jour. Indsl. Econs., Am. Econ. Rev.; mem. editorial bd. Managerial and Decision Econs.; contbr. numerous papers to profl. jours. Recipient Dow Jones award Wall St. Jour., 1965; AT&T grantee, 1971-72, Brookings Instl. grantee, 1968-69; NDEA fellow, 1965-69. Mem. AAAS, Am. Econ. Assoc., Econometric Soc., Royal Econ. Soc., Am. Statis. Assn., European Assn. for Rsch. in Indsl. Econs., Soc. for the Promotion of Econ. Theory, Math. Assn. Am. Congregationalist. Home: 9228 Farnsworth Dr Potomac MD 20854-4503 Office: Econsult Corp 901 15th St NW Ste 370 Washington DC 20005

REYNOLDS, ROBERT LOUIS, financial services executive; b. San Francisco, Nov. 5, 1939; s. James Clinton and Betty (Harris) R.; m. Sandra Benvenuto, June 14, 1980. B.B.S., U. Calif.-Berkeley, 1961. Exec. v.p. Chrysler Capital Corp., Stamford, Conn., 1975—; also dir. Mem. Am. Mgmt. Assn., Am. Assn. Equipment Lessors, S.W. Area Conn. Industry Assn. (advisor), Burning Tree Country Club (Greenwich), Bear Lakes Country Club (West Palm Beach, Fla.). Avocations: golf; music. Office: Chrysler Capital Corp 225 High Ridge Rd Stamford CT 06905-3000

REYNOLDS, ROGER LEE, composer; b. Detroit, July 18, 1934; s. George Arthur and Katherine Adelaide (Butler) R.; m. Karen Jeanne Hill, Apr. 11, 1964; children: Erika Lynn, Wendy Claire. BSE in Physics, U. Mich., 1957, MusB, 1960, MusM, 1961. Assoc. prof. U. Calif. San Diego, La Jolla, 1969-73, prof., 1973—, founding dir. Ctr. Music Expt. and Related Rsch., 1972-77; George Miller Prof. Amherst (Mass.) Coll., 1988; vis. prof. Yale U., New Haven, 1981; Rothschild composer in residence Peabody Conservatory of Music, 1992-93; sr. rsch. fellow ISAM, Bklyn. Coll., 1985. Author: MIND MODELS: New Forms of Musical Experience, 1975, A Searcher's Path: A Composer's Ways, 1987, A Jostled Silence: Contemporary Japanese Musical Thought, 1992-93; contbr. numerous articles and revs. to profl. jours. Bd. dirs. Am. Music. Ctr., Meet the Composer, Fromm Found. Harvard U.; mem. bd. govs. Inst. Current World Affairs. Recipient citation Nat. Inst. Arts and Letters, 1971, NEA awards, 1975, 78, 79, 86, Pulitzer prize for music, 1989; sr. fellow Inst. Studies in Am. Music, 1985, fellow Rockefeller Found., Guggenheim Found.; Fulbright scholar. Office: U Calif San Dieg Dept Music 0326 La Jolla CA 92093

REYNOLDS, SCOTT WALTON, academic administrator; b. Summit, N.J., July 15, 1941; s. Clark Leonard and Shirley (Hill) R.; m. Margaret Ann Johnson, July 5, 1969; children: Jane, Amy, David. B.A., Trinity Coll., Hartford, Conn., 1963; M.B.A., Harvard U., 1965. Mng. dir. corp. staff Bankers Trust Co., N.Y.C., 1967-94; asst. to the pres. St. Peter's Coll., Jersey City, 1994—. Chmn. fund campaign Montclair (N.J.) ARC, 1974; chmn. bus. and fraternal group Montclair Bicentennial Com., 1976; bd. fellows Trinity Coll., 1982-88, trustee, 1992—, sec., exec. com., 1993—. 1st lt. U.S. Army, 1965-67. Recipient 150th Anniversary award Trinity Coll., 1978, Alumni medal for Excellence, 1988, Pres.' Leadership medal, 1993. Mem. Montclair Jaycees (treas. 1973), Trinity Coll. Alumni Assn. N.Y. (pres. 1972-73). Episcopalian. Club: Harvard (N.Y.C.). Office: St Peters Coll 2641 John F Kennedy Blvd Jersey City NJ 07306

REYNOLDS, STEPHEN CURTIS, hospital administrator; b. Little Rock, May 1, 1946; married. BA, Ark. State U., 1968; MA, Washington U., 1972. Adminstrv. resident Baptist Meml. Health Care System, Memphis, 1971-72, adminstrv. asst., 1972-75, asst. v.p., 1975-80, v.p., 1980-86, sr. v.p., 1986-89, exec. v.p., 1992; exec. v.p. Baptist Meml. Hosp., Memphis, 1990-92, pres., 1992—. With Armed Forces, 1968-70. Mem. Tenn. Hosp. Assn. (chmn., 1989-90, bd. dirs. 1986-91). Home: 461 Princeton Wood Cove Memphis TN 38117 Office: Bapt Meml Hosp 899 Madison Ave Memphis TN 38146

REYNOLDS, THOMAS A., JR., lawyer; b. Chgo., Aug. 30, 1928. AB, Georgetown U., 1948; JD, U. Mich., 1951. Bar: Ill. 1954. Ptnr. Winston & Strawn, Chgo. Mem. ABA, Ill. State Bar Assn., Chgo. Bar Assn. Office: Winston & Strawn 35 W Wacker Dr Chicago IL 60601-1614

REYNOLDS, THOMAS A., III, lawyer; b. Evanston, Ill., May 12, 1952. BSBA, Georgetown U., 1974; JD, Emory U., 1977. Bar: Ill. 1977, U.S. Dist. Ct. (no. dist.) Ill. 1978, U.S. Ct. Appeals (7th cir.) 1979, U.S. Dist. Ct. (no. dist. trial bar) Ill. 1983. Ptnr. Winston & Strawn, Chgo. Office: Winston & Strawn 35 W Wacker Dr Chicago IL 60601-1614

REYNOLDS, THOMAS HEDLEY, university president; b. N.Y.C., Nov. 23, 1920; s. Wallace and Helen (Hedley) R.; m. Jean Fine Lytle, Apr. 24, 1943; children: Thomas Scott, David Hewson, John Hedley, Tay. Grad., Deerfield (Mass.) Acad., 1938; A.B., Williams Coll., 1942; LL.D. (hon.), 1978; M.A. in History, Columbia U., 1947, Ph.D. in History, 1953; LL.D., U. Maine, 1968, Bowdoin Coll., 1969, Colby Coll., 1969; DHL (hon.), Bates Coll., 1990, Middlebury Coll., 1992. Instr. history Hunter Coll., 1947-48; staff historian ARC, Washington, 1948-49; mem. faculty Middlebury Coll., 1949-67, chmn. dept. history, 1957-67, dean of coll., 1964-67; pres. Bates Coll., Lewiston, Maine, 1967-89, U. New Eng., Biddeford, Maine, 1991-95; mem. Edn. Commn. of States, 1969-80; mem. Higher Edn. Coun., 1971—, Commn. on Maine's Future, 1975—; dir. New Eng. Bd. Higher Edn., 1976—, mem. exec. com., 1977—; chmn. Gov.'s Commn. on Status of Edn. in Maine, 1983—. Bd. advisors AIDS project; bd. dirs. SALT, Inc.; mem. Vt. Hist. Sites Commn., 1964-66; mem. New Eng. Colls. Fund, pres., 1971-72; chmn. Com. on Jud. Responsibility and Disability, 1982—; trustee WCBB Ednl. TV, 1974—; bd. dirs. Nat. Assn. Ind. Colls. and Univs., 1977. Capt. AUS, 1942-46; col. Res. Mem. Am. Hist. Assn., Am. Antiquarian Soc., AAUP, Maine Hist. Soc., Vt. Hist. Soc., Maine Ptnrs. Alliance for Progress. Office: U New Eng 11 Hills Beach Rd Biddeford ME 04005

REYNOLDS, VALRAE, museum curator; b. San Francisco, Dec. 18, 1944; d. Ralph Stanley and Valberta May (Eversole) R.; m. Richard Lee Huffman, Sept. 14, 1974; children: Elizabeth Anne, Margaret Lee. BA in Fine Arts with honors, U. Calif., Davis, 1966; MA, NYU, 1969. Asst. curator Asian collections Newark (N.J.) Mus., 1969-70, curator Asian collections, 1970—; cons. SITES Exhibition, 1988; lectr., presenter in field. Editor: Newark Mus. Quar., 1976, Tibetan Jour., 1976, Asia Soc., 1977, Arts of Asia, 1989, Explore Tibet, 1992; contbr. over 36 articles and revs. to profl. jours.; prodr. multimedia prodns. in field. Grantee NEA, NEH, 1972-74, 82-83, 85-86, 88-91, 89-92, J. Paul Getty grantee, 1986, 89-91, Travel grantee Asian Cultural Coun., 1989. Mem. Assn. Asian Studies (chmn. art history sect. Mid-Atlantic regional conf. 1973), China Inst. Am. (art com.), Japan Soc. (art com.). Home: 229 Baltic St Brooklyn NY 11201-6403 Office: Newark Mus PO Box 540 49 Washington St Newark NJ 07102-3109

REYNOLDS, WARREN JAY, retired publisher; b. Chgo., Mar. 10, 1918; s. Bradford Jay and Bessie Pearl (Bon Durant) R.; m. Mary Ellen Seaman, June 29, 1940; children: William, Nancy, David, Linda. BA, DePauw U., 1939. Retail salesman Gen. Foods Corp., Chgo., 1939-41; advt. salesman Capper Publs., Chgo., 1941-42, 45-47; with Parade Publs., Inc., N.Y.C., 1947—; pub. dir. Parade Publs., Inc. (Parade Mag.), 1967-83; pub. emeritus Parade Publs., Inc., 1983—. Served to lt. comdr. USN, 1942-45. Recipient Alumnus of Yr. award DePauw U., 1968. Republican. Club: Venice Yacht (Fla.). Home: 312 Yacht Harbor Dr Osprey FL 34229-9151 Office: 711 3rd Ave New York NY 10017-4014

REYNOLDS, WILLIAM BRADFORD, lawyer; b. Bridgeport, Conn., June 21, 1942; s. William Glasgow and Nancy Bradford (DuPont) R.; m. Marguerite Lynn Morgan, June 27, 1964 (div. Feb. 1987); children: William Bradford Jr., Melissa Morgan, Kristina DuPont, Wendy Riker; m. Clare Alice Conroy, Aug. 29, 1987; 1 child, Linda Matisan. BA, Yale U., 1964; LLB, Vanderbilt U., 1967. Bar: N.Y. 1968, D.C. 1973, U.S. Supreme Ct. 1971. Assoc. Sullivan and Cromwell, N.Y.C., 1967-70; asst. to Solicitor Gen. U.S. Dept. Justice, Washington, 1970-73; ptnr. Shaw, Pittman, Potts &

Trowbridge, Washington, 1973-81; asst. atty. gen. Civil Rights div. U.S. Dept. Justice, Washington, 1981-88, counselor to Atty. Gen., 1987-88; ptnr. Ross & Hardies, 1989-91, Dickstein, Shapiro & Morin, 1991-94, Collier, Shannon, Rill & Scott, 1994—; chmn. Archtl. Transp. Barriers Compliance Bd., 1982-84. Editor-in-chief Vanderbilt Law Rev., 1966. Disting. scholar Free Congress Found., 1989-93, Disting. fellow Nat. Legal Ctr. for Pub. Interest, Washington, 1989-90. Mem. ABA, Fed. Bar Assn., D.C. Bar Assn., Order of Coif. Republican. Episcopalian.

REYNOLDS, WILLIAM CRAIG, mechanical engineer, educator; b. Berkeley, Calif., Mar. 16, 1933; s. Merrill and Patricia Pope (Galt) R.; m. Janice Erma, Sept. 18, 1953; children—Russell, Peter, Margery. B.S. in Mech. Engring., Stanford U., 1954, M.S. in Mech. Engring., 1955, Ph.D. in Mech. Engring., 1957. Faculty mech. engring. Stanford U., 1957—, chmn. dept. mech. engring., 1972-82, 89-93, Donald Whittier prof. mech. engring., 1986—, chmn. Inst. for Energy Studies, 1974-81; staff scientist NASA/Ames Rsch. Ctr., 1987—. Author: books, including Energy Thermodynamics, 2d edit, 1976; contbr. numerous articles to profl. jours. NSF sr. scientist fellow Eng., 1964, Otto Laporte awd., Am. Physical Soc., 1992. Fellow ASME, Am. Phys. Soc. Am. Acad. Arts Sci.; mem. AAUP, AIAA, Nat. Acad. Engring, Stanford Integrated Mfg. Assn. (co-chmn. 1990-94), Sigma Xi, Tau Beta Pi. Achievements include research in fluid mechanics and applied thermodynamics. Office: Stanford U Dept Mechanical Engineering Stanford CA 94305

REYNOLDS, WILLIAM FRANCIS, mathematics educator; b. Boston, Jan. 31, 1930; s. William Leo and Grace Regina (Devlin) R.; m. Pauline Jane Fitzgerald, Aug. 5, 1962; children—Nancy, Jane. A.B. summa cum laude, Holy Cross Coll., 1950; A.M., Harvard, 1951, Ph.D., 1954. Instr. Holy Cross Coll., Worcester, Mass., 1954-55; instr. Mass. Inst. Tech., Cambridge, 1955-57; asst. prof. math. Tufts U., Medford, Mass., 1957-60, assoc. prof., 1960-67, prof., 1967—, Walker prof. math., 1970—. Contbr. articles to math. jours. Mem. Am. Math. Soc., Math. Assn. Am., Sigma Xi. Achievements include research on modular and projective representations of finite groups. Home: 3 Preble Gardens Rd Belmont MA 02178-3460 Office: Dept Math Tufts U Medford MA 02155

REYNOLDS, WILLIAM HAROLD, music educator, choral conductor, music critic; b. Hermosa Beach, Calif., July 19, 1925; s. Frank Harold and Elma Katherine (Williams) R.; m. Mary Lee Kingman, June 19, 1949; children: Christopher, Joel, Ellen, Anne Marie, Susan, Martha. B.A. with highest honors, UCLA, 1949; M.F.A., Princeton U., 1952. Asst. music critic L.A. Times, 1948-50; asst. instr. music Princton (N.J.) U., 1951-52; instr. music Vassar Coll., Poughkeepsie, N.Y., 1952-54; asst. prof. U. Calif., Riverside, 1954-60, assoc. prof., 1960-66, prof., 1966-91, chmn. dept. music, 1961-67, 77-82, chmn. acad. senate, 1968-70, mem. statewide acad. coun., 1968-70, assoc. dean Coll. Humanities and Social Scis., 1989-94, prof. emeritus, 1991—; appointed dir. U. Calif. Scandinavian Study Ctr. at Lund U. (Sweden) and Copenhagen U., 1987-89; assoc. Danforth Found., 1958—. Author: Common Practice Harmony, 1985; contbr. articles on Danish composers to Grove's Dictionary of Music; contbr. articles to New Grove Dictionary of Opera, 1992. Recipient E. Harris Harbison prize for disting. teaching Danforth Found., 1969, Riverside Arts Coun. award for music, 1979; grantee Am. Philos Soc., 1960-61, 75-76, Statewide U. Calif. Humanities Inst., 1967-68, Creative Arts Inst., 1974, Danmarks Nat. Bank, 1975, Am. Scandinavian Found., 1982-83. Mem. Coll. Music Soc. (v.p. 1972-75, pres. 1975-77), Calif. Music Execs. (pres. 1981-82), Internat., Am. musicol. socs., Am. Choral Dirs. Assn., Calif. Choral Condrs. Guild (pres. Riverside-San Bernardino chpt. 1956-57), Phi Beta Kappa (hon., pres. Iota chpt. 1985-86). Democrat. Episcopalian. Home: 741 Spruce St Riverside CA 92507-2518 *Music is a field of great diversity, involving historical scholarship as well as the creative areas of performance and composition. It has been my good fortune to be able to combine scholarship and performance so that music is for me not merely an academic field nor a life of concert giving: it is both, and thus truly a liberal art.*

REYNOLDS, WILLIAM HENRY, film editor; b. Elmira, N.Y., June 14, 1910. Grad., Princeton Univ. Swing gang laborer Fox Film Corp., 1934; asst. editor Paramount, 1936-37, editor, 1937-42; editor Twentieth Century-Fox, 1947-62; free-lance editor, 1962—. Asst. editor: (films) The Farmer Takes a Wife, 1935, The Gay Deception, 1935, Big Brown Eyes, 1936, Her Master's Voice, 1936, Palm Springs, 1936, Spendthrift, 1936, John Meade's Woman, 1937, Honeymoon in Bali, 1939, A Night at Earl Carroll's, 1940, Typhoon, 1940; editor: (films) (with Otto Lovering) 52nd Street, 1937, (with Lovering) Algiers, 1938, So Ends Our Night, 1941, Moontide, 1942, Carnival in Costa Rica, 1947, Give My Regards to Broadway, 1948, The Street with No Name, 1948, You Were Meant for Me, 1948, Come to the Stable, 1949, Mother Is a Freshman, 1949, Halls of Montezuma, 1951, The Day the Earth Stood Still, 1951, The Frogmen, 1951, Take Care of My Little Girl, 1951, The Outcasts of Poker Flat, 1952, Red Skies of Montana, 1952, Beneath the 12-Mile Reef, 1953, Dangerous Crossing, 1953, The Kid from Left Field, 1953, Desiree, 1954, Three Coins in the Fountain, 1954, Daddy Long Legs, 1955, Good Morning, Miss Dove, 1955, Love Is a Many-Splendored Thing, 1955, Bus Stop, 1956, Carousel, 1956, In Love and War, 1958, Beloved Infidel, 1959, Blue Denim, 1959, Compulsion, 1959, Wild River, 1960, Tender Is the Night, 1961, Fanny, 1961 (Academy award nomination best film editing 1961), (with Gene Milford, Eda Warren, and Folmar Blangsted) Taras Bulba, 1962, Kings of the Sun, 1963, Ensign Pulver, 1964, The Sound of Music, 1965 (Academy award best film editing 1965), Our Man Flint, 1966, The Sand Pebbles, 1966 (Academy award nomination best film editing 1966), Star!, 1968, Hello, Dolly!, 1969 (Academy award nomination best film editing 1969), The Great White Hope, 1970, What's the Matter with Helen?, 1971, (with Peter Zinner) The Godfather, 1972 (Academy award nomination best film editing 1972), Two People, 1973, The Sting, 1973 (Academy award best film editing 1973), The Great Waldo Pepper, 1975, (with Danford Greene) The Master Gunfighter, 1975, The Seven-Percent Solution, 1977, The Turning Point, 1977 (Academy award nomination best film editing 1977), Old Boyfriends, 1979, A Little Romance, 1979, (with Lisa Fruchtman, Gerald Greenberg, and Tom Rolf) Heaven's Gate, 1980, Nijinsky, 1980, Making Love, 1982, Author! Author!, 1982, Yellowbeard, 1983, (with Raja Gosnell) The Lonely Guy, 1984, The Little Drummer Girl, 1984, (with Herve De Luze) Pirates, 1986, Dancers, 1987, (with Richard A. Cirincione and Stephen A. Rotter) Ishtar, 1987, A New Life, 1988, Rooftops, 1989, Taking Care of Business, 1990, Newsies, 1992; prodr.: (films) (with Richard Widmark) Time Limit, 1957. Office: The Gersh Agency 232 N Canon Dr Beverly Hills CA 90210*

REYNOLDS, WILLIAM LEROY, lawyer, educator; b. Balt., July 26, 1945; s. Austin Leroy and Doris (Hill) R.; m. Theodora Hoe, Sept. 3, 1966; children: William, Megan, Sarah. A.B., Dartmouth Coll., 1967; J.D., Harvard U., 1970. Bar: Md. 1972, U.S. Supreme Ct. 1975. Clk. to judge U.S. Dist. Ct. Md., 1970-71; asst. prof. law U. Md., 1971-74, assoc. prof., 1974-77, prof., 1977—; of counsel Piper & Marbury, Balt., 1992—; bd. dirs. Md. Jud. Inst. Author: Judicial Process in a Nutshell, 2d edit., 1991, Understanding the Conflict of Laws, 1984, 2d edit., 1993, Cases and Materials on Conflict of Laws, 1990. Mem. Am. Law Inst., Md. State Bar Assn. Am. Judicature Soc. Clubs: Serjeants' Inn, Wranglers (Balt.); St. Regis Yacht (Paul Smiths, N.Y.), Hamilton St. Office: U Md Sch Law 500 W Baltimore St Baltimore MD 21201-1786

REYNOLDS, W(YNETKA) ANN, university system administrator, educator; b. Coffeyville, Kans., Nov. 3, 1937; d. John Ethelbert and Glennie (Beanland) King; m. Thomas H. Kirschbaum; children—Rachel Rebecca, Rex King. BS in Biology-Chemistry, Kans. State Tchrs. Coll., Emporia, 1958; MS in Zoology, U. Iowa, Iowa City, 1960, PhD, 1962; DSc (hon.), Ind. State U., Evansville, 1980; LHD (hon.), McKendree Coll., 1984, U. N.C., Charlotte, 1988, U. Judaism, L.A., 1989, U. Nebr., Kearney, 1992; DSc (hon.), Ball State U., Muncie, Ind., 1985. Emporia (Kans.) State U., 1987; PhD (hon.), Fu Jen Cath. U., Republic of China, 1987; LHD (hon.), U. Nebr., Kearney, 1992, Colgate U., 1993. Asst. prof. biology Ball State U., Muncie, Ind., 1962-65; asst. prof. anatomy U. Ill. Coll. Medicine, Chgo., 1965-68, assoc. prof. anatomy, 1968-73, research prof. ob-gyn. from 1973, prof. anatomy, from 1973, acting assoc. dean acad. affairs Coll. Medicine, 1977, assoc. vice chancellor, dean grad. coll., 1977-79; provost, v.p. for acad. affairs, prof. ob-gyn. and anatomy Ohio State U., Columbus, 1979-82; chancellor Calif. State Univ. system, Long Beach, 1982-90, prof. biology,

1982-90; bd. dirs. Abbott Labs., Maytag, Owens-Corning, Humana, Inc.; clin. prof. ob/gyn. UCLA, 1985-90; chancellor CUNY, 1990—; mem. Nat. Rsch. Coun. Com. Undergrad. Sci. Edn., 1993—; co-chair Fed. Task Force on Women, Minorities and Handicapped in Sci. and Tech., 1987-90, Pacesetter Program Reform for Secondary Sch. Coll. Bd., 1992—; adv. bd. Congl. Black Caucus Inst. Sci., Space and Tech., 1987-91; Calif. Labor Employment and Tng. Corp., 1993—; Contbr. chpts. to books, articles to profl. jours; assoc. editor Am. Biology Tchr., 1964-67. Active numerous civic activities involving edn. and the arts; mem. nat. adv. bd. Inst. Am. Indian Arts, 1992—; bd. dirs. Calif. Econ. Devel. Corp., 1984-90; trustee Internat. Life Scis. Inst.-Nutrition Found., 1987—, Southwest Mus., L.A. County High Sch. for Arts Found., 1985-90; bd. dirs. UAW Calif. Recipient Disting. Alumni award Kans. State Tchrs. Coll., 1972, Calif. Gov.'s Award for the Arts for an Outstanding Individual in Arts in Edn., 1989, Prize award Cen. Assn. Obstetricians and Gynecologists, 1968; NSF Predoctoral fellow, 1958-62, Woodrow Wilson Hon. fellow, 1958. Fellow ACOG; mem. AAAS, Perinatal Rsch. Soc., Soc. Gynecol. Investigation (sec./treas. 1980-83, pres. 1992-93), Nat. Assn. Systems Heads (pres. 1987-88), Sigma Xi. Office: CUNY Office of the Chancellor 535 E 80th St New York NY 10021-0795

REYNOLDSON, WALTER WARD, state supreme court chief justice; b. St. Edward, Nebr., May 17, 1920; s. Walter Scorer and Mabel Matilda (Sallach) R.; m. Janet Aline Mills, Dec. 24, 1942 (dec. 1986); children: Vicki (Mrs. Gary Kimes), Robert; m. Patricia A. Frey, June 3, 1989. BA, State Tchrs. Coll., 1942; JD, U. Iowa, 1948; LLD (hon.), Simpson Coll., 1983, Drake U. 1987. Bar: Iowa 1948. Justice Iowa Supreme Ct., 1971-78, chief justice, 1978-87, sr. judge, 1989-93; of counsel Reynoldson Law Firm, Osceola, Iowa, 1993—; adj. prof. law Drake U., 1989-93; county atty., Clarke County, Iowa, 1953-57. Contbg. author: Trial Handbook, 1969. Pres. Nat. Ctr. for State Cts., 1984-85. Served with USNR, 1942-46. Recipient Osceola Community Svc. award, 1968. Mem. Iowa Bar Assn. (chmn. com. on legal edn. and admission to bar 1964-71), ABA, Am. Judicature Soc. (bd. dirs. 1983-87, Herbert Harley award 1990), Iowa Acad. Trial Lawyers, Conf. Chief Justices (pres. 1984-85), Am. Coll. Trial Lawyers. Office: Reynoldson Law Firm 200 W Jefferson St Osceola IA 50213

REZAC, PAMELA JEAN, hospital executive; b. Lesterville, S.D., Dec. 23, 1947; d. Melvin E. and Esther A. (David) Lee; m. Robert L. Rezac; children: Angel, Annie, Charles. RN, Meth. Sch. Nursing, 1969; BA in Health Care Adminstrn., U. Minn., 1978, MHA, 1981; postgrad., Harvard U., 1987—. Adminstr. Landman-Jungeman Hosp., Scotland, S.D., 1972-80; asst. adminstr. Sacred Heart Hosp., Yankton, S.D., 1980-82, interim chief exec. officer, 1982, v.p., 1982—; presenter nat. symposium Am. Coll. Health Care Mktg., Orlando, Fla., 1987, 89. Bd. dirs. S.D. Homes for Aging, 1984—, sec., 1984-86; mem. Gov.'s Resource and Devel. Coun., S.D., 1978—. Bush Found. fellow, 1987-88. Mem. Am. Hosp. Assn. (governing coun. for sect. of long term care and aged 1990—, med. staff forum 1989, presenter nat. symposium for health care mktg. 1988, 89), Am. Coll. Health Care Execs. (adv. coun. 1988, Cert.), Interchange Bus. and Profl. Orgn., S.D. Hosp. Assn. Profl. Practice Coun., Yankton C. of C. (subcom. chair health com. 1987-88, planning commn. 1989), Kiwanis, Hillcrest Golf Country Club. Democrat. Roman Catholic. Avocation: golf. Home: RR 1 Box 67 Yankton SD 57078-9415 Office: Presentation Health System Ste 1 Box 38 Yankton SD 57078

REZAC, STEPHAN ROBERT, trade association executive; b. Sioux Falls, S.D., Dec. 4, 1953; s. Gerald Robert and Nila Jean (Kunkel) R.; m. Donna Gail Blumenfeld, May 24, 1986. Student, S.D. State U., 1972-74, U. Wyo., 1984, Casper Coll., 1984. Dir. promotion, edn. S.D. Credit Union League, Sioux Falls, 1975-76; mktg. dir. Chanute Credit Union, Rantoul, Ill., 1976-80; dir. edn., mktg. Wyo. Credit Union League, Casper, 1980-86; pres., chief exec. officer N.Mex. Credit Union League, Albuquerque, 1986—; N.Mex. Credit Union League Services Corp., Albuquerque, 1986—; nat. dir. Credit Union Nat. Assn., Madison, Wis., 1986—; lobbyist N.Mex. Credit Union League, 1987—. Mem. AMA, Assn. Credit Union League Execs., N.Mex. Soc. Assn. Execs., Albuquerque C. of C. (govtl. affairs policy com. 1988—). Republican. Baptist. Avocations: fly-fishing, rock climbing, backpacking, snow skiing. Home: 5966 Curry Rd Ext Schenectady NY 12303-2800 Office: NMex Credit Union League 9426 Indian School Rd NE Albuquerque NM 87112-2843

REZAK, RICHARD, geology and oceanography educator; b. Syracuse, N.Y., Apr. 26, 1920; s. Habib and Radia (Khoury) R.; m. Hifa Hider, July 1, 1944 (div. Mar. 1965); 1 child, Christine Sara; m. Anna Lucile Nesselrode, Mar. 12, 1965. MA, Washington U., St. Louis, 1949; PhD, Syracuse U., 1957. Geologist U.S. Geol. Survey, Denver, 1952-58; rsch. assoc. Shell Devel. Co., Houston, 1958-67; assoc. prof. oceanography Tex. A&M U., College Station, Tex., 1967-71; prof. Tex. A&M U., College Station, 1971-91, prof. emeritus, 1991—; mem. edit. bd. Geo-MArine Letters, N.Y.C., 1981—; coun. SEPM, Tulsa, Okla., 1968-69; mem. gov. adv. panel Offshore Oil & Chem. Spill Response, Austin, Tex., 1984-85. Co-author: Reefs and Banks of the Northwest Gulf of Mexico, 1985; co-editor: Contributions on the Geological/Oceanography of the Gulf of Mexico, 1972, Carbonate Microfabrics, 1993; contbr. articles to profl. jours. Comdr. USNR, 1942-64. Rsch. grantee various fed. agys., 1968-90. Mem. Svc. Corps of Ret. Execs., Lions (Southwestern Div.). Episcopalian. Home: 3600 Stillmeadow Dr Bryan TX 77802-3324 Office: Tex A&M U Dept Oceanography College Station TX 77843

REZNECK, DANIEL ALBERT, lawyer; b. Troy, N.Y., Apr. 26, 1935; s. Samuel and Elizabeth (Fishburne) R.; m. Beverly Ann Macht, Mar. 7, 1971; children: Jonathan Noah, Abigail Rebecca. BA, Harvard U., 1956, JD, 1959. Bar: N.Y. 1959, D.C. 1961. Rsch. asst. Harvard U. Law Sch., Cambridge, Mass., 1959-60; law clk. to Justice William J. Brennan U.S. Supreme Ct., Washington, 1960-61; asst. U.S. atty. Dept. Justice, Washington, 1961-64; assoc. Arnold & Porter, Washington, 1964-68, ptnr., 1969—; adj. prof. law Georgetown U., Washington, 1963—; mem. D.C. Commn. on Jud. Disabilities and Tenure, 1979-86, D.C. Bd. Profl. Responsibility, 1994—; trustee D.C. Pub. Defender Svc., 1981-87. Contbr. articles to profl. jours. Contbr. articles to profl. jours. Named Young Lawyer of Yr. for D.C., 1971. Fellow Am. Coll. Trial Lawyers, Am. Bar Found.; mem. ABA, D.C. Bar (pres. 1975-76, pres. found. 1994—), Bar Assn. D.C., Am. Judicature Soc., Asst. U.S. Attys. Assn., D.C. B'nai Brith. Jewish. Avocations: American history; reading; writing. Home: 2852 Albemarle St NW Washington DC 20008-1036 Office: Arnold & Porter 555 12th St NW Washington DC 20004-1202

REZNICEK, BERNARD WILLIAM, power company executive; b. Dodge, Nebr., Dec. 7, 1936; s. William Bernard and Elizabeth (Svoboda) R.; m. Mary Leona Gallagher; children—Stephen B., Michael J., Charles W., Mary E., Bernard J., James G. BSBA, Creighton U., 1958, MBA, U. Nebr. 1979. With Omaha Public Power Dist., pres., chief exec. officer, from 1981; exec. Sierra Pacific Power, Reno, 1979-80; now pres., chief operating officer Boston Edison Co.; dir. Inst. Nuclear Power Ops., Atlanta, Atomic Indsl. Forum, Guarantee Mut. Life Ins. Co. Trustee Father Flanagans Boys' Home, 1984. Mem. C. of C. (bd. dirs. 1981, treas. 1986-87), Beta Gamma Sigma. Republican. Roman Catholic. Club: Oak Hills Country (sec. 1985, v.p. 1986). Lodge: Rotary (bd. dirs. 1984-86), Ak-Sar-Ben. Office: Boston Edison Co 800 Boylston St Boston MA 02199-8001

REZNIKOV, HANON, theater director, actor; b. N.Y.C., Sept. 23, 1950; s. Bernard and Harriette (Wexler) Reznikov; m. Judith Malina, May 6, 1988. BA, Yale U., 1972. Actor Living Theatre, N.Y.C., 1973-84, exec. dir., 1984—. Author, dir.: (plays) The Hellow Methuselah, 1982, Poland/1931, 1988, The Tablets, 1989, The Body of God, 1990, Rules of Civility, Anarchia, 1993, Utopia, 1995; author: (plays) Waste, The Zero Method. Recipient Ninth Centennial medal U. Bologna, 1988, Obie award Village Voice, 1989. Mem. Dramatists Guild. Home: 800 W End Ave New York NY 10025-5467

RHA, Y. B., electronics executive. With Kamsung Group, Korea, 1972-91; sr. v.p.-sales & marketing Samsung Semiconductor Inc., San Jose, Calif., 1991—. Office: Samsung Semiconductor Inc 3655 N 1st St San Jose CA 95134-1707

RHAME, THOMAS GENE, army officer; b. Winnfield, La., Jan. 27, 1941; s. Thomas Elton and Mary Sue (Blair) R.; m. Linda Ann Saunders, Jan. 21, 1961; children: Rebecca Jean Rhame Barton, Thomas Gregory. BS, La. State U., 1963; MBA, Syracuse U., 1970. Commd. 2d lt. U.S. Army, 1963, advanced through grades to lt. gen., 1993; co. comdr., advisor 1st Cavalry Div., Republic of Vietnam, 1967-71; student Armed Forces Staff Coll., Norfolk, Va., 1975; bn. comdr. 2d Armored Div., Ft. Hood, Tex., 1976-78; advisor Calif. N.G. 40th Inf. Div., L.A., 1979-80; student Army War Coll., Carlisle, Pa., 1981; brigade comdr. 3d Inf., Kitzingen, Fed. Republic Germany, 1981-83; chief of staff 3d Armored Div., Frankfurt, Fed. Republic Germany, 1983; community comdr., asst. div. comdr. U.S. Army Europe, Hanau, Fed. Republic Germany, 1985-86; dep. chief of staff for pers. U.S. Army Staff, Washington, 1986-89; comdr. 1st Inf. Div., Ft. Riley, Kans., 1989-91; Operation Desert Storm chief U.S. Mil. Tng. Mission, U.S. Cen. Command, Riyadh, Saudi Arabia, 1991-93; dir. Def. Security Assistance Agy., Washington, 1993—. Mem. Transatlantic coun. Boy Scouts Am., Fed. Republic Germany, 1985-86; bd. dirs. Soc. Big Red One, 1989-91. Decorated Legion of Merit, Bronze Star (3), Silver Star (2), M.S.M. (3), Army D.S.M. (2), Defense D.S.M.; named to La. State U. Hall of Disting. Grads., 1991. Mem. Assn. U.S. Army. Republican. Baptist. Avocations: stamp collecting, hunting, fishing.

RHAME, WILLIAM THOMAS, land development company executive; b. Wantagh, N.Y., Aug. 14, 1915; s. Frank Phipps and Eleanora May Sanger (Davis) R.; m. Thelma Scorgie, Aug. 13, 1939 (div. 1964); children—Frank Scorgie, Frederick Taylor. B.A., U. Cin., 1936; M.B.A., Harvard, 1938, D.C.S., 1942. Mem. faculty Harvard Grad. Sch. Bus. Adminstrn., 1938-40; partner Robert Heller & Assos., Cleve., 1940-45; bus. cons. N.Y.C., 1945-48; pres. Texstar Corp., San Antonio, 1948-65, Merger Consultants of Am., Inc., 1965—; partner Investment Realty Co.; chmn. finance com., dir. ICN Pharms., Inc., Irvine, Calif., 1960-76; dir. T.O. Corp.; Hallmark Realty Corp., Mountain Top Estates Inc. Pres. Guadalupe Com. Center, 1956-57, The Argyle, 1957-58; chmn. bd. dirs. Mind Sci. Found. Mem. Phi Beta Kappa, Sigma Alpha Epsilon, Sigma Sigma, Tau Kappa Alpha. Republican. Episcopalian. Clubs: San Antonio Country, Argyle, University. Home: 4001 N New Braunfels Ave San Antonio TX 78209-6349 Office: 1635 North East Loop 410 San Antonio TX 78209

RHEIN, MURRAY HAROLD, management consultant; b. N.Y.C., June 7, 1912; s. Aaron and Celia (Hagler) R.; m. Miriam Eisenstadt, Dec. 22, 1940; children: Alan A., Barbara (Mrs. Allan D. Kramer). B.A., U. Ark., 1932, postgrad., 1932-33. Jr. exec. R.H. Macy & Co., N.Y.C., 1934-39; with Platt & Munk Co., N.Y.C., 1940-78, sales mgr., 1958-64, exec. v.p., 1964-67, pres., 1967-77; v.p. Questor Edn. Products Co., 1969-78; with M & M Rhein (mgmt. consultants to pub. industry), 1978—. Pub.: The Little Engine that Could. Served with USCGR, 1943-46. Jewish (trustee, v.p. temple).

RHEINBOLDT, WERNER CARL, mathematics educator, researcher; b. Berlin, Sept. 18, 1927; came to U.S., 1956; s. Karl L. and Gertrud (Hartwig) R. Dipl Math, U. Heidelberg, Fed. Republic Germany, 1952; Dr rer nat, U. Freiburg, Fed. Republic Germany, 1955. Mathematician Computer Lab. Nat. Bur. Standards, Washington, 1957-59; asst. prof. math., dir. Computer Ctr., Syracuse (N.Y.) U., 1959-62; dir. Computer Sci. Ctr., U. Md., College Park, 1962-65, prof. math. and computer sci., 1965-78, dir. applied math. program, 1974-78; A.W. Mellon prof. math. U. Pitts., 1978—; cons. various orgns., 1965—; cons. editor Acad. Press, Inc., N.Y.C., 1987—; mem. adv. panel NSF, Army Rsch. Office, Office Naval Rsch., NASA. Author: (with J. Ortega) Iterative Solution of Nonlinear Equations in Several Variable, 1970; Methods of Solving Systems on Nonlinear Equations, 1974, Numerical Analysis of Parametrized Equations, 1985; also over 130 articles. With German Army, 1943-45. Recipient Av. Humboldt Disting. Scientist award, Alexander von Humboldt Found., Germany; grantee NSF, 1965—, Office Naval Rsch., 1972—. Fellow AAAS; mem. Am. Math. Soc., Soc. for Indsl. and Applied Math. (editor 1964—, v.p. pubs. 1976, pres. 1977-78, coun. 1979-80, trustee, 1982, chmn. bd. trustees 1985-90). Office: U Pitts Dept Math and Stats 612 Thackeray Building Pittsburgh PA 15260-4146

RHEINSTEIN, PETER HOWARD, government official, physician, lawyer; b. Cleve., Sept. 7, 1943; s. Franz Joseph Rheinstein and Hede Henrietta (Neheimer) Rheinstein Lerner; m. Miriam Ruth Weissman, Feb. 22, 1969; 1 child, Jason Edward. BA with high honors, Mich. State U., 1963, MS, 1964; MD, Johns Hopkins U., 1967; JD, U. Md., 1973. Bar: Md., D.C.; diplomate Am. Bd. Family Practice. Intern USPHS Hosp., San Francisco, 1967-68; resident in internal medicine USPHS Hosp., Balt., 1968-70; practice medicine specializing in internal medicine Balt., 1970—; instr. medicine U. Md., Balt., 1970-73; med. dir. extended care facilities CHC Corp., Balt., 1972-74; dir. drug advt. and labeling div. FDA, Rockville, Md., 1974-82, acting dep. dir. Office Drugs, 1982-83, acting dir. Office Drugs, 1983-84, dir. Office Drug Standards, 1984-90; dir. medicine staff, Office Health Affairs FDA, 1990—; chmn. Com. on Advanced Sci. Edn., 1978-86, Rsch. in Human Subjects Com., 1990-92; adj. prof. forensic medicine George Washington U., 1974-76; WHO cons. on drug regulation Nat. Inst. for Control Pharm. and Biol. Products, People's Republic of China, 1981—; advisor on essential drugs WHO, 1985—; FDA del. to U.S Pharmacopeial Conv., 1985-90. Co-author: (with others) Human Organ Transplantation, 1987; spl. editorial advisor Good Housekeeping Guide to Medicine and Drugs, 1977—; mem. editorial bd. Legal Aspects Med. Practice, 1981-89, Drug Info. Jour., 1982-86, 91; contbr. articles to profl. jours. Recipient Commendable Svc. award FDA, 1981, Group award of merit, 1983, 88, Group Commendable Svc. award, 1989, 92, 95, Commr.'s Spl. Citation, 1993. Fellow Am. Coll. Legal Medicine (bd. govs. 1983-93, treas., chmn. fin. com. 1985-88, 90-91, chmn. publs. com. 1988-93, chmn. jud. coun. 1993—, Pres.'s awards 1985, 86, 89, 90, 91, 93), Am. Acad. Family Physicians; mem. AMA, ABA, Drug Info. Assn. (bd. dirs. 1982-90, pres. 1984-85, 88-89, v.p. 1986-87, chmn. ann. meeting 1991, 94, N.Am. steering com. 1991—, Outstanding Svc. award 1990), Fed. Bar Assn. (chmn. food and drug com. 1976-79, Disting. Svc. award 1977), Med. and Chirurgical Faculty Md., Balt. City Med. Soc., Johns Hopkins Med. and Surg. Assn., Am. Pub. Health Assn., Md. Bar Assn., Math. Assn. Am., Soc. Indsl. and Applied Math., Mensa (life), U.S. Power Squadrons, Mich. State U. Alumni Assn. (life), U. Md. Alumni Assn. (life), Johns Hopkins U. Alumni Assn., Fed. Exec. Inst. Alumni Assn. (life), Chartwell Golf and Country Club, Annapolis Yacht Club, Johns Hopkins Club, Delta Theta Phi. Avocations: boating, electronics, physical fitness, real estate investments. Home: 621 Holly Ridge Rd Severna Park MD 21146-3520 Office: FDA Office of Health Affairs Dir Medicine Staff 5600 Fishers Ln Rockville MD 20857-0001

RHETT, HARRY MOORE, JR., investment executive; b. Huntsville, Ala., Mar. 3, 1912; s. Harry Moore and Marie Louise (Rison) R.; m. Sharon Barbour, June 14, 1952 (dec. May 1972); children: Louise Rhett Orem, Harry Moore III, William Warren Barbour, Leslie Rhett Crosby. AB, Washington & Lee U., 1935; MBA, Harvard U., 1937; LHD (hon.), U. Ala., 1995. Asst. underwriter Accident & Casualty Ins. Co., N.Y.C., 1937-39; spl. agt. Accident & Casualty Ins. Co., L.A., 1939-41; asst. to pres. Rison Banking Co., Huntsville, 1946-48; prin. H. M. Rhett Jr., Huntsville, 1948—; bd. dirs. emeritus First Ala. Bank, Huntsville, First Ala. Bancshares, Birmingham. Mem. Army Community Rels. Com., Redstone Arsenal, Ala, 1955—; treas. U. Ala. Huntsville Found., 1979—; chmn. Huntsville Waterworks Utility Bd., 1954-95, Huntsville Gas Utility Bd., 1954-95. Maj. U.S. Army, 1941-46, ETO. Recipient Outstanding Citizen award Huntsville-Madison County C. of C., 1973; Harry Moore Rhett Jr. Solarium named in his honor Huntsville Hosp., 1987. Mem. Masters of Foxhound Assn. (bd. dirs. Leesburg, Va.), Nat. Steeplechase and Hunt Assn. Md., Huntsville-Madison County C. of C. (pres. 1952), Harvard Club of N.Y.C. (Chatham (Mass.) Beach and Tennis Club (pres. 1977-82), Byrd Spring Rod and Gun Club, Rotary (pres. Huntsville club 1952). Democrat. Episcopalian. Avocations: tennis, fox hunting. Home: 603 Adams St SE Huntsville AL 35801-3704 Office: 200 W Court Sq Huntsville AL 35801 Address: PO Box 526 Huntsville AL 35804

RHETT, HASKELL EMERY SMITH, foundation executive, educator; b. Evanston, Ill., Aug. 29, 1936; s. Haskell Smith and Eunice Campbell (Emery) R.; m. Roberta Teel Oliver, Sept. 9, 1961 (div. 1973); children: Kathryn Emery, Cecily Coffin; m. Anita Leone, May 30, 1983 (div. 1993). AB, Hamilton Coll., 1958; MA, Cornell U., 1967, PhD, 1968. Asst. to the pres. Hamilton Coll., Clinton, N.Y., 1961-64; rsch. asst. Cornell U.,

Ithaca, N.Y., 1964-66; rsch. assoc. U. London, 1966-67; dir. program devel. Ednl. Testing Svc., Princeton, N.J., 1967-73; asst. chancellor N.J. Dept. Higher Edn., Trenton, 1973-85; v.p. The Coll. Bd., N.Y.C., 1985-90; pres. The Woodrow Wilson Nat. Fellowship Found., Princeton, 1990—. Author: Going to College in New Jersey, 1978; contbg. author: Government's Role in Supporting College Savings, 1990. Commr. N.J. Pub. Broadcasting Authority, Trenton, 1983-85; mem. Nat. Task Force on Student Aid Problems, Washington, 1974-75; mem. Gov's. Adv. Panel on Higher Edn. Restructuring, State of N.J., 1994; trustee Dominican Coll., San Rafael, Calif., 1990—; del. Dem. Nat. Conv., Miami, 1972; sr. warden Trinity Episcopal Ch., Princeton, 1988-92, vestryman, 1979-82, dep. Gen. Conv., Detroit, 1988, Phoenix, 1991; mem. standing com. Episcopal Diocese of N.J. 1992; trustee Trenton State Coll., 1992—, Gov. Dummer Acad., Mass., 1993—. Heartland Edn. Cmty., Ohio, 1992—. Lt. USNR, 1958-61. Nat. Def. fellow U.S. Govt., 1966-67, Eliot-Winant fellow Brit.-Am. Assocs., 1982, Harvard U. fellow, 1985, faculty fellow Wilson Coll., Princeton U., 1993—. Mem. Am. Assn. for Higher Edn., Nat. Assn. State Scholarship and Grant Programs (pres. 1976-78), Nassau Club, Cornell Club (N.Y.), Springdale Golf Club. Avocations: tennis, golf, sailing, classic automobiles. Home: 64 River Dr Titusville NJ 08560-1726 also: PO Box 53 Blue Hill Falls ME 04615 Office: The Woodrow Wilson Nat Fellowship Found CN 5281 Princeton NJ 08543-5281

RHETT, JOHN TAYLOR, JR., government official, civil engineer; b. Fort Benning, Ga., Feb. 20, 1925; s. John Taylor and Bessie (Grier) R.; m. Helen Watson, Nov. 5, 1949; children—Elizabeth, John Taylor III. B.S. in Mil. Engring., U.S. Mil. Acad., 1945; M.E. in Civil Engring., U. Calif.-Berkeley, 1952; M.S. in Internat. Relations, George Washington U., 1965. Registered civil engr., Fla., D.C. Commd. 2d lt. U.S. Army, 1942, advanced through grades to col., 1967; chief engring. U.S. Army Constrn. Agy., Vietnam, 1968-69; dist. engr. C.E., U.S. Army, Louisville, Ky., 1969-72; resident mem. Rivers and Harbors Bd., C.E., U.S. Army, 1972-73; ret. U.S. Army, 1973; dep. asst. adminstr. water program ops. EPA, Washington, 1979-86; self-insp. Alaska Natural Gas Transp. System, Washington, 1979-86; self-employed cons. Arlington, Va., 1986—. Decorated Legion of Merit; recipient Gold medal EPA, 1976, Disting. Career award EPA, 1979. Fellow ASCE; mem. Am. Acad. Environ. Engrs. (diplomate), Soc. Mil. Engrs. Presbyterian.

RHIND, JAMES THOMAS, lawyer; b. Chgo., July 21, 1922; s. John Gray and Eleanor (Bradley) R.; m. Laura Haney Campbell, Apr. 19, 1958; children: Anne Constance, James Campbell, David Scott. Student, Hamilton Coll., 1940-42; A.B. cum laude, Ohio State U., 1944; LL.B. cum laude, Harvard U., 1950. Bar: Ill. bar 1950. Japanese translator U.S. War Dept., Tokyo, Japan, 1946-47; congl. liaison Fgn. Operations Adminstrn., Washington, 1954; atty. Bell, Boyd & Lloyd, Chgo., 1950-53, 55—, ptnr., 1958-92, of counsel, 1993—; Bd. dirs. Kewaunee Scientific Corp., Statesville, N.C., Lindberg Corp., Rosemont, Ill., Microseal Corp., Zion, Ill., Griffith Labs., Inc., Alsip, Ill. Commr. Gen. Assembly United Presbyn. Ch., 1963; life trustee Ravinia Festival Assn., Hamilton Coll., Clinton, N.Y., U. Chgo.; Northwestern Univ. Assocs.; chmn. Cook County Young Republican Orgn., 1957; Ill. Young Rep. nat. committeeman, 1957-58; v.p., mem. bd. govs. United Rep. Fund Ill., 1965-84; pres. Ill. Childrens Home and Aid Soc., 1971-73, life trustee; bd. dirs. E.J. Dalton Youth Center, 1966- 69; governing mem. Orchestral Assn., Chgo.; mem. Ill. Arts Council, 1971-75; mem. exec. com. div. Met. Mission and Ch. Extension Bd., Chgo. Presbytery, 1966-68; trustee Presbyn. Home, W. Clement and Jessie V. Stone Found., U. Chgo. Hosps. Served with M.I. AUS, 1943-46. Mem. ABA, Ill. Bar Assn., Chgo. Bar Assn. (bd. mgrs. 1967-69), Fed. Bar Assns., Chgo. Council on Fgn. Relations, Japan Am. Soc. Chgo., Legal Club Chgo., Law Club Chgo., Phi Beta Kappa, Sigma Phi. Presbyterian (elder). Clubs: Chicago (Chgo.), Glen View (Chgo.), Commercial (Chgo.), Attic (Chgo.), Economic (Chgo.). Home: 830 Normandy Ln Glenview IL 60025-3210 Office: Bell Boyd & Lloyd 3 First National Pla 70 W Madison St Ste 3200 Chicago IL 60602-4284

RHINES, PETER BROOMELL, oceanographer, atmospheric scientist; b. Hartford, Conn., July 23, 1942; s. Thomas B. and Olive (Symonds) R.; m. Marie Louise Lenos, Oct. 12, 1968; (div. 1983); m. Linda Jean Mattson; 1 child, Andrew Nelson. B.S., M.S., M.I.T., Cambridge U., 1964; Ph.D., Trinity Coll., Cambridge U., Eng., 1967. Asst. prof. oceanography M.I.T., Cambridge, 1968-71; rsch. asst. dept. applied math. and theoretical physics Cambridge U., Eng., 1971-72; scientist Woods Hole Oceanographic Inst., Woods Hole, Mass., 1972-84; prof. oceanography and atmospheric scis. U. Wash., Seattle, 1984—; vis. fellow Christ's Coll., Cambridge, Eng., 1979-80, 1983. Recipient de Florez research award MIT, 1963; NSF fellow, 1963-64; Guggenheim fellow, 1979-80; Queen's fellow in marine scis., Australia, 1988; A.E. Sloan Research scholar MIT, 1960-63; Marshall scholar Cambridge, 1964-67; Green scholar U. Calif., San Diego, 1981. Fellow Am. Geophys. Union, Am. Meterol. Soc.; mem. Nat. Acad. Scis. Avocations: guitar, walking, studying the global environment. Home: 5753 61st Ave NE Seattle WA 98105-2037 Office: Sch Oceanography U Wash WB-10 Seattle WA 98195

RHINES, WALDEN C., information system specialist; b. 1948. With Tex. Instruments, Dallas, 1972-93, exec. v.p. semiconductor group; with Mentor Graphics Corp., Wilsonville, Oreg., 1993—, now CEO, pres. Office: Mentor Graphics Corp 8005 SW Boeckman Rd Wilsonville OR 97070*

RHINESMITH, STEPHEN HEADLEY, international management consultant; b. Mineola, N.Y., Dec. 13, 1942; s. Homer Kern and Winifred Headley (Long) R.; m. Kathleen Alys Law, Aug. 28, 1965; children: Chrisopher Law, Colin Headley. BA (Baker scholar), Wesleyan U., 1965; M in Pub. and Internat. Affairs, (Heinz fellow), U. Pitts., 1966, PhD (NDEA fellow), 1972. Dir. internat. svcs. McBer and Co., Cambridge, Mass., 1969-71; pres. AFS Intercultural Programs, N.Y.C., 1972-80, 87-89, Holland Am. Cruises, N.Y.C., 1980-82, Moran, Stahl, Boyer, N.Y.C., 1982-84, Rhinesmith & Assocs. Inc., N.Y.C., 1984—; named amb., coord. Pres.'s US-Soviet Exch. Initiative, 1986-87; chmn. dept. orgnl. sociology Moscow State U., 1991—. Author: Bring Home the World: A Management Guide for Community Leaders of International Programs, 1975, 85; A Manager's Guide to Globalization: Six Keys to Success in a Changing World, 1993. Mem. ASTD (chair 1994), Met. Club (Washington), Stamford Yacht Club, Union League (N.Y.C.). Office: 1 Devonshire Pl PH10 Boston MA 02109

RHOADES, FLOYD, real estate and property manager. Pres. ARA Living Ctrs., Inc., Houston. Office: ARA Living Ctrs Inc 15415 Katy Fwy Houston TX 77094-1816

RHOADES, JOHN SKYLSTEAD, SR., federal judge; b. 1925; m. Carmel Rhoades; children: Mark, John, Matthew, Peter, Christopher. AB, Stanford U., 1948; JD, U. Calif., San Francisco, 1951. Prosecuting atty. City of San Diego, 1955-56, dep. city atty., 1956-57; pvt. practice San Diego, 1957-60; ptnr. Rhoades, Hollywood & Neil, San Diego, 1960-85; judge U.S. Dist. Ct. (so. dist.) Calif., San Diego, 1985—. With USN, 1943-46. Office: US Dist Ct 940 Front St San Diego CA 92101-8705

RHOADES, WARREN A., JR., retired mechanical engineer; b. 1924. BSME, La. State U. registered P.E. Tex., La. Engr. with Cooper-Bessemer Corp., 1948-65; mgr. engring. De Laval Turbine Inc., 1965-80; gen. mgr. CentriMarc. div. IMO Industries Inc., 1980-92. Served PTO, W. W. II. mem. ASME (Diesel & Gas Power Award, 1972, George Westinghouse Gold Medal, 1988), Soc. Automotive Engrs., Soc. Naval Architects and Marine Engrs. Address: 3420 Hillview St Denton TX 76201

RHOADS, GEORGE GRANT, medical epidemiologist; b. Phila., Feb. 11, 1940; s. Jonathan Evans and Teresa (Folin) R.; m. Frances Ann Secker, June 5, 1965; children: Thomas C., James E. MD, Harvard U., 1965; MPH, U. Hawaii, 1970. Intern Hosp. of U. Pa., Phila., 1965-66, resident in internal medicine, 1966-68; resident in preventive medicine U. Hawaii Sch. Pub. Health, 1968-71; epidemiologist Japan-Hawaii Cancer Study, Honolulu, 1974-75; assoc. prof. U. Hawaii, Honolulu, 1974-79, chair dept. pub. health sci., 1978-81, dir. gen. preventive medicine, 1978-81, prof. pub. health, 1979-82; chief epidemiology br. Nat. Inst. Child Health and Human Devel./NIH, Bethesda, Md., 1982-89; prof., dir. grad program in pub. health U. Medicine and Dentistry N.J.-Robert Wood Johnson Med. Sch., Piscataway, 1989—.

Contbr. more than 120 articles on the epidemiology of non-infectious diseases to profl. jours. Recipient Dirs. award NIH, 1987, EEO award NICHD, 1984. Fellow Am. Coll. Physicians; mem. Am. Epidemiol. Soc. Mem. Soc. of Friends. Achievements include research on the protective effect of high density Lipoprotein in the blood against development of heart attacks. Office: Environ and Occupl Health Scis Inst PO Box 1179 681 Frelinghuysen Rd Piscataway NJ 08855-1179

RHOADS, GERALDINE EMELINE, editor; b. Phila., Jan. 29, 1914; d. Lawrence Dry and Alice Fegley (Rice) R. A.B., Bryn Mawr Coll., 1935. Publicity asst. Bryn Mawr (Pa.) Coll., 1935-37; asst. Internat. Students House, Phila., 1937-39; mng. editor The Woman mag., N.Y.C., 1939-42; editor Life Story mag., 1942-45, Today's Woman mag., N.Y.C., 1945-52, Today's Family Mag., N.Y.C., 1952-53; lectr. Columbia U., 1954-56; assoc. editor Readers Digest, 1954-55; producer NBC, 1955-56; assoc. editor Ladies Home Jour., 1956-62, mng. editor, 1962-63; exec. editor McCall's mag., 1963-66; editor Woman's Day mag., 1966-82, editorial dir., 1982-84; editorial dir. Woman Day Resource Center, 1984-89; v.p. Woman's Day mag., 1972-77, 78-84, CBS Consumer Publs., 1977-84; cons. Woman's Day, N.Y.C., 1989-91; editorial cons., dir. Nat. Mag. Awards, 1991-94. Author: (with others) Woman's Day Help Book, 1988. Recipient award for profl. achievement Diet Workshop Internat., 1977; Elizabeth Cutter Morrow award YWCA Salute to Women in Bus., 1977; Recipient Econ. Equity award Women's Equity Action League, 1982; March of Dimes Women Editor's citation, 1982. Mem. Nat. Press Club (dir.), Fashion Group (bd. govs. 1977-79, 87-88, chmn. bd. govs. 1978-80, treas. bd. govs. 1983-85, bd. govs. 1987, bd. dirs. Found. 1980-81), Am. Soc. Mag. Editors (chmn. exec. com. 1971-73), N.Y. Women in Communications (Matrix award 1975), Advt. Women in N.Y. (bd. govs. 1983-85, 2d v.p. 1985-87, 1st v.p. 1987-89, bd. dirs. 1989-90, Pres.'s award 1987), Women's Forum (bd. dirs. 1985-87), YWCA Acad. Women Achievers, Literacy Vols. of N.Y.C. (bd. dirs. 1986-93), Turtle Bay Assn. (bd. dirs. 1989-92), Bryn Mawr Coll. Alumnae Assn. (bd. dirs. 1989-94), Bryn Mawr Club of N.Y.C. (bd. dirs. 1994—). Home: # 21M 185 West End Ave New York NY 10023

RHOADS, JAMES BERTON, archivist, former government official, consultant, educator; b. Sioux City, Iowa, Sept. 17, 1928; s. James Harrison and Mary (Keenan) R.; m. S. Angela Handy, Aug. 12, 1947; children: Cynthia Patrice Neven, James Berton, Marcia Marie MacKellar. Student, Southwestern Jr. Coll., 1946-47, Union Coll., Lincoln, Neb., 1947-48; BA, U. Calif.-Berkeley, 1950, MA, 1952; PhD, Am. U., 1965. With GSA-Nat. Archives and Records Service, Washington, 1952-79; asst. archivist for civil archives GSA-Nat. Archives and Records Service, 1965, dept. archivist U.S., 1966-68, archivist U.S., 1968-79; chmn. Nat. Archives Trust Fund Bd., 1968-79; chmn. adminstrv. com. Fed. Register, 1968-79; mem. Nat. Hist. Publs. and Records Commn., 1968-79; mem. Fed. Council on Arts and Humanities, 1970-79; pres. Rhoads Assos. Internat., 1980-84; dir. grad. program in archives and records mgmt. Western Wash. U., Bellingham, 1984-94, prof. history, 1989—; dir. Ctr. for Pacific N.W. studies, 1994—. Trustee Woodrow Wilson Internat. Center for Scholars, 1969-79; v.p. Intergovtl. Coun. UNESCO Info. Program, 1977-79; mem. adv. bd. Wash. State Hist. Records, 1990—. Recipient Meritorious and Disting. Service awards GSA, 1966, 68, 79. Fellow Soc. Am. Archivists (pres. 1974-75); mem. Internat. Coun. Archives (pres. 1976-79), Am. Antiquarian Soc., Am. Coun. Learned Socs. (com. Soviet-Am. archival coop. 1986-91), Orgn. Am. Historians, Mass. Hist. Soc. (corr.), Wash. State Hist. Soc. (trustee 1986-95), Acad. Cert. Archivists (pres. 1992-94). Office: Western Wash U Ctr Pacific NW Studies Bellingham WA 98225

RHOADS, JONATHAN EVANS, surgeon; b. Phila., May 9, 1907; s. Edward G. and Margaret (Ely Paxson) R.; m. Teresa Folin, July 4, 1936 (dec. 1987); children: Margaret Rhoads Kendon, Jonathan Evans Jr., George Grant, Edward Otto Folin, Philip Garrett, Charles James; m. Katharine Evans Goddard, Oct. 13, 1990. BA, Haverford Coll., 1928, DSc (hon.), 1962; MD, Johns Hopkins U., 1932; D. Med. Sci., U. Pa., 1940, LLD (hon.), 1960; DSc (hon.), Swarthmore Coll., 1969, Hahnemann Med. Coll., 1978, Duke U., 1979, Med. Coll. Ohio, 1985; DSc (Med.) (hon.), Med. Coll. Pa., 1974, Georgetown U., 1981, Yale U., 1990; LittD (hon.), Thomas Jefferson U., 1979. Intern Hosp. of U. Pa., 1932-34, fellow, instr. surgery, 1934-39; asso. surgery, surg. research U. Pa. Med. Sch., Grad. Sch. Medicine, 1939-47, asst. prof. surg. research, 1944-47, asst. prof. surgery, 1946-47, assoc. prof., 1947-49; J. William White prof. surg. research U. Pa., 1949-51; prof. surgery Grad. Sch. Medicine, U. Pa., 1950—; prof. surgery and surg. research U. Pa. Sch. Med., 1951-57, prof. surgery, 1957-59; provost U. Pa., 1956-59, provost emeritus, 1977—; John Rhea Barton prof. surgery, chmn. dept. surgery, 1959-72, prof. surgery, 1972—, asst. dir. Harrison dept. surg. research, 1946-59, dir., 1959-72; chief surgery Hosp. U. Pa., 1959-72, chmn. med. bd., 1959-61; dir. surgery Pa. Hosp., 1972-74; surg. cons. Pa. Hosp., Germantown (Pa.); mem. staff Hosp. of U. Pa.; mem. bd. pub. edn., City of Phila., 1965-69; co-chmn. Phila. Mayor's Commn. on Health Aspects of Trash to Steam Plant, 1986, chief justice Pa. Com. on Phila. Traffic Ct.; former mem. bd. mgrs. Haverford Coll., chmn., 1963-72, pres. corp., 1963-78, emeritus bd. mgrs. 1989—; bd. mgrs. Friends Hosp. of Phila.; trustee Coriell Inst. Med. Rsch., 1957-90, v.p. sci. affairs, 1964-76, life trustee, 1990—; trustee GM Cancer Rsch. Found.; chmn. bd. trustees Measey Found.; trustee emeritus Bryn Mawr Coll.; mem. com. in charge Westtown Sch., 1962-94; treas. Germantown Friends Sch.; cons. Bur. State Services, VA, 1963; cons. to divsn. med. scis. NIH, 1962-63; nat. adv. gen. medical scis. council USPHS, 1963; adv. council Life Ins. Med. Research Fund., 1961-66; Pres. Phila. div., 1955-56; chmn. advisory commn. on research on pathogenesis of cancer Am. Cancer Soc., 1956-57, del., 1956-61, dir. at large, 1965—, pres., 1969-70, past officer dir., 1970-77, hon. life mem., 1977—; chmn. surgery adv. com. Food and Drug Adminstrn., 1972-74; chmn. Nat. Cancer Adv. Bd., 1972-79; Mem. Am. Bd. Surgery, 1963-69, sr. mem., 1969—. Co-editor: Surgery: Principles and Practice, 1957, 61, 65, 70; author: (with J.M. Howard) The Chemistry of Trauma; mem. editorial bd. Jour. Surg. Rsch., 1960-71, Oncology Times, 1979—; co-editor: Accomplishments in Cancer Research, 1979-94; editor Jour. Cancer, 1972-91, editor emeritus, 1991—; editorial bd. Annals of Surgery, 1947-77, emeritus, 1977—, chmn., 1971-73; editorial adv. bd. Guthrie Bull., 1986—; contbr. articles to med. jours., chpts. to books. Trustee John Rhea Barton Surg. Found. Recipient Roswell Park medal, 1973, Papanicolaou award, 1977, Phila. award, 1976, Swanberg award, 1987, Benjamin Franklin medal Am. Philos. Soc., Medal of the Surgeon Gen. of U.S., Disting. Alumnus award U. Pa., 1993, Russell W. Richie award Friends Hosp. Phila., 1994, Presdl. award Nat. Assn. Psychit. Health Systems, 1994; hon. Benjamin Franklin fellow Royal Soc. Arts; patient care pavilion at Hosp. U. Pa. named the Jonathan Evans Rhoads Pavilion, 1994. Fellow Am. Med. Writers Assn., Am. Philos. Soc. (sec. 1963-66, pres. 1977-84), ACS (regent, chmn. bd. regents 1967-69, pres. 1971-72), Royal Coll. Surgeons (Eng.) (hon.), Royal Coll. Surgeons Edinburgh (hon.), Deutsches Gesellschaft für Chirurgie (corr.), Am. Surgeons India (hon.), Royal Coll. Physicians and Surgeons Can. (hon.), Coll. Medicine South Africa (hon.), Polish Assn. Surgeons (hon.), Royal Coll. Surgeons in Ireland (hon.), AAAS (sec. med. sci. sect. 1980-86); mem. Hollandscheatschappij der Wetenschappen (fgn.), Am. Public Health Assn., Assn. Am. Med. Colls. (chmn. council acad. socs. 1968-69, disting. service mem. 1974—), Fedn. Am. Socs. Exptl. Biology, Am. Assn. Surgery Trauma, Am. Soc. Clin. Nutrition, Am. Trauma Soc. (founding mem., chmn. bd. dirs. 1986-94), AMA (co-recipient Goldberger award 1970, Dr. Rodman and Thomas G. Sheen award 1980), Pa. Med. Soc. (mem. jud. coun. 1991-94, vice chmn. 1994—, Disting. Svc. award 1975), Phila. County Med. Soc. (pres. 1970, Strittmater award 1968), Coll. Physicians Phila. (v.p. 1954-57, pres. 1958-60, Disting. Svc. award 1987), Phila. Acad. Surgery (pres. 1964-66), Phila. Physiol. Soc. (v.p. 1945-46), Am. Surg. Assn. (pres. 1972-73, Disting. Service medal, trustee found., vice chmn. 1992-94), Pan Pacific Surg. Assn. (v.p. 1975-77), So. Surg. Assn., The Internat. Surg. Group (pres. 1958), Internat. Fedn. Surg. Colls (v.p. 1972-78, pres. 1978-81, hon. pres. 1987—), Fellows of Am. Studies, Soc. of U. Surgeons, Soc. Clin. Surgery (pres. 1966-68), Am. Assn. for Cancer Research, Am. Chem. Soc., Am. Physiol. Soc., Coun. Biology Editors, Internat. Soc. Surgery (hon.) N.Y. Acad. Scis., Surg. Infection Soc. (pres. 1984-85), Surgeons Travel Club (pres. 1976, hon. mem.), Am. Inst. Nutrition, World Med. Assn., Am. Acad. Arts and Scis., Inst. of Medicine (sr.), Soc. for Surgery Alimentary Tract (pres. 1967-68), Southeastern Surg. Congress, Soc. Surg. Chmn. (pres. 1966-68), Buckingham Mountain Found. (sec., treas.), James IV Soc. (hon.), Phi Beta Kappa, Alpha Omega Alpha, Sigma Xi. Clubs: Rittenhouse, Union League, Philadelphia, Cosmos (D.C.). Achievements include demonstration that protein malnutri-

tion could retard callus formation in experimental fractures and that positive nitrogen balance could be induced in protein deficient patients who could not take things by mouth. Office: 3400 Spruce St Philadelphia PA 19104-4220

RHOADS, PAUL KELLY, lawyer; b. La Grange, Ill., Sept. 4, 1940; s. Herbert Graves and Mary Margaret (Gurrie) R.; m. Katheryn Virginia Reissaus, Sept. 14, 1963; children: Elizabeth R. Saline, Katheryn R. Meek, Julia S. BA, Washington & Lee U., 1962; JD, Loyola U., Chgo., 1967. Bar: Ill. 1967, U.S. Dist. Ct. (no. dist.) Ill. 1967, U.S. Tax Ct. 1980. Trust officer 1st Nat. Bank Chgo., 1963-69; with Schiff Hardin & Waite, Chgo., 1969—, ptnr., 1973—; bd. dirs. McKay Enterprises, Chgo., Haymarsh Corp., Glen Ellyn, Ill., Philanthrophy Roundtable, Indpls. Author: Starting a Private Foundation, 1993; contbr. articles to profl. jours. and chpts. to books. Trustee Ill. Inst. Tech., 1985—, Western Springs (Ill.) Hist. Soc., 1983-92; bd. dirs. Cyrus Tang Scholarship Found., 1984-91; bd. overseers Ill. Inst. Tech. Chgo.-Kent Coll. Law, 1985—; pres., bd. dirs. Grover Hermann Found., Chgo., 1984—; sec., bd. dirs. Western Springs Svc. Club, 1976-86; sec. Vandivort Properties, Inc., Cape Girardeau, Mo; mem. adv. com. estate, tax and fin. planning Loyola U., 1986-92; adv. com. Thomas A. Roe Inst. for Econ. Policy Studies, Heritage Found., 1989—. Mem. Ill. State Bar Assn., Chgo. Bar Assn., Union League, Salt Creek Club (Hinsdale, Ill.) (pres. 1982, bd. dirs. 1981-83), Portage Lake Yacht Club (Onekama, Mich.) (commodore 1988, bd. dirs. 1985-89), Manistee (Mich.) Golf and Country Club. Republican. Avocations: sailing, golf, tennis. Office: Schiff Hardin & Waite 233 S Wacker Dr Chicago IL 60606

RHOADS, RICHARD H., printing company executive. MBA, Columbia U., 1962. Staff cons. Arthur D. Little Inc., N.Y.C., 1962-65, v.p., 1965-71, pres., 1971-75, CEO, 1975-91; chmn. bd. New Eng. Bus. Svc. Inc., Groton, Mass., 1991—. Office: New Eng Bus Svc Inc 500 Main St Groton MA 01471*

RHOADS, STEVEN ERIC, political science educator; b. Abington, Pa., May 12, 1939; s. John Reginald and Barbara Ann (Dugan) R.; m. Diana Cabanis Akers, May 17, 1944; children—Christopher, Nicholas, John. B.A., Princeton U., 1961; M.P.A., Cornell U., 1965, Ph.D., 1972. Mem. staff Office Mgmt. and Budget, Washington, 1965-66; asst. prof. dept. govt. and fgn. affairs U. Va., Charlottesville, 1970-76, assoc. prof., 1977-86, prof. 1986—. Served to lt. (j.g.) USN, 1961-63. Fellow NEH, Inst. Ednl. Affairs, Earhart Found., Bradley Found., Olin Found. Mem. Am. Polit. Sci. Assn., Assn. Pub. Policy and Mgmt. Author: Policy Analysis in the Federal Aviation Administration, 1974; Valuing Life: Public Policy Dilemmas, 1980; The Economist's View of the World: Government, Markets and Public Policy, 1985, Incomparable Worth: Pay Equity Meets the Market, 1993; contbr. articles to profl. publs. Home: 3190 Dundee Rd Earlysville VA 22936-9621 Office: U Va Dept Govt and Fgn Affairs Cabell Hall 232 Charlottesville VA 22903

RHODE, ALFRED SHIMON, business consultant, educator; b. Vienna, Austria, July 31, 1928; s. Aron and Olga (Schwarz) Rothkirch; came to U.S., 1940, naturalized, 1949; m. Phyllis Mazur, Dec. 28, 1959; children: Yael, Tamar, Yvette, Liane. BCE, CUNY, 1950; MEA, George Washington U., 1959; PhD, Am. U., 1973. Engr., Bur. of Reclamation, Sacramento, 1950-52; various engring. positions U.S. Govt., 1954-63; head logistics rsch. Navy Supply Systems Command, Washington, 1963-68; head support forces, manpower and logistics br. Navy Program Planning Office, Washington, 1968-75; sr. v.p. nat. security analysis and warfare support group Info. Spectrum, Inc., Arlington, Va., 1976-89, cons., 1989-92; professorial lectr. George Washington U., Washington, 1969-75; adj. faculty Sch. Bus. Adminstrn. George Mason U., Fairfax, Va., 1990—; pretrial screener Office State's Atty., Montgomery County, Md. Contbr. articles to profl. jours. Served to capt. USAF, 1952-54. Congl. fellow, 1962. Registered profl. engr., Md. Fellow Mil. Ops. Rsch. Soc. (1st v.p., dir.); mem. Inst. Ops. Rsch. and Mgmt. Scis. (chmn. mil. applications sect.), Washington Ops. Rsch. Sci. Coun., Internat. Inst. Strategic Studies. Home: 8305 Fox Run Potomac MD 20854-2576

RHODE, DAVID LELAND, mechanical engineering educator, consultant; b. Kingsville, Tex., Apr. 24, 1950; s. Robert David and Dorothy (Kidd) R.; m. Carol Day Rivers, Mar. 12, 1977; children: Courtney Day, Allison Rene. BSME, U. Tex., 1973, MSME, 1978; PhD, Okla. State U., 1981. Registered profl. engr., Tex. Mfg. engr. Friedrich div. Wylain Inc., San Antonio, 1973-74, design engr., 1974-76; rsch. asst. Ctr. for Energy Studies, U. Tex., Austin, 1977-78; teaching asst. Okla. State U., Stillwater, 1980, rsch. assoc., 1980-81; asst. prof. Tex. A&M U., College Station, 1981-87, assoc. prof., 1987—; cons. Sundstrand Aerospace, Rockford, Ill., 1991—, I.A.P. Rsch. Corp., Dayton, Ohio, 1992—. Contbr. numerous papers and articles to profl. jours. Sunday sch. tchr. 1st Bapt. Ch., Bryan, Tex., 1984-85. Recipient Halliburton Excellence award Halliburton Found., 1985, Faculty Assistance award Exxon Found., 1983, 85, Cert. of Recognition and Cash award NASA Lewis, 1983, NASA Marshall, 1984. Mem. ASME (sec. fluid machinery com. 1988-89), AIAA, Am. Soc. for Engring. Edn., Phi Kappa Phi. Avocations: jogging, racquetball. Office: Tex A&M U Mech Engring Dept College Station TX 77843

RHODE, DEBORAH LYNN, law educator; b. Jan. 29, 1952. BA, Yale U., 1974, JD, 1977. Bar: D.C. 1977, Calif. 1981. Law clk. to judge U.S. Ct. Appeals (2d cir.), N.Y.C., 1977-78; law clk. to Hon. Justice Thurgood Marshall U.S. Supreme Ct., D.C., 1978-79; asst. prof. law Stanford (Calif.) U., 1979-82, assoc. prof., 1982-85, prof., 1985—; dir. Inst. for Rsch. on Women and Gender, 1986-90, Keck Ctr. of Legal Ethics and The Legal Profession, 1994—; trustee Yale U., 1983-89; chmn. profl. responsibility sect. Am. Assn. Law Schs., co-chmn. ABA com. profl. responsibility. Author several books; contbr. articles to profl. jours. Office: Stanford U Law Sch Stanford CA 94305

RHODE, EDWARD ALBERT, veterinary medicine educator, veterinary cardiologist; b. Amsterdam, N.Y., July 25, 1926; s. Edward A. and Katherine (Webb) R.; m. Dolores Bangert, 1955; children: David E., Peter R., Paul W., Robert M., Catherine E. DVM, Cornell U., 1947. Diplomate Am. Coll. Veterinary Internal Medicine. Prof. emeritus vet. medicine U. Calif., Davis, 1964—, assoc. prof. vet. medicine, 1968-71, assoc. dean instrn. Sch. Vet. Medicine, 1971-77, 78-81, dean sch. Vet. Medicine, 1982-91. Mem. AAAS, Nat. Acad. Practices, Am. Coll. Vet. Internal Medicine, Am. Vet. Medicine Assn., Basic Sci. Coun., Am. Heart Assn., Am. Acad. Vet. Cardiology, Am. Physiol. Soc., Calif. Vet. Medicine Assn. Office: U Calif Sch Vet Medicine Davis CA 95616

RHODEN, MARY NORRIS, educational center director; b. Greenville, S.C., Jan. 3, 1943; d. Tony and Carrie Thelma (Reuben) Norris; 1 adopted child, Scottie Brooks-Rhoden. BS in Biology, Allen U., 1966; postgrad., Atlanta U., 1967-68. Dir., tchr. MSR Learning Ctr., Riverdale, Ga., 1989—. Author poetry. Bd. dirs. William H. Borders Aftercare Ctr., Atlanta, 1994, Big Bethel's Richard Allen Outreach Ctr., Atlanta, 1994; vol. Buffalo Soldiers Monument Commn., Ft. Leavenworth, Kans., 1991—, devel. letters to petition Congress, Postmaster Gen. to issue Buffalo Soldiers Stamp. Recipient Cert. Appreciation NAACP, Greenville, S.C., 1979, Wheat St. Bapt. Ch., Atlanta, 1989. Democrat. African Meth. Episcopal Ch. Avocations: jogging, writing, swimming, skating, skiing. Office: MSR Learning Ctr 7037 Shangrila Tr Riverdale GA 30296-2138

RHODES, ALFRED WILLIAM, former insurance company executive; b. Manchester, Eng., Dec. 20, 1922; came to U.S., 1930, naturalized, 1943; s. William Henry and Agnes Anna (King) R.; m. Joan Helen LaVine, Oct. 12, 1947; children: Alfred William, Ellen Jeanne, Thomas John, Phyllis Irene, Kenneth James. BS, Hofstra U., 1947; AMP, Harvard U., 1967. With John Hancock Mut. Life Ins. Co., Boston, 1942-85; regional supr. John Hancock Mut. Life Ins. Co., 1953-54, field v.p., 1954-69, 2d v.p., 1969-71, v.p., 1971-74, sr. v.p., 1974-85; ret., 1985. Past pres. Needham (Mass.) Youth Soccer Program; host family Mass. chpt. Am. Field Service, 1971-72, pres., 1972-75; mem. Town of Needham Finance Com., 1973-80. Served with AUS, 1943-46. Decorated Bronze Star. Mem. AARP (instr. and counselor tax counseling for the elderly), Nat. Assn. Life Underwriters, Gen. Agts. and Mgrs. Conf., Life Underwriter Tng. Coun. (past trustee), Life Ins. Mktg. and Rsch. Assn. (past bd. dirs.), CLUs, Club Med, Sandpiper Golf Club. Episcopalian. Home: 1761 SE Adair Rd Port Saint Lucie FL 34952-5739

RHODES, CHARLES HARKER, JR., lawyer; b. Chgo., May 24, 1930; s. Charles Harker and Claire (Hepner) R.; m. Mae Ellen Svoboda, Apr. 19, 1952; children: Charles Harker, James Albert, Edward Joseph. BA, U. Chgo., 1948, JD, 1951. Bar: Ill. 1951. Assoc. Schatz & Busch, Chgo., 1951-53; assoc. Sonnenschein Nath & Rosenthal, Chgo., 1953-60, ptnr., 1961—; dir. Ill. Inst. for Continuing Legal Edn., Springfield, 1977-84, 86-88; pres. Ill. Bar Automated Rsch., N.Y.C., 1976-94; pres. B.R. Ryall YMCA, Glen Ellyn, Ill., 1967. Fellow Am. Bar Found. (devel. com. 1988—), Chgo. Bar Found. (pres. 1977-80), Ill. Bar Found. (fellows chmn. 1990-91); mem. ABA (mem. tort and ins. practice sect., long range planning com. 1991-92, mem. pub. editorial bd. com. 1993—), Ill. State Bar Assn. (bd. govs. 1975-79, chmn. liaison com. Atty. Registration and Disciplinary Commn. 1992-93), Chgo. Bar Assn. (libr., bd. mgrs. 1969-72), Am. Arbitration Assn. (arbitrator), Nat. Conf. Bar Founds. (trustee, pres. 1987-88), Met. Club Chgo. Republican. Presbyterian. Avocations: world travel, photography. Home: 267 N Montclair Ave Glen Ellyn IL 60137-5508 Office: Sonnenschein Nath & Rosenthal Ste 8000 233 S Wacker Dr Chicago IL 60606

RHODES, DARRYL W., bank executive. With Farm Credit Systems, 1972—; sr. v.p., CFO Farm Credit Bank of Wichita. Mem. Fed. Land Bank Assn. Office: Farm Credit Bank of Wichita 245 N Waco St Wichita KS 67202*

RHODES, DENNIS EARL, public relations executive; b. Jersey City, Jan. 24, 1954. B.A., St. Peter's Coll., 1976; Earl L. and Marion A. (Visco) R. Editor, William H. Wise & Co., Union City, N.J., 1976-78; sr. editorial asst. Am. Mgmt. Assn., 1978-80; account exec. Ruder, Finn & Rotman, N.Y.C., 1980-81; sr. v.p. Lobsenz-Stevens, N.Y.C., 1981-89, account supr. Geltzer & Co., 1989—. Editor book New Jersey Wildlife Illustrated, 1977. Mem. Public Relations Soc. Am., Authors Guild, Inc., Publicity Club N.Y. Roman Catholic. Home: 51 W 76th St New York NY 10023-1538 Office: Lobsenz-Stevens Inc 460 Park Ave S New York NY 10016-7315

RHODES, DONALD ROBERT, musicologist, retired electrical engineer; b. Detroit, Dec. 31, 1923; s. Donald Eber and Edna Mae (Fulmer) R.; children: Joyce R. Bridges, Jane E., Roger C., Diane R. Herran. BEE, Ohio State U., 1945, MS, 1948, PhD, 1953. Research assoc. Ohio State U., Columbus, 1945-54; research engr. Cornell Aero. Lab., Buffalo, 1954-57; head basic research dept. Radiation, Inc., Orlando, Fla., 1957-61; sr. scientist Radiation, Inc., Melbourne, Fla., 1961-66; Univ. prof. N.C. State U., Raleigh, 1966-94, prof. emeritus, 1994—. Author: Introduction to Monopulse, 1959, 2d edit., 1980, Synthesis of Planar Antenna Sources, 1974, A Reactance Theorem, 1977. Co-founder Central Fla. Community Orch., Winter Park, 1961, pres., 1961-62. Recipient Benjamin G. Lamme medal Ohio State U., 1975; Eminent Engr. award Tau Beta Pi, 1976; named to N.C. State U. Acad. Outstanding Tchrs., 1980. Fellow AAAS, IEEE (John T. Bolljahn award 1963, pres. Antenna and Propogation Soc. 1969); mem. Am. Musicological Soc. Home: 625 Cardinal Gibbons Dr Apt 101 Raleigh NC 27606-3255 Office: PO Box 7911 Raleigh NC 27695

RHODES, ERIC FOSTER, real estate and insurance executive, consultant; b. Luray, Va., Feb. 5, 1927; s. Wallace Keith and Bertha (Foster) R.; m. Barbara Ellen Henson, Oct. 19, 1946; children: Roxanne Jane, Laurel Lee; m. Lorraine Endresen, July 29, 1972; m. Daisy Chun, May 31, 1980. AA, George Washington U., 1949, AB, 1950, MA, 1952, EdD, 1967. Tchr. high sch. Arlington, Va., 1950-52; counselor Washington Lee High Sch. Arlington, Va., 1952-53, dir. publs., 1953-54, chmn. dept. English, 1954-55; exec. sec. Arlington Edn. Assn., Arlington, Va., 1952-53, Montgomery County (Md.) Edn. Assn., Rockville, Md., 1955-57; lectr. edn. George Washington U., Washington, 1955-60, 65-70; salary cons. NEA, Washington, 1957-58, asst. dir. membership div., 1958-60; dir. N.Y. regional office, N.Y.C., 1960-64; ednl. cons. Ednl. Rsch. Svcs., White Plains, N.Y., 1964-65; pres. Ednl. Svc. Bur., Inc., Arlington, Va., 1965-72, chmn. bd., 1972-80; pres. Negotiations Consultation Svcs., Inc., Arlington, 1969-80, Eastern States Advt. Inc., Arlington, 1970-79, EFR Corp., Arlington, 1972-90; exec. dir. Assn. Negotiators and Contract Adminstrs., Arlington, 1981-89; area coord. U.S. Legal Protection Co., 1989—; pres. Employee Futures Rsch., Arlington, 1980—, Waterfront Only Real Estate, New Port Richey, Fla., 1988—, Inst. for Negotiations Tng., New Port Richey, 1989—, Asset Protection Co., 1991—; asst. supt. for adminstrn. Brighton Schs., Rochester, N.Y., 1983-88; owner Frederick Foster Galleries, Arlington, 1974-80; cons. Va. Dept. Community Colls., Richmond, 1965-77; vice chancellor Va. Community Coll. System, 1970-71; employee rels. ofcl. City of Orlando, 1980-83; lectr. edn. Frostburg (Md.) State Coll., 1967. Author: Negotiating Salaries, 41 Ways to Cut Budget Costs, Making Good Things Happen Through Negotiation; editor: Inside Negotiations, Wages and Benefits, Employers' Negotiating Service. Mem. Civil Rights Commn., Franklin Twp., N.J., 1962-64; mem. Franklin Twp. Bd. Edn., 1964-65; mem. adv. bd. Keep Am. Beautiful, 1964-75, nat. chmn., 1968; bd. dirs., v.p. Unitarian-Universalist Ch., Tarpon Springs, Fla., 1990-94, pres. 1994—. With AUS, 1945-47. Mem. Am. Assn. Sch. Adminstrs., Internat. Assn. Sch. Bus. Officials, NEA, Edn. Press Assn., Nat. Assn. Ednl. Negotiators (exec. dir. 1971-81), Am. Arbitration Assn. (labor arbitrator), Indsl. Rels. Rsch. Assn., United C. of C. of Pasco County (sec., treas. 1989-90, exec. dir. 1990-91), Am. Legion, Fed. Schoolmen's Club, N.Y. Schoolmen's Club, Lions (v.p. N.Y.C. club 1964-65), Kiwanis (pres. West Pasco club 1991-93), Order of St. John of Jerusalem, Phi Delta Kappa (chpt. pres. 1959-60). Home: 5617 Palmetto Rd New Port Richey FL 34652-1707

RHODES, FRANK HAROLD TREVOR, federal science agency administrator, former academic administrator, geologist; b. Warwickshire, Eng., Oct. 29, 1926; came to U.S., 1968, naturalized, 1976; s. Harold Cecil and Gladys (Ford) R.; m. Rosa Carlson, Aug. 16, 1952; children: Jennifer, Catherine, Penelope, Deborah. BSc, U. Birmingham, 1948, PhD, 1950, DSc (hon.), 1963; LLD (hon.), Wooster Coll., 1976, Nazareth Coll. Rochester, 1979, Skidmore Coll., 1989, U. Mich., 1990, Clemson U., 1991, Dartmouth Coll., 1993; LHD (hon.), Colgate U., 1980, John Hopkins U., 1982, Wagner Coll., 1982, Hope Coll., 1982, Rensselaer Poly Inst., 1982, LeMoyne Coll., 1984, Pace U., 1986, Alaska Pacific U., 1987, Hamilton Coll., 1987, SUNY, 1992, Canisius Coll., 1994; DSc (hon.), U. Wales, Eng., 1981, Bucknell U., 1985, U. Ill., 1986, Reed Coll., 1988, Elmira Coll., 1989, U. Southampton, 1989; DLitt (hon.), U. Nev., 1982; EdD (hon.), Ohio State U., 1992; D. Univ. (hon.), U. Stirling, 1994. Post-doctoral fellow, Fulbright scholar U. Ill., 1950-51, vis. lectr. geology, summers 1951-52; lectr. geology U. Durham, 1951-54; asst. prof. U. Ill., 1954-55, assoc. prof., 1955-56; dir. U. Ill. Field Sta., Wyo., 1956; prof. geology, head geology dept. U. Wales, Swansea, 1956-68, dean faculty of sci., 1967-68; prof. geology and mineralogy Coll. Lit., Sci. and Arts, U. Mich., 1968-77, dean, 1971-74, v.p. for acad. affairs, 1974-77; pres., prof. geology Cornell U., Ithaca, N.Y., 1977-95; chmn. Nat. Science Foundation, Washington, D.C., 1995—; Gurley lectr. Cornell U., 1960; Bownocker lectr. Ohio State U., 1966; Case lectr. U. Mich., 1976; dir. NSF, Am. Geol. Inst., summer field inst., 1963; Australian vice-chancellors' visitor to Australian univs., 1964; vis. fellow Clare Hall, Cambridge, Summer 1982; Bye fellow Robinson Coll., Cambridge, Summers, 1986, 87; Am. Fulbright Disting. fellow, Kuwait, 1987. Author: The Evolution of Life, 1962, 2d edit., 1976, Fossils, 1963, Geology, 1972, Evolution, 1974, Language of the Earth, 1981; author numerous articles and monographs on sci. and edn. Trustee Carnegie Found. for Advancement Teaching, 1978-86, vice chmn., 1983-85, chmn. 1985-86; trustee The Freedom Forum, 1983-93; trustee Com. for Econ. Devel., 1984-93; bd. trustees Andrew W. Mellon Found., 1984—; bd. dirs. KMI Continental, Inc., 1979-86, Tompkins County Trust Co., 1984—, Gen. Electric Co., 1984—, Nat. Broadcasting Corp., 1986—, Am. Council on Edn., 1983-88, vice chair, 1985-86, chair, 1986-88; bd. overseers Meml. Sloan-Kettering Cancer Ctr., 1979-91; chmn. adv. bd. Freedom Forum Media Studies Ctr., 1984-93; mem. Nat. Sci. Bd., 1987—, chair, 1994—, Internat. Exec. Service Corps Council, 1984—. NSF sr. vis. rsch. fellow, 1965-66. Fellow Geol. Soc. London (council 1963-66, Bigsby medal 1967); mem. Palaeontol. Assn. (v.p. 1963-68), Brit. Assn. Advancement Sci., Geol. Soc. Am., Am. Assn. Petroleum Geologists, Soc. Econ. Paleontologists and Mineralogists, Phi Beta Kappa (hon.). Office: Nat Science Bd Office of the Chairman 4201 Wilson Blvd Arlington VA 22230

RHODES, GARY LYNN, food company executive; b. Kalamazoo, July 1, 1941; s. Jay Richard and Vivian Mabel (Stevens) R.; m. Lova Lydia Kuhlmann, May 9, 1964; children: Todd Alan, Eric Richard. BSME,

Purdue U., 1964. Plant supt. Gen. Foods Corp., Houston, 1967-74, mgr. engring., 1974-76; mgr. engring. Borden Foods, Plymouth, Wis., 1976-77, plant mgr., 1977-79; v.p. ops. Fisher Cheese Co., Wapakoneta, Ohio 1979-83, pres., 1983-87; pres. chief exec. officer Maplehurst, Inc., Indpls., 1987-92; CEO Sodiaal North Am. Corp., Harleysville, Pa., 1992—. Republican. Methodist. Lodge: Masons. Avocation: flying. Office: Sodiaal N Am Corp 832 Harleyville Pike Harleysville PA 19438

RHODES, GERALDINE BRYAN, secondary school administrator; b. Asheville, N.C., Dec. 7, 1941; d. Robert Gerald and Myrtle (Bartlett) B.; m. Gayle Dean Rhodes, May 27, 1967; children: Jennifer Ellen, Leah Rebecca. BM, So. Meth. U., 1967; MA, Columbia U., 1987, MEd, 1988, postgrad., 1988—. Permanent tchr. cert., N.Y. Music tchr. Dallas Ind. Sch. Dist., 1967-69, Yamaha Music Sch., Poughkeepsie, N.Y. 1971-75, Hudson Valley Philharmonic Music Sch., Poughkeepsie, 1986-88; music tchr. Poughkeepsie Day Sch., 1987-90, dir. music edn., 1990-92; tchr. fine arts Ctrl. Tex. Coll., Youngsan U.S. Army Base, Seoul, 1992-94; tchr., cons. Dutchess Arts Camp, Poughkeepsie, 1986-92, Hollingworth Pre-sch., Columbia U., N.Y.C., 1987-88; tchr., dir. Inter-generation Chorus N.Y. State Coun. Arts, Poughkeepsie, 1988-92. Mem. Music Educators Nat. Congress, N.Y. State Sch. Music Assn., Am. Orff Schulwerk Assn. Republican. Episcopalian.

RHODES, JAMES T., electric power industry executive; b. 1941. BS, N.C. State U., 1963; MS, Cath. U., 1968; PhD, Purdue U., 1972. Nuclear physicist Va. Electric & Power Co., 1971-72, supr. nuclear fuel, 1972-75, dir. nuclear fuel, 1975-78, dist. mgr. nuclear tech. svcs., 1980-81, v.p. adminstrv. svcs., 1981-84, v.p. pers. then sr. v.p. fin., 1984-89, pres., CEO, 1989—. Office: Va Electric & Power Co 1 James River Plz Richmond VA 23219

RHODES, JOHN BOWER, management consultant; b. Pitts., July 8, 1925; s. John Bower and Mary Lucile (Lewis) R.; m. Joan Ann Black, June 11, 1955; children: John Bower, III, Mark Lewis, Lydia Black. B.S. in Mech. Engring, Princeton U., 1946; postgrad., N.Y. U. Law Sch., 1953-55. With internat. ops. California Texas Oil Co., N.Y.C., 1946-59; mgr. ops. in California Texas Oil Co., Arabia, 1947-50, Calif. Tex. Oil Co., India, 1955-59; mng. officer Europe Booz, Allen & Hamilton Internat. NV, Zurich, Switzerland, 1959-63, Dusseldorf, Fed. Republic of Germany, 1963-68; v.p. internat. affairs Booz, Allen & Hamilton Inc., N.Y.C., 1968-70, vice chmn., 1970-90, of counsel, 1990—. Mgr. N.Y. Inst. for Edn. of Blind, 1976—. Served with USMC, 1943-45, 51-52. Mem. Internat. C. of C. (U.S. council), Council Fgn. Relations, Orgn. Econ. Coop. and Devel. Clubs: Princeton, N.Y. Yacht, Colonial, Nantucket (Mass.) Yacht. Office: Booz Allen Hamilton Inc 101 Park Ave New York NY 10178-0053

RHODES, JOHN JACOB, lawyer, former congressman; b. Council Grove, Kans., Sept. 18, 1916; s. John Jacob and Gladys Anne (Thomas) R.; m. Mary Elizabeth Harvey, May 24, 1942; children: John Jacob 3d, Thomas H., Elizabeth C. Rhodes Reich, James Scott. B.S., Kans. State U., 1938; LL.B., Harvard U., 1942. Bar: Kans. 1942, Ariz. 1945, D.C. 1965. Mem. 83d-97th congresses from 1st Dist. Ariz., chmn. Republican policy com. 89th-93d congresses, house minority leader, 1973-81; of counsel Hunton & Williams, Washington; mem. bd. overseers Hoover Instn., 1984-92; chmn. platform com. Nat. Rep. Conv., 1972, permanent chmn., 1976, 80. Mem. Ariz. Bd. Pub. Welfare, 1951-52. Served with AUS, World War II; Col., ret. Mem. Mesa C. of C. (pres. 1950), SAR, Am. Legion, Beta Theta Pi (internat. pres. 1984-87). Republican. Methodist. Clubs: Ariz, Mesa Golf and Country; Capitol Hill, Metropolitan (Washington), Burning Tree (Bethesda, Md.); Plaza, Pinetop Country. Lodges: Masons; York Rite; Scottish Rite (33 deg., grand cross); K.P.; Elks; Moose; Rotary. Office: Hunton & Williams 2000 Pennsylvania Ave NW Washington DC 20006-1812

RHODES, LAWRENCE, artistic director; b. Mt. Hope, W.Va., Nov. 24, 1939. Studied with Violette Armand. Joined Ballet Russe de Monte Carlo, 1958-60; from dancer to prin. dancer Joffrey Ballet, N.Y.C., 1960-64; prin. dancer Harkness Ballet, 1964-68, dir., prin. dancer, 1968-70; tchr. dance dept. NYU, 1978—, prin. ballet tchr., 1981—, chmn. dance dept., 1981-91; prin. dancer, ballet master, choreographer, tchr., artistic dir. Les Grands Ballets Canadiens, Montreal, 1989—; guest artist Het Nationale Ballet, Amsterdam, 1970-71, Pa. Ballet, 1971-76, Feld Ballet, N.Y.C., 1973-75. Danced with Makarova, Hayden and Fracci; danced for Butler, Joffrey, Ailey, Lubovitch, Harkavy, Nault, Van Dantzig and Mac Donald; featured dancer in film A Dancer's Vocabulary, PBS's Dance Am. series, CBS's Camera Three. Office: Les Grands Ballets Canadiens, 4816, rue Rivard, Montreal, PQ Canada H2J 2N6

RHODES, LINDA JANE, psychiatrist; b. San Antonio, May 23, 1950; d. George Vernon and Lucy Agnes (O'Dowd) R.; m. Timothy Robin Stacey, Dec. 29, 1972 (div. Apr. 1975). BA, Trinity U.; MD, U. Tex. Diplomate Am. Bd. Pediat. Resident in pediat. U. Tex. Med. Br., Galveston, 1975-78; fellow in ambulatory pediat. U. Tex. HSC, Houston, 1978-80; pediatrician Kelsey Seybold Clinic, P.A., Houston, 1980, on leave; resident in psychiatry U. Tex. HSC, San Antonio, 1990-92, child and adolescent psychiatrist, fellow in biology, 1992—; pediat. rep. Tex. Lay Midwifery Bd. Tex. Dept. Health, Austin, 1994—. Active San Antonio Conservation Soc., San Antonio Zool. Soc., San Antonio Mus. Assn. Fellow Am. Acad. Pediat.; Am. Psychiat. Assn. Ambulatory Pediat. Assn. Tex. Pediat. Soc., Tex. Soc. Psychiat. Physicians, Tex. Acad. Child and Adolescent Psychiat., Am. Med. Women's Assn. Office: UTHSC-SA Dept Psychiatry/Divsn Biol 7703 Floyd Carl Dr San Antonio TX 78284

RHODES, MARY, mayor; m. Donald A. Rhodes; children: Bryan, Randy. Grad., Youngstown Hosp. Assn. Mem. council: City of Corpus Christi, Tex., mayor, 1991—. Mem. LWV, Bus. and Profl. Womens Assn. Presbyterian. Office: Office of the Mayor PO Box 9277 1201 Leopard St Corpus Christi TX 78401-2162

RHODES, MILTON, arts association administrator; b. Apr. 7, 1945; s. Theodore Milton and Frances (Fulmer) R.; m. Mattie Menefee, June 10, 1967; children: Milt, Ben, Addrian. BA, Wofford Coll., 1967; MFA, NYU, 1969. Bus. mgr. Winston-Salem (N.C.) Symphony, 1968-69; exec. dir. The Arts Council Inc., Winston-Salem, 1971-85; pres. Am. Council for the Arts, N.Y.C., 1985—; chmn. Nat. Assembly Local Arts Agencies, Washington, 1976-78; mem. city spirit panel Nat. Endowment Arts, Washington, 1975-76, mem. fed. state partnership panel, 1978-79; mem. adv. bd. Sharp Found., Colorado Springs, Colo., 1983-85. Columnist Horizon mag. Served to lt. U.S. Army. Recipient Career Service award Arts Mgmt. Inc., 1983; gallery named in his honor by The Arts Council Inc., 1985. Avocation: sports. Office: Am Coun Arts 3rd Fl Area M 1285 Avenue Of The Americas New York NY 10019-6028 Office: 1319 F St NW Ste 307 Washington DC 20004-1106

RHODES, PETER EDWARD, label company executive; b. Rochester, N.Y., Sept. 25, 1942; s. Robert A. and Anne (Ward) R.; m. Cassandra Durkee, May 26, 1962 (div. Sept. 1991); children: Tamara, Amy, Brian. B.S., Rochester Inst. Tech., 1964, M.B.A., 1970. With Touche Ross & Co., Rochester, 1962-69; sr. auditor Touche Ross & Co., to 1969; with Xerox Co., Rochester, 1969, Fay's Drug Co., Inc., Liverpool, N.Y., 1970-87; exec. v.p. Fay's Drug Co., Inc., 1974-87, also dir.; exec. v.p. Syracuse Label Co., Inc., Liverpool, 1987—, also bd. dirs.; dir. Byrne Dairy Inc. Mem. N.Y. State Soc. C.P.A.s, Am. Inst. C.P.A.s, Fin. Execs. Inst. Club: Belevue Country.

RHODES, RICHARD LEE, writer; b. Kansas City, Kans., July 4, 1937; s. Arthur and Georgia Saphronia (Collier) R.; m. Linda Iredell Hampton, Aug. 30, 1960 (div. 1974); children: Timothy James, Katherine Hampton; m. Mary Magdalene Evans Nov. 26, 1976 (div. 1988); m. Ginger Kay Untrif, Oct. 3, 1993. BA cum laude, Yale U., 1959; LHD (hon.), Westminster Coll. Fulton, Mo., 1988. Author: The Inland Ground, 1970, The Last Safari, 1970, The Ungodly, 1973, The Ozarks, 1974, Holy Secrets, 1978, Looking for America, 1979, Sons of the Earth, 1981, The Making of the Atomic Bomb, 1987, Farm, 1989, A Hole in the World, 1990, Making Love, 1992, Nuclear Renewal, 1993, How to Write, 1995, Dark Sun, 1995; contbr. articles to nat. mags. Trustee Andrew Drumm Inst., Independence, Mo., 1991—.

Recipient Nat. Book Critics Cir. award for nonfiction, Nat. Book award for nonfiction, 1987, Pulitzer prize, 1988; Guggenheim fellow, 1974-75, fellow Nat. Endowment for Arts, 1978-79, Ford Found., 1981-83, Sloan Found., 1985, 89, 91, 92, MacArthur Found., 1990-91. Office: Janklow & Nesbit Assoc 598 Madison Ave New York NY 10022-1614

RHODES, SAMUEL, violist; b. Long Beach, N.Y., Feb. 13, 1941; s. Bernard and Martha (Ephraim) R.; m. Hiroko Yajima, Dec. 30, 1968; children—Amy, Harumi. B.A., Queen's Coll., CUNY, 1963; M.F.A., Princeton U., 1967; D.F.A. (hon.), Mich. State U., 1984; D.Music (hon.), Jacksonville U., 1986. Mem. faculty Juilliard Sch., N.Y.C., 1969—, Mich. State U., East Lansing, 1977-85, SUNY-Purchase, 1982-86; violist Marlboro Festival, 1960-68, 78-81, 91—, Galimir String Quartet, 1961-68, Juilliard String Quartet, 1969—; mem. faculty Tanglewood Music Ctr., 1988—. Office: Juilliard Sch Music Lincoln Ctr New York NY 10023

RHODES, WILLIAM REGINALD, banker; b. N.Y.C., Aug. 15, 1935; s. Edward R. and Elsie R.; divorced; 1 child, Elizabeth. BA in History, Brown U., 1957. Sr. officer internat. banking group-Latin Am. and Caribbean Citibank, N.A., N.Y.C., 1977-80, sr. corp. officer Latin Am. and Caribbean, 1980-84, chmn. restructuring com., 1984-90, group exec., 1986-90, also chmn. bank adv. coms. for Brazil, Argentina, Peru, and Uruguay, 1982-90, co-chmn. bank adv. com. for Mexico, 1982-90, sr. exec.-internat., 1990-91; vice chmn. Citicorp, N.Y.C., 1991—; vice chmn. Inst. Internat. Fin., Met. Mus. Bus. Com.; mem. exec. com. Bretton Woods Com., U.S.-Russia Bus. Coun.; past chmn. adv. com. Export-Import Bank of U.S.; chmn. U.S. Sect., Venezuela-U.S. Bus. Coun., External Adv. bd. for Columbia U. Program in Econ. Policy Mgmt.; active U.S.-Egyptian Pres. Coun.; bd. dirs. Citicorp/ Citibank; Pvt. Export Funding Corp. Trustee Brown U.; chmn. Northfield-Mt. Hermon Sch.; bd. dirs. N.Y. Hosp., N.Y.C. Partnership; bd. overseers of Watson Inst. for Internat. Studies; active Lincoln Ctr. Corporate Leadership Com. Decorated comdr. Nat. Order of the Southern Cross, Brazil, chevalier Legion of Honor, France, Orden de Mayo, Argentina, officer Order Francisco Miranda 1st and 3rd classes, Order Merito en el Trabajo 1st class, Venezuela. Mem. Americas Soc. (bd. dirs.), Coun. of Ams. (trustee), Inst. for EastWest Studies (bd. dirs.), Bankers Assn. for Fgn. Trade (past pres.), Coun. Fgn. Rels., Venezuelan-Am. C. of C. (past pres.), Bankers Roundtable. Avocations: reading history, jogging, swimming. Office: Citicorp 399 Park Ave New York NY 10043-0001

RHODES, YORKE E(DWARD), organic chemistry educator; b. Elizabeth, N.J., Mar. 25, 1936; s. Yorke Edward and Helen (Pyper) R.; m. Mechthilde Weggemann, May 24, 1975; children—Yorke Edward III, Christopher A., Matthias Raabe, Timothy A. B.S., U. Del., 1957, M.S., 1959; Ph.D., U. Ill., 1963. Chemist, Thiokol Chem. Corp., Elkton, Md., 1959; lectr. Yale U., New Haven, 1964-65; asst. prof. chemistry NYU, N.Y.C., 1965-71, assoc. prof., 1971—, asst. dean Coll. Arts and Sci., 1987-89, dir. NYU-Stevens Dual Degree Program in Sci. and Engring., 1988—; vis. prof. Universitat Freiburg, Fed. Republic Germany, 1972-73, Technische Universitat Munich, Fed. Republic Germany, 1977, Université Grenoble, 1987; named Humboldt vis. prof. tech. U. Munich, 1978; Dept. State sci. exchange visitor Zagreb, Yugoslavia, and Prague, Czechoslovakia, 1977. Contbr. articles to profl. publs. Englewood Democratic committeeman, N.J., 1968-72. NIH fellow Yale U., 1964-65; NASA summer faculty fellow Jet Propulsion Labs., Pasadena, Calif., 1980, 81. Mem. Am. Chem. Soc., Royal Chem. Soc., Planetary Soc., N.Y. Acad Scis., Sigma Xi. Avocations: opera; photography; travel; gardening; railroads. Office: NYU Dept Chemistry 100 Washington Sq E New York NY 10003

RHODIN, THOR NATHANIEL, educational administrator; b. Dec. 9, 1920; m. Elspeth Lindsay, Sept. 21, 1949; children: Robert, Ann, Lindsay, Jeffrey. BS in Chemistry, Haverford Coll., 1942; AM in Chem. Physics, Princeton U., 1945, PhD in Chem. Physics, 1946. Rsch. asst. Manhattan Project, Princeton U., 1944-46; rsch. assoc. James Franck Inst., Chgo., 1946-51; jr. faculty dept. chemistry U. Chgo., 1946-51; rsch. assoc. E.I. duPont de Nemours & Co., Inc., Wilmington, Del., 1951-58; assoc. prof. applied engring. physics Cornell U., Ithaca, N.Y., 1958-65, prof. applied engring. physics 1965-91, acting assoc. dean grad. rsch. and edn. Coll. Engring., 1988-89, assoc. dean and dir. continuing edn. Coll. Engring., 1989-90, dir. master of engring. program, chmn. grad. profl. program, 1989-90, assoc. dir. Mario Einaudi Ctr. for Internat. Studies, 1991-94; prof. emeritus applied and engring. physics Cornell U., 1991—; vis. prof. materials sci. and solid state physics MIT, 1973, Japan Soc. for Promotion of Sci., U. Tokyo, 1976, U. Osaka, 1992; cons. Kodak, IBM, duPont; referee reviewer of proposals and pubs. Am. Chem. Soc., Am. Phys. Soc., NSF, Surface Sci. Surface Sci. Letters; co-prin. investigator synchrotron radiation beamline (U16-B), Nat. Synchrotron Light Source, Brookhaven Nat. Lab., 1985—. Editor: Stress-Corrosion Fracture, 1959; co-editor: Nature of the Surface Chemical Bond, 1979, Proceedings Microphysics of Beams, Adsorbates and Surfaces, 1989; author: Chemistry and Physics of Surfaces and Interfaces, 1992; adv. editor Surface Sci., Physics Status Solidi(a), Progress in Surface Sci., Langmuir Surface Chemistry Jour.; contbr. over 150 articles to profl. jours. NSF sr. fellow, 1964-65, NATO sr. fellow, 1975; named Disting. Vis. Faculty, NATO Adv. Study Inst. on Electron Structure and Reactivity of Metal Surfaces, Namur, Belgium, 1971-75; Humboldt Sr. Scientist Inst. of Phys. Chemistry, Maximillian U., Munich, 1985; others. Fellow Am. Phys. Soc., Am. Vacuum Soc.; mem. Am. Chem. Soc., Am. Soc. for Materials Rsch. Office: Cornell Univ 217 Clark Hall Ithaca NY 14853

RHODY, RONALD EDWARD, banker, communications executive; b. Frankfort, Ky., Jan. 27, 1932; s. James B. and Mary M. (Clark) R.; m. Patricia Schupp, Apr. 23, 1955; children: Leslie K., Mary M., Virginia K., Ronald C. Student, Georgetown Coll., Ky., 1950-52, U. Ky., 1953-55. Accredited pub. relations Pub. Relations Soc. Am. Pub. relations dir. Kaiser Aluminum & Chem. Corp., Ravenswood, W.Va., 1959-62, N.Y.C., 1962-67; corporate v.p. Kaiser Aluminum & Chem. Corp., Oakland, Calif., 1967-83; sr. v.p. corp comm. Bank of Am. NT&SA, San Francisco, 1983—, exec. v.p., 1992-94; CEO Rhody, Inc., 1994—. Contbr. articles to profl. jours. Mem. exec. steering com. St. Mary's Coll., Moraga, Calif.; mem. adv. bd. U. Tex. Sch. Journalism and Mass Communications; chmn. media adv. coun., Media Inst., Washington. Named Pub. Relations Profl. of Yr. Pub. Relations News, 1981. Mem. Pub. Relations Soc. Am. (pres.'s adv. council Rex Harlow award), Internat. Assn. Bus. Communicators (Gold Quill award 1980), Pub. Relations Roundtable San Francisco (bd. govs., awards 1980, 85). Clubs: San Francisco Press; International (Washington); Nat. Press (Washington). Office: 712 Bancroft Rd Walnut Creek CA 94598

RHONE, DOUGLAS PIERCE, pathologist, educator; b. Bloomsburg, Pa., Mar. 27, 1940; s. Wilbur Clayton and Marian Faye (Shaffer) R.; m. Leta Daiva Budelskis, Sept. 27, 1969; children: Jennifer Ann, Todd Brader. BS, Ill. Benedictine Coll., 1965; MD, MS in Pathology, U. Ill., 1969. Diplomate Am. Bd. Pathology. Attending pathologist Ill. Masonic Med. Ctr., Chgo., 1976, chmn. dept. pathology, 1976—; asst. prof. pathology U. Ill. Coll. Medicine, Chgo., 1976-80, assoc. prof. pathology, 1980—; dir. residency pathology Ill. Masonic Med. Ctr., Chgo., 1976-90, U. Ill. Metro. Hosps., Chgo., 1990—; assoc. dir. med. affairs, 1992—; pres. Ill. Masonic Med. Ctr. Pathologists, S.C., Chgo., 1977—, Lab. Cons., Ltd., Chgo., 1977—. Contbr. articles to profl. jours. Maj. U.S. Army, 1971-76. Recipient Raymond B. Allen award U. Ill. Coll. Medicine, 1979, 80, 95, C. Thomas Bombeck award, 1991. Fellow Am. Soc. Clin. Pathologists (Sheard-Sanford Rsch. award 1969), Coll. Am. Pathologists; mem. Chgo. Pathology Soc., Ill. Soc. Pathologists. Roman Catholic. Avocations: antiquities, gardening, oil painting, classical music and opera, Russian history and culture. Home: 222 S Spring Ave LaGrange IL 60525 Office: Ill Masonic Med Ctr Dept Pathology 836 W Wellington Ave Chicago IL 60525

RHONE, SYLVIA, recording industry executive; b. Philadelphia, PA, Mar. 11, 1952; d. James and Marie (Christmas) R.; 1 daughter, Quinn. M.A., Wharton Sch. of Comm., U. of Pa, 1974. Dir. nat. black music promotion Atlantic Records, New York, N.Y., 1985-88; Sr. V.P. Atlantic Records, New York, N.Y., 1988-91; chair/CEO EastWest Records America, New York, N.Y., 1991—; chair Elektra Music, New York, N.Y., 1994—. mem. bd. of dir. Alvin Ailey Amer. Dance Theater, Phoenix House Found., Rock n'Roll Hall of Fame, R&B Found. Became 1st black female recording industry executive when appointed Sr. V.P. at Atlantic in 1988. Office: EastWest Records America 75 Rockefeller Plz New York NY 10019-6907*

RHOTON, ALBERT LOREN, JR., neurological surgery educator; b. Parvin, Ky., Nov. 18, 1932; s. Albert Loren and Hazel Arnette (Van Cleve) R.; m. Joyce L. Moldenhauer, June 23, 1957; children: Eric L., Albert J., Alice S., Laural A. BS, Ohio State U., 1954; MD cum laude, Washington U., St. Louis, 1959. Diplomate Am. Bd. Neurol. Surgery (bd. dirs. 1985-91, vice chmn. 1991). Intern, Columbia Presbyn. Med. Ctr., N.Y.C., 1959; resident in neurol. surgery Barnes Hosp., St. Louis, 1961-65; cons. neurol. surgery Mayo Clinic, Rochester, Minn., 1965-72; chief div. neurol. surgery U. Fla., Gainesville, 1972-80, R.D. Keene prof. and chmn. dept. neurol. surgery, 1980—; developer microsurg. tng. ctr.; guest lectr. Neurol. Socs. Switzerland, Japan, Venezuela, France, Columbia, Middle East, Brazil, Japan, Mex., Can., Costa Rica, Uruguay, Korea, Australia, Egypt, Argentina, Hong Kong; invited faculty and guest lectr. Harvard U., Washington U., Emory, U., UCLA, U. Calif., San Francisco, U. Miami, U. Okla., U. So. Calif., U. Mich., Northwestern U., U. Chgo., U. Pa., Johns Hopkins U., Ohio State U., Temple U., Duke U., Cornell U., NYU, U. Cin., Tulane U., Vanderbilt, U. Minnesota, U. Md., U. Pa., Albany Med. Coll., Cleve. Clin. Found., St. Louis U., Henry Ford Med. Found., Med. Coll. N.Y., Jefferson Med. Coll., Hahnamann Med. Coll., U. P.R., U. Calif., Irvine, U. Hong Kong, La. State U. Recipient Disting. Faculty award U. Fla., 1981, Alumni Achievement award Washington U. Sch. Medicine, 1985, Jones award for outstanding spl. med. exhibit of yr. Am. Assn. Med. Illustrators, 1969; grantee NIH, VA, Am. Heart Assn.; awarded hon. memberships neurosurg. socs. of Brazil, Japan, Mex., Can., Uruguay, Venezuela, Tex., Okla., Wis., Ga., Rocky Mountain. Mem. ACS (bd. govs. 1978-84), Congress Neurol. Surgeons (pres. 1978, honored guest 1993), Nat. Found. for Brain Rsch. (bd. dirs. 1990—), Nat. Coalition for Rsch. in Neurol. Disorders (bd. dirs. 1990-94), Fla. Neurosurgical Soc. (pres. 1978), Am. Assn. Neurol. Surgeons (chmn. vascular sect., treas. 1983-86, v.p. 1987-88, pres. 1989-90, exec. com. 1993), Soc. Neurol. Surgeons (treas. 1975-81, pres. 1993), So. Neurol. Soc. (v.p. 1976), Alachua County Med. Soc. (exec. com. 1978), AMA (Billings Bronze medal for sci. exhibit 1969), Fla. Med. Assn., Am. Surg. Assn., Soc. Univ. Neurosurgeons, Am. Heart Assn. (stroke coun., Outstanding Achievement award 1971), North Am. Skull Base Soc. (pres. 1993-94), Am. Acad. Neurol. Surgery, Neurol. Soc. Am., Acoustic Neuroma Assn. (med. adv. bd. 1983—, chmn. 1992—), Trigeminal Neurol. Assn. (med. advisor bd. 1992—). Designed over 200 microsurgery instruments; mem. editorial bd. Neurosurgery, Jour. Microsurgery, Surgical Neurology, Jour. Fla. Med. Assn., Am. Jour. Otology, Skull Base Surgery; contbr. numerous articles to profl. jours. Home: 2505 NW 22nd Ave Gainesville FL 32605-3819 Office: U Fla Shands Hosp Gainesville FL 32610

RHYNE, CHARLES SYLVANUS, lawyer; b. Charlotte, N.C., June 23, 1912; s. Sydneyham S. and Mary (Wilson) R.; m. Sue Cotton, Sept. 16, 1932 (dec. Mar. 1974); children: Mary Margaret, William Sylvanus; m. Sarah P. Hendon, Oct. 2, 1976; children: Sarah Wilson, Elizabeth Parkhill. BA, Duke U., 1934, LLD, 1958; JD, George Washington U., 1937, DCL, 1958; LLD, Loyola U., Calif., 1958, Dickinson Law Sch., 1959, Ohio No. U., 1966, De Paul U., 1968, Centre, 1969, U. Richmond, 1970, Howard U., 1975, Belmont Abbey, 1982. Bar: D.C. 1937. Pvt. practice Washington; sr. ptnr. Rhyne & Rhyne; gen. counsel Nat. Inst. Mcpl. Law Officers, 1937-88, of counsel; prof. govt. and aviation law George Washington U., 1948-53; prof. govt. Am. U., 1939-44; gen. counsel Fed. Commn. Jud. and Congl. Salaries, 1953-54; spl. cons. Pres. Eisenhower, 1957-60; Dir. Nat. Savs. & Trust Co., 1941-76, ACCIA Life Ins. Co., 1966-84; Mem. Internat Commn. Rules Judicial Procedures, 1959-61, Pres.'s Commn. on UN, 1969-71; spl. ambassador, personal rep. of Pres. U.S. to UN High Commr. for Refugees, 1971-73. Author: Civil Aeronautics Act, Annotated, 1939, Airports and the Courts, 1944, Aviation Accident Law, 1947, Airport Lease and Concession Agreements, 1948, Cases on Aviation Law, 1950, The Law of Municipal Contracts, 1952, Municipal Law, 1957, International Law, 1971, Renowned Law Givers and Great Law Documents of Humankind, 1975, International Refugee Law, 1976, Law and Judicial Systems of Nations, 1978, Law of Local Government Operations, 1980; editor Mcpl. Atty., 1937-88; contbr. articles to various publs. Trustee George Washington U., 1957-67, Duke U., 1961-85, now trustee emeritus. Recipient Freedoms Found. award for creation Law Day-U.S.A., 1959; Alumni Achievement award George Washington U., 1960; Nat. Bar Assn. Stradford award, 1962; 1st Whitney M. Young award, 1972; Harris award Rotary, 1974; U.S. Dept. State appreciation award, 1976; Nansen Ring for refugee work, 1976, 1st Peacemaker award Rotary Internat., 1988. Mem. ABA (pres. 1957-58, chmn. ho. dels. 1956-58, chmn. commn. world peace through law 1958-66, chmn. com. aero. law 1946-48, 51-54, chmn. internat. and comparative law sect. 1948-49, chmn. UN com., chmn. commn. on nat. inst. justice 1972-76, nat. chmn. Jr. Bar Conf. 1944-45, Grotius Peace award 1958, ABA Gold medal 1966), D.C. Bar Assn. (pres. 1955-56, Disting. Svc. award 1976), Inter-Am. Bar Assn. (v.p. 1957-59), Am. Bar Found. (pres. 1957-58, chmn. fellows 1958-59), Internat. Bar (founder patron 1947, v.p. 1957-58), Am. Judicature Soc. (dir. life), Am. Law Inst. (life), Am. Soc. Internat. Law (life), World Peace Through Law Ctr. (pres. 1963-89), World Jurist Assn. (life, pres. 1989-91, hon. pres. for life), Nat. Aero. Assn. (dir. 1945-47), Washington Bd. Trade, Duke U. Alumni Assn. (chmn. nat. coun. 1955-56, pres. 1959-60), Barristers, Met. Club (life), Nat. Press Club, Congl. Country Club (life), Nat. Lawyers Club (life), Univ. Club, Delta Theta Phi (life), Order of Coif (life), Omicron Delta Kappa, Scribes. Home and Office: 1404 Langley Pl Mc Lean VA 22101-3010

RHYNE, VERNON THOMAS, III, electrical engineer, consultant; b. Gulfport, Miss., Feb. 18, 1942; s. Vernon T. and Elizabeth (Brame) R.; m. Glenda Pevey, June 5, 1961; children: Amber Ruth, Tommy. BSEE, Miss. State U., 1962; MEE, U. Va., 1964; PhD, Ga. Inst. Tech., 1967. Registered profl. engr., Tex. Mem. tech. staff NASA Langley Rsch. Ctr., Hampton, Va., 1962-65; prof. elec. engring. Tex. A&M U., College Station, 1967-83; v.p. R&D MCC, Austin, Tex., 1983-94; mgr. strategic programs, semiconductor products sector Motorola, Austin; patent cons., expert witness, N.Y.C., Houston, L.A., 1975—. Author: Fundamentals of Digital Systems Design, 1973 (Terman award Am. Soc. Engring. Edn. 1980). Pres. bd. trustees Eanes Ind. Sch. Dist., Austin, 1987-90, trustee, 1990—. Fellow IEEE (bd. dirs. 1990-95, treas. 1994—), Accreditation Bd. for Engring. and Tech. Baptist. Home: 3410 Day Star Cv Austin TX 78746-1433 Office: Motorola MD: TX30/OE14 6501 William Cannon Dr W Austin TX 78735

RIASANOVSKY, NICHOLAS VALENTINE, historian, educator; b. Harbin, China, Dec. 21, 1923; came to U.S., 1938, naturalized, 1943; m. Arlene Ruth Schlegel, Feb. 15, 1955; children—John, Nicholas, Maria. B.A., U. Oreg., 1942; A.M., Harvard U., 1947; D.Phil., Oxford (Eng.) U., 1949. Mem. faculty U. Iowa, 1949-57; mem. faculty U. Calif., Berkeley, 1957—, prof. history, 1961—, Sidney Hellman Ehrman prof. European history, 1969—; trustee Nat. Council Soviet and E. European Research, 1978-82; mem. Kennan Inst. Acad. Council, 1986-89; vis. research prof. USSR Acad. Scis., Moscow, 1969, Moscow and Leningrad, 1974, 79. Author: Russia and the West in Teaching of the Slavophiles: A Study of Romantic Ideology, 1952, Nicholas I and Official Nationality in Russia, 1825-1855, 1959, A History of Russia, 1963, 5th edit., 1993, The Teaching of Charles Fourier, 1969, A Parting of Ways: Government and the Educated Public in Russia, 1801-1855, 1976, The Image of Peter the Great in Russian History and Thought, 1985, The Emergence of Romanticism, 1992, Collected Writings 1947-94, 1994; co-editor: Calif. Slavic Studies, 1960—; editl. bd. Russian Rev., Zarubezhnaia Periodicheskaia Pechat' Na Russk Iazyke; contbr. articles to profl. jours. Served to 2d lt. AUS, 1943-46. Decorated Bronze Star; recipient Silver medal Commonwealth Club Calif., 1964; Rhodes scholar, 1947-49; Fulbright grantee, 1954-55, 74, 79; Guggenheim fellow, 1969; sr. fellow Nat. Endowment Humanities, 1975; Fulbright sr. scholar, sr. fellow Ctr. Advanced Studies in Behavioral Scis., 1984-85; sr. fellow Woodrow Wilson Internat. Ctr. for Scholars, 1989-90. Mem. AAAS, Am. Assn. Advancement Slavic Studies (pres. 1973-76, Disting. Contbr. award 1993), Am. Hist. Assn. (award for Scholarly Distinction 1995).

RIAZZI, RICHARD, gas industry executive; b. 1954. BA, U. Pitts., MBA. Various positions Equitable Resources, Inc., Pitts., 1980-91, v.p. corporate devel., from 1991; now prin. Equitable Resources Mktg. Co., Pitts. Office: Equitable Resources Mktg Co 420 Blevard of the Allies Pittsburgh PA 15219*

RIBBANS, GEOFFREY WILFRID, Spanish educator; b. London, Apr. 15, 1927; came to U.S. 1978; s. Wilfrid Henry and Rose Matilda (Burton)R.; m. Magdalena Willmann, Apr. 21, 1956; children: Madeleine Elizabeth, Helen Margaret, Peter John. BA with 1st class hons., Kings Coll., U. London,

1948, MA, 1953. Asst. lectr. U. Sheffield, Eng., 1954-56; lectr. U. Sheffield, 1956-61, sr. lectr. Spanish, 1961-63; Gilmour prof. Spanish U. Liverpool, Eng.; 1963-78 Mellon prof. Spanish, U. Pitts., 1970-71; Wm. R. Kenan Jr. U. prof. Spanish Brown U., Providence, 1978—, chmn. dept., 1981-84; editor Bull. Hispanic Studies, 1964-78; vis. prof. U. Salamanca, Spain, 1995. Author: Catalunya i Valencia al Segle XVIII, 1955, 2d edit., 1993, Niebla y Soledad: Aspectos de Unamuno y Machado, 1971, Galdos: Fortunata y Jacinta, 1977 (Spanish transl. 1988); editor: Antonio Machado, Soledades, Galerias, Otros Poemas, 1984, 12th edit., 1994, Campos de Castilla, 1989, 4th edit., 1993, History and Fiction in Galdos's Narratives, 1993; also articles. Hispanic studies in his honour, Liverpool, 1992. Mem. MLA (internat. Assn. Hispanists (v.p. 1974-80), Internat. Assn. Galdós Scholars (pres. 1988-89). Office: Brown U Dept Hispanic Studies PO Box 1961 Providence RI 02912-1961

RIBBLE, JOHN CHARLES, medical educator; b. Paris, Tex., July 26, 1931; s. Elbert Alfred and Dorothy (Pyeatt) R.; m. Anne Blythe Hoerner; 1 stepchild, Helen Blythe Strate. MD, U. Tex., 1955. Diplomate Am. Bd. Internal Medicine. Asst. prof. medicine Cornell U., N.Y.C., 1962-66, assoc. prof. pediatrics, 1966-78, assoc. dean, 1974-78; assoc. dean Med. Sch., U. Tex., Houston, 1978-86, dean, 1986—; interim pres. U. Tex. Health Sci. Ctr., Houston, 1987-89; mem. Nat. Adv. Coun. Gen. Med. Scis. NIH, Bethesda, Md., 1988-91. Mem. Infectious Disease Soc. Episcopalian. Home: 6200 Willers Way Houston TX 77057-2808 Office: U Tex Med Sch 6431 Fannin St Houston TX 77030-1501

RIBBLE, RONALD GEORGE, psychologist, educator, writer; b. West Reading, Pa., May 7, 1937; s. Jeremiah George and Mildred Sarah (Folk) R.; m. Catalina Valenzuela (Torres), Sept. 30, 1961; children: Christina, Timothy, Kenneth. BSEE, U. Mo., 1968, MSEE, 1969, MA, 1985, PhD, 1986. Cert. psychologist, Tex. Enlisted man USAF, 1956-60, advance through grades to lt. col., 1976; rsch. dir. Coping Resources, Inc., Columbia, Mo., 1986; pres. co-owner Towers and Rushing Ltd., San Antonio, 1986—; referral devel. Laughlin Pavilion Psychiat. Hosp., Kirksville, Mo., 1987; program dir. Psychiat. Insts. of Am., Iowa Falls, Iowa, 1987-88; lead psychotherapist Gasconade County Counseling Ctr., Hermann, Mo., 1988; lectr. U. Tex., San Antonio, 1989—; assessment clinician Afton Oaks Psychiat. Hosp., San Antonio, 1989-91; psychologist Olmos Psychol. Svcs., Inc., San Antonio, 1991-93; vol. assessor Holmgreen Children's Shelter, San Antonio, 1992-93; condr. seminars, revs. for maj. pub.s. Contbr. essays to psychol. reference books and poetry to anthologies periodicals, lyrics to popular music; columnist Feelings, 1993—; public access TV appearances, 1991—. Del. Boone County (Mo.) Dem. Conv., 1984; vol. announcer pub. radio sta., Columbia, 1993; contbg. mem. Dem. Nat. Com., 1983-92, Presdl. Congl. Task Force, 1994; vol. counselor Cath. Family and Children's Svc., San Antonio, 1989-91; chpt. advisor Rational Recovery Program for Alcoholics, San Antonio, 1991-92; mem. Pres. Leadership Circle, 1994. Mem. APA, AAUP, NEA, ACLU, Internat. Soc. for Study of Individual Differences, Internat. Platform Assn., Bexar County Psychol. Assn., Air Force Assn., Ret. Officers Assn., People for the Am. Way. Roman Catholic. Avocations: running and fitness, poetry, singing, pub. speaking. Home: 14023 N Hills Village Dr San Antonio TX 78249-2531 Office: U Tex Div Cultural And Sc San Antonio TX 78249 also: Towers and Rushing Ltd San Antonio TX 78249

RIBERO, MICHAEL ANTONIO, marketing executive; b. Miami, Fla., May 16, 1956; s. Miguel and Zoe (Prio) R.; m. Brenda Starr, Sept. 8, 1979; children: Michael, Kristen. BS in Ops. Research, U. Fla., 1979. Analyst mktg., mgr. through brand mgr. The Procter & Gamble Co., Cin., 1979-85; from dir. to v.p. Eastern Airlines, Miami, 1985-88; sr. v.p. mktg. Hilton Hotels Corp., Beverly Hills, Calif., 1988—; bd. dirs. Compass Comuter Corp., Hilton Svc. Corp. Bd. dirs. Miami Project to Cure Paralysis, 1987. Republican. Roman Catholic. Avocations: golf, fishing, other sports. Office: Hilton Hotels Corp 9336 Civic Center Dr Beverly Hills CA 90210-3964

RIBICOFF, ABRAHAM A., lawyer, former senator; b. New Britain, Conn., Apr. 9, 1910; s. Samuel and Rose (Sable) R.; m. Ruth Siegel, June 28, 1931 (dec.); children: Peter, Jane; m. Lois Mathes, 1972. Student, NYU; LL.B. cum laude, U. Chgo., 1933. Bar: Conn. 1933, N.Y. 1981, US. Ct. Appeals (D.C. cir.) 1982, U.S. Supreme Ct. 1981. Mem. Conn. Ho. of Reps., 1939-42; mcpl. judge Hartford, Conn., 1942-43, 45-47; chmn. Conn. Assembly Mcpl. Ct. Judges, 1942; mem. 81st—82d congresses from 1st Conn. Dist., mem. com. fgn. affairs; gov. Conn., 1955-61; sec. HEW, 1961-62; mem. U.S. Senate from Conn., 1963-81, mem. fin., joint econ. coms., chmn. govt. affairs com.; spl. counsel firm Kaye, Scholer, Fierman, Hays & Handler, N.Y.C. and Washington, 1981—; dir. Hartford Ins. Group, United Television, Inc. Author: Politics: The American Way, 1967, America Can Make It, 1972, The American Medical Machine, 1972. Democrat. Office: 425 Park Ave New York NY 10022-3506

RIBLE, MORTON, manufacturing executive, lawyer; b. Los Angeles, July 30, 1938; s. Ulysses Floyd and Ruth (Morton) R.; m. Ann Martin, June 22, 1963; children: Kimberly, Kristen. AB cum laude, Princeton U., 1961; JD, Stanford U., 1964; MBA, U. So. Calif., 1973. Bar: Calif. 1964. Ptnr. Darling, Mack, Hall & Call, Los Angeles, 1965-69; v.p., gen. counsel, sec. The Leisure Group Inc., Los Angeles, 1969-76; sr. v.p., gen. counsel, dir. Calif. Life Corp., Los Angeles; sec. PS Group Inc., San Diego, 1978-87; sr. v.p., gen. counsel Jet Air Lines, San Diego, 1978-85, v.p. human resources and adminstrn., 1985-87; v.p., gen. counsel, sec. PS Group Inc., San Diego, 1978-87; sr. v.p., gen. counsel, chief adminstrv. officer AM Internat., Inc., Chgo., 1988-94; chmn. San Diego Travel Group, Inc., 1994—. Bd. dirs. San Diego C. of C., 1983-86, Rancho Santa Fe (Calif.) Community Found., 1981-89; pres. Palos Verdes (Calif.) Community Arts Assn., 1976-77; trustee Rancho Santa Fe Youth Inc., 1980-82. Mem. ABA, Calif. Bar Assn., Am. Soc. Corp. Secs., Exec. Club. Avocations: running, skiing. Home: 70 E Cedar St Chicago IL 60611-1133 also: PO Box 945 Rancho Santa Fe CA 92067

RIBLET, ROBIN L., judge; b. 1949. BA cum laude, Univ. of Fla., 1971; JD cum laude, Univ. of San Diego, 1975; LLM, N.Y.U., 1979. With Stutman, Treister & Glatt, 1979-88; bankruptcy judge U.S. Bankruptcy Ct. (Calif. ctrl. dist.), 9th circuit, Santa Barbara, 1988—. Mem. L.A. Bar Assn., L.A. County Bar Assn., San Diego Bar Assn. Office: US Courthouse 222 E Carrillo St Rm 104 Santa Barbara CA 93101

RIBMAN, RONALD BURT, playwright; b. N.Y.C., May 28, 1932; s. Samuel M. and Rosa (Lerner) R.; m. Alice S. Rosen, Aug. 27, 1967; 2 children. BBA, U. Pitts., 1954, MLitt, 1958, PhD, 1962. Asst. prof. English lit. Otterbein Coll., 1962-63. Author plays including: Harry, Noon and Night, 1965, The Journey of the Fifth Horse, 1966 (Obie award Best Play, 1965-66), The Ceremony of Innocence, 1967, Passing Through From Exotic Places (includes The Son Who Hunted Tigers in Jakarta, Sunstroke, The Burial of Esposito), 1969, Fingernails Blue as Flowers, 1971, A Break in the Skin, 1972, The Poison Tree, 1976 (Straw Hat award Best New Play, 1973), Cold Storage, 1977 (Elizabeth Hull-Kate Warriner award Dramatists Guild 1977), Buck, 1983 (Playwrights USA award 1984), The Cannibal Masque, 1987, A Serpent's Egg, 1987, Sweet Table at the Richelieu, 1987, The Rug Merchants Of Chaos, 1991, Dream of the Red Spider, 1993, (screenplays) The Final War of Olly Winter, 1967 (Emmy award nomination 1967), The Angel Levine, 1969, Seize The Day, 1986; (miniseries) The Sunset Gang, 1991. With AUS, 1954-56. Rockefeller Found grantee, 1966, 68; Guggenheim fellow, 1970; Nat. Endowment Arts fellow, 1974, 86-87; Rockefeller Found. awardee for contbn. to Am. Theatre, 1975. Office: care Samuel Gelfman BDP & Assocs 10637 Burbank Blvd North Hollywood CA 91601 Address: 263 Stone Meadow South Salem NY 10590

RIBNER, HERBERT SPENCER, physicist, educator; b. Seattle, Apr. 9, 1913; s. Joseph Herman and Rose Esther (Goldberg) R.; m. Lelia Carolyn Byrd, Oct. 29, 1949; children—Carol Anne, David Byrd. B.S., Calif. Inst. Tech., 1935; M.S., Washington U., St. Louis, 1937; Ph.D., Washington U., 1939. From physicist to dir. lab. Brown Geophys. Co., Tex., 1939-40; from physicist to head stability sect. Langley Lab., NACA, Va., 1940-49; cons. to head boundary layer sects. Lewis Lab. NACA, Cleve., 1949-54; research assoc. Inst. aerospace studies U. Toronto, Ont., Can., 1955-56; asst. prof. U. Toronto, 1956-57, assoc. prof., 1957-59, prof., 1959-86, prof. emeritus, 1986—; vis. prof. U. Southampton, 1960-61; staff scientist NASA Langley Research Ctr., 1975-76, disting. rsch. assoc., 1979—; chmn. sonic boom

panel Internat. Civil Aviation Orgn., 1969-70; adviser com. on hearing, bioacoustics and mechanics Nat. Acad. Scis., 1972-74. Contbr. over 100 articles to profl. jours. Recipient Can. 125th Commemorative medal, 1993, Pub. Svc. medal NASA, 1994. Fellow AIAA (Aero-Acoustics award 1976, Dryden lectr. 1981), Royal Soc. Can., Am. Phys. Soc., Acoustical Soc. Am., Can. Aero. and Space Inst. (Turnbull lectr. 1968); mem. Can. Acoustical Assn. (chmn. 1966-68). Office: U Toronto Inst Aerospace Studies, 4925 Dufferin St, Downsview, ON Canada M3H 5T6

RICARD, JOHN H., bishop, educator; b. Baton Rouge, Feb. 29, 1940; s. Maceo and Albanie (St. Amant) R. BA, St. Joseph Sem., 1962, MA, 1968; MS, Tulane U., 1970. Ordained priest Roman Cath. Ch., 1968. Pastor Holy Redeemer Ch., Washington, 1972-75, Holy Comforter Ch., Washington, 1975-84; ordained titular bishop of Rucuma, 1984; aux. bishop Balt., 1984; assoc. prof. Cath. U. Am., Washington, 1973—; mem. priest's senate Archdiocese of Washington, 1974—, mem. shc. bd., 1976—. Mem. Secretariat of Black Caths. Office: St Francis Xavier Rectory 1501 E Oliver St Baltimore MD 21213-2910*

RICARDI, LEON JOSEPH, electrical engineer; b. Brockton, Mass., Mar. 21, 1924; s. Philip Julius and Eva Isabel (DuBois) R.; m. Angelena Marie Giorgio, Jan. 19, 1947; children: Eva Marie, John Philip, Richard Christopher. B.S. in Elec. Engring, Northeastern U., 1949, M.S., 1952, Ph.D., 1969. Engr. Andrew Alford Cons. Engrs., Boston, 1950-51; project engr. Gabirel Labs., Needham, Mass., 1951-54; group leader, head Tech. Adv. Office, MIT-Lincoln Lab., Lexington, Mass., 1954-84; pres. L.J. Ricardi, Inc., El Segundo, Calif., 1985—; part-time lectr. Northeastern U., Boston, 1969-80; cons. U.S. Air Force, 1965-85. Served with USAF, 1943-45. Fellow IEEE. Roman Catholic. Office: L J Ricardi Inc 360 N Sepulveda Blvd Ste 2030 El Segundo CA 90245 Listen as much as possible but never fail to speak when you feel that you are right and what you have to say is more than of average importance.

RICARDO-CAMPBELL, RITA, economist, educator; b. Boston, Mar. 16, 1920; d. David and Elizabeth (Jones) Ricardo; m. Wesley Glenn Campbell, Sept. 15, 1946; children: Barbara Lee, Diane Rita, Nancy Elizabeth. BS, Simmons Coll., 1941; MA, Harvard U., 1945, PhD, 1946. Instr. Harvard U., Cambridge, Mass., 1946-48; asst. prof. Tufts U., Medford, Mass., 1948-51; labor economist U.S. Wage Stabilization Bd., 1951-53; economist Ways and Means Com. U.S. Ho. of Reps., 1953; cons. economist, 1957-60; vis. prof. San Jose State Coll., 1960-61; sr. fellow Hoover Instn. on War, Revolution, and Peace, Stanford, Calif., 1968—; lectr. health svc. adminstrn. Stanford U. Med. Sch., 1973-78; bd. dirs. Watkins-Johnson Co., Palo Alto, Calif., Gillette Co., Boston; mgmt. bd. Samaritan Med. Ctr., San Jose, Calif. Author: Voluntary Health Insurance in the U.S., 1960, Economics of Health and Public Policy, 1971, Food Safety Regulation: Use and Limitations of Cost-Benefit Analysis, 1974, Drug Lag: Federal Government Decision Making, 1976, Social Security: Promise and Reality, 1977, The Economics and Politics of Health, 1982, 2d edit., 1985; co-editor: Below-Replacement Fertility in Industrial Societies, 1987, Issues in Contemporary Retirement, 1988; contbr. articles to profl. jours. Commr. Western Interstate Commn. for Higher Edn. Calif., 1967-75, chmn., 1970-71; mem. Pres. Nixon's Adv. Coun. on Status Women, 1969-76; mem. task force on taxation Pres.'s Coun. on Environ. Quality, 1970-72; mem. Pres.'s Com. Health Services Industry, 1971-73, FDA Nat. Adv. Drug Com., 1972-75; mem. Econ. Policy Adv. Bd., 1981-90, Pres. Reagan's Nat. Coun. on Humanities, 1982-89, Pres. Nat. Medal of Sci. com., 1988-94; bd. dirs. Inds. Colls. No. Calif. 1971-87; mem. com. assessment of safety, benefits, risks Citizens Commn. Sci., Law and Food Supply, Rockefeller U., 1973-75; mem. adv. com. Ctr. Health Policy Rsch., Am. Enterprise Inst. Pub. Policy Rsch., Washington, 1974-80; mem. adv. coun. on social security Social Security Adminstrn., 1974-75; bd. dirs. Simmons Coll. Corp., Boston, 1975-80; mem. adv. coun. bd. assocs. Stanford Librs., 1975-78; mem. coun. SRI Internat., Menlo Park, Calif., 1977-90. Mem. Am. Econ. Assn., Mont Pelerin Soc. (bd. dirs. 1988-92, v.p. 1992-94), Harvard Grad. Soc. (coun. 1991), Phi Beta Kappa. Home: 26915 Alejandro Dr Los Altos CA 94022-1932 Office: Stanford U Hoover Instn Stanford CA 94305-6010

RICART, PAUL F., SR., automotive retail executive; b. 1919. With Ricart Ford, Groveport, Ohio, 1953—, now chmn. bd.; with Capital Jeep Eagle, Inc., Columbus. Office: Ricart Ford Inc 4255 S Hamilton Rd Groveport OH 43125*

RICART, RHETT C., retail automotive executive; b. 1956. Grad., Ohio State U., 1977. Prin. Ricard Ford, Groveport, Ohio, 1977—, pres., treas., 1988—. Office: Ricart Ford Inc 4255 S Hamilton Rd Groveport OH 43125*

RICCARDS, MICHAEL PATRICK, academic administrator; b. Hillside, N.J., Oct. 2, 1944; s. Patrick and Margaret (Finelli) R.; m. Barbara Dunlop, June 6, 1970; children: Patrick, Catherine, Abigail. BA, Rutgers U., 1966, MA, 1967, MPhil, 1969, PhD, 1970. Spl. asst. to chancellor Dept. Higher Edn., Trenton, N.J., 1969-70; from asst. prof. to assoc. prof. SUNY, Buffalo, 1970-77; dean U. Mass., Boston, 1977-82; provost, prof. Hunter Coll., CUNY, 1982-86; pres. St. John's Coll., Santa Fe, 1986-89, Shepherd Coll., Shepherdstown, W.Va., 1989—. Author: The Making of the American Citizenry, 1973, A Republic If You Can Keep It, 1987, The Ferocious Engine of Democracy, 2 vols., 1995—; co-editor: Reflections on American Political Thought, 1973. Chmn. N.Mex. Endowment for Humanities, 1989; mem. nat. adv. com. Ctr. for Study of Presidency, 1987—; mem. bd. trustees Albuquerque Acad.; mem. Coun. Humanities W.Va. Fulbright fellow 1973, Huntington Libr. fellow 1974, NEH fellow Princeton U. 1976-77. Office: Shepherd Coll Shepherdstown WV 25443

RICCI, KENNETH, architect; b. N.Y.C., Feb. 19, 1943; s. Fred Q. and Mary Rita (Vaccaro) R.; m. Annalea Canzoniero, Apr. 26, 1970; children: Marco, Lea, Maria. BArch, Pratt Inst., 1964. Registered architect. Jr. architect Raymond & Rado, N.Y.C., 1964-65; vol. Peace Corps, Colombia, S.Am., 1965-66; freelance architect N.Y.C., 1966-67; jr. architect Mascioni & Behrman, N.Y.C., 1967-69; pres. Ricci Architects, N.Y.C., 1969-76, 88—; v.p. Ehrenkrantz Group, N.Y.C., 1976-88; cons. faculty Nat. Vail Ctr., Boulder, Colo., 1989—. Designer correctional facility for Westchester, 1989, Phila., 1983; co-designer correctional facility for Dutchess County, 1994. Founder, chmn. Svcs. Through Organized People, Bronx, N.Y., 1969-81; chmn. devel. com. Providence Rest Nursing Home, Bronx, 1994—. Mem. AIA (citation, 1990, chmn. justice facilities com. N.Y. chpt. 1994—). Roman Catholic. Avocation: wine making. Office: Ricci Architects 130 W 30th St New York NY 10001

RICCI, ROBERT RONALD, manufacturing company executive; b. N.Y.C., Jan. 11, 1945; s. George and Mary Pauline (Barbieri) R.; m. Sandra Piccione, Jan. 18, 1948; children: Jason, Sean. AAS, S.I. Community Coll., 1972; BBA, Bernard Baruch Coll., 1974, MBA, 1976. Sales mgr. G.A.F. Photo, Elizabeth, N.J., 1974-76; v.p. Photo Drive Thru, Pennsauken, N.J., 1976-80; head nat. accounts Berkey Photo, Phila., 1980-85; dir. nat. account sales Qualex, Inc., Durham, N.C., 1988-92, v.p sales east, 1993—; v.p. new acct. devel. sales National, 1995—; pres. Sanjasean, Inc., Marlton, N.J., 1978-86. Served with USN, 1966-70. Mem. Photo Mktg. Assn. Republican. Roman Catholic. Avocations: photography, carpentry, computers. Home: 1001 Clingmans Pl Raleigh NC 27614 Office: Qualex Inc 3404 N Duke St Durham NC 17704

RICCI, RUGGIERO, violinist, educator; b. San Francisco, July 24, 1918; s. Pietro Ricci and Emma Bacigalupi; m. Ruth Rink, 1942; m. Valma Rodriguez, 1957; m. Julia Whitehurst Clemenceau, 1978; 5 children. Pupil, Louis Persinger, Mishel Piastro, Paul Stassevitch, Georg Kulenkampff. Began career as child prodigy; N.Y. debut Manhattan Symphony, 1929; performed concert engagements throughout world including unaccompanied violin recitals, 1st European tour, 1932, specializes in violin solo, introduced Ginastera, von Einem and Veerhoff violin concerti, U.S. premiere Paganini, 6th violin concerto; prof. music Ind. U., 1971-74, Juilliard Sch., 1974-79, U. Mich., (Ann Arbor, 1982-87; prof. Mozarteum, Salzburg, Austria, 1989—. Recordings include The Great Violinist Series, The Making of a Legend, Vols. 3, 4, Portrait of an Artist, Vol. 4, Vol. 6, Ruggiero Ricci, Virtuoso Recital. Served with USAAF, 1942-45. Decorated Knight Order of Merit Italy. Mem. Royal Acad. Music (hon.). Made first complete recording of Paganini's Caprices. Office: Intermusica Stephen Lumsden, 16 Duncan Terr,

London N1 8B2, England also: One-Eleven Ltd c/o Albany Music Distrs Inc P O Box 5011 Albany NY 12205 also: c/o John Gingrich Mgmt Inc P O Box 1515 New York NY 10023*

RICCIARDI, LAWRENCE R., food products company executive, lawyer. BA, Fordham U., 1962; JD, Columbia U., 1965; course in executive program, Stamford U., 1978. Bar: N.Y. 1967. Assoc. Gilbert, Segall & Young, 1965-69; counsel Overseas Pvt. Invest Corp/US Dept. State Internat. Devel., 1969-73; internat. counsel Am. Express, 1973-75; gen. counsel Internat. Banking Corp., 1975-77, Travel Related Svcs., 1977-89; exec. v.p., gen. counsel RJR Nabisco, Inc., N.Y.C., 1989-93, pres., 1993—. Mem. Assn. of Bar of City of N.Y. Office: RJR Nabisco Holdings Corp 1301 Ave of the Americas New York NY 10019-6022*

RICCIARELLI, KATIA, soprano; b. Rovigo, Italy, Jan. 18, 1946; m. Pippo Baudo, 1986. Grad. summa cum laude, Benedetto Marcello Conservatory, Venice, Italy. Operatic debut as Mimi in La Boheme, Mantua, Italy, 1969, also Covent Garden, London, 1974, I Due Foscari, Lyric Opera, Chgo., 1972; appeared in Suor Angelica, La Scala, Milan, 1976, La Boheme, Met. Opera Co., N.Y.C., 1975; other roles include Donizetti's Caterina Cornaro, Maria de Rohan and Lucrezia Borgia, and Bellini's Imogene, Elisabeth de Valois in Don Carlos, Covent Garden, 1989; numerous appearances in maj. opera houses throughout U.S. and Europe including San Francisco Opera, Paris Opera, Verona Festival; leading roles in Anna Bolena; recs. include I Due Foscari, Turandot, Carmen, Aida, Un Ballo in Maschera, Falstaff, Il Trovatore, La Boheme, Tosca, Pavarotti and Ricciarelli Live, Duetti d'Amore with Jose Carreras; also appears as Desdemona in Franco Zeffirelli's video Otello. Office: ICM Artists Ltd 40 W 57th St New York NY 10019 Office: Via Magellana 2, I-20097 Corsica Italy*

RICE, (ETHEL) ANN, publishing executive, editor; b. South Bend, Ind., July 3, 1933; d. Walter A. and Ethylan Maude (Worden) R. A.B., Nazareth Coll., Kalamazoo, 1955. Editorial asst. Ave Maria mag., Notre Dame, Ind., 1955-63, asst. editor, 1963-64; asst. editor Today mag., Notre Dame, 1963-64, Scott, Foresman & Co., Chgo., 1964-67; editor U. Notre Dame Press, 1967-74, exec. editor, 1974—. Democrat. Roman Catholic. Office: U Notre Dame Press Notre Dame IN 46556

RICE, ANNE, author; b. New Orleans, Oct. 14, 1941; d. Howard and Katherine (Allen) O'Brien; m. Stan Rice, Oct. 14, 1961; children: Michele (dec.), Christopher. Student, Tex. Woman's U., 1959-60; BA, San Francisco State Coll., 1964, MA, 1971. Author: Interview with the Vampire, 1976, The Feast of all Saints, 1980, Cry to Heaven, 1982, The Vampire Lestat, 1985, The Queen of the Damned, 1988, The Mummy or Ramses the Damned, 1989, The Witching Hour, 1990, Tale of the Body Thief, 1992, Lasher, 1993, Taltos, 1994, Memnoch the Devil, 1995; (as A.N. Roquelaure) The Claiming of Sleeping Beauty, 1983, Beauty's Punishment, 1984, Beauty's Release: The Continued Erotic Adventures of Sleeping Beauty, 1985, (as Anne Rampling) Exit to Eden, 1985, Belinda, 1986; screenwriter: Interview with a Vampire, 1994. Office: care Alfred A Knopf Inc 201 E 50th St New York NY 10022-7703*

RICE, ARGYLL PRYOR, Hispanic studies and Spanish language educator; b. Va.; d. Theodorick Pryor and Argyll (Campbell) R. BA, Smith Coll., 1952; MA, Yale U., 1956, PhD, 1961. Spanish instr. Yale U., New Haven, 1959-60, 61-63; asst. prof. Spanish, Conn. Coll., New London, 1964-67, assoc. prof., 1967-72, prof., 1972—, chair dept. Hispanic Studies, 1971-74, 77-84. Author: Emilio Ballagas: poeta o poesia, 1967, Emilio Ballagas, Latin American Writers III; editor in chief Carlos A. Sole, Charles Scribner's Sons, 1989. Mem. MLA, Am. Assoc. Tchrs. of Spanish and Portuguese, New Eng. Coun. Latin Am. Studies, U.S. Tennis Assoc. (New England hall of fame), Phi Beta Kappa. Avocations: music, tennis. Home: 292 Pequot Ave 2L New London CT 06320

RICE, CHARLES DUNCAN, university official; b. Aberdeen, Scotland, Oct. 20, 1942; came to U.S., 1969; s. James Inglis and Jane Meauras (Scrogie) R.; m. Susan Ilene Wunsch, July 5, 1967; children: James Duncan, Samuel Duncan, Jane Emma. MA with 1st class honors, U. Aberdeen, 1966; PhD, U. Edinburgh, Scotland, 1969. Lectr. history U. Aberdeen, 1966-69; asst. prof. history Yale U., New Haven, 1970-76, assoc. prof., 1976-79; prof. history Hamilton Coll., Clinton, N.Y., 1979-85, dean, 1979-85; prof. history, dean faculty of arts and sci. NYU, 1985-95, vice chancellor, 1991—. Author: Rise and Fall of Black Slavery, 1975, The Scots Abolitionists, 1982; assoc. editor: Slavery and Abolition, 1979-86; contbr. articles and revs. in field. Trustee The Peddie Sch., Hightstown, N.J., 1973-82, 86—. C. & J. Henry Fund fellow, 1965-66, Am. Coun. Learned Socs. fellow, 1969-70, Morse fellow, 1974-75. Home: 29 Washington Sq W Apt 15C New York NY 10011-9199 Office: NYU/Vice Chancellor 70 Washington Sq S New York NY 10012

RICE, CHARLES EDWARD, banker; b. Chattanooga, Tenn., Aug. 4, 1936; s. Charles Edward and Louise (Goodson) R.; m. Dianne Tauscher; children: Danny, Celeste, Michelle. B.B.A. U. Miami, 1958; M.B.A., Rollins Coll., Winter Park, Fla., 1964; grad., Advanced Mgmt. Program, Harvard U., 1975. Vice pres., then pres. Barnett Bank, Winter Park, 1965-71; exec. v.p. Barnett Banks Fla., Inc., Jacksonville, 1971-73, pres., from 1973, chief exec. officer, 1979—, now also chmn., bd. dirs.; bd. dirs. Sprint Corp., CSX Corp. Trustee Univ. of Miami, Rollins Coll. Office: Barnett Banks Inc 50 N Laura St Jacksonville FL 32202-3637

RICE, CLARE I., electronics company executive; b. Rice Lake, Wis., Nov. 3, 1918; s. Chris Nilson and Ingeborg (Haug) R.; m. Virginia M. Bateman; children: Karen Bateman, Carol Rice Brannon, David Alan; m. Elaine Spurrier. B.S. in Elec. Engring. U. Wis., 1943; B.S. in Law, St. Paul Coll. Law, 1950; D.Engring., Rose-Hulman Inst. Tech., 1979. Registered profl. engr., Minn., D.C. Supr. aircraft radio engring. Northwest Airlines, Inc. Mpls., 1946-51; staff engr. Aero. Radio, Inc., Washington, 1951-53; aviation sales mgr., gen. mgr. Bendix Avionics Div., Balt., 1953-62; pres. Sunbeam Electronics, Inc., Ft. Lauderdale, Fla., 1962-66; v.p. Nova U., Ft. Lauderdale, 1966-68; asst. v.p., v.p., sr. v.p. Collins Radio Co., pres. Collins Avionics group Rockwell Internat. Corp., Cedar Rapids, Iowa, 1968-83; dir. Rockwell-Collins Internat., Inc., Dallas. Chmn. United Way, Cedar Rapids, 1973-74; trustee Coe Coll., 1979-83, Hoover Presdl. Libr.; bd. dirs. St. Luke's Hosp., 1976-82, Mchts. Nat. Bank, 1977-83; chmn. Mcpl. Airport Commn., Cedar Rapids, 1980-84; charter mem. Aviation Hall of Fame; capt. Hon. Dep. Sheriffs Assn., 1987—; pres. Cmty. Assn. Rancho Bernardo Heights, 1988-91; dir. Rancho Bernardo Cmty. Found. Lt. comdr. USNR, 1943-46. Recipient Disting. Svc. citation U. Wis., 1979, 84; Pioneer award Milw. Sch. Engring., 1981. Sr. mem. IEEE; mem. Wis. Alumni Assn. (bd. dirs. 1975-81), Gen. Aviation Mfrs. Assn. (dir. 1970-81, chmn 1979), U. Wis. Alumni Assn. (chmn. 1981-82, pres. 1980-81, Disting. Service award 1984). Republican. Presbyn. Clubs: Wings (N.Y.C.); Nat. Aviation (Washington); Rancho Bernardo Heights Country. Lodge: Royal Order of Jesters (dir. 1979). Home: 12201 Fairway Pointe San Diego CA 92128-3230

RICE, DARREL ALAN, lawyer; b. Denver, Jan. 8, 1947; s. Dale Harvey and Dorothy (Enewold) F.; m. Jeffrey Lynn Taylor, May 31, 1970; children: Ashley, Justin, Chandler. BSIE, U. Ark., 1969; JD, So. Meth. U., 1972. Bar: Tex. 1972. Assoc. Butler & Binion, Houston, 1972-75, Winstead, McGuire, Sechrest & Minick, P.C., Dallas, 1975-78; dir., shareholder Winstead, Sechrest & Minick, P.C. (formerly Winstead, McGuire, Sechrest & Minick, P.C.), Dallas, 1978—. Trustee 1st Presbyn. Ch. Found., Dallas, 1982—; adv. dir. Spl. Camps for Spl. Kids, Dallas, 1987-90, bd. dirs., mem. exec. com., 1990—; bd. dirs. Tex. Bus. Law Found., 1989—; bd. dirs., mem. exec. com. Dallas CASA, 1989—; mem. exec. com. bd So. Meth. U. Law Sch., 1991—. Mem. ABA, Tex. Bar Assn., State Bar Tex. (chmn. legal opinions com. 1989-92, mem. coun. bus. law sect. 1992-94), Dallas Bar Assn., Tex. Assn. Bank Counsel, Tower Club. Office: Winstead Sechrest & Minick PC 5400 Renaissance Tower 1201 Elm St Dallas TX 75270-2016

RICE, DENIS TIMLIN, lawyer; b. Milw., July 11, 1932; s. Cyrus Francis and Kathleen (Timlin) R.; children: James Connelly, Tracy Ellen. A.B., Princeton U., 1954; J.D., U. Mich., 1959. Bar: Calif. 1960. Practiced in San Francisco, 1959—; assoc. firm Pillsbury, Madison & Sutro, 1959-61, Howard & Prim, 1961-63; prin. firm Howard, Rice, Nemerovski, Canady, Robertson,

---

Falk & Rabkin, 1964—; dir. Gensler & Assocs., Inc., San Francisco; chmn., mng. com. San Francisco Inst. Fin. Svcs., 1983-92. Councilman, City of Tiburon, Calif., 1968-72, mayor, 1970-72, dir., Marin County Transit Dist., 1970-72, 77-81, chmn., 1979-80; supr. Marin County, 1977-81, chmn., 1979-80; commr. Marin Housing Authority, 1977-81; mem. San Francisco Bay Conservation and Devel. Commn., 1977-83; bd. dirs. Planning and Conservation League, 1981—, Marin Symphony, 1984-92, Marin Theatre Co., 1987—, Marin Conservation League, 1995—, Digital Village Found., 1995—; mem. Met. Transp. Commn., 1980-83; mem. bd. visitors U. Mich. Law Sch. Served to 1st lt. AUS, 1955-57. Recipient Freedom Found. medal, 1956. Fellow Am. Bar Found.; mem. ABA (fed. regulation of securities com.), State Bar of Calif., San Francisco Bar Assn., Am. Judicature Soc., Bankers Club, Tiburon Peninsula Club, Nassau Club, Olympic Club, Order of Coif, Phi Beta Kappa, Phi Delta Phi. Home: 1850 Mountain View Dr Belvedere Tiburon CA 94920-1810 Office: 3 Embarcadero Ctr Ste 700 San Francisco CA 94111-4065

RICE, DONALD BLESSING, former secretary of air force, corporate executive; b. Frederick, Md., June 4, 1939; s. Donald Blessing and Mary Celia (Santangelo) R.; m. Susan Fitzgerald, Aug. 25, 1962; children: Donald Blessing III, Joseph John, Matthew Fitzgerald. BSChemE, U. Notre Dame, 1961, DEng (hon.), 1975; MS in Indsl. Adminstrn., Purdue U., 1962, PhD in Mgmt. and Econs., 1965, D. Mgmt. (hon.), 1985; LLD (hon.), Pepperdine U., 1989; LHD (hon.), West Coast U., 1993. Dir. cost analysis Office Sec. Def., Washington, 1967-69, dep. asst. sec. def. resource analysis, 1969-70, asst. dir. Office Mgmt. and Budget, Exec. Office Pres., 1970-72; pres., CEO The Rand Corp., Calif., 1972-89; sec. USAF, 1989-93; pres., COO Teledyne, Inc., L.A., 1993—; bd. dirs. Teledyne, Inc., Vulcan Materials Co., Wells Fargo Bank, Wells Fargo & Co.; mem. Nat. Sci. Bd., 1974-86; chmn. Nat. Commn. Supplies and Shortages, 1975-77; mem. Nat. Commn. on U.S.-China Relations; mem. nat. adv. com. oceans and atmosphere Dept. Commerce, 1972-75; mem. adv. panel Office Tech. Assessment, 1976-79; adv. council Coll. Engring., U. Notre Dame, 1974-88; mem. Def. Sci. Bd., 1977-83, sr. cons., 1984-88; U.S. mem. Trilateral Commn.; dir. for sec. def. and Pres. Def. Resource Mgmt. Study, 1977-79. Author articles. Served to capt. AUS, 1965-67. Recipient Sec. Def. Meritorious Civilian Service medal, 1970, Def. Exceptional Civilian Svc. medal, 1993, Forrestal award, 1992; Ford Found. fellow, 1962-65. Fellow AAAS; mem. Council Fgn. Relations, Inst. Mgmt. Scis. (past pres.), Tau Beta Pi. Office: Teledyne Inc 2049 Century Park E 15th Fl Los Angeles CA 90067

RICE, DONALD SANDS, lawyer; b. Bronxville, N.Y., Mar. 25, 1940; s. Anton Henry and Lydia Phipps (Sands) R.; m. Edgenie Higgins, Aug. 27, 1966; children: Alice Higgins, Edgenie Reynolds. AB magna cum laude, Harvard U., 1961, LLB cum laude, 1964; LLM in Taxation, NYU, 1965. Bar: N.Y. 1964, U.S. Ct. Claims 1965, U.S. Supreme Ct. 1981. Law clk. to judge U.S. Ct. Claims, 1965-67; assoc. Barrett, Smith, Schapiro & Simon, N.Y.C., 1967-71; ptnr. Barrett, Smith, Schapiro, Simon & Armstrong, N.Y.C., 1971-86; vice chmn. bd. The Bowery Savs. Bank, N.Y.C., 1986-88; also bd. dirs. The Bowery Savs. Bank; ptnr. Chadbourne & Parke, N.Y.C., 1988—; lectr. Nat. Assn. Real Estate Investment Trusts, Bank Adminstrs. Inst., Bank Tax Inst., 1971-86; chmn., bd. dirs. Corp. of Yaddo, 1986—; co-chmn. Soviet-Am. Banking Law Working Group, 1991—; v.p., treas., bd. dirs. Soviet Bus. and Comml. Law Edn. Found., 1991—; vol. lectr. Fin. Svcs. Vol. Corps Mongolian Bank Tng. Program, 1993, Georgetown Internat. Law Inst., NYU Sch. Continuing Edn., Russian Trade Fair-U.S. Dept. Commerce, 1994; mem. real estate adv. bd. to N.Y. State Comptr., 1987-93. Bd. dirs. African Meml. Rsch. Found., 1978—; trustee Marimed Found., 1984—, Chapin Sch., 1980-91, The Hackley Sch., 1974-81, St. Philip's Episcopal Ch., Mattapoisett, Mass., 1987—; trustee Nat. Com. Am. Fgn. Policy, 1994—. Mem. ABA, Internat. Bar Assn., N.Y. State Bar Assn. (chmn. fin. instns. com. tax sect. 1984-86), Bar Assn. City of N.Y., Century Assn., Harvard Club, N.Y. Yacht Club, River Club. Home: 1120 Fifth Ave New York NY 10128-0144 Office: Chadbourne & Parke 30 Rockefeller Plz New York NY 10112-0001

RICE, DOROTHY PECHMAN (MRS. JOHN DONALD RICE), medical economist; b. Bklyn., June 11, 1922; d. Gershon and Lena (Schiff) Pechman; m. John Donald Rice, Apr. 3, 1943; children: Kenneth D., Donald B., Thomas H. Student, Bklyn. Coll., 1938-39; BA, U. Wis., 1941; DSc (hon.), Coll. Medicine and Dentistry N.J., 1979. With hosp., and med. facilities USPHS, Washington, 1960-61; med. econs. studies Social Security Adminstrn., 1962-63; health econs. br. Community Health Svc., USPHS, 1964-65; chief health ins. rsch. br. Social Security Adminstrn., 1966-72, dep. asst. commr. for rsch. and statistics, 1972-75; dir. Nat. Ctr. for Health Stats., Rockville, Md., 1976-82; prof. Inst. Health & Aging U. Calif., San Francisco, 1982-94, prof. emeritus, 1994—; developer, mgr. nationwide health info. svcs.; expert on aging, health care costs, disability, and cost-of-illness. Contbr. articles to profl. jours. Recipient Social Security Adminstrn. citation, 1968, Disting. Service medal HEW, 1974, Jack C. Massey Found. award, 1978. Fellow Am. Public Health Assn. (domestic award for excellence 1978, Sedgwick Meml. medal, 1988), Am. Statis. Assn.; mem. Inst. Medicine, Assn. Health Scvs. Rsch. (President's award 1988), Am. Econ. Assn., Population Assn. Am., LWV. Home: 13895 Campus Dr Oakland CA 94605-3831 Office: U Calif Sch Nursing Calif # N631 San Francisco CA 94143

RICE, EDWARD EARL, former government official, author; b. Saginaw, Mich., Feb. 6, 1909; s. William Edward and Katherine Marie (Meyer) R.; m. Mary June Kellogg, Oct. 26, 1942. Student, U. Wis., 1926-28; BS, U. Ill., 1930, postgrad., 1934-35; postgrad., U. Mex., 1931, Coll. Chinese Studies, also pvt. tutors, Beijing, 1935-37. Joined Fgn. Svc., Dept. State, 1935; lang. attache Beijing, 1935-37; vice consul Canton, China, 1938-40; consul Foochow, China, 1940-42; 2d sec. Am. Embassy, Chungking, China, 1942-45; asst. chief div. Chinese affairs Dept. State, 1946-48, asst. chief div. Philippine affairs, 1948-49; 1st sec., consul Am. Embassy, Manila, 1949-51; consul gen. Stuttgart, Fed. Republic Germany, 1952-56; fgn. svc. insp. Dept. State, 1956-58, dep. dir. pers., 1959, mem. plicy planning coun., 1959-61, dep. asst. sec. of state for Far Ea. affairs, 1962-63; consul gen., min. Hong Kong, 1964-67; diplomat in residence with rank of prof. U. Calif. Berkeley, 1968-69, rsch. assoc. Ctr. for Chinese Studies, 1969—; vis. prof. Marquette U., 1973; advisor U.S. del. 3d, 4th and 5th sessions Econ. Commn. for Asia Far East, 1948-49. Author: Mao's Way, 1972, Wars of the Third Kind, 1988. Recipient Gold medal for non-fiction Commonwealth Club, 1973. Mem. Beta Gamma Sigma. Home: 1819 Lagoon View Dr Belvedere Tiburon CA 94920-1807 Office: U Calif Ctr for Chinese Studies Berkeley CA 94720

RICE, EMILY JOY, retired secondary and adult educator; b. Terrell, Tex., Aug. 30, 1928; d. Martin Alexander Joy Jr. and Susan Martha (Helen) Ruth Joy; m. LeRoy Noonon Rice Jr., May 30, 1951; children: Edna Anne Rice-Padhi, Margaret Elizabeth (dec.). BS, Tex. Woman's U.; postgrad., U. Tex., Tex. A&I U. Tchr. adult bible studies First United Meth. Ch., Austin, Tex., Bellaire United Meth. Ch., Houston; instr. Austin C.C., 1982-90; tchr. Austin Ind. Sch. Dist., 1982-92, Bellaire United Meth. Ch., Houston. Vol. Meth. Hosp., Houston; mem. scholarship com. U. Tex. Mem. AAUW, Delta Kappa Gamma. Home: 5220 Weslayan # 201 Houston TX 77005

RICE, EUGENE FRANKLIN, JR., history educator; b. Lexington, Ky., Aug. 20, 1924; s. Eugene Franklin and Lula (Piper) R.; m. Charlotte Bloch, Aug. 26, 1952 (dec. Oct. 1982); children: Eugene, John, Louise. BA, Harvard U., 1947, MA, 1948, PhD, 1953; postgrad., Ecole Normale Superieure, 1951-52. Instr. Harvard U., Cambridge, Mass., 1953-55; asst. prof. Cornell U., Ithaca, N.Y., 1955-59, assoc. prof., 1959-63; prof. Cornell U., Ithaca, 1963-64; prof. Columbia U., N.Y.C., 1964-74, William R. Shepperd prof., 1974—; chmn. dept. history Columbia U., 1970-73; advisor in history Random House, Knopf, N.Y.C., 1964-90; chmn., founder seminar Columbia U. Seminar Homosexualities. Author: The Renaissance Idea of Wisdom, 1958, The Foundations of Early Modern Europe, 1970, The Epistles of Lefevre d'Etaples, 1972, St. Jerome in the Renaissance, 1985; contbr. articles to profl. jours. Staff sgt. U.S. Army, 1943-45, ETO. Guggenheim Found. fellow Inst. for Advanced Study, 1959-60, 62-63, NEH fellow, 1974-75. Mem. Am. Hist. Assn. (v.p. nomination com. 1979-84), Renaissance Soc. Am. (exec. dir. N.Y.C. chpt. 1966-88), Soc. for Reformation Rsch. Democrat. Home: 560 Riverside Dr Apt 12J New York NY 10027-3214 Office: Columbia U Dept Of History New York NY 10027

RICE, FERILL JEANE, writer, civic worker; b. Hemingford, Nebr., July 4, 1926; d. Derrick and Helen Agnes (Moffatt) Dalton; m. Otis LaVerne Rice, Mar. 7, 1946; children: LaVeria June McMichael, Larry L. Student, U. Omaha, 1961. Dir. jr. and sr. choir Congl. Ch., Tabor, Iowa, 1952-66; tchr. Fox Valley Tech. Inst., Appleton, Wis., 1970-77; activity dir. Family Heritage Nursing Home, Appleton, Wis., 1972-75; dir. activity Peabody Manor, Appleton, Wis., 1975-76. Editor: Moffatt and Related Families, 1981; asst. editor (mag.) Yester-Year, 1975-76; contbr. articles to profl jours. Chmn. edn. Am. Cancer Soc., Fremont County, 1962, 63, 64; founder Mothers Club Nishna; 1st pres. valley chpt. Demolay Boys. Mem. DAR, Internat. Carnival Glass Assn., Heart Am. Carnival Glass Assn., Nat. Cambridge Collectors, Heisey Collectors Am., Iowa Fedn. Women's Clubs (Fremont county chmn. 1964, 65, 66, 67, 7th dist. chmn. libr. svcs. 1966-67), Tabor Women's Club (pres. 1962, 63, 64), Jr. Legion Aux. (founder, 1st dir. 1951-52), Fenton Art Glass Collectors Am. (co-founder 1977, sec., editor newsletter 1976-86, editor/sec. 1988-93, pres./editor 1993—), Mayflower Soc., John Howland Soc., Ross County Ohio Geneal. Soc., Iowa Geneal. Soc., Dallas County Mo. Geneal. Soc., Imperial Collectors Am., Clay County (Ind.) Geneal. Soc., Owen County (Ind.) Geneal. Soc., Fenton Finders of Wis. (chpt. #1, pres. 1988-90). Republican. Methodist. Lodge: Order of Eastern Star (worthy matron 1959, 64), Rainbow for Girls (bd. dirs. 1964), Internat. Order Jobs Daughters (honored queen 1945). Home: 302 Pheasant Run Kaukauna WI 54130-1802 Office: Rice Enterprises & Rice & Rice 1665 Lamers Dr # 305 Little Chute WI 54140-2519

RICE, FREDERICK COLTON, environmental management consultant; b. Exeter, N.H., Aug. 8, 1938; s. Frederick Nott and Mary (Colton) R.; m. Joan Alis Lambrecht, June 25, 1962; children: Frederick Lambrecht, Janelle Alis. BS, U.S. Mil. Acad., 1960. Registered environ. assessor. Commd. 2d lt. U.S. Army, 1960, advanced through grades to maj., 1967, resigned, 1970; supr. Pacific Bell, San Bruno, Calif., 1970-71; area mgr. Sta-Power Industries, San Francisco, Phoenix and Balt., 1971-73; v.p. Getty Synthetic Fuels, Signal Hill, Calif., 1974-83; dir. land resources The Irvine Co., Newport Beach, Calif., 1983-84; pres. F. C. Rice & Co., Inc., Orange, Calif., 1984-88; nat. tech. dir. HDR Engring., Inc., Irvine, 1988-89; So. Calif. mgr. R. W. Beck and Assocs., Irvine, 1990-91; pres. F.C. Rice & Co., Laguna Hills, Calif., 1991-92; project dir. Roy F. Weston, Inc., Wilmington, Mass., 1993—. Contbr. articles to profl. jours. Mem. nat. referee com. Am. Youth Soccer Orgn., Tustin, Calif., 1978-79; admissions rep., U.S. Mil. Acad. Admissions Office, 1975-87, area coord., Orange County, Calif., 1987-92, So. Calif. coord., 1992-93. Mem. Solid Waste Assn. N.Am. (so. Calif. chpt. bd. dirs. 1989-91, chmn. landfill gas com. 1979-80, resource recovery com. 1981-83, control tech. com. 1988-89, landfill gas div. 1991-93, Profl. Achievement award 1994), Internat. Solid Waste Assn., West Point Soc. Orange County (pres. 1975-76, bd. govs. 1975-93, Duty, Honor, Country award 1987), U.S. Mil. Acad. Assn. Grads. (trustee-at-large 1992—, societies com. 1991—, chmn. mem. subcom. 1994—). Republican. Roman Catholic. Avocations: skiing, golf, backpacking. Home: 15 Heather Ln Hampton NH 03842-1118 Office: Roy F Weston Inc 187 Ballardvale St Wilmington MA 01887

RICE, H. WAYNE, food products executive; b. 1942. With R.B. Rice Co., Lee's Summit, Mo., 1965-78, pres., CEO, 1978-86; prin. H. Wayne Rice Cons., 1986-88; pres. Farmland Foods, Inc., Kansas City, Mo., 1988—. Office: Farmland Foods Inc Ste 270 10150 NW Executive Hills Blvd # 200 Kansas City MO 64153-2314

RICE, JAMES A., investment company executive; b. Somerville, N.J., Apr. 5, 1948; s. David R. and Helen (Kramer) R.; m. Susan B. Rice, Oct. 11, 1972. BA in Fin., Southwest Mo. State U., 1971; MBA in Fin., U. Ark., 1972. With Trust Co. Ga., Atlanta, 1974-77; a.v.p. Dean Witter, N.Y.C., 1977-79; v.p. Donaldson Lofkin Jennrette, N.Y.C., 1979-81; pres. Aubrey G. Lanston & Co. Inc., N.Y.C., 1981—, also bd. dirs.; mem. exec. com. primary dealer divsn. PSA, N.Y.C. Sgt. USMC, 1966-72. Office: Aubrey G Lanston & Co Inc One Chase Manhattan Plz New York NY 10005-2601

RICE, JAMES ROBERT, engineering scientist, geophysicist; b. Frederick, Md., Dec. 3, 1940; s. Donald Blessing and Mary Celia (Santangelo) R.; m. Renata Dmowska, Feb. 28, 1981; children by previous marriage: Douglas, Jonathan. B.S., Lehigh U., 1962, Sc.M., 1963, Ph.D., 1964. Postdoctoral fellow Brown U., Providence, 1964-65, asst. prof. engring., 1965-68, assoc. prof., 1968-70, prof., 1970-81, Ballou prof. theoretical and applied mechanics, 1973-81; McKay prof. engring. sci. and geophysics Harvard U., Cambridge, Mass., 1981—. Recipient awards for sci. publs. ASME, awards for sci. publs. ASTM, awards for sci. publs. U.S. Nat. Com. Rock Mechanics. Fellow ASME, AAAS; mem. NAS, NAE, ASCE, Am. Geophys. Union. Research contbns. to solid mechanics, materials sci. and geophysics. Office: Harvard U Div Applied Sci Cambridge MA 02138

RICE, JERRY LEE, professional football player; b. Starkville, Miss., Oct. 13, 1962; m. Jackie Rice; 1 child, Jaqui. Student, Miss. State Valley U. Football player San Francisco 49ers, 1985—. Named MVP, Super Bowl XXIII, 1989, Sporting News NFL Player of Yr., 1987, 90; named to Sporting News Coll. All-Am. team, 1984, Sporting News All-Pro team, 1986-92, Pro Bowl team, 1986-93. Holder NFL career records for most touchdown receptions (118), 1986; most consecutive games with one or more touchdowns (13), 1987; NFL single-season record for most touchdown receptions (22), 1987; shares NFL single-game record for most touchdown receptions (5), 1990. Office: care San Francisco 49ers 4949 Centennial Blvd Santa Clara CA 95054*

RICE, JERRY MERCER, medical research center administrator; b. Washington, Oct. 3, 1940; s. John Earle Rice and Leona (Mercer) Greiner; m. Mary Jane Janocha, Jan. 10, 1978; children: Stacey Lynn, Stephen Mark. BA, Wesleyan U., 1962; PhD, Harvard U., 1966. Commd. officer USPHS; research scientist Nat. Cancer Inst., Bethesda, Md., 1966-81; chief Lab. of Comparative Carcinogenesis, Frederick, Md., 1981-94; assoc. dir. Frederick Cancer Rsch. and Devel. Ctr., Nat. Cancer Inst., Frederick, Md., 1994—; lectr. univs., profl. groups, med. socs. Editor: Perinatal Carcinogenesis, 1979. Co-editor: Organ and Species Specificity in Chemical Carcinogenesis, 1983, Perinatal and Multigeneration Carcinogenesis, 1989; contbr. rsch. articles and revs. in mechanisms of chem. carcinogenesis to profl. jours. Mem. Am. Soc. Microbiology, Am. Chem. Soc., Am. Assn. Cancer Research, Am. Soc. Investigative Pathology, Teratology Soc., Phi Beta Kappa, Sigma Xi. Avocation: viticulture. Home: 3213 Coquelin Ter Bethesda MD 20815-4840 Office: Nat Cancer Inst Frederick Cancer R & D Ctr Frederick MD 21702

RICE, JERRY W., insurance company executive; b. 1962. With I.C.H. Corp., Louisville, Ky., 1986—; chmn. bd. Consolidated Fidelity Life Ins. Co., Louisville, Ky., 1991—. Office: Consoldted Fdelty Life Insur Co 4211 Norbourne Blvd Louisville KY 40207-4048

RICE, JOHN RISCHARD, computer scientist, researcher, educator; b. Tulsa, June 6, 1934; s. John Coykendal Kirk and Margaret Lucille (Rischard) R.; m. Nancy Ann Bradfield, Dec. 19, 1954; children: Amy Lynn, Jenna Margaret. BS, Okla. State U., 1954, MS, 1956; PhD, Calif. Inst. Tech., 1959. Postdoctoral fellow Nat. Bur. Standards, Washington, 1959-60; rsch. mathematician GM Rsch. Labs., Warren, Mich., 1960-64; prof. Purdue U., West Lafayette, Ind., 1964-89; head dept. computer sci. Purdue U., West Lafayette, 1983—, disting. prof., 1989—; editor-in-chief ACM Trans. Math. Software, N.Y.C., 1975-93; chmn. ACM-Signum, N.Y.C., 1977-79; dir. Computing Rsch. Bd., Washington, 1987-94; chair Computing Rsch. Assn., Washington, 1991-93. Author: The Approximation of Functions, 1964, Vol. 2, 1969, Numerical Methods, Software and Analysis, 1983; author and editor: Mathematical Software, 1971; editor: Intelligent Scientific Software Systems, 1991. Fellow AAAS; mem. ACM (George Forsythe Meml. lect. 1975), IFIP (working group 2.5, vice chmn. 1977-91), Soc. Indsl. and Applied Math., Nat. Acad. Engring., Phi Kappa Phi. Home: 112 E Navajo St West Lafayette IN 47906-2153 Office: Purdue U Computer Sci Dept West Lafayette IN 47907

RICE, JOHN THOMAS, architecture educator; b. New London, Conn., Feb. 4, 1931; s. Clarence Benjamin and Emily (Gudal) R. BS in Engring., U. Conn., 1952; MSME, Newark Coll. Engring., 1958; D.Sc. in Engring., Columbia U., 1962. Registered profl. engr., N.Y. Test equipment designer propeller div. Curtiss-Wright Corp., Caldwell, N.J., 1952-54; stress analyst Wright Aeronautical div. Curtiss-Wright Corp., Woodridge, N.J., 1954-59;

chief structural mechanics Gen. Dynamics/Electric Boat, Groton, Conn., 1962-64; asst. prof. mech. engring. Pratt Inst., Bklyn., 1964-66, assoc. prof., 1966-74, prof., 1974—, chmn. dept. mech. engring., 1981-90. Mem. ASME (chmn. mech. engring. dept. heads com. region II 1987-89, chmn. profl. devel. region II 1989-93, mem. exec. com. met. sect. 1990—, vice chmn. 1991-92, chmn. 1992-93, sec. region II 1993—), Pi Tau Sigma, Tau Beta Pi. Office: Pratt Inst Dept of Architecture 200 Willoughby Ave Brooklyn NY 11205-3899

RICE, JONATHAN C., educational television executive; b. St. Louis, Feb. 19, 1916; s. Charles M. and May R. (Goldman) R.; m. Kathleen Feiblman, Aug. 6, 1946 (dec. June 1964); children: Jefferson Charles, Kit (dec.), May Nanette. AB, Stanford U., 1938. War photographer, reporter Acme Newspix/NEA Svc., PTO of WWII, 1941-43; picture book editor Look Mag., N.Y.C., 1947-48; news/spl. events dir. Sta. KTLA-TV, L.A., 1948-53; program mgr. Sta. KQED-TV, San Francisco, 1953-67, dir. program ops., 1967-78, asst. to pres., 1978-90, bd. dirs., 1990—; cons. NET, PBS, Corp. for Pub. Broadcasting, Ford Found., TV Lima Peru, Sta. WGBH-TV, Boston, Sta. WNET-TV, N.Y.C., French TV, Europe Eastern Edn. TV, Dept. Justice, 1955-90; lectr. Stanford U., 1958-77. Editor: Look at America, The South, Official Picture Story of the FBI, 1947. Bd. dirs. NATAS, San Francisco, Planned Parenthood, San Francisco and Marin County, Calif. Maj. USMC, 1943-47, PTO. Recipient George Foster Peabody award, 1956, Thomas Alva Edison award for best station, N.Y.C., 1960, Gov.'s award NATAS, 1972-73, Ralph Lowell award Corp. for Pub. Broadcasting, 1972; Jonathan Rice Studio named in his honor, 1986. Avocations: rowing, bicycling, cooking, photography, travel. Home: 1 Russian Hill Pl San Francisco CA 94133-3605

RICE, JOSEPH ALBERT, banker; b. Cranford, N.J., Oct. 11, 1924; s. Louis A. and Elizabeth J. (Michael) R.; m. Katharine Wolfe, Sept. 11, 1948; children: Walter, Carol, Philip, Alan. B.Aero. Engring., Rensselaer Poly. Inst., 1948; M.Indsl. Engring., NYU, 1952, MA, 1968. With Grumman Aircraft Engring. Corp., 1948-53; with IBM, N.Y.C., mgr. ops., real estate, constrn. divs., 1963-65; dep. group exec. N.Am. comml. telecommunications group, pres. telecommunications div. ITT, N.Y.C., sr. v.p. Irving Trust Co., N.Y.C., 1967-69, exec. v.p., 1969-72, sr. exec. v.p., 1972-73, vice chmn., 1973-74, pres., from 1974, chmn., 1984-88; exec. v.p. Irving Bank Corp., 1971-74, vice chmn., 1974-75, pres., 1975-83, chmn. bd., CEO, 1984-88; bd. dirs. Avon Products, Inc., Apache Corp. Trustee John Simon Guggenheim Meml. Found., Hist. Hudson Valley, Insts. Religion and Health. Mem. Coun. Fgn. Relations, N.Y. Acad. Scis., University Club, Links, Sky Club.

RICE, JOSEPH LEE, III, lawyer; b. Bklyn., Feb. 24, 1932; s. Joseph Lee Jr. and Frances (Plunkett) R.; m. Franci Blassberg, Jan. 4, 1992; children: Kimberley, Daniel, Lee Ann. BA, Williams Coll., Williamstown, Mass., 1954; LLB, Harvard U., 1960. Assoc Sullivan & Cromwell, N.Y.C., 1960-66; v.p. Laird Inc., N.Y.C., 1966-68, McDonnell & Co., N.Y.C., 1968-69; founding ptnr. Gibbons, Green & Rice, N.Y.C., 1969-78; founder, pres. Clayton, Dubilier & Rice, Inc., N.Y.C., 1978—. Trustee Williams Coll., 1988—. Lt. USMC, 1954-57. Mem. Bronxville Field Club, Maidstone Club, The Links Club, River Club, Univ. Club. Office: Clayton Dubilier & Rice Inc 126 E 56th St New York NY 10022-3613

RICE, JOY KATHARINE, psychologist, educational policy studies and women's studies educator; b. Oak Park, Ill., Mar. 26, 1939; d. Joseph Theodore and Margaret Sophia (Bednarik) Straka; m. David Gordon Rice, Sept. 1, 1962; children: Scott Alan, Andrew David. B.F.A. with high honors, U. Ill., Urbana, 1960; M.S., U. Wis., Madison, 1962, U. Wis., Madison, 1964; Ph.D., U. Wis., Madison, 1967. Lic. clin. psychologist. USPHS predoctoral fellow dept. psychiatry Med. Sch. U. Wis.-Madison, 1964-65, asst. dir. Counseling Ctr., 1966-74, dir. Office Continuing Edn. Services, 1972-78, prof. ednl. policy studies and women's studies, 1974—; pvt. practice psychology Madison, 1967—; mem. State Wis. Ednl. Approval Bd., Madison, 1972-73; mem. Adult Edn. Commn., U.S. Office Career Edn., Washington, 1978. Author: Living Through Divorce, A Developmental Approach to Divorce Therapy, 1985, 2d edit., 1989; editl. bd. Lifelong Learning, 1979-86; cons. editor Psychology of Women Quar., 1986-89, assoc. editor, 1989-94; cons. editor: Handbook of Adult and Continuing Education, 1989; contbr. articles to profl. jours. Knapp fellow U. Wis.-Madison, 1960-62, teaching fellow, 1962-63; recipient Disting. Achievement award Ednl. Press Assn. Am., 1992. Fellow APA (exec. bd. Psychology of Women divsn. 1994—); mem. Nat. Assn. Women in Edn. (editl. bd. jour. 1984-88, cons. editor Initiatives 1988-91), Am. Ednl. Rsch. Assn., Internat. Coun. Psychologists, Am. Assn. Continuing and Adult Edn. (meritorious svc. award 1978-80, 82), Wis. Psychol. Assn., Phi Delta Kappa. Avocations: interior design, collecting art, gardening, travel. Home: 4230 Waban Hl Madison WI 53711-3711 Office: Dept Ednl Policy Studies 2727 Marshall Ct Madison WI 53705

RICE, JULIAN CASAVANT, lawyer; b. Miami, Fla., Dec. 31, 1923; s. Sylvan J. and Maybelle (Casavant) R.; m. Dorothy Mae Haynes, Feb. 14, 1958; children—Scott B., Craig M. (dec.), Julianne C., Linda D., Janette M. Student, U. San Francisco, 1941-43; JD cum laude, Gonzaga U., 1950. Bar: Wash. 1950, Alaska 1959, U.S. Tax Ct. 1988. Pvt. practice law Spokane, 1950-56, Fairbanks, Alaska, 1959—; prin. Law Office Julian C. Rice (and predecessor firms), Fairbanks, 1959; bd. dirs. Key Bank of Alaska, Anchorage; founder, gen. counsel Mt. McKinley Mut. Savs. Bank, Fairbanks, 1965—, chmn. bd., 1979-80; v.p., bd. dirs., gen. counsel Skimmers, Inc., Anchorage, 1966-67; gen. counsel Alaska Carriers Assn., Anchorage, 1970-71, Alaska Transp. Conf., 1960-67. Mayor City of Fairbanks, 1970-72. Served to maj. USNG and USAR, 1943-58. Decorated Bronze Star, Combat Infantryman's Badge. Fellow Am. Bar Found. (life); mem. ABA, Wash. Bar Assn., Alaska Bar Assn., Transp. Lawyers Assn., Spokane Exchange Club (pres. 1956). Office: Ste 102 1008 16th Ave Fairbanks AK 99701-4896 Office: PO Box 70516 Fairbanks AK 99707

RICE, LACY I., JR., lawyer; b. Martinsburg, W.Va., Dec. 29, 1931; s. Lacy Isaac and Anna (Thorn) R.; m. Linda Watkins, Mar. 2, 1957; children: Anne W., Lacy I. III, William T. BA, Princeton U., 1953; LLB, U. Va., 1956. Bar: W.Va. 1956, U.S. Dist. Ct. (no. Dist.) W.Va. 1956, U.S. Cir. Ct. Appeals (3d and 4th cirs.) 1968. Ptnr. Lacy I. Rice Sr. law firm & Rice, Hannis & Rice & successors, Martinsburg, 1956-89; sr. ptnr. Bowles, Rice, McDavid, Graff & Love, Martinsburg, 1989—; pres. Old Nat. Bank of Martinsburg, 1978, chmn. bd.; chmn., CEO One Valley Bank-East N.A.; vice chmn. One Valley Bancorp, Inc.; bd. dirs. Continental Brick Co., C&P Telephone Co., W.Va. Mem. W.Va. Bar Assn. (pres. 1984-85). Home: 600 N Tennessee Ave Martinsburg WV 25401-9281 Office: PO Drawer 1419 105 W Burke St Martinsburg WV 25401

RICE, LESTER, electronics company executive; b. Detroit, Feb. 23, 1927; s. Carvel Lester and Irene R.; m. Barbara Helen Winston, June 27, 1957; children—Scott W., Jody I., Jeffrey C., Judy A., Timohty D. B.S.E.E., U. Mich., 1951. Gen. sales mgr. Westinghouse Semicondr. Div., Youngwood, Pa., 1951-68; pres. Airco Speer Elec. div. Airco Inc., Bradford, Pa., 1968-80; vice chmn., dir. KOA Speer Electronics, Inc., Bradford, 1980—; bd. dir. DeFond No. Am. Inc., ASJPTE Ltd., Singapore; chmn. bd. Lester Rice, Inc., Bradford, 1980—. Adv. bd. U. Pitts. With USN, 1945-46. Mem. IEEE, Electronics Industries Assn. (bd. govs.), Am. Legion, Masons. Republican. Home: 2 Vista Avenue Ext Bradford PA 16701-2759 Office: PO Box 547 Bradford PA 16701-0547

RICE, LINDA JOHNSON, publishing executive; b. Chgo., Mar. 22, 1958; d. John J. and Eunice Johnson; m. Andre Rice, 1984. BA Journalism, Univ. Southern California, Los angeles, 1980; MBA, Northwestern Univ., Evanston, 1988. With Johnson Pub. Co., 1980—, past v.p. and asst. pub., 1987—, also chief oper. officer. Office: Johnson Pub Co Inc 6408 1/2 Brynhurst Ave Los Angeles CA 90043-3840

RICE, LOIS DICKSON, former computer company executive; b. Portland, Maine, Feb. 28, 1933; d. David A. and Mary D. Dickson; m. Alfred B. Fitt, Jan. 7, 1978 (dec. 1992); children: Susan, John Rice. A.B. magna cum laude, Radcliffe Coll., 1954; postgrad. (Woodrow Wilson fellow), Columbia U., 1954-55; LL.D. (hon.), Brown U., 1981, Bowdoin Coll., 1984. Dir. counseling services Nat. Scholarship Service and Fund for Negro Students, N.Y.C., 1955-59; with The Coll. Bd., N.Y.C. and Washington, 1959-81; v.p.

The Coll. Bd., Washington, 1973-81; sr. v.p. govt. affairs, bd. dirs. Control Data Corp., 1981-91; guest scholar The Brookings Inst., Washington, 1991—; bd. dirs. McGraw Hill Inc., Bell Atlantic, Washington, Hartford Steam Boiler Inspection and Ins. Co., Internat. Multifoods, Shawmut Nat. Corp., UNUM Corp.; overseer Tuck Sch. Mgmt. Dartmouth Coll., 1990-94; mem. Pres. Fgn. Intelligence adv. bd., 1993—; trustee George Washington U., 1992-94. Contbr. articles on edn. to profl. publs.; editor: Student Loans: Problems and Policy Alternatives, 1977. Mem. Gov.'s Commn. on Future of Postsecondary Edn. in N.Y. State, 1976-77; mem. Carnegie Coun. on Higher Edn., 1975-80; bd. dirs. Potomac Inst., 1977-92, German Marshall Fund, 1984-94, Joint Ctr. Polit. and Econ. Studies, 1991-94, Harry Frank Guggenheim Found., 1990—, Reading is Fundamental, 1991—; trustee Radcliffe Coll., 1969-75, Stephens Coll., Mo., 1976-78, Beauvoir Sch., Washington, 1970-76, Children's TV Workshop, 1970-73; chmn. adv. bd. to dir. NSF, 1981-89, chair 1986-89. Recipient Disting. Service award HEW, 1977. Mem. Cosmos Club, Phi Beta Kappa. Episcopalian. Home: 2332 Massachusetts Ave NW Washington DC 20008-2801 Office: The Brookings Instn 1775 Massachussetts Ave NW Washington DC 20036

RICE, MICHAEL LEWIS, business educator; b. Ann Arbor, Mich., Jan. 7, 1943; s. Edwin Stevens and Elaine (Ivey) R.; m. Eileen Lynn Barnard, July 7, 1961. BS, Fla. State U., 1971, MBA, 1972; PhD, U. N.C. 1975. Asst. prof. U. N.C., Chapel Hill, 1974-80; assoc. prof. Wake Forest U., Winston-Salem, N.C., 1980-83; prof., dean U. Alaska, Fairbanks, 1983-91, vice chancellor adminstrv. svcs., 1991—. Contbr. numerous articles on fin. topics. Pres. United Way of Tanana Valley, Fairbanks, 1986-91. Mem. Am. Mgmt. Assn., Am. Mktg. Assn., Am. Econs. Assn., Am. Assembly Collegiate Schs. Bus., Western Assn. Collegiate Schs. Bus. (sec.-treas.), Rotary (bd. officer Fairbanks 1986-92, pres. 1992-93). Avocations: flying, amateur radio. Office: U Alaska Vice Chancellor Adminstrv Svcs Fairbanks AK 99775-7900

RICE, NORMAN B., mayor; b. 1943. With govt. City of Seattle, 1978—, city councilman, 1978-89, mayor, 1990—. Office: Office of the Mayor Municipal Bldg 12th Fl 600 4th Ave Seattle WA 98104-1826

RICE, PAUL JACKSON, lawyer, educator; b. East St. Louis, Ill., July 15, 1938; s. Ray Jackson and Mary Margaret (Campbell) R.; m. Carole Jeanne Valentine, June 6, 1959; children: Rebecca Jeanne Ross, Melissa Ann Hansen, Paul Jackson Jr. BA, U. Mo., 1960, JD, 1962; LLM, Northwestern U., 1970; student, Command and Gen. Staff Coll., 1974-75, Army War Coll., 1982-83. Bar: Mo. 1962, Ill. 1969, U.S. Dist. Ct. (no. dist.) Ill. 1970, U.S. Supreme Ct. 1972, U.S. Ct. Appeals (D.C. cir.) 1991, D.C. 1993. Commd. 1st lt. U.S. Army, 1962, advanced through grades to col., 1980; asst. judge advocate 4th Armored Div., Goeppingen, Fed. Republc Germany, 1966-69; dep. staff judge advocate 1st Cavalry Div., Republic Vietnam, 1970-71; instr., prof. The Judge Adv. Gen. Sch., Charlottesville, Va., 1971-74, commdt., dean, 1985-88; br. chief Gen. Law Br., Pentagon, 1975-78; chief adminstrv. law div. Office Judge Adv. Gen., Pentagon, Washington, 1978-79; staff judge adv. 1st Inf. Div., Ft. Riley, Kans., 1979-82, V Corps U.S. Army, Frankfurt, Fed. Republic Germany, 1983-85, USACAC, Ft. Leavenworth, Kans., 1989-90; faculty Insdl. Coll. Armed Forces, 1988-89; chief counsel Nat. Hwy. Traffic Safety Adminstrn., Washington, 1990-93; with Arent Fox Kintner Plotkin & Kahn, Washington, 1993—. Contbr. articles to profl. jours. Granted Legal Svc. award State of Hessen, Weisbaden, Fed. Republic Germany, 1985, Cert. Merit U. Mo. Alumni Assn., 1987. Mem. ABA, Fed. Bar Assn. (pres. local chpt. 1986-88), Mo. Bar Assn., Ctr. For Law and Nat. Security, U. Va. Sch. Law (1985-89), Lion Tamers, Phi Delta Phi. Methodist. Avocations: writing, reading, sports. Home: 7835 Vervain Ct Springfield VA 22152-3107 Office: Arent Fox Kintner Plotnick 1050 Connecticut Ave NW Washington DC 20036-5339

RICE, RICHARD CAMPBELL, retired state official, retired army officer; b. Atchison, Kans., Dec. 11, 1933; s. Olive Campbell and Ruby Thelma (Rose) R.; m. Donna Marie Lincoln, Aug. 4, 1956; children: Robert Alden, Holly Elizabeth. BS in History, Kans. State U., 1955; MA in Social Studies, Eastern Mich. U., 1965; grad. U.S. Army Command and Gen. Staff Coll., 1968, U.S. Army War Coll., 1977, FBI Nat. Exec. Inst., 1990, grad. program for sr. execs. in state and local govt., Harvard U., 1985. Commd. 2d lt. U.S. Army, 1955; advanced through grades to col., 1976; with Joint Chiefs of Staff, Washington, 1975-76; faculty U.S. Army War Coll., Carlisle Barracks, Pa., 1977-79; chief of staff Hdqrs. 3d ROTC Region, Ft. Riley, Kans., 1982-83; ret. 1983; dir. Mo. State Emergency Mgmt. Agy., Jefferson City, 1983-85, dir. Mo. Dept. Pub. Safety, Jefferson City, 1985-93; trustee Mo. State Employees Retirement System, 1990-93; bd. visitors Nat. Emergency Mgmt. Inst., 1991-92. Grad. Leadership, Mo., 1991; mem. Coordinating Coun. Health Edn., Mo.'s Children and Adolescents., Mo. Jail and Prison Overcrowding Task Force, Gov.'s Domestic Violence Task Force, Gov.'s Conf. Health Needs Children, Gov.'s Commn. on Crime, Gov.'s Adv. Coun. on Driving While Intoxicated, Mo. Children's Svcs. Commn., Blue Ribbon Commn. on Svcs. to Youth, Campaign to Protect Our Children; mem. policy com. Mo. Youth Initiative; chmn. Gov.'s Cabinet Coun. for Justice Adminstrn., Mo. Statistical Analysis Ctr. adv. bd., adv. bd. Mo. Criminal Hist. Records; bd. dirs. Mo. Law Enforcement Meml. Found, Gt. Rivers coun. Boy Scouts Am., 1993—; peer rev. cons. Nat. Inst. of Justice; chmn. Alliance for Uniform Hazmat Transp. Procedures, 1991-93. Decorated Legion of Merit, Bronze Star (3), Meritorious Service medal (4), Air medal (2), Joint Service Commendation medal, Army Commendation medal (2); Republic of Vietnam Cross of Gallantry with Silver Star; recipient Conspicuous Svc. medal State of Mo. Mem. Nat. Eagle Scout Assn., Assn. U.S. Army, Soc. First Div., Am. Legion, VFW, Disabled Am. Vets., AMVETS, Mil. Order of World Wars, Nat. Soc., Sons Am. Revolution, The Retired Officers Assn., Nat. Criminal Justice Assn. (bd. dirs. 1987-93), Rotary (Paul Harris fellow), St. Andrews Soc., Theta Xi. Republican. Avocation: sailing.

RICE, RICHARD LEE, retired architect; b. Raleigh, N.C., May 4, 1919; s. Robert Edward Lee and Grace Lucille (Betts) R.; m. Cora Belle Stegall, Apr. 12, 1946; children—Richard Lee, Westwood Carter, David Sinclair. BS in Archtl. Engring., N.C. State U., 1941; grad., U.S. Army Command and Gen. Staff Coll., 1961. Assoc. Cooper-Shumaker, Architects, Raleigh, 1946-47; prin. Richard L. Rice, Architects, Raleigh, 1947-48; assoc. Cooper, Haskins & Rice and predecessor firm, Raleigh, 1948-52, ptnr., 1953-54; ptnr. Haskins & Rice, Architects, Raleigh, 1954-85; prin. Haskins, Rice, Savage & Pearce, Architects, 1985-91, pres., 1985-91; U.N. Design Found., 1973; pres. N.C. Archtl. Found., 1975; mem. Raleigh Arts Commn., 1978-82, Raleigh Hist. Properties Commn., 1990-92, Raleigh Hist. Dists. Commn., 1991-92. Archtl. works include renovations, Raleigh Meml. Auditorium, 1964, 78, 91 (SE Regional AIA award of merit 1964), Auditorium, 4 high schs. and 13 elem. schs., Raleigh Civic Ctr., stack addition Wilson Libr. U. N.C., Chapel Hill, 1977, Reidsville, N.C. Jr. High Sch.; assoc. architect Raleigh Radisson Hotel, 1980, One Hanover Sq. Office Bldg., 1985, Two Hannover Sq. Office Bldg., 1990, additions and renovations to Raleigh Meml. Auditorium, 1989, 3 indsl. plants, 7 bldgs., Wake Tech. C.C., 50 chs. Pres. Wake County (N.C.) Hist. Soc., 1973-74; mem. N.C. Gov.'s Com. for Facilities for Physically Handicapped, 1970-73. Served with inf. and C.E. U.S. Army, 1941-46, ETO; Col. USAR; ret. Decorated Silver Star; Legion of Merit; Bronze Star; Purple Heart. Fellow AIA (pres. N.C. chpt. 1970, Disting. Svc. award N.C. chpt. 1975); mem. Raleigh Council Architects (pres. 1950), Nat. Trust for Hist. Preservation, N.C. Symphony Soc., N.C. State Art Soc., Raleigh C. of C., Res. Officers Assn. U.S., Ret. Officers Assn. U.S. (pres. Triangle chpt. 1983), N.C. State U. Gen. Alumni Assn. (pres., chmn. bd. 1960-61, pres. Class 1941, 1986-91), Carolina Country Club, Lions, Torch Club (pres. 1982-83), Phi Eta Sigma, Phi Kappa Phi. Democrat. Baptist.

RICE, ROBERT ARNOT, school administrator; b. San Francisco, Apr. 4, 1911; s. Abraham Lincoln and Mary Eugenia (Arnot) R.; m. Frances Von Dorsten, Aug. 15, 1936 (dec. Sept. 1986); m. Esther Pauline Railton, July 11, 1989. BA, U. Calif., Berkeley, 1934, MA, 1947; postgrad., Columbia U., 1948. Various ednl. positions, 1935-61; supr. sci. math. Berkeley Unified Sch. Dist., 1961-64; adminstr. NSF Summer Insts. for Sci. Tchr., U. Calif., Berkeley, 1957-65; dir. On Target Sch., Berkeley Unified Sch. Dist., 1971-73; coord. pub. programs Lawrence Hall of Sci, 1964-70; work experience edn. coordr. Berkeley Unified Sch. Dist., 1973-75; exec. dir. Calif. Sci. Tchrs. Assn., 1964-90; dir. No. Calif.-Western Nev. Jr. Sci. and Humanities Symposium, 1962-93; cons. Berkley Unified Sch. Dist., 1964-70; bd. dirs. San Francisco Bay Area Sci. Fair, 1960—; mem. steering com. Chem. Study, 1960-75; coord. Industry Initiatives for Sci. and Math. Edn. Program, 1985-86; dir.

Industry Initiatives for Sci. and Math. Edn. Acad., 1987; mem. Internat. Sci. and Engring. Fair Coun., Sci. Svc., Inc., 1959-68; dir. 18th Internat. Sci. and Engring. Fair, San Francisco, 1967; exec. dir. San Francisco Bay Area Sci. Fair, 1954-59; resource cons. Calif. Farm Bur. Fedn.-Youth Power Conf. Asilomar, 1966; judging chair Nat. Jr. Sci. and Humanities Symposium, 1993—. Contbr. articles to profl. publs. Bd. dirs. Calif. Heart Assn., 1966-71, Alameda County Heart Assn., 1966-71; mem. Cen. Calif. Sci. Com., 1965-70; mem. rsch. com. Alameda County TB and Health Assn., 1965-69, mem. adv. com., 1965-69. Recipient Benjamin Ide Wheeler medal, 1985, San Francisco Bay Area Sci. Fair award of honor Calif. Acad. Sci., 1970, Armed Forces Chem. Assn. award for outstanding chemistry tchr. in San Francisco Bay Area, 1965; named to Berkeley H.S. Hall of Fame, 1994. Mem. NEA, Nat. Sci. Tchrs. Assn. (region VIII dir. 1955-57, Calif. state dir. 1949-56, mem. chemistry com. 1956-60, pres. 1960-61, Disting. Svc. to Sci. Edn. award 1986), No. Calif. Com. on Problem Solving in Sci., Calif. Sci. Tchrs. Assn. (pres. no. sect. 1949-50, Disting. Svc. to Sci. Teaching award 1981), Calif. Tchrs. Assn., Bay Area Curriculum Coords. (N.C. Sci. Specialists), Berkeley Kiwanis Club, Phi Delta Kappa (pres. Lambda chpt. 1963). Office: U Calif Berkeley Lawrence Hall of Sci Berkeley CA 94720-5200

RICE, ROBERT H., principal; b. Coatesville, Pa., June 14, 1937; s. Samuel W. and Iva (Simpson) R.; m. Judith Bugar, May 27, 1961; 1 child, Laura Anne. BS, West Chester U., 1959; MA, Villanova U., 1965; EdD, Temple U., 1984. Tchr. West Chester (Pa.) Sch. Dist., 1960-65, guidance counselor, 1965-68; guidance counselor Wallingford (Pa.)/Swarthmore Sch. Dist., 1968-71, prin., 1971—; site vis. U.S. Dept. Edn. Blue Ribbon Schs. Award Program, Ill., N.J., 1992-93. With U.S. Army, 1960-65. Recipient Elem. Sch. Recognition award U.S. Dept. Edn., 1989-90. Mem. Nat. Assn. Elem. Prins., Del. County Prins. Assn., Pa. Prins. Assn. Home: 914 N Hill Dr West Chester PA 19380-4319 Office: Wallingford/Swarthmore Sch Dist 20 S Providence Rd Wallingford PA 19086-6224

RICE, ROGER DOUGLAS, television executive, artist; b. Spokane, Wash., Feb. 20, 1921; s. Leland L. and Bernice B. (Metcalf) R.; m. Molly Herron, Feb. 22, 1946; children: Stephannie Lee, Roger Douglas. B.S., U. Wash., 1944. With KING Radio, Seattle, 1947-51, 53-54; sta. mgr. KTVW-TV, Seattle, Tacoma, 1954-55; gen. sales mgr. WIIC-TV, Pitts., 1955-66; gen. mgr. WIIC-TV, 1966-68; v.p., gen. mgr. Cox Broadcasting Corp. KTVU, San Francisco, Oakland, Calif., 1968-74; pres., chief exec. officer TV Bur. Advt., N.Y.C., 1974-88; also abstract artist. Chmn. U.S./Japan Cultural Exchange, 1974; mem. Japan-U.S. Friendship Commn.; bd. dirs. Advt. Council. Mem. Nat. Assn. Broadcasters (bd. dirs. TV code rev. bd. 1971-74). Clubs: Pres. Com. of 25 (v.p.), Thunderbird Country (bd. dirs., Rancho Mirage, Calif.)

RICE, RONALD JAMES, hospital administrator; b. Springfield, Mo., Feb. 5, 1944; s. Glen Elwood and Alice Jeanett (Robinson) R. BSBA, Cen. Mo. State U., 1966, MABA, 1969, Specialist, 1972. Lic. nursing home adminstr.; lic. risk mgr. Unit mgr. Bapt. Med. Ctr., Kansas City, Mo., 1970-71; dir. unit mgmt. Ind. Health Ctr., Independence, Mo., 1971-72; adminstrv. officer Meth. Hosp., Jacksonville, Fla., 1972-73, dir. personnel, 1973-74; assoc. adminstr. Humana Hosp. Orange Park (Fla.), 1974-77; adminstr. Cathedral Rehab. Hosp., Jacksonville, 1977-79, Marion County Gen. Hosp., Hamilton, Ala., 1979-80, Nassau Gen. Hosp., Fernandina Beach, Fla., 1980-85, Reception Med. Ctr., Lake Butler, Fla., 1985-91; regional adminstr. health svcs. Dept. Corrections, Gainesville, Fla., 1991—; cons. Clay Meml. Hosp., Green Cove Springs, Fla., 1976-77, Allied Health Care, Jacksonville, 1989. Mem. Polit. Action Com., Fla. Hosp. Assn., 1990, Coun. on Crime and Delinquency, Gainesville, 1990, Human Resources Com., Orlando, 1991. With U.S. Army, 1967-69. Decorated Army Commendation medal. Fellow Am. Coll. Health Care Execs.; mem. Am. acad. Med. Adminstrs., Am. Coll. Health Care Adminstrs., Am. Soc. Personnel Adminstrs., Fla. Hosp. Assn., Rotary (pres. 1984-86). Democrat. Unity Sch. Christianity. Avocations: boating, auto collecting model, antique juke box collecting, reading. Home: 1744 Horton Dr Orange Park FL 32073-2757

RICE, RONALD MAX, superintendent. Supt. Ames Community Sch. Dist., Ames, Iowa. Recipient State Finalist for Nat. Supt. of Yr. award, 1992. Office: Ames Community Sch Dist 120 S Kellogg Ave Ames IA 50010-6700

RICE, STANLEY TRAVIS, JR., poet, English language educator; b. Dallas, Nov. 7, 1942; s. Stanley Travis and Margaret Nolia (Cruse) R.; m. Anne O'Brien, Oct. 14, 1961; children: Michele (dec.), Christopher. BA, San Francisco State U., 1963, MA, 1965. Asst. prof. San Francisco State U., 1965-71, assoc. prof., 1971-76, prof. English and creative writing, 1977-88, asst. dir. Poetry Ctr., 1964-72, chmn. dept. creative writing, 1980-88, ret. Author: Some Lamb, 1975, Whiteboy, 1976 (Edgar Allen Poe award Acad. Am. Poets 1977), Body of Work, 1983, Singing Yet: New and Selected Poems, 1992, Fear Itself, 1995; one-man show of paintings Gallerie Simone Stern, New Orleans, La., 1992. Nat. Endowment Arts grantee, 1966, writing fellow, 1972; recipient Joseph Henry Jackson award San Francisco Found., 1968.

RICE, STEPHEN LANDON, engineering educator; b. Oakland, Calif., Nov. 23, 1941; s. Landon Frederick and E. Genevieve (Hunt) R.; m. Penny Louise Baum, Dec. 29, 1965; children: Andrew Landon, Katherine Grace. BS, U. Calif., Berkeley, 1964, MEngring., 1969, PhD, 1972. Registered profl. engr., Fla. Design engr. Lawrence Berkeley Lab., 1964-69; asst. prof. U. Conn., Storrs, 1972-77, assoc. prof., 1977-82, prof., 1982-83; prof., chmn. U. Central Fla., Orlando, 1983-88, assoc. dean, rsch. dir., 1988—; participant Fulbright program for adminstrs. in internat. edn., Germany, 1995; program evaluator ASME/ABET, N.Y.C., 1988-93; NASA predoctoral fellow, 1969-72; U.S. del. to Internat. Rsch. Group, Orgn. for Econ. Cmty. Devel., 1993—. Inventor impact wear apparatus, 1975. Named Outstanding Young Faculty Dow/ASEE, 1975, Eminent Engr., Tau Beta Pi, 1988; Fulbright rsch. scholar U. South Pacific, 1978-79. Fellow ASME; mem. Am. Soc. Engring. Edn., Orlando C. of C. (mem. Goals 2000 1988-92), Theta Delta Chi. Avocations: sailing, tennis. Office: U Central Fla Dean's Office 1 University Blvd Orlando FL 32816-0450

RICE, STUART ALAN, chemist, educator; b. N.Y.C., Jan. 6, 1932; s. Harry L. and Helen (Rayfield) R.; m. Marian Ruth Coopersmith, June 1, 1952; children—Barbara, Janet. B.S., Bklyn. Coll., 1952; M.A., Harvard, 1954, Ph.D., 1955. Jr. fellow Harvard, 1955-57; faculty U. Chgo., 1957—, prof. chemistry, 1960-69, Louis Block prof. phys. scis., 1969—, chmn. dept. chemistry, 1971-76, Frank P. Hixon disting. service prof., 1977—, dean phys. scis. div., 1981, dir. Inst. Study Metals, 1962-68; mem. Nat. Sci. Bd., 1980-86; nat. Phi Beta Kappa lectr., 1994-95. Author: Polyelectrolyte Solutions, 1961, Statistical Mechanics of Simple Liquids, 1965, Physical Chemistry, 1980; bd. dirs.: also numerous articles. Bull. Atomic Scientists. Guggenheim fellow 1960-61; Falk-Plautt lectr. Columbia U., 1964; Riley lectr. Notre Dame U., 1964, NSF sr. postdoctoral fellow 1965-66; USPHS spl. postdoctoral fellow U. Copenhagen,1970-71; Univ. lectr. chemistry U. Western Ont., 1970, Seaver lectr. U. Tex., Austin, 1975; Foster lectr. SUNY, Buffalo, 1976; Frank T. Gucker lectr. Ind. U., 1976; Fairchild lectr. Calif. Inst. Tech., 1979, Baker lectr. Cornell U., 1985-86, Centenary lectr. Royal Soc. Chemistry, 1986-87, Phi Beta Kappa Nat. Lectr., 1994-95. Fellow Am. Philos. Soc.; mem. Am. Chem. Soc. (award Pure Chemistry 1963, Leo Hendrik Baekeland award 1971, Peter Debye award 1985, Hildebrand award 1987), Nat. Acad. Sci., Am. Acad. Sci., Am. Phys. Soc., AAAS, Faraday Soc. (Marlowe medal 1963), N.Y. Acad. Scis. (A. Cressy Morrison prize 1955), Danish Acad. Sci. and Letters (fgn.).

RICE, SUE ANN, dean, industrial and organizational psychologist; b. Ponca City, Okla., Sept. 17, 1934; d. Alfred and Helen (Revard) R. BS in Edn., U. Okla., 1956; MA, Cath. U., 1979, PhD, 1988. Ensign USN 1956, advanced through grades to comdr., 1973; ednl. svcs. officer 9th Naval Dist., Great Lakes, Ill., 1956-58; adminstr., asst. staff, comdr. in-chief Pacific Fleet, Honolulu, 1958-61; head edn. div. Naval Air Sta., Lemoore, Calif., 1961-63; instr., acad. dir. Women Officers' Sch., Newport, R.I., 1963-66; head. tng. div. Naval Command Systems Support Activity, Washington, 1966-70; head, ops. support sec., comdr.-in-chief Lant, Norfolk, Va., 1970-74; sr. U.S. rep. NATO, subgroup 5 joint. JCS, Washington, 1974-77; ret. USN, 1977; head vocation office Archdiocese of Washington, 1977-78; con. Notre Dame Inst., Arlington, Va., 1989—, dean of students, 1990—; lectr. Cath. U. Am.,

Washington, 1983-84; bd. dirs. Villa Cortona Apostolic Ctr., Bethesda, 1984-94. Tech. reviewer Personnel Administration, 1964; editor (newsletter) Vocation News, 1978. Conoco scholarship Continental Oil Co., 1952-56; recipient Meritorious Svc. medal Pres. of U.S., 1977, rsch. grant Cath. U. Sigma Xi, 1986. Mem. Washington Acad. Scis., Cath. War Vets. (nat. dir. chmn. nat. pub. rels. com., nat. youth act subcom., combined Nat. Vets. Assn. rep.), Lay Women's Assn. (nat. pres.), Potomac Ch. Human Factors Soc. (assoc.), Kappa Delta Pi, Gamma Phi Beta. Roman Catholic. Avocations: travel, music, gardening, woodworking. Office: PO Box 1035 Falls Church VA 22041-0035

RICE, SUSAN F., zoological park executive; b. Chgo., Dec. 10, 1939. BA, St. Mary's Coll., 1961; MPA, UCLA, 1976; EdD, Pepperdine U., 1986. Pres. YWCA, Santa Monica, Calif., 1978, League of Women Voters Calif. San Francisco, 1979-81; sr. fundraising profl. administr., instr. Santa Monica (Calif.) Coll., 1978-81; dir. govtl. rels. UCLA Alumni Assn., 1981-82; dir. devel. UCLA Grad. Sch. Mgmt., 1982-89; dep. dir. mktg. and devel., dir. major gifts Spl. Olympics Internat., Washington, 1989-90; v.p. devel. Bus. Exec. Nat. Security, Washington, 1991-92; pres., CEO Greater L.A. Zoo Assn., 1992—. Co-author: Women as Donors, Women as Philanthropists, 1994. Bd. dirs. St. Mary's Coll. Alumnae Assn., Notre Dame, Ind., 1982-84, Santa Monica Coll. Assocs., 1984-94, Internat. Human Rights Law Group, 1990-92; trustee, chair pers. compensation com. L.A. Mus. Nat. History Found., 1982-89; treas. Women's Commn. Refugee Women, 1990—; vice chmn. pers. commn. Santa Monica Coll. Dist., 1985-89. Recipient Disting. Alumna award St. Mary's Coll., 1986. Mem. Nat. Soc. Fund Raising Execs. (bd. dirs. 1990—). Office: Greater Los Angeles Zoo Assn 5333 Zoo Dr Los Angeles CA 90027

RICE, T. WALKER, actor, theatre adminstrator; b. N.Y.C., June 14, 1963. Student, Union Coll., 1981-83; BFA in Theatre with honors, NYU, 1986. Profl. actor N.Y.C., 1983—; asst. co. mgr. Nat. Shakespeare Co., Inc., N.Y.C., 1991-92, tour dir., 1992—; instr. N.Y.C. Refugee Employment Project, 1992—. Actor: (stage prodns.) The Brothers Karamazov, The First Lulu, The Idiot, Much Ado About Nothing, A Dream Deferred, M & M/ Mars Industrial, 4 AM (Open All Night), Cheers, City of Steel, Moby Dick, Beyond the Horizon, The Taming of the Shrew, Macbeth, She Stoops to Conquer, Hamlet, The Tempest, (film and TV) Rotten to the Core, Bottom of the Barrel, Operation Desert Storm Windows, Hannah's Garden, Law and Order, Banned, The Mind's Eye, Polygram Industrial; author (screenplay) Winter Coat, 1993. Mem. AFTRA. Presbyterian. Avocations: reading, rock climbing, bicycling, juggling, guitar. Office: Nat Shakespeare Co 414 W 51st St New York NY 10019-6503

RICE, THOMAS JAMES, III, health care executive, hospital administrator; b. Richmond, Va., Mar. 1, 1952; s. Thomas James, Jr. and Betty Larus (Morrissette) R.; m. Linda Kay Beaver, May 29, 1976; children: Kathryn Anne, Thomas Johnathan, Michael Benjamin. B.A. in English, Coll. William and Mary, 1974, M.B.A., 1976; M.H.A., Med. Coll. Va., 1978. Sales interpreter Colonial Williamsburg Found., Va., 1972-77; evening supr. Petersburg Gen. Hosp., Va., 1977-78; v.p. Health East, Inc., Roanoke, Va., 1978—; asst. adminstr. Wythe County Community Hosp., Wytheville, Va., 1978-79; adminstr. Lonesome Pine Hosp., Big Stone Gap, Va., 1979-85, Southside Community Hosp., Farmville, Va., 1985-90; sr. v.p. operations, Holston Valley Hosp. and Med. Ctr., 1991; bd. dirs. Lions Club; Mountain Region Speech & Hearing, pres. 1994-95; mem. Am. Hosp. Assn, Tenn. Hosp. Assn. Avocations: sailing, golf, photography, skiing. Home: 105 Cannongate Rd Kingsport TN 37660-7219 Office: Holston Valley Hosp & Med Ct PO Box 238 Kingsport TN 37662-0238

RICE, SIR TIMOTHY MILES BINDON, lyricist; b. Amersham, Eng., Nov. 10, 1944; s. Hugh Gordon and Joan Odette (Bawden) R.; m. Jane McIntosh, Aug. 19, 1974; children: Eva Jane Florence, Donald Alexander Hugh. Student, Lancing Coll., Sussex, 1958-62. Solicitor's articled clk. Pettit & Westlake, London, 1963-66; mgmt. trainee E.M.I. Records Manchester Sq., London, 1966-68; record prodr. Norrie Paramor Orgn., London, 1968-69; ind. writer, record producer London, 1969—; broadcaster BBC Radio and TV, Ind. TV, U.K., 1973—; founder, dir. GRRR Books, 1978—, Pavilion Books, 1981—. Host: (TV) Friday Night Saturday Morning, Musical Triangles, Disco; lyricist for Marvin Hamlisch, Rick Wakeman, Vangelis, Paul McCartney, Mike Batt, Francis Lai, John Barry, Freddie Mercury, Richard Kerr, Graham Gouldman; lyricist for stage musicals: (with music by Andrew Lloyd Weber) Joseph and the Amazing Technicolor Dreamcoat, 1968, rev. 1973 (Tony award nominations best book of musical and best original cast 1982, Grammy award nomination best cast show album 1982), Jesus Christ Superstar, 1970 (Grammy award nomination album of the year 1971, Tony award nomination best original score 1972), Evita, 1976, rev. 1978 (Tony awards best book of musical and best original score 1980, Grammy award best cast show album 1980), Cricket, 1986, (with music by Stephen Oliver) Blondel, 1983, (with music by Benny Andersson and Björn Ulvaeus) Chess, 1984, rev. 1986, (with music by Michel Berger) Tycoon, 1992, (with music by Alan Menken) Beauty and the Beast, 1994; lyricist for film musicals: (with music by Menken) Aladdin, 1992, (with music by Elton John) The Lion King, 1994; lyricist for songs: (from Aladdin, with Menken) A Whole New World, 1992 (Academy award best original song 1992, Grammy award song of the year 1993), (from The Lion King, with John) Can You Feel the Love Tonight, 1994 (Academy award best original song 1994), Circle of Life, 1994 (Academy award nomination best original song 1994), Hakuna Matata, 1994 (Academy award nomination best original song 1994); prodr.: (stage musical) Anything Goes, 1989; author: Heartaches Cricketers' Almanack (yearly), 1975—, (with others) The Guiness Book of British Hit Singles, 1977, The Guiness Book of Hits of the Seventies, 1980, Treasures of Lord's, 1989; editor: Lord Taverners Sticky Wicket Book, 1980. chmn. Stars Orgn. for Spastics, 1983-85, Shaftesbury Ave. Centenary Com., 1984-86, Found. for Sport and the Arts, 1991—; pres. Lord's Taverners, 1988-90. Recipient 10 Ivor Novello awards. Mem. Marylebone Cricket Club, Heartaches Cricket Club, Garrick, Saints and Sinners Club. Address: 31 The Terrace, London SW13 ONR, England*

RICE, VICTOR ALBERT, global industrial company executive; b. Hitchin, Hertfordshire, Eng., Mar. 7, 1941. With Ford Motor Co., U.K., 1957-64, Cummins Engines, U.K., 1964-67, Chrysler Corp., U.K., 1968-70; comptroller N. European ops. Perkins Engines Group Ltd., Peterborough, U.K., subsequently Group's dir. fin., Group dir. sales, and dep. mng. dir. ops., 1970-75; comptroller world-wide Varity Corp. (formerly Massey-Ferguson Ltd.) Toronto, Ont., Can., 1975-77; v.p. staff ops. Varity Corp., Toronto, Ont., Can., 1977-78, pres., chief operating officer, 1978-80; chmn., chief exec. officer Varity Corp., Buffalo, N.Y., 1980—, also bd. dirs. Mem. Chief Execs. Orgns., World Pres. Orgns., Toronto Club, Toronto Golf Club, Country Club of Buffalo, Buffalo Club. Office: Varity Corp 672 Delaware Ave Buffalo NY 14209-2202

RICE, WALTER HERBERT, federal judge; b. Pitts., May 27, 1937; s. Harry D. and Elizabeth L. (Braemer) R.; m. Bonnie Rice; children: Michael, Hilary, Harry, Courtney Elizabeth. BA, Northwestern U., 1958; JD, MBA, Columbia U., 1962; LLD (hon.), U. Dayton, 1991. Bar: Ohio 1963. Asst. county prosecutor Montgomery County, Ohio, 1964-66; assoc. Gallon & Miller, Dayton, Ohio, 1966-69; 1st asst. Montgomery County Prosecutor's Office, 1969; judge Dayton Mcpl. Ct., 1970-71, Montgomery County Ct. Common Pleas, 1971-80, U.S. Dist. Ct. (so. dist.) Ohio, 1980—; adj. prof. U. Dayton Law Sch., 1976—; bd. visitors, 1976—; chmn. Montgomery County Supervisory Council on Crime and Deliquency, 1972-74; vice chmn. bd. dirs. Pretrial Release, Inc., 1975-79. Author papers in field. Pres. Dayton Area Coun. on Alcoholism and Drug Abuse, 1971-73; chmn. bd. trustees Stillwater Health Ctr., Dayton, 1976-79, Family Svc. Assn. Dayton, 1978-80; chmn. RTA in 2000 Com., 2003 Com. Designed To Bring Nat. Park to Dayton To Honor Wright Bros. and Birth of Aviation; chmn. Martin Luther King Jr. Meml. Com.; trustee Montgomery County Vol. Lawyers Project, Miami Valley Cultural Alliance, Sinclair Community Coll. Found., U.S. Air & Trade Show, Barbara Jordan Com. Racial Justice. Recipient Excellent Jud. Service award Ohio Supreme Ct., 1976, 77, Outstanding Jud. Service award, 1973, 74, 76, Man of Yr. award Disting. Service Awards Council, Dayton, 1977, Outstanding Jurist in Ohio award Ohio Acad. Trial Lawyers, 1986, Pub. Ofcl. of Yr. award Ohio region of Nat. Assn. Social Workers, 1992, Humanitarian award NCCJ, 1993. Mem. Dayton Bar Assn.

RICE, WILLIAM EDWARD, newspaper columnist; b. Albany, N.Y., July 26, 1938; s. Harry Edward, Jr. and Elizabeth (Lally) R.; m. Carol Timmon, June 3, 1978 (div.); m. Jill Van Cleave, Aug. 20, 1983. BA in History, U. Va., 1960; MS with honors, Columbia U., 1963. Reporter, editorial writer, critic Washington Post, 1963-69; student LeCordon Bleu, Paris, 1969-70; dir. L'Ecole de Cuisine, Bethesda, Md., 1971-72; freelance writer, restaurant critic Washingtonian Mag., 1971-72; exec. food editor Washington Post, 1972-80; editor-in-chief Food and Wine Mag., N.Y.C., 1980-85; food and wine columnist Chgo. Tribune, 1986—; Dining In columnist Gentlemen's Quarterly, 1987-89; chmn. restaurant awards com. James Beard Found., 1993—. Author: Feasts of Wine and Food, 1986; editor: (with others) Where to Eat in America, 1978, 2d edit., 1980, 3d edit., 1987. Served with USN, 1960-62. Recipient Vesta award as outstanding newspaper food editor, 1979, Ordre du Merite Agricole (France), 1983. Home: 3000 N Sheridan Rd Chicago IL 60657-5553 Office: Chgo Tribune Co Po Box 25340 435 N Michigan Ave Chicago IL 60611-4001

RICE, WILLIAM PHIPPS, investment counselor; b. Bronxville, N.Y., Mar. 27, 1944; s. Anton Henry Jr. and Lydia Phipps (Sands) R.; m. Lynn Lucas Rice, May 21, 1972; children: William Phipps Jr., Paige Sands Rice. BA cum laude, Kenyon Coll., 1966. Analyst Spencer Trask & Co., N.Y.C., 1960-67; v.p., portfolio mgr. Endowment Mgmt. and Rsch. Corp., Boston, 1969-77, Ft. Hill Investors Mgmt. Corp., Boston, 1977-83; pres., founder Anchor Capital Advisors Inc., Boston, 1983—, Anchor/Russell Capital Advisors, Boston, 1989—. Pres., trustee Mass. Bible Soc., Boston, 1985-89; trustee of donations Episcopal Ch. Diocese of Mass., Boston, 1989—. With U.S. Army, 1967-69. Mem. Assn. for Investment Mgmt. and Rsch., Assn. Investment Mgmt. Sales Execs., Boston Security Analysts Soc., Boston C. of C. Avocations: skiing, boating, woodworking. Home: PO Box 1599 Duxbury MA 02331-9999 Office: Anchor Capital Advisors Inc 1 Post Office Sq Boston MA 02109

RICER, N. DEAN, park superintendent; b. Stewartsville, Ohio, Nov. 1, 1936; s. Newell D. and Cleo (Dean) R.; m. Will Anne Moeller, Oct. 29, 1956; children: Karen, Wendy. BS in Floriculture, Tex. A&M U., 1965. Supt. grounds C.W. Murchison Jr., Dallas, 1965-68, U. Mont., Missoula, 1968-72; park supt. Living Desert Zool. and Bot. State Park, Carlsbad, N.Mex., 1972—. Mem. Riverfront Devel. Com., Carlsbad, 1987; field coordinator N.Mex. State Police Search and Rescue Plan, Carlsbad, 1980—. Mem. Am. Assn. of Bot. Gardens and Arboreta, Carlsbad Caverns Nat. History Assn. (bd. dirs. 1975-86, Service award 1986), Carlsbad C. of C. (hon. bd. dirs. 1978—), Masons. Avocations: hiking, photography, gardening. Home: 1506 Monroe St Carlsbad NM 88220-4141 Office: Living Desert State Park Skyline Dr Carlsbad NM 88220

RICH, ADRIENNE, writer; b. Balt., May 16, 1929; d. Arnold Rice and Helen Elizabeth (Jones) R.; m. Alfred H. Conrad (dec. 1970); children: David, Paul, Jacob. AB, Radcliffe Coll., 1951; LittD (hon.), Wheaton Coll., 1967, Smith Coll., 1979, Brandeis U., 1987, Coll. Wooster, Ohio, 1988, CCNY, Harvard U., 1990, Swarthmore Coll., 1992. Tchr. workshop YM-WHA Poetry Ctr., N.Y.C., 1966-67; vis. lectr. Swarthmore Coll., 1967-69; adj. prof. writing divsn. Columbia U., 1967-69; lectr. CCNY, 1968-70, instr., 1970-71, asst. prof. English, 1971-72, 74-75; Fannie Hurst vis. prof. creative lit. Brandeis U., 1972-73; prof. English Douglass Coll., Rutgers U., 1976-79; Clark lectr., disting. vis. prof. Scripps Coll., 1983-84; A.D. White prof.-at-large Cornell U., 1981-87; disting. vis. prof. San Jose State U., 1984-85; prof. English and feminist studies Stanford U., 1986-93; Marjorie Kovler vis. lectr. U. Chgo., 1989. Author: A Change of World, 1951, The Diamond Cutters and Other Poems, 1955, Snapshots of a Daughter-in-Law, 1963, Necessities of Life: Poems, 1962-65, 1966, Leaflets, Poems, 1965-68, Necessities of Life: Poems, 1965-68, 1969, The Will to Change, 1971, Diving into the Wreck, 1973, Poems Selected and New, 1950-74, 1975, Of Woman Born: Motherhood as Experience and Institution, 1976, 10th anniversary ed., 1986, The Dream of a Common Language: Poems, 1974-1977, 1978, others. Mem. nat. adv. bd. Bridges, Boston Women's Fund, Sisterhood in Support of Sisters in South Africa. Recipient Yales Series of Young Poets award, 1951, Ridgely Torrence Meml. award Poetry Soc. Am., 1955, Nat. Inst. Arts and Letters award poetry, 1961, Bess Hokin prize Poetry mag., 1963, Eunice Tietjens Meml. prize, 1968, Shelley Meml. award, 1971, Nat. Book award, 1974, Fund for Human Dignity award Nat. Gay Task Force, 1981, Ruth Lylly Poetry prize, 1986, Brandeis U. Creative Arts medal for Poetry, 1987, Nat. Poetry Assn. award, 1989, Elmer Holmes Bobst award arts and letters NYU, 1989, others. Mem. PEN, Am. Acad. Arts and Letters (dept. of lit. 1990—), Nat. Writers Union, The Authors Guild, Am. Acad. Arts and Scis. Office: care W W Norton Co 500 Fifth Ave New York NY 10110-0002

RICH, ALAN, music critic, editor, author; b. Boston, June 17, 1924; s. Edward and Helen (Hirshberg) R. A.B., Harvard, 1945; M.A., U. Calif-Berkeley, 1952. Alfred Hertz Meml. Traveling fellow in music Vienna, Austria, 1952-53; Asst. music critic Boston Herald, 1944-45, N.Y. Sun, 1947-48; contbr. Am. Record Guide, 1947-61, Saturday Rev., 1952-53, Mus. Am., 1955-61, Mus. Quar., 1957-58; tchr. music U. Calif. at Berkeley, 1950-58; program and music dir. Pacifica Found., FM radio, 1953-61; asst. music critic N.Y. Times, 1961-63; chief music critic, editor N.Y. Herald Tribune, 1963-66; music critic, editor N.Y. World Jour. Tribune, 1966-67; contbg. editor Time mag., 1967-68; music and drama critic, arts editor N.Y. mag., 1968-81, contbg. editor, 1981-83; music critic, arts editor Calif. (formerly New West mag.), 1979-83, contbg. editor, 1983-85; gen. editor Newsweek mag., N.Y.C., 1983-87; music critic L.A. Herald Examiner, 1987-89, L.A. Daily News, 1989-92, L.A. Weekly, 1992—; tchr. New Sch. for Social Rsch., 1972-75, 77-79, U. So. Calif. Sch. Journalism, 1980-82, Calif. Inst. Art, 1982-94, UCLA, 1990-91; artist-in-residence Davis Ctr. for Performing Arts CUNY, 1975-76. Author: Careers and Opportunities in Music, 1964, Music: Mirror of the Arts, 1969, Listeners Guides to Classical Music, Opera, Jazz, 3 vols., 1980, The Lincoln Center Story, 1984, Play-by-Play: Bach, Mozart, Beethoven, Tchaikovsky, 4 vols., 1995, American Pioneers, 1995; author interactive CD-ROM computer programs: Schubert's Trout Quintet, 1991, So I've Heard: Bach and Before, 1992, So I've Heard: The Classical Ideal, 1993, So I've Heard: Beethoven and Beyond, 1993; contbr. articles to entertainment mags. Recipient Deems Taylor award ASCAP, 1970, 73, 74. Mem. Music Critics Circle N.Y. (sec. 1961-63, chmn. 1963-64), N.Y. Drama Critics Circle, Am. Theatre Critics Assn., Music Critics Assn., PEN. Home: 2925 Greenfield Ave Los Angeles CA 90064-4019

RICH, ALEXANDER, molecular biologist, educator; b. Hartford, Conn., Nov. 15, 1924; s. Max and Bella (Shub) R.; m. Jane Erving King, July 5, 1952; children: Benjamin, Josiah, Rebecca, Jessica. A.B. magna cum laude in Biochem. Scis, Harvard U., 1947, M.D. cum laude, 1949; Dr. (hon.), Fed. U. Rio de Janeiro, 1981; PhD honoris causa, Weizmann Inst. Sci., Rehovot, Israel, 1992; DSc (hon.), Eidgenössische Technische Hochschule, Zurich, Switzerland, 1993. Research fellow Gates and Crellin Labs., Calif. Inst. Tech., Pasadena, 1949-54; chief sect. phys. chemistry NIMH, Bethesda, Md., 1954-58; vis. scientist Cavendish Lab., Cambridge (Eng.) U., 1955-56; asso. prof. biophysics MIT, Cambridge, 1958-61; prof. biophysics MIT, 1961—, William Thompson Sedgwick prof. biophysics, 1974—; Fairchild disting. scholar Calif. Inst. Tech., Pasadena, 1976; mem. AAAS (coun. mem. 1967-71), Biophysical Soc (coun. mem. 1960-69), com. career devel. awards NIH, 1964-67, mem. postdoctoral fellowship bd., 1955-58; mem. com. exobiology space sci. bd. NAS, 1964-65; mem. U.S. nat. com. Internat. Orgn. Pure Applied Biophysics, 1965-67; mem. vis. com. dept. biology Weizmann Inst. Sci., 1965-66, co-chmn. sci. and adv. com. 1987-91; mem. vis. com. biology dept. Yale U.1963; mem. life scis. com. NASA, 1970-75, mem. lunar planetary missions bd., 1968-70; mem. biology team Viking Mars Mission, 1969-80; mem. corp. Marine Biol. Lab., Woods Hole, Mass., 1955-67, 87—; mem. sci. rev. com. Howard Hughes Med. Inst., Miami, Fla., 1978-90; mem. vis. com. biology div. Oak Ridge Nat. Lab., 1972-76; chmn. com. on USSR and Ea. Europe Exch. Bd. NAS, 1973-76; mem. Internat. Rsch. and Exchs. Bd. Am. Coun. Learned Socs., N.Y.C., 1973-76, mem. panel judges N.Y. Acad. Sci. ann. book award for children's scis. books, N.Y.C.,1973-90; chmn. nominating com. Am. Acad. Arts and Sci., 1974-77, adv. bd., acad. forum NAS, 1975-82; mem. sci. adv. bd. Stanford Synchrotron Radiation Project, 1976-80, Mass. Gen. Hosp., Boston, 1978-83; mem. U.S. Nat. Sci. Bd., 1976-82; mem. bd. govs. Weizmann Inst. Sci., 1976—; mem. research com. Med. Found., Boston, 1976-80; mem. U.S.-USSR Joint Commn. on Sci. and Tech., Dept. State, Washington, 1977-82; sci. coms. Office of Sci. and Tech. Policy, Exec. Office of Pres., Washington, 1977-81; mem. council Pugwash Confs. on Sci. and World Affairs, Geneva, 1977-82; chmn. basic research com. Nat. Sci.

Bd., Washington, 1978-82; mem. U.S. Nat. Com. for Internat. Union for Pure and Applied Biophysics, NAS, 1979-83; mem. nominating com. NAS, 1980; bd. dirs. Med. Found., Boston, 1981-90; mem. vis. com. for Div. Med. Sci., Harvard U., 1981-87; mem. exec. com. of council, 1985-88, mem. govt.-univ.-industry research round table, 1984-87; chmn. sci. adv. com. dept. molecular biology Mass. Gen. Hosp., Boston, 1983-87; mem. governing bd. NRC, 1985-88; mem. nat. adv. com. Pew Scholars program Pew Meml. Trust, 1986-88; mem. com. on USSR and Eastern Europe Nat. Research Council, Washington, 1986—; mem. external adv. com. Ctr. for Human Genome Studies, Los Alamos Nat. Lab., N.Mex., 1989—, Nat. Critical Techs. Panel, Office of Sci. & Tech. Policy, Exec. Office of Pres., Washington, 1990-91; mem. vis. com. NASA Ctr. Exobiology, La Jolla, Calif., 1992—; fgn. mem. Russian Acad. Scis., Moscow, 1994—; vis. prof. Collège de France, Paris, 1987. Editor: (with Norman Davidson) Structural Chemistry and Molecular Biology, 1968;mem. editorial bd. Biophys. Jour., 1961-63, Currents Modern Biology, 1966-72, Science, 1963-69, Analytical Biochemistry, 1969-81, Bio-Systems, 1973-86, Molecular Biology Reports, 1974-85, Procs. NAS, 1973-78, Jour. Molecular and Applied Genetics, 1980-84, DNA, 1981-89, EMBO Jour., 1988-90, Jour. Biotech., 1987—, Genomics, 1987—, Proteins, Structure, Function and Genetics, 1986-91, Jour. Molecular Evolution, 1983—; Springer Series on Molecular Biology, 1980-88; editorial advisory bd. Jour. Molecular Biology, 1959-66, Accounts of Chemical Research, 1980-82, Jour. Biomolecular Strucure and Dynamics, 1983—, PAABS Revista, 1972-77, Biopolymers, 1963-74; contbr. articles to profl. jours. Served with USN, 1943-46. Recipient Skylab Achievement award NASA, 1974, Theodore von Karmin award Viking Mars Mission, 1976, Presidential award N.Y. Acad. Scis., 1977, Jabotinsky medal Jabotinsky Found., 1980, James R. Killian Faculty Achievement award MIT, 1980, Lewis S. Rosenstiel award in basic biomed. research Brandeis U., 1983; NRC fellow, 1949-51; Guggenheim Found. fellow, 1963; mem. Pontifical Acad. Scis. The Vatican, 1978. Fellow Am. Acad. Arts and Scis., AAAS; mem. NAS (chmn. biotech. program, com. on scholarly communication with the Peoples Republic China 1986—, exec. com. 1985—, com. on sci. communication and nat. security 1982—), Am. Chem. Soc. (exec. com. divsn. Biol. Chemistry 1962), Biophys. Soc. (council 1960-69), Am. Soc. Biol. Chemists, Am. Crystallographic Soc., Internat. Soc. for Study of Origin of Life, French Acad. Scis. (fgn. mem.), European Molecular Biology Orgn. (assoc.), Japanese Biochem. Soc. (hon. mem.), Physicians for Social Responsibility (nat. adv. bd. 1983—), Am. Philos. Soc., Inst. of medicine (sr. mem. 1990), Phi Beta Kappa, Alpha Omega Alpha. Office: MIT Dept Biology 77 Massachusetts Ave Rm 68-233 Cambridge MA 02139-4307

RICH, ARTHUR LOWNDES, music educator; b. Woodcliff, N.J., May 7, 1905; s. Frank Joseph and Ruth (Lowndes) R.; m. Helen Wall, July 26, 1934; children: Arthur Lowndes, Ruth Anne. A.B., Rutgers U., 1926; A.M., Columbia U., 1928; Ph.D., NYU, 1940; diploma, Julliard Sch. Music, 1928; licentiate, Royal Schs. Music (Royal Acad. Music, Royal Coll. of Music), London, 1939; spl. study, Harvard, 1943, Christiansen Choral Sch., 1948, 52. Prof. music Catawba Coll., Salisbury, N.C., 1928-43; dir. music Belhaven Coll., Jackson, Miss., 1943-44, Mercer U., Macon, Ga., 1944—; Roberts prof. music Mercer U., 1945-74, prof. emeritus, dir. concert series and cultural affairs, 1974—; Choral condr., adjudicator, Ga. and S.E.; music critic Macon News; corr. Mus. Am.; pres. Tudor Apts., Biscayne Apts., Inc. Author: Lowell Mason, the Father of Singing Among the Children, 1945; Contbr. articles to ednl., music jours., reference books. Bd. dirs. Macon Arts Council, Middle Ga. Symphony Orch. Life hon. mem. Community Concert Assn. (dir.); mem. Mark Twain Soc. (hon.), Am. Assn. Coll. and Univ. Concert Mgrs., Nat. Assn. Schs. Music, Phi Mu Alpha Sinfonia Soc., Macon Morning Music Club (hon.), Macon Federated Music Club (hon.). Lodge: Rotary. Home: 369 Candler Dr Macon GA 31204-2450

RICH, BEN ARTHUR, lawyer, university official; b. Springfield, Ill., Mar. 27, 1947; s. Ben Morris and Betty Lorraine (Ingalls) R.; m. Caroline Rose Castle, Oct. 4, 1984 (div. Nov. 1988). Student, U. St. Andrews, Scotland, 1967-68; BA, DePauw U., 1969; JD, Washington U., 1973; postgrad., U. Colo. Bar: Ill. 1973, N.C. 1975, Colo. 1984. Rsch. assoc. U. Coll. Law, Urbana, 1973-74; staff atty. Nat. Assn. Attys. Gen., Raleigh, N.C., 1974-76; prin. Hollowell, Silverstein, Rich & Brady, Raleigh, 1976-80; dep. commr. N.C. Indsl. Commn., Raleigh, 1980-81; counsel N.C. Meml. Hosp., Chapel Hill, 1981-84; assoc. univ. counsel U. Colo. Health Scis. Ctr., Denver, 1984-86; gen. counsel U. Colo., Boulder, 1986-89, spl. counsel to the regents, 1989-90; asst. prof. attendent U. Colo. Sch. Med., 1986-91, asst. clin. prof. 1992—, adj. instr. Sch. Law, 1988—, vis. assoc. prof., 1990-91, lectr. U. Denver Coll. Law. Contbr. articles to jours., chpt. to book. Mem. Am. Coll. Legal Medicine (assoc.,-in-law 1987—), Am. Soc. Law, Am. Philos. Assn., Soc. for Health and Human Values, Medicine and Ethics (health law tchrs. sect.), Toastmaster Internat. (pres. Raleigh chpt. 1978). Unitarian. Avocations: sailing, jogging, tennis. Home: 222 S Elm St Denver CO 80222-1133 Office: U Colo Dept Philosophy Box 232 Boulder CO 80309

RICH, BEN ROBERT, aerospace executive, aero-thermodynamicist; b. Manila, Philippines, June 18, 1925; came to U.S., 1941; s. Isadore and Annie (Kupfermann) R.; m. Faye Mayer, June 25, 1950 (dec. Aug. 1980); m. Hilda Herman, July 1, 1982; children: Michael D., Karen Rich Erbeck. B.S., U. Calif.-Berkeley, 1949; M.S., UCLA, 1950; Advanced Mgmt. Program, Harvard U., 1968. Teaching assoc. UCLA, 1949-50; engr. Electro Film, North Hollywood, Calif., 1950; program mgr. advanced devel. projects Lockheed Calif. Co., Burbank, 1965-69, chief engr. advanced design, 1969, chief preliminary design, 1969-71, v.p. advanced design, 1972-75, v.p., gen. mgr. advanced devel. projects, 1975-84; pres. Lockheed Advanced Aeros. Co., Burbank, 1984-91, sr. cons., 1991—; lectr. Wright Bros. AIAA, Royal Aero. Soc., 1988; bd. dirs Raycomm Transworld Industries, Inc. Recipient Peter Recchia Omni Meml. award 1981, Aviation Week & Space Tech's. Aero/Propulsion Laurel award, 1988, Silver Knight award Nat. Mgmt. Assn., 1989; named Engr. of Yr. San Francisco Engring. Soc., 1981, Alumnus of Yr. UCLA, 1982. Fellow AIAA (Orgn's. Nat. Aircraft Design award 1972, Sylvanus A. Reed Aeronautics award 1994), Inst. for the Advancement Engring., Nat. Acad. Engring., Inst. Aero. Scis., Tau Beta Pi. Office: Lockheed Advanced Devel Co 1011 Lockheed Way Palmdale CA 93599-0001 also: Lockheed Corp 4500 Park Granada Woodland Hls CA 91399*

RICH, BRUCE MILLER, lawyer, environmental foundation executive; b. Buffalo, Feb. 21, 1947; s. Paul John Jr. and Doris Deanne (Miller) R. Student, U. Munich, 1967-68; BA cum laude, Yale U., 1970; student, Ecole Pratique Hautes Etudes, Paris, 1975-76; JD, U. Pa., 1981. Bar: D.C. 1982. Atty. Natural Resources Def. Coun., Washington, 1981-85; sr. atty., dir. internat. program Environ. Def. Fund, Washington, 1985—; cons. U.S. Agy. for Internat. Devel., Brazzaville, Congo; cons. Office Environ. Affairs, World Bank; cons. internat. fin. instns. and pesticide use World Resources Inst.; cons. Mediterranean Action Plan, UN Environ. Program, Tunesia, France; cons. U.S. Congress Office of Tech. Assessment; cons. devel. and resources mgmt. Union Conservation of Nature and Natural Resources, Belize, Cen. Am.; cons. conservation and devel. World Wildlife Fund, U.S., Chiapas, Mex. Author: Mortgaging the Earth, 1994; contbr. numerous articles on environment and devel. to profl. jours. including World Policy Jour., The Nations, New Internationalist, The Ecologist. Recipient Global 500 award UN Environment Program, 1988, World Hunger Media award, 1988. Mem. D.C. Bar Assn. Avocations: reading, traveling, hiking. Home: 1909 New Hampshire Ave NW Washington DC 20009 Office: Environment Def Fund Ste B-1 1875 Connecticut Ave NW Washington DC 20009

RICH, CHARLES ALLAN, singer; b. Forrest City, Ark., Dec. 14, 1932; s. Wallace Neville and Helen Margaret (West) R.; m. Margaret Ann Greene, May 25, 1952; children: Renee Annette Rich Bennett, Charles Allan, Laurie, Rich Lee, Jack Michael. Student, U. Ark. Farmer nr. West Memphis, Ark. Appeared in piano bars and clubs, Memphis; session musician, Sun Records, rec. artist, Epic Records; recs. include Behind Closed Doors, 1973 (Gold record), The Most Beautiful Girl (Platinum record). Recipient Grammy award as best country male vocalist 1973, named Male Vocalist of Yr., Country Music Assn. 1973, Entertainer of Yr. 1974, Favorite Country Male Vocalist 1974, Pop Single Male Vocalist, Billboard mag. 1974), Boss Man, Classic Rich, Nobody But You, Silver Linings, American Originals, 1989, Midnight Blue, Pictures and Paintings, 1992, The Complete Smash Sessions, 1992, Unchained Melody, 1992; profile in Smithsonian Inst., 1992. Office: Charlie Rich Enterprises Inc #460 6584 Poplar Memphis TN 38138*

RICH, DANIEL HULBERT, chemist; b. Fairmont, Minn., Dec. 12, 1942; married, 1964; 2 children. BS, U. Minn., 1964; PhD in Organic Chemistry, Cornell U., 1968. Rsch. assoc. organic chemist Cornell U., 1968; rsch. chemist Dow Chem. Co., 1968-69; rsch. assoc., organic chemist Stanford U., 1969-70; asst. prof. pharm. chemistry U. Wis., Madison, 1970-75, assoc. prof., 1975-81, prof. dept. medical chemistry, 1981—, prof. dept. organic chemistry, 1988—, Ralph F. Hirschmann prof. medicinal and organic chemistry, 1994—; cons. biorganic natural product study sect., NIH, 1980—, mem., 1981—. Recipient H.I. Romnes award, 1980, Vincent du Vigneaud award, 1990, Hitchings award for innovative methods in drug design, 1992, Alexander von Humboldt award, 1993; fellow NIH, 1968. Fellow AAAS, Am. Chem. Soc. (Ralph F. Hirschmann award in Peptide Chemistry 1993, Divsn. Medicinal Chemistry award 1991), Am. Assn. Pharm. Sci. (Rsch. Achievement award 1992). Achievements include research in synthesis in peptides and hormones, inhibition of peptide receptors and proteases, characterization, synthesis and mechanisms of action of peptide natural products. Office: U Wis Dept Chemistry 425 N Charter St Madison WI 53706

RICH, DAVID BARRY, city official, auditor, accountant, entertainer; b. Bronx, N.Y., July 3, 1952; s. Steven and Gizella (Kornfeld) R.; 1 child, Suzanne Stephanie. BS in Health Adminstrn., Ithaca Coll., 1976; postgrad. in acctg., Bryant and Stratton Coll., Buffalo, 1977. Office mgr. Rubin Gorewitz, CPA, N.Y.C., 1977-78; auditor State of Ariz., Phoenix, 1979-83; internal auditor City of Phoenix, 1983-84; sales use tax auditor City of Mesa (Ariz.), 1984—; pres. Clovis Acctg. Inc., Mesa, 1980-94; rep. H.D. Vest Investment Inc., Irving, Tex., 1984-94; owner D.B. Rich Enterprises Import/ Export, Mesa, 1992—; stage name Barry Rich, Stand-up Comedy, 1994—. Treas., bd. dirs. Missing Mutts Inc., Tempe, Ariz., 1986-88. With USAF, 1971-76. Fellow Nat. Assn. Tax Preparers; mem. Toastmasters (treas. Mesa 1986-87), Phi Beta Kappa.

RICH, FRANCES LUTHER, sculptor; b. Spokane, Wash., Jan. 8, 1910; d. Elvo Elcourt Deffenbaugh and Irene (Luther Deffenbaugh) Rich. BA, Smith Coll., 1931; art student, Paris studios, 1933-35, Boston Mus. Sch. Art, 1935-36, Cranbrook Acad. Art, Bloomfield Hills, Mich., 1937-40, Claremont (Calif.) Coll., 1946-47, Columbia U., 1946-47; pupil of, Malvina Hoffman, Carl Milles, Alexandre Iacovleff. Dir. pub. relations Smith Coll., 1947-50; with pvt. studios Rome, 1950-52, Paris, 1960-62. Pub. and pvt. marble sculpture include Army-Navy-Air Force Nurses Arlington Nat. Cemetery, Washington, 1938, Terra Cotta, Benedictine Abbey Chapel, Mt. Angel, Oreg., 1954, Bronze Pelican, Earle C. Anthony Bldg., U. Berkeley, Calif. 1958, St. Joseph, Guadelupe Coll., Los Gatos, Calif., 1966; Bronze series St. Francis of Assisi, 4' St. Francis, Little Austria Terrace, Millesgården, Lid- ingö, Sweden, 1960; 6'7" St. Francis, St. Margaret's Episcopal Ch., Palm Desert, Calif., 1970, 7'6" Pierce-Deree Coll., Mt. Hymettus, Athens, Greece, 1970, 7'6" St. Francis, Pres.'s Garden Smith Coll., Northampton, Mass., 1978, 4'4" bronze Cranbrook Acad. Art Mus., Bloomfield Hills, Mich. 1983, 10' bronze "Our Lady of Combermere" grounds, The Madonna House Lay Apolstolate Tng. Ctr., Combermere, Ont., Can., 1960, 19" bronze "Our Lady of Combermere", Madonna House Chapel, Edmonton, Can.; medals of Our Lady of Combermere at Combermere Madonna House Tng. Ctr., and 22" bronze "St. Catherine of Siena" (Santa Catalina Sch., Monterey, Calif.), 1968, 89, " Crucifix, The Madonna Chapel, Grace Cathedral, San Francisco, 1972, 30" bronze crucifix St. Margaret's Episcopal Ch., Palm Desert, Calif., 1990, bronze "The Healer", David L. Reeves Meml. Libr., Cottage Hosp., Santa Barbara, Calif., 1973, 15 bronze "Birds in Flight", Living Desert Reserve, Palm Desert, Calif., 1978; reliefs include: 6 nine ' stone panels Union Bldg., Purdue U., Lafayette, Ind., 1939; bronze 4'x 6' panel "Nunc Dimittis", St. Peter's Episcopal Ch., Redwood City, Calif., 1957; 8' "Our Lady Seat of Wisdom", St. Cecelia Ch., Stanwood, Wash., 1965; 8' bronze "Christ of the Sacred Heart", St. Sebastian's Ch., West Los Angeles, Calif. 1972; portraits include: Margaret Sanger, 1957 and Pres. Herbert Davis, 1950, Nielson Libr., Smith Coll., Northampton, Mass., Prof. Henry Russel Hitchcock, marble bust Alice Stone Blackwell, Boston Pub. Library, 1961; 3'6" terra cotta figure Katharine Hepburn, Shakespeare Mus., 1962 and bronze bust of Hepburn, 1961, both as Cleopatra, at Am. Shakespeare Theatre, Stratford, Conn.; also bronze head Lawrence Langner, Shakespeare Theater Foyer, 1963; bronze head Virgil Thomson, Virgil Thomson Room, NYU, 1977; Smith Coll. Mus. Art collection includes bronze portraits of Katharine Hepburn as Cleopatra, Lotte Lehman, Diego Rivera, 1978, terra cotta portrait of Margaret Sanger, cotta portrait of Lotte Lehman; bronze portrait of Pres. Herbert Davis and bronze bas relief of Laura Scales; marble bust of Alice Stone Blackwell; further sculpture collections Smith Coll. Mus. Art and Cranbrook Acad. Art, 1981; one man shows: Art Ctr., Phoenix, 1954, Santa Barbara Mus. Art, 1955, Calif. Palace Legion of Honor, San Francisco, 1955, Laguna Blanca Sch., Santa Barbara, 1955, Palm Springs Desert Mus., 1969, 77, Smith Coll Mus. Art, 1981, Cranbrook Acad. Art Mus., 1983; group exhbns.: Am. Art Exhibit, World's Fair, N.Y., 1939, First Nat. Biennale Contemporary Religious Art, Set Hall Coll., Pa., 1953, Denver Liturgical Art Show, 1952, De Young Mus., Calif Liturgical Artists, 1952, Grace Cathedral, San Francisco, 1957, Knoedler's Gallery, N.Y.C., 1962, Members Exhibit, Archtl. League, N.Y.C., 1962, Boston Pub. Libr.; 10 bronzes Nat. Liturgical Art Week, Seattle World's Fair, 1962; 8 bronzes "Students of Carl Milles" Exhibit, Millesgården, Lidingö, summer 1986; Milles as Mentor: The Work of Cranbrook Sculptors, 1931-51, 5 bronzes Cranbrook Acad. Art, Bloomfield Hills, Mich., summer, 1990;12 1/2" bronzes of Our Lady of Combermere in each of 27 Madonna House Chapels Lay Apostolates Worldwide, 1989, 4'5" bronze St. Francis of Assisi, Botanic Garden Ctr., Fort Worth. 1990; 15" bronze of St. Margaret of Scotland St. Margaret's Episcopal Ch., Palm Desert, 1990, Canongate Kirk, Edinburgh, 1991; 18" bronze crucifix Canongate Kirk Manse; life size bronze bust Dr. George Bass, underwater archaeologist, 1993; numerous portraits, fountains, small bronzes and silvers for pvt. collectors. Served to lt. comdr. USNR, 1942-46. Mem. Archtl. League N.Y.C., Smith Coll. Alumnae Assn., Cosmpolitan Club (N.Y.C.). Home and Studio: 1208 E Bolivar St Payson AZ 85541 also: 4385 Marina Dr Santa Barbara CA 93110*

RICH, FRANK HART, critic; b. Washington, June 2, 1949; s. Frank Hart Rich and Helene Bernice (Aaronson) Fisher; m. Alexandra Rachelle Witchel, 1991; children from previous marriage: Nathaniel Howard, Simon Hart. B.A. in Am. History and Lit. magna cum laude, Harvard U., 1971. Co-editor Richmond (Va.) Mercury, 1972-73; sr. editor, film critic New Times mag., N.Y.C., 1973-75; film critic N.Y. Post, N.Y.C., 1975-77; film and TV critic Time mag., N.Y.C., 1977-80; chief drama critic N.Y. Times, N.Y.C., 1980-93; columnist N.Y. Times Sunday Mag., N.Y.C., 1993; Op-Ed columnist N.Y. Times, N.Y.C., 1994—. Author: (with others) The Theatre Art of Boris Aronson, 1987. Office: The NY Times 229 W 43rd St New York NY 10036-3913

RICH, GILES SUTHERLAND, federal judge; b. Rochester, N.Y., May 30, 1904; s. Giles Willard and Sarah Thompson (Sutherland) R.; m. Gertrude Verity Braun, Jan. 10, 1931 (dec.); 1 child, Verity Sutherland Grinnell (Mrs. John M. Hallinan); m. Helen Gill Field, Oct. 10, 1953. SB, Harvard, 1926; LLB, Columbia, 1929; LLD (hon.), John Marshall Law Sch., Chgo., 1981, George Washington U., 1989, Franklin Pierce Law Ctr., 1993. Bar: N.Y. 1929, U.S. Patent Office 1934. Pvt. practice N.Y.C., 1929-56; ptnr. special- izing patent and trademark law Williams, Rich & Morse, 1937-52, Churchill, Rich, Weymouth & Engel, 1952-56; assoc. judge U.S. Ct. Customs and Patent Appeals, 1956-82; cir. judge U.S. Ct. Appeals (Fed. cir.), 1982—; lectr. patent law Columbia, 1942-56, N.Y. Law Sch., 1952; adj. prof. Ge- orgetown U. Law Sch., 1963-69. Contbr. articles to profl. jours. Recipient Jefferson medal N.J. Patent Law Assn., 1955, Kettering award Patent Trademark and Copyright Inst. George Washington U., 1978, Founder's Day award for disting. govt. svcs., 1970, Freedom Found. award Am. Inst. Chemists, 1967, Eli Whitney award Conn. Patent Law Assn. 1972, Columbia U. Sch. Law medal for Excellence, 1994, Licensing Execs. Soc. of U.S.A. and Can. award, 1994. Mem. ABA, Assn. of Bar of City of N.Y., Am. Intellectual Property Law Assn., N.Y. Patent Law Assn. (pres. 1950- 51), Rochester Patent Law Assn. (hon. life), L.A. Patent Law Assn. (hon.), San Francisco Patent Law Assn. (hon. life). Clubs: Harvard (Washington), Cosmos. Office: US Ct Appeals Fed Cir 717 Madison Pl NW Washington DC 20439-0002

RICH, HARRY E., footwear and specialty retailing financial executive; b. Wichita, Kans., Mar. 5, 1940; s. Hubert E. and Lorene (Sadler) R.; m. Elfreda Elizabeth Babcock, Aug. 8, 1964; children—Lisa G., Carey E.,

Ashley H. B.A., Harvard U., 1962, M.B.A., 1968. Pres. instrumentation div. Baxter Travenol, Deerfield, Ill., 1977-78; group v.p. Mallinckrodt, Inc., St. Louis, 1978-83; sr. v.p., chief fin. officer Brown Group, Inc., St. Louis, 1983-88, exec. v.p., chief fin. officer, 1988—; also dir.; bd. dirs. Boatmen's Nat. Bank of St. Louis. Bd. dirs. Repertory Theatre, 1984—, pres. bd. dirs., 1988-90; treas. V.P. Fair Found., 1985-88; bd. trustees Mary Inst., 1986-90, Mary Inst./St. Louis Country Day Sch., 1990—. Lt. USN, 1962-66. Avo- cations: tennis, jogging, sailing. Home: 101 Fair Oaks Saint Louis MO 63124-1514 Office: Brown Group Inc 8300 Maryland Ave Saint Louis MO 63105-3647

RICH, HOWARD, retail executive; b. 1937. CEO, pres. Rich's Dept. Store, Salem, Mass. Office: Rich's Dept Stores Inc 35 Congress St Salem MA 01970*

RICH, J(AY) PETER, lawyer; b. Santa Monica, Calif., July 28, 1953; s. Jay Baum and Claire Louise (Niessen) R.; m. Elizabeth Ann Higdon, Dec. 27, 1980; children: Jennifer Jeanne, Natalie Amanda, Megan Elizabeth. AB summa cum laude, UCLA, 1974; JD, Harvard U., 1977. Bar: Calif. 1977, U.S. Dist. Ct. (ctrl. dist.) Calif. 1978, U.S. Ct. Appeals (9th cir.). Assoc. Memel, Jacobs, et al, L.A., 1978-84, ptnr., 1984-87; ptnr. McDermott, Will & Emery, L.A., 1987—; pres., bd. dirs. Univ. Religious Conf. UCLA, L.A., 1986-89, dir., 1989—; mem., bd. govs. Unicamp UCLA, L.A., 1986—. Author: Alternative Forms of Healthcare Delivery Systems: HMOs and PPOs, 1983, State Laws and Regulations Governing Preferred Provider Or- ganizations, 1986; contbr. chpts. to books and articles to profl. jours. Mem. Hillcrest Country Club, Phi Beta Kappa. Avocations: golf, basketball, coaching youth soccer, military history, cinema. Office: McDermott Will & Emery 2049 Century Park E # 3400 Los Angeles CA 90067-3036

RICH, JOHN, film and television producer, director; b. Rockaway Beach, N.Y., July 6, 1925; s. Louis and Jennie (Rich) R.; children: Catherine Lee, Anthony Joseph, Robert Lawrence. AB, U. Mich., 1948, MA, 1949. Ind. TV dir., 1959—; sec. Dirs. Guild Am. and Benevolent Found., 1959—. Exec. producer TV series MacGyver, 1985—; director (films) Wives and Lovers, 1963, The New Interns, 1964, Roustabout, 1964, Boeing-Boeing, 1965, Easy Come, Easy Go, 1967; (television) Academy Awards, The Dick Van Dyke Show, All in the Family, Mr. Sunshine, Dear John. Served to capt. USAAF, 1943-46. Recipient Outstanding Comedy Direction awards Acad. TV Arts and Scis. for The Dick Van Dyke Show, 1963, All in the Family, 1972, 73; Sesquicentennial award U. Mich., 1967; Dirs. Guild Am. award for most outstanding directorial achievement, 1972, Robert B. Aldrich award, 1992; Golden Globe awards for All in the Family, 1972, 73, Emmy award 1972; Christopher award for Henry Fonda as Clarence Darrow 1974. Mem. Dirs. Guild Am. (bd. dirs., founding trustee DGA-Producers Pension Plan, chmn. 1964-65, 68-69), Phi Beta Kappa, Phi Kappa Phi.

RICH, JOHN MARTIN, humanities educator, researcher; b. Tuscaloosa, Ala., Dec. 14, 1931; s. Emanuel Morris and Bertha (Rose) R.; m. Martha Elaine Schur, June 6, 1955 (div. June 1966); children—Jeffrey Brian, Suzanne Elon; m. Joyce Ann Stegemoller, Aug. 28, 1967 (div. Mar. 1985); m. Audrey Faye Arnold, Aug. 1, 1987. B.A., U. Ala., 1954, M.A., 1955; Ph.D., Ohio State U., 1958. Grad. asst. Ohio State U., Columbus, 1955; asst. instr. edn. Ohio State U., 1956-58; asst. prof. edn. U. Tenn.-Martin, 1958-60; assoc. prof. edn. Coll. SUNY-Oneonta, 1960-61; from asst. prof. to assoc. prof. Iowa State U., Ames, 1961-66; assoc. prof. social and philos. studies U. Ky., Lexington, 1966-69; prof. cultural founds. edn. U. Tex., Austin, 1969—, chmn. dept. cultural founds. edn., 1969-75; vis. lectr. Nat. Kaohsiung (Taiwan) Normal U., 1993. Author: books Education and Human Values, 1968, Humanistic Foundations of Education, 1971, Portugese translation, 1975, Korean translation, 1985, Challenge and Response, 1974, New Direc- tions in Educational Policy, 1974, Discipline and Authority in School and Family, 1982, Professional Ethics in Education, 1984, Innovative School Discipline, 1985, Foundations of Education, 1992; co-author: Theories of Moral Development, 1985 (named an Outstanding Book of 1985-86 Choice Mag.), 2nd edit. 1994, Helping and Intervention, 1988, Competition in Education, 1992; editor: Readings in the Philosophy of Education, 1966, 2d edit., 1972, Conflict and Decision, 1972, Innovations in Education, 6th edit., 1992; co-editor, editorial adv. bd. Ednl. Studies, 1970-74, 77-80, 89-91; bd. contbg. editors Rev. Edn., 1977-85; editorial bd. Focus on Learning, 1980- 84, Educational Foundations, 1985-91; bd. cons. Jour. Rsch. and Devel. in Edn., 1982—, Ednl. Theory, 1991-95; contbr. articles to profl. jours., U.S., Can., Eng., Australia. Recipient Faculty Research Assignment award Univ. Research Inst., Austin, Tex., 1983-84; vis. scholar U. London, 1977; Univ. Research Inst. grantee, 1981-82, 84-85. Mem. North Central Philosophy of Edn. Soc. (pres. 1966-67), Ohio Valley Philosophy of Edn. Soc. (pres. 1967- 68), Philosophy of Edn. Soc. (exec. bd. 1967-68, 80-82, Cert. Significant Svc.), Am. Ednl. Studies Assn. (exec. council 1972-74, pres. 1975-76). Home: 1801 Lavaca St Apt 8M Austin TX 78701-1307 Office: U Tex Edn Bldg 406 Austin TX 78712

RICH, JOSEPH JOHN, accountant; b. Detroit, Sept. 5, 1944; s. John H. and Edna R. (Swallow) R.; m. Carolyn A. Atkinson, Nov. 3, 1962 (div. Dec. 19, 1983); children: Marcella, Loren; m. Darlene E. Kornfehl, Aug. 2, 1985. A of Commerce, Alpena Community Coll.; A in Ins. Law, Am. Edn. Inst. Pres. Tax Svcs., Inc., Portland, Mich., 1965—; claim specialist State Farm Ins., Marshall, Mich., 1966-80; owner Someplace Else Travel Ctr., Portland, 1990—; labor cons. Portland Pub. Schs., 1972—; exec. sec. Mich. Theatre Assn., Portland, 1979-86, Community Theatre Assn. of Mich., Port- land, 1981-91; investment adviser H.D. Vest Investments, Irving, Tex., 1987—. Author: Insurance Guide for Theatres, 1977, Accounting for Non- Profit Theatres, 1976. Chmn. Ionia (Mich.) County Commn., 1986-90; mem. Ionia Social Svcs. Bd., 1992, Ionia Planning Commn., 1986, Portland Area Mcpl. Authority, 1992. Named one of Outstanding Young Men in Am., 1981. Mem. Portland Kiwanis Club, Ind. Accts. Assn. of Mich. Republi- can. Avocations: theatre, travel. Office: Tax Svcs Inc 200 W Bridge St Portland MI 48875

RICH, JUDE T., management consulting firm executive; b. Atlantic City, Aug. 4, 1943; s. Samuel John and Mary Elizabeth (Miller) R.; m. Mary Theresa Bosies, Apr. 28, 1979; children: Victoria Elizabeth, Jessica Anne; children from previous marriage: Denise Marie, Jude T. Jr., Dina Marie. BS in Econs. cum laude, Rutgers U., 1966, MBA cum laude, 1974. Coll. recruiter Johnson & Johnson, New Brunswick, N.J., 1966; pers. mgr. NL Industries, N.Y.C., 1968-72; pers. dir. RCA, N.Y.C., 1972-74; ptnr., human resources practice head McKinsey & Co., N.Y.C., 1974-84; chmn. Sibson & Co., Princeton, N.J.; chm. dir. Assn. Mgmt. Cons. Firms. Co-author: (rsch. publ.) Productivity in the Public Schools, 1982; contbr. articles to profl. jours. Pres. Gramercy Spire Assn., N.Y.C., 1980-82; bd. dirs. Recording for Blind. Mem. Human Resource Planning Soc., Assn. of Mgmt. Cons. (bd. dirs.), Univ. Club. Episcopalian. Avocations: sailing, scuba, military history. Office: Sibson & Co Inc 504 Carnegie Ctr Princeton NJ 08543-5211

RICH, KENNETH MALCOLM, executive search and management con- sultant; b. Newark, N.J., Aug. 17, 1946; s. Lucien Ludwell and Grace (Hardy) R.; m. Sandra Ann Arrington; children: Stephen Montgomery, Khristine Nicole. AB in Chemistry, Lafayette Coll., 1967; MBA in Fin. Mktg., U. Chgo., 1969; cert. in acctg., NYU, 1979. Assoc., corp. fin. Kuhn, Loeb & Co., N.Y.C., 1969-73; special asst. to the asst. sec. policy, devel. and rsch. HUD, Washington, 1973-74; mng. dir. fgn. investments The Dornbush Co. Atlanta, 1974; resident v.p. Citibank, N.A., N.Y.C., Athens and Dubai, U.A.E., 1975-78; mng., cons. div. Peat, Marwick, Mitchell & Co., N.Y.C. 1978-80; mng., strategic planning Gen. Elec. Credit Corp., Stamford, Conn. 1981-83; ptnr. Paul Ray Berndtson Inc., N.Y.C., 1983—; mem. mktg. com. Paul R. Ray & Co., Inc., N.Y.C., 1985-88, chmn. fin. svcs. practice com., 1989-92, mem. compensation com., 1989—; mem. stk. com., bd. dirs. prac- tice group; also bd. dirs. Paul Ray Berndtson Inc., N.Y.C., 1989—; trustee Lafayette Coll., Easton, Pa., 1970-75. Chief umpire Ridgefield (Conn.) Little League, 1980-89; mem. Lafayette Leadership Coun., 1993—; bd. dirs. Juvenile Diabetes Found. Internat., 1993—; Assn. Exec. Search Cons. 1994—. Standard Oil of N.J. fellow U. Chgo., 1967-69; named one of N.Am.'s top exec. recruiters The New Career Makers (by John Sibbald), 1994. Presbyterian. Avocations: reading, music, cross training. Home: 66 St Johns Rd Ridgefield CT 06877-5524 Office: Paul Ray Berndtson Inc 101 Park Ave New York NY 10178-0001

RICH, LEE, entertainment industry executive; b. Cleve.; m. Ilene Graham; children by previous marriage: Jessica, Miranda. B.A., Ohio U., hon. degree in communications, 1982; LL.D. (hon.), Southwestern U., 1983. Advt. exec., resigned as sr. TV v.p. Benton & Bowles to become pres. Mirisch Rich TV, 1965-67; with Leo Burnett Agy., 1967-69; pres., co-owner Lorimar Prodns., Culver City, Calif., 1969-86; chmn., chief exec. officer MGM/UA Com- munications Co., Beverly Hills, Calif., 1986-88; now chmn. bd. Lee Rich Prodns., Burbank. Prodr: (TV movie) Sybil, (films) Helter Skelter, Green Eyes, Eric, The Homecoming, The Blue Knight, Skag, Two of a Kind, (TV series) Dallas, The Waltons (Emmy awards), Eight is Enough, Knots Landing, Falcon Crest; film prodr.: Being There, The Big Red One, The Postman Always Rings Twice, Who Is Killing the Great Chefs of Europe, Victory, S.O.B., Hard to Kill, 1990, Passenger 57, 1992, Innocent Blood, 1992, Little Panda, 1994, Just Cause, 1994. Recipient Disting. Citizenship award Southwestern U. Sch. Law, 1983. Office: Bldg 81 Rm 200 4000 Warner Blvd Burbank CA 91522

RICH, MARY D., women's health nurse; b. Lynchburg, Va., Dec. 10, 1952; d. Samuel Bernard Jr. and Virginia Lucille (Guill) Doss; m. Tollie West Rich Jr., May 20, 1978; 1 child, Dustin Samuel West. Diploma, Va. Bapt. Hosp., 1974; BS, Old Dominion U., 1980. RN, Va. Staff nurse ob-gyn., emergency dept. Norfolk (Va.) Gen. Hosp.; nurse mgr. Sentara Norfolk Gen. Hosp., dir. nursing. Mem. NAACOG (Tidewater chpt., cert. inpatient obstetric nurse, Nurse of Yr. 1984, past sec.-treas.), AONE, Va. Perinatal Assn.

RICH, MICHAEL DAVID, research corporation executive, lawyer; b. Los Angeles, Jan. 23, 1953; s. Ben Robert and Faye (Mayer) R.; m. Debra Paige Granfield, Jan. 12, 1980; children: Matthew, William. AB, U. Calif., Berkeley, 1973; JD, UCLA, 1976. Bar: Calif., 1976. Law clk. to judge U.S. Dist. Ct., Boston, 1976; staff mem. RAND, Santa Monica, Calif., 1976-85, dir. resource mgmt. program, 1980-85, dep. v.p., 1986, v.p. nat. security rsch. and dir. Nat. Def. Rsch. Inst., 1986-93; sr. v.p. RAND, 1993—. Author numerous classified and unclassified reports and articles. Immediate past pres., bd. dirs. WISE Sr. Svcs. Mem. Internat. Inst. Strategic Studies, Council Fgn. Relations. Office: RAND PO Box 2138 1700 Main St Santa Monica CA 90401-3208

RICH, MICHAEL JOSEPH, lawyer; b. N.Y.C., June 19, 1945; s. Jesse and Phyllis (Sternfeld) R.; m. Linda Christine Kubis, July 19, 1969; children: David Lawrence, Lisa Diane. BA, Gettysburg Coll., 1967; JD, Am. U., 1972. Bar: Del. 1973, U.S. Dist. Ct. Del. 1973, U.S. Supreme Ct. 1976, Pa. 1981. Law clk. Del. Supreme Ct., Georgetown, 1972-73; assoc. Tunnell & Raysor, Georgetown, 1973-76; ptnr. Dunlap, Holland & Rich, P.A., Ge- orgetown, 1976-80; gen. counsel Pearlette Fashions, Inc., Lebanon, Pa., 1981-83; assoc. Morris, Nichols, Arsht & Tunnell, Georgetown, 1983-86, ptnr., 1987-91; ptnr. Twilley, Street, Rich, Braverman & Hindman, P.A., Dover, Del., 1991-95; state solicitor, 1995—; mem. Del. Bar Examiners, Del., 1986—, vice chair, 1994—; minority counsel Del. Ho. of Reps., Dover, 1977- 79; mem. Del. Gov's Magistrate Commn., 1980, 83-86; sec. Del. Gov's. Jud. Nominating Commn., 1986-89. Bd. dirs. People's Place II, Inc., Milford, Del., 1973-77; pres. Bi-County United Way, Inc., Milford, 1977-78; mem. Partnership Greater Milford Commn., 1987-89, Friends Milford Library. Served to 1st lt. U.S. Army, 1967-69, Vietnam. Dean's fellow Am. U., 1971- 72. Mem. ABA, Am. Acad. Hosp. Attys., Am. Judicature Soc., Del. Bar Assn. (pres. 1990-91), Sussex County Bar Assn. (pres. 1987-89), Kent County Bar Assn. Republican. Office: Dept Justice 820 N French St Wilm- ington DE 19801

RICH, PHILIP DEWEY, publishing executive; b. Nashua, N.H., Feb. 1, 1940; s. John Parker and Olive Frances (Hussey) R.; m. Leslie Ann Burke, June 14, 1974 (div. 1982). AB magna cum laude, Harvard U., 1961; MA, NYU, 1962; postgrad., Princeton U., 1962. Editor Houghton Mifflin Co., Boston, 1964-73; asst. mng. editor UpCountry Mag. Berkshire Eagle, Pitts- field, Mass., 1976-77; editor Book Creations Inc., Canaan, N.Y., 1977-80, editor-in-chief, 1980-91, v.p., exec. editor, 1991-92; cons. editor Berkshire Ho. Publs., Stockbridge, Mass., 1992-93, mng. editor, 1993—. Office: Berk- shire House Pubs PO Box 297 Stockbridge MA 01262-0297

RICH, R(OBERT) BRUCE, lawyer; b. N.Y.C., Oct. 28, 1949; s. John J. and Sylvia (Berkenblit) R.; m. Melissa Jo Saxe; children—Meghan, Alexander. A.B., Dartmouth Coll., 1970; J.D., U. Pa., 1973. Bar: N.Y. 1974, U.S. Dist. Ct. (so. and ea. dists.) N.Y. 1974, U.S. Ct. Appeals (2d cir.) 1980, U.S. Supreme Ct. 1980, U.S. Ct. Appeals (D.C. cir.) 1985. Assoc. firm Weil, Gotshal & Manges, N.Y.C., 1973-81, ptnr., 1981—. Contbg. author: Cul- tivating the Wasteland: Can Cable Put the Vision Back in TV?, 1983. Contbr. articles to profl. jours. Bd. advisers Communications and the Law, Westport, Conn., 1983—. Mem. ABA (antitrust law sect., forum com. on communications law), Assn. Bar City N.Y. (com. on trade regulation 1982- 85, communications law com. 1985-88), Phi Beta Kappa. Office: Weil Got- shal & Manges 767 Fifth Ave New York NY 10153-0002

RICH, ROBERT C., manufacturing executive; b. 1944. BA, Brigham Young U., 1969; MBA, Northwestern U. 1971. Fin. analyst, supr. Ford Motor Co., Dearborn, Mich., 1971-75; divsn. contr. Pullman, Inc., Chgo., 1975-81; v.p. fin. men's apparel group Hartmarx Corp., Chgo., 1981-87; v.p. fin. Tonka Corp., Minnetonka, Minn., 1987-88; sr. v.p. Masterbrand Indus- tries, 1988-92; exec. v.p. ops. Master Lock Co., Milw., 1993—. Office: Master Lock Co 2600 N 32nd St Milwaukee WI 53210*

RICH, ROBERT E., SR., frozen foods company executive; married. Grad., U. Buffalo, 1935. Owner Wilber Farms Dairy, 1935; founder, chmn. bd. dirs. Rich Products Corp., Buffalo, 1944—. Office: Rich Products Corp 1150 Niagara St Buffalo NY 14213-1713

RICH, ROBERT E., JR., food products company executive; b. 1941. Student, Williams Coll.; MBA, U. Rochester. Pres., bd. dirs. Rich Products Corp., Buffalo; also vice-chmn. bd. dirs. Buffalo Sabres Hockey Club. Office: Rich Products Corp 1145 Niagara St Buffalo NY 14213-1713 also: Buffalo Sabres Meml Auditorium 140 Main St Buffalo NY 14202-4190

RICH, ROBERT EDWARD, lawyer; b. Corbin, Ky., Feb. 4, 1944; s. Ed- ward Bluch and Marjorie Brooks (Wentworth) R.; m. Janet Sue Shearer, May 14, 1966; children: Susan M., Christopher R., David E., Sarah M. AB, U. Ky., 1966; JD, Harvard U., 1969. Bar: Ohio 1970. Jud. clk. U.S. Ct. Appeals for 6th Cir., Louisville, 1969-70; assoc. Taft, Stettinius & Hollister, Cin., 1970, ptnr., 1978—. Vice pres. New Life Youth Svcs., Inc., Cin., 1985; trustee Ky. Youth Assn., State YMCA, Frankfort, Ky., 1990; pres. Bob Hope House, Inc., Mt. Healthy, Ohio, 1991, Cin. Bar Found., 1991. Mem. ABA, Cin. Bar Assn. Republican. Presbyterian. Home: 215 Hilltop Ln Wyoming OH 45215-4121 Office: 1800 Star Bank Ctr 425 Walnut St Cincinnati OH 45202-3957

RICH, ROBERT REGIER, immunology educator, physician; b. Newton, Kans., Mar. 7, 1941; s. Eldon Stahly and Margaret Joy (Regier) R.; m. Susan Jepson Solliday, Mar. 22, 1974; children from previous marriage: Kenneth Eldon, Cathryn Louise. AB, Bethel Coll., 1962; M.D., U. Kans., 1966. Diplomate Am. Bd. Internal Medicine (bd. dirs. 1990-93), Am. Bd. Allergy and Immunology (bd. dirs. 1987-93, chmn. 1991), cert. spl. qualifi- cation Diagnostic Lab. Immunology. Intern, resident in internal medicine U. Wash., Seattle, 1966-68; clin. asso., chief clin. asso., sr. staff fellow NIH, Bethesda, Md., 1968-71; research assto. Harvard Med. Sch., Boston, 1971-73; asst. in medicine Peter Bent Brigham Hosp., 1972-73; asst. prof., asso. prof., prof. microbiology, immunology and internal medicine Baylor Coll. Medicine, Houston, 1973-78, prof., 1978-95, head immunology sect., 1978—, chief clin. immunology, 1979-91, prof. medicine, 1979-95, Disting. svc. prof. microbiology, immunology and medicine, 1995—; v.p., dean of rsch. Baylor Coll. Medicine, 1990—; investigator Howard Huges Med. Inst., Bethesda, Md., 1977-91; mem. immunobiology study sect. NIH, 1977-81; mem. med. staff Harris County Hosp. Dist., Meth. Hosp., Houston; mem. transplanta- tion biology and immunology com. Nat. Inst. Allergy and Infectious Disease, 1982-86, chmn., 1984-86; mem. nat. ctr. grants com. Arthritis Found., 1983- 86, chmn., 1984-86; nat. tech. com., 1984-89, chmn., 1986-89, ho. of dels., 1985-91; mem. rsch. adv. com. Nat. Multiple Sclerosis Soc., 1989-94, chmn., 1993-94. Assoc. editor: Jour. Immunology, 1978-82, sect. editor, 1991—; assoc. editor: Jour. Infectious Diseases, 1984-88; adv. editor: Jour. Exptl.

Medicine, 1980-84; editorial bd. Jour. Clin. Immunology, 1989—; contbr. articles to profl. jours. Served with USPHS, 1968-70. Recipient Research Career Devel. award NIH, 1975-77, Merit award NIH, 1987. Fellow ACP, Am. Acad. Allergy and Immunology (chmn. basic and clin. immunology interest sect. 1992-93), Infectious Diseases Soc. Am.; mem. AMA, AAAS, Am. Bd. Internal Medicine (diplomate, bd. dirs. 1990-93), Am. Bd. Allergy and Immunology (diplomate, bd. dirs. 1987-93), Assn. Am. Physicians, Am. Soc. Clin. Investigation, Am. Soc. Histocompatibility and Immunogenetics, Am. Assn. Immunologists (chmn. pub. affairs com. 1994—), Am. Assn. Investigative Pathology, Transplantation Soc., Am. Soc. Microbiologists, So. Soc. Clin. Investigation, Am. Fedn. Clin. Rsch., Am. Clin. Climatological Assn., Harris County Med. Soc., Tex. Med. Assn., Clin. Immunology Soc. (coun. 1990—, pres. 1995—), Alpha Omega Alpha, Sigma Xi. Office: Baylor Coll Medicine One Baylor Pla Houston TX 77030

RICH, ROBERT STEPHEN, lawyer; b. N.Y.C., Apr. 30, 1938; s. Maurice H. and Natalie (Priess) R.; m. Myra N. Lakoff, May 31, 1964; children: David, Rebecca, Sarah. AB, Cornell U., 1959; JD, Yale U., 1963. Bar: N.Y. 1964, Colo. 1973, U.S. Tax Ct. 1966, U.S. Supreme Ct. 1967, U.S. Ct. Claims 1968, U.S. Dist. Ct. (so. dist.) N.Y. 1965, U.S. Dist. Ct. (ea. dist.) N.Y. 1965, U.S. Dist. Ct. Colo. 1980, U.S. Ct. Appeals (2d cir.) 1964, U.S. Ct. Appeals (10th cir.) 1978; conseil juridique, Paris, 1968. Assoc. Shearman & Sterling, N.Y.C., Paris, London, 1963-72; ptnr. Davis, Graham & Stubbs, Denver, 1973—; adj. faculty U. Denver Law Sch., 1977—; adv. bd. U. Denver Ann. Tax Inst., 1985—; adv. bd. global bus. and culture divsn. U. Denver, 1992—, Denver World Affairs Coun., 1993—; bd. dirs. Clos du Val Wine Co. Ltd., Danskin Cattle Co., Areti Wines, Ltd., Taltarni Vineyards, Christy Sports, Copper Valley Assn., pres.; bd. dirs. several other corps.; mem. Colo. Internat. Trade Adv. Coun., 1985—, tax adv. com. U.S. Senator Hank Brown; mem. Rocky Mountain Dist. Export Coun. U.S. Dept. Commerce, 1993—. Author treatises on internat. taxation; contbr. articles to profl. jours. Bd. dirs. Denver Internat. Film Festival, 1978-79, Alliance Française, 1977—; actor, musician N.Y. Shakespeare Festival, 1960; sponsor Am. Tax Policy inst., 1991—; trustee, sec. Denver Art Mus., 1982—; mem. adv. bd. Denver World Affairs Coun., 1993—. Capt., AUS, 1959-60. Fellow Am. Coll. Tax Counsel (bd. regents 10th cir. 1992—); mem. ABA, Internat. Bar Assn., Colo. Bar Assn., N.Y. State Bar Assn., Assn. of Bar of City of N.Y., Asia-Pacific Lawyers Assn., Union Internationale des Avocats, Internat. Fiscal Assn. (pres. Rocky Mt. br. 1992—, U.S. regional v.p. 1988—), Japan-Am. Soc. Colo. (bd. dirs., 1989—, pres. 1991-93), Confrerie des Chevaliers du Tastevin, Meadowood Club, Denver Club, Cactus Club Denver, Yale Club, Denver Tennis Club. Office: Cherry Creek Sta PO Box 61295 Denver CO 80206-8295

RICH, S. JUDITH, public relations executive; b. Chgo., Apr. 14; d. Irwin M. and Sarah I. (Sandock) R. BA, U. Ill., 1960. Staff writer, reporter Economist Newspapers, Chgo., 1960-61; asst. dir. pub. rels. and communications Coun. Profit Sharing Industries, Chgo., 1961-62; dir. advt. and pub. rels. Chgo. Indsl. Dist., 1962-63; account exec., account supr., v.p., sr. v.p., exec. v.p. and nat. creative dir. Daniel J. Edelman Inc., Chgo., 1963-85; exec. v.p., dir. Ketchum Pub. Rels., Chgo., 1985-89, exec. v.p., exec. creative dir. USA, 1990—; frequent spkr. on creativity and brainstorming. workshop facilitator, spkr. in field. Mem. adv. bd. U. Chgo. Grad Sch. Bus., Roosevelt U., Chgo., DePaul U., Chgo., Gov.'s State U. Mem. Pub. Rels. Soc. Am. (Silver Anvil award, judge Silver Anvil awards), Counselors Acad. of Pub. Rels. Soc. Am. (exec. bd.), Chgo. Publicity Club (8 Golden Trumpet awards). Avocations: theatre, swimming, cycling, racquetball. Home: 2500 N Lakeview Ave Chicago IL 60614-1836 Office: Ketchum Pub Rels 142 E Ontario St Chicago IL 60611-2818

RICH, WILLIS FRANK, JR., banker; b. Ft. Dodge, Iowa, July 26, 1919; s. Willis Frank and Agnes Reed (Paterson) R.; m. Jo Ann Rockwell, Apr. 12, 1947; children: Ronald Rockwell, Roxanne, Andrew Paterson. B.A., Princeton U. 1941. Credit analyst Northwestern Nat. Bank, Mpls., 1947-52; asst. cashier Northwestern Nat. Bank, 1952-55, asst. v.p., 1955, v.p., 1955-57; pres. N.W. Nat. Bank, Bloomington-Richfield, Minn., 1952-58; v.p., cashier N.W. Nat. Bank, 1957-60, v.p. div. A, 1960-68, sr. v.p. nat. and internat. divs., 1968-73; exec. v.p. N.W. Nat. Bank, Mpls., 1973-81, vice chmn. bd. dirs., chief credit officer, 1981-84; fin. cons., 1984—; dir. Advance Acceptance Corp. Pres. Viking coun. Boy Scouts Am., 1970-71, trustee found., 1971-86; mem. exec. bd. Minn. Community Rsch. Coun., 1969-77; dir. Minn. Zoo, 1987—; trustee St. Martin's Found., 1986-90; vestry mem. St. Martin's-By-The-Lake Ch. Served with AUS, 1941-46. Decorated Bronze Star. Mem. Robert Morris Assocs. (nat. pres. 1977-78). Episcopalian. Clubs: Woodhill, Swan Lake Country. Home: 4770 Manitou Rd Excelsior MN 55331-9400

RICHARD, ALISON FELTES, anthropology educator; b. Great Britain, Mar. 1, 1948. BA, Cambridge U., 1969; PhD, London U., 1973. Asst. prof. anthropology Yale U., New Haven, 1972-76, assoc.prof. anthropology, 1976-85, prof. anthropology, 1985—. Office: Office of the Provost Yale U New Haven CT 06520-8118

RICHARD, ANN BERTHA, nursing administrator; b. Hartford, Conn., Mar. 21, 1944; d. Victor Charles and Theresa (Gasper) R.; children: Elena Skrinak, Judith Dunn. Diploma, Capital City Sch. Nursing, Washington, 1965; BSN summa cum laude, U. Hartford, Bloomfield, Conn., 1982; MS, U. Conn., 1986. RN, Conn.; cert. nurse adminstr., med.-surg. nurse. Staff nurse D.C. Gen. Hosp., Washington, 1965-66; staff nurse Hartford Hosp., 1972-73, asst. head nurse, 1973-74, head nurse, 1974-83, nutritional support clinician, 1983-85; total nursing care project cons. Hosp. of St. Raphael, New Haven, 1986-88, assoc. dir. gen. surg. nursing and spltys., 1986-88; v.p. for nursing svcs. Manchester (Conn.) Meml. Hosp., 1988—. Contbr. chpt. to book. Passini scholar, 1985. Mem. ANA (nursing adminstrn. coun. 1986—), Conn. Orgn. Nurse Execs., Conn. Nurses Assn. (govt. rels. com. 1984-88, bd. dirs. 1990-94), Conn. Orgn. Nurse Execs. (nominating com. 1988-88), Am. Coll. Healthcare Execs., Conn. Hosp. Assoc. (chairperson nurse exec. conf., 1993-95, bd. dirs. 1995—), Sigma Theta Tau (program com. 1986-88, nominating com. 1988-89), Alpha Chi, Conn. League Nursing (bd. dirs. 1990-92), Nat. League Nursing. Office: Manchester Meml Hosp 71 Haynes St Manchester CT 06040

RICHARD, DEBRAH JANE, environmental planner; b. Lynn, Mass., July 8, 1956; d. Edmund Darryl and Dorothy Louise (Green) R. BA in Geography, U. Maine, 1978; MA in Geography, U. Oreg., 1982. Preservation planner Town Farmington, Maine, 1979-80; teaching fellow U. Oreg., Eugene, 1980-82; asst. dir. Greater Portland Landmarks, Maine, 1983-85; dir. planning and community devel. City of Lewiston, Maine, 1986-88; dir. bur. of land quality Dept. of Environ. Protection, Maine, 1988—; bd. dirs. Lewiston-Auburn Econ. Growth Coun., 1986-89. Author: Historic Resources Inventory, 1980. Fund raiser festival series Portland Symphony Orch., Lewiston, 1986—; mem. Maine Nuclear Referendum Coun., Augusta, 1980-81, Payson Gallery Art, Portland, 1985—, Lewiston Hist. Preservation Rev. Bd., 1988—. Mem. Am. Planning Assn., Nat. Trust for Hist. Preservation, Am. Assn. Geographers, Maine Real Estate Devel. Assn. (bd. dirs. 1987-88), Maine Assn. Planners (exec. mem. 1987—, cert. of excellence for pub. participatory procession govt. 1987—, outstanding project award 1988). Republican. Mem. Soc. of Friends. Avocations: skiing, golf, biking. Office: Dept Environ Protection State House Sta 17 Augusta ME 04333

RICHARD, EDWARD H., manufacturing company executive, former municipal government official; b. N.Y.C., Mar. 15, 1937; s. Henry and Ida Richard; B.A., Antioch Coll., 1959. Pres., chmn. bd. dirs. Magnetics Internat. Inc., Maple Heights, Ohio, 1967-86, exec. v.p. Stearns Magnetics S.A., Brussels, Belgium, 1974-77; prin. Edward H. Richard & Assocs., Cleve., 1967-92; pres., treas. David Round & Son, Inc., Cleve; exec. adminstrv. asst. to mayor City of Cleve., 1979-87, dir. dept. pub. utilities, 1981-89, dep. to mayor, chief adminstrv. officer, 1986-89; dir. airports and port control City of Cleve., 1988-90; pres., CEO David Round & Son, Inc., Solon, Ohio, 1989—; chmn. Cleve. dist. adv. council Small Bus. Adminstrn., 1975-79; former mem. nat. adv. council Dept. Treasury; cons. and advisor in field; del. world trade fairs. Former trustee Regional Econ. Devel. Council, Met. Cleve. Jobs Council, Cleve. Devel. Found., Cleve. Better Bus. Bur.; former trustee Hiram House, Antioch U., N.E. Ohio Regional Sewer Dist., Greater Cleve. Domed Stadium Corp., Cleve. Conv. and Vis. Bur.; former trustee, vice-chmn. Cleve. Center Econ. Edn.; pres. Bratenahl Con-

dominium Assn.; mem., chmn. fin. com. Bratenahl Bd. Edn., 1971-75. Office: PO Box 39456 Solon OH 44139

RICHARD, ELLEN, theater executive; b. Bridgeport, Conn., Dec. 12, 1957; d. Laurent and Anne (Markham) R. Bus. mgr. Atlas Scenic Studio, Bridgeport, 1977-82; theater mgr. Stamford (Conn.) Ctr. for Arts, 1980-83; bus. mgr. Westport (Conn.) Country Playhouse, 1982-84; gen. mgr. Roundabout Theatre Co. Inc., N.Y.C., 1983—. Mem. N.Y. Cycling Club. Republican. Avocations: cycling, skiing. Office: Roundabout Theatre Co 1530 Broadway New York NY 10036-4002

RICHARD, HAROLD IRVIN, agricultural business executive; b. Lodi, Ohio, Mar. 13, 1935; s. Charles Irvin and Thelma (Grier) R.; m. Nancy Hutchinson, Oct. 4, 1959; children—David Scott, Julia Lynn, Douglas Alan, Bryce Noel. B.Sc., Ohio State U., 1959. Owner, mgr. Dowler Farm, Ashville, Ohio, 1959-74; European dir. Am. Soybean Assn., Brussels, Belgium, 1975-79; pres. Farmers Commodity Corp., West Des Moines, 1979-84, Agri Industries, West Des Moines, 1984-85; v.p. Ill. Futures Co., Chgo. 1982—; dir. Farmers Export Co., Kansas City, Mo., 1984—; chmn. bd. Farmers Commodity Corp., West Des Moines, 1984—, Agri Fin. Services, West Des Moines, 1984—. Served with U.S. Army, 1953-55, Korea. Mem. Nat. Feed & Grain Dealers (dir. 1985—), Iowa Farm Bur., Nat. Futures Assn. (arbitration com. 1983—), Commodity Futures Trading Commn. (arbitration commn. 1985—). Republican. Mem. Reformed Ch. Club: Des Moines Country. Avocations: Golf; raquetball; travel. Home: 14266 Wildwood Dr Des Moines IA 50325-7702 Office: Farmers Grain Dealers Inc 2829 Westown Pky 240 West Des Moines IA 50266

RICHARD, MARK M., government official, lawyer; b. N.Y.C., Nov. 16, 1939; s. Louis and Rae (Karnefsky) R.; m. Sheila Levitan, Aug. 6, 1960; children: Cara, Alisa, Daniel. B.A., Bklyn. Law Sch., 1961, J.D., 1967. Bar: N.Y. 1968. Trial atty. fraud sect., criminal div. Dept. Justice, Washington, 1967-75; exec. sec. Atty. Gen.'s White Collar Crime Com., Washington, 1975-76; chief fraud sect., criminal div. Dept. Justice, Washington, 1976-79, dept. asst. atty. gen. criminal div., 1979—; mem. econ. crime com. ABA, Washington, 1977-79. Recipient Legal award Assn. Fed. Investigators, 1981, Meritorious Exec. award Pres. of U.S., 1980. Home: 912 Burnt Crest Ln Silver Spring MD 20903-1340 Office: Dept Justice Criminal Divsn 10th Constitution Ave NW Washington DC 20530

RICHARD, OLIVER GONZARD, III (RICK RICHARD), lawyer, business executive; b. Lake Charles, La., Oct. 11, 1952; s. Oliver Gonzard and Mary Jean (Turvey) R.; m. Donna Margaret Guzman, July 6, 1974; 1 child, David Turvey. B.A., La. State U., 1974, J.D., 1977; M.L.T., Georgetown U. 1981. Bar: La. 1977, U.S. Dist. Ct. (ea. dist.) La. 1977, U.S. Dist. Ct. (we. dist.) La. 1977, U.S. Dist. Ct. (mid. dist.) La. 1977, U.S. Supreme Ct. 1981. Assoc., Sanders, Downing, Kean & Cazedessus, Baton Rouge, 1977; legis. asst. to U.S. Senator J. Bennett Johnston, Washington, 1977-81; ptnr. Hayes Durio & Richard, Lafayette, La., 1981-82; mem. FERC, Washington, 1982-85; v.p., gen. counsel Tenngasco Corp. div. Tenneco, 1985-87, v.p. regulatory and competitive analysis, 1987—. Fellow Council Econ. Regulation; mem. ABA, Omicron Delta Kappa. Democrat. Roman Catholic. Office: No Natural Gas Co 2223 Dodge St Omaha NE 68102-1228

RICHARD, PAUL, art critic; b. Chgo., Nov. 22, 1939. BA, Harvard U., 1961; student, U. Pa. Art critic Washington Post, 1967—. Office: Washington Post Co 1150 15th St NW Washington DC 20071-0002

RICHARD, ROBERT JOHN, library director; b. Oakland, Calif., Sept. 20, 1947; s. John Argyle and Vern Elizabeth (Bauer) R.; m. Anne Elizabeth Terrell, June 8, 1968 (div. 1982); children: Jennifer Lynn, Laura Ellen, Constance Anne, Andrea Lee. Student, Fullerton Coll., 1965-67; B.A. in Biology, Chapman Coll., Orange (Calif.), 1972; M.S.L.S., Calif. State U.-Fullerton, 1973. Cert. county librarian, Calif. Audiovisual specialist Fullerton Pub. Libr., 1969-72, asst. to city librarian, 1972-73, librarian, 1973-76; br. librarian Orange County Pub. Libr., Orange, 1976-78; regional administr. Orange County Pub. Libr., 1979-80; assoc. dir. Long Beach Pub. Libr., Calif., 1980-81; dir. Sacramento Pub. Libr., 1981-86, Santa Ana (Calif.) Pub. Libr., 1986—. Mem. ALA, Pub. Library Execs. Assn So. Calif., Calif. Library Assn., Library Adminstrn. and Mgmt. Assn., Library Info. and Tech. Assn., Pub. Library Assn. Office: Santa Ana Pub Libr 26 Civic Center Plz Santa Ana CA 92701-4010

RICHARD, SCOTT F., portfolio manager; b. Chgo., Dec. 13, 1946; s. Jerome and Sue (Selig) Richard; m. Susan L. Diamond, June 15, 1969 (div. May 1983); children: Rebecca, Michael; m. Roberta C. Meyerson, Oct. 1, 1983. BS, MIT, 1968; D Bus. Adminstrn., Harvard U., 1972. Prof. fin. Carnegie-Mellon U., Pitts., 1972-87; v.p. fixed income rsch., co-dir. rsch. and model devel. Goldman, Sachs & Co., N.Y.C., 1987-92; portfolio mgr. Miller, Anderson & Sherrerd, West Conshohocken, Pa., 1992—, ptnr., 1993—; vis. prof. fin. MIT, Cambridge, Mass., 1986-87; advt. bd. Jour. of Portfolio Mgmt., 1989—, Jour. of Fixed Income, 1991—. Author: (with A.H. Meltzer and A. Cukierman) Political Economy, 1991; assoc. editor: Jour. of Fin., 1983-88, Jour. Fin. Econs., 1976-83, Mgmt. Sci., 1977-78; contbr. articles to profl. jours. Mem. Am. Econs. Assn., Am. Fin. Assn., The Econometric Soc., Inst. Mgmt. Sci. Office: Miller Anderson & Sherrerd One Tower Bridge West Conshohocken PA 19428

RICHARD, SUSAN MATHIS, trade association executive; b. Detroit, June 21, 1949; d. Robert Louis and Maybelle Ann (Kromm) Engel; m. Paul Carl Mathis, May 12, 1973 (div. 1982); m. Robert Stephen Richard, Oct. 26, 1985. BA, U. Mich., 1971. Cert. tchr., Mich. Tchr. Carl Brablec High Sch., Roseville, Mich., 1971-73; anchorperson, producer Sta. WNCC-Cable TV, East Lansing, Mich., 1973-76; press asst. Ford-Dole Presdl. Campaign, Washington, 1976; TV and radio reporter Cox Communications, Washington, 1977-81; dep. dir. media rels. White House, Washington, 1981-84, spl. asst. to Pres., dir. media rels., 1985-87; mgr. media rels. Walt Disney World, Lake Buena Vista, Fla., 1987-88; v.p. industry communications Nat. Cable TV Assn., Washington, 1989; dep. assoc. adminstr. for pub. affairs Nat. Aeros. and Space Adminstrn., 1990-93; v.p. comm. The Personal Comm. Industry Assn., 1993—; mem. exec. com. Radio-TV Corrs. Galleries, Washington, 1978-81. Dir. promotions Action for Children's TV, East Lansing, 1975; mem. strategic Planning Adv. Coun. of the Orange County (Fla.) Pub. Schs., 1988; communications dir. Bush-Quayle Fla. Campaign, 1988. Named Outstanding Young Working Woman, Lansing C. of C., 1975, Outstanding Working Woman, Washington Woman mag., 1985. Mem. AAUW (bd. dirs. Lansing chpt. 1974), Nat. Assn. Execs., Am. Soc. Assn. Execs. (Pub. Rels. trophy 1994), Radio-TV News Dirs. Assn., Fla. Youth and Family Svcs. Network (bd. dirs. 1988), Acad. TV Arts and Scis. (pub. rels. com. 1989), Women in Aerospace, Women in Wireless, U. Mich. Alumni Assn. (bd. dirs. 1983-85), Gamma Phi Beta Alumnae Assn. Episcopalian. Avocations: doll houses, decorating.

RICHARDI, RALPH LEONARD, airline executive; b. Jersey City, Oct. 10, 1947; s. Nicholas Frank and Genevieve (Miele) R.; m. Cathy A. Himmelberger, Apr. 11, 1981. BS in Indsl. Mgmt., Fairleigh Dickinson U., 1969, MBA, 1976; cert. advanced mgmt. program, Harvard U., Boston, 1991. Indsl. engr. Ford Motor Co., Mahwah, N.J., 1969-72, Chase Manhattan Bank, N.Y.C., 1974-76; indsl. engr. Am. Airlines, Dallas-Ft. Worth, 1976-80, dir. indsl. engring., 1980-83, dir. quality of work life, 1983-85, asst. v.p. labor rels., 1985-87; gen. mgr. reservations Am. Airlines, L.A., 1987-88; gen. mgr. San Francisco Airport Am. Airlines, 1988-89, v.p. Dallas-Ft. Worth Airport, 1989-95; pres. Simmons Airlines/Am. Eagle, 1995—. Vice chmn. fund drives United Way, Dallas-Ft. Worth Airport, 1989-91. Avocation: golf. Address: 6103 Mimosa Ln Dallas TX 75230-5041 Office: Am Airlines Inc PO Box 619616 Dallas TX 75261-9616

RICHARDS, BERNARD, investment company executive; b. N.Y.C., July 12, 1927; s. Charles and Sadie (Rubin) R.; m. Arlene Kaye, Dec. 23, 1948; children: Carol Leslie, Patricia Ellen, Lori Gale. BBA, Baruch Coll., 1949. CPA, N.Y. Acct. Eisner & Lubin, N.Y.C., 1949-53, S.D. Leidesdorf, N.Y.C., 1953-56; from controller to treas. to v.p. fin. to pres. Slattery Group Inc., N.Y.C., 1956-87; pres. Slattery Investors Corp., N.Y.C., 1988—; chmn. bd. dirs. Slattery Assocs., Inc., N.Y.C., 1968-87. Trustee Temple Sinai, Roslyn, N.Y., 1987-89; bd. dirs. Variety Boys Club, Queens, N.Y.C., 1972—;

bd. dirs. N.Y.C. Indsl. Devel. Bd., 1973-76; pres., bd. dirs. Baruch Coll. Fund, N.Y.C., 1975—, Man Yr., 1972. Recipient Heavy Constrn. award United Jewish Appeal, 1980, Pres.'s medal Baruch Coll., 1989; named Outstanding Alumnus of Yr. Baruch Coll., 1979, Man of Yr. United Jewish Appeal, 1980, March of Dimes, 1983; Wood fellow Baruch Coll., 1979. Mem. AICPA, N.Y. State Soc. CPAs, Moles, Beavers (bd. dirs. 1982—), Marco Polo Club, Shelter Rock Tennis Club. Republican. Jewish. Avocations: tennis, travel, cycling, swimming, hiking. Home: 18 Applegreen Dr Old Westbury NY 11568-1203 Office: Slattery Investors Corp 1 Hollow Ln Ste 311 New Hyde Park NY 11042-1215

RICHARDS, CHARLES A., government official; b. Irvona, Pa., May 6, 1940; s. Charles A. Sr. and Genevieve H. (Peterson) R.; m. Mary Gale Davis, May 10, 1980; children: Amy, Antonina. BS in Edn., Indiana U. Pa., 1963. Tchr. history Woodbridge Twp, N.J., 1963-68; nat. rep. Am. Fedn. Tchrs., Washington, 1968-74, asst. to pres., dir. organizing, 1974-82; dir. field activities Pub. Employee Dept. AFL-CIO, Washington, 1982-92; nat. labor coord. Clinton/Core Campaign, Little Rock, 1992; labor coord. Presdl. Transistion Team Clinton/Gore, Washington, 1992-93; dep. asst. sec. U.S. Dept. Labor, Washington, 1993—. Coach Little League. Avocations: skiing, reading. Office: US Dept Labor 200 Constitution Ave Washington DC 20210

RICHARDS, CORY, demographic think-tank executive. V.p. for pub. policy Alan Guttmacher Inst. Wash. Office, Washington, D.C. Office: Alan Guttmacher Inst Washington Office 2010 Mass Ave NW 5th fl Washington DC 20036

RICHARDS, DANIEL THOMAS, library director; b. Salisbury, N.C., Dec. 13, 1945; s. Eric Kenneth and Martha Emaline (Camp) R. BS, U. Maine, 1967; MS, U. Wis., 1969; postgrad., U. Md., 1970-71; cert., Nat. Libr. Medicine, Bethesda, Md., 1971. Reference libr. Brown U., Providence, 1969-70; libr. assoc. Nat. Libr. Medicine, 1970-71, collection devel. officer, 1988-91; cataloger UCLA Biomed. Libr., 1971-72, head acquisitions div., 1972-79, asst. to biomed. libr., 1972-78, collection devel. officer, 1979-81; asst. health scis. libr. for resources and reference svcs. Columbia U., N.Y.C., 1981-88, acting health scis. libr., 1982-83; dir. biomed. librs. Dartmouth Coll., Hanover, N.H., 1991—; lectr. UCLA Grad. Sch. Libr. and Info. Sci., 1973-81, Columbia U. Sch. Libr. Svc., 1982-83, Cath. U. Am. Sch. Libr. and Info. Scis., Washington, 1989; instr. Internat. Fedn. Libr. Assns., Sydney, Australia, 1988; tutor Dartmouth Med. Sch., 1993—; mem. librs. adv. bd. John Wiley & Sons, Inc., N.Y.C., 1991—; mem. bd. libr. advisors Doody's Health Scis. Book Rev. Jour., Chgo., 1993—; cons. Meml. Sloan-Kettering Cancer Ctr., N.Y.C., 1989, U. Ariz., 1991, McGill U., Montreal, 1992, also others. Author: Development and Assessment of Collections in Health Sciences Libraries, 1989, rev. edit., 1991, (with D. Morse) Collection Development Policies for Health Sciences Libraries, 1992, (with others) Collection Development Manual of the National Library of Medicine, 3d edit., 1993, (with D. Eakin) Collection Development in Health Sciences Libraries, 1995; contbr. articles to profl. jours., chpts. to books. Pres., chmn. bd. dirs. Choo-San Goh and H. Robert Magee Found., Washington, 1989—; pres. Culinary Historians N.Y., N.Y.C., 1987-89. Mem. ALA (chmn. chief collection devel. officers large rsch. librs. discussion group 1990), Med. Libr. Assn. (nat. nominating com. 1987, nat. bd. dirs. 1993-96Louise Darling medal, 1989, founding chmn. collection devel. sect. 1986, mem. coms. and bds. for 4 regional chpts. 1971—), Am. Assn. Acad. Health Scis. Libr. Dirs., Am. Assn. for History Medicine, Coun. Biology Editors, Friends Dartmouth Coll. Libr., Friends Nat. Libr. Medicine. Democrat. Roman Catholic. Avocations: collecting John Updike books, culinary and medical history. Home: PO Box 401 Hanover NH 03755 Office: Dartmouth Coll Dana Biomedical Library Hanover NH 03755

RICHARDS, DANIEL WELLS, company executive; b. Taylor, Pa., Dec. 16, 1928; s. Daniel Wells and Bernice (Robling) R.; m. Helen Reilly, Feb. 10, 1979; children: Kenneth, Deborah, Thomas. BA, Dickinson Coll., 1950; postgrad., U. Pitts., 1953-54. Mgr. advt. prodn. Miller Machine Co., Pitts., 1954-55; mgr. sales promotion Gen. Paper Co., Pitts., 1955-57; advt. and product mgr. Harris Seybold Co., Cleve., 1957-67; v.p. mktg. Colwell Systems Inc., Champaign, Ill., 1967-86, pres., 1986-91; Disting. lectr., exec. in residence Ill. State U. 1991-93; pres. D.W. Richards & Assocs., 1994—. Mem. Urbana (Ill.) City Council, 1975-77; budget dir. Ill. Humanities Council, 1980-84; bd. dirs. United Way Champaign County, 1987—, Sinfonia da Camert, 1987—. Served to lt. U.S. Army, 1950-53. Unitarian. Home: 1704 Coventry Dr Champaign IL 61821-5242

RICHARDS, DAVID A. J., lawyer, educator; b. 1944. AB, Harvard U., 1966, JD, 1971; PhD (Knox Meml. fellow), Oxford U., Eng., 1970. Bar: N.Y., 1972. Assoc. Cleary, Gottlieb, Steen & Hamilton, N.Y.C., 1971-74; assoc. prof. Fordham U. N.Y.C., 1974-77; vis. prof. philosophy Barnard Coll., N.Y.C., 1974-77; assoc. prof. law NYU, 1977-79, prof., 1979—. Author: A Theory of Reasons for Action, 1971, The Moral Criticism of Law, 1977, Sex, Drugs, Death and the Law, 1982 (named best book in criminal justice ethics, 1982), Toleration and the Constitution, 1986, Criminal Legal Education. Rockefeller grantee Austinian Soc. and Ctr. for Study of Law and Soc., Berkeley, Calif., 1974; Mellon fellow Aspen Inst. for Humanistic Studies. Mem. Soc. for Philosophy and Pub. Affairs (bd. dirs. N.Y. chpt. 1975-76), Austinian Soc. (pres. 1974). Club: Tuesday Evening. Office: NYU Law Sch 40 Washington Sq S New York NY 10012-1099

RICHARDS, DAVID ALAN, lawyer; b. Dayton, Ohio, Sept. 21, 1945; s. Charles Vernon and Betty Ann (Macher) R.; m. Marianne Catherine Del Monaco, June 26, 1971; children: Christopher, Courtney. BA summa cum laude, Yale U., 1967, JD, 1972; MA, Cambridge U., 1969. Bar: N.Y., 1973. Assoc. Paul, Weiss, Rifkind, Wharton & Garrison, N.Y.C., 1972-77, Coudert Bros., N.Y.C., 1977-80, ptnr., 1981-82; ptnr., head real estate group Sidley & Austin, N.Y.C., 1983—; gov. Anglo-Am. Real Property Inst. U.S./U.K., 1983-88, sec., 1988, chair, 1993; mem. Chgo. Title N.Y. Realty Adv. Bd., 1992—. Contbr. articles to profl. jours. Trustee Scarsdale Pub. Libr. , 1984-89, pres., 1988-89. Fellow Am. Bar Found.; mem. ABA (real property, probate and trust sect., chair 1991-92), Am. Coll. Real Estate Lawyers (chmn. amicus curiae brief com. 1985-88, gov. 1987-93), Internat. Bar Assn., Assn. of Bar of City of N.Y. (real property com. 1978-80, 84-87), Shenorock Shore Club (Rye, N.Y.). Democrat. United Ch. of Christ. Home: 18 Forest Ln Scarsdale NY 10583-6464 Office: Sidley & Austin 875 3rd Ave New York NY 10022-6225

RICHARDS, DAVID GLEYRE, German educator; b. Salt Lake City, July 27, 1935; s. Oliver L. and Lilian Marie (Powell) R.; m. Annegret Horn, Sept. 3, 1959 (div. 1992); 1 child, Stephanie Suzanne. BA, U. Utah, 1960, MA, 1961; PhD, U. Calif.-Berkeley, 1968. Asst. prof. German SUNY, Buffalo, 1968-74, assoc. prof., 1974-84, prof., 1984—. Author: Georg Buchners Woyzeck, 1975, George Buchner and the Birth of the Modern Drama, 1976, The Hero's Quest for the Self: An Archetypal Approach to Hesse's Demian and other Novels, 1987; editor: (with H. Schulte) Crisis and Culture in Post-Enlightenment Germany: Essays in Honor of Peter Heller. SUNY grantee, 1973; NEH grantee, 1977-78, Fulbright Commn. grantee, 1980; Rsch. Found. of SUNY fellow, 1982. Mem. MLA, Am. Assn. Tchrs. German. Democrat. Avocation: photography. Office: SUNY Buffalo Dept Modern Langs & Lits 910 Clemens Hall Buffalo NY 14260

RICHARDS, DAVID JOHN, food distribution company executive; b. Wilkes-Barre, Pa., 1948. Grad., Univ. Pa., 1970, Wayne State U., 1975. Sr. v.p. store devel. Scrivner Inc., Oklahoma City. Home: 11209 Shady Glen Rd Oklahoma City OK 73162-3406 Office: Scrivner Inc Box 26030 5701 N Shartel Ave Oklahoma City OK 73118-5930

RICHARDS, DAVID KIMBALL, investor; b. Portland, Maine, May 14, 1939; s. Robert Ladd and Janice (Kimball) R.; m. Carol Ann Liebich, May 27, 1967; children: Adam, Peter. A.B. cum laude, Harvard U., 1961, M.B.A., 1965; B.A., Wadham Coll., Oxford, Eng., 1963. Research analyst H.C. Wainwright & Co., N.Y.C., 1965-71, ptnr., 1971-73; sr. v.p., dir. Capital Research & Mgmt. Co., Los Angeles, 1973-85; v.p. Income Fund of Am., Los Angeles, 1976-85; pres. Fundamental Investors Inc., Los Angeles, 1982-85; vice chmn. Primecap Mgmt., Pasadena, Calif., 1985-91; pvt. investor, 1991—. Republican. Home: 109 Esparta Way Santa Monica CA 90402-2137

RICHARDS, EDGAR LESTER, psychologist, educator; b. Albany, N.Y., Apr. 20, 1942; s. Edgar Lester and Gertrude Veronica (Halpin) R.; B.S. in Biology, Siena Coll., 1966, M.S. in Edn., 1968; M.A., U. Pa., 1975; C.A.S., Wesleyan U., 1976; M.Phil., Columbia U., 1977, Ph.D., 1981; m. Ruth Anne Farrar, Dec. 21, 1968; children—Edgar Lester, Christopher Hartington, James Gerald, Ruth Anne. Tchr. secondary sch. biology Stillwater Central Sch. Dist. (N.Y.), 1966-71; NSF grantee, 1969, 70; adminstrv. asst. to supt. City Sch. Dist., Watervliet, N.Y., 1971-72, supt. schs., 1972-74; research and devel. assoc. Ctr. for Sch. Study Councils Grad. Sch. Edn., U. Pa., Phila., 1974-75; research scientist N.Y. State Psychiat. Inst., 1975-77; asst. dir. for research and evaluation coordinator Research for Better Schs., Inc., Phila., 1979-80, coordinator field support services, 1980-81, specialist in evaluation and devel., 1981-82; adj. asst. prof. Grad. Sch. Edn., Fordham U., N.Y.C., 1985-86, 88, adj. assoc. prof., 1990—; asst. supt. schs. Mahopac Central Sch. Dist. (N.Y.), 1982—; cons. Nat. Tng. and Evaluation Center, N.Y.C., 1977-79, N.Y.C. Bd. Edn., 1977-79, Research for Better Schs., Inc., 1974-75, 84. Cert. secondary sch. biology and gen. sci. tchr., sch. dist. adminstr., secondary prin., N.Y. State; cert. secondary sch. biology, chemistry, and gen. sci. tchr., prin., Mass. Mem. Am. Assn. Sch. Adminstrs., Am. Assn. Sch. Pers. Adminstrs., Am. Ednl. Research Assn., Am. Psychol. Assn., Assn. for Supervision and Curriculum Devel., Nat. Council on Measurement in Edn., Phi Delta Kappa. Democrat. Roman Catholic. Author: Career Education Linking Agents: Perspectives and Roles, 1981, Career Education Program Design, 1981, Perceptions of the Preparation of Youth for Work: Report of a Three State Survey, 1980, Sharing Career Education Resources with Schools: An Exploratory Study of Employer Willingness, 1980; contbr. articles to profl. jours. Home: 26 Nevins Rd Mahopac NY 10541 Office: Mahopac Pub Schs Dist Cen Office Mahopac NY 10541

RICHARDS, FRED TRACY, finance company executive; b. Waverly, N.Y., Feb. 8, 1914; s. Parke and Lois (Tracy) R.; m. Gladys Bucher Albright, Aug. 1, 1942 (div. 1973); children: Fred Tracy, John Harvey; m. Jean Hunter, June 16, 1973. B.S. in Engring. with honors, Princeton U., 1935. Supr. maintenance way, spl. purchasing agt. Pa. R.R. Co., Phila., 1935-47; supr. materials Dept. Interior and Defel. Transp., 1941-42; chmn. bd., chief exec. officer Central Supply Co. Va. Inc., Phila., 1947-55; asst. to chmn. Avco Corp., Greenwich, Conn., 1955-79; pres. Richards Resources, Inc., Greenwich, 1979—. Pres., bd. dirs. U.S.O., N.Y., 1973-80; v.p. Nat. Exec. Service Corps, N.Y.C., 1981-86. Served to lt. col. C.E. AUS, 1942-46. Mem. Soc. Mayflower Descs. State N.Y., S.R., The Pilgrims, Princeton Club (N.Y.C.). Home: 100 Putnam Pk Greenwich CT 06830-5777

RICHARDS, FREDERIC MIDDLEBROOK, biochemist, educator; b. N.Y.C., Aug. 19, 1925; s. George and Marianna Richards; m. Heidi Clarke, 1948 (div. 1955); children: Sarah, Ruth Gray; m. Sarah Wheatland, 1959; 1 child, George Huntington. BS, MIT, 1948; PhD, Harvard U., 1952; DSc (hon.), U. New Haven, 1982. Rsch. fellow in phys. chemistry Harvard Med. Sch., Cambridge, Mass., 1952-53; NRC postdoctoral fellow Carlsberg Lab., Denmark, 1954; NSF fellow Cambridge U., Eng., 1955; asst. prof. biochemistry Yale U., New Haven, Conn., 1955-59, assoc. prof., 1959-62, prof., 1963-89, Henry Ford II prof. molecular biophysics, 1967-89, Sterling prof. molecular biophysics, 1989-91, Sterling prof. emeritus, 1991—, chmn. dept. molecular biology and biophysics, 1963-67, chmn. dept. molecular biophysics and biochemistry, 1969-73; dir. Jane Coffin Childs Meml. Fund Med. Rsch., 1976-91; mem. Nat. Adv. Rsch. & Resources Coun., 1983-87; mem. corp. Woods Hole Oceanographic Inst., 1977-83, 84-90; mem. bd. advisors Whitney Marine Lab., 1979-84, Purdue U. Magnetic Resonance Lab., 1980-84, Biology divsn. Argonne Nat. Lab., 1982-84, Brookhaven Nat. Lab., Nat. Synchrotron Light Source; mem. sci. adv. bd. structural biology Howard Hughes Med. Inst., 1988-89, adv. bd., 1989-92; mem. sci. adv. bd. Donaghue Found. Med. Rsch., 1991-92. Mem. editorial bd. Jour. Biol. Chemistry, 1963-69, 82-84, Jour. Molecular Biology, 1973-75, Advances in Protein Chemistry, 1963—; contbr. articles on protein and enzyme chemistry to profl. jours. Sgt. U.S. Army, 1944-46. Recipient Pfizer-Paul Lewis award in enzyme chemistry, 1965, Kai Linderstrom-Lang prize in protein chemistry, 1978; Guggenheim fellow, 1967-68. Fellow AAAS, Am. Acad. Arts and Scis.; mem. NAS, Am. Philos. Soc., Am. Soc. Biochemistry and Molecular Biology (Merck award 1988), Protein Soc. (Stein and Moore award 1988), Internat. Union Pure and Applied Biophysics (mem. coun. 1975-81), Am. Soc. Biol. Chemists (pres. 1979-80), Biophys. Soc. (pres. 1972-73), Am. Chem. Soc., Am. Crystallographic Assn. Roman Acad. Sci. and Engring. Avocations: sailing, skiing. Home: 69 Andrews Rd Guilford CT 06437-3715 Office: Yale U Dept Molecular Biophysics 260 Whitney Ave PO Box 208114 New Haven CT 06520-8114

RICHARDS, GALE LEE, communications educator; b. Long Run, W.Va., July 31, 1918; s. Robert Amaziah and Edna Jane (Scott) R.; m. Barbara Lee Neely, Apr. 19, 1944; children—Robin Lee, Wendell Scott, Jeffrey Marshall. B.A. (Pixley scholar), U. Akron, O., 1940; M.A. (C.S. Knight Meml. scholar), U. Ia., 1942, Ph.D. 1950. Instr. speech U. Akron, 1941-42; asst. prof. speech Drake U., 1947-48; asst. prof. English U. Nev., 1948-52; asst. prof. speech U. Wash., 1952-58; assoc. prof. speech U. So. Calif., 1958-65; prof. communication Ariz. State U., Tempe, 1965—, chmn. dept. speech and theatre, 1965-73; Pub. relations cons. Red Feather campaign United Fund, Los Angeles, 1955-58; mgmt. and tng. cons. various profl. and comml. orgns., 1955—. Cons. editor: Western Speech, 1957-61, 62-65, 69-72, Jour. of Communication, 1961-67; Contbr. articles profl. jours. Bd. dirs. Phoenix Little Theatre. Served to lt. USNR, 1942-45, PTO. Recipient Distinguished Alumni award Radio Sta. WSUI, 1942. Mem. Speech Communication Assn. (adminstrv. coun., legis. coun., chair commn. on Am. Parliamentary procedures, 1988, emeritus 1991), Internat. Communication Assn. (adminstrv. coun.), Am. Inst. Parliamentarians, Western States Communication Assn. (2d v.p. 1956, 71, pres. Execs. club 1975, Disting. Svc. award 1989), Ariz. Communication and Drama Assn. (pres. 1967, editor jour. 1984-87), Blue Key, Phi Kappa Phi, Delta Sigma Rho. Democrat. Presbyn. Club: Rotarian. Home: 614 E Bishop Dr Tempe AZ 85282-2325

RICHARDS, HERBERT EAST, minister emeritus, commentator; b. Hazleton, Pa., Dec. 30, 1919; s. Herbert E. and Mabel (Vannaucker) R.; m. Lois Marcey, Jan. 1, 1942; children: Herbert Charles, Marcey Lynn, Robyn Lois, Fredrick East, Mark Allen. AB, Dickinson Coll., 1941; BD, Drew U., 1944; MA, Columbia, 1944; DD, Coll. of Idaho, 1953; postgrad., Union Theol. Sem., 1941-48, Bucknell U., 1943-44. Accredited news reporter Nat. Assn. Broadcasters. Ordained to ministry Methodist Ch., 1944; pastor in Boiling Springs, Pa., 1937-40, West Chester, Pa., 1940-41, Basking Ridge, N.J., 1941-47; mem. faculty Drew U. and Theol. Sem., 1944-51, assoc. prof. homiletics and Christian criticism, chmn. dept., assoc. dean, 1947-51; spl. lectr. religion Howard U., 1947; minister 1st Meth. Cathedral, Boise, Idaho, 1951-69, 1st United Meth. Ch., Eugene, Oreg., 1969-78; minister Tabor Heights United Meth. Ch., Portland, Oreg., 1978-86, minister emeritus, 1986—; weekly radio broadcaster Sta. KBOI, Sta. KIDO, 1941—; weekly TV broadcaster CBS, 1945—, ABC, 1969—, NBC, 1973; pres. Inspiration, Inc., TV Found., 1965—, TV Ecology, 1973; producer Life TV series ABC, 1974-85, also BBC, Eng., Suise Romande, Geneva; chmn. Idaho bd. ministerial tng. Meth. Conf., 1954-60, TV, Radio and Film Commn., 1942-64, Oreg. Coun. Public Broadcasting, 1973; del. Idaho Conf. Meth. Gen. Conf., 1956, Jurisdictional Conf., 1956, World Meth. Coun., 1957, 81, World Meth. Conf., 1981, mem. Gen. Conf., 1956-60, Jurisdictional Conf., 1956, 60; meml. chaplain Idaho Supreme Ct., 1960; chaplain Idaho Senate, 1960-68; mem. Task Force on TV and Ch., 1983. Author: In Time of Need, 1986; contbr. articles to religious publs.; composer: oratorios Prophet Unwilling, 1966, Meet Martin Luther, 1968, Dear Jesus Boy, 1973. Mem. Commn. on Centennial Celebration for Idaho, 1962-63; committeeman Boy Scouts Am.; bd. dirs. Eugene chpt. ARC, 1954-73; trustee Willamette U., Cascade Manor Homes; adv. bd. Medic-Alert Found. Recipient Alumni citation in religious edn. Dickinson Coll., 1948, Golden Plate award Am. Acad. Achievement, 1965, Jason Lee Mass Media TV award, 1983; named Clergyman of Yr., Religious Heritage Am., 1964. Mem. AAUP, CAP (chaplain Idaho wing, lt. col.), Am. Acad. Achievement (bd. govs. 1967—), Am. Found. Religion and Psychiatry (charter gov.), Greater Boise Ministerial Assn. (pres.), Eugene Ministerial Assn. (pres. 1978), Masons (33 degree, editor Pike's Peak Albert That Is), Shriners, Elks, Rotary (editor Key and Cog, pres. dist. 510 Pioneer Club), Kappa Sigma (Grand Master of Beta Pi). Home: 10172 SE 99th Dr Portland OR 97266-7227 Office: Tabor Heights United Meth Ch 6161 SE Stark St Portland OR 97215-1935 *When a person presses his face against the window pane of life, he becomes as a child waiting for his father's return;*

simple, trusting and infinitely wiser. In our present time of growth/conflict, such a face-pressing is essential to get us safely from where we are to where we ought to be.

RICHARDS, HILDA, academic administrator; b. St. Joseph, Mo., Feb. 7, 1936; d. Togar and Rose Avalynne (Williams) Young-Ballard. Diploma nursing St. John's Sch. Nursing, St. Louis, 1956; BS cum laude, CUNY, 1961; MEd, Columbia U., 1965, EdD, 1976; MPA, NYU, 1971. Dep. chief dept. psychiatry Harlem Rehab. Ctr., N.Y.C., 1969-71; prof., dir. nursing Medgar Evers Coll., CUNY, N.Y.C., 1971-76, prof., assoc. dean, 1976-79; dean Coll. Health and Human Service, Ohio U., Athens, 1979-86; provost, v.p. for acad. affairs Indiana U., Pa., 1986-93; chancellor Ind. U. N.W., Gary, 1993—; bd. dirs. Sta. 56-TV; active N.W. Satir Inst., Execs. Coun. N.W. Ind., ACE Commn. on Minorities in Higher Edn., AASCU Com. on Diversity and Social Change. Author: (with others) Curriculum Development and People of Color: Strategies and Change, 1983; editor Black Conf. on Higher Edn. Jour., 1989-93. Bd. dirs. Avanta Network, 1984—, Urban League N.W. Ind., 1993, N.W. Ind. Forum, 1993, Bank One Regional Bd., Merrillville, Ind., 1994, The Meth. Hosps., Inc., Gary.Merrillville, 1994, Lake Area United Way, 1994, Boys and Girls Clubs N.W. Ind.; life mem. Gary chpt. NAACP; exec. com. Pa. Black Conf. on Higher Edn., 1988-93. Recipient Rockefeller Found. award Am. Council Edn., Washington, 1976-77, Black Achiever award Black Opinion Mag., 1989, Athena award Bus. and Profl. Women's Club Ind., 1991; Martin Luther King grantee NYU, N.Y.C., 1969-70, Gunt Found. grantee Harvard Inst. Ednl. Mgmt., Cambridge, Mass., 1981. Fellow Am. Acad. Nursing; mem. ANA (Outstanding Woman of Color award 1990), AAHE, AAUW, APHA, Am. Assn. State Colls. and Univs., Nat. Assn. Allied Health Profls., Am. Assn. Univ. Adminstrs., Assn. Black Nursing Faculty in Higher Edn. (bd. dirs. 1989—), Pa. Nurses Assn., Assn. Black Women in Higher Edn., Inc., Nat. Black Nurses Assn. (bd. dirs., 1st v.p. 1984—, editor jour. 1985—, Spl. Recognition award 1991, Disting. African-Am. Nurse Educator award Queens County chpt., 1991), Nat. Assn. Women in Edn., Am. Coun. Edn. (exec. com. coun. fellows), Internat. Assn. Univ. Pres., N.W. Rotary, N.W. Kiwanis, Phi Delta Kappa, Sigma Theta Tau, Zonta Club of Ind. County. Democrat. Avocations: needlepoint, travel. Home: 7807 Hemlock Ave Gary IN 46403-2164 Office: Ind U NW Office of Chancellor 3400 Broadway Gary IN 46408-1197

RICHARDS, HUGH TAYLOR, physics educator; b. Baco County, Colo., Nov. 7, 1918; s. Dean Willard and Kate Bell (Taylor) R.; m. Mildred Elizabeth Paddock, Feb. 11, 1944; children: David Taylor, Thomas Martin, John Willard, Margaret Paddock, Elizabeth Nicholls, Robert Dean. BA, Park Coll., 1939; MA, Rice U., 1940, PhD, 1942. Research assoc. Rice U., Houston, 1942; scientist U. Minn., Mpls., 1942-43, U. Calif. Sci. Labs., Los Alamos, N.Mex., 1943-46; research assoc. U. Wis., Madison, 1946-47, mem. faculty, 1947-52, prof., 1952-88, prof. emeritus, 1988—, physics dept. chairperson, 1960-63, 66-69, 85-88; assoc. dean Coll. Letters and Sci., U. Wis, 1963-66. Author: Through Los Alamos 1945: Memoirs of a Nuclear Physicist, 1993; contbr. articles to profl. jours. Fellow Am. Phys. Soc.; mem. Am. Assn. Physics Tchrs. Unitarian-Universalist. Achievements include neutron measurements first A-Bomb test; fission neutron (and other) spectra by new photo-emulsion techniques; mock fission neutron source; spherical electrostatic analyzer for precise reaction energy measurements; negative ion sources for accelerators (He ALPHATROSS, SNICS); accurate proton, deuteron, and alpha particle scattering and reaction cross sections; systematics mirror nuclei; isospin violations in nuclear reactions. Home: 1902 Arlington Pl Madison WI 53705-4002 Office: Univ of Wis Dept Of Physics Madison WI 53706

RICHARDS, J. SCOTT, rehabilitation medicine professional. BA in Psychology cum laude, Oberlin Coll., 1968; Cert. in Elem. Edn., Wayne State U., 1969; MS in Resource Ecology, U. Mich., 1973; PhD in Psychology, Kent State U., 1977. Elem. tchr. Detroit Pub. Schs., 1968-71; rsch. asst. Inst. Fisheries Rsch., 1971-73; teaching asst. Kent State U., 1973-74; psychology intern, 1973-77; dir. psychology and instr. dept. rehab. medicine, co-dir. pain control program SRC with depts. psychiatry and psychology U. Ala., Birmingham, 1977—, from asst. to assoc. prof. dept. rehab. medicine, 1980-90, prof., 1990—, dir. tng. med. rehab. rsch. tng. ctr., 1985-87, dir. rsch., 1987—, co-dir. UAB-SCI Care System and Nat. SCI Statis. Ctr., 1989—; cons. Ctrs. Disease Control, Nat. Inst. Disability & Rehab. Rsch. Contbr. articles to profl. jours. Fellow APA. Office: U Ala Sch Medicine Rehab Medicine 1717 7th Ave S Birmingham AL 35294-0001

RICHARDS, JAMES E., pharmaceutical executive. Chmn. bd., ceo Tenn. Wholesale Drug Co., Nashville, Tenn., 1940—. Office: Tennessee Wholesale Drug Co 200 Cumberland Bnd Nashville TN 37228-1804

RICHARDS, JEANNE HERRON, artist; b. Aurora, Ill., Apr. 8, 1923; d. Robert Watt and Ida (Herron) R. B.F.A., U. Iowa, 1952, M.F.A., 1954. instr. art State U. Iowa, 1955-56; instr. U. Nebr., 1957-59, asst. prof., 1959-63; instr. Ascension Acad., Alexandria, Va., 1967-68. One-woman shows include U. Nebr. Art Galleries, Lincoln, 1959, U. Ill., Champaign-Urbana, 1969, group shows include Library of Congress, 1947-61, Corcoran Gallery, Washington, 1974; represented in permanent collections Lessing J. Rosenwald Collection, Library of Congress, Nat. Mus. Am. Art, Smithsonian Instn. Served with USNR, 1943-46. Fulbright grantee, 1954-55. Mem. Am. Graphic Artists, Soc. Washington Printmakers, Gamma Phi Beta. Address: 9526 Liptonshire Dr Dallas TX 75238-2727

RICHARDS, JERRY LEE, academic administrator, religious educator; b. Lawrenceville, Ill., Nov. 4, 1939; s. Russell O. and Elvessa A. (Goodman) R.; m. Susan Richards, Apr. 25, 1986; children: Mark, Renee, Teresa, Angela. B.A., Lycoming Coll., 1965; B.D., Evang. Congregational Sch. Theology, 1967; M.Div., Garrett Theol. Sem., 1968; D.Ministry, St. Paul Sch. Theology, 1975. Ordained to ministry Meth. Ch., 1968. Pastor chs. Pa., 1960-65, Williamsport, Iowa, 1965-70; mem. faculty Iowa Wesleyan U., Mt Pleasant, 1970-85; prof. religion, dir. responsible social involvement Iowa Wesleyan U., Mt. Pleasant, 1975-85, v.p. for acad. affairs, 1975-82, pres., 1982-85; dir. spl. gifts U. Wis., Eau Claire, 1985—. Pres. Mental Health Inst. Aux., Mt. Pleasant, 1976; dir. spl. gifts U. Wis.-Eau Claire, 1985—. Mem. Phi Alpha Theta. Office: U Wis Office of Devel 213 Schofield Hall Eau Claire WI 54701

RICHARDS, JOHN M., wood and paper products company executive; b. 1937. BA, Stanford U., 1959; MBA, Harvard U., 1961. With Fernwood Tie Co., 1962-64, v.p.; with St. Maries Plywood Co., 1964-69, v.p., gen. mgr.; with Potlatch Corp., San Francisco, 1969—, sales mgr., wood products group mktg. div., 1970-72, v.p., wood products group western div., 1972-76, sr. v.p. fin., 1976-83, sr. v.p. fin. adminstrn., 1983-87, exec. v.p. fin. adminstrn., 1987-89, pres., chief oper. officer, 1989—. Office: Potlatch Corp PO Box 3591 1 Maritime Plz San Francisco CA 94111-3404

RICHARDS, JOSEPH EDWARD, artist; b. Des Moines, Oct. 10, 1921; s. Earl L. and Ivanore M. (Shelledy) R.; m. Elizabeth Anne Morrow, Mar. 23, 1943. Student Am. Acad. Art, Chgo., 1946-49, Art Inst. Chgo., 1949-50, Pa. Acad. Fine Arts, 1950-52. Exhbns. include: Butler Inst. Am. Art, Youngstown, Ohio, 1976, 77, 78, 81, Tex. Fine Arts Assn./Laguna Gloria Art Mus., Austin, Tex., 1977, NAD, N.Y.C., 1978, Silvermine Guild Artists, New Cannan, Conn., 1978, 79, Pa. Acad. Fine Arts, Phila., 1978, 80, 94, Va. Mus., Richmond, 1979, O.K. Harris Gallery, N.Y.C., 1982, 89, 92, 94, O.K. Harris West Gallery, Scottsdale, Ariz., 1981, 82, Robert Kidd Galleries, Birmingham, Mich., 1984, Soghor, Leonard & Assocs. Gallery, N.Y.C., 1985, O.K. Harris South, Miami, Fla., 1986, Butler Inst. Am. Art, Youngstown, Ohio, 1987, Tortue Gallery, Santa Monica, Calif., 1988, Art Expo, Tokyo, 1990, Art Now Gallery, Gothenburg, Sweden, 1990, Louis Stern Gallery, Beverly Hills, Calif., 1991, Bobbitt Visual Arts Ctr. Albion (Mich.) Coll., 1991. Represented in private and corp. collections in U.S., Can., Europe. Recipient Disting. artists award Va. Mus. Fine Art, 1979. Fellow Pa. Acad. Fine Arts. Home: PO Box 374 Hillsdale NY 12529-0374

RICHARDS, KEITH, musician; b. Dartford, Kent, Eng., Dec. 18, 1943; s. Bert and Doris Richards; m. Anita Pallenberg; children: Marlon, Angela; m. Patti Hansen, Dec. 18, 1983; children: Theodora, Alexandra. Student Sidcup Art Sch. Lead & rhythm guitarist, vocalist, Rolling Stones, 1962—; films include: Sympathy for the Devil, 1970, Gimme Shelter, 1970, Ladies and Gentlemen, the Rolling Stones, 1974, Let's Spend the Night Together, 1983, film mus. dir. (with Chuck Berry, Eric Clapton and friends) Hail! Hail! Rock & Roll, 1987; composer (with Mick Jagger) numerous songs and albums, 1964—, including (albums) The Rolling Stones, Now!, 1964, Aftermath, 1966, Flowers, 1967, Beggars Banquet, 1968, Let It Bleed, 1969, Sticky Fingers, 1971, Hot Rocks, 1972, Exile on Main Street, 1972, Goat's Head Soup, 1973, It's Only Rock and Roll, 1974, Metamorphosis, 1975, Black and Blue, 1976, Some Girls, Emotional Rescue, 1980, Tatoo You, 1981, Still Life, 1982, Under Cover, 1983, Dirty Work, 1986, Steel Wheels, 1989, Flashpoint, 1991, Voodoo Lounge, 1994 (Grammy award Best Rock Album); (songs) Wild Horses, Angie, Start Me Up, Honky Tonk Woman, Jumpin' Jack Flash, (I Can't Get No) Satisfaction, Before They Make Me Run, Miss You, Happy, Shattered, Paint It Black, Waiting On a Friend, Ruby Tuesday, You Can't Always Get What You Want, Brown Sugar, Tumbling Dice, Faraway Eyes, Mixed Emotions, Rock and a Hard Place, Highwire; producer (soundtrack album) Hail! Hail! Rock 'N Roll, 1987; solo albums: Talk Is Cheap, 1988, Keith Richards & The X-Pensive Winos Live At The Hollywood Palladium, Dec. 15, 1988, 1991, Main Offender, 1992. Recipient Living Legend award Internat. Rock; inducted into Rock and Roll Hall of Fame, 1989. Address: care Raindrop Svcs 1776 Broadway New York NY 10019-2001

RICHARDS, LACLAIRE LISSETTA JONES (MRS. GEORGE A. RICHARDS), social worker; b. Pine Bluff, Ark.; d. Artie William and Geraldine (Adams) Jones; m. George Alvarez Richards, July 26, 1958; children: Leslie Rosario, Lia Mercedes, Jorge Ferguson. BA, Nat. Coll. Christian Workers, 1953; MSW, U. Kans., 1956; postgrad. Columbia U., 1960. Diplomate Clin. Social Work, Am. Bd. of Examiners in Clin. Social Work, Nat. Assn. Social Workers; cert. gerontologist. Psychiat. supervisory, teaching, community orgn., adminstrv. and consultative duties Hastings Regional Ctr., Ingleside, Nebr., 1956-60; supervisory, consultative and adminstrv. responsibilities for psychiat. and geriatric patients VA Hosp., Knoxville, Iowa, 1960-74, field instr. for grad. students from U. Mo., EEO counselor, 1969-74, 78-90, conn. 1969-70, Fed. women's program coordinator, 1972-74; sr. social worker Mental Health Inst., Cherokee, Iowa, 1974-77; adj. asst. prof. dept. social behavior U. S.D.; instr. Dept. of Psychiatry U. S.D Sch. of Medicine, 1988—, Augustana Coll., 1981-86; outpatient social worker VA Med. and Regional Office Center, Sioux Falls, S.D., 1978-90; med., surg. & intensive care social worker, 1990-92, surg. & intermediate care social worker, 1992—; EEO counselor. Mem. Knoxville Juvenile Adv. Com., 1963-65, 68-70, sec., 1965-66, chmn., 1966-68; sec. Urban Renewal Citizens' Adv. Com., Knoxville, 1966-68; mem. United Methodist Ch. Task Force Exptl. Styles Ministry and Leadership, 1973-74, mem. adult choir, mem. ch. and society com.; counselor Knoxville Youth Line program; sec. exec. com. Vis. Nurse Assn., 1979-80; canvasser community fund drs., Knoxville; mem. Cherokee Civil Rights Commn.; bd. dirs., pub. relations, membership devel. and program devel. cons. YWCA, 1983-85; bd. dirs. Family Svc. Agy., 1989-90, Food Svcs. Ctr. Inc., 1992—; mem. S.D. Symphonic Choir, 1991—. Named S.D. Social Worker of Yr., 1983. Mem. NAACP (chmn. edn. com. 1983-85), AAUW (sec. Hastings chpt. 1958-60), Nat. Assn. Social Workers (co-chmn. Nebr. chpt. profl. standards com. 1958-59), Acad. Cert. Social Workers, S.D. Assn. Social Workers (chmn. minority affairs com., v.p. S.E. region 1980, pres. 1980-82 exec. com. 1982-84, mem. social policy and action com.), Nebr. Assn. Social Workers (chmn. 1958-59), Seventh Dist. S.D. Med. Soc. Aux., Coalition on Aging., Nat. Assn. Social Workers (qualified clin. social worker 1991—), Methodist (Sunday sch. tchr. adult div.; mem. commn. on edn.; mem. Core com. for adult edn.; mem. Adult Choir; mem. Social Concerns Work Area). Home: 1701 E Ponderosa Dr Sioux Falls SD 57103-5019

RICHARDS, LISLE FREDERICK, architect; b. Merrick, N.Y., Dec. 28, 1909. B.Arch., U. So. Calif., 1934. Draftsman H.C. Nickerson, 1935, Lawrence Test, 1936-40, Raimond Johnson, 1937; with Richards & Logue (architects); practice as L.F. Richards Santa Clara, Calif., 1947-78. Prin. works include Labor Temple, San Jose, Calif., 1948, Swimming Center, Santa Clara, 1949, C.W. Haman Sch, Santa Clara, 1952, Scott Lane Sch, Santa Clara, 1953, W.A. Wilson Sch, Santa Clara, 1954, Westwood Sch, Santa Clara, 1955, Civic Center, Santa Clara, 1962, Santa Clara Internat. Swim Center, 1970. Mem. Santa Clara County Appeals Bd., 1952; mem. Santa Clara Code Com., 1954. Fellow AIA (pres. Coast Valleys chpt. 1956, pres. Calif. Council 1958, Disting. Service award 1959, Disting. Service citation Santa Clara Valley chpt. 1982, Testimonial Appreciation 1990). Home: 4985 Ponderosa Ter Campbell CA 95008-5751 *As I look back on the past seventy years—what a wonderful and terrible time it has been to live.*

RICHARDS, LLOYD GEORGE, theatrical director, university administrator; b. Toronto, Ont., Can.; came to U.S., 1923; s. Albert George and Rose Isabella (Coote) R.; m. Barbara Davenport, Oct. 11, 1957; children: Scott, Thomas. Student, Wayne U., 1943-44. Head actor tng. NYU Sch. Arts, N.Y.C., 1966-72; artistic dir. Nat. Playwrights Conf., Eugene O'Neill Meml. Theatre Ctr., Waterford, Conn., 1969—; prof. theatre and cinema Hunter Coll., N.Y.C., 1972-79; dean Yale U. Sch. Drama, New Haven, 1979-91; artistic dir Yale Repertory Theatre, New Haven, 1979-91; prof. emeritus Sch. Drama, 1991—; artistic dir. Yale Repertory Theater, 1979-91; pres. Theater Devel. Fund; head actor tng. Sch. Arts NYU, 1966-72; lectr., cons. in field; bd. dirs. Theatre Comm. Group, U.S. Bicentennial World Theatre Festival; mem. various profl. adv. groups, task forces; mem. playwrights selection com. Rockefeller Found.; mem. new Am. plays program com. Ford Found.; mem. com. on profl. theater tng. Nat. Endowment Arts. Actor on radio, TV and theater, 1941—; including Broadway plays The Egghead, 1957, Freight, 1956; disc jockey, Detroit; dir. for: radio, TV, film and theater, including Broadway plays A Raisin in the Sun, 1958, The Long Dream, 1960, The Moon Besieged, 1962, I Had a Ball, 1964, The Yearling, 1966, Paul Robeson, 1977-78, Ma Rainey's Black Bottom, 1984, Fences, 1987 (Tony award 1987), Joe Turner's Come and Gone, 1986, The Piano Lesson, 1990, Two Trains Running, 1992; and TV prodns. include: segment of Roots: The Next Generation, 1979, Bill Moyers' Jour, 1979, Robeson, 1979, Hallmark Piano Lesson 95. Served with USAAF, 1943-44. Recipient Pioneer award AUDELCO, 1986-87, Frederick Douglas award, 1986-87, Golden Plate award, 1987, Nat. Medal of Arts, 1993. Mem. Soc. Stage Dirs. and Choreographers (pres.), Actors Equity Assn., AFTRA, Dirs. Guild Am. Office: 18 W 95th St New York NY 10025-6708

RICHARDS, MAX DE VOE, management educator, consultant, researcher, author; b. Nova, Ohio, May 23, 1923; s. Paul Leroy and Dorothy Charlotte (Daniels) Richards; m. Winona Marie Petersen, Mar. 3, 1950 (div. Dec. 1974); children: Cassandra, Elizabeth; m. Ruth Sara Nixon, Nov. 12, 1977. M.B.A., Stanford U., 1947; Ph.D., U. Ill., 1955. Indsl. engr. Nat. Tube div. U.S. Steel Co., 1948-49; instr. mgmt. U. Ill., Urbana, 1949-54; assoc. prof., head dept. mgmt. U. Wichita, Kans., 1954-56; assoc. prof., head div. mgmt. Pa. State U., University Park, 1956-64, prof., head dept. mgmt., 1964-67, 78-81, prof., asst. dean, dir. grad. programs Coll. Bus. Adminstrn., 1966-77; disting. prof. mgmt. Rollins Coll., Winter Park, Fla., 1981-85; organizational and strategic mgmt. cons., program speaker, U.S., internationally, 1954—; bd. dirs. Inst. for Adminstrv. Research, 1967-69; evaluator Middle States Accrediting Assn., Newark, 1973—. Author: Organizational Goal Structures, 1978, Intermediate and Long Term Credit Small Corporations, 1980, Setting Strategic Goals and Objectives, rev. edit. 1986; co-author: Management Decisions and Behavior, 2d edit. 1973; editor: Readings in Management, 7th edit. 1986. Ford Found. faculty fellow, 1965-66; Nat. Social Sci. Research Council fellow, 1966. Fellow Acad. Mgmt. (dir. 1961-68, v.p., program chmn. 1965-66, pres. 1966-67, chmn. policy and planning div. 1975, dir. div. 1974-78); mem. Strategic Mgmt. Soc. (editorial bd. 1983—), Order of Artus, Sigma Iota Epsilon (trustee 1968), Beta Gamma Sigma, Beech Mountain Club (N.C.), Tuscawilla Country Club (Winter Springs, Fla.), Elks. Home: 1117 Winged Foot Cir W Winter Spgs FL 32708-4201 Office: Crummer Grad Sch Bus Rollins Coll Winter Park FL 32789

RICHARDS, MERLON FOSS, retired diversified technical services company executive; b. Farmington, Utah, May 18, 1920; s. Ezra Foss and Mertie Malinda (Hunt) R.; m. Carlye Jane Vandenberg, July 18, 1945 (dec. 1994); children: Craig M., Cathy Jean, Cynthia Jane, Julie Ann. BS, U. Utah, 1942; MBA, Harvard U., 1947. CPA, Ill. Pub. acct. Arthur Andersen & Co., Chgo., 1947-52; asst. treas. to exec. v.p. Land-Air, Inc., Chgo., 1952-59; from v.p. to vice chmn., chief exec. officer DynCorp (formerly Dynalectron Corp.), Washington 1959-85, bd. dirs., mem. exec. com., 1971-88; consulting fin. officer Indsl. Tng. Corp., Herndon, Va., 1988-89; former dir. over 20

DynCorp subs.; mem. adv. bd. Sycom Inc., 1986-88; dir. Riggs Nat. Bank, 1979-81. Chmn., vice chmn. membership Potomac dist. Nat. Capital Area coun. Boy Scouts Am., 1989—; pub. affairs dir. Washington region LDS Ch., 1984-94; mem. fin. com. Interfaith Conf. of Met. Washington, 1992—. Maj. F.A., U.S. Army, 1941-54, ETO. Decorated Bronze Star, Silver Star. Mem. Pi Kappa Alpha. Republican. Home and Office: 5502 Newington Rd Bethesda MD 20816-3318

RICHARDS, MICHAEL, actor, comedian; b. 1949; 1 child. TV appearences include Fridays, 1980-82, Marblehead Manor, 1987, Seinfeld, 1990— (Emmy award, Outstanding Supporting Actor in a Comedy Series, 1993, 94); films include Young Doctors in Love, 1982, Transylvania 6-5000, 1985, UHF, 1989, Problem Child, 1990, Coneheads, 1993, Unstrung Heroes, 1995. Office: APA 9000 Sunset Blvd/Ste 1200 Los Angeles CA 90069*

RICHARDS, NORMAN BLANCHARD, lawyer; b. Melrose, Mass., May 27, 1924; s. Henry Edward and Annie Jane (Blanchard) R.; m. Diane Maionchi, July 9, 1977; children—Terri, Jeffrey. B.S., Bowdoin Coll., 1945; J.D., Stanford U., 1951. Bar: Calif. bar 1951. Mem. firm McCutchen Doyle Brown & Enersen, San Francisco, 1951—; partner McCutchen Doyle Brown & Enersen, 1960—; mem. faculty Tulane Admiralty Law Inst., Hastings Coll. Advocacy. Bd. visitors Stanford Law Sch. With USN, 1943-46. Fellow Am. Coll. Trial Lawyers; mem. Am. Bar Assn., Calif. State Bar, San Francisco Bar Assn., Maritime Law Assn. U.S., World Trade Club. Home: 85 Platt Ave Sausalito CA 94965-1897 Office: McCutchen Doyle Brown & Enerson 3 Embarcadero Ctr San Francisco CA 94111-4003

RICHARDS, PAUL A., lawyer; b. Oakland, Calif., May 27, 1927; s. Donnell C. and Theresa (Pasquale) R.; m. Ann Morgans, May 20, 1948 (dec. 1984); 1 child, Paul M. BA, U. Pacific, 1950; JD, U. San Francisco, 1953. Bar: Nev. 1953, U.S. Dist. Ct. Nev. 1953, U.S. Supreme Ct. 1964, U.S. Ct. Claims 1976, U.S. Ct. Appeals (9th cir.) 1982. Pvt. practice, Reno, 1953—, prin. Paul A. Richards, Ltd.; prof. environ. law Sierra Nevada Coll., 1970-80. Mem. Washoe Dem. Central Com., 1959-74, chmn., 1964-66, vice chmn., 1966-68; trustee Sierra Nevada Coll., 1970-82, Ducks Unltd., 1964-72; trustee emeritus, 1974—; mem. Fed. Land Law Commn., Nev., 1973-80; bd. dirs. Reno Rodeo Assn., 1963, pres., 1979. Served with U.S. Navy, 1945-46. Recipient Pres.'s Buckle and award Reno Rodeo Assn., 1979. Mem. Nev. Bar Assn., Washoe County Bar Assn. Democrat. Roman Catholic. Club: Lodge: Elks, Masons. Office: 248 S Sierra St Richards Bldg Ste 1 Reno NV 89501

RICHARDS, PAUL GRANSTON, geophysics educator, seismologist; b. Cirencester, Eng., Mar. 31, 1943; came to U.S., 1965; s. Albert George and Kathleen Margaret (Harding) R.; m. Judy Margaret Porterfield, June 1, 1968; children: Mark, Jessica, Gillian. BA, Cambridge (Eng.) U., 1965; MS, Calif. Inst. Tech., Pasadena, 1966, PhD, 1970. Prof. geol. scis. Columbia U., N.Y.C., 1971—, chmn. dept. geol. scis., 1980-83; Co-author: Quantitative Seismology, 2 vols., 1980. Guggenheim Found. fellow, 1977-78, MacArthur Found. fellow, 1981-86. Fellow Royal Astron. Soc.; mem. Am. Geophys. Union (Macelwane award 1976), Coun. Fgn. Rels. Episcopalian. Office: Lamont-Doherty Earth OBS Palisades NY 10964

RICHARDS, PAUL LINFORD, physics educator, researcher; b. Ithaca, N.Y., June 4, 1934; s. Lorenzo Adolph and Zilla (Linford) R.; m. Audrey Jarratt , Aug. 24, 1965; children: Elizabeth Anne, Mary-Ann. AB, Harvard U., 1956; PhD, U. Calif., Berkeley, 1960. Postdoctoral fellow U. Cambridge (Eng.), 1959-60; mem. tech. staff Bell Telephone Labs., Murray Hill, N.J., 1960-66; prof. physics U. Calif., Berkeley, 1966—, Faculty Rsch. lectr., 1990-91; faculty sr. scientist Lawrence Berkeley Lab., 1966—; advisor NASA, 1975-92, Conductus Inc., Mountain View, Calif., 1988—; hon. prof. Miller Inst. Rsch. in Phys. Scis., Berkeley, 1969-70, 87-88; vis. prof. Ecole Normale Superieure, Paris, 1984, 92; vis. astronomer Paris Obs., 1984. Contbr. over 300 articles to profl. jours. Guggenheim Meml. Found. fellow, Cambridge, Eng., 1973-74; named Calif. Scientist of Yr. Mus. Sci., L.A., 1981; recipient sr. scientist award alexander von Humboldt Found., Stuttgart, Fed. Republic Germany, 1982; Berkeley Faculty Rsch. lectr. 1991. Fellow NAS, Am. Phys. Soc., Am. Acad. Arts and Scis. Avocations: vineyardist, wine making.

RICHARDS, RAYMOND SEARS, scientist, company executive; b. Somerville, N.J., July 10, 1928; s. Herbert E. and Gladys (Stowe) R.; m. Judy Danton, June 20, 1952 (div. 1967); children: Christopher, Dustin, Mark; m. Norma Jean Speak, Jan. 29, 1971. BS in Chem. Engring., Antioch Coll., 1951; MS in Metal Engring., Ill. Inst. Tech., 1953. Project engr. IITRI, Armour Rsch. Found., Chgo., 1951-54; project engr., head Timet, Titanium Metals Corp., Henderson, Nev., 1954-57; chief, glass project Owens Ill. Inc., Toledo, 1957-83; pres. Assoc. Tech. Cons., Toledo, 1983—; sr. scientist Glasstech. Inc., Toledo, 1989—. Contbr. articles to profl. jours. Mem. Am. Soc. Metals, Am. Ceramic Soc., Am. Inst. Mining, Metallurgied Petrolium Engrs. Home: 8050 Holstein Rd Toledo OH 43617 Office: Assoc Tech Cons 2375 Dorr St Ste I Toledo OH 43607-3406

RICHARDS, REUBEN FRANCIS, natural resource company executive; b. Aug. 15, 1929; s. Junius A. and Marie R. (Thayer) R.; m. Elizabeth Brady, Nov. 28, 1953; children: Reuben Francis, Timothy T., Andrew H. AB, Harvard U., 1952. With Citibank, N.A., N.Y.C., 1953-82, exec. v.p., 1970-82; chmn. Terra Industries Inc., N.Y.C., 1982—; bd. dirs. Ecolab, Inc., St. Paul, Potlach Corp., San Francisco, Minorco, Luxembourg, Santa Fe Energy Resources, Inc., Houston, Engelhard Corp., Iselin, N.J.; chmn., pres., CEO Minorco (U.S.A.) Inc. With USNR, 1948-50. Office: Terra Industries Inc 250 Park Ave New York NY 10177-0001

RICHARDS, RILEY HARRY, insurance company executive; b. North Judson, Ind., Oct. 6, 1912; s. Harry J. and Chestie (Johnson) R.; m. Eloise Quinn Smith, May 4, 1940; children: Roy, Lynne. A.B., U. Calif.-Berkeley, 1934; M.B.A., Harvard U., 1937. Chartered fin. analyst. Fin. analyst Savs. Bank Trust Co. N.Y.C., 1937-40, SEC, Washington, Phila., 1940-45; accountant U.S. Steel Corp., Pitts., 1945-47; with Equitable Life Ins. Co. Iowa, Des Moines, 1947-77; v.p. finance Equitable Life Ins. Co. Iowa, 1961-73, v.p., sec., treas., 1973-76, sr. v.p., sec., treas., 1976-77; dir. mem. exec. com. Equitable of Iowa Cos., 1977-84; pres. Westminster House, Inc., 1989—; dir. F.M. Hubbell Sons & Co., 1977-85. Mem. Des Moines Plan and Zoning Commn., 1959-70, chmn., 1968-69; mem. bd. pensions U.P. Ch. in U.S.A., 1960-72, chmn. finance com., 1963-72; trustee United Presbyn. Found., 1979-87, vice chmn., 1981-83, chmn., 1983-87; bd. regents Life Officers Investment Seminar, 1969-70; trustee Thompson Trust, 1976—, Frederick M. Hubbell Estate, 1977-85. Mem. Am. Coun. Life Ins. (chmn. fin. sect. 1970), Iowa Soc. Fin. Analysts (pres. 1965-67), Sigma Alpha Epsilon. Republican. Club: Des Moines. Lodges: Masons, Rotary. Home: 2880 Grand Ave Apt 311 Des Moines IA 50312-4274

RICHARDS, ROBERT WADSWORTH, civil engineer, consultant; b. Beacon, N.Y., Jan. 26, 1921; s. Parke and Lois Richmond (Tracy) R.; m. Cynthia Elizabeth Pigot, May 31, 1952; children: Sarah Palmer Richards Graves III, Robert Wadsworth, Tracy Leigh Richards Purdy. BS, Princeton U., 1943, MCE, 1944. Registered profl. engr., Ga. Instr. civil engring. Swarthmore (Pa.) Coll., 1944-45; rsch. engr. The Budd Co., Phila., 1945-50; assoc. charge Atlanta office Howard, Needles, Tammen & Bergendoff, 1950-88; cons. engr. Tech. & Creative Writing, 1988—. Contbr. articles to tech. and bus. jours. Named Eminent Engr., Tau Beta Pi. Fellow ASCE; mem. Am. Soc. Engring. Edn. (life), Princeton Campus Club. Home: 1051 Winding Branch Ln Atlanta GA 30338-3947

RICHARDS, ROY, JR., wire and cable manufacturing company executive. Chmn.; CEO, dir. Southwire Co., Carrollton, Ga. Office: Southwire Co Inc PO Box 1000 Carrollton GA 30119-1000*

RICHARDS, STANFORD HARVEY, advertising agency executive, design studio executive; b. Phila., Nov. 8, 1932; s. Jack and Ruth (Stein) R.; m. Betty Jo Pugh, July 12, 1957; children—Grant Leonard, Bradford Craig. Student, Pratt Inst., 1950-53. Creative dir. Bloom Advt., Dallas, 1954-55; owner Stan Richards & Assocs., Dallas, 1955-75; owner, pres. The Richards Group, Inc., Dallas, 1975—, also bd. dirs.; instr. E. Tex. State U., Commerce, 1976-77; assoc. bd. mem. Cox Sch. Bus., So. Meth. U., Dallas, 1980-84, 88—. Author: Hobo Signs, 1965. Trustee Dallas Symphony, 1978,

Dallas Ballet, 1978; bd. dirs. Episcopal Sch., Dallas, 1981—, Dallas Arboretum, 1984-86, The Sci. Pl., 1987-90; mem. Dallas Citizens Council, adv. council Salvation Army Adult Rehab. Ctr., 1986—, adv. bd. Dallas County Salvation Army, 1987—; exec. com. United Way, 1990—; bd. dirs. YMCA, 1990—. Recipient alumni achievement award Pratt Inst., Bklyn., 1985. Club: Aerobic Activity Ctr. Avocations: deep sea fishing, running, skiing. Office: The Richards Group 10000 N Central Expwy Ste 1200 Dallas TX 75231

RICHARDS, STEPHEN HAROLD, engineering educator; b. Austin, Tex., July 19, 1952; s. Harold Richards Jr. and Janice Valerie (Mahone) Jackson; m. Mary Kathryn King Coleman, Aug. 15, 1974 (div. July 1981); 1 child, Adam King. BSCE, U. Tex., 1976; MCE, Tex. A&M U., 1977; PhDCE, U. Tenn., 1989. Registered profl. engr., Tenn., Tex. Rsch. asst. Tex. Transp. Inst., Tex. A&M U., 1976-77, engring. rsch. assoc., 1977-81, asst. rsch. engr., 1982-84; asst. dir. transp. ctr. U. Tenn., Knoxville, 1984-87, acting dir. transp. ctr., 1987-89, dir. transp., 1989—, assoc. prof. civil engring., 1989—; traffic engring. cons., 1976—; engr., mgr. Walton & Assocs./Cons. Engrs., Inc., Houston, 1981-82; lectr. in civil engring. U. Houston, 1982, Tex. A&M U., 1978-81, 83-84; instr. Tex. Engring. Extension Svc., Tex. A&M U., 1978-84; Dwight D. Eisenhower Fellowship Rev. Com., Tenn. State U., 1993, N.C. A&T Univ., 1992; Bicentennial planning Com. U. Tenn., 1993, dir. program for minority student recruitment into transp. careers, 1992—, coll. engring. awards com., 1991—, chmn. spl. events traffic planning com., 1985—. Contbr. numerous articles to profl. jours. Mem. Cumberland Gateway Com., 1993—; edn. com. Southeastern Transp. Ctr., 1992—; exec. dir. Southeastern Consortium of U. Transp. Ctrs., 1992—; chmn. Knoxville Transp. Authority, 1992-94, vice-chmn., 1990-92, commr., 1989-93; rep. Coun. of Univ. Transp. Ctrs. U. Tenn., 1987—, bd. dirs. 1992—; adv. com. Ga. State u. Transp. Ctr., 1989—; traffic control device subcom. Transp. Rsch. Bd., 1989-91, traffic control devices, 1991—, many other coms. Hwy. Safety fellowship Fed. Hwy. Adminstrn., U.S. Dept. Transp., 1976-77. Mem. ASCE, Inst. of Transp. Engrs. (chmn. tech. com. Tenn. sect. 1988—, area coord. Tex. sect. 1982-84, guidelines for driveway design and location), Transp. Rsch. Bd., Soc. Profl. Engrs., Am. Road and Transp. Builders Assn. (edn. com. 1988—), Phi Kappa Phi, Chi Epsilon. Office: U Tenn Knoxville Transt Ctr 357 S Stadium Hall Knoxville TN 37996-0700

RICHARDS, SUZANNE V., lawyer; b. Columbia, S.C., Sept. 7, 1927; d. Raymond E. and Elise C. (Gray) R. AB, George Washington U., 1948, JD with distinction, 1957, LLM, 1959. Bar: D.C. 1958. Sole practice, Washington, 1974—; lectr. in family and probate law. Recipient John Bell Larner award George Washington U., 1958; named Woman Lawyer of the Yr., Women's Bar Assn. D.C., 1977. Mem. Bar Assn. D.C. (pres. 1989-90), Women's Bar Assn. (pres. 1977-78), Trial Lawyers Assn. of D.C. (bd. govs. 1978-82, 85—, treas. 1982-85), D.C. Bar, Fed. Bar Assn., Nat. Assn. Women Lawyers, ABA (mem. ho. dels. 1988-90), D.C. Jud. Conf. Office: 1701 K St NW Washington DC 20006-1409

RICHARDS, THOMAS CARL, air force officer, governmental official; b. San Diego, Feb. 13, 1930; m. Meredyth Sweda. B.S., Va. Poly. Inst., 1956; M.A., Shippensburg State Coll., 1973. Commd. 1st lt. U.S. Air Force, 1958; advanced through grades to gen., 1986; pilot 524th bombardment squadron Homestead AFB, Fla.; co-pilot B-47, 659th bombardment squadron Homestead AFB; aircraft commdr. B-47, 32nd and 352nd bombardment squadrons Lockbourne AFB, Ohio, 1961-64; aircraft commdr. B-52, 20th bombardment squadron Barksdale AFB, La., 1964-65, Carswell AFB, Tex., 1965-67; forward air controller Bien Hoa Air Base, Republic of Vietnam, 1967-68; forward air controller 56th commando wing and 56th spl. ops. wing Udorn Royal Thai AFB, Thailand, 1968-69; exec. officer U.S. Air Force Acad., Colo.; air officer commdg. cadet squadron U.S. Air Force Acad., group air officer, vice commandant of cadets, 1977-78, commandant of cadets, 1978-81; wing dep. commdr., later commdr. Basic. Mil. Tng. Sch., Lackland AFB, Tex. 1973-75; chief motivation and communications br., directorate of personnel plans Office of Dep. Chief of Staff for Personnel, Hdqrs. U.S. Air Force, Washington, 1975-76; chief leadership and motivation div. Office of Dep. Chief of Staff for Personnel, Hdqrs. U.S. Air Force, 1976; commdr. Hdqrs. Air Reserve Personnel Ctr., Denver, 1976-77; commdr. U.S. Air Force recruiting service, dep. chief of staff recruiting air tng. command Randolph AFB, Tex., 1981-82; commdr. Keesler Tech. Tng. Ctr., Air Tng. Command, Keesler AFB, Miss., 1982-83; vice commdr. 8th Air Force strategic air command Barksdale AFB, La., 1983-84; commdr. Air U., Maxwell AFB, Ala., 1984-86; dep. commdr., chief U.S. European Command, Stuttgart, Germany, 1986-89; administr. Fed. Aviation Adminstrn., Washington, D.C., 1992—. Commr. Aviation Security and Terrorism Commn., 1989-90. Decorated D.S.M., Silver Star with 1 oak leaf cluster, Legion of Merit with 1 oak leaf cluster, D.F.C., Bronze Star with V device and 1 oak leaf cluster, Meritorious Service medal, Air medal with 17 oak leaf clusters, Purple Heart with 1 oak leaf cluster, Air Force Outstanding Unit award ribbon with 12 oak leaf clusters, Combat Readiness medal, Nat. Def. Service medal with 1 service star, Korean Service medal, Vietnam Service medal with 5 service stars, Air Force Service award ribbon with 5 oak leaf clusters, Republic of Vietnam campaign medal; Army of Occupation medal (Japan). Avocations: fishing; bicycling.

RICHARDS, TOM, III, real estate manager. Gen. ptnr. Sunrise Mall Assocs., Citrus Heights, Calif. Office: Sunrise Mall Assocs 6041 Sunrise Mall Citrus Heights CA 95610*

RICHARDS, VINCENT PHILIP HASLEWOOD, librarian; b. Sutton Bonington, Nottinghamshire, Eng., Aug. 1, 1933; emigrated to Can., 1956, naturalized, 1961; s. Philip Haslewood and Alice Hilda (Moore) R.; m. Ann Beardshall, Apr. 3, 1961; children: Mark, Christopher, Erika. A.L.A., Ealing Coll., London, 1954; B.L.S. with distinction, U. Okla., 1966. Cert. profl. librarian, B.C. Joined Third Order Mt. Carmel, Roman Catholic Ch., 1976; with Brentford and Chiswick Pub. Libraries, London, 1949-56; asst. librarian B.C. (Can.) Pub. Library Commn., Dawson Creek, 1956-57; asst. dir. Fraser Valley Regional Library, Abbotsford, B.C., 1957-67; chief librarian Red Deer (Alta., Can.) Coll., 1967-77; dir. libraries Edmonton (Alta.) Pub. Library, 1977-89; libr. and book industry cons. Ganges, Can., 1990—; pres. Faculty Assn. Red Deer Coll., 1971-72, bd. govs., 1972-73. Contbr. articles to profl. jours., 1954—. Vice pres. Jeunesses Musicales, Red Deer, 1969-70; bd. dirs. Red Deer TV Authority, 1975-76, Alta. Found. Lit. Arts, 1984-86; mem. Reform Party Can. Served with Royal Army Ednl. Corps, 1951-53. Dedication to public service, in spite of its frustrating aspects, diversity of experience, people and places, and the avoidance of overspecialization are great contributors to an enjoyable working life.

RICHARDS, WALTER DUBOIS, artist, illustrator; b. Penfield, Ohio, Sept. 18, 1907; s. Ralph DuBois and Ruby Mildred (Smith) R.; m. Glenora Case, June 20, 1931; children: Timothy, Henry Tracy. Grad.- Cleve. Sch. Art, 1930. With Sundblom Studios, Chgo., 1930-31, Tranquillini Studios, Cleve., 1931-36, Charles E. Cooper Studios, N.Y.C., 1936-50. Freelance artist, 1950—; executed paintings and illustrations for leading indsl. corps., nat. mags.; designed: U.S. postage stamps including Frederick Douglas 25 cent stamp; block of 4 stamps on beautification of Am.; Am. bald eagle-Mus. Natural History with commemorative; Cape Hatteras Nat. Parks Centennial block of four stamps; Paul Lawrence Dunbar Am. Poets commemorative; block of 4 stamps on Am. trees, 1978, blocks of 4 stamps on Am. architecture, 1979, 80, 81, 82; co-designer anti-pollution block of four stamps; James Hoban stamp, 1981, Timberline Lodge 50th Anniversary U.S. comerorative stamp, 1987; exhibited, Cleve. Mus. Art, Art Inst., Chgo., Met. Mus., N.Y.C., Pa. Acad. Fine Arts, Bklyn. Mus., N.A.D., Whitney Mus., 200 Years Watercolor Painting, Met. Mus., 1966, 200 Years Am. Illustration, N.Y. Hist. Soc., 1976; represented in permanent collection, Whitney Mus., New Britain Mus. Am. Art, Cleve. Mus. Art, William A. Farnsworth Library and Art Mus., West Point Mus., Worcester (Mass.) Art Mus., Yale U. Art Gallery-New Haven, Conn. Bd. dirs. Rowayton Art Center, Historic New Orleans Collection, 1989. Recipient highest award in lithography Cleve. Mus. Art, ann. 1935-38; Spl. Honor USAF, 1964; ann. Environ. Improvement award, 1983; named to Rocky River (Ohio) High Sch. Hall of Fame, 1991. Mem. Am. Watercolor Soc. (2d v.p. 1965-67), Conn. Watercolor Soc., NAD (assoc.), Soc. of Illustrators. Clubs: Fairfield Watercolor Group (pres., founder), Westport Artists. Address: Po Box 1134 87 Oak St New Canaan CT 06840

RICHARDS-KORTUM, REBECCA RAE, biomedical engineering educator; b. Grand Island, Nebr., Apr. 14, 1964; d. Larry Alan and Linda Mae (Hohnstein) Richards; m. Philip Ted Kortum, May 12, 1985; children: Alexander Scott, Maxwell James. BS, U. Nebr., 1985; MS, MIT, 1987, PhD, 1990. Asst. prof. biomed. engring. U. Tex., Austin, 1990—. Named Presdl. Young Investigator NSF, Washington, 1991; NSF presdl. faculty fellow, Washington, 1992; recipient Career Achievement award Assn. Advancement Med. Instrumentation, 1992, Dow Outstanding Young Faculty awd., Am. Soc. for Engineering Education, 1992. Mem. AAAS, Am. Soc. Engring. Edn. (Outstanding Young Faculty award 1992), Optical Soc. Am., Am. Soc. Photobiology. Achievements include research in photochemistry, photobiology, applied optics and bioengring. Office: U Tex Dept Elec & Computer Engring Austin TX 78712

RICHARDSON, ANN BISHOP, foundation executive, lawyer; b. New Rochelle, N.Y., Dec. 15, 1940; d. Arthur Hewes (Stuart) Heilemann; m. James K. Bishop, Jr., Nov. 30, 1960 (div. 1972); children: Timothy William, Lynn Patricia, Melanie Elizabeth; m. John P. Richardson, Apr. 16, 1972 (div. 1994). BA summa cum laude, Georgetown U., 1977; JD, George Washington U., 1984; cert. Oxford U., Eng. 1986. Bar: Md. 1988, DC 1989. Student counselor Amideast, Beirut, 1967-68, program specialist 1970-73; adminstrv. asst. UN Devel. Program, Yaounde, Cameroon, 1968-70; adminstrv. mgr. Antioch Sch. Law, Washington, 1977-79; chief adminstrv. officer for internat. ops. Peace Corps, Washington, 1980-84; dir. adminstrn. and fin. African Devel. Found., Washington, 1984-87; atty. Karr and McLain, Washington, 1987-92; v.p., gen. counsel Time Dollar, Inc., Washington, 1992—; adj. prof. law D.C. Sch. Law, Washington, 1994—. Mem. Neighbors, Inc., Washington, 1976—. Recipient spl. achievement award Peace Corps, 1981, 82, African Devel. Found., 1986. Mem. ABA, ACLU, D.C. Bar Assn., Assn. Am. Women Univ. Grads., Soc. for Internat. Devel. Phi Beta Kappa. Office: Time Dollar Inc 5500 39th St NW Washington DC 20015-2904

RICHARDSON, ARTEMAS P(ARTRIDGE), landscape architect; b. Phila., May 24, 1918; s. Eugene Stanley and Jessica (Ripple) R.; m. Frederica McAfee, Sept. 2, 1945; children: Steven, David, Ann, Vida, Stanley. BA in Fine Arts, Williams Coll., 1940; student, Pa. State U., 1940-42; BS in Landscape Architecture, Iowa State U., 1947. Registered landscape architect, Conn., Fla., Md. Mass., Miss., N.Y., Ohio, R.I., Tenn. Asst. landscape architect McCloud & Scatchard, Lilitz, Pa., 1947-48; asst. landscape architect Olmsted Bros., Brookline, Mass., 1949-50, ptnr., 1950-61; ptnr. Olmsted Assocs., Brookline, 1961-64, pres, treas., 1964-80; owner The Olmsted Office, Fremont, N.H., 1980—; lectr. Harvard U., Cambridge, 1961; mem., chair Bd. Registration Landscape Architects, Mass., 1968-77. Illustrator: Trees for Every Purpose, 1980. Mem., chair Planning Bd., Needham, Mass., 1956-62, Conservation Commn., Fremont, 1982—, chair, 1984—; mem. N.H. Gov.'s Task Force on Community Trees, Concord, 1989-91. Lt. USNR, 1942-46, ETO. Fellow Am. Soc. Landscape Architects, Boston Soc. Landscape Architects (pres. 1952-56); mem. N.H. Landscape Assn. (bd. dirs. 1984-87), Granite State Landscape Architects (vice chair 1990-91), Herb Soc. Am. (life), Scarab, Rotary (pres. local club 1965-66, dist. trustee 1968-69, dist. gov. 1970-71, bd. dirs. R.I. 1978-80), Delta Phi, Tau Sigma Delta, Pi Gamma Alpha. Avocations: photography, woodworking, gardening. Home: 106 North Rd Fremont NH 03044-3100 Office: The Olmsted Office 106 North Rd Fremont NH 03044-3100

RICHARDSON, BINGLEY GERALDO, territory legislator; b. St. Thomas, V.I., Sept. 18, 1935; s. Bingley G. and Lillian M. (Smith) R.; m. Marilyn Donovan; children: Janice, Laura Richardson Ofoha, Bingley G. Jr., Shirley, Stephanie, Sekou, Taiwo. Student, U. Md., 1955-56; diploma, Seaman's Ch. Inst., N.Y.C., 1973. Cert. aquatic inst., 300 ton ocean operator capt. Teletype operator Hudson Pulp & Paper Corp., N.Y.C., 1958-63; comm. specialist ITT, N.Y.C., 1963-68; statis. clk. V.I. Dept. Housing, St. Thomas, 1969-71, V.I. Dept. Health, St. Thomas, 1971-72; dir. Sea Explorers Boy Scouts Am., St. Thomas, 1972-73; mgr. Lindberg Bay Ctr., Inc., St. Thomas, 1973-78; owner, pres. Charger Inc., St. Thomas, 1978-89; maritime instr. Caribbean Maritime Inst., 1991-93; mem. V.I. Ho. of Reps., Charlotte Amalie, 1987-91, 93—, pres., 1993—. Contbr. articles to travel mag. Organized free beach, St. Thomas, 1969-72; coun. mem. Boy Scouts Am. 1984-86; pres., organizer Self-Help Inc., St. Thomas, 1989-94. With USAF, 1954-58. Recipient pub. svc. award Caribbean Am. League Reichold Ctr., 1984, Carlos Cooks award African Diaspora Youth Devel. Found., 1984, pub. sch. vol. svc. award V.I. Dept. Edn., 1987, Award from Guam, St. Thomas, 1993. Democrat. Avocations: scuba diving, cycling, boating. Home: PO Box 304463 Charlotte Amalie VI 00803 Office: Legislature of VI Capitol Bldg Charlotte Amalie VI 00802

RICHARDSON, BRENDA, museum administrator; BA, U. Mich., 1964; MA, U. Calif.-Berkeley, 1966. Curator, asst. dir. University Art Mus., Berkeley, 1964-75, Balt. Mus. Art, 1975—. Author: Dr. Claribel & Miss Etta: The Cone Collection, 1985, Brice Marden Cold Mountain, 1992; (exhbn. catalogues) Mel Bochner, 1976, Frank Stella, 1976, Barnett Newman, 1979, Bruce Nauman: Neons, 1982, Gilbert & George, 1984, Oskar Schlemmer, 1986, Scott Burton, 1986. Recipient Disting. Alumni Lectureship, U. Calif.-Berkeley, 1973. Office: Balt Mus Art Art Museum Dr Baltimore MD 21218-3898

RICHARDSON, BRUCE LEVOYLE, dentist; b. Corvallis, Oreg., Jan. 28, 1950; s. Richard LeVoyle Richardson and Bonney Willard (Blair) Williams; m. Rhonda Kay Stratton, Sept. ll, 1976; children: Zachary LeVoyle, Nicklis Emery Christopher, Jessica Christine. BS, U. Oreg., 1972; DDS, U. Oreg., Portland, 1977. Pvt. practice Newport, Oreg., 1977—. Chmn. Lincoln County Extension Citizens Adv. Com., 1980-82; trustee Pacific Communities Hosp. Found., 1991; bd. dirs. Lincoln County YMCA, 1983—, chmn. advance gifts campaign, 1984, active current support campaign, 1985, mem. bldg. com., 1985—. Fellow Nat. Acad. Gen. Dentistry (mem. long-range planning coun. 1988-88, mem. ann. meeting coun. 1991—, Mastership award 1987); mem. Oreg. Dental Assn. (mem. ho. dels. 1983-87, trustee 1984-87, v.p. 1987-88, pres. 1989—, Oreg. Young Dentist award 1990). Advanced Periodontic Study Club, Lincoln County Study Club, Newport C. of C., Rotary. Republican. Methodist. Avocations: whitewater rafting, camping, fishing, biking, raising cattle. Home: 333 NW Beaver Valley Dr Seal Rock OR 97376-9523 Office: 123 SE Douglas St Newport OR 97365

RICHARDSON, CAMPBELL, lawyer; b. Woodland, Calif., June 18, 1930; s. George Arthur and Mary (Hall) R.; m. Patricia Packwood, Sept. 3, 1958 (dec. Oct. 1971); children: Catherine, Sarah, Thomas; m. Carol Tamblyn, June 1975 (div. Dec. 1977); m. Susan J. Linbert, May 3, 1980; 1 child, Laura. AB, Dartmouth Coll., 1952; JD, NYU, 1955. Bar: Oreg. 1955, U.S. Dist. Ct. Oreg. 1957. Ptnr. Stoel Rives, Portland, 1964—. Co-author: Contemporary Trust and Will Forms for Oregon Attorneys; contbr. articles to profl. jours. Mem. Portland/Metro Govt. Boundary Commn., 1976; mem. Oreg. Adv. Com. to U.S. Commn. on Civil Rights, 1976-84; bd. dirs. Ctr. for Urban Edn., Portland, 1980-84, Dorchester Conf., Inc., Bend, Oreg., 1982, Friends of the Zoo, 1993—; chmn. planned giving com. St. Vincent Med. Found., 1988—; planned giving com. Oregon Health Scis. Found., 1993—; trustee Met. Family Svc. Found., 1990—. Served with U.S. Army, 1955-57. Mem. ABA, Oreg. Bar Assn., Multnomah County Bar Assn., Estate Planning Coun. Portland (pres. 1978), Am. Coll. Trust and Estate Counsel, City Club, Multnomah Athletic Club (Portland). Republican.ican. Home: 1500 SW 5th Ave Unit 1701 Portland OR 97201-5430 Office: Stoel Rives Boley Jones & Gray 900 SW 5th Ave Ste 2300 Portland OR 97204-1268

RICHARDSON, CHARLES CLIFTON, biochemist, educator; b. Wilson, N.C., May 7, 1935; s. Barney Clifton and Florence Elizabeth (Barefoot) R.; m. Ute Ingrid Hanssum, July 29, 1961; children—Thomas Clifton, Matthew Wilfrid. B.S.M., Duke U., 1959, M.D., 1960; A.M. (hon.), Harvard U., 1967. Intern internal medicine Duke U., Durham, N.C., 1960-61; postdoctoral fellow dept. biochemistry Stanford U. Med. Sch., Calif., 1961-63; asst. prof. biol. chemistry Harvard Med. Sch., Boston, 1964-67, assoc. prof., 1967-69, prof. biol. chemistry, 1969—, chmn. dept. biol. chemistry, 1978-87, Edward S. Wood prof., 1979—; mem. physiol. chemistry study sect. NIH, 1970-74; mem. Fachbeirat of Max-Planck Inst. für Molekulare Genetik, Berlin, Fed. Republic Germany, 1980-89; mem. Genetics Inst., Cambridge, Mass., 1986—; mem. Nat. Bd. Med. Examiners, 1973-76; mem. nucleic acids and protein adv. com., Am. Cancer Soc. Inst., 1975-78; mem. vis. com.

Boston Biomed. Rsch. Found., 1985—; assoc. Helicon Found., San Diego, Calif., 1983—; bd. dirs. Amersham Life Sci., Inc. Editor: Ann. Rev. Biochemistry, 1983— (assoc. editor 1973-82) ; mem. editorial bd. Jour. Biol. Chemistry, 1968-73, 84-88, Jour. Molecular Biology, 1976-79. Recipient Career Devel. award NIH, 1967-76, Merit award, 1986. Fellow Am. Acad. Arts and Scis., Inst. of Medicine; mem. Nat. Acad. Scis., Am. Chem. Soc. (Eli Lilly Co. biol. chem. award 1968), Am. Soc. Biol. Chemists (mem. nominating com. 1974-75, 1983-84), Am. Cancer Soc. (coun. for rsch. and clin. investigation 1989-92).

RICHARDSON, CURTIS J., ecology educator; b. Gouverneur, N.Y., July 27, 1944; s. Nilie John and Rose Marie (LaPierre) R.; m. Carol Bartlett, Aug. 22, 1972; children: John, Suzanne. BS in Biology, SUNY, Cortland, 1966; PhD in Ecology, U. Tenn., 1972. Asst. prof. resource ecology Sch. Natural Resources U. Mich., Ann Arbor, 1972-77; asst. prof. plant ecology U. Mich., Biologican Station, Mich., summer 1973; assoc. prof. resource ecology Sch. Forestry and Environ. Studies Duke U., Durham, N.C., 1977-87, prof. resource ecology, 1988—; dir. Wetland Ctr., 1990—; sr. rsch. fellow in applied ecology and forestry U. Edinburgh, Scotland, 1982; mem. sci. adv. bd. Nat. Wetland Rsch. Plan, U.S. EPA, Washington, 1991, chmn. Nat. Wetland EMAP rev. panel, 1992; panel mgr. competitive grants program water quality USDA, Washington, 1990-91. Mem. AAAS, Am. Inst. Biol. Scis., Am. Soc. Agronomy, Ecol. Soc. Am., Soc. Wetland Scientists (v.p. 1986-87, prs. 1987-88, assoc. editor 1987-93). Avocations: jogging, hiking, fishing. Office: Duke U Wetland Ctr Sch Environ LSRC Research Dr Durham NC 27708-0333 Home: 717 Anderson St Durham NC 27705

RICHARDSON, DANA ROLAND, video producer; b. Mason City, Iowa, Jan. 11, 1945; s. Dana Roland Richardson and Louise Marion (Duke) Sarles; m. Sandra Anderson, June 12, 1966; children: Patricia Nan, Dana Roland, Jr. BS, UCLA, 1966, MBA, 1967. CPA, Calif., N.Y. Staff acct. Arthur Young, L.A., 1967-72, mgr., 1972-76; prin. Arthur Young, N.Y.C., 1976-78; ptnr. Ernst & Young, N.Y.C., 1978-94; pres. Dream Street Prodns., New Canaan, Conn., 1994—. Author: A Manager's Guide to Computer Timesharing, 1975, Audit and Control of Information Systems, 1987. Staff sgt. Reserves USANG, 1967-73. Named one of Techology 100 Top 100 Achievers in Technology in Am., Technology Mag., 1982. Mem. AICPA, Calif. Soc. CPA's. Republican. Episcopalian. Avocations: boating, fishing, music, videography, multimedia. Office: Dream St Prodns PO Box 73 New Canaan CT 06840

RICHARDSON, DANIEL PUTNAM, headmaster, history, economics and criminal law educator; b. Boston, Sept. 17, 1941; s. Frederick Leopold William Jr. and Helen (Warren) R.; m. Patricia Randle, Apr. 6, 1962; children: Daniel Putnam Jr., Randle Bayard, Mary Elizabeth. BA in Econs. and History, U. Denver, 1965; MEd, Harvard U., 1982. Tchr., dir. ops. Woodstock (Vt.) Country Sch., 1970-73; tchr., asst. headmaster Barlow Sch., Amenia, N.Y., 1975-76; tchr., head of sch. Wykham Rise Sch., Washington, Conn., 1976-80; interim head of sch. St. Michael's Sch., Newport, R.I., 1980-81; tchr., head of upper sch. Tatnall Sch., Wilmington, Del., 1982-87; dir. athletics 1985-86; tchr., head of sch. Cape Henry Collegiate Sch., Virginia Beach, Va., 1987—; mgr. Gillette Co., 1965-70; pres. Real Estate and Contrn. Co., 1973-75. Chmn. bd. dirs. Urban League, Hampton Road, Va., 1990—; treas. Chesapeake Bay Acad.; active NCCJ. Mem. Nat. Assn. Prins. Schs. for Girls, Va. Assn. Ind. Schs. (treas.), Two Dans Discussion Group (co-founder 1991—). Office: Cape Henry Collegiate Sch 1320 Mill Dam Rd Virginia Beach VA 23454-2306

RICHARDSON, DAVID BACON, writer, journalist; b. Maplewood, N.J., July 13, 1916; s. Percy Bacon and Elizabeth (Jones) R.; m. Ruth Cummings (dec.); children: Hilary C., Julia R. Neilson, Francesca Richardson-Allen; m. Anne Phelan Werner, Oct. 8, 1994. BA, Ind. U., 1940; postgrad. press fellow, Princeton U., 1953-54. Sports reporter Daily Courier, Orange, N.J., 1934-36; mng. editor, editor-in-chief Ind. Daily Student, 1939-40; editorial staff N.Y. Herald Tribune, N.Y.C., 1940-41; combat corres. Yank, The Army Weekly, PTO, 1942-45; corr. Time Mag., India, Fed. Republic Germany, U.K., Mideast, Mexico, 1945-56; bur. chief S.Am. U.S. News & World Report, Buenos Aires, 1959-64; chief domestic news burs. U.S. News & World Report, Washington, 1964-73; chief European corr. U.S. News & World Report, Rome, 1974-81; chief nat. corr. U.S. News & World Report, Washington, 1981-82; freelance writer Washington, 1983—; lectr. in field, 1986—. Contbr. to books The Best From Yank, 1945, Yank, the GI Story of the War, 1947. V.p., bd. dirs. Iona Sr. Svcs., 1993—; pres., bd. dirs. Greenbriar Condominium, Washington, 1984-87. Decorated Legion of Merit, Bronze Star; recipient Valor medal of Nat. Headliners Club. Mem. Coun. Fgn. Rels., Washington Inst. Fgn. Affairs, Overseas Writers Assn., Soc. Profl. Journalists, Merrill's Marauders Assn., Internat. Combat Camera Assn., Cosmos Club. Episcopalian. Home and Office: #1014 E 4201 Cathedral Ave NW Washington DC 20016

RICHARDSON, DAVID JOHN, ballet dancer, educator; b. Middletown, N.Y., Mar. 2, 1943; s. Fred and Helen (Anderson) R. Grad., high sch., Pine Bush, N.Y. Dancer Am. Ballet Theatre, N.Y.C., 1961-63, ballet master, 1983—; dancer N.Y.C. Ballet, 1963-83, asst. ballet master, 1976-83. Repertoire includes (with N.Y.C. Ballet) Jerome Robbins' The Goldberg Variations, George Balanchine's The Four Temperaments, Firebird, Episodes, Antony Tudor's Dim Lustre; staged various ballets including Circus Polka, Paris Opera Ballet, 1974, San Francisco Ballet, 1979, Royal Danish Ballet, 1984, Le Tombeau de Couperin, Paris Opera Ballet, 1975, Coppelia, Asami Maki Ballet, Tokyo, 1981, The Leaves Are Fading, Star Dancers Ballet, Tokyo, 1991, Bruch Violin Concert No. 1, Scottish Ballet, 1993; staged annual performances of George Balanchine's The Nutcracker, Stamford City Ballet, Pa. Ballet, 1988, Pittsburgh Ballet Theatre, 1990, Miami City Ballet, 1992; TV credits include Choreography by Balanchine Parts I and II, PBS, Coppelia, PBS, A Tribute to George Balanchine, PBS, The Nutcracker, CBS, Edward Villella's Little Women, NBC, Lee Theodore's Kiss Me, Kate, NBC, (children's choreographer) Baryshnikov at the White House. Office: Am Ballet Theater 890 Broadway New York NY 10003-1211*

RICHARDSON, DAVID WALTHALL, cardiologic educator, consultant; b. Nanking, China, Mar. 22, 1925; s. Donald William and Virginia (McIlwaine) R.; m. Frances Lee Wingfield, June 12, 1948; children—Donald, Sarah, David. B.S., Davidson Coll., 1947; M.D., Harvard U., 1951. Diplomate Am. Bd. Internal Medicine, Am. Bd. Cardiology. Intern, resident Yale New Haven Hosp., Conn., 1951-53; resident, fellow Med. Coll. Va., Richmond, 1953-56, assoc. prof. to prof. medicine, 1962-95, prof. emeritus, 1995—, chmn. div. cardiology, 1972-87; interim chmn. dept. medicine, 1973-74; chief cardiology, assoc. chief staff for rsch. VA Hosp., Richmond, 1956-61; dir. cardiology tng. program, 1990-95; vis. scientist Oxford U., Eng., 1961-62; vis. prof. U. Milan, Italy, 1972-73. Contbr. articles to profl. jours. Moderator Hanover Presbytery, Presbyterian Ch. U.S., Richmond, 1970; chmn. events com. NHLBI Cardiac Arrhythmia Suppression Trial, 1983-92. Served with USN, 1944-46. Fellow Am. Coll. Cardiology (gov. VA. 1970-72); mem. Am. Heart Assn. (council clin. cardiology); mem. Am. Soc. Clin. Investigation, Am. Clin. and Climatol. Assn. Home: 5501 Queensbury Rd Richmond VA 23226-2121

RICHARDSON, DEAN EUGENE, retired banker; b. West Branch, Mich., Dec. 27, 1927; s. Robert F. and Helen (Husted) R.; m. Barbara Trytten, June 14, 1952; children: Ann Elizabeth, John Matthew. AB, Mich. State U., 1950; JD, U. Mich. 1953; postgrad. Stonier Grad. Sch. Banking, 1965. With Indl. Nat. Bank, Detroit, 1953-55; with Mfrs. Nat. Bank, Detroit, 1955-90; v.p. adminstrn. Mfrs. Nat. Bank, 1964-66, sr. v.p. 1966-67, exec. v.p., 1967-69, pres., 1969-73, chmn. bd. dirs., 1973-89, chmn. exec. com., 1989-90; chmn. bd. dirs. Mfrs-Detroit Internat. Corp., 1973-90; chmn. exec. com. Mfrs. Nat. Bank, 1989-90; bd. dirs. Detroit Edison Co., Tecumseh Products Co., Ford Holdings, Inc., AAA of Mich. Served with USNR, 1945-46. Mem. Mich. Detroit bar assns. Episcopalian. Clubs: Masons, KT, Detroit Athletic, Detroit, Country of Detroit. Office: Comerica Bank Bldg 20180 Mack Ave Grosse Pointe MI 48236-1839

RICHARDSON, DON ORLAND, agricultural educator; b. Auglaize County, Ohio, May 12, 1934; s. Dana Orland and Mary Isabell (Bowersock) R.; m. Shirley Ann Richardson (div. 1982); children: Daniel, Bradley, Eric, Laura. BS, Ohio State U., 1956, MS, 1957, PhD, 1961. Asst. prof. to prof.

U. Tenn., Knoxville, 1963—, head Animal Sci. Dept., 1982-88, dean Agrl. Exptl. Sta., 1988—. Mem. Am. Dairy Sci. Assn. Am. Soc. Animal Sci., Coun. Agrl. Sci. and Tech., Holstein Assn. Am., Rotary Club Knoxville. Office: Tenn Agrl Exptl Sta 103 Morgan Hall PO Box 1071 Knoxville TN 37901-1071

RICHARDSON, DONALD CAMPBELL, land planner, landscape architect; b. Summit, N.J., Dec. 3, 1934; s. Donald and Margaret (Campbell) R.; Nancy Richardson, Aug. 3, 1957; children: Donald William, Martha Ann. BS, Delaware Valley Coll., 1956; M Landscape Architecture, Harvard U., 1961. Lic. landscape architect, N.J., N.Y., Conn., Pa., Mass., profl. planner, N.J. Landscape architect Fletcher Steele, Boston, 1959, Sasaki Walker Assocs., Watertown, Mass., 1961, Zion & Breen Assocs., Imlaystown, N.J., 1962—; land planner Lexington (Mass.) Planning Bd., 1960; pvt. practice landscape architect, planner, cons. Maplewood, N.J., 1965—; adj. prof. landscape architecture CUNY, 1973-75, Rutgers U., 1973-76; vis. critic Urban Design Studio, U. Pa., 1991; juror Temple U., Ambler Campus, 1991; lectr. Princeton U., 1976-80, U. Conn., 1958, U. Conn., 1958. Mem. planning bd. Twp. of Maplewood, 1983—, mem. bd. adjustment, 1980-83; mem. Legis. Commn., State of N.J., 1973. Recipient award of Merit, Hyde Park Urban Renewal Agy., citation AIA, award State of N.Y. and Gov. Rockefeller, honor U.S. Dept. HUD, 1st Honor award FHA, Urban Renewal Project award Urban Renewal Adminstrn. Fellow Am. Soc. Landscape Architects (chair N.Y. state coun. 1973, v.p. N.Y. chpt. 1969-71, pres. 1971-73, chair comms. newsletter and programs 1966-69, Honor award N.J. chpt., Silver award, Merit award). Avocations: reading, skiing, tennis, sailing, photography. Home: 27 Roosevelt Rd Maplewood NJ 07040 Office: Zion & Breen Assoc Inc PO Box 34 Main St Imlaystown NJ 08526

RICHARDSON, DONALD EDWARD, neurosurgery educator; b. Vicksburg, Miss., Oct. 5, 1931; s. Edward K. and Ina Mae (Cooper) R.; children: Donna Richardson Boas, Scott, David. W. Jeffrey, Cooper E.H. BS in Chemistry, Millsaps Coll., 1953; MD, Tulane U., 1957. Diplomate Am. Bd. Neurol. Surgery. Intern in surgery Charity Hosp., New Orleans, 1957-58, resident in neurosurgery, 1961-62; resident in neurosurgery Ochsner Found. Hosp., New Orleans, 1958-60, VA Hosp., New Orleans, 1960-61; instr. Dept. Neurosurgery, Tulane U., New Orleans, 1962-64, asst. prof., 1964-67, assoc. prof., 1967-74, prof., chmn., 1980—, adj. prof. biomed. engring., 1984—; clin. assoc. prof. dept. neurosurgery La. State U., New Orleans, 1974-80; dir. Pain Treatment Ctr. Hotel Dieu Hosp., New Orleans, 1978-93, mem.-at-large exec. com., 1978-84, chmn. spl. procedures com., 1984-93; chief neurosurgery sect. Charity Hosp. La. New Orleans, 1980—, VA Hosp. New Orleans, 1980—; mem. neurosurgery staff, Toure Infirmary, So. Bapt. Hosp., Pendelton Meml. Meth. Hosp., St. Jude Med. Ctr.; chmn. Neurosurgery dept. Tulane U. Med. Ctr. Hosp., 1980—, oper. rm. and exec. coms., 1980—; lectr. in field. Contbr. articles to profl. jours. Fellow ACS; mem. AAAS, Am. Assn. Neurol. Surgeons, AMA, Am. Pain Soc., Am. Soc. for Stereotactic and Functional Neurosurgery, Assn. for Acad. Surgery, Congress Neurol. Surgeons, Internat. Assn. for Study Pain, Internat. Neurosurg. Soc., La. Neurol. Soc. (pres. 1979), La. State Med. Soc., Neuroelectric Soc., N.Y. Acad. Sci., Orleans Parish Med. Soc., Research Soc. Neurol. Surgeons, Royal Soc. Medicine, Soc. for Neurosci., So. Med. Assn., So. Neurosurg. Assn., Oscar Creek Surg. Soc., Midwest Pain Soc., Can. Neurosurg. Soc., Am. Acad. Pain Medicine, Alton Ochsner Med. Found. Soc., Soc. Neurol. Surgeons, La. Med. Rev. Found., Am. Acad. Clin. Neurophysiology, Alpha Omega Alpha. Lodge: Rotary. Avocations: skiing, travel, collecting art. Office: Tulane U Sch of Medicine Dept of Neurosurgery 1430 Tulane Ave New Orleans LA 70112-2699

RICHARDSON, DOUGLAS FIELDING, lawyer; b. Glendale, Calif., Mar. 17, 1929; s. James D. and Dorothy (Huskins) R.; m. Leni Tempelaar-Lietz, June 26, 1959; children—Arthur Wilhelm, John Douglas. A.B., UCLA, 1950; J.D., Harvard U., 1953. Bar: Calif. 1953. Assoc. O'Melveny & Myers, Los Angeles, 1953-68, ptnr., 1968-86, of counsel, 1986—. Author: (with others) Drafting Agreements for the Sale of Businesses, 1971, Term Loan Handbook, 1983. bd. govs. Town Hall of Calif., L.A., 1974-87, sec., 1977, v.p., 1978-79, pres., 1984, mem. adv. coun., 1987—, chmn. sect. on legis. and adminstrn. of justice, 1968-70, pres. Town Hall West, 1975, mem. exec. bd. 1973-93; bd. dirs. Hist. Soc. Soc. Calif., 1976-82, pres., 1980-81; bd. dirs. Alliance Francaise de Pasadena, treas., 1993—. Mem. ABA (com. on devels. in bus. financing, com. state regulation of securities, com. corp. law and acctg., com. employee benefits and exec. compensation of sect corp. banking and bus. law.), Calif. Bar Assn., Los Angeles County Bar Assn. (chmn. com. Law Day 1968, exec. com. commnl. law sect. 1974-78, exec. com. corp. law sect. 1975-86), Kiwanis, Phi Beta Kappa. Republican. Presbyterian (elder). Clubs: California, Harvard So. Calif. Home: 1637 Valley View Rd Glendale CA 91202-1340 Office: O'Melveny & Myers 400 S Hope St Los Angeles CA 90071

RICHARDSON, EDWARD JAMES, federal government agency official; b. Bethesda, Md., Oct. 7, 1954; s. James Franklin and Jane Elizabeth (Warner) R.; m. Jean Margaret Sanderhoff, Aug. 8, 1952; children: James Carr, Luke Edward, Scott Marshall. AA, U. S. Fla., 1974, BBA cum laude, 1975. CPA, Fla. Acct. Taylor, Edenfield, Gilliam & Whitshire CPA's, Ft. Myers, Fla., 1975-77, GTE Corp., Tampa, Fla., 1978; official U.S. Dept of Justice, Miami and Tampa, Fla., 1978—. Adv. to Explorer post Miami council Boy Scouts Am., 1980-82. Named Eagle Scout Boy Scouts Am., 1969, Disting. Expert Nat. Rifle Assn., 1968. Mem. Fla. Inst. CPA's, Am. Inst. CPA's. Republican. Methodist. Avocations: jogging, weightlifting, scuba diving, fishing, hunting, spectator sports. Office: US Dept of Justice 500 E Zack St Rm 610 Tampa FL 33602-3919

RICHARDSON, ELLIOT LEE, lawyer; b. Boston, July 20, 1920; s. Edward P. and Clara (Shattuck) R.; m. Anne F. Hazard, Aug. 2, 1952; children: Henry, Nancy, Michael. AB cum laude, Harvard U., 1941, LLB cum laude, 1947, LLD (hon.), 1971; other hon. degrees. Bar: Mass. 1949, D.C. 1980. Law clk. Judge Learned Hand, U.S. Ct. Appeals (2d cir.), N.Y., 1947-48, Supreme Ct. Justice Felix Frankfurter, 1948-49; assoc. Ropes, Gray, Best, Coolidge & Rugg, Boston, 1949-53, 55-56; asst. to Mass. Senator Leverett Saltonstall, 1953-54; acting counsel to Mass. Gov. Christian A. Herter, 1956; asst. sec. legis. HEW, 1957-59; U.S. atty. for Mass., 1959-61, spl. asst. to atty. gen. U.S., 1961; ptnr. Ropes & Gray, Boston, 1961-64; lt. gov. Mass., 1965-67, atty. gen. Mass., 1967-69, under sec. state, 1969-70; sec. HEW, 1970-73; sec. def., 1973, atty. gen. U.S., 1973; fellow Woodrow Wilson Internat. Ctr. for Scholars, Washington, 1974-75; ambassador Ct. St. James's, London, 1975-76; sec. commerce, 1976-77; ambassador-at-large, spl. rep. of pres. Law of Sea Conf., Washington, 1977-80; sr. ptnr. Milbank, Tweed, Hadley & McCloy, Washington, 1980-92; personal rep. SG of UN for Nicaraguan Elections, 1989-90; spl. rep. of Pres. of U.S. for multilateral assistance in The Philippines, 1989-94; bd. dirs. Crop Genetics Internat., Oak Industries, BNFL Inc.; mem. environ. adv. bd. Riedel Environ. Tech.; mem. adv. bd. Am. Flywheel Systems; former dir. John Hancock Life Ins. Co. Author: The Creative Balance, 1976; contbr. numerous articles to profl. jours. and others. Former trustee Radcliffe Coll., Mass. Gen. Hosp.; hon. trustee Roger Tory Peterson Inst.; pres. World Affairs Coun., Boston; dir. Mass. Bay United Fund, past chmn. Greater Boston United Fund Campaign; mem. bd. overseers Harvard Coll.; chmn. overseers com. to visit John F. Kennedy Sch. Govt., Harvard U.; mem. overseers com. to visit Harvard U. Law Sch.; bd. dirs. U.S. Coun. Internat. Bus., Urban Inst.; chmn. Coun. on Ocean Law, Hitachi Found., Japan-Am. Soc. Washington; co-chmn. Nat. Coun., UN Assn. U.S.; chmn. overseers com. to visit Harvard Med. Sch. and Sch. Dental Medicine; vice chmn. Citizens Network Fgn. Affairs; mem. Compt. Gen.'s cons. panel; chmn. quality rev. bd. GAO; mem. adv. com. for commemoration World War II, Dept. Def.; bd. dirs. Am. Acad. Diplomacy. Served to lt. inf. U.S. Army, 1942-45. Decorated Bronze Star, Purple Heart with oak leaf cluster, Légion d'Honneur; recipient Jefferson award Am. Inst. Pub. Svc., Thomas Hart Benton award Kansas City Art Inst., Emory R. Buckner medal Fed. Bar Coun., Penn Club award, Albert Lasker Spl. Pub. Svc. award, Neptune award, Meritorious Pub. Svc. award USCG, Harry Truman Good Neighbor award, Thomas Paine P. O'Neill Jr. award for pub. svc., Sam Rayburn award, and other awards. Fellow AAAS, Am. Bar Found., Mass. Bar Found.; mem. ABA, ASPA, D.C. Bar Assn., Mass. Bar Assn., Harvard U. Alumni Assn. (former elected dir.), Coun. on Fgn. Rels., Am. Law Inst., Am. Soc. Internat. Law, Bretton Woods Com., Am. Acad. Diplomacy, Am. Acad. Social Ins., Internat. Law Assn., Nat. Acad. Pub. Adminstrn., DAV, VFW, Am. Legion, Alfalfa Club, F Street Club.

Office: Milbank Tweed Hadley McCloy 1825 I St NW Ste 1100 Washington DC 20006-5492

RICHARDSON, ELSIE HELEN, retired elementary educator; b. Vancouver, Wash., Feb. 1, 1918; d. Anthony William and Marie Julia (Dusek) Podhora-Clark; m. Clyde Stanley Richardson, Oct. 16, 1944 (dec. 1989). BA, Cen. Washington Coll. Edn., 1939. Cert. jr. high sch. prin.; cert. life elem. tchr., Calif., life spl. secondary to teach mentally retarded; cert. psychometrist, Calif. Tchr. 2d and 3d grades Randle (Wash.) Sch. Dist., 1939-40; remedial tchr. Randle, 1940-41; 2d grade tchr. Seattle Sch. Dist., 1941-44; remedial tchr., child guidance Vancouver, Wash., mental tester, 1944-45; tchr. 3nd grade Lancaster (Calif.) Sch. Dist., 1946-48; tchr. spl. edn. Bakersfield (Calif.) Sch. Dist., 1948-49; tchr. 2d grade Norco (Calif.) Sch. Dist., 1950-51; tchr. 4th grade Chino (Calif.) Sch. Dist., 1951-55, tchr. spl. edn., 1955-79, ret., 1979. Leader Girl Res., Camp Rimrock, Wash., summer 1939; leader Bluebird Club, 1939. Recipient Cert. of Appreciaiton, State Assembly of Calif., 1979. Mem. NEA, AAUW, Am. Assn. Ret. Persons, Calif. Tchrs. Assn. (rep.), Calif. Ret. Tchrs. Assn., Vancouver Edn. Assn., Chino Tchrs. Assn. (past v.p., sec.), PTA (life), Fun After Fifty Club, Delta Kappa Gamma.

RICHARDSON, EVERETT VERN, hydraulic engineer, educator, administrator; b. Scottsbluff, Nebr., Jan. 5, 1924; s. Thomas Otis and Jean Marie (Everett) R.; m. Billie Ann Kleckner, June 23, 1948; children—Gail Lee, Thomas Everett, Jerry Ray. B.S., Colo. State U., 1949, M.S., 1960, Ph.D., 1965. Registered profl. engr., Colo. Hydraulic engr. U.S. Geol. Survey, Wyo., 1949-52; hydraulic engr. U.S. Geol. Survey, Iowa, 1953-66; rsch. hydraulic engr. U.S. Geol. Survey, Ft. Collins, Colo., 1956-63, project chief, 1963-68; prof. civil engring., adminstr. engring. rsch. ctr. Colo. State U., Ft. Collins, 1968-82, prof. in charge of hydraulic program, 1982-88, prof. civil engring., 1988-94, prof. emeritus, 1994—, dir. hydraulic lab. engring. rsch. ctr., 1982-88, dir. Egypt water use project, 1977-84, dir. Egypt irrigation improvement project, 1985-90; dir. Egypt Water Rsch. Ctr. Egypt Water Rsch. Ctr. Project, Ft. Collins 1988-89; sr. assoc. Resource Consultants and Engrs., Inc., Ft. Collins, Colo., 1989—; dir. Consortium for Internat. Devel., Tucson, Ariz., 1972-87; cons. in field. Editor: Highways in the River Environment, Fed. Hwy. Adminstrn., 1975, 90; contbr. articles to profl. jours., chpts. in books. Mem. Ft. Collins Water Bd., 1969-84; mem. N.Y. State Bridge Safety Assurance Task Force, 1988-91. Decorated Bronze Star, Purple Heart; Combat Infantry Badge, U.S. Govt. fellow MIT, 1962-63. Fellow ASCE (J.D. Stevens award 1961, chair task com., hydraulics divsn. excellence award 1993); mem. Internat. Congress for Irrigation and Drainage (bd. dirs.), Sigma Xi, Chi Epsilon, Sigma Tau. Home: 824 Gregory Rd Fort Collins CO 80524-1504 Office: Resource Cons and Engrs PO Box 270460 Fort Collins CO 80527-0460

RICHARDSON, F. C., academic administrator; b. Memphis, Sept. 22, 1936; m. Bernice Tanner. AB in Biology, Rust Coll., 1960; MS in Biology, Atlanta U., 1964; PhD in Botany, U. Calif., Santa Barbara, 1967. Asst. prof. botany Ind. U. N.W., Gary, 1967-71, assoc. prof., 1971-82, prof., 1982-84, chair dept. biology, 1971-72, chair div. arts and scis., 1972-84; prof. Jackson (Miss.) State U., 1984-85, v.p. for acad. affairs, 1984-85; v.p. for acad affairs Moorhead (Minn.) State U., 1985-89; prof. SUNY Coll. at Buffalo, 1989, pres., 1989—; cons. evaluator North Ctrl. Assn., 1987-89; mem. commn. on elem. schs. Mid. States Assn., 1990—; mem. Commn. on Minorities in Higher Edn., Am. Coun. on Edn.; mem. task force on outcomes and accountability Coun. on Postsecondary Edn., 1991—. Mem. editorial bd. Negro Ednl. Rev., 1977—, exec. editor, 1981—; contbr. numerous articles to profl. jours. Mem. fellowship selection com. for Martin Luther King, Jr. Fellowship Program, Woodrow Wilson Nat. Fellowship Found., Chgo., 1969-74; bd. dirs. Lake County Assn. for Retarded Citizens, 1969-75; chair Ind. U. N.W./Community Adv. Bd. for Spl. Svcs., 1970-74; mem. Gary Air Pollution Control Adv. Bd., 1970-84, chair; chair steering com. for creation of Gary Neighborhood Svcs., Inc., 1970-71, bd. dirs., 1971-84; mem. N.W. Ind. Clean Air Coordinating Com., N.W. Ind., 1970-73, Comprehensive Health Planning Coun., 1971-75, Com. on Sci. and Tech. R&D, State of Minn., 1987, Moorhead Chamber Edn. Task Force, 1987-88; mem. Gary Bd. Health, 1972-82, sec., 1976-79, pres., 1979-82; bd. dirs. Meth. Hosps., Gary, 1973-84, Med. Ctr. of Gary, Inc., 1975-81, Greater Buffalo Devel. Found., 1989—, Buffalo State Natural Scis., 1989—, Western N.Y. Tech. Devel. Ctr., Inc., 1991—, Buffalo Fine Arts Acad., 1991—; mem. Lake area planning and allocation com. United Way, 1981-83, chair Lake area campaign exec. group, 1982-83, bd. dirs. United Way Buffalo and Erie County, 1990—; mem. local organizing com. World Univ. Games 1993, 1989—; mem. bd. govs. NCCJ of Western N.Y., 1989—. Univ. scholar Atlanta U., 1962-64; fellow NSF, 1966, U. Calif., 1967-68. Mem. Am. Inst. Biol. Scis., Bot. Soc. Am., Internat. Soc. Plant Morphologists, Am. Assn. State Colls. and Univs. (SCAN team 1986). Home: 152 Lincoln Pky Buffalo NY 14222-1012 Office: SUNY Coll at Buffalo Office of Pres 1300 Elmwood Ave Buffalo NY 14222

RICHARDSON, FRANK H., retired oil industry executive; b. Mar. 15, 1933. BS, South Dakota Sch. Mines, 1955. With Shell Oil Co., Houston, 1955-93, exec. v.p., 1983-88, pres., CEO, 1988-93. Address: Ste 504 2001 Kirby Houston TX 77019

RICHARDSON, FRANK KELLOGG, lawyer, former state justice; b. St. Helena, Calif., Feb. 13, 1914; s. Channing Alonzo and Jessie May (Kellogg) R.; m. Elizabeth Kingdon, Jan. 23. 1943; children: Stuart Channing, Paul Kellogg, Eric Kingdon, David Huntington. Student, U. Pa., 1931-32; A.B. with distinction, Stanford U., 1935, LL.B., 1938; LL.D. (hon.), Western State U., San Diego, 1976, Mid-Valley Coll. Law, Los Angeles, 1977, Pepperdine U., Los Angeles, 1981. Bar: Calif. 1938. Sole practice Oroville, Calif., 1939-42, Sacramento, Calif., 1946-71; presiding justice Calif. Ct. of Appeal (3d Dist.), 1971-74; assoc. justice Calif. Supreme Ct., Sacramento, 1974-83; solicitor U.S. Dept. Interior, 1984-85; prof. law U. Pacific., 1946-51; disting. vis. prof. law Pepperdine U., Los Angeles, 1984; dir. Fedco, Inc. Pres. Methodist Hosp., Sacramento, 1965-71, Sacramento Community Welfare Council, 1956-57, Sacramento YMCA, World Affairs Council Sacramento, 1970-71; bd. visitors, mem. exec. com. law sch. Stanford (Calif.) U., 1966-69; bd. dirs. Meth. Hosp. of Sacramento Valley Health Care Found. Served with USAAF, 1942-43; Served with U.S. Army, 1943-45. Fellow Am. Coll. Probate Counsel, Am. Bar Found., Am. Coll. Trust and Estate Counsel Found.; mem. Calif. Judges Assn., State Bar Calif. (mem. exec. com. 1965-69, Presiding Justice Cts. Appeal, Sacramento County Bar Assn. (pres. 1962-63), Order of Coif (hon.), Phi Beta Kappa, Delta Theta Phi, Pi Sigma Alpha, Phi Delta Phi (hon.). Methodist. Club: Sutter (hon.). Home: 4140 Elderberry Ln Sacramento CA 95864-6062

RICHARDSON, GISELE, management company executive; b. Willow Bunch, Sask., Can., July 5, 1929; d. Donat and Julienne (Lavallee) Boucher; m. Howard Richardson, Dec. 14, 1952; 1 child, Marc. Student, McGill Univ., Montreal, Can., 1972-75. Editorial officer UN Devel. Programme, Bangkok, Thailand, 1967-70, Tokyo, 1970-72; pres. Richardson Mgmt. Assn., Montreal, Quebec, Can., 1973—; bd. dirs. Internat. Cons. Found., Washington, Can. Commercial Corp., O.D. Can.; v.p. Quebec C. of C., 1990-92; internat. vis. lectr., spkr. in field. Bd. dirs. Soc. de Musique Contemporaire, Montreal; contbr. articles to profl. jours. Founding mem. Internat. Cons. Found.; bd. dirs.; bd. dirs. Centre de droit préventif, Orgn. Devel. Inst. Mem. Acad. Mgmt. Avocations: languages, white water rafting, travel, skiing, gardening. Office: Richardson Mgmt Assoc Ltd, 2054 Sherbrooke St W Ste 102, Montreal, PQ Canada H3H 1G5

RICHARDSON, HERBERT HEATH, mechanical engineer, educator, institute director; b. Lynn, Mass., Sept. 24, 1930; s. Walter Blake and Isabel Emily (Heath) R.; m. Barbara Ellsworth, Oct. 6, 1973. SB, SM with honors, MIT, 1955, ScD, 1958. Registered profl. engr., Mass., Tex. Research asst., research engr. Dynamic Analysis and Control Lab. MIT, 1953-57, instr. Dept. Mech. Engring., 1957-58, mem. faculty, 1958-84, prof. mech. engring., 1968-85, head dept., 1974-82, assoc. dean engring., 1982-84; Disting. prof. engring. Tex. A&M U., 1984—; Regents prof. Tex. A&M U. System, College Station, 1993—; dean, vice chancellor engring. Tex. A&M U., 1984-85, dep. chancellor, dean, dir. Tex. Engring. Expt. Sta., 1985-91; chancellor Tex. A&M U. System, College Station, 1991-93, assoc. vice chancellor engring., 1993—; assoc. dean engring., 1993—; with Ballistics Rsch. Lab. Aberdeen Proving Ground, Md., 1958; chief scientist U.S. Dept. Transp., 1970-72; bd. dirs. Foster-Miller Inc.,

Mass., Ten X Inc., Tex. Utilities Co., Tex. Inst. for Advancement of Chem. Tech.; chmn. adv. com. for engring. NSF, 1987-89, adv. com. basic energy scis. U.S. Dept. Energy, 1987-91. Author: Introduction to System Dynamics, 1971; contbr. articles to profl. publs. Trustee S.W. Rsch. Inst. Officer U.S. Army, 1968. Recipient medal Am. Ordnance Assn., 1953, Gold medal Pi Tau Sigma, 1963, Meritorious Service award and medal Dept. Transp., 1972. Fellow AAAS, ASME (Moody award fluid engring. divsn. 1970, Centennial medallion 1983, Rufus Oldenberger medal 1984, Meritorious Svc. medal 1986, Disting. Svc. award 1986, hon. mem. 1987); mem. NAE (coun. 1986-92, com. on engring. edn.), Am. Soc. Engring. Edn. (Disting. Svc. medal 1993), N.Y. Acad. Sci., Inst. Transp. Engrs., Nat. Rsch. Coun. (gov. bd. 1986-92, chmn. transp. rsch. bd. 1988-89), Sigma Xi, Tau Beta Pi. Office: Tex A&M U Sys CE/TTI Bldg MS 3135 College Station TX 77843-3135

RICHARDSON, IRENE M., healthcare company executive; b. Columbia, Tenn., Oct. 22, 1938; d. John Frank and Beatrice (Hill) Murphy; m. Joseph Richardson, Dec. 27, 1960; children: Pamela, Joseph, John, Karen. BS, Ramapo Coll., Mahwah, N.J., 1981; MBA, Farleigh Dickinson U., 1987; nursing diploma summa cum laude, St. Thomas Sch. of Nursing, Nashville, 1959. RN, N.J.; cert. sr. profl. in human resources. Clin. instr. St. Thomas Hosp., Nashville; coord. edn., staff nurse St. Clare's Hosp., Denville, N.J.; dir. edn. St. Clares Riverside Med. Ctr., Denville; pres. Cygnus Assocs., Inc., Kinnelon, N.J., 1986—; dir. edn. & tng. Northwest Covenant Med. Ctr., Denville, N.J., 1995—. Author: RN Job Satisfaction. Recipient U.S. Pub. Health Svc. scholarship. Mem. Am. Soc. for Health Care Edn. and Tng., Soc. for Health Care Edn. and Tng. N.J. (bd. dirs.), Women's Svc. Orgn. (pres. 1995-96). Home: 65 Fayson Lake Rd Kinnelon NJ 07405-3129

RICHARDSON, JEROME JOHNSON, food service company executive; b. 1936; married. AB, Wofford Coll., Spartanburg, S.C., 1959. Profl. football player Balt. Colts, 1959-61; pres. Spartan Food Systems Inc., Spartanburg, S.C., 1962-86, Spartan Food Systems div. TWS, Spartanburg, 1986-89; pres. chief exec. officer Spartan Food Systems Inc., Spartanburg, 1989—, chmn., 1990—; pres., chief exec. officer Denny's, Inc., 1988, chmn., 1989—; pres., chief exec. officer Canteen Corp., 1989—; pres. TWS, Spartanburg, 1987-89, pres., chief exec officer, 1989—, also bd. dirs.; pres., chief exec. officer TWH, Spartanburg, 1989—; chmn., dir. Flagstar Cos.; bd. dirs. Isotechnologies Inc., Sonat Inc., Spartan Mills. Bd. dirs. NCAA Found. Address: Canteen Corp 222 N LaSalle St Chicago IL 60601*

RICHARDSON, JOAN, reporter. Edn. reporter Detroit Free Press. Office: Detroit Free Press 321 W Lafayette Detroit MI 48226

RICHARDSON, JOHN, retired international relations executive; b. Boston, Feb. 4, 1921; s. John and Hope (Hemenway) R.; m. Thelma Ingram, Jan. 19, 1945; children: Eva Selek Teleki, Teren de Cossy, Hope Richardson Gravely, Catherine Richardson Munch, Hetty L. A.B., Harvard U., 1943, J.D., 1949. Bar: N.Y. 1949. Assoc. Sullivan & Cromwell, N.Y., 1949-55; with Paine, Webber, Jackson & Curtis, N.Y., 1955-69, gen. ptnr., 1958-61, ltd. ptnr., 1961-69; pres., chief exec. officer Free Europe, Inc. (Radio Free Europe), 1961-68; asst. sec. for ednl. and cultural affairs Dept. State, 1969-77, also acting asst. sec. state for pub. affairs, 1971-73; exec. dir. for social policy Ctr. for Strategic and Internat. Studies; research prof. internat. communication Sch. Fgn. Service, Georgetown U., Washington, 1977-78; pres., chief exec. officer Youth for Understanding, Inc., 1978-86, bd. dirs. 1986—, vice chmn., 1989—; counselor U.S. Inst. of Peace, 1987-90; spl. advisor Aspen Inst. Humanistic Studies, 1977-80. Mem. Council Fgn. Relations, 1957—, Citizens Commn. on S.E. Asian Refugees, 1978—; founder Polish Med. Aid Project, 1957-61; co-founder, chmn. bd. Am. Com. to Aid Poland, 1989—; pres. Internat. Rescue Com., 1960-61, bd. dirs., 1958-61, 78—; chmn. N.Y.C. Met. Mission, United Ch. of Christ, 1966-69, Am. Council for United Nations U., 1977-87, Consortium for Internat. Citizens Exchange, 1980-84; bd. dirs. Coun. for the Advancement of Citizenship, 1991—, Delphi Internat., 1991—, chmn. 1995—, Freedom House, 1963-69, pres., 1977-84; chmn. Nat. Endowment for Democracy, 1984-88, 91-92, bd. dirs., 1984-92, chmn. emeritus, 1992—; bd. dirs. Kennedy Ctr. for Performing Arts, 1970-77, Inter-Am. Found., 1970-77, East-West Ctr., 1975-77, Fgn. Policy Assn., 1958-68, 77-86, Japan-U.S. Friendship Commn., 1976-77, Am. Forum, 1977—, Social Sci Found., U Denver, 1992—, Meridian House Internat., 1978-83, Atlantic Council of U.S., 1982-84, Fgn. Student Service Council, 1978-82. Served with paratroops U.S. Army, World War II. Decorated Bronze Star with v device, Order of the Sacred Treasure, Gold and Silver Star, Japan; Commdr.'s Cross, Order of Merit Fed. Republic Germany. Home: 7401 Bradley Blvd Bethesda MD 20817-2131

RICHARDSON, JOHN CARROLL, lawyer, tax legislative consultant; b. Mobile, Ala., May 3, 1932; s. Robert Felder and Louise (Simmons) R.; m. Cicely Tomlinson, July 27, 1961; children—Nancy Louise, Robert Felder III, Leslie. B.A., Tulane U., 1954; LL.B. cum laude, Harvard U., 1960. Bar: Colo. 1960, N.Y. 1965, D.C. 1972. Assoc. Holland & Hart, Denver, 1960-64; legal v.p. Hoover Worldwide Corp., N.Y.C., 1964-69; v.p., gen. counsel Continental Investment Corp., Boston, 1969; dep. tax legis. counsel U.S. Treasury Dept., Washington, 1970-71, tax legis. counsel, 1972-73; ptnr. Brown, Wood, Ivey, Mitchell & Petty, N.Y.C., 1973-79, LeBoeuf, Lamb, Leiby & MacRae, N.Y.C., 1979-88, Morgan, Lewis & Bockius, N.Y.C., 1988-93; ret., 1993; tax legis. cons., Oxford, N.H., 1993—; adj. prof. Fordham Law Sch., 1990-94. Served to lt. comdr. USN, 1954-57. Mem. ABA (chmn. com. adminstrv. practice tax sect. 1984-86), N.Y. State Bar Assn. (exec. com. tax sect. 1975-84), D.C. Bar Assn., Am. Coll. Tax Counsel, N.Y. Athletic Club, Royal Automobile Club. Office: RR 1 Box 2070 Oxford NH 03777-9727

RICHARDSON, JOHN REGINALD, physics educator; b. Edmonton, Alta., Oct. 31, 1912; Married 1938; 2 children. AB, U. Calif. L.A., 1933, PhD physics, 1937; DSc, U. Victoria, Can. Nat. rsch. coun. fel physics U. Mich., 1937-38; asst. prof. U. Ill., 1938-42; physicist Manhattan proj. U. Calif., 1942-46; dir. Tri U. Meson Facility, U. BC, 1971-76, vis. sci., 1976—. Recipient Robert R. Wilson prize for Achievement in the Physics of Particle Accelerators Am. Physical Soc., 1991. Fellow Am. Phys. Soc., Sigma Xi. Office: TRIUMF, 4004 Westbrook Mall, Vancouver, BC Canada V6T 2A3*

RICHARDSON, JOHN THOMAS, university chancellor, clergyman; b. Dallas, Dec. 20, 1923; s. Patrick and Mary (Walsh) R. B.A., St. Mary's Sem., Perryville, Mo., 1946; S.T.D., Angelicum U., Rome, Italy, 1951; M.A., St. Louis U., 1954. Prof. theology, dean studies Kenrick Sem., St. Louis, 1951-54; lectr. Webster Coll., 1954; dean Grad. Sch. DePaul U., Chgo., 1954-60, exec. v.p., dean faculties, 1960-81, pres., 1981-93; prof. DePaul U Coll. Law, Chgo., 1955; chancellor DePaul U., Chgo., 1993—. Trustee DePaul U., Chgo., 1954—. Home: 2233 N Kenmore Ave Chicago IL 60614-3504 Office: De Paul U 1 E Jackson Blvd Chicago IL 60604

RICHARDSON, JOHN VINSON, JR., library science educator; b. Columbus, Ohio, Dec. 27, 1949; s. John Vinson Sr. and Hope Irene (Smith) R.; m. Nancy Lee Brown, Aug. 22, 1971. BA, Ohio State U., 1971; MLS, Vanderbilt U., 1972; PhD, Ind. U., 1978. Asst. prof. UCLA, 1978-83, assoc. prof., 1983—; editor The Libr. Quar., 1994—, chair grad. coun., 1995—; fellow advanced rsch. Inst. U. Ill., 1991; pres. Info. Transfer, Inglewood, Calif., 1988—; mem. editorial bd. Ref. Svcs. Rev., Ann Arbor, Mich., 1991—, Jour. Govt. Info., Oxford, Eng., 1975—, Index to Current Urban Documents, Westport, Conn., 1987—, U. Calif. Press Catalogues and Bibliographies series, 1993—; vis. fellow Charles Sturt U. NSW Australia, 1990; chmn. Calif. Pacific Ann. Conf. Com. on Archives and History, 1992—. Author: Spirit of Inquiry, 1982, Gospel of Scholarship, 1992, Knowledge-based Systems for General Reference Work, 1995; editor elect The Libr. Quar. 1994-95, editor, 1995—. Mem. UCLA Grad. Coun., 1992— (chair 1995—), U. Calif. systemwide coord. com. on grad. affairs, 1993—; pres. Wesley Found., L.A., 1981-87; lay del. Cal-Pac Conf. United Meth. Ch., 1985, 86, 92—. Rsch. grantee Coun. on Libr. Resources, 1985, 90; Harold Lancour scholar Beta Phi Mu, 1986; recipient Louise Maxwell award Ind. U. Alumni Assn., 1995. Mem. ALA (Justin Winsor prize 1990, Ref. and Adult Svcs. divsn. Outstanding Paper award 1992), AAAS, Assn. Libr. and Info. Sci. Educators (rsch. paper prize 1986, 91), Am. Statis. Assn., Sigma Xi. Democrat. Avocations: wine tasting,reading, fgn. travel, lilac point Siamese.

Office: UCLA GSLIS PO Box 951520 300 Circle Dr N Ste 204 Los Angeles CA 90095-1520 *By our common action, we can bend the flow of history.*

RICHARDSON, JOSEPH HILL, physician, medical educator; b. Rensselaer, Ind., June 16, 1928; s. William Clark and Vera (Hill) R.; m. Joan Grace Meininger, July 8, 1950; children: Lois N., Ellen M., James K. MS in Medicine Northwestern U., 1950, M.D., 1953. Intern, U.S. Naval Hosp., Great Lakes, Ill., 1953-54; fellow in medicine Cleve. Clinic, 1956-59; individual practice medicine specializing in internal medicine and hematology, Marion, Ind., 1959-67, Ft. Wayne, Ind., 1967—; assoc. clin. prof. medicine, Ind. U. Sch. Medicine, 1993—. Served to lt. MC USNR, 1953-56. Diplomate Am. Bd. Internal Medicine. Fellow ACP, AAAS; mem. AMA, Masons. Contbr. articles to med. jours. Home and Office: 8726 Fortuna Way Fort Wayne IN 46815-5725

RICHARDSON, LAUREL WALUM, sociology educator; b. Chgo., July 15, 1938; d. Tyrrell Alexander and Rose (Foreman) R.; m. Herb Walum, Dec. 27, 1959 (div. 1972); children: Benjamin, Joshua; m. Ernest Lockridge, Dec. 12, 1981. AB, U. Chgo., 1955, BA, 1956; PhD, U. Colo., 1963. Asst. prof. Calif. State U., Los Angeles, 1962-64; postdoctoral fellow Sch. Medicine Ohio State U., Columbus, 1964-65, asst. prof. sociology, 1970-75, assoc. prof., 1975-79, prof. sociology, 1979—; asst. prof. sociology Denison U., Granville, Ohio, 1965-69; mem. editorial bd. Jour. Contemporary Ethnography, Symbolic Interaction, Gender & Soc., Qualitative Sociology, Sociol. Quar. Author: Dynamics of Sex and Gender, 1977, 3d edit. 1988, The New Other Woman, 1985, Die Neve Andere, 1987, A Nova Outra Mulher, 1987, Writing Strategies: Reaching Diverse Audiences, 1990, Gender and University Teaching: A Negotiated Difference, 1991n; editor: Feminist Frontiers, 1983, 2d edit., 1989, 3rd. edit., 1992; contbr. over 100 research articles and papers. Ford Found. fellow, 1954-56; NSF dissertation fellow, 1960-62; post doctoral fellow Vocat. Rehab., Columbus, 1964; grantee Ohio Dept. Health, 1986-87, Nat. Inst. Edn., 1981-82, NIMH, 1972-74, NSF, 1963-64, NEH, 1992; recipient Disting. Affirmative Action award Ohio State U., 1983. Mem. Am. Sociol. Assn. (com. on coms. 1980-81, com. on pub. info. 1987—), North Ctrl. Sociol. Assn. (pres. 1986-87), Sociologists for Women in Soc. (coun. mem. 1978-80), Ctrl. Ohio Sociologists for Women in Soc. (past pres.), Women's Poetry Workshop, Soc. for Study of Symbolic Interaction (publs. com.). Democrat. Avocations: hiking, poetry, reading, antiques. Office: Ohio State Univ Dept of Sociology 190 N Oval Mall Columbus OH 43210-1321

RICHARDSON, LAWRENCE, JR., Latin language educator, archeologist; b. Altoona, Pa., Dec. 2, 1920; married. B.A., Yale U., 1942, Ph.D. in Classics, 1952. Instr. classics Yale U., New Haven, 1946-47, instr. to assoc. prof., 1955-66; prof. Duke U., Durham, N.C., 1966-78, James B. Duke prof. Latin, 1978-91, prof. emeritus, 1991—; field archeologist Am. Acad. Rome, 1952-55, Mellon prof., 1980-81; mem. Inst. Advanced Study, 1967-68. Author: Pompeii: An Architectural History, 1988, A New Topographical Dictionary of Ancient Rome, 1992; contbr. articles to profl. jours. Guggenheim fellow, 1958-59; Am. Council Learned Socs. fellow, 1967-68, 72-73; NEH fellow, 1979-80. Mem. German Archeol. Inst. (corr.), Am. Philol. Assn., Archeol. Inst. Am. Office: Duke U West Campus Dept Classical Studies Durham NC 27708

RICHARDSON, LORETTA M., college dean, medical/surgical nurse; b. Idamay, W.Va., June 12, 1930. Diploma, Provident Hosp. Sch. Nursing, Balt., 1954; BSN, U. Md., Balt., 1965, MS in Nursing, 1971; PhD, Union Inst., Balt., 1979. RN, Md. Coord. health Balt. City Pub. Schs.; assoc. exec. dir. Md. Bd. Nursing, exec. dir.; dean div. nursing Coppin State Coll.; chmn. Md. RN-BSN Validation Com. Contbg. author: Contemporary Minority Nurse, Collaboration for Articulation. Recipient Disting. Alumni award U. Md., 1989, Woman of Yr. in Edn. award Zeta Phi Beta. Mem. Md. Coun. Dirs. Baccalaureate and Higher Degree Programs (v.p.). Home: 3404 Cedardale Rd Baltimore MD 21215-7302

RICHARDSON, MARGARET MILNER, federal agency administrator, lawyer; b. Waco, Tex., May 14, 1943; d. James W. and Margaret Wiebusch Milner; m. John L. Richardson, July 22, 1967; 1 child, Margaret Lawrence. AB in Polit. Sci., Vassar Coll., 1965; JD with honors, George Washington U., 1968. Bar: Va. 1968, D.C. 1968, U.S. Dist. Ct. D.C. 1968, U.S. Ct. Appeals (4th, 5th, D.C. and Fed. cirs.) 1968, U.S. Claims Ct. 1969, U.S. Tax Ct. 1970, U.S. Supreme Ct. 1971. Clk. U.S. Ct. Claims, Washington; with Office Chief Counsel IRS, Washington, 1969-77; with Sutherland, Asbill and Brennan, Washington, 1977-80, ptnr., 1980-93; commr. IRS, Washington, 1993—; mem. commr.'s adv. group IRS, 1988-90, chair, 1990; mem. fed. tax adv. group Prentice Hall. Contbr. articles to profl. jours. Assisted Clinton 1992 gen. election campaign; served as team leader Justice Dept./Civil Rights Cluster during Presdl. Transition. Mem. ABA, D.C. Bar Assn. (tax sect.), Va. State Bar Assn., Fed. Bar Assn. (coun. taxation), Fin. Women's Assn. N.Y. Avocations: foreign travel, collecting antiques, needlepoint, gardening. Office: IRS 1111 Constitution Ave NW Washington DC 20224-0001

RICHARDSON, MAURICE M., manufacturing executive; b. 1933. Exec. v.p., COO Engraph Inc., Atlanta, 1983—. Office: Engraph Inc 2635 Century Pky NE Atlanta GA 30345-3112*

RICHARDSON, MAURINE JANET, reading educator; b. Portland, Maine, May 17, 1944; d. Maurice Joseph and Rena (Prevost) Vaillancourt; m. James Alexander Richardson, Apr. 30, 1966. AA, Palm Beach Jr. Coll., Lake Worth, Fla., 1964; BA, Fla. Atlantic U., 1966; MEd, U. Ark., 1979, EdD, 1981. Tchr. Pewamo-Westphalia Sch. Dist., Pewamo, Mich., 1967-69, River Valley Sch. Dist., Three Oaks, Mich., 1974-76; asst. prof. tchr. edn. Bethel Coll., McKenzie, Tenn., 1981-88; asst. prof. reading edn. U. Tenn., Martin, 1988-89, U. S.D., Vermillion, 1989—. Author: Directed Reading, Writing, and Art Activity, 1990, Imagery Format, 1987. Mem. adv. bd. Area 7 Spl. Olympics, Martin, 1988-89. Named Duchess of Paducah City of Paducah, Ky., 1987. Mem. Internat. Reading Assn., Nat. Coun. Tchrs. English, S.D. Reading Coun. (chair studies and rsch.), Vermillion Valley Reading Coun. (pres. 1992-93), Epsilon Sigma Alpha, Delta Kappa Gamma, Phi Delta Kappa. Avocations: reading, traveling, sailing, stamp collecting. Home: 902 Ridgecrest Dr Vermillion SD 57069-3531 Office: U SD 414 E Clark St Vermillion SD 57069-2307

RICHARDSON, MIDGE TURK, magazine editor; b. Los Angeles, Mar. 26, 1930; d. Charles Aloysius and Marie Theresa (Lindekin) Turk; m. Hamilton Farrar Richardson, Feb. 8, 1974. BA, Immaculate Heart Coll., L.A., 1951, MA, 1956; postgrad., U. Calif., Santa Barbara, Duquesne U., U. Pitts. Mem. Immaculate Heart Community, Roman Catholic Ch., 1948-66; asst. to dean Sch. Arts, NYU, 1966-67; coll. editor Glamour mag., N.Y.C., 1967-74; editor-in-chief Co-Ed mag.; also editorial dir. Forecast and Co-Ed mags., N.Y.C., 1974-75; editor-in-chief Seventeen mag., N.Y.C., 1975—; lectr. Tishman seminars Hunter Coll., N.Y.C., 1975-77. Host, guest TV and radio programs.: Author: The Buried Life: A Nun's Journey, 1971, Gordon Parks: A Biography for Children, 1971; also articles. Bd. dirs. YMCA, N.Y.C., 1972-73, Timothy Dwight Sch., 1979-83, Girl Scout council Greater N.Y., 1979-82; life trustee Internat. House. Recipient award Outstanding Women in Pub., 1982; winner ASME Nat. Mag. award for fiction, 1984. Mem. Am. Soc. Mag. Editors, Fashion Group. Democrat. Clubs: River, Meadow. Office: Seventeen Mag 200 Madison Ave New York NY 10016

RICHARDSON, MIRANDA, actress; b. Lancashire, Eng., 1958. Studied, Drama Program Bristol. Stage performances London: Moving, All My Sons, Who's Afraid of Virginia Woolf, The Life of Einstein, A Lie of the Mind; others include The Changling, Mountain Language; TV appearances: The Hard World, Sorrel and Son, A Woman of Substance, Underworld, Death of the Heart, (series) Black Adder II, Sweet as You Are, (miniseries) Die Kinder; films: Dance with a Stranger, 1985, The Innocent, 1986, Empire of the Sun, 1987, Eat the Rich, 1987, Twisted Obsession, 1990, The Bachelor, 1991, Enchanted April, 1992, Damage, 1992, The Crying Game, 1992 (Acad. award nominee for best supporting actress), Fatherland, HBO, 1994 (Golden Globe award), Tom & Viv, 1994 (Acad. award nominee for best actress 1995). Office: care Susan Smith & Assocs 192 Lexington Ave New York NY 10016*

RICHARDSON, NATASHA JANE, actress; b. May 11, 1963; d. Tony Richardson and Vanessa Redgrave; m. Liam Neeson, July 3, 1994; 1 son: Micheál Richard Antonio. Acting debut on stage at Leeds (England) Playhouse, 1983; appearences include (plays) A Midsummer's Night Dream, Hamlet, 1985, The Seagull, 1985, High Society, 1987, Anna Christie, 1993 (Tony award nominee 1993, Drama Desk award), (films) Every Picture Tells a Story, 1984, Gothic, 1987, A Month in the Country, 1987, Patty Hearst, 1988, Fat Man and Little Boy, 1989, The Handmaid's Tale, 1990, The Comfort of Strangers, 1991, The Favor, The Watch and the Very Big Fish, 1992, Past Midnight, Widows' Peak, 1994, Nell, 1994, (TV) In a Secret State, 1984, The Copper Beaches, 1984, Ghosts, 1986, Suddenly Last Summer, 1992, Hostages, 1993, Zelda, 1993. Recipient Most Promising Newcomer award Plays & Players, 1986; named Best Actress by London Theatre Critics, Plays & Players, 1990, Evening Standard Best Actress, 1990.

RICHARDSON, NOLAN, university athletic coach. Head coach U. Arkansas Razorbacks, 1985—. Coach NCAA championship team 1994, NCAA 2nd place team, 1995; recipient Naismith award for Best NCAA Divsn. IA coach, 1994. Office: Univ Arkansas Broyles Athletic Ctr Fayetteville AR 72701*

RICHARDSON, PATRICIA, actress; b. Bethesda, Md., Feb. 23, 1951; d. Laurence Baxter and Elizabeth (Howard) R.; m. Raymond Baker, June 20, 1982; children: Henry, Roxanne, Joseph. BFA, So. Meth. U., 1972. Appearences include (Broadway) Gypsy, Loose Ends, The Wake of Jamie Foster; (off-Broadway) The Collected Works of Billy the Kid, The Frequency, Vanities, The Coroner's Plot, Hooters, Company, Fables for Friends, The Miss Firecracker Contest, Cruise Control; (regional theatre) King Lear, The Killing of Sister George, Relatively Speaking, The Importance of Being Earnest, Of Mice and Men, The Philadelphia Story, Room Service, Fifth of July, About Face; (nat. tours) Gypsy, Vanities; (films) Gas, 1972, You Better Watch Out, Lost Angels, 1988, In Country, 1988; (TV) Double Trouble, 1984, Eisenhower & Lutz, 1988, FM, 1989-90, Home Improvement, 1991—(Lead Actress in a Comedy Series Emmy award nominee, 1994, Golden Globe award nominee, 1993, 94). Office: William Morris Agy 151 El Camino Beverly Hills CA 90210*

RICHARDSON, PETER DAMIAN, mechanical engineering educator; b. West Wickham, Eng., Aug. 22, 1935; came to U.S., 1958; s. Reginald W. and Marie S. (Ouseley) R. B.Sc. in Engring, Imperial Coll., U. London, 1955, A.C.G.I., 1955, Ph.D. (Unwin scholar), 1958, D.I.C., 1958; D.Sc. in Engring. U. London, 1974, D.Sc. in Physiology, 1983. Demonstrator dept. mech. engring. Imperial Coll., U. London, 1955-58; vis. lectr. Brown U., Providence, 1958-59; research asso. Brown U., 1959-60, asst. prof. engring., 1960-65, asso. prof., 1965-68, prof., 1968-84, prof. engring. and physiology, 1984—, chmn. faculty, 1987-88; chmn. exec. com. Center Biomed. Engring., 1972—; cons. to industry, U.S. govt. agys; on leave at U. London, 1967, U. Paris, 1968, Orta Dogu Teknik Universitesi, Ankara, Turkey, 1969, Medizinischen Fakultat, RWTH, Aachen, Germany, 1976, U. Paris XIII, 1991. Contbr. numerous articles on engring., physics, geology, biology and medicine to profl. publs. Recipient Sr. Scientist award Alexander Von Humboldt Found., 1976; named Laureate in Medicine, Jung Found., 1987. Fellow ASME, Royal Soc., Am. Inst. Med. Biol. Engring.; mem. Am. Soc. Engring. Edn., Am. Soc. Artificial Internal Organs (past assoc. editor jour.), European Soc. Artificial Organs., Biomed. Engring. Soc. Office: Brown U Box D 79 Waterman St Providence RI 02912-9079

RICHARDSON, RAND MICHAEL, public relations executive; b. Detroit, May 9, 1949. BA in Distributive Edn., Wayne State U., 1970, BS in Mktg., 1971. Dir. mktg. adminstrn. Playboy, Inc., 1972-75; exec. v.p. Ritter/Geller Commns., 1975-86, Smith Mktg., 1987-89; exec. v.p. gen. mgr. Rowland Co./West, L.A., 1989-92, pres., COO, 1992—. Mem. Pub. Rels. Soc. Am. Office: Rowland Co West 5700 Wilshire Blvd Los Angeles CA 90036

RICHARDSON, RICHARD JUDSON, political science educator; b. Poplar Bluff, Mo., Feb. 16, 1935; s. Jewell Judson and Naomi Fern (Watson) R.; m. Sammie Sue Cullum, Dec. 29, 1961; children: Jon Mark, Anna Cecile, Ellen Elizabeth, Megan Leigh. BS, Harding Coll., 1957; cert., U. Dublin, 1958; MA, Tulane U., 1961, PhD, 1967. Instr. Tulane U., 1962-65; asst. prof. polit. sci. Western Mich. U., Kalamazoo, 1965-67; assoc. prof. Western Mich. U., 1967-69; vis. assoc. prof. U. Hawaii, 1967-68; asso. prof. U. N.C., Chapel Hill, 1969-72, prof., 1972-77, Burton Craige prof., 1977—, assoc. chmn. dept., 1972-73, chmn. dept., 1975-80, 85-90, chmn. curriculum in justice, 1990—, assoc. v.p. acad. affairs univ. gen. adminstrn., 1991-92; adj. prof. Duke U., Durham, 1972-74; cons. in field. Author: (with Kenneth Vines) The Politics of Federal Courts, 1971, (with Darlene Walker) People and the Police, 1973, (with Marian Irish, James Prothro) The Politics of American Democracy, 1981. Del. County Dem. Conv., 1972, 83; vice chmn. Dem. Party Precinct, 1983-85; chmn. bldg. fund YMCA, 1976; chmn. Carolina Challenge for endowment U. N.C., Chapel Hill, 1979-80; chmn. U. N.C. Bicentennial Observance, 1991-94; chmn. United Way, 1983, pres., 1985; pres. PTA County Coun., 1984. Recipient Edward S. Corwin award Am. Polit. Sci. Assn., 1967, Tanner Disting. Teaching award U. N.C., 1972, Univ. award for Outstanding Teaching, 1981, Thomas Jefferson award, 1987, Alumni Faculty Disting. Svc. award, 1994, James Johnston Disting. Teaching award, 1993; Edgar Stern fellow, 1959-61; NEH grantee, 1970. Mem. N.C. Polit. Sci. Assn. (pres. 1978-79), Am. Polit. Sci. Assn., So. Polit. Sci. Assn., ACLU (bd. dirs. local chpt. 1985-88, state bd. dirs. 1988-89), Order of Janus, Order of the Long Leaf Pine, Order of Golden Fleece, Order of the Grail. Home: RR 1 Box 282 Pittsboro NC 27312-8108 Office: U NC Dept Polit Sci Chapel Hill NC 27514

RICHARDSON, ROBERT, cinematographer. Cinematographer: (films) Salvador, 1986, Platoon, 1986 (Academy award nomination best cinematography 1986), Wall Street, 1987, Dudes, 1988, Eight Men Out, 1988, Talk Radio, 1988, Born on the Fourth of July, 1989 (Academy award nomination best cinematography 1989), City of Hope, 1991, The Doors, 1991, JFK, 1991 (Academy award best cinematography 1991), A Few Good Men, 1992, Heaven and Earth, 1993, Natural Born Killers, 1994, (TV spl.) To the Moon, Alice, 1990; cameraman: (films) Repo Man, 1984, Making the Grade, 1984. Office: care Spyros Skouras Sanford Skouras Gross & Assocs 1015 Gayley Ave 3rd Fl Los Angeles CA 90024*

RICHARDSON, ROBERT CHARLWOOD, III, management consultant, retired air force officer; b. Rockford, Ill., Jan. 5, 1918; s. Robert Charlwood, Jr. and Lois (Farman) R.; m. Anne Waln Taylor, Sept. 13, 1952; children: Anne Newbold, Robert Charlwood, Lydia Farman. B.S., U.S. Mil. Acad., 1939; grad., Nat. War Coll., 1956. Commd. 2d lt. U.S. Army, 1939; advanced through grades to brig. gen. USAF, 1960; squadron comdg. officer Ascension Island, 1942-43; (Army Air Force Bd.), Orlando, Fla., 1943- 44; assigned U.K. and France, 1944-45; comdg. officer 365th Fighter Group, 9th Air Force, 1945-46; assigned joint war plans com. Joint Chiefs Staff, NATO, 1946-49, Washington and Paris, 1949-54; U.S. mil. rep. European Def. Community, 1954-55, comdg. officer 83d and 4th Fighter Wing, Tactical Air Command, 1956-58, assigned plans div. Hdqrs. USAF, 1958-61, mil. rep. NATO Council Paris, 1962-64, dep. chief staff for sci. and tech. Air Force Systems Command, 1964-66; dep. comdr., field command Def. Atomic Support Agy. Sandia Base, 1966-67, ret., 1967; sr. assoc. Schriever & McKee Assos., Inc., 1967-70; policy cons., pres. Encabulator Corp., 1970-80; pres. Global Activities Ltd.; v.p. Cons.'s Internat. Inc., 1973-77; dep. dir. High Frontier Inc., 1981—; pres. Exim Corp., 1977-82. Contbr. numerous articles on atomic warfare, NATO, strategy and concepts. Bd. dirs., sec./treas. Am. Cause, 1975-80, Security and Intelligence Fund, 1977-90; exec. dir. Am. Fgn. Policy Inst., 1976-86; bd. dirs., sec-treas. Space Transp. Assn., 1991—. Decorated Legion of Merit with oak leaf cluster, Air medal, Army Commendation medal; Croix de Guerre with silver star France). Home: 212 S St Asaph St Alexandria VA 22314-3744

RICHARDSON, ROBERT COLEMAN, physics educator, researcher; b. Washington, June 26, 1937; s. Robert Franklin and Lois (Price) R.; m. Betty Marilyn McCarthy, Sept. 2, 1962; children: Jennifer, Pamela. BS in Physics, Va. Poly. Inst. and State U., 1958, MS, 1960; PhD in Physics, Duke U., 1966. Research assoc. Cornell U., Ithaca, N.Y., 1966-67, asst. prof., 1968-71, assoc. prof., 1972-74; prof., 1975—; chmn. internat. Union Pure and Applied Physics Commn. (C-5), 1981-84; mem. bd. assessment Nat. Bur. Standards, 1983—. Mem. editorial bd. Jour. of Low Temperature Physics,

1984—. Served to 2d lt. U.S. Army, 1959-60. Guggenheim fellow 1975, 83; recipient Simon Meml. prize Brit. Phys. Soc., 1976. Fellow AAAS, Am. Phys. Soc. (Oliver E. Buckley prize 1981); mem. Nat. Acad. Scis. Avocations: photography, gardening. Office: Cornell Univ Dept Physics Clark Hall Ithaca NY 14853

RICHARDSON, ROBERT DALE, JR., English language educator; b. Milw., June 14, 1934; s. Robert Dale and Lucy Baldwin (Marsh) R.; m. Elizabeth Hall, Nov. 7, 1959 (div. 1987); m. Annie Dillard, Dec. 10, 1988; children: Elisabeth, Anne. AB magna cum laude in English, Harvard U., 1956, PhD in English Lit., 1961. Instr. English Harvard U., Cambridge, Mass., 1961-63; asst. prof. English U. Denver, 1963-68, assoc. prof., 1968-72, prof., 1972-87, Lawrence C. Phipps prof. humanities, 1979-82, chmn. dept., 1968-73, pres. Univ. senate, 1972-73, assoc. dean grad. studies, 1975-76; prof. English, U. Colo., Boulder, 1987; vis. prof. letters Wesleyan U., Middletown, Conn., 1989-94; vis. prof. Harvard U., summer 1976, CUNY, 1978, Sichuan U., 1983; vis. fellow Huntington Libr., 1973-74; vis. instr. Yale U., 1988; bd. dirs. David R. Godine Pub. Author: Literature and Film, 1969, Henry Thoreau: A Life of the Mind, 1986, Emerson: The Mind on Fire, 1995, Myth and Literature in the American Renaissance, 1978, (with Burton Feldman) The Rise of Modern Mythology 1680-1860, 1972. Trustee Meadville-Lombard Theol. Sch., 1981-87. Guggenheim fellow, 1990. Mem. MLA, Rocky Mountain MLA, Am. Studies Assn., Soc. Eighteenth Century Studies, Melville Soc., Author's Guild, Thoreau Soc., Emerson Soc. Democrat. Unitarian.

RICHARDSON, ROBERT JANECEK, library director; b. Savannah, Ga., July 30, 1945; s. William Blakely and Mildred Ann (Salcedo) R.; m. Janice Amelia Neder, June 10, 1967; children: Robert Jr., Mary Neder Salcedo. AA, Mid. Ga. Coll., 1965; BA, West Ga. Coll., 1967; MSc, Fla. State U., 1971. Tchr. social studies Dublin (Ga.) City Schs., 1967-70; libr., instr. Ga. Coll., Milledgeville, 1971-78; asst. libr. dir. Chattahoochee Valley Regional Libr., Columbus, Ga., 1979-80; libr. dir. Young Harris (Ga.) Coll., 1980—; mem. evaluation team So. Assn. Colls. and Schs., Atlanta, 1983—; cons. Ga. Mil. Coll. Libr., Milledgeville, 1986. Mem. adminstrv. coun. Sharp Meml. Meth. Ch., Young Harris, 1984-88; trustee Towns County Libr., Hiawassee, Ga., 1980-84, 92—, chmn. 1995—; bd. dirs. Towns-Union Credit Union, Young Harris, 1986—. Mem. Ga. Libr. Assn. (pres. 1989-91, Nix-Jones Svc. award 1993), Ga. Assn. Instrnl. Tech. Democrat. Methodist. Avocations: camping, gardening. Office: Young Harris Coll 1 Duckworth Blvd Young Harris GA 30582

RICHARDSON, R(OSS) FRED(ERICK), insurance executive; b. Renfrew, Ont., Can., Feb. 4, 1928; came to U.S., 1980; s. Garfield Newton and Grace Mary (MacLean) R.; m. Betty Blanche Betts, Feb. 4, 1972; children by previous marriage—Sheri Joan, Robert John, Paul Frederick. BA in Math. and Physics with honors, Queens U., 1950. Actuarial asst. Empire Life Ins. Co., Kingston, Ont., Can., 1950-55; sec. Maritime Life Ins. Co., Halifax, N.S., Can., 1955-59, dir. sales, 1959-65, chief exec. officer, 1967-72; mng. dir., chief exec. officer Abbey Life Ins. Co., U.K., 1972-80; group gen. mgr. Hartford Europe Group, 1975-80; sr. v.p., dir. worldwide life ins. ops. Hartford Ins. Group, Conn., 1980-83, dir. worldwide life ins. ops., 1983-88; pres., chief operating officer Hartford Life Cos., 1983-88; pvt. ins. cons. Boca Raton, Fla., 1988; pres., chief exec. officer Crown Life Ins. Co., 1988-93; cons. INSCE, Boca Raton, 1993—. Fellow Soc. Actuaries; mem. Inst. Actuaries Gt. Britain, Companion Brit. Inst. Mgmt. CLU. Home and Office: 17047 Boca Club Blvd 165B Boca Raton FL 33487

RICHARDSON, RUDY JAMES, toxicology and neurosciences educator; b. May 13, 1945. BS magna cum laude, Wichita State U., 1967; Sc.M., Harvard U., 1973, Sc.D., 1974. Diplomate Am. Bd. Toxicology. Research geochemist Columbia U., N.Y.C., summer 1966; NASA trainee SUNY, Stony Brook, 1967-70; research biochemist Med. Research Council, Carshalton, Eng., 1974-75; asst. prof. U. Mich., Ann Arbor, 1975-79, assoc. prof., 1979-84, prof. toxicology, 1984—, assoc. prof. neurotoxicology neurology dept., 1987—, acting dir. dept. Toxicology, 1993; dir., 1994—; bd. dirs. Trillium Enterprises Inc.; vis. scientist Warner-Lamber Co., Ann Arbor, 1982-83; vis. prof. U. Padua, Italy, 1991; cons. NAS, Washington, 1978-79, 84, Office Tech. Assessment, US Congress, 1988-90, Nat. Toxic Substance Disease Registry, 1990—; mem. sci. adv. panel on neurotoxicology EPA, 1987-89; chmn. work group on neurotoxicity guidelines Orgn. for Econ. Coop. and Devel., 1990, Nat. Inst. Orgnl. Safety and Health, 1990, 94. Contbr. articles to profl. jours., chpts. to books; mem. editorial bd. Neurotoxicology, 1980—, Toxicology and Indsl. Health, 1986—, Toxicology and Applied Pharmacology, 1989—. Mem. Mich. Lupus Found., Ann Arbor, 1979—. Grantee NIH, 1977-86, EPA, 1977-86; invited speaker Gordon Conf., Meriden, N.H., 1984, Cholinesterase Congress, Bled, Yugoslavia, 1983. Mem. AAAS, Soc. Toxicology (pres. neurotoxicology sect. 1987-88, councilor 1988-89), Soc. for Neurosci., Am. Diabetes Assn., Am. Chem. Soc., Internat. Soc. Neurochemistry, Internat. Brain Rsch. Orgn. Achievements include co-discoverer (with B.R. Dudek) of lymphocyte neurotoxic esterase (NTE); development of lymphocyte NTE as biomarker of exposure to neuropathic organophosphates; refinement of NTE assay for use in neurotoxicity testing. Office: U Mich Toxicology Program M 7525 Sph # 2 Ann Arbor MI 48109

RICHARDSON, SALLY KEADLE, state health care administrator; b. Huntington, W.Va., Mar. 2, 1933; d. Okey P. and Viola Miriam (Graybeal) Keadle; m. Don Kule Richardson, Dec. 15, 1961; children—Miriam Paige, Ruth Evan. A.B., Vassar Coll., Poughkeepsie, N.Y., 1954. Regional pub. info. rep. Columbia Gas System, Charleston, 1958-62; dir. Children's Mus., Charleston, 1963; coordinator space-related sci. project Kanawha County Schs., Charleston, 1967-68; vol. dir. Rockefeller for Gov. Campaign, Charleston, 1972, program dir., 1976, 1980; dir. admissions W.Va. Wesleyan Coll., Buckhannon, 1974-75; spl. asst. Office of Gov. State of W.Va., 1977, dep. commr. Dept. Welfare, 1978-79, dep. dir. Dept. Health, 1979-83; chmn. W.Va. Health Care Cost Rev. Authority, Charleston, 1983—; W.Va. rep. Task Force on So. Children, So. Growth Policies Bd., 1978-79; co-chmn. exec. com. W.Va. Internat. Yr. of Child, 1979; staff mem. Com. on Human Resources Nat. Gov. Assn., 1983—. Mem. Am. Health Planning Assn., W.Va. Pub. Health Assn. Democrat. Episcopalian. Office: W Va Health Care Cost Rev Authority State Capital Charleston WV 25305

RICHARDSON, SYLVIA ONESTI, physician; b. San Francisco, Sept. 12, 1920; d. Silvio J. and Johanna (Kristoffy) Onesti; m. William R. Richardson, Sept. 8, 1951 (dec. 1994); children: William Charles, Christopher Lee. B.A., Stanford, 1940; postgrad., U. Wash., 1940-41; M.A., Columbia U., 1942; M.D., McGill U., 1948; D.Litt. (hon.), Emerson Coll. Intern Children's Meml. Hosp., Montreal, 1948-49; resident Children's Med. Center, Boston, 1949-50; instr. spl. edn. Columbia, 1942-43; supr. hearing handicapped New Rochelle (N.Y.) Pub. Schs., 1942-43; clin. fellow in medicine Boston Children's Med. Center, 1949-51, dir. speech clinic, 1950-52, asso. physician, 1951-52, research fellow in surgery, 1954-55; instr. speech dept. Boston U., 1950-52, San Diego State Coll., 1952-54; teaching fellow in medicine Harvard U., 1951-52; asst. clin. prof. pediatrics State U. N.Y., Downstate Med. Center, Bklyn., 1957-58; asso. prof. pediatrics and psychiatry, dir. child study center U. Okla. Sch. Medicine, 1958-65; asst. clin. prof. pediatrics U. South Fla. Med. Sch. Medicine, 1965-67, asso. prof., 1967-80; dir. learning disabilities program Center for Developmental Disorders, 1966-80; disting. profl. communication scis. and disorders, clin. prof. pediatrics U. South Fla., 1980—; cons. dept. child health and maternal welfare State of Okla., 1957-65; spl. cons. Nat. Inst. Nervous Diseases and Blindness, 1960-62; spl. cons. on mental retardation Okla. State Dept. Pub. Welfare, 1963-65; cons. Bur. State Services, USPHS, Bur. Edn. Handicapped, U.S. Office Edn. Editor: Children's House mag, 1966-67; mem. editorial bd. Jour. Learning Disbailities, Topics in Lang. Disorders. Mem. Okla. gov.'s com. White House Conf., 1960, White House Conf. on Children, 1970; Okla. citizen's com. Adequate Higher Edn., 1958-62. Recipient award for mental health planning Gov. of Okla., 1966; Distinguished Service award Internat. Assn. Children with Learning Disabilities, 1969; Old Master award Purdue U., 1972; named Okla. Woman of the Year, 1964; Talisman Service award Ohio Assn. Children with Learning Disabilities, 1974; Newell Kephart award for services to exceptional children, 1976. Fellow Am. Speech and Hearing Assn. (mem. exec. council 1957-59, chmn. elect ho. of dels. 1965, pres. 1973, honor award 1988), Royal Soc. Health, Internat. Assn. Rsch. in Learning Disabilities, Multidisciplinary Acad. for

Clin. Edn., Internat. Assn. for Logopedics and Phoniatrics; mem. AMA, Mass. Speech and Hearing Assn. (co-founder, pres. 1950-52), Okla. Speech and Hearing Assn. (exec. council), Orton Dyslexia Soc. (bd. dirs. 1978-84, pres. 1984-88, Samuel T. Orton award 1992), Ohio Speech and Hearing Assn., Oklahoma County Council Mentally Retarded Children (bd. dirs. 1960-65), Oklahoma County Mental Health Assn. (profl. adv. bd. 1961-65), Okla. Hearing Soc. (v.p., bd. dirs. 1959-61), Soc. Research in Child Devel., Assn. Children with Learning Disabilities (chmn. profl. adv. bd.), Council Exceptional Children, Cin. Pediatric Soc. Home: 4141 Bayshore Blvd Apt 1701 Tampa FL 33611-1802

RICHARDSON, THOMAS HAMPTON, design consulting engineer; b. St. Louis, Nov. 25, 1941; s. Claude Hampton and Pearl Lily (Burks) R.; m. Lois Louise Atteberry June 8, 1963; children: Shelley Ann, David Hampton, Stephanie Lynn. BTEE, Wash. U., St. Louis, 1974. Registered profl. engr., Mo., Ill., Ind., Kans., Calif., Fla., Ky., Miss. Elec. project designer Fruco Engrs. Inc., St. Louis, 1967-68; mgr., mech./elec. engr. MBA Engrs. Inc., St. Louis, 1968-74, Kenneth Balk and Assocs., St. Louis, 1974-76; instr. elec. engring. Wash. U., St. Louis, 1976; v.p., chief engr. John F. Steffen Assoc., St. Louis, 1976-79; prin. ptnr. Keeler, Webb and Richardson, St. Louis, 1979-94; pres./owner The Richardson Engring. Group, St. Louis, 1979—. Contbr. articles to profl. jours. Recipient Internat. Lgt. Des. award Illuminating Engr. Soc. St. Louis 1985, Edwin F. Guth award of Merit Illuminating Engr. Soc. N.Am. 1986. Mem. NSPE, ASHRAE, Am. Cons. Engr. Coun., Illuminating Engring. Soc. Past pres.), Soc. for Mkt. Profl. Svcs. (v.p.), Profl. Svcs. Mgmt. Assn. (bd. dirs.), Mo. Soc. Profl. Engrs. (govt. rels. com.), Nat. Fire Protection Assn., Green Turtle Bay Yacht Club, Grand Lake Yacht Club, Ky. Lake Club. Avocations: sailing, flying, horses, photography. Office: The Richardson Engring 1700 Gilsinn Dr Fenton MO 63026-2004

RICHARDSON, W. FRANKLYN, religious organization administrator. Gen. sec. Nat. Baptist Convention, USA, Mount Vernon, N.Y. Address: 52 S 6th Ave Mount Vernon NY 10550

RICHARDSON, WALTER JOHN, architect; b. Long Beach, Calif., Nov. 14, 1926; s. Walter Francis and Ava Elizabeth (Brown) R.; m. Marilyn Joyce Brown, June 26, 1949 (div. 1982); children: Mark Steven, Glenn Stewart; m. Mary Sue Sutton, Dec. 4, 1982. Student, UCLA, 1944-45, Long Beach City Coll., 1946; BA, U. Calif., Berkeley, 1950. Registered architect, Ala., Ariz., Calif., Colo., Fla., Hawaii, Ill., Kans., Md., Mass., Nev., N.J., N.Y., Okla., Oreg., Tex., Utah, Vt., Va., Wash. Draftsman Wurster, Bernardi, Emmons, San Francisco, 1950-51, Skidmore, Owings & Merrill, San Francisco, 1951; designer Hugh Gibbs Architect, Long Beach, 1952-58; ptnr. Thomas & Richardson Architects, Long Beach, Costa Mesa, 1958-70; pres. Walter Richardson Assocs. Architects, Newport Beach, Calif., 1970-74; cmn. bd. Richardson, Nagy, Martin Architects and Planners, Newport Beach, 1974—. Co-author: The Architect and the Shelter Industry, 1975. Chmn. Planning Commn., City of Orange, Calif., 1967-68. With USAF, 1945. Recipient over 200 Gold Nugget Design awards Pacific Coast Builders Conf., San Francisco, 1969-94, 12 Builders Choice Design awards Builder Mag.; named Architect of Yr. Profl. Builder mag., 1986. Fellow AIA (pres. Orange County chpt. 1970, chmn. nat. housing com. 1976, 7 design awards); mem. Nat. Assn. Home Builders, Nat. Coun. Archtl. Registration Bds., Alpha Tau Omega. Republican. Avocations: photography, downhill skiing, travel, tennis. Office: Richardson Nagy Martin 4611 Teller Ave Ste 100 Newport Beach CA 92660

RICHARDSON, WILLIAM BLAINE, congressman; b. Pasadena, Calif., Nov. 15, 1947; m. Barbara Flavin, 1972. BA, Tufts U., Medford, Mass., 1970; MA, Fletcher Sch. Law and Diplomacy, 1971. Mem. staff U.S. Ho. of Reps., 1971-72, Dept. State, 1973-75; mem. staff fgn. relations com. U.S. Senate, 1975-78; exec. dir. N. Mex. State Democratic Com., 1978, Bernalillo County Democratic Com., 1978; businessman Santa Fe, N. Mex., 1978-82; mem. 98th-103rd Congresses from 3rd N.Mex. dist., Washington, 1982—; democratic chief dep. majority whip 103d Congress; ranking minority mem. Resources Com. on Nat. Pks., Forests and Lands; mem. Select Com. on intelligence, Helsinki Commn. Vice chair Dem. Nat. Com.; active Big Bros.-Big Sisters, Santa Fe. Mem. Santa Fe Hispanic C. of C., Santa Fe C. of C., Council Fgn. Relations, NATO 2000 Bd., Congl. Hispanic Caucus, Am. G.I. Forum. Office: 2209 Rayburn House Office Bldg Bldg Washington DC 20515-0001*

RICHARDSON, WILLIAM CHASE, university administrator; b. Passaic, N.J., May 11, 1940; s. Henry Burtt and Frances (Chase) R.; m. Nancy Freeland, June 18, 1966; children: Elizabeth, Jennifer. B.A., Trinity Coll., 1962; M.B.A., U. Chgo., 1964; Ph.D., 1971. Research assoc., instr. U. Chgo., 1967-70; asst. prof. health services U. Wash., 1971-73, assoc. prof., 1973-76, prof., 1976-84, chmn. dept. health services, 1973-76; dean U. Wash. Sch. Public Health, 1976-81, acting dean, 1977, 78; dean U. Wash. Grad. Sch., vice provost, 1981-84; exec. v.p., provost prof. dept. family and community medicine Pa. State U., 1984-90; pres. Johns Hopkins U., Balt., 1990—, prof. dept. health policy, mgmt.; cons. in field: Author: books, including Ambulatory Use of Physicians Services, 1971, Health Program Evaluation, 1978; contbr. articles to profl. jours. Kellogg fellow, 1965-67. Fellow Am. Public Health Assn.; mem. Inst. Medicine, Nat. Acad. Scis. Office: Johns Hopkins U Office of Pres Charles # 34th Sts Baltimore MD 21218*

RICHARDSON, WILLIAM F., lawyer; b. Harvey, Ill., Apr. 20, 1948; s. Donald and Dorothy (Warren) R. BS, U. Ill., 1970, JD, 1973. Bar: Ill. 1973. Ptnr. Peterson and Ross, Chgo., 1973-94, Blatt, Hammesfahr & Eaton, Chgo., 1994—. Mem. ABA. Office: Blatt Hammesfahr & Eaton 333 W Wacker Dr Ste 1900 Chicago IL 60606

RICHART, JOHN DOUGLAS, investment banker; b. Urbana, Ill., Jan. 16, 1947; s. Frank Edwin and Elizabeth Norma (Goldthorp) R.; m. Nan Jackson, June 27, 1970. BS in Engring., U. Mich., 1967, MS in Engring., 1968; MBA, Harvard U., 1973. V.p. Donaldson, Lufkin and Jenrette Securities Corp., N.Y.C., 1973-82; mng. dir. Chase Investment Bank div. Chase Manhattan Bank, N.A., N.Y.C., 1982-89; 1st v.p. mgr. mergers and acquisitions Australia and New Zealand Banking Group, N.Y.C., 1989-91; pres. Richart & Co., Upper Montclair, N.J., 1991—. Lt. (j.g.) USCG, 1968-71. Mem. Harvard Bus. Sch. Club N.Y., Montclair Golf Club, Bradford Bath and Tennis Club, PGA West. Republican. Avocations: golf, platform tennis. Home: 15 Bradford Way Cedar Grove NJ 07009-1933 also: 54-981 Southern Hills La Quinta CA 92253 Office: Richart & Co Ste 379 551 Valley Rd Montclair NJ 07043-1850

RICHART, CAROLYN MAE, mathematics educator; b. Catskill, N.Y., Aug. 12, 1945; d. George R. and Frances (Reynolds) Eden; m. Lynn A. Richart, Aug. 15, 1987. BS, SUNY, Genesee, 1967, MEd, 1982; PhD, U. Albany, 1992. Cert. math. tchr., elem. tchr., N.Y. Tchr. Wolcott St. Sch., Le Roy, N.Y., 1967-69; math. tchr. Le Roy Cen. High Sch., 1969-72, Attica (N.Y.) Mid. Sch., 1978-84; assoc. prof. Genesee C.C., Batavia, N.Y., 1984-87; grad. asst. U. Albany, 1987-90; asst. prof. Russell Sage Coll., Troy, N.Y., 1990-92, SUNY, New Paltz, 1992—; project dir. grades kindergarten through 6, N.Y. State Math Mentor Network. Contbr. articles to profl. jours. Mem. Nat. Coun. Tchrs. Math. (speaker), Assn. Math. Tchrs. N.Y. State (pres. 1995-96, pres.-elect 1994-95, corr. sec. 1991-92, rec. sec. 1988-89, dir. workshop 1992, chairperson workshop program 1989, chairperson Wyo. County sect. 1985-88), N.Y. State Assn. Two-Yr. Colls. (exec. bd. 1986-90, legis. chairperson 1986-89, curriculum chairperson 1989-90). Home: 25 Martha's Ct Saugerties NY 12477 Office: SUNY at New Paltz Old Main New Paltz NY 12561-2499

RICHBURG, KEITH BERNARD, journalist, foreign correspondent; b. Detroit, May 19, 1958; s. Walter Arthur and Katie Lee (Clemons) R. BA in Polit. Sci., U. Mich., 1980; MSc in Internat. Rels., London Sch. Econs. 1984. Met. staff reporter Washington Post, 1980-83, nat. staff corr., 1984-86; S.E. Asia bur. chief Washington Post, Manila, 1986-90; Africa bur. chief Washington Post, Nairobi, Keyna, 1991-94; Hong Kong bur. chief Washington Post, 1995—. Recipient fgn. reporting award Nat. Assn. Black Journalists, 1993, UN reporting award Korn-Ferry, 1993, George Polk award for fgn. reporting L.I. U., 1994; Harry S Truman scholar Truman Found., 1978. Mem. Am. Friends London Sch. Econs., U. Mich. Alumni

Assn., Phi Beta Kappa. Home and Office: Washington Post (Fgn Desk) 1150 15th St NW Washington DC 20071-0001

RICHELSON, PAUL WILLIAM, curator; b. Montpelier, Idaho, Sept. 27, 1939; s. Paul Newton and June (Quayle) R. BA, Yale U., 1961; MFA, Princeton U., 1967, PhD, 1974. Asst. prof. Lawrence U., Appleton, Wis., 1970-77, U. Denver, 1977-84; asst. dir., curator Trisolini Gallery of Ohio U., Athens, 1984-87; chief curator Grand Rapids (Mich.) Mus., 1987-91; curator of Am. art Mobile Mus. Art, Mobile, Ala., 1991—. Author: (book) Studies in the Personal Imagery Collection of 20th Prints Ohio University, 1985; (catalogue) The Golden Age 19th Century Prints by David Roberts, 1988, Lee Loring: A Southern Sophisticate, 1992, Modernism and American Painting of the 1930s, 1993, ThirtySomething, 1994, Alabama Impact: Contemporary Artists with Alabama Ties, 1995. Lt. (j.g.) USN, 1961-63. Fulbright-Hays fellow to Italy, 1967-69; Mus. Purchase Plan grantee Nat. Endowment for the Arts, 1991. Mem. Southeastern Museums Conf. Home: 6427 Grelot Rd Apt 405 Mobile AL 36695-2630 Office: Mobile Museum of Art PO Box 8426 Mobile AL 36689-0426

RICHENBURG, ROBERT BARTLETT, artist, retired art educator; b. Boston, July 14, 1917; s. Frederick Henry and Shary (Bartlett) R.; m. Libby Chic Peltyn, Nov. 11, 1942 (dec. 1977); 1 child, Ronald P.; m. Margaret Kerr, Feb. 9, 1980; stepchildren: William Blakeley Kerr, David Garrett Kerr, Margaret Frances Kerr. Student, Boston U., George Washington U., Corcoran Sch. Art, Art Students League N.Y., Ozenfant Sch. Fine Arts, Hans Hofmann Sch. Art. Tchr. painting Schrivenham Am. U., Eng., 1945; instr. Coll. City N.Y., 1947-52, Cooper Union, 1955-65; instr. Bklyn.-Queens Central YMCA, 1947-51; instr. NYU, 1960-61, Pratt Inst., Bklyn., 1951-64; assoc. prof. art Cornell U., Ithaca, N.Y., 1964-67; prof. art Hunter Coll., N.Y.C., 1967-70, Aruba (Netherlands Antilles) Research Center, 1970; prof. art Ithaca Coll., 1970-83, mem. council on arts; panelist various orgns. One-man shows Hendler Gallery, Phila., N.Y. Artists Gallery, Tibor DeNagy Gallery, Hansa Gallery, N.Y., Dwan Gallery, Los Angeles, Santa Barbara Mus. (Calif.), Dayton Art Inst., Dana Arts Center Colgate U., Ithaca Coll. Mus. Art, Grad. Sch. Bus. Cornell U., others; exhibited in group shows Mus. Modern Art, Solomon Guggenheim Mus., N.Y.C., Chrysler Art Mus., Yale Art Gallery, Whitney Mus., N.Y.C., Univ. Art Mus., Austin, Tex., Balt. Mus., Cocoran Mus. Art, Washington, Bklyn. Mus., Knox Albright Mus., Buffalo, Larry Aldrich Mus., Seattle Art Mus., Boston Mus. Fine Arts, numerous others; represented in permanent collections Chrysler Mus. Art, Norfolk Mus. Art, Coll. of William and Mary, Whitney Mus., Phila. Mus. Art, Pasadena Mus. Fine Art, Mus. Modern Art, Univ. Art Mus., U. Calif.-Berkeley, U. Tex. Art Mus., Austin, Ithaca Coll. Mus., Hirschorn Mus., Smithsonian Instn., Washington, many others. Served with AUS, 1942-45. Mem. Am. Assn. U. Profs., Coll. Art Assn., Internat. Platform Assn., Art Students League N.Y. (life). Club: (N.Y.C.). Home: 1006 Springs Fireplace Rd East Hampton NY 11937-1432

RICHERSON, HAL BATES, physician, internist, allergist, immunologist, educator; b. Phoenix, Feb. 16, 1929; s. George Edward and Eva Louise (Steere) R.; m. Julia Suzanne Bradley, Sept. 5, 1953; children: Anne, George, Miriam, Julia, Susan. BS with distinction, U. Ariz., 1950; MD, Northwestern U., 1954. Diplomate Am. Bd. Internal Medicine, Am. Bd. Allergy and Immunology, Bd. Diagnostic Lab. Immunology; lic. physician, Ariz., Iowa. Intern Kansas City (Mo.) Gen. Hosp., 1954-55; resident in pathology St. Luke's Hosp., Kansas City, 1955-56; trainee in neuropsychiatry Brooke Army Hosp., San Antonio, 1956; resident in medicine U. Iowa Hosps., Iowa City, 1961-64, fellow in allergy and immunology, 1964-66; fellow in immunology Mass. Gen. Hosp., Boston, 1968-69, instr. internal medicine, 1964-66, asst. prof., 1970-76, assoc. prof., 1977-74, prof., 1974—, acting dir. Div. Allergy and Applied Immunology, dept. Internal Medicine, 1970-72, dir. Allergy and Clin. Immunology sect., 1972-78, dir. Allergy and Immunology div., 1978-91; gen. practice, asst. to Gen. Surgeon Ukiah, Calif., 1958; gen. practice medicine Holbrook, Ariz., 1958-61; vis. lectr. medicine Harvard U. Sch. Medicine, Boston, 1968-69; vis. prof. & rsch. scientist U. London & Brompton Hosp., London, 1984; prin. investigator Nat. Heart, Lung and Blood Inst., 1971—, Nat. Inst. Allergy and Infectious Diseases, 1983-94; dir. NIAID Asthma and Allergic Diseases Ctr., U. Iowa, 1983-94; mem. VA Merit Rev. Bd. in Respiration, 1981-84, Pulmonary Diseases Adv. Com., Nat. Heart, Lung, and Blood Inst., 1983-87, Residency Rev. Com. for Allergy & Immunol., 1980-84, vice chmn., 1983-84; mem. com. NIH Gen. Clin. Rsch. Ctrs., 1989—; bd. scientific advisers Merck Inst., 1990-94; presenter lectures, seminars, continuing edn. courses; numerous univ., coll. and hosp. com. memberships, 1970—; cons. Merck Manual, 1982, 87, 92; mem. rev. reserve NIH, 1993—. Contbr. numerous articles and revs. to profl. jours., chpts. to books; reviewer Sci., Jour. Immunology, Jour. Allergy and Clin. Immunology, Am. Rev. Respiratory Disease, New Eng. Jour. Medicine, Ann. Internal Medicine. Served to capt. U.S. Army, 1956-58. NIH fellow 1968-69. Fellow ACP, Am. Acad. Allergy; mem. AMA, AAAS, Iowa Med. Soc., Iowa Thoracic Soc. (chmn. program com. 1964-65, 69-71, pres. 1972-73, exec. com. 1972-74), Am. Thoracic Soc. (bd. dirs. 1981-82, councillor assembly on allergy and immunology 1980-81, nominating com. 1988-90), Iowa Clin. Med. Soc., Am. Fedn. Clin. Research, Am. Assn. Immunologists, Cen. Soc. Clin. Research (chmn. sect. on allergy-immunology 1980-81, council mem. 1981-84), Alpha Omega Alpha. Avocations: reading, swimming, handball, scuba diving. Home: 331 Lucon Dr Iowa City IA 52245-3300 Office: U Iowa Hosps and Clinics Dept Internal Medicine SE 630 Gen Hosp Iowa City IA 52242

RICHERT, PAUL, law educator; b. Elwood, Ind., Aug. 31, 1948; s. Clarendon George and Margaret Ann (Cummins) R.; m. Catherine George Stanton, June 24, 1972; children: John Cummins, William Stanton. AB, U. Ill.-Urbana, 1970, MS, 1971; JD, Tulane U., 1977. Bar: Ohio 1977. Asst. law librarian U. Akron, 1977-78, law librarian, asst. prof. law, 1978-83, assoc. prof., 1983-87, prof. law, 1987—; cons. to cts. Served with U.S. Army, 1971-74. Mem. Am. Assn. Law Libraries, Akron Bar Assn., ABA. Mem. United Churches of Christ. Editor: Ohio Appellate Decision on Fiche, 1981; indexer Publs. Clearing House Bull., vols. 1-4. Home: 2030 Ganyard Rd Akron OH 44313-6050 Office: U Akron Sch of Law Libr 150 University Ave Akron OH 44325-2902

RICHETTA, FRED J., manufacturing and operations executive; b. Mt. Clements, Mich., Sept. 28, 1949; s. Frank and Erma A. (Bertonsin) R.; m. Gayle A. Prieur, Apr. 21, 1972; children: Brett J., Blake F. BS in Mech. Engring., U. Mich., 1971; MS in Engring. Mgmt., U. Louisville, 1975; MBA, Bellarmine Coll., 1980. Registered profl. engr., Mich. With mfg. mgmt. program GE, Louisville, 1971-73; mfg. engr. GE, Kissimmee, Fla., 1973-76; advanced mfg. quality GE, Louisville, 1976-78, mfg. productivity, 1978-79, plant unit mgr., 1979-80; corp. cons. GE, Bridgeport, Conn., 1980-81; mgr. productivity and quality strategy GE, Louisville, 1981-82; mgr. advanced mfg. Herman Miller, Holland, Mich., 1982-83, mgr. strategic planning, 1984, dir. mfg. svcs., 1984-85, dir. engring., 1985-86; mgr. mfg. devel. Briggs & Stratton, Milw., 1986-87; v.p. mfg. Pa. House, Lewisburg, 1987, v.p. ops., 1988-90; sr. v.p. Drexel (N.C.) Heritage Furniture, 1990—. Mem. Assn. Mfg. Excellence. Office: Drexel Heritage 101 N Main St Drexel NC 28619

RICHETTE, LISA AVERSA, judge; b. Phila., Sept. 11, 1928; d. Domenico and Maria (Giannini) Aversa; m. Lawrence J. Richette, Apr. 15, 1958 (div. Apr. 1971); 1 child, Lawrence Anthony II. BA summa cum laude, U. Pa., 1949; LLB, Yale U., 1952. Bar: Pa. 1954. Rsch. assoc. Yale U. Law Sch., 1952, instr., 1952-54; asst. dist. atty. Dist. Atty.'s Office, Phila., 1954-64; chief family ct. div., 1956-64; judge Ct. Common Pleas, Phila., 1972—; lectr. Temple U. Law Sch., 1972—; adj. prof. law, 1972—; adj. prof. sociology dept. St. Joseph's U.; clin. prof. law Villanova (Pa.) U. Law Sch., 1970-72. Author: The Throwaway Children, 1969. Co-founder, bd. dirs. Big Sisters, Phila. YWCA, Nat. Commn. Child Abuse; pres. Phila. Health and Welfare Coun., 1958-60. Decorated Star of Solidarity (Italy); recipient Disting. Dau. of Pa. award Commonwealth Pa., 1991, St. Thomas More Lawyer of Yr. award, 1994. Mem. Phila. Bar Assn. (vice chmn. chancellor's commn. on drug abuse 1972-75), Justinian Soc., U. Pa. Women's Alumna Soc. (pres. 1966-70), Mortar Bd., Phi Beta Kappa, Phi Alpha Theta. Office: Ct Common Pleas Phila 294 City Hall Philadelphia PA 19107-3202

RICHETTI, JOHN JOSEPH, English educator, writer, editor; b. N.Y.C., Nov. 14, 1938; s. Miguel and Maria Louisa (Braconi) R.; m. Frances Ellyn

Palminteri, Sept. 14, 1960 (div. 1986); children: Dion, Noel; m. Deirdre Ada Whitaker, Aug. 4, 1987. BA, St. Francis Coll., 1960; MA, Columbia U., 1961, PhD, 1968. Instr. St. John's U., Bklyn., 1961-65; asst. prof. Columbia U., N.Y.C., 1967-70; assoc. prof. Rutgers U., New Brunswick, N.J., 1970-74, prof., 1975-87; Sugarman prof. U. Pa., Phila., 1987—, chmn. dept. English, 1991—. Author: Popular Fiction Before Richardson, 1969, Defoe's Narratives, 1975, Philosophical Writing, 1983; editor: Cambridge Univ. Studies in Eighteenth-Century Literature and Thought, Cambridge, Eng., 1967—. Guggenheim Found. fellow, 1971, Am. Coun. Learned Soc. fellow, 1976, NEH sr. fellow, 1990. Office: U Pa 34th And Walnut St Philadelphia PA 19104

RICHEY, CHARLES ROBERT, federal judge; b. Logan County, Ohio, Oct. 16, 1923; s. Paul D. and Miriam (Blaine) R.; m. Agnes Mardelle White, Mar. 25, 1950; children: Charles R. Jr., William Paul. BA, Ohio Wesleyan U., 1945; LLB, Case-Western Res. U., 1948. Bar: Ohio 1949, D.C. 1951, U.S. Supreme Ct. 1952, Md. 1964. Legis. counsel former congresswoman Frances P. Bolton, Ohio, 1948-49; practice in Washington and Chevy Chase, Md., 1950-71; founding partner firm Richey & Clancy, Washington and Chevy Chase, Md., 1964-71; gen. counsel Md. Pub. Service Commn., 1967-71; judge U.S. Dist. Ct. D.C., 1971—; sat by designation as mem. U.S. Ct. Appeals for D.C., 1972-75, 77-85; mem. Temporary U.S. Emergency Ct. Appeals, 1983-84, Commn. on Criminal Law and Adminstrn. of Probation System of Jud. Conf. U.S., 1954-55; adj. prof. trial advocacy-practice Georgetown Law Ctr., 1976-74, mem. adv. bd. CLE Program, 1979—; mem. faculty Nat. Coll. State Judiciary, 1973-75, Fed. Jud. Ctr., 1976-86, U.S. Atty. Gen. 's Advocacy Inst., Washington, 1977-85; spl. counsel councilmanic redistricting, Montgomery County Govt. 1965-66; vice chmn. Charter Revision Commn., 1967-68; frequent lectr. ABA and ATLA ann. meetings, CLE programs of Am. Law Inst., ABA Practicing Law Inst. and other Bar and civic groups throughout U.S.; mem. Jud. Coun. D.C. Cir. 1988-94; co-chair D.C. 1st and 3d cirs. Sentencing Insts., 1984, D.C. 3d and 7th cirs. Sentencing Insts, 1992. Author: Manual on Employment Discrimination and Civil Rights Actions, 1994; contbr. articles to profl. jours. Legal counsel Boys' Clubs Greater Washington, 1966-71; affiliate mem. D.C. Urban Renewal Council and Citizens Housing Commn., 1961-64; chmn. parents assns. Sidwell Friends Sch., Washington, 1968-70; mem. Montgomery County Bd. Appeals, 1965-67, chmn., 1966-67; trustee Immaculata Coll., Washington, 1970-73, Suburban Hosp. Bethesda, Md., 1967-71; pres. PTA, Potomac, Md., 1966-67. Recipient Outstanding and Dedicated Public Service award Montgomery County, Md., 1966, 68; Cert. Disting. Citizenship award Gov. Md., 1971; Annual Award of Merit by Adminstrv. Law Judges of U.S., 1979; Outstanding U.S. Fed. Trial Judge, Am. Trial Lawyers Assn., 1979; Humanitarian of Yr. award, Howard U. Law Sch. Alumni Assn., 1979, Justice Harold Hitz Burton Award, Cleveland Club of Washington, 1990, Judge H. Carl Moultrie Award of Jud. Excellence, D.C. Area Trial Lawyers Assn., 1990, Outstanding Spkr. award Fla. Bar Assn., 1991, Ben A. Arneson Dist. Pub. Career award Ohio Wesleyan U., 1994. Fellow Am. Bar Found. (life); mem. ABA (ho. of dels. 1981-85, chmn. com. on alcohol and drug abuse 1973-76, chm. com. on sentencing probation and parole 1976-77, mem. coun. criminal justice sect. 1976-85, chmn. nat. adv. com. Project ADVOCATE 1976-80, chmn. nat. conf. fed. trial judges 1980-81, officer and mem. exec. com. 1975-85, mem. coun. jud. adminstrv. divsn. 1980-81, ATLA (faculty Nat. Coll. Advocacy 1975-77), Bar Assn. of D.C., Md. Bar Assn., Am. Judicature Soc., Supreme Ct. Hist. Soc. (founding mem.), Edward Bennett Williams Am. Inn of Ct. (master, charter), Charlotte E. Ray Am. Inn of Ct. (master, charter), Soc. of Benchers of Case-Western Res. U. Sch. Law, Omicron Delta Kappa, Delta Sigma Rho, Pi Delta Epsilon, Phi Delta Phi, Phi Gamma Delta (gen. counsel 1960-63). Methodist. Club: Nat. Lawyers (Washington). Lodge: Masons (33rd degree). Home: 8101 Connecticut Ave Apt C-501 Chevy Chase MD 20815-2806 Office: US Dist Ct US Courthouse 3rd & Constitution Ave NW Washington DC 20001

RICHEY, CLARENCE BENTLEY, agricultural engineering educator; b. Winnipeg, Manitoba, Can., Dec. 28, 1910; s. Raus Spears and Emily Cornelia (Bentley) R.; m. Marguerite Anne Jannusch, Dec. 27, 1936; children: David Volkman, Stephen Bentley. BS in Agrl. Engring., Iowa State U., 1933; BS in Mech. Engring., Purdue U., 1939. Registered agrl. engr., Calif. Instr. agrl. engring. Purdue U., West Lafayette, Ind., 1936-41; asst. prof. dept. agrl. engring. Ohio State U., Columbus, 1941-43; head devel., engr. Electric Wheel Co., Quincy, Ill., 1943-46; project engr. Harry Ferguson, Inc., Detroit, 1946-47; sr. project engr. Dearborn Motors Corp., Detroit, 1947-54; supt., chief rsch. engr. Ford Tractor Divsn., Birmingham, Mich., 1954-62; chief engr. Fowler (Calif.) divsn. Massey-Ferguson Ltd., 1964-69; product mgmt. engr. Massey-Ferguson Ltd., Toronto, Ont., Can., 1970-71; assoc. prof. agrl. engring. Purdue U., West Lafayette, 1971-76, prof. emeritus, 1976—; farm equipment cons. Ford Found., Allahabad, India, 1963. Author: (autobiography) Fifty Years of Engineering Farm Equipment, 1989; editor-in-chief: Agricultural Engineer's Handbook, 1961; contbr. bulls. and articles to profl. jours. Fellow Am. Soc. Agrl. Engrs. (Cyrus Hall McCormick Gold medal 1977); mem. Lafayette Kiwanis. Achievements include patent for farm equipment; holder or co-holder of 79 patents. Home: 2217 Delaware Dr West Lafayette IN 47906-1917

RICHEY, DONALD L., retail executive; b. 1943. Pres. Cloth World, St. Louis, 1990—; also with Hancock Fabrics, Tupelo, Miss., 1996—. Office: Cloth World Inc 8300 Maryland Ave Saint Louis MO 63105*

RICHEY, EVERETT ELDON, religion educator; b. Claremont, Ill., Nov. 1, 1923; s. Hugh Arthur and Elosia Emma (Longnecker) R.; m. Mary Elizabeth Reynolds, Apr. 9, 1944; children: Eldon Arthur, Clive Everett, Loretta Arlene, Charles Estel. ThB, Anderson U., 1946; MDiv, Sch. Theology, Anderson, Ind., 1956; ThD, Iliff Sch. of Theology, Denver, 1960. Pastor Ch. of God, Bremen, Ind., 1946-47, Laurel, Miss., 1947-48; pastor First Ch. of God, Fordyce, Ark., 1948-52; prof. Arlington Coll., Long Beach, Calif., 1961-68; pastor Cherry Ave. Ch. of God, Long Beach, 1964-68; prof. Azusa (Calif.) Pacific U., 1968-93; mem. Christian Ministries Tng. Assn., 1968; mem., chmn. Commn. on Christian Higher Edn./Ch. of God, 1982-93; pres. Ch. Growth Investors, Inc., 1981—. Author: ednl. manual Church Periodical--Curriculum, 1971-83. Mem. Assn. Profs. and Rschrs. Religious Edn., Christian Ministries Tng. Assn. Republican. Avocation: gardening. Home and Office: 413 N Valencia St Glendora CA 91741-2418

RICHEY, HERBERT SOUTHALL, II, coal company executive; b. Cleve., June 26, 1922; s. Francis O. and Helen (Betteridge) R.; m. Martha J. Ewig, June 20, 1944; children: Suzanne, Francis O. II. BS, U. Mich., 1944. With Valley Camp Coal Co., Cleve., 1946—, pres., 1960—, chief exec. officer, 1964—, also bd. dirs.; pres. Richey Coal Co., Hot Springs, Va., 1979—; dir. mem. exec. com., mem. compensation com. Union Savs. Assn., until 1979, Oglebay Norton Co., Sifco Industries, Inc.; bd. dirs., mem. compensation com., chmn. audit com. Fairchild Corp.; dir. mem. audit com., mem. ethics com. Fairchild Industries; v.p., dir. Washington Energy Processing, Inc., 1982. Bd. dirs., mem. compensation com. Nat. Ctr. for Productivity, Washington, 1976-77. Lt. USNR, 1943-46. Mem. U.S. C. of C. (dir. 1968-82, chmn. 1976-77, chmn. exec. com. 1977-78, mem. sr. coun., budget, exec. U.S.-Can. pub. affairs, pension plan investment coms., investment adv. coun.), Nat. Coal Assn. (dir., chmn. 1971-72), Ohio Coal Assn. (dir.), W.Va. Coal Assn. (dir.), Bituminous Coal Opers. Assn. (exec. com., dir., vice chmn. 1st del. of coal execs. to visti USSR coal mines 1970), Union Club, Va. Hot Spring Golf and Tennis Club. Home: PO Box 1010 Hot Springs VA 24445-1010

RICHEY, PHIL HORACE, former manufacturing executive, consultant; b. Detroit, July 30, 1923; s. Lawrence Kennedy and Hazel Annsonia (Stuckey) R.; children: Karen L. Richey Forrester, Ann C. Richey Zepke; stepchildren: Gregory F. Lloyd, Charles E. Lloyd III.; m. Mary Elizabeth McCulloch, June 30, 1984; stepchildren: Julie Ann McCulloch Beal, Mary Elizabeth McCulloch, Claire May Thompson. B.A. with distinction, U. Mich., 1948. With Detrex Chem. Industries Inc., Detroit, 1948-56; group v.p. Detrex Chem. Industries Inc., 1962-71; with Allied Research Products Co., 1956-59, v.p. fin., 1958-59; with U.S. Chem. Milling Co., Manhattan Beach, Calif. 1959-61; v.p. U.S. Chem. Milling Co., 1960-61; with Olin Corp., Stamford, Conn., 1971-81; corp. v.p., pres. Winchester group, 1978-81; mgmt. cons., 1981—; bd. dirs. Assn. Chems. and Svcs., Inc. 1st lt. AUS, 1942-46. Mem. Phi Kappa Phi, Beta Gamma Sigma. Home and Office: 342 Winamar Ave La Jolla CA 92037-6549

RICHEY, RONALD KAY, insurance company executive, lawyer; b. Erie, Kans., June 16, 1926; s. Earle Jacob and Mary Wintress (Oakleaf) R.; m. Florence E. Kane, Nov. 24, 1949; children: Linda, Robert, Chris. B.A., Washburn U., 1949, LL.B., 1951. Bar: Kans. 1951, Ill. 1958, Okla. 1965. Vice pres. Central Plains Ins. Group, Hutchinson, Kans., 1955-57; legis. mgr. Am. Mut. Ins. Alliance, Chgo., 1957-64; exec. v.p. Globe Life and Accident Ins. Co., Oklahoma City, 1964-78, chmn. bd., 1978—, chief exec. officer, 1978-82; pres. Torchmark Corp., Birmingham, Ala., 1982-85, pres., chief operating officer, 1985-86, chmn. bd., chief operating officer, 1986—, also dir.; dir. Liberty Nat. Life Ins. Co., Birmingham, United Am. Ins. Co., Dallas. Served with U.S. Army, 1944-46. Mem. Am. Coun. Life Assn. (bd. dirs.), ABA, Okla. Bar Assn., Okla. City C. of C. (bd. dirs.), HIAA (bd. dirs.). Republican. Clubs: Quail Creek Golf and Country (Oklahoma City); Oaktree Golf and Country (Edmond, Okla.); Shoal Creek Golf and Country (Birmingham). Office: Torchmark Corp 2001 3rd Ave S Birmingham AL 35233-2187

RICHIE, JEROME PAUL, surgeon, educator; b. San Antonio, 1944. MD, U. Tex., 1969. Surg. intern UCLA, 1969-70, resident in gen. surgery, 1970-71, resident in urology, 1971-75, fellow surg. urology, 1974-75; asst. clin. prof. U. Calif., San Diego, 1975-77; asst. prof. urology Harvard U., 1977-80, assoc. prof., 1980-86, prof., 1986—, Elliott C. Cutler prof. surgery, 1987—, chmn. program in urology, 1987—; chief urol. oncology Brigham and Women's Hosp., Boston, 1977—; cons. Sidney Farber Cancer Ctr., Boston, 1977—. Lt. comdr. M.C., USN, 1975-77. Mem. ACS, Am. Assn. Genito-Urinary Surgeons, Am. Urol. Assn., Assn. Acad. Surgery, Am. Soc. (Clin.) Oncology. Office: Brigham & Womens Hosp 45 Francis St #ASB II 3 Boston MA 02115-6195

RICHIE, LEROY C., lawyer, automotive executive; b. Buffalo, N.Y., Sept. 27, 1941; s. Leroy C. and Mattie A. (Allen) R.; m. Julia Thomas Richie, June 10, 1972; children: Leroy, Lamont, Loren, Brooke, Darcy. BA magna cum laude, CCNY, 1970; JD, NYU, 1973. Bar: Mich. 1985, N.Y. 1974, U.S. Ct. Appeals (2nd cir.) 1974. Atty. White & Case, N.Y.C., 1973-78; dir. Fed. Trade Commn. N.Y. Regional Office, N.Y.C., 1978-83; asst. gen. counsel Chrysler Corp., Highland Park, Mich., 1983-84; assoc. gen. counsel Chrysler Corp., Highland Park, 1984-86, v.p., gen. counsel, 1986—; chmn. Vis. Nurses Assn., Detroit, 1988-90, Highland Park (Mich.) Devel. Corp., 1988—; chmn. bd. trustees Marygrove Coll., Detroit, 1994—; treas. Nat. Jud. Coll., Reno. With U.S. Army, 1961-64, Germany. Fellowship award, Arthur Garfield Hayes Civil Liberties, NYU, 1972. Mem. Am. Corporate Counsel Assn. (bd. dirs. Mich. chpt. 1987—), Detroit Bar Assn. Office: Chrysler Motors Corp 12000 Chrysler Dr Detroit MI 48288-0002

RICHIE, LIONEL B., JR., singer, songwriter, producer; b. Tuskegee, Ala., June 20, 1949; s. Lyonel B. Sr. and Alberta (Foster) R.; m. Brenda Harvey, 1975. BS in Econs., Tuskegee U., 1971, MusD (hon.), 1985; MusD (hon.), Boston Coll., 1986. Pres. Brockman Music, L.A. Mem. group The Mystics (name changed to The Commodores), 1969-81; writer, producer songs for Commodores including: Easy, Three Times a Lady (Am. Music award 1979, People's Choice award for best song 1979), Still (People's Choice award for best song 1980), Sail On, Lady (Nat. Music Pubs. award 1980, 81, People's Choice award for best composer 1981); songwriter, producer album for Kenny Rogers; albums (with The Commodores) include Midnight Magic, Machine Gun, Movin' On, Commodores, Caught in the Act, Hot on the Tracks, Natural High, Heroes, (solo albums) Lionel Richie, Can't Slow Down, 1984 (Grammy award Album of Yr. 1985), Dancing on the Ceiling, 1986, Back to Front, 1992; producer, composer: (songs) Truly (Grammy award 1982, 2 Am. Music awards 1982, People's Choice award Best Song, 1983), All Night Long (Nat. Music Pubs. award 1984, 3 Black Gold awards 1984, Am. Music award 1984, Hello (2 Am. Music awards 1985), Say You, Say Me (ASCAP Pop award 1987, Am. Music award 1987, Oscar award Best Song 1986, Golden Globe award Best Song 1986), Dancing on the Ceiling (3 Am. Music awards 1987), (duet with Diana Ross) Endless Love (Grammy award 1982, 2 Am. Music awards 1982, Am. Movie award 1982, Rojo award Gold Status in Hong Kong 1982, People's Choice award Best Song 1982), (sung by Kenny Rogers) Lady, (with Michael Jackson) We Are The World, 1985 (Grammy awards Best Song, Record of Yr. 1986, People's Choice award Best Song 1986). Recipient Best Young Artist in Film award, 1980, 2 NAACP image awards, 1983, Favorite Male Vocalist Pop/Rock award Am. Music Acad., 1987, Favorite Male Vocalist Soul/R&B award Am. Music Acad., 1987; named Man of Yr. Children's Diabetes Found., 1984, Alumnus of Yr. United Negro Coll. Fund, 1984, Favorite Male Singer People mag. Readers Poll, 1985, Entertainer of Yr., NAACP, 1987. Mem. ASCAP (Writer of Yr. 1984, 85, 86, Pub. of Yr. 1985). *

RICHIE, SHARON I., army nursing officer; b. Phila., Dec. 14, 1949; d. William Joseph and Helen Lucille (Oglesby) R.; m. Paul Henri, Jan. 1, 1986. BS, Wagner Coll., 1971; MS, U. Tex. Grad. Sch. Nursing, San Antonio, 1976; postgrad. George Washington U., 1987—;student Army War Coll., 1987-88. Commd. 2d lt. U.S. Army, advanced through grades to col., 1988; clin. staff nurse Walter Reed Army Med. Ctr., Washington 1971-74; hosp. pschiat. nurse cons., head nurse 5th Gen. Hosp., Landstuhl, Germany, 1976-77; psychiat. clin. nurse specialist Alcholism Treatment Facility, Stuttgart, Germany, 1977-79; cons. alcohol and drug abuse nursing U.S. Army Surg. Gen., The Pentagon, Washington, 1980, also clin. liaison officer; asst. dir. edn. and rehab. Office Drug and Alcohol Abuse Prevention, Dept. Def., Pentagon, 1980-82; White House fellow, 1982-83; asst. chief nurse evenings/nights Letterman Army Med. ctr., San Francisco, 1983-84; chief ambulatory nursing service, 1984-85; dir. quality assurance, dept. nursing, 1985-86; PROFIS chief nurse, 8th Evacuation Hosp., Fort Ord, Calif., 1984-86; asst. chief nurse Kimbrough Army Hosp., Ft. Meade, Md., 1986, chief dept. nursing, 1986-87; chief clin. nursing svc. Walter Reed Army Med. Ctr., Washington, 1988-90; chief dept. nursing Letterman Army Med. Ctr., San Francisco, 1990-91; dir. med. directorate U.S. Army Recruiting Command, Ft. Sheridan, Ill., 1991; dir Health Svcs. Directorate U.S. Army Recruiting Command, Ft. Knox, Ky., 1991-93; chief nurse S.E. Regional Health Svcs. Support Area and dir. Nursing Eisenhower Army Med. Ctr., Fort Gordon, Ga., 1993—; cons. Regional Commrs. Pres's Commn. on White House Fellow, 1985-86, sec. White House Fellow Assn. and Found. Bd. Named Alumni of Yr., Wagner Coll., S.I., 1983; White House fellow, 1982; recipient Meritorious medal sec. Def., 1982, A Prefix U.S. Army Surgeon Gen., 1992, Legion of Merit 1993, Presdl. Svc. Badge (white house) 1993. Mem. Nat. Black Nurses Assn., Am. Nurses Assn., Am. Nurses Found., Assn. U.S. Army, Assn. U.S. Mil. Surgeons, Sigma Theta Tau. Clubs: Presidio Officers (former v.p.) Avocations: weight lifting, collecting miniature camels, indoor gardening. Home: 3019 Bransford Rd Augusta GA 30909 Office: Eisenhower Army Med Ctr Dept Nursing Augusta GA 30905

RICHKIN, BARRY ELLIOTT, financial services executive; b. N.Y.C., Apr. 14, 1944; s. Harry and Celia (Goldberg) R. BA, Bklyn. Coll., 1964. CLU, cert. in personal fin. planning, NASD. Auditor First Nat. Bank of N.Y., N.Y.C., 1968-70; sr. supr. ABC, N.Y.C., 1970-73; account rep. Met. Life Ins. co., Atlanta, 1973-74; rep. Mixon-Baker Fin. Svcs., Atlanta, 1974-78; owner Barry Richkin Fin. Svcs., Roswell, Ga., 1978—; owner Barry Richkin Philatelics, Roswell, 1991—; cons., owner Benefit Cons. Group, Roswell, 1989—; cons., pres., bd. dirs. Am. Health Network, Roswell, 1982—. Author: Guide to Preferred Provider Organizations, 1986. Mem. Am. Soc. CLU and ChFC, Am. Philatelic Soc., Manuscript Soc., U.S. Postal Hist. Soc., Conn. Hist. Soc. Avocations: manuscripts, philatelics, jogging. Office: Barry Richkin Fin Svcs 600 Houze Way Bldg C-6 Roswell GA 30076

RICHLER, MORDECAI, writer; b. Montreal, Que., Can., Jan. 27, 1931; s. Moses Isaac and Lily (Rosenberg) R.; m. Florence Wood, July 27, 1959; children: Daniel, Noah, Emma, Martha, Jacob. Student, Sir George Williams U., 1948-50. vis. prof. Carleton U., Ottawa, Ont., 1972-74; assoc. judge for Can., Book-of-the-Month Club, 1974-88, also mem. editorial bd., N.Y. Author: (novels) The Acrobats, 1954, Son of a Smaller Hero, 1955, A Choice of Enemies, 1957, The Apprenticeship of Duddy Kravitz, 1959, Stick Your Neck Out, 1963, Cocksure, 1967, St. Urbain's Horseman, 1971, Joshua Then and Now, 1980, Solomon Gursky Was Here, 1990, (essays) Notes on an Endangered Species, 1974, Home Sweet Home, 1984, Oh Canada!, Oh Quebec! A Lament for a Divided Nation, 1992, (stories) The Street, 1975, (nonfiction) Oh Canada! Oh Quebec! Requiem for a Divided Country, 1992, This Year in Jerusalem, a memoir, 1994; children books Jacob Two-Two

Meets The Hooded Fang, 1975, Jacob Two-Two and the Dinosaur, 1987; film The Apprenticeship of Duddy Kravitz, 1974 (Acad. award nomination 1974, Writers Guild of Am. award 1974), Joshua, Then and Now, 1985, Jacob Two-Two's First Spy Case, 1995; editor: The Best of Modern Humor, 1983, Writers on World War II, 1991; contbr. articles to profl. jours. Recipient Gov.-Gen.'s award for lit., 1968, 71, Paris Rev. Humour prize, 1968, Commonwealth Writer's prize, 1990; Guggenheim fellow, 1961; various Can. Coun. fellowships. Mem. Montreal Press Club. Home: Apt 80 C, 1321 Sherbrooke St W, Montreal, PQ Canada H3Y 1J4

RICHLIN, W. GAR, investment banking executive, lawyer; b. N.Y.C., July 7, 1945; s. Padie and Sylvia (Salzman) R.; m. Margaret Goodman, June 7, 1967; children: Kimberly A., Jenny R. AB with honors, Wesleyan U., 1967; JD, Georgetown U., 1971. Law clk. to Hon. Harrison L. Winter, U.S. Ct. Appeals, 1971-72; assoc. Piper & Marbury, Balt., 1972-79, ptnr., 1979-89; mgr., gen. counsel Alex Brown & Sons Inc., Balt., 1989-91, head investment banking, mgr., 1991—, also bd. dirs. Home: 11425 High Hay Dr Columbia MD 21044-1027 Office: Alex Brown & Sons Inc 135 E Baltimore St Baltimore MD 21202-1607

RICHMAN, ALAN, magazine editor; b. Bronx, N.Y., Nov. 12, 1939; s. Louis and Sonia (Carity) R.; m. Kelli Shor, June 21, 1964; children: Lincoln Seth Shor, Matthew Mackenzie Shor. B.A., Hunter Coll., 1960. Reporter Leader-Observer (weekly newspaper), N.Y.C., 1960-61; asst. editor Modern Tire Dealer (publ.), N.Y.C., 1962-64; assoc. editor ASTA Travel News, N.Y.C., 1964-65; pub. relations rep. M.J. Jacobs, Inc. (advt. agy.), N.Y.C., 1965-66; mng. editor Modern Floor Coverings, N.Y.C., 1966-68; editor Bank Systems & Equipment, N.Y.C., 1968-79, Health Care Products News, N.Y.C., 1976; asso. pub. Bank Systems & Equipment, 1969-71, co-pub., 1971-73, pub., 1973-79; editorial dir. Nat. Jeweler, N.Y.C., 1979-81; editor Health Foods Bus.; editorial dir. Army/Navy Store and Outdoor Merchandiser, 1981-88, The Pet Dealer, 1983-88; editor Cabinet Mfg. and Fabricating KBC Publs., 1988—; program dir. Cabinet Mfg. Fair, 1989—; adj. faculty NYU, 1989—, Brookdale Community Coll., 1992—, Bergen County Community Coll., 1992—. Exec. editor: Kitchen and Bath Design News, 1992-93; editor-in-chief Wood Digest, PTN Pub. Co., 1992-94; editor: Whole Foods, 1994—; author: Czechoslovakia in Pictures, 1969, A Book on the Chair, 1968. Served with AUS, 1961-62. Recipient Jesse H. Neal certificate merit Am. Bus. Press, 1973. Mem. Internat. Platform Assn.

RICHMAN, ARTHUR SHERMAN, sports association executive; b. N.Y.C., Mar. 21, 1926; s. Samuel Abraham and Clara (Ganbarg) R.; m. Martha Landgrebe, Nov. 9, 1979. Student, Bklyn. Coll., 1942-44. Baseball writer, columnist N.Y. Mirror, N.Y.C., 1943-63; acct. exec. Grey Pub. Rels., N.Y.C., 1963-65; dir. promotions, pub. rels., traveling sec., spl. asst. to gen. mgr. N.Y. Mets, Flushing, 1965-89; sr. v.p. N.Y. Yankees, Bronx, 1989—. Contbr. articles to profl. and popular jours. Leader baseball groups USO/U.S. Dept. Def., Vietnam, Thailand, Japan, Korea, Philippines, Guam, Hawaii and Greenland, 1965-74;. Recipient Ben Epstein Good Guy award N.Y. Baseball Writers, 1983, Long and Meritorious Svc. award Major League Baseball Scouts, 1984, Good Guy award N.Y. Press Photographers, 1988; elected to Bklyn. Coll. Athletic Hall of Fame, 1984, St. Louis Browns' Baseball Media Hall of Fame, 1986. Mem. Assn. Profl. Baseball Players Am. (v.p. 1986—). Jewish. Office: NY Yankees Yankee Stadium E 161st St & River Ave Bronx NY 10451

RICHMAN, DAVID PAUL, neurologist, researcher; b. Boston, June 9, 1943; s. Harry S. and Anne (Goodkin) R.; m. Carol Mae von Bastian, Aug. 31, 1969; children—Sarah Ann, Jacob Charles. A.B., Princeton U., 1965; M.D., Johns Hopkins U., 1969. Diplomate Am. Bd. Psychiatry and Neurology. Intern, asst. resident in medicine Albert Einstein Coll. Medicine, N.Y.C., 1969-71; resident in neurology Mass. Gen. Hosp., Boston, 1971-73; chief resident in neurology, 1973-74; instr. neurology Harvard Med. Sch., Boston, 1975-76; asst. prof. neurology U. Chgo., 1976-80, assoc. prof. dept. neurology, mem. immunology and neurobiology coms., 1981-85, prof. dept. neurology and com. on immunology, 1985-91, Straus prof. neurol. scis., 1988-91; prof., chair dept. neurology U. Calif., Davis, 1991—; mem. com. Nat. Inst. Aging, NIH, 1984-85, mem. immunogical scis. study sect., 1986-90. Mem. AAAS, Am. Assn. Immunologists, Am. Acad. Neurology, Am. Neurol. Assn., Phi Beta Kappa, Sigma Xi. Office: U Calif Davis Medical Ctr Dept Neurology 2315 Stockton Blvd Sacramento CA 95817-2201*

RICHMAN, FREDERICK ALEXANDER, lawyer; b. Pasadena, Calif., Oct. 18, 1945; s. Matthew and Ruth (Beckman) R.; m. Judith R., Oct. 24, 1971; children—Robert, David. A.B. cum laude, Harvard U., 1967; J.D. cum laude, NYU, 1970. Bar: Calif. 1971. Assoc. firm O'Melveny & Myers, Los Angeles, 1970-77; ptnr. O'Melveny & Myers, 1978—. Mem. ABA, Calif. Bar Assn., Los Angeles County Bar Assn. Office: O'Melveny & Myers 1999 Ave of the Stars 7th Fl Los Angeles CA 90067

RICHMAN, HAROLD ALAN, social welfare policy educator; b. Chgo., May 15, 1937; s. Leon H. and Rebecca (Klieman) R.; m. Marlene M. Forland, Apr. 25, 1965; children: Andrew, Robert. AB, Harvard U., 1959; MA, U. Chgo., 1961, PhD, 1969. Asst. prof., dir. Ctr. for Study Welfare Policy, Sch. Social Svc., U. Chgo., 1967-69, dean, prof. social welfare policy, 1969-78, Hermon Dunlap Smith prof., 1978—, dir. of ctr., 1978-81, dir. Children's Policy Rsch. Project, 1978-84, dir. Chapin Hall Ctr. for Children, 1985—, chmn. univ. com. on pub. policy studies, 1974-77; chmn. Univ. Lab. Schs., 1985-88; cons. to gov. State of Ill., Edna McConnell Clark Found., 1984-95, Lilly Endowment, 1987—, Ford Found., 1987—. Chmn. editorial bd. Social Svcs. Rev., 1970-79; contbr. articles to profl. jours. Bd. dirs. Chgo. Com. Fgn. and Domestic Policy, 1969-78, S.E. Chgo. Commn., 1970—, Jewish Fedn. Met. Chgo., 1970-75, Ill. Facilities Fund, 1989-94, Welfare Coun. Met. Chgo., 1970-72, Erikson Inst. Early Childhood Edn., 1972-79, Nat. Urban Coalition, 1975-86, Family Focus, 1980-89, Jewish Coun. Urban Affairs, 1982-87, Ctr. for Study Social Policy, 1983-92, Nat. Family Resource Coalition, 1990-93, Pub./Pvt. Ventures, 1992—, Benton Found., 1994—; bd. dirs. Israel Ctr. on Children, chmn., 1995—. Capt. USPHS, 1961-63. White House fellow, Washington, 1965-66; recipient Disting. Svc. citation U.S. Dept. Health, Edn. & Welfare, 1970, Quantrell award U. Chgo., 1990. Mem. White House Fellows Assn. (v.p. 1976-77), Am. Pub. Welfare Assn. (bd. dirs. 1989-92). Home: 5715 S Dorchester Ave Chicago IL 60637 Office: U Chgo Chapin Hall Ctr for Children 1155 E 60th St Chicago IL 60637-2745

RICHMAN, HOWARD, surgeon; b. N.Y.C., Oct 11, 1927; s. Morton and Beatrice (Antel) R.; m. Barbara Renee Richman, Dec. 1947 (dec. 1958); children—Leslie Francine, Michael Edward; m. 2d Thelma Miriam Richman, Nov. 1969 (dec. 1980); m. 3d Barbara Susan Richman, Oct. 1985. B.A., NYU, 1949, M.D., 1953. Intern, NYU/Bellevue Med. Ctr., 1953-54, resident, 1954-58 practice medicine, specializing in surgery, N.Y.C., 1975—; chief of surgery N.Y. Infirmary/Beekman Downtown Hosp., N.Y.C., 1975—; prof. clin. surgery NYU Med. Center, 1960—. Contbr. articles to profl. jours. Served with USAF, 1946-47. Fellow ACS, AMA, Am. Bd. Surgery, Internat. Coll. Surgeons, N.Y. Acad. Sci. Democrat. Jewish. Club: NYU. Office: 170 William St New York NY 10038-2612

RICHMAN, JOAN F., television consultant; b. St. Louis, Apr. 10, 1939; d. Stanley M. and Barbara (Friedman) R. B.A., Wellesley (Mass.) Coll., 1961. Asst. producer Sta. WNDT, N.Y.C., 1963-65; researcher CBS News, N.Y.C., 1961-64, researcher spl. events unit, 1965-67; mgr. rsch. CBS News (Rep. and Dem. nat. convs.), N.Y.C., 1968; assoc. producer CBS News, N.Y.C., 1972-75; exec. producer Sports Spectacular CBS, N.Y.C., 1975-76; exec. producer CBS Evening News weekend broadcasts CBS News, N.Y.C., 1976-81, v.p. spl. events, 1982-87, v.p. news coverage, 1987-89; fellow Inst. Politics, John F. Kennedy Sch. Govt., Harvard U., 1990. Mem. nat. patrons com. Opera Theatre St. Louis. Recipient Emmy award for CBS News space coverage nat. TV Acad. Arts and Scis., 1970-71; Alumnae Achievement award Wellesley Coll., 1973. Mem. Coun. on Fgn. Rels., Wellesley Coll. Alumnae Assn. (pres. class of 1961, 1966-70). Home: 14 Tinicum Creek Rd Erwinna PA 18920-9246

RICHMAN, JOHN MARSHALL, lawyer, business executive; b. N.Y.C., Nov. 9, 1927; s. Arthur and Madeleine (Marshall) R.; m. Priscilla Frary, Sept. 3, 1951; children: Catherine Richman Wallace, Diana H. BA, Yale U.,

1949; LLB, Harvard U., 1952. Bar: N.Y. 1953, Ill. 1973. Assoc. Leve, Hecht, Hadfield & McAlpin, N.Y.C., 1952-54; mem. law dept. Kraft, Inc., Glenview, Ill., 1954-63; gen. counsel Sealtest Foods div. Kraft, Inc., Glenview, 1963-67, asst. gen. counsel, 1967-70, v.p., gen. counsel, 1970-73, sr. v.p., gen. counsel, 1973-75, sr. v.p. adminstrn., gen. counsel, 1975-79, chmn. bd., chief exec. officer, 1979; chmn. bd., chief exec. officer Dart & Kraft, Inc. (name changed to Kraft, Inc. 1986), Glenview, 1980; chmn. Kraft Gen. Foods, Glenview, Ill., 1988-89; counsel Wachtell, Lipton, Rosen & Katz, Chgo., 1990—; bd. dirs. BankAm. Corp. and Bank of Am. Nat. Trust and Savs. Assn., R.R. Donnelley & Sons. Co., USX Corp.; mem. Bus. Coun. Chmn. bd. trustees Chgo. Symphony Orch.; trustee Northwestern U.; trustee Johnson Found.; bd. dirs. Evanston Hosp. Corp., Chgo. Coun. on Fgn. Rels., Lyric Opera Chgo. Mem. Comml. Club, Econ. Club, Chgo. Club, Casino Club (Chgo.); Union League Club (N.Y.C.); Westmoreland Country Club (Wilmette, Ill.); Old Elm Club (Ft. Sheridan, Ill.); Lost Tree Club (N. Palm Beach, Fla.), Shoreacres, Lake Bluff, Ill. Congregationalist. Office: Wachtell Lipton et al 227 W Monroe St Ste 4825 Chicago IL 60606-5016

RICHMAN, MARC HERBERT, forensic engineer, educator; b. Boston, Oct. 14, 1936; s. Samuel and Janet (Gordon) R.; m. Ann Raeshel Yoffa, Aug. 31, 1963. B.S., MIT, 1957, Sc.D., 1963; M.A., Brown U., 1967. Registered profl. engr., Conn., Mass., R.I.; cert. forensic examiner. Cons. engr., 1957—; engr. shipbldg. div. Bethlehem Steel Corp., Quincy, Mass., 1957; instr. metallurgy MIT, Cambridge, 1957-60, research asst. dept. metallurgy, 1960-63; instr. metallurgy div. univ. extension Commonwealth of Mass., 1958-62; asst. prof. engring. Brown U., Providence, 1963-67, assoc. prof., 1967-70, prof., 1970—, dir. central electron microscopy facility Materials Research program, 1971-86, dir. undergrad. program in engring., 1991—; pres. Ednl. Aids of Newton Inc., Providence, 1968-71, Marc H. Richman Inc., Providence, 1981—; guest scientist Franklin Inst., Phila., 1959; vis. rpof. U.R.I., Kingston, 1970-71; biophysicist dept. medicine Miriam Hosp., Providence, 1974-87; bioengr. dept. orthopaedics R.I. Hosp., 1979-93. Author: Introduction to Science of Metals, 1967; also articles; editor Soviet Physics: Crystallography, 1970-94; mem. editorial adv. bd. Metallography, 1970—; mem. editorial adv. bd. Jour. Forensic Engring., 1985-88. Maj. Ordnance Corps, U.S. Army, 1963. Served to maj. Ordnance Corps, U.S. Army, 1963. Fellow Nat. Acad. Forensic Engrs. (cert.), Am. Coll. Forensic Examiners (cert.), Am. Inst. Chemists; mem. ASCE, AIME, NSPE, ASEE (Outstanding Young Faculty award 1969), NAFE (bd. cert. diplomate in forensic engring.), Inst. Materials (U.K.), ASM (sec.-treas. 1965-68, chmn. R.I. chpt. 1968-69, Albert Sauveur Meml. award 1968, 69), Providence Engring. Soc. (pres. 1991-92, Freeman award for engring. achievement 1989), B'nai B'rith, Sigma Xi, Tau Beta Pi. Home: 291 Cole Ave Providence RI 02906-3452 Office: Brown U Divsn Engring Box D Providence RI 02912 also: One Richmond Sq Providence RI 02906

RICHMAN, MARTIN FRANKLIN, lawyer; b. Newark, Feb. 23, 1930; s. Samuel L. and Betty E. (Goldstein) R.; stepson Doris (Bloom) R.; m. Florence E. Reif, May 6, 1962; children—Judith, Andrew. B.A. magna cum laude, St. Lawrence U., 1950; LL.B. magna cum laude, Harvard U., 1953. Bar: N.Y. 1953, D.C. 1981. Law clk. to judge Calvert Magruder and Chief Justice Earl Warren, 1955-57; assoc., mem. firm Lord Day & Lord, Barrett Smith (and predecessors), N.Y.C., 1957-66, 69-94; of counsel Kirkpatrick & Lockhart, N.Y.C., 1994—; dep. asst. atty. gen. Office Legal Counsel, Dept. Justice, Washington, 1966-69; Public mem. Adminstrv. Conf. U.S., 1970-76; bd. dirs. Community Action for Legal Services, 1977-80. Trustee St. Lawrence U., 1979-95, vice chmn. bd., 1988-95; bd. dirs. Friends of Law Libr. of Congress, 1992—. Recipient Alumni citation St. Lawrence U., 1977. Fellow Am. Bar Found., N.Y. Bar Found.; mem. ABA (chmn. sect. adminstrv. law 1983-84), N.Y. State Bar Assn. (ho. of dels. 1983-84), Assn. of Bar of City of N.Y. (sec. and mem. exec. com. 1976-79, chmn. com. fed. legislation 1972-75, com. lawyer's pro bono obligations 1977-81), Am. Law Inst. Office: Kirkpatrick & Lockhart 1251 Ave of the Americas New York NY 10020

RICHMAN, MARVIN JORDAN, real estate developer, investor, educator; b. N.Y.C., July 13, 1939; s. Morris and Minnie (Graubart) R.; m. Amy Paula Rubin, July 31, 1966; children: Mark Jason, Keith Hayden, Susanne Elizabeth, Jessica Paige. BArch, MIT, 1962; M Urban Planning, NYU, 1966, postgrad., 1967-69; MBA, U. Chgo., 1977; U.S. Dept. State fellow U. Chile, 1960. Architect, planner Skidmore, Owings & Merrill, N.Y.C., 1966, Conklin & Rossant, N.Y.C., 1965-67; ptnr. Vizbaras & Ptnrs., N.Y.C., 1968-69; v.p. Urban Investment & Devel. Co., Chgo., 1969-79, sr. v.p., 1979; pres. bd. dirs. First City Devels. Corp., Beverly Hills, Calif., 1979-80; pres. Olympia & York (U.S.) Devel. (West), 1987-89, Olympia & York Calif. Equities Corp., L.A., 1981-87, Olympia & York Calif. Devel. Corp., 1981-87, Olympia & York Hope St. Mgmt. Corp., 1982-87, Olympia & York Homes Corp., 1983-89, Olympia & York Constrn. Corp., 1986-89, The Richman Co., L.A., 1989—, pres. Richman Real Estate Group, Salt Lake City, 1995—; dean Sch. Bus. and Mgmt. Woodbury U., Burbank, Calif., 1993—; lectr. NYU, 1967-69, UCLA, 1989-90, Nat. Humanities Inst., other univs. Adv. NEA. Bd. advisors UCLA Ctr. Fin. and Real Estate. With USAF, 1963-64. Registered architect; lic. real estate broker. Mem. AIA, Am Planning Assn., Internat. Coun. Shopping Ctrs., L.A. World Affairs Coun., Urban Land Inst., Nat. Assn. Office and Indsl. Parks, Chief Exec.'s Round Table, Air Force Assn., Lambda Alpha.

RICHMAN, PAUL, semiconductor industry executive, educator; b. N.Y.C., Nov. 17, 1942; s. Harry and Molly (Armel) R.; m. Ellen Margaret Kleiman, July 3, 1966; children: Lee Stuart, Alyson Michelle, Daniel Noah. B.S.E.E., MIT, 1963; M.S.E.E., Columbia U., 1964. V.p. R & D Standard Microsystems Corp., Hauppauge, N.Y., 1971-76, pres., 1976-81, pres., chief exec. officer, 1981-83, pres., chmn. bd., chief exec. officer, 1983—; co-founder Toyo Microsystems Corp., Tokyo, 1987—; pres. The Consortium for Tech. Licensing, Ltd., Nissequogue, N.Y., 1994—; vis. prof. elec. engring. SUNY, Stony Brook, 1976-85; dir. MOSAID Tech., Inc., Ottawa, Ont., Can. Author: Characteristics and Operation of MOS Field Effect Devices, 1967, MOS Field Effect Transistors and Integrated Circuits, 1974; inventor: COPLAMOS tech. Recipient ann. award for achievement in electronics, Electronics Mag., 1978; named one of 30 most Important Contbrs. in the world to devel. integrated cir. tech., Elec. Engring. Times/Elec. Buyers' News/V.L.S.I. Systems Design, 1988. Fellow IEEE (award for outstanding tech. achievement 1980).

RICHMAN, PETER, electronics executive; b. N.Y.C., Nov. 7, 1927; s. Emil H. and Janet (Seidler) R.; m. Vivian Hoffman, July 29, 1951; children: Meredith, Eugene. BS, MIT, 1946; MS, NYU, 1953. Asst. chief engr. Reeves Instrument Corp., Garden City, N.Y., 1948-58; chief engr. Epsco, Inc., Cambridge, Mass., 1959-60; v.p., co-founder Rotek Instrument Corp., Watertown, Mass., 1960-64; v.p. Weston-Rotek, Lexington, Mass., 1964-67; cons. electronics engr. Lexington, 1967—; bd. dirs. Thermo Voltek Corp.; founder, pres. KeyTek Instrument Corp., 1975-93; mem. NRC/NAS/Nat. Acad. Engring. Evaluation Panel for electricity divsn. Nat. Bur. Standards; mem. sci. adv. groups for several indsl. and sci. orgns. Patentee in precision electronic instrumentation; pioneer in precision dc and audio-frequency measurements, surge electrostatic discharge generation and electrostatic discharge measurements; contbr. articles to profl. jours. Mem. bd. overseers Boston Mus. Sci. Fellow IEEE; mem. Electromagnetics Acad., Instrument Soc. Am. (sr.), Sigma Xi, Tau Beta Pi.

RICHMAN, PETER MARK, actor, painter, writer; b. Phila., Apr. 16, 1927; s. Benjamin and Yetta Dora (Peck) R.; m. Theodora Helen Landess, May 10, 1953; children: Howard Bennett, Kelly Allyn, Lucas Dion, Orien, Roger Lloyd. BS in Pharmacy, Phila. Coll. Pharmacy and Sci., 1951; student of Lee Strasberg, N.Y.C., 1952-54; mem., Actors' Studio, N.Y.C., 1954—. Registered pharmacist, Pa., N.Y. Appeared in little theater, Phila., 1946-51, on stage radio and in live TV, Phila., N.Y.C., and Los Angeles, 1948-65, including Have I Got a Girl for You (pre-Broadway tryout) Biltmore Theater, L.A., 1962, The Deputy, Ctr. Theater Group, L.A., 1965; appeared at Grove Theater, Nuangola, Pa., 1952, Westchester Playhouse, 1953, Drury Lane, Chicago, 1957, Strand, N.J., 1957, Capri, 1959, Ogonquit (Maine) Playhouse, 1955-62, Matunuck, R.I., 1955, Falmouth, Mass., 1953-55, Westport, Conn., 1955, Harrison, Maine, 1962, Dennis, Mass., 1955-62, Phila. Playhouse in the Park, 1962-63; Broadway plays include End as a Man, 1953, Hatful of Rain, nat. tour, 1956-57, Masquerade, 1959; off-

Broadway plays include End as a Man, 1953, The Dybbuk, 1954, The Zoo Story (400 performances), 1960-61; numerous other theater appearances, including Rainmaker, Private Lives, Angel Street, Arms and the Man, Funny Girl, Hold Me, Equus, Night of the Iguana, Blithe Spirit, Twelve Angry Men, Henry Fonda Theatre, L.A. 1985, Babes in Toyland, Calif. Mus. Theater, 1988, Ray Bradbury's Next in Line, L.A., 1992, others; writer, performer (one man show) 4 Faces, 1995; motion pictures include Friendly Persuasion, 1956, The Strange One, 1956, Black Orchid, 1958, The Dark Intruder, 1965, Agent for HARM, 1965, For Singles Only, 1967, The Third Hand, 1988, Friday the 13th, Part 8 (Jason Takes Manhattan), 1989, Naked Gun 2 1/2 (The Smell of Fear), 1991; appeared on TV series as Nick Cain in Cain's Hundred, 1961-62, as David in David Chapter III for CBC, 1966, as Duke Page in series Longstreet, 1971-72, as Andrew Laird in series Dynasty, 1981-84, as Channing Capwell in series Santa Barbara, 1984, voice of God series Heroes of the Bible, 1979, voice of the Phantom in animated series Defenders of the Earth, 1986, as Madros in Berlin series Mystery of the Keys, 1991; guest star over 500 TV shows, including Hotel, Dallas, Hart to Hart, Fantasy Island, Murder She Wrote, T.J. Hooker, Three's Company, Knight Rider, Star Trek: The Next Generation, Matlock, Beverly Hills 90210, others; starred in TV movies House on Greenapple Road, 1968, McCloud, 1969, Yuma, 1970, Nightmare at 43 Hillcrest (Wide World of Entertainment), 1974, Mallory, 1975, The Islander, 1978, Greatest Heroes of the Bible, 1979, Blind Ambition, 1979, The PSI Factor, 1981, Dynasty, 1981, Dempsey, 1983, City Killer, 1984, Bonanza, The Next Generation, 1988; one-man shows (paintings) Am. Masters Gallery, L.A., 1967, Orlando Gallery, L.A., 1966, McKenzie Gallery, L.A., 1969, 73, Hopkins Gallery, L.A., 1971, Goldfield Gallery, L.A., 1979, Galerie des Stars, L.A., 1988, Crocker Mus., Sacramento, Calif., 1967, others; group shows include Bednarz Gallery, L.A., 1968, Dohan Gallery, L.A., 1966, Celebrity Art Exhibits, 55-city tour, 1964-65, Parkhurst Gallery, Seal Beach, Calif., 1991; represented in permanent collections Crocker Mus., Sacramento, Calif., 1968, SUNY, Albany, also numerous pvt. collections U.S. and abroad; playwright: Heavy Heavy What Hangs Over?, 1971, A Medal for Murray, 1991; dir. plays Apple of His Eye, 1954, Glass Menagerie, 1954; featured in book Actors as Artists, 1992, Guide to Artists in Southern California, 1994. Trustee Motion Picture and TV Fund. Served with USN, 1945-46. Recipient Silver Medallion award Motion Picture TV Fund, 1990, Sybil Brand Humanitarian award Jeffrey Found., 1990. Mem. SAG, AFTRA, Actors Equity Assn., Assn. Can. TV and Radio Artists, Acad. Motion Picture Arts and Scis., Acad. TV Arts and Scis. Office: c/o Budd Moss Shapiro Lichtmann Agy 8827 Beverly Blvd Los Angeles CA 90048 *I have always been grateful to be able to work in more than one medium. In a way they are all related, each solidifying and nurturing the other. I have a strong belief in God...and spiritual values. This, along with my marriage, children, and family life, has helped me enormously to express my own individuality as an artist.*

RICHMAN, PHYLLIS CHASANOW, newspaper critic; b. Washington, Mar. 21, 1939; d. Abraham and Helen (Lieberman) C.; m. Alvin Richman, June 5, 1960 (div. 1984); children—Joseph, Matthew, Libby. B.A., Brandeis U., 1961; postgrad., U. Pa., 1961-63, Purdue U., 1966-70. Restaurant critic Washington Post, 1976—; exec. food editor, 1980-88, food critic, 1988—. Author: Barter, 1976, Best Restaurants, 1980, 82, 85, 89. Mem. Washington Ind. Writers (adv. bd.). Home: 2118 O St NW Washington DC 20037-1007 Office: Washington Post 1150 15th St NW Washington DC 20071-0002

RICHMAN, STEPHEN ERIK, lawyer; b. Austin, Tex., Mar. 10, 1945; s. Allen A. and Erika (Zimmerman) R.; m. Frances Ellen Sharpe, Aug. 29, 1971; children: Joshua Eric, Wendy Michelle. BA magna cum laude, Amherst Coll., 1967; JD cum laude, Harvard U., 1970. Bar: N.Y. 1971, Wis. 1972. Assoc. Webster Sheffield, N.Y.C., 1970-72; assoc. Quarles & Brady, Milw., 1972-78, ptnr., 1978—. Pres. Milw. Youth Symphony Orch., 1985-87; mem. exec. com. Milw. Jewish Fedn., 1990—; chair summer task force and artistic affairs com. Milw. Symphony Orch., 1993—, mem. exec. com., 1992—; bd. dirs. Jewish Cmty. Found., Milw., 1992—. Mem. ABA, Nat. Assn. Bond Lawyers, State Bar Wis., Phi Beta Kappa. Home: 709 E Carlisle Ave Milwaukee WI 53217-4835 Office: Quarles & Brady 411 E Wisconsin Ave Milwaukee WI 53202-4409

RICHMAN, STEPHEN I., lawyer; b. Washington, Pa., Mar. 26, 1933; m. Audrey May Gefsky. BS, Northwestern U., 1954; JD, U. Pa., 1957. Bar: Pa. 1958, U.S. Dist. Ct. (we. dist.) Pa. With McCune Greenlep & Richman, 1960-63, Greenlee Richman Derrico & Posa, 1963-84, ptnr. Ceisler, Richman, Smith Law Firm, P.A., Washington, 1985—; bd. dirs. Three Rivers Bank; lectr. U. South Fla. Sch. Medicine, Mine Safe Internat. Chamber of Mines of Western Australia, W.Va. U. Med. Ctr. Grand Rounds, Am. Coll. Chest Physicians, Pa. Thoracic Soc., Am. Thoracic Soc., The Energy Bur., Coll. of Am. Pathologists, Allegheny County Health Dept., APHA, Internat. Assn. Ind. Accident Bds. and Commns., Indsl. Health Found., Nat. Coun. Self-Insurers Assn., Am. Iron and Steel Inst., Can. Thoracic Soc., I.L.O./N.I.O.S.H., Univs. Associated for Rsch. and Edn. in Pathology, Am. Ceramics Soc., Nat. Sand Assn.; mem. adv. com. U.S. Dist. Ct. Western Dist. Pa., 1994—; lectr. in field. Author: Meaning of Impairment and Disability, Chest, 1980, Legal Aspects for the Pathologist, in Pathology of Occupational and Environmental Lung Disease, 1988, A Review of the Medical and Legal Definitions of Related Impairment and Disability, Report to the Department of Labor and the Congress, 1986, Medicolegal Aspects of Asbestos for Pathologists, Arch. Pathology and Laboratory Medicine, 1983, Legal Aspects of Occupational and Environmental Disease, Human Pathology, 1993, Impairment and Disability in Pneumoconiosis, State of the Art Reviews in Occupational Medicine-The Mining Industry, 1993, other publs. and articles; author House Bills 2103 and 885 co-author Act 44 amending Pa. Workmen's Compensation Act. Mem. legal com. Indsl. Health Found., Pitts.; bd. dirs. Pitts. Opera Soc., 1994—, Pitts. Jewish Fedn., 1994—. Mem. ABA (vice chair workers compensation and employers liability law com., toxic and hazardous substance and environ. law com., lectr.), Pa. Bar Assn. (former mem. coun. of worker's compensation sect., lectr., contbg. author bar assn. quarterly 1992, 93), Assn. Trial Lawyers Am., Pa. Chamber Bus. and Industry (workers' compensation com., chmn. subcom. on legis. drafting, lectr.). Home: 620 E Beau St Washington PA 15301-2906 Office: Washington Trust Bldg Ste 200 Washington PA 15301 *Notable cases include: Beth Energy Mines vs. Wofford; Strube vs. Consol. Coal Co., Skirpan vs. Beth Energy Mines.*

RICHMAN, WILLIAM SHELDON, furniture company executive; b. Far Rockaway, N.Y., Aug. 5, 1921; s. Joseph and Mollye (Josephson) R.; m. Marilyn Melvoin, Dec. 27, 1951; children: Daniel, Elizabeth, Ruth. BS, CCNY, 1941; MBA, Harvard U., 1943. Asst. buyer Kresge-Newark, 1946-49; buyer, mdse. mgr. Mandel Bros., Chgo., 1949-56; sales mgr. Futorian Corp., Chgo., 1957-64, exec. v.p., 1965-70, pres., dir. 1971-86; vice-chmn. Mohasco Upholstered Furniture Corp., Chgo., 1986—, bd. dirs. NCCJ, Chgo., 1979—, nat. bd. dirs., 1982—. Recipient Champion of Youth award B'nai B'rith, 1975; recipient Brotherhood award NCCJ, 1979. Mem. Nat. Assn. Furniture Mfrs. (dir. 1975—), Upholstered Furniture Action Coun. Home: 525 Sheridan Rd Glencoe IL 60022-1715 Office: Mohasco Upholstered Furniture Corp 680 N Lake Shore Dr Chicago IL 60611-3057

RICHMOND, ALLEN MARTIN, speech pathologist, educator; b. N.Y.C., July 24, 1936; m. Deborah Moll. BS, SUNY, Geneseo, 1958; MEd, Pa. State U., 1961; PhD, Ohio U., 1965. Instr. N.Y.S. Public Schools, 1958-60, Penn. Rehab. Ctr., 1960-62, Buffalo Hearing and Speech Ctr., 1969-88; clin. instr. dept. otolaryngology SUNY Med. Sch., 1980—; speech pathologist dept. otolaryngology SUNY, Buffalo, 1989—; vis. prof. U. Md., 1968; adj. asst. prof. comm. disorders dept., 1989—; staff Sisters of Charity Hosp.; advisor New Voice Club of Niagara Frontier, Buffalo, 1980-90; cons. Bry-Lin Hosp., Buffalo, 1989—, W.B. Saunders Co., 1988. Contbg. author: An Atlas of Head and Neck Surgery. Participant Very Spl. Arts, Niagara, 1990—. Mem. Am. Speech-Lang.-Hearing Assn. Avocations: running, baseball, reading, travel. Home: 423 Walton Dr Buffalo NY 14225-1005 Office: Sisters Hosp Head and Neck Ctr 2157 Main St Buffalo NY 14214

RICHMOND, ANTHONY HENRY, sociologist, emeritus educator; b. Ilford, Essex, Eng., June 8, 1925; s. Henry James and Ellen Bertha (Hankin) R.; m. Freda Williams, Mar. 29, 1952; 1 dau., Glenys Catriona Richmond Troth. BSc in Econs., London Sch. Econs., 1949; MA, U. Liverpool (Eng.), 1951; PhD, U. London, 1965. Rsch. officer U. Liverpool, 1949-51; lectr. dept. social study U. Edinburgh, Scotland, 1952-63; reader in sociology

Bristol (Eng.) Coll. Sci. and Tech., 1963-65; prof. sociology York U., Toronto, Ont., Can., 1965-89; prof. emeritus, sr. scholar York U., Toronto, 1989—; dir. York U. (Inst. Behavioral Rsch.), 1979-82; social rsch. cons.; vis. prof. Australian Nat. U., Canberra, 1971, 77, St. Antony's Coll., Oxford, Eng., 1984-85. Author: Colour Prejudice in Britain, 1954, 2d edit., 1971, The Colour Problem: A Study of Racial Relations in Britain, Africa and the West Indies, 1955, rev. edit., 1961, Post-War Immigrants in Canada, 1967, (with others) Immigrant Integration and Urban Renewal in Toronto, 1973, Migration and Race Relations in an English City, 1973, (with W. E. Kalbach) Factors in the Adjustment of Immigrants and Their Descendants, 1980, Immigration and Ethnic Conflict, 1988, Caribbean Immigrants: A Demoeconomic Analysis, 1989, Global Apartheid: Refugees, Racism and the New World Order, 1994; editor: Readings in Race and Ethnic Relations, 1972, (with D. Kubat) Internal Migration: The New World and the Third World, 1976; contbr. chpts. to books, articles to profl. jours. Recipient research grants and scholarships. Fellow Royal Soc. Can.; mem. Can. Sociology and Anthropology Assn., Can. Population Soc. Mem. Soc. of Friends. Avocations: classical music, photography. Office: York U, Dept Sociology, 4700 Keele St, North York, ON Canada M3J 1P3

RICHMOND, DAVID WALKER, lawyer; b. Silver Hill, W.Va., Apr. 20, 1914; s. David Walker and Louise (Finlaw) R.; m. Gladys Evelyn Mallard, Dec. 19, 1936; children: David Walker, Nancy L. LL.B., George Washington U., 1937. Bar: D.C. 1936, Ill. 1946, Md. 1950. Partner firm Miller & Chevalier, Washington; lectr. fed. taxation. Contbr. to profl. jours. Served from ensign to lt. comdr. USNR, 1942-46. Decorated Bronze Star; recipient Disting. Alumni Achievement award George Washington U., 1976. Fellow Am. Bar Found., Am. Coll. Trial Lawyers, Am. Coll. Tax Counsel; mem. ABA (chmn. taxation sect. 1955-57, ho. of dels. 1958-60), Am. Law Inst., Lawyers' Club of Washington, Union League (Chgo.), Bird Key Yacht Club (Sarasota), Masons. Republican. Methodist. Home: 988 Blvd Of The Arts Sarasota FL 34236 Office: 655 15th St NW Washington DC 20005-5701

RICHMOND, EERO, music librarian, composer; b. Tacoma, Wash., Jan. 5, 1938; s. Orin August and Esther Maija (Johnson) R. BA in music, U. Wash., 1961, MLS, 1966. Music libr. N.Y.C. Pub. Libr., 1966-68, head music cataloger, 1969-80; dir. info. svcs. Am. Music Ctr., N.Y.C., 1982-93, head music cataloger, 1994—; pianist Slavic Arts Ensemble, N.Y.C., 1985—, Inoue Chamber Ensemble, N.Y.C., 1993—. Composer musical works performed throughout U.S., Europe, South Am., Japan; contbr. articles to profl. jours. Mem. ASCAP, Internat. Soc. for Contemporary Music (v.p. 1986-90), Sibelius Soc. (v.p. 1985—), Phi Mu Alpha Sinfonia, Beta Phi Mu. Democrat. Lutheran. Avocations: travel (especially Berlin); reading. Office: Am Music Ctr 30 W 26th St # 1001 New York NY 10010-2011

RICHMOND, GAIL LEVIN, law educator; b. Gary, Ind., Jan. 9, 1946; d. Herbert Irving and Sylvia Esther (Given) Levin; children: Henry, Amy. AB, U. Mich., 1966, MBA, 1967; JD, Duke U., 1971. Bar: Ohio 1971, U.S. Claims Ct. 1986, U.S. Ct. Mil. Appeals, 1994; CPA, Ill. Acct. Arthur Andersen & Co., Chgo., 1967-68; assoc. Jones, Day, Cleve., 1971-72; asst. prof. Capital U. Law Sch., Columbus, Ohio, 1972-73, U. N.C. Law Sch., Chapel Hill, 1973-78; vis. asst. prof. U. Tex. Law Sch., Austin, 1977-78, Nova U. Law Ctr., Ft. Lauderdale, Fla., 1979-80; assoc. prof. Nova U. Law Ctr., Ft. Lauderdale, 1980-81, assoc. prof., assoc. dean, 1981-85, prof., assoc. dean., 1985-93, prof., acting dean, 1993—. Author: Federal Tax Research, 4th edit., 1990; contbr. articles to profl. jours. Pres. Greater Ft. Lauderdale Tax Coun., 1987-88; chair Law Sch. Admission Coun. Audit Com., 1991-93; chair Assn. Am. Law Schs. Audit Com., 1992; trustee Law Sch. Admission Coun., 1994-97. Mem. ABA, Am. Assn. of Attys.-CPAs (dir. Fla. chpt. 1992-95), Assn. Am. Law Schs. (mem. audit com. 1990-92, pres. S.E. chpt. 1993-94), Broward County Women Lawyers Assn. Democrat. Jewish. Avocation: reading. Office: Nova Southeastern U Shepard Broad Law Ctr 3305 College Ave Fort Lauderdale FL 33314-7721

RICHMOND, HAROLD NICHOLAS, lawyer; b. Elizabeth, N.J., Apr. 5, 1935; s. Benjamin I. and Eleanor (Turbowitz) R.; m. Elaine Zemel, June 16, 1957 (div. Nov. 1972); children: Bonnie J. Ross, Michele Weinfeld; m. Marilyn A. Wenrich, Aug. 26, 1973; children: Eric L., Kacy L. BA, Tulane U., 1957; LLB, NYU, 1961, LLM in Taxation, 1965. Estate tax examiner IRS, Newark, 1963-65; tax mgr. Puder & Puder/Touche Ross & Co., CPAs, Newark, 1965-73; ptnr. Sodowick Richmond & Crecca, Newark, 1973-84; prin. Harold N. Richmond, West Orange, N.J., 1984-86; ptnr. Wallerstein Hauptman & Richmond, West Orange, 1986-91, Hauptman & Richmond, West Orange, 1992—. With U.S. Army, 1959-60. Mem. ABA (tax sect. closely held bus. com., real property and probate sect.), N.J. Bar Assn. (tax, real property and probate sects.), Essex County Bar Assn. (chmn. tax com. 1989, real property and probate sect.). Avocations: running, tennis. Office: Hauptman & Richmond 200 Executive Dr West Orange NJ 07052-3303

RICHMOND, JAMES ELLIS, restaurant company executive; b. Chgo., Feb. 16, 1938; s. Kenneth E. and Irene M. (Anderson) R.; m. Karen Ann Ryder, Oct. 6, 1956; children: Scott, Brian, Ann, Susan. BBA, Case Western Res. U., 1960. CPA, Ohio. Sr. auditor Ernst & Ernst, Cleve., 1960-64; treas. Cook United, Inc., Cleve., 1964-75; treas. Fairmont Foods Co., Houston, 1975-80, v.p. ops., 1980-82; v.p., treas. U-tote-M, Inc., 1982-84; mktg. exec. Circle K Convenience Stores, 1984-86; v.p. Consol. Products, Inc., Indpls., 1986—. Lutheran. Home: 13088 Tarkington Common Carmel IN 46033-9352 Office: Consol Products Inc 36 S Pennsylvania St Indianapolis IN 46204-3634

RICHMOND, JULIUS BENJAMIN, retired physician, health policy educator emeritus; b. Chgo., Sept. 26, 1916; s. Jacob and Anna (Dayno) R.; m. Rhee Chidekel, June 3, 1937 (dec. Oct. 9, 1985); children: Barry J., Charles Allen, Dale Keith (dec.); m. Jean Rabow, Jan. 11, 1987. BS, U. Ill., 1937, MS, MD, 1939; DSc (hon.), Ind. U., 1978, Rush-Presbyn.-St. Luke Med. Ctr., 1978, U. Ill., 1979, Georgetown U., 1980, Syracuse U., 1986, U. Ariz., 1991; DMS (hon.), Med. Coll. Pa., 1980; D in Pub. Svc. (hon.), Nat. Coll. Edn., Evanston, Ill., 1980; LHD (hon.), Tufts U., 1986. Intern Cook County Hosp., Chgo., 1939-41, resident, 1941-42, 46; resident Mcpl. Contagious Disease Hosp., Chgo., 1941; mem. faculty U. Ill. Med. Sch., Chgo., 1946-53, prof. pediatrics, 1950-53; dir. Inst. Juvenile Research Inst. Juvenile Rsch., Chgo., 1952-53; prof., chmn. dept. pediatrics Coll. Medicine, SUNY at Syracuse, 1953-65; dean med. faculty, chmn. dept. pediatrics, 1965-70; prof. child psychiatry and human devel., prof. chmn. dept. preventive and social medicine Harvard Med. Sch., 1971-77, prof. health policy, 1981-88, div. divsn. health policy rsch. and edn., 1983-88, prof. health policy emeritus, 1988—; also faculty Harvard Sch. Pub. Health; psychiatrist-in-chief Children's Hosp. Med. Center, Boston, 1971-77, adv. on child health policy, 1981—; dir. Judge Baker Guidance Center, Boston, 1971-77; asst. sec. health and surgeon gen. HHS, 1977-81; mem. Pres.'s Commn. on Mental Health, 1977. Author: Pediatric Diagnosis, 1962, Currents in American Medicine, 1969. Nat. dir. Project Head Start; dir. Office Health Affairs OEO, 1965-66. Edn., Evanston, Ill., 1980; LHD (hon.), Tufts U., 1986. Served as flight surgeon USAAF, 1942-46. Recipient Agnes Bruce Greig Sch. award, 1966, Parents Mag. award, 1966, Disting. Service award Office Econ. Opportunity, 1967, Family Health Mag. award, 1977, Myrdal award Assn. For Evaluation Rsch., 1977, award for disting. sci. contbn. Soc. for Research in Child Devel., 1979, Dolly Madison award Inst. on Clin. Infants Programs, 1979, Public Health Disting. Service award HEW, 1980, Illini Achievement award U. Ill. Alumni Assn., 1982, Community Service award Health Planning Council Greater Boston, 1985, Lemuel Shattuck award Mass. Pub. Health Assn., 1985, 1st Ann. Ronald McDonald Children's Charities award for Outstanding Contbns. to Child Health and Welfare, 1986, Sedgwick award APHA, 1992. Fellow Am. Orthopsychiat. Assn. (Ittleson award 1994), Am. Psychiat. Assn. (disting.); mem. Am. Acad. Child Psychiatry (hon.), New Eng. Coun. Child Psychiatry (assoc.), Inst. Medicine of NAS (1st Ann. Gustav O. Lienhard award 1986), AMA (AMA-ERF award in health edn. 1988), Am. Pediatric Soc. (John Howland award 1990), Am. Acad. Pediatrics (C. Anderson Aldrich award 1966, ann. award sect. on community pediatrics 1977, Outstanding Contbn. award sect. community pediatrics 1978), Soc. Pediatric Rsch., Am. Psychosomatic Soc., APHA (Martha May Eliot award 1970, Sedgwick Medal 1992), Sigma Xi, Alpha Omega Alpha, Phi Eta Sigma.

RICHMOND, MARILYN SUSAN, lawyer; b. Bethesda, Md., Oct. 19, 1949; d. Carl Hutchins Jr. and Elizabeth Adeline (Saeger) R. BA with honors, U. Fla., 1971; JD, Georgetown U., 1974. Bar: Md. 1974, D.C. 1975.

Atty. Office of Gen. Counsel, FTC, Washington, 1974-77, antitrust atty. Bur. of Competition, 1977-81; counsel, consumer subcom. of com. on commerce, sci. and transp. U.S. Senate, Washington, 1981-85; assoc. Heron, Burchette, Ruckert & Rothwell, Washington, 1985-87, ptnr., 1987-90; dep. asst. sec. for govtl. affairs U.S. Dept. Transp., Washington, 1990-91, acting asst. sec. for govtl. affairs, 1991-92; cons. Raffaelli, Spees, Springer & Smith, Washington, 1993-94; asst. exec. dir. govt. rels. APA Practice Directorate, 1995—; lectr. Brookings Instn. Ctr. for Pub. Policy Edn., Washington, 1985-88. Active Lawyers for Bush-Quayle, Washington, 1988. Mem. ABA (antitrust, adminstrv. law sect., vice chair transp. industry com. antitrust sect. 1992-95). Republican. Methodist. Avocations: horseback riding, tennis. Home: Apt 503 I 2725 Connecticut Ave NW Washington DC 20008-5305

RICHMOND, PHYLLIS ALLEN, library and information science educator; b. Boston, Jan. 5, 1921; d. Charles Francis Hitchock and Alberta (Currie) Allen; m. James Hugh Richmond, Sept. 24, 1949 (dec. 1951). B.A. Western Reserve U., 1942; M.A., U. Pa., 1946, Ph.D., 1949; M.S. in Library Sci., Western Reserve U., 1956. Curator of history Rochester, N.Y. Mus., 1943-47; research asst. to dir. Welch Inst. Johns Hopkins U., Balt., 1952; librarian U. Rochester, N.Y., 1955-68; prof. Syracuse U., N.Y., 1969, Case Western Reserve U., Cleve., 1970-84; vis. prof. UCLA, 1985, Columbia U., 1986; speaker, U.S. Can., Europe, 1960—; cons. to profl. groups, 1965—; with Rochester Pub. Libr., 1953-54. Author: Precis for North American Usage, 1982; co-editor Theory of Subject Analysis: A Sourcebook, 1985; mem. editorial bd. Internat. Classification, Germany, 1970-84; contbr. articles to profl. jours. Mem. ALA (recipient Margaret Mann citation 1978), Am. Soc. for Info. Sci. (recipient award of merit 1972, Pioneer Info. Sci. award 1987), History of Sci. Soc., Am. Radio Relay League. Republican. Presbyterian. Avocations: travel; stamp collection; bird watching. Home: 206 Hamlet Hills Dr Bldg 8 Chagrin Falls OH 44022-2806

RICHMOND, RICHARD THOMAS, journalist; b. Parma, Ohio, May 16, 1933; s. Arthur James and Frances Marie (Visosky) R.; m. Charlotte Jean Schwoebel, Dec. 19, 1933; children: Kris Elaine, Leigh Alison, Paul Evan. AB, Washington U., St. Louis, 1961. Bur. mgr. UPI News Pictures, St. Louis, 1957-62; asst. picture editor Post-Dispatch, St. Louis, 1962-64, editor color sect., 1964-80, columnist, 1971—, editor calendar sect., 1983-94; asst. entertainment editor, 1995—; v.p. Golden Royal Enterprises, St. Louis, 1976-78; pres. Oroquest Press, St. Louis, 1977-80; dir. U.S. Mortgage & Investment Corp., Hilton Head Island, N.C., 1977-81; pres. Magalar Mining, Texarkana, Ark., 1979-83. Co-author: Treasure Under Your Feet, 1974, In the Wake of the Golden Galleons, 1976, Diabetes: The Facts That Will Let You Regain Control of Your Life, 1986. Avocation: undersea treasure hunting. Home: 307 Lebanon Ave Belleville IL 62220-4126 Office: St Louis Post-Dispatch 900 N Tucker Blvd Saint Louis MO 63101-1099

RICHMOND, ROBERT LINN, management consultant; b. Columbus, Ohio, Apr. 10, 1920; s. Loren Magee and Ruth Winifred (Shannon) R.; m. Ruth Felton Morrison, Dec. 6, 1943; children: Robert Morrison, Bates Carleton. BSBA, Ohio State U., 1942. CPA, cert. internal auditor. Sr. auditor Keller, Kirschner, Martin & Clinger (C.P.A.s), Columbus, Ohio, 1946-52; div. v.p., gen. auditor B.F. Goodrich Co., Akron, Ohio, 1952-78; pres., chief operating officer Inst. Internal Auditors, Altamonte Springs, Fla., 1979-81; cons. mgmt. controls systems Naples, Fla., 1981—; bd. regents Cert. Internal Auditor Exams., 1976-78. Editor: Internal Auditor, 1963-68. Speaker seminars and meetings; Active Little Hoover Commn. Task Force, Summit County, Ohio, 1969-70; mem. Citizens Com., Task Force, Ohio, 1968-70. Served to capt., Signal Corps U.S. Army, 1942-45. Mem. AICPA (spl. adv. com. on internal acctg. control 1977-79, auditing standards adv. coun. 1978-81), Ohio Soc. CPAs, Inst. Internal Auditors (hon., Cadmus Meml. award 1978), Citrus Club, Masons, Shriners, Kiwanis (Kiwanian of Yr. award 1985). Republican. Episcopalian. Home: 1300 Gulf Shore Blvd N Apt 610 Naples FL 33940-4904 Office: 660 9th St N Ste 34A Naples FL 33940-8139

RICHMOND, RONALD LEROY, aerospace engineer; b. L.A., Aug. 16, 1931; s. William Paul and Martha Emelia (Anderson) R.; m. Mary Louise Gates, Jan. 2, 1955; children: Pandora Deanne Richmond Perry, Steven Lee. BSME, U. Calif., Berkeley, 1952; MS in Aero. Engring., Calif. Inst. Tech., 1953, PhD in Aero. Engring., 1957. Aerodynamicist Lockheed Aircraft Co., Burbank, Calif., 1952-54; teaching/rsch. asst. Calif. Inst. Tech., Pasadena, 1952-57; asst. group leader aero. performance Douglas Aircraft Co., Long Beach, Calif., 1957-59; chief engr. adv. devel. Ford Aerospace, Newport Beach, Calif., 1959-87; adj. assoc. prof. Sch. Engring., U. Calif., Irvine, 1987-88; dir. engring. Brunswick Def., Costa Mesa, Calif., 1988-94; aerodynamics cons. Douglas Aircraft, 1956-57, Shelby-Am. (Ford) Auto., L.A., 1960-62; subgroup leader NATO Indsl. Adv. Group #16, Brussels, Belgium, 1984-86. Res. dep. Orange County Sheriff's Dept., 1976—. Calif. Inst. Tech. Rsch. assistantship, 1953, 54, 55, 56, 57, teaching asst., 1955, 56, 57, grantee, 1955, 56, 57. Assoc. fellow AIAA (Orange County sect. chmn. 1989-90); mem. Western States Assn. Sheriff's Air squadrons (comdr. 1987-88), Skylarks of So. Calif. (pres., chmn. bd. 1987-88). Republican. Achievements include experimentally proved that skin friction forces on long, slender cylinders was several times that on flat plates, at Mach 5.8 for both laminar and turbulent boundary layers. Home: 1307 Seacrest Dr Corona Del Mar CA 92625-1227

RICHMOND, SAMUEL BERNARD, management educator; b. Boston, Oct. 14, 1919; s. David E. and Freda (Braman) R.; m. Evelyn Ruth Kravitz, Nov. 26, 1944; children: Phyllis Gail, Douglas Emerson, Clifford Owen. AB cum laude, Harvard U., 1940; MBA, Columbia U., 1948, PhD, 1951. Mem. faculty Columbia U., 1946-76; assoc. prof., 1957-60, prof. econ. and statistics, 1960-76; assoc. dean Grad. Sch. Bus. Columbia U., 1971-72, acting dean, 1972-73; dean prof. mgmt. Owen Grad. Sch. Mgmt. Vanderbilt U., Nashville, 1976-86, Ralph Owen prof. mgmt., 1984-88, Ralph Owen prof. mgmt. emeritus, 1988—, dean emeritus, adj. prof., 1988—; vis. prof. U. Sherbrooke, Que., 1967, U. Buenos Aires, Argentina, 1964, 65, Case Inst. Tech., Cleve., 1958-59, Fordham U., N.Y.C., 1952-53; dir. IMS Internat. Inc., N.Y.C., 1978-88; 1st Am. Corp., Nashville, 1981-86, Winners Corp., Nashville, 1983-89, Corbin Ltd., N.Y.C., 1970-85, Ingram Industries Inc., Nashville, 1981-92; cons. to maj. comml., ednl., profl. and govtl. orgns. Author: Operations Research for Management Decisions, 1968, Statistical Analysis, 1957, 2d. edit., 1964, Regulation and Competition in Air Transportation, 1961; talk show host Nashville Bus. Edit., WDCN-TV, 1984-86. Trustee Ramapo Coll., N.J., 1975-76; bd. dirs. Jewish Fedn. Nashville and Middle Tenn; trustee Endowment Fund Jewish Fedn. Nashville and Mid. Tenn. 1st lt. USAAF, 1943-45. Recipient Honor award CAB, 1971, Alumni award for outstanding svc. Grad. Sch. Bus., Columbia U., 1973. Mem. Am. Econ. Assn., Inst. Mgmt. Sci., Ops. Rsch. Soc. Am., Beta Gamma Sigma. Home: 5404 Camelot Rd Brentwood TN 37027-4113 Office: Vanderbilt U Owen Grad Sch Mgmt Nashville TN 37203

RICHMOND, WILLIAM PATRICK, lawyer; b. Cicero, Ill., Apr. 5, 1932; s. Edwin and Mary (Allger) R.; m. Elizabeth A., Jan. 9, 1954 (div.); children: Stephen, Janet, Timothy; m. Magda, June 8, 1992. A.B., Albion Coll., 1954; J.D., U. Chgo., 1959. Bar: Ill. 1959, N.Y. 1985. Assoc. Sidley & Austin, Chgo., 1960-67, ptnr., 1967—. Served with U.S. Army, 1954-56. Fellow Am. Coll. Trial Lawyers; mem. Soc. Trial Lawyers, Chgo. Bar. Assn., Ill. State Bar Assn., ABA. Republican. Methodist. Clubs: Mid-Day; Legal; Ruth Lake Country (Hinsdale, Ill.). Home: 4 Tartan Ridge Rd Burr Ridge IL 60521-8904 Office: Sidley & Austin 1 First Nat Plz Chicago IL 60603

RICHSTEIN, ABRAHAM RICHARD, lawyer; b. N.Y.C., Apr. 18, 1919; s. Morris and Ida (Stupp) R.; m. Rosalind Bauman; children: Eric, Jonathan. B.S., CCNY, 1939; J.D., Fordham U., 1942; LL.M. in Internat. Law, NYU, 1956; M.S. in Internat. Affairs, George Washington U., 1966; diploma, Command and Gen. Staff Coll., 1958, Nat. War Coll., 1966. Bar: N.Y. 1942, U.S. Supreme Ct 1956, D.C. 1977. Enlisted as pvt. U.S. Army, 1942, advanced through grades to col., 1966; served with Mil. Intelligence, U.S. 9th Army U.S. Army, Europe, 1944; legal staff U.S. War Crimes Commn. U.S. Army, Ger., 1946; staff officer UN Command (U.S. Army), Far East, 1951-53; mil. law judge (Hdqrs. First Army), 1954-57; chief internat. affairs Office Judge Adv., Hdqrs. US Army Europe U.S. Army, 1960-63; chief plans office Office Judge Adv. Gen., Washington, 1963-64; Judge Adv. Hdqrs. U.S. Army Combat Devels. Command, 1964-66; ret., 1969;

asst. gen. counsel AID, State Dept., 1969-81; gen. counsel ACDA, Washington, 1981-83; mem. faculty Nat. War Coll., 1966-68; adj. prof. Def. Intelligence Coll., Washington, 1989-91; joint staff planner, policy and planning directorate Joint Chiefs Staff, Washington, 1968-69. Mem. editorial bd. Mil. Law and Law of War Rev., 1960-63, Fed. Bar News Jour., 1988-89; book rev. editor: Fordham U. Law Rev., 1941-42. Decorated Bronze Star.; recipient AID Superior Honor award, 1980, ACDA Meritorious Honor award, 1983. Mem. Am. Soc. Internat. Law. Home: 8713 Mary Lee Ln Annandale VA 22003-3659

RICHTER, BURTON, physicist, educator; b. N.Y.C., Mar. 22, 1931; s. Abraham and Fanny (Pollack) R.; m. Laurose Becker, July 1, 1960; children: Elizabeth, Matthew. B.S., MIT, 1952, Ph.D., 1956. Research assoc. Stanford U., 1956-60, asst. prof. physics, 1960-63, assoc. prof., 1963-67, prof., 1967—; Paul Pigott prof. phys. sci., 1980—, tech. dir. Linear Accelerator Ctr., 1982-84, dir. Linear Accelerator Ctr., 1984—; cons. NSF, Dept. Energy; bd. dirs. Varian Corp., Litel Instruments; Loeb lectr. Harvard U. 1974; DeShalit lectr. Weizmann Inst., 1975. Contbr. over 300 articles to profl. publs. Recipient E.O. Lawrence medal Dept. Energy, 1975; Nobel prize in physics, 1976. Fellow Am. Phys. Soc. (pres. 1994), AAAS; mem. NAS, Am. Acad. Arts and Scis. Achievements include research in elementary particle physics. Office: Stanford Linear Accel Ctr PO Box 4349 Stanford CA 94309

RICHTER, DONALD PAUL, lawyer; b. New Britain, Conn., Feb. 15, 1924; s. Paul John and Helen (Racoske) R.; m. Jane Frances Gumpright, Aug. 10, 1946; children: Christopher Dean, Cynthia Louise. A.B., Bates Coll., 1947; LL.B., Yale U., 1950. Bar: N.Y. 1951, Conn. 1953. Assoc. Winthrop, Stimson, Putnam & Roberts, N.Y.C., 1950-52; ptnr. Murtha, Cullina, Richter and Pinney, Hartford, Conn., 1954-94, counsel, 1994—. Trustee Bates Coll., 1962—, Manchester (Conn.) Meml. Hosp., 1963—; Hartford Sem., 1973-85; Trustee Suffield Acad., 1974—, pres., 1982-89; bd. dirs. Met. YMCA Greater Hartford, 1970—, pres., 1976-81; mem. nat. council YMCA, 1978-82; bd. dirs. Church Homes, 1967-81; trustee, v.p. Silver Bay Assn., 1971—. Served with USNR, 1943-46. Fellow Am. Coll. Trust and Estate Counsel; mem. ABA, Conn. Bar Assn., Univ. Club, Hartford Club, Rotary, Phi Beta Kappa, Delta Sigma Rho. Congregationalist. Home: 140 Boulder Rd Manchester CT 06040-4508 Office: Murtha Cullina Richter & Pinney City Place I 185 Asylum St Hartford CT 06103-3469

RICHTER, EARL EDWARD, manufacturing company executive; b. Twin Lakes, Wis., Oct. 16, 1923; s. John Benjamin and Emma Augusta (Kautz) R.; m. Carlista Mae Dean, Sept. 12, 1943; children: Susan Dianne, Robert Dean. B.B.A., U. Wis.-Madison, 1948. C.P.A., Wis. With Modine Mfg. Co., Racine, Wis., 1948—, v.p. gen. mgr., 1963-74, pres., 1974—, chief operating officer, 1974, chief exec. officer, 1974—; dir. M&I Bank of Racine, Portec Inc. Served with USAAF, 1943-45. Mem. Racine Mfrs. Assn. (dir.), Conf. Bd., Am. Mgmt. Assn. Lutheran. Clubs: Racine Country, Milw. Athletic. Office: Modine Mfg Co 1500 De Koven Ave Racine WI 53403-2552

RICHTER, GEORG, book publishing executive. Pres. Bantam Doubleday Dell Books for Young Readers, N.Y.C. Office: Bantam Doubleday Dell Books 1540 Broadway New York NY 10036-4039

RICHTER, GERHARD, artist; b. Dresden, Germany, Feb. 9, 1932; m. Isa Genzken, 1982; 1 child, Betty. Student, Hochschule fur Bildende Kunste, Dresden, 1952-57; studied with, Karl-Otto Gotz Staatliche Kunstakademie, Dusseldorf, 1961-64. Scenery painter Stadttheatre Zittau, East Germany, 1949-50; commercial artist numerous firms Zittau, 1950-51; photolab. technician Dresden, 1957-60; painter Dusseldorf, 1963—; prof. Staaliche Kunstakademie, Dusseldorf, 1971—; lectr. in field. One man shows include Mobelhaus Berges, Dusseldorf, 1963, Galerie Heiner Friedrich, Munich, 1964, 67, 70, 72, Galerie Rene Block, 1965, 69, 74, White Wide Space Gallery, Antwerp, 1967, Galerie Ricke, Kassel, 1968, Galleria del Naviglio, 1969, Palais des Beaux-Arts, Brussels, 1970, Galerie Konrad Fischer, Dusseldorf, 1970, 72, 75, 83, Mus. Folkwang, Essen, 1970, 80, Kunstverein, Dusseldorf, 1971, Galerie Thomas Borgmann, Cologne, 1971, 84, Galerie Rudolph Zwirner, Cologne, 1972, Galerie Serial, Amsterdam, 1973, Onnasch Gallery, N.Y., 1973, Galleria La Bertesca, Milan, 1973, Galerie Rolf Preisig, Basle, 1975, Nova Scotia Coll. Art, Halifax, 1978, Whitechapel Art Gallery, London, 1979, Sperone-Westwater-Fischer, N.Y., 1980, 83, Kunsthalle, Dusseldorf, 1981, Galerie Hetzler, 1982, Padiglione d'Arte Contemporanea, Milan, 1982, Galleria Lucio Amelio, Naples, 1983, Galleria Maria Pieroni, Rome, 1983, Musée d'Art et d'Industrie, St. Etienne, France, 1984, Marian Goodman Gallery, N.Y., 1985, Sperone-Westwater, N.Y., 1985, Anthony d'Offay Gallery, London, 1988, Art Gallery Ont., 1988, others; exhibited in group shows at Whitechapel Art Gallery, London, Stedelijk Mus., Amsterdam, Kunsthalle, Royal Acad. London, L.A. County Mus. Art; represented in permanent collections Kunstmuseum, Dusseldorf, Neue Gallery, Mus. Folkwang, Nationalgalerie, Berlin, Kunstmuseum, Basle, Guggenheim Mus., N.Y.; author: Bericht uber eine Demonstr., 1963, Gerhard Richter: Atlas von de fot., 1972, Gerhard Richter: Atlas der Fotos, Collgen und Skizzen, 1976. Recipient Kunstpreis Junger Westen, Recklinghausen, 1967, Arnold Bode prize, Kassel, 1982. Office: Kaiserwerther Strasse 115, 4000 Dusseldorf Germany also: Am European Art Assoc Inc 22 E 72nd St Ste 5B New York NY 10021

RICHTER, JAMES MICHAEL, physician, clinical investigator; b. Ann Arbor, Mich., Oct. 26, 1950; s. James Burton and Doris Jean (Barber) R.; m. Claudia Jo Upchurch, Aug. 23, 1974; children: James Andrew, Laura Emily. BS in Chemistry, U. Tex., 1972; MD, Southwestern Med. Sch., 1976; MA, U. Tex., 1976. Diplomate Am. Bd. Internal Medicine. Intern Mass. Gen. Hosp., Boston, 1976-77, resident, 1977-79, fellow, 1979-81, physician, 1981—, chief gastrointestinal clinic, 1981—; v.p. med. dir. Mass. Gen. Physicians, Boston, 1992—; instr. medicine Harvard U. Med. Sch., Boston, 1981-85, asst. profl, 1985—; cons. Policy Analysis Inc., Brookline, Mass., 1986—. Contbr. articles to profl. jours. Coach Winchester Soccer Club, Scout Master Boy Scouts of Am. Troop 503. Fellow ACP, Am. Coll. Gastroenterology; mem. Soc. Gen. Internal Medicine, Soc. for Med. Decision Making, Am. Gastroent. Assn., Appalachian Mountain Club, Alpha Omega Alpha. Congregationalist. Office: Mass Gen Hosp 15 Parkman St Boston MA 02114-3139

RICHTER, JUDITH ANNE, pharmacology educator; b. Wilmington, Del., Mar. 4, 1942; d. Henry John and Dorothy Madelyn (Schroeder) R. BA, U. Colo., 1964; PhD, Stanford U., 1969. Postdoctoral fellow Cambridge (Eng.) U., 1969-70, U. London, 1970-71; asst. prof. pharmacology Sch. Medicine Ind U., Indpls., 1971-78, assoc. prof. pharmacology and neurobiology, 1978-84, prof., 1984—; vis. assoc. prof. U. Ariz. Health Sci. Ctr., Tucson, 1983; mem. biomed. rsch. rev. com. Nat. Inst. on Drug Abuse, 1983-87. Mem. editorial bd. Jour. Neurochemistry, 1982-87; contbr. numerous articles to sci. jours. Scholar Boettcher Found., 1960-64; fellow Wellcome Trust, 1969-71. Mem. AAAS, Am. Soc. for Pharmacology and Exptl. Therapeutics (exec. com. neuropharmacology div. 1989-91), Am. Soc. for Neurochemistry, Internat. Soc. for Neurochemistry (sec. for Neurosci., Women in Neurosci., Assn. Women in Sci., Phi Beta Kappa, Sigma Xi. Achievements include research in neuropharmacology, especially barbiturates and neurobiology of mutant mice. Office: Ind U Sch Medicine 791 Union Dr Indianapolis IN 46202-4887

RICHTER, MICHAEL THOMAS, professional hockey player; b. Phila., Sept. 22, 1966. Student, U. Wisconsin. With N.Y. Rangers 1985—; goalie U.S. Nat. Team, 1987-88, U.S. Olympic Team, 1987-88. Recipient WCHA Rookie of the Yr. award, 1985-86; named MVP, All-Star Game, 1994. Played in NHL All-Star Game, 1992-93, Stanley Cup Championship, 1994. Office: NY Rangers 4 Pennsylvania Plz New York NY 10001*

RICHTER, PETER CHRISTIAN, lawyer; b. Opava, Czechoslovakia, June 13, 1944; came to U.S., 1951; s. Hanus and Alzbeta (Kindlarova) R.; m. Leslie Diane Rousseau, Nov. 25, 1967; children: Timothy Jason, Lindsey Berta. BS, U. Oreg., 1967, JD, 1971. Bar: Oreg. 1971, U.S. Dist. Ct. 1972, U.S. Ct. Appeals (9th cir.) 1972, U.S. Supreme Ct. 1983. Assoc. Veatch, Lovett & Stiner, Portland, Oreg., 1971-73; with Miller, Nash, Wiener, Hager & Carlsen, Portland, 1973—; adj. prof. law trial advocacy Northwestern Sch.

of Law, Lewis and Clark Coll., Portland, 1986—; pro tempore judge Multnomah County Cir. Ct., Portland, 1985—, Oreg. State Bar Trial Advocacy Seminars, 1988—. Author: (handbook) Oregon State Bar, 1987, 88, 89; co-author: (chpt. in book) Oregon State Bar Damage Manual, 1985, 90; editor, program planner Sales: The Oregon Experience, 1989. Trustee, bd. dirs. Parry Ctr. for Children, Portland, 1990; former bd. dir. Boy Scouts of Am., Columbia Pacific Coun., Portland, Nat. Conf. Christians and Jews, Portland, 1983. With Oreg. Army N.G., 1967-75. Recipient Cert. of Appreciation Northwestern Sch. of Law, 1990. Fellow Am. Bar Found. (mem. trial techniques com.); mem. ABA (trial techniques com.), Fed. Bar Assn. (Oreg. chpt.), Am. Bd. Trial Advocates (advocate), Oreg. Bar Assn. (lectr. trial advocacy seminars 1988—, mem. jud. adminstrn. com.), Multnomah Bar Assn. (ct. liaison com.), Oreg. Assn. Def. Counsel (cert. of appreciation 1987, 89), Inns of Ct., Multnomah Athletic Club, Arlington Club. Avocations: squash, tennis, skiing, golf, reading. Office: Miller Nash Wiener Hager & Carlsen 111 SW 5th Ave Portland OR 97204

RICHTER, RICHARD PAUL, academic administrator; b. Bryn Mawr, Pa., Mar. 6, 1931; s. Manuel DeWitt and Emma Margaret (Theilacker) R.; m. Margot Denithorne, Sept. 5, 1953; children: Karen Lee, Kurt Richard. BA, Ursinus Coll., 1953, LLD (hon.), 1976; MA, U. Pa., 1957; cert., Inst. Ednl. Mgmt., Harvard U., 1974; DHL (hon.), Tohoku Gakuin U., Sendai, Japan, 1986, Muhlenberg Coll., 1989. Editor Provident Mut. Life Ins. Co., Phila., 1956-58; supr. employee communications Gas Works div. UGI Corp., Phila., 1958-65; alumni dir. Ursinus Coll., Collegeville, Pa., 1965-67, asst. to pres., 1967-69, v.p. adminstrv. affairs, 1969-76, pres., 1976-94; pres. emeritus, 1995—; instr. in English Ursinus Coll., Collegeville, Pa., 1965-73, asst. prof. English, 1973-86; prof. of coll. Ursinus Coll., Collegeville, Pa., 1986—; chmn. Commn. for Ind. Colls. and Univs. Pa., 1984, Found. for Ind. Colls. of Pa., Harrisburg, 1985; past chmn. Coun. for Higher Edn. United Ch. of Christ; bd. dirs. Covenant Life Ins. Co., CenterCore. Contbtr. articles, poems to various publs. Chmn. CMMC, Inc. Montgomery Hosp., Norristown, Pa. Recipient Gold Quill award Am. Assn. Indsl. Editors, 1964, Lindback award for excellence in teaching Ursinus Coll., 1973, Silver Beaver award Boy Scouts Am., 1985. Mem. Pa. Assn. Colls. and Univs. (bd. dirs.), Del. Valley Assn. Communicators (past treas.), Pa. Folklife Soc., Montgomery County Hist. Soc. Home: 236 6th Ave Collegeville PA 19426-2510 Office: Ursinus Coll Box 1000 Collegeville PA 19426

RICHTER, W. D., screenwriter, director, producer; b. New Britain, Conn., Dec. 7, 1945; s. Walter Oswald and Hedwig (Duch) R.; m. Susan Booth, June 22, 1968. BA, Dartmouth Coll., 1968; postgrad., U. So. Calif., 1968-70. Freelance writer, producer, director, 1973—. Screenwriter: Slither, 1973, Peeper, 1975, Nickelodeon, 1976, Invasion of the Body Snatchers, 1978, Dracula, 1979, Brubaker, 1980 (Academy award nomination best original screenplay 1980), All Night Long, 1981, Big Trouble in Little China, 1986, Needful Things, 1993; prodr., dir.: (films) Buckaroo Banzai, 1984, Late for Dinner, 1991. Mem. Writers Guild Am., Dirs. Guild Am. Office: The Shapira/Lichtman Agency 8827 Beverly Blvd Los Angeles CA 90048*

RICHTER, WILLIAM, JR., aerospace company executive; b. Bklyn., Aug. 20, 1934; s. William and Emma (Zehender) R.; m. Eleanor E. Wharton, Nov. 1956; children: Mike S., John E., Kathryn L. AAS, N.Y. C.C., 1956; BSEE, NYU, 1957; MBA, U. Ala., 1970. Program mgr., group engr. Walleye, GPS, Mil Systems, Titan, Gemini Martin Marietta, Denver, 1960-67; program mgr. Skylab Martin Marietta, Huntsville, Ala., 1967-75; from dir. mil. space systems, program dir. space station, mgr. system integration .MX to program mgr. Manned Manuvering Unit Martin Marietta, Denver, 1975-89; mgr. program devel., space and launch systems SCI Systems Inc., Huntsville, 1989—; assoc. prof. Met. State U., Denver, 1964-67. Mem. sch. bd. Cherry Creek, Colo., 1976. Recipient Collier trophy, 1982, Group Achievement award NASA, 1987, Pub. Svc. Group Achievement medal NASA, 1988. Mem. AIAA (sr.), Am. Soc. Quality Control (pres. 1963-65), Am. Def. Preparedness Assn., Armed Forces Comms. and Electronics Assn. Avocations: skiing, flying. Home: 1715 Drake Ave SE Huntsville AL 35802 Office: PO Box 1000 Mail Stop 206 8600 S Meml Pkwy Huntsville AL 35807

RICHTOL, HERBERT HAROLD, science foundation program director; b. Bklyn., Aug. 13, 1932; s. Israil and Pearl (Boshnack) R.; m. Iris Gloria Klar, Aug. 11, 1956; children: Nancy Anne, Susan Gail, Elise Carol, Michael Bruce. BS, St. Lawrence U., 1954; PhD, NYU, 1961. Instr. Queens (N.Y.) Coll., 1960-61; chemistry prof. Rensselaer Poly. Inst., Troy, N.Y., 1961-85, dean undergrad. coll., 1985-94; program dir. Divsn. Undergrad. Edn. NSF, Arlington, Va., 1994—. Contbr. articles to profl. jours. Bd. dirs. Temple Beth El, Troy, 1980-85. Served with U.S. Army, 1954-56. Mem. Am. Chem. Soc., AAAS, Am. Assn. Higher Edn., Woodrow Wilson Soc., Sigma Xi. Democrat. Jewish. Avocations: theater, squash. Home: 15 Detroit Ave Troy NY 12180-2419 Office: NSF Divsn Undergrad Edn 4201 Wilson Blvd Arlington VA 22230

RICHWINE, DAVID ALAN, marine corps officer; b. Oakland, Calif., Oct. 4, 1943; s. David William and Violet Elaine (Cohoon) R.; m. Gayle Lydia Kreutzer, June 30, 1968; children—Heather Louise, Carrie Anne. B.A., U. Kans., 1965; student Basic Sch., 1965, Flight Tng. Sch., 1969-70, Amphibious Warfare Sch., 1973, Air Command and Staff Coll., 1978-79, Nat. War Coll., 1984-85. Commd. 2d lt. U.S. Marine Corps, 1965, advanced through grades to col., 1986; platoon comdr., co. comdr. 3d Bn. 4th Marine regiment, 1966-67, officer selection officer 9th Marine Corps Dist., 1967-69, basic tng. officer fighter/attack tng. Squadron 201, 1970-71, asst. maintenance officer Tng. Squadron 4, 1971-72, Fighter/Attack Squadron 232, 1973-74; standardization officer Fighter/Attack Squadron 212, 1974-76, aide-de-camp to comdg. gen. and plans officer Fleet Marine Force Pacific Hdqrs., 1976-78, exec. officer hdqrs. and maintenance squadron, Beaufort, S.C., 1979-80, comdg. officer Fighter/Attack Squadron 251, 1980-81, exec. officer Marine Aircraft Group 15, Japan, 1981-82, spl. ops. officer Hdqrs., Arlington, Va., 1982, spl. analyst Office Undersec. Def., Washington, 1983-84, comdg. officer Air Sta., Beaufort, 1985-87; asst. br. head Aviation Plans & Policies Br. Hdqrs. USMC, 1987—. Mem. Partnerships in Edn., Beaufort, 1985; mem. Japan-Am. Community Council, Japan, 1981-82; mem. PTA, Burke, Va., 1982-85; mem. Low Country council Boy Scouts Am., 1986; bd. dirs. Big Bros./Big Sisters of Beaufort, 1986. Decorated Silver Star, Purple Heart, Defense Meritorious Service medal; recipient Chgo. Tribune award, 1965, DAR award, 1965. Mem. U.S. Marine Corps Assn., U.S. Naval Aviation Mus. Soc., Marine Corps Aviation Assn., Beaufort C. of C. (Pres.'s award 1987), Phi Delta Theta. Lodge: Rotary. Avocations: Woodworking; scuba diving; sports; running. Home: 5420 Rilian Ct Burke VA 22015-2171 Office: USMC Office Of Brig Gen Cherry Point NC 28533

RICK, CHARLES MADEIRA, JR., geneticist, educator; b. Reading, Pa., Apr. 30, 1915; s. Charles Madeira and Miriam Charlotte (Yeager) R.; m. Martha Elizabeth Overholts, Sept. 3, 1938 (dec.); children: Susan Charlotte Rick Baldi, John Winfield. B.S., Pa. State U., 1937; AM, Harvard U., 1938, Ph.D., 1940. Asst. plant breeder W. Atlee Burpee Co., Lompoc, Calif., 1936, 37; instr., jr. geneticist U. Calif., Davis, 1940-44; asst. prof., asst. geneticist U. Calif., 1944-49, assoc. prof., assoc. geneticist, 1949-55, prof., geneticist, 1955—; chmn. coordinating com. Tomato Genetics Coop., 1950-82; dir. CMR Tomato Genetics Resource Ctr., 1975—; mem. genetics study sect. NIH, 1958-62; mem. Galapagos Internat. Sci. Project, 1964; mem. genetic biology panel NSF, 1971-72; mem. nat. plant genetics resources bd. Dept. Agr., 1975-82; Guy. Edn. Bd. vis. lectr. N.C. State U., 1956; Faculty Research lectr. U. Calif., 1961; Carnegie vis. prof. U. Hawaii, 1963; vis. prof. Universidade São Paulo, Brazil, 1965; vis. scientist U. P.R., 1968; centennial lectr. Ont. Agr. Coll. U. Guelph, Ont., Can., 1974; adj. prof. Univ. de Rosario, Argentina, 1980; univ. lectr. Cornell U., 1987; mem. Plant Breeding Research Forum, 1982-84. Contbr. numerous articles in field to books and sci. jours. Recipient award of distinction Coll. Agr. and Environ. Scis., U. Calif., Davis, 1991, Disting. Svc. award Calif. League Food Processors, 1993, Alexander von Humboldt award Alexander von Humboldt Found., 1993; grantee NSF, USPHS/NIH, Rockefeller Found., 1953-83; Guggenheim fellow, 1948, 50, Pa. State U. Alumni fellow, 1991; C.M. Rick Tomato Genetics Resource Ctr. at U. Calif., Davis named in his honor, 1990. Fellow Calif. Acad. Sci., AAAS (Campbell award 1959), Indian Soc. Genetics and Plant Breeding (hon.), Am. Soc. Horticultural Sci.; mem. Nat. Acad. Scis. Bot. Soc. Am. (Merit award 1976), Am. Soc. Hort. Sci. (M.A. Blake award 1974, Vaughan Research award 1946), Mass. Hort. Soc. (Thomas Roland medal 1983), Soc. Econ. Botany (named Disting. Econ. Botanist 1987), Nat.

Council Comml. Plant Breeders (Genetic and Plant Breeding award 1987), Am. Genetics Assn. (Frank N. Meyer medal 1982). Office: U Calif Davis CA 95616

RICKARD, LISA ANN, lawyer; b. Englewood, N.J., Oct. 22, 1955; d. Joseph Mitchell and Ann Marie (Samen) Moore; m. J. Scott Rickard, June 18, 1977; children: Jack Taylor, Justin Moore. BA in Govt. and French, Lafayette Coll., 1977; JD, Am. U., 1982. Legis. asst. Bank of Am., Washington, 1977-78; spl. asst. and press asst. to Sen. Richard Stone, Washington, 1978-80; legis. asst. to Sen. Frank Murkowski, Washington, 1981; assoc. and ptnr. Akin, Gump, Strauss, Haver & Feld, Washington, 1982-87; v.p. federal affairs Ryder System, Inc., Washington, 1993—; mem., corp. adv. coun. Women's Rsch. and Edn. Inst., Washington, 1991—. Polit. fundraiser various fed. dem. candidates. Diplome D'Etudes Francaises Cours Moyen, Deuxieme Degres, U. Strasbourg, France, 1976. Mem. D.C. Bar Assn. Episcopalian. Avocation: travel. Home: 10112 Darmuid Green Dr Potomac MD 20854 Office: Ryder System Inc Ste 580 1100 New York Ave NW Washington DC 20005

RICKARD, NORMAN EDWARD, office equipment company executive; b. Rochester, N.Y., Apr. 6, 1936; s. Norman E. and Florentine (Jensen) R.; m. Patricia Chester, Jan. 19, 1963 (dec. March 7, 1966); children: Anne, Margaret; m. Carol Miller, Apr. 6, 1968 (div. March 24, 1981); children: Sarah, Catherine, Elizabeth; m. Margaret S., June 6, 1981; stepchildren: Lee Ann, Sarah W. BA, St. John Fisher Coll., 1958; MBA, St. John's U., 1962; postgrad. study, NYU, 1962-64. Instr. St. John's U., N.Y.C., 1962-63; various fin. functions Oxford Paper Co., Rumford, Maine and N.Y.C., 1963-66; various positions planning, fin. Xerox Corp., Rochester, N.Y., 1966-71; controller, N.E. region Xerox Corp. U.S. Mktg., White Plains, N.Y., 1971-73; dir. internat. fin. Xerox Corp., Stamford, Conn., 1974-75; controller Xerox Corp., Rank Xerox, London, 1975-78; v.p. planning & control Xerox Corp., Worldwide Mfg., Stamford, 1978-81; dir. Xerox Corp., Stamford, 1981-87, v.p. quality, 1987-92; pres. Xerox Bus. Svcs., 1992—; trustee St. John Fisher Coll.; co-chair Total Quality Mgmt. Ctr., bd. dirs. Sr. examiner Malcolm Baldrige Nat. Quality Award, 1992-93. With U.S. Army, 1958-60. Mem. Assn. for Quality and Participation (bd. dirs. 1991-94), Whippoorwill Country Club, Stratton Mounty Country Club, Manchester Country Club. Republican. Roman Catholic. Office: Xerox Corp PO Box 1600 800 Long Ridge Rd Stamford CT 06902-1227

RICKARD, RUTH DAVID, retired history and political science educator; b. Fed. Republic Germany, Feb. 20, 1926; came to U.S., 1940; d. Carl and Alice (Koch) David; m. Robert M. Yaffe, Oct. 1949 (dec. 1959); children: David, Steven; m. Norman G. Rickard, June 1968 (dec. 1988); 1 stepson, Douglas. BS cum laude, Northwestern U., 1947, MA, 1948. Law editor Commerce Clearing House, Chgo., 1948; instr. history U. Ill., Chgo., 1949-51; instr. extension program U. Ill., Waukegan, 1960-67; instr. history Waukegan (Ill.) Schs., 1960-69; original faculty, prof. western civilization, polit. sci. Coll. of Lake County, Grayslake, Ill., 1969-92; mem. Inter-Univ. Seminar on Armed Forces and Soc. Author: History of College of Lake County, 1987 (honored by city of Waukegan 1987), (poem) I Lost My Wings, 1989, Au Revoir from Emeritusdom, 1993, Where are the Safety Zones, 1994; spkr. on various ind. radio and TV programs; contbr. articles to profl. jours. Mem. Econ. Devel. Commn., Waukegan, 1992-93. Scholar Freedoms Found. Am. Legion, Valley Forge, Pa., 1967. Mem. AAUW (pres. Waukegan chpt. 1955-57, scholarship named for her 1985; mem. McLean chpt. 1993—), LWV (charter, v.p.), Nat. Press Club (D.C.), Phi Beta Kappa. Avocations: writing, travel, reading, theater.

RICKARDS, LEONARD MYRON, oil company executive; b. Canton, N.C., Aug. 17, 1927; s. James Cooper and Ethel Naomi (Trull) R.; m. Pauline Hope Murray, Feb. 28, 1953; children—Tim Paul, Lisa Diane. BS, U. Kans., 1950; postgrad., European Inst. Bus. Adminstrn., Fountainbleau, France, 1974. With Phillips Petroleum Co., Bartlesville, Okla., 1950—; sr. v.p. Europe-Africa Phillips Petroleum Co., London, 1973-76; mgr. N.Am. exploration and prodn. div. Phillips Petroleum Co., Bartlesville, 1976-77, v.p. N.Am., 1977-80, sr. v.p. exploration and production, 1980-85, exec. v.p., bd. dirs., 1985-89, ret., 1989. Served with U.S. Coast Guard, 1945-46. Mem. Am. Assn. Petroleum Geologists, Am. Petroleum Inst. (past, bd. dirs.), Okla. Soc. Profl. Engrs., Sigma Tau, Tau Beta Pi, Theta Tau.

RICKART, CHARLES EARL, mathematician, educator; b. Osage City, Kans., June 28, 1913; s. Charles Day and Ola May (Brewer) R.; m. Annabel Esther Erickson, Mar. 31, 1942; children: Mark Charles, Eric Alan, Thomas Melvin. B.A., U. Kans., 1937, M.A., 1938; Ph.D., U. Mich., 1941. Peirce instr. math. Harvard U., 1941-43; mem. faculty Yale U., 1943—; prof. math., 1959-83, chmn. dept., 1959-65, Percey F. Smith prof. math., 1963-83, prof. emeritus, 1983—. Author: General Theory of Banach Algebras, 1960, Natural Function Algebras, 1979, Structuralism and Structures, 1994. Mem. AAAS, AAUP, Conn. Acad. Arts and Scis., Am. Math Soc., Math . Assn. of Am. Home: Evergreen Woods Apt 173 88 Notch Hill Rd North Branford CT 06471 Office: Yale U Dept Math New Haven CT 06520

RICKE, DAVID LOUIS, agricultural and environmental consultant; b. Greensburg, Ind., Aug. 21, 1942; s. Louis Vincent and Lois (Malone) R.; m. Susan Jane Spenceman, July 20, 1968; children: Stephanie, Elizabeth, Sarah, Emily. BS in Agri. Econs., Purdue U., 1964. Cert. to registry of environ. and agrl. profls. Nat. Alliance Profl. Crop Cons. Pres. R & R Farms, Inc., Greensburg, Ind., 1967-81; prin. David L. Ricke Cons. Svcs., Greensburg, Ind., 1981—. 1st Lt. U.S. Army, 1965-67. Mem. Am. Soc. Agronomy, Ind. Assn. Profl. Crop Cons. (pres. 1991-92), Am. Soc. Agrl. Cons. (cert. mem.), Nat. Alliance of Ind. Crop Cons., Optimists. Home and Office: 601 E Hendricks St Greensburg IN 47240

RICKELS, KARL, psychiatrist, physician, educator; b. Wilhelmshaven, Germany, Aug. 17, 1924; came to U.S., 1954, naturalized, 1959; s. Karl E. and Stephanie (Roehrhoff) R.; m. Rosalind Wilson, June 27, 1964; children: Laurence Arthur, Stephen W., Michael R. M.D., U. Frankfurt, 1951. Intern Dortmund (Germany) Hosp., 1951-52; postgrad. tng. U. Erlangen, U. Frankfurt, City Hosp. Kassel, 1952-54; resident in psychiatry Mental Health Inst., Cherokee, Iowa, 1954-55, Hosp. U. Pa., Phila., 1955-57; from instr. to assoc. prof. U. Pa., Phila., 1957-69; prof. psychiatry U. Pa., 1969—, prof. pharmacology, 1976—, Stuart and Emily B.H. Mudd prof. human behavior, 1977—, chief mood and anxiety disorders program, 1964—; chmn. com. on studies involving human beings U. Pa., Phila., 1985—; chief psychiatry Phila. Gen. Hosp., 1975-77. Editor, author 7 books; contbr. over 500 articles to profl. publs. Fellow Am. Coll. Neuropsychopharmacology (charter), Am. Coll. Clin. Pharmacology, Am. Psychiat. Assn., Coll. Physicians Phila., Collegium INternat. Neuro-Psychopharmacologicum; mem. Arbeits Gemeinschaft Neuro-Psychopharmacology, Internat. Soc. Investigation of Stress, European Coll. Neuropsychopharmacology (corr.). Home: 1324 Youngsford Rd Gladwyne PA 19035-1231 Office: U Pa Dept Psychiatry 803 Sci Ctr 3600 Market St Philadelphia PA 19104-2641

RICKER, JOHN BOYKIN, JR., insurance counselor; b. Augusta, Ga., Nov. 20, 1917; s. John B. and Emily Clark (Denny) R.; m. Jane Duncan Darling, Sept. 30, 1950; children: John, Robb Duncan. B.A., Southwestern Coll., 1938. Mgr. Cotton Fire and Marine Underwriters, Memphis, 1955-63; pres., chief exec. officer Marine Office of Am., N.Y.C., 1964-74; chmn. bd., pres., chief exec. officer Continental Corp., N.Y.C., 1976-82; with Internat. Ins. Counselors, Essex Fells, N.J., 1983—. Trustee Rhodes Coll., 1986—. Served with USNR, 1942-46. Decorated Bronze Star. Mem. Am. Inst. Marine Underwriters (past pres.), Essex Fells Country Club. Republican. Episcopalian. Office: 11th Fl 180 Maiden Ln New York NY 10038

RICKER, WILLIAM EDWIN, biologist; b. Waterdown, Ont., Can., Aug. 11, 1908; s. Harry Edwin and Rebecca Helena (Rouse) R.; m. Marion Torrance Cardwell, Mar. 30, 1935; children—Karl Edwin, John Fraser, Eric William, Angus Clemens. B.A., U. Toronto, 1930, M.A., 1931, Ph.D., 1936; D.Sc. (hon.), U. Man., 1970; LL.D., Dalhousie U., 1972. Sci. asst. Fisheries Research Bd. Can., Nanaimo, B.C., 1931-38; editor publs. Fisheries Research Bd. Can., Nanaimo, 1950-62, biol. cons. to chmn. and staff, 1962-63; acting chmn. Fisheries Research Bd. Can., Ottawa, 1963-64; chief scientist Internat. Pacific Salmon Fisheries Commn., New Westminster, B.C., 1938-39; asst. prof., assoc. prof., prof. zoology Ind. U., 1939-50; dir. Ind. Lake and Stream Survey Ind. Dept.

Conservation, 1939-50; vol., contract investigator Pacific Biol. Sta., Nanaimo, 1973-95. Contbr. articles to profl. jours. Decorated officer Order of Can., 1986; named Eminent Ecologist Ecol. Soc. Am., 1990; recipient Murray Newman award Vancouver Aquarium, 1995. Fellow Royal Soc. Can. (Flavelle medal 1970), AAAS; mem. Wildlife Soc. (awards 1956, 59), Profl. Inst. Pub. Service Can. (gold medal 1966), Am. Fisheries Soc. (award of excellence 1969), Can. Soc. Zoologists (F.E.J. Fry medal 1983), Am. Soc. Limnology and Oceanography (pres. 1959), Arctic Inst. N.Am., Can. Soc. Wildlife and Fishery Biologists, Entomol. Soc. B.C., Internat. Assn. Limnology, Marine Biol. Assn. India, Ottawa Field-Naturalists Club, Wilson Ornithol. Club, Explorers Club, Sigma Xi. Home: 3052 Hammond Bay Rd, Nanaimo, BC Canada V9T 1E2

RICKERD, DONALD SHERIDAN, foundation executive; b. Smiths Falls, Ont., Can., Nov. 8, 1931; s. Harry M. and Evaline Mildred (Sheridan) R.; m. Julie Rekai, Dec. 14, 1968; 1 child, Christopher. Student, St. Andrews U., Scotland, 1951-52; BA, Queen's U., Can., 1953; LLD, Queen's U., 1985; BA (Rotary Found. fellow), Oxford U., Eng., 1955, MA, 1963; DCL, Mount Allison U., Can., 1985; LLD, Trent U., Can., 1986; LLB, York U., Can., 1991. Bar: Ont. 1959; apptd. Queen's Counsel, 1978. Assoc. Fasken & Calvin, Toronto, 1957-61; registrar, lectr. history, asst. prof. law Faculty of Adminstrv. Studies York U., Toronto, 1961-68; pres. Donner Can. Found., Toronto, 1968-89, W.H. Donner Found., Inc., N.Y.C., 1971-87, Max Bell Found., Toronto, 1989—; chmn. bd. dirs. Draeger Can. Ltd.; bd. dirs. ICWI Found., Kingston, Jamaica. Former chmn. coun. Ont. Coll. Art., Toronto; bd. dirs., chmn. Ctrl. Hosp.; mem. Royal Commn. concerning Activities of Royal Can. Mounted Police, 1977-81; former bd. govs. Upper. Can. Coll., Toronto; trustee Queen's U.; former bd. regents Mt. Allison U. Decorated Order of Can. Mem. Can. Bar Assn., County of York Law Assn., Toronto Lawyers Club, Bd. Trade Met. Toronto, Univ. Club. Office: Max Bell Found, PO Box 105, 79 Wellington St W, Toronto, ON Canada M5K 1G8

RICKERT, JONATHAN BRADLEY, foreign service officer; b. Washington, July 23, 1937; s. Van Dusen and Margaret Eleanor (Bradley) R.; m. Ulla Gerd Margareta Granstrand, June 20, 1969; children: Ulla Margaret, Jonathan Bernt. AB cum laude, Princeton U., 1959; diploma Russian lang., U.S. Army Lang. Sch., 1962; student, Harvard U., 1976-77; MA, George Washington U., 1982. Rotational jr. officer Exec. Sec. State Dept., 1963-65; consular officer Embassy, London, 1965-66; staff aide to amb., polit. officer Embassy, Moscow, 1966-68; exchanges officer Office Soviet and Eastern European Exchanges State Dept., 1969-70, with Romanian Lang. Tng. FSI, 1971; consular officer Embassy Bucharest, 1971-73, polit. officer, 1973-74; spl. asst. to U.S. Rep. U.S. Delegation MBFR, Vienna, 1974-76; polit./labor officer Embassy Port Spain, 1977-80; desk officer Trinidad, Guyana, Suriname, acting dir. Office Caribbean Affairs State Dept., 1980-82, desk officer Romania, Office Eastern European and Yugoslav Affairs, 1982-84, with Bulgarian Lang. Tng., 1984-85; dep. chief mission Embassy Sofia, 1985-88; chief European assignments divsn. State Dept., 1988-90; legis. asst. to Sen Bob Packwood, 1990-91; dep. chief mission Embassy Bucharest, 1991-95. With U.S. Army, 1961-62. Mem. Am. Fgn. Svc. Assn. Episcopalian.

RICKETTS, GARY EUGENE, animal scientist; b. Willard, Ohio, Aug. 2, 1935; s. Franklin Edward and Berthalda Marie (Albright) R.; m. Audrey May Wheeler, Sept. 14, 1958; children—Dawn, John, Mark. B.S., Ohio State U., 1957, M.S., 1960, Ph.D., 1963. Livestock extension specialist dept. animal sci. U. Ill., Urbana-Champaign, 1964-86, sheep extension specialist and extension program leader, 1986—. Contbr. articles to profl. jours. and livestock publs. Active Little League Baseball, 8 yrs.; leader 4-H Club, 11 yrs. Served with Army N.G., 1958-64. Recipient Beef Booster award Ill. Red Angus Assn., 1973, G. R. Carlisle Extension award, 1979, Outstanding Leadership and Recognition award Ill. Sheep Industry, 1984, Sustained Excellence award in extension Ill. Coop. Extension Service, 1984, J.C. Spitler award Epsilon Sigma Phi, 1984, Guy Green award Am. Corriedale Assn., 1992. Mem. Am. Soc. Animal Sci. (Young Scientist award Midwest sect. 1971, Extension award 1984), Am. Registry Profl. Animal Scientists. Republican. Methodist. Home: 2506 S Cottage Grove Ave Urbana IL 61801-6820 Office: 128 ASL 1207 W Gregory Dr Urbana IL 61801-3838

RICKETTS, THOMAS ROLAND, bank executive; b. Detroit, Mar. 4, 1931; s. Samuel Charles and Lillian May (Schwab) R.; m. Priscilla Anne Irving, Aug. 10, 1957; children: Robert T., Karen L. B.B.A., U. Mich., 1953, J.D., 1956. Bar: Mich. 1956. With Standard Fedn. Bank, Troy, Mich., 1956—; branch mgr. Standard Fed. Savs. Bank, Troy, Mich., 1958-62, v.p. advertising, pub. relations, personnel, 1962-70, sr. v.p., treas., 1970-72, exec. v.p., chief adminstrv. officer, 1972-73, pres., chief adminstrv. officer, 1973-74, pres., mng. officer, 1974-81, chmn. bd., pres., mng. officer, 1981—, also bd. dirs.; pres. Savs. Instns. Mktg. Soc. Am., 1968, bd. dirs., 1965-69; pres. Mich. Savs. and Loan League, 1976, bd. dirs. 1975-78; mem. adv. com. Fed. Savs. and Loan Ins. Corp., 1989. Trustee Olivet Coll. 1973-87, Savs. and Loan Found., 1978-82, Detroit Symphony Orch., 1980—, Citizens Rsch. Coun. Mich., 1981—; bd. dirs. United Found., Detroit, 1978—, Detroit-Wayne County Port Authority, 1984-88, Detroit Econ. Growth Corp., 1984—, Detroit Econ. Growth Fund, 1984—; bd. dirs. New Detroit, Inc., 1978—, chmn. Mich. Infrastructure Coalition, 1993-87; mem. Gov.'s Commn. on Jobs and Econ. Devel., 1983-90. Mem. State Bar Mich., U.S. League of Savs. Instn. (govt. affairs com. 1976-93, bd. dirs. 1983-86), Mich. League of Savs. Instn. (legis. and legis. policy coms. 1971-93), Econ. Club Detroit (Bd. dirs. 1989-93). Office: Std Fed Bank 2600 W Big Beaver Rd Troy MI 48084-3323

RICKEY, GEORGE WARREN, artist, sculptor, educator; b. South Bend, Ind., June 6, 1907; s. Walter J. and Grace (Landon) R.; m. Edith Leighton, May 24, 1947; children: Stuart Ross, Philip J. L. Ed., Trinity Coll., Glenalmond, Scotland, 1921-26; B.A., Balliol Coll., Oxford U., 1929, M.A., 1940; postgrad., Académie Lhote, Paris, 1929-30, Inst. Fine Arts, NYU, 1945-46, Stale U. Iowa, 1947, Inst. Design, Chgo., 1948-49; hon. doctorates, Union Coll., Schenectady, 1973, Ind. U., 1974, Kalamazoo Coll., 1977, York U., Can., 1978, Tulane U., 1983, Rensselaer Polytechnic Inst., Troy, N.Y., 1990. Tchr. Groton Sch., 1930-33; artist-in-residence Olivet Coll., 1937-39, Kalamazoo Coll., 1939-40, Knox Coll., 1940-41; head dept. art Muhlenberg Coll., 1941-42, 46-48; assoc. prof. design Ind. U., Bloomington, 1949-55; prof. Tulane U., New Orleans, 1955-61, head dept., 1955-59; prof. art Sch. Architecture Rensselaer Poly. Inst., Troy, N.Y., 1962-65. Sculptor, DAAD Art Program, Berlin, Germany, 1968-69, 71-72. Exhibited Denver Mus., 1945, 48, Met. Mus. Art, 1951, Pa. Acad. Ann., 1952-54, Whitney Mus., 1952-53, 64, Mus. Modern Art, 1959, Albright-Knox Gallery, 1965, Mus. Modern Art Internat. Council, 1965, Stedelijk Mus., Amsterdam, Holland, 1965, Mus. Tel Aviv, 1965, St. Louis Bicentennial Sculpture Exhbn., 1965, Dag Hammerskjold Plaza, N.Y.C., 1977, Pier and Ocean, Hayward Gallery, London, 1980, Whitney Mus., 1983, Neuer Berliner Kunstverein, 1987, Am. Fedn. Arts, 1991, Found. Maeght, France, 1992, other U.S. and fgn. galleries; one man shows: John Herron Art Mus., Indpls., 1953, Delgado Mus., New Orleans, 1955, Kraushaar Gallery, 1955, 1959, Amerika Haus, Hamburg, Germany, 1957, Santa Barbara Mus., 1960, Kunstverein, Düsseldorf, Fed. Republic Germany, 1962, Kunsthalle, Hamburg, 1962, Inst. Contemporary Arts, Boston, 1964, Corcoran Gallery, Washington, 1966, UCLA, 1971, Kestner Gesellschaft, Hannover, 1973, Nationalgalerie, Berlin, 1973-74, Amerika Haus, Berlin, 1979, Guggenheim Mus., 1979, Montreal Musée d'Art Contemporain, 1981, Nat. Sculpture Trust, Glasgow, Scotland, 1982, Sculpture Park, Yorkshire, Eng., 1982, Fairweather Hardin Gallery, 1982, Tulane U. Art Gallery, New Orleans, 1983, Bauhaus Archiv., Berlin, Fed. Republic Germany, 1984, Josef Albers Mus., Bottrop, Fed. Republic Germany, 1984, George Rickey in South Bend, 1985, Neuer Berliner Kunstverein, Berlin, 1986, Neuberger Mus., Purchase, N.Y., 1987, Veranneman Found., Holland, 1988, Mus. Boymans-van Beuningen, Rotterdam, Holland, 1989, Gallery Kasahara, Osaka, Japan, 1989, Artcurial, Paris, 1990, Katonah Mus. Art, 1991, Berlinische Galerie, Berlin, 1992, Foundation Maeght, Vence, France, 1992, UCLA Wright Art Gallery, L.A., 1993, Harenberg Verlag Dortmund, Germany, 1994, numerous others; represented in permanent collections: Dallas Mus., Kunsthalle, Hamburg, Whitney Mus., Mus. Modern Art, Albright-Knox Gallery, Tate Gallery, London, U. Glasgow, U. Heidelberg, Nationalgalerie, Berlin, Corcoran Gallery of Arts, Washington, Louisiana Mus., Humlebaek, Denmark, Auckland City Art Gallery, New Zealand, Tokyo City Hall, Japan, City of Nurnberg, Germany, Nat. Mus. Fine Art, Osaka, Japan, New Theatre, Rotterdam, Parliament Bldg., Dusseldorf, Fed. Republic Germany, Hara Mus., Tokyo, Berlinische

Galerie, Berlin, others, also pvt. collections; executed commns. Ft. Worth City Hall, 1974, Fed. Courthouse, Honolulu, 1976. Tech. U., Ulm, Germany, 1977, Ruhr U., Bochum, Ger., 1978, K.B. Plaza, New Orleans, 1978, Central Trust Center, Cin., 1979, Nat. City Ctr., Cleve., 1980, Pitts. Nat. Steel Ctr., 1982, Gerald Ford Library, Ann Arbor, Mich., 1982, Musée de Grenoble, France, 1991, Nat. Gallery, Washington, 1992, Martin Gropius Bau, Berlin, 1992, Nat. Mus. of Fine Arts, Osaka, 1993, Met. Mus. of Art, N.Y.C., 1994; author: Constructivism: Origins and Evolution, 1967, 95; contbr. to pubis. in field. Decorated Order of Merit 1st Class, Germany, 1993; recipient Fine Arts medal AIA, 1972, Skowhegan medal for sculpture Skowhegan Sch. Painting and Sculpture, 1973, Ind. Arts. Commn. award for sculpture, 1975, Creative Arts Award medal Brandeis U., 1979; Guggenheim fellow, 1960-62. Mem. Am. Acad. Arts and Letters (Gold medal for sculpture 1995), Coll. Art Assn., Akademie der Kunste (Berlin). Episcopalian. Club: Century Assn. (N.Y.C.).

RICKLES, DONALD JAY, comedian, actor; b. L.I., N.Y., May 8, 1926; s. Max S. and Etta (Feldman) R.; m. Barbara Sklar, Mar. 14, 1965; children: Mindy Beth, Lawrence Corey. Grad., Am. Acad. Dramatic Arts, N.Y.C. Appeared in TV shows The Don Rickles Show, 1971-72, C.P.O. Sharkey, 1976-77, Foul-Ups, Bleeps and Blunders, 1984, Daddy Dearest, 1993; appeared in movies Run Silent, Run Deep, 1958, The Rabbit Trap, 1959, The Rat Race, 1960, Where It's At, 1969, Innocent Blood, 1992, Kelly's Heroes, 1992, Casino, 1995, Toy Story, 1995, others; appeared as comedian at MGM Grand Hotel, Las Vegas, Nev., Harrah's Club, Reno and Lake Tahoe, Nev., Caesar's Palace, Atlantic City, numerous other nightclubs; numerous appearances TV variety shows; rec. albums include Don Rickles Speaks. Served with USN, 1943-45. Named Entertainer of Yr., Friars Club, 1974. Jewish. Avocation: golfing. Office: care Shefrin Co 800 S Robertson Blvd Los Angeles CA 90035-1606

RICKLIN, ARTHUR H., hospital administrator; b. N.Y.C., Aug. 30, 1934; s. Solomon and Betty (Hirsch) R.; m. Janet Jacobson, Nov. 24, 1954; children: Jonathan H., Leslie J. BS, NYU, 1956; postgrad., NYU Sch. Pub. Adminstrn., 1964-69. Lic. physiotherapist; lic. nursing home adminstr., N.Y. Chief phys. therapist Misericordia Hosp., Bronx, N.Y., 1958-64; adminstrv. asst. Misericordia-Fordham Hosp., Bronx, 1964-65; dir. Albert Einstein Hosp., Evelyn & Joseph I. Lubin Rehab. Ctr., Bronx, 1965-66; asst. adminstr. Hosp. of Albert Einstein Coll. Medicine, Bronx, 1967-72, sr. asst. adminstr., 1972-73, adminstr., 1973-79; assoc. dir. Montefiore Hosp. Med. Ctr., Bronx, 1979-83; adminstr. Blvd. Hosp., Long Island City, N.Y., 1983-84; assoc. hosp. dir. NYU Med. Ctr., 1984-85; pres. Rehab. Resources Inc., 1985—; prin. assoc. dept. rehab. medicine, assoc. dept. community health Albert Einstein Coll. Medicine; asst. prof. allied health div. phys. therapy Ithaca Coll., 1973—; clin. assoc. Health Professions Inst., Herbert H. Lehman Coll., CUNY; chmn. com. on weekend admission policy for Bronx Profl. Standards Rev. Orgn., 1979; cons., chmn. bd. Health Care Facilities Rehab. Programs U.S.A., Inc.; cons., lectr. in field. Lavanburg Cornerhouse scholar NYU. Mem. Am. Hosp. Assn., Am. Pub. Health Assn., Hosp. Execs. Club N.Y., Greater N.Y. Hosp. Assn., Am. Phys. Therapy Assn. (vice chmn. Greater N.Y. dist. 1965-67, dist. dir. 1968-72, Disting. Svc. award N.Y. state chpt. 1972), Royal Soc. Health (London), Pub. Health Assn. N.Y.C., Am. Soc. Law and Medicine, Am. Coll. Utilization Rev. Physicians. Home and Office: 19 Lookout Pl Ardsley NY 10502-1201

RICKMAN, ALAN, actor; b. London, 1946. Student, Royal Acad. of Dramatic Arts. Stage appearances: Measure for Measure, Mephisto, Les Liaisons Dangereuses, 1985, 87 (Tony award Best Actor 1987), Tango at the End of Winter, 1991, Desperately Yours (also director), 1980; TV: Romeo and Juliet, Masterpiece Theater-Therese Raquin, Smiley's People, Barchester Chronicles; films: Die Hard, 1988, The January Man, 1989, Robin Hood: Prince of Thieves, 1989, Quigley Down Under, 1990, Truly, Madly, Deeply, 1991, Closet Land, 1991, Close my Eyes, 1991, Bob Roberts, 1992, Mesmer, 1994, An Awfully Big Adventure, 1995. Office: Jusy Holland Interlatent Agy Penthouse 25 9200 Sunset Blvd Los Angeles CA 90069*

RICKMAN, TOM, screenwriter, director; b. Sharpe, Ky., Feb. 8, 1940; s. Marshall and Mattie Colleen (Johnston) R. BA, Murray State Coll., 1965; MA, U. Ill., 1969. Fellow Am. Film Inst., Beverly Hills, Calif., 1969-71; founder, dir. Squaw Valley (Calif.) Screenwriters Workshop, 1975—; resource advisor Sundance (Utah) Inst., 1981—, trustee, 1981-88; instr. grad. course in screenwriting U. So. Calif., L.A., 1987. Writer, dir. (short film) What Fixed Me, 1971 (Best Film award Nat. Student Assn. 1971), (feature film) The River Rat, 1984, (TV movie) Shannon's Deal: Wrongful Death, 1991; writer (feature films) The Laughing Policeman, 1973, W.W. and the Dixie Dancekings, 1975, Coal Miner's Daughter, 1980 (Academy award nomination best adapted screenplay 1980), Everybody's All-American, 1988; cowriter (feature films) Kansas City Bomber, 1972, The White Dawn, 1974, Hooper, 1978; author (play) The Collaborators, 1981. Served with USMC, 1958-61. *

RICKS, DONALD JAY, agricultural economist; b. Lansing, Mich., Sept. 14, 1936; s. Glenn L. and Evelyn N. R.; m. Joanne M. Burr, Aug. 24, 1968; children: Mark, Craig. B.S. with highest honors, Mich. State U., 1958, M.S., 1960; Ph.D., Oreg. State U., 1965. Instr. econs. Oreg. State U., 1962-63, asst. in agrl. econs., 1963-64; asst. prof. agrl. econs. Mich. State U., 1964-70, assoc. prof., 1970-76, prof., 1976—, extension mktg. economist, 1973—; project leader, extension mktg., 1976-82; chmn. Fed. Cherry Adminstrv. Bd.; mem. Mich. Apple Com. Contbr. numerous articles to various pubis. Recipient State Extension Team award, 1971, Man of Yr. award Nat. Cherry Industry, 1989. Mem. Am. Agrl. Econs. Assn., Extension Specialists Assn., Mich. Assn. County Agts. (Outstanding Extension Specialist award 1982), Mich. Extension Specialists Assn. (Outstanding Extension Specialist award 1989), Phi Kappa Phi, Epsilon Sigma Phi, Phi Eta Sigma, Alpha Zeta. Home: 953 Barry Rd Haslett MI 48840-9104 Office: Room 23 Agr Hall Mich State U East Lansing MI 48823

RICKS, MARY FRANCES, university administrator, anthropologist; b. Portland, Oreg., July 6, 1939; d. Leo and Frances Helen (Corcoran) Samuel; m. Robert Stanley Ricks, Jan. 7, 1961; children: Michael Stanley, Allen Gilbert. BA, Whitman Coll., 1961; MA, Portland State U., 1977, MPA, 1981, PhD, 1995. Asst. to dir. auxiliary services Portland State U., 1975-79, instnl. researcher, 1979-85, dir. instnl. research and planning, 1985—, rsch. assoc. prof., 1994—. Contbr. articles and presentations to profl. socs. Vol. archeologist BLM-USDI, Lakeview, Oreg., 1983—. Fellow Soc. Applied Anthropology; mem. Soc. Am. Archaeology, Soc. Coll. and U. Planning, Pacific N.W. Assn. Instnl. Rsch. and Planning (pres. 1990-91), Assn. Oreg. Archaeologists (v.p. 1988-90), Assn. Instnl. Rsch., City Club of Portland, Sigma Xi. Home: 5466 SW Dover Loop Portland OR 97225-1033 Office: Portland State U Office Instnl Rsch/Planning PO Box 751 Portland OR 97207-0751

RICKS, THOMAS EDWIN, accounting executive; b. Salt Lake City, May 4, 1946; s. Ben E. and Afton (Bawden) R.; m. Virginia Richey, Aug. 21, 1968; children: Leslie, Thomas Jr., Brian, Brent, Susannah, Stephen. BS in Acctg. cum laude, Weber State Coll., 1972. CPA, Calif., Tex. Audit sr. Arthur Anderson & Co., Los Angeles, 1972-75; internal audit supr. So. Calif. Edison Co., Rosemead, 1975-77; internal audit mgr. El Paso (Tex.) Natural Gas Co., 1977-80, gen. acctg. mgr., 1982-83; fin. forecast dir., 1982-83; asst. v.p. acctg. Burlington No. Co., Seattle, 1983-85; v.p., controller, chief acctg. officer El Paso (Tex.) Natural Gas Co., 1985—. Active Boy Scouts Am., El Paso, 1977; dir. Jr. Achievement, El Paso, 1985—. Mem. Am. Gas Assn. (mem. adv. com.), Interstate Natural Gas Assn., Am. Inst. CPA's, Tex. Soc. CPA's, Phi Kappa Phi. Republican. Mormon. Avocations: fishing, hunting, camping, sports, old car collecting. Home: 6364 La Posta Dr El Paso TX 79912 Office: El Paso Natural Gas Co PO Box 1492 El Paso TX 79978-0001

RIDDELL, MATTHEW DONALD RUTHERFORD, consulting environmental engineer; b. Toronto, Ont., Can., Mar. 13, 1918; s. Matthew Rutherford and Edith (Downs) R.; m. Dorothy Jane Williams, Oct. 2, 1948; children: James, David, Ann. S.B., Harvard U., 1940, M.S. in San. Engring., 1946. Registered profl. engr., Ill., Mich., Wis. With Greeley & Hansen, Chgo., 1946—; ptnr. Greeley & Hansen, 1957-85, cons., 1986—; mem. water resources tech. adv. com. Northeastern Ill. Planning Commn., 1968—. Pres., bd. dirs. Glenview (Ill.) Pub. Library, 1970-71. Served with USNR, 1941-46.

Named Chgo. Civil Engr. of Year, 1975. Mem. ASCE, Am. Acad. Environ. Engrs. (trustee 1969-75, pres. 1980-81), Am. Water Works Assn., Central States Water Pollution Control Assn., Am. Pub. Works Assn., Inst. Water Resources (pres. 1979-80, hon. 1986), Phi Beta Kappa, Delta Omega, Tau Beta Pi. Clubs: Union League (Chgo.). Home: 1215 Elm St Glenview IL 60025-2809 Office: 100 S Wacker Dr Chicago IL 60606-4003

RIDDELL, RICHARD ANDERSON, naval officer; b. Cambridge, Md., Nov. 20, 1940; s. Edward Leo and Katherine Francis (Insley) R.; m. Anne Price Fortney, May 10, 1986; children: Joel Anderson, Amy Kirsten. BS, U.S. Naval Acad., 1962. Commd. ensign USN, 1962, advanced through grades to rear adm., 1991; exec. officer USS Spadefish USN, Norfolk, Va., 1973-76; comdg. officer USS Nautilus USN, New London, Conn., 1976-80, dep. comdr. submarine squadron 2, 1980-81; spl. asst to dir. naval nuclear propulsion program Dept. Navy USN, Washington, 1981-84, dep. dir. strategic policy div. Dept. Navy, 1984-86; comdr. submarine squadron 1 USN, Pearl Harbor, Hawaii, 1986-88, chief of staff Pacific submarine force, 1988-90; dir. strategic submarine div. Dept. Navy USN, Washington, 1990-92; comdr. Submarine Group 9/Comdr. Naval Base, Seattle, 1992-94; dir. spl. programs OPNAV Dept. Navy, The Pentagon, Washington, 1994—. Mem. U.S. Naval Inst. Office: The Pentagon Spl Programs OPNAV Navy Dept 5D660 Washington DC 20350-2000

RIDDELL, RICHARD HARRY, retired lawyer; b. Seattle, Nov. 29, 1916; s. Charles F. and Kathryn (Wykoff) R.; m. Dolores Gloyd, Feb. 10, 1970; children by previous marriage: Dorothea R. Alleyne, Wendy, Kathryn R. Reeves, Mark W. A.B., Stanford, 1938; LL.B., Harvard, 1941. Bar: Wash. 1941. Ptnr. Riddell, Williams, Bullitt and Walkinshaw and predecessor firms, Seattle, 1941-92; ret., 1992. Chmn. Seattle Transit Commn., 1971. Fellow Am. Coll. Trial Lawyers; mem. ABA, County Bar Assn. (pres. 1963-64), Wash. State Bar Assn. (pres. 1976-77). Clubs: Seattle Tennis, Rainier (Seattle), Spanish Trail Golf (Las Vegas). Home: 7833 Rancho Mirage Dr Las Vegas NV 89113

RIDDER, BERNARD HERMAN, JR., newspaper publisher; b. N.Y.C., Dec. 8, 1916; s. Bernard Herman and Nell (Findley) R.; m. Jane Delano, Feb. 24, 1939; children: Laura, Paul A., Peter, Robin, Jill. B.A., Princeton U., 1938. Advt. dir. Duluth News-Tribune, 1941-42, gen. mgr., 1947-52; pub., 1952-72; pub. St. Paul Dispatch-Pioneer Press, 1959-73; pres. Ridder Publs., Inc., 1969—; chmn. bd. Knight-Ridder Newspapers, 1979-83; dir. AP, 1954-64, Seattle Times;. Served from ensign to lt. USNR, 1942-45. Recipient Journalism award U. Minn., also Regents award. Mem. U.S. Golf Assn. (mem. exec. com. 1958-64), Inland Daily Press Assn. (pres. 1954). Clubs: Royal and Ancient Golf (St. Andrews, Scotland); Somerset Country (St. Paul); Augusta Nat. Golf (Ga.), Gulf Stream Golf (Delray Beach, Fla.). Office: St Paul Pioneer Press NW Publ Inc 345 Cedar St Saint Paul MN 55101-1014

RIDDER, DANIEL HICKEY, newspaper publisher; b. N.Y.C., May 3, 1922; s. Bernard Herman and Nell (Hickey) R.; m. Frani Cooper Ackerman, Oct. 13, 1971; children by previous marriage: Daniel Hickey, Randy Helen, Richard J. AB, Princeton U., 1943. Reporter N.Y. Jour. Commerce, Grand Forks (N.D.) Herald; pub. St. Paul Dispatch and Pioneer-Press, 1952-58; co-pub. Long Beach (Calif.) Ind. Press-Telegram, 1958-69, pub., 1969-88; chmn. Long Beach (Calif.) Ind. Press-Telegram, Long Beach, Calif., 1988-90; mem. operating com. Knight-Ridder, Inc., Long Beach, Calif., 1989-94; bd. dirs. AP, 1975-84; v.p. Knight-Ridder, Inc., 1975-89. Chmn. bd. St. Mary Med. Ctr., 1987-92; past bd. dirs. Sta. KCET, L.A. 1988; Newspaper Advt. Bur., L.A. County Mus. Art, Calif., 1974-84; past chmn. bd. trustees Calif. State U. and Colls.; trustee Long Beach Mus. Art; vice chmn. bd. govs. Calif. Community Found. Lt. (j.g.) USN, 1942-46, ETO, PTO. Clubs: Virginia Country (Long Beach, Calif.); El Dorado Country (Palm Springs, C(life); L.A. Country; Cypress Point (Pebble Beach, Calif.). Home: 5531 Bryant Dr E Long Beach CA 90815-4111 Office: Knight-Ridder Inc 604 Pine Ave Long Beach CA 90844-0001

RIDDER, ERIC, newspaper publisher; b. Hewlett, L.I., N.Y., July 1, 1918; s. Joseph E. and Hedwig (Schneider) R.; m. Ethelette Tucker, 1939 (div.); children: Eric, Susan; m. Madeleine Graham, 1955 (dec. Nov. 1991). Student, Harvard U., 1936-37. Entire career in newspaper work; dir. Seattle Times Co., Knight-Ridder Newspapers, Inc. Trustee South St. Seaport Mus. Republican. Roman Catholic. Clubs: Seawanhaka-Corinthian Yacht (N.Y.C.), Piping Rock (N.Y.C.), N.Y. Yacht (N.Y.C.), India House (N.Y.C.); Royal Swedish Yacht. Home: Piping Rock Rd Locust Valley NY 11560-2208 Office: 2 World Trade Ctr Fl 27 New York NY 10048-0298

RIDDER, PAUL ANTHONY, newspaper executive; b. Duluth, Minn., Sept. 22, 1940; s. Bernard H. and Jane (Delano) R.; m. Constance Louise Meach, Nov. 6, 1960; children: Katherine Lee Pennoyer, Linda Jane, Susan Delano Cobb, Paul Anthony, Jr. B.A. in Econs., U. Mich., 1962. Staff writer With Aberdeen (S.D.) Am. News, 1962-63; With Pasadena (Calif.) Star News, 1963-64; with San Jose (Calif.) Mercury News, 1964-86, bus. mgr., 1968-75, gen. mgr., 1975-77, pub., 1977-86, pres., 1979-86; pres. Knight-Ridder Newspaper Div., Miami, Fla., 1986—; pres. Knight-Ridder, Inc., Miami, 1989—, also bd. dirs.; bd. dirs. Seattle Times, Knight-Ridder, Inc., Newspaper First. B. dirs. United Way; mem. adv. bd. Ctr. for Econ. Policy Devel. Stanford U., U. Mich.; mem. pres.' adv. bd. U. Mich. Named Calif. Pub. of Yr., 1983, Newspaper Exec. of Yr., Ad Week, 1991. Mem. Fla. C. of C. (bd. dirs., coun. of 100), Cypress Point Club, Indian Creek Club, Pine Valley Golf Club. *

RIDDERHEIM, DAVID SIGFRID, hospital administrator; b. Providence, Apr. 26, 1936; married. BA, Brown U., 1958; MA, U. Minn., 1960. Adminstrv. res. St. Luke's Hosp., Cleve., 1959-60, adminstrv. asst., 1960; assoc. adminstr. Parkview Meml. Hosp., Ft. Wayne, Ind., 1963-77, adminstr., 1977-84, exec. v.p., 1985-91, pres., 1989-91, pres., CEO, 1991—; adj. educator in field. Contbr. articles to profl. jours. Mem. Ind. Hosp. Assn. (community svc.). Home: 8508 Gerig Rd Leo IN 46765 Office: Parkview Meml Hosp 2200 Randallia Dr Fort Wayne IN 46805-4699

RIDDICK, DANIEL HOWISON, obstetrics and gynecology educator, priest; b. Lynchburg, Va., Dec. 12, 1941; s. Joseph Henry and Nancy Eloise (Gordon) R.; m. Louisa McIntosh Spruill, June 9, 1963; children: Ellen, Daniel. BA, Duke U., 1963, MD, 1967, PhD in Physiology, 1969. Diplomate Am. Bd. Ob-Gyn, Am. Bd. Reproductive Endocrinology; ordained priest Episc. Ch., 1969. Asst. prof. physiology Duke U., Durham, N.C., 1973-74; asst. prof. ob-gyn U. Conn. Sch. Medicine, Farmington, 1974-76, dir. reproductive endocrinology and infertility, 1974-85, assoc. prof. ob-gyn, 1976-81, prof. ob-gyn, 1981-85; prof., chmn. ob-gyn dept. U. Vt., Burlington, 1985—, assoc. dean grad. med. edn., 1987-88. Editor: Reproductive Endocrinology in Clinical Practice, 1987; editor: (with others) Pathology of Infertility, 1987. Mem. ACOG, Am. Fertility Soc. (pres. 1992-93), Am. Gynecol. and Obstet. Soc. Avocation: sheep-raising. Home: 680 Mayo Rd Huntington VT 54462 Office: Fletcher Allen Health Care Dept of Obstetrics & Gynecology 111 Colchester Ave Burlington VT 05401-1473

RIDDICK, DOUGLAS SMITH, horticultural industrialist, industrial designer; b. High Point, N.C., Sept. 28, 1942; s. Delmar Smith and Irene Douglas (Sparks) R.; m. Marcia Ann, Feb. 24, 1968; children: Eric Smith, Adrea Anne. Student, Columbus (Ohio) Coll. Art and Design, 1961-65, U. Bridgeport, 1965-66; BFA, U. Del., 1978. Indsl. designer Harper Landell & Assocs., Phila., 1967-70, ILC Industries, Dover, Del., 1970-75, Leeds Travelwear, Clayton, Del., 1975-76, DuPont Co., Glasgow, Del., 1976-79, Consumer Electronics Div. RCA, Indpls., 1979-80; designer Brayton Internat. Coll., High Point, N.C., 1981; owner Riddick Landscape Nursery, Archdale, N.C., 1980—; greenhouses and nursery mgr. Riddick Garden Ctr. and Landscaping, Inc., Archdale, N.C., 1980—. Patentee; designer insdl. instruments in field. Mem. Dover Bicentennial Com., 1975-76, Gov. DuPont's Com. Promotion of Solar Energy and subcom. Consumer Protection, 1978-79. Recipient Best in Packaging award Print Casebooks III, Washington. 1977, Excellence in Advt. award Am. Assn. Nurserymen, 1981. Mem. AAAS, Am. Horticultural Soc., Nat. Space Soc., Planetary Soc. Baptist. Club: Bicycle Club Del. (coordinator 1974-78, pres. 1979). Avocation: bicycling. Home and Office: 7125 Turnpike Rd Archdale NC 27263-7726

RIDDICK, FRANK ADAMS, JR., physician, health care facility administrator; b. Memphis, June 14, 1929; s. Frank Adams and Falba (Crawford) R.; m. Mary Belle Alston, June 15, 1952; children: Laura Elizabeth Dufresne, Frank Adams III, John Alston. BA cum laude, Vanderbilt U., 1951, MD, 1954. Diplomate: Am. Bd. Internal Medicine (bd. govs. 1973-80). Intern Barnes Hosp., St. Louis, 1954-55, resident in medicine, 1957-60; fellow in metabolic diseases Washington U., St. Louis, 1960-61; staff Ochsner Clinic (Ochsner Found. Hosp.), New Orleans, 1961—; head sect. endocrinology and metabolic disease Ochsner Clinic (Ochsner Found. Hosp.), 1976-83, asst. med. dir., 1968-72, assoc. med. dir., 1972-75, med. dir., 1975-92; clin. prof. medicine Tulane U., New Orleans, 1977—; trustee Alton Ochsner Med. Found., 1973—, CEO, 1991—; chmn. bd. Ochsner Health Plan, 1983-92; pres. Orleans Svc. Corp., 1976-80, South La. Med. Assocs., New Orleans, 1978—; dir. Brent House Corp., New Orleans, 1980—; pres. Am. Group Practice Assn., 1992-94. Trustee St. Martin's Protestant Epis. Sch., Metairie, La., 1970-84; bd. govs. Isidore Newman Sch., New Orleans, 1987-93. Recipient Disting. Alumnus award Castle Heights Mil. Acad., 1979; recipient teaching award Alton Ochsner Med. Found., 1969, Physician Exec. award Am. Coll. Med. Group Adminstrs., 1984, Disting. Alumnus award Vanderbilt U. Sch. Med., 1988. Fellow ACP, Am. Coll. Physician Execs. (pres. 1987-88); mem. Am. Soc. Internal Medicine (trustee 1970-76, disting. internist award), AMA (ho. of dels. 1971, chmn. coun. on med. edn. 1983-85), Endocrine Soc., Am. Diabetes Assn., Nat. Acad. Scis. Inst. Medicine, Soc. Med. Adminstrs. (pres. 1995—), Accreditation Coun. on Grad. Med. Edn. (chmn. 1986-87), Nat. Resident Matching Program (v.p. 1986-90, accreditation coun. on med. edn. 1988-90), Boston Club, New Orleans Country Club, Cosmos Club, Intern. Home: 1923 Octavia St New Orleans LA 70115-5651 Office: Ochsner Clinic 1514 Jefferson Hwy New Orleans LA 70121-2483

RIDDIFORD, LYNN MOORHEAD, zoologist, educator; b. Knoxville, Tenn., Oct. 18, 1936; d. James Eli and Virginia Amalia (Berry) Moorhead; m. Alan Wistar Riddiford, June 20, 1959 (div. 1966); m. James William Truman, July 28, 1970. AB magna cum laude, Radcliffe Coll., 1958; PhD, Cornell U., 1961. Rsch. fellow in biology Harvard U., Cambridge, Mass., 1961-63, 65-66, asst. prof. biology, 1966-71, assoc. prof., 1971-73; instr. biology Wellesley (Mass.) Coll., 1963-65; assoc. prof. zoology, U. Wash., Seattle, 1973-75, prof., 1975—; mem. study sect. tropical medicine and parasitology NIH, Bethesda, Md., 1974-78; mem. Competitive Grants panel USDA, Arlington, Va., 1979, 89, 95; mem. regulatory biology panel NSF, Washington, 1984-88; mem. governing coun. Internat. Ctr. for Insect Physiology and Ecology, 1985-91, chmn. program com., 1989-91; chmn. adv. com. SeriBiotech, Bangalore, India, 1989; mem. bio. adv. com. NSF, 1992-95. Contbr. articles to profl. jours. Mem. editorial bd. profl. jours. NSF fellow, 1958-60, 61-63; grantee NSF, 1964—, NIH, 1975—, Rockefeller Found., 1970-79, USDA, 1978-82, 89—; fellow John S Guggenheim, 1979-80, NIH, 1986-87. Fellow AAAS, Am. Acad. Arts and Scis., Royal Entomol. Soc.; mem. Am. Soc. Zoologists (pres. 1991), Am. Soc. Biochem. and Molecular Biology, Entomol. Soc. Am., Am. Soc. Cell Biology, Soc. Devel. Biology. Methodist. Home: 16324 51st Ave SE Bothell WA 98012-6138 Office: U Wash Dept Zoology Box 351800 Seattle WA 98195-1800

RIDDLE, CHARLES ADDISON, III, state legislator, lawyer; b. Marksville, La., June 8, 1955; s. Charles Addison Jr. and Alma Rita (Gremillion) R.; m. Margaret Susan Noone, Mar. 24, 1978; children: Charles Addison IV, John H., Michael J. BA, La. State U., 1976, JD, 1980. Bar: La. 1980, U.S. Dist. Ct. (mid. and we. dists.) La. 1983, U.S. Ct. Appeals (5th cir.) 1988, U.S. Supreme Ct. 1991, U.S. Ct. Vets. Appeals 1994. Assoc. Riddle & Bennett, Marksville, 1980; pvt. practice Marksville, 1981—; mem. La. Ho. of Reps., Baton Rouge, 1992—. Elected La. State Dem. Cen. com., Avoyelles Parish, 1983-87, Parish Exec. Demo. Com. 1987-91. Mem. Avoyelles Bar Assn. (pres. 1987-88), Bunkie Rotary (bd. dirs.), Marksville Lions, Marksville C. of C. (pres. 1988-92). Office: 208 E Mark St Marksville LA 71351-2416

RIDDLE, DONALD HUSTED, former university chancellor; b. Bklyn., Jan. 22, 1921; s. William Ewing and Ruth (Husted) R.; m. Leah Dunlap Gallagher, June 20, 1942; children: Susan Lee and Judith Lee (twins). AB magna cum laude, Princeton U., 1949, MA (Woodrow Wilson fellow), 1951, PhD (Ford Found. fellow), 1956; LLD (hon.), Am. U., 1980, John Jay Coll. Criminal Justice, 1990. Asst. prof. dept. govt. Hamilton Coll., 1952-58; dir. rsch., assoc. prof., prof. politics Eagleton Inst. Politics, Rutgers U., 1958-65; dean faculty John Jay Coll. Criminal Justice, CUNY, 1965-68, pres., 1968-76; chancellor U. Ill. - Chgo., 1976-83, chancellor emeritus, 1983—; staff asst. Conn. Commn. on State Govt. Organ., 1949; staff mem. Survey Field Services, Dept. Interior, 1950; staff U.S. Senator Paul H. Douglas, 1955-56; cons. N.Y. State Spl. Com. on Constl. Revision and Simplification, 1958. Author: The Truman Committee: A Study in Congressional Responsibility, 1964; Editor, co-author: The Problems and Promise of American Democracy, 1964, Contemporary Issues of American Democracy, 1969; Editor: American Society in Action, 1965. Mem. bd. edn., Princeton, N.J., 1962-64; mem. Mayors Criminal Justice Coordinating Council, N.Y.C., 1968-73; life mem. U. Ill. Press Council. Served to 1st lt. USAAF, 1942-46. Recipient Presdl. medal John Jay Coll. Criminal Justice, 1979. Mem. Acad. Criminal Justice Scis. (pres. 1970-71; hon. life, Presdl. Disting. award for contbg. to criminal justice edn. 1979), Phi Beta Kappa, Phi Sigma Alpha.

RIDDLE, JAMES DOUGLASS, college administrator; b. Austin, Tex., Oct. 8, 1933; s. Prebble Elmer and Jewel Lee (Nalley) R.; m. Marilyn Brown Moore, Sept. 8, 1956; children: Mary Elizabeth, Margaret Allison, Charles Douglass. BA in History and Govt., Southwestern U., 1958; MDiv in Theology and Social Ethics, Boston U. Sch. Theology, 1962; postgrad., Boston U., 1962-65; D Ministry, San Francisco Theol. Sem., 1991. Ordained to ministry Meth. Ch., 1963, transferred to United Ch. of Christ, 1966. Co-pastor The First Parish Ch., Lincoln, Mass., 1963-67; sr. pastor The Community Ch., Chapel Hill, N.C., 1967-80, First Ch. of Christ Congl. United Ch. of Christ, Springfield, Mass., 1980-89; v.p. devel. Am. Internat. Coll., Springfield, 1989—; teaching fellow, lectr. in human rels. Boston U. Sch. Bus., 1960-64; mem. Chapel Hill-Carrboro Bd. Edn., Chapel Hill, 1975-80. Mem. governing bd. Nat. Coun. Chs., 1969-72, commn. on faith and order, 1969-72, com. on future ecumenical structure, 1971-72; chmn. commn. on ecumenical study and svc. United Ch. of Christ, 1969-75, del. gen. synod, mem. exec. coun., 1969-75; pres. N.C. Legal Def. Fund, 1969-80, Orange-Chatham Counties Community Action Agy., 1970-76, Chapel Hill-Carrboro Inter-Ch. Coun. Housing Corp., 1969-77; mem. bd. Community Care Mental Health Ctr., 1980-90, chair, 1985-88; chair Downtown Ministry Project, 1981-84; mem. governing bd. Greater Springfield Coun. Chs., 1980-86, Downtown Econ. Devel. Corp., Springfield Cen., 1981—; StageWest Regional Theatre Co., 1982-92, Springfield YMCA, 1982-87, City of Springfield 350th Anniversary, 1984-87, Springfield Adult Edn. Coun., 1984—; corporator Zone Arts Ctr., 1986—. Named Person of Yr. NOW, 1987; recipient 350th Anniversary Medallion, City of Springfield, 1986. Mem. ACLU, Coun. for Advancement and Support of Edn., Nat. Soc. Fund Raising Execs., Estate Planning Coun. Hampden Country, New Eng. Devel. Rsch. Assn., Acad. Religion and Mental Health, Congl. Christian Hist. Soc. (mem. bd. 1987—), Assn. Humanistic Psychology, Common Cause, The Reality Club of Springfield, Springfield Rotary. Democrat. Avocations: backpacking, sailing, travel, cooking. Office: Am Internat Coll 1000 State St Springfield MA 01109-3151

RIDDLE, LYNNE, judge; b. L.A., Sept. 9, 1938; d. James Edgar and Lois Elaine (Marrish) R. BA, Calif. State Univ., L.A., 1960, MA, 1963; EdD, Syracuse Univ., 1966; JD, Hastings Coll. of Law, Univ. of Calif., 1977. Bar: Calif. 1978. Asst. prof. Calif. State Univ., Long Beach, 1966-68, Univ. of Iowa, 1968-69, Univ. of Calif., Santa Barbara, 1970-71, Dalhouse Univ., Halifax, Nova Scotia, 1971-73; atty. Santa Ana, 1978-88; bankruptcy judge U.S. Bankruptcy Ct. (cen. dist.) Calif. Santa Ana, 1988, San Bernardino, 1989-94, Santa Ana, 1994—; dir. Orange County Bankruptcy Forum; mem. Inland Empire Bankruptcy Forum; mem. Orange County Women Bankruptcy Lawyers. Office: 506 Fed Bldg 34 Civic Center Plz Santa Ana CA 92701

RIDDLE, STURGIS LEE, minister; b. Stephenville, Tex., May 26, 1909; s. Lee and Linda (McKinney) R.; m. Elisabeth Pope Sloan, Oct. 14, 1939. B.A. magna cum laude, Stanford U., 1931; student, Gen. Theol. Sem. N.Y.C., 1931-32; B.D. cum laude, Episcopal Theol. Sch., Cambridge, Mass.,

1934; D.D., Seabury Western Theol. Sem., Evanston, Ill., 1957. Ordained deacon P.E. Ch., 1934, priest, 1935; Episcopal chaplain U. Calif. 1934-37; instr. church Div. Sch. of Pacific, 1934-37; rector Caroline Ch., Setauket, L.I., 1937-40; asst. minister St. Thomas Ch., N.Y.C., 1940-46; rector St. James Ch., Florence, Italy, 1947-49; dean Am. Cathedral of Holy Trinity, Paris, France, 1949-74; dean emeritus Am. Cathedral of Holy Trinity, 1974—; exchange preacher Trinity Ch., N.Y.C., 1956-57, 62, St. Bartholomew's Ch., N.Y.C., 1958, 63, 73, St. John's Cathedral, Denver, 1959, Grace Cathedral, San Francisco, 1960, Nat. Cathedral, Washington, 1961, Trinity Ch. Boston, 1964, St. Andrew's Cathedral, Honolulu, 1965, St. John's Ch., Washington, 1966, 67, 68, 70, 73, St. Thomas' Ch., N.Y., 1968, 73, St. Paul's Cathedral, Boston, 1969; clerical dep. Europe to Gen. Conv. P.E. Ch., 1949-60, 64, 70. Author: One Hundred Years, 1950; contbg. Author: We Believe in Prayer, 1958, That Day with God, 1965. Hon. gov. Am. Hosp. in Paris; fellow Morgan Library, N.Y.C., trustee bd. fgn. parishes; chmn. Friends of the Am. Cathedral in Paris. Decorated Legion of Honor France; grand cross and grand prelate Sovereign Order St. John of Jerusalem Knights of Malta; grand cross Ordre du Milice de Jesus Christ; Patriarchal Order Mt. Athos. Mem. Nat. Inst. Social Sci., Am. Soc. French Legion of Honor, Phi Beta Kappa. Clubs: Union, University, Pilgrims, Spouting Rock Beach Assn. Home: 870 Fifth Ave New York NY 10021-4953

RIDDLE, VERYL LEE, lawyer; b. Campbell, Mo., Dec. 6, 1921; s. Elvis Lloyd and Etter Whitehead (Wood) R.; m. Mary J. Riggs, Jan. 15, 1941 (div. 1967); children—Kay Riddle Campbell, Jo Riddle McCarver, Janet Lee Riddle, Veryl Lee, Jr.; m. Janet Lewis, Nov. 24, 1985. Student, Southeast Mo. U., 1939-41; student, U. Buffalo, 1942, 45-46; J.D., Washington U., St. Louis, 1948. Bar: Mo. 1948, U.S. Dist. Ct. (ea. and we. dists.) Mo. 1949, U.S. Ct. Appeals (8th cir.) 1949, U.S. Supreme Ct. 1969, U.S. Ct. Appeals (7th cir.) 1970, U.S. Ct. Appeals (5th cir.) 1974, U.S. Ct. Appeals (3d cir.) 1975. Investigator Dept. Justice, N.Y.C., Buffalo and El Paso, Tex., 1942-43; U.S. atty. Eastern Dist. Mo. Dept. Justice, St. Louis, 1967-69; ptnr. Riddle, Baker & O'Herin, Malden, Mo., 1948-67; sr. ptnr. Bryan Cave, St. Louis, 1969—; pros. atty. Dunklin County, Mo., 1950-53; chmn. merit selection panel for U.S. Magistrate, St. Louis, 1983-84. Del., Nat. Democratic Conv., Chgo., 1956, Los Angeles, 1960. Served with U.S. Army, 1943-45. Recipient Disting. Alumni award Washington U. Sch. Law, 1993. Fellow Am. Coll. Trial Lawyers, Internat. Acad. Trial Lawyers; mem. Acad. Mo. Squires. Baptist. Clubs: Bellerive Country, Noonday, Round Table (St. Louis). Office: Bryan Cave 211 N Broadway Saint Louis MO 63102-2733

RIDDLEBERGER, HUGH COMPTON, III, headmaster; b. Poughkeepsie, N.Y., May 13, 1947; s. Hugh Compton and Jane (Joscelyn) R.; m. Louise Wesheldt McIlhenny, Apr. 24, 1976; children: Emily, Sarah, James. BA, U. Mich., 1970; EdM, Harvard U., 1974. Tchr. Charles River Sch., Dover, Mass., 1970-73, Newton (Mass.) Pub. Schs., 1976-79; prin. Metairie (La.) Park Country Day Sch., 1979-87; headmaster Sheridan Sch., Washington, 1987—; trustee Assn. Ind. Schs. Greater Washington, 1989—; dir. Project Seed, Washington, 1987—. Edn. Policy fellow Harvard U. and Ford Found., Washington, 1975-76. Mem. Nat. Assn. Elem. Sch. Prins., Assn. Curriculum and Supervision. Episcopalian. Avocations: jogging, sailing, carpentry, summers in Maine. Home: 6100 33rd St NW Washington DC 20015-2404 Office: Sheridan Sch 4400 36th St NW Washington DC 20008-4299

RIDDOCH, GREGORY LEE, professional baseball manager; b. Greeley, Colo., July 17, 1945; s. William Perry and Ruth C. (Gregory) R.; m. Linda Marcella Andre, Mar. 2, 1968; children: Rory David, Raliegh Davin. BBA, U. No. Colo., 1968; MA in Ednl. Adminstrn., Colo. State U., 1983. Minor league baseball player Cin. Reds, 1967-71, minor league mgr., 1973-80; scout Cin. Reds, Colo., Kans., Nebr., Wyo., 1981-83; asst. dir. player devel. and scouting Cin. Reds, 1984, dir. minor leagues, 1985; dir. instrn. San Diego Padres, 1986, coach, 1987-90, mgr., 1990—; substitute tchr. Greeley (Colo.) Sch. Dist., 1971-83; speaker in field. Writer videotapes: Tony Gwynn Fielding, 1989, Tony Gwynn Hitting, 1989. Vol. March of Dimes, Greeley, 1970—, Children's Hosp., San Diego, 1986—; Say No to Drugs, 1986—; fundraiser UNICEF, Greeley, 1970—. Named Mgr. of Yr., N.W. League, 1975-78; mgr. winning team State Spl. Olympics Boys Basketball Champions, 1975. Mem. Profl. Baseball Players Assn., NEA. Avocations: hunting, fishing, stained glass, jogging. Home: 1711 Glen Meadows Dr Greeley CO 80631-6831

RIDE, SALLY KRISTEN, physics educator, scientist, former astronaut; b. Los Angeles, May 26, 1951; d. Dale Burdell and Carol Joyce (Anderson) R.; m. Steven Alan Hawley, July 26, 1982 (div.). B.A. in English, Stanford U., 1973, B.S. in Physics, 1973, Ph.D. in Physics, 1978. Teaching asst. Stanford U., Palo Alto, Calif.; researcher dept. physics Stanford U.; astronaut candidate, trainee NASA, 1978-79, astronaut, 1979-87; on-orbit capsule communicator STS-2 mission Johnson Space Ctr. NASA, Houston; on-orbit capsule communicator STS-3 mission NASA, mission specialist STS-7, 1983, mission specialist STS-41G, 1984; sci. fellow Stanford (Calif.) U., 1987-89; dir. Calif. Space Inst. of U. Calif. San Diego, La Jolla, 1989—; prof. Physics U. Calif. San Diego, La Jolla, 1989—; mem. Presdl. Commn. on Space Shuttle, 1986, Presdl. Com. of Advisors on Sci. and Tech., 1994—. Author: (with Susan Okie) To Space and Back, 1986, (with T.O'Shaughnessy) Voyager: An Adventure to the Edge of the Solar System, 1992, The Third Planet: Exploring the Earth From Space, 1994. Office: Calif Space Inst 0221 Univ Calif San Diego La Jolla CA 92093-0221

RIDENHOUR, JOSEPH CONRAD, textile company executive; b. Rowan County, N.C., Aug. 12, 1920; s. Martin Luther and Mary Virginia (Schaeffer) R.; m. Julia Claire Thorne, Dec. 21, 1943; 1 child, Janis Claire. Student, Duke U., 1938-40; L.H.D., Lenoir Rhyne Coll., 1974. Asst. sec. Cannon Mills Co., Kannapolis, N.C., 1953-63; asst. v.p. Cannon Mills Co., 1959-60, v.p., 1960-71, sr. v.p., dir. mktg., 1971-82, vice chmn. bd., 1981-83, also dir. Mem. Kannapolis Bd. Edn., 1954-65; sec. Home Mission Found., N.C. synod United Lutheran Ch. in Am., 1953-68, dir., 1953—, pres., 1968—; mem. bd. Luth. Theol. So. Sem., 1964-85. Served with arty AUS, World War II, ETO. Home and Office: Oaklynn 420 Idlewood Dr Kannapolis NC 28083-3630

RIDENOUR, WINDSOR ALLEN, newspaper editor; b. Skiatook, Okla., Sept. 21, 1938; s. Robert Warren and Juanita Mae (DeShazer) R.; m. Mary Kathryn Cummings, Jan. 7, 1958; children: Rebeccah Lynn, Robert Allen. BS in Journalism, Okla. State U., 1964. Reporter San Diego Union, 1964-65; reporter The Tulsa Tribune, 1965-73, city editor, 1973-82, asst. mng. editor, 1982-83, mng. editor, 1983-90, exec. editor, 1990—. Mem. AP Okla. News Editors (pres. 1986), Tulsa Press Club (pres. 1985). Avocation: ranching. Home: Star Rte A Skiatook OK 74070 Office: Tulsa Tribune Co 2407 E Skelly Dr Tulsa OK 74105-6006

RIDEOUT, PATRICIA IRENE, operatic, oratorio and concert singer; b. St. John, N.B., Can., Mar. 16, 1931; d. Eric Aubrey and Florence May (Chase) R.; m. Rolf Edmund Dissmann, Sept. 3, 1955 (dec. 1975); m. Leonard R. Rosenberg, May 25, 1987. Ed., U. Toronto Opera Sch., Royal Conservatory Music, 1952-55. Tchr. voice Queen's U., Kingston, Ont., 1980-86, Royal Conservatory Music, Toronto, 1980-91. Singer Can. Opera Co., Toronto, 1954-85; leading roles in operas, Stratford, Ont., Vancouver, B.C., Guelph, Ont., 1956-85, 1958-90. Mem. Actors Equity Assn., Assn. Radio and TV Artists, Toronto Heliconian Club. Unitarian.

RIDEOUT, PHILIP MUNROE, publishing company executive; b. Boston, June 24, 1936; s. Allen MacDonald and Allene Lucille (Holman) R.; m. Sylviane R.L. Eldin, Aug. 7, 1959; 1 dau., Nicole MacDonald. BA, Williams Coll., 1958. With Addison-Wesley Pub. Co., 1961-77; gen. mgr. W.A. Benjamin, Inc., Menlo Park, Calif., 1972-77; gen. mgr. health scis. div. Addison-Wesley Co., Menlo Park, 1975-77; pres. Cummings Pub. Co., Inc., Menlo Park, 1968-77; v.p. Coll. Mktg. Group, Inc., 1977-78; v.p., editor-in-chief Larousse U.S.A., Inc., N.Y.C., 1979-85; v.p., pub. Keystone Publs., N.Y.C., 1986-91; CEO Monroe Allen Pubs. Inc., N.Y.C., 1991—; bd. dirs. Monroe Allen Pubs., Inc., 1990—. Served with U.S. Army, 1958-61. Decorated Disting. Svc. medal. Mem. S.A.R. Home: 67-25 Dartmouth St Forest Hills NY 11375 Office: 370 W 58th St New York NY 10019

RIDEOUT, WALTER BATES, English educator; b. Lee, Maine, Oct. 21, 1917; s. Walter John and Helen Ruth (Brickett) R.; m. Jeanette Lee Drisko, Aug. 2, 1947; children: Linda Carolyn, Richard Bates, David John. A.B. Colby Coll., 1938; M.A., Harvard U., 1939, Ph.D., 1950. Teaching fellow English Harvard U., 1946-49, asst. prof., summer 1954; prof., summer 1969; from instr. to assoc. prof. Northwestern U., Evanston, Ill., 1949-63, dir. program Bell System execs., 1957-58, 59-61; prof. English U. Wis., Madison, 1963–, Harry Hayden Clark prof. English, 1972–, chmn. dept., 1965-68, sr. vis. prof. Inst. Research in Humanities, 1968-69; vis. prof. U. Hawaii, summer 1977; Disting. lectr. English Kyoto Am. Studies Summer Seminar, Kyoto, Japan, 1981. Author: The Radical Novel in the United States, 1900-1954, 1956; editor: (with Howard Mumford Jones) Letters of Sherwood Anderson, 1953, (with James K. Robinson) A College Book of Modern Verse, 1958, A College Book of Modern Fiction, 1961, The Experience of Prose, 1960, I. Donnelly-Caesar's Column, 1960, (with G.W. Allen and J.K. Robinson) American Poetry, 1965, Sherwood Anderson: Collection of Critical Essays, 1974. Recipient MidAm. award Soc. for Study of Midwestern Lit., Mich. State U., 1983, Outstanding Educator award, 1993; fellow Newberry Libr., 1951, Guggenheim fellow, 1957; Fulbright grantee to Kyoto, 1981. Mem. ACLU, MLA (mem. nat. exec. council 1970-73), Phi Beta Kappa. Home: 1306 Seminole Hwy Madison WI 53711-3728 Office: Dept English U Wis 600 N Park St Madison WI 53706-1403

RIDEOUTTE, JOSEPH GREEN, highways and public transportation administrator; b. Columbia, S.C., Mar. 1, 1933; s. Joseph Green and Ruth (Joyner) R.; m. Marion Smith, June 27, 1956; children: Tammy Batson, Joseph Green Jr. BS in Acctg. and Fin., U.S.C., 1955. With S.C. Dept. Hwys & Pub. Transp., Columbia, S.C., 1957–; previously jr. acct. S.C. Dept. Hwys & Pub. Transp., Columbia, then acct., then acctg. mgr., then dir. fin., then sec.-treas., now exec. dir. Office: Hwys & Pub Transp Dept 955 Park St Box 191 Columbia SC 29202

RIDER, BRIAN CLAYTON, lawyer; b. San Antonio, Oct. 8, 1948; s. Ralph W. and Emmie (Kott) R.; m. Patsy Anne Ruppert, Dec. 27, 1970; children: Christopher, David, James, Andrew. BA, Rice U., 1969; JD, U. Tex., 1972. Bar: Tex. 1972. Assoc. then ptnr. Dow, Cogburn & Friedman, Houston, 1972-83; ptnr. Brown, McCarroll & Oaks Hartline, Austin, Tex., 1983–. Contbr. articles to profl. jours.; lectr. in field. Mem. Am. Coll. REal Estate Lawyers, Travis County Bar Assn. (bd. dirs. 1986-88, chmn. Travis County real estate sect. 1986-88), State Bar of Tex. (coun. real estate and probate sect. 1992–). Home: 2906 Hatley Dr Austin TX 78746-4613 Office: Brown McCarroll & Oaks Hartline 111 Congress Ave Ste 1400 Austin TX 78701-4049

RIDER, JANE LOUISE, artist, educator; b. Brownfield, Tex., Sept. 11, 1919; d. Oscar Thomas and Florence Myrtle (Bliss) Halley; m. Rolla Wilson Rider Jr., Mar. 26, 1944 (dec. July 1992); 1 child, Dorothy Jo Neil. BA, UCLA, Westwood, 1943, tchg. diploma in secondary art; postgrad., Chgo. Art Inst., 1945, Chouniards, L.A., U. Oreg.; Scripps Claremont, Calif. Art supr., elem. and jr. high art tchr. Tulare (Calif.) City Schs. Dist., 1943-44, 44-45; art tchr. Beverly Hills (Calif.) High Sch., 1946-47; art tchr. jr. high gen. art and ceramics Santa Barbara City Schs., Goleta, Calif., 1964-66; head art dept., tchr. Morro Bay (Calif.) Jr.-Sr. High Sch. Dist., 1967-70; pvt. practice studio potter Cambria, Calif., 1961-85; artist, Santa Rosa, Calif., 1985–; founder, dir., tech. La Canada (Calif.) Youth House Art Program, 1953-60; dir. Pinedorado Art Show, Allied Arts Assn., Cambria, 1970-80. Exhibited in group shows Wine Country Artist's Spring Show, 1991, 92, 93, 94, 95, Gualala Art in Redwoods, 1986, 87, 88, Rodney Strong Vineyards Art Guild, 1994; revolving exhibits Berger Ctr. and Chalais-Oakmont, Santa Rosa, 1985-95, statewide art show Spring Palettes Mumm Cuvee Winery, Napa, Calif. 1994), Santa Rosa Art Guild show, 1986-94. Mem. Nat. League Am. Pen Woman, Inc. (artist 1994, 95), Santa Rosa Art Guild (rec. sec. 1989), Ctrl. Coast Watercolor Soc. (charter 1977), Oakmont Art Assn. (Women Creating Luther Burbank Ctr., Santa Rosa 1994). Republican. Avocations: photography, gardening, listening to music, traveling, tennis. Home: 7019 Overlook Dr Santa Rosa CA 95409-6376

RIDER, JOHN ALLEN, II, business educator, paralegal; b. Gage, Okla., Mar. 11, 1928; s. George Henry Rider and Laurenna Agnes Meek; m. Audrey Claudine Barker, July 16, 1961; children: Michelle Renee Rider Brown, John Allen III. BS, Northwestern Okla. State U., 1952; MA, U. Wyoming, 1956; EdD, U. Nebr., 1966; postgrad., U. Ky. Cert. profl. tchr., Tenn., Iowa. Court reporter, stenographer USN, 1946-48; dep. ct. clk., ct. reporter Ellis County, Okla., 1948-49; tchr. bus. Rozel (Kans.) Rural High Sch., 1952-53, Norwich (Kans.) High Sch., 1953-54, Bluff City (Kans.) High Sch., 1954-56; instr. Black Hills State Coll., Spearfish, S.D., 1956-58; tchr. bus. Balboa (C.Z.) High Sch., 1958-60; instr. Northwestern Coll., Orange City, Iowa, 1958-60, chair divsn. edn., 1962-64; asst. prof. Northwestern State Coll., Alva, Okla., 1962-63; teaching asst. U. Nebr., Lincoln, 1963-64; head bus. edn. program, assoc. prof. U. N.Mex., Albuquerque, 1966-70; prof. West Tex. State U., Canyon, 1970-74; chair profl. occupational edn. divsn. Coffeyville (Kans.) Community Jr., 1974-75; assoc. prof. East Tenn. State U., Johnson City, 1975-94, coord. bus. edn. program, 1985-94; ret., 1994; cons. various bus. Active Johnson City Literacy Coun., v.p./tutor trainer, 1978-80; relief worker, registrar Mid-Am. yearly meeting Friends Ch., Wichita, 1981; cons. yearly meeting N.C. Soc. Friends, 1987. Recipient Meritorious award West Tex. Bus. Tchr., 1970-74, Outstanding Edn. Grad. award Northwestern Okla. State U. Alumni Assn., 1995; named Tchr. of Yr., Dist. 16 Tex. Bus. Edn. Assn., 1973. Mem. NEA (life), Am. Vocat. Assn. (life), Nat. Bus Edn., Nat. Assoc. Tchr. Edn. (life, bus. and office edn.), Tex. State Edn. Assn., Tenn. Bus. Edn. Assn. (treas., pres.-elect, pres., past pres., Educator of Yr. 1986), So. Bus. Edn., Kiwanis (Johnson City exec. bd. 1975-80, 92), Am. Legion (King's Mt. post), SAR (former sec., pres. Panhandle-Plains chpt., Tex. sec.), Holt County (Mo.) Hist. Soc. (charter, life). Republican. Avocations: genealogy, history, photography. Home: 1505 Baxter St Johnson City TN 37601-3307 Office: East Tenn State U PO Box 24507 Johnson City TN 37614-0124

RIDGE, MARTIN, historian, educator; b. Chgo., May 7, 1923; s. John and Ann (Lew) R.; m. Marcella Jane VerHoef, Mar. 17, 1948; children: John Andrew, Judith Lee, Curtis Cordell, Wallace Karsten. AB, Chgo. State U., 1943; AM, Northwestern U., 1949, PhD, 1951. Asst. prof. history Westminster Coll., New Wilmington, Pa., 1951-55; from asst. prof. to prof. San Diego State Coll., 1955-66; prof. history Ind. U., Bloomington, 1966-79, Calif. Inst. Tech., 1980–; vis. prof. UCLA, summer 1963, Northwestern U., summer 1959; editor Jour. Am. History, 1966-77; sr. research assoc. Huntington Library, 1977–; bd. dirs. Calif. Hist. Landmarks Commn., 1954-64; cons. in field; Tanner lectr. Mormon Hist. Assn., 1991; Whitsett Meml. lectr., Calif. State U., 1992. Author: Ignatius Donnelly: Portrait of a Politician, 1962, 91, The New Bilingualism: An American Dilemma, 1981, Frederick Jackson Turner: Wisconsin's Historian of the Frontier, 1986, Atlas of American Frontiers, 1992, My Life East and West, 1994; co-author: California Work and Workers, 1963, The American Adventure, 1964, America's Frontier Story, 1969, Liberty and Union, 1973, American History after 1865, 1981, Westward Expansion, 1982; editor: Children of Ol'Man River, 1988, Westward Journeys, 1989, History, Frontier and Section, 1993. Served with U.S. Maritime Service, 1943-45. William Randolph Hearst fellow, 1950; fellow Social Sci. Research Council, 1952; fellow Guggenheim Found., 1965; fellow Am. Council Learned Socs., 1960; Newberry fellow, 1964; Huntington fellow, 1974; Annenberg scholar U. So. Calif., 1979-80; recipient Best Book award Phi Alpha Theta, 1963, Gilberto Espinos prize N.Mex. Historical Review, 1989, Ray Allan Billington prize Western History Assn., 1991. Mem. Am. Hist. Assn. (Best Book award Pacific Coast br. 1963), Orgn. Am. Historians, Western History Assn. (v.p. 1985-86, pres. 1986-87), So. History Assn., Agrl. History Soc., Social Sci. History Soc., Hist. Soc. So. Calif. (pres. 1994–), Am. Hist. Assn. (v.p. Pacific coast br. 1994). Democrat. Address: Huntington Library San Marino CA 91108

RIDGE, MICHELE MOORE, librarian; b. Erie, Pa., Feb. 25, 1947; d. Howard William and Margaret Frances (Nagle) Moore; m. Jerry Lewis Stephenson, Aug. 19, 1972 (div. 1976); m. Thomas Joseph Ridge, Sept. 28, 1979. BA, Seton Hill Coll., 1969; MLS, U. Pitts., 1971. Adult svcs. libr. Prince Georges County Meml. Libr., Hyattsville, Md., 1971-73; br. mgr. Erie City and County Libr., Pa., 1976-78, head pub. svcs., 1978-79; libr. dir. Erie County Libr., 1979–. Trustee, rec. sec. Erie Art Mus., 1980–; trustee Erie Art Mus., Foodbank of Erie, Inc. Mem. ALA, Pa. Libr. Assn. (chmn.

intellectual freedom com. 1980-82), N.W. Interlibrary Coop. (chair steering com. 1982-84), Erie County Hist Soc. (trustee), Erie Club. Republican. Roman Catholic. Office: Erie County Libr System 27 S Park Row Erie PA 16501-1102

RIDGE, THOMAS JOSEPH, governor, former congressman; b. Munhall, Pa., Aug. 26, 1945; m. Michele Moore, 1979. B.A., Harvard U., 1967; J.D., Dickinson Coll. Law, Carlisle, Pa., 1972. Bar: Pa. 1972. Sole practice Erie, Pa., 1972-82; mem. 98th-103rd Congresses from Pa. 21st dist., Washington, D.C., 1983-1995; mem. Banking, Fin., Urban Affairs com., subcoms. Econ. Growth and Credit Formation, Housing and Community Devel., Veteran's Affairs com.; former dist. atty. Erie County; mem. subcom. Hosps. and Healthcare, Oversight and Investigation, Post Office and Civil Svc. com., subcom. Census and Population, Civil Svc.; former legal instructor Erie County; gov. State of Penn., 1995–. Mem. Erie County Republican Com.; bd. dirs. St. Mary's Home, Erie, Cathedral Prep Sch. Alumni Assn., Greater Erie Community Action Com., Greater Erie Golf Classic; exec. dir. Erie County Library. Served with inf. U.S. Army, 1968-70, Vietnam. Office: Office of the Gov 245 Main Capitol Bldg Harrisburg PA 17120*

RIDGEWAY, JAMES FOWLER, journalist; b. Auburn, N.Y., Nov. 1, 1936; s. George L. and Florence (Fowler) R.; m. Patricia Carol Dodge, Nov. 1966; 1 son, David Andrew. A.B., Princeton U., 1959. Assoc. editor New Republic, Washington, 1962-68, contbg. editor, 1968-70; editor Hard Times, 1968-70, Elements, 1974-78; assoc. editor Ramparts, 1970-75; assoc. fellow Inst. for Policy Studies, 1973-77; mem. Pub. Resource Center, 1977–; staff writer Village Voice, 1973–. Author: The Closed Corporation, 1969, Politics of Ecology, 1970, The Last Play, 1973, New Energy, 1975, Energy-Efficient Community Planning, 1979, Who Owns the Earth, 1980 (with Arthur Cockburn) Smoke, 1978, Political Ecology, 1979, Powering Civilization, 1983, Blood in the Face, 1991, The March to War, 1991, (with Jean Casella) To Cast A Cold Eye, 1991, The Haiti Files, 1994, (with Jasminka Udovicki) Yugoslavia's Ethnic Nightmare, 1995; prodr., dir. Blood in the Face, 1991, Feed, 1992. Served with Army N.G., 1959. Home: 3103 Macomb St NW Washington DC 20008-3325

RIDGLEY, ROBERT LOUIS, gas company executive, lawyer; b. Ft. Wayne, Ind., Mar. 4, 1934; s. Charles Herbert and Margaret (Sparling) R.; m. Marilyn A. Hester, Aug. 24, 1957; children: Gregory C., Derek W. A.B., Cornell U., 1956; J.D., Harvard, 1959. Bar: Oreg. bar 1959. Practice in Portland, 1960-84; assoc. Stoel, Rives, Boley, Fraser and Wyse (and predecessors), 1960-66, ptnr., 1966; exec. v.p. N.W. Natural Gas Co., 1984, pres., chief exec. officer, 1985–. Co-editor: Pleading and Practice Handbook, 1964. Mem. Nat. Adv. Council for Edn. Disadvantaged Children, 1969-70; mem. Nat. Commn. on Reform of Secondary Edn.; mem. Multnomah County Republican Exec. Com., 1962-66; alt. del. Nat. Conv., 1964; Chmn. bd. dirs. Portland Sch. Dist.; bd. dirs. Cornell U. Council, Nat. Pub. Affairs Center for TV; trustee Cornell U., 1970-76; trustee Lewis and Clark Coll., 1975-88, chmn. bd. dirs., 1985-88; chmn. bd. visitors Northwestern Sch. Law, 1975-76; bd. dirs. Oreg. Symphony Assn., 1981-84; mem. Exposition-Recreation Commn., 1980-85; chmn. gov. com. on sch. funding reform. Served to 1st lt., arty. AUS, 1959-60. Named Jr. First Citizen Portland, 1968, First Citizen Portland, 1987. Mem. Nat. Sch. Bds. Assn. (dir.), Oreg. Sch. Bds. Assn. (pres.), Portland C. of C. (dir. 1981– vice chmn. 1986-88, chmn. 1989). Lodge: Portland Rotary (dir. 1983-85, v.p. 1986-87, pres. 1987-88). Home: 4927 SW Downs View Ct Portland OR 97221-2124 Office: NW Natural Gas Co 220 NW 2nd Ave Portland OR 97209-3943

RIDGLEY, THOMAS BRENNAN, lawyer; b. Columbus, Ohio, Apr. 29, 1940; s. Arthur G. and Elizabeth (Tracy) R.; m. Nancy Vaughan, June 27, 1964; children: Elizabeth, Jennifer, Kathryn. BA, Princeton (N.J.) U., 1962; JD with honors, U. Mich., 1965. Bar: Pa. 1965, Ohio 1968, U.S. Dist. Ct. (so. and no. dists.) Ohio, U.S. Dist. Ct. (ea. dist.) Pa., U.S. Ct. Appeals (6th, 3d and 10th cirs.), U.S. Supreme Ct. Assoc. Dechert, Price and Rhoades, Phila., 1965-67; ptnr. Vorys, Sater, Seymour and Pease, Columbus, 1967–. Author: Interstate Conflicts and Cooperation, 1986, (with others) Fending Off Corporate Raiders, 1987. Bd. dirs., mem. exec. com. United Way of Franklin County, Columbus, 1986–, Cmty. Shelter Bd., 1992–. Fellow Am. Coll. Trial Lawyers. Office: Vorys Sater Seymour & Pease 52 E Gay St Columbus OH 43215-3161

RIDGWAY, BRUNILDE SISMONDO, archaeology educator; b. Chieti, Italy, Nov. 14, 1929; came to U.S., 1953, naturalized, 1963; d. Giuseppe G. and Maria (Lombardo) Sismondo; m. Henry W. Ridgway Jr., Sept. 6, 1958; children: Conrad W., Eric R., Kevin P., Christopher L. Laurea in Lettere Classiche, Messina U., Italy, 1953; MA in Classical Archaeology, Bryn Mawr Coll., 1954, PhD, 1958; HHD, Georgetown U., 1992; LLD, Union Coll., 1992. Asst. prof., head dept. classics Hollins (Va.) Coll., 1960-61; Asst., then instr. archaeology Bryn Mawr (Pa.) Coll., 1957-60, mem. faculty, 1961–, prof. classical archaeology, 1970–, Rhys Carpenter prof. archaeology, 1977-93, prof. emerita, 1993–; dir. Summer Sch. in Greece Am. Sch. Classical Studies, Athens, 1967, 71; Disting. Andrew Mellon vis. prof. U. Pitts., 1978; Disting. vis. prof. George Washington U. Art Dept. 1986; E. Whitehead prof. Am. Sch. Classical Studies, Athens, Greece, 1988; Cecil H. and Ida Green vis. prof. classics dept. U. B.C., Vancouver, Can., 1990; H.L. Hooker Disting. vis. prof. McMaster U., Hamilton, Can., 1992; vis. prof. Archeol. Inst. Australia, Athens, Australia, 1992; Hanes-Willis vis. prof. dept. Art., U. N.C., Chapel Hill, 1995; ann. mem. Inst. Advanced Study, Princeton, N.J., 1967-68; Thomas Spencer Jerome lectr. U. Mich., Ann Arbor and Am. Acad. in Rome, 1981-82; guest curator Allentown Art Mus., Pa., 1979; Geddes-Harrower Chair, U. Aberdeen, Scotland, fall term 1989. Author: The Severe Style in Greek Sculpture, 1970; Classical Sculpture, 1972; The Archaic Style in Greek Sculpture, 1977, 2d rev. edit., 1993; (with G.F. Pinney) Aspects of Ancient Greece, 1979; Fifth Century Styles in Greek Sculpture, 1981; Roman Copies of Greek Sculpture, The Problem of the Originals, 1984; (with C.J. Eiseman) The Porticello Shipwreck: A Mediterranean Merchant Vessel of 415-385 B.C., 1987; Hellenistic Sculpture I: The Styles of ca. 331-200 B.C., 1990; (with others) Greek Sculpture in the Art Mus., Princeton U.; Greek Originals, Roman Copies and Variants, 1994; contbr. articles to profl. jours., (others), editor-in-chief Am. Jour. Archaeology, 1977-85; editor: (with others) Ancient Anatolia, 1986. Recipient Christian R. and Mary F. Lindback Found. award for disting. teaching, 1981, Gold medal Coun. for Advancement and Support Edn., 1989; named Fla. Prof. of Yr., 1989; Guggenheim fellow, 1974-75; Kress Sr. fellow Ctr. Advanced Study in Visual Arts, Nat. Gallery of Art , 1986. Mem. Archaeol. Inst. Am. (life, Disting. Archeol. Achievement Gold medal 1988), Internat. Assn. Classical Archaeology, German Archaeol. Inst. (corr.), Am. Philos. Soc. Home: 601 Montgomery Ave Bryn Mawr PA 19010-3529 Office: BrynMawr Coll Dept Archaeology 101 N Merion Ave Bryn Mawr PA 19010-2899

RIDGWAY, ROZANNE LEJEANNE, government executive, former diplomat; b. St. Paul, Aug. 22, 1935; d. H. Clay and Ethel Rozanne (Cote) R.; m. Theodore E. Deming. BA, Hamline U., 1957, LLD (hon.), 1978; LLD (hon.), George Washington U., 1986; hon. degree, U. Helsinki, Elizabethtown Coll., Albright Coll., Coll. of William and Mary, Hood Coll. Career diplomat U.S. Fgn. Svc., 1957-89, amb. at large for oceans and fisheries, 1975-77; amb. to Finland, 1977-80; counselor of the Dept. State, Washington, 1980-81; asst. sec. to asst. state, 1981; amb. to German Dem. Republic, 1982-85; asst. sec. state Europe and Can., 1985-89; pres. The Atlantic Coun. U.S., Washington, 1989-92, co-chair, 1993–; chair Baltic-Am. Enterprise Fund, 1994–; bd. dirs. 3M Corp., RJR Nabisco, Union Carbide Corp., Bell Atlantic, Citicorp, Citibank, Emerson Electric Co., The Boeing Corp., Sara Lee Corp., Nat. Geog. Soc., Internat. Bd. Advisors, New Perspective Fund. Trustee Hamline U.; bd. dirs. Am. Acad. Diplomacy, Coun. on Ocean Law, Ptnrs. for Democratic Change, Catalyst, Aspen Inst., Bookings Instn. Recipient Profl. awards Dept. State, Presdl. Disting. Performance award, Joseph C. Wilson internat. rels. achievement award, 1982, Sharansky award Union Couns. Soviet Jewry, 1989, Grand Cross of the Order of the Lion, Finland, 1989; named Person of Yr., Nat. Fisheries Inst., 1977, Knight Comdr. of the Order of Merit, Fed. Republic Germany, 1989, U.S. Presdl. Citizens Achievement medal, 1989. Fellow Nat. Acad. Pub. Adminstrn.; mem. Met. Club, Army-Navy Country Club. Office: The Atlantic Coun of The US 910 17th St NW Ste 1000 Washington DC 20006

RIDINGS, DOROTHY SATTES, communications executive, newspaper publisher; b. Charleston, W.Va., Sept. 26, 1939; d. Frederick L. and Katharine E. (Backus) Sattes; m. Donald Jerome Ridings, Sept. 8, 1962; children: Donald Jerome Jr., Matthew Lyle. Student, Randolph-Macon Woman's Coll., 1957-59; BSJ, Northwestern U., 1961; MA, U. N.C.-Chapel Hill, 1968; D.Pub. Svc. (hon.), U. Louisville, 1985; LHD (hon.), Spalding U., 1986. Reporter Charlotte Observer, N.C., 1961-66; instr. U. N.C. Sch. Journalism, 1966-68; freelance writer Louisville, 1968-77; news editor Ky. Bus. Ledger, Louisville, 1977-80, editor, 1980-83; communications com., editor, 1983-86; mgmt. assoc. Knight-Ridder Inc., Charlotte, N.C., 1986-88; pres., publisher The Bradenton (Fla.) Herald, 1988–; adj. prof. U. Louisville, 1982-83; v.p. Nat. Mcpl. League, 1985-86; bd. dirs. com. on Constl. System, Nat. Com. Against Discrimination in Housing, 1982-87, Com. for Study of Am. Electorate, 1982-89; bd. dirs. Ind. Sector, 1983-88, 92–; mem. exec. com. Leadership Conf. Civil Rights, 1982-86. Pres. LWV U.S., 1982-86, 1st v.p. 1980-82, human resources dir., 1976-80, chair edn. fund, 1982-86, 1st vice chair, 1980-82, trustee, 1976-80, pres. Louisville/Jefferson County, 1974-76, bd. dirs. 1969-76; trustee Louisville Presbyn. Theol. Sem., 1992–, Ford Found., 1990–, Manatee Community Coll., 1992–; bd. dirs. Benton Found., 1987–, Fla. Press Assn., 1994–; mem. ABA Accreditation Com., 1987-93, Gov.'s Council Ednl. Reform, 1984-85; chair Prichard Com. Acad. Excellence, 1985-86; bd. dirs. Leadership Ky., 1984-87, Leadership Louisville, 1983-86, Louisville YWCA, 1978-80, Jr. League Louisville, 1972-74; mem. Gov.'s Commn. Full Equality, 1982-83; mem. state adv. council U.S. Commn. Civil Rights, 1975-79; mem. steering com. Task Force for Peaceful Desegregation, 1974-75; elder 2d Presbyn. Ch., 1972-75, 78-81; mem. adv. council on ch. and soc. United Presbyn. Ch. in USA, 1978-84; mem. bd. visitors U. N.C., 1992–. Recipient Northwestern U. Alumni Merit award, 1994, Leadership award Nat. Assn. Cmty. Leadership Orgns., 1986, Alumnae Achievement award Randolph-Macon Woman's Coll., 1985, Disting. Citizens award Nat. Mcpl. League, 1983. Home: 3412 Avenida Madera Bradenton FL 34210 Office: The Bradenton Herald PO Box 921 Bradenton FL 34206-0921

RIDLEN, SAMUEL FRANKLIN, agriculture educator; b. Marion, Ill., Apr. 24, 1916; s. Will and Leoma Josephine (Sneed) R.; m. Helen Louise Camp, Apr. 17, 1946; children: Judith Elaine, Barbara Jo, Mark Ellis. BS, U. Ill., 1940; MS, Mich. State U., 1957. Agr. instr. Westville (Ill.) Twp. High Sch., 1940-43; gen. mgr. Honegger Breeder Hatchery, Forrest, Ill., 1953-56; assoc. prof. poultry sci. U. Conn., Storrs, 1957-58; from asst. prof. to prof. poultry extension U. Ill., Urbana-Champaign, 1946-86, prof. emeritus poultry extension, 1986–, asst. head dept. animal scis., 1978-86. Author: An Idea and An Ideal-Nabor House Fraternity 1939-1989, 1989; poultry editorial cons. Successful Farming, Wonderful World Ency., 1960; poultry editor Am. Farm Youth, 1949-53, Ill. Feed Folks, 1949-53. Founding mem., charter mem. Nabor House Frat. Recipient Superior Svc. award U.S. Dept. Agr., 1982, Paul A. Funk Recognition award Coll. Agr. U. Ill., 1983, numerous others. Fellow Poultry Sci. Assn.; mem. World's Poultry Sci. Assn., Ill. State Turkey Growers Assn., Ill. Poultry Industry Coun., Ill Egg Market Devel. Coun. (adv. mem.), Ill. Animal Industry Coun., Coun. for Agr. Sci. and Tech., Ill. Alumni Assn. (life), DAV (life), Alpha Tau Alpha, Epsilon Sigma Phi, Gamma Sigma Delta (pres. 1982-83). Home: 1901-C Lakeside Dr Champaign IL 61821

RIDLEY, CAROLYN FLUDD, social studies educator; b. Nashville, Jan. 21, 1942; d. Quitman Daniel and Glennora Elizabeth (Cannon) F.; m. Raymond Bennett, June 23, 1962 (div. 1984); 1 child, Karen Elizabeth Bennett Moore; m. Cornelius Theodore Ridley, July 16, 1988; stepchildren: Constance Maria Ridley Smith, William Keith. BA, CUNY, 1973; MEd, Tenn. State U., 1985. Cert. tchr., prin., Tenn.; N.Y. Tchr. N.Y.C. Bd. Edn., 1973-75, Dickson (Tenn.) County Bd. Edn., 1976-77, Hickman County Bd. Edn., Centerville, Tenn., 1977-86, Met. Nashville Bd. Edn., 1986–; dir. Hickman County Career Day, 1982-83; bd. dirs. Assn. Retarded Citizens, Centerville, 1982-86; adv. com. Hickman County Bicentennial Com., Centerville, 1984-86, initiator commemorative quilt; participant NEH lectr. Author: A Black History of Hickman County, 1985. Campaign worker Met. Nashville Bd. Edn., 1991; campaigner Met. Nashville Edn., Assn., 1992; attendant Dem. Socialization Meeting, Nashville, 1992; participant Nat. Endowment for the Humanities Summer Inst. Furman U., Greenville, Tenn., 1995. Grantee Mid. Tenn. State U., Murfreesboro, 1990, Tenn. State U., Nashville, 1992; James R. Stokeley Inst. fellow U. Tenn., 1993; participant NEH Summer Inst. at Furman U., Greenville, Tenn., 1995. Fellow Taft Inst. (cert. 1992); mem. AAUW, NEA, NASA Space Inst. (cert. 1990), Smithsonian Instn., Internat. Platform Assn., Nat. Historic Preservation Soc., Nat. Geographic Soc., Nat. Coun. Social Studies, Internat. Platform Assn. Democrat. Mem. Ch. of Christ. Avocations: travel, reading, music, studying quilting folk art. Home: 4348 Setters Rd Nashville TN 37218-1839 Office: Haynes Mid Sch 510 W Trinity Ln Nashville TN 37207-4944

RIDLEY, CLARENCE HAVERTY, lawyer; b. Atlanta, June 3, 1942; s. Frank Morris Jr. and Clare (Haverty) R.; m. Eleanor Horsey, Aug. 22, 1969; children: Augusta Morgan, Clare Haverty. BA, Yale U., 1964; MBA, Harvard U., 1966; JD, U. Va., 1971. Bar: Ga. 1971. Assoc. King & Spalding, Atlanta, 1971-77, ptnr., 1977–; bd. dirs. Haverty Furniture Cos., Inc., mem. exec. com., 1992–. Author: Computer Software Agreements, 1987, 2d edit., 1993; exec. editor Va. Law Rev., 1970-71. Chmn. St. Joseph's Hosp. Found., Atlanta, 1986-89; trustee St. Joseph's Health Svcs., 1987–; chmn. fin. com., 1992–; bd. dirs. Atlanta Opera Co., 1979-89, Atlanta Ballet Co., 1993–. Lt. U.S. Army, 1966-68, Korea. Roman Catholic. Home: 2982 Habersham Rd NW Atlanta GA 30305-2854 Office: King & Spalding 191 Peachtree St Atlanta GA 30303

RIDLOFF, RICHARD, real estate executive, lawyer, consultant; b. N.Y.C., July 18, 1948; s. Sol and Daisey (Metz) R.; m. Caren Sara Berger, Mar. 27, 1977; children: Michael Joshua, Daniel Joseph. BA cum laude, Queens Coll., 1969; JD, Cornell U., 1972. Bar: N.Y. 1973. Assoc. counsel MONY, N.Y.C., 1972-79; sr. v.p., gen. counsel, sec. MONY Real Estate Investors, N.Y.C., 1979-85; v.p. investments MONY Fin. Svcs., N.Y.C., 1985-87; pres. MONY Realty Ptnrs. Inc., Glen Point, N.J., 1985-91; v.p. for investment mgmt. MONY Real Estate Investment Mgmt., N.Y.C., 1988-91; exec. v.p. Tibor Pivko and Co., Clifton, N.J., 1991-94; pres., dir. Growth & Income Inc., 1993-94; spl. projects dir. Kimco Realty Corp., 1995–; bd. dirs. Growth & Income Inc.; mem. adv. commn. on real property ins. to Calif. Sen. Com. on Ins. Claims and Corps., 1986-92; adv. com. N.Y. chpt. Nat. Assn. Corp. Real Estate Execs., 1990. Author: A Practical Guide to Construction Lending, 1985; editor Real Estate Financing Newsletter, 1980-85 ; contbr. articles to profl. jours. Mem. secondary sch. interviewing com. Cornell U., Ithaca, N.Y., 1981–; chmn. fed. legis. com. Nat. Assn. Real Estate Investment Trusts, Washington, 1981-82. Mem. ABA (mem. real property com., fin. sect. real property, probate and trustlaw 1979–), N.Y. Bar Assn., Oakwood-Princeton Park Civic Assn., Omicron Delta Epsilon, Pi Sigma Alpha, Alpha Epsilon Pi.

RIEBMAN, LEON, electronics company executive; b. Coatsville, Pa., Apr. 22, 1920; s. Abraham Benjamin and Bertha (Aisikovitz) R.; m. Claire Jay Edeson, Feb. 27, 1944; children: Barbara Lynne, Robert Alvin. B.E.E., U. Pa., 1943, MS, 1947, Ph.D., 1951. Sr. engr. Philco, Phila., 1946; research asso., part-time instr. U. Pa., 1948-51; a founder, pres. Am. Electronic Labs., Colmar and Lansdale, Pa., 1950–; dir. Ampal, Old York Rd. Bank. Served to lt. (j.g.) USNR, 1943-46. Recipient State of Israel Bond award, 1968, Atwater Kent award, 1943. Fellow IEEE; mem. Am. Technion (pres. Phila. chpt.), Sigma Xi, Tau Beta Pi, Etta Kappa Nu, Pi Mu Epsilon. Patentee in field. Home: 1380 Barrowdale Rd Jenkintown PA 19046-2418 Office: Am Electronic Labs Inc 305 Richardson Rd Lansdale PA 19446-1485

RIECHMANN, FRED B., retired newspaper publisher; b. Evansville, Ind., Oct. 30, 1915; s. George Edward and Helen (Umbach) R.; m. Pauline Ashby, Nov. 11, 1939; children—Fredrica Ann Riechmann Wellborn, Paul F. Student, U. Evansville, 1931-33; M.E., U. Cin., 1938. Registered profl. engr., Ohio. Bookkeeper Nat. City Bank, Evansville, 1933-35; product exec. Servel Inc., Evansville, 1935-59; v.p., treas. Miller Block Co., Evansville, 1960-70; pres., dir. Evansville Courier, 1970-87. Served to maj. Ordnance Dept., U.S. Army, 1941-46. Republican. Lutheran. Home: 510 Bse Riverside Dr Evansville IN 47713

RIECK, THEODORE J., city official; b. Holyoke, Mass., Apr. 9, 1956; s. Theodore A. and Claire C. (Brooks) R.; m. Maria C. Silva, June 6, 1987; 1 child, John. AS, N.H. Coll., 1976; BA, U. N.H., 1978; M City and Regional Planning, Ohio State U., 1980; MBA, Rockhurst Coll., Kansas City, Mo., 1987. Transp. planner I Southeastern Mich. Transp. Authority, Detroit, 1980-82, transp. planner II, 1982-84, coord. planning, 1984; mgr. planning Kansas City Area Transp. Authority, 1984-88; nat. sales mgr. Mayflower Contract Svcs., Overland Park, Kans., 1988-92; gen. mgr. Indpls. Pub. Transp. Corp., 1992—. Mem. Am Pub. Transp. Assn., Kiwanis. Office: Indpls Pub Transp Corp 1501 W Washington St Indianapolis IN 46222-4553

RIECKE, HANS HEINRICH, architect; b. Münster, Westfalia, Germany, Mar. 30, 1929; came to U.S., 1955; s. Hans Joachim and Hildegard (Schwarze) R.; m. Elvira Maria Magdalena Kaatz, Nov. 30, 1954; children: Christine, Annette, Monica, Ralph, Heidi. Student architecture, Technische Hochschule, Hannover, Fed. Republic. Germany, 1953; BA in Architecture, U. Calif., Berkeley, 1957. Registered architect, Calif., Hawaii. Draftsman Orinoco Mining Co., Puerto Ordaz, Venezuela, 1954-55, H.K. Ferguson Co., San Francisco, 1956-57; architect, ptnr. Hammarberg and Herman, Oakland, Calif., 1957-74; prin. Hans Riecke, Architect Inc., Kahului, Maui, Hawaii, 1974-78, Riecke Sunnland Kono Architects Ltd, Kahului, Maui, Hawaii, 1978—. Bd. dirs. Kihei Community Assn., Maui, Hawaii, 1975-77, Seabury Hall, Makawao, Maui, 1980-82; chmn. Mayor's Com. on Housing, County of Maui, 1984. Recipient Merit award Pacific Coast Builders Con., Kahului, Hawaii, 1990. Fellow AIA (pres. Maui chpt. 1990); mem. Am. Arbitration Assn. (panel of arbitrators 1980). Avocations: biking, gardening. Office: Riecke Sunnland Kono Architect PO Box 1627 Kahului HI 96732-7627

RIECKEN, HENRY WILLIAM, psychologist; research director; b. Bklyn., Nov. 11, 1917; s. Henry William and Lilian Antoinette (Nieber) R.; m. Frances Ruth Manson, Aug. 7, 1955; children—Mary Susan, Gilson, Anne. A.B., Harvard U., 1939, Ph.D., 1950; M.A., U. Conn., 1941. Social sci. analyst Dept. Agr., 1941-46; teaching fellow Harvard U., 1947-49, lectr. social psychology, research assoc. clin. psychology, 1949-54; assoc. prof. then prof., sr. mem. lab. research social relations U. Minn., 1954-58; program dir. social sci. research NSF, Washington, 1958-59; head Office Social Sci., Washington, 1959-60, asst. dir. social scis., 1960-64, assoc. dir. sci. edn., 1964-66; v.p. Social Sci. Research Council, N.Y.C., 1966-69; pres. Social Sci. Research Council, 1969-71; prof. behavioral scis. U. Pa., Phila., 1972-85, prof. emeritus, 1985—; assoc. dir. for planning Nat. Library Medicine, Bethesda, Md., 1985-87; fellow Ctr. Advanced Study Behavioral Scis., Stanford, Calif., 1971-72; Paterson Meml. lectr. U. Minn., 1970; Jensen lectr. Duke U., 1973; mem. adv. com. to dir. NIH, 1966-70, chmn. internat. ctrs. com., 1968-73; pres. Am. Psychol. Found., 1971-73; vice chmn., chmn. com. nat. needs for biomed. and behavioral rsch. pers. NRC, 1975-80; mem. commn. sociotech. systems Nat. Acad. Scis., 1976-79; adj. prof. psychiatry U. Tex. Med. Br., 1988—. Author: The Volunteer Work Camp, 1952, When Prophecy Fails, 1956, Social Experimentation, 1974, Experimental Testing of Public Policy, 1976; contbr. articles to profl. jours. Bd. dirs. Found. Child Devel. (formerly Assn. Aid Crippled Children), N.Y.; trustee W.T. Grant Found., N.Y. Served with USAAC, 1943-45. Fellow Am. Psychol. Assn. (Harold M. Hildreth award 1971), Am. Acad. Arts and Scis.; mem. Am. Assn. Pub. Opinion Research, Sociol. Research Assn. (pres. 1966), Nat. Acad. Scis., Inst. Medicine. Clubs: Harvard (N.Y.C.); Cosmos (Washington). Office: Kezar Assocs Washington DC

RIEDEBURG, THEODORE, management consultant; b. Milw., June 7, 1912; s. Theodore and Elva Pauline (Wolf) R.; m. Margaret Anna Louise Oertel, Dec. 24, 1937 (dec.); children: Theodore, Charles Howard; m. Ruth Jones Keith, May 3, 1980. BS, Marquette U., 1934, MS, 1936. Dist. sales mgr. Philip Morris & Co., 1937-42; asst. mgr. fumigants dept. Dow Chem. Co., Midland, Mich., 1942-45; sales mgr. agrichems. Westvaco Chem., N.Y.C., 1945-50; mng. dir. Theodore Riedeburg Assocs., N.Y.C., 1950-80; ind. forensic chemist-pesticides St. Simons Island, Ga., 1980—. Contbr. articles to profl. jours. Pres. Citizens League White Plains (N.Y.), 1962. Fellow Soc. Profl. Mgmt. Cons. (past pres.); mem. Am. Arbitration Assn., Nat. Bur. Profl. Mgmt. Cons. (exec. adv. bd. 1989), Chemists Club (N.Y.C.). Home: 2507 Demere Rd Apt 2 Saint Simons Island GA 31522 Office: PO Box 21158 Saint Simons Island GA 31522-5426

RIEDEL, ALAN ELLIS, manufacturing company executive, lawyer; b. Bellaire, Ohio, June 28, 1930; s. Emil George and Alberta (Shafer) R.; m. Ruby P. Tignor, June 21, 1953; children: Ralph A., Amy L., John T. AB magna cum laude, Ohio U., 1952, LLD (hon.), 1994; JD, Case Western Res. U., 1955; grad., Advanced Mgmt. Program, Harvard, 1971. Bar: Ohio 1955, Tex. 1968. Assoc. Squire, Sanders & Dempsey, Cleve., 1955-60; gen. counsel Cooper Industries Inc. (formerly Cooper Bessemer Co.), Mt. Vernon, Ohio, 1960-63, sec., 1963-68, 1963-68, v.p. indsl. rels., 1968-73; sr. v.p. adminstrn. Cooper Industries, Inc., Houston, 1973-92; dir. Cooper Industries Inc., Houston, 1981-94, vice chmn., 1992-94; bd. dirs. Standard Products Co., Cleve., Arkwright Mut. Ins. Co., Waltham, Mass., Belden Inc., St. Louis, First Knox Nat. Bank Corp.; bd. dirs. Gardner Denver Machinery Inc., Quincy, Ill., chmn. bd. dirs. 1994—. Former chmn. bd. dirs. Jr. Achievement of S.E. Tex.; former chmn. bd. trustees Ohio U. Endowment Found. Mem. Order of Coif, Phi Beta Kappa, Omicron Delta Kappa, Delta Tau Delta. Home: 803 Creekwood Way Houston TX 77024

RIEDEL, BERNARD EDWARD, retired pharmaceutical sciences educator; b. Provost, Alta., Can., Sept. 25, 1919; s. Martin and Naomi E. (Klingaman) R.; m. Julia C. McClurg, Mar. 5, 1944 (dec. Mar. 1992); children: Gail Lynne, Dwain Edward, Barry Robert. BS in Pharmacy, U. Alta., Edmonton, 1943, MS in Pharmacology, 1949; PhD in Biochemistry, U. Western Ont., 1953, DSc (hon.), U. Alta., 1990. Lectr., asst. prof. Faculty of Pharmacy U. Alta., Edmonton, 1946-49, asst. prof. then assoc. prof., 1953-58, prof., 1959-67, exec. asst. to v.p., 1961-67; dean, prof. Faculty Pharm. Scis. U. B.C., Vancouver, 1967-84, coordinator Health Scis. Centre, 1977-84; mem. sci. adv. com. Health Rsch. Found. of B.C., 1991—. Contbr. numerous articles on pharmacology to profl. jours. Elder Ryerson United Ch.; mem. exec. bd. Boy Scouts Can., Edmonton Region, Alta.; mem. Cancer Control Agy. of B.C., trustee 1979-86, v.p., 1984, pres. 1985-86; bd. dirs. B.C. Lung Assn., 1988—, v.p. 1989, pres., 1990-91; chmn., bd. dirs. B.C. Organ Transplant Soc., 1986-89. Wing comdr. RCAF, 1943-46, 49-67. Recipient Gold medal in Pharmacy, 1943; Centennial medal, 1967, 75th Anniversary medal U. B.C., 1990; Can Forces decoration, 1965; Commemorative medal for 125th Anniversary of the Confedn. of Can., 1992. Mem. Alta. Pharm. Assn. (hon. life), Can. Pharm. Assn. (hon. life), Assn. of Faculties of Pharmacy of Can. (hon. life, chmn. 1959, 69), Can. Biochem. Soc., Pharmacol. Soc. Can., Can. Assn. of Univ. Tchrs., Can. Soc. Hosp. Pharmacists, B.C. Coll. Pharmacists (hon. life), U. B.C. Profs. Emeriti Divsn. Alumni Assn. (pres. 1993—). Home: 8394 Angus Dr, Vancouver, BC Canada V6P 5L2

RIEDERS, FREDRIC, forensic toxicologist; b. Vienna, Austria, July 9, 1922; came to U.S., 1939; s. Kalman and Ethel Julia (Quastler) Rozsa; m. Betty Jean Stockwell, Apr. 28, 1955; children: Eric F., Michael F., Carl W., Julia H. AB, Wash. Sq. Coll., 1948; MS, NYU, 1949; PhD, Thomas Jefferson U., 1952. Diplomate Am. Bd. Forensic Toxicology, Am. Bd. Clin. Chemistry. Jr. toxicologist Office of Chief Med. Examiner, N.Y.C., 1946-49; fellow in indsl. toxicology Jefferson Med. Coll., Thomas Jefferson U., Phila., 1949-52; from instr. to assoc. prof. dept. pharmacol. Jefferson Med. Coll., Phila., 1952-56, prof. pharmacology and toxicology, 1960—; chief toxicologist Dept. of Health, Med. Examiner, Phila., 1956-70, dir. poison info., 1956-70; dir. labs. Universal Med. Svcs. Inc., King of Prussia, Pa., 1969-70; lab. dir. Nat. Med. Svcs. Inc., Willow Grove, Pa., 1970—. Contbr. articles to profl. jours. Cpl. U.S. Army, 1942-46, ETO. Recipient Disting. Alumnus award Thomas Jefferson U. Coll. Grad. Studies, 1992. Fellow Am. Acad. Forensic Scis. (chmn. toxicology sect. 1957—, A.O. Gettler award 1986), Am. Chem. Soc.; mem. Am. Soc. Pharm. Exptl. Therapeutics, Internat. Assn. Forensic Toxicologists (charter). Republican. Lutheran. Office: Nat Med Svcs Inc 2300 Stratford Ave Willow Grove PA 19090-4123

RIEDL, JOHN ORTH, university dean; b. Milw., Dec. 9, 1937; s. John O. and Clare C. (Quirk) R.; m. Mary Lucille Priestap, Feb. 4, 1961; children: John T., Ann E., James W., Steven E., Daniel J. BS in Math. magna cum laude, Marquette U., Milw., 1958; MS in Math., U. Notre Dame, 1960, PhD in Math., 1963; postgrad., Northwestern U., 1963. Asst. prof. math. Ohio

State U., Columbus, 1966-70, assoc. prof., 1970—, asst. dean Coll. Math. and Phys. Sci., 1969-74, assoc. dean, 1974-87, acting dean, 1984-86, spl. asst. to provost, 1987, dean, dir. Mansfield (Ohio) Campus, 1987—, coord. dean regional campus, 1988—; panelist sci. edn. NSF, 1980-91; cons. Ohio Dept. Edn., 1989. Pres., v.p., exec. com. Univ. Community Assn., Columbus, 1970-78; mem. edn. commn. St. Peter's Schs., Mansfield, 1989—; mem. bus. adv. com. Mansfield City Schs., 1991—; trustee Rehab. Svc. North Cen. Ohio, Mansfield, 1990—, v.p., 1993; pres. Ohio Assn. Regional Campuses, 1993. NSF grad. fellow, 1960, 61, 62; recipient Faculty Svc. award Nat. U. Continuing Edn. Assn., 1988, Creative Programming award, 1988. Mem. Math. Assn. Am. (chair com. on minicourse 1981-87), Rotary Internat. Democrat. Roman Catholic. Avocations: fishing, woodworking, handball, gardening. Home: 745 Clifton Blvd Mansfield OH 44907 Office: Ohio State U 1680 University Dr Mansfield OH 44906

RIEDLINGER, BRIAN A., principal. Prin. Jean Gordon Elem. Sch., New Orleans. Recipient Elem. Sch. Recognition award U.S. Dept. Edn., 1989-90. Office: Jean Gordon Elem Sch 6101 Chatham Dr New Orleans LA 70122-2743

RIEDLSPERGER, MAX ERNST, history educator; b. San Luis Obispo, Calif., July 7, 1937; s. Helmuth Georg and Jean (Bennett) R.; m. Deanna Beckmann, Feb. 12, 1966; 1 child, Gretchen. AB, Wabash Coll., 1959; MA, U. Mich., 1961; PhD, U. Colo., 1969. Tchr. Eastern High Sch., Detroit, 1961-63, Day de Noc Community Coll., Escanaba, Mich., 1963-66; teaching assoc. U. Colo., Denver, 1966-67; instr. Colo. Women's Coll., Denver, 1967-68; asst. prof. Calif. Poly. State U., San Luis Obispo, 1969-72, assoc. prof., 1977-82, prof., 1983—, chmn. history dept., 1985-91; dir. internat. programs Calif. State U., Heidelberg, Fed. Republic Germany, 1983-84. Author: Lingering Shadow of Nazism, 1978; contbr. articles to profl. publs., chpts. to books. Bd. dirs. San Luis Obispo Mozart Festival, 1979-83, 84-85, v.p., 1985-86. Austrian Ministry of Edn. fellow, 1968-69; grantee Am. Coun. Learned Socs., 1972, NEH, 1976, U.S. Dept. Edn., 1986-88. Mem. Am. Hist. Assn., German Studies Assn. Democrat. Avocations: swimming, skiing, tennis, music. Office: Calif Poly State U Dept History San Luis Obispo CA 93407

RIEDY, MARK JOSEPH, finance educator; b. Aurora, Ill., July 9, 1942; s. Paul Bernard and Kathryn Veronica R.; m. Erin Jeanne Lynch, Aug. 29, 1964; children: Jennifer Erin, John Mark. BA in Econs. maxima cum laude, Loras Coll., 1964; MBA, Washington U., St. Louis, 1966; PhD, U. Mich., 1971. Asst. prof. bus. adminstrn. U. Colo., Boulder, 1969-71; sr. staff economist Council of Econ. Advisers, Washington, 1971-72; spl. asst. to chmn. Fed. Home Loan Bank Bd., Washington, 1972; v.p., dir. research PMI Investment Corp., San Francisco, 1973; v.p.; chief economist Fed. Home Loan Bank of San Francisco, 1973-77; exec. v.p., chief operating officer Mortgage Bankers Assn. of Am., Washington, 1978-84; pres., chief operating officer Fed. Nat. Mortgage Assn., Washington, 1985-86, cons., 1986-87; pres., chief operating officer J.E. Robert Cos., Alexandria, Va., 1987-88; pres., chief exec. officer Nat. Coun. Community Bankers, Washington, 1988-92, also bd. dirs.; Ernest W. Hahn prof. real estate fin. U. San Diego, 1993—; bd. dirs. Real Estate Rsch. Coun. No. Calif., 1974-76; mem. adv. coun. Credit Rsch. Ctr., Purdue U., 1981-82; bd. dirs. Fed. Nat. Mortgage Assn., Am. Residential Mortgage Corp., Continental Savs. Bank, Neighborhood Bancorp, Noble Broadcast Group, Drayton Ins. Cos., Perpetual Savs. Bank, Ctr. for Fin. Studies; mem. San Diego Mayor's Renaissance Commn. Vice chmn. St. Vincent De Paul Village. Woodrow Wilson scholar, 1964; Nat. Def. scholar, 1964-66; U.S. Steel Found. fellow, 1966-68; Robert G. Rodkey Found. fellow, 1966-69; Earhart Found. fellow, 1968-69. Mem. Am. Econs. Assn., Am. Fin. Assn., Nat. Assn. Bus. Economists, Am. Soc. Assn. Execs., Lambda Alpha Internat., Alpha Kappa Psi (hon.). Office: U San Diego Sch Bus Adminstrn 5998 Alcala Pk San Diego CA 92110-2492

RIEFF, DAVID SONTAG, editor, writer, critic; b. Boston, Sept. 28, 1952; s. Philip and Susan (Sontag) R. B.A., Princeton U., 1978. Dir. publs. N.Y. Inst. for Humanities, 1977-80, fellow, 1980—; program dir., 1984—; sr. editor Farrar, Straus & Giroux Inc., N.Y.C., 1979—. Author: Texas Boots, 1979; contbr. numerous articles, short stories to various publs. Club: Princeton (N.Y.C.). Office: Pentagram Design 212 Fifth Ave New York NY 10010

RIEFF, PHILIP, sociologist; b. Chgo., Dec. 15, 1922; s. Gabriel and Ida (Hurwitz) R.; m. Alison Douglas Knox, Dec. 31, 1963; 1 son by previous marriage, David. BA, U. Chgo., 1946, MA, 1947, PhD, 1954. Teaching fellow U. Chgo., 1946, instr., 1947-52; asst. prof. Brandeis U., Waltham, Mass., 1952-57; fellow Ctr. for Advanced Study in Behavior Scis., Palo Alto, Calif., 1957-58; assoc. prof. sociology U. Calif., Berkeley, 1958-61; prof. U. Pa., Phila., 1961—, Univ. prof. sociology, 1965-67, Benjamin Franklin Prof. Sociology, 1967-93, prof. emeritus, 1993—; dir. psychiatry Med. Coll. Pa., Phila., 1993—; chief editorial cons. Beacon Press, Boston, 1952-58; vis. assoc. prof. Harvard U., 1960; vis. fellow Ctr. for Study of Dem. Instns., Santa Barbara, Calif., 1963-64; Gauss lectr. Princeton U., 1975; Terry lectr. Yale U., 1976-77; prof. psychiatry and preventive medicine, Med. Coll. Pa., 1993—; vis. professorial lectr. Naval Acad., 1994. Author: Freud: The Mind of the Moralist, 1959, rev. edit., 1961, The Triumph of the Therapeutic: Uses of Faith After Freud, 1966, Fellow Teachers, 1973, The Feeling Intellect, 1990; editor The Collected Papers of Sigmund Freud (10 vols.), 1961; assoc. editor Am. Sociol. Rev., 1958-61; founding editor Jour. Am. Acad. Arts and Scis., 1956-59, Daedalus. Chief cons. planning dept. Nat. Coun. Chs., 1961-64. Named Fulbright Prof. U. Munich, 1959-60, Guggenheim fellow, 1970, Sometime fellow All Souls Coll., Oxford. Fellow Royal Soc. Arts London; mem. Libr. Co. Phila., Am. Sociol. Assn., Soc. Sci. Study Religion (mem. coun.), Societe Europeene de Culture, Garrick Club of London. Office: Med Coll Pa Dept Psychiatry 3200 Henry Ave Philadelphia PA 19129

RIEFLER, DONALD BROWN, financial consultant; b. Washington, Nov. 10, 1927; s. Winfield W. and Dorothy (Brown) R.; m. Patricia Hawley, Oct. 12, 1957; children: Duncan, Linda, Barbara. BA, Amherst Coll., 1949. With Morgan Guaranty Trust Co. of N.Y., N.Y.C., 1952—; v.p. Morgan Guaranty Trust Co. of N.Y., 1962-68, sr. v.p., 1968-77, chmn. market risk com., 1977-91; fin. mkts. cons., 1991—; bd. dirs. Liberty Brokerage Inc., Niagara Mohawk Power Corp., Bank of Tokyo Trust Co. With U.S. Army, 1950-52. Mem. John's Island Club, Riomar Country Club, Country Club of the Rockies (Edwards, Colo.). Home: 512 Bay Dr Vero Beach FL 32963-2107 Office: J P Morgan 109 Royal Palm Way Palm Beach FL 33480-4249

RIEGEL, BYRON WILLIAM, ophthalmologist; b. Evanston, Ill., Jan. 19, 1938; s. Byron and Belle Mae (Huot) R.; BS, Stanford U., 1960; MD, Cornell U., 1964; m. Marilyn Hills, May 18, 1968; children—Marc William, Ryan Marie, Andrea Elizabeth. Intern, King County Hosp., Seattle, 1964-65; asst. resident in surgery U. Wash., Seattle, 1965; resident in ophthalmology U. Fla., 1968-71; pvt. practice medicine specializing in ophthalmology, Sierra Eye Med. Group, Inc., Visalia, Calif., 1972—; mem. staff Kaweah Delta Dist. Hosp., chief of staff, 1978-79; mem. staff Visalia Community Hosp. Bd. dirs., asst. sec. Kaweah Delta Dist. Hosp., 1983-90. Served as flight surgeon USN, 1966-68. Co-recipient Fight-for-Sight citation for research in retinal dystrophy, 1970. Diplomate Am. Bd. Ophthalmology, Nat. Bd. Med. Examiners. Fellow ACS, Am. Acad. Ophthalmology; mem. AMA, Calif. Med. Assn. (del. 1978-79), Tulare County Med. Assns., Calif. Assn. Ophthalmology (v.p. 3d party liaison 1994—), Am. Soc. Cataract and Refractive Surgery, Internat. Phacoemulsification and Cataract Methodology Soc. Roman Catholic. Club: Rotary (Visalia). Home: 3027 W Keogh Ct Visalia CA 93291-4228 Office: 2830 W Main St Visalia CA 93291-4300

RIEGEL, JOHN KENT, corporate lawyer; b. Olean, N.Y., Sept. 24, 1938; s. Forrest M. and Lena (Zilkofsky) R.; m. Betty Ann Eden, Mar. 16, 1968; children: John Kent, Geoffrey. BA, Alfred U., 1961; LLB, Syracuse U., 1963. Bar: N.Y. 1963, Md. 1971. Military lawyer USMC, 1964-68; atty. advisor USN, Washington, 1968-71; asst. atty. gen. State of Md., Annapolis, 1971-72, gen. counsel dept. agriculture, 1972-74; atty. regulatory law ICI Ams. Inc., Wilmington, Del., 1974-76, atty. law dept., 1976-85; gen. counsel ICI Ams. Inc., Wilmington, 1986-93, also bd. dirs., exec. com., 1986—, pres., gen counsel, 1993—; bd. overseers Widener U. Sch. Law, 1987—; bd. trustees Med. Ctr. Del., 1987—; bd. dirs. Child Care Connection, 1991-94.

Mem. ABA, N.Y. State Bar Assn., Am. Corp. Counsel Assn. (bd. dirs. Del. Valley chpt. 1987-90, pres. 1989), European-Am. C. of C. (bd. dirs. 1995—). Office: ICI Americas Inc 3411 Silverside Rd Wilmington DE 19850-5391

RIEGEL, KURT WETHERHOLD, environmental protection, occupational safety and health; b. Lexington, Va., Feb. 28, 1939; s. Oscar Wetherhold and Jane Cordelia (Butterworth) R.; children: Tatiana Suzanne, Samuel Brent Oscar, Eden Sonja Jane. BA, Johns Hopkins U., 1961; PhD, U. Md., 1966; PMD, Harvard U., 1977. Asst. prof. astronomy UCLA, 1966-74; prof. astronomy U. Calif. Extension, Los Angeles, 1968-74; mgr. energy conservation program Fed. Energy Adminstrn., Washington, 1974-75; chief tech. and consumer products energy conservation Dept. Energy, Washington, 1975-78, dir. consumer products div., conservation and solar energy, 1978-79; assoc. dir. environ. engring. and tech. EPA, 1979-82; head Astronomy Ctrs. NSF, 1982-89; dir. Environ. Protection Office USN, 1989-94; dir. environ. tech. USN, Washington, 1994—; cons. Aerospace Corp., El Segundo, Calif., 1967-70, Rand Corp., Santa Monica, Calif., 1973-74; vis. fellow U. Leiden, Netherlands, 1972-73; Mem. Casualty Council Underwriters Labs., Nat. Radio Astron. Observatory Users Com., 1964-73. Contbr. articles to profl. jours. Mem. AAAS, Am. Phys. Soc., Sierra Club, Audubon Soc., Internat. Radio Sci. Union, Am. Astron. Soc., Internat. Astron. Union, Assn. of Scientists and Engrs. Home: 3019 N Oakland St Arlington VA 22207-5320

RIEGEL, T. E., manfacturing executive, light; b. 1942. Degree, Southwest Mo. State U., 1965. With O'Sullivan Industries, Inc., Lamar, Mo., 1965—, now exec. v.p. Office: O'Sullivan Industries Inc 1900 Gulf St Lamar MO 64759*

RIEGER, MITCHELL SHERIDAN, lawyer; b. Chgo., Sept. 5, 1922; s. Louis and Evelyn (Sampson) R.; m. Rena White Abelmann, May 17, 1949 (div. 1957); 1 child, Karen Gross Cooper; m. Nancy Horner, May 30, 1961 (div. 1972); stepchildren: Jill Levi, Linda Hanan, Susan Perlstein, James Geoffrey Felsenthal; m. Pearl Handelsman, June 10, 1973; stepchildren: Steven Newman, Mary Ann Malarkey, Nancy Halbeck. A.B., Northwestern U., 1944; J.D., Harvard U., 1949. Bar: Ill. 1950, U.S. Dist. Ct. (no. dist.) Ill. 1950, U.S. Supreme Ct. 1953, U.S. Ct. Mil. Appeals 1953, U.S. Ct. Appeals (7th cir.) 1954. Legal asst. Rieger & Rieger, Chgo., 1949-50, assoc., 1950-54; asst. U.S. atty. No. Dist Ill., Chgo., 1954-60; 1st asst. No. Dist Ill., 1958-60; assoc. gen. counsel SEC, Washington, 1960-61; ptnr. Schiff Hardin & Waite, Chgo., 1961—; instr. John Marshall Law Sch. Chgo., 1952-54. Contbr. articles to profl. jours. Mem. Chgo. Crime Commn., 1965-93; pres. Park View Home for Aged, 1969-71; Repr. precinct commiteeman, Highland Park, Ill., 1964-68; bd. dirs. Spertus Mus. Judaica, 1987-91, vis. com., 1991—. Lt. (j.g.) USNR, 1943-46, PTO. Fellow Am. Coll. Trial Lawyers; mem. ABA, FBA (Chgo. chpt. 1959-60, nat. v.p. 1960-61), Chgo. Bar Assn., Ill. Bar Assn., Am. Judicature Soc., 7th Circuit Bar Assn., Standard Club, Law Club Chgo., Cliff Dwellers Club, Vail Racquet Club, Phi Beta Kappa. Jewish. Avocations: photography; skiing; sailing. Home: 4950 S Chicago Beach Dr Chicago IL 60615-3204 Office: Schiff Hardin & Waite 7200 Sears Towers Chicago IL 60606

RIEGER, PHILIP HENRI, chemistry educator, researcher; b. Portland, Oreg., June 24, 1935; s. Otto Harry and Carla (Oertli) R.; m. Anne Bioren Lloyd, June 18, 1957; 1 child, Christine Lloyd. B.A., Reed Coll., 1956; Ph.D., Columbia U., 1962. Prof. chemistry Brown U., Providence, 1962—. Contbr. articles to profl. jours. Mem. Am. Chem. Soc. (chmn. R.I. sect. 1978), Royal Soc. Chemistry, New Eng. Assn. Chemistry Tchrs. Episcopalian. Home: 119 Congdon St Providence RI 02906-1462 Office: Brown U Dept Chemistry Box H Providence RI 02912

RIEGER, STEVEN ARTHUR, state legislator, business consultant; b. Pullman, Wash., May 14, 1952; s. Samuel and Olga (Skoblikoff) R.; m. Karen Jean Gibson, July 5, 1992. AB, Harvard U., 1974, MBA, 1976. Asst. to v.p. Crowley Maritime Corp., Seattle, 1976-79; asst. v.p. Seattle-Northwest Securities Corp., Anchorage, 1980-81; spl. asst. Alaska State Legislature, Juneau, 1981-82; v.p. William Kent Co., Anchorage, 1983-84; mem. Alaska Ho. Reps., Juneau, 1985-91; pres. S. Rieger & Co., Anchorage, 1991-92; mem. Alaska State Senate, Juneau, 1993—; dir. AJCH, Inc., Anchorage, 1991—. Republican. Avocations: running, skiing, outdoor activities. Office: Alaska State Legislature Box V Capitol Juneau AK 99811

RIEGERT, PETER, actor; b. N.Y.C., Apr. 11, 1947. BA in English, U. Buffalo. Appearances include (theatre, Off-Broadway) Minnie's Boys, (debut), Dance With Me, 1975, Sexual Perversity in Chicago, 1976, Censured Scenes From King Kong, 1980, Isn't It Romantic, 1984, La Brea Tar Pits, 1984, A Hell of a Town, 1984, A Rosen By Any Other Name, 1986, (Broadway) The Nerd, 1987, (films) National Lampoons Animal House, 1978, Americathon, 1978, Chilly Scenes of Winter, 1982, National Lampoon Goes to the Movies, 1982, The Big Carnival, 1983, Local Hero, 1983, The City Girl, 1984, A Man in Love, 1987, The Stranger, 1987, Crossing Delancy, 1988, That's Adequate, 1990, A Shock to the Systems, 1990, The Object of Beauty, 1991, Oscar, 1991, Passed Away, 1992, Utz, 1993, The Mask, 1994; (TV series) Middle Ages, 1992, (TV movies) Ellis Island, 1984, News at Eleven, 1986, Barbarians at the Gate, 1993 (Emmy award nominee 1993), Gypsy, 1993. Office: United Talent Agy 9560 Wilshire Blvd 5th Fl Beverly Hills CA 90212*

RIEGERT, ROBERT ADOLF, law educator, consultant; b. Cin., Apr. 21, 1923; s. Adolf and Hulda (Basler) R.; m. Roswitha Victoria Bigalke, Oct. 28, 1966; children—Christine Rose, Douglas Louis. BS, U. Cin., 1948; LL.B. cum laude, Harvard U., 1953; J.U.D. magna cum laude, U. Heidelberg, Fed. Republic Germany, 1966; postgrad., U. Mich., Harvard U., Yale U., MIT. Bar: D.C. 1953, Cts. Allied High Commn. Germany 1954. Mem. Harvard Legal Aid Bur., 1952-53; sole practice Heidelberg, 1954-63; vis. assoc. prof. So. Meth. U. Law Sch., Dallas, 1967-71; prof. law Cumberland Law Sch., Samford U., Birmingham, Ala., 1971—; dir. Cumberland Summer Law Program, Heidelberg, 1981—; Disting. vis. prof. Salmon P. Chase Coll. Law, 1983-84. Author: (With Robert Braucher) Introduction to Commercial Transactions, 1977, Documents of Title, 1978; contbr. articles to profl. jours. Chmn. subcom. on com. laws Ala. Pattern Jury Instruction Com. Served to 1st lt. USAAF, 1943-46. Grantee Dana Fund for Internat. and Comparative Law, 1979; grantee Am. Bar Found., 1966-67; German Acad. Exchange, 1953-55, mem. Harvard Legal Aid Bur., Salmon P. Chase Coll. law scholar, 1950; Pres.'s scholar U. Cin., 1941. Mem. ABA (com. on new payment systems), Internat. Acad. Comml. and Consumer Law, Am. Law. Inst., Ala. Law Inst. (coun.), mem. Am. Law Schs. (chmn. sect. internat. legal exchs.), Ala. Pattern Jury Instrns. Com., German Comparative Law Assn., Acad. Soc. German Supreme Cts., Army-Navy Club (Washington). Club: Army-Navy (Washington). Office: Samford U Cumberland Law Sch Birmingham AL 35229

RIEGLE, LINDA B., federal judge; b. 1948. BS, Shepherd Coll., Shepherdstown, W.Va.; JD, Union U., Albany, N.Y. Admitted to bar, 1978. Bankruptcy judge U.S. Dist. Ct. Nev., Las Vegas, 1988-94, chief bankruptcy judge, 1994—. Office: US Dist Ct 300 Las Vegas Blvd S Las Vegas NV 89101-5812

RIEGSECKER, MARVIN DEAN, pharmacist, state senator; b. Goshen, Ind., July 5, 1937; s. Levi and Mayme (Kauffman) R.; m. Norma Jane Shrock, Aug. 3, 1958; children: Steven Scott, Michael Dean. BA in Pharmacy, U. Colo., 1967. Pharmacist Parkside Pharmacy, Goshen, Ind., 1967-73; pharmacist, mgr. Hooks Drugs, Inc., Goshen, 1973-94; coroner Elkhart County, Goshen, 1977-84; mem. Ind. Senate, Indpls., 1988—; pharmacist Walgreens, Goshen, 1994—; bd. dirs. Goshen Gen. Hosp., 1985-94. Rep. commr. Elkhart County, 1985-88; bd. commrs. pres., 1987-88; past adv. bd. dirs. Oaklawn Hosp.; past chmn. Michiana Area Coun. of Govts. Mem. Elkhart County Pharm. Assn., Ind. Pharm. Assn. Republican. Mennonite. Avocation: jogging. Home: 801 S 6th St Goshen IN 46526-4010 Office: Ind Senate Statehouse 4-D N 200 W Washington St Indianapolis IN 46204

RIEHECKY, JANET ELLEN, writer; b. Waukegan, Ill., Mar. 5, 1953; d. Roland Wayne and Patricia Helen (Anderson) Polsgrove; m. James Jay Riehecky, Aug. 2, 1975; 1 child, Patrick William. BA summa cum laude, Ill. Wesleyan U., 1975; MA in Communication, Ill. State U., 1978; MA in

English, Northwestern U., 1983. Tchr. English Blue Mound (Ill.) High Sch., 1977-80, West Chicago (Ill.) High Sch., 1984-86; editor The Child's World Pub. Co., Elgin, Ill., 1987-90; freelance writer Elgin, 1990—. Author: Dinosaur series, 24 vols., 1988, UFOs, 1989, Saving the Forests, 1990, The Mystery of the Missing Money, 1995, The Mystery of the UFO, 1995, Irish Americans, 1995, others. Recipient Summit award for best children's nonfiction Soc. Midland Authors, 1988. Mem. Soc. Am. Magicians, Children's Reading Round Table, Soc. Children's Book Writers and Illustrators, Mystery Writers of Am., Phi Kappa Phi. Democrat. Baptist. Avocations: reading, hiking, dinosaur hunting.

RIEKE, ELIZABETH ANN, federal agency administrator; b. Buffalo, July 10, 1943; divorced; children: Frederick Martin, Eowyn Ann. BA in Polit. Sci. summa cum laude, Oberlin Coll., 1965; JD with highest distinction, U. Ariz., 1981. Rsch. asst. S.W. Environ. Svc., Tuscon, 1976-79; law well & Wilmer (formerly Bilby, Shoenhari, Warnock & Dolph), Tuscon, 1979; law clk. Office of Solicitor Divsn. Conservation and Wildlife, Dept. Interior, Washington, 1980; law clk. to Hon. William C. Canby Jr. U.S. Ct. Appeals (9th cir.), 1981-82; dep. legal counsel Ariz. Dept. Water Resources, 1982-85, chief legal counsel, 1985-87, dir., 1991-93; assoc. Jennings, Strouss & Salmon, Phoenix, 1987-89, ptnr., 1989-91; asst. sec. for water and sci. Dept. Interior, Washington, 1993—; adj. prof. Ariz. State U., Phoenix, 1989; speaker in field. Recipient Disting. Alumnus award U. Ariz., 1986. Office: Dept Interior 1849 C St NW Washington DC 20240-0001

RIEKE, PAUL VICTOR, lawyer; b. Seattle, Apr. 1, 1949; s. Luvern Victor and Anna Jane (Bierstedt) R.; m. Judy Vivian Farr, Jan. 24, 1974; children: Anna Katharina, Peter Johann. BA, Oberlin Coll., 1971; postgrad. U. Wash., 1971, Shoreline C.C., 1972-73; JD, Case Western Res. U., 1976. Bar: Wash. 1976, U.S. Dist. Ct. (we. dist.) Wash. 1976, U.S. Tax Ct. 1978. Assoc. Hatch & Leslie, Seattle, 1976-82, ptnr., 1982-91; ptnr. Foster, Pepper & Shefelman, 1991—. Exec. notes editor Case Western Res. U. Law Rev., 1975-76. Mem. exec. bd. dist. council N. Pacific dist. Am. Luth. Ch., Seattle, 1978-83, council pres. 1983, Am. Luth. Ch. pub. bd., 1984-87; v.p. Northwest Wash. Synod of Evangelical Luth. Ch. Am., Seattle, 1988-90, mem. Synod Coun., 1990-92, del. ELCA Nat. Assembly, 1991, ELCA Northwest Synod Regional Rep., 1992—, region one coun. mem., 1994—. Mem. ABA, Wash. State Bar Assn., Seattle-King County Bar Assn., Order of Coif. Democrat. Lodge: Seattle Downtown Central Lions. Home: 321 NE 161st St Seattle WA 98155-5741 Office: Foster Pepper & Shefelman 34th Fl 1111 3rd Ave Seattle WA 98101

RIEKE, WILLIAM OLIVER, foundation director, medical educator, former university president; b. Odessa, Wash., Apr. 26, 1931; s. Henry William and Hutoka S. (Smith) R.; m. Joanne Elynor Schief, Aug. 22, 1954; children: Susan Ruth, Stephen Harold, Marcus Henry. B.A. summa cum laude, Pacific Luth. U., 1953; M.D. with honors, U. Wash., 1958. Instr. anatomy U. Wash. Sch. Medicine, Seattle, 1958; asst. prof. U. Wash. Sch. Medicine, 1961-64, adminstrv. officer, 1963-66, assoc. prof., 1964-66; prof., head dept. Coll. Medicine U. Iowa, Iowa City, 1966-71; dean protem Coll. Medicine U. Iowa (Coll. Medicine), 1969-70, chmn. exec. com., 1969-70; vice chancellor for health affairs, prof. anatomy U. Kans. Med. Center, Kansas City, 1971-73; exec. vice chancellor, prof. anatomy U. Kans. Med. Center, 1973-75; affiliate prof. biol. structure U. Wash. Sch. Medicine, Seattle, 1975—; pres. Pacific Lutheran U., Parkland, Wash., 1975-92; pres. emeritus, 1992—; exec. dir. Ben B. Cheney Found., 1992—; Mem. interdisciplinary gen. basic sci. test com. Nat. Bd. Med. Examiners, 1968-72, chmn. anatomy test com., 1972-75, mem. at large, 1975-79; spl. cons. NIH, 1970-72; mem. adv. com. Inst. Medicine, Nat. Acad. Scis., 1974-76; mem. Commn. on Colls., NW Assn. Schs. and Colls., 1979-84. Editor: Procs. 3d Ann. Leucocyte Culture Conf, 1969; editorial bd.: Am. Jour. Anatomy, 1968-71. Bd. dirs. Luth. Ednl. Council N. Am., 1980-83, pres., 1982-83; chmn. Wash. Friends Higher Edn., 1983-91. Named one of Most Effective Coll. or Univ. Pres., Bowling Green State U. Research Study, 1986, Disting. Alumnus Pacific Luth. U., 1970, Disting. Alumnus Pi Kappa Delta, 1977, Disting. Alumnus U. of Washington Med. Alumni, 1989; decorated Knight First Class Royal Norwegian Order of Merit, 1989. Lutheran (mem. ch. council 1967-73). Home: 13905 18th Ave S Tacoma WA 98445-1006 Office: Ben B Cheney Found 1st Interstate Plz Ste 1600 Tacoma WA 98402

RIELLY, JOHN EDWARD, association executive; b. Rapid City, S.D., Dec. 28, 1932; s. Thomas J. and Mary A. (Dowd) R.; m. Elizabeth Downs, Dec. 28, 1957 (marriage annulled 1976); children: Mary Ellen, Catherine Ann, Thomas Patrick, John Downs; m. Irene Diedrich, Aug. 1, 1987. B.A., St. John's U., Collegeville, Minn., 1954; postgrad. (Fulbright scholar), London Sch. Econs. and Polit. Sci., 1955-56; Ph.D., Harvard U. 1961. Faculty dept. govt. Harvard U., 1958-61; with Alliance for Progress programs Dept. State, Washington, 1961-62; fgn. policy asst. to Sen. then Vice Pres. Hubert Humphrey, Washington, 1963-69; cons. office European and internat. affairs Ford Found., N.Y.C., 1969-70; sr. fellow Overseas Devel. Council, Washington, 1970-71; exec. dir. Chgo. Council on Fgn. Relations, 1971-74; pres., 1974—; cons. NSC; mem. adv. bd. Grad. Sch. Arts and Scis., Harvard U.; bd. dirs. Am. Council on Germany, Nat. Com. on U.S.-China Relations, China Council of Asia Soc.; Trilateral Commn., commn. on, U.S.-Brazilian Relations; past pres. Nat. Council Community World Affairs Orgns. Contbr. articles to profl. jours.; editor: American Public Opinion and U.S. Foreign Policy, 1975, 2d edit., 1979, 83, 87, 91, 95; editl. bd. Fgn. Policy Quar., 1974—. Trustee St. John's U. Mem. Am. Polit. Sci. Assn., Council on Fgn. Relations, N.Y.C. Home: 2021 Kenilworth Ave Wilmette IL 60091-1519 Office: 116 S Michigan Ave Chicago IL 60603-6001

RIEMEN, DAVID CLARENCE, chief of police; b. Ft. Wayne, Ind., Mar. 8, 1944; s. Albert Joseph and Beulah Mary (Patterson) R.; m. Diane Mae Gebhard, July 11, 1964; children—David, Michael, Jennifer, Sara. A.S., Ind. U., 1981. With Ft. Wayne (Ind.) Police Dept., 1967—, chief of police, 1981—; tng. instr. Police Sch. Liaison Officers Clinic, Flint, Mich., Internat. Assn. Chiefs of Police Developing Computer Capabilities, Nashville. Mem. adv. bd. Ft. Wayne Women's Shelter. Mem. Internat. Assn. Chiefs of Police. Roman Catholic. Club: Toastmasters. Office: Office Police Chief 1 E Main St Rm 280 Fort Wayne IN 46802-1804

RIEMENSCHNEIDER, ALBERT LOUIS, engineering educator; b. Cody, Nebr., May 18, 1936; s. Albert L. and Agnes E. (Schilling) R.; m. Norma Mae Geisler, June 24, 1962; children: Richard L., David F., Barbara J. BSEE, S.D. Sch. Mines and Tech., 1959, MSEE, 1962; PhD, U. Wyo., 1969. Registered profl. engr., S.D. Engr. Sperry Utah Corp., Salt Lake City, 1959-60; design engr. Dakota Steel & Supply Co., Rapid City, S.D., 1960-61; instr. U. Wyo., Laramie, 1961-67; chief engr. Dunham Assocs., Rapid City, 1974-80; grad. tchg. asst. S.D. Sch. Mines and Tech., Rapid City, 1961-62, asst. prof., 1967-73, assoc. prof., 1973-74, 80-84, prof., dept. head, 1983—; cons. ALR Engring., RE/SPEC, Inc., Rapid City, 1987—. Mem. IEEE, Am. Soc. Engring. Edn., Nat. Soc. Profl. Engrs. Democrat. Lutheran. Lodge: Elks. Avocations: electronics, computers, hunting, fishing. Home: 4051 Corral Dr Rapid City SD 57702-9228 Office: South Dakota Sch of Mines 501 E St Joseph St Rapid City SD 57701-3995

RIEMENSCHNEIDER, DAN LAVERNE, religious organization administrator; b. Pontiac, Mich., July 21, 1952; s. Henry LaVerne and Sarah Lou R.; m. Rebecca Joy Fruth, June 26, 1976; 1 child, Derek Henri. BA in Social Work, Mich. State U., 1974, PhD in Family Ecology, 1985; MA in Religion Edn., Asbury Seminary, Wilmore, Ky., 1976. Min. of Edn. Spring Arbor (Mich.) Free Meth. Ch., 1977-85; asst. prof. social work and family sci. Spring Arbor Coll., 1985-87; exec. dir. dept. edn. Free Meth. Ch. of North Am., Indpls., 1987—; chmn. Samaritan Counseling Ctr., Jackson, Mich., 1985-87. Bd. dirs. Mich. Council on Family Relations, Lansing, Mich., 1985-87. Mem. Nat. Council Family Relations, Nat. Assn. Evangelicals, Nat. Christian Edn. Assn. (bd. dirs.), Nat. Task Force on Family (bd. dirs.). Office: Free Meth World Hqdrs PO Box 535002 770 N High School Rd Indianapolis IN 46214-3756

RIEMENSCHNEIDER, PAUL ARTHUR, physician, radiologist; b. Cleve., Apr. 17, 1920; s. Albert and Selma (Marting) R.; m. Mildred McCarthy, May 12, 1945; children: Barbara Anne, Nancy Emelia, David Andrew, Paul Albert, Mary Elizabeth, Sarah Bache. BS magna cum laude, Baldwin-Wallace Coll., 1941; MD, Harvard U., 1944. Diplomate Am. Bd. Radiology (trustee 1973-85), Nat. Bd. Med. Examiners. Prof., chmn. dept. radiology

SUNY, Syracuse, 1945-64; chief diagnostic radiology Santa Barbara (Calif.) Cottage Hosp., 1964-89, bd. dirs., 1984-90; vis. prof. in residence SUNY, Syracuse, 1983—; Radiology Soc. of No. Am. Internat. vis. prof. of Radiology, Univ. Malaya, 1990-91. Co-editor: N.Y. State Jour. Medicine, 1960-64; mem. editorial adv. bd. Yearbook of Cancer, 1960-64; contbr. articles to profl. jours. Mem. appropriations com. Santa Barbara Found., 1984-93; vestryman All Saints Episcopal Ch., 1970-76, sr. warden, 1973; bd. dirs. ARC, Santa Barbara, 1968-72, Am. Cancer Soc., Santa Barbara, 1967-70; bd. dirs. Casa Dorinda Retirement Residence, 1975-76, 89—, pres., 1993—; bd. dirs. Wood Glen Hall Retirement Residence, 1980—, sec., 1987; bd. dirs. Cancer Found. Santa Barbara, 1966-82, 89-95, chmn. equipment com., 1973-82. Lt. comdr. USNR, 1945-47, 54-56. Recipient Alumni Merit award Baldwin-Wallace Coll., 1985. Fellow Am. Coll. Radiology (cancer com. 1952-54, council 1956-64, bd. chancellors 1967-73, chmn. commn. standards in radiologic practice 1968-71, v.p. 1972, pres. 1974, chmn. commn. manpower 1972-86, chmn. com. manpower in armed svcs. 1975-86, Gold medal 1982); mem. AMA, Calif. Med. Assn., Santa Barbara County Med. Soc. (chmn. med. sch. com. 1967-71), Am Roentgen Ray Soc. (mem. publs. com. 1965-75, chmn. 1970-75, exec. council 1970-75, 77-82, chmn. program com. 1977-79, pres.-elect 1977-79, pres. 1979, Gold medal award 1986), South Coast Radiol. Soc. (pres. 1967), Assn. Univ. Radiologists (sec. 1960, pres. 1961, com. resident tng. 1984-88), Radiol. Soc. N.Am. (Gold medal award 1990), Am. Soc. Neuroradiology, Soc. Pediatric Radiology, Eastern Radiol. Soc. (pres.-elect 1987, pres. 1988-89), Calif. Radiol. Soc., So. Calif. Radiol. Soc., Detroit Roentgen Soc. (hon.), Bluegrass Radiol. Soc. (hon.), Pacific N.W. Radiol. Soc. (hon.), Alpha Omega Alpha. Republican. Clubs: Birnamwood Golf (Santa Barbara); Skaneateles Country (N.Y.). Avocations: tennis, swimming. Home: 112 Olive Mill Rd Santa Barbara CA 93108-2424

RIEMKE, RICHARD ALLAN, mechanical engineer; b. Vallejo, Calif., Oct. 11, 1944; s. Allan Frederick and Frances Jewell (O'Brien) R. BA in Physiology, U. Calif., Berkeley, 1967, MA in Physiology, 1971, PhD in Engring. Sci., 1977. Postdoctoral fellow U. So. Calif., Los Angeles, 1977-78; rsch. engr. Del Mar Avionics, Irvine, Calif., 1979; staff fellow NIH, Bethesda, Md., 1980; sr. engring. specialist Nat. Engring. Lab., Lockheed Idaho Techs., Inc., Idaho Falls, 1980—. Served with U.S. Army, 1969-75. Mem. AAAS, ANS, Am. Soc. Mech. Engrs., Biomed. Engring. Soc., Soc. Computer Simulation, Soc. Math. Biology, Soc. Engring. Sci., Order of Golden Bear, Alpha Sigma Phi. Republican. Roman Catholic. Avocations: swimming, surfing. Home: 1727 Grandview Dr # 4 Idaho Falls ID 83402-5016 Office: Lockheed Ida Techs Inc Idaho Nat Engring Lab Idaho Falls ID 83415-3880

RIENNER, LYNNE CAROL, publisher; b. Pitts., Aug. 3, 1945; d. David and Molly (Rice) R. B.A., U. Pa., 1967. Exec. v.p., assoc. publisher, editorial dir. Westview Press Inc., Boulder, Colo., 1975-84; pres. Lynne Rienner Pub. Inc., Boulder, Colo., 1984—; pub. series various orgns.; lectr. U. Denver Pub. Inst. 1981-84, 93; panelist nat. meetings. Bd. dirs. Boulder Breast Cancer Coalition, 1993—. Mem. Soc. Scholarly Pub., Assn. Am. Pubs. (bd. dirs. 1992—). Office: Lynne Rienner Pub Inc 1800 30th St Ste 314 Boulder CO 80301-1026

RIEPE, DALE MAURICE, philosopher, writer, illustrator, educator, Asian art dealer; b. Tacoma, June 22, 1918; s. Rol and Martha (Johnson) R.; m. Charlene Williams, 1948; children: Kathrine Leigh Riepe Herschlag, Dorothy Lorraine. B.A., U. Wash., 1944; M.A., U. Mich., 1946, Ph.D., 1954; postgrad. (Rockefeller-Watamull-McInerny fellow), U. Hawaii, Banaras and Madras, India, Tokyo and Waseda, Japan, 1949. Instr. philosophy Carleton Coll., 1948-51; asst. prof. U.S.D. 1952-54; asso. prof. U. N.D., 1954-59, prof., 1959-62, chmn. dept., 1954-62; prof., chmn. C.W. Post Coll., 1962-63; prof. philosophy SUNY, Buffalo, 1963—; chmn. dept. social scis., assoc. dean SUNY (Grad. Sch.), 1964—; exchange lectr. U. Man., 1955; vis. lectr. Western Wash. U. 1961; instr. marine electricity Naval Tng. Program, Seattle, 1943-45; mem. nat. screening bd. South Asia, Fulbright Selection, 1968-73, Asia, 1970-72; chmn. Fulbright Selection Com. for Asia, 1972, 82; vis. Fulbright lectr. Tokyo U., 1957-58, vis. lectr. Delhi U., 1967; exchange lectr. Moscow State U., 1979, Beijing Higher Edn. Inst., 1984; docent Albright-Knox Art Gallery; cons. Ctr. for Sci., Tech. and Devel., Council of Sci. adn Indsl. Rsch., Govt. India, 1978—, Inst. Fang Studies, 1987—; ed. Cuban-N.Am. Philosophy Conf., Cuban Inst. Social Sci., 1982, Fang Centennial, Taiwan Nat. U., Taipeh, 1987, Hungarian-Am. Philos. Conf., Budapest, 1988; sports columnist The Town Crier. Author: The Naturalistic Tradition in Indian Thought, 1961, The Philosophy of India and its Impact on American Thought, 1970, Indian Philosophy Since Independence, 1979, The Owl Flies by Day, 1979, Asian Philosophy Today, 1981, Objectivity and Subjectivism in the Philosophy of Science, 1985, Philosophy and Revolutionary Theory, 1986, also articles in field.; editor: Phenomenology and Natural Existence, 1973, Philosophy and Political Economy; co-editor: The Structure of Philosophy, 1966, Contributions of American Sankritists in the Spread of Indian Philosophy in the United States, 1967, Radical Currents in Contemporary Philosophy, 1970, Reflections on Revolution, 1971, Philosophy at the Barricade, 1971, Contemporary East European Philosophy, 1971, Essays in East-West Dialogue, 1973, Explorations in Philosophy and Society, 1978; illustrator The Quick and the Dead, 1948; editorial com. Chinese Studies in History, 1970—, Chinese Studies in Philosophy, 1970—; publs. bd. Conf. for Asian Affairs; Editor various series.; editl. bd. Philos. Currents and Revolutionary World, 1972-86, Soviet Studies in Philosophy, 1979-87, Marxist Dimensions, 1987—; Mem. com. overseers Chung-an U., Korea; bd. dirs. Evergreen Coll. Cmty. Orgn., 1988—; bd. dirs Friends of Evergreen Coll. Libr., 1992—; active Henry Gallery, Frye Gallery; mem. Capital Mus. and Art Soc., Wash. State Hist. Soc., Seattle Art Mus. Fulbright scholar India, 1951-52; Fulbright lectr. U. Tokyo, 1957-58; U. Mich. fellow, 1945-48, Carnegie Corp. fellow Asian Studies, 1960-61; Am. Inst. Indian Studies research fellow, 1966-67; grantee 4th East-West Philosophers Conf., 1964; Penrose fund Am. Philos. Soc., 1963; SUNY Research Found., 1965, 66, 67, 69, 72, 73, Bulgarian Acad. Sci., 1975, London Sch. Oriental and African Studies grantee, 1971. Fellow Royal Asiatic Soc., Far Eastern Inst. (Tokyo); mem. AAAS, ACLU, Conf. Asian Affairs (sec. 1955), Am. Oriental Soc., Am. Philos. Soc., Indian Inst. Psychology, Philosophy and Psychical Research (hon. adviser), Soc. for Am. Philosophy (chmn. 1960), Am. Inst. Indian Studies (trustee 1965-66), Soc. for Creative Ethics (sec.), Am. Archaeol. Soc., Am. Assn. Asian Studies, Am. Math. Soc., Am. Aesthetics Soc., Internat. Soc. for Aesthetics, Am. Soc. Comparative and Asian Philosophy, Asiatic Soc. (Calcutta), Soc. for Philos. Study Dialectical Materialism (founding sec.-treas. 1962—), Soc. for Philos. Study Marxism (publs. sec. 1973-86), Union Am. and Japanese Profls. against Nuclear Omnicide (treas. U.S. sect. 1985—), Internat. House of Japan, t. Philosophers for Prevention Nuclear Omnicide, United Univ. Profs of SUNY-Buffalo (v.p.), Johnson Soc., Kokusai Bunka Shinkokai, Palm Springs Desert Mus., Seattle Art Mus., Tumwater Valley Golf Club, Alpha Pi Zeta. Office: SUNY 605 Baldy Hall Buffalo NY 14261

RIEPE, JAMES SELLERS, investment company executive; b. Bryn Mawr, Pa., June 25, 1943; s. Henry Brunt and Marjorie (Sellers) R.; m. Gail Nelms Petty, Sept. 14, 1968; children: Christina, James, Jr. B.S., Wharton Sch., U. Pa., 1965, M.B.A., 1967. Mem. audit staff Coopers & Lybrand, C.P.A.s, Phila., 1967-69; asst. to pres. Wellington Mgmt. Co., Phila., 1969-72; v.p. Wellington Mgmt. Co., 1972-75; exec. v.p. Vanguard Group, Inc., Valley Forge, Pa., 1975-82; dir. Vanguard Group, Inc., 1979-82; mng. dir., mem. mgmt. com. T. Rowe Price Assocs., Inc., Balt., 1982—; pres. T. Rowe Price Investment Services, 1982—; chmn. TRP Trust Co., 1982—, TRP Retirement Plan Svcs., 1982—; dir. Rhône-Poulenc Rorer. Trustee, chmn. Balt. Mus. Art.; trustee U. Pa.; mem. exec. com., mem. exec. com. health sys.; pres. Gilman Sch., 1994—. Mem. Balt. Equitable Soc., Nat. Assn. Security Dealers (gov.), Investment Co. Inst. (gov.). Clubs: Greenspring Valley Hunt, Maryland. Office: T Rowe Price Assocs Inc 100 E Pratt St Baltimore MD 21202-1009

RIEPER, ALAN GEORGE, brokerage company executive; b. S.I., N.Y., May 2, 1941; s. Henry Jay and Marian Francis (Tilman) R.; m. Kathryn Ruth Young, Sept. 26, 1970; children: Karen Elizabeth, Mark Edward. BS in Bus., Lehigh U., 1962; MBA, Columbia U., 1964. Asst. cashier First Nat. City Bank, N.Y.C., 1964-72; v.p. Sentinel Advs., Inc., Montpelier, Vt., 1972-79; v.p. Cowen & Co., Boston, 1979-83, spl. ltd. ptnr., 1983-87, ptnr. 1987-91, mng. dir., 1991-93; prin. Morgan Stanley & Co., Inc., 1993—. Bd. dirs. First Ch. of Christ, Scientist, Marblehead, Mass., 1983-84, pres. 1985; bd. dirs. Green Mountain council Boy Scouts Am., Burlington, Vt., 1977-79.

Served to capt. USNR, 1965-67, Res. ret. Fellow Fin. Analysts Fedn.; mem. N.Y. Soc. Security Analysts, Electronic Analysts N.Y., Electronic Analysts Boston, Naval Res. Assn. Republican. Mem. Ch. Christ Scientist. Avocations: sailing, photography, travel, fly fishing. Home: 19 Dodge Rd Marblehead MA 01945-1405 Office: Cowen & Co One Exchange Pl Boston MA 02109

RIEPL, FRANCIS JOSEPH, utilities executive; b. Sayreville, N.J., Feb. 7, 1936; s. Frank Joseph and Adeline (Farley) R.; m. Jacqueline Ann York, Dec. 29, 1956; children: Timothy, Frank, Glenn. BS in Econs., U. Pa., 1958. Mgr. adminstrv. systems Pub. Service Electric and Gas, Newark, 1970-72, asst. treas., 1972-80, gen. mgr. systems, 1980-87, v.p., treas., 1987—. Office: Pub Svc Electric & Gas Co 80 Park Plz Newark NJ 07102-4106

RIERSON, ROBERT LEAK, broadcasting executive, television writer; b. Walnut Cove, N.C., Sept. 5, 1927; s. Sanders C. and Anna (Cox) R.; m. Barbara Eugenia McLeod, Sept. 23, 1950 (dec. Feb. 1988); children: Barbara Elaine, Richard Troy. Student, Duke U., 1945-46, Davidson Coll., 1946-47; BS in Speech cum laude, Northwestern U., 1948. Program dir., program ops. mgr. WBT Radio and WBTV, Charlotte, N.C., 1948-66; program mgr. WJBK-TV, Detroit, 1966-69, WTOP-TV, Washington, 1969-71; dir. broadcasting WCBS-TV, N.Y.C., 1971-73; pres. Rierson Broadcast Consultants, N.Y.C., 1973-75; program exec. Grey Advt., N.Y.C., 1975-77; v.p., dir. programming Dancer-Fitzgerald-Sample, N.Y.C., 1977-80; exec. producer Corinthian Prodns., N.Y.C., 1980-82; dir. news programming CNN TV, Atlanta, 1982—. Producer-creator TV show ABCs of Democracy, 1965; producer, writer TV show George Washington's Mt. Vernon, 1970; creator, writer TV series 24 Days of Christmas, 1978. Bd. dirs. Mich. Coun. Chs., Detroit, 1968-69, ARC, Charlotte, 1960-62; 1st v.p. Charlotte Oratorio Singers, 1960-66. Lt. USNR, 1952-54. Recipient Edn. award Charlotte Jr. Woman's Club, 1961, George Washington Honor medal Freedoms Found., 1970; named Young Man of Yr., 1960. Mem. Nat. Assn. Radio-TV Program Execs. (charter mem., bd. dirs. 1964—), Radio-TV News Dirs. Assn., Order of Long Leaf Pine. Republican. Mem. Moravian Episcopal Ch. Avocations: reading, travel, movies. Home: 3068 Vinings Ridge Dr NW Atlanta GA 30339-3771 Office: Turner Program Svcs 1 CNN Center Plz Atlanta GA 30335-4201

RIES, EDWARD RICHARD, petroleum geologist, consultant; b. Freeman, S.D., Sept. 18, 1918; s. August and Mary F. (Graber) R.; student Freeman Jr. Coll., 1937-39; A.B. magna cum laude, U. S.D., 1941; M.S., U. Okla., 1943, Ph.D. (Warden-Humble fellow), 1951; postgrad. Harvard, 1946-47; m. Amelia D. Capshaw, Jan. 24, 1949 (div. Oct. 16, 1956); children: Rosemary Melinda, Victoria Elise; m. Maria Wipfler, June 12, 1964. Asst. geologist Geol. Survey S.D., White River area, 1941; geophys. interpreter Robert Ray Inc., Western Okla., 1942; jr. geologist Carter Oil Co., Mont., Wyo., 1943-44, geologist Mont., Wyo., Colo., 1944-49; sr. geologist Standard Vacuum Oil Co., Assam, Tripura and Bangladesh, India, 1951-53, sr. regional geologist N.V. Standard Vacuum Petroleum, Maatschappij, Indonesia, 1953-59, geol. adviser for Far East and Africa, White Plains, N.Y., 1959-62; geol. adviser Far East, Africa, Oceania, Mobil Petroleum Co., N.Y.C., N.Y., 1962-65; geol. adviser for Europe, Far East, Mobil Oil Corp., N.Y.C., 1965-71, sr. regional explorationist Far East, Australia, New Zealand, Dallas, 1971-73, Asia-Pacific, Dallas, 1973-76, sr. geol. adviser Rsch. Geology, 1976-79, assoc. geol. advisor Geology-Geophysics, Dallas, 1979-82, sr. geol. cons., 1982-83; ind. internat. petroleum geol. cons. Europe, Africa, Sino-Soviet and S.E. Asia, 1986—. Grad. asst., teaching fellow U. Okla., 1941-43, Harvard, 1946-47. Served with AUS, 1944-46. Mem. AAAS, Am. Assn. Petroleum Geologists (assoc. editor 1978-83, 50 Yr. Mem. Svc. award 1993), Geol. Soc. Am., Am. Geol. Inst., Nat. Wildlife Fedn., Nat. Audubon Soc., N.Y. Acad. Sci., Soc. Exploration Geophysicists, Wilderness Soc., Am. Legion, Phi Beta Kappa, Sigma Xi, Phi Sigma, Sigma Gamma Epsilon. Republican. Mennonite. Club: Harvard (Dallas). Author numerous domestic and internat. proprietary and pub. hydrocarbon generation and reserve evaluations, reports and profl. papers. Home and Office: 6009A Royal Crest Dr Dallas TX 75230-3434

RIES, MARTIN, artist, educator; b. Washington, Dec. 26, 1926; s. Martin Frank and Kathryn (Stretch) R.; m. Dianys d'Arcy Frobisher, June 8, 1953; children: d'Arcy, Von, Gannett, Nicole. BFA, Am. U., 1950; MA in Art History, Hunter Coll., 1968, postgrad. in mus. adminstrn., 1968. Asst. dir. pub. rels. Nat. Congl. Com., Washington, 1951; asst. dir. Hudson River Mus., 1957-67; advisor Westchester Cultural Ctr., 1965-66; curator instnl. art exhibits, prof. art L.I. U., Bklyn., 1967-94. One-man shows include Atelier Gallery, N.Y.C., 1968, Paul Gallery, Tokyo, 1968, Atelier Terre d'Ocre, France, 1973, Unicorn Gallery, Soho, N.Y., 1976, Ganesh Gallery, Lenox, Mass., 1978, Belanthi Gallery, Bklyn., 1984, Stamford Mus., Stamford, Conn., 1981, Raja Idris Gallery, Melbourne, Australia, 1989, Robb St. Gallery, Bairnsdale, Australia, 1989, Salena Gallery, L.I.U.; exhibited in group shows Smithsonian Inst., 1952, Mus. of Modern Art, N.Y.C., 1956, SUNY-Albany, 1967, Casa de la Cultura Ecuatoriana in Cuayaquil, Ecuador, 1979, Hammer Gallery, N.Y.C., 1980, Muestra Internacional de Obra Grafica, Spain, 1982, Aaron Berman Gallery, N.Y.C., 1983, Kenkeleba Gallery, N.Y.C., 1985, Inst. of Contemporary Art, London, 1988; contbr. editor Arts Mag., 1974-75; contbr. articles, revs., catalog introductions, and artists' statements to publs. Art editor Greenwich Village News, 1976-77. With U.S. Army, 1945-46. Mem. Artists Representing Environ. Art (bd. dirs.), Assn. Internationale des Critiques d'Art (Am. sect.), Am. Soc. Contemporary Artists (bd. dirs.). Home: 36 Livingston Rd Scarsdale NY 10583-6845

RIES, STANLEY K., plant physiologist, university educator; b. Kenton, Ohio, Sept. 6, 1927; s. Edwin John and Gertrude (Hanna) R.; m. Mary Isabelle Kinsel, June 19, 1949; children: Carol, Don, Kathleen. BS, Mich. State Coll., East Lansing, 1950; PhD, Cornell U., 1954. Rsch. asst. Cornell U., Ithaca, N.Y., 1950-53; asst. prof. Mich. State U., East Lansing, 1953-58; assoc. prof. Mich. State U., 1958-65, prof., 1965—; cons. agrl. bus., 1954—, several chem. cos., 1960—. Contbr. articles to profl. pubs. With USAF, 1945-46. Fellow AAAS, ASHS; mem. Phi Kappa Phi, Sigma Xi. Achievements include patents for Cucumber Harvester, Tomato Harvester; discovery of two natural plant growth regulators. Home: 1529 Cahill Dr East Lansing MI 48823-4724 Office: Mich State U Dept Horticulture East Lansing MI 48824

RIESBECK, JAMES EDWARD, glass company executive; b. Corning, N.Y., Oct. 11, 1942; s. Paul E. and Isadora F. (Quinn) R.; m. Joyce K. Luta, June 8, 1962; 1 child, Bryan. A.A.S., Corning Community Coll., 1962; B.S., U. Ky., 1966; postgrad. Harvard Bus. Sch., 1976. With Corning Glass Works, N.Y., 1966—, asst. corp. controller, 1977-80, v.p., controller, 1981—. Mem. Fin. Execs. Inst. Republican. Home: RR 2 Corning NY 14830-9802 Office: Corning Glass Works Houghton Park Corning NY 14831

RIESENBACH, MARVIN S., automotive corporation executive; b. 1929; married. BA, Pa. State U., 1951; MBA, Rutgers U., 1954. Acct. Haskins & Sells, 1957-62; v.p. Inst. for Sci. Info., 1962-68; v.p., treas. 3i Co., 1968-72; mem. staff Subaru of Am., Cherry Hill, N.J., 1972-76, v.p., contr., 1976-77, sr. v.p., 1977-83, exec. v.p., 1983, exec. v.p., chief fin. officer, 1986—. Served with U.S. Army, 1954-56. Office: Subaru of Am Inc PO Box 6000 Cherry Hill NJ 08034-6000

RIESENFELD, STEFAN ALBRECHT, law educator, consultant; b. Breslau, Ger., June 8, 1908; came to U.S. 1934, naturalized, 1940; s. Conrad Ernst and Margarethe (Landecker) R.; m. Phyllis B. Thogrimson, Dec. 23, 1943; children—Peter William, Stefan Conrad. J.U.D., U. Breslau, 1932, U. Milan, 1934; LL.B., U. Calif.-Berkeley, 1937; S.J.D., Harvard U., 1940; B.S., U. Minn., 1943; D.h.c., U. Cologne (Ger.), 1970. Bar: Minn. 1939, U.S. Supreme Ct. 1978. Prof. law U. Minn., Mpls., 1938-52; prof. law U. Calif.-Berkeley, 1952—; Emanuel S. Heller prof., 1954-75, prof. emeritus, 1975—; prof. law U. Calif., Hastings Coll. Law, San Francisco, 1975—; cons. to U.S. Bd. Econ. Warfare, 1942, UN ad hoc com., 1952; counselor on internat. law Dept. Def., 1955, Dept. State, 1977-82; mem. Adv. Com. on Bankruptcy Rules, 1961-72; vis. prof. various U.S. and fgn. univs.; cons. Calif. law revision commn., 1970-81, Legal Ref. Bur. of Hawaii, 1968-74. Served with USN, 1943-46. Recipient Silver medal Dept. State, 1979, 84; Verdienstkreuz, Fed. Republic of Germany, 1975. Mem. ABA, Nat. Bankruptcy Conf., Am. Acad. Arts and Scis., Am. Soc. Internat. Law, Internat. Law Assn. (Am. br.), Soc. Legal History. Lutheran. Author: Protection of Fisheries Under

International Law, 1943, Modern Social Legislation, 1950, (with Hetland, Maxwell and Warren) California Secured Land Transactions, 4th edit., 1992, Creditors' Remedies and Debtors' Protection, 4th edit., 1986. Home: 1129 Amador Ave Berkeley CA 94707-2632 Office: U Calif Berkeley Law Sch Boalt Hall Berkeley CA 94720

RIESER, JOSEPH A., JR., lawyer; b. Pitts., Aug. 28, 1947; s. Joseph Alexander and Ruth Margaret (Piper) R.; m. Susan Jean Irving, Feb. 28, 1976; 1 child, Alexander H.I. AB, Princeton U., 1969; JD, Harvard U., 1974, MPP, 1974. Bar: Pa. 1974, D.C. 1976, U.S. Supreme Ct. 1979. Assoc. Reed Smith Shaw & McClay, Pitts. and Washington, 1974-82; ptnr. Reed Smith Shaw & McClay, Washington, 1983—. Chmn. nat. alumni assn. Kennedy Sch. Govt., Cambridge, Mass., 1979-82; bd. dirs. Harvard U. Alumni Assn., 1982-84; gen. counsel 1984 Dem. Nat. Conv., Washington, 1983-84, Nat. Dem Party, Washington, 1985-89; spl. counsel Clinton/Gore '92, Inc.; mem. Clinton-Gore 1992 presdl. transition team. Mem. D.C. Bar (chmn. bus. related taxes com. 1989-92, tax policy steering com., chmn. D.C. Bar Nat. Fed. Tax Inst. 1991, 92, chmn. state and local taxes com. 1994—), Harvard-Yale-Princeton Club, Cosmos Club. Presbyterian. Home: 3517 Davis St NW Washington DC 20007-1426 Office: Reed Smith Shaw & McClay Ring Bldg 1200 18th St NW Washington DC 20036-2506

RIESER, LEONARD MOOS, college administrator, physics educator; b. Chgo., May 18, 1922; s. Leonard Moos and Margaret (Wallerstein) R.; m. Rosemary Littledale, July 16, 1944; children: Leonard, Timothy Savage, Abigail Wild; 1 adopted child, Kenneth Willis. S.B., U. Chgo., 1943; Ph.D., Stanford, 1952; A.M. (hon.), Dartmouth, 1963. Research asst., then research assoc. Stanford, 1949-52; mem. faculty Dartmouth, 1952—, prof. physics, 1960—, dir. grad. study, 1961-66, dean arts and scis., provost, 1967-71, v.p., dean of faculty, 1971-80, provost, 1979-82, dir. Dickey Endowment, 1982—; Pres. New Eng. Conf. Grad. Edn., 1965; mem. com. grants Research Corps, N.Y., 1961-66; chmn. bd. Bull. Atomic Scientists, 1985—; vis. scholar MacArthur Found., 1990. Trustee Hampshire Coll., 1984—, Latin Am. Students in Am. Univs., 1990—. Served with AUS, World War II. Mem. AAAS (chmn. com. sci. edn. 1965, bd. dirs. 1967-75, pres. 1973, chmn. bd. 1974, chmn. com. new directions 1975—, chmn. com. sci. freedom), Interciencia Assn. (v.p. 1976-80, pres. 1980-84), Am. Assn. Physics Tchrs., Am. Phys. Soc., Sigma Xi, Phi Beta Kappa. Home: Elm St Norwich VT 05055 Office: Baker Library Dartmouth Coll Hanover NH 03755

RIESKE, GORDON, food products executive; b. 1937. With Price Waterhouse, L.A., 1966-71, Memorex Corp., L.A., 1971-77; v.p., COO Wilsey Foods Inc., La Puente, Calif., 1977—. Office: Wilsey Foods Inc 14840 Don Julian Rd La Puente CA 91746*

RIESMAN, DAVID, lawyer, social scientist; b. Phila., Sept. 22, 1909; s. David and Eleanor L. (Fleisher) R.; m. Evelyn Hastings Thompson, July 15, 1936; children: Paul (dec.), Jennie, Lucy, Michael. AB, Harvard U., 1931, LLB, 1934; LLD, Marlboro Coll., 1954; LL.D., Grinnell Coll., 1957, Temple U., 1962, U. Sussex, Eng., 1965, Muhlenberg Coll., 1967, U. Calif., Berkeley, 1968, U. Pa., 1972, Fordham U., 1972, Lafayette Coll., 1974, Harvard U., 1990; LHD (hon.), Williams Coll., Williamstown, Mass., 1977; L.H.D. (hon.), St. Ambrose Coll., 1966, Franklin and Marshall Coll., 1976; D.C.L., Lincoln U., 1962; Ed.D., R.I. Coll., 1959; D.Litt., Wesleyan U., 1960; also hon. degrees, Ohio State U., SUNY, Carleton Coll., Tufts U., Suffolk U., Skidmore Coll., Boston U., Harvard U. Bars: Mass., D.C. 1935, N.Y. 1939. Research fellow Harvard U., Boston, 1934-35; law clk. to Mr. Justice Brandeis U.S. Supreme Ct., Washington, 1935-36; assoc. Lyne, Woodworth & Evarts, Boston, 1936-37; prof. law U. Buffalo, 1937-41; vis. research fellow Columbia U. Law Sch., N.Y.C., 1941-42; dep. asst. dist. atty. N.Y. County, 1942-43; asst. to treas., war contract termination dir. Sperry Gyroscope Co. Lake Success, L.I., 1943-46; vis. assoc. prof. Coll. Social Scis., U. Chgo., 1946-47, prof. social scis., 1949-58; dir. research project on mass communications Com. Nat. Policy, Yale U., New Haven, 1948-49; Deiches lectr. Johns Hopkins U., Balt., 1954; Henry Ford II prof. social scis. Harvard U., 1958—; fellow Ctr. for Advanced Study in Behavioral Scis., 1968-69; mem. Inst. Advanced Study, Princeton, N.J., 1971-72; mem. Carnegie Commn. for Study Higher Edn., 1967-75. Author: The Lonely Crowd: A Study of the Changing American Character, 1950, Faces in the Crowd, 1952, Thorstein Veblen, 1953, Individualism Reconsidered and Other Essays, 1954, Constraint and Variety in American Education, 1956, Abundance for What? and Other Essays, 1963, rev. edit., new preface, 1993; (with Evelyn Thompson Riesman) Conversations in Japan: Modernization, Politics and Culture, 1967; (with Christopher Jencks) The Academic Revolution, 1968; (with Joseph Gusfield and Zelda Gamson) Academic Values and Mass Education: the Early Years of Oakland and Monteith, 1970; (with Seymour M. Lipset) Education and Politics at Harvard, 1975; (with Gerald Grant) The Perpetual Dream: Experiment and Reform in the American College, 1978; (with Gerald Grant and others) On Competence: A Critical Analysis of Competence-Based Reforms in Higher Education, 1979, On Higher Education: The Academic Enterprise in an Era of Rising Student Consumerism, 1980, (with Judith Block McLaughlin) Choosing a College President: Opportunities and Constraints, 1991; editor: (with Verne Stadtman) Academic Transformation, 1973; contbr. articles to profl. jours. Mem. adv. coun. Marlboro Coll., Vt., Hampshire Coll., Amherst, Mass.; hon. fellow New Coll., Sarasota, Fla., Cowell Coll., U. Calif., Santa Cruz. Mem. Am. Sociol. Assn., Eastern Sociol. Assn., Assn. Studies in Higher Edn., Nat. Acad. Edn., A. Acad. Arts and Scis., Am. Philos. Soc., Tocqueville Soc. (pres. emeritus). Office: Harvard U Dept Sociology Rm 508 484 William James Hall Cambridge MA 02138

RIESS, GEORGE FEBIGER, lawyer, educator; b. New Orleans, Oct. 22, 1943; s. Frank and Jane (Kelleher) R.; m. June 22, 1968 (div. June 1976); 1 child, Katherine Cody; m. Maida Magee, Aug. 23, 1980; children: Frank Henry, Carson Magee, Maida Jean. BA, Tulane U., 1965; JD, La. State U., 1969. Bar: La. 1969, Mich. 1972, U.S. Dist. Ct. (ea., we. and mid. dists.) La. 1970. Mng. ptnr. Johnson & Riess Law Firm, New Orleans, 1970-76; ptnr. Monroe & Lemann Law Firm, New Orleans, 1976—; bd. dirs. Plaquemines Oil and Devel. Corp., New Orleans; adj. prof. law Tulane U. Law Sch., New Orleans, 1987-94. Sec. of vestry St. Martin Episcopal Ch., Metairie, La., 1992—. Recipient Ford Found. grant, 1969. Fellow La. State Bar Found.; mem. ABA, Am. Judicature Soc., Fed. Bar Assn., La. Assn. Def. Counsel, La. State Bar Assn., New Orleans Assn. Def. Counsel, So. Yacht Club, New Orleans Lawn Tennis Assn. Office: Monroe and Lemann 201 Saint Charles Ave Ste 3300 New Orleans LA 70170-1000

RIESS, GORDON SANDERSON, management consultant; b. Salonika, Macedonia, Greece, Feb. 25, 1928; came to U.S., 1932; s. Lewis William and Dorothy Onward (Sanderson) R.; m. Priscilla Rich, June 2, 1951; children: Mark C., Kimberly A., Blake G. AB with highest honors, Whitman Coll., 1949; MBA cum laude, Harvard U., 1951. Cert. mgmt. cons.; registered profl. cons.; accredited profl. cons. Mgmt. trainee Ford Internat. Div., N.Y.C., 1951-53; asst. fin. mgr. Ford Motor Co., Mid. East, Alexandria, Egypt, 1953-57; gen. sales mgr. Ford Motor Co., Rome, Italy, 1957-60; regional fin. mgr. Ford Motor Co., Scandinavia, Copenhagen, Denmark, 1960-62; gen. mgr. Ford Motor Co., European, Brussels, Belgium, 1962-67; v.p. Internat. Paper Co., Zurich, Switzerland, 1967-71; exec. v.p. Cinema Internat. Corp., London, 1971-75; chmn., pres. Stewart-Riess Labs. Inc., Tarzana, Calif., 1976-83; pres., CEO Intercontinental Enterprises Ltd., Beverly Hills, Calif., 1983—; chmn. Vis. Nurse Found., L.A., 1985—; bd. dirs., chmn. Vis. Nurse Assn., L.A., 1976—; bd. dirs. Beverly Found., Pasadena, Calif., 1990—; vice chmn. of bd., Whitman Coll., Walla Walla, Wash., 1985—. Inventor/patentee pre-fillable hypodermic syringe. Chmn. Inter-Community Sch. Zurich, 1968-71; trustee Am. Sch. London, 1972-75; vice chmn. Krafterliner Mfgs. Assn., Zurich, 1968-71; bd. dirs. Vols. in Tech. Assistance, Arlington, Va., 1986-93; bd. overseers Muhlenberg Coll., 1993—; internat. bd. Czechoslovak Mgmt. Ctr., 1990—. Sgt. U.S. Army, 1946-47. R.H. Macy scholar, Harvard Bus. Sch., 1949. Mem. Am. Assn. Profl. Cons., Am. Cons. League, L.A. World Affairs Coun., Hollywood Radio & Television Soc., Inst. Mgmt. Cons., Lic. Execs. Soc. Avocations: skiing, scuba diving. Office: Intercontinental Ent Ltd 256 S Robertson Blvd Ste 3194 Beverly Hills CA 90211-2898

RIESS, J. M., gas and oil industry executive; b. 1942. BSBA, Drake U., 1964. With The Gates Rubber Co., Denver, 1965—, pres., CEO, 1994—.

Office: The Gates Rubber Co PO Box 5887 900 S Broadway Denver CO 80209-4010*

RIESS, SUSAN ELIZABETH, lawyer; b. Chgo., Oct. 21, 1956; d. Robert John and Helen Elizabeth (Hughson) Riess; m. Lloyd Perry Korn, June 21, 1986. B in Gen. Studies, U. Miami, Fla., 1978, JD, 1982. Bar: Fla., 1983, Tex., 1984, Calif., 1987. Gen. counsel Roma Corp., Dallas, 1982-86; assoc. McCutchen, Black, Verleger & Shea, L.A., 1987-89; pvt. practice L.A., 1989-91; sr. counsel Nissan Motor Corp., Carson, Calif., 1991-93, Nissan N. Am., Inc., Torrance, Calif., 1994—. Mem. Law Review U. Miami. 1980-82. U. Miami Honor scholar, 1976, 77, 79, Harvey T. Reid scholar, 1979, 80, 81. Mem. ABA, L.A. County Bar Assn., Fla. Bar Assn., Calif. Bar Assn., Am. Corp. Counsel Assn. Avocations: gardening, travelling, cooking, skiing. Home: 4616 Glencoe Ave # 2 Marina Del Rey CA 90292 Office: Nissan N Am Inc PO Box 2814 Torrance CA 90509-2814

RIESZ, PETER CHARLES, marketing educator, consultant; b. Orange, N.J., Apr. 30, 1937; s. Kolman and Ellen (Wachs) R.; m. Elizabeth Strider Dunkman, Dec. 28, 1968; children—Sarah Kathleen. B.S., Rutgers Coll., 1958; M.B.A., Columbia U., 1963, Ph.D., 1971. Asst. prof. U. Iowa, Iowa City, 1968-73, assoc. prof., 1973-80, prof. mktg., 1980—, chmn. dept. mktg., 1981-84, 85-87, Williams prof. tchg., 1994—; vis. prof. Boston U., 1974-75, Duke U., Durham, N.C., 1984-85; cons. in field. Contbr. articles to profl. jours. Recipient Teaching Excellence award HON Industries, 1989; named MBA Prof. of Yr., 1990; Old Gold fellow U. Iowa, 1972. Mem. Am. Chem. Soc., Am. Mktg. Assn. Democrat. Presbyterian. Avocations: photography. Home: 2411 Tudor Dr Iowa City IA 52245-3638 Office: U Iowa Iowa City IA 52242

RIFENBURGH, RICHARD PHILIP, investment company executive; b. Syracuse, N.Y., Mar. 3, 1932; s. Russell D. and Edna (MacKenzie) R.; m. Doris Anita Hohn, June 24, 1950; children: David, Susan, Robert. Student, Wayne State U. With Mohawk Data Scis. Corp., Herkimer, N.Y., 1964-74, pres., 1970-74, chmn., 1974; chmn. Moval Mgmt. Corp., Herkimer, 1968—; CEO, GCA Corp., Andover, Mass., 1986-87; gen. ptnr. Hambrecht and Quist Venture Ptnrs., 1987-90; chmn. Miniscribe Corp., Longmont, Colo., 1988-91, Ironstone Group Inc., 1988-91; dir. Libr. Bur. Inc., Herkimer, 1976—; chmn. St. G Crystal Ltd., Jeannette, Pa., 1985—; bd. dirs. Concurrent Computer Corp.; dir. Glasstech Inc., 1995—; chmn. Ross Cosmetics Distbn. Ctrs., Inc. (now named Tristar Corp.), 1992—. With USAF, 1951-55. Address: Moval Mgmt Corp 2637 Atlantic Blvd Ste 133 Pompano Beach FL 33062

RIFFATERRE, MICHAEL, foreign language educator, writer; b. France, Nov. 20, 1924; s. Camille and Marie R.; m. Hermine Bilfeld, May 15, 1965; children: Lee, Jason. Ed., U. Lyons, France, 1941, U. Paris, 1945-50; Ph.D., Columbia U., 1955. Asst. prof. French Columbia U., N.Y.C., 1955-58, assoc. prof., 1958-64, prof., 1964-75, Univ. prof., 1982—, chmn. dept., 1974-83, Blanche W. Knopf prof. French lit., 1975-82; vis. prof. Johns Hopkins U., Balt., 1980, 89, Coll. de France, Paris, 1981, Yale U., New Haven, 1983, Harvard U., 1985-86, CUNY, 1985, U. Pa., 1989; sr. fellow Dartmouth Coll. Sch. Criticism and Theory, 1979—, dir., 1987—; vis. sr. fellow St. John's Coll., Oxford, Eng., 1991. Author: Le Style de Gobineau, 1957 (Ansley award), Stylistique Structural, 1971, Semiotics of Poetry, 1978, Text Production, 1983, Litterature et Realité, 1982, Fictional Truth, 1989; gen. editor: Romanic Rev., 1971—. Dir. Reid Hall, Inc., from 1978. Decorated officer Order Palmes Academiques, France, 1977; recipient U. Helsinki medal, 1994, Columbia Grad. Faculties Alumni award for excellence, 1984; Guggenheim fellow, 1962, 79. Fellow Am. Acad. Arts and Scis.; mem. Am. Assn. Tchrs. of French (pres. chpt. 1962-64), Am. Assn. Study of Dada and Surrealism (pres. 1965-66, 73-79), Acad. Lit. Studies (pres. 1978-79), Semiotic Soc. Am. (pres. 1985-86), Toronto Semiotic Circle (hon.). Home: 300 West End Ave New York NY 10023 Office: Dept French Columbia U New York NY 10027

RIFKIN, ARNOLD, film company executive; m. Rita George; two children. BA, U. Cin. Founder Rifkin-David, 1974-80; merged to form Rifkin/David/Kimble/Parseghian, 1980-81, DHKPR, 1981-84; head motion picture dept. Triad Artists, Inc., 1984-92; sr. v.p., worldwide head motion picture divsn. William Morris Agy., Beverly Hills, Calif., 1992—; lectr. UCLA. Office: William Morris Agy 151 S El Camino Dr Beverly Hills CA 90212-2704*

RIFKIN, HAROLD, physician, educator; b. N.Y.C., Sept. 10, 1916; s. Jack and Rose (Zuckoff) R.; m. Beatrice Weiss, Nov. 25, 1945; children—Janet, Matthew, Phyllis. B.A., U. Mo., 1935; M.D., Dalhousie U., 1940. Diplomate Am. Bd. Internal Medicine. Intern Jewish Hosp., Bklyn., 1940-41; resident in internal medicine Montefiore Hosp., N.Y.C., 1942-43, 46-47; practice medicine specializing in internal medicine and diabetes N.Y.C., 1947—; clin. prof. medicine Albert Einstein Coll. Medicine, N.Y.C., 1974-93, disting. univ. prof. of medicine emeritus, 1993—; prof. clin. medicine NYU Sch. Medicine, 1975—; chief of diabetes svc. emeritus Montefiore Med. Ctr., N.Y.C., 1993—; cons. emeritus Lenox Hill Hosp., N.Y.C., 1992—. With U.S. Army, 1943-46. Fellow ACS, N.Y. Acad. Medicine, N.Y. Acad. Scis.; mem. AMA, Internat. Diabetes Fedn. (chmn. N.Am. region 1985—, assoc. editor-in-chief Bull. 1985—, v.p. 1988—, hon. pres. 1994—), Am. Diabetes Assn. (bd. dirs. 1973—, pres. 1985-86), N.Y. Diabetes assn. (past pres., bd. dirs. 1970—), N.Y. County Med. Soc., N.Y. State Med. Soc., Am. Soc. Clin. Rsch., Harvey Soc. Home: 885 Park Ave New York NY 10021-0325

RIFKIN, LEONARD, metals company executive; b. N.Y.C., Apr. 10, 1931; s. Irving W. and May (Goldin) R.; m. Norma Jean Smith, Aug. 22, 1954 (dec. Jan. 1983); children: Daniel Mark, Richard Sheldon, Martin Stuart; m. Ariel Kalisky, Jan. 14, 1984. B.S., Ind. U., Bloomington, 1952. Pres. Omni Source Corp., Fort Wayne, Ind., 1960—. Served with U.S. Army, 1956-58. Office: Omni Source Corp 1610 N Calhoun St Fort Wayne IN 46808-2788

RIFKIN, NED, museum director; b. Florence, Ala., Nov. 10, 1949; s. Arthur Robert and Ina Blanche (Steinberg) R.; m. Diann Carole Kleinman, Mar. 4, 1976; children: Moses Kleinman, Amos Kleinman. BA, Syracuse U., 1972, MA in Art History, U. Mich., 1973, PhD in Art History, 1976. Asst. prof. dept. art U. Tex., Arlington, 1977-80; curator, asst. dir. New Mus. Contemporary Art, N.Y.C., 1980-84; curator contemporary art Corcoran Gallery Art, Washington, 1984-86; chief curator exhbns. Hirshhorn Mus. and Sculpture Garden, Washington, 1986-90, chief curator, 1990-91; dir. High Mus. Art, Atlanta, 1991—.

RIFKIN, ARLEEN B., physician, researcher; b. N.Y.C., June 29, 1938; d. Michael C. and Regina (Gottlieb) Brenner; m. Robert S. Rifkind, Dec. 24, 1961; children: Amy, Nina. BA, Bryn Mawr Coll., 1960; MD, NYU, 1964. Intern Bellevue Hosp., N.Y.C., 1964-65, resident, 1965; clin. assoc. Endocrine br. Nat. Cancer Inst., 1965-68; research assoc., asst. resident physician Rockefeller U., 1968-71; asst. prof. medicine Cornell U. Med. Coll., N.Y.C., 1971-82, assoc. prof. medicine, 1983—, asst. prof. pharmacology, 1973-78, assoc. prof. 1978-82, prof., 1983—; chmn. Gen. Faculty Council Cornell U. Med. Coll., 1984-86; mem. Nat. Inst. Environ. Health Scis. Rev. Com., 1981-85, chmn., 1985-86; mem. toxicology study sect. Nat. Inst. Health, 1989-91, chmn. 1991-93; bd. sci. counselors USPHS Agy. for Toxic Substances and Disease Registry, 1991—. Mem. editorial bd. Drug Metabolism and Disposition, 1994—; contbr. articles to profl. jours. Chmn. Friends of the Library, Jewish Theol. Sem. Am.; trustee Temple Dalton Sch., 1986-92; mem. Environ. Health and Safety Coun. Am. Health Found., 1990—. Recipient Andrew W. Mellon Tchr.-Scientist award, 1976-78; USPHS spl. fellow, 1968-70, 71-72. Mem. Endocrine Soc., Am. Soc. Clin. Investigation, Am. Soc. Pharmacology and Exptl. Therapeutics, AAAS, Internat. Assn. Study Xenobiotics, Soc. Toxicology. Office: Cornell U Med Coll Dept Pharmacology 1300 York Ave New York NY 10021-4805

RIFKIND, ROBERT S(INGER), lawyer; b. N.Y.C., Aug. 31, 1936; s. Simon H. and Adele (Singer) R.; m. Arleen Brenner, Dec. 24, 1961; children: Amy, Nina. BA, Yale U., 1958; JD, Harvard U., 1961. Bar: N.Y. 1961, U.S. Supreme Ct. 1965. Asst. to solicitor gen. Dept. Justice, 1965-68; assoc. firm Cravath, Swaine & Moore, N.Y.C., 1962-65, 68-70; ptnr. Cravath, Swaine & Moore, 1971—. Trustee Dalton Sch. N.Y.C., 1975-83, hon. trustee, 1983—, pres., 1977-79; trustee The Loomis Inst., 1987—; Citizens Budget Commn.; bd. dirs. Charles H. Revson Found., 1991—, Jewish Theol.

Sem. Am., 1983—, Benjamin N. Cardozo Sch. Law, 1984-89; pres. Am. Jewish Com., 1994—. Recipient Stanley M. Isaacs Human Rels. award Am. Jewish Com., 1983. Fellow Am. Coll. Trial Lawyers, N.Y. Bar Found.; mem. ABA, Am. Law Inst., Assn. of Bar of City of N.Y., Phi Beta Kappa. Democrat. Office: Cravath Swaine & Moore Worldwide Pla 825 8th Ave New York NY 10019-7416

RIFKIND, SIMON HIRSCH, lawyer; b. Meretz, Russia, June 5, 1901; came to U.S., 1910, naturalized, 1924; s. Jacob and Celia (Bluestone) R.; m. Adele Singer, June 12, 1927 (dec. Apr. 1984); children: Richard Allen, Robert Singer. B.S., CCNY, 1922; LL.B., Columbia U., 1925; Litt.D., Jewish Theol. Sem., 1950; LL.D., Hofstra Coll., 1962, Brandeis U., 1977, CCNY, 1978; J.D., Hebrew U. of Jerusalem, 1980. Bar: N.Y. 1926, Ill. 1957. Legislative sec. to U.S. senator Robert F. Wagner, 1927-33; ptnr. firm Wagner, Quillinan and Rifkind, N.Y.C., 1930-41; fed. judge So. N.Y. Dist., 1941-50; 3d dep. police commr. City of N.Y., 1951; mem. firm Stevenson, Rifkind & Wirtz, Chgo., 1957-61; ptnr. Paul, Weiss, Rifkind, Wharton & Garrison, 1950—; adviser to Gen Eisenhower on Jewish matters in Am. occupation zone, 1945; Herman Phleger vis. prof. law Stanford, 1975; spl. master Colo. River litigation U.S. Supreme Ct.; chmn. Presdl. R.R. Commn., 1961-62; mem. State Commn. Govtl. Operations City N.Y., 1959-61; co-chmn. President's Commn. on Patent System, 1966-67; mem. mayors mediation panel N.Y. City teachers strike, 1963. Mem. Bd. Higher Edn. City N.Y., 1954-66; chmn. adminstrv. bd. Am. Jewish Com., 1953-56, chmn. exec. bd., 1956-59; former chmn. bd., now hon. chmn. exec. com. Jewish Theol. Sem.; bd. dirs. Beth Israel Med. Center, N.Y.C., 1975-86, now emeritus; chmn. bd. Charles H. Revson Found., Inc., 1975-87, bd. dirs., 1987-90; pres. bd. dirs. Tudor Found., Inc., 1945-90; bd. dirs., pres. Norman and Rosita Winston Found., Inc., 1975-87, bd. dirs., 1987-90. Recipient Medal of Freedom, 1946. Mem. Assn. of Bar of City of N.Y., Am. Coll. Trial Lawyers (regent 1967-71, pres. 1976-77), Phi Beta Kappa. Democrat. Jewish. Club: Harmonie (N.Y.C.). Office: Paul Weiss Rifkind Wharton & Garrison 1285 Ave of the Americas New York NY 10019-6064

RIGALI, JUSTIN F., archbishop. ordained priest April 25, 1961. Bishop Diocese of Bolsena, 1985-94; archbishop Diocese of St. Louis, 1994—. Office: Archdiocese of St Louis Chancery Office 4445 Lindell Blvd Saint Louis MO 63108*

RIGBY, KATHRYN JILL (JILL RIGBY), newspaper editor, travel journalist; b. St. Catharines, Ont., Can., Mar. 7, 1954; d. Thomas Alexander Rigby and Joan Elizabeth (Stewart) Clarke. Student, U. Montpellier, France, 1972; BA, U. Toronto, Ont., 1975; MS in Journalism, Columbia U., 1980; postgrad., Banff (Alta.) Sch. Fine Arts, 1981. Writer Toronto Star, 1978-80; assoc. prodr. Ripley's Believ It or Not, Paris, 1981-82; prodn. mgr. Sta. CFTO-TV/Glen Warren, Toronto, 1982-84; dir. corp. comm. Oxford Devels., Toronto, 1984-86; travel editor Toronto Sun, 1986—. Avocations: skiing, sailing, trekking, tennis. golf. Office: The Toronto Sun, 333 King St E, Toronto, ON Canada M5A 3X5

RIGBY, PAUL CRISPIN, artist, cartoonist; b. Melbourne, Australia, Oct. 25, 1924; came to U.S., 1977; s. James Samuel and Violet Irene (Wood) R.; m. Marlene Anne Cockburn, Nov. 16, 1956; children: Nicole, Pia, Peter, Paul, Danielle. Student, Brighton Tech. Sch., Australia, Art Schs., Victoria, Victoria Nat. Gallery, Australia. Free lance artist, 1940-42; illustrator West Australian News, Ltd., 1948-52; editorial cartoonist Daily News Australia, 1952-69; daily cartoonist London Sun and News of the World, 1969-74; editorial cartoonist New York Post, 1977-84, 93—, New York Daily News, 1984-93. Illustrator numerous books; represented in exhbns. of painting in, Australia, Europe and U.S.A.; Contbr. work to numerous publs., U.S., Europe, Asia. Served with Royal Australian Air Force, 1942-46. Decorated knight commdr. Order of St. John, Knights of Malta; recipient Walkley award Australia, 1960, 61, 63, 66, 69; N.Y. Press Club award for art, 1981, 83, Page One award for excellence in journalism Newspaper Guild, 1982, 83, 84, 85. Mem. Ch. of Eng. Clubs: Rolls Royce Owners, Royal Freshwater Bay Yacht; Friars, Players (N.Y.C.). Home: 72 Kenyon Rd Hampton CT 06247 Office: NY Post 210 South St New York NY 10002

RIGBY, PAUL HERBERT, management educator, college dean; b. Humboldt, Ariz., Aug. 6, 1924; s. John Herbert and Grace Irene (Dailey) R.; m. Dorothy Ann Sall, Dec. 18, 1954; children—Peter Nathan, Mark Herbert. B.B.A., U. Tex.-Austin, 1945; M.B.A., 1948, Ph.D., 1951. Rsch. assoc., asst. prof. U. Ala., Tuscaloosa, 1952-54; dir., assoc. prof. Ga. State U., Atlanta, 1954-56; dir. rsch., prof. U. Houston, 1956-62; bus. rsch. dir., assoc. prof. U. Mo., Columbia, 1962-64; dir. div. rsch., asst. dean rsch. and grad. program, prof. mgmt. sci. Pa. State U., University Park, 1964—; treas., bd. dirs. Centre Community Hosp., State College, Pa., 1978-87, pres., chmn. 1987-91; pres. U. Houston Senate, 1961-62. Author: Conceptual Foundations of Business Research, 1965, Models in Business Analysis, 1969; (with others) Corresponding Education in U.S., 1968; contbr. articles to profl. jours. Chmn. Centre Area Transp. Authority, State College, 1975-80. Served to cpl. U.S. Army, 1945-46. Mem. Inst. Mgmt. Sci. (vice-chmn. Coll. on Mgmt. Policy and Philosophy 1987, chmn. 1988), Am. Statis. Assn., Am. Inst. Decision Scis., Associated Univs. for Bus. and Econ. Research (pres. 1969). Democrat. Unitarian. Home: 131 Legion Ln State College PA 16801-6434 Office: Pa State U Smeal Coll Bus Administrn 801D Bus Adminstrn Bldg University Park PA 16802

RIGBY, PERRY GARDNER, medical center administrator, educator, former university dean, physician; b. East Liverpool, Ohio, July 1, 1932; s. Perry Lawrence and Lucille Ellen (Orin) R.; m. Joan E. Worthington, June 16, 1957; children: Martha, Peter, Thomas, Matthew. B.S. summa cum laude, Mt. Union Coll., 1953, D.Sc. hon., 1976; M.D., Western Res. U. 1957. Diplomate: Am. Bd. Internal Medicine. Intern in medicine U. Va. Hosp., Charlottesville, 1957-58, asst. resident in medicine, 1958-60; research fellow in hematology Mass. Meml. Hosp., Boston, 1960-62; clin. asst. in medicine Boston City Hosp., 1961-62; research assoc. in medicine Mass. Meml. Hosp., Boston U. Med. Ctr., 1961-62; asst. prof. internal medicine and anatomy U. Nebr., Omaha, 1964-66, assoc. prof. internal medicine and anatomy, 1966-69, prof. internal medicine, 1969-78, prof. anatomy, 1969-74, prof. med. edn., 1973-74, head sect. hematology Eugene C. Eppley Inst. for Research in Cancer and Allied Diseases, 1964-68, dir. hematology div., 1968-74, asst. dean for curriculum Coll. Medicine, 1971-72, assoc. dean for acad. affairs, 1972-74, dir. office ednl. services, 1972-74, acting assoc. dean for allied health professions, 1973-74, vice chmn. dept. med. and ednl. adminstrn., 1974, dean, 1974-78, chmn. dept. med. and ednl. adminstrn., 1974; prof. internal medicine La. State U., Shreveport, 1978—, assoc. dean acad. affairs Sch. Medicine, 1978-81, acting dean, 1981-82, dean, 1982-85; chancellor La. State U., 1985-94; dir. Health Care Systems La. State U., New Orleans, 1994—; mem. clin. bd. Univ. Hosp. La. State U., 1978—, chmn. clin. bd., 1978—, program dir. biomed. research support grant program, 1980-81; chmn. dean's com. VA Hosp., 1978—; mem. courtesy staff Immanuel Med. Ctr.; bd. dirs. Health Planning Council of Midlands, Omaha, 1976-78; cons. WHO, Kabul, Afghanistan, 1976. Bd. dirs. Fontenelle Forest, Omaha, 1976-78; bd. dirs. River Cities High Tech. Group, Shreveport, 1982—. Served as capt. M.C. U.S. Army, 1962-64. Markle scholar, 1965. Fellow ACP; mem. Am. Fedn. Clin. Research (councillor 1971), AMA (del.), Am. Soc. Hematology, N.Y. Acad. Scis., Am. Assn. Med. Colls. (council of deans of Midwest-Gt. Plains 1974-78, chmn. Midwest-Gt. Plains 1976), Am. Assn. Cancer Research, AAAS, Am. Heart Assn., Central Soc. Clin. Research, Internat. Soc. Hematology, Health Edn. Media Assn., Am. Assn. Physicians' Assts., So. Soc. Clin. Investigation, Shreveport C. of C. (dir. 1982—), Sigma Xi, Alpha Omega Alpha, Phi Rho Sigma. Office: La State U Med Ctr Resource Ctr 433 Bolivar St New Orleans LA 70112-2223

RIGDON, IMOGENE STEWART, nursing educator, dean; b. St. Joseph, Mo., Apr. 2, 1937; d. George Francis and Mary Elizabeth (Byrne) Stewart; m. Michael Allen Rigdon, Nov. 1, 1973; 1 child, Mary Lisa. BSN, Marillac Coll., 1961; MSN, Cath. U. Am., 1973; PhD, U. Utah, 1985. Cert. clin. specialist in adult psychiat.-mental health nursing Am. Nurses Assn. Asst. dir. nursing St. Anthony Hosp., Oklahoma City, 1974-76; regional teaching nurse III Shands Teaching Hosp., Gainesville, Fla., 1977-78; asst. prof. U. Fla., Gainsville, 1978-82; teaching fellow U. Utah Coll. Nursing, Salt Lake City, 1983-85; clin. specialist U. Hosp., Salt Lake City, 1985-87, vol. aux. faculty, assoc. prof., 1987—; dean, assoc. prof. St. Mark's Westminster Sch. Nursing, Salt Lake

City, 1987—; co-therapist North Cen. Fla. Community Mental Health Ctr., 1978-80; vol. nurse-psychotherapist North Cen. Fla. Community Mental Health Ctr., 1980-82; mem. Advanced Practice task force, 1990—, Utah Nursing Resources task force, 1988-90, Utah State Bd. Regents' Com. on Nursing Edn., 1988-89, Psychiat.-Mental Health Nursing Conf. Group; mem. Advanced Psychiat.-Mental Health Nursing Adv. Com. to the State Bd. Nursing, 1986-89; mem. Intermountain Health Care Home Health Adv. Com., 1988; group leader grief edn. groups Holy Cross Grief Ctr., 1990—; others. Contbr. chpts. to books and articles to profl. jours. Mem. Citizens Adv. Com., New Directions Group Home, 1980-81; mem. Girl Scouts Am., 1980-83; campaign vol., 1983—; bd. mem. Holy Cross Bereavement Program Adv. Coun., 1989—; mem. Utah Com. for Am.-Soviet Rels., 1988—; mem. campaign com. Paula Julander for Utah Legis., 1988, 90, co-chair Neighborhood Walking, 1988, 90. Capt. USAFR, 1972-82. Mem. AAUW, Am. Assn. Colls. Nursing, Nat. League Nursing, Am. Orthopsychiatric Assn., Soc. for Edn. and Rsch. in Psychiat. Nursing, Coun. Clin. Specialists in Psychiat.-Mental Health Nursing, Utah Citizens League for Nursing (bd. mem. 1989—), Utah Nurses' Assn. (Utah health agenda task force 1988-89, gov. bd. 1986-89, dist. 1 treas. 1985-87), Mental Health Assn., Sierra Club, ACLU, Amnesty Internat., Sigma Theta Tau (Kappa chpt., Iota Iota chpt.). Democrat. Roman Catholic. Avocations: guitar playing, cross country skiing, gardening, walking. Home: 3196 Millcreek Canyon Rd Salt Lake City UT 84109 Office: Westminster Coll 1840 South 1300 East Salt Lake City UT 84105

RIGG, CHARLES ANDREW, pediatrician; b. Hamilton, Vic., Australia, Oct. 18, 1926; came to U.S., 1963; s. Arthur Oscar and Mary Eileen (Wingrove) R. B in Medicine, Surgery with honors, Sydney U., 1951. Staff adolescent medicine Children's Hosp., Boston, 1964-65; chief dept. adolescent medicine Children's Hosp., Washington, 1967-80, Boston City Hosp., 1981-83; med. dir. Outer Cape Health, Provincetown, Mass., 1983-88, Medicenter Five, Harwich, Mass., 1988—; from asst. to assoc. prof. child health George Washington Med. Sch., Washington, 1967-80; cons. Nat. Naval Med. Ctr., Bethesda, Md., 1967-80, Walter Reed Army Med. Ctr., Washington; assoc. prof. pediatrics Boston U. Med. Sch., 1981-83; courtesy staff Medicine Childrens Hosp., Boston, 1983—. Editor: Adolescent Medicine Present and Future Concepts, 1980; contbr. articles to profl. jours. Mem. AIDS edn. review panel Mass. Dept. Edn., Boston, 1989—; Lt. Col. USAR, 1985-88. Model Tng. Program in Adolescent Medicine grantee Maternal and Child Health Svcs.-U.S. Govt., 1967-80, Comprehensive Health Svcs. Adolescent Ctr. grantee Mass. Dept. Pub. Health, 1981-83. Fellow Am. Acad. Pediatrics, Royal Australasian Coll. Physicians, Soc. Adolescent Medicine (charter mem., treas., chmn., legis. com.); mem. Royal Sydney Golf Club (sydney N.S.W.), City Tavern Club (Washington). Episcopalian. Avocations: historic preservation, gardening, theater, music, walking. Office: Medicenter Five 525 Long Pond Dr Harwich MA 02645

RIGG, DIANA, actress; b. Doncaster, Yorkshire, Eng., July 20, 1938; d. Louis and Beryl (Helliwell) R.; m. Menahem Gueffen, July 6, 1973 (div. Sept. 1976); m. Archibald Hugh Stirling, Mar. 25, 1981 (div.); 1 child, Rachael Atlanta. Grad., Fulneck Girls' Sch., Pudsey, Yorkshire; student, Royal Acad. Dramatic Art, London; D (hon.), Stirling U., Eng., 1988, Leeds U., Eng., 1992. Stage debut as Natella Abashwili in The Caucasian Chalk Circle, Theatre Royal, York, Eng., 1957; joined Royal Shakespeare Co., Stratford-on-Avon, 1959, debut as Andromache in Troilus and Cressida, 1960; London debut as Philippe Trincant in The Devils, London, 1961; numerous repertory appearances; joined Nat. Theatre, 1972; appeared in Jumpers, Macbeth, 1972, The Misanthrope, 1973, Pygmalion, 1974, Phaedra Britannica, 1975, Night and Day, 1978, Collette, 1982, Heartbreak House, 1983, Little Eyolf, 1985, Antony and Cleopatra, 1985, Wildlife, 1986, Follies, 1987, Love Letters, 1990, All for Love, 1991, Putting It Together, 1992, Berlin Bertie, 1992, Medea, 1992 (Tony award, Broadway prod., 1994); film appearances include A Midsummer Night's Dream, The Assassination Bureau, On Her Majesty's Secret Service, Julius Caesar, The Hospital, Theatre of Blood, A Little Night Music, The Great Muppet Caper, Evil Under the Sun, A Good Man in Africa; co-starred as Emma Peel in Brit. TV series The Avengers, 1965-67; star TV series Diana, 1973-74; numerous TV movies including This House of Brede, 1975, Hedda Gabler, 1981, Little Eyolf, 1982, Witness for the Prosecution, 1982, King Lear, 1983, Bleak House, 1984, A Hazard of Hearts, 1987, Worst Witch, 1987, Unexplained Laughter, 1989, Mother Love (Broadcasting Guild Award), 1989, Citizen Cohn, 1990; host PBS series Mystery, 1989—; author: No Turn Unstoned, 1982, U.S. edit., 1983. Decorated comdr. Brit. Empire; created dame, 1994; recipient Tony award nomination as best actress in Abelard and Heloise and The Misanthrope; Plays and Players award for Phaedra Britannica and Night and Day; Variety Club Gt. Britain award for best actress for Evil Under the Sun; Brit. Acad. Film and TV Arts award for best TV actress in Mother Love, 1989. Mem. United Brit. Artists (co-founder, dir. 1982—). Office: care London Mgmt, 235 Regent St, London W1A 2JT, England also: c/o Lionel Larner, Ltd 130 W 57th St New York NY 10019*

RIGGINS-EZZELL, LOIS, museum administrator; b. Nashville, Nov. 18, 1939; d. Percy Leon and Lula Belle Prather (Traughber) Von Schmittou; 1 son, Nicholas. B.S., Belmont Coll., 1968; postgrad., U. Western Ky., 1969-72, George Washington U., 1978. Cert. tchr., Ky., Tenn. Tchr. Ky. Pub. Schs., Adairville, 1962-71; tour supr. Tenn. State Capitol, Nashville, 1972-74; curator of extension services Tenn. State Mus., Nashville, 1975-77, curator edn., 1977-81, exec. dir. 1981—. Chmn. Nashville Flight of Tenn. Friendship Force, Caracas, Venezuela, 1977, Tenn. Am. Revolution Bicentennial Arts Competition, 1976, Gov.'s Quicentennial Com., 1991-92; bd. dirs. Tenn. State Mus. Found., Inc., 1981—, Zool. Soc. Mid. Tenn., 1986-88, So. Folk Cultural Revival Project, 1986-93, Tenn. Pres. Trust, 1989—, Hist. Coun., Girl Scouts U.S.; mem. commning. com. USS Tenn., 1990; keynote speaker nat. forums Corp. Philanthropy Report, Chgo., Atlanta, 1991. Named Woman for Lears, Lears Mag., 1990, Tenn. Woman of Distinction, 1993. Mem. Southeastern Mus. Conf. (edn. com., rep. to Am. Assn. Mus. council, publs. advt. com. 1983), Inter Mus. Council of Nashville (chmn. edn. 1980-81), Am. Assn. Mus., Am. Assn. State and Local History (edn. com. 1988-90). Office: Tenn State Mus 505 Deaderick St Nashville TN 37243-1120

RIGGIO, LEONARD, book publishing executive; b. 1941. Merchandise mgr. NYU Bookstore, N.Y.C., 1962-65; pres., CEO, bd. dirs. Barnes & Noble Bookstores, Inc., 1965—; chmn. bd., CEO, pres., treas. Barnes & Noble Inc., N.Y.C., 1986—; chmn. bd., prin. beneficial owner Software Etc. Stores, Inc., Mpls., MBS Textbook Exchange, Inc., Columbia, Mo. Office: Barnes & Noble Inc 122 Fifth Ave New York NY 10011-5605 Address: MBS Textbook Exchange Inc 2711 W Ash St Columbia MO 65203

RIGGIO, STEPHEN, book store chain executive; married; 3 children. BA in Anthropology, Bklyn. Coll., 1974. Buying, mktg. areas Barnes & Noble Bookstores, Inc., N.Y.C., 1974-78, gen. mdse. mgr., 1978-81, head direct mail bus., 1981-86, exec. v.p. merchandising, 1986-90, exec. v.p., chief oper. officer, 1990—; originator Children With Special Needs collection books about and for children with learning disabilities. Bd. dirs. N.Y. chpt. Assn. Help Retarded Children. Office: Barnes & Noble Bookstores Inc 122 5th Ave Fl 4 New York NY 10011-5605

RIGGLEMAN, JAMES DAVID, professional baseball team manager; b. Ft. Dix, N.J., Dec. 9, 1952. Degree in Physical Edn., Frostburg State U. Minor league baseball player, 1974-81, minor league baseball mgr., 1982-88, 91-92; dir. player devel., then coach St. Louis Cardinals, 1988-90; mgr. San Diego Padres, 1993-94, Chicago Cubs, 1995—. Office: Wrigley Field 1060 W Addison St Chicago IL 60613-4397*

RIGGS, ANDY J., JR., newspaper publishing executive. V.p. prodn. The Daily News, N.Y.C. Office: The Daily News 220 E 42 st Ste 817 New York NY 10017*

RIGGS, ARTHUR JORDY, retired lawyer; b. Nyack, N.Y., Apr. 3, 1916; s. Oscar H. and Adele (Jordy) R.; m. Virginia Holloway, Oct. 15, 1942 (dec.); children: Arthur James (dec.), Emily Adele Riggs Freeman, Keith Holloway, George Bennett; m. Priscilla McCormack, Jan. 16, 1993. AB, Princeton U., 1937; LLB, Harvard U., 1940. Bar: Mass. 1940, Tex. 1943; cert. specialist in labor law to 1992. Assoc. Warner, Stackpole, Stetson & Bradlee, Boston, 1940-41; staff mem. Solicitors Office U.S. Dept. Labor, Washington and Dallas, 1941-42; mem. Johnson, Bromberg, Leeds & Riggs, Dallas, 1949-81;

of counsel Geary & Spencer, Dallas, 1981-91. Mem. ABA, State Bar Tex., Phi Beta Kappa. Avocations: Maya archeology, photography, scuba diving. Home and Office: 4116 Amherst Ave Dallas TX 75225-6901

RIGGS, BENJAMIN CLAPP, JR., building products manufacturing company executive; b. Boston, Sept. 29, 1945; s. Benjamin Clapp and Norma (Campanaro) R.; m. Cheryl Pusey, July 3, 1970 (div. 1987); children: Sonia Campanaro, Anne Elizabeth; m. Lee Thornton Ainsworth, Feb. 25, 1989. BA, Boston U., 1968. Commd. ens. U.S. Navy, 1969, advanced through grades to capt., 1990, served as pilot and aero. engr., 1969-76, now res.; exec. v.p. Resource Mgmt. Corp., Boston, 1976-78; br. mgr. Reynolds Aluminum Co., Mt. Kisco, N.Y., 1978-80; mktg. dir. Am. Abrasive Metals Co., Irvington, N.J., 1980-83; v.p. gen. mgr. Glen-Gery Corp., River Edge, N.J., 1984-90; dir. Resource Mgmt. Co., Oakland, N.J., 1990—; pres. HAPCO div. Kearney-Nat., Abington, Va., 1992-93; CEO, mng. dir. Resource Mgmt. Co., Bristol, Tenn., 1993—. Mem. Res. Officers Assn. Republican. Episcopalian. Avocations: sailing, ocean cruising, tennis, skiing, writing. Office: Resource Mgmt Co 1270 Volunteer Pkwy # F17 Bristol TN 37620

RIGGS, BYRÓN LAWRENCE, JR., physician, educator; b. Hot Springs, Ark., Mar. 24, 1931; s. Byron Lawrence and Elizabeth Ann (Patching) R.; m. Janet Templeton Brewer, June 24, 1955; children: Byron Kent, Ann Templeton. B.S., U. Ark., 1953, B.S. in Medicine, 1955, M.D., 1955; M.S. in Medicine, U. Minn., 1962. Diplomate: Am. Bd. Internal Medicine. Intern Letterman Army Hosp., San Francisco, 1958-59; resident in internal medicine Mayo Grad. Sch. Medicine Hosp., Rochester, Minn., 1958-61; asst. to staff Mayo Clinic and Found., Rochester, 1961, mem. staff internal medicine and metabolism, 1962—; mem. faculty U. Minn. Med. Sch., Rochester, 1962—, assoc. prof., 1970—; Purvis and Roberta Tabor prof. med. rsch. Mayo Clinic and Med. Sch., Rochester, 1974—, chmn. divsn. endocrinology and metabolism, 1974-84; mem. gen. medicine B study sect. NIH, 1979-82; nat. adv. bd. NIAMS/NIH, 1987-91. Contbr. articles to med. jours. Dist. investigator Mayo Found., 1991—. Served with M.C. AUS, 1956-58. Recipient Mayo Found. postgrad. travel award, 1961; Kappa Delta award Am. Acad. Orthopedic Surgery, 1972; traveling fellow Royal Soc. Medicine, 1973. Fellow ACP; mem. AMA, AAAS, Am. Soc. Clin. Investigation, Endocrine Soc. (Rorer Clin. Investigator award 1989), Am. Fedn. Clin. Rsch. (councillor Midwest sect. 1969-71), Am. Soc. for Bone and Mineral Rsch. (pres. 1985-86, Barttter Clin. Investigation award 1990, Career Recognition award, 9th Workshop on Vitamin D rsch.), Ctrl. Soc. Clin. Rsch. (councillor), Assn. Am. Physicians (councillor 1972-74). Home: 432 10th Ave SW Rochester MN 55902-2911 Office: Mayo Clinic 200 1st St SW Rochester MN 55905-0001

RIGGS, DAVID FOSTER, museum curator, historian; b. Trenton, N.J., Feb. 26, 1950; s. Grennell Merrill and Grace Marie (Foster) R.; m. Susan Elizabeth Agee, Apr. 24, 1976. BA, Lock Haven U., 1972; MA, Pa. State U., 1974. Cert. archivist. Archivist Lock Haven (Pa.) U., 1970; grad. asst. Pa. State U., State College, 1973-74; archivist Kenmore Assn., Fredericksburg, Va., 1974; archivist, cataloger manuscripts Va. Hist. Soc., Richmond, 1974-78; park technician Fredericksburg & Spotsylvania Nat. Mil. Park Nat. Park Svc., 1978; park technician Jefferson Nat. Expansion Meml., Nat. Park Svc., St. Louis, 1978-80, Vicksburg (Miss.) Nat. Mil. Park, Nat. Park Svc., 1980-81; mus. curator Vicksburg (Miss.) Nat. Mil. Park, 1981-85, Colonial Nat. Hist. Park, Nat. Park Svc., Jamestown, Va., 1985—; book reviewer in field. Author: East of Gettysburg, 1970, 7th Virginia Infantry, 1982, 13th Virginia Infantry, 1988; co-author: Vicksburg Battlefield Monuments, 1984, Dictionary of American Military Biography, 1984; contbr. articles to profl. jours. Recipient Award of Merit Confederate Meml. Lit. Soc., 1978, Achievement and Performance awards Nat. Park Svc., 1984—, Alumni Achievement award Lock Haven U., 1989. Mem. Am. Assn. Mus., Va. Hist. Soc., Williamsburg Hist. Records Assn., Assn. for Preservation of Civil War Sites, Soc. Mil. History Acad. Cert. Archivists, Soc. Am. Baseball Rsch., Mid-Atlantic Regional Archives Conf. Methodist. Avocation: major league baseball. Office: Colonial Nat Hist Park PO Box 210 Yorktown VA 23690-0210

RIGGS, DONALD EUGENE, librarian, university dean; b. Middlebourne, W.Va., May 11, 1942; m. Jane Vasbinder, Sept. 25, 1964; children: Janna Jennifer, Krista Dyonis. BA, Glenville State Coll., 1964; MA, W.Va. U., 1966; MLS, U. Pitts., 1968; EdD, Va. Poly. Inst. and State U., 1975. Head librarian, tchr. sci. Warwood (W.Va.) High Sch., 1964-65; head librarian, audiovisual dir. Wheeling (W.Va.) High Sch., 1965-67; sci. and econs. librarian California State Coll. of Pa., 1968-70; dir. library and learning center Bluefield State Coll., 1970-72; dir. libraries and media services Bluefield State Coll., Concord Coll., Greenbrier Community Coll., and So. campus W.Va. Coll. of Grad. Studies, 1972-76; dir. libraries U. Colo., Denver, Met. State Coll., and Community Col. of Denver—Auraria Campus, 1976-79; univ. librarian Ariz. State U., 1979-88, dean univ. libraries, 1988-90; prof. info. and libr. sci., dean univ. libr. U. Mich., Ann Arbor, 1991—; adj. prof. Calif. State Coll. 1968-70, W.Va. U., 1970-72, U. Colo., 1977-79, U. Ariz., 1985; fed. rels. coord. Am. and W.Va. Libr. Assns., 1970-75; chmn. bd. dirs. Cen. Colo. Libr. System, 1976-79; chmn. Colo. Coun. Acad. Librs., 1977-78; mem. exec. bd. Colo. Alliance Rsch. Librs., 1978-79; fgn. assignments in Xi'an, People Republic of China, 1988, Guadalajava, Mexico, 1990, Budapest, Hungary, 1991, Hong Kong, 1992, 94, San Juan, Puerto Rico, 1993, Melbourne, Australia, 1994; cons. to librs.; fgn. assignments in Xi'an People's Repr. China, 1988, Gaudalajava, Mex., 1990, Budapest, Hungary, 1991, Hong Kong, 1992, 94, San Juan, Puerto Rico, 1993, Melbourne, Australia, 1994, Guangzru, Repr. Crimea, Ukraine, 1995; bd. govs. Rsch. Librs. Group, Inc., Mountain View, Calif., 1991-92; vice-chmn. mgmt. com. William L. Clements Libr., 1991—. Editor: W.Va. Librs., 1973-75, Library Hi Tech, 1993—; founding editor: Libr. Adminstrn. and Mgmt., 1987-89; assoc. editor: Southeastern Librarian, 1973-75; contbg. author: Libraries in the Political Process, 1980, Options for the 80's, 1982, Library and Information Technology: At the Crossroads, 1984; contbg. author, editor: Library Leadership: Visualizing the Future, 1982; author: Strategic Planning for Library Managers, 1984, (with Helen Godfrey) Time Management in Academic Libraries, 1986, (with Gordon Sabine) Libraries in the 90's: What the Leaders Expect, 1988, Creativity, Innovation, and Entrepreneurship in Libraries, 1989, Library Communication: The Language of Leadership, 1991, (with Rao Aluri) Expert Systems in Libraries, 1990, Cultural Diversity in Libraries, 1994; mem. editorial bd. Am. Librs., 1987-89, Jour. Libr. Adminstrn., 1987—; Coll. and Rsch. Librs., 1990—. Trustee Mesa (Ariz.) Pub. Library, 1980-86, chmn., 1985-86; mem. Ariz. State Library Adv. Council, 1981-84; bd. dirs. Documentation Abstracts, Inc., 1986-90. Recipient Alumnus of Yr. award Glenville State Coll., 1992; named Outstanding Young Educator, Ohio County Schs., 1966; Coun. on Libr. Resources grantee, 1985; sr. fellow UCLA, 1989. Mem. ALA (councilor-at-large 1982-86, 89-93, chmn. coun.'s resolutions com. 1985-86, pub. com. 1988-92, Hugh Atkinson award 1993), Ariz. Libr. Assn. (pres. coll. and univ. div. 1981-82, pres. 1983-84, Spl. Svc. award 1986, Disting. Svc. award 1990), Colo. Libr. Assn. (pres. 1978-79), W.Va. Libr. Assn. (pres. 1975-76), Assn. Coll. and Rsch. Librs. (pres. Tri-State chpt. 1972-74, Ariz. chpt. 1981-82), So. Libr. Assn. (chmn. coll. and univ. sect. 1982-83), Assn. Rsch. Librs. (100th meeting planning com. 1982, mgmt. of rsch. libr. resources com. 1990-93), AMIGOS Bibliograph Coun. (trustee 1986-90, chmn. bd. trustees 1988-89), Libr. Adminstrn. and Mgmt. Assn. (bd. dirs. 1987-89, pres.-elect, 1993-94, pres. 1994-95), Libr. Info. and Tech. Assn. (bd. dirs. 1989-93, councilor 1989-93), Ctr. for Rsch Librs. (councilor 19), Mountain Plains Libr. Assn. (bd. dirs. 1987-90, pres. elect 1990-91), Beta Phi Mu, Chi Beta Phi, Phi Delta Kappa, Phi Kappa Phi. Office: U Mich Hatcher Grad Libr Office of Dean Arbor MI 48109-1205

RIGGS, DOUGLAS A., lawyer; b. Rigby, Idaho, Aug. 20, 1944; s. Ursel and Elsie Groom Riggs; m. Heidi Bankart Eddy, Dec. 27, 1985; 1 child, Nathan Whittlesey. BS, Brigham Young U., 1966; MS, W.Va. U., 1967; JD, Cornell U., 1973. Bar: Alaska 1974, D.C. 1985. Assoc. Johnson, Christensen & Schamberg Inc., Anchorage, 1974-75; gen. counsel Alaska State Housing Authority, Anchorage, 1975-76, exec. dir., 1976-77; spl. counsel to the gov. State of Alaska, Washington, 1977-79; counsel Citizens for Mgmt. for Alaska Lands Inc., Washington, 1979; sole practice Anchorage, 1979-80; ptnr. Bogle & Gates, Anchorage, 1980-83; spl. asst. to pres. for pub. liaison The White House, Washington, 1983-85; gen. counsel U.S. Dept. Commerce,

Washington, 1985-87; v.p. corp. planning, communications and external affairs, mem. corp. mgmt. com. Pitney-Bowes, Inc. World Hdqrs., Stamford, Conn., 1988-93, v.p. comms., planning, sec., gen. counsel, corp. mgmt. com., 1993—. Counsel Senator Frank H. Murkowski campaign, Anchorage, 1980; mem. exec. com. Senator Ted Stevens re-election campaign, Anchorage, 1982-83. Served to sgt. U.S. Army, 1967-70. Mem. Alaska Bar Assn., D.C. Bar Assn. Republican. Home: 18 Weir Farm Ln Ridgefield CT 06877-6000 Office: Pitney Bowes Inc World Hdqrs Stamford CT 06926

RIGGS, FRANK, congressman; b. Louisville, Ky., Sept. 5, 1950; m. Cathy Anne Maillard; three children: Ryan, Matthew, Sarah Anne. BA, Golden Gate U. With Veale Investment Properties, until 1987; co-founder (with wife) Duncan Enterprises; mem. 102nd Congress 1st Calif. Dist., 1991-92, mem. 104th Congress, 1995—. With U.S. Army, 1972-75. Republican. Office: US House Reps 114 Cannon House Office Bldg Washington DC 20515-0501

RIGGS, FRANK LEWIS, foundation executive; b. Indpls., Apr. 1, 1937; s. Frank Lloyd Riggs and Marie Loretta (Shaner) Ellis; m. Gail Evelyn Kershner, July 28, 1960 (div. 1987). BS in Bus. Adminstrn., U. Ariz., 1961, EdD, 1976; MBA, George Washington U., 1964. Mktg. adminstr. TRW Systems, L.A., 1964-67; assn. exec. Electric League Ariz., Phoenix, 1967-68; pub. affairs adminstr. Ariz. Regional Med. program Coll. of Medicine, U. Ariz., Tucson, 1968-73; dir. community affairs Tucson Med. Ctr., 1973-82; dir. pub. rels. Good Samaritan Med. Ctr., Phoenix, 1982-85; pres. The Lew Riggs Co., Phoenix, 1985-88; chief exec. officer Tucson Osteo. Med. Found., Tucson, 1988—; adj. prof. U. Ariz. Coll. Edn., Tucson, 1976-79; cons. to hosps. and physicians in group practice nationally; presenter in field. Editor: Public Relations Handbook, 1982; co-author booklets; contbr. articles to profl. jours. Chmn. pub. rels. Nat. Arthritis Found., Atlanta, 1985-87; participant Ariz. Strategic Planning and Econ. Devel., 1991-92. Lt. col. USAFR, 1987. Recipient Silver Anvil award Pub. Rels. Soc. Am., Golden Mike award Am. Legion Aux., MacEachern citation Acad. Hosp. Pub. Rels., Pres.'s citation Pub. Rels. Soc. Mem. Nat. Assn. Osteo. Founds. (pres. 1991—), Student Osteo. Med. Assn. (found. bd. dirs. 1990—), Acad. Hosp. Pub. Rels. (treas. 1980-81), Rotary. Republican. Methodist. Home: 5050 E South Regency Cir Tucson AZ 85711 Office: Tucson Osteo Med Found 4280 N Campbell Ave # 200 Tucson AZ 85718

RIGGS, GINA GINSBERG, educational association administrator; b. Berlin, Germany, Mar. 29, 1921; came to U.S., 1945; d. Hugo Herz and Elisabeth Herrmanns; m. Sidney Ginsberg, Dec. 24, 1954 (dec. (Sept. 1974); children: Matt, Jill; m. Sheldon K. Riggs, June 5, 1976 (dec. Oct. 1985). Sales mgr. Consolidated Bus. Systems, N.Y.C., 1950-54; exec. dir. Gifted Child Soc., Glen Rock, N.J., 1968—; project dir. Parent Info. Network for Gifted; con. Nat. Rsch. Ctr. on Gifted and Talented. Contbr. articles to profl. publs. Charter mem. Leadership N.J., 1989—. Recipient cert. of merit U.S. Office Edn., 1980. Avocations: internat. peace, artificial intelligence. Home: 59 Glen Gray Rd Oakland NJ 07436 Office: Gifted Child Soc Inc 190 Rock Rd Glen Rock NJ 07452

RIGGS, HENRY EARLE, college president, engineering management educator; b. Chgo., Feb. 25, 1935; s. Joseph Agnew and Gretchen (Walser) R.; m. Gayle Carson, May 17, 1958; children: Elizabeth, Peter, Catharine. BS, Stanford U., 1957; MBA, Harvard U., 1960. Indsl. economist SRI Internat., Menlo Park, Calif., 1960-63; v.p. Icore Industries, Sunnyvale, Calif., 1963-67, pres., 1967-70; v.p. fin. Measurex Corp., Cupertino, Calif., 1970-74; prof. engring. mgmt. Stanford U., Calif., 1974-88, Ford prof., 1986-88, v.p. for devel., 1983-88; pres. Harvey Mudd Coll., Claremont, Calif., 1988—; bd. dirs. Mutual Funds of Capital Rsch. Group. Author: Accounting: A Survey, 1981, Managing High-Tech Companies, 1983, Financial and Cost Analysis, 1994; contbr. articles to Harvard Bus. Rev. Bd. dirs. Mt. Baldy Coun. Boy Scouts Am., 1993—. Baker scholar Harvard Bus. Sch., Boston, 1959; recipient Gores Teaching award Stanford U., 1980. Mem. Stanford U. Alumni Assn. (bd. dirs. 1990-94, chmn. 1993), Calif. Club, Pauma Valley Club, Sunset Club, Phi Beta Kappa, Tau Beta Pi. Congregationalist. Office: Harvey Mudd Coll Kingston Hall # 201 Claremont CA 91711

RIGGS, JAMES ARTHUR, financial executive; b. Atlantic, Iowa, Mar. 27, 1936; s. LaVerne Albert and Grace Christine (Wesgaard) R.; m. Roberta Rose Lattanzi, Sept. 28, 1967; children: Kristen, James, Emily. BSBA, U. Ill., 1958; MBA, U. New Haven, 1979. Fin. analyst Ford Motor Co., Dearborn, Mich., 1961-65; supr. cost analysis Olin Corp., New Haven, 1965-67, mgr. fin. analysis, 1967-69; controller ammunition Olin Corp., East Alton, Ill., 1969-71, Olin Ski Co., Middletown, Conn., 1971-73; fin. officer recreation products Olin Corp., New Haven, 1973-79, fin. officer Winchester Group, 1979-81; fin. officer chem. group Olin Corp., Stamford, Conn., 1981-86, v.p., comptroller, 1986-90, sr. v.p., chief fin. officer, 1990—. Served with U.S. Army, 1959-61. Office: Olin Corp 120 Long Ridge Rd Stamford CT 06902-1839

RIGGS, JOHN B., architect; b. Tucson, Ariz., June 26, 1942; s. John Stark and Anna Lee (McAleb) R.; m. Barbara Wynn Bettner, Sept. 1, 1966 (div. Dec. 1976); children—Jeff, Bran; m. Jennifer J. Jewett, June 9, 1979; children—Courtney, Jennifer. B.Arch., U. Ariz., 1966. Registered architect, Ariz., Colo., Utah, Wash., Nev. Draftsman Terry Atkinson, Tucson, 1966-68, CNWC Architects, Tucson, 1968-69; designer Freidman & Jobusch, Tucson, 1969-70; prin., pres. Architecture One Ltd., Tucson, 1970—; mem. Ariz. State Bd. Tech. Registration, Phoenix, 1980-87, chmn., 1983-84; mem. exam. com. Nat. Council Architectural Registration Bds., 1981-86, asst. coordinator exam. A com., 1984, coordinator, 1985, mem. examination planning com., 1986-87. Bd. dirs., v.p. Ariz. Theatre Co., Tucson, 1980—; adv. com. U. Ariz. Coll. Architecture, 1983—. Recipient numerous awards in field. Mem. AIA (bd. dirs. So. Ariz. chpt. 1976-77), Western Conf. Archtl. Bds. (chmn. 1986-87, bd. dirs., v.p. Ariz. chpt.). Democrat. Methodist. Club: Plaza (bd. govs. 1985—). Office: Architecture One Ltd 6303 E Tanque Verde Rd Ste 200 Tucson AZ 85715-3859

RIGGS, JOHN HUTTON, JR., lawyer; b. Plainfield, N.J., Nov. 21, 1936; s. John Hutton and Helen Virginia (Butler) R.; m. Dominique Lacoste, Dec. 28, 1965; children: Emilie L., Francis L., Jennifer C. BA, Yale U., 1958; JD, U. Va., 1964. Bar: N.Y. 1965, U.S. Dist. Ct. (so. and ea. dists.) N.Y. 1976, Conseil Juridique France 1976. Assoc. Haight, Gardener, Poor & Havens, N.Y.C., 1964-67; assoc. White & Case, N.Y.C., 1967-68, Paris, 1968-71; ptnr. White & Case, N.Y.C., 1972-75, Paris, 1976—. Trustee Am. Library Paris; bd. dirs. Am. C. of C. in France; bd. dirs. Am. Hosp. Paris. Served to lt. USN, 1958-61. Mem. ABA, Internat. Bar Assn., Assn. of Bar of City of N.Y., Am. Soc. Internat. Law, Union Internat. des Avocats. Episcopalian. Clubs: Cercle Interallie, Polo, American (Paris) (pres. 1982-84). Home: 8 Ave Frederic Le Play, Paris 75007, France

RIGGS, LORRIN ANDREWS, psychologist, educator; b. Harput, Turkey, June 11, 1912; parents Am. citizens; s. Ernest Wilson and Alice (Shepard) R.; m. Doris Robinson, 1937 (dec.); children: Douglas Rikert, Dwight Alan; m. Caroline Cressman, 1994. A.B., Dartmouth Coll., 1933; M.A., Clark U., 1934, Ph.D., 1936. NRC fellow biol. scis. U. Pa., 1936-37; instr. U. Vt., 1937-38, 39-41; with Brown U., 1938-39, 41—, from asst. to assoc. prof., 1938-51, prof., 1951—, L. Herbert Ballou prof., 1960-68, E.J. Marston Univ. prof., 1968-77, prof. emeritus, 1977—; Guggenheim fellow U. Cambridge, 1971-72. Author sci. articles on vision, physiol. psychology. Recipient Kenneth Craik award Cambridge U., 1979, Prentice medal Am. Acad. Optometry, 1973. Mem. AAAS (chmn., v.p. sect. 1 1964), APA (div. pres. 1962-63, Disting. Sci. Contr. award 1974), Eastern Psychol. Assn. (pres. 1975-76), Optical Soc. Am. (Tillyer medal 1969, Ives medal 1982), Nat. Acad. Scis., Am. Physiol. Soc., Internat. Brain Rsch. Orgn., Soc. for Neurosci., Soc. Exptl. Psychologists (Howard Crosby Warren medal 1957), Assn. Rsch. in Vision and Ophthalmology (pres. 1977, Friedenwald award 1966), Am. Acad. Arts and Scis, Am. Psychol. Soc. (William James fellow 1989), Sigma Xi (chpt. pres. 1962-64). Home: Kendal at Hanover # 1020 80 Lyme Rd Hanover NH 03755-1225

RIGGS, MICHAEL DAVID, magazine publisher, writer; b. Frankfort, Ky., Apr. 30, 1951; s. Homer David and Helen Marion (Webber) R.; m. Elizabeth Susan Borman, Apr. 24, 1983; children: David B., William B. AB, Washington U., 1973. Chief trader Thomte & Co., Boston, 1975-77; tech. writer Saddlebrook Corp., Cambridge, Mass., 1977-79; assoc. editor Mini-Micro

Systems Mag., Boston, 1979-80; editor High Fidelity Mag., N.Y.C., 1980-89; exec. editor Stereo Review Mag., N.Y.C., 1989—. Author: Understanding Audio and Video, 1989. Mem. Audio Engring. Soc., Am. Society of Magazine Editors., Boston Audio Soc. Office: Stereo Review 1633 Broadway New York NY 10019-6708

RIGGS, RITA, costume designer; b. Boone County, Ark., Sept. 2, 1930; s. J. Almus and Ida V. (Keeling) Riggs; m. Charles S. Sharp, May 9, 1982 (dec. Sept. 1982). AA in Theatre Prodn., Santa Ana Coll., 1950; BA in Theatre Prodn., U. Ariz., 1952, MFA, 1954. Freelance designer Norman Lear's Tandem Prodns., L.A., 1970-80; costumer designer, pres. Rita Riggs Inc. Design Studio, L.A., 1980—; owner The Loft design studio, L.A., 1967—, Eureka Springs Train Sta., Ark., 1980—. Costume designer for numerous film, TV and theatrical prodns., including Marnie, Divorce, American Style, Seconds, The Professionals, The Model Shop, Petulia, The Lawyer, Happy Ending, Cold Turkey, Pro, Cinderella Liberty, Bite the Bullet, Electra Glide in Blue, Domino Principle, Night Moves, All in The Family, Sanford and Son, Maude, The Jeffersons, Good Times, One Day at a Time, Nancy Walker, All's Fair, Mary Hartman, Mary Hartman, Cattle Annie & Little Britches, The Idol Maker, Yes Giorgio, An Officer and A Gentleman, Deal of the Century, Women of Valor, Off Limits, Mr. North, Texasville, Broadway Bound, A Part of the Family, A Thing Called Love, The Last Outlaw, The Hunted. Home: The Loft Costume Studio 100 N Irving Blvd Los Angeles CA 90004 Office: Rita Riggs Inc 5971 W 3d St Los Angeles CA 90036

RIGGS, SONYA WOICINSKI, elementary school educator; b. Newhall, Calif., Oct. 9, 1935; d. Jack Lewis Woicinski and Mittie Mozelle (Bennett) Gillett; m. Eugene Garland Riggs, Dec. 21, 1956; children: Georgia Ann, Madeline Sue, Dana Eugene. BS in Elem. Edn., U. Tex., 1970; MEd in Reading Edn., S.W. Tex. State U., 1980. Cert. elem. tchr. English, Tex., cert. reading specialist K-12. Sec. state govts., Nebr./Tex., 1955-57; piano instr. Elgin, Tex., 1961-66; tchr. 1st grade Elgin Elem. Sch., Elgin, 1967-69, tchr. Music 3rd/4th grades, 1971-72, tchr. 4th grade, 1973-77; sec. region office Planned Parenthood/World Population, Austin, 1975-76; tchr. 8th-12th grades Giddings (Tex.) State Sch., 1976-78; tchr. 4th/5th grades Thorndale (Tex.) Ind. Sch. Dist., 1979-80; tchr. remedial reading Brazosport Ind. Sch. Dist., Freeport, Tex., 1980-81; tchr. 6th grade reading and chpt. I Bastrop (Tex.) Mid. Sch., 1981—; pres. El Tesoro Internacionale, Inc., 1973-74. Contbr. articles to Shih Tzu Reporter, 1993 French Bulldog Ann., Golden Retriever World, 1994-95, The Boston Quarterly, 1995. Mem. Elgin Band Boosters, 1970-83, sec., 1976; active South Ctrl. Regional Hearing Com., 1995. Mem. Assn. Tex. Profl. Educators, Austin Kennel Club (bd. dirs. 1990-91, 95—), Am. Shih Tzu Club (edn. and rescue com., regional hearing com.), French Bulldog Club Am. (rescue com.), Mission City Ring Stewards Assn., Internat. Soc. of Poets. Avocations: exhibiting dogs to Am. Kennel Club championships, writing poetry, playing piano, drawing, painting.

RIGGS, TIMOTHY ALLAN, museum curator; b. New Haven, Conn., Feb. 15, 1942; s. Douglas Shepard and Robin (palmer) R.; divorced; 1 child, Emma. BA, Swarthmore Coll., 1964; MA, Yale U., 1966, PhD, 1971. Rschr. Print Coun. Am., 1970-73; asst. curator Worcester (Mass.) Art Mus., 1973-76, curator prints and drawings, 1976-84; asst. dir. Ackland Art Mus., Chapel Hill, N.C., 1984—, acting dir., 1986, 94; adj. prof. U. N.C., Chapel Hill., 1984—. Contbr. catalogs. Mem. Print Coun. Am. (bd. dirs. 1981-84), Historians Netherlandish Art. Office: Ackland Art Mus U NC Chapel Hill CB # 3400 S Columbia St near Franklin St Chapel Hill NC 27599-3400

RIGGSBY, DUTCHIE SELLERS, education educator; b. Montgomery, Ala., Oct. 26, 1940; d. Cleveland Malcolm and Marcelia (Bedsole) Sellers; m. Ernest Duward Riggsby, Aug. 25, 1962; 1 child, Lyn. BS, Troy (Ala.) State Coll., 1962, MS, 1965; postgrad. George Peabody Coll., 1963; EdD, Auburn U., 1972. Cert. tchr., Ala., Ga.; cert. libr., Ga. Tchr. Montgomery Pub. Sch.s, 1962-63, Troy City Schs., 1963-67; instr. Auburn (Ala.) U., 1968-69; asst. prof. Columbus (Ga.) Coll., 1972-77, assoc. prof., 1977-83, prof., 1983—; vis. prof. U. P.R., Rio Piedras, 1972, 73; cons. schs. Columbus and Ft. Benning, Ga., 1980; leader various workshops, 1989, 93—; software reviewer Nat. Sci. Tchrs. Assn. Photographer: (book) Families, Professionals and Exceptionality, 1986, (textbook) Counseling Parents of Exceptional Children, 1986; contbr. more than 80 articles on state, regional, nat., and internat. programs to profl. jours., 1968—; reviewer instrnl. materials. Educator internal aerospace CAP, Maxwell AFB, 1980-90; dir. Air and Space Camp for Kids, 1990—. Recipient STAR Tchr. award Nat. Sci. Tchrs. Assn., Washington, 1968. Mem. Assn. for Ednl. Comms. and Tech. (nonperiodical pubs. com. 1994-96, awards com. 1994-96), Nat. Congress on Aviation and Space Edn. (dir. spl. promotions 1986-90), World Aerospace Edn. Orgn., Ga. Assn. Instrnl. Tech. (bd. dirs. 1982-84), Phi Delta Kappa (pres. Chattahoochee Valley chpt. 1986-87, Svc. award 1989, Svc. Key award 1993). Baptist. Avocations: photography, mining for gemstones. Home: 1709 Ashwood Ct Columbus GA 31904-3009 Office: Columbus Coll Sch Edn 4225 University Ave Columbus GA 31907-5645

RIGGSBY, ERNEST DUWARD, science educator; b. Nashville, June 12, 1925; s. James Thomas and Anna Pearl (Turner) R.; m. Dutchie Sellers, Aug. 25, 1964; 1 child, Lyn-Dee. BS, Tenn. Polytech. Inst., 1948; BA, George Peabody Coll. Tchrs., 1952, George Peabody Coll. Tchrs., 1953; MA, George Peabody Coll. Tchrs., 1956, EdS, 1961, EdD, 1964. Vis. grad. prof. U. P.R., Rio Piedras, George Peabody Coll., 1963-64; prof. Auburn (Ala.) U., Troy (Ala.) State U., Columbus (Ga.) Coll.; pres. Ednl. Developers, Inc., Columbus, Ga.; vis. grad. prof. George Peabody Coll. 1963-64; vis. lectr. Fla. Inst. Tech., summers 1967-77. Contbr. articles to profl. jours. Col., USAF, 1944-85. Named to Aerospace Crown Cir., 1984; elected to Aerospace Edn. Hall of Fame, 1982. Fellow AAAS; mem. Nat. Sci. Tchrs. Assn., World Aerospace Edn. Assn. (v.p. for the Ams.). Home: Columbus Coll Columbus GA 31993-2399

RIGHTER, WALTER CAMERON, bishop; b. Phila., Oct. 23, 1923; s. Richard and Dorothy Mae (Bottomley) R.; m. Nancy Ruth DeGroot, Aug. 22, 1992; children: Richard, Rebecca. BA, U. Pitts., 1948; MDiv, Berkeley Div. Sch., New Haven, 1951, DD, 1972; DCL, Iowa Wesleyan U., 1982; DD, Seabury Western Sem., 1984. Ordained priest Episcopal Ch., 1951, consecrated bishop, 1972; lay missioner St. Michael's Ch., Rector, Pa., 1947-48; priest-in-charge All Saints Ch., Aliquippa, Pa., 1951-54, St. Luke's, Georgetown, Pa., 1952-54; rector Ch. of Good Shepherd, Nashua, N.H., 1954-71; bishop Diocese of Iowa, Des Moines, 1972-89; asst. bishop Dio. of Newark, 1989-91; interim rector St. Elizabeth's, Ridgewood, N.J., 1991; mem. exec. coun. Protestant Episcopal Ch. U.S.A., 1979-85; spl. adv. NH Cursillo, 1994—. Mem. N.H. com. White House Conf. on Youth, 1962, Regional Crime Commn., Hillsboro County, N.H., 1969-71; trustee Nashua Libr., 1968-71, Seabury Western Sem., 1986-89; founding trustee The Morris Fund, Des Moines; planning com. Town of Alstead, N.H., 1993—. Fellow Coll. Preachers, Washington Cathedral.

RIGHTS, GRAHAM HENRY, minister; b. Winston-Salem, N.C., Jan. 14, 1935; s. Douglas LeTell and Cecil Leona (Burton) R.; m. Sybil Critz Strupe, Sept. 7, 1963; children: Susan Elizabeth, John Graham. BA, U. N.C., 1956; BD, Yale U., 1959; postgrad., Moravian Theol. Sem., 1959-60, U. Edinburgh, Scotland, 1965-66; DD (hon.), Wofford Coll., 1989. Ordained to ministry Moravian Ch., 1960. Pastor Union Ch., Managua, Nicaragua, 1960-63, Managua Moravian Ch., 1960-65, Mayodan (N.C.) Moravian Ch., 1966-72, Messiah Moravian Ch., Winston-Salem, 1972-81; exec. dir. Bd. World Mission Moravian Ch., Bethlehem, Pa., 1981-83; pres. exec. bd. so. province Moravian Ch., Winston-Salem, 1983-95; pres. exec. bd. world-wide Moravian Chs., 1991-94; pastor First Moravian Ch., Greensboro, N.C., 1995—. Author: On the Roof of the World, 1961. Trustee Moravian Coll., Bethlehem, 1983-95, Moravian Theol. Sem., Bethlehem, 1983-95; bd. dirs. Crisis Control Ministry, Winston-Salem, 1976—. Home: 208 W Elam Ave Greensboro NC 27403 Office: Drawer O 304 S Elam Ave Greensboro NC 27403

RIGOLOT, FRANÇOIS, French literature educator, literary critic; b. Château-du-Loir, Sarthe, France, May 21, 1939; s. Paul and Madeleine (Overnoy) R.; m. Carol Nolan, Sept. 5, 1970; children—Sophie, Stephanie. Diplôme, Hautes Etudes Commerciales, Paris, 1961; MA in Econs., Northwestern U., 1963; Ph.D. in French, U. Wis.-Madison, 1969.

Asst. prof. U. Mich, Ann Arbor, 1969-74; bicentennial preceptor Princeton U., N.J., 1974-77, assoc. prof. dept. romance langs. and lits., 1977-79, prof., 1979-81, Meredith Howland Pyne prof. French lit., chmn. dept.; 1984-91; chair Renaissance studies Princeton U., 1993—; prof. French, Middlebury (Vt.) Coll., 1973; dir. NEH seminar for coll. tchrs., Princeton, 1981, 84, 86, 88, 90; vis. prof. Johns Hopkins U., 1981; vis. mem. Inst. for Advanced Study, Princeton, 1982-83; dir. seminar The Folger Inst., Washington, 1987; prof. Institut d'Etudes Françaises, Avignon, 1989-95; ofcl. lectr. Alliance Française, 1994-95. Author: Les Langages de Rabelais, 1972, Poétique et Onomastique, 1977, Le Texte de la Renaissance, 1982 (Gilbert Chinard Lit. prize 1984), Les Métamorphoses de Montaigne 1988; editor: Complete Works of George Louise Labé, 1986, Journal de Voyage of Montaigne, 1992; co-editor: A New History of French Literature, 1989 (MLA James Russell Lowell prize 1990), De la Littérature Française, 1993; collaborator: Sémantique de La Poésie, 1979. Recipient Médaille de la ville de Bordeaux, Médaille de la ville de Tours, 1992, Officier des Plames Académiques, 1993, Howard T. Behrman award for Disting. Achievement in the Humanities, 1993; NEH fellow, 1979-80, Guggenheim Found. fellow, 1982-83. Mem. Acad. Literary Studies, Am. Assn. Tchrs. French, Renaissance Soc. Am., MLA, Assn. Internat. des Etudes Françaises. Home: 81 Pretty Brook Rd Princeton NJ 08540-7537 Office: Princeton U East Pyne Dept Romance Langs and Lits Princeton NJ 03544-5264

RIHA, WILLIAM EDWIN, beverage company executive; b. New Brunswick, N.J., Sept. 15, 1943; s. William Edwin and Grace Blue (McDowell) R.; m. Joan Ann Murphy, June 25, 1967; children: William Edwin III, Jennifer Dawn. BS, Rutgers U., 1965, MS, 1969, PhD, 1972. Mgr. product devel. Hunt-Wesson Foods, Inc., Fullerton, Calif., 1972-76; dir. tech. svcs. Cadbury N.Am., Hazleton, Pa., 1976-78; mgr. food tech. Peter Paul Cadbury, Inc., Naugatuck, Conn., 1978-80; group mgr. U.S. product devel. PepsiCo, Valhalla, N.Y., 1980-84, dir. internat. product devel., 1984-89; v.p. R&D J. E. Seagram & Sons, Ltd., White Plains, N.Y., 1989-93; v.p. rsch. & tech. svc. Tropicana Products Inc., Bradenton, Fla., 1993—. Capt. USAR, 1965-73. Mem. Inst. Food Technologists (grad. fellowship Nestle 1968), Indsl. Rsch. Inst. (membership com. 1990-92), Sigma Xi. Avocations: golf, tennis, baseball memorabilia. Home: 3243 Dick Wilson Dr Sarasota FL 34240 Office: Tropicana Products Inc 1001 13th Ave E Bradenton FL 34208-2656

RIHANI, FUAD AKIL, civil engineer, researcher; b. Al-Husn, Jordan, Sept. 30, 1937; s. Akil Odeh and Tamam Bidaiwi (Ayyoub) R.; m. Katherine Elizabeth Ketner, Aug. 23, 1969; children: Elizabeth Tamam, Kristin Awatif, John Akil. B of Civil Engring., Am. U., Beirut, 1959; MS in Transp., N.C. State U., 1964, PhD in Transp., 1974. Project engr. Ministry of Pub. Works, Jordan, 1959-63; project mgr. M. Binladin Orgn., Saudi Arabia, 1965-68; hwy. planning engr. N.C. DOT, Raleigh, 1968-73, chief transp. systems planning, 1973-75; assoc. prof. N.C. State U., Raleigh, 1975-78; chief engr. M. Binladin Orgn., Saudi Arabia, 1978-82, dir. R & D, 1982-90; dir. R & D Saudi Binladin Group, Saudi Arabia, 1990—. Dir. Mid. East Policy Coun., Washington, 1992—. USAID scholar, 1954-59, Fulbright scholar, 1963-64. Mem. ASCE, Inst. Transp. Engrs., Transp. Rsch. Bd. Republican. Lutheran. Home: 4320 4th Street Cir NW Hickory NC 28601-9021 Office: Saudi Binladin Group, Prince Abdullah St, Jeddah 21483, Saudi Arabia

RIKER, WALTER F., JR., pharmacologist, physician; b. N.Y.C., Mar. 8, 1916; s. Walter F. and Eleanore Louise (Scafard) R.; m. Virginia Helene Jaeger, Nov. 28, 1941; children: Donald K., Walter F., Wayne S. BS, Columbia U., 1939; MD, Cornell U., 1943; D.Sc. (hon.), Med. Coll. Ohio, 1980. Instr. pharmacology Cornell U. Med. Coll., N.Y.C., 1944-47; instr. medicine Cornell U. Med. Coll., 1945-46, asst. prof. pharmacology, 1947-50, assoc. prof., 1950-56, prof., chmn. dept. pharmacology, 1956-83, Revlon chair pharmacology and toxicology, 1980-83, prof. emeritus, 1983-86; mem. study sect. NIH, 1956-63, 65-68; mem. Nat. Inst. Gen. Med. Scis. Council., 1963-64, Nat. Inst. Environ. Health Scis. Council, 1971-75, Pres.'s Sci. Adv. Com. on Toxicology, 1964-65; vis. prof. pharmacology U. Kans. Med. Coll., 1953; mem. Unitarian Service Med. Exchange Program, Japan, 1956; mem. sci. adv. com. Pharm. Mfrs.'s Assn. Found., 1966-87; adj. mem. Roche Inst. Molecular Biology, 1972-80; med. advisor on drugs Nat. Football League, 1973-84; adv. com. Irma T. Hirschl Found., N.Y.C., 1973—; bd. sci. advisors Sterling Drug, 1973-76; dir. Richardson-Vicks Inc., 1979-85. Recipient Teaching award Cornell U. Med. Coll., 1968, 78, citation Pharm. Mfrs.'s Assn. Found., 1972, 87, Award of Distinction Cornell U. Med. Coll. Alumni Assn., 1981, Maurice R. Greenberg Svc. award N.Y. Hosp./Cornell U. Med. Ctr., 1990; Sterling Drug vis. professorship established in honor at Cornell U. Med. Coll., 1979; named Hon. Fellow, Am. Coll. Clin. Pharmacology, 1987. Fellow AAAS, N.Y. Acad. Medicine, Harvey Soc.; mem. Am. Soc. Pharmacology and Exptl. Therapeutics (chmn. membership com. 1956-59, councillor 1959-62, bd. publs. trustees 1962-64, chmn. bd. publs. trustees 1962-70, chmn. com. ednl. and profl. affairs 1972-74, John Jacob Abel award 1951, Publs. citation 1970, Torald Sollman award 1986, Oscar B. Hunter award 1990), Japanese Pharmacology Soc., Am. Soc. Clin. Pharmacology and Therapeutics, N.Y. Acad. Scis., Sigma Xi, Alpha Omega Alpha. Office: Cornell U Med Coll 1300 York Ave New York NY 10021-4896

RIKER, WILLIAM KAY, pharmacologist, educator; b. N.Y.C., Aug. 31, 1925; s. Walter Franklin and Eleanore Louise (Scafard) R.; m. Carmela Louise DePamphilis, Dec. 21, 1947 (dec. 1981); children: Eleanor Louise, Gainor, Victoria; m. Leena Mela, Aug. 13, 1983. B.A., Columbia U., 1949; M.D., Cornell U., 1953. Intern 2d Cornell med. div., Bellevue Hosp., 1953-54; practice medicine, specializing in pharmacology Phila., 1954-69, Portland, Oreg., 1969—; instr., asst. prof. dept. pharmacology U. Pa. Sch. Medicine, 1954-61; spl. fellow dept. physiology U. Utah Sch. Medicine, 1961-64; assoc. prof., prof., chmn. dept. pharmacology Woman's Med. Coll., Phila., 1964-69; prof., chmn. dept. pharmacology U. Oreg. Sch. Medicine, U. Oreg. Health Scis. Center, 1969-91, prof. emeritus, 1991—; asst. dean. for admissions, 1986-89; mem. neurol. disorders program project com. NIH, 1975-79. Editor: Jour. Pharmacology and Therapeutics, 1969-72; contbr. articles to biomed. jours. Served with USNR, 1943-46. Recipient Christian R. and Mary F. Lindback Found. award for disting. teaching, 1968; Pa. Plan scholar, 1957-61; Nat. Inst. Neurol. Diseases and Blindness spl. fellow, 1961-64; USPHS-NIH research grantee, 1958-83. Mem. Am. Soc. Pharmacology and Exptl. Therapeutics (sec.-treas. 1978-81, pres. 1985-86), Western Pharmacol. Soc. (pres. 1976), Japanese Pharmacol. Soc., Assn. Med. Sch. Pharmacologists (sec-officio 1976-78), Epilepsy Assn. Am., Pharm. Mfrs. Assn. Found. (chmn. pharmacology-morphology adv. com., sci. adv. com. 1976-92), Cosmos Club. Home: 4326 SW Warrens Way Portland OR 97221-3246 Office: 3181 SW Sam Jackson Park Rd Portland OR 97201-3011

RIKKERS, LAYTON F., surgeon; b. Fond du Lac, Wis., 1944. MD, Stanford U., 1970. Diplomate Am. Bd. Surgery (vice chmn. 1993-94, chmn. 1994—). Intern U. Utah Hosp., 1970-71, resident gen. surgery, 1971-73, 74-76; fellow hepatology Royal Free Hosp., London, 1973-74; surgeon U. Nebr. Hosp., Omaha; prof., chmn. U. Nebr. Coll. Medicine. Fellow ACS; mem. Am. Surg. Assn., Soc. Clin. Surgery, Soc. Surgery of Alimentary Tract, Soc. Univ. Surgeons. Office: U Nebr Med Ctr Dept Surgery 600 S 42d St Omaha NE 68198-3280

RIKKERS, LAYTON FREDERICK, surgeon; b. Fond du Lac, Wis., Jan. 31, 1944; s. Judson John and Dorothy (Layton) R.; m. Diane Lynn Foster, Aug. 20, 1966; children: Steven, Kristin. BS, U. Wis., 1966; MD, Stanford U. Sch. Medicine, 1970. Diplomate Nat. Bd. Med. Examiners, Am. Bd. Surgery. Intern U. Utah Sch. Medicine, Salt Lake City, 1970-71, surgical residency, 1971-76; instr. surgery Emory U. Sch. Medicine, Atlanta, 1976-77; rsch. assoc. Salt Lake Vet. Adminstrn. Hosp., 1977-79; from asst. prof. surgery to acting chmn. div. gen. surgery U. Utah Sch. Medicine, Salt Lake City, 1977-84; prof., chmn. dept surgery U. Nebr. Med. Ctr., Omaha, 1984—; interim dean college of medicine U. Nebr. Coll. Medicine, 1991-93, M.M. Musselman prof. surgery, 1990—; cons. Omaha Vet. Adminstrn. Ctr., 1984—, NIH, 1992, Gov.'s Blue Ribbon Coalition on Health Care, Nebr., 1993-94. Editor: Surgical Clinics of North America, 1990; contbr. articles to profl. jours. Mem. Am. Surgical Assn., Am. Coll. Surgeons (com. chair 1993-95), Am. Bd. Surgery (clin. chmn. 1994-95), Soc. Clin. Surgery (pres.-elect 1994-95). Episcopalian. Avocations: hiking, reading, skiing, travel. Office: U Nebr Med Ctr Dept Surgery 600 S 42d St Omaha NE 68198

RIKLI, DONALD CARL, lawyer; b. Highland, Ill., June 16, 1927; s. Carl and Gertrude Louise (Stoecklin) R.; m. Joan Tate, Oct. 10, 1953; children: Kristine, David. AB, Ill. Coll., 1951; JD, U. Ill., 1953. Bar: Ill. 1953, U.S. Dist. Ct. (so. dist.) Ill. 1961, U.S. Ct. Appeals (7th cir.) 1968, U.S. Supreme Ct. 1974. Pvt. practice law Highland, 1953—; atty. City of Highland, 1956-59. Author: The Illinois Probate System, 1974, 75, 77, 78; bd. editors Illinois Real Property I, 1966, 71, Lawyers World, 1970-72, Law Notes, 1981-83, The Compleat Lawyer, 1985-87. Mem. consistory United Ch. Christ, 1960-62, 93—. With U.S. Army, 1945-47. Fellow Am. Coll. Trust and Estate Counsel, Ill. Bar Found., Am. Bar Found.; mem. ABA (sec. chairperson gen. practice sect. 1990-91, Ho. of Dels. 1991-93, mem. coun. 1981-93, Sole Practitioner of Yr. 1990), Ill. Bar Assn. (chmn. Bill of Rights com. 1967-68, coun. estate planning probate and trust sect. 1976-81, sec. 1980-81), Madison County Bar Assn. (pres. 1966-67); bd. gov. Am. Acad. of Estate Planning Attorneys, 1994—. Home: 1312 Old Trenton Rd Highland IL 62249-2028 Office: 914 Broadway Highland IL 62249-1811

RIKLIS, MARCIA, retail executive. Formerly vice-chmn. Schenley Industries Inc., Dallas; exec. v.p. EII Holdings, Rapid Am. Corp., N.Y.C.

RIKLIS, MESHULAM, manufacturing and retail executive; b. Turkey, Dec. 2, 1923; came to U.S., 1947, naturalized, 1955; s. Pinhas and Betty (Guberer) R.; children: Simona Riklis Ackerman, Marcia Riklis Hirschfeld, Ira Doron, Kady Zadora Riklis, Kristofer Riklis. Student, U. Mexico, 1947; BA, Ohio State U., 1950, MBA, 1968. Co-dir. youth activities and mil. tng. Hertzlia High Sch., Tel-Aviv, 1942; tchr. Hebrew Talmud Torah Sch., Mpls., 1951; research dept. Piper, Jaffray & Hopwood, 1951-53, sales rep., 1953-56; vice chmn. McCrory Corp., N.Y.C., 1960-69, vice chmn. exec. com., from 1970, chmn., 1975-85, dir., former pres.; with Rapid-Am. Corp., N.Y.C., 1956—, chmn., 1956—, pres., chief exec. officer, 1957-73, chmn., chief exec. officer, 1973-76, chmn., pres., chief exec. officer, 1976—; E-II Holdings, 1988-90. Served Brit. 8th Army, 1942-46. Mem. Pi Mu Epsilon. Jewish. Office: McCrory Corp 888 7th Ave New York NY 10106 also: Riklis Family Corp 2901 Las Vegas Blvd S Las Vegas NV 89109

RIKOSKI, RICHARD ANTHONY, engineering executive, electrical engineer; b. Kingston, Pa., Aug. 13, 1941; s. Stanley George and Nellie (Gober) R.; m. Giannina Batchelor Petrullo, Dec. 18, 1971 (div. 1979); children: Richard James, Jennifer Anne. BEE, U. Detroit, 1964; MSEE, Carnegie Inst. Tech., 1965; PhD, Carnegie-Mellon U., 1968; postdoctoral student, Case-Western Res. U./NASA, 1971. Registered profl. engr., Ill., Mass., Pa. Engr. 1st communication satellite systems Internat. Tel. & Tel., Nutley, N.J., 1961-64; engr. Titan II ICBM program Gen. Motors, Milw., 1964; trainee NASA, 1964-67; instr. Carnegie-Mellon U., Pitts., 1966-68; asst. prof. U. Pa., Phila., 1968-74; assoc. prof., dir. hybrid microelectronics lab., chmn. ednl. TV com. IIT, Chgo., 1974-80, chmn. ednl. TV com., 1974-80; rsch. engr. nuclear effects ITT Rsch. Inst., Chgo., 1974-75; pres. Tech. Analysis Corp., Chgo., 1980—; engr. color TV colorimetry Hazeltine Rsch., Chgo., 1969; engr. Metroliner rail car/roadbed ride quality dynamics analysis U.S. Dept. Transp., ENSCO, Inc., Springfield, Va., 1970; pres. Tech. Analysis Corp., Chgo., 1978-91; contractor analysis of color TV receiver safety hazards U.S. Consumer Product Safety Commn., 1977, analysis heating effect in aluminum wire Beverly Hills Supper Club Fire, Covington, Ky., 1978; engr. GFCI patent infringement study 3M Corp., St. Paul, 1979-81; elec. systems analyst Coca-Cola Corp., Atlanta, 1983-91; fire investigator McDonald's Corp., Oak Brook, Ill., 1987-90; engring. analyst telephone switching ctrs. ATT, Chgo., 1990-91; expert witness numerous other govtl. and corp. proc. Author: Hybrid Microelectronic Circuits, 1973; editor: Hybrid Microelectronic Technology, 1973; contbr. articles to profl. jours. Officer Planning Commn., Beverly Shores, Ind., 1987-93, trustee town coun., 1992—, police liason 1993—; mem. Chgo. Coun. Fgn. Rels., USAF SAC Comdrs. Disting. Vis. Program; adv. coun. Nat. Park Svc. Ind. Dunes Nat. Lake Shore, 1993—. NASA fellow, 1964-67, 70. Mem. IEEE (sr. ednl. activities bd. N.Y.C. 1970-74, USAB career devel. com. 1972-74, editor Soundings 1973-75, Cassette Colloquia 1973-74, del. Popov Soc. Tech. Exch. USSR, mgr. Dial Access Tech. Edn. program 1972), Assn. for Media Based Continuing Engring. Edn. (bd. dirs.), Nat. Fire Protection Assn., Sigma Xi, Tau Beta Pi, Eta Kappa Nu. Republican. Avocations: sailing, travel. Home: One E Lakefront Dr Beverly Shores IN 46301-0444 Office: Tech Analysis Corp 3600 N Lake Shore Dr Chicago IL 60613-4656

RILES, WILSON CAMANZA, educational consultant; b. Alexandria, La., June 27, 1917; m. Mary Louise Phillips, Nov. 13, 1941; children: Michael, Narvia Riles Bostick, Wilson, Phillip. B.A. No. Ariz. U., 1940; M.A., 1947, LL.D., 1996; LL.D., Pepperdine Coll., 1965, Claremont Grad. Sch., 1972, U. So. Calif., 1975, U. Akron, 1976, Golden Gate U., 1981; L.H.D., St. Mary's Coll., 1971, U. Pacific, 1971, U. Judaism, 1972. Tchr. elem. schs., adminstr. pub. schs. Ariz., 1940-54; exec. sec. Pacific Coast region Fellowship of Reconciliation, Los Angeles, 1954-58; with Calif. Dept. Edn., 1958-83, dep. supt. pub. instrn., 1965-70, supt. pub. instruction, 1971-83; pres. Wilson Riles & Assocs., Inc., 1983—; dir. emeritus Wells Fargo Bank, Wells Fargo Co. Past mem. editorial adv. bd.: Early Years mag. Ex-officio mem. bd. regents U. Calif. 1971-82; ex-officio trustee Calif. State Univs. and Colls., 1971-82; nat. adv. council Nat. Schs. Vol. Program; former mem. council Stanford Research Inst.; former mem. adv. council Stanford U. Sch. Bus.; former mem. adv. bd. Calif. Congress Parents and Tchrs.; former trustee Am. Coll. Testing Program; former mem. Edn. Commn. of States; past 2d v.p. Nat. PTA.; former trustee Found. Teaching Econs.; former mem. Joint Council Econ. Edn.; former mem. Nat. Council for Children and TV. With USAF, 1943-46. Recipient Spingarn medal NAACP, 1973. Mem. Assn. Calif. Sch. Adminstrs., Cleve. Conf., NAACP (Spingarn medal 1973), Nat. Acad. Pub. Adminstrn., Phi Beta Kappa. Office: 400 Capitol Mall Ste 1540 Sacramento CA 95814 Is growing up in rural Louisiana during the depression as an orphan, poor and black, attending a segregated school, a handicap? I have never thought so. Maybe it's because of the superb teachers who never let me feel sorry for myself. As I recall, some did not even have college degrees, but they believed I could learn. Because they did, it never occurred to me that I couldn't. Forrest Paul Augustine, the principal, admonished us to get as much education as we could because, "that is one thing no one can ever take away from you". I chose education as a career because those humble public schools gave me a chance. I want all boys and girls to have a chance, too.

RILEY, ANN J., state legislator, technology specialist; b. Memphis, Oct. 27, 1940; m. Ray T. Riley, Apr. 28, 1962. BSBA, U. Albuquerque, 1985; MBA, Webster U., 1988; cert. in pub. policy, Harvard U., 1994. Loan officer Ravenswood Bank, Chgo., 1970-74; mgr. dist. sales Security Lockout, Chgo., 1974-77; owner AR Fasteners, Albuquerque, 1977-82; tech. transfer agt. Sandia Nat. Labs., Albuquerque, 1983—; mem. N.Mex. Senate, Santa Fe, 1993—; resolutions chair energy com. Nat. Order of Women Legil. Nat. Conf. State Legislators. Bd. dirs. All Faiths Receiving Home. Albuquerque, 1989-92, Law Enforcement Acad., Santa Fe, 1991-92; active Leadership Albuquerque, 1991, state federal task force U.S. Office Sci. & Tech., 1995. Pub. Policy Inst. fellow John F. Kennedy Sch. Govt. Harvard U. Democrat. Avocations: running, bicycling, politics, reading. Home: 10201 Karen NE Albuquerque NM 87111-3635

RILEY, ANTHONY WILLIAM, German language and literature educator; b. Radcliffe-on-Trent, Eng., July 23, 1929; s. Cyril Frederick and Winifred Mary (White) R.; m. Maria Theresia Walter, July 16, 1955; children: Christopher, Katherine, Angela. B.A. with honors, U. Manchester, Eng., 1952; Dr. Phil., U. Tübingen, Fed. Republic Germany, 1958. Lectr. U. Tübingen, 1957-59, 60-62; asst. lectr. Queen Mary Coll., U. London, Eng., 1959-60; asst. prof. German lang. and lit. Queen's U., Kingston, Ont., Can., 1962-65; asso. prof. Queen's U., 1965-68, prof. 1968-92; emeritus prof. Queen's U., Kingston, Ont., Can., 1993—; head dept. German lang. and lit. Queen's U., 1967-76, acting head dept., 1979-80, 86-87. Author: Elisabeth Langgässer Bibliographie mit Nachlassbericht, 1970; also articles on Elisabeth Langgässer, Alfred Döblin, Thomas Mann, Herman Hesse, Frederick Philip Grove; co-editor: The Master Mason's House (F.P. Grove), 1976, Echoes and Influences of German Romanticism, 1987, Muse and Reason, The Relation of Arts and Sciences 1650-1850, 1994; co-translator, co-editor: Fanny Essler, 2 vols. (Grove), 1984; editor: Der Oberst und der Dichter/Die Pilgerin Aetheria (Alfred Döblin), 1978, Der unsterbliche Mensch/Der Kampf mit dem Engel (Alfred Döblin), 1980, Jagende Rosse/Der schwarze Vorhang (Alfred Döblin), 1981, Wadzeks Kampf mit der Dampfturbine (Alfred Döblin), 1982, Kleine Schriften I (1902-1921) (Döblin), 1985, Kleine Schriften II (1922-24) (Döblin), 1990, Schicksalsreise (Alfred Döblin), 1993. Served with Brit. Army, 1947-49. Summer fellow Weil Inst. for Studies in Religion and the Humanities, Cin., 1965; Can. Council Leave fellow, 1969-70, 76-77, 83-84. Fellow Royal Soc. Can. (sec. acad. humanities and social scis. 1992-95); mem. Can. Assn. Univ. tchrs. German (v.p. 1973-75, pres. 1975-76, Hermann Boeschenstein medal 1987, Konrad Adenauer rsch. award Alexander von Humboldt Found. 1989), Deutsche Schillergesellschaft Humanities Assn. Can., internat. Alfred Döblin-Gesellschaft (v.p. 1984-95), Internat. Assn. for Germanic Studies, Elisabeth Langgässer-Gesellschaft (Darmstadt), Soc. for acad. Freedom and Scholarship. Home: 108 Queen Mary Rd, Kingston, ON Canada K7M 2A5

RILEY, ARTHUR ROY, consulting engineer; b. Wink, Tex., Oct. 10, 1930; s. Lincoln Harold and Wylie Edna (Box) R.; m. Betty Lynn Weddle, Jan. 24, 1953; children: Cynthia Lynn, Nina Marion, Julia Beth, Arthur Roy Jr. BSME, Miss. State U., 1953. Registered profl. engr., La., Tex. Petroleum engr. ea. divsn. Exxon Corp. USA, New Orleans, 1955-62; tech. sales rep. Exxon Chem. Co., Lafayette, La., 1962-70; pres. Arthur Chems., Inc., Lafayette, 1970-75; pres. Arthur Engrs., Inc., Lafayette, 1975-80, Spring, Tex., 1980—; pres. McCain Prodn. Co., Inc., Spring, 1985-92, Gopher Tool Co., Spring and Lafayette, 1980, Chart-X Corp., Spring, 1990—; cons. petroleum engr. various drilling and prodn. cos., La., Tex. and N.Mex., 1975-90; cons. drilling engr. DOE-SPR, New Orleans, 1979-80, DOE-Las Vegas-Geothermal, S.W. La., Houston, 1981, Vertec divsn. Bow Valley Ind., Denver, 1984-85. Del. Tex. Dem. Conv., Houston, 1988. 1st lt. USAF, 1953-55, Korea. Mem. Soc. Petroleum Engrs., Inst. Shaft Drilling Tech. Republican. Baptist. Avocations: genealogy, auto repair, carpentry and home repair, golf. Office: Arthur Engrs Inc 9530 Enstone Cir Spring TX 77379-6605

RILEY, CARROLL LAVERN, anthropology educator; b. Summersville, Mo., Apr. 18, 1923; s. Benjamin F. and Minnie B. (Smith) R.; m. Brent Robinson Locke, Mar. 25, 1948; children: Benjamin Locke, Victoria Smith Evans, Cynthia Winningham. A.B., U. N.Mex., 1948, Ph.D., 1952; M.A. UCLA, 1950. Instr. U. Colo., Boulder, 1953-54; asst. prof. U. N.C., Chapel Hill, 1954-55; asst. prof. So. Ill. U., Carbondale, 1955-60, assoc. prof., 1960-67, prof., 1967-86, Disting. prof., 1986-87, Disting. prof. emeritus, 1987—, chmn. dept., 1979-82, dir. mus., 1972-74; rsch. assoc. lab. anthropology Mus. N.Mex., 1987-90, sr. rsch. assoc., 1990—; rsch. collaborator Smithsonian Instn., 1988—; adj. prof. N.Mex. Highlands U., 1989—. Author: The Origins of Civilization, 1969, The Frontier People, 1982, expanded edit., 1987, Rio del Norte, 1995; editor: Man Across the Sea, 1971, Southwestern Journals of Adolph F. Bandelier, 4 vols., 1966, 70, 75, 84, Across the Chichimec Sea, 1978 and others; contbr. numerous articles to profl. jours. Served in USAAF, 1942-45. Decorated 4 battle stars; grantee Social Sci. Research Council, NIH. Am. Philos. Soc., Am. Council Learned Socs., NEH, others. Home and Office: 1106 6th St Las Vegas NM 87701-4311

RILEY, DANIEL EDWARD, air force officer; b. Flint, Mich., Aug. 18, 1915; s. Daniel Edward and Elva (Kirby) R.; m. Margaret E. Marengo, Nov. 28, 1938; children—Dennis M., Patricia A., Daniel R. B. Aero. Engring., U. Detroit, 1940; M.B.A., U. Mich., 1951; postgrad., Indsl. Coll. of Armed Forces, 1959. Commd. 2d lt. USAAF, 1936; advanced through grades to maj. gen. USAF, 1968; chief of plans and ops. (7290th Procurement Squadron at), Rhein/Main Air Base, Germany, 1951-1952; dep., later chief of procurement and prodn. div. (Hdqrs. USAF in), Europe; also comdr. (7290th Procurement Squadron), 1952-54; dep. chief of staff materiel (Directorate of Procurement and Prodn., Hdqrs. USAF), 1954-58; program dir. (MACE missile Air Research and Devel. Command), Wright-Patterson AFB, Ohio, 1959-60; program dir. SAC C&C Systems AFSC, 1961-63; vice comdr. (Electronics Systems div. AFSC), Bedford, Mass., 1965; comdr. (Air Force Contract Mgmt. Div.), Los Angeles, 1965-69; asst. dir. (Def. Supply Agy.), Washington, 1969-70; asst. to pres. Novatronics Inc., Pompano Beach, Fla., 1976-77. Decorated Legion of Merit with 2 oak leaf clusters. Mem. Air Force Assn., Ret. Officer Assn., Embry-Riddle Aero U. Bd. of Visitors, Indsl. Coll. Armed Forces Assn., Mil. Order World Wars, Lindbergh Fund, Halifax River Yacht Club, Beta Gamma Sigma, Phi Kappa Phi. Home: 1566 Poplar Dr Ormond Beach FL 32174-3414

RILEY, DOROTHY COMSTOCK, state supreme court justice; b. Detroit, Dec. 6, 1924; d. Charles Austin and Josephine (Grima) Comstock; m. Wallace Don Riley, Sept. 13, 1963; 1 child, Peter Comstock. B.A. in Polit. Sci., Wayne State U., 1946, LL.B., 1949; LLD (hon.), Alma Coll., 1988, U. Detroit, 1990. Bar: Mich. 1950, U.S. Dist. Court (ea. dist.) Mich. 1950, U.S. Supreme Court 1957. Atty. Wayne County Friend of Court, Detroit, 1956-68; ptnr. Riley & Roumell, Detroit, 1968-72, 73-76; judge Wayne County Circuit, Detroit, 1972, Mich. Ct. Appeals, Detroit, 1976-82; assoc. justice Mich. Supreme Court, Detroit, 1982-83, 85—; chief justice Mich. Supreme Court, Lansing, 1987-91; mem. U.S. Jud. Conf. Commn. on State-Fed. Ct. Rels.; chmn. tort reform com. Conf. of Chief Justices; bd. dirs. Nat. Ctr. for State Cts., Thomas J. Cooley Law Sch. Co-author manuals, articles in field. Mem. steering com. Mich. Children Skillman Found., 1992; mem. multistate profl. responsibility exam. com. Nat. Conf. Bar Examiners, 1992. Recipient Disting. Alumni award Wayne U., 1990; Headliner award Women of Wayne, 1977; Donnelly award, 1946; Law Enforcement Commendation medal Nat. Soc. Sons of Am. Revolution, 1991; inducted in Mich. Women's Hall of Fame, 1991. Mem. ABA (family law sect. 1965—, vice chmn. gen. practice sect. com. on juvenile justice 1975-80, mem. jud. adminstrn. sect. 1973—, standing com. on fed. ct. improvements, mem. judges adv. com. of standing com. on ethics and profl. responsibility 1992), Am. Judicature Soc., Fellows Am. Bar Found., Mich. State Bar Found., State Bar Mich. (civil liberties com. 1954-58), Detroit Bar Assn. (pub. rels. com. 1955-56, author Com. in Action column, Detroit Lawyers 1955, chmn. friend of ct. and family law com. 1974-75), Nat. Women Judges Assn., Nat. Women Lawyers Assn., Women Lawyers Assn. Mich. (pres. 1957-58), Mich. Sup. Ct. Hist. Soc., Karyatides, Pi Sigma Alpha. Republican. Roman Catholic. Avocations: reading; gardening. Office: Mich Supreme Ct 500 Woodward Ave 20th Fl Detroit MI 48226

RILEY, EDWARD JOHN, protective services official; b. Rochester, N.Y., June 7, 1954; s. John Joseph and Dorothy Marie (Graham) R.; m. Cheryl Lee Williams, Sept. 27, 1980; children: Kevin Timothy, Meghan Rose. AS in Liberal Arts, Monroe C.C., Rochester, 1975, AAS in Fire Protection, 1976; BS in Fire Adminstrn., SUNY, Rochester, 1986. Fire fighter Eastmand Kodak Co., Rochester, 1977-86; fire coord. Monroe County, Rochester, 1986—; vol. fire fighter Lake Shore Fire Dist., Rochester, 1972—, fire. commr., 1992—; mem. HAZMAT response team Monroe County, 1987—; course evaluator Empire State Coll., SUNY, 1986—. Recipient Heroic Act award Greece Safety Coun., 1986. Mem. N.Y. State Fire Coords. Assn. (v.p. 1993—). Republican. Roman Catholic. Avocations: antique watch collection, local history, genealogy. Home: 1650 Edgemere Dr Rochester NY 14612-1516 Office: Monroe County Fire Bur 111 Westfall Rd Rochester NY 14620

RILEY, GEORGIANNE MARIE, lawyer; b. Chgo., Feb. 5, 1953. BA in Psychology, Drake U., 1974, JD, 1978. Bar: Ill., 1978. Chief counsel Ill. Commn., Chgo., 1979-83; dep. chief counsel Ill. Dept. Transp., Chgo., 1983-89; counsel Chem. Waste Mgmt., Oakbrook, Ill., 1989-91, sr. counsel, 1991-92; gen. counsel, v.p., sec. Rust Indsl. Svcs., Westchester, Ill., 1993—. Office: Waste Mgmt Inc 3003 Butterfield Rd Oak Brook IL 60521

RILEY, HAROLD JOHN, JR., manufacturing executive; b. Syracuse, N.Y., Nov. 13, 1940; s. Harold John and Esther Emma (Denmark) R.; m. Diane Marie Slattery, June 15, 1963; children—Beth Ann, Thomas, Patrick. B.S. in Indsl. Engring., Syracuse U., 1961; postgrad., Harvard Bus. Sch., 1985. Mfg. tng. program Gen. Elec. Co., various locations, 1961-63; various mfg. assignments Crouse-Hinds Co., Syracuse, 1963-74; gen. mgr. Midwest Elec., Chgo., 1974-77; v.p., gen. mgr. Crouse-Hinds Distbn. Equipment Div., Earlysville, VA., 1977-79; v.p. Crouse-Hinds Co., Syracuse, 1979-82; exec. v.p. Cooper Industries Inc., Houston, 1982-92, pres., chief oper. officer, 1992—, also bd. dirs.; bd. dirs. Wyman-Gordon Co., North Grafton, Mass. Bd. dirs. Jr. Achievement Southeast Tex., Houston Ctrl., Houston Symphony, Sch. Mgmt. Syracuse U. Mem. Mfrs. Alliance for Productivity Improvement, Houston Club, Lakeside Country Club (Houston), Farmington County Club (Charlottesville, Va.). Republican. Roman Catholic. Home: 3669 Chevy

Chase Houston TX 77019 Office: Cooper Industries Inc PO Box 4446 Houston TX 77210-4446

RILEY, HARRIS DEWITT, JR., pediatrician; b. Clarksdale, Miss., Nov. 12, 1924; s. Harris DeWitt and Louise (Allen) R.; m. Margaret Barry, Sept. 16, 1950; children: Steven Allen, Mark Barry, Margaret Ruth. B.A., Vanderbilt U., 1945, M.D., 1948. Intern Balt. City Hosps., Johns Hopkins Hosp., 1948-49; resident in pediatrics Babies and Children's Hosp., Univ. Hosp., Cleve., 1949-50, Vanderbilt U. Hosp., 1950-51; instr., fellow in pediatrics Vanderbilt U. Med. Sch., 1953-57; prof. pediatrics, chmn. dept. U. Okla. Med. Sch., 1958—; med. dir. Children's Meml. Hosp., 1972—; disting. prof. pediatrics U. Okla., 1976; prof. pediatrics Vanderbilt U. Sch. of Medicine, Nashville, 1991—. Served as capt. M.C. USAF, 1951-53. Office: Children's Hosp of Vanderbilt Vanderbilt Univ Med Ctr Nashville TN 37232

RILEY, HELENE MARIA KASTINGER, Germanist; b. Vienna, Austria, Mar. 11, 1939; came to U.S., 1959; d. Josef and Helene (Friedl) Kastinger; m. Edward R. Riley, Nov. 6, 1957 (div. May 1970); children: India Helene, John Edward, Jesse Dale, Michael Rutledge; m. Darius G. Ornston, May 11, 1983. Grad., bus. coll., Vienna, 1955; BA in Music, North Tex. State U., 1970; MA in Germanics, Rice U., 1973, PhD in Germanics, 1975. Teaching asst. Rice U., Houston, 1971-75; asst. prof. German Yale U., New Haven, Conn., 1975-78, head summer lang. inst., 1979-81, assoc. prof., 1979-85; chmn. Dept. Fgn. Langs. Wash. State U., Pullman, 1981-82; head Dept. Langs. Clemson (S.C.) U., 1985-86, prof., 1985—; guest prof. Middlebury (Vt.) Coll., 1976; speaker in field. Author: Achim von Arnim, 1979, Virginia Woolf, 1983, Clemens Brentano, 1985, Die Weibliche Muse, 1986, Max Weber, 1991, others; contbr. numerous articles to profl. jours. Grantee Griswold Found., 1975-76, 78, S.C. Dept. Edn., 1986, NEH, 1986, Provost's award, Clemson U., 1989, Hilles Fund, 1976, 79, 82; NDEA fellow, 1972, 73; Rice fellow, 1971, 74; Morse fellow, 1977-78; Deutscher Akademischer Austausch-Dienst, 1979; sr. faculty fellow Yale U., 1981-82; Holland Fund, 1982; Deutsche Forschungsgemeinschaft, 1982; recipient German-Am. Friendship award Consul Gen. of the German Fed. Republic, 1989; Mesda fellow, 1993. Fellow Davenport Coll., Yale U.; mem. AAUP (v.p. 1987-88, pres. 1988-89), MLA, Am. Assn. Tchrs. German, So. Comparative Lit. Assn., others. Democrat. Avocations: reading, writing, sports, needlecraft, painting. Office: Clemson U Dept Langs 717 Strode Twr Clemson SC 29634-1515

RILEY, HENRY CHARLES, banker; b. Newton, Mass., Mar. 23, 1932; s. Charles Matthew and Marine Anna (Armstrong) R.; m. Patricia Ann Buchanan, Mar. 3, 1962; children: Lauren Elizabeth, Carolyn Ann, Julie Louise. A.B., Yale U., 1954; M.B.A., Boston Coll., 1965. With BayBank Harvard Trust Co., Cambridge, Mass., 1958-89, treas., sec., 1967-70, v.p., treas., 1970-72, sr. v.p., sec., 1972-82; exec. v.p. BayBank Harvard Trust Co., 1982-87; mng. dir. community banking BayBank Systems Inc., Waltham, Mass., 1987-90; exec. v.p., dir. community banking BayBank Boston, 1990-92; exec. v.p. BayBank Systems, Inc., Waltham, 1992—. Trustee, treas. Longy Sch. Music, 1970-92; bd. dirs. Richard Warren Surg. Rsch. and Ednl. Fund Inc., 1984—; bd. dirs., pres. Cambridge Econ. Devel. Corp., 1982-87; corporator, past asst. treas. Mt. Auburn Hosp.; past mem. exec. bd. Gettysburg Coll. Parents Assn.; past treas. St. John's Episcopal Ch., sr. warden, Westwood, Mass., 1982-85; mem. St. Paul's Cathedral chpt., Boston, 1990-93. Wiht USNR, 1956-57. Mem. Am. Bankers Assn. (chmn. 1991-92, exec. com. br. adminstrv. divsn. 1992, chmn. nat. retail banking conf. 1990), Nat. Br. Adminstrs. Roundtable, Boston Coll. Sch. Mgmt. Alumni Assn. (past dir., pres.), Harvard Sq. Bus. Assn. (past dir.), Cambridge C. of C. (dir., past treas., v.p. 1975-87), Rotary (club dir. 1976-80, pres. 1979-80), Yale Club (Boston), Harvard Club (Boston), Dennis Yacht Club (mem. bd. govs., treas. 1993-94), The Meadows Country Club (Sarasota, Fla.). Episcopalian. Home: 33 York Way Westwood MA 02090-2633 Office: BayBank Systems Inc One BayBank Technology Pl Waltham MA 02154-7438

RILEY, IVERS WHITMAN, stock exchange executive; b. L.A., Sept. 28, 1932; s. Ivers Whitman and Lillian Lucille (Bendig) R.; m. Barbara Joann Bensley, June 18, 1955; children: Michael George, Steven Ivers, Christine Susan. BS., UCLA, 1955; LLB, La Salle Extension U., Chgo., 1963. C.L.U. Stockbroker Merrill Lynch Pierce Fenner & Smith, 1963-69; ins./equities product planning and edn. Aetna Life & Casualty, 1969-74; sr. v.p. Chgo. Bd. Options Exchange, 1974-78, Paine Webber Co., N.Y.C., 1978-81; ptnr. The Options Group, N.Y.C., 1981-83; exec. v.p. N.Y. Stock Exchange, N.Y.C., from 1983; sr. exec. v.p. Am. Stock Exchange, N.Y.C., 1986—; bd. dir. Options Clearing Corp., Chgo. Comdr. USNR, 1955-75. Fellow Life Mgmt. Inst.; mem. N.Y. Options Soc. Republican. Avocations: bridge, stein collecting. Office: Am Stock Exchange Inc 86 Trinity Pl New York NY 10006-1818

RILEY, JACK, actor, writer; b. Cleve., Dec. 30, 1935; s. John A. and Agnes C. (Corrigan) R.; m. Ginger Lawrence, May 18, 1975; children: Jamie, Bryan. BS in English, John Carroll U., 1961. Mem.: Rolling Along of 1960, Dept. Army Travelling Show; co-host: Baxter & Riley, Sta.-WERE, Cleve., 1961-65; numerous TV appearances, including: as Mr. Carlin on Bob Newhart Show, CBS-TV, 1972-78; Occasional Wife, 1966, Mary Tyler Moore, 1972, Barney Miller, 1979, Diff'rent Strokes, 1979, Hart to Hart, 1980, Love Boat, 1984, Night Court, 1985-91, St. Elsewhere, 1986, Babes, 1991, Evening Shade, 1992, Family Matters, 1993, Hangin' with Mr. Cooper, 1993, Dave's World, 1994, Married with Children, 1994, The Boys are Back, 1995; appeared in feature films including Catch-22, 1969, McCabe and Mrs. Miller, 1970, Long Goodbye, 1972, Calif. Split, 1974, World's Greatest Lover, 1978, High Anxiety, 1978, Butch and Sundance: The Early Years, 1979, History of the World, Part I, 1981, Frances, 1983, To Be or Not To Be, 1983, Finders Keepers, 1984, Spaceballs, 1987, Rented Lips, 1987, Gleaming the Cube, 1988, C.H.U.D. II, 1988, The Player, 1992, Dangerous Woman, 1993, T-Rex, 1995; plays West Coast premier of Small Craft Warnings, 1975, Los Angeles revival of 12 Angry Men, 1985, Zeitgeist, 1990, House of Blue Leaves, at Cleve. Playhouse and tour Ea. Europe, 1993; TV writer: Don Rickles Show, 1968, Mort Sahl Show, 1967; writer commls. for, Blore & Richman Inc., Los Angeles, 1966-84; numerous radio commls. and TV voice-overs, Rugrats (cartoon series), 1993. Served with U.S. Army, 1958-61. Mem. Screen Actors Guild, Actor's Equity, AFTRA, Writers Guild Am., Acad. Motion Picture Arts and Scis., Acad. TV Arts and Scis. Office: care Ho of Reps 9911 Pico Blvd Ste 1060 Los Angeles CA 90035

RILEY, JAMES KEVIN, lawyer; b. Nyack, N.Y., July 21, 1945; s. Charles A. and Mary Lenihan R.; m. Joan Leavy Riley, Oct. 4, 1969; children: Carolyn, Tara, Sean. AB, Fordham Coll., 1967; JD, Rutgers U., 1970. Bar: N.Y. 1971, N.J. 1983, U.S. Supreme Ct. 1984; cert. fin. planner., estate planner. Asst. dist. atty. Rockland County, New City, N.Y., 1973-74; ptnr. Amend & Amend, N.Y.C., 1974-78, O'Connell & Riley, Pearl River, N.Y., 1978—; pub., pres. 1099 Express Software, 1099 Express Ltd., Pearl River, 1987—; adj. prof. estate planning Pace Univ., White Plains, N.Y. Bd. dirs. United Way of Rockland County, N.Y., 1974-80, Rockland Family Shelter for Victims of Domestic Violence, 1981-85, literacy vols. Rockland County, 1989—; chmn. bd. dirs. New Hope Manor, Barryville, N.Y., 1985-88. Mem. ABA, Am. Soc. Hosp. Attys., Nat. Coun. Sch. Dist. Attys., N.Y. State Bar Assn. (ho. of dels. 1988-92), Rockland County Bar Assn. (bd. dirs. 1986—), Internat. Platform Assn., Rotary. Democrat. Roman Catholic. Home: 145 Franklin Ave Pearl River NY 10965-2510 Office: O'Connell & Riley 144 E Central Ave Pearl River NY 10965-2532 also: 111 Chestnut Ridge Rd Montvale NJ 07645-1710

RILEY, JERLENA, church administrator. Fin. dir. Ch. of God of Prophecy Admin. Com. Office: Church of God of Prophecy PO Box 2910 Cleveland TN 37320-2910

RILEY, JOE, real estate executive. Pres. Coldwell Banker Ira E. Berry, St. Louis. Office: Coldwell Banker Ira E Berry 530 Maryville Centre Dr Saint Louis MO 63141*

RILEY, JOHN GRAHAM, economics educator; b. Christchurch, New Zealand, Dec. 8, 1945; came to U.S., 1969; s. Charles Graham and Patricia (White) R.; m. Rita Jane Stulin, July 5, 1971 (div. 1981); m. Beverly Fong Lowe, Oct. 16, 1982; 1 child, Alexandra Lowe Riley. BSc, U. Canterbury, Christchurch, 1967, M in Commerce, 1969; PhD, MIT, 1972. Instr. Boston

Coll., 1971-72, asst. prof., 1972-73; asst. prof. econs. UCLA, 1973-76, assoc. prof., 1976-80, prof., 1980—, chmn. dept., 1987-90, 92—. Assoc. editor Am. Econs. Rev., 1983-85, co-editor, 1985-87; contbr. numerous articles to profl. jours. Co-chair Ch. and Synagogue Assocs. Inc. Erskine fellow U. Canterbury, 1987; NSF grantee, 1975-89. Fellow Econometrics Soc. Office: UCLA Dept Econs 2263 Bunche Hall Los Angeles CA 90024

RILEY, JOHN WINCHELL, JR., consulting sociologist; b. Brunswick, Maine, June 10, 1908; s. John Winchell and Marjorie Webster (Prince) R.; m. Matilda White, June 19, 1931; children: John Winchell III, Lucy Ellen. AB, Bowdoin Coll., 1930, LLD, 1972; MA, Harvard U., 1933, PhD, 1936. Mem. faculty Marietta Coll., 1933-35, Wellesley Coll., 1935-37, Douglass Coll., 1937-45; mem. faculty Rutgers U., 1945-60, prof. sociology, chmn. dept., 1945-60; v.p., dir. social research Equitable Life Assurance Soc. of U.S., N.Y.C., 1960-68, v.p. corp. relations, 1968—, sr. v.p. corp. relations, 1968-72, sr. v.p. social research, 1972-73, cons., 1973—; mem. faculty Harvard U., 1955; cons. Market Rsch. Co. Am., 1940-45, Columbia Broadcasting Co., 1945-50, Ford Motor Co., 1965, Am. Coun. Life Ins., 1973-90, WHO, 1984—, Internat. Fedn. Aging, 1983—, Scripps Found., 1987—, Max Planck, 1989, numerous others; sr. cons. Matthew Greenwald & Assocs., 1990—, Project Age and Structural Change Nat. Inst. Aging, 1994—; vis. scholar Ctr. for Advanced Study in Behavioral Sci., 1978-79; mem. adv. bd. Carnegie Corp. Aging Soc. project, 1982—, U. Mich. Inst. Gerontology, 1987—, U. So. Calif. Intergenerational Project, 1990; lectr. in field. Author: (with Bryce Ran, Marcia Lifshitz) The Student Looks at His Teacher, 1950 (with Wilbur Schramm) The Reds Take A City, 1951 (with Matilda W. Riley, Jackson Toby) Sociological Studies in Seale Analysis, 1954 (with Matilda W. Riley, Marilyn Johnson) Aging and Society, Vol. II, 1969; editor: The Corporation and Its Publics, 1963; contbr. Our Aging Soc., 1986, Nationalization of the Social Sciences, 1987, Ency. of Aging, 1990, The Changing Contract Among Generations, 1993, others. Former trustee Am. Found. Blind, Inst. Edn. Devel., Nat. Urban League, Boethner Rsch. Inst.; trustee Industrywide Network Social Rural and Rural Efforts; mem. capital campaign com. Bowdoin Coll., 1984; rsch. adv. bd. The Am. Coll., 1989—. With OWI, Psychol. Warfare Divsn., AUS, 1944, Far Ea. Rsch. Group, USAF, 1950-51. Recipient Stuart A. Rice Merit award, 1990, numerous other awards for profl. excellence. Fellow AAAS; mem. Sociol. Research Assn. (pres. 1964-65), Oliver Wendall Holmes Assn. (former trustee), Am. Sociol. Assn. (sec. 1950-55, Disting. Career award for practice 1983), Eastern Social Soc., Osborne Assn. (former trustee), Am. Assn. Pub. Opinion Research (pres. 1961-62, Disting. Career award 1983), Market Research Council, Am. Assn. Internat. Aging (former trustee), Am. Sociol. Found. (incorporator, mem. adv. com. 1987—), D.C. Sociol. Soc. (co-pres. 1984-85). Home and Office: 4701 Willard Ave Apt 1607 Chevy Chase MD 20815-4630

RILEY, JOSEPH HARRY, retired banker; b. Pitts., May 13, 1922; s. Joseph John and Frances P. (Wacker) R.; m. Anna Belle Hepler, May 2, 1957 (dec. May 1994); 1 child, Michelle Patricia. B.C.S., Benjamin Franklin U., 1950; postgrad., Grad. Sch. Banking, Rutgers U., 1954. With Crestar Bank, N.A. (name formerly Nat. Savs. & Trust Co.), Washington, 1947—; exec. v.p. Crestar Bank, N.A. (name formerly Nat. Savs. & Trust Co.), 1970-73, sr. exec. v.p. 1973-76, pres., 1976-80, chmn., pres., 1980-84, also bd. dirs. Treas. Heroes; bd. dirs. Anthony Francis Lucas Spindletop Found., Anson Mills Found., Jr. Achievement Washington, Boys Club Greater Washington; bd. dirs., pres. Kiwanis Found.; past pres. Met. Washington Bd. Trade. Served with USMCR, 1942-46, 50-51. Mem. D.C. Bankers Assn. (past pres.), Am. Bankers Assn., Mortgage Bankers Assn., Washington Conv. and Visitors Bur. (past pres.), Soc. Friendly Sons St. Patrick (past pres.), Congl. Country Club (Washington), Univ. Club (Washington), Met. Club (Washington), Burning Tree Club, Rolling Rock Club (Ligonier, Pa.). Home: 10116 Iron Gate Rd Potomac MD 20854-4728 Office: 1445 New York Ave NW Washington DC 20005-2134 *If one guideline stood out in my life it would be my belief in contributing. I feel you should voluntarily offer to give of yourself in any endeavor in which you are a participant whether it be business, community or social. If you fail to make such an effort you have forfeited the right to complain regardless of the final result.*

RILEY, KEVIN M., principal. Prin. Gretna (Nebr.) Jr. Sr. High Sch. Recipient Blue Ribbon award U.S. Dept. Edn., 1990-91. Office: Gretna Jr-Sr High Sch 805 S County Rd Gretna NE 68028-4777

RILEY, LAWRENCE JOSEPH, bishop; b. Boston, Sept. 6, 1914; s. James and Ellen (Ryan) R. A.B., Boston Coll., 1936, LL.D., 1965; S.T.B. Gregorian U., 1939; S.T.D., Catholic U. Am., 1948; LL.D., Stonehill Coll., 1957. Ordained priest Roman Cath. Ch., 1940. Prof., rector St. John's Sem., Boston, 1941-66; prof. Emmanuel Coll., 1965-66; chaplain Harvard Cath. Club, 1950-54; vice officialis Met. Tribunal, Archdiocese of Boston 1950-76; sec. to archbishop of Boston, 1951-58; aux. bishop Archdiocese of Boston, 1972-90; aux. bishop emeritus Archdiocese of Boston, 1990—; asst. at Pontifical Throne, 1986—; vicar gen. emeritus Archdiocese of Boston; pastor emeritus Most Precious Blood Parish, Hyde Park, Mass. Decorated Knight Comdr. with star Holy Sepulchre of Jerusalem; decorated Knight Order of Star of Italian Solidarity. Mem. Cath. Theol. Soc. Am. (past pres.), Mariological Soc. Am., Canon Law Soc. Am., Dante Alighieri Soc. Mass. (past v.p.), Nat. Cath. Edn Assn., Fellowship of Cath. Scholars, Pope John XXIII Med.-Moral Ctr. Address: 43 Maple St Hyde Park MA 02136-2738

RILEY, MATILDA WHITE (MRS. JOHN W. RILEY, JR.), sociology educator; b. Boston, Apr. 19, 1911; d. Percival and Mary (Cliff) White; m. John Winchell Riley, Jr., June 19, 1931; children: John Winchell III, Lucy Ellen Riley Sallick. BA, Radcliffe Coll., 1931, MA, 1937, DSc (hon.), 1994 DSc, Bowdoin Coll., 1972; LHD (hon.), Rutgers U., 1983. Rsch. asst. Harvard U., Cambridge, Mass., 1932; v.p. Market Rsch. Co. Am., 1938-49; chief cons. economist WPB, 1941; rsch. specialist Rutgers U., 1950, prof., 1951-73, dir. sociology lab., chmn. dept. sociology and anthropology, 1959-73, emeritus prof., 1973—; Daniel B. Fayerweather prof. polit. econ. and sociology Bowdoin Coll., 1974-78, prof. emeritus, 1978—; assoc. dir. Nat. Inst. on Aging, 1979-91, sr. social scientist, 1991—; mem. faculty Harvard U., summer 1955; staff assoc., dir. aging and society Russell Sage Found., 1964-73, staff sociologist, 1974-77; chmn. com. on life course Social Sci. Rsch. Coun., 1977-80; sr. rsch. assoc. Ctr. for Social Scis., Columbia U., 1978-80; adv. bd. Carnegie Aging Soc. Project, 1985-87; mem. Commn. on Coll. Retirement, 1982-86; vis. prof. NYU, 1954-61; cons. Nat. Coun. on Aging, Acad. Ednl. Devel.; mem. study group NIH, 1971-79, Social Sci. Rsch. Coun. Com. on Middle Years, 1973-77; chmn. NIH Task Force on Health and Behavior, 1986-91; cons. WHO, 1987—; Winkelman lectr. U. Mich., 1984, Selo lectr. U. No. Calif., 1987, Boettner lectr. Am. Coll., 1990, Claude Pepper lectr. Fla. State U., 1993, Disting. lectr. Southwestern Social Scis. Assn., 1990, Standing lectr. SUNY, 1992, Inaugural lectr. Cornell U., 1992; lectr. Internat. Inst. of Sociology, Plenary, 1993, Inter-Univ. Consortium Pol. and Social Rsch., U. Mich., 1993, Duke U., 1993. Author: (with P. White) Gliding and Soaring, (with Riley and Toby) Sociological Studies in Scale Analysis, 1954, Sociological Research, vols. I, II, 1964, (with others) Aging and Society, vol. I, 1968, vol. II, 1969, vol. III, 1972, (with Nelson) Sociological Observation, 1974, Aging from Birth to Death: Interdisciplinary Perspectives, 1979, (with Merton) Sociological Traditions from Generation to Generation, 1980, (with Abeles and Teitelbaum) Aging from Birth to Death: Sociotemporal Perspectives, 1982, (with Hess and Bond) Aging in Society, 1983; editor: (with M. Ory and D. Zablotsky) AIDS in an Aging Society: What We Need to Know, 1989; co-editor: Perspectives in Behavioral Medicine: The Aging Dimension, 1987, (with J. W. Riley) The Quality of Aging, 1989, The Annuals, 1989; sr. editor: Structural Lag, 1994; editorial com.: Ann. Rev. Sociology, 1978-81, Social Change and the Life Course, vol. 1, Social Structures and Human Lives, (with B. Huber and B. Hess) Sociological Lives, vol. II, 1988; contbr. chpts. to books, articles to profl. jours. Former trustee The Big Sisters Assn. Recipient Lindback Rsch. award Rutgers U., 1970, Social Sci. award Andrus Gerontology Ctr., U. So. Calif., 1972, Radcliffe Alumnae award, 1982, Commonwealth award 1984, Kesten Lecture award U. So. Calif., 1987, Sci. Achievement award Washington Acad. Scis., 1989, Disting. Sci. award, 1989, Disting. Creative award Gerontol. Soc. Am., 1990, Presdl. Meritorious award, 1990, Stuart Rice award Columbia Sociol. Soc., 1992, Kent award Gerontol. Soc. Am., 1992; fellow Advanced Study in Behavioral Scis., 1978-79; Matilda White Riley award in rsch. and methodology established in her honor Rutgers U., 1977; Matilda White Riley prize established Bowdoin Coll., 1987. Fellow AAAS (chmn. sect. on social and econ. scis. 1977-78); mem. NAS, Inst. Medicine of NAS (sr.), Acad. Behavioral Medicine Rsch., Am. Sociol. Assn. (exec. officer

1949-60, v.p. 1973-74, pres. 1986, 91, chmn. sect. on sociology of aging 1989, Disting. Scholar in Aging 1988, Career award 1992), Am. Assn. Public Opinion Rsch. (sec.-treas. 1949-51, Disting. Svc. award 1983), Eastern Sociol. Soc. (v.p. 1968-69, pres. 1977-78, Disting. Career award 1986), Soc. for Study Social Biology (bd. dirs. 1986-92), Am. Acad. Arts and Scis., D.C. SI. Soc. (co-pres. 1983-84), Sociol. Rsch. Assn., Internat. Orgn. Study Human Devel., Am. Philos. Soc. (membership lectr. 1987), Phi Beta Kappa, Phi Beta Kappa assocs. Home: 4701 Willard Ave Apt 1607 Chevy Chase MD 20815-4630 Office: NIH Nat Inst on Aging 7201 Wisconsin Ave Bethesda MD 20814-4808

RILEY, MICHAEL JOSEPH, government official; b. Rochester, N.H., Mar. 14, 1943; s. Matthew Howard and Agnes Riley; m. Nancy Sarah Mason, July 25, 1970; children: Shawn, Paul, James, Sarah. B.S., U.S. Naval Acad., 1965; M.B.A., U. So. Calif., Los Angeles, 1972; D. Bus. Adminstrn. in Fin., Harvard U., 1977. Acct. Teradyne, Boston, 1972-73; asst. controller Northeast Utilities, Berlin, Conn., 1976-83; treas. Mich. Bell Telephone Co., Detroit, 1983-85; sr. v.p. fin., chief fin. officer United Airlines, Elk Grove Village, Ill., 1985-87; v.p. fin. Lee Enterprises, Inc., Davenport, Iowa, 1987-93; CFO, sr. v.p. U.S. Postal Svc., Washington, 1993—; lectr. fin. U. Conn., 1977-81, U. Mich., 1985. Author: (with Dwight B. Crane) NOW Accounts: Strategy for Financial Institutions, 1978. Bd. dirs. Group Health Plan Southeast Mich., 1983-85; bd. trustees Mich. 4-H, 1983-86. Served to lt. USN, 1965-70, Vietnam. Mem. Fin. Execs. Inst. (nat. membership com. 1982-86, sec.-treas. Hartford chpt. 1981-83), Fin. Mgmt. Assn. (dir. 1983-85). Office: US Postal Svc 475 L'Enfant Pla SW Washington DC 20260-5000

RILEY, NANCY MAE, retired vocational home economics educator; b. Grand Forks, N.D., May 1, 1939; d. Kenneth Wesley and Jeanne Margaret Olive (Hill) R. BS in Edn., Miami U., 1961; postgrad., Ohio U., 1964-69; MA, Marietta Coll., 1989. Cert. high sch. tchr. Tchr. home econs. Malta-McConnelsville (Ohio) High Sch., 1961-66; tchr. home econs. Waterford (Ohio) High Sch., 1967-92; advisor Malta-McConnelsville Future Homemakers, 1961-66, Waterford Future Homemakers Am., 1968-92; advisor to state officer Ohio Future Homemakers Am., McConnelsville, 1963, Waterford, 1976. Leader Girl Scouts Am., McConnelsville, 1962-66, camp counselor, 1962-76; fair judge Waterford Cmty. Fair, Waterford, 1970-85. Mem. NEA, Am. Vocat. Assn. (life), Ohio Edn. Assn. (life, del. 1979), Ohio Vocat. Assn. (life), DAR, Daus. Union Vets. (del. 1992, 93, dist. jr. v.p. 1993-94), Daus. of War of 1812 (pres. 1991—), Ohio Geneal. Soc., Order of Eastern Star (worthy matron 1967-68, dep. grand matron 1978), White Shrine Jerusalem (worthy high priestess 1979-81, 83). Republican. Baptist. Avocations: ceramics, genealogy, camping, reading, handcrafts. Home: PO Box 137 Waterford OH 45786-0137

RILEY, PATRICK JAMES, former professional basketball coach; b. Rome, N.Y., Mar. 20, 1945; s. Leon R.; m. Chris Riley; children: James Patrick, Elisabeth. Grad., U. Ky., 1967. Guard San Diego Rockets, 1967-70; guard Los Angeles Lakers, 1970-75, asst. coach, 1979-81, head coach, 1981-90; head coach N.Y. Knicks, 1991-95; guard Phoenix Suns, 1975-76; broadcaster Los Angeles Lakers games Sta. KLAC and Sta. KHJ-TV, Los Angeles, 1977-79, NBC Sports, 1990-91; player NBA Championship Team, 1972, coach, 1982, 85, 87, 88. Author: The Winner Within: A Life Plan for Team Players, 1993. Named NBA Coach of Yr., 1990. Office: care NY Knickerbockers Madison Sq Garden 2 Pennsylvania Plz New York NY 10121-0091*

RILEY, RANDY JAMES, banker; b. Waukegan, Ill., May 5, 1950; s. Francis James and Florence Josephine (Belec) R.; m. Joanne M. Lehtola (div.); 1 child, Tara Lynn; m. Marge Witte Hagen. Student, Elmhurst Coll., 1969-70, U. Wis. Grad. Sch. Banking, 1975-76, U. Colo. Sch. of Bank Mktg., 1984-85. Mgmt. trainee Am. Nat. Bank, Waukegan, 1971-73; v.p. 1st Nat. Bank, Eagle River, Wis., 1973-85, M&I Western State Bank, Oshkosh, Wis., 1985-88; sr. v.p. Community Nat. Bank, Titusville, Fla., 1988-89, Citrus Bank, N.A., Vero Beach, Fla., 1989—; treas. Brevard Small Bus. Assistance Coun., Indian River Chamber Small Bus. Task Force, 1990, Legis. Task Force, 1992, vice-chmn. 1994. Pres. Eagle River C. of C., 1981, Oshkosh Comml. Devel. Corp., 1987; pres., founder Eagle River Community Theatre, 1983, Headwater's Performing Arts, Eagle River, 1983; affordable housing subcom. mem. Indian River County; bd. dirs., treas. Jr. Achievement, 1992, vice-chmn. 1993. Mem. Am. Inst. Banking, Robert Morris Assocs., Lions (v.p. Oshkosh club 1987), Elks, Kiwanis (v.p. 1992, pres. 1993). Avocations: golf, skiing, sailing. Home: 965 4th Ln Vero Beach FL 32962-1586 Office: Citrus Bank NA 1717 Indian River Blvd Vero Beach FL 32960-0867

RILEY, RICHARD WILSON, U.S. secretary of education; b. Greenville, S.C., Jan. 2, 1933; s. Edward Patterson and Martha Elizabeth (Dixon) R.; m. Ann Osteen Yarborough, Aug. 23, 1957; children: Richard Wilson, Anne Y., Hubert D., Theodore D. B.A., Furman U., 1954; J.D., U. S.C., 1960. Bar: S.C. 1960. Partner firm Riley & Riley, Greenville, 1959-78; gov. S.C., 1978-86; ptnr. Nelson, Mullins, Riley & Scarborough, Greenville and Columbia, S.C., 1987-93; U.S. Sec. of Edn. Washington, 1993—; spl. asst. to subcom. U.S. Senate Jud. Com., 1960; mem. S.C. Ho. of Reps., 1963-66, S.C. Senate senate from Greenville-Laurens Dist., 1966-76. Lt. (j.g.) USNR, 1954-56. Named Outstanding Young Man of Greenville and S.C., Jr. C. of C., 1965, recipient Harold W. McGraw, Jr. Prize in Education, McGraw-Hill, 1989. Mem. S.C., Greenville bar assns., Furman U. Alumni Assn. (pres. 1968-69). Rotarian. Office: US Dept Edn Washington DC 20202-0001

RILEY, ROBERT BARTLETT, landscape architect; b. Chgo., Jan. 28, 1931; s. Robert James and Ruth (Collins) R.; m. Nancy Rebecca Mills, Oct. 5, 1956; children: Rebecca Hill, Kimber Bartlett. PhB, U. Chgo., 1949; BArch, MIT, 1954. Chief designer Kea, Shaw, Grimm & Crichton, Hyattsville, Md., 1959-64; prin. partner Robert B. Riley (A.I.A.), Albuquerque, 1964-70; campus planner, asso. prof. architecture, dir. Center Environ. Research and Devel., U. N.Mex., 1966-70; prof. landscape architecture and architecture U. Ill., Urbana-Champaign, 1970—, head dept. landscape architecture, 1970-85; sr. fellow landscape architecture studies Dumbarton Oaks/Harvard U., 1992—; mem. rev. panel landscape architects Fed. Civil Service-Nat. Endowment Arts. Assoc. editor Landscape mag., 1967-70; editor Landscape Jour., 1987—. Served with USAF, 1954-58. Nell Norris fellow U. Melbourne, Australia, 1977; project fellow Nat. Endowment Arts, 1985. Fellow Am. Soc. Landscape Architects (Nat. Honor award 1979); mem. Coun. of Educators in Landscape Architecture (pres. 1984-85, chmn. bd. dirs. 1985-86, Outstanding Educator award 1992, Pres.'s award 1994), AIA (Design award Md. 1962, N.Mex. 1968, Environ. Svc. award N.Mex. 1970), Environ. Design Rsch. Assn. (chmn. bd. 1990-91), Phi Beta Epsilon. Unitarian. Home: 407 E Mumford Dr Urbana IL 61801-6231 Office: Univ Ill 214 Mumford Hall 1301 W Gregory Dr Urbana IL 61801-3608

RILEY, ROBERT EDWARD, financial services company executive; b. Boston, Feb. 19, 1930; s. Edward Gerard and Nina Loretta (Wolfe) R.; m. Ann Elizabeth McCourt, Nov. 10, 1956 (div. 1972); children: Robert Edward, David, Thomas; m. Carol Lee Anthony, June 22, 1974; children: Michael, Brian. A.B., Holy Cross Coll., 1951; M.B.A., Harvard U., 1953. Pres., chief exec. officer Putnam Mgmt. Co., Boston, 1970-80, Marsh & McLennan Asset Mgmt. Co., Boston, 1974-81; sr. v.p. Am. Express Co., N.Y.C., 1981-84; sr. v.p. group pensions Prudential Ins. Co. Am., Newark, 1984-85; pres. Prudential Asset Mgmt. Co., Newark, 1985-86; exec. v.p. Prudential Investment Corp., Newark, 1986-94; chmn. Prudential Realty Group, Newark, 1986-90; pres., chief exec. officer Loomis, Sayles and Co., Boston, 1990; chmn., CEO Prudential Residential Svcs. Co., Boston, 1990-93, Prudential Reins. Co., 1993-94; pres., COO Dreyfus Corp. Assoc. trustee Holy Cross Coll.; trustee Joseph P. Kennedy Trusts; reserve Tufts U. Sch. Medicine; dir. John F. Kennedy Libr.; corporator N.E. Deaconess Hosp. Lt. comdr. USNR, 1953-56, Korea. Named Chief Exec. Officer of Yr. Fin. World Mag., 1975, 79. Republican. Roman Catholic. Clubs: Union (Boston); Univ. (N.Y.C.). Avocations: boating, skiing, ice hockey. Office: Prudential Ctr Ste 4365 800 Boylston St Boston MA 02199

RILEY, STEPHEN THOMAS, historian, librarian; b. Worcester, Mass., Dec. 28, 1908; s. John and Mary (Ward) R.; m. Alice Amelia Riehle, July 2, 1949. A.B., Clark U., 1931, A.M., 1932, Ph.D. in Am. History, 1953, L.H.D. (hon.), 1981; grad., U. Pa. Army Specialized Tng. Program, 1943-44. Asst. librarian Mass. Hist. Soc., Boston, 1934-47; librarian Mass. Hist. Soc.,

1947-62, dir., 1957-76, dir. emeritus, 1977—; mem. Mass. Revolutionary War Bi-Centennial Commn., 1965-91, Mass. Gov.'s Commn. on Need of New Mass. Archives Bldg., 1974, Mass. Archives Adv. Com., 1978-91; mem. adminstrv. bd. Adams Family Papers, 1956-91, George Washington Papers, 1969-91, Daniel Webster Papers, 1966-89; mem. vis. com. Boston Coll. Library, 1964, 67-68, Harvard U. History Dept., 1962-68, Harvard U. Press, 1965-71; cons. N.Y. State Hist. Assn., 1978, Va. Hist. Soc., 1981. Author: The Massachusetts Historical Society, 1791-1959, 1959, Stephen Thomas Riley: The Years of Stewardship, 1976; editor: (with Edward W. Hanson) The Papers of Robert Treat Paine, Vol. I 1746-1756, Vol. II 1757-1774, 1992; contbr. articles and revs. to hist. jours. Bd. dirs. Freedom Trail, Boston, 1965-91; trustee Clark U., 1963-74, hon. trustee, 1974—. Served with U.S. Army, 1942—44; USAAF, 1944-45. Fellow AAAS; mem. Archives Am. Art (adv com. New Eng. br. 1972-91), Am. Antiquarian Soc., Am. Bostonian Soc., Colonial Soc. Mass. (v.p. 1980-91), Mass. Hist. Soc., New Eng. hist. Geneal. Soc. (corr. sec. 1973-81), Weston (Mass.) Hist. Soc. (pres. 1977-84), Odd Vols. (Boston, v.p. 1979-83), Grolier Club (N.Y.C.), Phi Beta Kappa. Democrat. Roman Catholic. Clubs: of Odd Vols. (Boston) (v.p. 1979-83), St. Botolph (Boston); Grolier (N.Y.C.). Home: 334 Wellesley St Weston MA 02193-2620 Office: 1154 Boylston St Boston MA 02215-3695

RILEY, TERRY, composer, musician; b. Colfax, Calif., June 24, 1935. Student, San Francisco State Coll., 1955-57; MA, U. Calif., Berkeley, 1961. mem. creative assoc. program SUNY, Buffalo, 1969; mem. faculty Mills Coll., 1972-87. Plays keyboards and soprano saxophone; performer, tchr. North Indian vocal music; composer, performer U.S., Europe, 1963—; guest Swedish Radio and Acad. Music, 1967; compositions include In C, 1964, The Keyboard Studies, 1965, Dorian Reeds, 1966, Untitled Organ, 1966, Poppy Nogood and the Phantom Band, 1968, A Rainbow in Curved Air, 1969, Music with Balls, 1969, Genesis (ballet), 1970, Persian Surgery Dervishes, 1971, Shri Camel, 1976, G-Song for string quartet, 1980, Songs from the Old Country, 1980-81, Song of the Emerald Runner, 1983, Songs for Ten Voices of the Two Prophets, 1983, The Medicine Wheel for piano, voice, synthesizer, sitar, and tabla, 1983, Cadenza on the Night Plain for string quartet, 1984, The Harp of New Albion for solo piano, 1985, Salome Dances for Peace, parts I and II, for string quartet, 1985, 86, The Room of Remembrance for vibraphone, marimba, piano, and soprano saxophone, 1987, Chanting the Light of Foresight for saxophone quartet, 1987, The Crows Rosary for keyboard and string quartet, 1988, The Jade Palace Orchestral Dances for large symphony orch., 1989, Cactus Rosary for mixed instruments, 1990, The Sands concerto for string quartet and orch., 1991, June Buddhas concerto for chorus and orch., 1991, The Saint Adolf Ring, 1992, 4 Wölfli sketches for chamber ensemble, 1992, Embroidery, Eastern Man, Chorale of the Blessed Day, Ritmos and Melos for piano, violin, percussion, 1993, El Hombre for String Quartet and Piano, 1993, Ascencion for solo guitar, 1993, Chorus 193 for large mixed vocal ensemble, 1993, The Heaven Ladder, others. Nat. Endowment Arts grantee, 1977; Guggenheim fellow, 1979; Koussevitzky Music Found. grantee, 1991. *

RILEY, THOMAS JACKSON, lawyer; b. New Hebron, Miss., July 19, 1933; s. James Arthur and Mary (Baker) R.; m. Helen Gayle Anderson, Feb. 1, 1958 ;(dec. Mar. 1981); m. Billie Anderson, Nov. 1, 1981; children: Thomas Jackson Jr., Mark Riley, Franklin Lawrence. BS, U. So. Miss., 1958; LLB, U. Miss., 1961, JD, 1968. Bar: Miss. 1961, U.S. Dist. Ct. Miss. 1965, U.S. Ct. Appeals (5th cir.) 1965. Atty. State of Miss., 1961—; sch. bd. atty. Perry County Schs., New Augusta, Miss., 1975—, Richton (Miss.) Schs., 1970—. Prosecutor City of Hattiesburg, 1965, Forrest County, Hattiesburg, 1969; bd. dirs. YMCA, pres., 1972-74. With U.S. Army, 1953-56. Republican. Baptist. Avocations: fishing, hunting, gardening. Home: 54 Cabin Rd Hattiesburg MS 39401

RILEY, THOMAS LESLIE, retired college president; b. Ghent, Ky., Jan. 2, 1927; s. Carey Judson and Mary Elizabeth (Sebree) R.; m. Margaret Leslie Crim, June 21, 1947; children: Clark, David, Patrick, Susannah, John. BA, Hanover Coll., 1954; BS, U. Ky., 1949, MS, 1955; PhD, U. Chgo., 1965. Tchr. Jefferson County Schs., Madison, Ind., 1949-52; county agrl. extension agt. Kenton County, Covington, Ky., 1952-62, Cuyahoga County, Cleve., 1962-65; pres. Hopkinsville Community Coll., Ky., 1965-89; ret., 1989. Pres., campaign chmn. Hopkinsville Christian County United Way, 1975, 77. With USMC, 1944-46. Mem. SAR (pres. 1987—, Ky. chpt. 1991), Ky. Assn. Community Colls. (pres. 1968-69), Hopkinsville-Christian County C. of C. (pres. 1980-81), Pennyrile Rose Soc. (pres. 1976), Assn. U.S. Army (pres. 1977-83), Athanaeum Soc. (pres. 1982-83), Christian County U. Ky. Alumni Assn. (sec. 1985-88), Soc. Cincinnati Md., Philatelic Soc. (pres. 1975-76), Ky. Hist. Soc. (pres. 1993—), Rotary, Masons. Democrat. Baptist. Avocations: gardening, antiques, genealogy, local history. Home: 2527 Cox Mill Rd Hopkinsville KY 42240-1576

RILEY, TOM JOSEPH, lawyer; b. Cedar Rapids, Iowa, Jan. 9, 1929; s. Joseph Wendell and Delma B (Kyle) R.; m. Nancy Evans, Jan. 21, 1952; children: Pamela, Peter, Lisa, Martha, Sara, Heather. BA, U. Iowa, 1950, JD, 1952. Bar: Iowa 1952, U.S. Dist. Ct. (no. dist.) Iowa 1952, U.S. Ct. Appeals (8th cir.) 1960, U.S. Supreme Ct. 1966. Assoc. Simmons, Perrine, Allbright & Ellwood, Cedar Rapids, 1952-60, ptnr., 1960-80; pres. Tom Riley Law Firm, P.C., Cedar Rapids, 1980—; adj. prof. trial advocacy Coll. Law, U. Iowa, Iowa City, 1979. Author: Proving Punitive Damages, 1981, The Price of a Life, 1986. Mem. Iowa Ho. of Reps., 1960-64, Iowa Senate, 1965-74. First lt. USAF, 1952-54. Named Outstanding Freshman Legislator, Des Moines Press and Radio Club, 1961. Fellow Iowa Acad. Trial Lawyers (bd. govs. 1982-91); mem. Cedar Rapids Country Club, U. Athletic Club, Iowa City, Des Moines Club, Masons. Republican. Presbyterian. Avocations: tennis, sailing, downhill skiing. Home: 5300 Lakeside Rd Rural Route Marion IA 52302 Office: 4040 1st Ave NE Cedar Rapids IA 52402-3140

RILEY, VICTOR J., JR., financial services company executive; b. Buffalo, Aug. 29, 1931; s. Victor J. and Gwenevieve Riley; m. Marilyn A. Felrath, Aug. 8, 1954; children—Victor J. III, Karen, Patricia, Kevin, Shawn, Mary Katherine. BA in Econs., U. Notre Dame; LLD, Coll. St. Rose, 1983. With trust div. 1st Nat. Bank Miami, Fla., 1955-62; mgr. Miami office Bowles, Andrews & Towne, 1962-64; trust officer Nat. Comml. Bank (now Key Bank N.A.), Albany, N.Y., 1964-73; pres., chief exec. officer KeyCorp (formerly Key Banks Inc.), Albany, from 1973—, now chmn., pres., chief exec. officer, also bd. dirs.; also dir.; chmn. bd. Key Bank N.A., Albany, 1984—, Ctr. Econ. Growth; dir. Albany Med. Ctr., Interstate Banking Commn. for State of N.Y., 1986—. Hon. chmn. Capital Dist. Cerebral Palsy Telethon, Albany, 1981-87; bd. dirs. Pop Warner Football League; chmn. various fund raising drives. Served with U.S. Army, 1953-55. Apptd. civilian aide to Sec. Army, 1985—. Decorated Knight of Malta. Mem. N.Y. State Bankers Assn. (long-range planning com.), Interstate Banking Com. State N.Y. Republican. Roman Catholic. Avocations: travel, fishing, cooking. Home: 5 Hemlock Ln East Greenbush NY 12061-2035 Office: KeyCorp 1 Keycorp Pla Towers Albany NY 12207*

RILEY, WILLIAM, corporate executive, writer; b. Indpls., June 30, 1931; s. Leo Michael and Edna (Wilhelm) R.; m. Laura Etz, Apr. 20, 1957. AB, U. Notre Dame, 1952; LLB, Yale U., 1955. V.p., dir., chmn. Ivy Corp., Atlanta, 1960-80; chmn. Moore-Handley, Inc., Birmingham, Ala., 1981—; bd. dirs. Tru-Die, Inc., Franklin Pk., Ill., Fabco-Air, Inc., Gainesville, Fla. Author: (with Laura Riley) Guide to the National Wildlife Refuges, 1979 (Pulitzer prize nominee). Trustee The Raptor Trust, Basking Ridge, N.J., 1980—; bd. dirs. Nat. Wildlife Refuge Assn., Potomac, Md., 1985—, Hawk Mountain Sanctuary Assn., Kempton, Pa., 1989—. Net. Audubon Soc., N.Y.C., 1990-94. With U.S. Army, 1957-58. Mem. Met. Club of N.Y.C. Office: 745 Fifth Ave Ste 1803 New York NY 10151-1803

RILEY, WILLIAM FRANKLIN, mechanical engineering educator; b. Allenport, Pa., Mar. 1, 1925; s. William Andrew and Margaret (James) R.; m. Helen Elizabeth Chilzer, Nov. 5, 1945; children—Carol Ann, William Franklin. B.S. in Mech. Engring., Carnegie Inst. Tech., 1951; M.S. in Mechanics, Ill. Inst. Tech., 1958. Mech. engr. Mesta Machine Co., West Homestead, Pa., 1951-54; research engr. Armour Research Found., Chgo., 1954-61; sect. mgr. IIT Research Inst., Chgo., 1961-64, sci. advisor 1964-66; prof. Iowa State U., Ames, 1966-78, Disting. prof. engring., 1978-88, prof. emeritus, 1989—; ednl. cons. Bihar Inst. Tech., Sindri, India, 1966, Indian Inst. Tech., Kanpur, summer 1970. Author: (with A.J. Durelli) Introduction to Photomechanics, 1965; (with J. W. Dally) Experimental Stress Analysis,

1991; (with D. Young, K. McConnell and T. Rogge) Essentials of Mechanics, 1974; (with A. Higdon, E. Ohlsen, W. Stiles and J. Weese) Mechanics of Materials, 4th edit., 1985; (with J. Dally and K. McConnell) Instrumentation for Engineering Measurements, 1993; (with L.W. Zachary) Introduction to Mechanics of Materials, 1989, (with L.D. Sturges) Engineering Mechanics- Statics and Dynamics, 1993; also numerous articles and tech. papers. Served to lt. col. USAAF, 1943-46. Fellow Soc. for Exptl. Mechanics (hon. mem.); mem. Soc. for Exptl. Stress Analysis (hon., M.M. Frocht award 1977). Home: 1518 Meadowlane Ave Ames IA 50010-5547

RILL, JAMES FRANKLIN, lawyer; b. Evanston, Ill., Mar. 4, 1933; s. John Columbus and Frances Eleanor (Hill) R.; m. Mary Elizabeth Laws, June 14, 1957; children: James Franklin, Roderick M. AB cum laude, Dartmouth Coll., 1954; LLB, Harvard, 1959. Bar: D.C. bar 1959. Legis. asst. Congressman James P. S. Devereux, Washington, 1952; pvt. practice Washington, 1959-89; assoc. Steadman, Collier & Shannon, 1959-63; ptnr. Collier, Shannon & Rill, 1963-69, Collier, Shannon, Rill & Scott, 1969-89; asst. atty. gen., antitrust div. U.S. Dept. Justice, Washington, 1989-92; ptnr. Collier, Shannon, Rill & Scott, Washington, 1992—. Contbr. articles to profl. jours. Trustee Bullis Sch., Potomac, Md. Served to 1st lt. arty. AUS, 1954-56. Mem. ABA (founder antitrust law sect. spl. com. to study role of FTC, past chmn. legis. com., mem. council, past chmn. sect. of antitrust law, vice chmn. com. agy. adjudication sect. adminstrv. law), D.C. Bar Assn., Phi Delta Theta. Clubs: Met., Loudon Valley. Home: 7305 Masters Dr Rockville MD 20854-3850 Office: Collier Shannon Rill & Scott Ste 400 3050 K St NW Washington DC 20007

RILLING, JOHN ROBERT, history educator; b. Wausau, Wis., Apr. 28, 1932; s. John Peter and Esther Laura (Wittig) R.; m. Joanne Marilyn McCrory, Dec. 21, 1953; children—Geoffrey Alan, Andrew Peter. B.A. summa cum laude, U. Minn., 1953; A.M., Harvard U., 1957, Ph.D. 1959. Asst. prof. history U. Richmond, Va., 1959-62, assoc. prof. history, 1962-68, prof. history, 1968—, chmn. dept. history, 1977-83; chmn. Westhampton Coll. dept. history, 1965-71. Served with U.S. Army, 1953-55. Woodrow Wilson fellow, 1955-59; Harvard U. Travelling fellow, 1958; Coolidge fellow, 1955-56; Folger Library fellow, 1960; recipient U. Richmond Disting. Educator award, 1975, 76, 77, 80, 87. Mem. Am. Hist. Assn., Econ. History Soc., Conf. Brit. Studies, Phi Beta Kappa, Omicron Delta Kappa. Presbyterian. Contbr. articles to profl. jours. Home: 1507 Wilmington Ave Richmond VA 23227-4429 Office: U Richmond Richmond VA 23173

RIM, B. C., wholesale distribution executive, retail executive. MBA, NYU, 1981. Sec. Jindo Am., Inc., Lyndhurst, N.J., 1981—. Office: Jindo Am Inc 165 Chubb Ave Lyndhurst NJ 07071*

RIMA, INGRID HAHNE, economics educator; d. Max F. and Hertha G. (Grunsfeld) Hahne; m. Philip W. Rima; children: David, Eric. BA with honors, CUNY, 1945; MA, U. Pa., 1946, PhD, 1951. Prof. econs. Temple U., Phila., 1967—. Author: Development of Economic Analysis, 1967, 5th edit., 1991, Labor Markets Wages and Employment, 1981, The Joan Robinson Legacy, 1991, The Political Economy of Global Restructuring, Vol. I, Production and Organization, Vol. II, Trade and Finance, 1993, Measurement, Quantification and Economic Analysis, 1994, Labor Markets in a Global Economy, 1995. Fellow Ea. Econ. Assn.; mem. Am. Econ. Assn., History of Econs. Soc. (pres. 1993-4), Phi Beta Kappa. Office: Temple U Broad & Montgomery Ave Philadelphia PA 19122

RIMBACH, EVANGELINE LOIS, music educator; b. Portland, Oreg., June 28, 1932; d. Raymond Walter and Viola Clara (Gaebler) Rimbach. BA, Valparaiso (Ind.) U., 1954; MMus, Eastman Sch. Music, Rochester, N.Y., 1956; PhD, Eastman Sch. Music, 1967; student, Pacific Luth. U., Parkland, Wash., 1950-52. Vocal music instr. Goodwin Jr. High Sch., Redwood City, Calif., 1956-57; music instr. Calif. Concordia Coll., Oakland, Calif., 1957-62; prof. music Concordia U., River Forest, Ill., 1964—, chmn. dept., 1989—. Contbg. editor: Church Music, 1965-80; editor book: Johann Kuhnau: Magnificat, 1980; editor cantata: Johann Kuhnau: Lobe den Herrn, 1993; contbr. articles to profl. jours. Bd. dirs. Civic Symphony of Oak Park-River Forest, 1974-80, concert com. chmn., 1976-78, prog. annotator, 1976-80; mem. choir Grace Luth. Ch., River Forest, 1964—. AAUW postdoctoral fellow, 1969-70; DAAD grantee, Munich, 1980; recipient Rose of Honor award, Sigma Alpha Iota, 1987. Mem. Am. Musicol. Soc., Am. Recorder Soc., Luth. Edn. Assn., Sigma Alpha Iota. Republican. Lutheran. Avocations: travel, cooking, needlework. Home: 1115 Bonnie Brae Pl River Forest IL 60305-1515 Office: Concordia U 7400 Augusta St River Forest IL 60305-1402

RIMEL, REBECCA WEBSTER, foundation executive. BS, U. Va., 1973; MBA, James Madison U., 1983. RN, Va. Head nurse, emergency dept. U. Va. Hosp., Charlottesville, 1973-74, coord. med. out-patient dept., 1974-75, nurse practitioner dept. neurosurgery, 1975-77, instr. in neurosurgery, 1975-80, asst. prof., 1981-83; program mgr. health Pew Charitable Trusts, Phila., 1983-84; asst. v.p. Glenmede Trust Co., Pew Charitable Trusts, Phila., 1984-85; v.p. for programs Pew Charitable Trusts, Phila., 1985-88, exec. dir., 1988-94; pres., 1994—; mem. Coun. on Founds., Washington; prin. investigator dept. neurosurgery U. Va., 1981-85; adv. com. for U.S. Olympics on Boxing, 1983-86; also v.p. Nat. Inst. of Neurol. Disorders & Strokes, 1988-91, also bd. dirs.; bd. dirs. Nat. Environ. Edn. and Tng. Found., Inc., Washington, Thomas Jefferson Meml. Found., Ind. Sector, Washington. Contbr. articles and abstracts to profl. jours., chpts. in books. Recipient Disting. Nursing Alumni award U. Va., 1988; Kellogg Nat. fellow, 1982. Mem. APHA, ANA, Va. State Nurses Assn. (membership and credentials com. 1982-86), Am. Acad. Nursing, Am. Assn. Neurosurg. Nurses, Emergency Dept. Nurses Assn.

RIMER, JOHN THOMAS, foreign language educator, academic administrator, writer, translator; b. Pitts., Mar. 2, 1933; s. John T. and Naomi (Bowser) R.; m. Laurence E. Mus., Apr. 18, 1964; children: John, Mark. B.A., Princeton U., 1954; M.A., Columbia U., 1969, Ph.D., 1971. Asst. cultural officer USIA, Laos, Japan; then dir. Am. Cultural Ctr. Kobe, Japan, 1958-67; assoc. prof., then prof. Japanese lang. and lit. Washington U., St. Louis, 1973-83, chmn. dept. Chinese and Japanese, 1973-83; chief Asian div. Library of Congress, Washington, 1983-86; chmn. Hebrew and East Asian langs. and lits. U. Maryland, College Park, 1986-91; chmn. East Asian langs. and lits. U. Pitts., 1991—; mem. Am. adv. bd. Japan Found., 1984—. Author: Toward a Modern Japanese Theatre, 1974, Traditions in Modern Japanese Fiction, 1978; translator: stories Mori Ogai, 2 vols., 1977, Mask and Sword: Two Plays for the Contemporary Japanese Theatre, 1980, On the No Drama, 1983, Pilgrimages, 1988, A Reader's Guide to Japanese Literature, 1988; editor: Multiple Meanings, 1987; editor, contbr.: Culture and Identity, Japanese Intellectuals during the Interwar Years, 1990, Shisendo, 1991, Youth and Other Stories by Mori Ogai, 1994. Served with U.S. Army, 1954-58. NEH fellow France, 1976-77; NEH grantee, 1979-81. Mem. Social Sci. Research Council (joint com. on Japan studies 1979-83). Episcopalian. Home: 1400 N Negley Ave Pittsburgh PA 15206-1118 Office: U Pitts Dept East Asian Langs and Lits 1501 CL Pittsburgh PA 15260

RIMERMAN, IRA STEPHEN, banker; b. N.Y.C., Apr. 28, 1938; s. Samuel David and Dorothy (Hoffman) R.; m. Iris Jacqueline, Mar. 10, 1962; children: Traci, Randi-Sue, Judith. BA in Indsl. Engring., Syracuse U., 1960; MBA, U. Pa., 1961; profl. degree indsl. engring., Columbia U., 1968. Tech. data processor ITT, Paramus, N.J., 1962-65, CBS, N.Y.C., 1965-67, Allied Chem., N.Y.C., 1967-69, Computer Usage Corp., N.Y.C., 1969-71; data processing mgr. Citicorp, N.Y.C., 1971; CFO Citicorp subs. Citicorp, Columbus, Ohio, 1971-73; dir., v.p. econ. devel. ctr. Citicorp, N.Y.C., 1974-75, chief of staff, v.p. N.Y. banking group, 1975-76; bus. mgr., v.p. consumer bus. Citicorp, Hong Kong, 1976-81; div. head bank cards Citibank USA div. Citicorp, N.Y.C., 1981-85, group exec. comsumer svc. internat., 1985-87, group exec. card products, 1987-89, sr. v.p. adminstrn., 1989—, sr. v.p., 1992—; sr. account mgr. for Citicorp Wharton Bus. Sch. U. Pa., 1986—. Trustee The Community Synagogue, 1982-88; bd. dirs. Vis. Nurse Svc., N.Y., treas., 1987—, comm. fin. com., 1988—; bd. dirs. Beth Israel Med. Ctr. 1989—; mem. Wharton Grad. Exec. Bd., 1989—; bd. dirs. Wharton Entrepreneurial Ctr., 1990—. Mem. Am. Inst. Indsl. Engrs., Wharton Alumni Assn. (bd. dirs. 1976-89), Hong Kong Club. Democrat. Jewish. Avocations: swimming, reading. Home: 63 Sands Point Rd Sands

Point NY 11050-1645 Office: Citicorp 399 Park Ave New York NY 10043-0001

RIMMER, JACK, retired chemical company executive; b. N.Y.C., Mar. 1, 1921; s. Sigmund and Esther (Grumet) R.; m. Mae Haskin, Oct. 31, 1942; children: Phyllis Ellen, Carole Ruth, Ann Rhoda. B.S. in Chemistry, Bklyn. Coll., 1946. Prodn. mgr. Winthrop Labs., Rensselaer, N.Y., 1946-57; dir. ops. B.T. Babbitt, Inc., Albany, N.Y., 1957-61; with W.R. Grace & Co., N.Y.C., 1961-85; exec. v.p. W.R. Grace & Co., 1980-85, also dir.; pres. The Grey Group, 1988; bd. dirs. W.R. Grace & Co., Dearborn Chem. Co., Dearborn-U.K. Ltd., E.J. Killam Assocs., Teroson K.K. (Japan), The Grey Group; lectr. Georgetown U.; instr. Hudson Valley Tech. Inst., Northwood Univ. Vice-pres., trustee Arts-in-Edn. Found. of N.J.; trustee Bklyn. Coll. Found. Score. Served with U.S. Navy, 1944-46. Mem. Am. Chem. Soc., Am. Inst. Chem. Engrs., World Trade Assn. Home: 123 Lakeshore Dr North Palm Beach FL 33408-3614

RIMMEREID, ARTHUR V., bishop. Bishop N.W. Minn. Synod Evang. Luth. Ch., Moorhead. Office: Evangelical Lutheran Church-Am PO Box 678 Moorhead MN 56561-0678

RIMOIN, DAVID LAWRENCE, physician, geneticist; b. Montreal, Que., Can., Nov. 9, 1936; s. Michael and Fay (Lecker) R.; m. Mary Ann Singleton, 1962 (div. 1979); 1 child, Anne; m. Ann Pilani Garber, July 27, 1980; children: Michael, Lauren. BSc, McGill U., Montreal, 1957, MSc, MD, CM, 1961; PhD, Johns Hopkins U., 1967. Asst. prof. medicine, pediatrics Washington U., St. Louis, 1967-70; assoc. prof. medicine, pediatrics UCLA, 1970-73, prof., 1973—, chief med. genetics, Harbor-UCLA Med. Ctr., 1970-86; dir. dept. pediatrics, dir. Med. Genetics and Birth Defects Ctr., 1986—; Steven Spielberg chmn. pediatrics Cedars-Sinai Med. Ctr., L.A., 1989—; chmn. coun. Med. Genetics Orgn., 1993. Co-author: Principles and Practice of Medical Genetics, 1983, 90; contbr. articles to profl. jours., chpts. to books. Recipient Ross Outstanding Young Investigator award Western Soc. Pediatric Research, 1976, E. Mead Johnson award Am. Acad. Pediatrics, 1976. Fellow ACP; mem. Am. Fedn. Clin. Rsch. (sec.-treas. 1972-75), Western Soc. Clin. Rsch. (pres. 1978), Western Soc. Pediatric Rsch. (pres. 1995), Am. Bd. Med. Genetics (pres. 1979-83), Am. Coll. Med. Genetics (pres. 1991—), Am. Soc. Human Genetics (pres. 1984), Am. Pediatric Soc., Soc. Pediatric Rsch., Am. Soc. Clin. Investigator, Assn. Am. Physicians, Johns Hopkins Soc. Scholars, Inst. Medicine. Office: Cedars-Sinai Med Ctr 8700 Beverly Blvd Los Angeles CA 90048

RIMPEL, AUGUSTE EUGENE, JR., management and technical consulting executive; b. St. Thomas, V.I., Aug. 25, 1939; s. Auguste Eugene and Leah Eudora (Harris) R. B.A. magna cum laude, Inter-Am. U. P.R., 1957; M.S. in Ch.E., M.I.T., 1961; Ph.D., Carnegie Inst. Tech., 1964; M.B.A., Columbia U., 1964-65; m. Maria Czernetski, Sept. 23, 1966; children: Nicole, Christopher. Research chem. engr. Am. Cyanamid Co., Stamford, Conn., 1961-62; with Arthur D. Little, Inc., Cambridge, Mass., 1965-75, sr. staff mem., 1973-75; commr. of commerce, spl. advisor to gov. for econ. affairs Govt. U.S. V.I., St. Thomas, 1975-78; mem. corp. spl. staff Arthur D. Little, Inc., Cambridge, 1978-81, also v.p. Arthur D. Little Internat., Inc.; v.p. Booz-Allen and Hamilton, Inc., 1981-83; v.p., ptnr., Price Waterhouse, 1983—. Bd. dirs. Caribbean/Lat. Am. Action, 1979-94; mem. U.S. del. World Bank Conf. on Caribbean Econ. Devel., 1977-78; mem. subcoms. on internat. econ. devel. U.S. C. of C., 1980-83; V.I. rep. White Ho. Conf. on Balanced Nat. Growth and Econ. Devel., 1978; bd. dirs. travel adv. bd. U.S. Dept. Commerce, 1977-78; pres. Caribbean Tourism Assn. 1977-78; bd. dirs., mem. exec. com. Caribbean Tourism Research Center, 1976-78. Mem. Am. Inst. Chem. Engrs., Am. Chem. Soc., Am. Inst. Chemists, Soc. Internat. Devel., Sigma Xi. Office: 1801 K St NW Washington DC 20006-1394

RIMROTT, FRIEDRICH PAUL JOHANNES, engineer, educator; b. Halle, Germany, Aug. 4, 1927; emigrated to Can., 1952; s. Hans and Margarete (Hofmeister) R.; m. Doreen McConnell, Apr. 7, 1955; children: Karla, Robert, Kira, Elizabeth-Ann. Dipl. Ing., U. Karlsruhe, Germany, 1951; MASc, U. Toronto, Ont., Can., 1955; PhD, Pa. State U., 1958; Dr Ing., Tech. U., Darmstadt, Germany, 1961; P.Eng., Ontario Prov., 1954; C.Eng. (hon.), U.K., 1987; D.Eng. (hon.), U. Victoria, 1992. Asst. prof. engring. mechanics Pa. State U., 1958-60; mem. faculty dept. mech. engring. U. Toronto, 1960—, assoc. prof., 1962-67, prof., 1967-93, prof. emeritus, 1993—; vis. prof. Tech. U. Vienna, Austria, 1969-70, 86, Tech. U. Hanover, Germany, 1970, U. Bochum, Germany, 1971, U. Wuppertal, Germany, 1987, 89, U. Lanzhou, People's Republic of China, 1989, Otto-von-Guericke-U. Magdeburg, 1992, 93, 94, 95; mng. dir. German Lang. Sch. (Metro Toronto) Inc., 1967-91; pres. 15th Internat. Congress Theoretical and Applied Mechanics, 1980; pres. CSME Mech. Engring. Forum, 1990. Author: Introductory Attitude Dynamics, 1988, Introductory Orbit Dynamics, 1989 (with K.Y. Yeh) Orbital Mechanics Introduction, Chinese edit., 1993, (with B. Tabarrok) Variational Methods and Complementary Formulations in Dynamics, 1994; editor: (with J. Schwaighofer) Mechanics of the Solid State, 1968, (with L.E. Jones) Proceedings CANCAM 67, 1968, (with J.T. Pindera, H.H.E. Leipholz, D.E. Gierson) Experimental Mechanics in Research and Development, 1973, (with W. Eichenlaub) Was Du ererbt, 1978, (with B. Tabarrok) Theoretical and Applied Mechanics, 1980. Mem. Can. Council on Multiculturalism, 1972-79. NRC postdoctorate fellow, 1959, Alexander von Humboldt sr. fellow, 1962, NRC sr. rsch. fellow, 1969-70; recipient Can. Congress Applied Mechanics award, 1989, Alexander von Humboldt Rsch. award, 1994. Fellow ASME, Instn. Mech. Engrs., Engring. Inst. Can., Can. Soc. Mech. Engring. (pres. 1974-75), Can. Aero. and Space Inst.; mem. Can. Congress Applied Mechanics (pres. 1971-72), Soc. German Engrs. (Germany), Soc. for Applied Math. and Mechanics (Germany) (dir. 1971-79). Home: 6 Thurgate Cres, Thornhill, ON Canada L3T 4G3 Office: U Toronto, Dept Mech Engring, Toronto, ON Canada M5S 1A4

RIMSZA, SKIP, mayor; b. Chgo.; m. Kim Gill; children: Brian, Jenny. Owner Rimsza Realty; mem. Phoenix City Coun., 1990-94; vice mayor City of Phoenix, 1993, mayor, 1994—; former pres. Bd. Realtors. Mem. several cmty. bds. Office: Office of the Mayor 251 W Washington St Phoenix AZ 85003*

RINALDINI, LUIS EMILIO, investment banker; b. Cambridge, Eng., July 29, 1953; came to U.S., 1964; s. Luis Maria and Fanny Josefina (Lopez) R.; m. Elaine Nash McHugh, June 22, 1974 (div. 1987); m. Julie Sayre Short, Aug. 1, 1987. BSE, Princeton U., 1974; MBA, Harvard U., 1980. Architect Johnson Burgee Architects, N.Y.C., 1974-78; assoc. Lazard Freres & Co., N.Y.C., 1980-85, gen. ptnr., 1986—. Mem. Piping Rock Club (Locust Valley, N.Y.), Meadowbrook Club (Jericho, N.Y.), Lyford Cay Club (Bahamas), Raquet and Tennis Club (N.Y.C.). Home: 124 E 64th St New York NY 10021-7307 Office: Lazard Freres & Co 1 Rockefeller Plz New York NY 10020-2001

RINAMAN, JAMES CURTIS, JR., lawyer; b. Miami, Fla., Feb. 8, 1935; s. James Curtis and Ruth Marie (Rader) R.; m. Gloria Margaret Kaspar; children: James, Mark, Christine, Karen. BA, U. Fla., 1955, JD, 1960. Bar: Fla. 1960, U.S. Dist. Ct. (so. dist.) Fla. 1960, U.S. Ct. Appeals (5th cir.) 1960, U.S. Supreme Ct. 1963, U.S. Dist. Ct. (mid. dist.) Fla. 1967, U.S. Dist. Ct. (no. dist.) Fla. 1981, U.S. Ct. Appeals (11th cir.) 1981, U.S. Ct. Claims 1991, U.S. Ct. Mil. Appeals 1994. With Marks, Gray, Conroy & Gibbs, Jacksonville, Fla., 1960—; gen. counsel Fla. Bd. Architecture, 1965-79, City of Jacksonville, 1970-71, Jacksonville C. of C., 1973-76, 90; adj. prof. Coll. Architecture, U. Fla., 1975-90. Pres. Jacksonville Community Coun. Inc., 1985, Leadership Jacksonville, Inc., 1987; mem. Jacksonville Transp. Authority, 1971-80. Brig. gen. AUS ret., 1992. Named to U. Fla. Hall of Fame. Fellow Am. Coll. Trial Lawyers, Am. Bar Found., Fla. Bar Found. (bd. dirs. 1982-87, Disting. Svc. award 1983, 86, Medal of Honor 1988); mem. ABA (mem. ho. of dels. 1982-86), The Fla. Bar (pres. 1982-83), Jacksonville Bar Assn. (pres. 1972-73), Assn. Def. Trial Attys. (nat. pres. 1976-77), Fla. Def. Lawyers Assn. (pres. 1973), Def. Rsch. Inst. (so. regional v.p. 1980-83, bd. dirs. 1976-78, 83-87), Am. Judicature Soc. (Herbert Harley award 1987), Fla. Coun. Bar Pres.' (Outstanding Past Pres. award 1989), Lawyers for Civil Rights (pres. 1988-91, chmn. bd. dirs. 1991-94), Civil Lawyers Resource Ctr. of Fla. (pres. 1984-89, chmn. bd. dirs. 1989-93), So. Conf. of Bar (pres. 1982—), Nat. Conf. of Bar (pres. 1982—), Jacksonville C. of C. (chmn. 1994), Fla. Blue Key, Meninack Civic Club (pres. 1986), San

Jose Country Club, River Club, Univ. Club, Jacksonville Commodores League, Phi Gamma Delta, Phi Alpha Delta. Democrat. Methodist. Office: Marks Gray Conroy & Gibbs Ste 800 1200 Riverplace Blvd Jacksonville FL 32207 also: PO Box 447 Jacksonville FL 32201-0447

RINCK, ELIZABETH APPEL, editor; b. Indpls., Apr. 14, 1961; d. Wilbur Lewis and Myrna Jeanne (Pipes) Appel; m. Jeffrey Bliss Rinck, May 11, 1985. BS, Butler U., 1983. Asst. editor Internat. Computer Programs, Indpls., 1982; coord. community rels. John County Meml. Hosp., Franklin, Ind., 1983-85; editor Children's Playmate Children's Digest Mag., Indpls., 1985-94; editl. dir. Children's Better Health Inst., 1994—; editor Turtle Mag. for Presch. Kids, 1994—; speaker Reader's Digest/ U. S.C. Mag. Writing Workshop, 1993. Guest editor Pacific N.W. Writer's Conf., 1994; contbg. editor Children's Mag. Mkt., 1992. Bd. advisors Young Writer's Contest Found., McLean, Va., 1985-91. Recipient Edn. Press Disting. Achievement award for Excellence in Edn. Journalism, 1991. Mem. Soc. Profl. Journalists, Ednl. Press Assn. Am. (Ednl. Journalism Disting. Achievment award 1991). Office: Children's Better Health Inst PO Box 567 1100 Waterway Blvd Indianapolis IN 46206

RINDEN, DAVID LEE, editor; b. Lake Mills, Iowa, Aug. 1, 1941; s. Oscar Henry and Iva (Stensrud) R.; m. Gracia Elizabeth Carlson, Sept. 11, 1966; children: Jonathan, Elizabeth, Amy. BA, Moorhead State U., 1964; diploma, Luth. Brethren Sem., 1966; postgrad., Seattle Pacific U., 1973. Ordained to ministry Luth. Ch., 1967. Pastor Bethesda Luth. Ch., Eau Claire, Wis., 1968-72, Maple Pk. Luth. Ch., Lynnwood, Wash., 1972-79; v.p. Ch. of the Luth. Brethren, Fergus Falls, Minn., 1991—; editor Faith & Fellowship, Fergus Falls, Minn., 1979—; exec. dir. ch. svcs. Ch. of the Luth. Brethren, Fergus Falls, 1979—; chmn. com. on commitment Ch. of Luth. Brethren, Fergus Falls, 1981-82, com. on role of women in ch., 1984-86, chmn. com. on 90th anniversary, 1989—, chmn. bd. pubils., 1968-78. Editor: Explanation of Luther's Small Catechism, 1988; author: Biblical Foundations, 1981. Founding com. JAIL, Inc., Fergus Falls, 1991; pres. bd. dirs. Fergus Falls Fed. Community Credit Union, 1987—. Mem. Fergus Falls Ministerial Assn. (sec. 1989-90, v.p. 1991-92, pres. 1992-93), Kiwanis (pres. 1994-95). Home: 701 W Channing Ave Fergus Falls MN 56537-3218 Office: Ch of the Luth Brethren 1007 Westside Dr, Box 655 Fergus Falls MN 56538

RINDER, GEORGE GREER, retired retail company executive; b. Chgo., Feb. 3, 1921; s. Carl Otto and Jane (Greer) R.; m. Shirley Laurine Latham, Dec. 21, 1946; children: Robert Latham, Carl Thomas, Susan Jane Sitrick. M.B.A., U. Chgo., 1942. C.P.A., Ill. With Gen. Electric Co., 1941-42; with Marshall Field & Co., Chgo., 1946-86; asst. to gen. mgr. Marshall Field & Co., 1959-62, v.p., comptroller, 1962-67, v.p. finance, 1967-71, exec. v.p. fin., 1971-74, exec. v.p., 1974-78, sr. exec. v.p., 1978-81, vice chmn., 1981-86, dir., 1972-83; ret., 1986. Nat. trustee McCormick Theol. Sem.; mem. coun. Grad. Sch. Bus., U. Chgo. Served to capt. AUS, 1942-46. Recipient Alumni Svc. citation U. Chgo., 1990, Alumni Svc. medal U. Chgo., 1995. Mem. Fin. Execs. Inst., Phi Beta Kappa, Delta Upsilon, Beta Gamma Sigma. Clubs: Chicago (Chgo.), University (Chgo.), Economic (Chgo.); Hinsdale (Ill.) Golf). Home: 736 Cleveland Rd Hinsdale IL 60521-4806

RINDFUSS, RONALD RICHARD, sociology educator; b. Buffalo, Dec. 11, 1946; married Aug. 1968; 2 children. BA, Fordham U., 1968; PhD, Princeton U., 1974. Rsch. asst. Nat. Fertility Study, Office Population Rsch., Princeton U., 1971-73; rsch. assoc. Ctr. Demography and Ecology U. Wis., Madison, 1973-76; asst. prof. sociology U. N.C., Chapel Hill, 1976-79, assoc. prof., 1979-84; prof. sociology U. N.C., 1984—; dir. Carolina Population Ctr., Chapel Hill, 1991—; cons. in field. Contbr. numerous articles to profl. jours.; assoc. editor Social Forces, 1976—; cons. editor Am. Jour. Sociology, 1977-80; contbg. editor Social Biology, 1974; referee for numerous jours. NIH traineeship, 1968-71. Mem. Am. Sociol. Assn. (chmn. sociology of population sect. 1989-90, mem. pubs. com. 1983-84), Population Assn. Am. (pres. 1991, mem. Mindel C. Sheps award com. 1990, bd. dirs. 1984-87), Internat. Union for Sci. Study Population, Nat. Coun. on Family Rels., So. Regional Demographic Group, So. Sociol. Soc., Coun. on Family Rsch. Office: Carolina Population Ctr. CB # 8120 University Sq 123 W Franklin St Chapel Hill NC 27516-3997

RINDLAUB, JOHN WADE, advertising agency executive; b. Lancaster, Pa., July 26, 1934; s. Willard Weaner and Jean (Wade) R.; m. Laurette Lukens, June 22, 1956; children: John Wade, Curtis Clay, David Landis. BA, Yale U., 1956. Copywriter, supr. Young & Rubicam, N.Y.C., 1956-68; v.p., creative dir. Toronto, 1968-71; assoc. creative dir. N.Y.C., 1971-73; creative dir. Stockholm and Frankfurt, Fed. Republic Germany, 1973-77; mng. dir. Holter, Young & Rubicam, Oslo, 1977-78; assoc. dir. mktg. Young & Rubicam, N.Y.C., 1978-80, sr. v.p., mgr. creative services, 1980-84, assoc. creative dir., 1984-88, sr. v.p., dir. corp. rels., 1988-90, dir. industry and govt. rels., 1990—. Mem. Yale Club, Riverside Yacht Club. Episcopalian. Home: 8 Hill Lane Ave Riverside CT 06878-2500 Office: Young & Rubicam 285 Madison Ave New York NY 10017-6401

RINE, SUSAN, principal. Prin. Centennial Elem. Sch. Office: Centennial Elem Sch 38501 Centennial Rd Dade City FL 33525

RINEARSON, PETER MARK, journalist, author, software developer; b. Seattle, Aug. 4, 1954; s. Peter Morley and Jeannette Irene (Love) R.; m. Jill Chan, Sept. 15, 1991; 1 child, Tess. Student, U. Wash., 1972-78. Editor Sammamish Valley News, Redmond, Wash., 1975-76; reporter Seattle Times, 1976-78, govt. and polit. reporter, 1979-81, aerospace reporter, 1982-84, Asian corr., 1985-86; pres. Alki Software Corp., Seattle, 1990—. Author: Word Processing Power with Microsoft Word (4th edit. Running Microsoft Word 5.5, 1991), Microsoft Word Style Sheets, 1987, Quick Reference Guide to Microsoft Word, 1988, Microsoft Word Companion Disk, 1988, Masterword, 1990, 91, 92. Recipient Spl. Paul Myhre award-series Penney-Mo. Newspaper awards, 1983, Disting. Writing award Am. Soc. Newspaper Editors, 1984, Pulitzer prize for feature writing, 1984, Lowell Thomas Travel Writing award, 1984, John Hancock award,1985, semi-finalist NASA Journalist-in-Space Project, 1986; U.S.-Japan Leadership Program fellow Japan Soc., 1988. Office: 300 Queen Anne Ave N # 410 Seattle WA 98109-4599

RINEHART, CHARLES R., savings and loan association executive; b. San Francisco, Jan. 31, 1947; s. Robert Eugene and Rita Mary Rinehart; married; children: Joseph B., Kimberly D., Michael P., Scott. BS, U. San Francisco, 1968. Exec. v.p. Fireman's Fund Ins. Cos., Novato, Calif., 1969-83; pres., CEO Avco Fin. Services, Irvine, Calif., 1983-89, H.F. Ahmanson & Co., Irwindale, Calif., 1989—; chmn., CEO Home Savs. of Am., Irwindale. Trustee San Francisco; mem. adv. com. Drug Use is Life Abuse. Served to 2d lt. U.S. Army, 1968-69. Fellow Casualty Actuarial Soc.; mem. Am. Mgmt. Assn., Am. Acad. Actuaries. Republican. Roman Catholic. Avocations: athletics, gourmet cooking, model trains. Office: Ho Savs Am/H F Ahmanson & Co 4900 Rivergrade Rd Irwindale CA 91706-1438

RINEHART, JONATHAN, public relations executive; b. N.Y.C., Apr. 19, 1930. BA in Internat. Rels., Yale U., 1952. Corr., bur. chief, chief mil. corr. Time Mag., 1956-62; dep. chief corrs., gen. editor Newsweek, 1962-65; sr. v.p. public rels. Ea. Airlines, 1965-73; pres. Jonathan Rinehart Group, Inc., 1974-77; pres. Adams & Rinehart, 1977-87, chmn., CEO, 1987-92; chmn. Ogilvy Pub. Rels. Group, 1987-92, Ogilvy Adams & Rinehart, 1992—; also bd. dirs. Ogilvy & Mather Worldwide. Office: Ogilvy Adams & Rinehart 708 3rd Ave New York NY 10017-4103

RINEHEART, GARY, mortgage company executive; b. 1943. Pres. Sunshine Mortgage Corp., Smyrna, Ga. With USAF, 1967-70. Office: Sunshine Mortgage Corp 2401 Lake Park Dr Ste 300 Smyrna GA 33080*

RINES, JOHN RANDOLPH, automotive company executive; b. Balt., Aug. 3, 1947; s. John William and Betty (Singer) R.; m. Peggy J. Daugaard, Sept. 19, 1969 (dec. 1978); m. Katherine M. Duff, Nov. 29, 1980; children: Jacqueline J., Sharon W. BS in Econs., Colo. State U., 1970; MBA, U. Va., 1977. With GM, 1970-75, 77—; fin. analyst GM, Detroit, 1977-78, dir. product programs, 1978-80, asst. to pres., 1980-81, gen. dir. fin., 1981-82; exec. dir. GM, Sao Paulo, Brazil, 1982-84; dir. fin. Buick/Oldsmobile/Cadillac group GM, Flint, Mich., 1984-85; gen. mgr. motors holding div.

and GM auction GM, Detroit, 1985-91, gen. mgr. parts ops., 1991—; pres. GM Acceptance Corp., Detroit, 1992—. Trustee Arts Found. Mich., Detroit. Mem. Grosse Pointe (Mich.) Club, Old Club (Harsen's Island), Birmingham Athletic Club. Office: GM 3044 W Grand Blvd Detroit MI 48202-3091

RINES, S. MELVIN, investment banker; b. Berlin, N.H., Aug. 26, 1924; s. William James and Gladys Olive (Estes) R.; m. Mary Jo Marcy, Feb. 27, 1954; children: Pamela Marcy, Jeffrey William, David Melvin. BA, U. N.H., 1947; OD, No. Ill. Coll., 1950. Asst. v.p. Kidder, Peabody & Co., Inc., N.Y.C., 1970, v.p., 1972—, shareholder, 1973—; mng. dir. Kidder, Peabody & Co. Inc., 1986—; adj. prof. Am. U., Washington, 1986—. Co-editor: The Supranationals, 1986; contbr. articles to profl. jours. Mem. Bretton Woods Com., Washington, 1987—. Served to lt. USN, 1943-46, 50-54, Korea. Mem. Boston Exec. Assn. (pres. 1970-71). Republican. Clubs: Downtown (pres. 1974-81), Bond (Boston) (pres. 1976-77); Met. (Washington); DTA (N.Y.). Avocations: tennis, skiing, sailing, swimming, riding. Home: 21 Sudbury Rd Weston MA 02193-1332 Office: Kidder Peabody & Co Inc 10 Hanover Sq New York NY 10005

RINEY, HAL PATRICK, advertising executive; b. Seattle, July 17, 1932; s. Hal Patrick and Inez Marie R.; m. Elizabeth Kennedy; children: Benjamin Kennedy, Samantha Elizabeth. BA, U. Wash., Seattle, 1954. From art dir./writer to v.p., creative dir. BBDO, Inc., San Francisco, 1956-72; exec. v.p., creative dir. Botsford Ketchum, San Francisco, 1972-76; sr. v.p., mng. dir., creative dir. Ogilvy & Mather, San Francisco, 1976-81; exec. v.p. Ogilvy & Mather West, 1981-86; chmn. Hal Riney & Ptnrs., Inc., San Francisco, 1986—. Recipient 5 Lion d'Or du Cannes awards, 17 Clio awards, 15 Addy awards, Grand Prix du Cannes; named to Creative Hall of Fame. Mem. Am. Assn. Advt. Agys., San Francisco Advt. Club, San Francisco Soc. Communicating Arts, Wild Goose Club, Meadow Club, St. Francis Yacht Club. Home: 1 Los Pinos Nicasio CA 94946-9701 Office: Hal Riney & Ptnrs Inc 735 Battery St San Francisco CA 94111-1501

RING, ALICE RUTH BISHOP, physician; b. Ft. Collins, Oct. 11, 1931; d. Ernest Otto and Mary Frances (Drohan) Bishop; m. Wallace Harold Ring, July 26, 1956 (div. 1969); children: Rebecca, Eric, Mark; m. Robert Charles Deifenbach, Sept. 10, 1977. BS, Colo. State U., 1953; MD, U. Colo., 1956, MPH, U. Calif., Berkeley, 1971. Physician cons. Utah State Div. HEalth, Salt Lake City, 1960-65; med. dir., project head start Salt Lake City Community Action Program, 1965-70; resident Utah State Div. Health, 1969-71; asst. assoc. reg. health dir. U.S. Pub. Health Svc., San Francisco, 1971-75; med. cons. U.S. Pub. Health Svc., Atlanta, 1975-77, dir. primary care, 1977-84; dir. div. diabetes control Ctrs. Disease Control, Atlanta, 1984-88; dir. WHO Collabor Ctr., Atlanta, 1986-91; dir. preventive medicine residency Ctrs. Disease Control, Atlanta, 1988-94; exec. dir. Am. Bd. Preventive Medicine, 1993—; trustee Am. Bd. Preventive Medicine, 1990-92 (diplomate); lectr. Emory U. Sch. Pub. Health, 1988-94. Co-author: Clinical Diabetes, 1991. Bd. dirs. Diabetes Assn. Atlanta, 1985-90, med. adv. com., 1990-94. Fellow Am. Coll. Preventive Medicine (bd. dirs. 1990-94); mem. AMA, Am. Pub. Health Assn., Am. Acad. Pediatrics, Sigma Xi. Home: 245 Vantage Rd The Sea Ranch CA 95499 Office: Am Bd Preventive Medicine 9950 Lawrence Ave Schiller Park IL 60176*

RING, ALVIN MANUEL, pathologist; b. Detroit, Mar. 17, 1933; s. Julius and Helen (Krolik) R.; m. Cynthia Joan Jacobson, Sept. 29, 1963; children—Jeffrey, Melinda, Heather. BS, Wayne State U., 1954; MD, U. Mich., 1958. Intern Mt. Carmel Hosp., Detroit, 1958-59; resident in pathology Michael Reese Hosp., Chgo., 1960-62; asst. pathologist Kings County Hosp., Bklyn., 1962-63; assoc. pathologist El Camino Hosp., Mountain View, Calif., 1963-65; chief pathologist, dir. labs. St. Elizabeth's Hosp., Chgo., 1965-72, Holy Cross Hosp., Chgo., 1972-87, Silver Cross Hosp., Joliet, Ill., 1990—; instr. SUNY, 1962-63, Stanford U., 1963-65; asst. prof. pathology U. Ill., Chgo., 1966-69, assoc. prof., 1969-78, 1978—; adj. clin. prof. No. Ill. U., 1981-87; adj. prof. med. edn. U. Ill. Coll. Medicine, 1988—; chmn. histotech. Nat. Accrediting Agy. for Clin. Lab Scis., 1977-81; mem. spl. adv. com. Health Manpower, 1966-71; pres. Spear Computer Users Group, 1981-82; mem. adv. com. Mid-Am. chpt. ARC, 1979-85; pres. Pathology and Lab Cons., Inc., 1985—; adj. prof., med. dir. Med. Tech., Moraine Valley C.C., 1994—; originator, coord. pathology, med. decision-making courses Nat. Ctr. for Advanced Med. Edn., 1981—, others. Author: Laboratory Correlation Manual, 1968, 82, 86, Laboratory Assistant Examination Review Book, 1971, Review Book in Pathology, Anatomic, 1986, Review Book in Pathology, Clinical, 1986; mem. editorial bd. Lab. Medicine, 1975-87; contbr. articles to med. jours. Fellow Coll. Am. Pathology (insp. 1973—), Am. Soc. Clin. Pathology; mem. AMA, Ill. Med. Soc., Chgo. Med. Soc. (alt. councilor 1980-85, mem. adv. com. on health care delivery), Ill. Pathol. Soc., Chgo. Pathol. Soc. (censor 1980-88, exec. com. 1985-89, program. com. 1987—), Am. Assn. Blood Banks, Assn. Brain Tumor Rsch. (cons.), Exec. Svc. Corps (exec. cons. 1988—), Phi Lambda Kappa. Home: 100 Graymoor Ln Olympia Fields IL 60461-1213 Office: Silver Cross Hosp 1200 Maple Rd Joliet IL 60432-1439

RING, GERALD J., real estate developer, insurance executive; b. Madison, Wis., Oct. 6, 1928; s. John George and Mabel Sarah (Rau) R.; m. Armella Marie Dohm, Aug. 20, 1949; children: Michael J., James J., Joseph W. Student public schs., Madison. With Sub-Zero Freezer Co., Madison, 1948-70; mfr.'s rep. Sub-Zero Freezer Co., 1954-70; founder, pres. Parkwood Hills Corp., Madison, from 1965, Park Towne Devel. Corp., Madison, from 1969, Ring Devel. Co., 1992—; bd. dirs. CUNA Mut. Ins. Soc., CUNA Mut. Ins. Group, CUNA Mut. Investment Corp., CUDIS Ins. Soc., all Madison, 1968—, exec. com., 1973-83, chmn. bd., 1979-81; bd. dirs. CUMIS Ins. Soc., mem. exec. com., 1973-83, chmn. bd., 1977-79; bd. dirs. CMCI Corp., mem. exec. com., 1974-83, chmn. bd., 1981-83; treas. CUNADATA Corp., 1974-81; bd. dirs. Wis. Credit Union League, 1958-79, pres., 1965-67; mem. Wis. Credit Union Rev. Bd., 1967-83, chmn., 1973-76, 82-83; bd. dirs. CUNA Credit Union Nat. Assn., Inc., 1964-81, League Life Ins. Co., League Gen. Ins. Co., Southfield, Mich., CUNA Mut. Fin. Svcs. Corp., Century Ins. Co. Am., Waverly., Iowa. Chmn. Greater Madison C. of C., 1980, bd. dirs., 1976-89, v.p. econ. devel., 1983-85, v.p. govtl. affairs, 1985-89, mem. capital fund raising com., 1983—, chmn. 1983-86; mem. Mayor's Emergency Housing Com., 1984-85; chmn. fin. com. St. Patrick's Congregation, 1983-89. Served with USMC, 1951-53. Mem. Aircraft Owners and Pilots Assn. Roman Catholic. Lodge: Rotary. (bd. dirs. 1981-83). Home: 607 Farwell Dr Madison WI 53704-6029 Office: 402 S Gammon Rd Madison WI 53719-1002

RING, JAMES EDWARD PATRICK, mortgage banking consulting executive; b. Washington, Feb. 12, 1940; s. Edward Patrick and Eleanor (Sollers) R.; m. Kathleen Murphy, Aug. 10, 1979; children: Christopher James, Daniel Edward Patrick. Student, Holy Cross Coll., Worcester, Md., 1958-59; BSEE, U.S. Naval Acad., 1963; MBA in Fin., Wharton Sch. Bus., U. Pa., 1972. Lic. securities broker, comml. pilot. Fin. analyst Exec. Office of the President, Washington, 1972-74; sr. budget analyst Bd. Govs. Fed. Res. System, Washington, 1974-77; fin. plng. Fed. Home Loan Mortgage Ins., Washington, 1977-83; dir. mktg. Ticor Mortgage Ins., Falls Church, Va., 1983-84, G.E. Mortgage Ins., Mc Lean, Va., 1985-86; sr. v.p. First Chesapeake Mortgage, Beltsville, Md., 1986-88; v.p. G.E Capital Mortgage Corp., McLean, 1988-94; cons. Mortgage Dynamics, McLean, 1994—. Vol. Big Bros. Am., Washington, 1973-81; pres. U.S. Naval Acad. Class of 1963 Found., 1983-95. Lt. USN, 1963-69. Mem. Wharton Club (Washington), U.S. Naval Acad. Alumni Assn., Army-Navy Country Club. Republican Roman Catholic. Home: 1716 Stonebridge Rd Alexandria VA 22304-1039 Office: 1355 Beverly Rd Ste 300 Mc Lean VA 22101-5723

RING, JAMES WALTER, physics educator; b. Worcester, N.Y., Feb. 24, 1929; s. Carlyle Conwell and Lois (Tooley) R.; m. Agnes Elizabeth Muir, July 18, 1959; 1 son, Andrew James. AB, Hamilton Coll., 1951; PhD (Root fellow), U. Rochester, 1958. Asst. prof. physics Hamilton Coll., Clinton, N.Y., 1957-62, assoc. prof., 1962-69, prof., 1969—, Winslow prof., 1975—, chmn. dept. physics, 1968-80, 87-88, 91-92, radiation safety Officer, 1964-84, engring. liaison officer, 1984—; attached physicist Atomic Energy Rsch. Establishment, Harwell, Eng., 1965-66; vis. physicist Phys. Chemistry Lab. Oxford (Eng.) U., 1973; vis. fellow Ctr. for Energy and Environ. Studies, Princeton U., 1981; vis. scientist Lab. for Heating and Air Conditioning, Danish Tech. U., Copenhagen, 1987. Contbr. articles to profl. jours. and books in physics, chemistry, solar energy, environ. sci., health physics and engring. Recipient prize Acad. Edn./Devel., 1980; NSF grantee, 1959-66; NSF sci. faculty fellow, 1965-66. Mem. AAUP (chpt. pres. 1987-92), Am. Phys. Soc., Am. Assn. Physics Tchrs., Interant. Solar Energy Soc., Internat. Soc. Indoor Air Quality and Climate, Phi Beta Kappa, Sigma Xi. Achievements include solar house design and testing, and indoor air studies in radon dangers and thermal comfort. Office: Hamilton Coll Dept Physics Clinton NY 13323

RING, MICHAEL WILSON, lawyer; b. Phoenix, Feb. 14, 1943; s. Clifton A. and Leona (Wilson) R. BA, U Wash., 1964; JD, U. Calif., Berkeley, 1968. Bar: Calif. 1969. Assoc. Sheppard, Mullin, Richter & Hampton, L.A., 1968-76, ptnr., 1976-87; ptnr. Mayer, Brown & Platt, L.A., 1987-92, Sonnenschein Nath & Rosenthal, L.A., 1992—. Mem. ABA, L.A. County Bar Assn., Am. Coll. Real Estate Lawyers, Urban Land Inst. (assoc.), Internat. Coun. Shopping Ctrs. (assoc.), L.A. Hdqrs. City Assn. Home: 3658 Mountain View Ave Los Angeles CA 90066-3129 Office: Sonnenschein Nath & Rosenthal 601 S Figueroa St Ste 1500 Los Angeles CA 90017-5720

RING, RENEE E., lawyer; b. Frankfurt, Germany, May 29, 1950; arrived in U.S., 1950; d. Vincent Martin and Etheline Bergetta (Schoolmeesters) R.; m. Paul J. Zofnass, June 24, 1982; Jessica Renee, Rebecca Anne. BA, Catholic U. Am., 1972; JD, U. Va., 1976. Bar: N.Y. 1977. Assoc. Whitman & Ransom, N.Y.C., 1976-83; assoc. Carro, Spanbock, Fass, Geller, Kaster & Cuiffo, N.Y.C., 1983-86, ptnr., 1986; ptnr. Finley Kumble Wagner et. al., N.Y.C., 1987; of counsel Kaye, Scholer, Fierman, Hays & Handler, N.Y.C., 1988; ptnr. Kaye Scholer Fierman Hays & Handler, N.Y.C., 1989—. Mem. exec. com. Lawyers for Clinton, Washington, 1991-92; team capt. Clinton Transition Team, Washington, 1992-93; mem. Nat. Lawyers Coun. Dem. Nat. Com., 1993—. Mem. ABA (chmn. programs subcom. for partnerships com., sect. bus. law), N.Y. Women's Bar Assn. Democrat. Roman Catholic. Office: Kaye Scholer Fierman Hays & Handler 425 Park Ave New York NY 10022-3506

RING, RODNEY EVERETT, religion educator; b. Sioux City, Iowa, May 13, 1927; s. Everett Irwin and Pearl Olive (Rubeck) R.; m. Naomi Ruth Korn, Sept. 11, 1949; children: Alexander Everett, Angela Catherine. MA, U. Chgo., 1950, PhD, 1954. Prof. Muhlenberg Coll., Allentown, Pa., 1950-51, 55-90, Thiel Coll., Greenville, Pa., 1954-55. Author: Solving Biblical Problems, 1988; editor ELNA bull., 1970-72; contbr. articles to religious jours. Sgt. U.S. Army, 1946-48. Grantee Muhlenberg Coll., 1964, Mack Trucks Inc., 1968. Mem. Soc. Bibl. Lit., Am. Acad. Religion. Home: 250 Deer Run Rd Kutztown PA 19530-9432

RING, TERRY WILLIAM, company executive, environmentalist; b. Lewiston, Idaho, Nov. 11, 1955; s. Robert L. and Irene M. (Sullivan) R. BA, Boise State U., 1979. Pres. Silver Creek Outfitters, Inc., Ketchum, Idaho, 1980—. Bd. dirs. Idaho Nature Conservancy, Ketchum, 1982—, chmn., 1986-2; bd. dirs. The Peregrine Fund, Boise, Idaho, 1994—. Recipient Oak Leaf Awd., 1993, Nature Conservancy. Mem. Nature Conservancy (Oak Leaf Awd. 1993). Home: PO Box 1096 Sun Valley ID 83353-1096 Office: Silver Creek Outfitters Inc 500 N Main St Ketchum ID 83340

RINGEL, DEAN, lawyer; b. N.Y.C., Dec. 12, 1947; m. Ronnie Sussman, Aug. 24, 1969; children: Marion, Alicia. BA, Columbia Coll., 1967; JD, Yale U., 1971. Bar: N.Y. 1972, U.S. Ct. Appeals (6th cir.) 1972, U.S. Ct. Appeals (2d and D.C. cirs.) 1974, U.S. Supreme Ct. 1976, U.S. Ct. Appeals (10th cir.) 1982. Law clk. to Judge Anthony J. Celebrezze U.S. Ct. Appeals (6th cir.), 1971-72; assoc. Cahill Gordon & Reindel, N.Y.C., 1972-79; ptnr. Cahill, Gordon & Reindel, N.Y.C., 1979—. Mem. ABA (vice chmn. com. on freedom of speech and press 1978-79), Assn. Bar of City of N.Y. (comm. com., fed. legis. com.), N.Y. State Bar Assn. (chmn. antitrust com., sect. on comml. and fed. litigation), Pub. Edn. Assn. (bd. trustees). Office: Cahill Gordon & Reindel 80 Pine St New York NY 10005-1701

RINGEL, ELEANOR, film critic; b. Atlanta, Nov. 3, 1950; d. Herbert Arthur and Sara (Finklestein) R.; m. John Gillespie, Nov. 18, 1989. BA magna cum laude, Brown U., 1972. With Alliance Theatre, 1974, S.C. Open Road Ensemble, 1974-75, N.Y. Shakespeare Festival, 1975-78, Children's TV Workshop, 1975-77; obituary writer Atlanta Jour., 1978; critic, editor Atlanta Jour.-Constitution Film, 1978—. Named Best Local Critic Atlanta Mag., 1990, Best of Cox Newspapers Critisims, 1987, Finalist Citations Critisims, 1984-85, Merit award, 1987. Mem. Nat. Soc. Film Critics (elected 1994). Home: 235 1/2 East Wesley Rd Atlanta GA 30305 Office: Atlanta Journal Constitution Entertainment Desk 72 Marietta St NW Atlanta GA 30303-2804

RINGEL, ROBERT LEWIS, university administrator; b. N.Y.C., Jan. 27, 1937; s. Benjamin Seymour and Beatrice (Salis) R.; m. Estelle Neuman, Jan. 18, 1959; children—Stuart Alan, Mark Joseph. B.A., Bklyn. Coll., 1959; M.S., Purdue U., 1960, Ph.D., 1962. cert. speech pathologist. Rsch. scientist, laryngeal rsch. lab. Ctr. Health Scis., UCLA, 1962-64; asst. prof. communication disorders U. Wis., 1964-66; mem. faculty Purdue U., 1966—, prof., head dept. audiology and speech sci., 1970-73, dean Sch. Humanities, Social Sci. and Edn. (Sch. Liberal Arts), 1973-86, v.p., dean Grad. Sch., 1986-90, exec. v.p. for acad. affairs, 1991—; vis. prof. Inst. Neurology and Nat. Hosps. Coll. Speech Scis., U. London, 1985; cons. NIH, NEH, Bur. Edn. Handicapped of U.S. Office Edn. Author sci. articles; contbr. to monographs and textbooks. Bd. dirs. Lafayette Home Hosp., 1978-87, Lafayette Symphony Orch., 1983-85. Recipient Research Career Devel. award Nat. Inst. Dental Research, 1967-70, Award for highest merit for sci. article Jour. Speech and Hearing Research, 1979, Disting. Alumnus award Bklyn. Coll., 1985. Fellow Am. Speech and Hearing Assn. (v.p. Found. 1990—); mem. AAUP, Nat. Assn. State Univs. and Land Grant Colls. (exec. com. 1988-91, rsch. policy and grad. edn., exec. com. coun. on acad. affairs 1991—, exec. com. provosts institutional cooperation com., 1991—), Sigma Xi (v.p. 1986—). Office: Purdue U West Lafayette IN 47907-1073

RINGEN, CATHERINE OLESON, linguistics educator; b. Bklyn., June 3, 1943; d. Prince Eric and Geneva Muriel (Leigh) Oleson; m. Jon David Ringen, Nov. 22, 1969; children: Kai Mathias, Whitney Leigh. Student, Cornell U., 1961-63; BA, Indiana U., 1970, MA, 1972, PhD, 1975. Vis. lectr. U. Minn., Mpls., 1973-74; asst. prof. U. Iowa, Iowa City, 1975-79, assoc. prof., 1980-87, prof., 1988—, chair linguistics, 1987-93. Author: Vowel Harmony: Theoretical Implications, 1988; contbr. articles to profl. jours. Sr. Fulbright prof. Trondheim, Norway, 1980, Poznan, Poland, 1994-95. Mem. AAAS, Linguistic Soc. Am., Phi Beta Kappa. Office: U Iowa Dept Linguistics Iowa City IA 52242

RINGER, JAMES MILTON, lawyer; b. Orlando, Fla., July 9, 1943; s. Robert T. and Jessie M. (Rowe) R.; m. Jaquelyn Hope, Apr. 10, 1965; children—Carolyn Hope, James Matthew. A.B., Ohio U., 1965; J.D., Cornell U., 1968. Bar: N.Y. 1968, U.S. Dist. Ct. (no. dist.) N.Y. 1968, U.S. Dist. Ct. (so. and ea. dists.) N.Y. 1972, U.S. Ct. Appeals (2d cir.) 1972, U.S. Ct. Claims 1976, U.S. Dist. Ct. (we. dist.) N.Y. 1978, U.S. Ct. Appeals (4th cir.) 1981, U.S. Ct. Appeals (9th cir.) 1983. Assoc. Rogers & Wells, N.Y.C., 1968-78, ptnr., 1978—; instr. bus. law U. Alaska, 1970-71. Editor Cornell Law Rev., 1967-68. Served to lt. JAGC, USNR, 1969-72. Republican. Episcopalian. Office: Rogers & Wells 200 Park Ave New York NY 10166-0153

RINGER, JEROME, public relations executive; b. L.A., Mar. 1, 1935; s. Arthur and Alice (Olds) R.; m. Shirley A. O'Neal, Jan. 5, 1955; children: Julie Ann Webster, Kellie Lynn Burns. BSBA, Calif. State U., Northridge, 1967. Reporter Glendale (Calif.) News, 1956-58; pub. relations Northrop, Van Nuys and Thousand Oaks, Calif., 1956-64; pub. relations and advt. mgr. Walter Kidder Webber A/C Div., Burbank, Calif., 1964-67; account exec. Smith Klitton Advt. Agy., Santa Monica, Calif., 1967-68; asst. to pres. Cubic Corp., San Diego, 1968—; pub. rels. trustee San Diego, 1985—; teaching assoc. pub. rels. U. Calif., San Diego, 1984-94; bd. dirs. Jr. Achievement, San Diego, 1971-90. Pres. San Diego chpt. Nat. Football Found., 1972—; bd. dirs. U.S. Olympic Tng. Sight Task Force, San Diego, 1986-92. Sgt. U.S. Army, 1954-56. Named Profl. of Yr. Pub. Relations Club, 1986. Mem. Press Club of San Diego (v.p., Best. Com. Rels. Program award 1975, 78, 80, Man of Yr. 1986), Fin. Analyst Soc., Aviation Space Writers Assn., Pub.

Rels. Soc. Am., U. So. Calif. Trojan Club (San Diego). Avocations: jogging, sports, gardening, helping youth. Office: Cubic Corp 9333 Balboa Ave San Diego CA 92123

RINGER, LARRY JOEL, statistics educator; b. Cedar Rapids, Iowa, Sept. 24, 1937; s. Joel Burnett and Frances Margaret (Hummer) R.; m. Jean Bradley, Nov. 26, 1960; children: Margaret, Michael, Susan. BS in Math., Iowa State U., 1959, MS in Statistics, 1962; PhD in Statistics, Tex. A&M U. 1966. From instr. to prof. dept. statistics Tex. A&M U., College Station, 1965—, asst. head dept. statistics, 1977—. Pres. College Station Recreation Coun., 1974-76; councilman City of College Station, 1976-83, mayor, 1986—; program chair summer rsch. conf. So. Regional Coun. Stats., 1983, treas., 1983-85, pres.-elect, 1993—. Mem. Am. Statistical Assn. (pres. Southwest chpt. 1967-68, 71-72), Am. Soc. Quality Control, Kiwanis (pres. College Station club 1979, Kiwanian of Yr. 1977). Avocations: athletics, gardening, reading. Office: Tex A&M U Dept Stats College Station TX 77843-3143

RINGGOLD, FAITH, artist; b. N.Y.C., Oct. 8, 1930. B.S., CCNY, 1955; M.A., 1959; DFA (hon.), Moore Coll. Art, Phila., 1986, Coll. Wooster, Ohio, 1987, Mass. Coll. Art, Boston, 1991, CCNY of CUNY, 1991, DSc (hon.), Brockport (N.Y.) State U., 1992, Calif. Coll. Arts. and Crafts, Oakland, Calif., 1993, RISD, 1994. Art tchr. N.Y. Pub. Schs., 1955-73; lectr. Bank St. Coll. Grad. Sch., N.Y.C., 1970-80; prof. art U. Calif., San Diego, 1984—. Solo exhbns. include Spectrum Gallery, N.Y.C., 1967, 70, 10 year retrospective, Voorhees Gallery, Rutgers U., 1973, Summit Gallery, N.Y.C., 1979, 20 year Retrospective, Studio Mus. in Harlem, N.Y.C., 1984, Bernice Steinbaum Gallery, N.Y.C., 1987-88, Balt. Mus., Deland (Fla.) Mus., Faith Ruggold 25 Yr. Survey Fine Arts Museum L.I., Hempstead, 1990-93; exhibited in group shows at Meml. Exhibit for MLK, Mus. Modern Art, N.Y.C., 1968, Chase Manhattan Bank Collection, Martha Jackson Gallery, N.Y.C., 1970, Am. Women Artists, Gedok, Kunstalle, Hamburg, Ger., 1972, Jubilee, Boston Mus. Fine Arts, 1975, Major Contemporary Women Artists, Suzanne Gross Gallery, Phila., 1984, Committed to Print Mus. Modern Art, N.Y.C., 1988, The Art of Black Am. in Japan, Terada Warehouse, Tokyo, Made in the USA, Art in the 50s and 60s U. Calif. Berkeley Art Mus., Craft Today Poetry of the Physical, Am. Craft Mus., N.Y.C., Portraits and Homage to Mothers Hecksher Mus. Huntington, 1987; works in collections at Chase Manhattan Bank, N.Y.C., Philip Morris Collection, N.Y.C., Children's Mus., Bklyn., Newark Mus., The Women's House of Detention, Rikers Island, N.Y., The Studio Mus., N.Y.C., High Mus., Atlanta, Guggenheim Mus., Met. Mus. Art, Boston Mus. Fine Arts, MOMA. Author: Tar Beach, 1991, Aunt Harriet's Underground Railroad in the Sky, 1992; contbr. articles to profl. jours. Recipient AAUW travel award to Africa, 1976, Caldecott honor award, Coretta Scott King award best illustrated children's books Tar Beach, 1991; John Simon Guggenheim Meml. Found. Fellowship (painting), 1987, N.Y. Found. for Arts award (painting), 1988, Nat. Endowment Arts award (sculpture) 1978, (painting) 1989, La Napoule Found. award (painting in So. of France) 1990, Arts Internat. award (travel to Morocco) 1992. Office: Marie Brown Assocs 625 Broadway New York NY 10012-2611

RINGLE, BRETT ADELBERT, lawyer; b. Berkeley, Calif., Mar. 17, 1951; s. Forrest A. and Elizabeth V. (Darnall) R.; m. Sue Kinslow, May 26, 1973. B.A., U. Tex., 1973, J.D., 1976. Bar: Tex. 1976, U.S. Dist. Ct. (no. dist.) Tex. 1976, U.S. Supreme Ct. 1980, U.S. Ct. Appeals (5th cir.) 1984. Ptnr., Shank, Irwin & Conant, Dallas, 1976-86, Jones, Day, Reavis & Pogue, Dallas, 1986—; adj. prof. law So. Meth. U., Dallas, 1983. Author: (with J. W. Moore and H. I. Bendix) Moore's Federal Practice, Vol. 12, 1980, Vol. 13, 1981, (with J. W. Moore) Vol. 1A, 1982, Vol. 1A Part 2, 1989. Mem. Dallas Bar Assn. Home: 3514 Gillon Dallas TX 75205 Office: Jones Day Reavis & Pogue 2001 Ross Ave PO Box 660623 Dallas TX 75266

RINGLEE, ROBERT JAMES, consulting engineering executive; b. Sacramento, Apr. 23, 1926; s. Francis and Marie N. R.; m. Helen Laura Carleton, Aug. 27, 1949; children—Sarah N., Jane C., Robert K. B.S.E.E., U. Wash., 1946, M.S.E.E., 1948; Ph.D. in Mechanics, Rensselaer Poly. Inst., 1964. Registered profl. engr., N.Y., Mass. With advanced engring. program Gen. Electric Co., 1948-51, advanced devel. engr., power transformer dept., 1951-55, supr. power transformer design, 1955-60, sr. analytical engr., 1960-65, mgr. system and equipment reliability, 1965-69; prin. engr. dir. Power Technologies, Inc., Schenectady, 1969-86; prin cons. Power Technologies, Inc., 1986-93; TAG assoc. Power Techs., Inc., 1993-94; assoc. cons., 1994—. Contbr. articles to profl. publs. Mem. Schalmont Bd. Edn., 1966-70, pres., 1968-69. Served with USNR, 1944-46. Recipient Managerial award Gen. Electric Co., 1953. Fellow IEEE (3 prize paper awards), AAAS; mem. Internat. Conf. on High Voltage Power Systems (expert advisor, Attwood Assoc.), Adirondack Mountain Club (pres. 1990-93, acting exec. dir. 1994). Democrat. Unitarian. Patentee. Home: 315 Juniper Dr Schenectady NY 12306-1705 Office: PO Box 1058 Schenectady NY 12301-1058

RINGLER, DANIEL HOWARD, lab animal medicine educator; b. Oberlin, Ohio, Aug. 19, 1941. DVM, Ohio State U., 1965; MS, U. Mich., 1969; diploma, Am. Coll. Lab. Animal Medicine, 1971. From instr. to assoc. prof. lab. animal medicine U. Mich., Ann Arbor, 1969-79, prof., 1979—; cons. animal resources br. divsn. rsch. resources NIH, 1973—; mem. adv. coun. inst. lab. animal resource Nat. Rsch. Coun.-NAS, 1975-78. Mem. Am. Assn. Lab. Animal Sci. (Griffin award), Am. Vet. Medicine Assn., Am. Assn. Accreditation Lab. Animal Care. Achievements include research in spontaneous diseases of laboratory animals, use of animals in biomedical research, diseases and husbandry of amphibians, pathogenic bacteriology. Office: U Mich Unit Lab Animal Medicine Animal Rsch Facility Ann Arbor MI 48109

RINGLER, JAMES M., cookware company executive; b. 1945. BS, U. Buffalo, 1967, MBA, 1968. Mgr., cons. Arthur Andersen & Co., 1968-76; v.p. appliance group Tappan Co., Mansfield, Ohio, 1976-78, gen. v.p., mgr. appliance div., 1978-87, pres., chief operating officer, 1987—, also bd. dirs.; pres., COO Premark Internat., Inc., Deerfield, Ill. Office: Premark Internat Inc 1717 Deerfield Rd Deerfield IL 60015 also: Premark Internat Inc 1717 Deerfield Rd Deerfield IL 60015*

RINGLER, LENORE, educational psychologist; d. Albert Haendel and Ida (Brafstein) Haendel; 1 son., Adam. BA, Bklyn. Coll.; MA, Queens Coll., 1954; PhD, NYU, 1965. Tchr., then reading specialist N.Y.C. Bd. Edn.; prof. NYU, 1965—, chair dept. ednl. psychology, 1974-79; ednl. cons. Psychol. Corp., Council on Interracial Books for Children, N.Y.C. Bd. Edn. Author: Skills Monitoring System-Reading, 1977, A Language-Thinking Approach to Reading, 1984; author reading series for Holt Rhinehart & Winston, 1989; contbr. articles to profl. jours. Mem. Citizens Com. for Children; mem. Commn. on Reading Nat. Acad. Edn., 1983-85. Grantee U.S. Office Edn., 1968-69, Newspapers in Edn., 1990. Mem. Am. Psychol. Assn., Am. Ednl. Rsch. Assn., Internat. Reading Assn. (past pres. Manhattan coun.), Nat. Reading Conf. (v.p. 1982-84, pres. 1984-85), Pi Lambda Theta (chpt. fellow 1963-64), Kappa Delta Pi. Office: NYU 239 Greene St Rm 400 New York NY 10003

RINGWOOD, BOB, costume designer. Costume designer: (TV movies) The Corn Is Green, 1979, (films) Excalibur, 1981, The Draughtsman's Contract, 1983, Dune, 1984, Santa Claus: The Movie, 1985, Solarbabies, 1986, Prick Up Your Ears, 1987, Empire of the Sun, 1987 (Academy award nomination best costume design 1987), (with Linda Henrikson) Batman, 1989, Chicago Joe and the Showgirl, 1990, Alien 3, 1992, Batman Returns, 1992, Demolition Man, 1993. Office: care Costume Designer's Guild 13949 Ventura Blvd Ste 309 Sherman Oaks CA 91423*

RINK, LAWRENCE DONALD, cardiologist; b. Indpls., Oct. 14, 1940; s. Joe Donald and Mary Ellen (Rand) R.; m. Eleanor Jane (Zimmerly, Aug. 10, 1963; children: Scott, Virginia. BS, DePauw U., 1962; MD, Ind. U., 1966. Diplomate Am. Bd. Internal Medicine, Am. Bd. Cardiology, Critical Care Medicine. Clin. asst. prof. Ind. U. Med. Sch., Indpls., 1973-79, clin. assoc. prof., 1979-85; clin. prof. med. Ind. Univ. Med. Sch., Indpls., 1985—; cardiologist Internal Medicine Assocs., Bloomington, Ind., 1974—, pres.; dir. cardiac rehab. Bloomington Hosp., 1976—, dir. med. edn. Bloomington Hosp., 1976—; med. dir. Track and Field Pan Am. Games, 1987; U.S. Olympic physician Olympic Sports Festival, 1989, World Univ. Games,

1990, Olympic Games, Barcelona, 1992; N.Am. continent rep. Fed. Internat. Student Univ. Sports. Bd. dirs. J.O. Ritchie Soc., Ind. U. Med. Sch. Bd. dirs., dean's coun. Ind. U. Med. Sch., 1992—. Recipient Quality of Life award Major Bloomington, 1978; named Most Outstanding Flight Surgeon, USN, 1968. Fellow Am. Coll. Cardiology, Am. Heart Assn., Am. Soc. Critical Care, Am. Coll. Sports Medicine; mem. AMA, Ind. U. Med. Alumnae Assn. (pres. 1986-87, exec. alumna coun.). Avocations: reading, writing, golf, tennis. Office: Internal Medicine Assn 719 S Rogers St Bloomington IN 47403-2368

RINK, WESLEY WINFRED, banker; b. Hickory, N.C., June 14, 1922; s. Dewey Lee and Mabel E. (Yount) R.; m. Doreen M. Warman, Sept. 7, 1946; children: Rebecca S., Christopher L. B.S. in Accountancy, U. Ill., 1947, M.S., 1948. Acct., Glidden Co., Chgo., 1948-58; admnstrv. mgr. Central Soya Co., Chgo., 1958-65; v.p., comptroller State Nat. Bank, Evanston, Ill., 1965-71; exec. v.p., dir. Pioneer Trust & Savs. Bank, Chgo., 1971-76; corp. v.p. Exchange Bancorp., Inc., Tampa, 1977-82; sr. v.p. NCNB Nat. Bank Fla., Tampa, 1982-86; fin cons. Temple Terrace, Fla., 1986—; dir. Terr. Bank Fla., Temple Terrace, Lady Lake of the Villages, Lady Lake, Fla. Served to capt. USAAF, 1942-46. Home: 523 Garrard Dr Tampa FL 33617-3819 Office: 5140 E Fowler Ave PO Box 16828 Temple Terrace FL 33687-6828

RINKER, MARSHALL EDISON, SR., cement company executive; b. Cowan, Ind., Dec. 8, 1904; s. Jacob E. and Alberta May (Neff) R.; m. Vera Lea Keesling, Nov. 26, 1925 (dec. Mar. 1985); children: Marshall Edison, David B., John J.; m. Ruby Marian Stewart, Aug. 27, 1987. Student in teaching, Ball State U., 1921-23; HHD (hon.), Palm Beach Atlantic Coll., 1988. With Rinker Materials Corp. (purchased by CSR), 1988; chief exec. officer, chmn. bd. Rinker Materials Corp., West Palm Beach, Fla., 1926-88, chmn. emeritus, 1988-93; chief exec. officer, chmn. bd. Rinker Realty Corp., West Palm Beach, 1988—. Chmn., chief exec. officer M.E. Rinker Sr. Found., Inc., 1988; chmn. West Palm Beach Community Chest, 1954; bd. dirs. West Palm Beach chpt. ARC, 1930-50, Fla. East Coast Industries, 1978—; trustee emeritus Stetson U.; trustee DeLand, Fla., Palm Beach Atlantic coll., 1990; chmn. bd. deacons 1st Bapt. Ch., West Palm Beach, 1960-62. Recipient Free Enterprise medal Palm Beach Atlantic Coll., 1985; named John D. MacArthur Bus. Leader of Yr., 1985; ednl. instns. named in his honor include M.E. Rinker Sr. Sch. Bus. Palm Beach Atlantic Coll., 1989, M.E. Rinker Sr. Sch. Bldg. Constrn. U. Fla., 1989, M.E. Rinker Sr. Inst. Tax and Accountancy Stetson U., 1989. Mem. Nat. Concrete Masonry Assn. (bd. dirs., pres. 1954), Nat. Ready Mixed Concrete Assn. (pres. 1973, Joseph E. Carpenter award 1990), Fla. Concrete and Products Assn. (pres. 1967), West Palm Beach C. of C. (pres. 1954-55), Sigma Lambda Chi. Clubs: Everglades, Old Guard Soc., Govs.' (life) (Palm Beach); Garden of Gods (Colorado Springs, Colo.); Ocean Reef (Key Largo, Fla.); River (Jacksonville, Fla.). Lodge: Rotary (Paul Harris fellow 1988). Avocations: golf, reading. Home: 561 Island Dr Palm Beach FL 33480-4746 Office: 310 Okeechobee Blvd West Palm Beach FL 33401-6432

RINKER, RUBY STEWART, foundation administrator; b. Dayton, Ohio, June 11, 1936; d. Encle Stewart and Addie (Hamilton) Stewart-Smith; children: William Bertram Klawonn, Elizabeth Lynn Dennis, William Stewart-Bradley Klawonn. Human relations counselor Palm Beach County Sch. System, West Palm Beach, Fla., 1974-84; admnstrv. asst. Bohmfalk Estate, Palm Beach, Fla., N.Y.C, Newport, R.I., 1984—; hon. counselor U.S. Naval Acad., U.S. Air Force Acad. Trustee Bohmfalk Charitable Found. Mem. Phi Delta Kappa. Home: 561 Island Dr Palm Beach FL 33480-4746

RINKEVICH, CHARLES FRANCIS, federal official; b. Grand Rapids, Mich., June 28, 1940; s. Peter Paul and Mabel (Knauf) R.; m. Sara Frances Rees, Aug. 2, 1969; children: Charles Francis, Monica. AA, Grand Rapids Jr. Coll., 1960; BS in Police Administrn., Mich. State U., 1962; MPA, Ga. State U., 1985. Patrolman Mich. State U. Police Dept., East Lansing, 1963-65; lt. Savannah (Ga.) Police Dept., 1965-67; law enforcement cons. U. Ga., 1967-68; police mgmt. cons. Internat. Assn. Chiefs Police, Washington, 1968-69; exec. dir. Pa. Crime Commn., Harrisburg, 1969-71; regional admnstr. Law Enforcement Assistance Adminstrn., Justice Dept., Phila., 1971-74, regional admnstr., Atlanta, 1974-83; dir. Fed. Law Enforcement Tng. Ctr., Glynco, Ga., 1983—. Mem. law enforcement exploring com. Boy Scouts Am. Recipient Presdl. Meritorious and Disting. Rank awards. Mem. Nat. Sheriff's Assn., Internat. Assn. Chiefs Police. Office: Dept Treasury Fed Law Enforcement Tr Ctr Glynco GA 31524

RINSCH, CHARLES EMIL, insurance company executive; b. Vincennes, Ind., June 28, 1932; s. Emil and Vera Pearl (White) R.; m. Maryann Elizabeth Hitchcock, June 18, 1964; children: Christopher, Daniel, Carl. BS in Stats., Ind. U., 1953; MS in Bus., Butler U., 1959; MBA, Stanford U., 1960. Budget analyst Chrysler Corp., Indpls., 1955-57; sr. fin. analyst Ford Motor Co., Indpls., 1957-59; budget dir. Nat. Forge Co., Warren, Pa., 1960-61; div. controller and asst. to v.p., fin. Norris Industries, L.A., 1961-65; v.p., treas., sec. Teledyne Inc, L.A., 1965-88; pres., chief exec. officer Argonaut Group Inc., L.A., 1988—. Cubmaster Pack 721, Boy Scouts Am., L.A., 1987-88, treas. 1981-87; mem. dean's adv. coun. Ind. U. Sch. Bus. 1st lt. U.S. Army, 1953-55. Mem. Acad. Alumni Fellows Ind. U. Sch. Bus., L.A. Treas.'s Club. Avocations: photography, travel. Home: 19849 Greenbriar Dr Tarzana CA 91356-5428 Office: Argonaut Group Inc 1800 Ave Of The Stars Ste 1175 Los Angeles CA 90067

RINSLAND, ROLAND DELANO, university official; b. Low Moor, Va., Apr. 11, 1933; s. Charles Henry and Lottie (Parks) R.; AB. with distinction, Va. State U., 1954; A.M., Tchrs. Coll., Columbia U., 1959, profl. diploma, 1960, Ed.D., 1966. Asst. to dean of men Va. State Coll., Petersburg, 1952-54; asst. purchasing agt. Glyco Products Co., Inc., N.Y.C., 1956-57; asst. office of registrar Tchrs. Coll., Columbia U., N.Y.C., 1957-66, tchr. cert. advisor, 1959—, registrar, 1966-71, asst. dean for student affairs, also registrar, dir. office doctoral studies, 1971—; mem. Tchrs. Coll. Devel. Council, 1974-76 91—; rep., presenter of degrees Tchrs. Coll., Japan, 1989, 91, 93, 94. Served to 1st lt. AUS, 1954-56. Designated Important and Valuable Human Resource of USA Am. Heritage Research Assn. First Am. Bicentennium. Mem. N.Y. State Personnel and Guidance Assn., Am. Coll. Personnel Assn., Nat. Soc. Study Edn., Am. Ednl. Research Assn., Middle States, Am. assns collegiate registrars and admission officers (inter-assn. rep. to state edn. depts. on tchr. cert. 1973-74, mem. com. on orgn. and adminstrn. registrars activities 1973, 74-76), Assn. Records Execs. and Admnstrs. (charter mem., by-laws and program chmn. 1969), Am. Acad. Polit. and Social Sci., Am. Assn. Higher Edn., Assn. Instl. Research, Internat. Assn. Applied Psychology, Soc. Applied Anthropology, Am. Assn. Counseling and Devel., Assn. Study of Higher Edn., AAAS, N.Y. Acad. Scis., Met. Opera Guild, NEA (Leah B. Sykes award for life mem.), Scabbard and Blade, Kappa Phi Kappa, Phi Delta Kappa, Kappa Delta Pi. Home: 25 W 68th St New York NY 10023-5302 Office: 525 W 120th St New York NY 10027

RINTELMANN, WILLIAM FRED, audiology educator; b. Chgo., June 22, 1930; s. Henry Detrich and Caroline (Ohlhorst) R.; children by previous marriage: Russell Thomas, Lindsey Ann; m. sandra Jean Baier, Feb. 1, 1986; stepchildren: Robert Walter Hartwick, Richard William Hartwick. BS cum laude, Ariz. State U., 1952, MA, Ind. U., 1957, PhD, 1960; MA (hon.), U. Pa., 1976. asst. prof. U. N.D., Grand Forks, 1959-61; postdoctoral fellow Northwestern U., Evanston, Ill., 1961-63, asst. prof., 1963-66; assoc. prof. Mich. State U., East Lansing, 1966-70, prof., 1970-75; prof., chmn. audiology sect., dept. otorhinolaryngology U Pa. Sch. Medicine, Phila., 1975-80; prof., chmn. audiology dept. Wayne State U. Sch. Medicine, Detroit, 1980—; dir. audiology svc. Harper Hosps. U. Health Ctr., Detroit, 1980—; dir. infant hearing testing program Hutzel Hosp., Detroit, 1986—; dir. Audiology Research Lab. Mich. State U., 1972-75, Speech and Hearing Ctr. Hosp. Univ. Pa., 1976-80. Editor: Hearing Assessment, 1979, 2d edit., 1991; co-editor: Principles of Speech Audiometry, 1983; contbr. articles to profl. jours., chpts. to books. Mem. scientific adv. bd. Nat. Retinitis Pigmentosa Found., 1983—. Served to 1st lt. U.S. Army, 1952-55. Recipient Editor's award Jour. Speech and Hearing Disorders, 1976. Fellow Am. Speech-Lang.-Hearing Assn. (cert. clin. competence in audiology), Am. Acad. Audiology; mem. Am. Auditory Soc. (exec. com. 1986-93), Acad. Rehabilitative Audiology, John Morgan Soc. Republican. Office: Wayne State U Sch Medicine Dept of Audiology 4201 St Antoine St Detroit MI 48201-2194

RINZEL, DANIEL FRANCIS, lawyer; b. Hartford, Wis., Dec. 30, 1942; s. Arthur Zeno and Marie Rose (Lorenz) R.; m. Kathleen Marie Saunders, Aug. 31, 1968 (div. 1987); children—Daniel, Laura, Joseph. B.A., Marquette U., 1965; J.D., U. Wis., 1968. Bar: Wis., 1968, D.C. 1982. Staff atty. Wis. Legis. Council, Madison, 1968-69; trial atty. U.S. Dept. Justice, Washington, 1969-79; chief criminal sect. U.S. Dept. Justice, 1979-83, dep. asst. atty. gen., 1995—; staff dir., chief counsel U.S. Senate Permanent Subcom. on Investigations, 1984-86, chief counsel for minority, 1986-94; adj. faculty Columbia Sch. Law Cath. U. Am., 1989—. Supr. Dane County Bd. Suprs., Wis., 1968-69. Recipient Atty. Gen.'s Disting. Service award U.S. Dept. Justice, 1983. Mem. Wis. Bar Assn., D.C. Bar Assn. Republican. Roman Catholic. Office: Permanent Subcom on Investigations Room 193 Senate Russell Bldg Washington DC 20510

RINZLER, ALLAN, consulting company executive; b. Atlanta, May 18, 1941; s. Harry and Florence (Raab) R.; m. Brenda Joan Schear, Aug. 19, 1962; children: Harley S., S. Barrett. Student, Emory U., 1959-61; %, %, 1962-65; student, Ohio State U., 1961-62; BA, Emory U., 1964, LLB, 1965. CPA; bar: Ga. 1964, U.S. Dist. Ct. Ga. 1965, U.S. Ct. Appeals 1965. Tax sr. Arthur Andersen & Co., Atlanta, 1965-68; v.p. fin. Super Food Svcs., Inc., Dayton, Ohio, 1968-69; v.p. treas. Schearbrook Land and Livestock, Inc., Dayton, 1969-72; pres., chief exec. officer Rinzler and Assocs., Dayton, 1972—; bd. dir. Chapel Electric Co., Dayton 1982—, Dynamic Industris Inc., Detroit 1983-88, DECOR Corp., Columbus 1984-86, So. Calif. Savs., 1984. Trustee Wright State U., Dayton, 1985-94, vice chmn. bd., 1991-92, bd. trustees chmn., 1992-93; bd. dirs., pres. Hillel Acad. Dayton; trustee Friends Clambake Found., Gov. coun., 1988-90. Mem. Ga. Bar Assn., Ga. Soc. CPAs, Meadowbrook Country Club (treas. 1987-88), Gainey Ranch Golf Club, Racquet Club, Beta Gamma Sigma. Jewish. Avocations: golf, bridge. Office: Rinzler & Assocs Inc 230 Talbott Towers Dayton OH 45402

RIOPELLE, ARTHUR JEAN, psychologist; b. Thorp, Wis., Apr. 22, 1920; s. Wilfred Gaspar and Ann Marie (Schroeder) R.; m. Mary Jane Astell, May 2, 1942; children—Mary Ann, James Michael, Jean Elizabeth. B.S., U. Wis., 1941, M.S., 1948, Ph.D., 1950. Asst. prof., then assoc. prof. Emory U., 1950-57; dir. psychology div. U.S. Army Med. Research Lab., Ft. Knox, Ky., 1957-59; dir. Yerkes Labs. Primate Biology, Orange Park, Fla., 1959-62, Delta Regional Primate Research Ctr., Covington, La., 1962-71; prof. psychology La. State U., Baton Rouge, 1972—, Boyd prof., 1977-89, Boyd prof. emeritus, 1989—; mem. NRC panel on manganese, Com. on Med. and Biol. Effects of Environ. Pollutants. Editor: Jour. Gen. Psychology, 1978—; asst. editor: Animal Behavior, 1962-65; cons. editor: Jour. Genetic Psychology and Genetic Psychology Monograph, 1978—; contbr.: chpts. Marvels of Animal Behavior, 1972, Dewsbury's Comparative Psychology, 1973, Orbach's Neuropsychology after Lashley, 1982—, Fitzgerald's Child Nurturance, vol. 3, 1982, Watts' Nonhuman Primate Models for Human Growth and Development, 1985. La. Bd. Examiners of Psychologists, 1972-75; mem. panel on Air Force tng. Nat. Acad. Sci.-NRC, 1955-56; primate research study sect. Am. Inst. Biol. Scis.-NASA, 1959-63; chmn. sub-com. on man Lunar Receiving Lab. Study, 1970-71; chmn. U.S.-Japan Conf. Primate Research, 1963-64; chmn. sub-com. primate standards inst. Lab. Animal Resources, NRC, 1964-69. Served with USAAF, 1942-46, ETO. Mem. Am. Psychol. Assn., Am. Physiol. Soc., Soc. Philosophy and Psychology, Internat. Primatological Soc., AAAS, Psychonomic Soc., Southeastern Psychol. Assn., Sigma Xi, Phi Kappa Phi, Sigma Chi. Home: 9710 Highland Rd Baton Rouge LA 70810-4031 Office: La State U Dept Psychology Baton Rouge LA 70803

RIORDAN, GEORGE NICKERSON, investment banker; b. Patchogue, N.Y., May 16, 1933; s. E. Arthur and Constance E. (Whelden) R.; m. Ann Wiggins, Jan. 4, 1958; children—Susan M., Peter G. B.S., Cornell U., 1955; M.B.A., Harvard U., 1960. Vice-pres. Lehman Bros., N.Y.C., 1960-71; mng. dir. Blyth Eastman Paine Webber, Los Angeles and N.Y.C., 1971-81, Prudential-Bache Securities, Los Angeles, 1981-88, Bear Stearns & Co., Inc., L.A., 1988-89, Dean Writer Reynolds Inc., 1989-91; bd. dirs. MacNea Schwendler Corp., L.A., Pancho's Mexican Buffet, Inc., Ft. Worth, Lewis Galoob Toys, Inc. Served to capt. USAF, 1955-57. Mem. Calif. Club, Quoque Field Club, Athenaeum Club, Valley Hunt Club (Pasadena, Calif.). Office: 3300 Hyland Ave Costa Mesa CA 92626-0820

RIORDAN, JAMES QUENTIN, retired company executive; b. Bklyn., June 17, 1927; s. James A. and Ruth M. (Boomer) R.; m. Gloria H. Carlson, June 23, 1951; children: Harris, Susan, James, Ruth. Ba, Bklyn. Coll., 1945; LLB, Columbia U., 1949. Bar: N.Y. 1951, U.S. Supreme Ct 1954. Atty. Winthrop, Stimson, Putnam & Roberts, N.Y.C., 1949-51; mem. staff Ways and Means sub-com., Washington, 1951-52; atty. tax div. Justice Dept., Washington, 1952-55; atty. Chadbourne, Parke, Whiteside & Wolff, N.Y.C., 1955-57; various positions to vice chmn., chief fin. officer Mobil Corp., 1957-89; pres. Bekaert Corp., 1989-92; ret., 1992; bd. dirs. Dow Jones & Co., Inc., The Bklyn. Union Gas Co., Tri-Continental Corp. and other J & W Seligman mutual funds, Pub. Broadcasting Svc. Bd. dirs. Com. Econ. Devel., Tax Foun., Inc.; trustee Bklyn. Mus. Mem. Rembrandt Club (N.Y.C.), Blind Brook Club, Sailfish Point (Fla.). Office: 675 3rd Ave New York NY 10017-5704

RIORDAN, JOHN FRANCIS, oil and gas corporate executive; b. Medina, N.Y., Jan. 12, 1936; s. Francis J. and Harriet (Stork) R.; m. Judith Kathryn Wokna, Feb. 5, 1967; children: Michael, Timothy, Allison. B.A. in Chemistry, Niagara U., 1958; M.B.A., SUNY-Buffalo, 1975. Chemist Durez div. Occidental Chem. Corp., North Tonawanda, N.Y., 1958-61, field sales rep., 1961-67; product mgmr. Durez div. Occidental Chem. Corp., North Tonawanda, N.Y., 1967-75; dir. corp. devel. Occidental Chem. Corp., Grand Island, N.Y., 1965-76; v.p., gen. mgr. internat. Occidental Chem. Corp., Niagara Falls, N.Y., 1976-78, v.p., gen. mgr. ECD, Hooker Chems. Plastic Corp., 1978-80, v.p. employee rels. Hooker Corp., Houston, 1980-81, pres. ICG, Hooker Corp., 1981-85; exec. v.p. Occidental Chem. Corp., Niagara Falls, 1985-86; exec. v.p. NGL Group Cities Service Oil & Gas Corp., Tulsa, 1986-88; pres. MidCon Corp., Lombard, Ill., 1988, chief exec. officer, 1990—; exec. v.p. Occidental Petroleum Corp., 1990—; dir. Occidental Petroleum Corp. Roman Catholic. Office: MidCon Corp 701 E 22nd St Lombard IL 60148-5009

RIORDAN, RICHARD J., mayor; b. Flushing, N.Y., 1930; m. Eugenia Riordan; 6 children (2 dec.); m. Jill Riordan. Attended, U. Calif., Santa Clara; grad., Princeton U., 1952; JD, U. Mich., 1956. With O'Melveny & Myers, L.A.; owner, operator Original Pantry Cafe; founder Total Pharmaceutical Care, Tetra Tech; mayor L.A., 1993—. Co-founder LEARN, 1991; sponsor Writing to Read computer labs Riordan Found.; active Eastside Boys and Girls Club. Lt. U.S. Army, Korea. Office: Los Angeles City Hall 200 N Spring St Los Angeles CA 90012-4801*

RIORDAN, WILLIAM F., lawyer; b. Wichita, Kans., Mar. 26, 1941. B.B.A., U. N.Mex., 1965, J.D., 1968. Bar: N.Mex. 1968, U.S. Tax Ct. 1972, U.S. Supreme Ct. 1971. Legal aid atty. Albuquerque, 1968-69; asst. atty. gen. N.Mex., 1969; asst. dist. atty. Bernalillo County, N.Mex., 1969-72; judge 2d Jud. Dist. of N.Mex., Albuquerque, 1972-80; justice N.Mex. Supreme Ct., Santa Fe, 1980-85; chief justice N.Mex. Supreme Ct., 1986-87; pvt. practice law Albuquerque, 1987—. Office: 20 First Plaza Ctr NW Ste 402 Albuquerque NM 87102-3351

RIORDAN, JOHN BERNARD, museum director; b. Bathurst, N.B., Can., Dec. 4, 1947; s. Thomas Francis and Mary Antoinette (Quinn) R.; m. Marie Lilliane Theriault, June 14, 1973; children: Melissa, Thomas, Edward, Jillian. BA, St. thomas U., Fredericton, N.B. 1970; postgrad., St. Mary's U., Halifax, N.S., 1973. Gallery asst. St. Mary's U. Art Gallery, Halifax, 1971-73; curator Centennial Art Gallery, N.S. Mus. Fine Arts, Halifax, 1973-75; dir. Art Gallery N.S., Halifax, 1975—; expert examiner (fine art) Cultural Property Export and Import Rev. Bd., Ottawa, 1986-90. Author: (exhbn. catalogs) Francis Silver, 1982, C. Anthony Law: A Retrospective, 1989, Nova Scotia Folk Art: Canada's Cultural Heritage, 1989. Past chmn. Jr. Achievement Halifax, 1982; past chmn. bldg. com. Children's Aid soc., 1986; mem. Art Allocation Com., Halifax, 1987-89. Recipient art mus. tour of U.S. U.S. Info. Agy., 1986. Mem. Visual Arts Nova Scotia (ad hoc), Internat. Coun. Museums, Can. Museums Assn., Can. Art Mus. Dirs. Assn. (treas. 1986-89), The Smithsonian Instn., Arts atlantic (Charlottetown, adv. bd. 1980-90), Am. Assn. Museums, Halifax Bd. Trade. Avocations:

gardening, farming, woodworking. Home: 25 Crestview Dr, Halifax, NS Canada B3P 1G1 Office: Art Gallery NS, 1741 Hollis St at Cheapside, Halifax, NS Canada B3J 3C8

RIOS, ALBERTO ALVARO, English educator; b. Nogales, Ariz., Sept. 18, 1952; s. Alberto Alvaro and Agnes (Fogg) R.; m. Maria Guadalupe Barron, Sept. 8, 1979; 1 child, Joaquin. BA in Lit. & Creative Writing with honor, U. Ariz., 1974, BA in Psychology with honors, 1975, MFA in Creative Writing, 1979. Asst. prof. English Ariz. State U., Tempe, 1982-85, assoc. prof., 1985-89, prof., 1989—, dir. creative writing program, 1986-89, 92—; mem. editorial bd. New Chicano Writing, 1990—; corr. editor Manoa, 1989—; bd. dirs. Libr. of Congress/Ariz. Ctr. for the Book, 1988—, vice chair, 1989—. Author: Elk Heads on the Wall, 1979, Sleeping on Fists, 1981, Whispering to Fool the Wind, 1982, The Iguana Killer, 1984, Five Indiscretions, 1985, The Lime Orchard Woman, 1988, The Warrington Poems, 1989, Teodoro Luna's Two Kisses, 1990 (Pulitzer prize nomination); editor Ploughshares, 1991-92, advisory editor, 1992—; poetry editor Colorado Review, 1993; editorial bd. New Chicana/Chicano Writing, 1990—, Equinox, 1992—; contbr. poems and stories to numerous jours. and anthologies. Guggenheim fellow, 1988-89; recipient Western States Book award for Fiction, Walt Whitman award Acad. Am. Poets, Pushcart Prize, 1986, 88, 89, 93, Community Appreciation award Chicanos Por La Causa, 1988, Gov.'s Arts award State of Ariz., 1991; named Author of Yr. Mountain Plains Libr. Assn., 1991; NEA fellow; Ariz. State U. grantee. Office: Ariz State U Dept English Tempe AZ 85287-0302

RIOS, EVELYN DEERWESTER, columnist, musician, artist, writer; b. Payne, Ohio, June 25, 1916; d. Jay Russell and Flossie Edith (Fell) Deerwester; m. Elden Tietjen Rios, Sept. 19, 1942 (dec. Feb. 1987); children: Jane Evelyn, Linda Sue Rios Stahlman. BA with honors, San Jose State U., 1964, MA, 1968. Cert. elem., secondary tchr., Calif. Lectr. in music San Jose State U., 1969-75; bilingual cons., then assoc. editor Ednl. Factors, Inc., San Jose, 1969-76, mgr. field research, 1977-78; writer, editor Calif. MediCorps Program, 1978-85; contbg. editor, illustrator The Community Family Mag., Wimberly, Tex., 1983-85; columnist The Springer, Dripping Springs, Tex., 1985-90; author, illustrator, health instr. textbooks elem. schs., 1980-82. Choir dir. Bethel Luth. Ch., Cupertino, Calif., 1965-83; organist Holy Spirit Episc. Ch., Dripping Springs, Tex., 1987-94; music dir. Cambrian Park (Calif.) Meth. Ch., 1961-64; chmn. planning and zoning commn. City of Dripping Springs, 1991-93. Mem. AAUW, Am. Guild Organists (dean 1963-64), Phi Kappa Phi (pres. San Jose chpt. 1973-74). Episcopalian. Avocations: weaving, stitching, painting. Home and Office: 23400 FM 150 Dripping Springs TX 78620

RIOUX, CLAUDE, economics educator; b. Tracadie, N.B., Can., Sept. 4, 1955; s. Joseph and Yvonne (Mercure) R.; m. Sylvaine Gesseaume, July 26, 1982; children: Marie, Camille, Mathilde. B Social Sci., U. Moncton, N.B., 1977, MSc in Econs., 1978; D Econs. Sci., U. Dijon, France, 1982. Prof. dept. econs. and mgmt. U. Que. (Can.), Rimouski, 1991—, head dept., 1991—. Office: University of Quebec, 300 Allee des Ursulines, Rimouski, PQ Canada G5L 3A1

RIPKEN, CALVIN EDWIN, JR. (CAL RIPKEN), professional baseball player; b. Havre de Grace, Md., Aug. 24, 1960. Baseball player minor league teams Bluefield, Miami, Charlotte, Rochester, 1978-81; baseball player Balt. Orioles, 1978—. Recipient Rookie of Yr. award Internat. League, 1981, Rookie of Yr. award Baseball Writers Assn., Am. League, 1982; named Am. League Rookie of the Yr. The Sporting News, 1982, Player of the Yr., 1983, 91, Am. League Most Valuable Player, 1983;91; Major League Player of Yr., The Sporting News, 1983, 91; named to Am. League All-Star Team, 1983-94; recipient Gold Glove award, 1991-92; recipient Silver Slugger award, 1983-86, 89, 91, 93-94. Second player to play in 2,000 consecutive games. Office: care Balt Orioles Memorial Stadium 333 W Camden St Baltimore MD 21201*

RIPLEY, EDWARD FRANKLIN, investment company executive; b. Cohasset, Mass., June 26, 1927; s. Sheldon Nichols Ripley and Marguerite (Albertson) Giles; m. Elizabeth Robertson Tucker, Dec. 19, 1964; children: Peter Hobart, Elizabeth Stockton. BA, Lafayette Coll., 1950; MA, Columbia U., 1953; cert. Sch. of Banking of South, La. State U., 1961. Sr. investment officer Mfrs. Hanover Bank, N.Y.C., 1953-57, Va. Nat. Bank, Norfolk, 1957-61; v.p. Studley, Shupert & Co., Phila., 1961-69; pres. Resource Mgmt. Group, Phila., 1969-72; v.p. First Pa. Bank, Phila., 1972-79; adj. prof. Phila. Coll. Textiles and Sci., 1979-91; v.p. Gruntal & Co./E.W. Smith, Phila., 1979-82, Legg, Mason, Wood, Walker, Inc., Phila., 1982-91; v.p. Walnut Asset Mgmt. Inc. Phila., 1991—; cons. Educator Mut. Life Ins. Co., Lancaster, Pa., 1972—, Cigna Corp. Phila., 1980-82, Oppenheimer Capital Corp., N.Y.C., 1981, Meridian Bancorp., Reading, Pa., 1984-85. Vestryman, St. Martin-in-the-Fields Episcopal Ch., Phila., 1980; treas. Voyage House, Phila., 1983; bd. dirs. All Saints Hosp. and Springfield Retirement Home, Phila., Planned Parenthood of Pa.; convener, Ea. Pa. Episc. Synod of Am. Fellow Fin. Analysts Fedn.; mem. Phila. Securities Assn., Mayflower Soc., Soc. Colonial Wars, Mil. Order Fgn. Wars. Republican. Avocations: tennis; tree farming; hiking. Home: 300 W Gravers Ln Philadelphia PA 19118-3715 Office: Walnut Asset Mgmt Inc Ste 500 One Penn Ctr Philadelphia PA 19103

RIPLEY, RANDALL BUTLER, political scientist, educator; b. Des Moines, Jan. 24, 1938; s. Henry Dayton and Aletha (Butler) R.; m. Grace A. Franklin, Oct. 15, 1974; children: Frederick Joseph, Vanessa Gail. B.A., DePauw U., 1959; M.A., Harvard, 1961, Ph.D, 1963. Teaching fellow Harvard, 1960-62; mem. staff Brookings Inst., Washington, 1963-67; research asst. Brookings Inst., 1963-64, research assoc., 1964-67; intern Office of Democratic Whip, U.S. Ho. of Reps., Washington, 1963; assoc. prof. dept. polit. sci. Ohio State U., Columbus, 1967-69, prof., 1969—, chmn., 1969-91, dean Coll. Social and Behavioral Scis., 1992—; lectr. Cath. U., Washington, 1963-64; professorial lectr. Am. U., Washington, 1964-67; vis. prof. U. Okla., 1969-91. Author: Public Policies and Their Politics, 1966, Party Leaders in the House of Representatives, 1967, Majority Party Leadership in Congress, 1969, Power in the Senate, 1969, The Politics of Economic and Human Resource Development, 1972, Legislative Politics U.S.A., 1973, American National Government and Public Policy, 1974, Congress: Process and Policy, 1975, 4th edit., 1988, Policy-making in the Federal Executive Branch, 1975, Congress, the Bureaucracy, and Public Policy, 1976, 5th edit., 1991, National Government and Policy in the United States, 1977, A More Perfect Union, 1979, 4th edit., 1989, Policy Implementation and Bureaucracy, 1982, 2d edit., 1986, CETA: Politics and Policy, 1973-82, 1984, Policy Analysis in Political Science, 1985, Readings in American Government and Politics, 1989, 2d edit. 1993, Congress Resurgent, 1993; contbr. articles to profl. jours. Active various polit. campaigns. Woodrow Wilson fellow, 1959-60; Danforth fellow, 1959-63; recipient Sumner prize Harvard, 1963. Mem. Am. Polit. Sci. Assn. (sec. 1978), Midwest Polit. Sci. Assn., Phi Beta Kappa. Democrat. Home: 2685 Berwyn Rd Columbus OH 43221-3207

RIPLING, EDWARD JOSEPH, metallurgical engineer, researcher; b. Lewistown, Pa., Feb. 25, 1921; s. Hyman and Edith (Koons) R.; m. Marcella Hansburg, July 4, 1943; children: James Martin, Earl Michael, Nancy Faith. BS in Metallurgy, Pa. State U., 1942; MS in Metallurgy, Case Western Reserve U., 1948, PhD in Metallurgy, 1952. Metallurgist Westinghouse Electric Mfg. & Co., E. Pitts., 1942-43, Copperweld Steel Co., Glassport, Pa., 1943-44; asst. prof. Case Western Reserve U., Cleve., 1946-55; lab. dir. Continental Can Co., Chgo., 1955-60; pres., dir. rsch. Materials Rsch. Lab., Glenwood, Ill., 1960—; mem. Nat. Materials Adv. Bd. Com., Washington; chmn. various Blue Ribbon Panels for Projection Malfunction, U.S. Army. Co-author: (with N.H. Polakowski) Strength and Structure of Engineering Materials, 1966; contbr. more than 70 articles to profl. jours. With U.S. Navy, 1944-46, PTO. Recipient David McFarland award, Pa. State U., State Coll. Pa., 1984. Fellow Am. Soc. for Metals. Republican. Jewish. Achievements include 8 patents on various aspects of metal forming. Home: 2051 Cummings Ln Flossmoor IL 60422-1310 Office: Materials Rsch Lab Inc 2051 Cummings Ln Flossmoor IL 60422-1310

RIPPE, PETER MARQUART, museum administrator; b. Mpls., Dec. 16, 1937; s. Henry Albert and Gladis (Marquart) R.; m. Maria Boswell Wornom, Aug. 10, 1968. BA, U. Puget Sound, 1960; MA, U. Del., 1962. Dir. Confederate Mus., Richmond, Va., 1962-68; exec. dir. Harris County Her-

itage Soc., Houston, 1968-79, Roanoke Mus. Fine Arts (Va.), 1979-89, P. Buckley Moss Mus., Waynesboro, Va., 1989—; mem. Roanoke Arts Commn., 1983-90. Fellow Old Deerfield Found., 1958, H.F. duPont Winterthur Mus., 1960-62, chmn. Blue Ridge TV, Roanoke; bd. dirs. Augusta-Staunton-Waynesboro Visitors Bur. Mem. Am. Assn. Mus. (chmn. small mus. com. 1981-83, sr. examiner, 1983—, councillor-at-large 1985-88), Tex. Assn. Mus. (pres. 1975-77, Tex. award 1979), Va. Assn. Mus. (pres. 1983-84), Southeast Mus. Conf. (chmn. awards com. 1986-89), Rotary (Waynesboro chpt.), Waynesboro Club. Democrat. Lutheran. Home: 149 Brook Ct Waynesboro VA 22980-5559 Office: P Buckley Moss Mus 2150 Rosser Ave Waynesboro VA 22980-9406

RIPPEL, CLARENCE W., academic administrator. Acting pres. Lincoln U. Office: Lincoln U Office of President 281 Masonic Ave San Francisco CA 94118

RIPPEL, HARRY CONRAD, mechanical engineer, consultant; b. Phila., Feb. 19, 1926; s. Philip and Emma (Metzger) R.; m. Dorothy Ann Tartala, Nov. 20, 1948; children—Linda Jean, Richard Peter. B.M.E., Drexel U., Phila., 1952, M.S., 1957. Registered profl. engr., Pa. With Franklin Research Center, div. Franklin Inst., Phila., 1952-87, Inst. fellow, 1978—; cons. in tribology, 1987—; resident consultant Rotor Bearing Tech. & Software Inc., 1987—; mem. Com. on Sci. and the Arts, Franklin Inst., Phila. Author manuals and articles in field. Active local Boy Scouts Am.; Sunday sch. tchr.; layreader St. James Episcopal Ch., Phila.; bd. dirs. Turbo Rsch. Found. Served with AUS, World War II, ETO. Decorated Bronze Star. Fellow ASME, Soc. Tribologists and Lubrication Engrs.; mem. Sigma Xi, Pi Tau Sigma. Home: 1434 Sharon Park Dr Sharon Hill PA 19079-2218 Office: Rotor Bearing Tech & Software Inc Lee Park 1100 E Hector St Consholhocken PA 19428-2374

RIPPEL, JEFFREY ALAN, library director; b. Moberly, Mo., June 19, 1945; s. Charles Kenneth and Mildred Agnes (Dodge) R.; m. Mary Elizabeth Burton, Oct. 25, 1969; children: Sarah, Andrew. BA, Fla. State U., 1967; MLS, U. Tex., 1973. Cert. county librarian, Tex., profl. librarian, S.C. Br. librarian Waco (Tex.) Pub. Library, 1974-76; dir. Victoria (Tex.) Pub. Library, 1976-78; dep. dir. Greenville (S.C.) County Library, 1978-81; dir. Longview (Tex.) Pub. Library, 1981-88, Lubbock (Tex.) City-County Library, 1988—. Contbr. articles to profl. jours. Bd. dirs. Lubbock Area Coalition for Literacy. Capt. USAF, 1967-72. Mem. ALA, Tex. Library Assn., Lubbock Area Library Assn. (past pres.), Rotary. Home: 2627 22nd St Lubbock TX 79410-1615 Office: Lubbock City-County Libr 1306 9th St Lubbock TX 79401-2798

RIPPETEAU, DARREL DOWNING, architect; b. Clay Center, Nebr., Jan. 14, 1917; s. Claude LaVerne and Eva (Downing) R.; m. Donna Doris Hiatt, Jan. 8, 1939 (dec. 1988); children: Bruce Estes, Darrel Downing, Jane Upson Heffron; m. Joyce Spencer, May 18, 1991. B.A. in Architecture, U. Nebr., 1941. Staff architect FHA, Omaha, 1941-42; project mgr., mng. ptnr. Sargent-Webster-Crenshaw & Folley, Archs. and Engrs., Watertown, Buffalo, Syracuse, N.Y., Burlington, Vt, Bangor, Maine, 1946-81; treas., dir. Empire Forest System, Albany, N.Y., 1984-89; ret., 1990; bd. dirs. Archtl. Corp. Atlanta, Key Bank No. N.Y., Watertown. Assn. Island Recreational Corp.; commr. N.Y. State Coun. Architecture, U. Nebr., 1975-85; mem. N.Y. State Forest Practice Bd., 1980—, chmn., 1994-96; nat. adv. bd. mem. Remington Art Mus., Ogdensburg, N.Y., 1983—. Prin. works include Justice Bldg, Albany, N.Y. State Office Bldg Watertown, Toomey Abbott Towers Syracuse, State U. N.Y. Cortland, U.S. P.O. Facility Syracuse. Mem. nat. fin. com. Rep. Party, 1971-73; bd. dirs. The Antique Boat Mus., Clayton, N.Y., 1973—, Glenn Curtiss Mus., Hammondsport, N.Y. Maj. U.S. Army, 1942-46; lt. col. Corps of Engrs. Recipient North Country citation St. Lawrence U., Canton, N.Y., 1971; Sears-Roebuck scholar, 1936-37; U. Nebr. Dept. Architecture grantee, 1940-41; Nebr. master U. Nebr., 1971. Fellow AIA (nat. dir. 1969-73, trustee AIA Found. 1972-76); mem. Greater Watertown C. of C. (past pres.), N.Y. State Assn. Indsl. Devel. Agencies (past v.p.), N.Y. State Assn. Architects (pres. 1968-69, polit. action com. 1980—), Bldg. Research Inst., Res. Officers Assn. (past pres.), Am. Tree Farm Assn., Jefferson County Hist. Soc. (dir. 1974-78), OX-5 Aviation Pioneers (chpt. pres.), Assn. U.S. Army (chpt. pres. 1985-86). Republican. Presbyterian. Home: 1011 NW 3rd Ave Delray Beach FL 33444 Home and Studio: River Oaks 45650 Landon Rd Wellesley Island NY 13640-9722

RIPPEY, DONALD TAYLOR, education educator; b. Aztec, N.Mex., Jan. 1, 1927; s. Charles Elwell and Lydia (Hulbert) R.; m. Margaret Simonton, Dec. 18, 1968 (div.); children: John, Jane Parson; m. Gwen Oglesby Rippey; children: Gary, Albert, Kim, Kelly Hall. BA, U. N.Mex., 1950, MA, 1952; EdD, U. No. Colo., 1963. Cert. tchr., adminstr. N.Mex., Wash. Tchr. Roswell (N.Mex.) Jr. High Sch., 1950-53; prin. Washington Elem. Sch., Roswell, 1953-61; dir. Roswell Community Coll., 1958-62; pres. Columbia Basin Coll., Pasco, Wash., 1962-66, El Centro Coll., Dallas, 1966-76; prof. edn. adminstrn. U. Tex., 1976-90, W.K. Kellogg prof., 1990-94, prof. emeritus, 1994—; acting pres. U. Tex.-Permian Basin, Odessa, 1982-83; exec. dir. Nat. Coun. C.C. Bus. Ofcls., 1984-89. Author: Some Called It Camelot, 1987; (monograph) What is Student Development, 1981; contbr. articles on tech. and devel. edn. to profl. jours.; mem. editorial bd. Jour. Devel. Edn., 1979-95. Chmn. bd. dirs. Dallas Young Adult Inst., 1969-74; pres. Benton/Franklin Mental Health Assn., Pasco, 1964, Dallas Council on Alcoholism, 1973. Served as cpl. USAF, 1944-46, PTO. Recipient Appreciation award Ala. Dept. Postsecondary Edn., 1986, Disting. Service award Council Colls. and Univs., Washington, 1987, Master Tchr. award Nat. Inst. award Staff and Organizational Devel., 1989. Mem. Phi Delta Kappa. Methodist. Avocations: reading, traveling, hunting, fishing. Home: 6110 Mountainclimb Dr Austin TX 78731-3824 Office: Univ of Tex at Austin Dept of Edn Adminstrn Univ Station Austin TX 78712

RIPPLE, HELEN BERNICE, nursing administrator; b. Rochester, Minn., Jan. 22, 1936; d. Alexander Morris and Mary Magdalen (Marcus) R. BSN, St. Louis U., 1968, MSN, 1970. Rn, Mo., Va., Calif. Assoc. adminstr./dir. nursing City Hosp., St. Louis, 1969-73; dir. nursing U. Va. Med. Ctr., Charlottesville, 1974-80; assoc. adminstr./dir. nursing, clin. prof. U. Calif. Med. Ctr., San Francisco, 1980—; mem. Blue Ribbon Com. on Long Term Care, San Francisco; mem. Commr's com. JointCommn. on Accreditation Healthcare Orgn., 1988—. With USAF, 1965-69, col. USAR. Mem. Am. Nurses Assn. (cert. in nursing adminstrn.), Calif. Nurses Assn., Va. Nurses Assn., Am. Orgn. Nurse Execs. (pres. 1984-85), Am. Assn. Nurse Administrs. (pres. Va. chpt. 1977), Am. Hosp. Assn., Nat. League Nurses, Va. Hosp. Assn., Golden Gate Nurses Assn. Republican. Roman Catholic. Home: 1 Hoffman Ave San Francisco CA 94114 Office: U Calif Med Ctr 505 Parnassus Ave San Francisco CA 94143-6505

RIPPLE, KENNETH FRANCIS, federal judge; b. Pitts., May 19, 1943; s. Raymond John and Rita (Holden) R.; m. Mary Andrea DeWeese, July 27, 1968; children: Gregory, Raymond, Christopher. AB, Fordham U., 1965; JD, U. Va. 1968; LLM, George Washington U., 1972, LLD (hon.), 1992. Bar: Va. 1968, N.Y. 1969, U.S. Supreme Ct. 1972, D.C. 1976, Ind. 1984, U.S. Ct. Appeals (7th cir.), U.S. Ct. Mil. Appeals, U.S. Dist. Ct. (no. dist.) Ind. Atty. IBM Corp., Armonk, N.Y., 1968; legal officer U.S. Supreme Ct., Washington, 1972-73, spl. asst. to chief justice Warren E. Burger, 1973-77; prof. law U. Notre Dame, 1977—; judge U.S. Ct. Appeals (7th cir.), South Bend, 1985—; reporter Appellate Rules Com., Washington, 1978-85; commn. on mil. justice U.S. Dept. Def., Washington, 1984-85; cons. Supreme Ct. Ala., 1983, Calif. Bd. Bar Examiners, 1981; cons. Anglo-Am. Jud. Exch., 1977, mem., 1980; adv. com. Bill of Rights to Bicentennial Constn. Commn., 1989; mem. adv. com. on appellate rules Jud. Conf. U.S., 1985-90, chmn. 1990-93. Author: Constitutional Litigation, 1984. Mem. bd. visitors 208 US Courthouse 204 S Main St South Bend IN 46601-2122 also: Fed Bldg 219 S Dearborn St Apt 2660 Chicago IL 60604-1803

RIPPLEY, ROBERT, wholesale distribution executive; b. 1968. BS in Bus. pub. adminstrn., U. Mo., 1972. Exec. v.p., CEO Affiliated Food Stores Inc., Tulsa, Okla., 1989—. Office: Affiliated Food Stores Inc 4433 W 49th St Tulsa OK 74107*

RIPPON, THOMAS MICHAEL, art educator, artist; b. Sacramento, Apr. 1, 1954; s. Samuel Joseph Jr. and June Evelyn (Garnet) R.; m. Sarah Sterrett, Dec. 22, 1980; children: Adam Michael, Peter Thomas. MFA, Art Inst. Chgo., 1979. Instr. Columbia Coll., Chgo., 1978-79; asst. prof. Montana State U., Bozeman, 1980, Calif. State U., Sacramento, 1981; assoc. prof. Tenn. Tech. U., Cookeville, 1982-87; asst. prof. U. Nev., Reno, 1987-89; assoc. prof. U. Montana, Missoula, 1989—, chair dept. art, 1990—; artist in residence U. Nevada, Reno, 1988; vis. prof. U. Calif., Davis, 1989; lectr. in field, 1973—. Solo exhbns. include Quay Gallery, San Francisco, 1975, 77, 81, 85, Rochester (Minn.) Art Ctr., 1979, Betsy Rosenfield Gallery, Chgo. 1980, 82, 84, Drake U., Des Moine, Iowa, 1985, Cross Creek Gallery, Malibu, Calif., 1987, 88, Judith Weintraub Gallery, Sacramento, 1990, Huntington (W.Va.) Mus. Art, 1991, Kohler Art Ctr., Sheboygan, Wis., 1992, Yellowstone Art Ctr., Billings, Mont., 1993, Missoula Mus. Arts, 1994, others; group exhbns. include San Francisco Mus. Modern Art, 1972, Davis (Calif.) Art Ctr., 1973, Oakland Mus., 1974, Evanston (Ill.) Art Ctr., 1974, Fendrick Gallery, Washington, 1975, Campbell Mus., Camden, N.J., 1976, Montana State U., Bozeman, 1976, De Young Mus., San Francisco, 1978, Am. Craft Mus., N.Y.C., 1978, 81, Phila. Mus. Modern Art, 1980, Craft and Folk Mus., L.A., 1980, Indpls. Mus. Art, 1982, Impressions Today Gallery, Boston, 1982, Elements Gallery, N.Y.C., 1983, Tampa (Fla.) Mus., 1983, Hyde Park Art Ctr., Chgo., 1983, 85, Traver-Sutton Gallery, Seattle, 1984, Erie (Pa.) Art Mus., 1985, Fay Gold Gallery, Atlanta, 1986, Seattle Art Mus., 1987, Candy Store Art Gallery, Folsom, Calif., 1987, Crocker Art Mus., Sacramento, 1988, Lang Gallery Scripps Coll., Claremont, Calif., 1988, Sherley Koteen & Assoc., Washington, 1989, 90, Eve Mannes Gallery, Atlanta, 1989, Art Gallery Western Australia, 1989, Joanne Rapp Gallery, Scottsdale, 1990, Missoula Mus. of Arts, 1991, 92, Sutton West Gallery, Missoula, 1992, Yellowstone Art Ctr., 1992, Natsoulas Gallery, Davis, Calif., 1993, many others; represented in pvt. collections; pub. collections include San Francisco Mus. Art, L.A. County Mus. Art, Sheldon Meml. Collection U. Nebr., Mus. Fine Arts, Salt Lake City, Ch. Fine Arts Collection U. Nev., Reno, Kanzawa-Shi, Hokkoku Shinbun, Kyoto, Japan, Renwick Gallery Smithsonian Institution, Contemporary Art Mus., Honolulu, J.B. Speed Art Mus., Louisville, Ky., U. Iowa, Ames, Missoula Mus. Arts, others. Recipient Kingsley Art Club award Crocker Art Mus., Sacramento, 1971, Crocker-Kingsley award, 1972; NEA fellow, 1974, 81, Nelson Raymond fellow Art Inst. Chgo., 1979. Office: Univ of Montana Dept Of Art Missoula MT 59812

RIPPS, RODNEY, artist; b. N.Y.C., Dec. 6, 1950; m. Helene Verin. Student, Hunter Coll., 1974; B.A., York Coll., 1972. Exhibited one man shows Nancy Lurie Gallery, Chgo., 1976, 1977; exhibited one man shows Brooke Alexander Gallery, Chgo., 1977, 1978; exhibited one man shows Galerie Daniel Templon, Paris, 1978, 1980, 1982; exhibited one man shows Gallery Bruno Bishofberger, Zurich, 1979, Galerie Hans Mayer, Dusseldorf, W.Ger., 1979, 1980; exhibited one man shows Holly Solomon Gallery, N.Y.C., 1980, 1981; exhibited one man shows Galeri Walmer, Malmo, Sweden, 1980, Akira Ikeda Gallery, Nagoya, Japan, 1981, Galleria Schema, Florence, Italy, Dart Gallery, Chgo., Gallery 121, Antwerp, Belguim, Gallery G7, Blogna, Italy, 1982, Munson-Williams Procter Inst., Utica, N.Y., 1983, Carl Solway Gallery, Cin., 1983, Carnegie Mellon U., Pitts., 1984, Marisa Del Re Gallery, N.Y.C., 1985; group shows Whitney Bienial, 1979, Venice Bienial, 1980. Nat. Endowment Arts grantee, 1980. Home: 350 Stockbridge Rd Lenox MA 01240

RIPPY, FRANCES MARGUERITE MAYHEW, English educator; b. Ft. Worth, Sept. 16, 1929; d. Henry Grady and Marguerite Christine (O'Neill) Mayhew; m. Noble Merrill Rippy, Aug. 29, 1955 (dec. Sept. 1980); children: Felix O'Neill, Conrad Mayhew, Marguerite Hailey. BA, Tex. Christian U., 1949; MA, Vanderbilt U., 1951, PhD, 1957; postgrad., U. London, 1952-53. Instr. Tex. Christian U., 1953-55; instr. to asst. prof. Lamar State U., 1955-59; asst. prof. English Ball State U., Muncie, Ind., 1959-64; assoc. prof. English, Ball State U., 1964-68, prof., 1968—; dir. grad. studies in English, 1966-87; editor Ball State U. Forum, 1960-89; vis. asst. prof. Sam Houston State U., 1957; vis. lectr., prof. U. P.R., summers 1959, 60, 61; exch. prof. Westminster Coll., Oxford, Eng., 1988; cons.-evaluator North Cen. Assn. Colls. and Schs., 1973—, commn.-at-large, 1987-91; cons.-evaluator New Eng. Assn. Schs. and Colls., 1983. Author: Matthew Prior, 1986; contbr. articles to profl. jours., encys., ref. guides, chpts. to anthology; contbr. to Dictionary of Literary Biography. Recipient McClintock award, 1966; Danforth grantee 1964, Ball State U. Rsch. grantee, 1960, 62, 70, 73, 76, 87, 88, 89, 90, 92, 93, 95, Lilly Libr. Rsch. 1978; Fulbright scholar U. London, 1952-53; recipient Outstanding Faculty award Ball State U., 1992, Phi Delta Kappa Rsch grants 1992, 94. Mem. MLA, AAUP, Coll. English Assn, Nat. Coun. Tchrs. English, Am. Soc. 18th Century Studies, Am. Fedn. Tchrs., Ind. Coll. English Assn. (pres. 1984-85, Ind. Tchr./Scholar of 1994), Johnson Soc. Midwest (sec. 1961-62). Home: 4709 W Jackson St Muncie IN 47304-3514 *I have found all of the worlds which the above biographical paragraph touches upon—familial, academic, literary—lively and stimulating and thoroughly satisfying. Each world demands a great deal and offers a great deal in return.*

RIPSTEIN, CHARLES BENJAMIN, surgeon; b. Winnipeg, Man., Can., Dec. 13, 1913; came to U.S., 1949; s. Hyman Mendel and Bertha (Benjamin) R.; m. Barbara Adelman, Dec. 26, 1950; children: Ellen Joan, Linda Hope. B.S., U. Ariz., 1936; M.D., C.M., McGill U., 1940. Diplomate: Am. Bd. Surgery, Am. Bd. Thoracic Surgery, Am. Bd. Colon and Rectal Surgery. Intern medicine Royal Victoria Hosp., Montreal, 1940-41; residency in surgery Royal Victoria and Montreal Gen. hosps., 1945-48; demonstrator surgery McGill U., 1948-49; asso. clin. surgery SUNY, Bklyn., 1949-52; prof. surgery SUNY, 1952-54; prof. surgery, also exec. officer dept. surgery Albert Einstein Coll. Medicine, Yeshiva U., 1954-58, prof. clin. surgery, 1958—; clin. prof. surgery U. Miami Sch. Medicine, 1972; chief divs. gen. and thoracic surgery Bronx Mcpl. Hosp. Center, N.Y.C., 1954-58; dir. surg. service Beth-El Hosp., Bklyn., 1958—; dir. surgery Brookdale Hosp. Center, Bklyn.; cons. in surgery Maimonides Hosp., Bklyn., Bronx VA Hosp., surgeon Miami Heart Inst.; attending surg. Lebanon Hosp.; clin. prof. surgery U. Miami, Fla.; cons. cardiac surgery Health Ins. Plan N.Y.; vis. prof. surgery U. Tel Aviv, 1969-70. Author chpt. on cardiac surgery in textbook. Served as squadron leader RCAF, 1941-45. Fellow ACS, Royal Coll. Surgeons (Can.), N.Y. Acad. Medicine, Am. Coll. Chest Physicians; mem. AMA, Soc. Univ. Surgeons, Am. Assn. Thoracic Surgery, Am. Heart Assn., N.Y. Surg. Soc., Alpha Omega Alpha, Zeta Beta Tau. Home: 500 Bayview Dr Apt 932 Miami FL 33160-4749

RIRIE, CRAIG MARTIN, periodontist; b. Lewiston, Utah, Apr. 17, 1943; s. Martin Clarence and VaLera (Dixon) R.; m. Becky Ann Ririe, Sept. 17, 1982; children: Paige, Seth, Theron, Kendall, Nathan, Derek, Brian, Amber, Kristen. AA, San Bernadino Valley Coll., 1966; DDS, Creighton U., 1972; MSD, Loma Linda U., 1978. Staff mem. Flagstaff (Ariz.) Med. Ctr. 1974—; pvt. practice dentistry specializing in periodontics Flagstaff, 1974—; assoc. prof. periodontics No. Ariz. U., Flagstaff, 1979—, chmn. dept. dental hygiene, 1980-81; med. examiner No. Ariz. U., W.L. Gore, Flagstaff, 1983—. Contbr. articles to profl. jours. V.p. bd. dirs. Grand Canyon coun. Boy Scouts Am., 1991—. Health professions scholarship Creighton U., Omaha, 1969-71; recipient Mosby award Mosby Pub. Co., 1972; research fellowship U. Bergen, Norway, 1978-79. Mem. ADA, Am. Acad. Periodontology (cert.), Western Soc. Periodontology (chmn. com. on research 1982—), bd. dirs. 1983—), No. Ariz. Dental Soc., Am. Acad. Oral Implantologists, Internat. Congress Oral Implantologists, Ariz. Dental Assn., Am. Cancer Soc. (bd. dirs.), Flagstaff C. of C., Rotary. Avocations: skiing, tennis, golf. Home: 1320 N Aztec St Flagstaff AZ 86001-3004 Office: 1050 N San Francisco St Flagstaff AZ 86001-3259

RIS, HANS, zoologist, educator; b. Bern, Switzerland, June 15, 1914; came to U.S., 1938, naturalized, 1945; s. August and Martha (Egger) R.; m. Hania Wislicka, Dec. 26, 1947 (div. 1971); children: Christopher Robert, Annette Margo; m. Theron Caldwell, July 14, 1980. Diploma high sch. teaching, U. Bern, 1936; Ph.D., Columbia, 1942. Lectr. zoology Columbia U., 1942; Seessel fellow in zoology Yale U., 1942; instr. biology Johns Hopkins U., 1942-44; asst. Rockefeller Inst., N.Y.C., 1944-46; assoc. Rockefeller Inst., 1946-49; assoc. prof. zoology U. Wis., Madison, 1949-53; prof. U. Wis., 1953-84, prof. emeritus, 1984—. Fellow AAAS; mem. Am. Acad. Arts Scis., Nat. Acad. Scis. Achievements include research on mechanisms of nuclear division, chromosome structure, nuclear envelope, cell ultrastructure, electron microscopy. Office: U Wis Zoology Rsch 1117 W Johnson St Madison WI 53706-1705

RIS, HOWARD C., JR., nonprofit public policy organization administrator. BA in Math., Duke U., 1970, postgrad., 1972; MLA, SUNY, Syracuse, 1974. Sr. assoc. Roy Mann Assocs., Inc., Cambridge, Mass., 19774-76; sr. planner Mass. Office Coastal Zone Mgmt., Boston, 1976-78; program mgr. New Eng. River Basins Commn., Boston, 1980-81; dep. dir. Union Concerned Scientists, Inc., Cambridge, 1981-84, exxec. dir., 1984—; bd. dirs. Ris Paper Corp., Inc.; founding dir. Profls.' Coalition for Nuclear Arms Control, Internat. Network Engrs. and Scientists for Global Responsibility. Mem. Energy and Transp. Task Force, President's Coun. on Sustainable Devel., New Eng. Bus. Coun.; mem. adv. bd. Living on Earth Prodns. Office: Union of Concerned Scientists 2 Brattle Sq Cambridge MA 02238

RIS, WILLIAM KRAKOW, lawyer; b. Dubuque, Iowa, June 11, 1915; s. Rinehart F. and Anna W. (Krakow) R.; m. Patty S. Nash, Dec. 28, 1940; children: Frederic N., William Krakow Jr. AB, U. Colo., 1945, LLB, 1939. Bar: Colo. 1939. Practice in Denver, 1939-43, 46-86; with firm Wood, Ris & Hames, P.C., 1948-86, of counsel, 1986—; mem. Commn. on Jud. Qualifications, 1973-77, chmn., 1977. Served with AUS, 1943-46. Fellow Am. Bar Found., Am. Coll. Trial Lawyers (bd. regents 1982-83); mem. Colo. Bar Assn. (pres. 1962-63), Denver Law Club (pres. 1956-57), Order of Coif. Episcopalian. Home: 635 Eudora St Denver CO 80220-5113 Office: 1775 Sherman St Ste 1600 Denver CO 80203-4317

RISCASSI, ROBERT W., career military officer. Gen. AUS. Office: Dept Def Office of Chief Staff The Pentagon Washington DC 20310-1000 also: US Forces Korea/CG EUSA APO AP 96301

RISCH, JAMES E., lawyer; b. Milw., May 3, 1943; s. Elroy A. and Helen B. (Levi) R.; m. Vicki L. Choborda, June 8, 1968; children—James E., Jason S., Jordan D. B.S. in Forestry, U. Idaho, 1965, J.D., 1968. Dep. pros. atty. Ada County, Idaho, 1968-69, chief dep. pros. atty., 1969-70, pros. atty., 1971-75; mem. Idaho Senate, 1974-88, 95—, majority leader, 1977-82, pres. pro tem, 1983-88; ptnr. Risch Goss & Insinger, Boise, Idaho, 1975—; prof. law Boise State U., 1972-75. Chmn. George Bush Presdl. Campaign, Idaho, 1988; mem. Gen. Coun. Idaho Rep. Party, 1991-95. Mem. ABA, Idaho Bar Assn., Boise Bar Assn., Am. Judicature Soc., Nat. Dist. Attys. Assn. (bd. dirs. 1977), Idaho Pros. Attys. Assn. (pres. 1976), Ducks Unlimited, Nat. Rifle Assn., Nat. Cattlemans Assn., Idaho Cattlemans Assn., Am. Angus Assn., Idaho Angus Assn., Boise Valley Angus Assn., Phi Delta Theta, Xi Sigma Pi. Republican. Roman Catholic. Avocations: hunting; fishing; skiing; horseback riding; tennis. Home: 5400 S Cole Rd Boise ID 83709-6401 Office: Risch Goss & Insinger 407 W Jefferson St Boise ID 83702-6079

RISCH, MARTIN DONALD, marketing-management consulting company executive; b. Bklyn., Oct. 7, 1929; s. Rene and Lillian (Grant) R.; m. Joan Nattrass, Dec. 26, 1955; children: Lillian, David. BA, Colgate U., 1951; MBA, Harvard U., 1955. Dir. mktg. devel. Riegel Paper Co., N.Y.C., 1959-60, Fitchburg (N.Y.) Paper Co., 1960-64; dir. planning speciality paper div. Litton Industries, Fitchburg, 1965-69, 70-71, v.p. planning paper printing div., 1971-76; pres. Lincoln Assocs., Lexington, Mass., 1976—. 1st lt. USAF, 1951-53, Korea. Mem. TAPPI, Graphic Arts Tech. Found., Packaging Internat., Harvard Club, Oak Hill Country Club. Home: 71 Winter St Lincoln MA 01773-3502 Office: Lincoln Assocs 35 Bedford St Ste 4 Lexington MA 02173-4451

RISCH, RICHARD WILLIAM, horticultural manager; b. Milw., Jan. 8, 1941; s. Frederick William and Sophia (Banker) R. BS, U. Wis., Milw., 1965. Asst. floriculturist Mitchell Park Conservatory, Milw., 1968-72, asst. hort. dir., 1972-81, conservatory dir., 1981—. Editor, photographer: Mitchell Park Conservatory Souvenir Booklet, 1975, 81. Mem. Am. Assn. Bot. Gardens and Arborea (chmn. conservatory com. 1984-86), Milw. Bonsai Soc. (June Kelley award 1982). Office: Mitchell Pk Conservatory 524 S Layton Blvd Milwaukee WI 53215-1295

RISEBROUGH, DOUG, professional hockey team executive; b. 1954; m. Marilyn Risenbrough; children: Allison, Lindsay. Former player Montreal (Que.) Canadiens, for 8 years; former player Calgary (Alta., Can.) Flames, for 5 years, former asst. coach, 1987-89, asst. gen. mgr., 1989-90, head coach, 1990-92; General Manager Calgary (Alt., Can.) Flames, 1992—. *

RISEN, WILLIAM MAURICE, JR., chemistry educator; b. St. Louis, July 22, 1940. ScB, Georgetown U., 1962; PhD, Purdue U., 1967. Asst. prof. chemistry Brown U., Providence, 1967-72, assoc. prof. chemistry, 1972-75, prof. chemistry, 1975—, chmn. chemistry dept., 1972-80, chmn. of faculty, 1993-94; cons. in field. Contbr. over 100 articles to profl. jours. Grantee in field. Mem. Am. Chem. Soc., Am. Phys. Soc., Am. Ceramic Soc. Office: Brown U Dept of Chemistry 324 Brook St Providence RI 02912-0001

RISHE, MELVIN, lawyer; b. Chgo., June 16, 1940. BS, Roosevelt U., 1963; JD, DePaul U., 1967. BAr: Ill. 1967, D.C. 1974, U.S. Supreme Ct. 1974, U.S. Claims Ct. 1974, U.S. Ct. Appeals (D.C. cir.) 1974. Dep. gen counsel Dept. Navy, 1967-74; ptnr. Sidley & Austin, Washington; contbr. articles to profl. jours. Mem. ABA, D.C. Bar Assn., Pi Gamma Mu. Office: Sidley & Austin 1722 I St NW Washington DC 20006

RISHEL, JAMES BURTON, manufacturing executive; b. Omaha, Apr. 27, 1920; s. James Blaine and Elizabeth Helen (Kerr) R.; m. Alice Jane Snyder, June 30, 1945; children: James Richard, Sara Jane Rishel Fields. BSME, U. Nebr., 1946. Profl. engr., Ohio. Pres. Corp. Equipment Co., Cin., 1962-82; chmn. bd. Systecon Inc., Cin., 1982—. Author: The Water Management Manual; patentee hydraulic systems; contbr. numerous articles to profl. jours. Capt. USAF, 1942-46, 51-52. Fellow ASHRAE; mem. Am. Water Works Assn., Water Environment Fedn. Avocations: philanthropy, golf, walking. Home: 7570 Thumbelina Ln Cincinnati OH 45242 Office: Systecon Inc 9750 Crescent Park Dr West Chester OH 45069

RISHEL, RICHARD CLINTON, banker; b. Oreland, Pa., June 7, 1943; S. Herbert Beale and Evelyn (Lauer) R.; m. Carol Staub, Apr. 3, 1965; children: Christian Daniel, Peter James. B.A., Pa. State U., 1965; postgrad., Drexel Inst. Tech., 1965-66. Credit analyst 1st Pa. Banking & Trust Co., Phila., 1965-69; comml. lending officer Nat. Bank of Chester County, West Chester, Pa., 1969; asst. v.p. Continental Bank of Norristown, Pa., 1969-70; sec. Continental Bank of Norristown, 1970-71, v.p., 1971-73, sr. v.p., chief fin. officer, 1973-75, exec. v.p., chief fin. officer, 1975-81, vice chmn., 1981-83, pres., chief adminstrv. officer, 1984-89, also dir.; pres., chief exec. officer Continental Bank, Continental Bancorp, 1990-92; vice chmn. bd. Continental Bank, 1981-84; pres. parent co. Continental Bancorp., 1981-92; dir. Barnett Inst. U. North Fla., 1993-94; sec. of banking Commonwealth of Pa., 1995—. Office: 4567 Saint Johns Bluff Rd S Jacksonville FL 32224-2646

RISHER, JAMES A., electronics executive; b. 1943. MS in Econs. and Stats., U. Tex., 1943. With IBM Corps., 1969-80; v.p. Wang Labs., 1980-84; sr. v.p. Motorola Computer Systems, Inc., 1984-86; pres., CEO Exide Electronics Group, Inc., Raleigh, N.C., 1986—, now pres., CEO; with Exide Electronics Corp. Office: Exide Electronics Corp 8521 Six Forks Rd Raleigh NC 27615-2963*

RISHER, JOHN ROBERT, JR., lawyer; b. Washington, Sept. 23, 1938; s. John Robert and Yvonne Gwendolyn (Jones) R.; m. Carol Adrienne Seager, June 9, 1974; children—John David, Michael Temple, Mark Eliot, Conrad Zachary. B.A., Morgan Coll., 1960; LL.B., U. So. Calif., 1963; postgrad. John F. Kennedy Sch., Harvard U., 1977. Bar: Calif. 1963, D.C. 1967, U.S. Supreme Ct. 1975. Mem. staff Pres.'s Com. on EEO, Washington, 1965; atty. criminal fraud sect. Dept. Justice, Washington, 1965-68; assoc. Arent, Fox, Kintner, Plotkin & Kahn, Washington, 1968-75; ptnr. Arent, Fox, Kintner, Plotkin & Kahn, 1975-76; corp. counsel D.C., 1975-78; ptnr. Arent, Fox, Kintner, Plotkin & Kahn, Washington, 1978—; chmn. D.C. Criminal Justice Coordinating Bd., 1976-78, D.C. Bar spl. com. on fed. judiciary, 1985-87; v.p., trustee Supreme Ct. Hist. Soc., 1990—; fellow Am. Bar Found. 1994—. Chmn. budget com. Jewish Social Svc. Agy., 1980-85;

chmn. D.C. Commn. on Licensure to Practice Healing Arts, 1976-78; chmn. nominating com. D.C. Bd. Elections and Ethics, 1974-76; bd. dirs. D.C. Pub. Defender Svc., 1974-76; chmn. Montgomery County Civil Liberties Union, 1970-71; mem. exec. com. Nat. Capital Area Civil Liberties Union, 1969-71; pres. D.C. Jewish Cmty. Ctr., 1985-87, bd. dirs., 1985—; trustee, bd. dirs. capital camps United Jewish Appeal Fedn., 1987-93; dir. Washington Symphony Orch., 1990—. Mem. ABA, Bar Assn. D.C., Calif. Bar Assn., Fed. Bar Assn., Washington Bar Assn.. DePriest 15. Democrat. Jewish. Home: 3311 Cleveland Ave NW Washington DC 20008-3456 Office: Arent Fox Kintner Plotkin Kahn 1050 Connecticut Ave NW 6th Floor Washington DC 20036-5339

RISI, LOUIS J., JR., business executive; b. Highland Park, Ill., July 2, 1936; s. Louis J. and Ann E. R.; m. Mary Jean Anson, Jan. 15, 1957; children—Steven, Janet, Andrew. B.S., Bradley U., 1958; MBA, U. Chgo. With Arthur Young & Co., Chgo., 1959-69; exec. asst. mgmt. Norin Corp., Miami, Fla., 1968-69; exec. com. dir. Maple Leaf Mills Ltd., Toronto, Can., 1970-81, Corp. Foods, Inc., 1970-81, also dir., chief exec. officer Nat. Investors Fire & Casualty Co., 1975-77; exec. com. dir. Investors Equity Life Ins. Co. of Hawaii, 1970-75; pres., dir. The Abbey, Lake Geneva, 1970-75; exec. comm., dir. Upper Lakes Shipping, Ltd., Toronto, Can., 1970-76; pres., dir. The Pioneer Resort, Lake Okshosh, 1971-76; exec. comm., dir. Port Weller and St. Lawrence Dry Dock, Ltd., St. Catharines, Can., 1971-76; pres., dir. Homosassa Springs Resort, Fla., 1971-78; exec. v.p., dir. Ivan Tors Films Inc., Culver City, Calif., 1972-76, Ivan Tors Studios Inc., Miami, Fla., 1976-80; exec. com. dir. Midland Nat. Bank, 1976-80; pres., dir. Norris Grain Co., 1980-82; chmn. bd., chief exec. officer CTC Corp., 1981-83; chmn. bd. dirs., CEO Red Wing Co., Oklawaha Farms, Inc., Assured Security Co.; dir. Breckinridge Resorts Group; exec. v.p., bd. dirs. Detroit Red Wings Hockey Club, Inc., 1978-82; bd. govs. Nat. Hockey League, 1978-82; bd. dirs. Chgo. Rock Island and Pacific R.R., dir. exec. com., Bankmgrs. Corp.; lt. comdr. U.S.N.R., 1959-67; U.S rep. Grain negotiations with USSR; U.S. rep. Feedstuffs negotiations with China; mem. adv. com. Am. Stock Exch.; mem. Agrl. Processors Liaison com. FTC; mem. adv. bd. Nat. Millers Assn. Trustee Fairchild Tropical Garden, Miami, Fla. Mem. Ocean Reef Yacht Club (Key Largo, Fla.), Santa Rosa (Calif.) Country Club, Riviera Country Club (Coral Gables, Fla.), Anabelle's Club (London), St. James Club (London). Home: 10915 SW 53rd Ave Miami FL 33156-4209 Office: 200 NE 2nd Dr Homestead FL 33030-6119

RISINGER, PAUL N., electronics executive; b. 1933. V. chmn. Synmetricom, Inc., San Jose. Office: Silicon General Inc 85 W Tasman Dr San Jose CA 95134*

RISK, JOHN FRED, banker, investment banker; b. Ft. Wayne, Ind., Dec. 1, 1928; s. Clifford and Estella (Kline) R.; m. Viola Jean Tompt, July 12, 1953; children: Nancy Jean, John Thomas. B.S. cum laude, Ind. U., 1949, LL.B., J.D., 1951; postgrad., Nortwestern U.; LL.D., Ind. State U. With Harris Trust & Savs. Bank, Chgo., 1951-54, W.T. Grimm & Co., 1954-56; with Ind. Nat. Bank of Indpls., 1956-76, exec. v.p. dir., 1965-68, pres., 1968-76, chmn., 1971-76; mem. Forum Group, Inc., 1976-91, Sovereign Group Inc., 1980—, Sargent & Greenleaf Inc., 1993—; bd. dirs. Steak 'n Shake, Inc., Standard Locknut, Inc., Somerset Corp., Nat. Homes Corp., Amli Realty Co., Security Group, Inc., Keystone Distbn., Inc. Lacy Diversified Industries, Inc., Excepticon, Inc., L. R. Nelson Corp., Breckenridge Corp., Canterbury Corp., Cygnet Enterprises, Inc., Franklin Corp., Haag Drug Co., Inland Container Corp., ind. Bell Tel. Co., Ransburg Corp., Hook Drug Co., Northwestern Mut. Life Ins. Co., Consolidated Products Inc., Safemasters Co., Inc., Howard Sams Co. Bd. dirs. Hanover Coll., 1966-72, Ind. U. Found., 1968—, United Student Aid Fund; chmn. Indpls. Ctr. for Advanced Rsch., Ind. State Scholarship Coms., 1968-72. Capt. inf. U.S. Army, 1950-51. Mem. Am., Ind., Res. City bankers assns., Ind. Indpls. bar assns. Methodist. Clubs: Meridian Hills Country (Indpls.); Royal Poincianna Golf (Naples, Fla.); Quail Creek Country (Naples). Office: Sovereign Group Inc 8900 Keystone Xing Ste 1150 Indianapolis IN 46240-2135

RISK, RICHARD R., health facility administrator; b. Chgo., Sept. 15, 1947; s. Clement Albert and Mary Catherine (Clarke) R.; m. Rebecca Ann Sandquist, Jan. 11, 1969 (div. Sept. 1984); children: Michael, Daniel, Laura; m. Louise L. Lawson, Dec. 1, 1984; stepchildren: Carrie Lawson, Valerie Lawson. BS in Econs., U. Ill., 1968; MBA in Health Adminstrn., U. Chgo., 1971. Asst. adminstr. U. Ill. Hosp., Chgo., 1969-72, Ctrl. DuPage Hosp., Winfield, Ill., 1972-74; mgmt. cons., v.p Tribrook Group, Inc., Oak Brook, Ill., 1974-81; v.p. cons. svcs. Parkside Med. Svcs., Park Ridge, Ill., 1981-83; prin. health and med. divsn. Booz, Allen, & Hamilton, Inc., Chgo., 1983-84; with EHS Health Care, Oak Brook, 1984—, now pres., CEO; mem. faculty Healthcare Fin. Mgmt. Assn., 1978-86, Am. Assn. Hosps. Cons., 1978-84; lectr. grad. program social scis. No. Ill. U., 1982-88; lectr., adv. bd. multihosp. system study Kellogg Sch. Health Mgmt. Program Northwestern U., 1985—; lectr. Grad. Program in Health Adminstrn., U. Chgo. 1982—. Mem. access com. Gov.'s Task Force on Health Reform, 1992—. Sgt. USAR, 1968-74. Fellow Am. Assn. Hosp. Cons. (bd. dirs., treas., chmn. govt. rels. com., chmn. membership task force, liaison Nat. Coun. Community Hosps.); mem. Am. Healthcare Systems (bd. dirs., ad hoc ins. com.), Am. Hosp. Assn. (alternate del. healthcare systems sect.), Ill. Hosp. Assn. (chmn. coun. on health fin., mem. strategic plan com.), U. Chgo. Hosp. Adminstrn. Alumni Assn. (pres. exec. com. alumni coun., chmn. 50th ann. com.). Home: 801 N Clinton Pl River Forest IL 60305 Office: EHS Health Care 2025 Windsor Dr Oak Brook IL 60521

RISKAS, HARRY JAMES, construction company executive; b. Shelton, Wis., Mar. 27, 1920; s. James and Anna (Pappeonou) R.; student St. Mary's Naval Coll., 1941-43; m. Joan Evelyn Clark, Aug. 1, 1964; children—Lawrence, Douglas, Kimberly. Pres. Pacific Western Contractors, Inc., Millbrae, Cal., from 1951; pres., dir. Riskas Baker Riskas Devel. Corp., San Luis Properties, Inc.; pres., chmn. bd. Pacific Western Contractors, Inc., Sanfo-Bay Corp., H.J.R. Developers, Inc., Windrock Corp. Dir., Am. Properties, & Investment Fund, 1970. Lt. comdr. USNR, 1942-46. Mem. Young Pres.'s Orgn., Bankers Club, K.C. (San Francisco). Home: 237 Thatcher Ln San Mateo CA 94404-3950 Office: 1650 S Amphlett Blvd Ste 226 San Mateo CA 94402-2515

RISKE, WILLIAM KENNETH, cultural services consultant; b. Lamont, Alta., Can., May 9, 1949; s. Norman Elmer and Clara Jeanette (Krause) R.; m. Barbara Elizabeth Malcolm, Apr. 28, 1973; children: Elizabeth Nicola, William Norman Malcolm. BFA, U. Alta., 1969. Stage mgr. Royal Winnipeg Ballet, Man., Can., 1971-73; prodn. stage mgr. Royal Winnipeg Ballet, 1973-76, prodn. mgr., 1976-77, assoc. gen. mgr., 1978-79, gen. mgr., 1979-92, cultural svcs. cons., 1992—; assoc. prodr., gen. mgr. Cirque Du Soleil-Mystère, 1994—. Mem. Assn. Cultural Execs., Can. Assn. Profl. Dance Orgns. (pres. 1985-88), Dancevision (pres. 1990). Home: 59 Kingsway Ave, Winnipeg, MB Canada R3M 0G2

RISKIND, KENNETH DAY, metals company executive; b. Chgo., Nov. 6, 1937; s. Phillip A. and Idah (Steinberg) R.; m. Judith Hexter, Nov. 30, 1963; children: Patricia, Peter, Michael, Susan. B.A., Cornell U., 1959; M.B.A., Columbia U., 1961. Pres., chief exec. officer Fullerton Metals Co., Northbrook, Ill., 1962—. Bd. overseers Bus. Sch., Ill. Inst. Tech.; mem. coun. Cornell U., 1991—. Served to 1st lt. U.S. Army, 1969. Mem. Nat. Assn. Aluminum Distbrs. (pres.). Clubs: Economic (Chgo.); Northmoor Country. Home: 1428 Green Bay Rd Highland Park IL 60035-3613 Office: Fullerton Metals Co 3000 Shermer Rd Northbrook IL 60062-7796

RISLEY, LARRY L., air transportation executive. CEO, pres. bd. dirs. Mesa Airlines. Office: Mesa Airlines 2325 E 30th St Farmington NM 87401-8900

RISLEY, TODD ROBERT, psychologist, educator; b. Palmer, Alaska, Sept. 8, 1937; s. Robert and Eva Lou (Todd) R.; 1 child, Todd Michael. A.B. with distinction in Psychology, San Diego State U., 1960; M.S., U. Wash., 1963, Ph.D., 1966. Asst. prof. psychology Fla. State U., Tallahassee, 1964-65; research assoc. Bur. Child Research, U. Kans., Lawrence, 1965-77, sr. scientist, 1977—; asst. prof. dept. human devel., 1967-69, assoc. prof., 1969-73, prof., 1973-84; prof. psychology U. Alaska, Anchorage, 1982—; dir. Ctr. for Applied Behavior Analysis, 1970-82; dir. Johnny Cake Child Study Ctr., Mansfield, Ark., 1973-74; vis. prof. U. Auckland (N.Z.), 1978; acting dir. Western Carolina Ctr., Morgantown, N.C., 1981; dir. Alaska Div. Mental Health and Devel. Disabilities, 1988-91; cons. in field to numerous orgns. and instns. Co-author: The Infant Center, 1977, Shopping with Children: Advice for Parents, 1978, The Toddler Center, 1979; editor: Jour. Applied Behavior Analysis, 1971-74; mng. editor: Behavior Therapy, The Behavior Therapist, Behavioral Assessment, 1977-80; mem. editorial bds. of numerous profl. jours.; contbr. revs. and numerous articles. Co-chmn. Fla. task force on use of behavioral procedures in state programs for retarded, 1974—; mem. resident abuse investigating com. div. retardation Fla. Dept. Health and Rehab. Services, 1972—; mem. adv. com. Social Research Inst., U. Utah, 1977—; mem. Alaska Gov.'s Council on Handicapped and Gifted, 1983-88, NIH Mental Retardation Research Com., 1987-88, Alaska Mental Health Bd., 1988. Grantee NIMH, 1971-72, 72-73; research grantee Nat. Ctr. Health Services, 1976-79; grantee Nat. Inst. Edn., 1973, NIH, 1967—. Fellow Am. Psychol. Assn. (coun. of reps. 1982-85, pres. div. 25, 1989); mem. AAAS, Am. Psychol. Soc., Am. Assn. Mental Deficiency, Assn. Advancement of Behavior Therapy (dir. 1975-80, pres. 1976-77, chmn. profl. rev. com. 1977—, series editor Readings in Behavior Therapy 1977—), Soc. Behavioral Medicine, Assn. Behavior Analysis, Sigma Xi. Office: U Alaska-Anchorage Dept Psychology 3211 Providence Dr Anchorage AK 99508-4614

RISMAN, MICHAEL, lawyer, business executive, securities company executive; b. Everett, Mass., Apr. 2, 1938; s. Morris Charles and Doris (Rosenbaum) R.; m. Rebecca R. Fuchs, Mar. 23, 1974; 1 stepchild, Ian Carlton Murray; children: Matthew Craig, Deborah Gayle, Jared Evan. BA, U. Mich., 1960; LLB, Georgetown U., 1964. Bar: D.C. 1964. Staff mem. Democratic Nat. Com., Washington, 1964-66; atty. U.S. Fgn. Claims Settlement Commn., Washington, 1964-66, SEC, Washington, 1966-67; counsel Seaboard Planning Corp., Beverly Hills, Calif., 1967-72, pres., 1970-72; v.p. Seaboard Corp., Beverly Hills, Calif., 1970-72; sec. B.C. Morton Realty Trust, 1967-71; with Arlington Investments Corp., Santa Monica, Calif., 1979-86; founder The Quincey Group, 1986; owner, pres. Armstrong Kitchens, San Francisco, 1988-90; sr. v.p. AFC Am. Housing Corp., L.A., Calif., 1991—; bd. dir. Competitive Capital Fund, Income Fund Boston, Inc., Admiralty Fund. Home: 1133 Centinela Ave Santa Monica CA 90403-2316

RISOM, JENS, furniture designer, manufacturing executive; b. Copenhagen, May 8, 1916; came to U.S., 1938; naturalized, 1944; s. Sven J. and Inger Risom; m. Iben Haderup, Dec. 12, 1939 (dec. Jan. 1977); children: Helen Ann, Peggy Ann, Thomas Christian, Sven Christian; m. Henny Panduro, May 12, 1979. Freelance furniture designer, 1939-43; founder, pres. Jens Risom Design Inc., 1946-71; pres. Jens Risom Design, Inc. (became subs. Dictaphone Corp. 1971), N.Y.C., 1946-73; v.p. Dictaphone Corp., 1971-73; pres. Design Control, New Canaan, Conn., 1973—; cons. design, mktg., space planning. Trustee RISD, New Canaan Libr., others. With AUS, 1943-45, ETO. Recipient awards Archtl. League, Am. Inst. Internat. Design, Lifetime Achievement award Bklyn. Mus. Art, 1994, numerous Danish and Am. design awards. Mem. Indsl. Designers Soc. Am. Home and Office: 103 Chichester Rd New Canaan CT 06840-3913 also: PO Box 596 Block Island RI 02807-0596

RISOM, OLE CHRISTIAN, publishing company executive; b. Copenhagen, Denmark, Oct. 3, 1919; came to U.S., 1941, naturalized, 1942; s. Sven and Inger (Henriques) R.; m. Agnes Grafin von Rechberg u Rothenloewen, May, 1947; children: Christopher, Camilla, Charles Nicholas. Art dir. Interior Design Mag., N.Y.C., 1948-50; assoc. art dir. McCall, Better Living Mag., N.Y.C., 1950-52; v.p., art dir. Golden Press Western Pub., N.Y.C., 1952-72; v.p., assoc. pub. juvenile div. Random House, N.Y.C., 1972-90. Author: I Am a Bunny, 1963 Little Bunny Follows its Nose, 1971, Max the Nosey Bear, 1972, Do You Know Colors, 1979, others. Served to sgt. U.S. Army, 1942-46, ETO. Decorated Bronze Star. Mem. Nat. Arts Club, Soc. Illustrators, Racquet and Tennis Club, Seawanhaka Corinthian Yacht Club, Royal Danish Yacht Club. Lutheran. Home: 160 Harbor Ln Roslyn NY 11576-1119

RISON, ANDRE, football player; b. Flint, Mich., Mar. 18, 1967. Student, Mich. State U. With Indpls. Colts, 1989, Atlanta Falcons, 1990-95, Cleve. Browns, 1995—. Named to Pro-Bowl, 1990, 91, Sporting News All-Pro team, 1990. Office: Cleveland Browns 80 First Ave Berea OH 44017-0679*

RISPETTOSO, GEORGE ALPHONSE, vocational educator, diesel technology consultant; b. Arlington, Mass., Feb. 21, 1941; s. Samuel and Marie (Valeriano) R.; m. Mary Ann C. Tempesta, Oct. 11, 1987. BS in Edn., Fitchburg (Mass.) State Coll., 1984, MS in Edn., 1988. Cert. tchr., supt. and dir. vocat. tech. high sch., Mass. Tchr. Blue Hills Regional Vocat. Tech. High Sch., Canton, Mass., 1978-85; asst. prof. Massasoit C., Canton, 1985-88; industry instr. Caterpillar Corp., Hopkinton, Mass., 1988; tchr. diesel tech. Southeastern Regional Tech. High Sch., Easton, Mass., 1988—; cons. Diesel Tech. Mgmt. Inc., Kingston, Mass., 1982— Curriculum writer. Charter mem. Rep. Presdl. Task Force, Washington, 1982—. With USAF, 1962-66. Mem. Masons (3d and 32d degrees), Shriners (mem. Shriners Burn Ctr. Motorcycle Drill Team). Roman Catholic. Avocations: cars, boating, motorcycling. Home: 4 Bay View Ave Kingston MA 02364-1712

RISS, ERIC, psychologist; b. Vienna, Austria, Oct. 10, 1929; s. David S. and Rebecca (Schneider) R.; came to U.S., 1940, naturalized, 1945; B.A., Bklyn. Coll., 1950; Ph.D., NYU, 1958; diplomate Am. Bd. Psychotherapy; m. Miriam Barbara Schoen, July 22, 1956; children: Arthur, Suzanne, Wendy. Pvt. practice psychotherapy, family therapy, marriage counseling, N.Y.C., 1952—; sr. psychologist N.Y.C. Diagnostic Center, 1954-57; with Marriage and Family Life Inst., N.Y.C., 1956-92; cons., 1956-58, dir. pub. edn., 1960-73, chmn. bd. dirs., 1961-73, dir., 1973-92; mem. attending staff, supr. psychotherapy and family therapy Payne Whitney Psychiat. Clinic, N.Y. Hosp., N.Y.C., 1971-78; clin. instr. psychology and psychiatry Cornell U. Med. Coll., 1971-72, clin. assoc. prof., 1973-78; dir. Inst. for Exploration of Marriage, 1976-84; chief psychologist Artists, Writers and Performers Psychotherapy Center, 1978-92; lectr. Bklyn. Coll., 1955-62; cons. Fordham Hosp., 1956-68; psychotherapist N.Y. Neuropsychiat. Center, 1958-60; psychotherapist Community Guidance Service, N.Y.C., 1958-61. Mem. Am. Acad. Psychotherapy, N.Y. State Marriage, Family and Child Counseling Assn. (pres. 1971-72), Nat. Registry of Health Providers in Psychology, Acad. Family Psychology, Am., N.Y. State psychol. assns. Contbr. numerous articles to profl. jours. Office: 174 E 73rd St New York NY 10021-4352

RISS, MURRAY, photographer, educator; b. Stryj, Poland, Feb. 6, 1940; came to U.S., 1951, naturalized, 1958; s. Elias and Dora (Feit) R.; m. Karen Mason; children: Shanna, Adya. Student, CCNY, 1958-63; B.A., Cooper Union, 1966; M.F.A., R.I. Sch. Design, 1968. Prof., chmn. dept photography Memphis Acad. Arts, 1969—; lectr. film and photography Southwestern U., Memphis, 1972—; artist-in-residence U. Syracuse, N.Y., 1980, U. Haifa, Israel, 1976. One man shows include Art Inst., Chgo, 1971, Mpls. Inst. Fine Arts, 1971, U. Rochester, N.Y., 1975, Photographers Gallery, London, 1977, Afterimage Gallery, Dallas, 1979, Visual Studies Workshop, Rochester, 1980, Hampshire (Mass.) Coll., 1981, Loomis Inst., Conn., 1984; group shows include Mus. Modern Art, N.Y.C., 1970, 71, New Orleans Mus. Art, 1975, Nexus Gallery, Atlanta, 1981, Askew Nixon Gallery; touring show So. Arts Fedn., 1985-86; conceived, organized, dir. Southern Eye, Southern Mind, A Photographic Inquiry, Memphis, 1981; illustrator: History of Memphis Architecture until 1900, 1983, Guide to Mud Island, 1989; curator, dir. Emerging Southern Photographers, Memphis Coll. Art Gallery, 1992, Memphis Brooks Mus. Art, 1994. Nat. Endowment for Arts fellow, 1979. Mem. Soc. Photographic Edn. Home: 1306 Harbert Ave Memphis TN 38104-4514 Office: Murray Riss Photography 516 S Main St Memphis TN 38103-4443 Had I designed the events and outcomes of my life I would not have done as well as my fate has done for me.

RISS, ROBERT BAILEY, insurance company executive; b. Salida, Colo., May 27, 1927; s. Richard Roland and Louise (Roberts) R.; married; children: Edward Stayton, G. Leslie, Laura Bailey, Juliana Warren. BSBA, U. Kans., 1949. Pres. Riss Internat. Corp., Kansas City, Mo., 1950-80, chmn. bd., 1964-86; founder, chmn. bd., pres. Republic Industries, Inc., Kansas City, Mo., 1969-86; chmn. bd. Grandview Bank and Trust Co., 1969-86,

Commonwealth Gen. Ins. Co., 1986-93; Chmn. bd. dirs., exec. com. Heart of Am. Fire and Casualty Co.; chmn. bd. dirs. Comml. Equipment Co. Vice chmn. bd. trustees Kansas U. Endowment Assn., 1980-89. Recipient Silver Beaver award Kansas City Area coun. Boy Scouts Am., 1972; Disting. Svc. citation U. Kans., 1976; Fred Ellsworth medal U. Kans., 1979; named Most Outstanding Young Man in Mo. U.S Jr. C. of C., 1956. Mem. Kans. U. Alumni Assn. (nat. pres. 1969-70), Sigma Nu. Episcopalian.

RISSE, GUENTER BERNHARD, physician, historian, educator; b. Buenos Aires, Argentina, Apr. 28, 1932; s. Francisco B. and Kaete A. R.; m. Alexandra G. Paradzinski, Oct. 14, 1961; children—Heidi, Monica, Alisa. MD, U. Buenos Aires, 1958; PhD, U. Chgo., 1971. Intern Mercy Hosp., Buffalo, 1958-59; resident in medicine Henry Ford Hosp., Detroit, 1960-61, Mt. Carmel Hosp., Columbus, Ohio, 1962-63; asst. prof. medicine U. Chgo., 1963-67; asst. prof. dept. history of medicine U. Minn., 1969-71; asso. prof. dept. history of medicine and dept. history of sci. U. Wis., Madison, 1971-76; prof. U. Wis., 1976-85, chmn. dept. history of medicine, 1971-77; prof., chmn. dept. history health scis. U. Calif., San Francisco, 1985—; Mem. project com. Ctr. for Photog. Images in Medicine and Health Care. Author: Paleopathology of Ancient Egypt, 1964, Hospital Life in Enlightenment Scotland, 1986; editor: Modern China and Traditional Chinese Medicine, 1973, History of Physiology, 1973, Medicine Without Doctors, 1977; mem. editorial bd. Jour. History of Medicine, 1971-74, 90-93, Clio Medica, 1973-88, Bull. History of Medicine, 1980-93, Medizinhistorisches jour., 1981—, Med. History, 1989—, Communicationes de Historia Artis Medicinae, 1991—, Asclepio, 1995—. Served with Argentine Armed Forces, 1955. NIH grantee, 1971-73, 82-83, WHO grantee, 1979,-. Mem. Am. Assn. History of Medicine (pres. 1988-90, William H. Welch medal 1988), History Sci. Soc., Internat. Acad. History Medicine, Deutsche Gesellschaft fur Geschichte der Medizin, European Assn. History of Medicine, Am. Soc. Eighteenth-Century Studies, Mexican Soc. History and Philosophy of Medicine, Peruvian Assn. Med. Ethnology and History, Brit. Soc. for Social History of Medicine, Argentine Ateneo de Historia de la Medicina, AIDS History Group (co-chair 1988-94, pres. 1994—), Bay Area Med. Hist. Club (pres. 1994—). Home: 600 Noriega St San Francisco CA 94122-4616 Office: Univ of Calif Dept History Health Scis 513 Parnassus Ave San Francisco CA 94143-0726

RISSER, ARTHUR CRANE, JR., zoo administrator; b. Blackwell, Okla., July 8, 1938; s. Arthur Crane and Mary Winn (Stevenson) R.; children: Michelle W., Stephen C., Michael R. BA, Grinnell Coll., Iowa, 1960; MA, U. Ariz., Tucson, 1963; PhD, U. Calif., Davis, 1970. Mus. technician, Smithsonian Instn., Washington, 1963-64; research assoc. Sch. Medicine U. Md., Balt., 1964-65; grad. teaching asst. U. Calif., Davis, 1965-70; asst. prof. biology U. Nev.-Reno, 1970-74; asst. curator birds Zool. Soc. San Diego, 1974-76, curator birds, 1976-81, gen. curator birds, 1981-86; gen. mgr. San Diego Zoo, 1986—; co-chmn. Calif. Condor Working Group on Captive Breeding and Reintroduction, 1983-85; mem. Calif. Condor Recovery Team, 1984-86. Treas., Planned Parenthood, Reno, 1972; bd. dirs. Internat. Found. Conservation Birds, 1979-88, Conservation Rsch. Found. of Papua New Guinea, 1991—. Fellow Am. Assn. Zool. Parks and Aquariums. Office: San Diego Zoo PO Box 551 San Diego CA 92112

RISSER, JAMES VAULX, JR., journalist, educator; b. Lincoln, Nebr., May 8, 1938; s. James Vaulx and Ella Caroline (Schacht) R.; m. Sandra Elizabeth Laaker, June 10, 1961; children: David James, John Daniel. BA, U. Nebr., 1959, cert. in journalism, 1964; JD, U. San Francisco, 1962. Bar: Nebr. 1962. Pvt. practice law Lincoln, 1962-64; reporter Des Moines Register and Tribune, 1964-85, Washington corr., 1969-85, bur. chief, 1976-85; dir. John S. Knight fellowships for profl. journalists, prof. communication Stanford U., 1985—; lectr. Wells Coll., 1981; mem. com. on agrl. edn. in secondary schs. Nat. Acad. Scis., 1985-88. Trustee Reuters Found., 1989—; mem. Pulitzer Prize Bd., 1990—. Pulitzer Journalism fellow Stanford U., 1973-74; recipient award for disting. reporting public affairs Am. Polit. Sci. Assn., 1969; Thomas L. Stokes award for environ. reporting Washington Journalism Center, 1971, 79; Pulitzer prize for nat. reporting, 1976, 79; Worth Bingham Found. prize for investigative reporting, 1976; Raymond Clapper Meml. Assn. award for Washington reporting, 1976, 78; Edward J. Meeman award for Conservation Reporting, 1985. Mem. Nebr. Bar Assn., Soc. Environ. Journalists, Soc. Profl. Journalists (Disting. Svc. award 1976), Investigative Reporters and Editors Assn. Club: Gridiron. Home: 382 Everett Ave Palo Alto CA 94301 Office: Stanford U Communication Dept Stanford CA 94305-2050

RISSER, PAUL GILLAN, botanist, academic administrator; b. Blackwell, Okla., Sept. 14, 1939; s. Paul Crane and Jean (McCluskey) R.; children: David, Mark, Stephen, Scott. BA, Grinnell Coll.; MS in Botany, U. Wis., PhD in Botany and Soils. From asst. prof. to prof. botany U. Okla., 1967-81, also asst. dir. biol. sta., chmn. dept. botany and microbiology, 1977-81; dir. Okla. Biol. Survey, 1971-77; chief Ill. Natural History Survey, 1981-86; program dir., ecosystem studies NSF; provost and v.p. acad. affairs U. N.Mex., 1989-92; pres. Miami U. Oxford, Ohio, 1993—. Author: (with Kathy Cornelison) Man and the Biosphere, 1979, (with others) The True Prairie Ecosystem, 1981; research, numerous pubs. in field. Trustee Pioneer Multi-County Library Bd. Mem. Am. Acad. Arts and Scis., Ecol. Soc. Am. (pres.), Brit. Ecol. Soc., Soc. Range Mgmt., Southwestern Assn. Naturalists (pres.), Am. Inst. Biol. Sci. (pres.), Torrey Bot. Club. Presbyterian. Office: Miami U Roudebush Hall Oxford OH 45056

RISSETTO, HARRY A., lawyer; b. Dec. 1, 1943. AB, Fairfield U., 1965; JD, Georgetown U., 1968. Bar: N.Y. 1969, D.C. 1970. Law clk. to Hon. John J. Sirica U.S. Dist. Ct. D.C., 1968-69; law clk. to Chief Justice Warren E. Burger U.S. Supreme Ct., 1969-70; ptnr. Morgan, Lewis & Bockius, Washington; adj. prof. law Georgetown U. Law Ctr., 1986-89. Mem. ABA (co-chmn. railway labor act com. sect. of labor and employment law 1987-89). Office: Morgan Lewis & Bockius 1800 M St NW Washington DC 20036-5869

RISSING, DANIEL JOSEPH, hospital administrator; b. Fort Wayne, Ind., Mar. 25, 1944; married. BA, Ind. U., 1966; MA, Xavier U., 1968. Adm. res. Parkview Meml. Hosp., Fort Wayne, Ind., 1967-68, administrv. asst., 1968-69; administr. PHS Indian Hosp., Tuba City, Ariz., 1969-71; extern William N. Wishard Meml. Hosp., Indpls., Ind., 1971-73; administr. Dearborn County Hosp., Lawrenceburg, Ind., 1974-78; pres. Good Samaritan Med. Ctr., Zanesville, Ohio, 1978-88, Hosp. St. Raphael, New Haven, Conn., 1988-91, Toledo (Ohio) Hosp., 1991—; adj. educator in field. Lt. Comdr. U.S. Army, 1969-71. Mem. NEHA, Conn. Hosp. Assn. (community svc.), Ohio Hosp. Assn. (bd. dirs.), Ind. Hosp. Assn. (bd. dirs.), various healthcare orgns. Home: 4529 Woodhill Rd Toledo OH 43615-2254 Office: The Toledo Hosp 2142 N Cove Blvd Toledo OH 43606

RISSMAN, BURTON RICHARD, lawyer; b. Chgo., Nov. 13, 1927; s. Louis and Eva (Lyons) R.; m. Francine Greenberg, June 15, 1952; children: Lawrence E., Thomas W., Michael P. BS, U. Ill., 1947, JD, 1951; LLM, NYU, 1952. Bar: Ill. 1951, U.S. Dist. Ct. (no. dist.) Ill. 1954, U.S. Ct. Appeals (7th cir.) 1978, U.S. Supreme Ct. 1982. Assoc. Schiff, Hardin & Waite, Chgo., 1953-59, ptnr., 1959—, mem. mgmt. com., 1984-92, chmn. mgmt. com., 1986-90; mem. faculty Practicing Law Inst. Bd. editor U. Ill. Law Forum, 1949-51; contbr. articles to profl. jours. Trustee Crow Canyon Archaeol. Ctr. 1st lt. JAGC, USAF, 1952-54. Food Law fellow, 1951. Mem. ABA, Ill. State Bar Assn., Chgo. Bar Assn., Chgo. Coun. Lawyers, Am. Judicature Soc., Green Acres Country Club (Northbrook, Ill.), Met. Club, Carlton Club. Office: Schiff Hardin & Waite 233 S Wacker Dr Chicago IL 60606-6473

RIST, ROBERT G., religious publishing executive. Pres. Warner Press Inc. Office: Warner Press Inc PO Box 2499 Anderson IN 46018-2499

RISTAU, KENNETH EUGENE, JR., lawyer; b. Knoxville, Tenn., Feb. 14, 1939; s. Kenneth E. and Frances (Besch) R.; m. Mary Emily George, Nov. 27, 1967 (div. Apr. 1987). children: Heidi, Mary Robin, Kenny, Michael, Robert; m. Emily Pettis, Mar. 31, 1990; 1 child, James Patrick. BA, Colgate U., 1961; JD, NYU, 1964. Bar: U.S. Ct. Appeals (9th cir.) 1968, U.S. Ct. Appeals (D.C. cir.) 1974, U.S. Supreme Ct. 1974, U.S. Dist. Ct., Southern Dist. of Calif., 1993. Assoc. Gibson, Dunn & Crutcher, L.A., 1964-69; ptnr. Gibson, Dunn & Crutcher, Newport Beach, Calif., 1969—. Mem. Merchants

and Mfrs. Assn. (adv. bd.), Orange County Indsl. Rels. Rsch. Assn. (pres. 1992-93), Big Canyon Country Club, Rancho Las Palmas Country Club, Newport Beach Tennis Club, Santa Fe Hunt Club (pres., bd. dirs.), Ridgeline Country Club. Office: Gibson Dunn & Crutcher Jamboree Ctr 4 Park Plz Irvine CA 92714

RISTINE, JEFFREY ALAN, reporter; b. Ann Arbor, Mich., Apr. 21, 1955; s. Harold G. and Amelita (Schmidt) R. BA, U. Mich., 1977. Reporter The Midland (Mich) Times, 1978-79, Johnstown (Pa.) Tribune-Dem., 1979-80, San Diego Tribune, 1980-92, San Diego Union-Tribune, 1992—. Recipient Appreciation award Am. Planning Assn., San Diego sect., 1988; named Best polit./govt. reporter San Diego Press Club, 1986. Avocations: puzzlesolving, bicycling, cat photography. Office: San Diego Union-Tribune 350 Camino de la Reina San Diego CA 92112-4106

RISTOW, GEORGE EDWARD, neurologist, educator; b. Albion, Mich., Dec. 15, 1943; s. George Julius and Margaret (Beattie) R.; 1 child, George Andrew Martin. BA, Albion Coll., 1965; DO, Coll. Osteo. Medicine and Surgery, Des Moines, 1969. Diplomate Am. Bd. Psychiatry and Neurology. Intern, Garden City Hosp., 1969-70; resident Wayne State U., 1970-74; fellow U. Newcastle Upon Tyne, 1974-75; asst. prof. dept. neurology Wayne State U., Detroit, 1975-77; assoc. prof. Mich. State U., East Lansing, Mich., 1977-83, prof., 1983-84, 95—, prof., chmn., 1984-95. Fellow Am. Acad. Neurology, Royal Soc. Medicine; mem. AMA, Am. Osteo. Assn., Pan Am. Med. Assn., Am. Coll. Neuropsychiatrists (sr.). Home: 2070 Riverwood Dr Okemos MI 48864 Office: Mich State U Dept Internal Medicine 305 E Fee Hall East Lansing MI 48824-1316

RITCH, HERALD LAVERN, finance company executive; b. Los Angeles, Feb. 13, 1951; s. Herald Lester and Caroline (Lillevold) R.; m. Linda Suzanne Lundberg, June 11, 1972; children: Eleanor Loring, Seth Alden. BA in Econs., Stanford U., 1973; MBA, U. Pa., 1975. Assoc. Dean Witter Reynolds, Inc., N.Y.C., 1975-79, v.p., 1979-82, mng. dir., mgr. merger and acquisition dept., 1982-83; v.p. Kidder, Peabody & Co, Inc., N.Y.C., 1983-86, mng. dir., 1987-88; gen. ptnr. Freeman Spogli & Co., N.Y.C., 1988-90; managing dir. Donaldson Lufkin & Jenrette, N.Y.C., 1991-94, mng. dir. and dir. mergers and acquisitions, 1994—. Contbr. articles to profl. jours. Pres. Greenwich Assn. Retarded Citizens; elder 1st Presbyn. Ch., Greenwich. Mem. Stanwich Club, Met. Club. Avocations: tennis, skiing, reading. Office: Donaldson Lufkin & Jenrette 140 Broadway New York NY 10005-1101

RITCH, KATHLEEN, diversified company executive; Harbor Beach, Mich., Jan. 23, 1943; d. Eunice (Spry) R.; BA., Mich. State U., 1965: student Katharine Gibbs Sch., 1965-66. Exec. sec., adminstrv. asst. to pres. Katy Industries, Inc., N.Y.C., 1969-70; exec. sec., adminstrv. asst. to chmn. Kobrand Corp., N.Y.C., 1970-72; adminstrv. asst. to chmn. and pres. Ogden Corp., N.Y.C., 1972-74; asst. sec., adminstr. office services, asst. to chmn. Ogden Corp., N.Y.C., 1974-81, corporate sec., adminstr. office services, 1981-84, v.p. corporate sec., adminstr. office services, 1984-92, v.p. corp. sec., 1992—; part-owner Unell Mfg. Co., Port Hope, Mich., 1986-87. Bd. dir. Young Concert Artists, Inc., 1984-92. Mem. Am. Soc. Corporate Secs. Home: 500 E 77th St New York NY 10162-0025 Office: Ogden Corp Two Pennsylvania Pla New York NY 10121

RITCHESON, CHARLES RAY, university administrator, history educator; b. Maysville, Okla., Feb. 26, 1925; s. Charles Frederick and Jewell (Vaughn) R.; m. Shirley Marie Spackman, June 13, 1953 (div. July 1964); children: Charles Brendan, Mark Frederick; m. Alice Luethi, Oct. 11, 1965; children: Philip Luethi, Steven Whitefield, Andrew Shepherd, Peter Lorentz. B.A., Okla. U., 1946; postgrad., Zurich U., Switzerland, 1946-47, Harvard U., 1947-48; Ph.D. (Fulbright fellow), Oxford U., Eng., 1951; D.Litt. (hon.), Leicester U., Eng. Asst. prof. history Okla Coll. for Women, 1951-52, assoc. prof., 1952-53; assoc. prof. Kenyon Coll., Gambier, Ohio, 1953-60; prof. Kenyon Coll., 1960-64, chmn. dept. history, 1964; chmn., dir. grad. studies in history So. Meth. U., 1965-70; dir. Center Ibero-Am. Civilization, 1967-68; dir. with rank of dean Library Advancement, 1970-71; Colin Rhys Lovell Prof. Brit. history U. So. Calif., 1971-74, Lovell Disting. prof., 1977-84, Univ. prof., Univ. librarian, dean Univ. library, vice provost, spl. asst. to pres., 1984-90, Univ. prof. emeritus, Univ. librarian emeritus 1990—; prin., 1991—; cultural attaché Am. Embassy, 1974-77; pres. Soc. Conf. on Brit. Studies, 1967-70, Pacific Coast br. Conf. on Brit. Studies, 1971-73; exec. sec. Nat. Conf. Brit. Studies, 1973-74; presdl. appointee Nat. Council on Humanities, 1982-86, Bd. of Fgn. Scholarships, 1986-88, Nat. Council on Humanities, 1988-90; Fulbright prof. Edinburgh U., Cambridge U., 1963-64. Author: British Politics and the American Revolution, 1954, Era of the American Revolution, 1968, British Policy Toward the U.S, 1783-1795, 1968; Contbr. articles to learned jours. Chmn. U.S.-U.K. Ednl. Commn., 1974-77; ofcl. observer Brit. Bicentennial Liaison Com., 1974-76; mem. internat. adv. coun. U. Buckingham, Eng.; v.p. Am. Friends of Covent Garden, 1982-85, Fund for Arts and Culture in Ea. Europe, 1992—, exec. v.p.; mem. adv. coun. Ditchley Found.; chmn. Brit. Inst. U.S., 1978-81. Lt. (j.g.) USNR, 1942-45. Univ. award for creative scholarship, 1980; Social Sci. Research Council Faculty fellow, 1956-59; Eli Lilly-Clements Library fellow, 1960; Am. Council Learned Socs. fellow, 1963-64. Fellow Royal Hist. Soc.; mem. Conf. Brit. Studies (exec. sec. 1968-70), Tex. Inst. Letters, Phi Beta Kappa. Clubs: Calif. Club (L.A.), Brooks, Beefsteak (London), Pilgrims (N.Y.C.), Cosmos (Washington). Address: 85 Blvd Haussmann, Paris France

RITCHEY, JAMES SALEM, office furniture manufacturing company executive; b. Birmingham, Ala., June 15, 1950; s. Salem E. and Edna (George) R.; m. Rhonda Waddell, Jan. 20, 1989; children: Barry, John. BS in Acctg., U. Ala., 1972, MBA, 1981. CPA, Ala. Staff acct. Ernst & Young, Birmingham, 1971-74; asst. contr. United Chair Co., Inc., Leeds, Ala., 1974-81, contr., 1981-83; v.p. fin. Office Group Am. (United Chair Co. and Anderson Hickey Co.), Leeds, 1983-89, exec. v.p., 1989-91; pres. Office Group Am. (United Chair Co. and Anderson Hickey Co.), Leeds, 1991—; CPA. Named Acctg. Alumni of Yr., U. Ala., Birmingham, 1987. Mem. AICPA, Ala. Soc. CPA's, Nat. Assn. Accts. (past chpt. pres., Branhart-Strawn award 1982), Alpha Beta Psi. Avocations: golf, tennis, chess. Office: Office Group Am 114 Churchill Ave NW Leeds AL 35094

RITCHEY, PATRICK WILLIAM, lawyer; b. Pitts., July 9, 1949; s. Joseph Frank and Patricia Ann (Giovengo) R. BA, Haverford Coll., 1971; JD, Yale U., 1974. Bar: U.S. Dist. Ct. (we. dist.) Pa. 1974, U.S. Ct. Appeals (3d. cir.) 1976, U.S. Supreme Ct. 1980, U.S. Ct. Appeals (4th cir.) 1981, U.S. Ct. Appeals (6th cir.) 1982, U.S. Dist. Ct. (ea. dist.) Wis. 1987, U.S. Ct. Appeals (7th cir.) 1991, U.S. Ct. Appeals (D.C. cir.) 1993, U.S. Ct. Appeals (8th cir.) 1993. Assoc. Reed Smith Shaw & McClay, Pitts., 1974-82, ptnr., 1982—; mem. Pitts. Personnel Assn., Pitts., 1982—; U.S. Dist. Ct. Rules Task Force, Pitts., 1988. Mem. ABA (labor law sect.), Allegheny County Bar Assn. (labor law and fed. ct. sects.), Harvard-Yale-Princeton Club, Duquesne Club. Office: Reed Smith Shaw & McClay James H Reed Bldg 435 6th Ave Pittsburgh PA 15219-1809

RITCHEY, WILLIAM MICHAEL, chemistry educator; b. Mt. Vernon, Ohio, June 2, 1925; s. Joseph David and Minnie (Tanury) R.; m. Minetta Hoover, July 27, 1947; children: Stephen, Joseph, Mark. With Standard Oil of Ohio Research Ctr., Clev., 1955-68; prof. chemistry and macromolecular sci. Case Western Res. U., Clev., 1968—; researcher nuclear magnetic resonance; cons. Co-editor: Atlas of Spectral Data and Physical Constants for Organic Compounds, 1978. Asst. scoutmaster Troop 424, Greater Clev. Council; active Lyndhurst Baptist Ch., (Ohio). Served with U.S. Army, 1943-46. Mem. Am. Chem. Soc., Soc. Applied Spectroscopy, Sigma Xi. Home: 851 Haywood Dr South Euclid OH 44121-3403 Office: Millis Sci Center Adelbert Rd Cleveland OH 44106-7078

RITCHIE, ALBERT, lawyer; b. Charlottesville, Va., Sept. 29, 1939; s. John and Sarah Dunlop (Wallace) R.; m. Jennie Wayland, Apr. 29, 1967; children: John, Mary. BA, Yale U., 1961; LLB, U. Va., 1964. Bar: Ill. 1964. Assoc. Sidley & Austin, Chgo., 1964-71, ptnr., 1972—. Bd. dirs. Erie Neighborhood House, Chgo., 1978-88; bd. dirs. United Charities of Chgo., 1979-90. Capt. U.S. Army, 1965-67. Mem. ABA, Am. Coll. Real Estate Lawyers, Chgo. Legal Aid Soc., Legal Club Chgo. (pres. 1986-87), U. Va. Law Sch. Alumni Assn. (v.p. 1989-93, pres. 1993-95), LaSalle Club, Indian Hill Club. Episcopalian. Office: Sidley & Austin 1 First Nat Plz Chicago IL 60603

RITCHIE, ANNE, educational administrator; b. Grants Pass, Oreg., July 1, 1944; d. William Riley Jr. and Allie Brown (Clark) R.; m. Charles James Cooper, Sept. 4, 1968 (div. 1985); children: Holly Anne, Wendy Nicole. BA in Edn. with honors, Calif. State U., Sacramento, 1981. Cert. elem. tchr., Calif. CEO El Rancho Schs., Inc., Carmichael, Calif., 1981—; citizen amb. del. People to People Internat., Russia, Lithuania, Hungary, 1993, China, 1994. Active Sacramento Symphony Assn., Crocker Art Mus.; mem. Rep. Senatorial Inner Circle, Washington, 1995. Mem. AAUW, Nat. Assn. Edn. for Young Children, Profl. Assn. Childhood Educators, Nat. Child Care Assn. Episcopalian. Avocations: traveling, skiing, reading.

RITCHIE, CEDRIC ELMER, banker; b. Upper Kent, N.B., Can., Aug. 22, 1927; s. E. Thomas and Marion (Henderson) R.; m. Barbara Binnington, Apr. 20, 1956. Student pub. schs., Bath, N.B. With The Bank of N.S., Bath, 1945—; chief gen. mgr. The Bank of N.S., Toronto, Ont., Can., 1970-72, pres., 1972-79, chief exec. officer, 1972-93, chmn. bd. dirs., 1974-95; chmn. bd., dir. The Bank N.S. Jamaica Ltd., The Bank N.S. Trust Co. Trinidad and Tobago Ltd., The West India Co. Mcht. Bankers Ltd., The Bank N.S. Trinidad & Tobago Ltd., Scotiabank Jamaica Trust and Mcht. Bank Ltd.; dir., chmn. exec. com. The Bank N.S.; mem. adv. coun. for Can. Exec. Svc. Orgn.; dir. Can. Life Assurance Co., Can. Nat. Rlwys., Ingersoll-Rand Co., Maduro & Curiel's Bank N.V., J. Ray McDermott, S.A., Mercedes-Benz Can., Inc., Minorco, Moore Corp., Ltd., NOVA Corp., Alta., Pacific Basin Econ. Coun. Can. Coun., Solidbank Corp., The Japan Soc., MacMillan Bloedel Ltd. Mem. hon. com. Can. Orgn. for Devel. through Edn.; internat. adv. coun. Ctr. for Inter-Am. Rels.; chmns. coun. Ams. Soc.; dir.-at-large Jr. Achievement Can.; gov. Olympic Trust Can, Asian Inst. Mgmt., Dalhousie U.; chmn. Can.-Philippines Coun, Can. Bus. Com. on Jamaica; mem. adv. coun. Can. Exec. Svc. Orgn.; hon. dir. Save Our Northwest Atlantic Resources. Decorated Officer Order of Can., 1981; recipient Sikatuna award Can. Fedn. for Humanities, 1993; named Bus. Man of Yr., Harvard Bus. Sch. Club, 1993, Bus. Leader of Yr., Western Bus. Sch. Club Toronto, 1993. Mem. Am. Soc. Edn. (mem. hon. com.), Spencer Hall Found. (pres., trustee). Clubs: Canadian, Donalda, Mt. Royal, Mid Ocean, National, Toronto, York, Lyford Cay. Office: Scotia Plz 44 King Street W, Toronto, ON Canada M5H 1H1

RITCHIE, DANIEL LEE, university administrator; b. Springfield, Ill., Sept. 19, 1931; s. Daniel Felix and Jessie Dee (Binney) R. B.A., Harvard U., 1954, M.B.A., 1956. Exec. v.p. MCA, Inc., Los Angeles, 1967-70; pres. Archon Pure Products Co., Los Angeles, 1970-73; exec. v.p. Westinghouse Electric Corp., Pitts., 1975-78; pres. corp. staff and strategic planning Westinghouse Broadcasting Co., 1978-79, pres., chief exec. officer, 1979-81, chmn., chief exec. officer; chmn., chief exec. officer Westinghouse Broadcasting & Cable, Inc., 1981-87; owner Grand River Ranch, Kremmling, Colo., 1977—, Rancho Cielo, Montecito, Calif., 1977—; chancellor U. Denver, 1989—. With U.S. Army, 1956-58. Office: U Denver Office of the Chancellor University Park Denver CO 80208

RITCHIE, GARRY HARLAN, television broadcast executive; b. Earling, W.Va., Aug. 18, 1938; s. Edgar Harlan and Elsie Pearl (Meador) R.; m. Nancy Lee Gladwell, June 14, 1958; children: Arthur Harlan, Michael Lee. Student, U. Charleston, 1956-60; student, Baldwin-Wallace Coll., 1965; BA, Thomas Edison State Coll., 1979. Engr., reporter Sta. WTIP Radio, Charleston, W.Va., 1956-60; sta. mgr. Sta. WRON Radio, Ronceverte, W.Va., 1960-63; reporter, newscaster Stas. WDOK AM & FM Radio, Cleve., 1963-65, Sta. WHK AM & FM Radio, Cleve., 1965-67; reporter, assignment editor Scripps-Howard Broadcasting Co., Sta. WEWS-TV, Cleve., 1967-69; from news dir. to sta. mgr. Scripps-Howard Broadcasting Co., Sta. WEWS-TV, 1969-82; cable news mgr. corp. office Scripps-Howard Broadcasting Co., Westport, Conn., 1982-83; asst. gen. mgr. Scripps-Howard Broadcasting Co., Sta. WCPO-TV, Cin., 1983-84; v.p., gen. mgr. Diversified Communications, Sta. WCJB-TV, Gainesville, Fla., 1984-86, Diversified Communications, Sta. WYOU-TV, Scranton, Pa., 1986-91; pres. broadcast div. Diversified Communications, Portland, Maine, 1991-93; v.p., gen. mgr. Gateway Comms., Inc., Sta. WOWK-TV, Huntington, W.Va., 1993—. Bd. dirs. Hippodrome Theatre, Gainesville, 1985-86, Vol. Ctr. Alachua County, Gainesville, 1985-86, Crimetrac Gainesville, Fla., 1985-86, Police Adv. Commn., Gainesville, 1985-86, Barnett Bank Alachua County, Gainesville, 1986, Scranton chpt. ARC, 1988-91, Better Bus. Bur. N.E. Pa., Scranton, 1988-91, Untied Way Lackawanna County, Scranton, 1989-91, Cabell Huntington (W.Va.) Hosp. Found., 1993—; bd. dirs., v.p. Girls Club Alachua County, Gainesville, 1985-86; mem. adv. bd. Scranton Area Found., 1989-91; trustee Keystone Jr. Coll. Laplume, Pa., 1991-92. Recipient 5 Emmy awards Cleve. chpt. NATAS, 1973-80. Mem. Nat. Assn. Broadcasters, Nat. Assn. TV Programming Execs., W.Va. Broadcasters Assn., Pa. Assn. Broadcasters (bd. dirs. 1989-91), Greater Scranton C. of C. (bd. dirs. 1987-90), Downtown Scranton Bus. Assn. (bd. dirs. 1989-91), Rotary (Scranton) (bd. dirs. 1989-91), Rotary (Huntington, W.Va.). Republican. Methodist. Avocations: ham radio, astronomy, computers, reading. Home: 19 Pinecrest Dr Huntington WV 25705

RITCHIE, J. MURDOCH, pharmacologist; b. Aberdeen, Scotland, June 10, 1925; came to U.S. 1956; s. Alexander Farquharson and Agnes Jane (Bremner) R.; m. Brenda Rachel Bigland; children: Alasdair J., A. Jocelyn. BSc, Aberdeen (Scotland) U., 1944, U. Coll. London, 1949; PhD, U. Coll. London, 1952, DSc, 1960; MA, Yale U., 1968; DSc, Aberdeen U., 1987. Lectr. physiology U. Coll. London, 1949-51; vis. staff Nat. Inst. Med. Rsch., London, 1951-55; asst. prof. to prof. Albert Einstein Coll. Medicine, N.Y.C., 1954-63, prof. pharmacology, 1963-68; prof. and chmn. pharmacology Yale U., New Haven, 1968-74, dir. biol. scis., 1975-78, prof. pharmacology, 1968—. Contbr. articles to profl. jours.; editor sci. books and jours. Fellow Royal Soc., Univ. Coll. London. Home: 47 Deepwood Dr Hamden CT 06517-3414 Office: Yale Univ Sch Medicine 333 Cedar St New Haven CT 06510-3206

RITCHIE, JAMES E., hotel executive; b. 1936. Exec. v.p. corp. mgt. Mirage Resorts Inc., Las Vegas. Office: Mirage Resorts Inc 3400 Las Vegas Blvd S Las Vegas NV 89109*

RITCHIE, MICHAEL BRUNSWICK, film director and producer; b. Waukesha, Wis., Nov. 28, 1938; s. Benbow Ferguson and Patricia (Graney) R.; m. Jimmie Bly, Oct. 1982; children from previous marriage: Lauren, Steven, Jessica; stepchildren: Lillian, Miriam, Nelly, Billy. A.B., Harvard U., 1960. Television dir., 1963-68, now dir. films. Dir.: Downhill Racer, 1969, Prime Cut, 1972, The Candidate, 1972, Smile, 1975, Bad News Bears, 1976, Semi Tough, 1977, The Island, 1980, Bette Midler's Divine Madness, 1980, The Survivors, 1983, Fletch, 1985, Wildcats, 1986, The Golden Child, 1986, The Couch Trip, 1987, Fletch Lives, 1989, Diggstown, 1989, Cops and Robbersons, 1994, The Scout, 1994; dir., writer: The Bad News Bears Go to Japan, 1978, An Almost Perfect Affair, 1979; (TV series) Profiles in Courage (also prod.), Man from U.N.C.L.E., Run for Your Life, Dr. Kildare, The Big Valley, others; TV films include The Positively True Adventures of the Alleged Texas Cheerleader-Murdering Mom, 1993; films invited to Venice Film Festival and U.S. Film Festival. Mem. Dirs. Guild Am. Office: care Marvin Freedman Freedman Kinzelberg & Broder 2121 Avenue Of The Stars Los Angeles CA 90067-5010 also: ICM 8942 Wilshire Blvd Beverly Hills CA 90211-1908*

RITCHIE, RICHARD LEE, communications company executive, former railroad and forest products company executive; b. Grand Rapids, Mich., July 20, 1946; s. Robert George and Gertrude (Dryer) R.; m. Marlene Barton, Nov. 16, 1969; children: Gabrielle Gay, Steven Barton. B.A., Mich. State U., 1968, M.B.A., 1972; P.M.D., Harvard U., 1982. C.P.A., Mich. Sr. acct. Peat, Marwick, Mitchell & Co., Detroit, 1968-69, 72-74; mgr. corp. acctg. Grand Trunk Western R.R., Detroit, 1974-76; treas. Grand Trunk Western R.R., 1976-79, asst. v.p.-treas., 1980-83; v.p., treas. James River Corp., Richmond, Va., 1984-86; sr. v.p. fin., chief fin. officer Harte Hanks Communications, San Antonio, 1987—; prof. Oakland Community Coll., Farmington, Mich. Served with AUS, 1969-71. Mem. AICPA, Mich. Assn. CPAs, Am. Acctg. Assn., Beta Alpha Psi, Beta Gamma Sigma. Jewish. Office: Harte Hanks Comm 200 Concord Plz Dr # 800 San Antonio TX 78216

RITCHIE, ROBERT FIELD, lawyer; b. Dallas, July 9, 1917; s. Robert Allan and Sallie Bowen (Field) R.; m. Catherine Canfield, Sept. 14, 1949;

children—Allan, Lee, Ann, Kate, Sara, Beth. B.S., So. Meth. U., 1939, LL.B., 1941; LL.M., U. Mich., 1942, S.J.D., 1953. Bar: Tex. 1941. Ptnr. Ritchie Ritchie & Crosland, Dallas, 1946-66; ptnr. Ritchie Crosland & Egan, Dallas, 1966-82, Andrews & Kurth, Dallas, 1982—. Author: Integration of Public Utility Holding Companies, 1954. Elder Presbyn. Ch., Dallas, 1976—. Recipient Silver Beaver award Boy Scouts Am., 1970, Disting. Eagle Scout award, 1975, Order of San Jacinto, Sons Republic of Tex., 1979. Mem. ABA, Dallas Bar Assn., Tex. Bar Found., Crescent Club, Dallas Country Club, Tower Club, Kappa Alpha (Court of Honor 1974). Avocation: photography. Home: 3939 Marquette St Dallas TX 75225-5432 Office: Andrews & Kurth 4400 Thanksgiving Towers Dallas TX 75201

RITCHIE, ROBERT OLIVER, materials science educator; b. Plymouth, Devon, U.K., Jan. 2, 1948; came to U.S. 1974; s. Kenneth Ian and Kathleen Joyce (Sims) R.; m. Connie Olesen (div. 1978); 1 child, James Oliver; m. HaiYing Song, 1991. BA with honors, U. Cambridge, Eng., 1969, MA, PhD, 1973, ScD, 1990. Cert. engr. Goldsmith's rsch. fellow Churchill Coll. U. Cambridge, 1972-74; Miller fellow in basic rsch. sci. U. Calif., Berkeley, 1974-76; assoc. prof. mech. engring. MIT, Cambridge, 1977-81; prof. U. Calif., Berkeley, 1981—; dir. Ctr. for Advanced Materials Lawrence Berkeley Lab., Cambridge, 1987—; dep. dir. materials sci. div. Lawrence Berkeley Lab., Berkeley, 1990-94; cons. Alcan, Allison, Boeing, Chevron, Exxon, GE, Grumman, Instron, Northrop, Rockwell, Westinghouse, Baxter, Carbomedics, Med. Inc., Shiley, St. Jude Med. Editor seven books; contbr. over 250 articles to profl. jours. Recipient Curtis W. McGraw Rsch. award Am. Soc. Engring. Educators, 1987, Mathewson Gold medal Minerals, Materials, Metals, Soc., 1985, Rosenhain medal Inst. Materials London, 1992; named one of Top 100 Scientists, Sci. Digest mag., 1984. Fellow Inst. Materials (London), Am. Soc. Metals Internat., Internat. Congress on Fracture (hon., v.p.); mem. Minerals, Materials and Metals Soc., Am. Orchid Soc. Avocations: skiing, orchids, tennis. Home: 590 Grizzly Peak Blvd Berkeley CA 94708-1238 Office: U Calif Dept Materials Sci & Mineral Engring Berkeley CA 94720

RITCHIE, ROYAL DANIEL, economic development executive; b. Takoma Park, Md., Dec. 28, 1945; s. Thomas Joseph and Dorothy Queen (Royal) R.; m. Karen Louise Turner; children: Kimberly, Matthew, Jessica, Heather. Student Glassboro State U., 1965-66, Columbia Union Coll., 1966-67. V.p., dir. Assoc. Developers Internat., Inc., Washington, 1968-75, Internat. Fin. and Mgmt. Corp., Washington, 1975-77; project mgr. Sheraton Corp., Washington, 1977-78; v.p. East Balt. Developers, Inc., 1979-82, East Balt. Contractors, Inc., 1979-82; dir. econ. devel. East Balt. Community Corp., 1979-82, Stouffer Harbor Place Hotel, Balt., 1986-88, project mgr., 1988—; dir. devel. Somerset House, Inc., 1982-86; mng. gen. ptnr. HFA Homes for Ams.; ltd. ptnr. C & R Contracting Assocs.; pres. RDR Contracting Assn., Inc.; pres. Hanlon Park Condominimum Assn., Inc.; 1st v.p. Prince George's Rep. Club, 1982-85; chmn. Com. for Better Govt., Riverdale, Md., 1984—; mem. 22d legis. dist. Md. State Rep. Cen. Com., 1982-86; 2d v.p. Prince George's County Civic Fedn., Inc., 1984, pres. 1985-86, 88; chmn. Quality Health Care Action Com., Inc. Mem. Am. Concrete Inst. (com. on rehabilitation, repair of concrete com.), Montgomery County C. of C. (econ. devel. com.), Prince George's County Bd. Trade, Balt. Coun. on Fgn. Affairs, Lions (v.p. Riverdale club). Adventist. Home: 7934 Sly Fox Ln Manassas VA 22111 Office: Somerset House Inc 5560 Friendship Blvd Chevy Chase MD 20815-7200

RITCHIE, WALLACE PARKS, JR., surgeon, educator; b. St. Paul, Nov. 4, 1935; s. Wallace Parks and Alice Ransome (Otis) R.; m. Barbara Carey Jewell, Aug. 10, 1960; children: Stephanie, David, Jessica. BA, Yale U., 1957; MD, Johns Hopkins U., 1961; PhD, U. Minn., 1971. Diplomate Am. Bd. Surgery. Intern, resident in surgery Yale U., New Haven, 1961-63; resident in surgery U. Minn. Hosps., Mpls., 1963-69, instr. in surgery, 1969-70; from asst. prof. to prof. surgery U. Va. Sch. Medicine, Charlottesville, 1973-83; prof., chmn. dept. surgery Temple U. Sch. Medicine, Phila., 1983-93; exec. dir. Am. Bd. Surgery, Phila., 1994—. Editor textbook: Essentials of Surgery, 1994; contbr. over 125 sci. articles to profl. jours. Lt. col. Med. Corps U.S. Army, 1970-73. USPHS grantee, 1974-85. Office: Am Bd Surgery Inc 1617 JFK Blvd Ste 860 Philadelphia PA 19103-1847

RITCHIE, WILLIAM PAUL, lawyer; b. Columbus, Ohio, June 3, 1946; s. Austin Everett and Helen (Drake) R.; m. Diane Smith, Aug. 2, 1969; 1 child, Elizabeth Drake. BS in Bus. Adminstrn., Ohio State U., 1968, JD, U. Va., 1971. Bar: Ohio 1971, Calif. 1973, Ill. 1987. Assoc. Jones, Day, Reavis & Pogue, Cleve., 1971-77, ptnr., 1977—, ptnr.-in-charge, Chgo., 1987—. Served to lt. USAR, 1972. Mem. ABA, Ohio Bar Assn., Calif. Bar Assn., Chgo. Bar Assn., Mayfield Country Club (Cleve.), Chgo. Club. Republican. Home: 55 W Goethe St # 1252 Chicago IL 60610-2233 Office: Jones Day Reavis & Pogue 77 W Wacker Chicago IL 60601-1692

RITER, STEPHEN, university administrator, electrical engineer; b. Providence, Mar. 7, 1940; s. Max and Jeannette (Finn) R.; m. Eve R. Hirsch, Aug. 11, 1963; children—Heidi L., Theodore H. B.A., Rice U., Houston, 1961, B.S. in Elec. Engring, 1962; M.S., U. Houston, 1967, Ph.D., 1968. Registered profl. engr., Tex. Dir. Center Urban Programs, Tex. A&M U., 1974-76, mem. univ. faculty, 1968-80, prof. elec. engring., 1976-80; dir. Tex. Energy Extension Service, 1976-79; prof. elec. engring., chmn. dept. elec. engring. and computer sci. U. Tex., El Paso, 1980-89, dean engring., 1989-95, dir. Ctr. for Environ. Resource Mgmt., 1989—; interim v.p. acad. affairs U Tex, El Paso, 1995; Active El Paso Utility Regulatory Bd., 1982-89; cons. in field. Author papers in field.; Editor: Trans. Geosci. Electronics, 1972-76. Mem. policy adv. com. Tex. Dept. Community Affairs, 1979-81; Tex. Border Health and Environ. Issues Task Force, 1990—. Served with U.S. Army, 1962-64. Mem. IEEE, Am. Soc. Engring. Edn. Home: 836 Cherry Hill Ln El Paso TX 79912-3325 Office: Univ Tex Office of VP Acad Affairs El Paso TX 79968

RITSCH, FREDERICK FIELD, academic administrator, historian; b. Covington, Va., Nov. 25, 1935; s. Frederick Field and Harriet Curtis (Miller) R.; m. Jeannette McClung, June 14, 1957 (dec.); children: Frederick Field III, Lise Catherina; m. Debra Ronning, Dec. 21, 1991; 1 child, Anne Ronning. BA, U. Va., 1956, MA, 1959, PhD, 1964; student, Univ. de Strasbourg, France, 1957-58. Instr. Randolph-Macon Women's Coll., Lynchburg, Va., 1959; vis. lectr. Sweet Briar (Va.) Coll., 1959-60; from asst. prof. to prof. Dana history and humanities Converse Coll., Spartanburg, S.C., 1960-83, dir. ctr. for humanities, head div. humanities; dean of faculty Elizabethtown (Pa.) Coll., 1984-85, provost, 1986—; cons. Ednl. Services, Inc., Washington, 1975-77; vice chmn. Communication Services, Inc., Spartanburg, 1978-82; dir. Ctr. for Study Contemporary Humanities, Spartanburg, 1972-81. Author: French Left and European Idea, 1967; author, editor: Issues and Commitment, 1976; editor: (with M. Goldberg) Probes and Projections, 1974; contbr. articles to profl. jours. and collections. Elder Donegal Presbyn. Ch., Mt. Joy, Pa. Fulbright fellow, 1957-58; NEH grantee, 1969; recipient Cert. Merit, Inst. Internat. Edn., 1978. Mem. Am. Hist. Assn., Pa. Acad. Deans Conf. (program chmn. 1984), So. Humanities Conf. (editor jour. Humanities in the South 1971-83, chmn. 1984), Phi Beta Kappa. Home: 600 S Spruce St Elizabethtown PA 17022-2552 Office: Elizabethtown Coll 1 Alpha Dr Elizabethtown PA 17022

RITT, DAVID LAWRENCE, symphony musician; b. Manhasset, N.Y., July 15, 1957; s. Lawrence and Alisha (Lewin) R.; m. Heather Diana Woods, Dec. 16, 1991. BMus, Eastman Sch. Music, Rochester, N.Y., 1975. Registered hypnotist/hypnotherapist. Prin. trombone Singapore Symphony, 1978-79, Ft. Wayne (Ind.) Philharmonic, 1979-80, Seattle Symphony, 1981—, Seattle Opera, 1981—; bass trumpet Pacific N.W. Wagner Festival, Seattle, 1982—, Met. Opera, N.Y.C., 1990-91. Composer 120 Melodious Accompaniments, 1994. Democrat. Office: Seattle Symphony Seattle Center House 305 Harrison St 4th Fl Seattle WA 98109

RITT, PAUL EDWARD, communications and electronics company executive; b. Balt., Mar. 3, 1928; s. Paul Edward and Mary (Knight) R.; m. Dorothy Ann Wintz, Dec. 30, 1950; children: Paul Edward, Peter M., John W., James T., Mary Carol, Matthew J. BS in Chemistry, Loyola U., Balt., 1950, M.S. in Chemistry, 1952; Ph.D. in Chemistry, Georgetown U., 1954. Research asso. Harris Research Lab., Washington, 1950-52; aerospace research chemist Melpar, Inc., Falls Church, Va., 1952-60; research dir. Melpar, Inc., 1960-62, v.p. research, 1962-65, v.p. research and engring.,

1965-67; v.p., gen. mgr. Tng. Corp. Am., 1965-67; pres. applied sci. div., applied tech. div. Litton Industries, 1967-68; v.p., dir. research GTE Labs., Waltham, Mass., 1968-86; dir. acad. affairs Babson Coll., Wellesley, Mass., 1986—; bd. dirs. Abex Inc., N.Y.C. subs. IC Industries, 1983-89; bd. dirs. Pneumo/Abex Inc., Boston, 1986-89. Contbr. articles to profl. jours. Mem. dean's adv. coun. U. Mass. Sch. Engring.; mgmt. bd. advs. Worcester Poly. Inst.; adv. coun. Stanford U.; mem. Mass. High Tech. Coun.; trustee Waltham-Weston Hosp., 1983—, New Eng. Coll. Fund., 1980-86. Fellow Am. Inst. Chemists, AAAS; mem. Am. Phys. Soc., Royal Soc. Chemistry, IEEE, Am. Inst. Physics, Electrochem. Soc., Am. Vacuum Soc., Am. Ceramic Soc., Am. Chem. Soc., Washington Acad. Sci., N.Y. Acad. Sci., Tech. Transfer Soc., Sigma Xi. Patentee in field. Home: 36 Sylvan Ln Weston MA 02193-1028 Office: Babson Coll Wellesley MA 02154

RITT, ROGER MERRILL, lawyer; b. N.Y.C., Mar. 26, 1950; m. Mimi Santini, Aug. 25, 1974; children: Evan Samuel, David Martin. BA, U. Pa., 1972; JD, Boston U., 1975, LLM, 1976. Bar: Mass. 1977, Pa. 1975, U.S. Tax Ct. Sr. ptnr. Hale and Dorr, Boston; adj. prof. grad. tax program Boston U.; panelist Am. Law Inst., Mass. Continuing Legal Edn., World Trade Inst., NYU Inst. on Fed. Taxation; mem. exec. com. Fed. Tax Inst. New Eng. Editor tax highlights Boston Bar jour. Treas. Found. for Tax Edn. Mem. ABA (tax sect.), Boston Bar Assn. Office: Hale and Dorr 60 State St Boston MA 02109-1801

RITTBERG, ERIC JOSEPH, political consultant; b. Queens, N.Y., Nov. 21, 1962; s. Samuel Herman and Ida Gerri (Turk) R.; m. Barbara Jean Carpenter, Jan. 28, 1982. BA in Polit. Sci., Fla. State U., 1990. Mem. rep. Fla. C. of C., Tallahassee, 1991-93; advance man/travel aide Ron Paul for Pres., Houston, 1987-88; exec. dir. Republican Liberty Caucus, Tallahassee, 1993—. Author: Activism for Liberty, 1995. Nat. committeeman Libertarian Party, 1986-87; precinct committeeman Leon County Rep. Party, Tallahassee, 1992—; chmn. County Conservation Dist. Bd. of Suprs., 1995—. With USN, 1981-85. Decorated Expiditiary medal USN, 1984. Mem. Vols. for Am. (pres. 1995—), Jews for the Preservation of Firearms Ownership, Young Reps. Republican. Jewish. Avocations: books, traveling, computer debate forums. Home: 1549 A Willow Bend Way Tallahassee FL 32301 Office: Rep Libery Caucus # 434 1717 Apalachee Pkwy Tallahassee FL 32301

RITTER, ALFRED, aerospace consultant; b. Bklyn., Mar. 15, 1923; s. Max and Anna Ritter; m. Joyce Rimer, June 15, 1947; children: Michael Glenn, Erica Anne, Theodore William. BS in Aerospace Engring., Ga. Inst. Tech., 1943, MS in Aerospace Engring., 1947; PhD, Cornell U., 1951. Rsch. engr. Office of Naval Rsch., Washington, 1951-54; supr. aerophysics Rsch. Inst. Ill. Inst. Tech., Chgo., 1954-58, instr. calculus and fluid mechanics, 1956-58; pres. Therm Advanced Rsch., Inc., Ithaca, N.Y., 1958-68; asst. head applied mechanics dept. Calspan Corp. (formerly Cornell Aero. Lab.), Buffalo, 1968-70, asst. head aerodynamic rsch. dept., 1970-78, head aerodynamic rsch. dept., 1978-80; dir. tech. Arnold Engring. Devel. Ctr. div. Calspan Corp. (formerly Cornell Aero. Lab.), Tullahoma, Tenn., 1980-86; sr. assoc. Booz Allen & Hamilton, Huntsville, Ala., 1986-88; pres. A. Ritter, Inc., Huntsville, 1988—; vis. lectr. Cornell U., 1965; instr. aerospace U. Ala., Huntsville, 1985, 87, 88, adj. prof. aerospace engring., 1988—; exec. dir. Calspan Ctr. for Aerospace Rsch., U. Tenn., 1984-86, chmn. nat. adv. bd. Space Inst., 1987—; mem. gov.'s task force So. Mid. Tenn. High Tech. Initiative, 1985-86; reviewer Applied Mechanics Revs., 1955-84; presenter seminars many ednl. instns. Contbr. articles to profl. publs. Mem. Ithaca (N.Y.) Bd. Edn., 1967. 2nd lt. U.S. Army AC, 1943-46. Fellow AIAA (nat. v.p. tech. activities 1981-85, bd. dirs. 1981-85, mem. various coms., participant confs.); mem. AAAS (rep. to atmospheric and hydrospheric scis. sect. 1978-80), U.S. Air Force Assn. (gen. H.H. Arnold chpt. 1985-86, medal of merit 1986), Internat. Coun. Aero. Scis., Nat. Rsch. Coun. (mem. earthquake engring. com. 1984, mem. assessment of nat. aero. wind tunnel facilities com. 1987-88), Strategic Def. Initiative Orgn. (blue ribbon panel to review missile programs 1989, 92), N.Y. Acad. Scis., Rotary, Sigma Xi. Avocations: reading, music, sports, swimming, cross-country skiing. Home: 10148 Dunbarton Dr SE Huntsville AL 35803-1252

RITTER, ALFRED FRANCIS, JR., cable television executive; b. Norfolk, Va., Dec. 31, 1946; s. Alfred Francis Ritter and Lucile Grey (Thomas) Woodward; m. Caroline Buchanan O'Keefe, Aug. 10, 1968; children: Alfred F. III, Caroline O'Donnell. BA, Coll. of William and Mary, 1968. CPA, Va. Staff acct. Goodman & Co. CPAs, Norfolk, Va., 1971-76; corp. controller Landmark Communications, Norfolk, 1976-78, v.p., controller, 1978, v.p. fin., 1978; v.p. fin. TeleCable Corp., Norfolk, 1983-89, exec. v.p., 1989—. Mem. exec. com. Health, Welfare and Recreation Planning Coun., Hampton Roads, Va., 1991—; trustee Norfolk Acad., 1991—, Hermitage Found., 1991—; bd. dirs. Norfolk Forum, 1991—. Lt. USN, 1968-71. Mem. AICPAs, Va. Soc. CPAs. Episcopalian. Avocations: fishing, golf. Home: 1133 S Bay Shore Dr Virginia Bch VA 23451-3807 Office: TeleCable Corp 999 Waterside Dr Norfolk VA 23510-3300

RITTER, BRUCE, Commodities Company executive. Exec. v.p. Louis Dreyfus Corp., Wilton, Conn., 1973—. Office: Louis Dreyfus Corp 10 Westport Rd Wilton CT 06897-4522

RITTER, CHARLES EDWARD, lawyer; b. Detroit, July 24, 1938; s. Kenneth Eugene and Mary Elizabeth (Klinsmann) R.; m. Donna Lou Monroe, Mar. 20, 1965; children: Jeffrey Munro and Matthew Alan. B in Archtl. Engring., U. Detroit, 1961; JD, Wayne State U., 1966. Bar: Mich. 1966, U.S. Dist. Ct. (we. dist.) Mich. 1967, U.S. Ct. Appeals (6th cir.) 1988, U.S. Supreme Ct. 1988. Assoc. Adams, Burgie, Scott, Ritter & Brenton, P.C. and predecessors, Kalamazoo, 1966-69, ptnr., 1970-83; ptnr. Brown, Colman & DeMent, P.C., Kalamazoo, 1983-84; ptnr. Miller, Canfield, Paddock and Stone, Kalamazoo, 1984—, resident ptnr., 1988-90; group leader Western Mich. Litigation, 1994—. Sr. warden St. Martin of Tours Episc. Ch., Kalamazoo, 1990. Fellow Mich. Bar Found.; mem. Fed. Bar Assn., Kalamazoo Bar Assn. (bd. dirs. 1985-89, pres. 1988-89), Def. Rsch. Inst., Nature Conservancy (life). Avocations: cross country skiing, photography, outdoor activities. Office: Miller Canfield Paddock & Stone 444 W Michigan Ave Kalamazoo MI 49007-3752

RITTER, DALE FRANKLIN, geologist, research association administrator; b. Allentown, Pa., Nov. 13, 1932; s. C. Century and Elizabeth (Bowden) R.; m. Jacqueline Leh, Aug. 15, 1953 (dec. Jan. 1961); children: Duane, Darryl, Glen; m. Esta Virginia Lewis, Nov. 23, 1962; 1 child, Lisa Diane. BA in Edn., Franklin and Marshall Coll., 1955, BS in Geology, 1959; MS in Geology, Princeton U., 1963, PhD in Geology, 1964. From asst. to assoc. prof. geology Franklin and Marshall Coll., Lancaster, Pa., 1964-72; prof. geology So. Ill. U., Carbondale, 1972-90; exec. dir. Quaternary Sci. Ctr. Desert Rsch. Inst., Reno, Nev., 1990—. Author: Process Geomorphology, 2d edit., 1986. Fellow NSF, 1968-69; recipient Lindback award Disting. Teaching, Lindback Found., 1970, Outstanding Teaching award Amoco Found., 1979. Fellow Geol. Soc. Am. (chmn. quaternary geol./geomorphology divsn. 1988-89); mem. Am. Quaternary Assn., Assn. Am. Geographers, Yellowstone-Big Horn Rsch. Assn. (pres. 1983-85). Office: Quaternary Sci Ctr Desert Rsch Inst 7010 Dandini Blvd Reno NV 89512

RITTER, DANIEL BENJAMIN; lawyer; b. Wilmington, Del., Apr. 6, 1937; s. David Moore and Bernice Elizabeth (Carlson) R.; m. Shirley F. Sether, Jan. 29, 1971; 1 child, Roxane Elise. AB with honors, U. Chgo., 1957; LLB, U. Wash., 1963. Bar: Wash. 1963, U.S. Dist. Ct. (we. dist.) Wash. 1963, U.S. Tax Ct. 1965, U.S. Ct. Appeals (9th cir.) 1963. Assoc. Davis, Wright Tremaine (formerly Davis, Wright and Jones), 1963-69, ptnr., 1969—; lectr. Bar Rev. Assocs. Wash., Seattle, 1964-86; chmn. internat. dept. Davis, Wright and Jones, Seattle, 1984-85, chmn. banking dept., 1986-89. Casenote editor U. Wash. Law Rev., 1962-63; contbg. author: Washington Commercial Law Desk Book, 1982, rev. edit., 1987, Washington Community Property Desk Book, 1977. Trustee Cathedral Assoc., Seattle, 1980-86; legal counsel Wash. State Reps., Bellevue, 1983-92; bd. dirs. U. Chgo. Club Puget Sound, Seattle, 1982—, pres. 1984-86; bd. dirs. Am. Lung Assn.-Wash., Seattle, 1992; mem. vis. com. U. Wash. Law Sch., 1984-88; trustee U. Wash. Law Sch. Found., 1989-92; chmn. alumni rels. coun. U. Chgo., 1986-88; mem. statute law com. State of Wash., 1978-87; bd. dirs. Seattle Camerata, 1991-93; bd. dirs. Early Music Guild, Seattle, 1993—. Mem. ABA (bus. law sect.), Wash. State Bar Assn. (chmn. bus. law sect.

1988-89, uniform comml. code com. 1980—, chmn. 1980-86, chmn. internat. law com. 1979-81, judicial recommendations com. 1991-93), Seattle-King County Bar Assn. (chmn. internat. and comparative law sect. 1980-82), Rainier Club, Order of Coif. Republican. Lutheran. Avocation: reading, theater, early music. Home: 1204 22nd Ave E Seattle WA 98112-3535 Office: Davis Wright Tremaine 2600 Century Sq 1501 4th Ave Seattle WA 98101-1662

RITTER, DEBORAH ELIZABETH, anesthesiologist, educator; b. Phila., May 16, 1947; d. Charles William and Elizabeth Angeline (Coffman) R. BA, Susquehanna U., 1968; MS, U. Pa., 1969; MD, Med. Coll. Pa., 1973. Diplomate Am. Bd. Anesthesiology (assoc. examiner oral bds. 1990, 92). Intern Thomas Jefferson Univ. Hosp., Phila., 1973-74, resident in anesthesia, 1974-76, clin. fellow in anesthesiology, 1976-77; affiliate resident in anesthesia Children's Hosp. Pa., Phila., 1975; assoc. in anesthesiology Frankford Hosp., Phila., 1977-78; clin. instr. anesthesiology Med. Coll. Pa., Phila., 1977-78; clin. instr. anesthesiology Thomas Jefferson U., 1978-80, clin. asst. prof., 1980-86, clin. assoc. prof., 1986—, vice chmn. dept. anesthesiology, 1985—. Contbr. articles to profl. jours. Named Top Doc, Phila. Mag., 1994. Mem. AMA, Am. Women's Med. Assn., Am. Soc. Anesthesiologists, Internat. Anesthesia Rsch. Soc., Soc. Edn. Anesthesia, Am. Anesthesia Clin. Dirs. Lutheran. Avocations: gardening, music, history, wilderness preservation, American Indian culture. Office: Thomas Jefferson U Dept Anesthesiology 111 S 11th St Ste 6460G Philadelphia PA 19107

RITTER, DONALD LAWRENCE, environmental policy institute administrator; b. N.Y.C., Oct. 21, 1940; s. Frank and Ruth R.; m. Edith Duerksen; children: Jason, Kristina. B.S. in Metall. Engring., Lehigh U., 1961; M.S. in Phys. Metallurgy, MIT, 1963, Sc.D., 1966. Mem. faculty Calif. State Poly. U., also contract cons. Gen. Dynamics Co., 1968-69; mem. faculty dept. metallurgy and materials scis., asst. to v.p. for research Lehigh U., 1969-76; mgr. research program devel., 1976-79, mem. 96th-102d congresses from 15th Pa dist., 1979-93; scientist, chmn., pres. Nat. Environ. Policy Inst., Washington, 1994—; mem. energy and commerce com. and subcoms. telecommunications and fin.; ranking minority mem. transp. and hazardous materials; mem. sci., space and tech. com. and subcoms. environment and tech. and competitiveness; chmn. house Rep. task force on tech. and policy; co-chair Cngl. High Tech. Caucus; ranking minority mem. house Commn. on Security and Cooperation in Europe (Helsinki Commn.), mem. 1980-93; co-chmn. ad hoc com. on Baltic states and Ukraine; treas. Congl. steel caucus; mem. Congl. textile and apparel caucus; mem. environ. and energy study conf.; sci. exchange fellow U.S. Nat. Acad. Scis.-Soviet Acad. Sci., Baikov Inst., Moscow, 1967-68. Contbr. articles to sci., engring. and quality jours. Bd. dirs. Baum Art Sch., Bach Choir Bethlehem, Pa.; ex officio mem. bd. assocs. Muhlenberg Coll., Allentown; mem. polit. sci. vis. com. MIT, 1982-85. Recipient award for disting. pub. svc. IEEE, 1990. Fellow Am. Inst. Chemists (hon scroll award); mem. NSPE, Am. Soc. for Metals (disting. life), Sigma Xi, Tau Beta Pi, Pi Mu Epsilon. Unitarian. Home: 2746 Forest Dr Coopersburg PA 18036-9253 Office: Nat Environ Policy Inst 1101 16th St NW Ste 502 Washington DC 20036-4803

RITTER, FRANK NICHOLAS, otolaryngologist, educator; b. New Albany, Ind., July 30, 1928; s. Carl Joseph and Kathleen Mary (Wolfe) R.; m. Gertrude Erlacher; children: Raymond, Kathleen, Lawrence, Mary Elizabeth, Teresa, Joseph, Sharon, Michael. BS, Notre Dame U., 1949; MD, St. Louis U., 1953; MS, U. Mich., 1959. Diplomate Am. Bd. Otolaryngology (pres. 1990-93). Intern Mercy Hosp., Ohio, 1953-54; resident in otorhinolaryngology U. Mich. Hosp., 1954-60; asst. otolaryngology U. Mich., Ann Arbor, 1960-65, assoc. prof., 1966-70, clin. prof., 1971—. Author: The Surgical Anatomy and Technique of Surgery on the Paranasal Sinuses, 1978, 3d edit. 1992; contbr. articles to profl. jours. Capt. USAF, 1955-57. Recipient Sr. award Med. Sch., U. Mich., 1965, Shovel award U. Mich. Med. Students, 1967. Mem. Am. Laryngol. Assn., Am. Otological Soc., Am. Acad. Otolaryngology, Head and Neck Surgery, Am. Bronchoesophagological Assn. (pres. 1985), Mich. Otolaryn. Soc. (pres. 1968), Soc. Univ. of Otolaryngologists, Triological Soc. (exec. sec. 1985-89, pres. 1993), Centurian (pres. 1984), Walter Wark Soc. (pres. 1986). Roman Catholic. Avocations: golf, fishing. Office: Reichert Health Bldg 5333 Mcauley Dr Ste 4016R Ypsilanti MI 48197-1087

RITTER, HAL, newspaper editor. Mng. editor money sect. USA Today, Arlington, Va., now mng. editor news, 1995—. Office: USA Today 1000 Wilson Blvd Arlington VA 22229°

RITTER, JAMES WILLIAM, architect, educator; b. Richmond, Va., June 14, 1942; s. James William and Catherine (Luck) R.; m. Betty Ann Mauck, June 19, 1965; 1 child, Mark Channing. BArch., Va. Poly. Inst. and State U., 1965. Registered architect Va., Md., D.C., Del., Ky., W.Va., N.C., Pa. Assoc. Wilkes and Faulker, Architects, Washington, 1967-70, Winesett/Duke,Architects, Springfield, Va., 1970-74; prin. James William Ritter Architect, Alexandria, Va., 1974—; adj. prof. architecture Va. Poly. Inst. and State U., 1981—. 1st lt. U.S. Army, 1965-67. Recipient Design award Masonry Inst., 1987, 1st Pl. Residential award Va. Masonry Coun., 1989, Grand award for nat. housing innovations, 1984; included in Am. Architects, 1989. Fellow AIA (bd. dirs. No. Va. chpt. 1976-78, 83-85, pres. 1988-89, bd. dirs., 1st v.p. Va. Soc. 1990-91, pres. 1993, various awards 1977—); mem. Am. Arbitration Assn. (mediator 1984—), Alexandria C. of C., Mensa. Avocation: leader Buck Creek Jazz Band. Office: 705 King St Alexandria VA 22314-3014

RITTER, JOHN(ATHAN) (SOUTHWORTH), actor; b. Burbank, Calif., Sept. 17, 1948; s. Tex and Dorothy Fay (Southworth) R.; m. Nancy Karen Morgan, Oct. 16, 1977. BFA, U. So. Calif., 1971. Actor: (films) The Barefoot Executive, 1970, The Other, 1972, Nickelodeon, 1976, Americathon, 1979, Wholly Moses, 1980, Hero at Large, 1980, They All Laughed, 1981, Real Men, 1987, Skin Deep, 1989, Problem Child, 1990, Noise's Off, 1992, Stay Tuned, 1992; (plays) Feiffer's People, Butterflies Are Free, The Glass Menagerie, The Tempest, As You Like It, The Unvarnished Truth, Love Letters, (TV shows) Who's Happy Now, Theatre in America, The Lie, Playhouse 90, Life With Lucy, (TV spl.) John Ritter: Being of Sound Mind and Body, 1980; (TV movies) Leave Yesterday Behind, The Comeback Kid, In Love With An Older Woman, Pray TV, Sunset Limousine, Love Thy Neighbor, Letting Go, Unnatural Causes, The Last Fling, A Prison for Children, My Brother's Wife, Dreamer of Oz: The Frank Baum Story, 1990, The Summer My Father Grew Up, 1991, It, 1991, The Only Way Out, 1993, Gramps, 1995; star (TV series) Three's Company, 1977-84 (Emmy award for best actor, Golden Globe award for best actor), Three's A Crowd, 1984-85, Hooperman, 1987-89 (Emmy nomination Best Actor, People's Choice award), Hearts Afire, 1992-95; prodr.: (series) Have Faith, 1989, Anything But Love, 1989-90, (TV movies) Downpayment on Murder, Daughter of The Streets. Bd. dirs. United Cerebral Palsy Assn. Mem. Screen Actors Guild, AFTRA, Actor's Equity. Office: care Robert Myman 11777 San Vicente Blvd Los Angeles CA 90049-5011°

RITTER, ROBERT FORCIER, lawyer; b. St. Louis, Apr. 7, 1943; s. Tom Marshall and Jane Elizabeth (Forcier) R.; m. Karen Gray, Dec. 28, 1966; children: Allison Gray, Laura Thompson, Elisabeth Forcier. BA, U. Kans., 1965; JD, St. Louis U., 1968. Bar: Mo. 1968, U.S. Dist. Ct. (ea. and we. dists.) Mo. 1968, U.S. Ct. Mil. Appeals 1972, U.S. Supreme Ct. 1972, U.S. Ct. Appeals (8th cir.) 1980, U.S. Dist. Ct. (so. dist.) Ill. 1982. Assoc. Gray & Sommers, St. Louis, 1968-71; ptnr. Gray & Ritter, 1974—; bd. dirs. United Mo. Bank of St. Louis; adv. com. 22d cir. Supreme Ct., 1985-92; mem. Supreme Ct. com. on civil jury instrns., U.S. Dist. Ct. adv. com.; lectr. author in field. Bd. dirs., Cystic Fibrosis Found., Gateway Chpt. (pres. 1991). Served to capt. USAR, 1968-74. Recipient Law Week award Bur. Nat. Affairs, 1968. Fellow Internat. Soc. Barristers (bd. govs. 1994), Am. Coll. Trial Lawyers, Internat. Acad. Trial Lawyers; mem. Bar Assn. Met. St. Louis (chmn. trial sect., 1978-79, exec. com 1980-82, award of merit 1976, award of achievement 1982, chmn. bench bar conf. 1983), Mo. Bar Assn. (coun. practice and procedure com. 1972—, coun. tort law com. 1982—, bd. govs. 1984-91, fin. com. 1984-91), Mo. Bar Found. (outstanding trial lawyer award, 1978), ABA, Lawyers Assn. St. Louis (exec. com. 1976-81, pres. 1977-78), Mo. Assn. Trial Attys. (bd. govs. 1984—), Am. Judicature Soc., Assn. Trial Lawyers Am., Am. Bd. of Trial Advocates (advocate), Noonday Club, Old Warson Country Club, Bellerive Country Club, John's Island Club, Racquet Club (bd. govs. 1988-93, pres. 1991-92). Presbyterian (elder

1992—). Contbr. articles to law jours. Office: Gray & Ritter PC 701 Market St Fl 8 Saint Louis MO 63101-1850

RITTER, ROBERT JOSEPH, lawyer; b. N.Y.C., Aug. 11, 1925; s. Robert Reinhart and Mary (Mandracchia) R.; m. Barbara Willis Foust, Oct. 1, 1955 (div. May 1977); children: Robert Thornton, Jan Willis Ritter Kelly, Nancy Carol Ritter dePoortere. Student, Bklyn. Poly. Inst., 1943; BA cum laude, Queens Coll., 1949; JD, NYU, 1953, LLM in Internat. Law, 1955. Bar: N.Y. 1953. Acct. UN Secretariat, N.Y.C., 1949-54; asst. counsel RCA Corp., N.Y.C., 1955-58; atty. CIBA-GEIGY Corp., Ardsley, N.Y., 1958-60, AT&T Bell Tel. Labs., Inc., Murray Hill, N.J., 1960-70; tax atty. AT&T Techs., Inc., N.Y.C., 1970-85; mgr. fin. AT&T Corp. Hdqrs., Parsippany, N.J., 1985-87; asst. sec. 14 subs. telephone cos. AT&T, 1985-87; v.p. CPPS Tax Cons., N.Y.C., 1987—. Contbr. articles to legal jours. Pres. Harry B. Thayer chpt. Tel. Pioneers Am., N.Y.C., 1983-84; trustee, sec. United Way Cen. N.J., Milltown, 1989—, chmn. community div. govt. rels. allocations coms., 1990—; corp. program dir. Vol. Action Ctr. of Middlesex County, N.J., 1988; mem. adv. bd. Dept. Human Svcs., State of N.J., 1991—; mem. adv. coun. Project Resources, State of N.J., 1987—; bd. dirs. Somerset Hills YMCA, Bernardsville, N.J., 1971-73, Greater Raritan Pvt. Industry Coun., New Brunswick, N.J., 1989—; Dem. cand. N.Y. State Assembly, Westchester County, N.Y., 1965; chmn. Am. Cancer Soc. Fund Drive, Bronxville, N.Y., 1964. With USAAF, 1943-46. Recipient Crusade award Am. Cancer Soc., 1965, Masonic Svc. award, 1947, Am. Legion Citizenship award, 1943, Vol. of Yr. award United Way, 1991. Mem. ABA (sr. lawyers divsn. 1990—), Nat. Tax Assn.-Tax Inst. Am. (chmn., advisor state sales and use taxation com. 1984-88, chmn. prodn. exemption subcom. 1978-84), Nat. Eagle Scouts Assb., Assn. of Bar of City of N.Y., Internat. Platform Assn., Legal Aid Soc., NYU Law Alumni Assn., Rossmoor Old Guard (pres. 1994-95), Perth Amboy (N.J.) C. of C. (exec. dir. 1988-89), Rossmoor Tennis Club (pres. 1987-88), Church Club of N.Y., Kiwanis (1st v.p. 1970-71), Sigma Alpha. Democrat. Episcopalian. Home: 3-N Village Mall Jamesburg NJ 08831-1534 Office: CPPS Tax Cons Yorkville Sta PO Box 7022 New York NY 10128-0010

RITTER-CLOUGH, ELISE DAWN, publishing company executive, consultant; b. Balt., Aug. 14, 1952; d. Nelson Fred and Marjorie Jean (Corke) Ritter; m. Philip Anthony Gibson, Apr. 7, 1979 (div. Feb. 1990); 1 child, Christopher Ritter Gibson; m. Victor Wayne Clough, Jr., Mar. 3, 1990; stepchildren: Wesley T., Lindsay, Sharon. Student, Austro-Am. Inst., Vienna, Austria, 1973; BS, U. Kans., 1974. Researcher, Impeachment Inquiry Staff U.S. Ho. of Reps., Washington, 1974; researcher APA, Washington, 1975; editor prodn. The New Republic Mag., Washington, 1976-77; copy editor Time-Life Books, Alexandria, Va., 1977-79, assoc. editor, 1979-83, series adminstr., 1983-87, asst. dir. editorial resources, 1988-90; dir. editorial resources Time Warner, Time-Life Books, Alexandria, 1990-94; mem. bd. dirs. Arlington's Ministering to Emergency Needs, 1995. Bd. dirs. Arlingtonians Ministering to Emergency Needs (AMEN), 1995—; mem. outreach commn. Mt. Olivet Meth. Ch., Arlington, 1994—.

RITTERHOFF, C(HARLES) WILLIAM, retired steel company executive; b. Balt., Nov. 1, 1921; s. Ernest F. and Anna M. (Luerssen) R.; m. Margery A. McKenney, June 24, 1944 (dec. May 1987); children: Leslie, William, James; m. Marita C. Halsey, Feb. 20. 1988. B.S. in Mech. Engring. Mass. Inst. Tech., 1947; grad., Advanced Mgmt. Program, Harvard, 1973. Asst. engr. mech. dept., then various supervisory positions Bethlehem Steel Co., Sparrows Point, Md., 1948-57; asst. supt. Sparrows Point plate mills, 1957-60, asst. chief engr. plant engring. dept., 1960-63; asst. chief engr. Burns Harbor project, 1963, asst. gen. mgr., 1963-67; gen. mgr. Burns Harbor plant, 1967-70; v.p. manufactured products and West Coast steel plants, 1970-71, v.p. steel operations-prodn., 1971-74, dir., 1974-82, exec. v.p., 1974-77, vice chmn., 1977-80, exec. v.p. steel ops., 1980-82. Served to 1st lt. U.S. Army, 1943-46. Mem. NAM (past bd. dirs.), Am. Iron and Steel Inst., Assn. Iron and Steel Engrs., Hwy. Users Fedn. (past bd. dirs.), Moorings Club, Bridgehampton Club (N.Y.). Home: 150 Anchor Dr Vero Beach FL 32963-2957

RITTERHOUSE, KATHY LEE, librarian; b. Hutchinson, Kans., May 24, 1952; d. Fayne Lee and Elizabeth Rose (Tener) R.; m. Michael Raymond Demmitt, July 8, 1972 (div. Apr. 1990). BA in English, Kans. State U., 1974; MLS, U. Okla., 1979. Circulation libr. Grand Prairie (Tex.) Meml. Libr., 1979-80, libr. dir., 1980—. Bd. dirs. Grand Prairie Arts Coun., 1980-95, pres., 1989. Named Pub. Svc. Employee of Yr. Grand Prairie C. of C., 1989. Mem. ALA, Tex. Libr. Assn. (Tex./SIRS Intellectual Freedom award 1993), Metro Rotary Club (bd. dirs. 1992-95), Beta Phi Mu. Office: Grand Prairie Meml Libr 901 Conover Dr Grand Prairie TX 75051-1521

RITTERMAN, STUART I., speech pathologist, educator; b. Bklyn., May 21, 1937; s. Nathan and Ettie (Fried) R.; m. Sharen Bruneau, 1977; children: Moriah, Joshua. B.A., NYU, 1959; postgrad., CUNY, 1962-64; Ph.D., Case Western Res. U., 1968. Speech clinician Bklyn. Coll. Clinic, CUNY, Bklyn., 1963, Bergen Pines County Hosp., Paramus, N.J., 1963-64; Vocat. Rehab. adminstrn. trainee Cleve. Hearing and Speech Center, 1964-66; speech clinician Benjamin Rose Hosp., Cleve., 1965-66; NIH career investigator trainee Case Western Res. U., Cleve., 1966-68; research asso. in dental edn. Case Western Res. U., 1967-68; asst. rsch. dept. communication disorders U. Okla. Med. Center, Oklahoma City, 1968-69; dir. diagnostic services in speech pathology U. Okla. Med. Center, 1968-69; asst. prof. dept. communication sci. and disorders U. South Fla., Tampa, 1969-71; assoc. prof. U. South Fla., 1972-76, prof., 1976—; dir. diagnostic services, 1969-71, dir. research in communicology, 1976—, acting dir. program in speech pathology and audiology Coll. Social and Behavioral Sci., 1971, dir., 1971; prof., program developer communicative disorders and scis. Sch. Med. Rehab., U. Man., Winnipeg, Can., 1991—; vis. prof. phonetics U.E.R. Angellier U. Lille (France), 1984; pres Cypher Research Consortium. Contbr. articles to profl. jours. HEW grantee, 1971; Office of Edn. grantee, 1971; Fla. Dept. Edn. grantee, 1971. Fellow Royal Soc. Health, Acad. for Forensic Application of Communication Process; mem. Am. Speech and Hearing Assn., Fla. Speech and Hearing Assn., Internat. Soc. Phonetic Sci., Inst. for Advanced Study of Communication Process, Computer Users Speech & Hearing. Home: 6008 Ellerbee Rd Zephyrhills FL 33544-4206 Office: Bee St # 241 Tampa FL 33611-1449

RITTERSKAMP, DOUGLAS DOLVIN, lawyer; b. St. Louis, July 7, 1948; s. James Johnstone Jr. and Linn M. (Dolvin) R.; m. Linda S. Vansant, Mar. 23, 1974; 1 child, Tammy. AB, Washington U., 1970, JD, 1973; LLM in Taxation, NYU, 1978. Bar: N.Y. 1974, Mo. 1979. Assoc. Patterson, Belknap, Webb & Tyler, N.Y.C., 1974-78; jr. ptnr. Bryan Cave, St. Louis, 1978-82, ptnr., 1983—. Capt. USAR, 1970-79, active duty reg., 1973. Mem. ABA (employee benefits com. of sect. of taxation 1987-91), Bar Assn. of Met. St. Louis (employee benefits com. of employee benefits 1989—), Masons (32 degree), Shriners. Methodist. Home: 5223 Sutherland Ave Saint Louis MO 63109-2338

RITTINGER, CAROLYNE JUNE, newspaper editor; b. Swift Current, Sask., July 19, 1942; d. George Kelly Gaetz and Eva Evelyn (Hiebert) Olson; m. Robert Edward Rittinger, Aug. 16, 1958; children: Robert Wade, Angela Alison, Lisa Michelle. Women's editor Swift Current Sun, 1967-68; city editor Medicine Hat (Alta.) News, 1969-70; reporter Kitchener-Waterloo Record, Kitchener, Ont., 1972-75, copy editor, 1976, women's editor, then dist. editor, entertainment editor, wire editor, 1976-85, city editor, 1985-86, asst. mng. editor, 1986-89, mng. editor, 1989-93, editor, 1992—. Recipient News Story of Yr. award Calgary Women's Press Club, 1969, Best Feature Story on Fine Art award, 1970, Honorable Mention for A.R. McKenzie award for Info. Story, 1970; named Oktoberfest Woman of Yr., 1992. Mem. AP Mng. Editors, Can. Mng. Editors Conf. (bd. dirs. 1990-92). Avocations: downhill skiing, travel, live theatre. Office: Kitchener-Waterloo Record, 225 Fairway Rd, Kitchener, ON Canada N2G 4E5

RITTMER, ELAINE HENEKE, library media specialist; b. Maquoketa, Iowa, Feb. 4, 1931; d. Herman John and Clara (Luett) Heneke; m. Sheldon Lowell Rittmer, June 11, 1950; children: Kenneth, Lynnette, Robyn (dec.), infant son (dec.). BA, Marycrest Coll., 1973; MS, Western Ill. U., 1980. Permanent teaching cert. K-14, Iowa; cert. libr. media specialist K-14, Iowa. Sch. libr. Calamus-Wheatland (Iowa) Community Schs., 1970-74; high sch. libr. media specialist, libr. coord. Camanche (Iowa) Community Sch.,

1974—; ind. tech. cons., 1988—. Mem. Iowa Edn. Media Assn., Iowa State Edn. Assn., Camanche Edn. Assn., Camanche Cmty. Schs. Tech. Com., Media Tech. Cons. Republican. Avocations: reading, walking, political activities, future technology developments. Home: 3539 230th St De Witt IA 52742-9208 Office: Camanche High Sch PO Box 160 937 9th St Camanche IA 52730

RITTMER, SHELDON, farmer, senator; b. DeWitt, Iowa, Sept. 5, 1928; s. Elmer and Lois (Hass) R.; m. Elaine Heneke, June 11, 1950; children: Kenneth S., Lynnette Rittmer Jones, Robyn Jon (dec.). County supr. Clinton (Iowa) Conty Bd. Suprs., 1978-90; chmn. Clinton County Title III Com., 1987-90; v.p. Iowa Assn. County Suprs., Des Moines, 1989-90; senator dist. 19 State of Iowa, 1990—; mem. local govt. com., state govt. com., human svcs. appropriations subcom., 1990—; ranking mem. transp. com. Chmn. 1st Luth. Ch., Maquoketa, Iowa, 1964-68; active Clinton County Hist. Soc., 1980—. Recipient Spl. Recognition award Nat. Fedn. Ind. Bus., 1991-92, Spl. Recognition Iowa Soil Conservation award, 1994. Mem. Izaak Walton League Iowa, DeWitt Lions, Ducks Unlimited U.S.A, Clinton County Pork Prodr's. Assn., Clinton County Cattlemen's Assn., Pheasants Forever, City of Clinton C. of C., DeWitt C. of C, Bettendorf C. of C. Republican. Avocations: public speaking, governmental research, reading, farming. Home: 3539 230th St De Witt IA 52742-9208 Office: State Senate of Iowa State Capital Des Moines IA 50319

RITTNER, CARL FREDERICK, educational administrator; b. Boston, Feb. 28, 1914; s. Philip and Augusta (Beich) R.; m. Eunice Carin, 1940; 1 child, Stephen. BS in Edn., Boston U., 1936, EdM, 1937. Ednl. cons. Boston, 1940's; founder dir. Rittners Floral Sch., Boston, 1947—. Coauthor: Flowers for the Modern Bride, 1965, Arrangements for All Occasions, 1966, Flowers for the Modern Bride (In Living Color), 1968, Rittner's Silver Anniversary Book, 1972, Dried Arrangements, 1978, Rittners Guide to Permanent Flower Arranging, 1978, Vase Arrangements for the Professional Florist, 1979, Christmas Designs, 1979, Flowers for Funerals, 1980, Manual of Wedding Design Styles, 1980, Contemporary Floral Designs, 1983, Floral Designs for That Special Occasion, 1985, Inexpensive Bread & Butter Designs, 1986. Mem. Am. Floral Svcs., Soc. Am. Florists, Florist Transworld Delivery Svc., Phi Delta Kappa. Office: 345 Marlborough St Boston MA 02115-1799

RITTNER, EDMUND SIDNEY, physicist; b. Boston, May 29, 1919; s. Philip and Augusta (Beich) R.; m. Marcella Weiner, Oct. 6, 1942; 1 child, Leona. B.S., MIT, 1939, Ph.D., 1941. Research assoc. MIT, Cambridge, 1942-45; sect. chief Philips Labs., Briarcliff Manor, N.Y., 1946-62; dir. Dept. Physics, 1962-67, dir. exploratory research, 1967-69; exec. dir. phys. scis. COMSAT Labs., Clarksburg, Md., 1969-84; A.D. Little postdoctoral fellow MIT, 1941-42. Contbr. articles to profl. jours. Fellow Am. Phys. Soc., IEEE (Photovoltaic Pioneers award, 1985). Home: 700 New Hampshire Ave NW 116-S Washington DC 20037

RITVO, EDWARD ROSS, psychiatrist; b. Boston, June 1, 1930; s. Max Ritvo; m. Riva Golan, Sept. 11, 1989; children: Deborah, Eva, Anne, Matthew, Victoria, Skylre, Max. BA, Harvard U., 1951; MD, Boston U. Sch. Medicine, 1955. Diplomate Am. Bd. Psychiatry and Neurology, Am. Bd. Child Psychiatry. Prof. UCLA Sch. Medicine, 1963—. Author 4 books; contbr. over 150 articles to profl. jours. Capt. U.S. Army, 1959-61. Recipient Blanche F. Ittleson award Am. Psychiat. Assn., 1990. Mem. Nat. Soc. for Autistic Children, Profl. Adv. Bd. (chmn.). Office: UCLA Sch Medicine Dept Psychiatry 760 Westwood Plz Los Angeles CA 90024-1759

RITVO, ROGER ALAN, university dean, health management-policy educator; b. Cambridge, Mass., Aug. 12, 1944; s. Meyer and Miriam R.S. (Meyers) R.; m. Lynn Lieberman; children: Roberta, Eric. BA, Western Res. U., 1967; MBA, George Washington U., 1970; PhD, Case Western Res. U., 1976. Asst. adminstr. N.Y. Mental Health System, 1968-70; asst. prof., asst. dean Sch. Applied Social Scis. Case Western Res. U., Cleve., 1976-79, assoc. prof., 1981-84; assoc. prof., founding dir. Grad. Program in Health Adminstrn. Cleve. State U., 1984-87; prof. health mgmt. and policy, dean Sch. Health and Human Svcs. U. N.H., Durham, 1987—; sr. health policy analyst to sec. DHHS, Washington, 1980-81; vis. rsch. scholar WHO, Copenhagen, 1978; vis. prof. Am. U., Washington, 1980-81, U. W.I., 1993; vis. scholar U. Sheffield, Eng., 1985; cons. to numerous orgns. on profit and non-profit strategic planning. Editor 4 books; contbr. articles to profl. jours. Trustee Hosp. Sisters of Charity, Cleve., 1980-85, Greater Seacoast United Way, 1991-93; chmn. health care adv. com. Ohio Senate, 1983-85; bd. mem. Fairmount Temple, Beachwood, Ohio, 1980-85; trustee Leadership Seacoast, 1991-93, bd. dirs., 1992—; bd. dirs. N.H. chpt. United Way, 1992—. Recipient Outstanding Adminstr. award, 1992; Govt. fellow Am. Coun. Edn., 1980-81. Mem. Nat. Tng. Labs. Inst. (bd. dirs 1981-85, 92—), Cert. Cons. Internat., Jewish Philatelic Club, Hist. Soc. N.Y.C. Avocations: philatelist, white water rafting. Office: U NH Sch Health and Human Svcs Durham NH 03824

RITZ, ESTHER LEAH, civic worker, volunteer, investor; b. Buhl, Minn., May 16, 1918; d. Matthew Abram and Jeanette Florence (Lewis) Medalie; m. Maurice Ritz, Apr. 8, 1945 (dec. 1977); children—David Lewis, Peter Bruce. B.A. summa cum laude, U. Minn, 1940, postgrad., 1940-41; postgrad., Duke U., 1941-42. Adminstrv. analyst, economist Office of Price Adminstrn., N.Y., Washington and Chgo., 1942-46. Pres., Nat. Jewish Welfare Bd., 1982-86; v.p. Council of Jewish Fedns., 1981-84; pres. World Conf. Jewish Community Ctrs., 1981-86; bd. dirs. Am. Jewish Joint Distbn. Com., 1977-93, bd. dirs. (hon. life mem.) Joint Distbn. Com., 1994; trustee United Jewish Appeal, 1982-87; vice-chmn. bd. dirs. Jerusalem Ctr. Pub. Affairs, 1984—; bd. dirs. Wurzweiler Sch. Social Work Yeshiva U., 1984-89, HIAS, 1983-86; mem. Jewish Agy. Com. on Jewish Edn., 1984-90, bd. govs., 1988-92; bd. dirs. Legal Aid Soc., Milw. County, 1983-85; mem. Community Issues Forum, Milw.; vice chmn. bd. United Way Greater Milw., 1977-81; pres. Florence G. Heller Jewish Welfare Bd. Research Ctr., 1979-83; pres. Mental Health Planning Council of Milw. County, 1976-79; vice chmn Large City Budgeting Conf., 1976-82; pres. Jewish Community Ctr. Milw., 1966-71; pres. Milw. Jewish Fedn., 1978-81; bd. dirs. Shalom Hartman Inst., 1989—; bd. dirs.; mem. exec. coun., policy com. Nat. Jewish Dem. Coun., 1991—; vice-chmn. bd. dirs., 1994—; bd. dirs. Nat. Jewish Ctr. for Learning and Leadership, 1988-92, Ams. Peace Now, 1989—, vice-chmn. bd. dirs., 1995—; Coun. Initiatives Jewish Edn., 1990—; Friends of Labor Israel (steering com. 1988—, chair 1988-90); bd. vis. Ctr. for Jewish Studies U. Wis., Madison, 1994—. Named to Women's Hall of Fame YWCA, 1979; recipient Cmty. Svc. award Wis. Region NCCJ, 1977, William C. Frye award Milw. Found., 1984, Telesis award Alverno Coll., Milw., 1984, Hannah G. Solomon award. Nat. Coun. Jewish Women, ProUrbe award Mt. Mary Coll., Evan P. Helfer award Milw. chpt. Nat. Soc. of Fund Raising Execs., 1994, Margaret Miller award Planned Parenthood of Wis., 1994. Mem. LWV, NAACP, NOW, Hadassah, Na'amat, Common Cause, Nat. Women's Polit. Caucus, Nat. Coun. Jewish Women, Planned Parenthood. Democrat. Avocations: golf, music, bridge, art collecting. Home: 626 E Kilbourn Ave Milwaukee WI 53202

RITZ, LORRAINE ISAACS, nursing administrator; b. Wheeling, W.Va.; d. John and Anna (Julian) Isaacs; m. Robert H. Ritz, Apr. 24, 1953; children: Chris Casuccio, Bonnie, Amy. Diploma nursing, Wheeling Hosp.; BS in Nursing, W. Liberty State Coll.; MS in Nursing, W.Va. U. Staff nurse Wheeling Hosp. supr.; DON Wheeling (W.Va.) Hosp., 1980-88, asst. adminstr. nursing, 1988-94; mem. adv. bd. West Liberty State Coll., 1984-87, W.Va. No. C.C., 1981-92; pres. W.Va. Bd. Examiners, 1993, 94; bd. dirs. Wheeling Health Right, sec., 1992, 93, 94. Bd. dirs. Florence Crittenton, 1984-91, sec., 1990-91. Mem. ANA, Nat. League Nurses, W.Va. Orgn. Nurse Execs. (v.p. 1988-89, pres., 1991, 92, 93, W.Va. Exec. of Yr. 1991), Am. Orgn. Nurse Execs. Office: Wheeling Hosp Inc Med Park Wheeling WV 26003

RITZ, RICHARD ELLISON, architect, architectural historian, writer; b. Colfax, Wash., Dec. 8, 1919; s. Henry Clay and Katharine Fredericka (Failing) R.; m. Evelyn R. Robinson, Sept. 21, 1940; children: Margaret Karen Ritz Barss, Susan Elizabeth Ritz Williams. Student, Whitman Coll., 1936-37. Registered architect, Oreg. Draftsman, job capt. Pietro Belluschi, Architect, Portland, Oreg. 1946-51; project mgr., chief prodn. Belluschi and Skidmore, Owings & Merrill, Portland, 1951-56; project mgr., then gen. mgr.

Skidmore, Owings & Merrill, Portland, 1956-82; pvt. practice architecture Portland, 1982—; founder Greenhills Press, 1991. Author: A History of the Reed College Campus, 1990, An Architect Looks at Downtown Portland, 1991; editor: A Guide to Portland Architecture, 1968; contbr. articles to profl. jours. Bd. dirs. Architecture Found., Portland, 1982-85; mem. Portland Hist. Landmarks Commn., 1987—. Sgt. USAF, 1942-45. Fellow AIA (bd. dirs. Portland chpt. 1975-79, pres. 1978, mem. handbook com. Ft. Mgmt. for Architects 1980); mem. Soc. Archtl. Historians, Oreg. Coun. Architects (del. 1975-79), Portland Art Mus., Oreg. Hist. Soc., Lang Syne Soc., City Club Portland, Univ. Club (Portland), Multnomah Athletic Club. Republican. Presbyterian. Home and Office: 4550 SW Greenhills Way Portland OR 97221-3214

RITZHEIMER, ROBERT ALAN, educational publishing executive; b. Trenton, Ill., Dec. 29, 1931; s. Leslie H. and Hilda M. (Fochtmann) R.; m. Shirley Ann Wharrie, Sept. 11, 1954; children: Kim E. Ritzheimer Chase, Gina C. Ritzheimer Hartle, Scott D., Susan L. Ritzheimer Kelly. BS in Edn., Ill. State Normal U., 1953, MS in Edn., 1960; postgrad., Columbia U., 1955. Cert. tchr., supr., k-12, Ill. Tchr. Bloomington (Ill.) Pub. Schs., 1955-57; prin., elem. and jr. high sch. Wesclin Community Unit #3, New Baden, Ill., 1957-62; ednl. sales rep. Scott Foresman Co., Bradford Woods, Pa. 1962-81; field sales mgr. Scott Foresman Co., Sunnyvale, Calif., 1981-91; mgr. sales support Scott Foresman Co., Sunnyvale, 1992-93; ret., 1993; cons., pub. Calif. State Bd. Edn., Sacramento, 1981-93; guest lectr. Stanford U., Palo Alto, Calif., 1983, Santa Clara (Calif.) U., 1992. Treas Little League, New Baden, Ill., 1958-62; pres. Ill. Edn. Assn., Kaskaskia Div., E. St. Louis, 1961. With U.S. Army, 1953-55. Mem. ASCD, NEA (life), Calif.Sci. Teachers Assn. Republican. Avocations: travel, swimming, plate collecting. Home: 1566 Deerfield Dr San Jose CA 95129-4707

RITZIE, ROBERT F., metal products executive. V.p. fin. Bull Moose Tube Co., Chesterfield, Mo., 1988—. Office: Bull Moose Tube Co 1819 Clarkson Rd Chesterfield MO 63017*

RIVA, J. MICHAEL, art director, production designer. Prodn. designer: (films) I Never Promised You a Rose Garden, 1977, Bare Knuckles, 1978, Fast Charlie...the Moonbeam Rider, 1979, Halloween II, 1981, The Hand, 1981, Bad Boys, 1983, The Adventures of Buckaroo Banzai: Across the 8th Dimension, 1983, The Goonies, 1985, The Slugger's Wife, 1985, The Color Purple, 1985 (Academy award nomination best art direction 1985), The Golden Child, 1986, Lethal Weapon, 1987, Scrooged, 1988, Lethal Weapon 2, 1989, Tango & Cash, 1989, Radio Flyer, 1992, Dave, 1992, A Few Good Men, 1992, (TV movies) Callie & Son, 1981; art dir.: (films) Ordinary People, 1980, Brubaker, 1980; visual cons.: (films) Stranger's Kiss, 1984. Office: Innovative Artists 1999 Ave of the Stars Ste 2850 Los Angeles CA 90067*

RIVARD, GILLES, government official, lawyer; m. Lucie Rondeau; 5 children. Law degree, Laval U., 1958. Called to Bar of Que. 1958. Pvt. law practice; sr. ptnr. Rivard, Rivard; mem. Nat. Postal Mus. Adv. Com., 1987, Com. for Devolution of Inquiry on Soc. Alcools du Que., 1987-92; dir. Que. Indsl. Loan Office, 1987-92; chmn. Nat. Transp. Act Rev. Commn., Ottawa-Hull, Can., 1992; chmn., CEO Nat. Transp. Agy. Can., 1993—; pres. Hydro-Pontiac Inc.; bd. dirs. Coun. of Can. Adminstrv. Tribunals; pres. Que. Jr. Bar Assn.; mem. gen coun., exec. com. Que. Provincial Bar Assn., 1966-68, 74-76; batonnier Que. Bar, 1975-76. Founder, pres. Pavillion of Prevention of Heart Diseases. Named to Queen's Counsel, 1973. Mem. Can. Bar Assn., C. of C., Que. Garrison Club, Que. Rotary Club (pres. 1973-74), Ducks Unltd. (bd. dirs. 1980). Office: Nat Transp Agy Can, Office of Chmn, Ottawa, ON Canada K1A 0N9

RIVARD, PAUL EDMUND, museum director; b. Sanford, Maine, Aug. 21, 1943; s. Joseph Paul and Claire Rachael (Demers) R.; B.A., U. Maine, 1965; postgrad. Clark U., Worcester, Mass., 1965-66; M.A., SUNY, 1967. postgrad. Cooperstown Grad. program, 1966-67; m. Suk Hi Lee, Jan. 14, 1970; children—Sonya Lee, Christopher Lee. Supr. interpretation Mystic (Conn.) Seaport, 1967; dir. Slater Mill Historic Site, Pawtucket, R.I., 1969-74; dir. Rockwell Corning Mus., Corning, N.Y., 1974-77, Maine State Mus., Augusta, 1977-91; dir. Mus. Am. Textile History, North Andover, Mass., 1991—; cons. in field. Served with U.S. Army, 1967-69. Recipient Jaycee Outstanding Young Man award, Pawtucket, 1973. Mem. Am. Assn. Mus., Am. Assn. State and Local History, Soc. Indsl. Archeology. Author: Pawtucket at 300, 1971, Guidebook to the Slater Mill Historic Site, 1972, Samuel Slater, 1973, Weaving Exhibition Catalogue, 1974, The Painter's West, 1976, Made in Maine, 1985, Lion, 1987, Maine Sawmills, 1991. Office: Mus Am Textile History 800 Massachusetts Ave North Andover MA 01845

RIVARD, WILLIAM CHARLES, mechanical engineering educator; b. Detroit, Sept. 2, 1942; s. William John and Ruby Marie (Theel) R.; m. Betty L. Slocum, Nov. 21, 1964; children: Michele, Traci. BS, U. Detroit, 1965, MS, 1966; PhD, Ill. Inst. Tech., 1968. Staff mem. explosive systems div. Los Alamos (N.Mex.) Nat. Lab., 1968-71, assoc. group leader theoretical div. 1971-80; v.p., co-owner Flow Sci., Inc., Los Alamos, 1980-87; dir. Arthur O. Willey prof. mech. engring. U. Maine, Orono, 1987—; pres. Fluid Systems, Inc., East Holden, Maine, 1988—; cons. Exxon Rsch. Ctr., Florham Park, N.J., 1989—, McDonnell Douglas Space Systems, Huntington Beach, Calif., 1987—, Aerospatiale, Les Mereaux, France, 1989—, Technischer Uberwachungs-Verein, Hanover, Fed. Republic of Germany, 1985-88. Contbr. articles to profl. jours. Grad. fellow NSF, 1967, NASA, 1968. Office: U Maine Mech Engring Dept Orono ME 04469

RIVAS-VAZQUEZ, ANA VICTORIA, federal official; b. Miami, Fla., Aug. 25, 1963; d. Rafael A. and Ana (Albarran) R. BA in Govt., Georgetown U., 1985, MA in Latin Am. Studies, 1987. Staffer Times of the Americas, Washington, 1987-88; press aide Dukakis-Bentsen Campaign Hdqrs., Boston, 1988; assignment editor Univision, Miami, 1989; news prodr. Sta. WLTV-Channel 23, Miami, 1990-92; elections prodr. Univison News, Miami, 1992; asst. press sec. White House Press Office, Washington, 1992—. Avocations: tennis, photography, movies, travel. Office: White House Press Office 1600 Pennsylvania Ave NW Washington DC 20500

RIVENBARK, JAN MEREDITH, corporate executive; b. Spartanburg, S.C., Feb. 22, 1950; s. George Meredith and Audrey Isabel (Frady) R.; m. Barbara N. Newton, Sept. 25, 1976; children: Abigail, Justin, Patrick. BS in Math., Duke U., 1972; postgrad., Ga. State U., 1980. Mgmt. trainee Citizens & So. Nat. Bank, Atlanta, 1972, br. mgr., 1974, employee relations mgr., 1975-77, v.p. compensation, benefits, payroll and data mgmt., 1977-80; mgr. personnel First Tenn. Bank, Memphis, 1980-81; dir. compensation and benefits Hanes Group, Consol. Foods Corp. (now Sara Lee Corp.), Winston-Salem, N.C., 1981-83, exec. dir. compensation and benefits, Chgo., 1983-84; exec. dir. internat. staff Sara Lee Corp., 1985, exec. dir. corp. planning, 1985-87; sr. v.p. PYA/Monarch div. Sara Lee Corp., Greenville, S.C., 1987-89; pres., chief oper. officer JP Foodservice, Hanover, Md., 1989-92; CEO, PCA Internat., Inc., Charlotte, N.C., 1992—. Mem. Alpha Tau Omega (chpt. pres. 1971-72). Republican. Home: 2500 Greenbrook Pky Matthews NC 28105-7790 Office: PCA International Inc 815 Matthews Mint Hill Rd Matthews NC 28105-1705

RIVERA, ANGEL (ANDY) MANUEL, retired career officer, city official; b. Arecibo, P.R., Dec. 24, 1942; s. Ramon and Domitila (Viruet) R.; m. Rose Marie Wuchina; children: Tina Nikkole, Marc Anthony. BBA, U. P.R., Rio Pedras, 1960; MBA, Inter-Am. U. P.R., San German, 1969. Commd. 2d lt. USAF, 1965, advanced through grades to col., 1987; various positions SAC, Tng. Command, Airlife Command, 13th Air Force, Vietnam and U.S., 1965-77; wing exec. 1605th Air Base Wing Lajes Field, Azores, Portugal, 1978; instr., liaison officer U.S Army Sch. Ams., Ft. Gulick, Panama, 1978-79; sec. joint staff U.S. So. Command, Quarry Heights, Panama, 1979-80; ops. officer U.S./Panama U.S. So. Commd., Quarry Heights, Rep. of Panama, 1980-82; chief pers. div. 42d Combat Support Group, Loring AFB, Maine, 1982-84; asst. dep. chief staff for pers. 8th Air Force, Barksdale AFB, La., 1984-87; comdr. 7th Combat Support Group, Carswell AFB, Tex., 1987-89; comdr., prof. aerospace studies Tex. Christian U., Ft. Worth, 1989-91; ret. 1991; exec. asst. to chancellor U. North Texas, Denton, 1991-92; dir. airport sys. City of Ft. Worth, 1992—; adj. faculty La. Tech. U., Barksdale AFB, 1986-87, U. Md. Lajes Field Azores, 1976-78, Ctrl. Tex. Coll., Lajes Field, 1976-78, Park Coll., Lajes Field, 1975-76, Big Bend C.C., Scott AFB, 1974-75; mem. civilian adv. coun. No. Maine Vocat. Tech. Inst., Presque Isle,

1983-84; instr. mgmt. and ligistics U.S. Army Sch. Ams., 1978-79. Mem. Ft. Worth Airshow Com., Airport Minority Adv. Coun., Vets. Adv. Com., 12th Congl. Dist., Def./Mil. Adv. Com., Ft. Worth Congl. 6th Congl. Dist. Adv. Com., Ft. Worth Lulac Coun. 601, Image of Ft. Worth, Am. G.I. Forum of Tarrant County, Forum Ft. Worth, Hispanics Friends of U. Tex.; past mem. Metroplex Fed. Exec. Bd., Ft. Worth Crimestoppers Com., Star-Telegram Citizens Adv. Bd., Peru's Coun. U. North Tex.; past athletic trustee U. North Tex.; past exec. bd. dirs. Longhorn Coun. Boy Scouts Am., past chmn. Silver Star dist.; past bd. dirs. Frontiers of Flight Mus., Love Fields, Dallas; past mem. subcom. Ft. Worth chpt. Rev. Com.; assoc. Greater Ft. Worth Civil Leaders Assn., United Hispanic Coun. Ft. Worth; past mem. exec. com. Sunshine dist. Girl Scouts Am., Panama Canal Zone; active Big Bros. and Big Sisters of Tarrant County, Ft. Worth Citizens Organized Against Crime, Alzheimers Assn. Tarrant County, Multiple Sclerosis Assn. Tarrant County. Decorated Legion of Merit with oak leaf cluster, Bronze Star, Def. M.S.M., A.F.C.M. with oak leaf cluster; Armed Forces Honoe medal 1st class, Air Svc. medal honor class, Gallentry Cross with palm (Vietnam). Mem. Tex. Assn. Airport Execs., Am. Assn. Airport Execs., Air Force Assn. (life), Navy League, Ft. Worth Airpower Coun., Ft. Worth Hispanic C. of C., Ft. Worth C. of C., Forum Ft. Worth (vice chmn.), U. North Tex. Parents Assn. (chmn.), Rotary (treas. Ft. Worth), Phi Beta Delta. Republican. Avocations: golf, sports. Office: Ft Worth Dept Aviation 4201 N Main St Ste 228 Fort Worth TX 76106-2749

RIVERA, ARMANDO REMONTE, utilities engineer; b. Oas, Albay, Philippines, Jan. 27, 1940; came to U.S., 1969; s. Venancio Rey Rivera and Eugenia (Raneses) Remonte; m. Carmelita Lim Chan, Dec. 11, 1971. BSME, U. of the Philippines, Quezon City, 1962; MBA, U. of the Philippines, Manila, 1967; postgrad., U. So. Calif., L.A., 1972. Registered profl. engr., Calif. Engr. Fluor Corp., L.A., 1969-71; energy svcs. engr. So. Calif. Edison Co., Rosemead, Calif., 1972-76; project engr. Aramco Overseas Co., Hague, Netherlands, 1976-82, London, 1982-84; sr. project engr. electric systems Anaheim (Calif.) Pub. Utilities, 1984—. EPA grantee U. So. Calif. 1972. Mem. ASME, Am. Assn. Cost Engrs., Nat. Soc. Profl. Engrs. Republican. Roman Catholic. Avocations: antique, religious art, Japanese prints. Home: 1523 N Pacific Ave Glendale CA 91202 Office: Anaheim Pub Utilities 201 S Anaheim Blvd Anaheim CA 92805-9999

RIVERA, CHITA (CONCHITA DEL RIVERO), actress, singer, dancer; b. Washington, Jan. 23, 1933; d. Pedro Julio Figuerva del Rivero; m. Anthony Mordente. Student, Am. Sch. Ballet, N.Y.C. Broadway debut: Call Me Madam, 1952; appeared on stage in: Guys and Dolls, Can-Can, Seventh Heaven, Mister Wonderful, West Side Story, Father's Day, Bye Bye Birdie, Three Penny Opera, Flower Drum Song, Zorba, Sweet Charity, Born Yesterday, Jacques Brel is Alive and Well and Living in Paris, Sondheim-A Musical Tribute, Kiss Me Kate, Ivanhoe, Chicago, Bring Back Birdie, Merlin, Jerry's Girls, 1985, The Rink, 1984 (Tony award 1984), Can-Can 1988, Kiss of the Spider Woman (Tony award, Best Actress in a musical) 1993; performs in cabarets and nightclubs around world; starred in: film Sweet Charity, 1969; numerous TV appearances include Kojak and the Marcus Nelson Murders, 1973, The New Dick Van Dyke Show, 1973-74, Kennedy Ctr. Tonight-Broadway to Washington!, Pippin, 1982, The Mayflower Madam, 1987, Sammy Davis Jr.'s 60th Birthday Celebration, 1990. Mem. AFTRA, SAG, Actors Equity Assn. Office: William Morris Agy 1350 Ave Americas New York NY 10019*

RIVERA, GERALDO, television personality, journalist; b. N.Y.C., July 4, 1943; s. Cruz Allen and Lillian (Friedman) R.; m. Sheri Rivera (div. 1984); m. C.C. Dyer, 1987; children: Gabriel Miguel, Isabella, Simone. BS, U. Ariz., 1965; JD, Bklyn. Law Sch., 1969; postgrad., U. Pa., 1969, Sch. Journalism, Columbia U., 1970. Bar: N.Y. 1970. Mem. anti-poverty neighborhood law firms Harlem Assertion of Rights and Community Action for Legal Svcs., N.Y.C., 1968-70; with Eyewitness News, WABC-TV, N.Y.C., 1970-75; reporter Good Morning America program, ABC-TV, 1973-76, corr.; host Good Night America program, 1975-77, corr., sr. producer 20/20 Newsmag., 1978-85; host syndicated talk show Geraldo, N.Y.C., 1987—; host investigative show Rivera Live, N.Y.C., 1994—. Author: Willowbrook, 1972, Island of Contrasts, 1974, Miguel, 1972, A Special Kind of Courage, 1976, Exposing Myself, 1991; host numerous syndicated TV spls.; film appearances: The Bonfire of the Vanities, 1990; television movie: Perry Mason: The Case of the Reckless Romeo. Recipient 7 Emmy awards, Peabody award, Kennedy Journalism award, 1973, 75, numerous others; named Broadcaster of Yr. N.Y. State AP, 1971, 72, 74; Smith fellow U. Pa., 1969. Jewish. Office: Geraldo Investigative News Group 555 W 57th St New York NY 10019-2925*

RIVERA, RICHARD E., food products executive; b. Jan. 6, 1947; m. Leslie Suzanne Pliner, Nov. 18, 1984. BA, Washington & Lee U., 1968. Credit analyst Nat. Bank Commerce, Dallas, 1970-71; from mgmt. trainee to exec. v.p., dir. Steak Ale Restaurants of Am., Dallas, 1971-80; pres. restaurant div. El Chico Corp., 1980-82; exec. v.p., chief operating officer T.J. Applebee's and Taco Villa Mexican Restaurant, Dallas, 1982-87; exec. v.p. ops. TGI Friday's Inc., Dallas, 1987-88, pres., chief exec. officer, 1988—. Office: TGI Friday's Inc Apt 74 7540 Lyndon B Johnson Fwy Dallas TX 75251-1008

RIVERA, ROSALIND THERESA, nurse, educator; b. Fulton, N.Y.; d. Ralph R. and Domenica Volotta; children: Denise, Deborah, Janice. Diploma, Gen. Hosp. Syracuse; BS, MEd, Johns Hopkins U.; EdD, U. So. Calif., 1982. Asst. dean career and tech. edn., chair div. allied health Anne Arundel Community Coll., Arnold, Md.; bd. dirs. Providence Ctr., Inc. Mem. Anne Arundel County Health Planning Bd.; mem. adv. bd. Project Linc. Mem. Orgn. for Advancement of Assoc. Degree Nursing, Nat. League Nursing, Johns Hopkins Alumnae Orgn., Zonta Internat. (pres.-elect).

RIVERA-ORTIZ, GILBERTO, senator; b. Humacao, P.R., Apr. 20, 1932; s. Gervasio and Perfecta (Ortiz) R.; m. Melania Rivera, Dec. 6, 1955; children: Erving, Wanda, Wilma. BA, U. P.R., 1959; MA, Northwestern U., 1962. Tchr. high sch. P.R. Dept. Instrn., 1959-60; prof. U. P.R., Rio Piedras, 1960-71; U.S. senator from P.R., 1971—; senate majority leader P.R.; disting. participant on edn. Oxford U., London, 1991. Contbr. over 75 articles to profl. jours. With U.S. Army, 1953-55, Korea. Named one of More Disting. Legislators in U.S.A. during last decade Nat. Conf. State Legislators, 1990. Mem. Nat. Conf. State Legislators, Nat. Tchrs. Assn., Edn. Commn. of States, Aries Club. Democrat. Roman Catholic. Avocations: baseball, reading. Home: 2-K-14 Villa Universitaria Humacao PR 00661 Office: Senate of PR Capitol Bldg San Juan PR 00904

RIVERS, JOAN, entertainer; b. N.Y.C., June 8, 1937; d. Meyer C. Molinsky; m. Edgar Rosenberg (dec.), June 15, 1965; 1 child, Melissa. BA, Barnard Coll., 1958. Formerly fashion coordinator Bond Clothing Stores. Debut entertaining, 1960; mem. From Second City, 1961-62; TV debut Tonight Show, 1965; Las Vegas debut, 1969; nat. syndicated columnist Chgo. Tribune, 1973-76; creator: CBS TV series Husbands and Wives, 1976-77; host: Emmy Awards, 1983; guest hostess: Tonight Show, 1983-86; hostess The Late Show Starring Joan Rivers, 1986-87, Hollywood Squares, 1987—, (morning talk show) Joan Rivers (Daytime Emmy award 1990) 1989—, Can We Shop? Home Shopping Netwrk, 1994—; originator, screenwriter TV movie The Girl Most Likely To, ABC, 1973; other TV movies include: How to Murder A Millionaire, 1990, Tears and Laughter: The Joan and Melissa Rivers Story, 1994; cable TV spl. Joan Rivers and Friends Salute Heidi Abromowitz, 1985; film appearances include The Swimmer, 1968, Uncle Sam, The Muppets Take Manhattan, 1984; co-author, dir.: (films) Rabbit Test, 1978 (also acted), Spaceballs, 1987; actress: theatre prodn. Broadway Bound, 1988, Sally Marr...and her escorts, 1994; recs. include: comedy album What Becomes a Semi-Legend Most, 1983; author: Having a Baby Can be a Scream, 1974, The Life and Hard Times of Heidi Abromowitz, 1984, (autobiography with Richard Meryman) Enter Talking, 1986, (with Richard Meryman) Still Talking, 1991; debuted on Broadway (play) Broadway Bound, 1988, creator Seminar You Deserve To Be happy, 1989. Nat. chmn. Cystic Fibrosis, 1982—, benefit performer for AIDS, 1984. Recipient Cleo awards for commls., 1976, 82, Jimmy award for best comedian, 1981; named Hadassah Woman of Yr., 1983, Harvard Hasty Pudding Soc. Woman of Yr., 1984. Mem. Phi Beta Kappa. Office: care Dorothy Melvin DTM Mgmt 145 S Fairfax Ave Ste 201A Los Angeles CA 90036-2166*

RIVERS, JOHN MINOTT, JR., real estate developer; b. Charleston, S.C., May 28, 1945; m. Kathleen Hudson, Nov. 10, 1979. AB in Polit. Sci., U. N.C., 1967. Pres. Rivers Enterprises, Inc., Riverwood Devel. Corp., Chattooga Devel. Corp.; mem. adv. com. urban studies Coll. Charleston, 1975, exec. com. Miss U.S.A./Universe, 1978, sustaining mem. Trident 2000, nat. devel. coun. U. N.C., Chapel Hill; chmn. CBS Television Network Affiliates, 1982-83, govt. rels. com., 1980-87; organizer Bank S.C., 1987. Explorer, mem. adv. bd. Charleston Coun. Boy Scouts Am., 1973-74; mem. com. Roper Hosp. Fund Drive, 1973-74; div. pres. United Way, 1974, vice chmn. budget bd., 1974, chmn., 1975, pacesetter div., 1976, mem. exec. com., 1975; fund raiser Spoleto U.S.A., 1978; bd. dirs. YMCA Mil. Svcs. Ctr., 1972-78, chmn. publicity com., 1977; treas. Charleston Travel Industry Devel. Coun., 1976, bd. dirs., 1977-78; mem. City Charleston All-Am. Com., 1977-78, chmn., 1978; co-chmn. Charleston Area Campaign United Negro Coll. Fund, 1977-78; mem. City Charleston Clean Community System Com., 1977-79, chmn. subcom., 1978-79; mem. Charleston Area Community Rels. Com., 1977-88, vice chmn., 1979-82; mem. bd. trustees Ashley Hall, 1983-92; mem. adv. bd. The Citizens & So. Nat. Bank S.C., 1974-86, The Citizens & So. Nat. Bank S.C. Trust, 1974-86, bd. dirs., 1981-86; mem. Gibbes Mus. Art, S.C. Hist. Soc., St. Cecilia Soc., St. Philips Episcopal Ch. Mem. S.C. Broadcasters Assn. (bd. dirs. ednl. found. 1982-83), Charleston Indsl. Assn. (sec. 1975-80, bd. dirs. 1975-86, v.p. 1981-86), S.C. State C. of C. (bd. dirs. 1978-81), U. N.C. Alumni Assn. (life, bd. visitors 1989-92), U.S. Naval Supply Corps Alumni Assn., Nat. Audubon Soc., Carolina Yacht Club, Yeaman's Hall Club, Wade Hampton Golf Club, Cedar Creek Racquet Club, High Hampton Golf and Country Club, Chattooga Club, U.S. Croquet Assn. Office: PO Box 21050 Charleston SC 29413-1050

RIVERS, KENNETH JAY, judicial administrator, consultant; b. N.Y.C., Feb. 13, 1938; s. Alexander Maximillian and Albertina Ray (Gay) R.; m. Leah B. Files, Sept. 21, 1957 (div.); children: Londa Denise, Nancy Laura, Terrie Ruth, Kenneth J. Jr. AAS in Criminal Justice, St. Francis Coll., Bklyn., 1978, BS in Criminal Justice, 1978; MPA, L.I. Univ., 1981. Correction officer N.Y.C. Dept. Correction, 1965-69; ct. officer N.Y. State Unified Ct. System, N.Y.C., 1969-71, asst. ct. clk., 1971-73, sr. ct. clk., 1973-85, assoc. ct. clk., 1985-88, prin. ct. clk., 1988-90, dep. chief clk., 1991-95; tng. instr. N.Y. State Unified Ct. System, N.Y.C., 1985—, pers. assessor, 1985—; lectr. John Jay Coll. NYU, N.Y.C., 1987. Author: Juvenile Crime Survey, 1982, New York State Jury Selection, 1984. Bd. dirs. Parkway Consumers Med. Coun., Bklyn., 1983—, Cen. Bklyn. Tenant's Rights, 1988—. Recipient Leadership award Tribune Soc., N.Y. State Cts. 1987, Svc. award, 1988, Cert. of Merit award Fedn. Afro-Am. Civil Svc. Orgns., 1987. Mem. ASPA, Internat. Pers. Mgmt. Assn., Acad. Polit. Sci., Conf. Minority Pub. Adminstrs., Masons. Democrat. Methodist. Avocation: jazz musician.

RIVERS, LYNN N., congresswoman; b. Augres, Mich., Dec. 19, 1956. BA, U. Mich., 1987; JD, Wayne State U., 1992. Mem. sch. bd. City of Ann Arbor, Mich., 1984-92; mem. Mich. House of Reps., 1992-94. married; 2 children. Office: US House Reps 2107 Rayburn House Office Bldg Washington DC 20515-0513

RIVERS, MARIE BIE, broadcasting executive; b. Tampa, Fla., July 12, 1928; d. Norman Albion and Rita Marie (Monroe) Bie; m. Eurith Dickinson Rivers, May 3, 1952; children—Eurith Dickinson, III, Rex B., M. Kells, Lucy L., Georgia. Student, George Washington U., 1946. Engaged in real estate bus., 1944-51, radio broadcasting, 1951—; pres., CEO, part owner Sta. WGUN, Atlanta, 1951—, Stas. KWAM and KJMS, Memphis, Sta. WEAS-AM-FM, Savannah, Ga., Stas. WGOV and WAAC, Valdosta, Ga., Sta. WSWN and Sta. WBGF, Belle Glade, Fla.; owner, chairperson, pres., CEO Sta. WCTH, Islamorado, Fla.; pres., CEO The Gram Corp., real estate com. Creative Christian Concepts Corp., 1985, pres., CEO Ocala, 1986; owner Suncoast Broadcasting Inc. Author: A Woman Alone, 1986; contbr. articles to profl. jours. Mem. Fla. Assn. Broadcasters (bd. dirs.), Coral Reef Yacht (Coconut Grove, Fla.), Palm Beach Polo and Country Club, Kappa Delta. Roman Catholic. Avocations: travel, music writing, canines, horses. Office: 11924 W Forest Hill Blvd Ste 1 West Palm Beach FL 33414-6257 It is my hope in life that no one will ever be worse off for having known me.

RIVERS, RICHARD ROBINSON, lawyer; b. Dallas, June 9, 1942; s. Stewart Robinson and Madge (Fiske) R.; divorced; children: Laura Ellen, Jonathan Stewart. BA, Tulane U., 1964; JD, Cath. U. of Am., 1974. Bar: D.C. 1974. Writer Bauerlein, Inc., New Orleans, 1965-68; staff asst. Office of House Majority Whip, Washington, 1968-70, Office of House Majority Leader, Washington, 1971-73; internat. trade counsel Com. on Fin. U.S. Senate, Washington, 1973-77; gen. counsel Office Spl. Trade Rep., Washington, 1977-79; ptnr. Akin, Gump, Hauer & Feld, Washington, 1979—; instr. Dalian (Peoples Republic of China) Inst. Tech., Aug. 1986. Mem. ABA, D.C. Bar Assn., Coun. Fgn. Rels. Democrat. Episcopalian. Home: 1600 Avon Pl NW Washington DC 20007 Office: Akin Gump Strauss Hauer & Feld Ste 700 1333 New Hampshire Ave NW Washington DC 20036-1564

RIVERS, RONALD D., manufacturing executive; b. Washington, Ohio, July 10, 1933; s. Baxter Harmon and Gladys Ann (Meade) R.; m. Romona Williams, (div. May 1986); 1 child, Rochele. Student high sch. Pres. Mid Ohio Chem. Co., Washington Court House, Ohio, 1963—. Named 1990 Entrepreneur of Yr., Ernst and Young Inc. Mag. Office: Mid-Ohio Chemical Co Inc 717 Robinson Rd Washington Court House OH 43160-1844

RIVERS, WILGA MARIE, foreign language educator; b. Melbourne, Australia, Apr. 13, 1919; came to U.S., 1970; d. Harry and Nina Diamond (Burston) R. Diploma in edn, U. Melbourne, 1940, BA with honours, 1939 MA, 1948; License es L., U. Montpellier, France, 1952; PhD, U. Ill., 1962; MA (hon.), Harvard U., 1974; D Langs. (hon.), Middlebury Coll., 1989. High sch. tchr. Victoria, Australia, 1940-48; asst. in English lang. France, 1949-52; tchr. prep. schs., 1953-58; asst. prof. French No. Ill. U., DeKalb, 1963-64; assoc. prof. Monash U., Australia, 1964-69; vis. prof. Columbia U., 1970-71; prof. French U. Ill., Urbana-Champaign, 1971-74; prof. Romance langs. and lit., coord. lang. instrn. Harvard U., 1974-89, prof. emerita, 1989—; cons. NEH, Ford Found., Rockefeller Found., others; lectr 38 countries and throughout U.S.; adv. coun. Modern Lang. Ctr., Ont. Inst. for Studies in Edn., Nat. Fgn. Lang. Ctr., Lang. Acquire Rsch. Ctr., San Diego. Author: The Psychologist and the Foreign-Language Teacher, 1964, Teaching Foreign-Language Skills, 1968, 2d edit., 1981, A Practical Guide to the Teaching of French, 1975, 2d edit., 1988; co-author: A Practical Guide to the Teaching of German, 1975, 2d edit., 1988, A Practical Guide to the Teaching of Spanish, 1976, 2d edit., 1988, A Practical Guide to the Teaching of English as a Second or Foreign Language, 1978, Speaking in Many Tongues, 1972, 3d edit., 1983, Communicating Naturally in a Second Language, 1983, Teaching Hebrew: A Practical Guide, 1989, Opportunities for Careers in Foreign Languages, 1993, others; editor and contbr.: Interactive Language Teaching, 1987, Teaching Languages in Coll.: Curriculum and Content, 1992, writing translated into 9 languages; editorial bd. Studies in Second Language Acquisition, Applied Linguistics, Language Learning, System; mem. adv. com. Can. Modern Lang. Rev.; contbr. articles to profl. jours. Recipient Nat. Disting. Fgn. Lang. Leadership award N.Y. State Assn. Fgn. Lang. Tchrs., 1974. Mem. MLA, Am. Assn. Applied Linguistics (charter pres.), Am. Coun. on Teaching Fgn. Langs. (Florence Steiner award 1977, Anthony Papalia award 1988), Mass. Fgn. Lang. Assn. (Disting. Svc. award 1983), Tchrs. of English to Speakers of other Langs., Am. Assn. Tchrs. French, Linguistic Soc. Am., Am. Assn. Univ. Suprs. and Coords. Fgn. Lang. Programs Northeast Conf. (Nelson Brooks award 1983), Internat. Assn. Applied Psycholinguistics (v.p. 1983-89), Japan Assn. Coll. English Tchrs. (hon.), Am. Assn. Tchrs. German (hon.), Internat. Assn. Lang. Labs. (hon.). Episcopalian. Home and Office: 84 Garfield St Watertown MA 02172-4916

RIVES, STANLEY GENE, university president emeritus; b. Decatur, Ill., Sept. 27, 1930; s. James E. and Frances (Bunker) R.; m. Sandra Lou Belt, Dec. 28, 1957; children: Jacqueline Ann, Joseph Alan. B.S., Ill. State U., 1952, M.S., 1955; Ph.D., Northwestern U., 1963. Instr. W. Va. U., 1955-56, Northwestern U., 1956-58; asst. prof. Ill. State U., Normal, 1958-63; assoc. prof. Ill. State U., 1963-67; prof. Ill. State U., Normal, 1967-80, asst. dean Coll. Arts and Scis., 1968-69, Am. Council on Edn. Fellows Program, 1969-70, assoc. dean faculties, 1970-72, dean undergrad. instrn., 1972-80, dir. W.K. Kellogg Faculty and Instructional Devel. Program, 1977-80, assoc. provost, 1976-80, acting provost, 1979-80; provost, v.p. acad. affairs, prof.

Eastern Ill. U., Charleston, 1981-83, pres., 1983-92, pres. emeritus, 1992—; vis. prof. U. Hawaii, 1963-64. Author: (with Donald Klopf) Individual Speaking Contests: Preparation for Participation, 1967, (with Gene Budig) Academic Quicksand. Trends and Issues in Higher Education, 1973, (with others) Academic Innovation: Faculty and Instructional Development at Illinois State University, 1979, The Fundamentals of Oral Interpretation, 1981; contbr. articles to profl. jours. Bd. dirs. Ill. State Univs. Retirement System, 1992—, Ea. Ill. Univ. Found., 1993—, East Ctrl. Ill. Devel. Corp., 1983-92, Charleston Area Econ. Devel. Found., 1986-92, Coles Together, 1988-92; mem. pres. commn. NCAA, 1985-91; trustee Nat. Debate Tournament, 1967-75. With U.S. Army, 1952-54. Mem. Am. Assn. State Colls. and Univs., Ill. State C. of C. (bd. dirs. 1990-92), Charleston C. of C. (bd. dirs. 1985-88), Rotary, Theta Alpha Phi, Phi Kappa Delta, Pu Gamma Mu. Home: 2231 Andover Pl Charleston IL 61920-3807

RIVETTE, GERARD BERTRAM, manufacturing company executive; b. Syracuse, N.Y., May 18, 1932; s. George Francis and Helen (McCarthy) R.; m. Patricia Anne Yates, June 20, 1953; children: Kevin Gerard, Brian Yates. A.B., Syracuse U., 1954; postgrad., U. Buffalo, 1957-59, Rutgers U., 1962-65. Owner-mgr. Rivette Sales and Svc., Syracuse, 1950-54; sales rep. Sperry-Rand, Inc., Elmira, N.Y., 1954-55; with Hewitt-Robins Inc., Buffalo, 1955-62; mgr. conveyor equipment sales Hewitt-Robins Inc., Passaic, N.J., 1962-65; pres. Hewitt-Robins (Can.) Ltd., Montreal, 1965-69, also dir.; Can. regional mgr. Hewitt-Robins, 1965-69; pres. Conergics Corp., Kansas City, Kans., 1970-86, Mid-West Conveyer Co., 1970-86, Alpine Metals Co., Salt Lake City, Con Cal Corp., Orange, Calif.; chmn. bd. Versa Corp., Mt. Sterling, Ohio, 1972-86, Baker Erection Co., Kansas City, Mo., 1971-86, Arrowhead Conveyer Corp., Oshkosh, Wis., 1979-86, Conveyer Sales and Mfg., Seattle, 1983-86; chmn. bd., pres. Conveyer Corp. Am., Ft. Worth, 1978-86, Mayfran Internat. Inc., Cleve., 1984-86, Mayfran Limburg B.V., The Netherlands, 1984-86, Guardian Devel. Corp., Palo Alto, Calif., 1982—; chmn. bd. Jeffrey Chain Co., Morristown, Tenn., 1985—, Whitney Chain Corp., Morristown, 1985—; chmn. bd., pres. Guardian Resources Ltd., Redwood City, 1966-91, Jeffrey Chain Can. Inc., Toronto, 1987—; chmn. bd. Intelligent Software Internat. Inc., Redwood City, 1985—, Tsubakimoto Mayfran, Osaka, Japan, 1984-86, Greaves Midwest Engring. Ltd., Bangalore, India, 1977-86; bd. dirs. Jeffrey Chain Can., Toronto. Trustee U. Kansas City, 1983—, Midwest Rsch. Inst., 1984—; bd. dirs. Monterey Inst. Internat. Studies, 1989—. Mem. AIME. Office: PO Box 60367 Palo Alto CA 94306-0367

RIVKIND, PERRY ABBOT, federal railroad agency administrator; b. Boston, Jan. 22, 1930; s. Samuel Alexander and Mae Edna (Polisnor) R.; m. Dolores Russo; children: Robert Douglas, Valerie Jean; m. Kathleen Marie Lysher, Aug. 14, 1989. AA, Miami (Fla.) Community Coll., 1963; BA, Fla. State U., 1965; MA, Fla. Atlantic U., 1966; postgrad., Nat. War Coll., Washington, 1981. Comml. charter pilot, 1956-58; police officer Met. Police Dept., Miami, 1958-61; chief investigator Dade County State Atty. Office, Miami, 1961-67; prof. air. dept. Cen. Piedmont Coll., Charlotte, N.C., 1967-68; asst. dir. Fed. Bur. Narcotics, Washington, 1968-74; asst. adminstr. Law Enforcement Assistance Adminstrn., Washington, 1974-81; assoc. commr. U.S. Immigration and Naturalization Svc., Washington, 1981-84; dist. dir. U.S. Immigration and Naturalization Svc., Miami, 1984-88; safety mgr. Miami Herald Pub. Co., 1988-89; dep. adminstr. Fed. R.R. Adminstrn., Washington, 1989—; chmn. com. on trng. Pres.'s Coun. on Drug Abuse, Washington, 1971-74; chmn. com. on rsch. Working Group on Terrorism Nat. Security Coun., Washington, 1978-81. With U.S. Army, 1951-53. Perry A. Rivkind Day established in his honor City of Miami/Dade County/City of Miami Beach, 1985-89. Republican. Avocations: boating, hunting, fishing, motorcycling, camping.

RIVLIN, ALICE MITCHELL, economist; b. Phila., Mar. 4, 1931; d. Allan C. G. and Georgianna (Fales) Mitchell; m. Lewis Allen Rivlin, 1955 (div. 1977); children: Catherine Amy, Allan Mitchell, Douglas Gray; m. Sidney Graham Winter, 1989. B.A., Bryn Mawr Coll., 1952; Ph.D., Radcliffe Coll., 1958. Mem. staff Brookings Instn., Washington, 1957-66, 69-75, 83-93; dir. econ. studies Brookings Inst., 1983-87; dir. Congl. Budget Office, 1975-83; prof. pub. policy George Mason U., 1992; dep. dir. U.S. Office Mgmt. and Budget, 1993-94; dir., 1994—; dep. asst. sec. program coordination HEW, Washington, 1966-68, asst. sec. planning and evaluation, 1968-69; mem. Staff Adv. Commn. on Intergovtl. Rels., 1961-62. Author: The Role of the Federal Governemnt in Financing Higher Education, 1961, (with others) Microanalysis of Socioeconomic Systems, 1961, Systematic Thinking for Social Action, 1971, (with others) Economic Choices 1987, 1986, (with others The Swedish Economy, 1987, (with others) Caring for the Disabled Elderly: Who Will Pay?, 1988, Reviving the American Dream, 1992. MacArthur fellow, 1983-88. Mem. Am. Econ. Assn. (nat. pres. 1986). Office: U S Office Mgmt and Budget Office of the Director Old Exec Office Bldg Washington DC 20503

RIVLIN, BENJAMIN, political science educator; b. Bklyn., July 10, 1921; s. Moses and Esther (Ribnick) R.; m. Leanne Green, July 9, 1957; 1 child, Marc Alexander. BA, Bklyn. Coll., 1942; MA, Harvard U., 1947, PhD, 1949. With OSS, 1943-45; teaching fellow Harvard U., 1948; mem. trusteeship dept. UN Secretariat, 1948, 50, 52; research assoc. Hoover Commn., 1948; mem. faculty Bklyn. Coll. of CUNY, 1949-75, prof. polit. sci., 1962-70, chmn. dept., 1966-70; mem. Grad. Sch. faculty CUNY, 1970-85, exec. officer Ph.D. program, 1970-75, dean research and univ. programs Grad. Sch. and Univ. Center, 1975-78, dir. Ralph Bunche Inst. on UN; vis. lectr. Johns Hopkins Sch. Advanced Internat. Studies, 1956; vis. prof. African and Middle East Insts., Columbia U., 1963-88. Author: The United Nations and The Italian Colonies, 1950, Self-Determination and Dependent Areas, 1955, (with J.S. Szyliowicz) The Contemporary Middle East: Tradition and Innovation, 1965, Ralph Bunche: The Man and His Times, 1990, (with Leon Gordenker) The Challenging Role of the UN Secretary-General, 1993; also articles. Served with AUS, 1942-45. Grantee Social Sci. Research Council, 1951, 54, 64; Fulbright scholar France and N. Africa, 1956-57. Fellow African Studies Assn., Middle East Studies Assn.; mem. Internat. Studies Assn. (pres. Middle Atlantic region 1978-80), Am. Polit. Sci. Assn., Acad. Coun. on UN System (vice chair 1990-91, dir. N.Y. liaison office). Office: CUNY 33 W 42d St New York NY 10036

RIVLIN, RICHARD SAUL, physician, educator; b. Forest Hills, N.Y., May 15, 1934; s. Harry Nathaniel and Eugenie (Graciany) R.; m. Barbara Melinda Pogul, Aug. 28, 1960 (div.); children: Kenneth Stewart, Claire Phyllis; m. Rita Klausner, Feb. 29, 1976; children: Michelle Elizabeth, Daniel Elliott. A.B. cum laude in Biochem. Scis., Harvard U., 1955; M.D. cum laude in Biochem. Scis., 1959. Diplomate Am. Bd. Internat Medicine. Intern Bellevue Hosp., N.Y.C., 1959-60; asst. resident in medicine Johns Hopkins U. Hosp., Balt., 1960-61; asst. resident Johns Hopkins U. Hosp., 1963-64; clin. assoc. endocrinology br. Nat. Cancer Inst., NIH, Bethesda, Md., 1961-63; fellow dept. physiol. chemistry, medicine Johns Hopkins U. Sch. Medicine, Balt., 1964-66; lectr. clin. medicine Johns Hopkins U. Sch. Medicine, 1965-66; attending physician med. service Balt. City Hosps., 1964-66; assoc. in medicine Columbia U. Coll. Physicians and Surgeons, N.Y.C., 1966-67; asst. prof. medicine Columbia U. Coll. Physicians and Surgeons, 1967-71, assoc. prof. medicine, 1971-79; mem. Inst. Human Nutrition, 1972-79; chief endocrinology, asst. physician Francis Delafield Hosp., N.Y.C., 1966-75; asst. physician Presbyterian Hosp., N.Y.C., 1966-73; assoc. attending physician Presbyterian Hosp., 1973-79; chief nutrition service Meml. Sloan-Kettering Cancer Ctr., N.Y.C., 1979—; prof. medicine Cornell U. Med. Coll., 1979—; chief div. nutrition dept. medicine N.Y. Hosp. -Cornell Med. Center, 1979—; NSF grant reviewer, 1967—; vis. prof. Creighton U., 1974, U. Guadalajara (Mexico), 1974; vis. prof. N.J. Coll. Medicine and East Orange VA Hosp., Newark Med. Sch., N.J., 1974, 1976, 1983; Upjohn vis. prof. in nutrition Med. Coll. Ga., 1976; vis. prof. Syracuse U. 1980; Nat. Dairy Council vis. prof. in nutrition U. Mich., Ann Arbor, 1982; vis. prof. Washington U.-Jewish Hosp., St. Louis, 1983; external examiner in physiology Calcutta U., India; vis. physician Rockefeller U., N.Y.C., 1979—; prin. investigator coop. core labs. amd clin. nutririon rsch. unit Meml. Sloan-Kettering Cancer Ctr., N.Y.C. Editor: Riboflavin, 1975, Contemporary Issues in Clinical Nutrition (series), 1981—; profl. conf. procs., referee numerous profl. jours.; contbr. articles to profl. jours. Served with USPHS, 1961-63. Recipient Grace A. Goldsmith Lectre award Am. Coll. Nutrition, 1981. Fellow ACP; mem. Am. Fedn. Clin. Research, Endocrine Soc., AAAS, Harvey Soc., Am. Thyroid Assn., Am. Physiol. Soc., Am. Soc. Clin.

Investigation, Am. Inst. Nutrition, Soc. Exptl. Biology and Medicine. Home: 30 Farragut Rd Scarsdale NY 10583

RIVLIN, RONALD SAMUEL, mathematics educator emeritus; b. London, May 6, 1915; came to U.S., 1952, naturalized, 1955; s. Raoul and Bertha (Aronsohn) R.; m. Violet Larusso, June 16, 1948; 1 son, John Michael. BA, St. John's Coll., Cambridge U., 1937, MA, 1939, ScD, 1952; D.Sc. h.c., Nat. U. Ireland, 1980, Nottingham U., 1980, Tulane U., 1982; Dr. h.c., Sch. Tech. U. Thessaloniki, 1984. Rsch. physicist GE, Eng., 1937-42; sci. officer Telecom. Rsch. Establishment, Ministry Aircraft Prodn., Eng., 1942-44; rsch. physicist, head phys. rsch., supt. rsch. Brit. Rubber Prodrs. Rsch. Assn., 1944-52; head rsch. group Davy-Faraday Lab., Royal Instn., London, 1948-52; cons. Naval Rsch. Lab., Washington, 1952-53; prof. applied math. Brown U., 1953-63, L. Herbert Ballou U. prof., 1963-67, prof. applied math. and engring sci., 1963-67, chmn. divsn. applied math., 1958-63; professeur associé U. Paris, 1966-67; Centennial Univ. prof., dir. Ctr. for Application of Math. Lehigh U., Bethlehem, Pa., 1967-80; prof. emeritus Lehigh U., Bethlehem, 1980—, adj. Univ. prof., 1980-88; co-chmn. Internat. Congress Rheology, 1963; Russell Severance Springer vis. prof. U. Calif.-Berkeley, 1977; fellow Inst. Advanced Study, Berlin, 1984-85; Disting. vis. prof. U. Del., 1985-86. Contbr. articles profl. jours.; mem. editorial com. Jour. Rational Mechanics and Analysis, 1952-57, Archive for Rational Mechanics and Analysis, 1957-72, Jour. Math. Physics, 1960, Jour. Applied Physics, 1960-63, Acta Rheologica, 1963—, Internat. Jour. Biorheology, 1972-74, Mechanics Research Communications, 1974—, Jour. Non-Newtonian Fluid Mechanics, 1975—, Meccanica, 1975-94, Internat. Jour. Solids and Structures, 1990—, Zietschrift für Angewandte Mathematik und Mechanik, 1992—. Recipient Panetti prize, 1975, von Humboldt Sr. award, 1981, Charles Goodyear medal Am. Chem. Soc., 1992, von Karman medal ASCE, 1993; Guggenheim fellow, 1961-62. Fellow ASME (mem. exec. com. applied mechanics divsn. 1975-80, vice-chmn. and sec. 1978-79, chmn. 1979-80, Timoshenko Medal 1987), Acad. Mechanics, Am. Phys. Soc.; mem. NAE, Soc. Natural Philosophy (chmn. 1963-64), Am. Acad. Arts and Scis., Inst. Physics (gov. 1974-76), Soc. Rheology (exec. com. 1957-59, 71-77, Bingham medal 1958, v.p. 1971-73, nat. com. theoretical and applied mechanics 1973-82, chmn. 1976-78, vice chmn. 1978-80), Internat. Union Theoretical and Applied Mechanics (gen. assembly 1975-82, chmn. U.S. del. 1978), Coun. Sci. Pres. (sec.-treas. 1975, exec. bd. 1975-77), Mex. Soc. Rheology (hon.), Accademia Nazionale dei Lincei (fgn.), Royal Irish Acad. (hon.). Home: 1604 Merryweather Dr Bethlehem PA 18015-5249 Office: Lehigh U Bethlehem PA 18017

RIZK, MOHAMMED M., import/export executive. Pres. Rizkozaan, Inc., N.Y.C., 1987. Office: Rizkozaan Inc 211 E 43rd St Ste 1002 New York NY 10017*

RIZZO, FRANCIS, arts administrator, writer, stage director; b. N.Y.C., Nov. 8, 1936; s. Patrick Charles and Mary Katherine (McTigue) R. AB, Hamilton Coll., 1958; student, Yale Sch. Drama, 1958-60. Gen. dir. (U.S.) Festival of Two Worlds, Spoleto, Italy, 1968-71; artistic adminstr. Wolf Trap Farm Park for the Performing Arts, Vienna, Va., 1972-78, artistic cons., 1985-94; artistic dir. The Washington Opera, 1977-87; free-lance stage dir. various U.S. cos. including N.Y.C. Opera, Houston Grand Opera, Santa Fe Opera, Opera Theater of St. Louis, others; com. NEA, Washington, 1974—. Contbr. articles to Opera News, 1968—; translator supertitles, various U.S. opera cos., 1984—. Mem. Am. Guild Mus. Artists. Home: 590 West End Ave New York NY 10024-1747

RIZZO, MARY ANN FRANCES, international trade executive, former educator; b. Bryn Mawr, Pa., Jan. 11, 1942; d. Joseph Franklyn and Armella Louise (Grubenhoff) R. BA magna cum laude (N.Y. State scholar), Marymount-Manhattan Coll., 1963; MA (fellow), Yale U., 1965, PhD (Lounsbury-Cross fellow), 1969; postgrad. Harvard U. Bus. Sch., 1979. Instr. Romance langs. and lit. Yale U., New Haven, 1966-70; asst. prof. Finch Coll., N.Y.C., 1971-73; v.p. Joseph F. Rizzo Co., Fla., 1969-87; owner, pres., 1987—; minister of the Word coordinator Our Lady of Perpetual Help Ch., Scottsdale, Ariz., 1986—, eucharistic min.; mem. bd. adv. Assn. Internat. des Etudiants en Sciences Economiques et Commerciales, Ariz. State U. Vice chmn., charter mem. bd. regents Cath. U. Am.; mem., coord. export counseling svc. Ariz. Dist. Export Coun.; 2d v.p. bd. advisors sch. bus. mgmt. Ariz. State U., Phoenix; bd. advisors bus. studies Paradise Valley (Ariz.) C.C. Mem. Il Circolo Italian Cultural Club (Palm Beach, Fla.), Fgn. Trade Coun. Palm Beach County (charter mem.), World Affairs Coun. of Ariz., Scottsdale C. of C. (internat. bus. devel. com.), World Trade Ctr., Alpha Chi. Republican. Roman Catholic (community coun. 1972-74). Clubs: Harvard Bus. Sch. Greater N.Y., Yale (N.Y.C. and Phoenix), Alliance Francaise (Phoenix), Ariz., Yale of Palm Beaches, Cercle Français de Palm Beach (Fla.), Ariz. Harvard Bus. Sch. Translator: From Time to Eternity, 1967; bibliographer: Italian Literature-Roots and Branches, 1976. Home: Villa Serein 2170 Ibis Isle Rd Palm Beach FL 33480-5323 Address: 5665 N 74th Pl Scottsdale AZ 85250-6416 Office: 7436 E Stetson Dr Ste 180 Scottsdale AZ 85251

RIZZO, PAUL J., information processing company executive; b. Utica, N.Y., Jan. 4, 1928; s. Dominick and Jennie (Grande) R.; m. Sidna Chockley, Oct. 14, 1929; children: David, Ann, Beverley. B.S., U. N.C., 1950. C.P.A. Va. With Lybrand, Ross & Montgomery, 1950-51; asst. to controller Dan River Mills, 1951-58; now vice chmn. bd. IBM Corp., Armonk, N.Y.; dir. Johnson & Johnson, New Brunswick, N.J., Burlington Industries, Greensboro, N.C., Continental Ill. Bank, Chgo. Trustee Hollins Coll.; bd. dirs. United Way Tri-State, Nat. Action Council Minorities Eng., Bus. Council N.Y. State. Office: IBM Corp Old Orchard Rd Armonk NY 10504-1709

RIZZO, RICHARD C., lawyer; b. Phila., 1944. BA summa cum laude, LaSalle Coll., 1966; JD magna cum laude, U. Pa., 1969. Bar: Pa. 1970. Law clerk 3d cir. U.S. Ct. Appeals, 1969-70; ptnr. Dechert Price & Rhodes, Phila. Comment editor U. Pa. Law review, 1968-69. Mem. Order of Coif. Office: Dechert Price & Rhoads 4000 Bell Atlantic 1717 Arch St Philadelphia PA 19103-2713

RIZZO, RONALD STEPHEN, lawyer; b. Kenosha, Wis., July 15, 1941; s. Frank Emmanuel and Rosalie (Lo Cicero) R.; m. Mary Catherine Conrad, Sept. 10, 1963; children: Ronald Stephen Jr., Michael Robert. BA, St. Norbert Coll., 1963; JD, Georgetown U., 1965, LLM in Taxation, 1966. Bar: Wis. 1965, Calif. 1967. Assoc. Kindel & Anderson, L.A., 1966-71, ptnr., 1971-86; ptnr. Jones, Day, Reavis & Pogue, L.A., 1986-93, Chgo., 1993—; bd. dirs Reid Plastics, Inc., Monrovia, Calif., Guy LoCicero & Son Inc., Kenosha, Wis. Contbg. editor: ERISA Litigation Reporter. Schulte zur Hausen fellow Inst. Internat. and Fgn. Trade Law, Washington, 1966. Fellow Am. Coll. Tax Coun.; mem. ABA (chmn. com. on employee benefits sect. on taxation 1988-89), L.A. County Bar Assn. (chmn. com. on employee benefits sect. on taxation 1977-79, exec. com. 1977-78, 90-92), State Bar Calif. (co-chmn. com. on employee benefits sect. on taxation 1980), Nat. Ctr. Employee Ownership, West Pension Conf. (steering com. L.A. chpt. 1980-83). Avocations: reading, golf, travel. Home: 4803 83rd Pl Kenosha WI 53142 Office: Jones Day Reavis & Pogue 77 W Wacker Chicago IL 60601-1692

RIZZO, SOCRATES, Mexican governor; b. Linares, Nuevo Leon, Mex., Sept. 14, 1945; m. Alma Elisa Reyes de Rizzo, Sept. 15, 1971; children: Socrates, Cordelia, Tesalia. Baccalaureate, U. Auto. N.L., Monterrey; M in Econs., Colegio de Mex.; postgrad., U. Chgo. Dir. treas. politics Govt. Mex., 1979-81, Dir. econ. politics, 1982, dir. econ. program 1982-83, dir. econ. & social programs, 1982-85; congressman 53d legis., 1985-88; pres. Partido Revolucionario Institucional, Nuevo Leon, 1988; cons. Banco Nacional de Obras y S, Banco Nacional de Commercio Exterior, BANCRESER, NAFINSA, FOMEX and FONEl., 1989; mayor City of Monterrey, 1989-91; gov. State of Nuevo Leon, 1991—. Author: Generation and Allocation of Oil Economic Surplus, 1984, Panorama Económico del México Actual, 1986. Partido Revolucionario Institucional. Office: Gobierno del Estado de Nuevo Leon, 5 de Mayo y Zaragoza, 64000 Monterrey Mexico

RIZZO, WILLIAM OBER, lawyer; b. Boston, Aug. 19, 1948; s. Nicholas Daniel and Edith Katherine (Kepler) R.; m. Susan J. Parker, May 17, 1984; 1 child, Aura E.P. AB, Lawrence U., 1970; JD, Columbia U., 1973. Bar:

Mass. 1974, U.S. Dist. Ct. (fed. dist.) Mass. 1975. Law clk. to Hon. Irving R. Kaufman U.S. Ct. Appeals (2d crct.) N.Y., 1973; assoc. Ropes & Gray, Boston, 1974-81; ptnr. McDermott & Rizzo, Boston, 1981-90, Kirkpatrick & Lockhart, Boston, 1990—. Bd. dirs. Lawrence U. Alumni Assn., 1980-86, Beacon Hill Civic Assn., 1977-91, chmn. zoning and licensing com., 1977-84, pres., 1984-86, chmn. bd. dirs., 1986-88; trustee Thompson Island Edn. Ctr. 1981—; chmn. Boston Groundwater Trust, 1986-91; active Beacon Hill Archtl. Commn., 1991-93. Avocations: reading, Italian opera, collecting prints and antiques, tennis. Office: Kirkpatrick & Lockhart One Internat Pl 13th fl Boston MA 02110

RIZZOLO, LOUIS B. M., artist, educator; b. Ferndale, Mich., Oct. 8, 1933; s. Louis and Bella Lonita (Bronson) R.; m. Patricia Ann, June 30, 1956 (div. 1982); children: Connie Lucille, Louis Matthew, Marc Angelo; m. Linda Talbot, Dec. 3, 1982; stepchildren: Heather MacIntyre, Cameron Smith, Jennifer Talbot, Meghan Smith. BS in Art, Western Mich. U., 1956; MA in Fine Art, U. Iowa, 1960; postgrad., U. Ga., 1969. Tchr. art Petoskey (Mich.) Pub. Schs., 1956-64; tchr. history, art studio North Ctrl. Mich. Coll., Petoskey, 1959-64; grad. teaching asst. U. Iowa, Iowa CIty, 1958-60; tchr. painting Kalamazoo Inst. Art, 1970-85; prof. art Western Mich. U., Kalamazoo, 1964—; tchr. patinging, drawing, interdisciplinary/multi-media, installation/performance/exhbn., lectr. internat. workshops, Switzerland, Austria, Can., France, Hawaii, Scotland, 1989—; artistic/gen. dir. Rizzolo and Assocs.: Inflatable Light Workshop, Kalamzoo, 1990-96; co-dir. rsch. Creative Learning Program, Kalamazoo, 1986-96; R.W.S. London Watercolor Del. Rep. of China. Capt. AUS, 1958-68. Grantee Ford Found., Dow Corning, Du Pont, UpJohn, Mich. Coun. Arts, Mich. Found. Arts, W.K. Kellogg, Kalamazoo Arts Coun., Nat. Exhbn./Collections; Western Mich. U. fellow. Mem. Internat. Soc. Art & Tech., Mich. Watercolor Soc., World Forum of Acoustic Ecology, Laser Inst. Am. Independent. Home: PO Box 62 Glenn MI 49416

RIZZUTO, LEANDRO PETER, corporate executive; b. N.Y.C., Apr. 10, 1938; s. Julian and Josephine (Rizzo) R.; children—Susan, Leandro P. Jr., Denis, Rita. Student, St. Johns U. Pres., chmn. bd. Conair Corp., Edison, N.J., 1959—. Bd. dirs. St. Jude's Children's Hosp., Memphis, 1971—. Recipient Man of Yr. award Boys Town of Italy, 1980, Achievement award Italian Legions of Merit, 1983, Man of Yr. award Am. Beauty Assn., 1987; named Humanitarian of Yr., Cabrini Hosp., 1985; faculty fellow U. Brideport, 1984. Roman Catholic. Club: Columbus (N.Y.C.). Office: Conair Corp 1 Cummings Point Rd Stamford CT 06902-7900

RIZZUTO, PHILIP FRANCIS (SCOOTER), sports broadcaster, former professional baseball player; b. Brooklyn, N.Y., 1917; s. Fiore Francesco Rizzuto and Rose. m. Cora, 4 children, 2 grandchildren. Shortstop N.Y. Yankees, N.Y.C., 1941-43, 46-56; radio and TV broadcaster, 1956-94. USN, Pacific theatre, 1943-45. MVP 1950; Baseball Hall of Fame, 1994. Office: c/o NY Yankees Yankee Stadium E 161 St & River Ave Bronx NY 10451

ROACH, SISTER ANN DOMINIC, school system administrator. Supt. schs. Archdiocese of Boston. Office: Office Schs Supt 468 Beacon St Boston MA 02115-1098

ROACH, ARVID EDWARD, II, lawyer; b. Detroit, Sept. 6, 1951; s. Arvid Edward and Alda Elizabeth (Buckley) R. BA summa cum laude, Yale U., 1972; JD cum laude, Harvard U., 1977. Bar: D.C. 1978, N.Y. 1978, U.S. dist. ct. D.C. 1978, U.S. dist. ct. (so. dist.) N.Y. 1978, U.S. Ct. Appeals (10th cir.) 1980, U.S. Ct. Appeals (2d cir.) 1981, U.S. Ct. Appeals (D.C. cir.) 1981, U.S. Ct. Appeals (7th and 9th cirs.) 1982, U.S. Supreme Ct. 1983, U.S. Dist. Ct. Md., 1985, U.S. Ct. Appeals (3d, 4th, 5th, 6th, 8th, 11th cirs.) 1988, U.S. Ct. Appeals (1st cir.) 1992. Law clk. to judge U.S. Dist. Ct., 1977-78; assoc. Covington & Burling, Washington, 1978-85, ptnr., 1985—. Mem. ABA. Contbr. articles to legal jours. Office: Covington & Burling PO Box 7566 Washington DC 20044-7566

ROACH, EDGAR MAYO, JR., lawyer; b. Pinehurst, N.C., June 2, 1948; s. Edgar Mayo Sr. and Rhuamer (Richardson) R.; m. Deborah Day, Oct. 10, 1970; children: Edgar Mayo III, John Clifton. BA, Wake Forest U., 1969; JD with honors, U. N.C. 1974. Bar: N.C. 1974, Va. 1976, U.S. Ct. Appeals (4th cir.) 1976. Law clk. to judge U.S. Ct. Appeals (4th cir.), Abingdon, Va., 1974-75; assoc. Hunton & Williams, Richmond, Va., 1975-80; ptnr. Hunton & Williams, Raleigh, N.C., 1981-94; v.p. Va. Power, Richmond, Va., 1994—. Home: 3142 Monument Ave Richmond VA 23221 Office: Va Power 1 James River Plz Richmond VA 23261

ROACH, JAMES RICHARD, university president. V.p. acad. affairs North Adams State Coll., Mass., until 1986; pres. U. Maine, Presque Isle, 1986-92, Western Conn. State U., Danbury, 1992—. Office: Western Conn State Univ 181 White St Danbury CT 06810

ROACH, JAMES ROBERT, retired political science educator; b. Rock Rapids, Iowa, Aug. 25, 1922; s. Paul Ramsey and Doris (Kline) R. BA, U. Iowa, 1943; AM, Harvard U., 1948, PhD, 1950. Mem. faculty, adminstrn. U. Tex., Austin, 1949—, prof. govt., 1965-95, prof. emeritus, 1995—, dir. spl. programs, 1965-69, vice provost, dean interdisciplinary programs, 1971-72, dean divsn. gen. and comparative studies, 1972-74; counselor for cultural affairs Am. embassy, New Delhi, 1974-78; Fulbright vis. lectr. polit. sci. Rajasthan U., India, 1961-62; mem. Bd. Fgn. Scholarships, 1965-74, chmn., 1969-71; mem. U.S. Commn. for UNESCO, 1966-69. With USNR, 1943-46. Fulbright rsch. grantee, Australia, 1951-52, Ford Found. fgn. fellow, India, 1956-57. Mem. Assn. Asian Studies, Phi Beta Kappa, Kappa Tau Alpha, Sigma Delta Chi, Phi Kappa Psi. Democrat. Conglist. Home: 8604 Dorotha Ct Austin TX 78759-8113 Office: U Tex Dept Of Govt Austin TX 78712-1087

ROACH, SISTER JEANNE, S.C., nun, hospital administrator; b. Denver, Aug. 25, 1934. R.N., Regina Sch. Nursing, 1956; BS, Coll. Mt. St. Joseph, 1964; MS, Trinity U., 1973. Joined Sisters of Charity, Roman Catholic Ch., 1951; med. supr. St. Mary-Corwin Hosp., Pueblo, Colo., 1956-58; operating room supr. San Antonio Hosp., Kenton, Ohio, 1958-61; dir. nursing service Mt. San Rafael Hosp., Trinidad, Colo., 1961-67; speciality supr. Penrose Hosp., Colorado Springs, Colo., 1967-69, dir. nursing service, 1969-70, asst. adminstr., 1970-71, asst. adminstr. profl. services, 1973-75; assoc. adminstr. and coordinator St. Joseph Hosp., Mt. Clemens, Mich., 1975-78; v.p. Good Samaritan Hosp., Cin., 1978-82; adminstr. Our Lady of the Way Hosp., Martin, Ky., 1982-85, Mother Margaret Hall Nursing Home, 1990—; CEO St. Joseph Hosp., Huntingburg, Ind., 1985-89. Trustee, treas. Ohio Valley Renal Disease Network, Inc., Louisville, 1981-83; bd. dirs. Mud Creek Clinic, Grethel, Ky., 1982-85, St. Mary-Corwin, Pueblo, Colo., Sunny Acres, Denver, St. Joseph's Home, Cin. Fellow Am. Coll. Health Care Adminstrs.; mem. Am. Mgmt. Assn., Am. Hosp. Assn., Cath. Health Assn., Ky. Hosp. Assn., Nat. League for Nursing. Office: Mother Margaret Hall 5900 Delhi Rd Mount Saint Joseph OH 45051-1500

ROACH, JOHN D. C., manufacturing company executive; b. West Palm Beach, Fla., Dec. 3, 1943; s. Benjamin Browning and Margaret (York) R.; m. Pam Flebbe, Dec. 29, 1967 (div. Aug. 1982); children: Vanessa, Alexandra; m. Elizabeth Louise Phillips, Aug. 28, 1982; children: Bruce Phillips, Bryce Phillips, Brian Phillips. BS in Indsl. Mgmt., MIT, 1965; MBA, Stanford U., 1967. Dir. mgmt. acctg. and info. systems Ventura div. Northrop Corp., Thousand Oaks, Calif., 1967-70; co-founder, mgr. Northrop Venture Capital, Century City, Calif. 1970-71; v.p., dir. Boston Consulting Group, Boston and Menlo Park, Calif., 1971-80; v.p., world-wide strategic mgmt. practice mng. officer Booz, Allen, Hamilton, San Francisco, 1980-82; Houston, 1982-83; vice chmn., mng. dir. Braxton Assocs., Houston, 1983-87; sr. v.p., chief fin. officer Manville Corp., Denver, 1987-88, exec. v.p. ops., 1988-91; pres. Manville Sales Corp., Denver, 1988-90, Manville Mining and Minerals Group, Denver, 1990-91, Celite Corp., Denver, 1990-91; chmn., pres. chief exec. officer Fibreboard Corp., Walnut Creek, Calif., 1991—; bd. dirs. Magma Power Corp. Author: Strategic Management Handbook, 1983; contbr. articles to profl. jours. Bd. dirs. Cystic Fibrosis, Houston, 1986-87, Am. Leukemia Soc., Houston, 1986, Denver C. of C., Denver, 1987-91, Bay Area Coun., San Francisco; bd. trustees Alta Bates Med. Ctr.; mem. exec. com. San Francisco Opera Assn. Mem. N.Am. Soc. Strategy Planners, Greater Denver C. of C. (bd. dirs.), Geol. Energy and Minerals Assn. (bd.

dirs.), Colo. Forum, Soc. Corp. Planners (charter), Fin. Execs. Inst., Stanford Grad. Sch. Bus. Club, MIT Alumni Club, Met. Racquet Club (Houston), Denver Athletic Club, Cherry Hills Country Club (Englewood, Colo.), Contra Costa Country Club, Claremont Country Club. Avocations: running, bicycling, golf, snow skiing, hunting. Home: 125 Guilford Rd Piedmont CA 94611-3804 Office: Fibreboard Corp 2121 N California Blvd Ste 560 Walnut Creek CA 94596-7306

ROACH, JOHN HENDEE, JR., bank executive, investment banker; b. N.Y.C., Oct. 24, 1941; s. John Hendee and Julia (Casey) R.; m. Joan Hayden Muchmore, Sept. 23, 1972; children: Hayden, Cameron, John, Lauriston, Schuyler. BA, Washington & Jefferson Coll.; postgrad., Aspen Inst., 1987, Harvard U., 1989. With Chem. Bank, N.Y.C., 1968-71, v.p. Wall St. div., 1972-74, v.p. corp. bank, 1974-80; pres. Chem. N.Y. Corp. U.S.A., Chgo., 1980-87; mng. dir. Chem. Bank, N.Y.C., 1987-92; ret. 1992; sr. mng. dir., vice chmn. The Geneva Cos., N.Y.C., 1992—. Capt. U.S. Army, 1964-66. Mem. Field Club (Greenwich, Conn.), Racquet and Tennis Club, Onwentsia (Lake Forest, Ill.), Chgo. Club, Round Hill Club. Republican. Roman Catholic. Home: 513 Lake Ave Greenwich CT 06830 Office: The Geneva Cos 425 Park Ave New York NY 10022

ROACH, JOHN ROBERT, archbishop; b. Prior Lake, Minn., July 31, 1921; s. Simon J. and Mary (Regan) R. B.A., St. Paul Sem., 1946; M.A., U. Minn., 1957; L.H.D. (hon.), Gustavus Adolphus Coll., St. Mary's Coll., St. Xavier U., Villanova U. Ordained priest Roman Catholic Ch., 1946; instr. St. Thomas Acad., 1946-50, headmaster, 1958; named domestic prelate, 1966; rector St. John Vianney Sem., 1968-71; aux. bishop St. Paul and Mpls., 1971; consecrated bishop, 1971; pastor St. Charles Borromeo Ch., Mpls., 1971-73, St. Cecilia Ch., St. Paul, 1973-75; archbishop of St. Paul, 1975—; appointed vicar for parishes, 1971, vicar for clergy, 1972—; Episc. moderator Nat. Apostolate for Mentally Retarded, 1974; Mem. Priests Senate, 1968-72; pres. Priests Senate and Presbytery, 1970; chmn. Com. on Accreditation Pvt. Schs. in Minn., 1952-57; mem. adv. com. Coll. Entrance Exam. Bd., 1964; Episc. mem. Bishops and Pres.'s Com.; chmn. Bishops Com. to Oversee Implementation of the Call to Action Program, 1979-80; chmn. priestly formation com.; mem. Cath. Charity Bd. Trustee St. Paul Sem. Sch. Div., 1971—, now chmn.; trustee Cath. U. Am., 1978-81, Coll. St. Catherine; chmn. bd. trustees St. Thomas Acad., U. St. Thomas, St. John Vianney Sem.; v.p. Nat. Conf. Cath. Bishops, 1977-80, pres., 1980-83, chmn. ad hoc com. on call to action, 1977; chair internat. policy com. U.S. Catholic Conf., 1990-93. Mem. Am. Coun. Edn. (del. 1963-65), Minn. Cath. Edn. Assn. (past pres.), Assn. Mil. Colls. and Schs. U.S. (past pres.), North Cen. Assn. Colls. and Secondary Schs., Nat. Conf. Cath. Bishops (adminstrv. com., priestly formation com., chmn. vocations com., priorities and plans com., com. on sexual abuse), U.S. Cath. Conf. (com. on social devel. and world peace 1990-93, priorities and plans com.), Nat. Cath. Edn. Assn. (chmn. bd. dirs.), Nat. Cath. Rural Life Conf. (past chmn. task force on food and agr. 1987-89). Address: Chancery Office 226 Summit Ave Saint Paul MN 55102

ROACH, JOHN VINSON, II, retail company executive; b. Stamford, Tex., Nov. 22, 1938; s. John V. and Agnes M. (Hanson) R.; m. Barbara Jean Wiggin, Mar. 31, 1960; children: Amy, Lori. BA in Physics and Math., Tex. Christian U., 1961, MBA, 1965. V.p. Radio Shack, 1972-75, Radio Shack Mfg., 1975-78; exec. v.p. Radio Shack, 1978-80; gen. mgr. data processing Tandy Corp., Ft. Worth, 1967-73, pres., 1980—, chief exec. officer, 1981—, chmn., 1982—, also bd. dirs.; bd. dirs. Justin Industries. Bd. dirs. Van Cliburn Found.; chmn. bd. Tex. Christian U. Mem. Ft. Worth Club, City Club, Colonial Country Club, Rotary. Office: Tandy Corp 1800 1 Tandy Ctr Fort Worth TX 76102

ROACH, MARGOT RUTH, biophysicist, educator; b. Moncton, N.B., Can., Dec. 24, 1934; d. Robert Dickson and Katherine (McMillan) R.;. B.Sc. in Math. and Physics with honors, U. N.B., Fredericton, Can., 1955; M.D., C.M. cum laude, McGill U. Montreal, Can., 1959; Ph.D. in Biophysics, U. Western Ont., Can., 1963; D.Sc. (hon.), U. St. John, Can., 1981. Jr. intern Victoria Hosp., London, Ont., Can., 1959-60, fellow in cardiology, 1962-63, asst. resident in medicine, 1963-64; asst. resident in medicine Toronto Gen. Hosp., 1964-65; mem. faculty, dept. biophysics U. Western Ont., London, Ont., Can., 1965—, head dept. biophysics, 1970-78, prof., 1971—, asst. prof. medicine, 1965-72, assoc. prof., 1972-78, prof., 1978—; mem. staff dept. medicine Victoria Hosp., 1967-72, U. Hosp., London, 1972—; Commonwealth vis. sci. dept. applied math. theoretical physics Cambridge U., 1975; vis. sci. Bioengring. Inst., Chonqing U., People's Republic of China, 1991; mem. bioengring. grants com. Med. Rsch. Coun. Can., 1993—; cons. and lectr. in field. Active civic orgns. and coms. including Univ. Rsch. Coun., 1976-79; mem. interview bd. London Conf. of United Ch., 1967-90; steward United Ch. Can., 1967-73, elder, 1973—; chmn. stewardship devel. com. Colborne St. United Ch. 1990-93. Recipient A. Wilmer Duff prize in physics U. N.B., 1955, Cushing prize in pediatrics, 1959, Ciba Found. award for research in aging, 1959, Teaching award Faculty of Medicine U. Western Ont., 1990; Med. Research Council fellow U. Western Ont., 1960-62; numerous other fellowships and grants in medicine. Fellow Royal Coll. Physicians (Can.), Am. Coll. Cardiology (Young Investigator's award 1963); mem. Can. Physiol. Soc., Can. Cardiovascular Soc. (off council), Can. Clin. Investigation Soc. (council 1980-84), Can. Biophys. Soc., Can. Soc. Internal Medicine. Home: 223 University Crescent, London, ON Canada N6A 2L7

ROACH, MAXWELL LEMUEL, musician; b. Elizabeth City, N.C., Jan. 10, 1924; s. Alphonzo and Cressie (Saunders) R.; m. Mildred Wilkinson, Jan. 14, 1949 (div.); children: Daryl, Maxine; m. Abbey Lincoln, Mar. 3, 1962 (div.). Student, Manhattan Sch. Music, N.Y.C.; Mus.D. (hon.), New Eng. Conservatory Music, 1982. Prof. music U. Mass., from 1973. Adapted use of tympani in jazz; musician specializing percussion instruments; with Charlie Parker, 1946-48, later appeared with Thelonious Monk, Bud Powell, Dizzy Gillespie; co-leader Max Roach-Clifford Brown Quintet; with Sonny Rollins, Harold Land, 1954-56, later with Booker Little, Ray Bryant, Eric Dolphy; appearances at Paris Jazz Festival, 1949, Newport Jazz Festival, 1972; composer: integration of jazz and dance Freedom Now suite; albums include: Percussion Bitter Sweet, It's Time, Drums Unlimited, Speak Brother Speak, The Loadstar, Conversations, Long as You're Living, Survivors, The Long March, Jazz in 3/4 Time, Scott Free, To the Max!, 1991, (with Dizzy Gillespie) Max and Dizzy: Paris 1989; producer, dir. and choreographer. Recipient Best Record of Year award Down Beat mag. 1956; winner Down Beat poll 1955, 57, 58, 59, 60, 84, metronome poll 1951-54. Mem. Jazz Artists Guild Inc. (organizer), Am. Acad. and Inst. of Arts and Letters (Hon.), 1992. Office: care PSI 810 7th Ave New York NY 10019-5818*

ROACH, THOMAS ADAIR, lawyer; b. Akron, Ohio, May 1, 1929; s. Edward Thomas and Mayme Bernice (Turner) R.; m. Sally Jane Bennett, July 11, 1953; children: Thomas, David, James, Dorothy, Steven, Patrick. AB, U. Mich., 1951, JD with distinction, 1953. Bar: Mich. 1953. Assoc. McClintock, Fulton, Donovan & Waterman (and successor firms), Detroit, 1956-62, ptnr., 1962-87; counsel Bodman, Longley & Dahling, Detroit and Ann Arbor, Mich., 1988-90; ptnr. Bodman, Longley & Dahling, Detroit and Ann Arbor, Mich., 1990—; bd. dirs. Ferndale Labs, Inc., Acme Abrasive Co. Contbr. articles to profl. jours. Vice chmn. 14th Congl. Dist. Democratic Orgn., 1971-75; chmn. platform and resolution com. Mich. Dem. Party, 1971-74, treas., 1975-87; permanent chmn. Dem. State Conv., 1976; mem. platform com. and drafting subcom. Dem. Nat. Conv., 1972, mem. rules com., 1980, alt. del., 1984; Bd. regents U. Mich., 1975-90; bd. dirs. Mich. Tech. Coun., 1983-92, vice chmn. 1984-86, south-ctrl. region 1992-95; pres. 9th Dist. Res. Policy Bd. 1976-77; nat. chmn. Am. Giving U., Mich., 1987—; mem. Mich. Higher Edn. Assistance Authority, Mich. Higher Edn. Student Loan Authority, 1990-94, Great Saulk Trail Coun., 1993—; bd. dirs. Wolverine Coun. Boy Scouts Am., 1991-93; officer Compensation Commn. Pittsfield Twp., 1991-93. Served to capt. USCGR, 1953-56; res. group comdr., 1974-77. Mem. ABA, FBA, Mich. Bar Assn. (chmn. constrn. law com. 1983-85), Detroit Bar Assn., Washtenaw County Bar Assn., Res. Officers Assn., Order of Coif, Thomas M. Cooley Club, U. Mich. Club (gov. 1970-74), U. Mich. Alumni Assn. (bd. dirs. 1991-94, pres. 1995—), Rotary Club (bd. dirs. Ann Arbor chpt. 1991—, pres. 1994-95). Anglican. Home: 11825 Durston Pinckney MI 48169-9502 Office: Bodman Longley & Dahling Ste 300 110 Miller Ann Arbor MI 48104

ROACH, WAYNE E., retail automotive executive; b. 1946. Pres., COO Fred Jones Co., Inc., Oklahoma City, 1991—. Office: Fred Jones Cos Inc 123 S Hudson Ave Oklahoma City OK 73102*

ROACH, WESLEY LINVILLE, lawyer, insurance executive; b. Norlina, N.C., Oct. 8, 1931; s. Joseph Franklin and Florence G. (Sink) R.; m. Mary Jon Gerald, Aug. 13, 1955; children: Gerald, Mary Virginia. B.S., Wake Forest U., 1953, J.D., 1955. Bar: N.C. 1955. With Pilot Life Ins. Co., Greensboro, N.C., 1958-86, also bd. dirs.; sr. v.p., gen. counsel Jefferson-Pilot Life Ins. Co., Greensboro, 1986-88; sec. Great Ea. Lif. Ins. Co., 1975-85; of counsel Smith, Anderson, Blount, Dorsett, Mitchell & Jernigan, Attys. at Law, Raleigh, N.C., 1988—; former chmn. bd. dirs. N.C. Life and Accident and Health Ins. Guaranty Assn., Va. Life, Accident and Health Guaranty Assn., S.C. Life, Accident and Health Guaranty Assn.; sec. JP Investment Mgmt. Co., Jefferson-Pilot Equity Sales, Inc., Spl. Services Agy., Inc., 1974-84; mem. exec. com., bd. dirs. N.C. Ins. Found., 1978—. Mem. fin. com. Greensboro United Fund, 1964-65; mem. fin. com. Greensboro 1st Bapt. Ch., 1963-66, 83-86, chmn., 1983-85, chmn. bd. deacons, 1974-76, 80-81; nat. chmn. alumni coun. coll. fund Wake Forest U., 1971-76, pres. nat. alumni coun., 1975-76, trustee univ., 1978-82; trustee So. Bapt. Theol. Sem., Louisville, 1973-84; trustee Bapt. Retirement Homes N.C., Inc., 1992—, chmn., 1993-94 With USNR, 1955-58. Mem. ABA, N.C. Bar Assn., Raleigh Bar Assn., Assn. Life Ins. Counsel (bd. govs. 1984-88), Greensboro C. of C. (chmn. nat. legis. com. 1973—), Nat. Orgn. Life Guaranty Assn. (bd. dirs. 1982-87). Democrat. Home: PO Box 1490 601 Selma Rd Wendell NC 27591-8648 Office: 2500 First Union Capitol Ctr PO Box 2611 Raleigh NC 27602-2611

ROACH, WILLIAM RUSSELL, training and education executive; b. Bedford, Ind., Jan. 1940; s. George H. and Beatrice M. (Schoenlaub) R.; m. Margaret R. Balogh, 1961 (div. 1994); children: Kathleen L., Keith W. BS in Fin. and Acctg., UCLA, 1961. CPA, Calif. Internal auditor Hughes Aircraft Co., L.A., 1961-62, Lockheed Aircraft Corp., L.A., 1962; sr. acct. Haskins & Sells, L.A., 1962-66; asst. to group v.p., asst. corp. contr. Lear Siegler, Inc., Santa Monica, Calif., 1966-71; exec. v.p., corp. sec., dir. Optimum Systems Inc., Santa Clara, Calif., 1972-79; pres., dir. Banking Systems Inc., subs. Optimum Systems Inc., Dallas, 1976-79, BancSystems, Inc., Santa Clara, 1976-79, DMA/Optimum, Honolulu, 1978-79; v.p. URS Corp., San Mateo, Calif., 1979-81; pres. URS Internat., Inc., 1980-81; pres., CEO, dir. Advanced Systems, Inc., from 1981, Applied Learning Internat., Inc. (formed from merger of Advanced Systems, Inc. and Deltak Training Corp.), Naperville, Ill., 1981-88; sr. v.p., bd. dirs. Nat. Edn. Corp. (parent co. Applied Learning Internat.), Irvine, Calif., 1988—; chmn. bd., pres., chief exec. officer TRO Learning Inc., (acquisition tng. and edn. group Control Data Corp.), Schaumburg, Ill., 1989—; bd. dirs. Mil. Profl. Resources, Inc., Sch. Properties, Inc.; guest speaker numerous industry related funtions including Rep. Platform Com., 1988. Mem. AICPA, Calif. Soc. CPAs, Theta Delta Chi, Commonwealth Club (San Francisco); The Meadow Club (Chgo.). Home: 45 Hawthorne Ln Barrington Hills IL 60010-5109 Office: TRO Learning Inc Woodfield Corp Ctr 150 N Martingale Rd Ste 700 Schaumburg IL 60173-2079

ROACHE, EDWARD FRANCIS, retired manufacturing company executive; b. Morristown, N.J., May 2, 1923; s. Vincent D. and Cecelia R. (Kennedy) R.; m. Beth Davidson, Aug. 8, 1948; children: Marc E., Steven P., Kevin J. B.S. in Economics, Fordham U., 1947; postgrad., Sienna Coll., 1953. With Gen. Electric Co., 1947—; mem. fin. mgmt. program, corporate audit staff, mgr. fin. various depts., gen. mgmt. assignments in electronics, computers, aircraft engine and intern Gen. Electric Co., Syracuse, N.Y., Phoenix, Lynn, Mass., Fairfield, Conn., 1978-83; v.p., gen. mgr. internat. constrn. bus. div. Gen. Electric Co., 1978-83, ret., 1983; dir. Gen. Electric Co., Italy, Australia, S. Korea, U.K. Served with USMC, 1943-46. Mem. Fin. Execs. Inst. Clubs: Pinnacle; Landmark (Stamford, Conn.). Home: 1161 Mill Hill Rd Southport CT 06490-1041

ROACHE, FRANCIS MICHAEL, law enforcement official; b. Boston, Aug. 3, 1936; s. Francis J. and Barbara M. (McKeon) R.; m. Barbara M. Campers, June 13, 1959; children—Barbara, Donna, Paula, Michael, Lori. M. Pub. Mgmt., Boston State Coll., 1981, BS in Law Enforcement; grad., Fed. Bur. Investigation Nat. Acad., Quantico, Va., 1982. Officer Boston Police Dept., 1968-75, sgt., 1975-83, acting lt., 1984-85, commr., 1985—; mem. Gov.'s Statewide Anti-Crime Council (Mass.), 1985—; mem. The Partnership, Inc., Boston, 1985—. Cons., lobbyist Mass. landmark civil rights legis., 1979; active Greater Boston Civil Rights Coalition, 1980, Norfolk County Human Rights Council (Mass.), 1983; bd. dirs. Boy Scouts Am., Boston, 1985. Served to cpl. USMC, 1955-59. Mem. FBI Nat. Exec. Inst., Internat. Assn. Chiefs Police (coord. New Eng. region), Mass. Chiefs of Police Assn., NE Assn. Chiefs of Police, FBI Nat. Acad. Assocs., Nat. Criminal Justice Honor Soc. of Northeastern U., KC, Omega Epsilon chpt. Alpha Phi Sigma. Roman Catholic. Avocation: marathon running. Office: Boston Police Hdqrs 154 Berkeley St Boston MA 02116-5196

ROADEN, ARLISS LLOYD, higher education executive director, former university president; b. Bark Camp, Ky., Sept. 27, 1930; s. Johnie Samuel and Ethel Nora (Killian) R.; m. Mary Etta Mitchell, Sept. 1, 1951; children: Janice Arletta Roaden Skelton, Sharon Kay Roaden Hagen. Grad., Cumberland Coll., 1949; AB, Carson Newman Coll., 1951; MS, U. Tenn., 1958, EdD, 1961; PhD (hon.), Cumberland Coll., 1986; DLitt (hon.), Tusculum Coll., 1992. With Oak Ridge Inst. Nuclear Studies, 1957-59, Auburn U., 1961-62; mem. faculty Ohio State U., 1962-74, prof. edn., 1967-74, acting dean Coll. Edn., 1968-70, vice provost for research, dean Grad. Sch., 1970-74; pres. Tenn. Tech. U., 1974-85; dir. Tenn. Higher Edn. Commn., 1985—; pres. emeritus Tenn. Tech. U., 1985—; summer vis. prof. Marshall U., 1961, U. So. Calif., 1964, Ind. U., 1967; cons. ednl. instns., 1961—; mem. Tenn. Coll. Assn., 1978; chmn. sci. and tech. com. Am. Assn. State Colls. and Univs., 1980; chmn. task force on program and instl. assessment State Higher Edn. Exec. Officers', 1987, pres. 1993-94, chmn. coun. postsecondary accreditation liaison com., 1986-88, exec. com., 1988-95, pres. elect 1992-93; mem. exec. bd. trustees Southern Assn. Colls. and Schs., 1986—, chair communications com., 1990—, mem. task force, 1990—; mem. Southern Regional Edn. Bd., 1985—; chmn. procedures com. for reviewing bylaw changes and revisions, 1988-89; mem. exec. com., state rep., treas., chair Internal Audit Com., 1990-91, Edn. Commn. States, 1987-90; mem. Tenn. Econ. Cabinet Coun., 1988—, chmn.m 1988-91, bd. dirs. 1988—Fgn. Lang. Inst.; treas. chair Internal Audit Com., 1990-91; mem. Performance Standards in Vocat.-Tech. Edn. Working Group, U.S. Dept. Edn., 1990. Coauthor: The Research Assistantship: Recommendations for Colleges and Universities, 1975; editor: Problems of School Men in Depressed Urban Areas, 1967; contbr. articles to profl. jours. State chmn. Tenn. Am. Cancer Soc. Crusade, 1986-88, bd. dirs., 1987; mem. exec. bd., coun. commr. Middle Tenn. coun. Boy Scouts Am., 1987-88, nat. coun., 1988—, chair scouts membership rels. com.; mem. Phi Delta Kappa Found., 1965—, past chmn. bd. govs., mem. futures and diamond jubilee coms., 1989—; chair Blue Ribbon com. to respond to edn. goals, 1990; bd. dirs. Nat. Project 714, 1986—, pres.-elect, 1987-88, chmn., 1988-89; pres. Alumni Assn. Bd. Cumberland Coll., 1987-88; adult Sunday sch. tchr. Woodmont Bapt. Ch., chmn. pers. com., 1989—. With AUS, 1951-53. Research grantee Phi Delta Kappa Internat., 1968; named Distinguished Alumnus Cumberland Coll., 1970; recipient Distinguished Alumni and Faculty Centennial medallion Coll. Edn., 1970, Distinguished Service award Council Grad. Students, 1974; both Ohio State U.; recipient Silver Beaver award Boy Scouts Am., Rotarian of Yr., 1984; Eagle Scout honoree Middle Tenn. Coun. Boy Scouts Am., 1989, others. Fellow Oxford Soc. Scholars; mem. AAAS, Am. Assn. Higher Edn., Acad. Polit. and Social Scis., Am. Ednl. Rsch. Assn. (chmn. publs. com. 1979-80), Nat. Soc. Study Edn., Nat. Assn. State Colls. and Land Grant Univs., Order of Lion and Eagle, Lions (Nashville bd. dirs. 1988-90, pres. 1991-92, zone chmn. 1992-93), Rotary (bd. dirs.), Phi Kappa Phi, Phi Delta Kappa (Disting. Svc. award Ohio State U. chpt. 1974), Kappa Phi Kappa, Kappa Delta Pi. Baptist. Office: Tenn Higher Edn Commn Ste 2100 404 James Robertson Pky Nashville TN 37243-0830

ROAF, WILLIAM LAYTON, professional football player; b. Pine Bluff, Ark., Apr. 18, 1970; s. Clifton George and Andree Yvonne (Layton) R. Left offensive tackle New Orleans Saints, 1993—. Named All-American, Sports Writers, 1993, finalist Outland Trophy, Sports Writers, 1993; named to All-Rookie Team, Football News, 1994, Pro-Bowl Alt., 1994. Episcopal. Dr.

Z's All-Pro team, 1994. Office: New Orleans Saints 6928 Saints Dr Metairie LA 70003

ROAN, JAMES CORTLAND, JR., air force officer; b. St. Louis, Apr. 10, 1937; s. James Cortland and Marguerite L. (Johnson) R.; m. Connie R. Brown, Nov. 10, 1962; children: James Bradley, Brian Edward. BSBA, JD, Washington U., St. Louis, 1960. Bar: Mo. 1960. Commd. 1st lt. USAF, 1960, advanced through grades to brig. gen., 1990; staff judge adv. Air Force Aero. Systems Div., Dayton, Ohio, 1982-85, Hdqrs. Air Force Logistics Command, Dayton, 1991-92, Hdqrs. Air Force Systems Command, Washington, 1985-87, 1990-91; staff judge adv. Air Force Electronic Systems Div., Boston, 1987-90; comdr. Hdqrs. Air Force Contract Law Ctr., Dayton, 1991-92; staff judge adv. Hdqrs. Air Force Materiel Command, Dayton, 1992—. Recipient Stuart R. Reichart award as outstanding sr. atty. in USAF, Air Force Assn., 1989. Mem. Fed. Bar Assn. (pres. Beverly Hills chpt. 1980-81). Avocation: woodworking. Home: 523 Johnson Dr Dayton OH 45433-1129 Office: HQ Air Force Material Command AFMC/JA Wright-Patterson AFB OH 45433

ROARK, CHARLES ELVIS, healthcare executive; b. Port Arthur, Tex., Feb. 11, 1946; s. Chris C. and Alene (Adams) R.; m. Marlene Jones, Jan. 18, 1969; children: Cari Joann, Carolyn Dianne, Charles Eric. BBA, Lamar U., Beaumont, Tex., 1969; MS, Trinity U., San Antonio, 1971; EdD, Tex. Tech U., 1994. Asst. adminstr. Hotel Dieu Hosp., El Paso, 1969-76; dir. planning Tex. Hosp. Assn., Austin, 1976-79; adminstr. Gulf Coast Hosp., Wharton, Tex., 1979-81; pres. Charles E. Roark & Assocs., El Paso, 1980—; exec. dir. Hospice of El Paso Inc., 1990—; bd. dirs. Bien Vivir Health Svcs. Pres. N.E. Civic Leaders Coun., Inc., 1986-90; mem. adv. bd. Anytown USA, 1987-88; mem. City of El Paso Sanitation Adv. Bd., 1987-88; bd. dirs. Keep El Paso Beautiful, 1986-88. Fellow Am. Coll. Healthcare Execs. (cert.); Mem. Rotary Club of El Paso, N.E. Civitan (pres. 1975-76, dist. gov. 1988-89), S.W. Healthcare Execs. (pres. 1991-92). Baptist. Avocations: sports, hunting, fishing. Office: Hospice of El Paso Inc 3901 N Mesa Ste 400 El Paso TX 79902

ROARK, EDITH HUMPHREYS, private school language arts educator, reading specialist; b. Raleigh, N.C., Jan. 26, 1943; d. Sidney Frederick and Jennie Mildred (Swain) Humphreys; m. Larry Alden Roark, Nov. 27, 1964; children: Jonathan Laurance, Nancy Elaine, Naomi Elizabeth. BS, Appalachian State U., 1965; MA, East Tenn. State U., 1980, postgrad., 1986-88. Cert. elem. tchr., Tenn. Tchr. Memphis City Schs., 1966, Wake County Schs., Garner, N.C., 1967, Dover (N.J.) Twp. Schs., 1968, Kingsport (Tenn.) Christian Sch., 1974-77; tchr. Tri-Cities Christian Sch., Kingsport, 1983-84, reading tutor, 1980-84; reading tutor Ashley Acad., Johnson City, Tenn., 1984-87, tchr., 1987—; ofcl. judge Odyssey of the Mind, Tenn., 1991, 94, coach, 1992, regional judge, 1993-95; state judge 1994-95; leader Gt. Books, Johnson City, 1988; participant NIE Playshop, Kingsport, summers 1989-94, Slingerland Multisensory Reading Tchr. Tng. Mem. Internat. Reading Assn., Orton Dyslexia Soc., Kappa Delta Pi, Delta Kappa Gamma (chair literacy com. 1991—, corr. sec. 1994—). Baptist. Avocations: reading, collecting newspaper trivia, gardening, decorating, teaching Sunday school. Home: 222 Norwood Dr Johnson City TN 37615 Office: Ashley Acad 816 Lacy St Johnson City TN 37604

ROARK, TERRY PAUL, university president; b. Okeene, Okla., June 11, 1938; s. Paul J. and Erma K. (Morrison) R.; m. Beverly Brown, Sept. 7, 1963; 1 child, David. C. BA in Physics, Oklahoma City U., 1960; MS in Astronomy, Rensselaer Poly. Inst., 1962, PhD in Astronomy, 1966. Asst. provost for curricula Ohio State U., Columbus, 1977-79, assoc. provost for instrn., 1979-83; prof. physics Kent (Ohio) State U., 1983-87, v.p. acad. and student affairs, 1983-87, provost, 1985-87; pres. U. Wyo., Laramie, 1987—; bd. dirs. Rocky Mountain Fed. Savs. Bank, chmn. audit com., 1989-93; commr. Western Interstate Commn. for Higher Edn., 1987—, chmn., 1991; bd. dirs. Associated Western Univs., 1987-94, chmn., 1991, bd. trustees, 1994—; mem. adv. bd. Wyo. Geol. Survey, 1987—; mem. Warren AFB Civilian Adv. Coun., 1987—; bd. dirs. First Interstate Bank of Wyo. Mem., treas. Ctr. for Pub. Edn., Columbus, 1980-83; mem. fin. adv. com. LWV, Kent, 1986; mem. long range planning com. Cleve. Urban League, 1985-86; mem. adv. com. Battelle youth sci. program Columbus and Ohio Pub. Schs., 1982; bd. dirs. Ivinson Hosp. Found., 1987—. Mem. AAUP, Am. Astron. Soc., Astron. Soc. Pacific, Internat. Astron. Union, Nat. Assn. State Univs. and Land Grant Colls. (bd. dirs. 1994—, chair commn. on internat. affairs 1995), Am. Assn. for Higher Edn., Sigma Xi, Phi Kappa Phi, Omicron Delta Kappa. Avocations: photography, music, hiking. Home: 1752 Edward Dr Laramie WY 82070 Office: U Wyo Office of Pres PO Box 3434 Laramie WY 82071-3434

ROATH, KENNETH B., investment company executive. Pres., chmn. bd., CEO Health Care Property Investors, L.A., 1978—. Office: Health Care Property Investors 10990 Wishire Blvd Los Angeles CA 90024*

ROATH, ROBERT S., food products executive; b. N.Y.C., Jan. 27, 1943; children: David, Jessica. BA, U. Md., 1966; postgrad., Amos Tuck Sch., 1979. CPA, N.Y. Audit mgr. Price Waterhouse, N.Y.C., 1966-73; asst. corp. controller GAF, Wayne, N.J., 1973-75, Gen. Foods Corp., White Plains, N.Y., 1975-81; internat. controller Gen. Foods Internat., Rye, N.Y., 1981-84; v.p. fin. and bus. devel. Gen. Foods, Can., Toronto, 1984-88; v.p. corp., contr. Colgate Palmoolive Co., N.Y.C., 1988-90, RJR Nabisco, Inc., N.Y.C., 1990—. Served to sgt. USAF, 1960-64. Mem. Am. Inst. CPA's, N.Y. Soc. CPA's, Fin. Execs. Inst., Council Fin. Execs. (conf. bd. Can.). Home: 7 Covlee Dr Westport CT 06880-6406 Office: RJR Nabisco 1301 Ave Of The Americas New York NY 10019-6022

ROBAK, KIM M., state official; b. Columbus, Nebr., Oct. 4, 1955; m. William J. Mueller; children: Katherine, Claire. BA with distinction, U. Nebr., 1977, JD with high distinction, 1985. Tchr. Lincoln (Nebr.) Pub. Schs., 1978-82; clerk Cline Williams Wright Johnson & Oldfather, Lincoln, 1983; summer assoc. Cooley Godward castro Huddleson & Tatum, San Francisco, 1984, Steptoe & Johnson, Washington, 1985; ptnr. Rembolt Ludtke Parker & Berger, Lincoln, 1985-91; legal counsel Gov. E. Benjamin Nelson/State of Nebr., Lincoln, 1991-92, chief of staff, 1992-93; lt. gov. State of Nebr., Lincoln, 1993—; chair Prairie Fire Internat. Symposium on Edn. 1986. Fellow Leadership Lincoln, 1986-87, program com., 1987-90; chair program com. Leadership Lincoln Alumni Assn., 1987, selection com., 1990; chair Landfill Alternatives and Ops. Task Force, 1986-87; chair Gladys Forsyth award subcom. YWCA Tribute! to Women, 1987, chair nominations, 1991; mem. adv. com. U.S. Constitution Bicentennial Competition, 1987; gen. Dem. Counsel, Nebr., 1985-93; bd. women's ministries First Plymouth Congl. Ch., 1988-91, bd. trustees, 1991-94. Mem. Nat. Conf. Lt. Govs. (fed. practice com. 1989-92), Nat. Inst. Trial Attys., Nebr. State Bar Assn. (ethics com. 1987-92, vice chair com. on pub. rels. 1988-92, chair com. on yellow page advt. 1988, ho. dels. 1989—, ways and means com. 1991-94), Lincoln Bar Assn., U. Nebr. Coll. Law Alumni Assn. (bd. dirs. 1988—), Order of Coif, Updowntowners. Office: Lt Gov's Office PO Box 94863 Lincoln NE 68509-4848

ROBAK, ROSTYSLAW WSEWOLOD, psychologist, educator; b. Passau, Germany, Nov. 15, 1948; s. Bohdan and Maria R.; m. Loretta J. Tallon; children: Marika, Boyan. BA, Seton Hall U., 1970; MA, Fairleigh Dickinson U., 1973; PhD, Hofstra U., 1976. Lic. psychologist N.Y., Pa., Mass. Prof. Pace U. Pleasantville, N.Y., 1988—; dir. M.S. program in substance abuse counseling Pace U., 1992—; adj. prof. Orange County Community Coll., Middletown, N.Y. 1985-88; founding faculty advisor Pace U. chpt. Psi Chi Nat. Honor Soc., 1991—. Author: A Primer for Today's Substance Abuse Counselor, 1991. Mem. APA, Am. Orthopsychiat. Assn., Nat. Register Health Svc. Providers in Psychology, Assn. Death Edn. and Counseling. Office: Pace Univ Pleasantville NY 10570

ROBARDS, JASON NELSON, JR., actor; b. Chgo., July 26, 1922; s. Jason Nelson and Hope (Glanville) R.; m. Eleanore Pitman, May 7, 1948; children: Jason III, Sarah Louise, David; m. Lauren Bacall, July 4, 1961 (div.); 1 son, Sam; m. Lois O'Connor; children: Shannon, Jake. Student, Am. Acad. Dramtic Arts, 1946; D.H.L., Fairfield U., 1982; D.F.A., Williams Coll., 1983. Bd. dirs. Am. Acad. Dramatic Arts, 1957—. Broadway plays include Stalag 17, 1951-53, The Chase, 1952, The Iceman Cometh, 1956, Long Day's Journey Into Night, 1956-58, 76, 88, The Disenchanted, 1958, 1958-59, Toys in the Attic, 1960, Big Fish, Little Fish, 1961, A Thousand Clowns, 1962, After the Fall, 1964, But for Whom, Charlie, 1964, Hughie, 1964, The Devils, 1965, We Bombed in New Haven, 1968, The Country Girl, 1972, A Moon for the Misbegotten, 1973, A Touch of the Poet, 1977-78, A Month of Sundays, 1987, No Man's Land, 1993; other plays include Henry IV, Part I, Stratford (Ont., Can.), 1958, Macbeth, Stratford, Conn., You Can't Take It With You, 1983, Love Letters, 1989, Park Your Car in Harvard Yard, 1991; motion picture appearances include The Journey, 1959, By Love Possessed, 1961, Long Day's Journey into Night (Cannes Internat. Film Festival, Best Actor Award, 1962), A Thousand Clowns, Big Hand for the Little Lady, 1966, Any Wednesday, 1966, St. Valentine's Day Massacre, 1967, Night They Raided Minsky's, 1968, Hour of the Gun, 1967, Loves of Isadora, 1969, Once Upon a Time in the West, 1969, Ballad of Cable Hogue, 1970, Johnny Got His Gun, 1971, Murders in the Rue Morgue, 1971, The War Between Men and Women, 1972, Pat Garrett and Billy the Kid, 1973, All the President's Men, 1976, Julia, 1977, Comes a Horseman, 1978, Hurricane, 1979, Melvin and Howard, 1979, Something Wicked This Way Comes, 1983, Max Dugan Returns, 1983, Square Dance, 1987, The Good Mother, 1988, Parenthood, 1989, Quick Change, 1990, Storyville, 1992, The Trial, 1993, The Adventures of Huck Finn, 1993, Philadelphia, 1993, Little Big League, 1994, The Paper, 1994, Crimson Tide, 1995; TV appearance in For Whom the Bell Tolls, CBS, 1959; starred in TV films including: The Iceman Cometh, 1961, One Day in the Life of Ivan Denisovitch, 1963, Washington Behind Closed Doors, 1977, F.D.R.: The Last Year, 1980, The Day After, 1983, Sakharov, 1984, Johnny Bull, 1986, Inherit the Wind, 1988 (Emmy award, 1988), The Christmas Wife, 1988, Chernobyl: The Final Warning, 1991; appeared in TV miniseries Haywire, 1980, The Atlanta Child Murders, 1985. Served with USN, 1939-46. Recipient ANTA award for outstanding contbn. to living theater, 1959, Antoinette Perry award as best actor, 1959, Obie award, 1956, Tony award for best dramatic actor, 1959, Acad. awards for best supporting actor, 1976, 77, N.Y. Film Critics Circle award for best supporting actor, 1976, Presdl. citation. Club: Players (N.Y.C.). Address: C/O Paradigm Talent Agy 25th FL 10100 Santa Monica Blvd Los Angeles CA 90067*

ROBB, A. M., glass manufacturing executive. Chmn. bd. Pilkington Holding Inc., Toledo. Office: Pilkington Holdings Inc 811 Madison Ave Toledo OH 43624-1626

ROBB, BRUCE, former insurance company executive; b. Norman, Okla., July 28, 1919; m. Betty Jane Sharrar, May 6, 1950; children: Elizabeth (dec.), Bruce. B.S., U.S. Naval Acad., 1941; M.B.A., Columbia U., 1949. Security analyst Clark, Dodge & Co., Inc., 1947-51, 1948-52, 53-62; asst. treas. SAFECO Corp., Seattle, 1962-66; v.p., treas. SAFECO Corp., 1966-72, sr. v.p., treas., 1972-84. Mem. Wash. State Fin. Adv. Com., 1970-80. Investment Com., Diocese of Olympia. Mem. Seattle Found., Seattle Mus. History and Industry, Beta Gamma Sigma. Club: Sand Point Country. Home: 6307 NE 57th St Seattle WA 98105-2011

ROBB, CHARLES SPITTAL, senator, lawyer; b. Phoenix, AZ, June 26, 1939; s. James Spittal and Frances Howard (Woolley) R.; m. Lynda Bird Johnson, Dec. 9, 1967; children: Lucinda Desha, Catherine Lewis, Jennifer Wickliffe. Student, Cornell U., 1957-58; B.B.A., U. Wis., 1961; J.D., U. Va., 1973. Bar: Va. 1973, U.S. Supreme Ct. 1976. Law clk. to presiding justice U.S. Ct. Appeals, 1973-74; atty. Williams Connolly & Califano, 1974-77; lt. gov. Va., 1978-82, gov., 1982-86; ptnr. Hunton & Williams, Richmond, Norfolk, and Fairfax, Va., Washington; U.S. Senator from Va., 1989—; chmn. Nat. Conf. Lt. Govs., 1979-80, Am. Coun. Young Polit. Leaders Dels. to Peoples Republif of China, 1979, edn. Commn. of the States, 1985; vis. prof. pub. affairs George Mason U., spring 1987. Chmn. Jobs for Am.'s Grads. Inc., 1985-90, Dem. Leadership Coun., 1986-88; gov. Atlantic Inst. for Internat. Affairs, 1987. With USMC 1961-70. Decorated Bronze Star, Vietnam Service medal with 4 Stars; Vietnamese Cross of Gallantry with Silver Star; recipient Raven award, 1973, Seven Soc. award U. Va. Mem. ABA, Va. Bar Assn., So. Govs. Assn. (chmn.), Dem. Govs. Assn. (chmn.), Coalition for Dem. Majority, Res. Officers Assn., USMC Res. Officers Assn., U.Fa. La. Alumni Assn. (bd. dirs. 1974-85), Am. Legion, Raven Soc., Navy League U.S., Coun. on Fgn. Rels., Omicron Delta Kappa. Episcopalian. Office: US Senate 493 Russell Senate Office Bldg Washington DC 20510-4603*

ROBB, DAVID BUZBY, JR., financial services company executive, lawyer; b. Phila., Nov. 30, 1935; s. David Buzby and Sarah Whelan (Carson) R.; m. Patricia Ann Irons, Sept. 14, 1979; children: Steven C., David S.; stepchildren: Donald Irons, Steven Irons. B.A., Princeton U., 1958; J.D., U. Va., 1963; A.M.P., Harvard Bus. Sch., 1978. Bar: Pa., 1963. Assoc. firm Ballard, Spahr, Andrews, Ingersoll, Phila., 1963-69; sr. v.p., chief operating officer trust div., 1976-82, sr. v.p., gen. counsel Nat. Corp., Phila., 1970-76; dir., vice chmn. Provident Instl. Mgmt. Corp., 1977-82; dir., chmn., chief exec. officer Provident Capital Mgmt., 1982-87; exec. v.p. SEI Corp., Wayne, Pa., 1982-89; pres., chief exec. officer Trust Funds Group, 1982-89; dir., pres., chief exec. officer Premier Systems, Inc., Wayne, Pa., 1989-91; pres., CEO J.P. Morgan Fla., 1991—. Bd. dirs. Landmark Soc., Phila. City Inst., 1981-85, Friends Hosp., Pa. Acad. Fine Arts, ARC S.E. Pa., Econ. Coun. Palm Beach County. Served to lt. USN, 1958-60. Mem. ABA, Phila. Bar Assn., Sunnybrook G.C., P.G.A. Nat. G.C., P.B. Yatch Club. Republican. Episcopalian. Office: JP Morgan Florida FSB 109 Royal Palm Way Palm Beach FL 33480-4249

ROBB, DAVID METHENY, JR., art historian; b. Mpls., Apr. 12, 1937; s. David Metheny and Jane (Howard) R.; m. Frances Louise Osborn, Feb. 12, 1965; children: Andrew Osborn, Matthew Howard. B.A., Princeton U., 1959; MA, Yale U., 1967; mus. mgmt. inst., U. Calif., Berkeley, 1983. Research asst. Soc. for Preservation of New Eng. Antiquities, Boston, 1959, Nat. Gallery Art, Washington, 1963; curator Paul Mellon Collection, Upperville, Va., 1963-65; curatorial fellow Walker Art Ctr., Mpls., 1967-69; research curator Kimbell Art Mus., Ft. Worth, 1969-74, chief curator, 1974-83, acting dir., 1979-80; dir. Telfair Acad. Art & Scis., Savannah, Ga., 1983-85, Huntsville (Ala.) Mus. Art, 1985-94. Co-author: Star-Spangled History—Joseph Boggs Beale, 1975; editor: Kimbell Art Museum: Catalogue of the Collection, 1972, Kimbell Art Museum: Handbook of the Collection, 1981; author: catalogue Louis J. Kahn: Sketches for the Kimbell Art Museum, 1978, preface Elisabeth Louise Vigée Le Brun, Ft. Worth, 1982. Mem. adv. com. S.E. Inst. for Edn. in Visual Arts, Chattanooga, 1987—, Leadership 2000 Program, Huntsville, 1989-90. Comdr. USNR, 1960-63. Heritage Found. fellow, 1958, Ford Found. fellow, 1967-69. Mem. Am. Assn. Mus. Coll. Art Assn., Ala. Mus. Assn. (chmn. long-range plans com. 1989), Tallulah Bankhead Soc. (treas. 1991—), Huntsville Club, Rotary, Princeton Alumni Schods Com.

ROBB, FELIX COMPTON, association executive, consultant; b. Birmingham, Ala., Dec. 26, 1914; s. Felix Compton and Ruth (Nicholson) R.; m. Virginia Lytle Threlkeld. A.B. summa cum laude, Birmingham-So. Coll., 1936; M.A., Vanderbilt U., 1939; postgrad., George Peabody Coll., 1939-40; Ed.D., Harvard U., 1952; D.Ped., W.Va. Wesleyan Coll., 1968; LL.D., Mercer U., 1968, U. S.C., 1978; D.H.L., U. Ala. System, 1975, Jacksonville U., 1981; H.H.D., Birmingham So. Coll., 1979. Tchr. jr. high sch. Irondale, Ala., 1936-37; tchr. Ensley High Sch., Birmingham, 1937-38; instr. English Birmingham-So. Coll., 1940-42, successively alumni sec., registrar, 1946; asst. to pres. Peabody Coll., 1947-51, acting dir. Libr. Sch., 1947-48, acting dean of coll. Libr. Sch., 1948-49, assoc. prof. higher edn. Libr. Sch., 1950-53, prof. Libr. Sch., 1953-66, acting dir. surveys and field svcs. Libr. Sch., 1951, dean instrn. Libr. Sch., 1951-61, coll. pres. Libr. Sch., 1961-66; dir. So. Assn. Colls. and Schs., Atlanta, 1966-79; exec. dir. So. Assn. Colls. and Schs., 1979-82, exec. dir. emeritus, 1982—; pres. Ginge, Inc., 1982—; interim pres. Tallulah Falls Sch., 1988-89; sec., treas. So. Edn. Exec. Search Assocs.; coord. edn. project, Republic of Korea, 1956-58, bd. dir. Carnegie fellowships in teaching, 1950-60, Peabody Bldg. Fund Campaign, 1958; chief of staff The Study of Coll. and Univ. Presidency, 1958-60; mem. Tenn. Adv. Coun. on Tchr. Edn. and Certification, 1954-58; case writer Inst. for Coll. and Univ. Administrs., Harvard, 1955; nat. selection com. Fulbright awards, 1955-57; bd. dir. workshops in TV, ednl. TV program series, Nashville, chmn. gov.'s conf. sch. beyond high sch., 1958; mem. com. specialized pers. Dept. Labor, Tenn. Common Human Rels., 1964-66; exec. com. Met. Action Commn., 1965-66; chmn. S.E. Manpower Adv. Com., 1965-68; mem. bd. So. Edn. Reporting Svc., 1961-69; mem. nat. adv. com.

Acad. of Sr. Profls. at Eckerd Coll., 1974-76; cons. Profl. Assn. Ga. Educators. Author: America's Urgent Agenda, 1990. Trustee, chmn. scholarship com. Presser Found.; trustee, chmn. fin. com. United Meth. Children's Home, 1985-88; trustee Longview Found., Reinhardt Coll.; mem. Cleve. Conf.; mem. devel. coun. Birmingham-So. Coll., adv. bd. Southall Trust; trustee, chmn. administr. bd. Meth. ch., 1974. Mem. So. Coun. Tchr. Edn. (pres. 1956-57), Am. Soc. Assn. Execs., Loulie Compton Sem. Alumni Assn. (pres.), Phi Beta Kappa, Omicron Delta Kappa, Phi Delta Kappa, Kappa Phi Kappa, Pi Gamma Mu, Kappa Alpha Order, Kappa Delta Pi (Laureate mem., mem. ednl. found.), Rotary. Home: 377 Camden Rd NE Atlanta GA 30309-1513

ROBB, GARY CHARLES, lawyer; b. Kansas City, Mo., May 17, 1955; s. George Albert and Gabriela (Kleotzel) R.; m. Anita Candace Porte, Apr. 30, 1983. B.A. with distinction in Polit. Sci. and Communications, U. Mo.-Kansas City, 1977, M.A. in Econs., 1978; J.D. cum laude, U. Mich., 1981. Bars: Ill. 1981, U.S. Dist. Ct. (no. dist) Ill. 1981, Mo. 1982, U.S. Dist. Ct. (we. dist.) Mo. 1982, U.S. Ct. Appeals (8th cir.) 1982. Assoc. Mayer, Brown & Platt, Chgo., 1981-82, Shughart, Thomson & Kilroy, Kansas City, Mo., 1982-84; ptnr. Robb & Robb, Kansas City, Mo., 1984—; adj. prof. law U. Mo., Kansas City; lectr., program chmn. Nat. Conf. on Products Liability Law, Chgo., 1983, lectr., 1984. Contbg. author: Tort Law, Missouri Bar Handbook, 1982; Products Liability, 1984. Exec. articles editor U. Mich. Jour. Law Reform, 1980-81; contbg. editor Products Liability, 1983; mem. bd. editors Products Liability Newsletter, 1982—; mem. bd. experts Lawyers Alert Newsmag. Contbr. articles to profl. jours. Mem. ABA (chmn. future programs and projects subcom., trial evidence com., sect. litigation, mem. products liability and consumer law com., tort and ins. practice sect.), Kansas City Bar Assn., Mo. Bar Assn. (fed. practice com.), Lawyers Assn. Kansas City, Assn. Trial Lawyers Am. (tort and aviation sects.), Mo. Assn. Trial Attys., Univ. Mo.-Kansas City Alumni Assn. (chmn. career planning com.), Phi Kappa Phi, Omicron Delta Epsilon, Pi Sigma Alpha (pres.), Pi Kappa Delta. Republican. Club: Kansas City. Office: 1200 Main St Ste 3900 Kansas City MO 64105

ROBB, JAMES ALEXANDER, lawyer; b. Huntingdon, Que., Can., May 3, 1930; s. Alexander George and Irma Mary (Martin) R.; m. Katherine Ann Teare, June 26, 1960; children: Laura, John, andrew. B.A., McGill U., 1951, B.C.L., 1954; postgrad., U. Montreal, 1961-63. Bar: Que. 1955, queen's counsel 1970. Lectr. comml. law and taxation Sir George Williams U., 1958-60; ptnr. Stikeman, Elliot and predecessor firm Stikeman, Elliott, Tamaki, Mercier & Robb, Montreal, 1967—; bd. dirs. Robapharm (Can.), Ltd., Itochu Can. Ltd., Majorich Investments Inc., YKK Can. Inc., Hitachi (HSC) Can. Inc., NGK Spark Plugs Can. Ltd., Hitachi Credit (Can.) Inc., Domtar Inc., Descente Can. Inc., Klockner Stadler Hurter, Ltd.; pres. Que.-Japan Bus. Forum, 1993—. Mem. Protestant Sch. Bd. Greater Montreal, mem. central parents com.; chmn. bd. trustees Martlet Found., 1967-69; v.p. Que. Liberal Party, 1976-79; mem. adv. com. McGill Ctr. for Study of Regulated Industries; bd. dirs. Montreal Mus. Fine Arts, 1987-90; bd. govs. McGill U., 1991—. Mem. Bar Que., Consumers Assn. Can. (past chmn. regulated industries program), Grad. Soc. McGill U. (v.p.), Can. Club Montreal (bd. dirs. 1988, pers. 1990-91), Univ. Club, Kanawaki Golf Club (Que.), Royal Montreal Curing Club, Hillside Tennis Club. Home: 9 Renfrew Ave, Westmount, PQ Canada H3Y 2X3 Office: 1155 René Lévesque Blvd W, Suite 3900, Montreal, PQ Canada H3B 3V2

ROBB, JAMES WILLIS, Romance languages educator; b. Jamaica, N.Y., June 27, 1918; s. Stewart Everts and Clara Johanna (Mohrman) R.; m. Cecilia Uribe-Noguera, 1972. Student, Inst. de Touraine, Sorbonne, 1937-38; B.A. cum laude, Colgate U., 1939; postgrad., U. Nacional de Mex., 1948; M.A., Middlebury Coll., 1950; Ph.D., Catholic U. Am., 1958. Instr. Romance langs. Norwich U., 1946-50; asst. prof. Romance langs. George Washington U., Washington, 1950-58, assoc. prof., 1958-66, prof., 1966-88, prof. emeritus, 1988—. Author: El Estilo de Alfonso Reyes, 1965, 78, Repertorio Bibliográfico de Alfonso Reyes, 1974, Prosa y Poesia de Alfonso Reyes, 1975, 84, Estudios sobre Alfonso Reyes, 1976, Por los Caminos de Alfonso Reyes, 1981, Imágenes de América en Alfonso Reyes y en Germán Arciniegas, 1990; contbr. articles to profl. jours. With U.S. Navy, 1942-44, USNR, 1944-46, PTO. Recipient Alfonso Reyes Internat. Lit. prize, 1978; Lit. Diploma of Merit, State of Nuevo León and City of Monterrey, Mex., 1979; OAS grantee, 1964; Am. Philos. Soc. grantee, 1977. Mem. MLA, Assoc. Internat. De Lit Iberoamericana, Am. Assn. Tchrs. Spanish and Portuguese, Assn. N.Am. de Colombianistas, Phi Beta Kappa. Office: George Washington U Romance Langs Dept Washington DC 20052

ROBB, JOHN WESLEY, religion educator; b. Los Angeles, Dec. 1, 1919; s. Edgar Milton and Alta (Boger) R.; m. Ethel Edna Tosh, June 13, 1942; children: Lydia Joan Robb Durbin, Judith Nadine Robb Eggerman. A.B., Greenville Coll., 1941; Th.M., U. So. Calif., 1945, Ph.D., 1952; L.H.D., Hebrew Union Coll.-Jewish Inst. Religion, 1977. Asst. prof. philosophy and religion Dickinson Coll., Pa., 1948-51; fellow Fund for Advancement Edn., 1951-52; assoc. prof. U. So. Calif., L.A., 1954-62, chmn. dept. religion, 1954-67; assoc. dean humanities Coll. Letters, Arts and Scis. U. Calif., L.A., 1963-68, Leonard K. Firestone prof., 1974-75; prof. U. So. Calif., L.A., 1962-87, prof. emeritus, 1987—; prof. Sch. Medicine U. So. Calif., 1981-87; coun. mem. Inst. of Lab. Animal Resources Nat. Acad. Scis. Nat. Rsch. Coun., 1986-93; prof. emeritus U. So. Calif., 1991—; vis. disting. prof. USAF Med. Ctr., Wilford Hall, Tex., 1985; mem. rev. com. NIH Guide for the Care and Use of Lab. Animals, NRC, NAS, 1993—; advisor/tutor med. disciplinary bd. Dept. Health, State of Wash., 1994—; adj. prof. bioethics Sch. Medicine, U. So. Calif., 1989-91, prof. emeritus, 1991—. Author: Inquiry Into Faith, 1960; co-editor: Readings in Religious Philosophy; The Reverent Skeptic, 1979. Served as lt. (j.g.) USNR, 1945-47; to lt. 1952-54. Recipient award for excellence in tchg. U. So. Calif., 1960-74, Dart award for acad. innovation, 1970, Raubenheimer Disting. Faculty award div. humanities, 1980, Outstanding Faculty award Student Senate, 1988, Disting. Emeritus award, 1995; Robert Fenton Craig award Blue Key, 1980. Fellow Soc. for Values in Higher Edn.; mem. Am. Acad. Religion (v.p. 1966, pres. 1967), Am. Philos. Assn., AAUP (v.p. Calif. Conf. 1977, pres. 1978-79), Phi Beta Kappa (hon.), Phi Kappa Phi, Phi Chi Phi. Methodist. Home: 8001 Sand Point Way NE # C35 Seattle WA 98115-6356

ROBB, LYNDA JOHNSON, writer; b. Washington, Mar. 19, 1944; d. Lyndon Baines and Claudia Alta (Taylor) Johnson; m. Charles Spittal Robb, Dec. 9, 1967; children: Lucinda Desha, Catherine Lewis, Jennifer Wickliffe. BA with honors, U. Tex., 1966. Writer, McCall's mag., 1966-68; contbg. editor Ladies Home Jour., 1968-80; lectr. bd. dirs. Reading Is Fundamental, 1968—, Lyndon B. Johnson Family Found., 1969—. Mem. Va. State Coun. on Infant Mortality, Va. Maternal & Child Health Coun., Nat. Commn. to Prevent Infant Mortality, 1987-93; chmn. Pres.'s Adv. Com. for Women, 1979-81; bd. dirs. Nat. Home Libr. Found., Ford Theatre; chmn. Va. Women's Cultural History Project, 1982-85; mem. adv. bd. Commn. Presdl. Debates. Mem. Nat. Wildflower Rsch. Ctr., Zeta Tau Alpha. Democrat. Episcopalian.

ROBB, NATHANIEL HEYWARD, JR., national guard officer, real estate executive; b. Columbia, S.C., Sept. 10, 1942; s. Nathaniel Heyward Robb and Dorothy Claiborne (Cabell) Dortch; m. Louise Taber Rivers, Sept. 26, 1964; children: Elizabeth T., Nathaniel Heyward III, Catherine Pease. BSBA, The Citadel, 1964; grad. Realtors Inst., U. N.C., 1972; grad., Command and Gen. Staff Coll. Pres. Robb Realty, Charleston, N.C., 1972—; adj. gen. of N.C., 1989-93; dep. commdr. in chief U.S. Atlantic Command, 1993—; exec. sec. Gov.'s Adv. Commn. Mil. Affairs, 1985-89; mem. Raleigh Bd. Realtors, 1975-85; dir. state property office N.C. Dept. Administrn., 1975-77; pres., founding mem. Raleigh Comml. Listing Svc., 1975-85; asst. sec. N.C. Dept. Crime Crontrol and Safety, Raleigh, 1985-89; bd. dirs. Aerial Images, Inc., Raleigh. Dir. Mordecai Sq. Hist. Soc.; mem. Raleigh Hist. Dists. Commn., 1973-78; dir., v.p. Raleigh Hist. Properties Commn., 1973-78; mem. Gov.'s Mgmt. Coun., Raleigh, 1985-89, Gov.'s Waste Mgmt. Bd., 1985-89; mem. Gov.'s Drug Cabinet, 1988-89; mem. Nat. Rep. Com., 1970—. Maj. gen. inf., U.S. Army N.G., 1964-70, Vietnam; N.C. N.G., 1970—. Decorated D.S.M., N.C. D.S.M. with one device, Legion of Merit, Bronze Star with v device and one oak leaf cluster, Meritorious Svc. medal; Nat. Def. medal with star, USAR Components Achievement medal with four oak leaf clusters; Republic Vietnam Cross of Gallantry with bronze and silver stars and palm, other mil. awards; recipient Disting. Milit. Grad. award The Citadel,

---

Humanitarian Svc. medal, Legion de Lafayette of Hist. Socs. of Militia and N.G. Mem. N.G. Assn. U.S., N.C. N.G. Assn., 2500 Club. Episcopalian. Avocations: skiing, pistol shooting. Home: 2115 Banbury Rd Raleigh NC 27608-1123 Office: USACOM JO1RC 1562 Mitscher Ave Ste 200 Norfolk VA 23551-2488

ROBB, WALTER LEE, retired electric company executive, management company executive; b. Harrisburg, Pa., Apr. 25, 1928; s. George A. and Ruth (Scantlin) R.; m. Anne Gruver, Feb. 27, 1954; children: Richard, Steven, Lindsey. BS, Pa. State U., 1948; MS, U. Ill., 1950, PhD, 1951; DEng (hon.), Milw. Sch. Engring., 1994; Worcester Poly. Inst., 1988. With GE, 1951-93; mgr. R & D dept. silicone products GE, Waterford, N.Y., 1966-68; venture mgr. med. devel. ops. GE, Schenectady, N.Y., 1968-71; sr. v.p., group exec. med. sys. group GE, Milw., 1973-86; sr. v.p. corp. R & D GE, Schenectady, 1986-93; cons., pres. Vantage Mgmt., Schenectady, N.Y., 1993—; bd. dirs. Celgene Corp., Marquette Electronics, Inc., Cree Rsch., Inc.; chmn. Neopath, Inc. Recipient Nat. medal of tech., 1993. Mem. NAE. Achievements include patentee in field of membranes and gas separation; rsch. in permeable membranes, diagnostic imaging equipment. Home: 1358 Ruffner Rd Niskayuna NY 12309-2500 Office: Vantage Mgmt 1222 Troy-Schenectady Rd Schenectady NY 12309

ROBBIE, TIMOTHY JOHN, professional football team executive; b. Minneapolis, MN, Aug. 24, 1955; s. Joseph and Elizabeth Ann (Lyle) R.; m. Ann Marie Franklin, July 15, 1989. BA, Tulane U., 1977. Dir. pub. rels. Ft. Lauderdale (Fla.) Strikers Profl. Soccer Team, 1978, asst. gen. mgr., 1978, gen. mgr., 1980-83; gen. mgr. Minn. Strikers Profl. Soccer Team, Mpls., 1984-87; v.p. pub. affairs Miami (Fla.) Dolphins, 1987-89; pres. Miami Dolphins Ltd., 1990—; chmn. bd. Robbie Stadium Corp., Miami, 1990—. Trustee Fla. Internat. U., Miami, 1990—. Democrat. Roman Catholic. Avocations: reading, traveling, golf. Office: care Miami Dolphins Joe Robbie Stadium 2269 NE 199th St Miami FL 33180*

ROBBINS, ALLEN BISHOP, physics educator; b. New Brunswick, N.J., Mar. 31, 1930; s. William Rei and Helen Grace (Bishop) R.; m. Shirley Mae Gernert, June 14, 1952 (div. 1978); children: Catherine Jean, Marilyn Elizabeth, Carol Ann, Melanie Barbara; m. Alice Harriet Ayars, Jan. 1, 1979. Student, Oberlin Coll., 1948-49; B.S., Rutgers U., 1952; M.S., Yale U., 1953, Ph.D., 1956. Research fellow U. Birmingham (Eng.), 1957-58, lectr., 1960-61; instr. physics Rutgers U., New Brunswick, N.J., 1956-57; asst. prof. physics Rutgers U., 1957-60, assoc. prof., 1960-68, prof., 1968—, chmn. dept. physics and astronomy, 1979—. Contbr. articles on nuclear physics to profl. jours. Recipient Lindbach Christian and Mary F. Lindbach Found., Rutgers U., 1975. Fellow Am. Phys. Soc.; mem. Am. Assn. Physics Tchrs., AAAS, Phi Beta Kappa, Sigma Xi. Office: Rutgers U Dept Physics & Astronomy PO Box 849 Piscataway NJ 08855-0849

ROBBINS, ANNE FRANCIS See REAGAN, NANCY DAVIS

ROBBINS, CHANDLER S(EYMOUR), research biologist; b. Belmont, Mass., July 17, 1918; s. Samuel Dowse and Rosa Margaret (Seymour) R.; A.B., Harvard U., 1940; M.S., George Washington U., 1950; m. Eleanor Graham Cooley, Apr. 16, 1948; children: Jane S., Stuart B., George C., Nancy E. Wildlife rsch. biologist U.S. Fish and Wildlife Svc., Nat. Biol. Survey, Patuxent Wildlife Rsch. Ctr., Laurel, Md., 1945—; bd. dirs. Hawk Mountain Sanctuary Assn. Recipient Arthur A. Allen award Cornell Lab. Ornithology, 1979; Paul Bartsch award Audubon Naturalist Soc., 1979; Disting. Service award U.S. Dept. Interior, 1979, 87; Ludlow Griscom award Am. Birding Assn., 1984; Eugene Eisenmann medal Linnaean Soc. N.Y., 1987, Chuck Yeager award Nat. Fish and Wildlife Found., 1990. Fellow Am. Ornithologists' Union; mem. Am. Meteorol. Soc., Internat. Ornithol. Congress, Wilson Ornithol. Soc., Cooper Ornithol. Soc., Eastern Bird Banding Assn., Western Bird Banding Assn., Brit. Trust for Ornithology, Nature Conservancy, Mass. Audubon Soc. Democrat. Author: Birds of North America, 1966; co-author: Birds of Maryland and the District of Columbia, 1958. Editor: Maryland Birdlife, 1947—; tech. editor Audubon Field Notes/American Birds, 1954-89. Home: 7900 Brooklyn Bridge Rd Laurel MD 20707-2822 Office: Patuxent Wildlife Research Ctr Laurel MD 20708

ROBBINS, CONRAD W., naval architect; b. N.Y.C., Oct. 11, 1921; s. Girard David and Ethyl Rae (Bergman) R.; m. Danae Gray McCartney, Jan. 8, 1923 (dec. Jan. 1971); children: Lorraine, Linton, Jennifer; m. Melissa Jahn, Apr. 15, 1971 (dec. Mar. 1992). BSE, U. Mich., 1942. Estimator Pacific Electric Co., Seattle, 1946-47; pres. Straus-Dupanquet, Lyons-Alpha, Albert Pick, N.Y.C. and Chgo., 1947-67, C.W. Robbins, Inc., Carefree, Ariz., 1967—; cons. in field. Capt. floating drydock USN, 1942-46. Avocations: travel, gardening, gourmet cooking. Home: PO Box 2208 Carefree AZ 85377-2208 Office: CW Robbins Inc 7500 Stevens Rd Carefree AZ 85377

ROBBINS, CORNELIUS (VAN VORSE), education administration educator; b. Wilmington, Del., Nov. 2, 1931; s. Cornelius V. and Irene (Tatman) R.; m. Janet Porter, Aug. 1953; children: Eva Robbins Burke, Susan Robbins, Laurel Robbins Truax, Melissa Robbins Beegle. B.A. in Polit. Sci, U. Del., 1953, M.Ed. in Social Scis, 1961; Ed.D. in Ednl. Adminstrn, U. Pa., 1964. Mem. faculty U. Del., 1957-58; tchr. Marshallton (Del.) Sch. Dist., 1958-60, Mt. Pleasant (Del.) Sch. Dist., 1960-62; asst. to dir. sch. study councils U. Pa., 1962-64; dean instrn. Ocean County Coll., 1965-67; dean of coll. Community Coll. of Delaware County, Pa., 1967-69; sr. assoc., coll. div. dir. McManis Assocs., Washington, 1969-70; pres. Genesee Community Coll., 1970-75; assoc. chancellor for community colls. SUNY, 1975-85; acting pres. Potsdam State Coll. (N.Y.), 1982-83; pres. Cobleskill (N.Y.) Coll. Agr. & Tech., 1985-92; prof. edn. adminstrn. SUNY, Albany, N.Y., 1992—; cons. Middle States Assn. Colls.; area liaison officer U.S. Mil. Acad., 1972; chmn. SUNY West Pres.'s Council and mem. Chancellor's Council, 1973, 85, 91. Contbr. articles to profl. publs. Served with U.S. Army, 1954-56. Recipient Outstanding Educator's award N.Y. State Assn. Jr. Colls., 1975, Disting. Svc. award Faculty Coun. Community Colls., 1988. Mem. Am. Assn. Higher Edn., State Dirs. of Community Colls. Assn., Phi Delta Kappa. Office: Educ 329 SUNY at Albany Albany NY 12222

ROBBINS, DONALD MICHAEL, lawyer; b. Woonsocket, R.I., Oct. 2, 1935; s. Robert Sidney and Nancy Ruth (Medoff) R.; m. Esther Sharp, Aug. 30, 1959; children: Jeffrey, Benjamin. Student, Brandeis U., 1953-55; A.B., U. Mich., 1957; LL.B., Boston U., 1960. Bar: Mass. 1961, R.I. 1962. Individual practice law, 1961-68; v.p., sec., gen. counsel Hasbro, Inc., Pawtucket, R.I., 1968-91, sr v.p., gen. counsel, corp. sec., 1992—. Bd. dirs., past chmn. Big Bros. R.I.; bd. dirs. Miriam Hosp., New Eng. Legal Found.; past pres. Temple Emanu-El; chmn. Israel Bonds State of R.I.; v.p. Jewish Fedn. of R.I. Mem. Am. Soc. Corp. Secs., Mass. Bar Assn., R.I. Bar Assn. Home: 83 Cambridge Pky # 803 W Cambridge MA 02142 Office: Hasbro Inc 1027 Newport Ave Pawtucket RI 02861-2500

ROBBINS, EDITH SCHULTZ, microscopy educator; b. Galveston, Tex., July 4, 1941; d. Leon and Sara (Major) Schultz; m. Peter L. Robbins, May 26, 1966; 1 child, George M. AB, Barnard Coll., N.Y.C. 1962; MS, NYU Grad. Sch. Arts & Scis., 1965, PhD, 1970. Instr. CUNY, N.Y.C., 1968-71; asst. prof. Borough Manhattan Community Coll., N.Y.C., 1973-75; assoc. prof. CUNY, N.Y.C., 1975-82, prof.; adj. asst. prof. NYU Sch. Medicine, 1970-73, adj. asst. prof., 1973-75, adj. assoc. prof. 1975—. Recipient grants NYU Sch. Medicine, Dept. Energy. Mem. AAAS, N.Y. Soc. Exptl. Microscopists, N.Y. Acad. Sci. Microscopy Soc. Am., Am. Soc. Cell Biology. Jewish. Avocation: photography. Home: 12 Myrtle Dr Great Neck NY 11021-1808 Office: NYU Sch Medicine/Cell Biol 550 1st Ave New York NY 10016-6481 also: Borough of Manhattan CC 199 Chambers St New York NY 10007

ROBBINS, FRANCES ELAINE, educational administrator; b. Prescott, Mich., Oct. 27, 1928; d. Arlington Clifford and Anna Maria (Melrose) Osborne; m. Robert Allen Robbins, July 29, 1950 (dec. Feb. 1992); children: Gloria Jean, Reginald David, Eric Lynn. Student, Cen. Mich. U., 1948; BS, No. Mich. U., 1967, MA, 1974. Cert. elem. Mich., prin. Mich. Tchr. kindergarten Rose City (Mich.) Elem. Sch., 1948-51; tchr. Rudyard (Mich.) Elem. Sch., 1961-62, Pickford (Mich.) Elem. Sch., 1962-64, Skandia (Mich.) Elem. Sch., 1964-66; tchr. kindergarten Brimley (Mich.) Elem. Sch., 1966-69, tchr., coord., 1969-70, prin. 1970—; Mem. Ea. Upper Peninsula Substance

Abuse Adv. Bd., Sault Ste. Marie, Mich., 1975-77; owner Robbins Refinishing and Repair, Brimley, 1985—. Dir. choir, Sunday sch. tchr. Brimley Congl. Ch., 1970—; vol. Superior Twp. Ambulance Corp., Brimley, 1972-91. Recipient Celebrate Literacy award Internat. Reading Assn., 1986. Mem. NAESP, Mich. Elem. and Mid. Sch. Prins. Assn., Ea. Upper Peninsula Reading Assn., Ea. Upper Peninsula Elem. Prins. Assn. (pres. 1990-91), Brimley Hist. Soc., Delta Kappa Gamma (state rec. sec. 1989-91, Woman of Distinction award Alpha Tau chpt. 1988). Avocations: knitting, travel, grandchildren.

ROBBINS, FRANK ERNEST, linguistics educator, administrator; b. Elmira, N.Y., May 12, 1926; s. David Earl and Anna Evelyn (Dunning) R.; m. Ethel Louise Anderson, Aug. 23, 1947; children: Sara, Larry, Anna Jo, David. BA in Greek and Latin, Houghton Coll., 1949, LittD (hon.), 1991; MA in Linguistics, Cornell U., 1960, PhD in Linguistics, 1965. Br. dir. Summer Inst. Linguistics, Mexico City, 1965-72; v.p. acad. affairs Summer Inst. Linguistics, Internat., 1972-75, exec. v.p., 1976-84; area dir. for Africa, rsch. supr. Summer Inst. Linguistics, Nairobi, Kenya, 1984-89; pres., bd. dirs. Summer Inst. Linguistics, Dallas, 1990—; dir. Okla. Summer Inst. Linguistics Sch. U. Okla., Norman, 1972-73; dir. Tex. Summer Inst. Linguistics Sch. U. Tex., Arlington, 1971-73; adj. prof. U. Tex., Arlington, 1990—; cons. in field; bd. dirs Ctr. for Applied Linguistics, 1976-84, vice chmn., 1983-84; mem. literacy adv. bd. Summer Inst. Linguistics, 1991—. Author: Quiotopec Chinantec Grammar; Training in Linguistics, SIL, Its Works and Contributions, 1977; contbr. articles to profl. jours. NDFL fellow, 1962-64. Mem. Linguistic Soc. Am., West African Linguistic Soc. Presbyterian. Office: Summer Inst Linguistics 7500 W Camp Wisdom Rd Dallas TX 75236-5628

ROBBINS, FREDERICK CHAPMAN, physician, medical school dean emeritus; b. Auburn, Ala., Aug. 25, 1916; s. William J. and Christine (Chapman) R.; m. Alice Havemeyer Northrop, June 19, 1948; children: Alice, Louise. AB, U. Mo., 1936, BS, 1938; MD, Harvard U., 1940; DSc (hon.), John Carroll U., 1955, U. Mo., 1958, U. N.C., 1979, Tufts U., 1983, Med. Coll. Ohio, 1983; LLD, U. N.Mex., 1968. Diplomate Am. Bd. Pediatrics. Intern Children's Hosp., Boston, 1941-42, resident, 1940-41, resident pediatrican, 1946-48; sr. fellow virus disease Nat. Rsch. Coun., 1948-50; staff rsch. div. infectious diseases Children's Hosp., Boston, 1948-50, assoc. physician, assoc. dir. isolation svc., asso. rsch. div. infectious diseases, 1950-52; instr., assoc. in pediatrics Harvard Med. Sch., 1950-52; dir. dept. pediatrics and contagious diseases Cleve. Met. Gen. Hosp., 1952-66; prof. pediatrics Case Western Res. U., 1950-80, dean Sch. Medicine, 1966-80, univ. prof., dean emeritus, 1980—, univ. prof. emeritus, 1987—; pres. Inst. Medicine, NAS, 1980-85; vis. scientist Donner Lab., U. Calif., 1963-64. Served as maj. AUS, 1942-46; chief virus and rickettsial disease sect. 15th Med. Gen. Lab. investigations infectious hepatitis, typhus fever and Q fever. Decorated Bronze Star, 1945; recipient 1st Mead Johnson prize application tissue culture methods to study of viral infections, 1953; co-recipient Nobel prize in physiology and medicine, 1954; Med. Mut. Honor Award for 1969; Ohio Gov.'s award, 1971. Mem. Assn Am. Med. Colls. (Abraham Flexner award 1987), Nat. Acad. Scis., Am. Acad. Arts and Scis., Am. Soc. Clin. Investigation (emeritus mem.), Am. Acad. Pediatrics, Soc. Pediatric Research (pres. 1961-62, emeritus mem.), Am. Pediatric Soc., Am. Philos. Soc., Phi Beta Kappa, Sigma Xi, Phi Gamma Delta. Office: Case Western Res U Sch Med 10900 Euclid Ave Cleveland OH 44106-1712*

ROBBINS, GARY SAMUEL, airport manager; b. Ellensburg, Wash., July 10, 1937; s. Harold William and Catherine May (Randall) R.; m. Patricia Ann Morrison, July 14, 1957; children: Teresa Ann, Becky Jo, Michael Guy. BA in Edn., Cen. Wash. U., 1960; MA in Psychology, U. No. Colo., 1980. Commd. U.S. Air Force, 1960, advanced through grades to lt. col., 1977, ret., 1980; mgr. Yakima (Wash.) Air Terminal, 1980—. Mem. Wash. Airport Mgmt. Assn. Republican. Methodist. Office: Yakima Air Terminal 2400 W Washington Ave Yakima WA 98903-1134

ROBBINS, GEORGE WILLIAM, III, chemical company executive; b. Norfolk, Va., July 25, 1940; s. George William Jr. and Edna Ruth (Craft) R.; m. Elizabeth Waddell Loving, Nov. 25, 1967; children—George William IV, Elizabeth Loving, Sarah Waddell. B.A. in Biology, Va. Mil. Inst., 1962. Sales devel. mgr. Gen. Electric Plastics, Pittsfield, Mass., 1974-75, mktg. mgr. Lexan div., 1975-77; mktg. dir. Avery Internat., Painesville, Ohio, 1977-78, div. v.p., gen. mgr., 1978-82; group v.p., gen. mgr. SCM Corp. Organic Chems., Jacksonville, Fla., 1982-86; pres. SCM Glidco Organics, Jacksonville, 1986—. Mem. Mayor's Council on Econ. Devel., Jacksonville, 1984—; vestry mem. Ch. of Our Saviour, 1984-87; mem. diocesan planning com. Episcopal Ch. Served as 1st lt. U.S. Army, 1964-66. Mem. Pulp Chems. Assn., Chem. Mfrs. Assn., Soc. Chems. Industry, Jacksonville C. of C. (bd. dirs. 1985—, project leader Far East Task Force 1985), Rotary (bd. dirs., sec. 1990). Republican. Avocations: flying; tennis; skiing. Home: 12550 Mandarin Rd Jacksonville FL 32223-1819 Office: SCM Glidco Organics 435 Clark Rd Jacksonville FL 32218-5596

ROBBINS, HAROLD, author; b. N.Y.C., May 21, 1916; m. Lillian Machnivitz (div.); m. Grace Palermo (div.); children: Caryn, Adreana; m. Jann Stapp. Student pub. schs., N.Y.C. In food factoring bus., until 1940; shipping clk. Universal Pictures, N.Y.C., 1940-46. Author: Never Love a Stranger, 1948, The Dream Merchants, 1949, A Stone for Danny Fisher, 1951, Never Leave Me, 1953, 79 Park Avenue, 1955, Stiletto, 1953, The Carpetbaggers, 1961, Where Love Has Gone, 1962, The Adventurers, 1966, The Inheritors, 1969, The Betsy, 1971, The Pirate, 1974, Lonely Lady, 1976, Dreams Die First, 1977, Memories of Another Day, 1979, Goodbye, Janette, 1981, Spellbinder, 1982, Descent from Xanadu, 1984, The Storyteller, 1985, The Piranhas, 1991, The Raiders, 1994. Office: Ernst Cane Berner & Gitlin 919 Third Ave New York NY 10022-3903 also: care Simon & Schuster 1230 6th Ave New York NY 10020-1513

ROBBINS, HENRY ZANE, public relations and marketing executive; b. Winston-Salem, N.C., Jan. 17, 1930; s. Romulus Mayfield and Vera Ethel (Daniel) R.; m. Barbara Anne Brown, Jan. 19, 1955; children: Zane Scott, Jill Stewart, Gail Ruth. AB, U. N.C., 1952; student, Emory U., 1952. Reporter Atlanta Constn., 1952; exhibit specialist Gen. Electric Co., Schenectady, 1952; employee relations specialist Gen. Electric Co., Cin., 1955; editor Gen. Electric Co. Schenectady, 1955; account supr. Gen. Electric Co., Winston-Salem, 1956-58; group supr. Gen. Electric Co. Schenectady, 1958-60; v.p., gen. mgr. Burson-Marsteller, Pitts. and Chgo., 1960-70, sr. v.p., 1970; pres., chief exec. officer SL&H-Robbins Inc., Chgo., 1970-72; also dir.; pres., chief exec. officer Beveridge Kraus Robbins & Manning, Chgo., 1973-75; also dir.; pres., dir., chief exec. officer Beveridge and Robbins Inc., Chgo., 1975-77; pres., chief exec. officer Financial Advt. of Ill., Inc., Chgo.; mng. dir. Sports Mgmt. Group, Chgo., 1975-77; dir. communications Arthur Andersen & Co., Chgo. and Geneva, Switzerland, 1977-81; dir. mktg. support services Arthur Andersen & Co., Chgo. and Geneva, 1981-89, dir. mktg. and commns., 1989-91; mem. Worldwide Alpha Group, 1991—; prin. Arthur Andersen & Co., 1980—; Mem. journalism adv. com. Harper Coll.; pub. relations com. Chgo. Met. Crusade Mercy; mem. Nat. Task Force on Environment; cons. sec. Dept. Health, Edn. and Welfare, 1970; chmn. pub. relations com. Honor Am. Day Com., 1970. Author: Vision of Grandeur, 1988; contbr. articles to profl. jours. Counselor Council of Mojave, 1972-74; gen. chmn. Chgo. Children's Classic Golf Tournament, 1974-77; chmn. Chgo. fin. com. Am.'s Freedom Train, 1976; chmn. fund devel. com. Presbytery of Chgo., 1977-83, maj. mission fund, 1977-79; dist. commr. Boy Scouts Am., 1976-79, chmn. Wildcat dist., 1980-83; mem. exec. bd. N.E. Ill. council, 1980-85; mem. Republican Citizens Com. Ill., 1960-61, Allegheny County (Pa.) Rep. Com., 1962-65; Trustee Roycemore Sch., Evanston, 1971-74; trustee, v.p. devel. Child and Family Services Chgo.; bd. dirs. Fellowship of Christian Athletes, U. N.C. Alumni Ill., Stockbrokers Assn. Chgo. Served to 1st lt. AUS, 1952-54. Elected to N.C. Pub. Rels. Hall of Fame, 1994. Mem. Pub. Relations Soc. Am., Nat. Investor Relations Inst., Midwest Travel Writers Assn., Chgo. Ednl. TV Assn., Pub. Relations Counselors Roundtable, Am. Mgmt. Assn.; Environ. Writers Assn. Am., Chgo. Assn. Commerce and Industry, Art Inst. Chgo., Univ. Club, Sunset Ridge Country Club, Chi Psi. Republican. Presbyterian. Home: 2759 Broadway Ave Evanston IL 60201-1556 Office: 69 W Washington St Chicago IL 60602-3002

ROBBINS, HULDA DORNBLATT, artist, printmaker; b. Atlanta, Oct. 19, 1910; d. Adolph Benno and Lina (Rosenthal) Dornblatt. Student, Phila. Mus's. Sch. Indsl. Art, 1928-29, Prussian Acad., Berlin, 1929-31, Barnes Found., Merion, Pa., 1939. Poster designer and maker ITE Circuit Breaker Co. Inc., Phila., 1944; instr. serigraphy Nat. Serigraph Soc. Sch., N.Y.C., 1953-60; instr. creative painting Atlantic County Jewish Community Centers, Margate and Atlantic City, N.J., 1960-67. One-man shows, Lehigh U. Art Galleries, 1933, ACA Galleries, Phila., 1939, 8th St. Gallery, N.Y.C., 1941, Serigraph Gallery, N.Y.C., 1947, Atlantic City Art Center, 1961, 71, numerous group shows, 2d Nat. Print ann. Bklyn. Mus., Carnegie Inst., Library of Congress, LaNapoule Art Found.; Am. Graphic Contemporary Art; represented in permanent collections, including, Met. Mus. Art, N.Y.C., Mus. Modern Art, N.Y.C., Bibliotheque Nationale, Smithsonian Instn., Art Mus. Ont., Can., Victoria and Albert Mus., London, U.S. embassies abroad, Lehigh U., Princeton (N.J.) Print Club. Recipient Purchase prize Prints for Children, Mus. Modern Art, N.Y.C., 1941; prize 2d Portrait of Am. Competition, 1945; 2d prize Paintings by Printmakers, 1948. Mem. Am. Color Print Soc., Print Club, Graphics Soc., Serigraph Soc. (mem. founding group, charter sec., Ninth Ann. prize 1948, 49). Home and Office: 16 S Buffalo Ave Ventnor City NJ 08406-2635 *To cherish and express living through devotion to art.*

ROBBINS, JANE BORSCH, library science educator, information science educator; b. Chgo., Sept. 13, 1939; d. Reuben August and Pearl Irene (Houk) Borsch; 1 child, Molly Warren Robbins. B.A., Wells Coll., 1961; M.L.S., Western Mich. U., 1966; Ph.D., U. Md., 1972. Asst. prof. library and info. sci. U. Pitts., 1972-73; asso. prof. Emory U., Atlanta, 1973-74; cons. to the bd. Wyo. State Library, 1974-77; asso. prof. La. State U., Baton Rouge, 1977-79; dean La. State U. (Sch. Library and Info. Sci.), 1979-81; prof., dir. Sch. Library and Info. Studies U. Wis., Madison, 1981-94; dean, prof. Sch. Libr. and Info. Studies Fla. State U., Tallahassee, 1994—. Author: Public Library Policy and Citizen Participation, 1975, Public Librarianship: A Reader, 1982, are We There Yet?, 1988, Libraries: Partners in Adult Literacy, 1990, Keeping the Books: Public Library Financial Practices, 1992, Balancing the Books: Financing American Public Library Services, 1993, Evaluating Library Programs and Services: A Manual and Sourcebook, 1994; editor Libr. and Info. Sci. Rsch., 1982-92; contbr. articles to profl. jours. Mem. ALA (councilor 1976-80, 91-95), Am. Soc. Info. Sci., Assn. for Libr. and Info. Sci. Edn. (dir. 1979-81, pres. 1984), Wis. Libr. Assn. (pres. 1986). Democrat. Episcopalian. Office: Fla State U Sch Libr and Info Studies Louis Shores Bldg Tallahassee FL 32306

ROBBINS, JEFFREY HOWARD, media consultant, research writer, educator; b. N.Y.C., Mar. 29, 1941; s. Stanley Samuel and Miriam (Cooper) R.; m. Marsha Sue Rimler, Nov. 3, 1984; 1 child, Nina Camille. BSME, Carnegie Mellon U., 1962; MS in Physics, U. N.Mex., 1966, ABD in Physics, 1967; postgrad., U. Calif., Berkeley and L.A., 1963-64. Summer rsch. assoc. Linde Co., Tonawanda, N.Y., 1961; rsch. engr. N.Am. Aviation (Rockwell), Downey, Calif., 1962-64; summer rsch. assoc. Los Alamos (N.Mex.) Nat. Lab., 1965; sr. engr. Radio Engring. Labs., L.I., N.Y., 1968-70; engring. cons. PRD Electronics, Syosset, N.Y., 1972-73; sr. cons. Bendix Corp., Teterboro, N.J., 1974-76; sr. engr. Giordano Assocs., Franklin Lakes, N.J., 1977-81; sr. applications engr. Racal-Redak, Mahwah, N.J., 1981-83; tech. media cons. Allied Signal Corp., Teterboro, 1983-92, U.S. Army, Picatinny Arsenal, N.J., 1992, Ford Motor Co., Lansdale, Pa., 1992—; cons., rsch. writer media literacy programs Packer Collegiate Inst., Bklyn., N.Y.C., 1992-93, On TV, Inc., N.Y.C., 1992—, moderator Media Literacy Forum, 1995; evening sch. instr. New Sch. for Social Rsch., N.Y.C., 1979-85; presenter in field. Author: On Balance and Higher Education, 1970; contbr. articles to profl. jours. Organizer, co-moderator Future Impact of Artificial Intelligence, Robotics Forum, 1984; initiator, moderator Media Literacy Forum, The Packer Collegiate Inst., 1995. Recipient 1st prize for essay The World and I Mag., 1990; nominee Grawemeyer award in Edn., 1988; NDEA fellow, 1966-67, others. Mem. IEEE (presenter Internat. Symposium in Tech. and Soc. 1993, Internat. Soc. Sys. Scis. Conf. 1993, initiator, moderator, media literacy forum Packer Collegiate Inst. 1995). N.Y. Acad. Scis., Sigma Xi, Phi Kappa Phi, Pi Tau Sigma. Home: 215 Adams St # 10A Brooklyn NY 11201 Office: Cassiopeia Cons Inc Box 335 Long Beach NY 11561

ROBBINS, JEROME, choreographer, director; b. N.Y.C., Oct. 11, 1918; s. Harry and Lena (Rips) R. Student, NYU, 1935-36, hon. degree, 1985; D.F.A. (hon.), Ohio U., 1975; studied ballet, modern, Spanish and Oriental dance.; hon. degree, CUNY, 1980. Mem. panel N.Y. Council on Arts, 1973-77, Nat. Council on Arts, Nat. Endowment for Arts, 1974-80; Ballet Theatre (N.Y.C.), 1940-44, soloist, 1941-44; choreographer N.Y.C. Ballet, 1944—, assoc. artistic dir., 1949-59, ballet master, 1969-83, co-ballet master-in-chief, 1983-89; dir., Ballet U.S.A. 1958-61, Jerome Robbins Chamber Dance Co., tour Peoples' Republic of China (sponsored by U.S. Internat. Communications Agency), 1981; ballets also in repertories of Am. Ballet Theatre, Joffrey Ballet, Royal Swedish Ballet, Batsheva Ballet, Royal Danish Ballet, Boston Ballet, Nat. Ballet of Canada, Harkness Ballet, Royal Winnipeg Ballet, London Ballet, Australian Ballet, San Francisco Ballet, Pennsylvania Ballet, Dance Theatre of Harlem, Paris Opera Ballet, Bayerischen Staatsoper (Munich), La Scala, Opernhaus (Surich), Finnish Ballet, Star Dancers Kinov Foundation.; Debut as dancer Sandor-Sorel Dance Center, 1937; dancer Broadway musicals Great Lady, 1939, Straw Hat Review, 1939, Keep Off the Grass, 1940; dancer ballets Helen of Troy, 1942, Petrouchka, 1944, Three Virgins and a Devil, 1944, Romeo and Juliet, 1944, Concert Varieties, 1945, Summer Day, 1947, Facsimile, 1947, Bouree Fantasique, 1949, The Prodigal Son, 1950, The Age of Anxiety, 1950, The Pied Piper, 1951, Circus Polka, 1971, George Abbott...A Celebration, 1976; tours include Gypsy, 1959, 81, Fiddler on the Roof, 1964, 80, Peter Pan, 1981, Jerome Robbins Chamber Dance Company, 1981; ballets choreographed include Fancy Free, 1944, Interplay, 1945, Afterthought, 1946, Facsimile, 1946, Summer Day, 1947, Pas de Trois, 1948, The Guests, 1949, (with Balanchine) Jones Beach, 1950, Age of Anxiety, 1950, Pied Piper, 1951, The Cage, 1951, Ballade, 1952, Fanfare, 1953, Afternoon of a Faun, 1953, Wonderful Town, 1953, The Tender Land, 1954, Quartet, 1954, The Concert, 1956, N.Y. Export: Opus Jazz, 1958, Moves, 1959, Les Noces, 1965 (City of Paris award, Internat. Dance Festival 1971), 3X3, 1961, Events, 1961, (with Balanchine) Firebird, 1970, Dances at a Gathering, 1969, In the Night, 1970, The Goldberg Variations, 1971, Requiem Canticles, 1972, (with Balanchine) Dumbarton Oaks, 1972, (with Balanchine) Pulcinella, 1972, Watermill, 1972, Scherzo Fantastique, 1972, Circus Polka, 1972, Interplay, 1972, An Evening's Waltzes, 1973, Celebration: The Art of the Pas de Deux, 1973, Beethoven Pas de Deaux, 1973, Dybbuk Variations, 1974, Introduction & Allegro for Harp, 1975, Une Barque Sur L'Ocean, 1975, Concerto in G (later in G Major), 1975, Ma mere l'oye, 1975, Chansons Madecasses, 1975, Concert for the Royal Ballet, 1975, Introduction, 1975, Allegro For Harp, 1975, Mother Goose, 1975, Other Dances, 1976, A Sketchbook, 1978, (with Peter Martins and Jean-Pierre Bonnefous) Tricolore, 1978, The Dreamer, 1979, Le Bourgeois Gentilhomme, 1979, The Four Seasons, 1979, Opus 19: The Dreamer, 1979, Suite of Dances, 1980, Rondo, 1981, Andantino, 1981, Piano Pieces, 1981, (with Pulchinella 1972 and Firebird 1970) Allegro con Grazia, 1981, The Gershwin Concerto, 1982, Four Chamber Works, 1982, Glass Pieces, 1983, I'm Old Fashioned, 1983, Antique Epigraphs, 1984, (with Twyla Tharp) Brahms/Handel, 1984, Eight Lines, 1985, In Memory Of..., 1985, Quiet City, 1986, Piccolo Balletto, 1986, Ives, Songs, 1988, N.Y.C. Retrospective of Jerome Robbins' Ballets, 1989, (with Mikhail Baryshnikov) A Suite of Dances, 1994, 2 Part Inventions, 1994; choreographer of Broadway musicals Billion Dollar Baby (Donaldson award 1946), 1946, High Button Shoes (Tony award best choreographer 1948, New York Drama Critics' award 1948), 1947, Miss Liberty, 1949, The King and I, 1951 (Donaldson award 1952), Two's Company (Donaldson award 1952), 1952; dir. and choreographer stage musicals Look Ma, I'm Dancin' 1948, Call Me Madam, 1950, Peter Pan, 1954, Bells Are Ringing, 1956 (Tony award nomination best choreographer 1957), West Side Story, 1957 (Tony award best choreographer 1958, London Evening Standard Drama award 1958), Gypsy (Tony award nomination best director of musical 1960), 1959, Fiddler on the Roof (Drama Critics' Circle award best musical 1965, Tony award best choreographer 1965, Tony award best director of musical 1965), 1964, Jerome Robbins' Broadway (Tony award best director of musical 1989), 1989-90; dir. plays that include That's the Ticket, 1948, The Pajama Game (Donaldson award 1954), 1954, Oh Dad, Poor Dad, Mama's Hung You in the Closet and I'm Feelin So Sad, 1962; choreographer and creator On the Town, 1944; creator of The Small House of Uncle Thomas, 1951; dir. and producer (with Cheryl Crawford) Mother Courage and Her Children (Tony

award nomination best play 1963, Tony award nomination best producer 1963), 1963; choreographer motion pictures The King and I (Box Office Blue Ribbon award 1956), 1956, West Side Story, 1960 (SBI Gold Owl award 1961, Outstanding Directorial Achievement award for feature films Directors Guild of Am. 1961, Academy award best director 1961, Laurel award Writer's Guild of Am. West 1961); TV credits include Ford 50th Anniversary Show (Sylvania award 1953), 1953, Peter Pan (Emmy award best choreographer 1955), 1955, 56, 60, Two Duets, 1980, Live from Studio 8H: An Evening of Jerome Robbins' Ballets, 1980. Decorated chevalier Order of Arts and Letters (France), comdr., 1964; chevalier Legion of Honor (France); Dance Magazine award for outstanding achievement 1950, 57, City of New York Citation, 1959, Hon. Award for Brilliant Achievements in the Art of Choreography on Film, Acad. Motion Picture Arts and Scis., 1961, Capezio Dance award, 1976, recipient Handel medallion N.Y.C., 1976, American-Israel Arts, Sciences, and Humanities award, 1979, Kennedy Ctr. honors, 1981, Brandeis U. Creative Arts award, 1984, Astaire Lifetime Achievement award, 1985, Nat. medal of Arts, 1988, H.C. Andersen Ballet Prize, Royal Danish Theatre, 1988, Drama Desk award, 1989, Commonwealth award of distinguished svc. in the dramatic arts, Bank of Delaware, 1990; named best choreographer Theatre des Nations, 1959. Mem. Am. Acad. and Inst. Arts and Letters (hon., Commonwealth award 1990, Commandeur de l'Ordre des Arts et des Lettres 1990), French Legion of Honor, 1993. Office: care NYC Ballet NY State Theater Lincoln Ctr Plz New York NY 10023

ROBBINS, JERRY HAL, educational administration educator; b. De-Queen, Ark., Feb. 28, 1939; s. James Hal and Barbara I. (Rogers) R. B.A. in Math, Hendrix Coll., 1960; M.Ed., U. Ark., 1963, Ed.D., 1966. Tchr. math. and music Clinton (Ark.) pub. schs., 1960-61; prin. Adrian (Mo.) High Sch., 1961-63; exec. sec. Ark. Sch. Study Council, Fayetteville, 1963-65; mem. faculty U. Miss., University, 1965-74; prof. ednl. adminstrn. U. Miss., 1970-74, chmn. dept. ednl. adminstrn., 1970-74; dean Coll. Edn., U. Ark., Little Rock, 1974-79; asso. v.p. for acad. affairs Ga. State U., Atlanta, 1979-84, dean Coll. Edn., 1984-90, prof. ednl. adminstrn., 1990-91; dean. Coll. Edn. Ea. Mich. U., Ann Arbor, 1991—. Co-author: (with S. B. Williams Jr.) Student Activities in the Innovative School, 1969, School Custodian's Handbook, 1970, Administrator's Manual of School Plant Administration, 1970. Mem. NEA, Am. Assn. Sch. Adminstrs., Am. Assn. Colls. Tchr. Edn. (dir. 1979-82), Nat. Assn. Secondary Sch. Prins., So. Regional Council Ednl. Adminstrn. (pres. 1970-71), Phi Delta Kappa, Kappa Delta Pi (v.p. chpt. devel. 1978-80, pres. elect 1980-82, pres. 1982-84, past pres. 1984-86). Mem. United Meth. Ch. Home and Office: 3323 Breckland Ct Ann Arbor MI 48103-9734 Office: Ea Mich U Boone Hall Ypsilanti MI 48197

ROBBINS, JESSIE EARL, metallurgist; b. York, Ala., Feb. 17, 1944; s. Elbert Jessie and Ella Lee (Hurst) R.; m. Dolly Marie Welch, Apr. 7, 1977; children: Angela Michelle, Amanda Leigh. BS in Engring., U. Ala., 1974. Registered profl. engr. Tex. Welding engr. Chicago Bridge & Iron Co., Brimingham, Ala., 1974-77; metallurgist AMF Tuboscope, Houston, 1977-78; plant metallurgist Tubular Finishing Works, Navajoto, Tex., 1978-80; welding engr. Daniel Inds., Houston, 1980-82; welding engr., metallurgist TRW-Mission, Houston, 1982-85; quality assurance engr. Vincotte USA, Houston, 1986-87; welding engr. LTV Missiles & Electronics, Camden, Ark., 1987-90; mgr. tech. svcs. Mavrick Tube Corp., Conroe, Tex., 1990—. With USN, 1961-65. Mem. Am. Petroleum Inst. (com. mem. 1992), Am. Soc. Testing and Materials (com. mem. 1992), Nat. Assn. Corrosion Engrs. (com. mem. 1992), Soc. Petroleum Engring., Grangerland Lions Club (charter). Independent.

ROBBINS, JOHN CLAPP, management consultant; b. Cleveland, Jan. 22, 1921; s. John Clapp and Esther Turner (Holland) R.; m. Louise Severance Nash, Jan. 10, 1951 (div. Oct. 1974); children: Anne Millikin, Julia Severance, John Nash; m. Beatrice Blair, Aug. 2, 1975 (dec. July 1994). A.B., Harvard U., 1942. Copy boy, reporter, writer, promotion editor Cleve. Press, 1946-57; exec. internat. div. Mobil Oil Corp., N.Y.C., Istanbul, 1957-70; chief exec. officer Planned Parenthood/World Population, N.Y.C., 1970-75; prin. mgmt. cons. Stanford Research Inst., 1976-83; v.p. GPA Inc., N.Y.C., 1983—; pres. John Robbins Assocs. Author: Too Many Asians, 1959. Bd. dirs., pres. Am. Hosp., Istanbul; treas. Sex Info. and Edn. Coun. U.S., Harvard Libr. in N.Y.C. Capt. AUS, 1942-45. Decorated Bronze Star, Purple Heart; Reid fellow, 1953. Mem. Internat. Planned Parenthood Fedn. London. Republican. Unitarian. Club: Harvard (N.Y.C.). Home: 115 E 9th St New York NY 10003 Office: 98 Riverside Dr New York NY 10024-5323

ROBBINS, JOHN MICHAEL, JR., mortgage company executive; b. Phoenix, June 16, 1947; s. John Michael and Dorothy Louise (Hollenbeck) R.; m. Laura Rohe, Oct. 5, 1968; children—James S., Deanna M. Student, Phoenix Coll., 1965-66, 70-71. V.p. Colonial Mortgage Co., Phila., 1971-80; regional v.p. Advance Mortgage Co., Southfield, Mich., 1980-82; sr. v.p. Central Fed. Mortgage, San Diego, 1982-83; exec. v.p. Imperial Corp. Am., San Diego, 1983-88; pres., chmn. Am. Residential Mortgage Corp., La Jolla, 1983—; chmn. bd. Am. Mortgage Investment Corp., Fieldstone Co. Zone chmn. Ducks Unltd., San Diego, 1975-78; pres. Encinitas Union Sch. Dist. Ednl. Facilities Corp., 1975-78; bd. dirs. Child Abuse Prevention Found., San Diego YMCA, Polinsky's Children's Ctr., Old Globe Theatre. Mem. Mortgage Bankers Assn. Am. (bd. govs.), San Diego C. of C. (bd. dirs.), Century Club San Diego (bd. dirs. 1992—), Univ. Club San Diego. Republican. Lutheran. Avocations: golf, hunting, deep sea fishing. Office: Am Residential Mortgage Corp 11119 N Torrey Pines Rd La Jolla CA 92037-1085

ROBBINS, KEITH CRANSTON, research scientist; b. Berwyn, Ill., Feb. 3, 1944; s. Ollice Cranston and Edith Eileen Robbins; m. Barbara Anne Byrne, June 17, 1967; children: Christine Anne, Nancy Edith, Elizabeth Erin. BA, Ind. U., 1967; MS.Am. U., 1972; PhD, George Washington U., 1977. Staff scientist Hazleton Labs., Vienna, Va., 1972-80; cancer expert Nat. Cancer Inst., Bethesda, Md., 1980-85, sect. chief, 1985-88; sect. chief Nat. Inst. Dental Rsch., Bethesda, 1988—, lab. chief, 1992—; invited lectr. Australian Biochem. Soc., Am. Heart Assn., Nat. Geriatric Soc., Am. Soc. Biochemistry & Molecular Biology, Argentine Congress on Cancer, Sci. Frontiers in Clin. Dentistry, Am. Soc. Microbiology, Mich. Cancer Found., S.Am. Symposium on Signal Transduction, Cellw Growth and Cancer, Upjohn Pharms., Pfizer Pharms., Sterling Drug, Nova Pharms., Cor Therapeutics, Pfizer Inc., also numerous univs.; ad hoc mem. various sci. study sects., NIH, NRSA, NCI. Contbr. over 100 articles to profl. jours. Vestryman United Christian Parish, Reston, Va., 1993. Mem. AAAS. Achievements include discovery of gene specifying platelet-derived growth factor; discovered a number of oncogenes; 2 patents. Office: Natl Inst of Dental Health 9000 Rockville Pike Bldg 30 Bethesda MD 20892-0001

ROBBINS, KENNETH L., advertising agency executive; b. Berkeley, Calif., Aug. 28, 1935; BA, U. Pa. With J.W. Thompson, 1963-80; Exec. v.p. SSC&B (now Lintas Worldwide), N.Y.C., 1980—; now chmn., CEO Lintas Worldwide; bd. dirs. The Interpublic Group of Cos. Office: Lintas Worldwide 1 Dag Hammarskjold Plz New York NY 10017-2201

ROBBINS, LAWRENCE HARRY, anthropologist; b. Washington, Nov. 22, 1938; s. Maurice and Edith R.; m. Martha Ann Edwards, Dec. 16, 1967; children: Daniel, Brian, Michael, Mark. A.B., U. Mich., 1961, A.M., 1962, Ph.D., U.Calif., Berkeley, 1968. Acad. dir. U. Utah, 1967; mem. faculty Mich. State U., East Lansing, 1968—; prof. anthropology and African studies Mich. State U., 1977—, chairperson ANP dept., 1992-95; vis. research asso. U. Nairobi, Kenya, 1969-70. Nat. Mus. Kenya, 1975-76; Fulbright vis. prof. U. Botswana, 1982-83; vis. archaeologist Nat. Mus. and Art Gallery, Botswana, 1982-83. Author: Stones, Bones and Ancient Cities, 1990; contbr. articles to profl. jours. Grantee NSF, 1965-66, 69-70, 75-77, 91—, Nat. Geographic Soc., 1987, 89. Fellow Am. Anthropol. Assn.; mem. Soc. Africanist Archeologists in Am., So. African Archeol. Soc., Botswana Soc. Officer: Dept Anthropology Mich State U East Lansing MI 48824

ROBBINS, MARION LE RON, agricultural research executive; b. Inman, S.C., Aug. 18, 1941; s. Jack Dennis and Christina (Champion) R.; m. Margaret Elanor Wilson, Sept. 25, 1965; children: Jack, Rona, Jeff, Kyle. BS, Clemson U., 1964; MS, La. State U., 1966; PhD, U. Md., 1968. Asst. prof. Iowa State U., Ames, 1968-72; rsch. scientist Clemson U., Charleston, S.C., 1972-83; resident dir. Sweet Potato Rsch. Sta., Chase, La., 1984-88, Calhoun (La.) Rsch. Sta., 1988—; advisor Farm Bur., Monroe, La., 1988-90, Agribus.

Coun., Monroe, 1988—. Editor: Jour. of Vegetable Crop Prodn., 1992—; assoc. editor: (jour.) Crop Prodn., 1972-90; contbr. more than 200 articles, abstracts, rsch. papers and revs. to profl. jours. Delegation leader People to People Internat., Spokane, Wash., 1985—. Mem. Am. Soc. for Hort. Sci. (dir., pres. so. region 1982-83), Rsch. Ctr. Adminstrs. Soc. (dir. 1985), Calhoun Civic Club (pres. 1994-95) Rotary Club (pres. 1987-88), Exch. Club (pres. 1976-77). Presbyterian. Achievements include development of 22 varieties and genetic lines of crop plants, including 2 All-American winners and an All-Am. designate. Office: Calhoun Rsch Sta 321 Highway 80 E Calhoun LA 71225-9703

ROBBINS, NANCY LOUISE See MANN, NANCY LOUISE

ROBBINS, OREM OLFORD, insurance company executive; b. Mpls., Feb. 5, 1915; s. Douglas Ford and Grace (Rorem) R.; m. Annette Strand Scherer, May 17, 1992; children: Ford M., Ross S., Gail R. Tomei, Cynthia R. Rothbard. BBA with distinction, U. Minn., 1936; BS in Law, William Mitchell Coll. Law, 1946, JD, 1948. Comml. rep. NW Bell Telephone Co., Mpls., 1936-48; dep. dir. U.S. Treas. Dept., Mpls., 1948-49; sales rep. Conn. Gen. Life Ins. Co., Mpls., 1949-56; founder, chmn. Security Life Ins. Co. Am., Mpls., 1956—. Bd. dirs., past pres. Family and Children's Svcs., Mpls., 1968—; bd. govs., past chmn. Meth. Hosp., Mpls., 1960—; past treas., bd. dirs Goodwill/Easter Seals, St. Paul, 1958-68, 75-88; life trustee Hamline U., St. Paul, 1979—, chmn. bd. trustees, 1990-91. Col. U.S. Army, 1941-46. Decorated Legion of Merit. Fellow Life Mgmt. Assn.; mem. Am. Soc. CLU (pres. Mpls. chpt. 1959), Health Underwriters Assn., Chartered Fin. Cons., Am. Legion, Skylight Club (Mpls.), Mpls. Minikahda, Hole in the Wall Golf Club, Naples Yacht Club, Masons. Republican. Methodist. Office: Security Life Ins Co Am 10901 Red Circle Dr Minnetonka MN 55343-9137

ROBBINS, ORREN BOURNE, newspaper publisher; b. Hyannis, Mass., July 20, 1932; s. Percy Burton and Sara Hatch (Jones) R.; m. Bonnie Jean Eldredge, Apr. 24, 1952; children: Orren Bourne Jr., David Mervyn, Stephen Wayne. Grad., Barnstable High Sch., Hyannis. Advt. sales rep. Cape Cod Standard-Times, Hyannis, 1958-71; gen. mgr. Press-Rep., Plattsburgh, N.Y., 1971-74; Gen. mgr. Cape Cod Standard-Times, Hyannis, 1974-79; pub. The Traverse City (Mich.) Record-Eagle, 1979-86, The Standard-Times, New Bedford, Mass., 1987—. Bd. dirs. United Way Greater New Bedford, 1987—, Downtown New Bedford, Inc., 1988—. Mem. Am. Newspaper Pubs. Assn., New Eng. Newspapers Assn., Mass. Newspaper Pubs. Assn., New Bedford Area C. of C., Country Club New Bedford, Rotary, Elks. Republican. Avocation: bluegrass music. Office: Standard-Times Pub Co 555 Pleasant St New Bedford MA 02740-6235

ROBBINS, PHILLIPS WESLEY, biology educator; b. Barre, Mass., Aug. 10, 1930; married, 1953; 2 children. AB, Depauw U., 1952; PhD in Biochemistry, U. Ill., 1955. Rsch. assoc. Mass. Gen. Hosp., Boston, 1955-57; asst. prof. Rockefeller Inst., N.Y.C., 1957-59; from asst. prof. to prof. MIT, 1959-77, Am. Cancer Soc. prof. biochemistry, 1977—. Recipient Eli Lilly award in biol. chemistry, 1966. Mem. Am. Soc. Biol. Chemistry, Am. Chem. Soc., Am. Acad. Arts and Scis. Office: Mass Inst Tech Ctr for Cancer Rsch Dept Biology E 17-233 Cambridge MA 02139-4325*

ROBBINS, RAY CHARLES, manufacturing company executive; b. Syracuse, N.Y., Sept. 15, 1920; s. Frederick and Mary Elizabeth (Field) R.; children: Sandra Robbins Jannetta, Ray Charles Jr., Eric L. With Lennox Internat. Inc. (formerly Lennox Furnace Co.), 1940-48; asst sales mgr. Lennox Industries Inc. (formerly Lennox Furnace Co.), Syracuse, 1948-52; gen. mgr. new factory and sales office, Lennox Industries, Inc. (formerly Lennox Furnace Co.), Toronto, Ont., Can., 1952-67; dir. Lennox Can. and Timeplan Fin. Co. Ltd., 1953-65; pres. Lennox Can., 1965-69; exec. v.p. Lennox-Worldwide, 1969-70; pres., CEO, 1970-77; chmn. bd. Lennox Internat. Inc., 1976-92; chmn. bd., chief exec. officer Lennox Industries Inc., 1977-80, chmn. bd., 1980-91, chmn. emeritus 1991—; bd. dirs. Lennox Internat., First Interstate of Iowa, Inc., Hawkeye Security Ins. Co., Des Moines, Fin. Security Group, Inc., Des Moines, Q-Dot, Garland, Tex.; pres., founder, bd. dirs. Exec. Inst., Inc., Dallas, 1983—; bd. advisor Internat. Exec. Svc. Corp., 1993—. Bd. dirs. Metro Toronto Big Bros., 1964-69, Queensway Gen. Hosp., 1957-69, Texx Found., 1979-81, Bus. Industry Polit. Action Com.; bd. govs., mem. exec. com. Iowa Coll. Found., 1975-78; v.p., mem. exec. bd. Mid-Iowa County Boy Scouts Am., 1972-78; mem. Pres.' Phys. Fitness Council, from 1979; exec. bd. Circle 10 council Boy Scouts Am., from 1979; mem. Dallas Citizens Council; bd. of govs. Nat. Women's Econ. Alliance Found.; bd. dirs. North Tex. Commn. Served with AUS, 1942-45, PTO. Mem. ASHRAE (life), Am. Refrigeration Inst. (bd. dirs 1973-74, 78, life from 1979, v.p. 1975-76, chmn. 1977), NAM (bd. dirs. 1974-75, dir. at large 1976, dir. State of Iowa 1977-78, dir. State of Tex. 1979-92), Nat. Mgmt. Assn. (exec. adv. com. 1979-92), Gas Appliance Mfrs. Assn. (past bd. dirs.), Can. Gas Assn. (pres.), Can. Mfg. Assn. (chmn. Toronto dist.), U.S.C. of C. (Can.-U.S. sect.), Bus.-Industry Polit. Action Com. (bd. dirs. 1991), Internat. Exec. Svc. Corps (bd. advs. 1993). Clubs: Park Cen., Landmark Athletic, Aerobics Activity Ctr. (Dallas); Canyon Creek Country (Richardson, Tex.). Office: Lennox Internat Inc PO Box 799900 Dallas TX 75379

ROBBINS, RICHARD, composer. Film scores include The Europeans, 1979, Jane Austen in Manhattan, 1980, Quartet, 1981, Heat and Dust, 1983, The Bostonians, 1984, A Room with a View, 1986, My Little Girl, 1986, Sweet Lorraine, 1987, Maurice, 1987, The Perfect Murder, 1988, Slaves of New York, 1989, Bail Jumper, 1990, Mr. and Mrs. Bridge, 1990, The Ballad of the Sad Cafe, 1991, Howards End, 1992 (Academy Award nomination best original score 1993), The Remains of the Day, 1993 (Academy Award nomination best original score 1993), Jefferson in Paris, 1995. Office: Creative Artists Agency 9830 Wilshire Blvd Beverly Hills CA 90210*

ROBBINS, ROBERT B., lawyer; b. Canton, Ohio, Aug. 31, 1951; s. Nathan H. and Evelyn (Cohen) R.; m. Melinda Abbot Street, Oct. 18, 1981; children: Julia Bates, Katherine Melinda, Caroline Rachel, Eli Street. AB, Cornell U., 1972; JD, Harvard U., 1975. Bar: D.C. 1975. Ptnr. Shaw, Pittman, Potts & Trowbridge, Washington, 1976—, also vice chmn. corp. group; chmn. D.C. Bar Commn. on Broker-Dealer Regulation, 1985-90; trustee and mem. exec. bd. Greater Washington Rsch. Ctr., 1993—; cochmn. ann. course study on pvt. placement Am. Law Inst.-ABA. Mem. D.C. Bar (steering com. sect. corp., fin. and securities law 1991-94, chmn. 1993-94). Office: Shaw Pittman Potts & Trowbridge 2300 N St NW Washington DC 20037-1122

ROBBINS, ROBERT JOHN, biologist, computer scientist, educator; b. Niles, Mich., May 10, 1944; s. Robert Addison and Aura M. (McKinney) R.; m. Coreen Amelia Kelly, July 1, 1984. AB, Stanford U., 1966; BS, Mich. State U., 1973, MS, 1974, PhD, 1977. Asst. prof. Mich. State U., East Lansing, 1979-82, assoc. prof., 1982-87; staff assoc. NSF, Washington, 1987—; postdoctoral researcher U. Calif., Davis, 1978-79. Author: Genetics: A Brief Introduction, 1981, The Sweep of Life, 1983, Chordate Development, 1985. Fellow NSF, U. Calif., Davis, 1978. Mem. IEEE, Assn. Computing Machinery, Genetics Soc. Am., Am. Soc. Microbiology, Am. Inst. Biological Scis., Philosophy of Sci. Assn. Home: 1300 Southview Rd Baltimore MD 21218-1425 Office: Nat Sci Found Div of Biotic Systems and Resources 1800 G St NW Washington DC 20550-0002

ROBBINS, STEPHEN J. M., lawyer; b. Seattle, Apr. 13, 1942; s. Robert Mads and Aneita Elberta (Melby) R.; m. Nina Winifred Tanner, Aug. 11, 1967; children: Sarah E.T., Alicia S.T. AB, UCLA, 1964; JD, Yale U., 1971. Bar: D.C. 1973, U.S. Dist. Ct. D.C. 1973, U.S. Ct. Appeals (D.C. cir.) 1973, U.S. Ct. Appeals (3d cir.) 1973, U.S. Dist. Ct. (ea. and no. dists.) Calif. 1982, U.S. Dist. Ct. (cen. dist.) Calif. 1983, Supreme Ct. of Republic of Palau, 1994. Pres. U.S. Nat. Student Assn., Washington, 1964-65; assoc. Steptoe & Johnson, Washington, 1972-75; chief counsel spl. inquiry com. on nutrition U.S. Senate, Washington, 1975; v.p., gen. counsel Straight Arrow Pubs., San Francisco, 1975-77; dep. dist. atty. City and County of San Francisco, 1977-78; regional counsel U.S.SBA, San Francisco, 1978-80; spl. counsel Warner-Amex Cable Communications, Sacramento, 1981-82; ptnr. McDonough, Holland and Allen, Sacramento, 1982-84; v.p Straight Arrow Pubs., N.Y.C. 1984-86; ptnr. Robbins & Livingston, Sacramento, 1986—; gen. legal counsel Govt. of State of Koror, Republic of Palau, Western Caroline Islands, 1994-95. Staff sgt. U.S. Army, 1966-68. Mem. Nat. Inst. Mcpl. Law Officers

(assoc.), D.C. Bar, State Bar of Calif., ABA (sect. of urban, state and local govt. law-land use, planning and zoning, com., sect. of real property, probate and trust law, sect. natural resources energy, environ. law, forum com. on affordable housing and cmty. devel.), Urban Land Inst. (assoc.), Am. Planning Assn. (planning and law divsn., internat. divsn.), Internat. Urban Devel. Assn. Unitarian. Avocations: theatre, art, hiking. Office: Robbins & Livingston 3300 Douglas Blvd Roseville CA 95661

ROBBINS, TIM (TIMOTHY FRANCIS ROBBINS), actor; b. N.Y.C., Oct. 16, 1958. BA, UCLA, 1981. Founder, artistic dir. The Actor's Gang, 1981—. Actor: (films) No Small Affairs, 1984, Toy Soldiers, 1984, Fraternity Vacation, 1985, The Sure Thing, 1985, Howard the Duck, 1986, Top Gun, 1986, Five Corners, 1987, Bill Durham, 1988, Tapeheads, 1989, Eric The Viking, 1989, Twister, 1989, Miss Firecracker, 1989, Cadillac Man, 1990, Jacob's Ladder, 1990, Jungle Fever, 1991, The Player, 1992 (Cannes Best Actor award 1992), Short Cuts, 1993, The Hudsucker Proxy, 1994, The Shawshank Redemption, 1994, Ready to Wear (Prêt-à-Porter), 1994, I.Q., 1994; Dir., writer, actor: Bob Roberts, 1992; (TV movies) Quarterback Princess, 1983, Malice in Wonderland, 1985; dir., actor: (play) Ubu Roi (L.A. Weekly Dir. award); dir. (plays) A Midsummer's Night Dream, Methusalem, the Eternal Bourgeois, The Good Woman of Setzuan (L.A. Drama Critics Circle nominee); co-writer: Alagazam, After the Dog Wars, Violence: The Misadventures of Spike Spangle, Farmer, Carnage, A Comedy. Office: Care ICM 8942 Wilshire Blvd Beverly Hills CA 90211*

ROBBINS, TOM, author; b. Blowing Rock, N.C., 1936; m. Terrie Hemingway (div.); 1 child, Fleetwood Starr. Student, Washington and Lee U., 1954-56, U. Wash., 1963; degree in social sci., Va. Commonwealth U., 1959. Former copy editor Richmond (Va.) Times-Dispatch, Seattle Post-Intelligencer; art critic Seattle Times. Author: (biography) Guy Anderson, 1965, (fiction) Another Roadside Attraction, 1971, Even Cowgirls Get the Blues, 1976, Still Life with Woodpecker, 1980, Jitterbug Perfume, 1984, Skinny Legs and All, 1990, Half Asleep in Frog Pajamas, 1994. With USAF. Office: PO Box 338 La Conner WA 98257

ROBBINS, WILLIAM DAVID, retired police officer; b. Martins Ferry, Ohio, Dec. 22, 1930; s. Harold David and Hazel Clareice (Burnett) R.; m. Marion M. Ruckh May, 1953; children: Christine Diana Gary, David Rock; m. Evelyn Clair Farley, Nov. 19, 1977; 1 child, Michael Allen. Student, U. Louisville, 1978, U. Ga., 1980. Officer Wheeling (W.va.) Police Dept., 1957-76, detective, 1976-91, lt., 1991-94. With U.S. Army, 1952-53, Korea. Decorated Bronze Star; recipient numerous citations and commendations for police work. Mem. Fraternal Order of Police, Masons. Democrat. Roman Catholic. Avocations: shooting, golf, photography. Home: 58 Mount Wood Rd Wheeling WV 26003

ROBBINS, WILLIAM RANDOLPH, minister; b. West Hartford, Conn., May 22, 1912; s. Harry E. and Matilda Sydney (Franklin) R.; m. Sarah Craig Wright, June 6, 1942 (dec. Dec. 25, 1986); children: Henry Craig, Sarah Franklin Robbins Jenks Coate, Thomas Nelson. BA, Princeton U., 1934; MDiv, Yale U., 1941, STD (hon.), 1984; postgrad., Oxford U., Eng., 1946-47, 82. Ordained priest Episcopal Ch., 1942. Asst. min. St. George's Ch., N.Y.C., 1941-43; rector St. Peter's Ch., Cazenovia, N.Y., 1943-49, St. Thomas's Ch., New Haven, 1949-84; founder St. Thomas's Day Sch., 1956, pres. sch. corp., 1956-84, headmaster emeritus, 1984—; chaplain Mil. Order Fgn. Wars U.S., past chaplain gen.; chaplain in chief Mil. Order Loyal Legion U.S.; chaplain le comite français de Souvenir de Lafayette, Civil Def. New Haven area, Old Guard City of N.Y., 2d co. Gov.'s Foot Guard, Conn., New Haven County Sheriff's Assn. Founder Christian Community Action, New Haven; sec. New Haven Archdeaconry; mem. Berkeley Divinity Sch. coun., Yale U.; bd. dirs. Lord's Day Alliance, New Haven Vis. Nurse Assn. 1st lt. U.S. Army, to lt. col. N.Y. N.G., to capt. USCG Aux. Recipient Alumni Disting. Ministry award Berkeley Div. Sch., Disting. Mil. Svc. award N.Y. State Guard, Outstanding Achievement award Princeton U. Class of 1934; assoc. fellow Trumbull Coll., Yale U. Mem. Conn. Acad. Arts and Scis., Soc. Descendants Colonial Govs. (chaplain gen.), Soc. Descendants Colonial Clergy (past chaplain gen.), The Soc. the Cin. (chaplain), Soc. Colonial Wars (chaplain), Soc. Descendents Knights of Garter, The Pilgrims, Dartmouth House English-Speaking Union (London), Most Venerable Order St. John's Hosp. Jerusalem, Berkeley Divinity Sch. Alumni (past pres.), St. Nicholas Soc. (N.Y. chaplain), Order of Knighthood, St. John of Jersulaem (chaplain), Order of Hist. Mil. Commands (chaplain), Union Club of N.Y., Royal Tennis Court (Hampton Court Palace, Eng.), Royal Tennis Ct. Club, Hampton Ct. Palace, Princeton Club, Union Club (N.Y.C.), Elizabethan of Yale Club, Royal Bermuda Yacht Club, Grad. Club (New Haven). Home: 24 Battis Rd New Haven CT 06514-2908 One of the greatest blessings in our time is the neutralizing of militant, atheistic Communism by the moral and ethical influences of Religion and the freedom of the individual for which it stands.

ROBE, THURLOW RICHARD, engineering educator, university dean; b. Petersburg, Ohio, Jan. 25, 1934; s. Thrulow Scott and Mary Alice (McKibben) R.; m. Eleanora C. Komyati, Aug. 27, 1955; children: Julia, Kevin, Stephen, Edward. B.S.C.E., Ohio U., 1955, M.S. in Mech. Engring., 1962; Ph.D. in Applied Mechanics, Stanford U., 1966. Engr. Gen. Electric Co., Niles, Ohio, Cleve., Erie, Pa., Evendale.Ohio, 1954-60; instr. Ohio U., Athens, 1960-63; asst. prof to prof., assoc. dean U. Ky., Lexington, 1965-80; dean Ohio U., Athens, 1980—, Cruse W. Moss prof. Engring. Edn., 1992—; dir. Innovation Ctr. Authority Ohio U., 1983—; pres., chmn. bd. Q.E.D. Assocs., Inc., Lexington, 1975-83; dir. Databeam Corp., Lexington; bd. dirs. Accreditation Bd. for Engring. and Tech., 1988-90; trustee Engring. Found. Ohio, 1988-94; bd. govs. Edison Materials Tech. Ctr., 1987—. Contbr. articles to profl. jours.; patentee trailer hitch. Bd. dirs. Athens County Community Redevel. Corp., 1980-86; treas. South Lexington Little League, 1976-80; vice chmn. Thoroughbred dist., Boy Scouts Am., 1975-77; pres. Tates Creek High Sch. PTA, Lexington, 1975-76; bd. dirs. U. Ky. Athletics Assn., 1975-80. Served to maj. USAF Res. (ret.). Recipient Alumni medal of merit Ohio U., 1993; Am. Coun. on Edn. Adminstrn. fellow, 1970-71. Mem. ASME, NSPE (Profl. Engring. in Edn. exec. bd., ctrl. region vice-chmn. 1987-89), Am. Soc. Engring. Edn. (Outstanding Contbn. in Rsch. award 1966), Athens Country Club, Athens Reading Club, Athens Symposiarchs, Assn. of Ohio Commodores, Rotary, Sigma Xi, Tau Beta Pi Omicron Delta Kappa, Alpha Lambda Delta. Office: Russ Coll Engring & Tech Ohio U Athens OH 45701

ROBECK, MILDRED COEN, educator; b. Walum, N.D., July 29, 1915; d. Archie Blane and Mary Henrietta (Hoffman) Coen; m. Martin Julius Robeck, Jr., June 2, 1936; children: Martin Jay Robeck, Donna Jayne Robeck Thompson, Bruce Wayne Robeck. BS, U. Wash., 1950, MEd, 1954, PhD, 1958. Ordnance foreman Sherman Williams, U.S. Navy, Bremerton, Wash., 1942-45; demonstration tchr. Seattle Pub. Schs., 1946-57; reading clinic dir. U. Calif., Santa Barbara, 1957-64; vis. prof. Victoria Coll., B.C., Can., summer 1958, Dalhousie U., Halifax, summer 1964; rsch. cons. State Dept. Edn., Sacramento, Calif., 1964-67; prof., head early childhood edn. U. Oreg., Eugene, Oreg., 1967-86; vis. scholar West Australia Inst. Tech., Perth, 1985; v.p. academic affairs U. Santa Barbara, Calif., 1987-94; exec. prod. psychology of reading U. Santa Barbara, Calif., 1987—; trainer, evaluator U.S. Office of Edn. Head Start, Follow Thru, 1967-72; cons., evaluator Native Am. Edn. Programs, Sioux, Navajo, 1967-81; cons. on gifted Oreg. Task Force on Talented and Gifted, Salem, 1974-76; evaluator Early Childhood Edn., Bi-Ling Petroleum and Minerology, Dhahran, Saudi Arabia, 1985; writer, rschr. in field. Author: Materials KELP: Kgn. Evaluation Learning Pot, 1967, Infants and Children, 1978, Psychology of Reading, 1990; contbr. articles to profl. jours. Evaluation cons. Rosenburg Found. Project, Santa Barbara, 1966-67; faculty advisor Pi Lambda Theta, Eugene, Oreg, 1969-74; guest columnist Oreg. Assn. Gifted and Talented, Salem Oreg., 1979-81; editorial review bd. ERQ, U.S. Calif., L.A., 1981-91. Recipient Nat. Dairy award H-4 Clubs, Wis., 1934, scholarships NYA and U. Wis. Madison, 1934-35, faculty rsch. grants U. Calif., Santa barbara, 1958-64, NDEA Fellowship Retraining U.S. Office Edn., U. Oreg., 1967-70. Mem. APA, Am. Ednl. Rsch. Assn., Internat. Reading Assn., Phi Beta Kappa, Pi Lambda Theta. Democrat. Avocations: historical research, duplicate bridge, hist. rsch., photography. Home and Office: 452 Venado Dr Santa Barbara CA 93111 also: 95999 Hwy 101 S Yachats OR 97498

ROBEK, MARY FRANCES, business education educator; b. Superior, Wis., Jan. 30, 1927; d. Stephen and Mary (Hervert) R. BE, U. Wis., 1948; MA, Northwestern U., 1951; MBA, U. Mich., 1962, PhD, 1967. Tchr. Bergland (Mich.) High Sch., 1948; Tchr. Tony (Wis.) High Sch., 1948-50, Sch. Vocat. and Adult Edn., Superior, 1950-58; prof. bus. edn. and office tech. Ea. Mich. U., Ypsilanti, 1958-93; instr. Jazyckova Gymnasium, Banská, Štiavnicá, Slovakia, 1994. Author: Information and Records Management, 1995. Assn. of Records Mgrs. and Adminstrs. fellow, 1992. Mem. Assn. Records Mgrs. and Adminstrs. (life), Inst. Cert. Mgrs. (pres. 1980-81), Cath. Daus. Am., Delta Pi Epsilon, Delta Kappa Gamma, Pi Lambda Theta. Republican. Roman Catholic. Home: 108445 Nakota Rd Solon Springs WI 54873 Opportunity to do creative and innovative things without infringing on the rights of others is limited only by priorities set considering people and technology.

ROBENALT, JOHN ALTON, lawyer; b. Ottawa, Ohio, May 2, 1922; s. Alton Ray and Kathryn (Straman) R.; m. Margaret Morgan Durbin, Aug. 25, 1951 (dec. July 1990); children: John F., William A., James D., Robert M., Mary K., Margaret E., Thomas D.; m. Nancy Leech Kidder, Sept. 21, 1991. B.A., Miami U., 1943; LL.B., Ohio State U., 1948, J.D., 1948. Bar: Ohio 1948. Asst. atty. gen. Ohio, 1949-51; practice in Lima, Ohio, 1951-59; partner Robenalt, Daley, Balyeat & Balyeat, 1959-82; ptnr. Robenalt, Kendall & Robenalt, 1983-85, Robenalt, Kendall, Rodabaugh & Staley, 1985-92, Robenalt & Robenalt, 1993—. Chmn. Lima March of Dimes, 1957-58; Bd. dirs. Lima Civic Center, pres., 1971-72; bd. dirs Lima Rotating Fund; trustee Allen County Regional Transit Authority, Lima, pres., 1975—. Served with AUS, 1943-45. Mem. ABA, Ohio Bar Assn., Allen County Bar Assn. (pres. 1969-70), Am. Legion, Lima Automobile Club (bd. dirs., pres. 1975-82), Shawnee Country Club (pres. 1968-70), Ohio Automobile Club (trustee 1982—, chmn. 1995—), Elks (bd. trustees 1991—), Rotary, Delta Tau Delta, Phi Delta Phi. Home: 1755 Shawnee Rd Lima OH 45805-3857 Office: 211215 N Elizabeth St Lima OH 45801-4300

ROBERSON, BRUCE H., lawyer; b. Wilmington, Del., Mar. 7, 1941; s. A. L. and Virginia Amelia (Heerdt) R.; m. Mary E. Abrams; children: Cheryl Anne, David B., Douglas M. B.S. cum laude, Washington and Lee U., 1963; J.D., U. Va., 1966. Bar: Va. 1966, Del. 1966, Fla. 1966. Mem. Morris, Nichols, Arsht & Tunnell, Wilmington, 1966-67; with Holland & Knight, Tampa, Fla., 1969—, ptnr., 1975—. Contbg. editor Warren, Gorham and Lamont Banking and Lending Institution Forms, 1992-95. Served to capt. U.S. Army, 1967-69. Decorated Bronze Star. Fellow Am. Bar Found., Fla. Bar Found. (corp. banking and bus. law sect. exec. coun. 1978-86, chmn. banking law com. 1982-84); mem. ABA (bus. law sect. com. on consumer fin. svcs. 1976—, banking law com. 1980—, savs. instns. com. 1989—), Hillsborough County Bar Assn., Del. Bar Assn., Va. Bar Assn., Am. Judicature Soc., Univ. Club, Tampa Yacht and Country Club, Lambda Chi Alpha. Republican. Methodist. Office: Holland & Knight 400 N Ashley Dr Ste 2300 PO Box 1288 Tampa FL 33601

ROBERSON, JAMES O., foundation executive; m. JoAnn Roberson; children: Melanie Merrill, Sharyl Ritucci, James Jr., Trisha Summersheim, Joel. AB in Journalism, Baylor U., 1956; student Indsl. Devel. Inst., U. Okla.; student Inst. Orgnl. Mgmt., U. Houston. Cert. indsl. developer. Dir. info. West Tex. C. of C., Abilene, 1956-59; area devel. mgr. Mo.-Kans.-Tex. R.R., 1959-63; exec. dir. Albuquerque Indsl. Devel. Svc., 1963-65; dir. N.Mex. Dept. Devel., Albuquerque, 1965-69; mgr. Forward Metro Denver, 1969-72; dir. R.I. Dept. Econ. Devel., Providence, 1972-77; v.p., dir. new bus. devel. Howard Rsch. and Devel. Corp. subs. Rouse Co., Columbia, Md., 1977-79; sec. Md. Dept. Econ. and Community Devel., Annapolis, 1979-83; pres. Louisville C. of C., 1983-88; pres., CEO Rsch. Triangle Found. N.C., 1988—; bd. dirs. Charlotte br. Fed. Res. Bank Richmond; cons., speaker in field. Editor West Tex. Today mag., 1956-59. Bd. dirs N.C. Citizens for Bus. and Industry, N.C. Biotech. Ctr. Fellow Am. Econ. Devel. Coun. (past chmn.); mem. Indsl. Devel. Rsch. Coun., Nat. Assn. State Devel. Agys. (past pres.). Office: Rsch Triangle Found NC PO Box 12255 2 Hazen Ct Durham NC 27712-9590

ROBERSON, NATHAN RUSSELL, physicist, educator; b. Robersonville, N.C., Dec. 13, 1930; s. Nathan Russell and Myrtle (Taylor) R.; m. Ruth Haislip, June 19, 1954; children: David Wintner, Michael Taylor, Mary Russell. BS, U. N.C., 1954, MS, 1955; PhD, Johns Hopkins U., 1960. Jr. instr. Johns Hopkins U., Balt., 1955-60; research assoc. Princeton (N.J.) U., 1960-63; asst. prof. physics Duke U., Durham, N.C., 1963-68, assoc. prof., 1968-74, prof., 1974—; bd. dirs. Triangle Univs. Computation Ctr., 1975-81; mem. instrumentation subcom. Nuclear Sci. Adv. Com., 1982-85; mem. energy sci. network steering com. Dept. Energy, 1987-90, nuclear physics panel on computer networks, 1988-90, dep. dir. Triangle U. Nuclear Lab., 1990-92; dir. Triangle Univs. Nuclear Lab., 1992—. Contbr. articles on physics to profl. jours. Treas. N.C. Council Chs., 1974-79. Fellow Am. Phys. Soc.; mem. IEEE, Am. Assn. Physics Tchrs., Phi Beta Kappa. Presbyterian. Home: 3406 Ogburn Ct Durham NC 27705-5427 Office: Dept Physics Duke U Durham NC 27708

ROBERSON, PATT FOSTER, mass communications educator; b. Middletown, N.Y., Dec. 3, 1934; d. Gilbert Charles and Mildred Elizabeth (O'Neal) Foster; m. Murray Ralph Roberson Jr., May 10, 1963 (dec. 1968). AA, Canal Zone Jr. Coll., 1954; BA in Journalism, La. State U., 1957, MA in Journalism, 1973; MA in Media, So. U., Baton Rouge, 1981; PhD in Mass Communication, U. So. Miss., 1985. Exec. sec. Lionel H. Abshire and Assocs., AIA, Architects, Baton Rouge, 1958-60, Murrell and Callari, AIA, Architects, Baton Rouge, 1960-63; bus. mgr. So. Rev. La. State U., Baton Rouge, 1963-69; free-lance researcher, ind. contractor Baton Rouge, 1969-74; rep. dept. info. State of La., Baton Rouge, 1974-75; asst. prof. mass. comm. So. U., 1976-86, assoc. prof. mass comm., 1986-93, prof. mass comm., 1993—; reviewer Random House Pubs., N.Y.C., 1981; profl. devel. intern Baton Rouge Morning Advocate, 1991, Baker Observer, 1991-92; cons. advt. Baton Rouge Little Theater, 1971—; reporter-photographer Canal Record, Seminole, Fla., 1967—; biographer of Edward Livermore Burlingame, John H. Johnson, Daniel Kimball Whitaker, (book) American mag. journalists series, Dictionary Literary Biography, Detroit, 1986-87; tutor Operation Upgrade, 1978-82. Co-editor: La. State U. cookbook Tiger Bait, 1976; biographer Frank E. Gannett in Biographical Dictionary of American Journalism, 1987; freelance writer/editl. cons.; editl. bd. Am. Journalism, 1986-87; reviewer Longman Publs. 1991-92; contbr. articles to profl. jours. Mem. poll commn. East Baton Rouge Parish Govt., 1971—; pres. Our Lady Lake Regional Med. Ctr., 1971-72; bd. dirs. Dist. Atty.'s Rape Crisis Commn., 1976-79, Plan Govt. Study Commn., 1973-76, Selective Svc. System Bd. 8, Baton Rouge, 1986—; docent Greater Baton Rouge Zoo, 1974-77; vol. ARC, 1989—; mem. East Baton Rouge Parish Commn. on Govtl. Ethics, 1992-93; mayoral appointee Baker Mobile Home Rev. Bd., 1990—; v.p. Baker Hist. and Cultural Found., 1990-93; mem. Baker Interclub Coun., 1990-91; organizer human-animal therapy svc. Baker Manor Nursing Home, 1994; mem. 1st class Citizens Basic Police Tng. Acad., Baton Rouge Police Dept., 1994. Mem. AAUP (sec.-treas. La. state conf. 1988-89, sec. La. state conf. 1992-93, chmn. pub. rels. La. state conf. 1994—), Assn. Edn. Journalism and Mass Communication, Am. Newspapers Pubs. Assn. (nat. coop. com. on edn. in journalism 1989-92), Women in Communications (pres. Baton Rouge chpt. 1982, nat. judge Clarion awards 1987), Pub. Rels. Assn. La., La. State U. Journalism Alumni Assn. (pres. 1977), Soc. Profl. Journalists (Sigma Delta Chi, pres. 1982 SE La. chpt.), Am. Journalism Historians Assn., La. State U. Alumni Assn. (East Baton Rouge Parish chpt. pres. 1978-80), Popular Culture Assn., Investigative Reporters and Editors Assn., Baker C. of C., Toastmasters Internat. (adminstrv. v.p. Baton Rouge 1977), Pilot Club Internat. Home: 2801 Allen Ct Baker LA 70714-2253

ROBERSON, ROBERT STEPHEN, investment company executive; b. Mt. Kisco, N.Y., Nov. 30, 1942; s. Robert H. and Mercedes C. (Stack) R.; m. Barbara Colbert Drane, Oct. 21, 1967; children: Elizabeth de V., Merritt B., Barbara D. BS, NYU, 1964; MBA, Coll. William and Mary, 1973. Various positions in fin. and bldg. industries, 1964-67; mem. N.Y. Produce Exchange, 1965-66; with Weaver Bros., Inc., Newport News, 1967—, now pres., dir.; bd. dirs. First Peninsula Bank & Trust Co., Hampton, Va., 1977-78. Former mem. Newport News Rep. City Com.; past dir. Peninsula Unit Am. Cancer Soc., Newport News; past dir. Heritage Coun. Girl Scouts U.S.A., Hampton; former trustee Newport News Pub. Libr., Va. Living Mus., Am. Assn. Mus.,

Newport News; former trustee Hampton Roads Acad., Newport News; former mem. bd. visitors to George Washington's Mt. Vernon Nat. Shrine; hon. dep. chief N.Y.C. Fire Dept. Mem. S.R., Newcomen Soc. of the U.S., Hon. Fire Officers Assn., Gen. Soc. Colonial Wars, St. Nicholas Soc. of the City N.Y., Colonial Order Acorn, Sovereign Mil. Order of the Temple of Jerusalem, Mil. Order Fgn. Wars of U.S., Squadron A Assn., Pilgrims of the U.S., Blue Key, Union Club, Church Club (N.Y.C.), Hay Harbor Club (Fishers Island, N.Y.), Farmington Country Club (Charlottesville, Va.), James River Country Club, Hampton Roads German Club, The Hundred Club (Newport News, Va.), N.Y. Yacht Club, Fishers Island Yacht Club, Rotary Internat. (Paul Harris fellow), Delta Sigma Pi. Episcopalian. Home: PO Box 66 Williamsburg VA 23187-0066

ROBERT, BRUCE G., manufacturing executive, light. Chmn. bd., CEO Siegel Robert, Inc., Saint Louis. Office: Siegel Robert Inc 8645 S Broadway Saint Louis MO 63111*

ROBERT, LESLIE LADISLAS, research center administrator, consultant; b. Budapest, Hungary, Oct. 24, 1924; s. Louis and Elizabeth (Bardos) R.; m. Barbara Klinger, Nov. 19, 1949 (dec.); children: Marianne, Catherine, Elisabeth; m. Jacqueline Labat, Dec. 20, 1976. Student, U. Szeged, Budapest, Hungary, 1944-48; MD, U. Paris, 1953; PhD, U. Lille, France, 1977; D (hon.), Med. U. Budapest, 1991. Mem. med. faculty dept. biochemistry U. Paris, 1950-59; postdoctoral rsch. fellow dept. biochemistry Sch. Medicine U. Ill., 1959-60; postdoctoral rsch. assoc., spl. fellow Columbia U., N.Y.C., 1960-61, 67; dir. biochemistry lab. Inst. for Immunobiology INSERM/CNRS, Broussais Hosp., Paris, 1962-66; founder 1st rsch. ctr. on connective tissue biochemistry CNRS, U. Paris XII, Créteil, France, 1966-94; adminstr. Cell Biology Lab. U. Paris VII, 1995—; rsch. dir. French Nat. Rsch. Ctr., Paris, 1974-94, hon. rsch. dir., 1995—; founder rsch. ctr. for clin. and biol. rsch. on aging Charles Foix-Jean Rostand Hosp., Ivry, France, 1993—; cons. several pharm. firms; mem. Sci. Coun. Arteriosclerosis Rsch. Inst., U. Munster, Fed. Republic of Germany, 1970—. Author 5 books on biology of aging, monograph series: Frontier of Matr's Biology, 11 vols.; mem. editorial bd. several sci. jours.; contbr. over 750 articles on connective tissues, biochemistry and pathology to sci. jours. Recipient Spl. Sci. prize Sci. Writer, 1966, Reiss prize in Opthalmology, 1970, Verzar medal for gerontol. rsch. U. Vienna, Austria, 1994. Mem. French Atherosclerosis Soc. (pres. 1993—), Hungarian Acad. Scis. (fgn. mem.). Home: 7 Rue Lully, 94440 Santeny France Office: Univ Paris Dept Cell Biology, 2 Pl Jussieu-Tour 23/33, 75005 Paris France

ROBERT, PATRICK, playwright; b. Kilgore, Tex., Sept. 27, 1937; s. Robert and Beulah (Goodson) O'Connor. Author numerous plays produced off-off Broadway, off-Broadway, Broadway, also abroad including Robert Patrick's Cheep Theatricks, (23 plays), 1972, Simultaneous Transmissions, 1973, Play-By-Play, 1975, The Golden Circle, 1975, Kennedy's Children, 1975, Let Me Tell It To You, Dr. Paroo, 1976, One Man, One Woman (6 plays), 1978, T-Shirts, 1979, Mercy Drop and Other Plays (5 plays), 1980, My Cup Ranneth, 1984, Big Sweet, 1985, Untold Decades, (7 plays), 1988, Drowned Out, 1990, Connie, 1991, Michelangelo's Models, 1994; author: (novels) Temple Slave, 1986, Echo, 1990; contbr. poems, articles, stories. Recipient Show Bus. Best Playwright award 1968-69, Glasgow Citizens' Theatre Best World Playwright award, 1974, Omni-Act One award, 1975, Robbie award, 1976, Founders award Internat. Thespians Soc., 1980, Blue is for Boys weekends in Manhattan, 1983, 86; Rockefeller grantee, 1974, N.Y. State CAPS grantee, 1975. Home: 1837 N Alexandria Ave Apt 211 Los Angeles CA 90027-4068 *No object or action has any meaning except that given to it by a writer. Writers create the consciousness of humanity, which in turn creates our world. Writers write the world.*

ROBERT, STEPHEN, investment firm executive; b. Haverhill, Mass., June 13, 1940; s. Samuel R.; m. Catherine Price; children: Tracey Alexandra, Elisabeth Amory. A.B. with honors, Brown U., 1962; postgrad., London Sch. Econs., 1962-63, Columbia Bus. Sch., 1963-64. Security analyst Faulkner Dawkins and Sullivan, 1965-67; v.p. Oppenheimer Funds, N.Y.C., 1968-76, chief portfolio mgr., 1969-76; gen. ptnr. Oppenheimer & Co., Inc., N.Y.C., 1970-82, dir. research, 1976-78, pres., 1979-83, chmn., chief exec. officer, 1983—; dir. NacRe Corp. Bd. dirs., chmn. fin. com. Wiltwyck Sch., 1968-78; bd. dirs. Joffrey Ballet, 1981—; trustee The Dalton Sch., 1984—, Brown U., 1984—. Club: Harmonie (N.Y.C.). Office: Oppenheimer & Co Inc Oppenheimer Tower World Fin Ctr New York NY 10281

ROBERTI, MARIO ANDREW, lawyer, former energy company executive; b. Denver, May 12, 1935; s. Emil and Elvira (Ligrano) R.; m. Patricia Ann Ludwig, Apr. 27, 1963; children: Andrea Louise, Paul Richard, Robert Raymond. B.S., Loyola U. (now Loyola Marymount U.), Los Angeles, 1957, J.D., 1960. Bar: Calif. 1961, Hawaii 1977, D.C. 1985. Dep. atty. gen. State of Calif., 1961-69; atty. Pacific Lighting Corp., Los Angeles, 1969-71; asst. gen. counsel, asst. sec. McCulloch Oil Corp., Los Angeles, 1971-76; v.p., gen. counsel Pacific Resources, Inc., Honolulu, 1976-88, sr. v.p., gen. counsel, 1988-92; with Reinwald, O'Connor, Marrack, Hoskins & Playdon, Honolulu, 1993—; bd. dirs. St. Francis Med. Ctr., Honolulu. Trustee Hawaii Sch. Girls, 1979-87; regent Loyola Marymount U., Chaminade U. Of Honolulu, 1982-93, chmn. bd. regents, 1987-89; adv. bd. Internat. Oil and Gas Ednl. Ctr., Southwestern Legal Found. Mem. ABA, D.C. Bar Assn., Hawaii Bar Assn. (chmn. corp. counsel sect. 1979), Calif. Bar Assn. Outrigger Canoe Club, Oahu County Club, Pacific Coast Gas Assn. (life, chmn. legal adv. com. 1983-84), Phi Alpha Delta, Phi Kappa Theta. Office: 24th Fl 733 Bishop St Fl 24 Honolulu HI 96813-4020

ROBERTI, WILLIAM VINCENT, retail executive; b. Bridgeport, Conn., Oct. 18, 1946; s. Armand E. and La Junta Juanita (Swindle) R.; m. Christina Gura, May 30, 1970; children—Jennifer A., Jessica M. BA, Sacred Heart U. Bridgeport, 1969; MBA, So. Meth. U., 1987. Buyer, D.M. Read's div. Allied Corp., Bridgeport, 1968-73; div. mdse. mgr. Robinson's Fla. div. Associated Dry Goods Co., St. Petersburg, 1973-77; exec. v.p. Maas Bros. div. Allied Corp., Tampa, Fla., 1977-83; v.p., gen. mdse. mgr. Mervyn's, Hayward, Calif., 1983-84; chmn., chief exec. officer Diversified Group Zale Corp., Dallas, 1984-87. Trustee Sacred Heart U., 1989—; bd. dirs. Jr. Achievement Tampa, 1982-83; mem. Pinellas County Com. 100, St. Petersburg, 1982-83; bd. govs. N.Y. chpt. Assn. U.S. Army; mem. Dept. Def. Clothing and Textile Bd.; mem. Nat. Multiple Sclerosis Soc.; mem. Vet. Corp Arty., N.Y.C. Lt. col. USAR, 1966—. Roman Catholic. Mem. West Point Soc. (N.Y. chpt.), Assn. U.S. Army. N.Y. Athletic Club (N.Y.C.), St. Petersburg Yacht Club (Fla.), Yale Club (N.Y.C.), Conn. Club (Easton). Office: Brooks Brothers 346 Madison Ave Fl 8 New York NY 10017-3703

ROBERTS, ALBERT GEORGE, academic administrator; b. Jersey City, Dec. 2, 1947; s. Albert F. and Helen M. (Matteucci) R.; m. Arlene Joan Kausch, Mar. 7, 1970; 1 dau., Karen. B.A., Jersey City State Coll., 1969; M.S., Fordham U., 1973; Ed.M., Columbia U., 1976, Ed.D., 1979. Cert. prin., tchr. Ohio, N.J.; cert. supr., N.J. Tchr. Teaneck (N.J.) schs., 1970-79; prin. Emerson sch., Teaneck, 1979-81, Lomond Sch., Shaker Heights, Ohio, 1981-87; asst. supt. of schs., Sparta, N.J., 1987-90; supt. Orange City Sch. Dist., Pepper Pike, Ohio, 1990—; cons. N.J. Dept. Edn., 1978; dir. children's programming cable TV, 1978-79. Dir. recreation Summer Outreach, 1977-78. Mem. Am. Assn. Sch. Adminstrs., Assn. Supervision and Curriculum Devel., Nat. Sci. Tchrs. Assn., Ohio Assn. Elem. Sch. Adminstrs., Nat. Assn. Elem. Sch. Prins., Phi Delta Kappa. Author numerous curriculum guides in math., reading, sci. Office: Orange City Sch Dist 32000 Chagrin Blvd Pepper Pike OH 44124

ROBERTS, ALBERT ROY, social work educator; b. Bronx, N.Y., May 22, 1944; s. Harry and Evelyn (Schwartz) R.; m. Beverly Jean Schenkman, July 5, 1971; 1 child, Herbert. BA in Sociology, L.I. U., 1966, MA in Sociology, 1967; D Social Welfare, U. Md. Balt., 1978. Lectr. Rider Coll., Lawrenceville, N.J., 1970-71; asst. prof., chmn. Coppin State Coll. Balt., 1971-74; project dir. Am. Correctional Assn., College Park, Md., 1975-76; asst. prof. N.Y. Inst. Tech., Old Westbury, N.Y., 1976-78, Bklyn. Coll., CUNY, 1978-79; assoc. prof. U. New Haven, West Haven, Conn., 1979-81, Seton Hall U., South Orange, N.J., 1981-83; assoc. prof., chmn. Ind. U. Sch. Social Work, Indpls., 1984-89; prof. social work, program dir. Rutgers U., New Brunswick, N.J., 1989—; manuscript reviewer Dorsey Press, Chgo., 1984-88, Hosp. and Community Psychiatry, Washington, 1986—; Longman Pubs., White Plains, N.Y., 1987-92; founding social work series editor

Springer Pub. Co., N.Y.C., 1980—. Author: Sourcebook on Prison Education, 1971, Sheltering Battered Women, 1981, Battered Women and Their Families, 1984, Runaways and Non Runaways in An American Suburb, 1987, Helping Crime Victims, 1990; editor: Juvenile Justice: Policies, Programs and Services, 1989 (main selection Behavioral Sci. Book Club 1990), Crisis Intervention Handbook, 1990, Critical Issues in Crime and Justice, 1994, Crisis Intervention and Time-Limited Cognitive Therapy, 1995, Helping Battered Women, 1996; founding editor-in-chief Crisis Intervention and Time-Limited Treatment Jour., 1992—. Bd. dirs. Ind. chpt. Nat. Com. for Prevention Child Abuse, Indpls., 1986-89; mem. state adv. bd. for probation N.J. Supreme Ct., Trenton, 1991—; mem. N.J. Gov.'s Juvenile Justice and Delinquency Prevention Commn., 1991-95. Recipient award for outstanding article Correctional Edn. Assn., 1975. Fellow Am. Orthopsychiat. Assn.; mem. NASW, Acad. Criminal Justice Scis. (life), Am. Soc. Criminology, Nat. Coun. Juvenile and Family Ct. Judges (assoc.), Alpha Delta Mu. Avocations: hiking, bicycling, reading. Office: Rutgers U Sch Social Work 536 George St New Brunswick NJ 08901-1167 *The primary objective of a scholar and educator is to build the knowledge base in a selected area of expertise and to transmit it to one's students. My life has been devoted to setting important goals, overcoming adversity and persevering in order to achieve major accomplishments in both my personal and academic life.*

ROBERTS, ALFRED WHEELER, III, law firm executive; b. N.Y.C., Aug. 3, 1938; s. Alfred Wheeler and Florence Henley (Kirk) R.; m. Pamela Anne Stover, June 29, 1967; children—Ashley Anne, Alfred Kirk, Michael Tyler. B.A., Dartmouth Coll., 1960. M.B.A., 1961. C.P.A., N.Y. With Arthur Young & Co., N.Y.C., 1961-89, ptnr., 1971-89, vice chmn., 1982-88; ptnr. RFE Investment Ptnrs., New Canaan, Conn., 1989-90; exec. dir. Winthrop, Stimson, Putnam & Roberts, N.Y.C., 1991—. Bd. dirs., treas. Legal Aid Soc. N.Y., 1981-88; bd. dirs. YMCA of Greater N.Y., 1983-89, vice chmn., 1987-89. Mem. Am. Inst. C.P.A.s. Congregationalist. Club: University (N.Y.C.).

ROBERTS, ALICE, reservations service executive. With Regent Ins. Adjustors, Wichita, Kans., 1962-63, Western Control, Wichita, 1963-65, McCormick, Mathers Pub., Wichita, 1965-66, Southwest Nat. Bank, Wichita, 1966-69, Kennedy & Coe, Wichita, 1969-73, Coors of Kans., Wichita, 1973-79, Terry Scanlon, Wichita, 1979-81, Profl. Agrl. Supply, Wichita, 1981-83; with Corp. Lodging Conss., Wichita, 1983—, chmn. bd. dirs. Office: Corp Lodging Conss 829 N Market St Wichita KS 67214*

ROBERTS, ARCHIBALD E., nonprofit corporation executive. Commd. U.S. Army, advanced through grades to col.; paratrooper 11th Airborne Divsn., 187th Airborne Regimental Combat Team, 101st Airborne Divs.; info. officer 3d Inf. Divsn., ret. 1965; founder Com. to REstore the Constn., Ft. Collins, Colo., 1965—; has addressed joint session of Ala., La. state legis.; testified before legis. coms. in 25 states, various pub. meetings, seminars; litigan in precedent-setting lawsuit against Sec. of Army Cyrus R. Vance involving freedom of speech of mil. pers.; writer, dir. 24th Inf. Divsn. Pro Blue troop info. program in Germany, 1959. Author: Rakksan, 1955, Screaming Eagles, 1956, The Marne Division, 1957; Victory Denied, 1966, The Anatomy of Revolution, 1968, Peace by the Wonderful People Who Brought You Korea and Viet Nam, 1972, The Republic: Decline and Future Promise, 1975, The Crisis of Federal Regionalism: A Solution, 1976, Emerging Struggle for State Sovereignty, 1979, Defend Your Money and Property, 1986, The Most secret Science; contbr. numerous articles to profl. jours.; pub. newsletter The Bulletin. Mem. SAR, Res. Officers Assn., 511th Parachute Inf. Assn., 187th Airborne Regimental Combat Team Assn., 11th Airborne Divsn. Assn. Office: Community To REstore Constn PO Box 986 Fort Collins CO 80522-0986

ROBERTS, ARCHIBALD EDWARD, retired army officer, author; b. Cheboygan, Mich., Mar. 21, 1915; s. Archibald Lancaster and Madeline Ruth (Smith) R.; grad. Command and Gen. Staff Coll., 1952; student U.S. Armed Forces Inst., 1953, U. Md., 1958; m. Florence Snure, Sept. 25, 1940 (div. Feb. 1950); children—Michael James, John Douglas; m. 2d, Doris Elfriede White, June 23, 1951; children—Guy Archer, Charles Lancaster, Christopher Corwin. Enlisted U.S. Army, 1939, advanced through grades to lt. col., 1960; served in Far East Command, 1942, 1953-55, ETO, 1943-45, 57-60; tech. info. officer Office Surgeon Gen., Dept. Army, Washington, 1950, Ft. Campbell, Ky., 1952-53, info. officer, Camp Chicamauga, Japan, Ft. Bragg, N.C., Ft. Campbell, Ky., 1953-56, Ft. Campbell, 1956-57, Ft. Benning, Ga., Wurzburg, Germany, 1957-58, spl. projects officer Augsburg, Germany, 1959-60, U.S. Army Info. Office, N.Y.C., 1960-61; writer program precipitating Senate Armed Services Hearings, 1962; ret., 1965; mgr., salesman Nu-Enamel Stores, Ashville, N.C., 1937-38; co-owner, dir. Roberts & Roberts Advt. Agy., Denver, 1946-49; pres. Found. for Edn., Scholarship, Patriotism and Americanism, Inc.; founder, nat. bd. dirs. Com. to Restore Constn., Inc., 1965—. Recipient award of merit Am. Acad. Pub. Affairs, 1967; Good Citizenship medal SAR, 1968; Liberty award Congress of Freedom, 1969; Man of Yr. awards Women for Constl. Govt., 1970, Wis. Legislative and Research Com., 1971; medal of merit Am. Legion, 1972; Speaker of Year award We, The People, 1973; Col. Arch Roberts Week named for him City of Danville, Ill., 1974; recipient Spl. Tribute State of Mich., 1979. Mem. Res. Officers Assn., Airborne Assn., SAR, Sons Am. Colonists. Author: Rakkasan, 1955; Screaming Eagles, 1956; The Marne Division, 1957; Victory Denied, 1966; The Anatomy of a Revolution, 1968; Peace: By the Wonderful People Who Brought You Korea and Viet Nam, 1972; The Republic: Decline and Future Promise, 1975; The Crisis of Federal Regionalism: A Solution, 1976; Emerging Struggle for State Sovereignty, 1979; How to Organize for Survival, 1982; The Most Secret Science, 1984; also numerous pamphlets and articles. Home: 2218 W Prospect PO Box 986 Fort Collins CO 80522-0986

ROBERTS, AUSTIN LEONARD, III, banker; b. Washington, Feb. 5, 1947; s. Austin Leonard and Barbara Fenella (Wahl) R.; m. Barbara Ann Powell, Nov. 2, 1974; 1 child, Austin Leonard. B.A., Coll. of William and Mary, 1969, M.B.A., 1971. Personnel interviewer United Va. Bank/State Planners, Richmond, 1969-70; v.p., comml. loan officer First and Mchts. Nat. Bank, Newport News, 1971-76; pres. First Peninsula Bank and Trust, Hampton, 1976-83; regional pres. First Am. Bank of Va., Hampton Roads, 1983—; dir. VAZ, Inc., Newport News, Hero Lands Co., New Orleans. Campaign chmn. United Way of Va. Peninsula, 1984, bd. dirs., 1978—; bd. dirs. Peninsula Planned Parenthood, 1974-82; Va. Peninsula Indsl. Council, 1976-79; treas. Va. Peninsula council Boy Scouts Am., 1975-76; pres. William and Mary Athletic Ednl. Found., 1980-83; bd. dirs. Future of Hampton Roads, 1983—, Hampton Roads Girls Club, 1981—, Va. State Co., 1984—, also others. Named Outstanding Young Man in Va., Jaycees, 1980, others. Mem. William and Mary Soc. Alumni (pres. 1983-). Episcopalian. Clubs: James River Country (Newport News); Town Point (Norfolk, Va.). Home: RR 2 Box 5120 White Stone VA 22578-9719 Office: Bank Lancaster 100 S Main St Kilmarnock VA 22482

ROBERTS, B. K., lawyer, former judge; b. Sopchoppy, Fla., Feb. 5, 1907; s. Thomas and Florida (Morrison) R.; m. Mary Newman, Aug. 20, 1937; children: Mary Jane, Thomas Frederick. J.D., U. Fla., 1928; LL.D., U. Miami, 1954; D.H.L., Fla. State U. 1980. Bar: Fla. 1928. Practiced in Tallahassee, 1928-49; justice Supreme Ct. of Fla., 1949-77, chief justice, 1953-54, 61-63, 71-72, ret., 1977; of counsel Ervin, Varn, Jacobs, Odom & Ervin, Tallahassee, Fla., 1977—; v.p. dir. Tallahassee Bank & Trust Co. (now Barnett Bank), 1948-49; Mem. awards jury Freedoms Found. at Valley Forge, 1962; mem. Fla. Constl. Revision Commn., 1966, 77; chmn. subcom. on human rights; chmn. Jud. Council Fla., 1962-77; mem. exec. com. Nat. Conf. Chief Justices, 1966, dep. chmn., 1972-73. Chmn. trustees Fla. State U. Found.; bd. counselors Fla. Presbyn. Coll. Served as lt. comdr. USCG; Served as lt. comdr. 1942-45 originating commr. 1943-45, Port Jacksonville, Fla. Recipient Disting. Citizen award Stetson U. Coll. Law (2); selected as Great Floridian, 1989, Mus. of Fla. History. Fellow Am. Bar Found.; mem. Internat. Bar Assn. (patron), Inter-Am., ABA (UN com., world order under law com.; ofcl. ct. rep. London meeting 1957), Fla. Bar Assn. (past v.p.), Tallahassee Bar Assn. (past pres.), Am. Judicature Soc., Am. Law Inst., Newcomen Soc. Eng., Am. Legion (mem. nat. distinguished guests com.), Alpha Kappa Psi, Fla. Blue Key, Fla State U. Gold Key, Soc. of Wig and Robe, Phi Alpha Delta, Delta Chi. Democrat. Presbyterian. Clubs: Governor's, Killearn Golf and Country, Hendersonville (N.C.) Country,

Capital City Country (Tallahassee). Lodges: Masons; Shriners; Elks; Odd Fellows; Kiwanis. Home: Westminster Village 4172 Covenant Ln Tallahassee FL 32308 Office: Ervin Varn Jacobs Odom & Ervin PO Box 1170 Tallahassee FL 32302-1170 also: 305 S Gadsden St Tallahassee FL 32302

ROBERTS, BERT C., JR., telecommunications company executive; b. 1942; married. BS, Johns Hopkins U., 1965. Project dir., mgr. Westinghouse Electric Corp., 1960-69; dir. Leasco Response Inc., 1969-72; with MCI Communications Corp., Washington, 1972—, v.p., 1974-76, sr. v.p., 1976-83, pres., 1983-85; chief operating officer MCI Telecommunications Corp., Washington, 1985-91, chief exec. officer, 1991—, chmn., 1992—. Office: MCI Comm Corp 1801 Pennsylvania Ave NW Washington DC 20006-3605*

ROBERTS, BILL GLEN, retired fire chief, investor, consultant; b. Deport, Tex., June 2, 1938; s. Samuel Westbrook and Ann Lee (Rhodes) R.; m. Ramona Ryall, June 1, 1963 (dec. Nov. 1988); 1 child, Renee Ann. Student, So. Meth. U., 1968, North Tex. State U., 1974; grad. paramedic course, U. Tex. Southwestern Med. Sch., 1974; grad. Exec. Program for Fire Service, Tex. A&M U., 1978; AAS, El Centro Jr. Coll., Dallas, 1980; grad. exec. fire officer program, Nat. Fire Acad., 1989. With Dallas Fire Dept., 1958-82, lt., 1964-67, capt., 1967-71, div. fire chief, 1971-79, asst. fire chief, 1979-83; fire chief Austin (Tex.) Fire Dept., 1983-94; tech. bd. dirs. Found. Fire Safety, Washington, 1982-85; adj. faculty Nat. Fire Acad., 1981-86; aft. State Life of Indpls., Dallas, 1962; owner Personnel Testing Lab., Dallas, 1963; real estate salesman Dale Copus Realtor, Dallas, 1963-66; salesman intercommunications equipment Chandler Sound, Dallas, 1966-67; field engr. IBM Corp., Dallas, 1968; cons. U. Tenn., 1974, Ga. Inst. Tech., 1974, Tex. Dept. Health Resources, 1973-78, Rand Corp., Washington, Mission Rsch., Santa Barbara, Calif., Macro. Author: EMS Dallas, 1978; (with others) Anesthesia for Surgery Trauma, 1976, EMS Measures to Improve Care, 1980; contbr. articles to periodicals. Com. chmn. Dallas Jaycees, 1962-65; mem. task force Am. Heart Assn., Austin, 1973-83; bd. dirs. Brackenridge Hosp., 1989, Rehab. Hosp. Austin, 1992-94, Austin Police Pensions Bd., 1989, Capitol Area coun. Boy Scouts Am., 1989-92. Recipient John Stemmons Service award Dallas Fire Dept., 1979; Internat. Assn. Fire Chiefs scholar, 1967. Mem. Internat. Assn. Fire Chiefs, Nat. Fire Protection Assn., Nat. Critical Care Inst., Am. Heart Assn., Am. Trauma Soc. (founder), Am. Assn. Trauma Specialists, Nat. Assn. Emergency Med. Technicians, Tex. Assn. Emergency Med. Technicians, ACS, North Tex. Coun. of Govts. (regional emergency svc. adv. coun. 1973-79), Internat. Rescue and First Aid Assn., Found. Fire Safety (tech. bd. dirs. 1982-85), Tex. Assn. Realtors, Austin World Affairs Coun., People to People Internat., Rotary Internat. Methodist. Home: 3 Highlander Rd Asheville NC 28804

ROBERTS, BRIAN LEON, communications executive; b. Phila., June 28, 1959; s. Ralph J. and Suzanne F. Roberts; m. Aileen Kennedy, Dec. 28, 1985; children: Sarah, Tucker, Amanda. Student, U. Pa., 1981. V.p. ops. Comcast Cable Communications, Inc., Phila., 1985-86; exec. v.p. Comcast Corp., 1986—, also bd. dirs., now pres.; bd. dirs. Turner Broadcasting System, QVC Network, Viewer's Choice, Calbe Labs. Vice chmn. The Walter Katz Found. Mem. Nat. Cable TV Assn. (bd. dirs., exec. com.). Office: Comcast Corp 1500 Market St Philadelphia PA 19102*

ROBERTS, BURTON BENNETT, administrative judge; b. N.Y.C., July 25, 1922; s. Alfred S. and Cecelia (Schanfein) R.; m. Gerhild Ukryn. B.A., NYU, 1943, LL.M., 1953; LL.B., Cornell U. 1949. Bar: N.Y. 1949. Asst. dist. atty. N.Y. County, 1949-66; chief asst. dist. atty. Bronx County, Bronx, N.Y., 1966-68; acting dist. atty. Bronx County, 1968-69, dist. atty., 1969-72; justice Supreme Ct. State N.Y., 1973—, adminstrv. judge criminal br. Bronx County 12th Jud. Dist., 1984—, adminstrv. judge civil br. Bronx County 12th Dist., 1988—. Pres. Bronx div. Hebrew Home for Aged, 1967-72. With U.S. Army, 1943-45. Decorated Purple Heart, Bronze Star with oak leaf cluster. Mem. Assn. Bar City N.Y., Am. Bar Assn., N.Y. Bar Assn., Bronx County Bar Assn., N.Y. State Dist. Attys. Assn. (pres. 1971-72). Jewish (exec. bd. temple). Home: 215 E 68th St Apt 19A New York NY 10021-5727 Office: Supreme Ct Bronx County 851 Grand Concourse Bronx NY 10451-2937

ROBERTS, C. FRANK, broadcast executive. Pres. The New York Times Broadcasting Group, Memphis, Tenn. Office: The New York Times Broadcasting 803 Channel 3 Dr Memphis TN 38103

ROBERTS, CARL GEOFFREY, lawyer; b. Boston, June 17, 1948; s. Simon Matthew and Ruth (Gorfinkle) R.; m. Sharon Ash, Mar. 24, 1979. BA, Harvard U., 1970; JD, U. Pa., 1974. Bar: Pa. 1974, U.S. Dist. Ct. (ea. dist.) Pa. 1974, U.S. Ct. Appeals (3d cir.) 1978, U.S. Supreme Ct. 1980, U.S. Ct. Claims 1980, U.S. Dist. Ct. (mid. dist.) Pa. 1986. Law clk. U.S. Dist. Ct. (ea. dist.) Pa., Phila., 1974-76; assoc. Dilworth, Paxson, Kalish & Kauffman, Phila., 1978-82, ptnr., 1982-92; ptnr. Ballard, Spahr, Andrews & Ingersoll, Phila., 1992—. Bd. dirs. Phila. Chamber Ensemble, sec., 1977-92, pres., 1992—. Mem. ABA (law practice mgmt. sect., computer div., vice chmn. techs. and facilities group). Office: Ballard Spahr Andrews & Ingersoll 1735 Market St 51st Fl Philadelphia PA 19103

ROBERTS, CAROL ANTONIA, county commissioner, real estate associate; b. Miami, Fla., June 22, 1936; d. Milton R. and Betty Shirley (Pallot) Klein; m. Aug. 9, 1953; children: David, Jonathan, Mark, Stephen, Scott, Pamela. Student, Tuft U., 1953-54, Palm Beach (Fla.) Jr. Coll., 1960-62, Palm Beach Atlantic Coll., 1971-72. Host radio program Sta. WPBR, Palm Beach, Fla., 1976-83; co-founder Denman Roberts & Ross, West Palm Beach, Fla., 1978-80; pres. Sunshine Acad. Press, Inc., West Palm Beach, 1978-82; pres. broker VIP Mgmt. and Realty, Inc., West Palm Beach, 1980—. Commr. City of West Palm Beach, Fla., 1975, 77, 82, 84, vice mayor, 1976-77, 84-85, mayor, 1985-86; chair Palm Beach County Bd. Commrs., 1987, 88; bd. dirs., chair women's div. Palm Beach County Comprehensive Community Mental Health Ctr. Bd., 1977-80, Jewish Fedn. Palm Beach County, 1978-80, Palm Beach Inst. Med. Rsch., Goodwill Industries, Cities in Schs., Anti-Defamation League, Adopt-A-Family; vice chair Tri-County Rail Authority, chmn. mktg. com.; vice chair Solid Waste Authority, 1977-78; chair art in Pub. Places, Artificial Reef com., Intracoastal Waterway com.; co-chair Water Resources Mgmt. Adv. Bd.; vice chair Fla. League of Cities Intergovtl. Rels. com.; mem. Palm Beach Sports Authority, So. Fla. Mental Health Consortium, Treasure Coast Regional Planning Coun.; mem Fla. Crime Prevention Commn., 1985; founder Jewish Cmty.Day Sch.of the Palm Beaches. John and Mabel Ringling Mus. Art grantee, Norton Art Gallery grantee, U. Ga. grantee, U. Fla. grantee, Tufts U. grantee, Fla. A&M U. grantee; named Woman of the Yr., Bus. and Profl. Women Palm Beaches, 1985, Leading Lady in Mcpl. Govt., Network Connection, 1985; recipient Appreciation award Tri-County Nat. Bus. League, 1985, Woman of the Yr. award Temple Beth El Sisterhood, 1986, Disting. medal Palm Beach Atlantic Coll., 1986, Disting mem. of Pres. Coun. U. Fla.; inducted into Fla.'s Hall of Fame, 1986. Mem. Fla. League of Cities (vice chair intergovtl. rels. com.), Fla. Assn. Counties (social svcs. policy com.), Fla. Assn. Counties Bd. Dirs., Nat. Assn. Counties (intergovtl. rels. com.), South Fla. Mental Health Consortium. Democrat. Jewish. Home: 6708 Pamela Ln West Palm Beach FL 33405-4175 Office: Office Bd County Commrs PO Box 1989 301 N Olive Ave West Palm Beach FL 33402-1989

ROBERTS, CAROLYN C., hospital administrator; b. Parkersburg, W.Va., Dec. 4, 1938; married. M, Northeastern U., 1981. Various positions, 1962-75; dir. clin. adminstrn. svcs. Sidney Farber Cancer Inst., Boston, 1975-82; pres., CEO Copley Health Sys., Morrisville, Vt., 1982—. Author books; contbr. articles to profl. jours. Recipient cmty. svc. awards. Fellow Am. Acad. Med. Administrs.; mem. Am. Hosp. Assn. (bd. dirs., chmn., del., trustee), Am. Soc. Healthcare Risk Mgmt. (coms.), Vt. Hosp. Assn. (coms., trustee). Home: RR # 2 Box 290 Morrisville VT 05661 Office: Copley Health Sys Box 760 RR # 3 Morrisville VT 05661

ROBERTS, CECIL KENNETH, lawyer; b. Tyler, Tex., Mar. 31, 1930; s. Cecil Kelly and Blanche Lulu (Cash) R.; m. Cary N. Thornton, Sept. 1, 1951; children: Kenneth Kelly, Cristina Cary. BBA, U. Tex., Austin, 1950, JD, 1951; LLM, U. Tex., 1953; AMP, Harvard U., 1971. Bar: Tex. 1952. Atty. Exxon Co., U.S.A., Houston, 1954-64, N.Y.C., 1964-65; chief atty. refining, environment and labor rels. law Houston, 1965-67, adminstrv. mgr. Baytown refinery, 1967-68, mgr. pub affairs dept., 1969-72; exec. asst. to pres. Exxon Corp., N.Y.C., 1972-73, dep. mgr. pub. affairs dept., 1973-74, assoc. gen. counsel, 1974-79; gen. counsel Exxon Co., U.S.A., Houston, 1979-92; v.p., gen. counsel Exxon Corp., Dallas, 1993-95; of counsel Fulbright & Jaworski, Houston, 1995—; bd. dirs. Nat. Ctr. for State Cts., 1986-89; mem. steering com. Com for Jud. Merit Election. Trustee Southwestern Legal Found., 1993—; U. Tex. Law Found., 1992—; bd. dirs. Landmark Legal Found., Kansas City, Mo., 1980—, vice chmn., 1987-93; mem. bd. visitors U. Tex. Law Sch., Austin, Stanford U. Law Sch., 1980-84, mem. law and econs. adv. com., 1983-87. Recipient Paul C. Reardon award Nat. Ctr. for State Cts., 1990; named Outstanding Alumni, U. Tex. Sch. Law, 1993. Fellow Am. Bar Found.; mem. ABA, Tex. Bar Assn., Houston Bar Assn., Am. Law Inst., Am. Petroleum Inst. (gen. com. on law), Assn. Gen. Counsel, Am. Arbitration Assn. (bd. dirs. 1993—), Petroleum Club (bd. dirs.), River Oaks Country Club, Las Colinas Country Club, Univ. Club (N.Y.C.), Monterey Peninsula Country Club. Office: Fulbright & Jaworski 1301 McKinney Ste 5100 Houston TX 77010-3095

ROBERTS, CHALMERS MCGEAGH, reporter; b. Pitts., Nov. 18, 1910; s. Franklin B. and Lillian B. (McGeagh) R.; m. Lois Hall, Sept. 11, 1941; children: David H., Patricia E. Roberts Monahan, Christopher C. A.B., Amherst Coll., 1933, L.H.D. 1963. Reporter Washington Post, 1933-34, Asso. Press., Pitts. bur., 1934-35, Toledo News-Bee, 1936-38, Japan Times, Tokyo, 1938-39; asst. mng. editor Washington Daily News, 1939-41; Sunday editor Washington Times-Herald, 1941; staff OWI, London, Washington, 1941-43, Life mag., 1946-47, Washington Star, 1947-49; staff writer Washington Post, 1949-71, reporter local and nat. news, 1949-53, chief diplomatic corr., 1953-71, contbg. columnist, 1971—; contbg. columnist San Diego Union, 1971-86. Author: Washington Past and Present, 1950, Can We Meet the Russians Half Way?, 1958, The Nuclear Years: The Arms Race and Arms Control 1945-70, 1970, First Rough Draft: A Journalist's Journal of Our Times, 1973, The Washington Post: The First 100 Years, 1977, rev. In the Shadow of Power: The Story of the Washington Post, 1989, How Did I Get Here So Fast? Rhetorical Questions and Available Answers from a Long and Happy Life, 1991; contbr. articles to popular mags. Capt. USAAF, 1943-46. Decorated Order of Merit (Germany); recipient Sigma Delta Chi award, 1953, nat. news award Washington Newspaper Guild, 1954, 60; citation Overseas Press Club, 1955, front page grand prize Washington Newspaper Guild, 1957, 60, Raymond Clapper Meml. award, 1957, Edward Weintal prize for diplomatic reporting, 1975, Frank Luther Mott Rsch. award Kappa Tau Alpha, 1978; named to Washington Journalism Hall of Fame, Sigma Delta Chi, 1982. Mem. Am. Newspaper Guild, State Dept. Corrs. Assn. (pres. 1958-59), Council on Fgn. Relations, Fgn. Policy Assn., Nat. Book Critics Circle. Home: 6699 MacArthur Blvd Bethesda MD 20816-2247

ROBERTS, CHARLES PATRICK, congressman; b. Topeka, Kans., Apr. 20, 1936; m. Franki Fann, 1970; children: David, Ashleigh, Anne-Wesley. B.A., Kans. State U., 1958. Pub. Litchfield Park, Ariz., 1962-67; adminstrv. asst. U.S. Senator Frank Carlson, 1967-68, U.S. Congressman Keith Sebelius, 1968-80; mem. 97th-104th Congresses from 1st Kans. Dist. 97th-103rd Congresses from 1st Kan. Dist., 1980—. Served with USMC, 1958-62. Office: 1126 Longworth HOB Washington DC 20515-1601

ROBERTS, CLYDE FRANCIS, business executive; b. Lawrence, Mass., Sept. 10, 1924; s. Clyde F. and Blanche (Fellows) R.; May 18, 1947; 1 dau., Michele. B.S.B.A., Boston U., 1947; postgrad., Am. U., Beirut, 1954. Commd. fgn. affairs officer Dept. State, 1948-57; v.p. NAM, Washington, 1957-75; pres. Indsl. Fasteners Inst., Cleve., 1975-82; founding prior. RBJ Technologies, 1982—; pres. Nat. Assets Mgmt. Enterprises, 1984—; mem. instl. rev. bd. Fairview Gen. Hosp., 1985—; mem. adv. bd. Tabac Assocs., 1986—, Phoenix Corp. 1989—. Served with U.S. Army, 1943-45, Africa, Sicily, Italy, Greece. Mem. Nat. Indsl. Coun., Coun. Small Enterprise. Roman Catholic. Office: 18827 Cliff Cir Cleveland OH 44126-1707

ROBERTS, CORINNE BOGGS (COKIE ROBERTS), correspondent, news analyst; b. New Orleans, Dec. 27, 1943; d. Thomas Hale and Corinne Morrison (Claiborne) Boggs; m. Steven V. Roberts, Sept. 10, 1966; children: Lee Harriss, Rebecca Boggs. BA with distinction in Polit. Sci., Wellesley Coll., 1964; hon. degrees. Amherst Coll., Columbia Coll., Loyola U. of the South. Assoc. prodr., host Altman Prodns., Washington, 1964-66; prodr. Altman Prodns., L.A., 1969-72; reporter, editor Cowles Communications, N.Y.C., 1967; prodr. Sta. WNEW-TV, N.Y.C., 1968, Sta. KNBC-TV, L.A., Greece, 1972-74; reporter CBS News, Athens, Greece, 1974-77; corr. Nat. Pub. Radio, Washington, 1977—; MacNeil/Lehrer Newshour, Washington, 1984-88; spl. Washington corr. ABC News, Washington, 1988—; interviewer, commentator This Week With David Brinkley, Washington, 1992—; lectr. in field. Co-host weekly pub. TV program on Congress, The Lawmakers, 1981-84; producer, host pub. affairs program Sta. WRC-TV, Washington; producer Sta. KNBC-TV Serendipity, L.A. (award for excellence in local programming, Emmy nomination for children's programming); contbr. articles to newspapers, mags. Bd. dirs. Dirksen Ctr., Pekin, Ill., 1988—; Everett Dirksen award, 1987; bd. dirs. Fgn. Students Svc. Ctr., Washington, 1990—, Manhattenville Coll., Purchase, N.Y., 1991—, Children's Inn at NIH, Bethesda, Md., 1992—. Recipient Broadcast award Nat. Orgn. Working Women, 1984, Everett McKinley Dirksen disting. reporting of Congress, 1987, Weintal award Georgetown U., 1988, Corp. Pub. Broadcasting award, 1988, Edward R. Murrow award Corp. Pub. Broadcasting, 1990, Broadcast award Nat. Women's Polit. Caucus, 1990, David Brinkley Comm. award, 1992, Mother of Yr. award Nat. Mothers' Day Com., 1992. Mem. Radio-TV Corrs. Assn. (pres. 1981-82, bd. dir. 1993—), U.S. Capitol Hist. Soc. Roman Catholic. Office: ABC News 1717 DeSales St NW Washington DC 20036 Office: Nat Pub Radio 2025 M St NW Washington DC 20036*

ROBERTS, DAVID, wholesale distribution executive; b. 1942. With Standard Liquors, Inc., Peoria, Ill., 1964-70, Heublein, Inc., Boston, 1971-87; with United Liquors Ltd., West Bridgewater, Mass., 1987—, pres., COO. Office: United Liquors Ltd 1 United Dr West Bridgewater MA 02379*

ROBERTS, DAVID GLENDENNING, state supreme court justice; b. Fort Fairfield, Maine, July 17, 1928; s. Melvin Philip and Ethel (Chamberlain) R.; m. Rose Marie Downie. Feb. 9, 1952; children: Michael, Mary, Dorothy, Catherine, Sarah, Joseph, Susan. A.B., Bowdoin Coll., 1950; LL.B., Boston U., 1956. Bar: Maine 1956, U.S. Dist. Ct. Maine 1959, U.S. Ct. Appeals (1st cir.) 1964. Ptnr. Pendleton and Roberts, Caribou, Maine, 1956-61; asst. U.S. atty. U.S. Dept. Justice, Bangor, Maine, 1961-66; pvt. practice Bangor, 1966-67; justice Maine Superior Ct., Bangor, 1967-80; assoc. justice Supreme Jud. Ct., Portland, 1980—; mem. Maine Jud. Council, Augusta, 1969-77, 80-86. Served to lt. U.S. Army, 1951-53. Democrat. Roman Catholic. Office: ME Supreme Jud Ct PO Box 269 142 Federal St Portland ME 04112

ROBERTS, DAVID HARRILL, English language educator; b. St. Petersburg, Fla., June 4, 1944; s. Thomas Harrill and Daphne Virginia (Spear) R.; m. Madonna Jean Richards, Sept. 16, 1967; children: Michael Anthony, Mark David. BA in English, Lander Coll., 1970; MA in Linguistics, U. S.C., 1973; PhD in Rhetoric, Ind. U. of Pa., Indiana, Pa., 1982. Corp. prodn. planner Abney Mills, Greenwood, S.C., 1965-70; secondary sch. tchr. Sumter, S.C., 1970-71; systems analyst, computer programmer ICI Am., Inc., Hopewell, Va., 1972-73; founder, dir. Baptist Lang. Centre, Bapt. Mission Zambia, Luanshya, 1973-76; dir. pub. and alumni rels., instr. English Bluefield Coll., Bluefield, Va., 1976-78; dir. McDowell Country Ctr., Bluefield State Coll., 1978-83; asst. prof. English Bluefield State Coll., 1978-83; founder, dir. SPICE Ctr., Bluefield State Coll., 1978-83; assoc. prof. English U. So. Miss., Hattiesburg, 1983-88; prof. English Samford U., Birmingham, Ala., 1988—; dir. univ. writing programs, 1989-94; bd. dirs. Office. Tech. Acad., Milw.; pres., owner Bus. and Edn. Computer Support, 1984-88; exec. bd. Mis. Writing/Thinking Inst., 1987-88; pres. Roberts & Richards, Inc. med. electronics, 1989—; writing adv. bd. Southeastern Ednl. Improvement Lab., Research Triangle Park, N.C., 1988-89. Mem. editorial bd. Focuses, 1986—, Writing Ctr. Jour., 1986-89; author: First Lessons in Bemba, 1974, First Lessons in Chichewa A Study Guide, 1975, A Guide to Computer Aided Writing Instruction, 1989, Writing: From Private to Public, 1993; co-author: The Ophthalmology Residency Tracker, 1992; editor: Tales from Tall Pines, Volume 3, 1988, Selected Papers fo the Southeastern Writing Center Association, 1984-85, 86, Tales from Tall Pines, vol. 1, 1986 Scribblings in the Pines, 1987, Impact '92: Anthology of Teachers' Writings, Bluefield Coll. Press, 1978, Rev. 1970; developer Borzoi Online Handbook

for Writers, 1990, McGraw-Hill Online Handbook, 1991, The Online Handbook for College Writers, 1992, Grammar Online!, 1993; contbr. articles to profl. jours. Recipient Rsch. award Nat. U. Continuing Edn. Assn., 1985, Exemplary Media Use award Bluefield State Coll., 1982; First Bapt. Ch. scholar, Bluefield, 1981, Charles B. Keesee scholar, 1973, Julian A. Hodgens scholar, 1973; J. F. Thompkins grantee, 1973; named Honary Alumnus, The Bapt. Theol. Sem. at Richmond, 1992. Mem. Nat. Writing Ctr. Assn. (exec. com. 1986—), Nat. Coun. Tchrs. English, Conf. on Coll. Composition and Comm., Ala. Coun. Tchrs. English, Southeastern Writing Ctr. Assn. (exec. com. 1984-88, v.p. 1984-85, pres. 1985-87), Soc. Tech. Comm., Phi Kappa Phi (life), Phi Delta Kappa. Avocations: hiking, music. Office: Samford U 800 Lakeshore Dr Birmingham AL 35229-2207

ROBERTS, DENNIS WILLIAM, association executive; b. Chgo., Jan. 7, 1943; s. William Owen and Florence Harriet (Denman) R. BA in Journalism, U. N.Mex., 1968; MA in Legal Studies, Antioch U., 1982; MA, St. John's Coll., 1984. Cert. assn. exec. Gen. assignment reporter Albuquerque Pub. Co., 1964, sports writer, 1960-64, advt. and display salesman, 1967-68; dir. info. N.Mex. bldg. br. Asso. Gen. Contractors Am., Albuquerque, 1968-79, asst. exec. dir., 1979-82, dir., 1982—. Active United Way, Albuquerque, 1969-78; chmn. Albuquerque Crime Prevention Council, 1982; bd. dir. ARC (Rio Grande chpt., 1992—). Recipient Pub. Relations Achievement award Assoc. Gen. Contractors Am., 1975, 78. Mem. N.Mex. Pub. Relations Conf. (chmn. 1975, 82-83), Pub. Relations Soc. Am. (accredited, pres. N.Mex. chpt. 1981, chmn. S.W. dist. 1984, chmn. sect. 1988), Am. Soc. Assn. Execs. (cert.), Contrn. Specifications Inst. (Outstanding Industry Mem. 1974, Outstanding Com. Chmn. 1978), Sigma Delta Chi (pres. N.Mex. chpt. 1969). Republican. Lutheran. Clubs: Toastmasters (dist. gov. 1977-78, Disting. Dist. award 1978, Toastmaster of Year 1979-80), Masons, Shriners, Elks. Home: 1709 Hiawatha St NE Albuquerque NM 87112-4519 Office: Assn Gen Contractors 1615 University Blvd NE Albuquerque NM 87102-1717 Personal philosophy: Set your priorities in life, then your goals. In pursuing your goals, visualize their accomplishment. Be persistent, and you will accomplish what you set out to accomplish. Learn to be fair to others and empathetic.

ROBERTS, DONALD ALBERT, advertising, public relations, marketing and media consultant; b. Boston, Dec. 17, 1935; s. Albert Arthur and Linette Violette (Ouelette) R.; m. Gabrielle Dorothy St. Laurent, Apr. 20, 1957; children: Lynne Dianne, Tammy Denise. Student, U. Maine, 1987-88, Liberty U., 1988-89. Program mgr. air sports Sta. WIMA-TV, Lima, Ohio, 1965-68; v.p., gen. mgr. Sta. WABK/WKME, Gardiner, Maine, 1968-74; pres., owner Sta. WRDO, Augusta, Maine, 1974-77; cons. group gen. mgr. Valley Communications, Bangor, Maine, 1977-78; pres., owner Roberts Advt. Agy., Augusta, 1977-78; v.p., gen. mgr. Sta. WLOB AM/FM, Portland, Maine, 1978-80, Sta. WKCG/WFAU, Augusta, 1980-83; pres., owner Roberts & Co., Augusta, 1983—; exec. v.p. mktg., programming and advt. sales State Cable TV Corp., Augusta, 1983-92; cons. New Eng. Ziebart Dealers Assn., 1982—. Contbr. articles to profl. jours. Pres. Auburn (Maine) City Coun., 1957-60; chmn. Jefferson-Jackson Dinner, Rockland, Maine, 1959, Preserve Augusta Neighborhood Assn., 1989—; del. Dem. State Conv., Bangor, 1980; city councilor-at-large of Augusta, 1990—. Named Maine Sportscaster of Yr. Nat. Sportscasters Assn., 1962, 63; recipient Tiger award Maine Broadcasting System, 1965. Mem. So. Kennebec Valley Realtors Assn., Cable Advt. Bur., Cable TV Adminstrs. and Marketers, Ohio Sportscasters Assn. (co-founder 1965), Maine Assn. Broadcasters (bd. dirs.), Kennebec Valley C. of C. (bd. dirs.). Avocations: politics, reading, golf. Home and Office: 44 Longwood Ave Augusta ME 04330-4131

ROBERTS, DONALD FRANK, JR., communications educator; b. Seattle, Mar. 30, 1939; s. Donald Frank Sr., and Ruth Amalia (Geiger) R.; m. Karlene Hahn, 1963 (div. 1981): 1 child, Donald Brett; m. Wendy G. Roberts, Aug. 26, 1983; stepchildren: Richard L., David L., Katherine M. AB, Columbia U., 1961; MA, U. Calif., Berkeley, 1963; PhD, Stanford U., 1968. Instr., dept. English U. Hawaii, Honolulu, 1963-64; asst. dir. ednl. svc. bur. The Wall Street Jour., Princeton, N.J., 1964-65; asst. prof., rsch. assoc. dept. comm., Inst. Comm. Rsch. Stanford (Calif.) U., 1970-76, assoc. prof., 1976-84, prof. Comm., 1984—, dir. Inst. Comm. Rsch., 1985-90, chmn. dept. Comm., 1990—; Thomas More Storke Prof., 1991—; cons. NIMH, 1970-71, Rand Corp., 1972-74, Sta. KQED-TV, 1975-77, Far West Lab. Ednl. Rsch. and Devel., 1978-79, FTC, 1978-80, Westinghouse Broadcasting, 1983-86, Soc. Nutrition Edn., 1984-86, The Disney Channel, 1986-87, WHO, 1988-89, SRI Internat., 1988-89, Carnegie Coun. Adolescence, 1989-90, NBC, 1992, Ctr. Disease Control, 1992, Software Pubs. Assn., 1994, Nickelodeon, 1994; bd. advisors Media Scope, 1992-94; v.p. Recreational Software Adv. Coun., 1994—; proposal reviewer NIMH, NSF, U.S. Agy. Internat. Devel., Can. Coun., John and Mary R. Markle Found., W.T. Grant Found.; speaker numerous seminars, confs., symposia. Co-author: Process and Effects of Mass Communication, 1971, Television and Human Behavior, 1978; mem. editl. bd. Jour. Broadcasting, 1980-88, Pub. Opinion Quarterly, 1981-86, Communicare, 1986—; editl. reviewer Commn. Rsch., Comm. Monograph, Comm. Yearbook, Human Comm. Rsch., Jour. Comm., Jour. Quarterly, Child Devel., Jour. Applied Psychology, Jour. Ednl. Psychology, Psychology Bull., Jour. Adolescent Health; contbr. articles to profl. jours, also monographs and book chpts. Fellow Human Scis. Rsch. Coun., Pretoria. South Africa, 1985, 1987, Fullbright Teaching fellow Inst. for Unterrichtstechnologie Und Medienpadagogic, Austria, 1987. Mem. APA, Internat. Comm. Assn., Assn. Edn. in Journalism and Mass Comm., Soc. Rsch. Child Devel., Soc. Personality and Soc. Psychology. Office: Stanford U Dept Comm McClatchy Hall Stanford CA 94305-2050

ROBERTS, DONALD JOHN, economics and business educator, consultant; b. Winnipeg, Man., Can., Feb. 11, 1945; came to U.S., 1967; s. Donald Victor and Margaret Mabel (Riddell) R.; m. Kathleen Eleanor Taylor, Aug. 26, 1967. B.A. (honours), U. Man., 1967; Ph.D., U. Minn., 1972. Instr. dept. managerial econs. and decision scis. J.L. Kellogg Grad. Sch. Mgmt., Northwestern U., Evanston, Ill., 1971-72, asst. prof. 1972-74; assoc. prof. J. L. Kellogg Grad. Sch. Mgmt., Northwestern U., Evanston, Ill., 1974-77; prof. J.L. Kellogg Grad. Sch. Mgmt., Northwestern U. Evanston, Ill., 1977-80, Grad. Sch. Bus., Stanford U., Calif., 1980; Jonathan B. Lovelace prof. grad. sch. bus. Stanford U., 1980—, assoc. dean grad. sch. of bus., 1987-90; dir. exec. program in strategy and orgn., 1992—; dir. Global Mgmt. Program, 1994—; vis. rsch. faculty U. Catholique de Louvain, Belgium, 1974-75; cons. bus., econs. and antritrust, 1976—; spl. econ. cons. U.S Dept. Transp., Washington, 1978-79; vis. fellow All Souls Coll., Oxford U., 1995. Assoc. editor: Jour. Econ. Theory, 1977-92, Econometrica, 1985-87, Games and Economics Behavior, 1988—; mem. editorial bd. Am. Econ. Rev., 1991-95, Jour. Econs. and Mgmt. Strategy, 1991—; co-author: Economics, Organization and Management, 1992; contbr. articles to profl. jours. NSF grantee, 1973-93; rsch. fellow Ctr. Ops. Rsch. and Econometrics, Heverlee, Belgium, 1974, fellow Ctr. for Advanced Study in the Behavioral Scis., 1991-92. Fellow Econometric Soc. (mem. coun. 1994—); mem. Am. Econ. Assn., Beta Gamma Sigma. Home: 835 Santa Fe Ave Palo Alto CA 94305-1022 Office: Stanford U Grad Sch Bus Stanford CA 94305

ROBERTS, DONALD MUNIER, banker, trust company executive; b. Paterson, N.J., Aug. 3, 1935; s. Edward and Dorothy (Munier) R.; m. Sally D. Ingram, Sept. 6, 1958 (dec. Feb. 1978); 1 dau., Sarah M.; m. Mary Ayer Gordon, June 23, 1978; children: Edward (dec.), John, Martha. B.S., Yale U., 1957; M.B.A., NYU, 1961. Exec. v.p., 1979-90; vice chmn., treas. U.S. Trust Co. N.Y., N.Y.C., 1990—; bd. dirs. York (Pa.) Internat. Corp., U.S. Trust Corp., Burlington Resources, Inc. Elder Brick Presbyn. Ch.; trustee St. Bernards Sch. Mem. Tau Beta Pi. Republican. Club: Links (N.Y.C.). Home: 10 Gracie Sq New York NY 10028-8031 Office: US Trust Co NY 114 W 47th St New York NY 10036-1510

ROBERTS, DORIS, actress; b. St. Louis, Nov. 4, 1930; d. Larry and Ann (Meltzer) R.; m. William Goyen, Nov. 10, 1963 (dec.); m. Michael E. Cannata, June 21, 1950; 1 child, Michael R. Student, NYU, 1950-51; studies with, Sanford Meisner, Neighborhood Playhouse, N.Y.C., 1952-53, Lee Strasberg, Actors' Studio, N.Y.C., 1956. Ind. stage, screen and TV actress, 1953—. Profl. stage debut, Ann Arbor, Mich., 1953; appeared in summer stock Chatham, Mass., 1955; Broadway debut in The Time of Your Life, 1955; other Broadway and off-Broadway appearances include The Desk Set, 1955, The American Dream, 1961, The Death of Bessie Smith, 1961, The Office, 1965, The Color of Darkness, 1963, Marathon 33, 1963, Secret Affair

of Mildred Wilde, 1972, Last of the Red Hot Lovers, 1969-71, Bad Habits, 1973 (Outer Circle Critics award 1974), Cheaters, 1976, Fairie Tale Theatre, 1985, The Fig Tree, 1987, It's Only a Play, 1992; movies include Something Wild, 1961, movies include Barefoot in the Park, 1968, No Way to Treat a Lady, 1973, A Lovely Way to Die, 1969, Honeymoon Killers, 1969, A New Leaf, 1970, Such Good Friends, 1971, Little Murders, 1971, Heartbreak Kid, 1972, Hester Street, 1975, The Taking of Pelham, One, Two, Three, 1974, The Rose, 1979, Good Luck, Miss Wyckoff, 1979, Rabbit Test, 1979, Ordinary Hero, 1986, #1 with a Bullet, 1987, For Better or for Worse-Street Law, 1988, National Lampoon's Xmas Vacation, 1989, Used People, 1992, The Night We Never Met, Momma Mia, 1994, Walking to Waldheim, 1995, The Grass Harp, 1995; TV debut on Studio One, 1958, Mary Hartman, Mary Hartman, 1975, Mary Tyler Moore Hour, 1976, Soap, 1978-79, Angie, 1979-80, Remington Steele, 1984-88, Lily Tomlin Comedy Hour, Barney Miller, Alice, Full House, Perfect Strangers, Sunday Dinner, A Family Man, The Fig Tree (Pub. Broadcasting System), 1987, (TV films) The Story Teller, 1979, Ruby and Oswald, 1978, It Happened One Christmas, 1978, Jennifer: A Woman's Story, 1979, The Diary of Anne Frank, 1982, A Letter to Three Wives, Blind Faith, 1989, The Sunset Gang, 1990, Crossroads, 1993, Dream On, 1993, The Boys, 1993, A Time To Heal, 1994, Murder She Wrote, Step By Step, Burk's Law Walker, Texas Ranger, 1994, Amazing Grace, 1995. Recipient Emmy award Nat. Acad. TV Arts and Scis., 1984, 85, Emmy nominations, 1986, 88, 91. Mem. Screen Actors Guild, AFTRA, Actors Equity Assn., Dirs. Guild Am.

ROBERTS, DORIS EMMA, epidemiologist, consultant; b. Toledo, Dec. 28, 1915; d. Frederic Constable and Emma Selina (Reader) R. Diploma, Peter Bent Brigham Sch. Nursing, Boston, 1938; BS, Geneva Coll., Beaver Falls, Pa., 1944; MPH, U. Minn., 1958; PhD, U. N.C., 1967. RN, Mass. Staff nurse Vis. Nurse Assn., New Haven, 1938-40; sr. nurse Neighborhood House, Millburn, N.J., 1942-45; supr. Tb Baltimore County Dept. Health, Towson, Md., 1945-46; Tb cons. Md. State Dept. Health, Balt., 1946-50; cons., chief nurse Tb program USPHS, Washington, 1950-57; cons. divsn. nursing USPHS, 1958-63; chief nursing practice br. Health Resources Adminstrn., HEW, Bethesda, Md., 1966-75; adj. prof. U. N.C. Sch. Pub. Health, 1975-92; cons. WHO, 1961-82. Contbr. articles to profl. jours. With USPHS, 1945-75. Recipient Disting. Alumna award Geneva Coll., 1971, Disting. Svc. award USPHS, 1971, Outstanding Achievement award U. Minn., 1983. Fellow APHA (v.p. 1978-79, Disting. Svc. award Pub. Health Nursing sect. 1975, Sedgwick Meml. medal 1979), Am. Acad. Nursing (hon. fellow); mem. Inst. Medicine of NAS, Common Cause, LWV, Delta Omega. Democrat. Episcopalian. Avocations: reading, needlepoint, gardening. Home: 6111 Kennedy Dr Bethesda MD 20815-6509

ROBERTS, E. F., lawyer, educator; b. 1930; m. Alice A. Dunn, July 4, 1955; children: Martha, Ernest III, Michael, Marianne. B.A., Northeastern U., Boston, 1952; LL.B., Boston Coll., 1954. Bar: Mass. 1954. Asst. prof. law Villanova U., Pa., 1957-59, assoc. prof. law, 1959-60, prof. law, 1960-64; prof. law Cornell U., Ithaca, N.Y., 1964—, Edwin H. Woodruff prof. law; vis. prof. Nottingham U., Eng., 1962-63, Harvard U., 1983; mem. edn. panel Environ. Law Reporter, 1971-80; cons. in field. Author: Public Regulation on Title Insurance, 1960, Land Use Planning, 2d edit., 1975, Law and the Preservation of Agricultural Land, 1982, (with Strong et al) McCormick on Evidence, 4th edit., 1992. Mem. Am. Law Inst. (life), Internat. Coun. of Environ. Law. Office: Cornell U Sch Law Ithaca NY 14853

ROBERTS, EARL JOHN, carbohydrate chemist; b. Magee, Miss., May 14, 1913; s. William J. and Mary E. (Kennedy) R.; m. Mary Kirk Lilly, Oct. 28, 1944; children: Mary Karyl, John William. BA, Miss. Coll., 1939; MS, La. State U., 1942. Cert. chemist. Jr. chemist U.S. Dept. Agrl., New Orleans, 1942-44, prin. chemist, 1944-47, sr. chemist, 1948-72; sr. rsch. chemist Sugar Processing Rsch. Inst., New Orleans, 1972—. Contbr. articles to profl. jours. Recipient Sugar Crystal award. Achievements include patents for preparation of glue from peanut protein, recovery of aconitic acid from molasses, preparation of derivatives of cotton cellulose.

ROBERTS, EDWARD BAER, technology management educator; b. Chelsea, Mass., Nov. 18, 1935; s. Nathan (dec.) and Edna (Podradchik) R.; m. Nancy Helen Rosenthal, June 14, 1959; children: Valerie Jo Roberts Friedman, Mitchell Jonathan, Andrea Lynne. BS and MS in Elec. Engring., MIT, 1958, MS in Mgmt., 1960, PhD in Econs., 1962. Founding mem. system dynamics program MIT, 1958-84, instr., 1959-61, asst. prof., 1961-65, assoc. prof., 1965-70, prof., 1970—, David Sarnoff prof. mgmt. of tech., 1974—, assoc. dir. research program on mgmt. of sci. and tech., 1963-73, chmn. tech. and health mgmt. group, 1973-88, chmn. mgmt. of tech. and innovation, 1988—, chmn. ctr. for entrepreneurship, 1992-94, co-dir. internat. ctr. rsch. mgmt. tech., 1993—; co-founder, pres. Pugh-Roberts Assocs., Inc., Cambridge, Mass., 1963-89, chmn., 1989—; co-founder dir. Med. Info. Tech., Inc., Westwood, Mass., 1969—; dir. MIT-Boston VA Joint Ctr. on Health Care Mgmt., 1976-80; dir. MIT Mgmt. of Tech. Program, 1980-89, co-chmn., 1989—; co-founder, gen. ptnr. Zero Stage Capital Group, 1981—; bd. dirs. Advanced Magnetics, Inc., Cambridge, High Point Sys., Inc., Lexington, Laser Scis., Inc., Newton, Digital Products Inc., Waltham, Mass., Selfcare Inc., Waltham. Author: The Dynamics of Research and Development, 1964, Systems Simulation for Regional Analysis, 1969, The Persistent Poppy, 1975, The Dynamics of Human Service Delivery, 1976, Entrepreneurs in High Technology, 1991; prin. author, editor: Managerial Applications of System Dynamics, 1978; editor (with others) Biomedical Innovation, 1981; editor: Generating Technological Innovation, 1987; mem. editorial bd. IEEE Trans. on Engring. Mgmt., Internat. Jour. Tech. Mgmt., Indsl. Mktg. Mgmt., Jour. Engring. and Tech. Mgmt., Jour. Product Innovation Mgmt., Tech. Forecasting and Social Change. Mem. IEEE, Inst. Mgmt. Sci., Sigma Xi, Tau Beta Pi, Eta Kappa Nu, Tau Kappa Alpha. Home: 300 Boylston St # 1102 Boston MA 02116 Office: MIT 50 Memorial Dr Cambridge MA 02139

ROBERTS, EDWARD GRAHAM, librarian; s. Samuel Noble and Frances Johnson (Boykin) R.; m. Anna Jean Walker, Nov. 12, 1949; children: Galer Walker, Edward Graham, John Boykin. B.A., U. South, 1943; B.A. in Library Sci., Emory U., 1948; Ph.D., U. Va., 1950. Curator manuscripts Duke U., Durham, N.C., 1948-52; dir. libraries (Drake U.), Des Moines, 1952-56; dir. Southeastern Interlibrary Research Facility, Atlanta, 1956-59; asst. prof. info. sci. Ga. Inst. Tech., Atlanta, 1963-66, assoc. prof., 1966-69, prof., 1969-73, assoc. dir. libraries, 1966-71, dir. libraries, 1971-84; dir. emeritus Ga. Inst. Tech., 1984—; chmn. info bank com. Ga. Tech. Service Program, Atlanta, 1965-67; mem. exec. bd. Southeastern Library Network, Atlanta, 1973-74; library cons. So. Regional Edn. Bd., Atlanta, 1958-59. Compiler, editor: Southeastern Supplement to the Union List of Serials, 1959; author: Literature of Science and Engineering, 1966, 2d edit.,1969. Served with U.S. Army, 1942-43. Mem. ALA, Southeastern Library Assn., Ga. Library Assn. Democrat. Episcopalian. Home: 1639 Adelia Pl NE Atlanta GA 30329-3807

ROBERTS, EDWARD MOXON, Canadian government official, lawyer, politician; b. St. John's, Newfoundland, Can., Sept. 1, 1940; s. Harry Duncan and Mary Katherine (Moxon) R.; m. Eve Hargraft; children: Catherine Elizabeth, Caroline Alexandra. BA, U. Toronto, 1960, LLB, 1964. Bar: Nfld. 1965, Queen's Coun. 1979, Master of Supreme Ct. Nfld. 1989. Assoc. pvt. sec. to Hon. J.W. Pickersgill Govt. of Nfld., 1963, exec. asst. to Hon. J.R. Smallwood, 1964-66, parliamentary asst. to premier of Nfld., 1966-68, min. pub. welfare, 1969-72, min. justice and atty. gen., 1972—; mem. from dist. White Bay North Ho. of Assembly, 1966-72, mem. from dist. Strait of Belle Isle, 1975-85, mem. from dist. Naskaupi, Labrador, 1992; joined Halley Hunt (formerly Halley, Hickman, Hunt and Adams), St. John's, 1978, various positions to sr. ptnr., until 1992; leader Liberal Party of Nfld. and Labrador, 1972-77; house leader Opposition, 1979-80; chmn. pub. accts. com., 1982-84; chmn. Com. Constn., 1991; chmn. bd. trustees Waterford Hosp., St. John's, 1990-91, The Gen. Hosp. Corp., St. John's, 1991-92; appointed Govt. Ho. Leader, 1992. Active United Ch. of Can. Mem. Can. Bar Assn., Can. Maritime Law Assn., Nfld. Game, Fish and Protection Soc., Nfld. Hist. Soc., Brigus Hist. Soc. (life). Avocations: reading, collecting Newfoundlandia. Home: Ponds Head, Hogan's Pond Rd, Saint John's, NF Canada A1A 2X9 Office: Dept Justice, PO Box 8700, Confederation Bldg, Saint John's, NF Canada A1B 4J6

ROBERTS, EDWIN ALBERT, JR., newspaper editor, journalist; b. Weehawken, N.J., Nov. 14, 1932; s. Edwin Albert and Agnes Rita (Seuferling) R.; m. Barbara Anne Collins, June 14, 1958; children: Elizabeth Adams, Leslie Carol, Amy Barbara, Jacqueline Harding. Student, Coll. William and Mary, 1952-53, NYU, evenings 1955-58; AA in Coll. & Cmty. Svc., St. Petersburg Jr. Coll., 1994. Reporter N.J. Courier, Toms River, 1953-54, Asbury Park (N.J.) Press, 1954-57; reporter Wall Street Jour., N.Y.C., 1957, editorial writer, 1957-63; news editor Nat. Observer, Silver Spring, Md., 1963-68, columnist, 1968-77; editorial writer, columnist Detroit News, 1977-78, editorial page editor, 1978-83; editor editorial page Tampa Tribune, 1983—. Author: Elections, 1964, 1964, Latin America, 1965, The Smut Rakers, 1966, Russia Today, 1967; Editor anthology: America Outdoors, 1965. Recipient Disting. Reporting Bus. award U. Mo., 1969; Pulitzer prize for distinguished commentary, 1974. Mem. Am. Soc. Newspaper Editors, Nat. Conf. Editorial Writers. Office: 202 S Parker St Tampa FL 33606-2308

ROBERTS, ELIZABETH PORCHER, library director; b. St. Louis, Jan. 17, 1928; d. Francis Davis and Mary (Callaway) Porcher; m. Lorin W. Roberts, June 11, 1949 (div. 1965). AA, William Woods Coll., Fulton, Mo., 1947; BA, U. Mo., 1949; MLS, Emory U., 1956. Reference librarian Emory U. A.W. Calhoun Med. Library, Atlanta, 1954-56; with classified staff sci. library Wash. State U., Pullman, 1957, reference librarian, 1958-62, head serial record sec., 1963-72, acting head sci. library, 1965-66, 69-70, head interlibrary loan, 1970, head sci. library, 1972-76, head Owen Sci. and Engring. Library, 1977—. Contbr. articles to profl. jours. USDA Northwest and Intermountain Regional Document Delivery System grantee, Fred Meyer Chairtable Trust, 1977—. Mem. ALA (sci. tech. sect. com. on comparison of sci. libraries, task for on preconf.), Wash. Library Assn. (com. state interlibrary loan code 1972, com. women's rights 1972), Am. Soc. Engring. Edn. (PNW chmn. engring. sch. libraries div. 1966-68, v.p., program chmn. 1969-70, pres. 1970-71), Am. Soc. Info. Sci. (chmn. mentoring catalyst program 1983-84), Assn. for Faculty Women (chmn. com. on temporary appointments 1984—, faculty status com. 1985—), Assn. Acad. and Rsch. Libraries (sec./treas. 1973, nominating com. 1980), Pacific Northwest Library Assn. Avocations: reading, bicycling. Home: 10423 W Ocotillo Dr Sun City AZ 85373-1647 Office: Wash State U Owen Sci and Engring Libr Pullman WA 99164-3200

ROBERTS, ELLIOTT C., SR., hospital administrator; b. Balt., Jan. 20, 1927; married. BA, Morgan State U.; MA, George Washington U. Bus. mgr. Provident Hosp., Balt., 1953-58, asst. adminstr., 1958-60; chief acct. Crownsville (Md.) Hosp. Ctr., 1960-62, asst. supr., 1962-65; exec. asst. Mercy-Douglass Hosp., Phila., 1965, exec. dir., 1965-69; exec. dir. Harlem Hosp. Ctr., N.Y., 1969-72; commr. hosps. Detroit Gen. Hosp., 1972-77; exec. dir., asst. sec. Charity Hosp. New Orleans, 1977-80; v.p., assoc. project dir. Hyatt Med. Mgmt. Svcs., Chgo., 1980-81; dir., CEO Cook County Hosp., Chgo., 1981-84; prof. dept. health systems mgmt. Tulane U., New Orleans, 1984—; adj. prof. La. State U. Med. Ctr.; prof. Coll. St. Francis; CEO Med. Ctr. La., New Orleans; active Pro Pac Commn., Washington, 1990—. Mem. Am. Coll. Healthcare Execs. (del.), Assn. Am. Med. Colls. (del., bd. dirs.), Am. Hosp. Assn. (life, trustee 1971-76, Honor award 1993, Life Membership award 1993), Ill. Hosp. Assn. (trustee 1982-84). Office: Med Ctr La at New Orleans 1532 Tulane Ave New Orleans LA 70140

ROBERTS, ERIC, actor; b. Biloxi, Miss., Apr. 18, 1956. Ed., Royal Acad. Dramatic Art, London, 1973-74, Am. Acad. Dramatic Art, N.Y.C. Appeared in stage prodns. Rebel Women, Streetcar Named Desire, others; TV appearances include Another World; films include King of the Gypsies, 1978, Raggedy Man, 1981, Star 80, 1983, The Pope of Greenwich Village, 1984, The Coca-Cola Kid, 1985, Runaway Train, 1985, Nobody's Fool, 1986, Rude Awakening, 1989, Blood Red, 1989, The Best of the Best, 1989, Final Analysis, 1992, The Best of the Best 2, 1993, Babyfever, 1994, The Specialist, 1994; TV films include Paul's Case, Miss Lonelyhearts, A Time to Heal, 1988, Love, Honor & Obey: The Last Mafia Marriage, 1993, Love, Cheat and Steal, 1993, others; Broadway plays include Burn This, 1988 (Theatre World award 1988). Office: United Artist Agy 9560 Wilshire Blvd Beverly Hills CA 90212*

ROBERTS, ERNST EDWARD, marketing consultant; b. Wheeling, W.Va., Dec. 19, 1926; s. Charles Emmitt and Virginia Mae (Stephenson) R.; m. Donna Clare Davis, Dec. 27, 1949; children: Ernst Edward II, Carol Lee Roberts Gaydac. BS, U.S. Mil. Acad., 1949; MBA, Xavier U., Cin., 1954; MS in Mech. Engring., U. So. Calif., 1957; grad. with distinction, Air War Coll., 1970. Commd. 2nd lt. U.S. Army, 1949, advanced through grades to brig. gen., 1971; served as officer in combat U.S. Army, Korea, 1950-52; prof. mil. sci. Xavier U., Cin., 1952-54; mgmt. asst. to asst. comdt. U.S. Army Air Def. Sch., Fort Bliss, Tex., 1957-60; admissions officer U.S. Mil. Acad., West Point, N.Y., 1961-62, asst. to supt. (pres.), 1962-64, dir. admissions, 1964-65; comdg. officer 3d Missile Battalion, 71st Arty., Fed. Republic of Germany, 1965-67; staff officer Gen. Staff U.S. Army, Washington, 1968-70; comdg. officer NATO Air Defense Arty. Group, Fed. Republic of Germany, 1970-71; comdg. gen. 38th Air Def. Arty. Brigade, Korea, 1971-72; asst. comdt. U.S. Army Air Def. Sch. and Ctr., Fort Bliss, Tex., 1972-74; retired U.S. Army, 1974; v.p. bldg. and property mgr. El Paso (Tex.) Nat. Bank and Corp., 1974-79, sr. v.p., dir. personnel and tng., 1979-83, exec. v.p., dir. mktg., 1983-92; mktg. cons., 1992—; mem. exec. mgmt. com. Tex. Commerce Bank, El Paso, 1983-92; vis. lectr. mktg. Webster U. Mem. bd. advisors SBA; mem. mayor's Citizens Com. on Police Dept. Matters, El Paso; mem. Task Force to Evaluate Mgmt. of Sheriff's Dept.; head bond-issue campaign, El Paso; adv. dir. Armed Services YMCA, past pres.; adv. dir. nat. bd. dirs. Armed Svcs. YMCA, El Paso Community Found.; past pres. U. Tex.-El Paso Eldorados; mem. bd., trustee Found. Lighthouse for Blind; chmn. adv. bd. dirs. El paso Bus. Com. for Arts; chmn. capital fund drive com. Rio Grande Girl Scouts Am., Plaza Theatre-Plaza Park Restoration bd.; past mem. campaign cabinet United Way El Paso County; chmn. Capital Fund Drive, Air Def. Artillery Mus., Ft. Bliss, Tex.; bd. dirs. City of El Paso, mem. steering com. Safe 2000; bd. dirs. Crimestoppers of El Paso. Decorated D.S.M., Legion of Merit, Silver Star, Meritorious Svc. medal; recipient Pro Eclesio Et Pontifice, Vatican, 1971; Conquistador award City of El Paso, Liberty Bell award Legal Community El Paso, 1988. Mem. Am. Inst. Banking, Assn. U.S. Army (gen. army Omar N. Bradley chpt.), El Paso C. of C. (mem. armed forces com., chmn. spl. task force to evaluate chamber mgmt.), El Paso Club (past pres., bd. dirs.), Rotary (past pres.), U.S. Army Air Def. Artillery Assn. (pres.). Republican. Roman Catholic. Home: 8212 Antero Pl El Paso TX 79904-2401

ROBERTS, EUGENE LESLIE, JR., newspaper executive, editor; b. Goldsboro, N.C., June 15, 1932; s. Eugene Leslie and Margaret (Ham) R.; m. Susan Jane McLamb, Feb. 23, 1957; children: Leslie Jane, Margaret Page, Elizabeth Susan, Polly Ann. AA, Mars Hill Jr. Coll., 1950-52; BA, U. N.C., 1952-54; postgrad., Harvard U., 1961-62; LLD (hon.), Colby Coll., 1989. Local govt. reporter Goldsboro News Argus, N.C., 1956-58; maritime reporter Norfolk Virginian-Pilot, Va., 1958-59; state capitol corr. Raleigh (N.C.) News & Observer, 1959-61, Sunday editor, 1962-63; labor writer Detroit Free Press, 1963-64, city editor, 1964-65; chief So. corr. N.Y. Times, 1965-67; war corr. N.Y. Times, Vietnam, 1968-69; nat. editor N.Y. Times, 1969-72; exec. editor, v.p. Phila. Inquirer and Phila. Newspapers, Inc., 1972-80, exec. editor, sr. v.p. 1980-86; prof. Coll. of Journalism U. Md., 1991-94; mng. editor New York Times, 1994—; mem. Pulitzer Prize bd., Columbia U., 1982-91, chmn., 1989-90; chmn. Am. com. Internat. Press Inst., 1987-93, internat. bd., 1990—; chmn. nat. adv. bd. UPI, Washington, 1986-91; bd. visitors Sch. Journalism U. Md., 1983-91, Sch. Journalism Pa. State U., 1983-89; chmn. bd. visitors Sch. Journalism U. N.C., 1989-91; chmn. bd. dirs. Knight Ctr. for Specialized Journalism, U. Md., 1987-91; bd. visitors U. Mich. Journalist-in-Residence program; bd. govs. Columbia U. Seminars and News Media on Soc. and Soc., Grad. Sch. Journalism; bd. advisors Ctr. for Fgn. Journalists, 1987—; bd. dirs. World Press Freedom Com., 1986-93; bd. dirs. Arthur Burns Fellowship, 1990—; chmn. Woods Hole sci. writing fellowship Marine Biol. Lab., 1993—; bd. dirs. Universal Press Syndicate, 1992-94. Author (with Jack Nelson) The Censors and the Schools, 1963; editor (with David R. Jones) Assignment America, 1973. With U.S. Army, 1954-56. Recipient William Allen White award U. Kans., 1985, John Peter Zenger award for Freedom of Press, U. Ariz., 1987, Disting. Contbns. to Journalism award Nat. Press Found., 1989, Elijah Parish Lovejoy award for Freedom of the Press, 1989; Disting. Achievement in Journalism award U. So. Calif., 1989, Reuben award for Disting. Contbns. to Newspaper Features, 1991;

Nieman fellow, 1961-62. Mem. Am. Soc. Newspaper Editors, Soc. Profl. Journalists, Cosmos Club (Washington), Nat. Press Club (4th Estate award 1993), Am. Antiquarian Soc., North Caroliniana Soc. Home: 2614 Woodley Pl NW Washington DC 20008-1523 Office: NY Times 229 W 43rd St New York NY 10036

ROBERTS, FRANCES CABANISS, history educator; b. Gainesville, Ala., Dec. 19, 1916; d. Richard H. and Mary (Watson) R. B.S., Livingston State U., 1937; M.A., U. Ala., 1940, Ph.D., 1956, LHD, 1993; postgrad., Vanderbilt U., 1949-50. Tchr. pub. schs. Huntsville, Ala., 1937-52; teaching fellow U. Ala., 1952-53; mem. faculty U. Ala. at Huntsville, 1953-80; prof. history U. Ala., 1961-80, prof. emeritus, 1980—, chmn. dept., 1966-70, dir. Acad. Advisement Center, 1972-80. Author: Shadows on the Wall, The Life and Works of Howard Weeden, 1962, Civics for Alabama Schools, 1968, rev., 1970, History of the Church of the Nativity, 1843-1993, 1992; editor Huntsville Historical Review, 1989—. Bd. mem. Huntsville Civic Symphony, 1958-85; Bd. mem. Twickenham Hist. Preservation Assn., pres., 1983-84; Ala. state dir. on exec. bd. So. Heritage Found., 1964-65; bd. dirs. Burritt Mus., Huntsville, 1958-80; mem. Huntsville Historic Preservation Commn., 1972—; Commn. Restoration Capitol Bldg., 1973, Ala. Com. on Humanities and Pub. Policy, 1972-79; chmn. bd. Constitution Hall Park, 1979-83, Cahaba Hist. Commn., 1980-90; chair edn. com. for Vision 2000, Huntsville, 1988-90; chair edn. Summit, Huntsville, 1991; chair adv. com. Coll. Liberal Arts U. Ala., Huntsville, 1988—. Recipient Livingston State U. Alumni award, 1964; Ala. Historic Commn. award, 1969, 78; N.Ala. Bar Assn. Liberty Bell award, 1970; Life Sharer's award Kiwanis, 1973; Service award U. Ala., Huntsville, 1975; award of merit Am. Assn. State and; Alumni Faculty Appreciation award, 1976, 80; Disting. Citizen award Huntsville C. of C., 1990; Favorite Tchr. award TV Channel 19, 1991; Chapel of the Four Chaplins Legion of Honor award, 1992. Mem. Ala. Edni. Assn., Huntsville Hist. Soc. (exec. bd. 1950—, pres. 1987-89), Ala. Council Social Studies (pres. 1947-48), Am. Hist. Assn., Ala. Hist. Assn. (pres. 1968-69, exec. bd. 1951-79), So. Hist. Assn., N. Hist. Assn. (exec. bd. 1956-64), Golden Key, Kappa Delta Pi, Phi Alpha Theta (scholarship award 1973), Phi Kappa Phi. Home: 603 Randolph Ave SE Huntsville AL 35801-4159

ROBERTS, FRANCIS DONALD, manufacturing company executive; b. Utica, N.Y., Jan. 18, 1938; s. Francis J. and Agnes E. (McDermott) R.; m. Nancy Anne Crowder, June 23, 1964; children—Christine, Karen, Susan, Katherine. B.A., Utica Coll., 1959; Ph.D., Cornell U., 1964. From research scientist to mgr. oral research Colgate Palmolive, N.Y.C., 1964-73, dir. purchasing, 1973-76; dir. research and devel. Kendall Co., Boston, 1976-81, v.p. research and devel., 1981-84, v.p. sci. affairs, 1984-87, v.p. tech. and planning, 1987-89; pres., CEO, Steadfast, Inc., Cambridge, Mass., 1989-92; pres. F.D. Roberts and Assocs., Dover, Mass., 1992-93, Periodontix, Inc., Watertown, Mass., 1993—; trustee Textile Research Inst., Princeton, N.J., 1984-89. Mem. Am. Chem. Soc., Dirs. Indsl. Rsch. Republican. Roman Catholic. Avocations: tennis; golf. Home: 2 Bridle Path Cir Dover MA 02030-2400

ROBERTS, FRANCIS JOSEPH, retired army officer, retired educational administrator, global economic advisor; b. Holyoke, Mass., July 26, 1918; s. Francis Raymond and Mary (Curry) R.; m. Mary Murray Prickett, May 30, 1942; children: Murray Francine Roberts Mux, Laurel Virginia Roberts Manning, Randall Curry, Phillip Raymond. BS, U.S. Mil. Acad., 1942; postgrad., George Washington U., 1960, Harvard U., 1964. Commd. 2d lt. U.S. Army, 1942, advanced through grades to brig. gen., 1966; comdg. officer (B Battery, 358th F.A.), 1942-43; ops. and tgn. staff 358th F.A., 1943-45; ops. and tng. staff officer (Hdqrs. III Corps), 1946; instr. tactics (U.S Mil. Acad.), 1946, instr. academics, 1950-53, grad. mgr. athletics, dir. athletics, 1956-59; intelligence staff officer, plans officer (Amphibious Force U.S. Atlantic Fleet), 1946-48; pers. staff officer (Hdqrs. 101st Airborne Div.), 1948; dep. chief of staff 101th Airborne Div., 1948-49; plans and ops. staff officer (Hdqrs. I Corps), Korea, 1953-54; comdg. officer (159th F.A.), Korea, 1954; plans and policy staff officer (J-3, Hdqs. Far East Command), Japan, 1954-55; chief pers. services div. (Office Asst. Chief of Staff for Pers.), Washington, 1960-61; mil. asst. to dep. sec. def. Washington, 1961-64; comdg. officer (4th Inf. Div. Arty.), 1964-66; chief war plans (SHAPE), 1966, chief strategic plans br., 1966-68; chief of staff (Alaskan Command), 1968-69; comdg. gen. (II Field Force Arty. Vietnam), 1969-70; chief of staff (Hdqs. II Field Force), Vietnam, 1970-71; chief (Europe-Middle East-Africa Div. Orgn. Joint Chiefs Staff), 1971-72; ret., 1972; dean of cadets N.Y. Mil. Acad., 1972, supt., 1972-82. Bd. dirs. Global Econ. Action Inst., 1980-93, Am. Child Guidance Found.; v.p. AMP 45, Harvard; bd. dirs., mem. exec. com. U.S Olympic Com.; mem. exec. com. Ea. Collegiate Athletic Conf.; mem. Western Alaska coun. Boy Scouts Am.; mem. nat. bd. trustees Boys and Girls Clubs Am.; mem. panel Golf Digest. Decorated D.S.M., D.F.C., Silver Star, Legion of Merit with 3 oak leaf clusters, 10 Air medals, Croix de Guerre avec Etoile de Argent, Legion of Honor, Army Disting. Order 1st Class medal Vietnam, Vietnam Gallantry Cross with Palm, Nat. Honor medal Vietnam, Royal Army Aiguillette Thailand, others; first inductee Nat. Alumni Hall of Fame, Boys and Girls Clubs Am. Mem. Assn. Grad. West Point, Harvard Alumni Assn., Grads. Nat. War Coll., U.S. Golf Assn. (sectional affairs com.), U.S. Srs. Golf Assn. (bd. govs., sec. internat. golf team), Internat. Srs. Amateur Golf Assn., Assn. U.S. Army (chpt. pres., chmn. nat. resolution com., bd. advisors), Ret. Officers Assn.(bd. dirs., exec. com.), So. Srs. Golf Assn., N.C. Srs Golf Assn., Global Econ. Action Inst. (bd. dirs.). Clubs: Army-Navy Country (Washington); Pinehurst (N.C.) Country; Union League (N.Y.C.); Harvard-Radcliffe of Hudson Valley (pres. 1976-80), Touchdown of Am. (dir.), Bryce Mountain (Va.) Golf and Country, Ambs. Club-Duke U. Address: PO Box 2017 Pinehurst NC 28374-2017

ROBERTS, FRANCIS JOY, secondary education educator, journalist; b. Marblehead, Mass., July 19, 1931; s. Roland Merritt and Carrie (Ramsdell) R.; m. Patricia Zanio, Dec. 25, 1953; children: Elizabeth, Katherine, Cynthia. BS, Mass. State Coll., 1953; MA, Wesleyan U., 1957; EdD, Harvard U., 1959. Cert. tchr., N.Y., Conn. Tchr. Middlefield (Conn.) Pub. Schs., 1952-53, 55-56; prof. Springfield (Mass.) Coll., 1957-60; prin. Cold Spring Harbor (N.Y.) High Sch., 1960-66; rsch. fellow Yale U., New Haven, 1973; supt. Stony Brook, N.Y., 1966-73; pres. Bank Street Coll., N.Y.C., 1973-79; asst. dir. NEH, Washington, 1980-83; NEH, Cold Spring Harbor, 1983—; cons. various ednl. orgns. Contbg. editor (columns and features) Parents mag., 1978—. Trustee Heckscher Mus. of Art, Huntington, N.Y., 1985—, vice chmn., 1990—. With U.S. Army, 1953-55. Recipient Golden Apple award, 1988. Mem. Am. Assn. Sch. Adminstrs., Nat. Soc. for Study Edn., Marblehead Arts Assn., Harvard Club (bd. dirs. Washington chpt. 1982-83). Democrat. Avocations: painting, travel, gardening, writing. Office: Cold Spring Harbor Schs Cold Spring Harbor NY 11724

ROBERTS, FRANCIS STONE, advertising executive; b. Scranton, Pa., Aug. 15, 1944; s. Gordon Link and Eleanor Swartz (Stone) R.; m. Anne Carter Housh, Dec. 21, 1974; children: Francis Stone, Link McGregor. B.A., Grove City (Pa.) Coll., 1966; A.M.P., U. Chgo., 1984. With media dept., then account exec. Compton Advt. Inc., N.Y.C., 1966-69; account exec. Tatham-Laird & Kudner Advt., N.Y.C., 1969-70; account supr., v.p. SSC&B Advt. Inc., N.Y.C., 1970-78, sr. v.p., mgmt. supr., 1978-81; exec. v.p. SSC&B: Lintas Advt. Worldwide, 1981-86, group exec. v.p., 1987-89; COO, pres. Lintas, N.Y., 1990—; mem. policy and ops. coms., chmn. strategy rev. bd. Lintas N.Y.; also bd. dirs. Lintas N.Y. and U.S.A.; CEO Gotham Group, N.Y.C., 1994—. Emergency rm. com. Lenox Hill Hosp. Mem. William Penn Charter Alumni Assn. (pres. N.Y. 1984-88), Ad Club N.Y. Republican. Presbyterian. Club: New Canaan Field, New Canaan Winter. Home: 208 Canoe Hill Rd New Canaan CT 06840-3707 Office: Lintas Worldwide Advt Inc 1 Dag Hammarskjold Plz New York NY 10017-2201 also: Gotham Group 79 5th Ave New York NY 10003

ROBERTS, FRANK EMMETT, financial executive; b. Lordsburg, N. Mex., June 1, 1930; s. John J. and Clova (Lovett) R.; m. Gloria Ann Marengo, June 30, 1953; children: Linda, Craig, Laura. BS, U. Calif., 1953, MBA, 1957; postgrad., Harvard U., 1981. Sr. fin. analyst Kaiser Industries Oakland, Calif., 1957-67; controller Consol. Freightways Inc., San Francisco, 1976-78, controller-treas., 1978-79, v.p., treas., 1979—. Served to lt. comdr. USNR, 1953-57. Mem. Fin. Execs. Inst. (pres., dir.). Republican. Office: Consol Freightways Inc 3240 Hillview Ave Palo Alto CA 94304-1201

ROBERTS, GARY, lawyer; b. Portland, Oreg., Dec. 12, 1947. BS, U. Oreg., 1969; JD, NYU, 1974. Bar: Oreg. 1974. Ptnr. Schwabe Williamson & Wyatt, Portland, Oreg.; adj. prof. Northwestern Sch. Law, 1977-78; lectr. in field. contbr. articles to profl. jours. Mem. Oreg. State Bar (numerous offices and coms.), Multnomah County Bar Assn. Office: Schwabe Williamson & Wyatt 1211 SW 5th Ave Portland OR 97204-3713

ROBERTS, GEORGE BERNARD, JR., business and government affairs consultant, former state legislator; b. Andover, Mass., June 13, 1939; s. George Bernard and Helene F. (Eversen) R.; m. Margaret Fay Edmunds, Aug. 26, 1967; children: Abigail Emerson, Jessica Swift. B.S., U. N.H., 1964, M.P.A., 1967. Ptnr. Roberts Real Estate Assocs., Gilmanton, N.H. 1966—; mem. N.H. Ho. of Reps., from 1967, majority leader, 1971-74, speaker, 1975-76, 77-78, 79-80; pres. Policy Mgmt. Assocs., govt. rels. cons., Concord, Concord Coach Soc. Del. Nat. Rep. Conv., 1972-76; mem. N.H. Constl. Conv., 1974, 84, N.H. Rep. Party Fin. Com.; pres. Nat. Conf. State Legislatures, 1979-80; chmn. exec. com. 1st Congl. Soc. Gilmanton. Mem. Nat. Rep. Legislators Assn. (founding, past pres.), Masons, Sigma Alpha Epsilon. Republican. Office: 4 Park St Ste 100 Concord NH 03301

ROBERTS, GEORGE R., venture capital company executive; married; 3 children. JD, U. Calif., San Francisco. With Bears, Stearns, New York, until 1976; now ptnr. Kohlberg, Kravis, Roberts, San Francisco; dir. Beatrice Co., Chgo., Houdaille Industries Inc., Northbrook, Ill., Malone and Hyde, Memphis, Union Tex. Petroleum Holdings Inc., Houston. Office: Kohlberg Kravis Roberts & Co 2800 Sand Hill Rd Ste 200 Menlo Park CA 94025*

ROBERTS, HAROLD ROSS, medical educator, hematologist; b. Four Oaks, N.C., Jan. 4, 1930; s. Walter Lee and Matilda Alicia (Daughtry) R.; m. Marilyn Claassen; children—Eric Michael, John Claassen. B.S., U.N.C., 1952, M.D., 1955. Research assoc. U. N.C., Chapel Hill, 1961-62, instr. medicine, 1962-64, asst. prof., 1964-67, assoc. prof., 1967-70, prof., 1970—, chief hematology, 1968-77, dir. Hemophilia Treatment Ctr., 1977-80, dir. Ctr. for Thrombosis and Hemostasis, 1978—, co-chief hematology and oncology, 1979-81, chief hematology, 1981—; vis. prof. U. Aarhus, Denmark, 1973-74; dir. clin. coagulation lab. N.C. Meml. Hosp., Chapel Hill, 1977—. Assoc. editor Thrombosis & Hemostasis, 1975-81; editor Hemostasis, 1975-83; mem. editorial bd. Blood, 1976-82, assoc. editor, 1983—; contbr. articles to profl. jours. Chmn. Orange County Bd. Adjustment, N.C. Recipient Disting. Career award Temple U. Health Sci. Ctr., Stockholm, 1983. Fellow ACP; mem. Assn. Am. Physicians, Am. Soc. for Clin. Investigation, AMA, Internat. Soc. on Thrombosis and Hemostasis. Anglican. Avocations: arborist; ornithology; philosophy. Home: 2502 Jones Ferry Rd Chapel Hill NC 27516 Office: U NC Chapel Hill Sch Medicine Ctr Thrombosis & Hemostasis Campus Box 7015 Chapel Hill NC 27514

ROBERTS, HARRY MORRIS, JR., lawyer; b. Dallas, June 10, 1938; s. Harry Morris and La Frances (Reilly) R.; m. Nancy Beth Johnson, Mar. 7, 1964; children: Richard Whitfield, Elizabeth Lee. BBA, So. Meth. U., 1960; LLB, Harvard U., 1963. Bar: Tex. 1963, U.S. Dist. Ct. (no. dist.) Tex. 1964, U.S. Ct. Appeals (5th cir.) 1972, U.S. Supreme Ct. 1971. Assoc. Thompson & Knight, Dallas, 1963-69, ptnr., 1970-75, sr. ptnr., 1975—; chmn. real estate, probate and trust law sect. State Bar Tex., 1984-85; vis. scholar U. Tex. Law Sch., 1986. Contbr. articles to legal jours. Trustee Shelter Ministries of Dallas, 1982— (chmn. bd. trustees 1992—). Mem. ABA, Dallas Bar Assn. (chmn. real estate sect. 1981), Am. Bar Found., Tex. Bar Found., Dallas Bar Found., Am. Coll. Real Estate Lawyers, Tex. Coll. Real Estate Attys. (vice chair, bd. dirs. 1990-93). Episcopalian. Clubs: Salesmanship (Dallas), Dallas Country. Office: Thompson & Knight 1700 Pacific Ave Ste 3300 Dallas TX 75201

ROBERTS, HARRY VIVIAN, statistics educator; b. Peoria, Ill., May 1, 1923; s. Harry V. and Mary (Pickels) R.; m. June H. Hoover, Nov. 19, 1943; children: Andrew H., Mary D. BA, U. Chgo., 1943, MBA, 1947, PhD, 1955. Market researcher McCann-Erickson, Inc., Chgo., 1946-49; mem. faculty Grad. Sch. Bus., U. Chgo., 1949—, prof. stats., 1959-88, Sigmund E. Edelstone prof. of stats. and quality mgmt., 1988-93, emeritus, 1993—; cons. in field, 1950—. Author: (with James Lorie) Basic Methods of Marketing Research, 1951, (with Allen Wallis) Statistics: A New Approach, 1956, Conversational Statistics, 1974, Time Series Analysis and Forecasting with IDA, 1983, Data Analysis for Managers with Minitab, 2d edit., 1991, (with Bernard Sergesketter) Quality is Personal, 1993; contbr. articles to profl. publs. Mem. rezoning commn. Village of Homewood, Ill., 1956-60, 71-73, mem. zone bd. appeals, 1962-75, chmn. zone bd. appeals, 1973-75, mem. plan commn., 1970-73; mem. mfg. bd., mem. sci. bd. Dept. Def., 1988-90. With AUS, 1943-45. Fellow AAAS (stats. sect.), Am. Statis. Assn. (census adv. com. 1973-78, asso. editor Jour. 1977-82); mem. Royal Statis. Soc., Inst. Math. Stats., Am. Econ. Assn. Home: 1353 Burr Oak Rd Homewood IL 60430-1908 Office: Univ Chgo Grad Sch Bus Chicago IL 60637

ROBERTS, HENRY REGINALD, management consultant, former life insurance company executive; b. Toronto, Ont., Can., June 2, 1916; came to U.S., 1945, naturalized, 1954; s. Alfred Reginald and Mary Margaret (Creighton) R.; m. Margaret Elizabeth Fisher, May 23, 1940; children: Michael Alfred, Barbara Elizabeth, William Henry, Margaret Jane. B.A. in Math. and Physics, U. Toronto, 1937; L.H.D. (hon.), Clarkson Coll. Tech., 1965; LL.D., Trinity Coll., 1970, U. Hartford, 1971. With Mfrs. Life Ins. Co., Toronto, 1937-45; with Conn. Gen. Life Ins. Co., Hartford, 1945-81; 2d v.p. Conn. Gen. Life Ins. Co., 1958-60, exec. v.p., dir., 1960-61, pres., 1961-76; chmn. bd. Aetna Ins. Co., subs., 1966-76; pres., dir. Conn. Gen. Ins. Corp. parent co., 1967-76; chmn. bd. CGIC, 1976-81, presiding dir., 1981; pres. Henry R. Roberts Co., Hartford, 1981-89; chmn. bd. DNA Plant Tech. Corp., 1987-88. Corporator St. Francis Hsop., Hartford Hosp.; mem. coun. Internat. Execs. Svc. Corps. Fellow Soc. Actuaries. Office: 171 Bloomfield Ave Hartford CT 06105-1008

ROBERTS, HOWARD L., wholesale distribution executive; b. 1922. Chmn., pres. Roberts & Dybdahl, Inc., Des Moines, Iowa, 1956—; bd. dirs. Astro Bldgs., Inc., Des Moines, Roberts Trading Corp., Des Moines. Office: Roberts & Dybdahl Inc 1350 Financial Ctr PO Box 1908 Des Moines IA 50306-1908*

ROBERTS, HOWARD RICHARD, food scientist, association administrator; b. Eldred, Pa., July 6, 1932; s. Edward Euclid and Irene Victoria (Bills) R.; m. Marylyn Ann Morrissey, Dec. 28, 1957; children: Cynthia Anne, Mark Edward, Mary Beth, John Michael. BS, George Washington U., 1955, MS, 1957, PhD, 1962. Cert. pub. analyst; grad. D.C. Instr. George Washington U., Washington, 1958-59; ops. analyst Johns Hopkins U., Bethesda, Md., 1958-59; rsch. dir. Booz, Allen & Hamilton, Washington, 1959-67; v.p. Booz, Allen & Hamilton, Kansas City, Mo., 1967-72; dir. nat. foods FDA, Washington, 1972-78; dir. sci. affairs Nat. Soft Drink Assn., Washington, 1978-85, sr. v.p. 1986—; cons. George Washington U. Med. Sch., Washington, 1958-59; adv. panel AMA, Chgo., 1974-80; food expert panel FDA, Washington, 1990-91. Author: Food Safety, 1981; co-author: Human Consumption of Caffeine, 1984, Agricultural & Food Chemistry, 1978; contbr. articles to Food Tech. Jour., Food Drug Cosmetic Law Jour. Coach, official Vienna (Va.) Youth Inc., 1971-74. With USNR, 1950-54. George Washington U. fellow, 1957; recipient FDA award of Merit, 1978. Fellow Am. Soc. Quality Control (chmn. 1968-70, Svc. award 1971); mem. AAAS, ASTM, Am. Coll. Toxicology (coun. 1985-87), Inst. Food Technologists (profl.), N.Y. Acad. Scis., Soc. Soft Drink Technologists, Assn. Food and Drug Ofcls., Internat. Soc. Regulatory Toxicology and Pharmacology, Sigma Xi, Omicron Delta Kappa. Republican. Achievements include rsch. in risk assessment, consumption estimation. Office: Nat Soft Drink Assn 1101 16th St NW Washington DC 20036-4803

ROBERTS, HUGH D., real estate company executive; b. 1946. With H. D. Roberts Real Estate Co., Albany, 1967—, now pres. Office: H D Roberts Real Estate Co 16 The Sage E St Albany NY 12204*

ROBERTS, HUGH EVAN, business investment services company executive; b. Marion, Ind., Aug. 29, 1923; s. Arthur Edwin and Georgina (Fankboner) R.; m. Ellen Langtree Gordon, Sept. 16, 1950; children: Ellen Langtree, Daniel Evan, Robert Gordon. BSME, U. Cin., 1950. With Procter & Gamble Co., 1950-63, Monsanto Co., 1963-69; with Binkley Co., 1969-81, v.p., div. mgr., 1971-73, pres., 1973-79; chief exec. officer Binkley Co., Warrenton, Mo., 1971-81, chmn. bd., 1979-81; assoc. Capital Assocs. Fund, St. Louis, 1982-85; chmn. bd. Grant Cooper & Assocs., St. Louis, 1985-90; ptnr. Lockett, McNearney & Roberts Inc., St. Louis, 1990-94; retired. Mem. bd. St. Louis County Spl. Sch. Dist., 1973-79, pres., 1976-79. Served to 1st lt., pilot USAAF, World War II. Decorated D.F.C., Air medal with 4 oak leaf clusters. Republican. Episcopalian. Clubs: Mo. Quail and Gun; Univ. (St. Louis). Patentee chemistry, mech. devices. Home: 17 Frontenac Est Dr Saint Louis MO 63131-2613

ROBERTS, HYMAN JACOB, internist, researcher, author, historian, publisher; b. Boston, May 29, 1924; s. Benjamin and Eva (Sherman) R.; m. Carol Antonia Klein, Aug. 9, 1953; children: David, Jonathan, Mark, Stephen, Scott, Pamela. M.D. cum laude, Tufts U., 1947. Diplomate Am. Bd. Internal Medicine. Intern, resident Boston City Hosp., 1947-49; resident Mcpl. Hosp., Washington, 1949-50; research fellow, instr. med. Tufts Med. Sch., Boston, 1948-49, Georgetown Med. Sch., Washington, 1949-50; fellow in medicine Lahey Clinic, Boston, 1950-51; mem. active staff Good Samaritan and St. Mary's Hosps., West Palm Beach, Fla., 1955—; dir. Palm Beach Inst. Med. Research, West Palm Beach, 1964—, pres., Sunshine Sentinel Press, Inc. lectr. two day seminar on The New Frontiers in Legal Medicine, Seminar on Def. Against Alzheimer's Disease. U.S. rep. Council of Europe for Driving Standards, 1972. Author: Difficult Diagnosis, Spanish and Italian edits, 1958; The Causes, Ecology and Prevention of Traffic Accidents, 1971, Is Vasectomy Safe?, 1979, Aspartame (NutraSweet): Is It Safe?, 1989, Sweet'ner Dearest, 1992, Is Vasectomy Worth the Risk?, 1993, Mega Vitamin E: Is It Safe?, 1994, The Spirit of Modern Taiwan, 1994, West Palm Beach: Centennial Reflections, 1994, Defense Against Alzheimers Disease, 1995; (play) My Wife, The Politician; assoc. editor: Tufts Med. Alumni Bull, Boston, 1978-87, Nutrition Health Rev.; contbr. sci. and med. articles to profl. and theol. jours. Pres. Jewish Community Day Sch., West Palm Beach, Fla., 1975-76; disting. mem. pres. council U. Fla., Gainesville, 1974—; founder, dir. Jewish Fedn. Palm Beach County, West Palm Beach, 1960-72. Served to lt. USNR, 1951-54. Named Fla. Outstanding Young Man Jr. C. of C. Fla., 1958; hon. Ky. col.; recipient Gold Share cert. and silver certs. Nat. Agr. and Food Scis., U. Fla., 1974-78; Paul Harris fellow Rotary Found., 1980. Fellow ACP, Am. Coll. Chest Physicians, Am. Coll. Nutrition, Stroke Council; mem. AMA, Am. Acad. Neurology, Endocrine Soc., Am. Diabetes Assn., Am. Heart Assn., Am. Fedn. Clin. Research, Am. Coll. Angiology (gov. 1981), Am. Coll. Legal Medicine, Pan Am. Med. Assn. (chmn. endocrinology 1982), So. Med. Assn., N.Y. Acad. Scis., Am. Physicians Fellowship of Israel Med. Assn., Confrerie de la Chaine des Rotisseurs, Alpha Omega Alpha, Sigma Xi. Club: Governors of West Palm Beach (a founder), Executive (founder). Lodges: Rotary; B'nai B'rith, Order St. George (knight of magistral grace 1992). Research in med. diagnosis, diabetes, hypoglycemia, postvasectomy state, Vitamin E metabolism, pentachlorophenol, heavy metal toxicity, narcolepsy, traffic accidents, thrombophlebitis, aspartame, Alzheimer's disease, brain tumors, nutrition and bioethics. Home: 6708 Pamela Ln West Palm Beach FL 33405-4175 Office: Palm Beach Inst Med Rsch 300 27th St West Palm Beach FL 33407-5202 also: Sunshine Sentinel Press Inc PO Box 17799 West Palm Beach FL 33416

ROBERTS, J. WENDELL, federal judge; b. Somerset, Ky., May 1, 1943; s. Earl C. and Dorothy (Whitaker) R.; children: Stephen A., Shannon L. BA, Ea. Ky. U., 1964; JD, U. Ky., 1966. Bar: Ky. 1966, U.S. Dist. Ct. (we. dist.) Ky. 1978, U.S. Ct. Appeals (6th cir.) 1983. Atty. Ky. Dept. Revenue, Frankfort, 1966; law clk. Ky. Supreme Ct., Frankfort, 1966-67; atty. Charles A. Williams & Assoc., Paducah, Ky., 1967, Westberry & Roberts, Marion, Ky., 1968-87; city atty. City of Marion, 1968-84; judge U.S. Bankruptcy Ct. Western Dist. Ky., Louisville, 1987—, chief judge, 1988—. Vice chmn. Pennyrile Area Devel. Dist., Hopkinsville, Ky., 1968-72. Mem. Ky. Bar Assn., Louisville Bar Assn., Nat. Conf. Bankruptcy Judges (bd. govs. 1991-94), Mcpl. Attys. Assn. Ky. (pres. 1983). Methodist. Avocations: travel, antiques. Office: US Bankruptcy Ct 528 US Courthouse 601 W Broadway St Louisville KY 40202-2238

ROBERTS, JACK EARLE, lawyer, ski resort operator, wood products company executive, real estate developer; b. L.A., Nov. 5, 1928; s. James Earle and Illa Ann (Morgan) R.; m. Marilyn Humphreys, Sept. 13, 1954; children: Ronda, Cyndi, Scott, Robynne, Craig. B.S. in Accounting and Bus. Adminstrn, Brigham Young U., 1952; J.D., George Washington U., 1955, LL.M. in Taxation (Teaching fellow), 1956. Bar: Calif. 1957; CPA, Ariz. Pvt. practice L.A.; atty. Office Chief Counsel, IRS, L.A., 1956-60; mem. firm Roberts, Carmack, Johnson, Poulson & Harmer, L.A. 1961-78; pres. Park West Ski Resort, Park City, Utah, 1975-88; pres., dir. Accudyne Corp., Los Angeles, 1972-89, Richmark Corp., Los Angeles, 1972-77; chmn., dir. Comml. Wood Products Co., Los Angeles, 1968—; pres., dir. Snyderville Devel. Co., Inc., Utah, 1978—, Community Water Co., Salt Lake City, 1987—, Roberts Mgmt. Corp., Salt Lake City, 1988—, Ste. Vacations, Inc., Salt Lake City, 1989—. Contbr. articles on legal subjects to tech. jours. Pres. Westwood Rep. Club, 1968; mem. cen. coms. Calif. State, L.A. County Rep. Party, 1974-77; mem. Utah State Cen. and Exec. Coms., 1981—; Summit County Rep. cen. and exec. coms., 1978-84; state sec. Utah Rep. Party, 1985-88, chmn., 1989; mem. Rep. Nat. Com., 1988—; chmn. Summit County Rep. Party, 1981-83. Mem. Calif. Bar Assn., D.C. Bar Assn. Office: 150 Virginia St Salt Lake City UT 84103-4315

ROBERTS, JACQUELINE, state legislator, political consultant; m. Curley Roberts; children: Lisa LaVon, Curlee LaFayette, Dwyane Keith. BS in Instl. Dietetics, U. Ark., Pine Bluff, 1967, cert. teaching, 1968, cert. libr. sci., 1970. Shipping and receiving supt. U. Ark., Pine Bluff, 1969-74; sales rep. Brown & Williamson Tobacco Co., Ark., 1979-83; office mgr. Dancy Oil Co., Pine Bluff, 1983-85; housing complex mgr. May's Property Mgmt., North Little Rock, 1985-89; polit. cons. Pan Ark, Inc., Little Rock, 1991—; state rep. Dist. 73 Ark. Legis., Little Rock, 1991—, sec. legis. black caucus, city county and local affairs com., 1991-94, jud. com., legis. coun., house mgmt. com., chair subcom. on hate-motivated crime. Mem. affirmative action com. Ark. Dem. State Party, state exec. com., black caucus; chmn. Jefferson County Ctrl. Dem. Com., mem. pub. rels. subcom.; vol. dep. vote registrar, organizer; vol. Neighborhood Clean-up; bd. dirs. Parents as Tchrs., Cornerstone, Pine Bluff Literacy Coun., Pine Bluff Hippy Bd., St. John Apts./ Alexander Town, U.S. Postal Svc., Coalition for Diversity in Edn.; mem. Ark. steering com. Minority Recruitment in Edn; founder Young Enhancement Svcs., Inc.; mem. performing arts com. Pine Bluf Arts Ctr.; active St. John A.M.E. Ch., Assn. for Communities Organized for Reform Now, Pine Bluff Downtown Devel., Ptnrs. for a Better Pine Bluff, Ark. Cancer Coalition/Breast Cervical Control, Top Ladies of Distinction, Pine Bluff Black Caucus. Recipient Recognition award Pine Bluff Frat. Order of Police, 1992, Assn. of Communities Organized for Reform Now (ACORN), 1990, Ark. Polit. Survivor citation, 1991, Capital citation, 1991, St. John A.M.E. Bible Sch., 1991, Order of Distinction Social Club, 1992, Blacks in Govt., 1992, M.L.K. Planning Commn. Ft. Smith, 1994, Pine Bluff Arsenal-Dr. Martin Luther King, 1994, Nat. Assn. Equal Opportunity in Higher Edn., among others. Mem. NAACP, Nat. Conf. State Legislators, Nat. Conf. Black State Legislators (com. on law and justice, com. on youth), Ark. Dem. Black Caucus, Ark. Women's Polit. Caucus (Uppity Woman award 1991), Women in Govt. (state dir. Ark.), Urban League of Ark., Pine Bluff C. of C. (chairmans club), Ctr. for Women in Am. Politics, Elks Daus. Office: Ark House of Reps State Capitol Little Rock AR 72201

ROBERTS, JAMES ALLEN, urologist; b. Beach, N.D., May 31, 1934; s. Earl Fernando and Maria Ellen R.; m. Hilda Peachy, Nov. 22, 1987; children from previous marriage: Jennifer Lou Roberts Walsh, Mary Ellen Roberts Wargo, Thomas J. M.D., U. Chgo., 1959. Diplomate: Am. Bd. Urology. Intern U. Chgo. Sch. Medicine, 1959-60, resident in urology, 1961-65; mem. faculty Tulane U. Med. Sch., New Orleans, 1971—; prof. urology Tulane U. Med. Sch., 1975—, assoc. chmn., 1986—; sr. research scientist head dept. urology Tulane Regional Primate Research Center, Covington, 1972—. Mem. editorial bd. Am. Jour. Kidney Diseases and Urol. Rsch.; contbr. articles to profl. jours. Bd. dirs. Highland Park Hosp., 1985-87. Recipient grants NIH. Fellow ACS; mem. St. Tammany Parish Med. Soc. (pres. 1979), Soc. Rsch. on Calculous Kinetics, La. Urol. Soc., Am. Urol. Assn., Soc. Univ. Urologists, Nat. Kidney Found., Soc. Exptl. Biology and Medicine, Sigma Xi. Office: 1323 S Tyler St Covington LA 70433-2338

ROBERTS, JAMES G., foundation executive; b. Lincoln, Nebr., May 20, 1922; s. Ellsworth James and Anna (Gillette) R.; m. Eleanor Ramsey, July 28, 1945; children—Kenneth James, Ellen Margaret. Student, Nebr. Wesleyan U., 1939-41; B.A., Colo U., 1942. Mgr. Littlefield C. of C., Tex., 1948-50; mgr. indsl. div. Amarillo C. of C., Tex., 1950-51; mgr. Plainview C. of C., Tex., 1951-53; mgr. Tulsa dist. U.S. C. of C., 1953-54; mgr. Southwestern div. U.S.C. of C., Dallas, 1954-58; gen. mgr. Greater Boston C. of C., 1958-59, exec. v.p., 1959-64; v.p. pub. info. New Eng. Mut. Life Ins. Co., Boston, 1964-67; pres. Roberts Assocs., 1968-72; exec. v.p. Greater Pitts. C. of C., 1972-75; gen. mgr. N.H. Bus. and Industry Assn., 1975-77, exec. v.p., 1977-83; pres. Gordon Coll. Found., Wenham, Mass., 1983-87; adminstr. St. Andrews Estates South, Boca Raton, Fla., 1988-91; 1st pub. Boston mag., 1962; pres. Back Bay Planning & Devel. Corp., Boston, 1965-67; bd. dirs. Wellesley Nat. Bank. Mem. exec. com Billy Graham Crusade, 1964; trustee Gordon Coll., Joslyn Diabetes Found., Historic Park Street Ch.; bd. dirs. Salvation Army; deacon Presby. Ch.; Pensacola Mayor's com. for Elderly Affairs. Served to 1st lt. USAAF, World War II. Mem. Soc. Advancement of Mgmt. (v.p. pub. relations), Boston Better Bus. Bur. (bd. dirs.), No. Shore C. of C. (bd. dirs.). Clubs: Wellesley (Mass.); Algonquin, Greater Boston Execs. (pres.)(Boston); Eastern Yacht (Marblehead, Mass.); Duquesne (Pitts.).

ROBERTS, JAMES HAROLD, III, lawyer; b. Omaha, Aug. 11, 1949; s. James Harold Jr. and Evelyn Doris (Young) R.; m. Marilyn Novak, June 29, 1974; children: Jessica Noël, Meredith Caitlin. BA, U. Notre Dame, 1971; JD, St. Louis U., 1974. Bar: Iowa 1974, U.S. Ct. Mil. Appeals 1974, U.S. Supreme Ct. 1979, D.C. 1981. Govt. contract atty. U.S. Gen. Acctg. Office, Washington, 1978-83, U.S. Dept. Treasury, Washington, 1983-88; pvt. practice Manatt Phelps & Phillips, Washington, 1988—. Editor St. Louis U. law rev., 1973-74. Served to capt. JAGC, U.S. Army, 1974-78, lt. col. USAR/ NG, 1978—. Mem. ABA (pub. contract law sect.), D.C. Bar Assn., Fed. Bar Assn. Roman Catholic. Home: 308 N Monroe St Arlington VA 22201-1736 Office: Manatt Phelps & Phillips Ste 700 1501 M St NW Washington DC 20005

ROBERTS, JAMES LEE, fire chief; b. Pecos, Tex., Aug. 7, 1940; s. William Clay and Suda Mae (Henson) Wall; m. Judith Ann Galyardt. AAS, Midland Coll., 1976. Licensed master firefighter. Firefighter City of Midland, Tex., 1960-67; fire inspector City of Midland, 1968-70, asst. fire marshall, 1971-75, asst. fire chief, 1976-82, fire chief, 1983—; mem. Midland Coll. Emergency Svc. Com., 1980—; appointee to fire protection standards and edn. State of Tex., 1989—. Chpt. chmn. Midland ARC, 1965-89; bd. dirs. Am. Heart Assn., Midland County, 1968-69. With USMC, 1958-66. Recipient Nat. Pub. Spirit award Am. Legion Auxiliary, 1988, Rescue award Nat. Fire Prevention Assn., 1987, Disting. Svc. award USMC, 1988. Mem. Internat. Assn. Fire Chiefs, Tex. Fire Chiefs Assn. (pres. 1989-90), Tex. Mcpl. League (bd. dirs. 1991—), Lions. Avocation: carpentry. Home: 1903 N D St Midland TX 79705-8710

ROBERTS, JAMES MCGREGOR, retired professional association executive; b. Moncton, N.B., Can., Nov. 24, 1923; came to U.S., 1949, naturalized, 1956; s. Roland M. and Edith M. (Shields) R.; m. Thelma E. Williams, May 6, 1944; 1 dau., Jana M. B.Commerce, U. Toronto, Ont., Can., 1949. Auditor Citizens Bank, Los Angeles, 1949-54; auditor Acad. Motion Picture Arts and Scis., Hollywood, Calif., 1954—; controller Acad. Motion Picture Arts and Scis., 1956-71, exec. dir., 1971-89, exec. sec. acad. found., 1971-89; exec. cons. Acad. Motion Picture Arts and Scis., Hollywood, Calif., 1989-92; exec. cons., 1990-93, ret., 1994. Served as pilot Royal Can. Air Force, World War II. Home: 4968 Lerkas Way Oceanside CA 92056-7428

ROBERTS, JAMES MILNOR, JR., association executive; b. Pitts., Sept. 16, 1918; s. James Milnor and Elizabeth (Bennett) R.; m. Virginia Lee Sykes, Mar. 15, 1947; children: James Milnor III, Mary Lee Roberts Newman, Deborah Lee Roberts Gillespie, Todd Osborn. Student, Lehigh U., 1936-40, U.S. Army Command and Gen. Staff Coll., 1962, Nat. Def. U., 1963, Army War Coll., 1970. Commd. 2d lt. inf. U.S. Army, 1940, advanced through grades to maj., 1944, discharged, 1945; mem. U.S. Army (Res.), 1946-70; with 1st battle group U.S. Army Res. 314th Inf. Regt., Pitts., 1947-62; comdr. combat command sect. 79th Command Hdqrs., Pitts., 1962-64; with Office Chief Info., Dept. Army, Washington, 1964-67; comdr. 99th Army Res. Command, Pitts., 1967-70; promoted to maj. gen. 99th Army Res. Command, 1971; dep. chief U.S. Army Res., Washington, 1970-71; chief U.S. Army Res., 1971-75; exec. dir. Res. Officers Assn. U.S., Washington, 1975-84; pub. The Officer mag., 1975-84; pres. Nat. Intelligence Study Ctr.; pres. Americans for High Frontier, Arlington, Va., 1987—. Chmn. Young Republicans, Allegheny County, Pa., 1952-54; exec. v.p. World Symphony Orch., Pitts., 1961-62; bd. dirs. Pitts. Civic Light Opera, 1958-70; chmn. Com. for Free Afghanistan, 1983—; v.p. Nat. Hist. Intelligence Mus. Decorated D.S.M., Legion of Merit, Bronze Star; Croix de Guerre with silver star France; Mil. Cross Czechoslovakia; recipient USN Disting. Pub. Svc. award, USCG Disting. Pub. Svc. award, USAF Exceptional Svc. award; named Significant Sig Sigma Chi, 1973. Mem. Res. Officers Assn. (past chpt. officer), Am. Security Council, Assn. U.S. Army, Mil. Order World Wars, Ret. Officers Assn., The Dwight D. Eisenhower Soc. (chair 1992—), Soc. of Cin., SAR, VFW, Am. Legion, Army-Navy Club (Washington), Ft. Myer (Va.) Officers Club, Capital Hill Club, Masons. Home: 11910 Parkside Dr Fairfax VA 22033 Office: High Frontier 2800 Shirlington Rd Ste 404 Arlington VA 22206-3601

ROBERTS, JAMES OWEN, financial planning executive, consultant; b. Madison, Wis., Aug. 19, 1930; s. John William and Sada (Buckmaster) R.; m. Georgianna Timmons, Jan. 30, 1954; children: Stephen, Susan, Ellen, Timmons. BS, Ohio State U., 1952; MBA, Case Western Res. U., 1970. With Owens-Ill., Inc., Toledo, Ohio, 1952, 54-55, salesman, Atlanta, 1955-58, N.Y.C., 1958-62, food div. mgr., N.Y.C., 1963-66, br. mgr., Cleve., 1966-71; mgr. corp. fin. Stone & Webster Securities Corp., Cleve., 1971-74; regional dir. Mgmt. Planning, Inc., Cleve., 1976-80, v.p., 1980-86, sr. v.p., 1986, pres., 1986—; lectr. valuation and bus. ownership succession in field. Contbr. articles to profl. jours. Trustee Soc. for the Blind, Cleve., 1983-86, Ohio Motorists Assn., 1985-94, chmn., 1990-92; pres. Children's Svcs., 1988-88; trustee Great Lakes Theater; elder Fairmont Presbyn. Ch. 1st Lt. USAF, 1952-54. Mem. Fin. Analysts Fedn., Cleve. Soc. Security Analysts, Cleve. Skating Club, Nassau Club, Huron Yacht Club, Chgo. Athletic Assn. Republican. Avocations: sailing, skiing, flying, hiking, photography. Home: 2323 Stillman Rd Cleveland OH 44118-3520 Office: Mgmt Planning Inc 545 Hanna Bldg Cleveland OH 44115 also: 101 Poor Farm Rd Princeton NJ 08540-1941

ROBERTS, JAY, pharmacologist, educator; b. N.Y.C., July 15, 1927; s. Harry and Evelyn R.; m. Marion Camenson, June 18, 1950; children—Hunt, Kathy. B.S., L.I. U., 1949; Ph.D., Cornell U., 1953. Asst. prof., then asso. prof. pharmacology Cornell U. Med. Coll., 1956-66; prof. pharmacology U. Pitts. Med. Sch., 1966-70; prof. pharmacology, chmn. dept. Med. Coll. Pa., 1970—; chmn. dept. Hahneman U. Sch. Medicine, 1994—; cons. to industry; mem. NIH Study Sect. Contbr. numerous articles to profl. jours.; reviewer for numerous sci. jours.; assoc. editor (Pharmacology) Jour. Gerontology; asst. editor Jour. Pharmacol. and Exptl. Therap. Served with USNR, 1945-46. Postdoctoral fellow N.Y. Heart Assn., 1953-57; Postdoctoral fellow USPHS, 1953-55; recipient Lindback Disting. Teaching award Med. Coll. Pa., 1973. Fellow Am. Coll. Cardiology, Am. Coll. Clin. Pharmacology, Coll. Physicians Phila. (chmn. geriatric sect. 1986-88), Gerontol. Soc. Am. (chmn. biol. sect. 1984); mem. Internat. Study Group Research Cardiac Metabolism, Am. Fedn. Clin. Research, AAAS, Am. Soc. Pharmacology and Exptl. Therapeutics, Soc. Exptl. Biology and Medicine, Cardiac Muscle Soc., Am. Heart Assn., Southeastern Pa. Heart Assn. (peer reviewer grants 1973-94, Sr. Investigation Achievement award 1990), Harvey Soc., Assn. Med. Sch. Pharmacology, Am. Coll. Clin. Pharmacology (chmn.), AAUP, U.S. Pharmacopeial Conv. (chmn. geriatric advisor panel 1980-90), Mid-Atlantic Pharmacology Soc. (pres. 1990-92), Sigma Xi. Home: Benson House 930 Montgomery Ave Bryn Mawr PA 19010-3044 Office: Med Coll Pa 3200 Henry Ave Philadelphia PA 19129-1137

ROBERTS, JEANNE ADDISON, literature educator; b. Washington; d. John West and Sue Fisher (Nichols) Addison; m. Markley Roberts, Feb. 19, 1966; children: Addison Cary Steed Masengill, Ellen Carraway Masengill Coster. A.B. Agnes Scott Coll., 1946; M.A., U. Pa., 1947; Ph.D., U. Va.,

1964. Instr. Mary Washington Coll., 1947-48; instr., chmn. English Fairfax Hall Jr. Coll., 1950-51; tchr. Am. U. Assn. Lang. Center, Bangkok, Thailand, 1952-56; instr. Beirut (Lebanon) Coll. for Women, 1956-57, asst. prof., 1957-60, chmn. English dept., 1957-60; instr. lit. Am. U., Washington, 1960-62; asst. prof. Am. U., 1962-65, asso. prof., 1965-68, prof., 1968-93; dean faculties Am. U., 1972-74; lectr. Howard U., 1971-72; seminar prof. Folger Shakespeare Library Inst. for Renaissance and 18th Century Studies, 1974; dir. NEH Summer Inst. for High Sch. Tchrs. on Teaching Shakespeare, Folger Shakespeare Library, 1984, 85, 86. Author: Shakespeare's English Comedy: The Merry Wives of Windsor in Context, 1979, The Shakespearean Wild: Geography, Genus and Gender, 1991; editor: (with James G. McManaway) A Selective Bibliography of Shakespeare: Editions, Textual Studies, Commentary, 1975; (with Peggy O'Brien) Shakespeare Set Free, vol. 1, 1993, vol. 2, 1994, vol. 3, 1995; contbr. articles to scholarly jours. Danforth Tchr. grantee, 1962-63; Folger Sr. fellow, 1969-70, 88. Mem. MLA (chmn. Shakespeare div. 1981-82), Renaissance Soc. Am., Milton Soc., Shakespeare Assn. Am. (trustee 1978-81, 87-89, pres. 1986-87), AAUP (pres. Am. U. chpt. 1966-67), Southeastern Renaissance Conf. (pres. 1981-82), Phi Beta Kappa, Mortar Board, Phi Kappa Phi. Episcopalian. Home: 4931 Albemarle St NW Washington DC 20016-4359 Office: Am U Dept Lit Washington DC 20016

ROBERTS, JERRY, newspaper editor. Polit. editor city desk San Francisco Chronicle, editl. pg. editor, 1995—. Office: San Francisco Chronicle 901 Mission St San Francisco CA 94103-2905*

ROBERTS, JO ANN WOODEN, school system administrator; b. Chgo., June 24, 1948; d. Tilmon and Annie Mae (Wardlaw) Wooden; m. Edward Allen Roberts Sr. (div.); children: Edward Allen Jr., Hillary Ann. BS, Wayne State U., 1970, MS, 1971; PhD, Northwestern U., 1977. Speech, lang. pathologist Chgo. Bd. Edn., 1971-78, adminstr., 1978-88; dir. spl. svcs. Rock Island (Ill.) Pub. Schs., 1988-90; supt. Muskegon Hts. (Mich.) Pub. Schs., 1990-93; deputy supr. Chgo. Pub. Schs., 1993—; instr. Chgo City Community Coll., 1976-77; project dir. Ednl. Testing Svc., Evanston, Ill., 1976-77; exec. dir. Nat. Speech, Lang. and Hearing Assn., Chgo., 1984-86; hon. guest lectr. Govs. State U., University Park, Ill., 1983-86; cons. in field. Author: Learning to Talk, 1974. Trustee Muskegon County Libr. Bd., 1990, Mercy Hosp. Bd., Muskegon, 1990, St. Mark's Sch. Bd. Dirs., Southborough, Mass., 1989, United Way Bd., Muskegon, 1990; mem. Mich. State Bd. Edn. Systematic Initiative in Math and Sci., 1991, Gov. John Engler Mich. 2000 Task Force, 1991, Chpt. II Adv. Commn., 1991. Recipient Leadership award Boy Scouts Am., 1990; named finalist Outstanding Young Working Women, Glamour Mag., 1984, Outstanding Educator, Blacks in Govt., 1990. Mem. Am. Assn. Sch. Adminstrs., Nat. Alliance Black Sch. Educators, Mich. Assn. Sch. Adminstrs., Assn. Supervision & Curriculum Devel., Phi Delta Kappa. Avocations: creative writing, peotry, modern dance, theater, drawing. Office: Chgo Pub Schs 1819 W Pershing Rd Chicago IL 60001

ROBERTS, JOAN I., social psychologist, educator. BA in English, U. Utah, Salt Lake City, 1957; MA in Social Psychology, Columbia U., 1960, EdD in Social Psychology, 1970. Teaching asst. in English U. Utah, Salt Lake City, 1956-57; cons. psychologist Herrold Assocs. Mgmt. Cons., N.Y.C., 1958-61; research staff mem. Makerere Coll., Kampala, East Africa, 1961-63; research assoc. Hunter Coll., N.Y.C., 1964-67; coordinator Tng. Project and Research in Intergroup Relations, Madison, Wis., 1970-73; asst. prof. dept. ednl. policy studies U. Wis., Madison, 1968-75; assoc. prof. social scis. Upstate Med. Ctr./SUNY, Syracuse, 1976-79; chairperson dept. child, family, and community studies Syracuse (N.Y.) U., 1978-80, assoc. prof. dept. child, family, and community studies, 1978-84, prof. dept. child, family, and community studies, 1985—, prof. emerita, 1994—; prof. internat. programs abroad Syracuse U, London, 1984-85, 1990; adj. prof. Syracuse U. Sch. Nursing, N.Y., 1976—; adj. assoc. prof. social scis. SUNY, 1979-83; project dir. model caregivers tng. project N.Y. State Dept. Social Services, 1981; lectr. and presenter of papers to various academic and profl. groups; coordinator, mem. Wis. Coordinating Council of Women in Higher Edn., 1971-74. Author: School Children in the Urban Slum: Readings in Social Science Reseach, 1966, 2d rev. edit., 1968, Group Behavior in Urban Classrooms, 1968, Scene of the Battle: Group Behavior in Urban Classrooms, 1970; Beyond Intellectual Sexism: A New Woman, A New Reality, 1976; author: (with Prof. Sherri Akinsanya) Educational Patterns and Cultural Configurations: The Anthropology of Education, Vol. I, 1976, Schooling in the Cultural Context: Anthropological Studies of Education, Vol. II, 1975, Feminism and Nursing: Historical Perspectives on the Status, Power, and Political Activism in Nursing Profession, 1995. Mem. APA, Am. Anthrop. Assn., Corinthian Club, Brit. U. Womens Club.

ROBERTS, JOHN BENJAMIN, II, public policy consultant, writer; b. Albrook AFB, C.Z., Oct. 10, 1955; s. Robert Benjamin and Mary Pauline (Porath) R.; 1 child; John Benjamin III. BA, U. Calif., Irvine, 1973; MA with honors, Oxford U., Eng., 1978. Assoc. editor Handgunner, Ltd., London, 1979-80; press aide Reagan-Bush Campaign, Arlington, Va., 1980, sr. policy analyst, Washington, 1984; dep. dir. communications Rep. Nat. Com., Washington, 1981, Nat. Rep. Congl. Com., 1991; dir. editorial policy U.S. Dept. Edn., Washington, 1981-83; assoc. dir. office planning and evaluation White House, Washington, 1983-84, assoc. dir. office polit. and govtl. affairs, 1985-86; sr. v.p. Russo, Watts & Rollins Inc., Washington, 1986-88, pres. Roberts Communications, Inc., Washington, 1988—; sr. v.p. Robinson, Lake/Sawyer Miller, Washington, 1991-94; TV producer McLaughlin Group, One on One, CNBC, 1986—. Author: Entitlement Spending, 1984. Contbr. articles to newspapers, mags. Bd. dirs. Inst. for Rsch. on Small Arms in Internat. Security, Washington, 1989. Internat. Exch. Coun. (bd. dirs.) Oxford U. Pistol Club (Half-Blue Varsity award 1978), U.K. Practical Shooting Assn. (founder, life mem.). Oxford Soc . Avocations: competitive marksmanship, backpacking, photography. Home and Office: 528 S Alfred St Alexandria VA 22314

ROBERTS, JOHN D., chemist, educator; b. L.A., June 8, 1918; s. Allen Andrew and Flora (Dombrowski) R.; m. Edith Mary Johnson, July 11, 1942; children: Anne Christine, Donald William, John Paul, Allen Walter. AB, UCLA, 1941, PhD, 1944; D in Natural Scis. (hon.), U. Munich, 1962; D.Sc. (hon.), Temple U., 1964, Notre Dame U., 1993, U. Wales, 1993. Instr. chemistry UCLA, 1944-45; NRC fellow chemistry Harvard U., 1945-46, instr. chemistry, 1946; instr. chemistry MIT, 1946, asst. prof., 1947-50, assoc. prof., 1950-52; vis. prof. Ohio State U., 1952, Stanford U., 1973-74; prof. organic chemistry Calif. Inst. Tech., 1953-72, Inst. prof. chemistry, 1972-88, inst. prof. chemistry emeritus, 1988—, dean of faculty, v.p., provost, 1980-83, lectr., 1988—, chmn. divsn. chemistry and chem. engring., 1963-68, acting chmn., 1972-73; Foster lectr. U. Buffalo, 1956; Mack Meml. lectr. Ohio State U., 1957; Falk-Plaut lectr. Columbia U., 1957; Reynaud Found. lectr. Mich. State U., 1958; Bachmann Meml. lectr. U. Mich., 1958; vis. prof. Harvard, 1958-59, M. Tishler lectr., 1965; Reilly lectr. Notre Dame U., 1960; Am.-Swiss Found. lectr. 1960; O.M. Smith lectr. Okla. State U., 1962; M.S. Kharasch Meml. lectr. U. Chgo., 1962; K. Folkers lectr. U. Ill., 1962; Phillips lectr. Haverford Coll., 1963; vis. prof. U. Munich, 1962; Sloan lectr. U. Alaska, 1967; Disting. vis. prof. U. Iowa, 1967; Sprague lectr. U. Wis., 1967; Kilpatrick lectr. Ill. Inst. Tech., 1969; Pacific Northwest lectr., 1969; E.F. Smith lectr. U. Pa., 1970; vis. prof. chemistry Stanford U., 1973-74; S.C. Lind lectr. U. Tenn.; Arapahoe lectr. U. Colo., 1976; Mary E. Kapp lectr. Va. Commonwealth U., 1976; R.T. Major lectr. U. Conn., 1977; Nebr. lectr. Am. Chem. Soc., 1977; Leermakers lectr. Wesleyan U., 1980; Iddles Meml. lectr. U. N.H., 1981; Arapahoe lectr. Colo. State U., 1981; Winstein lectr. UCLA, 1981; Gilman lectr. Iowa State U., 1982; Marvel lectr. U. Ill., 1982; vis. lectr. Inst. Photog. Chemistry, Beijing, People's Republic of China, 1983, King lectr. Kans. State U., 1984, Lanzhou U., People's Republic of China, 1985, Davis lectr. U. New Orleans, 1986, Du Pont lectr. Harvey Mudd Coll., 1987, 3M vis. lectr. St. Olaf Coll., 1987, Swift lectr. Calif. Inst. Tech., 1987, Berliner lectr. Bryn Mawr Coll., 1988; Friend E. Clark lectr. W. Va. U., 1990; George H. Büchi lectr. MIT, 1991; Henry Kuivala lectr. SUNY Albany, 1991, Fusón lectr. U. Nev., 1992; dir./cons. editor W.A. Benjamin, Inc., 1961-92; cons. E.I. du Pont Co., 1950—; mem. adv. panel chemistry NSF, 1958-60, chmn., 1959-60, chmn. divisional com. math., phys. engring. scis., 1962-64, mem. math. and phys. sci. div. com., 1964-66; chemistry adv. panel Air Force Office Sci. Research, 1959-61; chmn. chemistry sect. Nat. Acad. Scis., 1968-71; chmn. Nat. Acad. Scis. (Class I), 1976-78, councillor, 1980-83, nominating com., 1992; dir. Organic Syntheses, 1948-70. Author: Basic Organic Chemistry, Part I, 1955, Nuclear Magnetic Resonance, 1958, Spin-

Spin Splitting in High-Resolution Nuclear Magnetic Resonance Spectra, 1961, Molecular Orbital Calculations, 1961, (with M.C. Caserio) Basic Principles of Organic Chemistry, 1964, 2d edit., 1977, Modern Organic Chemistry, 1967, (with R. Stewart and M.C. Caserio) Organic Chemistry-Methane To Macromolecules, 1971; (autobiography) At The Right Place at the Right Time, 1990; cons. editor: McGraw-Hill Series in Advanced Chemistry, 1957-60; editor in chief Organic Syntheses, vol. 41; mem. editorial bd. Spectroscopy, Organic Magnetic Resonance in Chemistry, Asymmetry, Tetrahedron Computer Methodology. Trustee L.S.B. Leakey Found., 1983-92; bd. dirs. Huntington Med. Rsch. Insts., Organic Syntheses Inc., Coleman Chamber Music Assn.; mem. Calif. Competitive Tech. adv. com., 1989—. Guggenheim fellow, 1952-53, 55-56; recipient Am. Chem. Soc. award pure chemistry, 1954, Harrison Howe award, 1957, Roger Adams award in organic chemistry, 1967, Alumni Profl. Achievement award UCLA, 1967, Nichols medal, 1972, Tolman edal, 1975, Michelson-Morley award 1976, Norris award, 1978, Pauling award, 1980, Theodore Wm. Richrds medal, 1982, Willard Gibbs Gold medal, 1983, Golden Plate award Am. Acad. Achievement, 1983, Priestley medal, 1987, Madison Marshall award, 1989, (with W. v.E. Doering) Robert A. Welch award, 1990, Nat. Medal Sci., 1990, Glenn T. Seaborg medal, 1991, Award in nuclear magnetic resource, 1991, Svc. to Chemistry award, 1991, Arthur C. Cope award, 1994, Chem. Pioneer award, 1994, History Maker award from Pasadena Hist. Soc., 1994; named hon. alumnus Calif. Inst. Tech., 1990, SURF dedicatee, 1992. Mem. NAS (mem. com. on sci. and engring. pub. policy 1983-87), AAAS (councillor 1992-95), Am. Chem. Soc. (chmn. organic chemistry divsn. 1956-57), Am. Philos. Soc. (mem. coun. 1983-86), Am. Acad. Arts and Scis., Sigma Xi, Phi Lambda Upsilon, Alpha Chi Sigma. Office: Calif Inst Tech Div of Chem 164-30 CR Pasadena CA 91125

ROBERTS, JOHN DERHAM, lawyer; b. Orlando, Fla., Nov. 1, 1942; s. Junius P. and Mary E. (Limerick) R.; m. Malinda K. Swineford, June 11, 1965; 1 child, Kimberlyn Amanda. Cert., Richmond (Va.) Bus. Coll., 1960; BS, Hampden-Sydney (Va.) Coll., 1964; LLB, Washington & Lee U., 1968. Bar: Va. 1968, Fla. 1969, U.S. Supreme Ct. 1969, U.S. Ct. Customs and Patent Appeals 1970, U.S. Tax Ct. 1970, U.S. Ct. Appeals (5th cir.) 1970, U.S. Ct. Appeals (9th cir.) 1974, U.S. Supreme Ct. 1969. Law clk. U.S. Dist. Ct., Jacksonville, Fla., 1968-69; assoc. Phillips, Kendrick, Gearhart & Aylor, Arlington, Va., 1969-70; asst. U.S. Atty. mid. dist. Fla. U.S. Dept. Justice, Jacksonville, 1970-74; asst. U.S. Atty. Dist. of Alaska, Anchorage, 1974-77, U.S. magistrate judge, 1977—. Bd. dirs. Teen Challenge Alaska, Anchorage, 1984-93; chmn. Eagle Scout Rev. Bd., 1993; bd. dirs. Alaska Youth for Christ, 1993—; mem. exec. com. Gov.'s Prayer Breakfast, 1994—. Recipient Citizenship award DAR, Anchorage, 1984, plaque, U.S. Navy, Citizen Day, Adak, Alaska, 1980. Mem. ABA, Nat. Conf. Spl. Ct. Judges (exec. bd. 1985-92), 9th Cir. Conf. Magistrates (exec. bd. 1982-85, chmn. 1984-85), Alaska Bar Assn., Anchorage Bar Assn., Chi Phi, Psi Chi, Phi Alpha Delta. Republican. Office: US Magistrate Judge 222 W 7th Ave #46 Anchorage AK 99513-7504

ROBERTS, JOHN GLOVER, JR., lawyer; b. Buffalo, Jan. 27, 1955; s. John Glover and Rosemary (Podrasky) R. A.B. summa cum laude, Harvard U., 1976, J.D. magna cum laude, 1979. Bar: D.C. 1981, U.S. Ct. Appeals (fed. cir.) 1982, U.S. Ct. Appeals (D.C., 5th, 9th circs.) 1988, U.S. Ct. Claims 1982, U.S. Supreme Ct. 1987. Law clk. U.S. Ct. Appeals 2d cir., N.Y.C., 1979-80; law clk. to Justice William H. Rehnquist U.S. Supreme Ct., Washington, 1980-81; spl. asst. to U.S. atty. gen. Dept. Justice, Washington, 1981-82; assoc. counsel to Pres. U.S., Washington, 1982-86; assoc. Hogan & Hartson, Washington, 1986-87, ptnr., 1988-89, 93—; dep. solicitor gen. U.S. Dept. Justice, Washington, 1989-93. Editor: Harvard Law Rev., 1977-79. Mem. Am. Law Inst., Phi Beta Kappa. Republican.

ROBERTS, JOHN J., accounting firm executive; b. 1945. With Coopers & Lybrand, 1967—, ptnr., 1974—, dep. chmn., 1991—, chief oper. officer, 1994—. Office: Coopers & Lybrand 1251 Avenue Of The Americas New York NY 10020-1157

ROBERTS, JOHN JOSEPH, insurance company executive; b. Montreal, Que., Can., June 4, 1922; s. Peter Ovila and Irene May (Rich) R.; m. Nancy Lee Rhodes, June 14, 1947; children: John Peter, Christopher Lee. BA, Princeton U., 1945. With Am. Internat. Underwriters Corp., 1947-59, 69—; regional mgr. Europe and Am. Internat. Underwriters Corp., Middle East, to 1959; pres. Am. Internat. Underwriters Corp. (U.S. Overseas ops.), N.Y.C., 1969-75, chmn. bd., 1975—; v.p. for European affairs C.V. Starr & Co., Inc. (subs. Am. Internat. Group, Inc.), N.Y.C., 1960-63; dir. overall worldwide ops. C.V. Starr & Co., Inc. (subs. Am. Internat. Group, Inc.), 1963-68; chmn. bd. Am. Internat. Underwriters Overseas (subs. Am. Internat. Group), N.Y.C., from 1968; exec. v.p. Am. Internat. Group, Inc., N.Y.C., 1976-89; vice chmn., 1989—; bd. dirs. Am. Internat. Group, Inc., Am. Internat. Underwriters Corp., Am. Internat. Underwriters Overseas, Am. Internat. Reins. Co., Inc., Am. Internat. Marine Agy. N.Y., Inc., AIG Mktg., Inc., C.V. Starr & Co., Inc., Starr Internat. Co., Inc., Admas Express Co., Petroleum & Resources Corp.; mem. Internt. Rsch. & Exch. Bd. Trustee C.V. Starr Found., Corcoran Gallery, Juilliard Sch.; chmn. Internat. Ins. Adv. Coun. to U.S. C. of C., 1977-79, U.S. sect. Polish-U.S. Econ. Coun., 1980-86; 1st v.p. Federacao Interamericana de Empresas de Seguros; chmn. U.S. sect. Hungarian-U.S. Bus. Coun., 1986-92; chmn. Bus. Coun. for Internat. Understanding, 1990—; chmn. internat. corp. coun. Sch. Internat. an Pub. Affairs, Columbia U., 1991—; mem. Coun. on Fgn. Rels.; mem. Coun. for Ethnic Accord. 1st lt. U.S. Army, 1943-46, CBI. Mem. The Geneva Assn., India House, Union Club, Racquet and Tennis Club, Brook Club, Nassau Club, Down Town Assn. Office: Am Internat Group Inc 70 Pine St New York NY 10270-0199

ROBERTS, JOHN KENNETH, JR., life insurance company executive; b. Omaha, Mar. 4, 1936; s. John Kenneth and Vera Blanche (Graham) R.; m. Carol Jean Baer, July 1, 1961; children: John Kenneth III, Susan Beth. Student, Cornell Coll., Mount Vernon, Iowa; B.A. in Actuarial Sci., U. Iowa. With Pan-Am. Life Ins. Co., 1959—; pres., chief exec. officer Pan-Am. Life Ins. Co., New Orleans, 1984—; dir. Whitney Nat. Bank of New Orleans, Whitney Holding Corp. Bd. dirs., past chmn. United Way Greater New Orleans Area, also past campaign chmn.; bd. dirs. Children's Hosp., New Orleans, YMCA, New Orleans. Fellow Soc. Actuaries; mem. Am. Acad. Actuaries, Life Office Mgmt. Assn. (bd. dirs., pres. bd. trustees, past chmn.), Health Ins. Assn. Am. (bd. dirs., chmn. pub. rels. policy com. 1993-94), Am. Coun. Life Ins. (bd. dirs. 1992), New Orleans Country Club. Lutheran. Home: 453 Fairfield Ave Gretna LA 70056-7033 Office: Pan-Am Life Ins Co 601 Poydras St New Orleans LA 70130-6029

ROBERTS, JOHN PETER LEE, cultural advisor, administrator, educator, writer; b. Sydney, Australia, Oct. 21, 1930; s. Noel Lee and Myrtle Winifred (Reid) R.; m. Christina Van Oordt, July 28, 1962; children—Noel, Christina, Olga. Student, State Conservatorium Music, New South Wales; MA, Carleton U., 1988; DFA (hon.), U. Victoria, 1992. With CBC Radio, Toronto, Can., 1955—; producer CBC Radio, 1955—, head music and variety, 1971—, spl. adv. music and arts, 1975; sr. advisor cultural devel., head office Ottawa, 1983-87; mem. exec. bd. Internat. Music Centre, Vienna, 1968-80, first chmn. radio and comml. rec. group, 1969-70, hon. mem., 1980; mem. exec. bd. Internat. Inst. Music Dance and Theatre, Vienna, 1969-75; bd. govs. Can. Conf. Arts, 1970-76; exec. bd. Internat. Music Coun., Paris, 1973-79; v.p. Internat. Music Council, 1975, pres., 1978-79; pres. Can. Music Centre, Toronto, 1971-77; dir. gen. Can. Music Centre, 1977-81; pres. Can. Music Council, 1968-71, 75-77; dir. Festival Singers of Can., 1965-78, Elmer Iseler Singers, 1979-81, Toronto Mendelssohn Choir, 1969-81, Nat. Youth Orch. Can., 1973-80; chmn. 1st World Music Week, 1975, Internat. Music Day, 1975-82; v.p. Internat. Inst. Audio-Visual Communication and Cultural Devel. (Mediacult), Vienna, 1976-87, pres., 1987-93; pres. Internat. Rsch. Inst. for Media, Communication, Cultural Devel., Vienna, 1993-95; v.p. Musicians Internat. Mus. Aid Fund, Geneva, 1978, 79; pres. Les Jeunesses Musicales du Can., 1979-83; chmn. Internat. Vocal Competition, Rio de Janeiro, 1979; spl. advisor to chmn. Can. Radio-TV and Telecomms. Commn., 1981; sr. advisor cultural devel. CBC, 1983-87; dean of faculty of fine arts U. Calgary, 1987-95; vis. fellow Inst. for Study of Canada McGill U., Montreal, 1995-96; adj. prof. U. Calgary, 1995—; bd. dirs. Nickle Arts Mus., 1987-95, Calgary Philharm. Orch., 1988-94, Esther Howens Internat. Piano Competition, 1994. Mem. editorial bd. Can. Music Book, 1970-77. Mem. exec. bd. dirs. Can. Music Commn. for UNESCO, 1976-80; founding

pres. Glenn Gould Found., Toronto, 1983—. Decorated Order of Canada; Cross of Honour for Sci. and the Arts (Austria). Mem. Can. assn. Fine Arts Deans (chmn. 1989-93), Internat. Coun. Fine Arts Deans (bd. dirs. 1992-94). Office: U Calgary Faculty Fine Arts, 2500 University Dr NW, Calgary, AB Canada T2N 1N4

ROBERTS, JULIA FIONA, actress; b. Smyrna, Ga., Oct. 28, 1967; d. Betty and Walter Motes; m. Lyle Lovett, Jun. 27, 1993 (div. 1995). Film appearances include Blood Red, 1986, Satisfaction, 1987, Mystic Pizza, 1988, Steel Magnolias, 1989 (Acad. Award nominee, Golden Globe award), Pretty Woman,1990 (Acad. Award nominee, Golden Globe Award), Flatliners, 1990, Sleeping With the Enemy, 1991, Hook, 1991, Dying Young, 1991, The Player, 1992, The Pelican Brief, 1993, I Love Trouble, 1994, Ready to Wear (Prêt-à-Porter), 1994, Mary Reilly, 1995; TV movies include Baja Oklahoma, 1988. Named Female Star of the Yr., Nat. Assn. Theatre Owners, 1991. *

ROBERTS, KARLENE ANN, education educator; b. San Frapcisco, June 12, 1937; d. Carl Joachim and Doris Elizabeth (Hosman) Hahn; m. Sept. 7, 1963 (div. June 1981); 1 child, Charlene Arletta. BA, Stanford U., 1959; PhD, U. Calif., Berkeley, 1967. Rsch. assoc. Stanford (Calif.) U., 1967-69; lectr. U. Calif., Berkeley, 1967-70, asst. prof., 1970-73, assoc. prof., 1973-78, prof., 1978—; cons. in field; reviewer in field. Mem. editorial bd. Acad. Mgmt. Jour., 1976-81, Jour. of Applied Psychology, 1977-87, Jour. of Vocat. Behavior, 1974-76, Orgnl. Behavior and Human Decision Processes, 1978-87, Calif. Mgmt. Rev., 1981-88, Acad. Mgmt. Exec., 1987; author: Comparative Studies in Organizational Behavior, 1972, Communication in Organizations, 1977, Toward an Interdisciplinary Science of Organizations, 1978, New Directions in Methodology: Aggregation Issues in Organizational Science, 1980, Organizational Behavior, 1991, New Challenges to Understanding Orgns., 1993.

ROBERTS, KATHERINE CHRISTINA, real estate executive; b. 1946. With H. D. Roberts Real Estate Co., Albany, 1971—, now sec. Office: H D Roberts Real Estate Co 16 The Sage E St Albany NY 12204*

ROBERTS, KATHLEEN ANNE, judge. BA in English summa cum laude, U. Mass., Boston, 1971; PhD program in English Lit., Yale U., 1971-72, JD, 1977. Bar: N.Y., U.S. Dist. Ct. (so. dist.) N.Y., U.S. Ct. Appeals (2nd cir.). Rsch. dir. Conn. Citizen Rsch. Group, 1972-73; investigator, monitor, evaluator grants, cons. Found for City of N.Y., 1973-77; law clk. U.S. Dist. Ct. (so. dist.) N.Y., 1977-79; asst. U.S. atty. criminal div. So. Dist. N.Y., N.Y.C., 1979-83, asst. U.S. atty. civil div., 1983-85, U.S. magistrate, 1985—; law clk. San Francisco Neighborhood Legal Assistance Found., summer 1975, U.S. Attys. Office, So. Dist. N.Y., criminal div., summer 1976; adj. prof. law, trial advocacy instr. Bklyn. Law Sch., 1983—. Office: US Dist Ct US Courthouse Foley Square New York NY 10007

ROBERTS, KATHLEEN MARY, school system administrator; b. Syracuse, N.Y., Apr. 15, 1947; d. Casimer and Lorrayne Arletta (Molloy) Piegdon; m. James C. Roberts, June 29, 1968 (div. Sept. 1988). Ba. Gen. State U., Edmond, Okla., 1968, MEd, 1971; PhD, U. Okla., 1977. Cert. tchr., prin., supt., Okla.; cert. supt., N.Y. Tchr. Putnam City Schs., Oklahoma City, 1960-72; reading specialist Moore (Okla.) Pub. Schs., 1973-74; reading specialist Crooked Oak Pub. Schs., Oklahoma City, 1974-77, supt., 1990—; rsch. assoc. Oklahoma City Pub. Schs., 1977-80; supt. Okla. Dept. Corrections, Oklahoma City, 1980-86, Healdton (Okla.) Pub. Schs. 1986-90. Contbr. articles to profl. publs. Bd. dirs. United Meth. Prism Ministry, Oklahoma City, 1986—, Children's Shelter, Ardmore, Okla., 1989-90; mem. State Vocat. Edn. Coun., Oklahoma City, 1980-85. Recipient citation Okla. State Senate, 1986. Mem. ASCD, Internat. Reading Assn., Am. Assn. Sch. Adminstrs., Okla. Assn. Sch. Adminstrs., Phi Delta Kappa, Alpha Chi, Kappa Delta Phi. Democrat. Roman Catholic. Avocations: furniture refinishing, reading, gardening. Office: Crooked Oak Schs 1901 SE 15th St Oklahoma City OK 73129-6058

ROBERTS, KEITH EDWARD, SR., lawyer; b. White Hall, Ill., Apr. 27, 1928; s. Victor Harold and Ruby Harriet (Kelsey) R.; m. Marthan Dusch, Sept. 4, 1954; 1 child, Keith Edward. Student, Western Ill. U., 1946-47, George Washington U., 1947-48; BS, U. Ill., 1951, JD, 1953. Bar: Ill. 1953, U.S. Dist. Ct. (no. dist.) Ill. 1957, U.S. Dist. Ct. (so. dist.) Ill. 1961, U.S. Dist. Ct. (no. dist.) Ohio 1960, U.S. Ct. Mil. Appeals 1954, U.S. Ct. Appeals (7th cir.) 1968. Assoc. J.D. Quarant, Elizabethtown, Ill., 1953-56; staff atty. Pa. R.R. Co., Chgo., 1957-60; assoc. Henslee, Monek & Henslee, Chgo., 1960-67; sole practice, Naperville, Ill., 1967-68; ptnr. Donovan, Atten, Mountcastle, Roberts & DaRosa, Wheaton, Ill., 1968-77; pres. Donovan & Roberts, P.C., Wheaton, 1977—. Served to capt. U.S. Army, 1954-57. Mem. ABA, Internat. Soc. Barristers, Assn. Trial Lawyers Am., Ill. Bar Assn., DuPage County Bar Assn. (gen. counsel 1976-86). Presbyterian. Office: Donovan & Roberts PC PO Box 417 Wheaton IL 60189-0417

ROBERTS, KENNETH LEWIS, investor, banker, foundation administrator; b. Dungannon, Va., Dec. 12, 1932; s. Clarence Eugene and Katherine (Osborne) R.; m. Anne Foster Cook, Sept. 10, 1955; children—Kenneth L., Patrick Hagan Foster. B.A., Vanderbilt U., 1954, LL.B., 1959. Bar: Tenn. Assoc. prof. law Vanderbilt U., 1959-60; assoc. Walker, Lansden & Dortch, Nashville, 1960-66; exec. v.p. Commerce Union Bank, Nashville, 1966-71; pres., chief exec. officer, dir. Cen. Nat. Bank, Richmond, Va., 1971-76; pres., chief exec. officer First Am. Nat. Bank, Nashville, 1976-90; dir. First Am. Corp., Nashville, 1976-90, vice chmn., 1976-77, pres., chief exec. officer, 1977-79, chmn., chief exec. officer, 1979-90; pres., exec. dir. HCA Found., Nashville, 1991—; past pres., dir. Cen. Nat. Corp. Trustee Vanderbilt U.; bd. dirs. Leadership Nashville; mem. exec. bd. Middle Tenn. coun. Boy Scouts Am. Lt. Chem. Corps, AUS, 1955-57. Mem. ABA, Tenn. Bar Assn., Nashville Bar Assn., Lawyers Assn. to U.S. C. Clubs: Cumberland, Belle Meade Country, Ponte Vedra (Fla.) Inn & Club. Office: HCA Foundation 3319 W End Ave #900 Nashville TN 37203-1076

ROBERTS, KEVIN, recreational facility executive. Pres. American Golf Corp., Santa Monica, Calif. Office: Am Golf Corp 1633 26th St Santa Monica CA 90404*

ROBERTS, LARRY SPURGEON, zoologist; b. Texon, Tex., June 30, 1935; s. E. Fowler and Frances Wray (Huggins) R.; m. Maria Elek, Feb. 7, 1962; children: Gregory Lorinc, Bruce Tibor, Teresa Margit, Eric Miklos. B.S., So. Meth. U., 1956; M.S. (NSF predoctoral fellow), U. Ill., 1958; D.Sc. (NIH predoctoral fellow), Johns Hopkins U., 1961. Cert. scuba instr. Nat. Assn. Underwater Instrs. Asst. prof. zoology U. Mass., Amherst, 1963-69, assoc. prof., 1969-75, prof., 1975-79; prof. biol. scis. Tex. Tech U., Lubbock, 1979-90; chmn. dept. Tex. Tech U., 1979-84; adj. prof. biol. scis. U. Miami, 1990—, Fla. Internat. U., 1990-93. Author: (with others) Foundations of Parasitology, 1977, 5th edit., 1995, Integrated Principles of Zoology, 1979, 9th edit., 1993, Biology of Animals, 1982, 6th edit., 1994, The Underwater World of Sport Diving, 1991, Animal Diversity, 1994. Mem. Amherst Dem. Town Com., 1968-79, vice chmn., 1972-76; mem. Amherst Town Meeting, 1966-76; mem. Amherst Zoning Bd. Appeals, 1972-75, vice chmn., 1972-75; recorder West Tex. Devel. Stes., 1985-86; mem. Dade County Dem. Exec. Com., 1991—. NIH postdoctoral trainee, 1961-63; NIH fellow, 1969-70; recipient Disting. Service cert. Mass. Tchrs. Assn., 1979. Mem. AAAS, ACLU (vice chmn. Hampshire County chpt. 1966-68, bd. dirs. Lubbock chpt. 1985-89, vice chmn. 1988-89, bd. dirs. Miami, Fla. chpt. 1991—, Fla. State bd. dirs., Am. Soc. Parasitologists (Henry Baldwin Ward medal 1971, council mem. at large 1980-83, v.p. 1984-85), Am. Micros. Soc. (v.p. 1974-75, exec. sec. 1978-81), Mass. Soc. Profs. (pres. 1977-78), Soc. Protozoologists, Am. Soc. Tropical Medicine and Hygiene, Wildlife Disease Assn. Southwestern Assn. Parasitologists (v.p. 1982, pres. 1983), Southeastern Soc. Parasitologists (pres. elect 1993, pres. 1994), Internat. Soc. Reef Studies (trustean Soc., Am. Acad. Underwater Scis., Sigma Xi. Home: 27700 SW 164th Ave Homestead FL 33031-2846

ROBERTS, LAWRENCE GILMAN, telecommunications company executive; b. Dec. 21, 1937; s. Elliott John and Elizabeth (Gilman) R.; m. June Ellen Stuller, 1959 (div. 1973); children: Paul, Kenny. BS, MIT, 1959, MS, 1960, PhD, 1963. Staff mem. Lincoln Lab. MIT, dir. info. proc. U.S. Dept. Defense, Arlington, Va., 1969-73; pres., CEO GTE Telenet Corp., Vienna, Va., 1973-82; DHL Redwood City, Calif., 1982-83; chmn., CEO

NetExpress, Inc., Foster City, Calif., 1983-93; pres. ATM Systems, Foster City, Calif., 1993—; dir. NetExpress, Inc., Foster City, 1982—. Mem. IEEE, IEEE Computer Soc., Am. Fedn. Info. Processing (Harry Goode award), Assn. Computer Machinery, Sigma Xi. Office: ATM Systems 989E Hillsdale Blvd # 290 Foster City CA 94404

ROBERTS, LEIGH MILTON, psychiatrist; b. Jacksonville, Ill., June 9, 1925; s. Victor Harold and Ruby Harriet (Kelsey) R.; m. Marilyn Edith Kadow, Sept. 6, 1946; children: David, Carol Roberts Mayer, Paul, Nancy Mills. B.S., U. Ill., 1945, M.D., 1947. Diplomate: Am. Bd. Psychiatry and Neurology. Intern St. Francis Hosp., Peoria, Ill., 1947-48; gen. practice medicine Macomb, Ill., 1948-50; resident in psychiatry U. Wis. Hosps., Madison, 1953-56; staff psychiatrist Mendota (Wis.) State Hosp., 1956-58; mem. faculty U. Wis. Med. Sch., Madison, 1959-89; prof. psychiatry U. Wis. Med. Sch., 1971-89, acting chmn. dept., 1972-75; mem. spl. rev. bd. Wis. Parole Bd. Sex Crimes Law, 1962-88, forensic cons., 1988—; mem. Dane County Devel. Disabilities Bd., 1962-66, Wis. Planning Com. Mental Health, 1963-65, Wis. Planning Com. Health, 1969-71, Wis. Planning Com. Vocat. Rehab., 1966-68, Wis. Planning Com. Health Centers, 1967-71, Wis. Mental Health Adv. Com., 1973-78; bd. dirs. Methodist Hosp., Madison, Dane County Rehab. House, Dane County Assn. Mental Health; cons. in field. Editor: Community Psychiatry, 1966, Comprehensive Mental Health, 1968; contbr. articles profl. jours. Pres. Wis. Council Chs., 1976-78; bd. dirs. Madison Campus Ministry, St. Benedict Center; trustee N.Central Coll., Naperville, Ill. Served with USNR, 1943-45, 50-53. Decorated Bronze Star, Purple Heart. Fellow Am. Psychiat. Assn. (bd. trustees 1981-84), Wis. Psychiat. Assn. (pres. 1967). Methodist. Home and Office: 722A Sauk Ridge Trl Madison WI 53705-1157 *Life is a precious gift whose journey is molded and shaped by cumulative experiences and relationships. Religious belief and practice which provides future-oriented hope, disciplined accountability and living service are balanced by professional psychiatric vistas on the uniqueness and worth of each human person.*

ROBERTS, LEONARD H., retail executive; b. Chgo., Feb. 19, 1949; s. Jack and Goldie (Solomon) R.; m. Laurie Susan Osser, Aug. 20, 1967; children: Dawn, Adina, Melissa. BS in Chemistry and Mktg., U. Ill., 1971; JD, DePaul U., 1974. Food scientist Armour Foods, Chgo., 1968-71, Cen. Soya, Chgo., 1971-74; govt. lobbyist Ralston Purina Co., St. Louis, 1974-76, dir. mktg., 1976-78; mng. dir. Raltech Purina Co., Madison, Wis., 1978-81; v.p. food service ops. Ralston Purina Co., St. Louis, 1981-85; pres., chief exec. officer Arby's Inc., Atlanta, 1985-89; chmn. bd., chief exec. officer Shoney's Inc., 1989-93; pres. Radio Shack, Fort Worth, TX, 1993—; vice chmn. bd. dirs. DWG Corp., 1987-89. Holder numerous patents on Soya protein research. Active United Way Met. Tarrant County, 1994, Big Brothers/Big Sisters Am., 1986, Nat. Crime Prevention Coun., 1994, Clark U. Students in Free Enterprise, Girl Scouts U.S. Recipient Pvt. Sector Initiative award Office Pres. of U.S., Washington, 1987, Disting. Achievement award B'nai B'rith, Restaurant Bus. Leadership award, 1991, Golden Plate award Nations Restaurant News, 1991, Wall St. Bronze Critics award, 1992. Mem. ABA, Ill. Bar Assn. Home: 3516 Briarhaven Rd Fort Worth TX 76109-3128 Office: Radio Shack 1800 One Tandy Ctr Fort Worth TX 76102

ROBERTS, LORIN WATSON, botanist, educator; b. Clarksdale, Mo., June 28, 1923; s. Lorin Cornelius and Irene (Watson) R.; m. Florence Ruth Greathouse, July 10, 1947; children: Michael Hamlin, Daniel Hamlin, Margaret Susan. B.A., U. Mo.-Columbia, 1948, M.A., 1950, Ph.D. in Botany, 1952. Asst. prof., then assoc. prof. botany Agnes Scott Coll., Decaur, Ga., 1952-57; vis. asst. prof. Emory U., 1952-55; mem. faculty U. Idaho, 1957—; prof. botany, 1967-91, prof. botany emeritus, 1991—; Fulbright research prof. Kyoto (Japan) U., 1967-68; research fellow U. Bari, Italy, 1968; Cabot fellow Harvard, 1974; Fulbright teaching fellow North-Eastern Hill U., Shillong, Meghalaya, India, 1977; Fulbright sr. scholar and fellow Australian Nat. U., Canberra, 1980; sr. researcher U. London, 1984; pres. botany sect. 1st Internat. Congress Histochemistry and Cytochemistry, Paris, 1960; Alexander von Humboldt vis. fellow Australian Nat. U., 1992. Author: Cytodifferentiation in Plants, 1976, (with J.H. Dodds) Experiments in Plant Tissue Culture, 1982, 3d edit., 1995, (with P.B. Gahan and R. Aloni) Vascular Differentiation and Plant Growth Regulators, 1988; contbr. articles to profl. jours. Served with USAAF, 1943-46. Alexander van Humboldt fellow, 1992; Decorated chevalier de l'Ordre du Merite Agricole France, 1961. Fellow AAAS; mem. W.M. Sci. Assn. (pres. 1970-71), Bot. Soc. Am., Am. Soc. Plant Physiologists, Internat. Assn. Plant Tissue Culture, Am. Inst. Biol. Scis., Idaho Acad. Scis., Sigma Xi, Phi Kappa Phi, Phi Sigma. Home: 920 Mabelle St Moscow ID 83843-3834

ROBERTS, LOUIS DOUGLAS, physics educator, researcher; b. Charleston, S.C., Jan. 27, 1918; s. Louis Wigfall and Evelyn (Douglas) R.; m. Marjorie Violette Staveley-Lawson, Aug. 29, 1942; 1 child, Joyce Carol. AB with honors, Howard Coll., 1938; postgrad., John Hopkins U., 1938-39; PhD, Columbia U., 1941. Rockefeller Found. fellow Cornell U., Ithaca, N.Y., 1941-42; rsch. physicist GE, Schenectady, N.Y., 1942-46, U. Calif. at Berkeley, 1944-45; prin. physicist Oak Ridge (Tenn.) Nat. Lab., 1946-68; Ford Found. prof. U. Tenn., Knoxville, 1963-68; prof. physics U. N.C., Chapel Hill, 1968—, Alumni Disting. prof., 1980—. Contbr. articles on physics to profl. jours.; holder numerous patents in semiconductor devices, magnetron design, nuclear power, metals and alloys, etc. Recipient Tanner teaching award U. N.C., 1977; Fulbright fellow Oxford U., 1958-59, Guggenheim Found. fellow, 1958-59. Fellow Am. Phys. Soc. (mem. Southeastern sect., 1948—, vice chmn. 1954-55, chmn. 1955-56). Republican. Avocations: reading, music, travel, garden, photography. Home: 1116 Sourwood Cir Chapel Hill NC 27514-4912 Office: Univ NC Dept Physics and Astronomy Chapel Hill NC 27599-3255

ROBERTS, LOUIS WRIGHT, transportation executive; b. Jamestown, N.Y., Sept. 1, 1913; s. Louis Lorenzo and Dora (Wright) R.; m. Mercedes Pearl McGavock, June 8, 1938; children: Louis M., Lawrence E. BA, Fisk U., 1935, LLD (hon.), 1989; MS, U. Mich., 1937, postgrad., 1941; postgrad., MIT, 1946. Teaching asst. Fisk U., Nashville, 1935-36; instr. St. Augustine's Coll., Raleigh, N.C., 1937-40, assoc. prof., 1941-42; assoc. prof. Howard U., Washington, 1943-44; mgr. tube div. Sylvania Elec. Products Inc., Danvers, Salem and Boston, Mass., 1944-50; tube cons. rsch. lab. for electronics MIT, Cambridge, 1950-51, vis. sr. lectr., 1979-80; founder, pres. Microwave Assocs., Inc., Boston, 1950-55; engring. specialist, cons. Bomac Labs., Inc., Beverly, Mass., 1955-59; founder, v.p. dir. METCOM, Inc., Salem, Mass., 1959-67; pres. Elcon Labs., Peabody, Mass., 1962-66; cons. Addison-Wesley Press, Reading, Mass., 1963-67; chief microwave lab. NASA Electronics Rsch. Ctr., Cambridge, 1967-68, chief optics and microwave lab., 1968-70; dep. dir. Office Tech. Transp. Systems Ctr., Cambridge, 1970-72, dir. Office Tech., 1972-77, dir. Office Energy and Environ., 1977-79; dep. dir. Office Data Systems and Tech., 1980-82, dir. Office Adminstrn., 1982-83, assoc. dir. Office Ops. Engring., 1983-84, acting dep. dir., 1984, acting dir., 1984-85, dir., 1985-89; cons. Battelle Meml. Inst., Columbus, Ohio, 1989-92; coporator Wakefield Svcs. Bank, Mass., 1975-90; bd. dirs. Systems Resources Corp. Editor: Electronic Tubes, 1964; author, editor: Handbook of Microwave Measurements, 1966; contbr. articles to profl. jours. Mem. Mass. Gov.'s Commn. on Vocat. Rehab., 1966-68, Positive Program for Boston, 1967-75; pres. Wakefield Coun. Chs., 1967-70; mem. adv. bd. U. Mass., Amherst, 1972-90, Bentley Coll., Waltham, Mass., 1974-90; trustee Univ. Hosp., Boston, 1973—. Recipient Apollo Achievement award NASA, 1969, Meritorious Achievement award Sec. Transp. 1976, Outstanding Achievement award U. Mich., 1978, Meritorious Exec. award Pres. U.S. 1984. Fellow IEEE; mem. AIAA, AAAS, N.Y. Acad. Sci., Phi Beta Kappa Associates (life mem.), Sigma Pi Phi (treas. 1980-85, pres. 1986-89), Nat. Guardsmen Club (pres. 1986-90), Masons. Episcopalian. Home: 5 Michael Rd Wakefield MA 01880-3611

ROBERTS, LOUISE NISBET, philosopher; b. Lexington, Ky., Apr. 21, 1919; d. Benjamin and Helen L. Nisbet; m. Warren Roberts, June 14, 1952; children: Helen Ward Roberts Hill, Valeria Lamar Roberts Emmett. AB, U. Ky., 1942, MA, 1944; PhD, Columbia U., 1952. Instr. philosophy Fairfax Hall, Waynesboro, Va., 1943-44, Fairmount Casements, Ormond Beach, Fla., 1944-45; mem. faculty Newcomb Coll., Tulane U., 1948—, prof. philosophy, 1969-85, dept. head, prof. emeritus, 1985—. Chmn. Episc. Diocese HIV/AIDS Commn., 1993—. Contbr. articles to profl. jours. Univ. scholar, 1945-46. Mem. AAUW (fellow 1947-48, pres. New Orleans chpt.

1986-88), DAR (vice regent New Orleans chpt. 1987-90), So. Soc. Philosophy and Psychology, Phi Beta Kappa (chpt. pres. 1956-57), Delta Delta Delta (fellow 1946-47). Democrat. Episcopalian. Office: Tulane U Dept Of Philosophy New Orleans LA 70118

ROBERTS, MALCOLM JOHN, steel company executive; b. Widnes, U.K., Nov. 8, 1942; s. Thomas and Cicely (Prescott) R.; m. Margaret Irene Turner, Dec. 5, 1964; children: Kathryn, Christopher, Jillian. B Engring., U. Liverpool, Eng., 1963, PhD, 1966. Research assoc Cornell U. Ithaca, N.Y., 1966-67; research engr. Bethlehem (Pa.) Steel Corp., 1967-71, supr., 1971-79, sect. mgr., 1979-82, div. mgr., 1982-84, assoc. dir. research, 1984-85, dir. research, 1985—. Mem. AIME, Am. Soc. Metals, Am. Iron and Steel Inst., Indsl. Research Inst. (rep.). Office: Bethlehem Steel Corp Homer Rsch Labs 8th & Eaton Ave Bethlehem PA 18016

ROBERTS, MARGARET HAROLD, editor, publisher; b. Aug. 18, 1928. A.B., U. Chattanooga, 1950. Editor, pub. series Award Winning Art, 1960-70, New Woman mag., Palm Beach, Fla., 1971-84; editor, pub. Going Bonkers mag., 1992—. Author: juvenile book series Daddy is a Doctor, 1965. Office: PO Box 189 Palm Beach FL 33480-0189

ROBERTS, MARIE DYER, computer systems specialist; b. Statesboro, Ga., Feb. 19, 1943; d. Byron and Martha (Evans) Dyer; BS, U. Ga., 1966; student Am. U., 1972; cert. systems profl., cert. in data processing; m. Hugh V. Roberts, Jr., Oct. 6, 1973. Mathematician, computer specialist U.S. Naval Oceanographic Office, Washington, 1966-73; systems analyst, programmer Sperry Microwave Electronics, Clearwater, Fla., 1973-75; data processing mgr., asst. bus. mgr. Trenam, Simmons, Kemker et al, Tampa, Fla., 1975-77; mathematician, computer specialist U.S. Army C.E., Savannah, Ga., 1977-81, 83-85, Frankfurt, W. Ger., 1981-83; ops. rsch. analyst U.S. Army Contrn. Rsch. Lab., Champaign, Ill., 1985-87; data base administr., computer systems programmer, chief info. integration and implementation div. U.S. Army Corps of Engrs., South Pacific div., San Francisco, 1987-93; computer specialist, IDEF repository coord., Functional Process Improvement Expertise, Defense Info. Systems Agy., Arlington, Va., 1993—. instr. computer scis. City Coll. of Chgo. in Franfurt, 1982-83. Recipient Sustained Superior Performance award Dept. Army, 1983. Mem. Am. Soc. Hist. Preservation, Data Processing Mgmt. Assn., Assn. of Inst. for Cert. Computer Profls., Assn. Women in Computing, Assn. Women in Sci., NAFE, Am. Film Inst., U. Ga. Alumni Assn., Sigma Kappa, Soc. Am. Mil. Engrs. Author: Harris Computer Users Manual, 1983.

ROBERTS, MARKLEY, economist, educator; b. Shanghai, China, Sept. 3, 1930; s. Donald and Frances Charlotte (Markley) R.; m. Jeanne Addison, Feb. 19, 1966; children: Addison, Ellen. A.B., Princeton U., 1951; M.A., Am. U., 1960, Ph.D., 1970. Reporter Washington Star newspaper, 1952-57; legis. asst. Office of Senator Hubert Humphrey of Minn., Washington, 1957-62; legis. asst., economist AFL-CIO, Washington, 1962—; asst. dir. econ. rsch. dept., 1989—; bd. dir., vice chmn. Econ. Edn. Found. for Clergy, 1972-80; chmn. labor research adv. council Bur. Labor Stats.-Dept. Labor, 1972—; adj. prof. econs. U. Md., 1966—, George Washington U., 1972—. Contbr. numerous articles on labor and econ. affairs, tech., productivity to various publs.; author monographs in field. Mem. D.C. Democratic Central Com., 1964-68; ward III coordinator Washington Mayor Walter Washington, 1974-78; bd. dirs. Laymen's Nat. Bible Com. Inc., N.Y.C., 1972-82. Mem. Am. Econ. Assn., Indsl. Rels. Rsch. Assn. (exec. bd. 1975-77), Am. Polit. Sci. Assn., Nat. Acad. Social Ins., Assn. Evolutionary Econs., Am. Statis. Assn., Nat. Consumers League (bd. dirs. 1991—), Newspaper Guild, Ams. for Dem. Action (exec. bd. 1992—), Social Democrats USA. Democrat. Episcopalian. Home: 4931 Albemarle St NW Washington DC 20016-4359 Office: AFL-CIO 815 16th St NW Washington DC 20006-4104

ROBERTS, MELVILLE PARKER, JR., neurosurgeon, educator; b. Phila., Oct. 15, 1931; s. Melville Parker and Marguerite Louise (Reimann) R.; m. Sigrid Marianne Magnusson, Mar. 27, 1954; children: Melville Parker III, Julia Pell, Erik Emerson. BS, Washington and Lee U., 1953; MD, Yale U., 1957. Diplomate: Am. Bd. Neurol. Surgery. Intern Yale Med. Ctr., 1957, neurosurg. resident, 1958-60, 62-64, Am. Cancer Soc. fellow in neurosurgery, 1962-64, instr., 1964; asst. prof. surgery Sch. Medicine U. Va., Charlottesville, 1965-69; practice medicine specializing in neurol. surgery Hartford, Conn., 1970—; mem. sr. staff Hartford Hosp., John Dempsey Hosp.; asst. prof. surgery Sch. Medicine U. Conn., Farmington, 1970-71; assoc. prof. U. Conn., 1972-75, assoc. prof. neurology, 1974-77, chmn. divsn. neurosurgery, 1971-84, prof. surgery 1975—, acting chmn. dept. neurology 1973-77, acting chmn. dept. surgery, 1974-77, William Beecher Scoville prof. neurosurgery, 1976—; James Hudson Brown rsch. fellow Yale U., 1957. Author: Atlas of the Human Brain in Section, 1970, 2d edition, 1987; mem. editorial bd.: Conn. Medicine, 1973—; contbr. articles to profl. jours. Capt. M.C., U.S. Army, 1960-61. Fellow ACS, Royal Soc. Medicine (London); mem. AAUP, Am. Assn. Neurol. Surgeons, Soc. Neurol. Surgeons, Congress Neurol. Surgeons (bd. dirs. joint spinal sect. with Am. Assn. Neurol. Surgeons, chmn. ann. meeting 1987, sci. program chmn. ann. meeting 1988), Assn. for Rsch. in Nervous and Mental Diseases, New Eng. Neurosurg. Soc. (bd. dirs. 1976-79, pres. 1989-91), Soc. Brit. Neurol. Surgeons, Rsch. Soc. Neurol. Surgeons, Soc. Rsch. into Hydrocephalus and Spina Bifida, Conn. Acad. Arts and Sci., Vereinigung Schweizer Neurochirugen, Mory's Assn., Graduates Club (New Haven), Sloane Club (London), Beaumont Med. Club (pres. 1988), Naval Club (London), Farmington Country Club, La Grand Mare Golf Club (Guernsey, Channel Islands), Sigma Xi. Episcopalian. Office: Ste 707 85 Seymour St Hartford CT 06106-5501

ROBERTS, MERRILL JOSEPH, economist, educator; b. Glendive, Mont., Aug. 10, 1915; s. Merrill Joseph and Inez (Ludgate) R.; m. Janet Hunter Dion, Aug. 31, 1941; children: David, Michael, James, Patricia. B.A., U. Minn., 1938; M.B.A., U. Chgo., 1939, Ph.D., 1952. Transp. economist OPA, Washington, 1941, USDA, Washington, 1942-46, TVA, 1946-48; asst. prof. transp. and econs., then assoc. prof. U. Fla., Gainesville, 1948-54, prof., 1955-58; assoc. prof. transp. UCLA, 1954-55; vis. prof. econs. Mich. State U., 1956-57; prof. transp. and pub. utilities Grad. Sch. Bus., U. Pitts., 1958-72, head dept. transp. and pub. utilities, 1958-61, prof. econs., 1960-72, chmn. faculty, 1960-63; dir. Bur. Bus. Research, 1963-66; v.p., dir. econs. div. Wilbur Smith and Assocs., 1972-75; prof., chmn. transp., bus. and pub. policy U. Md., 1975-79, prof., 1979-82, prof. emeritus 1983—; research cons. Nat. Transp. Policy Study Commn., 1977-79; cons. ICC, 1979-84, Dept. Transp., Washington, 1982-84, Md. Dept. Transp., 1987-88; Disting. Research lectr., Iowa State U., 1986; econ. adv. Estudio Integral de Transport de Bolivia, 1979; mem. adv. panel, R.R. merger project Rail Services Planning Office, ICC; dir. study Penn Central R.R. bankruptcy U.S. Senate, 1971-72; Econ. cons. numerous fgn. govts. including, New Zealand, Thailand, Singapore, Hong Kong, Korea, Spain, Nicaragua, Algeria; cons. transp. to bus. and govt. agys.; research staff Commn. Money and Credit, 1959-60; mem. Venezuelan Commn. Economica Ferroviaria Nacional, 1959-60; participant transp. study conf. Nat. Acad. Sci.-NRC, 1960; research staff Nat. Planning Assn. study, 1962-63; participant Am. Assembly Conf. on the Future of Am. Transp., 1971; mem. research com. Transp. Assn. Am., 1965-72; v.p. Am. Transp. Research Forum, 1960-63; mem. legis. com. Allegheny Regional Adv. Bd., 1959-72; mem. com. applications of econs. Transp. Research Bd., Nat. Acad. Scis., 1973-80. Author: (with T.C. Bigham) Citrus Fruit Rates, 1950, Transportation, 1952, Taxation of Railroads and Other State-Assessed Companies in Florida, 1957, Evaluation of Rate Regulation, 1959, Transportation in Region in Transition, 1962, Freight Transport Coordination, 1966, The Penn Central and Other Railroads, 1973; contbr. numerous articles to profl. jours. Mem. Port Authority Allegheny County, 1962-69; Bd. visitors Amy Transp. Sch., 1959-60. Served to lt. (s.g.) USNR, 1942-46. Recipient Johnson award for outstanding research, Transp. Research Bd., Nat. Acad. Scis., 1986. Mem. Am. Econs. Assn. (sec.-treas. transp. and pub. utilities group 1957-61, chmn. 1963), Am. Soc. Traffic and Transp. (founder mem.), Nat. Def. Transp. Assn. (life), Delta Nu Alpha, Phi Delta Theta, Beta Gamma Sigma. Presbyterian. Club: Cosmos (Washington). Home: #113 3749 Sarasota Square Blvd Sarasota FL 34238

ROBERTS, MORTON SPITZ, astronomer; b. N.Y.C., Nov. 5, 1926; m. Josephine Taylor, Aug. 2, 1951; 1 dau., Elizabeth Mason. B.A., Pomona Coll., 1948; Sc.D. (hon.), 1979; M.Sc., Calif. Inst. Tech., 1950; Ph.D. (Lick Obs. fellow), U. Calif., Berkeley, 1958. Asst. prof. physics Occidental Coll. 1949-52; lectr. astronomy dept. U. Calif., Berkeley, 1959-60; lectr., research

asso. Harvard Coll. Obs., Harvard U., 1960-64; scientist Nat. Radio Astronomy Obs., Charlottesville, Va., 1964-78; dir. Nat. Radio Astronomy Obs., 1978-84, sr. scientist, 1978—; Sigma Xi nat. lectr., 1970-71; vis. educator SUNY, Stony Brook, 1968, Cambridge U., 1972, 86-87, U. Groningen, 1972. Bd. editors: Astronomy and Astrophysics, 1977-80; asso. editor: Astron. Jour, 1977-79. NSF postdoctoral fellow, 1958-59. Mem. AAAS, NAS, Am. Astron. Soc. (vis. prof. program 1965-73, v.p. 1971-72, mem. coun. 1983-86, publs. bd. 1979-80), Internat. Astron. Union (v.p. 1988-94), Internat. Sci. Radio Union. Home: 1826 Wayside Pl Charlottesville VA 22903-1631 Office: Nat Radio Astronomy Obs Edgemont Rd Charlottesville VA 22903

ROBERTS, NANCY, computer educator; b. Boston, Jan. 25, 1938; d. Harold and Annette (Zion) Rosenthal; m. Edward B. Roberts, June 14, 1959; children: Valerie Friedman, Mitchell, Andrea. AB, Boston U., 1959, MEd, 1961, EdD, 1975. Elem. tchr. Sharon (Mass.) Pub. Schs., 1959-63; asst. prof. Lesley Coll., Cambridge, Mass., 1975-79, assoc. prof., 1980-83, prof., 1983—; dir. grad. programs in computers in edn. Lesley Coll., Cambridge, Mass., 1980—; dir. Project Bridge, 1987-92; dir. Ctr. for Math., Sci. and Tech. in Edn., Cambridge, Mass., 1990-91; rsch. assoc. MIT, Cambridge, 1976-79; mem. nat. steering com. Nat. Edn. Computing Conf., Eugene, Oreg., 1979—, co-chmn. nat. conf., 1989, vice chmn. steering com., 1991—. Author: Dynamics of Human Service Delivery, 1976, Practical Guide to Computers in Education, 1982, Computers in Teaching Mathematics, 1983, Introduction to Computer Simulation, 1983 (J.W. Forrester award 1983), Integrating Computers into the Elementary and Middle School, 1987, Computers and the Social Studies, 1988, Integrating Telecommunications into Education, 1990; mem. editorial bd. Jour. Ednl. Computing, 1983—; Jour. Rsch. in Sci. Teaching; editor Computers in Edn. book series, 1984-89. Mem. Computer Policy Com., Boston, 1982-84, mem. adv. bd. Electronic Learning, 1989-91; bd. dirs. Computers for kids, Cambridge, 1983-85; mem. State Ednl. Tech. Adv. Coun., 1990—. NSF grantee, 1985—. Mem. System Dynamics Soc. (bd. dirs. policy com. 1987-89). Republican. Jewish. Home: 300 Boylston St # 1102 Boston MA 02116-3923 Office: Lesley Coll 29 Everett St Cambridge MA 02138-2790

ROBERTS, NEIL FLETCHER, management consulting company executive; b. Salem, Oreg., Feb. 4, 1914; s. Harold D. and Rhoda (Haynes) R.; m. Lee (Roberts) R., June 23, 1937; children—Stephen L., Susan A. (Mrs. J.B. Persson). A.B., Dartmouth Coll., 1935; M.B.A., Harvard U., 1937. With United Bank Denver N.A. (formerly U.S. Nat. Bank, merger with Denver Nat. Bank 1959, became Denver U.S. Nat. Bank), 1937—, v.p. 1948-54, exec. v.p., 1954-62, pres., 1962-69, vice chmn., 1971—, chief exec. officer, 1969-71; v.p. United Banks Colo., Inc. (formerly Denver U.S. Bancorp., Inc.), 1964-70, exec. v.p., 1971-72, pres., 1972-77, chief exec. officer, 1974-79, chmn. bd., 1977-79; chmn. United Mortgage Co., 1971-74, dir., 1968-71, 74-77; chmn. United Banks Service Co., 1971-75, dir., 1975-77. Trustee Mile High United Way, 1971-79, chmn., pres., 1969-71. Served as lt. (j.g.) USNR, 1944-46. Mem. Phi Kappa Sigma. Episcopalian. Home: 3165 S Hills Ct Denver CO 80210-6829

ROBERTS, NORMAN LESLIE, lawyer; b. Yakima, Wash., Jan. 17, 1935; s. Leslie Clement Roberts and Marie (Dietzen) Delger; m. Dorita Gale Rushton, June 6, 1959; children—Theresa, Monica, Deborah. LL.B., Gonzaga U., 1959. Bar: Wash. 1959, U.S. Supreme Ct. 1965, Calif. 1969. Counsel guidance and control systems Litton Industries, Woodland Hills, Calif., 1968-73, v.p. group counsel, Beverly Hills, Calif., 1973-78, staff v.p., asst. gen. counsel, 1978-86, staff v.p., assoc. gen. counsel, 1986-88, corp. v.p., 1988-90, corp. sr. v.p., gen. counsel, 1990—, chmn. bd. dirs. Litton Saudi Arabia Ltd., 1982—; dir. Litton Employee Fed. Credit Union, 1971—; editorial advisor pub. contracts report Bur. Nat. Affairs, 1979—. Served to maj. U.S. Army, 1959-62. Mem. ABA (council mem. pub. contract law sect. 1984-87, sect. sec. 1987-88, vice chmn., 1988-89, sect. chmn. 1990-91, chmn. internat. procurement com. 1982-84), Warner Ctr. Club (L.A.), Tower Club (Oxnard, Calif.), Pacific Corinthian Yacht Club (Oxnard). Home: Woodland # 22449 Woodland Hills CA 91367 Office: Litton Industries Inc 360 N Crescent Dr Beverly Hills CA 90210-4802

ROBERTS, (GRANVILLE) ORAL, clergyman; b. nr. Ada, Okla., Jan. 24, 1918; s. Ellis Melvin and Claudius Priscilla (Irwin) R.; m. Evelyn Lutman, Dec. 25, 1938; children: Rebecca Ann (dec.), Ronald David (dec.), Richard Lee, Roberta Jean. Student, Okla. Bapt. U., 1942-44, Phillips U., 1947; LLD (hon.), Centenary Coll., 1975. Ordained to ministry Pentecostal Holiness Ch., 1936, United Meth. Ch., 1968. Evangelist 1936-41; pastor Fuquay Springs, N.C., 1941, Shawnee, Okla., 1942-45, Toccoa, Ga., 1946, Enid, Okla., 1947; began worldwide evangelistic ministry thru crusades, radio, TV, printed page, 1947; founder Oral Roberts Evangelistic Assn., Inc., Tulsa, 1948, Univ. Village Retirement Center, 1970, City of Faith Med./Research Ctr., 1981, Healing Outreach Ctr., 1986; founder, pub. Abundant Life mag., Daily Blessing (quar. mag.); founder, chancellor Oral Roberts U., Tulsa, 1963—; founding chmn. Internat. Charismatic Bible Ministries. Author: over 50 books including: If You Need Healing, Do These Things, 1947, God is a Good God, 1960, If I Were You, 1967, Miracle of Seed-Faith, 1970, autobiography The Call, 1971, The Miracle Book, 1972, A Daily Guide to Miracles, 1975, Better Health and Miracle Living, 1976, How to Get Through Your Struggles, 1977, Receiving Your Miracle, 1978, Don't Give Up, 1980, Your Road to Recovery, 1986, Attack Your Lack, 1985, How I Learned Jesus Was Not Poor, 1989, How to Resist the Devil, 1989, Fear Not!, 1989, A Prayer Cover Over Your Life, 1990, Is God Your Source?, 1992, 11 Major Prophecies For You in 1992, 1992, Unleashing the Power of Praying in the Spirit, 1993; also numerous tracts and brochures, Bible commentaries. Recipient Indian of Yr. award Am. Broadcasters Assn., 1963; Okla. Hall of Fame, 1973; Oklahoman of Yr., 1974. Club: Rotary. Office: Oral Roberts U 7777 S Lewis Ave Tulsa OK 74171-0002

ROBERTS, PAUL CRAIG, III, economics educator, author, consultant; b. Atlanta, Apr. 3, 1939; s. Paul Craig and Ellen Lamar (Dryman) R.; m. Linda Jane Fisher, July 3, 1969; children: Pendaran Struan Sherman, Becky Ellen, Stephanie Bradford. BS, Ga. Inst. Tech., 1961; postgrad., U. Calif., Berkeley, 1962-63, Merton Coll., Oxford (Eng.) U., 1964-65; PhD (Earhart fellow), U. Va., 1967. Asst. prof. econs. Va. Poly. Inst., 1965-69; assoc. prof. U. N.Mex., 1969-71; rsch. fellow Hoover Instn., Stanford U., 1971-77, sr. rsch. fellow, 1978—; mem. U.S. Congl. Staff, 1975-78; asst. sec. of treasury for econ. policy Dept. Treasury, Washington, 1981-82; William E. Simon prof. polit. economy Georgetown U. Ctr. for Strategic and Internat. Studies, Washington, 1982-93; chmn. Inst. for Polit. Economy, 1985—, John M. Olin fellow, 1994—; disting. adj. scholar Ctr. Strategic and Internat. Studies Georgetown U., Washington, 1993—; adj. scholar Cato Inst., 1987-93, disting. fellow, 1993—; assoc. editor, columnist Wall St. Jour., N.Y.C., 1978-80; columnist Bus. Week, 1983—, Fin. Post, Can., 1988-89, Liberation, Paris, 1988-89, Erfolg, Fed. Rep. of Germany, 1988, Washington Times, 1988-, San Diego Union, 1988—, Le Figaro, Paris, 1992—; nationally syndicated columnist Scripps Howard News Svc., 1989—; contbr. editor: Nat. Rev., 1993—, Reason Mag., 1993—; mem. Pres.-elect Reagan's Task Force on Tax Policy, 1980; dir. Value Line Investment Funds, N.Y.C., A. Schulman, Akron, Ohio; cons. Morgan Guaranty Trust Co., Lazard Freres Asset Mgmt.; pres. Econ. & Communication Svcs. Inc.; cons. Dept. Commerce, 1983, Dept. Def., 1983-84; mem. adv. bd. Marvin and Palmer; mem. Wright Investors' Svc. Internat. Bd. Econ. and Investment Advisors; bd. dirs. Com. on Present Danger; trustee Intercollegiate Studies Inst., Com. on Developing Am. Capitalism; mem. selection com. Frank E. Seidman Disting. Award in Polit. Economy. Author: Alienation and the Soviet Economy, 1971, new edit., 1990, Marx's Theory of Exchange, 1973, new edit., 1983, The Supply-Side Revolution: An Insider's Account of Policymaking in Washington, 1984, The Cost of Corporate Capital in the U.S. and Japan, 1985, Meltdown: Inside the Soviet Economy, 1990; mem. editorial bd. Modern Age, Intercollegiate Rev.; contbg. editor Harper's Mag. Drafted original Kemp-Roth Bill, 1976. Recipient Meritorious Svc. award Dept. Treasury, 1982, Pub. Svc. award GSA, 1991, Warren Brookes award for Excellence in Journalism, 1992; Am. Philos. Soc. grantee, 1968; named to Chevalier de la Légion d'Honneur, 1987; Nat. Chamber Found. fellow, 1984-85. Mem. Mont Pelerin Soc., Beethoven Soc., Am. Soc. French Legion of Honor, U.S. C. of C. (taxation com.). Internat. Club Washington. Office: Cato Inst 1000 Massachusetts Ave NW Washington DC 20001-5400

ROBERTS, PETER A., banker; b. N.Y.C., Apr. 11, 1951; s. Louis Aaron and Ida Ann (Sterman) Rottenberg. B.A., Colgate U., 1973; M.B.A.,

Stanford U., 1976. Vol. VISTA, Louisville, 1973-74; v.p., investment banker Morgan Stanley & Co., N.Y.C., 1976-82; investment banker Lazard Freres, N.Y.C., 1982-86, gen. ptnr., 1985-86; chmn., chief exec. officer College Savs. Bank, Princeton, N.J., 1987—. Mem. N.Y. Athletic Club, Metedeconk Nat. Golf Club (Jackson, N.J.), Omicron Delta Epsilon. Office: College Savs Bank 5 Vaughn Dr Princeton NJ 08540-6313

ROBERTS, PETER ALLEN, physical education educator; b. Buffalo, Feb. 20, 1943; s. Hobart Vosburgh and Bertha Jane (Ash) R.; m. Sherri Ann Olson, Sept. 12, 1986; 1 child, Sarah Jane. BS, Mich. State U., 1966, MA, 1970. Cert. tchr., Mich.; cert. water safety instr. trainer, lifeguard instr. trainer, CPR instr. trainer, standard first aid instr.-trainer. Educator Alpena (Mich.) Pub. Sch., 1966-69; prof. Wayne State U., Detroit, 1970—; head coach swimming Wayne State U., Detroit, 1969-84; cons. in field. Bd. dirs. ARC, Detroit, chair aquatic com., 1972—, mem. aquatic enhancement adv. com., 1993; staff mem. Mich. Aquatic Sch., 1968—. Recipient Outstanding Svc. medal ARC, 1981, Fifteen Yrs. Outstanding Svc. award, 1985, Joan B. Warren award ARC, 1986, 30 Yr. Svc. Pin, ARC, 1992. Mem. AAHPERD, Mich. AHPERD, Coll. Swimming Coaches Assn., Phi Epsilon Kappa. Democrat. Methodist. Avocations: golf, swimming, racquetball, boating. Home: 23055 Beck Rd Novi MI 48374-3622 Office: Wayne State U 264 Matthaei Bldg Detroit MI 48202

ROBERTS, PRISCILLA WARREN, artist; b. Montclair, N.J., June 13, 1916; d. Charles Asaph and Florence (Berry) R. Student, Art Students League, 1937-39, Nat. Acad., 1939-43. Represented in permanent collections Met. Mus., Cin. Art Mus., Canton Art Inst., Westmoreland County Mus. Art, Pa., IBM, Dallaas Mus., Walker Art Ctr., Mpls., Butler Inst., Youngstown, Ohio, Nat. Mus. Am. Art, Washington. Recipient Proctor prize, 1947, popular prize Corcoran Biennial, 1947, prize Westmoreland County Mus., 3d prize Carnegie Internat., Pitts., 1950, Nat. Mus. Women in Arts, Washington, Snite Mus., U. Notre Dame, Ind. Mem. NAD (Hallgarten prize 1945), Allied Artists Am. (Zabriskie prize 1944, 46), Catherine Lorillard Wolfe Assn. (hon.). Address: PO Box 716 Georgetown CT 06829

ROBERTS, RALPH JOEL, cable television, telephone communications and background music company executive; b. N.Y.C., Mar. 13, 1920; s. Robert and Sara (Wahl) Roberts; m. Suzanne Fleisher, Aug. 23, 1942; children: Catherine, Lisa, Ralph Jr., Brian, Douglas. BS in Econs., U. Pa., 1941. Account exec. Aitken Kynett Advt., Phila., 1946-48; v.p. Muzak Corp., N.Y.C., 1948-50; pres., chief exec. officer Pioneer Industries, Inc., Darby, Pa., 1950-61; pres. Internat. Equity Corp., Bala Cynwyd, Pa., 1961-83; chmn. bd., Comcast Corp., Phila., 1969—; chmn., chief exec. officer Sural Corp. (merger with Internat. Equity Corp. 1983); trustee, chmn. conflict interest com. Albert Einstein Med. Ctr. Bd. dirs. regional NCCJ; trustee Brandywine Mus. and Conservancy, charter mem. World Bus. Coun.; past mem. mentor program and Benjamin Franklin assocs. U. Pa.; bd. dirs. Phila. Orch., 1993; past v.p. Family Svc. Phila.; past bd. dirs., mem. budget and fees com. State Coll. and Univ. Dirs.; mem. re-regulation and legis. affairs coms. Nat. Cable TV Assn.; past mem. Gov.'s Rev. of Govt. Mgmt., Inc. Lt. USNR, 1942-45. Reipient americanism award Anti-Defamation League of B'nai B'rith, Brotherhood award NCCJ, 1989, award for outstanding svc. to cable TV industry Walter Kaitz Found., 1990, Acres of Diamonds Entrepreneurial Excellence award Entrepreneurial Inst. Temple U., 1991, Disting. Vanguard award for leadership Nat. Cable TV Assn., 1993; named to Broadcasting and Cable Hall of Fame, 1993. Avocations: tennis, travel. Home: Sural Farm 1375 Fairview Rd Coatesville PA 19320-4431 Office: Comcast Corp 480 E Swedesford Rd # 1 Wayne PA 19087-1822*

ROBERTS, RALPH S., restaurant chain executive; b. 1942. Co-founder, pres. Rusty Scupper Restaurant, San Francisco, 1969-76; pres. Stouffer Hospitality divsn. Nestlé, 1976-80; dep. group exec. ops. W.R. Grace Restaurant Group, Irvine, Calif., 1980-86; with American Restaurant Group, Newport Beach, Calif., 1986—; pres., COO various subs., Newport Beach, Calif.; now pres., COO American Restaurant Group, Newport Beach, Calif. Office: Am Restaurant Group 450 Newport Center Dr Newport Beach CA 92660-7610*

ROBERTS, RICHARD, mechanical engineering educator; b. Atlantic City, N.J., Feb. 16, 1938; s. Harold and Marion (Hofman) R.; m. Rochelle S. Perelman, Oct. 2, 1960; children: Lori, Lisa, Scott. BSME, Drexel U., 1961; MSME, Lehigh U., 1962, PhD in Mech. Engring., 1964. Asst. prof. mech. engring. Lehigh U., Bethlehem, Pa., 1964-68, assoc. prof., 1968-75, prof., 1975—. Editor: Proceedings of the Thirteenth Nat. Symposium on Fracture Mechanics, 1980, ASME PVP Division's Design Handbook, Materials and Fabrication, Vol. III. Recipient W. Sparagen award Am. Welding Soc., 1972, Adams Meml. award, 1981. Home: 317 Bierys Bridge Rd Bethlehem PA 18017-1142 Office: Lehigh Univ MSE/200 W Packer Bethlehem PA 18015

ROBERTS, RICHARD D., cable station executive; b. 1934. BS, U.S. Naval Acad.; MBA, Harvard U. With Landmark Comm. Inc., Norfolk, Va., 1967-73; with Teleccable Corp., Norfolk, 1968—, pres., 1977-84, CEO, 1984—. Mem. Nat. Cable TV Assn. (bd. dirs. 1987, chair high definition TV com.). Office: Teleccable Corp 999 Waterside Dr Ste 900 Norfolk VA 23510-3306*

ROBERTS, RICHARD HEILBRON, construction company executive; b. Sacramento, Nov. 19, 1925; s. John Montgomery and Mary Lou (Heilbron) R.; m. Jo Anne Sydney Erickson, Feb. 25, 1950; children: Richard, Kurt, Tracy. BSCE, U. Calif., 1949. Registered profl. engr., Calif. Field and resident engr. Calif. Div. Hwys., San Luis Obispo, 1949-51; project and br. mgr. Granite Constrn. Co., Watsonville, Calif., 1951-68, v.p., mgr., 1968-79, pres. engring. constrn. div., 1979-83, exec. v.p., chief operating officer, 1983-89, vice chmn., 1989—, also bd. dirs. Pres. Nellie Thomas Inst. Learning, 1989-90. Served to corp. U.S. Army, 1944-46. Mem. Soc. Am. Mil. Engrs., Beavers (bd. dirs., pres. 1984, Golden Beaver award 1986, Moles Non-mem. award 1988). Republican. Presbyterian. Clubs: Monterey Peninsula Country (Pebble Beach, Calif.); Silverado Country (Napa, Calif.); Pauma Valley (Calif.) Country. Avocations: golf, tennis. Home: 3481 Taylor Rd Carmel CA 93923-8914 Office: Granite Constrn Co PO Box 50085 Watsonville CA 95077-5085

ROBERTS, RICHARD JOHN, molecular biologist, consultant; b. Derby, Eng., Sept. 6, 1943; came to U.S., 1969; s. John Walter and Edna Wilhelmina (Allsop) R.; m. Elizabeth Dyson, Aug. 21, 1965 (dec.); children: Alison, Andrew; m. Jean E. Tagliabue, Feb. 14, 1986; children: Christopher, Amanda. BS, Sheffield (Eng.) U., 1965, PhD, 1968. Rsch. fellow Harvard U., Cambridge, Mass., 1969-70, rsch. assoc., 1971-72; sr. staff investigator Cold Spring Harbor Lab., N.Y., 1972-87, asst. dir., 1987-92; rsch. dir. New England Biolabs, 1992—; cons. New Eng. Biolabs, Beverly, Mass., 1974-92; sci. adv. bd. Genex, Rockville, Md., 1977-85. Contbr. articles to profl. jours. Recipient Nobel prize in Physiology and Medicine, Nobel Foundation, 1993, John Simon Guggenheim Found. fellow, 1979. Fellow Royal Soc.; mem. Am. Soc. Microbiology, Am. Soc. Biol. Chemists. Office: New England Biolabs 32 Tozer Rd Beverly MA 01915

ROBERTS, RICHARD STEWART, lawyer; b. Columbus, Ohio, May 18, 1945; s. Kibler Richard and Mary Christene (Wolf) R.; m. Carol Ann Redrow, June 13, 1970; children: Charles Kibler, Eric Wesley. BA cum laude, Ohio Wesleyan U., 1967; JD, U. Mich., 1969. Bar: Ohio 1970, U.S. Dist. Ct. (so. dist.) Ohio 1970, U.S. Ct. Mil. Appeals 1971, U.S. Supreme Ct. 1980. Assoc. Taft, Stettinius & Hollister, Cin., 1970, 74-80, ptnr., 1980—. Trustee Community Improvement Corp. of Greater Cin., 1982—; active mem. Anderson Hills United Meth. Ch., Cin., 1984—. Capt. JAGC, USAF, 1970-74. Mem. Masons, Phi Beta Kappa, Omicron Delta Kappa, Delta Tau Delta. Republican. Avocation: photography. Home: 835 Shawneetrace Ct Cincinnati OH 45255 Office: 1800 Star Bank Ct 425 Walnut St Cincinnati OH 45202-3957

ROBERTS, RICHARD Y., federal agency administrator; b. Birmingham, Ala., July 3, 1951; m. Peggy Frew; 3 children. BEE, Auburn U., 1973; JD, U. Ala., 1976; ML in Taxation, George Washington U., 1981. Bar: D.C., Ala. Assoc. Law Offices of Richard Shelby, Tuscaloosa, Ala., 1976-78; admnistrv. asst., legis. dir. to Congressman Richard Shelby Washington, 1979-82, admnistrv. asst., legis. dir. to Senator Richard Shelby, 1987-90;

ptnr. Pappanastos, Samford & Roberts, Montgomery, Ala., 1983-84, Perry, Russell & Roberts, Montgomery, 1985-86, Miller, Hamilton, Snider & Odom, Washington, 1990; commr. SEC, Washington, 1990—; lectr. in field. Contbr. articles to profl. jours. Bd. dirs. Nat. Capital Area Coun., Boy Scouts Am.; active First Bapt. Ch., Alexandria, Va. Mem. D.C. Bar Assn., Ala. State Bar Assn., Phi Eta Sigma, Tau Beta, Pi, Eta Kappa Nu. Home: 4711 Tara Dr Fairfax VA 22032 Office: SEC Office of the Chairman 450 5th St NW Washington DC 20549

ROBERTS, ROBERT, engineering organization executive, think-tank executive. Pres. Syracuse Rsch. Corp., Syracuse, N.Y. Office: Syracuse Research Corp Merrill Ln Syracuse NY 13210

ROBERTS, ROBERT CHARLES, secondary education educator; b. Passaic, N.J., June 2, 1940; s. Frank Douglas and Johanna (Cornelisse) Ungemah; Marian Elizabeth Spittel, Nov. 17, 1962 (widowed Oct. 1985); children: Donn, Lynn; m. Jane Francis Purdy, Apr. 5, 1986; children: Christopher, Dustin, B.J. BS, Montclair State U., N.J., 1963, MA, 1967. Cert. phys. edn. and health educator N.J.; supr., N.J., prin., N.J. Tchr. Clifton (N.J.) Bd. Edn., 1963-79, football coach, 1964-78, basketball coach, 1963-73, lacrosse coach, 1975-79, dir. phys. edn. health and athletics, 1979—; exec. sec. No. N.J. Interscholastic League, 1984—; pres. N.J. Interscholastic Hockey League, 1982-83, N.J. lacrosse League, 1983-84. Lay Leader United Meth. Ch., Franklin Lakes, N.J., 1986-90. Mem. Nat. Interscholastic Athletic Adminstrn. Assn., AAHPERD, N.J. Prin. and Suprs. Assn., N.J. Edn. Assn., N.J. Assn. for Health, Phys. Edn., Recreation and Dance. Republican. Methodist. Avocation: golf. Office: Clifton High School 333 Colfax Ave Clifton NJ 07013-1701

ROBERTS, ROBERT WINSTON, social work educator, dean; b. Balt., July 23, 1932; s. Kelmer Swan Roberts and Lettie Mae (Collins) Johnston; m. Helen Elizabeth Perpich, Mar. 4, 1964. BA with high honors, San Francisco State U., 1957; MSW, U. Calif., Berkeley, 1959; D in Social Welfare, Columbia U., 1970. Caseworker Edgewood Protestant Orphanage, San Francisco, 1959-62, Jewish Family Service, San Francisco, 1962-63; research assoc. U. Calif., Berkeley, 1963-65; research analyst Family Service Assn. Am., N.Y.C., 1965-69; asst. prof. U. Chgo., 1967-70; prof. U. So. Calif., Los Angeles, 1970-90, dean sch. social work, 1980-88, dean emeritus, prof. emeritus, 1990—; vis. prof. Western Australia Inst. Tech., Perth, 1976-77, Chinese U. Hong Kong and U. Hong Kong, 1980; cons. Crittenton Services, Los Angeles, 1970-72, James Weldon Johnson Community Ctr., N.Y., 1966-67; bd. dirs. El Centro, Los Angeles. Editor: The Unwed Mother, 1966; co-editor: Theories of Social Casework, 1970, Child Caring: Social Policy and the Institution, 1973, Theories of Social Work with Groups, 1976, Theory and Practice of Community Social Work, 1980; editorial bd. Social Work Jour.; contbr. articles to profl. jours. Served to staff sgt. USAF, 1950-54. Fellow NIMH, 1957-58, 65-67, Crown Zellerbach Found., 1958-59; recipient Outstanding Educator award Los Amigos de la Humanidad, 1979; named Disting. Assoc., Nat. Acad. Practice in Social Work, 1985. Mem. Nat. Assn. Social Workers (chmn. social action com. 1960-61), Council on Social Work Edn. (bd. dirs. 1970-73, del. to assembly 1971-72, commn. minority groups 1972-73). Avocations: reading, travel, photography. Office: Univ So Calif Sch Social Work Rm 214 Montgomery Ross Fisher Bldg Los Angeles CA 90089-0411

ROBERTS, RUBY ALTIZER, poet, author, fiction; b. Floyd Co., Vt., Apr. 22, 1907; d. Waddy William and Dana Adeline (Cummings) Altizer; m. Laurence Luther Roberts, July 23, 1927; 1 child, Heidi. Grad., Christianburg (Va.) High Sch.; nursing course, Norfolk (Va.) Protestant Hosp.; DHL, Coll. William and Mary, 1961. Freelance writer, 1939—, newspaper corr.; rep. of Spirit of Va., 1993. Author (with Rosa Altizer Bray) Emera Altizer and His Descendants, 1937, 2 vols. poetry, Forever is Too Long, command the Stars, (biography) The Way It Was, 1979, The Way It Is, 1992; editor juvenile verse dept. Embers Mag., Batavia, N.Y., 1944—; owner, editor, pub. The Lyric Mag.; poetry columnist Va. newspaper; contbr. over 120 poems to anthologies, newspapers, mags, numerous articles to jours. Recipient First Poetry prize Sanctuary Mag., Ballaman award Disting. Svc. to Poetry, 1956, citation Disting. Svc. Poetry Khalsa Coll.; named poet laureate Va. Gen. Assembly, 1950, poet laureate Va. emeritus Gen. Assembly Va., 1992. 1st Woman to be named Poet Laureate of state. Home: 301 Roanoke St Christiansburg VA 24073

ROBERTS, SAMUEL ALDEN, secondary education educator; b. Kansas City, Kans., Oct. 30, 1930; s. Elester and Sadie Lillian (Lewis) R.; m. Sallie Senora, Aug. 26, 1962; children: Sadie, Alden, Samuel Jr., William, Tyrone; AB, Knoxville Coll., 1954; MDiv, Interdenominational Theol. Ctr, 1960; MS, Ind. State U., 1974; DMin, Chgo. Theol. Sem., 1981; EdS, Ind. State U., 1986. Cert. secondary English tchr., secondary prin. Supt. Lott Carey Bapt. Mission Sch., Haiti, 1964-68, Hardy Jr. High Sch., Chattanooga; tchr. Wirt High Sch., Gary, Ind.; asst. prin. Elston Jr. High Sch., Michigan City, Ind., athletic dir., 1976-80; tchr. Rogers High Sch., Michigan City. Mem. ASCD, Internat. Reading Assn., Nat. Coun. Tchrs. English, Michigan City Area Coun. (past pres.), Fedn. Block Units of Urban League N.W. Ind. (pres.), Ind. State Reading Assn. (secondary curriculum com.), Fedn. Block Clubs, Phi Delta Kappa (editor newsletter U. Chgo./DePaul U. chpt.). Home: 2300 Adams St Gary IN 46407-3042

ROBERTS, SAMUEL SMITH, television news executive; b. Port Chester, N.Y., Feb. 8, 1936; s. Robert M. and Lillian (Smith) R.; children by previous marriage: Nancy, Pamela; m. Harriet Rubin, July 27, 1975; children: Rachel, David. BS, Northwestern U., 1957. Reporter UPI, N.Y.C., 1961; news editor Capital Cities Broadcasting, Providence, 1962; with CBS News, 1962—; sr. prodr. CBS Evening News with Walter Cronkite, N.Y.C., 1978-81; nat. editor CBS News, 1982-84, fgn. editor, 1984-87; dir. programming, exec. prodr. CBS News Prodns., 1992—; exec. prodr. 20th Century with Mike Wallace, 1994—. Served to lt. USN, 1957-61. Avocations: baseball, history, jazz.

ROBERTS, SANDRA, editor; b. Humboldt, Tenn., July 22, 1951; d. Harold and Margaret (Headrick) R.; m. Parker W. Duncan Jr., Aug. 11, 1990. Student, Tex. Christian U., 1969-70; BS, U. Tenn., 1972; MLS, Peabody Coll. Libr. The Tennessean, Nashville, 1975-82, editorial writer, 1982-87, editorial editor, 1987—. Pres. Women's Polit. Caucus, Nashville, 1982. Recipient John Hancock award John Hancock Co., 1983, Freedom award Tenn. Trial Laywers Assn., 1988. Mem. Am. Soc. Newspaper Editors, Nat. Conf. Editorial Writers, Sigma Delta Chi (Nat. Headliner award 1982). Mem. Christian Ch. Office: The Tennessean 1100 Broadway Nashville TN 37203-3116

ROBERTS, SEYMOUR M. (SKIP ROBERTS), advertising agency executive; b. Detroit, Aug. 11, 1934; s. Jacob and Florence Rabinowitz; m. Carol Knight, Dec. 16, 1956; children: Bradley Alan, Tracey Knight, Kristen Sophia. B.S. in Advt., Mich. State U., 1955; M.A. in Journalism, Wayne State U., Detroit, 1956. With W.B. Doner & Co., Southfield, Mich., 1956-91; exec. v.p. W.B. Doner & Co., Southfield, 1973-84, exec. v.p., gen. mgr., 1984-91; dir. strategic planning N.W. Ayer, Detroit, 1992—, sr. ptnr., 1995—. Chmn. Vis. Nurse Assn. of Southeastern Mich. With AUS, 1957-59. Mem. NATAS, Am. Assn. Advt. Agys. (past chmn. Mich. coun.). Adcraft Club Detroit (pres.), Franklin Hills Country Club. Office: NW Ayer 2000 W Fisher Fwy Bldg Detroit MI 48216-1287

ROBERTS, SIDNEY, biological chemist; b. Boston, Mar. 11, 1918; s. Samuel Richard and Elizabeth (Gilbert) R.; m. Clara Marian Szego, Sept. 14, 1943. B.S., Mass. Inst. Tech., 1939; postgrad., Harvard U., 1939-41; M.S., U. Minn., 1942, Ph.D., 1943. Instr. physiology U. Minn. Med. Sch., 1943-44, George Washington U. Med. Sch., 1944-45; rsch. assoc. Worcester Found. Exptl. Biology, Shrewsbury, Mass., 1945-47; asst. prof. physiol. chemistry Yale U. Med. Sch., 1947-48; mem. faculty U. Calif. Med. Sch., Los Angeles, 1948—; prof. biol. chemistry U. Calif. Med. Sch., 1957—; chmn. acad. senate UCLA, 1989-90; mem. adv. panel regulatory biology NSF, 1955-57, adv. panel metabolic biology, 1957-59; mem. metabolism study sect. NIH, 1960-63; basic sci. study sect. Los Angeles County Heart Assn., 1958-63; cons. VA Hosp., Long Beach, Calif., 1951-55, Los Angeles, 1958-62; air conservation tech. adv. com. Los Angeles County Lung Assn., 1972-76. Author articles, revs.; editor med. jours. Served to 2d lt. AUS, 1944-48. Guggenheim fellow, 1957-58. Fellow AAAS; mem. Am. Physiol. Soc.,

ROBERTS, SIDNEY I., lawyer; b. Bklyn., Nov. 29, 1913; s. David I. and Ray (Bleicher) Robinovitz; m. Arlene Lee Aron, June 4, 1961; 1 son, Russell Lewis. B.B.A., CCNY, 1935; LL.B. magna cum laude, Harvard U., 1938. Bar: N.Y. 1938; C.P.A. N.Y. With Michael Schimmel & Co. (C.P.A.s), N.Y.C., 1938-39, S.D. Leidesdorf & Co. (C.P.A.s), N.Y.C., 1939-49; with firm Roosevelt, Freidin & Littauer, N.Y.C., 1950-56, Anderson & Roberts, N.Y.C., 1956-57, Roberts & Holland, N.Y.C., 1957-94; adj. prof. law Columbia U., 1971-78; mem. adv. council Internat. Bur. Fiscal Documentation. Author: (with William C. Warren) United States Tax Income Taxation of Foreign Corporations and Nonresident Aliens, 1966, (with others) Annotated Tax Forms: Practice and Procedure, 1970; editor: Legislative History of United States Tax Conventions, 16 vols., 1986—; contbr. articles to profl. jours. Mem. Internat. Bar Assn., ABA (sect. on taxation, council dir. 1970-73, chmn. com. on cooperation with state and local bar assns. 1968-70, chmn. com. on taxation of fgn. income 1963-64), N.Y. State Bar Assn. (tax sect. exec. com. 1967-87, chmn. com. on tax sect. planning 1968-70, chmn. com. on tax policy 1970-72), Assn. of Bar of City of N.Y., N.Y. State Soc. CPA's, Internat. Fiscal Assn. (mem. exec. com. 1972-77, pres. U.S.A. br. 1972-73). Jewish. Office: 145 Central Park West New York NY 10023

ROBERTS, TED, manufacturing executive; b. Mpls., Mar. 28, 1958; s. Walter Glen and Mary Jo (Cronin) R.; m. Lee Ann Gustafson, Nov. 9, 1985. BS in Bus., U. Minn., 1980, MBA in Mktg., 1984. Assoc. pub. Comm3l. West Mag. Mpls., 1980-82; v.p. mktg. Roberts Automatic Products, Chanhassen, Minn., 1982—; v.p., dir. Roberts Trading Corp., Des Moines, Iowa. Mem. Nat. Screw Machine Products Assn., N.W. Chi Psi Ednl. Found. (v.p.). Home: 4400 Garfield Ave Minneapolis MN 55409-1847 Office: Roberts Trading Corp 1350 Fin Ctr Des Moines IA 50309*

ROBERTS, THEODORE HARRIS, banker; b. Gillett, Ark., May 14, 1929; s. D. Edward and Gertrude (Harris) R.; m. Elisabeth Law, July 17, 1953; children: Susan, William, Julia, John. BA in Govt., Northwestern State U., 1949; MA in Polit. Sci., Okla. State U., 1950; attended, U. Chgo., 1956. With Harris Trust and Savs. Bank, Chgo., 1953-83; exec. v.p., sec., treas. Harris Bank and Harris Bankcorp Inc., 1971-82, dir., exec. com., 1975-82; pres. Fed. Res. Bank St. Louis, 1983-85; chmn. bd., chief exec. officer Talman Home Fed. Savs. & Loan, Chgo., 1985-92; pres. LaSalle Nat. Corp., 1992—; CEO, chmn. bd. LaSalle Talman Bank. Bd. dirs. Chgo. Ctrl. Area Com.; mem. Chgo. com. Chgo. Coun. Fgn. Rels., Leadership Com., Neighborhood Housing Svcs.; govt. affairs coun. Savings & Cmty. Bankers Assn. Mem. Chgo. Club, Comml. Club Chgo., Econ. Club Chgo., Exmoor Country Club (Highland Park, Ill.). Office: La Salle National Corp 135 S La Salle St Ste 340 Chicago IL 60603

ROBERTS, THOMAS G., lawyer; b. Bakersfield, Calif., May 25, 1949. BA, U. So. Calif., 1971, JD, 1974. Bar: Calif. 1974. Ptnr. Baker & Hostetler, L.A. Mem. ABA, State Bar Calif., L.A. County Bar Assn. (chair real estate fin. sect.), Am. Coll. Real Estate Lawyers, Am. Coll. Mortgage Attys. Office: Baker & Hostetler 600 Wilshire Blvd Los Angeles CA 90017

ROBERTS, THOMAS MORGAN, federal official; b. Memphis, Apr. 14, 1937; s. James T. and Emily K. (Allen) R.; m. Margaret Elizabeth Boyle, Jan. 14, 1967; children: André Lovell, Elizabeth Boyle, Elinor Edgeworth. B.S., Ga. Inst. Tech., 1959. Asst. v.p. So. Boiler & Tank Works, Inc., Memphis, 1962-68, v.p., 1968-69, chmn. bd., pres., 1969-78; treas. George Bush for Pres. campaign, Houston, 1979-80; pvt. investor Washington, 1980-81; mem. U.S. Nuclear Regulatory Commn., Washington, 1981—; underwriting mem. Lloyd's of London, 1979—. Pres. Memphis Orchestral Soc., 1975-76; trustee Washington Opera, 1982—. Served to lt. (j.g.) USN, 1959-62. Mem. James Smithson Soc. (life). Republican. Presbyterian. Clubs: Memphis Country, Memphis Hunt and Polo; Chevy Chase; Met.

ROBERTS, THOMASENE BLOUNT, entrepreneur; b. Americus, Ga., Sept. 5, 1943; d. Thomas Watson and Mary Elizabeth (Smith) Blount; m. Henry Lee Roberts, Apr. 24, 1970 (div. 1991); 1 child, Asha Maia. Student, Fisk U., 1960-63; BA, Morris Brown Coll., 1965; MA, Atlanta U., 1970, postgrad., 1979-82; postgrad., Clark Atlanta U. Social worker Gate City Day Nursery Assn., Atlanta, 1965-66; ticket agt. Delta Air Lines, Inc., Atlanta, 1966-68; clk. accounts payable Kraft Foods, Inc., Decatur, Ga., 1968; cons. family svcs. Atlanta Housing Authority, 1970-72, supr. family svcs., 1972-73, mgr. family relocation, 1974-79; grad. rsch. asst. Sch. Edn. Atlanta U., 1979-82; city coun. asst. City of Atlanta, 1984-88, rsch. asst. Dept. Pub. Safety, 1988; dir. govtl. rels. Morris Brown Coll., Atlanta, 1988-93; owner TBR Ent., Atlanta, 1993—; researcher/intern Project Focus Teen Mother Program, Atlanta, 1981-82; moderator Nat. Black Women's Health Project, Atlanta, 1985; workshop leader Assn. Human Resources Mgrs., Atlanta, 1989; pres.'s rep. U. Ctr. Devel. Corp., Inc., 1989-93; cons. entrepreneur devel. workshop Morris Brown Coll. Chairperson Ida Prather YWCA Cmty. Bd., Atlanta, 1985-90; bd. dirs. YWCA Met. Atlanta, 1986-90, Met. Atlanta Coalition 100 Black Women, 1988-90, 92—, Hammonds House Mus., 1995—; active fund dr. com. Jomandi Prodn., 1988-89; v.p. maj. gifts com. Camp Best Friends, City of Atlanta, 1989; mem. Multi-Cultural Leadership Group, Gov.'s Coun. on Developmental Disabilities. Mem. Atlanta-Trinidad/Tobago Exch. (sec., treas. 1983-89, Pt. of Spain cert. 1986), Nat. Polit. Congress Black Women (corr. sec. 1989-90), Nat. Assn. for Equal Opportunity Higher Edn. (coll. liaison 1988-93), Coun. for Advancement-Support of Edn., Info. Forum, Atlanta Urban League, Inc., Nat. Assn. for Equal Opportunity in Higher Edn. (Disting. Alumni award 1991), Nat. Soc. Fund-Raising Execs. (cert. 1992), Nat. Soc. Fund-Raising Execs. Leadership Inst., Friends of Morehouse Sch. Medicine, Delta Sigma Theta (pub. rels. asst. 1986-89). Avocations: dancing, theatre, music, film. Home: 1817 King Charles Rd SW Atlanta GA 30331-4909 Office: TBR Enterprises Ste A-3165 2740 Greenbriar Pky SW Atlanta GA 30331

ROBERTS, TONY (DAVID ANTHONY ROBERTS), actor; b. N.Y.C., Oct. 22, 1939; s. Kenneth and Norma R.; 1 child, Nicole. B.S., Northwestern U., 1961. Movie debut in The Million Dollar Duck, 1971; other film appearances include Star Spangled Girl, 1971, Play It Again, Sam, 1972, Serpico, 1974, The Taking of Pelham, One Two Three, 1974, Annie Hall, 1977, Lovers Like Us, 1977, Just Tell Me What You Want, Stardust Memories, 1980, A Midsummer Nights Sex Comedy, 1982, Question of Honor, 1982, Packin' It In, 1983, Amityville IIID, 1983, Hannah and her Sisters, 1986, 18 Again!, 1988, Popcorn, 1990, Switch, 1991; TV movies The Lindbergh Kidnapping Case, 1976, Girls in the Office, 1979, If Things Were Different, 1980, A Question of Honor, 1982, Our Sons, 1992, Not in My Family, 1993; regular on TV series The Edge of Night, 1963-65, Rosetti and Ryan, 1977, The Four Seasons, 1986, The Lucy Arnaz Show, 1987, The Thorns, 1989; other TV appearances include The Way They Were, 1980; Broadway debut in Something about a Soldier, 1962; toured with nat. co. of Come Blow Your Horn, 1962; other Broadway stage appearances Take Her, She's Mine, 1964, Never Too Late, Barefoot in the Park, The Last Analysis, 1964, Don't Drink the Water, 1966, How Now, Dow Jones, 1967 (nominated for Tony award), Play It Again, Sam, 1969 (nominated for Tony award), Promises, Promises, 1971, Sugar, 1972, Absurd Person Singular, 1974, Murder at the Howard Johnson's, 1979, They're Playing Our Song, 1981, Doubles, 1985, Arsenic and Old Lace, 1986, Jerome Robbins Broadway, 1990, The Seagull, 1992; London debut in Promises, Promises, 1969 (London Critics Poll award as Best Actor in Musical); 1974; appeared in: Darkroom, Yale Repertory Theatres, New Haven, Hamlet, Otterbein Coll. (Ohio) Winter Drama Festival, 1975, Taming of the Shrew, Atlanta, 1978, Let 'Em Eat Cake, Berkshire Theatre Festival, Serenading Louis, Acad. Festival Theatre; The Seagull, Saratoga Performance Arts Festival, 1985, Who's Afraid of Virginia Woolf, 1986. Served in U.S. Army. Mem. SAG (bd. dirs. 1990—), Actors Equity Assn. (governing coun. 1968-74). Office: care Agy for Performing Arts 888 7th Ave New York NY 10106-0001*

ROBERTS, VIRGIL PATRICK, lawyer, business executive; b. Ventura, Calif., Jan. 4, 1947; s. Julius and Emma D. (Haley) R.; m. Eleanor Green,

Aug. 28, 1973; m. Brenda Cecilia Banks, Nov. 10, 1979; children: Gisele Simone, Hayley Tasha. AA, Ventura Coll., 1966; BA, UCLA, 1968; JD, Harvard U., 1972. Bar: Calif. 1972. Assoc. Pacht, Ross, Warne Bernhardt & Sears, L.A., 1972-76; ptnr. Manning, Reynolds & Roberts, L.A., 1976-79, Manning & Roberts, 1980-81; exec. v.p., gen. counsel Solar Records, L.A., 1981—; pres. Dick Griffey Prodns., L.A., 1982—, Solar Records, 1988—; judge pro tem L.A., Beverly Hills Mcpl. Cts., 1975—; past bd. dirs. L.A. Black Leadership Coalition, L.A. Mus. African Am. Art, Beverly Hills Bar Assn., L.A. Legal Aid Found., others. Bd. dirs. Coro Found., 1984—, Calif. Cmty. Found., 1991—, L.A. Ednl. Alliance for Restructuring Now, Cmty. Build; past pres. Beverly Hills Bar Scholarship Found.; commr. Calif. Commn. for Tchr. Credentialing, 1980-83; chmn. L.A. Ednl. Partnership, 1989—, v.p. 1983-89; vice-chmn. Nat. Pub. Edn. Fund Network; chmn. bd. dirs. L.A. Annenberg Metropolitan Project. Trustee, Comm. Econ. Devel., 1991—. Recipient NAACP Legal Def. Fund Equal Justice award, 1988. Mem. Recording Industry Assn. Am., Black Entertainment and Sports Lawyers (treas., bd. dirs. 1982—). Lead atty. for NAACP in Crawford vs. Bd. Edn. desegregation case, L.A., 1979-80. Address: 4151 Charlene Dr Los Angeles CA 90043-1552 Office: Dick Griffey Prodns 1635 N Cahuenga Blvd Los Angeles CA 90028-6240

ROBERTS, WALTER HERBERT BEATTY, anatomist; b. Field, B.C., Can., Jan. 24, 1915; came to U.S., 1956, naturalized, 1965; s. Walter McWilliam and Sarah Caroline (Orr) R.; m. Olive Louise O'Neal, Sept. 1, 1937; children: Gayle, Sharon, David. M.D., Coll. Med. Evangelists (later Loma Linda U.), 1939. Intern St. Paul's Hosp., Vancouver, B.C., 1938-40; med. dir. Rest Haven Hosp. Sanitarium and Hosp., Sidney, Vancouver Island, B.C., 1940-53; post doctoral trg. White Meml. Hosp., Los Angeles, 1946-47, hosp., Edinburgh, Scotland, 1953-55; instr. in anatomy Loma Linda U., 1955-58, asst. prof. anatomy, 1959-62, assoc. prof., 1962-70, prof., 1971—, chmn. dept. anatomy, 1974-81; prof. emeritus. Mem. Am. Assn. Anatomists, Sigma Xi, Alpha Omega Alpha. Adventist. Home: 11366 Campus St Loma Linda CA 92354-3302 Office: Loma Linda U Dept Anatomy Loma Linda CA 92350

ROBERTS, WALTER RONALD, political science educator, former government official; b. Waltendorf, Austria, Aug. 26, 1916; came to U.S., 1939, naturalized, 1944; s. Ignatius and Elizabeth (Diamant) R.; m. Gisela K. Schmarak, Aug. 22, 1939; children: William M., Charles E., Lawrence H. M.Litt., Cambridge U. (Eng.), 1940, Ph.D. 1980. Research asst. Harvard U. Law Sch., 1940-42; writer, editor Voice of Am., 1942-49; press officer U.S. del. to Austrian Treaty talks, 1949, 55; fgn. affairs officer Dept. State, 1950-53; dep. asst. dir. USIA, 1954-60; counselor of embassy for pub. affairs Am. Embassy, Belgrade, Yugoslavia, 1960-66; diplomat-in-residence Brown U., Providence, 1966-67; counselor U.S. Mission to Internat. Orgns., Geneva, 1967-69; dep. assoc. dir. USIA, Washington, 1969-71, assoc. dir., 1971-74; diplomatic studies Ctr. Strategic and Internat. Studies Georgetown U., Washington, 1974-75; exec. dir. Bd. Internat. Broadcasting, Washington, 1975-85; diplomat-in-residence George Washington U., Washington, 1986—. Author: Tito, Mihailovic and the Allies, 1941-45, 73, paperback, 1987, (with Terry L. Deibel) Culture and Information: Two Foreign Policy Functions, 1976; contbr. articles to profl. pubs. Apptd. mem. U.S. Adv. Commn. on Pub. Diplomacy, 1991—; bd. dirs. Salzburg Seminar, 1993. Recipient Disting. Honor award USIA, 1974. Mem. Washington Inst. Fgn. Affairs, Council Fgn. Relations, Oxford-Cambridge Com. Club: Metropolitan. Home: 4449 Sedgwick St NW Washington DC 20016-2713 Office: George Washington U Elliott Sch Internat Affairs 2013 G St NW Washington DC 20052

ROBERTS, WARREN ERROL, history educator; b. Los Angeles, May 8, 1933; s. Hugh Cedric and Mildred (Howe) R.; m. Anne Findlay, July 22, 1957; children: Erin, James, Thomas, Peter. BS, U. So. Calif., 1954; BA, U. Calif., Berkeley, 1959, MA, 1960, PhD, 1966. Asst. prof. SUNY, Albany, 1963-71, assoc. prof., 1971-81, prof. history, 1981-83, Disting. Teaching prof., 1983—. Author: Morality and Social Class in 18th Century French Literature and Painting, 1974, Jane Austen and The French Revolution, 1979, Jacques-Louis David, Revolutionary Artist: Art, Politics and the French Revolution, 1989. Presbyterian. Avocations: running, tennis, squash. Home: 13 Norwood St Albany NY 12203-3410 Office: SUNY Dept of History 1400 Washington Ave Albany NY 12222-0001

ROBERTS, WILLIAM B., lawyer, business executive; b. Detroit, Aug. 23, 1939; s. Edwin Stuart and Marjorie Jean (Wardle) R.; m. Cathleen Anne Thompson, Sept. 1, 1962; children: Bradford William, Brent William, Katrina Marjorie. BA, Mich. State U., 1961; JD with distinction, U. Mich., 1963; China law diploma, U. East Asia, Macau, 1989. Bar: Mo. 1964, Fla. 1983. Mem. firm Thompson & Mitchell, St. Louis, 1963-67; atty. Monsanto Co., 1967-70; sr. exec. v.p. adminstrn., sec., gen. counsel Chromalloy Am. Corp. (successor Segua Corp. N.Y.), St. Louis, 1970-78; exec. v.p.-adminstrn., gen. counsel, sec. Chromalloy Am. Corp. (successor Segua Corp. N.Y.), Clayton, Mo., 1978-82; pvt. practice law, 1983-87; mng. ptnr. Roberts and Nordahl, St. Louis and Naples, Fla., 1988-89, Law Offices of William B. Roberts, St. Louis and Naples, 1989-90, Darrow & Roberts, P.A., Naples, 1992-93; pres., mng. dir. Law Offices of William B. Roberts, Naples, 1994—; pres., mng. dir. The Fairborne Group, Ltd., St. Louis and Naples, 1988-91, William B. Roberts & Assocs. Co., Merger and Acquisitions Specialists, 1982—; mem. exam. com. of policyowners Northwestern Mut. Life Ins. Co., Milw., 1978; del. to U.S.-China Joint Session on Trade Investment and Econ. Law, Beijing, 1987; sports rep. Steve Carlton, St. Louis Cardinals, Phila. Phillies baseball clubs, 1987-89; pres., CEO Tropical Tracks, Inc., Naples, 1994—. Mem. ABA, Mo. Bar Assn., St. Louis Bar Assn. (chmn. antitrust sect. 1973), Fla. Bar Assn., Collier County Bar Assn., Delta Theta Phi. Methodist. Home: 2294 Royal Ln Naples FL 33962 Office: 4532 Tamiami Trail E Naples FL 33962

ROBERTS, WILLIAM EVERETT, lawyer; b. Pierre, S.D., May 12, 1926; s. Everett David and Bonnie (Martin) R.; m. Cynthia Cline, July 18, 1953; children: Catherine C. Roberts-Martin, Laura M., Nancy F. Weinreich, David H. BS, U. Minn., 1947; LLB, Yale U., 1950. Bar: Ind. 1950, U.S. Supreme Ct. 1964. Employee, ptnr. Duck and Neighbours, Indpls., 1950-58; ptnr. Cadick, Burns, Duck & Neighbours, Indpls., 1958-60, Roberts, Ryder, Rogers & Scism, Indpls., 1960-85; ptnr. Barnes & Thornburg, Indpls., 1986-93, of counsel, 1994—. Pres., bd. dirs. Park-Tudor Sch., Indpls., 1982-83; elder Second Presbyn. Ch., Indpls., 1962—; trustee Indpls. Mus. Art, 1978—; pres. New Hope of Ind., Indpls., 1986-87. Fellow Am. Bar Found.; mem. ABA, Ind. Bar Assn., Indpls. Bar Assn., Rotary, Meridian Hills Country Club (pres. 1983-84), Skyline Club. Republican. Home: 33 E 73rd St Indianapolis IN 46240-3004 Office: Barnes & Thornburg 1313 Mchts Bank Bldg 11 S Meridian St Indianapolis IN 46204-3506

ROBERTS, WILLIAM HENRY, architect; b. Oswestry, England, Dec. 9, 1932; s. Henry Wyn and Lena Mary (Edwards) R.; m. Jean Mary Davies, Aug. 16, 1958; children: Huw Wynne, Richard Henry. BArch, U. Wales, 1957; M in Landscape Architecture, U. Pa., 1960. Architect London County Council, 1957-58; archtl. faculty mem. Washington U., St. Louis, 1960-63; ptnr. Wallace Roberts & Todd, Phila., 1963—; adj. faculty U. Pa., Phila., 1963-70; cons. various corps., 1970—; teaching various seminars, 1970-80. Mem. Am. Soc. Landscape Architecture, Am. Planning Assn. Democrat. Episcopalian. Clubs: Phila. Cricket (bd. govs. 1973-85), Peale. Avocations: painting, golf, theater. Home: 325 W Springfield Ave Philadelphia PA 19118-4034 Office: Wallace Roberts & Todd 260 S Broad St Philadelphia PA 19102-5023

ROBERTS, WILLIAM HUGH, III, library director, consultant; b. Ridley Park, Pa., Oct. 21, 1936; s. William Hugh Jr. and Alison (Rush) R.; m. Barbara Lee Howard, Aug. 29, 1959; children: Cynthia Hope, Gloria Faith, Laura Susan, William Hugh IV. Student, Princeton U., 1954-55; AB, Earlham Coll., 1958; postgrad., U. Pa., 1958-61; MLS, Drexel Inst., 1963. Law clk. Duane, Morris and Heckscher, Phila., 1959-61; librarian Free Library of Phila., 1961-65; library dir. Clinton (Iowa) Pub. Library, 1965-67, Roanoke (Va.) County Pub. Library, 1967-71, Forsyth County Pub. Library, Winston-Salem, N.C., 1971—; pres. W.H. Roberts & Assocs., libr. cons. co., Winston-Salem, 1975—; pres. Forsyth County Employees Credit Union, Winston-Salem, 1977—. Author New Orleans Branch Library Action Plan: To the Year 2000, 1991, various libr. action plans. Trustee Nature Sci. Ctr., Winston-Salem, 1972-78; regional fundraiser Princeton U., 1980—; bd. dirs.

Winston-Salem Arts Coun., 1972—; pres. Forsyth County 4-H Found., Winston-Salem, 1983—. Mem. ALA (coun. 1990—), N.C. Libr. Assn. (sec. 1974-78, Libr. Dir. of Yr. award 1988), Southeastern Libr. Assn. (treas. 1978-80), N.C. Pub. Libr. Dirs. Assn. (pres. 1986), Kiwanis (club pres. 1982, lt. gov. Carolinas dist. 1986, gov. 1990, internat. trustee 1992—), Elks. Avocations: golf, tennis, genealogy. Home: 3116 Burkeshore Rd Winston Salem NC 27106-5532 Office: Forsyth County Pub Libr 660 W 5th St Winston Salem NC 27101-2755

ROBERTS, WILLIAM M., publishing executive. Pres. Brooks/Cole Publishing Co., Pacific Grove, Calif. Office: Brooks Cole Pub Co 511 Forest Lodge Rd Pacific Grove CA 93950-5098

ROBERTS, WILLIAM WOODRUFF, JR., applied mathematics educator, researcher; b. Huntington, W.Va., Oct. 8, 1942; s. William Woodruff Sr. and Sarah Louise (Huddleston) R.; m. Linda Louise Nelson, June 17, 1967; children: William Woodruff III, David Christopher. SB, MIT, 1964, PhD, 1969. Asst. prof. Sch. Engring. and Applied Sci. U. Va., Charlottesville, 1969-74, assoc. prof. Sch. Engring. and Applied Sci., 1974-82, prof. Sch. Engring. and Applied Sci., 1982-92, dir. math.-computational modeling lab., 1990—, Commonwealth prof. engring. and applied sci., 1992—; vis. scientist Kapteyn Astron. Inst., U. Groningen, The Netherlands, 1974; NORDITA guest prof. Stockholms Observatorium, Saltsjabaden, Sweden, 1974-75; pres. Computational Modeling Technologies, Inc., 1991—. Contbr. over 100 papers to profl. jours.; author 5 books. Mem. AAAS, AIAA, Am. Astron. Soc., Am. Men and Women of Sci. (div. dynamical astronomy), Am. Inst. Physics, Fiber Soc., Internat. Astron. Union, Soc. for Indsl. and Applied Math., Va. Acad. Scis., Sigma Xi. Office: U Va-Thornton Hall Inst Applied Math and Dept Mech Aerospace & Nuclear Engring Charlottesville VA 22903

ROBERTSON, A. HAEWORTH, actuary, benefit consultant, foundation executive; b. Oklahoma City, May 10, 1930; s. Albert Haeworth and Bonnie Tennessee (Duckett) R.; m. Mary Adeline Kissee, Feb. 3, 1952 (div. July 1979); children—Valerie Lynn, Alan Haeworth, Mary Kathryn. B.A. in Math., U. Okla., 1951; M.A. in Actuarial Sci., U. Mich., 1953. Actuary Wyatt Co., Washington and Dallas, 1955-58; actuary Bowles, Andrews & Towne, Dallas, 1958-60; v.p., actuary W. Alfred Hayes & Co., St. Louis, 1960-63; pres. First Am. Security Life Ins. Co. Mo., St. Louis, 1964-68; prvt. practice internat. cons. actuary Barbados and Ghana, 1969-72; sr. actuary ILO, Geneva, Switzerland, 1973-75; chief actuary U.S. Social Security Adminstrn., Balt., 1975-78; mng. dir. William M. Mercer, Inc., Washington, 1978-88; prvt. practice, internat. cons., actuary Washington, Kuwait, Turkey, Guyana, Zimbabwe, The Philippines, 1988—; chmn. Retirement Bd. Actuaries, Dept. Def., 1984—; mem. Edn. Benefits Bd. Actuaries, 1985—; pres., founder Retirement Policy Inst. Inc., 1986—. Author: The Coming Revolution in Social Security, 1981, Social Security: What Every Taxpayer Should Know, 1992. Served to 2d lt. USAF, 1953-55. Recipient Commrs. Citation, Social Security Adminstrn., Washington, 1976, Arthur J. Altmeyer award HEW, Washington, 1978. Fellow Soc. Actuaries (bd. govs. 1979-81, v.p. 1985-87), Conf. Cons. Actuaries; mem. Am. Acad. Actuaries, Internat. Actuarial Assn., Internat. Assn. Cons. Actuaries, U.K. Inst. Actuaries (assoc.), Cosmos Club, Phi Beta Kappa, Phi Eta Sigma, Phi Kappa Sigma. Republican. Methodist.

ROBERTSON, ABEL L., JR., pathologist; b. St. Andrews, Argentina, July 21, 1926; came to U.S., 1952, naturalized, 1957; s. Abel Alfred Lazzarini and Margaret Theresa (Anderson) R.; m. Irene Kirmayr Mauch, Dec. 26, 1958; children: Margaret Anne, Abel Martin, Andrew Duncan, Malcolm Alexander. BS, Coll. D.F. Sarmiento, Buenos Aires, Argentina, 1946; MD suma cum laude, U. Buenos Aires, 1951; PhD, Cornell U., 1959. Fellow tissue culture div. Inst. Histoloty and Embryology, Sch. Medicine Inst. Histology and Embryology, 1947-49; surg. intern Hosp. Ramos Mejia, Buenos Aires, 1948-50; fellow in tissue culture research Ministry of Health, Buenos Aires, 1950-51; resident Hosp. Nacional de Clinicas, Buenos Aires, 1950-51; head blood vessel bank and organ transplants Research Ctr. Ministry of Health, Buenos Aires, 1951-53; fellow dept. surgery and pathology Sch. Medicine Cornell U., N.Y.C., 1953-55; asst. vis. surgery U. Hosp. N.Y., N.Y.C., 1955-60; asst. prof. research surgery Postgrad. Med. Sch. NYU, N.Y.C., 1955-56; asst. vis. surgeon Bellevue Hosp., N.Y.C., 1955-60; assoc. prof. research surgery NYU, 1956-60, assoc. prof. pathology Sch. Medicine and Postgrad Med. Sch., 1960-63; staff mem. div. research Cleve. Clinic Found., 1963-73, prof. research, 1972-73; assoc. clin. prof. pathology Case Western Res. U. Sch. Medicine, Cleve., 1968-72, prof. pathology, 1973-82, dir. interdisciplinary cardiovascular research, 1975-82; exec. head dept. pathology Coll. Medicine, U. Ill., Chgo., 1982-88; prof. pathology Coll. Medicine U. Ill., 1982-93, prof. emeritus, 1993—; research fellow N.Y. Soc. Cardiovascular Surgery, 1957-58; mem. research study subcom. of heart com. N.E. Ohio Regional Med. Program, 1969—. Mem. internat. editorial bd.: Atherosclerosis, Jour. Exptl. and Molecular Pathology, 1964—, Lab. Investigation, 1989—, Acta Pathologica Japonica, 1991—; contbr. articles to profl. jours. Recipient Research Devel. award NIH, 1961-63. Fellow Am. Coll. Cardiology, Am. Coll. Clin. Pharmacology, Am. Heart Assn. (established investigator 1956-61, nominating com. council on arteriosclerosis 1972), Royal Microscopical Soc., Royal Soc. Promotion Health (Gt. Britain), Am. Geriatrics Soc., N.Y. Acad. Scis., Cleve. Med. Library Assn.; mem. AMA, AAAS, AAUP, Am. Soc. for Investigative Pathology, Am. Inst. Biol. Scis., Am. Judicature Soc., Am. Soc. Cell Biology, Am. Soc. Pathologists, Am. Soc. Nephrology, Assn. Am. Physicians and Surgeons, Assn. Computing Machinery, Electron Microscopy Soc. Am., Assn. Pathology Chmn., Internat. Acad. Pathology, Soc. Cardiovascular Pathology, Internat. Cardiovascular Soc., Internat. Soc. Cardiology (sci. council on arteriosclerosis and ischemic heart disease), Internat. Fed. on Genetic Engring. and Biotechnology, Internat. Soc. for Heart Rsch., Internat. Soc. Nephrology, Internat. Soc. Stereology, Pan Am. Med. Assn. (life, councillor in angiology 1966), Ill. Registry Anatomical Pathology (treas. 1985-87), Chgo. Pathology Soc., Reticuloendothelial Soc. Leucocyte Biology, Soc. Cryobiology, Tissue Culture Assn., Ohio Soc. Pathologists, Electron Microscopy Soc. Northeastern Ohio (pres., trustee 1966-68), Heart Assn. Northeastern Ohio, N.Y. Soc. Cardiovascular Surgery, N.Y. Soc. Electron Microscopists, Cuyahoga County Med. Soc., Cleve. Soc. Pathologists, The Oxygen Soc., Sigma Xi. Home: 415 Lee Ave Half Moon Bay CA 94019-1367

ROBERTSON, ALVIN CYRRALE, professional basketball player; b. Barberton, Ohio, July 22, 1962; m. Jackie Robertson; 1 child, Alvin Jr. Student, Crowder Jr. Coll., Mo., U Ark., 1981-84. With San Antonio Spurs, 1984-89; player Milw. Bucks, 1989-93, Detriot Pistons, 1993, Denver Nuggets, 1993—; mem. NBA All-Star team, 1986-88, 91. Recipient Gold medal Olympics, L.A., 1984; ranked 1st in NBA for steals, 1985-87, 91; named NBA Defensive Player of Yr., 1986, Most Improved Player, 1986; named to NBA All-Defense First Team, 1987, 91. Office: Detroit Pistons Palace Alburn Hills Two Championship Dr Auburn Hills MI 48326°

ROBERTSON, ARMAND JAMES, II, lawyer; b. San Diego, Sept. 23, 1937; s. Armand James and Muriel H. R.; m. Marion Sperry, Aug. 11, 1962; children: Armand James, Laura Marie. A.M. in Econs, Stanford U., 1960; LL.B., Harvard U., 1965. Bar: Calif. 1966. Law clk. to Charles M. Merrill, U.S. Ct. Appeals (9th cir.), 1965-66; assoc. firm Howard, Prim, Rice, Nemerovski, Canady & Pollak, San Francisco, 1966-71; ptnr. Howard, Prim, Rice, Nemerovski, Canady & Pollak, 1971-77; dir. Howard, Rice, Nemerovski, Canady, Robertson & Falk (P.C.), San Francisco, 1977-95; judge city and county U.S. Superior Court, San Francisco, 1995—. Served to lt. (j.g.) USN, 1960-62. Mem. Am. Law Inst., ABA (antitrust sect.), Ctr. for Pub. Resources, Phi Beta Kappa. Home: 178 Edgewood Ave San Francisco CA 94117-3713 Office: 3 Embarcadero Ctr Ste 700 San Francisco CA 94111-4065

ROBERTSON, BEVERLY CARRUTH, steel company executive; b. Texarkana, Ark., May 16, 1922; s. Glenn C. Robertson (dec.) and Luda (Brownlee) R. (dec.); m. Ruth Mulcare, Oct. 31, 1945 (dec. Oct. 1993); children: Glenn J., Beverly R. Dodds, Rebecca A. Robertson Deans. In sales Nat. Supply Co., Laurel, Miss., 1941-51; purchasing agt. Kirby Petroleum co., Houston, 1951-54; exec. v.p. mktg. Lone Star Steel Co., Dallas, 1954-85; exec. v.p. Lone Star Steel Co., 1985-86; pres., dir., chief exec. officer LSSCO Trading Corp., 1985-86; owner BSEER Enterprises, Dallas, 1986—; ptnr. Clayton Equipment Co., Dallas, 1992—; chmn. Sir Alec Inc., 1985-94;

cons. Pipeco, Inc., Houston, 1986-88; exec. v.p. mktg. and procurement Nat. Pipe and Tube Co., Houston, 1988-89; pres., CEO Tex. Am. Pipe & Supply Co., Inc., Dallas, 1989—; cons. Ipsco Steel, Inc., Camanche, Iowa, 1991-92. Served to capt. USAF, 1943-46, ETO. Named Supplier of Yr. Petroleum Industry Buyers group Nat. Assn. Purchasing Mgmt., 1982. Mem. Dallas Country Club, Dallas Petroleum Club. Republican. Episcopalian. Home: PO Box 12688 Dallas TX 75225-0688

ROBERTSON, C. R., insurance company executive; b. 1930; married. BBA, U. Tex., 1952. Mgr. audit staff Ernst & Ernst, 1955-65; staff asst. Am. Nat. Ins. Co., Galveston, Tex., 1965-67, asst. sec., 1967-69, controller, asst. sec., 1969-70, v.p., controller, 1970-74, sr. v.p., controller, 1974-77, exec. v.p. adminstrn., 1977-86, sr. exec. v.p. home office adminstrn., 1986—. Office: Am Nat Ins Co 1 Moody Plz Galveston TX 77550-7948

ROBERTSON, CLIFF, actor, writer, director; b. La Jolla, Calif., Sept. 9, 1925; s. Clifford Parker and Audrey (Willingham) R.; m. Dina Merrill, Dec. 21, 1966 (div.); children: Heather, Stephanie. DFA (hon.), Bradford Coll., 1981, MacMurray Coll., 1986, Susquehanna U., 1988. Contbr. articles to various publs.; stage appearances include Late Love, Wisteria Trees, Orpheus Descending; films include Picnic, 1956, Autumn Leaves, 1956, The Naked and the Dead, 1958, The Girl Most Likely, 1958, Gidget, 1959, All in a Nights Work, 1961, The Big Show, 1961, Under-World, U.S.A., 1961, As the Sea Rages, 1961, The Interns, 1962, PT 109, 1963, Sunday in New York, 1964, The Best Man, 1964, 633 Squadron, 1964, Love Has Many Faces, 1965, Masquerade, 1965, Up From the Beach, 1965, The Honey Pot, 1967, The Devil's Brigade, 1968, Charly, 1968, (Academy award for Best Actor 1969), The Great Northfield Minnesota Raid, 1972, Ace Eli and Rodger of the Skies, 1973, Too Late the Hero, 1970, Man on a Swing, 1974, 3 Days of the Condor, 1975, Out of Season, Obsession, 1976, Shoot, 1976, Star 80, 1983, Brainstorm, 1983, Malone, 1987, Wild Hearts Can't Be Broken, 1991, Wind, 1992, The Sunset Boys, 1995; TV movies and miniseries appearances include The Days of Wine and Roses, 1958, The Sunshine Patriot, 1968, The Game, 1968 (Emmy award) The Man Without a Country, 1973, A Tree Grows in Brooklyn, 1974, My Father's House, 1975, Return to Earth, 1976, Washington: Behind Closed Doors, 1977, Overboard, 1978, Two of a Kind, 1982, The Key to Rebecca, 1985, Dreams of Gold, 1986, Ford: The Man and The Machine, 1987, Dead Reckoning, 1990, Dazzle, 1995; appeared in TV series Falcon Crest; writer, dir.: play The V.I.P.'s, 1981; J. W. Coop. Served to lt. (j.g.) USNR. Recipient Wallace award Am. Scottish Found., 1984, Sharples aviation award AOPA, 1983, Theatre World award, 1970, award Advt. Age, 1985. Mem. SAG (bd. dirs. N.Y. chpt. 1980—), Writers Guild Am. (mem. coun. 1984-86), Bath & Tennis Club Palm Beach, Maidstone Club. Presbyterian. Clubs: Players (N.Y.C.), River, Wings. Avocations: flying, skiing, soaring, tennis.

ROBERTSON, DAVID, clinical pharmacologist, physician, educator; b. Sylvia, Tenn., May 23, 1947; s. David Herlie and Lucille Luther (Bowen) R.; m. Rose Marie Stevens, Oct. 30, 1976; 1 child, Rose. B.A., Vanderbilt U., 1969, M.D., 1973. Diplomate Am. Bd. Internal Medicine, Am. Bd. Clin. Pharmacology. Intern, Johns Hopkins U., Balt., 1973-74, asst. resident, 1974-75, asst. chief service in medicine, 1977-78; fellow in clin. pharmacology Vanderbilt U., Nashville, 1975-77, asst. prof. medicine and pharmacology, 1978-82, assoc. prof., 1982-86, prof., 1986—, prof. neurology, 1991—; dir. clin. research ctr., 1987—; dir. Ctr. for Space Physiology and Medicine, 1989—; dir. Med. Sci. Tng. Program, 1993—; pclin. rsch. specializing in gene therapy and disorders of blood pressure regulation, Nashville, 1978—; mem. staff Vanderbilt Hosp., Burroughs Wellcome scholar in clin. pharmacology, 1985-91. Author: (with B.M. Greene and G.J. Taylor) Problems in Internal Medicine, 1980, (with C.R. Smith) Manual of Clinical Pharmacology, 1981, (with Italo Biaggioni) Disorders of the Autonomic Nervous System, 1995, Primer on the Autonomic Nervous System, 1995; editor-in-chief Drug Therapy, 1991-94; editorial bds. Jour. Autonomic Nervous System, Clin. Pharm. and Therapeutics, Clin. Autonomic Rsch., Am. Jour. Med. Sci., Current Topics in Pharmacology. Recipient Research Career Devel. award NIH, 1981, Grant W. Liddle award for leadership in rsch., 1991; Adolph-Morsbach grantee Bonn, Germany, 1968; Logan Clendening fellow Reykjavik, Iceland, 1969. Fellow Am. Heart Assn. Council Hypertension and Circulation, ACP (teaching and research scholar 1978-81); mem. Am. Autonomic Soc. (pres. 1992-94), Am. Acad. Neurology, Soc. Neurosci., Am. Inst. Aeronautics and Astronautics, U.S. Pharmacopeial Conv., Nat. Bd. Med. Examiners, Aerospace Med. Assn. (space station sci. and applications com.), FDA Consortium Rare Disorders, Rare Disorder Network, Am. Fedn. for Clin. Research, Am. Soc. Clin. Investigation, Assn. Am. Physicians, So. Soc. for Clin. Investigation, Am. Soc. for Clin. Pharmacology and Therapeutics, Phi Beta Kappa, Alpha Omega Alpha (hon.). Baptist. Home: 4003 Newman Pl Nashville TN 37204-4308 Office: Vanderbilt U Clin Rsch Ctr 21st Ave S Nashville TN 37232-2195

ROBERTSON, DAVID GOVAN, lawyer; b. Chgo., May 3, 1947. AB with great distinction, Stanford U., 1969; JD, Yale U., 1973. Bar: Calif. 1973, U.S. Dist. Ct. (no., cen., ea. and we. dists.) Calif. 1973, U.S. Supreme Ct. 1988. Law clk. to chief judge U.S. Dist. Ct., 1973-74; assoc. Morrison & Foerster, San Francisco, 1974-79, ptnr., 1979—. Danforth Found. Grad. fellow Yale, 1970-73. Mem. Phi Beta Kappa. Office: Morrison & Foerster 345 California St San Francisco CA 94104-2606

ROBERTSON, DAVID WYATT, lawyer, educator; b. Little Rock, Sept. 8, 1937; s. Lee W. and Thelma (Queen) R. B.A., La. State U., 1960, LL.B., 1961; LL.M., Yale U., 1965, S.J.D., 1968. Bar: La. 1961, D.C. 1961, Tex. 1976, U.S. Supreme Ct. 1978. Legis. asst. to Sen. Russell B. Long, Washington, 1961-62; asst. prof. law La. State U., Baton Rouge, 1962-64; lectr. law Leeds (Eng.) U., 1965-66; assoc. prof. U. Tex., Austin, 1966-68; prof. U. Tex., 1968-80; of counsel firm Mandell & Wright, Houston, 1979-80; mem. firm Gravel, Robertson & Brady, Alexandria, La., 1980-83; Albert Sidney Burleson prof. law U. Tex., Austin, 1983-86, Hines H. Baker and Thelma Kelley Baker Chair-in-Law, 1986-88, A.W. Walker Centennial chair, 1988—; M.D. Anderson Found. vis. prof. U. London, 1986-87. Author: Admiralty and Federalism, 1970, The Correspondence Between Leon Green and Charles McCormick, 1988, Tort Cases and Materials, 1989, The Louisiana Law of comparative Fault, 1991; contbr. articles to profl. jours. Mem. Assn. Am. Law Schs., Am. Law Inst., Maritime Law Assn. Order of Coif, Omicron Delta Kappa. Office: U Tex 727 E 26th St Austin TX 78705-3224

ROBERTSON, EDWARD D., JR., state supreme court chief justice; b. Durham, N.C., May 1, 1952; m. Renee Ann Beal; two children. BA, U. Mo., 1974, JD, 1977. Bar: Mo. 1977. assoc. atty. gen., 1978-79; assoc. mcpl. judge City of Belton, Mo., 1980-81; dep. atty. gen. City of Belton, 1981-85; justice Mo. Supreme Ct., Kansas City, 1985—; former chief justice Mo. Supreme Ct. Office: Mo Supreme Ct PO Box 150 Jefferson City MO 65102-0150

ROBERTSON, EDWIN DAVID, lawyer; b. Roanoke, Va., July 5, 1946; s. Edwin Traylor and Norma Burns (Bowles) R.; m. Anne Littelle Ferratt, Sept. 7, 1968, 1 child, Thomas Therit. BA with honors, U. Va., 1968, LLB, 1971. Bar: N.Y. 1972, U.S. Ct. Appeals (2d cir.) 1972, U.S. Dist. Ct. (ea. and so. dists.) N.Y. 1973, U.S. Supreme Ct. 1975, U.S. Dist. Ct. (ea. dist.) Mich. 1986. Assoc. Cadwalader, Wickersham & Taft, N.Y.C., 1972-80; ptnr. Cadwalader, Wickersham & Taft, N.Y.C., 1980—. dir. bds. Early Music Found. N.Y.C., 1983—, chmn., 1993—; bd. dirs. Oratorio Soc. of N.Y.C., 1988—, sec., 1991—. 1st lt. USAF, 1971-72. Mem. ABA, Fed. Bar Coun., N.Y. County Lawyers Assn. (chmn. bankruptcy com. 1983-87, bd. dirs. 1985-88, investment com. 1992—), Assn. Bar City N.Y. (com. on state cts. of superior jurisdiction 1987-90, fed. legis. com. 1990-93), Jefferson Soc., Order of Coif, Soc. Colonial Wars, Down Town Assn. (N.Y.C.), Phi Beta Kappa, Alpha Kappa Psi. Republican. Episcopalian. Home: 315 E 72nd St New York NY 10021-4674 Office: Cadwalader Wickersham & Taft 100 Maiden Ln New York NY 10038-4892

ROBERTSON, GEORGE LEONARD, lawyer; b. Austin, Tex., Aug. 28, 1922; s. George Leonard and Pensive (Cocke) R.; m. Elizabeth Lauretta Reilly, Dec. 28, 1946; children—Nancy, Patricia, George Philip, Carol, David. B.B.A., U. Tex., 1943, LL.B., 1948. Bar: Tex. 1948. Atty. Atlantic Refining Co., Dallas, 1948-52; ptnr. Barrow, Bland, Robertson & Rehmet, Houston, 1952-58, Butler & Binion, Houston, 1958—. Served to lt. USNR, 1943-46. Mem. ABA, State Bar Tex., Houston Bar Assn. Methodist. Club:

Petroleum (Houston). Home: 3105 Avalon Pl Houston TX 77019-5905 Office: Butler & Binion 1600 Allied Bank Plz Houston TX 77002

ROBERTSON, GEORGE LEVEN, retired association executive; b. Alexandria, La., Feb. 7, 1921; s. Ernest E. and Cornelia (La Croix) R.; m. Florence Horne, Feb. 7, 1943; children—Dana Carleton, Linda, Malcolm Ernest, Judy Elaine. B.S., La. State U., 1941; M.S., A. and M. Coll. Tex., 1947; Ph.D. (Gen. Edn. Bd. fellow 1949-50), U. Wis., 1951. Grad. asst. animal husbandry A. and M. Coll. Tex., 1941-42, instr., then asst. prof., 1946-49, assoc. prof., 1951-55; grad. asst. U. Wis., 1949-51; prof. animal sci., head dept. La. State U., 1955-77, chmn. grad. council, 1961; exec. dir. Honor Soc. of Phi Kappa Phi, 1977-92. Trustee Baton Rouge Gen. Hosp.; deacon, trustee First Bapt. Ch., Baton Rouge. Served to capt. AUS, 1942-46; col. Res. Named Outstanding Tchr. A. and M. Coll. Tex. Sch. Agr., 1948-49. Fellow AAAS; mem. Am. Soc. Animal Sci. (pres. So. sect. 1967-68), AAUP, Assn. Coll. Honor Socs. (v.p. 1987-89, pres. 1989-91), Sigma Xi, Alpha Zeta, Phi Kappa Phi (nat. pres.-elect 1974-77), Gamma Sigma Delta, Omicron Delta Kappa. Clubs: Masons, Kiwanis. Home: 7017 Perkins Rd Baton Rouge LA 70808-4320

ROBERTSON, GREGG WESTLAND, diversified company executive; b. Sydney, Australia, Jan. 16, 1934; s. Alexander and Lillian R.; BA in Econs., Fairleigh Dickinson U., 1964; postgrad. Harvard U., 1980; m. Elizabeth Stimper, Apr. 30, 1957; children—Gregg Westland, Lisa. Asst. v.p. Bankers Trust Co., N.Y.C., 1964-69; asst. treas. Dillingham Corp., Honolulu, 1970-73, treas., 1974-77, v.p-fin., treas., chief fin. officer, 1977-82, sr. v.p. strategic devel., 1982-83, pres., chief exec. officer, 1986—; pres., chief exec. officer Calif. Gas Corp. subs., Sacramento, 1983-84, exec. v.p. parent co., San Francisco, 1984-86; pres., CEO Robertson & Co., San Francisco, 1987-93, Honolulu, 1992-93; exec. v.p., COO Liberty Bank, Honolulu, 1990-92; v.p., Cadinha & Co., Honolulu, 1993—. Bd. dirs. Aloha United Way, 1980-82, Sacramento United Way, 1983-84. Mem. Fin. Execs. Inst. Clubs: Olympic (San Francisco), Outrigger Canoe (Honolulu), Pacific. Home: 1862 Halekoa Dr Honolulu HI 96821-1029

ROBERTSON, HARRY STEVENS, retired mechanical engineer; b. Pitts., Sept. 12, 1931; s. Harry Stevens and Sherley Eloise (Hurlbut) Robertson; m. Carolyn Margaret Young, Oct. 10, 1976. BS, Purdue U., 1953. Profl. engr., Ohio. Foreman Continental Can Co., Elwood, Ind., 1953-57; mfg. engr. Western Electric Co., Indpls., 1957-66, Globe Industries, Dayton, Ohio, 1966-72, Detroit Aluminum & Brass, Bellefontaine, Ohio, 1972-76; cons. engr. H.A. Williams Assoc., Columbus, Ohio, 1976—. Served in USAF, 1954-56. Mem. Am. Inst. Plant Engrs. (pres. 1985), Masons. Avocations: sailing, radio controlled model boats. Home: 2793 Shellwick Ct Columbus OH 43235

ROBERTSON, HORACE BASCOMB, JR., law educator; b. Charlotte, N.C., Nov. 13, 1923; s. Horace Bascomb and Ruth (Montgomery) R.; m. Patricia Lavell, Aug. 11, 1947; children—Mark L., James D. B.S., U.S. Naval Acad., 1945; J.D., Georgetown U., 1953; M.S., George Washington U., 1968. Commd. ensign U.S. Navy, 1945, advanced through grades to rear adm., 1972; line officer, 1945-55, law specialist, 1955-68; spl. counsel to sec. Navy, Washington, 1964-67; judge adv. Navy, 1968-76; spl. counsel to chief naval ops. Washington, 1970-72; dep. judge adv. gen. Navy Dept., Washington, 1972-75; judge adv. gen. Navy Dept., 1975-76; prof. law Duke U., 1976-89, sr. assoc. dean, 1986-89, ret., 1990; Chas H. Stockton chair of internat. law Naval War Coll., Newport, R.I., 1991-92. Decorated D.S.M. Mem. ABA, Fed. Bar Assn. (nat. council), Am. Soc. Internat. Law. Methodist. Home: 5 Stoneridge Cir Durham NC 27705-5510 Office: Duke U Sch Law Durham NC 27708

ROBERTSON, HUGH DUFF, lawyer; b. Grosse Pointe, Mich., Mar. 14, 1957; s. Hugh Robertson and Louise (Grey) Bollinger; m. Lynn Ann Wicker, June 10, 1978. BBA in Fin., U. Wis., Whitewater, 1978; JD, Whittier Coll., 1982. Bar: Calif. 1983, U.S. Tax Ct. 1984. Pres., CEO, A. Morgan Maree Jr. & Assocs., Inc., L.A., 1979—. Mem. ABA (forum com. on entertainment 1982—, forum com. on constrn. industry 1989) State Calif., L.A. County Bar Assn., Beverly Hills Bar Assn., Acad. TV Arts and Scis., Am. Film Inst., Phi ALpha Delta. Republican. Episcopalian. Avocations: sports, swimming, running, reading. Office: A Morgan Maree Jr & Assocs 4727 Wilshire Blvd Ste 600 Los Angeles CA 90010

ROBERTSON, JACK CLARK, accounting educator; b. Marlin, Tex., Apr. 27, 1943; s. Rupert Cook and Lois Lucille (Rose) R.; m. Caroline Susan Hughes, Oct. 23, 1965; children: Sarah Ellen, Elizabeth Hughes. Student, Rice U., 1961-63; B.B.A. with honors, U. Tex., Austin, 1965, M.in Profl. Acctg., 1967; Ph.D., U. N.C., 1970. C.P.A.; Tex. Tax acct. Humble Oil and Refining Co., Houston, 1964-65; auditor Peat, Marwick, Mitchell & Co., Houston, 1965-66; acct. Wade, Barton, Marsh C.P.A.s, Austin, Tex., 1966-67; asst. prof. U. Tex., Austin, 1970-74; assoc. prof. U. Tex., 1974-79, Price Waterhouse auditing prof., 1979-84, C.T. Zlatkovich Centennial prof. acctg., 1984—; acad. assoc. Coopers & Lybrand, N.Y.C., 1975-76; acad. fellow U.S. Securities and Exchange Commn. Office of the Chief Acct., Washington, 1982-83; Erskine fellow U. Canterbury, Christchurch, New Zealand, 1988; lectr. in field. Contbr. articles to profl. jours. Lay reader St. Matthews Episcopal Ch., Austin, 1972-75, mem. vestry, 1973-75, 77-79, 84-86, treas., 1974-75, 87—, chmn. bldg. fund, 1976-87, chmn. everymem. canvass, 1980, sr. warden, 1986; del. Diocese of Tex. Coun., 1993-95. Mem. AICPA, Am. Acctg. Assn. (chmn. auditing sect. 1978-79, chmn. auditing stds. com. 1980-81, chmn. SEC liaison com. 1983-84), Tex. Soc. CPAs (vice chmn., profl. ethics com. 1986-94, Presdl. citation 1994), Nat. Assn. Cert. Fraud Examiners (regent emeritus, cert.), Phi Kappa Phi, Beta Gamma Sigma, Beta Alpha Psi. Office: CBA Univ of Tex Cba 4M 202 Dept Of Acc Austin TX 78712

ROBERTSON, JAMES COLVERT, insurance company executive; b. Takoma Park, Md., Feb. 2, 1932; s. Charles Edwin and Mary Louise (Colvert) R.; m. Grace A. Shuler, May 7, 1971. BS in Econs., U. Md., 1957; LLB, George Washington U., 1959. Bar: D.C. 1960, Pa. 1965. Atty./analyst SEC, Washington, 1959-64; atty. McNees, Wallace & Nurick, Harrisburg, Pa., 1964-67; gen. counsel Consumers Life, Camp Hill, Pa., 1967-68; pres., chmn. bd. Consumers Life & Consumers Fin. Corp., Camp Hill, 1968—; dir. Consumers Fin. Bd. dirs. Harrisburg Hosp., 1982-86, Elizabethtown Coll., 1982—, Keystone Sports Found., 1983-88; treas. Susquehanna Art Mus. 1988—. With U.S. Army, 1951-53. Mem. Pa. Bar Assn., Fed. Bar Assn. West Shore Country Club (pres.). Republican. Home: 86 Greenwood Cir Wormleysburg PA 17043 Office: Consumers Life Ins Co PO Box 26 1200 Camp Hill By-Pass Camp Hill PA 17001-0026

ROBERTSON, JAMES IRVIN, JR., historian, educator; b. Danville, Va., July 18, 1930; s. James Irvin and Mae (Kympton) R.; m. Elizabeth Green, June 1, 1952; children—Mae Elizabeth, James Irvin III, Howard Wells. B.A., Randolph-Macon Coll., 1955, Litt.D., 1980; M.A., Emory U., 1956, Ph.D., 1959. Ordained deacon Anglican Cath. Ch. Editor Civil War History, U. Iowa, 1959-61; exec. dir. U.S. Civil War Centennial Commn., 1961-65; assoc. prof. history U. Mont., 1965-67; prof. Va. Poly. Inst. and State U., Blacksburg, 1967-76, chmn. dept. history, 1969-77, C.P. Miles prof. history, 1977-92, Alumni disting. prof., 1992—. Author: Civil War Sites in Virginia, 1982, General A.P. Hill, 1987, Soldiers Blue and Gray, 1988, Civil War Virginia, 1991, Civil War! America Becomes One Nation, 1992; contbr. articles to profl. jours. Recipient Harry S. Truman Hist. award, Bruce Catton award, Nevins Freeman award. Outstanding Faculty award Va. State Coun. Higher Edn., 1991, others. Mem. So. Hist. Assn., Va. Hist. Soc. Home: 405 Stonegate Dr Blacksburg VA 24060-3243 Office: Va Poly Inst History Dept Blacksburg VA 24061

ROBERTSON, JAMES WOOLSEY, lawyer; b. Ft. Sam Houston, Tex., Aug. 6, 1942; s. Robert Charles Lee and Marjorie Evelyn (Woolsey) R.; 1 child, William Angus; m. Laura Ann Koons, Apr. 24, 1993. BBA, U. Tex., 1966, JD, 1967. Bar: Tex.; cert. real estate law specialist. Ptnr. Liddell, Sapp, Zivley, Hill & Laboon, L.L.P., Houston, 1971—, chmn. fin. com., 1985-90, chmn. banking and real estate sect. and computer com., 1992—; Chancellor Episc. Ch. Holy Spirit, Houston, 1984-92, trustee, 1984-87. Lt. comdr. USCGR, 1968-71. Mem. State Bar Tex., Houston Bar Assn., Houston Real Estate Lawyers Coun. Republican. Avocations: golf, fly fishing, skiing, hunting. Office: Liddell Sapp Zivley Et Al 3400 Tex Commerce Tower 600 Travis St Houston TX 77002

ROBERTSON, JAQUELIN TAYLOR, architect, educator; b. Richmond, Va., Mar. 20, 1933; s. Walter Spencer and Mary Dade (Taylor) R.; m. Marianne Neese, Sept. 15, 1962. BA cum laude, Yale U., 1955-57, MArch. 1961; postgrad. (Rhodes scholar, Yale U. and Magdalen) Oxford U., 1957. Archtl. designer Sir Leslie Martin, Cambridge, Eng., 1961-62, Edward L. Barnes Assos., N.Y.C., 1963-66; lectr. architecture Yale U., 1964-65, Columbis U., 1965-67; prin. urban designer N.Y.C. Planning Commn., 1967-69; dir. Office Midtown Planning & Devel., N.Y.C., 1969-72; lectr. The New Sch., N.Y.C., 1973; city planning commr., N.Y.C., 1973; v.p. Arlen Realty Devel., N.Y.C., 1974-75; mng. dir. Llewelyn-Davies Va Shoraka, Tehran, Iran, 1975-77; chmn. Llewelyn-Davies Assoc., N.Y.C., 1977-78; prin. Jaquelin Taylor Robertson FAIA, N.Y.C., 1978-80; prin. Design Devel. Resources, N.Y.C., 1980-88, Eisenman-Robertson Archs., N.Y.C., 1980-88; ptnr. Cooper-Robertson, N.Y.C., 1988—; dean Sch. Architecture, U. Va., Charlottesville, 1980-88, Commonwealth prof. architecture, 1985-90; vis. faculty Salzburg (Austria) Seminar, 1974; vis. prof. archtl. design R.I. Sch. Design, Providence, 1979; William Henry Bishop prof. Yale U., 1980. Chmn. policy panel Design Arts Program, Nat. Endowment for Arts, 1979-83, founder Mayor's Inst. on City Design, Washington, 1986—; vis. com. Harvard Grad. Sch. Design, 1983-88; trustee Inst. Architecture and Urban Studies, N.Y.C., 1984-85; bd. dirs. Parks Council, N.Y.C., 1971-75, Mcpl. Arts Soc., N.Y.C., 1971-75, Archtl. League N.Y., 1972-75, 79-81, Ctr. for Study of Am. Architecture, Columbia U., 1984-87; adviser Aga Khan Program for Study of Islamic Art & Architecture, Harvard and MIT, 1983-90; trustee Va. Mus. of Fine Arts, 1985-90; mem. art and architecture rev. council State of Va., 1982-88; founder Jeffersonian Restoration Adv. Bd., Univ. of Va., 1985—; mem. Congress for the New Urbanism, 1993—. Recipient numerous awards for design. Fellow AIA; mem. Am. Inst. Cert. Planners, Am. Planning Assn., Bullingdon Club (Oxford), Knickerbocker Club (N.Y.C.), Pundits (Yale), Torch Hon. Soc. (Yale), St. Anthony Hall Club (Yale), Maidstone Club (Easthampton, N.Y.). Exhbns. include Inst. Architecture and Urban Studies, N.Y.C., 1975, Archtl. League and Mcpl. Arts Soc., 1969, Mus. Modern Art, N.Y.C., 1967, others. Contbr. articles to profl. jours., mags. Episcopalian. Home: 11 Dunemere Ln East Hampton NY 11937 also: 211 E 70th St New York NY 10021-5205 Office: Cooper Robertson & Ptnrs 311 W 43rd St New York NY 10036-6413

ROBERTSON, JERRY EARL, retired mining and manuracturing company executive; b. Detroit, Oct. 25, 1932; s. Earl Howard and Nellie (Wright) R.; m. Joanne Alice Wesner, Sept. 3, 1955; children: Scott Clark, Lisa Kay, Stuart Todd. B.S., Miami U., Oxford, Ohio, 1954; M.S., U. Mich., 1956, Ph.D., 1959. With Minn. Mining & Mfg. Co., St. Paul, 1963—; tech. dir. med. products div., 1973-74, dept. mgr. surg. products dept., 1974-75, gen. mgr. surg. products div., 1975-79, div. v.p. surg. products div., 1979-80, group v.p. health care products and services, 1980-84, exec. v.p. life scis. sector, 1984-86, exec. v.p. life scis. sector and corp. svcs., 1986-94; ret., 1994; bd. dirs. 3M Co., Cardinal Health Distbn., Inc., Haemonetics Corp., Braintree, Mass., Allianz Life Ins. Co. of N.Am.; trustee Minn. Med. Found., Mpls., 1981-87. Bd. reference MAP Internat., Brunswick, Ga., 1986-94; bd. dirs. Project HOPE, 1988—, Manor Care Inc., 1989—, Cardinal Distbn., Inc., 1991—. Mem. Pharm. Mfrs. Assn. (bd. dirs. 1984-89), Health Industry Mfrs. Assn. (bd. dirs. 1982-91, chmn. 1990-91). Unitarian. Office: Minn Mining & Mfg Co 3M Center Saint Paul MN 55144-1000

ROBERTSON, JOHN A., law educator; b. 1943. BA, Dartmouth U., 1964; JD, Harvard U., 1068. Bar: Mass. 1969, Wis. 1975. Law clk. Superior Jud. Ct. Mass., 1969-70; program dir. for cts. Mass. Gov's. Con on Law Enforcement and Adminstrn. of Criminal Justice, 1970-72, Russell Sage resident in law and social sci., 1972-73; asst. prof. U. Wis., 1973-76, assoc. prof., 1976-79, prof. law, 1979-82; Charles T. McCormick prof. U. Tex., Austin, 1982-83, Marrs McLean prof., 1983-84, Edward Clark Centennial prof., 1984-85, Baker & Botts prof., 1985-89, Anne Green regents chair, 1988-89, Thomas Watt Gregory prof., 1989—; teaching fellow Harvard U., 1972-73; Fulbright & Jaworski prof. U. Tex., 1981-82. Editor: Rough Justice: Perspectives on Lower Criminal Courts, (with Zinberg) Drugs and the Public, 1972, The Rights of the Critically Ill., 1983. Panel mem. fetal tissue transplantation rsch. NIH, 1988. Rsch. fellow in law and psychiatry Harvard U., 1968-69. Mem. Am. Fertility Soc., Fed. Task Force on Organ Transplantation, Law and Social Assn. (nat. com. for protection of human subjects of biomed. and behavioral sci. rsch.). Office: U Tex Sch Law 727 E 26th St Austin TX 78705-3224

ROBERTSON, JOHN ALDEN, agrologist, researcher; b. Minnedosa, Man., Can., Mar. 28, 1937; s. Lorne Edgar and Frances Mary (Jones) R.; m. Isobel Anne McDonald; children: David, Lesley, Trevor. BS in Agr., U. Man., Winnipeg, 1959, MSc, 1961; PhD, Massey U., Palmerston North, New Zealand, 1969. Lectr. U. Sask., Saskatoon, Can., 1964-65; rsch. scientist Agr. Can., Melfort, Sask., 1965-85; dir. Agr. Can., Kamloops, B.C., Can., 1985-91, Brandon, Man., 1991—. Office: Agr Can Rsch Sta, PO Box 1000A RR #3, Brandon, MB Canada R7A 5Y3

ROBERTSON, JOHN ARCHIBALD LAW, nuclear scientist; b. Dundee, Scotland, July 4, 1925; s. John Carr and Ellen (Law) R.; m. Betty-Jean Moffatt, June 26, 1954; children: Ean Stuart, Clare Deborah, Fiona Heather. B.A., Cambridge (Eng.) U., 1950, M.A., 1953. Sci. officer U.K. Atomic Energy Authority, Harwell, Eng., 1950-57; research officer Atomic Energy Can. Ltd., Chalk River, Ont., 1957-63; head reactor materials br. Atomic Energy Can. Ltd., 1963-70, dir. fuels and materials div., 1970-75, asst. to v.p., 1975-82; dir. program planning Atomic Energy Can. Ltd. (Research Co. Head Office), 1982-85; cons., 1985—; mem. Atomic Energy Control Bd.'s Adv. Com. on Nuclear Safety, 1988—. Author: Irradiation Effects in Nuclear Fuels, 1969; editor: Jour. Nuclear Materials, 1967-71. Served to capt., Royal Engrs. Brit. and Indian armies, 1943-47. Recipient W.B. Lewis medal Can. Nuclear Assn., 1987, W.J. Kroll Zirconium medal W.J. Kroll Inst. for Extractive Metallurgy, 1993. Fellow Royal Soc. Can.

ROBERTSON, JOSEPH W., JR., investment company executive; b. 1947. BA, Houston Bapt. U., 1971. With Weingarten Realty Investors, Houston, 1971—; sr. v.p. Office: Weingarten Realty Investors 2600 Citadel Plz Dr Houston TX 77008*

ROBERTSON, LEON H., management consultant, educator; b. Atlanta, Jan. 25, 1934; s. Grady Jospeh and Pearline (Chandler) R.; m. S. Ann Parker, Aug. 27, 1971; children: Sharon, Michael. B.S. in Indsl. Mgmt., Ga. Inst. Tech., 1957, M.S., 1959; postgrad., U. Okla.-Norman, 1958, U. Mich., 1961; Ph.D. in Bus. Adminstrn., Ga. State U., 1968. Mgr. mgmt. cons. div. Arthur Anderson & Co., Atlanta, 1960-65; prof. bus. adminstrn. Ga. State U., 1965-75; corp. v.p. Tex. Gas Corp., Owensboro, Ky., 1975-78, sr. v.p., 1982-83; chmn. chief exec. officer Am. Carriers, Inc., Overland Park, Kans., 1978-88; chmn. bd. dirs. Midwest Coast Transport, Overland Park, 1989; prof. mgmt., dir. div. bus. adminstrn. U. Mo., Kansas City, 1990—. Office: Univ of Mo-Kansas City Henry W Bloch Sch Bus & Pub Admn 5110 Cherry St Kansas City MO 64110-2426

ROBERTSON, LESLIE EARL, structural engineer; b. Los Angeles, Feb. 12, 1928; s. Garnett Roy and Tina (Grantham) R.; m. Saw-Teen See, Aug. 11, 1982; children: Jeanne, Christopher Alan, Sharon Miyuki, Karla Mei. BS, U. Calif., Berkeley, 1952; D in Engring. (hon.), Rensselaer Polytech. Inst., 1986; DSc (hon.), U. Western Ont., Can., 1988; DEng (hon.), Lehigh U., 1991. Lic. arch., Japan. Structural engr. Kaiser Engrs., Oakland, Calif., 1952-54, John A. Blume, San Francisco, 1954-57, Raymond Internat. Co., N.Y.C., 1957-58; mng. ptnr. Skilling, Helle, Christiansen, Robertson, N.Y.C., Seattle and Anchorage, 1958-82; chmn. Robertson, Fowler & Assocs., P.C., N.Y.C., 1982-85, Leslie E. Robertson Assocs., structural engrs., 1986—; chmn. Coun. on Tall Bldgs. and Urban Habitat; mem. Com. on Natural Disasters; commr., mem. U.S. Nat. Com. for the Decade for Natural Disasters Reduction; dir. Wind Engring. Rsch. Coun.; lectr. Rensselaer Poly. Inst., 1984, Johns Hopkins U., 1985, Nat. Bur. Standards, 1986, Cornell U., 1987, Hong Kong U., 1986, Technischische U., Delft, Holland, 1991, 93, Waseda (Japan) U., Musashi Inst. Tech., 1993, others; James L. Sherard lectr. U. Calif., Berkeley, 1991. Author papers in field. Bd. dirs. Architects/Designers/Planners for Social Responsibility; mem. Japan Structural Cons. Assn.; mem. human rights of scientists com. N.Y. Acad. Scis.; mem. U.S.

Nat. Com. for Decade for Nat. Disaster Reduction; mem. engring. coll. coun. Cornell U. Served with USNR, 1944-46. Recipient Inst. Honor award AIA, 1989, Mayor's award for excellence in sci. and tech. Mayor of City of N.Y./N.Y. Acad. Scis., 1993, John R. Parmer award, 1991, Disting. Engring. Alumnus award U. Calif., Berkeley, 1991, Prof. Gengo Matsui prize, Japan, 1993, World Trade. Ctr. Individual Svc. medal, 1993, Citation of Excellence, ENR, 1993, named Constrn. Man of Yr., 1989. Fellow ASCE (Raymond C. Reese Rsch. prize 1974); mem. Nat. Acad. Engring., Archtl. League of N.Y. (v.p.), NY Acad. Scis. (Mayor Awd. Excellence in Sci. & Tech., 1993). Home: 45 E 89th St Apt 25C New York NY 10128-1230 Office: 211 E 46th St New York NY 10017-2935

ROBERTSON, LINWOOD RIGHTER, electric utility executive; b. Reedville, Va., Feb. 10, 1940; s. Reginald Linwood and Alliene Dewer (Righter) R.; m. Mildred Swift, Apr. 10, 1965; 1 child, William S. B.S., Va. Commonwealth U., 1970. Comml. fisherman Smith Fisheries, Belford, N.Y., 1964; supr. Philip Morris Co., Richmond, Va., 1965-68; various positions to sr. v.p., chief fin. officer Dominion Resources, Inc. (formerly Va. Power), Richmond, 1969—. With USN, 1962-64. Mem. Hermitage Country Club. Methodist. Home: 11 Quail Run Dr Manakin Sabot VA 23103-2632

ROBERTSON, MARTHA RAPPAPORT, state senator, consultant; b. Boston, Sept. 14, 1952; d. Jerome Lyle and Nancy (Vahey) Rappaport; m. T.L. Robertson, Nov. 22, 1980; 1 child, Colby. BA, Franklin & Marshall Coll., 1974; MBA, U. Pa., 1976. Mktg. and new bus. devel. exec. Gen. Mills, Inc., Mpls., 1976-91; state senator State of Minn., 1993—. Republican. Office: State of Minn 125 State Office Building Bldg Saint Paul MN 55155-1201

ROBERTSON, MARY LOUISE, archivist, historian; b. L.A., May 19, 1945; d. Snell and Dorothy (Tregoning) R. BA, UCLA, 1966, MA, 1968, PhD, 1975. Teaching asst. dept. history UCLA, 1967-70; acting instr. UCLA Extension, 1973-74; acting instr. dept. history Pepperdine U., L.A., 1970, Calif. State U., Northridge, 1972-73; asst. curator manuscripts Huntington Libr., San Marino, Calif., 1975, assoc. curator, 1977, chief curator, 1979—; adj. prof. English Claremont Grad. Sch., 1994. Author: Guide to British Historical Manuscripts in the Huntington Library, 1982; co-author, editor: Guide to American Historical Manuscripts in the Huntington Library, 1979; contbr. articles on Tudor history to profl. jours. Mabel Wilson Richards dissertation fellow, 1970-72. Mem. Am. Hist. Assn., Soc. Am. Archivists, Soc. Calif. Archivists, N.Am. Conf. on Brit. Studies, Pacific Coast Conf. on Brit. Studies (tress. 1986-88, pres. 1988-90), Phi Beta Kappa. Office: Huntington Libr 1151 Oxford Rd San Marino CA 91108-1218

ROBERTSON, MARY VIRGINIA, retired elementary educator; b. Lincoln, Nebr., Oct. 1, 1925; d. Dean Leroy and Anna Charlotte (Boge) R. AB in Philosophy and Psychology, U. Nebr., Lincoln, 1949, BS in Elem. Edn., 1953; postgrad., U. Toronto, Ont., Can., 1949. Cert. elem. tchr., Nebr. Country sch. tchr. Lancaster County schs., Nebr., 1943-44, Otoe County schs., Palmyra, Nebr., 1944-45; 3d-5th grade tchr. Palmyra Schs., 1945-46; 3d grade tchr. Valley (Nebr.) Schs., 1953-57, Lincoln Pub. Schs., 1957-81; ret.; leader workshop in field; math. coord. Riley Elem. Sch., Lincoln, 1970-71. Author pamphlet A Letter for You, 1954. Mem. NEA, AAUW, Nebr. State Edn. Assn., Nat. Coun. Math. Tchrs., Am. Child Edn. Internat., Belmont PTA (life), Eastern Star, Lincoln Women's Club. Methodist. Avocations: reading, cats, rocks, bridge, writing children's stories.

ROBERTSON, MICHAEL BRIAN, advertising executive; b. Glasgow, Scotland, Feb. 18, 1948; came to U.S., 1953. s. John Todd and Sarah (O'Brien) R.; m. Dian Lemlein (div. Sept., 1986); m. Linda Sprague Maxwell. Apr. 2, 1988; children: Megan, Brendan, Charlotte. BA in English, Wilkes U., 1969. V.p., assoc. creative dir. Scali, McCabe, Sloves, N.Y.C., 1980-82; sr. v.p., assoc. creative dir. Needham/Harper Worldwide, N.Y.C., 1982-85; exec. v.p., creative dir. Della Femina, McNamee, N.Y.C., 1985-88; vice-chmn., creative dir. Young & Rubicam, N.Y.C., 1988-92; chmn., CEO, creative dir. McCaffrey & McCall Advt., N.Y.C., 1002—. Avocations: golf, tennis, music. Home: PO Box 299 West Redding CT 06896-0299 Office: McCaffrey and McCall 575 Lexington Ave New York NY 10022-6401

ROBERTSON, MICHAEL SWING, religious association administrator; b. Boston, July 20, 1935; s. Charles Stuart and Elizabeth (Swing) R.; m. Margaret Filoon, Sept. 17, 1960; children: Michael Swing, Ashlee Whipple, Christopher Filoon, Andrew Stuart. A.B., Harvard U., 1957, grad. Advanced Mgmt. Program, 1979. With Robertson Factories, Inc., 1962-80, exec. v.p., 1968-73, pres., 1973-79, chmn. bd., 1979-80; dir. Robertson-Swing Co., 1980—; pres. The Berkley Co. Inc., 1981-90, Reactions Inc., 1985-90; treas. Falmouth Marine Inc., 1981-88; pres., treas. Orchard Computer Inc., 1984-91, chmn., treas., 1991-93; exec. sec. Nat. Assn. Congl. Christian Chs., Oak Creek, Wis., 1991—. v.p. adv. council Coll. of Bus. and Industry, Southeastern Mass. U., North Dartmouth, Mass., 1979-91; selectman, Town of Berkley, Mass., 1974-80, chmn., 1979-80; mem. President's Adv. Com. for Trade Negotiations, 1983-86; bd. dirs. Mass. Easter Seal Soc., 1977-91, pres., 1982-83; bd. dirs. Nat. Easter Seal Soc., 1985-91, Wis. Easter Seal Soc., 1994—; chmn. Berkley Republican Town Com., 1977-91; mem. Pilgrim Congl. Ch., Taunton; Republican nominee U.S. Senate from Mass., 1976, nominee for Mass. state auditor, 1982; co-chmn. Mass. Reagan for Pres. Com., 1980; Bristol County coordinator Reagan/Bush campaign; co-chmn. Mass. Dole for Pres. Commn., 1987; chmn. Southeastern Mass. campaign Harvard Coll., 1981; chmn. Friends of Harvard Track, 1986-91; trustee Barnstable County Hosp., 1985-90, chmn., 1988. Mem. Harvard Varsity Club, Harvard Bus. Sch. Alumni Club of Wis. Home: 500 W Bender Rd # 51 Milwaukee WI 53217 Office: Nat Assn Congl Christian Ch 8473 S Howell Ave Oak Creek WI 53154-2922 *Accept responsibility with enthusiasm and gratitude. Our freedom of choice is unmatched in history, compelling us to remain true to our heritage.*

ROBERTSON, NAN, journalist, correspondent; b. Chgo., July 11, 1926; d. Frank and Eva (Morrish) R.; m. Allyn Baum, Feb. 24, 1950 (div. 1961); m. Stanley Levey, Aug. 27, 1961 (dec. 1971). B.S. in Journalism, Northwestern U., 1948. Spl. corr. Paris Herald Tribune, Paris, Berlin and London, 1948-55, Milw. Jour., Paris, Berlin and London, 1948-55, Stars and Stripes, Paris, Berlin and London, 1948-55, Am. Daily, Paris, Berlin and London, 1948-55; reporter, corr. N.Y. Times, N.Y.C., Washington and Paris, 1955-83; reporter culture N.Y. Times, N.Y.C., from 1983. Author: The Girls in the Balcony: Women, Men and The New York Times, 1992. Recipient Pulitzer prize for feature writing, 1983; recipient Page One award N.Y. Newspaper Guild, 1983, Front Page award N.Y. Newswomen's Club, 1961, 80, 82, N.Y. Press Club award, 1983; MacDowell Colony fellow, 1981, 83; Woodrow Wilson nat. fellow, 1983. Episcopalian. Address: care Kelly Susa Random House Inc 201 E 50th St New York NY 10022

ROBERTSON, NAT CLIFTON, chemist; b. Atlanta, July 23, 1919; s. Henry Booker and Eura Allen (Williams) R.; m. Elizabeth Bates Peck, Nov. 29, 1946; children: Henry Bartlett, Mary Amanda, Paul Edward. A.B., Emory U., 1939, Sc.D., 1970; Ph.D., Princeton U., 1942. Research asso. OSRD, 1942-43; chemist Standard Oil Co., N.J., 1943-47; group leader Celanese Corp. Am., 1947-51; dir. petrochems. dept. Nat. Research Corp., 1951-55; v.p., dir. research Escambia Chem. Corp., 1955-58; v.p. Spencer Chem. div. Gulf Oil Corp. (formerly Spencer Chem. Co.), Kansas City, Mo., 1958-66, Air Products & Chems., Inc., Allentown, Pa., 1966-69; sr. v.p. Air Products & Chems., Inc., 1966-77, also bd. dirs.; dir. Marion Labs., 1963-88. Trustee Midwest Research Inst.; bd. dirs. Kans. Research Found., 1963-66, pres., 1963-64. Mem. Am. Chem. Soc., Dirs. Indsl. Research, Indsl. Research Inst. Phi Beta Kappa, Sigma Xi. Democrat. Presbyterian. Club: Princeton (N.Y.C.). Home: 156 Philip Dr Princeton NJ 08540-5423

ROBERTSON, OSCAR PALMER (BIG O), former professional basketball player, chemical company executive; b. Charlotte, Tenn., Nov. 24, 1938. BBBA, U. Cin., 1960. Player U.S. Olympic Basketball Team, 1960; basketball player Cin. Royals, 1960-70, Milw. Bucks, 1970-74; founder, pres., CEO, Orchem, Inc., Cin., 1981—, Orpack-Stone Corp., Herrin, Ill., 1990—, Oscar Robertson Constrn., Indpls., 1975—; player NBA Championship Team, 1971. Named Sporting News Coll. Player of Yr. 1958, 59, 60, Sporting News All-Star First Team, 1958, 59, 60, NBA Rookie of Yr., 1961, All NBA First Team, 1961-69; player NBA All Star Games, 1961-72; named MVP, NBA, 1964, M VP in NBA All-Star Games, 1961, 64, 69; named to

NBA 35th Anniversary All-Star Team, 1980; elected to Naismith Meml. Basketball Hall of Fame, 1979. Office: Orchem Inc 4293 Mulhauser Rd Fairfield OH 45014*

ROBERTSON, PAT (MARION GORDON ROBERTSON), religious broadcasting executive; b. Lexington, Va., Mar. 22, 1930; s. A. Willis and Gladys (Churchill) R.; m. Adelia Elmer; children: Timothy, Elizabeth, Gordon, Ann. BA, Washington and Lee U., 1950; JD, Yale U., 1955; MDiv, N.Y. Theol. Sem., 1959; ThD (hon.), Oral Roberts U., 1983. Ordained minister So. Bapt. Conv., 1961-87. Founder, pres. Christian Broadcast Network, Virginia Beach, Va., 1960—; host 700 Club, 1968—; founder, pres. CBN Univ., 1977—; now regent; founder, pres. Continental Broadcasting Network, 1978—; bd. dirs. United Va. Bank, Norfolk; mem. Pres. Task Force on Victims of Crime, Washington, 1982. Author: (with Jamie Buckingham) Shout It From the Housetops: The Story of the Founder of the Christian Broadcasting Network, 1972, My Prayer for You, 1977, The Secret Kingdom, 1982, Answers to 200 of Life's Most Probing Questions, 1984, Beyond Reason, 1984, 85, America's Date with Destiny, 1986, The Plan, 1989, The New Millennium, 1990, The New World Order, 1991. Candidate for Rep. nomination for Pres. U.S., 1988. Recipient Disting. Merit citation NCCJ, Knesset medallion Israel Pilgrimage Com., Faith and Freedom award Religious Heritage Am., Bronze Halo award So. Calif. Motion Picture Council, Humanitarian award Food for the Hungry, 1982, George Washington Honor medal Freedoms Found. at Valley Forge, 1983; named Internat. Clergyman of Yr. Religion in Media, 1981, Man of Yr. Internat. Com. for Goodwill, 1981. Mem. Nat. Broadcasters (bd. dirs. 1973—). Office: The Christian Broadcasting Network CBN Ctr Virginia Beach VA 23463

ROBERTSON, PETER BARRIE, mayor; b. N.Y.C., Nov. 4, 1938; s. Robert Barrie and Rosemary (Mecca) R.; m. Jo-Anne Chalmers; children: Scott, Kirk, Jodi. BPHE, U. Toronto, Ont., Can., 1961, BA in Psychology, 1964; BEd, Ont. Inst. of Studies in Edn., Toronto, 1967. Tchr., coach Etobicoke Bd. Edn., 1962-66; cons. Toronto Bd. Edn., 1967-71; prof. faculty of edn. U. Toronto, 1972-95; councillor City of Brampton, Ont., Can., 1974-91, mayor, 1991—; chmn. GTA Mayor's Com. on Mcpl. Tax Reform, Greater Toronto area, 1994-95; rschr. on assisting street children; spkr. and workshop leader in field. Co-author: Health for Life, 1984, (multimedia kit) Sexually Transmitted Diseases, 1979, (video and teaching kit) Taking Control Family Violence, 1986. Sch. trustee, councillor Castlemore and Toronto Gore, Peel County, 1968-74; mem. nat. edn. nucleus com. Can. Cancer Soc.; founder Castlemore Cmty. Sch., Peel Dist. Health Coun., Victim Svcs. in Peel, Peel Drinking and Driving Awareness Com.; nat. bd. dirs. Inst. Prevention Child Abuse. Recipient Ministry of Health recognition Peel Dist. Health Coun., 1977-84, Silver Pin for Vol. Svc., Can. Cancer Soc., 1979-85, Multi Cultural award North American Sikh League, 1990. Mem. Can. Assn. Phys. Health and Recreation (nat. membership chmn.), Can. Mental Health Assn. (nat. bd. dirs.). Home: 11570 McVean Dr RR 9, Brampton, ON Canada L6T 3Z8 Office: City of Brampton, 2 Wellington St W, Brampton, ON Canada L6Y 4R2

ROBERTSON, RALPH S., secondary school principal. Prin. Richmond Sr. High Sch., Rockingham, N.C. Recipient Rlue Ribbon Sch. award U.S. Dept. Edn., 1990-91, Nat. award Dale Parnell Tech. Prep Program of Excellence, 1991; named Prin. of Yr., N.C. Burger King/Nat. Assn. of Secondary Sch. Prin., 1987. Office: Richmond Sr High Sch PO Box 1748 US Hwy 1 North Rockingham NC 28379

ROBERTSON, RICHARD BLAKE, management consultant; b. Ahoskie, N.C., July 28, 1929; s. James Henry and Janie Bell (Baker) R.; m. Elizabeth Parker Gardner, Aug. 19, 1941. BSEE, N.C. State U., 1951; MBA, U. Md., 1956. Design engr. Westinghouse Electric Co., Friendship Airport, Md., 1951-54; product planner Gen. Electric Co., Lynchburg, Pa., 1956-59; dir. mktg. Gen. Motors Corp., Milw., 1959-60; pres. Robertson and Assocs., Pinetops, N.C., 1960—. Mem. Phi Kappa Phi, Tau Beta Pi, Phi Eta Sigma, Theta Tau, Eta Kappa Nu. Office: Robertson & Assocs Inc PO Drawer B Pinetops NC 27864

ROBERTSON, RICHARD EARL, physical chemist, educator; b. Long Beach, Calif., Nov. 12, 1933; s. Earl Austin and A. Isobel (Roberts) R.; m. Joyce W. Conger, Sept. 4, 1955 (div. 1972); children: Christopher, Jill; m. Patricia L. Richmond, Apr. 20, 1974. BA, Occidental Coll., L.A., 1955; student, UCLA, 1955-56; PhD, Calif. Inst. Tech., 1960. Phys. chemist rsch. lab. GE, Schenectady, N.Y., 1960-70; staff scientist Ford Motor Co., Dearborn, Mich., 1970-86; prof. materials sci. and engring. U. Mich., Ann Arbor, 1986—. Contbr. articles to profl. jours. Postdoctoral fellow Washington U., St. Louis, 1959-60. Fellow Am. Phys. Soc.; mem. Am. Chem. Soc., Sigma Xi. Office: U Mich Dept Materials Sci Eng Ann Arbor MI 48109

ROBERTSON, RICHARD STUART, insurance holding company executive; b. Spokane, Wash., June 14, 1942; s. Stuart A. and Marjory (Moch) R.; m. Trudy Ann Prendergast, July 31, 1976; children: Thomas Stuart, Richard Andrew. B.S., Calif. Inst. Tech., 1963. Chief reinsurance actuary Lincoln Nat. Life Ins. Co., Ft. Wayne, Ind., 1963-74; sr. v.p., chief fin. officer Lincoln Nat. Corp., Ft. Wayne, 1974-86, exec. v.p., CFO., 1986-92, exec. v.p., corp. risk officer, 1992—; bd. dirs. 1st Penn-Pacific, Linsco Reins. Co. Fellow Soc. Actuaries (pres. 1985-86); mem. Am. Acad. Actuaries (v.p. 1980-81), Actuarial Stds. Bd. Episcopalian. Home: 12618 Aboite Center Rd Fort Wayne IN 46804-9725

ROBERTSON, R(ITA) KAE, nurse, administrator; b. Richland, Wash., Aug. 14, 1954; d. Richard Grant and Rita Ione (Woffinden) R. Diploma, Highland Hosp. Sch. Nursing, Rochester, N.Y., 1978; BSN, Alfred U., 1980; MS, SUNY, Buffalo, 1986; MBA, U. Rochester, 1992. RN, N.Y. Head nurse U. Rochester (N.Y.)-Strong meml. Hosp.; asst. v.p. nursing Highland Hosp., Rochester, 1986-88, v.p. nursing, 1988-93; sr. mgr. Ernst & Young LLP, Cleve., 1993—. Mem. Am. Orgn. Nurse Execs., Western N.Y. League Nursing (bd. dirs.).

ROBERTSON, ROBBIE, musician, popular; b. Toronto, 1943. Guitarist Ronnie Hawkins and The Hawks, 1959-63, The Hawks, 1963-65, The Band (with Bob Dylan), 1965-68; guitarist, songwriter The Band, 1968-76; solo performer, 1976—. Albums: (with The Band) Music from Big Pink, 1968, The Band, 1969, Stage Fright, 1970, Cahoots, 1971, Rock of Ages, 1972, Moondog Matinee, 1973, Northern Lights—Southern Cross, 1975, The Best of The Band, 1976, Islands, 1977, The Last Waltz, 1978, Anthology, 1978, (with Bob Dylan) Planet Waves, 1974, Before the Flood, 1974, The Basement Tapes, 1975, (solo) Robbie Robertson, 1987, Storyville, 1991; record prodr. for artists including: Neil Diamond, Jesse Winchester, Hirth Martinez; film composer: Raging Bull, 1980, The King of Comedy, 1983, The Color of Money, 1986; appearances in films: The Last Waltz, 1978, Carny, 1980. Group The Band inducted into Rock & Roll Hall of Fame, 1994. Office: Geffen Records 9130 Sunset Blvd Los Angeles CA 90069*

ROBERTSON, ROBERT GORDON, retired Canadian government official; b. Davidson, Sask., Can., May 19, 1917; s. John Gordon and Lydia Adelia (Paulson) R.; m. Beatrice Muriel Lawson, Aug. 14, 1943; children: John Lawson, Karen Martha. B.A., U. Sask., 1938; B.A. Juris, Oxford U., 1940, D.C.L., 1983; M.A., U. Toronto, 1941; LL.D., U. Sask., 1959, McGill U., 1963, U. Toronto, 1973, U. Dalhousie, 1977; Di de l'univ., U. Laval, 1975, Ottawa U., 1982, Carleton U., 1990. Mem. staff Dept. External Affairs, Govt. of Can., 1941-45; sec. to Office of Prime Minister, 1945-49; mem. staff Privy Council Office, 1949-53; dep. minister of No. Affairs and Nat. Resources; commr. Northwestern Territories, 1953-63; clk. Privy Council, sec. to cabinet, 1963-75, sec. to cabinet for fed.-provincial relations, 1975-79; chancellor Carleton U., 1980-90; ret., 1990; mem. Queen's Privy Coun. for Can., 1982. Decorated Companion of Order of Can. Fellow Royal Soc. Can. Mem. United Ch. of Can. Home: 20 Westward Way, Ottawa, ON Canada K1L 5A7

ROBERTSON, SAMUEL LUTHER, JR., special education educator, therapist; b. Houston, Apr. 28, 1940; s. Sam L. and Portia Louise (Burns) R.; children: Samuel Luther IV, Sean Lee (dec.), Ryan William, Susan Elizabeth (dec.); m. Gail Maureen Daniels, Dec. 15, 1987; 1 child, Henry

Philmore. BS, McMurry U., 1969; MA, Hardin-Simmons U., 1973; PhD, U. Tex., 1993. Cert. tchr., administr., counselor, Tex.; lic. chem. dependency counselor, lic. clin. mental health counselor, Tex. Instr., coach, athletic dir. Tex. and La. schs., 1969-94; social worker, supr. Children's Protective Svcs., Abilene, Tex., 1978-79; instr. adminstr. Harlandale Sch. Dist., San Antonio, 1980-84, 87-90; adminstr. night sch. Harlandale Ind. Sch. Dist., San Antonio, 1988-89; instr. Edgewood Ind. Sch. Dist., San Antonio, 1985-87; developer, instr., integrated unit program San Antonio, 1990—; CEO The Educative Inst., San Antonio, 1992—; educative therapist, Educative Therapeutic Processes, San Antonio, 1972—. Author: (play) The Challenged, 1965: (poem) Trains in the Night, 1969. State co-chmn. Youth for Kennedy-Johnson, Tex., 1960; mem. W. Tex. Dem. Steering Com., Abilene, 1962-63; founding dir. Way Off Broadway Community Theater, Eagle Pass, Tex., 1971-72; founding bd. dirs. Battered Women's Shelter, Abilene, 1978-79; v.p. bd. dirs. Mental Health Assn., San Antonio, 1980-83, bd. dirs Palmer Drug Abuse Program, San Antonio, 1985-87; pres., bd. dir. Alcoholic Rehab. Ctr., 1985-86, 1987-92; mem., vice chmn. Civilian and Mil. Addictive Programs, San Antonio, 1991-92; author, implementer Community Vitalization Program, 1994—. Named Tchr. of Yr. Southside Ind. Sch. Dist., San Antonio, 1970-71, Harlandale Alternative Ctr., San Antonio, 1987-88; Vol. of Yr., Mental Health Assn., San Antonio, 1982, Alcoholic Rehab. Ctr., San Antonio, 1992-93. Mem. ACA, NEA, Tex. State Tchrs. Assn., Am. Ednl. Rsch. Assn., Am. Assn. Sch. Adminstrs., Tex. Assn. Alcoholism and Drug Abuse Counselors, Nat. Alcoholism and Drug Abuse Counselors, N.Mex. Mental Health Counselors Assn., Phi Kappa Phi, Kappa Delta Pi. Methodist. Avocations: reading, writing, travel, theater, sports. Home: 11907 Gallant Forest San Antonio TX 78249 Office: Educative Therapeutic Processes 339 E Hildebrand San Antonio TX 78212

ROBERTSON, SARA STEWART, portfolio manager; b. N.Y.C., Feb. 4, 1940; d. John Elliott and Mary Terry (Schlamp) Stewart; m. James Young Robertson, Nov. 29, 1975 (dec. Mar. 1988). BA, Conn. Coll., 1961; MBA, Am. U., 1969. From trainee to officer First Nat. Bank/First Chgo. Corp., 1969-75, v.p., 1975-92; prin. Royall Enterprises, Chgo., 1992—; bd. dirs. Youth Guidance, Chgo., 1982-85, 92-95, chair individuals fundraising, mem. exec. com., 1993-95. Bd. dirs. Harbor House Condominium Assn. Chgo., 1990-92; bd. trustees Sherwood Conservatory Music, 1993—, chair bd. devel., 1993-95; mem. allocations com. and family priority grants com. United Way-Chgo., 1992-95. Home and Office: 6504 N Artesian Chicago IL 60645 Address (winter): 470 S Ocean Blvd Apt 5 Palm Beach FL 33480

ROBERTSON, STEWART, conductor; b. Glasgow, Scotland. Assoc. condr. apprentice program Des Moines Opera; music dir. Glimmerglass Summer Opera Festival, 1988; past music dir., prin. condr. Santa Fe (N.Mex.) Symphony; music dir. Inland Empire Symphony Orchestra, San Bernardino, Calif.; prof. conducting, dir. orchestral activities, U. N.Mex. Office: Inland Empire Symphony Orch 362 W Court St San Bernardino CA 92401*

ROBERTSON, TED ZANDERSON, judge; b. San Antonio, Sept. 28, 1921; s. Irion Randolf and Aurelia (Zanderson) R.; m. Margie Gardner. Student, Tex. A&I, 1940-42; LL.B., St. Mary's U., San Antonio, 1949. Bar: Tex. 1949. Chief civil dept. Dist. Atty.'s Office, Dallas County, Tex., 1960-65; judge Probate Ct. 2, Dallas County, 1965-69, Juvenile Ct. 2, Dallas County, 1969-75, 95th Dist. Ct., Dallas County, 1975-76, Ct. Civil Appeals, 5th Supreme Jud. Dist., Dallas, 1976-82, Supreme Ct. Tex., Austin, 1982; of counsel Frank Branson P.C., Dallas, 1989—; guest lectr. So. Meth. U., Dallas, Dallas County Juvenile Bd., Tex. Coll. of the Judiciary, 1970-82. Active Dallas Assn. for Retarded Children; active Dallas County Commn. on Alcoholism, Dallas County Mental Health Assn. Served as yeoman USCG, 1942-46. Recipient Golden Gavel St. Mary's U., San Antonio, 1979; named Outstanding Alumnus St. Mary's U., 1981. Mem. Am. Judicature Soc., Tex. Bar Assn., Dallas Bar Assn., Dallas County Juvenile Bd. Democrat. Methodist. Lodges: Masons; Lions. Home: 6233 Highgate Ln Dallas TX 75214-2157 Office: Frank Branson 4514 Cole Ave Dallas TX 75205-5412

ROBERTSON, THOMAS L., health facility administrator; b. June 23, 1943. AA, Nat. Bus. Coll., 1965; postgrad., St. Louis U., 1971-74. CPA Anderson and Reed, Roanoke, Va.; with Carilion Health System, 1969—; pres., CEO N000, 1986—; also bd. dirs. Carilion Health System; chmn. bd. dirs. SunHealth Corp.; bd. dirs. Roanoke Electric Steel, Roanoke Gas Co., Shenandoah Life Ins. Co., 1st Union Corp. Va., Roanoke Valley Devel. Corp., Ctr. In The Sq. Chmn. Roanoke Valley Bus. Coun., Renew Roanoke; co-chmn. The New Century Coun.; bd. dirs. Va. Found. Ind. Colls., Roanoke Coll. Mem. Am. Hosp. Assn. (mem. ho. dels., mem. regional policy bd.), Va. Hosp. Assn. (bd. dirs., past chmn.), Roanoke Area Hosp. Coun. (past pres.), Hosp. Fin. Mgmt. Assn. (past pres.-Va. chpt.), Roanoke Valley C. of C. (former pres.), Jaycees (past pres.), Roanoke Country Club (former pres.). Office: Carilion Health System PO Box 13727 Roanoke VA 24036-3727

ROBERTSON, TIMOTHY B., cable television executive; b. 1955. With Christian Broadcasting Network, Inc., Virginia Beach, Va.; with Internat. Family Entertainment, Inc., Virginia Beach, 1989—, pres., CEO. Office: Internat Family Entertainment 2877 Guardian Ln Virginia Beach VA 23452*

ROBERTSON, TIMOTHY JOEL, statistician, educator; b. Denver, Oct. 4, 1937; s. Flavel P. and Helen C. (Oliver) Girdner; m. Joan K. Slater, Aug. 18, 1959; children—Kelly, Jana, Doug, Mike. B.A. in Math., U. Mo., 1959, M.S. in Math., 1961, Ph.D. in Stats., 1968. Asst. prof. Cornell Coll., Mt. Vernon, Iowa, 1961-63; prof. stats. U. Iowa, Iowa City, 1965—; vis. prof. U. N.C., Chapel Hill, 1974-75, U. Calif.-Davis, 1983-84; Eugene Lukacs Disting. vis. prof. Bowling Green State U., 1991-92; vis. lectr. Com. Pres. Statis. Soc., 1971-74. Author: (with F.T. Wright and R.L. Dykstra) Order Restricted Statistical Inference; assoc. editor Am. Math. Monthly, 1977-81; mem. editorial bd. Communications in Stats., 1981-92; assoc. editor Jour. Am. Statis. Assn., 1990—; contbr. numerous articles to profl. jours. Recipient Collegiate Teaching award U. Iowa, 1990. Fellow Am. Statis. Assn. (council 1974-75), Inst. Math. Stats., Internat. Statis. Inst.; mem. Math. Assn. Am., Sigma Xi, Sierra Club. Democrat. Avocations: canoeing, camping, bicycling, walking. Home: 1811 Kathlin Dr Iowa City IA 52246-4617 Office: U Iowa Dept Stats And Sci Iowa City IA 52242

ROBERTSON, WILLIAM FRANKLIN, publishing executive; b. Richmond, Va., Sept. 1, 1917; s. Joseph William and Nancy Lucretia (Brooks) R.; m. Avis Dorothy Stillman, Aug. 7, 1943; children: Lynne Brooks, William Elden. BS, U. Richmond, 1938. Mgr. office Richmond Newspapers, Inc. 1941-46, credit mgr., contr., 1946-66, asst. treas., 1966-68, treas., asst. sec., 1968-87, cons., 1987-94; v.p., treas., asst. sec. Media Gen., Inc., 1977-87, cons. 1987—. Trustee Va. Bapt. Homes; trustee, treas. Bapt. Mins. Relief Fund Va.; endowment fund trustee Richmond Bapt. Assn. Mem. Inst. Newspaper Contrs. and Fin. Officers (past dir.). Adminstrv. Mgmt. Soc. (pres. Richmond chpt. 1964-65), Fin. Execs. Inst., Phi Delta Theta. Avocation: private pilot. Home: 4 Ralston Rd Richmond VA 23229-8022 Office: 333 E Grace St Richmond VA 23219

ROBERTSON, WILLIAM RICHARD, banker, holding company executive; b. Schenectady, N.Y., July 26, 1941; s. Bruce Manson and Mary Jo (Gillam) R.; m. Sarah Reed Parker, June 20, 1964; children: Deborah Graham, John William, Julie Elizabeth. AB, Colgate U., 1964; MBA, Case Western Res. U., 1967. Nat. City Bank/Nat. City Corp., 1964—; Exec. v.p., chief fin. officer Nat. City Corp., Cleve., 1982-89, dep. chmn. bd. dirs., 1986—; bd. dirs. Nat. City Corp., Capitol Am. Fin. Corp., Kirtland Capital Corp. Trustee Coll. of Wooster, Ohio, 1982-91, Fairmount Presbyn. Ch., Cleve., 1983-86, St. Luke's House, Cleve., 1984—, Cleve. Ballet, 1985-89, United Way, 1986-92, Karamu House, 1988—, Western Res. Hist. Soc., 1990—, Cleve. Mus. Art, 1991—, Salvation Army, 1985—, chmn. adv. bd., 1991-93; pres., trustee Big Bros. and Big Sisters, Cleve. 1973-80; chmn., bd. trustees United Way of Cleve., 1995—, trustee Musical Arts Assn., 1994—, chmn. vis. com. of Case Western Res. U. Weatherhead Sch. Mgmt., 1995—. Mem. Fin. Execs. Inst., Bankers Roundtable, Am. Bankers Assn., Cleve. Skating Club (pres. 1980-82), Union Club, Country Club, Tavern Club, Pepper Pike Club, Ottawa Club, Desert Mountain Club. Republican. Avocations: travel, skiing, shooting, golf, history. Home: 2700 Chesterton Rd

Shaker Heights OH 44122 Office: Nat City Corp Nat City Ctr 1900 E 9th St Cleveland OH 44114-3303

ROBERTSON, WILLIAM WITHERS, lawyer; b. Morristown, N.J., Nov. 3, 1941; s. Thomas Withers and Jessie (Swain) R.; children: Barbara Ellen, William Withers, Jessie Swain. B.A., Rutgers U., 1964, LL.B., 1967. Bar: N.J. 1968. Law sec. to judge Superior Ct. N.J., 1967-68; asst. U.S. atty., 1972-76, 1st asst. U.S. atty., 1978-80; U.S. atty. Dist. N.J., 1980-81; chief Newark Organized Crime Strike Force, 1976-78; ptnr. firm Hannoch Weisman, Roseland, N.J., 1981—. Mng. editor Rutgers Law Rev., 1966-67. Trustee Rutgers U., 1984-88. Served to capt. JAGC USAR, 1968-72. Mem. Nat. Assn. Former U.S. Attys. (bd. dirs. 1990-93), Rutgers U. Law Sch. Alumni Assn. (pres. 1990-91), Rutgers U. Alumni Fedn. (pres. 1981-83). Office: Hannoch Weisman PO Box 1040 Newark NJ 07101-1040

ROBFOGEL, SUSAN SALITAN, lawyer; b. Rochester, N.Y., Apr. 4, 1943; d. Victor and Janet (Rosenthal) Salitan; m. Nathan Joshua Robfogel, July 12, 1965; children: Jacob Morris, Samuel Salitan. BA cum laude, Smith Coll., 1964; JD, Cornell U., 1967. Bar: N.Y.1967, U.S. Dist. Ct. (we. dist.) 1968, U.S. Ct. Appeals (2d cir.) 1971, U.S. Supreme Ct. 1971, U.S. Dist. Ct. (no. dist.) 1974, D.C. 1982. Asst. corp. counsel, then sr. asst. corp. counsel City of Rochester, N.Y., 1967-70; assoc. Harris, Beach & Wilcox, Rochester, 1970-75; ptnr. Harris, Beach, Wilcox, Rubin & Levey, Rochester, 1975-85; ptnr., chair health svcs. practice Nixon, Hargrave, Devans & Doyle, Rochester, 1985—; panel mem., Fed. Svc. Impasses Panel, Washington, 1983-94; mem., past chair Data Protection Rev. Bd., Albany, N.Y., 1984—. Mem. trustees vis. com. U. Rochester Med. Sch., 1990; mem. mgmt. adv. panel SUNY, 1990. Recipient Brockport Coll. Found. Community award, 1989. Fellow Am. Bar Found.; N.Y. State Bar Found.; mem. ABA, N.Y. State Bar Assn., Washington D.C. Bar Assn., Monroe County Bar Assn. (Rodenbeck award 1988). Home: 1090 Park Ave Rochester NY 14610 Office: Nixon Hargrave Devans & Doyle Clinton Sq PO Box 1051 Rochester NY 14603-1051

ROBICHAUD, FERNAND, Canadian government official. Sec. of state for parliamentary affairs Govt. of Can., 1993—. Office: Justice Canada, Kent St at Wellington St, Ottawa, ON Canada K1A 0H8*

ROBICHAUD, LOUIS JOSEPH, Canadian senator; b. St. Anthony, N.B., Oct. 21, 1925; s. Amedee and Annie (Richard) R.; m. Lorraine Savoie, Aug. 9, 1951; children: Jean Claude (dec.), Paul, Louis-Rene, Monique. B.A., Sacred Heart U., 1947, Dr. Polit. Sci., 1960; postgrad., Laval U., 1947-49; LL.D., U. N.B., 1960, St. Joseph's U., 1961, U. Montreal, 1961, U. Ottawa, 1962, St. Dunstan's U., 1964, U. St. Thomas, 1965, McGill U., 1967, Dalhousie U., 1969; D.C.L., Mt. Allison U., 1961, Moncton U., 1973. Bar: N.B. bar, Queen's counsel 1960. Practiced in Richibucto, N.B., 1952-60; mem. N.B. Legislature, 1952-71, financial critic, 1957-58, leader of opposition, 1958-60, 70-71, premier, 1960-70, atty. gen. N.B., 1960-65; minister of youth, 1967; mem. Privy Council, 1967—; chmn. Canadian sect. Internat. Joint Commn., 1971-73; summoned to Senate of Can., 1973—; leader Liberal Party of N.B., 1958-71. Past pres. Ottawa Valley chpt. Kidney Found. Can., bd. dirs. found. Decorated companion Order of Canada; recipient gold medal Laval U. Alumni Assn., 1963. Mem. N.B. Barristers Soc. Mem. Liberal Party. Roman Catholic. Home: 7 Pineland Ave, Nepean, ON Canada K2G 0E5 Office: Senate of Ont, 266 East Block, Ottawa, ON Canada K1A 0A4

ROBIE, JOAN, elementary school principal. Prin. Monteith Elem. Sch., Grosse Pointe, Mich. Recipient Elem. Sch. Recognition award U.S. Dept. Edn., 1989-90. Office: Monteith Elem Sch 1275 Cook Rd Grosse Pointe MI 48236-2511

ROBILLARD, DONALD J., elementary school principal. Prin. Glenmont (N.Y.) Elem. Sch. Recipient Elem. Sch. Recognition award U.S. Dept. Edn., 1989-90. Office: Glenmont Elem Sch RR 9 # W Glenmont NY 12077

ROBILOTTI, GERARD DANIEL, hospital administrator; b. N.Y.C., Oct. 5, 1940; s. Joseph Gerard and Victoria Elizabeth (Ventimiglia) R.; m. Martha Eleanor Bianco, Aug. 31, 1965; children: Mark, Elizabeth. BS, Manhattan Coll., Bronx, 1965; MS, Columbia U., 1971; postgrad., Temple U., Phila., 1966-68, Fordham U., Bronx, 1965-66. Lic. tchr., N.Y., Conn. Teaching asst. history Temple U., Phila., 1966-68; substitute tchr. social studies N.Y.C. Pub. Schs., 1965-66; adminstrv. intern Cabrini Med. Ctr., N.Y.C., summers 1965-66; coord. med. records dept. St. Vincent's Hosp. and Med. Ctr., N.Y.C., 1968-69; adminstrv. resident/adminstrv. asst. N.Y. Downtown Hosp., N.Y.C., 1970-71; dir. med. svc. Danbury (Conn.) Hosp., 1977-81, v.p., 1981-84, exec. v.p., 1984-87, 1985-94; exec. v.p. Danbury Health Sys., 1994—; adj. asst. prof. health edn. Western Conn. State U., Danbury, 1975-79; adj. assoc. prof. health svcs. adminstrn. Quinnipiac Coll., Hamden, Conn., 1976-77; lectr. U. Conn. Sch. Bus. Health Care Sys., Storrs, 1972-73; preceptor program in health svcs. adminstrn. Ithaca (N.Y.) Coll., 1974-75; preceptor program health scis. adminstrn. Yale U., New Haven, 1981-82, 90-91; preceptor program in pub. adminstrn. NYU Grad. Sch. Pub. Adminstrn., 1974-75; bd. dirs. Danbury Health Care Affiliates, Inc., Bus. Sys., Inc., Danbury, sec., 1988—; incorporator Savs. Bank of Danbury, 1988—; mem. Danbury regional adv. bd. First Fidelity Bank, 1995—. Contbr. articles to profl. jours. Bd. dirs. Danbury Hosp., 1987—; ExcelCare Health Care Sys., Bronxville, N.Y., 1994—; bd. dirs. ARC, Western Conn. chpt., Danbury, 1974-83, disaster svcs. com., 1982-90; bd. dirs. Aetna Health Plan of So. New Eng., Inc., 1994—, mem. med. mgmt. com., 1994—; bd. dirs. Western Conn. Chap. Trauma Found., Danbury, 1991—, steering com. for grad. program in health svcs. adminstrn. 1994—); adv. coun. Regional Hospice of Western Conn., Danbury, 1986-91; mem. edn. adv. coun. Danbury Pub. Schs., 1982-89, co-chmn. Danbury 2000 Sch. to Work Task Force, 1994—; bd. dirs. Conn. Lung Assn., Fairfield County, 1975-76; pres. Boy Scouts Am., Norwalk, Conn., 1988-90, v.p. 1990-93, bd. dirs., 1984—; chmn. health svcs. divsn. ann. dr. United Way of No. Fairfield County, 1994-95. Recipient Silver Beaver award Boy Scouts Am., 1990; Temple U. teaching fellow, 1966-68. Fellow Am. Coll. Health Care Execs., N.Y. Acad. Scis., Royal Soc. Health (London); mem. Am. Hosp. Assn. (alt. del. teaching hosps. 1990-91, met. hosps. 1991-93, state of Conn. 1995—), Conn. Hosp. Assn. (bd. dirs. 1987-89, CEO Conf. vice chmn. 1994—, govt. com. 1992-93, 94—, chmn. com. on trauma 1991—, com. on med. manpower and med. edn. 1994—), Vol. Hosp. Assn. of So. New Eng. (treas., bd. dirs. 1994—), New Eng. Healthcare Assembly (bd. trustees 1989-90, edn. exec. com. 1977-90, chmn. 1987-90), Conn. Soc. Hosp. With Accredited Residency Programs (treas. 1990—), Met. Health Adminstrs. Assn. (charter), Conn. Med. Soc. (com. on continuing med. edn. 1976—), Greater Danbury C. of C. (Leadership Danbury Faculty 1984), Rotary, Columbia U. Alumni Club of Fairfield County (treas. 1989-94). Office: Danbury Hospl 24 Hospital Ave Danbury CT 06810-6099

ROBIN, CLARA NELL (CLAIRE ROBIN), English language educator; b. Harrisonburg, Va., Feb. 19, 1945; d. Robert Franklin and Marguerite Ausherman (Long) Wampler; m. Phil Camden Branner, June 10, 1967 (div. May 1984); m. John Charles Robin, Nov. 22, 1984 (div. Dec. 1990). BA in English, Mary Washington Coll., 1967; MA in English, James Madison U., 1974; postgrad., Jesus Coll., Cambridge, Eng., 1982, Princeton U., 1985-86; Auburn U., 1988, U. No. Tex., 1990-91. Cert. tchr. English, French, master cert., Tex. Tchr. 7th grade John C. Myers Intermediate Sch., Broadway, Va., 1967-68; tchr. 10th grade Waynesville (Mo.) H.S., 1968-70; tchr. 6th, 7th, 8th grades Mary Mount Jr. Sch., Santa Barbara, Calif., 1970-72; tchr. 9th grade Forest Meadow Jr. H.S. Richardson (Tex.) Ind. Sch. Dist., 1972-78, tchr. 10th grade Lake Highlands H.S., 1972-84; tchr. 11th, 12th grades Burleson (Tex.) H.S. Burleson Ind. Sch. Dist., 1986—; instr. composition Hill Coll., 1992-94. Contbg. author: (book revs.) English Journal, 1989-94, (lit. criticism) Voice, 1993. Vol. Dallas Theater Ctr., 1990—; mem. Kimbell Art Mus., Ft. Worth, 1990—, Modern Art Mus., Ft. Worth, 1992—, KERA Pub. TV, Dallas, 1990—. Fellow NEH, 1988, 89, 92, 95, Fulbright-Hays Summer Seminar, 1991; ind. study grantee Coun. Basic Edn., 1990. Mem. ASCD, NEA, Nat. Coun. Tchrs. English, Tex. State Tchrs. Assn., Epsilon Nu of Delta Kappa Gamma (1st v.p. 1988-94, v.p. 1992-94). Avocations: bicycling, traveling, reading, writing, theater. Home: 4009 W 6th St Fort Worth TX 76107-2032 Office: Burleson High Sch 517 SW Johnson Ave Burleson TX 76028-5395

ROBIN, RICHARD SHALE, philosophy educator; b. Stamford, Conn., Apr. 18, 1926; s. Edwin Joseph and Eva (Effron) R.; m. Joann Wilma Cohan, Jan. 29, 1961; children: David Seth, Deborah Elizabeth. B.A., Harvard U., 1948, Ph.D., 1958. Instr. philosophy U. Conn., Storrs, 1958-62; asst. prof. Mt. Holyoke Coll., South Hadley, Mass., 1962-66; assoc. prof. Mt. Holyoke Coll., 1966-71, prof., 1971—, chmn. dept., 1968-83; mem. grad. faculty U. Mass. at Amherst, 1963—. Co-editor, co-author: Studies in the Philosophy of Charles Sanders Peirce, 1963, From Time and Chance to Consciousness, 1994; editor: Annotated Catalogue of the Papers of Charles S. Peirce, 1967; editor trans.: Charles S. Peirce Soc., bd. advs.; Peirce edit. project; bd. cons. Arisbe Papers; mem. editorial bd. Jour. Speculative Philosophy; adv. bd. The Peirce Seminar Papers. Grantee Harvard, 1960-61, Henry P. Kendall Found., 1962, Mt. Holyoke Coll., 1969-70, 75-76; Danforth assoc., 1967—; John Dewey sr. research scholar, 1983-84; Fulbright sr. lectr. Tohoku U., 1984-85; lectr. Kyoto Am. Studies Seminar, 1984, Charles Warren Ctr., Harvard U., 1991. Mem. Charles S. Peirce Soc. (pres. 1965-67), Charles S. Peirce Found., Am. Philos. Assn., AAUP, Soc. Advancement Am. Philosophy (exec. circle). Home: 78 Woodbridge St South Hadley MA 01075-1129

ROBIN, THEODORE TYDINGS, JR., engineer; b. New Orleans, Aug. 29, 1939; s. Theodore Tydings and Hazel (Corbin) R.; m. Helen Jones, June 8, 1963; children: Corbin, Curry, Ted, Phil. BME, Ga. Inst. Tech., 1961, MS in N.E., 1963, PhD, 1967; LLB, Blackstone Sch. Law, 1979. Bar: Calif 1980, U.S. Patent and Trademark Office 1982; registered profl. engr., Ala., Calif. Rsch. engr. Oak Ridge Nat. Lab., 1967; asst. prof. radiology and physics Emory U., 1968-69; project engr. Atomic Internat. div. N.Am. Rockwell, Canoga Park, Calif., 1970-72; engr. mgmt. engring. div. So. Co. Svcs., Birmingham, Ala., 1972-83, mgr. nuclear support and quality assurance, 1989-90, mgr. quality assurance and resources, 1991-92; mgr. Hatch Design Configuration, 1993-94; program mgr. pooled inventory mgmt. program So. Electric Internat., Birmingham, 1984-88; bd. dirs. polit. action com., 1985-87, cons., 1994—. Mem. ABA, ASME (mem. nat. quality assurance subcom. on standards coordinating 1991-95), Am. Nuc. Soc. (chmn. Birmingham sect. 1987-88, nuclear power plant standards com. 1989-94). Presbyterian. Club: Mountain Brook Swim and Tennis. Lodge: Rotary (pres. Shades Valley club 1987-88, chmn. dist. 6860 internat. youth exchange com. 1989-90, R.I. dist. gov. 6860, 1994-95). Research on power plant performance and reliability and effect of coal quality, space radiation effects on human cells, boiling heat transfer, nuclear reactor safety, multi-utility contracting, reliability economics, benchmarking and total quality management; patent law. Home and Office: 4524 Pine Mountain Rd Birmingham AL 35213-1828

ROBINER, DONALD MAXWELL, lawyer; b. Detroit, Feb. 4, 1935; s. Max and Lucia (Chassman) R.; divorced; children: Steven Ralph, Lawrence Alan. BA, U. Mich., 1957; postgrad., Wayne State U., 1957-58; JD, Case Western Res. U., 1961. Bar: Ohio 1961, U.S. Supreme Ct. 1964, U.S. Ct. Appeals (6th cir.) 1965; bd. cert. civil trial adv., Nat. Bd. Trial Advocacy. Assoc. Metzenbaum, Gaines, Schwartz, Krupansky & Stern, Cleve., 1961-67; ptnr. Metzenbaum, Gaines, Krupansky, Finley & Stern, Cleve., 1967-72; v.p. Metzenbaum, Gaines, Finley & Stern Co., L.P.A., Cleve., 1972-77, Gaines, Stern, Schwarzwald & Robiner Co., Cleve., 1977-81; exec. v.p., sec. Schwarzwald, Robiner & Rock, Cleve., 1981-90; prin. Buckingham, Doolittle & Burroughs, Cleve., 1991-94; trustee U.S. Dept. of Justice region 9, Ohio, Mich., 1994—; v.p., sec., bd. dirs. Richard L. Bowen & Assocs., Inc., Cleve., 1969-94; acting judge Shaker Heights Mcpl. Ct., 1973; mem. bd. Bar Examiners, State of Ohio, Columbus, 1974-79; life mem. 6th Cir. Jud. Conf.; mediator alt. dispute resolution U.S. Dist. Ct. (no. dist.) Ohio, 1993—. Mem. exec. com. Cuyahoga County Rep. Orgn., 1978-94; sec., Friends of Beachwood (Ohio) Libr., Inc., 1981-88, trustee, 1981—. Recipient Cert. of Appreciation Ohio Supreme Ct., 1974-79, Appreciation award Am. Soc. of Appraisers 1975. Mem. ABA (forum com. on the constrn. industry 1980-94), Cleve. Bar Assn., Cuyahoga County Bar Assn. (Cert. of Appreciation 19856-87), Ohio State Bar Assn., (coun. dels. 1987—, legis. screening com. 1987-89, 91, sch. law com. 1981-94, legal edn. com. 1987-92), Am. Arbitration Assn. (Svc. award 1975), Cuyahoga County Law Dirs. Assn., Ohio Coun. Sch. Bd. Attys. (exec. com. 1990-94), Jud. Conf. 8th Appellate Dist. Ohio (charter, life), KP. Home: 23512 E Silsby Rd Beachwood OH 44122-1266 Office: US Dept Justice Office of US Trustee 113 St Clair Ave NE Ste 200 Cleveland OH 44114

ROBINETT, BETTY WALLACE, linguist; b. Detroit, June 23, 1919; d. Henry Guy and Beulah (Reid) Wallace; m. Ralph F. Robinett, Apr. 10, 1952 (dec. div. 1960); 1 child, Richard Wallace. BA, Wayne State U., 1940; MA, U. Mich., 1941, PhD, 1951. Instr. adminstrv. asst. English Lang. Inst., U. Mich., Ann Arbor, 1945-50; cons. Dept. Edn., San Juan, P.R., 1950-51, 52-57; lectr. English, U. Mich., 1951-52, 55-56; assoc. prof. English InterAm. U., San German, P.R., 1957-59; assoc. prof. English and linguistics Ball State U., Muncie, Ind., 1959-63; assoc. prof. English and linguistics English and linguistics Ball State U., 1963-67, prof., 1967-68; prof. dept. linguistics U. Minn., Mpls., 1968-88, dir. program in English as a second lang., 1968-80, acting asst. v.p. acad. affairs, 1979-80, asst. v.p. acad. affairs, 1980-84, assoc. v.p. acad. affairs, 1984-88, prof. emeritus, 1988; chmn. Univ. Senate Consultative Com., 1977-78; vis. prof. Pa. State U., 1994-95; chmn. adv. panel on English tchg. USIA, 1988-93. Author: (with C.H. Prator) Manual of American English Pronunciation, 1972, 4th edit., 1985, Teaching English to Speakers of Other Languages, Substance and Technique, 1978, (with J. Schachter) Second Language Learning: Contrastive Analysis, Error Analysis and Related Aspects, 1983; editor Tesol Quar., 1967-72. Internat. Programs travel grantee, 1972, 77; recipient Morse-Amoco award for Excellence in Teaching, 1977. Mem. Tchrs. English to Speakers of Other Langs. (pres. 1974, James Alatis Svc. award 1990), Assn. Tchrs. ESL (chmn. 1976-77), Am. Assn. Applied Linguistics (v.p., pres. 1980-82), Linguistic Soc. Am. Home: 1936 Park Forest Ave State College PA 16803-1329

ROBINETTE, GARY E., lumber executive, wholesale distribution executive, retail executive; b. 1948. Grad., Xavier U., 1972. With Procter & Gamble, Cin., 1972-75, Avon Products, Cin., 1975-80, Mutual Mfg. & Supply, Cin., 1980-88; v.p. Carolina Builders Corp., Raleigh, N.C., 1988-93; pres. ERB Lumber Inc., Birmingham, Mich., 1993—. Office: ERB Lumber Inc 375 S Eton St Birmingham MI 48009*

ROBINOWITZ, JOE REECE, publishing executive; b. Houston, Dec. 13, 1950; s. Milton Earl and June Pearl (Stone) R.; m. Elizabeth Ellen Beekman, June 28, 1975; children—Julie Ann, Sarah Ellen. B.S. in Journalism, Northwestern U., 1973. Reporter, copy editor San Antonio Express News, 1973-77; makeup editor The Star, N.Y.C., 1977-78; asst. mng. editor N.Y. Post, N.Y.C., 1978-82; editor Boston Herald, 1982-86; v.p., gen. mgr. Sta. WFXT-TV, Boston, 1987-89; now exec. v.p. TV Guide Mag., Radnor, Pa. Jewish. Avocations: jogging; amateur photography. Office: TV Guide News Am Pubs Inc 100 Matsonford Rd Wayne PA 19088

ROBINOWITZ, STUART, lawyer; b. Port Chester, N.Y., Apr. 6, 1929; s. Sam and Rose (Goldstein) R.; m. Anne, July 15, 1952; children: Cathy, Susan, Richard, Robert, Jane. B.A., Williams Coll.; LL.B., Yale U. Bar: N.Y. 1953. Ptnr. Rosenman, Colin, Kaye, Petscheck & Freund, N.Y.C., 1961-70, Paul Weiss, Rifkind, Wharton & Garrison, N.Y.C., 1970—; vis. lectr. Yale U. Law Sch., 1981-82. Mem. Am. Bar City N.Y. (sec. 1963-64), ABA, N.Y. State Bar Assn., N.Y. County Lawyers Assn., Phi Beta Kappa. Office: Paul Weiss Rifkind Wharton & Garrison 1285 Ave Of The Americas New York NY 10019-6064

ROBINS, EDWIN CLAIBORNE, SR., retired pharmaceutical company executive; b. Richmond, Va., July 8, 1910; s. Claiborne and Martha (Taylor) R.; m. Lora McGlasson, June 24, 1938; children: Lora Elizabeth Robins Porter, E. Claiborne, Ann Carol Robins Marchant. AB, U. Richmond, 1931; BS, Med. Coll. Va. Sch. Pharmacy, 1933, D in Pharm. Sci., 1958, LLD, 1960. Former chmn. bd. A. H. Robins Co., Inc., Richmond. Trustee emeritus Richmond Meml. Hosp., United Givers Fund, Crippled Children's Hosp.; mem. exec. com.; trustee U. Richmond, past pres. alumni council. Recipient Outstanding Alumnus award MCV Alumni Assn., 1986, Disting. Service award U. Richmond, 1960; Dean M. McCann award Pharm. Wholesalers Assn., 1968; Hugo H. Schaefer medal Am. Pharm. Assn., 1969; Liberty Bell award Richmond Bar Assn., 1970; Sertoma Club award, 1970; Thomas Jefferson award Pub. Relations Soc. Am., 1970; named Pharmacist of Year Va. Pharm. Assn., 1967; Bus. Leader of Year Sales and Mktg. Execs. Richmond, 1969; Disting. Service award Va. State Chamber, 1972; Jackson Davis award for disting. service to higher edn. in Va., 1976; Edward A. Wayne medal for Disting. Service Va. Commonwealth U., 1978; Wall of Fame award, Va. Sports Hall of Fame; Wall of Fame award, 1979; award U. Richmond Athletic Hall of Fame, 1980; Gt. Am. Traditions award B'nai Brith, 1982, Outstanding Alumnus award Med. Coll. Va./Va. Commonwealth U. Sch. Pharmacy, 1983, U. Richmond Paragon medal, 1986, Disting. Citizen award Boy Scouts Am., 1991. Mem. NAM, Am. Pharm. Assn. (hon. pres. 1992), Pharm. Mfrs. Assn. (past chmn.), Va. Mfrs. Assn., Va. Pharm. Assn., Newcomen Soc. N.Am., Richmond C. of C. (past pres.), Med. Coll. Va. Alumni Assn. (past pres., dir.), Phi Beta Kappa, Alpha Kappa Psi, Omicron Delta Kappa, Phi Delta Chi, Kappa Psi, Lambda Chi Alpha, Beta Gamma Sigma (hon.). Baptist (mem. bd. adminstrn.). Clubs: Rotary (past dir.), Commonwealth Forum, Country of Va. Home: Clear View River Rd Richmond VA 23226 Office: 1301 N Hamilton St Ste 212 Richmond VA 23230-3959

ROBINS, GERALD BURNS, education educator; b. Salem, Ark., Jan. 24, 1924; s. Gerald Alfred and Lucille (Burns) R.; m. Fay Ann Kennan, Sept. 1, 1946; children: Gerald Kennan, James Dow. B.S. in Edn. cum laude, U. Ark., 1948, M.S., 1950; Ed.D., U. Ga., 1954. Asst. prof., chmn. dept. distbv. edn., chmn. dept. bus. edn. U. Ga., 1950-57, prof. higher edn., 1970-73; pres. Augusta (Ga.) Coll., 1957-70; pres. Tex. A&I U., Kingsville, 1973-77, sr. prof., 1977-89, prof. emeritus, 1994—; owner RobArt Sculpture; cons. Air Force ROTC, 1954; chmn. edn. com. Ga.-S.C. Nuclear Council, 1969; acad. dean CAP Cadet Officers Sch., 1970-71. Author: Understanding the College Budget, 1973, Campus, 1980, 1975. Trustee Lawton B. Evans Ednl. Fund, Barrett Sch. Nursing, Augusta Prep. Sch.; bd. dirs., pres. Tex. A & I Fed. Credit Union; mem. Friends of John E. Conner Mus. Served with USAAF, 1943-46; lt. col. USAF Res. (ret.). Decorated Air medal; recipient Commendation Resolution, Ga. Ho. of Reps., 1965, Disting. Svc. award Tex. Hist. Commn., 1987, Disting. Alumnus award U. Ark., 1974, Silver Spur award Tex. A & I U.; named Col. Aide de Camp, Ga. Govs. Office, 1963; named to Hall of Honor, U. Ark., 1992; Donaghey fellow, 1943, Kellogg fellow, 1953-54, Paul Harris fellow. Mem. Am. Assn. State Colls. and Univs. (com. on studies), Assn. Tex. Colls. and Univs. (commn. on acad. affairs), Internat. Assn. U. Pres.'s, Internat. Council Edn. for Teaching, Nat. Collegiate Athletic Assn. (pres. Lone Star Conf.), U. Ark. Alumni Assn. (life), Kleberg (Tex.) Hist. Commn. (chmn.), So. Tex. Hist. Soc. (dir.), 8th Air Force Hist. Soc. (life), Ret. Officers Assn. (life, pres.), Navy League, Res. Officers Assn. (life), Ga. Ret. Tchrs. Assn. (life), Pinnacle Club, Kingsville Country Club, Javelina Club, Victory Club, Century Club, Masons (32d deg.), Rotary (pres. local club, pres. 1992, dist. parliamentarian, 1991—, dist. gov. 1982-83, scholarship trustee, instr. internat. assembly 1985, faculty Tex. pres.'s tng. 1987-89, 93, 95, del. coun. on legis. 1992, 95, benefactor), Kappa Sigma (alumni advisor), Kappa Delta Pi, Phi Kappa Phi, Omicron Delta Kappa, Psi Chi, Phi Delta Kappa (emeritus mem., charter chpt. pres.); charter mem. Tex. State Aquarium. Methodist (bd. higher edn., campus ministry). Home: 515 University Blvd Kingsville TX 78363-4242

ROBINS, LEE NELKEN, medical educator; b. New Orleans, Aug. 29, 1922; d. Abe and Leona (Reiman) Nelken; m. Eli Robins, Feb. 22, 1946 (dec. Dec. 1994); children: Paul, James, Thomas, Nicholas. Student, Newcomb Coll., 1938-40; BA, Radcliffe Coll., 1942, MA, 1943; PhD, Harvard U., 1951. Mem. faculty Washington U., St. Louis, 1954—, prof. sociology in psychiatry, 1968-91, prof. sociology, 1969-91, univ. prof. social sci., prof. social sci. in psychiatry, 1991—; past mem. Nat. Adv. Coun. on Drug Abuse; past mem. task panels Pres.'s Commn. on Mental Health; mem. expert adv. panel on mental health WHO; Salmon lectr. N.Y. Acad. Medicine, 1983. Author: Deviant Children Grown Up, 1966; editor 11 books; N.Am. Assoc. editor Internat. Jour. Methods in Psychiat. Rsch.; mem. editl. bd. Psychol. Medicine, Jour. Child Psychology and Psychiatry, Devel. and Psychopathology, Jour. Studies on Alcohol, Epidemiol. e Psychiat. Sociale, Criminal Behavior and Mental Health; contbr. articles to profl. jours. Recipient Rsch. Scientist award USPHS, 1970-90, Pacesetter Rsch. award Nat. Inst. Drug Abuse, 1978, Radcliffe Coll. Grad. Soc. medal, 1979, Sutherland award Soc. Criminology, 1991, Nathan B. Eddy award Com. on Problems of Drug Dependence, 1993; rsch. grantee NIMH, Nat. Inst. on Drug Abuse, Nat. Inst. on Alcohol Abuse and Alcoholism. Fellow Am. Coll. Epidemiology, Royal Coll. Psychiatrists (hon.); mem. APHA (Rema Lapouse award 1979, Lifetime Achievement award sect. on alcohol and drug abuse 1994), World Psychiat. Assn. (sect. com. on epidemiology and cmty. psychiatry, treas.), Soc. Life History Rsch. in Psychopathology, Am. Coll. Neuropsychopharmacology, Am. Sociol. Assn., Internat. Sociol. Assn., Inst. Medicine, Internat. Epidemiol. Assn., Am. Psychopath. Assn. (pres. 1987-88, Paul Hoch award 1978). Office: Washington U Dept Psychiatry Med Sch Saint Louis MO 63110

ROBINS, MARJORIE KAPLAN, newspaper editor. Entertainment editor Saturday edit., travel editor Sunday edit. Newsday, Melville, N.Y. Office: Newsday Inc 235 Pinelawn Rd Melville NY 11747-4226*

ROBINS, MICHAEL HARRY, theater executive producing director; b. St. Paul, Oct. 19, 1948; s. Irvin Lowell Robins and Malinda (Best) Lunde. BA cum laude, U. Minn., 1969; studies with Ella Jarocewicz, Paris, 1970-72, studies with Etienne Decroux, 1970-74. Founder, exec. producing dir. Illusion Theater, Mpls., 1974—; panel mem. Arts Devel. Fund United Arts, Minn. Dance Alliance, 5% Fund St. Paul Ramsey Arts and Sci. Coun.; bd. dirs. Minn. AIDS Project. Dir. plays Eavesdrop, 1984, Family, 1986, The Sea, 1987, Men Sing, 1989, I Don't Believe...We've Met, 1991, Miss Evers Boys, 1991, others; playwright Touch, 1978, For Adults Only, 1985, Lucy's Fire, 1987, Amazing Grace, 1988-89, Men Sing, 1989, Dance With An Angel, 1991, others; dir. video No Easy Answers, 1987, co-dir. Amazing Grace, 1988, Both Sides Now, 1990; producer video Touch, 1983, Project Abuse, 1985, No Easy Answers, 1987, Archie, 1988. Bd. dirs. So. Theater Found., Mpls., 1983-85; founding mem. Arts Over AIDS, Mpls., 1989—; mem. cultural pluralism task force Minn. State Arts Bd., 1990—. Recipient Sch. Bell award Minn. Edn. Assn., 1984; named Urban Guerilla, Downtown Mpls. Civic Orgn., 1987. Mem. Theater Communications Group. Jewish. Office: Illusion Theater 528 Hennepin Ave # 704 Minneapolis MN 55403-1810

ROBINS, NORMAN ALAN, strategic planning consultant, former steel company executive; b. Chgo., Nov. 19, 1934; s. Irving and Sylvia (Robbin) Robins; m. Sandra Rosa, June 10, 1956; children: Lawrence Richard, Sherry Lynn. BS in Chem. Engring., MIT, 1955, MS in Chem. Engring., 1956; PhD in Math., Ill. Inst. Tech., 1972. Asst. mgr. process systems and controls Inland Steel Co., East Chicago, Ind., 1962-67, assoc. mgr. process systems and controls, 1967-72, dir. process research, 1972-77, v.p. research, 1977-84, v.p. technol. assessment, 1984-86, v.p. strategic planning, 1986-91, ret., 1991; ind. cons. in strategic planning, 1991—. Mem. bd. edn. Homewood-Flossmoor High Sch., Ill., 1974-77. Mem. AIME (Nat. Open Hearth Conf. award 1972), AIChE, Midwest Soc. Profl. Cons., Planning Forum.

ROBINS, ROBERT SIDWAR, political science educator, administrator; b. Spangler, Pa., Apr. 20, 1938; s. Sidney and Katherine (Sidwar) R.; m. Marjorie McGann, Nov. 25, 1959; children: Anthony P., Nicholas A. BA, U. Pitts., 1959; MA, Duke U., 1961, PhD, 1963. Prof. polit. sci. Tulane U., New Orleans, 1965—, chmn. dept. polit. sci., 1979-90, dep. provost, 1991—; acad. visitor Inst. Commonwealth Studies, U. London, 1969-70, 78-79, mem. 1987-88; sr. assoc. mem. St. Antony's Coll., Oxford, Eng., 1972-73; vis. scholar Hastings Ctr., 1982; vis. scientist Tavistock Clinic, London, 1987-88. Author: Political Institutionalization and the Integration of Elites, 1976 (Carnegie Commn. report) Legislative Attitudes Toward Higher Education in Louisiana, 1968, Psychopathology and Political Leadership, 1977, Disease and Political Leadership, 1990; co-author: When Illness Strikes the Leader; contbr. articles to profl. pubs. Vice chmn. Elections Integrity Commn., State of La., 1981-82. Recipient Excellence in Teaching award Tulane U., 1978; Fulbright scholar, 1961-62. Mem. Am. Polit. Sci. Assn., Internat. Soc. Polit. Psychology, New Orleans Fgn. Relations Assn. (bd. dirs.). Avocations: carpentry; gardening. Home: 727 Pine St New Orleans LA 70118-5118 Office: Tulane U Gibson Hall Office of the Provost New Orleans LA 70118

ROBINSON, ALLAN RICHARD, oceanography educator; b. Lynn, Mass., Oct. 17, 1932; married, 1955; 3 children. BA, Harvard U., 1954, MA, 1956, PhD in Physics, 1959; Dr. honoris causa, U. Liege, Belgium, 1988. NSF fellow in meteorology and oceanography Cambridge U., 1959-60; asst. prof. to assoc. prof. Harvard U., Cambridge, Mass., 1960-68; dir. Ctr. Earth and Planetary Physics Harvard U., Cambridge, 1972-75, Gordon McKay prof. geophys. fluid dynamics, 1968—, chmn. com. oceanography, 1972-87; co-chmn. Mid-Ocean Dynamics Expdn. I Sci. Coun. NSF, 1971-74; U.S. chmn. U.S.-USSR Polymode Expdn., 1973-81; co-chmn. Phys. Ocean East Mediterranean, Intergovernmental Oceanographic Commission-UNESCO, 1983—; guest investigator Woods Hole (Mass.) Oceanographic Inst., 1979-80; CNOC prof. Naval Postgrad. Sch., 1982; vis. scientist Applied Physics Lab. Johns Hopkins U., Laurel, Md., 1986—; Slichter vis. prof. UCLA, 1987; Franqui vis. prof. U. Liege, Belgium, 1988. Editor-in-chief: Dynamics of Atmospheres and Oceans, 1976—. Guggenheim fellow Cambridge (Eng.) U., 1972-73. Fellow AAAS, Am. Acad. Arts and Scis. Office: Harvard U Dept Earth Sci Pierce Hall 29 Oxford St Cambridge MA 02138-6502*

ROBINSON, AMINAH BRENDA LYNN, artist; b. Columbus, Ohio, Feb. 18, 1940; d. Leroy Edward William and Helen Elizabeth (Zimmerman) R.; m. Clarence Adrian Robinson (div. 1981); 1 child, Sydney Edward (dec. July 17, 1994). Student, Columbus Coll. of Art & Design, 1956-60, Ohio State U., 1960-61, Franklin U., 1961-62, Bliss Coll., 1963. Asst. libr., illustrator, artist Ohio Pub. Libr., Columbus, 1958-64; draftsman Mountain State Telephone Co., Boise, Idaho, 1964-66; illustrator TV Oper. Br. TV, Miss., 1966-67; sr. illustrator N.Am. Rockwell Corp., Columbus, 1971; with City Recreation and Pks. Dept., Columbus, 1972—; lectr. to numerous orgns., 1971—; speaker numerous workshops, 1970—. One woman shows include Otterbein Coll., Worthington, Ohio, 1991, 1989, 1982, U. Wis., Greenbay, 1990, Columbus Mus. Art, 1990, 1983, So. Ohio Mus., Portsmouth, 1990, Akron Art Mus., 1987, 88, Esther Saks Gallery, Chgo., 1984; exhibited in group shows at Wexner Art Ctr., Columbus, 1992, Nat. Mus. Women in the Arts, Washington, 1990, 91, Memphis Brooks Mus. Art, 1991; represented in permanent collections Columbus Art Mus., Newark Art Mus., Otterbein Coll.; numerous others. Ohio Arts Coun. fellow 1979-80, 86-87, 88-89, 991-92, Travel-Study fellow Am. Forum for Internat. Study, 1979, PSI Residency fellow, 1989; recipient Gov.'s award for the visual arts in Ohio, 1984, Columbus Star of 1980 Achievement award, 1980; named Outstanding Citizen in the Community, Nat. Epicureans, 1974.

ROBINSON, ARTHUR HOWARD, geography educator; b. Montreal, Que., Can., Jan. 5, 1915; s. James Howard and Elizabeth (Peavey) R.; m. Mary Elizabeth Coffin, Dec. 23, 1938 (dec. Jan. 1992); children: Stephen Michael, Patricia Anne; m. Martha Elizabeth Rodabaugh Phillips, Feb. 6, 1993. BA, Miami U., Oxford, Ohio, 1936, LittD, 1966; MA, U. Wis., 1938; PhD in Geography, Ohio State U., 1947, DSc (hon.), 1984. Sec. to mem. Ohio Bd. Liquor Control, 1936; asst. geography U. Wis., 1936-38, Ohio State U., 1938-41; chief map div. OSS, 1941-46; mem. faculty U. Wis., 1945—, prof. geography, 1951-80, prof. emeritus, 1980—, chmn. dept., 1954-58, 66-68, Lawrence Martin prof. cartography, 1967—; dir. Univ. Cartographic Lab., 1966-73; hon. cons. cartography Library of Congress, 1974-80; Chief map officer U.S. Delegation Quebec and Cairo confs., World War II; pres. Internat. Cartographic Assn., 1972-76. Author: Look of Maps, 1952, Early Thematic Mapping in the History of Cartography, 1982; co-author: Elements of Geography, 4th edit., 1957, Elements of Cartography, 6th edit., 1995, Fundamentals of Physical Geography, 3rd edit., 1977, The Nature of Maps, 1976; co-editor: Cartographical Innovations, 1987; editor Am. Cartographer, 1974-76; also articles; designer Robinson map projection, 1963. Served to maj. AUS, 1944-45. Decorated Legion of Merit; recipient Carl Mannerfelt medal Internat. Cartographic Assn., 1981, Helen Culver Gold Medal Geog. Soc. Chgo., 1983, John Oliver LaGorce medal Nat. Geog. Soc., 1988, Silver medal Brit. Cartographic Soc., 1991; Guggenheim rsch. fellow, 1964, 78. Mem. Assn. Am. Geographers (council 1960-65, pres. 1963), Am. Congress Surveying and Mapping (hon.; chmn. cartography div. 1971). Home: 7438 Cedar Creek Trail Madison WI 53717

ROBINSON, BARBARA PAUL, lawyer; b. Oct. 19, 1941; d. Leo and Pauline G. Paul; m. Charles Raskob Robinson, June 11, 1965; children: Charles Paul, Torrance Webster. AB magna cum laude, Bryn Mawr Coll. 1962; LLB, Yale U., 1965. Bar: N.Y. 1966, U.S. Dist. Ct. (so. and ea. dists.) N.Y. 1975, U.S. Tax Ct. 1972, U.S. Ct. Appeals (2d cir.) 1974. Assoc. Debevoise & Plimpton (formerly Debevoise, Plimpton, Lyons & Gates) N,Y.C., 1966-75, ptnr., 1976—; mem. adv. bd., lectr. Practising Law Inst.; arbitrator Am. Arbitration Assn., 1987—, Am. Judicature Soc. Contbr. articles to profl. jours. Mem. adv. coun., bd. visitors CUNY Law Sch., Queens, 1984-90; trustee Trinity Sch., 1982-86, pres., 1986-88; bd. dirs. Found. for Child Devel., 1989—, chmn., 1991—; mem. Coun. on Fgn. Rels.; bd. dirs. Catalyst, 1993—; trustee The William Nelson Cromwell Found., 1993—. Fellow Am. Coll. Trust and Estate Counsel, Am. Bar Found., N.Y. Bar Found.; mem. ABA, N.Y. State Bar Assn. (vice chmn. com. on trust adminstrn., trusts and estates law sect. 1977-81, ho. of dels. 1984-87, 90-92, mem. com. ann. award 1993—), Assn. of Bar of City of N.Y. (chmn. com. on trusts, estates and surrogates cts. 1981-84, judiciary com. 1981-84, coun. on jud. adminstrn. 1982-84, chair nominating com. 1984-85, mem. exec. com. 1986-91, chair 1989-90, v.p. 1990-91, pres. 1994—; chair com. on honors 1993-94, mem. com. on long-range planning 1991-94), Assn. of Bar of City of N.Y. Fund, Inc. (bd. dirs., pres.), Am. Arbitration Assn. (bd. dirs. 1995—), Yale Coun., Yale Law Sch. Assn. N.Y. (mem. devel. bd., exec. com. 1981-85, pres. 1988-93), Yale Club, Washington Club. Office: Debevoise & Plimpton 875 3rd Ave New York NY 10022-6225

ROBINSON, BARRY R., lawyer; b. Dover, Ohio, Dec. 8, 1946. AB, Princeton U., 1969; JD cum laude, Ohio State U., 1972. Bar: Ohio 1972. Ptnr. Baker & Hostetler, Columbus, Ohio. Fellow Am. Coll. Trust and Estate Counsel; mem. ABA, Ohio State Bar Assn., Columbus Bar Assn. Office: Baker & Hostetler Capital Sq 65 E State St Ste 2100 Columbus OH 43215

ROBINSON, BINA AITCHISON, publisher, newsletter editor; b. Schenectady, N.Y., Aug. 31, 1923; d. Thomas Cant and Winifred Maud (Binless) Aitchison; m. David Dunlop Robinson, May 14, 1944; children: Challice Binless, Jean Aitchison, Andrew McLeod, Janet Davison. BA with honors, U. Rochester, 1944. Tchr. Phila. Pub. Schs., 1944-45, Brockport (N.Y.) Cen. Sch., 1946-47, Harley Sch., Rochester, N.Y., 1947-52; engring. asst. GE, Pittsfield, Mass., 1945-46; entrepreneur, developer, mgr. Swain (N.Y.) Ski Ctr., 1947-77; founder, coord., editor, prin. writer Coalition to Protect Animals in Parks & Refuges, Swain, 1985—; editor, prin. writer The Civil Abolitionist, 1985—; Am. cons. Drs. in Brit. Against Animal Experiments; vis. lectr. schs. and colls. Contbr. articles to publs. Past pres. Allegany County Soc. Prevention Cruelty Animals, Wellsville, N.Y., 1978—. Mem. Am. Anti-Vivisection Soc., Nat. Resources Def. Coun., Internat. Primate Protection League, Nat. Alliance for Animals, N.Y. State Coalition for Animals, Action on Smoking and Health, Union Concerned Scientists, Civis/Civitas (exec. dir. 1983-91). Avocations: skiing, mountain hiking, swimming, canoeing, gardening. Home and Office: 1 Main St Swain NY 14884-0026

ROBINSON, BOB LEO, international investment services executive; b. Franklin, Tenn., Sept. 9, 1933; s. W.A. and Cornelia Irene (Lampley) R.; m. Carolyn Overton, Dec. 18, 1955; children: Richard Glenn, Leigh Ann, Elizabeth Lynne. BS in Indsl. Mgmt., Tenn. Tech. U., 1955. Cert. property mgr. Quality control engr. Gates Rubber Co., Nashville, 1960; tech. rep. Home Ins. Co., 1961-65; civilian staff adminstrv. asst. Dept. Army, Nashville, 1965; exec. asst. to pres. Sullivan's Dept. Stores, Nashville, 1966-69; dir. engring. and devel. Venture Out in Am., Knoxville, Tenn., 1969; v.p., then exec. v.p. Hosp. Corp. Am., Nashville, 1970-79; pres., chief exec. officer Real Estate Group Inc., Nashville, 1974—, Fidelity Title Co., Nashville, 1974-83; pres. Internat. Bus. and Investment Services, Orlando, 1978—; gen. partner Union Sq. Ltd., Jacksonville, Fla., 1973-79; dir. Am. Travel Service, World Health Cons.; chmn. bd. emeritus Arnold Palmer Devel. Co., Orlando, Fla., 1988—; past vice chmn. bd. dirs., chief exec. officer Clin. Diagnostic Systems, Inc., Orlando, 1988-89; past vice chmn. Space Rail Corp., Orlando, 1991; speaker in field. Mem. Mayor Nashville Blue Ribbon Com., 1975-77; commr. City of Brentwood, Tenn., 1969-71, vice mayor, 1969-71, mayor, 1971, mem. planning commnn., 1970-71; bd. dirs. Goodwill Industries Ctrl. Fla.; exec. commn. ops. com.; chmn. bldg. fund St. Cecilia Acad., Nashville, 1978; vice chmn. Audubon council Boy Scouts Am., 1968; founder

Tenn. Tech. ROTC Gen.'s Cup Scholarship Found., 1986; aide U.S. Com. for Normandy Meml. Mus., Caen, France, 1987—; parachutist Israeli Def. Forces, 1989, Royal Thai Spl. Warfare Command, 1990; campaign dir. Drage for County Chmn., Orange County, Fla., 1990. Served as officer, master army aviator, parachutist, U.S. Army, 1955-60, USAR, 1960-83; maj. gen. (brevet) USAR, 1990. Decorated Army Commendation medal, Meritorious Service medal; recipient numerous public service awards; named to Tenn. Tech. ROTC Hall of Fame, 1988. Mem. Internat. Inst. Hosp. Cons., Inst. Real Estate Mgmt., Army Aviation Assn. Am., Res. Officers Assn., Internat. Assn. Airborne Vets., 82d Airborne Div. Assn. (dir. Spacecoast chpt.). Republican. Baptist (past v.p. bd. trustees). Clubs: Arnold Palmer's Bay Hill (Orlando); Shriners.

ROBINSON, BRUCE BUTLER, physicist; b. Chester, Pa., Oct. 13, 1933; s. George Senior and Dorothy Conerly (Butler) R.; m. Dorothy Ross, June 4, 1960; children: Douglas Ross, Christopher Scott. BS in Physics, Drexel U., 1956; PhD in Physics, Princeton U., 1961; MBA, Rider U., 1977. Rsch. assoc. U. Calif., San Diego, 1961-63; rsch. scientist RCA David Sarnoff Lab., RCA, Princeton, N.J., 1963-73; exec. dir., mem. commerce tech. adv. bd. U.S. Dept. Commerce, Washington, 1973-75; dir. policy integration, dir. coal and synfuels policy U.S. Dept. Energy, Washington, 1975-81; sr. science advisor to v.p. rsch. Exxon Rsch. and Engring. Co., Linden, N.J., 1981-84; dep. dir. Office Naval Rsch., Arlington, 1984-87, dir. rsch., 1987—; prin. author nat. energy policy plan U.S. Dept. Energy, 1981; U.S. rep. to internat. energy agy., govt. expert group on tech., Paris, 1979-81; mem. internat. team to rev. R&D programs Dutch Ministry Econs. and Fin., The Hague, The Netherlands, 1979; presenter sci. lectures. Contbr. articles to sci. jours. NSF fellow Princeton U., 1956-58, NSF internat. summer fellow, Varenna, Italy, 1962; recipient Meritorious Presdl. Rank award Pres. of U.S., 1989. Mem. IEEE, Am. Phys. Soc., The Oceanography Soc. (founding).

ROBINSON, CAROLE ANN, insurance executive, retired; b. Omaha, Dec. 21, 1935; d. Harry B. and Mildred (Daley) Baker; widowed Mar. 1989; 1 child, Pamela Fleming. Clk. Blue Cross/Blue Shield Colo., Denver, 1969-70; mgr. Blue Cross/Blue Shield Colo., 1970-72, asst. to treas., 1972-74, dir., 1974-79, treas., 1980-86, sr. v.p. treas., 1986-90; v.p., treas., chief investment officer Rocky Mountain Health Care (Holding Co.), Denver, 1991-93, sr. v.p., chief investment officer, CFO, 1986-93; ret., 1993; bd. dirs. Denver, Colo. Compensation Ins. Authority, Denver, Combined Health Appeal, Denver. Mem. investment com. City and County of Denver, 1988. Mem. Colo. Cash. Mgmt. Assn., Nat. Cash Mgmt. Assn., Life Office Mgmt. Assn. (treasury ops. com. 1985-93). Republican. Avocations: cooking, entertaining, gardening, reading. Office: Rocky Mountain Health Care 700 Broadway Ste 990 Denver CO 80203-3443

ROBINSON, CHARLES DAVID, financial services executive; b. Warren, Ohio, Sept. 26, 1944; s. Lee Elmo and Dora Mae (Wheeler) R.; m. Sharon Lynn Pemberton, Apr. 8, 1966 (div. July 1979); 1 child, Heather Lynn; m. Sharon Ann Dillon, June 20, 1980. Student, Ventura (Calif.) Jr. Coll., 1962, Harvard U., 1964; BA, Am. U., 1966; MA, Ohio State U., 1979. CFP. Mershon fellow Ohio State U., Columbus, 1966-72; dir. tng. NATPAC-SOUTH Inc., Washington, 1973-74; field underwriter N.Y. Life, Bailey's Cross-Roads, Va., 1974-75; dir. debate W.T. Woodson High Sch., Fairfax, Va., 1975-80; exec. account rep. VALIC, Fairfax, 1980-89, unit mgr., 1981-86; dist. mgr. VALIC, Phoenix, 1990-91, regional mgr., 1991-95; regional v.p. VAMCO, Phoenix, 1991-95; v.p. instl. markets VALIC, Houston, 1995—. Editor, author: (booklet) Mutual Fund Sales Kit, 1992, (brochures) New Mexico Alternative Retirement Plan, 1991, Arizona Optional Retirement Plan, 1991; co-developer: Portfolio Optimizer Asset Allocation Software, 1994. Asst. to chmn. conv. coms. Bush Campaign Republican Nat. Conv., New Orleans, 1988; chmn. Fairfax County Tchrs. for Vivian Watts, Va., 1979. Mem. Inst. Cert. Fin. Planners, Phi Alpha Theta, Alpha Tau Omega. Avocations: golf, tennis, skiing. Office: VALIC 2929 Allen Pkwy Houston TX 77019

ROBINSON, CHARLES E., building materials executive; b. 1941. BA, Northwestern U., Evanston, Ill., 1963; JD, U. Mich., 1966. V.p., gen. coun. Jim Walter, Corp., Tampa, Fla., 1990. Office: Jim Walter Corp 4010 W Boy Scout Blvd Tampa FL 33607*

ROBINSON, CHARLES PAUL, nuclear physicist, diplomat, business executive; b. Detroit, Oct. 9, 1941; s. Edward Leonard and Mary Opal (Edmondson) R.; m. Barbara Thomas Woodard, Sept. 1992; children by previous marriage: Paula S., Colin C. BS in Physics, Christian Bros. U., 1963; PhD in Physics, Fla. State U., 1967. Mem. nuclear test staff Los Alamos (N.Mex.) Nat. Lab., 1967-69, chief test operator, 1969-70, mem. advanced concepts staff, 1971-72, assoc. div. leader, lasers, 1972-76, div. leader, 1976-79, assoc. dir., 1980-85; sr. v.p., bd. dirs Ebasco Services Inc. subs. Enserch Corp., N.Y.C., 1985-88; ambass. to nuclear testing talks U.S. Dept. State, Geneva, 1988-90; v.p. Sandia Nat. Labs., Albuquerque, 1990—; mem. sci. adv. group Def. Nuclear Agy., Washington, 1981—; mem. nat. security bd. Los Alamos Nat. Lab., 1985—; chmn. Presdl. Tech. Adv. Bd., 1991; mem. U.S. Strategic Command Adv. Bd. Pres. Student Concerts Inc., Los Alamos, 1972-74; instr. U. N.Mex., Los Alamos, 1974-76; exec. bd. Boy Scouts of N.Mex. Mem. AAAS, Am. Phys. Soc., Am. Nuclear Soc., Rotary Internat. Avocation: choral singing. Office: Sandia Nat Labs Orgn 4000 PO Box 5800 # 4000 Albuquerque NM 87185

ROBINSON, CHARLOTTE HILL, artist; b. San Antonio, Nov. 28, 1924; d. Lucius Davis and Charlotte (Moore) Hill; m. Floyd I. Robinson, Mar. 1943; children: Floyd I. Jr., Lawrence H., Elizabeth H. Student, Incarnate Word Coll., 1943, 44, 45, NYU, 1947, 48, Corcoran Sch. Art, 1951-52. Painting instr. Art League No. Va., Alexandria, 1967-75; Condr. Art World Seminar-Washington Women's Art Ctr., 1975-80, drawing workshop Smithsonian Instn. Resident Assocs. Program, Washington, 1977; program dir. Nat. Women's Caucus for Art, 1979; project coord., exhbn. curator The Artist and the Quilt, nat. mus. traveling exhbn., 1983-86; vis. artist S.W. Craft Ctr., San Antonio, 1983-85; lectr. WFUV 90 FM, Fordham U., N.Y.C., 1990, San Antonio Art Inst., 1991, Nat. Mus. for Women in Arts, Washington, 1991, Iowa State U., Ames, 1991. Editor: The Artist and the Quilt, 1983; one-person shows include Thames Sci. Ctr., New London, Conn., 1991, Brunner Gallery & Mus., Iowa State U., 1991, 92, de Andino Fine Arts, Washington, 1992, Masur Mus. Art, Monroe, La., 1993, Lee Hansley Art Gallery, Raleigh, N.C., 1993, Sol Del Rio, San Antonio, 1995; exhibited in group shows at Franklin Square and Watkins Gallery, Washington, 1992, Rutgers U., New Brunswick, N.J., 1992, Brody's Gallery, Washington, 1992, Lee Hansley Art Gallery, Raleigh, 1993, Emerson Gallery, McLean, 1993, No. Va. C.C., 1994. Trustee Bronx (N.Y.) Mus., 1977; bd. dirs. Washington Women's Art Ctr., 1977; nat. bd. dirs. Women's Caucus for Art, 1983-84; bd. dirs. New Art Examiner, 1985-86. Recipient Concourse award Corcoran Sch. Art, 1952, Scholarship award Telfair Acad. Art, Savannah, Ga., 1959; Nat. Endowment for Arts grantee, 1977, 78-81; fellow Va. Ctr. for Creative Arts, Sweet Briar, Va., 1985.

ROBINSON, CHESTER HERSEY, retired dean; b. Yonkers, N.Y., Nov. 8, 1918; s. Sherman Alexander and Alice (Hersey) R.; m. Marguerite Davis, Dec. 14, 1945 (div. Oct. 1976); children—Barry, Roslyn; m. Heidemarie Höfler, Dec. 30, 1976. A.B., Union Coll., Schenectady, 1940; Ph.D., Stanford U., 1950. Asst. registrar Stanford U., 1949-50; dir. div. extension and summer session Miami U., Oxford, Ohio, 1950-54; assoc. prof. Sch. Gen. Studies, Hunter Coll., 1954-60; dir. Sch. Gen. Studies, Bronx campus, 1960-66, dean, 1966-68; dean Sch. Gen. Studies, Herbert H. Lehman Coll. CUNY, 1968-82, dean Continuing Edn., 1982-86. Served to lt. USNR, 1942-46. Mem. NEA, Beta Theta Pi, Phi Delta Kappa. Presbyterian. Lodge: Elks. Home: 1120 Warburton Ave Apt 4C Yonkers NY 10701-1033

ROBINSON, CHRISTINE MARIE, mathematics educator; b. Savannah, Ga.; d. Aaron Sr. and Lucille (Jones) Williams; m. Amos Robinson, Aug. 2, 1953; children: Michael Anthony, Pamela Michele. BS in Math. magna cum laude, Savannah State Coll., 1951; MA, U. Mich., 1965. Tchr. in math. Chatham County Bd. of Instruction, Savannah, 1951-64; instr. in math. Duval County Bd. of Instruction, Jacksonville, Fla., 1964-71, master and resource tchr., 1971-76; prof. math. Fla. C.C., Jacksonville, 1976—; mem. faculty task force Fla. Dept. Edn./Fla. Assn. C.C., Tallahassee, 1979-81; onsite coord. Fla. Devel. Edn. Assn. Conv., Jacksonville, 1986; chmn. Fla. C.C. EA/EO Com., Jacksonville, 1988, 89. Mem. YWCA, Jacksonville, 1989—;

vol. driver Wheels for Cancer-AKA Sorority, Jacksonville, 1986; chmn. United Way, Jacksonville, 1987. Recipient Outstanding Faculty Mem. award Fla. Community Coll., 1987, Teaching Excellence award U. Tex., 1988; scholar U. Mich., U. Ill.; grantee NSF. Mem. Am. Math. Assn. Two-Yr. Colls., Fla. Devel. Edn. Assn. (bd. dirs. Jacksonville chpt. 1983-86), Fla. Assn. C.C., Math. Assn. Am., So. Assn. Colls. and Schs. (Fla. com.), LWV, Alpha Kappa Alpha. Democrat. Roman Catholic. Avocations: reading, piano, dancing, bicycling. Home: 7426 Simms Dr Jacksonville FL 32209-1023 Office: Fla CC 3939 Roosevelt Blvd Jacksonville FL 32205-8945

ROBINSON, CHRISTOPHER THOMAS, artist; b. Cold Spring Harbor, N.Y., Mar. 18, 1951; s. Fred Marlin and Gladys (Langford) R.; m. Janet Thompson, Jan. 17, 1972; children: Justin Christopher, Sarah Williams. BFA, Fla. State U., 1973; MFA, U. Mass., 1975. Teaching assoc. U. Mass., Amherst, 1973-75; assoc. prof. U. S.C., Columbia, 1975—; dir. grad. studies; vis. artist U. Ala., Huntsville, 1977—, U. Cen. Ark., Conway, 1986—, McDowell Tech., Marion, N.C., 1986—, Coll. of Charleston, S.C., 1987—, U. N.C., 1987, Clemson U., 1989; ops. leader Operation Raleigh, Chile, 1985; expdn. leader U.S. Sci. Expdn., London, 1987-88, Global Patriots climb of Orizaba, Mex., 1990, Global Patriots climb of Aconcagua, Argentina, 1992; cons. S.C. State Mus., Columbia, 1986—; seminar speaker Internat. Leadership Seminar; guest artist Meadow Creek Project, Honors Program, Conway, 1987. Solo exhbns. include U. Mass., Amherst, 1974, 75, Heath Gallery, Atlanta, 1977, Greenville County Mus. Art, 1978, U. S.C. Museums, 1978, U. of the South, Sewanee, Tenn., 1980, Atlanta Art Workers Coalition Gallery, 1980, Columbia Coll., 1983, Coll. Charleston, S.C., 1987, U. N.C., Chapel Hill, 1987, S.C. State Mus., Columbia, 1989, Carolighting State House, Columbia, N.C., 1991, Fayetteville St. Mall, Raleigh, N.C., 1991, So. Bell Regional Hdqrs., Charlotte, N.C., 1991; exhibited in group shows at Seven Hills Gallery, Tallahassee, Fla., 1973, Fla. State U., 1973, Archives of Am. Art, 1975, Columbia Mus. of Art, 1976-77, 9th Nat. and Internat. Sculpture Conf., 1976, Southeastern Coll. Art, 1976, New Orleans Mus. Art, 1977, Nat. Sculpture Conf., Jonesboro, 1977, Arcosanti Festival, Cordes Junction, Ariz., 1978, 19th Nat. Art Roundup Las Vegas Mus. Art, 1979, Coll. Art Assn. Ann. Meeting, 1980, Appalachian State U., 1981, Eastern Ill. U., 1981, Southeastern Ctr. Contemporary Art, Winston-Salem, N.C., 1981, Netherlands/American Contemporary Print Exchange Exhibition, 1982, S.C. Arts Commn. Ann. Exhbn., 1976, 81, 83 (Purchase award-State Collection), Friends of Arts First Regional Juried Exhbn., Spartanburg, S.C., 1983, U.S. Nat. Fine Arts Competition, Tallahassee, Fla., 1984, Southeastern Ctr. Contemporary Art, Winston-Salem, N.C., 1984, Portrait of the South, Rome Exhibition, Palazzo Venezia, Rome Italy, 1984, Fact, Fiction and Fantasy: Recent Narrative Art in the S.E., Ewing Art Gallery, U. Tenn., 1987, Art in Transit, Arts Festival of Atlanta, 1989, Austin Peay State U., Clarksville, Tenn., 1993, Anderson County Arts Ctr., 1993 (Merit award 1993), S.C. State Mus., Columbia, 1994, Arts Festival Atlanta, 1994, Emblems, Yale U. Art Gallery. Bd. dirs. Lexington County Sch. Dist. 5, Ballentine, S.C., 1986—; vice chmn. sch. bd., Sch. Dist. 5, Lexington and Richland counties, chmn. bd. trusteees, 1993—; mem. boardmanship tng. cadre S.C. Sch. Bds. Assn., 1990; seminar speaker Hugh O'Brian Youth Found., Denver, 1987; treas. exec. bd. S.C. Sch. Bds. Assn., 1993—. Lt. candidate, USN, 1978. Artist grant S.C. Arts Com., 1976; grantee Southern Regional Edn. Bd., Atlanta, 1985-86; Faculty Devel. grantee U. S.C., 1986-87; recipient Merit award 18th Ann. Juried Show Anderson County Arts Ctr.; Venture Fund grantee U. S.C. Mem. Southern Assn. Sculptors, Nat. Sculpture Exhbn., World Coun., Sci. Exploration Soc. (hon. 1987-89). Youth Svc. Internat. (bd. dirs. 1991—). Avocations: flying, mountaineering. Leader Global Patriots Clime of south ridge St. Elias, 1993. Home: 300 Lost Creek Dr Columbia SC 29212-2487 Office: U SC Dept Art Columbia SC 29208

ROBINSON, D. THEODORE, insurance company executive. Chmn. bd. dirs., CEO N.Y. Ctrl. Mutual Fire Ins., Edmeston, N.Y., 1960—; bd. dirs. Ctrl. Nat. Bank, Canajoharie, N.Y. Office: NY Central Mutual Fire Ins 1899 Central Plz E Edmeston NY 13335*

ROBINSON, DANIEL BARUCH, banker; b. Hamilton, Ont., Can., Dec. 4, 1937; s. David A. and Zelda (Frank) R.; m. Marta A. Calero, May 7, 1960; children—Allegra, Robert. B.Commerce, McMaster U., Hamilton, Ont., 1960; postgrad., U. Mich., 1969, Harvard U., 1971, Pontif Universidade Católica do Rio de Janeiro, 1979, Georgetown U., 1994. Chartered acct. Vice pres. fin. Comsur, La Paz, Bolivia, 1971-72; fin. dir. Light Servicos, Rio De Janeiro, Brazil, 1972-78; sr. fin. analyst The World Bank, Washington, 1978-79; v.p. fin. Jari Florestal, Rio De Janeiro, 1979-80, Manalta Coal, Calgary, Alta, Can, 1981-82; exec.v.p. Atomic Energy Can. Ltd., Mississauga, Ont., 1983-85; rep. Interam. Devel. Bank, Barbados, 1985-89, Washington, 1989—. Pres. Canadian Club, Rio de Janeiro, 1974-75. Recipient Highest Standing prize Chartered Accts. Assn.; 1961; Price, Waterhouse and Co. scholar, 1959. Mem. Inst. Chartered Accts. Ont., Canadian Inst. Chartered Accts., Fin. Execs. Inst. Clubs: Rio de Janeiro Yacht, Jockey Club do Rio de Janeiro, Itanhangã Golf (Rio de Janeiro), Sandy Ln. Property Owners Assn. (Barbados). Avocations: reading; translating from Spanish and Portuguese to English. Home: 12 4th St NE Washington DC 20002-5930 Office: Interam Devel Bank Washington DC 20577

ROBINSON, DANIEL N., psychology educator; b. N.Y., Mar. 9, 1937; s. Henry S. and Margaret R.; children from a previous marriage: Tracey, Kimberly; m. Francine Malasko, 1967. BA, Colgate U., 1958; MA, Hofstra U., 1960; PhD, CUNY, 1965. Rsch. psychol. electronics rsch. labs. Columbia U., 1960-65, asst. dir. sci. honors program electronics rsch. lab., 1964-68, sr. rsch. psychol. electronics rsch. labs., 1965-68, asst. dir. of life scis. electronics rsch. labs., 1967-68; asst. prof. Dept. of Psychol. Amherst Coll., 1968-70, assoc. prof. Dept. Psychol., 1970-71; dir. grad. program Dept. Psychol. Georgetown Univ., 1981-83, chmn. Dept. Psychol., 1973-76, 1985-91, assoc. prof. Dept. Psychol., 1971-74, prof. Dept. Psychol., 1974—; vis. lectr. in Psychol. Princeton U., 1965-68; vis. prof. Folger Shakespeare Inst., 1977; vis. sr. mem. Linacre Coll., U. Oxford, 1991—; cons. NIH, 1967-70, NSF, 1965-75, PBS, 1978-84, 1985-88, MacArthur Found., 1985, Atty. Gen's. Task Force on Crime, 1980, Dept. Health and Human Svcs., NIH, 1988. Author: Psychology: A Study of Its Origins and Principles, 1972, The Enlightened Machine: An Anlytical Introduction to Neuropsychology, 1973, 80, Psychology: Traditions and Perspectives, 1976, An Intellectual History of Psychology, 1976, The Mind Unfolded: Essay's on Psychology's Historic Texts, 1978, Systems of Modern Psychology: A Critical Sketch, 1979, Psychology and Law: Can Justice Survive the Social Sciences?, 1980, An Intellectual History of Psychology-Revised Edition, 1981, Toward A Science of Human Nature: Essays on the Psychologies of Hegel, Mill, Wundt, and James, 1982, Philosophy of Psychology, 1985, Aristotle's Psychology, 1989, (with William R. Uttal) Foundations of Psychobiology, 1983, (with Sir John Eccles) The Wonder of Being Human: Our Mind and Our Brain, 1984; editor Heredity and Achievement, 1970, Readings in the Origins and Principles of Psychology, 1972, Significant Contributions to the History of Psychology, 1977-78, Annals of Theoretical Psychology, 1990, Social Discourse and Moral Judgment, 1992; contbr. chpts. to books, reference books, articles to profl. jours. Recipient Inst. for Advanced Study in the Humanities fellow, U. Edinburgh, 1986-87; Pres's. medal Colgate U., 1986, Pub. Svc. award Gen. Svcs. Adminstrn., 1986. Fellow Am. Psychol. Assn. (divsns 3, 24, 26), British Psychol. Soc.; mem. Sigma Xi, Psi Chi. Home: 300 E Main St Middletown MD 21769-7927 Office: Georgetown U Dept Psychology Washington DC 20057

ROBINSON, DANIEL THOMAS, brokerage company executive; b. Los Angeles, June 17, 1925; s. George Thomas and Helen Theresa (Walsh) R.; m. Diane W. Robinson; children—Marc David, Matthew Curtis. B.S., U. So. Calif., 1948; M.B.A., UCLA, 1950. Pres. Horton & Converse Inc., 1961—; v.p. Dart Industries, Inc., Los Angeles, 1972-82; v.p. Bergen Brunswig Corp., Los Angeles, 1972-80; dir. bus. devel. Merrill Lynch, Los Angeles, 1981-82; with Internat. Network Brokerage, 1983—; bd. dirs. K.D.L Corp., Home Interstate Bank Fin. Svcs., Healthbank Corp. Author: Medical Marketing of Seventies, 1968, Marketing Challenges of Biomedical Industry, 1969, Biomedical Marketing, 1975, Biomedical Representation, 1976, Real Estate Funding Principles, 1988, Desert Properties for a Future, 1988, Sea and Desert Investments, 1989, Principles of Network Brokerage Marketing, 1991, Medical Products Brokerage Avocation, 1993. Past pres., bd. dirs. Trojan Club, U. So. Calif.; past pres. Cardinal and Gold; past pres. U. So. Calif., bd. councillors. Mem. Am. Coll. Pharmacists (dir., past pres.), Am.,

Man. surg. trade assns., Health Industries Assn. Office: 32081 Via Flores San Juan Capistrano CA 92675-3867

ROBINSON, DAVID ADAIR, neurophysiologist; b. Boston, Dec. 9, 1925; s. Edwin Whitmore and Gladys (Mansley) Colby; m. Ellen Marie Rogus, June 13, 1980. B.A., Brown U., 1947; M.S., Johns Hopkins U., 1956, Dr.Engring., 1958. Project engr., dir. engring., v.p. charge research Airpax Electronics Inc., Ft. Lauderdale, Fla., 1951-61; mem. faculty Johns Hopkins U. Med. Sch., 1961—, prof. ophthalmology depts. ophthalmology and biomed. engring., 1975-93, prof. emeritus, 1993—; mem. vis. sci. study sect. div. research grants NIH, 1966-70, engring. in biology and med. tng. com., 1971-73; mem. communicative sci. cluster President's Biomed. Research Panel, 1975; mem. planning com. sensori-motor disorders vision Nat. Eye Inst., NIH, 1976, 81; cons. in field. Editorial bd.: Investigative Ophthalmology, Exptl. Brain Research, Vision Research, Jour. Neurophysiology. Served to ensign USN, 1947-49. Rsch. grantee Nat. Eye Inst., 1969—, Rsch. to Prevent Blindness, 1975-77. Mem. Am. Inst. Med. Biol. Engring., Assn. Research Vision and Ophthalmology, Soc. Neurosci., Bárány Soc. Democrat. Research and publs. on neurophysiology oculomotor system.

ROBINSON, DAVID BROOKS, naval officer; b. Alexandria, La., Oct. 26, 1939; s. Donald and Marion (Holloman) R.; m. Gene Kirkpatrick, Aug. 1, 1964; children: Kirk, David. Student, Tex. A&M U., 1958-59; BS, U.S. Naval Acad., 1963; MS in Physics, Naval Postgrad. Sch., Monterey, Calif., 1969. Commd. ensign USN, 1963, advanced through grades to vice admiral, 1993; comdg. officer USS Canon and USS Ready, Guam, 1969-71; adminstrv. aide to Chmn. Joint Chiefs Staff, Washington, 1971-74; comdg. officer USS Luce, Mayport, Fla., 1976-78; surface comdr. assignment officer. and dir. fiscal mgt. and procedural control divsn. Naval Mil. Pers. Cmd., 1979-81; mem. Fgn. Service Inst. Exec. Seminar, Washington, 1982; comdg. officer USS Richmond K. Turner, Charleston, S.C., 1983-84; chief of staff, comdr. Naval Surface Force, Atlantic Fleet, Norfolk, Va., 1984; exec. asst. and sr. aide to vice chief Naval Ops., Washington, 1985, dir. Manpower and Tng. div., 1986, dir. Surface Warfare div. 1987-88; comdr. cruiser destroyer group 8, 1988-89; vice dir. and subsequently dir. operational plans and interoperability directorate Joint Staff, Washington, 1989-91; dep., chief of staff to comdr. U.S. Pacific Fleet, 1991-93, comdr. naval surface force, 1993—. Decorated Navy Cross, Def. D.S.M., D.S.M., Legion of Merit with 4 gold stars, Bronze Star, Purple Heart. Mem. Optimists (pres. Oakton, Va. 1986-87). Methodist. Avocations: golf, cycling, stamp collecting, reading. Office: COMNAVSURFPAC 2421 Vella LaVella Rd San Diego CA 92135

ROBINSON, DAVID CLINTON, reporter; b. Goffstown, N.H., Nov. 5, 1963; s. Clinton and Barbara Lee (Ploss) R.; m. Karen Ruth Eckhardt, July 3, 1992; children: Laura Lee, Lindsay Lee. AB, Syracuse U., 1985. Reporter The Buffalo News, 1985—. Mem. Buffalo Newspaper Guild (exec. com. 1989-95, vice chmn. 1991-92). Office: The Buffalo News 1 News Plz Buffalo NY 14203-2930

ROBINSON, DAVID EARL, pharmaceutical executive; b. Indpls., Nov. 28, 1948; s. Howard Ambler and Irma Katherine (Jones) R.; m. Nancy Margaret Neumann, Feb. 14, 1970; children: David Edward, Robert Steven. BA in Polit. Sci. and Econs., Macquarie U., Australia, 1974; MBA in Fin. and Mktg., U. New South Wales, Australia, 1977. Sales rep. Schering A.G., Australia, 1972-74; various positions Abbott Labs., 1974-84; pres. Adria Labs. div. Erbamont, Columbus, Ohio, 1984-88; chief oper. officer Erbamont N.V., Stamford, Conn., 1988—. Bd. dirs. Columbus Assn. Performing Arts, 1988—. Mem. Pharm. Mfrs. Assn., Am. Social Health Assn. (bd. dirs. 1987—), Young Presidents Orgn., Pvt. Pilots Assn. (Columbus chpt.), Capital Club. Avocations: flying, sailing, tennis, scuba diving, foreign languages. Office: Erbamont 1266 Main St Stamford CT 06902-3546

ROBINSON, DAVID G., management consultant. Pres., CEO CSC Index, Cambridge, Mass., 1981—. Office: CSC Index 5 Cambridge Ctr Cambridge MA 02142-1493*

ROBINSON, DAVID MASON, cell physiologist; b. Barton, Eng., July 7, 1932; came to U.S., 1969, naturalized, 1979; s. Thomas Leon Mason and Mabel (Orr) R.; B.Sc. with 1st class honours, U. Durham, 1955, Ph.D (Philip Buckle Meml. scholar), 1958; m. Jean Marcia Smith, Sept. 10, 1965; children—Jane Leonie Mason, Simon Henry Mason. Mem. sci. staff Namulonge Research Sta., Kampala, Uganda, 1959-61; research officer, tutor Hope Dept. Zoology, Oxford (Eng.) U., 1961-63; mem. sci. staff, biophysics group Med. Research Council, Radiobiol. Research Unit, Harwell, Eng., 1963-66; prin. sci. officer, head cell biology Microbiol. Research Establishment, Porton, Eng., 1966-69; asst. research dir., head cell biology ARC Blood Research Lab., Bethesda, Md., 1969-73; prof. biology, assoc. mem. Vincent Lombardi Cancer Research Ctr., Georgetown U., Washington, 1974-80, adj. prof. anatomy and cell biology, Sch. of Medicine, 1982-90; professorial lectr. in liberal studies Georgetown U., 1980—; assoc. dir. for sci. programs, dir. heart and vascular disease Nat. Heart, Lung and Blood Inst., NIH, Bethesda, Md., 1980-94, acting dir., 1993, dir. vascular rsch. program, 1994—; mem. faculty biology and genetics NIH Grad. Sch., 1981-86; mem. faculty Brookings Inst., 1994—. Capt. 1st Royal Green Jackets, 43d and 52d, Brit. Ter. Army, 1962-65. Empire Cotton Growing Corp. postgrad. scholar, 1957. Recipient Vicennial medal Georgetown U., 1992. Mem. Biophys. Soc., Soc. Complex Carbohydrates, Soc. Cryobiology (sec. 1975), Am. Soc. Cell Biology, Sigma Xi (pres. Georgetown chpt. 1978), Alpha Sigma Nu (hon.). Democrat. Episcopalian. Club: Royal Green Jackets Officers. Author: (with G.A. Jamieson) Mammalian Cell Membranes, 5 vols., 1973-76; contbr. articles to profl. jours. Home: Stoneleigh Cottage PO Box 2164 Shepherdstown WV 25443-2164 Office: NIH Fed Bldg Rm 416 Bethesda MD 20892

ROBINSON, DAVID MAURICE (THE ADMIRAL), professional basketball player; b. Key West, Fla., Aug. 6, 1965. Grad., U.S. Naval Acad., 1987. Commd. ensign USN, 1987; with San Antonio Spurs, 1989—; mem. U.S. Olympic Basketball Team, 1988, 92. Recipient Naismith award, 1987, Wooden award, 1987, IBM award, 1990, 91, 94, Schick Pivotal Player award, 1990, 91; named to Sporting News All-Am. First Team, 1986, 87, Sporting News Coll. Player of Yr., 1987, NBA Rookie of Yr., 1990, All-NBA First Team, 1991, 92, All-Star team, 1990-94; named NBA Defensive Player of Yr., 1992, MVP, 1994-95. Office: care San Antonio Spurs 600 E Market St Ste 102 San Antonio TX 78205*

ROBINSON, DAVID WEAVER, surgeon, educator; b. Kansas City, Mo., Nov. 15, 1914; s. David Beach and Aileen (Weaver) R.; m. Margaret Sherwood, June 20, 1940 (dec. Feb. 1986); children: David S., Nancy K., Peter B., Mary A.; m. Alma L. Dallas Horner, Aug. 26, 1987 (dec. 1991). A.B., U. Kans., 1935, M.S., 1948; M.D., U. Pa., 1938. Diplomate: Am. Bd. Surgery, Am. Bd. Plastic Surgery. Intern Phila. Gen. Hosp., 1938-40; surg. trainee U. Kans. Med. Ctr., Kansas City, 1940-43, instr., 1941-43, asst. prof., 1948-50, assoc. prof., 1951-54, prof. surgery, 1954-85, Regents prof., 1973-85; disting. prof. emeritus U. Kans. Med. Ctr., 1985—, chmn. sect. plastic surgery, 1947-72, dir. U. Kans. Burn Ctr., 1972-83, vice chancellor clin. affairs, 1974-80, acting vice chancellor, 1975-76; mem. surg. study sect. NIH Research Council, 1962-65. Contbr. articles to med. jours. Trustee Kansas City Philharm. Assn., Kans., 1963—. Served to capt. M.C. AUS, 1943-45. Decorated Croix de Guerre France; recipient disting. alumni citation U. Kans., 1969. Mem. Am Kans. Plastic Surgeons (honoree of yr. award 1982), Am. Assn. for Surgery Trauma, ACS (gov. 1973-79 honoree of yr. award), Am. Soc. Plastic and Reconstructive Surgery (pres. 1966), Am. Trauma Soc. (founding mem.), Am. Surg. Assn. (2d v.p. 1965), Central Surg. Assn., Western Surg. Assn., AMA, Assn. for Cleft Palate Rehab., Kans. Med. Soc. Plastic Surgery Research Council, Rocky Mountain Traumatological Soc., Soc. for Surgery Head and Neck, Soc. Univ. Surgeons, Am. Bd. Plastic Surgery (chmn. examining bd. 1966-), Societe Internationale de Chirurgie, Sigma Xi, Nu Sigma Nu, Alpha Omega Alpha, Beta Theta Pi. Republican. Presbyterian (ruling elder 1953-). Home: 7930 Bristol Ct Shawnee Mission KS 66208-5220 Office: U Kans Med Ctr Kansas City KS 66103

ROBINSON, DAVID ZAV, foundation administrator; b. Montreal, Que., Can., Sept. 29, 1927; s. Benjamin and Antonia (Seiden) R.; m. Nan Senior, Sept. 6, 1954; children: Marc, Eric. AB, Harvard U., 1946, AM, 1947, PhD,

1950. Asst. dir. rsch. Baird-Atomic Inc., Cambridge, Mass., 1949-59, 60-61; sci. liaison officer Office Naval Rsch., London, 1959-60; sci. advisor staff Office of Pres., Washington, 1961-67; v.p. acad. affairs NYU, 1967-70; v.p. Carnegie Corp. N.Y., N.Y.C., 1970-80, exec. v.p., 1981-85, exec. v.p., treas., 1986-88; exec. dir. Carnegie Commn. on Sci Tech. and Govt., 1988—; dir. Urban Research Corp., Chgo., 1968-75; cons. Congressional Office of Tech. Assessment, 1975-78; mem. com. women in sci. NRC, 1975-82; mem. vis. com. dept. chemistry Harvard U., 1977-83; physics dept. Princeton U., 1970-76. Mem. N.Y. Energy Rsch. and Devel. Authority, 1971-77; trustee CUNY, 1976-81, Amideast, 1983-88, Citizen Union Found., 1985—, Inst. Schs. of the Future, 1986—, N.C. Sch. Sci. and Math., 1989—, Santa Fe Inst., 1987—, Prep for Prep, 1989—. Mem. AAAS, Optical Soc. Am., Coun. on Fgn. Rels., Am. Contract Bridge League, Harvard Club (N.Y.C.), Century Assn. (N.Y.C.). Office: 437 Madison Ave New York NY 10022

ROBINSON, DAVIS ROWLAND, lawyer; b. N.Y.C., July 11, 1940; s. Thomas Porter and Cynthia (Davis) R.; m. Suzanne Walker, June 11, 1966; children: Christopher Champlin II, Gracyn Walker. B.A. magna cum laude, Yale U., 1961; LL.B. cum laude, Harvard U., 1967. Bar: N.Y. 1968, D.C. 1971, U.S. Supreme Ct. 1972. Fgn. svc. officer Dept. State, Washington, 1961-69; assoc. Sullivan & Cromwell, N.Y.C., 1969-71; assoc., ptnr. Leva, Hawes, Symington, Martin and Oppenheimer, Washington, 1971-81; legal adviser Dept. State, Washington, 1981-85; ptnr. Pillsbury, Madison & Sutro, Washington, 1985-88, Le Boeuf, Lamb, Greene & MacRae, Washington, 1988—; adj. prof. Georgetown Univ. Law Ctr. Pres. Harvard Legal Aid Bur., 1966-67. Mem. ABA, Assn. of Bar of City of N.Y., Fed. Bar Assn., Am. Law Inst. (adviser fgn. rels. law of the U.S.), Am. Soc. Internat. Law, Coun. on Fgn. Rels., Phi Beta Kappa. Office: Le Boeuf Lamb Greene & MacRae 1875 Connecticut Ave NW Washington DC 20009-5728

ROBINSON, DEAN WENTWORTH, chemist, educator; b. Boston, July 22, 1929; s. Lawrence Dean and Doris Elizabeth (Prowse) R.; children: Dean W., Amy E., Jonas W. B.S., U. N.H., 1951, M.S., 1952; PhD., M.I.T., 1955. Mem. faculty Johns Hopkins, 1955—, prof. chemistry, 1967—, chmn. dept., 1976-83. Author research papers. Guggenheim fellow, 1966; Fulbright fellow, 1966. Fellow AAAS; mem. Am. Chem. Soc. Home: 10 Sonachan Ct Baltimore MD 21286-7910 Office: Johns Hopkins U Dept Chemistry Baltimore MD 21218

ROBINSON, DEBORAH A., judge; b. 1953. BS, Morgan State U.; JD, Emory Univ. Law Sch., 1978. Law clk. to chief judge Superior Ct. of D.C., 1978-79; asst. U.S Atty. Office, Washington, 1979-88; magistrate judge U.S. Dist. Ct., D.C. circuit, 1988—. Office: US Courthouse Rm 1207 333 Constitution Ave NW Washington DC 20001

ROBINSON, DIXIE FAYE, school system administrator; b. Lexington, Ky., Feb. 7, 1944; d. John David and Betty Lou (Taylor) Moore; m. Jim Darrell Robinson, June 25, 1978. BA, Georgetown (Ky.) Coll., 1966; MA in Edn., Ball State U., 1972; postgrad., Miami U., Oxford, Ohio, 1989—, Ind. U., 1990-92. Cert. tchr., Ind. Tchr. Richmond (Ind.) Community Schs., 1966-91, adminstr., 1991—; team leader Richmond Community schs., 1983-90, mentor tchr., 1989-91, coop. learning staff devel. mem., 1989-91, coord. ptnrship in edn., 1990-91, site-base convenor, 1990-91; v.p. Richmond Area Reading Coun., 1984. Pres. Historic Richmond, Inc., 1982; tour guide Richmond-Wayne County Tourism Bur., 1986-87; vice-chmn. Richmond Area Rose Festival, 1988-89; adv. bd. Palladium Item, Richmond, 1990. Recipient Hoosier Meritorious award Ind. Sec. of State, 1986, Nat. Energy Edn. Devel. award, Washington, 1991; grantee Newspapers in Edn., 1986. Mem. NEA, NAFE, ASCD, Nat. Middle Sch. Assn., Assn. Tchr. Educators, Nat. Coun. Tchrs. English (Ctr. of Excellence award 1988-91), Ind. Coun. Tchrs. of English (Hoosier Tchr. English 1991), Richmond Area Reading Coun., Kappa Delta Gamma, Phi Delta Kappa. Avocations: historic preservation, antiques, community affairs, reading, travel. Home: 100 NW 8th St Richmond IN 47374

ROBINSON, DONALD KEITH, physicist, educator; b. Truro, N.S., Can., Aug. 29, 1932; s. Travis Sylvanus and Georgietta (Carter) R.; m. Margaret Tompkins Bainbridge, June 12, 1965; children—Gregory Kenneth, Claire Carter. B.Sc., Dalhousie, Halifax, N.S., 1954, M.Sc., 1956; postgrad., Cambridge (Eng.) U., 1956-57; D.Phil., Oxford (Eng.) U., 1960. Research asso. Brookhaven (N.Y.) Nat. Lab., 1960-62, asst. physicist, 1962-63, asso. physicist, 1963-66; asso. prof. physics Case Western Res. U., 1966-71, prof., 1971—. Co-author: (with Philip R. Bevington) Data Reduction and Error Analysis for the Physical Sciences. Mem. Am. Phys. Soc., AAUP. Research in exptl. particle physics with bubble chambers and electronic counters, boson resonances, neutral K-meson decays, polarized proton interactions, proton-antiproton interactions, radiative production and decay of hyperons. Home: 2602 E Overlook Rd Cleveland OH 44106-2802 Office: Dept Physics Case Western Res U Cleveland OH 44106

ROBINSON, DONALD LEONARD, social scientist, educator; b. Buffalo, Dec. 28, 1936; s. Sidney Smith and Marion Esther (Hershiser) R.; m. Molly McCaslin Jahnige, Jan. 1, 1983; children: John Samuel, David Wynn; stepchildren: Katherine Jahnige, Paul Jahnige. BA, Yale U., 1958; MDiv, Union Theol. Sem., 1962; PhD, Cornell U., 1966. Instr. govt. Cornell U., Ithaca, N.Y., 1965-66; asst. prof. Smith Coll., Northampton, Mass., 1966-71, assoc. prof., 1971-78, prof., 1978— Sylvia Dlugasch Bauman chair Am. studies, 1990-93, dir. Am. studies, 1979-85; cons. Ford Found., 1986-88, 91-92, Media and Society, 1986-87, Comm. on Operation of U.S. Senate, 1976; dir. Project '87, 1977-78; vis. prof. Doshisha U., Kyoto, Japan, 1989. Author: Slavery in the Structure of American Politics, 1765-1820, 1971, To the Best of My Ability: The Presidency and the Constitution, 1987, Government for the Third American Century, 1989; mem. editorial bd. Presdl. Studies Quar., 1987—; editor: Reforming American Government: The Bicentennial Papers of the Committee on the Constitutional System, 1985. Adminstr. New Eng. Regional Commn., 1973; chmn. Dem. City Com., 1978-80, Northampton Planning Bd., 1980-82; warden St. John's Episcopal Ch., 1981-85; trustee Diocese of Western Mass., 1988—; chair bd. selectmen, Ashfield, Mass., 1992—. Rockefeller Bros. fellow, 1958-59; Kent fellow, 1962-66; Project '87 fellow, 1980; fellow Ctr. for Study Democratic Insts., 1971; Phi Beta Kappa vis. scholar, 1988-89; recipient Anisfield-Wolf award, 1971. Mem. Am. Polit. Sci. Assn., Cosmos Club, Phi Beta Kappa. Home: Norton Hill Rd Ashfield MA 01330 Office: Smith Coll Dept Govt Northampton MA 01063

ROBINSON, DONALD WALTER, university dean; b. Rockford, Ill.; s. Walter John and Viola (Anderson) R.; m. Betty Jane Zink, May 30, 1948; children: Deborah Beth, Galen Don, Darci Lynn, Gregory John. A.B., Carthage Coll., 1950; M.A., Bradley U., 1951, Ph.D., 1957. Various positions coll. and pub. sch. adminstrn., 1952-58; specialist in coll. adminstrn. U.S. Office of Edn., Washington, 1959-62; dir. mental retardation research centers program Nat. Inst. Child Health and Human Devel., Bethesda, Md., 1962-65; asst. dean, prof. higher edn. So. Ill. U., Carbondale, 1965-70; dean, prof. Coll. Edn. Youngstown (Ohio) State U., 1970-72; dean Coll. Edn., prof. psychology and higher edn. Okla. State U., Stillwater, 1972-88, dean, prof. emeritus, 1988; dean, prof. Sch. Edn. U. Mo., St. Louis, 1988-92, dean emeritus, 1967-93; cons. examiner North Ctrl. Assn. Schs. and Colls., 1967-93; bd. examiners Nat. Coun. Accreditation/Tchr. Edn., 1990-93; cons. New Eng. Assn. Schs. and Colls., USPHS, U.S. Office Edn., World Bank; bd. dirs. Holmes Group, 1987-88. Bd. dirs. Marymount U., Arlington, Va., 1962-66, St. Louis Sci. Ctr., 1989-92. Teen Challenge Ark., Cmty. Counseling Found., Hot Springs, Ark. trustee St. Louis Regional Edn. Partnership, 1989-92; ruling elder John Calvin Presbyn. Ch., Bridgeton, Mo., Kirk in Pines, Hot Springs Village, Ark. With USAAF, 1944-46. Mem. Am. Assn. Colls. Tchr. Edn. (govt. rels. com. 1977-79, 88-91, bd. dirs. 1988-90), North Ctrl. Assn. Colls. and Schs. (dir. 1975-79, chmn. coun. rsch. and svc. 1977-79), Am. Psychol. Assn., Am. Ednl. Rsch. Assn., Am. Assn. Higher Edn., Assn. Colls. and Schs. in State Univs., Land Grant Colls. and Affiliated Pvt. Univs. (sec. 1985-86, pres. elect 1987-88, pres. 1988-90, past pres., bd. dirs. 1990-92), Kiwanis. Home: 13 Malaga Cir Hot Springs National Park AR 71909

ROBINSON, DONALD WILFORD, mathematics educator; b. Salt Lake City, Feb. 29, 1928; s. Wilford Allen and Thirza (Cornick) R.; m. Helen Ruth Sorensen, Aug. 27, 1952; children: Diane, Allen Conrad, Karen, Janette, Marilyn, Lynae, David William. BS, U. Utah, 1948, MA, 1952;

PhD, Case Inst. Tech., 1956. Asst. prof. math. Brigham Young U., Provo, Utah, 1956-59; assoc. prof. Brigham Young U., Provo, 1959-62, prof., 1962—; sr. rsch. fellow Calif. Inst. Tech., Pasadena, 1962-63; vis. prof. U.S. Naval Postgrad. Sch., Monterey, Calif., 1969-70, Rijksuniversiteit, Ghent, Belgium, 1986; Fulbright-Hayes lectr. State Dept., Valencia, Venezuela, 1976-77. Contbr. articles in field to profl. jours. Dist. chmn. Rep. Party, Provo, 1972-74. NSF faculty fellow, Pasadena, 1962-63; recipient Karl G. Maeser Rsch. and Creative Arts award Karl G. Maeser Scholarship Svc., 1993. Mem. Math. Assn. Am. (chmn. Intermountain sect. 1982-84, sect. gov. 1986-89, Meritorious Svc. cert. 1995), Sigma Xi (pres. Brigham Young U. chpt. 1967-68). Republican. Mormon. Avocations: gardening, singing. Home: 2380 N 930 E Provo UT 84604-4165 Office: Brigham Young Univ 312 Tmcb Provo UT 84602-1044

ROBINSON, DOUGLAS GEORGE, lawyer; b. Hamilton, Mont., Feb. 24, 1943; s. Clarence Elijah and Frances Carolina (Alonzo) R.; children from previous marriage: Stephen Douglas, Katherine Marielle; m. Julia Elizabeth Sullivan, 1995. B.A. in Econs, U. Wash., 1965; J.D.; George Washington U., 1969. Bar: D.C. Legis. asst. Wash. State Legis. Council, Olympia, 1965-66; assoc. firm Arnold & Porter, Washington, 1969-74; dep. gen. counsel Fed. Energy Adminstrn., Washington, 1974-76; mem. issues staff Carter-Mondale Presdl. Campaign, Atlanta, 1976; mem. Carter-Mondale Transition Group, Washington, 1976-77; spl. asst. to adminstr. for maj. energy projects Fed. Energy Adminstrn., Washington, 1977; asst. administr. for regulations and emergency planning Econ. Regulatory Adminstrn., U.S. Dept. Energy, Washington, 1977-78; dep. administr. for policy Econ. Regulatory Adminstrn., U.S. Dept. Energy, 1978-80, spl. asst. to sec., dep. sec., 1980-81; ptnr. Skadden, Arps, Slate, Meagher & Flom, Washington, 1981—. Editor-in-chief: George Washington Law Rev, 1968-69. Recipient John B. Larner medal George Washington U. Law Sch., 1969; cert. of superior service Fed. Energy Adminstrn., 1974; Outstanding Service medal Dept. Energy, 1979; Disting. Service medal Dept. of Energy, 1981. Mem. ABA (Nat. Pro Bono Publico award 1994), D.C. Bar Assn., Fed. Energy Bar Assn. Office: Skadden Arps Slate Meagher & Flom 1440 New York Ave NW Washington DC 20005-2111

ROBINSON, (DAVID) DUNCAN, museum administrator, art historian; b. Kidsgrove, Staffordshire, Eng., June 27, 1943; came to U.S., 1981; s. Tom and Ann Elizabeth (Clarke) R.; m. Elizabeth Anne Sutton, Jan. 7, 1967; children: Amanda Jane, Thomas Edward, Charlotte Elizabeth. B.A., Clare Coll., U. Cambridge, Eng., 1965; M.A., Clare Coll., U. Cambridge, 1969, Yale U., 1967. Asst. keeper paintings and drawings Fitzwilliam Mus., Cambridge, 1970-76, keeper paintings and drawings, 1976-80; fellow, lectr. Clare Coll., 1975-81; chief exec. officer Paul Mellon Ctr. for Studies in Brit. Art, London, 1981—; dir. Yale Ctr. for Brit. Art, New Haven, 1981—; adj. prof. Yale U., 1981—; vis. com. dept. painting restoration Met. Mus. Art; mem. coun. mgmt. William Blake Trust, 1983—; bd. govs. Yale U. Press, 1987—; mem. arts and artifacts indemnity adv. panel to Fed. Coun. on Arts & Humanities, 1991-94, chmn., 1992-94. Author: A Companion Volume to the Kelmscott Chaucer, 1975, Stanley Spencer, 1979, Morris & Co. in Cambridge, 1980, Town, Country, Shore and Sea: British Watercolors from VanDyck to Nash, 1982, Stanley Spencer, 1990. Mem. adv. panel Arts Coun. Gt. Britain, 1978-81, vice chmn. art adv. panel, 1981, coun. mem., 1981. Mellon fellow, 1965. Fellow Royal Soc. Arts; mem. Walpole Soc. (coun. 1986-89), Conn. Acad. Arts and Scis., New haven Colony Hist. Soc. (bd. dirs. 1991-94), Athenaeum Club (London), Century Club, Knickerbocker Club (N.Y.C.), Am. Friends of the Georgian Group (bd. dirs. 1992-94). Home: 142 Huntington St New Haven CT 06511-2017 Office: Yale Ctr-British Art 1080 Chapel St New Haven CT 06510-2302

ROBINSON, E. B., JR., bank executive; b. Centreville, Miss., Sept. 14, 1941; s. Emerson B. and Dolly (McGehee) R.; m. Judy M. Treppendahl, Sept. 7, 1963; children: E.B. III, John Green. BS, Davidson Coll., 1963; MBA, Harvard U., 1967. Mgmt. trainee Deposit Guaranty Nat. Bank, Jackson, Miss., 1967-69, investment officer, 1969-71, asst. v.p., 1971-73, v.p., 1973-75, exec. v.p., 1976-79, pres., chief ops. officer, 1979-84; pres., chief ops. officer Deposit Guaranty Corp., Jackson, 1982-84; chmn. and chief exec. officer Deposit Guaranty Nat. Bank and Deposit Guaranty Corp., Jackson, 1984—; bd. dirs. Fed. Res. Bank of Atlanta. Chmn. Fin. com. Millsaps Coll., Jackson; treas. Council for Support of Pub. Higher Edn., Jackson; bd. dirs. Columbia Sem., Atlanta. Served with U.S. Army, 1963-65. J. Spencer Love fellow Harvard U., 1963. Mem. Young Pres.'s Orgn., Assn. of Res. City Bankers (govt. relations com.), Dealer Bank Assn. (Glass-Stegall com.), Jackson C. of C. (pres. 1987), Phi Beta Kappa. Presbyterian. Clubs: Country of Jackson; Harvard (N.Y.C.). Avocation: running. Office: Deposit Guaranty Corp PO Box 1200 Jackson MS 39215

ROBINSON, EDDIE GAY, college football coach; m. Doris Robinson; children: Lillian Rose, Eddie Jr. BA, Leland Coll., 1940; MS, U. Iowa; LLD (hon.), La. Tech. Coach football Grambling U., La., 1941—, v.p athletics; head coach East-West Shrine Game, 1977. Recipient Horatio Alger award, Nat. Football Found. award, NAACP award, VFW award, Bear Bryant award, Liberty Bowl award, others, Spl. Commendations from Pres. Ronald Reagan, Nat. Collegiate Athletic Assn., U.S. Congress, State of La., B'nai B'rith; holds record of most college football victories. Mem. Nat. Assn. Sports & Phys. Edn., Nat. Assn. Intercollegiate Athletics, Southwestern Athletic Conf., La. Sports Hall of Fame, Pop Warner, Sugar Bowl, Black Coll. Winner 10 nat. Black coll. football championships. Office: Grambling State Univ Athletic Dept Grambling LA 71245

ROBINSON, EDGAR ALLEN, oil company executive; b. Boston, Dec. 12, 1933; s. Herbert and Ruth (Solomon) R.; m. Ruth Enid Schwartz, July 24, 1956; children: Jeffrey Michael, Laurie Karen. AB, Brown U., 1955; MBA, Harvard U., 1960. Fin. analyst Exxon Corp., N.Y.C., 1960-66, asst. treas., 1966-70; corp. planning mgr. Esso Europe Inc., London, 1970-72; pres. Esso Africa Inc., London, 1972-75; dep. contr. Exxon Corp., N.Y.C., 1975-79; sr. v.p. Exxon Co. U.S.A., Houston, 1979-83; v.p., treas. Exxon Corp., Irving, Tex., 1983—. Bd. dirs. bus. Arts Fund, Houston, 1980-83, chmn., 1983; trustee Houston Ballet Found., 1980-83, Brown U., Providence, 1982-88; mem. Dean's adv. com. U. Chgo. Bus. Sch., 1984—, 1990-94; bd. dirs. Dallas Zoo, 1992—; bd. govs. Dallas Symphony, 1993—. Office: Exxon Corp 225 E John W Carpenter Fwy W Irving TX 75062

ROBINSON, EDWARD JOSEPH, cosmetics company executive; b. White Plains, N.Y., May 12, 1940; s. Edward D.J. and Christine (Walsh) R.; m. Gail Lee Robinson, June 15, 1963; 1 son, Michael. B.B.A., Iona Coll., 1962. CPA, N.Y. Supr. Peat, Marwick, Mitchell, N.Y.C., 1963-70; exec. v.p. fin., chief fin. officer RJR Nabisco, Inc., Atlanta, 1987-89; exec. v.p. fin., chief fin. officer Avon Products, N.Y.C., 1989-93, vice chmn., chief fin. and adminstrv. officer, 1993—. Trustee Iona Coll. Recipient Loftus award for Disting. Achievement Iona Coll., 1976. Mem. Am. Inst. CPA's, N.Y. Soc. CPA's, Winged Foot Country Club (Mamaroneck, N.Y.), Met. Club (N.Y.C.), N.Y. Athletic Club (N.Y.C.). Republican. •

ROBINSON, EDWARD LEE, retired physics educator, consultant; b. Clanton, Ala., Nov. 6, 1933; s. Alonzo Lee and Ollie Sarah (Mims) R.; m. Shirley Anne Burnett (div. Sept. 1972); children: Edward Lee Jr., James Allan, Paul David; m. Linda G. Moon, 1990. AB with honors, Samford U., 1954; MS, Purdue U., 1958, PhD, 1962. Asst. prof. physics, chmn. dept. Samford U., Birmingham, Ala., 1961-62, assoc. prof., chmn. dept., 1962-66, prof., chmn. dept., 1966-67; assoc. prof. U. Ala., Birmingham, 1967-77, co-radiation safety officer, 1967-85, acting chmn. dept., 1973-74, prof. physics, 1977-91, adj. prof. forensic sci., 1983-91; cons. Hayes Internat. Corp., Birmingham, 1963-68, So. Research Inst., Birmingham, 1968-69; researcher Oak Ridge (Tenn.) Nat. Lab, 1968, 74-75, 82, U. Md., College Park, 1966, 67. Active Birmingham YMCA. Mem. Am. Phys. Soc., Soc. Automotive Engrs., AAAS, Ala. Acad. Sci. (v.p. 1964-65), N.Y. Acad. Sci. Baptist. Achievements include discovery, co-discovery of six radioisotopes. Avocations: handball, scuba diving. Home: 1692 Monteagle Dr Birmingham AL 35244

ROBINSON, EDWARD T., III, lawyer; b. Glen Cove, N.Y., May 23, 1932; s. Edward Jr. and Helen (Rahilly) R.; m. Lynn Simmons; children: Edward IV, Wendy, Christopher, Jeffrey, Lesley, Michael. AB, Holy Cross Coll., 1954; JD, Georgetown U., 1960. Bar: N.Y. 1961, U.S. Ct. Appeals (2d cir.) 1966. Counsel Royal-Globe Ins. Co., Mineola, N.Y., 1960-64; pvt. practice,

---

Oyster Bay, N.Y., 1964-70, 91-94; ptnr. Robinson & Cincotta, Oyster Bay, 1970-85, Robinson & Lynch, Oyster Bay, 1985-91, Robinson, Bermingham & Donegan, Oyster Bay, 1994—; mem. adv. bd. Chgo. Title Ins. Co., N.Y.C., 1982—; Fleet Bank, 1989—, United Cerebral Palsy, 1980—; mem. Nassau County Commn. on Govt. Revision, 1983—; mem. County Exec. Blue Ribbon Panel on Criminal Justice; mem. exec. coun. N.Y. State Conf. Bar Leaders; counsel Oyster Bay-East Norwich Ctrl. Sch. Dist. Mem. Nassau County Traffic and Parking Violations Bur.; pres. Holy Cross Coll. Club, L.I., 1989-90; trustee Nassau County coun. Boy Scouts Am.; chmn. Forget-Me-Not Ball, United Cerebral Palsy. Recipient Community Svc. award Nassau County coun. Boy Scouts Am.; named Man of Yr. United Cerebral Palsy, Nassau County, 1979. Mem. N.Y. State Bar Assn. (del., v.p 1992—), Nassau County Bar Assn. (pres. 1986-87), C. of C. (past pres.), Meadowbrook Hunt Club. Republican. Roman Catholic. Avocations: golf, tennis, jazz music. Home: 60 Calvin Ave Syosset NY 11791-2106 Office: 34 Audrey Ave Oyster Bay NY 11771-1548

ROBINSON, ENDERS ANTHONY, geophysics educator, writer; b. Boston, Mar. 18, 1930; s. Edward Arthur and Doris Gertrude (Goodale) R.; m. Eva Arborelius, Sept. 9, 1962 (div. 1973); children: Anna, Erik Arthur, Karin; m. Joyce McPeake, Aug. 8, 1992. BS in Math., MIT, 1950, MS in Econs., 1952, PhD in Geophysics, 1954. Dir. geophys. analysis group MIT, Cambridge, Mass., 1952-54; geophysicist Gulf Oil Corp., Pitts., 1954-55; instr. math. MIT, Cambridge, Mass., 1955-56; petroleum economist Standard Oil Co. N.J., N.Y.C., 1956-57; asst. prof. stats. Mich. State U., East Lansing, 1958; asst. prof. math. U. Wis., Madison, 1958-61, assoc. prof. math. (with tenure), 1961-62; dep. prof. stats Uppsala (Sweden) U., 1960-64; v.p., dir. Digicon, Inc. Houston, 1965-70; pres. Robinson Rsch. Inc. Houston, 1970-82; vis. prof. theoretical and applied mechanics Cornell U., Ithaca, N.Y., 1981-82; McMan prof. geophysics U. Tulsa, 1983-93; Maurice Ewing and J.L. Worzel prof. geophysics Columbia U., N.Y.C., 1993—. Author 25 books on sci. and tech. including Einstein's Relativity in Metaphor and Mathematics, 1990; editor: Internat. Jour. of Imaging Systems & Tech., 1988—; assoc. editor: Jour. of Time Series Analysis, 1984—; editorial bd. Multidimensional Systems and Signal Processing, An Internat. Jour., 1990—. 2d lt. U.S. Army, 1950-51. Recipient Conrad Schlumberger award European Assn. of Exploration Geophysicsts, 1969, Donald G. Fink Prize award IEEE, 1984. Mem. NAE, Nat. Rsch. Coun. (com. on undiscovered oil and gas resources), Soc. Exploration Geophysicists (hon., Best Paper award, 1964, medal 1969). Home: 560 Riverside Dr Apt 20J New York NY 10027-3236 Office: Columbia U Krumb Sch Mines New York NY 10027

ROBINSON, FARREL RICHARD, pathologist, toxicologist; b. Wellington, Kans., Mar. 23, 1927; s. Farrel Otis and Norine (Sloan) R.; m. Mimi Agatha Hathaway, June 5, 1949; children: Farrel Richard, Kelly S., E. Scott, Brian A. B.S., Kans. State U., 1950, D.V.M., M.S., 1958; Ph.D., Tex. A&M U., 1965. Diplomate: Am. Coll. Vet. Pathologists, Am. Bd. Vet. Toxicology (v.p. 1971-74, pres. 1976-79). Served with USN, 1945-46; commd. 2d lt. USAF, 1951, advanced through grades to lt. col., 1971; vet. pathologist Aerospace Med. Research Labs., Wright-Patterson AFB, Ohio, 1958-68; chief Vet. Pathology div. Armed Forces Inst. Pathology, Washington, 1968-74; ret., 1974; scientist assoc. Univs. Associated for Research and Edn. in Pathology, Inc., 1972-74; asst. clin. prof. pathology George Washington U. Sch. Medicine, 1972-74; instr. NIH Grad. Program, 1973-74; prof. toxicology-pathology Sch. Vet. Medicine, Purdue U., 1974-93; dir. Animal Disease Diagnostic Lab., 1978-85, head dept. vet. sci., 1978-85, head dept. vet. microbiology, pathology and pub. health, 1986-88, chief toxicology service, 1984-91; emeritus, 1993; cons. vet. pathology USAF surg. gen. and asst. surg. gen. for vet. services, 1970-74. Mem. editorial bd. Human and Vet. Toxicology, 1976—. Contbr. sci. articles to profl. jours. Decorated USAF Commendation medal, Meritorious Service medal; recipient Aerospace Med. Research Labs. Scientist of Year award, 1967. Mem. AVMA, Am. Bd. Vet. Toxicology, Am. Coll. Vet. Pathology, Am. Assn. Vet. Lab. Diagnosticians (bd. govs.1980-85, v.p. 1986, pres. 1987), Wildlife Disease Assn., Conf. Rsch. Workers in Animal Disease, Soc. Toxicology, U.S. Animal Health Assn., Sigma Xi, Phi Kappa Phi, Alpha Zeta, Phi Zeta. Democrat. Methodist. Home: 201 W 600 N West Lafayette IN 47906-9727 Office: Purdue U Animal Disease Diagnostic Lab West Lafayette IN 47907

ROBINSON, FRANK, professional baseball team executive, former coach, former player; b. Beaumont, Tex., Aug. 31, 1935; s. Frank and Ruth (Shaw) R.; m. Barbara Ann Cole, Oct. 28, 1961; children: Frank Kevin, Nichelle. Student, Xavier U., Cin. Baseball player Cin. Reds, 1956-65, Balt. Orioles, 1966-71, L.A., 1972, Calif. Angels, 1973-74; baseball player Cleve. Indians, 1974-76, mgr., 1975-77; coach Calif. Angels, 1977; coach Balt. Orioles, 1978-80, 85-87, mgr., 1988-91, asst. to gen. mgr., 1991—; mgr. San Francisco Giants, 1981-84; batting coach Milw. Brewers, 1984. Author: (with Al Silverman) My Life is Baseball, 1967, (with Barry Steinbach) Extra Innings, 1989, Frank the First Year, 1976. Named Rookie of Yr. Nat. League, 1956, Most Valuable Player, 1961, Am. League, 1966, Am. League Mgr. of Yr., 1982, 89; mem. World Series Championship Team, 1966, 70, Nat. League All-Star Team, 1956-57, 59, 61-62, 65, Am. League All-Star Team, 1966-67, 69-71, 74; inducted into Baseball Hall of Fame, 1982. Office: care Balt Orioles 333 W Camden St Baltimore MD 21201-2435•

ROBINSON, FRANKLIN WESTCOTT, museum director, art historian; b. Providence, R.I., May 21, 1939; s. Charles Alexander Robinson Jr. and Celia (Sachs) Stillwell; m. Margaret Dredge, Aug. 14, 1967; 1 child, John Alexander. BA, Harvard U., 1961, MA, 1964, PhD, 1970. Instr. Wellesley Coll., 1968-69; asst. prof. Dartmouth Coll., 1969-75; assoc. prof. Williams Coll., 1975-79; dir. Williams Coll. Mus., 1976-79, Mus. of Art, R.I. Sch. Design, Providence, 1979-92, Herbert F. Johnson Mus. Art, Cornell U., Ithaca, N.Y., 1992—. Author: Gabriel Metsu, 1975, Seventeenth Century Dutch Drawings from American Collections, 1977, Dutch and Flemish Paintings from the Ringling Mus, 1980. Fulbright fellow, 1961-62; recipient Clairborne Pell award R.I. State Coun. Arts, 1992. Mem. Assn. Art Mus. Dirs., Coll. Art Assn. Clubs: Century, Hope. Office: Herbert F Johnson Mus Art Cornell University Ithaca NY 14853-4001

ROBINSON, FRED COLSON, English language educator; b. Birmingham, Ala., Sept. 23, 1930; s. Emmett Colson and Morwenna Hope (Bennett) R.; m. Helen Caroline Wild, June 21, 1959; children: Lisa Karen, Eric Wild. BA, Birmingham So. Coll., 1953; MA, U. N.C., 1954, PhD, 1961; DLitt (hon.), Williams Coll., 1985; MA (hon.), Yale U, 1989. Instr. Stanford (Calif.) U., 1960-61, asst. prof., 1961-65, assoc. prof., 1967-71, prof. English philology, 1971-72; asst. prof. Cornell U., Ithaca, N.Y., 1965-66, assoc. prof., 1966-67; prof. Yale U., New Haven, 1972-83, Douglas Tracy Smith prof., 1983—, chmn. medieval studies, 1975-78, 80; vis. prof. Harvard U., Cambridge, Mass., 1983; mem. pub. com. Medieval Acad. Monographs, Cambridge, 1987-90. Author: Old English Literature: Select Bibliography, 1970, Beowulf and the Appositive Style, 1985, The Tomb of Beowulf, 1993, The Editing of Old English, 1994; co-author: A Bibliography...on Old English Literature, 1980, Old English Verse Texts from Many Sources: A Comprehensive Collection, 1991, A Guide to Old English, 5th edit., 1992; editor Old English Newsletter, 1966-73, Early English MSS in Facsimile, 1971—, Anglo-Saxon England, 1972—, Anglistica, 1981—; contbr. over 70 articles to scholarly jours. Trustee Yale Univ. Library Assocs., New Haven, 1986-89, 91—. With U.S. Army, 1954-56. Fellow Guggenheim Found., 1974-75, Am. Coun. Learned Socs., 1968-69, Inst. Social and Econs. Rsch., Rhodes U., 1978, Japan Soc. for Promotion Sci., 1989; grantee NEH, 1976, 79, 81, 85, Am. Philos. Soc., 1973, 85. Fellow AAAS, Medieval Acad. Am. (pres. 1983-84, Haskins medal 1984), Brit. Acad. (corr.), Meddeleeue-verenigung van Suidelike Afrika (corr.); mem. New Eng. Medieval Conf. (pres. 1982-83), Conn. Acad. Arts and Scis. (pres. 1980-83), Elizabethan Club (bd. govs. 1989—, v.p. 1989-90, pres. 1990-92), Manuscript Club (v.p. New Haven chpt. 1990-92), Phi Beta Kappa. Episcopalian. Office: Yale Univ Dept of English New Haven CT 06520

ROBINSON, FREDERIC M., agricultural products company executive; b. 1934. With Hanes Corp., Winston-Salem, N.C., 1967-69, Pfizer Genetics, Olivia, Minn., 1969-77, Anderson Clayton Seed Co. Belmont, Iowa, 1977-79, Agrigenetics Corp., Wickliffe, Ohio, 1979-88; pres., COO Delta and Pine Land Co., Scott, Miss., 1988—. Office: Delta & Pine Land Co 1 Cotton Row Scott MS 38772

ROBINSON, G. WILSE, molecular spectroscopist, educator; b. Kansas City, Mo., July 27, 1924; s. George Wilse, Jr. R. and Elizabeth (Millett) Ivison; m. Ellen Elizabeth Johnson, June 5, 1950. B.S. in Chemistry, Ga. Inst. Tech., 1947, M.S. in Chemistry, 1949; Ph.D. in Chemistry, U. Iowa, Iowa City, 1952. Research asst. physics. chemistry U. Iowa, 1950-52; research fellow in chemistry U. Rochester, N.Y., 1952-54; asst. prof. chemistry Johns Hopkins U., Balt., 1954-59; assoc. prof. phys. chemistry Calif. Inst. Tech., Pasadena, 1959-61; prof. Calif. Inst. Tech., 1961-75; prof. phys. chemistry, dept. chmn. U. Melbourne, Australia, 1975-76; Robert A. Welch prof. chemistry, prof. physics Tex. Tech U., Lubbock, 1976—; FMC lectr. Princeton U., 1964; Bourke lectr., 1967, A.D. Little lectr., 1967; adv. to U.S. Army Research Office, Durham, 1969-72; Erskine fellow U. Canterbury, 1971; Guggenheim fellow, 1971-72. Editor: Chem. Physics, 1972-75; assoc. editor: Jour. Chem. Physics, 1963-65; mem. editl. adv. bd. Chem. Physics Letters, 1966-84, Jour. Molecular Spectroscopy, 1967-71, Photochemistry and Photobiology, 1971-75, Chem. Physics, 1975—, Jour. Phys. Chemistry, 1988-94; mem. editl. com. Ann. Rev. Phys. Chemistry, 1966-71; contbr. 280 sci. articles to profl. jours. Served with USN, 1944-46, Pacific area. Served with USN, 1944-46. Recipient Alexander von Humboldt prize, 1984. Fellow Am. Phys. Soc. Home: 4810 1st Pl Lubbock TX 79416-3150 Office: Tex Tech U Dept Chemistry PO Box 41061 Lubbock TX 79409-1061 *Many scientists are pioneers. A few are explorers. I like to think of myself as being in the latter category. It greatly increases the fun of doing science, but diminishes somewhat the recognition. Scientific developments are easy to remember. Not many persons remember the footprints.*

ROBINSON, GAIL PATRICIA, mental health counselor; b. Medford, Oreg., Dec. 31, 1936; d. Ivan T. and Evelyn H. (Hamilton) Skyrman; m. Douglas L. Smith; children: Shauna J., James D. BS in Edn., Oreg. State U., 1958, PhD in Counseling, 1978; MS in Counseling, Western Oreg. State Coll., 1974. Lic. profl. counselor, Oreg. Tchr. Monterey (Calif.) Pub. Schs., 1958-59; tchr. Corvallis (Oreg.) Pub. Schs., 1959-62, 69-75, counselor, 1977-81; pvt. practice Corvallis, 1977—; vol. therapist Children's Svcs. divsn., Linn and Benton Counties, 1982-83; asst. prof. Western Oreg. State Coll., 1977, counselor, 1982-83; mem. grad. faculty Oreg. State U., Corvallis, 1978—; presenter workshops; lectr. in field. Contbr. articles to profl. jours. Mem. Benton County Mental Health Citizens Adv. Bd., 1979-85, chairperson, 1982-83; mem. WCTU Children's Farm Home Bd. Trustees, 1979-84, chairperson child welfare com., 1982-83, pres., 1984; mem. Old Mill Sch. Adv. Bd., 1979-85, chairperson, 1979-81; bd. dirs. Cmty. Outreach, 1979-83; mem. Benton Com. for Prevention of Child Abuse, 1979-85, v.p., 1982; chair Oreg. Bd. Lic. Profl. Counselors and Therapists, 1989-90. Mem. Am. Counseling Assn. (govt. rels com. 1988-91, professionalization com. 1988-92, pres.-elect 1995—), Am. Mental Health Counselors Assn. (chairperson consumer and publ. rels. com. 1988-91, bd.. dirs. Western region 1989-91, chairperson strategic planning com. 1994-95, pres. 1992-93), Oreg. Counseling Assn. (chairperson licensure liaison com. 1985-91, exec. bd. 1985-88, steering com. 1986-87, register editorial com. 1985-86, Disting. Svc. award 1985, 87, Leona Tyler award 1989), Oreg. Mental Health Counselors Assn. (pres. 1986-87, Disting. Svc. award 1985), Oreg. Sch. Counselors Assn., Assn. Religion and Values in Counseling, Phi Delta Kappa (chpt. pres. 1979-80).

ROBINSON, GLEN O., law educator; b. Salt Lake City, June 6, 1936; s. Burgham H. and Fern (Osmond) R.; m. Kay Costley, Dec. 20, 1960; children: Dean, Jennifer. BA, Harvard U., 1958; JD, Stanford U., 1961. Bar: D.C. 1961. Assoc. Covington & Bowling, Washington, 1961-67; from asst. prof. to prof. law U. Minn., Mpls., 1967-74; commr. FCC, Washington, 1974-76; from prof. law to John C. Skinner prof. law U. Va., Charlottesville, 1976—; U.S. rep. world adminstrn. radion conf. Dept State, 1978-79; vis. prof. Boston U., 1983-84. Author: The Forest Service, 1975, American Bureaucracy, 1991; co-author: The Administrative Process, 1986. With U.S. Army, 1962-64. Mem. Order of Coif. Office: U Va Sch Law Charlottesville VA 22901

ROBINSON, GORDON PRINGLE, forester; b. Vancouver, B.C., Can., Apr. 7, 1911; came to U.S., 1920; s. Laforest George and Sarah Lawrence (Mitchie) R.; m. Adina Wiens, Feb. 7, 1943; children: Charlotte Wiens, Daniel Gordon, Lawrence Pringle. Student, J.C. Marin Jr. Coll., Kentfield, Calif., 1934; BS in Forestry, U. Calif., Berkeley, 1937. Forester So. Pacific Transp. Co., 1939-66; staff forester Sierra Club, 1966-79; cons. Tiburon, Calif., 1966—. Author: The Forest and the Trees: a guide to Excellent Forestry, 1988. Honored for life and work Lawrence Hall of Sci., Berkeley, 1993. Democrat. Unitarian. Avocation: artist. Home and Office: 16 Apollo Tiburon CA 94920

ROBINSON, HERBERT HENRY, III, educator, therapist; b. Leavenworth, Wash., May 31, 1933; s. Herbert Henry II and Alberta (Sperber) R.; m. Georgia Murial Jones, Nov. 24, 1954 (div. 1974); children: Cheri Dean Asbury, David Keith, Peri Elizabeth Layton, Tanda Rene Graff, Gaila Daire. Grad. of Theology, Bapt. Bible Coll., 1959; BA in Philosophy/ Greek, Whitworth Coll., 1968; MA in Coll. Teaching, Ea. Wash. U., 1976; postgrad., Gonzaga U., 1980—. Choir dir. Twin City Bapt. Temple, Mishawaka, Ind., 1959-61; min. Inland Empire Bapt. Ch., Spokane, 1961-73; tchr. philosophy Spokane (Wash.) C.C., 1969-72; dir. Alternatives to Violence, Women in Crisis, Fairbanks, Alaska, 1985-87; tchr. pub. rels. U. Alaska, Fairbanks, 1986-87; dir. Alternatives to Violence Men Inc., Juneau, 1988-89; tchr. leadership mgmt. U. Alaska S.E., Juneau, 1988-89; min. Sci. of Mind Ctr., Sandpoint, Idaho, 1989-92; dir., therapist Tapio Counseling Ctr., Spokane, 1991-93; cons. Lilac Blind/Alpha Inc./Marshall Coll., Spokane, 1975-85, Alaska Placer Mining Co., Fairbanks, 1987; tchr. Spokane Falls C.C., Spokane, 1979-85; seminar, presenter Human Resource Devel., Spokane and Seattle, Wash., Pa., 1980; guest trainer United Way/Kellogg Found. Inst. for Volunteerism, Spokane, 1983. First trombone San Diego Marine Band, 1953-56, Spokane Symphony, 1961; bd. dirs. Planned Parenthood, Spokane, 1984, Tanani Learning Ctr., Fairbanks, 1987; mem. consensus bldg. team Sci. of Mind Ctr., Sandpoint, 1989-92. Cpl. USMC, 1953-56. Mem. ACA, Assn. for Humanistic Edn. and Devel., Assn. for Religious Values in Counseling, Internat. Assn. Addictions and Offender Counselors, Internat. Assn. Marriage and Family Counselors, Am. Assn. Profl. Hypnotherapists. Home: 11611 E Maxwell Ave Spokane WA 99206-4867 Office: Tapio Counseling Svcs Yellow Flag Bldg #109 104 S Freya Tapio Ctr Spokane WA 99202

ROBINSON, HOBART KRUM, management consulting company executive; b. Quincy, Mass., Oct. 8, 1937; s. Hobart Krum and Charlotte Elizabeth (Hall) R.; m. Gerd Ingela Janhede, Oct. 17, 1964; children: Steven Whitney, Karina Jill, Peter Danforth. BA, Williams Coll., 1959; MBA, Columbia U., 1964. Market analyst Mobil Chem. Co., Richmond, Va., 1964-67; mgr. program analysis and control Polaroid Corp., Cambridge, Mass., 1967-69; exec. v.p. dir. Simplex Wire and Cable, Inc., North Berwick, Maine, 1969-73; sr. engagement mgr. McKinsey and Co., Inc., N.Y.C., 1973-76; prin. Copenhagen, 1977-81, N.Y.C., 1985-89, Stockholm, 1989-95; pres. and chief exec. officer Brink's Inc., Darien, Conn., 1989-93; dir. adminstrn. McKinsey & Co., Stockholm, Eastern Europe, 1993-95; dir. Burlington No. Air Freight, Inc., Newport Beach, Calif., 1982-84. Pres. Am. Club in Copenhagen, 1980-81; dir. Fulbright Commn., Copenhagen, 1980-81. Served as lt. USNR, 1959-62. Republican. Episcopalian. Clubs: Innis Arden Golf (Old Greenwich, Conn.) (pres. 1982-87, pres. 1986-87); Tournament Players (Ponte Vedra, Fla.); Ullna Golf (Akersberga, Sweden). Home: Ymervägen 28, 18263 Djursholm Sweden Office: McKinsey & Co Inc, Klarabergsviadukten 70, 10724 Stockholm Sweden

ROBINSON, HUGH GRANVILLE, consulting management company executive; b. Washington, Aug. 4, 1932; s. James Hill and Wilhelmina (Thomas) R.; m. Matilda Turner; 1 stepdau., Mia; children by previous marriage—Hugh Granville, Susan K. Student, Williams Coll., 1949-50; B.S., U.S. Mil. Acad., 1954; M.S., MIT, 1959; LL.D., Williams Coll., 1983. Commd. 2d lt. U.S. Army, 1954, advanced through grades to maj. gen. 1983; platoon leader, co. comdr. Co. B, 185th Engrs. Bn., Korea, 1955; platoon leader, ops. officer 74th Engr. Co., Korea, 1955-56; br. chief Engr. Supply Control Office, St. Louis, 1956-58; chief Catalog and Authorization div. Engr. Supply Control Agy., Orleans, France, 1960-62; co. comdr. 553d Engr. Bn., Orleans, 1962-63; chief combat br. War Plans div. Engr. Strategic Studies Group, Washington, 1963-65; Army asst. to armed forces aide to Pres. Washington, 1965-69; comdr. 39th Engr. Bn., Vietnam, 1969-70; br.

chief war plans div. Office Dep. Chief Staff for Ops., Washington, 1970-71; assigned Nat. War Coll., 1972; comdr. 3d regt. U.S. Corps Cadets, West Point, N.Y., 1973-74, U.S. Army Engr. Sch. Brigade, Fort Belvoir, Va., 1974-76; dist. engr. U.S. Army Engr. Dist., Los Angeles, 1976-78; dep. dir. civil works office Chief of Engrs., Washington, 1978-80; comdr. Southwestern Div., U.S. Army C.E., 1980-83; ret., 1983; v.p. Southland Corp., Dallas, 1983-88; pres. Cityplace Devel. Corp.; sr. v.p. Grigsby Brandford Powell, Inc., 1988—; now chmn., chief executive officer The Tetra Group, Inc., Dallas, 1989—; mem. Mississippi River Commn., 1980-83, bd. engrs. for rivers and harbors, 1980-83, Coastal Engring. Rsch. Bd., 1980-83; bd. dirs. Belo Corp., TU-Electric, Smith Environ. Tech, Inc., Columbus Realty Trust, Guaranty Fed.; chmn. Dallas Fed. Res. Bd., 1991. Mem. nat. bd. dirs. Keep Am. Beautiful, 1981-85; bd. dirs. Dallas Symphony, 1981-85, Dallas United Way, 1984-92, Baylor U. Med. Ctr. Found., 1983-91, Dallas Opera, 1983-90, Dallas Citizens Coun., 1987-91, Greater Dallas C. of C., 1986-91, Vietnam Vets Meml. Fund Tex.; chmn. African Am. Mus., Dallas Youth Svcs. Corp.; trustee Dallas Mus. Fine Arts, 1988-93. Mem. Am. Soc. Mil. Engrs. (past sec. Orleans chpt., regional v.p. Tex.), Assn. U.S. Army, Dallas Black C. of C., ASCE. Methodist. Office: The Tetra Group Inc 4140 Office Pky Dallas TX 75204-3674

ROBINSON, HUGH R., retired marketing executive; b. Syracuse, N.Y., Sept. 18, 1922; s. Frank J. and Gladys (Hunt) R.; m. Evelyn De Mattia, Nov. 24, 1949; children: Susan, Hugh R., Patrice. B.S., Syracuse U., 1949. Dist. mgr. Syracuse China, 1949-59; with Royal Worcester Porcelain Co., N.Y.C., 1959-77; v.p. sales Royal Worcester Porcelain Co., 1971-75, pres., 1975-76; pres. Royal Worcester Spode, Inc., 1977, Lance Internat., N.Y.C., 1977-84; v.p. dir. Caithness Glass Inc., N.Y.C., 1980-84; v.p. sales amnd mktg. Weil Ceramics & Glass Inc., 1985-86, chief exec. officer, exec. v.p., 1986-88; chief exec. officer Lladro U.S.A. Inc., 1988-91; bd. dirs. Lladro Collectors Soc., Inc.; v.p. Lladro Realty, Inc., 1988—, Lladro Galleries, Inc., 1988—; advisor Lladro Group, Valencia, Spain, 1991—. Served with USAAF, 1942-46. Mem. Alumni Assn. Syracuse U., Lladro Collectors Soc. (dir.). Home: 12 Drislane Rd Briarcliff Manor NY 10510-1006 also: 6101 34th St W Bradenton FL 34210 Office: Lladro USA Inc 1 Lladro Dr Moonachie NJ 07074

ROBINSON, IRWIN JAY, lawyer; b. Bay City, Mich., Oct. 8, 1928; s. Robert R. and Anne (Kaplan) R.; m. Janet Binder, July 7, 1957; children: Elizabeth Binder Schubiner, Jonathan Meyer, Eve Kimberly Wiener. AB, U. Mich., 1950; JD, Columbia U., 1953. Bar: N.Y. 1956. Assoc. Breed Abbott & Morgan, N.Y.C., 1955-58; asst. to ptnrs. Dreyfus & Co., N.Y.C., 1958-59; assoc. Greenbaum Wolff & Ernst, N.Y.C., 1959-65; ptnr. Greenbaum Wolff & Ernst, 1966-76; sr. ptnr. Rosenman & Colin, N.Y.C., 1976-90; of counsel Pryor, Cashman, Sherman & Flynn, 1990-92; sr. ptnr. Phillips, Nizer, Benjamin, Krim & Ballon, N.Y.C., 1992—; treas. Saarsteel, Inc., Whitestone, N.Y., 1970—. Bd. dirs. Henry St. Settlement, N.Y.C., 1960-85, Jewish Cmty. Ctr. Assn. N.Am., N.Y.C., 1967-94; bd. dirs. Heart Rsch. Found., 1989-94, pres., 1991-93. Mem. ABA, N.Y. State Bar Assn., Assn. of Bar of City of N.Y., Internat. Bar Assn., Philippine-Am. C. of C. (bd. dirs. 1970—), Thai-Am. C. of C. (founder, bd. dirs. 1992—, pres. 1992-95), Vietnam-Am. C. of C., Inc. (founder, bd. dirs., pres. 1992-95), Sunningdale Country Club (Scarsdale, N.Y.), Rockefeller Ctr. Club (N.Y.C.). Jewish. Home: 4622 Grosvenor Ave Bronx NY 10471-3305 Office: Phillips Nizer Benjamin Krim & Ballon 666 5th Ave New York NY 10019-6167

ROBINSON, JACK ALBERT, retail drug stores executive; b. Detroit, Feb. 26, 1930; s. Julius and Fannie (Aizkowitz) R.; m. Aviva Freedman, Dec. 21, 1952; children: Shelby, Beth, Abigail. B in Pharmacy, Wayne State U., 1952. Founder, chief exec. officer, chmn. bd. Perry Drug Stores, Inc., Pontiac, Mich., 1957—. Chmn. Wayne State U. Fund, Detroit, 1986, Concerned Citizens for the Arts in Mich., 1990, 91—; chmn. ann. fund Detroit Symphony Orch.; bd. dirs. United Way of Pontiac, Mich., 1986, United Found. of Detroit, 1986, Pontiac Area Urban League, Community Found., S.E. Mich., Detroit Svc. Group, Save Orch. Hall, Inc., Cranbrook Inst. Sci., Jewish Fedn. Apts., Wetzman Inst. Sci., Holocaust Meml. Ctr., Harper-Grace Hosp., Detroit; past dir. Pontiac Symphony Boys Club, Detroit Osteo. Hosp.; pres. United Jewish Found. Metro. Detroit, 1992; co-chmn. Greater Detroit Interfaith Roundtable of Nat. Conf. of Christians and Jews, 1992; pres. Jewish Fedn. Metro Detroit, 1992—. Recipient Disting. Alumni award Wayne State U. Coll. Pharmacy, 1975, Eleanor Roosevelt Humanities award from State of Israel, 1978, B'nai B'rith Youth Services Am. Tradition award, 1982, Wayne State U. Disting. Alumni award, 1985, Tree of Life award Jewish Nat. Fund, 1985, Disting. Citizen award Pontiac Boy Scouts Am., 1985, Corp. Leadership award Wayne State U., 1985, Booker T. Washinton Bus. Assn. Brotherhood award, 1986, Humanitarian award March of Dimes, 1987, award Weizmann Research Inst., 1987, Humanitarian award Variety Club, 1988, Fred M. Butzel award Jewish Fedn. Metro Detroit, 1991, B'nai B'rith Great Am. Traditions award, 1991; named Entrepreneur of Yr. Harvard U. Bus. Sch., Detroit, 1982. Mem. Am. Pharm. Assn., Am. Found. for Pharm. Edn. (bd. dirs.), Nat. Assn. Chain Drug Stores (chmn. 1987). Club: Economic (bd. dirs. Detroit chpt.). Avocations: skiing, jogging, photography, classical music, glass collecting. Office: Perry Drug Stores Inc PO Box 436021 Pontiac MI 48343-6021 also: Apex Drug Stores Inc 5400 Perry Dr Waterford MI 48329

ROBINSON, JACQUES ALAN, electric manufacturing company executive; b. London, June 7, 1947; came to U.S., 1968, naturalized, 1978; s. Henry Herbert and Janine Helene (Siour) R.; children: Amon Eric, Brendan Kyle, Sean Scott. B.Sc., London U., 1968; M.B.A. (Fulbright scholar 1968-70) Mellon fellow 1969-70), Carnegie Mellon U., 1970. Mgmt. cons. Arthur D. Little Inc., Cambridge, Mass., 1969-72; dir. planning Assos. Corp., South Bend, Ind., 1972-73; gen. mgr. U.K. Consumer Fin. Assos. Corp., London, 1973-75; v.p. corp. devel. Am. Investment, St. Louis, 1976-78; v.p. corp. planning Gen. Electric Credit Corp., Stamford, Conn., 1979-80, v.p., gen. mgr. real estate div., 1980-81; v.p. corp. exec. office Gen. Electric Co., Fairfield, Conn., 1981-82; v.p., gen. mgr. consumer electronics bus. ops. Gen. Electric Co., Portsmouth, Va., 1982-87, v.p. internat. bus., 1987—; pres. Carillon Tech. (formerly Finial Tech.), Sunnyvale, Calif., 1987-90; pres., chief exec. officer The Scotcrest Group, Inc., Los Altos, Calif., 1990—. Republican. Office: The Scotcrest Group Inc 101 1st St # 434 Los Altos CA 94022-2706 *My integrity and my freedom are the only two things I cannot afford to lose.*

ROBINSON, JAMES ARTHUR, university president emeritus, political scientist; b. Blackwell, Okla., June 9, 1932; s. William L. and Ethel Bell (Hicks) R.; children: Adelaide Ethel, William Luke Walton. AB, George Washington U., 1954, DPS (hon.), 1977; MA, U. Okla., 1955; PhD, Northwestern U., 1957; LLD (hon.), Kyungpook (Korea) Nat. U., 1979; cert. Inst. for Ednl. mgmt., Harvard U., 1986. Instr. polit. sci. Northwestern U., 1958-59, asst. prof., 1959-62, assoc. prof., 1962-64; prof. polit. sci. Ohio State U., Columbus, 1964-71; dir. Mershon Center, 1967-70, v.p. acad. affairs, provost, 1969-71; pres., prof. polit. sci. Macalester Coll., St. Paul, 1971-74; pres. U. West Fla., Pensacola, 1974-88, pres. emeritus, 1988—. Regents prof. polit. sci., mgmt., ednl. leadership, 1988—. Author: (with R. C. Snyder) National and International Decision Making, 1961, Congress and Foreign Policy Making, rev. edit, 1967, House Rules Committee, 1964. Recipient Manning Dauer award Fla. Polit. Sci. Assn., 1992; Congl. fellow Am. Polit. Sci. Assn., 1957-58. Club: Cosmos (Washington).

ROBINSON, JAMES DIXON, III, corporate executive; b. Atlanta, Nov. 19, 1935; s. James Dixon Jr. and Josephine (Crawford) R.; m. Bettye Bradley (div.); children: Emily E. Robinson-Cook, James Dixon IV; m. Linda Gosden, July 27, 1984. BS, Ga. Inst. Tech. 1957; MBA, Harvard U., 1961; LHD (hon.), Spelman Coll., 1982; LLD (hon.), Adelphi U., 1982. Officer various depts. Morgan Guaranty Trust Co. of N.Y., N.Y.C., 1961-66, asst. v.p., staff asst. to chmn. bd. and pres., 1967-68; gen. partner corp. fin. dept. White, Weld & Co., 1968-70; exec. v.p. Am. Express Co., N.Y.C., 1970-75, pres., 1975-77, chmn. bd. dirs., CEO, 1977-93; pres. J.D. Robinson, Inc., N.Y.C., 1993—; pres., chief exec. officer Am. Express Internat. Banking Corp., 1971-73; bd. dirs. Bristol-Myers Squibb Co., Coca Cola Co., Union Pacific Corp.; former chmn., mem. Adv. Com. Trade Policy and Negotiations; bd. dirs. N.Y.C. Partnership. Chmn. bd. mgrs., chmn. bd. overseers Meml. Sloan-Kettering Cancer Ctr.; mem. Brookings Instn. Lt. USNR, 1957-59. Mem. Bus. Roundtable (former co-chmn.), N.Y.C. C. of C. and Industry (bd. dirs.), Brookings Inst., Japan Soc. (bd. dirs.), Coun. on Com-

petitiveness, Econ. Club (N.Y.C.), Pilgrims of U.S. Club. Office: Am Express Co Am Express Tower C 200 Vesey St New York NY 10285

ROBINSON, JAMES G., film production executive; five children. Former owner automobile distributorship; businessman Balt.; founder, now chmn., chief exec. officer Morgan Creek Prodns. Co-exec. producer films Young Guns, 1988, Skin Deep, 1989, Enemies A Love Story, 1989, Renegades, 1989, Major League, 1989, Coupe de Ville, 1990, Nightbreed, 1990, Young Guns II, 1990, Pacific Heights, 1990, The Exorcist III, 1990, Robin Hood: Prince of Thieves, 1991, Freejack, 1992, White Sands, 1992, Stay Tuned, 1992, The Crush, 1993, True Romance, 1993, Ace Ventura: Pet Detective, 1994, Major League II, 1994, Trial By Jury, 1994, Silent Fall, 1994. Office: Morgan Creek Prodns 4000 Warner Blvd Bldg 76 Burbank CA 91522

ROBINSON, JAMES KENNETH, lawyer; b. Grand Rapids, Mich., Nov. 27, 1943; s. Kenneth and Marguerite (Anderson) R.; m. Marietta Sebree; children: Steven James, Renee Elizabeth. BA with honors, Mich. State U., 1965; JD magna cum laude, Wayne State U., 1968. Bar: Mich. 1968, U.S. Dist. Ct. (ea. and we. dists) Mich. 1969, U.S. Ct. Appeals (6th cir.) 1969, U.S. Supreme Ct. 1977. Law clk. to judge U.S. Ct. Appeals (6th cir.), 1968-69; assoc. Miller, Canfield, Paddock & Stone, Detroit, 1969-71; assoc., then ptnr. Honigman Miller Schwartz and Cohn, Detroit, 1972-77, ptnr., 1981-93, chmn. litigation dept.; U.S. atty. Ea. Dist. Mich., 1977-80; prof., dean Law Sch. Wayne State U., Detroit, 1993—; adj. prof. Detroit Coll. Law, 1970-73, Wayne State U. Law Sch., 1973-84; mem. evidence test drafting com.-multistate bar exam Nat. Conf. Bar Examiners, 1975—; mem. adv. com. on evidence rules Jud. Conf. U.S., 1993—; chmn. com. on rules of evidence Mich. Supreme Ct., 1975-78; lectr. Mich. Jud. Inst., 1977—, Mich. Inst. Continuing Legal Edn. Author: (with others) Introducing Evidence-A Practical Guide for Michigan Lawyers, 1988; (with others) Scope of Discovery, 1986; contbg. author Evidence in America - The Federal Rules in the States, 1987; also articles; editor in chief Wayne Law Rev., 1967-68. Chmn. Gov.'s Commn. on Future Higher Edn. in Mich., 1983-84; pres. State Bar of Mich., 1990-91, commr. 1980-81, 83-91. Recipient Disting. Alumni award Wayne State U. Law Sch., 1979, 1986. Fellow Am. Bar Found., Mich. Bar Found., Am. Coll. Trial Lawyers, Internat. Soc. Barristers; mem. ABA (litigation and criminal justice sects., lectr.), Fed. Bar Assn. (dir. 1975-81), Detroit Bar Assn. (bd. dirs. 1975-81), Nat. Assn. Former U.S. Attys. (pres. 1984-85), Nat. Assn. Criminal Def. Lawyers, Am. Law Inst., 6th Cir. Jud. Conf., Wayne U. Law Alumni Assn. (pres. 1975-76), Detroit Club, Detroit Yacht Club. Office: Wayne State U Law Sch Detroit MI 48202

ROBINSON, JAMES LEROY, architect, educator; b. Longview, Tex., July 12, 1940; s. Willie LeRoy and Ruby Nell R.; B.Arch., So. U., 1964; M.C.P. (Martin Luther King fellow, 1972), Pratt Inst., 1972; m. Annabell Hilton; children: James LeRoy II, Kerstin Gunilla, Maria Theresa Narvaez, Jasmin Marisol, Ruby Nell, Kenneth Arne. Architect, Port of N.Y. Authority, 1964; architect, store planner W.T. Grant, 1964; with Herbst & Rusciano, AIA, 1965; architect Carson, Lundin & Shaw, N.Y.C., 1966, Kennerly, Slomanson & Smith, N.Y.C., 1967-69, architect-on-bus., 1969; pres. Robinson Architects, N.Y.C., 1969—; pres. NAROB Devel. Corp.; vis. prof. CUNY; adj. prof. Pratt Inst. Bd. dirs. Boys Club. Served with U.S. Army, 1966. Decorated knight Order of St. John, Knights of Malta; recipient AIA design award, 1976. Mem. Am. Arbitration Assn. (arbitrator), N.Y. Council Black Architects. Democrat. Works include: Stuyvesant Heights Christian Church, David Chavis House, Fulton Ct. Houses, Sinclair Houses, Hamilton Heights Terr., Eliot Graham Houses, Sojourner Truth Houses, Nehemiah Plan, Casas Theresa, N.Y.C. Postal Data Ctr., Mt. Carmel Bapt. Ch., Consol. Edison Collection Center, Casas Theresa, Jasmin Houses, CityHomes CD&E. Home: 67 Murray St New York NY 10007-2126 Office: 5 Beekman St New York NY 10038

ROBINSON, JAMES WILLIAM, retired management consultant; b. Bklyn., Feb. 22, 1919; s. Charles Edward and Adelaide (Reimer) R.; m. Dorothy L. Luckow, July 5, 1946; 1 child, Joan Barbara. AB, Cornell U., 1940, LLB, 1942. Bar: N.Y. 1942. Pvt. practice N.Y.C., 1946—; assoc. atty. Whitman, Ransom & Coulson, 1946-57; with Westvaco Corp., N.Y.C., 1957-69, sec., 1966-69; prin., mng. dir. Georgeson & Co. Inc., N.Y.C., 1969-82; prin. Morrow & Co., N.Y.C., 1982-90; pres. J.W. Robinson Assocs., Inc., N.Y.C., 1990—; mem. adv. com. shareholder communications SEC; com. on shareowner communications N.Y. Stock Exch., 1986—. Editor: Tender Offers Handbook. Capt. AUS, 1942-46. Decorated Bronze Star medal. Mem. ABA, N.Y. State Bar Assn., Assn. Bar City N.Y., Am. Soc. Corp. Secs., Canterwood Country Club, Phi Delta Phi, Lambda Chi Alpha. Home and Office: 4820 Old Stump Dr NW Gig Harbor WA 98332-8899

ROBINSON, JANIE MONETTE, education educator; b. Merkel, Tex., Oct. 20, 1941; d. Orvin Leon and Velma Cleone (Rutledge) R.; div.; children: Gregory Blake Keller, Karel Blynn Keller. BS, Howard Payne U., 1963; MEd, U. Nev., Las Vegas, 1990; postgrad., U. Nev., Reno, 1991-92, Brigham Young U., 1990-91. Cert. tchr., N.Mex., Nev. Tchr., coach Eula Rural Sch., Clyde, Tex., 1961-63; tchr. Grand Lake High Sch., Lake Charles, La., 1964; instr. history Colo. Bapt. Coll., Denver, 1977-78; tchr. Lincoln County Sch. Dist., Caliente, Nev., 1978-86, Abilene (Tex.) Ind. Sch. Dist., 1986-87, Lander County Sch. Dist., Battle Mountain, Nev., 1990-93, Raton (N.Mex.) Mcpl. Sch. Dist., 1993—; instr. edn. Trinidad Jr. Coll., 1995; dir. day care A Child's World, North Las Vegas, Nev., 1988-89; dir. girls' group home Regina Hall, Henderson, Nev., 1989-90. Mem. NEA, ASCD, Coun. for Exceptional Children, N.Mex. Edn. Assn. Baptist. Avocations: quilting, camping, reading. Home: PO Box 522 Raton NM 87740 Office: Raton High Sch 1535 Tiger Cir Raton NM 87740

ROBINSON, JAY (THURSTON) (THURSTON ROBINSON), artist; b. Detroit, Aug. 1, 1915; s. Carter Boston and Marie Rose (Steger) R.; m. Dorothy June Whipple, Sept. 15, 1937 (dec. 1968); children: Theodore Carter, Thomas Whipple, James Jay; m. Anne Frances Helen Posch, Nov. 5, 1970. BA, Yale U., 1937; MFA, Cranbrook Acad. Art, 1943. Illustrator: (books) Seventeenth Summer (Maureen Daly), 1948, The New York Guide Book, 1964; contbr. illustrations to others; one-man shows include, Guggenheim Mus. Non-Objective Painting, N.Y.C., 1947, Milch Galleries, N.Y.C., 1948, 53, 54, 55, 56, J.B. Speed Art Mus., Louisville, 1953, Dayton Art Inst., 1953, Phila. Art Alliance, 1957, Monede Gallery, N.Y.C., 1961, 62, Raymond Burr Galleries, Beverly Hills, Calif., 1963, xxth Century West Gallery, N.Y.C., 1968, E. Kuhlik Gallery, N.Y.C., 1971, New Canaan Soc. for Arts, 1983, Broome St. Gallery, N.Y.C., 1994, group shows include, Guggenheim Mus., 1947, 49, Carnegie Inst., Pitts., 1949, Des Moines Art Center, 1950, Butler Inst., Youngstown, Ohio, 1953, also Audubon Artists, N.Y.C., Corcoran Gallery, Washington, Mich. Artists, Detroit, NAD, N.Y.C., Pa. Acad., Phila., Provincetown (Mass.) Annual, Va. Biennial, Richmond; represented in permanent collections, including, Detroit Inst. Art, Houston Mus. Fine Art, Witte Meml. Mus., San Antonio, Philbrook Art Center, Tulsa; Berea Coll., Goucher Coll., Fisk U.; represented in also corp. collections, including, IBM; Republic Steel Co., Prentice-Hall Pub., portrait painter, designer china and textiles. Served with OSS, 1943; Served with USN, 1943-46. Louis Comfort Tiffany Found. award, 1950; various purchase awards Am. Acad. Arts and Letters, 1951-64; Outstanding Alumnus award Detroit Country Day Sch, 1966. Mem. Artist Equity Assn. N.Y. Home and Studio: 305 East Landing Williamsburg VA 23185-8254 *I have always been drawn to the theme of Man in His Environment. By extension to our own time, I love jazz music, many of whose players I have painted; classic cars; Japanese gardens; good company and active social life. Travel enables me to see what others have done and are doing, all of us alike in trying to cope as best we can. In painting, I can not only portray but participate in what goes on on our planet.*

ROBINSON, JENS JOSEPH, college dean; b. Portland, Oreg., Jan. 5, 1937; s. James J. and Gladys E. (Masten) R.; m. Kathryn P. Robinson, June 10, 1961; children: Jodi, Jaymi, Jini, Jared, Jossie. BS, Pacific U., 1958; MS, Oreg. State U., 1960; PhD, U. Oreg., 1970. Supt. Woodburn (Oreg.) Sch. Dist., 1971-86, McMinnville (Oreg.) Sch. Dist., 1982-86; dean Sch. Edn. Ea. Oreg. State Coll., La Grande, 1986—; cons. Oreg. Sch. Bds. Assn., Salem, 1982—, Idaho Sch. Bds. Assn., Boise, 1984-86; bd. dirs. Oreg. Total Info. Systems, Eugene. Bd. dirs. McMinnville Community Hosp., 1986—. Mem. Confedn. Oreg. Sch. Adminstrs., Oreg. Assn. Sch. Execs. (mem. exec. com.). Republican. Roman Catholic. Avocation: outdoor activities. Office: Ea Oreg State Coll Sch Edn 8th & K La Grande OR 97850

ROBINSON, JERRY H., lawyer; b. Mason City, Iowa, Dec. 4, 1932; s. Moe Lester and Annette (Kropman) R.; m. Leona Esther Ohsman, Aug. 26, 1956 (dec.); children: Vicki Lynn, Brenda Jo, Andrew Franklin. B.Sc., U. Iowa, 1954; J.D., Stanford U., 1960. Bar: Calif. 1960; cert. tax specialist. Ptnr. Heller, Ehrman, White & McAuliffe, San Francisco, 1960—. Author, editor: Attorney's Guide to Pension & Profit Sharing Plans, 1973, 2d edit. 1978. Contbr. articles to profl. jours. Mem. exec. com. atty. sect. Jewish Community Fedn., San Francisco. Served to lt. U.S. Army, 1954-56; Germany. Fellow Am. Coll. Tax Counsel; mem. State Bar Tax Sect. (chmn. 1979, Jud Klein award 1984), ABA (tax sect.), Calif. State Bar Assn., San Francisco Bar Assn. (cmn. tax sect. 1970), Commonwealth Club of Calif. Democrat. Jewish. Avocations: photography, traveling, gardening, woodworking, piano. Home: 28 Roselyn Ter San Francisco CA 94118-4321

ROBINSON, JOHN ALAN, logic and computer science educator; b. Halifax, Eng., Mar. 9, 1930; came to U.S., 1952; naturalized citizen, 1990.; s. Harry and Clara (Pilkington) R.; m. Gwen Groves, Dec. 18, 1954; children: Alan Groves, Hugh Parke Custis, Gwen Owen. B.A. in Classics with honours, Corpus Christi Coll., Cambridge (Eng.) U., 1952; M.A., 1955; M.A. in Philosophy, U. Ore., 1953; M.A., Princeton, 1955, Ph.D., 1956; D in Applied Sci. honoris causa, Leuven, 1988; D in Philosophy honoris causa, Uppsala, 1994. Operations research analyst E.I. du Pont de Nemours & Co., Inc., 1956-60; post-doctoral research fellow U. Pitts., 1960-6l; mem. faculty Rice U., 1961-67, prof. philosophy, 1964-65, prof. computer sci. and philosophy, 1965-66, prof. computer sci., 1966-67; disting. prof. logic and computer sci. Syracuse U., 1967-84, Univ. prof., 1984-92, univ. prof. emeritus, 1993—; cons. in applied math. divsn. Argonne Nat. Lab., 1961-67, Stanford Linear Acceleration Ctr., 1966-68; vis. rsch. fellow Australian Nat. U., 1989; Fujitsu vis. prof. U. Tokyo, 1991-92. Author: Logic: Form and Function, 1979; founder, editor-in-chief Jour. Logic Programming, 1984-86; contbr. articles to profl. jours. Served with RAF, 1948-49. Recipient Sr. U.S. Scientists prize Humbolt Found., 1995; Guggenheim Found. fellow, 1967-68; hon. research fellow U. Edinburgh, 1967—. Fellow Am. Assn. for Artificial Intelligence; mem. Kokusai Bunka Kaikan (Tokyo). Office: 96 Highland Ave Greenfield MA 01301

ROBINSON, JOHN BECKWITH, development management consultant; b. Portland, Oreg., May 23, 1922; s. Jewell King and Arvilla Agnes (Beckwith) R.; m. Dilys Walters, Sept. 8, 1945; children—John Gwilym, David Gwyn. B.A., U. Oreg., 1944; postgrad., U. Shrivenham, Eng., 1945, U. Oxford, Eng., 1946, Am. U., 1947. Staff Bur. Budget, 1948, 51-52; sr. program and budget officer UNESCO, 1948-51; chief personnel policy Mut. Security Agy., Washington, 1952-54; program officer Mut. Security Agy., Guatemala, 1954-59; planning officer, later acting asst. dep. dir. for program and planning Mut. Security Agy., Washington, 1959-61; dep. U.S. rep. devel. assistance com. OECD, 1961-64; asst. dir. devel. policy Pakistan, 1964-68; dep. dir. North Coast Affairs, AID, State Dept., Washington, 1969-71; dep. mission dir. U.S. Econ. Aid Program, Colombia, 1971-73; mission dir. U.S. Econ. Aid Program, Dominican Republic, 1973-76, Honduras, 1976-79; privatization adviser Gov. of Costa Rica, 1986-88; prin. assoc. J.B. Robinson & Assocs. (devel. mgmt. cons.), 1979—; mem. faculty, fellow Harvard U., 1968-69; cons. NATO, 1951, UN, 1959. Served to 1st lt., inf. AUS, 1943-46, ETO. Mem. Oriental Club (London), DACOR BACON House (Washington), Minchinhampton Golf Club, Minchinhampton Probus Club (pres. 1983-84). Episcopalian. Address: Anglezarke, The Hithe, Rodborough Common, Stroud GL5 5BN Gloucestershire, England also: 7130 SW Gable Pky Portland OR 97225-2620

ROBINSON, JOHN BOWERS, JR., bank holding company executive; b. Laconia, N.H., Oct. 9, 1946; s. John Bowers and Lee (Osborn) R.; m. Jane Frances Moore, Aug. 31, 1968; children: John Paul, Claire Frances, David Moore, Leanne Elizabeth, Gregory Joseph, Peter August. BA, Fairfield U., 1968; MBA, Adelphi U., 1977. V.p., asst. to pres. Hempstead Bank, N.Y., 1977-79, exec. v.p., 1979-81, pres., 1981-82; v.p. planning Norstar Bancorp, Inc., Albany, N.Y., 1982-84, exec. v.p., 1984-87, pres., 1987-88; exec. v.p. Fleet Fin. Group, Albany, 1988—; bd. dirs. Fleet Securities, Inc.; mem. N.Y. State Banking Bd., 1990—, N.Y. State Bus. Coun., 1990—, Albany Med. Ctr., 1989—, Siena Coll., Loudonville, N.Y. 1989—. Mem. Ft. Orange Club, Schuyler Meadows Club. Home: 81 Old Niskayuna Rd Loudonville NY 12211 Office: Fleet Fin Group Peter D Kiernan Plz Albany NY 12207

ROBINSON, JOHN C., manufacturing executive, light; b. 1943. Pres., coo King Bearing Inc., Cleve., 1992—. Office: King Bearing Inc 3600 Euclid Ave Cleveland OH 44115-2515*

ROBINSON, JOHN DAVID, retired army officer; b. Concord, Mass., June 9, 1937; m. Roberta Jean Small; children: Mark D., Karen L. BA, U. Maine, 1961; MBA, U. Ala., 1972. Commd. 2d lt. U.S. Army, 1961, advanced through grades to maj. gen., 1990; student Naval War Coll., Newport, R.I., 1979-80; asst. tng. and doctrine, command systems mgr. U.S. Army Aviation Ctr., Ft. Rucker, Ala., 1980; dir. army model improvement program U.S. Army Combined Arms Ctr., Ft. Leavenworth, Kans., 1980-83; comdr. 9th Cav. Brigade, 9th Inf. Div., Ft. Lewis, Wash., 1983-85; dep. asst. comdt. U.S. Army Aviation Ctr., Ft. Rucker, 1985-86; comdg. gen. Tng. and Doctrine Analysis Command, Ft. Leavenworth, 1986-88; dep. dir. for force structure, resource and assessment Joint Staff, Washington, 1988-89, dir., 1989-91; comdg. gen. U.S. Army Aviation Ctr. Ft. Rucker, 1991-94; v.p. ops. Raytheon Aerospace, Madison, Miss., 1994—. Decorated Def. D.S.M., Army D.S.M., Legion of Merit (2), Air medal with V device, Bronze Star with oak leaf. Mem. Assn. U.S. Army (sr. v.p.), Army Aviation Assn. Am. (nat. exec. bd.). Home: 109 Clairemont Dr Ridgeland MS 39157 Office: Raytheon Aerospace 555 Industrial Dr S Madison MS 39110-9073

ROBINSON, JOHN GWILYM, conservationist; b. Paris, Nov. 22, 1949; s. John Beckwith and Dilys (Walters) R.; m. Linda Cox, June 8, 1974; children: David Andrew Cox, Amanda Sian Cox. BA in Zoology with honors, Swarthmore Coll., 1971; PhD in Zoology, U. N.C., 1977. Postdoctoral fellow dept. zool. rsch. Nat. Zool. Park, Smithsonian Instn., Washington, 1977-80, zoologist, 1980-83; affiliate assoc. curator Fla. Mus. Natural History, Gainesville, 1983—; affiliate assoc. prof. dept. wildlife and range scis. U. Fla., 1983-85, assoc. prof., 1985-90, courtesy prof., 1990—; dir. program for studies in tropical conservation, 1980-90; dir. wildlife conservation internat. Wildlife Conservation Soc. (former N.Y. Zool. Soc.), Bronx, N.Y., 1990-93, v.p. internat. conservation, 1993—; program dir. integrated approaches to tng. in conservation and sustainable devel. Pew Charitable Trusts, Phila., 1988-93; mem. steering com. Species Survival Commn., World Conservation Union, 1991-93, regional mem. N.Am. and Caribbean, 1991-93, primate specialist group Species Survival Commn., 1985—, sustainable use specialist group, 1992—. Mem. editl. bd. Primates, 1991—; bd. editors Conservation Biology, 1993—; sci. com. Conservation and Mgmt., 1993—; editor: (with L.D. Navarro) Diversidad Biológica en La Reserva de la Biosphera de Sian Ka'an, 1990, (with K. H. Redford) Neotropical Wildlife Use and Conservation, 1991; contbr. articles to profl. jours., chpts. to books. Tech. adv. bd. Fundaçao Biodiversitas, Brasil, 1989—; coun. advisors Branger Found., Venezuela; nat. bd. advisors Duke U. Ctr. for Tropical Conservation, 1991—; mem. bd. Wild Things Inc., 1992—, Global Coral Reef Alliance, 1992—, Greentree Group, Inc., 1993—, Sociedade Civil Mamirauá, Brasil, Sócio Efetivo, 1993—; bd. dirs. World Parks Endowment, Inc., 1994—. Mem. AAAS, Am. Soc. Primatologists (conservation com. 1984-88), Internat. Primatological Soc. (election com. 1990—, Martha T. Galante endowment overview com. 1989—, conservation com. 1986-92), Soc. Conservation Biology (editor search com. 1993), Assn. Tropical Biology, Fauna and Flora Preservation Soc. Office: Wildlife Conservation Soc 185th St and Southern Blvd Bronx NY 10460

ROBINSON, JOHN HAMILTON, civil engineer; b. Kansas City, Mo., Feb. 14, 1927; s. David Beach and Aileen March (Weaver) R.; m. Patricia Ann Odell, June 17, 1949; children: Dan Hamilton, Patricia Ann, Donna Marie, Clinton Odell. B.S., U. Kans., 1949. Registered profl. engr., Kans. With Black & Veatch (cons. engrs.), Kansas City, Mo., 1949—; ptnr. Black & Veatch (cons. engrs.), 1956—, exec. ptnr., 1971-92, mng. ptnr., 1983-92, chmn. emeritus, 1993. Trustee Johnson County Community Coll.; deacon, elder 2d Presbyterian Ch., Kansas City, Mo. Served with USNR, 1945-46. Fellow ASCE (hon. mem.); mem. Am. Cons. Engrs. Coun. (chmn. com. of fellows), Cons. Engrs. Coun. Mo. (dir. 1972—, pres. 1976-77), Mo. Soc. Profl. Engrs., Kans. Engring. Soc. (Kans. Engr. of Yr. award 1983), Am.

Water Works Assn. (v.p. 1985, pres. 1987, Fuller award 1983), U. Kans. Alumni Assn. (pres.), Water Pollution Control Fedn., Mission Hills Country Club, Vanguard Club, Mercury Club, Rotary, Tau Beta Pi, Sigma Tau, Omicron Delta Kappa, Beta Theta Pi. Home: 3223 W 67th St Shawnee Mission KS 66208-1846 Office: Black Veatch Engrs 8400 Ward Pky Kansas City MO 64114-2031

ROBINSON, JOHN HAYES, law educator; b. Providence, Apr. 4, 1943; s. William Philip and Dorothy Frances (Hayes) R.; m. Deborah Ann Deery, Aug. 15, 1981; children: Gena, John. BA, Boston Coll., 1967; MA, Notre Dame U., 1972, PhD, 1975; JD, U. Calif.-Berkeley, 1979. Bar: R.I. 1980. Asst. prof. U. San Francisco, 1973-76; instr. law U. Miami, Coral Gables, Fla., 1979-80; jud. clk. U.S. Dist. Ct., Hartford, Conn., 1980-81; asst. prof. law and philosophy U. Notre Dame (Ind.), 1981—. Office: U Notre Dame Law Sch T J White Ctr Law Govt Notre Dame IN 46556

ROBINSON, JOHN LEWIS, geography educator; b. Leamington, Ont., Can., July 9, 1918; s. William John and Emily Laverne (Dunphy) R.; m. Josephine Rowan, Oct. 14, 1944; children: David, Jo-Anne, Patricia. B.A., Western Ont. U., 1940; M.A., Syracuse U., 1942; Ph.D., Clark U., 1946; LLD (hon.), Western Ont. U., 1984; DSc (hon.), U. B.C., 1994. Geographer N.W.T. Adminstrn., Ottawa, Ont., 1943-46; prof., head dept. geography U. B.C., Vancouver, 1946-68, prof. geography, 1968-85, prof. emeritus, 1985—. Author 14 books on aspects of regional geography of Can., including British Columbia: 100 Years of Geographical Change, 1973, Themes in the Regional Geography of Canada, 1983, 2d edit., 1989; contbr. articles to profl. jours. Recipient citation of merit Assn. Am. Geographers, 1966; Massey medal Canadian Geog. Soc., 1971. Mem. Canadian Assn. Geographers (pres. 1956, citation for service to profession 1976). Office: U BC, Dept Geography, Vancouver, BC Canada V6T 1Z2

ROBINSON, JOHN MINOR, lawyer, retired business executive; b. Uniontown, Pa., Mar. 18, 1910; s. John M. and Martha (Downs) R. A.B., Harvard U., 1932, LL.B, 1935. Bar: Calif. 1936. Assoc. firm Macdonald & Pettit, 1935-41; partner firm Musick, Peeler & Garrett, 1947-77; v.p., sec. Consol. Western Steel div. U.S. Steel Corp. (and predecessors), 1941-57. Clubs: Calif. (past pres. L.A.), Pacific Union (San Francisco); Cypress Point (Pebble Beach, Calif.); The Old Capital (Monterey, Calif.); Royal and Ancient Golf of St. Andrews (Fife, Scotland). Office: 9500 Center St Carmel CA 93923-8552

ROBINSON, JOHN PETER, film composer, keyboardist; b. Fulmer, Eng., Sept. 16, 1945; s. John Lacey and Winifred Gertrude (Hayes) R.; m. Cecilia Karin Angela Gardtman, Nov. 4, 1983 (div. Jan. 1988); 1 child, Aimee-Jane Dadswell. Diploma, Royal Acad. Music, London, 1967. Founding mem., keyboardist Quatermass, 1969-71; keyboardist Stanley Clarke's School Days Band, 1977-78, Al Stewart, 1978-79; keyboardist Shawn Phillips, 1971-76, Stomu Yamashta, 1976-77, Al Jarreau, 1980-81, Eric Clapton, 1984, Phil Collins/Brand X, 1978-85. Composer for films The Believers, 1986, Cocktail, 1988 (Box Office award ASCAP 1988), Cadillac Man, 1990, Wayne's World, 1992 (Box Office award ASCAP 1992), Highlander 3, 1995. Recipient Best Music award nomination Acad. Sci. Fiction Fantasy/Horror Films, 1988. Home: care BMI 3767 Tracy St Los Angeles CA 90027

ROBINSON, JOSEPH EDWARD, geology educator, consulting petroleum geologist; b. Regina, Sask., Can., June 25, 1925; came to U.S., 1976; s. Webb Gabriel Wilton and Blanche Marion (Schiefner) R.; m. Mary Corrine Maclaughlin, Nov. 1, 1952 (div. 1977); children: Joseph Christopher, John Edward, Timothy Webb. B.Eng., McGill U., 1950, M.Sc., 1951; Ph.D., U. Alta., 1968. Registered profl. engr., Que., Can. Geophysicist Imperial Oil Ltd., Can., 1951-68; sr. geologist Union Oil Co. Can., Calgary, Alta., Can., 1968-76; cons. geologist J.E. Robinson & Assocs., Syracuse, N.Y., 1976—; prof. geology Syracuse U., 1976-91, prof. emeritus, 1991—. Author: Computer Applications in Petroleum Geology, 1982. Served with Can. Navy, 1943-46, ETO. Mem. Am. Assn. Petroleum Geologists, Soc. Exploration Geologists, Soc. Ind. Profl. Earth Scientists, Can. Assn. Petroleum Geologists, Internat. Assn. Math. Geology (assoc. editor 1976-78). Home: 837 Ackerman Ave Syracuse NY 13210-2906 Office: Syracuse U Dept Geology Syracuse NY 13244

ROBINSON, JULIAN B., church administrator. Dir. of bus. and records Ch. of God. Office: PO Box 2430 Cleveland TN 37320

ROBINSON, JUNE KERSWELL, dermatologist, educator; b. Phila., Jan. 26, 1950; d. George and Helen S. (Kerswell) R.; m. William T. Barker, Jan. 31, 1981. BA cum laude, U. Pa., 1970; MD, U. Md., 1974. Diplomate Am. Bd. Dermatology, Nat. Bd. Med. Examiners, Am. Bd. Mohs Micrographic Surgery and Cutaneous Oncology. Intern Greater Balt. Med. Ctr., Hanover, N.H., 1974; resident in medicine Greater Balt. Med. Ctr., 1974-75; resident in dermatology Dartmouth-Hitchcock Med. Ctr., Hanover, N.H., 1975-78, chief resident, clin. instr., 1977-78; instr. in dermatology Dartmouth-Hitchcock Med. Ctr., Hanover, 1978; fellow Mohs; chemosurgery and dermatologic surgery NYU Skin and Cancer Clinic, N.Y.C., 1978-79; instr. in dermatology NYU, N.Y.C., 1979; asst. prof. dermatology Northwestern U. Med. Sch., Chgo., 1979, asst. prof. surgery, 1980-85, assoc. prof. dermatology and surgery, 1985-91, prof. dermatology and surgery, 1991—; mem. consensus devel. conf. NIH, 1992; lectr. in field. Author: Fundamentals of Skin Biopsy, 1985, also audiovisual materials; mem. editl. bd. Archives of Dermatology, 1988—; sect. editor The Cutting Edge: Challenges in Med. and Surg. Therapeutics, 1989—; contbg. editor Jour. of Dermatol. Surgery and Oncology, 1985-88; editl. com. 18th World Congress of Dermatology, 1982; contbr. numerous articles, abstracts to profl. publs., chpts. to books. Bd. dirs. Northwestern Med. Faculty Found., 1982-84, chmn. com. on benefits and leaves, 1984, nominating com. 1988. Grantee Nat. Cancer Inst., 1985-91, Am. Cancer Soc., 1986-89, Skin Cancer Found., 1984-85, Dermatology Found., 1981-83, Northwestern U. Biomed. Rsch., 1981, Syntex, 1984. Fellow Am. Coll. Chemosurgery (chmn. sci. program ann. meeting 1983, chmn. publs. com. 1986-87, chmn. task force on edni. needs 1989-90, co-editor bull. 1984-87); mem. AMA, Am. Dermatol. Assn., Am. Acad. Dermatology (asst. sec.-treas. 1995—, Stephen Rothman Lectr. award 1992, Presdl. citation 1992), Dermatology Found. (trustee 1995—), Internat. Soc. Dermatol. Surgery, Am. Soc. Dermatoi. Surgery (pres. 1994-95), Soc. Investigative Dermatology, Women's Dermatol. Soc., Chgo. Dermatol. Soc., Am. Fedn. Clin. Rsch. Home: 910 N Lake Shore Dr # 1419 Chicago IL 60611 Office: Northwestern U Med Sch Dept Dermatology 303 E Chicago Ave # 767 Chicago IL 60611

ROBINSON, KENNETH LEONARD, JR., trade association executive; b. Lynn, Mass., Feb. 14, 1929; s. Kenneth Leonard Sr. and Frances Ruth (Leighton) R.; m. Marie Louise Cormier, Sept. 1, 1951; children: Edward K., Elaine F., Ruth M., Doris A., Gordon M. BA, Boston Coll., 1950; MS, George Washington U., 1969. Advanced through grades to maj. gen. USMC, 1979; commdg. gen. Marine Corp. Base USMC, Camp Butler, Okinawa, 1977-79; commdg. gen. 3d Marine div. USMC, Okinawa, 1980; commdg. gen. Marine Corp. Base USMC, Camp Pendleton, Calif., 1980-83; ret. USMC, 1983; pres., chief exec. officer Nat. Assn. Fed. Credit Unions, Washington, 1984—; bd. dirs. San Diego (Calif.) Navy Fed. Credit Union, San Diego, Calif., 1981-83, Washington, 1975-77. Columnist on fin. topics for trade mags.; contbr. articles to trade publs. Mem. Far East Coun. Boy Scouts Am., Okinawa, 1977-80, San Diego Coun., 1980-83. Recipient Golden Eagle award Far East Coun. Boy Scouts Am., 1980, Silver Beaver award San Diego Coun., 1982. Mem. Am. Soc. Assn. Execs., Greater Washington Soc. Assn. Execs., USMC Hist. Soc. Bd. dirs. 1987—, chmn. audit com. 1987—), Army-Navy Club, Exchequer Club (Washington). Republican. Roman Catholic. Avocations: tennis, golf, bowling, chess. Home: 2538 N Vermont St Arlington VA 22207-4126 Office: Nat Assn Fed Credit Unions PO Box 3769 3138 10th St N Arlington VA 22201-2149

ROBINSON, L. DONALD, advertising executive; b. N.Y.C., Aug. 28, 1938; s. Samuel Maurice and Janice (Levey) R.; m. Janet Einhorn, Oct. 15, 1976 (div. 1982). BS, NYU, 1960. Eastern sales mgr. Group W TV Sales, N.Y.C., 1970-74; v.p., gen. mgr. Kaiser Broadcasting, N.Y.C., 1974-77; exec. v.p. Field Communications, N.Y.C., 1977-80; pres., chief exec. officer Katz Ind. TV, N.Y.C., 1980-83; pres., dir., chief exec. officer Media Gen. Broadcast Services, N.Y.C., 1983—; dir. TV Bur. of Advt., N.Y.C., 1977-83, Station Rep. Assn., N.Y.C., 1978-80, Katz Communications, N.Y.C., 1980-

83. Served to cpl. U.S. Army, 1960-63. Mem. Nat. Assn. TV Program Execs., TV Bur. Advt., Ind. TV Assn., Proprietary Drug Assn. Republican. Jewish. Avocations: tennis; films. Home: 25 Sutton Pl S 10-P New York NY 10022 Office: Media Gen Broadcast Svcs 630 3rd Ave New York NY 10017-6705

ROBINSON, LARRY ROBERT, insurance company executive; b. Indpls., Feb. 7, 1936; s. Manuel H. Robinson and Barbara Dawson Robinson Trees; m. Sharon Moore, Aug. 3, 1957; children: Christopher, Lizbeth, Lara, Jeremy. BA, DePauw U., Greencastle, Ind., 1957. Actuarial trainee State Life Ins. Co., Indpls., 1957-63, asst. actuary, 1963-66, actuary, 1966-67, asst. v.p., actuary, 1967-70, v.p., actuary, 1970-80, sr. v.p., actuary, 1980-83, exec. v.p., 1983—, also bd. dirs.; chmn. cost disclosure com. Am. Coun. Life Ins., Washington, 1985-87, chmn. actuarial com., 1990-91. Bd. dirs. Marion County Assn. Retarded Citizens, Indpls., 1980-86. With U.S. Army, 1961-62. Fellow Soc. Actuaries; mem. Am. Acad. Actuaries, Indpls. Actuarial Club (past pres.), Actuarial Club Ind., Ky. and Ohio (past pres.), Phi Beta Kappa. Office: State Life Ins Co 141 E Washington St Indianapolis IN 46204-3649

ROBINSON, LAURIE OVERBY, lawyer; b. Washington, July 7, 1946; d. Kermit and Ethel Esther (Schlasinger) Overby; m. Craig Baab, Oct. 22, 1977; (div. 1991); 1 child, Teddy Baab; m. Sheldon Krantz, Dec. 8, 1991. BA in Polit. Sci. magna cum laude, Brown U., 1968. Desk editor Cmty. News Svc., N.Y.C., 1968-71; asst. staff dir. sect. criminal justice ABA, Washington, 1972-74, dir. sect. criminal justice, 1979-93; assoc. dep. atty. gen. U.S. Dept. Justice, Washington, 1993-94, asst. atty. gen. Office Justice Programs, 1994—; mem. ex-officio, bd. regents Nat. Coll. Dist. Attys., Houston, 1979-93; mem. adv. bd. Fed. Sentencing Reporter, N.Y.C., 1990—; chair Nat. Forum on Criminal Justice, Washington, 1991-93. Active Clinton Campaign Criminal Justice Com., 1992, Clinton Transition Com. Dept. Justice, 1992. Mem. ABA, Phi Beta Kappa. Democrat. Office: US Dept Justice 633 Indiana Ave NW Washington DC 20531

ROBINSON, LAWRENCE DEWITT, lawyer; b. Saginaw, Mich., Sept. 15, 1943; m. Lynne Howe; children: Tiffany, Julia. BS, Cen. Mich. U., 1965; JD, U. Mich., 1968. Bar: Mo. 1968, Tex. 1983. Atty. Stinson, May & Fizzell, Kansas City, Mo., 1968-89; ptnr. Bracewell & Patterson, Dallas, 1991—. Tchr. navigational class. Mem. ABA, Dallas Bar Assn. Office: Bracewell & Patterson Lincoln Plz 500 N Akard Ste 4000 Dallas TX 75201-3387

ROBINSON, LAWRENCE WAYNE, protective services official; b. Dallas, Jan. 9, 1947; s. Henry Sherrod and Mary Ellen (Bannon) R.; m. Virginia Elaine Morgan, Aug. 9, 1980; children: Matthew Sherrod, Meghan Michelle, Joshua Morgan; 1 child from a previous marriage, Lawrence Wayne, Jr. BS in Psychology, No. Tex. State U., 1974; MS in Interdisciplinary Studies, U. Tex., Tyler, 1985. Cert. instr., firearms instr. Police officer Dallas Police Dept., 1966-68; salesman Nat. Cash Register, Dallas, 1968-69; police officer Denton (Tex.) Police Dept., 1969-71; adminstrv. asst. to chief No. Tex. State U., Denton, 1971-75, chief of police, 1976-83; coord. basic police training No. Ctrl. Tex. Regional Acad., Arlington, 1975-76; chief police Tyler (Tex.) Police Dept., 1983-94; chmn. Gang Task Force, Tyler; founder S.T.A.R. elementary sch. program, Tyler, 1990—; co-founder Mayor's Anti-Crime Task Force, Greater Tyler Drug-Free Bus.; speaker in field. Leader Boy Scouts Am., Tyler, 1993—; asst. coach Tyler Soccer Assn., 1993—, Rose Capital East Little League, Tyler, 1993—; deacon First Baptist Ch., 1993—. With Tex. Air Nat. Guard, 1965-71. Recipient Outstanding Leadership and Founder award Drug Free Youth in Tex. Assn., 1993, Dir.'s Community Leadership award FBI, 1994. Republican. Avocations: running, back packing, camping, cycling. Office: Tyler Police Dept Office of Police Chief 711 W Ferguson Tyler TX 75702

ROBINSON, LEE HARRIS, lawyer; b. N.Y.C., Aug. 2, 1939; s. Bernard and Bess (Polotnick) R.; m. Marilyn Yudien, June 13, 1963 (div. June 1985); children: Shari, Brett; m. Susan Stroble, June 22, 1985; stepchildren: Michael, Jonathan. BA, Cornell U., 1961; LLB cum laude, Columbia U., 1964. Bar: N.Y. 1965, U.S. Dist. Ct. (so. dist.) N.Y. 1968, U.S. Ct. Appeals (2d cir.) 1968. Ptnr. Rosenman & Colin, N.Y.C., 1964—. Contbr. articles to profl. jours. Mem. exec. com. young men's divsn. Albert Einstein Coll. Medicine, N.Y.C., 1979—; mem. Cornell Assn. Class Officers, 1981—. Mem. ABA (mem. benefits subcom. sect. on taxation, mem. exec. compensation com. sect. on real property, probate and trust law), N.Y. State Bar Assn. (mem. spl. com. on pension simplification, mem. com. on exec. compensation), Old Oaks Country Club (Purchase, N.Y.). Republican. Jewish. Avocation: golf. Home: 437 Orienta Ave Mamaroneck NY 10543-3939 Office: Rosenman & Colin 575 Madison Ave New York NY 10022-2511

ROBINSON, LEONARD HARRISON, JR., international government consultant, business executive; b. Winston-Salem, N.C., Apr. 21, 1943; s. Leonard Harrison and Winnie Cornelia (Thomas) R.; children: Kimberly Michelle, Rani Craft. NSF cert., Bennett Coll., Greensboro, N.C., 1959; BA, Ohio State U., 1964; postgrad., SUNY, Binghamton, 1966-67, Am. U., 1982-89, Harvard U., 1991; LLD (hon.), Shaw U., Raleigh, N.C., 1983; LHD (hon.), Huston-Tillotson Coll., 1991. Vol. Peace Corps, Bihar, India, 1964-66; assoc. dir. for India Peace Corps, Madras, 1967-70; dir. recruitment Peace Corps., Washington, 1970-71; dir. inner-city programs EPA, Washington, 1971-72; dir. mgmt. Family Planning Internat. Assistance, N.Y.C., 1972-74; Africa dir. Family Planning Internat. Assistance, Accra, Ghana and Nairobi, Kenya, 1974-77; task force dir. U.S. Ho. Reps., Washington, 1977-78; dir. population Africa AID, Washington, 1978-79; dir. Internat. Devel. Ctr. Battelle Inst., Washington, 1979-83; dep. asst. sec. Dept. State, Washington, 1983-85; pres. African Devel. Found., Washington, 1985-90; dep. asst. sec. state, sr. exec. svc. Dept. State, Washington, 1990-93; vice chmn., COO Washington Strategic Consulting Group, Inc., Washington, 1993—; cons. area studies U. Mo. Peace Corps, summer 1966; mgmt. analyst ATAC, Washington, 1971; mem. U.S. presdl. del. to Dakar, Senegal, 1987, to Malawi, Mozambique, and Uganda, Sept. 1988, to Mali, Uganda, and Kenya, Dec. 1988, v.p.'s visit to Africa, 1991. Author: monographs Assessment and Analysis of Population Attitudes in Tanzania, 1981, Analyze African Official Attitudes Concerning U.S. Population Assistance in Lesotho, Tanzania, Senegal and Togo, 1981. Adviser Population Resource Ctr., N.Y.C., 1978-82; adviser internat. program for health and tng., U. N.C., Chapel Hill, 1980-84; vice-chmn. New Directions Task Force Rep. Party, Montgomery County (Md.), 1982-83; adv. council Nat. Coun. Returned Peace Corps Vols., 1987—; bd. dirs. Washington Ballet, 1982-85, 86-91, v.p. bd. dirs., 1988-90; bd. dirs. Friends of Smithsonian Mus. African Art, Washington, 1982-84, Coalition for Equitable Representation in Govt., Montgomery County, Montgomery County Bd. Soc. Services, 1986-89, Joint Agrl. Consultative Corp., 1985-86; bd. dirs. Alan Gutmacher Inst., 1992—. Decorated commandeur de l'Ordre National du Niger, 1989; recipient Africare Disting. Svc. award, 1990, Key to the City of Greensboro, N.C., 1991, Christian D. Maxwell Disting. Svc. award Liberian Com. for Relief, Resettlement and Reconstruction, 1993. Mem. Soc. Internat. Devel. (dir. 1982), Am. Pub. Health Assn. (sec. population sect. 1979-81), Coun. on Fgn. Rels., C. of C. of D.C. (dir. 1979-82), Metro Club Washington, Kappa Alpha Psi, Sigma Pi Phi. Office: Washington Strategic Consulting Group 10th Fl 805 15th St NW Fl 10 Washington DC 20005-2207

ROBINSON, LINDA GOSDEN, communications executive; b. L.A., Jan. 10, 1953; d. Freeman Fisher and Jane Elizabeth (Stoneham) Gosden; m. Stephen M. Dart (div. June 1977); m. James Dixon Robinson III. Student, UCLA, 1970-72; BA summa cum laude in Psychology, U. So. Calif., 1978. Dep. press sec. Reagan Presdl. Campaign, L.A., 1979; press sec., dir. pub. relations Rep. Nat. Com., Washington, 1979-80; dir. pub. affairs U.S. Dept. Transp., Washington, 1981-83; ptnr. pub. and govt. affairs Heron, Burchette, Ruckert & Rothwell, Washington, 1983; dep. to spl. envoy Office of the Pres., N.Y.C., 1985; sr. v.p. corp. affairs Warner Amex Cable Communications, N.Y.C., 1983-86; pres., chief exec. officer Robinson, Lake, Lerer & Montgomery, N.Y.C., 1986—; bd. dirs. Revlon Group, Inc., N.Y.C., Nat. Health Labs., Inc., N.Y.C., Bozell, Jacobs, Kenyon & Eckhardt, N.Y.C., Coro Found., N.Y.C. Trustee NYU Med. Ctr., N.Y.C.; del. Rep. Nat. Conv., 1985. Mem. Women Achievers Acad., Nat. Women's Econ. Coun., Phi Beta Kappa. Avocations: horse showing, tennis, golf.

ROBINSON, MALCOLM, gastroenterologist; b. Amarillo, Tex., July 25, 1942; s. H. Malcolm and Frances Pauline (Kohn) R.; m. Susan Laird Robinson, June 22, 1969. BS with honors, Tulane U., 1964; MD, Okla. U., 1968. Diplomate Am. Bd. Internal Medicine, Am. Bd. Gastroenterology. Intern Cleve. Clinic, 1968-69; GI fellow Duke U., Durham, N.C., 1969-71; asst. prof. U. Okla., Oklahoma City, 1975-76; chief GI fellowship Okla City Clinic, 1976-89; pres., dir. Okla. Found. for Digestive Rsch., Oklahoma City, 1989—; clin. assoc. prof. U. Okla., Oklahoma City, 1976-92, clin. prof., 1992—; mem. adv. bd. Glaxo, Inc., Merck-J&J, TAP Pharm., Inc., Procter & Gamble, Inc.; mem. internat. adv. bd. Alimentary Pharmacology and Therapeutics; reviewer Am. Jour. Gastroenterology, Gastroenterology, Digestive Diseases and Sci., Gastrointestinal Endoscopy. Maj. M.C., U.S. Army, 1971-74. Recipient Janssen award for Outstanding Achievement in Clin. Gastroenterology Am. Gastroenterol. Assn., 1995. Fellow ACP, Am. Coll. Gastroenterology; mem. Am. Soc. Gastrointestinal Endoscopy, Am. Gastroenterological Assn. Office: Okla Found Digestive Rsch Ste 501 711 Stanton L Young Blvd Oklahoma City OK 73118-8428

ROBINSON, MARGUERITE STERN, anthropologist, educator, consultant; b. N.Y.C., Oct. 11, 1935; d. Philip Van Doren and Lillian (Diamond) Stern; m. Allan Richard Robinson, June 12, 1955; children: Sarah Penelope, Perrine, Laura Ondine. BA, Radcliffe Coll., 1956; PhD, Harvard U., 1965. Assoc. scholar Inst. for Study (now Bunting Inst.) Radcliffe U., Cambridge, Mass., 1964-65; asst. prof. anthology Brandeis U., 1965-72, assoc. prof., 1972-78, prof., 1978-85; dean Coll. Arts and Scis., 1973-75; assoc. fellow Inst. Internat. Devel. Harvard U., Cambridge, 1978-80, fellow Inst. Internat. Devel., 1980-85, inst. fellow Inst. Internat. Devel., 1985—; dir. Cultural Survival Inc., 1981—; dir. Am. Inst. Indian Studies, Chgo., 1977—, chmn., 1983-84; cons. Ministry of Fin., Govt. of Indonesia, Jakarta, 1979-92, USAID, 1992-95, Banco Solidario, Bolivia, 1993-95, Bank Rakyat Indonesia, 1994-95, Bank Danamon Indonesia, 1995. Author: Political Structure in a Changing Sinhalese Village, 1975, Local Politics: The Law of the Fishes, 1988, Pembiayaan Pertanian Pedesaan, 1993; contbg. author: Cambridge Papers in Social Anthropology 3, 1962, Cambridge Papers in Social Anthropology 5, 1968, Enterprises for the Recycling and Composting of Municipal Solid Waste, 1993, The New World of Microenterprise Finance, 1994; contbr. articles to profl. jours. Pres. the Greatest Gift Corp. Fellow NIH, 1964-65; grantee NSF, 1966-70, Ford Found., 1972-74, 79, Calmeadow Found., 1994; fellow Indo-Am. Fellowship Program-Indo-U.S. Subcommn. on Edn. and Culture, 1976-77, Am. Inst. Indian Studies, 1976-77; grantee Calmeadow Found., 1994. Fellow Am. Anthrop. Assn., Soc. Bunting Inst. Fellows; mem. Assn. Asian Studies, India Internat. Centre. Office: Harvard U Inst Internat Devel One Eliot St Cambridge MA 02138

ROBINSON, MARK ALEXANDER, III, heavy construction, mining equipment executive; b. Boise, Idaho, June 13, 1941; s. Mark Alexander and Mary Margaret (Braxton) R.; m. Lois Jayne Springer, Sept. 7, 1963; children: Scott, Kathryn. BS in Bus., U. Idaho, 1963. Asst. fin. mgr. Caterpillar Tractor Co., Peoria, Ill., 1968-72; fin. mgr. Ziegler Inc., Mpls., 1972-74, sec.-treas., 1974-76; v.p. N.E. ops. Ziegler Inc., Hibbing, Minn., 1976-80; exec. v.p. Ziegler Inc., Mpls., 1980-86; treas. Whayne Supply Co., Louisville, 1986-87, v.p., treas., 1987-89, v.p. fin., CFO, 1989-90, exec. v.p., CFO, 1990—; also dir.; dir. Coop. Assn. Tractor Dealers, Bethesda, Md., 1968—. Capt. U.S. Army, 1963-68. Mem. Fin. Execs. Inst. (dir. 1991—), Cedar Lake Lodge (dir. 1987—), Louisville Rotary. Republican. Lutheran. Avocations: golf, walking, boating. Office: Whayne Supply Co 1400 Cecil Ave PO Box 35900 Louisville KY 40232

ROBINSON, MARSHALL ALAN, economics educator, foundation executive; b. Berkeley, Calif., Feb. 16, 1922; s. Webster Richard and Evelyn (Casey) R.; m. Ynid Douglas Rankin, June 5, 1944 (div. 1973); children: Joan Douglas, Margaret Elaine, Richard Webster; m. Flavia Derossi, Oct. 1974. A.B., U. Calif.-Berkeley, 1943; M.A., Ohio State U., 1948, Ph.D., 1950. Instr. econs. Ohio State U., 1948-50; asst. prof. econs. Tulane U., 1951-53; research asso. Nat. Bur. Econ. Research, 1951-52; asst. prof. econs. Dartmouth Coll., 1953-55; sr. staff mem., asst. to pres. Brookings Instn., 1955-60; prof. econs., dean Grad. Sch. Bus., U. Pitts., 1960-63; dir. econs. devel. and adminstrn. program Ford Found., 1964-67, program officer in charge higher edn. and research, 1967-71, dep. v.p. edn. and research, 1971-73, v.p. resources and environ., 1973-79; pres. Russell Sage Found., N.Y.C., 1979-86; vis. prof. Grad. Sch. CUNY, 1986-89; fellow Inst. Social and Policy Studies Yale U., 1989-91; v.p. Daniele Agostino Found., 1992—. Author: An Introduction to Economic Reasoning, 1956, 5th edit., 1981, The National Debt Ceiling, 1959. Bd. dirs. Belgium-Am. Edni. Found., 1987—; trustee Antioch U., 1987-90. Served to 1st lt. USMCR, 1943-45, PTO. Decorated Royal Order of Leopold, Belgium. Mem. Am. Econs. Assn., N.Y. Sci. Policy Assn., Coun. on Fgn. Rels., Century Assn., Alpha Delta Phi.

ROBINSON, MARTHA STEWART, retired legal educator; b. Topeka, Mar. 2, 1914; d. Robert Bigger and Lenora (Stubbs) Stewart; m. Albrecht Marburg Yerkes, July 3, 1940 (dec. 1963); children: Robert Stewart, William Marburg; m. Stephan B. Robinson, Jr., July 17, 1971. A.B. cum laude, Washburn U., 1934, LL.B., 1940; LL.M., Stanford U., 1953. Bar: Kans. 1940, Calif. 1945. Individual practice law Los Angeles, 1946-55; instr. law Southwestern U. Sch. Law, Los Angeles, 1946-55; cons. Los Angeles Superior Ct. Com. on Standard Jury Instrns., 1957-64; prof. law Loyola U. Sch. Law, Los Angeles, 1965-84, prof. emeritus, 1984—; judge pro tempore Los Angeles County Superior Ct., 1963. Mem. Am. Law Inst., Calif. Bar Assn., L.A. County Bar Assn. (trustee 1976-78), Women Lawyers Assn. L.A. (past pres.). Home: 625 Old Mill Rd Pasadena CA 91108-1737 Office: Loyola U Law Sch 1441 W Olympic Blvd Los Angeles CA 90015-3980

ROBINSON, MARTIN F., lawyer; b. Trenton, N.J., July 5, 1939. AB, Rutgers U., 1961; LLB, U. Pa., 1964. Bar: N.J. 1965, Ill. 1967. Law clk. to Hon. Joseph Halpern N.J. Superior Ct., 1964-65; atty. Office Gen. Coun. NLRB, 1965-66; ptnr. Sidley & Austin, Chgo.; instr. Chgo. Kent Coll. Law, 1975-79; mem. nat. adv. com. State of Ill., 1988-90. Mem. Nat. Assn. Bond Lawyers. Office: Sidley & Austin 1 First Nat Plz Chicago IL 60603

ROBINSON, MARY LOU, federal judge; b. Dodge City, Kans., Aug. 25, 1926; d. Gerald J. and Frances (Pierce) Strueber; m. A.J. Robinson, Aug. 28, 1949; children: Rebecca Aynn Gruhlkey, Diana Ceil, Matthew Douglas. B.A., U. Tex., 1948, LL.B., 1950. Bar: Tex. 1949. Ptnr. Robinson & Robinson, Amarillo, 1950-55; judge County Ct. at Law, Potter County, Tex., 1955-59, (108th Dist. Ct.), Amarillo, 1961-73; assoc. justice Ct. of Civil Appeals for 7th Supreme Jud. Dist. of Tex., Amarillo, 1973-77; chief justice Ct. of Civil Appeals for 7th Supreme Jud. Dist. of Tex., 1977-79; U.S. dist. judge No. Dist. Tex., Amarillo, 1979—. Named Woman of Year Tex. Fedn. Bus. and Profl. Women, 1973. Mem. Nat. Assn. Women Lawyers, ABA, Tex. Bar Assn., Amarillo Bar Assn., Delta Kappa Gamma. Presbyterian. Office: US Dist Ct 205 E 5th Ave Box F-13248 Amarillo TX 79101-1563

ROBINSON, MAURICE RICHARD, JR., publishing executive; b. Pitts., May 15, 1937; s. Maurice Richard and Florence (Liddell) R.; m. Helen V. Benham, Oct. 18, 1986; 1 child, John Benham. BA in English magna cum laude, Harvard U., 1959; postgrad., St. Catharines Coll., Cambridge U., 1959-60, Tchrs. Coll. Columbia U., 1959-61. Tchr. English, Evanston Twp. (Ill.) High Sch., 1960-62; asst. editor Lit. Cavalcade, Scholastic Inc., N.Y.C., 1962-63; editor Scholastic lit. units Lit. Cavalcade, Scholastic Inc., 1963-64; editor Scope mag., 1964-67, editorial dir. English, 1967-71, pub. sch. div., 1971-74, pres., chief exec. officer, 1974—, chmn., 1982—. Bd. dirs. Fund for Advancement and Support of Teaching English, Children's Mus. Manhattan; chmn. Capitol campaign, 1987; trustee Am. Health Found., 1988—; geography adv. com. Am. Express Found., 1989—. Mem. Nat. Coun. Tchrs. English, N.Y. Acad. Public Edn., Assn. Am. Pubs. (bd. dirs.1989—, exec. com.), Century Assn., Pubs. Lunch Club, University Club (N.Y.C.), Phi Beta Kappa. Home: 47 Woodside Ave Westport CT 06880-3029 Office: Scholastic Inc 730 Broadway New York NY 10003-9511

ROBINSON, MICHAEL HILL, zoological park director, biologist; b. Preston, Eng., Jan. 7, 1929; came to U.S. 1984; s. Samuel and Ethel (Hill) R.; m. Barbara Cragg Robinson, May 19, 1959S. BS., U. Wales, U.K., 1962 D.Phil., U. Oxford, Eng. 1966. Tchr. sci. U.K. Secondary Schs., 1953-60; sr. sci. master Camborne Grammar Sch., 1958-60; biologist Smith. Tropical Research Inst., Panama, 1966-71; vis. lectr. U. Pa., Phila., 1969; reader in biology New U. Ulster, No. Ireland, 1971; biologist Smithsonian Tropical

Research Inst., Panama, 1971-84; asst. dir. Smithsonian Tropical Research Inst., 1980, acting dir., 1980-81, dep. dir., 1981-84; adj. prof. U. Miami, Coral Gables, Fla., 1981—; dir. Nat. Zool. Park, Washington, 1984—. Contbr. articles to profl. jours. Sci. fellow Zool. Soc. London, 1956. Fellow Linnean Soc., Royal Entomol. Soc., Inst. Biology; mem. Papua New Guinea Sci. Soc., Brit. Arachnological Soc., Internat. Soc. Tropical Ecologists, Am. Arachnological Soc., Soc. for Study of Animal Behavior. Home: 2729 Ordway St NW Apt 5 Washington DC 20008-5052 Office: Nat Zool Pk 3000 Connecticut Ave NW Washington DC 20008-2598

ROBINSON, MICHAEL R., aeronautical engineer. With Rockwell Internat. Corp., Seal Beach, Calif. Recipient Aircraft Design award Am. Inst. Aeronautics & Astronautics, 1994. Office: Rockwell Internat Corp 2201 Seal Beach Blvd PO Box 4250 Seal Beach CA 90740-8250*

ROBINSON, NAN SENIOR, not-for-profit organization consultant; b. Salt Lake City, Jan. 11, 1932; d. Clair Marcil Senior and Lillian (Worlton) Senior Davis; m. David Zav Robinson; Sept. 6, 1954; children: Marc S. Robinson, Eric S. Robinson. BA with hons., Mills Coll., 1952; MA, Harvard U., 1953. Spl. asst. to undersec. Dept. Housing and Urban Devel., Washington, 1966-69; asst. to the pres. U. Mass. Statewide System, Boston, 1970-73, v.p. for planning, 1973-78; dep. commr. Conn. Bd. Higher Edn., Hartford, 1978-81; v.p. adminstrn. The Rockefeller Found., N.Y.C., 1981-90; mem. governing coun. Rockefeller Archive Ctr., Pocantico Hills, N.Y., 1986-89; mem. Coun. on Founds. N.Y. Regional Assn. Grantmakers, 1985-89; mem. nat. advisory panel on governance Carnegie Found. for the Advancement of Teaching, Princeton, N.J., 1980-82. Trustee, chmn. fin. com. Inst. for Current World Affairs, Hanover, N.H., 1987-90; trustee Calif. Sch. Profl. Psychology, San Francisco, 1985—. Recipient Centennial award Am. Assn. U. Women Hartford Br., 1981; named Woman of Yr. Hartford YWCA, 1980; named to Centennial Honor List of 100 Women Barnard Coll., 1989. Mem. Soc. for Coll. and U. Planning (com. chmn. 1985-86, nominating com. 1980-85, regional rep. 1975-77), Harvard Club, Phi Beta Kappa. Home: 622 Greenwich St Apt 5B New York NY 10014

ROBINSON, NATHANIEL DAVID, physician; b. Providence, May 21, 1904; m. Dorothy Mae McLaughlin, Mar. 27, 1940; children: Nathaniel David Jr., Judith A. (Mrs. Joseph F. Baugher), Nancy L. (Mrs. Robert W. VanTuyle). BS, Tufts U., 1928, MD, 1931; postgrad. ophthalmology, N.Y.U., 1945-46. Diplomate Am. Bd. Ophthalmology. Intern Gallinger Mcpl. Hosp., Washington, 1931-32; physician gen. medicine Marine Hosp., Balt., 1935-36; gen. practice medicine Providence, 1936-40; resident ophthalmology Bellevue Hosp., N.Y.C., 1946-49; asst. to prof. ophtalmology N.Y.U., N.Y.C., 1949; practice medicine specializing in ophthalmology Providence, 1949—; cons. staff R.I., Miriam, VA, Roger Williams, Chapin Hosps., Providence, Meml. Hosp., Pawtucket, R.I.; ophthalmologist Sr. Friendship Ctr., Naples, Fla. Served with USN, 1940-45, PTO, ret. capt. USNR, 1964. N.Y. Kiwanis Club grantee for ophthalmology. Mem. R.I., Providence, Collier County med. socs., R.I., New Eng., Pan Am. Ophthal. socs., AMA, Am. Acad. Ophthalmology, Pan. Am. Med. Assn., Soc. Eye Surgeons, R.I. Hist. Soc., English Speaking Union, Audobon Soc., Narragansett Bay Power Squadron, Ret. Officers Assn., Mil. Order Fgn. Wars, Navy League of the U.S. Unitarian. Clubs: University, Moorings Country. Home: 2880 Gulf Shore Blvd N Apt 308 Naples FL 33940-4326

ROBINSON, NEIL CIBLEY, JR., lawyer; b. Columbia, S.C., Oct. 25, 1942; s. Neil C. and Ernestine (Carns) R.; m. Judith Ann Hunter, Sept. 4, 1971 (div. Nov. 1979); 1 child, Hunter Leigh; m. Vicki Elizabeth Kornahrens, Mar. 2, 1985; children: Neil C. III, Taylor Elizabeth. BS in Indsl. Mgmt., Clemson U., 1966; JD, U. S.C., 1973. Bar: S.C. 1974, U.S. Ct. Appeals (4th cir.) 1974, U.S. Dist. Ct. S.C. 1976. Asst. to dean U.S.C. Law Sch., Columbia, 1973-74; law clk. to judge Charles E. Jr. Simons Jr. U.S. Dist. Ct. S.C., Aiken, 1974-76; assoc Grimball & Cabaniss, Charleston, S.C., 1976-78; ptnr. Grimball, Cabaniss, Vaughan & Robinson, Charleston, 1978-84; ptnr., pres. Robinson, Wall & Hastie, P.A., Charleston, 1984-91; ptnr., mem. exec. com. Nexsen, Pruet, Jacobs, Pollard & Robinson, Charleston, 1991—; permanent mem. 4th Cir. Jud. Conf., 1982—; pres. Coastal Properties Inst., Charleston, 1981—. Bd. dirs. Southeastern Wildlife Exposition, Charleston, 1987—, pres. 1994—, Charleston Maritime Festival, 1993—, pres. 1994—, Parklands Found. of Charleston County; pres. S.C. Tourism Coun., Columbia, 1991—. Cpl. USMCR, 1960-66. Mem. ABA, Urban Land Inst., Am. Residential and Resort Devel. Assn., S.C. Bar Assn., Fed. Bar Assn., S.C. Def. Trial Lawyers Assn., Hibernian Soc. (mem. mgmt. com. 1984—), Kaiwah Club, Haig Point Club, Country Club of Charleston, Phi Delta Phi. Presbyterian. Avocations: golf, hunting. Home: PO Box 121 Charleston SC 29402-0121 Office: Nexsen Pruet Jacobs Pollard & Robinson 200 Meeting St Ste 301 Charleston SC 29401-3156

ROBINSON, NELL BRYANT, nutrition educator; b. Kopperl, Tex., Oct. 15, 1925; d. Basil Howell and Lelia Abiah (Duke) Bryant; m. Frank Edward Robinson, July 14, 1945 (dec.); 1 child, John Howell Robinson. B.S., N. Tex. State U., 1945; M.S., Tex. Woman's U., 1958, Ph.D., 1967. Registered dietitian, Tex. Tchr. Comanche High Sch., Tex., 1945-46, Kopperl High Sch., Tex., 1946-48; county extension agt. Agrl. Extension Service, Tex., 1948-56; prof. nutrition Tex. Christian U., Fort Worth, 1957-92, chmn. dept. nutrition and dietetics, 1985-91, ret., 1992. Pres., bd. dirs. Sr. Citizens Svcs. of Greater Tarrant County, 1990-91. Contbr. chpt. to book. Named Top Prof., Tex. Christian U. Mortar Bd., 1978. Mem. Am. Dietetic Assn. (del. 1983-88, ethics com. 1985-88, coun. edn. 1988-90, chmn. coun. on edn. divsn. edn. accreditation/approval 1989-90, medallion award 1990), Am. Home Econs. Assn., Tex. Dietetic Assn. (pres., 1972-73, Disting. Dietitian 1981), Tex. Home Econs. Assn. (pres. 1978-80, Home Economist of Yr. 1975). Club: Fort Worth Women's. Lodge: Order Eastern Star. Home: 5729 Wimbleton Way Fort Worth TX 76133-3651

ROBINSON, NINA, nursing administrator; b. Elizabeth, N.J., Nov. 12, 1944; d. Louis and Nina (Santa Lucia) Ventre; m. Edward T. Robinson Jr., Aug. 20, 1966, children: Nina Anne, E. Thomas. Diploma in nursing, Muhlenberg Hosp., Plainfield, N.J., 1965; BS, Monmouth Coll., 1982, MBA, 1988. cert. Am. Bd. Quality Assurance and Utilization Rev. Physicians, Inc. Dir. admissions/utilization rev. Kimball Med. Ctr., Lakewood, N.J., quality assurance coord., v.p. patient care svcs., 1990—; exec. dir. Kimball Ambulatory Care Ctr., Whiting, N.J., v.p. patient care svcs., 1990—. Co-chmn. nursing task force Ocean County (N.J.) Bd. Freeholders. Mem. Orgn. Nurse Execs., Am. Coll. Healthcare Execs.

ROBINSON, OPAL ANNE, secondary education educator; b. St. Louis, Sept. 26, 1936; d. Gilbert Newton and Florence (Verdier) Thompson; m. Gary Floyd Robinson, Aug. 26, 1955; children: Kathryn, Sherryl, Karen, Gary Randall. BS, U. Mo., 1970; MS in Edn., U. Ark., 1989. Cert. English tchr., Ark. Reading tchr. Van Buren (Ark.) Pub. Schs., 1970-76; travel coord., owner Friendship Tours, Ft. Smith, Ark., 1977-81; English tchr. Ft. Smith (Ark.) Schs., 1981—. Recipient 1st place award Internat. Paper Econ. Awards Program, 1985, 91, hon. mention, 1989, 2nd place, 1994. Mem. NEA, Ark. Edn. Assn., Ft. Smith Tchrs. Assn., Phi Delta Kappa (Outstanding Secondary Educator, Ft. Smith 1992). Republican. Baptist. Avocations: travel, writing. Office: Darby Jr High 14th Grand Fort Smith AR 72903

ROBINSON, ORMSBEE WRIGHT, educational consultant; b. Bklyn., June 17, 1910; s. Harry Alexander and Claire (Wright) R.; m. Janet MacNaughton Miller, June 22, 1935; children: Heather (Mrs. Phillips Thorp), John Alexander. AB cum laude, Princeton U., 1932, MSS, New Sch. Social Work., 1937; MA, Columbia U. Tchrs. Coll., 1942, EdD, 1949. Exec. sec. Plainfield Inst., N.J., 1934-35; high sch. instr., 1935; dir. adult edn. Soc. Ethical Culture, N.Y.C., 1935-41; tchr. ethics Fieldston Sch., N.Y.C., 1935-42; exec. dir. Assoc. Jr. Work Camps, Inc., 1938-42; assoc. OPA, Region II, 1942-46; dir. admissions and pub. rels. Bard Coll., 1946-50, v.p., 1950-54; ednl. cons. for higher edn. Conn. State Dept. Edn., 1954-55, chief Bur. Higher and Adult Edn., 1955-57; exec. sec. Conn. Coun. Higher Edn., 1954-57; cons. in exec. devel., IBM, 1957-61; program dir. IBM Exec. Sch., 1962; dir. ednl. affairs IBM, 1962-70, dir. univ. rels. planning, 1970-75; dir. internat. program Nat. Coun. on Philanthropy, 1975-79, acting pres., 1977-78; cons. Eugenio Mendoza Found. and Venezuelan Fedn. Pvt. Founds., Caracas, Venezuela, 1979-83, Technoserve, Inc., 1980-83; assoc Columbia U. seminar on technology and social change, 1962-75; chmn. bus. edn. adv. bd.

Com. Econ. Devel., 1963-64, mem. Coun. Devel., Edn., Tng. Nat. Indsl. Conf. Bd., 1960-68; faculty Salzburg Seminar in Am. Studies, 1968; mem. U.S. Nat. Commn. UNESCO, 1971-74, exec. com., 1972-74, chmn. adv. com. on bus. and internat. edn., 1971-72, chmn. membership com., 1974; mem. standards com. Am. Assembly Coll. Schs. of Bus., 1971-72, chmn. internat. affairs com., 1973-75, bd. dirs., 1974-75; mem. task force bus. and internat. edn. Am. Coun. on Edn., 1975-76. Bd. dirs World Affairs Ctr., Hartford, 1982-83; adv. coun. Am. Ditchley Found., 1969-86, advisor Assn. for Internat. Practical Tng.; mem. Granby Bd. Edn., Conn., 1979-83; bd. founders U. Hartford; bd. dirs. United Way of Chatham County, 1985-91, United Way N.C., 1993—. Mem. Soc. Internat. Devel., S.R., Soc. Colonial Wars, Fearrington Garden Club. Co-author: Education in Business and Industry, 1966. Editorial adv. bd. Indian Adminstrv. and Mgmt. Rev., New Delhi, 1968-75. Contbr. to profl. jours. Home: Fearrington Post 241 Pittsboro NC 27312

ROBINSON, PAMELA, dancer. Attended, Ctrl. Pa. Youth Ballet, Cin. Conservatory of Music, Lexington Ballet, Nat. Acad. Arts, Chempaign, Ill. Dancer Cleve. Ballet, Ala. Ballet, 1982-85; dancer Ballet West, Salt Lake City, 1985-88, prin. dancer, 1988—. Dance performances include Anna Karenina, Rosalinda, Lady of the Camellias, The Nutcracker, Sleeping Beauty, Swan Lake, Giselle, Carmina Burana (John Butler). Office: Ballet West 50 West 200 South Salt Lake City UT 84101*

ROBINSON, PAUL ARNOLD, historian, educator, author; b. San Diego, Oct. 1, 1940; s. Joseph Cook and Beryl Marie (Lippincott) R.; m. Ute Brosche, Aug. 3, 1964 (div. Aug. 1967); 1 child, Susan Marie. B.A., Yale U., 1962; postgrad., Free U. Berlin, 1962; PhD, Harvard U., 1968. Asst. prof. history Stanford U. (Calif.), 1967-73, assoc. prof., 1973-80, prof. history, 1980—, Richard W. Lyman prof. in the humanities, 1994—. Author: The Freudian Left, 1969, The Modernization of Sex, 1976, Opera and Ideas: From Mozart to Strauss, 1985, Freud and His Critics, 1993; editor: Social Thought in America and Europe, 1970; contbg. editor The New Republic, 1979-85. Guggenheim fellow, 1970-71, Stanford Humanities Ctr. fellow, 1984-85, Inst. for Advanced Study fellow, 1990-91. Fellow Am. Acad. Arts and Scis.; mem. Am. Hist. Assn. Home: 671 Santa Ynez St Palo Alto CA 94305-8542 Office: Stanford Univ Dept History Stanford CA 94305

ROBINSON, PETER, paleontology educator, consultant; b. N.Y.C., N.Y., July 19, 1932; s. Edward and Carol Nye (Rhoades) R.; m. Patricia Ellen Fisher, Sept. 11, 1954 (div. Mar. 1980); children: Diane Elizabeth, Nathan; m. Paola D'Amelio Villa, Dec. 8, 1984. BS, Yale U., 1954, MS, 1958, PhD, 1960. Instr. Harpur Coll. SUNY, Binghamton, 1955-57; rsch. assoc. Yale Peabody Mus., New Haven, 1960-61; curator geology U. Colo. Mus., Boulder, 1961—, asst. prof. natural history, 1961-67, assoc. prof., 1967-71, prof., 1971—, dir. mus., 1971-82, prof. geol. sci., 1971—; geologist Colo. Nubian Expdn., Sudan, 1962-66; chief Colo. Paleontol. Expdn., Tunisia, 1967—; mem. geol. adv. group Colo. Bur. Land Mgmt., Denver, 1983—. Mem. AAAS, Soc. Vertebrate Paleontology (pres. 1977-78), Australian Mammal Soc., Soc. Española Paleontologia, Sigma Xi. Democrat. Home: 5110 Williams Fork Trl Apt 204 Boulder CO 80301-3408 Office: Campus Box 315 Mus U Colo Boulder CO 80309

ROBINSON, PETER CLARK, general management executive; b. Brighton, Mass., Nov. 16, 1938; s. Richard and Mary Elizabeth (Cooper) R.; m. Sylvia Phyllis Petchek, Aug. 26, 1961 (div. 1973); children: Marc Louis, Nicholas Daniel, Andrea Suzanne.; m. Sarah Lingham, Jan. 1, 1984. B.S in Fgn. Service, Georgetown U., 1961; M.B.A., Babson Inst., 1963; AMP, Harvard U., 1986. Asst. supt. prodn. Mass. Broken Stone Co., Weston, 1961-62; night shift supt. Mass. Broken Stone Co., 1962-65, v.p. ops., 1968, v.p. 1969-75, 85-94, sr. v.p., 1995—, also dir.; asst. gen. supt. Berlin Stone Co., 1965-67, v.p. ops., 1968; v.p. Holden Trap Rock Co., to 1975, also dir., v.p., 1985-94, sr. v.p., 1995—; pres. Blount Materials Inc., Saginaw, Mich., 1975-81; v.p. corp. mktg. Blount, Inc., Montgomery, 1978-79, v.p. corp. planning and mktg., 1979-92, v.p. corp. planning and devel., 1992-94; group exec., pres. Blount Agri/Indsl. Corp., 1984-90; pres. P.C. Robinson & Co., Montgomery, 1994—; mem. The Planning Forum; bd. dirs. Mass. Broken Stone Co. Mem. Nat. Stone Assn. (dir., exec. com., chmn. govt. affairs com., chmn. bd.), Am. Mgmt. Assn., Am. Soc. Agrl. Engrs., Newcomen Soc., Engring. Soc. Detroit, Pres. Assn., SME-AIME. Clubs: Montgomery Country, Capital City (Montgomery), Harvard (Boston). Home: 1822 Galena Ave Montgomery AL 36106 Office: Robinson & Co 1067-C Woodley Rd Montgomery AL 36106

ROBINSON, PHIL ALDEN, director; b. Long Beach, Mar. 1, 1950; s. S. Jesse and Jessie Francis (Roth) Robinson. BA, Union Coll., 1971. Newscaster Stas. WGY/WRGB-TV, Schenectady, 1969-71; freelance filmmaker Los Angeles, 1974—. Screenwriter All of Me, 1984, (with others) Rhinestone, 1984, (TV) 2 episodes Trapper John, M.D., 1981-82; writer, dir. In the Mood, 1987, dir. (TV) 2 episodes George Burns Comedy Week, 1986; screenwriter, dir. Field of Dreams (nomination Writers Guild, Dirs. Guild, Best Picture and Best Screenplay Adaption Acad. award nominations). Served to 1st lt. USAF, 1971-74. Named Screenwriter of Yr. Nat. Assn. Theatre Owners, 1990. Mem. Acad. Motion Picture Arts and Scis., Writers Guild Am. West, Dirs. Guild Am., ASCAP. Office: CAA 9830 Wilshire Bvld Beverly Hills CA 90212

ROBINSON, PREZELL RUSSELL, college administrator; b. Batesburg, S.C., Aug. 25, 1922; s. Clarence and Annie (Folks) R.; m. Lulu Harris, Apr. 9, 1950; 1 dau. A.B. in Econs. and Social Sci., St. Augustine's Coll., 1946; M.A. in Sociology and Econs., Cornell U., 1951, Ed.D. in Sociology-Ednl. Adminstrn., 1956; D.C.L. (hon.), U. of the South, 1970; L.H.D., Cuttington U. Coll., Monrovia, Liberia, Voorhees Coll., 1981, Episcopal Theol. Sem., 1982; LL.D. (hon.), Bishop Coll., 1979; D.C.L., Columbia U., 1980; DHL (hon.), Kenyon Coll., 1988. Tchr. social sci., French Bettis Jr. Coll., Trenton, S.C., 1946-48; sucessively registrar, tchr., acting prin. high sch., acting dean jr. coll., instr., dir. adult edn. Voorhees Jr. Coll., Denmark, S.C., 1948-56; exec. dean, dean coll. St. Augustine's Coll., Raleigh, N.C., 1956-64, exec. dean, 1964-66, acting pres., 1966-67, pres., 1967—; pres. United Negro Coll. Fund, Inc., 1978-81, Nat. Assn. Equal Opportunity Higher Edn., 1981-84, N.C. Assn. Coll. & U., Cooperating Raleigh Colls., 1981, 86—; bd. dirs. Learning Inst. N.C.; scholar-in-residence Nairobi (Kenya) U., 1973; vis. lectr. Dept. State del. to African nations, 1971, 73, 78; Dir. Wachovia Bank & Trust Co. Contbr. articles to profl. publs. Mem. exec. com. N.C. Edn. Com. on Tchr. Edn.; mem. N.C. Bd. Edn.; chmn. bd. Assn. Episcopal Colls.; mem. Mayor's Community Relations Com.; vice chmn. Wake County div. Occoneechee coun. Boy Scouts Am., 1959-67; chmn. Wake Occoneechee coun., 1963-66, mem. exec. com., from 1965; vice chmn. Wake County chpt. ARC; chmn. edn. div. United Fund of Raleigh, mem. budget com., 1965—; mem. exec. com. Wake County Libraries; trustee Voorhees Coll. Fulbright fellow to India, summer 1965; former U.S. Pres. George Bush appointee U.S. Rep. or Public Member Amb. U.N., N.Y., 1992. Served with AUS, 1942. Recipient Distinguished Alumni award Voorhees Coll., 1967, Silver Anniversary award N.C. Community System, 1989; decorated Star of Africia Liberia; recipient numerous service awards and citations; named one of the most effective coll. pres.s in U.S. Coun. for Advancement and Support of Edn., Washington, 1986; Univ. fellow Cornell U., 1954, rsch. fellow, 1955, 56; Fulbright fellow, 1965. Mem. AAAS, Nat. Assn. Collegiate Deans and Registrars, Am. Acad. Polit. and Social Sci., Am. Sociol. Soc., N.C. Sociol. Soc. (exec. com.), Ctrl. Intercollegiate Athletic Assn. (exec. com.), N.C. Assn. Ind. Colls. and Univs. (dir.), Raleigh C. of C. (A.E. Finley Disting. Svc. award 1989), So. Sociol. Assn., Am. Acad. Polit. Sci., N.C. Lit. and Hist. Soc., N.C. Hist. Soc., Phi Beta Kappa, Phi Delta Kappa, Phi Kappa Phi, Alpha Kappa Mu, Phi Beta Lambda, Delta Mu Delta. Protestant Episcopalian (lay reader). Office: St Augustine's Coll 1315 Oakwood Ave Raleigh NC 27610-2298

ROBINSON, R. CLARK, mathematician, educator; b. Seattle, Dec. 29, 1943; s. Rex J. and Ruth C. (Clark) R.; m. Peggie Crose, Aug. 20, 1966. From asst. prof. to assoc. prof. Northwestern U., Evanston, Ill., 1969-78, prof., 1978—. Author: Dynamical Systems: Stability Symnolic Dynamics, and Chaos, 1995; contbr. numerous articles to profl. jours. Mem. Am. Math. Soc., Math. Assn. Am., Soc. Indsl. and Applied Math. Presbyterian. Office: Math Dept Northwestern U 2033 Sheridan Rd Evanston IL 60208

ROBINSON, R. LARRY, gas industry executive. Pres. Columbia Gas Transmission Corp., Charleston, W. Va. Office: Columbia Gas Transmission Corp 1700 Maccorkle Ave SE Charleston WV 25314*

ROBINSON, RANDALL, think-tank executive. Exec. dir. Trans Africa Form, Wash., D.C. Office: TransAfrica 1744 R St NW Washington DC 20009-2410

ROBINSON, RAY CHARLES See CHARLES, RAY

ROBINSON, RAYMOND EDWIN, musician, music educator, writer; b. San Jose, Calif., Dec. 26, 1932; s. Elam Edwin and Zula Mai (Hatley) R.; m. Ruth Aleen Chamberlain, Mar. 12, 1954; children: Cynthia Rae, Greg Edwin, David L, Brent Steven, Jeffrey Vernon. BA, San Jose State U., 1956; MMus, Ind. U., 1958, D in Mus. Edn., 1969; LHD, Westminster Choir Coll., 1987. Instr. music Ind. U., Bloomington, 1958-59; music critic Portland Reporter, 1962-63, Balt. Evening Sun, 1964-68; founder, tchr. seminar for music adminstrs., 1972—; chmn. divsn. fine arts Cascade Coll., Portland, Oreg., 1959-63; dean Peabody Inst., Balt., 1963-69; pres. Westminster Choir Coll., Princeton, N.J., 1969-87; vis. fellow Wolfson Coll. U. Cambridge, Eng., 1987-89; disting. prof. choral studies, choral condr. Palm Beach Atlantic U., West Palm Beach, Fla., 1989—; mem. Prestige Publs. Inc., 1978—; music critic Palm Beach (Fla.) Post, 1991—; prof. Sch. Ch. Music Knox Theol. Sem., Ft. Lauderdale, Fla., 1989—; choral condr. Palm Beach C.C., Lake Worth, Fla., 1992-93; condr.-in-residence, dir. music First Presbyn. Ch., West Palm Beach, 1989—; spl. guest choral condr. Palm Beach Opera, 1990—; interim condr. Choral Soc. Palm Beaches, 1992, Ray Robinson Chorale, 1994—. Author: The Choral Experience, 1976, Choral Music, 1978; Krzysztof Penderecki, A Guide to His Works, 1983, A Study of the Penderecki St. Luke Passion, 1983, John Finley Williamson: A Centennial Appreciation, 1987; co-author: German Diction for the Choral Singer, 1992, A Bach Tribute: Bach Essays in Honor of William H. Scheide, 1993; editor The Choral Tradition Series, Hinshaw Music Inc., 1978—. Bd. dirs. Balt. Symphony Orch., 1967-69, Am. Boy Choir Sch., 1970-73, N.Y. Choral Soc., 1972—; Palm Beach Atlantic U. choral series Hinshaw Music Inc., 1990—; bd. dirs. Palm Beach County Coun. Arts, chmn. profl. artists com., mem. task force for master plan, 1990-92; mem. cultural plan com. Palm Beach County Cultural Coun., 1992—; mem. task force for edn. Fla. Philharm. Orch., 1994—. Recipient Disting. Alumni Merit award Ind. U., 1975, Disting. Alumni award Sch. Music, 1973, Disting. Alumni award San Jose State U., 1990. Mem. Coll. Music Soc. (life), Am. Choral Dirs. Assn. (life, chmn. rsch. and publs. com. 1986—), Internat. Heinrich Schütz Soc. (chmn. Am. sect. 1984-87), Univ. Club N.Y., Nassau Club Princeton, Govs. Club West Palm Beach. Presbyterian. Home: 2413 Medina Way West Palm Beach FL 33401-8019

ROBINSON, RICHARD, publishing company executive; b. 1937; married. Grad., Harvard U., 1959. Tchr. Evanston Twp. High Sch., Ill., 1960-62; v.p. Scholastic Inc., N.Y.C., 1971-74, pres., 1974—, now also chmn., chief exec. officer, dir. Office: Scholastic Inc 555 Broadway New York NY 10012-3999

ROBINSON, RICHARD CLARK, engineering company executive; b. Steubenville, Ohio, Oct. 29, 1940; s. James Clark and Emma Maria (Newell) R.; m. Glenda S. Ekes, Feb. 28, 1964; children: Jacqueline, Renée Robinson Lobono. BA, Grove City Coll., 1963. Office mgr. Pitts. Piping & Equipment, 1959-60, Eichleay Corp., Pitts., 1963-69; treas. Robert W. Hunt Co., Chgo., 1969-76, dir., 1970-76, pres., chief exec. officer, chmn. bd., 1976—. Mem. Masons, Shriners. Avocations: golfing, bowling, swimming, gardening. Office: Robert W Hunt Co 580 Waters Edge Oak Creek Ctr Lombard IL 60148

ROBINSON, RICHARD FRANCIS, writer, author; b. Passaic, N.J., June 13, 1941; s. Francis Ward and Evelyn (Burnett) R.; m. Brenda Kay Moore, Feb. 6, 1970; 1 child, Kelly. Student, Coll. of William & Mary, 1959-60; BA in Journalism, Mich. State U., 1964. Reporter, columnist North Jersey Herald News, Passaic, 1964-67; med. writer, reporter The Oakland Press, Pontiac, Mich., 1967-75; staff reporter Nat. Enquirer, Lantana, Fla., 1975-79; staff writer Hank Meyer Assocs., Miami, Fla., 1987-88; pres. Dick Robinson Co., Delray Beach, Fla., 1979—; bd. dirs. Krynova Enterprises, Inc., St. Petersburg, Fla. Editor: Foot & Leg Function, 1988-90; contbr. numerous articles to publs. Delegate Mich. State Rep. Conv., Detroit, 1970; mem. exec. bd. Mich. Fedn. Young Reps., 1970. Recipient First Pl. award AP, 1973. Mem. Am. Med. Writers Assn. (bd. dirs. 1984-85, chmn. trade book awards com. 1986, founding pres. Fla. chpt. 1983-84, pres. 1986-88), Nat. Assn. Sci. Writers, Fla. Freelance Writers Assn., Athletic Club Boca Raton, Delray Beach Tennis Ctr. Avocations: tennis, computers, photography. Home and Office: 250 S Ocean Blvd Apt 252 Delray Beach FL 33483-6752

ROBINSON, ROBERT ARMSTRONG, pension fund executive; b. Waterbury, Conn., Sept. 11, 1925; s. Robert and Ethel (Armstrong) R.; m. D. Ann Harding, June 7, 1947; 1 child, Gayllis Robinson Ward. A.B. magna cum laude, Brown U., 1950, M.A., 1952; postgrad., U. Ill., 1954-55; Litt. D., Episcopal Theol. Sem. Ky., 1971; D.C.L., U. South, 1972; LL.D., Nashotah House, Oconomowoc, Wis. Instr. English Brown U., 1950-53; instr. English, asst. prof. rhetoric U. Ill., 1953-56; trust officer Colonial Bank & Trust Co., Waterbury, 1956-63; v.p., trust officer Colonial Bank & Trust Co., 1963-65, sr. trust officer, 1965-66; v.p., sec. Ch. Pension Fund and Affiliates, Ch. Life Ins. Corp., Ch. Ins. Co., Ch. Agy. Corp., Ch. Hymnal Corp., 1966-67, exec. v.p., 1967-68, pres., dir., 1968-91; pres. emeritus Ch. Pension Fund and Affiliates, Ch. Life Ins. Corp., et al., 1991—; mgr. East Side House Settlement; bd. dirs. Seabury Press, Inc., Mariners Instl. Funds, Inc., Mariner Tax Free Instl. Fund, UST Master Funds, Morehouse Pub. Co. , Inc., Mariner Funds Trust, Mariner Equity Trust, Pigmy Corp., U.S.T. Master Tax Free Funds, U.S.T. Master Variable Series, Inc., Rosiclare Lead and Fluorspar Mining Co., others; cons. to exec. dir. Pension Benefit Guaranty Corp. Trustee Hillspeak, Eureka Springs, Ark., Canterbury Cathedral Trust in Am., Hoosac Sch. Washington Nat. Cathedral, Nashotah Theol. Sem., Wis., H.B. and F.K. Bugher Found., Living Ch. Found.; mem. exec. com. N.Y. couns. Boy Scouts Am., Ch. Pensions Conf.; mem. econ. adv. bd. Columbia U. Grad. Sch. Bus. Adminstrn, mem. John Carter Brown Libr. Assoc. With inf. AUS, 1943-46. Decorated Bronze Star, Purple Heart with oak leaf cluster, Mil. Order of the Purple Heart, Knights of Malta, Order St. John. Mem. Am. Numis. Soc. (councillor), Conn. Bankers Assn. (v.p., head trust divsn.), Am. Numis. Assn., Newsomen Soc., St. Andrew's Soc. (N.Y.C.), Brown Club (N.Y.C.), Union League Club (N.Y.C.), Church Club (N.Y.C.) (pres. 1991—), Country Club of New Canaan, Athenaeum Club (London), Pilgrims, Union, Met. Clubs (Washington), Yeaman's Hall Club (Charleston, S.C.), Phi Beta Kappa. Republican. Episcopalian (vestryman). Clubs: St. Andrew's Soc. (N.Y.C.), Brown (N.Y.C.), Union League (N.Y.C.), Church (N.Y.C.), Country of New Canaan, Athenaeum (London), Pilgrims, Union, Met. (Washington), Yeaman's Hall (Charleston, S.C.). Home: 2 Hathaway Common New Canaan CT 06840-5737 Office: 800 2nd Ave New York NY 10017-4709

ROBINSON, ROBERT BLACQUE, association executive; b. Long Beach, Calif., Apr. 24, 1927; s. Joseph LeRoi and Frances Hansel R.; m. Susan Amelia Thomas, Jan. 21, 1960; children: Victoria, Shelly, Blake, Sarah. Student, Oreg. State Coll., 1946; BA, UCLA, 1950; student, U. Hawaii. Partner, Pritchard Assocs. (Mgmt. Cons.), Honolulu, 1956-58; asst. dir. Econ. Planning and Coordination Authority, Hawaii, 1959; dep. dir. dept. econ. devel. State of Hawaii, 1960-63; asst. mgr. Pacific Concrete and Rock Co., Ltd, Honolulu, 1963-66, exec. v.p. and gen. mgr., 1966-68, pres. and gen. mgr., 1968-75; chmn. Pacific Concrete and Rock Co., Ltd., 1976-77; pres. C. of C. of Hawaii, Honolulu, 1977—. Bd. govs. Hawaii Employers Coun., 1969-74, mem. exec. com., 1969-74, vice chmn., 1973-74; bd. dirs. Pacific Aerospace Mus., 1982-86; mem. Hawaii Tourism Conf., 1977, chmn., 1981-82; bd. dirs. Aloha United Fund, 1970-76, sec., 1972, v.p., 1973-76; bd. dirs. Oahu Devel. Conf., 1970-75; treas., bd. dirs. Crime Stoppers Hawaii, 1981—; mem. Hawaii Joint Coun. on Econ. Edn., 1985—; bd. dirs. Jr. Achievement Hawaii, 1967-73, pres., 1969; bd. dirs. Hawaii Ednl. Coun., 1974-75, Health and Community Services Coun., 1982-84; mem. exec. com. Hawaii Conv. Ctr. Coun., 1984—, Interagency Energy Conservation Coun., State of Hawaii, 1978—; trustee Cen. Union Ch., 1983-86; bd. dirs. Waikiki Improvement Assn. Inc., 1986—; mem. Ctr. for Tropical and Subtropical Aquaculture industry Adv. Coun., 1987—; chmn. Mayor's Adv.

Com. on Pacific Nations Ctr., 1988-89. Lt. comdr. USNR, 1945-46, ret. Mem. Japan-Am. Conf. of Mayors and C. of C. Pres. (mem. Am. exec. com. 1974—), Am. Soc. Assn. Execs. (past dir. Hawaii chpt.), Hawaii Execs. Coun. (found. , Young Pres. Assn. (past mem.), Aloha Soc. Assn. Execs., C of C. Hawaii (dir. 1972-75, chmn. 1975), Coun. of Profit Sharing Industries (past dir. Hawaii sect.), Cement and Concrete Products Industry of Hawaii (pres. 1968), Hawaii Mfrs. Assn. (past dir.), Navy League of U.S. (Hawaii council), Engring. Assn. Hawaii, Pacific Club, Rotary, Sigma Chi. Home: 1437 Kalaepohaku St Honolulu HI 96816-1804 Office: C of C Hawaii 735 Bishop St Ste 220 Honolulu HI 96813-4816

ROBINSON, ROBERT JAMES, retired manufacturing executive; b. Pitts., Dec. 19, 1935; s. Robert S. and Mary Hazel (Beale) R.; m. Joyce Ann Cordt, Aug. 12, 1961; children: Wende Lynne, Brittany D., Robert S. II. BS, Carnegie Inst. Tech., 1957; MBA, U. Chgo., 1977. From engr. to gen. supt. Allegheny Ludlum Industries, Dunkirk, N.Y., 1957-74; from v.p. ops. to COO, exec. v.p. Axia Inc., Oak Brook, Ill., 1974-92; mgmt. cons. Colorado Springs, 1992—. Co-inventor bag closing machine. Mem. Union League. Republican. Methodist. Avocations: hunting, fishing, skiing, sport cars. Home and office: 8315 Bluffview Way Colorado Springs CO 80919

ROBINSON, ROBERT L., financial service company executive, lawyer; b. Ridgeway, Va., Feb. 22, 1936; s. Gerald L. and Annie (McBride) R.; m. Audrey M. Allen, July 30, 1960; children: Robert, Diane, Kelly. B.A., Va. State Coll., 1957; LL.B., Harvard U., 1960; M.B.A., U. Conn., 1976. Bar: N.Y. 1961, Pa. 1978. Atty. N.Y. Central Ry. Co., N.Y.C., 1960-63; asst. gen. counsel Crane Co., N.Y.C., 1963-71; counsel Xerox Corp., Stamford, Conn., 1971-77; v.p., asst. gen. counsel and sec. INA Corp., Phila., 1977-82; sr. v.p., gen. counsel investment group CIGNA Corp., Bloomfield, Conn., 1982-84, sr. v.p., asst. gen. counsel, corp. sec., 1984-87; sr. v.p., gen. counsel property & casualty group CIGNA Corp., Phila., 1987-88, sr. v.p., chief counsel litigation, 1988—. Dir. Com. of Seventy, Phila. Maritime Mus. Served to lt. U.S. Army, 1957. Mem. ABA, Pa. Bar Assn., Westchester-Fairfield Corp. Counsel Assn. (founder, bd. dirs. pres. 1976-77), Great Oak Yacht Cub, Harvard Club (N.Y.C.), Merion Cricket Club, Phila. Club. Republican. Office: CIGNA Corp 1601 Chestnut St Philadelphia PA 19192-0003

ROBINSON, RONALD ALAN, oil company executive; b. Louisville, Mar. 23, 1952; s. J. Kenneth and Juanita M. (Crosier) R.; B.S., Ga. Inst. Tech., 1974; M.B.A. with honors, Harvard U., 1978. Staff engr., asst. to exec. v.p. ops. Dual Drilling Co., Wichita Falls, Tex., 1978-80; v.p. Dreco, Inc., Houston, 1980-84, pres., dir. subs. Triflo Industries Internat. Inc.; pres., chief operating officer Ramteck Systems, Inc., 1984-87; chmn. and chief exec. officer Denver Techs. Inc., 1988—. Recipient Optimist Internat. Citizenship award, 1970; Gardiner Symonds fellow, 1977. Mem. Harvard Alumni Assn. Home: 4815 Newstead Pl Colorado Springs CO 80906-5935 Office: Denver Equipment Co 621 S Sierra Madre St Colorado Springs CO 80903-4096

ROBINSON, RONALD MICHAEL, health care financial executive, financial consultant; b. N.Y.C., May 1, 1942; s. Arthur John and Matilda (Siegel) R.; m. Mary Jane Reemelin, Feb. 25, 1972; children: Scott Edward, Elizabeth Drew. BS, Ohio State U., 1964; MBA, U. Pa., 1966. CPA, Pa. Fin. mgr. Am. Airlines, Inc., N.Y.C., 1969-72; mgmt. cons. Coopers & Lybrand, Phila., 1973-75; pres. Robinson Assocs., Inc., Paoli, Pa., 1975-81; dir. fin. and administr., chief fin. officer Decision Scis. Corp., Jenkintown, Pa., 1981-82; sr. v.p. fin., chief fin. officer Presbyn. Homes, Inc., Camp Hill, Pa., 1982—. Bd. dirs. Healthamerica. Mem. Carlisle (Pa.) Borough Council, 1988-92. Mem. AICPA, Pa. Inst. CPAs, Health Care Fin. Mgmt. Assn., Fin. Execs. Inst., Pa. Assn. Non-Profit Homes for Aging, Masons, Rotary. Home: 201 Graham St Carlisle PA 17013 Office: Presbyn Homes Inc 1217 Slate Hill Rd Camp Hill PA 17011-8034

ROBINSON, ROSCOE ROSS, nephrologist, educator; b. Oklahoma City, Aug. 21, 1929; s. Roscoe and Tennie (Ross) R.; m. Ann Allen, Aug. 24, 1952; children: Susan, Brooke. BS, U. Ctrl. Okla., 1949; MD, U. Okla., 1954, LHD, 1994. Diplomate: Nat. Bd. Med. Examiners, Am. Bd. Internal Medicine (asso. mem. bd. govs. 1975-78, mem. 1979-82, chmn. test com. on nephrology 1979-82). Intern in medicine Duke U. Med. Ctr., Durham, N.C., 1954-55, jr. asst. resident in medicine, 1955-56, chief resident, instr. medicine, 1957-58, assoc. in medicine, 1960-62, asst. prof. medicine, dir. div. nephrology, 1962-65, assoc. prof. medicine, dir. div. nephrology, 1965-69, prof. medicine, dir. div. nephrology, 1969-78, Florence McAlister prof. medicine, dir. div. nephrology, 1978-81, assoc. v.p., 1976-81; chief exec. officer Duke U. Hosp., 1976-81; prof. medicine, vice chancellor health affairs Vanderbilt U. Med. Ctr., Nashville, 1981—; Am. Heart Assn. rsch. fellow, vis. fellow dept. medicine Columbia-Presbyn. Med. Ctr., N.Y.C., 1956-57; clin. investigator Durham VA Hosp., 1960-62, attending physician, 1962-81; cons. nephrology Fayetteville and Asheville, N.C.; cons. nephrology Research Triangle (N.C.) Inst., 1964-81; nat. cons. to surgeon gen. USAF, 1970-89; chmn. N.C. Kidney Coun. Region 21, Dept. HEW, 1977-81; bd. dirs. Research!America, 1993—. Mem. editorial bd. Archives Internal Medicine, 1970-80, Seminars in Nephrology, 1972-93, Mineral and Electrolyte Metabolism, 1977—; mem. editorial com. Fogerty internat. com. Monograph on Prevention of Kidney and Urinary Tract Disease; cons. editor renal diseases: Cecil Textbook of Medicine, 15th edit., 16th edit.; contbr. articles to profl. jours. Bd. dirs. SunHealth Corp., 1986-92, 1st Am. Corp., Tenn., 1992—; trustee Montgomery Bell Acad., Nashville, 1983—, Duke U. 1994—. Fellow ACP; mem. Am. Clin. and Climatol. Assn., Am. Fedn. Clin. Rsch. (councillor So. sect. 1968-71), Assn. Am. Physicians, European Dialysis and Transplant Assn., Am. Heart Assn., N.C. Heart Assn. (sr. investigator 1962-74, exec. com., bd. dirs. 1971-72), Am. Soc. Clin. Investigation, So. Soc. Clin. Investigation (councillor 1977-80), Am. Physiol. Soc., Am. Soc. Artificial Internal Organs (councillor 1968-71), Internat. Soc. Nephrology (editor Kidney Internat. jour 1971-84, exec. com. 1972—, v.p. 1984-87, pres.-elect 1987-90, pres. 1990-93), Am. Soc. Nephrology (councillor 1977-80, pres.-elect 1980-81, pres. 1981-82), Nat. Kidney Found. (mem. sci. adv. bd. 1970-75), Kidney Found. N.C., Assn. Acad. Health Ctrs. (bd. dirs. 1985-91, chmn. 1989-90), Soc. Med. Adminstrs. (pres.-elect 1989-91, pres. 1991-93), Nat. Inst. Diabetes, Digestive and Kidney Diseases (mem. nat. adv. coun. 1987-90), Alpha Omega Alpha. Home: 501 Jackson Blvd Nashville TN 37205-3427 Office: Vanderbilt U Med Center Nashville TN 37232

ROBINSON, SAMUEL L., wholesale grocery company executive. With Super Food Services, Inc., Dayton, 1972—, merchandising mgr., then div. mgr., sr. v.p. Ohio ops., now pres., chief operating officer. Office: Super Food Svcs Inc 3233 Newmark Dr Miamisburg OH 45342-5422

ROBINSON, SHARON PATTYSON, English educator; b. Rockville Center, N.Y., Mar. 15, 1947; d. Jack Ward and Mary Margaret (Coogan) Pattyson; m. W. Bruce Robinson, July 18, 1971; 1 child, Margaret L. AB, Vassar Coll., 1969; MA, Johns Hopkins U., 1970; PhD, U. Toledo, 1976. Lectr. English dept U. Conn., Stamford, 1975-77; vis. asst. prof. U. Minn., Mpls., 1977-78; assoc. prof., chair English dept. Russell Sage Coll., Troy, N.Y., 1978—. Contbr. articles to profl. jours. Mem. N.Y. State Theatre Inst. Citizens Bd., Albany, N.Y., 1989—. Vis. humanities scholar NYU/ Mellon Found., 1990. Mem. MLA, AAUP (sec. 1989-90). Democrat. Office: Russell Sage Coll 45 Ferry St Troy NY 12180-4115

ROBINSON, SHARON PORTER, federal official; b. Louisville. B in Edn., English and Psychology, U. Ky., 1966, M in Edn.; Curriculum and Instrn., 1976, D in Ednl. Adminstrn. and Supervision, 1979. Tchr. Lexington, Ky., U.S. AFB, Bitburg, Germany; assoc. dir. Jefferson County Edn. Consortium, Ky., late 1970's; dir. instrn. and profl. devel. NEA, 1980-89, dir. R & D arm Nat. Ctr. Innovation, 1989-93; asst. sec. ednl. rsch. and improvement U.S. Dept. Edn., 1993—; cons. Nat. Bd. Profl. Teaching Standards; head tchr. edn. initiative Nat. Ctr. Innovation. Office: Dept of Education Educational Rsch & Improvement 555 New Jersey Ave NW Washington DC 20208-0001

ROBINSON, SMOKEY, singer, composer; b. Detroit; m. Claudette Rogers (div.); children: Berry William, Tamla Claudette. V.p. Motown Record Corp. Formed group, Smokey Robinson and the Miracles, with Miracles, 1957-72, performed Detroit nightclubs, co-founder, Tamla record label, 1959; numerous singles and album recs. including: Sweet Harmony, 1973, Virgin

Man, 1974, Agony and the Ecstasy, 1975, Quiet Storm, 1976, Open, 1976, There will Come a Day (I'm Gonna Happen to You), 1977; appearances at clubs, colls., also network TV shows including Shindig: star own TV spl., 1971; solo albums include Smokey, 1973, A Quiet Storm, Smokey's Family Robinson, Deep in My Soul, Smokin', Warm Thoughts, Being with You, 1989, Smokey's World, Shop Around, One Heartbeat, 1987, Love Smokey, 1990, Blame It on Love & All the Great Hits, 1990, Double Good Everything, 1992; appeared on Broadway in An Evening with Smokey Robinson, 1985; author: (autobiography with David Ritz) Smokey: Inside My Life, 1989. Inducted Rock 'n Roll Hall of Fame, 1986, Songwriters Hall of Fame, 1986; recipient Grammy award for best male rhythm & blues vocal perfomance, 1987, Founders award ASCAP, 1988. Office: care Michael Roshkind 6255 W Sunset Blvd Fl 18 Los Angeles CA 90028-7496*

ROBINSON, SPENCER, JR., retired service club executive, accountant; b. Bridgeport, Conn., Apr. 16, 1942; s. Spencer Robinson and Helen (Diesinger) McNeill; m. Sally Emptage, June 21, 1963; children: David Spencer, Todd Wallace, John Marshall, Sarah Ann. BSIM, Ga. Tech. U., 1963; BS in Acctg., Jacksonville U., 1969; MSHA, U. Ala., Birmingham, 1989. Mng. ptnr. Deloitte Haskins & Sells, N.Y.C., 1963-85; exec. v.p., chief operating officer U. Ala. Health Svcs. Found., Birmingham, 1985-90; gen. sec., chief adminstrv. officer Rotary Internat., Evanston, Ill., 1990-94. Contbr. articles to profl. jours. Gen. sec. Rotary Found., Evanston, 1990-94; mem. Gov's. Com. of 100, La., 1985; trustee Nat. Multiple Sclerosis Soc., La., 1984; sec., treas. Crimestoppers, Inc., New Orleans, 1983. Recipient Razzberry award Birmingham Press Club, 1989. Republican. Presbyterian. Home: PO Box 280 Montreat NC 28757-0280

ROBINSON, SPENCER T. (HERK ROBINSON), professional baseball team executive; b. June 25, 1940; m. Kathy Robinson; children: Ashley, Amanda. Student, U. Miami, Washington U., St. Louis. With Cin. Reds., 1962-67; asst. scouting dir. Kansas City Royals, 1969-72, Balt. Orioles, 1968; dir. stadium ops. Kansas City Royals, 1973-74, v.p., 1975-80, exec. v.p. adminstrn., 1985-90, exec. v.p., gen. mgr., 1990—; former mem. bd. dirs Office: Kans City Royals PO Box 419969 Kansas City MO 64141-6969*

ROBINSON, STEPHEN MICHAEL, applied mathematician, educator; b. Columbus, Ohio, Apr. 12, 1942; s. Arthur Howard and Mary Elizabeth (Coffin) R.; m. Chong-Suk Han, May 10, 1968; children: Diana Marie, James Andrew. BA, U. Wis., 1962, PhD, 1971; MS, NYU, 1963. Adminstr. U. Wis., Madison, 1969-72, asst. prof., 1972-75, assoc. prof., 1975-79, prof. indsl. engring. and computer scis., 1979—, chmn. dept. indsl. engring., 1981-84; cons. various agys. Dept. Def., 1971-86; cons. Battelle Meml. Labs., Columbus, 1980-81. Editor: Math. of Ops. Rsch., 1981-86, assoc. editor 1975-80, Jour. Ops. Rsch., 1974-86, Math. Programming, 1986-91; mem. bd. editors Annals Ops. Rsch., 1984—, Set-Valued Analysis, 1992—, Jour. Convex Analysis, 1994—; adv. editor Math. of Ops. Rsch., 1987—; contbr. numerous articles to profl. jours. Trustee Village of Shorewood Hills, Wis., 1974-76, mem. fin. com. , 1973-87; bd. overseers Simon's Rock Coll., Great Barrington, Mass., 1991—. Served to capt. U.S. Army, 1963-69, Korea, Vietnam. Decorated Legion of Merit, Bronze star, Air medal, Army Commendation medal with 2 oak leaf clusters. Mem. Inst. for Ops. Rsch. and Mgmt. Scis. (mem. Ops. Rsch. Soc. Am. coun. 1991-94), Inst. Indsl. Engrs., Soc. Indsl. and Applied Math., Math. Programming Soc. (mem.-at-large of coun. 1991-94), Madison Club. Home: 1014 University Bay Dr Madison WI 53705-2251 Office: U Wis Dept Indsl Engring 1513 University Ave Madison WI 53706-1572

ROBINSON, SUE LEWIS, federal judge; b. 1952. BA with highest honors, U. Del., 1974; JD, U. Pa., 1978. Assoc. Potter, Anderson & Corron, Wilmington, Del., 1978-83; asst. U.S. atty. U.S. Attys. Office, 1983-88; U.S. magistrate judge U.S. Dist. Ct. (Del. dist.), 1988-91, dist. judge, 1991—. Mem. Del. State Bar Assn. (sec. 1986-87). Office: US Dist Ct J Caleb Boggs Fed Bldg 844 King Street Rm 6124 Wilmington DE 19801

ROBINSON, SUMNER MARTIN, college administrator; b. Boston, Dec. 7, 1928; s. Eli and Fannie (Solov) R.; m. Leanore Reiss, Dec. 20, 1953; children: Andrew, Eric, Evan. A.B., U. Maine, 1949; B.S., Mass. Coll. Pharmacy, 1954, M.S., 1956, Ph.D. 1961. Asst. prof. pharmacology Mass. Coll. Pharmacy, Boston, 1961-65; research biologist-pharmacologist U.S. Army Research Inst. Environ. Medicine, Natick, Mass., 1965-76, cons., 1976—; dean Mass. Coll. Pharmacy, Boston, 1976-83; pres. St. Louis Coll. Pharmacy, 1983-93, Mass. Coll. Pharmacy & Applied Health Sci., Boston, 1993—. Recipient Coll. medal Mass. Coll. Pharmacy, 1983. Mem. Am. Assn. Colls. Pharmacy, Am. Pharm. Assn., Nat. Assn. Retail Druggists. Democrat. Home: 59 Whitewood Rd Westwood MA 02090 Office: Mass Coll Pharmacy and Allied Health Sci 179 Longwood Ave Boston MA 02115

ROBINSON, SUSAN MITTLEMAN, data processing executive; b. Bklyn., Nov. 18, 1941; d. Samuel and Ida (Priest) Mittleman; m. Sheldon N. Robinson, June 5, 1962; children: Edward Bruce, Nancy Michelle, Jonathan Scott, Karen Barbara, Judith Lynn. AAS in Computer Sci., BCC, Lincroft, N.J., 1981; BBA, CUNY, 1962; MS in Computer Sci., Fairleigh Dickinson U., 1983; postgrad., Seton Hall U., 1983-85. Engr. asst. United Technologies, East Hartford, Conn., 1962-64; programmer, systems analyst Litton Industries (Sweda), Pine Brook, N.J., 1981-83; asst. prof. data processing Mercer Coll., West Windsor, N.J., 1983-85; adj. instr. data processing Brookdale Community Coll., Lincroft, N.J., 1983—; coord. MIS N.J. Dept. Health, Trenton, N.J., 1985—, Novell Lan administr., 1994—; outsource cons. Medicare/Medicaid, Trenton, 1989—; cons. Health Care Fin. Authority, Balt., 1995—. Author (reference material) Info-Henco, 1987, Automated Survey Processing Environment Users Training Manual, 1993; developer computerized sys. to help patients and their family select a nursing home. Exec. bd. Temple Beth Am, Parsippany, N.J., 1972-80. Mem. SAS Users Group, N.J. DOH Prime Users Group. Avocations: knitting, puzzle-solving, travel. Office: NJ Dept Health CN 367 Trenton NJ 08625

ROBINSON, TERENCE VACHEL, secondary education educator; b. Yakima, Wash., Dec. 13, 1943; s. Claude Vachel and Sibyl Lucille (Terry) R.; m. Nancy Ann Main, June 27, 1965; children: Teri Suzanne, Andrew Tai, Melissa Kay, Gregory Scott, Nicholas Aaron. BS, Calif. State U., Fullerton, 1972; MEd, U. La Verne, 1991. Cert. elem. tchr. Tchr. ABC Unified Sch. Dist., Cerritos, Calif., 1972—. Bd. dirs. La Mirada Little League, La Mirada, Calif., 1985; deacon Ch. of Christ, Norwalk, Calif., 1987-90. With U.S. Army, 1962-65. Mem. ASCD, Assn. Calif. Sch. Adminstrs., Nat. Coun. Social Studies. Republican. Avocations: fishing, golf, R.V. camping, travel, heavy duty truck driving. Home: 15224 San Ardo Dr La Mirada CA 90638-5724 Office: Haskell Jr High Sch 11525 Del Amo Blvd Cerritos CA 90701-7404

ROBINSON, THEODORE CURTIS, JR., lawyer; b. Chgo., Jan. 22, 1916; s. Theodore Curtis and Edna Alice (Willard) R.; m. Marynel Werner, Dec. 28, 1940; children: Theodore Curtis III, Peter S. BA, Western Res. U. 1938, LLB, 1940. Bar: Ohio 1940, U.S. Dist. Ct. (no. dist.) Ohio 1946, U.S. Ct. Appeals (8th cir.) 1948, U.S. Dist. Ct. (we. dist.) Wis. 1950, U.S. Dist. Ct. (we. dist.) N.Y. 1950, U.S. Ct. Appeals (6th cir.) 1950, Ill. 1957, U.S. Dist. Ct. (no. dist.) Ill. 1957, U.S. Ct. Appeals (7th cir.) 1964, U.S. Supreme Ct. 1972. Assoc. Davis & Young, Cleve., 1940; law clk. no. dist. ct. div. U.S. Dist. Ct., Cleve., 1940-42; assoc. Leckie, McCreary, et al, Cleve., 1945-52; ptnr. McCreary, Hinslea & Ray, Cleve., 1953-57, McCreary, Hinslea, Ray & Robinson, Chgo., 1957-90; counsel Ray, Robinson, Hannin & Carle, Chgo., 1990-91, Ray, Robinson, Carle, Davies & Snyder, Chgo., 1991—; mem. exec. com. Maritime Law Assn. of U.S., N.Y.C., 1981-83; pres. Propellor Club of U.S., Chgo., 1966-67; sec., treas. Internat. Shipmasters Assn., Chgo., 1958-91. Lt. USCG, 1943-45. Fellow Am. Coll. Trial Lawyers; mem. ABA, Chgo. Bar Assn. (com. chmn. 1973), Internat. Assn. Def. Counsel, Order Coif, Traffic Club Chgo. (dir. 1986, 87), Whitehall Club (N.Y.), Nat. Eagle Scout Assn. Republican. Avocations: gardening, golf, reading. Office: Ray Robinson Carle Davies & Snyder 850 W Jackson Blvd Chicago IL 60607-3025

ROBINSON, THEODORE GOULD, golf course architect; b. Long Beach, Calif., May 17, 1923; s. Franklin Willard and Hope (Gould) R.; m. Barbara Henderson, Oct. 28, 1949; children: Theodore G. Jr., Kristine Robinson Monroe, Leigha Robinson Ramsey. BA, U. Calif. Berkeley, 1944; MS, U. So. Calif., 1948. With Gordon Whitnall & Assocs., L.A., 1941-51; prin.

Robinson Golf Design, Dana Point, Calif., 1951—. Designer 150 golf courses throughout world. Ensign USN, 1943-46. Recipient awards for best new courses Golf Digest. Mem. Am. Soc. Golf Course Architects (pres. 1983). Office: Robinson Golf Designs Inc 33971 Selva Rd Ste 135 Dana Point CA 92629-3788

ROBINSON, THOMAS BULLENE, retired civil engineer; b. Kansas City, Mo., Feb. 28, 1917; s. David Beach and Aileen March (Weaver) R.; m. Suzanne Callaway, May 24, 1941; children: Suzanne, Thomas Bullene, Alice Robinson Levy. B.S., Kans. U., 1939; M.S., Columbia U., 1940. Diplomate: Am. Acad. Environ. Engrs. Asst. engr. Black & Veatch (cons. engr.), Kansas City, 1940-43; prin. asst. engr., prin. engr. Black & Veatch (cons. engr.), 1946-56, partner, 1956-65, asst. mng. partner, 1965-72, mng. partner, 1973-82; chmn. bd. Black & Veatch Internat., 1973-82; cons., 1982—. Past pres. Heart of Am. United Campaign; trustee Kansas City U., U. Kans. Endowment Assn., Midwest Research Inst. Served to lt. Civil Engr. Corps, USNR, 1943-46. Recipient Honor award for disting. service in engring. U. Mo., 1971; Disting. Service citation U. Kans., 1975; Disting. Engring. Service award U. Kans., 1982. Fellow ASCE (hon. mem.), Am. Cons. Engrs. Council (pres. 1970-71); mem. Nat. Acad. Engring., Am. Soc. Profl. Engrs., Am. Water Works Assn. (hon.), Sigma Xi, Tau Beta Pi, Sigma Tau, Beta Theta Pi. Club: Kansas City Country (Kansas City). Home: 6401 Norwood St Shawnee Mission KS 66208-1826

ROBINSON, THOMAS CHRISTOPHER, academic administrator, educator; b. Buffalo, Oct. 16, 1944; s. Christopher Sidney and Eleanor Florence (Martin) R.; m. Helen Dare Tew, June 21, 1986; children: Diane Dawn, Kristen Elizabeth, Molly Lindsay, Norman Ashley. BA, SUNY, Buffalo, 1966, EdM, 1968, PhD, 1991; grad. mgmt. devel. program, Harvard U., 1989. N.Y. State sec. sch. cert in social studies. Admissions officer, office of admissions of record SUNY, Buffalo, 1966-72, assoc. dean Sch. Health Related Professions, 1975-78; asst. dir. Erie County Lab., Buffalo, 1972-75; assoc. dean Coll. Health Professions, U. Ky., Lexington, 1978-84, dean, 1984—; cons. MDS Labs., Hamilton, Ont., Can., 1973-75, Joint U.S.-Arabian Commn. on Econ. Cooperation, 1986-87, West Sussex Inst. Higher Edn., Bogner Regis, U.K., 1987, U. Wis. Sys. Ctrs. of Excellence Program, 1988, Pub. Health Svc. Health Resources Adminstrn., 1983, 90-91; mem. exec. com. Nat. Practitioner Data Bank, 1992-94. Contbr. articles to profl. jours. Mem. Health Sys. Agy. Coun., Buffalo, 1977-78, Western N.Y. Hemophilia Soc. Bd. Buffalo, 1977-78, Lexington-Fayette County Bd. Health, Lexington, 1987-91, program excellence project Ohio Bd. Regents, United Way of Bluegrass Healthcare Devel. Bd., 1991; mem. La. Bd. Regents, 1995, Univ. Wolverhampton, U.K. With N.Y. Army N.G., 1968-74. Recipient Svc. award Jour. Allied Health, 1986. Mem. Am. Soc. Allied Health Professions (bd. dirs. 1985-87, Svc. award 1987, Fellow award 1988), Ky. Allied Health Consortium (bd. dirs. 1985-93), So. Assn. Allied Health Deans (sec. 1986-88, chmn. 1988-90), Assn. Schs. Allied Health Professions (pres. 1991-94), Ky. Hosp. Assn., Ky. Assn. of Healthcare Facilities, Ky. Primary Assn., Lexington C. of C., Civil War Round Table, Sigma Phi Epsilon. Avocations: golf, travel, geneology, gardening. Home: 620 Centennial Ln Lexington KY 40502-2770 Office: U Ky Coll Allied Health Professions Med Ctr Anx # 2 Lexington KY 40536

ROBINSON, THOMAS NATHANIEL, pediatrician, educator, researcher; b. Detroit, May 11, 1960; s. Kenneth J. and Judith R. (Rattner) R. BS in Biol. Scis., Stanford U., 1983, MD with rsch. honors, 1988; MPH in Maternal and Child Health, U. Calif., Berkeley, 1987. Diplomate Nat. Bd. Med. Examiners, Am. Bd. Pediatrics. Intern dept. medicine Children's Hosp. and Harvard Med. Sch., Boston, 1988-89, jr. asst. resident, 1989-90, sr. asst. resident, 1990-91; clin. fellow in pediatric medicine Harvard Med. Sch., Boston, 1988-91; Robert Wood Johnson clin. scholar Sch. Medicine Stanford U., Palo Alto, 1991-93, clin. instr. divsn. gen. pediatrics dept. pediatrics, acting dir. youth studies Ctr. for Rsch. in Disease Prevention Sch. Medicine, 1992-93, acting. assoc. prof. divsn. gen. pediatrics dept. pediatrics, co-dir. youth studies Ctr. for Rsch. in Disease Prevention, 1993—; attending physician divsn. gen. pediatrics dept. pediatrics Stanford U. Hosp., Palo Alto, 1992—; Lucile Salter Packard Children's Hosp., Palo Alto, 1992—; clinician scientist Am. Heart Assn., 1993—; presenter in field. Contbr. articles to med. and sci. jours. Alumni Med. scholar Stanford U., 1985; grantee Met. Life Found., 1985-87. Fellow Am. Acad. Pediatrics (candidate, sch. health com. No. Calif. dist. 1992—, chair 1993—); mem. Am. Heart Assn. (grantee 1993—), phys. activity subcom. 1993—). Office: Stanford U Sch Med Ctr for Rsch Disease Prevention 1000 Welch Rd Palo Alto CA 94304

ROBINSON, THURSTON See ROBINSON, JAY (THURSTON)

ROBINSON, VAN NESS D., insurance company executive; b. 1935. Exec. v.p., sec., vice chmn. N.Y. Ctrl. Mut. Fire Ins., Edmeston, N.Y., 1957—. Office: NY Ctrl Mut Fire Ins 1899 Central Plz E Edmeston NY 13335*

ROBINSON, WALTER, newspaper editor. Asst. mng. editor local news, Metro Desk Boston Globe. Office: Boston Globe 135 Morrissey Boston MA 02107*

ROBINSON, WALTER GEORGE, arts management and funding consultant; b. London, June 8, 1911; s. Walter and Annie (Ledger) R.; m. Ruth V. Holden, Sept. 14, 1941 (dec. Mar. 1987); stepchildren: Malcolm D. Whitman III, Gail W. Hughes; m. Vesta H. Bogle, May 31, 1990. Student, NYU, 1943; D.F.A. (hon.), Mpls. Coll. Art and Design, 1975. Engaged in investment bus. N.Y.C., 1928-33; with Bass River Savs. Bank, South Yarmouth, Mass., 1934-60, pres., 1952-60; dir. Cape & Vineyard Electric Co., 1958-60, Hyannis Trust Co., until 1960; pres. Mpls. Soc. Fine Arts, governing and supporting orgn. for Mpls. Inst. Arts, Mpls. Coll. Art and Design, Children's Theatre Co., 1960-72, vice chmn., treas., sec., 1972-75; acting dir. Mpls. Sch. Art, 1962-63; acting pres. Mpls. Coll. Art and Design, 1974-75; dir. resource devel. Mus. Fine Arts, Boston, 1975-77; arts mgmt. and funding cons., 1977—; mem. Art Advocates, Inc., 1984-87; trustee Farmers & Mechanics Savs. Bank. Vice pres. Cape Cod Hosp., 1955-60; chmn. Mpls. Com. for Urban Environment, 1968-70, 72-74; mem. Minn. State Arts Council, 1967-73, Minn. Heritage Preservation Commn., 1972-75; chmn. Mpls. Bicentennial Commn., 1974-75; mem. Minn. Com. on Esthetic Environment, 1973-75; founding dir. E.B. Kelley Found., Hyannis, Mass., 1954-87, v.p., 1985-87; bd. dirs Tyrone Guthrie Theatre Found., Mpls., 1960-70; trustee Northwestern Hosp., 1967-74, Am. Assn. Museums, 1973-75. Clubs: Skylight, Minneapolis, Minnesota (Mpls.). Home: PO Box 490 Damariscotta ME 04543-0490

ROBINSON, WALTER STITT, JR., historian; b. Matthews, N.C., Aug. 28, 1917; s. Walter Stitt and Mary Irene (Jamison) S.; m. Constance Lee Mock, Mar. 18, 1944; children—Ethel Barry, Walter Lee. B.A. summa cum laude, Davidson (N.C.) Coll., 1939; M.A., U. Va., 1941, Ph.D. 1950. Asst. prof., then assoc. prof. history Florence (Ala.) State Coll., 1946-48; mem. faculty U. Kans., Lawrence, 1950—; prof. history U. Kans., 1959-88, dean emeritus, 1988—, chmn. dept., 1968-73; mem. Nat. Civil War Centennial Commn., 1961-65, Kans. Com. Humanities, 1971-78, chmn., 1976-77. Author: Land Grants in Virginia, 1607-1699, 1957, The Southern Colonial Frontier, 1607-1763, 1979, James Glen: From Scottish Provost to Royal Governor of South Carolina, 1985; editor: Indian Treaties of Colonial Virginia, 2 vols., 1983, Indian Treaties of Colonial Maryland, 1987; mem. editl. bd.: 18th century bibliography in Philos. Quar., 1975-78; contbr. articles to profl. jours. Mem. adminstrv. bd. First United Methodist Ch., Lawrence, 1952—; exec. com., bd. dirs. Menninger Found., 1959-60, Am. Philos. Soc., 1967, 83, NEH, 1994. Mem. Orgn. Am. Historians (chmn. program com. 1959), So. Hist. Assn., Kans. Soc. (bd. dirs., exec. com. 1989—), Douglas County Hist. Soc. (pres. 1979-81, pres. 1995, bd. dirs.), Raven Soc., Phi Beta Kappa, Phi Alpha Theta (assoc. editor U. Kans. faculty bull. 1980-81, 86-87, pres. 1984-85). Home: 801 Broadview Dr Lawrence KS 66044-2490 Office: Dept History U Kans Lawrence KS 66045

ROBINSON, WILKES COLEMAN, federal judge; b. Anniston, Ala., Sept. 30, 1925; s. Walter Wade and Catherine Elizabeth (Coleman) R.; m. Julia Von Poellnitz Rowan, June 24, 1955; children: Randolph C., Peyton H., Thomas Wilkes Coleman. A.B., U. Ala., 1948; LL.B., U. Va., 1951, J.D.,

1970. Bar: Ala. 1951, Va. 1962, Mo. 1966, Kans. 1983. Assoc. Bibb & Hemphill, Anniston, Ala., 1951-54; city recorder City of Anniston, 1953-55; judge Juvenile and Domestic Relations Ct. of Calhoun County, Ala., 1954-56; atty. legal dept. GM&O R.R., Mobile, Ala., 1956-58; commerce counsel, asst. gen. atty. Seaboard Air Line R.R., Richmond, Va., 1958-66; commerce counsel Monsanto Co., St. Louis, 1966-70; gen. counsel, v.p. Marion Labs., Inc., Kansas City, Mo., 1970-79; pres. Gulf and Gt. Plains Legal Found., Kansas City, Mo., 1980-85; atty. Howard, Needles, Tammen & Bergendoff, Kansas City, 1985-86, also bd. dirs.; v.p. S.R. Fin. Group, Inc., Overland Park, Kans., 1986-87; judge U.S. Ct. Fed. Claims, Washington, 1987—. Bd. govs. Kansas City Philharmonic Orch., 1975-77. Served with USNR, 1943-44. Mem. Army Navy Country Club, Skyline Club, Univ. Club, Masons, Scottish Rite, Phi Beta Kappa (past treas. Kansas City, Mo. chpt.), Phi Eta Sigma, Phi Alpha Theta, Kappa Alpha. Episcopalian. Home: 2353 S Queen St Arlington VA 22202-1550 Office: US Ct Fed Claims 717 Madison Pl NW Washington DC 20005-1011

ROBINSON, WILLIAM ANDREW, health service executive, physician; b. Phila., Jan. 13, 1943; s. Colonial Washington and Lillian Dorothy (Ivey) R.; m. Jacqueline Ellen Garcia, Mar. 28, 1980; 1 child, David Alan; 1 child by previous marriage, William Andrew Jr. BA, Hampton U., 1964; MD, Meharry Med. Coll., 1971; MPH, Johns Hopkins U., 1971. Diplomate Nat. Bd. Med. Examiners; lic. physician, Md. Rotating intern George W. Hubbard Hosp., Nashville, 1971-72, emergency rm. physician, 1972; med. officer gastrointestinal drug sect., bur. drugs FDA USPHS, Dept. Health, Edn. and Welfare, Rockville, Md., 1973-75; dep. dir. office health resources opportunity USPHS, Dept. Health and Human Svcs., Rockville, 1975-80, dep. dir. bur. health professions health resources administrn., 1980-87, chief med. officer health resources and svcs. adminstrn., 1987-89; dep. asst. sec. minority health, dir. office minority health USPHS, Dept. Health and Human Svcs., Washington, 1989-91; acting administr. health resources and svcs. administrn. USPHS, Dept. Health and Human Svcs., Rockville, 1993-94, chief med. officer health resources and svcs. adminstrn., 1991—; chmn. sr. execs. performance rev. bd. Office of Asst. Sec. for Health, 1990-91; pub. health svc. rep. 2d Internat. Conf. on Health Promotion, Adelaide, South Australia; health cons. com. on interior and insular affairs U.S. Ho. of Reps., Washington, 1982-83; appointed field faculty dept. family and comty. health Meharry Med. Coll., 1979; U.S. rep. to WHO Primary Health Care Conf., Alma Ata, Kazakhstan. Mem. nat. editl. bd. Jour. Health Care for the Poor and Underserved, 1991; contbr. articles to profl. jours. Capt. U.S. Army, 1964-67. Recipient Nat. Urban Coalition Comty. Health Svc. award, 1972, Letter of Appreciation, Chmn. Congl. Black Caucus Health Braintrust, U.S. Ho. of Reps., 1988. Mem. AMA, APHA, Am. Acad. Family Physicians, Blacks in Govt., Fed. Physicians Assn., Nat. Med. Assn., Sr. Execs. Assn., Delta Omega (Alpha chpt.). Office: 5600 Fishers Ln Rm 14-39 Rockville MD 20857

ROBINSON, WILLIAM FRANKLIN, retired legal consultant; b. Hammond, Ind., Feb. 10, 1916; s. William P. and Pauline M. (Hopkins) R.; m. Betty Jo Powell, Sept. 15, 1946; children: William Franklin, Stephen Powell, Michael Paul. BA with high honors, Ind. U., 1942, JD, 1944. Bar: Ind. 1944, Mich. 1946, Calif. 1957. Spl. atty. Office Chief Counsel IRS, Washington, Detroit, 1944-46; pvt. practice Detroit, 1946-51; asst. gen. counsel, asst. sec. Montgomery Ward & Co. Inc., Chgo., 1951-56; v.p., gen. counsel, sec., dir. Transam. Fin. Corp., L.A., 1956-82, ret., 1982; legal cons., 1982-83; spl. instr. Wayne State U. Law Sch., U. Detroit, 1947-51. Contbr. articles to profl. jours., chpts. to textbooks. Mem. sch. bd., Calumet City, Ill., 1945-55; apptd. to Gov.'s Credit Retail Adv. Com., 1981; mem., bd. dirs., past pres. Ocean Hills Country Club Homeowners' Assn. Mem. Calif. Loan and Fin. Assn. (chmn. laws and regulations com.), Nat. Consumer Fin. Assn., Conf. Personal Fin. Law, Am. L.A. County bar assns., Acacia, Phi Beta Kappa, Phi Delta Phi. Home: 4136 Andros Way Oceanside CA 92056-7401

ROBINSON, WILLIAM M., lawyer; b. Pitts., June 30, 1941. AB, Princeton U., 1963; LLB, U. Pa., 1966. Bar: Pa. 1967. Ptnr. Reed Smith Shaw & McClay, Pitts. Office: Reed Smith Shaw & McClay 435 6th Ave Pittsburgh PA 15219-1886

ROBINSON, WILLIAM P., academic administrator, consultant, speaker; b. Elmhurst, Ill., Sept. 30, 1949; s. Paul Frederick and Lillian (Horton) R.; m. Bonnie Van Laan, Aug. 10, 1974; children: Brenna Kay, Benjamin Paul, Bailley Kay. Student, Moody Bible Inst., Chgo., 1967-70; AB, U. No. Iowa, 1972; postgrad., Princeton (N.J.) Theol. Sem., 1972-73; MA, Wheaton Coll., 1975; PhD, U. Pitts., 1979. Assoc. minister First Presbyn. Ch., Pitts., 1975-77; instr. U. Pitts., 1977-79; asst. prof. sch. continuing studies Nat. Coll. Edn., Evanston, Ill., 1979-80, dean sch. continuing studies, 1980-84, sr. v.p., 1984-86; pres. Manchester Coll., North Manchester, Ind., 1986-93, Whitworth Coll., Spokane, Wash., 1993; bd. dirs. Coun. Indep. Colls., Ind. Colls. Wash., Whitworth Coll.; cons., speaker for U.S. corps. and svc. orgns. Bd. dirs. Wash. Friends of Higher Edn., Spokane Symphony; vol. various orgns., especially prion work and hunger projects. Recipient various acad. awards. Mem. Nat. Assn. Ind. Colls. and Univs., Coun. Ind. Colls., Spokane Country Club, Spokane Club. Presyterian. Avocation: sports. Home: 215 Hawthorne Rd Spokane WA 99218 Office: Whitworth Coll Spokane WA 99251

ROBINSON, WILLIAM PHILIP, III, lawyer; b. Providence, Jan. 30, 1940; s. William Philip and Dorothy Frances (Hayes) R.; m. Marlene H. Zieky, Sept. 1, 1974; children: Jeffrey, Kevin, Courtney. BA, U. de Louvain, Belgium, 1962; MA, U. R.I., 1966; PhD, U. Conn., 1971; JD, Boston Coll., 1975. Bar: R.I. 1975, Mass. 1985, U.S. Ct. Appeals (1st cir.) 1977, U.S. Supreme Ct. 1989. Instr. U. Conn., Storrs, 1967-71; law clk. U.S. Ct. Appeals, Boston, 1975-77; assoc. Edwards & Angell, Providence, 1977-81, ptnr., 1981—; bd. trustees Providence Country Day Sch., East Providence, 1991—. Mem. East Greenwich Sch. Com., 1988—, vice chmn., 1990-94; mem. exec. com. R.I. Assn. of Sch. Coms.; mem. East Greenwich Dem. Town Com., 1988—; mem. Fed. Bd. Bar Examiners, R.I., 1994—; mem. R.I. Jud. Performance Evaulation Com., 1993—. Mem. Boston Coll. Law Sch. Alumni Assn. (v.p. R.I. chpt. 1990-93, pres. 1993—); Order of Coif, Phi Beta Kappa. Democrat. Roman Catholic. Avocations: reading, skiing, golf. Office: Edwards & Angell 2700 Hospital Trust Tower Providence RI 02903

ROBINSON, WILLIAM R., health facility adminstrator; b. 1951. Controller Meml. Hosp., Worcester, Mass., 1972-82, Leonard Morse Hosp., Methuen, Mass., 1982-85, Valley Regional Health Sys., Inc., Methuen, Mass., 1985-88; treas. New England Daconess Hosp., Boston, 1988—. Office: New England Daconess Hosp 185 Pilgrim Rd Boston MA 02215*

ROBINSON, WILLIAM WHEELER, editor; b. Elizabeth, N.J., Oct. 4, 1918; s. Henry Pearson and Clare Stearns (Wheeler) R.; m. Jane Dimock, Feb. 27, 1942; children: William Wheeler Jr., Martha Robinson Bliss, Alice. B.A., Princeton U., 1939. Traffic rep., traffic dept. Eastern Airlines, N.Y.C., 1939-41; mgr. pub. relations Elco Yacht Div., Bayonne, N.J., 1945-47; sportswriter Newark Evening News, 1944-55; sportswriter, syndicated columnist Newark Star-Ledger, 1955-57; assoc. editor Yachting Mag., N.Y.C., 1957-67; editor, v.p. Yachting Mag., 1967-78, editor-at-large, 1979-86; editor-at-large Cruising World Mag., 1987—; mem. exec. bd. Sea Ventures, Ft. Hancock, N.J., 1974-77; writer radio, TV shows on boating; freelance writer. Author: The Science of Sailing, 1960, New Boat, 1961, A Berth to Bermuda, 1961, Where the Trade Winds Blow, 1963, Expert Sailing, 1965, Over the Horizon, 1966, The World of Yachting, 1966, Better Sailing for Boys and Girls, 1968, (with H.L. Stone) The America's Cup Races, 1970, Legendary Yachts, 1971, rev., 1978, The Sailing Life, 1974, Right Boat for You, 1974, Great American Yacht Designers, 1974, America's Sailing Book, 1976, A Sailor's Tales, 1978, Cruising, the Boats and the Places, 1981, South to the Caribbean, 1981, Where to Cruise, 1984, Islands, 1985, Caribbean Cruising Handbook, 1986, 80 Years of Yachting, 1987, Cruising the Easy Way, 1990, Best Sailing Spots Worldwide, 1991, Destruction at Noonday, 1992, The Sailing Mystique, 1994; contbr. numerous articles to profl. jours. Vice pres. Rumson (N.J.) Community Appeal, 1952; mem. Rumson-Fair Haven (N.J.) Regional Bd. Edn., 1955-60, Rumson Environ. Commn., 1973-77. Served with USNR, 1941-45. Decorated Bronze Star with gold star. Mem. Met. Squash Racquets Assn. (v.p. 1973-75), Cruising Club Am. (historian 1972-77), Corinthians (master afterguard 1951-52). Clubs: Princeton of N.Y. (pres. 1984-87), N.Y. Yacht, Royal Bermuda Yacht, Seabright Beach. Avocation: squash. Home: 14 Oyster Bay Dr Rumson NJ 07760-1822

ROBISON, ANDREW CLIFFE, JR., museum curator; b. Memphis, May 23, 1940; s. Andrew Cliffe and Elfrieda (Barnes) R.; 1 child, Claire Catherine. A.B., Princeton U., 1962, Ph.D., 1974; B.A. (Marshall scholar), Oxford U., 1965, M.A., 1968. Instr. philosophy U. Ill., 1970-73, asst. prof. philosophy, 1973-75; curator, head dept. prints and drawings Nat. Gallery Art, Washington, 1974—, sr. curator, 1983-91, Andrew W. Mellon sr. curator, 1991—; Fulbright research scholar, India, 1965-66. Author: Giovanni Battista Piranesi: Prolegomena to the Princeton Collections, 1970, Paper in Prints, 1977, Master Drawings, 1978, Giovanni Battista Piranesi: The Early Architectural Fantasies, 1978, The Museum Curator and Fine Prints: Past, Present and Future, 1984, German Expressionist Prints from the Collection of Ruth and Jacob Kainen, 1985, Piranesi: Early Architectural Fantasies: A Catalogue Raisonné of the Etchings, 1986, Dürer to Diebenkorn, 1992, The Glory of Venice, 1994; contbr. articles and revs. to lit. Danforth fellow, 1966-70. Mem. Print Council Am. (pres. 1975-81), Master Drawings Assn. (internat. editorial adv. bd. 1981—), Drawing Soc. (bd. dirs. 1984—), Internat. Adv. Com. of Keepers of Pub. Collections of Graphic Art (pres. 1984-88), Ateneo Veneto, Phi Beta Kappa. Club: Grolier. Office: Nat Gallery of Art Washington DC 20565

ROBISON, BARBARA ANN, retired newspaper editor; b. Portland, Oreg., July 15, 1933; d. Louis Keith and Marjorie (Work) R.; 1 child, Nancy. Student, Coll. Idaho, 1951-54, U. Utah, 1968-70. Reporter Caldwell (Idaho) News Tribune, 1951-54; sports editor LaGrande (Oreg.) Evening-Observer, 1954-55; reporter Idaho Daily Statesman, Boise, 1955-57; asst. women's editor Tacoma (Wash.) News Tribune, 1958-59; lifestyle editor Salt Lake Tribune, 1967-93. Episcopalian. Avocations: reading, walking, animals. Home: 4210 Caroleen Way Salt Lake City UT 84124-2507

ROBISON, FREDERICK MASON, financial executive; b. Danville, Ill., May 30, 1934; s. Frederick A. and Katherine L. (Mason) R.; m. Nancy Jane Potter, Aug. 18, 1956; children: Frederick B., Christopher M. BS, U. Ill., 1956, JD, 1959. Tax mgr. Arthur Andersen & Co., Chgo., 1959-65; treas. Warnaco, Inc., Bridgeport, Conn., 1965-76; v.p. Emery Air Freight, Wilton, Conn., 1976-86, treas., 1976-79, sec., 1979-82, controller, 1979-86; v.p., controller Burlington Air Express, Irvine, Calif., 1986-88; sr. v.p. fin., chief fin. officer Sebastain Internat., Inc., Woodland Hills, Calif., 1988—. Vice chmn. Town Council, Monroe, Conn., 1971-73, mem., 1969-73, bd. edn., Monroe, 1973-79, chmn., 1975-79. Mem. AICPAs, Conn. Soc. CPAs, Fin. Execs. Inst. (dir. So. Conn. chpt. 1973-83, pres. 1977-78). Republican. Congregationalist. Home: 935 Triunfo Canyon Rd Westlake Vlg CA 91361-1826 Office: Sebastian Internat Inc 6109 De Soto Ave Woodland Hills CA 91367-3709

ROBISON, JAMES EVERETT, management consulting company executive; b. Alfred, N.D., Nov. 22, 1915; s. John J. and Myrtle (Klundt) R.; m. Jeanette Hoffman, June 6, 1942 (dec.); 1 child, Martha Ann Davies. A.B., U. Minn., 1938; M.B.A., Harvard U., 1940; Sc. D. (hon.), Suffolk U., 1968. Salesman Nashua Mfg. Co., N.Y.C., 1940-41, Textron, Inc., N.Y.C., 1947-53; chief textile br. OPS, Washington, 1951; pres., chief exec. officer, dir. Indian Head, Inc., N.Y.C., 1953-67; chmn. bd., chief exec. officer Indian Head, Inc., 1967-72, chmn. fin. com., 1971-75; pres. Lonsdale Enterprises, Inc., 1975—. Mem. com. univ. resources Harvard U., 1966-69, mem. vis. com. Grad. Sch. Bus. Adminstrn., 1966-72, 73-79; chmn. bd. Assocs. Harvard Bus. Sch., 1968-70, bd. dirs., 1988-92; trustee Air Force Aid Soc., 1968-94, mem. fin. com., 1969-94; bd. dirs. Bus. Com. for Arts, 1973-80; trustee Com. Econ. Devel., 1965-74, Calif. Inst. Tech., 1970—; vice chmn. president's coun. U. Vt. Sch. Bus., 1982-89. Maj. USAAF, 1942-46. Decorated D.F.C., Air Medal with three oak leaf clusters; recipient Distinguished Service award Harvard Bus. Sch. Assn., 1969; Outstanding Alumni award U. Minn., 1974. Mem. Conf. Bd., Am. Textile Mfrs. Inst. (bd. dirs. 1961-64), Harvard Bus. Sch. Assn., Soaring Soc. Am., U.S.C. of C., Air Force Res. Assn., Harvard Club, Harvard Bus. Sch. Club Greater N.Y. (past bd. dirs., pres. 1967-68), Stanwich Club (Greenwich, Conn.), Bedford Golf and Tennis Club (N.Y.), Lyford Cay Club (Bahamas), Phi Delta Theta. Avocations: golf, skiing, soaring.

ROBISON, OLIN CLYDE, political science educator, former college president; b. Anacoco, La., May 12, 1936; s. Audrey Clyde and Ruby (Cantrell) R.; m. Sylvia Margaret Potter, Apr. 10, 1959; children: Gordon Reece, Blake Elliott, Mark Edward. BA, Baylor U., 1958, LLD, 1979; D.Phil., Oxford (Eng.) U., 1963; LHD (hon.), Ehrenburger-Johannes Gutenberb U., Mainz, Fed. Republic Germany, 1977, Monterey Inst. Internat. Studies, 1982, Hofstra U, 1988; LLD (hon.), U. Vt., 1989. Dean students San Marcos (Tex.) Acad., 1963-64; regional officer Peace Corps, Washington, 1964-65; dir. univ. affairs Peace Corps, 1965-66; spl. asst. dep. under-sec. for polit. affairs Dept. State, Washington, 1966-68; assoc provost for social scis. Wesleyan U., Middletown, Conn., 1968-70; provost, dean faculty, sr. lectr. govt. and legal studies Bowdoin Coll., Brunswick, Maine, 1970-75; prof. polit. sci. Middlebury (Vt.) Coll., 1975-95, pres., 1975-90; pres. Salzburg Seminar, 1991—; chmn. Am. Collegiate Consortium, 1987-94; cons. State Dept., 1968-72, 77-88; bd. dirs. Investment Co. Am., Am. Mut. Fund, TDX Corp., Bank of Vt., 1989-92, The Noel Group, N.Y.C., 1989-91; cons. Paine Webber Mitchell Hutchins Inc., Am. Coun. Life Ins., 1968-81, Washington Forum, Met. Life Ins. Co. Bd. dirs. Atlantic Info. Center for Tchrs., London, 1977-78, Am. Com. on U.S.-Soviet Rels., Washington; chmn. Vt. com. Rhodes Scholarship Trust, 1976-77; bd. dirs. Am. Coun. Young Polit. Leaders, 1968-78, 81-90, Inst. East-West Security Studies, N.Y.C., Nat. Spinal Cord Injury Assn., Washington, Atlantic Coun. U.S., 1973-78, 81-91, U.S. Commn. for United World Coll. Schs; mem. U.S. Adv. Commn. on Public Diplomacy, 1978-83, chmn., 1978-81, visiting comm. Harvard Div. Sch., Cambridge, Mass., 1980-86, adv. comm. Harvard U., Ctr for Middle Ea. Studies, Cambridge, 1992—; adviser U.S. del. Conf. on Security and Coop. in Europe, Belgrade, 1977-78; U.S. del. Conf. on Security and Coop. in Madrid, 1980, in Vienna, 1986-87; mem. Royal United Svcs. Inst. Def. Studies, London; bd. dirs. Nat. Endowment for Democracy, 1984-92; bd. dirs., chmn. Chatham House Found., 1985-93. Named Ehrenburger Johannes Gutenberg Universität, Mainz, Fed. Republic Germany, 1977; Rockefeller Found./Aspen Inst. fellow, 1978-79; Presdl. fellow Aspen Inst. Humanistic Studies, 1979-80, Harry Luce fellow Aspen Inst., 1982-83. Fellow Royal Inst. Internat. Affairs (London); mem. Internat. Inst. Strategic Studies (London), Soc. Values in Higher Edn., Council Fgn. Relations, UN Assn. U.S. (panel on approaches to collective security), Atlantic Treaty Assn. (Atlantic edn. com. 1972-1976). Baptist. Clubs: Federal City (Washington); Century (N.Y.C.); United Oxford and Cambridge (London). Office: Salzburg Seminar The Marble Works PO Box 886 Middlebury VT 05753

ROBISON, PAULA JUDITH, flutist; b. Nashville, June 8, 1941; d. David Victor and Naomi Florence R.; m. Scott Nickrenz; Dec. 29, 1971; 1 child, Elizabeth Hadley Amadea Nickrenz. Student, U. So. Calif., 1958-60; B.S., Juilliard Sch. Music, 1963. Founding artist, player Chamber Music Soc., N.Y.C., 1970-90, NY Côro Band, 1994; co-dir. chamber music Spoleto Festival, Charleston, S.C., 1978-88; Filene artist-in-residence Skidmore Coll., Saratoga Springs, N.Y., 1988-89; mem. faculty New Eng. Conservatory Music, 1991—. Soloist with various major orchs., including N.Y. Philharm.; player, presenter Concerti di Mezzogiorno, Spoleto (Italy) Festival, 1978—; commd. flute concertos by Leon Kirchner, Toru Takemitsu, Oliver Knussen, Robert Beaser, Kenneth Frazelle; author: The Paula Robison Flute Warmups Book, 1989, The Andersen Collection, 1994, Paula Robison Masterclass: Paul Hindemith, 1995; recs. on CBS Masterworks, Music Masters, Vanguard Classics, New World Records, Omega, Arabesque, Sony Classical. Recipient First prize Geneva Internat. Competition, 1966, Adelaide Ristori prize, 1967; named Musician of Month, Musical Am., 1979, House Musician for Isamu Noguchi Garden Mus., N.Y.C., 1982; Martha Baird Rockefeller grantee, 1966; Nat. Endowment for Arts grantee, 1978, 86; Fromm Found. grantee, 1980; Housewright Eminent scholar Fla. State U., 1990-91. Mem. Sigma Alpha Iota (hon.). Office: care Shaw Concerts 1900 Broadway New York NY 10023-7004

ROBISON, SUSAN MILLER, psychologist, educator, consultant; b. Chgo., Nov. 15, 1945; d. William Louis and Constance Mary (Maloney) Miller; m. Philip Dean Robison, Dec. 27, 1969; 1 child, Christine Alyssa. BS, Loyola U., Chgo., 1967; MS, Ohio U., 1969, PhD, 1971. Lic. psychologist, Md. Asst.

prof. psychology Ohio U., Lancaster, 1970-72; prof. psychology Coll. Notre Dame, Balt., 1972—; pvt. practice Ellicott City, Md., 1982—; leadership cons. Nat. Coun. Cath. Women, Washington, 1987—. Author: Sharing Our Gifts, 1987, 2d edit., 1992, Discovering Our Gifts, 1989, Thinking and Writing in College, 1991. Troop leader Girl Scouts U.S.A., Ellicott City, 1982-85, mem. adv. bd. Girl Scouts Central Md., 1987-88; mem. adv. bd. Archdiocese of Balt., 1986. Mem. Am. Psychol. Assn., Am. Assn. Sex Educators, Counselors and Therapists, Assn. for Advancement Behavior Therapy. Avocations: writing, skiing, dancing, jogging, sewing. Home: 3725 Font Hill Dr Ellicott City MD 21042-4932

ROBITAILLE, LUC, professional hockey player; b. Montreal, P.Q., Can., Feb. 17, 1966. With Hull Olympiques Major Jr. Hockey League, Que., 1983-84, L.A. Kings, 1984-94, Pitts. Penguins, 1994—; scored winning goal for nat. team of Can. at 1994 World Hockey Championship. Recipient Guy LaFleur trophy, 1985-86, Can. Hockey Player of Yr. award, 1985-86, Calder Meml. trophy, NHL Rookie of Yr., 1986-87; named to NHL All-Star team, 1987, 88, 90-91, 92-93. Office: Pitts Penguins Gate No 9 Pittsburgh PA 15219*

ROBLE, CAROLE MARCIA, accountant; b. Bklyn., Aug. 22, 1938; d. Carl and Edith (Brown) Dusowitz; m. Richard F. Roble, Nov. 30, 1969. MBA with distinction, N.Y. Inst. Tech., 1984. CPA, Calif., N.Y. Compt. various orgns. various orgns., 1956-66; staff acct. ZTBG CPA'S, L.A., 1966-67; sr. acct. J.H. Cohn & Co., Newark, 1967-71; prin. Carole M. Roble, CPA, South Hempstead, N.Y., 1971-90; ptnr. Roble & Libman, CPAs, Baldwin, N.Y., 1990-93; prin. Carole M. Roble, CPA, Baldwin, N.Y., 1993—; speaker, moderator Found. for Acctg. Edn., N.Y., 1971—; lectr. acctg. various schs. including New Sch., Queens Coll., Empire State Coll., Touro Coll., N.Y. Inst. Tech., N.Y.C., Parsons Sch., 1971—. Guest various N.Y. radio and TV stas. Treas. Builders Devel. Corp. of L.I., Westbury, N.Y., 1985; dir. Women Econ. Devels. of L.I., 1985-87. Recipient Sisterhood citation Nat. Orgn. Women, 1984, 85, cert. of Appreciation Women Life Underwriters, 1988, Women in Sales, 1982, 84; named top Tax Practitioner Money Mag., 1987. Mem. AICPA, Am. Acct. Assn. (auditing sect.), Am. Soc. Women Accts. (pres. N.Y. chpt. 1980-81), Am. Woman's Soc. CPAs, Nat. Conf. CPA Practitioners (trustee L.I. chpt. 1981-82, sec. 1982-83, treas. 1983-84, v.p 1984-85, 1st v.p. 1985-86, pres. 1986-87, nat. nominating com. 1983-84, 88-89, nat. continuing profl. edn. chmn. 1988-90, nat. treas. 1991-94, nat. v.p. 1994—), Calif. Soc. CPAs, N.Y. State Soc. CPAs (bd. dirs. Nassau chpt. 1981-86, 91-93, bd. dirs. profl. devel., 1982-86, sec., mem. fin. acctg. standards com. 1990—), Kiwanis (program chmn. County Seat chpt. 1989-90, sec. 1990-91, pres. 1991-92), Baldwin C. of C. (treas. 1990-93). Avocations: golf, gourmet cuisine, water skiing, music. Home: 626 Willis St Hempstead NY 11550-8000

ROBLIN, DUFF, Canadian senator; b. Winnipeg, Man., Can., June 17, 1917; s. C.D. and Sophia May (Murdoch) R.; m. Mary Linda MacKay, Aug. 30, 1958; children—Andrew, Jennifer. Student, St. John's Coll. Sch., U. Chgo.; LL.D., McGill U., Man. U., Winnipeg U. Mem. Man. Legislature, Can., 1949-68, premier, 1958-67, sworn to privy council, 1967; appointed companion Order of Can., 1970; senator Can. Parliament, 1978-82, dep. leader opposition, 1980-84, leader of Govt. in Senate, 1984-86; pres. Canadian Pacific Investments Ltd., 1970-75. Progressive Conservative. Anglican. Office: 977 Century St, Winnipeg, MB Canada R3H 0W4

ROBOCK, STEFAN HYMAN, economics educator emeritus; b. Redgranite, Wis., July 31, 1915; s. Samuel and Elizabeth (Kushner) R.; m. Shirley Bernstein, June 17, 1946 (div. Mar. 1980); children: Alan David, Jerry, Lisa (Mrs. Stephen Shaffer). B.A., U. Wis., 1938; M.A. (Adminstrn. fellow), Harvard U., 1941, Ph.D., 1948; Prof. Honoris Causa, U. Recife, Brazil, 1956; M. Honoris Causa, E.S.T.E., San Sebastian, Spain, 1974. Economist Nat. Resources Planning Bd., Washington, 1940-41; antitrust div. U.S. Dept. Justice, Washington, 1941-42, Boston, 1948-49; chief economist TVA, Knoxville, 1949-54; devel. adviser UN, Brazil, 1954-56; tech. asst. missions UN, Chile, 1955; active missions UN, Colombia, 1956, India, 1959; with Midwest Rsch. Inst., 1956-58; mem. Com. Econ. Devel., 1958-60; prof. internat. bus. Ind. U., Bloomington, 1960-67; R.D. Calkins prof. internat. bus. Columbia U., N.Y.C., 1967-84, prof. emeritus, 1984—; internat. economist Dept. Commerce, 1975-76; trustee Inst. Current World Affairs, 1981-86; cons. fgn. countries, 1959—; bd. dirs. Econs. Inst., Boulder, Colo., 1984-89; adv. bd. World Trade Inst., 1974-95; mem. bd. sci. and tech. NAS, 1969-72; vis. prof. Beijing Mgmt. Inst., 1985, U. Internat. Bus. and Econs., Beijing, 1989, Internat. Mgmt. Ctr., Budapest, Hungary, 1992. Author: Brazil's Developing Northeast, 1963, Brazil: A Study in Development Progress, 1975, International Business and Multinational Enterprises, 4th edit., 1989; Editorial bd.: Columbia Jour. World Bus, 1975-85. Served with USNR, 1942-46. Mem. Soc. Internat. Devel. (mem. council 1966-69), Am. Econ. Assn., Acad. Internat. Bus. (v.p. 1983-85), Latin Am. Studies Assn., Phi Kappa Phi, Beta Gamma Sigma, Phi Eta Sigma. Club: Columbia Tennis. Home: 560 Riverside Dr Apt 21J New York NY 10027

ROBOL, RICHARD THOMAS, lawyer; b. Norfolk, Va., Feb. 8, 1952; s. Harry James and Lucy Henley (Johnson) R.; m. Melissa Janet Sengstack, June 3, 1978; children: Thomas Coke, Robert Talbot, Charles Taliaferro. BA, U. Va., 1974; JD, Harvard U., 1978. Bar: Va. 1979, U.S. Dist. Ct. (ea. dist.) Va. 1979, U.S. Ct. Appeals (4th cir.) 1979, U.S. Dist. Ct. (we. dist.) Va. 1981, U.S. Supreme Ct. 1982, D.C. 1991. Law clk. to presiding justice U.S. Dist. Ct. (ea. dist.) Va., 1978-79; ptnr. Seawell, Dalton, Hughes & Timms, Norfolk, 1979-87, Hunton and Williams, Norfolk, 1987-92; exec. v.p., gen. counsel Columbus Am. Discovery Group, Inc., 1992—; pro bono counsel Nat. Commn. for Prevention Child Abuse, Norfolk, 1983, Tidewater Profl. Assn. on Child Abuse, 1983, Parents United Va., 1981-82, Sexual Abuse Help Line, 1983-86; mem. Boyd-Graves Conf. on Civil Procedure in Va., 1981-87. Contbr. articles to law revs.; contbg. editor: International Law for General Practitioners, 1981. Bd. dirs. Va. Opera Assn. Guild, Norfolk, 1983-87, Tidewater br. NCCJ, 1991—; deacon Cen. Bat. Ch., Norfolk, 1980-83. 1st lt. USAR, 1992—. Fulbright scholar, 1974. Mem. Va. State Bar Assn. (bd. dirs. internat. law sect. 1984-87, chmn. 1982-83), Va. Young Lawyers Assn. (cir. rep. 1984-88), Va. Assn. Def. Attys., Maritime Law Assn., Norfolk-Portsmouth Bar assn. (chmn. speakers bur. 1987-88), Assn. Def. Trial Attys. (chmn. Va. 1987), Def. Rsch. Inst., 1982-88. Avocations: camping, rowing, scuba diving. Home: 60 Kenyon Brook Dr Worthington OH 43085 Office: Columbus Am Discovery Group 433 W 6th Ave Columbus OH 43201-3136

ROBOLD, ALICE ILENE, mathematician, educator; b. Delaware County, Ind., Feb. 7, 1928; d. Earl G. and Margaret Rebecca (Summers) Hensley; m. Virgil G. Robold, Aug. 21, 1955; 1 son, Edward Lynn. B.S., Ball State U., 1955, M.A., 1960, Ed.D., 1965. Substitute elem. tchr. Am. Elem. Sch., Augsburg, Germany, 1955-56; instr. Ball State U., Muncie, Ind., 1960-61; teaching fellow Ball State U., 1961-64, asst. prof. math. scis., 1964-69, assoc. prof., 1969-76, prof., 1976—. Mem. Nat. Coun. Tchrs Math., Ind. Coun. Tchrs Math., Sch. Sci. and Math. Assn., Pi Lambda Theta. Mem. Ch. of God. Office: Ball State U Dept Math Scis Muncie IN 47306

ROBRENO, EDUARDO C., federal judge; b. 1945. BA, Westfield State Coll., 1967; MA, U. Mass., 1969; JD, Rutgers U., 1978. With antitrust divsn. U.S. Dept Justice, Phila., 1978-81; ptnr. Meltzer & Schiffrin, Phila., 1981-86, Fox, Rothschild, O'Brien & Frankel, Phila., 1987-92; fed. judge U.S. Dist. Ct. (ea. dist.) Pa., Phila., 1992—; mem. Jud. Conf. Com. on Bankruptcy Rules. Fellow Am. Bar Found., Am. Law Inst.

ROBSON, BARBARA S., elementary education educator; b. Phila., July 4, 1938; d. Robert John and Gladys Blodwyn (Williams) Smith; m. William John Robson, Oct. 1, 1960; children: William Charles, Robin Lynne, Robert Bruce. BS, West Chester U., 1960; postgrad., Pa. State U., Millersville U., Fla. State U. Cert. elem. edn. Tchr. Lansdowne (Pa.) Aldan Sch. Dist., No Lebanon Sch. Dist., Fredericksburg, Pa., Ea. Lebanon County Sch. Dist., Myerstown, Pa.; cooperating tchr., mentor Lebanon Valley Coll. Delta Kappa Gamma scholar. Mem. NEA, Internat. Reading Assn., Assn. Supervision and Curriculum Devel., Pa. Edn. Assn., Ea. Lebanon County Edn. Assn., Lebanon County Ednl. Honor Soc., Delta Kappa Gamma. Home: RR 2 Box 240 Myerstown PA 17067-2054

ROBSON, BRIAN, electronics executive. Internat. contr. No. Telecom, 1966-84; v.p. fin. Ascom Timplex Inc., Woodcliff Lake, N.J., 1984—. Office: Ascom Timeplex Inc 400 Chestnut Ridge Rd Woodcliff Lake NJ 07675*

ROBSON, CHARLES BASKERVILL, JR., lawyer; b. Durham, N.C., Oct. 24, 1938; s. Charles Baskervill and Harriet Eleanor (Hardison) R.; m. Lucie Lea White, Sept. 20, 1969; children: Charles B. III, Patrick Lea. Student, Freie U. of Berlin, 1958-59; BA, Yale U., 1961; JD with honors, U. N.C., Chapel Hill, 1966. Bar: N.C. 1966, U.S. Dist. Ct. (mid. and ea. dists.) N.C. 1967, U.S. Ct. Appeals (4th cir.) 1967, U.S. Tax Ct. 1968, Ga. 1972, Mich. 1974. Assoc. McLendon, Brim, Holderness & Brocks, Greensboro, N.C., 1966-71; mem. law faculty U. Ga., Athens, 1971-75; mgr. legal affairs Carolina Power and Light, Raleigh, N.C., 1975-80; v.p., gen. counsel Hosp. Affiliates Internat., Nashville, 1980-81; ptnr. Foster, Conner & Robson, Raleigh, 1983-88, Patton, Boggs & Blow, Raleigh, 1988—. Contbr. to profl. publs. Mem. Order of Coif. Republican. Episcopalian. Office: Patton Boggs & Blow PO Box 786 Raleigh NC 27602

ROBSON, DONALD, physics educator; b. Leeds, Eng., Mar. 19, 1937; came to U.S., 1963; s. Albert and Rose Hannah (Parbutt) R.; m. Joy Olivia Burkitt Findlay, Aug. 1960 (div. May 1971); children: Donald Peter, David Ian, Karen Joy; m. Martha Breitenlohner, Aug. 26, 1971. BSc, U. Melbourne, Australia, 1959, MSc, 1961, PhD, 1963. Rsch. assoc. Fla. State U., Tallahassee, 1963-64, asst. prof. physics, 1964-65, assoc. prof., 1965-67, prof., 1967—, chmn. dept. physics, 1985-91, Disting. prof., 1990—. Editor: (with J.D. Fox) Isobaric Spin in Nuclear Physics, 1966, Nuclear Analogue States, 1976; assoc. editor Nuclear Physics A., 1972-96; vice chmn. bd. trustees SURA, 1994—; contbr. more than 100 articles to profl. jours. Fulbright scholar, 1963-64; A.P. Sloan fellow, 1966-67; Alexander Von Humboldt sr. scientist, 1976-77. Fellow Am. Phys. Soc. (co-recipient Tom W. Bonner prize 1972). Avocations: chess, golf, running. Office: Fla State U Dept Physics Tallahassee FL 32306

ROBSON, JOHN MERRITT, library and media administrator; b. Gordon, Nebr., Sept. 22, 1930; s. John Wesley Robson and Martha Mildred (Shook) Belknap; m. Kathryn Mae Baker, Aug. 26, 1951; children: Deborah Dawn, Diana Lynn, Denise Anne. BS in Edn., U. Nebr., 1953; MA in Librarianship, Denver U., 1959. Ordained deacon Episc. Ch., 1991. Ref. asst. Lincoln (Nebr.) City Librs., 1957-58; ref. and inter libr. loan Denver U. Libr., 1958-59; cataloger humanities USAF Acad. Libr., Colo., 1959-61; cataloger St. Cloud (Minn.) U., 1961-63, acquisitions libr., 1963-66; libr. dir. Southwest State U., Marshall, Minn., 1966-71, dir. media svcs., 1971-81; head libr., prof. libr. and instructional tech. Nebr. Wesleyan U., Lincoln, 1981-91, dir. media svcs., 1991—; mem. S.E. Nebr. Regional Libr. Bd., Lincoln, 1983-84; steward teamsters Faculty /Adminstrv. Bargaining Unit, Marshall, 1977-78. Author: Index to Publications of the Hakluyt Society, 1963; contbr. articles to profl. jours. Mem. gov's. task force on librs. State of Minn., St. Paul, 1973. Mem. Nebr. Libr. Assn. (Mentor of Yr. 1989), Nebr. Ednl. Media Assn. (conv. planning com. 1984—), Nebr. Assn. for Ednl. Data Processing. Avocations: stained glass, wood working, photography. Home: 1620 Atlas Ave Lincoln NE 68521-1654 Office: Nebr Wesleyan U 5000 St Paul Ave Lincoln NE 68504-2760

ROBSON, JUDITH BIROS, state legislator; b. Cleve., Nov. 21, 1939; d. George John and Mary Grace (Millen) Biros; m. Arthur Robson, Sept. 2, 1961; children: Marybeth, Marc, Matthew. BSN, St. John Coll., Cleve., 1961; MS, U. Wis., 1976. RN. Staff nurse Beloit (Wis.) Hosp., 1967-73; nurse practitioner Dr. Ken Gold, Beloit, 1976-78; instr. Blackhawk Tech. Coll., Jonesville, Wis., 1978-87; mem. Wis. Assembly, 1987—. Mem. bd. Bedcore, Beloit, 1990, YWCA, Beloit, 1992; sec. Majority Party Caucus, 1990—. Recipient Clean 16 award Environ. Decade. Avocations: biking, skiing, gardening, photography. Office: State Legislature State Capital Madison WI 57708

ROBSON, MARTIN CECIL, surgery educator, plastic surgeon; b. Lancaster, Ohio, Mar. 8, 1939; children: Karen Iredell, Douglas Spears, Martin Cecil III. Student, Northwestern U., 1957-59; B.A., Johns Hopkins U., 1961, M.D., 1964. Diplomate Am. Bd. Surgery, Am. Bd. Plastic Surgery. Intern U. Chgo. Hosps. and Clinics, 1964-65; resident in surgery Balt. City Hosp., 1965-67, Brooke Gen. Hosp., Ft. Sam Houston, Tex., 1967-69; resident in plastic surgery Yale-New Haven Hosp., 1971-73; instr. dept. surgery Yale U. Sch. Medicine, New Haven, 1973-74, asst. prof. plastic surgery, 1973-74, assoc. prof., 1974; assoc. prof. plastic surgery U. Chgo., 1974-77, prof. and chief plastic and reconstructive surgery, 1977-83, dir. Burn Center, 1976-83; prof., chmn. divsn. plastic and reconstructive surgery Wayne State U., Detroit, 1983-88; dir. Detroit Med. Ctr. Burn Ctr., 1983-88; Truman Blocker Disting. prof., chief divsn. plastic surgery U. Tex. Med. Br., 1988-93; dir. surg. svcs. Shriners' Burn Inst., Galveston, Tex., 1988-93; prof. surgery U. South Fla., Tampa, 1993—; chair surg. svc. Bay Pines (Fla.) VA Med. Ctr., 1993—. Mem. editl. bd. Jour. Burn Care and Rehab.; editl. cons. bd.: Jour. Trauma. Served to maj. M.C. U.S. Army, 1967-71; col. USAR Med. Corps, 1991—. Recipient Writing award Am. Med. Technologists, 1979, 80, 81, 82; recipient Lancer Authors' award, 1981, 82, Fisher award, 1982. Fellow ACS, Royal Australasian Coll. Surgeons (hon.); mem. Plastic Surgery Rsch. Coun. (chmn. 1983-84), Am. Burn Assn. (pres. 1985-86, Disting. Svc. award), Am. Surg. Assn., Am. Assn. Plastic Surgery, Am. Soc. Plastic and Reconstructive Surgeons, Nu Sigma Nu, Phi Delta Theta, Alpha Omega Alpha. Office: Bay Pines VA Med Ctr Bay Pines FL 33504

ROBY, EDGAR MACLIN, electronic equipment manufacturing company executive; b. Silver Spring, Md., 1931; B.S. in E.E., U. Md., 1954; M.S. in E.E., U. Mex., 1958; postgrad. Bus. Sch. Harvard U. Staff mem. Bell Telephone Labs., 1954-55, Sandia Corp., 1957-58; with Gulton Industries Inc., Princeton, N.J., 1958—, corp. v.p., 1969-78, exec. v.p., chief operating officer, 1978-79, pres., 1979—, chief exec. officer, 1984—, also dir. Served to 1st lt. USAF. Office: Mark IV Industries Inc PO Box 450 501 John James Audubon Pkwy Amherst NY 14228

ROBY, JASPER, bishop. Sr. bishop, exec. head Apostolic Overcoming Holy Ch. of God, Inc., Birmingham, Ala. Office: Apostolic Overcoming Holy Church God Inc 1120 N 24th St Birmingham AL 35234-3194

ROBY, JOE LINDELL, investment banker; b. Metropolis, Ill., May 22, 1939; s. Gerald C. and Inez (DeLaine) R.; m. Elizabeth Shute, June 17, 1967 (dec. Oct. 1980); m. Hilppa Pirila, June 15, 1984. BA cum laude, Vanderbilt U., 1961; MBA with distinction, Harvard U., 1967. Asst. v.p. Kidder, Peabody & Co., N.Y.C., 1967-72; v.p. Donaldson, Lufkin & Jenrette, N.Y.C., 1972-75, sr. v.p., 1976-83, mng. dir. investment banking, 1984—, also bd. dirs.; bd. dirs. Sybron, Inc., Muskland Group, Inc. Served to lt. USN, 1961-65. Mem. Down Town Assn., Bond Club of N.Y. Club: Down Town Assn. (N.Y.C.). Office: Donaldson Lufkin & Jenrette Securities Corp 140 Broadway New York NY 10005-1101

ROCCO, RON, artist; b. Ft. Hood, Tex., Nov. 21, 1953; s. Raymond Anthony and Dorothy Ann (D'Angelo) R. Student, Fordham U., 1972; BFA, SUNY, Purchase, 1976; MS in Visual Arts, MIT Ctr. for Advanced Visual Studies, 1983. Artist-in-residence Exptl. TV Ctr., Owego, N.Y., 1982-87; guest lectr., artist-in-residence The Banff (Alta., Can.) Ctr., 1987; artist-in-residence Kunstlerhaus Bethanian, Berlin, 1991; artist-in-residence inter. studio program Kunst and Complex, Rotterdam, Netherlands, 1993; guest lectr. various univs., 1977-90; mem. UN Internat. Conf. on Communication Tech. and Traditional Cultures, N.Y.C., 1983, Art Corp. Am., N.Y.C., 1979-81. Performance at The Solomon R. Guggenheim Mus., N.Y.C., 1983; works exhibited UN: Comm. Ctr. of Population Inst., N.Y.C., 1983, The Asia Soc., N.Y.C., 1985, Internat. Exhibit of Computer Art Forms, Kortijk, Belgium, 1986, Inst. for Art and Urban Resources, N.Y.C., 1987, Found. Artgarden, Amsterdam, The Netherlands, 1989, The Katonah (N.Y.) Mus. Art, 1990, The Bklyn. Mus., 1990, Fundacao Rocha, Fortalesca, Brazil, 1991, Kunstlerhaus Bethanien, Berlin, 1991, Amerika Haus, Berlin, 1992; artistic dir. Laser Sculpture/Dance, 1981; producer: Zaroff's Tale, 1983 (N.Y. State Coun. on Arts grantee); co-dir., collaborator Buddah Meets Einstein at the Great Wall, 1985 (Nat. Endowment Arts award); collaborator, sculptor Light and Sound Sphere Study, 1986 (N.Y. State Coun. on Arts grantee). Founder, dir. Ithaca Artists Coop., 1977-80. Creative and Performing Arts Coun. grantee Cornell U., Ithaca, N.Y., 1977; expansion arts program grantee Nat. Endowment Arts, 1977-79; recipient Netherland-

Am. Found. award, 1989, Art Matters award, 1989, N.Y. Found. for the Arts award, 1989, The Found. for Contemporary Performance Arts award, 1989. Mem. ACLU. Buddhist. Studio: 59 Harrison Ave Brooklyn NY 11211

ROCCO, VINCENT ANTHONY, consulting firm executive; b. Hoboken, N.J., Mar. 13, 1945; s. Bernard James and Margaret Gloria (Monaco) R.; m. Mary Elizabeth Bathe, Oct. 1, 1969. BSME, Stevens Inst. Tech., Hoboken N.J., 1967; MSME, U. Tenn., Tullahoma, 1970; MBA, U. Tenn., Knoxville, 1973. Registered profl. engr., Conn., Mo., N.Y., Maine, N.C., Ill., Tenn., N.J., Tex., Wis., Minn., N.H. Dir. environ. planning Tenn. Dept. Transp., Nashville, 1972-73; sr. environ. engr. Rychman, Edgerley, Tomlinson & Assocs., St. Louis, 1973; dir. environ. affairs Wis. Electric Power Co., Milw., 1973-74; v.p., gen. mgr. ERT, Concord, Mass., 1975-79; chmn., chief exec. officer TRC Cos. Inc., East Hartford, Conn., 1979—; cons. USAF Advanced Air Base Design Com., Washington, 1986—; commr. Bradley Airport, Conn., 1989—. Contbr. articles to profl. jours.; patentee in field. Chmn. engrs. sect. United Givers Fund, Hartford, Conn., 1988; commr. Bradley Internat. Airport Commn., Hartford, 1989; chmn. bd. trustees Xavier High Sch., N.Y.C., 1986—; chmn. adv. bd. Stevens Ctr. for Environ. Engring. Capt. USAF, 1968-72. Decorated Legion of Merit, Meritorious Svc. medal, Air Force Commendation medal. Mem. NSPE, Air and Water Mgmt. Assn., Nat. Soc. Mech. Engrs., Hartford Canoe Club. Republican. Roman Catholic. Avocations: history, reading, antiques collection. Office: TRC Cos Inc 5 Waterside Crossing Windsor CT 06095-1561*

ROCEK, JAN, chemist, educator; b. Prague, Czechoslovakia, Mar. 24, 1924; came to U.S., 1960, naturalized, 1966; s. Hugo and Frida (Loebl) Robitschek; m. Eva Trojan, June 26, 1947; children: Martin, Thomas. M.S., Tech. U., Prague, 1949, Ph.D., 1953. Scientist Czechoslovak Acad. Sci., Prague, 1953-57; sr. scientist Czechoslovak Acad. Sci., 1957-60; vis. scientist U. Coll., London, 1958; research fellow Harvard U., 1960-62; assoc. prof., then prof. Cath. U. Am., 1962-66; prof. chemistry U. Ill., Chgo., 1966—; acting head dept. U. Ill., 1980-81, head dept., 1981-93; vice chancellor rsch., dean grad. coll. U. Ill., Chgo., 1993—; acting dean Grad. Coll. U. Ill., 1969-70, dean Grad. Coll., 1970-79, assoc. mem. Ctr. for Advanced Studies, 1968-69; vis. scholar Stanford U., 1979-80, Cambridge U., 1980. Contbr. articles to profl. jours. Mem. Am. Chem. Soc., AAAS, Czechoslovak Soc. Arts and Scis. in Am., AAUP, Sigma Xi (pres. chpt. 1976-77, 85-86), Phi Kappa Phi. Home: 2636 Laurel Ln Wilmette IL 60091-2202 Office: 1737 W Polk St Chicago IL 60612-7227

ROCHA, ARMANDINO CORDEIRO DOS SANTOS, accountant, educator, auditor; b. Porto, Portugal, Oct. 19, 1934; s. Mario dos Santos and Maria de Conceicão (Cordeiro) R.; m. Maria Laura Oliveira Silva, Sept. 1, 1957 (div. 1976); children: Isabel Maria, Mario Rui; m. Ana Rosalina Sa Ribeiro, July 2, 1977; 1 child, Ana Sofia. B in Acctg., Inst. Comercial, Porto, 1962; B in Social Polit., Inst. Estudos Sociais, Lisbon, Portugal, 1969; B in Sociology, Inst. Superior Ciencias, 1982; BBA, Inst. superior C. Trab. Empresas, 1975; PhD in Bus. and Econs. Scis., U. Minho-Braga, 1991. Fin. dir. Fabrica Fiacão E Tecidos Da Portela, Delães, Portugal, 1960-72, Tinturaria Vaz Ferreira, S. Mamede De Infesta, Portugal, 1962-73; regional dir. Companhia Seguros Bonanca, Porto, 1973-87; auditor Emaco, Sa, Lisboa, Porto, 1979-85, Imobur S.A. and Riguadiana S.A., Porto, 1979-85, Estaleiros Navais De Viana, Porto, 1979-82; auditor Efi-Ed Ferreirinha and Irmao S.A., Porto, 1984-88, Feruni-Siceidade de Fundicão S.A., Trofa, Portugal, 1984-93, Portocork, Internat., S.A., Feira, Portugal, 1987-91, Copo Antlantica, Industria De Poliurentano S.A., Santo Tirso, Portugal, 1987—; Vasconcelos Lyncke, LDA, Feira, Portugal, 1989—; CYC, S.A.-Vilamoura, Portugal, 1989-92, Ferreirinhas Maquinas, S.A., Trofa, Portugal, 1989, Textil Artificial de Porto, 1989-90, Arnaldo Trindade, 1989; prof. acctg. U. Do Minho, Braga, Portugal, 1980—. Author: Principios Do Seguro, 1982; contbr. articles to profl. jours. Mem. Assn. Para O Desenvowimento Economico E Social, Portugal Economists Assn., Portugal Mgmt. Assn., Inst. Dos Actuários Portugueses. Clubs: Vigorosa Sport, Fenianos. Avocations: chess, music, reading, traveling. Home: 357-2 Faria Guimaraes, P-4000 Porto Portugal Office: Universidade Do Minho, Gualtar, P-4119 Braga Portugal

ROCHA, GUY LOUIS, archivist, historian; b. Long Beach, Calif., Sept. 23, 1951; s. Ernest Louis and Charlotte (Sobus) R. BA in Social Studies and Edn., Syracuse U., 1973; MA in Am. Studies, San Diego State U., 1975; postgrad., U. Nev., 1975—. Cert. archivist Am. Acad. Cert. Archivists. Tchr., Washoe County Sch. Dist., Reno, Nev., 1975-76; history instr. Western Nev. C.C., Carson City, 1976; curator manuscripts Nev. Hist. Soc., Reno, 1976-81, interim asst. dir., 1980, interim dir., 1980-81; state administr. archives and records Nev. State Libr. and Archives, Carson City, 1981—; hist. cons. Janus Assocs., Tempe, Ariz., 1980, Rainshadow Assocs., Carson City, 1983—; mem. State Bd. Geographic Names. Co-author The Ignoble Conspiracy: Radicalism on Trial in Nevada, 1986, The Earp's Last Frontier: Wyatt and Virgil Earp in Nevada 1902-1905, 1988; contbr. to book and govt. study; host weekly radio talk show Sta. KPTL, Carson City, 1988—. Ex-officio mem. Nev. Commn. Bicentennial U.S. Constitution, 1986-91. Mem. Washoe Heritage Council, Reno, 1983-85; editorial bd. Nev. Hist. Soc., Reno, 1983—; mem. Washoe County Democratic Central Com., Reno, 1984-87. Mem. Conf. Intermountain Archivists (Council mem 1979-87, v.p. 1984-85, pres. 1985-86), No. Nev. Pub. Administrs. Group (pres. 1986-87), S.W. Labor Studies Assn., State Hist. Records Adv. Bd. (dep. coordinator 1984-86, coordinator 1986—), Westerners Internat. Nev. Corral (dep. sheriff 1980-81, sheriff 1984-85, mem. state coordinators steering com. 1985-87, vice chmn. 1986-87), Soc. Am. Archivists, Western History Assn., Nat. Assn. Govt. Archives and Records Adminstrs., Orgn. Am. Historians. Democrat. Home: 1824 Pyrenees St Carson City NV 89703-2331 Office: Nev State Libr & Archives 100 Stewart St Carson City NV 89710

ROCHA, PEDRO, JR., academic administrator; b. Indé, México, Dec. 25, 1939; came to U.S., 1955; s. Pedro Sr. and Maria (Hernández) R.; m. Maria-Cruz Molina, Dec. 6, 1969; children: Diana-Marie, Diana-Irene, Pedro-Hugo. BA in History, U. Tex., El Paso, 1967, MA in Spanish, 1969; PhD in Edn. Adminstrn., U. Tex., 1981. Cert. secondary tchr., supr., adminstr., supt., Tex. Textbook adminstr. Ysleta Jr. High Sch., El Paso, 1976; secondary tchr. Ysleta Ind. Sch. Dist., El Paso, 1969-77; grad. student asst. U. Tex., El Paso, 1976-77; rsch. assoc. U. Tex., Austin, 1979-80; adminstrv. intern Austin (Tex.) C.C., 1978, substitute assoc. dean, 1981-83; rsch. intern S.W. Ednl. Devel. Lab., Austin, 1980-81; tax examiner div. clk. IRS, Austin, 1982; dir., coord. Cook Community Sch., Austin, 1982-85; from ESL instr. to dir., coord. Brooke Community Sch., Austin, 1985-86; dean Mesabi C.C., Virginia, Minn., 1987-92; v.p. for instrn. Trinidad (Colo.) State Jr. Coll., 1992—; Spanish instr. Vermilion C.C., Ely, Minn., 1990; cons.-evaluator for Commn. on Instns. of Higher Edn. of North Ctrl. Assn. Colls. and Schs.; cons. Raton (N.Mex.) Arts and Humanities Coun., 1993, U. Tex., Austin, 1982-86, Tex. Assn. Chicanos in Higher Edn., Denton, 1982, Mexican Am. Legal Def. & Edn. Fund, San Antonio, 1982, Intercultural Rsch., Inc., El Paso, 1981. Author: Staff Orientation Program: Welcoming the Employee to Our Team. Active mem., bd. dirs. So. Colo. Coal Miners Meml. and Scholarship Fund, 1994; pres. Marquette Sch. Bd., Virginia, 1991-92; active San Juan Coun. Cmty. Agencies, Farmington, 1986-87; leader Quarterly Dates Group, Farmington, 1986-87; adv. bd. Austin Cmty. Gardens, 1985-86. With USAF, 1961-65. Richardson fellow U. Tex., 1977-79; nominated and selected for Nat. Cmty. Coll. Hispanic Coun. Leadership Tng. Program for Hispanic C.C. Adminstrs., 1994. Mem. Am. Assn. for Higher Edn., Am. Assn. Cmty./Jr. Coll., Minn. Chief Acad. Adminstrs., Colo. Coun. Acad. Deans and Vice Presidents, Colo. Ednl. Svcs. Coun., Kiwanis Club, Hispanic C. of C. (bd. dirs. Trinidad-Las Animas County Hispanic C. of C.), Kappa Delta Pi, Sigma Delta Pi. Democrat. Roman Catholic. Avocations: bowling, basketball, walking, travel. Home: 1209 Grant Ave Trinidad CO 81082-3720 Office: Trinidad State Jr Coll 600 Prospect St Trinidad CO 81082-2396

ROCHBERG, GEORGE, composer, educator; b. Paterson, N.J., July 5, 1918; s. Morris and Anna (Hoffman) R.; m. Gene Rosenfeld, Aug. 18, 1941; children—Paul Bernard (dec.), Frances Ruth. B.A., Montclair State Tchrs. Coll., 1939, L.H.D., 1962; B.Mus., Curtis Inst. Music, 1948; M.A., U. Pa., 1949, Mus.D. (hon.), 1988; Mus.D. (hon.), Phila. Mus. Acad., 1964, Curtis Inst. Music, 1988. Mem. faculty Curtis Inst. Music, 1948-54; Fulbright fellow Am. Acad., Rome, 1950-51; editor, dir. publs. Theo. Presser Co., Bryn

Mawr, Pa., 1951-60; chmn. Music dept. U. Pa., 1960-83, Annenberg prof. humanities, 1979. Commd. to compose ballet music for Anna Sokolov, Lincoln Center Fund, 1965; recordings include numerous others; (recipient Gershwin Meml. award 1952, Soc. for Publ. Am. Music award 1956, Koussevitzky commn. 1957, Naumberg Rec. award 1961); Composer: Symphony No. 1, 1948-49, Night Music, 1949, String Quartet No. 1, 1952, Serenata d Estate, 1955, Symphony No. 2, 1956, La Bocca della Verita, 1958, String Quartet No. 2, 1959-61, Blake Songs, 1961, Time-Span (II), 1962, Trio for Violin, Cello and Piano, 1963, Zodiac, 1964, Black Sounds, 1965, Contra Mortem et Tempus, 1965, Music for the Magic Theater, 1965, Symphony No. 3, 1969, Tableaux for chamber ensemble, 1968, String Quartet No. 3, 1972, Violin Concerto premiered by Isaac Stern, 1975, Piano Quintet (Nat. Endowment for Arts commn.), 1975, Symphony No. 4, 1976; monodrama Phaedra, 1976, String Quartet No. 4, 1979 (1st place Kennedy Center Friedheim award), The Confidence Man, an Opera, 1981, Piano Trio No. 2 (for Beaux Arts Trio), 1983, Symphony No. 5, Chgo. Symphony, 1986, Symphony No. 6, Pitts. Symphony, 1987, Muse of Fire for flute and guitar, 1989, Piano Trio No. 3 (for Beaux Arts Trio), 1991, Sonata for Violin and Piano, 1988, Sonata-aria for Cello and Piano, 1992, Concerto for Clarinet and Orchestra, 1994-95, others. Served to 2d lt., inf. AUS, 1942-45, ETO. Decorated Purple Heart with cluster; gold medal in music Brandeis Creative Arts award, 1985; Nat. Inst. Arts and Letters grant, 1962; Fromm Found. commn., 1965; Guggenheim fellow, 1957, 1966-67; Nat. Endowment for Arts grantee, 1972-73. Mem. Am. Acad. Arts and Scis., Am. Musicological Soc., ASCAP, Internat. Webern Soc. (v.p.), Am. Acad. Arts and Letters. I have always clung fast to these fundamentals: that music was given man so he could express the best he was capable of; that the best he was capable of had to do with his deepest feelings; that his deepest feelings are rooted in what I believe to be a moral order in the universe which underlies all real existence.

ROCHE, BURKE BERNARD, manufacturing company executive; b. Billings, Mont., Oct. 26, 1913; s. John Francis and Bertha (Buchanan) R.; m. Mary Constance Kayser, Aug. 5, 1950. Ph.B., Loyola U., 1936; postgrad. law, Northwestern U., 1937; LL.B., DePaul U., 1939, LL.D, 1973. Bar: Ill. 1940. With Binks Mfg. Co., Chgo., 1946-47, v.p., 1948-49, pres., 1949—, chief exec. officer, 1973—; also dir., chmn. bd., pres. Binks Mfg. Co., Franklin Pk., Ill.; pres., chmn. bd. Binks Internat., Brussels, Belgium, Binks Italia, Zingonia, Italy, Binks Deutschland GmbH, Mulheim, Fed. Republic Germany, Binks Can. Ltd., Toronto, Can., Binks Japan, Ltd., Tokyo, Binks Research and Devel. Corp, Boulder, Colo., Sames S.A., Grenoble, France; dir. Binks Bullows, Eng., Australia, Sweden, Binks de Mex., Mexico City. Served to lt. USN, 1943-46, PTO. Mem. Ill. State Bar Assn., Am. Mgmt. Assn., Soc. Plastics Industry. Republican. Clubs: Chgo. Athletic, Econ., Loyola U. Pres.'s, Carlton. Office: Binks Mfg Co 9201 Belmont Ave Franklin Park IL 60131-2807*

ROCHE, DANIEL F., retail executive; b. 1928. Chmn. bd. dird. Roche Bros. Supermarkets, Inc., Wellesley, Mass., 1952—. With USMC, 1948-50. Office: Roche Bros Supermarkets Inc 70 Hastings St Wellesley MA 02181*

ROCHE, DAVID ALAN, accounting firm executive; b. Inglewood, Calif., Feb. 6, 1946; s. Francis John and Christine Cora (Coolidge) R.; m. Theo Lucia Kuys, June 29, 1974; 1 child, Kevin. BA in Bus., U. Wash., 1972. CPA. Staff person Touche Ross & Co., Seattle, 1972-77, supr., 1977-79, mgr., 1979-83, ptnr., 1983-86; ptnr. Deloitte & Touche, Portland, Oreg., 1986—; bd. trustees Oreg. Sch. Arts and Crafts, Portland, treas., 1988-89, chmn.-elect, 1990-91, chmn., 1991-93; bus. adv. coun. Oreg. State U., Corvallis, Internat. Trade Inst., Portland, 1988—. Mem. Leadership Tomorrow C. of C., Seattle, 1985. With USN, 1967-72. Mem. Japan Am. Soc.(bd. dirs. Oreg. chpt.), Downtown Rotary. Republican. Roman Catholic. Avocations: golf, skiing. Office: Deloitte & Touche 3900 US Bancorp Tower Portland OR 97204

ROCHE, DOUGLAS DAVID, lawyer, bar examiner; b. Detroit, Oct. 29, 1936; s. James Michael and Louise Carolyn (McMillan) R.; widowed; children: Douglas Jr., Michael, Daniel, Thomas, Robert, Barbara. AB with honors, Holy Cross Coll., Worcester, Mass., 1958; JD, Harvard U. 1963. Bar: Mich. 1963, U.S. Supreme Ct., 1978. Ptnr. Dickinson, Wright, Moon, Van Dusen & Freeman, Detroit, 1963—. Lt. (j.g.) USNR, 1958-60. Mem. ABA, Can. Bar Assn., Fed. Bar Assn. (chmn. Detroit chpt. bankruptcy sect. 1991-92), Mich. Bar Assn., Detroit Bar Assn., Nat. Conf. Bar Examiners (chmn. 1987-88, bd. mgrs. 1981-89, chmn. multistate bar examination policy com. 1988-94), Mich. Bd. Law Examiners (pres. 1975-77), Orchard Lake (Mich.) Country Club, Detroit Athletic Club. Republican. Office: Dickinson Wright et al One Detroit Ctr Detroit MI 48226

ROCHE, GEORGE CHARLES, III, college administrator; b. Denver, May 16, 1935; s. George Charles, Jr. and Margaret (Stewart) R.; m. June Bernard, Feb. 11, 1955; children: George Charles, IV, Muriel Eileen, Margaret Clare, Jacob Stewart. B.S., Regis Coll., Denver, 1956; M.A., U. Colo., 1961, Ph.D., 1965. Tchr. jr. and sr. high schs. Salida, Colo., 1958-60; mem. faculty U. Colo., 1963-64, Colo. Sch. Mines, 1964-66; pres. Hillsdale (Mich.) Coll., 1971—; dir. seminars Found. Econ. Edn., N.Y.C., 1966-71, trustee, 1971-90. Author: Power, 1967, American Federalism, 1967, Education in America, 1969, Legacy of Freedom, 1969, Frederic Bastiat: A Man Alone, 1971, The Bewildered Society, 1972, The Balancing Act: Quota Hiring in Higher Education, 1974, America by the Throat: The Stranglehold of Federal Bureaucracy, 1983, Going Home, 1986, A World Without Heroes, 1987, A Reason for Living, 1989, One By One, 1990, The Fall of the Ivory Tower: Government Funding, Corruption, and the Bankrupting of American Higher Education, 1994; also articles, newspaper column. Chmn. acad. adv. council Charles Edison Meml. Youth Bd., Nat. Council Ednl. Research, 1982-85. Served to 1st lt. USMCR, 1956-58. Recipient Freedom Leadership award Freedoms Found., 1972. Mem. Nat. Hist. Assn., Am. Acad. Polit. and Social Sci., Am. Assn. Pres.'s Ind. Colls. and Univs., Mt. Pelerin Soc., Phila. Soc. Office: Hillsdale Coll 33 E College St Hillsdale MI 49242-1298

ROCHE, JAMES MCMILLAN, lawyer; b. Detroit, Apr. 16, 1934; s. James Michael and Louise Cullen (McMillan) R.; m. Laura Jane McMillion, Oct. 27, 1962; children: James, Laura, David, Elizabeth. AB, Holy Cross Coll., 1956; LLB, Harvard U., 1959; LLM, Georgetown U., 1962. Bar: Mich. 1959, Ill. 1962. Ptnr., mem. mgmt. com. McDermott, Will & Emery, Chgo., 1962—; bd. dirs. Time Med Labeling, Inc., Burr Ridge, Ill. Contbr. articles to profl. jours. Chmn. Chgo. Econ. Devel. Corp., 1979-81; pres. Village of Kenilworth, Ill., 1982-85; bd. dirs. St. Francis Hosp., Evanston, 1987—. Served to capt. USAF, 1959-62. Mem. ABA, Ill. Bar Assn., Chgo. Bar Assn., Mich. Bar Assn., Glen View (Ill.) Golf Club, Monroe Club (Chgo.), The Boulders Club (Ariz.). Roman Catholic. Avocations: golf, Indian art, wine. Office: McDermott Will & Emery 227 W Monroe St Chicago IL 60606-5019

ROCHE, JAMES RICHARD, pediatric dentist, university dean; b. Fortville, Ind., July 17, 1924; s. George Joseph and Nelle (Kinnaman) R.; m. Viola Marie Morris, May 15, 1949; 1 child, Ann Marie Roche Potter. DDS, Ind. U., 1947, MS in Dentistry, 1953. Diplomate Am. Bd. Pediat. Dentistry (exec. sec.-treas. 1982—). Prof. emeritus Ind. U. Sch. Dentistry, Indpls., 1968—, chmn. divsn. grad. pediat. dentistry, 1969-76, asst. dean faculty devel., 1976-80, assoc. dean faculty devel., 1980-87, assoc. dean for acad. affairs, 1987-88; cons. Dental Edn., Hosp. Dental Svc. and Commn. Accreditation, Chgo., 1977-83. Capt. U.S. Army, 1952-54. Recipient Disting. Teaching Recognition award Ind. U., 1976. Fellow Internat. Coll. Dentists, Am. Coll. Dentists, Am. Acad. Pediat. Dentistry (bd. dirs. 1967-70, Pierre Fauchard Acad.; mem. ADA (cons. Bur. Dental Health Edn. 1977, Ind. Dental Assn. (v.p. 1973-74, chmn. legis com. 1968-77, lobbyist 1970-77), Indpls. Dist. Dental Assn. (pres. 1967-68), Am. Soc. Dentistry for Children (award of excellence 1993), Ind. U.-Purdue U. Indpls. Sr. Acad. (charter), Masons, Omicron Kappa Upsilon. Home and Office: 1193 Woodgate Dr Carmel IN 46033-9232

ROCHE, JOHN EDWARD, human resources management consultant, educator; b. St. Albans, N.Y., Nov. 11, 1946; s. John F. and Carolyn C. (Miller) R.; m. Valerie Vastola; children: Christopher D., Danielle, Ryan J., Jennifer M. BA, Marist Coll., 1968, MBA, 1975; MS in Edn., SUNY, New Paltz, 1974. Tchr. Kingston (N.Y.) City Schs., 1968-76; employment supr. ACLI Internat. Inc., N.Y.C., 1976-78; dir. pers. Balfour MacLaine Internat., N.Y.C., 1978-80; mgr. employee rels. Harcourt Brace Jovanovich, N.Y.C.,

1980-82; nat. dir. pers. Hayt, Hayt & Landau, Great Neck, N.Y., 1982-86; pres. Pers. Mgmt. Svcs., Great Neck, N.Y., 1983-86, Martin-Roche Assocs., Inc., Levittown, N.Y., 1986-92; prof. edn. N.Y. Inst. Tech., Old Westbury, 1989—; pres. Human Resources Dept. Inc., Garden City, N.Y., 1994—; pres. Martin-Roche Internat. Ltd., Plainview, N.Y., 1992-94. Exec. dir. Jr. Achievement, Kingston, 1972-76, coach Syosset Baseball Assn., CYO Basketball Assn. Mem. ASTD, Am. Compensation Assn. (cert. compensation profl.), Soc. for Human Resource Mgmt. (cert. sr. profl. in human resources), KC (grand knight 1967-68). Republican. Roman Catholic. Avocations: astronomy, photography. Home: 17 Meadow Ln Syosset NY 11791-4126 Office: Human Resources Dept Inc 747 Zeckendorf Blvd Garden City NY 11530-2110 also: NY Inst Tech Dept Edn Old Westbury NY 11568-8000

ROCHE, JOHN J., banking company executive, corporate lawyer. BS, Manhattan Coll., 1957; LLB, Harvard U., 1963. Assoc., then ptnr. Shearman & Sterling, 1963-89; exec. v.p Citicorp/Citibank, N.A., N.Y.C., 1989—. Office: Citicorp/Citibank NA 399 Park Ave New York NY 10043-0001

ROCHE, JOHN JEFFERSON, lawyer; b. N.Y.C., Apr. 12, 1934; s. William and Florence E. (Garvey) R.; m. Judith J. Stackpole, Sept. 4, 1980; 1 child from previous marriage, Forrest B. A.B., Brown U., 1957; LL.B., Boston U., 1964. Bar: Mass. 1964, U.S. Tax Ct. 1976. Asst. atty. gen. Dept. Atty. Gen., Boston, 1964-67; ptnr. Hale and Dorr, Boston, 1967-90; pvt. practice Cambridge, Mass., 1991—. Trustee The Hotchkiss Sch., 1986-91; bd. dirs. Big Bros. Assn. Boston, Indian Soc. Served with U.S. army, 1959-62. Fellow Am. Coll. Probate Counsel, Internat. Acad. Estate and Trust Law; mem. ABA, Mass. Bar Assn., Boston Bar Assn. Republican. Congregationalist. Club: Wig and Penn (London); Winchester Country. Lodge: Masons. Office: Sigma St Kingston MA also: John J Roche & Assocs Ste 405 One Cambridge Ctr Cambridge MA 02142

ROCHE, (EAMONN) KEVIN, architect; b. Dublin, Ireland, June 14, 1922; came to U.S., 1948, naturalized, 1964; s. Eamon and Alice (Harding) R.; m. Jane Tuohy, June 10, 1963; children: Eamon, Paud, Denis, Anne, Alice. B.Arch., Nat. U. Ireland, 1945; D.Sc. (hon.), Nat. U. Ireland, 1977; postgrad., Ill. Inst. Tech., 1948; D.F.A. (hon.), Wesleyan U., 1981. With Eero Saarinen and Assocs., Hamden, Conn., 1950-66; partner Kevin Roche John Dinkeloo and Assocs., Hamden, from 1966. Prin. works include Ford Found. Hdqs., 1967, Oakland (Calif.) Mus, 1968, Met. Mus. Art, N.Y.C., Creative Arts Ctr., Wesleyan U., Middletown, Conn., 1971, Fine Arts Ctr., U. Mass., 1971, Union Carbide Corp. World Hdqs., Conn., Gen. Foods Corp. Hdqs., Rye, N.Y., 1977, 1978, Conoco Inc. Hdqs., Houston, 1979, Central Pk. Zoo, N.Y.C., 1980, DeWitt Wallace Mus. Fine Arts, Williamsburg, Va., 1980, Bouygues World Hdqs., Paris, 1983, J.P. Morgan and Co. Hdqs., N.Y.C., 1983, UNICEF Hdqs., N.Y.C., 1984, Leo Burnett Co. Hdqs., Chgo., 1989, Corning (N.Y.) Inc. Hdqs., 1986, Merck & Co. Inc. Corp. Office Facility, N.J., 1987, Dai Ichi Hdqs./Norinchukin Bank Hdqrs., Tokyo, 1989, Nations Bank Hdqs., Atlanta, 1989, N.Y.C. Exchs. Hdqs., 1989, Pontiac Marina Pvt. Ltd., Singapore, 1990, Metropolitano, Madrid, 1990, Borland Internat., Inc., Scotts Valley, Calif., 1990, Internat. Trade Ctr., Dusseldorf, Germany, 1991, Eczacibasi Group Hdqs. Istanbul, 1991, Hdqs. Tanjong & Binariang/Ampang Tower, Kuala Lumpur, Malaysia, 1993, Mus. of Jewish Heritage Holocaust Meml., N.Y.C., 1993, Tata Cummins Pvt. Ltd., Jamshedpur, India, 1994, Vis. Ctr., Columbus, Ind., 1994, Cummins Engine Co. APEX Mfg. Facility, 1994, DBS Devel., Beijing, China, 1994. Mem. Fine Arts Commn., Washington; trustee Am. Acad. in Rome, 1968-71; Woodrow Wilson Center for Scholars in Smithsonian Instn. Recipient Creative Arts award Brandeis U., 1967; A.S. Bard award City Club N.Y., 1968, 77, 79; award Gov. of Calif., 1968; N.Y. State award Citizens Union N.Y., 1968; total design award Am. Soc. Interior Design; Pritzker Archtl. prize, 1982; Albert S. Bard award, 1990. Fellow AIA (medal of honor N.Y. chpt. 1968, Gold Medal award 1993), AAAS; mem. NAD (academician), AAAL (pres. 1994-97), Am. Acad. and Inst. Arts and Letters (Brunner award 1965, Gold medal 1990), Académie d'Architecture (Grand Gold medal 1977), Mcpl. Art Soc. N.Y. (Brendan Gill prize 1989), Acad. di San Luca. Office: Kevin Roche John Dinkeloo & Assoc PO Box 6127 20 Davis St Hamden CT 06517-0127

ROCHE, KEVIN JOSEPH, finance executive; b. Newburyport, Mass., Mar. 31, 1935; s. Francis A. and Johanna (Murphy) R.; m. Arleen Ann Tangney, Oct. 16, 1965; children: Elizabeth, Edward. BBA, Merrimack Coll., 1962. Various positions Dow Jones & Co., Inc., N.Y.C., 1977-87; comptroller Dow Jones & Co., Inc., Princeton, N.J., 1987—; v.p. fin., chief fin. officer Dow Jones & Co., Inc., 1987—. Contbr. articles to profl. jours. Served to sgt. USAF, 1954-58. Mem. Fin. Exec. Inst., Internat. Newspaper Fin. Execs. Office: Dow Jones & Co Inc 200 Liberty St New York NY 10281-1003*

ROCHE, LISA RILEY, reporter; b. Las Vegas, Nev., Aug. 16, 1958; d. Joseph Thomas and Shirley Arlene (Schulz) Riley; m. Vaughn Stewart Roche, Jan. 1, 1986. BA with honors, U. Nev., 1980. Editor coll. newspaper U. Nev., Las Vegas, 1980-81; newspaper reporter Las Vegas Sun, 1981-84, Las Vegas Rev. Jour., 1984-86, Deseret News, Salt Lake City, 1987—. Winner 1st Pl., Nev. State Press Assn., 1984; recipient Spl. merit Deseret News, 1989.

ROCHE, MARK WILLIAM, German language educator; b. Weymouth, Mass., Aug. 29, 1956; s. Jason Bernard and Joan (Murphy) R.; m. Barbara Hampshire, June 13, 1981. BA, Williams Coll., 1978; MA, U. Tübingen, Germany, 1980, Princeton (N.J.) U., 1982; PhD, Princeton (N.J.) U., 1984. Asst. prof. German Ohio State U., Columbus, 1984-90, assoc. prof., 1990—, chair dept. German, 1991—. Author: Dynamic Stillness, 1987, Gottfried Benn's Static Poetry, 1991. Fulbright fellow Germany, 1978-80, Whiting fellow 1983-84, ACLS fellow 1985, NEH Summer Stipend grantee 1991, DAAD Study Visit Rsch. grantee 1991. Mem. Soc. for Philosophic Study of contemporary Visual Arts (vice pres. 1990-92). Home: 2019 Surrey Rd Blacklick OH 43004 Office: Ohio State U 312 Cunz Hall Columbus OH 43210

ROCHE, WILLIAM JOSEPH, lawyer; b. Middletown, Ohio, Aug. 28, 1927; s. John Joseph and Elizabeth (Hall) R.; m. Blanid June Brandes, Jan. 22, 1956; children—Nancy Elizabeth, Maureen Brandes, Suzanne Margaret, Kathleen Mary. A.B., U. Mich., 1950, J.D., 1951. Bar: Mich. 1951, Tex. 1960. Assoc. atty. Armstrong, Helm, Marshall & Schumann, Detroit, 1951-58; assoc. counsel Tex. Instruments Inc., Dallas, 1958-62, asst. sec., 1962-66, gen. atty., 1966-67, asst. v.p., 1967-72, v.p., gen. counsel, 1972-75, v.p., sec., gen. counsel, 1975-78, sr. v.p., sec., gen. counsel, 1978-82; ptnr. Johnson & Swanson (now Johnson & Gibbs, P.C.), Dallas, 1982—. Served as cpl. U.S. Army, 1945-46. Mem. ABA (com. on corp. law depts., sec. of corp., banking and bus. law), Southwestern Legal Found. (adv. bd. internat. and comparative law ctr.), Assn. Gen. Counsel (emeritus). Office: Johnson & Gibbs PC 900 Jackson St Dallas TX 75202-4404

ROCHELEAU, JAMES ROMIG, academic administrator; b. Anchorage, Mar. 21, 1940; s. James Albert and Sophia (Rivord) R.; m. Margaret Anne Sheehan, Nov. 28, 1981; children from previous marriage: Renee, Tanya, Andrea. BA, U. Idaho, 1968, MA, 1969; PhD, Wash. State U., Pullman, 1975. Account exec. Spokesman Rev., Spokane, Wash., 1963; sales rep. RJR Nabisco, Inc., Spokane, 1963-66; grad. asst. U. Idaho, Moscow and Wash. State U., Pullman, 1967-70; instr. history Wash. State U., 1970-71; asst. prof. history Buena Vista Coll., Storm Lake, Iowa, 1971-76, dir., 1976-81, dean continuing edn., 1981-84; pres. Upper Iowa U., Fayette, 1984-94, pres. emeritus, 1994—; cons. North Cen. Assn., Chgo., 1981—, Kellogg Found., 1994—. Active N.E.-Midwest Leadership Coun. Served with U.S. Army, 1958-61. Mem. Nat. Assn. Ind. Colls. and Univs., Iowa Assn. Ind. Colls. Univs., Coun. Ind. Colls., Iowa Coordinating Coun. for Post-High Sch. Edn., C. of C. Home: 14455 90th Ave N Seminole FL 34646 Office: PO Box 373 Indian Rocks Beach FL 34635

ROCHELL, CARLTON CHARLES, librarian; b. Lawrenceburg, Tenn., Nov. 2, 1933; s. William Frank and Mae (Crews) R.; children: Carlton Charles, Anne Leslie. B.S. in Math, Vanderbilt U. George Peabody Coll., 1959; M.L.S., Fla. State U., 1961, A.M.D. in L.S, 1974, Ph.D. in L.S. and Govt, 1976. Reference librarian, spl. asst. to dir. Nashville Pub. Library, 1957-60; dir. Hattiesburg (Miss.)-Forest County Pub. Library, 1961-63, Pub.

Library Anniston and Calhoun County, Ala., 1963-65, Pub. Library Knoxville and Knox County, Tenn., 1965- 68, Atlanta Pub. Libr., 1968-76; dean librs., NYU Press, Archives NYU, 1976—; chmn. N.Y. Regents Libr. Adv. Bd., 1977-85; pres. N.Y. Met. Reference and Research Libr. Agy., 1978-80; N.Y. del. White House Conf. on Librs. and Info. Svcs., mem. steering com., 1979; cons. NEH. Author: Practical Administration of Public Libraries, 1981, An Information Agenda for the 1980's, 1981, Dreams Betrayed: Working in the Technological Age, 1988, editor: In Praise of Libraries, 1989; contbr. articles to profl. jours. Served with USNR, 1953-57. Recipient spl. citation City Anniston, 1965; Effie award N.Y. Chpt. Am. Mktg. Assn., 1976; Andy award Advt. Club N.Y., 1976; Council on Library Resources fellow, 1973; Internat. Inst. Adminstr. Sci. fellow, 1979-81; scholar-in-residence Bellagio Study and Conf. Ctr. Rockefeller Found., summer 1982. Mem. Rsch. Librs. Group (chmn. bd. govs. 1987-89, ALA (coun. 1986-89), Assn. of Rsch. Librs. (bd. dirs. 1988-91). Democrat. Episcopalian. Office: NYU Elmer Holmes Bobst Libr 70 Washington Sq S New York NY 10012-1091

ROCHELLE, LUGENIA, academic administrator; b. Maple Hill, N.C., July 14, 1943; d. John Edward and Ruby Lee (Holmes) R. BA, St. Augustine's Coll., 1965; MS, N.C. A & T State U., 1969; D of Pedagogy, Barbar-Scotia Coll., 1993. Cert. tchr., N.C. Tchr. French, English Butler High Sch., Barnwell, S.C., 1965-67; instr. English N.C. A & T State U., Greensboro, 1970-77; instr. English St. Augustine's Coll., Raleigh, N.C., 1977-86, dir. freshman studies program, 1986-91, dean lower coll., 1991—, asst. to v.p. acad. affairs, 1991-92; dir. Mellon program St. Augustine's Coll., Raleigh, 1980-83; adv. bd. cooperating Raleigh Colls., 1986—, Off to Coll., Montgomery, Ala., 1993—. Author: English Manual of Writing, 1980. Judge oratorical contests, Optimist Club, Raleigh, 1985-93; chair pro tem Raleigh Bicentennial Hist. Com., Raleigh, 1991-92; initiated chartering of Phi Eta Sigma St. Augustine's Coll., 1995. Nat. teaching fellow N.C. A & T State U., Greensboro, 1968-70. NCTE. Fellow Nat. Coun. Tchrs. English; mem. ASCD (assoc.), Profl. Practices Commn. N.C. State Dept. Pub. Instrn. Avocations: reading, collecting antique birds, traveling. Home: 405 Hill St Raleigh NC 27610

ROCHER, LUDO, humanities educator; b. Hemiksem, Belgium, Apr. 25, 1926; s. Jules and Anna Van Den (Bogaert) R.; m. Rosane Debels, Apr. 1, 1961. B.A., U. Ghent, Belgium, 1946, M.A., 1948, LL.D., 1950, Ph.D., 1952. Agrege U. Ghent, 1958-59; prof. Sanskrit and comparative philology U. Brussels, 1959-67; prof. Sanskrit U. Pa., Phila., 1966—, W. Norman Brown prof. South Asian studies, 1981—; chmn. dept. Oriental studies U. Pa., 1967-75, 88-94, chmn. dept. South Asia regional studies, 1975-78; dir. Center for Study of South and S.E. Asia, U. Brussels, 1961-67. Author: A Hindu Legal Digest, 1956, Manual of Modern Hindi, 1958, Bibliography of Hindu Law, 1963, Smrticintamani, 1976, Paulinus a S. Bartholomaeo on the Sanskrit Language, 1977, Ezourvedam, 1984, The Puranas, 1985; contbr. articles to profl. jours. Served with Belgian Army, 1950-52. Research fellow Nat. Found. for Sci. Research, Belgium, 1952-58. Fellow Royal Acad. for Overseas Scis. Belgium, Asiatic Soc. Calcutta; mem. Am. Philos. Soc., Am. Oriental Soc. (pres. 1985-86), Assn. for Asian Studies, Royal Asiatic Soc. (Eng.). Home: 226 W Rittenhouse Sq #1506 Philadelphia PA 19103-5747

ROCHESTER, MICHAEL GRANT, geophysics educator; b. Toronto, Ont., Can., Nov. 22, 1932; s. Reginald Baillie Rochester and Ruth Ellen (Bonwick) Rochester Konrad; m. Elizabeth Manser, May 9, 1958; children—Susan, Fiona, John. B.A. (with honors), U. Toronto, 1954, M.A., 1956; Ph.D., U. Utah, 1959. Aerodynamicist A.V. Roe Can. Ltd., Malton, Ont., 1954-55; lectr. geophysics U. Toronto, 1959-60, asst. prof., 1960-61; asst. prof. U. Waterloo, Ont., 1961-65; assoc. prof. U. Waterloo, 1965-67, Meml. U. Nfld., St. John's, Can., 1967-70; prof. Meml. U. Nfld., 1970—, univ. research prof., 1986—. Mem., officer Nat. Spiritual Assembly of Baha'is of Can., 1963-92. Grantee NRC, Natural Scis. and Engring. Research Council Can. Fellow Royal Soc. Can.; mem. Internat. Union Geodesy and Geophysics (Can. nat. com. 1971-75, 84-88), AAAS, Am. Geophys. Union, Can. Assn. Physicists, Can. Geophys. Union (Tuzo Wilson medal, 1986), Internat. Astron. Union (commn. rotation of the Earth 1973—), Royal Astron. Soc. London, Sigma Xi. Avocations: hiking, swimming, history. Office: Meml Univ Nfld, Dept Earth Scis, Saint John's, NF Canada A1B 3X5

ROCHETTE, EDWARD CHARLES, retired association executive; b. Worcester, Mass. Feb. 17, 1927; s. Edward Charles and Lilia (Viau) R.; m. Mary Ann Ruland, July 29, 1978; children by previous marriage—Edward Charles, Paul, Philip. Student, Washington U., St. Louis, Clark U. Exec. editor Krause Publs., Iola, Wis., 1960-66; acting exec. dir. Am. Numismatic Assn., Colorado Springs, Colo., 1967-68, exec. v.p., 1972-87, ret.; 1987; editor jour. The Numismatist, Colorado Springs, Colo., 1968-72. Bd. overseers Inst. Philatelic and Numismatical Studies, Adelphi U., Garden City, N.Y., 1979-81; chmn. medals com. Colo. Centennial Bicentennial Commn., 1976; mem. adv. panel Carson City Silver Dollar program Gen. Services Adminstrn., 1979-80; mem. U.S. Assay Commn., 1965. Served with USN, 1944-46. Recipient Gold medal for syndicated column Numismatic Lit. Guild, 1980, 86-88. Mem. Am. Numis. Assn. (life, medal of merit 1972), Am. Soc. Assn. Execs., Colo. Soc. Assn. Execs. (pres. 1988-89). Democrat. Roman Catholic. Lodge: Pikes Peak Kiwanis (pres. 1987-88). Office: Am Numis Assn PO Box 7083 Colorado Springs CO 80933-7083

ROCHETTE, LOUIS, shipowner; b. Quebec City, Que., Can., Feb. 19, 1923; s. Evariste and Blanche (Gaudry) R.; m. Nicole Barbeau, Oct. 12, 1968; children: Louise, Ann, Guy. M. Commerce, Laval U., Que.; transl. Chartered Accountant, Que. Chief auditor retail sales tax Govt. Que. Quebec City, 1953-55; treas. Davie Shipbldg., Ltd., Lauzon, Que., 1955-65; exec. v.p. Marine Industries Ltd., Montreal, Que., 1965-76; chmn., chief exec. officer Davie Shipbldg. Ltd., Lauzon, Que., 1976-82; pres., chief exec. officer Soconav Inc., Quebec, 1982-86; vice chmn. Soconav Inc., Quebec, 1986—; pres. Gesconav Inc., 1986—; bd. dirs. Hawker Siddeley Can. Inc., Leader Industries, Inc; past chmn. Lloyd's Com. for Can. Author: Le Reve Separatiste, 1969. Bd. dirs. Gov. Coun. for Can. Unity; gov. Laval U. Found, Quebec Opera Found. Pilot RCAF, 1943-45, ETO. Named Hon. Col., Royal Can. Artillery. Fellow Inst. Chartered Accts. Can., Que. C. of C., Can. Inst. of Mgmt. Accts. Home and Office: 1155 Turnbull St #1002, Quebec, PQ Canada G1R 5G3 also: Socanav Inc, 1801 McGill Coll St Suite 1400, Montreal, PQ Canada H3A 2N4 *Whatever success I have met with throughout my career was mainly achieved through perseverance in the face of what often looked like insurmountable obstacles.*

ROCHLIS, JAMES JOSEPH, manufacturing company executive; b. Phila., Apr. 12, 1916; s. Aaron and Gussie (Pearlene) R.; m. Riva Singer, Mar. 21, 1943; children: Jeffrey A., Susan J. Ed. pub. schs. Salesman Mid-City Tire Co., Phila., 1945-46, gen. mgr., 1946-49; pres. Ram Rubber Co., Phila., 1948-49; rep. Blair & Co., Phila., 1949-61, bus. analyst, 1955-61; pres., chief exec. officer Baldwin-Montrose Chem. Co., Inc., N.Y.C., 1961-68; v.p. Chris-Craft Industries, Inc., N.Y.C., 1968-69; pres. Chris-Craft Corp., Pompano Beach, Fla., 1969-71; v.p. Chris-Craft Industries, Inc., N.Y.C., 1969-87, also bd. dirs.; pres. Baldwin-NAFI Industries div. Chris-Craft Industries, 1968—, Chris-Craft Internat., 1977-87; pres. Chris-Craft Indsl. Products, Inc., Pompano Beach, 1981-86, chmn., bd. dirs., cons., 1986—; bd. dirs. Montrose Chem. Co. Calif., Torrance and Mex., So. Mass. Cablevision Corp., N.Y.C., Piper Aircraft Corp., Lock Haven, Pa., Chris-Craft Pacific, Inc., Calif. Mem. AIAA, Fin. Analysts Soc. Mem. Soc. Naval Architects and Marine Engrs., Antique and Classic Boat Soc. Club: Lotus (N.Y.C.). Home: 150 E 69th St New York NY 10021-5704 also: 10601 Wilshire Blvd Los Angeles CA 90024 Office: Chris-Craft Industries Inc 767 Fifth Ave New York NY 10153

ROCHON, JOHN PHILIP, cosmetics company executive; b. Sept. 20, 1951; s. Philip Benjamin and Helena Sylvia (McCullough) R.; m. Donna J. Hewitt, Dec. 15, 1972; children: Heidi C., William J., Lauren. BS, U. Toronto, Ont., 1973, MBA, 1976. Plant mgr. Econs. Lab. Ltd., Toronto, 1976-80; dir. mfg. Mary Kay Cosmetics, Ltd. Toronto, 1980-82; contr. mfg. group Mary Kay Cosmetics, Inc., Dallas, 1982-84, corp. contr.-, 1984—, v.p. fin., chief fin. officer, 1984-85, exec. v.p., chief fin. officer, 1986-87, vice chmn. bd., 1987-93; pres., CEO Mary Kay Cosmetics Corp., Dallas, 1993—; also bd. dirs. Mary Kay Cosmetics, Ltd., Dallas; bd. dirs. Mary Kay Holding Corp., Dallas, Strategic Assessment, Inc.; mem. fin. com. U. Tex.,

Dallas, 1985—. Mem. Cosmetic, Toiletry and Fragrance Assn., Direct Selling Assn., Verandah Club. Republican. Home: 4315 Firebrick Ln Dallas TX 75287-5138*

ROCHWARGER, LEONARD, former ambassador; b. Buffalo, Aug. 3, 1925; s. Max and Sarah (Wallace) R.; m. Arlene Bassuk, June 19, 1949; children: Jeffrey Alan, Michelle. BS, U. Buffalo, 1949; PhD (hon.), Canisius Coll. Chief auditor Western N.Y. State, Buffalo, 1949-61; sr. ptnr. S. L. Horowitz & Co., Buffalo, 1961-65; chmn., chief exec. officer Rockmont Corp., Buffalo, 1965-87, 90—; U.S. amb. to Fiji, Republic of Kiribati, Kingdom of Tonga, and Tuvalu, 1988-90; chmn. bd. Indpls. Morris Plan Corp., Firstmark Fin. Corp., 1972-87; chmn. bd. Israel Am. Leasing Ltd., 1971-87; dir. Marine Midland Bank-Western, Nat. Fuel Gas Co.; adj. prof. SUNY, Buffalo; bd. chmn. Menorah Campus, 1993—. Past gen. chmn. United Way Buffalo and Erie Co., 1973; past trustee, past chmn. bd. regents Canisius Coll.; past chmn. United Jewish Appeal, Buffalo, 1969; past. pres., life dir. Buffalo Jewish Ctr.; past mem. nat. bd. dirs. NCCJ; past bd. dirs., hon. life pres. Nat. Jewish Welfare Bd.; life mem., past pres. Jewish Fedn. Greater Buffalo; past bd. dirs. Coun. Jewish Fedns.; mem. adv. coun. Johns Hopkins U. Sch. Adv. Internat. Studies, Washington, 1986-88, 90—; past pres. Found. Jewish Philanthropies, Buffalo; trustee U. Buffalo Found., Inc. With AUS, 1943-46. Decorated Bronze Star, Conspicious Service Cross. Jewish. Home: 81 Nottingham Ter Buffalo NY 14216-3620

ROCK, ALLAN MÍCHAEL, Canadian government official; b. Ottawa, Ont., Can., Aug. 30, 1947; s. James Thomas and Anne (Dane) R.; m. Deborah Kathleen, June 24, 1983; children: Jason, Lauren, Andrew, Stephen. BA, U. Ottawa, 1968, LLB, 1971. Certified specialist in civil litigation. Sr. ptnr. Fasken Campbell Godfrey and Fasken Martineau; min. of justice, atty. gen. Govt. of Can., 1993—; treas. Law Soc. U.C., 1992—; bencher Law Soc., 1983, 87, 91; former chmn. discipline and legal edn. coms.; chmn. litigation dept. Fasken Campbel Godfrey. Fellow Am. Coll. Trial Lawyers. Office: Justice Canada, Justice Bldg 239 Wellington St, Ottawa, ON Canada K1A 0H8*

ROCK, ANGELA, volleyball player; b. Carlsbad, Calif., Oct. 15, 1963. BA in Psychology, San Diego State U., 1994. Fire-fighter San Diego; profl. volleyball team player; mem. U.S.A. Nat. Team, 1987-90. Winner bronze medal Pan Am. Games, 1987; named USVBA Most Valuable Player, 1987, WPVA Best Hitter, 1991, Winner of the Miller Lite Ice Cup. Mem. Assn. Volleyball Profls., Women's Profl. Volleyball Assn. Competed Goodwill Games, 1987, Olympic, Seoul, 1988; compiled 18 WPVA Open Wins; won AVP Women's Tour Event with Linda Hanley, Ocean City, 1993, 1st ever with Holly McPeak, Phoenix, Miller Lite Opens, (receipient Miller Lite Ice Cup), Grand Haven and Nestea Opens, Atlanta, Dallas with Nancy Reno, Phoenix, 1994. Office: care Assn Volleyball Profls 15260 Ventura Blvd Ste 2250 Sherman Oaks CA 91003*

ROCK, ARTHUR, venture capitalist; b. Rochester, N.Y., Aug. 19, 1926; s. Hyman A. and Reva (Cohen) R.; m. Toni Rembe, July 19, 1975. BS, Syracuse U., 1948; MBA, Harvard U., 1951. Gen. ptnr. Davis & Rock, San Francisco, 1961-68, Arthur Rock & Assocs., San Francisco, 1969-80; bd. dirs. Argonaut Group, Inc., L.A., Echelon, Palo Alto, Calif., AirTouch Comm., San Francisco; mem. exec. com. Teledyne, Inc., L.A., 1961-94; founder, chmn. exec. com. bd. dirs., past chmn. bd. dirs. Intel Corp., Santa Clara, Calif. Trustee Calif. Inst. Tech.; bd. dirs. San Francisco Opera Assn., 1970-92, San Francisco Mus. Modern Art; mem. vis. com. Harvard U. Bus. Sch., 1982-88. Recipient Medal of Achievement Am. Electronics Assn., 1987, Am. Acad. Achievement, 1989; named to Jr. Achievement Hall of Fame, 1990, Calif. Bus. Hall of Fame, 1990. Office: 1 Maritime Plz Ste 1220 San Francisco CA 94111-3502

ROCK, DOUGLAS LAWRENCE, manufacturing executive; b. Glen Cove, N.Y., Jan. 25, 1947; s. Herb and Beatrice (Vyse) R.; m. Cindy Pegoraro, May 11, 1967 (div. Apr. 1973); 1 child, Jason; m. Mary Sue Bell, Mar. 23, 1991. BS in Psychology and Chemistry, Pa. State U., 1968; postgrad., U. Chgo., 1971-73. Rsch. chemist FMC Corp., Princeton, N.J., 1968-69; mfg. system project leader A.O. Smith Corp., Erie, Pa., 1969-71; dir. materials and info. systems Joy Mfg., Michigan City, Ind., 1971-74; dir. info. systems Smith Tool div. Smith Internat. Inc., Irvine, Calif., 1974-75, dir. materials, 1975-77, v.p. mfg., 1977-80, sr. v.p. ops., 1980-82, pres., 1985-87; pres. Drilco div. Smith Internat. Inc., Houston, 1982-85; pres., chief exec. officer Smith Internat. Inc., Houston, 1987—, chmn. bd., 1991—. Named Golden Knight, Nat. Mgmt. Assn., 1983. Mem. Internat. Assn. Drilling Contractors, Am. Petroleum Inst., Petroleum Equipment Suppliers Assn. (bd. dirs. Houston chpt. 1987—), Nat. Offshore Industries Assn. (fin. com. 1988—, audit com. 1989), Kingwood Country Club, Greenspoint Club . Avocations: golf, racquetball, reading. Office: Smith Internat PO Box 60068 16740 Hardy Rd Houston TX 77205-0068

ROCK, HAROLD L., lawyer; b. Sioux City, Iowa, Mar. 13, 1932; s. Harold L. and Helen J. (Gormally) R.; m. Marilyn Beth Rock, Dec. 28, 1954; children: Michael, Susan, John, Patrick, Michele, Thomas. BS, Creighton U., 1954, JD, 1959. Bar: Nebr., N.Y., Minn., Mont., Wyo. Law clk. to judge U.S. Ct. Appeals 8th Circuit, Omaha, 1959-60, Fitzgerald Hamer Brown & Leahy, Omaha, 1960-65; ptnr. Kutak Rock, Omaha, 1965—; chmn. Nebr. Bd. Bar Examiners, 1989—; bd. dirs. Mid City Bank, Omaha. Bd. dirs. Douglas County Hist. Soc., 1992—. Served to 1st lt. U.S. Army, 1954-56. Mem. ABA (ho. of dels. 1990—, bd. govs., 1992-95), Nebr. Bar Assn. (ho. of dels., bd. dirs. 1985—, pres. 1988, Nebr. Bar found. bd. dir., 1985—), Omaha Bar Assn. (pres. 1972-73), Omaha Legal Aid Soc. (pres. 1969-72), Nebr. State Bd. Pub. Accts. (bd. dirs. 1981-85). Roman Catholic. Office: Kutak Rock The Omaha Bldg 1650 Farnam St Omaha NE 68102-2103

ROCK, JOHN AUBREY, gynecologist and obstetrician, educator; b. Corpus Christi, Tex., Oct. 23, 1946; s. William A. and Burta (Wheeler) R.; m. Barbara McAlpine, Oct. 8, 1976; children: John Aubrey Jr., Deborah Ellen, Daniel Authur. BS in Zoology, La. State U., Baton Rouge, 1968; MD, La. State U., New Orleans, 1972. Asst. prof. Johns Hopkins U. Sch. Medicine, Balt., 1978-80, assoc. prof., 1980-87, prof. ob-gyn, 1987—; prof. pediatrics, 1988—; dir. reproductive endocrinology, 1979-91, dep. dir. med. sch., 1985-88; chmn. Union Meml. Hosp., Balt., 1991-92; James Robert McCord prof., chmn. dept. ob-gyn. Emory U. Sch. Medicine, Atlanta, 1992—; cons. Dept. Army, Washington, 1982-93, NASA, Houston, 1988—; chmn. ad hoc com. on in vitro fertilization State of Md., 1985. Author: Reparative and Constructive Surgery of the Female Generative Tract, 1983, Endometriosis, 1988, TeLinde's Operative Gynecology, 1991; mem. editorial bd. Fertility and Sterility jour., 1986—, Gynecology Surgery, 1989—. Fellow Am. Coll. Ob-Gyn; mem. Am. Gynecol. and Obstet. Soc., Soc. Gynecol. Surgeons, Am. Fertility Soc., (bd. dirs. 1989-92), Soc. Gynecologic Investigation, Soc. Reproductive Surgeons (pres. 1986), Phi Kappa Phi. Methodist. Office: Emory U Sch Medicine Atlanta GA 30303-9999

ROCK, KENNETH WILLETT, history educator; b. Abilene, Kans., Dec. 12, 1938; s. Kenneth Melvin and Marjorie (Taylor) R.; m. Mercedes Alice de Sola, Aug. 22, 1964; children: Kenneth Teodoro, Laurel Elizabeth. BA, U. Kans., 1960; MA, Stanford U., 1962, PhD, 1969. Instr. history Colo. State U., Ft. Collins, 1965-68, asst. prof., 1968-72, advisor Fulbright, Marshall, Rhodes scholarships, 1968-80, assoc. prof., 1972-83, prof., 1983—, acting dir. Office Internat. Edn., 1984-85. Author (booklet) German Footprints in Colorado, 1980; contbr. articles to profl. jours.; chpts. to books. Fulbright scholar Inst. Internat. Edn., Vienna, Austria, 1964-65; fellow NEH, Vienna, 1972-73, NEH, U. Va., 1978; assoc. Danforth Found., 1978-84. Mem. Am. Assn. Advancement Slavic Studies, Conf. Group Cen. European History, Am. Hist. Assn., Am. Hist. Soc. Germans from Russia, Rocky Mountain Slavic Studies Assn., Phi Beta Kappa, Phi Alpha Theta. Democrat. Avocations: reading, historical miniatures, travelling, photography, painting. Home: 3212 Shore Rd Fort Collins CO 80524-1688 Office: Colo State U Dept History Fort Collins CO 80523

ROCK, MILTON LEE, publisher; b. Phila., Feb. 25, 1921; s. Maurice and Mary (Lee) R.; m. Shirley Cylinder, Aug. 3, 1943; children: Susan Rock, Robert Henry. BA, Temple U., 1946, MS, 1947; Ph.D., U. Rochester, 1949. Mng. ptnr. Hay Group, Phila., 1949-85; chmn. MLR Enterprises, Inc., Phila., 1985—; pres. Assn. Mgmt. Cons. Firms, N.Y.C., 1972-73. Co-author: The Executive Perceptanalytic Scale, 1963, The Development of Bank

Management Personnel, 1969; editor: Handbook of Wage and Salary Administration, 1972, 2d edit., 1983, Compensation Handbook, 1990, The Mergers and Acquisitions Handbook, 1987, 2d edit., 1994, Corporate Restructuring, 1989. Chmn. Middle Atlantic Regional Manpower Adv. Com., Labor Dept., 1972-73; mem. Pres.'s Nat. Commn. for Manpower Policy, 1974-77; bd. govs. Temple U. Hosp., 1975—, chmn., 1985-92, trustee Univ., 1979—; bd. dirs. Phila. Orch., 1981-87, 89-94, Curtis Inst. Music, Phila., 1983—, chmn. 1989—, Pa. Ballet, 1983—, Phila. Mus. Art, 1986—, chmn. 94—, Fgn. Policy Rsch. Inst. 1987-90; mem. adv. coun. J.L. Kellogg Grad. Sch. Mgmt. Northwestern U., 1981—. Fellow Am. Psychol. Assn.; mem. Inst. Mgmt. Cons. (dir., founding). Home: Pocono Pines PA 18350 Office: MLR Enterprises Inc 229 S 18th St Philadelphia PA 19103-6144

ROCK, RICHARD RAND, lawyer, former state senator; b. Wichita Falls, Tex., Sept. 27, 1924; s. Parker Francis and Ruth Ann (Phillips) R.; m. Rosalee Deardorff, Aug. 23, 1947; children: Richard R. II, Darci Lee, Devon Ray, Robert Regan. BA, Washburn U., 1948, LLB, 1950, JD, 1970. Bar: Kans., U.S. Dist. Ct. Kans., U.S. Ct. Appeals (4th and 10th cirs.). Dir. indsl. rels. Maurer-Neuer Packers, Arkansas City, Kans., 1950-52, plant supt., 1952-54; atty. Rock, Smith & Mason, Arkansas City, Kans., 1955—; pres., owner Shreveport (La.) Packing Co., 1972-83, Amarillo (Tex.) Beef Processors, 1977-82, Lubbock (Tex.) Beef Processors, 1978-81, Montgomery (Ala.) Food Processors, 1978-91, Humboldt (Iowa) Sausage Co., 1985-92, Great Bend (Kans.) Packing Co., 1984—; state senator, asst. minority leader State of Kans., 1988—; chmn. bd. dirs. Roadside Mgmt. Co., Overland Park, Kans. Judge Cowley County, Kans., 1952-56; state rep. State of Kans., 1957-61; authority mem. Kans. Turnpike Authority, 1980-88, 93—; commr. Children with Spl. Health Care Needs, Kans., 1993—. Served USN Air Corps, 1943-45. Mem. Kans. Bar Assn., Nat. Counsel State Legislatures, Kans. C. of C., VFW. Democrat. Mem. Disciples of Christ. Avocations: golf, yard work.

ROCKART, JOHN FRALICK, information systems reseacher; b. N.Y.C., June 20, 1931; s. John Rachac and Janet (Ross) R.; m. Elise Jean Feldmann, Sept. 16, 1961; children: Elise B. Liesl, Scott F. AB, Princeton U., 1953; MBA, Harvard U., 1958; PhD, MIT, 1968. Sales rep. IBM, 1958-61, dist. med. rep., 1961-62, fellow in Africa, 1962-64; instr. MIT, Cambridge, Mass., 1966-67; asst. prof. IBM, Cambridge, Mass., 1967-70, assoc. prof., 1970-74, sr. lectr., 1974—; dir. MIT, Cambridge, 1976—; bd. dirs. Keane, Inc., Boston, Comshare, Inc., Ann Arbor, Mich., Transition Sys., Inc., Boston, Multiplex, St. Louis, Renaissance Solutions, Lincoln, Mass., Synon, Inc., Larkspur, Calif. Co-author: Computers & Learning Process, 1974, Rise of Managerial Computing, 1986, Executive Support Systems, 1988 (Computer Press Assn. 1989); contbr. articles to profl. jours. Trustee New Eng. Med. Ctr., Boston; mem. Mass. Gov. Adv. Coun. on Info. Tech., Boston. Lt. USN, 1953-56. Mem. Assn. for Computing Machinery, Inst. for Mgmt. Sci., Ops. Rsch. Soc. Am., Soc. for Info. Mgmt. (bd. dirs. mem. at large 1989-94), New Eng. Med. Ctr. Audit Com., Weston (Mass.) Golf Club, Lake Sunapee Country Club (New London, N.H.). Republican. Unitarian. Home: 150 Cherry Brook Rd Weston MA 02193-1308 Office: CISR MIT Sloan Sch Mgmt E40-187 77 Massachusetts Ave Cambridge MA 02139-4307

ROCKBURNE, DOROTHEA G., artist; b. Montreal, Que., Can. Student, Black Mountain Coll. Milton and Sally Avery Disting. prof. Bard Coll., 1986; trustee Ind. Curators Inc., N.Y., Art in Gen.; artist in residence Am. Acad. in Rome, 1991; vis. artist Skowhegan Sch. Printing and Sculpture, 1984. One-person shows include Sonnabend Gallery, Paris, 1971, New Gallery, Cleve., 1972, Bykert Gallery, N.Y.C., 1970, 72, 73, Galleria Toselli, Milan, Italy, 1972, 73, 74, Galleria D'Arte, Bari, Italy, 1972, Lisson Gallery, London, 1973, Daniel Weinberg Gallery, San Francisco, 1973, Galerie Charles Kriwin, Brussels, 1975, Galleria Schema, Florence, Italy, 1973, 75, 92, John Weber Gallery, N.Y.C., 1976, 78, Galleria la Polena, Geona, Italy, 1977, Tex. Gallery, Houston, 1979, 80, 81, Xavier Fourcade Gallery, N.Y.C., 1980, 82, 83, 85, 86, David Bellman, Toronto, 1980, 81, Margo Leavin, Calif., 1982, Arts Club of Chgo., 1987, André Emmerich Gallery, N.Y.C., 1988, 89, 91, 92, 94, 95, 10 yr. retrospective Rose Art Mus., 1989, P. Fong & Spratt Galleries, San Jose, Calif., 1991, Sony Music Hdqs., N.Y.C., 1993, Frederick Spratt Gallery, San Jose, 1994; group shows include Whitney Mus. Am. Art, 1970, 73, 77, 79, 82, Mus. Modern Art, Buenos Aires, 1971, Kolner Kunst Market, Cologne, Germany, 1971, Stedelijk Mus., Holland, 1971, Spoleto (Italy) Festival, 1972, Palazzo Taverna, Rome, 1973, Nat. Gallery Victoria, Melbourne, Australia, 1973, Art Gallery NSW, Sydney, 1973, Auckland (New Zealand) City Art Gallery, 1973, Inst. Contemporary Art, London, 1974, Mus. d'Arte de la Ville, Paris, 1975, Galerie Aronowitsch, Stockholm, 1975, Stadtiches Mus., Manchengladbach, Germany, 1975, Galleria D'Arte Moderna, Bologna, Italy, 1975, Art Gallery Ont., Toronto, Can., 1975, Mus. Fine Art, Houston, 1975, Contemporary Arts Ctr., Cin., 1973, 75, 81, Mus. Contemporary Art, Chgo., 1971, 77, 86, Corcoran Gallery of Art, Washington, 1975, 87, Städtisches Mus., Leverkusen, Germany, 1975, Cannaviella Studio d'Arte Rome, 1976, Phila. Coll. Art, 1976, 83, Balt. Mus. Art, 1976, New Mus., N.Y.C., 1977, 80, 84, 83, Renaissance Soc. of U. Chgo., 1976, Lowe Art Mus., U. Miami, Fla., 1976, Inst. Contemporary Art, Boston, 1976, Seibu Mus. Art, Tokyo, 1976, N.Y. State Mus., Albany, 1977, Drawing Ctr., 1977, Kansas City (Mo.) Art Inst., 1977, Smithsonian Inst., Washington, 1977, Kassel, Fed. Republic Germany, 1972, 77, Ackland Art Ctr., Chapel Hill, N.C., 1979, 84, Milw. Art Ctr., 1978, 81, Biblioteca Nacional, Madrid, 1980, Gulbenkian Mus., Lisbon, Portugal, 1980, Bklyn. Mus., 1981, 89, Guggenheim Mus., 1982, 88, 89, Albright Knox Art Gallery, Buffalo, 1979, 80, 88, 89, Kuustforeningen Mus., Copenhagen, 1980, Venice Biennale, 1980, Cranbrook (Mich.) Acad. Art, 1981, Mus. Fine Arts, Boston, 1983, Contemporary Arts Mus., Houston, 1983, Norman Mackenzie Art Gallery, U. Regina, Sask., Can., 1983, Galleriet, Sweden, 1983-84, Seattle Art Mus., 1979-84, Nat. Mus. Art., Osaka, Japan, 1984, Fogg Art Mus., Cambridge, Mass., 1984, Am. Acad. and Inst. Arts and Letters, N.Y.C., 1984, 87, L.A. County Mus. Art, 1984, 86, Wadsworth Atheneum, Hartford, Conn., 1981, 84, Everhart Mus., Pa., 1984, Grey Art Gallery, NYU, 1977, 84, 87, Avery Ctr. Arts, Bard Coll., N.Y., 1985, 87-88, Stamford (Conn.) Mus., 1985, Aldrich Mus., Conn., 1979, 82, Bronx Mus. Arts, N.Y.C., 1985, High Mus., Atlanta, 1975, 81, Phila. Mus. Art, 1986, Nat. Gallery Art, Washington, 1984, Mus. Art, Ft. Lauderdale, Fla., 1986, Nat. Mus. Women in Art, Washington, 1987, Xavier Fourcade Gallery, 1983, 87, L.A. County Mus. Modern Art, 1986-87, The Hague, The Netherlands, 1986, Carnegie-Mellon Art Gallery, Pitts., 1979, 87, Balt. Mus. Art, 1975, 76, 88, Ctr. for Fine Arts, Miami, 1989, Milw. Art Mus., 1989, Cin. Art Mus., 1989, New Orleans Mus., 1989, Denver Art Mus., 1989, Parrish Art Mus., South Hampton, N.Y., 1990, 91, Margo Leavin Gallery, L.A., 1991, Mus. of Modern Art, N.Y.C., 1991, Guild Hall Mus., East Hampton, N.Y., 1991, Am. Acad., Rome, 1991, Mus. Contemporary Art, L.A., 1991, Hunter Coll., N.Y., 1991, Centro Cultural/Arte Contemporanea, Mexico City, 1991, Hilton, San Jose, Calif., 1992, Hillwood Art Mus., L.I., N.Y., 1992, Am. Acad. and Inst. Arts and Letters, 1992, Neuberger Mus., 1992, Statue of Liberty Group, 1993, Foster Harmans Galliers of Am. Art, Sarasota, Fla., 1993, Kohn-Abrams Gallerie, L.A., 1993, The Gallery at Bristol Myers Squibb, N.J., 1993, Friends of Art and Preservation in Embassies, N.Y.C., 1993, Just Art, N.Y.C., 1993, Mus. Modern Art, N.Y.C., 1994, TZ Art and Co., N.Y.C., Andre Emmerich Gallery, N.Y.C., 1993, Nat. Gallery of Art, Washington, 1994, Fred Spratt Gallery, San José, Calif., 1994, RAAB Galarie, Berlin, 1994, Gallary at Bristol Myer Squibb, N.J., 1994, Moma, N.Y.C., 1994, N.Y. Studio Sch., N.Y.C., 1995, Aldrich Mus., Conn., 1995; represented in permanent collections Milw. Art Ctr., Mus. Modern Art N.Y.C., Fogg Mus., Cambridge, Mass., Phila. Mus. Art, High Mus. Art, Atlanta, Houston Mus. Fine Arts, Corcoran Gallery, Washington, Mpls. Art Inst., Mpls. Art Mus., Met. Mus. Art, N.Y.C., Guggenheim Mus., N.Y.C., Ludwig Mus., Aachen, Fed. Republic Germany, Holladay, Washington, Saatchi, London, Bard, Albright-Knox Art Gallery, Buffalo, Whitney Mus. Am. Art, N.Y.C., U. Mich., Ann Arbor, Ohio State U., Columbus, Gilman Paper Co., N.Y., Auckland (New Zealand) City Art Mus., Portland (Oreg.) Art Mus., Aaken Art Mus., Oberlin, Ohio, Highhold Internat., S. Africa, U. Ohio Art Gallery, Columbus, HHK Charitable Found., Milw., Art Gallery Ont., Toronto, Can., Nat. Mus. Women in Art, Washington, Chase Manhattan Bank, N.Y.C., Hilton Hotel, San Jose, Calif., Sony Music Hdqs. Mem. artists adv. bd. New Mus. of Contemporary Art, N.Y.C.; trustee Ind. Curators, N.Y.C. Recipient Witowsky prize 72d Am. Exhbn., Art Inst., Chgo., 1976, Creative Arts award Brandeis U., 1985, Bard Coll., 1986; Guggenheim fellow, 1972; Nat. Endowment Arts grantee, 1974, Am. Acad., Rome, 1991.

ROCKE, DAVID MORTON, statistician, educator; b. Chgo., June 4, 1946; s. Sol J. and Verva (Coleman) R.; m. Carrie Clausen, Dec. 30, 1971; children: Emily Carolyn, Miriam Ruth. AB, Shimer Coll., 1966; PhD, U. Ill., Chgo., 1972, postdoctoral, 1977-79. Vis. lectr. math. dept. U. Ill., Chgo., 1972-74; prof. Govs. State U., Park Forest South, Ill., 1974-80; assoc. prof. grad. sch. mgmt. U. Calif., Davis, 1980-86, prof., 1986—; cons. Calif. State Water Bd., Sacramento, 1987—, Calif. Air Resources Bd., Sacramento, 1988—, U.S. Bur. Reclamation, Sacramento, 1986, Sherwin-Williams Rsch. Ctr., Chgo., 1980. Contbr. articles to profl. jours. Recipient Youden prize for articles Technometrics, 1983. Mem. Am. Statis. Assn. (Interlab. Testing award 1985), Inst. Math. Stats., Royal Statis. Soc., Am. Soc. for Quality Control (Shewell award 1987), Biometric Soc., Bernoulli Soc., Am. Math. Soc., Soc. for Indsl. and Applied Math., Math. Assn. Am., AAAS. Office: U Calif Sch Mgmt Davis CA 95616

ROCKEFELLER, DAVID, banker; b. N.Y.C., June 12, 1915; s. John Davison Jr. and Abby Greene (Aldrich) R.; m. Margaret McGrath, Sept. 7, 1940; children: David, Abby A., Neva, Margaret D., Richard G., Eileen M. BS, Harvard Coll., 1936; student, London Sch. Econs.; LLD (hon.), Harvard U., 1969; PhD, U. Chgo., 1940; LLD (hon.), Columbia U., 1954, Bowdoin Coll., 1958, Jewish Theol. Sem., 1958, Williams Coll., 1966, Wagner Coll., 1967, Rockefeller U., 1980, Pace Coll., 1970, St. John's U., 1971, Middlebury, 1974, U. Liberia, 1979, Am. U., 1987, U. Miami, 1988; DEng (hon.), Colo. Sch. Mines, 1974, U. Notre Dame, 1987. Sec. to Mayor Fiorello H. La Guardia, 1940-41; asst. regional dir. Office Def., Health and Welfare Services, 1941-42; asst. mgr. for dept. Chase Nat. Bank, N.Y.C., 1946-47, asst. cashier, 1947-48, 2d v.p., 1948-49; v.p. Chase Nat. Bank, 1949-51, sr. v.p., 1951-55; exec. v.p. Chase Manhattan Bank (Chase Nat. Bank merged with Bank of Manhattan), 1955-57; vice chmn. bd. Chase Manhattan Bank, 1957-61, pres., chmn. exec. com., 1961-69, chmn., 1969-81, CEO, 1969-80; chmn. bd. dirs. Chase Internat. Investment Corp.,1961-81, Chase Internat. Adv. Com., 1980—, Rockefeller Group, Inc., 1981—, Rockefeller Ctr. Properties, Inc., 1986-92, N.Y. Clearing House, 1977-78, Ctr. for Inter-Am. Rels., 1966-70, Overseas Devel. Coun., U.S.-USSR Trade and Econ. Coun. Inc.; bd. dirs. Internat. Exec. Svc. Com., 1964-90, chmn., 1964-68. Author: Unused Resources and Economic Waste, 1940, Creative Management in Banking, 1964. Active Urban Devel. Corp., N.Y. State Bus. Adv. Coun., 1968-72, U.S. Adv. Com. on Reform of Internat. Monetary System, 1973-77, U.S. Exec. Com., Dartmouth Coll., Bd. Int. Internat. Econs., Am. Friends of LSE, U.S. Hon. Fellows LSE, Bus. Com. for Arts, founding mem., Commn. on White House Fellows, hon. mem., 1964-65; mem. exec. com. Downtown Lower Manhattan Assn., 1958—, chmn., 1958-75; trustee Rockefeller U., 1940—, chmn. bd., 1950-75, chmn. exec. com., 1975—; chmn. Rockefeller Bros. Fund, 1981-87, vice-chmn., 1968-80; trustee Carnegie Endowment Internat. Peace; hon. trustee Rockefeller Family Fund; life trustee U. Chgo.; trustee, chmn. bd., exec. com. Mus. Modern Art, 1962-72, 1987-93; bd. overseers Harvard Coll., 1954-60, 62-68, 73-74; co-founder Trilateral Commn., 1973-91, N.Am. chmn. 1981-92, hon. chmn., 1992; hon. chmn. Internat. House, 1940—, dir., 1940-63; pres. Morningside Heights, Inc., 1947-57, chmn., 1957-65; chmn. Ams. Soc., 1981-92, hon. chmn., 1992—, N.Y.C. Partnership, 1979-88; trustee Hist. Hudson Valley, 1981—. Capt. AUS, 1942-46, NATOUSA, ETO. Decorated Legion of Honor France; Order of Merit, Italy, Order of Southern Cross, Brazil, Order of the White Elephant and Order of Crown, Thailand, Order of the Cedar, Lebanon, Order of the Sun, Peru, Order of the Humane African Redemption, Liberia, Order of the Crown, Belgium, Nat. Order of Ivory Coast, Grand Cordon Order of Sacred Treasure, Japan, Order Bernardo O'Higgins, Chile; recipient Merit award N.Y. chpt. AIA, 1965, Gold medal Nat. Inst. Social Scis., 1967, AIA medal of Honor for City Planning N.Y.C., 1968, Charles Evans Hughes award NCCJ, 1974, World Brotherhood award Jewish Theol. Sem, 1953, C. Walter Nichols award NYU, 1970, Regional Planning Assn. award, 1971; Hadrian award, World Monuments Fund, 1994. Mem. Internat. Exec. Service Corps (dir., chmn. 1964-68), Center Inter-Am. Relations (dir., hon. chmn.), Council Fgn. Relations (dir. 1949-51, v.p. 1951-70, chmn. 1970-85), Century Club, Harvard, River Club, Univ. Club. Links Club, Knickerbocker Club, N.Y. Yacht Club. Avocation: sailing. Address: 30 Rockefeller Plz New York NY 10112-0001

ROCKEFELLER, EDWIN SHAFFER, lawyer; b. Harrisburg, Pa.; Sept. 10, 1927; s. Edwin S. and Nancy Rhea (McCullough) R.; m. Marilie Gould Wallace, Dec. 22, 1952; children: Ben Wallace, Edwin Palmer. AB, Yale U., 1948, LLB, 1951, M in Internat. Pub. Policy, Johns Hopkins U., 1989. Bar: Conn. 1951, D.C. 1956, U.S. Supreme Ct. 1957. Atty., FTC, 1956-61, asst. to gen. counsel, 1958-59, exec. asst. to chmn., 1960-61; pvt. practice, Washington, 1961—; ptnr. Schiff Hardin & Waite, Washington, 1981-93, of counsel, 1994—; mem. USIA Inspection Team, Pakistan, 1971; adj. prof. Georgetown U. Law Ctr., Washington, 1985-87. 1st lt. JAGC, U.S. Army, 1953-56. Mem. ABA (chmn. sect. antitrust law 1976-77, ho. of dels. 1979-82), Chevy Chase Club, Met. Club (Washington), Yale Club (N.Y.C.). Author: Antitrust Questions & Answers, 1974; Desk Book of FTC Practice & Procedure, 3d edit., 1979; Antitrust Counseling for the 1980s, 1983. Office: Schiff Hardin & Waite 1101 Connecticut Ave NW Ste 600 Washington DC 20036-4390

ROCKEFELLER, JOHN DAVISON, IV (JAY ROCKEFELLER), senator, former governor; b. N.Y.C., N.Y., June 18, 1937; s. John Davison III and Blanchette Ferry (Hooker) R.; m. Sharon Percy, Apr. 1, 1967; children: Jamie, Valerie, Charles, Justin. B.A., Harvard U., 1961; student, Japanese lang. Internat. Christian U., Tokyo, 1957-60; postgrad. in Chinese, Yale U. Inst. Far Eastern Langs., 1961-62. Apptd. mem. nat. adv. council Peace Corps, 1961, spl. asst. to dir. corps, 1962, ops. officer in charge work in Philippines, until 1963; desk officer for Indonesian affairs Bur. Far Eastern Affairs, U.S. State Dept., 1963; later asst. to asst. sec. state for Far Eastern affairs; cons. Pres.'s Commn. on Juvenile Delinquency and Youth Crime, 1964; field worker Action for Appalachian Youth program, from 1964; mem. W.Va. Ho. of Dels., 1966-68; sec. of state W.Va., 1968-72; pres. W.Va. Wesleyan Coll., Buckhannon, 1973-75; gov. State of W.Va., 1976-84; U.S. senator from W.Va., 1985—, mem. vets. affairs com., fin. com., commerce, sci. and transp. com., chmn. Sen. steel caucus, Bipartisan Com. on Comprehensive Health Care; chmn. Nat. Commn. on Children, natural resources and environ. com. Nat. Govs. Assn., 1981-84. Contbr. articles to mags. including N.Y. Times Sunday mag. Trustee U. Chgo., 1967—; chmn. White House Conf. Balanced Nat. Growth and Econ. Devel., 1978, Pres.'s Commn. on Coal, 1978-80, White House Adv. Com. on Coal., 1980; active Commerce, Sci., and Transp. Com., Fin. Com.; chmn. Vet. Affairs Com. Office: US Senate 109 Hart Senate Bldg Washington DC 20510*

ROCKEFELLER, MARGARETTA FITLER MURPHY (HAPPY ROCKEFELLER), widow of former vice president of U.S.; m. Nelson Aldrich Rockefeller (dec.); children: James B. Murphy, Margaretta H. Bickford, Carol Murphy Lyden, Malinda Murphy Menotti, Nelson A. Rockefeller, Jr., Mark F. Rockefeller. Dir. Archer-Daniels-Midland Co., Decatur, Ill.; alt. rep. of U.S. to 46th Session of UN Gen. Assembly, 1991, 47th Session, 1992.

ROCKEFELLER, SHARON PERCY, broadcast executive; b. Oakland, Calif., Dec. 10, 1944; d. Charles H. and Jeanne Dickerson Percy; m. John D. Rockefeller IV; children: John, Valerie, Charles, Justin. BA cum laude, Stanford U.; LLD (hon.), U. Charleston, 1977, Beloit Coll., 1978; LHD (hon.), West Liberty State Coll., 1980, Hamilton Coll., 1982, Wheeling Coll., 1984. Founder, chmn. Mountain Artisans, 1968-78; commr. Corp. Pub. Broadcasting, Washington, 1981-84; bd. dirs. Stas. WETA-TV-FM, Washington, 1987-89, pres., 1989—; bd. dirs. State. WETA-TV-FM, Washington, 1987-89, pres., 1989—; bd. dirs. Pub. Broadcasting Svc., W.Va. Edn. Broadcasting Authority. Mem.-at-large Dem. Nat. Conv., del., 1976, 80, 84; bd. dirs. Rockefeller Bros. Fund. Office: Sta WETA-FM 3700 S Four Mile Run Dr Arlington VA 22206-2304

ROCKENSIES, JOHN WILLIAM, mechanical engineer; b. N.Y.C., May 30, 1932; s. John William and Wilma (Mercz) R.; m. Marion Paulne Peachman, Sept. 16, 1956; children: Kenneth John, Karen Martha Rockensies Steinbock. B of Mech. Engring., CCNY, 1954, M of Mech. Engring., 1960; postgrad. Bklyn. Polytechni. Inst., 1955, Columbia U., 1956. Registered prof. engr., N.Y. Jet engine performance and compressor devel. Curtiss Wright Corp., Woodridge, N.J., 1954-56; product devel. engr. Sperry Gyroscope Corp., Lake Success, N.Y., 1956-60; sr. exptl. test engr. Pratt & Whitney Corp., East Hartford, Conn., 1960-62; project engr. Stratos Corp.,

Bayshore, N.Y., 1962; prin. propulsion engr. Republic Aviation Corp., Farmingdale, N.Y., 1963-64; power plant design engr., group and project leader, project engr., engr. specialist and mgr. Grumman Aerospace Corp., Bethpage, N.Y., 1964—; mem. SAE E-32 Engine Condition Monitoring com., 1983; instr. navigation Smithtown Bay Power Squadron. Author tech. papers in field. Deacon, trustee, elder First Presbyn Ch. of Smithtown. Recipient Apollo Achievement award NASA, Washington, 1970. Assoc. fellow AIAA; mem. NSPE, ASME, U.S. Power Squadrons (sr.). Avocations: sailing/boating, jogging, tennis, camping, model aircraft, travel. Home: 65 Parnell Dr Smithtown NY 11787-2428 Office: Grumman Aircraft Systems MS B69-001 Bethpage NY 11713-5820

ROCKENSTEIN, WALTER HARRISON, II, lawyer; s. Walter Harrison and Martha Lee (Morris) R.; m. Jodell Lynn Steinke, July 29, 1972; children: Martha Liv, Andrew Harrison. BA cum laude, Coll. of Wooster, 1965; LLB, Yale U., 1968. Bar: Minn. 1968, U.S. Dist. Ct. Minn. 1968, U.S. Ct. Appeals (8th crct.) 1977. Spl. asst. atty. gen., chief antitrust divsn. Office of Minn. Atty. Gen., 1970-72; assoc. Head & Truhn, 1972-73; alderman 11th ward Mpls. City Coun., 1974-83; assoc. Faegre & Benson, Mpls., 1984-85, ptnr., 1986—; mem. Capital Long-Range Improvements Com., 1974-82, Gov.'s Econ. Roundtable, 1980-82, Hennepin County Waste Disposal & Energy Recovery Adv. Com., 1976-77; chmn. devel. strategies com. League of Minn. Cities, 1979-80, bd. dirs., 1980-83; Mpls. del. Metro. Aircraft Sound Abatement Coun., 1977-90, chmn., 1982-90; mem. aviation subcom. of transp. tech. adv. com. Metro. Coun., 1977-83; mem. airport noise adv. bd. Minn. Pollution Control Agy., bd. dirs. noise com., 1982-85, mem. tech. adv. com., 1990; adv. com. Nat. League of Cities, steering com. Environmental Quality, 1975-79, vice chmn., 1976, chmn., 1978, steering com. Energy, Environment and Natural Resources, 1980-83, Energy Task Force, 1977-79, Nat. Urban Policy Com., 1978; mem. Noise Task Force, Nat. League of Cities/Nat. Assn. of Counties, 1977-80; regional dir. Nat. Org. to Insure a Sound-Controlled Environment, 1976-90, v.p. legal affairs, 1983-90; cons. groupe nuclear waste mgt., U.S. Dept. Energy, 1978. Elder Westminster Presby. Ch., 1975-80, trustee, 1982-87, chair stewardship com., 1989, chair pastor nominating com., 1992-94; bd. dirs. Loring Nicollet-Bethlehem Community Ctrs., Inc., 1984—, pres., 1988-92; bd. dirs. U. Minn. Underground Space Ctr. Adv. Bd., 1985—, chair, 1988—; bd. dirs. Minn. Ctr. for Book Arts, 1988-93; com. mem. Cub Scout pack 196, Diamond Lake Luth. Ch., 1988-91, com. chair, 1990-91; alumni trustee, alumni bd. dirs. The Coll. of Wooster, 1990—; com. mem. Boy Scout Troop 187. Recipient Cert. of Appreciation, Upper Midwest chpt. Acoustical Soc. Am., 1977, Resolution of Appreciation, City of Mpls., 1983, Citation of Honor, Hennepin County, 1983, Cert. of Recognition, League of Minn. Cities, 1983, Hope of Rotary award City of Lakes Rotary Club, 1989, WCCO Good Neighbor award, 1992. Mem. Minn. State Bar Assn., Hennepin County Bar Assn., Delta Sigma Rho-Tau Kappa Alpha, Phi Sigma Alpha. Republican. Presbyterian. Avocations: reading, backpacking, cross-country skiing, woodworking. Office: Faegre & Benson 2200 Norwest Ctr 90 S 7th St Minneapolis MN 55402-3901

ROCKETT, CARLTON LEE, biological sciences educator; b. Houston, June 29, 1941; s. Carlton A. and Rosalie (Bays) R.; m. Bonnie Sue Nolan, Nov. 13, 1961; children: David Lee, Derek Bays. BS, La. State U., 1963, MS, 1965, PhD, 1971. Prof. biol. scis. Bowling Green (Ohio) State U., 1971-77, asst. prof., 1977-88, dir. parasitology, entomology program, assoc. prof. biology, 1979-85, prof., 1988—. Contbr. numerous articles to profl. jours. Capt. M.S.C., U.S. Army, 1965-68. Mem. Ohio Mosquito Control Assn., Sigma Xi, Omicron Delta Kappa, Phi Kappa Phi. Republican. Avocations: tennis, music, biking, reading, ornithology. Home: 618 Hillcrest Dr Bowling Green OH 43402-3618 Office: Bowling Green State U Dept Biol Scis Bowling Green OH 43403

ROCKEY, JAY, public relations company executive. Chmn. Rockey Co., Inc., Seattle. Office: Rockey Co Inc 2121 5th Ave Seattle WA 98121-2510

ROCKEY, PAUL HENRY, physician, medical educator, university official; b. Idaho Falls, Idaho, Apr. 3, 1944; m. Linda Marie Miller, Dec. 27, 1964; 3 children. MD with honors, U. Chgo., 1970; BS in Biochemistry with high honors, Mich. State U., 1966; MPH, U. Wash., 1978. Diplomate Am. Bd. Internal Medicine. Nat. Bd. Med. Examiners, Am. Bd. Med. Mgmt. Rotating intern Harborview Med. Ctr., Seattle, 1970-71; dir. Indian Health Ctr., Rocky Boy Reservation, Box Elder, Mont., 1971-73; resident, then chief resident in medicine, 1973-76; Robert Wood Johnson clin. scholar, acting instr. U. Wash. Sch. Medicine, Seattle, 1976-78, instr., asst. prof., assoc. prof., 1978-88, asst. dean, 1983-87; adj. assoc. prof., adj. assoc. prof. dept. health sevs. U. Wash. Sch. Pub. Health and Cmty. Medicine, 1980-88; chief resident USPHS Hosp. (name now Pacific Med. Ctr.), Seattle, 1975-76, asst. chief medicine, residency coord., 1978-80, med. dir., 1980-86; assoc. prof., assoc. dean U. Mass. Med. Sch., Worcester, 1988-90; prof. depts. medicine and med. humanities So. Ill. U. Sch. Medicine, Springfield, 1991—, assoc. dean for clin. affairs, 1991—, acting chmn. dept. family practice, 1991-93; mem. med. staff No. Mont. Hosp., Havre, 1971-73, v.p. med. staff, 1973; mem. med. staff Pacific Med. Ctr., Seattle, 1976-88, U. Wash. Hosp., Seattle, 1978-87, Providence Med. Ctr., Seattle, 1987-88, Madigan Army Med. Ctr., Ft. Lewis, Wash., 1986-88, Meml. Med. Ctr., Springfield, 1991—, St. John's Hosp., Springfield, 1991—; sr. v.p. for med. affairs St. Vincent Healthcare Sys., Inc. and St. Vincent Hosp., Worcester, 1988-90; coord. rev. Joint Commn. on Accreditation Hosps., 1980-83, 88-90; mem. exec. com. of med. staff St. Vincent Hosp., 1988-90; pres. Pacific Health Assocs. of Seattle, 1981-87; dir., vice chmn., bd. dirs. Pacific Health Plans, HMO, 1985-87; mem. Group Health Plan Credentialing Com. for Ctrl. Ill., 1994—; cons. in quality assurance and utilization mgmt. Westminster Hosp., London, 1988; mem. adapt. med. team to U. del Norte and Hosp. Infantal San Francisco de Paula, Barranquilla, Colombia, 1989-90; presenter in field. Contbr. articles and abstracts to med. jours., chpts. to books. Pres., bd. dirs. N.W. GIRLCHOIR, 1982-85, mem. steering com. Seattle Area Program for Affordable Health Care, 1983; mem. Alpental Doctor Patrol, 1975-86, Ski Acres Doctor Patrol, Snoqualmie Pass, Wash., 1982-86; trustee Ill. Cancer Coun., 1991-92; bd. dirs. Ancilla Sys., Hobart, Ind., 1993—, mem. compensation com., 1995—; vol. physician Health First Clinic, 1994—; mem. Golden Rule Award Panel Springfield, 1994; participant med. edn. subcom. Ill. Gov.'s Medicaid Adv. Com., 1994—; chmn. bd. dirs. Ancilla Med. Found., 1995—; regional interviewer student selection com. U. Chgo. Pritzker Sch. Medicine, 1978-88. With USPHS, 1971-81; maj. Wash. Army N.G., 1986-88; lt. col. Mass. Army N.G., 1988—. Alumni disting. scholar Mich. State U., 1962-66, scholar U. Chgo., 1966-70. Fellow ACP, Am. Coll. Physician Execs.; mem. AMA, Soc. Gen. Internal Medicine, Ill. Med. Soc., Sangamon County Med. Soc., Alpha Omega Alpha, Phi Kappa Phi. Home: 1433 Williams Blvd Springfield IL 62704 Office: So Ill U Sch Medicine PO Box 19230 Springfield IL 62794-9230

ROCKHILL, JACK KERRIGAN, collections company executive; b. Alliance, Ohio, Sept. 10, 1930; s. Carl Columbus and Lovell Fanny (Brown) R.; m. Karen Sue Rocki, Aug. 30, 1969; children: Michele, Martha. Student, Canton Actual Bus. Coll., Ohio, 1955, Internat. Corr. Schs., 1960, Kent State U., Canton, Ohio, 1962-65. Lic. pvt. investigator, 1960. Player Washington Senators, 1948-49; collection unit mgr. Nationwide Audit & Investigations, Canton, Ohio, 1960-66; pres. Fidelity Collections & Investigations, Alliance, 1966—; cons. Fidelity Properties, Inc., Alliance, 1980—, pres., 1984—; pres. Med. Receivables Control Co., Alliance, 1990-92. With USMC, 1950-58. Mem. Alliance Country Club, Sleepy Hollow Golf Club (Alliance). Republican. Methodist. Avocations: golfing, yachting, scuba diving. Home: 1487 Glenking Ln Alliance OH 44601-3666 Office: Fidelity Collections PO Box 2055 Alliance OH 44601-0055

ROCKLAGE, SISTER MARY ROCH, health system executive; b. St. Louis, Mar. 5, 1935; d. Henry B. and Catherine (Lohman) R. RN, St. John's Sch. Nursing, St. Louis, 1959; BS in Nursing, St. Xavier Coll., Chgo., 1961; MHA, St. Louis U., 1963; LLD (hon.), Maryville Coll., 1983. Supr. Mercy Villa, Springfield, Mo.; tng. coord. St. John's Hosp., St. Louis; dir. cen. dispatch St. John's Mercy Hosp., St. Louis, 1962-65, supr. intensive care unit, 1965-67; dir. nursing svc. St. John's Mercy Hosp., 1967-69; adminstr. pres. ST. John's Mercy Med. Ctr., St. Louis, 1969-79; provincial adminstr. Sisters of Mercy, St. Louis, 1979-85; chief exec. officer Sisters of Mercy Health System, St. Louis, 1985—; vice chairperson bd. dirs. Holy Cross Health System, South Bend, Ind.; asst. prof. health care adminstn. Washington U., St. Louis, 1970-79; preceptor Washington U., St. Louis, 1970-79, St. Louis U., 1970-79, U. Mo., Columbia, 1976-79; bd. dirs. Health Care for the Homeless, St. Louis, 1984—; mem. health commn., govt. comm. Sisters of Mercy, Province St. Louis, local coord. St. Joseph's Convent of Mercy, St. Louis, 1969-76, 77-79, province personnel bd. 1973-75, health adv. bd., 1973—. Bd. trustees Maryville Coll, St. Louis, 1972-75, Mercy Hosp., Mercy Hosp., New Orleans, 1974-75; governing bd. St. John's Med. Ctr., Joplin, Mo., 1973-77, Mo. Hosp. Assn., Jefferson City, 1974-78, St. Edward Mercy Med. Ctr., Ft. Smith, Ark., 1975-80, Mercy Health Ctr., Oklahoma City, 1975-80, McAuley Hall, St. Louis, 1977-83, Mercy Hosp., Laredo, Tex., 1978-80, St. Anthony's Hosp., Alton, Ill., 1985—; pres. Greater St. Louis Health System Agy., 1976-77, bd. dirs. 1978-79. Named Woman of Achievement, St. Louis Globe-Democrat, 1974, to Nat. Register Prominent Citizens, 1975; recipient A.C.H.E. Kenrick award. Mem. Am. Nurses' Assn., Am. Coll. Hosp. Adminstrs., Catholic Health Assn. (bd. trustees 1980—, chairperson 1984-85, sec. 1981-84, bylaws, fin. and mission svcs. coms.), Catholic Hosp. Assn. (coun. on hosp. orgn. and adminstrn.). Home: Sisters of Mercy Health System-St Louis 2039 N Geyer Rd Saint Louis MO 63131

ROCKLAND, BARRY CLIFFORD, retail financial executive; b. N.Y.C., Feb. 6, 1943; s. Albert J. and Rose (Pickel) R.; m. Cynthia A. Payne, Aug. 12, 1974 (div. Dec. 1979); 1 child, Jason Lyle; m. Marcia D. Alderfer, May 1, 1986; 1 child, Michael Spencer. BBA in Acctg., City Coll., N.Y.C., 1965, MBA in Fin., 1976. CPA, N.Y. Various fin. W.R. Grace & Co., N.Y.C., 1967-81; sr. v.p. fin. United Dept. Stores, Inc., N.Y.C., 1981-83; v.p. fin., chief fin. officer Sizes Unlimited (div. of The Limited, Inc.), Secaucus, N.J., 1983-86; exec. v.p. fin. and adminstrn., CFO Jamesway Corp., Secaucus, N.J., 1986—. Office: Jamesway Corp 40 Hartz Way Secaucus NJ 07094-2406

ROCKLEN, KATHY HELLENBRAND, lawyer, banker; b. N.Y.C., June 30, 1951. BA, Barnard Coll., 1973; JD magna cum laude, New England Sch. Law, 1977. Bar: N.Y. 1978, U.S. Dist. Ct. (so. and ea. dists.) N.Y. 1982, U.S. Dist. Ct. (no. dist.) Calif. 1985. Interpretive counsel N.Y. Stock Exchange, N.Y.C.; 1st v.p. E.F. Hutton & Co. Inc., N.Y.C.; v.p., gen. counsel and sec. S.G Warburg (U.S.A.) Inc., N.Y.C.; counsel Rogers & Wells, N.Y.C.; pvt. practice N.Y.C. Office mgr. Com. to elect Charles D. Breitel Chief Judge, N.Y. Named one of Outstanding Young Women in Am. Mem. ABA, N.Y. State Bar Assn., N.Y. Women's Bar Assn., Assn. of Bar of City of N.Y. (sec. 2d century com., sex, and law com., young lawyers com., corp. law com., chair com. drugs and law., chair fed. legis. com., securities law com.), Athletic and Swim Club. Avocation: running. Office: Law Office 515 Madison Ave New York NY 10022

ROCKLER, WALTER JAMES, lawyer; b. Nov. 25, 1920; s. Nathan Rockler and Evelyn (Terfansky) Norian; m. Elsie Spira, June 14, 1942 (div. 1946); m. Aino Allekand, Aug. 16, 1949; children—Elliot, James, Nicolas, Julia. B.A., U. Chgo., 1940; J.D., Harvard U., 1943. Bar: Ill. 1947, N.Y. 1950, D.C. 1953. Pros. atty. Nuremberg (Germany) War Crimes Trials, 1947-49; assoc. Chapman, Bryson, et al., N.Y.C., 1949-51, Paul, Weiss, et al., N.Y.C. and Washington, 1951-53; ptnr. Lederer, Livingston, et al., Chgo., 1954-60, Pennish, Steele & Rockler, Chgo., 1961-63, Cotton, Watt, Rockler & Jones, Chgo., 1964-66, Arnold & Porter, Washington, 1966—; dir. Office of Spl. Investigations U.S. Dept. Justice, Washington, 1979-80. Contbr. articles to profl. jours. Served to 1st lt. USMC, 1943-46. Decorated Bronze Star. Mem. Chgo. Bar Assn. (chmn. tax com. 1958-59), ABA (mem. tax com. 1964—), Phi Beta Kappa. Democrat. Jewish. Avocations: tennis; bridge; piano. Home: 11129 Stephalee Ln Rockville MD 20852-3655 Office: Arnold & Porter 551 12th St NW Washington DC 20004-1202

ROCKLIN, ISADORE J., manufacturing executive, consultant, engineer; b. Chgo., Nov. 9, 1907; s. Michael E. and Ada (Lehman) R.; m. Rena Marco, Nov. 5, 1939; 1 child, James Mark. BSME, U. Iowa, 1930. Registered profl. engr., Iowa, Calif. Mfr. engr. Western Electric Co., Chgo., 1930-32; asst. chief mech. engr. Grigsby Grunow Co., Chgo., 1932-33; indsl. engr. Jensen Radio Mfg. Co., Chgo., 1933; chief engr. Sioux City (Iowa) Foundry & Boiler Co., 1933-34; pres. Remedy Inc., Sioux City, 1980—; pres. Rocklin Mfg. Co., Sioux City, 1934-80, chmn. bd., 1980—. Nat. coun. mem. Boy Scouts Am.; mem. Mt. Sinai Temple, Sioux City; pres. Brotherhood Mt. Sinai Temple, 1974, B'nai B'rith, Sioux City, 1975. Mem. Nat. Soc. Profl. engrs., ASME (life), Soc. Mfg. Engrs. (life), Am. Radio Relay League, Sioux City C of C. Jewish. Avocations: travel, reading, inventing. Office: Rocklin Mfg Co 100 S Jennings St Sioux City IA 51101-1836

ROCKOFF, MARK ALAN, anesthesiologist; b. Jersey City, Apr. 13, 1948; s. Aaron and Rose (Drescher) R.; m. Elizabeth Sceery, Aug. 6, 1978; children: Benjamin, Jillian, Michael. BS, MIT, 1969; MD, Johns Hopkins U., 1973. Diplomate Am. Bd. Pediatrics, Am. Bd. Critical Care Pediatrics, Am. Bd. Anesthesiology. Pediatric intern and resident Mass. Gen. Hosp., Boston, 1973-75, anesthesia resident, 1975-77, assoc. dir. pediatric ICU, 1979-81; neuroanesthesia fellow U. Calif., San Diego, 1978-79; assoc. dir. ICU Children's Hosp., Boston, 1981-89, assoc. anesthesiologist-in-chief, 1988—; assoc. prof. anesthesia/pediatrics Harvard Med. Sch., Boston, 1987—. Editor jours. Survey of Anesthesiology, 1984-94, Jour. Neurosurg. Anesthesiology, 1994—. Fellow Am. Soc. Anesthesiologists, Am. Acad. Pediatrics, Soc. Critical Care Medicine; mem. Soc. Pediatric Anesthesia (pres. elect 1994—). Office: Children's Hosp 300 Longwood Ave Boston MA 02115

ROCKOFF, S. DAVID, radiologist, physician, educator; b. Utica, N.Y., July 21, 1931; s. Samuel and Sarah (Rattinger) R.; m. Jacqueline Garsh; children—Lisa E., Todd E., Kevin D. A.B., Syracuse U., 1951; M.D., Albany Med. Coll., 1955; M.Sc. in Medicine, U. Pa., 1961. Diplomate: Am. Bd. Radiology. Intern U.S. Naval Hosp., Bethesda, Md., 1955-56; resident and fellow in radiology, USPHS trainee dept. radiology p of U. Pa., Phila., 1958-61; staff radiologist NIH, Bethesda, Md., 1961-65; asst. prof. radiology Yale U. Sch. Medicine, New Haven, 1965-68; assoc. prof. Yale U. Sch. Medicine, 1968; asst. attending radiologist Yale-New Haven Med. Center, 1965-68; assoc. prof. radiology Washington U. Sch. Medicine, St. Louis, 1968-71; asst. radiologist Barnes and Allied Hosps., St. Louis, 1969-71; cons. radiologist VA Hosp., St. Louis, 1969-71, Homer G. Phillips Hosp., St. Louis, 1968-71; prof. radiology George Washington U. Sch. Medicine, Washington, 1971—; chmn. dept. radiology George Washington U. Sch. Medicine, 1971-77, head pulmonary radiology, 1978—, interim chmn. dept. radiology, 1989-90, prof. emeritus radiology, 1993—; cons. NIH, 1972—; vis. prof. Hadassah U., Beersheba U., Rambam Hosp., Israel, 1977; cons. in radiology VA Hosp., Washington, 1972-77, U.S. Naval Med. Center, Bethesda, 1973-77; mem. diagnostic radiology adv. com. NIH, 1973-76; mem. Cancer Research Manpower Rev. Com., NIH, 1978. Editor-in-chief: Investigative Radiology, 1965-76; editor-in-chief emeritus, 1976—; editor Jour. Thoracic Imaging, 1985; Contbr. numerous articles to med. jours. Served with USN, 1955-58; Served with USPHS, 1961-63. Recipient numerous USPHS grants. Fellow Am. Coll. Radiology (pres.-elect D.C. chpt. 1976), Am. Coll. Chest Physicians; mem. Am. Fedn. Clin. Research, D.C. Med. Soc. (mem. med.-legal com. 1975-78), AMA, Radiol. Soc. N.Am., Assn. Univ. Radiologists, Soc. Thoracic Radiology (pres. 1983-84, exec. dir. 1984-87). Home: PO Box 675650 Rancho Santa Fe CA 92067-5650 Office: George Washington U Sch Medicine 901 23rd St NW Washington DC 20037-2377

ROCKRISE, GEORGE THOMAS, architect; b. N.Y.C., Nov. 25, 1916; s. Thomas S. and Agnes M. (Asbury) R.; m. Margaret Lund Paulson, June 12, 1948 (dec. Aug. 1957); children: Christina, Peter; m. Sally S. Griffin, Dec. 1959 (div.); 1 child, Celia; m. Anneliese Warner, Nov. 27, 1985. B.Arch., Syracuse U., 1938; M.S. in Architecture, Columbia U., 1941. Fellow architecture Columbia U., 1940-41; architect Army and Navy, Panama, 1941-45; designer Edward D. Stone, N.Y.C., 1945-46, UN Hdqrs. Planning Commn., 1946-47; archtl. assoc. Thomas D. Church, San Francisco, 1948-49; pvt. practice architecture San Francisco 1949-86, Glen Ellen, Calif., 1986-87; chmn. bd. Rockrise, Odermatt, Mountjoy Assocs. (architects and planners); lectr. Sch. Architecture, U. Calif., 1949-53; adviser to faculty com. Sch. Architecture, U. Venezuela, Caracas, 1954; mem. San Francisco Art Commn., 1952-56; cons. architect U.S. Dept. State, Japan, 1957-58, Fed. Republic Germany, Venezuela, Brazil, 1978-80, Bahrain, Brazil, Venezuela, Fed. Republic of Germany, 1980; architect U.S. embassy, Bahrain; vis. lectr. Cornell U., Clemson Coll., 1961, Syracuse U., U. Utah, Stanford U., 1962-

65, Nat. U. Mex.; lectr. urban design Spanish Ministry Housing and Devel., Madrid, 1978; mem. San Francisco Planning Commn., 1961-62; adviser to Sec. for design HUD, 1966-67; participant State Dept. AID Urban Seminars Latin Am., 1971; mem. U.S. del. Pan Am. Congress Architects, Caracas, 1980; vis. prof. Universidad Central, Mex., 1985. Mem. pres.'s adv. com. U. Mass., 1971; mem. adv. council San Francisco Planning Urban Renewal Assn.; bd. dirs. Telegraph Hill Dwellers Assn., 1985-86, v.p.; pres. Archtl. Found. No. Calif., 1986; apptd. San Francisco Art Commn., 1986-87. Recipient AIA nat. award for residential work, 1953, 59, prog. architecture award citation, 1956, award of honor and award of merit AIA Homes for Better Living Program, 1956, regional awards for residential architecture AIA, 1957, others; Fulbright fellow in urban design U. Rome, 1978-79. Fellow AIA (pres. No. Calif. chpt. 1961, nat. v.p. from 1969, mem. nat honor awards jury, mem. nat. commn. urban design and planning 1978); mem. Am. Soc. Planning and Housing Ofcls., Am. Inst. Cert. Planners, Am. Soc. Landscape Architects, Nat. Assn. Housing and Redevel. Ofcls., Delta Kappa Epsilon, Tau Sigma Delta, Lambda Alpha. Home: 468 Vallejo St San Francisco CA 94133-4113 Studio: 1280 Hill Rd Glen Ellen CA 95442

My adult life as architect and planner has been devoted to the construction and improvement of the man-made environment. I have come to believe through this endeavor, that it is the concern and responsibility of all thinking persons, whether professional or lay person to comprehend the forces for change in the environment and to work for the protection and enhancement of our cities and the natural environment.

ROCKSTEIN, MORRIS, science writer, editor, consultant; b. Toronto, Ont., Can., Jan. 8, 1916; came to U.S., 1923; s. David and Mina (Segal) R.; children: Susan M. Bumgarner, Madelaine Jo Sottile. AB magna cum laude, Bklyn. Coll., 1938; MA, Columbia U., 1941; PhD, U. Minn., 1948; cert., Oak Ridge (Tenn.) Inst. Nuclear Studies, 1950. Research asst. entomology U. Minn., St. Paul, 1941-42; asst. prof., assoc. prof. zoophysiology Wash. State U., Pullman, 1948-53; asst. prof., then assoc. prof. physiology NYU Sch. Medicine, N.Y.C., 1953-61; prof. physiology U. Miami Sch. Medicine, 1961-81, chmn. dept., 1967-71; pres. Cortisol Med. Research, Inc., 1983-85; chmn. sci. adv. bd. Anorexia Nervosa Inst., Melbourne, Fla., 1983-85, Fla. Med. Ctr., Lauderdale Lakes, 1971-78; cons. entomology APHA, 1961-78; del. White House Conf. on Aging, Washington, 1961, 71; cons. insect physiology Sect. Tropical Medicine and Parasitology NIH, Washington, 1962-66, NASA, 1980-92, BIOS, 1983-85; mem. corp. Marine Biol. Lab., 1961-63, trustee, 1961-93, life mem., trustee emeritus, 1993—; vis. lectr. Minority Insts. FASEB MARCPROG, 1983-88. Sr. author: Biology of Human Aging, 1978; editor: (with G.T. Baker) Molecular Genetic Mechanisms in Development and Aging, 1972, Development and Aging in the Nervous System, 1973, Physiology of Insecta, 6 vols., 1973-74, Theoretical Aspects of Aging, 1977; (with R.T. Goldman) Physiology and Pathology of Human Aging, 1978, Biochemistry of Insects, 1978; editor Miscellaneous Publs. and Thos Say Found. Monographs, 1983-92; contbr. articles to profl. jours. Mem. resource and mgmt. com. Area Agy. on Aging, 1988-90. Served with USAAF, 1942-46, as Scientist, USPHS, 1951-81. NRC fellow in natural scis. U. Minn., 1946-48; recipient Disting. Alumnus award Bklyn. Coll., 1959, Outstanding Alumnus Achievement award U. Minn., 1977; named knight comdr. of merit Knights of Malta, 1982. Fellow AAAS (mem. coun. 1962-64), Gerontol. Soc. (pres. 1965-66), Entomol. Soc. Am.; mem. Internat. Assn. Gerontology (mem. exec. coun. 1963-66), Internat. Assn. Prolongation of Human Life Span (v.p. 1974-92), Am. Physiol. Soc., Am. Soc. Zoologists, Soc. Gen. Physiologists, Sunflower Soc. Miami (v.p. 1986-88), People to People Fla., Army-Navy Club, Miami Internat. Press Club, Coral Gables Country Club (bd. dirs. Fleet 1994—), Phi Beta Kappa, Sigma Xi. Home: 600 Biltmore Way Apt 805 Miami FL 33134-7531

ROCKWELL, ALVIN JOHN, lawyer; b. Kalamazoo, Dec. 29, 1908; s. John S. and L. B. (DeVall) R.; m. Anne Hayward, Aug. 24, 1933; 1 son, John Sargent. A.B., DePauw U., 1929; J.D. (hon.), 1991; postgrad., London Sch. Econs., 1929-30; J.D., Harvard U., 1933. Bar: Mass. 1933, Calif. 1948. Spl. asst. to U.S. atty. gen., 1940-43; gen. counsel NLRB, 1944-45; legal adviser to U.S. Mil. Govt., Germany, 1946-48; partner firm Brobeck, Phleger & Harrison, San Francisco, 1948-79; of counsel Brobeck, Phleger & Harrison, 1979—. Trustee De Pauw U., 1958-80, life trustee, 1980—; trustee San Francisco Law Library, 1977-88; trustee, later pres. San Francisco Bar Assn. Found., 1976-80; mem. Commn. on Uniform State Laws, 1962-69. Fellow Am. Bar Found.; mem. Am. Law Inst, Harvard Law Sch. Assn. No. Calif. (past pres.), World Affairs Council No. Calif. (past pres.), Phi Beta Kappa. Clubs: Commonwealth (San Francisco), Pacific-Union (San Francisco), Bohemian (San Francisco); Cosmos (Washington). Home: 1400 Geary Blvd Apt 2403 San Francisco CA 94109-6574 Office: Spear St Tower 29th Floor One Market Plaza San Francisco CA 94105

ROCKWELL, BRUCE MCKEE, retired banker, retired foundation executive; b. Denver, Dec. 18, 1922; s. Robert B. and Florence (McKee) R.; m. Virginia Packard, Apr. 22, 1950; children—David, Jane, Sarah. B.A., Yale U., 1945. Exec. sec. to mayor City of Denver, 1947-51; pub. rels. and advt. account exec. William Kostka & Assocs., 1952-53; with Colo. Nat. Bank, Denver, 1953-85; pres. Colo. Nat. Bank, 1970-75, chmn., chief exec. officer, 1975-85, also dir.; pres. Colo. Trust, Denver, 1985-91; sr. cons. BBC, Inc., Denver, 1991. Chmn., bd. dirs. The Denver Partnership, Inc., Kaiser Permanente, 1980-92; bd. dirs. Am. Pub. Welfare Assn., 1989-91; chmn. Denver Urban Renewal Authority, 1958-68; mem. nat. council Salk Inst., 1978-84; trustee Community Coll. Denver, Com. Econ. Devel., 1979-85, Denver Symphony Orch., 1974-77, Denver Art Mus., 1965-72, 82-86. Served as ensign USNR, 1945-46. Named Colo. Bus. Man of Yr., Colo. Bus. Mag., 1976. Mem. Assn. Res. City Bankers (dir. 1975-85), Denver C. of C. Clubs: University, Tennis (Denver). Home: 815 Vine St Denver CO 80206-3741

ROCKWELL, BURTON LOWE, architect; b. Utica, N.Y., June 3, 1920; s. Burton Lowe and Blanch Louise (Taylor) R.; m. Ruth Aldrich, May 19, 1949; children: Peter Grant, Abbie. BArch, MIT, 1946, MArch, 1947. Registered architect, Calif., N.Y., Vt., Mich., Ind. Project architect John Lyon Reid, Architect, San Francisco 1947-53; ptnr. John Lyon Reid & Ptnrs., San Francisco, 1953-60, Reid Rockwell Banwell & Tarics, San Francisco, 1960-62, Rockwell & Banwell, San Francisco, 1962-70; pvt. practice Burton Rockwell, FAIA, San Francisco, 1970-88; ptnr. Rockwell, Chatham, Marshall, San Francisco, 1977-88, Rockwell & Rockwell, Architects, San Francisco, 1987—; faculty mem. U. Calif. Berkeley, Coll. Environ. Design, 1962-71; guest prof. MIT, 1969-70; juror Calif. Coalition for Adequate Sch. Housing, Archtl. Competition, 1991; chmn. Calif. Coun. Architects and Engrs., 1965. Architect-designer: Med. Rsch. Facilities, U. Calif., San Francisco, 1968 (AIA Honor 1971), sch. sanctuary Lafayette Orinda Presbyn. Ch., 1968 (AIA Bay Area Honor 1974), Ct. House, Govt. Ct., Santa Cruz County, 1967 (Progressive Architecture award); contbr. articles to profl. jours. Bd. dirs. Community Music Ctr., San Francisco, 1972-74, Eastshore Pk. Project, San Francisco, 1975-80, Friends of Recreation and Parks, San Francisco, 1993—; mem. citizens' adv. com. San Francisco Bay Conservation and Devel. Commn., 1966—; mem. archtl. edn. com. Calif. Coun. Higher Edn., Sacramento, 1968-70; mem. bd. examiners Dept. Pub. Works, San Francisco, 1977-78. Served to capt. U.S. Army, 1942-46. Recipient 22 nat. awards for archtl. excellence San Francisco Art Commn., 1953—. Fellow AIA (pres. San Francisco chpt. 1965, bd. dirs., other officers); mem. ASTM, Calif. Coun. Architects (pres. 1965, bd. dirs., other offices 1965—), Constrn. Specification Inst., Am. Soc. Testing and Materials, Internat. Coun. Bldg. Officials. Avocations: Morgan and Lancia automobiles, Scottish deerhounds. Home: 150 Edgewood Ave San Francisco CA 94117-3713 Office: Rockwell & Rockwell Architects 888 Post St San Francisco CA 94109-6013

ROCKWELL, DON ARTHUR, psychiatrist; b. Wheatland, Wyo., Apr. 24, 1938; s. Orson Arthur and Kathleen Emily (Richards) R.; m. Frances Pepitone-Arreola, Dec. 23, 1965; children: Grant, Chad. BA, Wash. U., 1959; MD, U. Okla., 1963; MA in Sociology, U. Calif., Berkeley, 1967. Diplomate Am. Bd. Psychiatry and Neurology. Intern in surgery San Francisco Gen. Hosp., 1963-64; resident in psychiatry Langley-Porter Neuropsychiatric Inst. U. Calif. Med. Ctr., San Francisco, 1964-67; instr. dept. psychiatry U. Calif. Sch. Medicine, Davis, 1969-70, asst. prof., 1970-74, assoc. prof., 1974-80, acting assoc., dean curricular affairs, 1979-80, acting assoc. dean student affairs, 1980, assoc. dean student affairs, 1980-82, prof., 1980-84; career tchr. NIMH, 1970-72; assoc. psychiatrist Sacramento Med. Ctr.; med. dir. U. Calif. Med. Ctr., Davis, 1982-84; prof., vice chmn. dept. psychiatry and biobehavioral scis. UCLA, 1984—; dir. univ. Neuropsychiat. Hosp., 1984—, exec. assoc. dir. univ. Neuropsychiat. Inst., 1984—; chief of

profl. staff Neuropsychiat. Inst., UCLA, 1984-85; chmn. U. Calif. Hosp. Dirs. Council, 1988-89; cons. Nat. Commn. on Marijuana, Washington, 1971-73. Co-author: Psychiatric Disorders, 1982; contbr. chpts. to books; articles to profl. jours. Bd. dirs. Bereavement Outreach, Sacramento, 1974-84, Suicide Prevention, Yolo County, 1969-84; bd. visitors U. Okla. Sch. Medicine; chmn. hosp. dirs. coun. U. Calif. Hosp.; governing coun. AHA Psychiat. Hosp. Fellow Am. Psychiat. Assn., Am. Coll. Psychiatrists, Am. Coll. Mental Health Adminstrs.; mem. AMA (gov. coun. psych. hosp.), Am. Sociologic Assn., Am. Coll. Psychiat. Assn. (sec.-pres. 1977-78), U. Okla. Alumni Assn. (trustee 1981-86), Alpha Omega Alpha. Home: 1816 E Las Tunas Santa Barbara CA 93103

ROCKWELL, ELIZABETH DENNIS, retirement specialist, financial planner; b. Houston; d. Robert Richard and Nezzell Alderton (Christie) Dennis. Student Rice U., 1939-40, U. Houston, 1938-39, 40-42. Purchasing agt. Standard Oil Co., Houston, 1942-66; v.p mktg. Heights Savs. Assn., Houston, 1967-82; sr. fin. planner Oppenheimer & Co., Inc., Houston, 1982—; 2d v.p. Desk and Derrick Club Am., 1960-61. Contbr. articles on retirement planning, tax planning and tax options, monthly article 50 Plus sect. for Houston Chronicle newspaper. Bd. dirs. ARC, 1985-91, Houston Heights Assn., 1973-77; named sr. v.p. Oppenheimer, 1986—; mem. Coll. Bus. U. found. bd. Houston, 1990, mem. million dollar roundtable, 1991—, mem. ct. of the table, 1991—, mem. sys. planned giving coun., 1992—, mem. coll. bus. adv. bd., 1992—, mem. alumni bd., 1987—; appointed trustee U. Houston Sys. Found., Inc. 1992. Named Disting. Alumnae Coll. Bus. Alumn. Assn. U. Houston, 1992; named YWCA Outstanding Woman of Yr., 1978. Mem. Am. Savs. and Loan League (state dir. 1973-76, chpt. pres. 1971-72; pres. S.W. regional conf. 1972-73; Leaders award 1972), Savs. Inst. Mktg. Soc. Am. (Key Person award 1974), Inst. Fin. Edn., Fin. Mgrs., Soc. Savs. Instns., U.S. Savs. and Loan League (com. on deposit acquisitions and adminstrn.), Houston Heights Assn. (charter, dir. 1973-77), Houston North Assn., Friends of Bayou Bend, Harris County Heritage Soc., U. Houston Alumni Orgn. (life), Rice U. Bus. and Profl. Women, River Oaks Bus. Womens Exchange Club, U. Houston Bus. Womens Assn. (pres. 1985), Forum Club, Greater Houston Women's Found. (charter). Office: Oppenheimer & Co Inc 333 Clay St Ste 4700 Houston TX 77002-4103

ROCKWELL, GEORGE BARCUS, financial consultant; b. Chgo., Jan. 5, 1926; s. Thomas S. and Irene G. (Barcus) R.; m. Lois Ladd, Sept. 30, 1950; children: Susan, Cynthia. A.B. in Econs, Harvard U., 1949, grad. Advanced Mgmt. Program, 1967. Salesman IBM, 1949, products mgr., 1956; asst. mgr. IBM, Boston, 1958; mgr. IBM, Albany, N.Y., 1960; v.p., div. head computer services State St. Bank & Trust Co., Boston, 1963; v.p., head mut. funds div. State St. Bank & Trust Co., 1966, sr. v.p., 1968, bank sales coordinator, 1968, exec. v.p., 1968, pres., 1970-75; vice chmn. bd. State St. Boston Fin. Corp., 1975-76; also industry dir.; v.p., mng. dir. fin. industries Arthur D. Little, Inc., Cambridge, Mass., 1976-89; v.p., dir. Webster-Atlas Bldg. Corp., Keane Assocs., Inc., 1970-75; pres., dir. State St. Bank Boston Internat., State St. Boston Securities Svcs. Corp., State St. Boston Credit Co., Inc., SSB Investments, Inc.; dir., exec. com. Nat. BankAmericard Inc., 1970-75, Royal Bus. Group, Inc., 1980-84, Computer Ptnrs., 1983-86; bd. dirs. Sandwich Coop. Bank, Lahey Ins. Co., Ltd. Bd. overseers Boys' Clubs Boston, 1969-75; trustee coun. Boston U. Med. Ctr., 1969-74, trustee Lahey Clinic, 1973-95, Lahey Hitchcock Clinic, 1995—. Served to 1st lt., inf. AUS, 1944-46. Mem. Greater Boston C. of C. (bd. dirs. 1969-76), Harvard Bus. Sch. Assn. Boston (bd. govs. 1969-72). Clubs: Wellesley Country, Rio Verde Country Club, Rotary. Home: 376 Glen Rd Weston MA 02193-1403

ROCKWELL, HAYS HAMILTON, bishop; b. Detroit, Aug. 17, 1936; s. Walter Francis and Kathryn (McElroy) R.; m. Linda Hullinger, Sept. 7, 1957; children: Keith, Stephen, Sarah, Martha. AB, Brown U., 1958; BD, Episcopal Theol. Sch., Cambridge, Mass., 1961; DD (hon.), Episcopal Theol. Seminary SW, Austin, Tex., 1984; BD, Kenyon Coll., 1974; HHD, St. Louis U., 1994. Ordained to ministry Episcopal Ch. as deacon, 1961, as priest, 1962; ordained bishop, 1991. Chaplain St. George's Sch., Newport, R.I., 1961-69, Univ. of Rochester, N.Y., 1969-71; dean Bexley Hall, Rochester, 1971-76; rector St. James' Ch., N.Y.C., 1976-91; bishop coadjutor Diocese of Mo., St. Louis, 1991-93, bishop, 1993—; dir. Union Theol. Seminary, N.Y.C., 1976, 87, 91. Author: Steal Away, Steal Away Home, 1985. Mem. Coun. on Fgn. Rels., N.Y.C., 1988; former trustee U. Rochester, N.Y.C.; trustee Mo. Bot. Garden, St. Luke's Hosp., Mo. Mem. Century Assn. (N.Y.C.). Office: Diocese of Missouri 1210 Locust St Saint Louis MO 63103-2322

ROCKWELL, JOHN SARGENT, arts administrator, music critic, writer; b. Washington, Sept. 16, 1940; s. Alvin John and Anne Sargent (Hayward) R. B.A., Harvard U., 1962; postgrad., U. Munich, 1962-63; M.A., U. Calif., Berkeley, 1964, Ph.D. 1972. Music and dance critic Oakland (Calif.) Tribune, 1969; asst. music and dance critic Los Angeles Times, 1970-72; freelance music critic N.Y. Times, 1972-74, staff music critic, 1974-91; European cultural corr. and prin. classical recordings critic N.Y. Times, Paris, 1992-94; dir. summer arts festival Lincoln Ctr. for the Performing Arts, N.Y.C., 1994—; lectr. in field. Author: All American Music: Composition in the Late 20th Century, 1983, Sinatra: An American Classic, 1984. Harvard-German Govt. fellow, 1962-63; Woodrow Wilson fellow, 1963-64. Mem. Music Critics Assn., Century Assn., Phi Beta Kappa. Home: 543 Broadway Apt 10 New York NY 10012-3934 Office: Lincoln Ctr Performing Arts 70 Lincoln Ctr Plaza New York NY 10023

ROCKWELL, RICHARD COOK, association executive; b. Tyler, Tex., June 1, 1942; s. Richard Stauffer and Louis (Cook) R.; m. Phyllis Rolston, Mar. 19, 1969 (div. 1986); children: Jeffrey David, Stephen Dane. BA, U. Tex., 1964, MA, 1966, PhD, 1970. Dir. Social Sci. DAta Libr., U. N.C., Chapel Hill, 1969-76; fellow Boys Town Ctr., Omaha, 1976-79; staff assoc. Social Sci. Rsch. Coun., N.Y.C., 1979-91; exec. dir. Inter-univ. Consortium for Polit. and Social Rsch., Ann Arbor, Mich., 1991—; mem. standing com. on START, Internat. Geospher/Biosphere Programs, Stockholm, 1990—; exec. com. Global Change Program, U. Mich., 1992—. Coantbr. articles to profl. jours.; editor: AIDS in Africa, 1988. Mem. AAAS, Am. Statis. Assn. (Bur. of Census adv. com. 1991—), Phi Beta Kappa. Democrat. Unitarian. Office: ICPSR/ISR U Mich 426 Thompson St Ann Arbor MI 48104-2321

ROCKWELL, R(ONALD) JAMES, JR., laser and electro-optics consultant; b. Cin., May 7, 1937; s. Ronald James and Mary Cornelius (Thornton) R.; m. Diane Lundin, Feb. 3, 1968; children: James Gregory, Christopher Derrick. BS, U. Cin., 1960, MS, 1964. Directing physicist, assoc. prof. laser scis., laser research labs. Med. Center, U. Cin., 1963-76; dir. continuing edn. services Electro-Optical Systems Design Jour., Cin., 1976-77; v.p. laser/electro-optics Control Dynamics, Inc., Cin., 1977-79; pres. Rockwell Assocs., Inc. (cons. lasers, optics and electro-optics), Cin., 1979-89; pres., chief exec. officer Rockwell Laser Industries (cons. lasers, optics and electro-optics), Cin., 1989—; exec. com. sate use lasers com. Am. Nat. Standards Inst., 1971—; exec. sec. Laser Inst. Am., 1976-77, 1972-92, pres., 1974; mem. adv. com. Laser History Project, 1983-89; dir. Laserworks, Inc., Rockwell Devel. Co.; cons. WHO, Internat. Electrotechnical Commn., founder Consortium of Laser and Tech. Cons., 1988; mem. tech. com. Laser Fire Protection of the Nat. Fire Protection Assn., 1991—. Co-author: Lasers in Medicine, 1971; author: Laser Safety Training Manual, 1982, Laser Safety in Surgery and Medicine, 1985, Laser Safety: Concepts, Analysis and Controls, 1992, Laser Safety: Modularized Training Package, 1994; created software program: Laser Hazard Analysis, 1987, LAZAN for Windows, 1995; contbr. chpts. to books and articles to profl. jours.; editor jours. in field; mem. editl. bd. Jour. Laser Applications, 1994—. Co-chmn. Internat. Laser Safety Conf., 1990, 92. Recipient Pres.' award Laser Inst. Am., 1985. Mem. IEEE, N.Y. Acad. Scis., Am. Soc. Laser Medicine and Surgery, Midwest Bio-Laser Inst., Internat. Laser Display Assn., Newcomen Soc., Sigma Xi (nat. lectr. 1971-75), Delta Tau Delta (D.S.C. award 1985, dir. acad. affairs, nat. bd. dirs. 1975-83). Methodist. Designer, builder portable laser entertainment system in laser light artistic shows; patentee in field. Home: 6282 Coachlite Way Cincinnati OH 45243 Office: PO Box 43010 7754 Camargo Rd Cincinnati OH 45243

ROCKWELL, THEODORE, nuclear engineer; b. Chgo., June 26, 1922; s. Theodore G. and Paisley (Shane) R.; m. Mary Juanita Compton, Jan. 25, 1947; children—Robert C., William T., Lawrence E., Juanita C. B.S. in Engring, Princeton U., 1943, Chem.E. (M.S.), 1945; grad. courses, Oak

Ridge, 1944-49; D.Sc. (hon.), Tri-State U., 1960. Registered profl. engr., D.C. Process improvement engr. Manhattan Project, Oak Ridge, 1944-45; head shield engring. group Oak Ridge Nat. Lab., 1945-49; nuclear engr., naval reactors br. AEC, also nuclear propulsion divs. Navy Bur. Ships, 1949-55, tech. dir., 1955-64; founding officer, dir. MPR Assos., Inc., Washington, 1964-87; sole practice, 1988—; research asso. Johns Hopkins U. Center Fgn. Policy Research, 1965-66; Chmn. Atomic Indsl. Forum Reactor Safety Task Force, 1966-72; mem. adv. group artificial heart program NIH, 1966; cons. to Joint Congl. Com. on Atomic Energy, 1967. Author: The Rickover Effect: How One Man Made a Difference, 1992; co-author: Shippingport Pressurized Water Reactor, 1958, Arms Control Agreements/Designs Verification, 1968; co-founder Princeton Engr.; editor: Reactor Shield Design Manual, 1956; contbg. editor New Realities, 1982; contbr. sci. articles to profl. publs., non-tech. articles nat. mags.; holder patents, patent applications for neutron-absorbing cermets, process for leaching uranium from slags, process for prodn. boron-containing plastic sheet, others. Mem. adv. council dept. chem. engring. Princeton U., 1966-72. Recipient Disting. Civilian Svc. medal USN, 1960, Disting. Svc. medal AEC, 1960, Lifetime Contbn. award Am. Nuclear Soc. (1st, now known as Rockwell award), 1986. Fellow Am. Soc. Psychical Rsch. (life); mem. AAAS (rep. of Parapsychol. Assn. to AAAS 1975-87), Soc. for Sci. Exploration, U.S. Psychotronic Assn. (dir. 1988-91), Authors Guild, Writers Ctr., Washington Ind. Writers, Cosmos Club (Washington), Nat. Press Club. Presbyterian (elder). Address: 3403 Woolsey Dr Chevy Chase MD 20815-3924

ROCKWELL, WINTHROP ADAMS, lawyer; b. Pittsfield, Mass., May 7, 1948; s. Landon Gale Rockwell and Ruth (Adams) Lonsdale; m. Barbara Washburn Wood, June 20, 1970; children: Samuel Adams, Madeline McCord. AB, Dartmouth Coll., 1970; JD, NYU, 1975. Bar: Minn. 1975, U.S. Dist. Ct. Minn. 1975. Asst. newsman fgn. desk N.Y. Times, N.Y.C., 1970-71; asst. to pres. Dartmouth Coll., Hanover, N.H. 1971-72; assoc. Faegre & Benson, Mpls., 1975-79; assoc. chief counsel Pres.'s Commn. on Accident at Three Mile Island, Washington, 1979; assoc. Faegre & Benson, Mpls., 1979-82, ptnr., 1983—; chair diversity com., 1990—. V.p., bd. dirs. Children's Theatre, Mpls., 1982-83; bd. dirs. Actors Theatre of St. Paul, 1975-79, Trinity Films, Mpls., 1978-82. Served to specialist grade 4 USNG, 1970-76. Brit.-Am. Project fellow, 1987. Mem. ABA, Hennepin County Bar Assn., Am. Agrl. Law Assn., Adirondack 46ers, Adirondack Mountain Club. Avocations: writing, tennis, mountaineering, gardening. Home: 1901 Knox Ave S Minneapolis MN 55405-2533 Office: Faegre & Benson 2200 Norwest Ctr 90 S 7th St Minneapolis MN 55402

ROCKWOOD, RUTH H., former library science educator; b. Chgo., Oct. 15, 1906; d. Charles Edward and Myrtle Isabelle (Wheeler) Humiston; m. George Herbert Rockwood, Apr. 14, 1928 (dec.); children: Charles Edward, Nancy Hoyt Rockwood Haigh, Alice Frances Rockwood Bethke. A.B., Wellesley Coll., 1927; M.S., U. Ill., 1949; Ed.D., Ind. U., 1960. Adminstrv. asst., instr. U. Ill. Library Sch., 1949-52; Fulbright lectr. Chulalongkorn U., Bangkok, Thailand, 1952-53; vis. asst. prof. Ind. U. Library Sch., 1958-59; prof. library sci. Fla. State U., 1953-79, prof. emeritus, 1979—. Mem. Fla. Trail Assn., Sierra Club, Beta Phi Mu. Club: Pilot (Tallahassee). Home: 4434 Meandering Way Apt 301 Tallahassee FL 32308-5859 Office: Sch Library Sci Fla State U Tallahassee FL 32306

ROCKWOOD, THOMAS JULIAN, management services executive, information technolgy consultant; b. Cleve., May 16, 1942; s. Charles W. and Marjorie J. (Engert) R.; m. Janet L. Hess, Nov. 26, 1966; children: Kim, Kevin. BS in Acctg., Lehigh U., 1965, BS in Mech. Engring., 1966; MBA in Corp. Fin., NYU, 1971. Engr. Gen. Steel, Homestead, Pa., 1966-67, Western Electric Co., N.Y.C., 1967-84; mgr. AT&T Network Systems, Morristown, N.J., 1984-89; pres. Rockwood Mgmt. Svcs., Chatham, N.J., 1989—. Mem. ASME, Am. Mktg. Assn., Am. Mgmt. Assn. Office: Rockwood Mgmt Svcs 52 Johnson Dr Chatham NJ 07928-1168

ROCO, MIHAIL CONSTANTIN, mechanical engineer, educator; b. Bucharest, Romania, Nov. 2, 1947; came to U.S., 1980; s. Constantin M. and Armande Ch.-Ad. (Cantacuzino) R.; m. Ecaterina (Cathy) Roco, July 24, 1986; children: Constance-Armanda M., Charles Michael. PhD, Polytechnic Inst., Bucharest, 1976; diploma strat. planning/exec. leadership, U.S. OPM, Washington, 1992; diploma leadership program, U. Md., 1994. Prof. U. Ky., Lexington, 1981—; program dir. engring. NSF, Washington, 1990—; part-time prof. Johns Hopkins U., Balt., 1993; vis. prof. U. Paderborn, Fed. Republic of Germany, 1979, U. Sask.-Can., 1990, Tohoku U., Sendai, Japan, 1988-89, Calif. Inst. Tech., Pasadena, 1988-89; cons. to industry in U.S., Can., Europe and Australia, 1981-92; cons. to U.S. govt. agys., 1983-89; lectr. postgrad. engring. Japan, Chile, Ga., Fla., 1982-91. Author: (with others) Principles and Practice of Slurry Flow, 1991, Particulate Two-Phase Flow, 1993; assoc. tech. editor Jour. Fluids Engring., 1985-89; contbr. over 100 articles to sci. and engring. jours and several articles symbolist poetry in literary jours. Recipient Carl Duisberg Soc. award, Fed. Republic Germany, 1979, Outstanding Rsch. Professorship award U. Ky., 1986-87, Outstanding Performance award NSF, 1994; grantee NSF, Rsch. Founds. USA, Can., Fed. Republic Germany, OAS, 1979-91. Fellow ASME (director internat. symposium series 1984-94, chmn. multiphase flow com. 1992-94), Particle Tech. Forum (vice chmn. 1994—); mem. AIChE, AIAA, Soc. Rheology, Acad. Mechanics, N.Y. Acad. Scis. Achievements include formulation of innovative numerical methods for fluid and particulate flows (finite volume, probabilistic, marching), computer-aided-engineering for centrifugal slurry pumps, hydrotransport of solids through pipelines, and electro-imaging (fast laser printers); 13 inventions of fluid machineries, wear resistant equipment, methods to increase pipe transport capacity, viscosimeter; research on multiphase flow modeling, laser Doppler anemometry, flow visualization, power stations, pumps, and wear mechanisms. Office: NSF 4201 Wilson Blvd Rm 525 Arlington VA 22230-0001

ROCQUE, VINCENT JOSEPH, lawyer; b. Franklin, N.H., Nov. 27, 1945; s. Francis Albert and Mary Helen (O'Grady) R.; m. Emily Adams Arnold, May 31, 1969; children: Amanda Adams, Peter O'Connor, Caroline Quin. AB magna cum laude, Georgetown U., 1967; JD, Columbia U., N.Y.C., 1970. Bar: D.C. 1971, U.S. Supreme Ct. 1973. Assoc. Hogan & Hartson, Washington, 1970-73; counsel, spl. asst. to commr. Barbara Franklin U.S. Consumer Product Safety Commn., Washington, 1973-77; asst. dir. bur. trade regulation U.S. Dept. Commerce, Washington, 1977-80; ptnr. Sullivan & Worcester, Washington, 1980-90; pvt. practice law Washington, 1990—. V.p., co-pres. Janney Pub. Elem. Sch. PTA, Washington, 1982-84; vol. coord. homeless shelters Cath. Charities, Washington and Silver Spring, Md., 1984-90. Staff sgt. USAR, 1969-75. Mem. ABA (adminstrv. law and regulatory practice sect., internat. law and practice sect.), Fed. Bar Assn. (adminstrv. law and internat. law sects.), Mid-Atlantic Literary Edification Soc., Nat. Capital YMCA, Phi Beta Kappa. Catholic. Avocations: reading, travel, American Civil War history, basketball. Office: 1155 Connecticut Ave NW Ste 400 Washington DC 20036-4306

RODBELL, CLYDE ARMAND, distribution executive; b. Atlanta, Aug. 16, 1927; s. Joseph Hirsch and Fannie (Turetzky) R.; m. Cecile Rosenson, Mar. 27, 1949 (div.); children: Marsha, Jeffrey, Keith, Kim; m. Robin Graham McKenzie Rodbell, Dec. 15, 1974; 1 child, Lindsey. BBA, Emory U., 1949. Pres. Apex Supply Co. Inc., Atlanta, 1949—. Co-chmn. George Bush Presdl. Fund Raising, Ga., 1988-89; mem. State of Ga. Electoral Coll., 1989, exec. commr. Am. Bicentennial Pres. Inaugural Bus. Adv., 1989, Pres' Commn. on White House Fellowships, 1989-92. With U.S. Army, 1945. Mem. Wholesale Assn. Ga., Southern Wholesalers Assn., Am. Supply Assn., Standard Club, Rotary Club. Republican. Jewish. Avocations: reading, gardening, antiquing, politics, fund raising.

RODBELL, MARTIN, biochemist; b. Balt., Dec. 1, 1925; s. Milton William and Shirley Helen (Abrams) R.; m. Barbara Charlotte Ledermann, Sept. 10, 1950; children: Paul, Suzanne, Andrew, Phillip. BA, Johns Hopkins U., 1949; PhD, U. Wash., 1954; DSc (hon.), U. Montpelier, 1992. Nutrition and endocrinology chemist NIH, Bethesda, Md., 1956—; chief lab. nutrition and endocrinology NIAMD, Bethesda, Md., 1972-84; sci. dir. Nat. Inst. Environ. Health Scis., Research Triangle Park, N.C., 1985-89, chief sect. signal transduction, 1989—. Recipient Supr. Svc. award HHS, 1974, Gairdner Found. award, 1984, Jacobeus award, 1973, Nobel Prize for Physiology or Medicine, 1994. Mem. NAS (Richard Lounsbery award 1987), Am. Soc. Biol.

Chemists., Am. Acad. Arts and Scis. Office: NIH Environmental Health Scis Research Triangle Park NC 27709

RODDIS, RICHARD STILES LAW, insurance company executive, consultant, legal educator; b. Washington, Mar. 18, 1930; s. Louis Harry and Winifred Emily (Stiles) R.; m. Joanne Margreta Hagen, Aug. 16, 1953; children: Kathryn Hazel Roddis Meyer, Linda Marie Roddis McGinley, Victoria Anne Roddis Hoefer, Margaret Mae Roddis Rumpeltes, Richard Louis Martin. A.B., San Diego (Calif.) State Coll., 1951; J.D., U. Calif.-Berkeley, 1954. Bar: Calif. 1955, Wash. 1981, U.S. Supreme Ct. 1959. Dep. atty. gen. Calif. San Francisco, 1954-58; dep. atty. gen., chief sect. bus. law and investment frauds unit Los Angeles, 1961-63; practiced law San Diego, 1958-61; chief dep. ins. commr. Calif. Los Angeles, 1963-65; ins. commr., 1966-68; prof. law U. Wash., Seattle, 1968—; dean U. Wash. (Sch. Law), 1970-78; chmn., chief exec. officer Unigard Security Ins. Co., Seattle, 1984-88; dir. Stewart Econs., Inc., 1988—; adviser U.S. Dept. Transp., 1968-70, Nat. Conf. Commrs. on Uniform State Laws, 1971-72; chmn. Gov. Wash. Task Force on Catastrophic Health Care Costs, 1973-74; mem. steering com. Med. Injury Compensation Study, Inst. Medicine NAS, 1976. Bd. dirs. Saul Haas Found.; bd. dirs. Crista Ministries, 1986-91. Mem. ABA (com. to improve liability ins. system 1988), State Bar Calif., State Bar Wash., Nat. Assn. Ins. Commrs. (chmn. blanks com., chmn. laws and regs. com., vice chmn. exec. com. 1966-68). Republican. Lutheran. Home: 15524 SE 53rd Pl Bellevue WA 98006-5102

RODDY, EDWARD JOSEPH, plastic pipe company executive; b. Pittsfield, Mass., Dec. 24, 1941; s. Clarence Joseph and Dorothy Mea (Fredrick) R.; m. Josephine Sonja Blazich, Aug. 1, 1964; children: Sonja Anna, Michael Joseph. B Chem. Engring., Cath. U. Am., 1963; MBA, U. Del., 1969. Cert. Internat. Mgmt. Devel., 1992. Prodn. supr. E.I. DuPont de Nemours & Co., Deepwater, N.J., 1969-74; planning analyst E.I. DuPont de Nemours & Co., Wilmington, Del., 1974-75, mktg. specialist, 1976-77, prodn. supt., 1977-78, mfg. mgr., 1981-83, mktg. mgr., 1983-86; mfg. supt. E.I. DuPont de Nemours & Co., Pontchartrain Works, La., 1978-81, bus. mgr. Aldyl piping systems, 1986-91; pres. Upmor Aldyl Ams., New Castle, Del., 1991—; chmn. Upmor Aldyl S.A., Buenos Aires, 1991—, Wirsbo Co., Mpls., 1992—; Upnor Phoenix, Ariz., 1995—; dir. Upnor ETI, 1994—. Mem. Urban League, Wilmington, 1968-73; treas. Civic Assn., Wilmington, 1970-71. Mem. Am. Gas Assn., Soc. Plastics Engrs. (assoc.), Plastic Pipe Inst. (adv. bd.), Urban League. Republican. Roman Catholic. Avocations: travel, theater, opera, literature, aerobic exercise. Home: 600 Westmont Dr Wilmington DE 19808-1537 Office: Upmor Aldyl Americas New Castle Corp Commons 57 Read's Way New Castle DE 19720

RODE, JAMES DEAN, banker; b. Cleve., Feb. 4, 1948; s. Andrew Joseph and Eileen M. (Costello) R.; m. Leslie Ann Biles, June 27, 1970. B.A. in Econs, Ohio U., Athens, 1969; M.B.A. in Fin, Case Western Res. U., 1974. With AmeriTrust Co., Cleve., 1969—; sr. v.p. consumer fin. AmeriTrust Co., 1979-80, exec. v.p. retail banking, 1980-83, sr. exec. v.p. banking services group, 1983, pres., 1984—; COO Nissan Motor Acceptance Corp., Torrance, Calif., 1992—; dir. AmeriTrust Corp. & Co. With USAFR, 1969. Mem. Skytop Club (Pa.). Roman Catholic. Office: AmeriTrust Corp 900 Euclid Ave 14943 Camarosa Dr Pacific Palisades CA 90272

RODE, LEIF, real estate personal computer consultant; b. Copenhagen, Aug. 24, 1926; came to U.S., 1948, naturalized, 1960; s. Stig and Kirsten (Bay) R.; m. Elsa B. Ringressy, Feb. 14, 1992; children from previous marriage: Christian, Lise. BS magna cum laude, Columbia U., 1959. ChFC; CLU; cert. internal auditor; lic. realtor assoc. GRI. Mgr. East Asiatic Co., N.Y.C., 1952-54; various auditing positions N.Y. Life Ins. Co., N.Y.C., 1954-70, asst. gen. auditor, 1970-71, gen. auditor, 1971-82, sr. v.p., gen. auditor, 1982-87, cons., 1987-89; real estate agt., Weichert Realtors, Holmdel, N.J., 1989-90, Fraybern Realtors, Holmdel, 1990-92, Colts Neck Realty, Colts Neck, 1992—. Bd. dirs. Sports Found., Inc., Colts Neck, N.J., 1973-75, pres., 1975-77; mem. Bd. dirs. Colts Neck, 1975-76, v.p., 1976-78; trustee Bayshore Community Hosp., Holmdel, N.J., 1986-87; mcpl. liaison to Colts Neck Twp. for N.J. Assn. Realtors, 1989-94, real estate personal computer cons., 1995—. Served with Royal Danish Navy, 1946-47. Recipient award of honor N.Y. State Soc. CPA's, 1960; Merle M. Hoover scholar, 1960. Mem. Inst. Internal Auditors, Am. Soc. of CLU and Chartered Fin. Cons., Monmouth County Bd. Realtors (constn. and by-laws com. 1989-92, co-chair 1991-92, strategic planning com. 1992-93), N.J. Assn. Realtors (bd. dirs. 1993, legis. com. 1990-93, vice-chair 1992, chmn. 1993, new products and tech. com. 1990-92), Nat. Assn. Realtors. Republican. Lutheran. Home: 47 Blackbriar Dr Colts Neck NJ 07722-1203 Office: Colts Neck Realty PO Box 128 Colts Neck NJ 07722-0128

RODE, REINHARD, political science educator; b. Ernsthofen, Hessen, Germany, Apr. 27, 1947; s. Karl and Else (Flügel) R.; m. Godrun Rückert, Feb. 1, 1977 (div. 1980); 1 child, Julian; m. Hilde Kremer, Aug. 13, 1991; 1 child, Johannes. Degree in Habilitation, Goethe-Universität, Frankfurt, Germany, 1989, PhD, 1975. Rsch. fellow Cath. Commn. Devel. and Peace, Mettmann, Germany, 1972-75. Peace Rsch. Inst. Frankfurt, 1976-89; vis. prof. Free U. Berlin, 1989-90; dir. Peace Rsch. Inst. Frankfurt, 1990-91; Konrad Adenauer prof. Georgetown U., Washington, 1991-92; prof. internat. rels. Martin Luther U., Halle, Germany, 1992—. Author: U.S. Trade Policy and Europe, 1980, Security and Business, 1986; editor: Economic Warfare or Detente, 1985, GATT and Conflict Management, 1990. Mem. Deutsche Vereinigung für Politikwissenschaft, Studienkreis Internat. Beziehungen, Internat. Studies Assn. Home: Waldstrasse 16, Muehltal Hessen, Germany 64367 Office: Martin Luther U, Postfach 8, Halle Schsen-Anhalt, Germany 06099

RODEFFER, STEPHANIE LYNN HOLSCHLAG, archaeologist, government official; b. Newark, Ohio, Oct. 5, 1947; d. Jerry Bernard and Joan Elizabeth (Dasher) Holschlag; m. Michael Joe Rodeffer, Sept. 11, 1971. BA, U. Ky., 1969; PhD, Wash. State U., 1975. Instr., then asst. prof. anthropology Lander Coll., Greenwood, S.C., 1974-77; archaeologist interagy. archaeol. svcs. Nat. Park Svc./Heritage Conservation and Recreation Svc., Atlanta, 1977-80; archaeologist divsn. cultural programs Heritage Conservation and Recreation Svc./Nat. Park Svc., Albuquerque, 1980-81; archaeologist div. cultural programs Nat. Park Svc., Santa Fe, N.Mex., 1981-82; archaeologist, acting chief preservation planning br. Nat. Park Svc., Phila., 1982-86; chief interagy. archaeol. svcs. br. div. nat. register programs Nat. Park Svc., San Francisco, 1986-90; chief mus. collections repository Western Archaeol. and Conservation Ctr. Nat. Park Svc., Tucson, 1990—. Muster Chmn. Star Ft. Hist. Com., Ninety Six, S.C., 1975. Recipient spl. achievement award Nat. Park Svc., 1980, 82, mgmt. award So. Ariz. Fed. Execs. Assn., 1992; Woodrow Wilson fellow, 1969. Mem. Soc. for Hist. Archeology (membership chmn. 1976-78, sec.-treas. 1978—, Carol Ruppé Disting. Svc. award 1994), Soc. for Am. Archaeology, Soc. Profl. Archaeologists, Phi Beta Kappa. Roman Catholic. Avocations: genealogical research, quilting. Office: Nat Park Svc Western Archaeol-Conservation Ctr 1415 N 6th Ave Tucson AZ 85705-6643

RODEMEYER, MICHAEL LEONARD, JR., lawyer; b. Balt., May 25, 1950; s. Michael Leonard and Claire Isabel (Gunther) R.; m. Dorrit Carolyn Green, June 7, 1975; children: Justin, Christopher. AB, Princeton U., 1972; JD, Harvard U., 1975. Bar: Md. 1977, D.C. 1980, U.S. Ct. Appeals (10th cir.) 1980. Atty. Fed. Trade Commn., Washington, 1976-81, atty. advisor 1981-84; counsel Subcom. on Natural Resources, Agr. Rsch. & Environ., Washington, 1984-88; staff dir., counsel U.S. Ho. of Reps., Washington, 1988-90, chief dem. counsel, 1990—. Bd. dirs. Glen Echo (Md.) Park Found., 1991. Democrat. Avocations: computing, bicycling. Home: 6000 Harvard Ave Glen Echo MD 20812-1114 Office: Com on Sci 822 O'Neill HOB Washington DC 20515

RODENBACH, EDWARD FRANCIS, lawyer; b. Phillipsburg, N.J., Apr. 16, 1951; s. L. Ernst and Harriett T. (Reinbold) R.; m. Joanne B. Pursell, Aug. 18, 1973; children: Megan, Kyle. AB, Lafayette Co., Easton, Pa., 1973; JD, Cornell U., 1976. Bar: Conn. 1976, U.S. Dist. Ct. Conn. 1976, U.S. Tax Ct. 1976. Assoc. Cummings & Lockwood, Stamford, Conn., 1976-84, ptnr., 1984-87; ptnr. in charge fiduciary acctg. group, 1984-90; ptnr. Cummings & Lockwood Greenwich, Conn., 1987—, mng. ptnr. Greenwich office, 1989—; v.p., mem. exec. com. Cummings & Lockwood, 1988—, mem. fin. com., 1993—. Mem. stewardship com. 1st Congl. Ch., Ridgefield,

Conn., 1987-90, chmn. 1988-90; mem. endowment com. YMCA of Ridgefield, 1986-90. Mem. ABA (estates and real property sect.), Conn. Bar Assn. (estates and probate sect.), Estate Planning Coun. Lower Fairfield County (exec. com. 1985-89, pres. 1988-89). Republican. Avocation: skiing. Home: 44 Golf Ln Ridgefield CT 06877-4819 Office: Cummings & Lockwood 2 Greenwich Plz Greenwich CT 06830-6390

RODENBERGER, CHARLES ALVARD, aerospace engineer, consultant; b. Muskogee, Okla., Sept. 11, 1926; s. Darcy Owen and Kathryn Martha (Percival) R.; m. Molcie Lou Halsell, Sept. 3, 1949; children: Kathryn Sue Wilcox, Charles Mark. Student, U. Ark., 1944-45; B.S. in Gen. Engring., Okla. State U., 1948; M.S.M.E., So. Meth. U., 1959; Ph.D. in Aero. Engring., U. Tex.-Austin, 1968. Registered profl. engr., Tex. Petroleum engr. Amoco Oil Co., Levelland, Tex., 1948-51; chief engr. McGregor Bros., Odessa, Tex., 1953; petroleum engr. Gen. Crude Oil Co., Hamlin, Tex., 1954; sr. design engr. Gen. Dynamics, Ft. Worth, 1954-60; aerospace engr. NASA, Houston, summer 1962; prof. aerospace engring. Tex. A&M U., College Station, 1960-82, prof. emeritus, 1982—; chmn. aerospace engring. Tex. A&M U., College Station, 1967-82; pres. JETS, Inc., N.Y.C., 1977-79; cons. Southwest Research Inst., Gen. Motors Corp., Gen. Dynamics. Patentee hypervelocity gun and orthotic device. Served with USAAF, 1945; served with USAF, 1951-53. NSF fellow, 1964-65; recipient Disting. Teaching award Tex. A&M U., 1962. Fellow AIAA (assoc.); mem. Nat. Soc. Profl. Engrs. (v.p. 1980-81), Tex. Soc. Profl. Engrs., ASME, Am. Soc. for Engring. Edn., Sigma Xi. Methodist. Home: HC 85 Box 60 Baird TX 79504-9603

RODENSCHMIT, HELEN JULIANA, elementary education educator; b. Cross Plains, Wis., Jan. 8, 1932; d. Frank William and Juliana Helen (Schmelzer) R. BS in Edn., Alverno Coll., 1962; MS in Edn., U. Wis., Whitewater, 1988. Cert. elem. tchr., reading tchr., bilingual tchr., Wis., elem. tchr., Costa Rica; lifetime elem. tchr., N.Y. Tchr. primary St. Bernardine Sch., Forest Pk., Ill., 1951-58, St. Cyprian Sch., River Grove, Ill., 1958-59; tchr. elem. St. Monical Sch., N.Y.C., 1959-64, Holy Spirit Sch., Milw., 1964-66, St. Joseph Sch., Phlox, Wis., 1966-67; tchr. sci. and art St. Clare Collegio, Moravia, Costa Rica, 1968; tchr. elem. St. Joseph Primary, Moravia, Costa Rica, 1969-80; tchr. Kindergarten St. Francis Colegio, Moravia, Costa Rica, 1981-84; elem. libr. Lincoln Colegio, Moravia, Costa Rica, 1985-86; tchr. migrant and bilingual Marshall (Wis.) Pub. Sch., 1988-94; ESL tchr. Westside Elem. Sch., Sun Prairie, Wis., 1994—; tchr. ESL Westside Elem. Sch., Sun Prairie, Wis.; rsch. project tchr. U. Minn., 1964-66; tchr. tng. English as fgn. lang. St. Joseph Primary, St. Francis Colegio, Moravia, Costa Rica, elem. coord. ESL, 1981-84; home tutor Costa Rica, 1975-86. Mem. St. Vincent DePaul Project, Barrio Corazon de Jesus, Moravia, Costa Rica, 1970-73. Mem. Assn. Childhood Internat., Tchrs. English as Second Lang., Nat. Assn. Bilingual Edn., Sch. Sisters of St. Francis. Avocations: fgn. travel, gardening. Home: 4517 County Trunk Hwy P Cross Plains WI 53528

RODER, RONALD ERNEST, accountant; b. Milw., Nov. 8, 1948; m. Marilyn L. Frederick, June 13, 1970; children: Lori A., Ronald J. BBA, U. Wis., 1970. CPA, Wis. Fin. svcs. officer U. Wis., Milw., 1973-79; asst. v.p. 1st Wis. Corp., Milw. 1973-79; sr. v.p., contr. 1st Wis. Nat. Bank, Madison, 1979-87; 1st v.p. mergers and acquisitions 1st Wis. Corp., Milw., 1987-88; sr. v.p. info. svcs. 1st Wis. Nat. Bank, Milw., 1988-89; pres. Firstar Info. Svcs. Corp., Milw., 1990—. Mem. Wis. Inst. CPAs. Office: Firstar Info Svcs Corp 16900 W Capitol Dr Brookfield WI 53005-2192

RODERICK, RICHARD MICHAEL, petroleum distribution and real estate company financial executive; b. Buffalo, Oct. 18, 1948; m. Patricia Suzanne Rosick, Oct. 2, 1971; children: Kristina, Thomas, Carolyn. BBA in Acctg., U. Notre Dame, 1970; MS in Computer Systems Mgmt., U.S. Naval Postgrad. Sch., 1971; postgrad., Harvard U., 1984; MBA, U. Maine, 1985. CPA, Maine. Acct. Arthur Young & Co., Portland, Maine, 1976-79; corp. contr. Dead River Co., Bangor, Maine, 1979-87, v.p., contr., 1987-90, v.p., CFO, treas., 1990-94, v.p., CFO, v.p. real estate, 1994—. Bd. dirs., exec. com. United Way of Penobscot Valley, 1990-94, pres. 1992-94. Lt. USN, 1970-76. Mem. Greater Bangor C. of C. (bd. dirs. 1989-94, treas. 1991-92). Roman Catholic. Office: Dead River Co 55 Broadway Bangor ME 04401-5200

RODERICK, ROBERT GENE, accountant, chief financial officer; b. Tulsa, June 27, 1944; s. William Paul and Iris Elizabeth (Reniker) R.; children: James Robert, Scott Alan. BSBA, U. Tulsa, 1968. CPA, Okla. Staff acct. Amerada Petroleum Corp., Tulsa, 1966-68, Elmer Fox and Co., CPA's, Tulsa, 1968-71; controller The NORDAM Group, Tulsa, 1971-80, treas., v.p., chief fin. officer, 1980—, also bd. dirs.; bd. dirs. LORI, Inc., Tulsa, TKI, Inc., Springdale, Ark., Brooks Aero. Svcs., Tulsa, World Aviation Assocs. Ltd., Tulsa, M & N Plastics, Inc., Ft. Worth, Aviation Mktg. Ltd., Barbados. Mem. master adv. bd. Tulsa Jr. Coll., 1984-92. Mem. AICPA, Okla. Soc. CPAs, Risk Ins. Mgmt. Soc., Tulsa Aerospace Alliance. Republican. Episcopalian. Avocations: travel, numismatics, history. Office: The NORDAM Group 510 S Lansing Ave Tulsa OK 74120-3636

RODERICK, ROBERT LEE, aerospace executive; b. Chgo., Oct. 19, 1925; s. Albert Lee and Betha Manilla (Powers) R.; m. Lisa Wolf, Dec. 28, 1950; children: Diane Gale, Robert Kirk. Student, Iowa State U.; 1943; BSEE, Ill. Inst. Tech., 1948; PhD, Brown U., 1951. V.p. Litton Industries, Beverly Hills, Calif., 1968-73; group v.p. Hughes Aircraft Co., Canoga Park, Calif., 1973-87; v.p. corp. tech. ctrs. Hughes Aircraft Co., L.A., 1987-90. Patentee instanteous vertical speed indicator. With USN, 1943-46. Recipient Spl. Recognition award Ill. Inst. Tech., 1967, named to Hall of Fame, 1983; recipient Pub. Svc. award NASA, 1967, Am. Machinist's award Am. Machinists Assn., 1970. Mem. Assn. U.S. Army, Am. Def. Preparedness Assn., Sigma Xi, Tau Beta Phi, Eta Kappa Nu. Avocations: tennis, personal computing. Home: 3426 Alginet Dr Encino CA 91436-4124

RODERICK, WILLIAM RODNEY, academic administrator; b. Chgo., Aug. 6, 1933; s. William Forrest and June Hazel (Kurtz) R.; m. Dorothy Jean Paetel, Oct. 21, 1965. BS in Chemistry, Northwestern U., 1954; SM in Chemistry, U. Chgo., 1955, PhD in Chemistry, 1957. Prof. chemistry U. Fla., Gainesville, 1958-62; rsch. chemist Abbott Labs., North Chicago, Ill., 1962-71; prof. chemistry Roosevelt U., Chgo., 1972—; assoc. dean acad. affairs Roosevelt U., Arlington Heights, Ill., 1993—. Mem. AAAS, Am. Chem. Soc. (Tour Speaker of Yr. award 1969, 71), Sigma Xi, Phi Beta Kappa. Home: 15193 W Redwood Ln Libertyville IL 60048-1447 Office: Roosevelt U 2121 S Goebbert Rd Arlington Heights IL 60005-4205

RODEWIG, JOHN STUART, manufacturing company executive; b. Westfield, N.J., Oct. 15, 1933; s. Louis F. and Vivian E. (Colyer) R.; m. Ann Sterling Taylor, June 16, 1956; children: Louis F. II, Margaret R. Layman, Ann C. Lane. BEE, Cornell U., 1956. With Eaton Corp., various locations, 1969—; gen. mgr. axle div. Eaton Corp., Cleve., 1978-79; v.p. truck components-Europe Eaton Corp., London, 1979-89; v.p. truck components ops.-worldwide Eaton Corp., Cleve., 1989-91, pres. truck components group, 1991-92, pres., 1992—; bd. dirs. Eaton Corp., Eaton Ltd., Hounslow, Eng., Eaton S.A., St. Nazaire, France, Eaton S.A., Pamplona, Spain, Eaton Mfrs. S.A., Toluca, Mex., FKI plc, West Yorkshire, Eng., Hayes Wheels Internat., Inc. Campaign chmn. Boy Scout Am., Farmington Hills, Mich., 1975, Girl Scouts U.S., Farmington Hills, 1977; vis. com. bus. adminstrn. Cleve. State U.; mem. adv. com. coll. engring. Cornell U.; mem. corp. coun. Cleve. Mus. Art. Mem. Soc. Automotive Engrs., Western Hwy. Inst. (exec. com.), Am. Trucking Assn., Soc. Motor Mfrs. and Traders in Europe. Avocations: travel, golf, vintage car restoration. Home: 14732 North Hillbrook Ln Chagrin Falls OH 44022 Office: Eaton Corp 1111 Superior Ave Cleveland OH 44114*

RODGERS, AGGIE GUERARD, costume designer; m. Peter Laxton; children: James, Thomas. Grad., Fresno State Coll., 1967; MA in Theatre Arts, Calif. State U., Long Beach. Former wardrobe supr. Am. Conservatory Theatre, San Francisco. Costume designer: (films) American Graffiti, 1973, The Conversation, 1974, One Flew Over the Cuckoo's Nest, 1975, Corvette Summer, 1978, More American Graffiti, 1979, Return of the Jedi, 1983, The Adventures of Buckaroo Banzai: Across the 8th Dimension, 1983, Pee Wee's Big Adventure, 1985, Warning Sign, 1985, Cocoon, 1985, The Color Purple, 1985 (Academy Award nomination best costume design 1985), Fatal Beauty, 1987, Leonard Part VI, 1987, The Witches of Eastwick, 1987, *batteries not included, 1987, My Stepmother is an Alien, 1988, Beetlejuice, 1988, I Love You to Death, 1989, In Country, 1989, Forever Young, 1992, Grand

Canyon, 1992, Benny and Joon, 1993, The Fugitive, 1993. Office: care Lawrence Mirisch The Mirisch Agency 10100 Santa Monica Blvd Ste 700a Los Angeles CA 90067*

RODGERS, ANTHONY D., hospital administrator. BA, UCLA, 1971, MS in Pub. Health, 1975, postgrad. Rsch. analyst capital projects divsn. L.A. County Dept. Health Svcs., 1973-77; assoc. hosp. administr. John Wesley County Hosp., L.A., 1978-79; administr. H. Claude Hudson Comprehensive Health Ctr., L.A., 1979-89; chief exec. officer Metro West County Health Ctrs., L.A., 1989; assoc. hosp. adminstr. ops. Olive View Med. Ctr., L.A., 1989-90; chief exec. officer Maricopa Med. Ctr., Phoenix, 1990—; drug testing cons. office commr. Major League Baseball, 1986-87; facility planning cons., Condelli Brown & Assocs., Santa Monica, Calif., 1985-87; program planning con., Omni Corp., Santa Monica, 1980-81; staff planner devel. svc. programs ambulatory care ctrs. Pres. JWCH Inst., Inc., L.A., 1987-89. Mem. Nat. Assn. Pub. Hosps. (exec. bd., fellow), Ariz. Hosp. Assn. (regional coun., bd. dirs. Blue Cross/Blue Shield). Home: 13229 S 48th St Phoenix AZ 85044-5037 Office: Maricopa Med Ctr PO Box 5099 Phoenix AZ 85010-5099

RODGERS, BERNARD F., JR., academic administrator, dean; b. Hazleton, Pa., Mar. 21, 1947; s. Bernard F. and Anna V. (Gulla) R.; m. Patricia Hick, Dec. 6, 1969 (div. June, 1982); m. Jane Powell, Oct. 27, 1984. BS in English and Edn., Mt. St. Mary's Coll., 1969; MA in English, U. Bridgeport, 1972; PhD in English with honors, U. Chgo., 1975. Tchr. Eng., dir. drama Somers Ctrl. High Sch., Lincolndale, N.Y., 1969-72; seminar coord. Shakespeare Inst. U. Bridgeport, 1972; lectr. Am. Lit. U. Chgo. Extension, 1975; instr., asst. prof. lit. and humanities City Colls. Chgo., 1975-82, spl. asst. to chancellor, 1984-85; faculty Eng. Simon's Rock Coll. of Bard, Great Barrington, Mass., 1985—, dean acad. affairs, 1985-87, v.p., dean, 1987—; chair lit. and humanities sect. coll. acceleration program Chgo. City-Wide Coll., 1977-78, chair coll. acceleration program, 1977-78, mem. adminstrv. coun., 1980-81; bd. overseers Simon's Rock Coll. of Bard, 1987; evaluator NEH Summer Insts. High Sch. English Tchrs., 1985, 86; proposal evaluator Fund for Emprovement Postsecondary Edn., 1984; mem. planning com. humanists Write On, Chgo., 1982-83; mem. nom. com. Eisenhower Fellowship, Am. Embassy, Warsaw, Poland, 1980; mem. writing panel artists-in-residence progrm Chgo. Coun. Fine Arts, 1978. Author: Philip Roth: A Bibliography, 1974, 2d edit., 1984, Contemporary American Fiction 1944-79: A Chronology, 1980; essayist, reviewer in field; contbr. essays, reviews Arts in Review, 1980-85; assoc. prodr. TV talk show U. Chgo., 1974-75, prodr., 1975-76; prodr.. host interview program City Colls. Chgo., 1981-82; speaker in field. Bd. dirs. Fairview Hosp., Great Barrington, 1988—, Mass. Found. for Humanities, 1989—, chair, 1992—, vice chair, 1992-93, chair program com., 1990-92, Friends of Chgo. Pub. Libr., 1982; mem. South County cabinet Berkshires United Way, 1988, mem. planning com. humanists Read Ill., 1984-85, ad hoc com. excellence Ill. Community Coll. Trustees Assn., 1984-85. U. Chgo. fellow, 1973, Ford Found. fellow, 1974-75, Fulbright-Hays sr. lectr. to Poland, 1979-80, Chgo. Pub. Libr. assoc. scholar, 1976-78. Mem. Southern Berkshire C of C. (bd. dirs. 1987-90), New Eng. Assn. Schs. and Colls. (evaluation team chair commn. instns. higher learning 1986—), North Ctrl. Assn. Colls. and Schs. (asst. dir. commn. instns. higher edn. 1982-84), Soc. Midland Authors (chair fiction award com. 1985), Lambda Iota Tau, Pi Delta Epsilon, Delta Epsilon Sigma. Home: PO Box 778 Great Barrington MA 01230-0778 Office: Simon's Rock Coll of Bard 84 Alford Rd Great Barrington MA 01230-9702

RODGERS, BRUCE E., writer; b. Rochester, N.Y., Oct. 25, 1949; s. Ellsworth C. and Virginia (Byrnes) R.; m. Susan L. Storch, Feb. 2, 1974. BS, SUNY, Potsdam, 1971; MA, ind. U., 1976. Lit. dir. GeVa Theatre, Rochester, N.Y., 1977-82; writer Lebanon, N.J., 1982—; resident playwright McCarter Theatre, Princeton, N.J., 1985—. Co-author: Innovation Inc, 1988; author: (play) Debut..., 1987, (play) Lost Electra, 1988. With U.S. Army, 1971-74. Recipient Disting. Artist award N.J. State Coun. on the Arts, 1988; fellow MacDowell Colony, 1988. Mem. Dramatists Guild. Avocations: windsurfing, boating.

RODGERS, DANIEL TRACY, history educator; b. Darby, Pa., Sept. 29, 1942; s. Oliver Eliot and Dorothy (Welch) R.; m. Irene Wylie, 1971; children: Peter Samuel, Dwight Oliver. AB, BS in Engring., Brown U., 1965; PhD in History, Yale U., 1973. Instr. history U. Wis., Madison 1971-73, asst. prof., 1973-78, assoc. prof., 1978-80; assoc. prof. history Princeton (N.J.) U., 1980-86, prof., 1986—, chair, 1988-95; Fulbright lectr., Frankfurt, Fed. Republic Germany, 1983-84. Author: The Work Ethic in Industrial America, 1860-1920 (Frederick Jackson Turner award 1979), 1978, Contested Truths: Keywords in American Politics since Independence, 1987. Recipient Chancellor's award U. Wis., Madison, 1978; Am. Coun. Learned Socs. fellow, 1976, NEH fellow, 1987-88, Ctr. for Advanced Study in Behavioral Scis. fellow, 1991-92. Office: Princeton U Dept History Princeton NJ 08544

RODGERS, EUGENE, writer; b. Bklyn., July 22, 1939; s. Thomas Aquinas and Catherine (Slattery) R.; m. Carol Diane Huber, 1977; children: Eric Eugene, Catherine Huber. BS, Villanova U., 1961; postgrad., U. Wis., 1961-63; MS, Va. Commonwealth U., 1991. Research asst. sci. writing U. Wis., Madison, 1961-63; pub. info. officer U.S. Antarctic Research Program, 1963-65; freelance writer Washington, 1965-67; mgr. sci. pub. relations Westinghouse Electric Corp., Pitts., 1967-75; editor Atomic Indsl. Forum Inc., Washington, 1975-76; speechwriter ERDA, Washington, 1976, IBM, Armonk, N.Y., 1977-79, United Techs. Corp., Hartford, Conn., 1979-82; free-lance writer, 1982-84; sr. writer Virginia Power, Richmond, Va., 1984-87; editor, pub. Electric RD&D Newsletter, Midlothian, Va., 1987-88; free-lance writer Midlothian, 1988—; adj. instr. Va. Commonwealth U., Richmond, 1991-92. Author: Beyond the Barrier: The Story of Byrd's First Expedition to Antarctica, 1990. Home: 2621 Ellesmere Dr Midlothian VA 23113-3939

RODGERS, FRAN SUSSNER, educational development specialist; b. N.Y.C., Dec. 14, 1946; m. Charles Rodgers, May 2, 1971. BA, Barnard Coll., 1967; MA, Tufts U., 1971; cert., Mass. Gen. Hosp., 1971. Cons. Edn. Devel. Ctr., Newton, Mass.; tng. specialist U.S. Dept. Health and Human Svcs.; fed. adminstr. N.J. and N.Y. Child Care and Community programs; pres. Work/Family Directions, Inc., Watertown, Mass.; mem. Mass. Children's Lobby. Mem. Nat. Assn. for Edn. Young Children, Am. Mgmt. Assn.

RODGERS, FRANK, librarian; b. Darlington, Eng., July 28, 1927; came to U.S., 1956; s. Charles Bede and Frances (Page) R.; m. Sarah Louise Edelson, Dec. 18, 1971; children: Hilda Marie, Norah Frances. BA with honors, King's Coll., U. Durham, 1947; diploma librarianship, London U., 1952. Libr. Poplar Tech. Coll., London, 1951-53, St. Martin's Sch. Art, 1953-56; sr. libr. adult svcs. divsn. Akron (Ohio) Pub. Libr., 1956-59; asst. reference libr. U. Ill., 1959-64; chief reference libr., then asst. dir. pub. svcs. Pa. State U. Librs., 1965-69; dir. Portland (Oreg.) State U. Libr., 1969-79; dir. librs. U. Miami, Fla., 1979—; mem. Oreg. adv. coun. librs., 1973-74 ; bd. dirs. Pacific N.W. Bibliog. Ctr., 1973-77; tech. adv. com. librs. Columbia Regional Assn. Govts., 1976-79; vis. fellow U. Southampton, Eng., 1975-76; pres. Oreg. Libr. Assn., 1974-75; mem. nominating com. Southeastern Libr. Network, 1984-85; bd. dirs. S.E. Fla. Libr. Info. Network, 1984—, pres. 1991-92; mem. exec. coun. Assn. Caribbean U. Rsch. and Instl. Librs., 1985-88; chmn. local organizing com. for 1981 and 1987 confs. in Miami; mem. Fla. Libr. Network Coun., 1985—; NEH challenge grant rev. panel, 1987, Howard U. ann. inspection team, 1989, Reaffirmation com., Tex. Christian U., 1993. Author, editor various libr. publs., guides. Sr. fellow Grad. Sch. Libr. and Info. Sci. UCLA, 1983; grantee Coun. Libr. Resources, 1975-76. Fellow Libr. Assn. U.K.; mem. ALA, Assn. Rsch. Librs. (office mgmt. studies adv. com. 1981-83, stats. and measurements com. 1993—), Assn. Specialized and Coop. Libr. Agys. (membership promotion com. 1994—, chair 1990 program com.), Assn. Southeastern Rsch. Librs. (chmn. membership com. 1982—), Multilines. Home: 5630 Twin Lakes Dr Miami FL 33143-2038 Office: U Miami Library Coral Gables FL 33124

RODGERS, FREDERIC BARKER, judge; b. Albany, N.Y., Sept. 29, 1940; s. Prentice Johnson and Jane (Weed) R.; m. Valerie McNaughton, Oct. 8, 1988; 1 child: Gabriel Moore. AB, Amherst Coll., 1963; JD, Union U., 1966. Bar: N.Y. 1966, U.S. Ct. Mil. Appeals 1968, Colo. 1972, U.S.

Supreme Ct. 1974, U.S. Ct. Appeals (10th cir.) 1981. Chief dep. dist. atty., Denver, 1972-73; commr. Denver Juvenile Ct., 1973-79; mem. Mulligan Reeves Teasley & Joyce, P.C., Denver, 1979-86; pres. Frederic B. Rodgers, P.C., Breckenridge, Colo., 1980-89; ptnr. McNaughton & Rodgers, Central City, Colo., 1989-91; county ct. judge County of Gilpin, 1987—; presiding mcpl. judge cities of Breckenridge, Blue River, Black Hawk, Central City, Edgewater, Empire, Idaho Springs and Westminster, Colo., 1978-95; chmn. com. on mcpl. ct. rules of procedure Colo. Supreme Ct., 1984—; mem. gen. faculty Nat. Jud. Coll. U. Nev., Reno, 1990—; elected to faculty coun., 1994—. Author: (with Dilweg, Fretz, Murphy and Wicker) Modern Judicial Ethics, 1992; contbr. articles to profl. jours. Mem. Colo. Commn. on Children, 1982-85, Colo. Youth Devel. Coun., 1989—, Colo. Family Peace Task Force, 1994—. Served with JAGC, U.S. Army, 1967-72; to maj. USAR, 1972-88. Decorated Bronze Star with oak leaf cluster, Air medal. Recipient Outstanding County Judge award Colo. 17th Judicial Dist. Victim Adv. Coalition, 1991; Spl. Community Service award Colo. Am. Legion, 1979. Mem. ABA (jud. adminstrn. div. exec. coun. 1989—, ho. dels. 1993—), Colo. Bar Assn. (bd. govs. 1986-88, 90-92, 93—), Continental Divide Bar Assn., Denver Bar Assn. (bd. trustees 1979-82), First Jud. Dist. Bar Assn., Nat. Conf. Spl. Ct. Judges (chmn. 1989-90), Colo. County Judges Assn. (pres. 1995—), Colo. Mcpl. Judges Assn. (pres. 1986-87), Colo. Trial Judges Coun. (v.p. 1995—), Denver Law Club (pres. 1981-82), Colo. Women's Bar Assn. Am. Judicature Soc., Nat. Coun. Juvenile and Family Ct. Judges, Univ. Club (Denver), Arlberg Club (Winter Park), Marines Meml. Club (San Francisco), Westminster Rotary Club. Episcopalian. Office: Gilpin County Justice Ctr 2960 Dory Hill Rd Golden Gate CO 80403

RODGERS, JAMES FOSTER, association executive, economist; b. Columbus, Ga., Jan. 15, 1951; s. Laban Jackson and Martha (Jackson) R.; m. Cynthia Lynne Bathurst, Aug. 20, 1975. B.A., U. Ala., Tuscaloosa, 1973; Ph.D., U. Iowa, 1980. Fed. intern Office Rsch. and Stats., Social Security Adminstrn., Washington, 1976-77; rsch. assoc. Ctr. Health Policy Rsch., AMA, Chgo., 1979-80, rsch. dir., 1980-82, asst. to dep. exec. v.p. AMA, 1982-85; dir. AMA Ctr. Health Policy Rsch., Chgo., 1985—. Contbr. articles on health econs. to profl. jours. Pharm. Mfrs. Assn. grantee, 1978; NSF grantee, 1978; Hohenberg fellow, 1969-70. Mem. Am. Econ. Assn., Am. Soc. Assn. Exec., Am. Statis. Assn., So. Econ. Assn., Western Econ. Assn. Home: 2233 N Orchard Chicago IL 60614 Office: AMA Ctr for Health Policy Rsch 515 N State St Chicago IL 60610

RODGERS, JOHN, geologist, educator; b. Albany, N.Y., July 11, 1914; s. Henry D. and Louise W. (Allen) R. B.A., Cornell U., 1936, M.S., 1937; Ph.D., Yale U., 1944. Geologist, U.S. Geol. Survey, 1938-46, intermittently, 1946—; sci. cons. U.S. Army Engrs., 1944-46; instr. geology Yale U., New Haven, 1946-47; asst. prof. Yale U., 1947-52, assoc. prof., 1952-59, prof., 1959-62, Silliman prof., 1962-83, Silliman prof. emeritus, 1983—; vis. lectr. Coll. de France, Paris, 1960; sec.-gen. commn. on stratigraphy Internat. Geol. Congress, 1952-60; commr. Conn. Geol. and Natural History Survey, 1960-71. Author: (with C.O. Dunbar) Principles of Stratigraphy, 1957, The Tectonics of the Appalachians, 1970; also articles in field.; editor Symposium on the Cambrian System, 3 vols., 1956, 61; recording artist: (with W. Ruff) The Harmony of the World, 1979; asst. editor Am. Jour. Sci., 1948-54, editor, 1954—. NSF Sr. postdoctoral fellow France, 1959-60; exchange visitor Geol. Inst., Acad. Scis. USSR, 1967; Guggenheim fellow Australia, 1973-74; recipient Medal of Freedom U.S. Army, 1947, James Hall medal N.Y. State Geol. Survey, 1986; exchange scholar Inst. of Geology Academia Sinica (Beijing) 1986; recipient Médaille Paul Fourmarier Académie Royale des Sciences, Lettres et Beaux-Arts de Belgique, 1987, William Clyde DeVane medal Phi Beta Kappa, 1990. Fellow AAAS, Geol. Soc. Am. (councillor 1962-65, pres. 1970, Penrose medal 1981), Am. Geophys. Union; mem. NAS, Am. Acad. Arts and Scis., Am. Assn. Petroleum Geologists, Conn. Acad. Sci. and Engring. (charter), Conn. Acad. Arts and Scis. (pres. 1969), Geol. Soc. London (hon.), Société géologique de France (assoc. mem., v.p. 1960, Prix Gaudry 1987), Am. Philos. Soc., Russian Acad. Scis. (hon. fgn. mem.), Academia Real de Ciencias y Artes Barcelona (fgn. corr. mem.), Sigma Xi, Phi Beta Kappa. Club: Elizabethan (New Haven). Office: Dept Geology Yale U P O Box 208109 New Haven CT 06520-8109

RODGERS, JOHN HUNTER, lawyer; b. Lubbock, Tex., Jan. 18, 1944; s. James O'Donnell Rodgers and Dorothy (Ulin) Carpenter; m. Anne C. Smith, Nov. 29, 1969; children; Anne Elizabeth, Catherine Hunter. BA, Tex. A&M, 1966; JD, U. Tex., 1969. Bar: Tex. 1969, U.S. Supreme Ct. 1973. Atty. The Southland Corp., Dallas, 1973-79, gen. counsel, 1979-91, sec., 1987—, sr. v.p., chief adminstrv. officer, 1991-93, exec. v.p., chief adminstrv. officer, 1993—. Mem. visual arts com. Tex. A&M U., 1985—, bd. dirs. student fund enrichment bd., 1986—; mem. exec. com. Jr. Achievement Dallas, 1988—; mem. Dallas Citizens Coun., 1992—; trustee Goals for Dallas, 1991-92, Nat. Bd. Boys & Girls Clubs Am., 1993—; mem. mktg. com. Dallas Mus. Art, 1994—. Capt. JAGC, U.S. Army, 1969-73, Vietnam. Mem. ABA, Tex. Bar Assn. (coun. mem. corp. counsel sect. 1988), Dallas Bar Assn., Southwestern Legal Found. (adv. bd. Internat. and Comparative Law Ctr., rsch. fellow 1986-94), Nat. Assn. Convenience Stores (bd. dirs. 1993—). Roman Catholic. Office: The Southland Corp 2711 N Haskell Ave Dallas TX 75204-2906

RODGERS, JOHN JOSEPH, III, school administrator; b. Jamaica, N.Y., Oct. 13, 1941; s. John Joseph Jr. and Edith (McInerney) R.; children: Janet, John Joseph IV. BS, Fordham U., 1962; Profl. diploma, St. Johns U., 1970, EdD, 1979; postgrad., CUNY, Flushing. Asst. prin. N.Y.C. Bd. Edn., 1972-82; prin. Howard T. Herber Sch., Malverne, N.Y., 1982-85, Norman Thomas High Sch., N.Y.C., 1988—. Mem. ASCD, Nat. Assn. Secondary Sch. Prins. Home: PO Box 1491 New York NY 10156-1491 Office: 111 E 33 St New York NY 10016

RODGERS, JOHNATHAN, broadcast executive; b. San Antonio, Jan. 18, 1946; s. Marion Alford and Barbara (Merriwether) R.; m. Royal Graves Kennedy, Sept. 27, 1976; children: David, Jamie. BA, U. Calif., Berkeley, 1967; MA, Stanford U., 1972; PhD (hon.), Columbia Coll., Chgo., 1991. Writer-reporter Sports Illustrated, N.Y.C., 1966-68; assoc. editor Newsweek, N.Y.C., 1968-72; producer WNBC-TV, N.Y.C., 1972-73; reporter WKYC-TV (NBC), Cleve., 1973-74; sta. mgr., news dir. KCBS-TV, L.A., 1978-83; exec. producer CBS News, N.Y.C., 1983-86; v.p., gen. mgr. WBBM-TV (CBS), Chgo., 1986-90; pres. CBS TV Stas., Chgo., 1990—. Bd. dirs. Jr. Achievement, Chgo., Sickle Cell Anemia Found., Chgo., 1986-90, Harold Washington Found., Chgo., 1988-90; advisor Make-A-Wish Found., Chgo. With U.S. Army, 1969-71, Korea. mem. Nat. Assn. Black Journalists. Home: 843 W Chalmers Pl Chicago IL 60614-3233 Office: CBS-TV 630 N Mcclurg Ct Chicago IL 60611-3074

RODGERS, LAWRENCE RODNEY, physician, educator; b. Clovis, N.Mex., Mar. 9, 1920; s. Samuel Frank and Lillian (O'Connor) R.; m. Ivy Lorna Piper, Aug. 6, 1943; children: Lawrence Rodney (dec.), Ivy Elizabeth, George Piper. B.S., West Tex. State U., 1940; M.D., U. Tex., 1943. Diplomate Am. Bd. Internal Medicine. Intern Phila. Gen. Hosp., 1943-44, resident in medicine, 1946-49; assoc. internist Tumor Inst., U. Tex. M.D. Anderson Hosp., Houston, 1949—; chmn. dept. medicine Hermann Hosp., Houston, 1966-71; assoc. prof. clin. medicine Baylor U., 1949—; prof. clin. medicine U. Tex., 1972—. Editor: Harris County Physician, 1976-80. Bd. dirs. Tex. Med. Found.; trustee Houston Mus. Med. Sci., 1981. Served to maj. M.C. AUS, 1944-46. Decorated Bronze Star with two oak leaf clusters; recipient Ashbel Smith Disting. Alumnus award U. Tex. Med. Br.-Galveston, 1993. Fellow ACP (gov. for Tex. 1979-83), Laureate Internist Tex. award 1994); mem. AMA (del.), Harris County Med. Soc. (exec. bd. 1978-82, v.p. 1984), Am. Heart Assn., Houston Soc. Internal Medicine (pres. 1974), Houston Acad. Medicine (pres. 1981), Houston Philos. Soc. (pres. 1993-94), Doctor's Club Houston (bd. govs. 1984-88, pres. 1986).

RODGERS, MARY COLUMBRO, university chancellor, English educator, author; b. Aurora, Ohio, Apr. 17, 1925; d. Nicola and Nancy (DeNicola) Columbro; m. Daniel Richard Rodgers, July 24, 1965; children: Robert, Patricia, Kristine. AB, Notre Dame Coll., 1957; MA, Western Res. U., 1962; PhD, Ohio State U., 1964; postgrad., U. Rome, 1964-65; EdD, Cath. Nat. Open U., 1975, DLitt, 1978. Tchr. English Cleve. elem. schs., 1945-52, Cleve. secondary schs., 1952-62; supr. English student tchrs. Ohio State U., 1962-64; asst. prof. English U. Md., 1965-66; assoc. prof. Trinity Coll., 1967-68; prof. English D.C. Tchrs. Coll., 1968—; pres. Md. Nat. U., 1972—;

chancellor Am. Open U., 1965—; dean Am. Open U. Acad. Author numerous books and monographs, latest works include: A Short Course in English Composition, 1976, Chapbook of Children's Literature, 1977, Comprehensive Catalogue: The Open University of America System, 1978-80, Open University of America System Source Book, V, VI, VII, 1978, Essays and Poems on Life and Literature, 1979, Modes and Models: Four Lessons for Young Writers, 1981, Open University Structures and Adult Learning, 1982, Papers in Applied English Linguistics, 1982, Twelve Lectures on the American Open University, 1982, English Pedagogy in the American Open University, 1983, Design for Personalized English Graduate Degrees in the Urban University, 1984, Open University English Teaching, 1945-85: Conceptual History and Rationale, 1985, Claims and Counterclaims Regarding Instruction Given in Personalized Degree Residency Programs Completed by Graduates of California National Open University, 1986, The American Open University, 1965 t0 1985: History and Sourcebook, 1986, New Design II: English Pedagogy in the American Open University, 1987, The American Open University, 1965 to 1985: A Research Report, 1987, The American Open University and Other Open Universities: A Comparative Study Report, 1988, Poet and Pedagogue in Moscow and Leningrad: A Travel Report, 1989, Foundations of English Scholarship in the American Open University, 1989, Twelve Lectures in Literary Analysis, 1990, Ten Lectures in Literary Production, 1990, Analyzing Fact and Fiction, 1991, Analyzing Poetry and Drama, 1991, Some Successful Literary Research Papers: An Inventory of Titles and Theses, 1991, A Chapbook of Poetry and Drama Analysis, 1992, Convent Poems, 1943-61, 93, Fables for Fiction Analysis, 3d edit., 1993, First Access List to the Open University Literary Trust, 1993, Catholic Marriage Poems, 1962-79, 1993, New Design Responses 1945-1993, 10 vols., 1993, Catholic Widow with Children Poems, 1979-93, 1994, others. Fulbright scholar U. Rome, 1964-65. Fellow Cath. Scholars; mem. Poetry Soc. Am., Nat. Coun. Tchrs. English, Am. Ednl. Rsch. Assn., Am. Acad. Poets, Ohioana Libr. Assn., Friends John Henry Newman Assn., Writer's Ctr. Md., Pi Lambda Theta. Home and Office: Coll Heights Estates 3916 Commander Dr Hyattsville MD 20782-1027 My life as a Catholic scholar has focused on the literate and humane. Both as a student and as a scholar I have made my work a disciplined commitment to English literature, English language, and English pedagogy. My life's goal has been the effective, everyday transmission of humane values defined in my Catholic heritage to younger generations through my teaching, research and writing. My epitaph should read: She saw with the writer's eye and worked with the scholar's tools before she spoke with the teacher's tongue.

RODGERS, PAUL, lawyer, government official; b. St. Augustine, Fla., Aug. 9, 1933; m. Barbara Broadrick, July 1, 1955; 3 children. A.B., Mercer U., 1955, J.D., 1957. Bar: Ga. 1956, U.S. Supreme Ct. 1961, U.S. Ct. Appeals (5th cir.) 1964, D.C. 1968, U.S. Ct. Appeals (D.C. cir.) 1968, U.S. Ct. Appeals (4th cir.) 1970, U.S. Ct. Appeals (9th cir.) 1973, U.S. Ct. Appeals (10th cir.) 1984. Atty. Atlanta Gas Light Co., 1957-60; asst. atty. gen. State of Ga., 1960-65; adminstrv. dir., gen. counsel Nat. Assn. Regulatory Utility Commrs., Washington, 1965—. Served to 2d lt. Inf. U.S. Army, capt. Res. Mem. ABA, D.C. Bar Assn., Ga. Bar Assn., Fed. Communications Bar Assn., Fed. Power Bar Assn. Office: Nat Assn Regulatory Utility Commrs 1102 1CC Bldg PO Box 684 Washington DC 20044-0684

RODGERS, THOMAS J., electronics executive. Pres., CEO Cypress Semiconductor Corp., San Jose, Calif. Office: Cypress Semiconductor Corp 3901 N 1st St San Jose CA 95134-1599*

RODGMAN, ALAN, chemist, consultant; b. Aberdare, Wales, Feb. 7, 1924; came to U.S., 1954, naturalized, 1961; s. Arch and Margaret (Llewellyn) R.; m. Doris Curley, June 7, 1947; children: Eric, Paul, Mark. B.A. in Chemistry, U. Toronto, 1949, M.A. in Organic Chemistry, 1951, Ph.D. in Organic Chemistry, 1953. Rsch. asst. med. rsch. dept. U. Toronto, 1947-51, rsch. assoc., 1951-54; tchr., courses in organic chemistry, phys. chemistry, math. Chem. Inst. Can., 1951-54; sr. rsch. chemist R.J. Reynolds Tobacco Co., Winston-Salem, N.C., 1954-65; head smoke rsch. sect. R.J. Reynolds Tobacco Co., 1965-75, mgr. analytical rsch., 1975-76, dir. rsch., 1976-80, dir. fundamental rsch. and devel., 1980-87; cons. in field, 1987—. Mem. editorial bd. Tobacco Sci., 1963-67 (Vol. 31 Tobacco Sci. dedicated in his name 1987), Beitrage zur Tabakforschung Internat., 1978-87. Mem. Tobacco Working Group, Nat. Cancer Inst., 1976-77, Tech. Study Group on Cigarette and Little Cigar Fire Safety, 1984-87, Sci. Commn. Cooperation Ctr. for Sci. Rsch. Relative to Tobacco, 1982-84. With Can. Navy, 1942-45. Mem. Chem. Inst. Can., Am. Chem. Soc., N.Y. Acad. Scis., N.C. Acad. Sci., Sigma Xi. Episcopalian. Club: Winston-Salem Sertoma (award 1972). Home: 2828 Birchwood Dr Winston Salem NC 27103-3410

RODIBAUGH, ROBERT KURTZ, federal judge; b. Elkhart County, Ind., July 2, 1916; s. Ralph Leedy and Rose (Kurtz) R.; m. Doris Ann Siekemeyer, Jan. 1, 1942 (dec.); children—David L., Bob K. m. 2d, Eunice Margaret Room, Nov. 25, 1972. B.S.C., U. Notre Dame, 1940, J.D., 1941. Bar: Ind. 1941, U.S. Dist. Ct. (no. dist) Ind. 1946, U.S. Ct. Appeals (7th cir.) 1972, U.S. Supreme Ct. 1965. Dep. pros. atty. 1st 60th Jud. Cir., St. Joseph County, 1948-50, 53-57; judge U.S. Bankruptcy Ct., No. Dist. Ind., South Bend, 1960—; lectr. in law U. Notre Dame, 1973; atty. St. Joseph County Bd. Zoning Appeals, 1958-60. V.p. No. Ind. council Boy Scouts Am., 1967-77; bd. dirs. St. Joseph County council. ARC, 1970-77. Capt. U.S. Army, 1941-46; PTO. Recipient Silver Beaver award Boy Scouts Am., 1969. Mem. ABA, Seventh Fed. Cir. Bar Assn., Ind. Bar Assn., St. Joseph County Bar Assn. (gov. 1953-56), Am. Judicature Soc., Comml. Law League, Nat. Conf. Bankruptcy Judges (dir. 1977-79), Exchange Club, Masons, DeMolay Club (Legion of Honor), Shriners. Office: US Bankruptcy Ct 204 S Main St Rm 201 South Bend IN 46601-2120

RODIMER, FRANK JOSEPH, bishop; b. Rockaway, N.J., Oct. 25, 1927; s. Frank Grant and Susan Elizabeth (Hiler) R. Student, St. Charles Coll., Catonsville, Md., 1944-45; B.A., St. Mary's Coll.-Sem., Balt., 1947; postgrad., Immaculate Conception Sem., Darlington, N.J., 1947-50; S.T.L., Cath. U. Am., 1951, J.C.D., 1954. Ordained priest Roman Catholic Ch., 1951; asst. chancellor, 1954-64, chancellor, 1964-77, apptd. papal chaplain, 1963; apptd. 6th Bishop of Paterson, N.J., 1977; consecrated 6th Bishop of Paterson, 1978, ordained, 1978—. Office: 178 Derrom Ave Clifton NJ 07540*

RODIN, ALVIN ELI, pathologist, medical educator, author; b. Winnipeg, Man., Can., Mar. 25, 1926; came to U.S., 1963; s. Paul and Bessie (Oretsky) R.; m. Bernice Block, Dec. 15, 1951 (div. Dec. 1973); children: Beverly, Paula, Mindy, Lisa; m. Jean Callaway, Feb. 10, 1974. MD, U. Man., Winnipeg, 1950, MSc in Medicine, 1960. Diplomate Am. Bd. Pathology, Am. Bd. Clin. Pathology. Sr. intern Shaughnessy Hosp., Vancouver, B.C., Can.; asst. resident in pathology, demonstrator in parasitology Deer Lodge Hosp., U. Man., Winnipeg, 1955-56, resident in clin. pathology, demonstrator in parasitology, 1957-58, rsch. assoc., 1958-59; resident in pathology, teaching fellow in pathology Queen's U., 1956-57; prt. practice medicine Minitonas, Man., 1951-54; asst. pathologist Royal Alexander Hosp., Edmonton, Alta., Can., 1959-60; dir. labs. Misericordia Hosp., Edmonton, 1960-63; prof. pathology, dir. pathology edn. U. Tex. Med. Br., Galveston, 1963-75; prof. pathology, chmn. dept. postgrad. edn. Sch. Medicine, Wright State U., Dayton, Ohio, 1975-88, emer. prof. postgrad. edn., 1977-; dir. med. edn. Green Meml. Hosp., Xenia, Ohio, 1976-92; mem. Miami Valley Health Improvement Coun., Dayton, 1986—. Author: 11 books; contbr. numerous articles to profl. jours. Recipient Golden Apple award Student Am. Med. Assn., 1969, 73-74, Tchr. of Month award Rotary, Galveston, 1974, Outstanding Community Svc. award United Health Svcs., Dayton, 1980. Fellow Royal Soc. Medicine; mem. Am. Osler Soc. (pres. 1992), Soc. for Health and Human Values, Group for Rsch. in Pathology Edn. (pres. 1971-73), Internat. Acad. Pathology (pres. Galveston club 1968-70). Home and Office: 3041 Maginn Dr Beavercreek OH 45434-5833

RODIN, BURTON, mathematics educator; b. St. Louis, June 19, 1933; s. Raymond and Gertrude (Lebowitz) R.; m. Miriam Jessica Horowitz, Aug. 8, 1962; children: Mari Lisa, Joseph Marc. BS, UCLA, 1955, PhD, 1961. Fellow Harvard U., Cambridge, Mass., 1961-63; asst. prof. U. Minn., Mpls., 1963-64, Stanford (Calif.) U., 1965-66; prof. of math. U. Calif., San Diego, 1964—. Author: Principal Functions, 1968; contbr. articles to profl. jours. Lt. USN, 1955-57. Office: U Calif San Diego Math Dept La Jolla CA 92093

RODIN, ERVIN YECHIEL LÁSZLO, mathematician; b. Budapest, Hungary, Jan. 17, 1932; came to U.S., 1956; s. Mor Rothmann and Rose (Deutsch) Kaufmann; m. Sarah Liebovitz, Mar. 15, 1956; children: Daphna Cynthia, Eytan Murray, Allon Kenneth. BA, U. Tex., 1960, PhD, 1964. Spl. instr. U. Tex., Austin, 1960-64; sr. mathematician Wyle Labs., Huntsville, Ala., 1964-66; prof. systems sci. Washington U., St. Louis, 1966—, dir. Ctr. for Optimization and Semantic Control, 1989—. Author: Mathematical Modelling, 1990; editor: Energy Methods, 1978, Mathematical Modelling in Science, 1985, 1988; founder: (jours.) Computers and Math. (editor in chief, 1968—), Mathematical and Computer Modelling (editor in chief, 1975—), Applied Math. Letters (mng. editor, 1987—), Holocaust and Genocide Studies (editor; editor: (jours.) Computers and Chemistry, Leonardo. Fellow Am. Inst. Aeronautics and Astronautics (assoc.); mem. Am. Math. Soc., Soc. for Indusl. and Applied Math., Math. Assn. Am., Soc. Engring Sci. (pres. 1978-79). Home: 31 Nantucket Ln Saint Louis MO 63132-4138 Office: Washington U Dept Systems Sci PO Box 1040 Saint Louis MO 63130

RODIN, JUDITH SEITZ, academic administrator, educator; b. Phila., Sept. 9, 1944; d. Morris and Sally R. (Winson) Seitz. AB, U. Pa., 1966; PhD, U. Columbia, 1970. Asst. prof. psychology NYU, 1970-72; assoc. prof. Yale U., 1975-79, prof. dir. grad. studies, 1982-89, Philip R. Allen prof. psychology, medicine and psychiatry, 1984-94, chmn. dept. psychology, 1989-91, dean Grad. Sch., 1991-92, provost, 1992-94; pres. U. Pa., Phila., 1994—, prof. psychology, medicine and psychiatry, 1995—; chmn. John D. and Catherine T. MacArthur Found. Rsch. Network on Determinants and Consequences of Health-Promoting and Health-Damaging Behavior, 1983-93. Author: (with S. Schachter) Obese Humans and Rats, 1978, Exploding the Weight Myths, 1982, Body Traps, 1992; chief editor Appetite Jour., 1979-92; contbr. articles to profl. jours. Note: Addition of professional and position titles to name in BAS section ("Dr." and "President") is not in accordance with our editorial style. Vice-chair coun. of pres. Univs. Rsch. Assn., 1994—; mem. Pa. Gov.'s keystone commn., 1994-95, White House Security Rev., 1994-95, PCAST, 1994—, Pa. Task Force on Higher Edn. Funding, 1994. Fellow Woodrow Wilson Found., 1966-67, John Simon Guggenheim Found., 1986-87; grantee NSF, 1973-82, NIH, 1981—. Fellow AAAS, Am. Acad. Arts and Scis., APA (bd. sci. affairs 1979-82), Soc. Behavioral Medicine; mem. Inst. Medicine of NAS, Acad. Behavioral Medicine Rsch., Ea. Psychol. Assn. (exec. bd. 1980-82, pres. divsn. 38 health psychology APA 1982-83, Outstanding Contbn. award 1980, Disting. Sci. award 1977), Phi Beta Kappa, Sigma Xi (pres. Yale chpt. 1986-87). Office: U Pa 121 College Hall Philadelphia PA 19104-6380

RODIN, MICHAEL F., lawyer, corporate; b. Norwalk, Conn., Sept. 18, 1954. AB with honors, U. Chgo., 1975; JD cum laude, NYU, 1979. Bar: Pa. 1979, U.S. Dist. Ct. (mid. dist.) Pa. 1979, Wash. 1981, U.S. Dist. Ct. (we. dist.) Wash. 1981. Law clk. to Hon. Malcolm Muir U.S. Dist. (mid. dist.) Pa., 1979-81; assoc. Preston Thorgrimson, Seattle, 1981-86, ptnr., 1987-90; gen. counsel Puget Sound Bancorp, Tacoma, Wash., 1990-93, Key Bank of Washington, Tacoma, 1993—; speaker in field. Author: (with others) Washington Practice Manual, 1986-89. Fellow securities instr., NYU, 1979. Mem. ABA, Wash. State Bar Assn. (chair ad hoc securities com. bus. law sect. 1990, mem. opinion letter com. 1991—), Seattle-King County Bar Assn. Office: Key Bank Washington 1119 Pacific Ave Tacoma WA 98402

RODITE, ROBERT R.R., engineering scientist; b. Easton, Pa., Oct. 17, 1942; s. Victor James and Alice Cecilia (Zatovich) R.; m. Patricia Ann Sule, Apr. 8, 1967; children: Colleen P., Robert J. BSEE, Lafayette Coll., 1964; MSEE, Cait. Inst. Tech., 1965. Rsch. engr., mgr. mfg. rsch. lab. IBM, Endicott, N.Y., 1965-70, mfg. engring. mgr. electronic packaging mfg., 1970-72, devel. engring. mgr. electronic packaging engring., 1972-77; program dir. corp. engring., programming & tech. staff IBM, Armonk, N.Y., 1977-79; product engring. mgr., sr. engr. multichip module devel. IBM, East Fishkill, N.Y., 1979-81; system mgr., sr. tech. staff mem. fin. industry devel. IBM, Charlotte, N.C., 1981-92; sr. tech. staff mem. corp. tech. strategy devel. staff IBM, Armonk, 1992-93; pres. Rodite Assocs., Charlotte, N.C., 1993—; workgroup mem. Am. Nat. Standards Inst. Com. X9B Stds. Com., 1991—; chmn. IBM Image Processing and Visualization Interdivisional Tech. Liaison Com., 1992-93. Contbr. articles to profl. jours.; patentee in field. Asst. scoutmaster Boy Scouts Am., Charlotte, 1991, 92; mid. sch. basketball coach, Charlotte, 1991, 92, 93, 94; com. mem. Town County Consolidation Com., Endicott, 1970s; Cath. sch. bd. mem. Diocese of Charlotte, 1988-90. Tau Beta Pi fellow Calif. Inst. Tech., 1964. Mem. IEEE (sr.), Assn. for Info. and Image Mgmt., Phi Beta Kappa, Tau Beta Pi, Eta Kappa Nu. Avocations: personal computers, camping. Home: 10022 Thomas Payne Cir Charlotte NC 28277-8872

RODMAN, DENNIS KEITH, basketball player; b. Trenton, May 13, 1961. Student, Cooke County Jr. Coll., Gainesville, Tex., 1982-83, Southeastern Okla. State U., 1983-86. With Detroit Pistons, 1986-93; forward San Antonio Spurs, 1993—. Named NBA Defensive Player of Yr., 1990, 91, NBA All-Defensive First Team, 1989, 90, 91, 92, 93, All-Star team, 1990, 92, NBA All-Defense Second Team, 1994. Office: San Antonio Spurs Alamodome 100 Montana St San Antonio TX 78203

RODMAN, HARRY EUGENE, architect, acoustical and illumination consultant; b. Plainfield, Iowa, Sept. 29, 1913; s. Harry Irwin and Iva (Reade) R.; m. Marion G. Rooney, Feb. 14, 1942; children—Harry Eugene, Bruce Ervin, Gerald Reade, Blair Douglas. B. Archtl. Engring., Iowa State U., 1936; M.Arch., Harvard, 1937. Instr. Wash. State U., 1937-41; designer Austin Co. Cleve., 1941-45; architect U. Ill. at Urbana, 1945-46; mem. faculty Rensselaer Poly. Inst., 1946-78, prof. architecture, 1955-78; vis. prof. Sch. Architecture and Environ. Design, Calif. Poly. State U., 1979-82; profl. practice Troy, N.Y., 1946-78; cons. in field, 1946—; Chmn. N.Y. State Bd. Examiners Architects, 1962-64; bd. dirs. Nat. Council Archtl. Registration Bds., 1964-71, sec., 1967-71, chmn. com. exams., 1965-70; sec. Nat. Archtl. Accrediting Bd., 1969-70; mem. tech. adv. com. Illuminating Engring. Research Inst., 1972-78; mem. U.S. nat. com. Internat. Commn. on Illumination. Contbr. to profl. jours. Mem. exec. bd. Uncle Sam council Boy Scouts Am., 1956-70. Recipient Profl. Achievement citation Iowa State U., 1980. Fellow AIA (pres. Eastern N.Y. chpt. 1952, bd. dirs. 1953), Illuminating Engring. Soc.; mem. N.Y. State Assn. Architects (bd. dirs. 1954); asso. Acoustical Soc. Am.; mem. Allied Arts Com., Illuminating Engring. Soc. (vice chmn. Mohawk-Hudson sect. 1956, bd. mgrs. 1971-74), Am. Arbitration Assn. (panel commn. arbitrators), Tau Beta Pi, Tau Sigma Delta, Scarab. Home: 196 Luneta Dr San Luis Obispo CA 93405-1552

RODMAN, JAMES PURCELL, astrophysicist, educator; b. Alliance, Ohio, Nov. 11, 1926; s. Clarence James and Hazel (Purcell) R.; m. Margaret Jane Kinsey, Aug. 14, 1950; children—William James, Jeffrey Kinsey, David Lawrence, Gretchen. B.S. in Physics, Chemistry and Math, Mt. Union Coll., 1949; M.A. in Nuclear Physics, Washington U., St. Louis, 1951; Ph.D. in Astrophysics, Yale U., 1963. Sec. Alliance Ware, Inc., 1954-55, Alliance Machine Co., 1959-69; v.p., treas. Alliance Tool Co., 1951-54, pres., 1954-59; instr. dept. physics and math. Mt. Union Coll., Alliance, 1951-59; assoc. prof. physics Mt. Union Coll., 1962-66, prof., 1966-92, head dept. physics, 1963-65, head dept. physics and astronomy, 1965-74, 77-85, staff astronomer, 1992-94; dir. Clarke Obs., 1953-94, Computer Center, 1967-74, 77; coll. marshal, 1979-92, prof. emeritus, 1993; rsch. assoc. astronomy Yale U., 1963-68, rsch. fellow, 1982; cons. astrophys. engr. astron. instrumentation, 1962—; chief engr., owner Rodman Rsch., 1988—; chmn. bd. Westmont Inc., 1984—; bd. dirs. United Nat. Bank & Trust Co., Canton, Ohio, UNB Corp. Author books; also contbr. articles to profl. jours.; leader JR4 Musical Combo, 1962—. Mem. Alliance Bd. Edn., 1957-59, pres., 1959; exec. com. Buckeye coun. Boy Scouts Am., 1963-77, mem. nat. scouting com., 1973-77; dept. sheriff Stark County, 1972-73; spl. police officer Alliance Police Dept., 1974-90, tech. insp., 1976-90; exec. com. Stark County Disaster Svcs., 1976-78, chmn., 1979; trustee Western Res. Acad., 1969-91; pres. Alliance Community Hosp., Inc., 1986; mem. Cape May Cottagers Assn. Inc., 1967—; grand marshal Carnation City Parade, 1986. With USNR, 1944-45. Recipient Gt. Tchr. award, 1976, Alliance Mayor's Award as outstanding citizen, 1978. Fellow AAAS, Royal Astron. Soc.; mem. Am. Phys. Soc., Am. Astron. Soc., Astron. Soc. Pacific, Am. Assn. Physics tchrs., Optical Soc. Am., Nantucket Maria Mitchell Assn. (bd. dirs. 1974), Masons (32 degree), Shriners, Corinthian Yacht Club, Beach Cape May Club, Alliance Country Club, Wranglers Club (pres. 1986—), Sigma Xi. Home: 1125

Fernwood Blvd Alliance OH 44601-3764 also: 1613 Beach Dr Cape May NJ 08204-3608

RODMAN, LEIBA, mathematics educator; b. Riga, Latvia, U.S.S.R., June 9, 1949; came to U.S., 1985; s. Zalman and Haya Rodman; m. Ella Levitan, Feb. 2, 1983; children: Daniel, Ruth, Benjamin, Naomi. Diploma in maths., Latvian State U., 1971; MA in Statis., Tel Aviv (Israel) U., 1976, PhD in Maths., 1978. Instr. Tel Aviv U., 1976-78, sr. lectr., 1981-83, assoc. prof., 1983-85; postdoctoral fellow U. Calgary, Can., 1978-80; from assoc. to full prof. Ariz. State U., Tempe, 1985-87; prof. math. Coll. William and Mary, Williamsburg, Va., 1987—. Author: Introduction to Operator Polynomials, 1989, (with others) Matrix Polynomials, 1982, Matrices and Indefinite Scalar Products, 1983, Invariant Subspaces of Matrices with Applications, 1986, Interpolation of Rational Matrix Functions, 1990, Algebraic Riccati Equations, 1995; co-editor: Contributions to Operator Theory and Its Applications, 1988. Mem. IEEE, Am. Math. Soc., Math. Assn. Am., Internat. Linear-Algebra Soc., Soc. Indsl. and Applied Maths. Office: Coll of William & Mary Dept Of Math Williamsburg VA 23187

RODMAN, LEROY ELI, lawyer; b. N.Y.C., Feb. 22, 1914; s. Morris and Sadie (Specter) R.; m. Toby Chertcoff, Mar. 14, 1943; children: John Stephen, Lawrence Bernard. AB, CCNY, 1933; J.D. (James Kent scholar), Columbia, 1936. Bar: N.Y. 1937. Practiced in N.Y.C., 1937-43, 46—; law sec. to U.S. dist. judge Bklyn., 1936; law asst. Am. Law Inst., N.Y.C., 1937; chief food enforcement unit N.Y. Regional Office, OPA, 1942-43; mem. firm Lawrence R. Condon, N.Y.C., 1937-42; ptnr. Joseph & Rodman, N.Y.C., 1946-53; sr. ptnr. Rodman, Maurer & Dansker, N.Y.C., 1964-73, Carro, Spanbock, Londin, Rodman & Fass, N.Y.C., 1973-78, Rodman & Rodman, N.Y.C., 1978-89, Teitelbaum, Hiller, Rodman, Paden & Hibsher, P.C., N.Y.C., 1990—; tchr. fed. taxation Pace Coll., N.Y.C., 1953-55; bd. dirs., v.p., sec. Francosteel Corp., N.Y.C.; sec. Ameribrom, Inc. Editorial bd.: Columbia Law Rev, 1934-36; Contbr. articles to legal jours. Bd. dirs. Manhattan coun. Boy Scouts Am., 1960—, v.p., 1961-68, pres., 1972-75; exec. bd. Greater N.Y. couns., 1972—. Served to capt. JAGC AUS 1943-46. Recipient Certs. Svc., Silver Beaver award Boy Scouts Am., 1962. Fellow Am. Coll. Trust and Estate Counsel; mem. ABA, N.Y. County Lawyers Assn., Assn. of Bar of City of N.Y., Judge Adv. Assn., Phi Beta Kappa. Jewish (trustee, v.p. synagogue, pres. brotherhood 1958-60). Clubs: Univ. (N.Y.C.); Metropolis Country (White Plains, N.Y.) (sec. 1976-77, 80-82, v.p. 1977-78, bd. govs. 1976-82). Home: 535 E 86th St New York NY 10028-7533 Office: 260 Madison Ave New York NY 10016-2401

RODMAN, OLIVER, newspaper publishing executive. V.p. advt. Globe Newspaper Co., Boston. Office: Globe Newspaper Co 135 Morrissey Blvd Boston MA 02107*

RODMAN, PETER WARREN, foreign policy specialist; b. Boston, Nov. 24, 1943; s. Sumner and Helen Rhoda (Morris) R.; m. F. Veronique Boulad, Apr. 13, 1980; children: Theodora, Nicholas. BA summa cum laude, Harvard U., 1964, JD, 1969; BA, MA, Oxford (Eng.) U., 1966. Staff mem. NSC, Washington, 1969-77; fellow in diplomatic studies Ctr. for Strategic and Internat. Studies, Washington, 1977-83; dir. rsch. Kissinger Assocs., Washington, 1982-83; mem. policy planning council Dept. of State, Washington, 1983-84, dir. policy planning staff, 1984-86; dep. asst. to pres. for nat. security affairs (fgn. policy) NSC, Washington, 1986-87, counselor, spl. asst. to pres. for nat. security affairs, 1987-90; fellow Johns Hopkins Fgn. Policy Inst., Washington, 1990-93; dir. Middle East and Eurasian studies Ctr. for Strategic and Internat. Studies, Washington, 1994-95; dir. nat. security programs Nixon Ctr. for Peace and Freedom, Washington, 1995—; sr. advisor on fgn. policy Rep. Platform Com., 1992. Sr. editor Nat. Rev., 1991—; contbr. articles to profl. jours. Mem. Coun. on Fgn. Rels., Internat. Inst. for Strategic Studies, Atlantic Coun. U.S., Cosmos Club. Office: Nixon Ctr for Peace and Freedom 1620 I St NW Ste 900 Washington DC 20006

RODMAN, R. ARLENE, journalist; b. Brussels, Apr. 20, 1929; came to U.S., 1939; d. Harry Hermann Wall and Hella Magdalena (Werner) Forster; m. Juan Benedict Gould, Sept. 4, 1947 (dec. June 1965); children: Veronica Jenny, Roy Daniel, Virginia Lynn; m. David C. Rodman, Jan. 18, 1974 (dec. July 1992). BA, U. Andes, 1954; postgrad., U. Miami, 1955-57. Stringer, corr. The N.Y. Times, Bogota, Colombia, 1962-66, Time Life News Svc., Bogota, Colombia, 1962-66; reporter Time, Inc., Washington, 1966-71, Life Espanol Internat., Washington, 1966-71; U.S. corr. Cromos Mag., Bogota, 1973-77; editor Washington Fact Finders, Mountainside, N.J., 1977-85; mem. editorial bd. Viewpointe, Boca Raton, Fla., 1992—. Mem. Nat. Press Club, Overseas Press Club. Democrat. Avocations: reading, tennis, travel. Home: 6407 Via Rosa Boca Raton FL 33433-6471

RODMAN, SUMNER, insurance executive; b. Malden, Mass., Aug. 5, 1915; s. Nathan Markel and Sara Ruth (Slater) R.; m. Helen Rhoda Morris, July 2, 1942; children: Peter Warren, John Slater. A.B. cum laude, Harvard, 1935. C.L.U. Agt. Aetna Life Ins. and Annuity Co., Boston, 1935—; with Rodman Ins. Agy., Inc., Newton Ctr., Mass.; life ins. adviser, 1953—; Pres. Boston Life Ins. and Trust Council, 1958-59. Bd. dirs. Jewish Family and Children's Service, Boston, 1953-85, Boston Estate Planning Council, 1960-85, Youth Tennis Found. New Eng., 1963-85, Simons-Gutman Found., 1965—, Alzheimers Assn. Ea. Mass., 1990—; hon. trustee Combined Jewish Philanthropies of Greater Boston, 1967—; mem. Am. Jewish Com., Anti-Defamation League of B'nai Brith; mem. World Affairs Coun. Boston; hon. trustee Temple Israel, Boston. Served to capt. AUS, 1941-46, ETO. C.L.U. Inst. fellow, 1952, 61; named to New Eng. Tennis Assn. Hall of Fame, 1992. Mem. The Am. Coll. (trustee 1971-74), Boston Life Underwriters Assn. (pres. 1965-66), Am. Soc. CLUs (pres. 1972-73), Million Dollar Round Table (life), New Eng. Lawn Tennis Assn. (bd. dirs. 1966-68), Golden Key Soc. Jewish (trustee temple). Clubs: Harvard (Boston), Harvard Varsity (Boston); Newton (Mass.) Squash and Tennis; Wightman Tennis Center (Weston, Mass.). Lodge: Masons. Home: 94 Vine St Chestnut Hill MA 02167-3050 Office: 75 Wells Ave Newton MA 02159

RODNEY, JOEL MORRIS, dean; b. Bklyn., Nov. 9, 1937; s. Samuel Seymour and Jane (Loorya) R.; m. Judith DeStefano; 1 child, Benjamin; children from previous marriage: Jonathan, Adam. BA cum laude, Brandeis U., 1959; PhD, Cornell U., 1965; attended, Inst. Edn. Mgmt. Harvard U., 1976. From instr. to assoc. prof. Wash. State U., Pullman, 1963-70; chmn. div. social scis., assoc. prof. history Elmira (N.Y.) Coll., 1970-72, coordinator flood relief and community planning, 1973; dean arts and sci., prof. history Widener Coll., Chester, Pa., 1973-76, acting chief acad. officer, dean, 1976-77, chief acad. officer, dean, 1977-81, dir. univ. grad. programs, 1979-81; v.p. acad. affairs Salisbury (Md.) State Coll., 1981-86; provost Rockford (Ill.) Coll., 1986-90; dean U. Wis. Ctr.-Washington County, West Bend, 1990—. Editor Albion, 1967-78; contbr. articles to profl. jours. Vice chmn. Md. Gov.'s Com. on Employment of Handicapped, 1985-86, chmn. and mem. Lower Shore div., 1983-86; chmn. adv. bd., mem. Crozer-Chester Med. Health Ctr., Chester, 1974-77; project evaluator NEH, 1986, RSA, 1993; mem., sec. Delaware County Mental Health/Mental Retardation Bd., 1975-81; adv. bd. Rehab. Inst. of Chgo., 1988-94; mem. coun. Ct. of Gov.'s Regents Coll., London, 1986-90, Rock Valley Coll. Indsl. Coun., Rockford, 1989-90; bd. dirs. Moraine Symphony Orch., 1992-93, Welcome Home, Inc., 1990, pres., 1992; citizens adv. bd. West Bend Bank One, 1991, Washington County Vol. Ctr., 1991-92; bd. dirs. The Threshold, 1992; appointed to State Wis. Coun. Phys. Disabilities, 1994, vice chmn., 1995; exec. com. Moraine area Tech. Prep. Coun., 1994; mem. Wis. Gov. Com. on Personal Disabilities, 1994; mem. adv. bd. S.E. Wis. Area Health Edn. Coun., 1995; mem. West Bend C. of C. Ambs., 1995. Recipient Disting. Service award Widener Meml. Sch., 1978, Award of merit Md. Gov.'s Com. on Employment of Handicapped, 1984; named to Legion of Honor, Chapel of Four Chaplains, 1978; honoree West Phila. Vets. and Handicapped Employment Com., 1977. Mem. Am. Assn. Acad. Deans, Conf. on Brit. Studies, Am. Assn. Univ. Adminstrs., Nat. Spinal Cord Injury Assn. (bd. dirs. Ill. chpt. 1988-90), Rotary, Phi Alpha Theta. Republican. Home: 229 Bittersweet Dr West Bend WI 53095-4907 Office: U Wis Ctr Washington County 400 S University Dr West Bend WI 53095-3619

RODNICK, ELIOT HERMAN, psychologist, educator; b. New Haven, Nov. 27, 1911; s. Louis D. and Bertha (Caplan) R.; m. Helen Percival Hollander, Nov. 20, 1940; children: Jonathan Eliot, Marion Percival Rodnick Bell. AB with high oration, Yale U., 1933, PhD, 1936. Asst.

research Yale U., 1934-36; research psychologist, research service Worcester (Mass.) State Hosp., 1936-46, dir. psychol. research, chief psychologist, 1946-49; acting dir. Worcester Child Guidance Clinic, 1946-47; instr. Mt. Holyoke Coll., 1939; asst. prof. psychology Clark U., 1942-46, assoc. prof., 1946-49; vis. lectr. summer session U. Wis., 1949, Harvard U., 1952, U. Colo., 1958; prof. psychology, dir. clin. tng. psychology Duke U., 1949-61, chmn. dept. psychology, 1951-61; prof. psychology, dir. clin. tng. psychology U. Calif. at Los Angeles, 1961-79, prof. emeritus, 1979—; cons. psychologist VA, 1949-79, mem. central office adv. com. to chief, dept. psychiatry and neurology, 1957-61; mem. mental health study sect. NIH, 1954-57, behavorial sci. study sect., 1957, mental health projects rev. commn., 1957-60, chmn. spl. mental health grants rev. com., 1960-62; bd. dirs. Los Angeles Psychiat. Service, 1961-66, Didi Hirsch Mental Health Center, 1973-82, Calif. Sch. Profl. Psychology, 1981-83; cons. Calif. Dept. Mental Hygiene; mem. com. on research tng. in biol. scis. Nat. Inst. Mental Health, 1962-66, chmn., 1965-66; mem. mental health council Western Commn. Higher Edn., 1961-66; adv. com. abuse of stimulant and depressant drugs FDA, 1966-68; sci. adv. com. on drug abuse U.S. Dept. Justice, 1968-75; Cons. Narcotics Control Commn. N.Y., 1969-75; cons. Calif. Sch. Profl. Psychology. Editorial bd.: Am. Jour. Orthopsychiatry, 1954-57, Jour. Personality, 1955-60, Jour. Abnormal and Social Psychology, 1957-62, Am. Jour. Community Psychology, 1972-77, Family Process, 1977-81. Trustee Calif. Sch. Profl. Psychology, 1981-83. Commd. officer USPHS Res. Recipient Stanley Dean prize for outstanding research in schizophrenia, 1967; Wilbur Lucius Cross medal for outstanding profl. performance Yale Grad. Sch. Assn., 1975. Fellow AAAS, APA (bd. dirs. 1962-65, Disting. Contbn. to Clin. Psychology award 1976), Western Psychol. Assn. (pres. 1966-67), Am. Psychol. Soc. (James McKeen Cattell fellow award), Calif. Psychol. Assn. (Disting. Sci. Contbns. in Psychology award 1975), Los Angeles County Psychol. Assn., N.C. Psychol. Assn. (past pres.), Am. Orthopsychiat. Assn. (bd. dirs. 1966-69, pres. 1967-68); mem. Cosmos Club (Washington), Phi Beta Kappa, Sigma Xi. Home: 7577 Oak Leaf Dr Santa Rosa CA 95409-6254 Office: Dept Psychology U Cal 405 Hilgard Ave Los Angeles CA 90024-1563

RODNUNSKY, SIDNEY, lawyer, educator, Prince of Kiev, Prince of Trabzon, Prince and Duke of Rodari, Duke of Chernigov, Count of Riga, Count of Saint John of Alexandria; b. Edmonton, Alta., Can., Feb. 3, 1946; s. H. and I. Rodnunsky; m. Teresita Asuncion; children: Naomi, Shawna, Rachel, Tevie, Claire, Donna, Sidney Jr. BEd, U. Alberta, 1966, LLB, 1973; MEd, U. Calgary, 1969, grad. diploma, 1990; BS, U. of State of N.Y., 1988; MBA, Greenwich U., 1990. Served as regional counsel to Her Majesty the Queen in Right of the Dominion of Can.; former gov. Grande Prairie Regional Coll.; now prin. legal counsel Can.; Alta. coord. for gifted children Mensa Can.; past pres. Grande Prairie and Dist. Bar Assn. Author: Breathalyzer Casebook; editor: The Children Speak. Decorated Knight Grand Cross Sovereign and Royal Order of Piast, Knight Grand Cross Order of St. John the Baptist; knight Hospitaller Order St. John of Jerusalem; named to Honorable Order of Ky. Colonels; named adm. State of Tex.; recipient Presidential Legion of Merit. Mem. Law Soc. Alta., Law Soc. Sask., Canadian Bar Assn., Inst. Can. Mgmt. Address: Box 53, Smith, AB Canada T0G 2B0

RODOVICH, ANDREW PAUL, lawyer, federal magistrate; b. Hammond, Ind., Feb. 24, 1948; s. Andrew H. and Julia (Makar) R.; m. Gail Linda Patrick, May 27, 1972; children: Caroline Anja, Mary Katherine, James Patrick. BA, Valparaiso (Ind.) U., 1970, JD, 1973. Bar: Ind. Ptnr. Hand, Muenich & Rodovich, Hammond, 1973-78; chief dep. prosecutor Lake County Prosecutor's Office, Crown Point, Ind., 1979-82; U.S. magistrate U.S. Dist. Ct., Hammond, 1982—; referee Hammond City Ct., 1978; adj. prof. Valparaiso Law Sch., 1985—. Fellow Ind. Bar Found.; mem. Nat. Coun. U.S. Magistrates, Delta Theta Phi. Republican. Avocations: sports. Home: 7207 Baring Pky Hammond IN 46324-2218 Office: US Dist Ct 136 Federal Bldg Hammond IN 46320-1529

RODOVICH, ARLENE GUYOTTE, administrator, small business owner; b. Springfield, Mass., Mar. 21, 1935; d. Walter L. Guyotte and Dorothy (Hawley) Bigelow; m. Robert F. Rodovich, Sept. 30, 1955; 1 child, Heidi E. Pepyne. AA, Greenfield (Mass.) Community Coll., 1977. Cert. profl. property mgr. Sec. bookkeeper Gordon E. Ainsworth Assocs., South Deerfield, Mass., 1954-60; from jr. clk. to dir. U. Mass. Property and Inventory Control, Amherst, 1966—; owner Conway (Mass.) Bus. Service, 1958—. Author: (manual) Property Management, 1972. Chmn. fin. com., zoning bd. appeals, Conway, 1975—; selectman, 1991—; vice chair Franklin/Hampshire Employment and Tng. Mem. Nat. Property Mgmt. Assn. (v.p. profl. devel. 1987—, v.p. fin. 1988, pres. 1989-90, Property Person of the Yr. 1984, Property Person of the Yr. Eastern region 1986), Mass. Fedn. Bus. and Profl. Women (2d v.p. 1986—, 1st v.p. 1987-88, pres. elect 1988—, pres. 1989-90). Avocations: needlepoint, travel. Home: Ashfield Rd Conway MA 01341 Office: U Mass Goodell Bldg Amherst MA 01341

RODOWSKY, LAWRENCE FRANCIS, judge; b. Balt., Nov. 10, 1930; s. Lawrence Anthony and Frances (Gardner) R.; m. Colby Fossett, Aug. 7, 1954; children: Laura Rodowsky Ramos, Alice Rodowsky-Seegers, Emily Rodowsky Savopoulos, Sarah Jones Rodowsky, Gregory, Katherine. A.B. Loyola Coll., Balt., 1952; LL.B., U. Md., 1956. Bar: Md. 1956. Ct. crier, law clk. U.S. Dist. Ct. Md., 1954-56; asst. atty. gen. State of Md., 1960-61; assoc., ptnr. Frank, Bernstein, Conaway & Goldman, Balt., 1956-79; assoc. judge Ct. Appeals Md., Annapolis, 1980—; mem. rules com. Ct. Appeals Md., 1969-80; lectr., asst. instr. U. Md. Law Sch., 1958-68, 87-91; reporter jud. dept. Md. Constl. Conv. Commn., 1966-67. Chmn. Gov. Md. Commn. Racing Reform, 1979. Fellow Am. Coll. Trial Lawyers; mem. Md. Bar Assn., Balt. Bar Assn. Roman Catholic. Home: 4306 Norwood Rd Baltimore MD 21218-1118 Office: Ct Appeals Md 620 C M Mitchell Jr CTHS Baltimore MD 21202

RODRICKS, DANIEL JOHN, columnist, television commentator; b. Brockton, Mass., Mar. 8, 1954; s. Joseph Allen and Rose Mary (Popolo) R.; m. Lillian M. Donnard, Sept. 6, 1980. B.A., U. Bridgeport, 1976. Reporter The Patriot Ledger, Quincy, Mass., 1973-75; wire editor Middletown Times Record, N.Y., 1975; reporter Balt. Evening Sun, 1976-79, columnist, 1979—; reporter, commentator Sta. WBAL-TV, Balt., 1980—. Recipient Heywood Broun award Newspaper Guild, 1983, Front Page award, 1983; awards from Sigma Delta Chi, Md.-Del.-D.C. Press Assn., Firefighters Internat., also others. Mem. Sigma Delta Chi. Democrat. Roman Catholic. Avocations: cooking, fishing, theater, operetta. Office: Baltimore Sun 501 N Calvert St Baltimore MD 21202-3660

RODRIGUE, GEORGE PIERRE, electrical engineering educator, consultant; b. Paincourtville, La., June 19, 1931; s. George Pierre and Catherine (Barstow) R.; m. Mary Merritt, June 25, 1955; children: George Pierre III, Edward, Catherine, Frances, Jane, Dorothy. B.S., La. State U., 1952, M.S., 1954; Ph.D. Harvard U., 1958. Grad. asst. La. State U., 1952-54, Harvard U., 1955-56; sr. staff engr. Sperry-Rand, Clearwater, Fla., 1958-61, research engr., 1961-68; prof. elec. engring. Ga. Inst. Tech., Atlanta, 1969-77, Regents prof., 1977—; dir., cons. Electromagnetic Scis. Inc., Atlanta; cons. Litton Industries, Los Alamos Nat. Lab. Patentee Microwave devices and materials. Named Outstanding Tchr. Ga. Inst. Tech., 1971, 72, 79, 95. Fellow IEEE (dir., v.p. publs. 1982-83, Centennial medal 1984, Outstanding Engring. Educator award Region III 1984); mem. IEEE Microwave Theory and Techniques Soc. (pres. 1976, Outstanding Service award 1985, Disting. Educator award 1995). Roman Catholic. Home: 1090 Kingston Dr Atlanta GA 30342 Office: Sch Elec Engring Ga Inst Tech Atlanta GA 30332

RODRIGUES, EUSEBIO L., humanities educator; m. Merlyn R. Meneze, Aug. 1966; children: Esme, Usha. MA, St. Xaviers, Bombay, India, 1957, Columbia U. 1953; PhD, U. Pa., 1970. Prof. Bombay U., India, 1948-60, Georgetown U., Washington, 1970—; reader Baroda U., India, 1960-64. Author: Quest for the Human in Saul Bellow's Fiction, 1981. Office: Georgetown U 37th And O St NW Washington DC 20057

RODRIGUES, JOSEPH E., grain company executive; b. 1936. Tchr. Helderberg Coll., Sommerset, West Africa, 1960-67; with Ford Motor Co., Port Elizabeth, South Africa, 1967-69; CFO Arbor Acres, South Africa, 1969-74; with Seaboard Flour Corp., Iran, 1974-80; CFO, CEO Seaboard Corp., 1980—; exec. v.p., treas., bd. dirs. Office: Seaboard Corp 200 Boylston St Chestnut Hill MA 02167-2008

RODRIGUEZ, ADOLFO, library director, historian; b. Piedras Negras, Coahuila, Mex., Mar. 28, 1942; s. José Valentin Rodríguez González and Guadalupe Gallardo de Rodríguez; m. María Mercedes del Carmen Villatoro A.; children: Ernesto Rodríguez Villatoro, Diego Rodríguez Villatoro. M History, El Colegio de Mêxico, México City, 1964; MLS, U. Texas, 1970. Info. coord. Armo Industry, Mexico City, 1970; subdir. Sec. de Edn. Pub. Nat. Sch. Libr. Scis., Mexico City, 1971; dir. Sec. de Edn. Pub. Nac. Sch. Libr. Scis., Mexico City, 1972-76, 1977, acad. coord., 1977-81; dir. Univ. Nac. Autonoma de Mex. Gen. Dir. of Librs., Mexico City, 1973-77, acad. coord., 1977-81, libr. assessor faculty Philosophy and Letters, 1979-81, dir. Centro Universitario de Investigaciones Bibliotecológicas, 1982-84, dir., 1985—. Author: Las bibliotecas en los informes presidenciales, 1990, Historia de la legislacion bibliotecaria de la UNAM, 1994; co-author Bibliografia comentada sobre educacion bibliotecologica en Mexico, 1987; contbr. articles to profl. jours. Named 1st level Nat. Investigator Nat. System Investigators, Mêxico, 1991, named 2d level, 1994. Mem. Internat. Fedn. Documentation (rep. 1973), Internat. Fedn. Assns. Librs. (Comité para Am. Latina com. 1987-92), Nat. Assn. Libr. (pres. 1981-83). Home: Cerrada de Iliada # 24, Col Axomiatla, DF 01820, Mexico Office: Biblioteca Central, Ciudad Universitaria, 04510 Mexico City Mexico

RODRIGUEZ, ARTURO SALVADOR, labor union official; b. San Antonio, June 23, 1949; s. Arthur Salvador and Felice (Quintero) R.; m. Linda Fabela Chavez, Mar. 30, 1974; children: Olivia, Julie, Arthur. BA in Sociology, St. Mary's U., 1971; MSW, U. Mich., 1973. Various positions United Farm Workers of Am., Keene, Calif., 1973-90, v.p., 1981-93, organizer, 1990-92; pres. United Farm Workers Am. AFL-CIO, Keene, 1993—. Chief instr. UFW Sch., Keene, 1978-79; coord. Edward Kennedy Presdl. Dr., San Antonio, 1980. Office: United Farm Workers Am AFL-CIO PO Box 62-La Paz 29700 Woodford Tehachapi Rd Keene CA 93531

RODRIGUEZ, BEATRIZ, ballerina; b. Ponce, P.R.. Attended, Newark Acad. Ballet, N.J. Sch. of Ballet; scholarship student, Joffrey Ballet Sch. Former dancer N.J. Ballet; dancer Richard Englund's Dance Repertory Co., 1970; mem. Joffrey II Dancers, 1971-72; mem., sr. dancer Joffrey Ballet, N.Y.C., 1972—. Repertory includes: Cakewalk, Dream Dances, Illuminations, Love Songs, Offenbach in the Underworld, Petrouchka, Return to the Strange Land, Rodeo, and The Green Table, Moves, Interplay, Deuce Coupe, As Time Goes By, Billy the Kid, The Dream, Taming of the Shrew, Wedding Bouquet, Force Field, Concerto Grosso, Valentine, Trinty, Kettentans, Fanfarita, The Rite of Spring, Cotillion, Romeo and Juliet, Forgotten Land, Le Sacre du Printemps, The Green Table. Recipient Dance Mag. award, 1993. Office: The Joffrey Ballet 130 W 56th St New York NY 10019-3818

RODRIGUEZ, CESAR, librarian; b. Callao, Peru, Oct. 23, 1945; came to U.S., 1957; s. Jose Rodriguez and Angela (Seminario) Tabarne; m. Daisy Rodriguez, June 21, 1969. AA, Concordia Coll., 1965; BA, Queens Coll., 1970, MLS, 1975; M in Internat. Affairs, Columbia U., 1983. Libr. acquisitions asst. McKinsey & Co., Inc., N.Y.C., 1971-73; acquisitions libr. Info. for Bus., Inc., N.Y.C., 1973-76; acquisitions libr. Yale U. Libr., New Haven, Conn., 1976-86, curator L.Am. Collection, 1986—; bd. dirs. L.Am. Bibliographic Found., Redlands, Calif.; mem. exec. bd. Casa Cultural Julia De Burgos, New Haven, 1993—. Contbr. to books. Corp. U.S. Marines, 1965-68, Vietnam. Mem. ALA, L.Am. Studies Assn., Seminar of L.Am. Libr. Materials (exec. bd. 1993—, chair coms. 1979—). Episcopalian. Office: Yale U L Am Collection Box 208240 130 Wall St New Haven CT 06520

RODRIGUEZ, CHI CHI (JUAN RODRIGUEZ), professional golfer; b. Bayamon, P.R., Oct. 13, 1935. Profl. golfer, 1960—. Contbg. columnist golf. mags. Winner PGA Tour Denver, 1963, Lucky Internat., 1964, Western Tour, 1964, Tex. Tour, 1967, Sahara Tour, 1968, Byron Nelson Tour, 1973, Greater Greensboro, 1973, KO Olina Invitational, 1992; named to Ryder Cup Team, 1973.Inducted into the World Sports Humanitarian Hall of Fame, 1994. Leading money winner on sr. tour, 1987; represented P.R. in 12 world cups; ranked # 5 on PGA sr. tour, 1992; ranked # 4 among scoring leaders PGA sr. tour, 1992. Office: PGAA 100 Avenue Of Champions Palm Bch Gdns FL 33418-3653*

RODRIGUEZ, ELIAS C., judge; b. Dallas, Sept. 7, 1919; s. Elias S. and Anna (Fernandez) R.; m. Alberta Lenore Durbin, Jan. 1, 1949; children—Michael, Robert, Richard. B.A., So. Meth. U., 1941; J.D., Georgetown Law Sch., 1948, LL.M., 1953. Bar: Tex. 1948, D.C. 1948. Atty. IMF, Washington, 1948-51; fgn. service officer Dept. State, Washington, 1952-69; 1st sec. Am. Embassy Rome, Italy, 1960-65; atty. CAB, Washington, 1971-78, adminstrv. law judge, 1977-84; chief adminstrv. law judge, CAB, 1982-84; chief adminstrv. law judge Dept. Transp., Washington, 1984-87. Served to lt. col. US Army, 1942-46, ETO.

RODRIGUEZ, FERDINAND, chemical engineer, educator; b. Cleve., July 8, 1928; s. José and Concha (Luís) R.; m. Ethel V. Koster, July 28, 1951; children: Holly Edith, Lida Concha. B.S., Case Western Res. U., 1950, M.S., 1954; Ph.D., Cornell U., 1958. Devel. engr. Ferro Corp., Bedford, Ohio, 1950-54; asst. prof. chem. engring. Cornell U., 1958-61, asso. prof., 1961-71, prof., 1971—; on sabbatical leave at Union Carbide Corp., 1964-65, Imperial Chem. Industries, Ltd., 1971, Eastman Kodak Co., 1978-79; cons. to industry. Author: Principles of Polymer Systems, 3d edit, 1989; contbr. numerous articles to profl. jours.; songwriter. Served with U.S. Army, 1954-56. Recipient Excellence in Teaching award Cornell Soc. Engrs., 1966, Edn. Achievement award Hispanic Engr. Mag., 1991. Fellow Am. Inst. Chem. Engrs.; mem. Am. Chem. Soc., Soc. Hispanic Profl. Engrs., Soc. Plastics Engrs. Lutheran. Home: 107 Randolph Rd Ithaca NY 14850-1720 Office: 230 Olin Hall Cornell U Ithaca NY 14853

RODRIGUEZ, GENO (EUGENE RODRIGUEZ), artist, arts administrator; b. N.Y.C., June 2, 1940; s. Eugenio and Juana (Lopez) R.; m. Janice Rooney, Oct., 1966; 1 dau., Samantha Marisol. Student, Internat. Peoples Coll., Elsinor, Denmark, 1961-62; nat. diploma in art, Hammersmith Coll. Art, London, 1966. Founder, pres., exec. dir. Alternative Center for Internat. Arts Alternative Museum, N.Y.C., 1975—; instr. photography Sch. Visual Arts, N.Y.C., 1978-82, Rutgers U., 1977-79; mem. Artists Cert. Appeals Bd., N.Y.C., 1979, spl. artist task force N.Y. State Council on Arts, 1981; panelist, cons. NEA, Dept. Cultural Affairs N.Y.C.; lectr. in field. Exhibited in one-man shows Il Diaframa Gallery, Milan, Italy, 1979, Mus. Contemporary Arts, Caracas, Venezuela, 1979, Real Art Ways Gallery, Hartford, Conn., 1980, Cayman Gallery, N.Y.C., 1980, CEPA Gallery, Buffalo, 1987, Sheldon Meml. Art Gallery U. Nebr., Lincoln, 1989; group shows include Autoren Gallery, Munich, 1980, Miss. Mus. Art, Jackson, 1981, Palacio de Minerias, Mexico City, 1981, J.A.M. Gallery, N.Y.C., 1981, Chrysler Mus., Norfolk, Va., 1981, Am. Indian Gallery, 1982, Roger Litz Gallery, N.Y., 1982, Tweed Gallery, N.J., 1983, Baumgartner Gallery, Washington, 1983, Municipality of Genoa, Italy, 1984, Phila. Arts Alliance, 1985, Jayne H. Baum Gallery, N.Y.C., 1985-86, Gerald Melberg Gallery, Charlotte, N.C., 1985, Eupherat Gallerty, Calif., 1986, N.Y. State Mus., Albany, 1986, Hillwood Art Gallery, N.Y., 1986, Stux Gallery, Boston, 1986, San Diego Mus. Art, 1987, Alternative Mus., N.Y.C., 1987, Graham Modern, N.Y.C., 1987, Internat. Ctr. Photography, N.Y.C., 1987, Haggerty Mus. Art Marquette U., Milw., 1988, Herter Art Gallery U. Mass., 1989, Nat. Mus. Am. Art Smithsonian Instn., 1989; represented in permanent collections Internat. Ctr. Photography, N.Y.C., Mus. City of N.Y., Met. Mus. Art, N.Y.C., Everson Mus. Art, Syracuse, N.Y., Am. Mus. Natural History, N.Y.C., Mus. Contemporary Art, Caracas, Venezula; author: The Islands: Worlds of the Puerto Ricans, 1974, Mira, Mira, Mira Puerto Rican New Yorkers, 1975. Active Clinton/Gore Presdl. Transition Team for Arts and Humanites, 1992. Served with USN, 1959-63. Recipient Phelps-Stokes Fund award, 1977; Ludwig Vogelstien Found. award, 1981; Nat. Endowment for Arts fellow, 1979. Mem. Am. Assn. Mus. (exec. mem. curators com. 1985). Office: Alternative Museum 594 Broadway Rm 402 New York NY 10012-3234

RODRIGUEZ, IVAN, professional baseball player; b. Vaga Baja, P.R., Nov. 30, 1971. With Tex. Rangers, 1988—; mem. Am. League All-Star Team, 1992-94, Am. League Silver Slugger Team The Sporting News, 1994. Recipient Gold Glove award, 1992-94. Office: Tex Rangers 1000 Ballpark Way Arlington TX 76011*

RODRIGUEZ, JOSEPH H., federal judge; b. 1930; m. Barbara Marriner. AB, La Salle Coll., 1955; JD, Rutgers U., 1958. Assoc. Brown, Connery et al, Camden, N.J., 1959-82; pub. advocate, pub. defender State of N.J., 1982-85; judge U.S. Dist. Ct. N.J., Camden, 1985—; instr. law Rutgers U., N.J., 1972-82, 93—; chmn. State Commn. Investigation, N.J., 1974-79. Chmn. State Bd. of Higher Edn., N.J., 1971-73. Mem. N.J. State Bar Assn. (pres. 1978-79). Office: US Dist Ct 1 John F Gerry Plz Camden NJ 08101

RODRIGUEZ, JUAN ALFONSO, technology corporation executive; b. Santiago, Cuba, Feb. 10, 1941; came to U.S., 1953; s. Alfonso and Marie Madeleine (Hourcadette) R. BEE, CCNY, 1962; MEE, NYU, 1963. Engr. IBM, Poughkeepsie, N.Y. and Boulder, Colo., 1963-68; engring. mgr. IBM, 1968-69; dir. tech. Storage Tech. Corp., Louisville, Colo., 1969-74, v.p. engring., 1974-77, v.p., gen. mgr. disk, 1977-79; v.p., gen. mgr. optical disk Storage Tech. Corp., Longmont, Colo., 1979-85; pres., CEO Exabyte Corp., Boulder, 1985-87, CEO, 1987-90; chmn., 1987-92; pres. Sweetwater Corp., 1992-93, chmn., 1992—, also bd. dirs.; prof. elec. and computer engring. and engring. mgmt. U. Colo., 1992—; chmn. Datasonix, 1992—; mem. devel. coun. Coll. Engring. U. Colo., 1990-92; Kapre Corp.; mem. engring. adv. bd. CCNY, bd. dirs. Colo. Advanced Tech. Enterprise, 1994—, co-exec. dir. Joint Ctr. for Entre Preneurship, U. Colo., 1994—; Robert J. Appel Disting. lectr. law and tech. Law Sch. U. Denver, 1990. Patentee in field. Bd. dirs. Boulder YMCA, 1982-87, U. Colo. Artist Series, 1988—; mem. bd. govs. Boulder County United Way, 1989-93, chairperson campaign, 1992; commr. Colo. Advance Tech. Inst., 1988-92. Recipient Ind. Quality award Rocky Mountain sect. Am. Soc. Quality Control, 1990, Gen. Palmer award for Outstanding Engr. in Industry The Am. Cons. Engrs. Coun. of Colo., 1995; named Boulder Spirit Entrepreneur of Yr., 1989, Entrepreneur of the Decade Boulder C. of C., 1994; finalist Entrepreneur of Yr., Arthur Young & Inc Mag., 1989. Fellow IEEE; mem. Computer Soc. of IEEE (mem. steering com. on mass storage 1981-93), Soc. Photo-Optical Instrumentation Engrs., Boulder C. of C. (chmn. entrepreneurs support program 1989), Greater Denver C. of C. (bd. dirs. 1990-91). Office: Univ Colo Box 425 Boulder CO 80309

RODRIGUEZ, JUAN GUADALUPE, entomologist; b. Espanola, N.Mex., Dec. 23, 1920; s. Manuel D. and Lugardita (Salazar) R.; m. Lorraine Ditzler, Apr. 17, 1948; children: Carmen, Teresa, Carla, Rosa. BS, N.Mex. State U., 1943; MS, Ohio State U., 1946, PhD, 1949. Asst. entomologist U. Ky., 1949-51, assoc. entomologist, 1951-61, prof. entomology, 1961—; adv. entomology U. de San Carlos, Guatemala, 1961; vis. scientist Warsaw U., 1961; sec. V Internat. Congress Acarology, 1978; del. internat. confs. Vienna, Moscow, San Jose, Costa Rica, Nottingham, Eng., Prague, Saalfelden, Austria, Kyoto, Japan, Edinburgh, Scotland, Hamburg, Fed. Republic Germany; bd. dirs. Ky. Sci. & Tech. Coun., 1990—; cons. to food industry, 1989—. Ky. steering com. Eisenhower Math/Sci. Consortium Appalachia Ednl. Lab., 1992—. Bd. dirs. Lexington Chpt. NCCJ, Ky. Sci. & Tech. Coun., 1989—, Ky. steering com. of Appalachia Edn. Lab., 1993—. Served with inf., AUS, World War II; ex POW. Recipient Disting. Research award U. Ky. Alumni Assn., 1963; Thomas Poe Cooper award U. Ky. Coll. Agr., 1972, Outstanding Acarologist award Am. Registry Profl. Entomologists, 1984. Fellow Royal Entomol. Soc. London, AAAS; mem. Am. Inst. Biol. Scis., Acarol. Soc. Am. (governing bd.), Ky. Acad. Sci. (pres. 1982-83); pres. Found. 1982—, Disting. Scientist award 1985, exec. sec. 1988—), Can. Entomol. Soc., Ont. Entomol. Soc., Entomol. Soc. Am. (br. sec.-treas. 1963-65, br. com. man at large 1968-71, br. pres. 1982-83, North Cen. States br. rep. to governing bd. 1984-87, chmn. centennial com. 1987-89, hon. mem. 1989), Order Ky. Cols., Ky. Dept. Am. ex-POWs (comdr. 1992—), Sigma Xi (pres. U. Ky. chpt. 1977, comdr. 1992-94), Gamma Alpha, Gamma Sigma Delta. Roman Catholic. Editor: Insect and Mite Nutrition, 1972, Recent Advances in Acarology, vols. I and II, 1979; coeditor: Current Trends in Insect Endocrinology and Nutrition, 1981, Leafhoppers and Planthoppers, 1985, Nutritional Ecology of Insects, Mites and Spiders, 1987; mem. editorial bd. Internat. Jour. Acarology; contbr. articles to profl. jours. Home: 1550 Beacon Hill Rd Lexington KY 40504-2304

RODRIGUEZ, LINDA TAKAHASHI, secondary education educator; b. L.A., June 22, 1941; d. Edward S. and Mary Takahashi; divorced; children: Regina Marie, Marla Sari. AA, Trinidad (Colo.) Jr. Coll., 1961; BA, We. State Coll., Gunnison, Colo., 1963; MA, U. Colo., Denver, 1991. Cert. tchr., adminstr., Colo. Tchr. Stratton (Colo.) Jr./Sr. High Sch., 1964-65, Pikes Peak Elem. Sch., Colorado Springs, 1966-68, Prince Sch., Tucson, 1968-70, Ipava (Ill.) Grade Sch., 1970-72, Macomb (Ill.) Schs., 1972-74, Colchester (Ill.) Jr./Sr. High Schs., 1973-79, Hazel Park (Mich.) Alternative Sch., 1984-85; tchr. 8th grade lang. arts and social studies Denver Pub. Schs., 1986-94, chair lang. dept., 1987-95, tchr. reading resource, 1987-92; creator, dir. Reading Summer Sch., 1987-91; presenter insvcs. Denver Pub. Schs., 1987-95; mentor Alternative Tchr. Cert. Program; mem. bd. dirs. Asian Cultural Ctr. Advisor Asian Edn. Adv. Bd., Denver, 1989-94; bd. dirs. Colo. Youthat-Risk, Denver, 1992-93. Mem. Landmark Edn. Forum, Highland Park Optimists, Delta Kappa Gamma. Avocations: reading, skiing, swimming, socializing, travel, Brittanys and adventure. Home: 1617 Daphne Broomfield CO 80020

RODRIGUEZ, LOUIS JOSEPH, university administrator; b. Newark, Mar. 13, 1933; m. Ramona Dougherty, May 31, 1969; children: Susan, Michael, Scott. BA, Rutgers U., 1955; MA, La. State U., 1957, PhD, 1963. Dean, Coll. Bus. Adminstrn., Alcee Fortier Disting. prof. Nichols State U., Thibodaux, La., 1958-71; dean Coll. Bus. U. Tex.-San Antonio, 1971-72, v.p. acad. affairs, dean faculty, 1972-73; dean Sch. Profl. Studies U. Houston-Clear Lake City, 1973-75, vice-chancellor, provost, 1975-80; pres. Midwestern State U., Wichita Falls, Tex., 1981—; Hardin Found. prof., 1994—; vice chmn. Coun. Tex. Pub. Univ. Pres. and Chancellors, 1992-93. Contbr. articles to profl. jours. Chmn. bd. Tex. Council on Econ. Edn., Houston, 1981-83; bd. dirs. Joint Council on Econ. Edn., N.Y.C., 1981-83, Goodwill Industries Am., Washington, 1976-82; pres. Wichita Falls Bd. Commerce and Industry, 1988-89, Clear Lake City Devel. Found., Houston, 1976-77, Goals for Wichita Falls, Inc., 1983. Recipient Tchr. Edn. Supportive Pres. award Am. Assn. Colls. Tchr. Edn., 1991; named Wichitan of the Yr., 1987; Ford Found. grantee, 1976; Fulbright fellow, 1976. Mem. Am. Assn. State Colls. and Univs. (bd. dirs.), So. Assn. Colls. and Schs. (Commn. on Colls.), Assn. Tex. Colls. and Univs. (pres. 1988-89), Rotary (pres. Downtown Wichita Falls club 1990-91). Mem. Ch. of Christ. Home: 2405 Midwestern Pky Wichita Falls TX 76308-2911 Office: Midwestern State U 3410 Taft Blvd Wichita Falls TX 76308-2095

RODRIGUEZ, MATT L., protective services professional. AA in Bus. Adminstrn. with high honors, Wright Coll., 1972; B in Pub. Adminstrn. with honors, Roosevelt U., 1975, MPA with honors, 1976; postgrad., Northwestern U., 1976-77. Joined Chgo. Police Dept., 1959, advanced through grades to capt., 1988, patrolman, 1959-60, investigator Organized Crime sect., 1960-70, patrol sgt., 1970-71, investigative sgt. Criminal Investigation div., 1971-73, watch comdr., advanced through grades, command unit Vice Control div., 1973-76, 77-78, field lt. Patrol div., 1979, commanding officer area 6 youth div. Bur. Investigative Svcs., 1979, commanding officer gambling sect. Vice Control div., 1979-80, adminstrv. asst. to supt., 1980, dep. supt. Bur. Tech. Svcs., 1980-92, supt., 1992—; adj. prof. criminal justive dept. U. Ill., Chgo., 1979—, mem. adv. com. office internat. criminal justice; mayoral appointee Chgo. Emergency Telephone Systems Bd.; chmn. bd. Hispanic Inst. Law Enforcement; mem. adv. coun. Atty. Gen./State of Ill. Victim Assistance Program; lectr. Pub. Svcs. U., Beijing, 1984, Acad. Criminal Justive Scis., Orlando, Fla., 1984, Bramhill Police Coll., Hampshire, Eng., 1986, Am. Soc. Criminology ann. conf., Chgo., 1988, numerous others; keynote speaker IRS, Chgo., 1987, Northwestern U. Traffic Inst., 1989; panelist Nat. Conf. Criminal Justice Info. Law and Policy, CHgo., 1984, U.S. Dept. Justice Community Rels. Svcs.; participant numerous seminars and internat. confs. Contbr. articles to profl. jours. Bd. advisors Cath. Charities, Archdiocese of Chgo.; bd. dirs. Chgo. chpt. March of Dimes Birth Defects Found., Mental Health Assn. Greater Chgo., Law Found. Ill.; mem. community adv. com. Sta. WYCC-TV; mem. adv. bd. Malcom X Coll. Recipient Man or Yr. award Puerto Rican Congess Law and Order, 1983, Man of Yr. award Mex. Am. Legal Def. Ednl. Fund, 1987, Outstanding Achievement award Puerto Rican Congress Mut. Aid, Inc., 1987, Cert. Appreciation Near North Kiwanis Chgo., 1988, Man of Yr. award Polonia Cares Found., 1989, Outstanding Alumnus award Wright Coll., 1989, Alumni award Holy Trinity High Sch., 1989,

Citation of Honor Jewish Nat. Fund, 1991, Cert. Appreciation Drug Enforcement Adminstrn., 1991. Mem. Hispanic Am. Police Command Officers Assn. (1st v.p.), Internat. Assn. Chiefs of Police (com. on civil rights, Cert. Appreciation for Outstanding Contbrs. Towards Professionalization Law Enforcement 1990), Latin Am. Police Assn. (bd. dirs., Man of Yr. award 1984). Office: Chgo Police Dept Office of Supt 1121 S State St Rm 400 Chicago IL 60605

RODRIGUEZ, PLACIDO, bishop; b. Celaya, Mex., Oct. 11, 1940; came to U.S., 1953; s. Eutimio and Maria Concepcion (Rosiles) R. STB, STL, Cath. U., Washington, 1968; MA, Loyola U., 1971. Ordained priest Roman Cath. Ch., 1968, ordained to bishop, 1983. Pastor Our Lady Guadalupe Ch., Chgo., 1972-75, Our Lady of Fatima Ch., Perth Amboy, N.J., 1981-83; vocat. dir. Claretians, Chgo., 1975-81; bishop aux. Archdiocese of Chgo., 1983-94; bishop Diocese of Lubbock, Tex., 1994—. Office: The Catholic Ctr PO Box 98700 Lubbock TX 79499-8700*

RODRIGUEZ, RITA MARIA, bank executive; b. La Havana, Cuba, Sept. 6, 1944; came to U.S., 1960; Tomas and Adela (Mederos) R.; m. E. Eugene Carter, Jan. 7, 1972; 1 child, Adela-Marie R. Carter. BBA, U. Puerto Rico, 1964; MBA, NYU, 1968, PhD, 1969. Bus. adminstrn. asst. prof., then assoc. prof. Harvard Bus. Sch., Cambridge, Mass., 1969-74, 74-78; fin. prof. U. Ill., Chgo., 1978-82; dir. Export-Import Bank of U.S., Washington, 1982—; cons. Polaroid Corp. and Indsl. Devel. Bank in Ecuador (Corporacion Financiera Nacional), 1978-82, U.S. IRS, 1982; bd. dirs. Acad. Ednl. Devel., Washington, 1989-93; bd. advisors Pew Econ. Freedom Fellows, Washington, 1991—. Author: (with E. Eugene Carter) International Financial Management, 1976, secondedit., 1979, 3rd edit., 1984, Foreign Exchange Markets: A Guide to Foreign Currency Operations, 1977, Foreign Exchange Management in U.S. Multinationals, 1980, (with Heinz Riehl) Foreign Exchange and Money Markets, 1983, Japanese, Spanish, Portuguese translations, The Export-Import Bank at Fifty, 1987; contbr. numerous fin. articles to profl. publs. Recipient Outstanding Achievement award, Nat. Coun. of Hispanic Women, 1986; Outstanding Hispanic Achievement award, Hispanic Corp. Achievers, 1988; National Leadership award-Government, The Nat. Network of Hispanic Women, 1989. Mem. Coun. Foreign Rels., Am. Econ. Assn. Roman Catholic. Avocations: gardening, music. Home: 3075 Ordway St NW Washington DC 20008-3255 Office: Export-Import Bank of U.S. 811 Vermont Ave NW Washington DC 20571-0002

RODRIGUEZ, VERONICA, special education educator; b. Ft. Worth, June 21, 1959; d. Joe and Helen (Guereca) Martinez; m. Javier Rodriguez, July 17, 1982. BS, Tex. Wesleyan U., 1981; MEd, U. North Tex., 1986. Cert. elem. tchr., Tex. Spl. Edn. resource tchr. Ft. Worth Ind. Sch. Dist., 1981—. Active Learning Disabilities Assn. Ft. Worth Coun. Reading. Mem. NEA, Internat. Reading Assn., Nat. Coun. Tchrs. English, Tex. State Tchrs. Assn., Delta Kappa Gamma.

RODRIGUEZ, VICTOR, school system administrator. Supt. San Antonio public schs. Office: San Antonio Sch Bd 141 Lavaca St San Antonio TX 78210-1039

RODRIGUEZ, VINCENT ANGEL, lawyer; b. Cayey, P.R., 1921; s. Vicente and Maria (Antonigiorgi) R. B.S., Harvard U., 1941; LL.B., Yale U., 1944. Bar: N.Y. 1947. Assoc. Sullivan & Cromwell, N.Y.C., 1944-56, ptnr., 1956—; dir. Deltec Internat. Ltd., Eng., Am. Investors, Inc., Bermuda. Mem. Council Fgn. Relations, ABA, Assn. Bar City N.Y., Am. Soc. Internat. Law. Club: River (N.Y.C.). Home: 4521 Fisher Island Dr Fisher Island FL 33109-0156 Office: Sullivan & Cromwell 125 Broad St New York NY 10004

RODRIGUEZ, YOLANDA ISABEL, elementary instructional administrator; b. Aug. 16, 1954. AA, Laredo (Tex.) Jr. Coll., 1974; BS in Elem. Edn., Tex. A&I U. Laredo, 1976; MS in Bilingual Edn., Laredo State U., 1985. Bilingual cert.; cert. in kindergarten, gifted and talented, Tex. tchr. appraisal system and instrnl. leadership. Campus instrnl. administr. Finley Elem. Sch., Laredo, 1992—; trainer Tex. Educators Cert. for Adminstrs. and Tchrs. test, 1985, Site Base, 1991, Austin; presenter in field. Active Leadership Laredo, Mexican Am. Hispanic Caucus. Mem. NEA, United Edn. Assn., Tex. State Tchrs. Assn., Tex. Assn. Bilingual Edn., Tex. Elem. Prins. and Suprs. Assn., Laredo Assn. Young Children, Laredo Assn. Bilingual Edn., Piasano Reading Coun., Parent Tchr. Club, Alpha Delta Kappa. Office: Finley Elem Sch 2001 Lowry Rd Laredo TX 78041-7040

RODRÍGUEZ-ARIAS, JORGE HERMINIO, retired agricultural engineering educator; b. Ponce, P.R., Apr. 24, 1915; s. Herminio Rodríguez Colón and Rosa María Arias Rís; m. Carmen Teresa Quiñones Sepúlveda, May 9, 1948; children: Jorge H., Jaime Osvaldo, Nelson Rafael. BS in Agriculture, U. P.R., Mayaguez, 1936; BS in Agrl. Engring., Tex. A&M U., 1945; MS in Agrl. Engring., Kans. State U., 1947; PhD in Agrl. Engring., Mich. State U., 1956; D (hon.), U. P.R., Mayaguez, 1986. Instr. vocat. agriculture P.R. Reconstruction Adminstrn., Aibonito, 1936-37; instr. horticulture U. P.R., Mayaguez, 1937-43, from asst. to assoc. to prof. agrl. engring., 1947-77, dir. agrl. engring. dept., 1948-77; panelist UN Program for Devel., Lima, Peru, 1959. With USN, 1945-46. Fellow Am. Soc. Agrl. Engrs. (life), Instn. of Agrl. Engrs.; mem. Am. Soc. for Engring. Edn. (life), Inst. of Food Technologists (profl.). Home and Office: U PR Faculty Residences # 3-b Mayaguez PR 00681

RODRIGUEZ-CAMILLONI, HUMBERTO LEONARDO, architect, historian, educator; b. Lima, Peru, May 30, 1945; came to U.S., 1963; s. Alfonso and Elda (Camilloni) R.; m. Mary Ann Alexanderson, July 1, 1972; children: Elizabeth Marie, William Howard. BA magna cum laude, Yale U., 1967, MArch, 1971, MPhil, 1973, PhD, 1981. Rsch. asst. Sch. Architecture Yale U., 1964-70, teaching fellow dept. history art, 1971-72, 74-75; chmn. research dept. Centro de Investigacion y Restauracion de Bienes Monumentales Instituto Nacional de Cultura, Lima, 1973; restoration architect OAS, Washington, 1976—; asst. prof. Sch. Architecture Tulane U., New Orleans, 1975-82; assoc. prof., dir. Henry H. Wiss Ctr. Theory and History of Art and Architecture, Coll. Architecture and Urban Studies Va. Poly. Inst. and State U., Blacksburg, 1983—, dir. Ctr. for Preservation and Rehab. Tech., Coll. Architecture, 1986—; vis. prof. U. Ill., Chgo., 1982-83; reviewer, cons. Choice, 1975—; mem. interim bd. dirs. Ctr. Planning Handbook Latin-Am. Art, 1978—; cons., adviser Internat. Exhbn. and Symposium Latin-Am. Baroque Art and Architecture, 1980; mem. adv. bd. Mountain Lake Symposium on Art and Architecture Criticism, 1985—, Internat. Symposium Luis Barragan, 1990; coord. advisor exhbn. Tradition and Innovation: Painting, Architecture and Music in Brazil, Mex. and Venezuela between 1950-80, 1991, Internat. Art History Colloquium, 1993, 48th Internat. Congress of Americanists, 1994. Author: (with Walter D. Harris) The Growth of Latin American Cities, 1971; (with Charles Seymour, Jr.) Italian Primitives, The Case History of a Collection and its Conservation, 1972, Religious Architecture in Lima of the Seventeenth and Eighteenth Centuries: The Monastic Complex of San Francisco el Grande, 1984; contbg. editor Handbook of Latin American Studies, 1987—, The Dictionary of Art, 1991—. Named Ellen Battell Eldridge fellow, 1970-72, Robert C. Bates Jr. fellow Jonathan Edwards Coll., Yale U., 1970-71, Social Sci. Rsch. Coun. fellow, 1972-74, Yale Concilium Internat. Studies fellow, 1972-73, Giles Whiting fellow, 1974-75, NEH fellow Columbia U., 1983, Hobart and William Smith Colls. fellow, 1987, U. Ill. fellow, 1990, Edilia De Montequin fellow, 1991, NEH fellow U. N.Mex., 1992. Mem. Soc. Archtl. Historians (bd. dir. 1977-80, past. pres., past sec. South Gulf chpt.) SE sect. Soc. Archtl. Historians, Coll. Art Assn., SE Coll. Art Conf., Latin Am. Studies Assn., Assn. Latin Am. Art. Assn. Preservation Va. Antiquities, New River Valley Preservation League (bd. dir. 1987—), Nat. Trust Historic Preservation, Save our Cemeteries (past dir.), Preservation Resource Ctr. (past bd. dir.), Assn. for Preservation Tech., Blacksburg Regional Art Assn. (bd. dir.) Roman Catholic. Office: Va Poly Inst and State U Coll Architecture & Urban Studies Blacksburg VA 24061

RODRIGUEZ-DEL VALLE, NURI, microbiology educator; b. San Juan, P.R., May 25, 1945; d. Paulino and Lucila (del Valle) Rodriguez-Rolan; m. Juan C. Perez-Otero, June 1, 1968; children: Juan Carlos, Claudia Rosalia. BS, U. P.R., 1967, MS, 1970, PhD, 1978. Rsch. asst. Coll. Pharmacy U. P.R. Rio Piedras, 1966-67, instr. biochemistry Med. Sch., 1970-78, asst. prof. microbiology, 1978-82, assoc. prof., 1982-92, prof.,

1992—; ad honorem asst. prof. biology, 1984—; prin. investigator MBRS-NIH Grant, 1981—. Tchr. adult catechism, 1992. Named Disting. Scientist Mobil Oil Co., San Juan, 1981, Disting. Prof. Student Rsch. Forum, San Juan, 1989. Mem. AAAS (coun. mem. Caribbean div. 1990-92, pres.-elect 1993, pres. 1994), Am. Soc. Microbiology (coun. mem. 1981-89, sec., pres. elect, pres. P.R. br. 1982-89, Dr. Arturo Carrion lectr. 1983), Soc. Exptl. Biology and Medicine, N.Y. Acad. Medicine, Sigma Xi. Roman Catholic. Office: U PR dept microbiology Med Sci Campus PO Box 365067 San Juan PR 00936-5067

RODRIGUEZ-ERDMANN, FRANZ, physician; b. Mexico City, Feb. 2, 1935; came to U.S., 1961; m. Irma Villarreal; 1 child, Foro. M.B., U. Heidelberg, Germany, 1958, M.D., 1960. Diplomate: Am. Bd. Internal Medicine. Intern Univ. Hosps., Heidelberg, 1958-61, Mercy Hosp., Detroit, 1962-63; research assoc. Wayne State U. Med. Sch., Detroit, 1961-62; jr. asst. resident in medicine Tufts U. New Eng. Med. Center, Boston, 1964-65; research fellow hematology Tufts U. New Eng. Med. Center, 1964, clin. fellow cardiology, 1965-66; resident in medicine Boston City Hosp., 1966-67; sr. resident in medicine Georgetown U., Washington, 1967-68; fellow in hematology Peter Bent Brigham Hosp., Boston, 1968-69; assoc. in medicine Peter Bent Brigham Hosp., 1969-71; practice medicine specializing in internal medicine and hematology; attending physician Boston City Hosp.; instr., then asst. prof. Harvard U. Med. Sch., 1969-71; prof. medicine U. Ill. Med. Sch., 1971—; chief hematology sect. and hemostasis unit Edgewater Hosp., Chgo., 1979-82. Contbr. numerous articles to profl. jours. Fellow A.C.P.; mem. Internat. Soc. Hematology, Am. Fedn. Clin. Research, Am. Soc. Hematology, Internat. Soc. Hemostasis and Thrombosis, Council on Thrombosis, World Fedn. Hemophilia, Brazilian Coll. Hematology, Mex. Nat. Acad. Medicine, Bolivian Soc. Internal Medicine, Colombian Soc. Hematology, Alpha Omega Alpha. Home: 3255 Brookdale Rd Northbrook IL 60062-7501 Address: 5015 N Paulina Ste 420 Chicago IL 60640

RODRIGUEZ GARCIA, JOSE A., agronomist, investigator; b. Toa Baja, PR, Nov. 1, 1946; s. Pedro R. Rodriguez-Gónzalez and Maria A. Garcia-Fóntanez. BSA, Coll. Agriculture and Mechanical Arts, Mayagúez, PR, 1967; MSA, U. Mayagúez, 1979. Tchr. agr. Dept. Pub. Instrn. of P.R., 1967-68; asst. investigations Sta. of Agrl. Expts., 1968-76, asst. agronomics, 1976-83, assoc. agronomics, 1983-89, agronomics investigator, 1989—, adminstr., 1985—. Contbr. numerous articles to profl. jours. Mem. Little League of P.R., Recreation Assn. of Toa Baja, Red Cross of P.R.; bd. dirs. Baseball Team of Toa Baja. Mem. Coll. Agronomics of P.R., P.R. Soc. Agrl. Scis., Am. Soc. Agronomics, Caribbean Food Crops Soc., Am. Soc. Tropical Horticulture. Home: Apt 128 Toa Baja PR 00951 Office: U P R HC02 Box 10322 Bo Padilla Corozal PR 00643

RODWELL, JOHN DENNIS, biochemist; b. Boston, Oct. 9, 1946; s. William Joseph and Lillian Catherine (Cunningham) R.; m. Ellen M. McCaffrey, Dec. 18, 1971; children: Elizabeth Ann, Sarah Catherine. BA in Chemistry, U. Mass., 1968; MS in Organic Chemistry, Lowell Technol. Inst., 1971; PhD in Biochemistry, UCLA, 1976. Postdoctoral fellow Sch. Medicine U. Pa., Phila., 1976-80; rsch. asst., prof. U. Pa. Sch. Medicine, 1980-81; with Cytogen Corp., Princeton, N.J., 1981—; v.p. discovery rsch. Cytogen Corp., 1987-88, v.p. R & D, 1989—; adj. asst. prof., then adj. assoc. prof. Sch. Medicine, U. Pa., 1981—; series editor, Marcel Dekker, Inc., N.Y.C. 1988—. Patentee, antibody conjugates for compound delivery, antibody metal ion complexes; editor: Antibody Mediated Delivery Systems, 1988; co-editor: Covalently Modified Antigens and Antibodies in Diagnosis and Therapy, 1989. Recipient Nat. Rsch. Svc. award NIH, 1978-80, Thomas Alva Edison Patent award, 1993. Mem. AAAS, Am. Assn. Immunologists, Am. Chem. Soc. (assoc. editor 1989-93), N.Y. Acad. Scis., Soc. Nuclear Medicine. Democrat. Avocations: boating, flying. Home: 1340 Eagle Rd New Hope PA 18938-9222 Office: Cytogen Corp 201 College Rd E Princeton NJ 08540-6603

RODZIANKO, PAUL, energy company executive; b. Washington, Oct. 22, 1945; s. Paul and Aimee Rodzianko; m. Chauncie McKeever, May 1988; children: Marina, Alexander. BA, Princeton U., 1967; MA, Inst. Critical Langs., 1967. With GE Co., 1967-76; pres. U.S. Geothermal Corp., N.Y.C., 1976-77, Geothermal Energy Corp., N.Y.C., 1977-83, Geothermal Food Processors, Inc., Fernley, Nev., 1979-82; exec. v.p. Grace Geothermal Corp., 1981-83, bd. dirs., 1981-83; pres. Bay Capital Corp., Oyster Bay, N.Y., 1983-85, Data Port Co., 1985-86; v.p. spl. projects Kvaerner Energy Devel., Inc., Dover, N.J., 1992—; bd. dirs. McGill Environ. Sys., Inc.; chmn. bd. dirs. Mt. Hope Hydro, Inc., 1986-92, Halecon, Inc., 1986-92, Kvaerner Venture Inc., 1992—; v.p. Little Horn Energy Wyo., 1993—. Vice chmn. Russian Orthodox Theol. Fund, 1978—; chmn. Mt. Hope Waterpower Project, 1989-92; mem. Town Coun., Tuxedo, N.Y., 1992—, co-chmn. revitalization com.; mem. Rockaway Twp. Econ. Devel. Com., 1995—. Fellow Royal Geog. Soc., Explorers Club, New Eng. Soc.; mem. Geothermal Resources Coun. (bd. dirs., chmn. audit com. 1980-82), Nat. Inst. Social Scis., Rockaway Area C. of C. (bd. dirs. 1988-92), Camp Fire Club, Tuxedo Club, Rotary (hon. Paul Harris fellow 1988-92), Lions (mem.-at-large). Office: 627 Mt Hope Ave Wharton NJ 07885 also: Kvaerner Venture Inc 100 First Stamford Dr Stamford CT 06902

ROE, BENSON BERTHEAU, surgeon, educator; b. L.A., July 7, 1918; s. Hall and Helene Louise (Bertheau) R.; m. Jane Faulkner St. John, Jan. 20, 1945; children: David B., Virginia St. John. AB, U. Calif., Berkeley, 1939; MD cum laude, Harvard U., 1943. Diplomate Am. Bd. Surgery, Am. Bd. Thoracic Surgery (dir. 1971-83, chmn. bd. 1981-83, chmn. exam. com. 1978, chmn. long-range planning com. 1980, chmn. program com. 1977). Intern Mass. Gen. Hosp., Boston, 1943-44, resident, 1946-50; nat. rsch. fellow dept. physiology Med. Sch., Harvard U., Boston, Mass., 1947, instr. surgery, 1950; Moseley Traveling fellow Harvard. U. at U. Edinburgh, Scotland, 1951; asst. clin. prof. surgery U. Calif., San Francisco, 1951-58, chief cardiothoracic surgery, 1958-76, prof. surgery, 1966-89, emeritus prof., 1989—; pvt. practice medicine specializing in cardiothoracic surgery San Francisco, 1952-85; cons. thoracic surgery VA Hosp., San Francisco Gen. Hosp., Letterman Army Hosp., St. Lukes Hosp., Blue Shield of Calif., Baxter Labs., Ethicon, Inc.; bd. dirs. Control Laser Corp.; vis. prof. U. Utah, U. Ky., U. Gdansk, Poland, Nat. Heart Hosp., London, U. Ibadan, Nigeria, Sanger Clinic, Charlotte, Rush-Presbyn. Hosp., Chgo., Penrose Hosp., Colorado Springs; bd. dirs. Internat. Bioethics Inst. Mem. editorial bd. Annals of Thoracic Surgery, 1969-82, Pharos; editor 2 med. texts; author 21 textbook chpts.; contbr. 172 articles to profl. jours. Bd. dirs. United Bay Area Crusade, 1958-70, mem. exec. com., 1964-65; bd. dirs. chmn. exec. com. San Francisco chpt. Am. Cancer Soc., 1955-57; bd. dirs. San Francisco Heart Assn., 1964-72, pres., 1964-65, chmn. rsch. com., 1966-71; mem. various coms. Am. Heart Assn., 1964-67; pres. Miranda Lux Found., 1982-94; trustee Avery Fuller Found.; bd. dirs. Internat. Bioethics Inst., Point Reyes Bird Observatory. Served with Med. Svc. Corps, USNR, 1944-46. Fellow Am. Coll. Cardiology, ACS (chmn. adv. coun. thoracic surgery, program chmn. thoracic surgery, cardiovascular com.), Polish Surg. Assn. (hon.); mem. Am. Assn. Thoracic Surgery (chmn. membership com. 1974-75), AMA (residency rev. com. for thoracic surgery), Am. Surg. Assn., Pacific Coast Surg. Assn., Calif. Acad. Medicine (pres. 1974), Calif. Med. Assn., Soc. Univ. Surgeons, Soc. Thoracic Surgerons (pres. 1972, chmn. standards and ethics com.), Soc. Vascular Surgery (v.p.). Clubs: Cruising of Am, Pacific Union, St. Francis Yacht, Calif. Tennis. Office: U Calif Div Cardiothoracic Surgery U Calif M593 San Francisco CA 94143-0118

ROE, BYRON PAUL, physics educator; b. St. Louis, Apr. 4, 1934; s. Sam S. and Gertrude Harriet (Claris) R.; m. Alice Susan Krauss, Aug. 27, 1961; children: Kenneth David, Diana Carol. B.A., Washington U., St. Louis, 1954; Ph.D., Cornell U., 1959. Instr: physics U. Mich., Ann Arbor, 1959-61, asst. prof., 1961-64, assoc. prof., 1964-69, prof., 1969—; guest physicist SSC Lab., 1991. Avocation: Probability and Statistics in Experimental Physics, 1992. CERN vis. scientist Geneva, 1967, 89; Brit. Sci. Rsch. Coun. fellow, Oxford, 1979; recipient inventor's prize CDC Worldtech, Edina, Minn., 1982, 83. Fellow Am. Phys. Soc. Home: 3610 Charter Pl Ann Arbor MI 48105-2825 Office: U Mich Physics Dept 500 E University Ave Ann Arbor MI 48109-1105

ROE, CAROLYN, nursing educator; b. Marquette, Mich., Nov. 6, 1946; d. Harry Otto and Ellie Emma (Wurm) Wonders; m. Harold Roe, Dec. 22, 1972; 1 child, Jason. ADN, Kalamazoo Valley Community Coll., 1973; BS in Nursing, Nazareth Coll., 1976; MA, Western Mich. U., 1979; MS in Nursing, Mich. State U., 1987. Cert. family nurse. Staff nurse Borgess Med. Ctr., Bronson Hosp., Kalamazoo; home health nurse VNA at Southwestern Mich.; faculty Kalamazoo Valley Community Coll. Capt. USAR, 1984—. Mem. Southwestern Dist. Nurses Assn., Sigma Theta Tau, Phi Kappa Phi. Office: Mesa Luth Hosp 525 W Brown Rd Mesa AZ 85201

ROE, CLIFFORD ASHLEY, JR., lawyer; b. Elyria, Ohio, Nov. 5, 1942; s. Clifford A. and Betty (Humphrey) R.; m. Mary Jo Loparo, Aug. 29, 1964; children: Mary, Kip, Michael, Cathleen, Danny, Beth. BS in English, Xavier U., Cin., 1964; JD, Notre Dame (Ind.) U., 1967. Bar: Ohio 1967, U.S. Dist. Ct. (so. dist.) Ohio 1970, U.S. Ct. Appeals (6th cir.) 1968. Assoc Dinsmore & Shohl, Cin., 1967-74, ptnr., 1974—. Author: The Ohio Corporation - Legal Aspects of Organization and Operation, 1989. Mem. Ohio Bar Assn., Cin. Bar Assn. (chmn. various coms.), Queen City Club, Western Hills Country Club. Republican. Roman Catholic. Avocations: tennis, golf, sailing, jogging. Home: 2089 Beech Grove Dr Cincinnati OH 45233-4915 Office: Dinsmore & Shohl 1900 Chemed Ct 255 E 5th St Cincinnati OH 45202

ROE, DAVID HARTLEY, insurance company executive, retired air force officer; b. Denver, Dec. 11, 1940; s. Jo Dick and Helen Lucille (Hill) R.; m. Ada Clason, Dec. 21, 1963; children: David Arne, Christie, Stephanie. BS, USAF Acad., 1962; 1st BM exam., Oxford (Eng.) U., 1964; MS, U. Ill., 1969, PhD, 1970. CPCU; CLU, ChFC; registered series 7, 24 and 63, Nat. Assn. Securities Dealers. Commd. 2d lt. USAF, 1962, advanced through grades to brig. gen., 1985; prin. dir. NATO policy Office Asst. Sec. Def. for Internat. Security Policy, Washington, 1985-86; int., 1986; exec. v.p., chief of staff, then pres. fin. svcs. div. USAA, San Antonio, 1986-89, pres. property and casualty ins., 1989-90, exec. v.p., CFO, 1990-91; pres. United Svcs. Life Ins. Co., Arlington, Va., 1991—, chmn., CEO, 1992-95; pres., COO, US-LICO Corp., Arlington, 1992—; sr. v.p. Reliaster, 1995—; CEO United Svcs. Life & Bankers Security Life, 1995—; chmn., CEO, Bankers Security Life, Arlington, 1992—. Mem., past chmn. adv. coun. U. Tex. Coll. Bus., San Antonio, 1986-91; trustee, mem. exec. com. San Antonio Med. Found. 1989-91; trustee Falcon Found., 1986—, White House Fellows Found., 1991—; bd. dirs. Army Retirement Residence Found., 1992—, USO Met. Wash., 1993—. Rhodes scholar, 1962-64; White House fellow, 1975-76. Mem. Assn. Grads. USAF Acad. (past pres.), Assn. Am. Rhodes Scholars, White House Fellows Assn., Nat. War Coll. Alumni Assn., Air Force Assn., Sigma Xi. Republican. Mem. Christian Ch. (Disciples of Christ). Avocations: running, golf, soccer, reading. Home: 6105 Still Water Way McLean VA 22101 Office: United Svcs Life Ins Co 4601 Fairfax Dr Arlington VA 22203

ROE, JOHN ANDREW (ROCKY), major league baseball umpire, consultant; b. Detroit, Aug. 16, 1950; s. W. Calvin and Elizabeth F. (Smith) R.; m. Jeanne Louise Winchester, Feb. 24, 1973; children: Christopher John, Emily Ann. Degree in bus. adminstrn., Ea. Mich. U., 1972; student, Bill Kinnamon Umpire Sch., 1977. Mgr. Maxwell and Assoc., Lancaster, Ohio, 1972-76; umpire Fla. State League Class A Minor League, 1977, Ea. League Class AA Minor League, 1977, Am. Assn. Class AAA Minor League, 1979; mem. umpiring staff Am. League, 1979—; mem. software and analyst sales staff Computer Methods Corp., Livonia, Mich., 1980-89; umpire Major League Playoffs, 1986, 91, World Series, 1990, All Star Game, 1994; owner major league music compact disc juke box co., Mich., 1989—; spkr. Merrill Lynch, 1992. Named Major League All-Star Game Umpire, 1984. Home: 2846 Tamwood Ct Milford MI 48382 Office: Major League Umpires Assoc 1735 Market St Ste 3420 Philadelphia PA 19103

ROE, JOHN H., manufacturing company executive; b. 1939. BA, Williams Coll., 1962; MBA, Harvard U., 1964. With Bemis Co. Inc., Mpls., 1964—, plant supt., 1964-67, sales rep., 1967-68, sales mgr., 1968-70, plant mgr., 1970-73, gen. mgr. film div., 1973-76, exec. v.p. ops., 1976-87, pres., chief oper. officer, from 1987, chief exec. officer, 1990—, also bd. dirs. Office: Bemis Co Inc 222 S 9th St Minneapolis MN 55402-3389

ROE, KENNETH KEITH, power and industrial engineering/construction company executive; b. Phila., Oct. 17, 1945; s. Kenneth Andrew and Hazel (Thropp) R.; m. Elizabeth Eaton, June 28, 1975; children: Kenneth Andrew, Whitney Elizabeth, Edward Scott, Graham Bradford. B.S. in Mech. Engring., Princeton U., 1968; Nuclear Engr., MIT, 1974, M.S. in Nuclear Engring., 1974; program in mgmt. devel., Harvard Bus. Sch., 1980. Registered profl. engr. Calif., N.Y., Wash., P.R., N.H., N.J., Ala., Fla., Ill. Engr., asst. project mgr. Burns and Roe, Inc., Hempstead, N.Y., 1971-75, Oradell, N.J., 1975-77; project engr., resident project mgr. Burns and Roe, Inc., P.R., Woodbury, N.Y., Richland, Wash., 1977-78; project engr. mgr., asst. project mgr. Burns and Roe, Inc., Oradell, 1978-79, asst. to pres., 1979-80, v.p., 1980-82, exec. v.p., 1982-85, dir., 1971—; pres. Burns and Roe Enterprises, Inc., 1985-90, pres., CEO, 1990—, chmn., 1991—. Chmn. pastor-parish rels. com. First Ch. of Round Hill, Greenwich, Conn., 1981-93, bd. trustees, 1983—; mem. adv. coun. dept. mech. engring. Columbia U., N.Y.C., 1982-84; vis. com. Dept. Nuclear Engring. MIT, 1990—. Lt. (j.g.) USN, 1969-71. Sloan Found. fellow, 1971; recipient MIT Indsl. Leadership award, 1987. Mem. ASME (sec. exec. com. met. sect. 1981-82, 82-83, region II 1987—, chmn. 1983-84, Outstanding Leadership award 1986-87, chmn. nat. agenda bd., chmn. industry adv. bd. 1987—, com. on investments 1990—, bd. trustees ASME found., Mel Purdy award 1979, Disting. Svc. award 1990), AIAA, ASCE, NSPE, Am. Mgmt. Assn. (Gantt bd. of awards 1989-92), U.S. Energy Assn., Am. Nuclear Soc., Colegio de Ingenieros (P.R.), Young Pres.'s Orgn., Constrn. Ind. Pres. Forum, Nat. Space Club, Princeton Club (N.Y.C.), Stanwich Club (Greenwich), Sankaty Head Golf Club (Nantucket, Mass.), Coral Beach and Tennis Club (Paget, Bermuda), Nantucket (Mass.) Yacht Club, Ridgewood (N.J.) Country Club, Army and Navy Club, Sigma Xi (hon. MIT chpt.). Republican. Office: Burns and Roe Enterpises Inc 800 Kinderkamack Rd Oradell NJ 07649-1506

ROE, MARK J., law educator; b. N.Y.C., Aug. 8, 1951; m. Helen Hsu, Aug. 12, 1974; children: Andrea Hsu, Jessica Hsu. BA, Columbia U., 1972; JD, Harvard U., 1975. Bar: N.Y. 1976. Atty. Fed. Res. Bank, N.Y.C., 1975-77; assoc. Cahill Gordon & Reindel, N.Y.C., 1977-80; assoc. prof. Rutgers U. Law Sch., Newark, 1980-85, prof., 1985-86, prof. U. Pa. Law Sch., 1986-88; prof. Sch. Law Columbia U., N.Y.C., 1988—. Author: Strong Managers, Weak Owners: The Political Roots of American Corporate Finance, 1994. Office: Columbia U Sch Law 435 W 116th St New York NY 10027-7201

ROE, THOMAS ANDERSON, building supply company executive; b. Greenville, S.C., May 29, 1927; s. Thomas Anderson and Leila (Cunningham) R.; m. Shirley Marie Waddell, Aug. 2, 1980; children: Elizabeth Overton Roe Mason, Thomas Anderson, Philip Stradley, John Verner; 1 stepchild, Amy Elizabeth Waddell Willcox. BS, Furman U., 1948, LLD, 1980; diploma in bus. mgmt., LaSalle Extension U., 1956. Cancer rsch. asst. Furman U., 1947-48; with Builder Marts of Am., Inc., Greenville, S.C., 1948-87, pres., 1961-69, chmn., 1969-87, CEO, 1969-78; chmn. First Piedmont Corp., 1967-74, First Piedmont Bank & Trust Co., 1967-74; bd. dirs. Swiss Tex. Mem. Greenville County Redevel. Authority, 1971-75; vice chmn. S.C. Republican Com., 1963-64, fin. chmn. 1986—; mem. Nat. Rep. Fin. Com., 1963-64; hon. asst. sgt.-at-arms Rep. Nat. Conv., Chgo., 1960; past bd. dirs. Nat. Found. Ileitis and Colitis, Greenville United Central Palsy, Greenville chpt. ARC; past chmn. adv. council Furman U.; pres. S.C. Policy Council, Columbia, 1986-90, now founding chmn., bd. dirs.; bd. govs. Council for Nat. Policy, 1984-94; past trustee Greenville Symphony, 1985-93, Inst. Rsch. on Econs. of Taxation, 1983-90; trustee Christ Ch. Episc. Sch., 1970-72, Coker Coll., 1975-81, Intercollegiate Studies Inst., 1983—, Heritage Found., 1985—, Free Congress Rsch. and Edn. Found., Washington, 1987—; mem. bd. govs. Found. Francisco Marroquin, Guatemala, Internat. Policy Forum, Washington, 1984-90; bd. dirs. mem. exec. com. Found. for Performing Arts, Greenville; founding chmn., bd. dirs. State Policy Network, Ft. Wayne, Ind.; pres. Charity Ball Bd., Rose Ball, Greenville, S.C. Named builder of yr. Greenville Home Builders Assn., 1962. Mem. Nat. Assn. Home Builders (internat. housing com.), Greenville Home Builders Assn. (v.p. 1962-63), Nat. Lumber Bldg. Material Dealers Assn., Carolina Bldg. Material Dealers Assn. (pres. 1965-66), Greenville Bldg. Materials Assn. (pres.), Mont. Pelerin Soc., Greenville C. of C. (dir. 1967-70, pres. 1970), Players Club (pres. 1951), Sertoma Club (pres. local club 1960-61, disting. svc. award 1959, superior

leaderhsip award 1961), World Trade Ctr. Club, Poinsett Club. Home and Office: 712 Crescent Ave Greenville SC 29601-4350

ROE, THOMAS COOMBE, former utility company executive; b. Dover, Del., Sept. 22, 1914; s. John Moore and Elizabeth Lindale (Cooper) R.; m. Emma Lillian Scotton, Oct. 16, 1937; children: Thomas C., Margaret Ruth (dec.). B.S. in Elec. Engring, U. Del., 1935; DHL (hon.), Wesley Coll., 1987. With Eastern Shore Public Service, 1936-43; with Delmarva Power & Light Co., 1943—; pres. subs. Delmarva Power & Light Co., 1971-76, chmn. bd., 1976-79, dir., 1971-80, ret., 1980. Hon. trustee Peninsula Gen. Hosp. Med. Center, Salisbury, Md.; trustee Wesley Coll., Dover, Del.; former chmn. Wesley Coll.; former trustee Wesley Theol. Sem., Washington. Served with AUS, 1941-45. Republican. Methodist. Club: Rotary (past pres.).

ROEBUCK, JOHN CLIFFORD, lawyer; b. Richmond, Calif., Mar. 26, 1950; s. John Meredith and Esther May (Hicks) R.; m. Keiko Koyama, July 20, 1980; children: John Keiichiro, Jeannie Tamaki. AB, Princeton U., 1972; JD, U. Mich., 1975. Bar: D.C., U.S. Dist. Ct. (fed. dist.) 1975. Assoc. Arnold & Porter, Washington, 1975-79, Coudert Bros., Hong Kong, Hong Kong, 1980-81, Coudert Bros. affiliate Nishi Tanaka & Takahashi, Tokyo, 1982-85; ptnr. Mayer, Brown & Platt, Tokyo, 1985—. Office: Mayer Brown & Platt 190 S La Salle St Chicago IL 60603-3410

ROEDER, EDWIN WOODS, geologist; b. Monsey, N.Y., July 30, 1919; s. Hans and Edna (Woods) R.; m. Kathleen Rea; children: Spencer, Lucy. BA, Lehigh U., 1941; MA, Columbia U., 1947, PhD, 1950; DSc (hon.), Lehigh U., 1976. Rsch. engr. Bethlehem Steel Corp., Bethlehem, Pa., 1941-46; predoctoral fellow Geophys. Lab., Carnegie Inst., Washington, 1946-47; asst. in geology Columbia U., N.Y.C., 1946-49; asst. prof., assoc. prof. U. Utah, Salt Lake City, 1950-55; chief solid state group U.S. Geol. Survey, Washington, 1955-60, staff geologist, 1960-62, geologist, 1962-73, rsch. geologist, 1974-87; assoc. Harvard U., 1987—; scientist emeritus U.S. Geol. Survey, Washington, 1987—; mem. or cons. various adv. bds, vis. coms., panels for U.S. govt. and several universities. Author: Composition of Fluid Inclusions, 1972, Fluid Inclusions, 1984; editor: Research on Mineral Forming Solutions, 1965, Fluid Inclusion Research (ann. book), 1968—; patentee in field. Recipient Exceptional Sci. Achievement medal NASA, 1973, Disting. Svc. medal U.S. Dept. Interior, 1978, Abraham Gottlob-Werner medaille Deutschen Min. Gesellschaft, 1985, Cyril Purkyne medal Czech Geol. Survey, 1991; first H.C. Sorby medal, 1993; grantee NSF, others. Fellow AAAS, Am. Geophys. Union (pres. V.G. and P. sect. 1978-80), Mineral Soc. Am. (v.p. 1981-82, pres. 1982-83, Washington A. Roebling medal 1986); mem. NAS, Geochem. Soc. (sec. 1967-70, v.p. 1975-76, pres. 1976-77), Soc. Econ. Geologists (R.A.F. Penrose medal 1988). Avocations: music, travel, stamp collecting. Office: Harvard U Dept Earth & Planetary Scis Cambridge MA 02138

ROEDEL, PAUL ROBERT, steel company executive; b. Millville, N.J., June 15, 1927; s. Charles Howard and Irene (Voorhees) R.; m. June Gilbert Adams, June 25, 1951; children—Beth Anne, Meg Adams. B.S. in Accounting, Rider Coll., 1949. With Carpenter Tech Corp., Reading, Pa., 1949—; asst. controller Carpenter Tech. Corp., 1957-65, controller, 1965-72, treas., 1972-73, v.p. fin., treas., 1973-75, exec. v.p., 1975-79, pres., 1979—, chief operating officer, 1979-81, chief exec. officer, 1981-92, dir., 1973—, chmn., CEO, 1987-92; dir. Meridian Bancorp Inc., 1974—, Gen. Public Utilities Corp., 1979—, P.H. Glatfelter Co., 1992—. Bd. dirs. Hawk Mountain coun. Boy Scouts Am., Pa. 2000 Edn. Coalition; trustee Gettysburg Coll.; pres. Wyomissing Found. With USNR, 1945-46. Home: # 416 Wheatland Ave Reading PA 19607-1326 Office: Carpenter Tech Corp 101 Bern St Reading PA 19601-1203

ROEDER, MARY ALICE, health facility administrator; b. Cin., Sept. 22, 1943; d. Joseph and Velma C. (Simko) Bredestege; m. Roland C. Roeder, Nov. 25, 1965; children: Roland, Carolyn, Robert, Mary, Marilyn. BSN, Coll. of Mount St. Joseph, Cin., 1965; MSN, Wayne State U., 1974; JD, U. Toledo, 1989. Instr., Sch. of Nursing Maumee Valley Hosp., Toledo, Owens Tech. Coll., Perrysburg, Ohio; asst. staff adn. coord. St. Charles Hosp., Oregon, Ohio; dir. Sch. of Nursing Providence Hosp., Sandusky, Ohio. Mem. ABA, NLN, Sigma Theta Tau.

ROEDER, MYRON A., agricultural products company executive. Pres. Tropicana Products Inc., Bradenton, Fla., 1982—. Office: Tropicana Products Inc 1001 13th Ave E Bradenton FL 34208-2656

ROEDER, RICHARD KENNETH, business owner, lawyer; b. Phila., Oct. 11, 1948; s. Walter August and Gloria (Miller) R.; m. Frederika Anne Beesemyer, June 25, 1983; 1 child, William Frederick. AB, Amherst Coll., 1970; JD, U. Calif., Berkeley, 1973, Cambridge U. 1973-74. Assoc. Paul, Hastings, Janofky & Walker, L.A., 1974-81, ptnr., 1981-90; ptnr. Aurora Capital Ptnrs., L.A., 1990—. Office: Aurora Capital Ptnrs 1800 Century Park E Ste 1000 Los Angeles CA 90067-1500

ROEDER, ROBERT GAYLE, biochemist, educator; b. Boonville, Ind., June 3, 1942; s. Frederick John and Helene (Bredenkamp) R.; m. Suzanne Himsel, July 11, 1964 (div. 1981); children: Kimberly, Michael; m. Cun Jing Hong, June 2, 1990. BA summa cum laude (Gilbert scholar), Wabash Coll., 1964, DSc (hon.), 1990; MS, U. Ill., 1965; PhD (USPHS fellow), U. Wash., 1969. Am. Cancer Soc. fellow dept. embryology Carnegie Instn. Washington, Balt., 1969-71; asst. prof. biol. chemistry Washington U., St. Louis, 1971-75; assoc. prof. Washington U., 1975-76, prof., 1976-82, prof. genetics, 1978-82, James S. McDonnell prof. biochem. genetics, 1979-82; prof. lab. biochemistry and molecular biology Rockefeller U., N.Y.C., 1982—; Arnold O. and Mabel S. Beckmann prof. molecular biology and biochemistry Rockefeller U., 1985—; cons. USPHS, 1975-79, Am. Cancer Soc., 1983-86. Grantee NIH, 1972—, NSF, 1975-79, Am. Cancer Soc., 1979-85; recipient Dreyfus Tchr.-Scholar award Dreyfus Found., 1976, Molecular Biology award NAS-U.S. Steel Found., 1986, Outstanding Investigator award Nat. Cancer Inst., 1986—, Rosensteil award for disting. work in basic med. scis., 1995, Passano award, 1995. Fellow AAAS, N.Y. Acad. Scis.; mem. NAS, Am. Chem. Soc. (Eli Lilly award 1977), Am. Soc. Biol. Chemists, Am. Soc. Microbiologists, Harvey Soc. (pres. 1994), Phi Beta Kappa. Home: 504 E 63rd St Apt 36P New York NY 10021-7929 Office: Rockefeller University 1230 York Ave New York NY 10021-6399

ROEDER, ROSS EUGENE, consulting company executive; b. Bay City, Mich., Feb. 25, 1938; s. Roscoe Charles and Lillian (Jones) R.; m. Margaret Dickey, Mar. 7, 1972 (div. May 1985). Student, Mich. Tech. U., 1956-59; BS, Mich. State U., 1960; MBA, UCLA, 1966. V.p. Baskin-Robbins Ice Cream, Burbank, Calif., 1965-71; pres., chief exec. officer Winchell's Donuts, La Mirada, Calif., 1972-77; exec. v.p., chief exec. officer Denney's, Inc., La Mirada, 1978-79; mng. dir. Mktg. Centre, St. Petersburg, Fla., 1980-81; chmn. bd. dirs., chief exec. officer, chief operating officer acctg. Fotomat Corp., St. Petersburg, 1982-85; pres. Fed. Constrn. Co., St. Petersburg, 1986-93; chmn., CEO MDR, Inc., St. Petersburg, Fla., 1994—; cons. Mktg., Designs and Research, Inc.; bd. dirs. SFI Corp., Los Angeles, Morgan Kaufmann Pubs., Los Altos, Calif., Human Technologies, Inc., St. Petersburg, chmn., 1987. Trustee Bayfront Med. Ctr., St. Petersburg 1983—. Served to capt. U.S. Army, 1962-64. Recipient Bd. Control Silver medal Mich. Tech. U., 1986. Mem. St. Petersburg Yacht Club, Racquet Club, California Club (L.A.), Calif. Yacht Club, Newport Harbor Yacht Club, Useppa Island Club (Fla.) (chmn. bd. govs. 1985—), Feather Sound Country Club (bd. dirs. 1994—), Phi Kappa Tau. Avocations: sailing, photography, tennis, music, reading. Home: 6901 16th St NE # B Saint Petersburg FL 33702 Office: MDR Inc Ste 203-C 1325 Snell Isle Blvd Saint Petersburg FL 33704

ROEDER, STEPHEN BERNHARD WALTER, chemistry and physics educator; b. Dover, N.J., Aug. 26, 1939; s. Walter Martin and Katherine E.R. (Holz) R.; m. Phoebe E. Barber, June 28, 1969; children: Adrienne H.K., Roland K.W. B.A., Dartmouth Coll., 1961; D.U. Wis., 1965. Postdoctoral fellow Bell Telephone Labs., Murray Hill, N.J., 1965-66; lectr. physics U. Oreg., Eugene, 1966-68; asst. prof. chemistry and physics San Diego State U., 1968-72, assoc. prof., 1972-75, prof., 1975—, chmn. dept. physics, 1975-78, chmn. dept. chemistry, 1979-86, acting dean. Master of Liberal Arts Program, 1987, 89, chmn. dept. physics, 1991-94; chmn. dept.

of chemistry San Deigo State U., 1995—; vis. staff mem. Los Alamos Nat. Labs., 1974—; vis. assoc. prof. chemistry U. B.C., Vancouver, Can., 1974-75; vis. prof. physics Tex A&M U., College Station, 1982; cons. Lovelace Med. Found., 1985—. Author: (with others) Experimental Pulse NMR, 1981. Recipient Outstanding Teaching award San Diego State U., 1971, Outstanding Prof. award San Diego State U., 1992; grantee Rsch. Corp., 1968, 71, 72. Mem. AAAS, Am. Chem. Soc., Am. Phys. Soc., Sigma Xi. Republican. Home: 6789 Alamo Way La Mesa CA 91941-5807 Office: San Diego State U San Diego CA 92182

ROEDERER, JUAN GUALTERIO, physics educator; b. Trieste, Italy, Sept. 2, 1929; came to U.S., 1967, naturalized, 1972; s. Ludwig Alexander and Anna Rafaela (Lohr) R.; m. Beatriz Susana Cougnet, Dec. 20, 1952; children: Ernesto, Irene, Silvia, Mario. Ph.D., U. Buenos Aires, 1952. Research scientist Max Planck Inst., Gottingen, W.Ger., 1952-55; group leader Argentine Atomic Energy Commn., Buenos Aires, 1953-59; prof. physics U. Buenos Aires, 1959-66, U. Denver, 1967-77; prof. physics U. Alaska, Fairbanks, 1977-93, prof. emeritus, 1993—, dir. Geophys. Inst., 1977-86, dean Coll. Environ. Scis., 1978-82; vis. staff Los Alamos Nat. Lab. 1969-81; chmn. U.S Arctic Research Com., 1987-91. Author: Dynamics of Geomagnetically Trapped Radiation, 1970, Physics and Psychophysics of Music, 1973, 3d edit., 1995; contbr. articles to profl. jours. Nat. Acad. Sci. NASA sr. research fellow, 1964-66. Fellow AAAS, Am. Geophys. Union; mem. Assn. Argentina de Geodestas y Geofisicos, Nat. Acad. Sci. Argentina (corr.), Nat. Acad. Sci. Austria (corr.), Third World Acad. Scis. (assoc.). Lutheran. Research on plasma and energetic particles in earth's magnetosphere, policy issues for Arctic, perception of music. Home: 105 Concordia Dr Fairbanks AK 99709-3029 Office: Geophys Inst U Alaska Fairbanks AK 99775-7320

ROEG, NICOLAS JACK, film director; b. London, Aug. 15, 1928; s. Jack Nicolas and Mabel Getrude (Silk) R.; m. Susan Rennie Stephen, May 12, 1957; children: Joscelin Nicolas, Nicolas Jack, Lucien John, Sholto Jules; m. Theresa Russell, 1985; children: Maximilian Nicolas Sextus, Statten Jack. Student Brit. schls.; LittD, Hull (Eng.) U., 1995. Cinematographer films The Caretaker, 1963, Masque of Red Death, 1964, Fahrenheit 451, 1966, A Funny Thing Happened on the Way to the Forum, 1966, Far from the Madding Crowd, 1967, Petulia, 1968; co-dir. Film Performance, 1970; dir. films Walkabout, 1970, Don't Look Now, 1973, Glastonbury Fayre, 1973, The Man Who Fell to Earth, 1976, Bad Timing, 1980, Eureka, 1982, Insignificance, 1985, Castaway, 1986, 89, Track 29, 1987, Aria, 1987, The Witches, 1988-89, Cold Heaven, 1990, Heart of Darkness, 1994, Two Deaths, 1994, Hotel Paradise, 1995, Full Body Massage, 1990; dir. TV films: Sweet Bird of Youth, 1989, Heart of Darkness, 1994; exec. producer Without You I'm Nothing, 1989, Young Indy, 1991. Fellow Brit. Film Inst.; mem. Dirs. Guild Am., Dir. Guild Gt. Britain, Acad. Motion Picture Arts and Scis., Assn. Cinematograph, TV and Allied Technicians. Office: care Robert Littman Beverly Hills CA 90210

ROEGNER, GEORGE PETER, industrial designer; b. Flushing, N.Y., Sept. 3, 1932; s. George Elmer and Margaret (Hanna) R.; B.F.A., Pratt Inst., 1954; m. Jane R. Kramer, Aug. 29, 1959; children—George Curtis, John Hanson, Nicholas Meade. Staff designer Gen. Motors Corp., 1954-55, Raymond Loewy Assocs., N.Y.C., Westinghouse Corp., Metuchen, N.J., 1960-66; product design mgr. RCA, Indpls., 1966-70; dir. design Lenox Inc., Trenton, 1972-74; pres. Curtis Hanson Meade Inc., Far Hills, N.J., 1974—; ptnr. Furniture Concepts Internat. Ltd.; dir. Cove House Corp. Bd. dirs. Clarence Dillon Library; vice chmn. Far Hills Bd. Adjustment; councilman Borough of Far Hills, 1982—, police chmn., 1984—. Served with U.S. Army, 1956-58. Recipient design awards ID Mag., Nat. Paper Box, Consumer Electronics Show, Printing Industries, Print Mag., Wescon. Mem. Indsl. Designers Soc. Am. (past nat. com. chmn.), Somerset Hills Assn., Raritan Valley Watershed Assn. Republican. Clubs: Eastward Ho Country, Stage Harbor Yacht. Designs shown at Mus. Modern Art, Smithsonian Instn., N.Y. World's Fair, Brussels, Zagreb Fairs, Indpls. Art Mus.

ROEHL, JERRALD J(OSEPH), lawyer; b. Austin, Tex., Dec. 6, 1945; s. Joseph E. and Jeanne Foster (Scott) R.; m. Nancy J. Meyers, Jan. 15, 1977; children: Daniel J., Katherine C., J. Ryan, J. Taylor. BA, U. N.Mex., 1968; JD, Washington and Lee U., 1971. Bar: N.Mex. 1972, U.S. Ct. Appeals (10th cir.) 1972, U.S. Supreme Ct. 1977. Practice of Law, Albuquerque, 1972—; pres. Roehl Law Firm P.C. and predecessors, Albuquerque, 1976—; lectr. to profl. groups; real estate developer, Albuquerque. Bd. dirs. Rehab. Ctr. of Albuquerque, 1974-78; mem. assocs. Presbyn. Hosp. Ctr., Albuquerque, 1974-82; incorporator, then treas. exec. com. Ctr. City Coun., 1991—. Recipient award of recognition State Bar N.Mex., 1975, 76, 77. Mem. ABA (award of achievement Young Lawyers div. 1975, council econs. of law practice sect. 1978-80, exec. council Young Lawyers div. 1979-81, fellow div. 1984—, council tort and ins. practice sect. 1981-83), N.Mex. Bar Assn. (pres. young lawyers sect. 1975-76), Albuquerque Bar Assn. (bd. dirs. 1976-79), N.Mex. Def. Lawyers Assn. (pres. 1983-84), Sigma Alpha Epsilon, Sigma Delta Chi, Phi Delta Phi. Roman Catholic. Clubs: Albuquerque Country, Albuquerque Petroleum. Bd. advs. ABA Jour., 1981-83; bd. dirs. editors Washington and Lee Law Rev., 1970-71. Home: 4411 Constitution Ave NE Albuquerque NM 87110-5721 Office: Roehl Law Firm PC 3d Central Plz Ste 2500 E 300 Central Ave SW Albuquerque NM 87102

ROEHL, JOSEPH E., lawyer; b. Albuquerque, Feb. 17, 1913; s. H.C. and Elizabeth J. (Walsh) R.; m. Jeanne F. Scott, Nov. 1, 1938; children: James F., Jerrald J., Virginia J. B.A., U. N.Mex., 1936, postgrad., 1936-37; LL.B., U. Tex., 1946. Bar: Tex. 1946, N.Mex. 1946. News columnist, bus. mgr. N.Mex. Lobo, Albuquerque, 1934-36; spl. events, sports announcer sta. KOB, Albuquerque, 1935-37; advt. mgr. N.Mex. Sentinel, Santa Fe, 1938-40; owner operator Gas Palace, Albuquerque, 1940-42; asst. administr. OPA, 1942-44; promotion, merchandising mgr. sta. KNOW, Austin, Tex., 1945-46; librarian Supreme Ct. Tex., Austin, 1945-46; practice in Albuquerque, 1946—; law clk. U.S. Circuit Judge Sam G. Bratton, Albuquerque, 1946-47; assoc. Simms & Modrall, 1947-53; mng. partner Modrall, Seymour, Sperling, Roehl & Harris, 1954-74; sr. dir. Modrall, Sperling, Roehl, Harris & Sisk, 1953—; chmn. com. uniform jury instrns. Supreme Ct. N.M., 1962-83; bd. dirs. Mountain States Mut. Casualty Ins. Co., 1977-93; Pres. Rio Grande Lumber Co., 1959-68; pres. Rico, Inc. Co-author, editor: New Mexico Civil Jury Instruction, 1966, 2d edit., 1981; Contbr. articles on law office econs. and mgmt. profl. jours.; speaker before profl. groups. Recipient First Nat. award for state bar activities, 1962. Fellow Am. Bar Found.; mem. ABA, Tex. Bar Assn., N.Mex. Bar Assn., Elks, Albuquerque Country Club, Albuquerque Petroleum Club, Sigma Chi. Roman Catholic. Home: 4010 Avenida La Resolana NE Albuquerque NM 87110 Office: 1000 SunWest Bldg Albuquerque NM 87102

ROEHLING, CARL DAVID, architect; b. Detroit, June 25, 1951; m. Barbara K. Jeffries; children: Carl Robert, Kristin Virginia. BS in Architecture, U. Mich., 1973, MArch, 1975. Registered arch., Mich.; cert. Nat. Coun. Archtl. Registration Bd. Architect Minoru Yamasaki and Assocs., Inc., Troy, Mich., 1976-77; TMP Assocs., 1977-81; architect Harley Ellington Pierce Yee Assocs., Inc., Southfield, Mich., 1981-83, Giffels/Hoyem Basso Assocs., Troy, 1983-87, Smith, Hinchman & Grylls Assocs., Inc., Detroit, 1987—; with Chrysler World Hdqs., 1994. Prin. works include CBS/Fox Video Hdqrs., Livonia, Mich. (Honor award Mich. Masonry Inst., 1985), First Ctr. Office Bldg., Southfield, Mich. (Honor award AIA Mich., 1988), Ind. U. Chemistry Bldg., Bloomington (Honor award AIA Detroit, 1990, AIA Mich., 1990), U. Mich. Aerospace Lab. Bldg., Ann Arbor, 1993, Los Alamos (N.Mex.) Materials Sci. Lab., 1993, others. George Booth travelling fellow U. Mich., 1976; Albert Kahn grad. scholar U. Mich., 1974-75. Mem. AIA (Mich. chpg. pres. bd. dirs. 1989, mem. nat. com. on environ. 1991, Detroit chpt. pres. 1994, initiated Place mag., Young Arch. of Yr., AIA Detroit, 1986, AIA Mich., 1991, regional dir. 1996—, nat. bd. dirs.), Mich. Archtl. Found. (chmn. pres. scholarship program 1990). Office: Smith Hinchman & Grylls 150 W Jefferson Ave Ste 100 Detroit MI 48226-4415

ROEHM, CAROLYNE JANE, fashion designer; b. Jefferson City, Mo., May 7, 1951; d. Kenneth Smith and Elaine C. (Beaty) Bresee; m. Axel Roehm, June 3, 1978 (div. 1981); m. Henry Raymond Kravis, Nov. 23, 1985. BFA, Washington U., St. Louis, Mo., 1973. Designer Kellwood Co., N.Y.C., 1974-75; asst. designer Oscar de la Renta Ltd., N.Y.C., 1975-84;

designer, owner Carolyne Roehm, Inc., N.Y.C., 1984—; design critic Fashion Inst. of Tech., N.Y.C., 1986, Parsons Inst., N.Y.C., 1988; mem. Fashion Group, 1988. Mem. of assn. Met. Opera, N.Y.C., 1988—; chairperson N.Y.C. Ballet Gala, Met. Opera Gala, 1987-88, Winter Antiques Fair for Eastside Settlement House, 1988; co-chair Fête de Famille (Aids), 1988-89, Sta. WNET TV Silver Anniversay Ball, 1988; patron Lions of Performing Arts Dinner N.Y. Pub. Libr., 1989; co-sponsor embassy benefit ball French Am. Found. for Med. Rsch., 1987. Recipient Key to St. Louis C. of C., 1988, Dallas C. of C., 1988, New Orleans C. of C., 1988, Chgo. Fashion awards, 1988; named Woman of Achievement Girl Scouts U.S., 1988, The Girls' Club, 1988. Mem. Coun. Fashion Designers (pres. 1989-90), N.Y. Pub. Libr. (bd. trustees), Carnegie Hall (steering com.), Kappa Kappa Gamma. Republican. Avocations: skiing, horseback riding, tennis, piano. Office: Carolyne Roehm Inc 257 West 39th St 4th Fl New York NY 10018-3203*

ROEHM, MACDONELL, JR., investment firm executive; b. Semerang, Indonesia, July 6, 1939; s. MacDonell and Mary Bennett (Cobb) R.; m. Nedra Ann Zeth, May 11, 1974. B.A., Colgate U., 1961; M.B.A., Harvard U., 1966. Fin. analyst Exxon Corp., 1966-68; asso. Lazard Freres, N.Y.C., 1968-71; gen. partner J. Bush & Co., N.Y.C., 1971-73; v.p. planning and devel. Cerro Corp., N.Y.C., 1973-75; v.p., treas. N L Industries, Inc., N.Y.C., 1976-79; sr. v.p. ops., devel. and planning N L Petroleum Services/ N L Industries, Inc., Houston, 1979-80; pres. N.L. Shaffer/NL Industries, Inc., 1980-82; exec. v.p. NL Industries, Inc., 1982-85; ptnr. AEA Investors, Inc., 1985-95; chmn., pres., CEO Bill's Dollar Stores, Inc., 1995—. Served with USN 1961-64. Decorated Silver Star, Bronze star, Purple Heart. Office: 65 E 55th St New York NY 10022-3219

ROEHRENBECK, CAROL, law librarian, educator; b. Montclair, N.J.; d. William Edward and Marjorie E. (Buhler) R.; divorced. BA, U. Del.; MLS, Rutgers U., Newark, JD. Libr. Pennie, Edmonds, Morton, Taylor & Adams, N.Y.C., 1967-69; rsch. libr. Fed. Res. Bank N.Y., N.Y.C., 1969-70; head pub. svcs. Rutgers Sch. Law, Newark, 1970-79; asst. dir. Mass. Continuing Legal Edn., Inc., 1979-80; law libr. dir., assoc. prof. law Nova Southeastern U. Ctr. for the Study of Law, Ft. Lauderdale, Fla., 1980—; sec.-treas. S.E. Fla. Libr. Info. Network, Ft. Lauderdale, 1991—, pres., 1990-91; chief Consortium of Southeastern Law Librs., 1990-91. Author: Florida Legislative Histories: A Practical Guide to Their Preparation, 1987; contbr. chpt. to book, articles to legal jours. Mem. ABA, ALA, Am. Assn. Law Librs., Broward County Women Lawyers Assn., Broward County Bar Assn., Soc. Am. Law Tchrs., Am. Soc. Info. Scis. Home: 2305 NE 12th Ct Fort Lauderdale FL 33304 Office: Nova U Law Libr 3305 College Ave Fort Lauderdale FL 33314-7721

ROEHRIG, C(HARLES) BURNS, internist, health policy consultant, editor; b. Brookline, Mass., Jan. 21, 1923; s. Gilbert Haven and Helen (Burns) R.; m. Patricia Joan Orme, July 22, 1952; children—Joan Russell Roehrig Vater, Jennifer Orme Roehrig Munn, Charles Burns, Jr. Student. Amherst Coll., 1941-43, Vanderbilt U., 1943-44; M.D., U. Md., 1949; cert. in internal medicine, U. Pa. Grad. Sch. Medicine, Phila., 1953. Diplomate Am. Bd. Internal Medicine. Intern Boston City Hosp., 1949-50; resident in internal medicine and diabetes Joslin Clinic, New Eng. Deaconess Hosp., Boston, 1952-54; practice medicine specializing in internal medicine and diabetes Boston, 1954—; chief of staff, pres. med. adminstrv. bd. New Eng. Deaconess Hosp., Boston, 1972-75; dir., mem. exec. com. Blue Shield of Mass., Inc., Boston, 1977-88, dir., 1989—; mem. exec. com. Met. Boston Hosp. Coun., 1982—; mem. physician adv. council Mass. Hosp. Assn., Burlington, 1982-86. Editor: The Internist: Health Policy in Practice, Washington, 1987—; contbr. med. articles to profl. jours. Bd. dirs. Camping Svcs. Bd., Greater Boston YMCA, 1966—; mem. physician adv. group Health Care Financing Adminstrn., Washington, 1983—; mem. adv. panel on physician payment and med. tech. Office of Technology Assessment, U.S. Congress, Washington, 1984-85; chmn. Federated Coun. for Internal Medicine, Washington, 1985-86; trustee New Eng. Deaconess Hosp. Served to capt. (flight surgeon) USAF, 1949-52. Fellow ACP; mem. AMA (chmn. coun. on long range planning and devel., Chgo.), New Eng. Diabetes Assn. (pres. 1963-64), Mass. Soc. Internal Medicine (pres. 1971-72), Am. Soc. Internal Medicine (pres. 1984-85). Republican. Episcopalian. Club: Wellesley Country (Mass.). Office: PO Box 812900 Boston MA 02181-0026

ROEL, RON, newspaper editor. Dep. bus. editor Newsday, Inc., Melville, N.Y., now dep. nat. editor, 1995—. Office: Newsday Inc 235 Pinelawn Rd Melville NY 11747*

ROELLIG, LEONARD OSCAR, physics educator; b. Detroit, May 17, 1927; s. Oscar Otto and Laura K. (Rutz) R.; m. B. Pauline Cowdin, June 20, 1952; children: Thomas Leonard, Mark Douglas, Paul David. A.B., U. Mich., 1950, M.S., 1956, Ph.D., 1959. From asst. prof. to prof. physics Wayne State U., Detroit, 1958-78; dean Wayne State U., 1971-72, asso. provost, 1972-76; pres. Central Solar Energy Research Corp., Detroit, 1977; prof. physics CCNY, 1978—; vice chancellor acad. affairs CUNY, 1978-83; vis. prof. Univ. Coll., London, 1968-69, Tata Inst. Fundamental Rsch., Bombay, India, 1973, Paul Scherrer Inst., Villigen, Switzerland, 1991-92; chmn. bd. advisers Midwest Regional Solar Energy Planning Venture, 1977. Co-author: Positron Annihilation, 1967; contbr. articles to profl. jours. Bd. dirs. Luth. Publicity Bur., 1981-91, v.p. 1984-85, pres., 1985-89; v.p. Grosse Pointe (Mich.) Human Rels. Coun., 1969-70. With USN, 1945-46, U.S. Army, 1950-52. Recipient Wayne State U. Fund Research Recognition award, 1963, Probus Club award for acad. achievement, 1968, Probus Club award for acad. leadership, 1977. Mem. Am. Phys. Soc., N.Y. Acad. Sci. Home: 167 E 67th St New York NY 10021 Office: Dept Physics CCNY 138th St and Convent Ave New York NY 10031

ROELOFS, WENDELL LEE, biochemistry educator, consultant; b. Orange City, Iowa, July 26, 1938; s. Edward and Edith (Beyers) R.; m. Donna R. Gray, Dec. 23, 1989; children by previous marriage: Brenda Jo, Caryn Jean, Jeffrey Lee, Kevin Jon. BA, Central Coll., Pella, Iowa, 1960, DSc (hon.), 1985; PhD, Ind. U., 1964, DSc (hon.), 1986; DSc (hon.), Hobart and William Smith Colls., 1988, U. of Lund, Sweden, 1989, Free U. Brussels, 1989. Asst. prof. Cornell U., Geneva, N.Y., 1965-69, assoc. prof., 1969-76, prof., 1976—, Liberty Hyde Bailey prof. insect biochemistry, 1978—, chmn. dept., 1991—. Contbr. over 250 articles to sci. jours. Recipient Alexander von Humboldt award in Agr., 1977, Outstanding Alumni award Central Coll., 1978, Wolf prize for agr., 1982, Disting. Alumnus award Ind. U., 1983, Nat. Medal of Sci., 1983, Disting. Svc. award USDA, 1986, Silver medal Internat. Soc. Chem. Ecology, 1990; postdoctoral fellow MIT, 1965. Fellow AAAS, Entomol. Soc. Am. (J. Everett Bussart Meml. award 1973, Founder's Meml. award 1980, Disting. Achievement award Ea. br. 1983); mem. NAS, Am. Chem. Soc. (Sterling B. Hendricks award 1994), Am. Acad. Arts and Sci., Sigma Xi. Republican. Presbyterian. Patentee in field (10). Home: 4 Crescence Dr Geneva NY 14456-1302 Office: Cornell U Geneva NY 14456

ROELS, OSWALD ALBERT, oceanographer, educator, business executive; b. Temse, Belgium, Sept. 16, 1921; came to U.S., 1958, naturalized, 1965; s. Ghisleen and Elvire (Heirwegh) R.; m. Dorothy Mary Broadhurst, Sept. 16, 1950; 1 dau., Margaret Ann Roels Talarico. B.S., U. Louvain, Belgium, 1940, M.S., 1942; Ph.D., 1944. Prof. Columbia U., N.Y.C., 1960-75, CCNY, 1969-76; prof., dir. dept. marine sci. U. Tex., Austin, 1976-80; chmn. Maritek Corp., Corpus Christi, Tex., 1980-92; pres. Bradley Barges Inc.; adj. prof. Rockefeller U., N.Y.C., 1969-80; vis. research prof. Laval U., Que., Can., 1972-80; dir. mariculture research Port Aransas (Tex.) Marine Lab., U. Tex. Marine Sci. Inst., 1976-80. Author numerous articles in field.; assoc. editor Nutrition Revs., 1961-68. Served with Belgian Army, 1940. Recipient Postdoctoral award U. Brussels, 1945, Postdoctoral award U. Liverpool, Eng., 1946, Postdoctoral award Sorbonne, 1957; Research Career Devel. award NIH, 1962-65; WHO fellow, 1957; Hoffman-LaRoche vis. lectr., 1974. Mem. AAAS, Am. Chem. Soc., Am. Inst. Nutrition, Am. Soc. Biol. Chemists, Am. Soc. Limnology and Oceanography, Chemici Lovanienses, Inst. Environ. Scis. Inst. Food Tech., Internat. Conf. Biochem. Lipids, Marine Tech. Soc., N.Y. Acad. Scis., N.Y. Lipid Club, Photoelectric Spectrometry Group Gt. Britain, World Mariculture Soc. Home: 28 Hewitt Dr Corpus Christi TX 78404-1663

ROELS, PHILIP, insurance company executive. V.p., dir. Dorinco Reinsurance Co., Midland, Mich., 1977—. Office: Dorinco Reinsurance Co 1320 Waldo Ave Ste 200 Midland MI 48642*

ROEMER, EDWARD PIER, neurologist; b. Milw., Feb. 10, 1908; s. John Henry and Caroline Hamilton (Pier) R.; m. Helen Ann Fraser, Mar. 28, 1935 (dec.); children: Kate Pier, Caroline Pier; m. Marion Clare Zimmer, May 24, 1980. BA, U. Wis., 1930; MD, Cornell U., 1934. Diplomate Am. Bd. Neurology. Intern Yale-New Haven Hosp., 1934-36; resident internal medicine N.Y. Hosp., 1936; resident neurology Bellevue Hosp., N.Y.C., 1936-38; instr. Med. Sch. Yale U., New Haven, 1935-36; asst. prof. neurology Cornell U., N.Y.C., 1936-41; prof. neurology U. Wis., Madison, 1946-64; chief of neurology Huntington Meml. Hosp., Pasadena, Calif., 1964-78; pvt. practice Capistrano Beach, Calif., 1978—; founder, dir. Wis. Neurol. Found., Madison, 1946-64; adv. bd. Wis. Multiple Sclerosis Clinic, Madison, 1946-64; adv. bd. Inst. Antiquities and Christianity, Claremont Grad. Sch., 1970—; dir. found. Univ Good Hope, S.Africa. Contbr. rsch. articles on multiple sclerosis, neuropathies to profl. jours. Lt. col. med. corps U.S. Army, 1941-46, ETO. Fellow ACP, Royal Coll. Medicine, L.S.B. Leakey Found.; mem. Rotary Internat., Annandale Golf Club, El Niguel Country Club, Nu Sigma Nu, Phi Delta Theta. Republican. Achievements include significant findings in field of anthropology and archaeology in Egypt and southwest U. S. relative to prehistory and PreColumbian European influences. Home: 35651 Beach Rd Capistrano Beach CA 92624

ROEMER, ELAINE SLOANE, real estate broker; b. N.Y.C., Apr. 23, 1938; d. David and Marion (Frauenthal) Aloane; m. David Frank Roemer, June 21, 1959; children: Michelle Sloane Wolf, Alan Sloane Roemer. BBA, U. Fla., 1959; MEd, U. Miami, 1960. CFP; cert. tchr. Tchr. math. and bus. Dade County Pub. Schs., Miami, 1959-80, Miami Dade Community Coll., 1968-80; tchr. edn. Fla. Internat. U., Miami, 1977-80; real estate broker Miami, 1978—; tchr. math. St. Leo's Coll., Miami, 1991-92; mortgage broker, Miami, 1986—; speaker in field. Contbr. articles to profl. jours. Mem. Kendall-Perrine Assn. Realtors (sec., treas. 1992-93, bd. dirs. 1991-92, grievance com. 1990, arbitration com. 1991, pres. elect 1994, pres. 1995), Fla. Assn. Realtors (rep. dist. 4 1992—), Nat. Assn. Realtors, NEA, Fla. Edn. Commn., Classroom Tchrs. Assn., Dade County Edn. Assn., Fla. Coun. Tchrs. Math., Fla. Bus. Edn. Assn., Assn. Classroom Educators, Dade County Assn. Ednl. Adminstrs., ASCD, Alpha Delta Kappa, Kappa Delta Pi. Home: 7705 SW 138th Ter Miami FL 33158-1120 Office: 9036 SW 152d St Miami FL 33157

ROEMER, ELIZABETH, astronomer, educator; b. Oakland, Calif., Sept. 4, 1929; d. Richard Quirin and Elsie (Barlow) R. B.A. with honors (Bertha Dolbeer scholar), U. Calif., Berkeley, 1950, Ph.D. (Lick Obs. fellow), 1955. Tchr. adult class Oakland pub. schs., 1950-52; lab technician U. Calif. at Mt. Hamilton, 1951-55; grad. research astronomer U. Calif. at Berkeley, 1955-56; research asso. Yerkes Obs. U. Chgo., 1956; astronomer U.S. Naval Obs. Flagstaff, Ariz., 1957-66; asso. prof. dept. astronomy, also in lunar and planetary lab. U. Ariz., Tucson, 1966-69; prof. U. Ariz., 1969—; astronomer Steward Obs., 1980—; chmn. working group on orbits and ephemerides of comets commn. 20 Internat. Astron. Union, 1964-79, 85-88, v.p. commn. 20, 1979-82, pres., 1982-85, v.p. commn. 6, 1973-76, 85-88, pres., 1976-79, 88-91; mem. adv. panels Office Naval Research, Nat. Acad. Scis.-NRC, NASA; researcher and author numerous publs. on astrometry and astrophysics of comets and minor planets including 79 recoveries of returning periodic comets, visual and spectroscopic binary stars, computation of orbits of comets and minor planets. Recipient Dorothea Klumpke Roberts prize U. Calif. at Berkeley, 1950, Mademoiselle Merit award, 1959; asteroid (1657) named Roemera, 1965; Benjamin Apthorp Gould prize Nat. Acad. Scis., 1971; NASA Spl. award, 1986. Fellow AAAS (council 1966-69, 72-73), Royal Astron. Soc. (London); mem. Am. Astron. Soc. (program vis. profs. astronomy 1960-75, council 1967-70, chmn. div. dynamical astronomy 1974), Astron. Soc. Pacific (publs. com. 1962-73, Comet medal com. 1968-74, Donohoe lectr. 1962), Internat. Astron. Union, Am. Geophys. Union, Brit. Astron. Assn., Phi Beta Kappa, Sigma Xi. Office: U Ariz Lunar and Planetary Lab Tucson AZ 85721

ROEMER, ELIZABETH K., lawyer; b. South Bend, Ind., Sept. 29, 1952; d. Thomas Joseph and Shirley Marie (Shoemaker) R. BA, Ind. U., 1974; MA, Princeton U., 1978; JD, Stanford U., 1981. Bar: Calif., 1981. Atty. Shartsis, Friese & Ginsburg, San Francisco, 1981-83; sr. counsel, asst. sec. Pacific Telesis Group, San Francisco, 1983—. Avocation: psychology. Office: Pacific Telesis Group 130 Kearny St Ste 3609 San Francisco CA 94108

ROEMER, MILTON IRWIN, physician, educator; b. Paterson, N.J., Mar. 24, 1916; s. Jacob and Mary (Rabinowitz) R.; m. Ruth Rosenbaum., Sept. 1, 1939; children: John, Beth. B.A., Cornell U., 1936, M.A., 1939; M.D., NYU, 1940; M.P.H., U. Mich., 1943. Diplomate: Am. Bd. Preventive Medicine. Intern Barnert Meml. Hosp., Paterson, 1940-41; with N.J. Health Dept., Trenton, 1941-42, USPHS, Washington, 1943-48; mem. faculty Yale U. Med. Sch., 1949-51; with WHO. Geneva, 1951-53, Sask. (Can.) Health Dept., 1953-56; mem. faculty Cornell U., 1957-61; prof. health adminstrn. U. Calif. Sch. Pub. Health, Los Angeles, 1962—; cons. in field. Author: numerous books, including Health Care Systems in World Perspective, 1976, Comparative National Policies on Health Care, 1977, Ambulatory Health Services in America, 1981, National Health Systems of the World: Vol. 1: The Countries, 1991, Vol. 2: The Issues, 1993. Mem. Inst. Medicine, Am. Pub. Health Assn. (award for excellence in internat. health 1977, Sedgwick medal 1983), Am. Coll. Preventive Medicine, Internat. Epidemiol. Assn., Physicians Forum, Group Health Assn. Am., Phi Beta Kappa, Sigma Xi, Alpha Omega Alpha, Phi Kappa Phi, Delta Omega. Home: 365 S Westgate Ave Los Angeles CA 90049-4207 Office: Univ Calif Sch Pub Health Los Angeles CA 90024

ROEMER, TIMOTHY J., congressman; b. South Bend, Ind., Oct. 30, 1956; m. Sarah Lee Johnston, 1989. BA in pol. sci, U. Calif., San Diego, 1979; MA, PhD in internat. rels., U. Notre Dame, 1986. Staff asst. to congressman John Brademas U.S Congress; def., trade and fgn. policy advisor to senator Dennis DeConcini; mem. prof. 102nd-103rd Congresses from 3rd Ind. dist., 1991—; mem. economic and ednl. opportunity com., mem. sci. com.; adj. prof. Am. U. Office: 407 Cannon House Office Bu Washington DC 20515 also: 217 N Main St South Bend IN 46601-1216*

ROEMER, WILLIAM FREDERICK, banker; b. Youngstown, Ohio, Sept. 21, 1933; s. James Alexander and Helen France (James) R.; m. Linda Jo Cooper, June 30, 1956; children: Karen Roemer Seese, James Cooper, Gail Irwin, Sarah. B.A., Princeton U., 1955. Various positions Mellon Bank, Pitts., 1959-69; pres. Bradford (Pa.) Nat. Bank, 1970-72, First Laurel Bank, St. Marys, Pa., 1972-75; pres. Pennbank, Titusville, Pa., 1975-82, chmn., 1982-85; pres., chief exec. officer Pennbancorp, 1980-88; pres., chief exec. officer Integra Fin. Corp., Pitts., 1989-90, chmn., chief exec. officer, 1991—; bd. dirs. Pitts. br. of Fed. Res. Bank Cleve., 1990-92. Bd. dirs. Titusville Hosp., 1977-86, pres., 1979-81; sr. warden, lay reader St. James Episcopal Ch., Titusville, 1968-88; various coms. Episcopal Diocese Northwestern Pa., 1979-88, diocesan coun., 1982-88, campaign chmn. for venture in mission capital fund drive, 1981; vestryman St. Stephens Episcopal Ch., Sewickley, 1990—; mem. standing com. Episcopal Diocese Pitts., 1992—; bd. dirs. Pitts. Symphony Orch., 1990—, United Way Southwestern Pa., 1990— campaign chmn. 1993, Greater Pitts. Coun. Boys Scouts Am., 1990—, Allegheny Conf. Community Devel., 1991—, Penn's S.W., 1990—. Lt. USN, 1955-58. Mem. Am. Bankers Assn. (govt. rels. coun. 1982-85, bank polit. action com. 1989-90), Bankers Roundtable, Pa. Bankers Assn. (dir. pub. affairs com. 1977-88, govt. rels. policy com. 1987-90, exec. com. 1989-90), Duquesne Club (bd. dirs. 1992-94), Allegheny Country Club, Laurel Valley Golf Club. Republican. Home: 900 Academy Pl Sewickley PA 15143-2068

ROEMING, ROBERT FREDERICK, foreign language educator; b. Milw., Dec. 12, 1911; s. Ferdinand August and Wanda E. (Radtke) R.; m. Alice Mae Voss, Aug. 30, 1941; 1 child, Pamela Alice. BA, U. Wis., 1934, MA, 1936, PhD, 1941. Mem. faculty Wis.-Milw., 1937—, prof. French and Italian, 1956—, assoc. dean Coll. Letters and Sci., asst. to provost for devel. of spl. programs, 1957-62, sole dir. dept. lang. labs., 1964-70, dir. English as 2d lang., 1967-70, founder and Ctr. Twentieth Century Studies, 1970-74, prof. emeritus, 1980—; founder, chief investigator Camus Bibliography Research Collection, Golda Meir Library, 1985; rep. D.C. Heath Co., 1943-

46; cons., 1946-50; cons. computer systems Harnischfeger Corp., Milw., 1953-57; chmn. tech. sect. Internat. Congress on Fgn. Lang. Tchg., Pädagogisches Zentrum, Berlin, summer 1964; guest InterAm. Congress of Linguists, Montevideo, Uruguay, 1966; ofcl. guest Romanian govt. 10th Internat. Congress Linguists, summer 1967; dir. Insts. in Adult Basic Edn., 1969, U.S. Office Edn.; pres., treas. Electronic Rsch. Instruments Co., Inc., Nashotah, Wis., 1969-93. Author: (with C.E. Young) Introduction to French, 1951, Camus, A Bibliography, 1969, rev. and augmented computer-microfiche 11th edit., 1993, Little Magazine Catalog (NEH grantee), 1976-77; editor Modern Lang. Jour., 1963-70; contbr. numerous monographs and articles to profl. jours., 72 taped radio programs on French Black lit. Chmn. bldg. commn. Village of Chenequa, Wis., 1972-88; trustee, chmn. Midwest chpt. Jose Greco Found. for Hispanic Dance, Inc., 1970-76; mem. Wis. Bd. Nursing, 1977-79, chmn., 1979; mem. numerous nat. conservation orgns. and local civic groups. Decorated chevalier, officier, commandeur Ordre Palmes Académiques (France); recipient Travel award Italian Govt., 1934. Mem. MLA (life, index com. 1970-79), Nat. Fedn. Modern Lang. Tchrs. Assn. (exec. com. 1963-70), Verband Deutscher Schriftsteller, Wis. News Photographers Assn. (hon. life, Pres.'s award 1972), Soc. des Etudes Camusiennes, Am. Assn. of French Acad. Palms, Wis. Assn. for the Blind and Physically Handicapped, Chenequa Country Club, Lake Country Racquet and Athletic Club, Phi Eta Sigma, Phi Kappa Phi, Tau Kappa Epsilon. Research in application of the computer to humanities, applied linguistics and contemporary French and Italian Lit. Home: 6078 N Oakland Hills Rd Nashotah WI 53058 Office: U Wis-Milw Golda Meir Libr W240 2311 E Hartford Ave Milwaukee WI 53211-3175

ROEN, PHILIP RUBEN, urologist, surgeon, medical educator; b. N.Y.C., Aug. 5, 1914; s. Nathaniel and Ida (Brickman) R.; m. Florence Sonia Gluck, Dec. 23, 1944; children: Janet Leslie. BA, Columbia Coll., 1934, MD, 1938. Diplomate Am. Bd. Urology. Fellow Cleve. Clinic; resident in urology N.Y. Hosp.; dir. urology St. Clare's Hosp., N.Y.C., 1959—; attending urologist Roosevelt Hosp., N.Y.C., 1980—; prof. clin. urology N.Y. Med. Coll. Valhalla, 1980—. Contbr. articles to profl. jours. Chmn. profl. rels. Blue Shield, N.Y.C., 1978-80. Mem. ACS, Am. Urol. Assn., N.Y. Urol. Assn., Princeton Club N.Y.C. Office: 220 Madison Ave New York NY 10016

ROEN, SHELDON R., publisher, psychologist; b. N.Y.C.; s. Morris Rosenthal and Gussie (Weininger) R.; m. Selma Lois Pollets, Feb. 21, 1954; children—Randa M., Marjorie A., Harris L. B.S., City U. N.Y., 1950, M.A., 1951; Ph.D., Columbia U., 1955; postgrad., New Sch. Social Research, 1951-53, Harvard Sch. Pub. Health, 1961-62. Diplomate: Am. Bd. Examiners in Profl. Psychology. Tchr. pub. schs. N.Y.C., 1950-53; chief Clin. Psychology Svc., Ft. Sill, Okla., 1955-58; instr. Cameron Coll., Okla. A. and M. U., 1956-58; asst. prof. U. N.H., 1958-60; asst. chief psychol. services Mass. Mental Health Center, Boston, 1960-63; instr. Harvard, 1961-63; rsch. assoc. Med. Sch., 1960-63; dir. rsch. S. Shore Mental Health Center, Quincy, Mass., 1962-66; assoc. prof. dept. psychology Tchrs. Coll., Columbia, N.Y.C., 1966-72; dir. Psychol. Consultation Center, 1966-72; chmn. bd. pres., psychologist Human Scis. Press, N.Y.C., 1972—; Lectr. L.I. U. summer 1958, Tufts U., 1961-62; mem. N.H. Gov.'s Com. on Spl. Edn., also Study Com. on Mental Health Reorgn., 1961-62; cons. VISTA program OEO, 1966-67; mem. juvenile problems research rev. com. NIMH, 1968-69; mem. research rev. com. Title III Elementary and Secondary Edn. Act project application Ohio Dept. Edn., 1969-72; mem. mental health coordinating com. local sch. dist. 5, N.Y.C., 1969-72; mem., research dir. work incentive program for welfare recipients Wharton Sch. Pa., U.S. Dept. Labor, 1969-72; mem. mental health and community control com. N.Y. Psychologists for Social Action, 1969-72. Authors, editor books.; Editor: Mass. Psychol. Assn. Newsletter, 1963-65, Community Mental Health Jour; contbr. articles to profl. jours. and chpts. to books. Chmn. bd. trustees Bristol Acres Sch., Taunton, Mass., 1965-67. Fellow Am. Psychol. Assn. (mem. com. pre-coll. behavioral scis. 1968-71, founder div. 27 community psychology div. 1969, chmn. subcom. pre-high sch. behavioral sci. 1969-72), Am. Pub. Health Assn., Am. Orthopsychiat. Assn. (com. on research edn. 1965-67), Am. Sociol. Assn.; mem. New Eng. Psychol. Assn. (steering com. 1965-68), N.H. Psychol. Assn. (legis. chmn. 1961-62). Office: 3205 Beacon St Pompano Beach FL 33062-1207

ROENICK, JEREMY, professional hockey player; b. Boston, Jan. 17, 1970. Center Chgo. Blackhawks, 1988—. Named The Sporting News NHL Rookie of the Yr., 1989-90. Played in NHL All-Star Games, 1991-94. Office: Chgo Blackhawks 1800 W Madison St Chicago IL 60612-2620*

ROENKE, HENRY MERRILL, JR., curator; b. Geneva, N.Y., Mar. 16, 1916; s. Henry Merrill and Pauline Margaret (Young) R.; m. Marion E. Guess, Oct. 4, 1943; children: Henry M. III, Karl Guess, Kathleen Guess. BA, Hobart Coll., 1938; MS in Retailing, NYU, 1939; HLD (hon.), Hobart Coll. 1983. Sales Gimbels, N.Y.C., 1939; buyer, mdse. mgr. J.W. Smith Dry Goods Co., Geneva, N.Y., 1946-60, pres., 1961-76; pres. Prouty-Chew House-Geneva House Mus.-Geneva Hist. Soc., 1961; dir. Rose Hill Restoration, Geneva, 1966—; adminstrn. designer Fund for Hist. Geneva, 1966-71; tchr. continuing edn. Geneva Bd. Edn., 1969-80; curator fine arts Hobart & William Smith Coll., Geneva, 1968—; trustee Geneva Savings Bank, 1957-92; adminstr. Rose Hill Mansion & John Johnson House Mus., Geneva, 1967—. Author: Rose Hill: A Greek Revival Mansion, 1984, Treasures of American Architecture, 1987. Vestryman, warden St. Peter's Ch., Geneva, 1955—; councilman Geneva City Coun., 1960-64; mem. adv. bd. Salvation Army, Geneva, 1968-72; mem. lakefront devel. com. Geneva City Govt., 1989—; comml. design adv. team City of Geneva, 1990—. Comdr. USNR, 1940-45. Recipient Nat. Trust for Hist. Preservation award for Significant Achievement in Hist. Preservation in the U.S., 1974; named Citizen of Yr., Geneva C. of C., 1988. Mem. Am. Legion, Rotary (treas. 1961-71), Masons, Theta Delta Chi (nat. adv. bd. 1968, treas. alumni chpt. 1954-76). Republican. Episcopalian. Home: 91 St Clair St Geneva NY 14456 Office: Rose Hill Mansion Box 464 Geneva NY 14456

ROEPER, RICHARD, columnist; b. Chgo., Oct. 17, 1959; s. Robert and Margaret R. BA, Ill. State U., 1982. Freelance writer, 1982-87; columnist Chgo.-Sun Times, 1987—; talk show host Sta. WLS-FM, Chgo.; commentator Fox Thing in the Morning, Sta. WFLD-TV, Fox TV, Chgo. Recipient Outstanding Columnist Ill. Press Assn., 1992, Nat. Headliner award for top columnist Atlantic City Press Club, 1992, Emmy award, 1994. Mem. Am. Fedn. TV & Radio Artists, Chgo. Newspaper Guild. Office: Chgo Sun-Times 401 N Wabash Ave Chicago IL 60611-3532

ROEPKE, NANCY JEAN, investment company executive; b. Arlington, Va., Jan. 16, 1955; d. Duane Henry and Helen (Smeltzer) R. Student, Radford (Va.) Coll., 1973-77. Staff asst. Capitol Investors, Ltd., Alexandria, Va., 1979-82; adminstr. DeRand Corp. Am., Arlington, 1982-88; sec. Bankwest Corp., Denver, 1977—; pres., bd. dirs. Pace Investments, Inc., Washington, 1988-90; bd. dirs. Unocam, Inc., Washington; gen. securities prin. Washington Investment Corp., 1990-94. Mem. chancel choir, deacon Columbia Bapt. Ch., Falls Church, Va. Home: 2205 Hunters Run Dr Reston VA 22091 Office: NV Comml Inc Ste 500 8230 Leesburg Pike Vienna VA 22182

ROER, ROBERT DAVID, physiologist, educator; b. N.Y.C., Oct. 15, 1952; s. Edwin Marvin and Dorothy Barbara (Blaymore) R.; m. Marjorie Elizabeth Smith, May 29, 1976; 1 child, Sara Elizabeth. BS, Brown U., 1974; PhD, Duke U., 1979. Asst. prof. U. N.C. Wilmington, 1979-85, assoc. prof., 1985-90, prof., 1990—. Contbr. articles to various jours. and publs. Grantee NSF, NASA, N.C. Biotech. Ctr., N.C. Sea Grant. Mem. AAAS, AAUP, Am. Physiol. Soc., Am. Soc. Zoologists, Crustacean Soc., Sigma Xi. Office: Univ North Carolina 7205 Wrightsville Ave Wilmington NC 28403-7296

ROERICK, WILLIAM (GEORGE) (WILLIAM ROEHRICK), actor, author; b. New Jersey, Dec. 17, 1912; s. William George and Josephine (Clark) Roehrick. BS, Hamilton Coll., 1934, DFA (hon.), 1971; student, Berkshire Playhouse Drama Sch., 1935. chmn. fine arts adv. com. Alumni Coun., Hamilton Coll.; bd. dirs. Berkshire Theatre Festival, Stockbridge, Mass. Broadway roles include: Romeo and Juliet, 1935, St. Joan, 1936, Hamlet, 1936, Our Town, 1938, The Land is Bright, 1941, This is the Army, 1942-45, Magnificent Yankee, 1946, Tonight at 8:30, 1948, Right Honourable Gentleman, 1961, Marat/Sade, 1967, The Homecoming, 1967,

Waltz of the Toreadors, 1973, Night of the Iguana, 1976-77; film appearances include The Other Side of the Mountain, This is the Army, Day of the Dolphin; numerous TV appearances including role as Henry Chamberlain in TV serial Guiding Light; co-author: (with Thomas Coley) play The Happiest Years, 1949, A Passage to E.M. Forster; dramatic reading, 1970; TV scripts for Climax, Mamma. Served with AUS, 1942-45. Mem. Actors Equity Assn. (council 10 years), Screen Actors Guild. AFTRA, Dramatists Guild, Actors Fund Am., Players Club, Century Club. Home: 145 W 79th St New York NY 10024-6468

ROESCH, CLARENCE HENRY, banker; b. Egg Harbor City, N.J., Aug. 22, 1925; s. Joseph Aloysius and Bertha (Heumann) R.; m. Helen Regina Owens, Sept. 25, 1954; children—Kathleen Marie, Helena Patricia, Maryanne Cornelia. B.B.A., Rutgers U., 1949, postgrad., 1961; certificate, Am. Inst. Banking, 1961; grad., Trust Sch., Bucknell U., 1971. Cert. internal auditor, data processing auditor. Bookkeeper, teller, head teller, asst. sec., trust officer, auditor Egg Harbor Bank & Trust Co., 1949-61; bank examiner Phila. Fed. Res. Bank, 1962-65; chief auditor Am. Bank & Trust Co. of Pa. (name changed to Meridian Bancorp Inc. 1985), Reading, 1966—, v.p. audit dept., 1968-88; ret. officer Am. Bank & Trust Co. of Pa. (name changed to Meridian Bancorp Inc. 1985), 1988; parish sec. St. Benedict Ch., Plowville, 1989—; sr. staff auditor Nat. Penn Bank, Boyertown, 1990—; mem. faculty Berks County chpt. Am. Inst. Banking, 1966-68; instr. bank auditing Bank Adminstrn. Inst., U. Richmond, 1968; pres., past mems. chpt. Am. Banking Inst., Atlantic County, N.J., 1958-59. Mem. budget com. Berks County chpt. United Way, 1967-73; bd. dirs. Berks Reading coun. Camp Fire, 1966-93, chmn. fin. com., 1973, 75, treas., 1974-84; instr. 55 Alive Program Am. Assn. Ret. Person, 1989—. Recipient John Johnston award as outstanding banker N.J., 1955; award U.S. Savs. Bond Com., 1961; Luther Halsey Gulick award for vol. services Camp Fire, 1975; John C. Collier award for outstanding bus. and fin. services, 1981, Blue Ribbon award for vol. services Camp Fire, 1984, award for corp. vol. of yr. Meridian Bancorp Inc., 1984, 85, Outstanding Svc. in Fin. Mgmt. award Camp Fire, 1988. Mem. Inst. Internal Auditors (dir. ctrl. Pa. chpt.), Berks County Bankers Assn., Travelers Protective Assn., Berks Reading C. of C., Bank Administration Inst. (past pres., dir. Penn-Jersey chpt.), Spring Lawn Optimist Club (bd. dirs. 1992, Key Mem. award 1992, chmn. fin. and budget com. 1992-94). Home: 24 Medinah Dr Flying Hills Reading PA 19607

ROESER, ROSS JOSEPH, audiologist, educator; b. Louisville, Nov. 14, 1942; s. Carl Henry and Yvonne Marie (Phillips) R.; m. Sharon Lynn Hill, June 9, 1962; children: Wendy Ann, Elizabeth Marie, Jennifer Yvonne. BS, Western Ill. U., 1966; MA, No. Ill. U., 1967; PhD, Fla. State U., 1972. Audiologist Anna (Ill.) State Hosp., 1967-69; chief of audiology Callier Ctr., Dallas, 1972-88, dir., 1988—; prof. audiology U. Tex., Dallas, 1975—; clin. prof. dept. otolaryngology U. Tex. Southwestern Med. Ctr., 1975—. Author: Auditory Disorders, 1982; founder Ear and Hearing jour., 1979. Recipient Alumni Achievement award Western Ill. U., 1978, Fla. State U., 1990. Mem. Tex. Speech-Lang.-Hearing Assn. (Jack L. Bangs award 1994), Acad. Dispensing Audiologists (Joel Wernick award 1990). Home: 1921 Marydale Rd Dallas TX 75208-3034 Office: Callier Ctr 1966 Inwood Rd Dallas TX 75235-7298

ROESLER, KARL, electronics executive; b. 1941. Grad., U. Notre Dame, 1962. With GE, Fairfield, Conn., 1963-90; v.p. fin. Therm-O-Disc Inc., Mansfield, Ohio, 1990—. Office: Therm-O-Disc Inc 1320 S Main St Mansfield OH 44907-0538*

ROESLER, ROBERT HARRY, city official; b. Hammond, La., Oct. 5, 1927; s. Albert N. and Hilda (Schwartz) R.; m. Cloe Alferez, May 7, 1955; children: Kim, Bob, Toby. Student, Tulane U. Mem. sports staff Times Picayune, New Orleans, 1949-94, sports editor, 1964-80; exec. sports editor Times Picayune and States-Item, 1980-94; sports coord. New Orleans Met. Conv. and Visitors Bur., 1994—. Vice chmn. Navy Recruiting Dist.; mem. assistance coun., New Orleans, 1992—. Served with USNR, World War II; Served with USNR, Korean conflict. Mem. Profl. Football Writers Assn. Am. (pres. 1976-77), Nat. Turf Writers Assn., Football Writers Am., Am. Legion, Navy League U.S., New Orleans Press Club (pres. 1959-60, sports writing awards). Home: 6958 Colbert St New Orleans LA 70124-2334 Office: 1520 Sugar Bowl Dr New Orleans LA 70112

ROESNER, LARRY AUGUST, civil engineer; b. Denver, Mar. 14, 1941; s. Walter George and Sarah Jane (Merrick) R.; m. Kathleen Ann Fahrenbruch, Dec. 13, 1964; children: David John, Kevin Walter, Nathan August, Melissa Jane. B.S., Valparaiso (Ind.) U., 1963; M.S., Colo. State U., 1965; Ph.D., U. Wash., Seattle, 1969. Registered profl. engr., Calif., Mich., Va., Md., Fla., Ohio. Part-time grad. research asst. Colo. State U., 1963-65, U. Wash., 1965-68; assoc. engr., then prin. engr. Water Resources Engrs., Inc., Walnut Creek, Calif., 1968-77; assoc., then v.p. Camp Dresser & McKee Inc., Annandale, Va., 1977-85; sr. v.p. and dir. water resources Camp, Dresser & McKee Inc., Maitland, Fla., 1985-92; chief tech. officer Camp Dreser & McKee Inc., Maitland, Fla., 1992—; chmn. Engr. Found. Conf. on Current Practice and Design Criteria Urban Runoff Quality Controls, 1988; guest lectr., cons. urban hydrology and surface water quality; invited lectr. NATO Adv. Rsch. Conf. on Urban Runoff Pollution, 1985; invited participant ASCE Rsch. Conf. Engring. in 21st Century, 1987; NRC exec. com. Wastewater Mgmt. in Urban Coastal Areas, 1992; chmn. task force com. on urban runoff quality mgmt. Water Environ. Fedn. Author rsch. reports, tech. revs., contbg. author on urban hydrology in several books. Fellow ASCE (control mem. rsch. and edn. com. water resources div., nat. chmn. 1995 water resources planning and mgmt. div. splty. conf., nat. Walter L. Huber civil engring. rsch. prize 1975); mem. NAE, Am. Acad. Environ. Engrs. (diplomate), Am. Water Resources Assn., Am. Cons. Engrs. Assn., Water Environ. Fedn. (chmn. nonpoint sources of pollution com., urban runoff task force), Tau Beta Pi (eminent engr.). Republican. Lutheran. Achievements include development of several widely used mathematical models for U.S. government agencies including QUAL-II stream quality model for the EPA; STORM, an urban stormwater management model for the U.S. Army CE; SWMM-EXTRAN, a dynamic hydraulics model for storm drainage and sewer systems for the EPA. Home: 205 Wild Creek Ct Longwood FL 32779-3351 Office: Camp Dresser & McKee Inc 590 Summit Park Dr Ste 300 Orlando FL 32810-5934 An environmental engineer is a caretaker in God's garden, the earth. The challenge for the environmental engineer is to maintain a balance between the needs of man and those of nature so that man may both use and enjoy the garden. It is the responsibility of the environmental engineer to leave the garden a little nicer than he found it.

ROESNER, PETER LOWELL, manufacturing company executive; b. Winchester, Ind., July 3, 1937; s. Lowell LeClair and Martha Christine (Overmyer) R.; children: Peter Lowell II, David Brandon, John Franklin. Student, Durham (Eng.) U., 1957-58; B.A., DePauw U., 1959; J.D., U. Mich., 1962; M.B.A., Harvard U., 1964. Bar: Ind. 1962, N.J. 1992. Asst. to pres. Overmyer Corp., Muncie, Ind., 1964-65, corp. sec., 1965-69, pres., 1969-84, also dir.; pres. Clinitemp Inc., Indpls., 1985-88; pres., owner Middletown (N.J.) Interiors Inc., 1993—; dir. Mchts. Nat. Bank, 1974-84. Trustee Purdue U., 1978. Mem. Ind. Mfrs. Assn. (dir. 1970-82, pres. 1975, chmn. Phoenix Award com. 1974), Glass Packaging Inst. (trustee 1981-84), ABA. Episcopalian. Office: Middletown Interiors 1270 Highway 35 Middletown NJ 07748

ROESS, ROGER PETER, engineering educator; b. Flushing, N.Y., Dec. 12, 1947; s. Charles Gordon and Theresa (Welchner) R.; m. Janet Elaine Mitchell, July 4, 1970; children: Roger Michael, Christopher John. BCE, Poly. Inst. N.Y., Bklyn., 1968, MS in Transp. Planning, 1969, PhD in Transp. Planning, 1972. Instr. Poly. Inst. N.Y., 1969-72, asst. prof., 1972-77, assoc., 1977-83, prof., 1983-86; prof. Poly. U., Bklyn., 1986—, dean engring., 1984-95, assoc. provost acad. affairs, 1990-93; v.p. for academic affairs Poly U., Bklyn., 1993-95. Contbr. articles to profl. jours. Vice pres. Garden City South Little League, N.Y., 1981-87; trustee Franklin Sq. Bd. Edn., N.Y., 1984-90, 94—. Recipient D. Grant Mickle award Transp. Research Bd., 1979. Mem. Transp. Research Bd. (hwy. capacity and quality service com. 1985—), Inst. Transp. Engrs. (assoc.), Sigma Xi, Chi Epsilon, Tau Beta Pi. Office: Poly U Dept Civil-Environ Engring Brooklyn NY 11201-2907

ROESSER, JEAN WOLBERG, state legislator; b. Washington, May 8, 1930; d. Solomon Harry Wolberg and Mary Frances Brown; m. Eugene Francis Roesser, Aug. 3, 1957; children: Eugene Francis, Mary Roessler Calderon, Anne. BA, Trinity Coll., Washington, 1951; postgrad. in econs., Cath. U. of Am., 1951-53. Congl. relations asst. U.S. Info. Agy., Washington, 1954-58; news reporter for Montgomery County Council Suburban Record, 1983-86; del. Md. Gen. Assembly, Annapolis, 1986-94; mem. State Senate, Md. Gen. Assembly, Annapolis, 1994—, mem. fin. com., ethics con., 1994—. Mem. Md. Gov.'s Task Force on Energy; former pres. Montgomery County Fedn. Rep. Women, Potomac Women's Rep. Club; former 3d v.p. Md. Fedn. Rep. Women; founding mem. Montgomery County Arts Coun.; alt. del. Rep. Nat. Convention, 1992. Recipient Cmty. Achievement awrd Washington Psychiat. Soc., 1994, Trinity Coll. Leadership award, 1994, Common Cause Md. award, 1993, Md. Underage Drinking Preventio Coalition award, 1994. Mem. Women Legislators Md., also area citizens assns. and chambers commerce. Republican. Roman Catholic. Home: 10830 Fox Hunt Ln Potomac MD 20854-1553 Office: James Senate Office Bldg State Capitol Annapolis MD 21401

ROESSLER, ERNEST CHRISTIAN, bank executive; b. Pitts., Apr. 7, 1941; s. Ernest George and Edna Melzena (Poor) R.; m. Constance Verne Benner, Jan 20, 1968; children: E. Christian Jr., Todd S., Victoria E. BA, Dartmouth U., 1962; MBA, Amostuck, 1963. Sr. v.p. Mellon Bank, Pitts., 1963-87; supr., chief fin. officer Lane Fin., Northbrook, Ill., 1987-88; pres., CEO Central Carolina Bank, Durham, N.C., 1988—. Pres. Life and Sci. Mus., Durham, 1992—; dir. C. of C., Durham, 1992—. Capt. Air Guard, 1963-72. Mem. Fin. Execs. Inst. (v.p. 1989, pres.), Rotary Internat. (dir.), Duquesne Club, Hope Valley Club. Republican. Presbyterian. Avocations: golf, skiing. Home: 3710 Northampton Rd Durham NC 27707-5080 Office: CCB Fin Corp 111 Corcoran St Durham NC 27701

ROESSLER, RONALD JAMES, lawyer; b. Kansas City, Mo., Aug. 10, 1939; s. Robert Louis and Eleanor Florence (Ramsdell) R.; m. Sally Jo Canfield, Aug. 18, 1962; children: Martha Lee, Elizabeth Ramsdell. BA in Govt., Miami U., 1961; postgrad. Law Sch., Duke U., 1961-62; JD, Wis. Law Sch., 1964; LLM, George Washington U., 1968. Bar: Wis. 1964, D.C. 1970, W.va. 1971, Md. 1972, N.Y. 1985. Atty. Dept. Agr., Washington, 1964-66, Office Gen. Counsel, CIA, Washington, 1966, 68-69, C & P Tel. Co., Washington, 1969-72; sr. v.p., gen. counsel Alexander & Alexander Services Inc., N.Y.C., 1972-81, Alexander & Alexander Svcs. Inc., N.Y.C., 1972-94; sr. counsel Rollins Hudig Hall, N.Y.C., 1995—; adj. prof. bus. law Towson State U., 1981-82. Trustee Bryn Mawr Sch., Balt., 1980-83. Served with USAF, 1966-68. Mem. ABA, Wis. Bar Assn., D.C. Bar Assn., W. Va. Bar Assn., Md. Bar Assn., Assn. of Bar of City of N.Y. Home: 15 Ferncliff Rd Cos Cob CT 06807-1206 Office: Rollins Hudig Hall Two World Trade Ctr New York NY 10048

ROESSNER, BARBARA, journalist; b. Elizabeth, N.J., Sept. 16, 1953; d. Gilbert George and Dorothy Anne (Hector) R.; m. Craig William Baggott, Jan. 20, 1982; children: Craig, Taylor, Liam, Katherine, Elizabeth. BA, Wesleyan U., 1975. Reporter, editor Meriden (Conn.) Record-Jour., 1975-78; reporter The Hartford (Conn.) Courant, 1978-81, chief polit. writer, 1981-86, columnist, 1986—; column distributed worldwide by L.A. Times-Washington Post News Svc. Recipient Best Mag. Column award Soc. Profl. Journalists, 1993, Best Mag. Feature award, 1993. Home: 22 Vanderbilt Rd West Hartford CT 06119 Office: Hartford Courant Co 285 Broad St Hartford CT 06115-2510

ROESSNER, ROLAND GOMMEL, architect, educator; b. Terre Haute, Ind., Nov. 19, 1911; s. Elmer George and Florence Carol. Roessner; m. Virginia Gail Humberger, Nov. 17, 1943 (dec. Oct. 1955); 1 son., Roland Gommel. BArch, Miami U., Oxford, Ohio, 19356; MArch, U. Cin., 1942. Registered architect Ohio, Fla., Tex., interior designer, Tex. Assoc. Grunkeymeyer & Sullivan & Assocs., Cin. 1935-42; designing architect; pvt. practice architecture schs., pvt. residences St. Petersburg, Fla., 1945-47, Austin, Tex., 1947—; prof. Sch. Architecture U. Tex., Austin, 1947-82, chmn. design dept., 1954-67, mem. grad. faculty, 1958-82, acting dir., 1966, founder, dir. profl. residency program, 1971-82, prof. emeritus, 1982; assoc. Creer & Roessner, Austin, 1958-63; prin. R. Gommel Roessner, 1977—; design cons. O'Connell, Probst, Grobe, Inc. Architects/Engrs., Austin, 1979—; cons. community standards com. Dept. Commerce; mem. rsch. unit Naval Res.; adviser design State Bd. Archtl. Registration, Tex., 1960-68. Contbr. articles to profl. jours. Lt. comdr. USNR, 1942-45. Recipient numerous awards, citations in Am., fgn. publs. for architecture. Fellow AIA (mem. design com.); mem. Am. Concrete Inst., Am. Mil. Inst., Tex., Ohio, Fla. archtl. assns., Nat. Coun. Archtl. Registration Bds., Univ. Coop. Soc. (chmn. bd. dirs.), Am. Legion, VFW A'telier, Optimist Club, Westwood Country Club, U. Tex. Faculty Club, Headliners, Tarryhouse, Delta Phi Delta, Alpha Rho Chi, Delta Upsilon. Roland G. Roessner Professorship established Sch. Architecture U. Tex. Home: 3416 Pecos St Apt A Austin TX 78703-1012

ROETHE, JAMES NORTON, lawyer; b. Milw., Jan. 27, 1942; s. Arthur Frantz and Bess Irma (Norton) R.; m. Nita May Dorris, July 15, 1967; children: Melissa Dorris, Sarah Rebecca. BBA, U. Wis.-Madison, 1964, JD, 1967. Bar: Wis. 1967, U.S. Dist. Ct. (we. dist.) Wis. 1967, Calif. 1968, U.S. Dist. Ct. (no. dist.) Calif. 1972, U.S. Ct. Claims 1975, U.S. Ct. Appeals (9th cir.) 1980, U.S. Dist. Ct. (ea. dist.) Calif. 1982, U.S. Dist. Ct. (cent. dist.) Calif. 1986, U.S. Ct. Appeals (4th cir.) 1988, U.S. Ct. Appeals (2nd cir.) 1989. Assoc., Pillsbury, Madison & Sutro, San Francisco, 1971-77, ptnr., 1978-92; sr. v.p., dir. litigation, Bank of Am., San Francisco, 1992—; staff atty. Commn. on CIA Activities within U.S., Washington, 1975. Editor: Africa, 1967; editor-in-chief Wis. Law Rev., 1966-67. Bd. dirs. Orinda Assn. (Calif.), 1984-85, pres. 1986. Commr. City Orinda Planning Commn., 1988-94, chmn., 1990, 93; bd. dirs. Calif. Shakespeare Festival, 1993—; bd. visitors U. Wis. Law Sch., 1994—. Served to lt. USNR, 1967-71. Fellow Am. Bar Found.; mem. ABA, Wis. Bar Assn., Calif. Bar Assn., Bar Assn. San Francisco, Orinda Country Club, Phi Kappa Phi, Order of Coif. Republican. Home: 36 Fallen Leaf Ter Orinda CA 94563-1209 Office: Bank of Am Legal Dept 555 California St San Francisco CA 94104-1502

ROETHEL, DAVID ALBERT HILL, consultant; b. Milw., Feb. 17, 1926; s. Albert John and Elsie Margaret (Hill) R.; children: Elizabeth Jane, Susan Margaret. BS, Marquette U., 1950, MS, 1952; cert., Oak Ridge Sch. Reactor Tech., 1953. Chem. engr. naval reactors br. AEC, Washington, 1952-57; mgr. profl. relations, asst. to exec. sec. Am. Chem. Soc., Washington, 1957-72; exec. dir. Nat. Registry in Clin. Chemistry, Washington, 1967-72, Am. Assn. Clin. Chemists, Washington, 1968-70, Am. Orthotic and Prosthetic Assn., 1973-76, Am. Acad. Orthotists and Prosthetists, Am. Bd. Cert. in Orthotics and Prosthetics, 1973-76; exec. dir., fellow Am. Inst. Chemists, Washington, 1977-90; bd. dirs., exec. com. Am. Inst. Chemists, 1981-90, exec. dir. Nat. Certification Commn. in Chemistry and Chem. Engring., 1977-90, exec. dir., trustee Am. Inst. Chemists Found., 1982-90, sec., 1990; pres. Peachtree Promotions, 1991—; dir. Chemical Heritage Found., 1992—; treas. Cons. Consortium, 1994—; vice chmn., then chmn. Intersoc. Com. on Health Lab. Svcs., 1966-72; v.p. Pensions for Profls., Inc., Washington, 1970-72; vice chmn., then chmn. Engrs. and Scientists Joint Commn. on Pensions, 1978-80, vice chmn., 1985-87, chmn., 1988-90, 94—; mem. Commn. Profls. in Sci. and Tech., 1978—; sec.-treas., 1979-82, bd. dirs. 1989—, v.p., 1990-91, exec. com., 1990-95; sec. gen. 7th Internat. Congress in Orthotics, and Prosthetics, 1975-76, 2d World Congress in Prosthetics and Orthotics, 1975-77; chmn. U.S. arrangements Can.-Am. Chem. Congress, 1982-84; bd. dirs. China- U.S. Sci. Exchanges, 1985-89. Editor: Almanac, 1973-76, Chemist, 1977-90. Mem. Md. Gov.'s Com. on Sci. Devel., 1969; bd. dirs. Episcopal Ctr. for Children, 1991—, sec., 1992-93, pres., 1993-95. Served with U.S. Army, 1944-46. CBI. Recipient Outstanding Svc. award Intersoc. Com. on Health Lab. Svcs., 1972, Appreciation award Nat. Reg. in Clin. Chemistry, 1972. Mem. Am Chem. Soc. (dir. fed. credit union 1967-70, pres. 1968-70), Coun. Engring. and Sci. Soc. Execs. (bd. dirs. 1983-86), Am. Inst. Chemists, Sports Car Am. Club (bd. dirs. 1964-67, 75-77, vice chmn., sec. 1967, 75-76, local officer 1960-74, historian 1989—), Alpha Chi Sigma (pres. Washington-profl. chpt. 1963-64, 89-90, bd. dirs. 1991—, Profl. Achievement award 1986, bd. mgrs. 1986-90, dist. counselor 1964-68, nat. profl. rep. 1986-92, grand profl. alchemist 1992-94), D.C. Inst. Chemists (sec. 1992-94, pres.-elect 1995—), Sigma Gamma Chi, Pi Mu Epsilon.

ROETHENMUND, OTTO EMIL, financial and banking executive; b. Thun, Switzerland, Sept. 1, 1928; came to U.S., 1951, naturalized, 1957; s. Franz and Berta (Dallenbach) R.; m. Ermina Grassi, May 7, 1955; children—Robert, Denise. M.A., U. Neuchatel, 1948. Mgmt. trainee Kantonalbank, Bern, 1948-51; exec. trainee J. Henry Schroeder Banking and Trust Corp., N.Y.C., 1951-56; with Deak-Perera Group, N.Y.C., 1956—; vice chmn., group partner Deak-Perera Group, 1962—; v.p., then sr. v.p. Deak & Co. (holding co.), 1962-74, exec. v.p., 1974-80, pres., chief exec. officer, 1980-86; pres., dir. Inter-Nation Capital Mgmt. Corp., 1986—; lectr. internat. monetary and investment seminars. Served to lt. Swiss Army, 1948-51. Decorated knight Mil. Order Sts. Salvador and Brigitta (Sweden). Mem. Explorers Club, Met. Club (N.Y.C.), Westchester Country Club. Home: 2 Shore Rd Rye NY 10580-1031 Office: Inter-Nation Capital Mgmt Corp 230 Park Ave Ste 650 New York NY 10169-0650

ROETMAN, ORVIL M., retired airplane company executive; b. Slayton, Minn., Aug. 28, 1925; s. Ernest Gilbert and Olava (Christianson) R.; m. Lavera Jones, Mar. 14, 1948; 1 child, Debra Roetman Caldwell. BA, U. Minn., 1950; BS in Aerospace Engring., U.S. Naval Post Grad. Sch., 1955; JD, George Washington U., 1965; postgrad. Naval War Coll., 1961. Bar: D.C. 1966. Commd. ensign U.S. Navy, 1945, advanced through grades to comdr., 1962, ret., 1965; sole practice law, Washington, 1965-66; in legal services Boeing Co., Seattle, 1966-67, dir. contract adminstrn., 1968, dir. internat. sales, 1971-79, v.p. internat. sales, 1979-83, v.p. contracts, 1983-87, corp. v.p. govt. and internat. affairs, 1988-90, ret., 1990. Mem. bd. regents, pres. adv. bd. Concordia Theol. Sem., Fort Wayne, Ind., 1979—. Mem. Navy League (life). Republican. Lutheran.

ROETT, RIORDAN, political science educator, consultant; b. N.Y.C., Sept. 10, 1938; s. Riordan Jr. and Marion (Underwood) R. BA, Columbia U., 1959, MIA, 1962, PhD, 1968. Postdoctoral fellow Ctr. for Internat. Studies, MIT, Cambridge, Mass., 1966-67; asst. prof., assoc. prof. polit. sci. Vanderbilt U., Nashville, 1967-73; prof. polit. sci. Sch. Advanced Internat. Studies, Johns Hopkins U., Washington, 1973—; sr. polit. analyst internat. capital markets Chase Manhattan Bank, N.Y.C., 1983-85; sr. advisor World Econ. Forum, Geneva; bd. dirs. Global Ptnrs. Income Fund, Asia Tigers Fund, Emerging Markets Income Fund I & II, Salomon Bros. Worldwide Income Fund. Editor, co-author: Latin America, Western Europe, and the U.S.: Reevaluating the Atlantic Triangle, 1985, Mexico and the U.S.: Managing the Relationship, 1988, Paraguay: The Legacy of Personalist Politics, 1990, Mexico's External Relations in the 1990's, 1991, Political and Economic Liberalization in Mexico, 1993. Fulbright fellow, 1962. Mem. Latin Am. Studies Assn. (v.p. 1977, pres. 1978), Coun. on Fgn. Rels., Cosmos Club. Democrat. Roman Catholic. Home: 2301 Connecticut Ave NW Apt 1B Washington DC 20008-1730 Office: Johns Hopkins U SAIS 1740 Massachusetts Ave NW Washington DC 20036-1984

ROETTGER, NORMAN CHARLES, JR., federal judge; b. Lucasville, Ohio, Nov. 3, 1930; s. Norman Charles and Emma Eleanora R.; children: Virginia, Peggy. BA, Ohio State U., 1953; LLB magna cum laude, Washington and Lee U., 1958. Bar: Ohio 1958, Fla. 1958. Assoc. Frost & Jacobs, Cin., 1958-59; assoc. firm Fleming, O'Bryan & Fleming, Ft. Lauderdale, Fla., 1959-63, partner, 1963-69, 71-72; dep. gen. counsel HUD, Washington, 1969-71; judge U.S. Dist. Ct. (so. dist.) Fla., Ft. Lauderdale, 1972—. Lt. (j.g.) USN, 1952-55; to capt. Res. 1972. Mem. ABA, Fed. Bar Assn., Fla. Bar Assn., Broward County Bar Assn., Am. Judicature Soc., Order of Coif, Masons, Coral Ridge Yacht Club, Omicron Delta Kappa, Kappa Delta Rho. Presbyterian. Clubs: Masons; Coral Ridge Yacht (Ft. Lauderdale). Office: US Dist Ct 299 E Broward Blvd Fort Lauderdale FL 33301-1944

ROFF, J(OHN) HUGH, JR., energy company executive; b. Wewoka, Okla., Oct. 27, 1931; s. Hugh and Louise Roff; m. Ann Green, Dec. 23, 1956; children—John, Charles, Andrew, Elizabeth, Jennifer. A.B., U. Okla., 1954, LL.B., 1955. Bar: Okla., Mo., N.Y. Law clk. to presiding justice U.S. Ct. Appeals (10th cir.), 1958; atty. Southwestern Bell Telephone Co., St. Louis, 1959-63, AT&T, N.Y.C., 1964-68; v.p., gen. atty. Long Lines, N.Y.C., 1969-73, gen. atty., 1973-74; chmn., pres., chief exec. officer United Energy Resources, Houston, 1974-86; chmn. PetroUnited Terminals Inc., Houston, 1986—. Past chmn. Cen. Houston Inc.; mem. adv. bd. Ctr. for Strategic and Internat. Studies, Washington; mem. coun. overseers Jones Sch. Bus. Adminstrn., Rice U.; trustee Baylor Coll. Medicine; mem. adv. bd. The Salvation Army, Houston. 1st lt. JAGC, U.S. Army, 1955-58. Mem. Order of Coif, Phi Beta Kappa, Beta Theta Pi. Clubs: Houston Country, Coronado, Houstonian. Office: 333 Clay St Ste 4300 Houston TX 77002-4103

ROFF, WILLIAM ROBERT, history educator, writer; b. Glasgow, Scotland, May 2, 1929; came to U.S., 1969; s. Robert Henry William and Isabella (Anderson) R.; m. Susanne Rabbitt, Aug. 2, 1978; children: Sarah, Emily. B.A., U. New Zealand, 1957, M.A., 1959; Ph.D., Australian Nat. U., 1965. Lectr. history Monash U., Australia, 1963-66; lectr., sr. lectr. U. Malaya, Malaysia, 1966-69; assoc. prof. Columbia U., N.Y.C., 1969-73, prof., 1973-90, prof. emeritus, 1990—; vis. prof. Yale U., 1971, L'Ecole des Hautes Etudes en Sciences Sociales, Paris, 1985; vis. fellow Australian Nat. U., 1974, Trinity Coll., Oxford U., Eng. 1981; hon. fellow Edinburgh U., Scotland, 1992—. Author: The Origins of Malay Nationalism, 1967, (with others) In Search of Southeast Asia, 1971, Bibliography of Malay and Arabic Periodicals, 1972; author, editor: Kelantan: Religion, Society and Politics, 1973; editor: Islam and the Political Economy of Meaning, 1987. Guggenheim Found. fellow 1973; Rockefeller Found. fellow, 1982. Mem. Royal Asiatic Soc. (life), Assn. for Asian Studies, Asian Studies Assn. Australia, Brit. Soc. for Middle East Studies, Middle East Studies Assn. Avocation: parenting. Home: 29 Shore St, Cellardyke Fife, Scotland

ROFFEY, ROBERT C., JR., insurance company executive; b. Gloucester, Mass., 1935. Exec. v.p., dir. Comml. Union Ins. Co., Boston. Office: Commercial Union Insurance Co 1 Beacon St Boston MA 02108-3106

ROFFMAN, HOWARD, motion picture company executive; b. Phila.. Student, U. Pa.; JD, U. Fla. Assoc. Morgan, Lewis & Bockius, Washington; from legal counsel to gen. counsel Lucasfilm, Ltd., San Rafael, Calif., 1980-84, acting chief operating officer, 1984-85, v.p. licensing, 1986-93, v.p. licensing, thx, 1993—. Author: Presumed Guilty, 1974, Understanding the Cold War, 1976. Mem. Calif. Bar Assn., Washington Bar Assn., Licensing Industry Merchandising Assn. Office: Lucasfilm Ltd PO Box 2009 San Rafael CA 94912-2009

ROGAL, PHILIP JAMES, physician; b. N.Y.C., Dec. 23, 1939; s. Abraham and Cecilia (Sandor) R.; m. Susan Regan, June 17, 1967; Michael James, Elizabeth. BA, Princeton (N.J.) U., 1960; MD, Columbia U., 1964. Diplomate Am. Bd. Internal Medicine, Am. Bd. Cardiology. Intern Yale-New Haven Hosp., 1964-65; resident Bellevue Hosp., N.Y.C., 1965-67, Presbyn. Hosp., N.Y.C., 1967-68; fellow Bronx Mcpl. Hosp., 1970-71; pvt. practice internist, cardiologist N.Y.C., 1971-88, Tampa, Fla., 1988—; admissions com. Albert Einstein Coll. of Medicine, N.Y.C., 1983-88; chief of medicine Meml. Hosp., Tampa, 1995—. Capt. USAF, 1968-70. Fellow Am. Coll. Cardiology; mem. ACP, Alpha Omega Alpha. Avocations: squash racquets, tennis, travel, music. Office: Palma Ceia Med Group Ste 106 2919 Swann Ave Tampa FL 33609

ROGALIN, ROGER RICHARD, publishing executive; b. N.Y.C., June 20, 1949; s. William A. and Paule (Deroo) R.; m. Elizabeth Grose; children: Eric, Sara, Andrew, Dylan. BS, Fairfield (Conn.) U., 1971; MA, Fairleigh Dickinson U., 1972. Cert. tchr., N.J. Sci. tchr. Bergen Cath. High Sch. Oradell, N.J., 1971-74; pharm. rep. Beecham Labs., Bristol, Tenn., 1974-75; editor Holt, Rinehart, Winston, N.Y.C., 1975-77, adminstrv. editor, 1977-81; exec. editor D.C. Heath & Co. div. of Raytheon, Lexington, Mass., 1981-84, editor-in-chief, 1984-86, sr. v.p., 1986-92; v.p. sch. div. Macmillan Pubs., N.Y.C., 1992—; instr. CBS Sch. mgmt., N.Y.C., 1979-80; cons. Ramapo Schs., Suffern, N.Y., 1975; bd. dirs. Concord Assabet Svcs., 1990-92. Editor: Modern Biology, 1977, General Science, 1978, Modern Health, 1980. Mem. Nat. Sci. Tchrs. Assn., Nat. Coun. Tchrs. English, Nat. Coun. Tchrs. Math. Roman Catholic. Office: Assoc Am Pub 71 5th Ave New York NY 10003-3001

ROGALLO, FRANCIS MELVIN, mechanical, aeronautical engineer; b. Sanger, Calif., Jan. 27, 1912; s. Mathieu and Marie Rogallo; m. Gertrude Sugden, Sept. 14, 1939; children: Marie, Robert, Carol, Frances. Degree in Mech. and Aero. Engring., Stanford U., 1935. With NACA (name changed to NASA), Hampton, Va., 1936-70, Kitty Hawk Kites, Nags Head, S.C.; lectr. on high lift devices, lateral control, flexible wings and flow systems. Contbr. articles to profl. jours. Active Rogallo Found. Recipient NASA award, 1963, Nat. Air and Space Mus. trophy, Lifetime Achievement award Smithsonian Instn., 1992; named to N.C. Sports Hall of Fame, 1987. Mem. Am. Kite Assn., U.S. Hang Gliding Assn. Episcopalian. Achievements include patents for Flexible Wing, Corner Kite, others; research in aerodynamics, wind tunnels. Home: 91 Osprey Ln Kitty Hawk NC 27949-3839 Office: Kitty Hawk Kites PO Box 1839 Nags Head NC 27959-1839

ROGALSKI, EDWARD J., university administrator; b. Manville, N.J., Feb. 16, 1942; s. Joseph Stanley and Wladyslawa (Kraszewski) R.; m. Barbara Ann Bogk, June 01, 1968; children: Edward, James, Daniel, David, Christopher. BA, Parsons Coll., 1965; MA, U. Iowa, 1968, PhD, 1985; LittD (hon.), Loras Coll., 1990. Dean of men, asst. dean of students Parsons Coll., Fairfield, Iowa, 1965-67; dean of students St. Ambrose Coll., Davenport, Iowa, 1968-74, v.p. adminstrn., 1974-80, sr. v.p., 1980-86, exec. v.p., 1986-87; pres. St. Ambrose U., Davenport, 1987—; bd. dirs., corp. sec. Genesis Med. Ctr., 1994—; bd. dirs. Firstar Bank Davenport N.A.; cons. ednl. div. Marriott Corp., 1988—. Vice chairperson Civil Rights Commn., Davenport, 1975; bd. dirs. Handicapped Devel. Ctr., Davenport, 1987, Jr. Achievement, 1988, Big Brothers-Big Sisters, 1988, Iowa Coll. Found., 1992—. Grantee Kettering Found., 1968. Mem. Iowa Assn. Ind. Colls. and Univs. (exec. com., treas. 1992—), Am. Assn. Higher Edn., Davenport C. of C. (bd. dirs. 1992), Rotary, Phi Delta Kappa. Roman Catholic. Home: 806 W Rusholme St Davenport IA 52804-1928 Office: St Ambrose U 518 W Locust St Davenport IA 52803-2829

ROGAN, ELEANOR GROENIGER, cancer researcher, educator; b. Cin., Nov. 25, 1942; d. Louis Martin and Esther (Levinson) G.; m. William John Robert Rogan, June 12, 1965 (div. 1970); 1 child, Elizabeth Rebecca. AB, Mt. Holyoke Coll., 1963; PhD, Johns Hopkins, 1968. Lectr. Goucher Coll., Towson, Md., 1968-69; rsch. assoc. U. Tenn., Knoxville, 1969-73; rsch. assoc. U. Nebr. Med. Ctr., Omaha, 1973-76, asst. prof., 1976-80, assoc. prof. Eppley Inst., dept. pharm. and dept. biochemistry and molecular biology scis., U. Nebr., 1980-90, prof., 1990—. Contbr. articles to profl. jours. Predoctoral fellow USPHS, Johns Hopkins U., 1965-68. Mem. AAAS, AAUP, Am. Assn. Cancer Rsch., Am. Soc. Biochem. Molecular Biology. Democrat. Roman Catholic. Home: 8210 Bowie Dr Omaha NE 68114-1526 Office: U Nebr Med Ctr Eppley Inst 600 S 42d St Omaha NE 68198-6805

ROGAN, PATRICK GOODE, lawyer; b. New Haven, May 4, 1944; s. Richard Robert and Mary (Goode) R.; m. Rilla L. Rothwell, Dec. 20, 1967; children: Kevin, Megan, Brendan. BA, Claremont McKenna Coll., 1966; JD, Loyola U., L.A., 1972. Bar: Calif. 1972, U.S. Dist. Ct. (cen. dist.) Calif. 1972, U.S. Dist. Ct. (so. dist.) Calif. 1984, U.S. Dist. Ct. (no. dist.) Calif. 1986. Trial atty. pub. defender's office Los Angeles County, 1972-78; assoc. Lillick, McHose & Charles, L.A., 1979-80, ptnr., 1980-90; ptnr. Pillsbury Madison & Sutro, L.A., 1990—. Served with Spl. Forces, U.S. Army, 1967-69, Vietnam. Fellow Internat. Soc. Barristers; mem. ABA (torts and ins. practice sect.), Assn. Trial Lawyers Am., Calif. Bar Assn. (disciplinary examiner 1994—), Assn. So. Calif. Def. Counsel, Los Angeles County Bar Assn. (conf. del. exec. com. 1985—, trial lawyer sect. 1978—, pub. affairs com. 1979—, legis. rev. com. 1984, lectr. 1979—, L.A Athletic Club, Malibu Surfing Assn. (pres. 1994). Democrat. Roman Catholic. Avocations: snow skiing, surfing, windsurfing. Office: Pillsbury Madison & Sutro 725 S Figueroa St Ste 1200 Los Angeles CA 90017-5413

ROGATZ, PETER, physician; b. N.Y.C., Aug. 5, 1926; s. Julian and Sally (Levy) R.; m. Marjorie Plaut, June 10, 1949; children—Peggy Joy, William Peter. B.A.. Columbia Coll., 1945; M.D., Cornell U., 1949; M.P.H., Columbia U., 1956. Intern Lenox Hill Hosp., N.Y.C., 1949-50; resident Lenox Hill Hosp., 1950-51, VA Hosp., Bronx, N.Y., 1951-52, N.Y. Hosp., N.Y.C., 1952-53; dep. dir. Montefiore Hosp., N.Y.C., 1960-63; dir. L.I. Jewish Med. Center, 1964-68, Univ. Hosp., SUNY, Stony Brook, 1968-71; sr. v.p. Blue Cross/Blue Shield of Greater N.Y., 1971-76; prin., founding ptnr. RMR Health and Hosp. Mgmt. Cons., Inc., Roslyn Heights, N.Y., 1976-84; v.p. med. affairs Vis. Nurse Service, N.Y., 1984-91; med. dir. Staff Builders, Inc., 1992—; prof. cmty. medicine SUNY, Stony Brook, 1968—; mem. N.Y.C. Mayor's Commn. on Delivery of Health Svcs., 1967; v.p. Health and Welfare Coun. of Nassau County, 1968-72; bd. dirs. Cmty. Coun. Greater N.Y., 1974-77; mem. Task Force on N.Y.C. Crisis, 1976-81; chmn. bd. dirs. Cmty. Health Program (affiliated with L.I. Jewish Med. Ctr.), 1989-94; chmn. bd. dirs. Managed Health Inc., 1990-94. Author: Organized Home Medical Care in New York City, 1956, (with Eli Ginzberg) Planning for Better Hospital Care, 1961; mem. editorial bd.: Preventive Medicine, 1975-81; contbr. articles to profl. jours. Bd. dirs. Choice in Dying, 1994—. Commonwealth Fund fellow, 1955; recipient Dean Conley award Am. Coll. Hosp. Admnstrs., 1975. Fellow ACP, N.Y. Acad. Medicine, Am. Public Health Assn., Am. Coll. Preventive Medicine; mem. Am. Hosp. Assn., N.Y. Public Health Assn., AMA, N.Y. State Med. Soc., N.Y. County Med. Soc. Home and Office: 76 Oakdale Ln Roslyn Heights NY 11577-1535

ROGENESS, MARY SPEER, state legislator; b. Kansas City, Kans., May 18, 1941; d. Frederic A. and Jeannette (Hybskmann) Speer; m. Dean Rogeness, Aug. 31, 1964; children: Emily, James, Paul. BA, Carleton Coll., 1963. Computer analyst Dept. Def., Ft. Meade, Md., 1963-66; freelance writer, editor Longmeadow, Mass., 1982-91; mem. Mass. Ho. of Reps., Boston, 1991—. Editor: Reflections of Longmeadow, 1983. Mem. Longmeadow Rep. Town Com., 1983—; Mass. alt. del. Rep. Nat. Conv., Houston, 1992. Mem. Jr. League Springfield, World Affairs Coun. of Western Mass. (bd. dirs. 1990—). Office: Mass House of Reps State House Boston MA 02133

ROGER, JERRY LEE, school system administrator; b. Chase, Kans., Mar. 11, 1945; s. LeRoy J. and Lottie E. (Mapher) R.; divorced. BS, U. Tulsa, 1966, MA, 1969, EdD, 1975. Cert. tchr., supt., Okla. Math. tchr. Kansas City (Mo.) Pub. Schs., 1966-67, Shawnee Mission (Kans.) Pub. Schs., 1967-71; rsch. asst. Tulsa Pub. Schs., 1972-73, rsch. coord., 1973-81, adminstrv. asst., 1981-90, rsch. dir., 1990-95, exec. dir. planning and assessment, 1995—; adj. instr. Tulsa Jr. Coll., 1975-88; adj. asst. prof. U. Tulsa, 1980-85. Contbr. book revs. to Tulsa Sunday World, 1990-92. Paul Harris fellow; Rotary benefactor. Mem. NEA, Nat. Book Critics Cir., Phi Delta Kappa, Pi Mu Epsilon, Kappa Mu Epsilon. Home: Apt 106K 7766 Riverside Dr Apt 106K Tulsa OK 74138 Office: Tulsa Pub Schs 3027 S New Haven Ave Tulsa OK 74114-6131

ROGER, JOHN W., parks and recreation director. Pres. Chgo. Park Dist. Office: Chicago Park Dist 425 E McFetridge Dr Chicago IL 60605*

ROGER, RICHARD R., personal care industry executive; b. 1943; s. Mary Kay Ash. Student, North Tex. State U. and So. Meth. U., 1962-63. Salesman Prudential Life Ins. Co., Houston, 1963; salesman Mary Kay Cosmetics Inc., 1963-67, pres., 1967-87, chmn. bd., CEO, 1987—. Office: Mary Kay Corp 8787 N Stemmons Fwy Dallas TX 75247

ROGERS, A. KAY, construction company executive; b. Phoenix, June 11, 1935; s. Arthur W. Rogers and Irene Higbee; m. Sandra M. Mageleby, Oct. 15, 1957; children: Kaylene Willis, Kathlene, Kristine. BS in Civil Engring., Ariz. State U., 1962. Registered profl. engr.; registered land surveyor. Estimator Tanner Bros. Constrn., Phoenix, 1962-65; gen. constrn. supt. The Tanner Cos., Phoenix, 1965-74, pres., 1974-83; owner, pres. A.K. Rogers Co., Phoenix, 1983—. Bishop LDS Ch. Mem. AGC (bd. dirs. Ariz. chpt. 1974-81, pres. 1982). Office: A K Rogers Co 1122 E Campbell Ave Phoenix AZ 85014

ROGERS, ALAN VICTOR, former career officer; b. Hannibal, Mo., Nov. 13, 1942; s. Julian Alan and Gladys Cuneo R.; m. Linda Rae Peterson, May 8, 1966; children: Kimberly Rae, Krista Anne, Peter Alan. BS in Mil. Sci., USAF Acad., 1964; MBA with distinction, Harvard Bus. Sch., 1972; grad. with distinction, Air War Coll., 1980. Commd. 2d lt. USAF, 1964, advanced

through grades to maj. gen., 1989, ret., 1993; combat fighter pilot 355th Tactical Fighter Wing, Takhli, Thailand, 1966-67; jet pilot instr. Flying Tng. Wing, Williams AFB, Ariz., 1967-69; student Harvard Bus. Sch., Cambridge, Mass., 1970-72; pers. officer Cols. Group USAF Pentagon, Washington, 1972-75; student Air War Coll, Maxwell AFB, Ariz., 1980; wing comdr. 5th Bomb Wing, Minot AFB, N.D., 1982-84, 96th Bomb Wing (1st B-1 Wing), Dyess AFB, Tex., 1984-86; dir. ops. SAC, Offutt AFB, Nebr., 1986-89; asst. chief of staff ops. Supreme HQ Allied Powers Europe, Mons, Belgium, 1989-91; dir. J-7 Joint Staff, Washington, 1991-93; assoc. Burdeshaw Assocs., Ltd., Bethesda, Md., 1993-94; prin. Gemini Consulting, McLean, Va., 1994—. Mem., mil. adviser C. of C., Minot, N.D., 1982-84, Abilene, Tex. 1984-86. Decorated D.S.M., Legion of Merit, D.F.C. with two oak leaf clusters, Purple Heart. Mem. Air Force Assn., Red River Valley Fighter Pilots Assn., Nat. Eagle Scout Assn., Daedalians (chpt. pres. 1986). Republican. Roman Catholic. Avocations: skiing, travel, antiques, Porsche-356B. Home: 2405 Lexington Rd Falls Church VA 22043-3222 Office: Gemini Consulting Ste 220 1420 Beverly Rd Mc Lean VA 22101

ROGERS, ARTHUR HAMILTON, III, lawyer; b. Florence, S.C., Apr. 19, 1945; s. Arthur Hamilton Jr. and Suzanne (Wilson) R.; m. Karen Lyn Hess, June 22, 1968; children: Sarah Elizabeth, Thomas Hess. BA, Rice U., 1967; JD, Harvard U., 1970. Bar: Tex. 1970. Assoc. Fulbright & Jaworski, Houston, 1970-74, participating assoc., 1974-77, ptnr., 1977—; gen. counsel Lifemark Corp., Houston, 1981-82; sec. Mosher, Inc., Houston, 1984—. Dir. Alley Theatre, Houston, 1990—, Autry House, 1994—; mem. exec. com. Rice U. Fund Coun., Houston, 1993—. Mem. ABA, State Bar Tex., Assn. of Rice Alumni (treas. 1995—), Ramada-Tejas Club. Episcopalian. Home: 5309 Bordley Dr Houston TX 77056-2323 Office: Fulbright & Jaworski 1301 Mckinney St Fl 51 Houston TX 77010-3095

ROGERS, ARTHUR MERRIAM, JR., banker; b. Rochester, Minn., Apr. 19, 1941; s. Arthur Merriam and Marguerite Wood (MacCoy) R.; m. Barbara Whitney, Nov. 27, 1965; children: Arthur, Alison, Whitney. B.A., Yale U., 1963. Mgr. Banca Morgan Vonwiller, Milan, Italy, 1967-71; dir. Morgan & Cie Internat., Paris, 1972-73; gen. mgr. Bank of Kuwait and the Middle East, Kuwait, 1976-78; asst. gen. mgr. Morgan Guaranty Trust Co. N.Y., London, 1978-82; sr. v.p. Morgan Guaranty Trust Co. N.Y., N.Y.C., 1982-86, exec. v.p., 1986-89; mng. dir. Morgan Guaranty Trust Co. N.Y., 1989-93; chmn. J.P. Morgan, Del., 1994—. Pres. Kips Bay Boys Club, N.Y.C., 1965—. Club: Links (N.Y.C.). Office: JP Morgan 60 Wall St New York NY 10005-2807

ROGERS, BERNARD WILLIAM, military officer; b. Fairview, Kans., July 16, 1921; s. William Henry and Lora (Haynes) R.; m. Ann Ellen Jones, Dec. 28, 1944; children: Michael W., Diane E., Susan A. Student, Kans. State Coll., 1939-40; B.S., U.S. Mil. Acad., 1943; B.A. (Rhodes scholar), Oxford (Eng.) U., 1950, M.A., 1954, D.C.L. (hon.), 1983; grad., Command and Gen. Staff Coll., 1954-55, Army War Coll., 1959-60; LL.D. (hon.), Akron U., 1978, Boston U., 1981. Commd. lt. U.S. Army, 1943, advanced through grades to gen., 1974; aide to supt. U.S. Mil. Acad., 1945-46, comdt. cadets, 1967-69; aide to high commr. Austria Gen. Mark W. Clark, 1946-47; bn. comdr. Korea, 1952; exec. to comdr.-in-chief Far East Command, 1953-54; mil. asst. to Chief Staff U.S. Army, 1956-59; exec. to chmn. (Joint Chiefs of Staff), 1962-66; asst. div. comdr. (1st Inf. Div.), Vietnam, 1966-67; comdg. gen. (5th Inf. Div.), Ft. Carson, Colo., 1969-70; chief legis. liaison Dept. Army, 1971-72, dep. chief of staff for personnel, 1972-74; comdg. gen. U.S. Army Forces Command, 1974-76; chief of staff U.S. Army, 1976-79; supreme allied comdr. Europe; comdr. in chief (U.S. European Command), 1979-87; ret. U.S. Army, 1987; bd. dirs. or trustee Atlantic Coun. U.S., George C. Marshall Found., Assn. U.S. Army. Decorated DSC, Def. DSM, DSM of Army, Navy and Air Force, Silver Star, Legion of Merit with 3 oak leaf clusters, D.F.C. with 2 oak leaf clusters, Bronze Star medal with V device, hon. fellow Univ. Coll., Oxford U.; recipient Dist. Service Citation U. Kans., 1984. Mem. VFW, Assn. U.S. Army (bd. dirs.), Assn. Am. Rhodes Scholars, Soc. 1st Inf. Divsn., Am. Soc. French Legion of Honor, Ret. Officers Assn., Mil. Order of World Wars, The Pilgrims, Army-Navy Country Club, Army and Navy Club, Alfalfa, Phi Delta Theta.

ROGERS, BRIAN DEANE, librarian; b. New London, Conn., June 26, 1937; s. Albert Nash and Janette (Loofboro) R.; m. Carol Priscilla Mallett, May 18, 1962; children: Alison, Paul, Amy. BA, Wesleyan U., 1959; MLS, Rutgers U., 1967. Asst. registrar Salem (W. Va.) Coll., 1964-66; reference librarian Wesleyan U., Middletown, Conn., 1967-69, head pub. services, 1969-75; librarian Conn. Coll., New London, 1975-93, spl. collections libr., 1993—; Mem. State Adv. Council on Libraries, Hartford, 1976, chair 1977; mem. library bd. Mystic Seaport Maritime Mus., Mystic, Conn., 1987—. Mem. accreditation teams New England Assn. Sch. & Colls., 1985-90. Served with U.S. Army, 1961-64. Mem. ALA, Assn. Coll. and Research Libraries (com. on coll. library standards 1982-86), Conn. Acad. Arts & Scis., Beta Phi Mu. Clubs: Columbiad (Meriden, Conn.); Acorn (Hartford, Conn.). Home: 114 Library St Mystic CT 06355-2420 Office: Conn Coll Library 270 Mohegan Ave New London CT 06320-4196

ROGERS, BRYAN LEIGH, artist, art educator; b. Amarillo, Tex., Jan. 7, 1941; s. Bryan Austin and Virginia Leigh (Bull) R.; m. Cynthia Louise Rice; 1 child, Kyle Austin Rogers. BE, Yale U., 1963; MS, U. Calif., Berkeley, 1966, MA, 1969, PhD, 1971. Design engr. Monsanto Co., Texas City, Tex., 1962; research engr. Rocketdyne, Canoga Park, Calif., 1963-64; research scientist Lawrence Livermore (Calif.) Lab., 1966; lectr. U. Calif., Berkeley, 1972-73; fellow Akademie der Bildenden Künste, Munich, 1974-75; prof. art San Francisco State U., 1975-88; dept. head., prof. art. Carnegie Mellon U., Pitts., 1988—; dir. Studio for Creative Inquiry, 1989—; fellow Ctr. Advanced Visual Studies MIT, Cambridge, Mass, 1981. Editor Leonardo Jour., San Francisco, 1982-85. One-man shows include: Laguna Beach (Calif.) Mus. Art, 1974, DeSaisset Art Gallery U. Santa Clara, Calif., 1974, San Francisco Mus. Modern Art, 1974, Baxter Art Gallery Calif. Inst. Tech., Pasadena, 1979, Contemporary Crafts gallery, Portland, Oreg., 1987; group exhbns. include: Berkeley (Calif.) Art Ctr., 1969, Hansen-Fuller Gallery, San Francisco, 1970, San Francisco Arts Commn. Gallery, 1984, Clocktower Gallery, N.Y.C., 1984, Otis-Parsons Gallery, Los Angeles, 1985, P.P.O.W. Gallery, N.Y.C., 1985, 18th Internat. Bienal, São Paulo, Brazil, 1985, MIT, Cambridge, 1990, Objects Gallery, Chgo., 1992, ARTEC 93 Internat Biennale, Nagoya, Japan, 1993, Chgo. Cultural Ctr., 1993, Am. Iron and Steel Expo., Pitts., 1993, Pitts. Ctr. for Arts, 1994. Fellow NEA, Washington, 1981, 82, Deutscher Akademischer Austauschdienst, Fed. Republic of Germany, 1974, NSF, Washington, 1965-69; recipient SECA award San Francisco Mus. Modern Art, 1974. Office: Carnegie Mellon U Art Dept Pittsburgh PA 15213

ROGERS, C. B., lawyer; b. Birmingham, Ala., July 10, 1930; s. Claude B. Rogers and Doris (Hinkley) Rogers Lockerman; m. Patricia Maxwell DeVoe, Dec. 22, 1962; children: Bruce Lockerman, Evelyn Best, Brian DeVoe. A.B., Emory U., 1951, LL.B., 1953. Bar: Ga. 1953. Adj. prof. litigation Emory U., 1968-70; assoc., then partner firm Powell, Goldstein, Frazer & Murphy, 1954-76; partner firm Rogers & Hardin, Atlanta, 1976—. Fellow Am. Coll. Trial Lawyers; mem. Am. Law Inst., Capital City Club (Atlanta). Democrat. Episcopalian. Home: 1829 W Wesley Rd NW Atlanta GA 30327-2019 also: Brandon Mill Rd Lakemont GA 30335 also: 1160 Swollow Pointe Big Canoe GA 30143 Office: Rogers & Hardin 2700 Cain Tower 229 Peachtree St NE Atlanta GA 30303-1602

ROGERS, CHARLES EDWIN, physical chemistry educator; b. Rochester, N.Y., Dec. 29, 1929; s. Charles Harold and Maybelle (Johnson) R.; m. Barbara June Depuy, June 12, 1954; children: Gregory Newton, Linda Frances, Diana Suzanne. BS in Chemistry, Syracuse U., 1954; PhD in Phys. Chemistry, SUNY at Syracuse U., 1957. Rsch. assoc. dept. chemistry Princeton U., 1957-59, Goodyear fellow, 1957-59; mem. tech. staff Bell Telephone Labs., Murray Hill, N.J., 1959-65; assoc. prof. macromolecular sci. Case Western Res. U., Cleve., 1965-74, prof., 1974—; sr. vis. fellow Imperial Coll., U. London, 1971; assoc. dir. Ctr. for Adhesives Sealants Coatings, Case Western Res. U., 1984-88, dir., 1988-91; co-dir. Edison Polymer Innovation Corp., Ctr. for Adhesives, Sealants and Coatings, 1991—; cons. to polymer and chem. industries; devel. overseas ednl. instns. Editor: Permselective Membranes, 1971, Structure and Properties of Block Copolymers, 1977; contbr. numerous articles to profl. jours.; patentee in field. Served with U.S. Army, 1946-49. Mem. Am. Chem. Soc., Am. Phys.

Soc., N.Am. Membrane Soc., Cleve. Coatings Soc., The Adhesion Soc. Home: 8400 Rockspring Dr Chagrin Falls OH 44023-4645 Office: Case Western Reserve U Dept Macromolecular Sc Cleveland OH 44106-7202

ROGERS, CHARLES FORD, II, architect; b. Middlebury, Vt., May 22, 1937; s. Benjamin Earle and Elsie (Jenney) R.; m. Marga Rapuano, 1960 (div. 1992); children: Mara, Charles III; m. Alice B. Hyde, Aug. 30, 1992. BArch, Cornell U., 1960, MArch, 1962. Registered architect, 1971. Archtl. designer Freeman, French & Freeman, Burlington, Vt., 1957-58; architect, designer Office Dan Kiley, Charlotte, Vt., 1959-60, Office Werner Seligman, Cortland, N.Y., 1961-62, Aebli & Hoesli, Zurich, Switzerland, 1963-65, Office Karl Fleigh, Zurich, 1963-65, Perry, Dean, Hepburn & Stewart, Boston, 1965-71; prin. Perry, Dean, Ptnrs., Boston, 1971-84; pres. Perry, Dean & Ptnrs., Boston, 1984-93, chmn. bd., 1993—; archtl. draftsperson Cornell-Harvard Archaeol. Expedition, Sardis, Turkey, 1959-60; assoc. prof. coll. architecture Cornell U., Ithaca, N.Y., 1963-65; asst. prof. Swiss Fed. Inst. Tech., Zurich, 1963-65; design critic in architecture Harvard U., 1980. Prin. works include Wellesley Coll. Sci. Ctr., 1976, Hall Mercer Children's Ctr., 1980, Seeley Mudd Chemistry Bldg., 1985, Roe Visual Arts Bldg., 1985, Wesleyan Olin Libr., 1986, Amherst Campus Ctr., 1987, William M. Bristol Jr. Pool, 1988, Catoctin Broodmare Barns, 1989, Kreitzberg Libr. Norwich U., 1992, U.S. Embassy, Amman, Jordan, 1992, Bienecke Student Village Hamilton Coll., 1994, Richard Riley Hall Furman U., 1994. Trustee New Eng. Bapt. Hosp., Boston, 1977-92, William M. Bristol Jr. Swimming Pool, 1988. Biddle Found. scholar, 1959. Mem. AIA. Episcopalian. Club: Union (Boston).

ROGERS, CHARLES RAY, minister, religious organization administrator; b. Grapevine, Tex., Nov. 26, 1935; s. Arlin Avery and Bessie Lorene (Deaton) R.; m. Oma Fay Hines, Aug. 21, 1954; children: Sheree Gay Rogers Saberjissa, Charles Denne Ray, Robin Celeste Rogers Eddins. MS in Christian Edn., Faith Bible Coll., 1980, DD in Humanities (hon.), 1981; D of Ministry in Humanities (hon.), Sem. of Theol. Missions, Escuintla, Guatemala, 1992. Pastor various Bapt. chs., Athens, Dallas, Ft. Worth, 1960-64, various interdenominational chs., Houston, Longview, 1965-69; pres. Evangelism in Action, Ft. Worth, 1969—; bd. dirs. World Ministry Fellowship, Plano, Tex., dir. world missions, 1970—; leader Over 100 Mission, humanitarian trips Evangelism in Action, Ft. Worth, 1976—. Author: Joy, 1979, Handbook for Victorious Living, 1980, How to Develop Christian Love, 1981; vocalist (rec.) Charlie, 1981. Republican. Avocations: golf, tennis, swimming, running, computers. Home: 6416 Parkman Dr Fort Worth TX 76180-4807 Office: Evangelism in Action PO Box 820724 Fort Worth TX 76182

ROGERS, CHARLIE ELLIC, entomologist; b. Booneville, Ark., Aug. 13, 1938; s. Robert Wesley and Parthenia Fern (Mahoney) R.; m. Donna Carol Ray, Jan. 29, 1971; children: Christian Edward, Cheryl Elaine. BS, Northern Ariz. U., 1964; MS, U. Ky., 1967; PhD in Entomology, Okla. State U., 1970. Cert. entomologist. Tchr. biology, social studies Dysart Pub. Sch., Glendale, Ariz., 1964-65; grad. rsch. asst. U. Ky., Lexington, 1965-67; grad. rsch. asst. Okla. State U., Stillwater, 1967-70, postdoctoral rsch. assoc., 1970-71; asst. prof. agrl. experimental station Tex. A&M U., College Station, 1971-75; rsch. entomologist SW Gt. Plains Rsch. Ctr., USDA Agrl. Rsch. Svc., Bushland, Tex., 1975-80; supervisory rsch. entomologist, rsch. leader Conservation & Prodn. Rsch. Ctr., USDA, Tifton, Ga., 1980-83; lab dir. Insect Biology & Population Mgmt. Rsch. Lab Agrl. Rsch. Svc. USDA, 1983—; editor Biol. Control Acad. Press, San Diego, 1990—; rsch. com. Sunflower Assn. Am., Fargo, N.D., 1981-83; dir. elect Bd. Cert. Entomologist Entomol. Soc. Am., Lantham, Md., 1992. Author: Sunflower Species of the United States, 1982; co-editor: The Entomology of Indigenous and Naturalized Systems in Agriculture, 1988; editor: Biological Control, 1990—; contbr. articles to profl. publs. Sch. bd. mem. Bushland Ind. Sch. Dist., 1981-83; tchr. First Bapt. Ch., Tifton, 1986-91; mem. Rotary Club, Vernon, Tex., 1974-76. With U.S. Army, 1958-61. Recipient Profl. Excellence award Am. Agrl. Econ. Assn., 1979, Leadership award USDA, 1987, Profl. Svc. award Am. Registered Profl. Entomologists, 1987, Outstanding Performance award USDA, 1991, Disting. Alumni award, 1992. Mem. Entomol. Soc. Am. (bd. cert. entomologist), Ga. Entomol. Soc., Entomol. Soc. S.C, Sigma Xi, Tifton Club (pres. 1992-93). Republican. Baptist. Achievements include study of biology, ecology, and control of sheep nose bot, oestrus ovis; biology and augmentation of Propylea 14-punctata against the green bug; control of guar midge Conterina texana; control of insect pests of sunflowers; more. Home: 1711 Sarah Dr Tifton GA 31793-0748 Office: USDA/ARS Insect Biology & Population Mgmt Rsch Lab PO Box 748 Tifton GA 31793*

ROGERS, CURTIS L., JR., wholesale distribution executive. Chmn. bd. Rogers Am. Co. Inc., Charlotte, N.C. Office: Rogers Am Co Inc 7315 Pineville Matthews R Charlotte NC 28226*

ROGERS, DAVID, apparel executive. With Pickwick Internat., Mpls.; pres. Wilson's House of Suede, Mpls., 1979—. Office: Rosedale Wilsons Inc 400 Highway 169 S Ste 600 Minneapolis MN 55426-1114

ROGERS, DAVID, playwright, novelist, actor; b. N.Y.C.; s. George and Deborah (Samuels) Rosenberg; m. June Lois Walker, Oct. 14, 1962; children—Dulcy Dru, Amanda Brooke. Student, Am. Theatre Wing Sch., 1948, 49. N.Y.C. prodns. include Ziegfld Follies, 1957, Vintage '60, 1960, New Faces of 1962, Fun City, 1967, Charlie and Algernon, 1980 (Tony award nomination); London prodns. include Jubilee Girl, 1956, Young at Heart, 1961, Flowers for Algernon, 1979, Killing Jessica, 1986; pub. plays include Tom Jones, 1964, Flowers for Algernon, 1969, Brave New World, 1970, F.L.I.P.P.E.D, 1971, Here and Now, 1973, Soft Soap, 1982, Rehearsal for Murder, 1983; pub. musicals include Best of Broadway, 1961, Cheaper by the Dozen, 1969, The Hobbit, 1972, The Truth About Cinderella, 1974, The Dream on Royal Street, 1981; TV The Hero; opera, 1966 (winner Prix d'Italia Concorso Internat. Per Opere Radiofoniche e Televisive), Carol Burnett show, 1970; novels Oh Eden, 1974, The Bedroom Set, 1976, Somewhere There's Music, 1977, The Great American Alimony Escape, 1979, The In-Laws, 1979; actor Broadway prodns. Doubles, 1985, George Abbott's Broadway, 1987, internat. tour Grand Hotel, 1991. Served with U.S. Army, 1951-52, Korea. Mem. Dramatists Guild, Writers Guild Am. East, AFTRA, Broadcast Music Inc., Actors Equity. Club: Theatre Artists Workshop (Westport, Conn.) (bd. dirs. 1985).

ROGERS, DAVID H., banker; b. White Plains, N.Y., May 28, 1943; m. Elizabeth B. Barrett; children: Abigail, Joshua T., John D. III. BA, U. N.H.; MA, U. R.I.; postgrad, Brown U. Sr. v.p. Bank East, Manchester, N.H., 1972-75; v.p N.H. Savs. Bank, Concord, 1975-81, sr. v.p. mktg., 1981-82; exec. v.p., sec. N.H. Savs. Bank Corp., Concord, 1982-87, pres., chief exec. officer, 1987—, also bd. dirs.; bd. dirs. Rockingham Country Trust Co., Salem, N.H., Seabrook Bank & Trust Co., N.H., Nat. Mortgage Co., Bedford, N.H., Cons. Systems and Mgmt. Corp., Concord, New Eng. Capital Corp., Avon, Conn., New Eng. Fin. Resources, Boston, Pocketbank Inc., Manchester, N.H. Trustee, chmn. Concord Hosp. and Capital Region Health Care Corp., 1984-87. Avocations: sailing, skiing. Office: NH Savs Bank Corp 27 N State St Concord NH 03301-6322

ROGERS, DAVID HUGHES, finance executive; b. Chgo., May 21, 1947; s. Joseph Gordon and Viola Winifred (Hughes) R.; m. Louise Sheryl Kershner, Jan. 23, 1982; 1 child, Kirsten Morgan. BA, U. Mich., 1968; PhD, Columbia U., 1975. Economist Fed. Res. Bank of Cleve., 1974-75; asst. treas. B.F. Goodrich Co., Akron, Ohio, 1975-82; exec. v.p., chief fin. officer First Tex. Savs. Assn., Dallas, 1982-83; sr. exec. v.p., chief operating officer PriMerit Bank, Las Vegas, 1984-87, pres., dir., 1987-91; vice chmn., 1991-92; chief oper. officer The Baird Cos., Las Vegas, Nev., 1992—. Author: Consumer Banking in New York, 1975; also articles. Mem. exec. bd. Boulder Dam Area coun. Boy Scouts Am., 1986—; bd. dirs. Nev. Sch. Arts, 1988—; Temple Beth Am, 1994—, Las Vegas Bus. Bank, 1995—. Office: The Baird Cos 3753 Howard Hughes Pky Las Vegas NV 89109-0938

ROGERS, DESIREE GLAPION, state official; b. New Orleans, June 16, 1959; d. Roy and Joyce Glapion; m. John Rogers, Jr.; 1 child, Victoria. B in Polit. Sci., Wellesley Coll., 1981; MBA, Harvard U., 1985. Customer svc. mktg. mgr. AT&T, N.J., 1985-87; dir. devel. Levy Orgn., Chgo., 1987-89; founder, pres. Mus. Ops. Consulting Assocs., Chgo., 1989-91; dir. Ill. State

Lottery, Chgo., 1991—. Bd. dirs. Sta. WTTW-Pub. TV, Chgo., The Marwen Found.; mem. The Chgo. Children's Mus., Old St. Patrick's Sch., Chgo. Mem. The Econ. Club, Harvard Bus. Sch. Club, Wellesley Club. Office: Ill State Lottery 676 St Clair Chicago IL 60611

ROGERS, DONALD ONIS, language educator; b. Springfield, Mo., Oct. 9, 1938; s. Onis Lee and Wilma (Gideon) R.; m. Mora Jeannine, Aug. 19, 1961; children—Donald Scott, Anne Margaret. B.S., SW Mo. State U., 1961; M.A., La. State U., 1968; Ph.D., Southwestern La. U., 1978. Lang. coordinator Ralls County Pub. Schs., Mo., 1961-66; grad. teaching asst. La. State U., Baton Rouge, 1966-68; asst. prof. La. State U., Eunice, 1968-74, assoc. prof., 1974-79, head div. liberal arts, dir. acad. affairs, 1973-78, prof. English, dean acad. affairs and services, 1979-91, prof. English, vice chancellor for acad. affairs, 1991—. Bd. dirs. Bayouland Library System, 1974-78. Served with USNR, 1957-59. Mem. Ralls County Tchrs. Assn. (pres. 1965-66), Coll. English Assn., La. Council Tchrs. English, S.W. Regional Conf. English in 2-Yr. Colls., MLA, South Central MLA. Democrat. Home: PO Box 301 Cheneyville LA 71325-0301 Office: PO Box 1129 Eunice LA 70535-1129

ROGERS, DONALD PATRICK, business administration educator; b. Tucson, Aug. 28, 1947; s. Patrick Joseph and Pearl Anna (Howarter) R.; m. Fran Carlin, Aug. 3, 1974; children: Tracy Lynn, Anne Marie. BS, U. Ariz., 1969; MBA, Ohio U., 1971, PhD, 1973. Sales rep. TMC, Tucson, 1966-68; asst. prof. SUNY, Buffalo, 1972-78; assoc. prof. SUNY, Genesseo, 1978-87; prof. bus. adminstrn. Rollins Coll., Winter Park, Fla., 1987—; dir. Survey Info. Rsch. Ctr., Geneseo, N.Y., 1978-87, dir. masters in human resources Rollins Coll., Winter Park, 1993—; rsch. cons. various cos., Winter Park, 1976—. Co-author: Auditing Organizational Communication, 1978; editor: Fundamental Concepts of Business, 1984; co-editor: Integrated Business Analysis, 1985; contbr. articles to profl. publs. Mem. Acad. Mgmt. (div. chmn. 1982-83, svc. award 1983), Assn. Bus. Communication. Democrat. Office: Rollins Coll Holt Ave Winter Park FL 32789

ROGERS, EARL LESLIE, artist, educator; b. Oakland, Calif., July 8, 1918; s. Robert Ray and Addie Myrtle (Dice) R.; m. Eileen Estelle MacKenzie, Apr. 9, 1945; children: Leslie Eileen, Brian Donald (dec.). Student, L.A. Valley Coll., 1949-52, Northridge State U., 1958-59, UCLA Extension, 1967, Sergei Bongart Sch. Art, 1967-68; AA, Pierce Coll., 1958. Cert. tchr., Calif. Various positions City of L.A., Van Nuys, Calif., 1948-55, Reseda, Calif., 1955-68; pvt. practice Canoga Park, Calif., 1948-68; art tchr. Mariposa (Calif.) County High Sch., 1969-70; art instr. Merced (Calif.) County Coll., 1970—; instr. Earl Rogers Studio Workshop, Mariposa, Calif., 1969—; art dir. Yosemite Nat. Park, Calif., 1973; art instr. Asilomar Conf. Grounds, Pacific Grove, Calif., 1980; juror various art orgns., 1971-95; demonstrator Clovic (Calif.) Art Guild, 1971, 89, Sierra Artists, Mariposa, 1972, 81, 82, 84, 91, Merced Art League, 1976, Yosemite Western Artists, Oakhurst, Calif., 1973, Madera (Calif.) Art Assn., 1978, Chowchilla (Calif.) Art Guild, 1983, 86, 87, 89, 91, Soc. Western Artists, 1981, 89, 93. One-man shows include L.A. City Hall, 1968, Merced Coll., 1969, Mariposa Title Co. Bldg., 1969, Coffee's Gallery, 1970, others; exhibited in group shows include West Valley Artists Assn., 1966-68, L.A. City Hall, 1967, Yosemite Nat. Park, 1973, Soc. Western Artists, 1977-78, Cannon Bldg. Rotunda, Washington, 1982, Mother Lode Gallery, Columbia, Calif., 1977, 78, Arbor Gallery, Merced, 1988, Gold Country Gallery, 1990, 91, Merced Coll., 1969-92, others; represented in permanent collections include John C. Freemont Hosp., Mariposa, Mariposa Family Med. Bldg., Bear Valley (Calif.) Mus., Mariposa County Libr., Mariposa County Arts Coun., Mariposa Mus. and History Ctr. Asst. scout master Boy Scouts of Am., Canoga Park, Calif., 1956-58; art instr. L.A. Recreation Corps, L.A. Parks and Recreation Dept., 1967. Mem. Soc. Western Artists (Neva Rall Meml. award 1978), Mariposa Mus. and Hist. Ctr. (life), Pastel Soc. West Coast. Avocations: piano and books. Home and Office: 5323 Hwy 49 North Mariposa CA 95338

ROGERS, EDDY J., lawyer; b. Belleville, Ill., Nov. 29, 1940. AB, Harvard U., 1962, LLB, 1965. Bar: Tex. 1965, U.S. Dist. Ct. (so. dist.) Tex. 1975. Ptnr. Mayer Brown & Platt, Houston. Contbr. articles to profl. jours. Mem. ABA, State Bar Tex., Houston Bar. Assn., Phi Beta Kappa. Office: Mayer Brown & Platt 190 S La Salle St Chicago IL 60603-3410

ROGERS, EDMUND PENDLETON, III, lawyer; b. N.Y.C., May 5, 1941; s. Edmund Pendleton Rogers Jr. and Beatrice (Brown) Guthrie; m. Cynthia Banks Alexandre, June 26, 1965; children: Edmund, James. BA, Yale U., 1965, JD, 1968. Assoc. Davis, Polk & Wardwell, N.Y.C., 1968-76; asst. resident counsel Morgan Guaranty Trust N.Y., N.Y.C., 1976-78, v.p., asst. resident counsel, 1978-86, sr. v.p., resident counsel, 1986—. Bd. health Borough of Far Hills, N.J., 1988. With USNR, 1960-66. Mem. ABA, N.Y. State Bar Assn., Bar Assn. City of N.Y. (audit com. 1987—), Somerset Hills County Club (gov. 1987—), Anglers Club N.Y. Republican. Episcopalian. Avocations: fishing, golfing. Office: Morgan Guaranty Trust Co 60 Wall St New York NY 10260-0001

ROGERS, EDWARD SAMUEL, communications company executive; b. Toronto, May 27, 1933; s. Edward Samuel and Velma Melissa (Taylor) R.; m. Loretta Anne Robinson, Sept. 25, 1963; children: Lisa Anne, Edward Samuel, Melinda Mary, Martha Loretta. BA, Trinity Coll., U. Toronto, 1956; LLB, Osgoode Hall Law Sch., 1961; DSc (hon.), Clarkson U., 1989; LLD, U. Victoria, 1990, York U., 1994. Bar: Ont., 1962. Founder, prin. Rogers Telecomm. Ltd., Toronto, 1960—; pres., CEO Rogers Comm. Inc., 1978—; vice-chmn. Rogers Cablesystems Ltd., Rogers Broadcasting Ltd.; bd. dirs. The Hull Group, The Toronto Dominion Bank, Can. Pub. Corp., Mercedes-Benz Can., Inc., Teleglobe Can., Inc.; Rogers Cable TV Ltd., Rogers Cablesystems Ltd., Rogers Broadcasting Ltd. Bd. dirs. Jr. Achievement Can. Mem. Royal Can. Yacht Club, Albany Club, Granite Club, York Club, Muskoka Golf & Country Club, Rideau Club Ottawa, Lyford Cay Club (gov.), Balboa Bay Club, Sigma Chi (Beta Omega chpt.). Progressive Conservative. Mem. Anglican Ch. Office: Rogers Comms Inc PO Box 1007, 40 King St W Ste 6400 Scotia Plz, Toronto, ON Canada M5H 3Y2

ROGERS, EDWIN EARL, newspaper editor; b. Carbondale, Pa., Sept. 7, 1929; s. William Earl and Jessie (Pethick) R.; m. Eleanor Louise Hopkins, Feb. 28, 1959; children: Karen, Kevin, Kyle, Kathryn. Sports editor News-Leader, Carbondale, Pa., 1944-46; bur. reporter, photographer The Scranton (Pa.) Tribune, 1946-51; bur. reporter, photographer The Scranton Times, 1953-54, reporter, 1954-66, state editor, 1966-73, city editor, 1973-80, mng. editor, 1980—. Trustee Steamtown Found., Scranton, 1984; bd. dirs. Lackawanna County RR Authority, Scranton, 1984. Cpl. U.S. Army, 1951-53. Mem. Soc. Newspaper Design, Pa. Assn. Press Mng. Editors (pres. 1985). Republican. Methodist. Avocations: railroading, travel. Office: The Scranton Times PO Box 3311 149 Penn Ave Scranton PA 18503

ROGERS, ELIZABETH BARLOW, municipal park administrator; b. San Antonio, Feb. 6, 1936; d. Caleb Leonidas and Elizabeth (Ewing) Browning; m. Edward Lee Barlow, July 6, 1957 (div. 1979); children: Elizabeth Ewing, David Browning; m. Theodore Courtney Rogers, June 28, 1984. BA in Art History, Wellesley Coll., 1957; MA in City Planning, Yale U., 1964. Open space cons. Parks Council N.Y., 1965-69; legis. asst. N.Y. State Senate, 1967-68; freelance journalist, author, 1969-74; screenwriter Time-Life Film Series, N.Y.C., 1974-75; exec. dir. Central Park Task Force, N.Y.C., 1975-79; adminstr. N.Y.C. Dept. Parks and Recreation, 1979—; founder, pres. Central Park Conservancy, 1980—. Author: The Forests and Wetlands of New York City, 1971, Frederick Law Olmsted's New York, 1972; co-author: East Hampton, A History and Guide, 1976, The Central Park Book, 1978, Rebuilding Central Park, A Management and Restoration Plan, 1985, others. Ptnr. N.Y.C. Partnership. Recipient John Burroughs medal, 1971, Honor award AIA, 1985, Urban Beautification award Am. Hort. Soc., 1987, Disting. Alumnae Achievement award Wellesley Coll., 1989, Hist. Preservation award and medal Garden Club Am., 1992, Citizen Leadership medal Nat. Park Found., 1994. Mem. Century Assn., Cosmopolitan Club, Georgica Assn. Home: 1112 Park Ave New York NY 10128-1235 Office: The Arsenal Central Park New York NY 10026

ROGERS, ERNEST MABRY, lawyer; b. Demopolis, Ala., Sept. 22, 1947; s. James B. and Ernestine B. (Brewer) R.; m. Jeanne Edwards, Dec. 15, 1979; children—Gilbert B., Katherine B., Mary C. B.A., Yale U., 1969; J.D.,

Harvard U., 1974. Bar: Ala. 1974, U.S. Dist. Ct. (no. dist.) Ala. 1975, U.S. Ct. Appeals (5th cir.) 1976, U.S. Ct. Appeals (11th cir.) 1981, U.S. Supreme Ct. 1981, U.S. Ct. Claims 1983, U.S. Ct. Appeals (6th cir.) 1987. Law clk. to judge U.S. Dist. Ct. (no. dist.) Ala., 1974-75; ptnr. Bradley, Arant, Rose & White, Birmingham, Ala., 1981—. Contbr. articles to profl. jours. Fellow, Am. Coll. of Constrn. Lawyers. Episcopalian. Lodge: Kiwanis. Office: Bradley Arant Rose & White PO Box 830709 Birmingham AL 35283

ROGERS, EUGENE CHARLES, investment firm executive; b. Bklyn., Sept. 29, 1932; s. Eugene Aloysius and Agnes Hilda (Scharbach) R.; m. Anita Therese Tobin, May 13, 1961; 1 son, Eugene Charles. B.B.A., St. John's U., Bklyn., 1954; M.B.A., N.Y. U., 1960. C.P.A., N.Y. Staff accountant Haskins & Sells (C.P.A.s), N.Y.C., 1954-60, Bache & Co., N.Y.C., 1960-62; controller, then chief fin. officer Reynolds Securities Inc., N.Y.C., 1962-72; v.p., treas. Reynolds Securities Inc., 1972—; 1st v.p., treas. Dean Witter Reynolds Inc., 1978-81, sr. v.p., treas., 1981—; guest lectr., panelist in field. Bd. advisors Coll. Bus. Adminstrn., St. John's U. Served with U.S. Army, 1954-56. Mem. N.Y. State Soc. C.P.A.'s, Fin. Execs. Instn., Fin. Club of N.Y. U. Grad. Sch. Bus., Securities Industry Assn. (past pres. fin. mgmt. div.), Sun and Surf Beach Club, World Trade Ctr. Club, Hempstead Golf and Country Club. Roman Catholic. Home: 15 Whitby Ct Rockville Centre NY 11570-1641 Office: Dean Witter Reynolds Inc 2 World Trade Ctr New York NY 10048

ROGERS, EUGENE JACK, medical educator; b. Vienna, Austria, June 13, 1921; came to U.S., 1937; s. Louis and Malvina (Haller) R.; m. Joyce M. Lighter, Feb. 9, 1952; children: Jay A., Robert J. B.S., CCNY; M.D., Chgo. Med. Sch., 1946, M.D., 1947. Diplomate Am. Bd. Phys. Medicine and Rehab. Intern Misericordia and Cabrini Meml. Hosps., N.Y.C., 1946-48; resident Madigan Hosp., Tacoma, 1951, Mayo Clinic, Rochester, Minn., 1951, N.Y. Med. Coll. Met. Med. Ctr., 1953-55; USPHS fellow, 1955-56; ship's surgeon U.S. Lines, Grace Lines, N.Y.C., 1948-49; indsl. physician Abraham & Strauss Stores, Bklyn., 1949-51; practice medicine specializing in phys. medicine and rehab. Bklyn., 1956-73; dir. rehab. service, attending physician N.Y. City Hosp. Dept., 1955-73; prof. and chmn. dept. rehab. medicine Chgo. Med. Sch., North Chicago, Ill., 1973—; cons. N.Y.C. Mayor's Adv. Com. for Aged, 1957; asst. prof. SUNY Downstate Med. Sch. Bklyn., 1958-73; med. dir. Schwab Rehab. Hosp., Chgo., 1973-75; acting chief rehab. service VA Center, North Chicgo, 1975-77; chmn. Ill. Phys. Therapy Exam. Com., 1977-87; examiner Am. Bd. Phys. Medicine and Rehab., 1983; sec., dir. Microtherapeutics, Inc., 1972. Editor: Total Cancer Care, 1975; contbr. articles to med. jours.; contbg. editor Ill. Med. Jour., 1983-89. Served to capt. U.S. Army, 1951-53. Recipient Bronze medal Am. Congress Rehab. Medicine, 1974. Fellow ACP, Am. Acad. Phys. Med. and Rehab.; mem. Chgo. Med. Sch. Faculty Assembly (spkr. 1983), Chgo. Med. Sch. Alumni Assn. (exec. com., asst. treas. 1983-93, Presdl. plaque Greater N.Y. chpt., Disting. Alumnus 1980, treas. 1993—), Ill. State Med. Soc. (chmn. workmen's compensation com. 1980-83), Ill. Soc. Phys. Medicine and Rehab. (pres. 1983-84), Phi Lambda Kappa (trustee 1980), Alpha Omega Lapha, Odd Fellow (pres. 1983-84). Home: 1110 N Lake Shore Dr Chicago IL 60611-1054 Office: Finch U Health Scis Chgo Med Sch 3333 Green Bay Rd North Chicago IL 60064-3095

ROGERS, FRED BAKER, medical educator; b. Trenton, N.J., Aug. 25, 1926; s. Lawrence H. and Eliza C. (Thropp) R. A.A., Princeton U., 1947; M.D., Temple U., 1948; M.S. in Medicine, U. Pa., 1954; M.P.H., Columbia U., 1957; spl. student, Johns Hopkins U., 1962. Diplomate: Am. Bd. Preventive Medicine. Intern Temple U. Hosp., Phila., 1948-49; chief resident physician Temple U. Hosp., 1953-54; USPHS fellow Temple U. Sch. Medicine, 1954-55, asst. prof. preventive medicine, 1956-58, assoc. prof., 1958-60, prof., 1960-90, prof. emeritus, 1991—, chmn. dept., 1970-77; lectr. epidemiology Columbia U. Sch. Pub. Health, 1957-68, Sch. Nursing, U. Pa., 1964-67; cons. USN Hosp., Phila., 1964-73. Author: A Syllabus of Medical History, 1958, Help-Bringers: Versatile Physicians of N.J, 1960, Epidemiology and Communicable Disease Control, 1963, Studies in Epidemiology, 1965, (with A.R. Sayre) The Healing Art, 1966, (with M.E. Cashel) Your Body is Wonderfully Made, 1974; mem. editorial bd. Am. Jour. Pub. Health, 1967-73; contbr. articles to profl. jours. Served with M.C. USNR, 1950-53, Korea. Recipient Chapel of Four Chaplains award, 1982. Fellow ACP; mem. AMA (past chmn. sect. preventive medicine), Am. Pub. Health Assn., Royal Soc. Medicine of London (hon.), Sigma Xi, Alpha Omega Alpha, Phi Rho Sigma. Clubs: Campus (Princeton); Franklin Inn (Phila.); Charaka (N.Y.C.); Osler (London). Home: 333 W State St Trenton NJ 08618-5722 Office: Temple U Sch Medicine Philadelphia PA 19140

ROGERS, FRED MCFEELY, television producer and host; b. Latrobe, Pa., Mar. 20, 1928; s. James Hillis and Nancy (McFeely) Flagg; m. Sara Joanne Byrd, July 9, 1952; children: James Byrd, John Frederick. MusB, Rollins Coll., 1951; MDiv, Pitts. Theol. Sem., 1962; DHL (hon.), Thiel Coll., 1969; HHD (hon.), Eastern Mich. U., 1973; LittD (hon.), St. Vincent Coll., 1973; DD (hon.), Christian Theol. Sem., 1973, Washington and Jefferson Coll., 1984, Westminster Coll., 1987; LHD (hon.), Yale U., 1974, Lafayette Coll., 1977, Washington and Jefferson Coll., 1984, Linfield Coll., 1982, Duquesne U., 1982, Slippery Rock Coll., 1982, U. S.C., 1985, MacMurray Coll., 1986, Drury Coll., 1986, Bowling Green State U., 1987; DFA (hon.), Carnegie-Mellon U., 1976; MusD (hon.), Waynesburg Coll., 1978, U. Ind., 1988; LLD (hon.), Hobart and William Smith Colls., 1985, U. Conn., 1991, Ind. U., Pa., 1992, Boston U., 1992, Moravian Coll., 1992; hon. degree, Goucher Coll., 1993, U. Pitts., 1993; DHL(hon.), U. W.Va., 1995. Adj. prof. U. Pitts., 1976; pres. Family Communications, Inc., Pitts.; asst. producer NBC, N.Y.C., 1951-53; exec. producer Sta. WQED, Pitts., 1953-62; producer, host CBC, Toronto, Ont., 1962-64; exec. producer, host Mister Rogers' Neighborhood (PBS), Pitts., 1965—; prodr., host Old Friends, New Friends PBS interview series, 1979-81; host Fred Rogers' Heros PBS, 1994. Author: Mister Rogers Talks with Parents, 1983, Mister Rogers' First Experiences Books, 1985, Mister Rogers' Playbook, 1986, Mr. Rogers Talks About Divorce, 1987, Mister Rogers-How Families Grow, 1988, You are Special, 1994; producer five audio cassettes of original songs-Many Ways to Say I Love You, audio cassettes Bedtime, 1992, Growing, 1992; composer: Mr. Rogers' Songbook; host, writer, producer five one hour videocassettes home videos CBS, 1987-88. Chmn. child devel. and mass media forum White House Conf. on Children; mem. Esther Island Preserve Assn.; bd. dirs. McFeely Rogers Found.; hon. chmn. Nat. PTA, 1992-94. Recipient Peabody award for finest children's TV program; award for excellence in children's programming Nat. Ednl. TV; Emmy award, 1980; Ohio State award, 1983, ACT award, 1984, The Christopher award, 1984, Ga. Assn. Broadcasters award, 1984; Lamplighter award Ednl. Press. Assn. Am., 1985; Disting. Service award Spina Bifida Assn. Am., 1985; Children's Book Council award, 1985, Emmy award for outstanding writing in children's series, 1985, Assn. Childhood Edn. award, 1986; Director's award-Ohio State award, 1986; Gold medal Internat. Film and TV Festival, 1986, award Nat. Assn. State Dirs. Migrant Edn., 1987, Ollie award Am. Children's TV Festival, 1987, Immaculata (Pa.) Coll. medal, 1988, Bronze medal Internat. Film and TV Festival, 1988, Outstanding Pa. Author award, 1988, Parent's Choice award, 1987, 88, Spl. Recognition award Nat. Assn. Music Mchts., 1989, PBS award in recognition of 35 yrs. in pub. TV, 1989, Hall of Fame award Action for Children's TV, 1988, Man. of Yr. award Pitts. Vectors, 1990, Peabody award, 1993, Disting Svc. medal, Colgate Rochester Divinity Sch., 1994, Eleanor Roosevelt Val-Kill medal, 1994, Joseph F. Mulach, Jr. award, 1995. Mem. Luxor Ministerial Assn. Presbyterian. Office: 4802 5th Ave Pittsburgh PA 15213-2957 *Every person in this life is so much more than meets the eye or ear. I'm continually surprised at the complexity of all those whom I'm fortunate enough really to get to know.*

ROGERS, GARTH WINFIELD, lawyer; b. Fort Collins, Colo., Nov. 4, 1938; s. Harlan Winfield and Helen Marie (Orr) R.; m. Joanne Kathleen Rapp, June 16, 1962; children: Todd Winfield, Christopher Jay, Gregory Lynn, Clay Charles. BS, U. Colo., 1958, LLB, 1962. Bar: Colo. 1962; U.S. Dist. Ct. Colo. 1962. Law clk. to presiding justice U.S. Dist. Ct., Denver, 1962-63; assoc. Allen, Stover & Mitchell, Ft. Collins, 1963-68; ptnr. Allen, Rogers Metcalf & Vahrenwald, Ft. Collins, 1968—. Articles editor Rocky Mountain Law Rev., 1961-62. Bd. advs. Salvation Army, Ft. Collins; past bd. dirs. United Way of Ft. Collins, Trinity Luth. Ch., Ft. Collins, others. Mem. Ft. Collins C. of C. (past bd. dirs.), ABA, Colo. Bar Assn., Larimer County Bar Assn. Avocations: sports, amateur writing, reading. Office: Allen Rogers Metcalf & Varenwald 125 S Howes St Fort Collins CO 80521-2737

ROGERS, GERALD D., electronics executive. Pres., CEO Cyrix Corp., Richardson, Tex. Office: Cyrix Corp 2703 N Central Expy Richardson TX 75080*

ROGERS, HAROLD DALLAS (HAL ROGERS), congressman; b. Barrier, KY, Dec. 31, 1937; m. Shirley McDowell, 1957; children: Anthony, Allison, John Marshall. BA, U. Ky., 1962, LLB, 1964. Bar: Ky. 1964. Pvt. practice Somerset, Ky., 1967-69; Commonwealth atty. Pulaski and Rockcastle counties, Ky., 1969-80; mem. 97th-104th Congresses from 5th Dist. Ky., 1981—; mem. appropriations coms., subcom. commerce and justice, energy and water. Mem. appropriations coms. Ky. N.G., 1957-64. Republican. Office: US Ho of Reps 2468 Rayburn Washington DC 20515*

ROGERS, HARRY, school system administrator. Supt. Valdez (Alaska) City Sch. Dist. State finalist Nat. Supt. Yr. award, 1993. Office: Valdez City Sch Dist PO Box 398 1112 W Klutina St Valdez AK 99686-0398

ROGERS, HARRY G., Canadian government official; b. Toronto, Ont., Can., Apr. 24, 1931; s. Lionel Trueman and Ethel Pearl (Gilmour) d.; m. Micheline Ouelette, Mar. 14, 1987; children: Tanya, Kim, Suzanne, Donald, Julia, Alan, Bruce, Jeane. B.A. in Econs. and Polit. Sci., U. Western Ont., London, 1954. With Ford Motor Co., 1955-69; sec.-treas. Ford Motor Co., Malaya and South Africa; staff exec. central fin. Ford Motor Co., Detroit; gen. mgr. Ford of Japan, Tokyo; with Xerox Corp., Stamford, Conn., 1969-78, mgr. internat. fin. ops.; asst. controller ops. Xerox Corp., Rochester, N.Y.; v.p. fin., mktg. and ops. Xerox Can. Inc., Toronto; comptroller gen. Treasury Bd. of Can., Ottawa, Ont., 1978-84; dep. minister taxation Govt. of Can., Ottawa, 1984-87; dep. minister Office of Fed. Devel., Privy Coun. Office, Ottawa, 1987-92; dep. minister Gov. Can. Fed. Prov. Rels. Office, Ontario, 1993—. Trustee, chmn. Ottawa Gen. Hosp., 1981-89. Home: 88A Glen Rd, Toronto, ON Canada M4W 2V6 Office: Office Fed Econ Devel, 1 Front St W 4th Fl, Toronto, ON Canada M5J 1A4

ROGERS, HERBERT F., manufacturing company executive; b. 1925; married. BS, Purdue U., 1949, D Engring. (hon.), 1979. With Gen. Dynamics Corp., 1949-91; v.p. mktg. Gen. Dynamics Corp., Ft. Worth, 1974-76, v.p. F-16 program, 1976-81, v.p. gen. mgr., 1981-87, exec. v.p. aerospace, 1987-88, pres., COO, 1988-90, vice chmn., 1990, ret., 1991.

ROGERS, HOWARD GARDNER, consultant, photographic company research director emeritus; b. Houghton, Mich., June 21, 1915; s. Gardner and Grace (Phillips) R.; m. Erdna M. Reggio, Jan. 17, 1940; children—Anne Cranford, Peter Nicholas, Mary Phillips Rogers Helmreich, Mark Howard, Lucinda Gardner. Student, Harvard Coll., 1933-35. With Polaroid Corp., Cambridge, Mass., 1936-85; dept. mgr. spl. color photographic research Polaroid Corp., 1954-74, v.p., sr. research fellow, 1976-78, sr. v.p., assoc. dir. research, 1978-80, sr. v.p., dir. research, 1980-85; cons. on photog. systems, light polarizers, 3-D imaging, new polymers. Inventor of instant color photographic systems, dye developers, new light-polarizers and other optical devices. Recipient Wetherill medal Franklin Inst., 1966, Edwin H. Land medal Optical Soc. Am./Soc. for Imaging Sci. and Tech., 1993. Fellow Am. Acad. Arts and Scis., Optical Soc. Am., Soc. for Imaging Sci. and Tech. (hon.), Photographic Hist. Soc. N.E. (hon.), Am. Inst. Chemists; mem. Indsl. Rsch. Inst. (Achievement award 1987). Home: 20 Newton St Weston MA 02193-2311

ROGERS, HOWARD H., chemist; b. N.Y.C., Dec. 26, 1926; s. Julian Herbert and Minnie (Jaffa) R.; m. Barbara Kniaz, Mar. 27, 1954 (div. 1978); children: Lynne, Mark David, Susan; m. Maureen Dohn, Dec. 28, 1978. BS in Chemistry, U. Ill., 1949; PhD in Inorganic Chemistry, MIT, 1953. Research group leader Allis-Chalmers Mfg. Co., West Allis, Wis., 1952-61; sr. tech. specialist Rocketdyne div., Rockwell, Canoga Park, Calif., 1961-70; chief research scientist Martek Instruments, Newport Beach, Calif., 1970-73; sr. scientist, engr. Hughes Aircraft Co., Torrance, Calif., 1973—. Developer nickel-hydrogen battery; patentee; contbr. sci. papers to profl. publs. in field. Served with USN, 1944-46. Recipient Lawrence A. Hyland Patent award Hughes Aircraft Co., 1987. Mem. Electrochem. Soc. (chmn. So. Calif./Nev. sect. 1976-78), Am. Chem. Soc., Sigma Xi. Home: 18361 Van Ness Ave Torrance CA 90504-5309 Office: Hughes Aircraft Co B231/1720 PO Box 2999 Torrance CA 90509-2999

ROGERS, ISABEL WOOD, religious studies educator; b. Tallahassee, Aug. 26, 1924; d. William Hudson and Mary Thornton (Wood) R. BA, Fla. State U., 1945; MA, U. Va., 1947; MRE, Presbyn. Sch. Christian Edn., 1949; PhD, Duke U., 1961; DD (hon.), Austin Coll., 1986; LLD (hon.), Westminster Coll., 1988; LHD, Centre Coll., 1989. Campus min. 1st Presbyn. Ch., Milledgeville, Ga., 1949-52; campus chaplain Ga. Coll., Milledgeville, 1952-61; prof. of applied Christianity Presbyn. Sch. Christian Edn., Richmond, Va., 1961—; elder Ginter Pk. Presbyn. Ch., Richmond, 1976-79, 89—; moderator of Gen. Assembly, Presbyn. Ch. U.S.A., 1987-88; lectr. Presbyn. chs. Author: The Christian and World Affairs, 1965, In Response to God, 1969, Our Shared Earth, 1980, Sing A New Song, 1981. Vol. Richmond Community Action Program, 1968-75, YWCA, Women's Advocacy Program, 1982—; bd. dirs. Presbyn. Outlook Found., Richmond, 1987—. Du Pont fellow U. Va., 1946. 47, Kearns fellow Duke U. Mem. Soc. Christian Ethics, Phi Kappa Phi, Phi Beta Kappa. Democrat. Avocations: hiking, jogging, tennis, gardening, stamp collecting. Home and Office: Presbyn Sch Christian Edn 1205 Palmyra Ave Richmond VA 23227-4417

ROGERS, JACK DAVID, plant pathologist, educator; b. Point Pleasant, W.Va., Sept. 3, 1937; s. Jack and Thelma Grace (Coon) R.; m. Belle C. Spencer, June 7, 1958. BS in Biology, Davis and Elkins Coll., 1960; MF, Duke U., 1960; PhD, U. Wis., 1963. From asst. prof. to prof. Wash. State U., Pullman, 1963-72, chmn. dept. plant pathology, 1986—. Contbr. articles to profl. jours. Recipient William H. Weston Teaching Excellence award Mycological Soc. Am., 1992. mem. Mycological Soc. of Am. (pres., 1977-78), Am. Phytopathol. Soc., Botanical Soc. Am., British Mycological Soc.

ROGERS, JAMES ALBERT, lawyer; b. Chgo., May 15, 1944; s. Albert Lee and Edith Jane (Magee) R.; m. Jane Austin Rughe, May 14, 1967 (div. 1980); m. Ellen Sheriff, Sept. 26, 1987; children: Alison Sheriff, Emily Sheriff. B.A., Carleton Coll., 1966; J.D., U. Mich., 1969. Bar: Minn. 1969, Wis. 1971, D.C. 1975. Law clk. Justice C. Donald Peterson, Supreme Ct. of Minn., 1969-70; asst. atty. gen. State of Wis., 1971-73; assoc. gen. counsel water and solid waste U.S. EPA, 1977-80; ptnr., head environment dept. Skadden, Arps, Slate, Meagher & Flom, Washington, 1981-91; ptnr. Wilmer, Cutler & Pickering, Washington, 1991—. Contbr. articles to profl. jours. Recipient Presidential award for meritorious sr. exec. service Pres. Carter, 1980. Mem. D.C. Bar Assn., Minn. Bar Assn., Wis. Bar Assn., Environ. Law Inst. (bd. dirs. 1982—, chmn. bd. 1987-90), Am. Law Inst. Democrat. Office: Wilmer Cutler & Pickering 2445 M St NW Washington DC 20037-1435

ROGERS, JAMES DEVITT, judge; b. Mpls., May 5, 1929; s. Harold Neil and Dorothy (Devitt) R.; m. Leanna Morrison, Oct. 19, 1968. AB, Dartmouth Coll., 1951; JD, U. Minn., 1954. Bar: Minn. 1954, U.S. Supreme Ct. 1983. Assoc. Johnson & Sands, Mpls., 1956-60; sole practice Mpls., 1960-62; judge Mpls. Municipal and Dist. Ct., 1959-91; mem. faculty Nat. Judicial Coll. Bd. dirs. Mpls. chpt. Am. Red Cross, chmn. service to mil. families and vets. com.; bd. dirs. Minn. Safety Council, St. Paul, 1988-91. Served to sgt. U.S. Army, 1954-56. Mem. ABA (chmn. nat. conf. spl. ct. judge, spl. com. housing and urban devel. law, traffic ct. program com., chmn. criminal justice sect., jud. adminstrn. div.), Nat. Jud. Coll. (bd. dirs.), Nat. Christmas Tree Grower's Assn. (pres. 1976-78), Mpls. Athletic Club. Congregational. Office: 14110 Prince Pl Minnetonka MN 55345-3027

ROGERS, JAMES EDWARD, paper company executive; b. Richmond, Va., Aug. 13, 1945; s. Olin Adair and Marjorie (Aiken) R.; children: James Edward Jr., Catherine, Margaret. BS in Physics, Va. Mil. Inst., 1967; MS in Nuclear Engring., U. Va., 1969; postgrad., Harvard U., 1987. Licensing engr. Va. Electric and Power Co., Richmond, 1969-71; sales engr., sales mgr., v.p. sales and mktg. James River Paper Co., Richmond, 1971-77, 79-82, sr. v.p., gen. mgr., 1977-82; v.p. corp. devel., 1982-87; sr. v.p., group exec., specialty paper bus. James River Corp., Richmond, 1987-92; pres., CEO Specialty Coatings Intl., Richmond, 1992-93; mng. dir. SCI Investors

Inc., Richmond, 1993—; chmn., bd. dirs. Custom Papers Group Inc., Richmond; bd. dirs. Owens and Minor, Inc., Richmond, Wellman, Inc., Shrewsbury, N.J., Caraustar Industries, Inc., Austell, Ga., Marine Devel. Corp., Richmond. Bd. dirs. Richmond Childrens Mus., Maymont Found., Richmond, 1987; mem. adv. coun. Va. Home, Richmond, Commonwealth Girl Scouts. Mem. Pub. Affairs Group, Storm Try Sail Club. Republican. Clubs: Commonwealth (Richmond); Fishing Bay Yacht (Deltaville, Va.) (commodore 1980); N.Y. Yacht (N.Y.C.). Office: SCI Investors Inc 823 E Main St Ste 1200 Richmond VA 23219

ROGERS, JAMES EUGENE, electric utility executive; b. Birmingham, Ala., Sept. 20, 1947; s. James E. and Margaret (Whatley) R.; m. Robyn McGill (div.); children: Chrissi, Kara, Ben; m. Mary Anne Boldrick, Oct. 28, 1977. BBA, U. Ky., 1970, JD, 1974. Asst. atty. gen. Commonwealth Ky., Louisville; asst. chief trial atty. Fed. Energy Regulation Commn., Washington, dep. gen. counsel litigation and enforcement; law clk. to presiding justice Supreme Ct Ky., Louisville; ptnr. Akin, Gump, Hauer & Feld, Dallas; sr. v.p. rates and regulatory affairs Fla. Gas Transm. Transwestern PL, Houston, 1985-86; formerly pres. Transwestern Pipeline, Houston; now with CINergy Corp. (formerly PSI Resources, Inc.), Cin.; bd. dirs. CINergy Corp., A O Irkutsk Energo, NBD Ind., Inc., Bankers Life Holding, Inc., Edison Electric Inst., Duke Realty Investments, Inc. Trustee Nat. Symphony Orch.; bd. dirs. Cin. Mus. Assn., The Nature Conservancy-Ind. chpt., Butler U., Indpls., U. Ky. Bus. Partnership Found. Mem. FBA, Young Pres.' Orgn., C. of C. Of U.S.A. (bd. dirs.), Ind. C. of C. (bd. dirs.), Ky. Bar Assn., D.C. Bar Assn., Skyline Club, Columbia Club, Meridian Hills Country Club, Crooked Stick Golf Club, Queen City Club, Bankers Club, Met. Club. Baptist. Avocations: tennis, biking, skiing, golf. Office: CINergy Corp 139 E 4th St 1406M Cincinnati OH 45202

ROGERS, JAMES FREDERICK, banker, management consultant; b. Centerville, Iowa, June 27, 1935; s. John W. and Mildred Holly (Morris) R.; m. Janet L. Marsden, June 27, 1957; children: Jennifer Burke, John William. AB, U. Mo., 1957; postgrad., Rutgers U. Grad. Sch. Banking, 1970-72. With Am. Security and Trust Co., Washington, 1959-85; exec. v.p. Am. Security and Trust Co., 1980-83; bd. dirs., pres. Am. Security Corp., 1983-85; cons. B.E.I.-Golembe Assoc., 1985-93; chmn. Nat. Bank of Va. Inc., 1988-89. Commr. Arlington County Planning Commn., 1979-80; asst. treas Kennedy Ctr. Performing Arts; pres., trustee Leonard Wood Found.; trustee Friends of Nat. Zoo, Greater Washington Rsch. Ctr., Washington Dulles Task Force, Arena Stage, Sch. Commerce U. Va. Officer AUS, 1958-59. Mem. D.C. Bankers Assn. (pres. 1984-85). Presbyn. Clubs: Metropolitan (Washington); Chevy Chase. Home: 4201 38th Rd N Arlington VA 22207-4554

ROGERS, JAMES VIRGIL, JR., retired radiologist and educator; b. Johnson City, Tenn., Oct. 7, 1922; s. James Virgil and Mary Ruth (Collins) R.; m. Mildred Vandivere, June 9, 1945 (div. 1985); children: Rebecca Jean, James V. III, Janet Marie, Susan Margaret; m. Mary Lujean Craven, Mar. 18, 1989. BS, Emory U., 1943, MD, 1945. Intern Kings County Hosp., N.Y.C., 1945-46; resident in radiology Grady Meml. Hosp., Altanta, 1947-48, Emory U. Hosp., Altanta, 1948-50; instr. Emory U. Sch. Medicine, Atlanta, 1950-51, assoc., 1950-53, asst. prof., 1954-60, assoc. prof., 1960-64, prof., 1965-93; ret.; chief radiology svc. Emory U. Hosp., Atlanta, 1971-80, vice chmn. dept. radiology 1973-78, assoc. chmn., 1978-80; dep. sect. head Emory Clinic, Atlanta, 1971-78, sect. head, 1978-80, chief radiology svc., 1982-91; cons. radiology 3d Army Hdqrs., Atlanta; examiner Am. Bd. Radiology, 1970-79, site inspector for residency programs, 1972-83. Contbr. articles to profl. jours. Pres. PHRC Ga., Atlanta, 1990. 1st It. U.S. Army, 1946-47. Fellow Am. Coll. Radiology (councilor); mem. Radiol. Soc. North Am., Am. Roentgen Ray Soc., So. Radiologic Conf. (past pres.), Ga. Radiologic Soc. (past pres.), Atlanta Radiologic Soc. (past. pres.), AMA, So. Med. Assn. (past pres. radiology sect.), Druid Hills Golf Club, Am. Legion. Republican. Methodist. Avocations: golf, fishing. Home: 1715 Silver Hill Rd Stone Mountain GA 30087-2212

ROGERS, JAMES WILSON, church official; b. Vancouver, BC, Canada, Feb. 18, 1943; m. Carol Haney; children: Amy, Darren. Student, L.I.F.E. Bible Coll. With real estate profession, 1963-69; br. mgr. Wall & Redekop Realty, 1969-74, v.p., gen. mgr., 1974-90; exec. asst. to pres. Internat. Ch. of Foursquare Gospel, 1990—; dir. bus. devel. Realty World Can.; con. to numerous offices, Western Can.; Western regional dir. Comml. Divsn. Coun. mem. Kingsway Foursquare Ch., Vancouver, B.C.; bd. dirs. Youth for Christ Greater Vancouver; mem. pres.'s adv. com. Trinity Western U.; bd. dirs., bd. regents L.I.F.E. Bible Coll. Can.; founding dir., officer Foursquare Ch. Can., nat. bd. dirs. 1979-90. Office: Internat Ch Foursquare Gospel 1910 W Sunset Blvd Ste 200 Los Angeles CA 90026-0176

ROGERS, JEFFREY, dancer. Attended, Sch. Am. Ballet. Dancer Ballet West, Salt Lake City, 1984-89; soloist Ballet West, 1989-91, prin. artist, 1991—; instr., guest artist Ballet West Conservatory. Dance performances include The Dream, Abdallah, Romeo & Juliet, Giselle, Sleeping Beauty, The Age of Anxiety (John Neumeier). Recipient Princess Grace Found. award, 1984. Office: Ballet West 50 West 200 South Salt Lake City UT 84101*

ROGERS, JERRY, principal. Prin. Westwood Elem. Sch., Springdale, Ark. Recipient DOE Elem. Sch. Recognition award, 1989-90. Office: Westwood Elem Sch 1800 Mcray Ave Springdale AR 72762-4024

ROGERS, JERRY L., federal agency administrator; b. Tex., Dec. 22, 1938; s. Ancell Robert and Grace Evalena (Coin) R.; m. Peggy Floretta Sifford, Apr. 6, 1963; children: Tiana Lynne Conklin, Elvin Houston, Jeffrey Martin. BA in History, Tex. Tech, 1962, MA, 1965. Historian Nat. Park Svc., Ft. Davis, Tex., 1965-66; historian Nat. Register Nat. Park Svc., Washington, 1967-69, chief registration, 1972-73, chief grants divsn., 1973-75, chief archeology and hist. preservation, 1975-79, assoc. dir. cultural programs, 1981-83, assoc. dir. cultural resources, 1983—; dir. Ranching Heritage Ctr. Tex. Tech Mus., Lubbock, 1969-72; dep. assoc. dir. Heritage Conservation Svc., Washington, 1979-81; internat. cons. in hist. preservation to Italy, Russia, Spain, China, India, Egypt. Contbr. articles to profl. jours. Mem. adv. com. on cemeteries and memls. VA, Washington, 1987—. Recipient Meritorious Svc. award Dept. Interior, 1992. Mem. AIA (mem. com. hist. resources, ex-officio mem.), Nat. Trust Hist. Preservation (trustee 1981—), Civil War Trust. Avocations: genealogy, classic automobiles. Home: 2221 Glenheather Dr Falls Church VA 22043 Office: Nat Park Svc PO Box 37127 1849 C St NW Washington DC 20240

ROGERS, JODY RAY, army officer; b. Mauston, Wis., Jan. 22, 1953; s. Edwin Burton and Betty Mae (Allen) R.; m. Sandra Joy Olson, Sept. 7, 1974; children: Catherine, Aaron. BS, U. Wis., Stevens Point, 1976; MSBA, Boston U., 1982; M Healthcare Adminstrn., Baylor U., 1985; PhD, U. Minn., 1993. Commd. 2d lt. U.S. Army, 1976, advanced through grades to lt. comdr.; lab officer Brooke Army Med. Ctr., San Antonio, 1976-79, adminstr., 1986-89; lab. officer 5th Gen. Hosp., Stuttgart, Fed. Republic Germany, 1979-82; resident Kimbrough Cmty. Hosp., Ft. Meade, Md., 1984; fellow Office of Surgeon Gen., Washington, 1985; inspector gen. Health Svcs. Command, San Antonio, 1989-90; strategic planner U.S. Army Med. Command, San Antonio, 1993—. Bd. dirs. Juvenile Diabetes Found., San Antonio, 1994—. Fellow Am. Coll. Healthcare Execs.; mem. Ret. Officer Assn. Home: 2054 Chittin Hollow San Antonio TX 78232 Office: US Army Med Command Office Strategic Planning Fort Sam Houston TX 78234

ROGERS, JOEL, law, political science and sociology educator; b. Long Branch, N.J., Mar. 19, 1952. BA, Yale, 1972, JD, 1976; MA, Princeton U., 1978, PhD, 1984. Prof. Sch. Law U. Wis., Madison; founder Mfg. Tng. Consortium; organizer Ctr. Wis. Strategy. Author and co-author of several books including Right Turn: The Decline of the Democrats and the Future of American Politics, 1986. MacArthur fellow, 1995. Office: Univ WI Sch of Law 975 Bascom Mall Madison WI 53706*

ROGERS, JOHN ALFROD, lawyer; b. Charleston, W.Va., Aug. 3, 1949; s. Hugh Henry and Annie Catherine (Delp) R. BA in History and Govt., U. W.Va. Inst. Tech., 1972; JD, W.Va. U., 1978. Bar: W.Va. 1978, U.S. Dist. Ct. (so. dist.) W.Va. 1978, U.S. Ct. Appeals (4th cir.) 1978. Staff counsel W.Va. Legis., Charleston, 1978-83, 1985-87; asst. disciplinary counsel W.Va.

State Bar, Charleston, 1983-84; dep. commr. W.Va. Dept. Motor Vehicles, Charleston, 1984-85; dir. criminal law rsch. div. Pub. Legal Svcs. Coun., Charleston, 1987—. Bd. dirs. Kanawha Players, Charleston, 1982-85, Children's Theater of Charleston, 1987—; mem. choir First Presbyn. Ch., Charleston, 1982—. Mem. ABA, W.Va. State Bar Assn. Democrat. Avocations: theater, music, gardening, jogging, cycling. Home: 103 Westview Dr Charleston WV 25311-1333 Office: Pub Legal Svcs Coun 1800 Washington St W Charleston WV 25312-2029

ROGERS, JOHN JAMES WILLIAM, geology educator; b. Chgo., June 27, 1930; s. Edward James and Josephine (Dickey) R.; m. Barbara Bongard, Nov. 30, 1956; children: Peter, Timothy. BS, Calif. Inst. Tech., 1952, PhD, 1955; MS, U. Minn., 1952. Lic. geologist, N.C. From instr. to prof. Rice U., Houston, 1954-75, master Brown Coll., 1966-71, chmn. geol. dept., 1971-74; W.R. Kenan Jr. prof. geology U. N.C., Chapel Hill, 1975—. Author: A History of the Earth, 1993; co-author: Fundamentals of Geology, 1966, Precambrian Geology of India, 1987; co-editor: Holocene Geology of Galveston Bay, 1969, Precambrian of South India, 1983, Basalts, 1984, African Rifting, 1989; regional editor Jour. African Earth Scis., 1982-93; contbr. articles to profl. jours. Fellow Geol. Soc. Am., Geol. Soc. India, Geol. Soc. Africa (hon.); mem. Mineral. Soc. Am., Am. Assn. Petroleum Geologists, Soc. Econ. Paleontologists and Mineralogists. Home: 1816 Rolling Rd Chapel Hill NC 27514-7502 Office: U of NC Dept Geology CB #3315 Chapel Hill NC 27599-3315

ROGERS, JOHN M., food Products executive. Pres., CEO B.C. Rogers Processors Inc., Morton, Miss. Office: B C Rogers Prcessors Inc 121 Old Highway 80 E Morton MS 39117*

ROGERS, JOHN S., union official; b. Scranton, Pa., Nov. 19, 1930. Student, U. Wis., 1959-61, U. Mich., 1963; student spl. studies, Am. U., 1965-66, Harvard U. Bus. Sch., 1967. Internat. rep. United Brotherhood of Carpenters and Joiners of Am., Washington, 1958-65, asst. to gen. pres., 1966-74, dir. edn., 1971-82, mem. gen. exec. bd., 1974-78, gen. sec., 1978-91; sec.-treas. Suffolk County (N.Y.) Dist. Coun. Carpenters, 1957-58; v.p.n N.Y. State Bldg. and Constrn. Trades Council, 1974-78, N.Y. State Fedn. Labor, 1974-78; pres. N.Y. State Coun. Carpenters, 1974-78; vice chmn. N.Y. State Commn. Jobs and Energy; mem. Suffolk County Pub. Employment Rels.s Bd.; vis. lectr. George Meany Ctr. Labor Studies. Author numerous trade union leadership mans. and instructional materials, 1966-79. Bd. dirs. L.I. action com. Help for Retarded Children, 1956-60; labor co-chmn United Cerebral Palsy, N.Y.C., 1977-78; v.p. Leukemia Soc. Mem. Harvard Trade Union Alumnae Assn. Home: 7026 Darby Towne Ct Alexandria VA 22310-4752

ROGERS, JOHN WASHINGTON, JR., investment management company executive; s. John W. Sr. and Jewel (Mankarious) R.; m. Desiree Glapion. BS in Econs., Princeon U. Broker William Blair & Co.; now pres. Ariel Capital Mgmt., Inc., Ariel Mut. Funds, Chgo. Bd. dirs. Chgo. Urban League, Chgo. Park Dist., Chgo. Symphony Orch., Rush Presbyn. St. Luke's Hosp., Nat. Assn. Securities Dealers, Aon Corp., Morrison Knudsen Inc., Am. Nat. Bank. Office: Ariel Capital Mgmt Ariel Mut Funds 307 N Michigan Ave Ste 500 Chicago IL 60601-5305

ROGERS, JUDITH W., federal judge. AB cum laude, Radcliffe Coll., 1961; LLB, Harvard U., 1964; LLM, U. Va., 1988; LLD (hon.), D.C. Sch. Law, 1992. Bar: D.C. 1965. Law clk. Juvenile Ct. D.C., 1964-65; asst. U.S. atty. D.C., 1965-68; trial atty. San Francisco Neighborhood Legal Assistance Found., 1968-69; atty. assoc. atty. gen.'s office U.S. Dept. Justice, 1969-71, atty. criminal divsn., 1969-71; gen. counsel Congl. Commn. on Organization of D.C. Govt., 1971-72; coordinator legis. program Office of Dep. Mayor D.C., 1972-74, spl. assist. to mayor for legis., 1974-79, corp. counsel, 1979-83; assoc. judge D.C. Ct. Appeals, 1983-88, chief judge, 1988-94; cir. judge U.S. Ct. Appeals-D.C. Cir., 1994—; mem. D.C. Law Revision Commn., 1979-83, Mayor's Commn. on Crime and Justice, 1982, grievance com. U.S. Dist. Ct. for D.C., 1982-83, exec. com. Conf. Chief Justices, 1993-94. Bd. dirs. Wider Opportunities for Women, 1972-74, Friends of the D.C. Superior Ct., 1972-74; mem. vis. com. Harvard U. Sch. Law, 1984-90; trustee Radcliffe Coll., 1982-88. Named Woman Lawyer of Yr., Women's Bar Assn. D.C., 1990; recipient citation for work on D.C. Self-Govt. Act, 1973, Disting. Pub. Svc. award D.C. Govt., 1983, award Greater Washington Area Women Lawyers divsn. Nat. Bar Assn., 1989, award Nat. Bar Assn., 1989. Fellow ABA; mem. D.C. Bar Assn., Nat. Assn. Women Judges, Conf. Chief Justices (bd. dirs. 1993-94). Office: US Ct Appeals 333 Constitution Ave NW Washington DC 20001-2866

ROGERS, JUSTIN TOWNER, JR., retired utility company executive; b. Sandusky, Ohio, Aug. 4, 1929; s. Justin Towner and Barbara Eloise (Larkin) R. AB cum laude, Princeton U., 1951; JD, U. Mich., 1954. Bar: Ohio 1954. Assoc. Wright, Harlor, Purpus, Morris & Arnold, Columbus, 1956-58; with Ohio Edison Co., Akron, 1958-93, v.p., then exec. v.p., 1970-79, pres., 1980-91, chmn. bd., 1991-93; ret., 1993; bd. dirs. 1st Nat. Bank Ohio, 1st Bancorp Ohio; past mem. coal adv. bd. Internat. Energy Agy. Past pres., trustee Akron Cmty. Trusts, Akron Child Guidance Ctr.; past chmn. Akron Assoc. Health Agys., U. Akron Assocs.; past chmn., trustee, mem. exec. com. trustees Akron Gen. Med. Ctr., Health Network Ohio; mem. adv. coun. Coll. Bus. Adminstrn. Kent (Ohio) State U.; trustee Sisler McFawn Found.; mem. Gt. Trail coun. Boy Scouts Am. Mem. Akron City Club, Portage Country Club, Mayflower Club, Rockwell Springs Trout Club (Castalia, Ohio), Princeton Club (N.Y.C.), Phi Delta Phi, Beta Gamma Sigma.

ROGERS, KATE ELLEN, educator; b. Nashville, Dec. 13, 1920; d. Raymond Lewis and Louise (Gruver) R.; diploma Ward-Belmont Jr. Coll., 1940; BA in Fine Arts, George Peabody Coll., 1946, MA in Fine Arts, 1947; EdD in Fine Arts and Fine Arts Edn., Columbia U., 1956. Instr., Tex. Tech. Coll., Lubbock, 1947-53; co-owner, v.p. Design Today, Inc., Lubbock, 1951-54; student asst. Am. House, N.Y.C., 1953-54; asst. prof. housing and interior design U. Mo., Columbia, 1954-56, assoc. prof., 1956-66, prof., 1966-85, emeritus, 1985—, chmn. dept. housing and interior design, 1973-85; mem. accreditation com. Found. for Interior Design Edn. Research, 1975-76 chmn. standards com., 1976-82, chmn. research, 1982-85. Mem. 1st Bapt. Ch., Columbia, Mo.; bd. dirs. Meals on Wheels, 1989-91. Nat. Endowment for Arts research grantee, 1981-82. Fellow Interior Design Educators Council (pres. 1971-73, chmn. bd. 1974-76, chmn. research com. 1977-78); mem. Am. Soc. Interior Designers, (hon., medal of honor 1975). Am. Home Econs. Assn., Columbia Art League (adv. bd. 1988-93), Pi Lambda Theta, Kappa Delta Pi, Phi Kappa Phi (hon.), Gamma Sigma Delta, Delta Delta Delta (Phi Eta chpt.), Phi Upsilon Omicron, Omicron Nu (hon.). Democrat. Author: The Modern House, USA, 1962; editor Jour. Interior Design Edn. and Research, 1975-78.

ROGERS, KATHERINE DIANE, political consultant, state legislator; b. Concord, N.H., Mar. 7, 1955; d. Albert A. and Alta (Whittier) R. BA, Clark U., Worcester, Mass., 1977. Mem. N.H. Ho. of Reps., Concord, 1992—; bd. dirs. N.H. Bus. Fin. Authority. Mem. City Coun., Concord, 1991—. Democrat. Lutheran. Home: 4 Jay Dr Concord NH 03301-7831

ROGERS, KENNETH NORMAN, retired foreign service officer, lawyer, international political and commercial consultant; b. Troy, N.Y., Oct. 21, 1931; s. Kenneth Norman and Marguerite Anne (McAuliffe) R.; m. Millicent Zella Pierce, June 19, 1959; 1 child, Katherine Marguerite. BS, Ohio State U., 1953; JD, George Washington U., 1958; grad., Nat. War Coll., 1979. Bar: W.Va. 1959, U.S. Dist. Ct. D.C. 1972, U.S. Ct. Mil. Appeals 1975, U.S. Ct. Appeals (D.C. cir.) 1972, U.S. Supreme Ct. 1973. Fgn. svc. officer Dept. of State, Hong Kong, Vietnam, Morocco, Angola and Jamaica, 1957-85, Washington, 1976-78; Am. consul. gen. Dept. of State, Tangier, Morocco, 1980-85; cons. on internat. polit. and comml. matters, 1985—. Editor: Human Rights, 1979. Trustee Dacor Bacon House Found., Washington. Served to lt. (j.g.) USN, 1953-55, Korea. Recipient award for valor Dept. of State, 1975; recipient Meritorious Honor award Vietnam, 1964, Morocco, 1985, Superior Honor award, 1976, 77, 80. Mem. Am. Fgn. Service Assn. (v.p. 1978-79), U.S. Naval Inst., Nat. War Coll. Alumni Assn., Diplomatic and Consular Officers Ret. (bd. govs. 1992—), Delta Theta Phi, Theta Chi. Home: 9911 La Duke Dr Kensington MD 20895-3140

ROGERS, KENNETH R., advertising executive; married; 1 child. BA magna cum laude, Hofstra U.; MBA, Columbia U. With Compton Advt., N.Y.C.; exec. v.p., bd. dirs. BBDO, Inc., N.Y.C.; exec. v.p. J. Walter Thompson Co., N.Y.C., until 1987; exec. v.p., multinat. mng. dir., regional dir. for L.Am. Backer Spielvogel Bates Worldwide, Inc., N.Y.C., 1987-90; mng. dir. N.Y. Office responsible for account svcs. Backer Spielvogel Bates, Inc., N.Y.C., 1990-91, pres., COO, from 1991; now vice chmn., multinat. client svcs. Bates Worldwide (formerly Backer Spielvogel Bates, Worldwide, Inc.), N.Y.C. Office: Bates Worldwide Inc Chrysler Bldg 405 Lexington Ave New York NY 10174-0002

ROGERS, KENNETH RAY, entertainer, recording artist; b. Houston, Aug. 21, 1938; s. Edward Floyd and Lucille (Hester) R.; 1 child by 1st marriage, Carol; 1 child by 2d marriage, Kenneth; m. Marianne Gordon; 1 child, Christopher Cody. Student, U. Houston. Appeared on American Bandstand, 1958; mem. Bobby Doyle Trio, 1959-66, Christy Minstrels, 1966-67, The First Edition, 1967-69, Kenny Rogers and The First Edition, 1969-75, pursued solo career, 1975—; performed numerous concerts in U.S., Can., Eng., Scotland, New Zealand, Australia, Japan; hosted TV spls. Kenny Rogers Classic Weekend, 1988, 89, 90, Kenny, Dolly & Willie, 1989, Kenny Rogers in Concert, 1989, Goodwill Games, 1990; starred in TV series Rollin' with The First Edition, 1972; appeared in movies Six Pack, 1982, Wild Horses, 1985; appearances Tonight Show; appeared in TV movies: Kenny Rogers as the Gambler, 1980, Coward of the County, 1981, Gambler, Part II, 1983, Gambler III: The Adventure Continues, 1987, Christmas in America, 1989, The Gambler Returns, The Luck of the Draw (Gambler IV), 1991; appeared in TV spl. Very Special Arts; (TV series): MacShayne, 1994—; rec. artist with Liberty Records, 1976-82, RCA Records, 1983—; toured Kenny & Dolly, Dollywood, 1990, British Isles, 1990; recs. include That Crazy Feeling (Gold single), I Don't Need You (Brit. Country Music Assn. award, Acad. Country Music award), Love is What We Make It, 1985, The Heart of the Matter, 1985, They Don't Make Them Like They Used To, What About Me, I Prefer the Moonlight, 1987, When You Put Your Heart in It, 1988 (ofcl. theme song U.S. Gymnastics Fedn.), Christmas in America, 1989, Love Is Strange, 1990, Greatest Country Hits, 1990, If Only My Heart Had a Voice, 1993, Greatest Hits, 1994; number #1 albums include Kenny Rogers-Lucille, 1976, Love or Something Like It, 1978, The Gambler, 1978, Kenny, 1979, Gideon, 1980, Share Your Love, 1981, Eyes That See in the Dark, 1983, Something Inside So Strong, 1989; author photographic works Kenny Roger's America, 1986, Your Friends and Mine, 1987; rec. artist Warner/Reprice, 1988—; TV host A&E The Real West, 1993. Hon. capt. 1988 U.S. Gymnastics Team. Named Cross-Over Artist of Year Billboard mag., 1977, named Top Male vocalist People mag., 1979, 80; recipient Country Music Assn. award, 1978, 79, Am. Music award, Best Male Vocalist, Best Album, 1984, Am. Music award, Best Male Country Vocalist, Best Album, 1985, Country Music Found. Roy Acuff award, 1985, UN Peace award, 1984, Rec. Industry Assn. Am. Most Awarded Artist award, 1984 (11 platinum, 18 gold albums), Grammy award for best male country vocal, 1977, 79, co-recipient (with Ronnie Milsap) for best country vocal duet, 1987, 1st Harry Chapin award for humanitarianism ASCAP, 1988, Horation Alger award, 1990; numerous other music awards. Address: care Kragen & Co 1112 N Sherbourne Dr Los Angeles CA 90069-2202

ROGERS, LAWRENCE H., II, retired television executive, investor, writer; b. Trenton, N.J., Sept. 6, 1921; s. Norman Tallman and Nancy (Titus) R.; m. Suzanne Long; children: Hallie, Suzanne, Lawrence H. III, Campbell, Natalie, Christian. Grad., Lawrenceville Sch., 1939; BA with honors in history, Princeton U., 1943; student, Harvard U., 1963. A pioneer broadcast editorials; built sta. WSAZ-TV Inc.; with Taft Broadcasting Co., Cin., 1960-76; pres. Taft Broadcasting Co., 1963-76; pres., CEO Omega Comms., Inc., Orlando, Fla., 1977-92; chmn. bd. dirs. Cin. br. Fed. Res. Bank of Cleve., 1975-82; bd. dirs. Cin. Fin. Corp.; Cardinal Group of Funds, Columbus, Ohio; past mem. TV Code Rev. Bd.; treas. TV Bur. Advt., then chmn. bd. dirs.; vice chmn. bd. Sta. NBC-TV Affiliates; v. dir. Assn. Maximum Svc. Telecaster, Washington; mem. info. com. Nat. Assn. Broadcasters, then editl. com.; mem. TV Code Rev. Bd.; cons. to USIA, Africa, 1967, USSR and Ea. Europe, 1971; mem. summit trip and SALT signing with Pres. Richard Nixon, 1972. Author: Business of Broadcasting, 1963, Orlando Shoot-Out, 1990. Vice chmn. trustees distbn. com. Greater Cin. Found.; Former Gov. W.Va. Econ. Devel. Agy.; bd. dirs. Theatre Devel. Fund; gen. chmn. Greater Cin. Fine Arts Fund. Served to capt. F.A. AUS, World War II, ETO. Recipient Distinguished Service award U.S. Jr. C. of C., 1956. Mem. Internat. Radio TV Exec. Soc., Newcomen Soc. Clubs: Queen City (Cin.); Camargo, N.Y. Yacht, Brook (N.Y.C.); Rolling Rock (Ligonier, Pa.); Commonwealth (Cin.). Home and Office: 4600 Drake Rd Cincinnati OH 45243-4118

ROGERS, LEE FRANK, radiologist; b. Colchester, Vt., Sept. 24, 1934; s. Watson Frank and Marguerite Mortimer (Cole) R.; m. Donna Mae Brinker, June 20, 1956; children—Michelle, Cynthia, Christopher, Matthew. B.S., Northwestern U., 1956, M.D., 1959. Commd. 2d lt. U.S. Army, 1959, advanced through grades to maj., 1967; rotating intern Walter Reed Gen. Hosp., 1959-60; resident radiology Fitzsimons Gen. Hosp., 1960-63; ret., 1967; radiologist Baptist Meml. Hosp., San Antonio, 1967-68, U. Tex. Med. Sch., San Antonio, 1968-71; dir. residency tng.; radiologist U. Tex. Med. Sch., Houston, 1972-74; prof., chmn. dept. radiology Northwestern U. Med. Sch., Chgo., 1975—; editor-in-chief Am. Jour. Roentgenology, Winston-Salem, N.C., 1995—. Fellow Am. Coll. Radiology (past pres.); mem. Am. Roentgen Ray Soc., Assn. U. Radiologists, Radiology Soc. N.Am., Am. Bd. Radiology, Alpha Omega Alpha. Episcopalian. Office: Am Jour Roenterology 101 S Stratford Rd #303 Winston Salem NC 27104 *The source of most problems is previous solutions.*

ROGERS, LEE JASPER, lawyer; b. Fort Monmouth, N.J., May 6, 1955; s. Peter and Ethel Mae (Williams) R.; m. Vanessa Walisha Yarbrough, Apr. 18, 1981 (div. Oct. 1988); 1 child, Stephanie Alexandria. Student, Drew U., 1975, Monmouth Coll., 1975; BA in History, Hampton Inst., 1977; JD, Howard U., 1980. Pvt. practice Red Bank, N.J., 1981-91, 95—; asst. dep. pub. defender Ocean County region, Toms River, N.J., 1991-92; mortgage loan officer Allied Fin. Svcs., Neptune, N.J., 1992-93, Mortgage Money Mart, Edison, N.J., 1993-94, Residential First, Inc., Shrewsbury, N.J., 1994-95, Fairmont Funding, Lakewood, N.J., 1995—; vol. counsel Pro Bono Legal Svcs., Red Bank, N.J., 1982-91; pres., chmn. bd. Jay-Mar Entertainment Enterprises, Inc., 1986—. Author numerous poems; vocal singing group Pizazz, 1991-94, Nu Eara, 1992. Pres. bd. dirs. Count Basie Learning Ctr., Red Bank, 1995—; del. dist. 9 Red Bank Rep. Com., 1995—. Mem. ABA, NAACP (exec. com. Red Bank chpt. 1983-88), Assn. Trial Lawyers Am. Elks (sec. ho. com. Bates lodge #220 1988-90, loyal knight 1990-91, esteemed loyal knight 1993-94, chmn. by-laws com. 1993-94). Baptist. Home: Apt 3 298 Shrewsbury Ave Red Bank NJ 07701-1319 *Mastery is achieved through the development of the spirit, and the resulting obtainment of bliss. We should all seek to be at one within ourselves and with the world around us. To do this, we must walk with God. Only then can we find true happiness!.*

ROGERS, LON B(ROWN), retired lawyer; b. Pikeville, Ky., Sept. 5, 1905; s. Fon and Ida (Brown) R.; BS, U. Ky., 1928, LLB, 1932; LHD (hon.), Pikeville Coll., 1979, LHD (hon.) Centre Coll. of Ky., 1992; m. Mary Evelyn Walton, Dec. 17, 1938; children: Marylon Walton, Martha Brown, Fon II. Bar: Ky. 1932. Practiced law in Lexington, 1932-38, Pikeville, 1939-80. Dir. East Ky. Beverage Co., Pikeville, 1940-90, Pikeville Nat. Bank & Trust Co. Elder, 1st Presbyterian Ch, Pikeville, Ky., 1947-75; mem. Pikeville City Council, 1951; mem. local bd. SSS, 1958-69; mem. Breaks Interstate Park Commn., Ky.-Va., 1960-68, chmn., 1960-62, 64-66, vice chmn., 1966-68; chmn. Community Services Commn., Pikeville Model Cities, 1969-71; mem. Ky. Arts Commn., 1965-72, Ky. Travel Council, 1967-70, 73-75; pres. Ky. Mountain Laurel Festival Assn., 1971-72. Chmn. bd. trustees Presbytery Ebenezer, U.S.A., 1950-71; trustee Pikeville Coll., 1951-72, 73-79, trustee emeritus, 1979—; trustee Presbytery of Transylvania, 1981-82; mem. bd. nat. missions United Presbyn. Ch. USA, 1954-66; trustee Appalachian Regional Hosps., Inc., 1963-67, Ky. Ind. Coll. Found., 1973-82; bd. dirs. Meth. Hosp. of Ky., 1966-82; mem., Presbyn. Ch., Lexington 1982—, trustee, 1989-91; am. mem., trustee 2nd Presbyterian Ch. Mem. Ky. C. of C. (regional v.p. 1962-64, 69-74), Ky. Hist. Soc., S.A.R., Civil War Round Table, Blue Grass Kiwanis (past lt. gov.), Filson Club, Blue Grass Automobile (pres. 1971-74, dir.), Sigma Alpha Epsilon, Phi Delta Phi. Republican. Home: 505 E Main

St Lexington KY 40508-2309 Office: 300 E Main St Ste 403 Lexington KY 40507-1539

ROGERS, LORENE LANE, university president emeritus; b. Prosper, Tex., Apr. 3, 1914; d. Mort M. and Jessie L. (Luster) Lane; m. Burl Gordon Rogers, Aug. 23, 1935 (dec. June, 1941). B.A., N. Tex. State Coll., 1934; M.A. (Parke, Davis fellow), U. Tex., 1946, Ph.D., 1948; D.Sc. (hon.), Oakland U., 1972; LL.D. (hon.), Austin Coll., 1977. Prof. chemistry Sam Houston State Coll., Huntsville, Tex., 1947-49; research scientist Clayton Found. Biochem. Inst. U. Tex., Austin, 1950-64, asst. dir., 1957-64, prof. nutrition, 1962-80, assoc. dean Grad. Sch., 1964-71, v.p. univ., 1971-74, pres., 1974-79, mem. exec. com. African grad. fellowship program, 1966-71; research cons. Clayton Found. for Research, Houston, 1979-81; Vis. scientist, lectr., cons. NSF, 1959-62; cons. S.W. Research Inst., San Antonio, 1959-62; mem. Grad. Record Exams Bd., 1972-76, chmn., 1974-75; adv. com. ITT Internat. Fellowship, 1973-83; dir. Texaco, Inc., Gulf States Utilities, Republic Bank, Austin. Bd. dirs. Tex. Opera Theatre, Austin Lyric Opera; chmn. bd. trustees Texaco Philanthropic Found.; chmn. council of presidents Nat. Assn. State Univs. and Land-Grant Colls., 1976-77, mem. exec. com., 1976-79; mem. com. on identification of profl. women Am. Council on Edn., 1975-79, mem. com. on govt. relations, 1978-79; mem. target 2000 project com. Tex. A&M U. System; mem. ednl. adv. bd. John E. Gray Inst., Lamar U., Beaumont, Tex. Eli Lilly fellow, 1949-50; Recipient U. Tex. Students Assn. Teaching Excellence award, 1963; Disting. Alumnus award N. Tex. State U., 1972; Outstanding Woman of Austin award, 1950, 60, 71, 80; Disting. Alumnus award U. Tex., 1976; Honor Scroll award Tex. Inst. Chemists, 1980. Fellow Am. Inst. Chemists; mem. AAAS, Am. Chem. Soc. (sec. 1954-56), Am. Inst. Nutrition, Am. Soc. Human Genetics, Nat. Soc. Arts and Letters, Assn. Grad. Schs. (internat. edn. com. 1967-71), Sigma Xi, Phi Kappa Phi, Iota Sigma Pi, Omicron Delta Kappa. Research in hydantoin synthesis, intermediatory metabolism, biochem. nutritional aspects of alcoholism, mental retardation, congenital malformations. Home: 4 Nob Hill Cir Austin TX 78746-3650

ROGERS, MALCOLM AUSTIN, museum curator, art historian; b. Scarborough, Yorkshire, Eng., Oct. 3, 1948; s. James Eric and Frances Anne (Elsey) R. M.A., Magdalen Coll., U. Oxford , Eng., 1973; D. Phil., Christ Ch., U. Oxford, 1976. Asst. keeper Nat. Portrait Gallery, London, 1974-83, dep. dir., 1983-94; dir. Mus. Fine Arts, Boston, 1994—. Author: Blue Guide: Museums and Galleries of London, 1983; also articles. Fellow Soc. Antiquaries. Avocations: wine and food; travel; opera. Home: 14 Talfourd Rd, London SE15 5NY, England Office: Mus Fine Arts 465 Huntington Ave Boston MA 02115

ROGERS, MARGARET ELLEN JONSSON, civic worker; b. Dallas, Aug. 7, 1938, d. John Erik and Margaret Elizabeth (Fonde) Jonsson; m. Robert D. Rogers; children: Emily, Erik, Laura. Student Skidmore Coll., 1956-57, So. Methodist U., 1957-60. Civic worker, Dallas; dir. Sta. KRLD radio, Dallas, 1970-74; dir. 1st Nat. Bank, Dallas, 1976-85, vice-chmn. dirs. trust com.; trustee Meth. Hosps., 1972-82, mem. exec. com., 1977-82, corp. bd. mem., 1990-94, mem. fin. com., 1990-93. Bd. dirs. Lamplighter Sch., 1967—; past mem. vis. com. dept. psychology MIT; mem. vis. com. Stanford U. Librs., 1984-90; bd. dirs. Callier Ctr. Communication Disorders, 1967-90, Winston Sch., 1973-85; bd. dirs., mem. exec. com. Episc. Sch., 1976-83; chmn. Crystal Charity Ball; co-chmn. nat. major gifts com. Stanford Centennial Campaign; bd. dirs. Children's Med. Center, Hope Cottage Childrens' Bur., Baylor Dental Sch., Dallas Health and Sci. Mus., Dallas YWCA, Day Nursery Assn.; mem. devel. bd. U. Tex., Dallas, 1988-90; bd. govs. The Dallas Found., 1988-95, chmn. investment com. 1991-92; trustee So. Meth. U., mem. investment com., 1988—, chmn. investment com., 1992—; mem. visiting com. Dedman Coll., 1989-90; life trustee Dallas Mus. Art, mem. investment com.; mem. collectors com. Nat. Gallery Art; bd. dirs. Dallas Arboretum, 1991-92; trustee Monterey Bay Aquarium. Margaret Jonsson Charlton Hosp. of Dallas named in her honor, 1973. Mem. Internat. Coun. Mus. of Modern Art., MJR Fund (pres.), Jonsson Found., Susan G. Komen Found. (mem. steering com.)

ROGERS, MARK CHARLES, physician, educator; b. N.Y.C., Oct. 25, 1942; s. Gerald and Inez (Kaufman) R.; m. Elizabeth Ann London, Dec. 30, 1972; children: Bradley, Meredith. BA, Columbia U., 1964; MD, SUNY, Syracuse, 1969; MBA, U. Pa., 1991. Diplomate Am. Bd. Anesthesiology (examiner 1982—); Am. Bd. Pediatrics. Intern Mass. Gen. Hosp., Boston, 1969-70, resident, 1973-75; resident Boston Children's Hosp., 1970-71; fellow Duke U. Med. Ctr., Durham, N.C., 1971-73; asst. prof. dept. anesthesiology and critical care medicine Johns Hopkins U., Balt., 1977-79, assoc. prof., 1979-80, prof., chmn. dept., 1980-93, assoc. dean Sch. Medicine, 1990-93, dir. pediatric ICU, 1977-93; vice chancellor, exec. dir. Duke U. Med. Ctr., 1993—; pres. Critical Care Found., Balt., 1981—; cons. WHO, Bangkok, 1982-83. Editor in chief: Yearbook of Critical Care, 1983—; Textbook of Pediatric Intensive Care, 1987, Principles and Practices of Anesthesiology, 1990; editor: Perioperative Management, 1989; dep. editor in chief Critical Care Medicine Jour., 1990—. Maj. U.S. Army, 1975-77. Recipient Club of Mainz award, Mainz, Fed. Republic of Germany, 1981, award Assn. Univ. Anesthetists, 1980; Fulbright scholar, Ljubljana, Yugoslavia, 1990. Fellow Am. Acad. Pediatrics, Am. Soc. Anesthesiology; mem. Am. Heart Assn., Soc. Pediatric Rsch., Soc. Critical Care Medicine, Am. Coll. Critical Care. Home: 4406 W Cornwallis Rd Durham NC 27705-8126 Office: Duke U Med Ctr PO Box 3708 Durham NC 27710

ROGERS, MARY MARTIN, publishing company executive; b. Nov. 22, 1945; married; 3 children. BA in English, U. Hawaii, 1967. Prodn. editor Academic Press, N.Y.C., 1968-70; asst. prodn. mgr. U. Miami Press, Coral Gables, Fla., 1970-75; mng. editor Am. Statis. Assn., Washington, 1976-78; prodn. mgr. Am. Anthropological Assn., Washington, 1978-79; prodn. editor, books Raven Press, Ltd., N.Y.C., 1981-84, book prodn. mgr., 1984-85, acquisitions editor, 1985-87, exec. editor acquisitions 1986-87, v.p., editor-in-chief, acquisitions 1987-91, pres., 1991-95; pres., CEO J.B. Lippincott Co., Phila., 1995—; comms. specialist So. Fla. Regional Planning Coun., Miami, 1970-75. Office: JB Lippincott Co 227 E Washington Sq Philadelphia PA 19106

ROGERS, MILLARD FOSTER, JR., art museum director; b. Texarkana, Tex., Aug. 27, 1932; s. Millard Foster and Jessie Bell (Hubbell) R.; m. Nina Olds, Aug. 3, 1963; 1 son, Seth Olds. BA with honors, Mich. State U., 1954; MA, U. Mich., 1958; studied with, John Pope-Hennessy; LHD, Xavier U., 1987. Gosline fellow Victoria and Albert Mus., London, Eng., 1959; curator Am. art Toledo Mus. Art, 1959-67; coord. Ford Found. intern program; dir. Elvehjem Art Ctr., prof. art history U. Wis.-Madison, 1967-74; dir. Cin. Art Mus., 1974-94, dir. emeritus, 1994—; vis. scholar Principia Coll., Elsah, Ill., 1982, 84; pres. Madnerant Preservation Found., Ohio, 1982-91; adj. prof. U. Cin., 1987-91. Author: Randolph Rogers, American Sculptor in Rome, 1971, Spanish Paintings in the Cincinnati Art Museum, 1978, Favorite Paintings from The Cincinnati Art Museum, 1980, Sketches and Bozzetti by American Sculptors, 1800-1950, 1988. Served with AUS, 1954-56. Named Outstanding Citizen of Mariemont, 1991. Mem. Assn. Art Mus. Dirs., Am. Assn. Mus., Ohio Mus. Assn., Phi Beta Kappa. Office: Cin Art Mus Eden Park Cincinnati OH 45202-1596

ROGERS, NATHANIEL SIMS, banker; b. New Albany, Miss., Nov. 17, 1919; s. Arthur L. and Elizabeth (Bouton) R.; m. Helen Elizabeth Ricks, July 3, 1942; children—Alice, John, Lewis. AB, Millsaps Coll., 1941; MBA, Harvard U., 1947. With Deposit Guaranty Bank and Trust Co., Jackson, Miss., 1947-69, 1st v.p., 1957-58, pres., dir.; pres. 1st City Nat. Bank Houston, 1969-81, chmn., 1982-84; pres. 1st City Bancorp. of Tex., Houston, 1970-83, chmn., 1983-85, also bd. dirs. Chmn. Jackson United Givers Fund, 1957, pres., 1959, bd. dirs., 1958-61; pres. Andrew Jackson area coun. Boy Scouts Am., 1962; trustee Nat. Found. Ind. Colls., 1959-69; past pres., trustee Millsaps Coll.; trustee Methodist Hosp., Houston; chmn. ofcl. bd. Meth. ch. Lt. (s.g.) USNR, 1942-46. Named Outstanding Young Man of Year Jackson Jr. C. of C., 1955. Mem. Am. Bankers Assn. (pres. 1969-70), Miss. Bankers Assn. (pres., v.p. banker sect. 1952-53, pres. 1964-65), Robert Morris Assocs. (pres. S.E. chpt. 1954-55, nat. dir. 1959-62), Assn. Res. City Bankers (bd. dirs. 1980-83), Jackson C. of C. (pres. 1962), Houston C. of C. (chmn. 1979-80), Young Pres.'s Orgn., Millsaps Coll. Alumni Assn. (pres. 1955-56), Newcomen Soc., Phi Beta Kappa, Omicron Delta Kappa, Kappa Alpha. Methodist.

ROGERS, PAUL GRANT, lawyer, former congressman; b. Ocilla, Ga., June 4, 1921; s. Dwight L. and Florence (Roberts) R.; m. Rebecca Bell, Dec. 15, 1962; 1 child, Rebecca Laing. B.A., U. Fla., 1942, J.D., 1948, LL.D.; LL.B. (hon.), Fla. Atlantic U., U. Md., Duke U., 1, George Washington U.; D.Sc. (hon.), U. Miami, Albany Med. Coll. of Union U., Commonwealth U. Va.; H.H.D. (hon.), Nova U.; L.H.D. (hon.), N.Y. Med. Coll., N.Y. Coll. Podiatric Medicine, Hahnemann Med. Coll.; D.Med. Sci. (hon.), Med. U. S.C. Bar: Fla. 1948. Partner Burns, Middleton, Rogers, Farrell & Faust, 1952-69; mem. 84th-95th congresses from 11th Dist. Fla., 1955-79; chmn. house subcom. on health and environ. Hogan & Hartson, Washington, 1979—, ptnr., 1979—; bd. dirs. Salick Health Care, Inc., D. Marion, Merrell, Dow, Inc. Trustee Cleve. Clinic Found., The Scripps Rsch. Inst.; bd. dirs. Am. Cancer Soc.; co-chmn. Nat. Leadership Coalition on Health Care Reform; chmn. bd. dirs. Nat. Coun. Patient Info. and Edn., Found. for Biomed. Rsch.; chmn. Nat. Osteoporosis Found.; Friends of Nat. Libr. Medicine; mem. health scis. coun. Sch. Medicine, U. Va.; mem. nat. coun. Washington U. Sch. Medicine; mem. coun. for the div. biol. scis. U. Chgo., vis. com. Harvard Sch. Pub. Health. Recipient Pub. Welfare medal Nat. Acad. Acis., 1982, Sea Grant award, 1985, Yr. 2000 award Nat. Cancer Inst., 1987, Albert Lasker award for pub. svc., 1993, Hugo Schaefer award APhA, 1994, Achievement award Allied Signal, 1994. Mem. ABA, Fla. Bar Assn. (gov. jr. sect. 1952-53), Palm Beach County Bar assn., D.C. Bar Assn., Inst. Medicine of NAS, Phi Delta Phi, Phi Delta Theta. Methodist (steward). Office: Hogan & Hartson 555 13th St NW Ste 1200 Washington DC 20004-1109

ROGERS, PETER NORMAN, food company executive; b. High Wycombe, Eng., June 23, 1938; came to U.S. 1973; s. Norman John and Constance Jane (Jordan) R.; m. Doreen M. Baker, Dec. 2, 1990; children by previous marriage: Bridget Jane, Simon John. B.Sc., U. Leicester, Eng., 1959, Ph.D., 1963. Pres. Curtiss Candy Co., Chgo., 1973-76, New Eng. Fish Co., Seattle, 1978-80; sr. v.p. Standard Brands, Inc., N.Y.C., 1980-81; pres. Life Savers div. Nabisco Brands, Inc., N.Y.C., 1981-83; pres. biscuit div. Nabisco Brands, Inc., Parsippany, N.J., 1983-85, sr. v.p., 1985-86, pres., 1986-87; pres. Internat. Nabisco Brands, Inc., East Hanover, 1987-88; chmn., chief exec. officer Nabisco Biscuit Co., East Hanover, 1988-89; prin. Basildon Enterprises, N.Y.C., 1989—; chief exec. officer E. J. Brach Inc., Chgo., 1990—; dir. Revell-Monogram, Corp. Compensation Plans Inc. Bd. dirs. Chgo. Econ. Devel. Commt. Mem. Nat. Confectioners Assn. (dir. 1973-76, 91—). Home: 219 E Lake Shore Dr Apt 3C Chicago IL 60611-1303 Office: E J Brach & Sons Inc One Tower Ln Villa Park IL 60181

ROGERS, PETER PHILIPS, environmental engineering educator, city planner; b. Liverpool, England, Apr. 30, 1937; came to U.S., 1960, naturalized, 1977; s. Edward Joseph and Ellen (Duggan) R.; m. Rosemarie Rogers, July 11, 1964; children: Christopher, Justin. B in Engring., Liverpool U., 1958; MS, Northwestern U., 1961; PhD, Harvard U., 1966. Asst. engr. Sir Alfred McAlpine & Sons Ltd., Cheshire, Eng., 1958-60; mem. faculty Harvard U., 1966—; Gordon McKay prof. environ. engring., 1974—; prof. city planning, 1974—; mem. Center Population Studies, Harvard U. Sch. Pub. Health, 1974—; cons. World Bank, UN, U.S. Agy. for Internat. Devel., Govt. India, Govt. Pakistan, Govt. Bangladesh, Govt. Nepal, Govt. Italy, Govt. Costa Rica, Commonwealth P.R. Co-author: Urbanization and Change, 1970, Land Use and The Pipe: Planning for Sewerage, 1975, Resource Inventory and Baseline Study Methods for Developing Countries, 1983, Systems Analysis for River Basin Management, 1985, Evaluacion de Projectos de Desarrollo, 1990, America's Waters, 1993, Water in the Arab World, 1994. Gordon McKay teaching fellow, 1961; Radley research student, 1962-64; doctoral dissertation fellow Resources for Future, 1964-65; recipient Clemens Herschel prize Harvard U., 1964; Guggenheim fellow, 1973. Mem. Third World Acad. Scis. (corr.), Indian Inst. Agrl. Engring. (life), Cosmos Club (Washington), Sigma Xi. Home: 20 Berkeley St Cambridge MA 02138-3410 Office: Harvard U 116 Pierce Hall Cambridge MA 02138

ROGERS, PHILIP VIRGILIUS, JR., headmaster; b. New Haven, Nov. 14, 1935; s. Philip V. and Anne (Fitzpatrick) Rogers; m. Claudia Lawrence Rogers, June 13, 1964; children: Jennifer, Philip, Alexander. BA, Trinity Coll., 1958. Faculty The Fessenden Sch., West Newton, Mass., 1961-70; head of middle sch. Mosses Brown Sch., Providence, 1970-73; headmaster The Kew-Forest Sch., Forest Hills, N.Y., 1973—; commr. Middle States Assn. of Colls. and Schs., 1989—; trustee Ind. Sch. Multi-Media Ctr., N.Y.C., 1978—; bd. dirs. Guild of N.Y. Ind. Schs., N.Y.C. Churchwarden Christ Ch., Manhasset. With U.S. Army, 1958-60. Mem. N.Y. State Assn. Ind. Schs., Nat. Assn. Ind. Schs., Nat. Assn. of Schs. for Girls. Episcopalian. Home: 18 South Dr Manhasset NY 11030-1425 Office: The Kew-Forest Sch 11917 Union Tpke Forest Hills NY 11375-6143

ROGERS, RALPH B., industrial business executive; b. Boston, 1909; married. Ed., Northeastern U. With Cummins Diesel Engine Corp., Edwards Co., Hill Diesel Engine Co., Ideal Power Lawnmower Co., Indian Motocycle Co., Rogers Diesel & Aircraft Corp., Rogers Internat. Corp., Armstrong Rubber Export Corp.; with Tex. Industries Inc., Dallas, 1950—, chmn. bd., pres., CEO, 1951-75, chmn. bd., 1975—; dir. numerous subsidiaries. Chmn. bd. dirs. Tex. Industries Found.; chmn. emeritus Pub. Communication Found. North Tex., Pub. Broadcasting Svc., Univ. Med. Ctr., Inc.; past bd. dirs. Nat. Captioning Inst.; trustee Northeastern U.; trustee, chmn. emeritus St. Mark's Sch. of Tex.; former chmn. bd. mgrs. Dallas County Hosp. Dist.; founding chmn., chmn. emeritus Dallas Arboretum and Bot. Soc.; pres. Dallas Found. for Health, Edn. and Rsch.; co-founder Children's TV Workshop; founder, chmn. Zale Lipshy Univ. Hosp. Mem. Masons. Office: Tex Industries Inc Ste 700W 1341 W Mockingbird Ln Dallas TX 75247-6913

ROGERS, RAYMOND JESSE, federal railroad associate administrator; b. Eugene, Oreg., Mar. 1, 1941; s. Raymond Everett and Virginia Elaine (Simpkins) R.; m. Joan Katherine Peterson, June 6, 1964 (div. Aug. 1974); 1 child, Virginia Arlene; m. Kim Lien Nguyen, Dec. 26, 1974; children: Kim Lan, Vincent Minh. Student, Santa Rosa (Calif.) Jr. Coll., 1960-61, U.S. Army Non-commd. Officer Acad., Anchorage, Alaska, 1963, U. Md., 1967-74, Fed. Exec. Inst., Charlottesville, Va., 1981. Lic. real estate agt., Va. Sr. asst. mgr. Household Fin. Corp., Md., 1964-67; contract specialist Dept. Navy, Washington, 1967-71; contract svcs. officer AID, Saigon, Vietnam, 1971-76; contracting officer Dept. Transp., Fed. R.R. Adminstrn., Washington, 1976-80, dir. fin. svcs., 1980-84, assoc. adminstr. for adminstrn., 1984—. Leader local group Boy Scouts Am., Vienna, Va., 1987-92, Izaac Walton League of Am., Am. Legion, Am. Assn. of Retired Persons. Sgt. U.S. Army, 1961-64. Decorated Vietnam Civilian Svc. medal. Mem. U.S. Sr. Exec. Svc., Fed. Exec. Inst. Alumni Assn. Avocations: fishing, hiking, camping, waterskiing. Home: 102 Yeonas Dr SW Vienna VA 22180 Office: Dept Transp Fed RR Adminstrn 400 7th St SW Washington DC 20590-0001

ROGERS, RICHARD DEAN, federal judge; b. Oberlin, Kans., Dec. 29, 1921; s. William Clark and Evelyn May (Christian) R.; m. Helen Elizabeth Stewart, June 6, 1947; children—Letitia Ann, Cappi Christian, Richard Kurt. B.S., Kans. State U., 1943; J.D., Kans. U., 1947. Bar: Kans. 1947. Ptnr. firm Springer and Rogers (Attys.), Manhattan, Kans., 1947-58; instr. bus. law Kans. State U., 1948-52; partner firm Rogers, Stites & Hill, Manhattan, 1959-75; gen. counsel Kans. Farm Bur. & Service Cos., Manhattan, 1960-75 (split U.S. Dist. Ct., Topeka, Kans., 1975—. City commr., Manhattan, 1950-52, 60-64, mayor, 1952, 64, county atty., Riley County, Kans., 1954-58, state rep., 1964-68, state senator, 1968-75; pres. Kans. Senate, 1975. Served with USAAF, 1943-45. Decorated Air medal. Dfc. Mem. Kans., Am. bar assns., Beta Theta Pi. Republican. Presbyterian. Club: Masons. Office: US Dist Ct 444 SE Quincy St Topeka KS 66683-0001

ROGERS, RICHARD F., construction company executive, architect, engineer; b. Chgo., July 25, 1942; s. Frank S. and Emily H. (Novak) R.; m. Christina L. Rogers, June 30, 1963; children: Mitchell, Cynthia. B in Architectural Engineering, U. Ill., Chgo., 1964. Registered architect, Ill., Wis., Mich., profl. engr., Ill. Architect Einstein Assocs. Inc., Skokie, Ill., 1963-69; v.p. Land Am. Corp., Chgo., 1969-70; project architect M.A. Lombard Constrn. Co., Alsip, Ill., 1970-73; sr. project mgr. W.E. O'Neil Constrn. Co., Chgo., 1973-78; pres. A.C.M. Assocs. Inc., Mt. Prospect, Ill., 1978—. Mem. AIA, Builders Assn. Chgo. Office: ACM Assocs Inc 322 N Wolf Rd Mount Prospect IL 60056-2724

ROGERS, RICHARD HILTON, hotel company executive; b. Florence, S.C., May 26, 1935; s. Leslie Lawton and Bessie (Holloway) R.; m. Evelyn Pascuito; children: Richard Shannon, Leslie Anne. Student, U. N.C., 1953-55; BA in Bus. Adminstrn. cum laude, Bryant Coll., 1962. Innkeeper Helmsley Spear, N.Y.C., 1961-62; v.p. Holiday Inns of Am., Memphis, 1962-73; exec. v.p. First Hospitality Corp., Hackensack, N.J., 1974-77; v.p., chief oper. officer Cindy's Inc., Atlanta, 1978-81; v.p. 1982 World's Fair, Knoxville, Tenn.; pres., chief exec. officer Hospitality Internat., Atlanta, 1982—; developer, operator The Warehouse Rest., Oxford, Miss., 1973-75, Beauregard's Rest., Hattiesburg, Miss., 1975-78, Walter Mitty's Rest., Auburn, Ala., 1980-83. Contbr. to profl. jours. Mem. adv. bd. Bethune-Cookman Coll. With USN, 1954-58, Korea. Mem. Am. Hotel/Motel Assn. (mktg. com. 1986—, adv. council 1987—, industry adv. bd.), Economy Lodging Council. Avocations: sailing, photography. Home: 245 Rhine Dr Alpharetta GA 30202-5455 Office: Hospitality Internat Inc 1726 Montreal Circle Tucker GA 30084-6809*

ROGERS, RICHARD HUNTER, lawyer, business executive; b. Flushing, N.Y., Sept. 11, 1939; s. Royden Harrison and Frances Wilma (Hunter) R.; m. Belinda Hogue, Apr. 14, 1991; children: Gregory P., Lynne A., Reade H. B.S. in Bus. Adminstrn, Miami U., 1961; J.D., Duke, 1964. Bar: Ill. 1964, Ohio 1973. Atty. Continental Ill. Nat. Bank, Chgo., 1964-65; sr. atty. Brunswick Corp., Chgo., 1965-70; corporate counsel The A. Epstein Cos., Inc. (real estate developers), Chgo., 1970-73; v.p., gen. counsel, sec. Price Bros. Co., Dayton, Ohio, 1973-82; v.p., div. mgr. Water Systems Tech. div. Price Bros. Co., Dayton, Ohio, 1982-85; v.p., div. mgr. Internat. div. Price Bros. Co., Dayton, Ohio, 1986-88; chmn. Rogers Internat. Inc., 1988—; pvt. practice law Dayton, 1988—. Pres. adv. coun. Miami U. Bus. Sch.; bd. dirs. Red and White Club, Miami U.; mem. Washington Twp. Task Force on Future Govt.; trustee Woodhaven, Inc.; mem., vice chmn. Washington Twp. Zoning Commn. Mem. ABA (forum com. on constrn.), Ill. Bar Assn., Ohio Bar Assn., Dayton Bar Assn. (chmn. corp. law dept. com. 1983-84, exec. com. 1986-87, editor Bar Briefs 1990-91), Miami U. Alumni Assn. (pres.), Miami U. Pres.'s Club, Sycamore Creek Country Club. Home: 221 Walnut Grove Dr Dayton OH 45458-4158 Office: 7333 Paragon Rd Ste 200 Dayton OH 45459-4157

ROGERS, ROBERT BURNETT, naval officer; b. Plainfield, N.J., May 25, 1931; s. Jack Willoughby and Margaret (Snyder) R.; m. Jeanne Weaver, Mr. 15, 1956 (dec. Sept. 1978); children: Robert Burnett, Steven Michael, John Weaver, Kathryn Patricia; m. Marolyn Maybelline Templeton, May 25, 1981. B.S., U.S. Naval Acad., 1954; M.S., George Washington U., 1968. Commd. ensign U.S. Navy, 1954, advanced through grades to rear adm., 1981; comdg. officer U.S.S. Austin, Norfolk, Va., 1977-78; asst. chief of staff Naval Surface Force Atlantic, Atlantic Fleet, Norfolk, 1978-80; dep. comdr. Naval Surface Force Atlantic, Norfolk, 1982-83; comdr. Destroyer Squadron Eight, Mayport, Fla., 1980-81; dep. chief of staff Supreme Allied Command Atlantic, Norfolk, 1981-82; comdr. Amphibious Group Two, Norfolk, 1983-86; dir. logistics Atlantic Fleet, Norfolk, 1986, ret., 1986. City Commr. Fernandina Beach, 1994. Decorated Legion of Merit with 4 gold stars; recipient William S. Sims award Navy League U.S. Mem. U.S. Naval Inst., Marine Corps. Assn. Roman Catholic. Home: 2056 Oak Marsh Dr Fernandina Beach FL 32034-2407

ROGERS, ROBERT D., steel company executive; b. 1936. Grad., Yale U., 1958; MBA, Harvard U., 1962. With Tex. Industries, Inc., Dallas, 1963—, v.p. ops., 1968-70, pres., chief adminstrv. officer, 1970-74, pres., CEO, 1974—, also bd. dirs.; chmn. bd. dirs. Chaparral Steel Co., Midlothian, Tex. Served with USN, 1958-60. Office: Tex Industries Inc 7610 N Stemmons Fwy Dallas TX 75247-4216 also: Chaparral Steel Co 300 Ward Rd Midlothian TX 76065

ROGERS, ROBERT ERNEST, medical educator; b. West Palm Beach, Fla., Nov. 16, 1928; s. Jessie H. and Willie L. (Bahr) R.; m. Barbara Ann Hill, May 16, 1950; children: Robert E. Jr., Stephanie Ann Thompson, Cheri Lee Heck. BS, John B. Stetson U., 1949; MD, U. Miami, 1957. Diplomate Am. Bd. Ob-Gyn. Commd. 1st lt. M.C., U.S. Army, 1952, advanced through grades to col., 1971; intern Brooke Gen. Hosp., San Antonio, 1957-58, chief resident in ob-gyn, 1960-61; resident in ob-gyn Jackson Meml. Hosp., Miami, Fla., 1958-60; fellow gynecology M.D. Anderson Hosp., Houston, 1965-66; asst. chief ob-gyn Tripler Army Med. Ctr., Honolulu, 1966-69; chmn. ob-gyn Walter Reed Med. Ctr., Washington, 1969-70, Madigan Army Med. Ctr., Tacoma, Wash., 1970-74; ret. U.S. Army, 1974; prof. Ind. U. Sch. Medicine, Indpls., 1974—, also chief gynecol. div., 1974—; chief ob-gyn svc. Wishard Meml. Hosp., Indpls., 1983-87. Contbr. articles on ob-gyn to profl. jours. Mem. AMA, Am. Coll. Ob-Gyn (chmn. gynecol. practice com., commr. practice), Soc. Gynecol. Surgeons (pres. 1983-84), Soc. Gynecol. Oncologists. Office: Ind U Sch Medicine Dept Ob-Gyn Rm 2440 550 University Blvd Indianapolis IN 46202-5149

ROGERS, ROBERT MARK, physician; b. Upper Darby, Pa., June 9, 1933; s. John Francis and Clara (Baumann) R.; m. Sandra Betz, Feb. 14, 1968; children: Janet Marie, Robert Mark, Linda, William Bradford, David Philip. B.A. cum laude, LaSalle Coll., Phila., 1956; M.D., U. Pa., 1960. Intern Hosp. U. Pa.; resident Case Western Res. U. Hosps., Cleve., 1961-63; fellow in pulmonary disease VA Hosp., Cleve., 1963-64; fellow in pulmonary disease U. Pa., 1964-65, postdoctoral trainee in physiology, 1966-68, asst. prof. medicine and assoc. in physiology, 1968-72; chief emergency services Hosp. of U. Pa., 1968-69, founder, dir. respiratory ICU, 1968-72, dir. pulmonary disease sect. trng. program, 1970-72; prof. medicine, asso. prof. physiology U. Okla. Health Scis. Center Coll. Medicine, 1972-80; also chief pulmonary disease sect., dept. medicine, dir. clin. pulmonary physiology lab. hosp. and clinics; prof. medicine, chief pulmonary, allergy & critical care medicine U. Pitts. Med. Sch., 1980—; dir. U. Pitts. Comprehensive Lung Ctr., 1990—; U.S. rep. in China Chinese Med. Assn.-A.C.P., 1979. Author rsch. papers in field; editor Respiratory Intensive Care, 1977; founding editor-in-chief audio-cassetts program: A.C.P., 1978-80; editorial bd. Current Opinion in Pulmonary Medicine and Critical Care. Mem. ACP, Am. Thoracic Soc. (founding dir. Learning Resources Ctr. 1971-77, dir . 1982—; presdl. commendation 1977), Am. Fedn. Clin. Rsch., Am. Coll. Chest Physicians (Am. Physiol. Soc., Soc. Critical Care Medicine, Am. Heart Assn., Cen. Soc. Clin. Rsch., So. Soc. Clin. Rsch., Pa. Thoracic Soc. (pres. 1985-88), Coll. Physicians of Phila. Home: 4116 Bigelow Blvd Pittsburgh PA 15213-1408 Office: U Pitts Sch Medicine 440 Scaife Hall Pittsburgh PA 15261-2004

ROGERS, RODNEY ALBERT, biologist, educator; b. Lucas, Iowa, Aug. 24, 1926; s. Harold A. and Ardis (Allen) R.; m. Frances A. Ritchey, July 1, 1956; children—Robert, William. B.A., Drake U., 1949, M.A., 1951; Ph.D., U. Iowa, 1955. Asst. prof. biology Drake U., Des Moines, 1955-60; asso. prof. Drake U., 1961-64, prof., 1964-65; chmn. biology dept., 1966-92; asso. program dir. NSF, 1967-68. Served with AUS, 1944-46, PTO. Mem. A.A.A.S., Am. Inst. Biol. Sci., Am. Soc. Parasitologists, Soc. Am. Microbiologists, Am. Soc. Zoologists, Am. Assn. U. Profs., Am. Soc. Tropical Medicine and Hygiene, Sigma Xi, Omicron Delta Kappa. Home: 4203 40th St Des Moines IA 50310-3702

ROGERS, ROSEMARY, author; b. Panadura, Ceylon, Dec. 7, 1932; came to U.S., 1962; naturalized citizen.; d. Cyril Allan and Barbara (Jansze) R. Summa Navaratnam (div.); children: Rosanne, Sharon; m. Leroy Rogers (div.); children: Michael, Adam; m. Christopher Kadison. B.A., U. Ceylon. Writer features and pub. affairs info. Associated Newspapers Ceylon, Colombo, 1959-62; sec. billeting office Travis AFB, Calif., 1964-69; sec. Solano County (Calif.) Parks Dept., Fairfield, 1969-74; part-time reporter Fairfield Daily Republic. Author: (novels) Sweet Savage Love, 1974, The Wildest Heart, 1974, Dark Fires, 1975, Wicked Loving Lies, 1976, The Crowd Pleasers, 1978, The Insiders, 1979, Lost Love, Last Love, 1980, Love Play, 1981, Surrender to Love, 1982, The Wanton, 1985, Bound by Desire, 1988; (with Sean Kelly) Saints Preserve Us!: Everything You Need to Know About Every Saint You'll Ever Need, 1993. Mem. Authors Guild of Authors League Am., Writers Guild Am. •

ROGERS, ROY (LEONARD FRANKLIN SLYE), country musician, actor; b. Cin., Nov. 5, 1911; s. Andrew E. and Mattie Martha (Womach) Slye; m. Arlene Wilkins, 1936 (dec. Nov. 1946); children: Cheryl Darlene, Linda Lou, Roy Jr., Marion, Scottish Ward; m. Dale Evans; children: Robin (dec.), John (dec.), Mary Little Doe, Deborah (dec.). pres. Roy Rogers Enterprises; past

owner Roy Rogers Apple Valley Inn; owner Roy Rogers Western World and Mus., Victorville, Calif.; franchised Roy Rogers Family Restaurants. Organized western group Sons of the Pioneers; appeared in numerous films including Under Western Stars, 1938, The Old Corral, Frontier Pony Express, Silver Spurs, My Pal Trigger, Son of Paleface, Mackintosh & T.J.; former radio singer; TV series, spls.; actor, prodr. TV films; host TV show The Great Movie Cowboys, 1975; many personal appearances rodeos, fairs; rec. artist Capitol Records, 20th Century Records, RCA Records; albums include, Best Of, 1990, Tribute, 1991; author: (with Dale Evans) Happy Trails: Our Life Story, 1994. Mem. AFTRA, SAG, Am. Guild Variety Artists, Musicians Union, Masons. Address: RCA/BMG Music 1 Music Circle N Nashville TN 37203-4310*

ROGERS, RUTHERFORD DAVID, librarian; b. Jesup, Iowa, June 22, 1915; s. David Earl and Carrie Zoe (Beckel) R.; m. E. Margaret Stoddard, June 4, 1937; 1 child, Jane Shelley. B.A., U. No. Iowa, 1936, Litt.D., 1977; M.A., Columbia, 1937, B.S. (Lydia Roberts fellow), 1938; D.Library Adminstrn. (hon.), U. Dayton, 1971. Asst. N.Y. Pub. Library, 1937-38; reference librarian Columbia Coll. Library, Columbia U., 1938- 41, acting librarian, 1941-42, librarian, 1942-45; research analyst Smith, Barney & Co., N.Y.C., 1946-48; dir. Grosvenor Library, Buffalo, 1948-52, Rochester Pub. Library, 1952-54; chief personnel office N.Y. Library, 1954-55; chief reference dept., 1955-57; chief asst. librarian of Congress, Washington, 1957-62; dep. librarian of Congress, 1962-64; dir. univ. libraries Stanford U., 1964-69; univ. librarian Yale U., 1969-85, univ. librarian emeritus, 1985—; Dir. H.W. Wilson Co., 1969—; founder, chmn. bd. dirs. Research Libraries Group, Inc.; Mem. Exam. Com. for Pub. Librarians' Certificates, N.Y. State, 1951-54; mem. U.S. Adv. Council Coll. Library Resources; Bd. govs. Yale U. Press; bd. dirs. H.W. Wilson Found.; chmn. programme mgmt. com. Internat. Fedn. Library Assns. Author: Columbia Coll. Library Handbook, 1941, (with David C. Weber) University Library Administration, 1971; also articles in profl. jours. Served from pvt. to 1st sgt. Air Transp. Command USAAF, 1943-45; from 2d lt. to capt., planning officer, chief, spl. Planning Div., Office Asst. Chief Staff, Plans, Air Transport Command 1943-46. Decorated officer de L'Ordre de la Couronne Belge; recipient U. No. Iowa Alumni Achievement award, 1958, Disting. Alumni award Columbia U. Sch. Libr. Svc., 1992. Fellow Am. Acad. Arts and Scis.; mem. A.L.A. (chmn. com. Intellectual Freedom 1950-51), (1950-60), (2d v.p. 1965-66), (mem. exec. bd. 1961-65), (trustee endowment fund), Assn. Research Libraries (dir. pres. 1967-68), N.Y. Library Assn., AAUP, Bibliog. Soc. Am., Assn. Coll. and Reference Libraries, Blue Key, Kappa Delta Pi, Sigma Tau Delta, Theta Alpha Phi. Clubs: Grolier; N.Y. Library (N.Y.C.), Columbia U. (N.Y.C.), Yale (N.Y.C.); Cosmos (Washington), Kenwood Country (Washington); Roxburghe (San Francisco); Book of Calif. Home: 1111 S Lakemont Ave Apt 605 Winter Park FL 32792-5474

ROGERS, SAMUEL SHEPARD See SHEPARD, SAM

ROGERS, SARAH JEANNE, curator; b. Buffalo, Aug. 8, 1956; 1 child, Molly Katherine. B.A, Wells Coll., 1978; MA, Northwestern U., 1980. NEA intern, Abby Grey fellow Walker Art Ctr., Mpls., 1980-81; asst. dir. The New Gallery Contemporary Art, Cleve., 1981-82; curator The Contemporary Arts Ctr., Cin., 1982-89; curator exhbns. Wexner Ctr. for the Arts, Columbus, Ohio, 1989-91, sr. curator, 1991-92; dir. exhbns., 1992—; panelist Ohio Arts Coun., Columbus, 1985; juror Columbus Met. Libr. Sculpture Project, 1990, Ohio State U. Cancer Hosp. Sculpture Project, 1990; mem. Ohio State Arts & Memls. com., 1993-95, Dublin Pub. Art com., 1994; panelist Colo. Coun. on Arts, 1995. Curated exhbns. include Maya Lin, Terry Allen, Amy Hamilton. Office: Wexner Ctr for the Arts 30 W 15th Ave Columbus OH 43210-1305

ROGERS, SHARON J., university administrator; b. Grantsburg, Wis., Sept. 24, 1941; d. Clifford M. and Dorothy L. (Beckman) Dickau; m. Evan D. Rogers, June 15, 1962 (div. Dec. 1980). BA summa cum laude, Bethel Coll., St. Paul, 1963; MA in Libr. Sci., U. Minn., 1967; PhD in Sociology, Wash. State U., Pullman, 1976. Lectr., instr. Alfred (N.Y.) U., 1972-76; assoc. prof. U. Toledo, 1977-80; assoc. dean Bowling Green (Ohio) State U. Librs., 1980-84; univ. libr. George Washington U., Washington, 1984-92, asst. v.p. acad. affairs, 1989-92, assoc. v.p. acad. affairs, 1992—, co-dir. Univ. Teaching Ctr., 1990—; mem. Online Computer Libr.Ctr. Users Coun., 1985-92, pres., 1989-90, mem. rsch. adv. com., 1990-92, trustee, 1992—. Contbr. articles to profl. jours. Bd. dirs. ACLU, Toledo, 1978-84, CapAccess, 1993—, treas., 1993—. Jackson fellow U. Minn., 1964-65; NSF trainee Wash. State U., 1969-72. Mem. ALA (exec. coun. 1987-91, pub. com. 1989-93, chair 1990-93), Assn. Coll. and Rsch. Librs. (pres. 1984-85), Am. Sociol. Assn., Washington Rsch. Libr. Consortium (bd. dirs 1987-90), Universal Serials and Book Exch. (bd. dirs., treas. 1987). Office: George Washington Univ Rice Hall Ste 602 2121 Eye St NW Washington DC 20052

ROGERS, STEPHEN, newspaper publisher; b. Lansing, Mich., Feb. 24, 1912; s. Anthony and Anna (Kruszewska) R.; m. Athenia A. Andros, Oct. 19, 1935; children: Stephen A., Christopher A., Elizabeth A. A.B., Mich. State Coll., 1933; LLD (hon.), Syracuse U., 1988. Writer Detroit Times, 1934-35; copy editor N.Y. Herald-Tribune (European edit.), Paris, France, 1936-37; spl. writer Newark Ledger, 1937-38; editorial writer, city editor Long Island Daily Press, 1938-41; editor Long Island Star-Jour., 1941-55; pub. Post Standard, Syracuse, N.Y., 1955-58, Herald-Journal, Herald-Am., Syracuse; and pres. The Herald Co., 1958—; dir. N.Y. Dental Service Corp., N.Y.C., Mchts. Nat. Bank; pres. Met. Devel. Assn., 1980—. Bd. dirs. Crouse-Irving Hosp., Syracuse. Mem. N.Y. State Pubs. Assn. (pres. 1963), Am. Newspaper Pubs. Assn. Roman Catholic. Office: Syracuse Newspapers Ltd Clinton Sq PO Box 4915 Syracuse NY 13221-4915

ROGERS, STEPHEN HITCHCOCK, former ambassador; b. Flushing, N.Y., June 21, 1930; s. Francis Walker and Julia (Wheeler) R.; m. Kent Brain, June 23, 1956; children: Kryston R. Fischer, F. Halsey, Julia L., John H. BA, Princeton U., 1952; MA, Columbia U., 1956; MPA, Harvard U., 1962. Fgn. svc. officer Dept. of State, 1956-93; econ. counselor Am. Embassy, London, 1970-72; counselor U.S. Mission to OECD, Paris, 1972-75; office dir. Bur. Inter.-Am. Affairs Dept. of State, Washington, 1975-78; econ. counselor Am. Embassy, Mexico City, 1978-82; prof. Nat. Def. U., Washington, 1982-85; econ. counselor Am. Embassy, Pretoria, South Africa, 1986-90; amb. Am. Embassy, Mbabane, Swaziland, 1990-93. Lt. (jg) USN, 1952-55. Mem. United Ch. of Christ. Home: 3803 Ivydale Dr Annandale VA 22003-2006

ROGERS, THEODORE COURTNEY, investment company executive; b. Lorain, Ohio, Aug. 25, 1934; s. William Theodore and Leona Ruth (Gerhart) R.; m. Elizabeth B. Barlow, June 28, 1984; children by previous marriage: Pamela Anne Rogers Harmon, Theodore Courtney Jr. BS in Social Sci., Miami U., Oxford, Ohio, 1957; MBA summa cum laude, Marquette U. 1968. With Armco Inc., 1958-80; pres. Olympic Fastening Systems, 1970-74, with Bathey Mfg. Co. subs., 1970, group v.p. indsl. products, 1971-74, exec. v.p. Nat. Supply Co. subs., Houston, 1974-76, pres., 1976-80, v.p. parent co., 1976-79, group v.p. parent co., 1979-80; pres., chief operating officer NL Industries, Inc., N.Y.C., 1980-82, pres., chief exec. officer, 1982-83, chmn., pres., chief exec. officer, 1983-87; ptnr. Am Indsl. Ptnrs., N.Y., 1987—; bd. dirs. Sweetheart Cup, Smith Steelite, Inc., San Joaquin Paper, Day Internat., Derby Internat., Nottingham, Eng.; chmn. bd. dirs. Sunshine Materials, Easco Aluminum, Triptych. Bd. dirs. United Cerebral Palsy Rsch. and Ednl. Found., Inc., Lincoln Ctr. for Performing Arts, Poets & Writers, Am. Alliance for Rights and Responsibilities, Nat. Ocean Industries Assn.; chmn. bd. Theatre for New Audience; former chmn. N.Y.C. Ballet. Lt. USN, 1956-58. Mem. Petroleum Equipment Suppliers Assn. (bd. dirs.), N.Y. Soc. Libr. (trustee), World Pres. Orgn., N.Y. Soc. Libr. (trustee), Century Assn. (N.Y.), Bus. Roundtable, Poets and Writers (bd. dirs.), Achilles Track Club (founder, bd. dirs.), Ramada Club, Houston Country Club, Links Club, Sky Club, Econ. Club (N.Y.), Met. Club (Washington), The Union Club (Cleve.), Century Assn., Beta Gamma Sigma (bd. dirs.), Kappa Phi Kappa, Sigma Chi. Office: Am Indsl Ptnr 551 5th Ave Ste 3800 New York NY 10176

ROGERS, THOMAS FRANCIS, foundation administrator; b. Providence, Aug. 11, 1923; s. Thomas Francis and H. Ann (Flaharty) R.; m. Estelle E. Hunt, July 6, 1946; children: Clare, Judith, Hope. BS cum laude, Providence Coll., 1945; MA, Boston U., 1949. Rsch. assoc. Radio Rsch. Lab. Harvard

U., Cambridge, Mass., 1944-45; TV engr. Bell and Howell Co., Chgo., 1945-46; electronics scientist AF Cambridge Rsch. Ctr., Cambridge, Mass., 1946-54; assoc. group leader MIT Lincoln Lab., Cambridge, 1951-53; lab. head AF Cambridge Rsch. Ctr., Bedford, Mass., 1954-59; div. head and steering com. mem. MIT Lincoln Lab., Bedford, 1959-64; asst. dir. def. rsch. and engring. Office of Sec. Def., Washington, 1964-65, dep. dir. def. rsch. and engring., 1965-67; dir. rsch. and tech. Office of Sec. HUD, Washington, 1967-69; v.p. The Mitre Corp., Washington, Bedford, 1969-72; pres. The Sophron Found., McLean, Va., 1980—; dir. U.S. Congress Office of Tech. Assessment Study on Civilian Space Stas. and U.S. Future in Space, Washington, 1982-84; pres. The Space Transp. Assn., Arlington, 1992—; founding chmn. bd. dirs. External Tanks Corp., Boulder, Colo.; bd. dirs. Internat. Radio Satellite Corp., Washington; chmn. bd. dirs. Luna Corp., Great Falls, Va.; chmn. POLARIS Command-Communications Co., USN, 1960-64; mem. Satellite Communications Panel, Pres.'s Sci. Adv. Com., 1961-63; mem. Dept. Def. NASA Satellite Communications Com., 1961-64; U.S.A. del. UN Conf. on Applications of Sci. and Tech. by Lesser Developed Nations, Geneva, 1963; mem. Fed. Aeronautics and Astronautics Coordinating Bd., 1965-67, Fed. Coun. on Sci. and Tech., 1967-69; mem. Space Program Adv. Coun., NASA, 1971-73, chmn. applications com., 1972-73; mem. NAS com. on regional emergency med. communications systems, 1976-78, space applications bd., 1974-86, space applications bd. com. on NASA space communications, 1986-87, com. on antenna, satellite broadcasting and emergency preparedness for Voice of Am., 1986-88; adv. com. study space transp. U.S. Congrl. Office Tech Assessment, 1994—. Contbr. articles to jours., chpts. to books. Recipient Outstanding Performance award CSC, 1957, cert. commendation Sec. Navy, 1961, Meritorious Civilian Svc. award and medal, Sec. Def., Constrn.'s Man of Yr. award Engring. News Record, 1969, Space Pioneer award Nat. Space Soc., 1988. Fellow IEEE (chmn. aerospace R & D policy com. 1991—); mem. Cosmos Club (Washington). Home and Office: 7404 Colshire Dr Mc Lean VA 22102-7404

ROGERS, TIMOTHY FOLK, lawyer; b. Orangeburg, S.C., Oct. 3, 1947; s. Wallace Williams and Frances Ruth (Folk) R.; m. Mary Page Lonnecker, July 18, 1980; children: John Franklin Folk, Lucinda Lee, Rebecca Page. BA in Polit. Sci., Clemson U., 1969; JD, U. S.C., 1973. Bar: S.C. 1976. Asst. dir. S.C. Coun. Human Rights, Columbia, 1970-72; assoc. editor Osceola Newsweekly, Columbia, 1973; exec. sec. ACLU S.C., Columbia, 1977-78; asst. solicitor Fifth Jud. Cir., Columbia, 1979-83; pvt. practice Columbia, 1983—; ptnr. Lewis, Rogers & Lark, PA, Columbia, 1991—. Mem. S.C. Ho. of Reps., Richland County, 1983—; elected House Majority Leader, 1992. Named Legislator of Yr. Common Cause S.C., 1986, 88, Vietnam Vets. S.C., 1988; recipient Legis. Leadership award S.C. Dept. Probation, Pardon & Parole, 1988. Mem. S.C. Trial Lawyers Assn., S.C. Bar, Richland Bar Assn. Democrat. Baptist. Avocations: sports and outdoors. Home: 1719 Hollywood Dr Columbia SC 29205-3215 Office: PO Box 5151 Columbia SC 29250-5151

ROGERS, VANCE DONALD, former university president; b. Frontenac, Minn., May 16, 1917; s. Azzy Floyd and Mary C. (Martinson) R.; m. Barbara Marie Yarwood, June 22, 1940; children: Nancy Ann Rogers Steele, Mary Lou Rogers Frederickson. Student, Gustavus Adolphus Coll., St. Peter, Minn., 1934-36; A.B., Hamline U., 1938, LL.D., 1976; postgrad., Northwestern U., 1940-41; M.Div., Garrett Bibl. Inst., 1941; D.D., Nebr. Wesleyan U., 1955; LL.D., Mt. Union Coll., 1958; L.H.D., Morningside Coll., 1960; Litt.D., Lane Coll., 1966; L.H.D., U. Nebr., 1968; S.T.D., Oklahoma City U., 1984. Ordained to ministry Methodist Ch., 1941; minister Meth. Ch., Dundee, Ill., 1941-43, Brookfield, Ill., 1946-53; minister Trinity Meth. Ch., Lincoln, Nebr., 1953-57; pres. Nebr. Wesleyan U., Lincoln, 1957-77; chmn. bd. Pure Water, Inc., 1978-80; ret., 1981; staff cons. Lincoln Found., Inc. (Nebr.), 1981-86; sr. assoc., v.p Larry Price & Assocs., Lincoln, 1986-87; adv. dir. Nat. Bank Commerce, Lincoln, 1986-94. Served as lt. comdr. Chaplains Corps, USNR, 1943-46. Mem. Nebr. Acad. Scis., Newcomen Soc. N.Am., Am. Legion, Blue Key, C. of C., Phi Kappa Phi, Phi Eta Sigma, Pi Kappa Delta. Clubs: Mason (Lincoln) (Shriner, K.T.), Univ. (Lincoln), Lincoln Country (Lincoln), Rotary (Lincoln). Home: 3731 Faulkner Dr #310 Lincoln NE 68516 *A successful life is one that is: disciplined (body, mind, and spirit); adventuresome (seeking new ideas, innovative approaches to problem solving, and new areas of exploration); dedicated (to personal standards that call for mature responses-to ideal patterns of behavior-to moral and spiritual ideals rooted in the Judeo-Christian tradition).*

ROGERS, VERN CHILD, engineering company executive; b. Salt Lake City, Aug. 28, 1941; s. Vern S. and Ruth (Child) R.; m. Patricia Powell, Dec. 14, 1962. BS, U. Utah, 1965, MS, 1965; PhD, MIT, 1969. Registered profl. engr. Assoc. prof. Brigham Young U., Provo, Utah, 1969-73; vis. assoc. prof. Lowell Tech. Inst., 1970-71; mgr. IRT Corp., San Diego, 1973-76; v.p. Ford, Bacon & Davis, Salt Lake City, 1976-80; pres. Rogers & Assocs. Engring. Corp., Salt Lake City, 1980—. Contbr. articles to profl. jours. Mem. Health Physics Soc., Am. Soc. Profl. Engrs., Am. Nuclear Soc., Am. Chem. Soc. Mormon. Office: Rogers & Assocs Engring Corp PO Box 330 Salt Lake City UT 84110-0330

ROGERS, WARREN JOSEPH, JR., journalist; b. New Orleans, May 6, 1922; s. Warren Joseph and Rose Agatha (Tennyson) R.; m. Hilda Kenny, Dec. 23, 1943 (dec.); children: Patricia Ann, Sean; m. Alla Bilajiw, Dec. 26, 1973; 1 son, Michael (dec.). Student, Tulane U., 1940-41, La. State U., 1951. Copy boy, cub reporter New Orleans Tribune, 1939-41; copyreader, reporter A.P., Baton Rouge, 1947-51; reporter A.P., Washington, 1951-53, diplomatic corr., 1953-59; mil., fgn. affairs corr. assignments abroad Wash. Bur. N.Y. Herald Tribune, 1959-63; chief Washington corr. Hearst Newspapers, assignments abroad, 1963-66; Washington editor LOOK mag., 1966-69, chief, 1969-70; mil., fgn. affairs corr. Washington bur. Los Angeles Times, 1970-71; Washington columnist Chgo. Tribune-N.Y. News syndicate, 1971-73; v.p. pub. affairs Nat. Forest Products Assn., Washington, 1973-76; editorial dir. Plus Publs., Washington, 1977-78; v.p., editor-in-chief Plus Publs., 1978-79; free-lance, 1979—; Washington bur. chief The Trib of N.Y., 1977-78; editor White House Weekly, 1981-89; exec. editor Associated Features, Inc., Washington editor, 1992—; editor This Week in the White House, 1989-90, Georgetown Courier, 1991-92; bd. dirs. Nat. Press Found.; founder Robert F. Kennedy Journalism awards; lectr. presdl. politics, mil. and fgn. affairs. Author: The Floating Revolution, 1962, Outpost of Freedom, 1965, (with others) An Honorable Profession: A Tribute to Robert F. Kennedy, 1968, (with Paul Watson) Sea Shepherd, 1982, When I think of Bobby: A Personal Memoir of the Kennedy Years, 1993. Served with USMCR, 1941-45. Recipient citation Overseas Press Club N.Y., 1963, Disting. Svc. award Nat. Press Found., 1991. Clubs: Nat. Press (pres. 1972), Federal City Club, Gridiron Club, Washington Ind. Writers. Home: 1622 30th St NW Washington DC 20007-2903

ROGERS, WERNER, state superintendent schools. State supt. schs. Ga. Dept. Edn., Atlanta. Office: State Edn Dept Rm 2066 Twin Towers E 205 Butler St SE Atlanta GA 30334-4910

ROGERS, WILLIAM CECIL, political science educator; b. Manhattan, Kans., 1919; s. Charles Elkins and Sadie (Burns) R.; m. Mary Jane Anderson, Aug. 31, 1941; children: Shelley, Faith, Mary Sarah. B.A., U. Chgo., 1940, M.A., 1941, Ph.D., 1943. Asst. to dir. Pub. Adminstrn. Clearing House, Chgo., 1943-47; lectr. internat. relations U. Chgo., 1945-47; asst. prof. U. Va., 1947-48; assoc. prof. polit. sci. Western Res. U., 1948-49; dir. World Affairs Center, U. Minn., Mpls., 1949-84; cons. Minn. Internat. Ctr., 1984—; dir. Program Info. on World Affairs, Mpls. Star and Tribune, 1951-73. Author: Community Education in World Affairs, 1956, A Guide to Understanding World Affairs, 1966, Global Dimensions in U.S. Education: The Community, 1972; co-author: The Winter City Book, 1980. Pres. Minn. Jazz Sponsors, 1966-67; chmn. Mpls. Com. on Urban Environ., 1976-80. Mem. Nat. Univ. Extension Assn. (past sec.-treas.), Winter Cities Assn. (co-founder 1982). Home: 3510 Mckinley St NE Minneapolis MN 55418-1511 Office: 711 E River Rd Minneapolis MN 55455-0331

ROGERS, WILLIAM DILL, lawyer; b. Wilmington, Del., May 12, 1927; m. Suzanne Rochford, Sept. 7, 1926; children: William Rogers, Daniel. B.A., Princeton U., 1948; LL.B., Yale U., 1951. Bar: D.C. 1952, U.S. Supreme Ct. 1954. Ptnr. Arnold & Porter, Washington, intermittently 1953—; dep. U.S. coordinator Alliance for Progress, AID, 1962-65; pres.

N.Y. Ctr. Inter.-Am. Relations, 1965-72; asst. sec. of state inter-Am. relations Dept. State, 1974-76, undersec. of state for econ. affairs, 1976-77; mem. law faculty Cambridge U., Eng., 1982-83; sr. counselor Bipartisan Commn. on Central Am., 1983-84; vice chmn. Kissinger Assocs. Inc. Author: The Twilight Struggle: The Alliance for Progress and U.S.-Latin-American Relations, 1967. Co-chmn. U.S.-Mexico Binat. Commn.; bd. dirs. Coun. Fgn. Rels., 1981-90. Mem. Am. Soc. Internat. Law (pres. 1971-73), ABA. Office: Arnold & Porter 1200 New Hampshire Ave NW Washington DC 20036-6802

ROGERS, WILLIAM RAYMOND, college president, psychology educator; b. Oswego, N.Y., June 20, 1932; s. William Raymond and A. Elizabeth (Hollis) R.; m. Beverley Claire Partington, Aug. 14, 1954; children: John Partington, Susan Elizabeth Howell, Nancy Claire Glassman. BA magna cum laude, Kalamazoo Coll., 1954; BD, U. Chgo. and Chgo. Theol. Sem., 1958; PhD, U. Chgo., 1965; MA (hon.), Harvard U., 1970. Cons., staff counselor Counseling and Psychotherapy Rsch. Ctr., U. Chgo., 1960-62; teaching fellow, counselor to students Chgo. Theol. Sem., 1961-62; asst. prof. psychology and religion, dir. student counseling Earlham Coll., Richmond, Ind., 1962-68; assoc. prof. psychology and religion, assoc. dean of Coll. Earlham Coll., 1968-70; vis. lectr. pastoral counseling Div. Sch. Harvard U., Cambridge, Mass., 1969-70, prof. religion and psychology Div. and Edn. Schs., 1970-80, faculty chmn. clin. psychology and pub. practice, 1970-72, chmn. counseling and cons. psychology, 1979-80; pres., prof. psychology and religious studies Guilford Coll., Greensboro, N.C., 1980—; bd. dirs. Br. Bank and Trust; mem. N.C. Postsecondary Eligibility Rev. Commn. Author: The Alienated Student, 1969, Project Listening, 1974, Nourishing the Humanistic in Medicine, 1979; Contbr. articles to profl. jours. Bd. dirs. Greensboro Symphony Soc., Greensboro Day Sch., Moses Cone Hosp., Mary Reynolds Babcock Found. Danforth Found. fellow, Blatchford Traveling fellow U. Chgo. and Chgo. Theol. Sem., 1958. Mem. APA, Soc. for Values in Higher Edn., Friends Assn. for Higher Edn., Am. Coun. on Edn., Nat. Assn. Ind. Colls. and Univs. (bd. dirs.), N.C. Assn. Ind. Colls. and Univs., So. Assn. Colls. and Schs., Rotary. Mem. Soc. of Friends. Home: 5400 Westfield Dr Greensboro NC 27410-9223 Office: Guilford Coll 5800 W Friendly Ave Greensboro NC 27410-4173

ROGGER, HANS JACK, history educator; b. Herford, Germany, Sept. 9, 1923; s. Max and Berni (Heilbronn) R.; m. Claire Ryan, Jan. 2, 1955; 1 son, Alexander. B.A., Sarah Lawrence Coll., 1948; Ph.D., Harvard U., 1956. Asst. prof. Sarah Lawrence Coll., Bronxville, N.Y., 1953-58; asso. prof. Sarah Lawrence Coll., 1958-61; asso. prof. UCLA, 1961-66, prof. history, 1966-92, chmn. dept., 1978-83, dir. Russian and East European Studies Center, 1962-66, prof. emeritus, 1992—; fellow Russian Rsch. Ctr., Harvard U., 1962; sr. mem. St. Antony's Coll., Oxford U., 1972; vis. scholar George Kennan Ctr. Advanced Russian Studies, 1975, mem. acad. coun., 1984-88; sr. assoc. fellow Oxford Ctr. Postgrad. Hebrew Studies, 1984—; co-dir. Rand/UCLA Ctr. Soviet Studies, 1989-93. Author: (with E. Weber) The European Right, 1965, 66, 74, (with H. Hyman) Heard Round the World, 1969, National Consciousness in 18th Century Russia, 1960, 70, Russia in Modernization and Revolution, 1881-1917, 1983, Jewish Policies and Right-Wing Politics in Imperial Russia, 1985; contbr. chpts. to book: Shared Destiny: Fifty Years of Soviet-American Relations, 1985, Pogroms: Anti-Jewish Violence in Modern Russia History, 1991, Hostages of Modernization, 1993, Guerre et Culture, 1994; mem. editl. bd.: Am. Hist. Rev., 1982-85, Slavic Rev., 1985-91, Contention, 1992—, also assoc. editor, 1993—. Served with USN, 1943-46. Recipient Guggenheim fellowship, 1964-65; Am. Council Learned Socs. fellow, 1962; Nat. Endowment Humanities fellow, 1975-76. Mem. AAUP, Am. Assn. Advancement Slavic Studies (bd. dirs. 1982-85), Am. Hist. Assn. Office: Dept History UCLA Los Angeles CA 90024

ROGGEVEEN, RICHARD, operation services executive, executive recruiter; b. 1942. Pres. Horsemans Guarantee Corp. Am., Palatine, Ill., Am. Data Ctr. Inc., Palatine, Ill. Office: Horsemans Guarantee Corp AM 25 W Palatine Rd Palatine IL 60067-5199 also: Am Data Centre Inc 25 W Palatine Rd Palatine IL 60067-5199*

ROGICH, SIG, advertising executive. Pres. R & R Advt., Las Vegas; asst. to Pres. of U.S. for initiatives & special activities Washington, D.C., 1989—. Office: R&R Advertising PO Box 80130 Las Vegas NV 89180-0130 Office: Pub Events & Initiatives Old Exec Ofc Bldg Washington DC 20500

ROGIN, GILBERT LESLIE, editor, author; b. N.Y.C., Nov. 14, 1929; s. Robert I. and Lillian Carol (Ruderman) R. Student, State U. Iowa, 1947-49; A.B., Columbia, 1951. Editor-at-large Time Inc. Ventures, N.Y.C., 1955—. Author: The Fencing Master, 1965, What Happens Next?, 1971, Preparations for the Ascent, 1980. Served with AUS, 1952-54. Recipient award for creative work in lit. Am. Acad. Inst. Arts and Letters 1972. Home: 43 W 10th St New York NY 10011-8701 Office: Time Inc Ventures Time & Life Bldg New York NY 10020

ROGLIANO, ALDO THOMAS, publishing executive; b. Tuckahoe, N.Y., Mar. 7, 1925; s. Alfred and Nancy (Morrone) R.; m. Bettie Eleanor Fehrs, June 13, 1948; children: Susan Rogliano Shortley, Betsy Rogliano Dyer, Guy, Barbara Rogliano Tracy, Robert. Student, Syracuse U., 1946-49. Newsstand promotion mgr. Fawcett Publs. Inc., Greenwich, Conn., 1949-54; promotion mgr. Fawcett Publs. Inc., 1957-68, MacFadden Pub. Co., N.Y.C., 1954-57; account exec., promotion mgr. Dell Pub. Co., 1968-71; v.p., dir. pub. relations MacFadden-Bartell Corp., N.Y.C., 1971-74; promotion dir. Internat. Circulation Distbrs., N.Y.C., 1974-77, Kable News Co., 1977-78; v.p., dir. promotion and publicity Publishers Distbg. Corp. (a Filmways co.), N.Y.C., 1978-80; advt. and promotion dir. Flynt Distbg. Co., Los Angeles, 1980-83. Served with USMCR, 1943-45. Decorated Purple Heart; recipient Pub. Relations Gold Key award, 1971. Home: 4417 San Lucian Ln North Fort Myers FL 33903

ROGLIERI, JOHN LOUIS, health facility administrator; b. Plainfield, N.J., June 24, 1939; s. Vito and Grace Mary (DeCristofaro) R.; m. Geraldine Ann Piller, June 15, 1963; children: Maria Roglieri Friedman, Anna, John. BSChemE, Lehigh U., 1961, AB in Applied Scis., 1960; MD, Harvard U., 1966; MS in Bus., Columbia U., 1978. Diplomate Nat. Bd. Med. Examiners. Intern Bellevue Hosp., Columbia U., Service, 1966-67; resident Presbyn. Hosp., N.Y.C., 1969-71, dir. divsn. ambulatory medicine, 1973-75, v.p. ambulatory svcs., 1975-82, dir. employee health svc., 1988-92; fellow Harvard Med. Sch., Boston, 1971-73; asst. dir. Lab. Computer Sci. Mass. Gen. Hosp., 1972-73, dir. Ambulatory Screening Clinic, 1972-73; med. dir. Sanus Health Plan of Greater N.Y., 1988-92; corp. med. dir. Sanus Corp. Health Systems, Ft. Lee, N.J., 1992—; cons. Nat. Ctr. Health Svc. Rsch. and Devel., 1973-75; dir. clin. scholar program Columbia U., 1975-77, asst. prof. clin. medicine Coll. Physicians and Surgeons, 1973—; health edn. cons. Basic Internat. Investments, 1975-76; v.p., bd. dirs. AMARCO Internat., N.Y.C., 1975-85; mem. adv. bd. Western and Upper Manhattan Regional Perinatal Network, Coll. Physicians and Surgeons, N.Y.C., 1975-80; appeared in various TV and radio programs. Author: Odds on Your Life, 1980; mem. editorial bd. Managed Care, 1992—; Jour. Applied Rsch. in Health Adminstrn., 1979-81; book rev. cons. Acad. Press, Inc., N.Y.C.; contbr. articles to profl. publs.; Capt. USPHS, 1967-69. Mem. APHA, Am. Fedn. Clin. Rsch., Am. Soc. Internal Medicine, N.Y. State Soc. Internal Medicine, Soc. for Rsch. and Edn. in Primary Care Internal Medicine, Nat. Assn. Managed Care Physicians. Roman Catholic. Avocations: surfcasting, woodworking, technical stock analysis. Office: Sanus Corp Health Systems 400 Kelby St Fort Lee NJ 07024-2937

ROGO, KATHLEEN, safety engineer; b. Carrollton, Ohio, Sept. 28, 1952; d. Silvio and Mary (Siragusano) R. Grad. high sch., Carrollton; PhD in Med. Sci. (hon.), Ohio Valley Pathologists, Inc., 1992. Cert. histotechnologist, emergency med. technologist, safety engr. Rsch. pathology trainee Aultman Hosp., Canton, Ohio, 1970-75, supr. anatomic pathology, 1974-75; lab. mgr. W. Morgan Lab., Canton, 1973-74; supr. anatomic pathology Dr.'s Hosp., Massillon, Ohio, 1975-78; emergency med. technician Canton Fire Dept., 1976-81; safety engr. Ashland Oil Co., Canton, 1980-82; rsch. pathologist assoc., med. cons. Ohio Valley Pathologists, Inc., Wheeling, W.Va., 1990—. Mem. Am. Soc. Clin. Pathology (cert. histotechnician), Am. Soc. Safety Engrs. (cert.), Am. Soc. Emergency Med. Technicians (cert.),

Ohio State Med. Soc., Internat. Platform Assn. Democrat. Roman Catholic. Avocations: professional model, dancer and musician.

ROGOFF, JEROME HOWARD, psychiatrist, psychoanalyst, forensic expert; b. Detroit, Dec. 21, 1938; s. Abraham Solomon and Sarah Riva (Epstein) R.; (div. 1983); m. Erika Kathleen Keller, Sept. 25, 1983. BA, Harvard Coll., 1960; MD, Case Western Reserve U., 1965. Diplomate Am. Bd. Psychiatry and Neurology. Physician Peace Corps USPHS, Kathmandu, Nepal, 1966-68; clin. fellow psychiatry Harvard Med. Sch., Boston, 1975-79; staff psychiatrist Westwood (Mass.) Lodge Hosp., 1972-74; assoc. clin. prof. psych. Tufts Med. Sch., Boston, 1977-86; assoc. chief, psychiatry and dir. inpatient Psychiatry, day hosp. Faulkner Hosp., Boston, 1975-94; cons. psychiatrist Mass. Parole Bd. Probate Ct. Plymouth County, Mass., LEAA, Washington, 1971-78; med. psychiat. dir. ct. diversion program Boston TASC-A, 1974-75; treas., bd. dirs. Guild for Continuing Edn., Boston, 1981—; founding dir. Law and Psychiatry Resource Ctr., Boston, 1983—; adj. prof. Simmons Sch. Social Work, Boston, 1981-85; lectr. on psychiatry Harvard Med. Sch., Boston, 1980-81, 84-94. Chmn. psychiatry team Combined Jewish Philanthropies, Boston, 1978-83, assoc. chmn. med. team, 1984-87, mem. social planning and allocations com., 1991—; bd. dirs. Jewish Vocat. Svc., Boston, 1987-91. Fellow Am. Psychiat. Assn. (pub. affairs rep. 1988-92, 93-94); mem. mass. Psychiat. Soc. (councillor 1988-94, chair pub. affairs com. 1988-92, 93—, chair nominating com. 1990), Am. Psychoanalytic Assn., Boston Psychoanalytic Soc., Am. Acad. Psychiatry and Law. Democrat. Avocations: cabinetry, carpentry, cooking, classical music, squash, languages. Home and Office: 659 Chestnut St Newton MA 02168-2035

ROGOFF, KENNETH S., economics educator; b. Rochester, N.Y., Mar. 22, 1953; s. Stanley Miron and June Beatrice (Goldman) R.; m. Evelyn Jane Brody, Aug. 18, 1979 (div. 1989); m. Natasha Lance, June 25, 1995. BA/MA in Econs., Yale U., 1975; PhD in Econs., MIT, 1980. Economist Internat. Monetary Fund, Washington, 1983; economist, sect. chief Internat. Fin. div., Bd. Govs. of the Fed. Res. Sys., Washington, 1979-84; assoc. prof. econs. U. Wis., Madison, 1985-89; prof. econs. U. Calif., Berkeley, 1989-92; prof. econs. and internat. affairs Princeton (N.J.) U., 1992—; vis. scholar San Francisco Fed. Res., 1990-92, World Bank, Washington, 1989, IMF, Washington, 1988-94. Contbr. articles to profl. jours. Alfred P. Sloan Rsch. fellow, 1986-87, Hoover Instn. Nat. fellow, 1986-87, NSF fellow, 1985—. Fellow Econometric Soc.; mem. Am. Econ. Assn., World Chess Fedn. Grandmasters Assn. Office: Princeton U Woodrow Wilson Sch Princeton NJ 08544-1013

ROGOSHESKE, WALTER FREDERICK, lawyer, former state justice; b. Sauk Rapids, Minn., July 12, 1914; m. Dorothy Heywood, Sept. 29, 1940; children: James, Thomas, Mark, Paul, Mary Alice. BA, U. Minn., 1937, LLB, 1939; LLD, William Mitchell Coll. Law. Bar: Minn. 1940. Gen. practice Sauk Rapids, 1940-50; dist. judge 7th Jud. Dist., 1950-62; assoc. justice Supreme Ct. Minn., 1962-80; lectr. law U. Minn. Law Sch., 1951-74, adj. prof., 1980-84; cons. arbitration and mediation proceedings, 1980-95. Chmn. Mpls.-St. Paul Met. Airports Commn., 1949-50; Mem. Minn. Ho. of Reps., 1943-49; Bd. dirs. Amicus, Inc.; past pres. Big Bros., St. Paul. Served with AUS, 1944-45. Fellow Am. Bar Found.; mem. ABA (chmn. adv. com. prosecution and def. function, criminal law project 1968-71, mem. council sect. criminal justice 1970-74), Minn. Bar Assn., 7th Dist. Bar Assn., Am. Judicature Soc., Inst. Jud. Adminstrn., U. Minn. Law Alumni Assn. (dir.). Lutheran. Home and Office: 138 Canabury Ct Saint Paul MN 55117-1503

ROGOSKI, PATRICIA DIANA, financial executive; b. Chgo., Dec. 29, 1939; d. Raymond Michael and Bernice Rose (Konkol) R. BS in Acctg. and Econs., Marquette U., 1961, postgrad., 1965-66; postgrad., NYU, 1966-68, St. John's U., N.Y.C., 1975-76; cert. mgmt. acct., 1979. Sr. fin. analyst Blackhawk Mfg. Co., Milw., 1961-66; mgr., sr. analyst Shell Oil Co., N.Y.C., 1966-71; mgr. data processing Bradford Nat./Penn Bradford, Pitts., 1971-75; asst. mgr. fin. controls ITT, N.Y.C., 1975-79; v.p., comptr. ITT Consumer Fin. Corp., Mpls., 1979-80; sr. v.p. fin. ITT Fin. Corp., St. Louis, 1980-84; v.p., exec. asst., group exec. ITT Coins, Secaucus, N.J., 1984-85; pres. Patron S., Ltd. Wilmington, Del., 1986—; CFO, sr. v.p. Guardsmark, Inc., Memphis, 1989-94; sr. v.p. Peoplemark, Inc., Memphis, 1989-94. Bd. dirs. St. Louis Repertory Theater, 1983-84. Named to Acad. Women Achievers, YWCA, N.Y.C., 1980. Mem. Fin. Execs. Inst., Inst. Mgmt. Acctg., Econ. Club. Avocation: duplicate bridge. Office: Patron S Ltd Ste 1000 201 Walnut St Wilmington DE 19801

ROGOVIN, MILTON, documentary photographer, retired optometrist; b. N.Y.C., Dec. 30, 1909; s. Jacob and Dora (Shainhouse) R.; m. Anne Setters, Apr. 7, 1942; children—Ellen, Mark, Paula. B.S. in Optics and Optometry, Columbia U., 1931; M.A. in American Studies, SUNY-Buffalo, 1972; DFA (hon.), U. Buffalo, 1994, Buffalo State Coll., 1994, Dyouville Coll., 1994. Optometrist, Buffalo, 1931-75; freelance documentary photographer, 1958—. Author: Milton Rogovin: The Forgotten Ones, 1985, Portraits in Steel, 1993, Triptychs Buffalo's Lower West Side Revisited, 1993. Served with U.S. Army, 1942-45. Recipient W. Eugene Smith Meml. Fund award, 1983. Home: 90 Chatham Ave Buffalo NY 14216-3109

ROGOVIN, MITCHELL, lawyer; b. N.Y.C., Dec. 3, 1930; s. Max Shea and Sayde (Epstein) R.; m. Sheila Ann Ender, Jan, 31, 1954; children: Lisa Shea, Wendy Meryl, John Andrew. AB, Syracuse U., 1951; LLB, U. Va., 1954; LLM, Georgetown U., 1959. Bar: Va. 1953, D.C. 1968, N.Y., 1990, U.S. Tax Ct., U.S. Ct. Appeals (1st, 2d, 4th, 5th, 9th, D.C. and fed. cirs.), U.S. Supreme Ct. Chief counsel IRS, Washington, 1965-66; asst. atty. gen. U.S. Dept. Justice, Washington, 1966-69; ptnr. Arnold & Porter, Washington, 1968-76, Rogovin, Huge & Schiller, Washington, 1976—; spl. counsel CIA, 1975-76; nuclear regulation com. spl. inquiry into Three Mile Island accident NRC, 1979-80; bd. dirs. United So. Assurance Co., Med. Rsch. Legal Def. Fund. Gen. counsel John Anderson Pres. Campaign, 1980; bd. Echo Hill Outdoor Sch. Served to capt. USMC, 1954-58. Mem. Ctr. for Law and Social Policy (chmn. bd. dirs.), Council on Fgn. Relations, The Wilderness Soc. (governing bd.). Home: 3226 Volta Pl NW Washington DC 20007-2731 Office: 1250 24th St NW Washington DC 20037-1124

ROGOW, BRUCE JOEL, information technology consultant; b. Phila., Aug. 22, 1945; s. Abraham I. and Eunice (Friedman) R.; m. Lois Lee Kutun, Aug. 20, 1967 (div. Mar. 1973); children: Mark Alan, Michelle Renee; m. Winnie Ruth Teitelbaum, Mar. 7, 1980; 1 child, Geoffrey Evan. BCE, U. Fla., 1967. Systems engr. IBM, Gainesville, Fla., 1968-69, mktg. rep., 1969-72; staff instr. IBM, Poughkeepsie, N.Y., 1973-77; cons. Nolan, Norton & Co., Lexington, Mass., 1977-79, prin., 1979-82; sr. mng. prin. Nolan, Norton & Co./Peat Marwick & Co., Lexington, 1982-87; v.p. analytic resources, 1988-90, exec. v.p. cons. svcs., 1991-92, fellow, 1992—; pvt. cons. firm Marblehead, Mass., 1992—; speaker info. tech. industry. Republican. Jewish. Avocations: reading, skiing, family. Home and Office: 220 Ocean Ave Marblehead MA 01945-3629

ROGOWAY, LAWRENCE PAUL, civil engineer, consultant; b. Portland, Oreg., Dec. 9, 1932; s. Phillip F. and Shirley G. (Goldstein) R.; children: Cathy L. Hucke, Karen G. Callow. BS in Civil Engring., Oreg. State U., 1954. Registered profl. engr. Ariz., Calif., Colo., Fla., Nev., Okla., Oreg., Va., Wash. Assoc. engr. Lockheed Aircraft Co., Burbank, Calif., 1956-57; civil engring. asst. Dept. Pub. Works, Bur. Engring., L.A., 1957-59; civil engr. G. Shuirman & Assocs., L.A., 1959-66; v.p. Shuirman, Rogoway & Assocs., L.A., 1966-79; pres. RBA Ptnrs., Inc., L.A., 1979—. Chmn. Citizens Adv. Bd. for Com. Planning, L.A., 1970-72. Lt. (j.g.) USNR, 1954-56, Korea. Fellow ASCE; mem. NSPE, Am. Cons. Engrs. Coun. (governing bd.). Home: 2251 Colby Ave Los Angeles CA 90064 Office: RBA Ptnrs Inc 3470 Wilshire Blvd Ste 900 Los Angeles CA 90010-3909

ROGOWSKY, ROBERT A., trade commission director; b. Vancouver, B.C., Can., Mar. 12, 1951; s. Michael Randall and Ruth Ann (Wellman) R.; m. Linda Sue George, June 17, 1972; children: Vanessa, Heather, Tara, Nichole, Alexis. BA in Econs., Boston U., 1973; MA in Econs., U. Va., 1975, PhD in Econs., 1982. Asst. prof. dept. econs. George Mason U., Fairfax, Va., 1977-78; rsch. economist Bur. Econs. FTC, Washington, 1979-83; econ. advisor to commrs. Consumer Product Safety Commn., Washington, 1983-84, acting

exec. dir., asst. to dir., 1984; pres. Econ. Edn. for Clergy, Inc., Bethesda, Md., 1985-86; exec. asst. to chmn. Internat. Trade Commn., Washington, 1986-87; dep. dir. Bur. Consumer Protection FTC, Washington, 1987-89; dir. office of industries U.S. Internat. Trade Commn., Washington, 1989-92, dir. ops., 1992—; instr. U. Va., 1976-77; econ. rschr. Am. Enterprise Inst., 1976; econ. rsch. analyst Econ. Policy Office, U.S. Dept. Justice, 1974-75; presenter in field. Contbr. articles to profl. jours. Mem. Am. Mgmt. Assn., Am. Econs. Assn., Assn. Christian Economists. Lutheran. Home: 729 Forest Park Rd Great Falls VA 22066 Office: US International Trade Comm Operations 500 E St NW Washington DC 20436-0003*

ROGULA, JAMES LEROY, consumer products company executive; b. Rock Island, Ill., Nov. 8, 1933; s. Andrew and Nellie Pearl (Cook) R.; m. Adelaide F. Dittbrenner, May 29, 1960; children: James Lyle, Adelaide Ann, John Andrew. BA, Knox Coll., 1955; MBA, NYU, 1964. Group product mgr. Am. Chicle Co., Long Island City, N.Y., 1958-66; v.p. new product devel. Carter Wallace, Inc., N.Y.C., 1966-72; v.p. new products J.B. Williams Co., N.Y.C., 1972-74; sr. v.p. E.J. Brach & Sons, Chgo., 1974-77; v.p., gen. mgr. A.E. Staley Mfg. Co., Oak Brook, Ill., 1977-80; exec. v.p. Booth Fisheries Corp., Chgo., 1980-82; v.p., gen. mgr. Arm & Hammer div. Church & Dwight, Inc., Princeton, NJ, 1982-90; pres. Am. Candy Co., Richmond, Va., 1990-94; sr. v.p. consumer bus. group Scotts Co., Marysville, Ohio, 1994—; bd. dirs Sterns Miracle Grow Co. Bd. dirs. Jr. Achievement, Mercer County, N.J., 1987-90. With U.S. Army, 1956-58. Mem. Sunset Ridge Country Club, Econ. Club Chgo., Commonwealth Club Richmond. Home: 1513 West Ave Richmond VA 23220-3721 Office: Scotts Co 6630 W Broad St 14111 Scottslawn Rd Marysville OH 43041

ROH, MYUNG JA, social worker; b. Seoul, Dem. Republic of Korea, Jan. 12, 1940; d. Young Shin and M. Ho Ja (Kim) Kim; m. Chang Shub Roh, July 15, 1962; children: Shikyung, Shiyoung. BA, Ewha Woman's U., Seoul, 1961; postgrad., Ewha Woman's U., 1966-68; MSW, Marywood Coll., 1975. Cert. Acad. Cert. Social Workers; qualified clin. social worker; lic. social worker. Social worker III Danville (Pa.) State Hosp., 1975—. Recipient Alcoholism grantee Nat. Inst. for Alcohol Abuse & Alcoholism, 1973-75, AMI award Ctrl. Susquehanna chpt., 1992. Mem. NASW (mem. nomination com. 1987-89, affirmative action com. Pa. chpt. 1991-93). Methodist. Home: 905 Cherry Hill Rd Bloomsburg PA 17815-8803

ROHATSCH, RALPH E., JR. (BOB ROHATSCH, JR.), career military officer; b. San Angelo, Tex., Nov. 19, 1940; s. Ralph Robert and Alice (Yowell) R.; m. Janie L. Westbrook, June 22, 1963; children: Robert, Beth. BS, USAF Acad., 1963; MBA, Auburn U., 1976; disting. grad., Squadron Officer Sch., 1968, Air Command and Staff Coll., 1976, Air War Coll., 1980. Commd. 2d lt. USAF, 1963, advanced through grades to maj. gen., 1991; T-38 instr. pilot, T-38 flight examiner USAF, Webb AFB, Tex., 1964-68; T-38 flight examiner 3250th pilot instr. tng. squadron USAF, Tyndall AFB, Fla., 1968-72; adv. South Vietnamese air force Military Assistance Adv. Group USAF, Tan Son Nhut Air Base, South Vietnam, 1972-73; T-38 flight examiner Air Tng. Command standardization and evaluation bd., HQ Air Tng. Command USAF, Randolph AFB, Tex., 1973-74, exec. officer to Air Tng. Command dep. chief staff ops., 1974-75; HQ USAF, Washington, 1976-77, dep. chief staff Senate Liaison Office, 1977-80; comd. 25th flying tng. squadron USAF, Vance AFB, Okla., 1980-81; dep. commandant ops. with commandant of cadets USAF, Air Force Acad., Colo., 1981-84; comdr. 64th air base group, HQ Air Tng. Command USAF, Reese AFB, Tex., 1984-1985; comdr. 12th flying tng. wing, HQ Air Tng. Command USAF, Randolph AFB, 1985-87; dir. requirements office of dep. chief staff plans and requirements ATC HQ USAF, 1987; comdr. Air Force Res. Officer Tng. Corps. USAF, Maxwell AFB, Ala., 1987-1988; comdr. Air Force Dist. USAF, Washington, 1988-90; comdr. U.S. logistics group, commdg. USAFE Ops. Desert Shield, Desert Storm, Oper. Provide Comfort USAF, Ankara, Turkey, 1990-92; chief joint U.S. Milit. Mission for Aid to Turkey USAF; comdr. 16th Air Force, U.S. Air Forces in Europe USAF, Aviano, Italy, 1992-94. Decorated Legion of Merit with oak leaf cluster, Bronze Star, Vietnam Gallantry Cross with Palm, Vietnam Campaign Medal, D.S.M., Meritorious Svc. Medal with 2 oak leaf clusters, Air Force Commendation Medal, Vietnam Svc. Medal with bronze star, Southwest Asia Svc. Medal with 2 bronze stars,.

ROHATYN, FELIX GEORGE, investment company executive; b. Vienna, Austria, May 29, 1928; came to U.S., 1942, naturalized, 1950; s. Alexander and Edith (Knoll) R.; m. Jeannette Streit, June 9, 1956; children: Pierre, Nicolas, Michael; m. Elizabeth Fly, May 31, 1979. BS, Middlebury (Vt.) Coll., 1948; LLD (hon.), Adelphi U., Bard Coll., Hofstra U., 1981, L.I. U., 1981, Middlebury Coll., 1982, Fordham U., 1983; LLB (hon.), NYU, 1979, Brandeis U., 1987. With Lazard Freres & Co., investment bankers, N.Y.C., 1948—, gen. ptnr, 1960—; bd. dirs. Pfizer Co., Howmet, Gen. Instrument. Served with AUS, 1951-53, Korea. Office: Lazard Freres & Co 1 Rockefeller Plz New York NY 10020-2001

ROHDA, RODNEY RAYMOND, insurance company executive; b. East Troy, Wis., Aug. 11, 1942; s. Raymond Francis and Mona Leown (Hoffbauer) F.; divorced; children: Marney, Gregor. BBA, U. Wis., 1964. Asst. actuary Northwestern Mut. Life Ins. Co., Milw., 1964-73; 2d v.p., actuary N.Y. Life Ins. Co., N.Y.C., 1973-75; v.p., actuary Mut. Benefit Life Ins. Co., Newark, 1975-81; exec. v.p., dir. Home Life Ins. Co., N.Y.C., 1981-87; pres. Fidelity Investments Life Ins. Co., Boston, 1987-93, chmn., 1993—. Foremr mem. exec. com., pres. N.J. Assn. Mental Health. Served to 2d lt. USAR, 1966-72. Fellow Soc. Actuaries; mem. Am. Acad. Actuaries. Home: 1600 Washington St Apt 315 Newton MA 02165-2239 Office: Fidelity Investments # R25C 82 Devonshire St Boston MA 02109-3614

ROHDE, RICHARD A., plant pathologist educator; b. Peekskill, N.Y., Sept. 28, 1929; s. Frederick Allen and Ruth Winifred (Gallaher) R.; m. Suzanne Eloise Walker, Oct. 11, 1956; children: Melissa, Leigh, Katherine, David. AB, Drew U., 1951; MS, U. Md., 1956, PhD, 1958. Asst. prof. U. Mass., Amherst, Mass., 1959-65, assoc. prof., 1965-68, prof., head dept plant pathology, 1968-81; assoc. dean, assoc. dir. Mass. Agrl. Exptl. Sta., U. Mass., Amherst, Mass., 1981—; prof. emeritus, 1994; vis. scientist Rothamsted Exp. Sta., Harpenden, 1967, U. Ariz., Tucson, 1974, USDA-CSRS, Washington, D.C., 1981. Editor: Plant-Parasitic Nematodes, 3 Vols., 1971-81; contbr. articles to profl. jours. Cpl. U.S. Army, 1952-54. Recipient Alumni Achievement award Drew U., 1970. Mem. Am. Phytopathological Soc. (councilor, pres.), Soc. Nematologists. Lutheran. Home: 18 Butter Hill Rd Pelham MA 01002 Office: University of Massachusetts Agricultural Experiment Sta 217 Stockbridge Hall Amherst MA 01003

ROHLF, F. JAMES, biometrician, educator; b. Blythe, Calif., Oct. 24, 1936. BS, San Diego State Coll., 1958; PhD in Entomology, U. Kans., 1962. Asst. prof. biology U. Calif., Santa Barbara, 1962-65; assoc. prof. statis. biology U. Kans., 1965-69; assoc. prof. biology SUNY, Stony Brook, 1969-72, prof., 1972—; chmn. dept. ecology and evolution, 1975-80, 90-91; statis. cons. N.Y. Pub. Svc. Commn., 1975-78, IBM, 1977-81, U.S. EPA, 1978-80, Applied Biomath Inc., 1984-92; vis. scientist IBM, Yorktown Heights, N.Y., 1976-77, 80-81. Mem. Biometric Soc., Assn. Computing Machinery, Soc. Systematic Biology, Classification Soc. Achievements include research in applications of multivariate analysis, cluster and factor analysis to systematics, morphometrics, and population biology. Office: SUNY at Stony Brook Dept Ecology and Evolution Stony Brook NY 11794-5245

ROHLF, PAUL LEON, urologist; b. Davenport, Iowa, June 15, 1937; s. Lester Charles and Vera Bernice (Fisher) R.; m. Karen Kay Schnede, Aug. 8, 1959; children: David P., Gregory C., Elizabeth K., Kathryn A. BA, U. Iowa, 1959, MD, 1962. Diplomate Am. Bd. Urology. Intern Phila. Gen. Hosp., 1962-63; resident surgery VA Hosp., Iowa City, Iowa, 1963; resident urology U. Iowa Hosp., Iowa City, 1966-69; physician, urologist Urol. Assocs., Davenport, 1969—; dir. sec. UroSurgery Ctr., Inc., Davenport, 1986—; peer rev. com. Iowa Found. Med. Care, Des Moines, 1982-88; founder, dir. Urosurgery Ctr., Inc. 1986; cons. Vis. Nurse Assn., Davenport, 1976-79, Com. for Affordable Healthcare, Des Moines, 1985-87; chmn. dept. surgery Mercy Hosp. Davenport, 1978, utilization rev. chair Mercy and St. Lukes Hosp., Davenport, 1978-85, surg. appraisal chair, 1983-89, chmn. dept. surgery, 1993—. Bd. dirs. Maternal Health Ctr., Davenport, 1979—; peer rev. com. Heritage Nat. Health Plan, Davenport, 1991—, Capt. USAF, 1964-66. Fellow ACS; mem. AMA, Am. Urologic Assn., Am. Fertility Soc.,

Am. Soc. Outpatient Surgery, Iowa Med. Soc., Scott County Med. Soc. (pres. 1980-81), Iowa Urologic Soc. (pres. 1981-82). Republican. Lutheran. Avocations: tennis, gardening, running, healthcare cost issues. Home: 2412 E River Dr Davenport IA 52803-3702 Office: Urol Assocs PC 3319 Spring St Davenport IA 52807-2125

ROHLF, ROBERT HENRY, retired library director, library consultant; b. Mpls., May 14, 1928; s. Henry E. and Helen (Mulcahy) R.; m. Joan Ann Peters, Sept. 17, 1949; children: Catherine Rohlf Stepanek, Cynthia Rohlf Molenaar, William R., John H., David R. BA, Coll. St. Thomas, St. Paul, 1949; BSLS, U. Minn., 1950, MA, 1953, Cert. pub. adminstrn., 1955. Librarian inst. agrl. U. Minn., 1950-51, librarian, 1951-53; librarian, adminstrv. asst. Mpls. Pub. Library, 1953-58; dir. Dakota/Scott Regional Library, West St. Paul, 1959-66, Ill. Library Devel. Project, Aurora, 1963; coordinator of bldg. plan Library of Congress, Washington, 1966-68, dir. adminstrn., 1968-69; dir. Hennepin County Library, Mpls., 1969-94; prin. ptnr. Profl. Libr. Cons., P.A.; cons. in library planning and mgmt., 1960—; U.S. rep. internat. exec. com. UNESCO, Alexandria, 1993—. Author: Plan for Public Library Development in Illinois, 1963, Public Libraries in San Diego, 1981. Active Met. Council, Mpls. Citizens League, Gov.'s Adv. Com. on Youth, Minn. Bd. Edn. Adv. Council. Named one of outstanding young men Mpls. Jaycees, 1954. Mem. ALA (life, div. pres. 1981) Minn. Libr. Assn. (life, pres., Libr. of Yr. 1967), Rotary (bd. dirs. Edina chpt. 1994—), Jaycees (sen.). Avocations: skiing, golf, reading, sailing, camping.

ROHLFING, FREDERICK WILLIAM, lawyer, judge; b. Honolulu, Nov. 2, 1928; s. Romayne Raymond and Kathryn (Coe) R.; m. Joan Halford, July 15, 1952 (div. Sept. 1982); children: Frederick W., Karl A., Brad (dec.); m. Patricia Ann Santos, Aug. 23, 1983. BA, Yale U., 1950; JD, George Washington U., 1955. Bar: Hawaii 1955, Am. Samoa 1978. Assoc. Moore, Torkildson & Rice, Honolulu, 1955-60; ptnr. Rohlfing, Nakamura & Low, Honolulu, 1963-68, Hughes, Steiner & Rohlfing, Honolulu, 1968-71, Rohlfing, Smith & Coates, Honolulu, 1981-84; sole practice Honolulu, 1960-63, 71-81, Maui County, 1988—; dep. corp. counsel County of Maui, Wailuku, Hawaii, 1984-87, corp. counsel, 1987-88; land and legal counsel Maui Open Space Trust, 1992—; prin. Frederick W. Rohlfing III, Honolulu; magistrate judge U.S. Dist. Ct. Hawaii, 1991—. Mem. Hawaii Ho. Reps., 1959-65, 80-84; Hawaii State Senate, 1966-75; U.S. alt. rep. So. Pacific Commn., Noumea, New Caledonia, 1975-77, 1982-84. Capt. USNR, 1951-87. Mem. Hawaii Bar Assn., Fed. Magistrate Judges Assn. Avocation: ocean swimming. Home and Office: RR #1 Box 398 Kekaulike Ave Kula HI 96790

ROHLIN, DIANE ELIZABETH, financial public relations executive; b. N.Y.C., June 18, 1958; d. Edward F. and Elaine (Wittenstein) R. BA, Mich. State U., 1979. Account exec. Prudential Bache, Chgo., 1980, A.G. Becker, Chgo., 1981-82; sr. ptnr. Fin. Rels. Bd., Chgo., 1983—. Republican. Avocations: reading, golfing, horseback riding. Office: Fin Rels Bd 875 N Michigan Ave Chicago IL 60611-1779

ROHM, CHARLES EDWARD, insurance company executive; b. Detroit, Oct. 8, 1935; s. John T. and Bernice L. (Shook) R.; m. Joy T. Gwinn, Sept. 8, 1956; 1 child, Barbara. BA, Wabash Coll., 1957; MA, U. Mich., 1958. CLU. Actuarial asst. Prin. Fin. Group, Des Moines, 1963-68, asst. actuary, 1968-70, actuary, 1970-72, 2d v.p., actuary, 1972-74, v.p., 1974-79, v.p., chief actuary, 1979-84, sr. v.p., 1984-92, exec. v.p., 1992—; chmn., pres., bd. dirs. Prin. Mut. Life. Chmn., bd. trustees Simpson Coll., Indianola, Iowa; past chmn. United Way of Cen. Iowa, Des Moines. Mem. Am. Acad. Actuaries, Am. Soc. CLUs, Soc. of Actuaries, Life Ins. Mktg. Rsch. Assn. (bd. dirs.) Office: The Prin Fin Group 711 High St Des Moines IA 50392-0001

ROHM, ROBERT HERMANN, sculptor, educator; b. Cin., Feb. 6, 1934; s. Hermann George and Anna Katherine (Sager) R.; m. Patricia Jean Cutlip, Dec. 6, 1959 (div. 1978); children: Hans Tobin, Kyle Curtis. B in Indsl. Design, Pratt Inst., 1956; MFA in Sculpture, Cranbrook Acad. Art, 1960. Instr. Columbus (Ohio) Coll. Art and Design, 1956-59, Pratt Inst., Bklyn., 1960-65; prof. art U. R.I., Kingston, 1965–; artist in residence Artpark, Lewiston, N.Y., 1977. One-man shows: O.K. Harris Gallery, N.Y.C., 1970, 72, 73, 75, 77, 80, 83, 84, 86, 89, 92, 94, Parker St. 470 Gallery, Boston, 1970, 72, Univ. Rochester, N.Y., 1971, N.S. Coll. Art, Halifax, 1970, Worcester Art Mus. (Mass.), 1978, Univ. R.I., 1981, 88, 94, Nielsen Gallery, Boston, 1985, 86, 92, La Jolla Mus. Contemporary Art, Calif., 1985, Lenore Gray Gallery, Providence, 1990, 93, 95; group shows include Boston Mus., 1974, Whitney Mus., N.Y.C., 1962, 64, 69, 70, 73, 83, Va. Mus., Richmond, 1970, Fogg Mus., Cambridge, Mass., 1971, Seattle Art Mus., 1969, Vancouver Art Mus., B.C., Can., 1970, N.J. State Mus., Trenton, 1969, R.I. State Coun. on Arts, 1973, 82, Vassar Coll., 1971, Inst. Contemporary Art, Boston, 1975, Miss. Mus. Art, Jackson, 1979-80, Grey Art Gallery, NYU, 1980, Montclair (N.J.) Art Mus., 1978, Aldrich Mus. Contemporary Art, Ridgefield, Conn.,1981, 82, SUNY-Plattsburgh, 1981, Zone Gallery, Springfield, Mass., 1982, Cumberland Gallery, Nashville, 1986, 93, Allan Frumkin Gallery, N.Y.C., 1985, Beitzel Fine Arts Inc., N.Y.C., Addison Gallery Am. Art, Andover, Mass., 1989, Nielsen Gallery, Boston, 1990-91, Soma Gallery, San Diego, 1993; represented in permanent collections Columbus Gallery Fine Art, Finch Coll., N.Y.C., Pa. State U., Kunsthalle, Zurich, Va. Mus. Fine Arts, Mus. Modern Art, N.Y.C., U. N.Mex., Albuquerque, Albright-Knox Gallery, Buffalo, Whitney Mus. Am. Art, N.Y.C., Met. Mus. Art, N.Y.C., Rose Art Mus., Brandeis U., Waltham Mass., Mus. Fine Art, Boston, Mus. of Contemporary Art, Chgo. Grantee Guggenheim Found., 1964, R.I. State Council on Arts, 1973, 82, 93, NEA, 1974, 86; recipient Cassandra Found. award, 1967, award Boston 200 Bicentennial Commn., 1975. Subject of numerous articles in jours. and catalogues. Office: U RI Art Dept Fine Arts Ctr Kingston RI 02881

ROHN, ELIZABETH G., banker; b. Hartford, Conn., May 25, 1948; d. Charles Alonzo and Julie (Gelston) Harrington; m. Douglas Jerome Gregor (div. 1980); m. William John Rohn, Aug. 29, 1980. AA, Hartford Coll. for Women, 1968; BA, U. Ill., Chgo., 1971; MBA, U. Minn., 1975; cert. in exec. program-Sloan Mgmt., MIT, 1988. Coord. svc. TIES-Computer Coop., St. Paul, 1971-73; mgr. svcs. Metro-II Computer Coop, Mpls., 1976-78; sr. cons. Plante & Moran-CPA/Mgmt. Cons., Southfield, Mich., 1979-82; sr. cons. Fed. Nat. Mortgage Assn., Washington, 1982-83, asst. to chief exec. officer and chmn. bd., 1983-84, dir. mortgage acquisition, 1984-86, v.p. mortgage ops., 1987-88; v.p., mgr. consumer lending Mellon Bank (East), Phila., 1988-89; v.p. mortgage products mid-Atlantic region Mellon Bank, 1990—. Avocations: classical music, Calif. wines. Office: Mellon Bank 7th and Market Sts Philadelphia PA 19101-7899

ROHN, REUBEN DAVID, pediatric educator and administrator; b. Israel, Apr. 12, 1945; came to U.S., 1954; s. Aryeh and Rachel (Brenner) R.; m. Judith Semel, Sept. 6, 1971; 1 child, Karen. BA cum laude, Bklyn. Coll., 1967; MD, N.Y. Med. Coll., 1971. Diplomate Am. Bd. Pediatrics, Adolescent Medicine, Am. Bd. Pediatric Endocrology, Am. Bd. Pediatric Adolescent Medicine, Nat. Bd. Med. Examiners. Intern in pediatrics Montefiore Hosp., Bronx, N.Y., 1971-72, resident in pediatrics, 1972-74; fellow in adolescent medicine U. Md. Hosp., Balt., 1974-76; preceptor in pediatrics Johns Hopkins U. Sch. Health Svcs., Balt., 1975-76; asst. prof. dept. pediatrics Ea. Va. Med. Sch., Norfolk, 1976-82; coord. pediatric clerkship Ea. Va. Med. Sch., Children's Hosp. of King's Daughters, Norfolk, 1977-90; prof. dept. pediatrics Ea. Va. Med. Sch., Norfolk, 1989—; adj. prof. chemistry Old Dominion U., Norfolk, 1984—; dir. adolescent medicine/endocrinology Children's Hosp. of King's Daughters, Norfolk, 1976—; mem. curriculum com. Ea. Va. Med. Sch., 1977-79, clerkship coords. com., 1977-90, genetics com., 1978-80, evaluation com., 1979-81, chmn. selectives com., 1981-82, ad hoc com. on consultation, 1982-83, student progress com., 1983-85, student health com., 1985-87, LCME com. on curriculum, 1990-92; mem. child abuse com. Children's Hosp. of King's Daughters, 1976-80, chmn. adolescent adv. com., 1976-80, patient care com., 1980-94, nutrition com., 1980-94, utilization review com., 1980-82, med. records com. 1987-89, gen. med./surg. task force com., 1987-88; speaker in field. Reviewer Jour. Adolescent Health Care, 1986—, mem. editorial bd., 1989-92; contbr. articles to profl. jours. Mem. Norfolk Sch. Health Coun., 1977—, mem. ad hoc com. infant screening program for hypothyroidism Commonwealth of Va., 1977-79 cons., 1979—; mem. cmty. adv. bd. Norfolk Adolescent Pregnancy Prevention Svcs. Project, 1981-83; bd. dirs. Elizabeth River chpt. Am. Diabetes Assn., 1982-85, South Hampton Roads chpt., 1985-93; mem. adv. com. Norfolk-

Virginia Beach Jr. League, 1987-88; judge ann. Health Edn. Fair, Norfolk, Pub. schs., 1980—. Recipient grant Bressler Rsch. Fund, 1975-76, Biomed. Rsch. Devel. grant Ea. Va. Med. Sch., 1978, 78-79, 79-80. 81-82, 83-84, Children's Health Found. grant, 1988-89. Fellow Am. Acad. Pediatrics (youth and adolescence com. Va. chpt. 1978—); mem. Soc. Adolescent Medicine (abstract reviewer 1984-91), Lawson Wilkins Pediatric Endocrine Soc., Sigma Xi. Avocations: photography, folk dancing. Home: 4653 Larkwood Dr Virginia Beach VA 23464 Office: Childrens Hosp Kings Daus 601 Childens Ln Norfolk VA 23464

ROHNER, RALPH JOHN, lawyer, educator, university dean; b. East Orange, N.J., Aug. 10, 1938. A.B., Cath. U. Am., 1960, J.D., 1963. Bar: Md. 1964. Teaching fellow Stanford (Calif.) U., 1963-64; atty. pub. health div. HEW, 1964-65; prof. law Cath. U. Am. Sch. Law, Washington, 1965—, acting dean, 1968-69, assoc. dean, 1969-71, dean, 1987-95; staff counsel consumer affairs subcom. U.S. Senate Banking Com., 1975-76; cons. Fed. Res. Bd., 1976-83, chmn. consumer adv. council, 1981; cons. FDIC, 1978-80; spl. counsel Consumer Bankers Assn., 1984—; cons. U.S. Regulatory Coun., 1979-80; bd. dirs. Hanover Funds, Inc., N.Y.C. Co-author: Consumer Law: Cases and Materials, 1979, 2d edit., 1991; co-author, editor The Law of Truth in Lending, 1984. Bd. dirs. Migrant Legal Action Program, Inc., Washington, Automobile Owners Action Coun., Washington, Credit Rsch. Ctr., Purdue U. Mem. ABA, Am. Law Inst. Home: 10909 Forestgate Pl Glenn Dale MD 20769-2047 Office: Cath U Sch Law 620 Michigan Ave NE Washington DC 20064 *We learn from those we teach, we are inspired to write by those who read, and we should serve as examples to those who aspire.*

ROHNER, THOMAS JOHN, JR., urologist; b. Trenton, N.J., Jan. 1, 1936; s. Thomas J. and Julia (Kanyo) R.; m. Jessie Rohner; children: Christopher, James. BA, Yale U., 1957; MD, U. Pa., 1961. Diplomate Am. Bd. Urology. Intern Hosp. U. Pa., Phila., 1961-62, resident in gen. surgery, 1962-64, resident in urology, 1964-67; asst. prof. surgery M.S. Hersey Med. Ctr., Pa. State U., Hershey, 1970-71, assoc. prof., 1971-75, 1975—, chief urol. div., 1970—; urologic cons. VA Hosp., Lebanon, Pa., 1970—; corp. mem. Pa. Blue Shield, 1991—, bd. dirs., 1993—. Contbr. articles to profl. jours. Served to maj. M.C., U.S. Army, 1967-69. USPHS fellow, 1969-70; grantee HEW, 1971-76, USPHS, 1971-76. Fellow ACS (pres. cen. Pa. chpt. 1983-84, bd. govs. 1991—); mem. AMA, Am. Urol. Assn. (pres. mid-Atlantic sect. 1986-87), Urol. Assn. Pa., Phila. Urol. Soc. (pres. 1980-81), Assn. Acad. Surgeons, Am. Bd. Urology (trustee 1995—), Pa. Med. Soc., Dauphin County Med. Soc., Soc. Pediat. Urology, Soc. Univ. Urologists (pres. 1990-91), Nat. Urol. Forum, Societe Internationale d'Urologie, Transamerican Urol. Rschrs., Internat. Continence Soc., Coll. Physicians of Phila. Home: 2907 Mt Gretna Rd Elizabethtown PA 17022-9689 Office: Milton S Hershey Med Ctr Pa State Univ PO Box 850 Hershey PA 17033-0850

ROHR, DANIEL C., banker; b. Chgo., Apr. 9, 1946; s. Edward C. and Rose V. (Murphy) R.; children: Rebecca, David, James, Robert. B.A., St. Ambrose Coll., Iowa, 1968; M.B.A., U. Notre Dame, South Bend, 1970. Group v.p. S.E. Continental Ill. Nat. Bank, Chgo., 1980-83, group v.p. East Coast 1983-85, departmental credit officer, 1984-86, chmn. loan com., 1985-87, sr. v.p., 1985-88, dept. head, energy and minerals, 1986-87, chief credit officer, chmn. credit policy com., 1988; exec. v.p., chief credit officer Columbia Savs. and Loan Assn., Beverly Hills, Calif., 1988-90; exec. v.p., mgr. Comml. Banking Group, First Bank System, Mpls., 1990—. Mem. Robert Morris Assocs., Minn. Zool. Bd. Republican. Roman Catholic. Avocations: golf, tennis, skiing. Home: 110 Groveland Ter Minneapolis MN 55403-4111 Office: First Bank System Inc First Bank Pl Ste 2900 601 Second Ave S Minneapolis MN 55402-4302

ROHR, DAVID BAKER, federal agency commissioner; b. Hartford, Conn., Apr. 18, 1933; s. Charles James and Margaret Elizabeth (Getzendanner) R.; m. Loretta Avonne French, Apr. 25, 1959 (dec. Sept. 1991); children: Sharon Elizabeth, Derek Robert. BS, Colo. State U., 1958, MS in Econs., 1963. Master scheduler Stanley Aviation Corp., Denver, 1959-60; internat. economist U.S. Dept. Commerce, Washington, 1961-70; pub. affairs fellow Stanford U., Palo Alto, Calif., 1967-68; dir. trade negotiations and agreements U.S. Dept. Commerce, Washington, 1970-74; profl. staff mem. Com. on Ways and Means U.S. Ho. of Reps., Washington, 1974-80, staff dir. subcom. on trade, 1980-84; commr. U.S. Internat. Trade Commn., Washington, 1984—. Bd. dirs. West Laurel (Md.) Civic Assn., 1970-80. With U.S. Army, 1953-55. Democrat. Episcopalian. Avocations: skiing, fishing, swimming. Office: US Internat Trade Commn 500 E St SW Washington DC 20436-0003

ROHR, DAVIS CHARLES, aerospace consultant, business executive, retired air force officer; b. Burlington, Wis., Oct. 29, 1929; s. Charles Davis Rohr and Dorothy Elizabeth (Hahn) Rohr Larson; m. Gayle Lynn White, Aug. 22, 1959; children—Ellen Louise, Jean Elizabeth. Student, Northwestern U., 1947-48; B.Sc., U.S. Mil. Acad., 1952; M.A., U. Wash., 1960. Commd. 2d lt. USAF, 1952, advanced through grades to maj. gen, 1980; fighter pilot USAF, Ohio, Korea, Japan, 1954-58; asst. prof. history USAF Acad., Colo., 1960-64; fighter pilot, squadron ops. officer Idaho and Fed. Republic Germany, 1965-69; fighter squadron comdr. Vietnam, 1969-70; country dir. S.Am. Office of Sec. of Def., Washington, 1970-73; exec. officer, dep. dir. maintenance Hdqrs. Tactical Air Command, 1973-75; tactical fighter wing comdr. Tex., Utah, 1976-79; chief Office of Mil. Coop., Cairo, 1979-81; dir. plans and policy U.S. European Command, Stuttgart, Fed. Republic Germany, 1981-84; dep. comdr. in chief U.S. Cen. Command, MacDill AFB, Fla., 1984-87, ret.; aerospace cons. air force, 1987—. U.S. Air Force Acad. Decorated Def. D.S.M., 2 Def. Superior Service medals, Legion of Merit with cluster, D.F.C., Meritorious Service medal, Air medal with 14 clusters, Air Force Commendation medal, Purple Heart.

ROHR, DONALD GERARD, history educator; b. Toledo, Oct. 10, 1920; s. Lewis Walter and Marie (Pilliod) R.; m. Joan Willis Michener, Sept. 14, 1948; children: Karen, Kristin. B.A., U. Toronto, Ont., Can., 1943, M.A., 1949; Ph.D., Harvard U., 1958. Instr., then asst. prof. Williams Coll., 1953-59; mem. faculty Brown U., 1959—, prof. history, 1963-86, emeritus, 1986—, chmn. dept., 1960-65, 66-69, 72-74, sec. faculty, 1969-72, assoc. dean faculty and acad. affairs, 1976-81; adminstv. dr. Howard Fedn., 1989-92. Author: The Origins of Social Liberalism in Germany, 1963, (with Robert Ergang) Europe Since Waterloo, 1967. Served with AUS, 1943-46, ETO. Mem. Am. Hist. Assn., Conf. Group Ctrl. European History, Providence Com. Fgn. Rels. (sec. 1968-81, chmn. 1981-92), Thomas Becket Fedn. (v.p. 1983-84, pres. 1984-86), English Speaking Union (pres. Providence br. 1986-88), U. Club, Faculty Club (Providence, pres. 1981-83). Democrat. Roman Catholic. Home: 71 Grotto Ave Providence RI 02906-5609

ROHR, JAMES EDWARD, banker; b. Cleve., Oct. 18, 1948; s. Charles E. and Loretta (Kramer) R.; m. Sharon Lynn Chambers, Dec. 29, 1970; children—Julie, James, Kristen. B.A., Notre Dame U., 1970; M.B.A., Ohio State U., 1972. Comml. banking officer Pitts. Nat. Bank, 1974-76, asst. v.p., 1976-77, v.p., 1977-83, sr. v.p., 1983-85, exec. v.p., 1985-88, pres., 1988-89, chmn., chief exec. officer, 1989-93, pres., CEO, 1993—; vice chmn. PNC Bank Corp., 1989-92, pres., 1992—; bd. dirs. Shadyside Hosp., Pitts., Allegheny Ludlum Corp., Pvt. Export Funding Corp., Student Loan Mktg. Assn. Mem. adv. bd. Salvation Army, Pitts., 1983—, NAt. Flag Found.; bd. dirs. St. Vincent Coll., Latrobe, Pa., 1984—, United Way, Allegheny Trails Coun. Boy Scouts Am., Pitts. Cultural Trust, Carnegie-Mellon U.; chair Civic Light Opera. Mem. Am. Bankers Assn., Bankers Roundtable, Allegheny Conf., Young Pres.' Orgn., Pa. Bus. Roundtable, Duquesne Club, Allegheny Club, Laural Valley Golf Club, Rolling Rock Club. Roman Catholic. Office: PNC Bank Corp 5th and Wood Sts. Pittsburgh PA 15265-0001

ROHRABACHER, DANA, congressman; b. June 21, 1947; s. Donald and Doris Rohrabacher. Student, L.A. Harbor Coll., 1965-67; BA in History, Long Beach State Coll., 1969; MA in Am. Studies, U. So. Calif., 1976. Reporter City News Svc./Radio West, L.A., 4 yrs.; editorial writer Orange County Register, 1979-80; asst. press. sec. Reagan for Pres. Campaign, 1976, 80; speechwriter, spl. asst. to Pres. Reagan White House, Washington, 1981-88; mem. 101st-103rd Congresses from 45th Calif. dist., 1989-92, 103d Congress from 45th dist. Calif., 1993—; U.S. del. Young Polit. Leaders Conf. USSR; disting. lectr. Internat. Terrorism Conf., Paris, 1985; mem. Internat.

Rels. com.; chmn. Sci. subcom. on energy and environ. Recipient Disting. Alumnus award L.A. Harbor Coll., 1987. Avocations: surfing, skiing, white water rafting. Office: US Ho of Reps Rayburn Bldg 2338 Washington DC 20515-0545*

ROHRBACH, N. J., paper company executive. With Fieldcrest Mills, N.Y.C., 1962-70, Lanven Charle of the Ritz, N.Y.C., 1970-75, Lenox Inc., Oshkosh, Wis., 1975-80; pres. CPS/Artfaire, Appleton, Wis., 1980-89, Paper Factory Wis. Inc. subs. Gibson Greetings Inc., Appleton, 1989-94; pres., CEO Cleo Inc., Memphis, 1994—. Office: Cleo Inc 4025 Viscount Ave Memphis TN 38118*

ROHRBACH, ROGER PHILLIP, agricultural engineer, educator; b. Canton, Ohio, Oct. 12, 1942; s. Clarence A. and Beatrice E. (Burens) R.; m. M. Jeanette Weishner, June 12, 1965; children: Sharon E., Gregory A., Sara L. BS in Agrl. Engring., Ohio State U., 1965, PhD, 1968. From asst. prof. to assoc. prof. N.C. State U., Raleigh, 1968-78, prof., 1978—. Author: Design in Agricultural Engineering, 1986, Engineering Principles of Agriculture Machines, 1993. Fellow Am. Soc. Agrl. Engrs. (Young Designer award 1981). Office: NC State U Biol and Agrl Engring Dept PO Box 7625 Raleigh NC 27695-7625

ROHRBACK, ROBERT LEE, JR., lawyer; b. Washington, Nov. 17, 1924; s. Robert Lee and Theresa Martha (Morrow) R.; m. Eileen Lenore Reese, Aug. 28, 1948; children: Steven, Karen, Christine, Eric, Kathleen. BSEE, U. Maryland, 1949; JD, Georgetown U., 1952. Bar: Ill. 1958, U.S. Ct. Appeals (7th cir.) Calif. 1953, U.S. Ct. Appeals (fed. cit.) Calif. 1982, U.S. Supreme Ct. 1960. Patent engr. Western Electric Co., Washington, 1949-50; patent solicitor U.S. Dept. Navy, Washington, 1950-52; patent atty., ptnr. Mason, Kolehmainen, Rathburn & Wyss., Chgo., 1952-87; pvt. practice Mt. Prospect, Ill., 1987—. Patentee in field. Chmn. bd. trustee, Methodist Ch., Des Plaines, Ill. 1959; pres. Men's Club Methodist Ch., Des Plaines, 1963; precinct capt. Republican Party, Mt. Prospect , Ill. 1964-68. Lt. JG U.S. Navy, 1942-46, 1949-52. Mem. ABA (IPL section, numerous chairs), Optimist Club (pres.),. Avocations: woodworking, golf.

ROHRBERG, RODERICK GEORGE, welding consultant; b. Minneola, Iowa, Sept. 26, 1925; s. Charles H. and Emma (Minsen) R.; BS in Naval Sci., Marquette U., 1946; BSCE, Iowa State U., 1949; m. Genevieve Mary Sogard, June 19, 1949; children: Karla (Mrs. George H. Witz, Jr.), Roderick K., Cheries (Mrs. Mark Sauer), Timothy, Christopher. Bridge design engr. Alaska Rd. Commn., U.S. Dept. Interior, 1949-51; sr. tech. specialist North Am. Rockwell, rsch., L.A., 1951-69; pres. Creative Pathways Inc., advanced welding svcs., equipment design and devel., Torrance, Calif., 1969—; pvt. practice, Torrance, Calif., 1972—. Served with USNR, 1944-46. Recipient 1st nat. Airco Welding award, 1966, commendation NASA, 1965, Engring. Profl. Achievement citation Iowa State U., 1973, 3d pl. Von Karman Meml. Grand award, 1974. Registered profl. engr., Calif. Mem. Am. Welding Soc. Lutheran. Patentee in field. Home: 2742 W 234th St Torrance CA 90505-3118 Office: Creative Pathways Inc 3121 Fujita St Torrance CA 90505-4006

ROHRBOUGH, ELSA CLAIRE HARTMAN, artist; b. Shreveport, La., Sept. 26, 1915; d. Adolph Emil and Camille Claire (Francis) Hartman; m. Leonard M. Rohrbough, June 19, 1937 (dec. Jan. 1977); children: Stephen, Frank, Leonard. Juried exhbns. (painting) Massur Mus. Art, Monroe, La., Mobile (Ala.) Art Gallery, Gulf Coast Juried Exhibit, Mobile, Juried Arts Nat., Tyler, Tex., Greater New Orleans Nat., La. Watercolor Soc. Nat., Ky. Watermedia Nat., So. Watercolor Ann., La. Women Artist, many others. One-woman shows include Le Petit Theatre du Vieux Carre, New Orleans World Trade Ctr.'s Internat. House, Singing River Art Assn., Pascagoula, Miss., La. Font Inn, Pascagoula, Mandeville (La.) City Hall, St. Tammany Art Assn., Covington, La., others; exhibited in groups shows at 1st Guaranty Bank, Hammond, La., St. Tammany Art Assn., Ft. Isabel Gallery, Covington. Mem. Nat. League Am. Pen Women (v.p. S.E. La. br. 1986-87, pres. 1987-92, 94—), St. Tammany Art Assn. (bd. dirs. 1985-86, 87, instr. 1977-78, classes chmn. 1986-88). Republican. Roman Catholic. Avocations: sewing, flower arranging, gardening, ethnic cooking. Home: 2525 Lakeshore Dr Mandeville LA 70448-5627

ROHRER, GEORGE JOHN, lawyer; b. Elmira, N.Y., Oct. 24, 1931; s. George J. and Lois (Hess) R.; m. Martha M. Jacobs, Jan. 6, 1952; children: Jacquelyn M. Berbusse, Michael A., John S. JD with distinction, Pacific Coast U., 1967. Bar: Calif. 1969, U.S. Dist. Ct. (ctrl. dist.) 1969. Incentive dir. Blue Chip Stamp Co., L.A., 1963-69; gen. ptnr. Songer, Leavell Rohrer, Bellflower, Calif., 1969-80; sr. ptnr. Rohrer & Holtz, Anaheim, Calif., 1980—; panel atty. Calif. Assn. of Realtors/State, Hotline, Calif. 1977—; Founder/Dir. Midcities Nat. Bank, Bellflower, 1981-90; trustee S.E. area Bar Assn., Norwalk, Calif., 1974-75. Pres. Bellflower Kiwanis Club, 1972-73; dir. Los Cerritos Y.M.C.A., Bellflower, 1977-78; vol. counsel Am. Radio Relay League, 1987-92. Mem. Orange County Bar Assn., Los Angeles County Bar Assn., Orange County Amicus (pro bono), Bellflower C. of C. (pres. 1975-76), Masons, Shriners. Republican. Avocations: amature radio, fishing, travel. Office: Rohrer & Holtz #401 421 N Brookhurst Street Anaheim CA 92801

ROHRER, HEINRICH, physicist; b. Buchs, Switzerland, June 6, 1933. Diploma in Physics, Swiss Inst. Tech., Zurich, 1955, PhD in Physics, 1960; D. Sci. (hon.), Rutgers U., 1987, Marseille U., 1988, Madrid U., 1988, Tsukuba U., 1994. Rsch. asst. Swiss Inst. Tech., Zurich, 1960-61; post-doc. Rutgers U., New Brunswick, N.J., 1961-63; with IBM Rsch. Lab., Zurich, 1963—; vis. scholar U. Calif., Santa Barbara, 1974-75; bd. dirs. Swiss Fed. Insts. Tech., 1993. Co-recipient King Faisal Internat. prize for sci., 1984, Hewlett Packard Europhysics prize, 1984, Nobel prize for Physics, 1986, Cresson medal Franklin Inst., Phila., 1987; Magnun Seal, U. Bologna, Italy, 1988; IBM fellow, 1986; named to Nat. Inventors Hall of Fame, 1994. Fellow Royal Microscopical Soc. (hon. 1988); mem. NAS (fgn. assoc.), Swiss Acad. Tech. Scis., Swiss Phys. Soc. (hon. 1990), Swiss Assn. Engring. and Architecture (hon. 1991), Zurich Phys. Soc. (hon. 1992). Office: IBM Rsch Divsn Zurich Rsch Lab, Saeumerstrasse 4, CH-8803 Rueschlikon Switzerland

ROHRER, RONALD ALAN, electrical and computer engineering educator, consultant; b. Oakland, Calif., Aug. 19, 1939; m. Catherine (Casey) Jones. BSEE, MIT, 1960; MSEE, U. Calif., Berkeley, 1961, PhDEE, 1963. Asst. prof. elec. engring. U. Ill., Urbana, 1963-65; asst. prof. applied analysis SUNY, Stony Brook, 1965-66; asst. prof. elec. engring. U. Calif., Berkeley, 1966-68, assoc. prof., 1968-72; prof. elec. engring. Carnegie Mellon U., Pitts., 1974-75; vis. lectr. U. Colo., Boulder, 1976-77; prof., chmn. dept. elec. engring. U. Maine, Orono, 1977-79, So. Meth. U., Dallas, 1979-80; prof., chmn. dept. elec. engring and computer sci. U. Colo., Colorado Springs, 1980-81; prof. elec. and computer engring. Carnegie Mellon U., Pitts., 1985-89, Wilkoff Univ. prof. 1989—; mem. tech. staff, sect. mgr. Fairchild R&D, Palo Alto, Calif., 1968-70; mgr. elec. engring. analysis programs SofTech Inc., Waltham, Mass., 1971-72; staff scientist GE, 1981, program mgr. Integrated Circuit Design Automation, 1982, dir. elec. products mktg., Calma Divsn., 1982-83; gen. mgr. MEDS divsn. Scientific Calculations, Inc., 1983-85; cons. Synopsys, Mountain View, Calif., 1987-89, Genesis Microchip, Markham, Ont., Can., 1995—; bd. dirs. Genesis Microchip, Inc., Greenbriar Acad., Durham, N.C. ISS, Inc., Research Triangle Park, N.C., (chmn.) Performance Signal Integrity, Inc., Pitts. Author: Circuit Theory: An Introduction to State Variable Approach, 1970; co-author: Theory of Linear Active Networks, 1967, Introduction to System Theory, 1972, Electronic Circuit and System Simulation Methods, 1995. Recipient Rsch. Paper award Nat. Elec. Conf., 1964, Best Paper award IEEE CAD Transactions, 1991, Best Paper award ACM/IEEE Design Automation Conf.; recipient Inventor Recognition award Semicondr. Rsch. Corp., 1990, Tech. Excellence award, 1991. Fellow IEEE (brosder J. Thompson award 1967)l mem. Cirs. and Systems Soc. of IEEE (pres. 1987, Guillemin-Cauer award 1970, founding editor Transactions on Computer Aided Design 1980-84, CAS Soc. award, 1990, IEEE Edn. medal 1993), NAE, Am. Soc. Engring. Edn. (Frederick Emmons Terman award elec. engring. div. 1978). Office: Carnegie-Mellon U Dept Elec & Computer Engr 5000 Forbes Ave Pittsburgh PA 15213-3890

ROHRER, SAMUEL EDWARD, state legislator; b. Dover, Ohio, Aug. 11, 1955; s. David A. and Edith A. (Paulus) R.; m. Ruth Ann Hastie, Aug. 13, 1977; children: Nathan, David, Jason, Julia. BS in Mgmt., Bob Jones U., Greenville, S.C., 1977. Gen. mgr. KCCV Radio, Independence, Mo., 1977-79; prodn. scheduler Graco Children's Products Inc., Elverson, Pa., 1979-81, dir. mkgt., 1981-92; mem. Pa. Gen. Assembly, Harrisburg, 1992—. Patentee in field. Mem. Am. Legis. Exch. Coun., Washington, 1992—. Mem. Berks C. of C. Republican. Office: PO Box 100 Reading PA 19607-0100

ROHSENOW, WARREN MAX, retired mechanical engineer, educator; b. Chgo., Feb. 12, 1921; s. Fred and Selma (Gorss) R.; m. Katharine Towneley Smith, Sept. 20, 1946; children—John, Brian, Damaris, Sandra, Anne. B.S., Northwestern U., 1941; M.Eng., Yale, 1943, D.Eng., 1944. Teaching asst., instr. mech. engring. Yale, 1941-44; mem. faculty Mass. Inst. Tech., 1946-85, prof. mech. engring., 1955-85, dir. heat transfer lab., 1954-85, prof. emeritus, 1985; bd. dirs. Dynatech Corp., Thermal Process System. Author: (with Choi) Heat Mass and Momentum Transfer, 1961; Editor: Developments in Heat Transfer, 1964, (with Hartnett) Handbook of Heat Transfer, 1973, 2d edit., 1985. Served as lt. (j.g.) USNR, 1944-46; mech. engr. gas turbine div. Engring. Expt. Sta. Annapolis, Md. Recipient Pi Tau Sigma gold medal Am. Soc. M.E., 1951; award for advancement sci. Yale Engring. Assn., 1952; merit award Northwestern Alumni, 1955. Fellow Am. Acad. Arts and Scis., Nat. Acad. Engring., Am. Soc. M.E. (hon. mem., Heat Transfer Meml. award 1967, Max Jakob Meml. award 1970); mem. Sigma Xi, Tau Beta Pi, Pi Tau Sigma. Home: 32 Carroll St Falmouth ME 04105-1908 Office: MIT Cambridge MA 02139

ROHWER, WILLIAM D., JR., university dean; b. Denver, Oct. 2, 1937. AB, Harvard U., 1959; PhD, U. Calif., Berkeley, 1964. Asst. prof. education U. Calif., Berkeley, 1964-68, assoc. prof., 1968-70, prof., 1970—, acting assoc. dean grad. div., 1969-70, assoc. dean, 1970, acting dir. Inst. Human Learning, 1971, chmn. div. ednl. psychology, vice-chmn. dept. edn., 1982, assoc. dean edn., 1983-86, acting dean, 1989-90, dean, 1990—; vis. lectr. psychology U. Wis., Madison, 1967; rsch. psychologist U.S. Naval Pers. Rsch. Activity, San Diego, 1964. Contbr. articles to profl. jours.; ad hoc reviewer Child Develop., Devel. Psychology, Jour. Ednl. Psychology, Jour. Exptl. Child Psychology, Psychol. Rev., Sci. Recipient Palmer O. Johnson Meml. award Am. Ednl. Rsch. Assn., 1972; fellow Van Leer Jerusalem Found., 1974-75, Ctr. Advanced Study Behavioral Scis. Stanford U., 1979-80; scientific adviser Bernard Van Leer Found., 1974-75; grantee U.S. Office Edn., OEO, NSF, Nat. Inst. Child Health and Human Devel. Office: U Calif Office Dean Edn 1501 Tolman Berkeley CA 94720

ROIN, HOWARD JAMES, lawyer; b. Chgo., Aug. 28, 1953; s. Dan Ronald and Maureen Elizabeth (Mintz) R.; m. Judith Carol Seidel, Dec. 18, 1976; children: Benjamin N., Catherine C. Katharine A. BA, Amherst Coll., 1975; JD, U. Chgo., 1978. Bar: Ill. 1978, U.S. Ct. Appeals (D.C. cir.) 1979, U.S. Ct. Appeals (7th cir.) 1982, U.S. Dist. Ct. (no. dist.) Ill. 1981. Law clk. to Judge George MacKinnon U.S. Ct. Appeals (D.C. cir.), Washington, 1978-79; spl. asst. to Judge William Webster, dir. FBI, Washington, 1979-81; assoc. Mayer, Brown & Platt, Chgo., 1981-84, ptnr., 1985-93. Trustee Village of Glencoe, Ill., 1985-93. Mem. Chgo. Council Lawyers. Democrat. Office: Mayer Brown & Platt 190 S La Salle St Chicago IL 60603-3410

ROITER, ERIC D., lawyer; b. Newton, Mass., Nov. 18, 1948; s. Irving J. and Hilda (Cohen) R.; m. Teddy Joan Roiter, July 8, 1973; children: Rebekah, Jonathan, David. BA, U. Rhode Island, 1970; JD, Georgetown U., 1973, MA, 1981. Bar: D.C. 1973, N.Y. 1984. Assoc. Williams & Jensen, Washington, 1973-76; atty., spl. counsel, asst. gen. counsel SEC, Washington, 1976-81; assoc. Debevoise & Plimpton, Washington, 1981-84, ptnr., 1985—. Contbr. articles to profl. jours. Mem. ABA (chmn. sect. adminstrv. law, com. securities, commodities and exchs. 1988-89). Democrat. Jewish. Avocations: running, tennis. Office: Debevoise & Plimpton 555 13th St NW Ste 1100E Washington DC 20004-1163

ROITMAN, JUDITH, mathematician; b. N.Y.C., Nov. 12, 1945; d. Leo and Ethel (Gottesman) R.; m. Stanley Lombardo, Sept. 26, 1978; 1 child, Ben Lombardo. BA in English, Sarah Lawrence Coll., 1966; MA in Math., U. Calif., Berkeley, 1971, PhD in Math., 1974. Asst. prof. math. Wellesley (Mass.) Coll., 1974-77; from asst. prof. to prof. math. U. Kans., Lawrence, 1977—. Author: Introduction to Modern Set Theory, 1990; contbr. articles to profl. jours. Grantee NSF, 1975-87, 92-95. Mem. Assn. Symbolic Logic, Am. Math. Soc., Assn. Women in Math. (pres. 1979-81), Kans. Assn. Tchrs. of Math., Nat. Assn. Tchrs. Math. Avocation: poetry.

ROIZMAN, BERNARD, virologist, educator; b. Chisinau, Rumania, Apr. 17, 1929; came to U.S., 1947, naturalized, 1954; s. Abram and Liudmilla (Seinberg) R.; m. Betty Cohen, Aug. 26, 1950; children: Arthur, Niels. B.A., Temple U., 1952, M.S., 1954; Sc.D. in Microbiology, Johns Hopkins, 1956; D.H.L. (hon.), Gov.'s State U., 1984; MD (hon.), U. Ferrara (Italy), 1991. From instr. microbiology to asst. prof. Johns Hopkins Med. Sch., 1956-65; mem. faculty div. biol. scis. U. Chgo., 1965—, prof. microbiology 1969-84, prof. biophysics, 1970—, chmn. com. virology, 1969-85, 88—, Joseph Regenstein prof., 1981-83, Joseph Regenstein Disting. Svc. prof., 1984—, chmn. dept. molecular genetics and cell biology, 1985-88; convener herpes virus workshop, Cold Spring Harbor, N.Y., 1972; lectr. Am. Found. for Microbiology, 1974-75; mem. spl. virus cancer program, devel. rsch. working group Nat. Cancer Inst., 1967-71, cons. inst., 1967-73; mem. steering com. human cell biology program NSF, 1971-74, cons. found., 1972-74; mem. adv. com. cell biology and virology Am. Cancer Soc., 1970-74; chmn. herpes virus study group Internat. Commn. Taxonomy of Viruses, 1971-93; mem. Internat. Microbiol. Genetics Commn. Internat. Assn. Microbiol. Scis., 1974-81; mem. sci. adv. coun. N.Y. Cancer Inst., 1971-88; med. adv. bd. Leukemia Rsch. Found., 1972-77; mem. herpes-virus working team WHO/FOA, 1978-81; mem. bd. sci. cons. Sloan Kettering Inst., N.Y.C., 1975-81; mem. study sect. exptl. virology NIH, 1976-80; mem. task force on virology Nat. Inst. Allergy and Infectious Disease, 1976-77; mem. external adv. com. Emory U. Cancer Ctr., 1973-81, Northwestern U. Cancer Ctr., 1979-89; cons. Inst. Merieux, Lyon, France, 1979-91; mem. com. to establish vaccine priorities Nat. Inst. Medicine, 1983-85; chmn. sci. adv. bd. Viral-Showa Univs. Ctr., Tampa Bay Inst. Biomed. Scis, 1983—, chmn. bd. dirs., 1991—. Author sci. papers, chpts. in books; editor: Herpes Viruses, Vol. 1, 1982, Vol. 2, 1983, Vols. 3 and 4, 1985, The Human Herpesviruses, 1993, Infectious Diseases in an Age of change, 1995; adv. editor Progress in Surface Membrane Science, 1972; editor-in-chief Jour. Infectious Agts. and Disease, 1992—; mem. editl. bd. Jour. Hygiene, 1985-61, Infectious Diseases, 1965-69, Jour. Virology, 1970—, Jour. Intervirology, 1972-85, Archives of Virology, 1975-81, Virology, 1976-78, 83—, Microbiologica, 1978—, Cell, 1979-80, Gene Therapy, 1994. Trustee Goodwin Inst. for Cancer Research, 1977—. Recipient Lederle Med. Faculty award, 1960-61, Career Devel. award USPHS, 1963-65, Pasteur award Ill. Soc. Microbiology, 1972, Esther Langer award for achievement in cancer research, 1974, Outstanding Alumnus in Pub. Health award Johns Hopkins U., 1984; named hon. prof. Shandong Acad. Med. Scis., People's Republic of China, 1985; Am. Cancer Soc. scholar cancer research at Pasteur Inst. Paris, 1961-62; ICN Internat. prize in virology, 1988; faculty research assoc., 1966-71; traveling fellow Internat. Agy. Research Against Cancer, Karolinska Inst., Stockholm, Sweden, 1970; grantee USPHS/NIH, 1958—, Am. Cancer Soc., 1962-90, NSF, 1962-79, Whitehall Found., 1966-74. Fellow Japanese Soc. for Promotion of Sci., Pan Am. Cancer Soc. (hon.); mem. Nat. Acad. Scis., Am. Acad. Arts and Scis., Am. Acad. Microbiology, Am. Assn. Immunologists, Am. Soc. Microbiology, Am. Soc. Virology, Am. Soc. Biol. Chemists, Brit. Soc. Gen. Microbiology, Johns Hopkins U. Soc. Scholars, Quadrangle Club (Chgo.). Club: Quadrangle (Chgo.). Home: 5555 S Everett Ave Chicago IL 60637-1968 Office: U Chgo Marjorie B Kouler Viral Oncology Labs 910 E 58th St Chicago IL 60637

ROIZMAN, OWEN, cinematographer; b. Brooklyn, N.Y., Sept. 22, 1936; s. Sol R.; m. Mona Lindholm, Dec. 6, 1964; 1 child, Eric. BA, Gettysburg Coll., 1958. Cinematographer: (films) The French Connection, 1971 (Academy award nomination best cinematography 1971), The Gang That Couldn't Shoot Straight, 1971, The Heartbreak Kid, 1972, Play It Again, Sam, 1972, (with Billy Williams) The Exorcist, 1973 (Academy award nomination best cinematography 1973), The Taking of Pelham One, Two, Three, 1974, The Stepford Wives, 1975, Three Days of the Condor, 1975, Independence, 1976, Network, 1976 (Academy award nomination best

cinematography 1976), The Return of a Man Called Horse, 1976, Sergeant Pepper's Lonely Hearts Club Band, 1978, Straight Time, 1978, The Electric Horseman, 1979, The Black Marble, 1980, Absence of Malice, 1981, True Confessions, 1981, Taps, 1981, Tootsie, 1982 (Academy award nomination best cinematography 1982), Vision Quest, 1985, I Love You to Death, 1990, Havana, 1990, Grand Canyon, 1991, The Addams Family, 1991, Wyatt Earp, 1994 (Academy award nomination best cinematography 1994), French Kiss, 1995, (TV spls.) Singer Presents Liza with a "Z", 1972 (Emmy award nomination best cinematography 1972). Office: Smith/Gosnell/Nicholson & Assoc PO Box 1166 1515 Palisades Dr Pacific Palisades CA 90272*

ROJ, WILLIAM HENRY, lawyer; b. Phila., Mar. 29, 1949; s. Joseph S. and Mary B. (Schmidt) R.; m. Mary Lynn Durham, Dec. 20, 1969; children: Wesley Durham, Douglas Durham. BA, Western Md. Coll., 1970; MA in Econs., Duke U., 1971; JD, U. Va., 1975. Bar: Ohio 1975. Assoc. Jones, Day, Reavis & Pogue, Cleve., 1975-82, ptnr., 1983—; sec., bd. dirs. Austin Powder Corp., Cleve., 1984—, DM&M Corp., Coeburn, Va., 1985—; bd. dirs. Erico Investment Corp., Schuylkill Holdings, Inc., Sinter Metals, Inc. Trustee Austin Powder Found., Cleve., 1984—, Am. Contemporary Music Devel. Corp.; sec. Rock and Roll Hall of Fame and Mus., Inc. 1st lt. U.S. Army, 1970-71. Nat. Def. Fellow Duke U., 1970. Office: Jones Day Reavis & Pogue North Point 901 Lakeside Ave Cleveland OH 44114

ROJAS, CARLOS, Spanish literature educator; b. Barcelona, Spain, Aug. 12, 1928; s. Carlos and Luisa (Vila) R.; m. Eunice Anne Mitcham, Mar. 19, 1966; children: Carlos, Eunice Anne. MA, U. Barcelona, 1951; PhD, U. Cen., Madrid, 1955; PhD (hon.), U. Simón Bólivar, Barranquilla, Colombia, 1985. Teaching asst. U. Barcelona, 1951-52; fgn. asst. U. Glasgow, Scotland, 1952-54; asst. prof. Rollins Coll., Winter Park, Fla., 1957-60; asst. prof. Emory U., Atlanta, 1960-63, assoc. prof., 1963-68, prof., 1968-80, Charles Howard Candler prof. Spanish lit., 1980—. Author: Auto de fe, 1968 (Premio Nacional de Literatura 1968), Azaña, 1973 (Planeta award 1973), El Igenioso Hidalgo y Poeta F.G. asciende a los infiernos, 1980 (Nadal award 1980), El Sueño de Sarajevo, 1982, El Jardín de las Hespérides, 1988, El Jardín De Atocha, 1990, Yo, Goya, 1990, Proceso A Godoy, 1992, Salvador Dalí, or the Art of Spitting on Your Mother's Portrait, 1993. Recipient Premio Espejo de España award, Madrid, 1984, Encomienda al Mérito Civil, King of Spain, 1986, Univ. Scholar/Tchr. award Emory U., 1987; honoree of yr. Philol. Assn. of Carolinas, 1987. Mem. MLA, Am. Assn. Tchrs. Spanish and Portuguese, Assn. Doctores y Licenciados Españoles en los Estados Unidos (bd. dirs.), South Atlantic MLA. Avocation: painting. Home: 1378 Harvard Rd NE Atlanta GA 30306-2413 Office: Emory U Dept Spanish Atlanta GA 30322

ROJAS, VICTOR HUGO, retired vocational education educator; b. Mollendo, Peru, Jan. 11, 1923; came to U.S., 1944; s. Mariano A. and Maria Santos (Macedo) R.; m. Mary Emily Bush, Apr. 28, 1945 (dec. 1984); m. Ellen Manuel Proimos, Dec. 26, 1990. AA, Miami-Dade C.C., 1982; BS in Vocat. Edn., Fla. Internat. U., 1986. Cert. tchr., Fla. Automotive mechanic various Ford dealerships, Miami, Fla., 1945-60; automotive technician East Tenn. Motors, Knoxville, 1960-63; automotive technician Tally-Embry Ford, Inc., Miami, 1964-66, shop foreman, then mgr., 1966-75, master technician, automotive instr., 1973-75; instr. automotive tech. Dade County Pub. Schs., Miami, 1975-91; ret., 1991; adviser, sponsor Vocat.-Indsl. Clubs Am., Miami, 1988-91. With Armada Peruana, 1940-44, USN, 1945. Recipient Cert. of Achievement Motor Age mag., 1961, 62, St. Mary's Cathedral, Miami, 1988, Automotive Svc. Excellence award Nat. Inst. Automotive Svc., 1975. Mem. Am. Legion (historian 1989), Elks. Democrat. Roman Catholic. Avocations: music, art, camping, ballroom dancing, stock car racing. Home: 2365 Ainsworth Ave Spring Hill FL 34609-4402

ROJAS, WALDEMAR, school superintendent. Supt. schs. San Francisco Sch. Dist. Office: San Francisco Bd Edn 135 Van Ness Ave Ste 120 San Francisco CA 94102-5207

ROJHANTALAB, HOSSEIN MOHAMMAD, chemical engineer, researcher; b. Tehran, Iran, Sept. 26, 1944; came to U.S., 1984; s. Mohammad Rojhantalab and Sakineh (Fakhri) Nasser-Ghandi; 1 child, Ayda. MS, Calif. State U., Hayward, 1972; PhD, Oreg. State U., 1976. Asst. prof. Ahwaz (Iran) U., 1976-77, Shiraz (Iran) U., 1977-82; cons., chemist Water-Con Co., Tehran, 1982-84; rsch. assoc. U. Oreg., Eugene, 1985-88; lithography engr. Intel Corp., Hillsboro, Oreg., 1988-91; thin film CVO Tungsten polish engr. Intel Corp., Aloha, Oreg., 1991—; transl. Popular Sci. Pub. Co., Tehran, 1980-83, UNESCO workshop, 1984; editor, CEO, DNA Pub. Co., Tehran, 1982-84; vis. prof. chemistry Ore. State U., 1985. Editor, translator 4 books on genetic code, controlled nuclear fusion to Farsi, 1981-84; contbr. articles to sci. jours. Scholar Calif. State U., 1971-72; grantee Oreg. State U., 1975-76, CENTO, 1978-79. Mem. Electrochem. Soc. Am. Achievements include patent on single pass graded NSG/BPSG glass for deep trench fill; development of thin BPSG film for defect detection in 0.2 - 10 microns. Home: PO Box 6652 Aloha OR 97007-0652

ROKKE, ERVIN JEROME, air force officer, university president; b. Warren, Minn., Dec. 12, 1939; s. Edwin K. and Joan (Ivery) R.; m. Pamela Mae Patterson, June 6, 1962; children: Lisa Mae, Eric Scott. Student, St. Olaf Coll., 1957-58; BS, USAF Acad., 1962; MPA, Harvard U., 1964, PhD in Polit. Sci., 1970. Commd. 2d lt. USAF, 1962, advanced through grades to lt. gen., 1994; intelligence officer Pacific Air Forces, Hawaii, Japan, 1965-68; assoc. prof. dept. polit. sci. USAF Acad., Colorado Springs, Colo., 1968-73, permanent prof., 1976-80, dean of faculty, 1982-86; plans officer NATO Hdqrs., Brussels, 1973-76; air attache Am. Embassy, London, 1980-82; def. attache Am. Embassy, Moscow, 1987-89; sr. staff Nat. Security Agy., Ft. Meade, Md., 1989-91; dir. intelligence Hdqrs. European Command, Stuttgart, Fed. Republic Germany, 1991-93; assigned to Hdqs. USAF, Washington, 1993-94; pres. Nat. Def. U., Ft. Lesley J. McNair, DC, 1994—; cons. Dept. State, 1969. Editor: American Defense Policy, 1973. Decorated Def. Disting. Svc. medal, Disting. Svc. medal, Def. Superior Svc. medal, Legion of Merit. Mem. Coun. on Fgn. Rels., Am. Polit. Sci. Assn. (assoc.). Lutheran. Avocations: reading, skiing, squash. Home: Qtrs 12 Ft Lesley J McNair Washington DC 20024 Office: Nat Def U Ft Lesley J McNair Washington DC 20319-6000

ROLAND, ANNE, registrar Supreme Court of Canada; b. Neuilly-sur-Seine, France, Feb. 27, 1947; d. Pierre Philippe Roland and Geneviève Lehman; m. Alphonse Morisette, Dec. 3, 1975; 1 child, Julien. BA Philosophy, Caen, France, 1965; diploma, Inst. Supérieur d'interprétation et de traduction, 1969; lic. in law, Paris, 1969; LLB, U. Ottawa, 1979. Bar: Quebec 1980. Legal trans., revisor Paris, 1971-75; chief trans. svcs. customs and excise Sec. of State, Can., 1975-76; spl. asst. to chief justice Can., 1976-81; chief law editor Supreme Ct. Can., 1981-88, dep. registrar, 1988-90, registrar, 1990. Mem. Can. Bar Assn., Assn. Can. Ct. Adminstrs., Assn. Francophone Jurists, Can. Inst. Adminstrn. Justice, Assn. Reporters Jud. Decisions. Office: Supreme Ct of Can Office Reg, Wellington St., Ottawa, ON Canada K1A 0J1

ROLAND, CHARLES GORDON, physician, medical historian, educator; b. Winnipeg, Man., Can., Jan. 25, 1933; s. John Sanford and Leona (McLaughlin) R.; m. Marjorie Ethel Kyles, 1953 (div. 1973); children: John Kenneth, Christopher Franklin, David Charles, Kathleen Siobhan; m. Connie Rankin, 1979. Student, U. Toronto, Ont., Can., 1952-54; MD, U. Man., 1958, BSc, 1958. Intern St. Boniface Hosp., Man., 1958-59; pvt. practice medicine specializing in family medicine Tillsonburg, Ont., 1959-60, Grimsby, Ont., 1960-64; sr. editor Jour. Am. Med. Assn., Chgo., 1964-69; head sect. publs. Mayo Clinic, 1969-70, chmn. dept. biomed. communications, 1970-77; prof. history medicine, prof. biomed. communications, coordinator family practice track, chmn. adminstrv. com. dept. family medicine Mayo Med. Sch., 1971-77; mem. admissions, edn. and curriculum coordinators coms., hon. mem. med. staff West Lincoln Meml. Hosp., Grimsby; mem. grants com. Hannah Inst. History of Medicine, Toronto, 1974-77, 87-91, mem. publs. com., 1991—; Jason A. Hannah prof. history of medicine McMaster U., Hamilton, Ont., Can., 1977—; assoc. mem. history. McMaster U.; chmn. archives com. Faculty of Health Scis. McMaster U., Hamilton, Ont., Can., 1983—; chmn. spl. grants com. Hannah Inst. for History of Medicine, 1981-85; Sid W. Richardson vis. prof. Inst. Med. Humanities U. Tex. Med. Br., Galveston, 1984. Author: (with L.S. King) Scientific Writing, 1968, (with J.P. McGovern) William Osler, The Con-

tinuing Education, 1969, Good Scientific Writing, 1971, William Osler's The Master Word in Medicine: A Study in Rhetoric, 1972, (with L.S. Baker) You and Leukemia: A Day at a Time, 1976, (with P. Potter) An Annotated Bibliography of Canadian Medical Periodicals, 1826-1975, 1979, Clarence Meredith Hincks 1885-1964: Mental Health Crusader, 1990, Courage Under Seige:: Starvation, Disease and Death in the Warsaw Ghetto, 1992, Harold Nathan Segall: Pioneer Canadian Cardiologist, 1994; editor: (E.P. Scarlett) In Sickness and In Health, 1972; co-editor: An Annotated Checklist of Osleriana, 1976, Sir William Osler 1849-1919: A Selection for Medical Students, 1982, Health Disease and Medicine: Essays in Canadian History, 1984, Bibliography of Secondary Sources in Canadian Medical History, 1985, (with J.P. McGovern) The Collected Essays of Sir William Osler (3 vols.), 1985; editor, author introduction: Medical Topography of Upper Canada, 1985; (with Richard Golden) Sir William Osler: An Annotated Bibiography with Illustrations, 1987; co-editor: The Persisting Osler, 1984, The Persisting Osler II, 1994; editor in chief Can. Bulletin of Med. History, 1987-90; mem. editorial adv. bd. Canadian Family Physician, 1964-72, Chest, 1966—, Med. Communications, 1971-75, Postgrad. Med. Jour., London, 1967-72, Mayo Clinic Procs., 1969-77, Bioscis. Communications, 1975-80, Ont. Med. Rev., 1979-84, HSTC Jour., 1980-87, Can. Bull. Med. History, 1983-90, Med. History (London), 1982-87, Jour. History of Medicine and Allied Scis., 1991-94. Mem. bd. curators Osler Library, McGill U., Montreal, 1981—. Recipient Jason A. Hannah medal Royal Soc. Can., 1994. Fellow AAAS (council 1969-74), Am. Med. Writers Assn. (pres. 1969-70); mem. Can. Med. Assn., Am. Assn. History Medicine (sec.-treas. 1976-80, publs. com. 1979-85), Acad. Medicine Toronto (Grogan lecture com. 1978-83), Am. Mil. Inst., Internat. Inst. Prisoners of War, Soc. Internat. d'Histoire de la Medicine (internat. del. for Can. 1983-86), Can. Soc. for History of Medicine (v.p. 1982-87, pres. 1993-95), Soc. Med. History Chgo. (sec.-treas. 1966-69), Can. Ctr. for Studies in Hist. Horticulture (exec. com. 1982-89), Council Biology Editors, Med. Hist. Club Toronto (pres. 1977-78), Ont. Hist. Soc., Can. Med. Hist. Assn., Bibliog. Soc. Can., Am. Osler Soc. (sec.-treas. 1975-85, v.p. 1985-86, pres. 1986-87), Japan Osler Soc. (hon.), Royal Soc. Medicine (London), Royal Can. Mil. Inst., Champlain Soc. (Toronto), History of Second World War (Can. com.), Soc. Army Hist. Research,a Xi. Clubs: Univ. (Rochester); Osler (London); Alpine of Can.; Literary (Chgo.). Office: McMaster U, 3N10-HSC Med Ctr 1200 Main St W, Hamilton, ON Canada L8N 3Z5

ROLAND, CRAIG WILLIAMSON, architect; b. Lincoln, Nebr., Feb. 20, 1935; s. Harold Eugene and Nell (Williamson) R.; m. Edith Shearman Shaw, July 30, 1960; 1 child, Leah. B.Arch., U. Wash. Pres. Roland/Miller/Assocs., Santa Rosa, Calif., 1966-93; vis. instr. U. Calif.-Berkeley, 1983-84. Mem., chmn. design rev. bd. City of Santa Rosa, 1973-76, mem. planning commn., 1976-78; pres. bd. Sonoma County YMCA, Santa Rosa, 1979—. Served with U.S. Army, 1957-58. Recipient numerous local, state and nat. archtl. design awards. Home: 5441 Buttercup Dr Santa Rosa CA 95404-9628 Office: Craig W Roland Arch 5441 Buttercup Dr Santa Rosa CA 95404-9628

ROLAND, DONALD EDWARD, printing company executive; b. Dalhart, Tex., Nov. 14, 1942; s. Vernon O. Roland and Doris M. (Cox) Roland Hutson; m. Kathleen Marie Bennett, Feb. 1, 1964; children—Aileen, Donald E., Jenny. B.S., Calif. State U.-Los Angeles, 1964; M.A., U. Calif.-Riverside, 1967; exec. mgmt. cert. UCLA, 1979, Claremont Grad. Sch., 1974. Dir. computer graphics Times Mirror Press, Los Angeles, 1966-78, plant mgr., 1978-81, v.p. prodn., 1981-83; group v.p. ops. Treasure Chest Advt., Glendora, Calif., 1983-84, sr. v.p. ops., 1984-93, exec. v.p. 1993—. Republican. Baptist. Home: 315 W Roughrider Rd La Verne CA 91750-2335 Office: Treasure Chest Advt PO Box 5016 Glendora CA 91740-0805

ROLAND, FRANK H., metal products executive, chemicals executive; b. 1935. BS, U. Ala., 1957. CPA. With AMCA Internat. Corp., Hanover, N.H., 1967-86, H.H. Robertson Co., Pitts., 1986-88; with Halstead Industries Inc., Greensboro, N.C., 1988—, pres. Office: Halstead Industries Inc 300 N Greene St Ste 400 Greensboro NC 27401*

ROLAND, WILLIAM ALFRED, accountant, nursing home administrator; b. Brockton, Mass., Feb. 25, 1924; s. William A. and Alice (Giles) Roland; m. Patricia Carroll, July 22, 1950 (dec. June 1984); children—Alyce A., Michael J., William F., Susan M. Patricia L., John C. B.S., Northeastern U., 1952. Owner, mgr. Acctg. Service, Brockton, Mass., 1953—; pres., owner Braemoor Nursing Home Inc., Brockton, 1966—; fir. Fin. Data Systems, Raynham, Mass., 1981—; pres. Aescure Med. Supply, West Bridgewater, Mass., 1982—; lectr. health Stonehill Coll., North Easton, Mass., 1982-83. Served with USAF, 1943-45. Republican. Roman Catholic. Mem. Brockton Art Assn. Club: Wychmere Harbor (Harwichport, Mass.).

ROLANDI, GIANNA, coloratura soprano; b. N.Y.C., Aug. 16, 1952; d. Enrico G. and Jane E. (Frazier); m. Andrew Davis, 1 child, Edward. Mus.B., artist diploma, opera cert., Curtis Inst. Music, 1975. Made operatic debut at, N.Y.C. Opera, 1975; numerous appearances N.Y.C. Opera, made Met. Opera debut, 1979, numerous appearances Met. Opera, 1979—; star roles in: Tales of Hoffman, Ariadne auf Naxos, Rigoletto, The Barber of Seville, Daughter of the Regiment, Giulio Cesare, The Cunning Little Vixen, Marriage of Figaro, Lucia di Lammermoon, others; appeared with major opera cos. and symphonies throughout U.S., England, France, Italy, Switzerland; (rec.) Marriage of Figaro-Mozart; (video) Anabella; numerous appearances on Live from Lincoln Ctr., PBS, including Lucididi Lammermoon, Cunning Little Vixen. Winner Met. Opera Audition; Rockefeller grantee; Nat. Opera Inst. grantee.

ROLETT, ELLIS LAWRENCE, medical educator, cardiologist; b. N.Y.C., July 10, 1930; s. Daniel Meyer and Mary Elaine (Warshaw) R.; m. Virginia Ann Vladimir, Mar. 25, 1956; children: Roderic Lawrence, Barry Vladimir, Daniel Alfred. B.S., Yale U., 1952; M.D. cum laude, Harvard U., 1955. Diplomate: Am. Bd. Internal Medicine, Am. Bd. Cardiovascular Disease. Intern, resident in medicine Mass. Gen. Hosp., Boston, 1955-56, 59-61; asst. resident N.Y. Hosp.-Cornell U. Med. Ctr., N.Y.C., 1956-57; Am. Heart Assn. research fellow Peter Bent Brigham Hosp., Boston, 1961-63; mem. faculty U. N.C., Chapel Hill, 1963-74, then prof., 1971-74; prof. UCLA, 1974-77; chief cardiology VA Wadsworth Hosp., Los Angeles, 1974-77; prof. Dartmouth Med. Sch., Hanover, N.H., 1977—; chief cardiology Dartmouth-Hitchcock Med. Ctr., Hanover, N.H., 1977-87; vis. scientist August Krogh Inst., Copenhagen, 1984; mem. merit rev. bd. cardiovascular studies VA, 1976-79, chmn., 1978-79; mem. regional rsch. rev. com. New Eng. Am. Heart Assn., 1978-83; mem. sci. bd. Stanley J. Sarnoff Endowment for Carciovascular Sci., 1992—, chmn., 1994-95. Contbr. articles to profl. jours. Bd. dirs. N.H. affiliate Am. Heart Assn., 1978-85; pres. N.H. affiliate Am. Heart Assn., 1983-85. Served to capt. M.C. USAF, 1957-59. Recipient Lederle Med. Faculty award, 1965-68, USPHS Career Devel. award, 1967-72; grantee USPHS/NIH, 1964-76, VA Merit Rev. Rsch. Program, 1975-77, Mathers Found., 1984-86, 93—, Am. Heart Assn., 1989-91. Mem. AAAS, Am. Coll. Cardiology, Am. Fedn. Clin. Research, Am. Heart Assn., Am. Physiol. Soc., Internat. Soc. Heart Research, Phi Beta Kappa, Alpha Omega Alpha. Home: 4 Balch Hill Ln Hanover NH 03755-1622 Office: Dartmouth-Hitchcock Med Ctr Dept Cardiology Lebanon NH 03756

ROLEY, JERRY, bank executive; b. 1946. With Avco Corp. Silver Spring, Md., 1969-72, U.S. Ho. Rep. Credit Union, Washington, 1972-90; pres. U.S. Senate Credit Union, Washington, 1990—. With USAF, 1966-70. Office: US Senate FCU PO Box 77920 Washington DC 20013

ROLF, TOM, film editor. Editor: (films) Lucky Lady, 1975, French Connection II, 1975, (with Marcia Lucas and Melvin Shapiro) Taxi Driver, 1976, Black Sunday, 1976, Blue Collar, 1978, Prophecy, 1979, Hard Core, 1979, (with Lisa Fruchtman, Jerry Greenberg, and William Reynolds) Heaven's Gate, 1980, Ghost Story, 1981, (with Glenn Farr, Fruchtman, Stephen A. Rotter, and Douglas Stewart) The Right Stuff, 1983 (Academy award best film editing 1983), Wargames, 1983, Thief of Hearts, 1984, 9 1/2 Weeks, 1986, Quicksilver, 1986, Outrageous Fortune, 1987, (with Michael Ripps) Stakeout, 1987, (with Seth Flaum and William Gordean) The Great Outdoors, 1988, Black Rain, 1989, Jacob's Ladder, 1990, Sneakers, 1992, (with Trudy Ship) The Pelican Brief, 1993, Mr. Jones, 1993. Home: 12417 Mulholland Dr Beverly Hills CA 90210 Office: Broder Kurland Webb Uffner Agency 9242 Beverly Blvd Ste 200 Beverly Hills CA 90210*

ROLFE, MICHAEL N., management consulting firm executive; b. Chgo., Sept. 9, 1937; s. Mark Alexander and Antoinette (Wittgenstein) R.; m. Judith Mary Lewis, June 16, 1959; children—Andrew, Lisa, James. A.B. in Econs., U. Mich., 1959; MBA, U. Chgo., 1996. Sales staff Lewis Co., Northbrook, Ill., 1961-62; systems mgmt. staff Brunswick Corp., Chgo., 1962-68; dir. Kearney Mgmt. Cons., Chgo., 1968-81; ptnr. KPMG/Peat Marwick, Chgo., 1981-92; v.p. Keystone Group, Evanston, Ill., 1992—. Author: AMA Management Handbook, 1969. Bd. dirs. Commn., Chgo., 1972-75, U. Chgo. Cancer Rsch., 1985-88, Am. Cancer Soc., Chgo., 1985—; trustee Michael Reese Med. Ctr., 1986-91; pres. Sch. Bd. Dist. 113, Highland Park, Ill., 1977-83. Lt. (j.g.) USNR, 1959-61. Clubs: Northmoor Country (Highland Park); Standard (Chgo.). Home: 800 Deerfield Rd Apt 109 Highland Park IL 60035 Office: Keystone Group 1007 Church St Evanston IL 60201

ROLFE, ROBERT MARTIN, lawyer; b. Richmond, Va., May 16, 1951; s. Norman and Bertha (Cohen) R.; m. Catherine Dennis Stone, July 14, 1973; children: P. Alexander, Asher B., Joel A., Zachary A. BA, U. Va., 1973, JD, 1976. Bar: Va. 1976, N.Y. 1985, U.S. Dist. Ct. (ea. and we. dists.) Va. 1976, U.S. Supreme Ct. 1979, U.S. Ct. Appeals (4th cir.) 1976, U.S. Ct. Appeals (2d cir.) 1979, U.S. Dist. Ct. (ea. dist.) Mich. 1985, U.S. Ct. Appeals (D.C. cir.) 1985, U.S. Dist. Ct. (so. dist. and ea. dist.) N.Y. 1985. Assoc. Hunton & Williams, Richmond, 1976-83, ptnr., 1983—. Contbr. articles to profl. jours. Bd. dirs. Jewish Family Svcs., Richmond, pres., 1993-95; bd. mgrs., 2d v.p. Congregation Beth Ahabah, 1995—. Mem. ABA (litigation sect., natural resources, energy and environ. law sect.), Va. Bar Assn., Va. State Bar, Richmond Bar Assn., Am. Arbitration Assn. (comml. arbitrators panel), Order of Coif (Alumni award for acad. excellence U. Va. 1976). Home: 18 Greenway Ln Richmond VA 23226-1630 Office: Hunton & Williams Riverfront Plz East Tower 951 E Byrd St Richmond VA 23219-4074 also: 200 Park Ave New York NY 10166-0136

ROLFE, ROBIN ANN, trade association executive, lawyer; b. Mineola, N.Y., July 10, 1949; d. Justin B. and Joan (Gussman) R.; m. Edward F. Simpson, Aug. 22, 1971 (div. Oct. 1976); m. Arnold L. Saltzman, May 12, 1985. BA, Pa. State U., 1971; JD cum laude, Seton Hall U., 1977. Bar: N.J. 1977. Paralegal Jackson and Nash, N.Y.C., 1971-73; paralegal Lowenstein, Sandler, Kohl, Fisher and Boylan, Roseland, N.J., 1973-77, assoc., 1977-80; trademark atty. Chesebrough-Pond's Inc., Greenwich, Conn., 1980-81; exec. dir. Internat. Trademark Assn. (formerly U.S. Trademark Assn.), N.Y.C., 1981—; pres. Brand Names Edn. Found., N.Y.C., 1988—. Mem. adv. bd. Ctr. for Legal Studies Montclair State Coll., 1983—; regional coord. alumni admissions program Pa. State U., No. N.J., 1986—. Mem. ABA, N.J. Bar Assn., Am. Soc. Assn. Execs. Home: 300 Gorge Rd Cliffside Park NJ 07010-2759 Office: Internat Trademark Assn 1133 Avenue Of The Americas New York NY 10036-6710

ROLFE, RONALD STUART, lawyer; b. N.Y.C., Sept. 5, 1945; s. Nat and Florence I. (Roth) R.; m. Yvonne Susan Quinn, Sept. 1, 1979; 1 child, Andrew Quinn. AB, Harvard U., 1966; JD, Columbia U., 1969. Bar: N.Y. 1969, U.S. Ct. Appeals (2d cir.) 1970, U.S. Dist. Ct. (so. and ea. dists.) N.Y. 1971, U.S. Supreme Ct. 1973, U.S. Ct. Appeals (9th cir.) 1977, U.S. Dist. Ct. (no. dist.) Calif. 1982, U.S. Ct. Appeals (5th cir.) 1982, U.S. Ct. Appeals (6th cir.) 1984, U.S. Dist. Ct. (ea. dist.) Ky. 1984, U.S. Ct. Appeals (fed. cir.) 1993. Law clk. to judge U.S. Dist. Ct. (so. dist.) N.Y., 1969-70; assoc. Cravath, Swaine & Moore, 1970-77, ptnr., 1977—. Sec. bd. trustees Allen-Stevenson Sch. 1981-91, pres., 1992—; trustee Lawrenceville Sch., 1987—; v.p., trustee Prep for Prep. Kent and Stone scholar, 1969; mem. bd. visitors Columbia Law Sch. Fellow Am. Bar Found.; mem. ABA, N.Y. State Bar Assn., Assn. of Bar of City of N.Y., Fed. Bar Coun. (trustee 1989-94), Am. Law Inst., Harvard Club, Univ. Club, Stanwich Club (Greenwich, Conn.), Turf and Field Club (N.Y.C.), Royal Automobile Club (London). Office: Cravath Swaine & Moore Worldwide Plz 825 8th Ave New York NY 10019-7475

ROLFE, STANLEY THEODORE, civil engineer, educator; b. Chgo., July 7, 1934; s. Stanley T. and Eunice (Fike) R.; m. Phyllis Williams, Aug. 11, 1956; children: David Stanley, Pamela Kay, Kathleen Ann. B.S., U. Ill., 1956, M.S., 1958, Ph.D., 1962. Registered profl. engr. Pa., Kans. Supr. structural-evaluation sect. ordnance products div. U.S. Steel Corp., 1962-69, div. chief mech. behavior of metals div., 1969; A.P. Learned prof. civil engring. U. Kans., 1969—, chmn. civil engring. dept., 1975—; Chmn. metall. studies panel ship research com. Nat. Acad. Scis., 1967-70. Co-author: Fracture and Fatigue Control in Structures—Applications of Fracture Mechanics; co-author: textbook Strength of Materials; Contbr.: numerous articles to profl. jours. T.R. Higgins lectr., 1980; Recipient Sam Tour award Am. Soc. Testing Materials, 1971, H.E. Gould Distinguished Teaching award U. Kans., 1972, 75, AWS Adams Meml. Educator award, 1974; U. Ill. Civil Engring. Disting. Service award, 1985, U. Ill. Coll. Engring. Alumni Honor award Disting. Service in Engring., 1987; U. Kans. Irvin E. Youngberg research award, 1985. Mem. Nat. Acad. Engring., ASCE (chmn. task force on fracture, State of Art award 1983), Am. Soc. Testing Materials, ASME, Soc. Exptl. Stress Analysis, Am. Soc. Engring. Edn., Chi Psi. Presbyterian. Home: 821 Sunset Dr Lawrence KS 66044-2433

ROLFES, HERMAN HAROLD, Canadian government official; b. Humboldt, Bask, Sask., Can., July 13, 1936; s. Joseph and Josephine (Heckmann) R.; m. Myrna Josephine Hopfner, Apr. 4, 1961; children: Debora Lynne, Brian Joseph. Student, St. Peter's Coll., Muenster, Sask., Tchrs. Coll. Sask., 1955-56; BA, U. Sask., 1961, BEd, 1965, MEd, 1971. Cert. tchr., Can. Mem. legis. assembly Saskatoon Nutana South, 1971-82, 86—; min. social svcs., 1975-79, min. continuing edn., 1978-79; min. health Sask., 1979-82; now spkr. legis assembly. Saskatoon Nutana South, 1991—. Mem. Sask. Elem. Tchrs. Assn. (past pres.), St. Thomas Moore Alumni Assn., KC Roman Catholic. Avocations: tennis, golf, curling. Home: 2802 Calder Ave, Saskatoon, SK Canada S7J 1W1 Office: Speaker, Legislative Bldg Rm 129, Regina, SK Canada S4S 0B3

ROLL, DAVID LEE, lawyer; b. Pontiac, Mich., May 1, 1940; s. Everett Edgar and Garnette (Houts) R.; m. Nancy E. Roll, Aug. 17, 1963; children: Richard, Molly. BA cum laude, Amherst Coll., 1962; JD, U. Mich., 1964. Bar: Mich. 1965, U.S. Dist. Ct. (ea. dist.) Mich. 1965, U.S. Ct. Appeals (6th cir.) 1969, D.C. 1974, U.S. Dist. Ct. D.C. 1975, U.S. Supreme Ct. 1975, U.S. Ct. Appeals (4th cir.) 1976, U.S. Ct. Appeals (D.C. cir.) 1983, U.S. Ct. Appeals (3rd and 11th cirs.) 1985, U.S. Ct. Appeals (9th cir.) 1992, U.S. Ct. Appeals (fed. cir.) 1993. Assoc. Hill, Lewis, Detroit, 1965-70, ptnr., 1970-72; asst. dir. gen. litigation Bur. of Competition Fed. Trade Commn., Washington, 1972-75; ptnr. Steptoe & Johnson, Washington, 1975-93, chmn., 1993—. Mem. ABA (chair Robinson Patman Act com., antitrust sect. 1984-86, Clayton Act com., antitrust sect. 1986-88, Energy Litigation com., litigation sect. 1992—, mem. task force on indsl. competitiveness 1987, coun., antitrust sect. 1988-91, author, editor antitrust sect.). Office: Steptoe & Johnson 1330 Connecticut Ave NW Washington DC 20036

ROLL, IRWIN CLIFFORD (WIN ROLL), advertising, marketing and publishing executive; b. N.Y.C., Aug. 23, 1925; s. Arnold and Bertha (Vogel) R.; m. Marilyn Witlin, Apr. 10, 1949; children: Richard J., Douglas W. B.B.A. magna cum laude, CCNY, 1948; postgrad., Columbia U., 1952. Asst. advt. mgr. Standard Motor Products, Inc., Long Island City, N.Y., 1948-50; advt. and sales promotion exec. RCA, Harrison, N.J., 1950-54; account exec. Fuller & Smith & Ross, Inc., N.Y.C., 1954-59; group v.p Fuller & Smith & Ross, Inc., 1959-66; pres., dir. Henderson & Roll, Inc., advt. and pub. relations agy., 1966-77; pres., chief exec. officer Henderson, Roll & Friedlich, Inc., 1977-79; chmn. bd., treas., chief exec. officer, dir. Listfax Corp., nat. computerized info. services co., 1966-79; pres., CEO Win Roll and Co., Inc., N.Y.C., 1979-89; chmn. bd. Roll-Bender Research, 1980-82, Devonshire Communications, Ltd., 1983-87; sr. v.p. Tradewell Industries, Inc., 1983-87; exec. v.p. Internat. Mktg. Sys. Inc., 1988-90; pres. Concord Cons. Group, 1990—; corp. devel. dir. Ind. Media Svcs., Inc., 1992—; pres., chief ops. officer, bd. dirs. Megaworld, Inc., 1993—. Mem. mktg. com. Nat. Multiple Sclerosis Soc.; bd. dirs. Westchester County chpt. Multiple Sclerosis Soc., 1983-89; pres. Rosdale Residential Assn. 1983-85, bd. dirs., 1980—. With U.S. Army, 1943-46, ETO. Mem. Ad-Net Nat. Advt. Orgn. (bd. dirs. 1983-90, pres. 1986-88), Adv. Club of N.Y., Beta Gamma Sigma (bd. dirs., v.p. N.Y. Alumni chpt. 1986-89, pres. 1989-91, adv. bd. 1991—), Alpha Delta Sigma. Home: 11 Cedarwood Rd White Plains NY 10605-5331

ROLL, JOHN MCCARTHY, lawyer; b. Pitts., Feb. 8, 1947; s. Paul Herbert and Esther Marie (McCarthy) R.; m. Maureen O'Connor, Jan. 24, 1970; children: Robert McCarthy, Patrick Michael, Christopher John. B.A., U. Ariz., 1969, J.D., 1972, LLM U. Va., 1990. Bar: Ariz. 1972, U.S. Dist. Ct. Ariz. 1974, U.S. Ct. Appeals (9th cir.) 1980, U.S. Supreme Ct. 1977. Asst. pros. atty. U.S. Atty. U.S. Atty.'s Office, Tucson, 1980-87; judge Ariz. Ct. Appeals, 1987-91, U.S. Dist. Ct. Ariz., 1991—; lectr. Nat. Coll. Dist. Attys. U. Houston, 1976-87; mem. criminal justice mental health standards project ABA, 1980-83. Contbr. to Trial Techniques Compendium, 1978, 82, 84, Merit Selection: The Arizona Experience, Arizona State Law Journal, 1991, The Rules Have Changed: Amendments to the Rules of Civil Procedure, Defense Law Journal, 1994. Coach, Frontier Baseball Little League, Tucson, 1979-84; mem. parish coun. Sts. Peter and Paul Roman Catholic Ch., Tucson, 1983-91, chmn., 1986-91; mem. Roman Cath. Diocese of Tucson Sch. Bd., 1986-90. Recipient Disting. Faculty award Nat. Coll. Dist. Attys., U. Houston, 1979, Outstanding Alumnus award U. Ariz. Coll. Law, 1992. Mem. Am. Judicature Soc., Fed. Judges Assn., Pima County Bar Assn. Republican. Lodge: K.C. (adv. coun. 10441). Office: US Dist Ct 55 E Broadway Blvd Tucson AZ 85701-1719

ROLL, TERESA J., restaurant chain executive; b. 1952. JD, U. Kans., 1982. Lawyer Wichita, Kans., 1982-86; with Lake Mich. Mgmt. Co., Milw., 1986—, pres., treas., 1989—. Office: Lake MI Mgmt Co 3333 N Mayfair Rd Ste 214 Milwaukee WI 53222-3219*

ROLLAND, IAN MCKENZIE, insurance executive; b. Fort Wayne, Ind., June 3, 1933; s. David and Florence (Hunte) R.; m. Miriam V. Flickinger, July 3, 1955; children: Cheri L., Lawrence D., Robert A., Carol Ann, Sara K. B.A., DePauw U., 1955; M.A. in Actuarial Sci., U. Mich., 1956. With Lincoln Nat. Life Ins. Co., Ft. Wayne, 1956—, sr. v.p., 1973-75, pres., 1977-81, chief exec. officer, 1977-91, chmn., pres., 1981-92, chmn., chief exec. officer, 1992—; pres. Lincoln Nat. Corp., 1975-91, CEO, 1977-91, chmn., CEO, 1992—; bd. dirs. K&K Ins. Cos., No. Ind. Pub. Svc., Lincoln Fin. Corp., GTE North, Inc., Tokheim Corp., Lincoln, Nat. Sales Corp., Am. States Inst. Cos., 1st Penn-Pacific Ins. Co., The Richard Leahy Corp., MPT Assocs., Inc.; past chmn. Am. Coun. Life Ins.; exec. com. Assn. Ind. Life Ins. Cos. Mem. adv. bd. Ind. U.-Purdue U., 1977, Fort Wayne Leadership, Fort Wayne Community Found., Corp. Innovation Devel. Ventures; bd. dirs. Associated Colls. Ind., Corp. Innovation Devel.; chmn. Ind. Fiscal Policy Com.; trustee Hudson Inst.; mem. Indiana Acad. Mem. Soc. Actuaries, Acad. Actuaries, Health Ins. Assn. Am., Am. Council Life Ins. (past chmn. bd. dirs.), Assoc. Ind. Life Ins. Cos. (exec. com.), Ind. Ins. Soc. (bd. dirs.), Internat. Ins. Soc. (bd. dirs.), Ind. C of C (mem. exec. com.). Office: Lincoln Nat Corp 200 E Berry St Fort Wayne IN 46802

ROLLAND, LUCIEN G., paper company executive; b. St. Jerome, Que., Can., Dec. 21, 1916; s. Olivier and Aline (Dorion) R.; m. Marie de Lorimier, May 30, 1942; children: Nicolas, Natalie, Stanislas, Dominique, Christine, Etienne, David. Student, Coll. Jean de Brebeuf, Montreal; Profl. Engr., Loyola Coll., U. Montreal, B.A., B.A.Sc., C.E., also D.C.Sc. (hon.), 1960. Registered profl. engr. With Rolland Paper Co. Ltd. (name changed to Rolland inc. 1979), 1942—, v.p., gen. mgr., 1952, pres., gen. mgr., 1952-78, pres., CEO, 1978—, chmn., pres., CEO, 1984, chmn., CEO, 1985, chmn., 1991; chmn. bd. dirs. Rolland Paper Corp.; pres. Tarascon Holdings, Inc. Bd. govs. Notre-Dame Hosp., Montreal Children's Hosp., Montreal Gen. Hosp., Hôpital Marie Enfant. Decorated Knight Comdr. Order St. Gregory, officer Order of Can. Mem. Can. Pulp and Paper Assn. (hon.), Corp. Profl. Engrs., Montreal Bd. Trade, Province of Que., C of C, Montreal C. of C., Engring. Inst. Can. Home: Apt B-60, 1321 Sherbrooke St W, Montreal, PQ Canada H3G 1J4 Office: Rolland Inc, 2 Rolland Ave, Saint Jerome, PQ Canada J7Z 5S1

ROLLANS, JAMES O., service company executive; b. Glendale, Calif., July 7, 1942; s. Henry Leo and Geraldine Ada (Berg) R.; children: Jodie Helene, Thomas James, Daniel Joseph. BS, Calif. State U., Northridge, 1967. Vice pres., dir. Chase Manhattan Bank, 1976-78; v.p. corp. communications Dart Industries, Los Angeles, 1978-80; v.p. bus. analysis and investor relations Dart & Kraft, Chgo., 1980-82; sr. v.p., chief adminstrv. officer Fluor Corp., Irvine, Calif., 1982—; bd. dirs. Plaza Comm., Lafayette Pharms. Corp., Irvine Med. Ctr. Mem. Fin. Execs. Inst. Episcopalian. Avocations: boating; skiing; fishing; hunting. Office: Fluor Corp 3333 Michelson Dr Irvine CA 92730-0001

ROLLASON, WENDELL NORTON, social services administrator; b. Winsted, Conn., Aug. 21, 1916; s. George Herbert Sanderson and Helen Hotchkiss (Norton) R.; m. Mary Jane Kemp, 1946 (div. 1971); children: Wendell, Frank, Raleigh; m. Barbara Louise Schott, Oct. 29, 1978. Grad. high sch., Winsted. Supr. Dade County Port Authority, Miami, Fla., 1946-51; exec. dir. Inter Am. Affairs Com., Miami, Fla., 1952-64; exec. dir. Redlands Christian Migrant Assn., Immokalee, Fla., 1966-90, exec. v.p., 1990—; chmn. Gov.'s Adv. Coun. on Farmworker Affairs, 1979, 86, 90; mem. Nat. Commn. on Migrant Edn. appt. by U.S. Senate, 1989-92. Vice chmn. Fla. Interagy. Coordinating Coun. for Infants and Toddlers, 1989-93; chmn. dist. adv. coun. Fla. Dept. Health Related Svcs., 1989-92. Petty officer 1st class USN, 1941-45. Recipient various awards, 1952-93; named One of Fla.'s Greatest Humanitarian Assets, Govor. of Fla., 1985; ann. health award created in his name, 1988; scholarship fund created in his name Migrant Parent Orgn., 1992. Mem. Fla. Assn. Community Health Ctrs. Democrat. Episcopalian. Avocations: reading, politics, outdoor activities. Home: 14940 Old Olga Rd Fort Myers FL 33905-4734

ROLLE, ANDREW F., historian, educator, author; b. Providence, Apr. 12, 1922; m. Frances Squires, Dec. 1945 (div.); children: John Warren, Alexander Frederick, Julia Elisabeth.; m. Myra Moss, Nov. 1983. BA, Occidental Coll., 1943; M.A., UCLA, 1949, Ph.D., 1953; grad., So. Calif. Psychoanalytic Inst., 1976. Am. vice consul Genoa, Italy, 1945-48; editorial asso. Pacific Hist. Rev., 1952-53; from asst. prof. to Cleland prof. history Occidental Coll., 1953-88; rsch. scholar Huntington Libr., San Marino, Calif., 1988—. Author: Riviera Path, 1946, An American in California, 1956, reprinted, 1982, The Road to Virginia City, 1960, reprinted, 1989, Lincoln: A Contemporary Portrait, 1961, (with Allan Nevins, Irving Stone) California: A History, 1963, rev. edits., 1969, 78, 87, Occidental College: The First Seventy-Five Years, 1963, The Lost Cause: Confederate Exiles in Mexico, 1965, 1992, The Golden State, 1967, rev. edit., 1978, 1989, California, A Student Guide, 1965, Los Angeles, A Student Guide, 1965; Editor: A Century of Dishonor (Helen Hunt Jackson), 1964, Life in California (Alfred Robinson), 1971; The Immigrant Upraised, 1968, The American Italians: Their History and Culture, 1972, Gli Emigrati Vittoriosi, 1973; (with George Knoles others) Essays and Assays, 1973, (with others) Studies in Italian American Social History, 1975, (with others) Los Angeles: The Biography of a City, 1976, 2d edit., 1991, (with Allan Weinstein and others) Crisis in America, 1977, The Italian Americans: Troubled Roots, 1980, 2d edit. 1985, Los Angeles: From Pueblo to Tomorrow's City, 1981, 2nd edit., 1995, Occidental College: A Centennial History, 1986, John Charles Frémont: Character as Destiny, 1991, Henry Mayo Newhall and His Times, 1992. Served to 1st lt. M.I. AUS, 1943-45, 51-52. Decorated Cavaliere Ordine Merito Italy; recipient silver medal Italian Ministry Fgn. Affairs; Commonwealth award for non-fiction; Huntington Library-Rockefeller Found. fellow; resident scholar Rockefeller Found. Center, Bellagio, Italy. Fellow Calif. Hist. Soc.; mem. Phi Beta Kappa. Office: Huntington Libr Rsch Div San Marino CA 91108

ROLLE, CHRISTOPHER DAVIES, lawyer; b. Tokyo, Dec. 25, 1951; s. Norman Benjamin and Mavis Cameron (Williams) R.; m. Dale Mitchem; children: Christopher Davies, Jr., Zachery B. BA, Ark. State U., 1974; JD, Stetson U., 1977. Bar: Fla. 1978, U.S. Dist. Ct. (mid. dist.) Fla. 1979, U.S. Dist. Ct. (no. and so. dists.) Fla. 1980, U.S. Ct. Appeals (5th cir.) 1979, U.S. Ct. Appeals (11th cir.) 1981, U.S. Supreme Ct. 1981. Asst. state's atty. 20th Jud. Cir., Ft. Myers Fla., 1978; atty. securities fraud unit and office compt. State of Fla., Tampa, 1978-79; asst. atty. gen. adminstrv. law sect. State of Fla., Tallahassee, 1979-83; ea. regional counsel Nat. Med. Enterprises, Inc., Tampa, 1983-84; gen. counsel, v.p. Retirement Corp. Am., Bradenton, Fla., 1984-85; with Holland & Knight, Bradenton and Orlando, Fla., 1985-88; assoc. Baker & Hostetler, Orlando, Fla., 1988-90; ptnr. Foley & Lardner, Orlando, 1990—; mem. health com. Orlando Naval Tng. Ctr. Reuse

Commn. Editorial bd. Physician's Mktg. and Mgmt. Chmn. Jim Smith's gubernatorial campaign, Bradenton, 1986; bd. dirs. Retirement Housing Coun., 1985-87, v.p., 1986-87, Health Care Ctr. for Homeless, Inc.; chmn. bd. dirs. Children's Wish Found., Orlando, 1988—; grad. Leadership Orlando, 1990-91. Named one of Outstanding Young Men Am., 1988. Mem. ABA (forum on health law), Fla. Bar Assn. (vice chmn. commn. on elderly 1990-91, pub. rels. com. 1988-92, vice chmn. health law com. 1987-88, adminstrv. law sect. exec. coun., founding mem., exec. coun. health law sect. 1988-90, chmn. 1989-90), Manatee County Bar Assn. (treas. 1987-88), Orange County Bar Assn., Fla. Hosp. Assn., Fla. Acad. Hosp. Attys. (bd. dirs.), Am. Hosp. Assn., Am. Acad. Hosp. Attys., Nat. Health Lawyers Assn., Greater Orlando C. of C., Lambda Chi Alpha. Office: Foley & Lardner 111 N Orange Ave Ste 1800 Orlando FL 32801-4801

ROLLE, ESTHER, actress; b. Pompano Beach, Fla., Nov. 8; d. Jonathan Rolle. Student, Spellman Coll., Hunter Coll., New Sch. for Social Research. Dancer, Shogola Obola Dance Co., then mem., Negro Ensemble Co.; off-Broadway debut: The Blacks, 1962; London stage debut: God is a (Guess What?), 1969; numerous stage appearances include Macbeth, Amen Corner, Blues for Mister Charlie, Don't Play Us Cheap; toured Scandinavia in stage prdn. The Skin of Our Teeth; toured Australia, New Zealand in stage prdns. Black Nativity; other stage prdns. The Member of the Wedding, 1988, Nothing But a Man, 1964, Cleopatra Jones, 1973, Don't Play Us Cheap, 1973, P.K. and the Kid, 1982, Driving Miss Daisy, 1989, The Mighty Quinn, 1989, Color Adjustment, 1991, House of Cards, 1993, Nobody's Girls, 1994; TV series include Maude, 1972-74, One Life to Live, 1972-74, Good Times, 1974-77, 78-79, Singer and Sons, 1990; TV appearances include Summer of My German Soldier, 1979 (Emmy award 1979), I Know Why the Caged Bird Sings, 1979, Age Old Friends, 1989, The Kid Who Loved Christmas, 1990, Dinah's Place, N.Y.P.D., Like It Is, East Side, West Side, To Dance with a White Dog, 1993, Message From Nam, 1993, Scarlet, 1994. Hon. chmn. Pres.'s Com. on Employment of Handicapped.; Grand Marshall Cherry Blossom Festival, Washington, 1975. Named Woman of Yr. 3d World Sisterhood, 1976; recipient Image awards, NAACP, 1973, 74, 79, Leadership award, 1990, Hall of Fame, 1987; guest Bahamian gov. dedication Nat. Bank, 1993. Office: William Morris Agy 152 El Camino Dr Beverly Hills CA 90212*

RÖLLER, HERBERT ALFRED, biology and medical scientist, educator; b. Magdeburg, Germany, Aug. 2, 1927; came to U.S., 1962; s. Alfred H. and Elfriede (Wartner) R.; m. Manuela R. Buresch, Dec. 20, 1957. Abiturium, Christian Thomasius Schule, Halle/Saale, 1946; Dr.rer.nat., Georg August U., Goettingen, 1962. Project assoc. zoology U. Wis., Madison, 1962-65; asst. prof. pharmacology U. Wis., 1965-66, research assoc. zoology, 1966-67, assoc. prof. zoology, 1967-68; prof. biology Tex. A&M U., 1968-83, prof. biochemistry and biophysics, 1974-83, dir. Inst. Devel. Biology, 1973-83, Disting. prof., 1977—, Alumni prof., 1980-85; v.p. research Zoecon Corp., Palo Alto, Calif., 1968-72, sci. adv., 1972-85, chief scientist, Zoecon Research Inst., Palo Alto, 1985-88; sci. adv. European Community, 1988—; sci. adv. Affymax Rsch. Inst., Palo Alto, 1989—; adv. panel regulatory biology, div. biol. and med. scis. NSF, 1969-72; mem. Internat. Centre Insect Physiology and Ecology, Nairobi, Kenya, 1970—, dir. research, 1970-75. Editorial bd.: Jour. Chem. Ecology, 1974—; Contbr. articles to profl. publs. Recipient Disting. Achievement award for research Tex. A&M U., 1976. Fellow Tex. Acad. Sci.; mem. Deutsche Akademie Naturforscher Leopoldina, AAAS, Am. Soc. Zoologists, Entomol. Soc. Am., Am. Soc. Devel. Biology, Sigma Xi. Home: 824 N Rosemary Dr Bryan TX 77802-4309

ROLLER, ROBERT DOUGLAS, III, psychiatrist; b. Charleston, W.Va., Nov. 17, 1928; s. Francis Oliver and Mary Elizabeth (Rice) R.; m. Anthonia Ijsselstein, Mar. 7, 1970; children: Robert Douglas IV, Katherine Willis, David Nelson, Anthonia Elizabeth, Alexander Robert, John Richard. BA, U. Va., 1950, MD, 1960; postgrad. in philosophy, U. Va., 1953-56. Tchr. Chestnut Hill Acad. Phila./Raven Soc., U. Va., 1953-56; intern U. N.C. Hosp., Chapel Hill, 1960-61, resident, 1961-62; resident Med. Coll. of Va., Richmond, 1963; NIMH research and teaching fellow U. Calif. Med. Ctr., San Francisco, 1963-66; pvt. practice Berkeley, 1966—; assoc. psychiatrist, rsch. psychiatrist U. Calif., Berkeley, 1965-71; clin. asst. prof. U. Calif. Med. Sch., San Francisco, 1970—; clin. instr. Stanford U. Med. Sch., Palo Alto, Calif., 1969-78, C.G. Jung Analytic Inst., 1964-72; mem. staff Alta Bates Hosp., Berkeley, Herrick Hosp., Berkeley, 1971-90, Lodi (Calif.) Meml. Hosp., 1971-86, Lodi Cmty. Hosp., 1965-72; chief psychiatrist Clear Water Ranch for Children, Santa Rosa, Calif., 1964-71. Mem. Episcopal and Presbyn. Ch. With USNR, 1950-51. Mem. Farmington Country Club (Charlottesville, Va.), U. Calif. Faculty Club, St. Anthony Club of N.Y., St. Elmo Club (Va.), Sleepy Hollow Tennis Club, Bankers Club of San Francisco, Phila. Cricket Club. Home: 757 San Diego Rd Berkeley CA 94707-2025 Office: 2999 Regent St Ste 422 Berkeley CA 94705-2119

ROLLER, THOMAS BENJAMIN, manufacturing company executive; b. Phila., Mar. 4, 1950; s. Clarence Thomas and Anne Dolores (Marrese) R.; m. Christine Louise Rebman, Oct. 14, 1978; children: Thomas Nathaniel, Laura Anne, Elizabeth Anne. BA, Clemson U., 1972; MBA, Duke U., 1974. Fin. analyst E.I. duPont de Nemours & Co., Wilmington, Del., 1974-75; sr. fin. analyst Rockwell Internat. Corp., Pitts., 1975-77; mgr. acquisitions Rockwell Internat. Corp., Troy, Mich., 1978, mgr. bus. planning, 1979; dir. worldwide bus. devel. Rockwell Internat. Corp., London, 1979-81; v.p. mktg. automotive div. United Techs., Lausanne, Switzerland, 1981-83; v.p. corp. planning carrier United Techs., Syracuse, N.Y., 1984-85, v.p., gen. mgr. replacement components div., 1985-87, pres. residential products div., 1988-90; pres., CEO Plywood Panels, Inc., New Orleans, 1990-92; CEO Fruehauf Trailer Corp., Indpls., 1992—. Com. mem. U.S. Dept. Commerce Indsl. Sector Adv. Com. Capital Goods, Washington, 1986-89; pres. adv. Clemson U., 1990—; bd. dirs. alumni assn. Fuqua Sch. Bus. Duke U., Durham, N.C., 1985-87. Republican. Avocations: fishing, N.Am. archaeology.

ROLLHAUS, PHILIP EDWARD, JR., diversified manufacturing corporation executive; b. Phila., Sept. 29, 1934; s. Philip Edward and Elizabeth Snow (Bedford) R.; m. Jacqueline Merrill, Feb. 13, 1965 (div. 1975); children: Natalie, Philip Edward III; m. Barbara Lynn Walker, Oct. 8, 1983. BA in English Lit., Wesleyan U., 1956. Dir. gen. Société Rollhaus, Paris, 1960-64; regional mgr. Bus. Internat., Chgo., 1964-67; mgr. pvt. placements Woolard & Co., Chgo., 1967-69; founder, chmn., pres., CEO Quixote Corp., Chgo., 1969—; bd. dirs. Chgo. Capital Fund., 1986-91, DeVry, Inc., 1987-90, Keller Grad . Sch. Mgmt., Chgo., 1974-87, Alliance Francaise de Chicago 1993—; mem. Am. Bus. Conf., Washington, 1987—; chmn. Starlight Found., Chgo., 1986-88, Gastro-Intestinal Rsch. Found., Chgo., 1984-90; trustee Inst. Psychoanalysis, Chgo., 1983-89, Nat. Symphony Orch., Washington, 1989-92; bd. assocs. Gallaudet U., Washington, 1993—. Served to lt. (j.g.) USN, 1956-60. Mem. Econ. Club of Chgo., Soc. Mayflower Descs., Chicago Club, Racquet Club, Tavern Club, Bath and Tennis Club (Palm Beach, Fla.), Palm Beach Yacht Club, Shelter Island (N.Y.) Yacht Club, Bohemian Club (San Francisco). Home: 1500 N Lake Shore Dr Chicago IL 60610-1624 Office: Quixote Corp 1 E Wacker Dr 30th Fl Chicago IL 60601-1801

ROLLIN, BERNARD ELLIOT, philosophy educator, consultant on animal ethics; b. N.Y.C., Feb. 18, 1943; s. Phillip and Yetta Ethel (Bookchin) R.; m. Linda Mae Schieber, Aug. 30, 1964; 1 child, Michael David Hume. BA, CCNY, 1964; PhD, Columbia U., 1972. Preceptor Columbia U., N.Y.C., 1968-69; asst. prof. philosophy Colo. State U., Ft. Collins, 1969-73, assoc. prof., 1973-78, prof., 1979—, prof. physiology and biophysics, 1980—, dir. bioethical planning, 1981—; cons. Can., Australian, The Netherlands and U.S. govts., various univs. and agys. including U. Calif., Berkeley, Wash. State U., U. Fla., USDA, 1980—, United Airlines, Denver, 1985—; lectr. on animal ethics, 1978—. Author: Natural and Conventional Meaning, 1976, Animal Rights and Human Morality, 1981, 2d edit., 1992 (Outstanding Acad. Book award Choice Mag. Am. Assn. U. Librs. 1982, Gustavus Meyers Ctr. award for study of human rights 1993), The Unheeded Cry, 1989, The Experimental Animal in Biomedical Research, 1990, vol. 2, 1995, The Frankenstein Syndrome: Ethical and Social Issues in the Genetic Engineering of Animals, 1995; mem. editl. bd. Jour. AVMA, Between the Species, Agrl. Ethics, Acta Semiotica et Linguistica, Studies in Animal Welfare Sci., numerous others; contbr. articles to profl. jours. Recipient Harris T. Guard award Colo. State U., 1981, honors prof., 1983; Waco F. Childers award Am. Humane Assn., 1982, svc. award Colo. Vet. Med. Assn., 1983, Disting. Faculty award Colo. State U. Coll. Vet. Med., 1993, Gustavus Meyers

Human Rights award 1994, Brownlee award Animal Welfare Found. Can., 1994. Jewish. Avocations: weightlifting, horseback riding, motorcycles. Office: Colo State U Dept Philosophy Fort Collins CO 80523

ROLLIN, BETTY, author, television journalist; b. N.Y.C., Jan. 3, 1936; d. Leon and Ida R.; m. Harold M. Edwards, Jan. 21, 1979. BA, Sarah Lawrence Coll., 1957. Assoc. features editor Vogue mag., 1964; sr. editor Look mag., 1965-71; network corr. NBC News, N.Y.C., 1971-80, contbg. corr., 1985—; network corr. ABC News Nightline, 1982-84; lectr. in field. Profl. actress on stage and television, 1958-64; Author: I Thee Wed, 1958, Mothers Are Funnier Than Children, 1964, The Non-Drinkers' Drink Book, 1966, First, You Cry, 1976, reissue, 1993, Am I Getting Paid for This?, 1982, Last Wish, 1985; columnist Hers, N.Y. Times; Contbr. articles to popular mags. Office: care NS Bienstock Inc 1740 Broadway New York NY 10019-4315

ROLLINS, ALDEN MILTON, documents librarian; b. Billerica, Mass., July 31, 1946; s. Alden Milton and Agnes Morgan (Simpson) R. BA, Am. U., 1968; MLS, U. R.I., 1973. Documents libr. U. Alaska Libr., Anchorage, 1973—. Author: The Fall of Rome: A Reference Guide, 1983, Rome in the Fourth Century A.D., 1991. With U.S. Army, 1969-71. Mem. ALA, New Eng. Hist. Geneal. Soc., N.H. Hist. Soc., Vt. Hist. Soc. (life), Piscataqua Pioneers (life). Avocation: genealogy. Home: 221 E 7th # 114 Anchorage AK 99501 Office: U Alaska Libr Govt Documents 3211 Providence Dr Anchorage AK 99508

ROLLINS, ALFRED BROOKS, JR., historian, educator; b. Presque Isle, Maine, May 28, 1921; s. Alfred Brooks and Clarissa (Jack) R.; m. Ernestine Emma McMullin, Nov. 6, 1942 (dec. Aug. 28, 1972); children: John Douglas, Nancy Jane, James Scott; m. Faith Kenyon, June 16, 1973 (dec. Mar. 1979); m. Helen Anrod Jones, Feb. 28, 1981. BA, Wesleyan U., Middletown, Conn., 1942, MA, 1946; PhD, Harvard U., 1953. From instr. to prof. history State U., N.Y. at New Paltz, 1948-63; prof., chmn. dept. history State U. N.Y. at Binghamton, 1964-67; dean U. Vt., Burlington, 1967-70; v.p. acad. affairs U. Vt., 1970-76; pres. Old Dominion U., Norfolk, Va., 1976-85; prof. history Old Dominion U., Norfolk, 1976-91, pres. emeritus, prof. emeritus, 1991—; Cons. oral history project John F. Kennedy Library, 1965. Author: Roosevelt and Howe, 1962; Editor narrative: Franklin D. Roosevelt and the Age of Action, 1960, Woodrow Wilson and the New America, 1965; Contbr. articles to profl. jours. Served to 1st lt. USAAF, 1943-46. Decorated D.F.C., Air medal with four clusters. Mem. Am. Hist. Assn., Orgn. Am. Historians, Phi Beta Kappa, Chi Psi.

ROLLINS, EDWARD TYLER, JR., newspaper executive; b. Durham, N.C., May 23, 1922; s. Edward Tyler and Bessie (Steed) R.; m. Frances Louise Page, Oct. 5, 1963; children: Edward Tyler III, William Lawson. AB, U. N.C., 1947. V.p.; asst. sec. Durham (N.C.) Herald Co., 1949-69, v.p., sec.-treas., 1969-81, pres., pub., 1982-88, chmn., bd. dirs., 1985—; pres. Durham Radio Corp. Stas. WDNC-AM, WDCG-FM, 1982-88. Bd. dirs. Chowan Coll. Graphic Arts Found., 1986—; bd. dirs. Sch. of Journalism Found. U. N.C., 1982-88; mem. adv. bd. Friends of Duke Art Mus., 1988—, N.C. Nat. Bank, 1979-89; mem. Duke Pres.'s Art Mus. Com., 1994—; trustee Meredith Coll., Raleigh, N.C., 1966-69, Durham Pub. Libr., 1961-81; former bd. dirs. Durham Salvation Army; pres. Durham YMCA, 1952; former bd. dirs. Family Svc. Assn., N.Y. Symphony. 1st lt. inf. U.S. Army, 1943-46. Mem. Durham C. of C. (bd. dirs. 1969), N.C. Press Assn., So. Newspaper Publishers Assn., Newspaper Assn. of Am., Kiwanis, Hope Valley Country Club, Treyburn Country Club, University Club, Carolina Club. Presbyterian. Office: Durham Herald Co Inc 2828 Pickett Rd Durham NC 27705-5613

ROLLINS, GARY WAYNE, service company executive; b. Chattanooga, Aug. 30, 1944; s. Orville Wayne and Grace (Crum) R.; m. Ruth Magness; children: Glen William, Ruth Ellen, Nancy Louise, Orville Wayne. BSBA, U. Tenn., 1967. Sales mgmt. Orkin Exterminating Co., Atlanta, 1967-72, v.p. ops., 1975-78, pres., 1978—; v.p., gen. mgr. Dwoskin, Atlanta, 1972-75; with Rollins, Inc., Atlanta, 1959—, v.p. 1972-84, pres., COO, 1984—, also bd. dirs.; pres. Rollins Supply, Inc., Atlanta; v.p. LOR, Inc., Atlanta, 1978—; bd. dirs. Rollins Leasing Co., Wilmington, Del., Rollins Energy Services, Atlanta, RPC Energy Svcs., Inc. Mem. Atlanta Symphony, 1970—, Atlanta Humane Soc., 1970—, Atlanta High Mus. Art, 1970—, Ga. Structural Pest Control Commn., 1967; founding dir. Tuxedo Park Civic Assn., Atlanta, 1984—. Recipient de Tocqueville Soc. award United Way, 1987. Mem. PADI Open Water Diving, Piedmont Driving Club. Methodist. Club: Cherokee (Atlanta). Avocations: hunting, camping, scuba diving, family activities. Office: Rollins Inc 2170 Piedmont Rd NE Atlanta GA 30324-4135

ROLLINS, HENRY, musician, author, publisher; b. Feb. 13, 1961. Prin., pub. 2.13.61, L.A.; prin. Human Pitbull Music Pub. Formerly with Black Flag; now songwriter, lead singer Rollins Band; albums with Rollins Band include Hot Animal Machine, 1987, Drive By Shooting, 1987, Life Time, 1988, Do It, 1989, Hard Volume, 1989, Turned On, 1990, The End of Silence, 1992, Electro Convulsive Therapy, 1993, Weight, 1994; albums with Black Flag include My War, 1983, Family Man, 1984, Slip It In, 1984, Loose '84, 1984, Loose Nut, 1985, The Process of Weeding Out, 1985, In My Head, 1985, Who's Got the 10, 1986; spoken word releases include Short Walk on a Long Pier, Big Ugly Mouth, Sweatbox, Live at McCabe's, Human Butt, The Boxed Life; video Talking From the Box; author: High Adventure in the Great Outdoors, 1984, Hallucinations of Grandeur, 1986, You Can't Run from God, 1986, Pissing in the Gene Pool, 1987, Works, 1988, Art to Choke Hearts, 1989, Bang!, 1990, One From None, 1991, Black Coffee Blues, 1992, See a Grown Man Cry, 1992, Now Watch Him Die, 1993; contbr. Details mag., Village Voice, Spin, Sounds, Melody Maker, The Face, various anthologies; film appearances include: The Chase, 1994, Johnny Mnemonic, 1995; spoken word performer, 1983—. Grammy nomination, Best Metal Performance for "Liar", 1995. Office: 2 13 61 PO Box 1910 Los Angeles CA 90078 also: care Imago Recording Co 152 W 57th St New York NY 10019*

ROLLINS, HENRY MOAK, former oil drilling equipment company executive, consultant; b. Gulfport, Miss., Sept. 11, 1921; s. Henry Martin and Sophie Palmer (Hutson) R.; m. Emogene Broaddus, Oct. 20, 1946; children: Joseph, Robert, Richard. BSME, Tex. A&M U., 1942; MBA, U. Tex., 1969, PhD in Bus. Adminstrn., 1972. Product engr. Hughes Tool Co., Houston, 1947-51; v.p. engring. and mfg. Drilco Oil Tools Inc., Midland, Tex., 1951-67; lectr., dept. fin. U. Tex., Austin, 1968-79; commr. Pub. Utility Commn. of Tex., Austin, 1978-82, chmn., 1982-83; sr. lectr., dept. fin. U. Tex., Austin, 1983-84; pres. Financo Inc., Austin, 1983-88; chmn., chief exec. officer Smith Internat. Inc., Newport Beach, Calif., 1987-88; chmn. Financo, Inc., Austin, 1989-91; ind. cons., 1991—; chmn. Gulf Fed. Savs. & Loan Assn., Metairie, La., 1986-88; bd. dirs. Smith Internat. Inc., Houston, Franklin Fed. Bancshares, Austin, Tex. Contbr. articles to mags. Trustee Schreiner Coll., Kerrville, Tex., 1986—, chmn., 1993—, Tex. Presbyn. Found., 1990—, Austin Community Found., 1991—; (pres. elect), bd. dirs. Austin Symphony. Capt. USAAC, 1942-46. Recipient Disting. Service award Internat. Assn. Drilling Contractors, Houston, 1967. Republican. Presbyterian. Clubs: Austin Country, Headliners (trustee 1986-89). Home: 4509 Cat Mountain Dr Austin TX 78731-3503 Office: Financo Inc 3445 Executive Center Dr Austin TX 78731-1680

ROLLINS, HOWARD ELLSWORTH, JR., actor; b. Balt., Oct. 17, 1950; s. Howard E. Sr. and Ruth R. Student, Towson State U. Appearances include (Broadway) We Interrupt This Program, (TV) Eliza: Our Story, 1975, All My Children, Another World (Emmy nomination), King, Roots, The Next Generation, For Us The Living, Moving Right Along, Thornwell, My Old Man, The Neigborhood, Doctor's Story, (series) In the Heat of the Night, 1988-94; (films) The House of God, 1978, Ragtime (Oscar nomination), 1981, A Soldier's Story, 1984, (theatrical prodns.) Streamers, Medal of Honor Rag, G.R. Point, The Mighty Gents. Office: care William Morris Agency 151 El Camino Beverly Hills CA 90212*

ROLLINS, JACK, motion picture producer; b. 1914. Co-founder talent mgmt. firm Rollins, Joffe, Morra, Brezner Prodns., N.Y.C. Producer films: (with Charles Joffe) Take The Money and Run, 1969, Bananas, 1971, Everything You Always Wanted to Know...But Were Afraid To Ask, 1972,

Sleeper, 1973, Love and Death, 1975, The Front, 1976, Annie Hall, 1977, Interiors, 1978, Manhattan, 1979, Stardust Memories, 1980, Zelig, 1983; producer, actor films: The Purple Rose of Cairo, 1985, Hannah and Her Sisters, 1986, Radio Days, 1986, September, 1987, Another Woman, 1988, New York Stories (Oedipus Wrecks), 1989, Crimes and Misdemeanors, 1989, Shadows and Fog, 1992, Husbands and Wives, 1992, Manhattan Murder Mystery, 1993; TV producer Dick Cavett Show, Late Night with David Letterman; mgmt. firm handles careers of Woody Allen, Mike Nichols, Elaine May, Robin Williams, Robert Klein, Dick Cavett, Billy Crystal. Office: Rollins Joffe Morra Brezner Productions 130 W 57th St New York NY 10019-3325

ROLLINS, JIMMY DON, school system administrator. Supt. Springdale (Ark.) Sch. Dist. State finalist Nat. Supt. Yr. award, 1992. Office: Springdale Sch Dist 202 W Emma Ave Springdale AR 72764-4307

ROLLINS, JOHN W., JR., transportation executive, environmental services administrator; b. 1942. BBA, So. Meth. U., 1942; MBA, Northwestern U., 1965. With Rollins Truck Leasing Corp., Wilmington, Del., 1965—, sr. v.p., 1973, exec. v.p., 1975, pres., COO, 1975; with Rollins Eviron. Svcs. Inc., Wilmington, 1982—, chmn. bd. dirs., 1982, vice chmn., 1983, sr. vice chmn., 1988; with Matlack Systems Inc., Wilmington, 1988—, chmn. bd. dirs. Office: Matlack Systems Inc 1 Rollins Plz Wilmington DE 19803*

ROLLINS, JUNE ELIZABETH, elementary education educator; b. Turin, N.Y., June 24, 1929; d. Jay Elihue and Mildred (Evans) Hoskins; m. Clair Austin Rollins, June 28, 1952; children: Timothy, Teri June, Scott, Tracy. BS in Music, Fredonia (N.Y.) State U., 1950. Cert. tchr. nursery, kindergartern, elem. edn., music, N.Y. Instrumental and vocal music tchr. Greenwood (N.Y.) Cen. Sch., 1950-58, 59-68, kindergarten tchr., 1965-68; vocal and instrumental music tchr. Greenwood Cen. High Sch., 1968-71; third grade thcr. Greenwood Cen. Sch., 1971—. Organist and choir dir. Greenwood Meth. Ch., 1972—; piano tchr. Bible sch. and Sunday sch. tchr. Greenwood Meth. Ch., 1972—. Recipient Spl. Mission Recognition award Meth. Ch. for Music, 1981, Spl. Recognition award Music Dean Dist. United Meth. Houghton Coll., 1992, Gen. Douglas MacArthur Youth award The Grand Lodge of the State of N.Y., 1994; featured in Evening Tribune, Hornell, N.Y., 1990, Corning Leader, 1992; named Outstanding Citizen West Greenwood Grange, 1992. Mem. Delta Kappa Gamma (publicity chair 1989—, sec. 1994-95). Methodist. Avocations: flower gardening, crafts, needlework, quilting, bike riding. Home: 2671 Main St Greenwood NY 14839 Office: Greenwood Cen Sch PO Box 936 Greenwood NY 14839-0936

ROLLINS, R. RANDALL, diversified services company executive. Sr. vice chmn. Rollins, Inc., Atlanta. Office: RPC Energy Svcs Inc 2170 Piedmont Rd NE Atlanta GA 30324-4135

ROLLINS, SHERRIE SANDY, television executive; b. Roanoke, Va., June 11, 1958; d. William Gresham and Charlotte (Weeks) Sandy; m. Edward John Rollins, Jr., May 2, 1987. BA, U. Va., 1980. Sr. v.p. ABC TV Network, Washington, 1980; advt. dir. Georgetown mag., Alexandria, Va., 1980-81; exec. dir. Bus. and Profl. Assn. Georgetown, Washington, 1981-84; v.p. communications The Oliver Carr Co., Washington, 1985-89; asst. sec. for pub. affairs HUD, Washington, 1989-90; dir. news info. ABC News, N.Y.C., 1990-92; asst. to Pres. of U.S. for pub. liason and intergovtl. affairs The White House, Washington, 1992; sr. v.p. U.S. News and World Report, Washington, 1992-94; sr. v.p. Network Comms. ABC TV Network, N.Y.C., 1994—; bd. dirs. Am. Coun. Young Pol. Leaders, Cities in Schs. Mem. U. Va. Alumni Assn. (bd. mgrs.). Home: 7732 Southdown Rd Alexandria VA 22308-1341 Office: Capital Cities/ABC 77 West 66th St New York NY 10023

ROLLINS, (THEODORE) SONNY, composer, musician; b. N.Y.C., Sept. 7, 1930; s. Walter and Valborg (Solomon) R.; m. Dawn Finney, 1956 (div.); m. Lucille Pearson, Sept. 7, 1959. Ed. high sch., N.Y.C.; ArtsD, Bard Coll., 1992. Condr. Sonny Rollins & Co. Orch., concert tours in Europe, Far East, 1973—; composed, scored and played music for motion picture Alfie; recs. for Milestone, Fantasy-Prestige compositions include Way Out West, also others. Recipient numerous awards Guggenheim fellow, 1972. Home: RR 9 # G Germantown NY 12526

ROLLINS, THOMAS MICHIELI, lawyer; b. Panama Canal Zone, Nov. 1, 1955; s. Thomas Walsh and Mary (Michieli) R. BA cum laude, Georgetown U., 1978; JD magna cum laude, Harvard U., 1982. Bar: Tex. 1985. Reporter New Times & Politics Today Mag., Washington, 1978-79; research asst. Sen. Jud. Com., Washington, 1978-79; law clk. U.S. Ct. Appeals (2nd cir.), Vt., 1982-83; assoc. Susman, Godfrey & McGowen, Houston, 1983-85; chief of staff, chief counsel U.S. Senate Commn. Labor & Human Resources, Washington, 1985-89; pres. The Coll. Co., Washington, 1989—. Contbr. articles to profl. jours. Mem. ABA, Tex. Bar, Leadership Council of Build Am. Home and Office: Coll Am Corp 2727 Duke St Apt 1401 Alexandria VA 22314-4541

ROLLMAN, STEVEN ALLAN, communication educator; b. N.Y.C., Aug. 3, 1947; s. Leo and Margot (Seelenberger) R.; m. Nancy Sue Toberen, June 15, 1973; 1 child. Benjamin Allan. BA, C.W. Post Coll., 1970; MA, Ohio U., 1972; PhD, Pa. State U., 1977. Instr. Pa. State U., University Park, 1976; asst. prof. James Madison U., Harrisonburg, Va., 1977-83, assoc. prof., 1983-95, coord. interpersonal communication, 1986-90, prof., 1995—; cons. various sch. dists., Va., 1978—; Swissair, Zurich, 1971-72; book reviewer Choice, 1982—. Contbr. articles to profl. jours.; editor: Virginia Journal of Communication, 1980-81. Mem. Speech Comm. Assn., So. States Comm. Assn., Va. Speech Comm. Assn., Internat. Listening Assn. Avocations: computers, music, film, automobiles, tennis. Home: 608 Wynham Woods Cir Harrisonburg VA 22801-1668 Office: James Madison U Dept Communication Harrisonburg VA 22807

ROLLO, F. DAVID, hospital management company executive, radiology educator; b. Endicott, N.Y., Apr. 15, 1939; s. Frank C. and Augustine L. (Dumont) R.; m. Linda Wood, June 1, 1991; children : Mindee, Alex. BA, Harpur Coll., 1959; MS, U. Miami, 1965; PhD, Johns Hopkins U., 1968; MD, Upstate Med. Ctr., Syracuse, N.Y., 1972. Diplomate Am. Bd. Nuclear Medicine. Asst. chief nuclear medicine services VA Hosp., San Francisco, 1974-77; chief nuclear medicine VA Hosp., Nashville, 1977-79; sr. v.p. med. affairs Humana Inc., Louisville, 1980-92; dir. nuclear medicine div. Vanderbilt U. Med. Ctr., Nashville, 1977-81; prof. radiology Vanderbilt U., Nashville, 1979—; pres., CEO Metricor Inc., Louisville, 1992—; mem. med. adv. com. IBT, Washington, 1984—; mem. pvt. sector liaison panel Inst. of Medicine, Washington, 1983—; bd. dirs. ADAC Labs., KBL Healthcare, Positron Corp., Inc., Raytel Med. Corp., Cambridge Heart. Editor: Nuclear Medicine Physics, Instruments and Agents, 1977; co-editor: Physical Basis of Medical Imaging, 1980, Digital Radiology: Focus on Clinical Utility, 1982, Nuclear Medicine Resonance Imaging, 1983; mem. editorial adv. bd. ECRI, 1981—. Pres. bd. dirs. Youth Performing Arts Council, Louisville, 1984-85; bd. dirs. Louisville-Jefferson County Youth Orch., 1983-85; sr. v.p., exec. com. USA Internat. Harp Competition, 1992—. Fellow Am. Coll. Nuclear Physicians (profl. com. 1982-84, chmn. 1984); mem. AMA, Soc. Nuclear Medicine (trustee 1979-83, 84—, Cassen Meml. lectr. western region 1980, 84), Radiol. Soc. N.Am., Am. Coll. Radiology, Ky. Sci. Tech. Coun. (exec. bd. 1987—), Advancement Med. Instrumentation (bd. dirs. 1986—), Louisville C. of C. (chmn. MIC com. 1987—). Avocations: racquetball, squash. Home: 5646 Bailey Grant Rd Jeffersonville IN 47130-8607 Office: 500 W Main St Ste 1900 Louisville KY 40202-2941

ROLLOW, THOMAS A., federal official. BS in Mech. Engring. cum laude, Tulane U., 1975; MS in Nuclear Engring., Bettis Atomic Power Lab., 1976; MS in Engring. Adminstrn., George Washington U., 1979. Dep. asst. sec. nuclear safety office environment, safety and health Dept. Energy, Washington. Lt. comdr. USN, 1975-80, lt. comdr. res. Mem. Tau Beta Pi. Office: Nuclear Safety 1000 Independence Ave SW Gaithersburg MD 20878

ROLLS, JOHN ALLISON, electronics company executive; b. Hamilton, Ont., Can., June 1, 1941; came to U.S., 1955, naturalized, 1963; s. James Allison and Mary Elizabeth (Kirkendale) R.; m. Betsy Ann Becker, Aug. 21, 1966; children: Jason Andrew, Michael Allison. B.S., Ohio State U., 1964;

M.B.A., Columbia U., 1968. Ea. regional supr. Fisher Body Craftsman's Guild; also instr. mgmt. devel. Gen. Motors Inst., Gen. Motors Corp., 1964-67; fin. analyst Ford Motor Co., 1968-69; asst. treas. Kenton Corp., N.Y.C., 1969-72, Penn Co., N.Y.C., 1973-74; with Monsanto Co., St. Louis, from 1974; asst. treas. Monsanto Co., 1974-75; dir. fin. Monsanto Co., Europe, 1975; dep. treas. Monsanto Co., St. Louis, 1978-79; former treas. Monsanto Co., from 1979; v.p., treas. RCA, N.Y.C., 1982-84, sr. v.p. fin., chief fin. officer, 1984-86; exec. v.p., chief fin. officer United Techs., Hartford, Conn., 1986—. Home: 4 Frog Rock Rd Armonk NY 10504-1012 Office: United Techs Corp United Techs Bldg Hartford CT 06101

ROLLWAGEN, JOHN A., federal official; b. 1940; married. BSEE, MIT, 1962; MBA, Harvard U., 1964. Mktg. rep. Control Data Corp., 1964-66; prodn. mgr. Monsanto Corp., 1966-68; v.p. Internat. Timesharing Corp., 1968-75; v.p. fin. Cray Rsch. Inc., 1975-76, v.p. mktg., 1976-77, pres., 1977-80, pres., chief exec. officer, 1980-88, chmn., chief exec. officer, 1981-1993, also bd. dirs.; dep. sec. Dept. of Commerce, Washington, 1993—; bd. dirs. Dayton Hudson Corp., Minn.; chmn. bd. dirs. Fed. Reserve Bank Minn. Office: Dept of Commerce 14th & Constitution Ave NW Washington DC 20230-0002 also: Cray Rsch Inc 608 2nd Ave S Ste 154 Minneapolis MN 55402-1910 also: Cray Rsch Inc 655 Alone Oak Dr Eagan MN 55121

ROLNIK, ZACHARY JACOB, senior editor, publisher; b. Bayonne, N.J., Oct. 2, 1961; s. Joseph and Katie (Simon) R. BA, U. Rochester, 1982; M. in Pub. Policy, Harvard U., 1984. Ops. analyst, presdl. mgmt. intern U.S. Dept. Treasury, Washington, 1984-85; sr. editor, pub. Kluwer Acad. Pubs., Norwell, Mass., 1985—. Home: 146 Pleasant St Hanover MA 02339-1844 Office: Kluwer Acad Pubs 101 Philip Dr Norwell MA 02061-1615

ROLONTZ, ROBERT, recording company executive; b. Phila., Dec. 14, 1920; s. David E. and Rose (Malis) R.; m. Susan P. Morgan, Aug. 29, 1959; children: Lee Alison, Robert Morgan. BS, Columbia U., 1952, postgrad., 1952-54. Record producer RCA Victor Records, 1955-58; music editor Billboard mag., 1962-63; exec. editor Music Bus. mag., 1964-65; dir. advt. and publicity Atlantic Records, N.Y.C., 1965—; v.p. advt. and publicity Atlantic Records, 1969-74; dir. corporate information Warner Communications Inc., N.Y.C., 1974-84; v.p. communications Cosmos Soccer Club, N.Y.C., 1977-84; lit. agt., 1988—. Author: How to Get Your Song Recorded, 1963; contbr. articles to mags. Chmn. Ralph J. Gleason Music Book Awards. With USAAF, 1942-45, ETO. Decorated Air medal with clusters. Mem. NARAS, Music Reporters Assn. (founder, v.p. 1953-55), Record Industry Assn. Am. Office: 115 E 92nd St New York NY 10128-1688

ROLSTON, HOLMES, III, theologian, educator, philosopher; b. Staunton, Va., Nov. 19, 1932; s. Holmes and Mary Winifred (Long) R.; m. Jane Irving Wilson, June 1, 1956; children: Shonny Hunter, Giles Campbell. BS, Davidson Coll., 1953; BD, Union Theol. Sem., Richmond, Va., 1956; MA in Philosophy of Sci., U. Pitts., 1968; PhD in Theology, U. Edinburgh, Scotland, 1958. Ordained to ministry Presbyn. Ch. (USA), 1956. Asst. prof. philosophy Colo. State U., Ft. Collins, 1968-71, assoc. prof., 1971-76, prof., 1976—; vis. scholar Ctr. Study of World Religions, Harvard U., 1974-75; lectr. Yale U., Vanderbilt U., others; official observer UNCED, Rio de Janiero, 1992. Author: Religious Inquiry: Participation and Detachment, 1985, Philosophy Gone Wild, 1986, Science and Religion: A Critical Survey, 1987, Environmental Ethics, 1988, Conserving Natural Value, 1994; assoc. editor Environ. Ethics, 1979—; mem. editorial bd. Oxford Series in Environ. Philosophy and Pub. Policy, Zygon: Jour. of Religion and Sci.; contbr. chpts. to books, articles to profl. jours. Recipient Oliver P. Penock Disting. Svc. award Colo. State U., 1983, Coll. Award for Excellence, 1991., Univ. Disting. Prof., 1992; Disting. Russell fellow Grad. Theol. Union, 1991, Disting. Lectr. Chinese Acad. of Social Scis., 1991, Disting. Lectr. Nobel Conf. XXVII. Mem. AAAS, Am. Acad. Religion, Soc. Bibl. Lit. (pres. Rocky Mountain-Gt. Plains region), Am. Philos. Assn., Internat. Soc. for Environ. Ethics (pres. 1989-94), Phi Beta Kappa. Avocation: bryology. Home: 1712 Concord Dr Fort Collins CO 80526-1602 Office: Colo State U Dept Philosophy Fort Collins CO 80523

ROLSTON, ROBERT JOHN, accountant, consultant; b. N.Y.C., June 28, 1944; s. Robert Joseph and Meta Loretta (Marshall) R.; m. Heide-Maria Aniszewski, Nov. 8, 1969 (div. Mar. 1975); m. Annie Teresa Cryan, Oct. 2, 1982 (div. Apr. 1991). BBA, Hofstra U., 1974. CPA, N.Y. Sr. acct. Fass, Tuchler & Muster, CPAs, Great Neck, N.Y., 1974-77, Seidman & Seidman, CPAs, N.Y.C., 1977-78, Kraft, Fischman & Assocs., CPAs, N.Y.C., 1978-80; supervising acct. David Tarlow & Co., CPAs, N.Y.C., 1980-81; fin. officer Allied Trading Corp., Secaucus, N.J., 1981-82; contr. Konishiroku Photo Industries, Enlwd Cliffs, N.J., 1982-84; mng. acct. Bachman, Schwartz, Abramson, CPAs, N.Y.C., 1984-86; corp. contr. Yarnell Group, N.Y.C., 1986-87; tax mgr. Lazar, Levine & Co., CPAs, N.Y.C., 1987-88; prin. Robert J. Rolston, CPA, Guttenberg, N.J., 1988—. Co-author (with others): Accounting II, 1974. Mgr. Richmond Hill (N.Y.) Little League, 1978; deacon Second Ref. Ch., Hackensack, N.J., 1986-89, ch. Sunday sch. tchr., 1988-89; mem. leadership group Marble Collegiate Ch., 1993—; chmn. Condo Govt. Affairs Com., Guttenberg, 1986-87; facilitator Compassionate Friends, Hackensack, 1991—; music dir. Galaxy Singers, Guttenberg, 1989; asst. music dir. Metrognomes Singing Group, 1988-93, bus. mgr., 1993—; mem. Univ. Glee Club of N.Y.C. Mem. AICPA, N.Y. State Soc. CPAs, Coop. Stock Brokers and Exchs. Com., Internat. Taxation Com., Beta Gamma Sigma. Democrat. Avocations: music, golf, art, history, coin and stamp collecting. Office: Robert J Rolston CPA 7004 Blvd E Ste 36B West New York NJ 07093

ROM, (MELVIN) MARTIN, securities executive; b. Detroit, Mar. 2, 1946; s. Jack and Thelma (Meyer) R.; m. Barbara Miller, July 12, 1970. BA magna cum laude, U. Mich., 1967. Founder MultiVest, Inc., Southfield, Mich., 1969; pres. MultiVest, Inc., Southfield, 1969-73; chmn. bd., chief exec. officer MultiVest, Inc., 1973-75; pres. Real Estate Securities and Syndication Inst., Nat. Assn. Realtors, Washington, 1975—; dir., bd. govs. Real Estate Securities and Syndication Inst., Nat. Assn. Realtors, 1972—; pres. Martin Rom Co., Inc., 1976—; vice chmn. Sports Illus. Ct. Clubs, Inc., 1977-79; bd. dirs. Mocatta Corp., Med. Informatics Corp.; mem. joint com. Nat. Assn. Securities Dealers-Nat. Assn. Realtors, 1975-76; mem. adv. com. on market instruments Commodity Futures Trading Commn. Author: Nothing Can Replace the U.S. Dollar . . . and It Almost Has, 1975; Adv. bd.: Housing and Devel. Reporter, Washington. Trustee U. Chgo. Found. Mem. Nat. Assn. Securities Dealers, Com. on Gold Regulations, Phi Beta Kappa. Home and Office: 60 Quarton Ln Bloomfield Hills MI 48304-3456

ROMAGOSA, ELMO LAWRENCE, clergyman, retired editor; b. Thibodaux, La., Jan. 11, 1922; s. Lawrence Gabriel and Lydie (Achee) R. Ed., St. Joseph Sem., Notre Dame Sem., New Orleans, 1947. Ordained priest Roman Cath. Ch., 1947. Asst. pastor Cut Off, La., 1947-50, New Orleans, 1950-58; chaplain Ursuline Convent and Nat. Shrine Our Lady of Prompt Succor, 1958-63; pastor St. John's Ch., New Orleans, 1963-70; asst. dir. Soc. for Propagation of Faith, 1950-60, dir., 1962; communications dir. Archdiocese New Orleans, 1962; founding editor Clarion Herald newspaper, 1963-74; priest in residence Sts. Peter and Paul Ch., New Orleans, 1970-72; pastor Holy Trinity Ch., New Orleans, 1972-74, St. Rose of Lima Ch., New Orleans, 1974-76, St. Clement of Rome Ch., Metairie, La., 1976-84; chaplain Port of New Orleans, 1984-88; pastor Ch. of Infant Jesus, Harvey, La., 1988—; nat. sec. Cath. Broadcasters Assn., 1963-65; mem. U.S. Cath. bishops subcoms. on Cath.-Jewish relations, 1965; named prelate of honor, 1980. Editor Airtime, 1963-64. Dir. Stella Maris Maritime Ctr., 1984-88; chaplain Harbor Police, Port of New Orleans, 1984-88; mem. Nat. Conf. Seafarers, 1984, pres., 1986—, mem. legal adv. com. Ctr. for Seafarers Rights, 1986; mem. Nat. Cath. Conf. for Seafarers, 1984, pres., 1986-88. Recipient First Place award for best editorial and best feature photo Press Club New Orleans, 1965, First Place award for best column Press Club New Orleans, 1972; named Prelate of Honor, Pope John II, 1980. Mem. Cath. Press Assn. (1st Place awards for gen. excellence 1963-65), Sociedad Espanola New Orleans (founding sec.-treas.), Equestrian Order of Holy Sepulchre of Jerusalem (knight 1978, knight comdr. 1983, master of ceremonies 1986, Gold Palms of Jerusalem medallion 1993). Republican. Home and Office: Ch of the Infant Jesus 700 Maple Ave Harvey LA 70058-4008

ROMAINE, HENRY SIMMONS, investment consultant; b. N.Y.C., May 30, 1933; s. Theodore Cole and Cornelia (Simmons) R.; m. Susan Donaldson; children: Henry, Hilary, Kathryn. BA, Harvard U., 1954. Asst. security analyst Mutual Life Ins. Co., N.Y.C., 1958-60, investment analyst, 1960-61, investment specialist, 1961-64, asst. dir. investments, 1964, dir. investments, 1964-66, asst. v.p. for securities investment, 1966-68, 2d v.p. for securities investment, 1969-71, v.p. for securities investment, 1971-72, sr. v.p., 1972-78, sr. v.p., chief investment officer, 1976-78, exec. v.p., 1978-81, pres., 1981-86; vice chmn., chief investment officer Am. Gen. Corp., Houston, 1986-93; dir. MONY Life Ins. Co. of Can.; chmn. bd. MONY Real Estate Investors, 1978-86; mem. adv. bd. Chem. Bank, 1974-93. Served with USN, 1954-57. Mem. Links Club, Harvard Club. Home: 7 Conquest Ave Sullivans Island SC 29482-9779

ROMAN, KENNETH, JR., corporate communications executive; b. Boston, Sept. 6, 1930; s. Kenneth J. and Bernice (Freedman) R.; m. Ellen L. Fischer, Mar. 27, 1953. BA, Dartmouth Coll., 1952. Asst. advt. promotion mgr. Interchem Crp., N.Y.C., 1952-55; mgr. advt. sales promotion Raymond Rosen Co., Phila., 1955-56; advt. mgr. Allied Chem. Corp., 1956-63; account mgr. Ogilvy & Mather, N.Y.C., 1963-79; pres. Ogilvy & Mather, U.S., 1979-85, Ogilvy and Mather Worldwide, 1985-89; chmn., chief exec. The Ogilvy Group, 1988-89; exec. v.p. corp. affairs and communications Am. Express Co., N.Y.C., 1989-91; bd. dirs. Compaq Computer Corp., IBJ Schroder Bank & Trust Co., Penncorp Fin. Group, CIA Group plc. (U.K.). Co-author: The New How to Advertise, 1992, Writing That Works, 1992. Bd. dirs. N.Y. Bot. Garden, Meml. Sloan-Kettering Cancer Ctr. Mem. Univ. Club (N.Y.C.), The Century Assn. Home: 7 Gracie Sq New York NY 10028-8030 Office: 866 3rd Ave Fl 26 New York NY 10022-6221

ROMAN, STANFORD AUGUSTUS, JR., medical educator, dean; b. N.Y.C.; s. Stanford Augustas and Ivy L. (White) R.; children: Mawiyah Lythcott, Jane E. Roman-Brown. AB, Dartmouth Coll., 1964; MD, Columbia U., 1968; MPH, U. Mich., 1975. Diplomate Nat. Bd. of Med. Examiners. Intern in medicine Columbia U.-Harlem Hosp. Ctr., 1966-69, resident in medicine, 1969-71, chief resident in medicine, 1971-73; assoc. dir. ambulatory care Columbia U. Harlem Hosp., N.Y.C., 1972-73; instr. in medicine Columbia U., N.Y.C., 1972-73; asst. physician Presbyn. Hosp., 1972-73; clin. dir. Healthco Inc., Soul City, N.C., 1973-74; dir. ambulatory care, asst. prof. medicine/sociomed. scis. Boston City Hosp., 1974-78; asst. prof. medicine U. N.C., Chapel Hill, 1973-74; asst. dean Boston U. Sch. Medicine, 1974-78; med. dir. D.C. Gen. Hosp., Washington, 1978-81; assoc. dean acad. affairs Dartmouth Med. Sch., Hanover, N.H., 1981-86; assoc. prof., 1981-87, dep. dean, 1986-87; dean, v.p., prof. medicine Morehouse Sch. Med., Atlanta, 1987-89; sr. v.p., med. and prof. affairs Health and Hosps. Corp., N.Y.C., 1989-90; dean med. sch., prof. community health and social medicine CUNY, 1990—; dir. Boston Comprehensive Sickle Cell Ctr., 1975-78; bd. dirs. Nat. Bd. Med. Examiners, Phila., 1988-92, Winifred Masterson Burke Rehab. Hosp., White Plains, N.Y.; mem. Dartmouth Hitchcock Med. Ctr. Bd. of Medicine, N.Y.; trustee Dartmouth Coll.; mem. N.Y. State Coun. on Grad. Med. Edn. Contbr. to book chpts. and profl. jours. and editls. Mem. AMA, APHA, Nat. Med. Assn., N.Y. State Coun. Grad. Med. Education, N.Y. State Dept. Edn. Bd. Medicine. Democrat. Episcopalian. Avocations: photography, travel, music. Office: CUNY Med Sch J 909 Convent Ave and 138th St New York NY 10031

ROMAN-BARBER, HELEN, corporate executive; b. Dec. 20, 1946. LLB, U. Paris, 1971, M of Internat. Law, 1972. Chmn., chief exec. officer Roman Corp. Ltd., Toronto, Ont., Can. Office: Roman Corp Ltd, 200 King St W Box 82, Toronto, ON Canada M5H 3T4

ROMANELLI, G. JACK, journalist; b. San Benedetto Del Tronto, Ascoli Piceno, Italy, Oct. 16, 1959; arrived in Can., 1965; s. Martino and Ida (Michetti) R.; m. Lily Bramante, Aug. 30, 1985; children: Alexa, Julian. BA in Journalism, Loyalist Coll., 1983. Reporter Alliston (Ont.) Herald, Can., 1983; reporter, columnist Burlington (Ont.) Gazette, 1983-84; copy editor Montreal (Que.) Gazette, Can., 1984-88, asst. sports editor, 1988-91; exec. sports editor Montreal (Que.) Gazette, 1991-95, asst. mng. editor sports and projects, 1995—; chmn. sports editors' com. Southam Newspaper Group, 1993—; chmn. Can. region AP Sports Editors, 1994—. Avocations: reading, golf, racquetball, baseball stats. analysis. Home: 1538 Baxter St, LaSalle, PQ Canada H8N 2T5 Office: The Montreal Gazette, 250 St Antoine St W, Montreal, PQ Canada H2Y 3R7

ROMANESE, GINO, real estate executive; b. Montreal, Que., Can., July 26, 1957; s. Bruno and Angelina (LePore) R.; m. Anna Rossi, May 3, 1980; children: Marisa, Michael. B of Commerce (hon.), Concordia U., 1979. Cert. Real Estate Inst. of Canada, Canadian Real Estate Assn. Sales rep. A.E. LePage, Montreal, 1975-79, br. mgr., 1979-81, regional mgr., 1981-86; sr. v.p., div. mgr. Royal LePage, B.C., 1986-87, Que., 1987-88; sen. v.p. Royal LePage, Ont., 1988—; lifetime mem. Montreal Real Estate Bd., pres., 1986. Avocations: reading, squash, hockey. Office: Royal LePage Real Estate Svcs, 39 Wynford Dr, Don Mills, ON Canada M3C 3K5

ROMANI, JOHN HENRY, health administration educator; b. Milan, Italy, Mar. 6, 1925; s. Henry Arthur and Hazel (Pettengill) R.; m. Barbara A. Anderson; children: David John, Paul Nichols, Theresa A. Anderson. BA, U. N.H., 1949, MA, 1949; PhD, U. Mich., 1955. Instr. U. N.H., 1950-51; instr. U. Mich., Ann Arbor, 1954-55, assoc. prof., asst. to assoc. dean Sch. Pub. Health, 1961-69, assoc. v.p., 1971-75, chmn. health planning and adminstrn., 1975-80, prof., 1971-93, prof. emeritus pub. health adminstrn., 1993—; interim chair Pub. Health Policy and Adminstrn., 1991-92; sr. assoc. Gini Assocs., 1984—; asst. prof. Western Mich. U., 1956-57; assoc. dir. Cleve. Met. Services Commn., 1957-59; assoc. prof. U. Pitts., 1959-61; vice chancellor, prof. U. Wis.-Milw., 1969-71; research fellow Brookings Instn., 1955-56; task force mem. Nat. Commn. on Orgn. Community Health Services, 1963-66; staff dir. Sec.'s Com. on Orgn. Health Activities, HEW, 1965-66; dir. Govtl. Affairs Inst., 1969-75, chmn., 1970-72; trustee Pub. Adminstrn. Service, 1969-75, chmn., 1973-75; bd. dirs. Delta Dental Plan Mich., 1972-78, chmn. consumer's adv. council, 1975-77; bd. dirs. Centre for Population Activities, 1975-81, chmn., 1975-81. Author: The Philippine Presidency, 1956; editor: Changing Dimensions in Public Administration, 1962; contbr. articles to profl. jours. Mem. Citizens League, Cleve., 1957-59; mem. Ann Arbor Citizens Council, 1965-69; bd. dirs. Southeastern Mich. Family Planning Project, 1975-77; trustee Congregational Summer Assembly, 1982-85; commr. Accrediting Commn. on Edn. for Health Svcs. Asminstrn., 1989—. Served with AUS, 1943-46, ETO. Fellow Am. Pub. Health Assn. (chmn. program devel. bd. 1975-77, mem. exec. bd. 1975-80, mem. governing coun. 1975—, pres. 1979, chmn. publs. bd. 1984-88), Royal Soc. Health (hon.), Am. Polit. Sci. Assn. (life); mem. Am. Soc. Pub. Adminstrn. (past mem. coun.), Phi Kappa Phi, Pi Sigma Alpha, Pi Gamma Mu, Delta Omega. Home: 2670 Bedford Rd Ann Arbor MI 48104 Office: PO Box 7903 Ann Arbor MI 48107-7903

ROMANKIW, LUBOMYR TARAS, materials engineer; b. Zhowkwa, Ukraine, Apr. 17, 1931. BSc, U. Alta., 1955; MSc and PhD in Metallurgy, MIT, 1962. Mem. rsch. staff materials and processes, Thomas J. Watson Rsch. Ctr. IBM Corp, Yorktown Heights, N.Y., 1962-63, mgr. magnetic components divsn., 1965-68, mgr. magnetic material and devices, 1968-78, mgr. material and process studies, 1981-91, dep. mgr.; fellow IBM Corp, 1986; head Ctr. for Electrochem. Tech. and Microfabrication IBM Corp, Yorktown Heights, N.Y., 1991—; instr. MIT, 1959-61; cons. East Fishkill Devel. Lab. & Mfg. IBM Corp, 1978-80, San Jose Devel. Lab. and Mfg. Recipient Perkin medal Am. Chem. Soc., 1993; IBM fellow, 1986, ECS fellow, 1990, IBM Acad. Tech. fellow, 1984. Mem. IEEE (Morris Liebman award 1994), Electrochem. Soc. (sec.-treas. 1979-80, Vittorio de Nora medal and award 1994), Am. Electroplaters Soc. award, Acad. Engring. Sci. of Ukraine, Sigma Xi. Achievements include research in magnetic thin films, deposition of thin films, ray lithography mask devel. dielectrics, magnetic device design, material selection and fabrication, electrodeposition, magnetic materials, electronic and magnetic device fabrication, chemical engineering, and metallurgy. Office: IBM-Thomas J Watson Research Ctr POB 218 Yorktown Heights NY 10598

ROMANO, DOMINICK V., food products executive; b. 1934. V.p. Ronetco Supermarkets, Inc. subs. Shoprite Supermarkets, Inc., Succasunna, N.J., 1953—; treas., bd. dirs., chmn. bd. Shoprite Supermarkets, Inc., Edison, N.J., 1985—. Office: Shoprite Supermarkets Inc 130 Campus Plz Edison NJ 08837-3936

ROMANO, ROBERTA, law educator; b. Bklyn., Jan. 27, 1952. AB with highest honors, U. Rochester, 1973; MA, U. Chgo., 1975; JD, Yale U., 1980. Law clk. U.S. Ct. Appeals (2d cir.), Hartford, Conn., 1980-81; asst. prof. Stanford (Calif.) U., 1981-84, assoc. prof., 1984-85; prof. of law Yale U., New Haven, Conn., 1985—, Allen Duffy prof. of law, 1991—. Co-editor Jour. Law, Econs., and Orgn., 1988—. Mem. Assn. Am. Law Schs. (exec. coun., bus. assns. sect. 1987-90, chmn. 1990), Phi Beta Kappa. Office: Yale Law Sch 127 Wall St Drawer 401A Yale Sta New Haven CT 06520

ROMANOFF, MILFORD MARTIN, building contractor, architectural designer; b. Cleve., Aug. 21, 1921; s. Barney Sanford and Edythe Stolpher (Bort) R.; student Coll. Arch., U. Mich., 1939-42; B.B.A., U. Toledo, 1943; m. Marjorie Reinwald, Nov. 6, 1945; children—Bennett S., Lawrence M., Janet Beth (dec.). Pres., Glass City Constrn. Co., Toledo, 1951-55, Milford Romanoff Inc., Toledo, 1956—. Co-founder, Neighborhood Improvement Found. Toledo, 1960; mem. Lucas County Econ. Devel. Com., 1979—; mem. citizens adv. bd. Recreation Commn. Toledo, 1973-86; mem. campus adv. com. Med. Coll. Ohio, 1980—; trustee Cummings Treatment Center for Adolescents, 1981—; mem. Children's Services Bd. Lucas County, 1981—; pres. Ohio B'nai Brith, 1959-60, Toledo Lodge, 1958-59; bd. dirs. Anti-Defamation League, 1955-60, Ohio Hillel Orgns., Lucas County Dept. Human Svcs.; chmn. Toledo Amateur Baseball and Softball Com., 1979-81; mem. Democratic Precinct Com., 1975-78, Arthritis Bd. Dirs.; trustee Temple Brotherhood, 1956-58, bd. dirs., 1981—; pres. Cherry Hill Nursing Home, 1964-85; cons. U.S. Care Corp., 1985—; mem. Crosby Gardens Bd. Advisors, 1983—; bd. govs. Toledo Housing for Elderly, 1982-84, sec., 1989, pres. bd. govs., 1990—, pres, 1991—; bd. advisors Ret. Sr. Vol. Program, 1987-89, chmn. 1988-90, 93—, sec. adv. bd., 1990—; mem. adv. bd. Salvation Army (vice chmn. 1986-87), Mental Health Adv. Bd., 1983-84, sec., 1989; bd. dirs. Kidney Found. Northwestern Ohio, 1986—, sec., 1989; bd. dirs. Toledo Urban Forestry Commn., 1991—, pres., 1993—. Lt. (j.g.) USN, 1943-46. Mem. U. Toledo Alumni Assn., Toledo Mus. Art (asso.), Econ. Opportunity Planning Assn. Greater Toledo, U. Mich. Alumni Assn., Toledo Zool. Soc., Zeta Beta Tau. Clubs: Masons; B'nai B'rith (pres. Toledo lodge 1958-59, statewide pres. 1959-60), Hadassah (assoc. Toledo chpt.). Home and Office: Milford Romanoff Inc 2514 Bexford Pl Toledo OH 43606-2414

ROMANOW, ROY JOHN, provincial government official, barrister, solicitor; b. 1939; s. Michael and Tekla R.; m. Eleanore Boykowich, 1967. Educated at Univ. of Sask. Mem. Sask. Legislative Assembly, 1967-82, 1986—; provincial sec., 1971-72, atty. gen. of province, 1971-82, minister of intergovernmental affairs, 1979-82, leader, Sask. New Dem. Party, 1987—; leader of the opposition, 1987-91, leader of the majority, 1991—; premier, 1991—; opposition house leader for New Dem. Party Caucus, 1986. Co-author: Canada Notwithstanding, 1984. Office: Legislative Assembly, 2405 Legislative Dr, Regina, SK Canada S4S 0B3

ROMANOWITZ, BYRON FOSTER, architect, engineer; b. Covington, Ky., Nov. 14, 1929; s. Harry Alex and Mildred (Foster) R.; m. Mildred Elaine Gize, June 15, 1957; children: Laura Ann, Mark Walter, Cynthia Ellen. B.S. in Civil Engring, U. Ky., 1951; M.F.A. in Architecture, Princeton, 1953. Instr. sch. architecture Princeton U., 1954; architect Brock & Johnson, Lexington, 1958-59, Johnson & Romanowitz, Architects, Lexington and Louisville, 1960—; Pres. Ky. Bd. Examiners and Registration of Architects, 1975-91. Prin. works include U. Ky. campus bldgs., 1959-91, Ea. Ky. U. campus bldgs., 1959-77, Centre Coll., Danville, Ky., campus bldgs., 1967-89, Georgetown (Ky.) Coll. campus bldgs., 1964-84, Asbury Coll., Wilmore, Ky., 1972-78, Asbury Theol. Sem., 1978-93, Berea Coll. bldgs., 1978-91, Transylvania U. bldgs., 1974-90, U. Louisville, 1990, 11 downtown Lexington office bldgs. Mem. Lexington Urban Renewal Commn., 1963-69; chmn. adv. bd. Salvation Army, 1971-72; trustee Midway (Ky.) Coll., 1986—. Served with USNR, 1955-58; lt. comdr. Res. Recipient award of merit nat. archtl. competition AIA/Ednl. Facilities Lab., 1966. Fellow AIA (1st honor awards Ky. archtl. competition 1959, 61, 68, 70, 73, 78, 80, 81, pres. East Ky. chpt. 1965); mem. Ky. Soc. Architects (pres. 1966), Masons, Rotary, Lexington Club, Lexington Country Club, Cotillion Club, Pendennis Club, Tau Beta Pi, Phi Mu Alpha, Phi Sigma Kappa. Home: 2057 Lakeside Dr Lexington KY 40502-3016 Office: Johnson Romanowitz/ Arch & Assoc 300 E Main St Ste 301 Lexington KY 40507-1513

ROMANOWSKI, THOMAS ANDREW, physics educator; b. Warsaw, Poland, Apr. 17, 1925; came to U.S., 1946, naturalized, 1949; s. Bohdan and Alina (Sumowski) R.; m. Carmen des Rochers, Nov. 15, 1952; children—Alina, Dominique. B.S., Mass. Inst. Tech., 1952; M.S., Case Inst. Tech., 1956, Ph.D., 1957. Rsch. assoc. physics Carnegie Inst. Tech., 1956-60; asst. physicist high energy physics Argonne Nat. Lab., Ill., 1960-63; assoc. physicist Argonne Nat. Lab., 1963-72, physicist, 1972-78; prof. physics Ohio State U., Columbus, 1964-92, prof. emeritus, 1992—; sr. scientist Argonne Nat. Lab., 1992. Contbr. articles to profl. jours. and papers to sci. meetings, seminars and workshops. Served with C.E. AUS, 1946-47. Fellow Am. Phys. Soc., AAAS; mem. Lambda Chi Alpha. Achievements include research in nuclear and high energy physics. Home: 4408 Morgan St Rockville MD 20853-6117 Office: Dept Energy Div High Energy Physic Washington DC 20585

ROMANS, DONALD BISHOP, corporate executive; b. Louisville, Apr. 22, 1931; s. Albert D. and Moneta (Bishop) R.; m. Marilyn Yvonne Neff, June 13, 1953; children: Rebecca Ann, Jennifer. BS, U. Louisville, 1953; MBA, Harvard U., 1958. Mgr. internal auditing and data processing, mem. contr. staff Container Corp. Am., Chgo., 1958-62; successively asst. to pres., asst. treas., treas., v.p. fin., sr. v.p. fin., exec. v.p Trans Union Corp., Chgo., 1962-81; exec. v.p., chief fin. officer Sunbeam Corp., Chgo., 1981-82, Bally Mfg. Corp., Chgo., 1982-87; fin. cons. Chgo., 1987; pres. Romans and Co., Chgo., 1987-93; chmn. Merlin Corp., Geneva, Ill., 1990; bd. dirs. Burnham Fund Inc., N.Y.C.; trustee Zweig Series Trust, N.Y.C.; life trustee St. Mary of Nazareth Hosp. Capt. USMCR, 1953-56. Mem. Econ. Club. Republican. Avocations: tennis, boating.

ROMANS, JOHN NIEBRUGGE, lawyer; b. Bklyn., May 23, 1942; s. John McDowell and Helen Pond (Niebrugge) R.; m. Caroline Ward; children: John A., Andrew C. BA, Williams Coll., 1964; LLB, Columbia U., 1967. Bar: N.Y. 1967, U.S. Dist. Ct. (so. and ea. dist.) N.Y. 1971, U.S. Ct. Appeals (2d cir.) 1971, U.S. Ct. Appeals (3rd cir.) 1976, U.S. Ct. Appeals (4th and 7th cirs.) 1987, U.S. Ct. Appeals (9th cir.) 1992, U.S. Supreme Ct. 1971. Ptnr. Curtis, Mallet-Prevost, Colt & Mosle, N.Y.C., 1982-90, Katten Muchin & Zavis, N.Y.C., 1990—; lectr. on air law topics at various seminars. Contbr. articles to profl. jours. Trustee Summit (N.J.) Unitarian-Universalist Ch., 1978; bd. dirs. Robert Sterling Clark Found., 1989—; bd. trustees Mamaroneck Pub. Libr. Dist., 1990—. Lt. USNR, 1968-71. Mem. Internat. Assn. Def. Counsel, Assn. of Bar of City of N.Y. (mem. aero. com. 1983-85, chmn. 1986-89, 92—, products liability com. 1989-91), Larchmont (N.Y.) Yacht Club. Avocations: sailing, tennis. Office: Katten Muchin & Zavis 40 Broad St New York NY 10004

ROMANSKY, MICHAEL A., lawyer; b. Washington, Apr. 26, 1952. BSS, Northwestern U., 1974; JD with honors, George Washington U., 1977. Bar: D.C. 1977. Ptnr. McDermott Will & Emery, Washington. Mem. D.C. Bar Assn., Phi Eta Sigma. Office: McDermott Will & Emery 1850 K St NW Washington DC 20006-2296

ROMANSKY, MONROE JAMES, physician, educator; b. Hartford, Conn., Mar. 16, 1911; s. Benjamin and Henrietta (Levine) R.; m. Evelyn Muriel Lackman, Jan. 10, 1943; children: Stephen, Gerald, Michael, Richard. A.B., U. Maine, 1933; M.D., U. Rochester, 1937. Diplomate: Am. Bd. Internal Medicine. Intern Strong Meml. Hosp.-U. Rochester, N.Y., 1937-38; asst. resident Strong Meml. Hosp.-U. Rochester, 1938-39, James Gleason Research fellow studies on relationship of kidneys to hypertension, 1939-40, chief resident, 1940-41, instr. in medicine, 1941-42; investigator Office Sci. Research and Devel., Surgeon Gen. U.S., 1941-42; chief biochemistry and antibiotic research Walter Reed Army Hosp., 1942-46; assoc. prof. Sch. Medicine, George Washington U., Washington, 1946—; prof. medicine Sch. Medicine George Washington U., 1957—; dir. infectious diseases research lab. and infectious diseases div. D.C. Gen. Hosp., 1950-69; cons. internal medicine antibiotics Walter Reed Army Hosp., Washington, 1946—;

Cons. internal medicine antibiotics VA Hosp., Washington, 1952—, NIH, Bethesda, Md., 1953—, Surgeon Gen. USAF, 1966—; mem. Asian influenza adv. com. D.C., 1956-61; mem. ad hoc adv. com. Bur. Medicine FDA, 1966-67; examiner Am. Bd. Internal Medicine, 1965, 67, 69. Editorial bd.: Antimicrobial Agts. and Chemotherapy, 1961-72; Contbr. to profl. jours. Trustees council U. Rochester, 1965—. Served with M.C., AUS, 1942-46. Decorated Legion of Merit; recipient Founders award Tau Epsilon Phi, Disting. Career award U. Maine. Fellow ACP (adv. bd. to gov. D.C. 1969—); mem. Am. Soc. Internal Medicine, Am. Fedn. Clin. Research, Soc. Exptl. Biology and Medicine, Am. Soc. Microbiology, Infectious Diseases Soc. (founding council 1963-66), Soc. Med. Cons. to Armed Forces, Sigma Xi, Alpha Omega Alpha. Club: Woodmont Country. Pioneer work in prolonging action of penicillin, requiring only single daily injection, Romansky Formula, 1944; nutritional studies in obesity as related to weight reduction. Home: 5600 Wisconsin Ave Chevy Chase MD 20815 Office: 5480 Wisconsin Ave Chevy Chase MD 20815

ROMBOUT, LUKE, museum designer, administrator; b. Amsterdam, Netherlands, May 4, 1933; emigrated to Can., 1954, naturalized, 1959; s. Louis and Aleida (VanBuren) R. B.F.A., Mt. Alison U., Sackville, N.B., 1967. Acting curator Owens Art Gallery/Mt. Allison U., 1965-67, dir., 1968-71; chmn., asst. prof. visual arts program York U., Toronto, Ont., 1972-74; mem. arts adv. panel Can. Council, Ottawa, Ont., 1969-70; dir. art bank Can. Council, 1972-74, head visual arts film sect., 1974-75; dir. Vancouver Art Gallery (B.C., Can.), 1975-84; lectr. Can. Art History/Mt. Allison U., 1968-71; lectr. art history N.S. Coll. Art Design (Can.), 1970-72; lectr. U. Ottawa, 1974-75; mem. adv. com. art Can. Dept. Pub. Works, 1973; mem. design adv. com. Can. Post., 1973; mem. fine arts com. Can. Dept. External Affairs, 1973-75; bd. dirs. Anna Wyman Dance Theatre, 1976-85; dir. McCord Mus. Can. History, Montreal, Can., 1990-94; dean, faculty of creative work George Brown Coll., Toronto, Can., 1994—. Prin. works include Owens Art Gallery, Mt. Allison Univ., Sackville, N.B., 1970, Art Bank Repository, Can. Coun., Ottawa, Ont., 1972, Vancouver (B.C.) Art Gallery, 1983, Palais de la Civilisation Ville de Montréal, 1985, Expo'86 Contemporary Art Mus. Roundhouse Renovation, Vancouver, 1986, Expo'86 Ramses II Pavilion, Vancouver, 1986, McCord Mus. Can. History, Montréal, 1992. Fellow Royal Soc. Arts; mem. Order of Can., Assn. Internat. Critiques d'Art. Home: Hazelton Lanes, 77 Ave Rd # 301, Toronto, ON Canada M5R 3R8 Office: George Brown Coll, PO Box W15 Station B, Toronto, ON Canada M5T 2T9

ROME, DONALD LEE, lawyer; b. West Hartford, Conn., May 17, 1929; s. Herman Isaac and Juliette (Stern) R.; m. Sheila Ward, Apr. 20, 1958; children: Adam Ward, Lisa, Ethan Stern. SB, Trinity Coll., 1951; LLB, Harvard U., 1954. Bar: Conn. 1954, U.S. Dist. Ct. 1955, U.S. Cir. Ct. Appeals 1965, U.S. Supreme Ct. 1965. Assoc. Ribicoff and Kotkin, Hartford, Conn., 1954-58, ptnr., 1958-67; ptnr. Rosenberg, Rome, Barnett, Sattin & Santos and predecessor, Hartford, 1967-83; now ptnr. Robinson & Cole, Hartford, 1983—; mem. Conn. Gov.'s Study Commn. on Uniform Consumer Credit Code, 1969-70; chmn. Conn. bar advisory com. of attys. to make recommendations to U.S. dist. ct. for proposed changes of bankruptcy rules in dist. Conn., 1975-77; mem. Bankruptcy Merit Screening Com. for Dist. Ct., 1980-81; mem. adv. com. Conn. Law Revision Commn. on article 2A for Uniform Comml. Code, 1987-89; lectr. in law U. Conn., 1974-54, 81-83; mem. faculty Sch. Banking of the South, La. State U., 1982-84; lectr. continuing legal edn. on secured creditors' rights, comml. fin., bankruptcy and uniform comml. code, 1958—; corp. adv. bd. dirs. Shawmut Bank. Prin. author, editor: Business Workouts Manual, 1985, 1992; co-author: A Comparative Analysis and Study of the Uniform Consumer Credit Code in Relation to the Existing Consumer Credit Law in Connecticut, 1970; contbg. author: Connecticut Practice Book, 1978, Collier Bankruptcy Practice Guide, 1981, Asset-Based Financing: A Transactional Guide, 1984; mem. bd. editors Jour. Bankruptcy Practice, 1991—; contbr. articles to profl. jours. Past mem. bd. dirs. New Eng. region Am. Jewish Com., also Hartford chpt., Hebrew Home for Aged, Hartford; past mem. bd. trustees Temple Beth Israel, West Hartford. Mem. ABA (bus. bankruptcy com. and comml. fin. services com., sect. on bus. law), Fed. Bar Assn. (bankruptcy law com.), Conn. Bar Assn. (chmn. sect. comml. law and bankruptcy 1977-80, mem. exec. com. banking law sect. 1977-83, chmn. spl. com. scope and correlation 1983-84), Hartford County Bar Assn., Conn. Bar Found., Assn. Comml. Fin. Attys. (pres. 1978-80), Am. Arbitration Assn. (mem. nat. panel comml. arbitrators, mediator), Am. Law Inst., Am. Coll. Comml. Fin. Lawyers (alternate dispute resolution com.), Am. Bankruptcy Inst., Comml. Law League Am., Harvard Law Sch. Assn. Conn. (pres. 1970-71). Clubs: Hartford, Harvard of U.N.Y.C, Trinity. Lodge: Masons (32 deg., rnial commn. Conn. grand lodge 1970-82). Home: 46 Belknap Rd West Hartford CT 06117-2819 Office: Robinson & Cole 1 Commercial Plz Hartford CT 06103-3599 *We are told by Kipling that success and failure are "imposters." I have found this fundamental teaching to be most helpful in the practice of law and in life generally. Concentration on long-term relationships and basic values is so much more important than ephemeral successes and failures.*

ROME, JOHN L., restaurant chain executive; b. Alliance, Ohio, 1954. Pres. internat. div. Wendy's Internat. Inc. Office: Wendy's Internat Inc 4288 W Dublin Granville Rd Dublin OH 43017-2093

ROMEI, LURA KNACHEL, magazine editor; b. Mansfield, Ohio, Nov. 17, 1947; d. Dale Conrad and L. Blanche (Nichols) Knachel; m. Richard Dale Romei, Sept. 13, 1968 (div. 1978); children: Christopher Dale, Craig Steven; m. Jerry L. Gumeny, June 7, 1992. B Music Edn., Otterbein Coll., 1970; Assoc., Lakeland Community Coll., 1974. Contract programmer Hunter Mfg. Co., Solon, Ohio, 1974; programmer Better Meat Products Co., Cleve., 1974-76, Childers Products Co., Beachwood, Ohio, 1976-77; analyst, programmer Cuyahoga County Data Ctr., Cleve., 1977-79; analyst, programmer Penton Pub., Cleve., 1979, assoc. editor Modern Office Tech., 1979-84; editor Mng. Office Tech., Cleve., 1984—. Contbr. over 300 articles to profl. jours.; editor over 400 articles. Recipient award Am. Soc. Bus. Press Editors, Ohio Excellence in Journalism award. Mem. Soc. Profl. Journalists. Methodist. Avocations: computers, reading, sewing. Office: Penton Pub 1100 Superior Ave E Cleveland OH 44114-2501

ROMEO, LUIGI, linguist, educator; b. Tropea, Italy, Sept. 20, 1926; came to U.S., 1953; s. Pasquale and Beatrice (Lo Torto) R.; m. Elenore Ruth Andersen, Aug. 10, 1983. B.A. in Fgn. Langs., Wash. State U., 1957; M.A. in Romance Langs., U. Wash., 1959, Ph.D., 1960. Instr. Romance langs. U. Wash., Seattle, 1959-60, acting asst. prof. Romance langs., 1960-61; asst. prof. Italian U. Toronto, 1961-65; assoc. prof. Italian U. Colo., Boulder, 1965-68, prof. linguistics, 1968-84, prof. linguistics emeritus, 1984—.

ROMEO, PETER JOHN, lawyer; b. Darby, Pa., Aug. 1, 1942; s. Joseph Paul and Rose Marie (Beckett) R.; m. Nancy Virginia Schmidt, July 15, 1972; children: Christopher, Jeffrey, Michael. BSBA, Georgetown U., 1964; JD, George Washington U., 1967, LLM, 1969. Bar: Va. 1968, U.S. Dist. Ct. D.C. 1969, U.S. Supreme Ct. 1972; CPA, D.C. Acct. Schumaker & Yates, Washington, 1964-69; atty. U.S. Securities and Exchange Comm., Washington, 1969-72, spl. counsel, 1972-79, chief counsel div. corp. finance, 1980-84; ptnr. Hogan & Hartson, Washington, 1984—. Author: Comprehensive Section 16 Outline, 1984 (updated annually), The Registration Process, 1985 (updated annually); co-author: Section 16 Reporting Guide, 1989, Section 16 Forms and Filing Handbook, 1991 (updated 1993), Section 16 Treatise and Reporting Guide, 1994; contbr. articles to profl. jours. Mem. ABA (mem. fed. regulation securities com., chmn. task force on sect. 16 devels.), D.C. Bar Assn., Va. State Bar. Roman Catholic. Office: Hogan & Hartson 555 13th St NW Washington DC 20004-1109

ROMER, PAUL MICHAEL, economics educator; b. Denver, Nov. 7, 1955; s. Roy R. and Beatrice A. (Miller) R.; m. Virginia K. Langmuir, Feb. 28, 1980; children: Geoffrey M., Amy J. BA in Math., U. Chgo., 1977, PhD in Econs., 1983. Asst. prof. econs. U. Rochester (N.Y.), 1982-88; prof. dept. econs. U. Chgo., 1988-90; fellow Ctr. for Advanced Study in Behavioral Scis., Stanford, Calif., 1989-90; prof. econs. U. Calif., Berkeley, 1990—. Fellow Econometric Soc.; mem. Am. Econs. Assn., Nat. Bur. Econ. Rsch. Office: NBER 204 Junipero Serra Blvd Stanford CA 94305-8006

ROMER, ROY R., governor; b. Garden City, Kans., Oct. 31, 1928; s. Irving Rudolph and Margaret Elizabeth (Snyder) R.; m. Beatrice Miller, June 10,

1952; children: Paul, Mark, Mary, Christopher, Timothy, Thomas, Elizabeth. B.S. in Agrl. Econs., Colo. State U., 1950; LL.B., U. Colo., 1952; postgrad., Yale U. Bar: Colo. 1952. Engaged in farming in Colo., 1942-52; ind. practice law Denver, 1955-66; mem. Colo. Ho. of Reps., 1958-62, Colo. Senate, 1962-66; owner, operator Arapahoe Aviation Co., Colo. Flying Acad., Geneva Basin Ski Area; engaged in home site devel.; owner chain farm implement and indsl. equipment stores Colo.; commr. agr. State of Colo., 1975, chief staff, exec. asst. to gov., 1975-77, 83-84, state treas., 1977-86, gov., 1987—; chmn. Gov. Colo. Blue Ribbon Panel, Gov. Colo. Small Bus. Council; mem. agrl. adv. com. Colo. Bd. Agr. Bd. editors Colo. U. Law Rev., 1960-62. Past trustee Iliff Sch. Theology, Denver; mem., past chmn. Nat. Edn. Goals Panel; co-chmn. Nat. Coun. on Standards and Testing. With USAF, 1952-53. Mem. Dem. Gov.'s Assn. (chmn.), Nat. Gov.'s Assn. (former chmn.), Colo. Bar Assn., Order of the Coif. Democrat. Presbyterian. Office: Office of Gov State Capitol Denver CO 80203*

ROMERO, CHRISTIANE, German language educator; married; 2 children. Matura mit auszeichnung, Realgymnasium, Vienna, 1959; lehramtsprüfung in German and English, PhD, U Vienna, 1963; diploma in French, La Sorbonne, Paris, 1964; MPhil in Comparative Lit., Yale U., 1967. Lectr. in German Yale U., 1964-67; asst prof. Emmanuel Coll., Boston, 1970-73; asst prof. Tufts U., Medford, Mass., 1973-78, assoc. prof., 1978-85, prof., 1985—, acting chair dept. German and Russian, 1983, chair dept. German, Russian, and Asian Langs. and Lits., 1988—; lectr. women's studies, social justice and peace program, intro. to inetrnat. rels. Tufts U., past mem. student honors com., undergraduate admissions and fin aid com., ednl. policy com., grad. sch. policy com., faculty personnel com., grievance panel com., univ. planning and budget proirities com., tenure and promotion com., mem. internat. rels. exec. com., women's program adv. bd. com., comm. cluster exec. com, com. on coms., 1991—, faculty rep. to trustee com. on acad. affairs, 1985-86, faculty rep. to trustee com. on devel., 1991—; vis. asst. prof. German Duke U., 1967-70; coord. sect. Internat. Symposium on GDR, Conway, N.H., 1978—; panelist on German films Goethe Inst. workshop Middlebury (Vt.) Coll., 1979; mem. selection com. U.S. Congress-German Bundestags Exch. Program, 1983-88; panelist Fourth New England Workshop on German Affairs, Boston, 1983, Ctr. for European Studies, Harvard U., 1984; mem. exec. com. Grad. Consortium in Women's Studies, Radcliffe Coll., 1991—; lectr. Bryn Mawr Coll., 1977, Fletcher Sch. Law and Diplomacy, 1981, Cornell U., 1981, Smith Coll. 1982, Simmons Coll., 1984, U. Mass., Amherst, 1989, MIT, 1989, Timburlane Regional High Sch., N.H., 1989, Mich. Symposium, Ann Arbor, 1990, ctr. for internat. studies U. Pitts. 1991. Author: Simone de Beuvoir, 1978, 12th rev. edit., 1994, Anna Seghers, 1993; editor: Kritische Intelligenz, 1982; contbr. articles to profl. jours.; presenter papers in field. Fellow Yale U., 1964-67; Summer Rsch. fellow Tufts U., 1975, 84, 95; grantee Am. Philos. Soc., 1981; summer grantee NEH, 1981; rsch. grantee Am. Coun. Learned Socs., 1981-82; grantee Dept. Edn. (FIPSE), 1989. Mem. MLA (chair seminars 1975, 1988 (two), mem. exec. com. divsn. 20th century German lit. 1986-90), AAUP (exec. com., past chair com. W, v.p., pres. Tufts chpt.), Am. Assn. Tchrs. German (pres. Mass. chpt. 1983-84, past. sec., v.p., pres.-elect), Northeast MLA (chair 19th century German lit. 1977, 81, v.p 1988-89, pres. 1989-90), Women in German. Office: Tufts U Dept German Russian and Asian Langs and Lits Medford MA 02155

ROMERO, GEORGE A., film director; b. N.Y.C., Feb. 4, 1940. Dir.: (films) Night of the Living Dead, 1968, There's Always Vanilla, 1972, The Crazies, 1972, Hungry Wives, 1973, Martin, 1978, Dawn of the Dead, 1979, Creepshow, 1982, Day of the Dead, 1985, Monkey Shines: An Experiment in Terror, 1988, Two Evil Eyes, 1990, The Dark Half, 1993; dir., screenwriter Knightriders, 1981; exec. producer, scriptwriter Tales from the Dark Side:The Movie, 1990, Night of the Living Dead, 1990; Television: (exec. prodr., screenwriter) Tales From the Darkside. Office: care The Gersh Agy 232 N Canon Dr Beverly Hills CA 90210-5302*

ROMERO, PETER FRANK, diplomat; b. N.Y.C., Mar. 10, 1949; s. José and Catherine Tobin (Nevers) R.; m. Ruth Frances Espey, July 7, 1982; 1 child, Alexander Baden. BS, Fla. State U., 1971, MA, 1972. Cert. tchr., Md. Tchr. Prince George Pub. Schs., Upper Marlboro, Md., 1972-77; vice-consul Dominican Republic State Dept., Washington, 1977-79, polit. analyst, 1979-82, desk officer, 1982-83, polit./econ. officer U.S. Consulate, Naples, Italy, 1984-87, exec. asst. to amb. U.S. Embassy, Rome, 1987-88, dep. dir. Ctrl. Am. affairs, 1988-90, dir. Ctrl. Am. Affairs, 1990-92, chief of mission U.S. Embassy, San Salvador, El Salvador, 1992-93; amb. to Ecuador Quito, 1993—; cons. Team Cons., Washington, 1977. Chmn. EEOC/U.S. Dept. State, Washington, 1992, Hispanic Coun./U.S. Dept. State, Washington, 1991-92. Mem. Fgn. Svc. Assn. (Baker-Wilkins award for Leadership). Roman Catholic. Avocations: pre-Colombian art and history, tennis, sailing. Office: Unit 5301 APO AA 34039-3420

ROMERO-BARCELÓ, CARLOS ANTONIO, former political party executive, former governor of Puerto Rico; b. San Juan, P.R., Sept. 4, 1932; s. Antonio S. Romero and Josefina Barceló; m. Kathleen Donnelly, Jan. 2, 1966; children: Juan Carlos, Melinda Kathleen; children by previous marriage: Carlos, Andrés. BA, Yale U., 1953; LLB, U.P.R., 1956; LLD (hon.), U. Bridgeport, 1977. Bar: P.R. 1956. Mem. Herrero-Frank & Romero-Barceló, 1956-58; ptnr. Rivera-Zayas, Rivera-Cestero & Rúa, San Juan, 1958-63, Segurola, Romero & Toledo, 1963-68; pres. Citizens for State 51, 1965-67; mayor, San Juan, 1969-77; gov. P.R., 1977-85, 92—; pres. New Progressive Party, 1974-85, 89-91; resident commr., 1991—. Recipient Hoey award for Interracial Justice, Cath. Interracial Council of N.Y., 1977, Spl. Gold Medal award Spanish Inst., N.Y., 1979, U.S. Atty.-Gen.'s medal, 1981. Mem. Nat. Govs. Assn., So. Govs. Assn. (chmn. 1980-81), Conf., Nat. League Cities (pres. 1975), U.S. Conf. Mayors (bd. dir.) Roman Catholic. Author: Statehood is for the Poor; contbr. articles to profl. jours. Office: 428 Cannon House Office Bldg Washington DC 20515

ROMEY, WILLIAM DOWDEN, geologist, educator; b. Richmond, Ind., Oct. 26, 1930; s. William Minter and Grace Warring (Dowden) R.; m. Lucretia Alice Leonard, July 16, 1955; children—Catherine Louise, Gretchen Elizabeth, William Leonard. A.B. with highest honors, Ind. U., 1952; student, U. Paris, 1950-51, 52-53; Ph.D., U. Calif. at Berkeley, 1962. Asst. prof. geology and sci. edn. Syracuse U., 1962-66, assoc. prof., 1966-69; exec. dir. earth sci. ednl. program Am. Geol. Inst., 1969-72; prof., chmn. dept. geology St. Lawrence U., Canton, N.Y., 1971-76; prof. St. Lawrence U., 1976—, prof., chmn. dept. geography, 1983-93; prof. emeritus, 1993—; ednl. cons., 1962—; NAS visitor USSR Acad. Sci., 1967; vis. geoscientist Am. Geol. Inst., 1964-66, 71; earth sci. cons. Compton's Ency., 1970-71; adj. prof. Union Grad. Sch., 1974—; mem. bd. rsch. advisers and readers Walden U., 1981—; prof. Grad. Sch. Am., 1993—; travel writer and cruise ship lectr., 1990—. Author: (with others) Investigating the Earth, 1967, (with J. Kramer, E. Muller, J. Lewis) Investigations in Geology, 1967, Inquiry Techniques for Teaching Science, 1968, Risk-Trust-Love, 1972, Consciousness and Creativity, 1975, Confluent Education in Science, 1976; co-editor: Geochemical Prospecting for Petroleum, 1959; assoc. editor: Jour. Coll. Sci. Teaching, 1972-74, Geol. Soc. Am. Bull, 1979-84, Jour. Geol. Edn, 1980—; editor-in-chief: Ash Lad Press, 1975—; contbr. articles on geology, geography and edn. to profl. publs. Bd. dirs. Onondaga Nature Centers, Inc., 1966-69. Served to lt. USNR, 1953-57; lt. comdr. Res. Woodrow Wilson Found. fellow, 1959-60, 61-62; NSF sci. faculty fellow U. Oslo, 1967-68. Fellow Geol. Soc. Am., AAAS; mem. Nat. Assn. Geology Tchrs. (v.p. 1971-72), N.Y. Acad. Scis., Nat. Assn. Geology Tchrs. (pres. 1972-73), Assn. Am. Geographers, Am. Geophys. Union, Geol. Soc. Norway, Assn. Educating Tchrs. of Sci., Can. Assn. Geographers, Assn. for Can. Studies in U.S., Phi Beta Kappa, Sigma Xi, Phi Delta Kappa. Home: PO Box 294 East Orleans MA 02643 Office: St Lawrence U Dept Geography Canton NY 13617

ROMINE, THOMAS BEESON, JR., consulting engineering executive; b. Billings, Mont., Nov. 16, 1925; s. Thomas Beeson and Elizabeth Marjorie (Tschudy) R.; m. Rosemary Pearl Melancon, Aug. 14, 1948; children—Thomas Beeson III, Richard Alexander, Robert Harold. Student, Rice Inst., 1943-44; B.S. in Mech. Engring, U. Tex., Austin, 1948. Registered profl. engr., Tex., Okla., La., Ga. Jr. engr. Gen. Engring. Co., Ft. Worth, 1948-50; design engr. Wyatt C. Hedrick (architect/engr.), Ft. Worth 1950-54; chief mech. engr. Wyatt C. Hedrick (architect/engr.), 1954-56; chmn., chief mech. engr. Thomas B. Romine, Jr. (now Romine Romine & Burgess, Inc. cons. engrs.), Ft. Worth, 1956—; mem. heating, ventilating,

and air conditioning controls com. NRC, 1986-88. Author numerous computer programs in energy analysis and heating and air conditioning field; contbr. articles to profl. jours. Mem. Plan Commn., City of Ft. Worth, 1958-62; mem. Supervisory Bd. Plumbers, City Ft. Worth, 1963-71, chmn., 1970-71; chmn. Plumbing Code Rev. Com., 1968-69; mem. Mech. Bd., City Ft. Worth, 1974-82, chmn., 1976-82; chmn. plumbing code bd. North Central Tex. Council Govts., Ft. Worth, 1971-75; Bd. mgrs. Tex. Christian U.-South Side YMCA, 1969-74; trustee Ft. Worth Symphony Orch., 1968—, Orch. Hall, 1975—. Served with USNR, 1943-45. Disting fellow ASHRAE (pres. Ft. Worth chpt. 1958, nat. committeeman 1974—); fellow Am. Cons. Engrs. Coun., Automated Procedures for Engring. Cons. (trustee 1970-71, 75, 1st v.p. 1972-73, internat. pres. 1974); mem. NSPE, Tex. Soc. Profl. Engrs. (bd. dirs. 1956, treas. 1967), Cons. Engrs. Coun. Tex. (pres. North Tex. chpt., also v.p. state orgn. 1965, dir. state orgn. 1967), Starfish Class Assn. (nat. pres. 1970-73, nat. champion 1976), Delta Tau Delta (v.p. West div. 1980-90), Pi Tau Sigma. Episcopalian (vestryman). Clubs: Colonial Country, Rotary. Home: 3232 Preston Hollow Rd Fort Worth TX 76109-2051 Office: Romine Romine & Burgess 300 Greenleaf St Fort Worth TX 76107-2392 It has long been my belief that, in this technological age, the general public can do little more than accept on faith the propriety of mechanical and electrical systems provided for use in their homes and businesses, and that without an understanding and knowledgeable agent to guide them this faith is often misplaced. It is thus incumbent upon the Professional Engineer to use his expertise in this field to insure competency and safety in those projects under his control, and to assist wherever possible in guiding and influencing appropriate legislation in this regard along sound engineering pathways.

ROMINGER, RICHARD, federal agency administrator; b. Woodland, Calif., July 1, 1927; M. Evelyne Rowe; children: Richard S., Charles A., Ruth E., Bruce J. BS in Plant Sci., U. Calif., Davis, 1949. Farmer Calif.; dir. Dept. Food and Agriculture, Calif., 1977-82; dep. sec. USDA, 1993—. Recipient Disting. Svc. award Calif. Farm Bur. Fedn., 1991; named Agriculturalist of Yr. Calif. State Fair, 1992; numerous others. Office: US Dept of Agriculture Office of the Deputy Secy 14th & Independence Ave SW Washington DC 20250-0002

ROMLEY, RICHARD M., lawyer; b. Tucson, Apr. 28, 1949; s. Henry Romley and Margaret (Meyers) Madrid; m. Carol Ann Haight, July 20, 1985; children: Darin, David, Aaron. AA, Glendale (Ariz.) Community Coll., 1972; BS, Ariz. State U., 1974, JD, 1981. Bar: Ariz. 1981, U.S. Ct. Appeals (9th cir.) 1982. Spl. prosecutor City of Phoenix, 1981-83, spl. prosecutor sex crimes unit, 1984-86; prosecutor narcotics unit Maricopa County Atty's. Office, Phoenix, 1987-88; county atty. Maricopa County, 1989—; mem. Ariz. Criminal Justice Commn., Phoenix, 1989—; mem. policy/legis. com. Nat. Dist. Attys. Assn., Arlington, Va., 1989; co-chmn. Maricopa County Teen Substance Abuse Task Force, Phoenix, 1989; bd. dirs. Crime Victim Found., Phoenix; spl. law prof. Phoenix Coll., 1987. Active Gov's. Task Force on Domestic Violence, Ariz. Community Punishment Coun. With USMC, 1968-70. Recipient County Achievement award Nat. Assn. Counties, 1990; Refnes scholar Glendale C.C. 1971. Mem. Internat. Assn. Chiefs, Law Enforcement Intelligence, Assn. Govt. Attys. Republican. Office: Maricopa County Attys Office 301 W Jefferson St Phoenix AZ 85003-2143

ROMNEY, CARL F., seismologist; b. Salt Lake City, June 5, 1924; m. Barbara Doughty; children: Carolyn Ann, Kim. B.S. in Meteorology, Calif. Inst. Tech., 1945; Ph.D., U. Calif., Berkeley, 1956. Seismologist U.S. Dept. Air Force, 1955-58; asst. tech. dir. Air Force Tech. Applications Center, 1958-73; dep. dir. Nuclear Monitoring Research Office, Def. Advanced Research Projects Agy., 1973-75, dir., 1975-79; dep. dir. Def. Advanced Research Projects Agy., 1979-83; dir. Ctr. Seismic Studies, 1983-91; v.p. Sci. Applications Internat. Corp., 1987—; tech. adviser U.S. reps. in negotiations Test Ban Treaty; mem. U.S. del. Geneva Conf. Experts, 1958, Conf. on Discontinuance Nuclear Weapons Tests, 1959, 60; negotiations on threshold Test Ban Treaty, Moscow, 1974; mem. U.S. del. Peaceful Nuclear Explosions Treaty, Moscow, 1974-75. Contbr. articles to tech. jours. Recipient Exceptional Civilian Service awards Air Force, 1959, Exceptional Civilian Service awards Dept. Def., 1964, 79; Pres.'s award for Distinguished Fed. Civilian Service, for outstanding contbns. to devel. of control system for underground nuclear tests, 1967; Presdl. Rank of Meritorious Exec., 1980. Research on earthquake mechanism, seismic noise; generation, propagation, detection seismic waves from underground explosions. Home: 4105 Sulgrave Dr Alexandria VA 22309-2629 Office: Ste 1450 1300 N 17th St Arlington VA 22209

ROMNEY, RICHARD BRUCE, lawyer; b. Kingston, Jamaica, Dec. 29, 1942; came to U.S., 1945, naturalized, 1956; s. Frank Oswald and Mary Ellen (Burton) R.; m. Beverly Cochran, Sept. 11, 1965 (dec. 1984); children: Richard Bruce, Jr., Stephanie Cochran; m. Lynthia H. Walker, Aug. 14, 1988; children: Alisa Dawn, Kristen Elizabeth. BA, U. Pa., 1964; JD, U. Va. 1972. Bar: N.Y. 1973, U.S. Ct. Appeals (2d cir.) 1975. Assoc. Dewey, Ballantine, Bushby Palmer & Wood, N.Y.C., 1972-80, ptnr., 1981—. Mem. editorial bd. U. Va. Law Rev., 1970-72. Served to lt. USN, 1964-68. Mem. ABA, N.Y. State Bar Assn., Assn. Bar City N.Y., Order of Coif. Republican. Home: 35 Deerfield Rd Chappaqua NY 10514-1604 Office: Dewey Ballantine 1301 Avenue Of The Americas New York NY 10019-6092

ROMNEY, SEYMOUR LEONARD, physician, educator; b. N.Y.C., June 8, 1917; s. Benjamin and Anne (Senter) R.; m. Shirley Gordon, Nov. 4, 1945; children: Benjamin, Mary Clark, Tim Hayes, Anne. A.B., Johns Hopkins, 1938; M.D., N.Y. U., 1942. Intern Beth Israel Hosp., Boston, 1942-43; resident Boston Lying-in Hosp., Free Hosp. for Women, Boston, 1946-51; fellow, instr. Harvard Med. Sch., 1947-51, asst. prof. obstetrics and gynecology, 1951-57; prof., chmn. dept. gynecology and obstetrics Albert Einstein Coll. Medicine, N.Y.C., 1957-72; prof. Albert Einstein Coll. Medicine, 1972-89, prof. emeritus, 1989—, dir. research gynecol. oncology, 1972—; dir. obstetrics and gynecology Bronx Mcpl. Hosp. Ctr., N.Y.C., 1957-72; cons. WHO. Chair Soc. of Physicians for Reproductive Choice and Health; mem. med. adv. com. Maternity Ctr. Assn.; bd. dirs. Planned Parenthood, N.Y.C. Served to lt. comdr. M.C. USNR, 1943-45. Mem. ACOG, AAAS, Am. Assn. Med. Colls. (life), Am. Gynecol. and Obstet. Soc., Soc. Gynecologic Investigation, Am. Assn. Cancer Rsch., Maternity Ctr. Assn., Population Assn. Am., N.Y. Obstet. Soc., N.Y. Acad. Medicine, N.Y. Acad. Sci. Home: 1300 Morris Park Ave Bronx NY 10605-5008 Office: Einstein Coll Morris Park Ave East Bronx NY 10461

ROMNEY, W. MITT, investment company executive; b. Detroit, Mar. 12, 1947; s. George W. and Lenore (Lafount) R.; m. Ann D., Mar. 21, 1969; children: Taggart, Matthew, Joshua, Benjamin, Craig. BA, Brigham Young U., 1971; JD, Harvard U., 1975, MBA, 1975. Cons. Boston Consuting Group, 1975-77; cons. Bain & Co., Boston, 1977-78, v.p., 1978-84, chmn., CEO, 1991—; mng. ptnr., CEO Bain Capital, Inc., Boston, 1984—; bd. dirs. Marriott Corp., Bethesda, Md., Staples Inc., Framingham, Mass., Babbages Inc., Dallas, Tex., Damon Corp., Needham, Mass. Pres. Boston Stake LDS Ch., 1986—; adv. bd. Brigham Young U. Sch. Bus., Provo, Utah, 1990—; vis. com. Harvard Bus. Sch., Cambridge, Mass; mem. nat. exec. bd. Boy Scouts Am.; trustee Belmont (Mass.) Hill Sch., 1989—. Baker scholar Harvard Bus. Sch., Cambridge, Mass., 1975. Mem. Belmont Hill CLub. Office: Bain Capital 2 Copley Pl Boston MA 02116

ROMO, SYLVIA, state legislator, accountant; b. San Antonio, Dec. 27; d. Alfred B. and Josephine (Jimenez) Sepulveda; children: David, Samuel, Randall, Daniel. BBA in Acctg., U. Tex., San Antonio, 1976, postgrad., 11981. CPA, Tex., Ill. Acting fiscal dir. Bexar County Mental Health and Mental Retardation, San Antonio, 1979-81; pres. Romo and Co., CPA's, San Antonio, 1981-93, Sylvia Romo & Assoc., Ltd., San Antonio, 1994—; mem. Tex. Ho. of Reps., Austin, 1993—; acct. adv. SBA, 1989; advisor Pres.'s Adv. Com. on Women's Bus. Ownership; seminar leader on instrn. minority bus. women Nat. Assn. Banking Women. Mem. adv. bd. U. Tex. Coll. Bus.; commr. Housing Authority Bexar County; mem. adv. coun. U. Tex. Health Sci. Ctr. Med. Sch.; chmn. San Antonio Mayor's Task Force on Small, Minority and Women's Bus. Devel.; mem. San Antonio Bd. Rev. for Hist. Dists.; commr., vice chmn. Bexar County Women's Ctr.; bd. dirs. AMC Cancer Rsch. Ctr., Epilepsy Found. Bluebonnet Region; mem. allocation com. United Way; chmn. Bexar County Dem. Commn., 1990; grad. Leadership

San Antonio, 1986, mem. steering com., 1986-88. Tarrant C.C. scholar, Bus. and Profl. Found. scholar U. Tex.; named One of Top 10 Women of Decade in U.S., Bus. and Profl. Women's Found. Outstanding Woman of South Tex. in bus. San Antonio Express-News, 1989, Legislator of Yr., League United L.Am. Citizens, 1993, Woman of Yr., Mexican Am. Bus. and Profl. Women San Antonio, 1993, Small Bus. Adv. of Yr., San Antonio Hispanic C. of C., 1994. Mem. Am. Women's Soc. CPA's, Am. Soc. Women Accts., Tex. Soc. CPA's, Ill. CPA Soc., San Antonio Assn. Hispanic CPA's, Phi Theta Kappa. Office: 4606 Centerview Ste 206 San Antonio TX 78228

ROMOFF, JEFFREY ALAN, university officer, health care executive; b. N.Y.C., Nov. 30, 1945; s. Richard Warren and Evelyn (Alter) R.; m. Vivian Irene Goodman, Aug. 25, 1966 (dec. June 1983); children: Jennifer Ann, Rebecca Lynn; m. Maxine Ketterer, July 28, 1984. B.S. magna cum laude in Social Scis., CCNY, 1967; M.Phil. in Polit. Scis., Yale U., 1971. Teaching fellow Yale U., 1969-70, teaching assoc., 1970-71; exec. dir. Central Naugatuck Valley Mental Health Council, Waterbury, Conn., 1971-73; regional programing dir. Western Psychiat. Inst. and Clinic (U. Pitts.), 1973-74, assoc. dir. div. edn. and research, 1974-75; assoc. dir. Western Psychiat. Inst. and Clinic, 1975—; adj. asst. prof. pub. health U. Pitts. 1981—, instr. psychiatry, 1982—, assoc. v.p. health scis., 1984-86, vice chancellor health scis., 1986-92; exec. v.p. U. Pitts. Med. Ctr., 1986-92; sr. vice chancellor for Health Adminstrn. U. Pitts., 1992—; pres. U. Pitts. Med. Ctr., 1992—. N.Y.C. Regents scholar CCNY, 1963-67. Mem. Am. Hosp. Assn. (governing coun. sect. for mental health and psychiat. svcs. 1986-89), Am. Psychiat. Assn. (chmn. joint com. with Am. Hosp. Assn. 1983-84), Hosp. Assn. Pa., Coun. Psychiat. Svc. Providers (exec. com. 1981-84). Jewish. Home: 3208 Fox Run Rd Allison Park PA 15101-1506 Office: U of Pitts Medical Ctr 3811 O'Hara St Pittsburgh PA 15213-2593

ROMOND, JAMES, principal. Prin. La Salle Inst., Troy, N.Y. Recipient Blue Ribbon Sch. award U.S. Dept. Edn., 1990-91. Office: La Salle Inst 174 Williams Rd Troy NY 12180-7799

ROMOSER, GEORGE KENNETH, political science educator; b. Kingston, N.Y., Sept. 14, 1929; s. Carl August and Alva (Becker) R.; m. Mechthild von Tresckow, Apr. 30, 1967; children: Alexandra Ada, Valerie Anna. A.B., Rutgers U., 1951; A.M., U. Chgo., 1954, Ph.D, 1958. Research asst. Nat. Opinion Research Center, 1953; asst. Polit. Sci. Inst., Freiburg U., Fed. Republic Germany, 1955-56; instr. Ohio State U., 1957-61; asso. prof. Conn. Coll., 1963-67; asst. prof., asso. prof., prof. polit. sci. U. N.H., Durham, 1961-62, 67—, chmn. dept., 1968-71, prof. internat. Affairs, 1986—, course dir. Internat. Perspective Ctr., 1986-88; Fulbright prof. Faculty of Law, Mainz U., Fed. Republic Germany, 1962-63; dir. Emigre Meml. German Internship Programs, 1965—; vis. prof. Free U., Berlin, 1964, Mannheim U., 1968, 82-83, Johns Hopkins, Bologna, Italy, 1969, Munich U., 1973-74, U. Pa., 1986, Kobe U., Japan, 1988-89, Bowdoin Coll., 1990, Freiburg U., Germany, 1993-94, Fulbright Sr. Prof., 1993-94; adj. prof. Mannheim U., Fed. Republic Germany, 1983—; Fulbright sr. rsch. fellow, 1974; Rockefeller fellow Aspen Inst. for Humanistic Studies, 1978-79; cons. Com. on Internat. Exchange of Persons, 1965-66; NEH fellow Yale U., 1993; co-founder Conf. Group on German Politics, 1968—, chmn., 1968-84, regional dir., 1984-87; founder, dir. New Eng. Workshops on German Affairs, 1980—; co-founder Pacific Coast Workshops on German Affairs, 1983-93; commuting fellow Ctr. European Studies Harvard U., 1983—; founder The Japanese Circle, 1989—. Co-author: West German Politics in the Mid-Eighties, 1985, Germany's New Policy, 1995; contbr. articles to profl. jours, books. Chmn. com. on govtl. reorgn. Democratic party N.H., 1962. Decorated Civilian Knight's Cross Fed. Republic of Germany). Mem. Am. Coun. on Germany, Phi Delta Theta, Pi Sigma Alpha, Delta Phi Alpha, Phi Alpha Theta. Home: Worster Rd Eliot ME 03903 Office: U NH Durham NH 03824

ROMPF, CLIFFORD G., JR., distillery executive; b. Louisville, Aug. 2, 1930; s. Clifford G. and Marie (Kiesel) R.; m. Sheryl Palmer, Feb. 23, 1957; children—Clifford, William, Barbara, John. B.S., U. Louisville, 1956, M.B.A., 1964. Systems analyst Brown Forman Corp., Louisville, 1956-72, asst. controller, 1962-68, dir. mgmt. info., 1968-75, v.p. fin. ops., 1975—. Served as sgt. USAF, 1951-55. Mem. Data Processing Mgmt. Assn., Fin. Execs. Inst. (officer 1978-81). Republican. Roman Catholic. Clubs: Big Spring Country (Louisville), Pendennis. Avocations: tennis; computers. Office: Brown Forman Corp 850 Dixie Hwy Louisville KY 40210-1038

ROMSDAHL, MARVIN MAGNUS, surgeon, educator; b. Hayti, S.D., Apr. 2, 1930; s. Conrad Magnus and Hilda Johanna (Shelsta) R.; m. Virginia McElvany; children: Christine Ann, Laura Marie. AB, U. S.D., 1952, BS, 1954; MD, U. Ill., Chgo., 1956; PhD, U. Tex., Houston, 1968. Diplomate Am. Bd. Surgery. Clin. assoc. NIH, NCI, Bethesda, Md., 1958-60; instr. surgery U. Ill., Chgo., 1963-64; asst. surgeon, asst. prof. surgery U. Tex./M.D. Anderson Cancer Ctr., Houston, 1967-69; assoc. grad. faculty mem. Grad. Sch. Biomed. Sci., U. Tex., Houston, 1969-72; assoc. surgeon/asso. prof. surgery U. Tex./M.D. Anderson Cancer Ctr., Houston, 1969-75; dep. dept. head U. Tex./M.D. Anderson Cancer Ctr., 1979-85; grad. faculty mem. U. Tex. Health Sci. Ctr., Houston; 1972—; prof. surgery U. Tex. Med. Sch., Houston, 1975—; surgeon, prof. surgery U. Tex./M.D. Anderson Cancer Ctr., Houston, 1975—; lectr. in field. Contbr. articles to profl. jours. Phizer scholar, 1953; recipient Sr. Clin. Traineeship award, USPHS, 1963, Spl. Fellowship award, 1964; ACS Mead Johnson award, 1965, Ann. Outstanding Tchr. award, Dept. Gen. Surgery, U. Tex. M.D. Anderson Cancer Ctr., 1988. Mem. ACS, AMA, Am. Assn. Cancer Rsch., Am. Radium Soc., Assn. for Acad. Surgery, Collegium Internationale Chirugiae Digestivae, Harris County Med. Soc., Houston Acad. Medicine, Houston Philos. Soc., Internat. Pigment Cell Soc., N.Y. Acad. Sci., Soc. for Surgery of Alimentary Tract, Soc. of Surg. Oncology, S.W. Sci. Forum, Tex. Med. Assn., Tex. Surg. Soc., Houston Surg. Soc., W.H. Cole Soc., Western Surg. Assn., Sigma Xi. Republican. Home: 4530 Verone St Bellaire TX 77401-5514 Office: UT M D Anderson Cancer Ctr 1515 Holcombe Blvd Houston TX 77030-4095

RONALD, ALLAN ROSS, internal medicine and medical microbiology educator, researcher; b. Portage, Man., Can., Aug. 24, 1938; s. David E. and Muriel M. (MacFarlane) R.; m. Myrna Jean Marchyshyn, Oct. 19, 1962; children: Wendy, Sandra, Vickie. BSc in Medicine, U. Man., Winnipeg, 1961, MD with honors, 1961. Resident in internal medicine U. Md., 1962-64; fellow in infectious disease and microbiology U. Wash., 1964-68; asst. prof. U. Man., 1968-72, assoc. prof., 1972-77, prof., head med. microbiology, 1976-85, Disting. prof., head dept. internal medicine, physician-in-chief Health Scis. Ctr., 1985-90; head infectious diseases St. Boniface Gen. Hosp., Winnipeg, 1991-94; assoc. dean rsch. faculty of medicine U. Manitoba, Winnipeg, 1993—; vis. prof., researcher AIDS epidemiology U. Nairobi, Kenya, 1980—; Malcolm Brown Meml. lectr. Can. Soc. Clin. Investigation, 1985; mem. Med. Rsch. Coun. Can., 1987-93. Contbr. articles to profl. jours. Decorated Officer of Order of Can., 1994; recipient Jubilee award U. Man. Alumni Assn., 1990, Thomas Parran award Am. Venereal Disease Assn., 1991, Ortho award Can. Infectious Disease Soc., 1991. Fellow ACP (gov. 1995); mem. Infectious Disease Soc. Am. (councillor 1990-93), Internat. Soc. Infectious Diseases (pres.-elect 1994), Am. Soc. Clin. Investigation, Am. Physicians, Can. Inst. Acad. Medicine. Home: 3232 Assiniboine, Winnipeg, MN Canada R3K 0B1 Office: Saint Boniface Gen Hosp, 400 Tache ave, Winnipeg, MB Canada R2H 2A6

RONALD, PETER, utility executive; b. Duluth, Minn., Aug. 26, 1926; s. George W. and Florence (Jones) R.; m. Mary Locke Boyd, Nov. 25, 1950; children: Peter Webb, Pauline Morton, Samuel Herschel. B.A. U. Va., 1950. With Louisville Gas & Electric Co., 1950-88, treas., 1962—, v.p., 1969-82, sr. v.p., 1982-88, dir., 1979-89. Bd. dirs., mem. exec. com. Bus. Devel. Corp. Ky., 1967-75, pres., 1971-72; bd. dirs. Louisville Community Chest, 1967-72, v.p., 1969-72; bd. dirs., v.p. Louisville Rehab. Ctr., 1964-82, pres., 1970-71; bd. overseers Louisville Country Day Sch., 1967-70; trustee Children's Hosp. Found., 1978-81, sec.-treas., 1978-81; bd. govs. Captiva (Fla.) Civic Assn., 1990-94, v.p. 1992. With USNR, 1945-46. Mem. Louisville Country Club, Pendennis Club, Captiva Yacht Club, Zeta Psi. Home: Mockingbird Valley Rd Louisville KY 40207 Home: 1112 Schefflera ct PO Box 893 Captiva FL 33924-0893

RONALD, THOMAS IAIN, financial services executive; b. Glasgow, Scotland, Feb. 16, 1933; s. Newton Armitage and Elizabeth (Crawford) R.; m. Cristina de Yturralde, Aug. 30, 1962; children: Christopher, Isobel. B in

Law, Glasgow U., 1956; MBA, Harvard U., 1963. Chartered acct. Pres., CEO Zellers, Inc., Winnipeg, Man., Can., 1982-85; exec. v.p., dir. Hudson's Bay Co., Winnipeg, Man., Can., 1985-87; pres. Mgmt. Svcs. Group CIBC, Montreal, 1987-88, Adminstrv. Bank CIBC, 1988-92; vice chmn. Adminstrv. Bank CIBC, Toronto, 1992-95 (ret.); dir. CIBC; adv. bd. dirs. Amdahl Can. Ltd., The North West Co. Inc., Loblaw Co. Ltd., Wittington Investments Ltd., Leon's Furniture Ltd., Mobil Oil Can. Ltd.; chmn. Commcorp Fin. Svcs. Inc., Can. Life Assurance Co., T.A.L. Investment Counsel Ltd. Bd. dirs. Toronto Symphony Orch. Served as lt. Royal Navy, 1956-58. Fellow Inst. Chartered Accts. Ont.; mem. Inst. Chartered Accts. Scotland. Presbyterian. Club: Granite (Toronto). Avocations: music, squash, tennis. Office: Can Imperial Bank of Commerce, Commerce Court, Toronto, ON Canada M5L 1A2

RONALD, WILLIAM, artist; b. Stratford, Ont., Can., Aug. 13, 1926; came to U.S., 1954, naturalized, 1964; s. William Stanley and Lillian M. (Plant) R.; m. Helen Marie Higgins, Sept. 6, 1952 (div. 1988); children: Suzanne Marie, Dianna Louise, ; m. Alana Michelle Harris, 1989 (div. 1994). Grad. with honors, Ont. Coll. Art, Toronto, 1952; pupil, Jock Macdonald. founding mem. Painters Eleven Group, Toronto, 1952; radio and TV broadcaster, from 1966; newspaper columnist, book reviewer. One man shows include Hart House, U. Toronto, 1954, Greenwich Gallery, Toronto, 1957, Laing Galleries, Toronto, 1960, Douglass Coll., New Brunswick, N.J., Kootz Gallery, N.Y.C., 1957-60, 62, 63, Princeton Mus., 1963, Issacs Gallery, Toronto, 1963, David Mirvish Gallery, Toronto, 1965, Dunkelman Gallery, Toronto, 1970, Tom Thompson Meml. Gallery, Owen Sound, Ont., 1971, Brandon (Man.) U., 1972, Morris Gallery, Toronto, 1975, Gustafssen Gallery, Brampton, Ont., Brampton Pub. Libr. and Art Gallery, Bramlea, Ont., 1976; retrospective exhbn. Ronald-25 Yrs. at Robert McLaughlin Gallery, Oshawa, Ont., 1975, Musee d'Art Contemporain, Montreal, Que., Can., Rodman Hall Arts Centre, St. Catherines Art Gallery and Mus., Charlottetown, P.E.I., Edmonton (Alta.) Art Gallery, Burnaby (B.C.) Art Gallery, 1976, Art Gallery of Windsor, Ont., Morris Gallery, Toronto, 1977, 78, 79, 80, Wells Gallery, Ottawa, Ont., 1982, Quan-King Gallery, Toronto ,Moore Gallery, Hamilton, Ont., 1990; exhbns. of work The Prime Ministers (of Can.) Art Gallery of Ont., Art Gallery of Windsor, 1984, Manulife Pl., Edmonton, 1984, The N.B. Mus., St. John, 1985, Art Gallery N.S., 1985, Can., Montreal Gallery of Contemporay Art, 1986, The Jolliette (Que.) Mus., 1988; group exhbns. include Trinity Coll., Toronto, 1951, Eglinton Gallery, Toronto, 1953, Biennial exhbns. Nat. Gallery Can., 1955, 57-58, Smithsonian Travelling Exhbn., 1956, Riverside Mus., N.Y.C., Contemporary Can. Painters, 1957, Carnegie Internat., 1957, Brussels World Fair and Travelling Show, Sao Paulo Biennale, 1959, Whitney Mus. Ann., Corcoran Biennial, 1962-63, Toysby Contemporary Artists, 1966, Artists on Campus, York U., Toronto, 1970, Toronto Painting, 1972, Robert McLaughlin Gallery, Oshawa, 1978; represented in permanent collections Art Gallery Ont., Bklyn. Mus., Carnegie Inst., Guggenheim Mus., Mus. Modern Art, Nat. Gallery Can., R.I. Sch. Design, Albright Knox Gallery, Buffalo, Aldrich Mus., Ridgefield, Conn., U. B.C., Art Inst. Chgo., Internat. Minerals and Chems. Corp., Skokie, Ill., James A. Michener Found., Allentown, Pa., Montreal Mus. Fine Arts, York U., David Rockefeller Collection, Nelson A. Rockefeller Collection, U. N.C., Phoenix Art Mus., Balt. Mus., Walker Art Ctr., Mpls., Williams Coll., Princeton Mus., Queens U., Kingston, Ont., Brandeis U., Wadsworth Atheneum, Hartford, Conn., Whitney Mus. Am. Art, Washington Gallery Modern Art, Newark Mus., N.J. State Mus., Trenton, U. Tex., Can. Coun. Collection, Can. Art Bank, Windsor Art Mus., Hudson River Mus., Pasadena (Calif.) Mus. Modern Art, Peel County Mus. Brampton, Wellington County Mus., Kitchener Waterloo Art Mus., Masters Sch. and Mercy Coll., Dobbs Ferry, N.Y., Toronto Dominion Bank, Notre Dame U., U. Okla. Art Mus., Norman, numerous others; commd. artist prime mins. Can. Recipient Hallmark Art award for watercolor, 1952, Guggenheim Mus. award Can. painting, 1956, Sr. Arts award Can. Coun., 1977; Ind. Order Daus. Empire scholar, Can., 1951, Can. Amateur Hockey Assn. scholar Can. Found., 1956. Mem. Royal Can. Acad. Home: 206 Robert St, Toronto, ON Canada M5S 2K7

RONAN, WILLIAM JOHN, management consultant; b. Buffalo, Nov. 8, 1912; s. William and Charlotte (Ramp) R.; m. Elena Vinadé, May 29, 1939; children: Monica, Diana Quasha. A.B., Syracuse U., 1934; Ph.D., N.Y. U., 1940, LL.D., 1969; certificate, Geneva Sch. Internat. Studies, 1933. Mus. asst. Buffalo Mus. Sci., 1928-30; with Niagara-Hudson Power Co., 1931; transfer dept. N.Y.C.R.R., 1932; Penfield fellow internat. law, diplomacy and belles lettres, 1935, Univ. fellow, 1936; editor Fed. Bank Service, Prentice-Hall, Inc., 1937; instr. govt. N.Y. U., 1938, exec. sec. grad. div. for tng. in pub. services, 1938, asst. dir., 1940, asst. prof. govt., dir. grad. div. for tng. pub. service, 1940, assoc. prof. govt., 1946-47, prof., 1947, dean, grad. sch. pub. adminstrn. and social service, 1953-58; Cons. N.Y.C. Civil Service Commn., 1938; prin. rev. officer, negotiations officer U.S. Civil Service Commn., 1942; prin. div. asst. U.S Dept. State, 1943; cons. Dept. State, 1948, Dept. Def., 1954; dir. studies N.Y. State Coordination Commn., 1951-58; project mgr. N.Y. U.-U. Ankara project, 1954-59; cons. ICA, 1955, N.Y. State Welfare Conf.; adminstrv. co-dir. Albany Grad. Program in Pub. Adminstrn.; 1st dep. city adminstr. N.Y.C., 1956-57; exec. dir. N.Y. State Temporary Commn. Constl. Conv., 1956-58; sec. to Gov. N.Y., 1959-66; chmn. interdept. com. traffic safety, commr. Port Authority N.Y. and N.J., 1967-90, vice chmn., 1972-74, chmn., 1974-77; with UTDC Corp., West Palm Beach, Fla.; trustee Crosslands Savs. Bank; chmn. bd. L.I. R.R., 1966-74; chmn. Tri-State Transp. Com., N.Y., N.J., Conn., 1961-67; chmn. interstate com. New Haven R.R., 1960-63; chmn. N.Y. Com. on L.I. R.R., 1964-65; mem. N.Y. State Commn. Interstate Coop., 1961, N.Y. State Com. Fgn. Ofcl. Visitors, 1961, N.Y. State Coordination Commn., 1960; mem. N.Y. Civil Svc. Commn., Temporary State Commn. on Constl. Conv., 1966-67; chmn. N.Y. State Met. Commuter Transp. Authority, 1965-68, Met. Transp. Authority, 1968-74, Tri-Borough Bridge and Tunnel Authority, 1968-74, N.Y.C. Transit Authority, 1968-74, Manhattan and Bronx Surface Transit Operating Authority, 1968-74; chmn. bd., pres. 3d Century Corp., 1974-94; mem. Commn. Critical Choices for Am., 1973—, acting chmn., 1975-; mem. urban transp. adv. com. U.S. Dept. Transp.; sr. adviser Rockefeller family, 1974-80; pres. Nelson Rockefeller Collection, Inc., 1977-80; trustee Power Authority of State of N.Y., 1974-77; cons. to trustees Penn Ctrl. Transp. Co.; vice chmn. bd. CCX, Inc.; sec.-treas. Sarabam Corp. N.V.; dir. UTDC (U.S.A.) Inc., 1987-88; chmn. UTDC Corp. 1989-94, Transit Svcs. Corp., 1989-94; cons. Herzog Transit Svcs., 1995—, Dime Savs. Bank, Metal Powder Products Inc., Prometech, Inc., Internat. Mining and Metals Inc., Quadrant Mgmt. Inc., 1990—, Ohio Highspeed Rail Authority, 1991-93; chmn. N.Y. and N.J. Inland Rail Rate Com.; dir. Nat. Mgmt. Coun., 1951. Author: Money Power of States in International Law, 1940, The Board of Regents and the Commissioner, 1948, Our War Economy, 1943, (with others), articles in profl. jours.; adviser: Jour. Inst. Socio-Econ. Studies. Mem. U.S. FOA, Am. Public Health Assn.; staff relations officer N.Y.C. Bd. Edn.; Mem. Nat. Conf. Social Work, Nat. Conf. on Met. Areas, Citizens Com. on Corrections, Council on Social Work Edn.; bd. dirs. World Trade Club; adv. bd. World Trade Inst.; mem. 42d St. Redevel. Corp., chmn., 1980-94; mem. Assn. for a Better N.Y.; bd. advisers Inst. for Socioecon. Studies, 1977—; dir. Nat. Health Council, 1980-86; dep. dir. policy Nelson Rockefeller campaign for Republican presdl. nomination, 1964; mem. N.Y. State Gov.'s Com. on Shoreham Nuclear Plant, 1983-85, Nassau County Indsl. Devel. Authority, 1982-90, U.S. Dept. Transp. Com. on Washington and Capital Dist. Airports, 1985-86; bd. dirs. Ctr. Study Presidency, 1986-90, Alcoholism Council of N.Y., 1986—; trustee N.Y. Coll. Osteopathic Medicine, 1986-91. Served as lt. USNR, 1943-46. Mem. NEA, Am. Polit. Sci. Assn., Acad. Pub. Adminstrn., Am. Soc. Pub. Adminstrn., Civil Svc. Assembly of U.S. and Can., Internat. Assn. Met. Rsch. and Devel., Nat. Mcpl. League, Mcpl. Pers. Soc., Citizens Union of N.Y., Nat. Civil Svc. League, Am. Acad. Polit. and Social Sci., L.I. Assn. Commerce and Industry (dir.), Internat. Inst. Adminstrv. Scis., Am. Fgn. Law Assn., Internat. Union Pub. Transport (mgmt. com.), Am. Pub. Transit Assn. (chmn. 1974-76), Nat. Def. Transp. Assn. (v.p.for Mass transit), Met. Opera Club, Maidstone Club, Devon Yacht Club, Knickerbocker Club, Metairie Club, Harvard Club, Creek Club, Wings Club, Traffic Club, Univ. Club, Am. Club Riviera, Beach Club (West Palm Beach), Everglades Club. Home: 525 S Flagler Dr West Palm Beach FL 33401-5922 Home: Villa La Pointe Du Cap, Ave de La Corniche, 06230 Saint Jean Cap Ferrat France

RONAYNE, MICHAEL RICHARD, JR., academic dean; b. Boston, Apr. 29, 1937; s. Michael Richard and Margaret (Fahey) R.; m. Joanne Maria, Aug. 7, 1971; 1 child, Michelle Eileen. BS, Boston Coll., 1958; PhD, U.

Notre Dame, 1962. Instr. chemistry Providence Coll., 1962-63, asst. prof. chemistry, 1963-64; rsch. chemist Panametrics, Inc., Waltham, Mass., 1964-66; asst. prof. chemistry Suffolk U., Boston, 1966-67, assoc. prof., 1967-70, prof., chmn. dept. chemistry, 1970-72, dean Coll. Liberal Arts and Sci., 1972—; reaccreditation vis. team mem. New Eng. Assn. Schs. and Colls., Winchester, Mass., 1974-80, Mass. Dept. Edn., Boston, 1975; mem. acad. adv. com. Mass. Bd. Higher Edn., Boston, 1977. Contbr. articles to sci. jours., profl. publs. Mem. Winchester Sch. Com., 1983-92, chmn., 1984-85, 86-87; mem. Winchester Town Meeting, 1983—, mem. town capital planning com., 1983-84, town coun. on youth, 1987-88, 89-90; mem. exec. com., bd. dirs. Mass. Bay Marine Studies Consortium, 1985-87; project dir. U.S. Dept. of Edn. Title III Grants. Shell Oil Corp. fellow, 1958-59, AEC fellow 1959-62; recipient Contbns. in Sci. and Edn. citation New Eng. Sch. Art and Design, Boston, 1991. Mem. AAAS, Am. Chem. Soc., Am. Conf. Acad. Deans, Coun. for Liberal Learning, Am. Assn. for Higher Edn., Sigma Xi, Phi Alpha Theta, Phi Gamma Mu, Sigma Tau Delta, Omicron Delta Epsilon, Sigma Zeta. Office: Suffolk U Beacon Hill Boston MA 02114

RONCA, LUCIANO BRUNO, geologist, educator; b. Trieste, Italy, Apr. 26, 1935; came to U.S., 1957, naturalized, 1966; s. Hugo Luciano and Olympia (Leeb) R.; m. Melissa A. Wing, May 6, 1989; children by previous marriage: Melinda, Erika, Roxane. Grad., Lyceum-Gymnasium, Trieste, 1953, U. Padua, Italy, 1957; M.S. (Fulbright scholar), U. Kans., 1959, Ph.D., 1963. Research asso. geophysics U. Kans., 1962-64; gen. phys. scientist A.F. Cambridge Research Labs., Bedford, Mass., 1964-67; sr. scientist Boeing Sci. Research Labs., Seattle, 1967-70; prof. geology Wayne State U., Detroit, 1971-95; prof. emeritus, 1995—, Koc Sch., Istanbul, Turkey, 1995—; mem. U. Kans. Antarctic Expedition, 1960-61; researcher U. Bern, Switzerland, 1961-62; vis. scientist Brookhaven Nat. Labs, Upton, N.Y., 1966, Lunar Sci. Inst., Houston, 1970-71; Nat. Acad. Scis. vis. scientist Vernadsky Inst., Moscow, 1976, 79-80, 84-85. Editor-in-charge: Modern Geology, 1970-84; assoc. editor: The Moon, 1971—; contbr. articles to profl. jours. Fellow Geol. Soc. Am., Internat. Assn. Planetologists (treas. 1975-78), Am. Geophysics Union, Antarctican Soc., Am. Polar Soc., Mich. Basin Geol. Soc. Mount Ronca in Antarctica is named after him. Office: Dept Geology Wayne State U Detroit MI 48202

RONDEPIERRE, EDMOND FRANCOIS, insurance company executive; b. N.Y.C., Jan. 15, 1930; s. Jules Gilbert and Margaret Murray (Moore) R.; m. M. Anne Lerch, July 5, 1952; children: Aimee S., Stephen C., Peter E., Anne W. BS, U.S. Mcht. Marine Acad., 1952; JD, Temple U., 1959. Bar: D.C. 1959, Conn. 1988, U.S. Supreme Ct. 1992. Third mate Nat. Bulk Carriers, 1952-53; field rep. Ins. Co. N.Am., 1955-59, br. mgr., 1959-61; asst. sec. underwriting Ins. Co. N.Am., Phila., 1965-67, asst. gen. counsel, 1967-70, sr. v.p., gen. counsel, 1970-76; v.p., dep. chief legal affairs INA Corp., Phila., 1976-77; v.p., gen. counsel Gen. Reins. Corp., Stamford, Conn., 1977-79; sr. v.p., corp. sec., gen. counsel, 1979-94, sr. v.p., 1994—; bd. dirs. Gen. Reins. Ltd. (UK), Tempest Re Ltd, Herbert Clough, Inc. Lt. USN, 1953-55. Lt. USN, 1953-55. Mem. ABA, Conn. Bar Assn., D.C. Bar Assn., Inter-Am. Bar Assn., Soc. CPCU, Internat. Assn. Def. Counsel (past bd. dirs.), AIDA Reins. and Ins. Arbitration Soc. (dir., pres.), Stamford Yacht Club. Roman Catholic. Office: Gen Re Corp 695 E Main St Stamford CT 06904-2350

RONDILEAU, ADRIAN, college president; b. N.Y.C., May 8, 1912; s. Leon J. and Bessie (Caspere) R.; m. Martha L. Denison, Aug. 15, 1936 (dec. 1983); m. Mary Masterson Hamblen, June 1, 1985. A.B., CCNY, 1932; M.A., Columbia U., 1934, Ph.D., 1942; L.H.D., Yankton Coll., 1982; D. Pub. Admstrn., Mass. Maritime Acad.; 1986; D. Pub. Svc., Bridgewater State Coll., 1989. Instr. Central Mich. Coll., 1935-37; adminstr. speech research, adult edn. and curriculum Mich. Dept. Pub. Instrn., 1937-41; dir. vocat. guidance and in-service tng. War Manpower Commn., 1941-43; spl. cons., lectr. Brazilian Ministry Edn. and coordinator inter-Am. affairs Rio de Janeiro and Sao Paulo, 1943-46; dean bus. adminstrn., chmn. dept. econs. Associated Colls. Upper N.Y., 1946-49; dean liberal arts Pace Coll., 1950-54; pres. Yankton (S.D.) Coll., 1954-62, Bridgewater (Mass.) State Coll., 1962-86, 88-89; chmn. coll. and univ. com. YMCA 6-State N. Central Area; dir. North Central Area YMCA; adv. bd. Upper Midwest Research and Devel. Council; pres. S.D. Found. Pvt. Colls.; v.p. S.D. Assn. Colls. and Univs.; mem. Lady Doak Coll. Funds Corp.; trustee Mass. State Colls. Adv. Commn. Author: (with Donald Hayworth) Research Studies in the Teaching of College Public Speaking, 1939; author: Education for Installment Buying, 1943, People and Scenes of Brazil, 1945, Public Higher Education in the City of New York: The Master Plan Study Report (with D.P. Cottrell), 1950, The Capital Plant Needs of American Higher Education, 1951, Reminiscences: Bridgewater State College (1960-89), Adventure in Excellence, 1991; also articles. Rackham fellow, 1935-36; Stevens scholar, 1934-35; Hoe scholar, 1933-34. Mem. Mass. State Coll. Council of Pres. (pres. 1976-78), N. Central Assn. Colls. and Secondary Schs., New Eng. Assn. Colls. and Secondary Schs., Mass. Council of Pub. Coll. Pres. and Chancellors, Southeastern Mass. Consortium Pub. and Pvt. Colls. (pres. 1976-77, 1984-85), S.D. Ednl. Assn., Am. Econ. Assn., Am. Coll. Pub. Relations Assn., Brazil-Am. Cultural Soc., NEA, C. of C., Phi Delta Kappa, Pi Kappa Delta. Congregationalist. Lodges: Masons, Shriners, Elks, Rotary (dir.). Home: 150 Lakeside Dr Bridgewater MA 02324-1018 Office: Bridgewater State College Office of Pres Emeritus Bridgewater MA 02324

RONDINELLI, DENNIS A(UGUST), business administration educator, research center director; b. Trenton, N.J., Mar. 30, 1943; s. August P. and Vincentia (Madalena) R.; m. Soonyoung Chang, Dec. 19, 1976; children: Linda, Lisa. BA, Rutgers U., 1965; PhD, Cornell U., 1969. Asst. prof. urban affairs U. Wis., Milw., 1971-73; assoc. prof. grad. sch. of mgmt. Vanderbilt U., Nashville, 1973-76; assoc. prof. planning Maxwell Sch. of Citizenship and Pub. Affairs Syracuse U., N.Y., 1976-79; prof. social scis., 1979-86; prin. scientist and sr. policy analyst Office for Internat. Programs, Research Triangle Inst., Research Triangle Park, N.C., 1986-90; Glaxo Disting. Internat. Prof. Mgmt. Kenan-Flagler Bus. Sch.; dir. Ctr. Global Bus. Rsch., Kenan Inst. Pvt. Enterprise U. N.C., Chapel Hill, N.C., 1990—. Author: Decentralization and Development: Policy Implementation in Developing Countries, 1983, Applied Methods of Regional Analysis: The Spatial Dimensions of Development Policy, 1985, Development Administration and U.S. Foreign Aid Policy, 1987, Urban Services in Developing Countries: Public and Private Roles in Urban Development, 1988, Planning Education Reforms in Developing Countries, 1990, Development Projects as Policy Experiments, 1993, Privatization and Economic Reform in Central Europe, 1994, Expanding Sino-American Business and Trade: China's Economic Transition, 1994, Great Policies: Strategic Innovations in Asia and the Pacific, 1995, Managing Privatization: Policies and Institutional Capacities, 1995; editorial bd. Jour. of Euro-Asian Mgmt., 1994—. Adv. Bd. Inst. Regional Devel. Studies, Kanpur, India, 1984—; editorial adv. bd. Bangladesh Jour. of Pub. Adminstrn., Dhaka, 1986—. Captain U.S. Army, 1965-72. Decorated Julio Lleras Order of Merit (Colombia); Sr. fellowship East-West Ctr., 1975-76; recipient Rural Development medal, Ethnic Minorities Devel. medal Republic of Vietnam, 1971. Avocations: gardening, writing nonfiction. Office: Kenan Inst Pvt Enterprise CB#3440 The Kenan Ctr U NC Chapel Hill NC 27599-3149

RONE, B. J., financial executive; b. Anchorage, Oct. 15, 1942; s. Broadway Jones and Vera Lucille (Carden) R.; m. Katie Elizabeth Cornwell, June 8, 1963; children: Denise Lynne and Dennis Lee (twins). BS in Acctg., McNeese State U., Lake Charles, La., 1965; MBA in Fin., Sam Houston State U., 1972. Chief acct. Carnation Co., Houston, 1965-67; group controller Tex. Instruments Inc., Dallas, 1967-80; sr. v.p., chief fin. officer UTC-Mostek Corp., Dallas, 1980-82, Net Am. Corp., Dallas, 1983—. Author: Memories and More, 1983. Mem. Singapore Bd., 1979-80; chmn. 1st United Meth. Fin. Com., Dallas, 1985-86. Fellow Nat. Assn. Credit Mgrs.; mem. Fin. Execs. Inst., Nat. Assn. Accts., Nat. Assn. Corp. Dirs. Republican. Methodist. Home: 6004 Still Forest Dr Dallas TX 75252-5320 Office: Advacare Inc 9696 Skillman St Ste 325 Dallas TX 75243

RONE, WILLIAM EUGENE, JR., newspaper editor; b. Atlanta, Nov. 7, 1926; s. William Eugene and Marguerite (Kellett) R.; m. Margaret Louise Banks, July 17, 1953; 1 child, James Kellett. AB, Wofford Coll., 1949; LLB, U. S.C. 1951; grad., U.S. Army Command and Gen. Staff Coll., 1974. With The State (newspaper), Columbia, S.C., 1950—, city editor, 1962-65, asso. editor, 1966-69, editorial page editor, 1969-90, sr. editor, 1990-93; consulting

editor, 1993—; S.C. corr. So. Edn. Reporting Service, Nashville, 1962-68; columnist Raleigh (N.C.) News & Observer, 1968-83, Atlanta Jour.-Constn., 1973-84. Author: Biography of Max Hirsch, 1956. Chmn. S.C. Athletic Hall of Fame, 1957-61. Served with USNR, 1945-46. Recipient S.C. AP award for reporting in depth, 1962. Mem. Am. Soc. Newspaper Editors, Nat. Conf. Editorial Writers, S.C. Bar, Phi Beta Kappa, Kappa Sigma, Phi Delta Phi. Episcopalian. Home: 726 Fairway Ln Columbia SC 29210-5715 Office: care State-Record Co Shop Rd PO Box 1333 Columbia SC 29202

RONEN, CAROL, state legislator. BS, Bradley U.; MA, Roosevelt U. Dir. legis. and cmty. affairs Chgo. Dept. Human Svcs., 1985-89; exec. dir. Chgo. Commn. on Women, 1989-90; dir. planning and rsch. Chgo.-Cook County Criminal Justice Commn.; asst. commn. Chgo. Dept. Planning, 1991, Chgo. Dept. Housing; mem. Ill. Ho. of Reps., 1993—. Former pres. Ill. Task Force on Child Support; bd. dirs. Cook County Dem. Women, St. Martin De Porres Shelter for Women and Children. Democrat. Home: 6033 N Sheridan Chicago IL 60660 Office: Ill Ho of Reps State Capitol Springfield IL 62706

RONEY, JOHN HARVEY, lawyer; b. L.A., June 12, 1932; s. Harvey and Mildred Puckett (Cargill) R.; m. Joan Ruth Allen, Dec. 27, 1956; children: Pam Peterson, J. Harvey, Karen Louise Hanke, Cynthia Allen Harmon. Student, Pomona Coll., 1950-51; B.A., Occidental Coll., 1954; LL.B., UCLA, 1959. Bar: Calif. 1960, D.C. 1976. Assoc. O'Melveny & Myers, L.A., 1959-67, ptnr., 1967-94, of counsel, 1994—; gen. counsel Pa. Co., 1970-78, Baldwin United Corp., 1983-84; dir. Coldwell Banker & Co., 1969-81, Brentwood Savs. & Loan Assn., 1968-80; spl. advisor to dep. Rehab. of Mut. Benefit Life Ins. Co., 1991-94; cons., advisor to Rehab. of Confederation Life Ins. Co., 1994—; mem. policy adv. bd. Calif. Ins. Commn., 1991-95. Served to 1st lt. USMCR, 1954-56. Mem. ABA, Calif. Bar Assn. (ins. law com. 1991-95, chmn. 1993-94), L.A. County Bar Assn., San Francisco Bar Assn., D.C. Bar Assn., Coun. Fgn. Rels. N.Y., L.A. Com. on Fgn. Rels., Conf. Ins. Counsel, Calif. Club, Sky Club. (N.Y.). Republican. Home: The Strand Hermosa Beach CA 90254 Office: Ste 1600 400 S Hope St Los Angeles CA 90071-2899

RONEY, PAUL H(ITCH), federal judge; b. Olney, Ill., Sept. 5, 1921; m. Sarah E. Eustis; children: Susan M., Paul Hitch Jr., Timothy Eustis. Student, St. Petersburg Jr. Coll., 1938-40; B.S. in Econs, U. Pa., 1942; LL.B., Harvard U., 1948; LL.D., Stetson U., 1977; LL.M., U. Va., 1984. Bar: N.Y. 1949, Fla. 1950. Assoc. Root, Ballantine, Harlan, Bushby & Palmer, N.Y.C., 1948-50; ptnr. Mann, Harrison, Roney, Mann & Masterson (and predecessors), St. Petersburg, Fla., 1950-57; pvt. practice law, 1957-63; ptnr. Roney & Beach, St. Petersburg, 1963-69, Roney, Ulmer, Woodworth & Jacobs, St. Petersburg, 1969-70; judge U.S. Ct. Appeals (5th cir.), St. Petersburg, 1970-81; judge U.S. Ct. Appeals (11th cir.), St. Petersburg, 1981-86, chief judge, 1986-89, sr. cir. judge, 1989—; mem. adv. com. on adminstrv. law judges U.S. CSC, 1976-77. With U.S. Army, 1942-46. Fellow Am. Bar Found.; mem. ABA (chmn. legal adv. com. Fair Trial-Free Press 1973-76, mem. task force on cts. and public 1973-76, jud. adminstrn. div., chmn. appellate judges conf. 1978-79, mem. Gavel Awards com. 1980-83), Am. Judicature Soc. (dir. 1972-76), Am. Law Inst., Fla. Bar, St. Peterburg Bar Assn. (pres. 1964-65), Nat. Jud. Coll. (faculty 1974, 75), Jud. Conf. U.S. (subcom. on jud. improvements 1978-84, exec com. 1986-89, com. to review circuit coun. conduct and disability orders 1991-93). Home: Bayfront Tower 1 Beach Dr SE Saint Petersburg FL 33701-3924 Office: US Ct Appeals 11th Circuit 601 Federal Bldg 144 1st Ave S Saint Petersburg FL 33701-4397

RONEY, ROBERT KENNETH, retired aerospace company executive; b. Newton, Iowa, Aug. 5, 1922; s. Louie Earl and Hazel Iona (Cure) R.; m. Alice Lorraine Mann, Oct. 6, 1951; children: Stephen P., Karen Margaret Dahl. BSEE, U. Mo., 1944; MSEE, Calif. Inst. Tech., 1947, PhD, 1950. Engr. rsch. Jet Propulsion Lab. Calif. Inst. Tech., Pasadena, 1948-50, Hughes Aircraft Co., Culver City, Calif., 1950-54; mgr. system analysis Hughes Aircraft Co., Culver City, 1955-59, dir. tech. R&D, 1960, assoc. mgr. space system div., 1961-68, mgr. space system div., 1968-70, v.p. asst. group exec., 1970-85, sr. v.p. corp. technology, 1986-88, ret., 1988. Mem. adv. bd. Dept. Transp. Commnl. Space Transp., 1984-87, Engring. Sch. U. Kans., 1988-91. Lt. (j.g.) USNR, 1944-46, PTO. Recipient Honor award for Disting. Svc. in Engring. U. Mo.-Columbia, 1979. Fellow IEEE; mem. AIAA, Nat. Acad. Engring., Caltech Assocs. Home: 1105 Georgina Ave Santa Monica CA 90402-2027

RONEY, SHIRLEY FLETCHER, retail company executive; b. Atlanta, Dec. 3, 1935; d. Grady Franklin and Grace Ilene (Camp) Fletcher; student public schs., Atlanta; m. Sept. 19, 1953 (div.); 1 son, Joseph Clay. Collection corr. GMAC, Atlanta, 1953-64; sales rep. Washburn Realty, Atlanta, 1964-67; sec.-treas. Frank Jackson Lincoln Mercury, Inc., Sandy Springs, Ga., 1967-79; sec. treas., 1971—, comptroller, 1979—, pres., gen. mgr., 1983—; v.p., dir. J&J Investment Corp., 1975—; v.p., dir. Rivergate Corp., 1979-86, pres. 1986—; sec. treas., dir. Ajax Rent a Car, Sandy Springs Toyota. Div. vice chmn. United Way, 1979; bd. dirs. Ga. Spl. Olympics. Mem. Am. Bus. Womens Assn., Am. Contract Bridge League. Office: 7555 Roswell Rd Atlanta GA 30350-4838

RONEY, WALLACE, musician; b. Phila., May 25, 1960. Studied with Sigmund Haring, Howard U.; student, Berklee Coll. Trumpeter Art Blakey's Jazz Messengers, Tony Williams Quintet. Recorded 8 albums under own name, Verses, 1987, Intuition, 1989, Obsession, 1991, Seth Air, 1992, Misterios, 1994; other recs. include Story of Neptune (with Tony Williams), Seth Air Tribute to Miles Davis (with Herbie Hancock, Wayne Sholter, Ron Carter and Tony Williams), Live at Montreux (with Miles Davis), Killer Joe (with Art Blakey). Nominee for Grammy award, 1994. Office: care Blue Horn Prodns PO Box 1546 New York NY 10011-1546*

RONSON, RAOUL R., publishing executive; b. Fiume, Italy, Mar. 22, 1931; came to U.S., 1951; s. Mirko and Margaret (Fischer) Ruzicka; m. Susan Kohn, July 22, 1962; 1 child, Paul. DBA, U. Rome, 1950; MA, New Sch Social Research, 1957; postgrad., Inst. for Advanced Internat. Studies, U. Miami, 1967-68, NYU, 1974. Fgn. corr., freelance writer, 1953-59; treas. Daron Enterprises, Inc., 1959-63; pres. Seesaw Music Corp., N.Y.C., 1963—, Okra Music Corp., N.Y.C., 1963-77, Ulsyra Prodn. Corp., N.Y.C., 1963—; pres. The Composers Press, 1972-76; acad. lectr. Am., Australian, New Zealand univs. and conservatories; vis. lectr. Youngstown (Ohio) State U., 1985—, Finch Coll., N.Y.C., Eastman Sch. Music, Rochester, N.Y., Wake Forest U., Winston-Salem, N.C. Producer documentary films, 1959—, classical music recs., 1963—; The Dana Recording Project (nominated 2 Grammy awards). Mem. Emergency Control Bd. Office of Mayor, N.Y.C., 1973-82, Fed. Emergency Mgmt. Agy., Washington, 1982-84; rsch. analyst Office of the Sec. Def., Res. Affairs, The Pentagon, Washington, 1984-91; liaison officer U.S. Mil. Acad., West Point, N.Y., 1988—. With M.I., AUS, 1952-54, USAR, N.Y., 1955-91, ret. 1991. Decorated Legion of Merit, Def. Superior Svc. medal, Def. Meritorious Svc. medal, Army Meritorious Svc. medal, Army Commendation medal, Def. Identification badge Office Sec.; recipient numerous other awards and decorations; Grammy award nominee for Classical Prodr. of the Yr., 1993. Mem. Am. Polit. Sci. Assn., Am. Acad. Polit. and Social Sci., Internat. Platform Assn., Civil Affairs Assn., Sibelius Soc. (bd. dirs. 1978-85), Nat. Acad. Rec. Arts and Scis., Masons. Home: 825 West End Ave New York NY 10025-5349 Office: 2067 Broadway New York NY 10023-2806

RONSTADT, LINDA MARIE, singer; b. Tucson, July 15, 1946; d. Gilbert and Ruthmary (Copeman) R. Rec. artist numerous albums including Evergreen 1967, Evergreen Vol. 2, 1967, Linda Ronstadt, The Stone Poneys and Friends, Vol. 3, 1968, Hand Sown, Home Grown, 1969, Silk Purse, 1970, Linda Ronstadt, 1972, Don't Cry Now, 1973, Heart Like a Wheel, 1974, Different Drum, 1974, Prisoner In Disguise, 1975, Hasten Down the Wind, 1976, Greatest Hits, 1976, Simple Dreams, Blue Bayou, 1977, Living in the U.S.A., 1978, Mad Love, Greatest Hits Vol. II, 1980, Get Closer, 1982, What's New, 1983, Lush Life, 1984, For Sentimental Reasons, 1986, Trio (with Dolly Parton, Emmylou Harris), 1986, 'Round Midnight, 1987, Canciones de Mi Padre, 1987, Cry Like a Rainstorm-Howl Like the Wind, 1989, Mas Canciones, 1991, Frenesi, 1992, Winter Light, 1993, Feels Like Home, 1995; starred in Broadway prodn. of Pirates of Penzance, 1981, also in film, 1983, off Broadway as Mimi in La Boheme, 1984. Recipient Am. Music awards, 1978, 1979, Grammy awards, 1975, 76, 87, 88 (with Emmylou

Harris and Dolly Parton), 1989 (with Aaron Neville), 1990 (with Aaron Neville), Emmy award, 1988-89, Acad. Country Music awards, 1987, 88. Office: care Peter Asher Mgmt Inc 644 N Doheny Dr West Hollywood CA 90069-5526

ROOBOL, NORMAN RICHARD, chemistry educator, industrial painting consultant; b. Grand Rapids, Mich., Aug. 19, 1934; s. Pleune and Henrietta (Sietsema) R.; m. Joan Lois Ezinga, Aug. 15, 1957; children—Kerri Linda, Michael Eric, Victoria May, Sara Elizabeth Angelique. B.S., Calvin Coll., 1958; Ph.D. in Organic Chemistry, Mich. State U., 1962. Rsch. chemist Shell Oil Co., Emeryville, Calif., 1962-65; asst. prof. chemistry GMI Engring. Inst., Flint, Mich., 1965-68, assoc. prof., asst. head dept. math., sci., 1968-72, prof., 1972-89; pres. NR Painting Cons. Co., Peachtree City, Ga., 1989—; Rhodes prof. Russelsheim, Fed. Republic of Germany, 1980-81; tchr. short course on paint; cons. on coatings application processes; frequent spkr. on indsl. painting methods to paint soc. meetings; painting advisor, instr. Bombardier of Can., 1988—, Compaq-Asia, Singapore, 1991—, Harley-Davidson, 1992—, Outboard Marine Corp., 1986—; adj. prof. Kent (Ohio) State U., 1986—, Okla. State U., 1994—. Author: Painting Problems Solved, 1987, Industrial Painting Principles and Practices, 1991; monthly columnist, tech. editor Industrial Finishing jour.; contbr. numerous articles to profl. jours.; patentee in field. Sr. adviser Flint Sci. Fair. Served with Signal Corps, U.S. Army, 1954-56. Johnson fellow, 1957-58; NSF fellow, 1960-62; Dow fellow, 1961-62. Fellow Am. Inst. Chemists; mem. AAUP, Am. Sci. Affiliation, Soc. Mfg. Engrs. (bd. dirs.), Assn. Finishings Proc. (v.p profl. devel. council), Sigma XI, Alpha Tau Omega, Pi Tau Sigma (chpt. sr. adviser 1979-86). Office: NR Painting Cons Co 507 Haddington Ln Peachtree City GA 30269-3340

ROOD, DAVID S., linguistics educator; b. Albany, N.Y., Sept. 14, 1940; s. J. Henry and Pearl B. (Stanley) R.; m. Juliette A. Victor; 1 child, Jennifer. AB, Cornell U., 1963; MA, U. Calif., Berkeley, 1965; PhD, U. Calif., 1969. Instr. U. Colo., Boulder, 1967-69, asst. prof., 1969-77, assoc. prof., 1977-82, prof., 1982—. Author: Wichita Grammar, 1975, Siouan Languages Archive, 1982; (with others) Beginning Lakhota, 1976; editor Internat. Jour. of Am. Linguistics, 1981—; contbr. numerous articles to profl. jours. NSF grantee, 1972—, NEH grantee, 1972—. Mem. Linguistic Soc. Am., Soc. for Study Indigenous Langs. Am., Soc. for Linguistic Anthropology, Tchrs. of English to Speakers Other Langs. Office: U of Colo Dept of Linguistics Campus Box 295 Boulder CO 80309-0295

ROOD, DON D, insurance executive; b. Flint, Mich., Apr. 3, 1930; s. William and Ruth R.; m. Rose Lorraine Giguere, Apr. 7, 1951; children: Lorraine Cheryl Rood Burris, Don D. B.S., Central Mich. U., 1952; postgrad., U. Mich., 1954-65. Agt. State Farm Ins. Co., Flint, 1955-60; agy. mgr. State Farm Ins. Co., 1960-61; tng. dir. State Farm Ins. Co., Marshall, Mich, 1961-62; agy. dir. State Farm Ins. Co., 1962-71; dep. regional v.p. State Farm Ins. Co., Springfield, Pa., 1971-74; v.p. agy. State Farm Ins. Co., Bloomington, Ill, 1974-76; agy. v.p. State Farm Ins. Co., 1976-87, sr. agy. officer, 1980—, sr. agy. v.p., 1987—; bd. dirs. State Farm Life & Accident Assurance Co., Bloomington, State Farm Internat. Svcs. Inc., State Farm Mut. Automobile Co., State Farm Life Ins. Co., State Farm Annuity and Life Ins. Co., State Farm Fire and Casualty Ins. Co.; underwriter State Farm Lloyds. Served with U.S. Army, 1952-54, Korea. Mem. Nat. Assn. Life Underwriters, Agy. Officers Round Table, Life Ins. Mktg. and Rsch. Assn. (bd. dirs. 1982-85). Office: State Farm Mut Automobile Ins Co 1 State Farm Pla Bloomington IL 61710

ROOF, BETTY SAMS, internist; b. Columbia, S.C., Apr. 13, 1926; s. Grover Melton Saunders and Lucinda Wood (Sams) R.; m. Herman Hugh Fudenberg (div.); children: Drew Douglas, Brooks Roberts, David Melton, Hugh Haskell. BS, U. S.C., Columbia, 1944; MD, Duke U., 1949. Diplomate Am. Bd. Internal Medicine, Am. Bd. Endocrinology and Metabolism. Vol. vis. investigator Rockefeller Inst., N.Y.C., 1949-50; intern Presbyn. Hosp., N.Y.C., 1950-51, asst. resident, 1951-53, asst. physician, 1953-55; attending physician Francis Delafield Hosp., N.Y.C., 1954-55; clin. and research fellow dept. medicine Mass. Gen. Hosp., Boston, 1955-56, research fellow dept. pathology, 1957-58; research fellow Harvard U., 1955-56; research assoc. dept. microbiology and pathology Rockefeller Inst., 1958-59; asst. research physician Cancer Research Inst. U. Calif., San Francisco, 1962-63, assoc. research physician, 1967-71; lectr. medicine, 1971-74, assoc. clin. prof., 1974; assoc. prof. medicine Med. U. S.C., 1974-80, prof., 1980—, asst. dean, 1989—. Mem. Library Bd., Mill Valley, Calif., 1965-68; mem. Tamalpais Nursery Sch. Bd., Mill Valley, Calif., 1968. Am. Cancer Soc. trainee, 1953-55; grantee Am. Cancer Soc., USPHS, Koebig Trust Fund; USPHS fellow, 1949-50. Mem. Am. Assn. Cancer Research, Western Soc. Clin. Research, Endocrine Soc., Internat. Endocrine Soc., Am. Soc. for Bone and Mineral Research, Charleston Med. Soc., ACP, Am. Fedn. Clin. Research, So. Soc. Clin. Investigation, Waring Library Soc., Soc. for Destitute Widows and Children of Dec. Physicians, Pilot Club of Charleston (S.C.) (v.p., 1988-89, pres. 1990-91), Phi Beta Kappa, Alpha Omega Alpha. Contbr. articles to profl. jours. Home: 675 Ft Sumter Dr Charleston SC 29412-4333 Office: Med U SC 171 Ashley Ave Charleston SC 29425-0001

ROOF, ROBERT L., broadcast executive, sales executive; b. Circleville, Ohio, Apr. 15, 1946; s. Roger A. and Doris (Kraft) R.; m. Linda Anderson, Nov. 28, 1969; children: Jennifer, Leslie. Ba, Franklin U. Sales, disc jockey Sta. WPKO Radio, Waverly, Ohio, 1969-72, Sta. WSCR Radio, Scranton, Pa., 1972-75; sales Sta. WSPD Radio, Toledo, Ohio, 1975-78; sales Sta. WTVN Radio, Columbus, Ohio, 1978-81, local sales mgr., 1981-83, gen. sales mgr., 1984-87; v.p., gen. mgr. Sta. WDVE Radio, Pitts., 1987-93, pres., gen. mgr., 1993—. Pres. Southwest PA Jr. Achievement, Pitts., 1994—. Recipient Bronze Leadership award Jr. Achievement, Pitts., 1994. Mem. Columbus Sales Club (pres. 1982), Pitts. Sales Club (pres. 1989), Pitts. Radio Orgn. (pres. 1994). Methodist. Avocations: golf, hunting, Am. history. Home: 916 Summit Dr Wexford PA 15090 Office: Sta WDVE-FM 200 Fleet St Pittsburgh PA 15220-2908

ROOKE, ALLEN DRISCOLL, JR., civil engineer; b. San Antonio, Oct. 5, 1924; s. Allen Driscoll and Jean Edna (Lackner) R.; m. Betty Ruth Whitson, Oct. 17, 1949; children: Victoria Lynn Lewis, Cornelia Ruth. BSCE, Tex. A&M U., 1957; MSCE, Miss. State U., 1980. Registered profl. engr., Miss. Enlisted U.S. Army, 1942, advanced through grades to brig. gen., ret., 1984; rsch. civil engr. U.S. Army Corps Engrs., Vicksburg, Miss., 1958-83; ptnr. F.B. Rooke & Sons, Woodsboro, Tex., 1964—; sr. engr. Sci & Tech. Corp., Vicksburg, Miss., 1984—; bd. dirs. First Nat. Bank, Woodsboro, 1985—. Author/co-author numerous tech. publs. Mem. Res. Officers Assn. U.S. (dept. pres. 1980-82, svc. award 1980, 84), Assn. of U.S. Army, Ret. Officer's Assn. (chpt. v.p. 1985-86), Soc. Am. Mil. Engrs. (post v.p. 1979). Episcopalian. Club: army band Vicksburg (pres. 1980, 82). Avocation: chess. Home: PO Box 732 Woodsboro TX 78393-0732

ROOKE, DAVID LEE, retired chemical company executive; b. San Antonio, Tex., May 2, 1923; s. Henry Levi, Jr. and Annie (Davidson) R.; m. Esthermae Litherland, June 2, 1945; children—Eugene, Mark, Paul, Bruce. B.S. in Chem. Engring. Rice Inst., Houston, 1944; postgrad., U. Houston. With Dow Chem., Midland, Mich., 1946-88, v.p., pres., 1977-78; pres. Dow U.S.A., 1978-82; v.p. Dow Chem. Corp., 1978-82, exec. v.p., 1982-83, sr. v.p., 1983-86, ret., 1988, also bd. dirs.; bd. dirs. Dow Corning Corp. nat. exec. bd. Boy Scouts Am., 1979-86; bd. dirs. Meth. Mission Home, San Antonio. Served with USNR, 1944-46. Mem. AICE, United Meth. Reporter Found. (Dallas). Methodist.

ROOKLIDGE, WILLIAM CHARLES, lawyer; b. Portland, Oreg., Aug. 10, 1957; s. Chester Herbert and Barbara Kathryn (Dodson) R.; m. Kathryn Elaine Roosa, Aug. 20, 1983; children: Elizabeth Jill, Matthew Joseph. BS, U. Portland, 1979; JD, Lewis & Clark, 1984; LLM, George Washington U., 1985. Bar: Oreg. 1985, U.S. Patent Office 1985, U.S. Ct. Appeals (fed. cir.) 1985, Calif. 1988, U.S. Dist. Ct. (cen. dist.) Calif. 1988, U.S. Ct. Appeals (9th cir.) 1988, U.S. Supreme Ct. 1993, U.S. Dist. Ct. (so. dist.) Calif. 1992, U.S. Dist. Ct. (so. dist.) Calif. 1989. Engr. Tube Forgings Am., Inc., Portland, 1978-82; jud. clk. U.S. Ct. Appeals (fed. cir.), Washington, 1985-87; assoc. Knobbe, Martens, Olson & Bear, Newport Beach, Calif., 1987-89, ptnr., 1990-94; ptnr. Howard, Rice, Nemerovski, Canady, Falk & Rabkin, Newport Beach, Calif., 1995—. Contbr. articles to profl. jours. Recipient Joseph Rossman Meml. award Patent & Trademark Office Soc., 1988,

Gerald Rose Meml. award John Marshall Law Sch., 1993. Mem. ABA (sect. intellectual property law, com. chair 1992—). Am. Intellectual Property Law Assn. (com. chair 1988-93, dir. 1994—, Robert C. Watson award 1987), Orange County Patent Law Assn. (bd. dirs. 1990-93, pres. 1994). Republican. Presbyterian. Office: Howard Rice Nemerovski Canady et al 610 Newport Ctr Dr Ste 450 Newport Beach CA 92660-6420

ROOKS, CHARLES SHELBY, minister; b. Beaufort, N.C., Oct. 19, 1924; s. Shelby A. and Maggie (Hawkins) R.; m. Adrienne Martinez, Aug. 7, 1946; children: Laurence Gaylord, Carol Ann. AB, Va. State U., 1949; MDiv, Union Theol. Sem., 1953; LHD (hon.), Howard U., 1981, Va. State U., 1984, Talladega Coll., 1989; DD (hon.), Coll. Wooster, 1968, Interdenominational Theol. Ctr. 1979, Va. Union U., 1980; LLD (hon.), Dillard U., 1986, Heidelberg Coll., 1990; LittD (hon.), Huston-Tillotson Coll., 1989. Ordained to ministry United Ch. of Christ, 1953. Pastor Shanks Village Ch., Orangeburg, N.Y., 1951-53; pastor Lincoln Meml. Congl. Temple, Washington, 1953-60; assoc. dir. Fund for Theol. Edn., Princeton, N.J., 1960-67, exec. dir., 1967-74; pres. Chgo. Theol. Sem., 1974-84; exec. v.p. United Ch. Bd. for Homeland Ministries, N.Y.C., 1984-92 ret., 1992; mem. exec. bd. dept. ministry Nat. Coun. Chs., 1962-70; chmn. bd. United Ch. of Christ Office of Comm., 1964-81, chmn. com. structure Ctrl. Atlantic Conf., 1962-64; mem. Union Theol. Sem. Alumni Coun., 1968-70, Theol. Perspectives Commn. on Nat. Com. Black Churchmen, 1968-74; vis. fellow Episc. Theol. Sem. S.W., Austin, Tex., 1966; lectr. in field., 1960-94. Author: Rainbows and Reality, 1984, The Hopeful Spirit, 1987, Revolution in Zion, 1990; editor: Toward a Better Ministry, 1965; mem. editorial bd. Theology Today, 1966, New Conversations, 1977; contbr. articles to religious jours. Chmn. planning com. Nat. Consultation Negro in Christian Ministry, 1965; trustee Bexley Hall Theol. Sem., Colgate-Rochester Div. Sch., 1968-73, Lancaster Theol. Sem., Pa., 1969-74, Eastern Career Testing Ctr., Lancaster, 1969-74; mem. Princeton Regional Sch. Bd., 1969-70, exec. bd. Nat. Com. Religion and Labor, 1987-91; bd. dirs. The Africa Fund, 1987-91, Wash. Urban League, 1955-60, chmn. housing com., 1956-60; chmn. ednl. adv. com. Chgo. Urban League, 1978-84; pres. Communications Improvement, 1971-81; vice chair Nat. Com. for Full Employment, 1987-91. Served with AUS, 1943-46, PTO. Recipient Elizabeth Taylor Byrd Fund Outstanding Community Service award, 1969. Mem. Va. State U. Nat. Alumni Assn. (pres. 1966-67), Soc. for Study Black Religion (pres. 1970-74, 80-84), Assn. Theol. Schs. (cons. Black ch. studies 1970-71, mem. commn. on accrediting 1976-82, chmn. 1980-82, exec. com. 1982-84, Disting. Svc. medal 1992).

ROOKS, JUDITH PENCE, family planning, maternal health care, midwifery consultant; b. Spokane, Wash., Aug. 18, 1941; d. Lawrence Cyrus and Christine Atrice (Snow) Pence; m. Peter Geoffrey Bourne, Mar. 1972 (div.); m. Charles Stanley Rooks, Sept. 21, 1975; 1 child, Christopher Robert. BS, U. Wash., 1963; MS, Cath. U. Am., 1967; MPH, Johns Hopkins U., 1974. Cert. edpidemiology, nursing, nurse-midwife, mediator. Staff nurse The Clin. Ctr., NIH, Bethesda, Md., 1965; asst. prof. nursing dept. San Jose (Calif.) State Coll., 1967-69; edpidemiologist Ctrs. for Disease Control, Atlanta, 1970-72, 74-78; asst. prof. ob-gyn. Oreg. Health Sci. U., Portland, 1978-79; expert Office of the Surgeon Gen., Dept. HHS, Washington, 1979-80; project officer U.S. AID, Washington, 1980-82; prin. investigator Columbia U. Sch. Pub. Health, N.Y.C., 1988-89; cons. Portland, 1982—; mem. tech. adv. com. Family Health Internat., Research Triangle Park, N.C., 1986—; mem. editorial adv. com. population info. program Johns Hopkins U., Balt., 1984—; mem. com. Inst. of Medicine NAS, Washington, 1983-85. Co-author: Nurse-Midwifery in America, 1986; contbr. articles to profl. jours. Bd. advisors World Affairs Coun. Oreg., Portland, 1987—; bd. dirs. Planned Parenthood of the Columbia/Willamette, Portland, 1987-90; chmn. Ga. Citizens for Hosp. Abortion, Atlanta, 1969-70. Mem. APHA (chair com. on women's rights 1982-83, governing coun. 1976-77, 79-82, Martha May Eliot award for svc. to mothers, children, 1993), Am. Coll. Nurse-Midwives (life, pres. 1983-85). Avocations: gardening, running, reading, traveling, cooking. Home and Office: 2706 SW English Ct Portland OR 97201-1622

ROOMANN, HUGO, architect; b. Tallinn, Estonia, Mar. 25, 1923; came to U.S., 1951, naturalized, 1957; s. Eduard August and Annette (Kask) R.; m. Raja R. Suursoho, Sept. 15, 1945; children—Katrin-Kaja, Linda-Anu. B.S. Inst. Tech. Carolo Wilhelmina, Braunschweig, W. Ger., 1950; M.F.A. in Arch. (scholar 1956-57) Princeton U., 1957. Archtl. engr. Austin Co., Roselle, N.J., 1951-54; archtl. designer Epple & Seaman, Newark, 1954-55, 57-61; propr. Hugo Roomann, Cranford and Elizabeth, N.J., 1961-66; partner A.M. Kinney Assocs. (Architects and Engrs.), Cin., N.Y.C. and Chgo., 1966-89; dir. architecture, v.p. corp. ops. A.M. Kinney, Inc., Cin., 1967, 77, 89; dir. Walter Kidde Constructors, Inc., 1973, A.M. Kinney, Inc., A.M. Kinney Assocs. Inc., Chgo.; pres. Design Art Corp., 1986. Prin. works include Grad. Rsch. Ctr. for Biol. Scis., Ohio State U., 1970, Lloyd Libr., Cin., 1968, offices, labs. and mfg. facilities, Miles Labs., West Haven, Conn., 1969, Am. Mus. Atomic Energy, Oak Ridge, 1975, Renton K. Brodie Sci. Ctr., U. Cin., 1970, EPA Nat. Labs., Cin., 1975, NALCO Tech. Ctr., Naperville, Ill., 1979, Brown & Williamson Corp. Hdqrs., Louisville, 1983, U. Cin. Kettering Lab., 1989. Pres. Citizens League, Elizabeth, N.J., 1966, Estonian Heritage Assn. Cin., 1991-94; bd. dirs., pres. Intern-Ethnic Coun. of Greater Cin., 1992—. Recipient Top Ten Plant award Factory mag., 1967, Top Ten Plant award Modern Mfg. mag., 1970. Mem. AIA (Ohio chpt. award for Renton K. Brodie Sci. Ctr. 1971, for NALCO Ctr. 1980), Soc. Archtl. Historians, Princeton Club. Lutheran. Office: 2856 Observatory Ave Cincinnati OH 45208-2340

ROOMBERG, LILA GOLDSTEIN, lawyer; b. Bklyn., Oct. 21, 1929; d. William H. and Mary (Abramowitz) Goldstein; m. Lawrence A. Simon (div. 1965); 1 child, Virginia Simon Feil; m. Gerald Armon Roomberg (dec. 1995). BA, NYU, 1949, JD, 1951. Bar: N.Y. 1952, Pa. 1963. Assoc. Ballard, Spahr, Andrews & Ingersoll, Phila., 1959-71, ptnr., 1971-91, of counsel, 1992—. Mem. ABA, Pa. Bar Assn., Phila. Bar Assn., Phila. Bar Found. (sec. 1984-87, trustee 1981-87). Home: 120 Spruce St Philadelphia PA 19106-4315 Office: Ballard Spahr Andrews & Ingersoll 1735 Market St Philadelphia PA 19103-7501

ROONEY, ANDREW AITKEN, writer, columnist; b. Albany, N.Y., Jan. 14, 1919; s. Walter S. and Ellinor (Reynolds) R.; m. Marguerite Howard, Mar. 21, 1942; children: Ellen, Martha, Emily, Brian. Student, Colgate U., 1942. Writer-producer CBS-TV News, 1959—; newspaper columnist Tribune Co. Syndicate, 1979—. Author: (with O.C. Hutton) Air Gunner, 1944, The Story of Stars and Stripes, 1946, Conquerors' Peace, 1947, The Fortunes of War, 1962, A Few Minutes with Andy Rooney, 1981, And More By Andy Rooney, 1982, Pieces of My Mind, 1984, Word for Word, 1986, Not That You Asked, 1989, Sweet and Sour, 1992, My War, 1995; TV programs include An Essay on War, Mr. Rooney Goes to Washington, Mr. Rooney Goes to Dinner; regular commentator-essayist: 60 Minutes, 1978—. Served with AUS, 1941-45. Decorated Air medal, Bronze Star.; recipient awards for best written TV documentary Writers Guild Am., 1966, 68, 71, 75, 76, Emmy awards, 1968, 78, 81, 82. Office: CBS News/60 Minutes 524 W 57th St New York NY 10019-2925

ROONEY, DANIEL M., professional football team executive; b. 1932; s. Arthur Joseph and Kathleen (McNulty) R. Former salesman advt., editor Pitts. Steelers Program; now pres. Pitts. Steelers; mem. exec. coms. NFL. Office: Three Rivers Stadium 300 Stadium Cir Pittsburgh PA 15212-5729*

ROONEY, FRANCIS CHARLES, JR., corporate executive; b. North Brookfield, Mass., Nov. 24, 1921; s. Francis Charles and Evelyn Fullerbrown (Murray) R.; m. Frances Elizabeth Heffernan, June 10, 1950; children: Peter, Michael, Stephen, Jean, William, Carol, Frances, Clare. BS in Econs., U. Pa., 1943; D of Comml. Sci. (hon.) Suffolk U., 1968, St. John's U., 1973; PhD (hon.), Boston Coll., 1984. Sales staff John Foote Shoe Co., Brockton, Mass., 1946-48; mem. sales staff Florsheim Shoe Co., Chgo., 1948-53; various positions Melville Shoe Co., N.Y.C., 1953—; pres. Thom McAn div. Melville Shoe Corp., N.Y.C. 1961-64; pres., chief exec. officer Melville Corp., Harrison, N.Y. and N.Y.C., 1964-77; chmn., pres., chief exec. officer Melville Corp., Harrison, 1977-80, chmn., chief exec. officer, 1980-86, former chmn. exec. com.; chmn. bd., CEO H.H. Brown Shoe Co., Inc., Greenwich, Conn.; dir. Bankers Trust Co., N.Y.C., Crystal Brands Inc., Southport, Conn., N.Y.C., The Neiman Marcus Group, Chestnut Hill, Mass. Bd. dirs. United Cerebral Palsy, N.Y.C., 1960, Smithsonian Assocs., 1975; overseers

Wharton Sch. U. Pa.; trustee N.Y. Med. Coll. Lt. (j.g.) USN, 1943-46. Republican. Roman Catholic. Clubs: Round Hill (Greenwich); Links (N.Y.C.); Winged Foot (Mamaroneck, N.Y.). Office: H H Brown Shoe Co Inc 124 W Putnam Ave Greenwich CT 06830*

ROONEY, GAIL SCHIELDS, college administrator; b. St. Francis, Kans., Feb. 15, 1947; d. Fred Harlan and Darlene Mary (Saint) Schields; m. Thomas Michael Rooney, June 27, 1970; children: Shane Michael, Shauna Meghan. BA, U. Colo., 1969; MS, George Williams Coll., 1974; PhD, U. Ill., 1982. Asst. dir. Spl. Svcs. Program Cleve. State U., 1970-71; admissions counselor George Williams Coll., Downers Grove, Ill., 1972-73; coord. of career exploration ctr. Women's Programs Cuyahoga Community Coll., Cleve., 1973-76; vis. asst. prof. Sch. Clin. Medicine U. Ill., Champaign, 1981-82; counselor, instr. Cuyahoga Community Coll., Cleve., 1982-84, dir. counseling, career and psychol. svcs., 1984-85; dir. career, counseling and health svcs. Briar Cliff Coll., Sioux City, Iowa, 1985-88, v.p. for student devel., 1988—; adj. instr. counselor edn. Wayne (Nebr.) State Coll., 1988; program presenter Myers Briggs Type Indicator, Sioux City, 1986—. Bd. dirs. Gordon Chem. Dependency Ctr., Sioux City, 1988-89, St. Luke's Gordon Recovery Ctr., Sioux City, 1991—. Mem. ACA, Am. Coll. Pers. Assn., Nat. Assn. Student Pers. Adminstrs. Home: 52 Red Bridge Dr Sioux City IA 51104-1061 Office: Briar Cliff Coll 3303 Rebecca St Sioux City IA 51104-2340

ROONEY, J. PATRICK, insurance company executive; b. Lawrenceville, Ill., Dec. 13, 1927; s. Michael Andrew and Mary Francis (Loftus) R.; married; children: Therese, Andrew, Cathleen, Christine. BA in Econs., St. John's U., 1948. CLU. With Golden Rule Ins. Co. (formerly Golden Rule Life Ins. Co.), Lawrenceville, Ill., 1946—, pres., 1955-59, chmn. bd., chief exec. officer, 1974—, chmn. bd. Golden Rule Fin. Corp., 1972—. Republican. Roman Catholic.

ROONEY, JOHN EDWARD, state legislator, electrical company executive; b. Bklyn., Apr. 23, 1939; s. John Patrick and Micheline Daisy (Maturlo) R.; m. Martha Elizabeth Bollmann, Dec. 23, 1962; children: Beth Elise, Patrick John. BS in Mgmt., Rutgers U., 1974. Sales mgr. Toshiba, N.Y. and N.J., 1984—; mayor Borough of Northvale, N.J., 1979-86, 90—; mem. N.J. State Assembly, 1983—. Councilman Borough of Northvale, 1976-78; commr. Bergen County Utilities Authority, Little Ferry, N.J., 1983-88. Served with USAF, 1961-65. Mem. Am. Legion (jr. vice commdr. 1978-79), Vietnam Vets for Am. Republican. Roman Catholic. Lodges: Elks, Sons of Italy. Office: NJ State Assembly Dist 39 Office 436 Old Hook Rd Emerson NJ 07630-1368

ROONEY, JOHN EDWARD, JR., communications company executive; b. Evergreen Park, Ill., Apr. 24, 1942; s. John Edward and Margaret Wilma (Stolte) R.; m. Germaine Rose Dettloff, June 26, 1965; children: Kathleen, John, Colleen. BS, John Carroll U., 1964; MBA, Loyola U., 1969. Credit analyst Fed. Res. Bank, Chgo., 1964-69, adminstrv. asst., 1969-70; asst. treas. Pullman Inc., 1970-73, asst. contr., 1973-78; v.p. fin. Pullman Standard, 1978-79; sr. v.p. fin. Trailmobile, Chgo., 1979-81; treas. Firestone Tire & Rubber Co., Akron, Ohio, 1981-87, v.p. retail fin. services, 1987-88, sr. v.p. MasterCare Svc. Ctrs., 1988-90; v.p., treas. Ameritech, Chgo., 1990-92; pres. Ameritech Cellular Svcs., Chgo., 1992—; instr. fin. Ill. Benedictine Coll., 1975-80. Mem. Ohio Mfrs. Assn. (trustee 1983-87), Ohio Pub. Expenditure Coun. (trustee 1986-87), Glen Oak Country Club (Glen Ellyn, Ill.), Boulders Club (Carefree, Ariz.), The Tavern Club (Chgo.). Home: 2S 311 Davis Ct Wheaton IL 60187 Office: Ameritech # 3H 70 2000 W Ameritech Center Dr Hoffman Estates IL 60195-5000

ROONEY, JOHN JOSEPH, lawyer, former state supreme court justice; b. Chadron, Nebr., Nov. 30, 1915; s. William Peter and Armena Mae (Broghamer) R.; m. Velma Kruse, July 13, 1937; children—Armena, Velma, Margaret, Kathryn, Regina, John. A.B., U. Minn., 1940; LL.B., U. Colo., 1940. Bar: S.D. 1940, Wyo. 1952. Sole practice law Hot Springs, S.D., 1940-41; spl. agent FBI, 1941-58; mem. Hickey Gray & Rooney, Cheyenne, Wyo., 1959-72, Rooney Horishey Bagley & Hickey, Cheyenne, Wyo., 1972-77; atty. gen. State of Wyo., Cheyenne, 1978; justice Wyo. Supreme Ct., Cheyenne, 1979-86, chief justice, 1983-85; mem. firm Rooney, Bagley, Hickey, Evans & Statkus, 1986-88, ret.; mem. Wyo. Parole Bd., 1964-70; city atty. City of Cheyenne, 1968-70; atty. Laramie County Sch. Dist. No. 1, Cheyenne, 1974-79. Mem. Wyo. Ho. of Reps., 1965-70; chmn. Wyo. Democratic Com., 1966-71. Mem. ABA. Home: 420 W 28th St Cheyenne WY 82001-2723 Office: Wyo Supreme Ct Supreme Ct Bldg Cheyenne WY 82002

ROONEY, JOHN PHILIP, law educator; b. Evanston, Ill., May 1, 1932; s. John McCaffery and Bernadette Marie (O'Brien) R.; m. Jean Marie Kliss, Feb. 16, 1974 (div. Oct. 1988); 1 child, Caitlin Mairin. BA, U. Ill., 1953; JD, Harvard U., 1958. Bar: Ill. 1958, Calif. 1961, Mich. 1975, U.S. Tax Ct. 1973. Assoc. lawyer Chapman & Cutler, Chgo., 1958-60, Wilson, Morton, San Mateo, Calif., 1961-63; pvt. practice San Francisco, 1963-74; prof. law Cooley Law Sch., Lansing, Mich., 1975—. Author: Selected Cases (Property), 1985; contbr. articles to profl. jours. Pres. San Francisco coun. Dem. Clubs, 1970. 1st lt. U.S. Army, 1953-55. Recipient Beattie Teaching award Cooley Law Sch. Grads., 1979, 90, 92. Mem. ABA (real estate fed. tax problems com. 1986—, teaching taxation com.), Mich. Bar Title Standards Com., Ingham County Bar Assn., Univ. Club. Democrat. Unitarian. Office: Cooley Law Sch 217 S Capitol Ave Lansing MI 48933-1586

ROONEY, KEVIN DAVITT, lawyer; b. Springfield, Mass., June 23, 1944; s. Davitt Michael and Elizabeth Isabel (Wlodyka) R.; m. Annette Eloise Benevento, Nov. 11, 1972; children: Kathryn Denise, Mary Elizabeth. B.A., St. Marys Coll., 1966; J.D., George Washington U., 1975. Bar: Va. 1975, D.C. 1977. Computer systems analyst VA, Washington, 1967-68, 70-73; chief legal programs and budget Dept. Justice, Washington, 1973-77, exec. asst. to assoc. atty. gen., 1977, asst. atty. gen. for adminstrn., 1977-84; prin. Rooney & Assocs, Washington, 1984-87, 90-94, Rooney & Barry, Washington, 1987-89; assoc. dir. Exec. Office for Immigration Rev., U.S. Dept. Justice, Falls Church, Va., 1995—; bd. dirs., v.p. Joint Action in Cmty. Svcs., Inc., Washington, 1988-94. Served with U.S. Army, 1968-70. Mem. ASPA, Fed. Bar Assn., Va. Bar Assn., D.C. Bar Assn. Office: US Dept Justice Office Immigration Review 5107 Leesburg Pike #2400 Falls Church VA 22041

ROONEY, MARGARET ELAINE, nurse, educator; b. Pueblo, Colo.; d. Joseph and Margaret (Jacketta) Rooney; children: Kate, Sean. Diploma, St. Mary-Corwin Sch. Nursing, 1965; BS with honors and distinction, U. So. Colo., 1968; MSN, U. Colo., 1975; postgrad., Colo. State U. RN, Colo. Charge nurse St. Mary-Conview Hosp., Pueblo, Colo., 1965-68, Colo. State Hosp., Pueblo, Colo., 1968-72; instr. nursing U. So. Colo., Pueblo, Colo., 1972-79; instr. Beth El Coll. of Nursing, Colorado Springs, Colo., 1979-82; nursing coord., instr. Pikes Peak Community Coll., Colorado Springs, Colo., 1982—; so. dir. Colo. Orgn. for Assoc. Degree Nursing; chair-faculty senate Pikes Peak Community Coll., Colorado Springs; mem. adv. bd. dirs. Pueblo Community Coll. U. So. Colo. 1989—; active farmer, 1982—. Contbr. articles to profl. jours. Com. woman Democrat. Party, Colorado Springs. Mem. Tae Kwan Do Fedn. Democrat. Roman Catholic. Avocations: archery, yoga, karate. Office: Pikes Peak C C 5675 S Academy Blvd Box 13N Colorado Springs CO 80906

ROONEY, MATTHEW A., lawyer; b. Jersey City, May 19, 1949; s. Charles John and Eileen (Dunphy) R.; m. Jean M. Alletag, June 20, 1973 (div. Dec. 1979); 1 child, Jessica Margaret; m. Diane S. Kaplan, July 6, 1981; children: Kathryn Olivia, S. Benjamin. AB magna cum laude, Georgetown U., 1971; JD with honors, U. Chgo., 1974. Bar: Ill. 1975, U.S. Dist. Ct. (no. dist.) Ill. 1975, U.S. Ct. Appeals (7th cir.) 1990. Law clk. to cir. judge U.S. Ct. Appeals (7th cir.), Chgo., 1974-75; assoc. Mayer, Brown & Platt, Chgo., 1975-80, ptnr., 1981—. Assoc. editor U. Chgo. Law Rev., 1973. Mem. ABA, 7th Cir. Bar Assn., Order of Coif, Phi Beta Kappa. Democrat. Roman Catholic. Avocations: jogging, golfing. Home: 2718 Sheridan Rd Evanston IL 60201-1754 Office: Mayer Brown & Platt 190 S La Salle St Chicago IL 60603-3410

ROONEY, MICHAEL FRANCIS, publisher; b. Bronxville, N.Y., July 4, 1953; s. Francis Charles and Frances (Heffernan) R.; m. Joann Paulsen, Apr. 30, 1977; children: Leigh Ann, Hank. BS in Mktg., Boston Coll., 1976. V.p. Paulsen Pub. Inc., N.Y.C., 1979-85; regional sales mgr. Field & Stream Mag., N.Y.C., 1985-87, pub.; pub. Outdoor Life, N.Y.C. Mem. Pharm. Adv. Coun., Larchmont Yacht Club, Winged Foot Golf Club. Roman Catholic. Avocations: running, golf. Office: Times Mirror Mags Inc Two Park Ave New York NY 10016-5695*

ROONEY, MICKEY (JOE YULE, JR.), actor; b. Bklyn., Sept. 23, 1920; s. Joe and Nell (Carter) Yule; m. Ava Gardner, Jan. 10, 1942 (div. May 1943); m. Betty Jane Rase, Sept. 30, 1944 (div. 1949); children: Mickey Jr., Timothy; m. Martha Vickers, June 3, 1949 (div.); m. Elaine Mahnken (div. 1958); m. Barbara Thomason, Dec. 1958; children: Kerry, Kyle, Kelly Ann, Kimmy Sue; m. Margie Lang, Sept. 1966 (div. 1967); m. Carolyn Hockett, (div.); 1 adopted child, Jimmy, 1 child, Jonell; m. Jan Chamberlin, July 28, 1978; stepchildren: Chris Aber, Mark Aber. Ed. in Dayton Heights and Vine Street grammar sch., Pacific Mil. Acad., under tutors. First appeared in vaudeville with parents; then appeared with Sid Gould, numerous TV programs; appeared in motion pictures Judge Hardy's Children, Hold That Kiss, Lord Jeff, Love Finds Andy Hardy, Boys Town, Stablemates, Out West With the Hardys, Huckleberry Finn, Andy Hardy Gets Spring Fever, Babes in Arms, Young Tom Edison, Judge Hardy and Son, Andy Hardy Meets Debutante, Strike Up the Band, Andy Hardy's Private Secretary, Men of Boystown, Life Begins for Andy Hardy, Babes on Broadway, A Yank at Eton, The Human Comedy, Andy Hardy's Blonde Trouble, Girl Crazy, Thousands Cheer, National Velvet, Ziegfeld Follies, The Strip, Sound Off, Off Limits, All Ashore, Light Case of Larceny, Drive A Crooked Road, Bridges at Toko-Ri, The Bold and Brave, Eddie, Private Lives of Adam and Eve, Comedian, The Grabbers, St. Joseph Plays the Horses, Breakfast at Tiffany's, Somebody's Waiting, Requiem For A Heavyweight, Richard, Pulp, It's a Mad, Mad, Mad, Mad World, Everything's Ducky, The Secret Invasion, The Extraordinary Seaman, The Comic, The Cockeyed Cowboys of Calico County, Skidoo, B.J. Presents, That's Entertainment, The Domino Principle, Pete's Dragon, The Magic of Lassie, Black Stallion, Arabian Adventure, Erik the Viking, My Heroes Have Always Been Cowboys, 1991, (voice) Little Nimo: Adventures in Slumberland, 1992; starred in TV prodns. Pinocchio, 1957, Leave 'Em Laughing, 1981, Bill, 1981 (Emmy, Golden Globe), Senior Trip!, 1981, Bill on His Own, 1983, Little Spies (Acad. Hon. award 1982), It Came upon the Midnight Clear, 1984, Bluegrass, 1988; appeared on stage in Sugar Babies, 1979, The Will Rogers Follies, 1993; appeared in TV series A Year at the Top, The Mickey Rooney Show; author: I.E. An Autobiography, 1965, Life Is Too Short, 1991, Search for Sonny Skies, 1994; fgn. films: Midsummer Nights Dream, 1937, Words and Music, 1946, Rachels, 1973, To Hong Kong with Love, 1975, Oddessy of the Pacific, 1979. With AUS, WWII. Recipient Spl. Acad. Award, 1940, Tony award for best mus. actor, 1980; named One of Top 10 Money-Making Stars, Herald-Fame Poll, 1938-43. Office: PO Box 3186 Thousand Oaks CA 91359*

ROONEY, PAUL C., JR., lawyer; b. Winnetka, Ill., Oct. 23, 1943; s. Paul C. and Mary K. (Brennan) R.; m. Maria Elena Del Canto, Sept. 6, 1980. BA, Harvard U., 1963, LLB. 1966. Bar: Mass. 1968, N.Y. 1972, Fla. 1980, Tex. 1980, U.S. Dist. Ct. (ea. and so. dists.) N.Y., U.S. Ct. Appeals (2d cir.). Ptnr. White & Case, N.Y.C., 1983—. Served to lt. USNR, 1966-69. Mem. ABA, N.Y. State Bar Assn., Fla. Bar Assn., Tex. Bar Assn., Dallas Bar Assn., Univ. Club (N.Y.C.), Harvard Club (N.Y.C.) Mamaroneck Preserve. Home: 417 Park Ave New York NY 10022-4401 Office: White & Case 1155 Ave Of The Americas New York NY 10036-2711

ROONEY, PAUL GEORGE, mathematics educator; b. N.Y.C., July 14, 1925; s. Geoffrey Daniel and Doris Elizabeth (Babcock) R.; m. Mary Elizabeth Carlisle, June 20, 1950; children: Francis Timothy, Elizabeth Anne, Kathleen Doris, John Edward, James Carlisle. B.Sc., U. Alta., 1949; Ph.D., Calif. Inst. Tech., 1952. Asst. prof. math. U. Alta., 1952-55; asst. prof. U. Toronto, 1955-60, assoc. prof., 1960-62, prof., 1962-91, prof. emeritus, 1991—; dir. Commonwealth Petroleum Co., Calgary, 1946-59. Editor in chief Can. Jour. Math. 1971-75; contbr. articles to profl. jours. Bd. dirs. Francis F. Reeve Found., 1944-58. Served with Can. Army, 1943-45. Fellow Royal Soc. Can.; Mem. Can. Math. Soc. (councillor 1960-64, 66-70, 76-78, v.p. 1979-81, pres. 1981-83), Am. Math. Soc., Math. Assn. Am. Office: U Toronto, Dept Math, Toronto, ON Canada M5S 1A1

ROONEY, PAUL MONROE, former library administrator; b. Buffalo, Apr. 16, 1918; s. John Francis and Marguerite (Cass) R.; m. Elizabeth Dorsey, Jan. 22, 1955; children: James, Thomas. B.S., State Tchrs. Coll., Buffalo, 1938; B.S. in L.S, U. Buffalo, 1940. Br. librarian Buffalo Pub. Library, 1940-42; head reference dept. Grosvenor Library, 1945-59; head tech. dept. Buffalo and Erie County Pub. Library, 1959-61, asst. dep. dir., 1961-63, dep. dir., 1963-75, dir., 1975-83; chmn. N.Y. State Pub. Librarians Certification Com., 1959-60; trustee Western N.Y. Library Resources Council, 1966-83, pres., 1969-70. Served with USAF, 1942-45. Mem. N.Y. Am. library assns., Grosvenor Soc. (dir.) Roman Catholic. Home: 522 Ashland Ave Buffalo NY 14222-1307

ROONEY, TERENCE, public relations executive; b. 1951. V.p. Morgen-Walke Assocs., 1983-87, sr. v.p., 1987-89, ptnr./dir. press rels. group, 1989—. Office: Morgen-Walke Assocs Inc 380 Lexington Ave New York NY 10168

ROONEY, WILLIAM RICHARD, magazine editor; b. New Brunswick, N.J., Mar. 12, 1938; s. William Richard and Bernadette (Huether) R.; m. Rita Ann Scherer, July 20, 1963; children—Karen, Kevin, Brian, Kristin. B.S. in English, St. Peter's Coll., Jersey City, 1959. Asst., then asso. editor Marine Engring./Log mag., N.Y.C., 1960-64; asso. editor Outdoor Life mag., N.Y.C., 1964-72; mng. editor Outdoor Life mag., 1972-76, sr. editor, 1976-77; editor Am. Forests mag., Washington, 1977-91, v.p. for publs., 1991—; editor articles Sports Afield ann. outdoor mags., 1983-90. Contbr. to: Complete Outdoors Ency, 1972; others. Served with AUS, 1959-60. Mem. Outdoor Writers Assn. Am. Roman Catholic. Home: 7916 Carrie Ln Manassas VA 22111-2548 Office: 1516 P St NW Washington DC 20005-1932

ROOP, JAMES JOHN, public relations executive; b. Parkersburg, W.Va., Oct. 29, 1949; s. J Vaun and Mary Louise (McGinnis) R.; m. Margaret Mary Kuneck (div. 1982); m. Susan Lynn Hoell (div. 1989); m. Daisy P. Billue, 1990. BS in Journalism, W. Va. U., 1971. Various account mgmt. postions Ketchum Pub. Rels., Pitts., 1972-77, v.p., 1977-79; v.p. Burson-Marsteller, Chgo., 1979-81; sr. v.p. Hesselbart & Mitten/Watt, Cleve., 1981-84, exec. v.p., 1984-86, pres., 1986-87; pres. Watt, Roop & Co. (formerly Hesselbart & Mitten/Watt), Cleve., 1987—. Contbr. articles to profl. jours. Bd. dirs. Ctr. for Families and Children; active Project LEARN. Fellow Pub. Rels. Soc. Am. (chmn. investor rels. sect. 1984-85, chmn. honors and awards com. 1995); mem. Nat. Investor Rels. Inst. (charter pres. Cleve./Akron chpt., sr. investor rels. roundtable), Urban League, Police Athletic League, Econs. Am., Leadership Cleve., Cleve. Skating Club, Mayfield Country Club. Republican. Home: 2574 Fairmount Blvd Cleveland Heights OH 44106 Office: Watt Roop & Co 1100 Superior Ave E Ste 1350 Cleveland OH 44114-2518

ROOP, RALPH GOODWIN, retired oil marketing company executive; b. Snowville, Va., June 23, 1915; s. Guy C. and Ora (Goodwin) R.; married; children: Nancie Roop Kennedy, Paterson Roop Webster. BS, Va. Poly. Inst., 1936; MS, Cornell U., 1937. Various positions So. States Corp., Richmond, Va., 1937-66; pres. and/or chmn. bd. Petroleum Marketers, Inc., Richmond, 1954-88, dir., mem. exec. com., 1988—; bd. dirs. Jefferson Nat. Bank, Charlottesville, Va., 1979—. Trustee Va. Wesleyan Coll., Norfolk, 1982—; bd. dirs. Suhor Found., 1988—, Trinity Found., Richmond, Va. Tech. Found., Blacksburg. Named Oil Man of Yr., Va. Petroleum Jobbers Assn., 1983. Mem. Va. Petroleum Council (chmn. 1964-67), Va. Oil Men's Assn. (pres. 1975-76), Am. Petroleum Inst., Richmond C. of C. (past bd. dirs.). Methodist. Avocations: travel, photography, fishing. Home: 203 Hollyport Rd Richmond VA 23229-7620

ROORDA, JOHN FRANCIS, JR., business consultant; b. Evanston, Ill., Jan. 16, 1923; s. John Francis and Sadie M. (Daley) R.; m. Elizabeth Mul-

cahy, July 2, 1949; children: Elizabeth Roorda Barker, John F., Ann Roorda Hollis. B.S. in Chem. Engring, Purdue U., 1943, Ph.D., 1949. With Shell Oil Co., 1949-83; gen. mgr. combined oil products/chem. econs. dept., 1973-74, v.p. planning and econs., 1974-77; v.p. Shell Devel. Co., Houston, 1977-78; v.p. corp. planning Shell Oil Co., 1978-83; pres. John Roorda, 1983—; coordinator Exec. Service Corps, Houston, 1985—. Served to lt. (j.g.) USNR, 1943-46. Recipient Disting. Engring. Alumnus award Purdue U., 1976, Outstanding Chem. Engr. award Purdue U., 1991. Mem. Sigma Xi. Roman Catholic. Office: 2401 Fountainview Suite 910 Houston TX 77057

ROOS, CASPER, actor; b. N.Y.C., Mar. 21, 1925; s. Jacob and Sabina (Uhlenbusch) R.; m. Shirley Anne Nicholson, June 27, 1953; 1 child, Pieter Nicholson. Student, N.Y. Coll. Music. treas. Actors Equity Found., N.Y.C., 1982-88; co-chmn. research subcom. Nat. Theater Com., N.Y.C., 1983—. Prin. actor Shenandoah, N.Y.C., 1975-78, Brigadoon, N.Y.C., 1979-80, My One and Only, N.Y.C., 1982-85, Into the Light, 1986, Man of La Mancha, Zurich, 1988, (Broadway prodn.) Shenandoah Revival, 1989; numerous regional theater prodns. Served with U.S. Mcht. Marines, 1943-46. Mem. Actors Equity (treas. 1982-88, councilor 1964-79, 88-93). Home: PO Box 11 Gilbertsville NY 13766-0011 *Don Quixote wanted to 'add a little grace to the world.' I, too, would like to add a 'little' to this world, whether it be grace or laughter or tears to an audience or service to my colleagues. If, like Don Quixote, I look a little foolish, so be it. I prefer a life of striving for the ultimate to the easier smug acceptance of the status quo.*

ROOS, DANIEL, civil engineering educator; b. Bklyn., Apr. 12, 1939; s. Sigmund and Anita (Sperling) R.; m. Eva Bonis, June 1, 1969; children—Richard Joseph, Linda Suzanne. B.S. in Civil Engring, M.I.T., 1961, M.S., 1963, Ph.D., 1966. Mem. faculty MIT, Cambridge, 1963—, assoc. prof. civil engring., 1970-76, prof., 1976—, head transp. systems div., 1977-78, dir. Ctr. for Transp. Studies, 1978-85, dir. Ctr. Tech., Policy and Indsl. Devel., 1985—, Japan Steel Industry prof., 1985—; mem. Commn. on Indsl. Productivity MIT, 1987-89; founder, dir. Multisystems Inc., Cambridge, 1965-85; chmn. com. to assess advanced vehicle and hwy. technols., NRC, 1990-91; mem. com. on fuel economy NRC, 1991-92; dir. Internat. Motor Vehicle Program, 1980—; co-dir. Lean Aircraft Initiative, 1992—. Author: ICES System Design, 1964; The Future of the Automobile, 1984, Auto Futures, 1990; co-author: Made in America, 1989, The Machine That Changed the World, 1990; contbr. articles to profl. jours. Mem. U.S. Task Force on Transp., 1969. Mem. ASCE (Frank M. Masters Transp. Engring. award 1989), Assn. Computing Machinery, Ops. Research Soc. (treas. transp. sci. sect. 1970-71), Transp. Research Bd. (chmn. para-transit com. 1974-80, group coun. 1980-84), Coun. Univ. Transp. Ctrs. (pres. 1983). Developer Dial-A-Ride transp. concept, 1965; dir. Internat. Motor Vehicle. Home: 28 Baskin Rd Lexington MA 02173-6929 Office: MIT Ctr Tech Policy & Indsl Devel 77 Massachusetts Ave Cambridge MA 02139

ROOS, ERIC EUGENE, plant physiologist; b. Charleroi, Pa., May 23, 1941; s. Carl F. and Isabelle (McPherson) R.; m. Lois Bonita Bruno, Aug. 24, 1964; children: Michael, Erin. Bs, Waynesburg Coll., 1963; PhD, W.Va. U., 1967. Supr. plant physiologist, rsch. leader Nat. Seed Storage Lab, Agrl. Research Service of USDA, Ft. Collins, Colo., 1967—. Fellow Am. Soc. Agronomy, Am. Soc. Hort. Sci., Crop Sci. Soc. Am.; mem. Sigma Xi, Gamma Sigma Delta. Office: USDA Agrl Research Service 1111 S Mason St Fort Collins CO 80521-4500

ROOS, FREDERICK RIED, film producer; b. Santa Monica, Calif., May 22, 1934; s. Victor Otto and Florence Mary (Stout) R. BA, UCLA, 1956. Producer Zoetrope Studios, San Francisco. Casting dir., story editor various cos., 1960-70, film producer, 1964—; producer: Back Door to Hell, 1964-65, Flight to Fury, 1964-65, The Conversation (Acad. award nomination), Godfather Part II, 1973-79 (Acad. award Best Picture), Apocalypse Now, 1979, The Black Stallion, Hammett, 1982, The Escape Artist, The Outsiders, 1983, Rumble Fish, One From the Heart, Cotton Club, 1984, One Magic Christmas, Seven Minutes in Heaven, 1986, Gardens of Stone, 1987, Barfly, 1986, Tucker: The Man and His Dream, 1988, New York Stories, 1989, Wait Until Spring Bandini, 1990, The Godfather Part III, 1990, Hearts of Darkness: A Filmaker's Apocalypse, 1991, The Secret Garden, 1993; assoc. producer: Drive He Said, 1970. Served with AUS, 1957-59. Office: 2980 Beverly Glen Cir Los Angeles CA 90077-1725

ROOS, NESTOR ROBERT, consultant; b. St. Louis, Aug. 19, 1925; s. Maurice and Fannie (Friedman) R.; m. Fay Weil, July 8, 1951; children: Marilyn Roos Hall, Eileen Roos Ruddell, Robert F. BBA, Washington U., St. Louis, 1948; MSBA, Washington U., 1949; D of Bus. Adminstrn., Ind. U., 1959. Instr. bus. La. State U., Baton Rouge, 1949-51; teaching fellow Ind. U., Bloomington, 1951-53; asst. prof. Ga. State U., Atlanta, 1953-55; prof. U. Ariz., Tucson, 1955-86, prof. emeritus, 1986; pres. Risk Mgmt. Pub. Co., Tucson, 1976-90, cons. editor, 1990—; cons., expert witness in field; bd. dirs. Blue Cross-Blue Shield Ariz., sec., 1993-95; mem. Ins. Dirs.' Adv. Com., Phoenix, 1987—, Reverse Mortgage Adv. Com., Tucson, 1988-90. Author: (with others) Multiple Line Insurers, 1970, Governmental Risk Management Manual, 1976, Industrial Accident Prevention, 1980. Bd. dirs. Handmaker Geriatric Ctr., Tucson, 1987-92; pres. Temple Emanu-El, Tucson, 1981-83. With U.S. Army, 1943-45, ETO. Grantee Nat. Inst. Occupational Safety and Health, 1975. Mem. Risk and Ins. Mgmt. Soc., Western Risk and Ins. Assn. (pres. 1972-73), Public Risk and Ins. Mgmt. Assn. (dir. edn. and tng. 1982-89). Democrat. Jewish. Avocations: gardening, golf. Home: 7311 E Camino De Cima Tucson AZ 85715-2212 Office: Risk Mgmt Pub Co 2030 E Broadway Blvd Ste 106 Tucson AZ 85719-5908

ROOS, THOMAS BLOOM, biological scientist, educator; b. Peoria, Ill., Mar. 19, 1930; s. Seymour G. and Clara Gertrude (Bloom) R.; m. Marilyn A. Siker, June 14, 1953; children: David S., Sara D. AB, Harvard U., 1951; MS, U. Wis., 1953, PhD, 1960; MA (hon.), Dartmouth Coll., 1971. Instr. U. Wis., Madison, 1959-60; instr. Dartmouth Coll., Hanover, N.H., 1960-61, asst. prof., 1961-66, assoc. prof., 1966-71, prof., 1971—; vis. prof. St. George's Med. Sch., London, 1973-75; Fulbright lectr. U. Delhi, U. Calcutta, Bhabha Atomic Rsch. Centre, Coun. Indsl. and Sci. Rsch. Labs., Calcutta, Hyderabad; vis. scientist Harvard Med. Sch., 1988; cons. Commn. on Undergrad. Edn. in Biol. Scis., Washington, 1967-71, St. George's Med. Sch., 1974—, CSP, Inc., Billerica, Mass., 1986—. Inventor Master Scan Image Analyzing Computer. Mem. Dem. Town Com., Hanover, N.H., 1961-68. With U.S. Army, 1954-56. Spl. postdoctoral fellow NIH, Leyden, Netherlands, 1965-66; hon. fellow Univ. Coll., London, 1972-73. Mem. AAAS, Am. Soc. Zoologists. Club: Faculty (Hanover, N.H.) (pres. 1981-85). Avocations: music, computer programming, poetry. Home: 19 Raylon Rd Hanover NH 03755-2211 Office: Dartmouth Coll Dept Of Biology Hanover NH 03755

ROOSEVELT, EDITH KERMIT, journalist; b. N.Y.C., Dec. 19, 1927; d. Archibald Bulloch and Grace Stackpole (Lockwood) R. Grad., Barnard Coll., 1948. Reporter UPI, San Francisco, L.A., 1951-53, Siskiyou Daily News, 1953, UPI, Washington, 1953-55; writer McCann Erickson Co., N.Y.C., 1956-57; assoc. editor Spadea Syndicate, N.Y.C., 1957-59; reporter, feature writer Newark Star Ledger, 1959-63; syndicated columnist numerous newspapers, 1963-80; Washington editor, corr. Nutrition & Health Review, 1980—; lectr. in field. Recipient J.C. Meriam, Ervin S. Cobb & Rupert Hughes award of merit Am. Acad. Pub. Affairs. Address: 1661 Crescent Pl NW Washington DC 20009-4048

ROOSEVELT, THEODORE, IV, investment banker; b. Jacksonville, Fla., Nov. 27, 1942; s. Theodore III and Anne Mason (Babcock) R.; m. Constance Lane Rogers, Aug. 1, 1970; 1 child, Theodore Roosevelt V. AB, Harvard U., 1965, MBA, 1972. Assoc. Lehman Bros., N.Y.C., 1972-76; corp. v.p. Lehman Bros. Kuhn Loeb, N.Y.C., 1976-82; sr. v.p. Lehman Comml. Paper Inc., N.Y.C., 1982-85; mng. dir. Lehman Brothers (formerly Shearson Lehman Bros., inc.), N.Y.C., 1985—; bd. dirs. The Student Conservation Assn., Lehman Bros. Fin. Products, Inc. Mem. Trout Unlimited, League of Conservation Voters; trustee of the Reservations, Mass.; mem. chmn.'s coun. Nat. Resources Def. Counsel, N.Y.C. Lt. comdr. USNR, 1965-67, Vietnam. Mem. Coun. Fgn. Rels., The Links (N.Y.C.), The Heights Casino Club (Bklyn.), Explorers Club, Harvard Club (N.Y.C.). Republican. Home: 1 Pierrepont St Brooklyn NY 11201-3361 Office: Lehman Brothers 3 World Fin Ctr New York NY 10285-1000

ROOT, ALAN CHARLES, diversified manufacturing company executive; b. Essex, Eng., Apr. 11, 1925; came to U.S., 1951, naturalized, 1959; s. Charles Stanley and Lillian (Collins) R. B.A., Oxford U., 1943; M.A., Cambridge U., 1951; M.B.A., Stanford U., 1953. Rsch. analyst Dow Chem. Co., Midland, Mich., 1954-55; mgr. mktg. rsch. Gen. Electric Co., 1955-61; v.p. bus. planning Mosler Safe Co., Hamilton, Ohio, 1961-70; v.p. corp. planning Am. Standard Inc., N.Y.C., 1970-76, sr. v.p. ops. svcs., 1976-86, sr. v.p., 1986-88, sr. advisor, 1989; bd. dirs. Am.-Standard Energy, Inc., Amstan Trucking Inc., 1976-86. Bd. dirs., pres. Brit. Schs. and Univs. Found., admission to Order of St. John of Jerusalem sanctioned by H.M. Elizabeth II, 1986; trustee, treas. N.J. Chamber Music Soc. Served to capt. AUS, 1944-48. Mem. Order St. John of Jerusalem (comdr.). Mem. AIChE (assoc. producer TV series Midland sect. 1955), Pilgrims U.S., Newcomen Soc. N.Am., Univ. Club (N.Y.C.). Clubs: Univ. (N.Y.C.). Home: 4934 Mt Pleasant Ln Las Vegas NV 89113-0114 *Good luck meant that my industrial career drew on the education I enjoyed as a young man. Professional advancement came by building on prior experience at each step and through long-term, managerial continuity.*

ROOT, ALLEN WILLIAM, pediatrician, educator; b. Phila., Sept. 24, 1933; s. Morris Jacob and Priscilla R.; m. Janet Greenberg, June 15, 1958; children: Jonathan, Jennifer, Michael. AB, Dartmouth Coll., 1955, postgrad. Med. Sch., 1954-56; MD, Harvard U., 1958. Diplomate Am. Bd. Pediatrics (mem. bd. 1986—), Am. Pediatric Endocrinology (mem. bd. 1985-90, chmn. 1990). Intern Strong Meml. Hosp., Rochester, N.Y., 1958-60; resident in pediatrics Hosp. U. Pa., Phila., 1960-62; fellow in pediatric endocrinology Children's Hosp. of Phila., 1962-65; assoc. physician in pediatrics U. Pa. Sch. Medicine, 1964-66, asst. prof. pediatrics, 1966-69; assoc. prof. pediatrics Temple U. Sch. Medicine, Phila., 1969-73; prof. Temple U. Sch. Medicine, 1973; asst. physician in endocrinology Children's Hosp. Phila., 1965-69; chmn. divsn. pediatrics Albert Einstein Med. Center., Phila., 1969-73; prof. pediatrics U. South Fla. Coll. Medicine, Tampa, 1973—; prof. biochemistry, 1987—; assoc. chmn. dept. pediatrics, 1974—, dir. sect. pediatric endocrinology, 1973—; dir. univ. tchg. svcs. All Children's Hosp., St. Petersburg, 1973-89; mem. Fla. Infant Screening Adv. Coun., 1979—, chmn., 1994—; mem. Hillsborough County Thyroid Adv. Com., 1980; mem. med. adv. com. Nat. Pituitary Agy., 1974-78, mem. growth hormone subcom., 1972-79, 81-85. Author: Human Pituitary Growth Hormone, 1972; editor: (with C. La Cauza) Problems in Pediatric Endocrinology, 1980; mem. editorial bd. Jour. Pediatrics, 1973-81, Jour. Adolescent Health Care, 1979—, Jour. Pediactic Endocrinology, 1985—, Jour. Clin. Endocrinology and Metabolism, 1993—, Growth, Genetics and Hormones, 1993—; assoc. editor Adolescent and Pediatric Gynecology, 1992—. USPHS grantee; Birth Defects Found. grantee. Mem. AAAS, Am. Pediatric Soc., Soc. Pediatric Rsch., Lawson Wilkins Pediatric Endocrine Soc. (treas. 1979-88, pres. 1988-89), Endocrine Soc., Am. Acad. Pediatrics, Am. Fedn. Clin. Rsch., Soc. Exptl. Biology and Medicine, Soc. Nuclear Medicine, N.Y. Acad. Scis., Phila. Coll. Physicians, Phila. Endocrine Soc. (bd. dirs. 1971-72, treas. 1973), Dartmouth Coll. Alumni Coun., Dartmouth Club. Office: 801 6th St S Saint Petersburg FL 33701-4816

ROOT, DORIS SMILEY, portrait artist; b. Ann Arbor, Mich., June 28, 1924; d. George O. and Hazel (Smith) Smiley. Student, Art Inst. of Chgo., 1943-45, N.Y. Sch. Design, 1976-77, Calif. Art Inst., 1984-85. Creative dir. All May Co.'s, L.A., 1962-63; advt. sales pro. dir. Seibu, L.A., 1963-64; v.p. Walgers & Assoc., L.A., 1964-70; owner, designer At The Root of Things, L.A., 1970-73; advt. sales pro. dir. Hs. of Nine, L.A., 1973-74; asst. designer MGM Grand, Reno, Nev., 1974-76; designer, office mgr. Von Hausen Studio, L.A., 1976-82; ABC libr. ABC/Cap Cities, L.A., 1982-89; portrait artist (also known as Dorian), AKA Dorian, art studio, L.A., 1982—. One-man shows include Cookeville, Tenn., 1989, Beverly Hills, Calif., 1991; artist in residence, Cookeville, 1989-90. Republican. Presbyterian. Avocations: painting, golf.

ROOT, EDWARD LAKIN, university dean, educator; b. Cumberland, Md., Dec. 5, 1940; s. Lakin and Edna Grace (Adams) R. BS, Frostburg (Md.) State Coll., 1962, MEd, 1966; EdD, U. Md., 1970. Cert. tchr., Md. Tchr. Allegany County Bd. of Edn., Cumberland, 1962-66; grad. fellow U. Md., College Park, 1966-67, fellow, 1967-69; with Frostburg State U., 1969—, prof., head edn. dept., 1980-87, dean, 1987—; adj. grad. prof. U. Md., 1980—; mem. Profl. Standards Bd. Md., Balt., 1980-87, 95-98, Cert. Rev. Bd. Md., Balt., 1987-90, Md. Task Force Adminstrn., Balt., 1985-88, Md. Task Force: Essentials in Tchr. Edn., Md. Task Force: Response to Prisoners of Time Nat. Report, Allegheny County Planning and Zoning Bd. of Appeals. Mem. Nat. Assn. Secondary Sch. Prins., Nat. Soc. for the Study of Edn., Mensa, Elks, Shriners, Masons, Phi Delta Kappa. Democrat. Methodist. Avocation: photography. Home: 100 Pennsylvania Ave Cumberland MD 21502-4236 Office: Frostburg State U College Ave Frostburg MD 21532-1724

ROOT, FRANKLIN RUSSELL, business educator; b. Hartford, Conn., Jan. 30, 1923; s. Albert Edward and Marie Rose (Benard) R.; m. Liliane Anny Weissbrod, Feb. 2, 1951 (dec. 1975); children: Michele, Peter, Valerie, Allan, Jonathan; m. Joyce Elinor Halfen, Aug. 1, 1976. BS, Trinity Coll., 1947; MBA, Wharton Sch., 1948; PhD, U. Pa., 1951. Instr. Wharton Sch. U. Pa., Phila., 1948-50; from assoc. to full prof. bus. Wharton Sch. U. Pa., 1956-93; asst. prof. U. md., College Park, 1951-55; rsch. economist UN, N.Y.C., summer 1949, 50; Fulbright prof. Copenhagen Sch. Econs. and Bus. Adminstrn., Denmark, 1963-64; prof. Naval War Coll., Newport, R.I., 1967-68; regional adv. UN, Santiago, Chile, 1970. Author: Strategic Planning for Export Marketing, 1964, International Trade and Investment, 1959, rev. edit., 1994, Entry Strategies for International Markets, 1982, rev. edit., 1994, International Strategic Management, 1992; contbr. articles to profl. jours. Cpl. AUS, 1943-46. Fellow Acad. Internat. Bus. (pres. 1981-83); mem. Am. Econ. Assn., Acad. Mgmt., Internat. Trade and Fin. Assn. (pres. 1991), Phi Beta Kappa. Independent. Unitarian. Avocations: carpentry, swimming. Office: U Pa Wharton Sch Philadelphia PA 19104

ROOT, JAMES BENJAMIN, landscape architect; b. Detroit, Jan. 26, 1934; s. William Jehial and Helen Elizabeth (English) R. BBA, Memphis State U., 1960; B in Landscape Architecture, U. Ga., 1966. Registered landscape architect; lic. real estate agt., Va. Asst. prof. W.Va. U., Morgantown, 1973-75, 93; pvt. practice Charlottesville, Va., 1976-85, 91—; site planner LBA, PH&R, Charles P. Johnson & Assocs., Fairfax, Va., 1986-90; pvt. practice as golf course architect, Charlottesville, 1976—; instr. Parkersburg C.C., 1975, Piedmont Va. C.C., 1981. Author: Fundamentals of Landscaping and Site Planning, 1985; contbr. articles to profl. jours. Mem. Planning Commn., Marietta, Ohio, 1972. Mem. Elks, Va. Writers Club. Avocation: playing piano. Office: PO Box 7017 Charlottesville VA 22906

ROOT, LARRY DONALD, utilities executive; b. Emmetsburg, Iowa, Dec. 13, 1936; s. Donald Fred and Opal Ruth (Burdick) R.; m. Mary Ann Asby, June 4, 1960; children: Cheryl, Allen, Kara. BME, Iowa State U., 1959; MBA, U. Santa Clara (Calif.), 1967. Lic. nuclear engr., Calif. Engr. Lockheed, Sunnyvale, Calif., 1959-61, Martin Marietta, Balt., 1961-62, United Tech., Sunnyvale, 1962-65; project engr. GE, San Jose, Calif., 1965-70; successively assoc. project mgr., mechanical/nuclear engr., div. engring., asst. v.p. nuclear, v.p. engring., sr. v.p. ops. and tech. services Iowa Electric Light and Power Co., Cedar Rapids, Iowa, 1970-85, v.p. ops. and prodn., 1985-90; pres., chief oper. officer Iowa Electric Light and Power Co., Cedar Rapids, 1992—; pres., group exec. IES Utilities subs. IES Industries, 1992—; bd. dirs. IE Industries, Inc., Cedar Rapids, Teleconnect, Cedar Rapids, Amana (Iowa) Enterprises, Long Lines Ltd., Sergeant Bluff, Iowa. Div. leader United Way, Cedar Rapids, 1985; bd. dirs. Cedar Rapids C. of C., Theatre Cedar Rapids, 1989. With U.S. Army Res., 1957-63. Mem. Am. Mgmt. Assn., Rotary. Republican. Presbyterian. Avocations: reading, travel, fishing. Office: IE Industries Inc 200 1st St SE # 351 Cedar Rapids IA 52401-1409

ROOT, LYNAL A., fast food company executive; b. Eagle Grove, Iowa, July 23, 1930; s. Arthur Wellington and Ruth Mary (Grandgeorge) R.; m. Betty McNaughton, Aug. 7, 1948 (div. 1972); children: Connie, Kathy, Diane, Randall; m. Deborah Kay Armstrong, Jan. 22, 1984; children: Christine Armstrong, Jennifer. Grad. Ea. Waterloo High Sch., 1948; student, Miltonvale Wesleyan Coll. Mgr. Rath Packing Co., Waterloo, Iowa, 1949-66; sr. v.p. McDonald's Corp., Oak Brook, Ill., 1966—. Republican. Home:

1215 Hawthorn Ln Hinsdale IL 60521-2908 Office: McDonald's Corp 1 Mcdonalds Plz Oak Brook IL 60521

ROOT, NINA J., librarian; b. N.Y.C., Dec. 22; d. Jacob J. and Fannie (Slivinsky) Root; BA, Hunter Coll.; MSLS, Pratt Inst.; postgrad. U.S. Dept. Agr. Grad. Sch., 1964-65, City U. N.Y., 1970-75. Reference and serials libr. Albert Einstein Coll. Medicine Libr., Bronx, N.Y., 1958-59; asst. chief libr. Am. Cancer Soc., N.Y.C., 1959-62; chief libr. Am. Inst. Aeros. and Astronautics, N.Y.C., 1962-64; head ref. and libr. svcs. sci. and tech. div. Libr. of Congress, Washington, 1964-66; mgmt. cons. Nelson Assocs., Inc., N.Y.C., 1966-70; dir. libr. svcs. Am. Mus. Natural History, N.Y.C., 1970—; free-lance mgmt. cons. and libr. planning, 1970—. Trustee Barnard Found., 1984-91; mem. libr. adv. coun. N.Y. State Bd. Regents, 1984-89, trustee Metro, 1987-92; bd. dirs. Hampden/Booth Libr., Players, 1990—; trustee Mercantile Libr. N.Y., 1993—. Recipient Meritorious Svc. award Libr. of Congress, 1965. Mem. ALA (preservation com. 1977-79, chmn. library/ binders com. 1978-80, chmn. preservation sect. 1980-81, mem. coun. 1983-86), Spl. Librs. Assn. (sec. documentation group N.Y. chpt. 1972-73, 2d v.p. N.Y. 1975-76, treas. sci. and tech. group N.Y. 1975-76, mus. arts and humanities div. program planning chairperson-conf. 1977), Archons of Colophon (convener 1978-79), Soc. Natural History (N.Am. rep. 1977-85), N.Y. Acad. Scis. (mem. publs. com. 1975-80, 89-91, archives com. 1976-78, search com. 1976). Home: 400 E 59th St New York NY 10022-2342 Office: Am Mus Natural Hist Libr 79th St Central Park St W New York NY 10024

ROOT, STANLEY WILLIAM, JR., lawyer; b. Honolulu, Mar. 2, 1923; s. Stanley William and Henrietta E. (Brown) R.; m. Joan Louise Schimpf, Sept. 3, 1949; children: Henry, Louise. AB, Princeton U., 1947; LLB, U. Pa., 1950. Bar: Pa. 1950, U.S. Ct. Mil. Appeals 1951, U.S. Supreme Ct. 1971. Ptnr. Foley, Schimpf & Steeley, Phila., 1952-69; ptnr. Ballard, Spahr, Andrews & Ingersoll, Phila., 1970-91, of counsel, 1992—; lectr. Pa. Bar Assn. 1970-80; bd. dirs. Boardman-Hamilton Co., sec. 1980—. Exec. v.p. Chestnut Hill Community Assn., Phila., 1978; with Whitpain Farm Assn., Blue Bell, Pa., 1987, 90, pres. 1992-94; with St. Paul's Ch. Vestry, Phila., 1969-75; bd. dirs. Lansdale (Pa.) Med. Group, 1972—, E.B. Spaeth Found. Wills Hosp. Phila., 1975-88, Chevalier Jackson Clinic, Phila., 1965-88; trustee Civil War Libr. and Mus., 1985-93, v.p., 1989, sec. 1992-93, mem. adv. bd., 1993—; trustee Soc. Protestant Episcopal Ch., Pa. Diocese, 1955—. Lt. col. U.S. Army, 1942-45, ETO, 1950-52, Korea. Decorated Bronze Star; recipient Pa. Commendation medal State of Pa., 1962; named Comdr., Mil. Order Fgn. Wars, 1972. Mem. Union League (pres. 1983-85), Phila. Cricket Club, Sunnybrook Golf Club, Royal Poinciana Golf Club, Brit. Officers Club, Mil. Order Loyal Legion. Republican. Episcopalian. Avocations: golf, tennis, fishing. Home: 16 Hounds Run Ln Blue Bell PA 19422-2456 Office: Ballard Spahr Andrews & Ingersoll 51st Fl 1735 Market St Fl 51 Philadelphia PA 19103-7501

ROOT, STUART DOWLING, lawyer, former banker and government official; b. Chagrin Falls, Ohio, Oct. 14, 1932; s. Elton Albert and Virginia Saxton (Dowling) R.; m. Jean D. Youse, Dec. 31, 1957 (div. Jan. 1972); children: Bryan, Kathleen, Timothy, Todd; m. Patricia Stoneman Graff, Apr. 24, 1976. BA, Ohio Wesleyan U., 1955; JD, Columbia U., 1960. Bar: N.Y. 1960. Assoc. Cadwalader Wickersham and Taft, N.Y.C., 1960-68, ptnr., 1969-81, 84-87; pres. Bowery Savs. Bank, N.Y.C., 1981-82, vice chmn., 1982-83; exec. dir. Office Fed Savs. and Loan Ins. Corp., Washington, 1988-89; chmn. bd. Fin. Instn. Svcs. Corp., Washington, 1989; lectr. ABA, Practicing Law Inst., Infocast, Am. Law Inst.; bd. dirs Bowest Corp., 1969-81. Contbr. articles to profl. jours. Chmn. bd. dirs. Harlem Sch. Arts, N.Y.C., 1974-83, Open Space Inst., 1976-80, 84-87, 89—, Nat. Choral Svc., N.Y.C., 1981-86; trustee emeritus Harlem Sch. Arts, 1984—; pub. interest dir. Fed. Home Loan Bank N.Y., N.Y.C., 1985-87. Served with U.S. Army, 1955-57. Mem. ABA, Down Town Assn. (N.Y.C.), Century Assn. (N.Y.C.). Republican. Episcopalian. Avocations: liturgical music, fly fishing, golf. Home: 18 Alden Pl Bronxville NY 10708-4813

ROOT, WILLIAM ALDEN, export control consultant; b. Boston, Sept. 20, 1923; s. John Alden and Louise Joy (Eppich) R.; m. Constance Hilda Young, Dec. 14, 1945; children: Carl David, Margaret Anne Root Bruck, John Alden, Christine Eppich Root Wiley. B.A., Colo. Coll., 1943; M. Internat. Affairs, Columbia, 1948; certificate, Russian Inst., 1948. Budget examiner Bur. Budget, Washington, 1948-50; mgmt. and budget officer Dept. State, Washington, 1950-52, Bonn, Germany, 1952-55; budget officer for Europe Dept. State, 1955-59; economist Am. embassy, Copenhagen, Denmark, 1959-63; dep. dir. Office East-West Trade, Dept. State, 1964-69; econ. officer Am. embassy, Vietnam, 1969-71; econ. counselor U.S. Mission, Berlin, 1971-74; dir. Office Soviet and Eastern European Sci. and Tech. Affairs Dept. State, 1974-76, dir. Office East West Trade, 1976-83; export control cons., 1983—; mem. Tech. Adv. Com., 1989—. Author: United States Export Controls, Aspen Law and Business. Served to lt. (j.g.) USNR, 1943-46. Mem. Phi Beta Kappa. Address: 4024 Franklin St Kensington MD 20895-3826

ROOT, WILLIAM LUCAS, electrical engineering educator; b. Des Moines, Oct. 6, 1919; s. Frank Stephenson and Helen (Lucas) R.; m. Harriett Jean Johnson, Dec. 10, 1918; children: William Lucas Jr., Wendy Elizabeth Root Cate. BEE, Iowa State U., 1940; MEE, MIT, 1943, PhD in Math., 1952. Staff mem. MIT Lincoln Lab., Lexington, Mass., 1952-61, group leader, 1959-61; lectr. Harvard U., Cambridge, Mass., 1958-59; visitor U. Wis., Madison, 1963-64; vis. prof. Mich. State U., East Lansing, 1966, 68, U. Calif., Berkeley, 1966-67; prof. aerospace engring. U. Mich., Ann Arbor, 1961-87, prof. emeritus, 1988—; vis. fellow U. Cambridge (Eng.), 1970; mem. U.S. Army Sci. Bd., 1979-82. Co-author: Random Signals and Noise, 1958 (Russian and Japanese transls.); assoc. editor: (IEEE) Information Theory Transactions, 1977-79; Soc. Indsl. and Applied Math. Jour. Applied Mathematics, 1962-72; contbr. 65 articles to profl. jours., book chpts. and conf. procs. Served to lt. USMCR, 1943-45. NSF Sr. postdoctoral fellow, 1970, vis. fellow Cambridge Clare Hall, 1970; named Shannon lectr. IEEE Internat. Symposium Info. Theory, 1986; recipient Career Achievement award ComCon Conf. Bd., 1987. Life fellow IEEE (vice chmn. administrv. com. info. theory group 1965-66); mem. Am. Math. Soc. Home: PO Box 3785 Ann Arbor MI 48106-3785 Office: U Mich Dept Aerospace Engring Ann Arbor MI 48109

ROOT, WILLIAM PITT, poet, educator; b. Austin, Minn., Dec. 28, 1941; s. William Pitt and Bonita Joy (Hilbert) R.; m. Judith Carol Bechtold, 1965 (div. 1970); 1 dau., Jennifer Lorca; m. Pamela Uschuk, 1987. B.A., U. Wash., 1964; M.F.A., U. N.C. at Greensboro, 1967; postgrad. (Wallace Stegner Writing fellow), Stanford, 1968-69. Asst. prof. Mich. State U., 1967-68; tchr. writing Mid-peninsula Free U., 1969; writer-in-residence Amherst Coll., U. Southwestern La., 1976, U. Mont., 1978, 80, 83-84; with poet-in-schs. program state art councils Oreg., Miss., Idaho, Ariz., Vt., Mont., Wyo. Wash., Tex., 1971—; Distinguished writer-in-residence Wichita State U., 1976; vis. writer in residence U. Mont., 1978, 80, 83-86, Hunter Coll., N.Y.C., 1986—; vis. writer NYU, 1986; vis. writer Westside Young Men's Hebrew Assn., N.Y.C., 1988, Pacific Lutheran U., 1990. Author: The Storm and Other Poems, 1969, Striking the Dark Air for Music, 1973, The Port of Galveston, 1974, Coot and Other Characters, 1977, 7 Mendocino Songs, 1977, A Journey South, 1977, Firecock, 1981, Reasons for Going It on Foot, 1981, In the World's Common Grasses, 1981, The Unbroken Diamond: Nightletter to the Mujahideen, 1983, Invisible Guests, 1984, Faultdancing, 1986; transl. Trace Elements from a Recurring Kingdom, 1994; collaborated with filmmaker Ray Rice) on poetry films Song of the Woman and the Butterflyman (Orpheus award 1st Internat. Poetry Film Festival 1975), 7 For a Magician, 1976, Faces, 1981. Rockefeller Found. grantee, 1969-70; Guggenheim Found. grantee, 1970-71; Nat. Endowment for Arts grantee, 1973-74; U.S./U.K. Bicentennial Exchange Artist, 1978-79, Wallace Stegner creative writing fellow Stanford U., 1968-69; recipient 1st prize univ. poetry contest Acad. Am. Poets, 1966, Atlantic Young Poet award, 1967, Stanley Kunitz Poetry award, 1981, Guy Owen Poetry Prize, 1982, Pushcart Prize (Poetry), 1977, 1980, 1985. Address: CUNY Hunter Coll Dept Eng 695 Park Ave New York NY 10021 With Rilke I believe the measure of one's life consists in a growing capacity to change life even as one is changed by it, to engage ever more fully in that dance between what we call will and what we call fate until the result is a contagion of vitality powerful enough to dissipate the spell of habits and to recreate in oneself that first spirit which is intuitive, sympathetic, and clear. Poems simply record the complex effort.

ROOT-BERNSTEIN, ROBERT SCOTT, biologist, educator; b. Washington, Aug. 7, 1953; s. Morton Ira and Maurine (Berkstresser) Bernstein; m. Michèle Marie Root-Bernstein, Sept. 2, 1978; children: Meredith Marie, Brian Robert. AB, Princeton U., 1975, PhD, 1980. Postdoctoral fellow Salk Inst. for Biol. Studies, La Jolla, Calif., 1981-82, rsch. assoc., 1983-84; asst. prof. Mich. State U., East Lansing, 1987-89, assoc. prof., 1989—; cons. Biolark, Inc., San Diego, 1988-89, Parke-Davis Pharm. Rsch. Divsn., Ann Arbor, 1990-95, Chiron Corp., 1992-95; mem. adv. bd. Soc. for Advancement Gifted Edn., Chgo., 1987-92; Sigma Xi nat. lectr., 1994—. Author: Discovering, 1989, Rethinking AIDS, 1993; columnist The Scis. mag., 1989-92; contbr. numerous articles to profl. jours. MacArthur Found. fellow, 1981-86; recipient D.J. Ingle Meml. Writing prize, 1988. Mem. Phi Beta Kappa (hon.). Avocations: drawing, painting, photography, cello. Office: Mich State U Dept Physiology Giltner Hall East Lansing MI 48824

ROOTMAN, JACK, ophthalmologist, surgeon, pathologist, oncologist, artist; b. Calgary, Alta., Can., June 22, 1944; s. Abraham S. and Lillian (Walman) R.; m. Jenny Puterman, June 20, 1965; children: Russel Mark, Kathryn Anne, Daniel Benson. MD, U. Alta., 1968. Res. ophthalmology U. Alta., Edmonton, 1973, clin. asst. prof. ophthalmology and pathology, 1973-75; from asst. prof. to assoc. prof. ophthalmology & pathology U. B.C., Vancouver, 1976-84, prof. ophthalmology & pathology, 1985—, chmn. ophthalmology, 1990—; cons. pathologist Vancouver Gen. Hosp., 1989; cancer pathology cons. Can. Reference Ctr. Cancer Pathology, Ottawa, Ont., 1989; mem. adv. com. Internat. Congress Ophthalmology, 1990—; reviewer Med. Rsch. Coun. Can., 1981, 83, 84, 89—. Author: Diseases of the Orbit: A Multidisciplinary Approach, 1988; contbr. chpts. books, numerous articles to profl. jours.; inventor Rootman Orbital Surgery Set, numerous orbital surgical procedures; reviewer Can. Jour. Ophthalmology, 1981—, Survey Ophthalmology, 1990—, Am. Jour. Ophthalmology, 1992, Cancer, 1992—, others in field; paintings exhbited group shows Vancouver Gen. Hosp. Gallery, 1988, Zack Gallery, Vancouver, 1989; one man shows include Taylor Gallery, Mayne Island, B.C., 1989, U. B.C. Faculty Club, 1990, C.J. Herman Galleries, Vancouver, 1991, 92. Chmn. Vancouver Talmud Torah, 1982-84; bd. dirs. Contemporary Art Gallery, Vancouver, 1991. Recipient 1st Prize (tied) Can. Fed. Artists 50th Anniversary Show, 1991; Can. Cancer Soc. fellow, 1i74, Med. Rsch. Coun. fellow, 1977-78, E.A. Baker Found. fellow, 1978, 82, 91; Vancouver Found. grantee, 1978, B.C. Cancer Found. grantee, 1978, McLean Found grantee, 1979, B.C. Health Care Rsch. Found. grantee 1979-81, 83-85, 87-89, 92, B.C. Med. Svcs. Found. grantee 1982-83, Med. Rsch. Coun. grantee, 1982-88, others. Fellow Royal College Surgeons; mem. Royal Coll. Pathologists (cert.), Am. Acad. Ophthalmology (cert.), Royal Coll. Physicians and Surgeons (specialty com. ophthalmology, accrediation surveys), B.C. Soc. Eye Physicians and Surgeons, Can. Med. Assn., Can. Ocular Pathology Study Group, Can. Oculoplastic Study Group, Can. Ophthalmol. Soc., Hogan Soc., Internat. Orbit Soc., Internat. Soc. Eye Rsch., N.Am. Skull Base Soc. (charter), Ophthalmol. Soc. U.K., Pan Am. Cong. Ophthalmology, Vancouver Med. Assn., Am. Assn. Ophthalmic Pathologists. Office: Univ BC Dept Ophthalmology, 2550 Willow St, Vancouver, BC Canada V5Z 3N9

ROOTS, ERNEST FREDERICK, scientific advisor emeritus; b. Salmon Arm, B.C., Can., July 5, 1923; s. Ernest and Margaret Frances (Sharpe) R.; m. June Christine Blomfield, Jan. 15, 1955; children: Charles, Frances, Hannah, Jane, Robin. BASc, U. B.C., Vancouver, 1946, MASc, 1947; PhD, Princeton U., 1949; DSc (hon.), U. Victoria, B.C., 1986. Asst. meteorologist Can. Meteorol. Br., Banff, Alta., 1938-40; topog. surveyor Nat. Parks Svc., various locations, B.C., various locations, Alta., 1940-41; student asst. Geol. Survey Can., Ottawa, Ont., 1942-46, geologist, 1947-49, 53-58; geologist Norwegian, Brit. and Swedish Antarctic Expdn., 1949-52; asst. prof. geology Princeton (N.J.) U., 1952-54; coord. polar continental shelf project Can. Dept. Energy, Mines and Resources, Ottawa, 1958-73; sci. advisor Dept. Environ. Can., Ottawa, 1973-90, spl. advisor, 1990—; chmn. Can. Environ. Assessment Rsch. Coun., Ottawa, 1986-91; co-chmn. environ. sci. rev. group Nuclear Waste Environ. Assessment Rev. Panel, Ottawa, 1990—; pres. Internat. Arctic Sci. Com., 1990-93; chmn. Man and Biosphere No. Sci. Network, UNESCO, Paris, 1992—. Contbr. over 130 articles to sci. jours., chpts. to books. Decorated officer Order of Can.; recipient Patron's medal Royal Geog. Soc., London, 1960, Polar medals, Norway, 1952, USSR, 1960, U.K., 1984, U.S., 1986. Fellow Royal Soc. Can. Home: RR 3, Wakefield, PQ Canada J0X 3G0 Office: Can Dept Environment, 25 Eddy Hull, Ottawa, ON Canada K1A 0H3

ROPE, WILLIAM FREDERICK, academic administrator; b. N.Y.C., Aug. 27, 1940; s. Frederick Thornton and Irene (King) R.; m. Priscilla Barnard, Feb. 18, 1967; children: Katherine Austin, Robert Whitney. BA in History, Yale U., 1962; MA in Govt., Georgetown U., 1970; postgrad., Nat. War Coll., 1977-78. Vice consul Am. Consulate Gen., Hong Kong, 1967-69, polit./econ. officer, 1971-73; econ./comml. officer U.S. Liaison Office, Beijing, 1973-75; chief N.E. Asia div. Bur. Intelligence and Rsch. U.S. Dept. State, Washington, 1975-77, dir. Ops. Ctr., 1978-80; dir. Office Internat. Security Policy, Washington, 1980-81; dir. Office Chinese and Mongolian Affairs Washington, 1981-83, dir. Office So. European Affairs, 1984-86; dep. chief of mission Am. Embassy, Ankara, Turkey, 1987-89; prin. dep. asst. sec. state for politic-mil. affairs. Dept. State, Washington, 1989-92; chargé d'Affaires Am. Embassy, Bandar Seri Begawan, Brunei Darussalam, 1993, Suva, Fuji, 1994; sr. adviser policy planning staff and to U.S. Mission to the U.N., 1993-95; ret. Fgn. Svc., 1995; Am. co-dir. Johns Hopkins U.-Nanjing U. Ctr. for Chinese and Am. Studies, Nanjing, China, 1995—; mem. State Dept. Sr. Seminar, Rosslyn, Va., 1983-84. Lt. USN, 1962-66. Recipient Superior Honor award Dept. State, 1982, 89, Sr. Performance award, 1983, 84, 88-92. Home: 3815 Woodley Rd NW Washington DC 20016-3701 Office: Dept State Bur Politico-Mil Affairs 2201 C St NW Washington DC 20520-0001 *I consider Martin Luther King the greatest American in my lifetime. He spoke, eloquently, of simple, important truths and led with great moral courage. The challenge to all Americans is to do their best to serve their country by speaking out for, and doing, what is right. I try to do that in the world of foreign policy and in my personal life.*

ROPER, BERYL CAIN, library director; b. Long Beach, Calif., Mar. 1, 1931; d. Albert Verne and Ollie Fern (Collins) Cain; m. Max H. Young, Aug. 22, 1947 (div. 1958); children: Howard, Wade, Debra, Kevin, John R., Christopher; m. George Albert Roper, Mar. 24, 1962 (dec. July 1978); children: Ellen, Georgianne; m. Jack T. Hughes, Sept. 21, 1993. BA, West Tex. State U., 1986; MA, Tex. Womans U., 1989. Libr. clk. Cornette Libr., West Tex. State U., Canyon, 1981-87; dir. Clarendon (Tex.) Coll. Libr., 1988—; lectr. in history and archaeology; co-owner Aquamarine Publs. Editor, pub.: In the Light of Past Experience, 1989, Transactions of the Southwest Federation of Archeological Societies, 1993; author, pub.: Trementina, 1990, Trementina Revisited, 1994; author articles on women and history. Mem. Clarendon Archaeol. Soc. (charter mem., v.p. 1990-91), Tex. Libr. Assn., Tex. Jr. Coll. Tchrs. Assn., Am. Soc. Indexers, Tex. Intertribal Indian Orgn. (charter mem.), Saints Roost Scribes, Pi Gamma Mu, Beta Phi Mu, Alpha Chi, Phi Alpha Theta. Republican. Mem. LDS Ch. Avocations: teacher Sunday sch., music, gardening, decorating, remodeling old houses. Office: Clarendon Coll Libr PO Box 968 Clarendon TX 79226-0968

ROPER, BURNS WORTHINGTON, retired opinion research company executive; b. Creston, Iowa, Feb. 26, 1925; s. Elmo Burns and Dorothy Camille (Shaw) R.; m. Elizabeth Kellock, Feb. 7, 1945 (div.); children: Bruce, David, Douglas; m. Helen Gillette Lanagan, Dec. 26, 1958 (dec. Apr. 1990); 1 child, Candace Gillette; m. Helen Grinnell Page, Sept. 19, 1991. Student, Yale U., 1942-43, 45-46. Rsch. asst. Elmo Roper, N.Y.C., 1946-48, project dir., 1948-55; ptnr. Elmo Roper & Assocs., N.Y.C., 1955-66; pres., chmn. bd. Roper Rsch. Assocs., N.Y.C., 1967-70, The Roper Orgn., Inc., N.Y.C., 1970-93; exec. v.p. Roper Starch Worldwide, Mamaroneck, N.Y., 1991-94; chmn. bd. The Roper Pub. Opinion Rsch. Ctr., Storrs, Conn., 1970-94, trustee 1947—. Contbr. numerous articles on polls to profl. jours., book chpts. Trustee Nat. Urban League, N.Y.C., 1955-64, UN Assn. N.Y.C., 1964—, Freedom House, N.Y.C., 1970—, 1st lt. USAAF, 1943-45, ETO. Decorated DFC, Air medal with five oak leaf clusters. Mem. Am. Assn. Pub. Opinion Rsch. (nat. pres. 1982-83, award 1988), Nat. Coun. on Pub. Polls (bd. dirs. 1969—, chmn. bd. trustees 1980-

93), Market Rsch. Coun. (pres. 1967-68, inducted into Hall of Fame 1990), Wings Club, Cosmos Club. Democrat. Home: 70 Old Dam Rd Bourne MA 02532

ROPER, JOHN LONSDALE, III, shipyard executive; b. Norfolk, Va., Jan. 19, 1927; s. John Lonsdale II and Sarah (Dryfoos) R.; m. Jane Preston Harman, Sept. 29, 1951; children: Susan Roper, John Lonsdale IV, Sarah Preston Roper Massey, Jane Harman Roper Van Sciver, Katherine Hayward Roper Stout. BSME, U. Va., Charlottesville, 1949; BS in Naval Architecture and Marine Engring., MIT, 1951. CEO, pres. Norfolk Shipbuilding & Drydock Corp., 1985-91, pres., CEO, 1991—, also bd. dirs.; dir. John L. Roper Corp., Cruise Internat., Inc., The Flagship Group Ltd.; pres., dir. Lonsdale Bldg. Corp. Marepcon Corp.-Internat. With USCG, 1945-46. Mem. Shipbuilders Coun. Am. (bd. dirs.). Episcopalian.

ROPER, JOHN MARLIN, federal magistrate judge; b. Greenville, Ala., Dec. 11, 1942; s. John Marlin and Pearl (Martin) R.; m. Virginia Gene Kerth, Apr. 2, 1966; 1 son, John Marlin. B.S. Auburn U., 1964; J.D., Tulane U., 1968. Bar: Ala. 1968, Miss. 1974. Counselor/program dir. Juvenile Delinquency Instn., New Orleans, 1966-69; sr. law clk. to judge U.S. Dist. Ct. (so. dist.) Miss., 1969-75, magistrate, 1975—. Mem. Fed. Magistrate Judges Assn. (dir. 5th cir. 1976-82, nat. officer 1982-86, nat. pres. 1986-87, security com. jud. conf. 1987-89, budget com. 1989—). Methodist. Office: US District Court PO Box 1164 Biloxi MS 39533-1164

ROPP, ANN L., nurse consultant; b. Cin., June 24, 1939; d. William Howard and C. Louise (Kloecker) R. Diploma in nursing, Good Samaritan Hosp. Sch. Nursing, Cin., 1960; BA, U. Minn., 1970; MS, Coll. St. Francis, Joliet, Ill., 1985. RN, Minn.; cert. in maternal-child nursing. Clin. nurse specialist Fairview Southdale Hosp., Edina, Minn., 1986-87; dir. nursing St. Mary's Hosp., Mpls., 1987; nursing cons. Mpls., 1986—; dir. maternal-child nursing svcs. Fairview Riverside Med. Ctr., Mpls., 1987-95; dir. perinatal svcs. Fairview Ridges Hosp., Burnsville, Minn., 1995—. Author: Guidelines for Education and Practice for Intrapartum Nurses, Quality Assurance for OGN Nurses. Mem. Assn. for Women's Health Obstetrics, Neonatal Nursing (pres. 1991), Am. Coll. Healthcare Execs., Sigma Theta Tau.

ROPSKI, GARY MELCHIOR, lawyer; b. Erie, Pa., Apr. 19, 1952; s. Joseph Albert and Irene Stefania (Mszanowski) R.; m. Barbara Mary Schleck, May 15, 1982. BS in Physics, Carnegie-Mellon U., 1972; JD cum laude, Northwestern U. Sch. Law, 1976. Bar: Ill. 1976, U.S. Patent and Trademark Office 1976, U.S. Dist. Ct. (no. dist.) Ill. 1976, U.S. Ct. Appeals (7th cir.) 1977, U.S. Dist. Ct. (ea. dist.) Wis. 1977, U.S. Ct. Appeals (3d cir.) 1981, U.S. Ct. Claims 1982, Pa. 1982, U.S. Ct. Appeals (Fed. cir.) 1982, U.S. Supreme Ct. 1982, U.S. Dist. Ct. (ea. dist.) Mich. 1984, U.S. Dist. Ct. (no. dist.) Calif. 1986. Assoc. Willian Brinks Hofer Gilson & Lione, Chgo., 1976-81, shareholder, 1981—; adj. prof. patents and copyrights Northwestern U. Sch. Law, Chgo., 1982—. Contbr. numerous articles to profl. jours. Mem. ABA, Am. Intellectual Property Law Assn., Patent Law Assn. Chgo., Chgo. Bar Assn. Roman Catholic. Clubs: University, Chgo. Yacht. Home: 1416 S Plymouth Ct Chicago IL 60605-2729 Office: Willian Brinks Hofer Gilson & Lione NBC Tower Ste 3600 455 N Cityfront Plaza Dr Chicago IL 60611-5503

ROQUE, MARGARITA, government administrator; b. El Paso; d. Jose Matias and Dolores (Rincon) R.; children: Daniel, Joseph, Elena, Williams. BA, Hood Coll., Frederick, Md., 1984. Fiscal asst. sec. Dept. of Commerce, NOAA, Rockville, Md., 1977-81; comms. specialist Hood Coll., 1981-84; staff asst. Chs. Com. for Voter Registration, Washington, 1984; program coord. Women's Vote Project, Washington, 1984; site supr., info. analyst The Maxima Corp., Washington, 1984-86; legis. dir. Congl. Hispanic Caucus, Washington, 1987-89, exec. dir., 1989-92; with pers. office Clinton/ Gore Transition Office, Washington, 1992-93; spl. asst. to sec. Dept. Edn., Washington, 1992; dir., exec. secretariat Dept. Transp., Washington, 1992—. Mem. Fed. Women's Program Adv. Com.; mem. Campaign 88-Women of Color Access Project; mem. Hispanic adv. com. A Woman's Place; mem. Up-County Citiznes Adv. Com.; mem. Planning Adv. Bd., Damascus, Md.; bd. dirs. D.C. Latino Civil Rights Task Force. Mem. Mexican Am. Women's Nat. Assn., League of United Latin Am. Citizens, Women of Color Leadership Coun. Office: Dept of Transportation Rm 10205 400 7th St SW Washington DC 20590

ROQUE, ROBERTO DIZON, city official; b. Manila, Mar. 22, 1929; came to U.S., 1968; s. Feliciano Trinidad and Concepcion (Dizon) R.; m. Herminia Petate Miranda, May 3, 1958; children: Marichu, Marichu, Robbie, Roel. AA, U. Santo Tomas, 1950; student, Ateneo de Manila Coll. Law, 1950-53; LLB, Philippine Law Sch., 1955; postgrad., Northwestern U., 1968-69. Adminstrv., legal, personnel, rsch. and teaching positions The Philippines, 1955-68; purchasing and warehousing asst. Lawson Products, Niles, Ill., 1968-69; shipping supr., asst. mgr. mail opening Aldens, Inc., Chgo., 1969-71; med. adminstr. L.D. Villafria Med. Ctr., Chgo., 1971-74; mgr. 69th and Ashland Currency Exchange, Chgo., 1974-78; asst. dir., cons. on spl. promotions and real estate Gen. Devel. Corp., Chgo., 1978-80; sales rep. Met. Ins. Co., Chgo., 1980; ins. producer, real estate cons. R.D. Roque & Assocs., Chgo., 1980-84; eligibility specialist City of Chgo., 1984, contract compliance officer, 1985—; founder, editor Ang Balita, Filipino-Am. newspaper, 1968-69; v.p., treas. Coroman Industries Inc., Chgo., 1986—; pres., gen. mgr. La-Ro Restaurant, Inc., Chgo., 1975-76, Miro Internat., Inc., 1982—. Pres. Asian Am. Polit. Coalition, Inc., Filipino-Am. Polit. Assn., Inc., 1970-76; v.p. Filipino Am. Coun. Chgo., Inc., 1969-71, Bagumbayan Assn. in Am., 1969-71, Bagumbayan Credit Union, 1969-71, N.W. Community Orgn.; chmn. CCHM Community Block Club, Chgo.; chmn. steering com. North, Western, California and Armitage Housing Orgn.; eucharistic minister St. John Berchmans Parish, Chgo.; bd. dirs. Failipino Am. Dem. Orgn. Cook County, 1987—; treas. Asian/Pacific Am. Dem. Coun. Ill., 1988—. Named Outstanding Citizen of Yr., Citizenship Coun. Met. Chgo., 1975, Leadership award Philippine Lawyers Assn. Midwest, 1979, svc. award N.W. Community Orgn. and NWCA Housing Orgn., 1982, Svc. and Appreciation award Camarines Norte Assn. in Am., 1990, Pub. Svc. award Cavite Assn. Am., 1992. Mem. KC (4th deg.), Lions (comm. dist. 1-A 1985-86, 86-87, past pres. Chgo., 100% Pres. award 1980, Appreciation award 1987), Knights Rizal (chpt. comdr. Malaya chpt. 1992, pub., editor-in-chief Tambuli USA, 1992, 4th degree 1995, area comdr. North Ctrl. U.S. 1992, Leadership award 1992, Plaque of Recognition 1993, coodr. Ctrl. U.S. 1993). Home: 2424 W Cortland St Chicago IL 60647-4306 Office: 3954 N Janssen Chicago IL 60613

ROREM, NED, composer, author; b. Richmond, Ind., Oct. 23, 1923; s. Clarence Rufus and Gladys (Miller) R. Student, Northwestern U., 1940-42, Curtis Inst., Phila., 1943; B.A., Juilliard Sch. Music, 1946, M.A., 1948; D.F.A. (hon.), Northwestern U., 1977. Slee prof., composer-in-residence Buffalo U., 1959-61; prof. composition U. Utah, 1965-67, Curtis Inst., 1980-94. Composer: symphonies No. 1, premiere Vienna, Austria, 1951, No. 2, premiere La Jolla, Calif., 1956, No. 3, premiere with Leonard Bernstein and N.Y. Philharmonic, 1959, Three Piano Sonatas, 1949, 50, 54, Lento for Strings, 1950, Design for Orch., 1954, Pilgrims for Strings, 1958, Eagles for Orch., 1958, Lions, 1964, Ideas for Easy Orch, 1961, Piano Concerto No. 2, 1951, 3d Piano Concerto, 1970, Eleven Studies, 1959, Water Music, 1966, Sun; for voice and orch., commd. by N.Y. Philharmonic, 1966, Air Music for Orch, 1974 (Pulitzer prize 1976), Assembly and Fall, 1975, Sunday Morning for Orch., 1977, Remembering Tommy, 1981; numerous chorus works, latest being Letters from Paris, 1965; for chorus and orch., commd. by Kousevitzky Found. in Library of Congress, Little Prayers, 1972, Whitman Cantata, 1982, An American Oratorio, 1983, Homer, 1986, Seven Motets, 1986, Te Deum, 1986, What is Pink?, 1987, The Death of Moses, 1987, Goodbye My Fancy, 1988; operas A Childhood Miracle, 1952, Three Sisters Who Are Not Sisters, 1969, Fables, 1970, Bertha, 1968, Miss Julie, 1964 (Ford Found. grantee), Hearing, 1976, Cycles: War Scenes, 1969, Six Songs for High Voice and Orchestra, 1954, Six Irish Poems, 1951, Poems of Love and the Rain, 1964, Ariel for Voice, clarinet and piano, 1971, Last Poems of Wallace Stevens for voice, cello and piano, 1971, Serenade for voice, violin, viola and piano, Women's Voices, 1975, The Nantucket Songs, 1979, Three Calamus Poems, 1982, The Schuyler Songs, 1987, Day Music and Night Music for Violin, 1972-73, Etudes for Piano, 1975, Book of Hours for flute and harp, A Quaker Reader for Organ, 1976, The Santa Fe Songs, 1980, Remembering Tommy, 1980, Views From the Oldest House for organ, 1981,

Winter Pages, 1981, Picnic on the Marne, 1982, Dances for Cello, 1983, Violin Concerto, 1984, Organ Concerto, 1985, String Symphony, 1985, Septet: Scenes from Childhood, 1985, Trio: End of Summer, 1985, Quintet: Bright Music, 1988, Diversions for Brass Quintet, 1989, Trio (Spring Music), 1990, Three Organbooks; The Auden Poems, Trio for Violin, Cello, Piano, 1990, Swords and Plowshares (for 4 solo voices and orch.), 1991, Third Quartet, 1991, Fourth Concerto for Piano (left hand) and Orch., 1991, Present Laughter for mixed chorus, piano and brass, 1993, Songs of Sadness for quartet of baritone, guitar, clarinet and cello, 1994; commns. for U.S. Bicentennial include compositions for, Cin. Symphony, N.C. Symphony, Nat. Endowment of the Arts, Am. Harp Soc.; Author: The Paris Diary of Ned Rorem, 1966, Music from Inside Out, 1967, The New York Diary, 1967, Music and People, 1968, Critical Affairs, 1970, Pure Contraption, 1973, The Later Diaries, 1974, An Absolute Gift, 1978, Setting the Tone, 1983, Paul's Blues, 1985, The Nantucket Diary, 1987, Settling the Score, 1988, Knowing When To Stop, 1994, also articles newspapers, mags., Recs. for, Columbia, Decca, Odyssey, Desto, Phillips, Premier, C.R.I., Westminster, Orion, New World Records. Recipient Music Libraries Assn. award for song Lordly Hudson 1948, Gershwin Meml. award 1949, Lili Boulanger award 1950, Nat. Inst. Arts and Letters award 1968, Pulitzer prize in music 1976, Grammy award for Best Orchestral Rec., 1989; Fulbright fellow Paris, 1951-52; Guggenheim fellow, 1957-58, 77-78. Mem. PEN, ASCAP, Am. Acad. and Inst. Arts and Letters. Mem. Soc. of Friends. Address: PO Box 764 Nantucket MA 02554-0764

RORER, LEONARD GEORGE, psychology educator; b. Dixon, Ill., Dec. 24, 1932; s. Leonard Gleason and Marion Emma (Geyer) R.; m. Gail Evans, Apr. 30, 1958 (div. May 11, 1964); children: Liat, Eric Evans; m. Nancy McKimens, Jan, 9, 1969 (div. Jan. 19, 1976); 1 child, Mya Noelani. BA, Swarthmore Coll., 1954; PhD, U. Minn., 1963 . Rsch. assoc., then assoc. dir. Oreg. Rsch. Inst., Eugene, 1963-75; prof. psychology Miami U., Oxford, Ohio, 1975-93, dir. clin. psychology trng. program, 1976-86; pres. Oreg. Psychol. Assn., 1973-75. NIMH spl. rsch. fellow, 1967-68; fellow Netherlands Inst. Advanced Study, 1971-72; postdoctoral fellow Inst. for Rational-Emotive Therapy, 1982-83. Fellow APA (coun. reps. 1968-72), Am. Psychol. Soc. (charter), We. Psychol. Assn.; mem. Midwestern Psychol. Assn., Assn. Advancement Behavior Therapy, Soc. Multivariate Exptl. Psychology. Author articles in field, mem. editorial bds. profl. jours. Home: PO Box 13383 Hamilton OH 45013-0383

RORIE, NANCY KATHERYN, elementary and secondary school educator; b. Union County, N.C., May 31, 1940; d. Carl Van and Mary Mildred (Pressley) R. BA, Woman's Coll. U. N.C., 1962; MEd, U. N.C., 1967; EdD, Duke U., 1977. Cert. curriculum and instrnl. specialist, social studies tchr. for middle and secondary levels, English tchr., N.C. Social studies and English tchr. Guilford County Schs., Greensboro, N.C., 1962-67; social studies instr. Lees-McRae Coll., Banner Elk, N.C., 1967-76; social studies tchr. Monroe (N.C.) City Schs., 1977-93; curriculum instrnl. specialist, social studies tchr. Union County Schs., Monroe, N.C., 1993—. Mem. Profl. Educators N.C. Democrat. Baptist. Home: 2401 Old Pageland-Monroe Rd Monroe NC 28112

RORIG, KURT JOACHIM, chemist, research director; b. Bremerhaven, Germany, Dec. 1, 1920; came to U.S., 1924, naturalized, 1929; s. Robert Herman and Martha (Grundke) R.; m. Helen Yonan, Mar. 20, 1949; children: James, Elizabeth, Miriam. BS, U. Chgo., 1942; MA, Carleton Coll., 1944; PhD, U. Wis., 1947. Lectr. Loyola U., Chgo., 1950-62; chemist to dir. Chem. Research G.D. Searle & Co., Chgo., 1947-87; pres. Chemo-Delphic Cons. Ltd., Chgo., 1987—; adj. prof. chemistry U. Ill., Chgo., 1989—. Patentee in field. Mem. Sch. Bd., Wilmette, Ill., 1969-71. Mem. Am. Chem. Soc. (dir. West. sect.), Am. Soc. Pharm. and Exptl. Therapeutics, N.Y. Acad. Scis., AAAS, Chgo. Chemists Club (past pres.). Presbyterian. Home and Office: 337 Hager Ln Glenview IL 60025-3329

RORIMER, LOUIS, lawyer; b. N.Y.C., Feb. 17, 1947; s. James J. and Katherine (Serrell) R.; m. H. Savery Fitz-Gerald, July 1, 1978; children: Sarah, James. Student, Phillips Acad., 1965; BA, Harvard U., 1969; JD, Case Western Res. U., 1975. Bar: Ohio 1975. Assoc. Jones, Day, Reavis & Pogue, Cleve., 1975-83, ptnr., 1984—. Served to 1t. (j.g.) USNR, 1969-71, PTO. Mem. ABA. Home: 17900 S Park Blvd Shaker Hts OH 44120-1717 Office: Jones Day Reavis & Pogue North Point 901 Lakeside Ave Cleveland OH 44114

RORKE, KEVIN HAYDEN, broadcasting executive; b. Washington, June 22, 1949; s. James Hayden and Sari (Schwartz) R.; m. Patricia Hardy, July 15, 1972; children: Kelly Ann, Jennifer Hayden, Kathryn Hayden. BS in Bus. Administrn., Washington U., St. Louis, 1971; MBA, U. Denver, 1976. System mgr. Albany office Am. TV and Communications Corp., Englewood, Colo., 1977-79, div. mgr., 1979-81, v.p. devel. systems, 1981-83, pres. Orlando div. and sr. v.p., 1983-84, exec. v.p., 1984—; dir. Cabletelevison Advt. Bur., 1986—, Cable Television Adminstrn. and Mktg. Soc., 1987—. Served to 1st lt. U.S. Army, 1971-75.

RORKE, LUCY BALIAN, neuropathologist; b. St. Paul, June 22, 1929; d. Aram Haji and Karzouhy (Ousdigian) Balian; m. Robert Radcliffe Rorke, June 4, 1960. A.B., U. Minn., 1951, M.A., 1952, B.S., 1955, M.D., 1957. Diplomate Am. Bd. Pathology. Intern Phila. Gen. Hosp., 1957-58, resident anat. pathology and neuropathology, 1958-62, asst. neuropathologist, 1963-67, chief pediatric pathologist, 1967-68, chief neuropathologist, 1968-69, chmn. dept. anat. pathology and chief neuropathologist, 1969-73, chmn. dept. pathology, 1973-77, pres. med. staff, 1973-75; practice medicine specializing in neuropathology Phila., 1962—; neuropathologist Children's Hosp., Phila., 1965—, pres. med. staff, 1986-88; cons. neuropathologist Wyeth Rsch. Labs., Radnor, Pa., 1961-87, Wistar Inst. Anatomy and Biology, Phila., 1967-93; assoc. prof. pathology U. Pa. Sch. Medicine, Phila., 1970-73, prof., 1973—; clin. prof. neurology, 1979—; forensic neuropathologist Office of Med. Examiner, Phila., 1977—. Author: Myelinization of the Brain in the Newborn, 1969, Pathology of Perinatal Brain Injury, 1982; mem. editorial bd. Jours. Neuropathology Exptl. Neurology, 1980-85, 93—, Pediatric Neurosurgery, 1984—, Child's Nervous System, 1984-88, Brain Pathology, 1990—; contbr. articles to profl. jours. NIH fellow in neuropathology, 1961-62; NIH grantee for study of neonatal brain, 1963-68. Fellow Coll. Pathologists; mem. Phila. Gen. Hosp. Med. Staff (pres. 1973-75), Phila. Neurol. Soc. (v.p. 1971-72, editor Transactions 1973, pres. 1975-76), Am. Assn. Neuropathologists (exec. council 1976-85, v.p. 1979-80, pres. 1981-82), Am. Neurol. Assn., AMA, Burlington County Med. Soc., Phila. Coll. Physicians. Home: 120 Chestnut St Moorestown NJ 08057-2937 Office: Children's Hosp of Philadelphia 324 S 34th St Philadelphia PA 19104-4303

RORSCHACH, RICHARD GORDON, lawyer; b. Tulsa, Aug. 9, 1928; s. Harold Emil and Margaret (Hermes) R.; m. Martha Kay King, Dec. 23, 1979; children by previous marriage: Richard Helm, Reagan Cartwright, Andrew Maxwell. BS, MIT, 1950; MS, U. Okla., 1952; JD, U. Houston, 1961. Bar: Tex. 1961. Cons. civil engr. Freese & Nichols, Ft. Worth, 1955; cons. engr. Freese, Nichols & Turner, Houston, 1955-56; petroleum engr. Marathon Oil Co., Bay City, Tex., 1956-57, Houston, 1957-61; atty. Marathon Oil Co., 1961-64; ptnr. Broady, Kells & Rorschsch, Houston, 1964-68; ptnr. Ragan, Russell & Rorschach, Houston, 1968-80, Kilgore, Tex., 1980—; mem. exec. com. Colonial Royalties Co., Tulsa, 1970-77; officer Little River Oil & Gas Co., 1980-88; mng. ptnr. Pentagon Oil Co., 1988—; pres. Nat. Assn. Royalty Owners Tex., 1979-93; mem. exec. com. Nat. Assn. Royalty Owners, Inc.; owner, breeder, exhibitor Arabian Horses Shadowbrook Farm, Kilgore, Tex., 1980—. Served to 1st lt. C.E., AUS, 1952-54, Korea. Mem. ASME, ASCE, Tex. Bar Assn., Rotary Club (pres. Kilgore chpt. 1984-85), Sigma Xi, Sigma Alpha Epsilon. Republican. Presbyterian. Home: RR 4 Box 210 Kilgore TX 75662-9023 Office: 1100 Stone Rd PO Box 1934 Kilgore TX 75663-1934

RORTY, RICHARD MCKAY, philosophy educator; b. N.Y.C., Oct. 4, 1931; s. James Hancock and Winifred (Raushenbush) R.; m. Amelie Sarah Oksenberg, June 15, 1954 (div. 1972); 1 son, Jay; m. Mary R. Varney, Nov. 4, 1972; children: Patricia, Kevin. BA, U. Chgo., 1949, MA, 1952; PhD, Yale U., 1956; DHL, Northwestern U., 1992, Fla. Internat. Univ., 1994. Instr. philosophy Yale U., 1955-57; instr. Wellesley Coll., 1958-60, asst. prof., 1960-61; mem. faculty Princeton U., 1961-82, prof. philosophy, 1970-

81, Stuart prof. philosophy, 1981-82; Univ. prof. humanities U. Va., 1982—. Author: Philosophy and the Mirror of Nature, 1979, Consequences of Pragmatism, 1982, Contingency, Irony and Solidarity, 1989, Objectivity, Relativism and Truth, 1991, Essays on Heidegger and Others, 1991. Served with AUS, 1957-58. Guggenheim fellow, 1973-74; MacArthur fellow, 1981-86. Mem. Am. Philos. Assn. (pres. Eastern div. 1979), Am. Acad. Arts and Scis. Home: 402 Peacock Dr Charlottesville VA 22903-9725 Office: 412 Cabell Hall Charlottesville VA 22903

ROSA, EDWARD A., principal. Prin. Mansfield (Mass.) High Sch. Recipient Blue Ribbon School award U.S. Dept. Edn., 1990-91. Office: Mansfield High Sch 250 East St Mansfield MA 02048-2599

ROSA, RAYMOND ULRIC, retired banker; b. New Britain, Conn., Jan. 30, 1927; s. Kenneth E. and Regina (Chenette) R.; m. Irene M. Asselin, Feb. 5, 1949; children: R. James, David M., Cathryn P., Michael F., Nancy A., Kenneth E. A.S., Hillyer Coll., 1949. C.P.A., Conn. Pvt. practice pub. accounting Manchester, Conn., 1949-52; auditor Auditors of Pub. Accounts, State of Conn., Hartford, 1952-65; dir. Fed.-State Relations Dept. Finance and Control, Conn., 1965-69; dep. commr. Finance and Control, Conn., 1969-71; sr. v.p., auditor Soc. Savings, Hartford, 1971-90, ret., 1990; Mem. Windsor Locks (Conn.) Bd. Finance, 1973-81; pres. Savs. Bank Forum, 1981-82. Treas. Mental Health Assn. Conn., 1974-77, v.p. 1977-80, pres., 1980-83; bd. dirs. Nat. Assn. Mental Health, 1977-85, v.p. region 1, 1982-83; bd. dirs. Combined Health Appeal of Greater Hartford, 1982-90. Served with USNR, 1944-46. Mem. AICPA, Conn. Soc. CPAs, Conn. Assn. Govtl. Accts., KC, Dunedin Country Club, Suffield Country Club (bd. govs. 1984-91). Home: 2060 Golfview Dr Dunedin FL 34698

ROSALDO, RENATO IGNACIO, JR., cultural anthropology educator; b. Champaign, Ill., Apr. 15, 1941; s. Renato Ignacio and Mary Elizabeth (Potter) R.; m. Michelle Sharon Zimbalist, June 12, 1966 (dec. Oct. 1981); children: Samuel Mario, Manuel Zimbalist; m. Mary Louise Pratt, Nov. 26, 1983; 1 child, Olivia Emilia Rosaldo-Pratt. AB, Harvard U., 1963, PhD, 1971. Asst. prof. cultural anthropology Stanford (Calif.) U., 1970-76, assoc. prof., 1976-85, prof., 1985—, Mellon prof. interdisciplinary studies, 1987-90, dir. Ctr. for Chicano Rsch., 1985-90; chair anthropology, 1994—, Lucie Stern prof. social scis., 1993—. Author: Ilongot Headhunting 1883-1974, 1980, Culture and Truth, 1989. Recipient Harry Benda prize Assn. for Asian Studies, 1983; Guggenheim fellow, 1993. Avocations: swimming, drawing, dancing. Home: 2520 Cowper St Palo Alto CA 94301-4218 Office: Stanford U Dept Anthropology Stanford CA 94305-2145

ROSAMOND, PATRICIA ANN, construction company executive; b. Columbia, S.C., June 19, 1947; d. Joseph William and Ethel Alice (Frossard) Ludwig; m. Denver Wade Rosamond, July 17, 1965; children: Jill Ann, Joy Christine. Student, Queens Coll., 1976-78. Inter co. sales Anixter Bros., Inc., St. louis, 1971-72; adminstrv. asst. Rodgers Builders, Inc., Charlotte, N.C., 1972-75, project mgr., 1975-78, v.p., 1978-82, exec. v.p., 1982-87; pres. Rodgers Builders, Inc., Charlotte, 1987—. Appointed mem. pvt. Industry Council, 1984-85; bd. dirs. Hornet's Nest Girl Scout Council, Charlotte, 1985-86, U N-Charlotte Athletic Found., 1986—, Mercy Hosp. South Adv. Council, Pineville, 1987—. Mem. Carolinas Assn. Gen. Contractors (bd. dirs. 1986—), Mecklenburg Gen. Contractors (bd. dirs. 1987—). Avocations: tennis, traveling. Office: Rodgers Builders Inc 5701 N Sharon Amity Rd Charlotte NC 28215-3998

ROSAND, DAVID, art history educator; b. Bklyn., Sept. 6, 1938; s. Johan Herbert and Frieda (Grotenstein) R.; m. Ellen Fineman, June 18, 1961; children: Jonathan, Eric. AB, Columbia Coll., 1959; MA, Columbia U., 1962, PhD, 1965. Instr. art history Columbia U., N.Y.C., 1964-67, asst. prof., 1967-69, assoc. prof., 1969-73, prof., 1973-95, chmn. Soc. of Fellows in the Humanities, 1979-83, Meyer Schapiro prof. art history, 1995—. Author: (with Michelangelo Muraro) Titian and the Venetian Woodcut, 1976, Titian, 1978, Painting in Cinquecento Venice: Titian, Veronese, Tintoretto, 1982, The Meaning of the Mark: Leonardo and Titian, 1988, (with Robert Cafritz and Lawrence Gowing) Places of Delight: The Pastoral Landscape, 1988; editor: (with Robert W. Hanning) Castiglione: The Ideal and the Real in Renaissance Culture, 1983, Titian: His World and His Legacy, 1982; editorial bd. Arion, Imago Musicae, Venezia Cinquecento. Mem. bd. advisors CASVA Nat. Gallery Art., 1990-94. Fulbright Commn. fellow, 1962-63; NEH fellow, 1971-72, 85-86, 91-92; John S. Guggenheim Meml. Found. fellow, 1974-75. Mem. Coll. Art Assn., Renaissance Soc. Am. (mem. exec. bd. 1981—), Ateneo Veneto (fgn.). Home: 560 Riverside Dr New York NY 10027-3202 Office: Columbia U Dept Art History and Archaeology 826 Schermerhorn Hall New York NY 10027

ROSATI, MARIO, mathematician, educator; b. Rome, Jan. 5, 1928; s. Aristide and Maria (Gabrielli) R.; m. Maria Luisa Marziale, Aug. 3, 1968; children: Francesca, Nicoletta, Giulio. Laurea in Math., U. Rome, 1950. Asst. prof. U. Rome, 1952-66; prof. math. U. Padua, Italy, 1966—; dir. Applied Math. Inst., Padua U., 1978-86, Dept. Pure Applied Math., 1987-92, Seminario Matematico, 1994—. Co-editor: (with G. Tedone) Collana di Informazione Scientifica, 1965-78; contbr. books and articles in field. Fellow U. Goettingen 1955. Mem. Italian Math. Union, Am. Math. Soc., Nat. Rsch. Ctr. Roman Catholic. Home: 43 G Leopardi, 35126 Padua Italy Office: Dept Pure Applied Math, 7 GB Belzoni, 35131 Padua Italy

ROSATO, FRANCIS ERNEST, surgeon; b. Phila., June 2, 1934; s. Ernest Lancelot and Mary Rita (Huggard) R.; m. Gertrude Blount Doman, Oct. 27, 1962; children—Ernest, Ann, Gertrude, Frank, Aimee. Student, St. Joseph's Coll., Phila., 1952-55; M.D., Hahnemann Med. Coll., Phila., 1959. Diplomate: Nat. Bd. Med. Examiners. Resident in surgery U. Pa.; mem. faculty to prof. surgery, 1965-74; prof. surgery, chmn. dept. Eastern Va. Med. Sch., Norfolk, 1974-78; prof., chmn. dept. surgery Jefferson Med. Coll. of Thomas Jefferson U., Phila., 1978—; Advanced clin. fellow Am. Cancer Soc. Author: Surgery of the Breast, 1986, Atlas of Surgical Technique, 1992; contbg. author: Cameron's Current Surgical Therapy, Ana Sabiston's Text of Surgery; contbr. articles to med. jours. Fellow ACS; mem. Soc. Univ. Surgeons, Am. Surg. Assn., So. Surg. Assn., Halstead Soc., Phila. Country Club, Merion Cricket Club, Union League, Friendly Sons of St. Patrick. Roman Catholic. Home: 900 Merion Square Rd Gladwyne PA 19035-1510 Office: Jefferson Med Coll 1025 Walnut St Philadelphia PA 19107-5083

ROSBE, WILLIAM LOUIS, lawyer; b. Evanston, Ill., Feb. 17, 1944; s. Robert L. and Margaret H. (Black) R.; 1 child, Kimberly. BA, Yale U., 1966; JD, Cornell U., 1975. Bar: Va. 1975, U.S.C. Appeals (4th cir.) 1977, U.S. Supreme Ct. 1979, U.S. Ct. Appeals (D.C. cir.) 1980, D.C. 1981. Ptnr. Hunton & Williams, Richmond, Va., 1975—. Asst. gen. coun. Robert E. Lee coun. Boy Scouts Am., Richmond, Va. Col. USMCR, 1988. Mem. ABA (vice chmn. electric power commn. natural resources sect. 1981-87), Va. State Bar (chmn. environ. law sect. 1984-85), Va. Bar Assn., Richmond Bar Assn. Home: 8510 Rivermont Dr Richmond VA 23229-6427 Office: Hunton & Williams Riverfront Plaza East Tower 951 E Byrd St Richmond VA 23219-4074

ROSBERG, CARL GUSTAF, political science educator; b. Oakland, Calif., Feb. 28, 1923; s. Carl Gustaf and Ethel (Moore) R.; m. Elizabeth Joanna Wilson, Oct. 23, 1954; children—James Howard, David Nils. B.S., Georgetown U., 1948, M.S., 1950; D.Phil., Oxford (Eng.) U., 1954. Asst. prof., research asso. African studies program Boston U., 1955-58; vis. asst. prof. U. Calif., Berkeley, 1958-59, asst. prof. dept. polit. sci., 1959-63, asso. prof., 1963-67, prof., 1967-91, prof. emeritus, 1991—, chmn. dept. polit. sci., 1969-74, dir. Inst. Internat. Studies, 1973-89. Author: (with John Nottingham) The Myth of Mau Mau: Nationalism in Kenya, 1966, (with George Bennett) The Kenyatta Election: Kenya, 1960-61, 1961, (with Robert Jackson) Personal Rule in Black Africa: Prince, Autocrat, Prophet, Tyrant, 1982; editor: (with James S. Coleman) Political Parties and National Integration in Tropical Africa, 1964, (with William H. Friedland) African Socialism, 1964, (with Thomas Callaghy) Socialism in Sub-Saharan Africa, 1979, (with Robert M. Price) The Apartheid Regime: Political Power and Racial Domination, 1980, (with David E. Apter) Political Development and the New Realism in Sub-Saharan Africa, 1994. Served with USAAF, 1943-45. Decorated Purple Heart, Air medal, Prisoner of War medal; Ford Found. fellow, 1954-55. Mem. Coun. Fgn. Rels., African Studies Assn. (past pres.). Home: 1015

Cragmont Ave Berkeley CA 94708-1411 Office: Dept Polit Sci U Calif Berkeley CA 94720

ROSBERG, DAVID WILLIAM, plant sciences educator; b. Superior, Wis., Jan. 3, 1919; s. Albert and Hulda (Sundin) R.; m. Helen Dana McDonald, Nov. 8, 1941; children—David William, Dana Karin. B.A., St. Olaf Coll., 1940; postgrad., Tex. A&M Coll., 1940-41; M.S., Ohio State U., 1947, Ph.D., 1949. Grad. asst. biology dept. Tex. A&M U., College Station, 1940-42, lab asst. Tex. Agrl. Exptl. Sta., 1942, asst. prof. plant physiology and pathology dept., 1949-54, asso. prof., 1954-58, prof., 1958-60, prof., head dept. plant scis., from 1960, prof. emeritus, 1981—; insp. R.R. Perishable Inspection Agy., N.Y.C., 1941; grad. asst. dept. botany Ohio State U., 1946-48, research asst.; Research Found., 1948-49; lab. asst. Battelle Meml. Inst., Columbus, O., 1948. Named Disting. Alumnus Ohio State U. 1972. Mem. AAAS, Am. Phytopath. Soc., Tex. Acad. Sci., Sigma Xi, Phi Kappa Phi, Gamma Sigma Delta. Home: 11630 Sh # 30 College Station TX 77845 Office: Dept Plant Scis Tex A&M U College Station TX 77843

ROSBOTTOM, RONALD CARLISLE, academic administrator, French culture and literature educator; b. New Orleans, July 15, 1942; s. Albert Carlisle and Marjorie Catherine (Chavez) R.; m. Betty Elane Griffin, Sept. 5, 1964; 1 child, Michael K. B.A., Tulane U., 1964; M.A., Princeton U., 1966, Ph.D., 1969; MA (hon.), Amherst Coll., 1990. Instr. U. Pa., Phila., 1967-69, asst. prof., 1969-73; assoc. prof. Ohio State U., Columbus, 1973-78, prof. French lit., 1978-89, chmn. Romance langs., 1982-88; dean of faculty Amherst (Mass.) Coll., 1989-95, prof. French lit. and European studies, 1989—. Author: Marivaux's Novels, 1974, Choderlos de Laclos, 1979 (Havens prize 1980); editor: Studies in 18th Century Culture, 1975, 76, Essays in the French Enlightenment, 1991; mem. editorial bds. Eighteenth Century: Theory & Interpretation, Romance Quarterly. Decorated Ordre des Palmes Académiques; Woodrow Wilson Found. fellow, 1964-65, 66-67; Am. Council Learned Socs. summer fellow, 1970. Mem. MLA, AAUP, Internat. Soc. 18th Century Studies (exec. com. 1978-83), Am. Soc. 18th Century Studies (exec. sec. 1978-83, 2d v.p. 1992-93, 1st v.p. 1993-94, pres. 1994-95), Am. Assn. Tchrs. of French, Phi Beta Kappa. Democrat. Home: 326 Shays St Amherst MA 01002-2943 Office: Amherst Coll Box 2255 Amherst MA 01002-5000

ROSCH, JOHN THOMAS, lawyer; b. Council Bluffs, Iowa, Oct. 4, 1939; s. H.P. and Phebe Florence (Jamison) R.; m. Carolyn Lee, Aug. 18, 1961; children: Thomas Lee, Laura Lee. B.A., Harvard U., 1961, LL.B., 1965. Bar: Calif. 1966, U.S. Dist. Ct. (no. dist.) Calif. 1966, U.S. Dist. Ct. (ea. dist.) Calif. 1967, U.S. Ct. Appeals (9th cir.) 1966. Assoc. McCutchen, Doyle, Brown & Enersen, San Francisco, 1965-72, ptnr., 1972-73, 75-93; ptnr. Latham & Watkins, San Francisco, 1994—; dir. Bur. Consumer Protection, FTC, Washington, 1973-75. Contbr. articles profl. jours. Fellow Am. Bar Found., Am. Coll. Trial Lawyers; mem. ABA (past chmn. antitrust sect.), State Bar of Calif. Assn., San Francisco Bar Assn., Calif. State Antitrust and Trade Regulation (chair-elect law sect.). Republican. Episcopalian. Office: Latham & Watkins 505 Montgomery St San Francisco CA 94111

ROSCH, PAUL JOHN, physician, educator; b. Yonkers, N.Y., June 30, 1927; s. Samuel Joseph and Mary (Gang) R.; m. Lorraine Marie Hunt, June 27, 1951; children: David Carl, Jonathan Hunt, Jane Ellen, Michael Edward, Richard Joseph, Donna Marie; m. Marguerite Delamater, Sept. 12, 1972. AB, Brown U., NYU, 1948; MA, NYU, 1950; MD, Albany Med. Coll., 1954. Diplomate Am. Bd. Internal Medicine. Fellow Inst. Exptl. Medicine and Surgery, U. Montreal, Que., Can., 1951; intern, asst. resident in medicine Johns Hopkins Hosp., 1954-56; resident in medicine, then chief dept. metabolism Walter Reed Med. Ctr., 1956-58; physician-in-charge nuclear medicine St. John's Riverside Hosp., Yonkers, 1959, vice chief of staff; chief endocrine clinic St. Joseph's Hosp., 1959, sr. cons. in medicine, 1980—; pres., chmn. Am. Inst. Stress, Yonkers, 1978—, sr. cons. in medicine, 1980—; clin. prof. medicine and psychiatry N.Y. Med. Coll., 1980—; adj. prof. medicine in psychiatry Sch. Medicine, U. Md. From asst. to assoc. editor Health Comm. and Informatics; editor Stress Medicine; mem. editorial bd. AMA Archives Internal Medicine, Folia Clinica Internat, Jour. Human Stress, Internat. Jour. Psychosomatics, Cardiovascular Revs. & Reports, Internat. Jour. Stress Mgmt., Comprehensive Therapy, Jour. Human Behavior; contbg. editor Creative Living; contbr. articles to profl. jours. Bd. govs. Jewish Community Ctr.; bd. dirs. Family Svc. Soc., Mensana Clinic, 1980—; chmn. bd. Internat. Found. Biosocial Devel. and Human Health, 1980—; mem. adv. bd. Image Inst., 1980—. Capt. AUS, 1956-58. Fellow ACP, Am. Coll. Cardiology, Internat. Acad. Medicine, Am. Coll. Angiology, N.Y. Diabetes Assn.; mem. Westchester Diabetes Assn. (past pres.), Internat. Law Enforcement Stress Assn. (adv. bd. 1980—), Yonkers Acad. Medicine (bd. govs., past pres.), N.Y. Cardiology Soc., Acad. Psychosomatic Medicine, Soc. Behavioral Medicine, N.Y. Acad. Scis., Endocrine Soc., Am. Diabetes Assn., Westchester Soc. Internal Medicine (Past pres.), Stress Mgt. Assn. (hon. v.p.), N.Y. State Soc. Internal Medicine (pres. 1981—), Soc. Nuclear Medicine (bd. dirs.), Am. Fedn. Clin. Rsch., Am. Soc. Internal Medicine, Am. Geriatrics Soc., Elmwood Country Club, Atlantis Country Club, Breakers Golf Club, St. Andrews Golf Club. Home: 124 Park Ave Yonkers NY 10703 also: 221 N Country Club Dr Atlantis FL 33462-1113

ROSCHER, NINA MATHENY, chemistry educator; b. Uniontown, Pa., Dec. 8, 1938; d. Charles Kenneth and Wilma Pauline (Solomon) Matheny; m. David Roscher, Dec. 27, 1964. BS in Chemistry, U. Del., 1960; PhD in Chemistry, Purdue U., 1964. Phys. chemist Nat. Bur. of Standards, 1958-61; rsch. and teaching asst. Purdue U., West Lafayette, Ind., 1960-64, fellow in chemistry, instr. chemistry, 1964-65; instr. U. Tex., Austin, 1965-67; sr. staff chemist Coca-Cola Export Corp., 1967-68; asst. prof. Douglass Coll., Rutgers U., The State U., 1968-74, asst. dean, 1971-74; dir. acad. adminstrn. Am. U., Washington, 1974-76, assoc. prof. chemistry, 1974-79, prof., 1979—, assoc. dean grad. affairs Coll. Arts and Scis., 1976-79, vice-provost acad. svcs., 1979-82, vice provost for acad. affairs, 1982-85, dean faculty affairs, 1981-85, chair chemistry dept., 1991—; program dir. sci. edn., NSF, 1986—; lectr. in field. Contbr. articles to profl. jours. Standard Oil fellow, 1961-62, David Ross fellow, 1963-64, Rutgers U. Rsch. Fund, Biomed. Support grantee. Fellow AAAS, Am. Inst. Chemists (profl. opportunities for women com., pres. dist. inst. chemists 1978-79, sec. 1976-77, fin. com. 1983-87, exec. com. bd. dirs. 1986); mem. Am. Chem. Soc. (treas. Monmouth County sect. 1970-72, chmn. 1974, pres. Washington sect. 1995, profl. programs planning and coord. com. 1976-78, admissions com. 1981-89, 91—, GM scholar 1956-60, Virgil F. Payne award, numerous others), N.Y. Acad. Sci., AAUA, Assn. Women in Sci., Soc. Applied Spectroscopy, Sci. Manpower Commn. Profls. in Sci. Home: 10400 Hunter Ridge Dr Oakton VA 22124-1616 Office: Am Univ Dept Chemistry Washington DC 20016-8014

ROSCOE, STANLEY NELSON, psychologist, aeronautical engineer; b. Eureka, Calif., Nov. 4, 1920; s. Stanley Boughton and Martha Emma (Beer) R.; m. Margaret Hazel Brookins, Dec. 21, 1948 (dec.); children: Lee Marin Roscoe Bragg, Jack; m. Elizabeth Frances Lage, Mar. 12, 1977 (dec.); 1 child, Catherine Marie; m. Gayle Buchanan Karshner, Mar. 15, 1990. AB in Speech and English, Humboldt State U. 1943; postgrad., U. Calif., Berkeley, 1942, 46; MA in Psychology, U. Ill. 1947, PhD in Psychology, 1950. Cert. psychologist, Calif. Research asst. U. Ill., Champaign, 1946-50, research assoc., 1950-51, asst. prof., 1951-52; assoc. dir. Inst. Aviation, head aviation research lab., Champaign, 1969-75; asst. prof. psychology and aero. astronautical engring., 1969-79, prof. emeritus, 1979—; prof. N.Mex. State U., Las Cruces, 1979-86, prof. emeritus, 1986—; with Hughes Aircraft Co., Culver City, Calif., 1952-69, 75-77, dept. mgr., 1962-69, sr. scientist, 1975-77; tech. adviser, cons. in field; pres. Illiana Aviation Scis. Ltd., Las Cruces, N.Mex., 1976—. Author: Aviation Psychology, 1980, Flightdeck Performance: The Human Factor, 1990; editor: Aviation Research Monographs, 1971-72, Heydays in Humboldt, 1991, From Humboldt to Kodiak, 1992; assoc. editor: Human Factors Jour., 1982—; cons. editor Internat. Jour. Aviation Psychology, 1991—; contbr. numerous articles to profl. jours. 1st lt. AC, U.S. Army, 1943-46. Fellow APA (Franklin V. Taylor award 1976), Human Factors Soc. (pres. 1960-61, Jerome H. Ely award 1968, 73, 89, 91, Alexander C. Williams award 1973, Paul M. Fitts award 1974, Pres.'s award 1990), Soc. Engring. Psychologists, Royal Aero Soc. (Eng.); mem. IEEE, AIAA, Inst. Navigation, Assn. Aviation Psychologists (ann. career award 1978), Aerospace Human Factors Assn. (Paul T. Hansen award 1994), Sigma Xi, Phi Kappa Phi, Phi Sigma, Chi Sigma

Epsilon. Patentee, inventor in field. Home: 2750 Sunnygrove Ave Arcata CA 95521-9226 Office: PO Box 4498 Las Cruces NM 88003-4498

ROSCOPF, CHARLES BUFORD, lawyer; b. Marvell, Ark., Apr. 21, 1928; s. Emmett Lee and Sally Virginia (King) R.; m. Mary Anne Maddox, Aug. 22, 1954; children—Charles David; Ann Karen. Student, Hendrix Coll., 1948-50; J.D., U. Ark., 1954. Bar: Ark. bar 1954, U.S. Dist. Cts 1955, 64, U.S. Supreme Ct. bar 1965. Pvt. practice Helena, Ark., 1954—; assoc. firm Burke, Moore & Burke, 1954-58; ptnr. firm Burke & Roscopf, 1958-64; sr. ptnr. Roscopf and Roscopf, P.A., 1964—; mem. Ark. Ho. of Reps., 1953-58; del. Ark. Constl. Conv., 1968; mem. Ark. Probate Drafting Com.; mem. Ark. State Bd. Law Examiners, 1973-79; spl. justice Ark. Supreme Ct. Served with USN, 1946-48; served with USAFR, 1962-68. Fellow Ark. Bar Found.; mem. ABA, Ark. Bar Assn. (pres. 1990-91), Am. Law Inst., Am. Trial Lawyers Assn., Kappa Sigma. Methodist. Clubs: Rotary (Paul Harris fellow), Masons, Shriners. Home: 117 Avalon Pl Helena AR 72342-1722 Office: Nat Bank Bldg 408 Helena PO Box # 610 Helena AR 72342

ROSDEITCHER, SIDNEY SAMUEL, lawyer; b. Bayonne, N.J., June 2, 1936; s. Morris and Lee (Rosenbluth) R.; m. Linda Latter, Aug. 28, 1960; children: Elizabeth, David, Emily. AB, Columbia U., 1958; LLB magna cum laude, Harvard U., 1961. Bar: N.Y., D.C., U.S. Dist. Ct. (so. and ea. dists.) N.Y., U.S. Claims Ct., U.S. Tax Ct., U.S. Ct. Appeals (1st, 2d, 3d, 4th, 8th, 9th, 10th and fed. cirs.), U.S. Supreme Ct. Atty. office of legal counsel U.S. Dept. Justice, Washington, 1961-62; advisor to commr. FTC, Washington, 1965-66; assoc. Paul, Weiss, Rifkind, Wharton & Garrison, N.Y.C., 1962-65, 66-72, ptnr., 1972—; adj. prof. civil liberties Bklyn. Law Sch., 1974-75; lectr. profl. responsibility Columbia Law Sch., 1990-93. Article editor Harvard U. Law Rev., 1960-61; contbr. articles to legal jours. Trustee Lawyers Com. for Civil Rights Under Law, 1992—; bd. dirs. NAPIL Fellows, 1992—, Human Rights Watch/Africa. Mem. D.C. Bar Assn. (model rules spl. com. 1982-85), Assn. of Bar of City of N.Y. (chmn. profl. and jud. ethics com. 1979-82, fed. cts. com. 1982-85, chmn. com. on internat. human rights 1991-94, civil rights com. 1994—, coun. on pub. svc. 1994—). Home: 90 Riverside Dr New York NY 10024-5306 Office: Paul Weiss Rifkind Wharton & Garrison 1285 Ave Of The Americas New York NY 10019-6064

ROSE, ADAM ZACHARY, economist, educator; b. Bergen-Belsen, Germany, Jan. 5, 1948; s. Isaac and Gusta Eugenia (Kaiser) R.; m. Anne Lynn Carver, Oct. 15, 1972; children: Eleanor, Jonathan. BA, U. Utah, 1970; MA, Cornell U., 1972, PhD, 1974. Sr. economist N.Y. Council Econ. Advisers, N.Y.C., 1974-75; asst. prof. U. Calif., Riverside, 1975-81; assoc. prof. W.Va. U., Morgantown, 1981-84; faculty assoc. Regional Research Inst., Morgantown, 1981-88; vis. assoc. EQL Calif. Inst. Tech., Pasadena, 1986; prof. mineral econs. W.Va. U., 1984-88, chmn. dept., 1981-83, 86-88; prof. mineral econs., head dept., Pa. State U., University Park, 1988—; faculty assoc. Earth System Sci. Ctr., 1993—; cons. Mayor's Office, City of L.A., 1980, NSF, Washington, 1980, U.S. Forest Svc., 1982-83, So. Calif. Gas Co., 1983, 85, U.S. Corps of Engrs., 1984, 92-93, San Francisco City Atty's Office, 1986, Nat. Coal Assn., 1990, U.S. Dept. Energy, 1990, EUREMCO, 1991-92, UNCTAD, 1991-92, Foster Wheeler, Inc., 1992, Air Products & Chemicals Inc., 1992-93, Ctr. Energy and Econ. Devel., 1994-95; expert witness U.S. Senate, Washington, 1985, W.Va. Pub. Svc. Commn., 1991, Pa. Utility Commn., 1992. Sr. author: Forecasting Gas Demand, 1987, Natural Resource Policy and Income Distribution, 1988, Combating Global Warming: A Global System of Tradeable Carbon Emission Entitlements, 1992; editor, author: Geothermal Energy and Regional Development, 1979, Frontiers of Input-Output Analysis, 1989; author (monograph): Dynamic Interindustry Model of Pollution Abatement, 1976; guest editor: Jour. Policy Modeling, 1989; Resource and Energy Economics, 1993; assoc. editor: Jour. Regional Sci., 1985—; editorial bd. mem. Resources Policy, 1989—, Resource and Energy Economics, 1993—. Recipient Outstanding Planning Program Honor award Am. Planning Assn., 1983; Woodrow Wilson Found. fellow, Cornell U., 1970-71, U. Calif., Riverside, 1979; grantee U.S. Dept. Energy, 1983-84, 95, grantee NSF, Washington, 1987-88, 90-91, 93—; grantee Nat. Ctr. Earthquake Engring. Rsch., 1992-95; grantee Argonne Nat. Lab., 1992-94. Mem. Am. Econ. Assn. (rep. to AAAS 1986-92), AAAS (mem. sect. K exec. com.), Regional Sci. Assn., Internat. Assn. Energy Economists, Assn. Resource & Environ. Economists, Mineral Econs. and Mgmt. Soc. Democrat. Jewish. Home: 1702 Princeton Dr State College PA 16803-3259 Office: Pa State U 222 Walker Bldg University Park PA 16802

ROSE, ALAN DOUGLAS, lawyer; b. Flushing, N.Y., Dec. 22, 1945; s. William Allen and Josephine (Grohe) R.; m. Janet Louise Clift, Aug. 20, 1966; children: Alan Douglas Jr., Windsor, Ainsley, Vanessa, Hillary, Lacey. BA, Harvard U., 1967; MSc, London Sch. Econs., 1969; JD, U. Va., 1972. Bar: Mass. 1974, U.S. Dist. Ct. Mass. 1975, U.S. Ct. Claims 1983, U.S. Ct. Appeals (1st cir.) 1976, U.S. Ct. Appeals (fed. cir.) 1986, U.S. Supreme Ct. 1991. Law clk. to judge U.S. Dist. Ct. Mass., Boston, 1972-73; assoc. Choate Hall & Stewart, Boston, 1973-75; asst. U.S. Atty. Dept. Justice, Boston, 1975-80; ptnr. Nutter McClennen & Fish, Boston, 1980-95; mgr. litigation dept., 1991-93; spl. asst. atty. gen. Commonwealth of Mass., 1992-93, State of Washington, 1993-94; lawyer Rose & Assocs., Boston, 1995—; lectr. Law Sch. Harvard U., Cambridge, Mass., 1981-82. Bd. dirs. Jericho Corp., Boston. Mem. ABA, Boston Bar Assn. (vice chair joint bar com. on jud. appointments 1991-92), City Mission Soc. (chmn., bd. dirs.). Democrat. Mem. United Ch. Christ. Home: 50 Bristol Rd Wellesley MA 02181-2728 Office: Rose & Assocs One Boston Pl Boston MA 02108

ROSE, BEATRICE SCHROEDER (MRS. WILLIAM H. ROSE), harpist, educator; b. Ridgewood, N.J., Nov. 15, 1922; d. Henry William and Ida (LeHovey) Schroeder; m. William Harrison Rose, Apr. 10, 1954; 1 child, Daniel. Student, Inst. Musical Art, 1940-41, Mannes Coll. Music, 1942-44; studies with, Lucile Lawrence and Carlos Salzedo. Concert and radio debut N.Y. World's Fair, 1939; soloist Damrosch Music Appreciation Hour broadcast, 1940, Duke of Windsor's Save the Children Fund, Nassau, The Bahamas, 1941; assoc. harpist Radio City Music Hall Orch., N.Y.C., 1944-50; various radio and solo performances N.Y. area, 1944-51; concert artist Italy, U.S. and Can., 1952; prin. harpist Houston Symphony, 1953-84; instr. harp U. Houston, 1953—; soloist Contemporary Music Soc., 1959, 60, Houston Chamber Orch., 1969; dir. Christmas Festival of Harps, Houston Harp Ensemble, PBS, 1978, Harps of Gold, 1983; instr. Shepherd Sch. Music, Rice U., 1977-93. Author: Troubadour Harp A Guide for Teachers and Students, 1976, rev. edits., 1982, 92; co-author: Outline of Six-Year Harp Course for Elementary, Junior and Senior High School, 1966; composer works include Enchanted Harp, rev. edit., 1975; recs. for Houston Symphony, Stokowski, Everest, Capitol, Comissiona, Vanguard Records. Recipient 1st prize Federated Music Clubs Contest, 1936; N.Y. Hour of Music award, 1945. Mem. Am. Harp Soc., Tex. Music Educators Assn. (adjudicator All-State competitions), Nat. Fedn. Music Clubs, Phi Beta. Home: 1315 Friarcreek Ln Houston TX 77055-6714 Office: U Houston Sch Music Houston TX 77004

ROSE, C. KIMBALL, judge. Presiding judge Ariz. Superior Ct., Phoenix. Office: US Superior Ct 201 W Jefferson St Phoenix AZ 85003

ROSE, CAROL MARGUERITE, law educator; b. Washington, Apr. 12, 1940; d. J. Hugh and Marie (Meenehan) R. BA, Antioch Coll., 1962; MA, U. Chgo., 1963, JD, 1977; PhD, Cornell U., 1970. Bar: Ill. 1977, Calif. 1978, D.C. 1978. Instr. history Ohio St. U., Columbus, 1969-73; assoc. dir. So. Govtl. Monitor Project, Atlanta, 1975-76; law clk. to judge U.S. Ct. Appeals (5th cir.), Austin, Tex., 1977-78; asst. prof. law Stanford (Calif.) U., 1978-80; acting prof. law U. Calif., Berkeley, 1980-82; prof. law Northwestern U., Chgo., 1982-88, Yale U., 1988—; bd. editors Found. Press, Mineola, N.Y., 1986—. Mem. Am. Assn. Law Schs., Am. Acad. Arts and Scis., Order of Coif.

ROSE, SISTER CECILIA, healthcare management administrator; b. Point Marion, Pa., Apr. 16, 1925; d. Fred Hazard and Yvonne Augusta (Bellette) R. BS in Nursing, Cath. U., 1952; MEd, Boston Coll., 1958; cert., St. Louis U., 1979. Instr. nursing Catherine Laboure Sch. Nursing, Boston, 1952-61, dir., 1962-63; dir. sch. nursing St. Mary's Hosp., Troy, N.Y., 1961-62, St. Vincent's Hosp., Bridgeport, Conn., 1965-69, St. Vincent's Med. Ctr., Jacksonville, Fla., 1969-71; dir. St. Vincent's Community Mental Health Ctr.,

Jacksonville, 1971-75; asst. adminstr. Sacred Heart Hosp., Cumberland, Md., 1975-78, pres., chief exec. officer, 1978-87; v.p. St. Agnes Hosp., Balt., 1987—; sec., bd. dirs. Providence Hosp., Washington, 1981—; bd. dirs. St. Vincent Med. Ctr., Jacksonville, S.S. Cooper Corp., Del., Anne Plume Herron Found., Norfolk, Va. Chmn. Associated Cath. Charities, Cumberland, Md., 1983-84; mem. Roundtable for the Future, Western Md., 1983-87; bd. dirs. Consultation Ctr., Balt., 1989. Fellow Am. Coll. Healthcare Execs.; mem. Am. Soc. Healthcare Risk Mgmt., Nat. Assn. of Quality Assurance Profls. Roman Catholic. Avocations: pianist, organist. Home and Office: St Agnes Hosp 900 S Caton Ave Baltimore MD 21229-5201

ROSE, CHARLES, television journalist. B in History, Duke U., JD; postgrad., NYU. Interviewer Sta. WPIX-TV, N.Y.C., 1972; mng. editor Bill Moyers Internat. Report, from 1974; exec. producer Bill Moyers Jour., from 1975; corr. U.S.A.: People in Politics, PBS, 1976; polit. corr. NBC News, 1976-77; co-host A.M. Chgo., 1978; host The Charlie Rose Show Sta. KXAS-TV, Dallas, Ft. Worth, 1979-81; host nationally syndicated The Charlie Rose Show Sta. WRC-TV, Washington, 1981-83; former host, interviewer CBS News Nightwatch, Washington, from 1984; now host "Charlie Rose" Rose Comms., Inc. for PBS, N.Y.C., 1994—. Producer: (TV program) A Conversation with Jimmy Carter (Peabody award). Recipient News and Documentary Emmy award for Conversation with Roger Payne, 1992, 14th Annual Cable ACE award, 1992. Office: 499 Park Ave 15th flr New York NY 10022

ROSE, CHARLES DAVID, consulting company executive; b. Corpus Christi, Dec. 28, 1939; s. Robert Chester and Gladys (Blackmon) R.; m. Mary Ann McKinney, Apr. 23, 1965; children: David, Elizabeth, Katherine. BS in Physics magna cum laude, La. Tech. U., 1964; postgrad., Iowa State U. From engr. to dist. level supr. staff ops. South Ctrl. Bell Telephone Co., 1964-70; mgr. sales and engring. Hycaloader Co., 1970-74; owner Charles Rose Cons., Monroe, La., 1974—. Contbr. numerous articles to profl. jours. Mem. ASTM (various coms.), Am. Statis. Assn., Am. Soc. for Quality Control. Achievements include devel. of fractal variogram model for use in geostatistics; designated U.S. expert for ISO on coal sampling. Home: 3370 Deborah Dr Monroe LA 71201 Office: Charles Rose Cons PO Box 4344 808 N 31st St Monroe LA 71211-4344

ROSE, CHARLES GRANDISON, III (CHARLIE ROSE), congressman; b. Fayetteville, N.C., Aug. 10, 1939; s. Charles Grandison, Jr. and Anna Frances (Duckworth) R.; children: Charles Grandison IV, Sara Louise, Kelly Josephine. AB, Davidson Coll., 1961; LLB, U. N.C., 1964. Bar: N.C. 1964. Chief prosecutor Dist. Ct., 12th Jud. Dist., 1967-70; mem. 93nd-104th Congresses from 7th N.C. dist., Washington, 1972—; mem. agrl. com., subcom. Specialty Crops and Natural Resources, Gen. Farm Commodities 93nd-104th Congresses from 7th N.C. dist.; co-founder Congl. Rural Caucus; founder Congl. Clearing House on the Future. Pres. N.C. Young Democrats, 1968. Presbyterian. Office: US Ho of Reps 242 Cannon Washington DC 20515-3307

ROSE, DANIEL, real estate company executive, consultant; b. N.Y.C., Oct. 31, 1929; s. Samuel B. and Belle (Bernstein) R.; m. Joanna Semel, Sept. 16, 1956; children: David Semel, Joseph Benedict, Emily, Gideon Gregory. Student, Yale U., 1947-50; cert. of proficiency in Russian lang., U.S. Air Force Program, 1951; B.A., Syracuse U., 1952; postgrad., U. Paris. With Dwelling Mgrs., Inc., N.Y.C., 1954—; pres. Dwelling Mgrs., Inc. 1960—; dir. Dreyfus Tax Exempt Bond Fund Inc., 1976-82, Dreyfus Money Market Fund, Inc., 1980-82; pres., CEO Rose Assocs., Inc., N.Y.C., 1980—; assoc. fellow Pierson Coll. Yale U., 1974—; bd. dirs. U.S. Trust Corp., Nat. Realty Com., Inst. Urban Design, Nat. Housing Conf., Nat. Humanities Ctr., Ventures in Edn.; bd. dirs., mem. grants com. Realty Found. N.Y.; vice chmn. Lionel Trilling seminars Columbia U., 1977—; trustee, mem. exec. and compensation and benefits coms. U.S. Trust Co. of N.Y., 1982-92; trustee, vice chmn. mixed use devel. coun. Urban Land Inst., 1986-93; trustee, mem. investment and compensation coms. Corp. Property Investors; mem. exec. com. Urban Land Found., 1989—; gov. 1993—; designated Cert. Property Mgr. Inst. for Real Estate Mgmt.; bd. govs. Technion-Israel Inst. Tech.; vice chmn., sec.-treas. Baltic-Am. Enterprise Fund, 1994—. Expert advr. to sec. HUD, 1972; expert/cons. to commr. edn. HEW, 1974; cons. HUD panel on urban devel., 1984-86; dir. N.Y. Coun. Humanities, 1980-86, N.Y. Conv. Ctr. Devel. Corp., 1980-90, Get Ahead Found., 1989—, Fifth Ave. Assn., 1989—; mem. Governor's Task Force on Housing, 1975, Task Force on Taxation, Mcpl. Assistance Corp., 1976-77, Planning Commn. Theatre Adv. Group, coun. of fellows, vis. com. to grad. faculty, bd. overseers Ctr. for Study of N.Y.C. affairs New Sch. for Social Rsch.; overseers com. to visit Ctr. Internat. Affairs Harvard U.; mem. advr. bd. CUNY-TV channel A, 1986—, Mcpl. Broadcasting System, 1977-78, MIT Ctr. for Real Estate Devel.; donor Daniel Rose chair urban econs., trustee NYU N.Y. Inst. for Humanistic Studies, Mus. of City of N.Y., 1984-90, Jewish Publ. Soc., Com. for Econ. Devel., N.Y.C. Rand Inst.; chmn. bd. trustees, Horace Mann-Barnard Sch.,1971-74, trustee, 1962-89, hon. trustee, 1989—; v.p. assoc. treas., bd. dirs. Police Athletic League of N.Y., vice chmn. Cen. Harlem Facility; pres. Harlem Ednl. Activities Fund Inc., YM & YWHA of the Bronx, 1963-67; v.p. N.Y. Landmarks Conservancy, bd. dirs. 1977-90; bd. dirs. Jewish Cmty. Ctrs. Assn., 1970—, pres. 1974-78, hon. pres. 1978—; v.p. World Confedn. of Jewish Cmty. Ctrs., 1977-83; former trustee and exec. com. mem. Fedn. of Jewish Philanthropies of N.Y., chmn. standing functional com. on cmty. ctrs., 1969-73; ptnr. N.Y.C. Partnership, 1990—; treas., bd. dirs. Citizens Housing and Planning Coun. of N.Y.; chmn. Dem. platform adv. com., 1984 Nat. Conv.; bd. advisors Dem. Leadership Coun., 1992—, Progressive Policy Inst.; trustee Dem. Nat. Com., 1988; chmn. Del. Svcs. Host Com., N.Y.C. Served with USAF, 1951-54. Mem. Internat. Inst. Strategic Studies (dir. Am. Com. for IISS 1987—), Coun. on Fgn. Rels., Fgn. Policy Assn. (bd. dirs. 1971—, chmn. fgn. policy assocs. 1972-75), Inst. for East-West Security Studies (bd. dirs. 1982—, treas. 1988—, co-chmn. fin. com. 1990—), Am. Soc. Real Estate Counselors (mem. publs.-rsch. com.), Real Estate Bd. of N.Y. Inc. (chmn. housing com. 1975—, mem. bd. govs. 1977-80, 90—), mem. REBNY Found.), Assn. of Yale Alumni (del.-at-large 1978-81, class of 1951 del., 1986-89), Econ. Club N.Y., Quaker Ridge Country Club, Noyac Country Club. Clubs: Century Assn., Coffee House, Yale (N.Y.C.); Cosmos (Washington); Racquet and Tennis, Union (Boston). Home: 895 Park Ave New York NY 10021-0327 Office: Rose Associates Inc 380 Madison Ave New York NY 10017-2593

ROSE, DAVID ALLAN, investment manager; b. N.Y.C., Feb. 15, 1937; s. Edward William and Marion (Nadelstein) R.; m. Frances Helaine Dushman, Aug. 16, 1959; children: Evan Denali, Mitchell Franklin. BS in Acctg., Queens Coll., 1958; MBA, Syracuse U., 1968. Fin. mgr. U.S. Army, Fort Richardson, Alaska, 1961-75; comptroller U.S. Army, Fort Richardson, 1975; exec. dir. Alaska Mcpl. Bond Bank Authority, Anchorage, 1975-82, Alaska Indsl. Devel. Authority, Anchorage, 1980; co-owner Downtown Investment Co., Anchorage, 1980—, Downtown Delicatessen, Inc. Anchorage, 1976—; CEO, Alaska Permanent Fund Corp., Juneau, 1982-92; chmn., CEO, Alaska Permanent Capital Mgmt. Co., Inc., Anchorage, 1992—; ptnr. Russian Alaska Export/Import Co., Anchorage, 1993—; fin. advisor Fin. Green Lake Dam, Sitka, Alaska, 1977, Fin. Dutch Harbor Port, Unalaska, Alaska, 1979-80, Fin. Kenai-Anchorage Pipeline, Anchorage, 1979-80, Fin. Pulp Mill Pollution Control, Ketchikan, Alaska, 1979-80, Govt. of Republic of Sakha, Russia, 1994—. Mem. City Coun., Anchorage, 1971-75, Borough Assembly, Anchorage, 1971-75, Mcpl. Assembly, Anchorage, 1975-80; pres. Alaska Mcpl. League, 1975, Mcpl. Assembly, Anchorage, 1975-77; vice chmn. endowment fund Alaska Pacific U., 1994—. Recipient Golden Man award Boys Club Alaska, Anchorage, 1974, Decoration for Meritorious Civilian Service, U.S. Army, 1975, Pub. Service award City and Borough, Juneau, 1986, Lions Internat. awards; named Pub. Adminstr. Yr., Am. Soc. Pub. Adminstrn., Alaska chpt., 1986. Mem. Rotary (awards). Republican. Jewish. Avocations: boating, raising ducks and geese, gardening. Office: Alaska Permanent Capital 900 W 5th Ave Ste 701 Anchorage AK 99501-2029

ROSE, DAVID CAMERON, discount store executive; b. Vance County, N.C., Nov. 10, 1942; s. Thomas Benton, Jr. and Kathryn (Hunt) R.; m. Margaret Diane Oakley, June 26, 1965; children: David Cameron, Thomas Benjamin. B.B.A., Wake Forest U., Winston-Salem, N.C., 1965; M.B.A. Wharton Sch., U. Pa., 1967. C.P.A., N.C. Staff accountant Haskins & Sells (C.P.A.s) Greensboro, N.C., 1967-69; with Rose's Stores, Inc., Henderson,

N.C., 1969—; controller Rose's Stores, Inc., 1971-72, treas., 1972—, v.p. fin. from 1975, also dir.; dir. Central Carolina Bank, Durham, N.C., CCB Fin. Corp., Durham. Chmn. Henderson/Vance County Parks and Recreation Commn., 1979—; pres. Vance Acad., Inc., Henderson, 1982-84; trustee Maria Parham Hosp., 1985. Mem. Am. Inst. C.P.A.s, N.C. Assn. C.P.A.s., Fin. Execs. Inst. Methodist. Club: Henderson Rotary. Home: 3205 Cameron Dr Henderson NC 27536-3816 Office: Rose's Stores Inc PO Box 947 Henderson NC 27536-0947

ROSE, DONALD JAMES, computer science educator; b. Santa Ana, Calif., May 25, 1944; 1 child, Tamar Rose. BA, U. Calif., Berkeley, 1966; AM, Harvard U., 1967, PhD, 1970. Instr. applied math. Harvard U., Cambridge, Mass., 1970; asst. prof. math. U. Denver, 1970-72; asst. prof. applied math. Harvard U., 1972-74, assoc. prof., 1974-77; prof., chmn. dept. computer sci. Vanderbilt U., Nashville, 1977-78; researcher Bell Labs., Murray Hill, N.J., 1978-84; prof., chmn. dept. computer sci. Duke U., Durham, N.C., 1984-91, prof., 1991—; cons. MCNC, Research Triangle Park, 1984-89, Bell Labs, Murray Hill, 1984—, Tanner Rsch. Pasadena, Calif., 1993-94. Co-editor: Sparse Matrices and Their Applications, 1972, Sparce Matrix Computations, 1976; contbr. more than 50 articles to profl. jours. Mem. IEEE, Am. Math. Soc., Math. Assn. Am., Assn. Computing Machinery, Soc. Indsl. Applied Math. Office: Duke U Dept Computer Sci D112A LSRC Box 90129 Durham NC 27708-0129

ROSE, DONALD MCGREGOR, lawyer; b. Cin., Feb. 6, 1933; s. John Kreimer and Helen (Morris) R.; m. Constance Ruth Lanner, Nov. 29, 1958; children: Barbara Rose Mead, Ann Rose Weston. AB in Econs., U. Cin., 1955; JD, Harvard U., 1958. Bar: Ohio 1958, U.S. Supreme Ct. 1962. Asst. legal officer USNR, Subic Bay, The Philippines, 1959-62; with Office of JAG USNR, The Pentagon, Va., 1962-63; assoc. Frost & Jacobs, Cin., 1963-70, ptnr., 1970-93; sr. ptnr., 1993—; co-chmn. 6th Cir. Appellate Practice Inst., Cin., 1983, 90, mem. 6th Cir. adv. com., chmn. subcom. on rules, 1990-94, chmn., 1994—. Trustee, chmn. Friends of Cin. Pks., Inc., 1986-89, pres. 1980-86; trustee Am. Music Scholarship Assn., Cin., 1985-88; pres. Social Health Assn. Greater Cin. Area Inc., 1969-72; co-chmn. Harvard Law Sch. Fund for So. Ohio, Cin., 1985-87; pres. Meth. Union, Cin., 1983-85; chmn. trustees Hyde Pk. Community United Meth. Ch., 1974-76, chmn. coun. on ministries, 1979-81, chmn. adminstrv. bd., 1982-84, chmn. mem. canvass, 1985, chmn. staff parish rels. com., 1988-90, chmn. commn. missions, 1993—; trustee Meth. Theol. Sch. Ohio, vice chmn. devel. com., 1990-94, sec. 1992-94, chmn. devel. com., 1994—. Lt. USNR, 1959-63. Mem. ABA (cochmn. advocacy tng. subcom., appellate practice com., litigation sect. 1988—), Ohio Bar Assn., Cin. Bar Assn., University Club (Cin.), Cowan Lake Sailing Assn. (Wilmington, Ohio), Cin. Country Club. Republican. Avocation: sailing (racing and cruising). Home: 8 Walsh Ln Cincinnati OH 45208-3423 Office: Frost & Jacobs 2500 PNC Ctr 201 E 5th St Cincinnati OH 45202-4117

ROSE, EDWARD W. (RUSTY ROSE), professional sports team executive. Gen. partner Texas Rangers, Arlington, TX. Office: care Texas Rangers 1000 Ballpark Way Arlington TX 76011*

ROSE, ELIHU, real estate executive; b. N.Y.C., Mar. 30, 1933; s. Samuel B. and Belle (Bernstein) R.; m. Susan Wechsler, Feb. 6, 1965; children: Amy, Isabel, Abigail. BS, Yale U., 1954; MA, NYU, 1969, PhD, 1978. Ptnr. Rose Assocs., N.Y.C., 1956—; trustee Tchrs. Coll., Columbia U. Contbr. articles to profl. mil. jours. Trustee Jewish Mus. of N.Y., 1992—, Internat. Ctr. Photography; bd. visitors Boston U. Med. Sch., 1978—, past chmn.; bd. dirs. Sta. WNET (PBS), Lincoln Ctr. Theater, 1992—. Mem. Internat. Inst. Strategic Studies, Council Fgn. Relations, Century Assn. Jewish. Clubs: Yale (N.Y.); Army and Navy (Washington). Office: Rose Assocs 380 Madison Ave New York NY 10017-2513

ROSE, ELIZABETH, author, satirist, poet, publisher, environmentalist; b. N.Y.C., Sept. 18, 1941; children: Kimberly, Dana. Nurse, Lenox Hill Hosp. Sch. Nursing, 1962; BA summa cum laude, U. Redlands, 1976. Asst. head nurse emergency room N.Y.C., 1963-66; head nurse San Pedro (Calif.) Hosp., 1968-69; pub. Butterfly Pub. Co., Santa Monica, 1985; radio and TV personality L.A., 1985—; founder Candida Anonymous, Santa Monica, 1985; cons. health profls. Author: Lady of Gray: Healing Candida-The Nightmare Chemical Epidemic, 1985, 2d edit. 1987, 3d edit. 1989, Sainthood and Single Motherhood, 1990. Recipient Internat. World Leader award Better Worlds Soc., Cambridge, Eng., 1989; N.Y. State Regents scholar, 1959. Mem. UCLA Alumni Assn. (life), Cousteau Soc., Tesla Soc., L.A. Blue Book Club. Avocations: plays and movies, ice skating, crossword puzzles, dancing, reading.

ROSE, ERNST, dentist; b. Oldenburg, Germany, July 22, 1932; s. William and Elsie (Lowenbach) R.; came to U.S., 1940, naturalized, 1946; m. Shirley Mae Glassman, Dec. 24, 1960; children: Ruth Ellen, Michele Ann, Daniel Scot, Seth Joseph. BS, Georgetown U., 1955; DDS, Western Res. U., 1963. Intern, Waterbury (Conn.) Hosp., 1964; pvt. practice dentistry, Hubbard, Ohio, 1964—; pres., treas. Dr. Ernst Rose, Inc. Lab. instr. Ohio State U., Columbus, 1956-57; dental adviser Assoc. Neighborhood Ctr. Mem. Liberty Twp. Zoning Commn., 1967-74, 1988-92, vice chmn.; chmn., 1970-74, chmn., 1990; chmn. Hubbard (Ohio) Urban Renewal Com., 1968-74. Mem. brotherhood bd., 1967—, treas. 1971-73, 88-90, pres. 1975-77, 90-92, temple bd. dirs. 1975-84, 89—. Served with AUS, 1957-59. Mem. ADA, Ohio Dental Assn., Corydon Palmer Dental Soc. (mem. coun. 1983-87), Warren Dental Soc., Hubbard C. of C. (bd. dirs. 1967—), Jewish Chatauqua Soc. (life), Alpha Omega (council mem. 1968—, sec. 1970-71, v.p. 1971-72, pres. 1972-73, pres. 1989-90). Lodges: B'nai B'rith (mem. 1970-71, trustee 1971—), Rotary (vice chmn. Kashrut com. 1983-85, chmn. Kashrut com. 1985—, vice chmn. Mikvah com. 1983-93). Home: 418 Arbor Cir Youngstown OH 44505-1916 Office: 30 N Main St Hubbard OH 44425-1653

ROSE, EVANS, JR., lawyer; b. Sewickley, Pa., Mar. 10, 1932; s. Evans and Jane Eline (Murphy) R.; m. Patricia Stallings, July 16, 1983; children: Virginia, Susan, Henry, Hilary, Jennifer. A.B., Yale U., 1954; J.D., U. Pitts., 1959. Bar: Pa. 1960. Assoc. firm Rose, Schmidt, Hasley & DiSalle, Pitts., Washington and Harrisburg, 1960-64; ptnr. Rose, Schmidt, Hasley & DiSalle, 1964-90, sr. ptnr., 1970-90, co-mng. ptnr., 1985-86, mng. ptnr., 1986-89, chmn., 1989-90; dir. Cohen & Grigsby, P.C., 1990—; exec. com., 1992—; bd. dirs. Dietrich Industries, Inc., The Stackpole Corp., Integra Trust Co.; chmn. Pa. Client Security Fund, 1994—; solicitor Borough of Sewickley Heights; sec. Fed. Ct. Nominating Commn. of Pa., 1977-81; chmn. Appellate Ct. Nominating Commn. of Pa., 1979-81, mem. Pa. Client Security Fund, 1992—. Article editor: U. Pitts. Law Rev., 1958-59. Trustee West Penn Hosp., Pitts., Carnegie Hero Fund Commn., U. Pitts.; chmn. Pa. Republican Fin. Com., 1979; del. Rep. Nat. Conv., 1976, 80; chmn. fin. com. Rep. Gov.'s Assn., 1985. Served with U.S. Army, 1954-56. Mem. Am. Law Inst., Law Allegheny County (Pa.) Bar Assn., ABA, Pa. Bar Assn. Presbyterian. Clubs: Duquesne, Rolling Rock, Allegheny Country. Home: Scaife Rd Sewickley PA 15143 Office: 2900 Cng Towers Pittsburgh PA 15222

ROSE, GEORGE MAX, chemical company executive; b. N.Y.C., Oct. 14, 1923; s. Morris and Sarah (Loseff) R.; m. Audra Lois Abresch, Apr. 10, 1949; children: Evan Andrew, Scott Morris. BChE, NYU, 1948. Registered profl. engr., Del. Foreman Koppers Co., Pitts., 1947-51; tech. svc. engr. Houdry Corp., Phila., 1951-56; supr. petrochems. Tidewater Oil Co., Delaware City, Del., 1956-65; dir. mktg. Standard Oil Co. (Ohio), Cleve., 1965-85; pres. Rose Cons., Cleve., 1985-89; sr. v.p. Global Octanes Corp., Houston, 1989—. Served with U.S. Army, 1942-46, PTO. Mem. AIChE, Nat. Petroleum Refiners Assn. (bd. dirs.), Oxygenated Fuels Assn. (bd. dirs.), Airplane Owners and Pilots Assn., Mooney Aircraft Owners Assn., Sweetwater Country Club, Houston City Club. Democrat. Unitarian. Avocations: flying, photography, travel, tennis, walking. Home: 15 Greenway Plz 17F Houston TX 77046 Office: Global Octanes Corp 1000 Louisiana # 5680 Houston TX 77002

ROSE, GILBERT PAUL, classics educator; b. N.Y.C., Aug. 6, 1939; s. William R. and Sylvia (Lanzet) Briefstein; m. Nancy Gorz, June 11, 1961; children: Dorothy, Rebecca. Student, Princeton U., 1957-60; A.B., U. Calif.-Berkeley, 1963, Ph.D., 1969; postgrad., U. Wis., 1963-64. Instr. to assoc. prof. Swarthmore Coll., Pa., 1967-81, prof. dept. classics, 1981—; vis. asst.

prof. Ohio State U., Columbus, 1969; vis. assoc. prof. U. Calif.-Berkeley, 1979. Editor: Plato's Crito, 1980, Plato's Symposium, 1981, Plato's Republic, Book I, 1983. Old Dominion fellow, 1970-71; Mellon grantee, 1974-75. Mem. Am. Philol. Assn.; AAUP, Phi Beta Kappa. Office: Swarthmore Coll Swarthmore PA 19081

ROSE, HENRY, lawyer; b. Olean, N.Y., Mar. 28, 1927; s. Irving and Sarah (Cohen) R.; m. Norma Lefcowitz, Feb. 16, 1957 (div. 1981); children: Benjamin, Andra, Jonathan. BA cum laude, U. Buffalo, 1950, LLB cum laude, 1951. Bar: N.Y. 1951, D.C. 1953, U.S. Ct. Appeals (D.C., 2nd, 3d, 4th, 5th, 6th, 9th, 10th cirs.), U.S. Dist. Ct. (we. and so. dists.) N.Y., U.S. Dist. Ct. (so. dist.) Tenn., U.S. Supreme Ct. 1956. Sterling fellow Yale U., New Haven, 1956-57; atty. NLRB, 1952-53; pvt. practice Buffalo, 1953-56; assoc. prof. U. Toledo, Ohio, 1957-58, Rutgers U., Camden and Newark, N.J., 1958-62; from spl. asst. to solicitor, dep. assoc. solicitor for legislation and legal counsel U.S. Dept. Labor, Washington, 1962-70, assoc. solicitor, 1970-74; gen. counsel Pension Benefit Guaranty Corp., Washington, 1974-84; ptnr., chmn. employee benefits dept. Epstein Becker & Green, P.C., Washington, 1985-92, of counsel, 1993—; teaching assoc. Northwestern U., 1951-52; part-time lectr. U. Buffalo, 1954-56, U.S. Va., 1968; guest lectr. Harvard U., Am. U., Cath. U., Georgetown U., George Washington U.; acad. visitor London Sch. Econs., 1971-72; speaker in field. Contbr. articles to profl. jours. Asst. spl. counsel emergency crime com. Chgo. City Coun., 1952. Rsch. grantee Ford Found., 1959. Mem. ABA (mem. labor and employment law sect., mem. taxation sect., mem. torts and ins. practice sect., chmn. employee benefits com. 1993-94, mem. real property, probate and trust law sect., chair ABA joint com. on employee benefits 1995—), D.C. Bar Assn. Home: 700 New Hampshire Ave NW Washington DC 20037-2406

ROSE, HERMAN, artist; b. Bklyn., Nov. 6, 1909; s. Charles and Bella (Washelevsky) Rappaport; m. Tilly Lomsky, Mar. 15, 1934 (div.); children: George, Andrew; m. Elia Braca, Oct. 18, 1955. Student, N.A.D., 1927-29. Mem. staff art project Works Progress Administrn., 1934-39; tchr. Hofstra Coll., 1959-60, Bklyn. Coll., 1949-51, 58-61; instr. New Sch. Social Research, 1954-55, 63—; artist-in-residence U. Va., 1966, U. N.Mex., 1970-71, Queens Coll., 1974. One man shows include Egan Gallery, 1946-47, 48, A.C.A. Gallery, 1952-55, Forum Gallery, 1962, U. Va., Charlottesville, 1966, Bard Coll., Annandale-on-Hudson, N.Y., 1967, Nova Scotia Coll. Art, 1969, Zabriskie Gallery, 1969-67, 71-74, Fishbach Gallery, 1983, 86, 89, Coll. William and Mary, Williamsburg, Va., 1984; group shows include Mus. Modern Art, 1952, Barcelona, 1955, Paris, 1955, Tate Mus., London, 1956, Pa. Acad., 1953, Whitney Mus., 1948, 49, 53, 55, 56, Nat. Inst. Arts and Letters, 1956, 70, 72, Parrish Mus., Southhampton, N.Y., 1975, San Francisco Mus. Modern Art, 1985, Mus. at Stony Brook, L.I., N.Y., 1990, Macon Coll., Fredericksburg, Va., 1990; works in permanent collection Mus. Modern Art, Whitney Mus., U. Tex., U. Calif., Smithsonian Instn. Print Collection, Washington, Commerce Bancshares, Kans. City, Cigna Corp., Hallmark Coll., Reader's Digest, N.Y., Allied Bank of Tex., Sheldon Meml. Art Gallery, U. Nebr., Lincoln,Hirshhorn Mus. and Sculpture Garden, Washington, Weatherspoon Art Gallery, N.C.Y, Munson-Williams-Proctor Inst., Utica, N.Y., Parrish Art Mus., Southampton, Vassar Coll., Poughkeepsie, N.Y., NAD, N.Y.C., Palm Desert Mus., Palm Springs, Calif. Recipient Longview award, 1959, 60, 61, award Inst. Arts and Letters, 1972, Childe Hassam award, 1970, 73, Adolph and Esther Gottlieb Found. award, 1989, Oscar Williams and Gene Derwood award N.Y. Community Trust, 1984; Yaddo Scholar, 1955; Nat. Endowment for arts grantee, 1976, 80; Pollack Krasner Found. grantee, 1989-90. Mem. N.A.D. (Benjamin Altman 1st prize landscape 1976, 83, Henry Ward Ranger Fund purchase 1977, 85, Grumbacher gold medal, 1982, 85, Emil and Dines Carlsen award 1989). Office: care Fishbach Gallery 24 W 57th St New York NY 10019-3918

ROSE, HUGH, management consultant; b. Evanston, Ill., Sept. 10, 1926; s. Howard Gray and Catherine (Wilcox) R.; m. Mary Moore Austin, Oct. 25, 1952; children: Susan, Nancy, Gregory, Matthew, Mary. BS in Physics, U. Mich., 1951, MS in Geophysics, 1952; MBA with highest distinction, Pepperdine U., 1982. Mgr. Caterpillar, Inc., Peoria, Ill., 1952-66; v.p., mktg. mgr. Cummins Engine Co., Columbus, Ind., 1966-69; pres., chief exec. officer Cummins Northeastern, Inc., Boston, 1969-77; pres. Power Systems Assocs., L.A., 1980-83, C.D. High Tech., Inc., Austin, Tex., 1984-87; mgmt. cons. Rose and Assocs., Tucson, 1984, 87—. Contbr. paleontol. articles to various publs. Bd. dirs. Raymond Alf Mus., Claremont, Calif., 1975—, Comstock Found., Tucson, 1988, Environ. Edn. Exch., 1991, Heart Ctr. U. Ariz., Tucson, 1992. With USAAF, WWII. Fellow AAAS; mem. Soc. Vertebrate Paleontology, Beacon Soc. Boston (pres. 1979-80), Algonquin Club Boston (v.p., bd. dirs. 1974-80), Duxbury Yacht Club, Longwood Cricket Club, Delta Mu Delta, Sigma Gamma Epsilon, Beta Beta Beta. Republican. Presbyterian. Office: Rose & Assocs 5320 N Camino Sumo Tucson AZ 85718-5132

ROSE, HUGH, retired economics educator; b. London, July 20, 1920; came to U.S., 1960, naturalized, 1977; s. William and Ann (Ogus) R. Student, Oxford (England) U. England, 1939-40, 45-47, Nuffield Coll., England, 1950-52. Lectr. in econs. Rhodes U., South Africa, 1947-50, lectr., 1952-53; lectr. in econs. Exeter U., England, 1954-60; assoc. prof. econs. U. Rochester, N.Y., 1961-63, prof., 1965-70; assoc. prof. econs. U. Toronto, Can., 1963-65; hon. rsch. assoc. Harvard U., Cambridge, Mass., 1969-70; prof. econs. Johns Hopkins U., Balt., 1970-91. Author: Macroeconomic Dynamics, 1991; contbr.a rticles to profl. jours. With British Army, 1940-45. Home: 112-D Cross Keyes Rd Baltimore MD 21210 Office: Johns Hopkins U Dept Econs 3400 N Charles St Baltimore MD 21218

ROSE, ISRAEL HAROLD, mathematics educator; b. New Britain, Conn., May 17, 1917; s. Abraham and Dora (Dubrow) R.; m. Pearl Nitzberg, Jan. 24, 1942 (div. Feb. 1956); 1 son, Steven Philip; m. Susan Ann Lazarus, Mar. 26, 1961; children: Dora, Eric. Student, CCNY, 1934-36; A.B. Bklyn. Coll., 1938, A.M., 1941; Ph.D., Harvard, 1951. Tutor, instr. Bklyn. Coll., 1938-41; instr. Pa. State Coll., 1942-46; asst. prof. U. Mass., 1948-54, assoc. prof., 1954-60; faculty Hunter Coll., 1960-68, prof. math., 1965-68, chmn. dept., 1966-68; prof. math. Lehman Coll., CUNY, 1968-82, prof. emeritus, 1983—; chmn. dept., 1968-72, 80-82, resident prof., 1983—; Vis. asst. prof. Mt. Holyoke Coll., 1951-52, vis. assoc. prof., 1954-55, 58-59; sci. cons. AID, India, summer 1965. Author: A Modern Introduction to College Mathematics, 1959, Algebra: An Introduction to Finite Mathematics, 1963, Vectors and Analytic Geometry, 1968, Elementary Functions: A Precalculus Primer, 1973, (with Esther R. Phillips) Elementary Functions, 1978. NRC predoctoral fellow Harvard, 1946-48; fellow Fund Advancement Edn., 1952-53. Mem. Am. Math. Soc., Math. Assn. Am. (Math. tchr. N.Y. sect. 1973-75), Nat. Council Tchrs. Math., Assn. Tchrs. Math. New Eng. (pres. Conn. Valley sect. 1956-57), Sigma Xi (pres. Hunter Coll. chpt. 1966-67). Home: 18 Floral Dr Hastings Hdsn NY 10706-1202 Office: Lehman Coll Bedford Park Blvd W Bronx NY 10468

ROSE, JAMES MCKINLEY, JR., lawyer, government official; b. N.Y.C., Aug. 8, 1927; s. James McKinley and Helen R.; m. Anne Louise Bourne, Aug. 19, 1960; children: Anne Clark, Louise Barnes. Grad., Phillips Exeter Acad., 1946; B.A., Princeton U., 1951; J.D., Harvard U., 1954. Bar: N.Y. 1955, D.C. 1977. With firm Dewey, Ballantine, Bushby, Palmer & Wood, N.Y.C., 1954-57; asst. U.S. atty. So. Dist. N.Y., 1957-61; legal asst. to pres. Atlantic Mut. Ins. Co., 1961-65, sec., counsel, 1965-71; asst. fed. ins. adminstr. U.S. Dept. Housing and Urban Devel., Washington, 1971-81; exec. asst. to adminstr. Fed. Ins. Adminstrn., Fed. Emergency Mgmt. Agy., Washington, 1981-93. Mem. men's com. Am. Mus. Natural History, 1968-71. Served with AUS, 1946-47. Mem. Bar Assn. City N.Y., St. Nicholas Soc., Prouts Neck Assn. (pres. 1979-85). Republican. Episcopalian (sr. warden) Clubs: Prouts Neck (Maine) Country; Chevy Chase (Washington). Home: 4913 Rodman St NW Washington DC 20016-3238

ROSE, JAMES TURNER, aerospace consultant; b. Louisburg, N.C., Sept. 21, 1935; s. Frank Rogers and Mary Burt (Turner) R.; m. Daniele Raymond, Sept. 15, 1984; children by previous marriage—James Turner, Katharine S. B.S. with high honors, N.C. State U., 1957. Aero. research engr. NASA, Langley Field, Va., 1957-59; project engr. NASA (Mercury and Gemini), Langley Field, Va. and Houston, 1959-64; program systems mgr. McDonnell Douglas Astronautics Co (MDAC), St. Louis, 1964-69; mgr. shuttle dev. and implementation (MDAC) McDonnell Douglas Astronautics Co., St. Louis, 1969-72; mgr. shuttle support (MDAC) St. Louis, 1972-74; dir. space shuttle

engring. NASA, Washington, 1974-76; mgr. space processing programs McDonnell Douglas Astronautics Co., St. Louis, 1976-83; dir. electrophoresis ops. in space McDonnell Douglas Astronautics Co (MDAC), St. Louis, 1983-86; asst. adminstr. comml. programs NASA, Washington, 1987-91; aerospace cons., 1992—. Recipient Lindberg award for mgmt. leadership AIAA, 1983, Presdl. Meritorious Rank award, 1989, NASA Exceptional Svc. medal, 1990, Laurels award Aviation Week, 1990, Aerospace Contribution to Soc. award AIAA, 1993. Mem. Phi Kappa Phi. Epsicopalian.

ROSE, JEFFREY RAYMOND, public servant, trade union executive, economist; b. Toronto, Ont., Can., Sept. 23, 1946; s. Albert and Thelma (Harris) R.; m. Sandra Black; 1 child, Andrew. B.A. with honors, U. Toronto, 1968, M.Indsl. Relations, 1983; postgrad., London Sch. Econs., 1968-69. Planner planning dept. City of Toronto, 1976-80; pres. local 79 Can. Union Pub. Employees, Toronto, 1980-83; nat. pres. Can. Union Pub. Employees, Ottawa, Ont., 1983-91; dep. minister Intergovtl. Affairs Govt. Ont., 1991—; gen. v.p. Can. Labour Congress, 1983-91. Exec. mem. Ont. New Democratic Party, 1982-91; bd. dirs. Inst. for Research on Pub. Policy, 1988-91; mem. fed. council of New Dem. Party, 1988-91. Home: 55 Sunnydene Crescent, Toronto, ON Canada M4N 3J5 Office: Ministry Intergovtl Affairs, 6th Fl Mowat Block, 900 Bay St, Mowat Block, Toronto, ON Canada M7A 1C2

ROSE, JENNIFER JOAN, lawyer; b. Dayton, Ohio, Oct. 25, 1951; d. Virginia Rose Kelly Apaydin. BA, Tarkio Coll., 1972; JD, Drake U., 1976. Bar: Iowa 1977, U.S. Dist. Ct. (so. and no. dists.) Iowa 1977, U.S. Ct. Appeals (8th cir.) 1978, U.S. Supreme Ct. 1980. Mem. 1984. Adminstrv. asst. State Ombudsman, Des Moines, 1975; spl. asst. county atty. Page and Taylor Counties, Iowa, 1977-78; city atty. Imogene, Iowa, 1977-78, 85-87; city atty. Essex, Iowa, 1981-88; pvt. practice, Shenandoah, Iowa, 1977-81; dir. Southwest Iowa Family Systems Project, 1978-80; adv. council southwest region Legal Svcs. Corp. Iowa, 1983-88. Contbr. articles to profl. jours. and popular press. Vice-pres. vol. coun. Planned Parenthood Mid Iowa, 1980-83. Fellow Am. Acad. Matrimonial Lawyers, Internat. Acad. Matrimonial Lawyers; mem. Page County Bar Assn. (pres. 1978-80, v.p. 1988—), Southwest Iowa Bar Assn., Iowa State Bar Assn. (sec. coun. family law sect. 1989-93, chmn. 1992-93, spl. com. young lawyers com. law and mental health, spl. com. on family law 1977-81, liaison to family law sect. 1991-92), ABA (chair GPS task force on sole & small firms 1991-92, mem. gen. practice sect., chmn. membership com. 1992-94, nominating com. 1993-94, Mead Data Task Force 1993-94, vice-chmn. family law com. 1988-91, chmn. family law com. 1989-91, editor Family Law Update 1990-92, GPS coun. 1993—, juvenile law com., exec. mem. marital property com. family law sect., newsletter editor 1989—), Inter-Am. Bar Assn., Am. Orthopsychiat. Assn., Nat. Coun. Juvenile and Family Ct. Judges, Nat. Assn. Counsel for Children, Nat. Assn. Vol. in Criminal Justice (bd. dirs.), Iowa Law Alert (family law editor 1990—), Internat. Soc. Family Law, Delta Theta Phi. Jewish. Home: RR 1 Shenandoah IA 51601-9801 Office: Rose Law Offices PO Box 616 Shenandoah IA 51601-0616

ROSE, JEROME GERALD, law and urban planning educator, lawyer, editor, consultant; b. N.Y.C., July 4, 1926; s. Robert and Ida (Lippman) R.; m. Naomi Lichtman, Nov. 11, 1956; children—Patricia Zeigler, Elizabeth, Theodore. A.B. in Govt. with distinction, Cornell U., 1948; J.D. cum laude, Harvard U., 1951. Bar: N.Y. 1951. Assoc. Roth & Margolis, N.Y.C., 1951-53; sole practice, Massapequa, N.Y., 1954-56, 57-69; exec. v.p. Robert Rose Bindery, Inc., N.Y.C., 1957-69; assoc. prof. urban planning Rutgers U., New Brunswick, 1969-72, prof., 1972—; cons. govtl. agencies. Mem. Princeton (N.J.) Regional Planning Bd., 1974-81; mem. Princeton Twp. Zoning Bd. Adjustment, 1976-79. Served with USN, 1943-45. Mem. Am. Planning Assn., Am. Inst. Cert. Planners, Phi Beta Kappa. Author: The Legal Adviser On Home Ownership, 1967; Landlords and Tenants, 1973; The Transfer of Development Rights, 1976; After Mt. Laurel, 1977; Legal Foundations of Urban Planning, 1979, Legal Foundations of Land Use Planning, 1979; Tax and Expenditure Limitations, 1982; editor/author: Legal Foundations on Environmental Planning, 1983; Tax and Expenditure Limitation, 1983; editor-in-chief Real Estate Law Jour., 1972—. Avocations: tennis, gardening, travel. Office: Warren Gorham & Lamont Inc One Penn Plaza Real Estate Law Jour New York NY 10119

ROSE, JOEL ALAN, legal consultant; b. Bklyn., Dec. 26, 1936; s. Edward Isadore and Adele R.; BS in Econs., N.Y.U., 1958; MBA, Wharton Grad. Sch., U. Pa., 1960; m. Isadora Fenig, Apr. 12, 1964; children: Susan, Terri. Asst. purchasing agt. Maidenform, Inc., N.Y.C., 1960-62; personnel dir. E.J. Korvette, Inc., N.Y.C., 1962-66; mgmt. cons. Daniel J. Cantor & Co., Inc., Phila., 1966—, sr. v.p., 1987—; prin. Joel Alan Rose & Assocs. Inc., Cherry Hill, N.J., 1987—; mgmt. cons. to legal profession; coordinator Conf. Am. Legal Execs. Served with U.S. Army, 1960, Res. 1960-66. Mem. Inst. Mgmt. Cons., Am. Arbitration Assn. (nat. panel), ABA (chmn. acquisition and mergers com., practice mgmt. sect.), Adminstrv. Mgmt. Soc. (past chpt. pres.), Am. Mgmt. Assn., Assn. Legal Adminstrs. Author: Managing the Law Office; mem. adv. bd. Law Office Economics and Management; contbg. columnist N.Y. Law Jour. Nat. Law Jour.; also articles. Office: Joel A Rose & Assoc Inc 1766 Rolling Ln PO Box 162 Cherry Hill NJ 08003-0162

ROSE, JOHN CHARLES, physician, educator; b. N.Y.C., Dec. 13, 1924; s. Hugh Stanley and Marie-Louise (Delury) R.; m. Dorothy Anne Donnelly, June 26, 1948; children—Nancy, Ellen, John Charles, Richard, Christopher. B.S., Fordham U. 1946; M.D. magna cum laude, Georgetown U., 1950, D.Sc. (hon.), 1973; LL.D. (hon.), Mt. St. Mary's Coll., 1973. Diplomate: Am. Bd. Internal Medicine, Am. Bd. Family Practice. Intern Walter Reed Army Hosp., 1950-51; resident, research fellow Georgetown U., VA hosps., Washington, 1954-57; established investigator Am. Heart Assn., 1954-57; instr., asst. prof. medicine Georgetown U., 1954-57, coord. med. edn., 1957-58, assoc. prof. physiology and biophysics, 1958-60, prof., 1960-91, chmn. dept. physiology and biophysics, 1958-63, dean Sch. Medicine, 1963-73, 78-79, prof. medicine, 1973-91, prof. emeritus, 1991—, vice chancellor Med. Ctr., 1984-87. Assoc. editor Am. Family Physician, 1955-62, chief med. editor, 1962-88; assoc. editor Acad. Medicine, 1992-95; contbr. articles to sci. publs. Bd. dirs. Charles E. Culpeper Found. Served to 2d lt. USAAF, 1943-45. Decorated Air medal. Fellow A.C.P.; mem. Am. Physiol. Soc., Biophys. Soc. (charter), Soc. Exptl. Biology and Medicine (nat. councillor 1962-63), Am. Heart Assn. (fellow sect. circulation). Club: Cosmos (Washington). Home: 5710 Surrey St Chevy Chase MD 20815-5520

ROSE, JOHN M., JR., advertising executive; b. Chelsea, Mass., Sept. 29, 1959; s. John M. and Catherine C. (Puleio) R. BA, Boston Coll., 1981. Account exec. Sta. WHUE-AM and FM radio, Boston, 1981-82; cons., producer Q. Mktg. Ltd. Communications, Dedham, Mass., 1982-84; pres., treas. Stephan/Rose, Inc., Woburn, Mass., 1984-86; pres., chief exec. officer Parsons, Friedmann, Stephan & Rose, Inc., Boston, 1986—; cons. Howard Johnson Company, Quincy, Mass., 1984. Office: 30 Newbury St Boston MA 02116-3201

ROSE, JOHN THOMAS, finance educator; b. Ft. Worth, Aug. 20, 1943; s. Paul Pittman and Francis Nan (White) R.; m. Sandra Kaye Rolen, Sept. 5, 1969; children: Melanie Ann, Leah Nan, Lynnelle Renee. BA with honors, Tex. A&M U., 1965; MA, Washington U., St. Louis, 1968, PhD, 1976. Economist Bd. Govs. of Fed. Reserve System, Washington, 1972-82, sr. economist, 1982-84; Harriette L. and Walter G. Lacy, Jr. prof. of banking Baylor U., Waco, Tex., 1984—. Contbr. articles to profl. jours. Bd. visitors Abilene (Tex.) Christian U., 1989-92. Capt. U.S. Army, 1969-71. Decorated Bronze Star U.S. Army; recipient Disting. Bus. Prof. award, 1988, Hankamer Sch. Bus. Baylor U., 1988; Econ. Devel. Adminstrn. U.S. Dept. of Commerce fellow, 1968-69; Ernst & Young Found. Rsch. grantee, 1991. Mem. Am. Fin. Assn., So. Fin. Assn., Southwestern Fin. Assn., Fin. Mgmt. Assn., Omicron Delta Epsilon, Beta Gamma Sigma. Mem. Ch. of Christ. Office: Baylor U Hankamer Sch of Bus Dept Fin Ins and Real Estate PO Box 98004 Waco TX 76798-8004

ROSE, JONATHAN CHAPMAN, lawyer; b. Cleve., June 8, 1941; s. Horace Chapman and Katherine Virginia (Cast) R.; m. Susan Anne Porter, Jan. 26, 1980; 1 son, Benjamin Chapman. A.B., Yale U., 1963; LL.B. cum laude, Harvard U., 1967. Bar: Mass. 1968, D.C. 1972, U.S. Supreme Ct. 1976, Circuit Ct. Appeals 1977, Ohio 1978. Law clk. Justice R. Ammi Cutter, Mass. Supreme Jud. Ct., 1967-68; spl. asst. to U.S. pres., 1971-73;

gen. counsel Council on Internat. Econ. Policy, 1973-74; assoc. dept. atty. gen. U.S. Dept. Justice, 1974-75; dept. asst. atty. gen. U.S. Dept. Justice (Antitrust Div.), 1975-77; asst. atty. gen. Office of Legal Policy, 1981-84; ptnr. firm Jones, Day, Reavis & Pogue, Washington, 1977-81, 84—. Prin. Ctr. for Excellence in Govt.; pres. Yale Daily News Found. 1st lt. U.S. Army, 1969-71. Mem. ABA, D.C. Bar Assn., Mass. Bar Assn., Ohio Bar Assn., Fed. Bar Assn., Am. Law Inst. Republican. Episcopalian. Clubs: Met, Chevy Chase, Union, Yale, Harvard. Office: Jones Day Reavis & Pogue 1450 G St NW Ste 600 Washington DC 20005-2088

ROSE, JOSEPH HUGH, clergyman; b. Jewett, Ohio, Nov. 21, 1934; s. Joseph Harper and Lottie Louella (VanAllen) R.; m. Nila Jayne Habig, Feb. 14, 1958; children: J. Hugh II, Stephanie Jayne, David William, Dawnella Jayne. ThB, Apostolic Bible Inst., St. Paul, 1955, DD, 1990. Ordained United Pentecostal Ch. Assoc. min. Calvary Tabernacle, Indpls., 1956-73; Ind. youth sec. United Pentecostal Ch., 1958-60, Ind. youth pres., 1960-72; bd. edin. United Pentecostal Ch., Hazelwood, Mo., 1974—; presbyter Ohio dist. United Pentecostal Ch., 1975—; pastor Harrison Hills Ch., Jewett, Ohio, 1973—. Editor, Ind. Dist. News, 1959-70; narrator radio svc. Harvestime, 1961—. Republican. Avocations: travel, classical music. Office: United Pentecostal Ch 8855 Dunn Rd Hazelwood MO 63042-2212

ROSE, LANCE HADEN, hospital administrator; b. Phila., June 13, 1943; s. George Mallinson and Lizzie Kate (Haden) R.; m. Ann Patricia Henegan, Dec. 27, 1966; children: Rachel Veronica, Christopher Sean, Andrew Haden. AA in Biology, Hinds Jr. Coll., Raymond, Miss., 1963; BS in Sci. Edn. and Zoology, U. Md., 1972; MS in Health Related Professions, U. Pitts., 1977, MPH in Hosp. Adminstrn., 1983. Nuclear medicine technician Cafritz Meml. Hosp., Washington, 1969-71; chief nuclear medicine technician Holy Cross Hosp., Silver Spring, Md., 1971-72; dir. nuclear medicine Community Med. Ctr., LaPlata, Md., 1972-73; tech. dir. nuclear medicine Presbyn. Univ. Hosp., Pitts., 1973-77, adminstrv. dir. nuclear medicine, 1977-83, acting v.p., 1973-83; adminstr. ops. Centre Community Hosp., State College, Pa., 1983-88, exec. dir., chief exec. officer, 1988-90, pres., chief exec. officer, 1990—; v.p. operating bd. dirs. Healthpass PPA; charter participant Leadership Pa. Program, 1990. Bd. dirs. Cen. chpt. Am. Cancer Soc. With USN, 1963-69, Vietnam. Fellow Am. Coll. Health Care Execs.; mem. Health Care Fin. Mgmt. Assn. (advanced), Hosp. Assn. Pa., Healthcare Adminstrs. Cen. Pa. Avocations: photography, camping, collecting antiques. Office: Centre Community Hosp 1800 E Park Ave State College PA 16803-6797

ROSE, LARRY LEE, newspaper executive; b. Holcomb, Mo., Aug. 17, 1943; s. Harry Rose and Elizabeth Elaine (Kephart) LaFemina; m. Lucinda Patricia Blumenfeld, Dec. 1969 (div. May 1980); 1 child, Kirsten Marie; m. Lauraine Francine Miller, Feb. 6, 1981. BS, Kent State U., 1971. Sect. editor Sun-Sentinel, Ft. Lauderdale, Fla., 1964-66, Miami (Fla.) Herald, 1971-79; news editor Washington Star, 1979-81; asst. mng. editor Dallas Morning News, 1981-87; exec. editor Corpus Christi (Tex.) Caller-Times, 1987-94, exec. v.p., gen. mgr., 1994—; adj. prof. Tex. A&M U., Kingsville, 1989—. With U.S. Army, 1966-69, Vietnam. Recipient Best Daily Newspaper award Press Club Dallas, 1989, 90, 91, 93, 94, 1st Amendment award Scripps Howard Found., 1991, Freedom of Info. award Tex. Associated Press, 1991. Fellow Amundsen Inst.; mem. Am. Soc. Newspaper Editors, Newspaper Assn. Am., Soc. Profl. Journalists, Corpus Christi Country Club, Corpus Christi Town Club. Avocations: photography, painting, travel. Office: Corpus Christi Caller-Times 820 N Lower Broadway St Corpus Christi TX 78401-2025

ROSE, LEATRICE, artist, educator; b. N.Y.C., June 22, 1924; d. Louis Rose and Edna Ades; m. Sol Greenberg (div.); children: Damon, Ethan; m. Joseph Stefanelli, Oct. 10, 1975. Student, Cooper Union, 1941-45, Arts Students League, 1946, Hans Hoffman Sch., 1947. Solo exhns. include Hansa Gallery, N.Y.C., 1954, Zabriskie Gallery, N.Y.C., 1965, Landmark Gallery, N.Y.C., 1974, Tibor de Nagy Gallery, N.Y.C., 1975, 78, 81, 82, Elaine Benson Gallery, Bridgehampton, N.Y., 1980, Armstrong Gallery, N.Y.C., 1985, Benton Gallery, Southampton, N.Y., 1987, Cyrus Gallery, N.Y.C., 1989; group exhns. include Sam Kootz Gallery, N.Y.C., 1950, Peridot Gallery, N.Y.C., 1952, Poindexter Gallery, N.Y.C., 1959, Tanager Gallery, N.Y.C., 1960, 62, Riverside Mus., N.Y.C., 1964, Frumkin Gallery, N.Y.C., 1964, Pa. Acad. Fine Arts, Phila., 1966, N.Y. Cultural Ctr., 1973, The Queens (N.Y.) Mus., 1974, 83, Nat. Acad. Design, N.Y.C., 1974, 75, 76, 92, 93, Weatherspoon Art Gallery, Greensboro, N.C., 78, 81, Whitney Mus. Am. Art, N.Y.C., 1978, Albright-Knox Gallery, Buffalo, 1978, 81, Met. Mus. Art, 1979, Vanderwoude Tananbaum Gallery, N.Y.C., 1982, Benton Gallery, 1986, 87; public collections include Albrect Gallery, St. Joseph, Mo., Guild Hall Mus., East Hampton, N.Y., Tibor de Nagy, Met. Mus. Art. Grantee N.Y. State Coun. Arts, 1974, The Ingram Merrill Found. 1974, AAUW, 1975, NEA, 1977, Esther and Adolph Gottlieb Found., 1980, 88; recipient Altman prize NAD, 1974, Phillips prize NAD, 1992, award AAAL, 1992, Am. Inst. Art award. Mem. NAD. Avocations: reading, walking. Office: 463 West St New York NY 10014

ROSE, LLOYD, theatre critic. Office: The Washington Post 1150 15th St NW Washington DC 20071-0001

ROSE, MARGARETE ERIKA, pathologist; b. Esslingen, Germany, Feb. 12, 1945; came to U.S., 1967; d. Wilhelm Ernst and Lina (Schurr) Pfisterer; m. Arthur Caughey Rose, Feb. 3, 1967; children: Victoria Anne, Alexandra Julia, Frederica Isabella. MD, U. So. Calif., L.A., 1972. Diplomate Am. Bd. Anatomic and Clin. Pathology. Pathologist St. Joseph Med. Ctr., Burbank, Calif., 1977-78, Glenview Pathology Med. Ctr., Culver City, Calif., 1979—; dir. anatomic pathology Glenview Mem. Pathology, Culver City, 1988—; dir. Life Chem. Lab., Woodland Hills, Calif., 1992—, Clin. Sci. Labs., North Hollywood, Calif.; co-dir. lab. Holy Cross Med. Ctr., Mission Hills, Calif., 1994—. Mem. Because I Love You, L.A., 1994. Fellow Am. Soc. Pathology, Coll. Am. Pathology. Avocations: cross-stitching, gardening, traveling. Office: Brotman Med Ctr Dept Pathology 3828 Hughes Ave Culver City CA 90231

ROSE, MARIANNE HUNT, business educator; b. Portsmouth, Ohio, Nov. 6, 1940; d. Harry Duke and B. Marie (Craycraft) Hunt; m. W. Craig Rose, Aug. 9, 1958 (dec. 1988); children: W. Stuart, Deirdre Anne. BS in Edn., Ohio U., 1962; postgrad., U. Va., James Madison U., George Mason U. Cert. tchr., Va., Ohio. Asst. editor Morehead (Ky.) News, 1962-63; mgr. Birthday Calendar Co., Morehead, 1963-64; bus. tchr. Clay Twp. Schs., Portsmouth, 1964-65, Prince William County Adult Edn., Woodbridge, Va., 1977-80, Prince William County Schs., Woodbridge, 1973-94; sec., 1994; cosponsor Future Bus. Leaders Am., Gar-Field Sr. H.S., Woodbridge, mentor TLC program, 1990-94; team mem. Tech-Prep. Consortium, No. Va. C.C., Woodbridge, 1992-94. Mem. Dale City Civic Assn., Woodbridge; elder, sec. 1st United Presbyn. Ch., Woodbridge, 1972—. Recipient Professionalism award Tchr. Recognition Com./Gar-Field, 1993. Mem. NEA, AAUW, Va. Edn. Assn., Va. Bus. Edn. Assn., Prince William Edn. Assn. (bldg. rep.). Avocations: reading, music, dancing. Home: 14415 Fairview Ln Woodbridge VA 22193

ROSE, MARK ALLEN, humanities educator; b. N.Y.C., Aug. 4, 1939; s. Sydney Aaron and Rose (Shapiro) R.; divorced; 1 son, Edward Gordon. A.B. summa cum laude, Princeton, 1961; B.Litt., Merton Coll., Oxford (Eng.) U., 1963; Ph.D., Harvard, 1967. From instr. to assoc. prof. English Yale, 1967-74; prof. English U. Ill., Urbana, 1974-77; prof. English U. Calif., Santa Barbara, 1977—, chmn. English dept., 1987-89; dir. U. Calif. Humanities Rsch. Inst., 1989-94. Author: Heroic Love, 1968, (fiction) Golding's Tale, 1972, Shakespearean Design, 1972, Spenser's Art, 1975, Alien Encounters, 1981, Authors and Owners, 1993; editor: Twentieth Century Views of Science Fiction, 1976, Twentieth Century Interpretations of Antony and Cleopatra, 1977, (with Slusser and Guffey) Bridges to Science Fiction, 1980, Shakespeare's Early Tragedies, 1994. Woodrow Wilson fellow, 1961, Henry fellow, 1961-62, Dexter fellow, 1966, Morse fellow, 1970-71, NEH fellow, 1979-80, 90-91. Mem. MLA, Renaissance Soc. Am., Shakespeare Soc. Am., Phi Beta Kappa. Home: 1135 Oriole Rd Montecito CA 93108-2438

ROSE, MASON H., IV, psychoanalyst; b. Charlevoix, Mich., July 4, 1915; s. Mason III and Catharine (DIebel) R.; m. Marlene Alexander,

1990. Student, Philips Exeter, 1932, U. Fla., 1933, Duke U., 1934, U. So. Calif., 1935; B.A., Inst. Religious Sci., 1939; MS, Calif. Inst. Advanced Studies, 1943, PhD, 1946; LL.D. (hon.), Asso. Univs., Hong Kong, 1959. Tennis profl. The Inn, Charlevoix, 1932-35; lectr. Inst. Religious Sci., 1937-43; pvt. practice psychoanalysis Los Angeles, 1941—; exec. dir. Nat. Found. Psychol. Research, 1940-60; psychol. cons. Med. Found. Am., 1948-62; leader Humanist Ch. of Religious Sci., 1957—; v.p., dean undergrad. sch. Calif. Inst. Advanced Study, 1959-65; chancellor Pacific Inst. Advanced Studies, 1965—; pres. Mason Rose & Assocs.; chmn. Gt. Books of Modern World, 1959—; exec dir. Olympic League Am., 1967—; bd. dirs. Ctr. Organic Ecology, 1968—, Everywoman's Village, 1960-70, Disease Prevention and Life Extension Ctr.; cons. World Ecology Corp., 1969—, World Environ. Systems, 1970—. Author: You and Your Personality, 1944, Community Plan for the Returning Serviceman, 1945, Sex Education from Birth to Maturity, 1948, Creative Education, 1953, Humanism as Religion, 1959, The Nutra-Bio-Zyme Soil Management System, 1969, The Nutra-Bio-Zyme Manutrol System, 1970, Bio-N-Gest Sewage Treatment and Water Reclamation System, 1970, Bio-N-Gest Wast Recycling System, 1970, Bio-Dynamics, 1970, The Island Tribe, 1971, New Hopes for the Emotionally Disturbed Child, 1974, 2d edit., 1977, Humanics Health System, 1975, Medical Survey of Nutrition for Pregnancy and Lactation, 1976, How to Provide Optimum Nutrition for You and Your Child, 1978, Suntanning, The World's Most Dangerous Sport, 1979, How to Scare Your Teenager Straight, 1980, Radiant Living, 1986, Multimodal System for the Management of Pain and Stress, 1987, Glasscrete System of Construction, 1987, Macho Manifesto, How to Avoid Rape, 1991, 2nd edit., 1994, Glamorous Hollywood- Fabulous Hollywood, 1994; syndicated newspaper column You and Your Child, 1950-54; TV programs, 1951-52. Mem. AAAS, NAACP, ACLU, Fedn. Am. Scientists, Soc. Social Responsibility in Sci., Aircraft Owners and Pilots Assn., Helms Athletic Found. (life), So. Calif. Olympic Games Com., Philips Exeter Acad. Alumni Assn., PEN, So. Calif. Publicists, Trojan Football Alumni, Athletic Club (L.A.), Press Club (L.A., adv. bd. 1952-75). During forty years of clinical psychoanalysis my constant preoccupation has been to develop a wholistic treatment individualized to the human person. This has resulted in the concept of human ecology which utilizes biopsyen, i.e. biological-psychological-environmental therapy.

ROSE, MERRILL, public relations counselor; b. Beaufort, N.C., Apr. 20, 1955; d. Robert Lloyd Rose and Betty Lou (Merrill) Ellis. Student, U. N.C., 1977. Reporter, editor Consumer News, Washington, 1978-79; v.p. Fraser/Assocs., Washington, 1979-82; sr. assoc. Porter/Novelli, Washington, 1982-85, v.p., 1985-87; sr. v.p., food practice leader Porter/Novelli, N.Y.C., 1989-91, exec. v.p., 1990—; gen. mgr. Chgo. Porter/Novelli, 1991—. Bd. dirs. CARE, 1991—; bd. visitors U. N.C. Sch. Journalism, Chapel Hill, 1992—; bd. dirs. Friends of Prentiss affiliate Northwestern Meml. Hosp., 1993—; mem. accrediting com. Accrediting Coun. for Edn. in Journalism and Comm., 1994—. Mem. Am. Inst. of Wine and Food, Pub. Rels. Soc. Am. Office: Porter/Novelli 303 E Wacker Dr 12th Fl Chicago IL 60601

ROSE, MICHAEL DAVID, hotel corporation executive; b. Akron, Ohio, Mar. 2, 1942; s. William H. and Annabel L. (Kennedy) R.; children: Matthew Derek Franco, Gabrielle Elaine Franco, Morgan Douglas. B.B.A., U. Cin., 1963; LL.B., Harvard U., 1966. Bar: Ohio 1966. Lectr. U. Cin., 1966-67; atty. firm Strauss, Troy & Ruehlmann, Cin., 1966-72; exec. v.p. Winegardner Internat., Cin., 1972-74; v.p. hotel group Holiday Inns, Inc., Memphis, 1974-76, pres. hotel group, 1976-78, corp. exec. v.p., 1978-79, pres., from 1979, chief exec. officer, 1981—, chmn. bd. dir., 1984—; chmn., CEO Holiday Corp., Promus Co. Inc., 1990—; dir. First Tenn. Nat. Corp., Gen. Mills, Inc., Ashland Oil, Inc. Bd. dirs. Memphis Arts Coun., from 1979; mem. Future Memphis, from 1979; mem. bd. advisors U. Cin., from 1979; hon. chmn. bd. trustees Jr. Achievement, Memphis. Mem. Ohio Bar Assn., Young Pres.' Orgn. Office: Embassy Stes Inc 1023 Cherry Rd Memphis TN 38117-5423*

ROSE, MICHAEL DEAN, lawyer, educator; b. Johnstown, Pa., Oct. 22, 1937; s. Theodore Earl and Geraldine Ethel (Boyer) R.; m. Veda Sue Garber, June 27, 1959; children: Christopher John, Susan Elizabeth. BA, Ohio Wesleyan U., 1959; JD, Case Western Res. U., 1963; LLM, Columbia U., 1967. Bar: Ohio 1963. Assoc. firm Porter, Stanley, Treffinger & Platt, Columbus, Ohio, 1963-66; asst. prof. law Ohio State U., Columbus, 1967-69, assoc. prof., 1969-72, prof., 1972—, Lawrence D. Stanley prof. law, 1987—; staff asst. to chief counsel IRS, Washington, 1970-71. Author: (with Leo J. Raskind) Advanced Federal Income Taxation: Corporate Transactions, 1978, (with Joseph S. Platt) A Federal Taxation Primer, 1973, Hornbook on Federal Income Taxation, 3d edit., 1988; editor Selected Federal Taxation Statutes and Regulations, 1973—. Trustee Ohio CLE Inst. Fellow Am. Coll. Trust and Estate Counsel; mem. Am. Law Inst. Home: 1327 Friar Ln Columbus OH 43221-1527 Office: Ohio State U 55 W 12th Ave Columbus OH 43210-1391

ROSE, MICHAEL THOMAS, state legislator, lawyer; b. Charleston, S.C., Oct. 13, 1947; s. Artman Alvin Rose and Lynnette Marguerite (Davis) Pullen; m. Vivian Osborn, May 25, 1985. BS, USAF Acad., 1969; JD, NYU, 1973; MBA, Harvard U., 1981. Bar: Calif., Colo., Minn., Pa., S.C., U.S. Supreme Ct. Atty. Robins, Davis & Lyons, St. Paul, 1977-79; exec. dir. Farmers Assistance Relief Mission Inc., Summerville, S.C., 1986—; mem. S.C. Senate, 1988—; vice chmn. Rep. Forum, 1989-91; S.C. chmn. Am. Legis. Exch. Coun., 1990-91. Editor NYU Law Rev., 1971-73; contbr. articles to profl. jours. Founder Save the Yorktown, Inc.; founder, dir. Adopt-A-Cow Program; chmn. Dorchester County Legis. Delegation, 1989-90, 94—; active Bethany United Meth. Ch.; project dir. Entrepreneurship Ctr. U. Charleston. Capt. USAF, 1969-74. Decorated Order of Palmetto, Gov. S.C.; named Outstanding State Legislator, Am. Legis. Exchange Coun., 1990. Mem. Summerville Noon Lions Club, Goose Creek Rotary Club, Summerville Lodge, Elks. Avocations: travel, sports, geneology. Home: 409 Central Ave Summerville SC 29483 Office: Rose Law Firm 500 Oakbrook Ln Ste D Summerville SC 29485

ROSE, MICHEL, construction materials company executive. Pres., CEO Lafarge Corp., Reston, Va., 1992—. Office: Lafarge Corp 11130 Sunrise Valley Dr Ste 30 Reston VA 22091-4329

ROSE, MILTON CURTISS, lawyer; b. Cleve., June 5, 1904; s. Benjamin Holly and Evelyn (Curtiss) R.; m. Emily White Mason, Sept. 6, 1930; children: Stephen Curtiss, Mason Curtiss, Jonathan Holly. Grad., Phillips Exeter Acad., 1923; A.B., Williams Coll., 1927; LL.B., Harvard, 1930. Bar: N.Y. bar 1932. Asso. Baldwin, Hutchins & Todd, N.Y.C., 1930-38; partner firm Mudge, Rose, Guthrie Alexander & Ferdon (and predecessor firms), N.Y.C., 1938—. Bd. dirs. Royal Soc. Medicine Found., Gustavus and Louise Pfeiffer Research Found.; life trustee Pfeiffer Coll.; trustee Shaker Community, Inc.; bd. overseers emeritus Simon's Rock; bd. dirs., v.p., sec. Mario Negri Inst. Found. Mem. ABA, N.Y. State Bar Assn., Assn. of Bar of City of N.Y., N.Y. County Lawyers Assn., Century Assn. (N.Y.C.), Grolier Club (N.Y.C.), University Club (N.Y.C.). Presbyterian. Home: PO Box 427 Great Barrington MA 01230-0427 Office: 180 Maiden Ln New York NY 10038-4925

ROSE, NOEL RICHARD, immunologist, microbiologist, educator; b. Stamford, Conn., Dec. 3, 1927; s. Samuel Allison and Helen (Richard) R.; m. Deborah S. Harber, June 14, 1951; children: Alison, David, Bethany, Jonathan. BS, Yale U., 1948; MA, U. Pa., 1949, PhD, 1951; MD, SUNY, Buffalo, 1964; MD (hon.), U. Cagliari, Italy, 1990; ScD (hon.), U. Sassari, Italy, 1992. From instr. to prof. microbiology SUNY Sch. Medicine, Buffalo, 1951-73; dir. Center for Immunology SUNY Sch. Medicine, 1970-73, dir. Erie County Labs., 1964-70; dir. WHO Collaborating Center for Autoimmune Disorders, 1968—; prof. immunology and microbiology, chmn. dept. immunology and microbiology Wayne State U. Sch. Medicine, 1973—82; prof. chmn. dept. immunology and infectious diseases Johns Hopkins U. Sch. Hygiene and Pub. Health, Balt., 1982-93, prof. medicine and environ. health scis., 1982—; prof. molecular microbiology and immunology, 1993—; prof. pathology, dir. immunology Johns Hopkins U. Sch. Medicine, 1994—; cons. in field. Editor: (with others) International Convocation on Immunology, 1969, Methods in Immunodiagnosis, 1973, 3d rev. edit., 1986, The Autoimmune Diseases, 1986, 2d edit., 1992, Microbiology, Basic Principles and Clinical Applications, 1983 Principles of Immunology, 1973, 2d rev. edit., 1979, Specific Receptors of Antibodies, Antigens and

Cells, 1973, Manual of Clinical Laboratory Immunology, 1976, 2d rev. edit., 1980, 4d edit. 1992, Genetic Control of Autoimmune Disease, 1978, Recent Advances in Clinical Immunology, 1983, Clinical Immunotoxicology, 1992; editor in chief Clin. Immunology and Immunopathology, 1988—; contbr. articles to profl. jours. Recipient award Sigma Xi, 1952, award Alpha Omega Alpha, 1976, Lamp award, 1975, Faculty Recognition award Wayne State U. Bd. Govs., 1979, Pres.'s award for excellence in teaching, 1979, Disting. Service award Wayne State U. Sch. Medicine, 1982, U. Pisa medal, 1986; named to Acad. Scholars Wayne State U., 1981; Josiah Macy fellow, 1979. Fellow Am. Public Health Assn.; Am. Acad. Allergy and Immunology, Am. Acad. Microbiology, mem. Acad. Clin. Lab. Physicians and Scientists, AAAS, Am. Assn. Immunologists, Am. Soc. Investigative Pathology, Am. Soc. Clin. Pathologists, Am. Soc. Microbiology (Abbott Lab. Clinical and Diagnostic Immunology award 1993), Brit. Soc. Immunology, Coll. Am. Pathologists, Société Française d'Immunologie, Can. Soc. Immunology, Soc. Exptl. Biology and Medicine Council, Clinical Immunology Soc. (sec., treas., pres. 1993), Sigma Xi (pres. Johns Hopkins U. chpt. 1988), Alpha Omega Alpha, Delta Omega. Office: Johns Hopkins U Sch H-PH Dept Molecular Micro-Immun 615 N Wolfe St Baltimore MD 21205-2103

ROSE, PAUL EDWARD, publishing company executive; b. Spokane, Wash., Apr. 27, 1947; s. Albert Edward and Karen (Murray) R.; m. Karen Pearl Rose, Aug. 23, 1971; children: Aaron, Alicia. BS, Brigham Young U., 1970, M in Acctg., 1971. CPA, N.Y., Ill. Auditor Ernst & Whinney, N.Y.C., 1971-75; budget mgr. Dun & Bradstreet, N.Y.C., 1975-77; contr., dir. circulation sales Offcl. Airline Guides, Oak Brook, Ill., 1977-82; fin. contr. John Morrell & Co., Northfield, Ill., 1982-83; v.p. fin. Standard Rate and Data Svc., Wilmette, Ill., 1983-85; v.p. Macmillan Directory Div., Wilmette, 1985-87, exec. v.p., 1987-89, pres. Nat. Register Pub. Co., 1989-91; exec. v.p., Directory Div. Reed Reference Pub., Wilmette, 1991; v.p. Landmark Communications, Inc., Norfolk, Va., 1992—; pres. Promotion Info. Mgmt., Chgo., 1992—. Recipient Outstanding Pianist award Wash. State Music Tchrs. Assn., 1968. Mem. AICPA. Office: Landmark Communications Inc 150 W Brambleton Ave Norfolk VA 23510-2018

ROSE, PETER EDWARD, former professional baseball player and manager; b. Cin., Apr. 14, 1941; s. Harry Rose; m. Karolyn Ann Englehardt (div.); children: Fawn, Peter; m. Carol Woliung, Apr. 1984; children: Cara, Tyler. Player Cin. Reds, 1963-78, player mgr., 1984-87, mgr., 1987-89; player Phila. Phillies, 1979-83, Montreal Expos, 1984; host weekly radio show Pete Rose on Baseball Sta. WCKY, Cin., 1992; now host syndicated show Talk Sports with Pete Rose Sta. WGTO-AM, Orlando, Fla. Author: (with Bob Hertzel) Charlie Hustle, 1975, Winning Baseball, 1976, (with Peter Golenback) Pete Rose on Hitting, 1985, (with Roger Kahn) Pete Rose: My Story, 1989. Named Nat. League Rookie of Yr., 1963, Most Valuable Player, 1973, Most Valuable Player World Series, 1975, Nat. League Player of Yr. The Sporting News, 1968, Ball Player of Decade, 1979; named to Nat. League All-Star Team, 1965, 67-71, 73-79, 80-81. Second player in baseball history to exceed 4000 hits, all time leader in hits. Office: Sta WGTO-AM 821 Marshall Farms Rd Ocoee FL 34761-3316 also: care Sta KCKY-AM 219 Mcfarland St Cincinnati OH 45202-2696*

ROSE, PETER ISAAC, sociologist, writer; b. Rochester, N.Y., Sept. 5, 1933; s. Aaron E. and Lillian (Feld) R.; m. Hedwig Hella Cohen, Mar. 25, 1956; children: Elisabeth Anne, Daniel Eric. AB, Syracuse U., 1954; MA, Cornell U., 1957, PhD, 1959. Instr. Goucher Coll., 1958-60; mem. faculty Smith Coll., Northampton, Mass., 1960—; prof., 1967—; chmn. dept. sociology and anthropology Smith Coll., 1967-74, 79-80, Sophia Smith prof., 1973—; dir. Am. Studies Diploma program, 1975—; mem. grad. faculty U. Mass., 1961—; Fulbright prof. U. Leicester, Eng., 1964-65, Kyoto (Japan) Am. Studies Inst., Flinders U., Australia, 1970; vis. prof. Wesleyan U., Middletown, Conn., 1966-67, U. Colo., 1968, Yale U., 1970, Clark U., 1970-71; vis. scholar Harvard U., 1983, 84-85, vis. prof., spring 1984; vis. scholar Chinese Acad. Social Sci., Beijing, 1986; resident scholar Rockefeller Study Ctr., Bellagio, Italy, summer 1987. Author: They and We, 1964, 4th edit., 1990, The Subject is Race, 1968, Strangers in their Midst, 1977, Mainstream and Margins, 1983; co-author: Sociology, 1977, 2d edit., 1982, Understanding Society, 1978, 3rd edit., 1988; editor: The Study of Society, 1967, 4th edit., 1977, The Ghetto and Beyond, 1969, Americans From Africa, 1970, Nation of Nations, 1972, reissued, 1981, Seeing Ourselves, 1972, rev. edit., 1975, Socialization and the Life Cycle, 1979; Working with Refugees, 1986, Interminority Relations in U.S., 1993; co-editor: Through Different Eyes, 1973. Mem. Am. Sociol. Assn. (mem. coun. 1974-77), Mass. Sociol. Assn. (pres. 1967-68), Soc. Study of Social Problems (v.p. 1968-69), Ea. Sociol. Soc. (v.p. 1970-71, pres. 1991-92). Home: 66 Paradise Rd Northampton MA 01060-2907

ROSE, PHYLLIS, English language professional, author; b. N.Y.C., Oct. 26, 1942; d. Eli and Minnie (Selesko) Davidoff; m. Mark Rose, (div. 1975); 1 son, Ted.; m. Laurent de Brunhoff, 1990. BA summa cum laude, Radcliffe Coll., 1964; M.A., Yale U., 1965; Ph.D., Harvard U., 1970. Teaching fellow Harvard U., Cambridge, Mass., 1966-67; acting instr. Yale U., New Haven, 1969; asst. prof. Wesleyan U., Middletown, Conn., 1969-76, assoc. prof., 1976-81, prof. English, 1981—; vis. prof. U. Calif., Berkeley, 1981-82; chmn. fiction jury Nat. Book Awards, 1993; bd. dirs. Wesleyan Writers Conf. Key West Literary Seminar. Author: Woman of Letters: A Life of Virginia Woolf, 1978, Parallel Lives: Five Victorian Marriages, 1983, Writing of Women, 1985, Jazz Cleopatra: Josephine Baker in Her Time, 1989, Never Say Goodbye: Essays, 1991; editor: The Norton Book of Women's Lives, 1993; book reviewer N.Y. Times Book Rev., The Atlantic; essayist. Nat. Endowment for Humanities fellow, 1973-74; Rockefeller Found. fellow, 1984-85; Guggenheim fellow, 1985. Mem. PEN, Nat. Book Critics Circle, Authors Guild. Home: 74 Wyllys Ave Middletown CT 06457-3243 Office: Wesleyan U Dept English Middletown CT 06457

ROSE, REGINALD, television writer, producer; b. N.Y.C., Dec. 10, 1920; s. William and Alice (Obendorfer) R.; children: Jonathan, Richard, Andrew and Steven (twins); m. Ellen McLaughlin, July 6, 1963; children—Thomas, Christopher. Student, Coll. City N.Y., 1937-38. pres. Defender Prodn., Inc., 1961—. Author TV plays, 1951—, including, Twelve Angry Men, 1954, The Sacco Vanzetti Story, 1959, The Defenders, 1961-65, Escape From Sobibor, 1987; film scripts include Crime in the Streets, 1956, Twelve Angry Men, 1957, Baxter!, 1973, Somebody Killed Her Husband, 1978, The Wild Geese, 1978, The Sea Wolves, 1980, Whose Life Is It Anyway?, 1981; plays include Black Monday, 1962, Twelve Angry Men, 1958, The Porcelain Year, 1965; books include Six TV Plays, 1956, The Thomas Book, 1972. Pres. Reginald Rose Found., 1963—. Served to 1st lt. AUS, 1942-46. Recipient Emmy awards, 1954, 62, 63; numerous others including Laurel award Writers Guild Am., 1987. Address: 20 Wedgewood Rd Westport CT 06880

ROSE, RICHARD LOOMIS, lawyer; b. Long Branch, N.J., Oct. 21, 1936; s. Charles Frederick Perrott and Jane Mary (Crotta) R.; m. Marian Frances Irons, Apr. 1, 1960; children: Linda, Cynthia, Bonnie. BA, Cornell U., 1958; JD, Washington and Lee U., 1963. Bar: N.Y. 1963, Conn. 1965, U.S. Dist. Ct. (so. dist.) N.Y. 1964, U.S. Dist. Ct. Conn. 1965, U.S. Ct. Appeals (2d cir.) 1965, U.S. Supreme Ct. 1970. Assoc. Cummings & Lockwood, Stamford, Conn., 1965-71; ptnr. Cummings & Lockwood, Stamford, 1971-91, Kleban & Samor, P.C., Southport, 1991-93; of counsel Whitman Breed Abbott & Morgan, Greenwich, Conn., 1993—; sec., bd. dirs. Index Corp., Laing Constrn. Svcs.; bd. dirs. TUV Rhineland N.Am. Inc.; v.p., bd. dirs. OCE Credit Corp.; mem. Adv. Com. to Conn. Banking Commr. on Conn. Securities Laws, 1982—; dir. Conn. World Trade Assn. Editor: Washington and Lee Law Rev. Chmn. Fgn. Trade Zone Com. to Mayor of City of Bridgeport, Conn., 1988-90; mem. fgn. trade awareness com. S.W. Area Industry and Commerce Assn., Task Force, 1987-88. 1st lt. U.S. Army, 1958-60, Korea. Mem. ABA, Conn. Bar Assn. (exec. com. banking sect.), Internat. Bar Assn., New Canaan Country Club, Campfire Club Am. (bd. govs.) Phi Delta Phi, Omicron Delta Kappa, Phi Beta Theta. Republican. Office: Whitman Breed Abbott & Morgan 2 Greenwich Plz Greenwich CT 06830-6353

ROSE, ROBERT CARLISLE, banker; b. Gutheria, Okla., Aug. 14, 1917; s. Warren Glenn and Elizabeth Aileen (Landenberger) R.; m. Maejeanne Harker, June 17, 1939; children—Sharon Sue, Barbara Ann. Student public schs.; diploma, Sch. Banking, U. Wis., 1962. With Am. Nat. Bank,

Vincennes, Ind., 1935—; chmn. bd. dirs. Am. Nat. Bank, 1975—, also dir. Bd. dirs. Vincennes Community Sch. Corp.; sec. Harmony Soc., Vincennes. Served with USNR, World War II. Mem. Ind. Bankers Assn., Independent Bankers Assn. (dir.), Am. Legion, Vincennes C. of C. (dir.). Democrat. Baptist. Club: Elks. Office: Am Nat Bank 302 Main St Vincennes IN 47591-1236

ROSE, ROBERT E(DGAR), state supreme court justice; b. Orange, N.J., Oct. 7, 1939. B.A. Juniata Coll., Huntingdon, Pa., 1961; LL.B., NYU, 1964. Bar: Nev. 1965. Dist. atty. Washoe County, 1971-75; lt. gov. State of Nev., 1975-79; judge Nev. Dist. Ct., 8th Jud. Dist., Las Vegas, 1986-88; justice Nev. Supreme Ct., Carson City, 1989—, chief justice, 1993—. Office: Nev Supreme Ct 201 S Carson St Carson City NV 89710

ROSE, ROBERT GORDON, lawyer; b. Newark, June 25, 1943; s. Harry and Ann Shirley (Gordon) R.; m. Ellen Nadley Berkowitz, July 2, 1966; children: Lisa Pauline, Michael Allan. BA, SUNY, Buffalo, 1965; MA, Columbia U., 1969; JD, Emory U., 1974. Bar: NJ. 1974, U.S. Dist. Ct. N.J. 1974, U.S. Ct. Appeals (3rd cir.) 1974, U.S. Ct. Appeals (2nd cir.) 1975. Law clk. to Hon. John J. Gibbons U.S. Ct. Appeals (3rd cir.), Newark, 1974-75; assoc. Pitney, Hardin, Kipp & Szuch, Morristown, N.J., 1975-80, ptnr., 1980—. Contbr. articles to profl. jours. Mem. ABA, N.J. Bar Assn., Morris County Bar Assn. (trustee 1989-90). Avocations: travel, philately. Office: Pitney Hardin Kipp & Szuch Pk Ave at Morris County PO Box 1945 Morristown NJ 07962-1945

ROSE, ROBERT JOHN, bishop; b. Grand Rapids, Mich., Feb. 28, 1930; s. Urban H. and Maida A. (Glerum) R. Student, St. Joseph Sem., 1944-50; B.A., Seminaire de Philosophie, Montreal, Que., Can., 1952; S.T.L., Pontifical Urban U., Rome, 1956; M.A., U. Mich., 1962. Ordained priest Roman Catholic Ch., 1955; dean St. Joseph Sem., Grand Rapids, 1966-69; dir. Christopher House, Grand Rapids, 1969-71; rector St. John's Sem., Plymouth, Mich., 1971-77; pastor Sacred Heart Parish, Muskegon Heights, Mich., 1977-81; bishop Diocese of Gaylord, Mich., 1981-89, Diocese of Grand Rapids, Mich., 1989—. Mem. Nat. Conf. Cath. Bishops. *

ROSE, ROBERT LAWRENCE, financial services company executive; b. N.Y.C., Mar. 10, 1945; s. Martin and Helen (Diamond) R.; m. Andrea Joan Hoffman, Dec. 27, 1964 (div. June 1972); 1 child, Dawn; m. Julia Frances Knipl, Jan. 2, 1974 (div. Mar. 1991; children—Justin, Adam, Andrew. BS, Mich. State U., 1966; JD, U. Mich., 1969; LLM in Taxation, NYU, 1978. Bar: N.Y., Conn., Calif. Assoc. Kindel & Anderson, 1969-72; owner, mgr. Carol's Restaurant, N.Y.C., 1972-74; assoc. gen. counsel Equitable Life Ins. Co., N.Y.C., 1974-77; tax counsel Conn. Gen. Life Ins. Co., Bloomfield, 1977-80, assoc. gen. counsel, 1980-82; chief counsel employee benefits and fin. services CIGNA Corp., Bloomfield, 1982-84, sr. v.p., chief counsel investment group, 1984-89; v.p. corp. acctg. and planning CIGNA Corp., Phila., 1989—. Author: Group Insurance Tax, 1980, Annual Meeting-Annuity Taxation, 1983, Tax Shelters, 1984; editor U. Mich. Law Rev., 1968-69, Duke U. Law Jour., 1978. Mem. Leadership Greater Hartford, 1984, Am. Leadership Forum, 1986. Mem. Am. Council Life Ins. (fin. regulatory policy subcom.), U. Conn. Sch. of Law Ins. Inst. (chmn.), Assn. Life Ins. Counsel, Calif. Bar Assn., Conn. Bar Assn., N.Y. Bar Assn. Avocations: skiing, tennis, travel. Home: 735 S 2nd St Philadelphia PA 19147-3424 Office: CIGNA Corp 1 Liberty Pl PO Box 7716 1650 Market St Philadelphia PA 19103

ROSE, ROBERT MICHAEL, materials science and engineering educator; b. N.Y.C., Apr. 15, 1937; s. Lawrence Lapidus and Lillian (Rosen) R.; m. Martha Gibbs, Oct. 15, 1961; children: Cynthia J., James L., Joshua S. S.B., MIT, 1958, Sc.D., 1961. Registered profl. engr., Mass. Asst. prof. materials sci. and engring MIT, Cambridge, 1961-66, assoc. prof., 1966-72, prof., 1972—; dir. MIT Concourse program, 1988—; prof. health scis. and tech. Harvard Med. Sch.- MIT, 1978-90; dir. Cryoelectro Assocs., Wenham, Mass., 1978-90; mem. Mass. Bd. Registration of Profl. Engrs. and Land Surveyors, 1991-93; bd. dirs. Data Tech., Woburn, Mass.; adj. prof. Tufts U. Sch. Vet. Medicine. Author: Structure and Properties of Materials, 1964, Practical Biomechanics for the Orthopedic Surgeon, 1979, 92, The Chicken from Minsk, 1995. Recipient Kappa Delta prize Am. Acad. Orthopedic Surgeons, 1973. Mem. Am. Soc. Metals (vice chmn. 1971-72, Bradley Stoughton prize, chmn. 1972-73), Metal Soc. AIME, Dolphin Yacht Club (Marblehead, Mass.), Boston Yacht Club. Jewish. Home: 18 Morgan St Wenham MA 01984-1114 Office: Room 4-132 MIT 77 Massachusetts Ave Cambridge MA 02139-4307 I would share my thoughts with you if I were satisfied with what I am. But I submit to you that anyone who is truly satisfied with his personal success doesn't understand the nature of his own achievement.

ROSE, ROBERT NEAL, brokerage house executive; b. Chgo., Feb. 27, 1951; s. James Allan Rose and Hazel (Gordon) Kaufman; m. Anna Yvette Trujillo, Aug. 23, 1981; children: David James, Michelle Elizabeth, Daniel Jonathan. BS, Georgetown U., 1973; MBA, Harvard U., 1995. Trader Salomon Bros., N.Y.C., 1974-75; regional coord. Latin Am. Merrill Lynch Govt. Securities, N.Y.C., 1975-76; dir. fed. govt. affairs Pub. Service of N.Mex., Albuquerque, 1977-78; exec. dir. Gov. Jerry Apodaca, Washington, 1979-80; expert cons. U.S. Dept. Commerce, Washington, 1980-81; asst. treas. Am. Express Internat. Bank, N.Y.C., 1981-82; sr. v.p. Refco, Inc., N.Y.C., 1982-84; v.p., mgr. Thomson McKinnon Securities, N.Y.C., 1984-88; sr. v.p. Lehman Bros., N.Y.C., 1988-92; mng. dir. Credit Agricole Futures Inc., N.Y.C., 1992-95; Bear Stearns, N.Y.C., 1995—; cons. BDM Corp., McLean, Va., 1981-88, GFTA Trendanalysen, Feusisberg, Switzerland, 1988—; Presdl. appointee J. William Fulbright Gfn. Scholarship Bd., 1993—. Mem. Dem. Nat. Bus. Coun., Washington, 1980-85, vice chmn., 1989-92; mng. trustee Dem. Nat. Com., 1989-94, mem. conv. site selection com., 1989-90; mem. arrangements com. Dem. Conv., San Francisco, 1984; exec. com. Wexner Heritage Found., N.Y.C., 1992-94; governing com. LEvitt Pavilion for the Performing Arts, Westport, Conn., 1989-90; mem. Dem. Town Com., Westport, Conn., 1990—; fin. chmn. Conn. State ctrl. Com., 1993; mem. exec. com. Am. Israel Pub. Affairs Com., 1993—; event chmn. N.Y. Presdl., Glal, N.Y.C., 1993; fin. co-chair PResdl. Transition Found., 1992; chmn. Dem. Gov.'s Assn. Presdl. Diner, 1994. Jewish. Avocations: skiing, horsemanship, sailing. Office: Bear Stearns 275 Park Ave New York NY 10167

ROSE, ROBERT R., JR., lawyer; b. Evanston, Ill., Nov. 1, 1915; s. Robert R. and Eleanor B. R.; m. Kathryn Lorraine Warner, June 14, 1948; children: Robert R. III, Cynthia Ann. JD, U. Wyo., 1941. Bar: Wyo. bar 1941. Atty. Dept. Justice, 1941; with UNRRA, China; asst. sec. Dept. Interior, 1951-52; sr. partner firm Rose, Spence, Dobos and Duncan, Casper, Wyo., 1968-75; justice Wyo. Supreme Ct., 1975-85, chief justice, 1981-82; assoc. Spence, Moriarity and Schuster, Cheyenne, Wyo., 1985—; organizer, past pres., chmn. bd. Title Guaranty Co. Wyo; faculty Nat. Coll. Criminal Def., 1977-90; founder, instr. Western Trial Advocacy Inst., 1977-93; vis. prof. trial practice U. Wyo. Coll. Law, 1985-86; Milward Simpson chair in polit. sci. U. Wyo., 1985-86; founder Western Trial Advocacy Inst., 1977—. Author legal articles. Past chmn. fund drive Casper Community Chest, Am. Cancer Soc.; mem. Wyo. Ho. of Reps., 1949-51; mayor of Casper, 1950-51; past trustee Casper Coll. Served with USAAF, World War II. Recipient Jud. Achievement award Nat. Assn. Criminal Def. Lawyers, 1983. Mem. Am. Law Inst., Order of Coif (hon.), Trial Lawyers Coll. (founder, treas. bd. dirs. 1994—), Land and Water L. Rev. (bd. advs.). Episcopalian. Address: PO Box 1006 Cheyenne WY 82003-1006

ROSE, RUBYE BLEVINS (PATSY MONTANA), singer; b. Hot Springs, Ark., Oct. 30; d. Augustus Marion and Victoria Amanda (Meeks) Blevins; m. Paul Edward Rose, July 3, 1934; children—Beverly (Mrs. Ralph Losey, Jr.), Judy Rose. Student public schs., Hope, Ark. Country and Western singer with appearances in 49 states, also U.K., The Netherlands, toured Eng. and Europe, 1972, 75, 76, 77, 78; concerts in Paris, Berlin, 1986; composer over 200 pub. songs including I Want to be a Cowboy's Sweetheart; rec. for over 200 pub. songs including Columbia, Decca, RCA, Birch, Look Records, Huddersfield, Eng., 1975, Munich Records, Holland, 1978, Cattle Records, W. Ger., 1981, Flying Fish Records, Chgo.; including million seller I Want to be a Cowboy's Sweetheart; performer: Wake Up and Smile, ABC, 1944 (Recipient Pioneer award Acad. Country and Western Music 1970, awards from Pres. Roosevelt 1937, Gov. Love of Colo. 1973, various from VFW), Library of Congress, Washington, 1987; guest on David Letterman show, NBC. Named Queen of Country and Western Music, 1973; named Ky. col., 1978, Ark. Hall of Fame, 1985, Nat. Cowgirl Hall of Fame, Hereford, Tex., 1987. Mem. VFW Aux., Screen Actor's Guild, AFTRA, ASCAP, Country Music Assn., Acad. Country and Western Music. Republican. First country and western female singer to have a million selling record. Avocations: swimming, music, meeting people. *Talent is God given, be humble. Fame is man given, be grateful. Conceit is self given, be careful.*

ROSE, SELWYN H., chemical company executive; b. N.Y.C., May 1, 1933; s. Rubin and Ruth Rosenthal; BS, CCNY, 1954; MS, Ohio State U., 1958, PhD, 1961; MBA with honors, U. Chgo., 1979; m. Helen Diana De Mov, July 25, 1957; children: Michelle, Wendy, Suzanne. Sr. rsch. chemist Pennwalt Corp., King of Prussia, Pa., 1961-65; dept. mgr. Horizons Inc., Beachwood, Ohio, 1965-72, dir. rsch., 1972-74; mgr. long range rsch. De Soto Inc., Des Plaines, Ill., 1974-79; dir. rsch., cen. rsch. lab. Borg-Warner Chems., Des Plaines, 1979-85; v.p. tech. Parker Chem. Co., Madison Heights, Mich., 1985-88; gen. mgr. rsch. and devel. Himont Inc., Wilmington, Del., 1988-91, v.p. product devel., 1991-93; pres. SHR Fin. Advisors, Wilmington, 1993—. Served as 1st lt. U.S. Army, 1954-56. Recipient IR 100 award Indsl. Rsch. mag., 1971; award Roon Found., 1979. Mem. Am. Chem. Soc., Internat. Assn. Fin. Planners. Contbr. articles to profl. jours.; patentee in field. Achievements include development of polyphosphazene polymers. Home: 1704 N Park Dr Wilmington DE 19806-2144

ROSE, SUSAN PORTER, federal commission administrator; b. Cin., Sept. 20, 1941; d. Elmer Johnson and Dorothy (Wurst) Porter; m. Jonathan Chapman Rose, Jan. 26, 1980; 1 child, Benjamin Chapman. BA, Earlham Coll., 1963; MS, Ind. State U., Terre Haute, 1970. Staff asst. Congressman Richard L. Roudebush, Washington, 1963-64; asst. dean George Sch., Bucks County, Pa., 1964-66; asst. dir. admissions Mt. Holyoke Coll., South Hadley, Mass., 1966-71; asst. dir. correspondence First Lady (Mrs. Nixon) The White House, 1971-72, appointments sec. to First Lady (Mrs. Nixon), 1972-74, to First Lady (Mrs. Ford), 1974-77; spl. asst. to asst. atty. gen. Office Improvements in Adminstrn. Justice, Washington, 1977-79, Justice Mgmt. div. U.S. Dept. Justice, 1979-81; chief of staff to Mrs. Bush, asst. to v.p. Office of V.P. of U.S. Washington, 1981-89; dep. asst. to Pres. of U.S., chief of staff to First Lady (Mrs. Bush) The White House, 1989-93; commr. U.S. Commn. Fine Arts, 1993—. Bd. dirs. Barbara Bush Found. for Family Literacy; bd. trustees Bush Presdl. Libr. and Ctr. Recipient Dist. Alumni award Earlham Coll., 1992, Ind. State U., 1991. Mem. Ind. Acad. Home: 501 Slaters Ln # 1001 Alexandria VA 22314

ROSE, T. T., bishop. Bishop of Cen. Ill., Ch. of God in Christ, Springfield.

ROSE, THOMAS ALBERT, artist, art educator; b. Washington, Oct. 15, 1942; s. Francis John and Ann Elizabeth (Voelkel) R.; m. Mary Melinda Moyer, Aug. 21, 1965; children: Sarah, Jessica. Student, U. Wis., 1960-62; B.F.A., U. Ill., 1965; M.A., U. Calif.-Berkeley, 1967; postgrad., Lund U., Sweden, 1967-68. Instr. U. Calif.-Berkeley, 1968-69, N Mex. State U., Las Cruces, 1969-72; faculty mem. U. Minn., Mpls., 1972—, prof. art, 1983—. Exhibited one-man shows: Clock Tower, N.Y.C., 1977, Truman Gallery, N.Y.C., 1977-78, Rosa Esman Gallery, N.Y.C., 1979, 81, 82, Marianne Deson Gallery, Chgo., 1984-86, Robert Thomson Gallery, Mpls., 1986, 91, 92, Deson Saunders Gallery, Chgo., 1989, Mpls. Inst. Art, 1992, Weisman Art Mus., Mpls., 1994; group shows: Walker Art Ctr., Mpls., 1974, 76, 77, Whitney Mus. Downtown, N.Y.C., 1978, Wave Hill, Bronx, N.Y., 1981, Hirshhorne Mus., Washington, 1981, Am. Ctr. in Paris, 1982, Harvard U. Sch. Architecture, 1983, The Cultural Ctr., Chgo., 1983, Hal Bromm Gallery, N.Y.C., Sheldon Mus., Lincoln, Nebr., 1989, Tampa (Fla.) Mus., 1988; represented permanent collections: Walker Art Ctr., Joslyn Mus., Omaha, Park St. Lofts, Springfield, Mass., U. Minn., Mpls., Am. Lung Assn. Target Ctr., Mpls., St. Lukes Episcopal Ch. Mpls.; set designer: Fool for Love, Cricket Theater, Mpls, 1985, Circus, Theater de Jeune Lune, 1986; project dir. Works of Art in Pub. Places for Humphrey Inst. Pub. Affairs, Mpls., 1988. Fellow Nat. Endowment for Arts, 1977, 81, Bush Found., 1979, Minn. State Arts Bd., 1979, 84, McKnight Found., 1981, McKnight Found. rsch., 1993-96, travel fellow Dayton-Jerome/Jerome, 1990, Jerome Found. Arts, 1993-94, Mellon Found., 1993; grantee Arts Bd. Opportunities, 1993; Rockefeller resident Bellagio, Italy, 1993. Home: 91 Nicollet St Minneapolis MN 55401 Office: Univ Minn 208 Studio Arts 23d Ave SE Minneapolis MN 55455

ROSE, VICTORIA LASDON, magazine publisher. Pub. YM/Young & Modern mag., N.Y.C. Office: YM/Young & Modern 685 Third Ave New York NY 10017*

ROSE, W. AXL (WILLIAM BRUCE BAILEY), singer; b. Lafayette, Ind., Feb. 6, 1962; s. L. Stephen (stepfather) and Sharon Bailey; m. Erin Everly, 1991 (div. 1992). Lead singer (band) Guns N' Roses; albums include Live Like A Suicide, 1986, Appetite For Destruction, 1987, GN'R Lies, 1988, Use Your Illusion I, 1991, Use Your Illusion II, 1991, The Spaghetti Incident?, 1993. Office: care of David Geffen Co 9130 W Sunset Blvd West Hollywood CA 90069-6197*

ROSE, WIL, foundation executive; b. Townsend, Ohio, Sept. 13, 1931; s. William Marion and Dorothy Louise (Arnold) R.; m. Anna Marie Thielmann, Mar. 4, 1952 (div. 1976); children: Sharon, Dan; m. Princess Pale Moon, Oct. 7, 1977; children: Michael, Robert, John Mark. AA in Comml. Photography, Santa Monica City Coll., 1956; LitD, Ashland U., 1982. With motion picture prodn. dept. Moody Inst. Sci., Santa Monica, Calif., 1955-57; pres., founder DATA Internat., Palo Alto, Calif., 1958-66; PlanAm. Consulting, Falls Church, Va., 1981—; pres. People to People, Inc., Kansas City, 1966-67; CEO Am. Indian Heritage Found., Falls Church, 1973—. Charitable devel. officer Nat. Heritage Found. Inc., Falls Church, Va., 1968—; pres., founder Nat. Found. Philanthropy, Mpls., 1978-80; bd. devel. officer Congrl. Awards for Youth, Fairfax, Va., 1978—; mem. presdl. task force Reagan Adminstrn., Washington, 1984. Staff sgt. USMC, 1950-54, Korea. Decorated Purple Heart; recipient Nat. Achievement award SERTOMA Internat., 1964; named Outstanding Young Man, Calif. Jaycees, 1962, Outstanding Young Man in U.S., U.S. Jaycees, 1966. Mem. Rotary Club (various com. chmn.). Avocations: writing, speaking. Office: Am Indian Heritage Foundation 6051 Arlington Blvd Falls Church VA 22044-2721

ROSE, WILLIAM ALLEN, JR., architect; b. Flushing, N.Y., Nov. 26, 1938; s. William Allen and Josephine (Grohe) R.; m. Sandra L. Latham, June 24, 1961; children: Lindsay E., Lesley A. AB cum laude, Harvard U., 1960; MArch, Columbia U., 1964. Architect Rose Beaton Corsbie Dearden & Crowe, N.Y. and White Plains, N.Y., 1964-69; ptnr. Rose Beaton & Rose, White Plains, 1969-92; prin. Einhorn Yaffee Prescott, White Plains, 1993—. Chmn. White Plains Citizens Adv. Com., 1970-73; pres. Hillair Circle Civic Assn., White Plains, 1972-76, Am. Inst. Architects Rsch. Council, 1980-81; mem. White Plains City Coun., 1974-78, pres., 1976-78; mem. White Plains Urban Renewal Agy., 1988—, White Plains Comprehensive Plan Management Group, 1994-95; bd. dirs. White Plains YMCA, 1970-73, chmn. bd. trustees, 1981-83; bd. govs. YMCA Cen. and No. Westchester, 1983—, vice-chmn., 1983-85, chmn., 1985-87; chmn. bd. mgrs. McBurney Sch., N.Y.C., 1973-76, trustee, 1981-85; trustee Rye Country Day Sch., N.Y., 1981-87; trustee Baldwin League of Ind. Schs., 1986-88; trustee Mercy Coll., 1980-91, vice-chmn., 1982-88, chmn. 1988-91; bd. dirs. Burke Rehab. Inst., 1979-84, v.p., 1981-84; chmn. Commn. Fed. Procurement of Archtl. and Engring. Svcs., 1983-84. Recipient Robert Ross McBurney medal McBurney Sch., 1956, Design award Bell Sys., 1971, 76, Honor award for Archtl. Excellence L.I. Assn., 1971, 76, award Westchester Easter Seals, 1976, Outstanding Citizenship award United Way White Plains, 1980, World Fellowship award YMCA, 1988; Upjohn fellow, 1991. Fellow AIA (pres. chpt. 1975-76, regional dir. 1978-81, nat. v.p. 1982, trustee polit. action com. 1981-82, bursar Coll. of Fellows 1986-88, vice chancellor 1989, chancellor 1990, gold medal Westchester chpt. 1983); mem. N.Y. State Assn. Architects (pres. 1977-78, trustee polit. action com. 1983-84, Del Gaudio award 1982, James W. Kideney award 1988), Columbia Archtl. Alumni Assn. (v.p. 1969), Am. Archtl. Found. (regent 1990), St. Andrew's Soc. N.Y., Rotary, New York Athletic Club (N.Y.C.), Harvard of Westchester Club, Sunningdale Golf Club (U.K.), Royal & Ancient Golf Club (St. Andrews, Scotland), John's

Island Club, Winged Foot Golf Club. Republican. Congregationalist. Office: Einhorn Yaffee Prescott 81 Main St White Plains NY 10601

ROSE, WILLIAM SHEPARD, JR., lawyer; b. Columbia, S.C., Mar. 9, 1948; s. William Shepard and Meta Cantey (Boykin) R.; m. Frances John Hobbs, Aug. 11, 1973; children: Katherine Cummings, William Shepard, III, Whitaker Boykin. BA in English, U. South, 1970; JD, U. S.C., 1973; LLM in Taxation, Georgetown U., 1976. Bar: S.C. 1973, Ohio 1977, D.C. 1974, U.S. Dist. Ct. D.C. 1976, U.S. Tax Ct. 1976, U.S. Supreme Ct. 1976, U.S. Claims Ct. 1978, U.S. Ct. Appeals (10th cir., 5th cir., 4th cir.) 1987, U.S. Ct. Appeals (3d, 6th, 7th, 8th, 9th and 11th cirs.) 1988. Trial atty. Office of Chief Counsel IRS, Washington, 1973-77; assoc. Frost & Jacobs, Cin., 1977-80, McNair & Sanford, PA, Hilton Head Island, S.C., and Washington, 1980-83, ptnr., 1983-87, 89—; asst. atty. gen., tax div. U.S. Dept. of Justice, Washington, 1987-89; chmn. and dir. Sea Pines Montessori Sch., 1983-86, Hilton Head Broadcasting, 1983-87, Hilton Head Planned Parenthood, 1985-87, MBR Corp., Adwell Corp., Links Group Inc., Hilton Head Prep. Sch., 1986-87, 89-93, dir. Boys & Girls Club of Hilton Head Island, 1992—, Hilton Head Humane Soc., 1985. Contbr. articles to profl. jours. Asst. to chmn. of bus. fund raising Beaufort County United Way, Hilton Head Island, 1984; vice-chmn. Beaufort County Rep. Party, 1991-92, 93, chmn. 1992-93, vice chmn. 1993-95; mem. Beaufort County Transportation Com., 1994-95; commr. Sea Pines Pub. Svc. Dist. Mem. ABA (past co-chmn. subcom. tax sect.), Ohio Bar Assn., D.C. Bar Assn., S.C. Bar Assn., Beaufort County Bar Assn., Hilton Head Bar Assn., Hilton Head Coun. Estate and Fin. Advisors. Republican. Episcopalian. Clubs: S.C. Yacht Club (bd. govs., exec. com., rear commodore); Hilton Head Cotillion, Ducks Unltd., Caroliniana Ball. Home: 11 Jessamine Pl Hilton Head Island SC 29928-4255 Office: Palmeto Bay Office 31 C Bow Circle PO Drawer 7787 Hilton Head Island SC 29938

ROSE, ZELDON E., public relations consultant; b. N.Y.C., Mar. 22, 1932; s. Abraham and Mildred (Amada) R.; m. Sally Ann Grossman, Dec. 20, 1953; children—Nancy S., Peter S., Linda J. BS, NYU, 1953. Wire editor Suffolk News Herald, Va., 1953; reporter, editor Asbury Park Press, N.J., 1953-58; unit publicist, asst. mag. editor ABC-TV, N.Y.C., 1958-64; account exec., v.p. Harshe-Rotman and Druck, N.Y.C., 1964-70; sr. v.p. John DiNigris Assocs., Inc., N.Y.C., 1970-71; pres. Porter, LeVay and Rose, Inc., N.Y.C., 1971-95. Pres. Congregation B'nai Sholom, West End, N.J. 1981-83. Mem. Breakwater Beach Club (N.J.), New Shrewsbury Racquet Club (Tinton Falls, N.J.). Avocations: tennis; reading. Home: 27 Hilltop Rd West Long Branch NJ 07764-1813 also: Sapphire Vlg Saint Thomas VI 00802 Office: Porter LeVay & Rose Inc 7 Penn Plz New York NY 10001

ROSE-ACKERMAN, SUSAN, law and political economy educator; b. Mineola, N.Y., Apr. 23, 1942; d. R. William and Rosalie (Gould) Rose; m. Bruce A. Ackerman, May 29, 1967; children: Sybil, John. B.A., Wellesley Coll, 1964; Ph.D., Yale U., 1970. Asst. prof. U. Pa., Phila, 1970-74; lectr. Yale U., New Haven, Conn., 1974-75, asst. prof., 1975-78, assoc. prof., 1978-82; prof. law and polit. economy Columbia U., N.Y.C., 1982-87, dir. Ctr. for Law and Econ. Studies, 1983-87; Ely prof. of law and polit. econ. Yale U., New Haven, 1987-92, Luce prof. jurisprudence (law and polit. sci.), 1992—; Mem. rev. panel Program on Regulation and Policy Analysis, NSF, Washington, 1982-84, rev. panel Am. studies program Am. Coun. Learned Socs., 1987-90; vis. prof. U. Rome, 1984. Author: (with Ackerman, Sawyer and Henderson) Uncertain Search for Environmental Quality, 1974 (Henderson prize 1982); Corruption: A Study in Political Economy, 1978; (with E. James) The Nonprofit Enterprise in Market Economies, 1986; editor: The Economics of Nonprofit Institutions, 1986; (with J. Coffee and L. Lowenstein) Knights, Raiders, and Targets: The Impact of the Hostile Takeover, 1988, Rethinking the Progressive Agenda: The Reform of the American Regulatory State, 1992, Controlling Environmental Policy: The Limits of Public Law in Germany and the United States, 1995; contbr. articles to profl. jours.; bd. editors: Jour. Law, Econs. and Orgn., 1984—, Internat. Rev. Law and Econs., 1986—, Jour. Policy Analysis and Mgmt., 1989—, Polit. Sci. Quar., 1988—. Guggenheim fellow 1991-92, Fulbright fellow, Free U. Berlin, 1991-92. Mem. Am. Law and Econs. Assn. (bd. dirs. 1993—), Am. Econ. Assn. (mem. exec. com. 1990-93), Am. Polit. Sci. Assn., Assn. Am. Law Schs.; Assn. Pub. Policy and Mgmt. (mem. policy coun. 1984-88). Democrat. Office: Yale U Law Sch 401A Yale Ave New Haven CT 06515

ROSEANNE, actress, comedienne, producer, writer; b. Salt Lake City, Nov. 3, 1952; d. Jerry and Helen Barr; m. Bill Pentland, 1974 (div.1989); children: Jessica, Jennifer, Brandi, Jake; m. Tom Arnold, 1990 (div. 1994); m. Ben Thomas, 1994. Former window dresser, cocktail waitress; prin. Full Moon & High Tide Prodns., Inc. As comic, worked in bars, church coffeehouse, Denver; produced showcase for women performers Take Back the Mike, U. Boulder (Colo.); performer The Comedy Store, L.A.; showcased on TV special Funny, 1986, also The Tonight Show; featured in HBO-TV spl. On Location: The Roseanne Barr Show, 1987 (Am. comedy award Funniest female performer in TV spl., 1987, Ace award funniest female in comedy, 1987, Ace award Best Comedy Spl. 1987); star of TV series Roseanne ABC, 1988— (U.S. Mag. 2d Ann. Readers Poll Best Actress Comedy series, 1989, Golden Globe nomination Outstanding lead actress comedy series 1989, Emmy award Outstanding Lead Actress in a Comedy Series, 1993); actress: (motion picture) She-Devil, 1989, Look Who's Talking Too (voice), 1990, Freddy's Dead, 1991, Even Cowgirls Get the Blues, 1994; TV movies: Backfield in Motion, The Woman Who Loved Elvis, 1993; author: Roseanne: My Life as a Woman, 1989, My Lives, 1994. Active various child advocate orgns. Recipient People award, People's Choice award, Golden Globe award, Am. Comedy award, Humanitas award. Office: Full Moon & High Tide Prodns 4024 Radford Ave Dressing Rms 916-917 Studio City CA 91604

ROSEBERG, CARL ANDERSSON, sculptor, educator; b. Vinton, Iowa, Sept. 26, 1916; s. Swan Bernard and Selma (Olson) R.; m. Virginia M. Gorman, Aug. 23, 1942. B.F.A., U. Iowa, 1939, postgrad., 1939-41, M.F.A., 1947; postgrad., Cranbrook Acad. Art, summers 1947-48, U. Hawaii, 1950-51, U. Va., summer 1964, Mysore (India) U., summer 1965, Tyler Sch. Art, Temple U., summer 1967. Faculty Coll. William and Mary, Williamsburg, Va., 1947—; prof. fine arts Coll. William and Mary, 1966-82, prof. emeritus, 1982—; William and Mary Heritage fellow, 1968-82; founding bd. mem. 20th Century Gallery, Williamsburg; active judge various art groups. Exhibited one man shows at Radford Coll., 1962, Roanoke Fine Art Gallery, 1962-63, Norfolk Mus., 1963, Asheville (N.C.) Gallery Art, 1963, Longwood Coll., 1966, Phi Beta Kappa Hall, William and Mary Coll., 1970; 35 yr. retrospective William and Mary Coll., 1982; retrospective Twentieth Century Gallery, 1983; exhibited in numerous group shows; represented in permanent collections at U. Iowa, Springfield (Mo.) Mus., Va. Mus. Fine Arts, Colonial Williamsburg, Chrysler Mus. Norfolk, Rockingham County Citizens Com., Longwood Coll., Farmville, Va., Thalhimer Bros., Inc., Swem Libr., Coll. William and Mary, others; designer, creator bronze meml. plaque honoring Donald W. Davis for, Millington Hall, Coll. William and Mary, 1970, bronze plaque honoring William Q. Guy, Rogers Hall, 1975; I.L. Jones, Jr., Bruton Parish Ch., 1985. designer: James City County Bicentennial Medallion, 1976; designer, creator Carter O. Lowance Bronze Medallion Marshall-Wythe Sch. Law Coll. William and Mary, 1989, Bronze Medallion honoring 300th Ann. Coll. William and Mary, 1991, Bronze Medallion honoring L. I'Anson Marshall-Wythe Sch. Law, 1991. Served to comdr. USNR, 1941-45, 50-52; ret. Res. Recipient Thomas Jefferson award, 1971, numerous art awards, Cheek award William & Mary, 1993. Fellow Internat. Inst. Arts and Letters; mem. Am. Audubon Soc., Alan Asian Soc., Fulbright Assn., Res. Officers Assn., Va. Watercolor Soc., Navy League U.S., Williamsburg German Club, Middle Plantation Club, Masons, Lambda Chi Alpha. Presbyterian. Home: 4998 Hickory Sign Post Rd Williamsburg VA 23185-2464

ROSEBERRY, DONALD G., chief administrator. Chief adminstr. So. Prairie Area Edn. Agency 15, Ottumwa, Iowa. Recipient State Finalist for Nat. Supt. of Yr. award, 1993. Office: So Prairie Area Edn Agy 15 900 Terminal Ave Ottumwa IA 52501-9413

ROSEBERY, RICHARD JAY, electronics company executive; b. Gary, Ind., May 5, 1935; s. William J. and Vivian Ethel (Schnell) R.; m. Charleen Annette Bennett, July 30, 1966; children: Susan Dare, Richard J., Jr. BS in Elec. Engring., Purdue U., 1957. Program mgr. Emerson Electric, St. Louis,

1957-62; v.p. elec. engring. and contracting group Dynalectron Corp., McClean, Va., 1962-72; v.p. corp. affairs Arthur Corp., Phoenix, 1972-74; v.p., treas., chief fin. officer Elcor Corp., Dallas, 1975-93, exec. v.p., chief fin. and adminstrv. officer, 1993—; exec. v.p. Elcor Svc. Corp.; pres., bd. dirs. Chromium Corp., Elk Corp., Am., The Ortloff Corp., Ortloff Internat. Corp., Ortloff Engrs., Ltd., Elk Corp. of Ala., Elk Corp. of Ark., Elk Corp. of Tex., Elk Corp. of Dallas, Ga. Indsl. Cos.; v.p., bd. dirs. Gory Assoc. industries, Inc. Mem. fin. com. United Way, Midland, Tex., 1985-87. Mem. Fin. Execs. Inst., Conf. Bd., Am. Mgmt. Assn., Nat. Assn. of Mfrs., U.S. C. of C., Tex. C. of C., Dallas C. of C. Home: 5703 Club Oaks Dr Dallas TX 75248-1119 Office: Elcor Corp 14643 Dallas Pky Dallas TX 75240-8800

ROSEBOROUGH, TERESA WYNN, lawyer; b. Iowa City, Iowa, Nov. 28, 1958; d. Robert Larry Wynn Jr. and Ethel (Crawford) Wynn; m. Joseph Anthony Roseborough, May 24, 1980. BA, U. Va., 1980; MEd, Boston U., 1983; JD with high honors, U. N.C., 1986. Bar: Ga. 1987, D.C. 1986 (4th cir.) 1987, U.S. Dist. Ct. (no. dist.) Ga. 1989, U.S. Ct. Appeals (11th cir.) 1989. Counselor U.S. Dept. of Army, Giebelstadt, Fed. Republic of Germany, 1980-83; law clk. to hon. judge J. Dickson Phillips U.S. Ct. Appeals (4th cir.), 1986-87; law clk. to hon. justice U.S. Supreme Ct., Washington, 1987-88; assoc. Sutherland, Asbill & Brennan, Atlanta, 1989-93; dep. asst. atty. gen. office legal counsel U.S. Dept. Justice, Washington, 1994—. Editor in chief U. N.C. Law Rev., 1985-86. Bd. dirs. Howard Schs., Atlanta, 1990—, Neighborhood Justice Ctr., 1993—; chair pro bono com. Atlanta Coun. Younger Lawyers, 1990-92, bd. dirs., 1990-93. Mem. ABA (vice chair young lawyers sect. pro bono com. 1990-92, vice chair water quality com. sect. on natural resources energy and environment 1992—). Avocations: skiing, golf. Office: US Dept Justice Office Legal Counsel 10th & Constitution Ave NW Washington DC 20530-0001

ROSEBROUGH, WALTER M., JR., manufacturing executive; b. Enid, Okla., Mar. 27, 1954; s. Walter M. and Mary Lou (Allman) R.; m. Carol Sue Waldron, Oct. 5, 1974; children: J. Benjamin, Elizabeth Erin. B in Indsl. Engring., Gen. Motors Inst., 1977; MBA, Stanford U., 1979. From coop. student to gen. foreman GM, Kansas City, Kansas and Fremont, Calif., 1972-79; staff analyst GM, Detroit, 1979-80, sr. staff analyst, 1980-81, staff asst. to group v.p., 1982; dir. strategic planning Hill-Rom, Hillenbrand Industries, Batesville, Ind., 1982-83, v.p. strategic planning, bus. devel., 1983-87; v.p. mktg. Support Systems Internat. aka SSI Med. Svcs., Inc., Charleston, S.C., 1987-88, pres., CEO, 1988-94; pres. Hill-Rom Co. Inc., Batesville, Ind., 1994—. Bd. dirs. Margaret Mary Hosp., Batesville, 1983-87, Charleston Symphony Orch., 1992-93; mem. adv. bd. Charleston So. U., 1991-92, bd. visitors, 1992—; mem. pres. adv. bd. Med. Univ. S.C. Mem. Health Industries Mfg. Assn. (chmn. health fin. com. 1988), Gen. Motors Inst. Alumni Assn. (bd. dirs. 1986-88), Sigma Chi. Methodist. Office: Hill Rom Co Inc 1069 St Rt 46E Batesville IN 47006

ROSEBUSH, JAMES SCOTT, international management and public affairs consultant, former government official; b. Flint, Mich., June 1, 1949; s. Kenneth F. and Jacqueline (Porter) R.; m. Nancy Paull, May 18, 1974; children: Claire Haisley, Lauren Culver. BA, The Principia, Elsah, Ill., 1971; MA, Boston U., 1973. Cons. Boston, 1972-76; v.p. Nat. Chamber Found., Washington, 1976-79; assoc. dir. corp. contbn. Standard Oil Co., Cleve., 1979-81; dir. Office Bus. Liaison, U.S. Dept. Commerce, Washington, 1981, spl. asst. to pres. for pvt. sector initiatives, Washington, 1981-82; dept. asst. to pres., chief staff for First Lady The White House, Washington, 1982-86; pres. James Rosebush & Co., 1986—; lectr. Georgetown U., Washington, 1977-79, George Washington U., Washington, 1977-79; presdl. appointee Nat. Mus. Svcs. Bd. Author: First Lady, Public Wife, 1987; contbr. articles to profl. jours. Mem. rev. com. United Way, Cleve., 1979; mem. community relations com. Cleve. Orch., 1979; bd. mem. Concord Art Assn., 1972. Recipient Internat. award Rotary Internat., 1970. Republican. Avocations: tennis, skiing, reading, travelling. Office: 1250 24th St NW Ste 300 Washington DC 20037-1124

ROSECRANCE, RICHARD NEWTON, political scientist, educator. BA with high honors, Swarthmore Coll., 1952; MA, Harvard U., 1954, PhD, 1957. Instr. polit. sci. UCLA, 1957-58, asst. prof., 1958-62, dir. security studies program, 1961-67, assoc. prof., 1962-67, prof. polit. sci., 1988—, assoc. dir. Ctr. Internat. and Strategic Affairs, 1988-92, assoc. dean Internat. Studies and Overseas Programs, 1992—; prof. U. Calif., Berkeley, 1967-70, dir. internat. security program, 1968-70; Walter S. Carpenter Jr. Prof. Internat. and Comparative Politics dept. govt. Cornell U., Ithaca, N.Y., 1970-88; mem. policy planning com. U.S. State Dept., Washington, 1967-68; vis. prof. dept. internat. rels. London Sch. Econs., 1973-74; rsch assoc. Internat. Inst. Strategic Studies, London, 1973-74; guest scholar Brookings Inst., 1987-88; guest Japanese Fgn. Ministry, 1976, 86; active Aspen Consortium on Arms Control, 1982, Wilson Ctr. Delegation to Japan and Korea, 1987. Author: America's Economic Resurgence: A Bold New Strategy, 1990; co-editor: Beyond Realism: Domestic Factors and Grand Strategy, 1993; contbr. articles to profl. jours. Fulbright scholar, 1954-56, Rockefeller Found. scholar, 1977; Rockefeller fellow, 1964-65, 79, Guggenheim fellow, 1973-74, Ford Found. fellow, 1977-78. Office: UCLA Dept Polit Sci Los Angeles CA 90024

ROSEGGER, GERHARD, economist, educator; b. Bruck/Mur, Austria, July 28, 1930; came to U.S., 1954, naturalized, 1961; s. Walter and Irmgard Elsa (Stark) R.; m. Clara Louise Tretter, July 17, 1954; children: Karin Andrea, Michael Lorenz, Nora Lynn, Thomas Martin. Dr.iur., U Graz, Austria, 1953; MBA, U. Pa., 1954. From instr. to asst. prof. Rutgers U. Coll. of S. Jersey, Camden, N.J., 1956-61; asst. prof. Case Inst. Tech., Cleve., 1962-65; assoc. prof. Case Western Res. U., 1965-75, prof. econs., 1975—, Frank Tracy Carlton prof. econs., 1978—; Fulbright vis. prof. U. Innsbruck, Austria, 1983-84, 91; vis. prof. U. Cin., 1988, U. Kassel, Germany, Helsinki (Finland) Sch. Econs., 1991, Vienna Tech. U., 1995; vis. rsch. scholar U. Waikato, Hamilton, N.Z. Author: The Economics of Production and Innovation, 1980, 2d edit., 1986, 3d edit., 1995, (with others) Evaluating Technological Innovations, 1980, Technological Progress and Industrial Leadership, 1984; contbr. chaps. to books, numerous articles to profl. jours. Fulbright scholar, 1950-51; recipient research and travel grants. Mem. Am. Econ. Assn., Inst. Mgmt. Scis., Sigma Xi. Mem. Christian Ch. (Disciples of Christ). Home: 15719 Chadbourne Rd Cleveland OH 44120-3333 Office: Case Western Res U Cleveland OH 44106

ROSEHART, ROBERT GEORGE, university president, chemical engineer; b. Owen Sound, Ont., Can., July 29, 1943; s. Clarence Daniel and Evaline (Sutton) R.; m. Rita June Purvis, Aug. 26, 1967; children—Robert George, William, Karen Ann. Ch.E., B.A.Sc., U. Waterloo, 1967, M.A.Sc., 1968, Ph.D., 1970. Registered chem. engr. Assoc. prof. chem. engring Lakehead U., Thunder Bay, Ont., Can., 1970-77, dean univ. schs., 1977-84, pres., 1984—; sci. counsellor Porter Royal Commn. on Electric Power Planning, 1975-77; mem. Thunder Bay Waferboard Study, Govt. Ont., 1986-87; chmn. Ont. Forest Resources Inventory Com.; govt. reviewer No. Labour Mgmt. Issues: bd. dirs. Rainy River Forest Products Ltd., Ont. Energy Corp. Contbr. articles to profl. jours. Chmn. com. on resource coms., 1985, Premiers Coun. Sci. and Tech. Grantee in field. Mem. Can. Pulp and Paper Assn., Assn. Profl. Engrs. Ont. Roman Catholic. Avocations: curling, skiing, boating. Home: 588 Riverview Dr, Thunder Bay, ON Canada P7C 1R7 Office: Lakehead U, Thunder Bay, ON Canada P7B 5E1

ROSELLE, DAVID PAUL, university administrator, mathematician; b. Vandergrift, Pa., May 30, 1939; s. William John and Esther Suzanne (Clever) R.; m. Louise Helen Dowling, June 19, 1967; children—Arthur Charles, Cynthia Dowling. BS, West Chester State Coll., 1961; PhD, Duke U., 1965; LLD, West Chester U., 1994. Asst. prof. math. U. Md., College Park, 1965-68; assoc. prof. math. La. State U., Baton Rouge, 1968-73, prof. U. State U., Blacksburg, 1974-87, dean grad. sch., 1979-81, dean research and grad. studies, 1981-83, provost, 1983-87; prof. U. Ky., 1987-90, pres., 1987-90; pres. U. Del., 1990—; chmn. commn. on rsch. Va. Poly. Inst. and State U., 1981-83, commn. on grad. studies, 1983-87; pres. COMPA, Inc., Lexington, Mass., 1986-95; bd. dirs. Bell Atlantic Del., Wilmington Trust Corp. Editor: Proc. of the First Louisiana Conf. on Combinatorics, Graph Theory and Computing, 1970, Proc. of the Second Louisiana Conf. on Combinatorics, Graph Theory and Computing, 1971; mem. editorial bd. The Bicentennial Tribute to American Mathematics, 1977; contbr. numerous research articles to profl. jours. Mem. Del. Roundtable,

1990-94, Bus./Pub. Edn. Coun. 1990—; trustee Winterthur Mus., 1991—; bd. dirs. Del. Acad. Medicine, 1991—, Med. Ctr. Del., 1991—. Named Outstanding Alumnus West Chester State Coll., 1979; Westinghouse Coop. scholar, 1957; NSF grantee, 1965-75; Teaching Excellence Cert., 1978; Digital Equipment grant, 1984; Nat. Coun. Tchrs. Math. Cert. of Appreciation, 1984; founding fellow of Inst. for Combinatorics and Its Applications, 1990; numerous invited addresses at univs. and profl. soc. meetings. Mem. Am. Math. Soc., Math. Assn. Am. (sec., fin. com., exec. com., com. on publs. 1975-84, com. on spl. funds 1985—; chmn. com. on accreditation 1985; numerous other coms.). Home: 47 Kent Way Newark DE 19711-5201 Office: U Del Hullihen Hall Newark DE 19716

ROSELLE, RICHARD DONALDSON, industrial, marine and interior designer; b. Garwood, N.J., Nov. 20, 1916; s. Ernest North and Mary Elizabeth (Donaldson) R.; m. Eunice Calpin, June 28, 1947 (div. Oct. 1981); children: Sheryn, Christina, Gail; m. Judith Marie Bishop, Nov. 13, 1982. Student, St. John's Mil. Acad., 1935, Aurora (Ill.) Coll. 1935-37, Bucknell U., 1937-39. Exec. trainee J.J. Newberry Co., N.Y.C. 1939-41, G. Fox & Co., Hartford, Conn., 1941-42; materials expeditor Pratt & Whitney Aircraft, Hartford, 1942-43; exec. trainee, indsl. engr. TWA Airline, N.Y.C. and Kansas City, 1943-47; with employee rels. staff R.H. Macy, N.Y.C., 1947-49; asst. tng. dir. J.C. Penney Co., N.Y.C., 1949-50; owner Roselle Tile Mfr., Seattle, 1950-56; sr. indsl. designer Walter Dorwin Teague Assocs., Seattle, 1956-63; owner Roselle Design Internat., Inc., Seattle, 1963—; dir. Roselle Design Tours Internat., Seattle, 1967-93; internat. bus. developer via confs., 1993—. Mem. Am. Soc. Interior Design (nat. edn. chair 1972-74), Indsl. Designers Soc. Am. (charter), Internat. Inst. Profl. Designers, Master Resources Coun. Internat. (founder, pres.), Soc. Am. Mil. Engrs., Rotary. Republican. Episcopalian. Achievements include design of airline coupon ticket form accept as transportation industry standard; white on fuselage of aircraft to accentuate graphics, standard airline office ticket counters, aircraft interiors, megayacht styling and interiors, passenger train interior and exterior graphics; packages for oysters and caviar; concrete "Flothaus" and trimaran/hydrofoil cruise ship, panelized building systems. Office: Roselle Design Internat Camelot Atelier 3854 140th Ave NE Bellevue WA 98005-1451

ROSELLE, WILLIAM CHARLES, librarian; b. Vandergrift, Pa., June 30, 1936; s. William John and Suzanne Esther (Clever) R.; m. Marsha Louise Lucas, Aug. 2, 1959; 1 child, Paul Lucas. BA, Thiel Coll., 1958; MLS, U. Pitts., 1963. Lic. profl. guide State of Mont., 1978. Mem. faculty Milton Hershey (Pa.) Sch., 1960-62; trainee Pa. State Library, 1962-63; asst. catalog librarian Pa. State U., 1963-65; engring., math. librarian U. Iowa, 1965-66, library adminstrv. asst., 1966-69, asst. dir. libraries, 1969-71; prof., dir. library U. Wis.-Milw., 1971-89; dir. univ. library system U. Pitts., 1989-90; pvt. cons. Thiensville, Wis., 1991—; chmn. Morris Fromkin Meml. Lectr. Com., 1972-89; chmn. planning task force on computing U. Wis. System, 1973-74, mem. library planning study com., 1978-79, co-chmn. library automation task force, 1983-85; chmn. computing mgmt. rev. team U. Wis.-Stout, 1976; chmn. Council for U.S. Libraries, 1981-82; library cons. Grambling (La.) State U., Viterbo Coll. LaCrosse, Wis., N.C. A&T U., Greensboro, Mt. Mary Coll., Milw., U. Ill. at Chgo., Milw. Sch. Engring., Bklyn. Coll., U. South Ala., Concordia Coll., Milw., Metrics Rsch. Corp., Cardinal Stritch Coll., Milw., N.Y. Inst. Tech., Indiana U. of Pa., Med. Coll. Wis., Wis. Luth. Coll., Milw.; participant Library Adminstrs. Devel. Program, U. Md., 1973, micrographics seminar Nat. Microfilm Assn., 1973, Mgmt. Skills Inst., Assn. Rsch. Libraries, Kansas City, Mo., 1977, Meadowbrook Symposium Midwest Library Network, 1976; mem. sect. geography and map libraries Internat. Fedn. Library Assns. and Instns., 1978-83; mem. bldg. com. Ctr. for Rsch. Libraries, 1980-82. Editorial cons. The Quest for Social Justice, 1983, Current Geographical Publications, 1978-89; contbr. articles to profl. jours. Pres. Thiensville (Wis.) Village Bd., 1987; bd. dirs. Charles Allis Art Mus., 1979-84. Served with AUS, 1958-60. Named Disting. Alumnus, Thiel Coll., 1985. Hon. fellow Am. Geog. Soc.; mem. Spl. Libraries Assn. (spl. citation 1979), ALA (life), Iowa Library Assn. (chmn. audit com. 1968-70, chmn. intellectual freedom com. 1969-70), Wis. Library Assn., Midwest Acad. Librarians Conf. (chmn. 1969-71), AAUP (treas. U. Iowa chpt. 1969-70), Coun. Wis. Libraries (chmn. 1973-74), Soc. Tympanuchus Cupido Pinnatus, Milw. Civil War Round Table, Beta Beta Beta, Beta Phi Mu, Phi Alpha Theta, Phi Kappa Phi, Phi Delta Kappa. Lutheran. Home: 324 Sunny Ln Thiensville WI 53092-1334

ROSEMAN, SAUL, biochemist, educator; b. Bklyn., Mar. 9, 1921; s. Emil and Rose (Markowitz) R.; m. Martha Ozrowitz, Sept. 9, 1941; children: Mark Alan, Dorinda Ann, Cynthia Bernice. B.S., CCNY, 1941; M.S., U. Wis., 1944, Ph.D., 1947; (hon.) M.D., U. Lund, Sweden, 1984. From instr. to asst. prof. U. Chgo., 1948-53; from asst. prof. to prof. biol. chemistry, also Rackham Arthritis Research Unit, U. Mich., 1953-65; Ralph S. O'Connor prof. biology Johns Hopkins U., Balt., 1965—; chmn. dept., 1969-73; dir. McCollum-Pratt Inst., 1969-73, chmn. dept. biology , dir., 1988-90; cons. NIH, NSF, Am. Cancer Soc., Hosp. for Sick Children, Toronto; sci. counselor Nat. Cancer Inst.; Lynch lectr. U. Notre Dame, 1989; Van Niel lectr. Stanford U., 1992. Author articles on metabolism of complex molecules containing carbohydrates and on solute transport.; former mem. editorial bd.: Biochemistry, Jour. Biol. Chemistry. Served with AUS, 1944-46. Recipient Sesquicentennial award U. Mich., 1967, T. Duckett Jones Meml. award Helen Hay Whitney Found., 1973, Rosenstiehl award Brandeis U., 1974, Internat. award Gairdner Found. award, 1981, Townsend Harris award CUNY, 1987, Spl. award 11th Internat. Symposium on Glycoconjugates, 1991, Karl Meyer award Soc. Glycobiology, 1993. Fellow Am. Acad. Microbiology; mem. Am. Soc. Biol. Chemists, Am. Soc. Cell Biology, Am. Acad. Arts and Scis., Nat. Acad. Scis., Am. Chem. Soc., Am. Soc. Microbiologists, Biochem. Soc. Japan (hon.). Office: Johns Hopkins U 34th Charles St Baltimore MD 21218

ROSEMARIN, CAREY STEPHEN, lawyer; b. Englewood, N.J., Aug. 19, 1950; s. Jack L. and Muriel Ruth (Gordon) R.; m. Joan Maxine Lafer, June 17, 1973; children: Benjamin Joseph, Meryl Ruth. BS, U. Mich., 1972; MS, Pa. State U., 1974; JD, U. Tenn., 1978. Bar: Tenn. 1978, Ill. 1982, U.S. Dist. Ct. (ea. dist.) Tenn. 1978, U.S. Dist. Ct. (no. dist.) Ill. 1982. Rsch. assoc. Union Carbide Corp., Oak Ridge Nat. Lab., 1974-80; asst. regional counsel U.S. EPA, Chgo., 1980-86; ptnr. Katten, Muchin, & Zavis, Chgo., 1986-90, Jenner & Block, Chgo., 1990—. Mem. ABA, Tenn. Bar Assn., Chgo. Bar Assn. (chmn. environ. law com. 1985-86), Environ. Law Inst. (assoc.). Avocations: licensed glider pilot, bicycling. Office: Jenner & Block 1 E Ibm Plz Chicago IL 60611-3608

ROSEMBERG, EUGENIA, physician, scientist, educator, medical research administrator; b. Buenos Aires, Argentina, Apr. 25, 1918; came to U.S., 1948, naturalized, 1956; d. Pedro and Fanny (Hestrin) R. BS, Liceo Nacional de Senoritas, Buenos Aires, 1936; MD, U. Buenos Aires, 1944. Intern Hosp. Pirovano, Buenos Aires, 1940-41; resident Hosp. Nacional de Clinicas, U. Hosp., U. Buenos Aires, 1941-44, assoc. in pediatrics, 1943-48; instr. in anatomy Hosp. Nacional de Clinicas, U. Hosp., U. Buenos Aires (Med. Sch.), 1940-46, instr. pediatrics, 1946-48; practice medicine specializing in pediatrics, 1946-48; research in endocrinology Balt., 1948-51, Worcester, Mass., 1955—; Mead Johnson fellow dept. endocrinology Johns Hopkins Med. Sch., Balt., 1948-49; vis. scientist Med. Sch., U. Montevideo, Uruguay, 1950; research fellow NIH, Bethesda, Md., 1951-53, Nat. Inst. Arthritis and Metabolic Diseases, 1951-53, Med. Research Inst. and Hosp., Oklahoma City, 1953; mem. staff Worcester Found. Exptl. Biology, Shrewsbury, Mass., 1953-62; research dir. Med. Research Inst. of Worcester, Inc., 1962—; cons. Center for Population Research, Nat. Inst. Child Health and Human Devel., NIH, 1969-70, chief contraceptive devel. br., 1970-71; prof. pediatrics U. Md. Med. Sch., Balt., 1970-73; prof. medicine U. Mass. Med. Sch., Worcester, 1972—; mem. staff Worcester City Hosp., 1955-85, sec. human experimentation com., 1965-83, chmn., 1984-85, dir. clin. research, 1972-85; Soc. subcom. on gonadotropins Nat. Hormone and Pituitary Program, Nat. Inst. Arthritis, Diabetes, Digestive and Kidney Diseases, 1965-69, chmn., 1969-85, mem. med. adv. bd., 1969-72, 73-85; sec. subcom. on standards endocrinology study sect., 1968. Author: Gonadotropins, 1968, (with C.A. Paulsen) The Human Testis, 1970, Gonadotropin Therapy in Female Infertility, 1973, (with C. Gual) Hypothalamic Hypophysiotropic Hormones—Physiological and Clinical Studies, 1973; Mem. editorial bd.: Giner, 1970—, Procs. 1st Ann. Meeting Am. Soc. Andrology, supplement, Vol. 8, 1976, Andrologia, 1978—, Jour. Andrology, 1979-82, Internat. Jour. Andrology, 1978—; assoc. editor: Reproduccion, 1970—, Andrologia jour, 1974-77; Contbr. articles

and book chpts. on research in endocrinology to med. texts and jours.; Translator: from Spanish Diagnosis and Treatment of Endocrine Disorders in Childhood and Adolescence (L. Wilkins). Patentee in field, U.S., Can., Europe. Fellow AAAS; mem. Am. Med. Women's Assn., Endocrine Soc. U.S. (mem. com. pub. affairs 1971, v.p. 1975-76), Soc. for Research in Biology of Reproduction, Soc. for Study of Reproduction, Am. Fertility Soc., Peru Fertility Soc. (fgn. corr.), N.Y. Acad. Scis., New Eng. Cardiovascular Soc., Am. Mass. heart assns., Argentine Endocrine Soc., Argentine Pediatric Soc., Sociedad Argentine Para El Estudio de la Esterilidad., Pan Am. Med. Women's Alliance, Am. Soc. Andrology (program chmn. 1975-76, exec. council 1976-78, chmn. publ. com. 1975-80, Disting. Andrologist award 1982), Internat. Com. for Study Andrology (exec. council 1976-79).

ROSEMONT, NORMAN, television and feature producer; b. N.Y.C., Dec. 12, 1924. Prodns. include A Tale of Two Cities, Brigadoon, Carousel, Kiss Me Kate, Kismet, Stiletto, The Man Without a Country, Miracle on 34th Street, A Tree Grows in Brooklyn, The Red Badge of Courage, The Count of Monte Cristo, The Man in the Iron Mask, The Mad Mad Mad Mad World of the Super Bowl, Captains Courageous, The Court Martial of George Armstrong Custer, Four Feathers, Les Miserables, All Quiet on the Western Front, Pleasure Palace, Little Lord Fauntleroy; TV miniseries: Master of the Game, 1984, Camille, 1985, The Secret Garden, 1987, The Tenth Man, 1988, Ironclads, 1991, Long Road Home, 1991, Shadow of a Doubt, 1991, Fergie and Andrew, 1992, Harmful Intent, 1993.

ROSEN, ALEXANDER CARL, psychologist, consultant; b. L.A., Feb. 2, 1923; s. Benjamin and Pauline (Katz) R.; m. Florence Friedman, Mar. 18, 1951 (div. Nov. 1973); children: Diane, Judith; m. Susan Margaret Gersbacher, Nov. 4, 1973; 1 child, Rebecca. AA, U. Calif., L.A., 1943; AB, U. Calif., Berkeley, 1946, PhD, 1953. Diplomate clin. psychology Am. Bd. Profl. Psychology; lic. psychologist. Psychologist Contra Costa County, Martinez, Calif., 1953-56; asst. rsch. psychologist Office Naval Rsch. and San Francisco State Coll., 1953-56, UCLA-Neuropsychiat. Inst., L.A., 1956-57; asst. prof. to prof. psychiatry and behavioral sci. UCLA Sch. Medicine, L.A., 1956-89; chief psychology UCLA Neuropsychiatric Inst., L.A. 1958-89; prof. emeritus UCLA Sch. Medicine, L.A., 1989—; pvt. practice psychology cons. L.A., 1973—; instr. San Francisco State Coll., 1955; instr. psychology Calif. Inst. Tech., Pasadena, 1969; staff assoc. Nat. Tng. Lab. Inst. Applied Behavioral Sci., 1962—; cons. tng. U.S. Veteran's Assn., Sepulveda (Calif.) Hosp., 1966—; bd. mem. L.A. Group Psychotherapy Tng. Inst., 1972-75; bd. mem., trustee Calif. Sch. Profl. Psychology, 1974-76, 78; nat. bd., regional bd. Cert. Cons. Internat. Cons. Cons. editor: Jour. Genetic Psychology and Genetic Psychology Monograph, 1984—; contbr. articles to profl. jours. Mem. gov. bd. Hillel Coun., So. Calif.; cons. San Fernando Valley Counseling Ctr., 1991-92, Pacific Ctr. for AIDS, L.A., 1991—; bd. dir. Valley Youth Symphony. Fellow APA, AAAS; mem. Calif. State Psychology Assn. (pres. 1977-78), Western Psychol. Assn. Avocations: photography, music, drama. Home: 6247 Sunnyslope Ave Van Nuys CA 91401

ROSEN, ARTHUR MARVIN, advertising executive; b. N.Y.C., Dec. 28, 1930; s. Joseph and Cornelia (Grob) R.; m. Maureen Elizabeth Reilly; children: Ellen Jessica, Deborah Lynn, Daniel Joshua. BA, Cony, 1952; MA, Yale U., 1953; postgrad., Columbia U., 1955-57. Analyst research Dancer-Fitzgerald-Sample, N.Y.C., 1955-56; supr. research Benton and Bowles, N.Y.C., 1956-61; account exec. Young and Rubicam, N.Y.C., 1961-66; v.p. account supr. Grey Advt., N.Y.C., 1966-69; pres. Met. Diagnostic, N.Y.C. 1969-73; v.p. group mgmt. Grey Advt., N.Y.C., 1973-81; exec. v.p. Sudler and Hennessey, N.Y.C., 1981-94; mktg. cons. Himmel Nutrition, Inc., 1994—, Martin Himmel, Inc., 1994—; spkr. in field. Contbr. articles to profl. jours. Pres. Temple Beth Or, Washington Twp., N.J., 1973-74; chmn. Soc. Families, Colgate U., 1983-84; served as cpl. U.S. Army, 1953-55. Republican. Jewish. Club: Yale.

ROSEN, ARYE, microwave, optoelectronics and medicine researcher; b. June 26, 1937. BSEE cum laude, Howard U., 1963; MScE, Johns Hopkins U., 1965; MSc in Physiology, Thomas Jefferson U., 1975; PhD in Elec. Engring., Drexel U., 1993. Registered profl. engr., B.C., Can. Sr. mem. tech. staff David Sarnoff Rsch. Ctr. (subs. of SRI), Princeton, N.J., 1967—; assoc. in medicine Jefferson Med. Coll., Phila., 1977—; adj. prof. elec. and computer engring. Drexel U., Phila., 1981—. Co-editor: High-Power Optically Activated Solid-State Switches, 1993, New Frontiers in Medical Device Technology, 1995; contbr. more than 150 articles to profl. jours. Recipient Microwave prize 16th European Microwave Conf., 1986. Fellow IEEE (mem. MTT-S tech. com. for light-wave tech. 1979—, mem. MTT-S tech. program com., chmn. MTT-S tech. com. on biol. effects and med. applications, mem. editorial bd., assoc. editor IEEE Jour. Light-Wave Tech., editorial bd. Transactions on Microwave Theory and Techniques, editorial bd. Microwave and Optical Tech. Letters, mem. tech. com. IEEE Internat. Conf. Microwaves in Medicine 1991, ednl. activities bd., mem.-at-large health care engring. policy com., Region One award for significant contbns. to microwave tech.by the invention and devel. of microwave balloon angioplasty, 1989), N.Y. Acad. Scis. Achievements include 45 patents in the fields of engineering and medicine, including Percutaneous Transluminal Microwave Catheter Angioplasty, Method and Apparatus for High Frequency Catheter Ablation, Catheter with Distally Located Integrated Circuit Radiation Generator, Electrical Phase Shifter Controlled by Light, Direct DC to RF Conversion by Impulse Excitation, Light Controlled Antennas, High Power Optical Switch, Radiation Protection Circuit for Protection Against Gamma Ray and Neutron Radiation. Office: David Sarnoff Rsch Ctr CN 5300 Princeton NJ 08543-5300

ROSEN, BARRY HOWARD, museum director, history educator; b. Phila., June 26, 1942; s. Robert R. and Sylvia (Chanin) R.; m. Ann Adair Gould, Feb. 14, 1970; 1 son, David Joshua. BS, Temple U., 1963, M.A., 1966; Ph.D., U.S.C., 1974. Asst. to provost U.S.C. Columbia, 1973-74, asst. to pres., 1974-77, dir. mus., univ. archivist dir. mus. mgmt. programs, 1975-82; exec. dir. Kansas City Mus., Mo., 1982-86; pres. N.J. Hist. Soc., Newark, 1986-88; pres., CEO Milw. Pub. Mus., 1988—; field reader Inst. Mus. Svcs., Washington, 1981-84. Bd. dirs., pres. Westown Assn., 1988—. Mem. Am. Assn. State and Local History, Am. Assn Mus. (accrediting com. 1982—), Assn. Sci. Mus. Dirs. (chmn. future planning com. 1990—), Natural History Museums 2000 (steering com., 1989—, Southeastern Wis. Amniotrophic Lateral Sclerosis Soc. (bd. dirs. 1990—). Home: 5043 N Lake Dr Milwaukee WI 53217-5749 Office: Milw Pub Mus 800 W Wells St Milwaukee WI 53233-1404 *Having devoted my life to education in its broadest possible definition, I feel that what success I have achieved has been through my philosophical belief that one must always pursue excellence and the highest standards of quality. Failure only occurs when one gives up this quest.*

ROSEN, BENEDICT PHILIP, engineering executive; b. Georgetown, S.C., Apr. 20, 1936; s. Sylvan Lowenthal and Erma (Levkoff) R.; m. Bernice Wekstein, Feb. 2, 1958; children: Andrew, Greg, Heidi. BSEE, MIT, 1958. Engr. Sprague Elec. Co., North Adams, Mass., 1958-61, spl. project engr., 1961-62, mgr. filter devel., 1963-71; plant mgr. Aerovox, North Adams, Mass., 1972; v.p. gen. mgr. AVX Corp., Branton, Mass., 1972-74; sr. v.p. AVX Corp., Myrtle Beach, S.C., 1975-82, exec. v.p., 1983-89, pres., 1990-92, pres., CEO, 1993—. Mem. IEEE. Republican. Jewish. Avocations: golf, travel, reading. Office: AVX Corp 17 Ave S Myrtle Beach SC 29577

ROSEN, BENJAMIN MAURICE, venture capitalist, computer company executive; b. New Orleans, Mar. 11, 1933; s. Isidore J. and Anna Vera (Leibof) R.; m. Alexandra Ebere, Sept. 29, 1967; children:—Jeffrey Mark, Eric Andrew. B.S., Calif. Inst. Tech., 1954; M.S., Stanford U., 1955; M.B.A., Columbia U., 1961. Engr. Raytheon Corp., Oxnard, Calif., 1955-56; engr. Sperry Corp., Great Neck, N.Y., 1957-59; v.p. Quantum Sci. Corp., N.Y.C., 1961-65; ptnr. Coleman & Co., N.Y.C., 1965-75; v.p. Morgan Stanley & Co., N.Y.C., 1975-80; pres. Rosen Research Inc., N.Y.C., 1980-83; ptnr. Sevin Rosen Mgmt. Co., N.Y.C., 1981—; chmn. bd., 1982—; also chmn. Compaq Computer Corp, Houston, TX; former founder dir. Lotus Devel. Corp.; mem. bd. overseers and mgrs. Meml. Sloan Kettering Cancer Ctr., N.Y.C.; mem. bd. overseers Columbia U. Grad. Sch. Bus., N.Y.C. Trustee Calif. Inst. Tech., 1985-89. Office: Sevin Rosen Mgmt Co 200 Park Ave New York NY 10166-0217 also: Compaq Computer Corp PO Box 692000 B Houston TX 77269-2000

ROSEN, BENSON, business administration educator; b. Detroit, Oct. 9, 1942; s. David and Laura R.; m. Brenda M. Leibroder, Dec. 17, 1966; children—Gregory Scott, David Loren. B.S., Wayne State U., 1964, M.A., 1968, Ph.D., 1969. Asst. prof. U. N.C., Chapel Hill, 1969-74; assoc. prof. U. N.C., 1974-80, prof. bus. adminstrn., 1980—, Hanes prof., 1992, dir. PhD program, 1995—; vis. prof. U. Minn., 1981; cons. to bus., industry, govt.; cons. EEOC. Author: Becoming Aware, 1976; Older Employees: New Roles for Valued Resources, 1985; mem. editorial rev. bd. Acad. Mgmt. Jour., 1978-84; contbr. articles to profl. jours. Bd. dirs. SHRM Found., 1994—. Recipient Young Scholars award Spencer Found., 1976, 78, Disting. Rsch. award, 1993, PhD Teaching award, 1994; NSF grantee, 1973-75; Adminstrn. on Aging grantee, 1978-80. Fellow Am. Psychol. Assn.; mem. Acad. Mgmt., Soc. Human Resource Mgmt. Office: Kenan Flagler Bus Sch U NC Chapel Hill NC 27599-3490

ROSEN, BERNARD H., chemical engineer; b. N.Y.C., Sept. 29, 1922; s. Max and Dorothy (Hildebr) R.; m. Anita Ruth Greenberg, Aug. 26, 1947; children: Jeffrey Paul, Seth Gordon, Lise Ann. B.S. in Chem. Engring., CCNY, 1943; M.S., NYU, 1947; postgrad., Harvard U., 1943-44, Okla. A&M U., 1949, Ill. Inst. Tech., 1949-50, Columbia U., 1955-56. Grad. asst. NYU, 1946-47; with Cities Service Research and Devel. Co., 1947-82; successively research chem. engr. Cities Service Research and Devel. Co., Tallant, Okla.; asso. chemist Cities Service Research and Devel. Co., East Chicago, Ind.; chem. engr. Cities Service Research and Devel. Co., Camden, N.J.; asst. v.p. Cities Service Research and Devel. Co., N.Y.C., 1947-57; mgr. products devel. Cities Service Research and Devel. Co., Cranbury, N.J., 1957-58; mgr. Cranbury Lab., 1958-65; dir. product and process research Cities Service Oil Co., 1965-71; mgr. research and planning, chems. and metals group Cities Service Co., N.Y.C., 1971-72; dir. research Cities Service Co., 1972-76; pres. Cities Service Research & Devel. Co., Cranbury, 1972-76; gen. mgr. tech. systems div. Cities Service Research & Devel. Co., Tulsa, 1976-78; gen. mgr. metal fabrication Cities Service Research & Devel. Co., Chester, N.Y., 1978-80; cons. Cities Service Research & Devel. Co., 1980-81; gen. engr. U.S. Army, Ft. Monmouth, N.J., 1982-91; cons., 1992—. Contbr. articles to profl. jours. Served as 1st lt. AUS, 1943-46; capt. Res. Mem. Sigma Xi. Patentee in field. Home: 13 Buena Vista Ave Rumson NJ 07760-1109

ROSEN, CAROL MENDES, artist; b. N.Y.C., Jan. 15, 1933; d. Bram de Sola and Mildred (Bertuch) Mendes; m. Elliot A. Rosen, June 30, 1957. BA, Hunter Coll., 1954; MA, CUNY, 1962. Tchr. art West Orange (N.J.) Pub. Schs., 1959-85; co-curator exhibit Printimaking Coun. N.J, Sommerville, 1981; exhibit curator 14 Sculptors Gallery, N.Y.C., 1988, Collection: Nat. Collection of Fine Arts, Smithsonian Instn., Newark Mus., N.J. State Mus., Bristol-Myers Squibb, AT&T. Contbr. articles to arts mags. Fellow N.J. State Coun. on Arts, 1980, 83; recipient Hudson River Mus. award, Yonkers, 1983. Jewish. Avocations: gardening, reading. Home: 10 Beavers Rd Califon NJ 07830-3433

ROSEN, CHARLES, production designer. Prodn. designer: (films) Charly, 1968, A Separate Peace, 1972, Heroes, 1977, Empire of the Ants, 1977, Big Wednesday, 1978, Invasion of the Body Snatchers, 1978, Last Embrace, 1979, The Main Event, 1979, Inside Moves, 1980, My Favorite Year, 1982, The Entity, 1983, Flashdance, 1983, The Whoopee Boys, 1986, Broadcast News, 1987, Touch & Go, 1987, My Stepmother Is an Alien, 1988, My Blue Heaven, 1990, Downtown, 1990, The Butcher's Wife, 1991, Stop! or My Mon Will Shoot, 1992, Free Willy, 1993, My Girl 2, 1993, (TV movies) City in Fear, 1981. Office: care Lawrence Mirisch The Mirisch Agency 10100 Santa Monica Blvd Ste 700 Los Angeles CA 90067*

ROSEN, CHARLES, II, lawyer; b. New Orleans, Jan. 29, 1925; s. Louis Leucht and Nita (Silverstein) R.; m. Mary Alice Waldauer (div. 1976); children: Charles III, Virginia, Jane, James Louis; m. Sandra Reed. BA, Tulane U., 1948, LLB, 1951. Bar: La. 1951. Assoc. Rosen, Kammer, Wolff, Hopkins & Burke, New Orleans, 1951-55; assoc. Jones, Walker, Waechter, Poitevent, Carrere & Denegre, New Orleans, 1955-58, ptnr., 1958-90; sole counsel Locke, Purnell, Rain, Harrell, New Orleans, 1990—; mem. exec. com., past chmn. Golf & Sports Attractions, Inc. Past trustee Touro Synagogue; hon. trustee Touro Infirmary; chmn. lawyers div. Jewish Fedn. Greater New Orleans, 1969; past chmn. lawyers div. United Fund. 1st lt. U.S. Army, 1944-46, PTO. Mem. ABA, La. Bar Assn., New Orleans Bar Assn., Am. Coll. Real Estate Attys., Anglo Am. Real Property Inst., So. Golf Assn. (past bd. dirs.), New Orleans Golf Assn. (past pres., past bd. dirs.), Tulane Green Wave Club (bd. dirs.), Lakewood Country Club (past pres., bd. dirs.). Republican. Avocation: golf. Home: 1750 St Charles Ave PH G New Orleans LA 70130 Office: Locke Purnell Rain Harrell 601 Poydras St Ste 2400 New Orleans LA 70130-6036

ROSEN, CHARLES WELLES, pianist, music educator; b. N.Y.C., May 5, 1927; s. Irwin and Anita (Gerber) R. B.A. summa cum laude, Princeton, 1947, M.A., 1949, Ph.D., 1951; Dr. Music honoris causa, Trinity Coll. Dublin, 1976, U. Leeds, 1976, U. Durham, Eng., 1980, U. Cambridge, Eng., 1992, U. Bristol, 1994. Asst. prof. modern langs. MIT, 1953-55; prof. music SUNY-Stony Brook, 1971-90; Ernest Bloch prof. U. Calif., Berkeley, 1977; Norton prof. poetry Harvard U., 1980-81; George Eastman prof. Balliol Coll., Oxford U., Eng., 1987-88; prof. music and social thought U. Chgo., 1988—; Messenger lectr. Cornell U., 1975. Author: The Classical Style: Haydn, Mozart, Beethoven, 1971, Schoenberg, 1975, Sonata Forms, 1980, (with Henri Zerner) Romanticism and Realism, 1984, The Musical Languages of Elliott Carter, 1985, Frontiers of Meaning, 1994, The Romantic Generation, 1995; New York debut at Town Hall, 1951; first rec. Debussy Etudes, 1951; recs. include Elliott Carter's Double Concerto, 16 Beethoven Sonatas; concertized throughout Europe and Am. Recipient Nat. Book award, 1972; Edison prize, 1974; Deems Taylor award ASCAP, 1972, 76, 81; Fulbright fellow, 1951-53; Guggenheim fellow, 1973-74. Mem. Nat. Acad. Arts and Scis.

ROSEN, COREY M., professional association executive; b. Denver, Nov. 26, 1948; s. Abraham and Dorothy Lillian (Bernstein) R.; m. Karen Young, Aug. 4, 1979; 1 child, Jessica. Ba, Wesleyan U., 1970; MA, Cornell U., 1972, PhD, 1973. Asst. prof. govt. Ripon (Wis.) Coll., 1973-75; congressional fellow U.S. Senate, Washington, 1975-76; staff prof. Sen. James Abourezk, Washington, 1976-78; com. staff Senate Sm. Bus. Com., Washington, 1978-81; exec. dir. Nat. Ctr. for Employer Ownership, Oakland, Calif., 1981—. Author: Employee Ownership in America, 1986, Employee Ownership at Work, 1986, Understanding Employee Ownership, 1991. Democrat. Jewish. Avocations: running, bicycling, racquetball, reading. Office: Nat Ctr Employee Ownership 1201 Martin Luther King Hwy Oakland CA 94612

ROSEN, DAVID MICHAEL, university administrator, public affairs consultant; b. Cambridge, Mass., Mar. 26, 1945; s. Maynard S. and Irma (Leavitt) R.; m. Nina J. Glick, Apr. 8, 1967; children: Michelle, Elisabeth. BA, Boston U., 1967, MS, 1977. Reporter The Day, New London, Conn., 1968-69, Boston Herald, 1969-73; polit. writer UPI, Boston, 1973-76, State House bur. chief, 1976-77; polit. commentator WGBH-TV, Boston, 1975-77; pub. affairs cons. Boston, 1977-79; pub. info. dir. U.S. Commodity Futures Trading Commn., Washington, 1979-80; dir. pub. rels. Harvard U., Cambridge, Mass., 1980-84; assoc. v.p. Harvard U. Cambridge, 1984-85, U. Chgo., 1986-88; v.p. Nicolazzo Assocs., Boston, 1988; chief of staff Office of Lt. Gov., Boston, 1988-89; v.p. Brandeis U., Waltham, Mass., 1989-93; cons. David Rosen Assocs., Boston, 1993; dir. pub. rels. Yeshiva U., N.Y.C., 1994—; cons. U.S. GAO, Washington, 1977-79, Mass. Ins. Divsn., Boston, 1977-78, Harvard U., 1977-80, Radcliffe Coll., 1993, New Eng. Bd. Higher Edn., 1993, Clark U., 1993, Pilgrim Health Care, 1993; substitute tchr. Boston Pub. Schs., 1967-68. Author: Protest Songs in America, 1977. Avocations: piano, running. Home: 28 Arapahoe Rd Newton MA 02165-2203 Office: Yeshiva Univ Pub Rels Dept 500 W 185th St New York NY 10033-3201

ROSEN, DAVID PAUL, book editor; b. Buffalo, May 23, 1959; s. Paul Maurice and Ethel A. (Witt) R. BA summa cum laude, Elmira Coll., 1981; MA, Temple U., 1984. Mktg. assoc. Temple U. Press, Phila., 1982-85; editor The Advocate, L.A., 1985-87, Ziff-Davis, N.Y.C., 1987-89; editor Book-of-the-Month Club/Time Warner, N.Y.C., 1989—; lectr. pub. course NYU, 1994-95. Editor (book series) Triangle Classics, 1993—. Recipient

Robertson prize Temple U., 1984, GLAAD award, 1994. Mem. Pub. Triangle, Wallace Stevens Soc., Phi Beta Kappa. Office: BOMC QPB 1271 Ave of Americas 3d Fl New York City NY 10020

ROSEN, ELLEN FREDA, psychologist, educator; b. Chgo., Jan. 28, 1941; d. Samuel Aaron and Clara Laura (Pauker) R. BA, Carleton Coll., 1962; MA, U. Ill., 1965, PhD, 1968. Instr. psychology U. Ill., Urbana, 1966-67; prof., dir. grad. studies in psychology Coll. William and Mary, Williamsburg, Va., 1967-93; cons. Ctr. for Teaching Excellence Hampton (Va.) U., 1988-94. Author: Ednl. Computer Software, (with E. Rae Harcum) The Gatekeepers of Psychology, 1993; contbr. articles to profl. jours. Mem. Soc. for Computers in Psychology, Psychonomic Soc., Va. Psychol. Assn., Eastern Psychol. Assn., C.G. Jung Soc. of Tidewater, Am. Psychol. Assn., Assn. for Anorexia and Bulimia of Va. Office: Coll of William and Mary Dept of Psychology Williamsburg VA 23187

ROSEN, FRED SAUL, pediatrics educator; b. Newark, May 26, 1930; s. Philip and Amelia (Feld) R. AB, Lafayette Coll., 1951; MD, Western Res. U., 1955; MA (hon.), Harvard U., 1970; DSc (hon.), Lafayette Coll., 1978. From asst. to assoc. prof. pediatrics Harvard Med. Sch., Boston, 1966-72; James L. Gamble prof. pediatrics, 1972—; chief. div. immunology Children's Hosp., Boston, 1968-85, program dir. Gen. Clin. Rsch. Ctr., 1977-91; pres. Ctr. for Blood Rsch., Boston, 1987—; chmn. sci. com. on immunodeficiencies WHO, Boston, 1988—. Author: Dictionary of Immunology, 1989. Pres. Am. Friends of Jenner Appeal, Boston, 1985—; Sr. asst. surgeon USPHS, 1957-59. Recipient E. Mead Johnson award for pediatric rsch. Am. Acad. Pediatrics, 1970, Gen. Clin. Rsch. Ctrs. Program 4th Ann. award NIH, 1992; John Simon Guggenheim Meml. Found. fellow, 1974. Mem. Am. Assn. Immunology, Am. Soc. Clin. Investigation, Am. Pediatric Soc., Assn. Am. Physicians, NAS Inst. Medicine, St. Botolph Club, Harvard Club, Somerset Club. Home: 101 Chestnut St Boston MA 02108-1032 Office: The Ctr for Blood Rsch 800 Huntington Ave Boston MA 02115-6303

ROSEN, GEORGE, economist, educator; b. St. Petersburg, Russia, Feb. 7, 1920; s. Leon and Rebecca (Rosenoer) R.; m. Sylvia Vatuk; 1 son, Mark. B.A., Bklyn. Coll., 1940; M.A., Princeton U., 1942, Ph.D., 1949. Prof. econs. Bard Coll., Annandale-on-Hudson, N.Y., 1946-50; economist Dept. State, Washington, 1951-54, Council Econ. Indsl. Research, Washington, 1954-55, MIT, Cambridge, 1955-59, UN, N.Y.C., 1959-60, Ford Found., N.Y.C., India, 1960-62, Rand Corp., Santa Monica, Calif., 1962-67; chief economist Asian Devel. Bank, Manila, Philippines, 1967-71; prof. econs. U. Ill.-Chgo., 1972-85, prof. econs. emeritus, 1985—, head dept., 1972-77; fellow Woodrow Wilson Internat. Ctr., Washington, 1989-90; adj. prof. Johns Hopkins U.-Nanjing U. Ctr. Chinese-Am. Studies, 1986-87; cons USAID, Egypt, 1994; book rev. editor Econ. Devel. and Cultural Change, 1988—; treas. Am. Com. for Asian Econ. Studies, 1990-95. Author: Industrial Change in India, 1958, Some Aspects of Industrial Finance in India, 1962, Democracy and Economic Change in India, 1966, 67, Peasant Society in a Changing Economy, 1975, Decision-Making Chicago-Style, 1980, Western Economists and Eastern Socs., 1985, Industrial Change in India 1970-2000, 1988, Contrasting Styles of Industrial Reform: China and India in the 1980s, 1992. Ford Found. fellow NYU, 1971-72; grantee U. Ill., 1977-78, Social Sci. Research Council and Am. Inst. Indian Studies, 1980-81, Am. Inst. Indian Studies, 1983-84, 87-88, Rockefeller Found. Bellagio Study Ctr., 1984. Office: U Ill Dept Econs M/C 144 601 S Morgan St Chicago IL 60607-7121

ROSEN, GERALD ELLIS, federal judge; b. Chandler, Ariz., Oct. 26, 1951; s. Stanley Rosen and Marjorie (Sherman) Cahn; m. Laurie DeMond. BA, Kalamazoo Coll., 1973; JD, George Washington U., 1979. Researchist Swedish Inst., Stockholm, 1973; legis. asst. U.S. Senator Robert P. Griffin, Washington, 1974-79; law clk. Seyfarth, Shaw, Fairweather & Gerardson, Wash., 1979; from assoc. to sr. ptnr. Miller, Canfield, Paddock and Stone, Detroit, 1979-90; judge U.S. Dist Ct. (ea. dist.) Mich., Detroit, 1990—; Jud. Evaluation Com. (co-chmn. 1983-88), Detroit; adj. prof. law Wayne State U., 1992, 93, U. Detroit Law Sch., 1994—; lectr. CLE confs., others. Contbr. articles to profl. jours. Rep. candidate for U.S. Congress, Mich., 1982; chmn. 17th Congl. Dist. Rep. Com., 1983-85; mem. Mich. Criminal Justice Commn., 1985-87. Fellow Kalamazoo Coll. (sr. 1972). Mem. Franklin Racquet Club. Jewish. Office: US Courthouse 231 W Lafayette Blvd Rm 802 Detroit MI 48226-2799

ROSEN, GERALD HARRIS, physicist, consultant, educator; b. Mount Vernon, N.Y., Aug. 10, 1933; s. David A. and Shirley (Schapiro) R.; m. Sarah Louise Sweet, June 8, 1963; children: Lawrence Alexander, Karlyn Penelope. B.S.E. (Guggenheim Jet Propulsion scholar, Whiton Engring.-Physics scholar), Princeton U., 1955, M.A. (NSF predoctoral fellow), 1956, Ph.D., 1958. NSF predoctoral fellow Inst. Theoretical Physics, Utrecht, Netherlands, 1957-58; research asso. dept. aero. engring. Princeton, 1958-59; NSF postdoctoral fellow Inst. Theoretical Physics, Stockholm, 1959-60; tech. cons. weapon systems evaluation div. The Pentagon, 1960; prin. scientist Martin-Marietta Aerospace div., Balt., 1960-63; cons. to a tech. v.p. Southwest Research Inst., 1963-66; prof. physics Drexel U., Phila., 1966-73; M.R. Wehr prof. physics Drexel U., 1973—; cons. fin., indsl. and govt. agys., 1966—. Author: Formulations of Classical and Quantum Dynamical Theory, 1969, A New Science of Stock Market Investing, 1990; assoc. editor Bull. Math. Biology, 1982—; contbr. revs., articles to Math. Revs., Am. Phys. Soc., other profl. jours. Sponsor San Antonio Chamber Music Soc., 1963-66; mem. Franklin Inst., 1967—; mem. publ. bd. Soc. Math. Biol., 1983—. Fellow Am. Phys. Soc., AAAS; mem. Am. Math. Soc. Patentee in field. Home: 415 Charles Ln Wynnewood PA 19096-1604 Office: Drexel U Dept Physics Philadelphia PA 19104 *The meaning of life has transcended human understanding up to the present time, but there are reasons to believe that future discoveries in science will illuminate the significance of life in nature. We must break completely free of non-rational dogma and illusion, and attempt to solve this mystery with factual clues revealed by scientific progress.*

ROSEN, GERALD ROBERT, editor; b. N.Y.C., Nov. 17, 1930; s. Sol and Essie (Shapiro) R.; m. Lois Lehrman, May 9, 1958; 1 son, Evan Mark. BS, Ind. U., 1951, MA, 1953. Intelligence analyst Dept. Def., N.Y.C., 1955-58; assoc. editor Challenge: The Mag. of Econ. Affairs, N.Y.C., 1959-61; mng. editor Challenge: The Mag. of Econ. Affairs, 1961-64, 65-66; sr. editor Dun's Rev., N.Y.C., 1964-65; nat. affairs editor, 1967—; exec. editor Dun's Rev. (now Bus. Month), 1978-90; editor IMF survey Washington, 1990-93; mng. dir. Global Insights Svcs., Washington, 1993—; fin. corr. Westinghouse Broadcasting Co. Served with CIC US Army, 1953-55. Mem. Soc. Am. Bus. and Econ. Writers, N.Y. Fin. Writers Assn., White House Corrs. Assn. Club: Nat. Press. Home: 3210 Grace St NW Washington DC 20007-3628 Office: 1700 K St NW Washington DC 20006

ROSEN, HARVEY SHELDON, economics educator; b. Chgo., Mar. 29, 1949; s. Edward and Eleanor (Altman) R.; m. Marsha E. Novick, June 20, 1976; children: Lynne, Jonathan. AB, U. Mich., 1970; AM, Harvard U., 1972, PhD, 1974. Asst. prof. Princeton (N.J.) U., 1974-80, assoc. prof., 1980-84, prof., 1984—, chmn. dept. econs., 1993—; dep. asst. sec. U.S. Treasury, 1989-91; vis. fellow Inst. Advanced Studies, Hebrew U., Jerusalem, 1978; vis. scholar Hoover Intsn., Stanford, Calif., 1981. Fellow Econometric Soc.; mem. Phi Beta Kappa. Office: Princeton U Dept Econs Princeton NJ 08544

ROSEN, JAMES MAHLON, artist, art historian, educator; b. Detroit, Dec. 3, 1933; s. Joseph and Lillian Rosen; children: Shira Del, Phyllis Dresser, Jeremy-Joseph. Student, Cooper Union, 1956; BS, Wayne State U., 1957; MFA, Cranbrook Acad. Art, 1958. Mem. faculty dept. art Wayne State U., 1961-63, U. Hawaii, 1965-67; mem. faculty Santa Rosa (Calif.) Jr. Coll., 1967-84, U. Calif., 1987-88; Wm. Morris Eminent scholar in art Augusta Coll., 1989—; artist-in-residence, guest lectr. Deep Springs Coll., R.I. Sch. Design, Montclair State Coll., San Bernardino State Coll., Pa. Acad. Fine Arts; artist-in-residence Ferrara, Italy. Author: Notes From a Painter's Journal, 1960, An American Homage to Piero Della Francesca, In the Realm of Light, William Bartram Sketches: The Field and the Image, Qualities of Camoflaging, 1970, On the Sheer Nonsense of Liking Anything, 1979; exhbns. include Betty Parsons Gallery, N.Y.C., Donald Morris Gallery, Detroit, Dana Reich Gallery, San Francisco, Mus. Modern Art Penthouse Show, Eva Gelfman Gallery, Thomas Babeor Gallery, La Jolla,

Calif., La Jolla Mus. Contemporary Art, Gallery Paule Anglim, San Francisco; dir., curator William Bartram Art Exhbn.; represented in permanent collections at Mus. Modern Art, N.Y.C., Whitney Mus. Am. Art, Ga. Mus. Art, Syracuse U., Ashmolean Mus., U. Calif. Berkeley Mus., San Francisco Mus. Modern Art, Cranbrook Mus. Art, Victoria and Albert Mus., London; bd. dirs. Arts Meridian - A Cultural Jour. Ams. Served with M.C. U.S. Army, 1953-55. Grantee Huntington Hartford Found., Yaddo, MacDowell Found., NEH, Djerassi Found. Arts, Ga. Coun. on Arts. Mem. Am. Soc. Art, Religion and Culture (bd. dirs.). Home: 824 Johns Rd Augusta GA 30904

ROSEN, J(OSHUA) PHILIP, lawyer; b. N.Y.C., Aug. 24, 1956; s. Irving and Tauba (Krieger) R. BA, Yeshiva U., 1978; JD, Georgetown U., 1981. Bar: N.Y. 1982. Law clk. U.S. Dist. Ct. (so. dist.) N.Y., N.Y.C., 1981-82; ptnr. Weil, Gotshal & Manges, N.Y.C., 1982—; bd. advisors N.Y. Real Estate Law Reporter, N.Y.C., 1987—; bd. dirs. Yeshiva Coll. of Yeshiva U. Contbr. articles to legal publs. Legal counsel, speaker on real estate topics N.Y. Holocaust Meml. Commn., N.Y.C., 1983—. Jewish. Avocation: tennis. Home: 145 W 67th St Apt 23D New York NY 10023-5936 Office: Weil Gotshal & Manges 767 5th Ave New York NY 10153-0001

ROSEN, JUDAH BEN, computer scientist; b. Phila., May 5, 1922; s. Benjamin and Susan (Hurwich) R.; children—Susan Beth, Lynn Ruth. BSEE, Johns Hopkins U., 1943; PhD in Applied Math., Columbia U., 1952. Rsch. assoc. Princeton (N.J.) U., 1952-54; head applied math. dept. Shell Devel. Co., 1954-62; vis. prof. computer sci. dept. Stanford (Calif.) U., 1962-64; prof. dept. computer sci. and math. rsch. ctr. U. Wis., Madison, 1964-71; prof., head dept. computer sci. U. Minn., Mpls., 1971—; fellow Supercomputer Inst. U. Minn., 1985-93; sr. fellow Supercomputer Ctr., San Diego, 1993; adj. rsch. prof. dept computer sci. and engrin. U. Calif. San Diego, La Jolla, 1992—; Fulbright prof. Technion, Israel, 1968-69, Davis vis. prof. 1980; invited lectr. Chinese Acad. Sci., Peking, 1980; lectr., cons. Argonne (Ill.) Nat. Lab.; mem. Nat. Computer Sci. Bd. Author: Topics in Parallel Computing, 1992; editor: Nonlinear Programming, 1970, Supercomputers and Large-Scale Optimization, 1988; assoc. editor Global Optimization, 1990—, Annals of Ops. Rsch., 1984—; contbr. articles to profl. jours. and procs. Grantee NSF, 1969—, Air Force Office of Scientific Rsch., 1987—. Mem. Assn. Computing Machinery, Soc. Indsl. and Applied Math., Math. Programming Soc. Research interests: supercomputers and parallel algorithms for optimization. Home: 10305 28th Ave N Plymouth MN 55441-3219 also: 322 Prospect St La Jolla CA 92037 Office: EE/CSci Bldg U Minn Minneapolis MN 55455-0100 also: Univ Calif-San Diego Dept Computer Sci Engring 9500 Gilman Dr La Jolla CA 92093-0114

ROSEN, KENNETH T., economist; b. 1948. BA, U. Conn., 1970; PhD, MIT, 1974. Chmn. Ctr. for Real Estate and Urban Econs. U. Calif., Berkeley, Calif.; bd. dirs. Golden West Fin. Corp., World Savs. and Loan Assn. Office: U Calif/Ctr for Real Estate & Urban Econs 2680 Bancroft Way # A Berkeley CA 94720-0001

ROSEN, LAWRENCE, anthropology educator; b. Cin., Dec. 9, 1941; s. George and Hannah (Persky) R. B.A., Brandeis U., 1963; M.A., U. Chgo., 1965, Ph.D., 1968, J.D., 1974. Bar: N.C. 1975, U.S. Supreme Ct. 1979. Asst. prof. anthropology U. Ill., Urbana, 1968-70; mem. Inst. for Advanced Study, Princeton, N.J., 1970-71; assoc. prof. anthropology Duke U., Durham, N.C., 1974-77; prof. anthropology Princeton U., N.J., 1977—; adj. prof. Columbia U. Law Sch., 1979—; vis. prof. Northwestern U. Law Sch., Chgo., 1985-87, U. Pa. Law Sch., Phila., 1985-86, Georgetown Law Ctr., 1994; Lewis H. Morgan lectr. U. Rochester, 1985. Co-author: Meaning and Order in Moroccan Society, 1978, Bargaining for Reality, 1984, The Anthropology of Justice, 1989; editor: The American Indian and the Law, 1974, Other Intentions, 1995. Legal asst. Native Am. Rights Fund., Boulder, Colo., 1973. Woodrow Wilson fellow, 1964; Guggenheim fellow, 1981; John & Catherine MacArthur Found. fellow, 1981; Fulbright fellow, 1991. Fellow Am. Anthrop. Assn.

ROSEN, LEE SPENCER, lawyer; b. Miami, May 23, 1961; s. Maurice and Virginia Lee (Philpot) R.; m. Lisa C., June 23, 1990. BA, U. N.C., 1983; JD, Wake Forest U., 1986. Bar: N.C. 1987, U.S. Dist. Ct. (ea. dist.) N.C. 1987, U.S. Ct. Appeals (4th cir.) 1987. Atty. Crisp, Davis et al, Raleigh, N.C., 1987-89; ptnr. Rosen & Robbins, P.A., Raleigh, N.C., 1989—. Contbr. articles to profl. jours. Mem. ABA (chairperson 1989-92), N.C. Bar Assn. (coun. mem. 1989-92). Office: Rosen & Robbins PA 4101 Lake Boone Trl Ste 105 Raleigh NC 27607-7506

ROSEN, LOUIS, physicist; b. N.Y.C., June 10, 1918; s. Jacob and Rose (Lipionski) R.; m. Mary Terry, Sept. 4, 1941; 1 son, Terry Leon. BA, U. Ala., 1939, MS, 1941; PhD, Pa. State U., 1944; DSc (hon.), U. N.Mex., 1979, U. Colo., 1987. Instr. physics U. Ala., 1940-41, Pa. State U., 1943-44; mem. staff Los Alamos Sci. Lab., 1944-90, group leader nuclear plate lab., 1949-65, alt. div. leader exptl. physics div., 1962-65, dir. meson physics facility, 1965-85, div. leader medium energy physics div., 1965-86, sr. lab. fellow, 1985-90, sr. fellow emeritus, 1990—; Sesquicentennial hon. prof. U. Ala., 1981; mem. panel on future of nuclear sci., chmn. subpanel on accelerators NRC of NAS, 1976, mem. panel on instnl. arrangements for orbiting space telescope, 1976; mem. U.S.A.-USSR Coordinating Com. on Fundamental Properties of Matter, 1971-90. Author papers in nuclear sci. and applications of particle accelerators; bd. editors: Applications of Nuclear Physics; co-editor Climate Change and Energy Policy, 1992. Mem. Los Alamos Town Planning Bd., 1962-64; mem. Gov.'s Com. on Tech. Excellence in N.Mex.; mem. N.Mex. Cancer Control Bd., 1976-80, v.p., 1979-81; co-chmn. Los Alamos Vols. for Stevenson, 1956; Dem. candidate for county commr., 1962; bd. dirs. Los Alamos Med. Ctr., 1977-83, chmn., 1983; bd. govs. Tel Aviv U., 1986. Recipient E.O. Lawrence award AEC, 1963; Golden Plate award Am. Acad. Achievement, 1964; N.Mex. Disting. Public Service award, 1978; named Citizen of Year, N.Mex. Realtors Assn., 1973; Guggenheim fellow, 1959-60; alumni fellow Pa. State U., 1978; Louis Rosen prize established in his honor by bd. dirs. Meson Facility Users Group, 1984. Fellow AAAS (coun. 1989), Am. Phys. Soc. (coun. 1975-78, chmn. panel on pub. affairs 1980, div. nuclear physics 1985, mem. subcom. on internat. sci. affairs 1988). Home: 1170 41st St Los Alamos NM 87544-1913 Office: Los Alamos Sci Lab PO Box 1663 Los Alamos NM 87545-0001 *I have come to believe that only after one has learned to manage and set worthy goals for himself should he attempt to do so for others.*

ROSEN, MARCELLA, advertising executive; b. N.Y.C., Sept. 29, 1934; d. Leo and Irma (Rothschild) Jung; m. E. David Rosen, Dec. 22, 1962 (dec. Feb. 1982); children: Burt, Lisa. BA, Barnard Coll., 1951-55; MA, Columbia U., 1957. Research assoc. Cunningham and Walsh, N.Y.C., 1957-62; account exec. Doyle Dane Bernbach, N.Y.C., 1962-63, Smith Greenland, N.Y.C., 1963-64; dir. mktg. services Altman Stoller, N.Y.C., 1964-66; mktg. cons. Marcella Rosen Assoc., Inc., N.Y.C., 1967-70; pres. Trager-Rosen, N.Y.C., 1970-77; v.p. assoc. mktg. services N.W. Ayer, N.Y.C., 1977-78; sr. v.p., mng. dir. media svcs. N.W. Ayer, Inc., N.Y.C., 1978-88, exec. v.p., mng. dir. media svcs., 1988-93; pres, CEO Network TV Assn. N.Y.C., 1993-95. Bd. dirs. United Jewish Appeal-Fedn., N.Y.C., 1986—, mem. exec. com. capital campaign, 1988-93; trustee Barnard Coll., 1992—, 92d St YWHA, 1992—; founder, chairperson The Deciding Vote, 1992. Recipient Silver Prism award Advt. Women N.Y., 1988, Matrix award Women in Communications, N.Y.C., 1986; named one of 25 Who Count in TV View Mag., N.Y.C., 1985, Disting. Grad. Pub. Edn. Assn., 1988. Mem. Advt. Research Found. (bd. dirs. 1984-88), Internat. Radio TV Soc. (bd. dirs. 1983-90), Am. Assn. Advt. Agys. (chmn. Media Policy Com. 1986-87), Coalition Leading Women's Orgn. (chmn. 1985-88), Barnard Coll. Bus. and Profl. Women (pres. 1980), Women's Forum (bd. dirs. 1983-85). Avocations: tennis, skiing, piloting, art, music. Office: Network TV Assn 825 7th Ave New York NY 10019-6014

ROSEN, MATTHEW STEPHEN, botanist, consultant; b. N.Y.C., Oct. 7, 1943; s. Norman and Lucille (Cass) R.; m. Deborah Louise Mackay, June 16, 1974 (div. Feb. 1983); children: Gabriel Mackay, Rebecca Mackay; m. Kay Eloise Williams, July 11, 1987. MFSc, Yale U., 1972; BS, Cornell U. 1967. Instr. ornamental horticulture SUNY-Farmingdale, 1968-69; landscape designer Manhattan Gardens, N.Y.C., 1969-70; instr. ornamental horticulture McHenry County Coll., Crystal Lake, Ill., 1972-74; coord. agrl. studies, asst. prof. biology, chemistry Mercer County Community Coll., West

Windsor, N.J., 1974-79; administr. Des Moines Botanical Ctr., 1979—; consulting dir. West Mich. Horticultural Soc., 1993; cons. in field. Contbr. articles to profl. jours. Vice chmn. United Way Cen. Iowa, 1982, div. chmn. 1983-86, 88-89, 91, group chmn. 1987, chmn. arts adv. com. 1985-86, pres. 1986, bd. dirs. Arts and Recreation Council, 1985-86, com. chmn., 1992; mem. career vocat. com. Des Moines Indsl. Sch. Dist., 1986, co-chmn., 1987, mem. Ptnrs. for Progress com., 1988-90, mem. sci. monitoring program, 1991, 92; chmn. Two Rivers Festival, 1987-88; active Des Moines Sister City Program, Kofu, Japan, 1984, delegation, 1989, Naucalpan, Mexico, 1986, 87, Shijiazhuang, China, 1986, 90, 92; mem. edn. com. Am. Assn. Botanical Gardens & Arboretum, mem. membership com., mem. conservation com. Mem. Am. Assn. Botanical Gardens and Arboreta (edn. com.), Greater Des Moines C. of C. (team leader 1984—, chmn. new mem. sales, chmn. 8 O'clock new, Pres. Cabinet award 1983, 84, 85, Achievement award C. of C. Fedn. 1986, mem. exec. com. 1995), East Des Moines C. of C. (bd. dirs. 1992—, v.p., sec. 1993—, pres.- elect 1994, pres. 1995, sister cities commn. 1994), Greater Des Moines Conv. and Visitors Bur. (chmn. new mem. sales com. 1988-89), Iowa Advt. Rev. Coun., Affiliate Pres.'s Coun. of Chambers (chair 1995), bd. of dirs. DM Gen. Hosp., 1994-95, Rotary, Phi Kappa Phi, Pi Alpha Xi. Democrat. Jewish. Avocations: photography, reading, model trains, collecting old books, writing. Home: 1042 22nd St West Des Moines IA 50265 Office: Des Moines Botanical Ctr 909 E River Dr Des Moines IA 50316-2897

ROSEN, MOISHE, religious organization administrator; b. Kansas City, Mo., Apr. 12, 1932; s. Ben and Rose (Baker) R.; m. Ceil Starr, Aug. 18, 1950; children: Lyn Rosen Bond, Ruth. Diploma, Northeastern Bible Coll., 1957; DD, Western Conservative Bapt. Sem., 1986. Ordained to ministry Bapt. Ch., 1957. Missionary Am. Bd. Missions to the Jews, N.Y.C., 1956; minister in charge Beth Sar Shalom Am. Bd. Missions to the Jews, Los Angeles, 1957-67; dir. recruiting and tng. Am. Bd. Missions to the Jews, N.Y.C., 1967-70; leader Jews for Jesus Movement, San Francisco, 1970-73, exec. dir., 1973—, founder, chmn., 1973—; speaker in field. Author: Saying of Chairman Moishe, 1972, Jews for Jesus, 1974, Share the New Life with a Jew, 1976, Christ in the Passover, 1977, Y'shua, The Jewish Way to Say Jesus, 1982, Overture to Armageddon, 1991, The Universe is Broken: Who on Earth Can Fix It?, 1991, Demystifying Personal Evangelism, 1992. Trustee Western Conservative Bapt. Sem., Portland, Oreg., 1979-85, 86-91, Bibl. Internat. Coun. on Bibl. Inerrancy, Oakland, Calif., 1979-89; bd. dirs. Christian Advs. Serving Evangelism, 1987-91. Office: Jews for Jesus 60 Haight St San Francisco CA 94102-5895

ROSEN, MYOR, harpist, educator; b. N.Y.C., May 28, 1917; s. Caesar and Rose (Seidenberg) R.; m. Esther Rosen, May 25, 1941; children: Linda, David. Diploma, Juilliard Sch. Music, 1940. Faculty Juilliard Sch. Music, 1947-69. Prin. harpist, Mexico Symphony Orch., 1941-42, Indpls. Symphony Orch., 1941-42, Mpls. Symphony Orch., 1943-44, staff harpist, CBS, Columbia Records and free lanced, 1945-60, prin. harpist, N.Y. Philharm., 1960-87; Composer incidental music for: NBC series Arts and the Gods, 1946, CBS Camera Three, 1947, Solomon, The King, 1948. Served with U.S. Army, 1945. Mem. Am. Fedn. Musicians, Bohemians. *Having been the fortunate recipient of a 7-year scholarship through the New York Philharmonic Symphony Society and the Juilliard School of Music when I began my career as a harpist, I can think of no greater honor than my privilege in having been accepted as principal harpist with the same organization which trained me. I now bend my efforts to train future harpists to excel in like manner. In my opinion, the most important function of a teacher is to teach his students how to teach themselves; self-development.*

ROSEN, NATHANIEL KENT, cellist; b. Altadena, Calif., June 9, 1948; s. David Leon and Frances Jean (Kaufman) R.; m. Jennifer Langham, Aug. 27, 1976 (div. 1986); m. Margo Shohl, May 21, 1989; children: Samuel Gregory, Stella Rosalie. Student, Pasadena (Calif.) City Coll., 1965-67; Mus.B., U. So. Calif., 1971. Teaching asst. U. So. Calif., 1968-75, mem. faculty 7th ann. Gregor Piatigorsky Seminar Sch. Music, 1984; asst. prof. Calif. State U. at Northridge, 1970-76; mem. faculty Manhattan Sch. Music, N.Y.C., 1982-88, 94—; now mem. faculty U. Ill., Urbana, 1988-94. Prin. cellist, Los Angeles Chamber Orch., 1970-76, Pitts. Symphony, 1977-79, concert cellist worldwide; recordings include Orientale: Romantic Music for the Cello. Recipient 1st prize Naumburg Competition, 1977, 1st prize Moscow Tchaikovsky Competition, 1978; Ford Found. grantee, 1970-71; Rockefeller Found. grantee, 1973-74. Mem. Violoncello Soc. N.Y., Century Assn. N.Y. Office: Shaw Concerts 1900 Broadway New York NY 10023 also: North Star Recordings 95 Hathaway St Providence RI 02907*

ROSEN, NORMAN EDWARD, lawyer; b. Providence, July 2, 1938; s. Albert and Lillian R.; m. Estelle Cutler, Sept. 5, 1966; children: James, Vanessa. AB, Harvard U., 1959; LLB, Columbia U., 1962; MA, George Washington U., 1965. Bar: N.Y. 1962, D.C. 1963, U.S. Supreme Ct. 1966. Trial atty. FTC, Washington, 1962-67; assoc. Paskus, Gordon & Hyman, N.Y.C., 1967-69; ptnr. Levin, Kreis, Ruskin & Gyory, N.Y.C., 1970-72; staff v.p., sr. counsel state regulation and licensing RCA, N.Y.C., 1972-82, Princeton, N.J., 1982-86; sr. v.p., gen. counsel Gen. Electric and RCA Licensing Mgmt. Operation, Inc., Princeton, 1986—, GE Trading Co., N.Y.C., 1989—. Contbr. articles to profl. jours. Mem. ABA (chmn. patent trademark and know-how com. antitrust sect. 1983-86, mem. com. antitrust sect. 1986-89, mem. task forces on Dept. Justice antitrust guidelines and mergers and know-how in European econ. community, spl. com. on internat. antitrust, vice chmn. antitrust sect. 1991-92), Am. Intellectual Property Law Assn., Harvard Club, Surf Club. Office: GE 2 Independence Way Princeton NJ 08540-6620

ROSEN, RAYMOND, health facility executive; b. Louisville, Feb. 5, 1950; s. Sam and Olga Rosen; m. Deborah Joy Rubinow, June 25, 1972; children: Lisa, Jessica. BS, Pa. State U., 1972; MA, George Washington U., 1974. Administrv. resident York (Pa.) Hosp., 1973-74; asst. to pres., 1974-75, asst. administr.-adminstrn., 1975-77, asst. administr.-med. affairs, 1977-79, administr.-med. affairs 1979-87, v.p. opers., 1987—. Pres. Young Adminstrs. Group Ctrl. Pa., 1980-82; pres. Community Transit, Inc., 1992—, vice chmn., 1989-92, chmn., 1992—; bd. dirs. Fedn. South Ctrl. Pa. Emergency Health Svcs., 1978-92, mem. adv. com., 1992-93, York County Emergency Health Svcs. Coun., 1978-92, Jewish Community Ctr., 1986-91; divsn. chmn. United Way York County, 1988, York County Transp. Auth., 1995—. Fellow Am. Coll. Healthcare Execs. (regent south ctrl. Pa. 1991—); mem. Am. Hosp. Assn., Hosp. Assn. Pa. (mem. com. planning 1992—). Office: York Health Sys 1001 S George St York PA 17403-3676

ROSEN, RHODA, obstetrician-gynecologist; b. Trenton, N.J., Jan. 17, 1933; d. Max and Gussie (Thierman) R.; m. Seymour Kanter, Aug. 19, 1956; children: Cynthia, Gregg, Larry, Brad. BA, U. Pa., 1954, MD, 1958. Diplomate Am. Bd. Obstetrics and Gynecology. Intern Albert Einstein Phila. Med. Ctr., 1958-59, resident, 1959-62; clin. prof. ob-gyn. Temple U. Med. Sch., Phila.; assoc. staff gyn. exec. com. Albert Einstein Med. Ctr., Phila.; attending physician Rolling Hill Hosp., Elkins Park, Pa.; pvt. practice obs/gyn Phila., 1962—; chmn. gynpathology com. Albert Einstein Med. Ctr., Phila. bd. trustee Joseph J. Peters Inst. Fellow ACOG, ACS; mem. AMA, Pa. Med. Soc., Phila. Colposcopy Soc. (past pres.), Ex-Residents Assn. (past pres. Albert Einstein Med. Ctr.), Philadelphia County Med. Soc. (com.), Phila. Bar Assn. (com.). Jewish. Avocations: tennis, biking, art, swimming, music. Home: 1011 Valley Rd Philadelphia PA 19027-1814

ROSEN, RICHARD LEWIS, lawyer, real estate developer; b. N.Y.C., Mar. 6, 1943; s. Morris and Lorraine (Levy) R.; m. Doris Ellen Bloom, Aug. 28, 1983. BA, Cornell U., 1965; JD, N.Y. Law Sch., 1968; cert. N.Y.U. Real Estate Inst., 1980. Bar: N.Y. 1968, U.S. Dist. Ct. (so. and ea. dists.) N.Y. 1972; lic. real estate broker. Sole practice, N.Y.C., 1971-73; ptnr. Rosen, Wise, Felzen & Salomon, N.Y.C., 1973-79; ptnr. Rosen & Felzen, N.Y.C., 1979-84, Rosen, Rudd, Kera, Graubard & Hollender, 1985-88, Bell, Kalnick, Klee and Green, N.Y.C., 1989-90, Rosen, Einbinder & Dunn, P.C., N.Y.C., 1990—. Mem. ABA (mem. franchising com. anti-trust div.), Am. Assn. Franchisees and Dealers (mem. legal steering com.), Assn. Bar City N.Y. (panel mem. com. on franchising), Red Key Hon. Soc., Cornell U., Sphinx Head Hon. Soc., Cornell U., Spiked Shoe Soc., Cornell U., Ea. Intercollegiate Athletic Assn. (named to Lightweight Football All Ea. Selection, 1963, 64). Named Ea. States Lightweight Weightlifting Champion, 1968. Avocations: tennis, skiing, phys. fitness, guitar, reading. Home: 1 Old Jericho

Tpke Jericho NY 11753-1205 also: Lamb Ave Quogue NY 11959 Office: Rosen Einbinder & Dunn PC 641 Lexington Ave New York NY 10022-4503

ROSEN, ROBERT ARNOLD, management company executive, real estate investor; b. N.Y.C., June 19, 1936; s. Louis and Helen (Weiss) R.; m. Florence Cohen, Oct. 23, 1960; children: David S., Kenneth A., Mark A., Emily B. B.B.A., CUNY, 1957, M.B.A., 1960; postgrad. (Ford Found. scholar), NYU, 1961; grad., Indsl. Coll. Armed Forces, Air War Coll., 1960, U.S. Air Force U.; various courses, Naval Edn. and Tng. Command. Sales promotion mgr. Leipzig & Lippe, Inc., 1956-58; advt. and sales promotion mgr. Zenith Radio, 1957-62; chmn., pres., founder Am. Bus. Resources Corp., 1963-64; v.p., dir. Royal Bus. Funds Corp., 1964-68; CEO, mng. dir. Rosen Assocs., Jericho, N.Y., 1960—; pres. Rosen Assocs. Mgmt. Corp., Jericho, N.Y., 1983—; v.p. corp. finance div., dir. Brand Grumet & Siegel, Inc., 1969-70; pres. Brand Grumet & Siegel Equities, Inc., 1970; former pres., chief operating officer Bell TV, Inc., N.Y.C.; pres., former chmn. bd. Holmes Protection, Inc.; former chmn. bd., pres. Union Small Bus. Investment Co., 1968-77, Skyway-Laguardia Corp.; dir. past chmn. bd. Okuraya Davos Internat., Inc.; chmn. bd., pres., chief exec. officer, treas. Suburban Broadcasting Corp., 1970-80; chmn., pres. Affiliated Communications Corp.; vice chmn., pres. Communication Services Corp.; pres. Wescom Corp.; pres. Androse Corp., 1983—; cons. Asian Devel. Bank, Albert Einstein Coll. Medicine, Nat. Housing Bank of Brazil; mem. U.S. Senatorial Bus. Adv. Bd.; lectr. Baruch Coll. Grad. Sch. Bus., CUNY, 1960-63; adj. prof. Fairleigh Dickinson U. Grad. Sch. Bus., 1968-75; pres., dean Internat. Inst. Real Estate Studies Ltd.; dir. Center for Real Estate Studies, Adelphi U.; adj. prof. mgmt. NYU; mem. faculty New Sch. for Social Research; guest lectr., mem. bd. advs. Fordham U.; prin. owner, developer shopping centers, comml. real estate throughout, U.S.; chmn. UN Trade and Tech. Adv. Mission to Israel, 1972, Econ. Devel. Com./UJA Fedn.; active Nat. Builder Mktg. Bd. Chmn. Borough Presidents of Manhattan Com. on Narcotics Addiction Control, 1970-75; N.Y. mem. adv. council U.S. Air Force Acad.; mem. editorial policy com. Internat. Property Investment Jour. Hofstra U. Law Sch.; mem. Navy Recruiting Dist., N.Y. Assistance Council; bd. dirs. The Film Forum, 1979-86, N.Y.C. Housing Partnership, Housing Partnership Devel. Corp., Intrepid Sea, Air and Space Mus.; chmn. Navy Task Force to Study Navy Budgeting, Acquisition and Procurement; mem. Pres.'s Pvt. Sector Survey on Cost Control (Grace Commn.); mem. N.Y. State's Gov.'s Bus. Adv. Coun.; pres. Zachary and Elizabeth M. Fisher Found., Fisher House Found., Inc.; chmn. econ. devel. com. United Jewish Appeal/Fedn. With USAFR and USNR, 1959-90, ret. as capt. USNR, 1990; rear adm. (ret. upper half) N.Y. Naval Militia. Mem. Am. Arbitration Assn., Nat. Assn. Corp. Real Estate Execs., Soc. Internat. Devel., Internat. Inst. Valuers (SCV designation), Nat. Rifle Assn., U.S., Nat. Def. Exec. Res., Chief Execs. Orgn., Met. Pres.'s Orgn., Young Pres.'s Orgn. (past chmn. Met. chpt.), Real Estate Bd. N.Y., Assn. for Better N.Y., Internat. Council Shopping Centers, Property Cons. Soc., Nat. Assn. Rev. Appraisers (cert. rev. appraiser), Air Force Assn., Res. Officers Assn., Nat. Guard Assn., Naval Res. Assn., U.S. Naval Inst., Navy League of U.S., Naval War Coll. Found. (assoc.), Naval Militia Assn., Alpha Delta Sigma, Phi Sigma Delta, Sigma Alpha. Home: 85-29 Wicklow Pl Jamaica Estates NY 11432 Office: 333 Jericho Tpke Jericho NY 11753-1104

ROSEN, ROBERT CHARLES, lawyer; b. Valley Forge, Pa., Oct. 4, 1945; s. Morris and Fanella Rosen; m. Theresa J. Rosen, Mar. 19, 1972; children: Diane, Joanne, Marlene, Edgar, Lesa, Mitchell, Patty, Charlene. BS, U. Minn., 1967; JD, Duquesne U., 1970; LLM, Harvard U., 1979. Bar: Calif., D.C., Pa., U.S. Dist. Ct., U.S. Ct. Appeals. Legal intern Law Offices of Goldring and Nernberg, 1968-69; rsch. fellow Fletcher Sch. Law and Diplomacy, Tufts U., Boston, 1971-72; asst. atty. gen. Bur. Consumer Protection, Dept. Justice, Pa., 1972-73; atty., trial atty.-fin., legal asst. to commr., sr. counsel U.S. SEC, Washington, 1973-85; ptnr. Lewis, D'Amato, Brisbois & Bisgaard, L.A., 1985-94; atty. pvt. practice, L.A., 1994—; program chmn. Glendon Tremain Symposium, L.A., 1991, Internat. Securities, Regulations, Trading and Transactions Symposium, L.A., 1991, Recent Devels. in Securities and Comml. Arbitration, L.A., 1989, Recent Devels. in Securities Class Actions, L.A., 1988; co-chmn. seminar Regulation of Internat. Securities Transactions, N.Y.C., 1989. Contbr. articles to profl. jours. Mem. ABA (internat. law sect., banking and bus. law sect., spl. task force on securities arbitration), Internat. Bar Assn. (com. on issues and trading in securities bus. law sect.), Inter-Am. Bar Assn., L.A. County Bar Assn. (internat. law sect., bus. and corps. law sect., exec. com. 1986—, chmn. 1993-94, chmn. securities law enforcement subcom.). Office: 555 S Flower St 29th Fl Los Angeles CA 90071

ROSEN, ROBERT THOMAS, analytical and food chemist; b. Concord, N.H., Nov. 5, 1941; s. Maurice J. and Miriam M. (Miller) R.; m. Sharon Lynne Beres, Apr. 23, 1972. BA (cum laude), Nasson Coll.; PhD, Rutgers U. Sr. rsch. scientist Chem. Rsch. and Devel. Ctr., FMC Corp., Princeton, N.J., 1966-84; program dir. analytical support facilities, 1984—; assoc. dir. Ctr. for Advanced Food Technology, Rutgers U., New Brunswick, N.J., 1993—; chmn. North Jersey ACS Mass Spectrometry Topical Group, 1987-88. Assoc. editor The Mass Spec Source, 1988-90; contbr. articles and book reviews to profl. jours. Fellow Am. Inst. Chemists; mem. Am. Soc. for Mass Spectrometry, Am. Chem. Soc., N.Y. Acad. Scis., N.Am. Native Fishes Assn., Inst. Food Technologists, Phi Lambda Upsilon (pres.). Achievements include research in gas and liquid chromatography, free and glycosidically bound organic compounds in fruits and vegetables, determination of nonvolatile and thermally labile pesticides and phytochemicals in food, related materials and the environment by liquid chromatography and mass spectrometry. Home: Keats Rd # 293 Pottersville NJ 07979 Office: Rutgers U Cook Coll Ctr for Advanced Food Tech New Brunswick NJ 08903

ROSEN, SAM, economics educator emeritus; b. Balt., Apr. 1, 1920; s. Louis and Belle (Kurtz) R.; m. Mary Berman, Mar. 5, 1943; children—Michael David, Laura Elizabeth, Jonathan Donald. A.B., U. Wis., 1942; M.A., Harvard U., 1948, Ph.D., 1952. Asst. prof. econs. U. Wyo., Laramie, 1949-51, U. Del., Newark, 1952-57; assoc. prof. U. N.H., Durham, 1957-63; prof. U. N.H., 1963-74, Nashua Corp. prof. econs., 1974-85, emeritus prof. econs., 1985—; vis. prof. Inst. Social Studies, Holland, 1969, People's Republic China, 1987; vis. Fulbright prof., Malta, 1975. Author: National Income, 1963, National Income and Other Social Accounts, 1972; Contbr. articles to profl. jours. Served to lt. USN, 1942-45. Mem. AAUP (pres. U. N.H. chpt. 1962-63, 72-73), Am. Econ. Assn., Internat. Assn. Rsch. in Income and Wealth, Am. Fin. Assn., Ret. Faculty Assn. (chmn., bd. dirs.), N.H. Assn. for the Elderly, Seacoast Jazz Soc. (bd. dirs.). Office: Whittemore Sch Bus-Econs Mcconnell Hall Durham NH 03824

ROSEN, SANFORD JAY, lawyer; b. N.Y.C., Dec. 19, 1937; s. Alexander Charles and Viola S. (Grad) R.; m. Catherine Picard, June 22, 1958; children: Caren E. Andrews, R. Durelle Schacter, Ian D., Melissa S. AB, Cornell U., 1959; LLB, Yale U., 1962. Bar: Conn. 1962, U.S. Supreme Ct. 1966, D.C. 1973, Calif. 1974. Law clk. to Hon. Simon E. Sobeloff U.S. Ct. Appeals, Balt., 1962-63; prof. sch. law U. Md., Balt., 1963-71; assoc. dir. Coun. on Legal Edn. Opportunity, Atlanta, 1969-70; vis. prof. law U. Tex., Austin, 1970-71; asst. legal dir. ACLU, N.Y.C., 1971-73; legal dir. Mex.-Am. Legal Def. Fund, San Francisco, 1973-75; ptnr. Rosen, Remcho & Henderson, San Francisco, 1976-80, Rosen & Remcho, San Francisco, 1980-82; prin. Law Offices of Sanford Jay Rosen, San Francisco, 1982-86; sr. ptnr. Rosen & Phillips, San Francisco, 1986-89; prin. Rosen & Assocs., San Francisco, 1990; sr. ptnr. Rosen, Bien & Asaro, San Francisco, 1991—; commr. Balt. Community Rels. Commn., 1966-69; mem. com. Patuxent Instn., Balt., 1967-69; ad hoc adminstrv. law judge Calif. Agrl. Labor Rels. Bd., San Francisco, 1975-80; interim monitor U.S. Dist. Ct. (no. dist.) Calif., San Francisco, 1989. Contbr. articles to profl. jours. Mem. Commn. on Adminstrn. of Criminal Justice, Balt., 1968; mem. adv. com. HEW, Washington, 1974-75; early neutral evaluator U.S. Dist. Ct. (no. dist.) Calif., San Francisco, 1987—; mediator, 1993—; judge pro tem San Francisco Superior Ct., 1991—; lectr. Balt. State Attys., 1965. Mem. ABA, Assn. Trial Lawyers Am. (chair civil rights sect. 1993-94), D.C. Bar Assn., Calif. Bar Assn., Bar Assn. San Francisco, Calif. Attys. for Criminal Justice. Avocations: reading, travel, movies. Office: Rosen Bien & Asaro 155 Montgomery St Fl 8 San Francisco CA 94104-4105

ROSEN, SAUL WOOLF, research scientist, health facility administrator; b. Boston, July 29, 1928; s. David Tsvi and Ida (Hannah) Sadwin; m. Mary

Jean Westfall, June 14, 1959 (div. 1986); children: Craig, Laura, David; m. Deborah Susan Kieffer, Nov. 3, 1989. BA cum laude, Harvard U., 1947, MD, 1956; PhD, Northwestern U., 1955. Intern U. Calif. Med. Ctr., San Francisco, 1956-57, resident, 1957-58, sr. res., 1960-61; clin. assoc. Nat. Inst. Arthritis and Metabolic Diseases, Bethesda, Md., 1958-60; sr. investigator NIH Nat. Inst. Arthritis and Metabolism Disease, Bethesda, Md., 1961-84; dept. dir. Clin. Ctr. NIH, Bethesda, Md., 1984-90; acting dir. NIH, Bethesda, 1990-94; vis. scientist Nat. Inst. Med. Rsch., London, Eng., 1975-76. Contbr. articles to profl. jours. U.S. Rubber Co. fellow, Northwestern U., 1950. Fellow ACP; mem. Assn. Am. Physicians, Endocrine Soc. Avocations: opera, lexicography, philately, weightlifting. Home: 7401 Westlake Ter # 1104 Bethesda MD 20817

ROSEN, SHERWIN, economist, educator; b. Chgo., Sept. 29, 1938; s. Joe W. and Nell (Rudy) R.; m. Sharon Ginsberg, June 11, 1961; children: Jennifer, Adria. BS, Purdue U., 1960; M.A., U. Chgo., 1962, Ph.D., 1966. Mem. faculty dept. econs. U. Rochester, N.Y., 1964-75, Kenan prof. econs., 1975-77; prof. econs. U. Chgo., 1977-83, Bergman prof. econs., 1984—, chmn. econ. dept., 1988-94; sr. rsch. fellow Hoover Instn.; vis. prof. U. Buffalo, 1970, Harvard U., 1971-72, Columbia U., 1973, Stanford U., 1976; bd. trustees Joint Coun. on Econ. Edn., 1990—. Editor: Jour. of Polit. Economy, 1986—; contbr. articles to profl. jours. Fellow Econometric Soc., Am. Acad. Arts and Scis.; mem. Am. Econ. Assn. (exec. com. 1985--88, v.p. 1994). Home: 5714 S Kimbark Ave Chicago IL 60637-1615 Office: U Chgo Dept Econs 1126 E 59th St Chicago IL 60637-1580

ROSEN, STANLEY HOWARD, humanities educator; b. Warren, Ohio, July 29, 1929; s. Nathan A. and Celia (Narotsky) R.; m. Francoise Harlepp, Sept. 5, 1955; children: Nicholas David, Paul Mark, Valerie. B.A., U. Chgo., 1949, Ph.D., 1955; student, Am. Sch. Classical Studies, Athens, Greece, 1955-56. Mem. faculty Pa. State U., 1956-94, prof. philosophy, 1966-94; Fulbright research prof. U. Paris, 1960-61; research fellow Humanities Research Inst., U. Wis., 1963-64; Inst. Arts and Humanities research sr. fellow Pa. State U., 1972—; Evan Pugh prof. philosophy, 1985-94; Bowne prof. philosophy Boston U., 1994—; vis. prof. U. Calif., San Diego, 1978, U. Nice, 1981; cos. lectr. U. Barcelona, Spain, 1992. Author: Plato's Symposium, 1968, Nihilism, 1969, G.W.F. Hegel, 1974, The Limits of Analysis, 1980, Plato's Sophist: The Drama of Original and Image, 1983, Hermeneutics as Politics, 1987, The Quarrel Between Philosophy and Poetry, 1988, The Ancients and the Moderns, 1989, The Question of Being, 1993, Plato's Statesman: The Web of Politics, 1995, The Mask of Enlightenment, 1995. Research grantee Am. Philos. Soc., 1961; Research grantee Earhart Found., 1971, 73, 81. Mem. Metaphys. Soc. Am (pres. 1990-91). Home: 117 Brook St Wellesley MA 02181-6632 Office: 745 Commonwealth Ave Boston MA 02215

ROSEN, STEVEN TERRY, oncologist, hematologist; b. Bklyn., Feb. 18, 1952; married, 1976; 4 children. MB, Northwestern U., 1972, MD, 1976. Genevieve Teuton prof., med. sch. Northwestern U., 1989—, dir. cancer ctr., 1989—; dir. clin. programs Northwestern Meml. Hosp., 1989—. Editor-in-Chief Jour. Northwestern U. Cancer Center, 1989—, Contemporary Oncology, 1990—. Mem. AAAS, ACP, AMA, Am. Soc. Hematology, Am. Soc. Clin. Oncology, Ctrl. Soc. Clin. Rsch. Achievements include research in cutaneous T-cell lymphomas, biology of lung cancer, biologic therapies, and hormone receptors. Office: Northwestern U Robert H. Lurie Cancer Ctr Olson Pavilion Rm 8250 303 E Chicago Ave Chicago IL 60611-3008

ROSEN, WILLIAM, English language educator; b. Boston, July 1, 1926; s. Louis H. and Alice (Goldstein) R.; m. Barbara Cooper, Aug. 13, 1960; children: Judith Anne, Susan Eleanor. AB, Harvard U., 1948, AM, 1949, PhD, 1958. Instr. U. Wis., Madison, 1956-60; asst. prof. U. Conn., Storrs, 1960-63, assoc. prof., 1963-65, prof. English, 1965-92; prof. emeritus, 1992—; coordinator English grad. studies U. Conn., Storrs, 1979-80, 81-84, head English dept., 1972-92; Old Dominion prof. humanities Hampton Inst., Va., 1969-70; vis. fellow Clare Hall, Cambridge U., Eng., 1980-81, 88-89. Author: Shakespeare and the Craft of Tragedy, 1960; co-editor: Julius Caesar, 1963; contbr. articles to profl. jours. Vol. long term care adv., obudsman program State of Conn., 1994—. Pvt. U.S. Army, 1953-55. Mem. Am. Assn. Univ. Profs. (v.p. 1974-75, pres. 1975-76, chief negotiator U. Conn. chpt. 1976-77), Shakespeare Assn., MLA, Renaissance Soc. Am. Democrat. Jewish. Avocations: reading, gardening. Home: 233 Hanks Hill Rd Storrs Mansfield CT 06268-2333 Office: U Conn Dept English Storrs CT 06268

ROSEN, WILLIAM WARREN, lawyer; b. New Orleans, July 22, 1936; s. Warren Leucht and Erma (Stich) R.; m. Eddy Kahn, Nov. 26, 1965; children: Elizabeth K., Victoria A. BA, Tulane U., 1958, JD, 1964. Bar: La. 1964, U.S. Dist. Ct. (ea. dist.) La. 1965, U.S. Ct. Appeals (5th cir.) 1965, U.S. Supreme Ct. 1984, U.S. Dist. Ct. (mid. dist.) La. 1985, Colo. 1989. Assoc. Dodge & Friend, New Orleans, 1965-68, Law Office of J.R. Martzell, New Orleans, 1968-70; pvt. practice New Orleans, 1970-79, 89-90; ptnr. Lucas & Rosen (and predecessor firms), New Orleans, 1979-87, Herman, Herman, Katz & Cotlar, New Orleans, 1987-88, Rosen and Samuel, New Orleans, 1990—; adj. prof. trial advocacy Law Sch. Tulane U., 1988—, mem. adv. com. paralegal studies program, 1977-86, instr. bus. orgns., 1978, instr. legal interviewing, 1980-81; mem. adv. com. Paralegal Inst. U. New Orleans, 1990—, instr. legal interviewing and investigations, 1986-87; lectr. legal and paralegal fields; lectr. real and demonstrative evidence Nat. Edn. Network, 1993. Author: (with others) Trial Techniques publ. La. Trial Lawyers Assn., 1981; columnist Briefly Speaking publ. New Orleans Bar Assn., 1993—. Mem. budget and planning com. Jewish Welfare Fedn., 1970-73; mem. adv. coun. on drug edn. La. Dept. Edn., 1973; mem. profl. adv. com. Jewish Endowment Found., 1982—; mem. exec. com. U.S. Olympic Com., La. 1982-84; bd. dirs. Planned Parenthood La., 1994—; pres. Dad's Club, Isidore Newman Sch., 1984-85, Uptown Flood Assn., 1982-85; bd. dirs. Jewish Children's Home Svc., 1973-76, Met. Crime Commn. New Orleans, 1976-82; spl. agt. Office Spl. Investigations USAF, 1958-61. Fellow, Inst. of Politics. Loyola U. Mem. ABA (vice-chmn. pub. rels. com. 1974-76), Fed. Bar Assn. (past bd. dirs., past officer), La. Bar Assn. (pub. rels. com. 1970-73, 88-89, past chmn. state youth drug abuse edn. program, vol. lawyers for arts 1986—), New Orleans Bar Assn. (continuing legal edn. com. 1990-91, chmn. 1991-92, Am. Inns of Ct. Master 1992—, columnist 1993—), Assn. Trial Lawyers Am. (keyperson com. 1986-89, paralegal mem. com., vice-chmn. 1989-91, family law adv. com. 1989-90, sec. family law sect. 1990-91, legal edn. lectr. 1990-92, 94, contbr. Trial mag. 1994), La. Trial Lawyers Assn. (life, bd. govs. 1982-85, pres.'s adv. coun. 1980-82, 85-88, legal edn. lectr. 1979, 81, 83-84, 86, 88), Am. Arbitration Assn., Nat. Fedn. Paralegal Assn. (adv. coun. 1989—), Assn. Atty. Mediators (pres. La. chpt. 1995—), Nat. Choice in Dying (legal adv. com. 1992—), Nat. Edn. Network (legal edn. lectr. 1993). Avocation: photography (included in Louisiana Photographers publ. Contemporary Arts Ctr. 1988). Office: Rosen and Samuel Ste 200 715 Girod St New Orleans LA 70130-3505

ROSENAU, JAMES NATHAN, political scientist, author; b. Philadelphia, Nov. 25, 1924; s. Walter Nathan and Fanny Fox (Baum) R.; m. Norah McCarthy, Aug. 5, 1955 (dec. July 1974); 1 child, Heidi Margaret; m. Pauline Vaillancourt, June 14, 1987 (div. 1993); m. Hongying Wang, Dec. 11, 1993. A.B., Bard Coll., 1948; A.M., Johns Hopkins U., 1949; Ph.D., Princeton U., 1957. Instr. Rutgers U., New Brunswick, N.J., 1949-54; asst. prof. Rutgers U., New Brunswick, 1954-60, assoc. prof., 1960-62, prof., 1962-70; prof. Ohio State U., Columbus, 1970-73; prof. polit. sci. U. So. Calif., Los Angeles, 1973-92; univ. prof. of internat. affairs George Washington U., 1992—; research asst. Inst. Advanced Study, Princeton, N.J., 1953-54; research assoc. Princeton U., N.J., 1960-70; dir. Sch. Internat. Relations U. So. Calif., Los Angeles, 1976-79; dir. Inst. for Transnat. Studies, U. Southern Calif., Los Angeles, 1973-92. Author: Public Opinion and Foreign Policy, 1961, National Leadership and Foreign Policy, 1963, The Dramas of Politics, 1973, Citizenship Between Elections, 1974, The Scientific Study of Foreign Policy, 1980, Turbulence in World Politics, 1990, The United Nations in a Turbulent World, 1992; co-author: American Leadership in World Affairs, 1984, Global Voices, 1993, Thinking Theory Thoroughly, 1995; co-editor: Journeys Through World Politics, 1989, Global Changes and Theoretical Challenges, 1989, Governance Without Government, 1992, (play) Kwangju: An Escalatory Spree, 1991. Trustee Bard Coll., Annandale-on-Hudson, 1968-70, Odyssey Theater Ensemble, Los Angeles, 1987-88. Served with U.S. Army, 1942-46. Ford Found. fellow, 1958-59;

research grantee NSF, 1970, 73, 78, 79, 83, 88, 92; Guggenheim fellow, 1987-88; recipient stipend NEH, 1976. Mem. Internat. Studies Assn. (pres. 1984-85), Am. Polit. Sci. Assn. (mem. exec. council 1975-77). Democrat. Office: 2110 G St NW Washington DC 20052

ROSENBAUM, ALLEN, art museum administrator; b. N.Y.C., Jan. 28, 1937. B.A., Queens Coll., 1958; M.A., NYU, 1962. Instr. Sch. Gen. Studies, Queens Coll., N.Y.C., 1961; lectr. Metropolitan Mus. Art, N.Y.C., 1964-69, sr. lectr., 1970-72; instr. Sch. Fine Arts, U. Calif.-Irvine, 1972; asst. dir. Schickman gallery, N.Y.C., 1972-73; asst. dir. Art Mus. Princeton U., N.J., 1974, dir. Art Mus., 1980—; bd. dirs. Ternbach-Godwin Mus. Queens Coll., 1982—. Contbr. articles on art to profl. jours.; author exhbn. catalogue, Nat. Gallery Art, 1979. Inst. Fine Arts scholar, 1960-62; grantee Inst. Fine Arts, 1961, Met. Mus. Art, 1966, 68, 70; Fulbright fellow, 1962-63. Mem. Assn. Art Mus. Dirs. Office: The Art Mus Princeton University Princeton NJ 08544

ROSENBAUM, ARTHUR ELIHU, radiologist, educator; b. Cleve., June 30, 1935; s. Lionel Clarence and Dora Beatrice (Heldman) R.; m. Rona C. Rosenbaum, Dec. 25, 1981; children: Jeffrey, Lisa. L. Anne. Student, Case-Western Res. U., 1953-54, A.B., 1958; student, U. Mex., 1954-56; M.D., U. Miami, 1962. Diplomate Am. Bd. Radiology. Med. intern Jefferson Davis-Ben Taub Hosps., Houston, 1962-63; asst. resident, resident, chief resident Montefiore Hosp. and Med. Center, N.Y.C., 1963-66; instr. in radiology Albert Einstein Coll. Medicine, N.Y.C., 1966-67; asst. vis. physician Bronx Mcpl. Hosp. Center, 1966-67; cons. in neuroradiology Bronx-Lebanon Hosps., 1966-67; radiologist-in-chief USPHS Hosp., Staten Island, N.Y., 1968-69; clin. instr. radiology Sch. Medicine, U. Calif., San Francisco, N.Y., 1969; asst. clin. prof. radiology Sch. Medicine U. Calif., San Francisco, 1969; vis. asst. prof. radiology Harvard Med. Sch., Boston, 1970, asst. to assoc. prof. radiology, 1970-75; chief neuroradiology sect. Peter Bent Brigham Hosp., Boston, 1970-75; lectr. radiology Tufts U. Sch. Medicine, Boston, 1974-75; chief neuroradiology sect. Beth Israel Hosp., Boston, 1971-75; prof. radiology U. Pitts. Sch. Medicine, 1975; chief neuroradiology div. Children's Hosp. of Pitts., 1977, dir. pediatric neuroradiology, from 1979; neuroradiologist-in-chief U. Pitts. Sch. Medicine and Affiliated Hosps. of U. Health Center, 1978-80; prof. radiology Johns Hopkins U. Sch. Medicine and Med. Instns., Balt., 1980-87; chmn. div. radiology Cleve. Clinic Found., 1988; prof. radiology, dir. neuroradiologic rsch. SUNY-Health Sc. Ctr., Syracuse, N.Y., 1989—; dir. neuroradiology div. SUNY Health Sci., Syracuse, 1992—; cons. Luth. Med. Ctr., Cleve., 1988-89, Cleve. Spine and Arthritis Inst.; spl. cons. to editor Neuroradiology, 1990—. Member editorial bd. Neuroradiology, 1974-82, Stroke, 1986-90; adv. editorial bd. Am. Jour. Neuroradiology, 1979-86; contbr. articles to profl. jours., presenter papers profl. confs. U.S., France, Mex., Uruguay, Can., Norway, Bermuda, Chile, lectr. in field, author (sci. exhibits profl. convs.), designer (radiologic equipment), developer (radiologic equipment). Trustee, mem. edn., benefits and devel. coms. Syracuse Symphony Orch., 1990-92, chmn. young orch. com., 1992—, chair youth orch., 1993-94, artistic divsn., 1993—; sec. Performing Arts Medicine of Ctrl. N.Y., 1990-91, exec. com., 1990-94. With USPHS Res., 1967-69. Fellow Am. Coll. Radiology (diplomate); mem. AAAS, Am. Soc. Neuroradiology (nat. sec. 1974-77, pres. 1982-83), Radiol. Soc. N.Am. (chair neuroradiology program com. 1978-81), Assn. Univ. Radiologists, Soc. Photo-Optical Instrumentation Egnrs., Am. Soc. Stereotactic and Functional Neurosurgery, World Soc. Sterotactic and Functional Neurosurgery, Itnernat. Med. Soc. for Advancement of Sci., Phi Sigma, Alpha Omega Alpha. Fellow Am. Coll. Radiology (diplomate); mem. AAAS, Am. Soc. Neuroradiology (nat. sec. 1974-77, pres. elect 1981, pres. 1982-83), Radiol. Soc. N.Am., Assn. Univ. Radiologists, Soc. Photo-Optical Instrumentation Engrs., Am. Soc. for Stereotactic and Functional Neurosurgery, Internat. Med. Soc. for Advancement of Sci., Phi Sigma, Alpha Omega Alpha. Office: SUNY Health Sci Ctr 750 E Adams St Syracuse NY 13210-2306

ROSENBAUM, IRVING M., retail store executive; b. Dresden, Germany, Apr. 20, 1921; came to U.S., 1938, naturalized, 1943; s. Max and Clara (Koerner) R.; m. Hanni Schein, Oct. 15, 1953; children: Eli M., Daniel S., Michael J. B.A. in Econs., New Sch. Social Research, 1953; M.A. in Econs., NYU, 1956. Stockman, S.E. Nichols Inc., N.Y.C., 1938-40; asst. store mgr. S.E. Nichols Inc., 1940-43, store mgr., 1946-48, buyer, 1949-56, mdse. mgr., 1957-60, chmn. mdse. bd., 1972-83, vice-chmn. bd., 1983-85, also bd. dirs.; v.p. Venture Israel Ltd., Balt., 1985—, Israel Pharms., Balt., 1976-83; chmn. bd. F.R. Schreiber Co., Lititz, Pa., 1975-82; adv. com. mem. AMIFID Ptnrs. L.P., N.Y.C. Bd. dirs. chmn. bd. overseers Solomon Schechter Day Sch., Nassau and Suffolk Counties, 1985-90; bd. dirs. United Jewish Appeal, Fedn. Jewish Philanthropies, Israel Bond Orgn. Greater N.Y.; nat. chmn. Friends of the Open U. Israel, 1989—. With U.S. Army, 1943-45. Recipient Prime Minister's medal Israel, 1976, 88. Mem. Nat. Mass Retailing Inst., U.S. C. of C. (govt. and regulatory affairs com. 1977-79, adminstrv. law coun. 1980-85). Club: Lake Mohawk Country (Sparta, N.J.). Only a person who appreciates his own background, traditions and values is able to appreciate those of others.

ROSENBAUM, JACOB I., lawyer; b. Cleve., Oct. 4, 1927; s. Lionel C. and Dora (Heldman) R.; m. Marjorie Jean Arnold, Apr. 20, 1952; children: Laura Rosenbaum, Alexander, Judith Bartell. JD, U. N.Mex., 1951. Bar: N.Mex. 1951, Ohio 1952. Pres. Ohio Savs. Assn., Cleve., 1955-60, sr. v.p., 1960-92, also dir.; ptnr. Burke, Haber & Berick, Cleve., 1955-79; chmn. bd. Mercury Holdings, Inc., Richmond Heights, Ohio, 1967—; ptnr. Arter & Hadden, Cleve., 1979—; mem. Nat. Transp. Safety Bd. Pres. Temple Emanu El, University Heights, Ohio, 1965-67; active Judson Retirement Cmty., Cleveland Heights, Ohio, 1990—, trustee, 1988-94, pres. 1990-92; trustee Cleve. Zool. Soc., 1983—; pres. adv. bd. Cleve Women's Orch., 1983—; trustee Cleve. Nat. Air Show, 1981—, pres., 1987-90. Mem. Lawyer-Pilots Bar Assn. (pres. 1981-82, editor jour. 1982—), Ohio Bar Assn. (chmn. aviation law com. 1981-84), Greater Cleve. Bar Assn., NTSB Bar Assn., Cleve. Execs. Assn. (pres. 1989, chmn. 1990), Kiwanis (pres. 1970-71). Democrat. Jewish. Avocation: flying. Home: 28050 N Woodland Rd Cleveland OH 44124-4518 Office: Arter & Hadden 1100 Huntington Bldg Cleveland OH 44115

ROSENBAUM, JAMES EDWARD, psychologist, educator; b. Plainfield, N.J., Dec. 11, 1943; s. Irving and Dorothy Louise (Berger) R.; m. Virginia Ruth Warcholik, Aug. 4, 1974; 1 child, Janet. BA, Yale Coll., 1966; PhD, Harvard U., 1973. Asst. prof. Yale U. New Haven, Conn., 1973-79; prof. Northwestern U., Evanston, Ill., 1979—; advisor commn. on youth and Am's. future, commn. on workforce quality U.S. Dept. Labor, Washington, 1988—, U.S. GAO, Washington, 1988—, U.S. Dept. HHD, Washington, 1990; cons. Leadership Coun., Chgo., 1982—. Author: Making INequality, 1976, Careers in Corporations, 1984, Blacks in White Suburbs, 1990, Transition from High School to Work, 1990. Grantee Spencer Found., 1982, Mott Found., 1989, Ford Found., 1989, U.S. Dept. Labor, 1977, Joyce Found., 1985. Mem. Am. Sociol. Assn., Am. Psychol. Assn. Office: Soc Dept Northwestern U 633 Clark St Evanston IL 60208

ROSENBAUM, JAMES MICHAEL, judge; b. Fort Snelling, Minn., Oct. 12, 1944; s. Sam H. and Ilene D. (Bernstein) R.; m. Marilyn Brown, July 30, 1972; children: Alexandra, Victoria and Catherine (twins). BA, U. Minn. 1966, JD, 1969. Bar: Minn. 1969, Ill. 1970, U.S. Supreme Ct. 1979. VISTA staff atty. Leadership Council for Met. Open Communities, Chgo., 1969-72; assoc. Katz, Taube, Lange & Frommelt, Mpls., 1972-77; ptnr. Rosenbaum & Rosenbaum, Mpls., 1977-79, Gainsley, Squier & Korsh, Mpls., 1979-81; U.S. dist. atty. U.S. Dept. Justice, Mpls., 1981-85; judge U.S. Dist. Ct. Hennepin County, Minn., 1985—. Author booklet: Guide to Practice Civil Rights Housing, 1972; co-author: U.S. Courts Design Guide, 1991—. Campaign chmn. People for Boschwitz, Minn., 1978. Mem. Fed. Bar Assn. (bd. dirs., pres. 1992-93). Republican. Jewish. Office: US Dist Ct 669 US Courthouse 110 S 4th St Minneapolis MN 55401-2216

ROSENBAUM, JOAN HANNAH, museum director; b. Hartford, Conn., Nov. 24, 1942; d. Charles Leon and Lillian (Sharasheff) Grossman; m. Peter S. Rosenbaum, July 1962 (div. 1970). A.A., Hartford Coll. for Women, 1962; B.A., Boston U., 1964; student, Hunter Coll. Grad Sch., 1970-73; cert., Columbia U. Bus. Sch. Inst. Non Profit Mgmt., 1978; DHL (hon.), Jewish Theol. Sem., 1993. Curatorial asst. Mus. Modern Art, N.Y.C., 1966-72; dir. mus. program N.Y. Council on Arts, N.Y.C., 1972-79; cons. Michal Washburn & Assocs., N.Y.C., 1979-80; dir. Jewish Mus., N.Y.C., 1980—;

mem. adv. bd. Pub. Ctr., N.Y.C. Bd. dirs. Artists Space, 1980—; officer Council Am. Jewish Mus., 1981—; mem. policy panel Nat. Endowment Arts, 1982-83. Knighted (Denmark), 1983; European travel grantee Internat. Coun. Mus., 1972; recipient Disting. Alumni award Boston U. Coll. Liberal Arts, 1994. Mem. Am. Assn. Mus. (cons. 1979—), Assn. Art Mus. Dirs., N.Y. State Assn. Mus. (mem. council). Office: Jewish Mus 1109 5th Ave New York NY 10128-0118

ROSENBAUM, JOSEPH IRVING, lawyer, educator; b. N.Y.C., Sept. 22, 1947; s. Paul and Claire (Wachs) R.; m. Renee Millstein, July 3, 1974; children: Adam, Jill, David. BS, CCNY, 1968, MS, 1971; JD, N.Y. Law Sch., 1977. Bar: N.Y. 1978, U.S. Dist. Ct. (so. dist.) N.Y. 1978. Tchr. N.Y.C. Sch. System, N.Y.C., 1968-78; sr. counsel Am. Express, N.Y.C., 1978-94; assoc. prof. law Fordham U., N.Y.C., 1984, N.Y. Law Sch., N.Y.C., 1990—; rep. U.S. Coun. for Internat. Bus., Washington and N.Y.C., 1990—. Mem. editorial bd. Internat. Computer Law Advisor; contbr. articles to legal jours. Mem. ABA (chmn. internat. data flow com. and coun., sci. and tech. sect.), N.Y. State Bar Assn., Computer Law Assn., Am. Corp. Counsel Assn. Avocations: tennis, skiing, music. Home: 17 Westerly Dr New City NY 10956-6652

ROSENBAUM, KENNETH E., journalist, editor; b. N.Y.C., Aug. 30, 1942; s. Abraham Rosenbaum and Lena (Sentner) Schroeder; m. Mary Hercelia Zeller, Aug. 30, 1964 (div. 1972); children: Sandra, Steven; m. Karen Marie Tiefenbach, June 14, 1980; stepchildren: Stephanie Kay Burket and Stacey Jo Burket. BA, Ohio State U., 1965. Editor Ohio Jewish Chronicle, Columbus, 1963-64; mng. editor Medina (Ohio) County Gazette, 1965-68; copy editor, reporter Akron (Ohio) Beacon Jour., 1968; news editor Cleve. Press, 1968-82; slotman, asst. news editor St. Louis Globe-Dem., 1982-84; systems editor Toledo Blade, 1984-87, asst. mng. editor, graphics, 1987-89, dir. photography, 1989-93, dir. news systems, 1993—; photography judge Medina Country Fair, 1977-82; instr. journalism Cuyahoga Community Coll., Cleve., 1982, Bowling Green State U., 1989, 91. Democrat. Jewish. Lodges: Lions (bd. dirs. Medina chpt. 1970-71), Masons (steward 1986-87), Shriner. Avocations: photography, golf, motorcycling, rotisserie baseball. Home: 7045 Leicester Rd Toledo OH 43617-1310

ROSENBAUM, LOIS OMENN, lawyer; b. Newark, Apr. 10, 1950; d. Edward and Ruth (Peretz) Omenn; m. Richard B. Rosenbaum, Apr. 4, 1971; children: Steven, Laura. AB, Wellesley Coll., 1971; JD, Stanford U., 1974. Bar: Calif. 1974, Oreg. 1977, D.C. 1974, U.S. Supreme Ct. 1990. Assoc., Fried, Frank, Harris, Shriver & Kampelman, Washington, 1974-75, Orrick, Herrington, Rowley & Sutcliffe, San Francisco, 1975-77, Stoel, Rives, Boley, Jones & Grey, Portland, Oreg., 1977-81, ptnr., 1981—; mem. U.S. Dist. Ct. Mediation Panel. Bd. dirs. Providence Med. Found., Robison Jewish Home; past mem. Nat. Legal Com. Am. Jewish Com. Wellesley Coll. scholar, 1971. Mem. ABA, Multnomah County Bar Assn. (arbitration panel), Am. Arbitration Assn (panel mem.). Clubs: Multnomah Athletic, Wellesley (Oregon) (pres. 1987-88). Office: Stoel Rives Boley et al 900 SW 5th Ave Ste 2300 Portland OR 97204-1232

ROSENBAUM, MICHAEL A., investor relations consultant; b. Chgo., May 13, 1953; s. Robert and Muriel (Caplan) R.; m. Jill Ann Rubenstein, Oct. 12, 1975; children: Susan Brooke, Stephanie Ilyse. BS in Communications, U. Ill., 1974; MBA, Roosevelt U., 1979. Reporter Peoria (Ill.) Jour. Star, 1974, Compass Newspaper, Hammond, Ind., 1974-75; corr. UPI, Chgo., 1975-78; mng. editor Purchasing World Mag., Barrington, Ill., 1978-79; chief Midwest bur. The Jour. of Commerce, Chgo., 1979-83; sr. assoc. The Fin. Rels. Bd., Inc., Chgo., 1983-85, ptnr., 1985-88, sr. ptnr., 1988-90, dep. mng. ptnr., chief oper. officer, 1990—. Author: Selling Your Story to Wall Street: The Art and Science of Investor Relations, 1994; contbr. articles to profl. jours. Chmn. capital campaign Congregation Beth Judea, Long Grove, Ill., 1984-87, v.p. programming & membership, 1993-94; mem. capital campaign com. Infant Welfare Soc., Chgo., 1990-92, dir., 1993—, v.p., 1994—. Recipient Ann. Report Excellence award Fin. World Mag., 1988-93, Nat. Assoc. of Investment Clubs, 1986, 88-93, Assn. of Publicly Traded Cos., 1988-93, Publicity Club of Chgo., 1989. Mem. Nat. Investor Rels. Inst., Nat. Assn. Corp. Dirs.. Jewish. Office: Financial Relations Bd John Hancock Ctr 875 N Michigan Ave Chicago IL 60611-1801

ROSENBAUM, RICHARD MERRILL, lawyer; b. Oswego, N.Y., Apr. 8, 1931; s. Jack M. and Shirley (Gover) R.; m. Judith Kanthor, June 1, 1958; children: Amy, Jill, Matthew, Julie. BA, Hobart Coll., 1952; JD, Cornell U., 1955. Bar: N.Y. 1956. Ptnr. Rosenbaum, Agnello, Agnello & Levine, Rochester, N.Y., 1955-70; justice Supreme Ct. N.Y. State, 1970-73; ptnr. Nixon, Hargrave, Devans & Doyle, Rochester, 1977-84, 88—; counsel to chmn. of bd., dir. govt. rels. and pub. affairs. Integated Resources, Inc., 1984-88, also bd. dirs.; dir. Integrated Resources, Inc.; past mem. econ. adv. bd. U.S. Dept. Commerce; bd. dirs. sec. Jonathan Inst. Contbr. writings in fields of politics and public affairs, legal opinions to publs., 1984-88. Trustee Hobart Coll., 1977—; nat. committeeman N.Y. State Rep. Nat. Com., 1977—, rules rev. com., subcom. chmn. conv. procedures, 1977—; del.-at-large Rep. Nat. Conv., 1980, 84, 88, congl. dist. del., 1968, chmn. N.Y. State del., 1976; chmn. Monroe County Rep. Com., 1968-70, N.Y. Rep. State Com., 1973-77, Northeastern Rep. State Chairmen's Assn., 1973-76, Nat. Rep. State Chairmen's Assn., 1975-77; justice of peace Town of Penfield (N.Y.), 1962-66; mem. and asst. majority leader Monroe County Legislature, 1966-68; former mem. coun. SUNY, Brockport; apptd. by Pres. Ronald Reagan, U.S. Holocaust Meml. Coun., reapptd. by Pres. George Bush; apptd. by U.S. Senate to Bd. of Fed. Jud. Ctr. Found., 1989—; bd. dirs. Cardozo Sch. Law Yeshiva U.; bd. dirs. Rochester Mus. & Sci. Ctr., 1978—; gen. chmn. devel. fund drive, 1977—; trustee Rochester Area Colls., 1979—; mem. coun. of governing bds. of Ind. Colls. of State of N.Y., 1979—; apptd. mem. N.Y. Mental Hygiene Council, 1973-77, Nat. Citizens Adv. Com. on Environ. Quality, 1977; past bd. dirs. Jewish Home for Aged, Rochester; exec. com. Cornell Law Sch; Rep. candidate for nomination for N.Y. state gov., 1994. Recipient Congl. Medal Honor Ellis Island, 1992, Hobart Coll. Alumni citation. Mem. ABA, N.Y. State Bar Assn. Jewish. Clubs: Royal Order of Jesters, Masons, Shriners. Home: 19 Denonville Ridge Rochester NY 14625-1611 Office: Nixon Hargrave Devans & Doyle Clinton Sq PO Box 1051 Rochester NY 14603

ROSENBAUM, ROBERT ABRAHAM, mathematics educator; b. New Haven, Nov. 14, 1915; s. Joseph and Goldey (Rostow) R.; m. L. Louise Johnson, Aug. 1, 1942; children: Robert J., Joseph, David; m. Marjorie Rice Daltry, Aug. 26, 1980. A.B., Yale U., 1936, Ph.D., 1947; L.H.D. (hon.), St. Joseph Coll., 1970, Wesleyan U., Middletown, Conn., 1981; DSc (hon.), Conn. State U., 1993. Henry Fund fellow St. John's Coll., Cambridge (Eng.) U., 1936-37; Gen. Edn. Bd. fellow Reed Coll., 1939-40, from instr. to prof. math., 1940-53; prof. math. Wesleyan U., 1953-85, chmn. dept. math., 1953-63, dean sci., 1963-65, provost, 1965-69, v.p. for acad. affairs, 1967-69, chancellor, 1970-73, univ. prof., 1977-85, univ. prof. emeritus, 1985—; vis. prof. Swarthmore Coll., 1950-51, U. Mass., 1973, Coll. of St. Thomas, 1983; dir. Project to Increase Mastery Math. and Sci., 1979-95, chmn., 1995—; mem. exec. com. Hartford Alliance for Math. and Sci. and Tech., 1988-92, mem. coordinating com. Project CONNSTRUCT, 1991—; bd. dirs. Conn. Acad. for Edn. in Math., Sci. and Tech., 1991—, pres., 1992—. Served with USNR, 1942-45. Named hon. alumnus Reed Coll.; recipient Baldwin medal Wesleyan U., 1985, Transylvania medal, 1992. Fellow AAAS, Soc. for Values in Higher Edn.; mem. AAUP (chpt. pres. 1959-61, coun. 1981-84), Math. Assn. Am. (2d v.p. 1961-62, editor 1966-68, Christie lectr. 1994), Am. Math. Soc., Conn. Acad. Sci. and Engring. (charter mem., treas., chair edn. com.), Phi Beta Kappa, Sigma Xi. Office: Wesleyan U Middletown CT 06459

ROSENBAUM, STEVEN IRA, public relations and publishing executive, photographer; b. N.Y.C., Feb. 8, 1946; s. Samuel Meyer and Mary (Slobodow) R.; m. Janet Marilyn Hart, July 12, 1970; children—Elizabeth Jean, Mark Edward. B.S., Rochester Inst. Tech., 1967. Tech. rep. E.I. DuPont de Nemours and Co., Inc., Wilmington, Del., 1967-72; pres. Photog. Pleasures, Inc., Great Neck, N.Y., 1972-75; East coast editor Photog. mag. Petersen Pub. Co., Los Angeles, Calif., 1975-77; account supr. Bozell & Jacobs Advt. Agy., N.Y.C., 1977-80; v.p., assoc. pub. Modern Photography mag. ABC Pub. Co., N.Y.C., 1980-81, v.p., pub. High Fidelity mag. Schwann Record and tape Guides, Mus. Am. Internat. Directory of Performing Arts, 1981-86, v.p. circulation, 1986, v.p., pub., editorial dir.

Modern Photography mag., 1986-89; v.p. mgmt. supr. Bozell Inc. Pub. Rels., N.Y.C., 1990—, sr. v.p., 1992—; faculty Winona Sch. Profl. Photography, Winona Lake, Ind., 1972-75. Contbr. articles to profl. jours. Mem. Northport Bay Estates Civic Assn., N.Y., 1971—. Mem. Profl. Photographers Am., Soc. for Imaging Sci. and Tech., Am. Photog. Hist. Soc. (life), Mag. Pubs. Assn., Bay Boat Club. Avocations: photography; reading; music; walking; cooking. Home: 21 Hawkins Dr Northport NY 11768-1527 Office: Bozell Pub Rels Inc 75 Rockefeller Plz New York NY 10019

ROSENBERG, A. RICHARD, supermarket company executive; b. Englewood, N.J., 1938. Grad., Lehigh U., 1959. With Big V Supermarket Inc., Florida, N.Y., 1959—, pres., from 1969, chief exec. officer, dir., from 1981, now chmn. bd. Office: Big V Supermarkets Inc 176 N Main St Florida NY 10921-1021

ROSENBERG, ALAN GENE, newspaper editor; b. Chgo., Sept. 14, 1957; s. Earl David and Lorraine Faith (Blum) R.; m. Avis Beth Gunther-Rosenberg, Apr. 8, 1984; children: Ethan Elijah, Rebecca Greer. BJ, Northwestern U., 1978. From state staff reporter to asst. features editor Providence (R.I.) Jour.-Bulletin, 1978—. Mem. Am. Assn. Sunday and Feature Editors. Office: Providence Jour-Bulletin 75 Fountain St Providence RI 02902

ROSENBERG, ALAN STEWART, lawyer; b. N.Y.C., Mar. 29, 1930; s. Louis and Sadye (Knobler) R.; m. Ilse Rosenberg/Klein, Aug. 15, 1963; children: Gary, Robert. BA, Stanford U., 1949; LLB, Columbia U., 1952; LLM, NYU, 1960. Bar: N.Y. 1955. Assoc. Wolf Haldenstein Adler & Freeman, N.Y.C., 1955-56; ptnr., chmn. tax dept. Proskauer Rose Goetz & Mendelsohn, N.Y.C., 1957-94; bd. dirs. PEC Israel Econ. Corp. Contbr. articles to profl. jours. Mem. exec. com., bd. visitors Stanford (Calif.) Law Sch., 1982-85; advisor Stanford U. Humanities Ctr., 1985—, Jewish Studies Program, 1986—; chmn. bd. N.Y. Alliance for the Pub. Sch., 1988-91; mem. adv. com. on pub. issues, The Advt. Coun., 1991—; bd. dirs., sec. Univ./ Urban Schs. Nat. Task Force Inc., 1991—; mem. bd. visitors Columbia Law Sch., 1991—. Served to lt. (j.g.) USN, 1952-55. Avocations: amateur opera singer; tennis. Home: 115 Central Park W New York NY 10023-4153

ROSENBERG, ALEX, mathematician, educator; b. Berlin, Germany, Dec. 5, 1926; came to U.S., 1949, naturalized, 1959; s. Theodore and Rela (Banet) R.; m. Beatrice Gershenson, Aug. 24, 1952 (div. Apr. 1985); children: Theodore Joseph, David Michael, Daniel Alex; m. Brunhilde Angun, June 14, 1985. B.A., U. Toronto, 1948, M.A., 1949; Ph.D., U. Chgo., 1951. From instr. to assoc. prof. math. Northwestern U., 1952-61; prof. math. Cornell U., Ithaca, N.Y., 1961-88; chmn. dept. Cornell U., 1966-69; prof., chmn. dept. U. Calif., Santa Barbara, 1986-87, prof., 1986—, prof. emeritus, 1994—; mem. com. undergrad. program math. Math Assn. Am., 1966-76; mem. Inst. Advanced Study, 1955-57; vis. prof. U. Calif., Berkely, 1961, 1979, U. Calif., Los Angeles, 1969-70, 82, U. London, Queen Mary Coll., 1963-64, U. Munich, 1975-76, E.T.H Zurich, 1976, U. Dortmund, 1984-85; trustee Am. Math Soc., 1973-83. Editor: Proc. Am. Math. Soc., 1960-66, Am. Math. Monthly, 1974-77; Contbr. articles to profl. jours. Recipient Humboldt Stiftung Sr. U.S. Scientist award U. Munich, 1975-76, U. Dortmund, 1981. Home: 1225 Plaza del Monte Santa Barbara CA 93101

ROSENBERG, ALEX JACOB, art dealer, curator, fine arts appraiser, educator; b. N.Y.C., May 25, 1919; s. Israel and Lena (Zar) R. Student, Albright Coll., 1935-37, Sch. Phila. Mus. Art, 1937-40; BS, Phila. Coll. Textiles and Sci., 1948; DHL (hon.), Hofstra U., 1989, postgrad., 1992—. Pres., Anserphone, 1959-66; sec., dir. Gen. Cablevision Inc., 1968-72; v.p., dir. Communicable, Inc., 1967-71, Five Beaches C.A.T.V. Corp., Fla., 1967-71; Gen. Cablevision Palatka, Fla., 1967-71, Beacon Cable Corp., 1966-71; pres., dir. Modern Cable Corp., 1966-71, B.F.C.-C.A.T.V. Corp., 1966-71; v.p., dir. Starfax Corp. Real Estate, 1968-70; gen. ptnr. Lakewood Plaza Assocs., N.J., 1973-92, Rostin Assocs. Austin, Tex., 1970-83; pres. Transworld Art Inc., Alex Rosenberg Gallery and Alba Edits., N.Y.C., 1968-89, Rostin Mgmt. Corp., 1986-89, The Abbot Group, 1987-89, Ardmore Affiliates Ltd., Alex Rosenberg Fine Art, 1985—, Neikrug-Rosenberg Assocs., 1989—; lectr. Parsons Sch. Design, N.Y.C., 1979-88; instr. appraising modern art NYU, 1992—, adj. prof. appraising NYU, 1995—; vis. prof. fine art Advanced Inst. Arts, Havana, Cuba, 1993—; organizer Henry Moore exhibition Mus. Budapest, Bratislava and Prague, 1993. Contbr. articles to profl. jours.; co-curator Romare Bearden as Printmaker 1992—; assoc. editor exhbn. catalogue; curator An American Portrait Mus. Fine Art, Havana, Cuba, 1992-93; co-curator Henry Moore Mother and Child Exhbn., 1987-88; trustee Alice Baber Art Fund, 1991-93, Phila. Coll. Textiles and Sci., 1992—. Bd. dirs. Artists' Rights Today, 1974-80; mem. adv. com. Inst. Study for Older Adults, 1983-86; mem. mus. adv. bd. Hofstra Mus., Hempstead, N.Y., 1987—; mem. collection and exhbn. com. Parrish Art Mus., Southhampton, N.Y., 1989—; trustee Guttman Inst., 1979-92; mem. exec. bd. Nat. Emergency Civil Liberties Com., 1970—, treas., 1981—; trustee Nat. Emergency Civil Liberties Found., 1984—, chmn., 1992—; nat. bd. dirs. and bd. dirs. local coun. SANE, 1974-83; trustee, treas. New Lincoln Sch., 1968-71; trustee Givat Haviva Ednl. Found., N.Y.C., 1969—, chmn. exec. com., 1992—; trustee Givat Haviva Inst., Hadera, Israel, 1993—, Stephen Wise Free Synagogue, 1967-70, 73-76, Mus. Borough Bklyn., 1986-89; del. 28th World Zionist Congress, Jerusalem, 1972; mem. Community Planning Bd. # 7, 1965-67, 70-72; mem. Lower West Side Anti-Poverty Bd., 1965-66, Lincoln Ctr. Community Coun., 1968-74, Com. for Ind. Civilian Police Rev. Bd., 1967; mem. steering com. Com. Pub. Edn. and Religious Liberty; chmn. Am. Israel Civil Liberties Coalition, 1988-89; Dem. dist. leader, 1964-74, state committeeman, 1970-73, mem. county exec. com., 1964-74; del. Dem. Nat. Conv., 1968, 72; former treas. bd. dirs. Raoul Wallenberg Commn. of U.S., 1989—, chmn., 1990-92; mem. print and drawing coun. Israel Mus., 1980-85; assoc. dir. Snug Harbor Cultural Ctr, S.I., 1982-88. 2d lt. USAAF, 1943-45. Recipient Spl. prize Grenschen Triennial, Switzerland, 1976, Israel prize, 1974. Mem. Am. Soc. Appraisers (sr., bd. examiners 1988—, personal property com. 1988-90), Appraisers Assn. Am. (cert. mem., bd. dirs. 1990—, v.p. 1992-94, 1st v.p. 1994, pres. 1994—), Fine Art Pubs. Assn. (v.p., bd. dir. 1981-83, pres. 1983-86, treas. 1986-89), Nat. Arts Club. Home and Office: PO Box 583 Water Mill NY 11976

ROSENBERG, ALEXANDER, philosophy educator, author; b. Salzburg, Austria, Aug. 31, 1946; came to U.S., 1949; s. Samuel Theodore and Blanca (Nebenzahl) R.; m. Merle Susan Kurzrock, Dec. 21, 1969; children: Eugene, Adrianne. BA, CUNY, 1967; PhD, The Johns Hopkins U., 1971. Asst. prof. Dalhousie U., Halifax, Can., 1970-76; assoc. prof. then prof. Syracuse (N.Y.) U., N.Y., 1976-86; prof. U. Calif., Riverside, 1986-95, chair philosophy dept., 1989-92; dir. honors program U Ga., 1995—; dir. Univ. Honors Program, 1992-95, hon. program U. Ga., 1995—; vis. prof. U. Minn., 1975; vis. assoc. prof. U. Calif., Santa Cruz, 1978-79, vis. lectr. Oxford U., 1994-95. Author: Structure of Biological Science, 1984, Philosophy of Social Science, 1987, Instrumental Biology: Or the Disunity of Science, 1994; co-author: Hume and Problem of Causation, 1981, Economics-Science of Diminishing Returen, 1992. Guggenheim fellow, 1982, Am. Coun. of Learned Socs. fellow, 1982; grantee U.S. Dept. Edn. 1988, NSF, 1989, NEH, 1991, Lakatos award in philosophy of sci., 1993. Mem. Am. Philos. Assn. (com. on status of profession 1988-92), Philos. of Sci. Assn. (program com. 1986), Phi Beta Kappa (pres. N.Y. chpt. 1983-84). Avocations: rock climbing, jogging. Home and Office: U Ga Athens GA 30602

ROSENBERG, ALISON P., public policy official; b. Miami, Fla., Sept. 5, 1945; d. Mortimer I. and Gail (Sklar) Podell; m. Jeffrey Alan Rosenberg, May 4, 1969; 1 child, Robert Aaron. BS in Econs., Smith Coll., 1967. Mng. officer Citibank, N.Y.C., 1967-69; legis. aide Senator Charles Percy, Washington, 1969-80; profl. staff mem. Senate Fgn. Rels. Com., Washington, 1981-85; assoc. staff adminstr. Agy. for Internat. Devel., Washington, 1985-87; dir. African affairs Nat. Security Coun., Washington, 1987-88; asst. sec. for Africa State Dept., Washington, 1988-92; asst. admnstr. for Africa Agy. for Internat. Devel., Washington, 1992-93; co-financing advisor to the v.p. for Africa The World Bank, Washington, 1993—.

ROSENBERG, ARTHUR JAMES, research science company executive; b. Boston, Dec. 8, 1926; s. Benjamin R. and Lillian (Wolfson) R.; m. Naomi C. Solomon, Oct. 16, 1949; children: Deborah L., Janis E., Mia B. B.S. magna cum laude, Tufts U., 1948; M.A., Harvard U., 1951, Ph.D., 1952. Research scientist Merck & Co., Inc., 1951-54; mem. tech. staff Lincoln Lab., MIT,

Cambridge, 1954-60; pres. Tyco Labs., Inc., Waltham, Mass., 1960-70, Epidyne, Inc., Hawthorne, Calif., 1972-79, Panatech Research and Devel. Corp., Los Angeles, 1980—. Office: Panatech Rsch & Devel Corp PO Box 23160 Albuquerque NM 87192-1160

ROSENBERG, BRUCE ALAN, English language educator, author; b. N.Y.C., July 27, 1934; s. Howard Alyne and Audrey (Olenick) R.; m. Ann Harleman Stewart, June 1981; children: Eric Peter, Seth Allan, Bradley Michael, Sarah Stewart. Student, Alfred U., 1952-54; B.A., Hofstra U., 1955; M.A., Pa. State U., 1962; Ph.D., Ohio State U., 1965. Mem. faculty U. Calif., Santa Barbara, 1965-67, U. Va. Charlottesville, 1967-69, Pa. State U., State College, 1969-77; prof. English lit. and Am. civilization Brown U., 1977—; Fulbright lectr. Warsaw, Poland, 1981. Author: The Art of the American Folk Preacher, 1970, Custer and the Epic of Defeat, 1976, The Code of the West, 1981, The Spy Story, 1987, Can These Bones Live?, 1988, Ian Fleming, 1989, Folklore and Literature, 1991, The Neutral Ground, 1994; asst. editor: Caucer Rev., 1967-79, Jour. Am. Folklore, 1970-79; contbg. editor: Oral Tradition, 1985—. Served with U.S. Army, 1955-57. Recipient James Russell Lowell prize, 1970; Chgo. Folklore prize, 1970, 76; Am. Council Learned Socs. fellow, 1967; Nat. Endowment Humanities fellow, 1976-77; Guggenheim fellow, 1982-83. Mem. MLA, Folklore Fellows Internat., Am. Folklore Soc., Medieval Acad. Am. Jewish. Home: 55 Summit Ave Providence RI 02906-2709 Office: Brown U 82 Waterman St Brown Sta Providence RI 02912-0001

ROSENBERG, BURTON M., apparel company executive. Chief fin. officer Style Undies, N.Y.C., 1960-69; pres. Henry I. Siegel Co., Inc. N.Y.C., 1969—. Office: Chic By HIS Inc 1372 Broadway Fl 12 New York NY 10018

ROSENBERG, CHARLES ERNEST, historian, educator; b. N.Y.C., Nov. 11, 1936; s. Bernard and Marion (Roberts) R.; m. Carroll Ann Smith, June 22, 1961 (div. 1977); 1 child, Leah; m. Drew Gilpin Faust, June 7, 1980; 1 child, Jessica. B.A., U. Wis., 1956; M.A., Columbia U., 1957, Ph.D., 1961. Fellow Johns Hopkins U., Balt., 1960-61; asst. prof. U. Wis., 1961-63; assoc. prof. U. Pa., Phila., 1965-68; prof. history U. Pa., 1968—, chmn. dept., 1974-75, 79-83; Bd. dirs. Mental Health Assn. Southeastern Pa., 1973-76, Library Co. of Phila., 1980—. Author: The Cholera Years: The United States in 1832, 1849 and 1866, 1962, The Trial of the Assassin Guiteau: Psychiatry and Law in the Gilded Age, 1968, No Other Gods: On Science and Social Thought in America, 1976, The Care of Strangers: The Rise of America's Hospital System, 1987, Explaining Epidemics and Other Studies in the History of Medicine, 1992; editor Isis, 1986-89. Nat. Inst. Health Research grantee, 1964-70; Guggenheim Found. fellow, 1965-66, 89-90; Nat. Endowment Humanities fellow, 1972-73; Rockefeller Found. humanities fellow, 1975-76; fellow Inst. Advanced Study, 1979-80, Ctr. Advanced Study in Behavioral Scis., 1982-83. Fellow Am. Acad. Arts and Scis.; mem. Inst. Medicine of NAS, Am. Assn. History of Medicine (William H. Welch medal 1969, coun. 1974-76, pres. 1992-94), History of Sci. Soc. (coun. 1972-75), Soc. Social History of Medicine (pres. 1981), Orgn. Am. Historians (exec. bd. 1985-88). Home: 746 Beacom Ln Merion Station PA 19066-1604 Office: U Pa Dept History & Sociology Philadelphia PA 19104

ROSENBERG, CHARLES HARVEY, otorhinolaryngologist; b. N.Y.C., June 10, 1919; s. Morris and Bessie (Greditor) R.; m. Florence Rich, Dec. 27, 1942; children: Kenneth, Ina Garten. BA cum laude, Alfred U., 1941; MD, U. Buffalo, 1944. Intern Jewish Hosp. Bklyn., 1944-45; resident otolaryngology Mt. Sinai Hosp. N.Y.C., 1945-46, 48-50; teaching faculty, sr. clin. asst. Mt. Sinai Hosp. and Med. Sch., N.Y.C., 1950-72; attending surgeon Stamford (Conn.) Hosp., St. Joseph's Hosp., 1953—; dir. dept. otolaryngology Stamford Hosp. and St. Joseph's Hosp., 1973-79. Campaign chmn. United Jewish Fedn., Stamford, 1978-81, pres. 1981-83, exec. com. 1978—; mem. pres.'s coun. Alfred (N.Y.) U., 1990—. Capt. U.S. Army, 1945-46. Fellow ACS; mem. AMA, Stamford Med. Soc., Fairfield Med. Soc., Conn. State Med. Soc., Am. Bd. Otolaryngology, Am. Acad. Ophthalmology and Otolaryngology. Democrat. Jewish. Home: 304 Erskine Rd Stamford CT 06903 Office: 810 Bedford St Stamford CT 06901-1115

ROSENBERG, CHARLES MICHAEL, art historian, educator; b. Chgo., Aug. 3, 1945; s. Sandor and Laura (Fried) R.; m. Carol Ann Weiss, June 25, 1967; children: Jessica Rachel, Jasper Matthew. BA, Swarthmore Coll., 1967; MA, U. Mich., 1969, PhD, 1974. Asst. prof. SUNY, Brockport, 1973-80; assoc. prof. U. Notre Dame, Ind., 1980—. Author: 15th Century North Italian Painting and Drawing: Bibliography, 1986, Art and Politics in Late Medieval and Early Renaissance Italy, 1990; contbr. articles to Art Bull., Renaissance Quar., others. Kress Found. fellow Kunsthistorisches Inst., Florence, Italy, 1971-73, Am. Coun. Learned Socs. fellow, 1977-78, NEH fellow, Brown U., 1979-80, Villa i Tatti, Florence, 1985-86. Mem. Coll. Art Assn., Renaissance Soc. Am., Centro di Studi Europa Della Corti. Office: Notre Dame U Dept Art Art History & Design Notre Dame IN 46556

ROSENBERG, CLAUDE NEWMAN, JR., investment adviser; b. San Francisco, Apr. 10, 1928; s. Claude Newman and Elza (Wolff) R.; m. Louise Jankelson, Dec. 19, 1968; children: Linda Kay, Douglas Claude. BA, Stanford U., 1950, MBA, 1952. Research analyst J. Barth & Co., San Francisco, 1955-62; partner charge research J. Barth & Co., 1962-70; investment adviser, pres. Rosenberg Capital Mgmt., San Francisco, 1970—; lectr. and mem. adv. council Grad. Sch. Bus., Stanford. Author: Stock Market Primer, 1962, rev., 1970, 76, 81, 87, The Common Sense Way to Stock Market Profit, 1968, rev., 1978, Psycho-Cybernetics and the Stock Market, 1970, Investing with the Best, 1986, rev., 1993, Wealthy and Wise, 1994. Bd. dirs. Jewish Welfare Fedn., Presbyn. Children's Cancer Research Center, Internat. Hospitality Center, Jewish Community Center; trustee San Francisco Ballet Assn., Univ. High Sch., San Francisco.; chmn. adv. council Stanford U. Sch. Bus. Served with USNR, 1951-53. Recipient Arbuckle award Stanford U. Grad. Sch. Bus., 1984, Bus. Statesman award Harvard Bus. Sch. Assn. of No. Calif., 1995. Mem. Financial Analysts San Francisco, Alumni Assn. Stanford U. Grad. Sch. Bus. (pres.). Republican. Jewish religion. Clubs: Family (San Francisco), Concordia-Argonaut (San Francisco), Calif. Tennis (San Francisco), Family (San Francisco). Home: 2465 Pacific Ave San Francisco CA 94115-1237 Office: Four Embarcadero Center 29th Floor San Francisco CA 94111

ROSENBERG, DALE NORMAN, psychology educator; b. St. Ansgar, Iowa, Dec. 12, 1928; s. Eddie Herman and Ella (Kirchgatter) R.; BS, Mankato State Coll., 1956; M.Ed., U. S.D., 1959; postgrad. Ball State Tchrs. Coll., 1962, U. Nebr., 1961, Colo. State Coll., 1963-67; D.Arts, U. Central Ariz., 1978; m. Delrose Ann Hermanson, Sept. 10, 1950; children—Jean Marie, James Norman, Julie Ann, Lisa Jo. Tchr. public schs., Holstein, Iowa, 1956-60; prin. guidance dir., Crystal Lake, Iowa, 1960-62; prin. Grafton (Iowa) Jr. High Sch., 1962-66; psychol. tester Dept. Rehab., State of Iowa, 1960-66; prof. psychology North Iowa Area Community Coll., Mason City, 1966—; vis. lectr. Buena Vista Coll., Storm Lake, Iowa, 1984; invited speaker Inst. Advanced Philosophic Research, 1984-85. Served with USAF, 1949-53. Mem. NEA, Iowa Edn. Assn., Kappa Delta Pi, Phi Delta Kappa. Lutheran. Author multi-media curriculum for teaching disadvantaged introductory welding; author textbook-workbook, 1985. Recipient Golden Apple award Iowa TV Channel 3, 1994. Home: RR 3 Box 295 12373 Thrush Ave Mason City IA 50401-9828 Office: N Iowa Area Community Coll Mason City IA 50401

ROSENBERG, DAVID, law educator. Prof. law Harvard U., Cambridge, Mass. Office: Law Sch Harvard U Cambridge MA 02138

ROSENBERG, DAVID ALAN, military historian, educator; b. N.Y.C., Aug. 30, 1948; s. Sidney and Fay (Breitman) R.; m. Deborah Lee Haines, July 1, 1973; 1 child, Rebecca Haines. BA in History, Am. U., 1970; MA in History, U. Chgo., 1971, PhD in History, 1983. Asst. historian, cons. Lulejian & Assocs., Inc., Falls Church, VA., 1974-75; instr. history U. Wis., Milw., 1976-78; pvt. practice cons. researcher Chgo., Washington, 1978-82; asst. prof. history U. Houston, University Park, 1982-83; sr. fellow Strategic Concepts Devel. Ctr., Nat. Def. U., Washington, 1983-85; prof. strategy and ops. U.S. Naval War Coll., Newport, R.I., 1985-90; assoc. prof. history Temple U., Phila., 1990—; mem. U.S. exec. com. Four Nation Nuclear History Program, project dir. Berlin Crisis, 1989—; cons. Office of Chief

Naval Ops., Washington, 1974-78, 85—, Office of Sec. Def., 1990-93. Co-editor: (15 vol. book set) U.S. Plans for War, 1945-1950, 1990; contbr. articles to Jour. Am. History (2 awards nat. hist. assns. 1980), 20 others, also 11 book chpts. With USNR, 1982—. Advanced rsch. scholar U.S. Naval War Coll., 1974-79; Ford Found grantee, 1985-86, MacArthur rsch. grantee 1987-88; MacArthur fellow 1988-93. Mem. Orgn. Am. Historians (Binkley-Stephenson article prize), Soc. for Historians of Am. Fgn. Rels. (Bernath article prize), Soc. for Mil. History, U.S. Naval Inst., Internat. Inst. for Strategic Studies. Jewish. Office: Temple U Dept History Philadelphia PA 19122

ROSENBERG, DAVID HOWARD, lawyer, mediator, marketing executive; b. Terre Haute, Ind., July 2, 1941; s. Al and Pearl (Eshowsky) R.; m. Helen Claire Stahl, Jan. 29, 1967; children: Lisa Sharon. Michelle Lynn, Alan Jay. Student, N. Tex. State U., Denton, 1963-65; J.D., U. Tex., 1968. Bar: Tex. 1968. Law clk. to U.S. dist. judge, 1968-69; practice in Dallas, 1969—; pres. Precision Mktg., Inc., 1978—; bd. dirs. Nexus Inc., pres., 1991—. Bd. dirs. Jewish Fedn. Greater, Dallas, 1972-74, 76-80; trustee N. Am. Jewish Students' Appeal, 1973-80. Served with AUS, 1960-63. Recipient I. Zesmer Leadership award Jewish Fedn. Dallas, 1972. Mem. ABA, Tex. Bar Assn., Dallas Bar Assn. Atty. Mediators (mem. Nat. Assn. Security Dealers bd., mem. Am Arbitration Assn. bd. arbitrators). Home: 7102 Dye Dr Dallas TX 75248-1507 Office: Ste 1200 1845 Woodall Rodgers Fwy Dallas TX 75201

ROSENBERG, DOUGLAS OWEN, healthcare management executive; b. Chgo., July 13, 1941; s. Owen Carl and Doris Raven (Ambrose) R.; m. Deloris Anne Anne Wimmer, Aug. 19, 1967; children: Kevin Douglas, Jeffrey Kendall. BS in Biology, U. Chgo., 1963, MBA in Hosp. Adminstrn., 1969. Adminstrv. asst., asst. adminstr., assoc. adminstr. Ohio State U. Hosps., Columbus, 1969-74; v.p. adminstrn. Ravenswood Hosp., Chgo., 1974-76; v.p. clin. svc., exec. v.p. ops., pres. Evanston (Ill.) Hosp. Corp. 1976-92; pres., CEO Howard Young Health Care, Woodruff, Wis., 1994—; grad. student preceptor various univs., 1980-92. Pres. Glenview (Ill.) Safety Com., 1979-83; v.p. Glenview chpt. Am. Cancer Soc., 1979-86; budget chmn. United Way, Northbrook, Ill., 1984-94. Capt. U.S. Army, 1964-67, Vietnam. Decorated Bronze Star; Inst. Medicine fellow, 1977-92. Mem. Wis. Hosp. Assn. Methodist. Avocations: history, numismatics, canoeing, tennis. Avocations: K P Mfg Co 7066 Hwy J Saint Germain WI 54558 Office: Howard Young Health Care PO Box 470 Woodruff WI 54568

ROSENBERG, GARY ARON, construction executive, lawyer; b. Green Bay, Wis., June 18, 1940; s. Ben J. and Joyce Sarah (Nemzin) R.; m. Gloria Davis, Nov. 1967 (div. 1975); children: Myra, Meredith; m. Bridgit A. Maile, Apr. 9, 1983. BS, Northwestern U., 1962, MBA, 1963; JD, U. Wis. 1966. Bar: Wis. 1966, Ill. 1967. Atty. U.S. SEC, Washington, 1966-67; pvt. practice Chgo., 1967-74; founder, chmn. bd., CEO UDC Homes, Inc. (formerly UDC-Universal Devel., L.P.), Chgo., 1968—; mem. adv. bd. Kellogg Grad. Sch. Mgmt. Northwestern U., Evanston, Ill., 1985—, founder, chmn. adv. bd. Real Estate Rsch. Ctr., 1986—, adj. prof., 1982—; founder Shadow Hill Entertainment Corp., Beverly Hills, Calif., 1990. Recipient Arts Edn. Svc. award Ill. Alliance for Arts Edn., Chgo., 1988, Kellogg Schaffner Disting. Alumni award Kellogg Grad. Sch. Mgmt., 1993. Mem. Nat. Assn. Home Builders (coun. 1989-90), John Evans Club. Avocations: skiing, hiking, climbing, tennis, golf, reading. Office: UDC Homes Inc 980 N Michigan Ave Ste 1590 Chicago IL 60611 also: UDC Homes Inc 4812 S Mill Ave Tempe AZ 85232

ROSENBERG, GEORGE A., public relations company executive; b. N.Y., Dec. 13, 1945. BA in Pub. Rels., The Am. U., 1967; student, Pace Coll. With Burson-Marsteller, 1969-85; pres., COO Cohn & Wolfe, 1992-93; pres., CEO, 1992-93; mng. dir. Ward Howell Internat., N.Y., 1993—. Office: Cohn & Wolfe 225 Peachtree St NE Atlanta GA 30303-1701*

ROSENBERG, HENRY A., JR., petroleum executive; b. Pitts., Nov. 7, 1929; s. Henry A. and Ruth (Blaustein) R.; children: Henry A. III, Edward Lee, Frank Blaustein; m. Dorothy Lucibello, June 30, 1984. B.A. in Econs., Hobart Coll., 1952. With Crown Cen. Petroleum Corp., Balt., 1952—, pres., 1966-75, chmn. exec. com., 1966—, chmn. bd., 1975—, also chief exec. officer; dir. Am. Trading & Prodn. Corp., USF&G Corp., Signet Banking Corp. Bd. dirs. Johns Hopkins Hosp., Goucher Coll., McDonogh Sch., Nat. Flag Day Found., YMCA Greater Balt., United Way Cen. Md., Crohn's and Colitis Found., Md., Nat. Aquarium Balt.; mem. nat. exec. bd., mem. N.E. regional bd., v.p. program group nat. coun., past pres., exec. bd., adv. coun. Balt. Area coun. Boy Scouts Am.; past chmn., mem. adv. bd. William Donald Schaefer Ctr. for Pub. Policy. Mem. Nat. Petroleum Refiners Assn. (chmn., bd. dirs., exec. com.), Nat. Petroleum Coun., Balt. Area Convention and Visitors Assn. (chmn. bd. dirs.), 25 Yr. Club Petroleum Industry. Office: Crown Cen Petroleum Corp 1 N Charles St PO Box 1168 Baltimore MD 21203

ROSENBERG, JAMES WILLIAM, marketing executive; b. Boston, Nov. 23, 1958; s. Sumner Harold and Ruth (Sheff) R.; m. Donna Gail Siskind, Oct. 23, 1982; children: Randall Alexandra, Bari Elizabeth. BBA, U. Mass., Amherst, Mass., 1980; MBA, Bentley Coll., Waltham, Mass., 1985. Fin. analyst Raytheon/Telex Data Systems, Norwood, Mass., 1980-85; direct mktg. dir. ISM, Strategic Mktg., Inc., Boston, 1985-92; exec. v.p. mktg. Berenson, Isham & Ptnrs., Boston, 1992—; bd. dirs. Leveathal-Siddman Jewish Cmty. Ctr., Newton, Mass., 1991—; mem. judging com. Direct Mktg. Assn., N.Y.C., 1989-91; guest speaker Fla. Direct Mktg. Assn., Ft. Lauderdale, 1990; instr. continuing profl. studies Bentley Coll. Contbr. articles to profl. jours.; speaker Integrated Direct Mktg. Am. Mktg. Assn. 1989. Mktg. chmn. Leventhal-Siddman Jewish Community Ctr., Newton, Mass., 1989-92. Recipient ECHO award Direct Mktg. Assn. N.Y., 1989-90; NEDMA award New Eng. Direct Mktg. Assn., Boston, 1989-94. Mem. Direct Mktg. Assn., New England Direct Mktg. Assn. Avocations: swimming, woodworking, restorations, automobiles. Office: Berenson Isham & Ptnrs Inc 31 Milk St Boston MA 02109

ROSENBERG, JEROME I., lawyer; b. Passaic, N.J., June 9, 1931; s. Emanuel and Sylvia S. (Schwartz) R.; m. Dorothy Elaine Tennirbaum, Aug. 21, 1955; children:—Peter, Michael. B.A., NYU, 1953; LL.B., Harvard U., 1956. Bar: N.Y. 1966, D.C. 1957, U.S. Supreme Ct. Tax law specialist IRS, Washington, 1960-63; mem. firm Hughes Hubbard & Reed, N.Y.C., 1968—; dir. 1016 Properties, Inc., N.Y.C.; lectr. NYU Tax Inst. Contbr. articles to Jour. of Taxation. Served as lt. USAF, 1957-60. Mem. N.Y. State Bar Assn., Assn. of Bar of City N.Y., D.C. Bar Assn., Phi Beta Kappa. Office: Hughes Hubbard & Reed One Battery Park Plz New York NY 10004-1466

ROSENBERG, JEROME LAIB, chemist, educator; b. Harrisburg, Pa., June 20, 1921; s. Robert and Mary (Katzman) R.; m. Shoshana Gabriel, Sept. 15, 1946; children—Jonathan, Judith. AB, Dickinson Coll., 1941; MA, Columbia U., 1944, PhD, 1948. Rsch. chemist S.A.M. Labs, 1944-46; Instr. chemistry Columbia U., 1946-48; rsch. assoc., asst. prof. Inst. Radiobiology and Biophysics, U. Chgo., 1950-53; mem. faculty U. Pitts., 1953-91, chmn. dept. biophysics and microbiology, 1969-71, prof. biol. scis., 1976-91, dean faculty arts and scis., 1970-86, vice provost, 1978-89, chmn. biol. scis., 1989-90, interim chmn. communication, 1991, assoc. dean faculty arts and scis., 1991-92, rsch. integrity officer, 1992—, prof. emeritus biol. scis., 1991—, dir. Jewish studies program, 1991—. Author: Photosynthesis, 1965; editor, reviser: Outline Theory and Problems of College Chemistry (Schaum), 1949, 58, 66, 80, 90; contbr. articles to profl. jours. NSF sr. fellow Technion Israel Inst. Tech., 1962-63, AEC fellow U. Chgo., 1948-50; recipient Pitts. award Am. Chem. Soc., 1978. Home: 1029 S Negley Ave Pittsburgh PA 15217-1045 (1968-69).

ROSENBERG, JEROME WILLARD, accounting and consulting company executive; b. Scranton, Pa., May 2, 1930; s. Sam and Helen (Jurkowitz) R.; m. Lois Jean Feldstein, Nov. 16, 1952; children: Barbara J. Richard. BS in Commerce, Pa. State U., 1952. CPA, Pa. Acct. Laventhol Krekstein & Co., Wilkes-Barre, Pa., 1952-60, ptnr., 1960-63, ptnr.-in-charge, 1963-67; nat. tax ptnr. Laventhol, Krekstein, Horwath & Horwath, Wilkes-Barre, 1968-70; ptnr.-in-charge Laventhol & Horwath, Wilkes-Barre, 1970-76; ptnr.-in-charge Laventhol & Horwath, Mpls., 1976-80, regional mng. ptnr., 1980; mng. ptnr. ops. Laventhol & Horwath, Phila., 1980-89; exec. v.p., sec.-treas. Valuation Counselors, Inc., Phila., 1989—. Mem. Am Inst. CPA's, Pa. Soc. CPA's.

Republican. Jewish. Office: Valuation Counselors Inc 1845 Walnut St Fl 10 Philadelphia PA 19103-4701

ROSENBERG, JERRY MARTIN, business administration educator; b. N.Y.C., Feb. 5, 1935; s. Frank and Esther (Gardner) R.; m. Ellen Young, Sept. 11, 1960; children: Lauren, Elizabeth. B.S., Coll. City N.Y., 1956; M.A., Ohio State U., 1957; certificate, Sorbonne, 1958; Ph.D., N.Y.U., 1963. Asst. prof. Cornell U. Sch. Indsl. and Labor Relations, 1961-64; asst. prof. Columbia U., 1964-68; pvt. practice cons. N.Y.C., 1968-71; assoc. prof. CUNY, 1971-74; prof. mgmt., chmn. dept. Poly. Inst. N.Y., N.Y.C., 1974-77; prof. mgmt. Lehman Coll., CUNY; prof. bus. adminstrn. and mgmt., chmn. dept. bus. adminstrn. Rutgers U., Newark, 1977-88, prof. grad. sch. mgmt., chmn. dept. internat. bus., 1988—; testified before U.S. senate on privacy, 1971. Author: Automation Manpower and Education, 1966, The Computer Prophets, 1969, The Death of Privacy, 1969, Dictionary of Business and Management, 1978, Dictionary of Banking and Financial Services, 1982, Inside the Wall Street Journal, 1982, Dictionary of Computers, Data Processing and Telecommunications, 1983, Investor's Dictionary, 1986, Dictionary of Artificial Intelligence and Robotics, 1986, The New Europe, 1991, Dictionary of Business Acronyms, Abbreviations and Initials, 1992, Dictionary of Wall Street Acronyms, Abbreviations and Initials, 1992, Dictionary of Information Technology and Computer Acronyms, Abbreviations and Initials, 1992, The New American Community, 1992, Dictionary of International Trade, 1994, Encyclopedia of NAFTA, The New American Community and Latin-American Trade, 1994, Dictionary of Marketing and Advertising, 1995. Recipient Fulbright and French Govt. awards, 1957. Known as Am.'s foremost bus. and tech. lexicographer. Home: 515 Tulfan Ter Bronx NY 10463-1705 Office: Rutgers U Mgmt Edn Ctr Newark NJ 07102

ROSENBERG, JOHN DAVID, English educator, literary critic; b. N.Y.C., Apr. 17, 1929; s. David and Dorothy Lilian (Shatz) R.; m. Barbara E. Hatch, 1952 (div. 1969); m. Maurine Ann Hellner, June 11, 1972; 1 child, Matthew John. BA, Columbia U., 1950, MA, 1951, PhD, 1960; BA, Clare Coll., Cambridge U., 1953, MA, 1958. Editor-in-chief Columbia Rev., 1949-50; lectr. English Columbia U., N.Y.C., 1953-54, asst. prof., 1962-65, assoc. prof., 1966-67, prof. English, 1967—, William Peterfield Trent prof., 1988—; instr. CCNY, 1954-62; chmn. Columbia Coll. humanities program, 1970-73, dir. grad. studies in English, 1986-89; vis. prof. English, Harvard U., summer 1968, U.C., summer 1970, Princeton U., 1978; vis. fellow Clare Hall, Cambridge (Eng.) U., 1969; guest lectr. U.S. Mil. Acad., Cambridge U., Queens U., Northwestern U. Author: The Darkening Glass: A Portrait of Ruskin's Genius, 1961, The Fall of Camelot: A Study of Tennyson's Idylls of the King, 1973, Carlyle and the Burden of History, 1985; editor: The Genius of John Ruskin, 1963, Mayhew, 1968, Swinburne: Selected Poetry and Prose, 1968, The Poems of Alfred, Lord Tennyson, 1975; contbr. essays and reviews on English lit. to N.Y. Times Book Rev., Harper's mag., Hudson Rev. and profl. jours. Recipient Clarke F. Ansley award Columbia U., 1960, Coun. for Rsch. in Humanities grant-in-aid, 1965; Euretta J. Kellett fellow Cambridge U., 1951-53; Edward Coe fellow, 1956-57; Samuel S. Fels fellow, 1959-60; Am. Council Learned Socs. fellow, 1965-66, 79; Lawrence H. Chamberlain fellow, 1965-66; Guggenheim fellow, 1968-69; Nat. Endowment Humanities fellow, 1982-83. Mem. MLA (chmn. exec. com. Victorian div. 1970, exec. com. 1979-83), Tennyson Soc., Ruskin Assn., Camp Rising Sun Alumni Assn., Columbia Coll. Alumni Assn. (dir. 1980-82), Phi Beta Kappa. Office: Columbia U Dept English New York NY 10027

ROSENBERG, JOHN K., lawyer; b. N.Y.C., May 13, 1945; s. Robert and Joyce (Kane) R.; m. Fern Kaufman; children: Joyce, Amie. BA, Pa. State U., 1967; JD, Columbia U., 1970. Bar: N.Y. 1971, Kans. 1980, U.S. Dist. Ct. (no. dist.) N.Y. 1971, U.S. Dist. Ct. Kans. 1980, U.S. Ct. Appeals (10th cir.) 1982, U.S. Ct. Appeals (5th cir.) 1986, U.S. Supreme Ct. 1990. Staff counsel N.Y. Pub. Svc. Commn., Albany, 1970-74; prin. atty. N.Y. Consumer Protection Bd., Albany, 1974-78; asst. gen. counsel The Kans. Power & Light Co., Topeka, 1977-89, v.p. gen. counsel, 1987-89, exec. v.p., gen. counsel, sec., 1989-92; exec. v.p., gen. counsel Western Resources, Inc., Topeka, 1992—; mem. legal com. Edison Elec. Inst., 1987—. Bd. dirs. Friends of the Topeka 20, 1983-89, 94—, pres., 1988; mem. Mayor's Commn. on Literacy, 1990-93. Mem. Am. Gas. Assn. (legal mng. com. 1986—). Avocations: golf, flyfishing, hiking. Office: Western Resources Inc 818 S Kansas Ave Topeka KS 66612-1217

ROSENBERG, JUDITH LYNNE, middle school educator; b. Bklyn., Nov. 1, 1944; d. Benjamin and Rose (Delbaum) Jackler; m. Joel Barry Rosenberg, Aug. 26, 1965; children: Jeffrey Alan, Marc David. BA in Edn., Queens Coll., Flushing, N.Y., 1966, MS in Edn., 1972. Lic. advanced profl. elem. and mid. sch. math., Md., elem. edn., N.Y. Elem. tchr. N.Y.C. and Cranston, R.I., 1966-68; tchr. math. Earl B. Wood Mid. Sch., Rockville, Md., 1981-82, Walt Whitman High Sch., Bethesda, Md., 1982-83, Robert Frost Mid. Sch., Rockville, Md., 1983-89; math. and interdisciplinary resource Julius West Mid. Sch., Rockville, 1989—. Mem. NEA, Nat. Coun. Tchrs. Math., Md. State Tchrs. Assn. Home: 16 Flameleaf Ct Gaithersburg MD 20878-5216 Office: Julius West Mid Sch Great Falls Rd Rockville MD 20850

ROSENBERG, JUDITH META, brokerage executive; b. N.Y.C., Sept. 17, 1964. BS in Fin., Lehigh U., 1986. With Morgan Stanley, N.Y.C. 1986; broker Bear Stearns & Co., N.Y.C., 1987, v.p., 1988, assoc. dir., 1989; mng. dir., 1990. Bd. dirs. Henry Kaufmann Campgrounds. Mem. N.Y. Jr. League, Lehigh Alumni Assn., Women's Nat. Rep. Club. Republican. Office: 245 Park Ave Fl 9 New York NY 10167-0002

ROSENBERG, KIM DAVID, banker; b. Harrisburg, Pa., Nov. 21, 1945; s. Abraham Leon and Jeanette (Woolf) R.; m. Linda Marcia Sulka, Aug. 24, 1968; children: Elise Diane, Laine Michelle, Evan James. BS in Econs., U. Pa., 1967, MS in Ops. Research, 1973. 2nd v.p. Chase Manhattan Bank, N.Y.C., 1975-76; v.p. Chase Manhattan Bank, 1976-78, mgmt. sci. div. exec., 1978-80, student loan div. exec., 1980-82, treas. consumer sector, 1982-83; treas. NYBD Citibank N.A., N.Y.C., 1983-84; treas. NED Citibank N.A., 1985-86; pres. Citicorp Homeowners Inc., St. Louis, 1986-87; vice chmn. Citicorp Mortgage, Inc., St. Louis, 1987—; chmn. Citicorp Mortgage Securities Inc., N.Y.C., 1987—; dir. Citibank FSB (DC), 1990-92. Lt. comdr. USN, 1968-72. Mem. U. Pa. Alumni Club of N.J. (bd. dirs. 1974-86), Mortgage Bankers Assn. (sec. mktg. com. 1988—), Jr. Achievement of the Miss. Valley (bd. dirs. 1989—). Avocations: tennis, windsurfing, Golfing. Home: 14056 Montrachet Ln Chesterfield MO 63017-8342 Office: Citicorp Mortgage Inc 12855 N Outer Forty Dr Saint Louis MO 63141

ROSENBERG, LEON EMANUEL, medical educator, geneticist, university dean; b. Madison, Wis., Mar. 3, 1933; s. Abraham Joseph and Celia (Mazursky) R.; m. Elaine Lewis, Aug. 29, 1954 (div. Nov. 1971); children—Robert, Diana, David; m. Diane Drobnis, July 4, 1979; 1 child, Alexa. B.U.Wis., Madison, 1954, MD, 1957, Dsc (hon.), 1989. Diplomate Am. Bd. Internal Medicine. Intern Columbia Presbyn. Med. Ctr., N.Y., 1957-58, resident, 1958-59; resident Yale U.- New Haven Hosp., 1962-63; fellow metabolism Nat. Inst. Health, Bethesda, Md., 1959-62; Asst. prof. medicine Yale Sch. Medicine, New Haven, 1965-68, assoc. prof. pediatrics and medicine, 1968-72, prof. human genetics, medicine and pediatrics chmn. dept. human genetics, 1972-84, dean Sch. Medicine, 1984—, C.N.H. Long prof., 1980—; now rsch. scientist Bristol-Myers Squibb Pharmacology Rsch. Inst., Princeton, N.J.; mem. adv. council NIADDK, 1980-83; mem. com. on infant health Robert Wood Johnson Found., 1982-90; mem. panel Inst. Medicine, NIH, 1983-84; chmn. adv. com. scholars program Hartford Found., N.Y., 1984-85. Author: Amino Acid Metabolism and Its Disorders, 1974; editor: Metabolic Control and Disease, 1981. Served to sr. surgeon USPHS, 1959-65. Recipient Disting. Alumnus citation U. Wis. Madison, 1982. Fellow NAS, Inst. Medicine of NAS, AAAS, Am. Acad. Arts and Scis.; mem. Am. Soc. Clin. Investigation (v.p. 1978-79), Am. Soc. Human Genetics (pres. 1980-81), Am. Soc. Biol. Chemists, Assn. Am. Med. Colls. (coun. deans, chair elect 1990-91, chair 1991—). Democrat. Jewish. Avocations: tennis; skiing; jogging. Office: Bristol-Myers Squibb Pharmacology Rsch Inst PO Box 4000 Princeton NJ 08543-4000*

ROSENBERG, LEON JOSEPH, marketing educator; b. Atlanta, Oct. 9, 1918; s. Harry Manville and Gertrude Dora (Hassenbusch) R.; m. Phylis Jane Israel, Feb. 6, 1943 (dec. Mar. 1976); children: Joanne Rosenberg

Larson, Paul Harvey; m. Louise Marjorie Nachman, Oct. 15, 1977. B.S. in Indsl. Mgmt., Ga. Inst. Tech., 1939; M.S. (Univ. scholar), Columbia U., 1940; Ph.D., N.Y. U., 1967. Mem. staff Nat. Retail Mchts. Assn., N.Y.C., 1947-49; sr. research analyst Federated Dept. Stores, Inc., Cin., 1949-52; research dir. Sanger Harris Dept. Store, Dallas, 1952-56; gen. supt. Sanger Harris Dept. Store, 1956-67; assoc. prof. Coll. Bus. Adminstrn., U. Ark., Fayetteville, 1967-74; prof., mktg. and transp. Coll. Bus. Adminstrn., U. Ark., 1975-89, dept. head, 1986-89; prof. emeritus U. Ark., 1989—; with Lindsey & Assocs. Inc., Fayetteville; real estate cons., 1990—; lectr. various univs. Contbr. articles to profl. jours. Pres. Jewish Family Svc., Dallas, 1960-62, Temple Shalom, Fayetteville, 1992—; mem. exec. com. Jewish Welfare Fedn., 1963-67; bd. dirs. New Orleans Jewish Children's Regional Svc., 1962-72, 75-94, Jewish Fedn. Ark., 1990—; bd. dirs. Washington County (Ark.) chpt. Am. Cancer Soc., 1979-86, pres., 1982-83. Capt. USAAF, 1940-46. Mem. Acad. Mktg. Sci., Am. Mktg. Assn., So. Mktg. Assn., S.W. Mktg. Assn., S.W. Small Bus. Inst. Assn., Econs. and Bus. History Soc. (trustee 1986-89), Masons, B'nai B'rith, Alpha Phi Omega (svc. award 1971), Beta Gamma Sigma, Delta Nu Alpha. Home: 1124 W Lakefront Dr Fayetteville AR 72703-2000 Office: Lindsey & Assocs Inc Po Box 1174 Fayetteville AR 72702

ROSENBERG, LEONARD See RANDALL, TONY

ROSENBERG, LEROY JOSEPH, hospital executive, former military officer; b. Charleston, S.C., Apr. 7, 1940; s. A. Harry and Jennie (Sokol) R.; m. Cheryl Binder, May 14, 1964; children: Owen, Paige, David. BS, The Citadel, 1962; MHA, Baylor U., 1974. Commd. 2 lt. US Army, 1964, advanced through grades to lt. col., various army assignments, 1964-76, chief med. supply Landstuhl (Ger.) Med. Ctr., 1976-78, chief logistics Augsburg (Ger.) Army Hosp., 1978-80; chief logistics Walson Army Hosp US Army, Ft. Dix, N.J., 1980-84; ret. US Army, 1984; v.p. Presbyn.-U. Pa. Med. Ctr., Phila., 1984-85; v.p. ops. Cooper Hosp. Univ. Med. Ctr., Camden, N.J., 1985-92, chief exec. officer, 1992—. Chmn. bd. The Alternative Sch., Cherry Hill, N.J., 1991—; mem. Dist. Environ. Ctr., Trenton, N.J., 1991-92. Decorated Bronze Star, Legion of Merit. Fellow Am. Coll. Healthcare Execs.; mem. Rotary Internat. (Paul Harris fellow 1990), Del. Valley Health Coun. (com. 1993). Avocations: skiing, racquetball, sailing, reading, physical training. Home: 500 Covered Bridge Rd Cherry Hill NJ 08034-3109 Office: Cooper Hospital Univ Med Ct 1816 Spruce St Philadelphia PA 19103-6603

ROSENBERG, MANUEL, retail company executive; b. Boston, Apr. 26, 1930; s. Israel and Lillian (Wirin) R.; m. Audray Merle Gold, Aug. 28, 1955; children: Peter Neal, Beth Susan. A.B., Harvard U., 1951, M.B.A., 1953. V.P. Filene's, Boston, 1967-73; pres., chief exec. officer Gimbel's, Phila., 1973-75, chmn. bd., chief exec. officer, 1975-77; exec. v.p Garfinckel, Brooks Bros., Miller & Rhoads, Inc., Washington, 1977-79, pres., 1979-82, also dir.; chmn. bd., chief exec. officer Morse Shoe, Inc., Canton, Mass., 1982-92. Trustee Beth Israel Hosp., Boston, Mass. Eye and Ear Infirmary, Boston, Judge Baker Guidance Ctr., Boston. Served to lt. USN, 1953-56. Clubs: Univ., Harvard (Boston). Home: 370 Beacon St Boston MA 02116-1002

ROSENBERG, MARIANNE, lawyer; b. N.Y.C., Aug. 30, 1954; d. Alexandre Paul and Elaine Lois (Sobel) R. Maitrise, U. Paris, 1977; LLM, U. Pa., 1980. Bar: N.Y. State 1981. Assoc. Cleary, Gottlieb, Steen & Hamilton, Paris, 1977-79; assoc. White & Case, N.Y.C., 1980-87, ptnr., 1987—. Mem. N.Y. State Bar Assn. Office: White & Case 1155 Ave of Americas New York NY 10036-2711

ROSENBERG, MARILYN ROSENTHAL, artist, visual poet; b. Phila., Oct. 11, 1934; m. Robert Rosenberg, June 12, 1955; 2 children. B in Profl. Studies in Studio Arts, SUNY, Empire State Coll., 1978; MA in Liberal Studies, NYU, 1993. Author, creator unique poetry/painting books; solo exhbns. include Irvine Gallery, State U. Calif., Irvine, 1981, The Sandor Tezsler Libr. Gallery, Spartanberg, S.C., 1983, U. Wis., River Falls, 1984, 361 Degrees Gallery, Greenfield, Mass., 1987; two-person exhbns. include SUNY Purchase Libr., 1982, The Hudson River Mus., Yonkers, N.Y., 1984, Women's Studio Workshop Inskirts Gallery, Rosendale, N.Y., 1986, Brownson Art Gallery, Purchase, N.Y., 1988, (with collaborator) Westchester County Gallery, White Plains, N.Y., 1989, Marymount Coll., Tarrytown, N.Y., 1993; group exhbns. include Long Beach (Calif.) Mus. Art, 1977, Kathryn Markel Fine Arts Gallery, N.Y., 1978, Pratt Graphic Ctr. Gallery, N.Y., 1978, Polytechnic State U. Gallery, San Luis Obispo, Calif., 1979, Phila. Art Alliance, Glassboro State Coll., Pa., 1979, Ridotte del Treatro Comunale, Italy, 1980, SUNY Purchase Gallery, 1982, Galerie Caroline Corre, Paris, 1983, Thorpe Intermedia Gallery, Sparkhill, N.J., 1983, U. Rochester Gallery, Rochester, N.Y., 1984, 14 Sculptors Gallery, N.Y.C., 1984, Georgetown U., Washington, 1984, Franklin Furnace, N.Y.C., 1986, Douglas & Cook Colleges, New Brunswick, N.J., 1985, City Without Walls, Newark, 1986, Galleri T.V., Malmo, Sweden, Post Machina Group and Am. Consulate, Bologna, Italy, 1986, Technical U. of Nova Scotia, Halifax, 1986, Museu Municipal, Figuira Da Foz, Portugal, 1987, King Stephen Mus., Szekesfehrvar, Hungary, 1987, Allen Meml. Art Mus., Oberlin, Ohio, 1987, Cultural Centre of San Paulo, Brazil, 1988, Centro Cultural de la Caja de Ahorros de Valencia, Spain, 1988, Cooper Union Art, N.Y.C., 1989, San Francisco Craft and Folk Art Mus., 1990, Alternatives Gallery, San Luis Obispo, Calif., 1990-91, San Antonio Art Inst., 1991, Sazama Gallery, Chgo., 1992, SUNY Oneonta, 1992, Ralston Fine Arts, Johnson City, Tenn., 1993, Va. Ctr. for Craft Arts, 1993, Libr. Can., 1993, Muée de la Post, Paris, 1993, Pratt Inst., N.Y.C., 1993, Musée de la Poste, Paris, 1993-94, Papertrail, Ottawa, Can., 1993-94, Nexus Found. for Arts, Phila., 1994, Va. Ctr. for Craft Arts, Richmond, 1994, Ormond Meml. Art Mus., Fla., 1994, Libr. Nat. Mus. Women, Washington, 1994-95, Spirit Sq. Ctr. Arts, Charlotte, N.C., 1994, Ellipse Arts Ctr., Arlington, Va., 1995, Montserrat Coll. Art Gallery, Beverly, Mass., 1995, Yale U. Art Gallery Sculpture Hall, New Haven, Conn., 1995, Harper Collins, N.Y.C., 1995, Brookfield Craft Ctr., Conn., 1995, Muscatine Art Ctr., Iowa, 1995, Sangre de Cristo Art Ctr., Pueblo, Colo., 1995, ; public collections and archives include Art Gallery New South Wales, Sydney, Australia, Artpool Art Rsch. Ctr., Budapest, Hungary, Bibliotheque Nationale, Paris, Canadian Postal Mus. Archive, Ottawa, Electrografia Museo Internacional, La Mancha, Cuenca, Spain, Fogg Art Mus., Cambridge, Mass., Mus. of Modern Art Libr., N.Y.C., The Ruth and Marvin Sackner Archive, Miami Beach, Fla., Tate Gallery Libr., London, Victoria and Albert Mus., London, Yale U. Libr., New Haven, Ct., Canberra Sch. Art Gallery, Australia, Cleve. Inst. Art Libr., Harvard U. Fogg Mus. and Houghton Libr., Cambridge, Mass., Rochester (N.Y.) Inst. Tech., Sch. Art Inst. Chgo. Libr., Amherst (Mass.) Coll. Libr., Atlanta Coll. of Art Libr., Brown U. Libr., Cleve. Inst. of Art Libr., Dartmouth Coll., Sherman Art Libr., Georgetown U. Library, The N.Y. Pub. Libr., Rhode Island Sch. of Design, Stanford U. Libr., Temple U. Library, Phila., U. Calif. at Davis, Santa Barbara Librs., U. Chgo. Libr., U. Utah, Mariott Libr., U. Va. Libr., U. Commonwealth U. Libr., Wellesley Coll. Libr., Libr. Mus. Fine Arts Boston, Sch. Mus. of Fine Art Libr., Boston; works included in various publs. and periodicals. Studio: 67 Lakeview Ave W Peekskill NY 10566-6415

ROSENBERG, MARK B., think-tank executive; b. Athens, Ohio, Aug. 15, 1949; married; 2 children. BA, Miami U., Ohio; PhD in Polit. Sci., U. Pitts. Asst. prof. polit. sci. Fla. Internat. U., Miami, 1976—, chairperson Caribbean L.Am. studies coun., 1977-79, founding dir. L.Am. and Caribbean Ctr., 1979—, founding/acting dean Coll. Urban and Pub. Affairs, 1994—; co-dir. Fla. Caribbean Inst., Fla. Mexico Inst. Author, editor, co-editor 6 books; contbr. articles to profl. jours. Mem. Greater Miami C. of C. (vice chairperson exec. com. for internat. econ. devel.). Office: Fla Internat Univ North Miami Campus ACI-200 Coll Urban and Pub Affairs Miami FL 33131

ROSENBERG, MARK LOUIS, lawyer; b. Lexington, Ky., Sept. 21, 1947; s. Edward George and Shirley Lee (Berkin) R.; m. Betty Adler, May 16, 1982; stepchildren—Aaron and Sarah Claxton; children: Eli, Daniel. B.A., U. Mich., 1969; J.D., Harvard U., 1973, LL.M. in Raxation, Georgetown U., 1985. Bar: D.C. 1973, U.S. Dist. Ct. D.C. 1973, U.S. Ct. Appeals (D.C. cir.) 1973. Asst. to v.p. George Washington U., 1973-75; counsel U.S. Ho. of Reps., Washington, 1975-77; sr. atty. FTC, Washington, 1977-85; atty. Ross & Duerk, Washington, 1985—. Mem. Fed. Bar Assn. (Disting. Service award 1982, 83, 87, dep. sect. coordinator), ABA (legis. monitor adminstrv. law sect.). Democrat. Jewish. Home: 6101 Shady Oak Ln Bethesda MD 20817-

6027 Office: Gordon,Feinblatt,Rothman,Hoffberger & Hollander 1800 K St NW Washington DC 20006-2202

ROSENBERG, MAURICE, lawyer, educator; b. Oswego, N.Y., Sept. 3, 1919; s. Samuel and Diana (Lishansky) R.; m. Ruth Myers, Dec. 7, 1941 (dec. Nov. 1945); 1 child, David Lee; m. Gloria Jacobson, Dec. 19, 1948; children: Joan Myra dec. Sept. 1988), Richard Sam. A.B., Syracuse U., 1940; LL.B. (editor-in-chief Law Rev.), Columbia, 1947. Bar: N.Y. 1947. Law sec. to judge N.Y. Ct. Appeals, 1947-49; asso. firm Cravath, Swaine & Moore, N.Y.C., 1949-53; assoc. firm Austrian, Lance & Stewart, N.Y.C., 1953-56; prof. Columbia U. Law Sch., 1956, Nash prof., Harold R. Medina prof. procedural jurisprudence, 1973-91; on leave, 1978-81; dir. Project Effective Justice, 1956-64, Walter E. Meyer Research Inst. Law, 1965-71; spl. asst. to atty. gen. U.S., 1976; vis. prof. Harvard U., 1969-70; cons. U.S. Dept. Justice, 1977-79, asst. atty. gen. U.S., 1979-81; lectr., U.S., Asia and Europe; mem. faculty Appellate Judges Sems., Nat. Jud. Coll., Fed. Jud. Ctr.; cons. Western Justice Rsch. Ctr., 1992—; Tech. and Govt., 1989—; cons. Long Range Planning Com. on Judicial Conf. U.S.; mem. Mayor N.Y.C. Com. on Judiciary, 1962-77; chmn. Author. Council Appellate Justice, 1970-75, Coun. on Role of Cts., 1978-80; bd. dirs. Pvt. Adjudication Ctr. Duke Law Sch., 1985—; dir. program for judges on scientific evidence, 1991-92. Author: (with Rochelle Dreyfuss and Hans Smit) Elements of Civil Procedure, 1962, 5th edit., 1990, (with Willis Reese and Peter Hay) Conflict of Laws, 9th edit, 1990, The Pretrial Conference and Effective Justice, 1964, (with Paul Carrington and Daniel Meador) Justice on Appeal, 1976, (with James D. Hopkins and Robert MacCrate) Appellate Justice in New York, 1982; Editor: Dollars, Delay and the Automobile Victim, 1968, (with Lloyd Ohlin) Law and Social Research, 1977. Trustee Practising Law Inst., 1979—. Served with AUS, 1941-45, ETO. Fellow Am. Acad. Arts and Scis., Inst. Jud. Adminstrn.; mem. ABA (commn. to reduce ct. delay and expenses 1979-84, adv. com. on rules of civil procedure to U.S. Supreme Ct. 1980-87, chmn. standing com. on fed. judicial improvements 1990-92), Assn. of Bar of City of N.Y., Am. Bar Found., Assn. Am. Law Schs. (pres. 1972-73), Am. Judicature Soc. Clubs: Century (N.Y.C.); Cosmos (Washington). Home: 10 Hunting Ridge Rd White Plains NY 10605-4508 Office: Columbia U Law Sch 435 W 116th St New York NY 10027-7201

ROSENBERG, MICHAEL, lawyer; b. N.Y.C., Oct. 13, 1937; s. Walter and Eva (Bernstein) R.; m. Jacqueline Raymonde Combe, Apr. 29, 1966; children: Andrew James, Suzanne Jennifer. AB in Econs. with honors, Ind. U., 1959; LLB, Columbia U., 1962. Bar: N.Y. 1963, U.S. Dist. Ct. (so. and ea. dists.) N.Y. 1966, U.S. Ct. Appeals (2d cir.) 1975, U.S. Dist. Ct. (ea. dist. so. div.) Mich. 1989. From. dep. asst. atty. gen. to asst. atty. gen. N.Y. State Dept. Law, N.Y.C., 1963-66; assoc. Hellerstein, Rosier & Rembar, N.Y.C., 1966-73; assoc. gen. counsel Gen. Instrument Corp., N.Y.C., 1973-78; from assoc. gen. counsel to dep. gen. counsel U.S. Filter Corp., N.Y.C., 1978-82; v.p., gen. counsel, sec. Alfa-Laval Inc., Ft. Lee, N.J., 1982-88; counsel Becker Ross Stone De Stefano & Klein, N.Y.C., 1988-89; ptnr. Rosenberg & Rich, White Plains, N.Y., 1989-95, Quinn, Marantis & Rosenberg, LLP, White Plains, 1995—. Mem. ABA, N.Y. State Bar Assn., Assn. of Bar of City of N.Y., Westchester County Bar Assn. Office: Quinn Marantis & Rosenberg 170 Hamilton Ave White Plains NY 10601-1702

ROSENBERG, MICHAEL JOSEPH, financial executive; b. Passaic, N.J., Apr. 19, 1928; s. Emanuel and Sylvia Sarah (Schwartz) R.; m. Judith Ann Melnick, Dec. 6, 1964 (div. 1983); children: Ann Kirsten, Emily Jeanne; m. Kathleen Ann Jennings, Mar. 3, 1990. BS, Upsala Coll., 1951; MBA, NYU, 1955, postgrad., 1955-59. Asst. v.p. Meinhard & Co., N.Y.C., 1953-58, A.J. Armstrong Co., N.Y.C., 1958-59, Sterling Nat. Bank, N.Y.C., 1959-61; exec. v.p. Rosenthal & Rosenthal, Inc., N.Y.C., 1961—; bd. dirs. D.V.L., Inc., N.Y.C. Contbr. numerous articles on comml. fin. to newspapers and mags. Bd. dirs., treas. Town Hall Found., N.Y.C., 1982—; treas. Citizens for Clean Air, N.Y.C., 1984. Capt. U.S. Army, 1951-53, Korea. Decorated Silver Star, Bronze Star; recipient Meritorious Svc. award NYU, 1983; Albert Gallatin fellow, 1981. Mem. Albert Gallatin Assocs. (chmn. 1984-87), NYU Bus. Forum (pres. 1981-82), NYU Grad. Sch. Bus. Adminstrn. Alumni Assn. (pres. 1978-79), NYU Ptnrs. (co-chmn. 1987-89, chmn. 1990-93), NYU Club (pres. 1975-77, 82-85). Avocations: skiing, tennis, running, sailing. Office: Rosenthal & Rosenthal Inc 1370 Broadway New York NY 10018-7302

ROSENBERG, NATHAN, economics educator; b. Passaic, N.J., Nov. 22, 1927; s. Joseph and Mary (Kaplan) R.; m. Rina Gordon, Jan. 12, 1954; children: Karen, Gordon, Jonathan, David. B.A., Rutgers U., 1950; M.A., U. Wis., 1952, Ph.D., 1955. Lectr. Ind. U., Bloomington, 1955-57; asst. prof. U. Pa., Phila., 1957-61; assoc. prof. Purdue U., West Lafayette, 1961-64, prof., 1964-67; vis. prof. Harvard U., 1967-69; prof. U. Wis., Madison, 1969-74; prof. Economic History Cambridge U., U.K., 1989-90; prof. econs. Stanford U., Calif., 1974—. Author: Technology and American Economic Growth, 1972, Perspectives on Technology, 1976, Inside the Black Box, 1982, (with L.E. Birdzell) How the West Grew Rich, 1985, (with David C. Mowery) Technology and the Pursuit of Economic Growth, 1989, Exploring the Black Box, 1994, The Emergence of Economic Ideas (Essays in the History of Economics), 1994; editor: Jour. Econ. History. Served as sgt./ C.E. U.S. Army, 1945-47, Korea. Fellow Am. Acad. Arts and Scis., Royal Swedish Acad. Engring. (fgn.); mem. Am. Econs. Assn., Econ. History Assn., Royal Econ. Soc. Jewish. Office: Stanford Univ Dept Econs Landau Bldg Stanford CA 94305

ROSENBERG, NORMAN, surgeon; b. N.Y.C., Apr. 25, 1916; s. Leo and Rose (Kamerman) R.; m. Ruth Harriet Feller, Nov. 30, 1940; children: Lois A. Rosenberg Ebin, Ralph. BA, U. Pa., 1934; MD, NYU, 1938. Diplomate Am. Bd. Surgery, Am. Bd. Gen. Vascular Surgery. Intern Mt. Sinai Hosp., N.Y.C., 1939-41; resident Mt. Sinai Hosp., 1942-43; practice medicine, specializing in vascular surgery New Brunswick, N.J., 1946-80; sr. attending surgeon St. Peters Med. Center, New Brunswick, from 1946, now emeritus sr. attending surgeon; chief staff Middlesex Gen. Hosp., New Brunswick, 1959-66, chief vascular surgery, 1960-86, dir. dept. surgery, 1975-81; cons. surgeon Roosevelt Hosp., Metuchen, N.J., 1956-87; Raritan Valley Hosp., Greenbrook, N.J., 1970-81, Somerset Hosp., Somerville, N.J., 1952-88; J.F. Kennedy Hosp., Edison, N.J., 1969-88; clin. prof. surgery Robert Wood Johnson Med. Sch., U. Medicine and Dentistry N.J., New Brunswick, 1972-81, chief vascular surgery sect., 1981-86, prof. surgery, 1981-91, prof. emeritus, 1991—; cons. Johnson & Johnson Research Center, New Brunswick, 1954-78. Author: Handbook of Carotid Artery Surgery Facts and Figures, 1989, 2d edit., 1994; contbr. articles to books and profl. jours.; co-inventor modified bovine arterial graft. Trustee Robert Wood Johnson Found., 1958—. Capt. M.C., AUS, 1943-46. Fellow A.C.S., Southeastern Surg. Congress; mem. Soc. Vascular Surgery, Internat. Soc. Cardiovascular Surgery, Soc. Surgeons N.J. Home: 48 North Dr East Brunswick NJ 08816-1122

ROSENBERG, NORMAN JACK, agricultural meteorologist, educator; b. Bklyn., Feb. 22, 1930; s. Jacob and Rae (Dombrowitz) R.; m. Sarah Zacher, Dec. 30, 1950; children: Daniel Jonathon, Alyssa Yael. BS, Mich. State U., 1951; MS, Okla. State U., 1958; PhD, Rutgers U., 1961. Soil scientist Israel Soil Conservation Service, Haifa, 1953-55, Israel Water Authority, Haifa, 1955-57; asst. prof. agrl. meteorology U. Nebr., Lincoln, 1961-64, assoc. prof., 1964-67, prof. agrl. meteorology, 1967—, prof. agrl. engring., 1975—, prof. agronomy, 1976—, George Holmes prof. agrl. meteorology, 1981-87, prof. emeritus, 1987—, leader sect. agrl. meteorology, 1975-79, acting asst. vice chancellor for research, 1983-85; sr. fellow, dir. climate resources program Resources for the Future, Washington, 1987-92; mgr. integrated earth studies Tech. Planning and Analysis Ctr./Battelle Pacific N.W. Labs., Washington, 1992—; cons. Dept. State AID, NOAA, Oak Ridge Assoc. Univs., 1986-87, Elec. Power Rsch. Inst. 1989-92, Sandia Nat. Labs., 1990; mem. numerous ad hoc coms. and mem. standing com. on atmospheric sci. Nat. Acad. Scis./NRC, 1975-78, mem. bd. on atmospheric sci. and climate, 1982-85, mem. U.S. com. Internat. Geosphere-Biosphere Program, 1984-86, mem. panel on policy implications of climate change, 1990-91; mem. bd. coun. Agrl. Sci. and Tech.; vis. prof. agrl. meteorology Israel Inst. Tech., Haifa, 1968; trustee Nat. Inst. Global Environ. Change, 1992, vice-chmn., 1992—. Author: Microclimate: The Biological Environment, 1974, 2d edit., 1983, Chinese transl., 1983, Malay transl., 1987; also numerous articles in profl. jours.; editor: North American Droughts, 1978, Drought in the Great Plains: Research on Impacts and Strategies, 1980, Greenhouse Warming: Abatement and Adaptation, 1989; editor: Toward an Integrated Impact As-

sessment of Climate Change: The MINK Study, 1993; tech. editor Agronomy Jour., 1974-79; cons. editor Agrl. and Forest Meteorology, Climatic Change, Jour. Climate. Mem. Intergovernmental Panel on Climate Change, 1993—. Recipient Centennial medal Nat. Weather Service, 1970; NATO sr. fellow in sci., 1968, U. Nebr. rsch. fellow, 1968, Lady Davis fellow Hebrew U., Jerusalem, 1977, Nat. Resources fellow Resources for the Future, 1986; grantee State of Nebr., 1970-73, NSF, 1971-87, U.S. Dept. Commerce, 1972-74, 80-82, 83-85 88-89, NASA, 1972-73, 85-86, U.S. Dept. Interior, 1974-75, 77-79, 88—, U.S. Dept. Agr., 1979-82, U. Nebr. Found., 1982, Nat. Ctr. Atmospheric Rsch., 1984-85, U.S. Dept. Energy, 1989-92, G. Gunnar Vetleson Found., 1987-92, UN Environ. Program, 1989, EPA, 1988-89. Fellow AAAS (com. climate 1984-89, com. global change 1992—, adv. panel Earth Explorer ency. 1992-95), Am. Soc. Agronomy, Am. Meteorol. Soc. (Outstanding Achievement in Bioclimatology award 1978, councilor 1981-84); mem. Am. Assn. State Climatologists (Nebr. rep. 1979-81), Arid Zone Soc. India, Sigma Xi, Alpha Zeta, Gamma Sigma Rho. Jewish. Club: Cosmos (Washington). Office: Battelle Pacific Northwest Labs 901 D St SW Washington DC 20024-2169

ROSENBERG, PAUL, physicist, consultant; b. N.Y.C., Mar. 31, 1910; s. Samuel and Evelyn (Abbey) R.; m. Marjorie S. Hillson, June 12, 1943; 1 child, Gale B.E. AB, Columbia U., 1930, MA, 1933, PhD, 1941. Chemist Hawthorne Paint & Varnish Corp., N.J., 1930-33; grad. asst. physics Columbia U., 1934-39, lectr.; 1939-41; instr. Hunter Coll., N.Y.C., 1939-41; rsch. assoc. elec. enging. MIT, Cambridge, 1941; mem. staff Radiation Lab., Nat. Def. Rsch. Com., 1941-45; pres. Paul Rosenberg Assocs. (cons. physicists), Larchmont, N.Y., 1945—; Instr. Nav., 1950-51; mem. war com. radio Am. Standards Assn., 1942-44; gen. chmn. joint meeting Radio Tech. Commn. for Aeros., Radio Tech. Commn. for Marine Services and Inst. of Nav., 1950; co-chmn. Nat. Tech. Devel. Com. for upper atmosphere and interplanetary nav., 1947-50; mem. maritime research adv. com. Nat. Acad. Scis.-NRC, 1959-60; chmn. cartography panel space programs Earth resources survey NRC, 1973-76; chmn. panel on nav. and traffic control space applications study Nat. Acad. Scis., 1968; bd. dirs. Ctr. for Environment and Man, 1976-85. Mem. editorial com. Jour. Aerospace Scis., 1952-60; contbr. chpts. to books, entries in encys., over 70 articles to sci. tech. publs.; patentee in field. Recipient James S. Cogswell award U.S. Dept. Def., 1986. Fellow AAAS (v.p. 1966-69, mem. coun. 1961-73), IEEE, AIAA (assoc.), Am. Inst. Chemists, Explorers Club; mem. Am. Phys. Soc., Am. Chem. Soc., Nat. Acad. Engring., Acoustical Soc. Am., Armed Forces Communication Assn., Optical Soc. Am., Am. Soc. Photogrammetry (Talbert Abrams Grand award 1955), Am. Assn. Physics Tchrs., N.Y. Acad. Scis., Inst. Navigation (hon., pres. 1950-51), Beach Point Yacht Club (Mamaroneck, N.Y.), Columbia U. Club, Sigma Xi, Zeta Beta Tau. Home: 53 Fernwood Rd Larchmont NY 10538-1705 Office: Paul Rosenberg Assocs PO Box 729 Larchmont NY 10538-0729

ROSENBERG, PHILIP, production designer. Prodn. designer: (films) The Owl and the Pussycat, 1970, The Anderson Tapes, 1971, The Possession of Joel Delaney, 1972, Child's Play, 1972, From the Mixed-Up Files of Mrs. Basil E. Frankweiler, 1973, The Gambler, 1974, Network, 1976, Next Stop, Greenwich Village, 1976, The Sentinel, 1977, (with Tony Walton) The Wiz, 1978 (Academy award nomination best art direction 1978), (with Walton) All That Jazz, 1979 (Academy award best art direction 1979), Eyewitness, 1981, Soup for One, 1982, Lovesick, 1983, Daniel, 1983, Garbo Talks, 1984, The Manhattan Project, 1986, Moonstruck, 1987, Running on Empty, 1988, The January Man, 1989, Family Business, 1989, Q & A, 1990, Other People's Money, 1992, Beyond Innocence, 1993, Guilty as Sin, 1993, The Pelican Brief, 1993; art dir.: (films) Forever Young, Forever Free, 1976. Office: Smith/Gosnell/Nicholson & Assoc PO Box 1166 1515 Palisades Dr Pacific Palisades CA 90272*

ROSENBERG, PIERRE MAX, museum director; b. Paris, Apr. 13, 1936; s. Charles and Gertrude (Nassauer) R.; m. Béatrice de Rothschild, July 29, 1981. Baccalauréat, Lycée Charlemagne, Paris; Licence, Law Faculty, Paris; Diplome, Louvre Sch., Paris. Chief curator dept. paintings Musée du Louvre, Paris, 1982-94, pres., dir. Musé du Louvre, 1994—. Author: Chardin, 1963; Peyron, 1983; (catalogue) La peinture française du XVIIe siècle dans les coll. américaines, 1981; (catalogue) Watteau, 1984, Fragonard, 1987, Fréres Le Nain, 1993, Poussin, 1994. Mem. Société de l'Histoire de l'Art Français (pres. 1982-84), Comité Français d'Histoire de l'Art (pres. 1984). Home: 35 rue de Vaugirard, 75006 Paris France Office: Musée du Louvre, 34 quai du Louvre, 75058 Paris France

ROSENBERG, RALPH, former state senator, lawyer, consultant, educator; b. Chgo., Oct. 7, 1949; s. Nathan Benjamin and Rhea (Matlow) R.; m. Teresa Marie Sturm, July 11, 1989; children: Jacob Louis, Joel Patrick. BS in Commerce and Bus. Adminstrn., U. Ill., 1972; JD, Drake Law Sch., 1974. Bar: Iowa 1974. Sole practice Rosenberg Law Firm, Ames, Iowa, 1974—; mem. Iowa Ho. of Reps., Des Moines, 1981-90, Iowa Senate, Des Moines, 1990-94; adj. faculty Des Moines Area C.C., 1989—, Drake Law Sch., 1992—, Upper Iowa U., 1993—, Iowa State U., 1994—; dir. Environ. Planning Rsch. Group, Ames, 1976-77; exec. dir. Story County Legal Aid Soc., Nevada, Iowa, 1977-78; asst. Story County atty. County Atty.'s Office, Nevada, 1979-81; exec. dir., mng. atty. Youth Law Ctr., Des Moines, 1989-92; coord. Leadership in Govt. Inst., 1994—. Author, editor: Public Interest Law, 1992; author: Family Theory, Law, Policy and Practice, 1994; editor: Descriptive Analysis of Iowa Environmental Agencies, 1977. Co-chair Midwest Leadership Inst. of Coun. of State Govt.; bd. dirs. Iowa Protection and Advocacy, regional adv. bd. Legal Svcs. Corp. Iowa, Child and Family Policy Ctr.; past bd. dirs. Co-op. Child Care Svcs., Ames Cmty. Action Rsch. Group, Rural Iowa. Recipient Outstanding Contbn. to Well-being of Children award Youth and Shelter Svcs., 1992, Excellence in Svc. award Legal Svcs. Group, 1993, Iowa LWV Cornerstone award, 1994, Iowa Farmers' Union Friend of the Farmer award, 1994, Iowa Consumer Action Network Citizen Svc. award, 1994; named LEgislator of Yr., Sierra Club, 1988, Isaak Walton League, 1993; named Legis. Conservationist of Yr., Wildlife Soc., 1988, Elected Ofcl. of Yr., Iowa Corrections Assn., 1984. Mem. Iowa State Bar Assn. (family law com. 1993—), Nat. Conf. State Legislators (criminal justice com. 1986-94). Home: 1202 Northwestern Ave Ames IA 50010 Office: PO Box 1114 Welch Ave Sta Ames IA 50010

ROSENBERG, RICHARD M., lawyer; b. Chgo., May 14, 1934. BA, Harvard U., 1956, LLB, 1959. Bar: Ill. 1960. Ptnr. Mayer, Brown & Platt, Chgo.; adj. prof. Loyola Law Sch. 1983—. Contbr. articles to profl. jours. Mem. ABA, Chgo. Bar Assn., Chgo. Coun. Lawyers, Phi Beta Kappa. Office: Mayer Brown & Platt 190 S La Salle St Chicago IL 60603-3410

ROSENBERG, RICHARD MORRIS, banker; b. Fall River, Mass., Apr. 21, 1930; s. Charles and Betty (Peck) R.; m. Barbara K. Cohen, Oct. 21, 1956; children: Michael, Peter. BS, Suffolk U., 1952; M.B.A., Golden Gate Coll., 1962, LL.B., 1966. Publicity asst. Crocker-Anglo Bank, San Francisco, 1959-62; banking services officer Wells Fargo Bank, N.A., San Francisco, 1962-65; asst. v.p. Wells Fargo Bank, N.A., 1965-68, v.p. mktg. dept., 1968, v.p. dir. mktg., 1969, sr. v.p. mktg. and advt. div., 1970-75, exec. v.p. from 1975, vice chmn., 1980-83; vice chmn. Crocker Nat. Corp., 1983-85; pres., chief operating officer Seafirst Corp., 1986-87, also dir.; pres., chief operating officer Seattle First Nat. Bank, 1985-87; vice chmn. bd. BankAm. Corp., San Francisco, 1987-90, chmn., chief exec. officer, 1990—; dir. Airborne Express, Potlatch Corp., Northrop Corp., PacTel; past. chmn. Mastercard Internat. Bd. dirs. Marin Ecumenical Housing Assn.; trustee Calif. Inst. Tech., U. So. Calif. Jewish. Office: BankAm Corp Dept 3018 PO Box 37000 # 3018 San Francisco CA 94137

ROSENBERG, ROBERT ALLEN, psychologist, educator, optometrist; b. Phila., July 31, 1935; s. Theodore Samuel and Dorothy (Bailes) R.; m. Geraldine Bella Tishler, Sept. 3, 1961; children: Lawrence David, Ronald Joseph. BA, Temple U., 1957, MA, 1964; BS, Pa. Coll. Optometry, 1960, OD, 1961. Lic. optometrist, psychologist, Pa. Instr. Pa. Coll. Optometry, Phila., 1962-65, asst. prof., 1965-67; asst. prof. psychology Community Coll. Phila., 1967-76, assoc. prof., 1976—; pvt. practice optometry, Roslyn, Pa., 1965—. Contbr. articles to profl. jours. Named Humanitarian Chapel of Four Chaplains Bapt. Temple, 1980. Fellow Am. Acad. Optometry; mem. Am. Optometric Assn., Pa. Optometric Assn., Bucks-Montgomery Optometric Assn., Alumni Assn. Pa. Coll. Optometry (v.p. 1991—, sec. 1992—). Avocations: singing, acting, photography, writing, public speaking.

Home: 970 Corn Crib Dr Huntingdon Valley PA 19006-3304 Office: Community Coll Phila 1700 Spring Garden St Philadelphia PA 19130-3991

ROSENBERG, ROBERT BRINKMANN, research organization executive; b. Chgo., Mar. 19, 1937; s. Sidney and Gertrude (Brinkmann) R.; m. Patricia Margaret Kane, Aug. 1, 1959 (dec. Feb. 1988); children: John Richard Debra Ann; m. Maryann Bartoli Manrot, June 25, 1989. B.S. in Chem. Engring. with distinction, Ill. Inst. Tech., 1958, M.S. in Gas Tech., 1961, Ph.D. in Gas Tech., 1964. Registered profl. engr., Ill. Adj. asst. prof. Ill. Inst. Tech., 1965-69; mem. staff Inst. Gas Tech., Chgo., 1962-77; v.p. engring. research Inst. Gas Tech., 1973-77; v.p. research and devel. Gas Research Inst., Chgo. 1977-78; exec. v.p. Gas Research Inst., 1978-84, v.p. 1984—; interim exec. dir. IEA Internat. Ctr. for Gas Tech. Info., 1994-95, also bd. dirs. Author. Mem. Hinsdale (Ill.) Home Rule Ad Hoc Com., 1975-77; bd. dirs. Hinsdale Arts Coun., 1977-85, dir. emeritus, 1985—; pres. Triangle Frat. Edn. Found., 1974—; mem. vis. com. dept. chemistry U. Tex.; mem. adv. coun. U. Tex. Coll. Natural Scis. Found., 1990-95. Recipient Gas Industry Research award, 1985, Energy Exec. of Yr. award, 1987, Triangle Frat. Svc. Key and Outstanding Alumnus awards, 1987. Mem. Am. Inst. Chem. Engrs., Am. Gas Assn. (operating sect. award of merit 1989), Inst. Gas Engrs., Combustion Inst. (past treas. bd. central states sect.), Atlantic Gas Research Exchange (chmn. mng. bd. 1980—), Internat. Gas Union (U.S. rep. subcom. F-2 1974-83), Gas Appliance Engrs. Soc. (past trustee), Air Pollution Control Assn. (past sect. com. residential pollution sources). Patentee in field. Home: 28 Lake Ridge Club Dr Hinsdale IL 60521-7937 Office: Gas Rsch Inst 8600 W Bryn Mawr Ave Chicago IL 60631-3505

ROSENBERG, ROBERT CHARLES, housing corporation executive; b. Bronx, N.Y., Oct. 21, 1934; s. Bernard L. and Flora (Popiel) R.; BS, N.Y. U., 1955; LLB, Columbia U., 1958; JD (hon.), 1995; m. Diane Stricof, Jan. 28, 1962 (dec.); children: Andrew, Scott; m. Frances Kaufman, Sept. 11, 1976; stepchildren: Michael Kaufman, Benjamin Kaufman. Bar: N.Y. 1959. Adminstrv. asst. N.Y. State Dept. Law, N.Y.C., 1957-58; assoc. firm Barron Rice & Rochmore, N.Y.C., 1959-62, Carro Spanbock & Londin, N.Y.C., 1962-68; first dep. commr. for devel. dept., N.Y.C. Housing and Devel. Adminstrn., 1968-73; dir., 1st sr. v.p. Starrett Housing Corp., N.Y.C., 1973—; gen. mgr. Starrett City; pres., chmn. bd. Grenadier Realty Corp., 1976—; lectr. Practicing Law Inst., Real Estate Bd. N.Y.C., others. Candidate for N.Y. State Assembly, 1958, 65; sec. N.Y. State Assn. Young Republican Clubs, 1959-61; bd. dirs. pres. Bklyn. Philharmonic; corp. rep. Nat. Com. U.S.-China Relations; mem. N.Y.C. Mayor's-Beijing (China) Sister City Com.; bd. dirs. Bklyn. Acad. Music; v.p. Citizen's Housing and Planning Council, exec. v.p. N.Y.C. Associated Builders and Owners; exec. commn. Nat. Housing Conf. Served with USAF, 1958. Mem. ABA, N.Y. State Bar Assn., Bronx Bar Assn., N.Y. County Lawyers Assn., Nat. Assn. Housing and Renewal Ofcls., N.Y. State Assn. Housing and Renewal Ofcls., Urban Land Inst. Author N.Y. acts for residential constrn., rent. Home: 70 E 77th St New York NY 10021-1811 Office: 909 3rd Ave New York NY 10022-4731 also: 1310 Pennsylvania Ave Brooklyn NY 11239-1915

ROSENBERG, ROBERT M., food chain executive; b. 1938. Pres., CEO Baskin Robbins, Inc., Glendale, Calif., 1992—. Office: Baskin Robbins Inc 31 Baskin Robbins Pl Glendale CA 91201*

ROSENBERG, ROBERT MICHAEL, restaurant franchise company executive; b. Boston, Mar. 4, 1938; s. William and Bertha (Greenberg) R.; children: James Lee, John Matthew, Jennifer Beth. BS in Hotel and Restaurant Adminstrn., Cornell U., 1959; MBA, Harvard U., 1963; DBA (hon.), Nathaniel Hawthorne Coll., Antrim, N.H., 1980; LLD (hon.), N.H. Coll., 1982; D in Food Svc. Mgmt. (hon.), Johnson and Wales U., 1990. Pres. Dunkin' Donuts Inc., Randolph, Mass., from 1963; now chmn.; CEO Allied Domecq Retailing, 1993—; bd. dirs. J. Lyons & Co., Ltd., Eng., Allied Lyons Retailing, Ltd., Eng., Sonic Industries. Co-author: Profits from Franchising, 1969. Bd. dirs., trustee Dana Farber Cancer Found.; mem. bd. overseers Mus. Fine Arts, Boston; past dir. Am. Bus. Dir. Recipient Outstanding Man of Yr. award Jr. C of Co., Boston, 1968, Bus. award Bryant and Stratton Coll., Boston, 1968, award of excellence Am. Acad. Achievement, 1968, Leadership award Restaurant Bus. Mag., 1987, Gold Plate Winner as Foodsvc. Op. of Yr. 1983 Internat. Food Svc. Mfrs. Assn. Mem. Nat. Restaurant Assn. (bd. dirs., Silver Plate award 1984, 86, 87), Internat. Franchise Assn. (past pres., bd. dirs.), Am. Bus. Conf., Harvard Bus. Sch. Assn. Office: Dunkin' Donuts Inc 14 Pacella Park Dr Randolph MA 02368-1756

ROSENBERG, ROGER NEWMAN, neurologist, educator; b. Milw., Mar. 3, 1939; s. Sol J. and Cora D. (Newman) R.; m. Adrienne Turick, June 24, 1962; children—Jennifer, Lara. Student, Tufts U., 1957-60; BS, Northwestern U., 1961, MD with distinction, 1964. Diplomate Am. Bd. Psychiatry and Neurology. Intern Harvard Med. Service, Beth Israel Hosp., Boston, 1964-65; resident in neurology Neurol. Inst., Columbia U., N.Y.C., 1965-67, instr. neurology, 1967-68; research assoc. Lab. of Biochem. Genetics, NIH, Bethesda, Md., 1968-70; clin. instr. Howard U. Med. Sch., Washington, 1969-70; asst. prof. neurosci. Sch. Medicine, U. Calif.-San Diego, 1970-71; assoc. prof. neuroscis. and pediatrics, attending neurologist Univ. Hosp., U. Calif.-La Jolla, 1971-74; prof., chmn. dept. neurology U. Tex. Southwestern Med. Ctr., Dallas, 1973-91, prof. physiology, 1976—, Zale Disting. chair, prof. neurology, 1990—, dir. Alzheimer's Disease Rsch. Ctr., 1989—; attending neurologist Parkland Meml. Hosp. and Children's Med. Ctr., Dallas, 1974—, Zale Lipshy Univ. Hosp., 1990—; mem. staff Presbyn. Hosp., Dallas, 1974—, St. Paul's Hosp., Dallas, 1974—; cons. staff VA Hosp., Dallas, 1974—; mem. nat. med. adv. bd. Nat. Ataxia Found., Mpls., 1971—, Myasthenia Gravis Found., 1973; chmn. med. adv. bd., dir. med. sci. research Internat. Joseph Diseases Found., Livermore, Calif., 1977—; lectr. Japanese Soc. Neurology, 1987, 94, Chinese Neurol. Soc., 1987, Spanish Neurol. Soc., 1992; chmn. bd. sci. councilors NIH, 1984-86; pres. (hon.), Intl. French Soc. of Neurology Charcot Centenary Symposium, 1993. Editor Jour. Neurogenetics; mem. editorial bd. Neurology, 1977-82, 91—, Trends in Neurosci., 1980-86, Current Opinion in Neurology & Neurosurgery, 1990—; contbr. articles to med. jours. Bd. dirs. Winston Sch., Dallas, 1974-80. Recipient 1st Woody Guthrie Scholar in Medicine award Sci. Bd. Com. to Combat Huntington's Disease, 1971; USPHS grantee. Fellow AAAS; mem. Am. Acad. Neurology (chmn. sci. program com. nat. meetings 1979-84, elected councillor exec. bd. 1984-89, pres. 1991-93), Am. Neurochem. Soc., Tissue Culture Soc., Soc. Neurosci., Am. Fedn. Clin. Rsch., Soc. Pediat. Rsch., Internat. Child Neurology Assn., Am. Neurol. Assn. (1st v.p. 1987), Ctrl. Soc. Neurol. Rsch., Can. Congress Neurol. Scis. (hon.), Spanish Neurol. Soc. (hon. 1994), Sigma Xi, Alpha Omega Alpha (Merit award Northwestern U. Alumni Assn. 1964). Home: 4425 Wildwood Rd Dallas TX 75209-2801 Office: U Tex Southwestern Med Ctr Dallas TX 75235

ROSENBERG, RUTH HELEN BORSUK, lawyer; b. Plainfield, N.J., Feb. 23, 1935; d. Irwin and Pauline (Rudich) Borsuk; children—Joshua Cohen, Sarah, Rebecca, Daniel, Miriam, Tziporah, Isaac. A.B., Douglass Coll., 1956; J.D., U. Pa., 1963. Bar: Pa. 1964, N.Y. 1967, D.C. 1986, Md. 1987, Va. 1994, Mass. 1995, U.S. Ct. Appeals (3d cir.), 1969, (4th cir.), 1994, U.S. Supreme Ct. 1969. Law clk. Ct. Common Pleas, Phila., 1963-64; assoc. Blank, Rudenko, Klaus & Rome, Phila., 1964-67; atty. Office Corp. Counsel, City of Rochester, 1967-68; assoc. Nixon, Hargrave, Devans & Doyle, Washington, 1968-74, ptnr., 1975—; vice chairperson character and fitness com. Appellate div. 4th dept. 7th Jud. Dist. N.Y. Supreme Ct., 1976-80, mem. grievance com., 1981-84; mem. Washington Bd. Trade. Bd. dirs. Soc. Prevention Cruelty to Children, 1976-77, N.Y. Civil Liberties Union, 1971-85, v.p. 1976-85; bd. dirs. Jewish Home and Infirmary, 1978-83, pres., 1980-83; v.p. Jewish Fedn. Rochester, 1983, Yachad, Inc., Jewish Cmty. Housing Devel. Corp., 1990-94; bd. dirs. Jewish Cmty. Coun. Greater Washington, 1989-93, Leadership Washington, 1990-91, Libr. Theatre, 1994—, Op. Understanding, D.C., 1994-95. Mem. ABA, D.C. Bar Assn., Md. Bar Assn., Va. Bar Assn., Phi Beta Kappa. Office: Nixon Hargrave Devans & Doyle 1 Thomas Cir NW Ste 700 Washington DC 20005-5898

ROSENBERG, SAMUEL NATHAN, French and Italian language educator; b. N.Y.C., Jan. 19, 1936; s. Israel and Etta (Friedland) R. AB, Columbia U., 1957; PhD, Johns Hopkins U., 1965. Instr. Columbia U., N.Y.C., 1960-61; lectr. Ind. U., Bloomington, Ind., 1962-65; asst. prof. Ind. U., Bloomington, 1965-69; assoc. prof. Ind. U., Bloomington, Ind., 1969-81; prof. dept. French and Italian Ind. U., Bloomington, 1981—, chmn. dept.,

1977-84. Author: Modern French CE, 1970; author: (with others) Harper's Grammar of French, 1983, (with W. Apel) French Secular Compositions of the 14th Century, 3 vols., 1970-72, (with H. Tischler) Chanter m'estuet: Songs of the Trouveres, 1981; translator: (with S. Danon) Ami and Amile, 1981, Lyrics and Melodies of Gace Brulé, 1985, (with H. Tischler) The Monophonic Songs in the Roman de Fauvel, 1991; translator: Lancelor-Grail Cycle, vol. 2, 1993. Pres. Mid-Am. Festival of the Arts, Inc., Bloomington, Ind., 1984-85. Woodrow Wilson Found. fellow, 1959-60; Fulbright fellow, 1960-61; Lilly Faculty fellow, 1986-87. Mem MLA, Am. Assn. Tchrs. French; mem. Medieval Acad. Am., Internat. Courtly Lit. Soc., Am. Literary Translators Assn., Phi Beta Kappa. Home: PO Box 1164 Bloomington IN 47402-1164 Office: Dept French and Italian Ind U Bloomington IN 47405

ROSENBERG, SARAH ZACHER, institute arts administration executive, humanities administration consultant; b. Kelem, Lithuania, Jan. 10, 1931; came to U.S., 1938; d. David Meir Zacher and Rachel Korbman; m. Norman J. Rosenberg, Dec. 30, 1950; children: Daniel, Alyssa. BA in History, U. Nebr., 1970, MA in Am. History, 1973. Rsch. historian U. Mid-Am., Lincoln, Nebr., 1974-78, program developer dept. humanities, 1978-79, asst. dir. div. acad. planning, 1980-81, dir. program devel., 1981-82; exec. dir. Nebr. Humanities Coun., Lincoln, 1982-87, Nebr. Found. for Humanities, Lincoln, 1984-87; exec. dir. Am. Inst. for Conservation Hist. and Artistic Works, Washington, 1987—, exec. dir. found., 1991—; program officer, spl. cons. mus. div. NEH, Washington, 1987, external reviewer, 1981, 89; lay participant long-range planning conf. Nebr. Bar Assn., Hastings, 1986. Co-editor: The Great Plains Experience: Readings in the History of a Region, 1978; contbr. articles to profl. jours. Action mem. Haddasah, Lincoln, 1961-87, Tifereth Israel Synagogue, 1961-87, Beth El Congregation, Bethesda, Md., 1988—; bd. dirs. Sta. KUCV, affiliate Nat. Pub. Radio, Lincoln, 1986-87, Lincoln Community Playhouse, 1986-87. NEH grantee, 1981, 86, merit awards, 1983, 87; Humanities Resource Ctr. grantee, Peter Kiewit Found., 1984. Mem. Am. Hist. Assn., Western Hist. Assn., Alpha Theta. Democrat. Home: 8102 Appalachian Terr Potomac MD 20854 Office: Am Inst for Conservation Ste 301 1717 K St NW Washington DC 20006

ROSENBERG, SAUL ALLEN, oncologist, educator; b. Cleve., Aug. 2, 1927. BS, Western Res. U., 1948, MD, 1953. Diplomate Am. Bd. Internal Medicine, Am. Bd. Oncology. Intern Univ. Hosp., Cleve., 1953-54; resident in internal medicine Peter Bent Brigham Hosp., Boston, 1954-61; research asst. toxicology AEC Med. Research Project, Western Res. U., 1948-53; asst. prof. medicine and radiology Stanford (Calif.) U., 1961-65, assoc. prof., 1965-79, chief div. oncology, 1965-93, prof., 1970—, Am. Cancer Soc. prof., 1983-89, assoc. dean, 1989-92; chmn. bd. No. Calif. Cancer Program, 1974-80. Contbr. articles to profl. jours. Served to lt. M.C. USNR, 1954-56. Master ACP; mem. Am. Assn. Cancer Research, Inst. Medicine Nat. Acad. Sci., Am. Assn. Cancer Edn., Am. Fedn. Clin. Research, Am. Soc. Clin. Oncology (pres. 1982-83), Assn. Am. Physicians, Calif. Acad. Medicine, Radiation Research Soc., Western Soc. Clin. Research, Western Assn. Physicians. Office: Stanford U Sch Medicine Div Oncology M-211 Stanford CA 94305*

ROSENBERG, SEYMOUR, psychologist, educator; b. Newark, Sept. 7, 1926; s. Morris and Celia (Weiss) R.; children: Harold Stanley, Michael Seth. B.S., The Citadel, 1948; M.A., Ind. U., 1951, Ph.D., 1952. Research psychologist USAF, San Antonio, 1952-58, U. Kans., Lawrence, 1958-59, Bell Telephone Labs., Murray Hill, N.J., 1959-65; vis. prof. psychology Columbia, N.Y.C., 1965-66; prof. psychology Rutgers U., New Brunswick, N.J., 1966—; chmn. dept. psychology Rutgers U., 1981-83, 94-95; adj. prof. Rutgers U. Med. Sch., 1974—; vis. scholar U. Leuven, Belgium, 1983, 92, Université de Provence, France, 1990; panel mem. NSF, 1970-72. Cons. editor Jours. Personality and Social Psychology, 1968-69; assoc. editor, 1970-73; contbr. articles to profl. jours. Served with USN, 1945-46. NSF grantee, 1965—; NIMH, 1966-68; NIMH research scientist grantee, 1968-73; Social Sci. Research Council fellow, 1973-74. Fellow Am. Psychol. Assn.; mem. Soc. Exptl. Social Psychology, Psychometric Soc., Classification Soc., N.Y. Acad. Sci., Eastern Psychol. Assn. Home: 689 Canal Rd Somerset NJ 08873-7309 Office: Rutgers U Dept Psychology ED Livingston Campus New Brunswick NJ 08903

ROSENBERG, SHELI ZYSMAN, lawyer, financial management executive; b. N.Y.C., Feb. 2, 1942; d. Stephen B. and Charlotte (Laufer) Zysman; m. Burton X. Rosenberg, Aug. 30, 1964; children: Leonard, Marcy. BA, Tufts U., 1963; JD, Northwestern U., 1966. Bar: Ill. 1966. Ptnr. Schiff, Hardin & Waite, Chgo., 1973-80; exec. v.p., gen. counsel Equity Fin. Mgmt., Chgo., 1980—; exec. v.p., gen. counsel Equity Group Investments, Inc., Chgo., 1988-95, pres., CEO, 1995—; pres., CEO Equity Fin. and Mgmt. Co., Chgo., 1995—; prin. Rosenberg & Liebentritt, P.C., Chgo., 1995—; bd. dirs. Gt. Am. Mgmt. & Investment, Chgo., 1984—, v.p., gen. counsel, 1985—, sec., 1983-90; bd. dirs. CFI Industries, Inc., Am. Classic Voyages Co., Revco, D.S., Inc., Jacor Comm., Inc., The Vigoro Corp., Itel Corp., Capsure Holdings Corp., Eagle Industries, Inc., Falcon Bldg. Products, Inc.; bd. trustees Equity Residential Properties Trust. Bd. dirs., pres. Chgo. Network.

ROSENBERG, STEPHEN, lawyer; b. N.Y.C., May 18, 1943; s. Leo A. and Freda (Block) R.; m. Lucille Susan Abrams, June 23, 1968; children: Jonathan Paul, Michele Sydney. AB, Columbia Coll., 1964; LLB, Harvard U., 1967. Bar: N.Y. Assoc. Delson & Gordon, N.Y.C., 1968-69; assoc. Carro, Spanbock, Kaster & Cuiffo, N.Y.C., 1969-76, ptnr., 1976-90, counsel, 1990-93; sec. Zahren Fin. Corp., Avon, Conn., 1990—, Zahren Alternative Power Corp., Avon, 1994—; ptnr. Newman Tannenbaum Helpern Syracuse & Hirschtritt, N.Y.C., 1993—; sec. Zahren Alternative POWER Corp., Conn., 1994—. Contbr. articles to profl. jours. Pres. Old Bridge (N.J.) Theater Guild, 1984-85, Timber Glen Civic Assn., Old Bridge, 1985-87; trustee Temple Emanuel, Westfield, N.J., 1992-94, v.p. 94—. Mem. ABA, N.Y. Bar Assn., Columbia Coll. Alumni Assn., Harvard Law Sch. Alumni Assn., B'nai B'rith (trustee 1988-89). Avocations: travel, tennis. Office: Newman Tannenbaum Helpern Syracuse & Hirschtritt 900 3rd Ave New York NY 10022-4728

ROSENBERG, STEVEN AARON, surgeon, medical researcher; b. N.Y.C., Aug. 2, 1940; s. Abraham and Harriet (Wendroff) R.; m. Alice Ruth O'Connell, Sept. 15, 1968; children—Beth, Rachel, Naomi. B.A., Johns Hopkins U., 1960, M.D., 1963; Ph.D., Harvard U., 1968. Resident in surgery Peter Bent Brigham Hosp., Boston, 1963-64, 68-69, 72-74; resident fellow in immunology Harvard U. Med. Sch., Boston, 1969-70; clin. assoc. immunology br. Nat. Cancer Inst., Bethesda, Md., 1970-72; chief surgery Nat. Cancer Inst., 1974—, assoc. editor Jour., 1974—; mem. U.S.-USSR Coop. Immunotherapy Program, 1974—, U.S.-Japan Coop. Immunotherapy Program, 1975—; clin. assoc. prof. surgery George Washington U. Med. Ctr., 1976—; prof. surgery Uniformed Services U. Health Scis. Contbr. articles to profl. jours. Author: The Transformed Cell: Unlocking the Mysteries of Cancer, 1992. Served with USPHS, 1970-72. Recipient Meritorious Service medal Pub. Health Service, 1981; co-recipient Armand Hammer Cancer prize, 1985; named 1990 Scientist of the Yr., R&D magazine. Mem. Soc. Univ. Surgeons, Am. Surg. Assn., Soc. Surg. Oncology, Surg. Biology Club II, Halsted Soc., Transplantation Soc., Am. Assn. Immunologists, Am. Assn. Cancer Research, Phi Beta Kappa, Alpha Omega Alpha. Office: Nat Cancer Inst 9000 Rockville Pike Bethesda MD 20892-0001

ROSENBERG, STEVEN H., health facility administrator; b. 1953. BS, U. Conn., 1975; MBA, U New Haven, 1981. Sr. v.p., CFO St. Francis Hosp. Med. Ctr., Hartford, Conn., 1986—. Office: St Francis Hosp Med Ctr 114 Woodland St Hartford CT 06105*

ROSENBERG, STUART, film director; b. Bklyn., Aug. 11, 1927; s. David and Sara (Kaminsky) R.; m. Margot Pohoryles, Aug. 4, 1950; 1 son, Benjamin. B.A., NYU, 1949. Editor, producer, dir. over 300 TV shows 1950-65, in films, 1965—; films directed include Murder, Inc., 1962, Cool Hand Luke, 1967, April Fools, 1969, WUSA, 1970, Voyage of the Damned, 1977, Amityville Horror, 1979, Brubaker, 1980, The Pope of Greenwich Village, 1984; (Recipient Emmy award for dramatic directing 1962, Dir.'s Guild award nominee 4). Served with USNR, 1945-47.

ROSENBERG, SYDNEY J., security company executive; b. San Francisco, Sept. 3, 1914; s. Morris and Gussie (Kaufman) R.; m. Joyce Wexler, Nov. 15, 1939 (div. Mar. 1968); children: Brad, Jill Rosenberg Hughes, Todd; m.

2d Jaclyn Barde, Mar. 22, 1968; stepchildren: Gregg Cobarr, Glenn Cobarr. B.A., Stanford U., 1936; M.B.A., Harvard U., 1938. Pres., chief exec. officer Am. Bldg. Maintenance Industries, Los Angeles, from 1938; now chmn. bd. Am. Bldg. Maintenance Industries, San Francisco; chmn. ABM Security Svcs.; bd. dirs. Craig Corp., AMPCO Parking Svcs., AMTECH Elevator Svcs., AMTECH Lighting Svcs., Comm. Air. Mech. Svcs., Easterday Supply Co., Rose Pest Control Co.; pres. OPTIC Fund. Bd. govs. Performing Arts Council; bd. govs. Los Angeles Music Ctr.; trustee Jewish Big Bros.; mem. dirs. council Children's Orthopaedic Hosp. Mem. Chief Execs. Orgn., Urban Land Inst., World Bus. Council. Republican. Jewish. Clubs: Hillcrest (Los Angeles); Big Canyon (Newport, Calif.). Office: American Building 50 Fremont St San Francisco CA 94105-2230

ROSENBERG, THEODORE ROY, financial executive; b. Nyack, N.Y., Aug. 6, 1933; s. Rebecca Sheer R.; m. Eleanor Schmalsteig, Feb. 19, 1956 (div); children: Bradley Scott, Martha Ann; m. Mary Frances McVay, Sept. 21, 1991. BS, U. Conn., 1955; MBA, U. Pa., 1964. Commd. 2nd lt. U.S. Army, 1955, advanced through grades to col., 1976, retired, 1982; portfolio mgr. The Burney Co., Falls Church, Va., 1979—, v.p. mktg., 1982-94, v.p., 1994—. Active exec. com. Our Daily Bread, Fairfax, Va., 1991—; bd. dirs. Army Transp. Mus. Decorated Legion of Merit, Bronze Star; recipient Vietnam Medal of Honor, Govt. of Vietnam, 1966; inducted into Alumni Hall of Fame, U. Conn. Sch. Bus. Adminstrn., 1994. Mem. U. Pa. Mid Atlantic Bd. Assoc. Alumni (trustee), Wharton Club (v.p.). Avocations: scuba diving, snorkeling. Office: The Burney Co 121 Rowell Ct Falls Church VA 22046-3126

ROSENBERG, WILLIAM, supermarket company executive; b. 1907; married. With Met. Life Ins. Co., Hackensack, N.J., 1923-33; ins. agt. C. Rosenberg Inc., Teaneck, N.J., 1933-41; pres., chief exec. officer Big V. Supermarkets, Florida, N.Y., 1941-69, chmn. dirs. chief exec. officer, 1969-87, chmn. exec. com. to 1989, chmn. emeritus, 1989—. Office: Big V Supermarkets Ind 176 N Main St # B Florida NY 10921-1098

ROSENBERGER, BRYAN DAVID, lawyer; b. Johnstown, Pa., Oct. 8, 1950; s. Clarence Haines and Ida Rae (Neiderheiser) R.; m. Barbara Leah Byer, July 4, 1977; children: Laura Michelle, Lisa Renee. BS, Juniata Coll., 1971; JD, Coll. of William and Mary, 1974. Bar: Pa. 1974. Assoc. Eckert Seamans Cherin & Mellott, Pitts., 1974-82, ptnr., 1983—, chmn. corp. and bus. dept., 1992—; mem. exec. com., 1994—. Active new leadership bd. Pitts. Symphony Soc., 1990—. Mem. ABA, Pa. Bar Assn., Allegheny County Bar Assn. Home: 1358 Oak Ledge Ct Upper Saint Clair PA 15241 Office: Eckert Seamans Cherin & Mellott 600 Grant St 42d Fl Pittsburgh PA 15219

ROSENBERGER, CAROL, concert pianist; b. Detroit, Nov. 1, 1935; d. Maurice Seiberling and Whilamet (Gibson) R. B.F.A., Carnegie-Mellon U., 1955; postgrad., Acad. Performing Arts, Vienna, 1956-59. Mem. artist faculty U. So. Calif.; vis. artist numerous colls. and univs. Internat. concert career, 1964—; New York debut, 1970; appeared several times at Carnegie Hall; soloist Am. Symphony, Nat. Symphony, Royal Philharmonic, San Diego Symphony, Detroit Symphony, Houston Symphony, St. Louis Symphony, Indpls. Symphony, Los Angeles Chamber Orch.; performed world premiere of Buenaventura; piano concerts with Philippine Philharmonic, 1977, Am. Symphony, 1977; recital series in Am., European, Asian music capitals; recordings include Hindemith's Four Temperaments with London Royal Philharm., Water Music of the Impressionists, works of Beethoven, Schubert, Szymanowski, Night Moods, 1989, Perchance To Dream, 1989, Reveries: Music of Chopin, others; contbr. articles to music publs. Recipient Steinway Centennial medal, 1954, Critics Choice award Gramophone mag., 1980. Mem. Nat. Acad. Rec. Arts and Scis. Chosen to represent Am. women musicians by Nat. Commn. on Observance Internat. Womens Year, 1976. Office: care Dorothy Cone Artist Rep 60 E 86th St New York NY 10028-1009 also: Delos Internat Inc 1645 N Vine St Ste 340 Los Angeles CA 90028*

ROSENBERGER, DAVID A., research scientist, cooperative extension specialist; b. Quakertown, Pa., Sept. 14, 1947; s. Henry and Ada C. (Geissinger) R.; m. Carol J. Freeman, July 29, 1973; children: Sara, Matthew, Nathan. BS in Biology, Goshen Coll., 1969; PhD in Plant Pathology, Mich. State U., 1977. Asst. prof. Hudson Valley lab. Cornell U., Highland, N.Y., 1977-84, assoc. prof., 1984—; supt. Cornell U., Highland, 1990—. Mem. AAAS, Am. Phytopathological Soc., Coun. Agrl. Sci. and Tech. Avocations: religious studies, gardening, hiking, jogging. Office: Cornell U Hudson Valley Lab PO Box 727 Highland NY 12528

ROSENBERGER, ERNST HEY, judge; b. Hamburg, Germany, Aug. 31, 1931; came to U.S., 1935, naturalized, 1943; s. Ferdinand and Edith (Heymann) R.; m. Judith Ann Brailey, June 10, 1978; children: John Brailey, Anne Elizabeth. B.A., CCNY, 1955; J.D. (scholar), N.Y. Law Sch., 1958; cert. criminal law and practice (scholar), Northwestern U., summer 1960; cert., Nat. Coll. State Judiciary, U. Nev., 1976. Bar: N.Y. 1958, U.S. Dist. Ct. 1959, 61, U.S. Ct. Appeals 1962, U.S. Customs Ct 1962, U.S. Supreme Ct. 1970. Assoc. Kunstler & Kunstler, N.Y.C., 1958-59; sole practice N.Y.C., 1959-69; ptnr. Ordover, Rosenberger & Rosen, N.Y.C., 1970-72; judge Criminal Ct. City of N.Y., 1972-76; acting justice Supreme Ct. N.Y., 1973-76, justice, 1977—; presiding justice Extraordinary Spl. and Trial Term of Supreme Ct., 1978-85; justice Appellate Div Supreme Ct. N.Y., 1985—; instr. courses for N.Y. State Supreme Ct. Justices, N.Y. Civil and Criminal Ct.; mem. faculty Hastings Coll. Law U. Calif., San Francisco, 1979; adj. prof. law N.Y. Law Sch., 1976—; guest lectr. Bklyn. Law Sch., St. John's Law Sch., John Jay Coll., New Sch., Pratt Inst., N.Y.C. Police Dept., NYU Postgrad. Med. Sch.; co-chmn. Criminal Trial Advocacy Course, Appellate Div., First Jud. Dept.; tech. assistance and evaluations cons. to dir. legal services OEO, Washington, 1970; U.S. rep. to W. Ger. to study youth laws and cts., 1975. Editor in chief: N.Y. Law Rev. (Moot Ct. award); contbr. book reviews to profl. jours. Trustee N.Y. Law Sch., Tng. Inst. Mental Health Practitioners, Postgrad. Ctr. Residence, Congregation Habonim; bd. dirs. The Blue Card. Served with U.S. Army, 1949-51. Recipient Faculty Disting. Svc. award N.Y. Law Sch., 1981, 86, 91, Charles W. Froessel award, 1989. Mem. Am. Bar Assn., Am. Judicature Soc., Am. Soc. Legal History, N.Y. State Bar Assn. (exec. com. criminal justice sect., award for work in Criminal Law Edn. 1980, award for outstanding jud. contbn. to criminal justice, 1989), Assn. Bar City N.Y., N.Y. County Lawyers Assn. (guest lectr.), Assn. Justices Supreme Ct. State of N.Y. Jewish. Home: 1165 Fifth Ave New York NY 10029 Office: Supreme Ct NY 27 Madison Ave New York NY 10010-2295

ROSENBERGER, FRANZ ERNST, physics educator; b. Salzburg, Austria, May 31, 1933; came to U.S., 1966; s. Franz and Hertha (Sompek) R.; m. Renate Hildegard Suessenbach; children: Uta, Bernd, Till. BS in Physics, U. Stuttgart, 1960, diploma in physics, 1964; PhD in Physics, U. Utah, 1970. Asst. prof. physics U. Utah, Salt Lake City, 1970-77, assoc. prof., 1977-81, prof., 1981-86; prof. physics U. Ala., Huntsville, 1986—, dir. Ctr for Microgravity and Materials Rsch., 1986—. Author: Fundamentals of Crystal Growth, 1979; editor Jour. Crystal Growth, 1981—; contbr. articles to profl. jours. Mem. Am. Phys. Soc., Am. Assn. for Crystal Growth. Avocations: windsurfing, skiing, photography, home improvements. Home: 171 Stoneway Trl Madison AL 35758-8543

ROSENBLATT, ALBERT MARTIN, state supreme court justice; b. N.Y.C., Jan. 17, 1936; s. Isaac and Fannie (Dachs) R.; m. Julia Carlson, Aug. 23, 1970; 1 dau., Elizabeth. B.A., U. Pa., 1957; LL.B. (J.D.), Harvard U., 1960. Bar: N.Y. 1961. Dist. atty. Dutchess County, N.Y., 1969-75, county judge, 1976-81; justice N.Y. State Supreme Ct., 1982-89, appellate div., 1989—; chief adminstrv. judge N.Y. State, 1987-89; vis. prof. Vassar Coll., 1993—; mem. N.Y. State Fair Trial Free Press Conf., 1973-75; creator Dutchess County 1st consumer protection bur., 1973; instr. newly elected state supreme ct. judges and county judges; chmn. curriculum head tng. programs state dist. attys., asst. dist. attys., 1974, 75; instr. N.Y. State Police Acad. law tng., 1981; lectr. Nat. Dist. Attys. Assn., 1968-74. Area fund raising rep. Harvard U. Law Sch., 1974; alumni fund raising chmn. U. Pa., 1965, 66; bd. dirs. United Way Community Chest, 1970; bd. dirs. Bardavon 1869 Opera House, Dutchess County Hist. Soc.; mem. adv. bd. Jewish Community Ctr., 1987—. With USAR, 1960-66. Mem. N.Y. State Bar Assn. (named Outstanding Prosecutor 1974), N.Y. State Dist. Attys. Assn.

(pres. 1974, Frank S. Hogan award 1987, Jud. Svcs. award, 1994), Profl. Ski Instrs. Am. (cert. 1984—). Republican. Jewish. Club: Baker St. Irregulars (former assoc. editor Baker St. Jour.). Mem. editorial bd. advisors N.Y. State Bar Jour., 1992—; contbr. to N.Y. State Bench Book for Trial Judges, 1986-87; contbr. articles on law to profl. jours. and popular mags. Home: 300 Freedom Rd Pleasant Valley NY 12569 Office: Supreme Ct Chambers 40 Garden St Poughkeepsie NY 12601-3106

ROSENBLATT, ARTHUR ISAAC, architect, former museum director; b. N.Y.C., Aug. 31, 1931; s. Harry and Helen (Satz) R.; m. Ruth Anne Turteltaub, Aug. 5, 1956; children: Paul Mark, Judith Alice. Diploma in architecture, Cooper Union, 1952; BArch, Carnegie-Mellon U., 1956. Registered architect, N.Y. Designer Katzman Assocs., N.Y.C., 1956-57, Isadore & Zachary Rosenfield, N.Y.C., 1957-60, Skidmore, Owings & Merrill-Harrison, Abramovitz, Pomerance and Breines, N.Y.C., 1960-61; chief designer Irwing S. Chanin, Architect, N.Y.C., 1961-65; first dep. commr. N.Y.C. Dept. Parks, Recreation and Cultural Affairs, 1966-68; v.p., vice dir. Met. Mus. Art, N.Y.C., 1968-86; dir. capital projects N.Y. Pub. Libr., N.Y.C., 1982-86; dir. U.S. Holocaust Meml. Mus., Washington, 1986-88; v.p. Grand Cen. Partnership, N.Y.C.; assoc. dir. Bryant Park Restoration Corp., 1989-95; v.p. 34th St. Partnership, 1991-95; faculty Sarah Lawrence Coll., Bronxville, N.Y., 1967-69; dir. capital projects N.Y. Pub. Libr., N.Y.C., 1982-86; cons. architect Whitney Mus. Am Art, N.Y.C., 1981, Butler Mus. Am. Art, 1980, Youngstown, Ohio, Chrysler Mus. Art, Norfolk, Va., 1982, Internat. Ctr. Photography, N.Y.C., 1985-86, Mus. and Archive Acad. Hebrew Lang., Jerusalem, Newport Harbor Art Mus., 1990-91, J.B. Speed Art Mus., Louisville, 1992, Museo de Arte de Ponce, Ponce, P.R., 1995, P.R. Tourism Co., Commonwealth of P.R., 1995. Author: Temple of Dendur, 1978; co-author: Movie Song Catalog, 1993; contbr. articles to mags. and jours. Vice chmn. cmty. planning bd. # 8, N.Y.C., 1964-66; trustee The Cooper Union, 1983-86; commr. N.Y.C. Coun. Environment; v.p. Met. Hist. Structures Assn.; presl. appointee Nat. Mus. Svc. Bd., 1995. With U.S. Army, 1953-55. Nat. Endowment for the Arts grantee, 1981. Fellow AIA (pres. N.Y. chpt. 1982-83, spl. citation 1978), Nat. Inst. for Archtl. Edn. (bd. dirs. 1978); mem. Mcpl. Art Soc., Archtl. League N.Y. (pres. 1970-72). Home and Office: 1158 5th Ave New York NY 10029-6917

ROSENBLATT, EDDIE, record company executive; b. Far Rockaway, N.Y., Nov. 6, 1934; m. Bobbie Rosenblatt, 1954; children: Michael, Steven, Peter, Gretchen. AA in Bus. Bklyn. Coll., 1954. With Macy's Dept. Store, 1956, Cosnat, Cleve., 1957-62; gen. mgr. Main Line, Cleve., 1962-67; sales mgr. A&M Records, Calif., 1967-70, TA Records, Calif., 1970; sales mgr. Warner Bros. Records, Calif., 1971-72, v.p., dir. nat. sales and promotion, then sr. v.p., 1972-80; pres. Geffen Records, Calif., 1980-90, DGC Records, Calif., 1990—; chmn. bd., CEO Geffen Records, 1995—; co-founder, developer WEA Distributing Corp. Served with U.S. Army, 1954-56. Mem. NARAS, Rec. Industry Assn. Am. Achievements include tennis, books, movies, professional basketball. Office: Geffen Records 75 Rockefeller Pla New York NY 10019

ROSENBLATT, GERD MATTHEW, chemist; b. Leipzig, Germany, July 6, 1933; came to U.S., 1935, naturalized, 1940; s. Edgar Fritz and Herta (Fisher) R.; m. Nancy Ann Kaltreider, June 29, 1957 (dec. Jan. 1982); children: Rachel, Paul; m. Susan Frances Barnett, Nov. 23, 1990. BA, Swarthmore Coll., 1955; PhD, Princeton U., 1960; Doctorate in Physics (hon.), Vrije Universiteit Brussel, 1989. Chemist Lawrence Radiation Lab., Univ. Calif., 1960-63, cons., guest scientist, 1968-84; from asst. to assoc. prof. chemistry Pa. State U., University Park, 1963-70, prof., 1970-81; assoc. div. leader Los Alamos (N.Mex.) Nat. Lab., 1982-85; chemistry div. leader, 1982-85; dep. dir. Lawrence Berkeley (Calif.) Lab., 1985-89, sr. chemist, 1985—; lectr. U. Calif., Berkeley, 1962-63; vis. prof. Vrije U. Brussels, 1973; vis. fellow Southampton U., 1980, King's Coll., Cambridge, 1980; adj. prof. chemistry U. N.Mex., 1981-85; cons. Aerospace Corp., 1979-85, Solar Energy Rsch. Inst., 1980-81, Xerox Corp., 1977-78, Hooker Chem. Co., 19766-78, Los Alamos Nat. Lab, 1978, mem. external adv. com. Ctr. for Materials Sci., 1985-93; mem. rev. com. chemistry div., 1985; mem. rev. com. for chem. engring. div. Argonne Univ. Assn., 1974-80, chmn. 1977-78; mem. rev. com. for chem. sci. Lawrence Berkeley Lab., 1984; chmn. rev. com. for chem. and material sci. Lawrence Livermore Nat. Lab., 1984-91; mem. bd. advs. Combustion Rsch. Facility, Sandia Nat. Lab., 1985-89; mem. bd. advs. rsch. and devel. div. Lockheed Missiles & Space Co., 1985-87; chmn. Internat. Sci. Found. Chemistry III Panel, 1994; mem. U.S. Nat. Com. Com. on Data for Sci. and Tech., 1986-92, Internat. Union of Pure and Applied Chemistry, 1986-92; mem. basic scis. lab. program panel Dept. Energy, 1985-89; sec. IUPAC Commn. on High Temperature and Solid State Chemistry, 1992—. Editor: (jour.) Progress in Solid State Chemistry, 1977—; mem. editorial bd. High Temperature Sci., 1979—; contbr. articles to profl. jours. Du Pont grad. fellow, Princeton U., 1957-58; fellow Solvay Inst., 1973, U.K. Rsch. Coun., 1980. Fellow AAAS; mem. Am. Chem. Soc., Am. Phys. Soc., Electrochem. Soc., Nat. Rsch. Coun. (chmn. high temperature sci. and tech. com. 1977-79, 84-85, panel on exploration of materials sci. and tech. for nat. welfare 1986-88, sci. and tech. info. bd. 1990-91, chmn. numerical data adv. bd. 1986-90, solid state scis. com. 1988-91, chmn. western regional materials sci. and engring. meeting 1990, panel on long-term retention of selected sci. and tech. records of fed. govt. 1993). Achievements include first use of imaging detectors to obtain Raman compositional profiles and two-dimensional maps of chemical compositions, of rotational Raman scattering as a temperature and state-population probe in high temperature and combustion systems; elucidation of role of crystal defects and molecular structure in the evaporation of solid materials; first experimental determination of how molecular polarizability anisotropies change with internuclear distance; estimation of thermodynamic properties and molecular structures for gaseous molecules. Home: 1177 Miller Ave Berkeley CA 94708-1754 Office: Lawrence Berkeley Lab U Calif Berkeley CA 94720-0001

ROSENBLATT, JASON PHILIP, English language educator; b. Balt., July 3, 1941; s. Morris D. and Esther (Friedlander) R.; m. Zipporah Marton, June 2, 1964; children: Noah David, Raphael Mark. BA, Yeshiva U., 1963; MA, Brown U., 1966, PhD, 1969. Asst. prof. English U. Pa., Phila., 1968-74; asst. prof. English Georgetown U., Washington, 1974-76, assoc. prof., 1976-83, prof. English, 1983—; vis. lectr. English lit. Swarthmore (Pa.) Coll., 1972-73; cen. exec. com. Folger Inst. / Folger Shakespeare Libr., Washington, 1976-88. Author: Torah and Law in "Paradise Lost," 1994; co-editor: Not in Heaven: Coherence and Complexity in Biblical Narrative, 1991; mem. editl. bd. Milton Studies, 1992—; contbr. articles to scholarly publs. Guggenheim Found. fellow, 1977-78; NEH fellow, 1990-91. Mem. MLA (del. assembly 1989-91, exec. com. div. religion and lit. 1982-86), Milton Soc. Am. (exec. com. 1977-80, James Holly Hanford award 1989), Milton Seminar, Phi Beta Kappa. Democrat. Jewish. Avocations: Talmud study, music, swimming. Office: Dept English Georgetown Univ 37th St at O St Washington DC 20057

ROSENBLATT, JOAN RAUP, mathematical statistician; b. N.Y.C., Apr. 15, 1926; d. Robert Bruce and Clara (Eliot) Raup; m. David Rosenblatt, June 10, 1950. AB, Barnard Coll., 1946; PhD, U. N.C., 1956. Intern Nat. Inst. Pub. Affairs, Washington, 1946-47; statis. analyst U.S. Bur. of Budget, 1947-48; rsch. asst. U. N.C., 1953-54; mathematician Nat. Inst. Standards and Tech. (formerly Nat. Bur. Standards), Washington, 1955—, asst. chief statis. engring., 1963-68, chief statis. engring. lab., 1969-78, dep. dir. Ctr. for Applied Math., 1981-88; dep. dir. Computing and Applied Math. Lab., Gaithersburg, 1988-93, dir. 1993—; mem. com. on indsl. rels. Dept. Stats. Ohio State U.; mem. adv. com. in math. and stats. USDA Grad. Sch. 1971—; mem. Com. Applied and Theoretical Stats., Nat. Rsch. Coun., 1985-88. Mem. editorial bd. Communications in Stats. 1971-79, Jour. Soc. for Indsl. and Applied Math. 1965-73, Nat. Inst. Stds. and Tech. Jour. Rsch., 1991-93; contbr. articles to profl. jours. Chmn. Com. on Women in Sci. Joint Bd. on Sci. Edn., 1963-64. Rice fellow, 1946, Gen. Edn. Bd. fellow, 1948-50; recipient Fed. Woman's award, 1971, Gold medal Dept. Commerce, 1976, Presdl. Meritorious Exec. Rank award, 1982. Fellow AAAS (chmn. stats. sect. 1982, sec. 1987-91), Inst. Math. Stats. (coun. 1975-77), Am. Statis. Assn. (v.p. 1981-83, dir. 1979-80, Founders award 1991), Washington Acad. Scis. (achievement award math. 1965); mem. AAUW, IEEE Reliability Soc., Am. Math. Soc., Royal Statis. Soc. London, Philos. Soc. Washington, Internat. Statis. Inst., Bernoulli Soc. Probability and Math. Stats., Caucus Women Stats. (pres. 1976), Assn. Women Math., Exec. Women Govt., Phi Beta Kappa, Sigma Xi (treas. Nat. Bur. Standards chpt. 1982-84). Home: 2939 Van Ness St NW Apt 702 Washington DC 20008-

4628 Office: Nat Inst Stds and Tech Rm B118 Technology Bldg Gaithersburg MD 20899-0001

ROSENBLATT, JOSEPH, poet, editor; b. Toronto, Ont., Can., Dec. 26, 1933; s. Samuel and Bessie (Tee) R.; m. Faye Carole Smith, Oct. 13, 1969; 1 son, Eliot Howard. Grad. pub. schs. Writer-in-residence U. Western Ont., 1979-80, U. Victoria, 1980-81, U. Rome and U. Bologna, Italy, 1987. Author: Voyage of the Mood, 1963, The LSD Leacock, 1966, Winter of the Luna Moth, 1968, Dream Craters, 1974, Top Soil, 1976, Loosely Tied Hands, 1978, Tommy and the Ant Colony, 1979, Sleeping Lady, 1979, Brides of the Stream, 1983, Escape from the Glue Factory, 1985, The Kissing Goldfish of Siam, 1989, Beds and Consenting Dreamers, 1994; author, illustrator: Greenbaum, 1971, The Bumblebee Dithyramb, 1972, The Blind Photographer, 1972, Virgins and Vampires, 1975; illustrator: Dr. Anaconda's Solar Fun Club, 1978, Snake Oil, 1978: editor: Jewish Dialogue, 1969—; poems included in Oxford Book of Canadian Verse, 1968, Poets of the Sixties, 1973, Poets of Canada, 1978, Gridi nel buio (Italian), 1990, other anthologies; exhibited ink drawings one-man show, Gadatsy Gallery. Canada Coun. grantee, 1966, 68, 73; recipient Ont. Arts Coun. poetry award, 1970, Governor General's award for poetry, 1976. Mem. Writers Union of Can.

ROSENBLATT, LESTER, naval architect; b. N.Y.C., Apr. 13, 1920; s. Mandell and Rosa (Wolff) R. BS, CCNY; BS in Naval Architecture and Marine Engring., U. Mich., 1942; DSc (hon.), Webb Inst. Naval Architecture, 1993. Registered profl. engr., N.Y., Mass. Naval architect John H. Wells, Inc., 1942-47; naval architect USN Pearl Harbor Navy Yard, 1944-46; co-founder, chmn., chief exec. officer, naval architect M. Rosenblatt & Son Inc., Naval Architects and Marine Engrs., N.Y.C. and throughout U.S., 1947—; designer maj. ships, U.S. and fgn. Contbr. numerous tech. papers. Trustee (hon.) Webb Inst. Naval Architecture; mem. United Jewish Appeal N.Y., Maritime Friends of Seamen's Ch. Inst. Recipient U. Mich. Sesquicentennial award in ship design, 1967, 1st Rosenblatt-Mich. award, U. Mich., 1992; Admiral's honoree SUNY Maritime Coll., 1992. Mem. Soc. Naval Archs. and Marine Engrs. (pres. 1978-80, nat. chmn. membership com. 1964-78, mem. coun. and exec. com., Land medalist, fellow, hon. mem., chmn. N.Y. sect. 1961-82), Am. Bur. Shipping, Am. Soc. Naval Engrs. (Harold Saunders award 1987), Marine Soc. N.Y. (hon.), Internat. Maritime Hall Fame, Soc. Marine Cons., N.Y. Yacht Club, Tau Beta Pi. Home: 8 E 83rd St Apt 12B New York NY 10028-0418 Office: M Rosenblatt & Son Inc 350 Broadway New York NY 10013-3911

ROSENBLATT, MICHAEL, medical researcher, educator; b. Lund, Sweden, Nov. 27, 1947; s. Arthur Rosenblatt and Jean (Strosberg) Bialer; m. Patricia Ellen Regenbogen, Aug. 23, 1969; children: Anna Miriam, Adam Richard. AB summa cum laude, Columbia U., 1969; MD magna cum laude, Harvard U., 1973. Diplomate Am. Bd. Internal Medicine. Intern then resident Mass. Gen. Hosp., Boston, 1973-75, clin. rsch. fellow in endocrinology and metabolism, 1975-77, chief endocrine unit, 1981-84; instr. in medicine Harvard U., Boston, 1976-78, asst. prof. medicine, 1978-82, assoc. prof. medicine, 1982-85; v.p. for biol. rsch. Merck Sharp & Dohme Rsch. Labs., 1984-87, v.p. for biol. rsch. and molecular biology, 1987-89; sr. v.p. rsch. Merck Sharp & Dohme Rsch. Labs., West Point, Pa., 1989-92; Ebert prof. molecular medicine Harvard Med. Sch., Boston, 1992—; dir. div. health scis. and tech. Harvard-MIT, 1992—; chief div. bone and mineral metabolism Beth Israel Hosp., Boston, 1992—. Editor: Atrial Natriuretic Factor Endocrinology and Metabolism Clinics of N.Am., 1987; contbr. numerous sci. articles on parathyroid hormone and calcium metabolism to leading sci. jours. Recipient Vincent du Vigneaud award Gordon Confs., Kingston, R.I, 1986, Fuller Albright award Am. Soc. for Bone and Mineral Rsch., 1986, citation Japan Endocrine Soc., Tokyo. Fellow AAAS; mem. The Endocrine Soc., Am. Soc. for Biochemistry and Molecular Biology, Am. Soc. for Clin. Investigation, Assn. Am. Physicians, Inter-Urban Clin. Club. Home: 130 Lake Ave Newton Centre MA 02159-2108 Office: Harvard Med Sch HST MEC 213 260 Longwood Ave Boston MA 02115

ROSENBLATT, MURRAY, mathematics educator; b. N.Y.C., Sept. 7, 1926; s. Hyman and Esther R.; m. Adylin Lipson, 1949; children—Karin, Daniel. B.S., CCNY, 1946; M.S., Cornell U., 1947, Ph.D. in Math., 1949. Asst. prof. statistics U. Chgo., 1950-55; assoc. prof. math. Ind. U., 1956-59; prof. probability and statistics Brown U., 1959-64; prof. math. U. Calif., San Diego, 1964—; vis. fellow U. Stockholm, 1953; vis. asst. prof. Columbia U., 1955; guest scientist Brookhaven Nat. Lab., 1959; vis. fellow U. Coll., London, 1965-66, Imperial Coll. and Univ. Coll., London, 1972-73, Australian Nat. U. 1976, 79; overseas fellow Churchill Coll., Cambridge U. Eng., 1979; Wald lectr., 1970; vis. scholar Stanford U., 1982. Author: (with U. Grenander) Statistical Analysis of Stationary Time Series, 1957, Random Processes, 1962, (2d edit), 1974, Markov Processes, Structure and Asymptotic Behavior, 1971, Studies in Probability Theory, 1978, Stationary Sequences and Random Fields, 1985, Stochastic Curve Estimation, 1991; editor: The North Holland Series in Probability and Statistics, 1980; mem. editorial bd. Jour. Theoretical Probability. Recipient Bronze medal U. Helsinki, 1978; Guggenheim fellow, 1965-66, 71-72. Fellow Inst. Math Statistics, AAAS; mem. Internat. Statis. Inst., Nat. Acad. Scis. Office: U Calif Dept Math La Jolla CA 92093

ROSENBLATT, PAUL GERHARDT, federal judge. AB, U. Ariz., 1958, JD, 1963. Asst. atty. gen. State of Ariz., 1963-66; adminstrv. asst. to U.S. Rep., 1967-72; sole practice, Prescott, 1971-73; judge Yavapi County Superior Ct., Prescott, 1973-84; judge, U.S. Dist. Ct. Ariz., Phoenix, 1984—. Office: US Dist Ct US Courthouse & Fed Bldg 230 N 1st Ave Ste 7012 Phoenix AZ 85025-0007

ROSENBLATT, PETER RONALD, lawyer, former ambassador; b. N.Y.C., Sept. 4, 1933; s. William and Therese Amalia (Steinhardt) R.; m. Naomi Henriette Harris, July 1, 1952; children: Therese Sarah Sonenshine, Daniel Harris, David Steinhardt. B.A., Yale U., 1954, LL.B., 1957; postgrad. fellow, Tel-Aviv U. 1971. Bar: N.Y. 1959, D.C. 1969. Teaching asst. history Yale U., New Haven, 1954-55; asst. dist. atty. N.Y. County, 1959-62; asso. Stroock & Stroock & Lavan, N.Y.C., 1962-66; dep. asst. gen. counsel AID, Washington, 1966; mem. White House staff, Washington, 1966-68; jud. officer, chmn. bd. contract appeals U.S. Post Office Dept., Washington, 1968-69; v.p., dir. EDP Technology, Inc., Washington, 1969-71; chmn. bd. Internat. Devel. Services, Washington, 1969-71; spl. cons. to Senator Edmund S. Muskie, 1970-72; practice law Washington, 1972-77, 81-91; ptnr. Heller & Rosenblatt, Washington, 1991—; personal rep. of Pres. (with rank ambassador) to conduct negotiations on future polit. status of Trust Ter. of Pacific Islands, Washington, 1977-81; mem. Mid. East study group Dem. Adv. Council of Elected Officials, 1974-76; bd. dirs. MediSense, Inc., 1983—. Sec., chmn. exec. com. Coalition for a Dem. Majority, 1973-77, pres., 1983-93; bd. dirs. Com. on Present Danger, 1976-77, 82-93; mem. U.S. Nat. Com. Pacific Econ. Cooperation, 1986, sec., 1987—; bd. govs. Haifa (Israel) U., 1990-94; sec.-treas. Fund for Democracy and Devel., 1991-94, pres., 1994—. 2d lt. QMC, AUS, 1957-58. Mem. ABA, N.Y., D.C. Bar, Coun. Fgn. Rels. Jewish. Office: Heller & Rosenblatt 1501 M St NW Washington DC 20005-1702

ROSENBLATT, ROGER, writer; b. N.Y.C., Sept. 13, 1940; m. Virginia Rosenblatt; children: Carl, Amy, John. PhD in English and Am. Lit., Harvard U.; hon. doctorates, U. Md., Claremont Grad. Sch., U. Utah, Pace U. Tchr. lit. and creative writing Harvard U., 1968-73; dir. editorial NEH, 1973-75; lit. editor The New Republic, 1975-78; columnist Washington Post, mem. editorial bd., 1976-79; essayist, sr. writer Time, 1980-88; essayist MacNeil/Lehrer News Hour, PBS, 1983—; columnist, editor-at-large Life mag., 1989-92; contbg. editor N.Y. Times Mag., New Republic, Vanity Fair, also others; editor-in-chief Columbia Journalism Rev.; dir. Delacorte Ctr. for Mag. Journalism, Columbia Grad. Sch. Journalism, 1994—. Author: Black Fiction, 1974, Children of War, 1983 (Robert F. Kennedy Book prize), Witness: The World Since Hiroshima, 1985, Life Itself: Abortion in the American Mind, 1992 (Melcher award), The Man in the Water, 1994, (plays) Free Speech in America, 1991, and, 1992, Bibliomania, 1993. Fulbright scholar, Dublin, Ireland, 1965; recipient numerous journalistic honors including two George Polk awards, George Foster Peabody award, Emmy award.

ROSENBLATT, STEPHEN PAUL, marketing and sales promotion company executive; b. N.Y.C., Feb. 13, 1935; s. Jack Aaron and Ruth (Kloth)

R.; m. Dorothy Freedman, Apr. 7, 1962; children: Gregg, Amy, Robert. BEd, NYU, 1957. Tchr. art N.Y.C. Schs., 1957-78; art dir. Morse Internat., N.Y.C., 1958-65; v.p. L.C. Gumbinner Advt., N.Y.C., 1966-71; group mktg. dir. Norcliff Thayer, Tarrytown, N.Y., 1971-75; pres. BMS Mktg. Services, Inc., N.Y.C., 1975-89, The Promotion Group Inc. subs. Doctus PLC, N.Y.C., 1989-91, SPQR Inc., Yorktown Heights, N.Y., 1991—. Home and Office: 1451 White Hill Rd Yorktown Heights NY 10598-3543

ROSENBLEETH, RICHARD MARVIN, lawyer; b. Phila., Mar. 20, 1932; s. Morris B. and Henrietta (Friedman) R.; m. Judith A. Alesker, June 20, 1954; children—Dori, Lyn. BS in Econs., U. Pa., 1954, JD, 1957. Bar: Pa. 1958, U.S. Supreme Ct. 1961. Asst. dist. atty. City of Phila., 1957-62; assoc. Richman, Price & Jamieson, 1962-65; ptnr. Blank, Rome, Comisky & McCauley, Phila., 1965—; mem. Civil Justice Reform Act Adv. Group, U.S. Dist. Ct. (ea. dist.) Pa., 1991—; co-chair Mayor Rendell's Transition Task Force on the Law Dept., 1991; judge pro tem Phila. Ct. Common Pleas, 1992—. Pres., Merion Park Civic Assn., Pa., 1967; mem. Citizens Crime Commn., Phila., 1979-85. Fellow Am. Coll. Trial Lawyers (chmn. Pa. state com. 1993-94), Internat. Acad. Trial Lawyers, Am. Bar Found.; mem. ABA, Pa. Bar Assn., Phila. Bar Assn., Phila. Bar Found. (pres. 1994). Avocations: golf; art collecting. Office: Blank Rome Comisky et al 1200 Four Penn Ctr Plz Philadelphia PA 19103

ROSENBLITH, WALTER ALTER, scientist, educator; b. Vienna, Austria, Sept. 21, 1913; came to U.S., 1939, naturalized, 1946; s. David A. and Gabriele (Roth) R.; m. Judy Olcott Francis, Sept. 27, 1941; children: Sandra Yvonne, Ronald Francis. Ingenieur Radiotelegraphiste, U. Bordeaux, 1936; Ing. Radioelectricien, Ecole Supérieure d'Electricité, Paris, 1937; ScD (hon.), U. Pa., 1976, S.D. Sch. Mines, 1980, Brandeis U., 1988, U. Miami, Fla., 1992; PhD (hon.), Fed. U. of Rio de Janeiro, 1976. Research engr. France, 1937-39; research asst. N.Y. U., 1939-40; grad. fellow, teaching fellow physics U. Calif. at Los Angeles, 1940-43; asst. prof., asso. prof., acting head dept. physics S.D. Sch. Mines and Tech., 1943-47; research fellow Psycho-Acoustic Lab., Harvard U., 1947-51, lectr. otology and laryngology, 1969—; assoc. prof. comm. biophysics MIT, Cambridge, Mass., 1951-57, prof., 1957-84, Inst. prof., 1975—, Rosenblith prof., 1995—; staff Research Lab. Electronics, 1951-69, chmn. faculty, 1967-69, asso. provost, 1969-71, provost, 1971-80; dir. Kaiser Industries, 1968-76; chmn. com. electronic computers in life scis. Nat. Acad. Scis.-NRC, 1960-64, mem. brain scis. com., 1965-68, chmn., 1966-67; mem. cen. coun. Internat. Brain Rsch. Orgn., 1960-68, mem. exec. com., 1960-68, hon. treas., 1962-67; cons. life scis. panel Pres.'s Sci. Adv. Com., 1961-66; mem. coun. Internat. Union Pure and Applied Biophysics, 1961-69; inaugural lectr. Tata Inst. Fundamental Rsch., Bombay, 1962; Weizmann lectr. Weizmann Inst. Sci., Rehovoth, Israel, 1962; U.S. Nat. Commn. on Pure and Applied Biophysics, 1964-69; mem. Pres.'s Com. Urban Housing, 1967-68; cons. communications scis. WHO, 1964-65; mem. bd. medicine NAS, 1967-70, Rosenblith lectr., 1992; charter mem. Inst. Medicine, 1970—, mem. coun., 1970-76; mem. adv. com. to dir. NIH, 1970-74; mem. governing bd. NRC, 1974-76; mem. adv. com. med. scis. AMA, 1972-74; mem. selection com. Tyler Prize for Environ. Achievement, 1973—; chmn. sci. adv. coun. Callier Ctr. for Communication Disorders, 1968-85; chmn. rsch. com of the Health Effects Inst., 1981-89, bd. dirs., 1989—; chmn. internat. adv. panel of Chinese U. Devel. Project, 1986-91; mem. gov. coun. Internat. Centre Insect Physiology and Ecology, Kenya, 1987-90; mem. Am. and internat. panels on UNESCO (UN Assn. U.S. Am.), 1988-89; mem. Com. on Scholarly Communication with People's Republic of China, 1977-86, Coun. on Fgn. Rels., 1983—. Bd. Fgn. Scholarships, 1978-81, chmn., 1980-81; co-chmn. NRC-IOM com. for study of saccharin and food safety policy, 1978-79; cons. Carnegie Corp. N.Y., 1986—, Carnegie Commn. on Sci., Tech. and Govt., 1988—; hon. consulting prof. U. of Electronic Sci. and Tech. of China, 1988. Bd. govs. Weizmann Inst. Sci., 1973-86; chmn. com. on rehab. of physically handicapped NRC, 1975-77; trustee Brandeis U., 1979—. Decorated croix du chevalier Legion of Honor (France); recipient Alexander von Humboldt medal, 1989. Fellow Acoustical Soc. Am., World Acad. Art and Sci., Am. Acad. Arts and Scis. (exec. bd. 1970-77), AAAS, IEEE; mem. Internat. Council Sci. Unions (v.p. 1984-88), Biophys. Soc. (council 1957-61, 69-72, exec. bd. 1957-61), NAE, NAS (fgn. sec. 1982-86), Soc. Exptl. Psychologists, Engring. Acad. of Japan (fgn. assoc.). Office: MIT Cambridge MA 02139

ROSENBLOOM, ARLAN LEE, physician, educator; b. Milw., Apr. 15, 1934; s. Harris Phillip and Esther (Schneider) R.; m. Edith Kathleen Peterson, Sept. 14, 1958; children: Eric David, Maliah Jo, Disa Lynn, Harris Phillip. BA, U. Wis., 1955, MD, 1958. Diplomate Am. Bd. Pediatrics, Am. Bd. Pediatric Endocrinology. Am. Coll. Epidemiology. Intern Los Angeles County Gen. Hosp., 1958-59; resident in gen. practice Ventura County Hosp., Ventura, Calif., 1959-60; physician-in-chief Medico Hosp., Kratie, Cambodia, 1960-61; med. officer Pahang, Malaysia, 1961-62; resident in pediatrics U. Wis. Hosp., Madison, 1962-63, 64-65; fellow in pediatric endocrinology U. Wis. Hosp., 1963-64, 65-66; asst. prof. pediatrics U. Fla., Gainesville, 1968-71; asso. prof. U. Fla. 1971-74, prof., 1974—; chief div. endocrinology, 1977—, mem. Ctr. for African Studies, mem. Ctr. for Latin Am. Studies; assoc. dir. Clin. Research Center, 1969-74, dir., 1974-80; dir. Nat. Found. March of Dimes Birth Defects Center, 1969-73; med. dir. Gainesville Youth Clinic, 1972-74; mem. adv. com. Nat. Disease and Therapy Index; mem. Fla. Com. Children and Youth, 1972; data work group chmn. Nat. Diabetes Commn., 1975; mem. epidemiology and disease control study sect. NIH, 1978-82; vis. prof. McMaster U. Med. Centre, 1974-75; cons. epidemiologist Boston U. Health Policy Inst., West Africa, 1983-84; mem. affiliate faculty dept. clin. psychology U. Fla., 1984—; pres., dir. Fla. Camp for Children and Youth with Diabetes, 1970-90; dir. N. Fla. Regional Diabetes Program Children and Youth, 1974-88; dir. U. Fla. Diabetes Rsch. Edn. and Treatment Ctr., 1977-90; clin. and sci. adv. bd. Children's Diabetes Found., Denver, 1978-86; dir. N. Fla. Regional Diabetes and Endocrine Program for Children and Youth, 1988—; asst. med. dir. Children's Med. Svcs., Dist. 3, 1986—; mem. nat. diabetes adv. bd. NIH, 1990-94; internat. cons. Inst. for Endocrinology, Metabolism and Reproduction, Quito, Ecuador, 1990—. Editor Acta Paediactrica Belgica, 1979-82, Today in Medicine (Diabetes), 1989—; mem. editl. bd. European Jour. Pediatrics, 1982—, Jour. Pediatric Endocrinology, 1983—, Clin. Pediatrics, 1989—, Diabetes Care, 1992-95, Jour. Clin. Endocrinology and Metabolism, 1995—; contbr. numerous articles to profl. jours. Chief med. officer Hole in the Wall Gang Fund/South, 1990-95. Epidemiologist small pox eradication program USPHS, Yaounde, Cameroon, 1966-68, comdr. inactive Res., 1968-69, capt. Ready Res., 1987—. Recipient Best Drs. in Am., 1992-94, Faculty Rsch. prize U. Fla., 1994, U. Wis. Med. Alumni Citation, 1995. Mem. Am. Acad. Pediatrics, Am. Fedn. Clin. Rsch., Am. Diabetes Assn. (bd. dirs. 1986-90), Brit. Diabetic Assn., Fla. Diabetes Assn. (dir.), Alachua County Med. Soc., Internat. Soc. Pediatric Adolescent Diabetes, Endocrine Soc., Nat. Coun. for Internat. Health, Lawson Wilkins Pediatric Endocrine Soc., Am. Pediatric Soc., Internat. Diabetes Epidemiology Group, Soc. Pediatric Rsch. Home: 2902 SW 1st Ave Gainesville FL 32607-3002 Office: Children's Med Svcs Ctr 1701 SW 16th Ave Rm 2163 Gainesville FL 32608-1153

ROSENBLOOM, BERT, marketing educator, consultant, writer; b. Phila., Feb. 2, 1944; s. Max and Dora (Cohen) R.; m. Pearl Friedman, Aug. 18, 1968; children: Jack Alan, Robyn. B.S., Temple U., 1966, M.B.A., 1968, Ph.D., 1974. Instr. mktg. Rider Coll., Trenton, N.J., 1968-72, asst. prof., 1972-74; asst. prof. mktg. Baruch Coll. CUNY, 1974-76; assoc. prof. Drexel U., Phila., 1976-80, prof., 1980-85, G. Behrens Ulrich prof. mktg., 1985—, assoc. dean grad. programs, 1994—; cons. editor mktg. Random House, N.Y.C., 1977—; cons. in field; mem. bd. dirs Reality Landscaping Co., 1991—, McKee Real Estate Devel. Corp., 1991—. Author: Marketing Channels, 1978, 3d edit., 1987, Market Functions and the Wholesaler Distribution, 1987, Marketing Channels: A Management View, 4th edit., 1991, 5th edit., 1995, Retail Marketing, 1981, Direct Selling Channels, 1993; editor: Journal of Marketing Channels, 1989—, Jour. Consumer Mktg., Jour. Global Mktg., Jour. Acad. Mktg. Sci.; contbr. articles to profl. jours. Named dist. Erskine fellow U. Canterbury, New Zealand, 1986; recipient outstanding educator award Chapel of Four Chaplains, 1984, rsch. award Distbn. Rsch. and Edn. Found., 1986, rsch. award Direct Selling Found., 1986, 91; Nat. Assn. Wholesaler Distbrs. grantee, 1991; honored as disting. prof Retail Mktg. Inst. of Australia, 1985; Vis. scholar Ecole Superiore de Commerce de Paris, 1993. Fellow Acad. Mktg. Sci. (bd. govs. 1978-89); mem. Internat. Mgmt. Devel. Assn. (pres. 1992—), Am. Mktg. Assn. (v.p.

Phila. chpt. 1978-79), Beta Gamma Sigma. Office: Drexel U Sch Bus 32d and Market Sts Philadelphia PA 19104

ROSENBLOOM, DANIEL, investment banker, lawyer; b. N.Y.C., Feb. 11, 1930; s. Sol and Florence (Vogel) R. BA, U. Va., 1951, JD, 1954; LLM, NYU, 1960. Bar: Va. N.Y. 1956. Atty. Paskus, Gordon & Hyman, N.Y.C., 1956-61; v.p., sec., gen. counsel Phila. & Reading Corp., N.Y.C., 1962-67; ptnr. First Manhattan Co., 1967—. Trustee Nat. Found. for Facial Reconstruction, NYU Med. Ctr., Univ. Va. Law Sch. Found. 1st lt. AUS, 1954-56. Mem. Sunningdale Country Club, Farmington Country Club, Harmonie Club, City Athletic Club, Atlantic Golf Club, Phi Alpha Delta, Phi Epsilon Pi. Jewish. Office: First Manhattan Co 437 Madison Ave New York NY 10022-7001

ROSENBLOOM, H. DAVID, lawyer; b. N.Y.C., May 26, 1941; s. Milton M. and Rose Gold R.; m. Carla L. Peterson, June 23, 1968; children: Sarah Alix, Julia Micol. A.B., Princeton U., 1962; postgrad. (Fulbright scholar), U. Florence, Italy, 1962-63; J.D., Harvard U., 1966. Bar: N.Y. 1967, D.C. 1968. Spl. asst. to Arthur J. Goldberg U.S. amb. to UN, 1966-67; law clk. to Abe Fortas U.S. Supreme Ct., 1967-68; assoc. Caplin & Drysdale, Washington, 1968-72, ptnr., 1972-77, 81—; spl. asst. to dep. asst. sec. for tax policy Dept. Treasury, Washington, 1977, internat. tax counsel, 1978-81; lectr. Harvard U. Law Sch., 1984-87, 90-93, 95—, Stanford U. Law Sch., 1988. Mem. D.C. Bar. Home: 2948 Garfield Ter NW Washington DC 20008-3507 Office: One Thomas Circle NW Washington DC 20005

ROSENBLOOM, LEWIS STANLEY, lawyer; b. Fort Riley, Kans., Feb. 28, 1953; s. Donald and Sally Ann (Warsawsky) R.; m. Rochelle Leavitt, Dec. 16, 1973; children: Micah, Shaina. BA, Lake Forest Coll., 1974; JD with high honors, DePaul U., 1977. Bar: Ill. 1977, U.S. Dist. Ct. (no. dist.) Ill. 1977, U.S. Ct. Appeals (7th cir.) 1979, U.S. Ct. Appeals (9th cir.) 1987, U.S. Ct. Appeals (3d cir.) 1993, U.S. Supreme Ct. 1983. Sr. acct. Gale, Takahasi & Channon, Chgo., 1973-74; law clk. to Hon. Robert L. Eisen U.S. Dist. Ct. (no. dist.) Ill., Chgo., 1976; assoc. Nachman, Munitz & Sweig, Ltd., Chgo., 1976-82, prin., 1982-87; ptnr., co-chmn. involvency, bankruptcy & bus. reorgn. dept. Winston & Strawn, Chgo., 1987-93; ptnr., sr. bankruptcy reorgn. counsel McDermott, Will & Emery, Chgo., 1994—; co-chmn. distressed transactions SBU; mem. bd. advisors to bankruptcy, comml. law advisor Bus. Laws, Inc., 1988—; lectr. in field. Contbr. articles to profl. jours. Mem. adv. com. and fin. subcom. Ill. Bd. Higher Edn., Springfield; mem. state edn. and legal aid subcom. Ill. Coun. on Children and Youth Welfare, Chgo. Coll. scholar Lake Forest Coll., 1973-74. Fellow Am. Coll. Bankruptcy; mem. ABA (bus. bankruptcy com. 1982—, chmn. new and pending bankruptcy legis. subcom. 1982-85, chmn. transp. reorganizations subcom. 1985-88), Chgo. Bar Assn. (bankrupcy reorganization com., co-chmn. subcom. on retention and fees 1987-88). Office: McDermott Will & Emery 227 W Monroe St Chicago IL 60606-5016

ROSENBLOOM, MORRIS VICTOR, author, publisher, public relations executive, government official; b. Pitts., Oct. 25, 1915; s. Alfred A. and Corinne (Lorch) R.; m. Ronda Rose Robins, May 16, 1953 (div. 1975). B.A., U. Pitts., 1936. Dir. research stats. for Edward L. Bernays, N.Y.C., 1937; asst. to pres. Ruffsdale Distilling Co., Braddock, Pa., 1937-39; founder, dir. Am. Industries Surveys, N.Y.C., 1939-41; reactivated as Am. Surveys, 1947, dir., 1947-54, pres., 1955—; pres. Am. Surveys Internat., 1965—; sabbatical yr. as bus. liaison officer U.S. Customs Service, Washington, 1983-84; sr. economist OPM, 1941-42; prin. indsl. specialist, chief consumers durable goods and service equipment WPB, later asst. to vice chmn. civilian requirements, 1942-43; v.p. charge sales Diamond Prodns., Inc., 1946-47; mktg. and sales cons. to pres. Publicker Industries, Inc., Phila.; sales mgr. subs. Publicker Industries, Inc., 1947-50; program coordinator, asst. to chmn. NSRB, 1950; spl. asst. dep. adminstr. DPA, 1951-52; founder, exec. dir. Inst. on Econs. Def. Moblzn., sponsored by Am. U., ODM, 1951-52; exec. dir. def. materials operating and policy coms. ODM, 1953; asso. Coates & McCormick, Inc., Washington and N.Y.C., 1954. Author: The Liquor Industry, 1935, rev. edit., 1937; Bottling for Profit (with A.B. Greenleaf), 1940; Peace Through Strength: Bernard Baruch and a Blueprint for Security, 1953 (Warner award); contbr.: Profitable Pub. Rels.; contbr. articles to profl. jours.; lectr. Dir. ops. Nat. Citizens Com. for Hoover Report; sponsor Atlantic Council; mem. pub. relations adv. com. Fair Campaign Practices Com.; mem. Nat Council, nat. pub. rels. com. Boy Scouts Am.; also mem. adv. bd. and chmn. pub. relations com. Nat. Capital Area Council; chmn. alumni regional council U. Pitts., 1960-61. Served with USNR, 1943-46, comdg. officer submarine chaser PTO. Recipient Silver Beaver award Boy Scouts Am., 1963. Fellow Pub. Relations Soc. Am. (accredited, chmn. govt. affairs adv. com. 1969, mem. exec. com. counselors academy, dir. Washington chpt., David Apter Meml. award Pub. Svc. 1990, Paul M. Lund Pub. Svc. award 1990); mem. Nat. Eagle Scout Assn., Def. Orientation Conf. Assn. (life, charter, v.p. 1955-56), Internat. Pub. Relations Assn. (charter), Res. Officers Assn. U.S. U.S. Naval Inst., Friends of Kennedy Ctr. (founder), Dominion Found. for Natural Areas (hon.), Mil. Order of World Wars, Am. Legion Press Post 20 (commdg. officer), Internat. Platform Assn., Pi Lambda Phi (Big PII award 1973). Clubs: Army and Navy (Washington), Pitt. (Washington). Home: Embassy Sq Suites Washington DC 20036 Office: Am Surveys Internat 2000 N St NW Washington DC 20036-2336 *Since boyhood days, my lodestar has been to serve humanity in both my personal and business life. This rewarding objective has been realized with the warmth and encouragement from friends and associates over the years, for which I am deeply appreciative.*

ROSENBLOOM, RICHARD SELIG, business administration educator; b. Springfield, Mass., Jan. 16, 1933; s. Irving J. and Lillian (Saks) R.; m. Ruth Miriam Friedlander, Oct. 14, 1956; children: Joshua, Daniel, Rachel. A.B. in Chemistry, Harvard U., 1954, M.B.A., 1956, D.B.A., 1960. Faculty, Harvard Bus. Sch., Boston, 1960—, dir. doctoral program, 1970-74, assoc. dean research and course devel., 1976-80, prof., 1967—; vis. prof. Hebrew U. of Jerusalem, Israel, 1974-75; founder Jerusalem Inst. Mgmt., Tel Aviv, 1974-88; bd. dirs. Lex. Svc. PLC, London, Arrow Electronics Inc., Exec. Info. Systems, Inc. Author: (with others): Technology and Information Transfer, Cases in Operations Management: A Systems Approach. Editor: Research on Technological Innovation, Management and Policy. Pres., Friends of Harvard/Radcliffe Hillel, Cambridge, Mass., 1985—; bd. dirs. Combined Jewish Philanthropies Greater Boston, 1988—. Mem. AAAS, Soc. for History of Technology. Jewish. Office: Grad Sch Bus Adminstrn Harvard U Cambridge MA 02138

ROSENBLOOM, SANFORD M., lawyer; b. Phila., Sept. 24, 1928; s. Fred L. and Pauline B. (Basen) R.; m. Irene Nelson, 1961 (div. 1974); m. Willa Glazer, Nov. 21, 1976. BS, U. Pa., 1951; JD, Rutgers U., 1955. Bar: Pa. 1956, U.S. Dist. Ct. (ea. dist.) Pa. 1956, U.S. Ct. Appeals (3d cir.) 1957. Ptnr. Schnader, Harrison, Segal & Lewis, Phila., 1955-93; retired. Mem. Phila. Bar Assn. (former chmn. com. real estate sect.), Pa. Bar Assn. (no. of dels., chmn. real property, probate and trust law sect. 1991-92), Am. Coll. Real Estate Lawyers, Vesper Club, Bala Golf Club (Phila.). Republican. Jewish. Avocations: tennis, golf. Home: The Philadelphian 2401 Pennsylvania Ave Philadelphia PA 19130-3061 Office: Schnader Harrison Segal et al 1600 Market St Ste 3600 Philadelphia PA 19103-7236

ROSENBLOOM, STEVE, sportswriter. Sports columnist Chgo. Sun Times. Office: Chgo Sun-Times 401 N Wabash Ave Chicago IL 60611

ROSENBLUM, CONSTANCE, newspaper editor. Arts and leisure sect. editor N.Y. Times, N.Y.C. Office: The NY Times 229 W 43rd St New York NY 10036*

ROSENBLUM, HAROLD ARTHUR, grocery distribution executive; b. Sharon, Pa., Jan. 5, 1923; s. H. David and Carol (Thaler) R.; m. Irene F. Rosen, June 25, 1950; children—Julia M., Mark A., Lee S., Joel N., Ruth C. (dec.). Student, Western Res. U., 1939-40; A.B. cum laude, Harvard, 1943, J.D., 1949. Bar: Pa. 1949. With Sharon div. Peter J. Schmitt Co. (formerly Golden Dawn Foods, Inc.), Sharon, 1950-85; pres. Golden Dawn Foods, Inc., 1961-80, chmn. bd., 1980-83, treas., 1961-73; dir., sec. H.M. Pollock Co., Kittanning, Pa. Mem. Mercer County Mental Health/Mental Retardation Bd., 1967-90, chmn., chief 70-80; sec.; 1984-90; mem. Community Council Com. Mental Health/Mental Retardation, 1965-67, Shenango Valley Jewish Fedn., 1964—; pres. Friends of Buhl Henderson Library, 1973-75;

treas. Mercer County Mental Health Assn., 1964-66; bd. dirs. Mercer County Cmty. Mental Health & Counseling Ctr., 1959-82, sec., 1961-63, pres., 1963-65; v.p. Mercer County Drug and Alcohol Coun., Inc., 1973-74; mem. exec. bd. Shenango Valley Human Rels. Coun., 1960-68; mem. econ. devel. com. Multi-County Manpower Devel. Corp., 1972-73; mem. Sharon Human Relations Commn., 1969-88 , sec., 1984, chmn. 1985-86; sec. Mercer County Comprehensive Health Planning Bd., 1972-74, mem. adv. com., 1971-74; charter mem. Pa. Freedom of Choice in Family Planning; mem. Mercer County Commn. on Drug and Alcohol Abuse, 1973-78; mem. adv. bd. Shenango Valley Campus, Pa. State U., 1976; exec. com. Mercer County br. NAACP, 1964-71; pres. bd. dirs. Playhouse 600, 1973-76; bd. dirs. Sharon Regional Health System (formerly Sharon Gen. Hosp.), 1964—; sec., 1966-77, chmn., 1977—, home health adv. com., 1973—; mem. Mayor's Com. for Arts, 1973-75; trustee-at-large Pa. council Union Am. Hebrew Congregations, 1966-76, 85-90; bd. dirs. Shenango Valley Urban League, 1971-73, Pa. Mental Health Assn., 1968-72; bd. dirs. Mercer County Edn. and Rehab. Ctr. (formerly Mercer County Crippled Children's and Adults Soc.), 1981-94, exec. com., 1983-94, sec., 1986-92; bd. dirs. Family and Children's Svc. of Youngstown Area Jewish Fedn., 1981—, sec., 1986-87, v.p., 1987-89, pres. 1990-92; bd. dirs. Temple Beth Israel, Sharon, 1951-63, 82-89, v.p., 1956-58, pres., 1958-63, 84-87 ; bd. dirs. Cmty. Food Warehouse, 1983-88 , pres., 1985-86; Youngstown State U. Human Services Devel. Adv. Bd., 1986-92; adv. bd. Behavioral Health Ctr., 1988—. Served with AUS, 1943-46. Buhl Day honoree, 1985. Mem. Nat. Am. Wholesale Grocers Assn. (bd. govs. 1964-66), Shenango Valley C. of C. (bd. dirs. 1969-71, treas. 1970, Person of Yr. 1985). Clubs: Rotary (Sharon) (pres. 1978-79), Sharon Country (Sharon), University (Sharon) (fin. sec., pres. 1978-79); F.H. Buhl (dir. 1977-79). Home: 1700 Hannah Ct Sharon PA 16146-3818

ROSENBLUM, JOHN WILLIAM, business educator; b. Houston, Jan. 1, 1944; s. H. William and Susan (Ullmann) R.; m. Carolyn Edith Jones, Sept. 12, 1964; children: J. Christopher, Kathryn, Nicholas. A.B., Brown U., 1965; M.B.A., Harvard U., 1967, D.B.A., 1972. Instr. Harvard U. Bus. Sch., Boston, 1969-72, asst. prof., 1972-75, assoc. prof., 1975-79; prof. Darden Grad. Sch. Bus. Adminstrn., U. Va., Charlottesville, 1979-80, assoc. dean, 1980-82, dean, 1982-93; Tayloe Murphy prof., 1993—; bd. dirs. Chesapeake Corp., Cadmus Comms., Inc., T. Rowe Price Assocs., Comdial Corp., Cone Mills Corp., The Providence Jour. Co. Co-author: Strategy and Organization, 1973, (2d edit.), 1977, Cases in Political Economy-Japan, 1980. Mem. Phi Beta Kappa. Home: Rt 3 Box 530 Crozet VA 22932 Office: Univ of Va Darden Grad Sch Bus PO Box 6550 Charlottesville VA 22906-6550

ROSENBLUM, M. EDGAR, theater director; b. Bklyn., Jan. 8, 1932; s. Jacob and Pauline (Feldman) R.; m. Cornelia Hartmann, May 1, 1960; 1 child, Jessica Alex. Student, Bard Coll., 1951-55. Prodr. Folk Rock Chamber Music Series, Woodstock, N.Y., 1956-72; dir. Polari Gallery, Woodstock, 1959-72; asst. to mgr. Nat. Music League, N.Y.C., 1958-59; stage mgr. Joffrey Ballet Nat. Tour, 1960; prodr. When I Was a Child, 41st St Theatre, N.Y.C., 1960-61, Woodstock Playhouse, 1960-73; stage mgr. Turn of the Screw Nat. Tour, 1961; exec. dir. Hudson Valley Repertory Theatre, Woodstock, 1964-67; exec. prodr. The Shadow Box, N.Y.C., 1977; exec. dir. Long Wharf Theatre, New Haven, 1970—; producer and owner, Woodstock (N.Y.) Playhouse, 1959-73; cons. Fedn. for Ext. and Devel. of Am. Profl. Theatre, N.Y.C., 1970, Arts Couns. of New Haven, R.I., Alaska, Conn., Ohio, 1971—; bd. trustees Am. Arts Alliance, chmn of bd. 1982-84; vis. lectr. Yale U., New Haven, 1985-91. With U.S. Army, 1953. Ezra Stiles Coll. fellow, Yale U., 1973. Mem. Am. Arts Alliance (chmn. 1982-84), League of Resident Theatres (mem. exec., liaison and negotiating coms. 1974, v.p. 1993—), Nat. Corp. Theatre Fund (founding pres. 1976), Conn. Advocates for the Arts (bd. dirs. 1978—), Greater New Haven C. of C. (bd. dirs.). Office: Long Wharf Theatre 222 Sargent Dr New Haven CT 06511-5955

ROSENBLUM, MARVIN, mathematics educator; b. Bklyn., June 30, 1926; s. Isidore and Celia (Mendelsohn) Rosenblum; m. Frances E. Parker, May 30, 1959; children: Isidore, Mendel, Jessie, Rebecca, Sarah. B.S., U. Calif.-Berkeley, 1949, M.A., 1951, Ph.D, 1955. Instr. math. U. Calif.-Berkeley, 1954-55; asst. prof. U. Va., Charlottesville, 1955-59, assoc. prof., 1960-65, prof., 1965—, now Commonwealth prof.; mem. Inst. Advanced Study, 1959-60. Served with USNR, 1944-46. Mem. Am. Math. Soc., Am. Math. Assn., Soc. Indsl. and Applied Math. Jewish. Office: Univ Va Math-Astro Bldg Dept Math Charlottesville VA 22903

ROSENBLUM, MICHAEL F., lawyer; b. N.Y.C., Sept. 23, 1940. BA, Harvard U., 1962; JD, Villanova U., 1968. Bar: D.C. 1968, Ill. 1971. Ptnr. Mayer, Brown & Platt, Chgo.; mem. Nat. Rels. Bd. appellate ct. divsn., 1968-71. Mem. ABA, Fed. Bar Assn., D.C. Bar. Office: Mayer Brown & Platt 190 S La Salle St Chicago IL 60603

ROSENBLUM, MYRON, chemist, educator; b. N.Y.C., Oct. 21, 1925; s. Julius and Miriam (Sandler) R.; m. Rachel Susan Jacobson, June 22, 1958; children: Miriam, Jonathan, Leah. AB, Columbia U., 1949; AM, Harvard U., 1950, PhD, 1954. Postdoctoral fellow Columbia U., N.Y.C., 1953-55; asst. prof. chemistry Ill. Inst. Tech., Chgo., 1955-58; asst. prof. Brandeis U., Waltham, Mass., 1958-60, assoc. prof., 1960-66, prof., 1966—. Author: (monograph) The Iron Group Metallocenes, 1967. Sgt. inf. U.S. Army, 1943-46, ETO. Guggenheim fellow, 1965, Fulbright fellow. Mem. Am. Chem. Soc., Brit. Chem. Soc. Avocation: woodworking. Office: Brandeis U Dept of Chemistry Waltham MA 02254

ROSENBLUM, ROBERT, art historian, educator; b. N.Y.C., July 24, 1927; s. Abraham H. and Lily M. (Lipkin) R.; m. Jane Kaplowitz, June 23, 1977; children: Sophie Isla, Theodore Abraham. BA, Queens Coll., 1948; MA, Yale U., 1950; PhD, NYU, 1956; MA (hon.), Oxford U., 1972; ArtsD (hon.), Queens Coll., 1992. Mem. faculty U. Mich., Ann Arbor, 1955-56, Princeton (N.J.) U., 1956-66, Yale U., New Haven, 1966-67; mem. faculty NYU, N.Y.C., 1967—; prof. fine arts NYU, 1967—. Author: Cubism and Twentieth Century Art, 1960, Transformations in Late Eighteenth Century Art, 1967, Ingres, 1967, Frank Stella, 1971, Modern Painting and the Northern Romantic Tradition, 1975, The International Style of 1800, 1976, Andy Warhol: Portrait of the 70s, 1979, 19th Century Art, 1984, The Dog in Art From Rococo to Post-Modernism, 1988, The Romantic Child From Runge to Sendak, 1989, Paintings in the Musee d'Orsay, 1989, The Jeff Koons Handbook, 1992, Andy Warhol Portraits, 1993, Mel Ramos: Pop Images, 1994, The Paintings of August Strindberg, The Structure of Chaos, 1995. Served with U.S. Army, 1945-46. Recipient Frank Jewett Mather award for art criticism, 1981. Fellow Am. Acad. Arts and Scis.; mem. Coll. Art Assn. Am. Office: NYU Dept Fine Arts Washington Sq N New York NY 10003-6635

ROSENBLUM, VICTOR GREGORY, political science and law educator; b. N.Y.C., June 2, 1925; s. George and Vera (Minster) R.; m. Louise Rann, Feb. 21, 1946; children: Susan, Ellen, Laura, Keith, Jonathan, Peter, Warren, Joshua. A.B., Columbia U., 1945, LL.B., 1948; Ph.D., U. Calif.-Berkeley, 1953; D.H.L., Hebrew Union Coll., 1970; D.L., Siena Heights Coll., 1982. Bar: Ill., N.Y., U.S. Supreme Ct. Lectr. polit. sci. U. Calif., Berkeley, 1949-52, asst. prof. polit. sci., 1953-57; assoc. prof. polit. sci. Northwestern U., 1958-63, prof. polit. sci. and law, 1963-68, 70-88, Nathaniel L. Nathanson prof., 1988—; pres. Reed Coll., Portland, Oreg., 1968-70; sr. legal cons. project on bankruptcy govtl. studies div. Brookings Instn., 1964-69; vis. Fulbright lectr. Sch. Law U. Louvain, Belgium, 1966-67, vis. prof., 1978-79, 91-92; mem. Adminstrv. Conf. U.S., 1982—. Editor in chief Adminstrv. Law Rev., 1958-62; author: Law As A Political Instrument, 1955, (with A.D. Castberg) Cases on Constitutional Law: Political Roles of the Supreme Court, 1973, (with Frances Zemans) The Making of a Public Profession, 1981; contbr. to law revs., also law and polit. sci. books. Staff assoc. Govtl. Affairs Inst., Washington, 1952-53; cons., assoc. counsel Subcom. on Exec. and Legis. Reorgn., Com. on Govt. Ops., U.S. Ho. of Reps., 1956-57; bd. dirs. Center for Adminstrv. Justice, 1972-78. Mem. ABA (council speci. adminstrv. law 1962-65, 72-75, chmn. 1977-78), Fed. Bar Assn., Am. Polit. Sci. Assn., Law and Soc. Assn. (pres. 1970-72), Am. Judicature Soc. (dir. 1982-90, chmn. bd. 1985-86), Assn. Am. Law Schs. (exec. com. 1984-88, pres. 1987), Consortium of Social Sci. Assns. (pres. 1987-88), Phi Beta Kappa, Pi Sigma Alpha. Democrat. Jewish. Home: 2030 Orrington Ave Evanston IL 60201-2912 Office: Northwestern U Sch Law 357 E Chicago Ave Chicago IL 60611-3069

ROSENBLUTH, LUCILLE MAXINE, health research facility administrator; b. N.Y.C., Sept. 18, 1931; d. David and Rhea (Farber) Moses; m. Sol Rosenbluth, June 8, 1952; children: Shelly Kratzer, Martin. BA in Polit. Sci., Bklyn. Coll., 1952; M in Pub. Adminstrn., NYU, 1953. Intern N.Y. State Adminstrn. Internship Program, 1953-54; rsch. aide N.Y. State Workmen's Compensation Bd., 1954-55; personnel asst. Dept. Personnel, N.Y.C., 1955-57; lectr. Bklyn. Coll., 1958, 59; rsch. asst. Temporary State Commn. on Operation N.Y.C. Govt., 1959-60; cons. Dept. Health, N.Y.C., 1960-61; rschr. study of profl., tech. and managerial manpower needs City of N.Y. Brookings Instn., 1961-63; cons. personnel utilization Dept. Health, N.Y.C., 1963-64; chief rschr. Med. and Health Rsch. Assn. N.Y.C., Inc., 1964-67, project coord., work com. chmn. systems study of sch. health records, 1967-70, project dir., policy com. chmn. N.Y.C. infant day care study, 1970-75, exec. v.p., 1975-86, pres., 1986—; cons. Commonwealth of Mass., 1982; mem. adj. faculty grad. sch. program in pub. health, dept. environ. and community medicine Rutger Med. Sch. U. Medicine and Dentistry N.J., 1984-86; mem. maternal and child health steering com. Sch. Pub. Health Columbia U., 1983—, lectr. pub. health, 1986—. Author: (with others) Caring Prescriptions: Comprehensive Health Care Strategies for Young Children in Poverty, 1993; contbr. articles to profl. jours. Fellow N.Y. Acad. Medicine (assoc., exec. com. on pub. health); mem. APHA (chair breastfeeding com. 1985, 86, 87), Family Planning Couns. Am. (chair grantee adv. com. Region II 1987, 88), N.Y. State Family Planning Advocates, N.Y. State Pub. Health Assn. (co-chmn. legis. com., bd. dirs. 1986—), Pub. Health Assn. N.Y.C., Soc. Rsch. Adminstrs., Health Care Execs. Forum (pres. 1988, 89), Hermann Biggs Soc., Women's City Club N.Y. (chair com. pub. health 1982-84). Office: Medical Health Rsch Assn of NYC 40 Worth St # 720 New York NY 10013-2904

ROSENBLUTH, MARSHALL NICHOLAS, physicist, educator; b. Albany, N.Y., Feb. 5, 1927; s. Robert and Margaret (Sondhein) R.; m. Sara Unger, Feb. 6, 1979; children by previous marriage—Alan Edward, Robin Ann, Mary Louise, Jean Pamela. BA, Harvard, 1945; MS, U. Chgo., 1947, PhD, 1949. Inst. Stanford U., 1949-50; staff mem. Los Alamos Sci. Lab., 1950-56; sr. research adviser Gen. Atomic Corp., San Diego, 1956-67; prof. U. Calif., San Diego, 1960-67, Inst. for Advanced Study, Princeton U., N.J., 1967-80; dir. Inst. for Fusion Studies, U. Tex., 1980-87; prof. U. Calif., San Diego, 1987-92; chief U.S. scientist Internat. Thermonuclear Engring. Reactor, 1992—; lectr. with rank prof. in astrophys. scis. Princeton U.; also vis. sr. research physicist Princeton U. (Plasma Physics Lab.), 1967-80; Andrew D. White vis. prof. Cornell U., 1976; cons. AEC, NASA, Inst. Def. Analysis. Served with USNR, 1944-46. Recipient E.O. Lawrence award, 1964, Albert Einstein award, 1967, Maxwell prize, 1976, Enrico Fermi award Dept. Energy, 1985. Mem. Am. Phys. Soc., Nat. Acad. Sci., Am. Acad. Arts and Scis. Home: 2311 Via Siena La Jolla CA 92037-3933 Office: U Calif at San Diego Dept Physics 9500 Gilman Dr La Jolla CA 92093*

ROSENBLUTH, MORTON, periodontist, educator; b. N.Y.C., Sept. 28, 1924; s. Jacob and Eva (Bigeleissen) R.; m. Sylvia Fradin, July 2, 1946; children: Cheryl Bonnie, Hal Glen. BA, NYU, 1943, grad. program in periodontia, oral medicine, DDS, 1946. Diplomate Am. Bd. Periodontology. Intern Bellevue Hosp. N.Y.C., 1946-47, resident, 1947; individual practice dentistry, N.Y.C., 1947-59; individual practice periodontia, North Miami Beach, Fla., 1960—; periodontist Mt. Sinai Hosp., N.Y., Polyclinic Hosp. and Med. Sch. N.Y., Mt. Sinai Hosp., Miami Beach, Fla., Parkway Gen. Hosp.; chief dental dept. North Miami Gen. Hosp.; chmn periodontia sect. Dade County Research Ctr.; clin. assoc. prof. div. oral and maxillofacial surgery U. Miami Sch. Medicine; assoc. clin. prof. Southeastern U. Health Scis.; lectr. throughout U.S.A., Israel, Mexico, Rome, Teheran, Bangkok, Hong Kong, Tokyo, Honolulu, Jamaica, Paris, London, Sicily, Budapest, Berlin, Luxembourg, South Africa, and others; vis. lectr. U. Tenn. Dental Coll., NYU Dental Coll.; cons. VA Hosp., Miami. Mem. adv. bd. U. Fla. Coll. Dentistry; mem. profl. adv. bd. North Dade Children's Center, Hope Sch. Mentally Retarded Children; mem. sci. adv. com. United Health Found.; chmn. Dental div. United Fund of Dade County, Combined Jewish Appeal; nat. chmn. Hebrew U. Sch. Dental Medicine; bd. dirs. Health Planning Council S. Fla. Contbr. articles to profl. jours. Pres. Condominium Assn.; bd. dirs. and bd. overseers Am. Friends of Hebrew U.; mem. med. adv. bd. Dade-Broward Lupus Found.; trustee Jewish Congregation, 1961-64. With AUS, 1943-44, as capt. USAF, 1951-52. Recipient Maimonides award State of Israel, 1979. Fellow Am. Coll. Dentists, Internat. Coll. Dentists; mem. ADA, Am. Acad. Periodontology, Am., Fla. socs. periodontists, Am. Assn. Hosp. Dental Chiefs, Am. Acad. Dental Medicine, Am. Soc. Advancement Gen. Anesthesia in Dentistry, Northeastern Soc. Periodontists, Fla. (chmn. council on legislation), Miami, Miami Beach, East Coast (sec.-treas. 1968, pres. 1971-72), North Dade (pres. 1963-64) dental socs., Fedn. Dentaire Internationale, Fla. Acad. Dental Practice Adminstrn., Alpha Omega (pres. 1967-68, internat. regent 1973-75, internat. editor 1975-77, internat. pres.-elect 1977-78, internat. pres. 1979, chmn. bd. Alpha Omega Found. 1985-90) Am. Dental Interfrat. Council (pres. 1981-82), Nocoma Club (pres. 1958-60), NYU Century Club (local chmn.), Jockey Club (bd. govs.), KP, Masons, Kiwanis (bd. dirs. 1965), Chaine Des Rotisseurs (Miami Beach charge de missions). Home: 11111 Biscayne Blvd Apt 857 Miami FL 33181-3494 Office: 1166 Kane Concourse Bal Harbour FL 33154

ROSENDAHL, BRUCE RAY, dean, geophysicist, educator; b. Jamestown, N.Y., Dec. 28, 1946; s. Raymond Leslie and Marjorie (Anderson) R.; m. Susan Andrews, June 14, 1969; children: Tana, Andrew. BS, U. Hawaii, 1970, MS, 1972; PhD in Oceanography, U. Calif. San Diego, La Jolla, 1976. Rsch. asst. U. Hawaii, Honolulu, 1970-72; rsch. asst. Scripps Instn. Oceanography, San Diego, 1972-76, postdoctoral fellow, 1976; from asst. prof. to assoc. prof. Duke U., Durham, N.C., 1976-88, prof., 1988-89; dean, Lewis Weeks chair in Marine Geology & Geophysics U. Miami, Fla., 1989—; v.p., chief exec. officer Internat. Oceanographic Found., Miami, 1989—; bd. govs. Joint Oceanographic Instns., Washington, 1989—, mem. exec. com. deep earth sampling, 1989—; bd. dirs. Marine Coun., Miami, 1990; bd. advisors Maritime Sci. and Tech. Acad., Miami, 1990; mem. Coun. on Ocean Affairs, 1989—. Author, editor: Initial Reports Deepsea Drilling, Leg 54, 1980, African Rifting, 1989; tech. editor Sea Frontiers Mag., 1989—; contbr. articles to profl. jours. Trustee Mus. Sci., Miami, 1990. Mem. Am. Geophys. Union, Am. Assn. Petroleum Geologists. Home: 601 Vilabella Ave Miami FL 33146-1719 Office: U Miami Rosenstiel Sch Marine & Atmospheric Scis 4600 Rickenbacker Cswy Miami FL 33149-1031

ROSENDALE, SUZANNE MOORE, library media specialist; b. Utica, N.Y., July 12, 1942; d. Clark Wilbur and Lynda Louise (Hokerk) Moore; m. Walter R. Rosendale Jr., June 18, 1966; children: Kristen, Jennifer. AA, Penn Hall Jr. Coll., Chambersburg, Pa., 1962; BS in Elem. Edn. and BS in English 7-12, SUNY, Oswego, 1980; MLS, Syracuse U., 1986. Cert. elem. edn. tchr., N.Y. English tchr. VVS Middle Sch., Verona, N.Y., 1980-85; libr. media specialist VVS Middle Sch., Verona, N.Y., 1986—. Co-author: Creative Mathematics, 1980. Bd. dirs. Sherrill-Kenwood Community Chest, Sherrill, N.Y., 1980-84; trustee/regent Sherrill-Kenwood Free Libr., 1992—, chmn. pers. com. 1992-94; mem. beautification com. City of Sherrill, 1992. Named 1st runner-up Vol. Yr. Oneida (N.Y.) Daily Dispatch, 1970. Mem. ASCD, Cen. N.Y. State Libr. Assn., Sherrill, N.Y. Garden Club (sec., treas. 90-93). Republican. Methodist. Avocations: fishing, gardening, antiquing, boating, refinishing. Home: 177 Willow Pl Sherrill NY 13461-1056

ROSENDHAL, JEFFREY DAVID, federal science agency administrator, astronomer; b. Bklyn., June 21, 1941; s. Louis and Beulah (Goldsmith) R.; m. Sharon E. Katzman, Dec. 27, 1964 (div. Jan. 25, 1989); children—Martin Andrew, Rachel Lynn; m. Ellen R. Anderson, Feb. 14, 1992. B.A., Williams Coll., 1962; M.S., U. Ill., 1963; Ph.D. (NASA fellow 1966-68), Yale U., 1968. Vis. asst. prof. astronomy U. Wash., Seattle, 1968-69; asst. prof. U. Wis., Madison, 1969-71, U. Ariz., Tucson, 1971-74; with NASA, Washington, 1974—; mgr. advanced programs and tech., astrophysics div. NASA, 1978-80; asst. assoc. adminstr. advanced planning Office Space Sci., 1980-81; asst. assoc. adminstr. for sci. Office Space Sci. and Applications, 1981-87, spl. asst. to assoc. adminstr. for space sci. and applications, 1987-89, 92-93; spl. asst. for policy Office of Exploration, 1989-90; asst. dir. for exploration (internat.) Office of Aeronautics, Exploration and Tech., 1990-91; asst. dir. strategic planning Astrophysics Divsn. Office of Space Sci., Washington, 1993—; vis. prof. internat. rels. George Washington U., 1988-89; staff member subcom. House Sci. Space and Tech. Com., 1992. Mem. editorial adv. bd. Jour. Brit. Interplanetary Soc., 1988—; contbr. articles to Astrophys. Jour., Astrophysics and Space Sci., Physics Today, Issues in Sci. and Tech., Acta Astronautica, other jours. and conf. procs. Recipient NASA Sr. Exec. Service Performance awards, 1980, 82-86, Outstanding Leadership medal, 1984, group achievement awards (2), 1986, European Space Agy. Team Achievement award, 1983, 85, 86, Presdl. award of Meritorious Exec. in Sr. Exec. Service, 1987; NSF grantee, 1971, 71-73; hon. Woodrow Wilson fellow, 1962. Mem. AIAA, Astron. Soc. Pacific, Am. Astron. Soc., Royal Astron. Soc., Internat. Acad. Astronautics (corr.), Internat. Astron. Union, Phi Beta Kappa. Club: Cosmos (Washington). Achievements include discovery of the variability of the microturbulence in early-type high luminosity stars; direction of the selection of flight experiments for every major NASA scientific mission 1980-88. Home: 11446 Links Dr Reston VA 22090 Office: NASA Hdqrs Astrophysics Divsn Office Space Sci Code SZ Washington DC 20546

ROSENDIN, RAYMOND JOSEPH, electrical contracting company executive; b. San Jose, Calif., Feb. 14, 1929; s. Moses Louis and Bertha C. (Pinedo) R.; m. Jeanette Marie Bucher, June 30, 1951 (dec. Feb. 1967); children: Mark R., Patricia A., Debra M., Cynthia C., David R.; m. Nancy Ann Burke, July 6, 1984; children: Raymond M., Callie R., Blake W. Student engring., San Jose State U., 1947-48; B.S.E.E., Heald's Engring. Coll., San Francisco, 1950. V.p., CEO Rosendin Electric, Inc., San Jose, Calif., 1953-59, exec. v.p., CEO, 1969-75, pres., CEO, 1975-94, chmn., CEO, 1995—; former dir. Community Bank, San Jose. Bd. fellows U. Santa Clara, Calif., 1966-93, pres. bd., 1969-72, bd. regents, 1972-82; bd. dirs. United Way, Santa Clara, 1970-74; O'Connor's Hosp., San Jose, 1979-85, Community Hosp., Los Gatos, Calif., 1968-74. Recipient Man of Yr. award Santa Clara Valley Youth Village, 1963, Optimist of Yr. award Optimist Club, San Jose, 1970. Mem. C. of C. Greater San Jose (past dir.), Nat. Elec. Contractors Assn. (past pres., gov., dir.). Republican. Roman Catholic. Club: St. Claire (San Jose). Avocation: boating. Office: Rosendin Electric Inc 880 Mabury Rd San Jose CA 95133-1021

ROSENFELD, ARNOLD SOLOMON, newspaper editor; b. N.Y.C., Apr. 18, 1933; s. William and Cohen (Cohen) R.; m. Ruth Doris Lilly, Sept. 30, 1956; children—William Bennett, Jonathan Andrew, Lauren. Student, U. Houston, 1951; Profl. Journalism fellow, Stanford U., 1967. Mem. staff Houston Post, 1953-67; assoc. editor Detroit mag., Detroit Free Press, 1967; editor Detroit mag., 1968; mng. editor Dayton Daily News, Ohio, 1968-76; editor Dayton Daily News, 1976-80, Dayton Daily News and Jour. Herald, 1980-84, Austin Am.-Statesman, Tex., 1984-88, Atlanta Jour.-Constitution, 1988-89; editor-in-chief Cox Newspapers, Atlanta, 1989—; dir. The Temple, Atlanta, 1994—. Editor: A Thomason Sketchbook, 1969. Pres. Temple Israel Dayton, 1984; bd. dirs. Antioch U., 1978-84, Huston-Tillotson Coll., 1987-89. With AUS, 1951-53. Recipient Editorial Writing award A.P. Mng. Editors Assn. Tex., 1966; Tex. Theta Sigma Phi award, 1969, 72; Media award Nat. Assn. Mental Health, 1976. Mem. Am. Soc. Newspaper Editors (bd. dirs.). Home: 5875 Riverwood Dr NW Atlanta GA 30328-3728 Office: Cox Newspapers PO Box 105720 Atlanta GA 30348-5720

ROSENFELD, ARTHUR H., lawyer, publisher; b. Bklyn., May 24, 1930; s. Abraham and Sadie (Albert) R.; m. Lois E. Glantz, Apr. 15, 1956; children: Felicia Ann, Carolyn Jane, Sara Ellen. Student, St. Andrew's U., 1950-51; AB, Union Coll., Schenectady, 1952; JD, Harvard U., 1955; postgrad., CCNY, 1962-63. Bar: N.Y. 1955. Pres. Warren, Gorham & Lamont, Inc., N.Y.C., 1970-81, Internat. Thomson Profl. Pub., N.Y.C., 1981-84; chmn. bd. Rosenfeld, Emanuel Inc., Larchmont, N.Y., 1984-88; pres. Prentice Hall Tax & Profl. Ref., N.Y.C., 1988-89, Maxwell Macmillan Profl. and Bus. Reference Div., Englewood Cliffs, N.J., 1989-92, Arthur H. Rosenfeld Assocs., 1991—; Civic Rsch. Inst., Inc., 1992—; of counsel Am. Assn. Legal Publishers, 1995—; exec. dir. Fund for Pub. Access to the Law, 1995—. Vice chmn., bd. dirs. Coun. Econ. Priorities, 1990—. Mem. ABA, N.Y. State Bar Assn., Am. Assn. Pubs. (exec. coun. 1991). Democrat. Club: Harvard. Office: 330 W 72nd St New York NY 10023

ROSENFELD, AZRIEL, computer science educator, consultant; b. N.Y.C., Feb. 19, 1931; s. Abraham Hirsh and Ida B. (Chadaby) R.; m. Eve Hertzberg, Mar. 1, 1959; children—Elie, David, Tova. B.A., Yeshiva U., 1950, M.H.L., 1953, M.S., 1954, D.H.L., 1955; M.A., Columbia U., 1951, Ph.D, 1957; D.Tech. (hon.), Linkoping U., Sweden, 1980; D of Tech. (hon.), Oulu U., Finland, 1994. Ordained rabbi, 1952. Physicist Fairchild Controls Corp., N.Y.C., 1954-56; engr. Ford Instrument Co., Long Island City, N.Y., 1956-59; mgr. research electronics div. Budd Co., Long Island City and McLean, Va., 1959-64; prof., dir. Ctr. for Automation Rsch., U. Md., College Park, 1964—, disting. univ. prof., 1995—; vis. asst. prof. Yeshiva U., N.Y.C., 1957-63; pres. ImTech, Inc., Silver Spring, Md., 1975-92. Author, editor numerous books; editor numerous jours. Fellow IEEE (Emanuel R. Piore award 1985), IEEE Computer Soc. (Harry Goode Meml. award 1995), Washington Acad. Scis. (Sci. Achievement award 1988), Am. Assn. for Artificial Intelligence (founding), Assn. Computing Machinery (founding); mem. Math. Assn. Am., Machine Vision Assn. (bd. dirs. 1984-88, Pres.'s award 1987), Internat. Assn. Pattern Recognition (pres. 1980-82, K.S. Fu award 1988, founding fellow 1994), Assn. Orthodox Jewish Scientists (pres. 1963-65), Nat. Acad. Engring. of Mex. (corr.). Home: 847 Loxford Ter Silver Spring MD 20901-1132 Office: U Md Ctr Automation Rsch Computer Vision Lab College Park MD 20742-3275

ROSENFELD, HARRY MORRIS, editor; b. Berlin, 1929; s. Sam and Esther Laja (Sherman) R.; m. Anne Hahn, Feb. 28, 1953; children: Susan, Amy, Stefanie. BA, Syracuse U., 1952; postgrad., NYU, 1954, Columbia U., 1955-59. With N.Y. Herald Tribune, 1954-66, fgn. editor, 1962-66; mng. editor Herald Tribune News Svc., 1959-62, 1962-66; with Washington Post, 1966-78, fgn. editor, 1967-69; asst. mng. editor Met. News, 1970-74, Nat. News, 1974-76, Outlook/Book World, 1976-78; editor Times Union and Knickerbocker News, Albany, N.Y., 1978-88, L.A. Herald Examiner, 1985, The Times Union and Sunday Times Union, 1978—; dir. daily Watergate coverage for Washington Post (newspaper awarded Pulitzer Gold medal for pub. svc.); vice chmn. N.Y. Fair Trial Free Press Conf., 1985-94; co-chmn. for N.Y. State, Reporters Com. for Freedom of Press; mem. adv. com. Harvard Journalism Fellowship for Advanced Studies in Pub. Health. Recipient Black United Front award, 1973, First Amendment award Anti-Defamation League-B'nai B'rith, L.A., Outstanding Alumni award, Syracuse U. Coll. of Arts and Scis., Media Responsibility award N.Y. State Martin Luther King Jr. Inst. for Non-Violence, 1993. Mem. Am. Soc. Newspaper Editors, N.Y. State AP Assn. (pres. 1983, 3d pl. column award 1983, 85, 1st pl. column award 1987), N.Y. State Soc. Newspaper Editors, Internat. Press Inst., UPI Fgn. News Com. (rep. for N.E., adv. com. on cameras in N.Y. Cts., Pulitzer Juror 1987-88), Soc. Profl. Journalists (adv. bd. Albany chpt.), Cameras in the Cts. (adv. com.). Office: Times Union PO Box 1500 Albany NY 12212

ROSENFELD, HERB, educational consultant; b. N.Y.C., Feb. 13, 1931; s. David and Bertha (Kutler) R.; m. Esther Halfon, Dec. 25, 1957; children: Michele Eve, Seth Zvi, Amy Lynn. BA in Math. and Physics, CUNY, 1960; MS in Math. Edn., Yeshiva U., 1963; postgrad., Pa. State U., 1963, Columbia U., 1964, Fordham U., 1965-67. Tchr. math. Walton High Sch., N.Y.C., 1960-63, New Rochelle (N.Y.) High Sch., 1963-64; tchr. math., dean students, dir. discovery program Bronx (N.Y.) High Sch. Sci., 1964-82, founder, dir. outreach program, 1974-82; mem. planning com., then chmn. math. dept. Manhattan Ctr. for Sci. and Math., N.Y.C., 1982-84; co-founder, asst. dir. Central Park East Secondary Sch., N.Y.C., 1984-89; founder, cons. Eastside Community High Sch., Wooster (Mass.) and Boston Sch. Dists., I.S. 184, N.Y.C., 1990—; cons. Panasonic Found., Coalition Essential Schs., Bank Street Coll., Lyndhurst (N.J.) Sch. Dist.; project dir. N.Y.C. Dist. 1 Secondary Sch. Project. Contbg. author: Teaching Advanced Skills to Educationally Disadvantaged Students; You Must Have a Dream to Create a School, 1993. Home and Office: 711 Amsterdam Ave Apt 17L New York NY 10025-6925

ROSENFELD, JOEL, ophthalmologist, lawyer; b. Jan. 27, 1957; s. Jacques Maurice and Mazal (Attia) R. BS with high honors, U. Mich., 1976, MD, 1980; JD cum laude, U. Detroit, 1993. Diplomate Nat. Bd. Med. Examiners, Am. Bd. Ophthalmology; bar: Mich. 1994. Intern Baptist Coll. Medicine, Houston, 1980-81; resident in ophthalmology Kresge Eye Inst./Wayne State U., Detroit, 1981-84; fellow in ultrasound U. Iowa, Iowa City, 1984; chief of ophthalmology Wheelock Hosp., Goodrich, Mich., 1984—, Huron Meml. Hosp., Bad Axe, Mich., 1988—; St. Joseph Mercy Hosp., Pontiac, Mich., 1989—; co-founder, pres., gen. counsel Mktg. Systems, Inc., 1994—. Author rsch. reports. Supporting mem. Boys and Girls Club Am., Pontiac, Mich., 1984—, Pontiac Rescue Mission, 1988—. Recipient Man of Yr. award Boys and Girls Clubs Am., 1988; named Hon. Citizen, Father Flanagan Boys Home, Boys Town, Nebr., 1991, Ptnr. of Conscience, Amnesty Internat., N.Y.C., 1991. Fellow AMA, Am. Acad. Ophthalmology, Am. Coll. Legal Medicine; mem. ABA, FBA, Am. Soc. Law, Medicine and Ethics, Mich. State Med. Soc., Nat. Health Lawyers Assn. Jewish. Avocations: internat. politics and fin., history, reading autobiographies, travel. Home: 4612 W Maple Rd Bloomfield Hills MI 48301-1415

ROSENFELD, JOEL CHARLES, librarian; b. Bklyn., June 16, 1939. B.A., U. Mich., 1961, A.M. in L.S., 1964. Br. librarian Flint Pub. (Mich.) Library, 1962-66; adult services cons. Lincoln Trail Libraries, Champaign, Ill., 1967-68; dir. Urbana (Ill.) Free Library, 1968-74; exec. dir. Met. Library Service Agy., St. Paul, 1974-79; exec. dir. Rockford (Ill.) Pub. Library 1980—; pres. Rockford Area Literary Council, 1986-88. Mem. ALA (chmn. constl. and bylaws com. 1988-89,95—), Ill. Library Assn., Pub. Library Assn. (dir.-at-large 1980-81, pres. met. library sect. 1979-80). Office: Rockford Pub Library 215 N Wyman St Rockford IL 61101-1023

ROSENFELD, MARK KENNETH, retail store executive; b. Jackson, Mich., Mar. 17, 1946; s. Nathan and Marjorie N. (Leopold) R.; children: Edward Robert, Zachary, Alix Caitlin. B.A., Amherst Coll., 1968; S.M., MIT, 1970. With Jacobson's, Jackson, 1972—, v.p. real estate group mgr., 1976-78, exec. v.p., 1978-82, pres, 1992-93; chmn. and CEO Jacobson's, Jackson, Mich., 1993—, chmn., CEO, 1993—; bd. dirs. Jacobson Stores, 275 N Woodward Co., Gt. Lakes Bancorp, TCF Fin. Corp. With U.S. Army, 1969-70. Jewish. Office: Jacobson Stores Inc 3333 Sargent Rd Jackson MI 49201-8847

ROSENFELD, RONALD MARVIN, advertising executive; b. Balt., July 13, 1932; s. Bernard and Bessie (Feinglass) R.; m. Toni Pagane; children: Bonnie, Ned. Student, Balt. City Coll., 1946-49. Copywriter, Applestein, Levinstein & Golnick, Balt., 1955-57; v.p., co-copy chief Doyle Dane Bernbach, N.Y.C., 1957-68; sr. v.p., creative mgmt. supr. J. Walter Thompson, N.Y.C., 1968-69; prin., co-chmn. bd., co-creative dir. Rosenfeld, Sirowitz & Lawson, Inc., N.Y.C., 1970—. Bd. dirs. Daytop Village, drug program, N.Y.C., 1974-76, Hope for Diabetics Found. Served with U.S. Army, 1953-55. Named to Copywriters Hall of Fame, 1971; recipient numerous awards, including Copy Club N.Y., Art Dirs. Club, Clio awards. Mem. One Show (co-chmn.), Copy Club (pres. 1970-71). Home: 300 Central Park W New York NY 10024-1513 Office: Rosenfeld Sirowitz Humphrey & Strauss Inc 111 5th Ave New York NY 10003-1005

ROSENFELD, STEPHEN SAMUEL, newspaper editor; b. Pittsfield, Mass., July 26, 1932; s. Jay C. and Elizabeth R.; m. Barbara Bromson, Oct. 28, 1962; children: David, Rebecca, Emmet, James. B.A., Harvard U., 1953;; M.A., Columbia U., 1959. Reporter Berkshire Eagle, Pittsfield, 1955-57; successively reporter, fgn. corr., editorial writer, columnist, dep. editor editorial page Washington Post, 1959—. Co-author: (with Barbara Rosenfeld) Return from Red Square, 1967; author: The Time of Their Dying, 1977. Served to 1st lt. USMC, 1953-55. Mem. Coun. on Fgn. Rels.; Alexandria Lit. Soc., Century Assn. Home: 202 S Saint Asaph St Alexandria VA 22314-3744 Office: Washington Post Co 1150 15th St NW Washington DC 20071-0002

ROSENFELD, STEVEN B., lawyer; b. N.Y.C., Apr. 12, 1943; s. Eugene David and Laura (Sipin) R.; m. Naomi Eve Winkler, Aug. 21, 1965; children: Kathryn Anne, Elizabeth Jane. BA, Columbia Coll., 1964; LLB, Columbia U., 1967. Bar: N.Y. 1967, D.C. 1984, U.S. Dist. Ct. (so. dist.) N.Y. 1969, U.S. Dist. Ct. (ea. dist.) N.Y. 1970, U.S. Ct. Appeals (2d cir.) 1971, U.S. Ct. Appeals (3d cir.) 1974, U.S. Ct. Appeals (Fed. cir.) 1978, D.C. 1979, U.S. Supreme Ct. 1979, U.S. Ct. Appeals (5th cir.) 1982, U.S. Ct. Appeals (6th and D.C. cirs.) 1984, U.S. Ct. Appeals (4th and 9th cirs.) 1987, U.S. Ct. Appeals (1st cir.) 1989, U.S. Ct. Appeals (10th cir.) 1991. Law clk. to Hon. Charles M. Metzner U.S. Dist. Ct. (so. dist.) N.Y., 1967-68; assoc. Rosenman & Colin, N.Y.C., 1968-71; dep. counsel N.Y. State Commn. on Attica, N.Y.C., Batavia, N.Y., 1971-72; assoc. Paul, Weiss, Rifkind, Wharton & Garrison, N.Y.C., 1972-75; ptnr., 1976—. Contbr. articles to profl. jours. Bd. dirs. N.Y. Assn. New Ams., N.Y.C. 1973-95; trustee Dalton Sch., N.Y.C., 1988-94. Mem. N.Y. State Bar Assn., Assn. of Bar of N.Y.C. (exec. com. 1992-96, past mem. various coms.), Legal Aid Soc. (pres. 1989-91, bd. dirs., exec. com. 1978-95). Democrat. Jewish. Avocations: opera and chamber music, theatre, tennis. Office: Paul Weiss Rifkind Wharton & Garrison 1285 Avenue Of The Americas New York NY 10019-6028

ROSENFELD, STEVEN IRA, artistic director, music publisher; b. Bklyn., May 24, 1949; s. Harry Allen and Rosina (DeStefano) R. BA, Southampton Coll., 1971; MFA, St. Francis Coll., Bklyn., 1975. V.p. mktg. JVC, Inc., Maspath, N.Y., 1972-74; dir. Yamaha Internat. Corp., Buena Park, Calif., 1974-75; v.p., gen. mgr. Audio Mktg. Cons., Yorktown, N.Y., 1976-88; pres. World Wide Mgmt., Yorktown, 1970—; dir. Parsec Electronics, Wilmington, Del., 1986-88; mng. dir. Westchester Shakespeare Festival, N.Y.C., 1987-90; dir. The Roger Hendricks Simon Studio, N.Y.C., 1987—; v.p. Barnett Labs., Houston, 1992-93. Editor (newspaper) The Windmill, 1968-69. Mem. Internat. Platform Assn., Audio Engring. Soc. (cert.), Soc. Audio Cons. (cert.), Nat. Trust, Nat. Acad. Rec. Arts and Scis. Jewish. Address: PO Box 599 Yorktown Heights NY 10598

ROSENFELD, WALTER DAVID, JR., architect, writer; b. N.Y.C., May 30, 1930; s. Walter David and Florence (Romann) R.; m. Marilyn Smith, Oct. 15, 1954; children: John W., Sarah E., Susannah, Elizabeth A. AB, U. Pa., 1952; postgrad. Ind. U., 1953-54, Yale U., 1954-55, 57-59. Registered architect, Mass., N.H., Pa.; cert. Nat. Coun. Archtl. Registration Bds.; cert. constrn. specifier. Draftsman, specifier Perry Dean Stewart, Boston, 1966-67; architect, specifier, v.p., prin. The Architects Collaborative, Cambridge, 1967-86, also dir., 1980-84, consulting architect Walter Rosenfeld, CSI, Newton, Mass., 1986—. Author: The Practical Specifier, 1985. Contbg. editor Progressive Architecture mag., 1980-94; contbr. articles to profl. jours. Pres. Friends of Newton Free Libr., Mass, 1970-72; chmn. Newton Ward 1 Dem. Com., 1974-80; vice chmn. designer selection com. City of Newton, 1976-86; bd. dirs. Mass. Audubon Soc., 1987—. With U.S. Army, 1955-57, Fed. Republic Germany. Mem. Constrn. Specifications Inst. (bd. dirs. Boston chpt. 1980-86, pres. Boston chpt. 1987-88), AIA, Boston Soc. Architects. Avocation: sailing. Office: Walter Rosenfeld CSI PO Box 380909 Cambridge MA 02238-0909

ROSENFELT, FRANK EDWARD, motion picture company executive; b. Peabody, Mass., Nov. 15, 1921; s. Samuel and Ethel (Litvack) R.; m. Judith Roman, Nov. 1, 1943; children: Fred, Peter, Karen. B.S., Cornell U., 1948, LL.B., 1950. Bar: N.Y. 1950, Mass. 1950, Calif. 1971. Atty. RKO Radio Pictures, 1950-55; with Metro-Goldwyn-Mayer, Inc., 1955—, pres., chief exec. officer, dir., 1973-90; chmn. bd., chief exec. officer Metro-Goldwyn-Mayer Film Co., 1980-83; vice chmn. bd. emeritus in charge European ops. Metro-Goldwyn-Mayer Film Co., London, 1983-85; vice chmn. bd. in charge European ops. MGM/UA Communications Co. (formerly MGM/UA Entertainment Co.), London, 1985-90; exec. cons. Metro-Goldwyn-Mayer Inc., Culver City, Calif., 1990—. Bd. editors: Cornell Law Quar, 1948-50. Served with inf. AUS, World War II. Decorated Purple Heart. Mem. Acad. Motion Picture Arts and Scis. (bd. govs. 1977-85), Order of Coif. Office: Metro-Goldwyn-Mayer Inc 10000 Washington Blvd Ste 3023 Culver City CA 90232-2706

ROSENFIELD, ALLAN, physician; b. Cambridge, Mass., Apr. 28, 1933; s. Harold Herman and Beatrice (Garber) R.; m. Clare Stein, July 31, 1966; children: Paul Allan, Jill Emilie. BA cum laude, Harvard U., 1955; MD, Columbia U., 1959. Diplomate Am. Bd. Ob-Gyn. Intern, surgical resident Beth Israel Hosp., Boston, 1959-61; resident in ob/gyn Boston Hosp. for Women (now Brigham and Woman's Hosp.), Boston, 1963-66; rep. med. advisor The Population Council and Ministry Pub. Health, Bangkok, 1967-73; asst. dir. tech. assistance div. The Population Council, N.Y.C., 1973-75; prof. ob-gyn Columbia U., N.Y.C., 1975-88, prof. pub. health, 1975-86, DeLamar Prof. pub. health, 1986—, dir. ctr. for population and family health, 1975-88, acting chmn. dept. ob-gyn., 1984-86, dean sch. pub. health, 1986—. Contbr. over 100 articles to profl. jours. Capt. USAF, 1961-63.

Fellow Am. Coll. Obstetricians and Gynecologists; mem. Inst. Medicine of NAS (several coms. and bds.), Am. Pub. Health Assn. Jewish. Avocations: tennis, skiing, music. Home: 4 Crosshill Rd Hartsdale NY 10530-3014 Office: Columbia U Sch Pub Health 600 W 168th St New York NY 10032-3702

ROSENFIELD, BRUCE ALAN, lawyer; b. Mpls., Apr. 30, 1951; s. Arnold M. and Phyllis M. (Fruchtman) R.; m. Bonnie S. Brier, Aug. 15, 1976; children: Rebecca, Elizabeth, Benjamin. AB, Dartmouth Coll., 1973; JD, Stanford U., 1976. Bar: Pa. 1976, U.S. Dist. Ct. (ea. dist.) Pa. 1976. Law clk. to Hon. Raymond Broderick U.S. Dist. Ct. (ea. dist.) Pa., Phila., 1976-78; assoc. Schnader, Harrison, Segal & Lewis, Phila., 1978-85, ptnr., 1986—; cons. Pa. Joint State Govt. Adv. Com. on Decedent and Estate Laws, 1991—; bd. dirs. Rittenhouse Fin. Svcs. Fellow Am. Coll. Trust and Estate Coun.; mem. Phila. Bar Assn. (chair probate sect. 1993). Home: 132 Fairview Rd Penn Valley PA 19072-1331 Office: Schnader Harrison Segal & Lewis 1600 Market St Ste 3600 Philadelphia PA 19103-7236

ROSENFIELD, JAMES HAROLD, communications executive; b. Boston, July 18, 1929; s. Harold and Beatrice (Garber) R.; m. Nancy Lee Stenbuck, Oct. 19, 1952; 2 children. BA, Dartmouth Coll., 1952; D of Comml. Sci. (hon.), St. John's U., 1981. TV network sales exec. NBC, N.Y.C., 1954-57; advt. mgr. Polaroid Corp., Boston, 1956-59; v.p. mktg. Airequipt, Inc., New Rochelle, N.Y., 1959-65; TV account exec. CBS, Inc., N.Y.C., 1965-67, dir. daytime sales, 1967-70, v.p. Ea. sales, 1970-75, v.p. network sales adminstrn., 1975-77, v.p.. nat. sales mgr., 1977, pres. TV Network Div., 1977-81; exec. v.p. CBS/Broadcast Group, N.Y.C., 1981-83; sr. exec. v.p., 1983-86; chmn., CEO John Blair Communications, Inc., N.Y.C., 1987-93; pres. JHR Assocs., Consulting, N.Y.C., 1993; mng. dir. Veronis, Suhler & Assocs., N.Y.C., 1994—. Mem. nat. bd. dirs. Jr. Achievement Inc.; past alumni trustee Roxbury Latin Sch., Mass.; bd. dirs., former chmn. Advt. Coun. With Signal Corps, AUS, 1950-53. Mem. NATAS (bd. dirs. internat. coun.), Internat. Radio and TV Soc. (past pres.).

ROSENFIELD, JAY GARY, publisher; b. Roslyn, N.Y., June 25, 1948; s. Maurice Ullman and Harriet Jessica (Obstfeld) R.; m. Lily Schwartzberg, Aug. 23, 1975; children—Adam, Amanda. B.A. in History, Ithaca Coll., 1970. Pres. Reese Communications, N.Y.C., 1970—, creator, founder, pub. Video mag., 1977—; pres. R.G.H. Pub. Inc., 1989—; pres., mem. bd. dirs. Art Levis Found. Bd. dirs. Denton Green Sr. Dwellings, Inc., New Hyde Park, N.Y., 1979—. Mem. ACLU, Whipporwill Assn. (bd. dirs. 1988—), Internat. Motoring Press Assn. Office: Video Mag Hachette Filipacchi Mags 1633 Broadway New York NY 10019.

ROSENFIELD, JOHN MAX, art educator; b. Dallas, Oct. 9, 1924; s. John M. and Claire (Burger) R.; m. Ella Hopper, Jan. 2, 1948; children—Sarah, Paul Thomas. Student, U. Tex., 1941-43; BA, U. Calif., Berkeley, 1945; BFA, So. Meth. U., 1947; MFA, U. Iowa, 1949; PhD, Harvard U., 1959. Instr. art U. Iowa, 1949, 52-54; asst. prof. UCLA, 1957-60; rsch. fellow Harvard U., 1960-65, faculty, 1965-91, prof. art, 1968-91, Abby Aldrich Rockefeller prof. East Asian Art, 1974-91, chmn. dept. fine arts, 1971-76, curator Asian Art, 1976-91, acting dir. Art Mus., 1982-85, emeritus, 1991—. Author: Dynastic Arts of the Kushans, 1967; Japanese Art of the Heian Period, 1967; co-author: Traditions of Japanese Art, 1970, Courtly Tradition of Japanese Art and Literature, 1972, Journey of Three Jewels, 1979, Song of the Brush, 1979, Masters of Japanese Calligraphy, 1984; editor: Archives of Asian Art, 1973-84, Japanese Arts Library, 1977-80. Trustee Mus. Fine Arts, Boston, 1975-77. Served with AUS, 1943-46, 50-51. Mem. Assn. Asian Studies, Coll. Art Assn., Am. Acad. Benares, Am. Acad. Arts and Scis. Research history Buddhist art and Japanese art. Home: 75 Coolidge Rd Arlington MA 02174-7737 Office: Harvard U 32 Quincy St Cambridge MA 02138-3845

ROSENFIELD, ROBERT LEE, pediatric endocrinologist, educator; b. Robinson, Ill., Dec. 16, 1934; s. Irving and Sadie (Osipe) R.; m. Sandra L. McVicker, Apr. 14, 1973. BS, Northwestern U., 1956, MD, 1960. Diplomate Am. Bd. Pediatric Endocrinology. Intern, Phila. Gen. Hosp. and Children's Hosp., Phila., 1960-63, 65-68; practice medicine specializing in pediatric endocrinology; prof. pediatrics, medicine U. Chgo., 1968—. Contbr. research articles to profl. jours. Served to capt. USMC, 1963-65. Fogarty Sr. Internat. fellow, USPHS, Weizmann Inst., Israel, 1977-78. Mem. Am. Bd. Pediatrics (sub.-bd. pediatric endocrinology 1983-86), Am. Pediatric Soc., Lawson Wilkins Pediatric Endocrinology Soc., Endocrine Soc., Soc. Gynecol. Investigation, Chgo. Pediatric Soc. (pres. 1981). Democrat. Jewish. Avocation: photography. Home: 5474 S Greenwood Ave Chicago IL 60615-5104 Office: U Chgo Med Ctr 5841 S Maryland Ave Chicago IL 60637-1470

ROSENGREN, WILLIAM R., lawyer, corporation executive; b. 1934; LL.B., U. Minn., 1959. Pvt. practice, 1959-67; instr. bus. U. Minn., 1963-69; Asst. sec. and sr. atty. Internat. Multifoods Corp., to 1973; with Ecolab Inc., St. Paul, 1973—, v.p., gen. counsel, 1973, v.p., sec., gen. counsel, 1974-83, sr. v.p., gen. counsel, sec., 1983-92; sr. v.p. law, gen. counsel, 1992—. Office: Ecolab Inc Ecolab Ctr 370 Wabasha St Saint Paul MN 55102

ROSENHAN, DAVID L., psychologist, educator; b. 1929. A.B., Yeshiva U., 1951, M.A., 1953; Ph.D., Columbia U., 1958. Asst. prof., Haverford (Pa.) Coll., 1960-62; psychologist Ednl. Testing Service, 1962-68; assoc. prof. Princeton (N.J.) U., 1963-68; prof. Swarthmore (Pa.) Coll., 1968-70; prof. law and psychology, Stanford (Calif.) U., 1970—; mem. NIMH, 1970-74; cons. trial tactics, juries, forensic psychology. Vis. fellow Wolfson Coll., Oxford, Eng., 1977-78. Fellow AAAS, Am. Psychol. Assn. (pres. div. psychology and law 1982); mem. Am. Psychology Law Soc. (trustee 1978-79), Am. Bd. Forensic Psychology. Author: (with London) Foundations of Abnormal Psychology, 1968; Theory and Research in Abnormal Psychology, 2d edit., 1975; (with Gergen, Nisbett, Clarr) Social Psychology, 1975; (with Seligman) Abnormal Psychology, 1984, 89; adv. editor Holt, Rinehart & Winston, 1965-76. Office: Stanford U Sch Law Nathan Abbott Way Stanford CA 94305

ROSENHEIM, DANIEL EDWARD, journalist, newspaper editor; b. Chgo., Aug. 12, 1949; s. Edward W. and Margaret Morton (Keeney) R.; m. Christina J. Adachi, May 10, 1976 (div. 1979); m. Cindy Catherine Salans, June 20, 1980; children: Joseph Michael, James Salans, Nicholas Edward. BA, Wesleyan U., 1971. Factory worker Pitts. and Chgo., 1972-77; reporter Sun-Jour., Lansing, Ill., 1977; bus./labor editor Hammond (Ind.) Times, 1977-80; bus. writer Chgo. Sun Times, 1980-82, spl. writer, 1982-84; bus. writer Chgo. Tribune, 1984-85; econs. editor San Francisco Chronicle, 1985-87, city editor, 1987-95, mng. editor, 1995—. Mem. Soc. Profl. Journalists, San Francisco Tennis Club. Avocations: tennis, golf, fly fishing. Office: San Francisco Chronicle 901 Mission St San Francisco CA 94103-2905*

ROSENHEIM, DONALD EDWIN, electrical engineer; b. N.Y.C., Mar. 23, 1926; s. Seymour Lawrence and Leah Rebecca (Rosenberg) R.; m. Judith Comfort Hyman, June 22, 1958; children—Micah Robert, Jay Aaron. B.S. in Elec. Engring. magna cum laude, Poly. Inst. Bklyn., 1949; M.S., Columbia U., 1957. Devel. engr. Servo Corp. Am., 1949-51; mem. research staff IBM Corp., 1951—; dir. San Jose (Calif.) Rsch. Lab., 1973-83, dir. tech. coord., 1983-84; asst. dir. Almaden Rsch. Ctr., San Jose, 1984-92; cons. to lab. dir. Almaden Rsch. Ctr., 1992—; lectr. CCNY, 1956, Columbia U., 1958. Fellow IEEE; mem. Sigma Xi, Tau Beta Pi, Eta Kappa Nu. Home: 128 Smith Creek Dr Los Gatos CA 95030-1634 Office: IBM Almaden Research Ctr K01/802 650 Harry Rd San Jose CA 95120-6001

ROSENHEIM, EDWARD WEIL, English educator; b. Chgo., May 15, 1918; s. Edward Weil and Fannie (Kohn) R.; m. Margaret Morton Keeney, June 20, 1947; children: Daniel Edward, James Morton, Andrew Keeney. B.A., U. Chgo., 1939, M.A., 1946, Ph.D., 1953. Publicity writer Pub. Relations Service, Chgo., 1939-40; instr. Gary (Ind.) Coll., 1946; faculty U. Chgo., 1947—, prof. English, 1962—, David B. and Clara E. Stern prof., 1980-88, prof. emeritus, 1988—, assoc. chmn. dept. English, 1967-75, dir. broadcasting for univ., 1954-57; dir. Nat. Humanities Inst., 1977-80; Disting. vis. prof. Pa. State U., 1961; Disting. lectr. Nat. Coun. Tchrs. English, 1967; mem. Ill. Humanities Coun., 1982—, pres. 1985-87. Author: What Happens

in Literature, 1960, Swift and the Satirist's Art, 1963; editor: Selected Prose and Poetry of Jonathan Swift, 1958, Jour. Gen. Edn., 1954-56; co-editor: Modern Philology, 1968-88. Served to capt. inf. AUS, 1941-46. Recipient Alumni Svc. medal U. Chgo., 1990; Willet Faculty fellow, 1962, Guggenheim Meml. fellow, 1967. Mem. Am. Soc. 18th Century Studies, Johnson Soc. (pres. Central region 1971). Clubs: Quadrangle, Wayfarers, Caxton. Home: 5805 S Dorchester Ave Chicago IL 60637-1730 Office: 1050 E 59th St Chicago IL 60637-1512

ROSENHEIM, HOWARD HARRIS, management consultant; b. Williamson, W.Va., Oct. 1, 1915; s. William Spiller and Frances Minerva (Harris) R.; m. Marjorie Jane Griffin, June 30, 1945; children: Cathy (Mrs. Mark Bustamante), William Spiller. B.S., Northwestern U., 1936, M.B.A., 1954; grad., Advanced Mgmt. Program, Harvard U. Grad. Sch. Bus., 1956. Civilian dir. indsl. planning div. USAF, Dayton, Ohio, 1947; pres. Internat. Register Co., elec. mfg. co., Chgo., 1948-70; pres. home study sch. Internat. Accts. Soc., Chgo., 1971; pres. Denoyer-Geppert Co. ednl. pub. subs. Times Mirror Co., Chgo., 1972-79, Internat. Assocs., Ltd., cons., 1980—; chmn. Camelot Controls, Ltd. (Eng.), Chgo.-Br. Extel Corp., Chgo., Tele-Communication Radio Inc., Chgo., Data One, Inc., Chgo.; Vis. prof. bus. Northwestern U., Evanston, Ill., 1956-71, trustee, 1968-70; cons. Presdl. Commn. Nat. Air Policy, 1947; adv. to ministry of edn. Kingdom of Saudi Arabia, 1976-79. Pub. over 800 titles of ednl. materials in Arabic for schs. in Saudi Arabia; author articles to profl. jours. Served to maj. USAF, 1942-46. Decorated Award of Merit; recipient Disting. Educator award Northwestern U., 1972. Mem. Am. Mktg. Assn., Northwestern U. Alumni Assn. (pres. 1966-67). Methodist (mem. ofcl. bd. 1965-70). Clubs: Union League (Chgo.); Park Ridge (Ill.) Country. Inventor various time switches. Home: 2411 Farrell Ave Park Ridge IL 60068-1167

ROSENHEIM, MARGARET KEENEY, social welfare policy educator; b. Grand Rapids, Mich., Sept. 5, 1926; d. Morton and Nancy (Billings) Keeney; m. Edward W. Rosenheim, June 20, 1947; children: Daniel, James, Andrew. Student, Wellesley Coll., 1943-45; J.D., U. Chgo., 1949. Bar: Ill. 1949. Mem. faculty Sch. Social Service Adminstrn., U. Chgo., 1950—, assoc. prof., 1961-66, prof., 1966—, Helen Ross prof. social welfare policy, 1975—, lectr., dean, 1978-83; vis. prof. U. Wsh., 1965, Duke U., 1984; acad. visitor London Sch. Econs., 1973; cons. Pres.'s Commn. Law Enforcement and Adminstrn. Justice, 1966-67, Nat. Advt. Commn. Criminal Justice Standards and Goals, 1972; mem. Juvenile Justice Standards Commn., 1973-76; trustee Carnegie Corp. N.Y., 1979-87, Children's Home and Aid Soc. of Ill., 1981—; dir. Nat. Inst. Dispute Resolution, 1981-89, Nuveen Bond Funds, 1982—; mem. Chgo. Network, 1983. Editor, contbr.: Justice for the Child, 1962, reprinted, 1977, Pursuing Justice for the Child, 1976, Early Parenthood and Coming of Age in the 1990s, 1992; contbr. articles and book revs. to profl. jours. Home: 5805 S Dorchester Ave Chicago IL 60637-1730 Office: 969 E 60th St Chicago IL 60637-2640

ROSENHOFFER, CHRIS, lawyer; b. Cin., Apr. 19, 1913; s. Joseph and Barbara (Stitzel) R.; m. Alberta Arlene Jarvis, Dec. 28, 1935 (div. Apr. 1992); children: Chris Jr., Dennis P., Gary A., John J., Nancy A., Todd D. BS Commerce, Salmon P. Chase Coll. Commerce, Cin., 1948; JD, Salmon P. Chase Coll. Law, Cin., 1951. Bar: Ohio, 1951, U.S. Dist. Ct. (so. dist.) Ohio 1952. Acct., log buyer Al J. Boehm Walnut Co., Kenova, W.Va., 1938-44; acct. The Green Embry Co., Cin., 1948-51; judge Clermont County Ct., Batavia, Ohio, 1958-62, 67-86; pvt. practice law Batavia, 1951—; spl. counsel Atty. Gen. of Ohio, Batavia, 1963-64. Treas. Clermont County Rep. Club, Batavia, 1957-58; team mem. Citizens Amb. Program, Seattle, 1988, 93; mem. sch. bd. West Clermont Local Sch. Dist., Amelia, Ohio, 1958-74. With U.S. Army, 1944-46. Mem. Ohio State Bar Assn., Ohio Acad. Trial Lawyers, Clermont County Bar Assn. (pres. 1962), Cin. Bar Assn., Am. Legion. Methodist. Avocations: fishing, hunting. Office: 97 Main St Batavia OH 45103

ROSENHOUSE, IRWIN J., artist, designer; b. Chgo.. B.F.A., Cooper Union, N.Y.C., 1950. Designer Mus. Modern Art, 1954-57, Harcourt, Brace & Co., 1957, Dell Books, 1963; tchr. art Mus. Modern Art, 1967-69, Pratt Graphic Center, N.Y.C., 1972, 85, Bklyn. Coll., 1972-73, Bklyn. Mus. Art Sch., 1974, Nassau C.C., 1972-95, N.Y. Tech. Coll., 1983-86; owner Rosenhouse Gallery, N.Y.C., 1963-72; lectr. art, book illustration, design; preparer graphics for Arab-Israeli peace confs.: The Road to Peace, Convocation for Peace, N.Y.C., 1982; dir. monthly ednl. lecture series N.Y. Artist Equity, 1989-91. One-man shows N.Y.C., Bklyn., Easthampton, N.Y., Dance Theater Workshop Gallery, N.Y.C., 1992, also various colls. and mus. in U.S.; exhibited in group shows numerous mus., painting socs. exhbns. throughout U.S.; represented in permanent collections Met. Mus., N.Y. Pub. Libr., Everhart Mus., Cooper Union Mus., Bklyn. Coll. Collection; illustrator: (juvenile) Have You Seen Trees?. Served with U.S. Mcht. Marine, 1944-51. Recipient Louis Comfort Tiffany Found. award, 2 Huntington Hartford Found. awards, Billboard Ann. award, Illustrators Club award, 1st prize Rome Collaborative; record cover designs included in Smithsonian ethnic music collection. Address: 256 Mott St New York NY 10012 *Humanist imagery has been my main concern and the pursuit of a simple, direct image of nature.*

ROSENKER, MARK VICTOR, trade association executive; b. Balt., Dec. 8, 1946; s. Stanley and Irene (Moss) R.; m. Heather Beldon. BA in Communications, U. Md., 1969, postgrad., 1970-71; grad., USAF Air Command and Staff Coll., 1986, USAF Air War Coll., 1990. Asst. to events producer, relief engr. ABC-TV News, Washington, 1968-69; dep. dir. radio and TV Com. Reelect Pres., Washington, 1972; staff asst. to sec. U.S. Dept. Interior, Washington, 1972-73; account exec. Daniel Edelman Pub. Relations, Inc., Washington, 1973-75; dir. communications Motorized Bicycle Assn., Washington, 1975; dep. press sec. Pres. Ford Com., Washington, 1976; v.p. Electronic Industries Assn., Washington, 1977—; bd. of vis. Cmty. Coll. USAF, Maxwell, Ala., 1981-86; apptd. commer. Am. Battle Monument Commn., 1990-94. Active Campaign to Elect Reagan/Bush, Washington, 1980, 84, Campaign to Elect Bush/Quayle, 1988, 92. 1st lt. USAF, 1969-72, col. USAFR, 1972—. Recipient Chuck Docekal Meml. award, 1987, Am. Battle Monuments Commn. Meritious Svc. award, 1994. Mem. Am. Soc. Assn. Execs., Greater Washington Soc. Assn. Execs., Res. Officers Assn. Club, Capitol Hill Club, Army Navy Club. Avocations: sailing, tennis, skiing, golfing. Home: 1626 Great Falls St Mc Lean VA 22101 Office: Electronic Industries Assn 2500 Wilson Blvd Arlington VA 22201

ROSENKOETTER, GERALD EDWIN, engineering and construction company executive; b. St. Louis, Mar. 16, 1927; s. Herbert Charles and Edna Mary (Englege) R.; m. Ruth June Beekman, Sept. 10, 1949; children: Claudia Ruth, Carole Lee. BSCE, Washington U., St. Louis, 1951; MSCE, Sever Inst. Tech., St. Louis, 1957. Registered profl. engr. Colo., Del., D.C., Fla., Ga., Idaho, Kans., Mass., Mich., Mo., N.C., N.J., Ohio, Pa., Tex., Utah, Wis. Sr. structural engr. Sverdrup & Parcel, Inc., St. Louis, 1951-56, project engr., 1956-60; engring. mgr. Sverdrup & Parcel, Inc., Denver, 1960-62; project mgr. Sverdrup & Parcel & Assocs., St. Louis, 1962-69, chief engr., 1969-74, v.p., 1974-80; pres. SPCM, Inc., St. Louis, 1980-85; exec. v.p. Sverdrup Corp., St. Louis, 1985-88, vice-chmn., 1988-93; pres. Sverdrup Hydro, Inc., 1988-93; engr. and fin. cons. Sacramento, 1993—; asst. prof. Washington U., 1955-60; ptnr. 3 Sverdrup Partnerships, 1977-93; expert witness Sverdrup & Parcel & Assocs., 1970-75; cons. engring. and constrn. projects, 1993—. Councilman City of Berkeley, Mo., 1956-58, councilman-at-large, 1958-60, chmn. city planning and zoning com., 1963-65; dir. Conservatory and sch. Arts, St. Louis, 1989-92. Sgt. U.S. Army, 1945-46. Engrs. Club of St. Louis scholar, 1950. Mem. ASCE (chmn. continuing edn. 1965-66, named Outstanding Sr. Engring. Student 1951), Forest Hills Country Club (St. Louis), Bent Tree Country Club (Sarasota, Fla.). Lutheran. Avocations: golfing, sailing.

ROSENKRANTZ, BARBARA GUTMANN, retired history educator; b. N.Y.C., Jan. 11, 1923; d. James and Jeanette (Mack) G.; m. David P. Bennett, Sept. 5, 1942 (div.); 1 child, Louise; m. Paul Rosenkrantz, Apr. 19, 1950 (dec. 1986); children: Judith, Deborah; m. J. Nathaniel Marshall, 1988. A.B., Radcliffe Coll., 1944; Ph.D., Clark U., 1970. Rsch. assoc. Harvard U., Cambridge, Mass., 1970-71, lectr., 1971-73, assoc. prof. history of sci., 1973-75, prof., 1975-93, chmn. history of sci. dept., 1984-89, master Currier House, 1974-79. Author: Public Health and the State, 1972, (with William A. Koelsch) American Habitat, 1973; editor for history Am. Jour.

Pub. Health, 1985-89. NIH research grantee, 1970-72; Rockefeller Found. fellow, 1979-80; Ctr. for Advanced Study in Behavioral Scis. fellow Stanford U., 1984, Inst. Medicine fellow; Sherman Fairchild Disting. Scholar, Calif. Inst. Tech., 1989. Fellow Am. Acad. Arts and Scis., Mass. Hist. Soc.; mem. Am. Hist. Assn., History of Sci. Soc., Am. Assn. for History of Medicine. Jewish. Office: Harvard U Dept History Sci Center 235 Cambridge MA 02138

ROSENKRANTZ, DANIEL J., computer science educator; b. Bklyn., Mar. 5, 1943; s. Harry and Ruth (Sirota) R.; m. Carole Jaffee, Aug. 2, 1969; children: Holly, Sherry, Jody, Andrew. BS, Columbia U., 1963, MS, 1964, PhD, 1967. With Bell Telephone Labs., Murray Hills, N.J., 1966-67; info. scientist GE Co. R & D Ctr., Schenectady, N.Y., 1967-77; prof. dept. computer sci. SUNY at Albany, 1977—, dept. chair, 1993—; prin. computer scientist Phoenix Data Systems, Albany, 1983-85. Author: (with P.M. Lewis II and R.E. Stearns) Compiler Design Theory, 1976. Fellow ACM (editor-in-chief jour. 1986-91, area editor for formal langs. and models of computation 1981-86, mem. numerous conf. coms.); mem. IEEE Computer Soc., ACM Spl. Interest Group on Automata and Computability Theory (sec. 1977-79). Home: 1261 Cranbrook Ct Niskayuna NY 12309-1203 Office: SUNY Dept Computer Sci Albany NY 12222

ROSENKRANZ, HERBERT S., environmental toxicology educator, cancer researcher; b. Vienna, Sept. 27, 1933; came to U.S., 1948; s. Samuel and Lea Rose (Marilles) R.; m. Deanna Eloise Green, Jan. 27, 1959; children: Pnina Gail, Eli Joshua, Maragalit E., Dara V., Jeremy Amiel, Sara C., Naomi, Tsilila. BS, CCNY, 1954; PhD, Cornell U., 1959. Postdoctoral fellow Sloan-Kettering Inst. for Cancer Rsch., 1959-60, U Pa., Phila., 1960-61; asst. prof. microbiology Columbia U., N.Y.C., 1961-65, assoc. prof., 1965-69, prof., 1969-76; prof., chmn. microbiology dept. N.Y. Med. Coll., Valhalla, 1976-81; prof. Case Western Res. U., Cleve., 1981-90, dir. Ctr. Environ. Health Sci., 1981-84, chmn. dept. environ. health sci., 1985-90; prof., chmn. dept. environ. and occupational health U. Pitts., 1990—, dir. Ctr Environ. and Occupational Health and Toxicology. Lalor Found. awardee, 1963; Nat. Cancer Inst. Research Career Devel. awardee, 1965-75. Mem. AAAS, Am. Assn. Cancer Research, Am. Soc. Biol. Chemists, Environ. Mutagen Soc., Soc. Toxicology. Jewish. Office: U Pitts Grad Sch Pub Health Dept Environ and Occup Health 260 Kappa Dr Pittsburgh PA 15238-2818

ROSENKRANZ, ROBERT BERNARD, military officer; b. Paterson, N.J., Sept. 26, 1939; s. Irving Morton and Lucille (Kane) R.; m Barbara Jean Larson, May 17, 1970; children: Stephen Robert, Deborah Anne, Diana Rebecca, Susan Leslie. BS, U.S. Mil. Acad., 1961; MA, U. Pa., 1969. Comd. 2d. lt. U.S. Army, 1961, advanced through grades to maj. gen., 1992; officer U.S. Army, Fed. Republic of Germany, 1962-65; battalion exec. officer U.S. Army, Korea, 1973-74; battery comdr. U.S. Army, Vietnam, 1966-67; battery and brigade comdr. U.S Army, Fed. Republic of Germany, 1977-79, 83-85; assoc. prof. U.S. Mil. Acad., West Point, N.Y., 1969-72; dir. soviet studies U.S. Army War Coll., Carlisle, Pa., 1981-83; sr. mil. asst. under sec. of def. Pentagon, Washington, 1986-88; dep. dir. Army Ops., Readiness and Mobilization U.S. Army Pentagon, Washington, 1988-89, dir. force programs, 1989-92; comdr. U.S. Army Optec, Washington, 1992—. Treas. PTA, Fairfax, Va., 1988—; mem. sports boosters Woodson High Sch., Fairfax, 1986—. Decorated Bronze Star, Air medal; recipient Superior Svc. medal U.S. Dept. Def., 1988, D.S.M., 1992. Mem. Internat. Inst. of Strategic Studies, Assn. of the U.S. Army., Mantua Club. Republican. Jewish. Avocations: jogging, reading, woodworking, fishing, racquetball. Home: 3222 Wynford Dr Fairfax VA 22031-2828 Office: USA Operational Test and Evaluation Command 4501 Ford Ave Alexandria VA 22302-1435

ROSENKRANZ, STANLEY WILLIAM, lawyer; b. N.Y.C., Aug. 20, 1933; s. Jacob and Adele R.; m. Judith Ossinsky, Aug. 14, 1960; children: Jack Michael, Andrew Lawrence. BS in Acctg, U. Fla., 1955, JD with honors, 1960; LLM (Kenneson fellow), NYU, 1961. Bar: Fla. 1960, Ga. 1970; cert. tax lawyer. Mem. firm Macfarlane, Ferguson, Allison & Kelly, Tampa, Fla., 1961-68, 71-79; with King & Spalding, Atlanta, 1969-71, Holland & Knight, Tampa, 1979-86, Shear, Newman, Hahn & Rosenkranz P.A., Tampa, 1986—; adj. prof. Sch. Law, U. Fla., 1975-79, Grad. Coll. Bus. Adminstrn., U. Tampa, 1989; dir. Life Savs. Bank, 1979-88. Pres. Congregation Schaarai Zedek, Tampa, 1981-83; bd. dirs. Union Am. Hebrew Congregations, 1990—, v.p. S.E. region, 1988-90, pres., 1992—. With U.S. Army, 1955-57. Named Young Man of Year Tampa Jaycees, Fla., 1967. Mem. ABA, Am. Coll. Tax Counsel, Am. Law Inst., Fla. Bar Assn., Ga. Bar Assn., Greater Tampa C. of C. (bd. govs., chmn. anti-drug task force). Home: 1125 Shipwatch Cir Tampa FL 33602-5785 Office: 201 E Kennedy Blvd Tampa FL 33602-5181

ROSENMAN, LEONARD, composer; b. Brooklyn, N.Y., Sept. 7, 1924. Condr. Rome, 1962-66; instr. U. So. Calif.; musical dir. New Muse Chamber Orch. Music dir., composer: (film scores) The Outsider, 1962, Barry Lyndon, 1975 (Academy award best adapted score 1975), Bound for Glory, 1976 (Academy award best adapted score 1976), The Lord of the Rings, 1978; music condr.: (TV movies) Sherlock Holmes in New York, 1976; composer: (film scores) The Cobweb, 1955, East of Eden, 1955, Rebel without a Cause, 1955, Bombers B-52, 1957, Edge of the City, 1957, The Young Stranger, 1957, Lafayette Escadrille, 1958, Pork Chop Hill, 1959, The Bramble Bush, 1960, The Crowded Sky, 1960, The Plunderers, 1960, The Rise and Fall of Legs Diamond, 1960, The Chapman Report, 1962, Convicts Four, 1962, Hell is for Heroes, 1962, A Covenant with Death, 1966, Fantastic Voyage, 1966, Countdown, 1968, The Savage Land, 1969, Beneath the Planet of the Apes, 1970, A Man Called Horse, 1970, The Todd Killings, 1971, Battle for the Planet of the Apes, 1973, Race with the Devil, 1975, Birch Interval, 1976, The Car, 1977, 9/30/55, 1977, An Enemy of the People, 1978, Promises in the Dark, 1979, Prophecy, 1979, Hide in Plain Sight, 1980, The Jazz Singer, 1980, Making Love, 1982, Cross Creek, 1983 (Academy award nomination best original score 1983), Heart of the Stag, 1984, Sylvia, 1985, Star Trek IV: The Voyage Home, 1986 (Academy award nomination best original score 1986), Robocop 2, 1990, Ambition, 1991, (TV movie scores) Banyon, 1971, In Broad Daylight, 1971, Vanished, 1971, The Bravos, 1972, The Cat Creature, 1973, Judge Dee and the Monastery Murders, 1974, Nakia, 1974, The Phantom of Hollywood, 1974, The First Thirty-Six Hours of Dr. Durant, 1975, Sky Heist, 1975, Kingston: The Power Play, 1976, Lanigan's Rabbi, 1976, Sybil, 1976 (Emmy award best music composition for dramatic underscore 1977), Mary White, 1977, The Possessed, 1977, The Other Side of Hell, 1978, Friendly Fire, 1979 (Emmy award best music composition for dramatic underscore 1979), Nero Wolfe, 1979, City in Fear, 1980, Murder in Texas, 1981, The Wall, 1982, Celebrity, 1984, Heartsounds, 1984, The Return of Marcus Welby, M.D., 1984, First Steps, 1985, Promised a Miracle, 1988, Where Pigeons Go to Die, 1990, Aftermath: A Test of Love, 1991, Keeper of the City, 1992, (TV series scores) Men from Shiloh, 1970, Primus, 1971, Nakia, 1974, Gibbsville, 1976, Holmes and Yoyo, 1976, Rafferty, 1977, Joshua's World, 1980, (musical works) Threnody on a Song of K.R., 1971, Chamber Music 5, 1979, Foci I, 1981. Office: care ASCAP 6430 Sunset Blvd Ste 1002 Los Angeles CA 90028*

ROSENN, HAROLD, lawyer; b. Plains, Pa., Nov. 4, 1917; s. Joseph and Jennie (Wohl) R.; m. Sallyanne Frank, Sept. 19, 1948; 1 child, Frank Scott. BA, U. Mich., 1939, JD, 1941; LLD (hon.), Coll. Misericordia, 1991. Bar: Pa. 1942, U.S. Supreme Ct. 1957. Ptnr. Rosenn & Rosenn, Wilkes Barre, Pa., 1948-54; ptnr. Rosenn, Jenkins & Greenwald, Wilkes Barre, 1954-87, of counsel, 1988—; mem. Pa. State Bd. Law Examiners, 1983-93, Pa. Gov.'s Justice Commn., 1968-73, Pa. Crime Commn., 1968-73, Fed. Jud. Nominating Com., Pa., 1977-79, Appellate Ct. Nominating Com., Pa., 1979-81; asst. dist. atty. Luzerne County, Pa., 1952-54. Chmn. ARC, Wilkes Barre, 1958-60; pres. Pa. Council on Crime and Delinquency, Harrisburg, 1969-71; bd. dirs. Coll. Misericordia, Dallas, Pa., 1976-86, emeritus, 1986—; Hoyt Library, Kingston, Pa., 1971-78, Nat. Council on Crime and Delinquency, N.Y.C., 1969-71; chmn. United Way Campaign of Wyoming Valley, 1975; pres. United Way, Wyoming Valley, 1978-80; comdr. post 395 Am. Legion, Kingston, Pa., 1948. Served to capt. USAAF, 1942-45, ETO. Decorated presdl. citation with cluster; recipient Erasmus medal Dutch Govt., Disting. Svc. award in Trusteeship, Assn. Governing Bds. Univs. and Colls., 1990; Disting. Community Svc. award Greater Wilkes-Barre Soc. Fellows Anti-Defamation League, 1991, Clara Barton honor award Wyoming Valley chpt. ARC, 1992, Lifetime Achievement award United Way of

Wyoming Valley, 1992; honoree Wyoming Valley Interfaith Coun., 1986; named Golden Key Vol. of Yr., United Way of Pa., 1989. Mem. ABA, Pa. Bar Assn., Am. Judicature Soc., The Pa. Soc. Republican. Jewish. Clubs: U. Mich. (N.E. Pa.) (pres. 1946-76), Westmoreland (Wilkes Barre). Lodge: B'nai Brith (pres. Wilkes Barre 1952-53, Community Service award 1976).

ROSENN, KEITH SAMUEL, lawyer, educator; b. Wilkes-Barre, Pa., Dec. 9, 1938; s. Max and Tillie R. (Hershkowitz) R.; m. Nan Raker, June 21, 1960; 1 child, Eva; m. Silvia R. Rudge, Mar. 21, 1968; children—Jonathan, Marcia. A.B. Amherst Coll. 1960; LL.B. Yale U., 1963. Bar: Pa. 1964, U.S. Ct. Appeals (3d cir.) 1979, Fla. 1981, U.S. Ct. Appeals (11th cir.) 1982. Law clk. to Judge Smith U.S. Ct. Appeals for 2d Circuit, 1963-64; asst. prof. law Ohio State U. Coll. Law, 1965-68, assoc. prof., 1968-70, prof., 1970-79; project assoc. Ford Found., Rio de Janeiro, 1966-68; assoc. Escritorio Augusto Nobre, Rio de Janeiro, 1979-80; prof. law U. Miami, Fla., 1979—; project coordinator Olin Fellowship Program Law and Econs. Ctr., U. Miami, Fla., 1980-81, assoc. dean Law Sch., 1982-83, dir. fgn. grad. law program, 1985—; cons. Hudson Inst., 1977, U.S. State Dept., 1981-82, World Bank, 1988-90; Fulbright lectr. Argentina, 1987, 88. Author: (with Karst) Law and Development in Latin America, 1975; Law and Inflation, 1982, Foreign Investment in Brazil, 1991; co-editor: A Panorama of Brazilian Law, 1992; advisor InterAm. Law Rev.; contbr. articles to law jours. Recipient Order of Democracy award Congress of Republic of Colombia, 1987, Lawyer of the Ams. award, 1989; grantee Social Sci. Rsch. Coun., 1970, Dana Found., 1982. Mem. Am. Law Inst., ABA, Fla. Bar Assn., Inter-Am. Bar Assn., Am. Soc. Comparative Law (bd. dirs.). Jewish. Office: U Miami Law Sch PO Box 248087 Coral Gables FL 33124

ROSENN, MAX, federal judge; b. Plains, Pa., Feb. 4, 1910; s. Joseph and Jennie (Wohl) R.; m. Tillie R. Hershkowitz, Mar. 18, 1934; children: Keith S., Daniel Wohl. BA, Cornell U., 1929; LLB, U. Pa., 1932. Bar: Pa. 1932, U.S. Supreme Ct. 1955, Cts. of Philippines 1946. Gen. practice Wilkes-Barre, Pa., 1932-41; dir. Franklin Fed. Savs. & Loan, Wilkes-Barre, 1937-70; spl. counsel Pa. Dept. Justice, 1939; asst. dist. atty. Luzerne County, 1942-44; also solicitor various mcpl. boroughs, ptnr. firm Rosenn & Rosenn, 1947-54, Rosenn, Jenkins & Grenwald, Wilkes-Barre, 1954-66, 67-70; sec. pub. welfare Pa., 1966-67; judge U.S. Ct. Appeals (3d cir.), 1970—, now sr. judge; former mem. criminal procedure rules com. Supreme Ct. Pa., 1958-85; mem. Pa. Commn. to Revise Pub. Employee Laws, 1968-69; Pa. chmn. White House Conf. on Children and Youth. Contbr. articles to legal publs. Mem. Pa. Bd. Pub. Welfare, 1963-66; chmn. Pa. Gov.'s Hosp. Study Commn., Pa. Gov.'s Coun. for Human Svcs., 1966-67; mem. exec. bd. Commonwealth of Pa., 1966-67; chmn. Commmn. Met. Govt., 1957-58; pres. Property Owners Assn. Luzerne County, 1955-57; chmn. Pa. Human Rels. Commn., 1969-70, Pa. Comm. Children and Youth, 1968-70, Legis. Task Force Structure for Human Svcs., 1970; alt. del. Rep. Nat. Conv., 1964; pres. Wyoming Valley Jewish Com., 1941-42; life trustee Wilkes-Barre Jewish Community Ctr.; chmn. Flood Recovery Task Force, 1972. Fellow Am. Coll. Trial Lawyers, Internat. Acad. Trial Lawyers; mem. ABA, Pa. Bar Assn., Luzerne County Bar Assn., Am. Law Inst., Am. Soc. Law and Medicine (charter mem., former assoc. editor jour.), Am. Judicature Soc., B'nai B'rith (pres. dist. grand lodge 1947-48, life bd. govs., former chmn. bd. dirs. Anti-Defamation League Pa., W.Va. and Del. 1955-58, nat. commr. 1964—), Westmoreland Club, Masons (33d degree), Alpha Epsilon Pi. Jewish. Office: US Ct Appeals 229 US Courthouse 197 S Main St Wilkes Barre PA 18701-1500

ROSENNE, MEIR, lawyer, government agency administrator; b. Iasi, Romania, Feb. 19, 1931; came to Israel, 1944; s. Jacob and Mina Rosenhaupt; m. Vera Ayal, June 9, 1959; children—Mihal, Dafna. M.A. in Polit. Sci., Inst. Polit. Sci., Paris, 1953; LL.B., Sorbonne, U. Paris, 1955, Ph.D. in Internat. Law with honors, 1957; grad., Inst. Internat. Studies, Paris, 1953. In govt. service Israel, 1953—; consul Israel Consulate, N.Y.C. 1967-69; sr. lectr. in polit. sci. U. Haifa, Israel, 1969-71; coordinator Atomic Energy Commn. Israel, 1969-71; chief legal adviser Fgn. Office Israel, Jerusalem, 1971-79; Israeli amb. to France, Paris, 1979-83; Israeli amb. to U.S. Washington, 1983-87; pres. State of Israel Bonds, N.Y., 1989-93; atty. Balter, Guth & Aloni, Jerusalem; with Feith & Zell, Washington. Contbr. articles to N.Y. Times, Washington Post, N.Y. Herald Tribune, also others. Chmn. internat. bd. govs. Share-Zedek Hosp., Jerusalem , 1989—. Sgt. Israeli Air Force, 1948-50. Recipient Harold Weil medal NYU Sch. Law. Mem. Internat. Law Soc. (France), Soc. Internat. Law, Israeli Bar Assn., Am. Soc. Internat. Law, French Assn. Internat. Law. Jewish. Club: Internat. (Washington). Avocations: volleyball; swimming. Office: Balter Guth & Aloni, 23 Hillel St, Jerusalem Israel also: Feith & Zell 2300 M St NW Ste 600 Washington DC 20037

ROSENOW, EDWARD CARL, III, medical educator; b. Columbus, Ohio, Nov. 2, 1934; s. Oscar Ferdinand and Mildred Irene (Eichelberger) R.; m. Constance Donna Grahame, Sept. 7, 1957; children: Sheryl Lynn, Scott Edward. BS, Ohio State U., 1955, MD, 1959; MS in Medicine, U. Minn., 1969. Diplomate Am. Bd. Internal Medicine (mem. pulmonary subbd. 1982-88); cert. in Subspecialty Pulmonary Diseases. Intern Riverside Meth. Hosp., Columbus, Ohio, 1959-60; resident in internal medicine Mayo Grad. Sch. Medicine, Rochester, Minn., 1960-65, clin. fellow in thoracic diseases, 1965-66; cons. in internal medicine (thoracic diseases) Mayo Clinic, Rochester, 1966; instr. in medicine Mayo Grad. Sch. Medicine, Rochester, 1969-73; asst. prof. medicine Mayo Med. Sch., Rochester, 1973-77, assoc. prof. medicine, 1977-80, prof. medicine, 1980-86; assoc. dir. internal medicine residency program Mayo Clinic, Rochester, 1977-79, program dir. internal medicine residency program, 1979-84; sec. staff, 1979, Arthur M. and Gladys D. Gray prof. medicine, 1987—; cons. NASA, Houston. Capt. M.C., U.S Army, 1962-64. Recipient Alumni Achievement award Coll. Medicine Ohio State U., 1989; Edward W. and Betty Knight Scripps Professorship named in his honor Mayo Med. Sch., 1994. Fellow ACP (gov. Minn. chpt. 1987-91, Ralph S. Claypoole Sr. award for Lifetime Dedication to Patient Care 1995, Minn. chpt. Laureate award 1994), Am. Coll. Chest Physicians (editl. bd. CHEST 1973-78, editor spl. case reports 1975-90, com. on postgrad. med. edn. 1978-84, sci. program com. 1982, com. on undergrad. med. edn. 1981-82, co-chmn. sci. program com. Internat. Coll. Chest Physicians meeting, Sydney, Australia, 1985, regent 1984-88, pres. elect 1988-89, pres. 1989-90); mem. AMA, So. Minn. Med. Assn., Minn. Thoracic Soc., Am. Thoracic Soc., Sigma Xi. Office: Mayo Clinic Div Thoracic Diseases 200 1st St SW Rochester MN 55905-0001

ROSENOW, JOHN EDWARD, foundation executive; b. Lincoln, Nebr., Sept. 15, 1949; s. Lester Edward and Lucille Louise (Koehler) R.; m. Nancy Kay Hadley; children: Matthew, Stacy. BS in Agrl. Engring., U. Nebr., 1971. Dir. of tourism Nebr. Dept. Econ. Devel., Lincoln, 1971-79, interim dept. dir., 1985; founder Nat. Arbor Day Found., 1972; exec. dir. millionmem. Nat. Arbor Day Found., Lincoln and Nebraska City, 1979-94; pres. Nat. Arbor Day Found., 1994—. Co-author: (book) Tourism: the good, the bad, and the ugly, 1979. Democrat. Mem. United Ch. of Christ. Office: Nat Arbor Day Found 211 N 12th St Lincoln NE 68508-1497

ROSENOW, JOHN HENRY, surgeon, educator; b. Chgo., Sept. 16, 1913; s. Edward Carl and Lydia Barbara (Senty) R.; m. Jane Dexter, June 8, 1938; children: Joan (Mrs. Charles Jackson), Peter Dexter, Philip John, Charles Edward, Margaret (Mrs. Theodore Hope), Barbara (Mrs. Derek Von Schlegall). B.A., Carleton Coll., Northfield, Minn., 1934; M.D., Harvard U., 1938; M.S. in Surgery, Mayo Found., U. Minn., 1944. Diplomate: Am. Bd. Surgery. Intern Presbyn. Hosp., Chgo., 1939-40; fellow in surgery Mayo Clinic, 1941-43, 46-47; pvt. practice medicine specializing in gen. surgery Mpls., 1947-63; part-time editor Modern Medicine Publs, Inc., Mpls., 1955-63; sr. med. editor Modern Medicine Publs., Inc., 1963-75; clin. instr. surgery U. Minn. Med. Sch., 1955—; chief med. officer Mil. Entrance Processing Sta., Mpls., 1975-88; mem. staff Abbott-Northwestern Hosp., Fairview-Southdale hosps., Hennepin County Med. Center. Contbr. articles to med. jours. Mem. diocesan standing com. Episcopal Ch., 1961-64, 70-73. Served with M.C. USNR, 1943-46, PTO. Decorated Bronze Star. Fellow A.C.S.; mem. Am. Minn. med. assns., Hennepin County Med. Soc., Minn. Surg. Soc., Mpls. Acad. Medicine.

ROSENQUIST, GLENN CARL, pediatrician; b. Lincoln, Nebr., Aug. 29, 1931; s. Carl E. and Mable M. (Lundy) R.; m. Patricia Bechan, Sept. 6, 1953; children: Jane, Peter, John, Anne, Thomas, Matthew. B.A., U. Nebr., 1953; M.D., U. Nebr. Med. Sch., 1957. Diplomate: Am. Bd. Pediatrics, Am.

Bd. Pediatric Cardiology. Intern Phila. Gen. Hosp., 1957-58; resident in pediatrics Univ. Calif., San Francisco, 1960-63; fellow USPHS, Carnegie Inst. Washington, 1963-65; fellow pediatric cardiology Johns Hopkins Med. Sch., Balt., 1965-67; mem. faculty dept. pediatrics Johns Hopkins Med. Sch., 1967-76; chmn. dept. pediatrics Univ. Nebr. Coll. Medicine, Omaha, 1976-80; dir. research Children's Nat. Med. Center, Washington, 1980-93; gen. pediatric clinic Children's Nat. Med. Center, 1993—. Contbr. articles to various publs. Served with M.C. USAF, 1958-60. Recipient Research grants NIH, 1967-84, Career Devel. award, 1971-75. Mem. Am. Acad. Pediatrics, Am. Coll. Cardiology, Teratology Soc., Am. Assn. Anatomists, Soc. Pediatric Research, Am. Pediatric Soc., Soc. Developmental Biology, Phi Beta Kappa, Alpha Omega Alpha. Office: Children's Nat Med Ctr 11 Michigan Ave NE Washington DC 20002-1011

ROSENQUIST, JAMES ALBERT, artist; b. Grand Forks, N.D., Nov. 29, 1933; s. Louis A. and Ruth C. (Hendrickson) R.; m. Mary Lou Adams, June 5, 1960; 1 child, John Adams; m. Melinda Thompson, Apr. 18, 1987; 1 child, Lily McLean. Student, Art Students League, 1954-55. Lectr. Yale Sch. Art, 1964; artist in residence (Aspen (Colo.) Inst. Humanist Studies), 1965. Engaged as comml. artist painting gas tanks, billboards, 1952-60; one-man shows include Green Gallery, N.Y.C., 1962, 64, Mus. Modern Art, 1963, Sperone Gallery, Turin, Italy, 1964, Sonnabend Gallery, Paris, 1964, 67, 68, Dwan Gallery, Los Angeles, 1964, Moderna Museet, Stockholm, 1965, 66, Castelli Gallery, N.Y.C., 1965, 66, 68, 69, 70, 73, 74, 78, 85, 88, 91, Mus. Modern Art, Turin, 1965, Nat. Gallery Can., Ottawa, Ont., 1968, Met. Mus. Art, N.Y.C., 1968, Max Protech, Washington, 1974, Nat. Gallery, Victoria, Australia, 1978, Sable-Castelli Gallery, Toronto, 1978, Colo. State U., Ft. Collins, 1982, Castelli/Fergen/Corcoran, N.Y.C., 1982, Mayer Gallery, London, 1982, Mus. Contemporary Art, Houston, 1982, Whitney Mus. Am. Art, N.Y.C., 1982, Mus. Fine Arts, Houston, 1983, 88, U. South Fla., 1984, Butler Inst. Am. Art, 1988, Wetterling Gallery, Stockholm, 1989, Mus. Modern Art, Austin, Tex., 1990, Cen. Hall of Artists, Moscow, 1991, IVAM Centre Julio Gonzales, Valencia, Spain, 1991, others; exhibited in numerous group shows U.S. and Europe, including 16 Ams. at, Mus. Modern Art, 1963, Artist and Object at, Guggenheim Mus., 1963, São Paulo, Brazil, 1967, Mus. Modern Art, Tokyo, 1967, Musée des Arts Decoratives, Palais Louvre, 1967, Haywood Gallery, London, 1969, Albright-Knox Gallery, Buffalo, 1971, Mus. Contemporary Art, Chgo., 1972, Met. Mus. Art, N.Y.C., 1969-70, Whitney Mus. Am. Art, N.Y.C., 1974, biennial, Whitney Mus. Am. Art, N.Y.C., 1981, including 16 Ams. at, Mayer Gallery, London, 1978, U. Mich. Mus., 1978, Fitzwilliam Mus., Cambridge, Eng., 1978, Bklyn. Mus., 1981, Va. Mus., Richmond, 1981, Haus der Kunst, 1982, Nat. Gallery, Victoria, B.C., Can., 1982; represented in permanent collections Pasadena Mus., Modern Museet, Stockholm, Stadtlicht, Amsterdam, Holland, Whitney Mus., Albright-Knox Gallery, Mus. Modern Art, N.Y.C., Met. Mus. Art, N.Y.C., Nat. Gallery Can., Wallraf-Richartz Mus., Cologne, Germany, others; recipient Norman Waite Harris award Chgo. Art Inst. 1963, Prix di Tella, Argentina 1965, Graphics prize 6th Internat. Biennial Exhbn. Prints, Nat. Mus. Modern Art, Tokyo 1968, 7th Internat Expn. Graphics, Moderna Gallery, Ljubiana, Yugoslavia 1967); painting of bomber F-111. Bd. dirs. Nat. Endowment for Arts. Recipient Golden Plate award Am. Acad. Achievement, 1988. Mem. Municipal Art Soc., N.Y.

ROSENSAFT, MENACHEM ZWI, lawyer, author, community activist; b. Bergen-Belsen, Germany, May 1, 1948; came to U.S., 1958, naturalized, 1962; s. Josef and Hadassah (Bimko) R.; m. Jean Bloch, Jan. 13, 1974; 1 child, Joana Deborah. BA, MA, Johns Hopkins U., 1971; MA, Columbia U., 1975, JD, 1979. Bar: N.Y. 1980. Adj. lectr. dept. Jewish studies CCNY, 1972-74, professorial fellow, 1974-75; rsch. fellow Am. Law Inst., 1977-78; law clk. to judge U.S. Dist. Ct. (so. dist.) N.Y., N.Y.C., 1979-81; assoc. Proskauer, Rose, Goetz & Mendelsohn, N.Y.C., 1981-82, Kaye, Scholer, Fierman, Hays & Handler, N.Y.C., 1982-89; v.p., sr. assoc. counsel Chase Manhattan Bank, N.Y.C., 1989-93; spl. counsel Hahn & Hessen, N.Y.C., 1994—. Author: Moshe Sharett, Statesman of Israel, 1966, Fragments, Past and Future (poetry), 1968, Not Backward to Belligerency, 1969; editor: Bergen Belsen Youth mag., 1965; book rev. editor Columbia Jour. Transnat. Law, 1978-79; co-editor (with Yehuda Bauer) Antisemitism; Threat to Western Civilization, 1988; contbg. editor: Reform Judaism, 1993; contbr. to various publs. including N.Y. Times, Newsweek, N.Y. Post, L.A. Times, Phila. Inquirer, Maimi Hearld, Internat. Herald Tribune, Jerusalem Post, Liberation, Paris, Davar, Tel Aviv, El Diario, Snatiago de Chile, Columbia Human Rights Law Rev., Jewish Social Studies, Leo Baeck Inst. Year Book XXI, Columbia Jour. Environ. Law, (with Michael I. Saltzman) Tax Planning Internat. Rev., Fellowship, Reform Judaism, United Synagogue Rev., Forward, Midstream, N.Y. Jewish Week, Jewish Telegraphic Agy. Bull.; subject of profile "Survivor's Son" in Present Tense mag., 1990. Chmn. Internat. Network Children Jewish Holocaust Survivors, 1981-84, founding chmn., 1984—; pres. Labor Zionist Alliance, 1988-91; chmn. commn. human rights World Jewish Congress, 1986-91, chmn. exec. com. Am. sect., 1986-90; mem. Gen. Coun. World Zionist Orgn., 1987-92; mem. U.S. Holocaust Meml. Coun., 1994—, chmn. content com., 1994—; mem. N.Y.C. Holocaust Meml. Commn., 1982—, chmn. collections com., 1987-89; mem. Am. Zionist Tribunal, 1988-90, chmn., 1990; sec. Am. Zionist Fedn., 1990-93; bd. dirs. Am. Jewish Joint Distbn. Com., 1988-91, Mercaz, 1991—; N.Y. Met. region United Synagogue Conservative Judaism, 1991—, also chmn. United Synagogue delegation to Nat. Jewish Cmty. Rels. Adv. Coun., 1994—; mem. exec. com. Nat Jewish Cmty. Rels. Adv. Coun., 1994—; mem. N.Y. county Dem. com., 1981-85; organizer, leader demonstration against Pres. Reagan's visit to Bitbnurg Cemetery and Bergen-Belsen concentration camp, 1985; del. meeting on recognition of Israel between five Am. Jews and reps. of Palestine Liberation Orgn., Stockholm, 1988; mem. adv. coun. Park Ave. Synagogue, 1993-94, trustee, 1994, chmn. Sherr Inst. Adult Jewish Studies, 1993—. Recipient Abraham Joshua Heschel Peace award, 1989, Parker Sch. recognition of achievement with honors in internat. and fgn. law, 1979; Harlan Fiske Stone scholar, 1977-79. Mem. ABA, Assn. of Bar of City of N.Y., Phi Beta Kappa. Home: 179 E 70th St New York NY 10021-5154 Office: Hahn & Hessen 350 5th Ave Ste 3700 New York NY 10118-0075

ROSENSHINE, ALLEN GILBERT, advertising agency executive; b. N.Y.C., Mar. 14, 1939; s. Aaron and Anna (Zuckerman) R.; m. Suzan Weston-Webb, Aug. 31, 1979; children: Andrew, Jonathan. A.B., Columbia Coll., 1960. Copywriter J.B. Rundle (advt.), N.Y.C., 1962-65; copywriter Batten, Barton, Durstine & Osborn, N.Y.C., 1965, copy supr., 1967, v.p., 1968, asso. creative dir., 1970, sr. v.p., creative dir., 1975-77, exec. v.p., 1977-80, pres., 1980-82, chief exec. officer, 1981-86, chmn., 1983-86, also dir., mem. exec. com.; pres., chief exec. officer BBDO Internat., N.Y.C., 1984-86, also bd. dirs.; pres., chief exec. officer Omnicom Group, N.Y.C., 1986-88; chmn., chief exec. officer BBDO Worldwide, N.Y.C., 1988—; lectr. gen. studies Bklyn. Coll., 1961-65. Office: BBDO Worldwide Inc 1285 Avenue Of The Americas New York NY 10019-6028

ROSENSTEEL, GEORGE T., physics educator, nuclear physicist; b. Balt., Sept. 30, 1947; s. Walter St. George and Marie Emily (White) R. BSc, U. Toronto, Can., 1973, PhD, 1975. Can. fellow NRC, 1976-78; prof. physics Tulane U., New Orleans, 1978—, chmn. dept., 1985-91; vis. fellow Brit. Sci. and Engring. Coun., U. Sussex, Eng., 1986; vis. prof. Nat. Inst. Nuclear Theory, U. Washington, 1992. Contbr. 95 articles to profl. jours. Delivered grad. sch. commencement address Tulane U., 1987; recipient 7 grants NSF, 1979—. Mem. Am. Phys. Soc., Am. Math. Soc., Sigma Xi (young scientist award 1987). Office: Tulane U Dept of Physics New Orleans LA 70118

ROSENSTEEL, JOHN WILLIAM, insurance company executive; b. Chgo., June 4, 1940; s. Harold Eugene and Alice (Shanahan) R.; m. Judith; children: Elizabeth, Margaret, Jill. BS in Econs., Holy Cross Coll., 1962. Chartered life underwriter. Home office rep. Aetna Life and Casualty, Chgo., 1967-72; regional dir., 1972-75; dir. Aetna Life and Casualty, 1975-81; nat. dir. Aetna Life and Casualty, Hartford, 1981-83, v.p., 1983-86; sr. v.p. European region Aetna Internat., Inc., Hartford, 1986-90; sr. v.p. European region & United Kingdom Aetna Internat., Hartford, London & Madrid; now chief exec. officer Keyport Life Insurance Co., Boston, Mass., 1993—; bd. dirs. Aetna Internat. K.V., London, La Estrella de Seguros, Madrid, 1988. Lt. USN, 1963-66, Vietnam. Mem. Nat. Assn. Life Underwriters. Republican. Roman Catholic. Avocations: golf, swimming, reading. Home: 13 Glen Oak Dr Wayland MA 01778-3921 Office: Keyport Life 125 High St Boston MA 02110-2704

ROSENSTEIN, BERYL JOEL, physician; b. Boston, Jan. 5, 1937; s. Benjamin and Doris (Goldhagen) R.; m. Carolyn S., Aug. 31, 1958; children: Susan Eileen, Jonathan David. BA, Boston U., 1957; MD, Tufts U., 1961; M Adminstrv. Sci., Johns Hopkins U., 1987. Diplomate Am. Bd. Pediatrics. Intern in pediatrics Johns Hopkins Hosp., Balt., 1961-62, resident in pediatrics, 1962-64, dir. cystic fibrosis clinic, 1972—, v.p. med. affairs, 1994—; prof. pediatrics Johns Hopkins Sch. Med., Balt., 1989—; med. dir. Mt. Washington Pediatric Hosp., Balt., 1988-93; med. adv. coun. Cystic Fibrosis Found., Bethesda, Md., 1980-88, trustee, 1986—. Author: Pediatric Pearls: Handbook of Pediatrics, 1989, Primary Care of the Newborn, 1992; contbr. over 100 articles to profl. jours. and chpts. to books. Lt. comdr. USPHS, 1964-66. Fellow Am. Acad. Pediatrics, Ambulator Pediatric Assn.; mem. Am. Thoracic Soc., Am. Pediatric Soc., Alpha Omega Alpha. Avocations: tennis, bicycling, antique cars, travel, art. Office: Johns Hopkins Hosp Park 315 Baltimore MD 21287-2533

ROSENSTEIN, IRA M., beverage products executive; b. 1940. Grad., Calif. State U., Long Beach, 1965. Contr. Armco, Inc., L.A., 1965-69, Lear Siegler, Inc., L.A., 1969-70; v.p. fin. and adminstrn. Early Calif. Foods, Inc., L.A., 1970-76; v.p., dir. Comml. Internat. Corp., L.A., 1976-79; exec. v.p., dir. Dr. Pepper Co. Inc., 1980-88; exec. v.p. Dr. Pepper/Seven-Up Corp., 1988—. Office: Dr Pepper/Seven-Up Cos 8144 Walnut Hill Ln Dallas TX 75231

ROSENSTEIN, JAMES ALFRED, lawyer; b. Phila., Jan. 4, 1939; s. Louis Charles and Natalie Selma (Stern) R.; m. Linda Merle Lederman, Sept. 7, 1969; 1 child, Judith Esther. A.B., Harvard U., 1961, J.D., 1968. Bar: Pa. 1968. Assoc. Wolf, Block, Schorr and Solis-Cohen, Phila., 1968-76; ptnr. Wolf, Block, Schorr and Solis-Cohen, 1976—; mem. adv. com. task force on condominiums Joint State Govt Commn., Pa. Gen. Assembly, 1977-79; mem. condominium-coop. steering com. Phila. City Planning Commn., 1980-81. Contbr. articles to profl. jours. Trustee exec. com. Jewish Fedn. of Greater Phila., 1977—, chmn. com. on local svcs., 1986-89, sec., 1987-88, v.p., 1988-94, chmn. com. on allocations and planning, 1989-92; v.p. jewish Cmty. Rels. Coun., 1982-85, 89-90; trustee United Way of Greater Phila., 1979-84, bd. dirs., 1982-85, 91—. Lt. USN, 1961-64. Mem. ABA (chmn. devel. and financing of condominium project), Pa. Bar Assn. (chmn. common interest ownership com. 1980-93, chmn. real property divsn. 1993-95, chmn. real property probate and trust law sect. 1995—), Phila. Bar Assn., Am. Coll. Real Estate Lawyers, Coll. of Cmty. Assn. Lawyers, Coun. Jewish Fedns. (bd. dirs. 1986—, chmn. com. on svcs. to aging 1991—). Office: Wolf Block Schorr and Solis-Cohen Packard Bldg 12th Fl 111 S 15th St Philadelphia PA 19102-2678

ROSENSTEIN, MARVIN, public health administrator; b. Sept. 5, 1939. BSChemE, U. Md., 1961; MS in Environ. Engring., Rensselaer Poly. Inst., 1966; PhD in Nuclear Engring., U. Md., 1971. Rschr. U.S. Bur. Mines/College Park (Md.) Metall. Rsch. Sta., 1961; commd. ensign Commd. Corps Pub. Health Svc., 1962, advanced through grades to capt., 1983; with N.E. Radiological Health Lab., Winchester, Mass., 1962, program coord. analytical quality control svc. divsn. radiological health, 1962; with data collation and analysis sect. radiation surveillance ctr. Divsn. Radiological Health, Washington, 1966; chief radiation exposure intelligence sect. standards and intelligence br. Nat. Ctr. for Radiological Health, Rockville, Md., 1967; dep. chief radiation measurements and calibration br. divsn. electronic products Bur. Radiological Health, Rockville, 1971, spl. asst. to dir. divsn. electronic products, 1972, dep. dir. divsn. electonic products, 1973, sr. sci. advisor, 1979; dep. assoc. commr. for policy coordination office policy coordination FDA, Rockville, 1978; dir. office health physics Ctr. for Devices and Radiological Health, Rockville, 1982-95, sr. staff fellow, 1995—; mem. USASI Standards Com. N101, 1968-69; guest worker Ctr. for Radiation Rsch., Nat. Bur. Standards, 1969-74; faculty rsch. assoc. lab. for polymer and radiation sci. dept. clin. engring. U. Md., 1971-74; asst. clin. prof. radiology sch. medicine and scis. George Washington U., 1977-90. Contbr. over 70 publs. to profl. and sci. jours. Recipient Fed. Engr. of Yr. award NSPE/Dept. Health and Human Svcs., 1987. Mem. Nat. Coun. on Radiation Protection and Measurements (coun. 1988—, com. SC44 1976—, com. SC62 1980-85, chmn. com. SC46-12 1992—), Health Physics Soc. (publs. com. 1967-77, del. to 4th Internat. Congress Internat. Radiation Protection Assn. 1977, contbg. editor newsletter 1982—) Com. on Interagency Radiation Rsch. and Policy Coordination (alt. HHS policy panel 1984—, vice chmn. sci. panel 1985-94, exec. com. 1985-94, mem. subpanel on use BEIR V and UNSCEAR 1988 in risk assessment 1989-92), Internat. Commn. on Radiological Protection (com. 3 on radiological protection in medicine 1985—, corresp. mem. task group on revision publ. 21, 1979-88), Internat. Commn. on Radiation Units and Measurements (mem. report com. on dosimetry in diagnostic radiology for the patient, 1994—), Commd. Officers Assn., Sigma Xi. Achievements include patent for radiation dosimeter; research in absorbed dose from medical X rays, radiation risk estimates, dosimetry for epidemiological studies, absorbed dose to the public from radiation emergencies, electron depth-dose and dosimetry, radiochemistry and environmental health, radioactivity in food, general radiological health. Office: FDA Ctr Devices & Radiol Health 2094 Gaither Rd Rockville MD 20850

ROSENSTEIN, PETER DANIEL, association executive, medical educator; b. N.Y.C., Jan. 23, 1947; s. Heinz and Dorrit (Politzer) R. B.A., CCNY, 1969; M.P.A., Baruch Coll., 1978. Adminstrv. asst. Congresswoman Bella S. Abzug, N.Y.C., 1972-74; coordinator local govt. N.Y.C. Mayor's Office, N.Y.C., 1974-77; exec. dir. White House Conf. on Handicapped Individuals, Washington, 1978-80, Am. Acad. Physician Assts., Washington, 1981-84; exec. dir. Accts. for Pub. Interest, Washington, 1985—; adj. assoc. prof. G.W. Sch. Med. and Health Sci., Washington, 1983—; travel agt. Champion-Kail Travel Group, Washington, 1986—. Mem. exec. com. Scouting for the Handicapped, Washington, 1980—; campaign coordinator Bella Abzug for Mayor, N.Y.C., 1977; runoff coordinator Cuomo for Mayor, N.Y.C., 1977. Mem. Am. League Lobbyists, Profl. Conf. Mgrs. Assn., Am. Soc. Assn. Execs., Washington Soc. Assn. Execs., Ams. for Democratic Action. Avocation: travel. Home: 1717 P St NW Washington DC 20036-1307

ROSENSTEIN, SAMUEL M., federal judge; b. 1909. Student, U. Ky., 1927-28; JD, U. Cin., 1931. Assoc. Sen. Mills M. Logan Law Office, Frankfort, Ky., 1933-35, Smith, Reed & Leary, Frankfort, 1935-46, Milliken, Handmaker & Rosenstein, Louisville, 1946-68; sr. judge U.S. Ct. Internat. Trade, N.Y.C., 1968-72, Ft. Lauderdale, Fla., 1972—. Spl. counsel Ky. Dept. Revenue and Welfare, 1933-43; gen. counsel Ky. Fair Bd., 1956-63. With U.S. Army. Office: US Ct Internat Trade 2200 S Ocean Ln Ste 1508 Fort Lauderdale FL 33316

ROSENSTOCK, MORTON, librarian; b. N.Y.C., Feb. 7, 1929; s. Samuel and Frieda (Hut) R.; m. Charlotte Smilon, July 11, 1945 (dec. Nov. 1993); children: Kenneth, Jason. BA, Harvard U., 1949; MA, Columbia U., 1951, MS, 1952, PhD, 1963. Libr. Bklyn. Pub. Libr., 1950-52, Bklyn. Coll., 1952-53, Queens Coll., Flushing, N.Y., 1955-57; chief libr., prof. history Bronx (N.Y.) Community Coll., 1958-66, assoc. dean, 1967-75, acting pres., 1976-77, chief libr., 1979-94; dean CUNY, 1977-78; vis. faculty history Columbia U., N.Y.C., 1973-74. Author: Louis Marshall, Defender of Jewish Rights, 1965; contbr. articles to profl. jours. With U.S. Army, 1953-55. Mem. Am. Jewish Hist. Soc. (acad. coun. 1971—), Jewish Hist. Soc. N.Y. Home: 100 Winston Dr Apt 10HN Cliffside Park NJ 07010 Office: Bronx Community Coll University Ave Bronx NY 10453

ROSENSTOCK, SUSAN LYNN, orchestra manager; b. Bklyn., Nov. 2, 1947. BS, SUNY, Cortland, 1969; MBA, So. Meth. U., 1977, MFA, 1978. Cert. fund raising exec. Asst. mgr. Columbus (Ohio) Symphony Orch., 1978-82; grants program dir., info. officer Greater Columbus Arts Coun., 1982-83, asst. dir. grants and adminstrn., 1983-84; dir. annual giving and spl. events Columbus Symphony Orch., 1984-86, dir. devel., 1986-90, orch. mgr., 1990—; panelist Ohio Arts Coun. Music Panel, 1986, 87, Challenge Grants Panel, 1991, J.C. Penney Gold Rule Award Judges Panel, 1993, 94. Mem. Am. Symphony Orch. League (devel. dirs. steering com. nat. conf. 1987, 88), Nat. Soc. Fund Raising Execs. (program com. Ctrl. Ohio chpt. 1988—, chmn. program com. 1993, 94, bd. dirs. 1993—, treas. 1995). Office: Columbus Symphony Orch 55 E State St Columbus OH 43215

ROSENSWEIG, RONALD ELLIS, research scientist; b. Hamilton, Ohio, Nov. 8, 1932; s. Herman and Deana (Meisel) R.; m. Ruth Evelyn Cohen, Sept. 5, 1954; children—Scott Elliot, Beth Ellen, Perry Ethan. Chem. Engr., U. Cin., 1955; S.M., MIT, 1956, Sc.D., 1959. Asst. prof. dept. chem. engring. MIT, Cambridge, 1959-62; prin. scientist Avco Corp., Wilmington, Mass., 1962-69; pres., tech. dir., co-founder Ferrofluidics Corp., Burlington, Mass., 1969-73, also dir., 1969-85; rsch. assoc. Exxon Corp., Annandale, N.J., 1973-78, sr. rsch. assoc., 1978-85, sci. advisor, 1985—; vis. prof. U. Minn., Mpls., 1980, U. Chgo., 1990. Author: Ferrohydrodynamics, 1985; contbr. articles to profl. jours.; patentee in field. Fellow NSF, MIT, 1955-56; recipient IR-100 awards Indsl. Rsch. Pubs., 1968, 69, 71; named Young Engr. of Yr., Avco Corp., 1966, Disting. Engring. Alumnus U. Cin., 1986. Mem. Nat. Acad. Engring., Am. Inst. Chem. Engrs. (Alpha Chi Sigma award for rsch. 1985), Am. Phys. Soc., Magnetic Fluids Conf., Internat. Steering Com. (chmn. 1977-92). Jewish. Home: 34 Gloucester Rd Summit NJ 07901-3023 Office: Exxon Corp Research Labs Rte 22E Annandale NJ 08801

ROSENSWEIG, STANLEY HAROLD, retail executive; b. Phila., May 5, 1918; s. Emanuel Martin and Jennie (Hoffman) R.; m. Elaine Gordon Decker, Dec. 4, 1967; children by previous marriage—Susan, Ellen, Tod, Lisa. A.B. in Bus. Adminstrn., George Washington U., 1939. Chmn. bd. Electronics Wholesalers Co., Washington, 1947-68; chmn. bd. CWF Corp., Washington, 1963-73; pres. Sun Appliance Wholesalers, Washington, 1950-69; pres. Gem Internat. Inc., St. Louis, 1961-65, chmn. exec. com., 1963-66; bd. dirs. St. Louis Blues, 1966-74; chmn. bd. Lewis & Thomas Saltz Clothiers, Inc., Washington, 1977-84; dir. St. Louis Arena Inc., Action Leasing Inc. Trustee Boys Club, Greater Washington Jewish Community Found.; exec. bd. United Jewish Appeal, Washington; bd. dirs. Jewish Social Services Agy., Washington; bd. dirs. Nat. Symphony Orch., Child Guidance Clinic, Washington. Lt. U.S. Navy Res., 1941-45, PTO, 1944-45. Mem. Young Pres. Orgn. Clubs: Standard (Chgo.); Woodmont Country, Circus Saints and Sinners (Washington). Home: Fern Hill McClean VA 22101 Office: 3201 New Mexico Ave NW Washington DC 20016-2756

ROSENTHAL, AARON, management consultant; b. N.Y.C., July 12, 1914; s. Zelig and Sarah (Shapinsky) R.; m. Edna Blanche Finkel, Sept. 3, 1940; children—Stephen Mark, Marjorie Ann. B.A., Coll. City N.Y., 1934, M.S. in Edn, 1935; postgrad., Georgetown U. Law Sch., 1937-39, Am. U., 1950-53. Dir. Internal Audit Service, VA, Washington, 1953-58; controller VA, 1958-60; dir. financial mgmt. NASA, 1960-61; comptroller NSF, 1961-69, Nat. Acad. Scis., 1969-76; exec. cons. Coopers & Lybrand; fin. cons. to Ctr. for Devel. and Population Activities; fin. and mgmt. cons. to Joint Oceanographic Instns. Inc.; U.S. rep. supr. Radiation Effects Rsch. Found., Hiroshima, Japan; mem. nat. adv. coun. nat. Ctr. for Higher Edn. Mgmt. Systems; bd. dirs. TCOA, Inc., Manchester Center, Vt. Trustee Sci. Service Inc. Served with AUS, 1943-45. Recipient Exceptional Service award VA, 1960; Merit citation Nat. Civil Service League, 1957; Distinguished Service award NSF, 1969. Fellow AAAS; mem. Am. Soc. Pub. Adminstrn., Assn. Govt. Accts. Home: 3001 Veazey Ter NW Washington DC 20008-5454 Office: 2101 Constitution Ave NW Washington DC 20418-0007

ROSENTHAL, ALAN SAYRE, government official; b. N.Y.C., Sept. 30, 1926; s. Morris S. and Elizabeth (Ralph) R.; m. Helen Miller, Sept. 8, 1951; children: Edward S., Susan L., Richard M., James M. A.B., U. Pa., 1948; LL.B., Yale U., 1951. Bar: N.Y. 1952. Asst. in instrn. Yale U. Law Sch., 1950-51; law clk. to U.S. Circuit Judge Henry W. Edgerton, Washington, 1951-52; atty. appellate sect., civil div. Justice Dept., 1952-72, asst. chief, 1958-72; adminstrv. judge atomic safety and licensing appeal panel AEC (now Nuclear Regulatory Commn.), Washington, 1972-91, chmn., 1972-88; adminstrv. judge pers. appeals bd. GAO, Washington, 1991—, chmn., 1992-94; mem. ethics panel Montgomery County Bd. Edn., 1987-93; lectr. law U. Pa., 1981-83, Am. U., 1991-92. Pres. Kensington Elem. Sch. PTA, 1966-67; pres. North Chevy Chase Swimming Pool Assn., 1974-76; chmn. trustees Cedar Ln. Unitarian Ch., 1970-71; bd. dirs. Montgomery chpt. ACLU, 1967-69. Served with USAAF, 1944-46. Recipient John Marshall award Justice Dept., 1969, Disting. Svc. award Nuclear Regulatory Commn., 1988. Mem. Order of Coif, Phi Beta Kappa, Pi Gamma Mu, Delta Sigma Rho. Home: 3203 Kent St Kensington MD 20895-3210 Office: GAO GAO Pers Appeals Bd UCP II Washington DC 20548

ROSENTHAL, ALBERT JAY, advertising agency executive; b. Chgo., Sept. 30, 1928; s. Harry and Jennie (Comm) R.; m. Rhoda R. Rosenstein, June 18, 1950; children: Jayne, Michael, James, Nancy. BA, U. Ill., 1950. Reporter Transradio Press., Chgo., 1950-51; columnist Lerner Newspapers, Chgo., 1951-53; creative dir. Elliot, Jaynes & Baruch, Chgo., 1953-61; chmn. Albert Jay Rosenthal & Co., Chgo. and N.Y.C., 1961-85; chmn. Midwest div. HBM/Creamer-Albert Jay Rosenthal, Chgo., 1985-88, Della Femina, McNamee WCRS, Inc., Chgo., 1988-93; chmn. DFM/Tatham, Chgo., 1993; founder, pres. Franchising & Licensing World Ctr., Chgo., 1994—. Bd. dirs. Ill. Arts Alliance Found., Ill. Arts Alliance, Court Theatre U. Chgo.; mem. sustaining fund com. Ravinia Festival Assn.; mem. mktg. com. World Bus. Coun., Washington; vice chmn. Chgo. Internat. Film Festival; v.p. Gastro-Intestinal Rsch. Found. U. Chgo. Named one of Chgo. Ten Outstanding Young Men, Chgo. Jr. Assn. of Commerce, 1962, Advt. Man of Yr., Alpha Delta Sigma, 1978, Communicator of Yr., Jewish United Fund, 1988. Jewish. Home: 179 E Lake Shore Dr Chicago IL 60611-1351 Office: Franchising & Licensing World Ctr 840 N Lake Shore Dr Chicago IL 60611

ROSENTHAL, ALBERT JOSEPH, university dean, law educator, lawyer; b. N.Y.C., Mar. 5, 1919; m. Barbara Snowden, June 30, 1953; children: Edward H., Thomas S., William I. B.A., U. Pa., 1938; LL.B., Harvard U. 1941. Bar: N.Y. 1942, U.S. Supreme Ct. 1947. Law clk. to judge U.S. Ct. Appeals 1st Circuit, Boston, 1941-42; spl. appellate atty. OPA, Washington, 1946-47; law clk. to Justice Frankfurter U.S. Supreme Ct., Washington, 1947-48; asst. loan officer IBRD, Washington, 1948-50; atty. Dept. Justice, Washington, 1950-52; gen. counsel Small Def. Plants Adminstrn., Washington, 1952-53; ptnr. Golden Wienshienk & Rosenthal, N.Y.C., 1953-64; prof. law Columbia U., N.Y.C., 1964-89, Maurice T. Moore prof., 1974-89, dean Sch. Law, 1979-84, prof. emeritus, dean emeritus, 1989—; hearing officer N.Y. State Dept. Environ. Conservation, 1975, 77; mem. N.Y. State Law Revision Commn., 1987—; vis. prof. law St. John's U., 1989-92, disting. prof. 1992—; spl. master U.S. Dist. Ct. N.Y., 1990—. Author: (with H. Korn and S. Lubman) Catastrophic Accidents in Government Programs, 1963, (with F. Grad and G. Rathjens) Environmental Control: Priorities, Policies and the Law, 1971, Federal Regulation of Campaign Finance, 1972, (with F. Grad and others) The Automobile and the Regulation of Its Impact on the Environment, 1975; editor: (with L. Henkin) Constitutionalism and Rights: The Influence of the U.S. Constitution Abroad, 1989; contbr. articles to law jours. Mem. Logan Airport Master Plan Study Team, 1975. Served to capt. U.S. Army Air Corps, 1942-45. Fellow Am. Acad. Arts and Scis., Am. law Inst. Home: 15 Oakway Scarsdale NY 10583 Office: Columbia U Law Sch 435 W 116th St New York NY 10027-7201

ROSENTHAL, AMNON, pediatric cardiologist; b. Gedera, Israel, July 14, 1934; came to U.S., 1949, naturalized, 1959; s. Joseph and Rivka Rosenthal; m. Prudence Lloyd, July 22, 1962; children: Jonathan, Eben, Nathaniel. M.D., Albany Med. Coll., 1959. Intern Buffalo Children's Hosp., 1959-60; resident in pediatrics Children's Hosp. Med. Center, Boston, 1960-62; resident in pediatric cardiology Children's Hosp. Med. Center, 1965-68; asso. prof. pediatrics Children's Hosp. Med. Center and Harvard U. Med. Sch., Boston, 1975-77; dir. pediatric cardiology, prof. pediatrics C.S. Mott Children's Hosp., U. Mich., Ann Arbor, 1977—, assoc. dir. dept. pediatrics, 1989-92. Served to capt. M.C. USAF, 1962-65. Amnon Rosenthal endowed professorship U. Mich., 1994. Mem. Am. Acad. Pediatrics, Soc. for Pediatric Rsch., Am. Pediatric Soc., Am. Heart Assn., Am. Coll. Cardiology, Am. Bd. Pediatrics, Am. Bd. Pediatric Cardiology (chmn. 1987-88). Office: CS Mott Children's Hosp Ann Arbor MI 48109-0204

ROSENTHAL, ANDREW, newspaper editor. Washington bur. editor N.Y. Times. Office: The NY Times Washington Bur 1627 Eye St NW 7th fl Washington DC 20006°

ROSENTHAL, ARNOLD H., film director, producer, writer, graphic designer; b. Chgo., Jan. 31, 1933; s. Gus and Sara (Ariel) R.; children: Michel, Jason, Anthony. B.A., U. Ill., 1954. Graphic designer Whitaker-

Guernsey Studios, Chgo., 1954-55; art dir. Edward H. Weiss Advt., Chgo., 1956-60; owner Arnold H. Rosenthal & Assos., Chgo., 1960-70; partner, creative dir., pres. Meyer & Rosenthal Inc. (mktg. communications), Chgo., 1970-75; sr. v.p., creative dir. Garfield-Linn & Co. (Advt.), Chgo., 1975-81; pres., exec. producer/dir. Film Chicago div. Rosenthal Prodns., Inc., 1981—; TV jury chmn. Chgo. Internat. Film Festival, 1977, 78, 79, 87, mem. governing bd., 1984—, represented at Moscow Film Fest, 1990; TV jury chmn. U.S. Festival, 1980; lectr. Columbia Coll., Purdue U., U. Ill., Ohio State U. Contbr. articles to profl. publs. Bd. dirs. Jewish United Fund. Served with AUS, 1955-56. Recipient creative awards Communication Clubs Chgo., N.Y.C., 1960—, Silver medal N.Y. Film Festival, 1986, Clio award, 1981. Mem. Soc. Typographic Arts (design awards 1958—, pres. 1971-72), Am. Inst. Graphic Arts (spl. award 1974), Dirs. Guild Am., Jazz Inst. Chgo. (charter, jazz drummer), Tau Epsilon Phi, Alpha Delta Sigma.

ROSENTHAL, ARTHUR JESSE, publisher; b. N.Y.C., Sept. 26, 1919; s. Arthur J. and Grace (Ellinger) R.; m. Margaret Ann Roth, Dec. 12, 1975; children: James, Kathryn, Paul. BA, Yale U., 1941; postgrad., Harvard U. Bus. Sch., 1942. Spl. asst. to U.S. ambassador to Israel, Jerusalem, 1948; pres., editor in chief Basic Books, Inc., N.Y.C., 1949-72; dir. Harvard U. Press, Cambridge, 1972-90; pub. Hill and Wang, N.Y.C., 1990—; founding trustee Bank St. Coll. Edn., 1952-68. Editorial bd.: Pub. Interest, 1961-72, Harvard Bus. Rev, Family Process. Trustee Austen Riggs Center, Stockbridge, Mass., Nat. Commn. on Resources for Youth. Served to capt., M.I. U.S. Army, 1942-46. Clubs: Century Assn. (N.Y.C.); St. Botolph (Boston).

ROSENTHAL, CHARLES MICHAEL, financial executive; b. Bklyn., Nov. 21, 1935; s. David B. and Edna (Cohen) R.; m. Eva F. Sonnenberg, July 7, 1963; children: Andrea (dec.), Nicole. BA, Colgate U., 1957. Rsch. asst. Fed. Res. Bank N.Y., N.Y.C., 1960-62; v.p. L.M. Rosenthal & Co., Inc., 1962-74; ptnr. 1st Manhattan Co., N.Y.C., 1974—. Trustee Brown U., Providence, 1992—. Capt. USAF, 1957-60. Mem. Investment Assn. N.Y., Security Traders Assn. N.Y., Am. Coun. on Germany, East Hampton Tennis Club. Jewish. Home: 784 Park Ave New York NY 10021-3553 Office: 1st Manhattan Co 437 Madison Ave New York NY 10022-7001

ROSENTHAL, DAVID, physician; b. Phila., Sept. 30, 1929; m.; Suzanne Rosenthal; children: Michael, Samuel, Abrielle. Student, Julliard Sch. Music, 1948-49, George Washington U., 1953-54, Temple U., 1954-56; DO, Phila. Coll. Osteopathic Med., 1960. Diplomate Am. Bd. Osteopathic Rehabilitation Medicine. Internship Youngstown (Ohio) Osteopathic Hosp., 1960-61; resident VA Hosp. U. Pa., 1970-73; asst. medical dir. Moss Rehabilitation Hosp., Phila., 1974-77; gen. practice Phila., 1960-70; chmn. div. physical medicine & rehabilitation Suburban Gen. Hosp., Norristown, Pa., 1977—; medical dir. Medical Ctr. Performing Artists, Norristown, Pa., 1984—; medical dir. The Rehab Station, Norristown, Pa., 1988—, exec. dir., 1994—; asst. instr. in physical medicine & rehabilitation U. Pa., 1972-73, asst. prof., Temple U., 1973-77, asst. clinical prof., 1977—, Phila. Coll. Ostopathic Medicine, Phila., 1978-81, adj. clinical prof., N.Y. Coll., 1980-84, clinical assoc. prof. Phila. Coll., 1981—; hosp. affiliation Moss Rehabilitation Hosp., Albert Einstein Medical Ctr., Frankford Hosp., Suburban Gen. Hosp.; chmn. Medical Audit Com. Moss Rehabilitation Hosp., 1974-77, chmn. medical records com., 1974-77. Contbr. articles to profl. jours. Profl. Standards Review Orgn. Health Systems of South Eastern Pa., 1977-82; cons. to com. Rehabilitation and Spl. Devices Food and Drug Adminstrn., 1979-84, panel mem. com. 1979-84. Mem. Am. Osteopathic Assn., Pa. Osteopathic Medical Assn., Dist. X Pa. Osteopathic Medical Assn., Am. Osteopathic Coll. Rehabilitation Medicine (trustee 1975-79, vice chmn. 1977-78, pres. 1979-80, past pres. 1980-81), Am. Congress Rehabilitation Medicine, Phila. Soc. Physical Medicine and Rehabilitation (sec.-treas. 1975-76, v.p. 1975-77, pres. 1977-78), Am. Geriatrics Soc., Pan-Am. Medical Assn., Am. Coll. Sports Medicine, Am. Osteopathic Acad. Sports Medicine, Am. Acad. Clinical Neurophysiology. Home: 210 W Rittenhouse Sq Apt 2506 Philadelphia PA 19103 Office: Physiatric Assn Ltd 2705 Dekalb Pike Norristown PA 19401-1852

ROSENTHAL, DONALD B., political scientist, educator; b. N.Y.C., July 14, 1937; s. Max and Bessie Dora (Silverman) R. AB, Bklyn. Coll., 1958; AM, U. Chgo., 1960, PhD, 1964. Asst. prof. polit. sci. SUNY, Buffalo, 1964-68, assoc. prof., 1968-72, prof., 1972—, chmn. dept., 1978-80, 86-91. Author: The Limited Elite, 1970, The Expansive Elite, 1977, (monograph) Sticking Points and Ploys in Federal-Local Relations, 1979; Urban Housing and Neighborhood Revitalization, 1988; co-author: The Politics of Community Conflict, 1969, (monograph) Local Power and Comparative Politics, 1974; editor: The City in Indian Politics, 1976, Urban Revitalization, 1980; contbr. articles to profl. jours. Fellow Am. Inst. Indian Studies, 1963-64, 70, Nat. Assn. Schs. Pub. Affairs and Adminstrn., 1977-78, Rockefeller Inst., 1983; NSF grantee, 1974-75. Mem. Am. Polit. Sci. Assn., Am. Soc. Pub. Adminstrn. Democrat. Jewish. Office: SUNY Buffalo Amherst Campus Dept of Polit Sci Buffalo NY 14260

ROSENTHAL, DOUGLAS EURICO, lawyer, author; b. N.Y.C., Feb. 12, 1940; s. Jacob and Edna Louise (Muir) R.; m. Erica Switzen Kremen, Nov. 12, 1967; children: Benjamin Muir, Rachel Elizabeth. BA summa cum laude, Yale U., 1961, LLB, 1966, PhD in Polit. Sci, 1970; postgrad., Oxford (Eng.) U., 1962; MA, Columbia U., 1963. Bar: N.Y. 1968, U.S. Supreme Ct. 1976, D.C. 1980. Project dir. Russell Sage Found., N.Y.C., 1968-70; assoc. Fried, Frank, Harris, Shriver & Jacobson, N.Y.C., 1970-74; asst. chief fgn. commerce sect., antitrust div. Dept. Justice, Washington, 1974-77, chief, 1977-80; ptnr. Sutherland, Asbill & Brennan, Washington, 1980-88, Coudert Bros., 1989-94, Sonnenschein, Nath & Rosenthal, Washington, 1994—; reporter Am. Law Inst.-Am. Bar Assn. Model Lawyer Peer Rev. System, 1980; adj. prof. Tokyo U. Law Sch., 1992; speaker USIA, Australia, Eng., Can., Fed. Republic Germany, Japan; escrow agt., Boesky settlement funds paid to U.S. Govt. Author: (with Baker and others) Antitrust Guide for International Operations, 1977, Lawyer and Client: Who's in Charge?, 1974, 2d rev. edit., 1977, (with Knighton) National Law and International Commerce: The Problem of Extraterritoriality, 1982, Competition Policy in Hufbauer, Europe 1992: An American Perspective, 1990; chmn. bd. advisors Euro Watch; mem. bd. advisors Antitrust and Trade Regulation Reporter, George Washington Jour. Law and Econs., Can. Competition Policy Record; contbr. articles to profl. publs. Committeeman Nassau County (N.Y.) Dem. Com., 1963-65; lifetime mem. corp. Culinary Inst. Am. Recipient Edward S. Corwin award Am. Polit. Sci. Assn., 1971; Henry fellow Balliol Coll., Oxford U., 1962, Nobel Internat. fellow and Woodrow Wilson fellow Columbia U., 1963. Mem. ABA (internat. law, litigation and antitrust sect.), Coun. on Fgn. Rels., The European Inst., Am. Law Inst. (adv. com. law governing lawyers), Confrerie des Chevaliers du Tastevin, Oxford and Cambridge Club, Mory's Assn., Phi Beta Kappa. Jewish. Office: Ste 600 1301 K St NW Washington DC 20005

ROSENTHAL, EARL EDGAR, art history educator; b. Milw., Aug. 26, 1921; s. Edgar Ernst and Reneé (Wyler) R. B.S., U. Wis. at, Milw., 1943; Ph.D., NYU, 1953; Doctor honoris causa, U. Granada, 1994. Asst. dir. Milw. Art Inst., also Layton Art Gallery, Milw., 1952-53; vis. lectr., dept. art history U. Chgo., from 1953, prof., 1968-91, prof. emeritus, 1991—. Author: The Cathedral of Granada, 1961; The Palace of Charles V in Granada, 1985, translated to Spanish 1988, Arquitectura imperial, 1988. Contbr. articles to profl. publs. Served to lt. (j.g.) USNR, 1943-46, PTO. Recipient Gold medal in Fine Arts King of Spain, 1989, medal of honor Fundación Rodríguez Acosta (Granada), 1989; Spanish govt. grantee, 1948-49; Fulbright grantee Italy, 1949-50; Fulbright grantee Spain, 1963-64; Guggenheim grantee Italy, 1963-64. Mem. Hispanic Soc. Am., Coll. Art Assn., Soc. Archtl. Historians (dir. 1957-58, 66-69), Academia de San Fernando (Madrid) (corr.), Academia de Bellas Artes (Granada) (corr.). Office: Cochrane-Woods Art Center 5540 S Greenwood Ave Chicago IL 60637-1506

ROSENTHAL, FRANZ, language educator; b. Berlin, Aug. 31, 1914; came to U.S., 1940, naturalized, 1943; s. Kurt W. and Elsa (Kirschstein) R. Ph.D., U. Berlin, 1935; DHL (hon.), Hebrew Union Coll.; PhD (hon.), Hebrew U., Tel Aviv U., U. Tübingen. Asst. prof. Semitic langs. Hebrew Union Coll., Cin., 1940-48; prof. Arabic, U. Pa., 1948-56; Louis M. Rabinowitz prof. Yale U., 1956-67, Sterling prof. Near Eastern Langs., 1967-85, prof. emeritus, 1985—. Author: Aramaistische Forschung, 1939, Technique and Approach of Muslim Scholarship, 1947, Hist. of Muslim Historiography, 1952, Humor in Early Islam, 1956, Ibn Khaldun, The Muqaddimah, 1958, The Muslim Concept of Freedom, 1960, Fortleben der Antike im Islam,

1965, Knowledge Triumphant, 1970, The Herb: Hashish versus Medieval Muslim Society, 1971, Gambling in Islam, 1975, Sweeter than Hope, 1983, History of al-Tabari 38, 1985, 89, Muslim Intellectual and Social History: A Collection of Essays, 1990. Served with AUS, OSS, 1943-45. Fellow AAAS, Brit. Acad. (corr.); mem. Am. Philos. Soc., Am. Oriental Soc. (pres. 1964-65), Accademia Nazionale dei Lincei, Société Asiatique (hon.), Deutsche Morgenländische Ges. Home: 80 Heloise St Hamden CT 06517-3422

ROSENTHAL, HAROLD LESLIE, biochemistry educator; b. Elizabeth, N.J., Mar. 26, 1922; s. Isadore and Sophia (Shapiro) R.; m. Rose Schwartz, June 7, 1947; children: Jenifer Ann, Pamela Susan. B.Sc., U. N. Mex., 1944; Ph.D., Rutgers U., 1951. Rsch. asst. Rutgers U., New Brunswick, N.J., 1948-51; instr. Tulane U., New Orleans, 1951-53; chief biochemist Rochester Gen. Hosp., N.Y., 1953-58; prof. biomed. scis. Washington U., St. Louis, 1958-87, prof. emeritus, 1987—; vis. scientist Minerva Found., Finland, 1966, Nat. Acad. Sci., Hungary, 1974. Served with USN, 1943-46. Fellow AAAS; mem. Am. Chem. Soc. (emeritus), Am. Inst. Nutrition, Am. Soc. for Biochemistry and Molecular Biology, Sigma Xi. Avocations: gardening; oenology. Home: 7541 Teasdale Ave Saint Louis MO 63130-3923

ROSENTHAL, HELEN NAGELBERG, county official, advocate; b. N.Y.C., June 6, 1926; d. Alfred and Esther (Teichholz) Nagelberg; m. Albert S. Rosenthal, Apr. 10, 1949; children: Lisa Rosenthal Michaels, Apryl Meredith Rosenthal Stuppler. BS, CUNY, 1948; MA, NYU, 1950; postgrad., Adelphia U., L.I. U., Lehman Coll., 1975. Cert. early childhood and gifted edn. tchr., N.Y., N.J., elem. and secondary tchr., Fla. Tchr. gifted students N.Y. Bd Edn., Bklyn., 1949-77, 79-87, Baldwin (N.Y.) Pub. Schs., 1977-79; rep. community affairs County of Dade, Fla., 1988-92; ret., 1992. Author: Criteria for Selection and Curriculum for the Gifted, 1977, Science Experiments for Young Children, 1982, Music in the Air...and in Our Minds. Dir. Condominium, 1989-91. Recipient Departmental award, 1948. Mem. CCEGT (officer), AGATE, AICR, Bklyn. Coll. Alumni Assn. (pres. Dade and Broward counties 1995-96).

ROSENTHAL, HOWARD LEWIS, political science educator; b. Wilkinsburg, Pa., Mar. 4, 1939; s. Arnold Sidney R. and Elinor (Kaufman) (Rosenthal) Lewis; m. Annie Regine Lunel, June 30, 1960 (div. Nov., 1967); children: Illia Rebecca, Jean Laurent; m. Margherita Guastoni Spampinato, Feb. 6, 1968; 1 son, Gil Guastoni. B.S., MIT, 1960, Ph.D., 1964. Asst. prof. polit. sci. U. Calif.-Irvine, 1965-66; asst. prof. and assoc. prof. polit. sci. Carnegie-Mellon U., Pitts., 1966-71, prof., 1971-93; Roger Williams Straus prof. social scis. Princeton U., N.J., 1993—; vis. prof. Hebrew U., Jerusalem, 1968-69, U. Calif., San Diego, 1976-77, MIT, Cambridge, 1989-90, U. Paris I, 1990; vis. grad. lectr. Fondation Nat. des Scis. Politiques, Paris, 1972-73. Author: Prediction Analysis of Cross Classifications, 1977, Analysis of Ordinal Data, 1977, Partisan Politics, Divided Government and the Economy, 1994; mem. editorial bd. Pub. Choice, Econs. and Politics. Fellow NSF, 1969-92; fellow Ford Found., 1972-73, Social Sci. Rsch. Coun., 1964-65; Nat. fellow Hoover Instn., Stanford U., 1979-80; Sherman Fairchild disting. scholar Calif. Inst. Tech., 1982-83; fellow Internat. Ctr. for Econ. Rsch., Turin, Italy, 1991-93, Ctr. for Advanced Study in the Behavioral Scis., 1991-92, ECARE U. Libre de Brussels (Belgium), 1995. Fellow Am. Acad. Arts and Scis.; mem. Pub. Choice Soc. (Duncan Black award 1979), Am. Polit. Sci. Assn. (CQ Press award 1985), French Polit. Sci. Assn. Office: Princeton Univ Politics Dept Princeton NJ 08544

ROSENTHAL, IMRE, financial company executive. Chmn. bd. Rosenthal Inc., N.Y.C., 1964—. Office: Rosenthal Inc 1370 Broadway New York NY 10018

ROSENTHAL, IRA MAURICE, pediatrician, educator; b. N.Y.C., June 11, 1920; s. Abraham Leon and Jean (Kalotkin) R.; m. Ethel Ginsburg, Oct. 17, 1943; children: Anne, Judith. Student, CCNY, 1936-38; A.B., Ind. U., 1940, M.D., 1943. Intern Lincoln Hosp., N.Y.C., 1943-44; resident in pathology Albert Einstein Hosp., Phila., 1947-48; resident in pediatrics Fordham Hosp., N.Y.C., 1948-49; practice medicine specializing in pediatrics Bklyn., 1950-52; instr. U. Ill. Coll. Medicine, Chgo., 1953; asst. prof. U. Ill. Coll. Medicine, 1953-55, assoc. prof., 1955-63, prof. pediatrics, 1963-90, prof. emeritus, 1990—, head dept., 1973-82; clin. prof. pediatrics Stritch Sch. Medicine Loyola U., Chgo., 1990-91, lectr., 1991-93; clin. assoc. in pediatrics U. Chgo., 1990-91, clin. prof. pediatrics, 1991—; mem. med. service adv. com. Nat. Found. March of Dimes, 1975-80. Served to capt. U.S. Army, 1944-46. Mem. Am. Pediatric Soc., Soc. Pediatric Research, Acad. Pediatrics, Lawson Wilkins Pediatric Endocrine Soc., Endocrine Soc. Home: 5490 S South Shore Dr Chicago IL 60615-5984 Office: U Chgo Dept Pediatrics 5841 S Maryland Ave # 118 Chicago IL 60637-1463

ROSENTHAL, JACK, broadcasting executive; b. Chgo., Aug. 7, 1930; s. Samuel J. and Celia (Weinberg) R.; m. Elaine Lois Brill, May 2, 1954; children: Michael Bruce, Robert Joseph, Richard Scott. BA in History, U. Wyo., 1952, LLD (hon.), 1993. Sec. treas. Buffalo Theatre Corp., 1952-57, No. Wyo. Broadcasting Corp., 1957-64; v.p., gen. mgr. Sta. KTWO Radio and TV, Casper, Wyo., 1964-69; exec. v.p. Harriscope Broadcasting Corp., 1969-77; pres. broadcast div. Harriscope Broadcasting Corp., Los Angeles, 1977-87; pres. Wyo. Radio Network, 1987—, Clear Channel Radio, Inc., 1988—; chmn. Wyo. industry adv. com. FCC; dir. Wyo. Nat. Bank, Affiliated Bank Corp. of Wyo.; dir. TV Info. Office, 1984; designer U.S. Postage stamps 15 cent Buffalo Bill Cody, 1988, 25 cent Wyo. Centennial commemorative, 1990, 29 cent Oreg. Trail Commemorative, 1993; mem. ct. of honor World Stamp Expo '89, World Columbian Expo 1992, ct. of honor, Granada, Spain, 1992. Producer (TV film) Conrad Schwiering-Mountain Painter (Western Heritage award 1974). Mem. Wyo. Travel Commn., 1969-71, Wyo. Land and Water Commn., 1965-66, Yellowstone Nat. Park Centennial Commn., 1972, Wyo. Coun. Arts, 1969, City of Casper Art Fund, 1979-80; bd. dirs. Milward Simpson Endowment, U. Wyo. Found., 1970—; adv. Nat. Park Svc. Dept. Interior, 1974-76; mem. jud. planning com. Wyo. Supreme Ct., 1976-77; mem. citizens stamp adv. com. U.S. Postal Svc., 1985-89, chmn. 1990-92; trustee The Philatelic Found.; advisor, Nat. Postal Mus. Smithsonian Inst., 1993—. Served to 1st lt. U.S. Army, 1952-54, Korea. Recipient Alfred I. DuPont Found. award broadcast journalism, 1965, U.S. Conf. Mayors award for outstanding community service, 1966, Disting. Alumnus award U. Wyo., 1982, Commendation Casper C. of C., 1984, Disting. Alumnus award Coll. Arts and Scis., U. Wyo., 1991, chmn. football centennial, 1993; named hon. mem. Shoshoni and Arapahoe Indian Tribes, 1965. Mem. Nat. Assn. Broadcasters (nat. chmn. TV and radio polit. action com. 1977-79, Grover C. Cobb meml. award 1983), Wyo. Assn. Broadcasters (pres. 1963), Rocky Mountain States Ednl. TV Com. Office: 150 Nichols Ave Casper WY 82601-1816

ROSENTHAL, JACOB (JACK ROSENTHAL), newspaper editor; b. Tel-Aviv, June 18, 1935; came to U.S., 1938, naturalized, 1945; s. Manfred and Rachel (Kaplan) R.; m. Holly Russell, Dec. 21, 1985; children by previous marriage: John, Ann; stepchildren: Christopher Russell, Andrew Russell. A.B., Harvard U., 1956. Reporter, editor Portland Oregonian, Reporter, 1950-61; asst. dir., dir. public info. U.S. Dept. Justice, Washington, 1961-66; exec. asst. to Undersec. of State, 1966-67; Kennedy fellow Harvard Inst. Politics, 1967-68; nat. urban corr. Life Mag., N.Y.C., 1968-69; urban corr. N.Y. Times, Washington, 1969-73; asst. Sun. editor, mag. editor N.Y. Times, N.Y.C., 1973-77, dep. editorial page editor, 1977-86, editorial page editor, 1986-93; mag. editor, 1993—. Prin. author: Kerner Commn. Report on Urban Riots, 1968. Mem. Harvard Crimson Grad. Bd. Recipient Best Editorial award Internat. Labor Press Assn., 1961, Loeb award, 1973, Pulitzer prize for editorials, 1982. Office: NY Times Co 229 W 43rd St New York NY 10036-3913

ROSENTHAL, JAMES D., government and non-profit executive, former U.S. ambassador; b. San Francisco, Jan. 15, 1932. B.A., Stanford U., 1954; student Fgn. Service Inst., 1960-61, Nat War Coll., 1974-75. With U.S. Fgn. Service, 1956-90, adminstrv. officer, Port of Spain, Trinidad, 1958-60; polit officer, Saigon, Vietnam, 1961-65; faculty U.S. Mil. Acad., 1965-67; internat. relations officer Vietnam affairs Dept. State, 1967-70; mem. U.S. dele. to Vietnam Peace Talks, Paris, 1970-72; dep. chief of mission, Bangui, 1972-74; dir. Vietnam, Laos and Cambodia affairs Dept. State, 1975-77; dep. chief of mission Kuala Lumpur, Malaysia, 1977-79; dep chief mission, Manila, 1979-83; ambassador to Guinea, Conakry, 1983-86, dep. dir. mgmt. ops. Dept. State, Washington, 1986-90; exec. dir. Commonwealth Club of Calif.,

1990—. Office: Commonwealth Club of Calif 595 Market St San Francisco CA 94105-2802

ROSENTHAL, JULIAN BERNARD, lawyer, association executive; b. N.Y.C., July 4, 1908; s. Alex Sidney and Katherine (Goodman) R.; m. Frances Stone, Nov. 14, 1941; children—Brian, John L. Student, Columbia, 1925-26; LL.B., Fordham U., 1929. Bar: N.Y. 1931. Practiced in N.Y.C., 1931-72, Ga., 1972-78; mem. firm Javits & Javits, 1968-72, of counsel, 1972-74; mem. Air Force Assn., 1945—, life mem., 1946—, sec., 1946-59, chmn. bd. dirs., 1959-60, chmn. constn. com., 1946-71, chmn. resolutions com., 1946-61, permanent bd. dirs., 1960-84, dir. emeritus, 1984—; chmn. bd. dirs. Aerospace Edn. Council, N.Y.C., 1965-73; mem. Atlanta consumer adv. panel Gulf Oil Corp.; Govt. appeal agent SSS, 1943-44; chmn. steering com., Ga. joint legis. com. Am. Assn. Ret. Persons-Nat. Ret. Tchrs. Assn., 1975-78, mem. Ariz. joint state legis. com., 1978-81; mem. motion picture div. Dem. Nat. Com., 1940; past treas., dir. Lydia M. Morrison Found.; former sec. bd. dirs. Herbert I. and Shirley C. Rosenthal Found.; former v.p., treas., dir. Vanguard Found.; past trustee, sec. Aerospace Edn. Found.; mem. tech. adv. com. Health Planning Agy., Ga., 1987. Vol. legal aide North Cen. Legal Assistance Program, Durham, N.C., 1990—. Served with USAAF, 1944-45. Recipient Man of Year award Air Force Assn., 1953. Mem. ABA, Am. Assn. Ret. Persons (mem. nat. legis. adv. com. 1977, capitol task force Ga. 1987-89). Address: 2701 Pickett Rd Apt 4014 Durham NC 27705

ROSENTHAL, LEE H., federal judge; b. Nov. 30, 1952; m. Gary L. Rosenthal; children: Rebecca, Hannah, Jessica, Rachel. BA in Philosophy with honors, U. Chgo., 1974, JD with honors, 1977. Bar: Tex. 1979. Law clk. to Hon. John R. Brown U.S. Ct. Appeals (5th cir.), 1977-78; assoc. Baker & Botts, 1978-86, ptnr., 1986-92; judge U.S. Dist. Ct. (so. dist.) Tex., 1992—. Editor topics and comments Law Rev. U. Chgo., 1977-78. Active vis. com. Law Sch. U. Chgo., 1983-86, 94—; mem. devel. coun. Tex. Children's Hosp., 1988-92; pres. Epilepsy Assn. Houston/Gulf Coast, 1989-91; trustee Briarwood Sch. Endowment Found., 1991-92; bd. dirs. Epilepsy Found. Am., 1993—. Fellow Tex. Bar Found.; mem. ABA, Am. Law Inst., Texas Bar Assn., Houston Bar Assn. Office: US Dist Ct US Courthouse Rm 8631 515 Rusk Ave Houston TX 77002

ROSENTHAL, LEIGHTON A., aviation company executive; b. Buffalo, Jan. 27, 1915; s. Samuel and Sadie (Dosberg) R.; m. Honey Rousuck, June 30, 1940; children: Cynthia, Jane. Student, Phila. Textile Sch.; grad. Wharton Sch., U. Pa.; hon. doctorate, Cleve. Coll. Jewish Studies, 1973. Pres. Cleve. Overall Co., 1956-61, Work Wear Corp., 1961-86, The Purity Uniform Service Inc., 1986-89, Lars Mgmt. div. Purity Uniform Service Inc., 1986-89, Lars Aviation Inc., 1990—; chmn. architecture com. City of Palm Beach. Trustee Jewish Community Fedn. Cleve., Leighton A. Rosenthal Family Found., Samuel Rosenthal Found., Preservation Found. Palm Beach; bd. dirs. Ohio Motorists Assn. Fellow Am. Assn. Jewish Edn., Oakwood Club, Union Club, Poinciana Club, Marks Club, Annabels Club. Office: Lars Aviation Inc 1228 Euclid Ave Ste 310 The Halle Bldg Cleveland OH 44115

ROSENTHAL, LUCY GABRIELLE, writer, editor, educator; b. N.Y.C.; d. Henry Moses and Rachel (Tchernowitz) R. AB, U. Mich., 1954; MS in Journalism, Columbia U., 1955; MFA, Yale Sch. Drama, 1961; postgrad. Writers Workshop, U. Iowa, 1965-68. Asst. editor Radiology mag., Detroit, 1955-57; free-lance editorial cons. various pub. houses, lit. agts. N.Y.C., 1957-73; mem. admissions staff U. Iowa Writers Workshop, Iowa City, 1965-68; editor Book-of-the-Month Club, N.Y.C., 1973-74, mem. editorial bd. judges, 1974-79; sr. editorial advisor Book-of-the-Month Club, 1979-87; mem. biography jury Pulitzer Prize, 1980; mem. bd. Am. Book Awards, 1981-82; adj. prof. English, NYU, 1986—; mem. guest faculty in writing Sarah Lawrence Coll., 1988—; lectr. writing program Columbia U. Sch. Gen. Studies, 1990—, Humanities faculty, 92nd St. YM/YWCA, 1987; fiction workshop The Writer's Voice, West Side YMCA, summer 1991; adj. prof. NYU Sch. Continuing Edn., 1988; mem. faculty Sarah Lawrence Ctr. for Continuing Edn., 1989, 90; instr. fiction writing course Art Workshop Internat., Assisi, Italy, summer 1993. Plays produced at Eugene O'Neill Meml. Theater Ctr., 1966, 67; author: The Ticket Out, 1983; editor: Great American Love Stories, 1988, The World Treasury of Love Stories, 1995; contbr. articles and revs. to various mags. and periodicals including Washington Post and Chgo. Tribune Book World, Saturday Rev., Ms. mag., Mich. Quar. Rev., N.Y. Times Book Rev. Pulitzer fellow critical writing, 1968. Mem. Authors Guild, Authors League, Nat. Book Critics Circle, Women's Media Group (bd. mem. 1979-81), PEN, Associated Writing Programs, Eugene O'Neill Meml. Theater Ctr., Phi Beta Kappa, Phi Kappa Phi. Office: care of Wendy Weil Agy Inc 232 Madison Ave Ste 1300 New York NY 10016-2901

ROSENTHAL, LYOVA HASKELL See GRANT, LEE

ROSENTHAL, MACHA LOUIS, author, educator; b. Washington, Mar. 14, 1917; s. Jacob and Ethel (Brown) R.; m. Victoria Himmelstein, Jan. 7, 1939; children: David, Alan, Laura. B.A., U. Chgo., 1937, M.A., 1938; Ph.D., N.Y. U., 1949. Faculty Mich. State U., 1939-45; faculty NYU, N.Y.C., 1945—; prof. NYU, 1961-87, English prof. emeritus, 1987—; Moss chair of excellence in English Memphis State U. (now Memphis U.), 1989; founder, dir. NYU Poetics Inst., 1977-79; poetry editor The Nation, 1956-61, Humanist, 1970-78, Present Tense, 1973-91; vis. specialist U.S. Cultural Exchange Programs, Germany, 1961, Pakistan, 1965, Poland, Rumania, Bulgaria, 1966, Italy and France, 1980, 88; lectr. New Zealand univs., 1989; vis. prof. U. Pa., 1974, U. Zurich, 1984, U. Bologna, 1995; vis. poet, Israel, 1974, Yugoslavia, 1980, World Poetry Festival, Can., 1993; Disting. Scholar Exchange Program, China, 1982, World Poetry Festival, Toronto, 1993; dir. summer seminar NEH, 1981, 83, dir. NEH Inst., 1985; mem. adv. com. Nat. Book Com., 1964-67; mem. Bollingen award com. 1968-70; chmn. Delmore Schwartz Meml. award, 1970—; mem. creative arts awards lit. jury Brandeis U., 1976. Author: (with A.J.M. Smith) Exploring Poetry, 1955, 73, The Modern Poets: A Critical Introduction, 1960, A Primer of Ezra Pound, 1960, Blue Boy on Skates: Poems, 1964, The New Poets: American and British Poetry since World War II, 1967, Beyond Power: New Poems, 1969, The View from the Peacock's Tail: Poems, 1972, Randall Jarrell, 1972, Poetry and the Common Life, 1974, 83, She: A Sequence of Poems, 1977, Sailing into the Unknown: Yeats, Pound, and Eliot, 1978, Poems, 1964-80, 1981, (with Sally M. Gall) The Modern Poetic Sequence: The Genius of Modern Poetry, 1983, Be The Poet's Art, 1987, As for Love: Poems and Translations, 1987, Our Life in Poetry: Selected Essays and Reviews, 1991, Running to Paradise: Yeats' Poetic Art, 1994; editor: The Macmillan Paperback Poets, 1957-62; Selected Poems and Two Plays of W.B. Yeats, 1962, 73, The William Carlos Williams Reader, 1966, The New Modern Poetry: An Anthology of American and British Poetry since World War II, 1967, 69, 100 Postwar Poems, British and American, 1968, Selected Poems and Three Plays of William Butler Yeats, 1986; co-editor: Chief Modern Poets of Britain and America, 1970; gen. editor Poetry in English: An Anthology, 1987; editor Persea Books Lamplighters Series, 1982-92, Works-in-Progress (issue Ploughshares mag.), 1991; translator: The Adventures of Pinocchio: Tale of a Puppet, 1983; poetry adviser Macmillan Co., 1957-62; contbr. articles and poems to profl. publs. Recipient Explicator Found. award, 1984, 1st Yeats Soc. award for Disting. Contbns. to Yeats Scholarship, 1993; Fellow Am. Coun. Learned Socs., 1942, 50-51, Guggenheim Found., 1960-61, 64-65, Rockefeller Found. Rsch Ctr., Bellagio, Italy, 1988. Mem. AAUP, MLA, PEN, Poetry Soc. Am. (v.p. 1989-92), Am. Lit. Assn., Yeats Soc., Phi Beta Kappa. Home: 17 Bayard Ln Suffern NY 10901 Office: NYU Dept English 19 University Pl New York NY 10003-4501

ROSENTHAL, MARK ELLIOTT, hospital administrator; b. Columbus, Ohio, May 30, 1952; s. Bert L. and Betty L. (Robbins) R.; m. Phyllis Bidnick, Aug. 3, 1975; children—Heather, Emily. B.A. in Pre-med. Sci., U. Mo., 1974, M.S. in Pub. Health-Health Services Mgmt., 1977. Adminstrv. staff asst. Meml. Med. Ctr., Springfield, Ill., 1977-79, adminstrv. dir. phys. medicine and rehab., 1979-81; adminstr. Rehab. Inst. Okla.-Oklahoma City, 1981-83; assoc. adminstr. Dallas Rehab. Inst., 1983-86, COO, 1986-89; adminstr. Rehab. Hosp. Austin, 1989; adminstr., CEO CPC Capital Hosp., 1990-93; asst. adminstr. rehab. svcs. & adminstrn. Ctr. Rehab. Medicine Emory U., 1993—; regents adv. bd. ACHE, 1993—; bd dirs GARF, 1993—, adminstrv. surgeon, 1993—; sec. GAHE, 1995; mem. consumer cons. com. Tex. Rehab. Commn., 1983-85; mem. nat. adv. com. Commn.

Accreditation of Rehab. Facilities; mem. Ill. Gov's. steering com. Internat. Yr. Disabled Persons, 1981, chmn. Springfield Mayor's Exec. Com., 1981; mem. Plano Cable TV Adv. Bd., Tex., 1984-86. Named one of Outstanding Young Men of Am., 1982. Fellow Am. Coll. Healthcare Execs.; mem. Assn. Med. Rehab. Dirs. and Coordinators (Tex. Lone Star region rep. 1984), Am. Hosp. Assn., U. Mo. Grad. Studies Health Svcs. Mgmt. Alumni Assn. Jewish. Avocations: golf, water sports, photography, computers. Office: Emory Univ Hosp 1441 Clifton Rd NE Atlanta GA 30322

ROSENTHAL, MARTHA NEWMAN, museum executive; b. N.Y.C., Oct. 8, 1956; d. Norman and Janice (Newman) R.; m. Adorno Sclano, Mar. 2, 1978 (div.). B.A., Sarah Lawrence Coll., 1978. Jr. copywriter McCann-Erickson, Inc., N.Y.C., 1978-80; office mgr. Ed Libonati Prodns. Inc., N.Y.C., 1980-82; dir. spl. events and pub. relations Sch. Am. Ballet, N.Y.C., 1982-85; spl. cons., assoc. dir. of jr. council and new ballet audiences of Am. Ballet Theatre, N.Y.C., 1986, asst. dir., 1986-87; dir. Sch. Classical Ballet of Am. Ballet Theatre, N.Y.C., 1987-91; exec. devel. officer Cooper-Hewitt Mus., Nat. Mus. Design, Smithsonian Inst., N.Y.C., 1991—. Writer, editor, designer newsletters, 1982; writer, designer mailing pieces, 1982; editor, designer advt. jour., 1985. Club: Doubles. Avocations: travel, languages, cultural institutions.

ROSENTHAL, MARVIN BERNARD, pediatrician, educator; b. Bklyn., Jan. 1, 1930; s. Robert Alexander and Barbara (Gartner) Rosenthal Dreyfuss; m. Janet H. Swerlick, dec. 31, 1959; 1 child, Robert G. BA, Alfred U., 1951; MD, Leiden U., The Netherlands, 1957. Diplomate Nat. Bd. Med. Examiners, Am. Bd. Pediatrics. Intern Kings County Hosp., Bklyn., 1957-58, resident in pediatrics, 1958-60; fellow in hematology Children's Hosp. Phila., 1962; pediatrician Somerset Pediatric Group, Bridgewater, N.J., 1963-84; chief pediatrics Somerset Hosp., Somerville, N.J., 1983-84; assoc. dir. family practice residency Warren Hosp., Phillipsburg, N.J., 1984—; chief pediatrics, 1991—, dir. med. edn., sec.-treas. hosp. staff; mem. cons. staff Morristown (N.J.) Meml. Hosp., 1989—; clin. assoc. prof. Robert W. Johnson Med. Sch., New Brunswick, N.J., 1980—; mem. adj. faculty U. New England Coll. Osteopathics, Biddeford, Maine, 1988. Capt. USAF, 1960-62. Recipient Silver medallion Am. Heart Assn., 1976, 78. Fellow Am. Acad. Pediatrics, Am. Acad. Family Practice; mem. N.J. Med. Soc., Acad. Medicine N.J., N.J. Pediatric Soc., Warren County Med. Soc., Tchrs. Family Medicine, Ambulatory Pediatric Assn., Assn. Hosp. Med. Educators, Eagle Scout Assn. Home: 500 Spring Valley Rd Easton PA 18042-6872 Office: Warren Hosp Roseberry St Phillipsburg NJ 08865-1628

ROSENTHAL, MEYER L(OUIS), lawyer; b. Wilkes-Barre, Pa., May 27, 1944; s. Samuel J. and Lottie G. (Goncher) R; m. Susan M., Aug. 19, 1967; children: Norman, Bonnie. BA, Rutgers U., 1966, JD, 1969. Bar: N.J. 1969, U.S. Dist. Ct. N.J. 1969, Calif. 1975, U.S. Dist. Ct. (cen. dist.) Calif. 1981, U.S. Dist. Ct. (ea. dist.) N.Y. 1980, U.S. Dist. Ct. (so. dist.) N.Y. 1981, U.S. Ct. Appeals (9th cir.) 1981. Law sec. Hon. Leon Milmed N.J. Superior Ct., Newark, 1969-70; assoc. Kaufman & Kaufman, Elizabeth, N.J., 1970-76; ptnr. Trueger & Rosenthal, Morristown, N.J., 1976-82; atty. pvt. practice, Morristown, N.J., 1982—. Editor Rutgers Law Rev. Cub scout leader Morris Area Boy Scouts Am., Randolph, N.J., 1980; chmn. Morris City Human Rels. Commn., Morristown, 1992—. Mem. Comml. Law League Am., Calif. Bar Assn., N.J. Bar Assn., B'nai B'rith (bd. govs. 1975—, pres. dist. 3 1988-89, Internat. Young Leadership award 1982, Internat. Founders award 1985). Office: 161 Washington St Morristown NJ 07960-3753

ROSENTHAL, MICHAEL ROSS, academic administrator, dean; b. Youngstown, Ohio, Dec. 2, 1939; s. Samuel Herman and Frances Vance (Schlesinger) R.; m. Linda Gabler, Sept. 6, 1963; children: Heidi, Erika, Nicolas Gabler. AB, Case Western Res. U., 1961; MS, U. Ill., 1963, PhD, 1965. Asst. prof. chemistry Bard Coll., Annandale, N.Y., 1965-68, assoc. prof. chemistry, 1968-73, prof. chemistry, 1973-84, assoc. dean acad. affairs, 1980-84; v.p. acad. affairs St. Mary's Coll. of Md., St. Mary's City, 1984-89; provost, dean faculty, prof. chemistry Southwestern U., Georgetown, Tex., 1989—; acad. cons. and. and as rep. of Assn. Am. Colls. Author or co-author of numerous articles in jours. of inorganic chemistry and chem. edn. Chmn. Environ. Mgmt. Coun., Dutchess County, N.Y., 1978-84; founding chmn. Heritage Task Force for Hudson River Valley, 1980-84; pres., bd. dirs. Hudson River Heritage, N.Y., 1978-84; bd. dirs. Hudson River Rsch. Coun., 1976-84; teaching assoc. Danforth Found., 1980. Recipient Outstanding Community Svc. award, Dutchess County (N.Y.) Legislature, 1980. Mem. Am. Chem. Soc., The Royal Society (Chemistry, London), Am. Conf. Acad. Deans, Hudson River Environ. Soc., Sigma Xi, Phi Beta Kappa, Phi Lambda Upsilon. Democrat. Office: Southwestern U Office of Provost PO Box 770 Georgetown TX 78627-0770

ROSENTHAL, MILTON FREDERICK, minerals and chemical company executive; b. N.Y.C., Nov. 24, 1913; s. Jacob C. and Louise (Berger) R.; m. Frieda Bojar, Feb. 28, 1943; 1 child, Anne Rosenthal Mitro. BA, CCNY, 1932; LLB, Columbia U., 1935. Bar: N.Y. 1935. Rsch. asst. N.Y. State Law Revision Commn., 1935-37; law sec. Fed. Judge William Bondy, 1937-40; assoc. atty. Leve, Hecht & Hadfield, 1940-42; sec., treas. Hugo Stinnes Corp., 1946-48, exec. v.p., treas., 1948-49, pres., dir., chief exec. officer, 1949-64; pres., dir., chief exec. officer Minerals and Chems. Philipp Corp., N.Y.C., 1964-67; pres., dir., COO Engelhard Minerals & Chem. Corp., N.Y.C., 1967-71; chmn., pres., CEO, dir. Engelhard Minerals & Chems. Corp., N.Y.C., 1971-81. Trustee Mt. Sinai Med. Ctr. and Mt. Sinai Hosp.; bd. dirs. United Cerebral Palsy Rsch. and Ednl. Found., Inc.; ret. trustee Am. Fedn. Arts, Manhattanville Coll., Purchase Coll. Found. 1st lt. JAG dept. U.S. Army, 1942-45. Mem. Assn. of Bar of City of N.Y., Chgo. Bar Assn., Columbia Law Sch. Alumni Assn., Judge Adv. Assn., Phi Beta Kappa. Home: 450 Woodlands Rd Harrison NY 10528-1220 Office: 450 Park Ave Ste 2701 New York NY 10022-2605

ROSENTHAL, MURRAY WILFORD, chemical engineer, science administrator; b. Greenville, Miss., Feb. 25, 1926; s. Monnie and Esther (Bernstein) R.; m. Miriam Sylvia Teplit, Aug. 7, 1949; children: Elaine, Douglas I. B-SChemE, La. State U., 1949; PhDChemE, MIT, 1953. Devel. engr. heat transfer rsch., reactor exptl. engring. div. Oak Ridge (Tenn.) Nat. Lab., 1953-55, group leader aqueous homogeneous reactor analysis, 1955-59, group leader analysis advanced reactors, reactor div., 1959-61, project engr., 1961-63, chief planning and analysis sect., 1963-65, dir. planning, 1965, dir. molten salt reactor program, 1966-73, acting dep. dir., 1973, assoc. dir. advanced energy systems, 1974-89, dep. dir., 1989-93, lectr. in reactor engring. sch. reactor tech., 1955; cons., 1994—; vis. prof. chem. engring. MIT, Boston, 1961; tech. asst. to asst. gen. mgr. AEC, Washington, 1966. Vice chmn. Oak Ridge Charter Commn., 1955-56, chmn., 1962-63; mem. Oak Ridge Human Rels. Adv. Bd., 1963-65, Adv. Task Force on Tenn. Energy Future, Oak Ridge, 1978. Lt. (j.g.) USN, 1943-46. Recipient Disting. Career award Fusion Power Assocs., 1993, Disting. Svc. award Nat. Mgmt. Assn., 1994; inducted into Engring. Hall of Distinction, La. State U., 1982; Humble fellow MIT, 1950, Std. Oil fellow, 1951, Pan Am. fellow, 1952. Fellow Am. Nuclear Soc. (bd. dirs. 1970-73, exec. com. 1971-73); mem. NAE, AAAS, Sigma Xi. Home: 124 Carnegie Dr Oak Ridge TN 37830-7732

ROSENTHAL, MYRON MARTIN, retired electrical engineer, educator; author; b. Bklyn., Nov. 5, 1930; s. Murray Morris and Selma Locke (Belsky) R.; m. Charlene Powell, Sept. 16, 1989; children from previous marriage: Lynn, Debbie, Richard; stepchildren: Christi Ackerson, Michael Ackerson. BEE, CCNY, 1953; MS, Adelphi U., 1957. Registered profl. engr., N.J., Pa., N.J. Sr. engr. Republic Aviation Corp., Farmingdale, L.I., 1955-61; pres. Myron M. Rosenthal & Staff, Farmingdale, L.I., 1957-61; program mgr. Loral Electronics, Bronx, N.Y., 1962-64; engring. mgr. Singer-Kearfott div. The Singer Co., Wayne, N.J., 1964-87 prof. Poly. U., Bklyn., N.J., 1954-87; bd. dirs. Electronics and Aerospace Conv., 1971-82, treas., 1972-82, chmn. bd., 1974; bd. dirs. Nat. Aerospace and Electronics Conf., 1972-75; notary pub., N.J., N.Y., Fla. Patentee inflatable antenna, cylindrical flat plate 35 GHz antenna, rotating lens antenna seeker-head. Founder Randal Carter PTA cultural workshop, Wayne, 1965; lighting commr. Wayne, 1956. Recipient Picatinny Arsenal U.S. Army Engring. and Leadership commendations, 1969, 71, 73; Poly. U. N.Y. faculty award, 1975 Disting. Faculty award, 1982; Nat. Aerospace and Electronics Conf. award, 1968, 75, 76; Electronics and Aerospace Conv. award, 1974, 80, 82; Poly Service award, 1984. Mem. IEEE (sr. mem., award 1972, 74, Centennial medal 1984, life), NSPE, AIAA, ASME, ASCE, ASTM, Illuminating Engring. Soc., Am. Assn. Clin. Chemistry, Am. Inst. Indsl. Engrs., Audio Engring. Soc., Cincinatus Soc., Forest Products Rsch. Soc., Am. Inst. Chemists, Nat. Fire Protection Assn., Nat. Rehab. Assn., Assn. U.S. Army, Navy League, U.S. Naval Inst., Marine Corps Assn., Am. Def. Preparedness Assn., Air Force Assn., Aerospace Electronics and Systems Soc. (bd. govs. 1968-82, v.p. 1972, chmn. N.Y.-N.J. Met. chpt. 1972-82, Disting. Service award 1974, 79, 82), Armed Forces Communications and Electronics Assn., AAUP, N.Y. Acad. Sci., Am. Soc. Indsl. Security, Am. Chem. Soc., Am. Assn. Physics Tchrs., Am. Physics Soc., Am. Soc. Safety Engrs. (profl. mem.), Am. Vocat. Assn. (life), Constrn. Specifications Inst., Am. Soc. Public Adminstrn., Am. Public Works Assn., Am. Assn. Cost Engrs., Am. Ceramic Soc., Nat. Mgmt. Assn. (certified), Nat. Council Tchrs. of Math., Nat. Council Tchrs. of English, Adult Edn. Assn., Inst. Cert. Profl. Mgrs. (cert.), Am. Radio Relay League, Nat. Assn. Accts., Nat. Soc. Public Accts., ALA, Soc. Automotive Engrs., Am. Craft Council, Nat. Soc. Architects, Am. Soc. Interior Design, Nat. Sci. Tchrs. Assn., Soc. Plastics Engrs., Audio Engring. Soc., Internat. Assn. Assessing Officers, Am. Hist. Assn., Am. Philos. Assn., MLA, Inst. of Nav. (program com. 1978), Am. Judicature Soc., Aircraft Owners and Pilots Assn., Refrigeration Service Engrs. Soc., AAAS, Boat Owners Assn., Am. Assn. Higher Edn., Nat. Aeros. Assn., Nat. Assn. Social Workers, Nat. Council Young Israel, Am. Rose Soc., Nat. Audubon Soc., Am. Sch. of Deaf, Nat. Eye Research Found., Am. Council for Blind, Am. Diabetes Assn., Nat. Rehab. Assn., Am. Jewish Congress, Workmen's Circle, Am. Council Museums, Triple Nine Soc., Mensa, Intertel, Am. Nuclear Soc., Gold Coast Amateur Radio Club, United Otomy Assn., Sigma Xi, Eta Kappa Nu. Republican. Jewish. Clubs: B'nai B'rith (trustee 1976-77), Toastmasters (pres. 1969, areas gov. 1970, best speaker of the year 1967, 68, 69, 75, 77). Avocation: amateur radio operator. Home: 6858 Giralda Cir Boca Raton FL 33433-7734

ROSENTHAL, NAN, curator, author; b. N.Y.C., Aug. 27, 1937; d. Alan Herman and Lenore (Fry) R.; m. Otto Piene (div.); m. Henry Benning Cortesi, Sept. 5, 1990. BA, Sarah Lawrence Coll., 1959; MA, Harvard U., 1970, PhD, 1976. Asst. prof. art history U. Calif., Santa Cruz, 1971-77, assoc. prof., 1977-84, prof., 1985-86, chair dept. art history, 1976-80; curator 20th-century art Nat. Gallery Art, Washington, 1985-92; cons. Dept. of 20th Century Art, Metro. Mus. of Art, N.Y.C., 1993—; vis. prof. art history Fordham U., Lincoln Ctr., 1981, 85; vis. scholar N.Y. Inst. for Humanities, NYU, 1982-83; vis. lectr. visual arts Princeton U., 1985, 88, 92. Author: George Rickey, 1977; also exhbn. catalogues, catalogue essays and articles; art editor Show, 1963-64; assoc. editor, then editor at large and contbg. editor Art in Am., 1964-70. Radcliffe Inst. fellow, 1968-69, scholar, 1970-71; travelling fellow Harvard U., 1973-74, rsch. fellow U. Calif., 1978, Ailsa Mellon Bruce curatorial fellow Nat. Gallery of Art, 1988-89; rsch. and travel grantee U. Calif., Santa Cruz, 1974, 77-80, 82-85. Office: Met Mus of Art 20th Century Art 1000 Fifth Ave New York NY 10028-0113

ROSENTHAL, PAUL EDMOND, lawyer; b. Miami, May 1, 1951; s. David and Helen (Kaplan) R. BA, U. Fla., 1973, JD, 1976. Bar: Fla. 1977, U.S. Dist. Ct. (mid. dist.) Fla. 1977. Asst. city atty. City of Orlando (Fla.), 1977-79, asst. to mayor and council, 1979-80; assoc. Van den Berg, Gay & Burke, Orlando, 1980-81; ptnr. Van den Berg, Gay, Burke, Wilson & Arkin, Orlando, 1982-85, Foley & Lardner, Orlando, 1985—; mem., chmn. 9th Jud. Cir. Nominating Commn., Orlando, 1984-88; atty. City of Ocoee, Fla., 1988—. Mem. ABA, Orange County Bar Assn., Delta Upsilon (sec. alumni club). Democrat. Jewish. Office: Foley & Lardner 111 N Orange Ave Ste 1800 Orlando FL 32801-4801

ROSENTHAL, PETER, public relations executive; b. N.Y.C., Nov. 1, 1946; s. Walter and Rita (Horn) R.; m. Terri Thompson; children: Daniel, Joel. BA, Lehman Coll., 1969; MA, Ball State U., 1972. Tchr., N.Y.C. Bd. Edn., 1969-71; reporter Bklyn. Today, 1972-73; asst. dir. pub. rels. St. Vincents Hosp., N.Y.C., 1973-76; account exec. Howard Rubenstein Assocs. N.Y.C., 1976-78, v.p., 1978-81, sr. v.p., 1981-84, exec. v.p., 1984-87, sr. exec. v.p., 1987—. Mem. Internat. Assn. Bus. Communications, Nat. Assn. Real Estate Editors, Nat. Assn. Real Estate Investment Trust, Urban Land Inst. (assoc.) Jewish. Avocations: reading, theater, travel. Office: Howard J Rubenstein Assocs Inc 1345 Avenue Of The Americas New York NY 10105-0010

ROSENTHAL, RICHARD SCOTT, information management company executive; b. Phila., July 21, 1952; s. Stanley and Irene Marlyn (Yeager) R.; m. Arlen Sue Morris, Oct. 3, 1982; children: Rachel Ilise, Lisa Danielle. BA, Bowling Green State U., 1974, MA, 1976. Lectr., instr. criminal justice U. Md., College Park, 1977-80; cons. U.S. Dept. Justice, Washington, 1978; mgr. Aspen Systems Corp., Rockville, Md., 1980-85, v.p. justice programs, 1985—. Mem. Montgomery County (Md.) Juvenile Ct. Com., Rockville, 1984-90. Office: Aspen Systems Corp 1600 Research Blvd Rockville MD 20850

ROSENTHAL, ROBERT, psychology educator; b. Giessen, Germany, Mar. 2, 1933; came to U.S., 1940, naturalized, 1946; s. Julius and Hermine (Kahn) R.; m. Mary Lu Clayton, Apr. 20, 1951; children: Roberta, David C., Virginia. A.B., UCLA, 1953, Ph.D., 1956. Diplomate: clin. psychology Am. Bd. Examiners Profl. Psychology. Clin. psychology trainee Los Angeles Area VA, 1954-57; lectr. U. So. Calif., 1956-57; acting instr. UCLA, 1957; from asst. to assoc. prof., coordinator clin. tng. U. N.D., 1957-62; vis. assoc. prof. Ohio State U., 1960-61; lectr. Boston U., 1965-66; lectr. clin. psychology Harvard U., Cambridge, Mass., 1962-67, prof. social psychology, 1967—, chmn. dept. psychology, 1992-95. Author: Experimenter Effects in Behavioral Research, 1966, enlarged edit., 1976, (with Lenore Jacobson) Pygmalion in the Classroom, expanded edit., 1992, Meta-analytic Procedures for Social Research, 1984, rev. edit., 1991, Judgement Studies, 1987; (with others) New Directions in Psychology 4, 1970, Sensitivity to Nonverbal Communication: The Pons Test, 1979; (with Ralph L. Rosnow) The Volunteer Subject, 1975, Primer of Methods for the Behavioral Sciences, 1975, Essentials of Behavioral Research, 1984, 2d edit., 1991, Understanding Behavioral Science, 1984, Contrast Analysis, 1985, Beginning Behavioral Research, 1993; (with Brian Mullen) BASIC Meta-analysis, 1985; editor: (with Ralph L. Rosnow) Artifact in Behavioral Research, 1969, Skill in Nonverbal Communication, 1979, Quantitative Assessment of Research Domains, 1980, (with Thomas A. Sebeok) The Clever Hans Phenomenon: Communication with Horses, Whales, Apes and People, 1981, (with Blanck and Buck) Nonverbal Communication in the Clinical Context, 1986, (with Gheorghiu, Netter, and Eysenck) Suggestion and Suggestibility: Theory and Research, 1989. Recipient Donald Campbell award Soc. for Personality and Social Psychology, 1988, James McKeen Cattell Sabbatical award, 1995-96; Guggenheim fellow, 1973-74, fellow Ctr. for Advanced Study in Behavioral Scis., 1988-89; sr. Fulbright scholar, 1972. Fellow AAAS, (co-recipient Sociopsychol. prize 1960, co-recipient Behavioral Sci. Rsch. prize 1993), APA (co-recipient Cattell Fund awrd 1967), Am. Psychol. Soc.; mem. Soc. Exptl. Social Psychology, Ea. Psychol. Assn. (Disting. lectr. 1989), Midwestern Psychol. Assn., Mass. Psychol. Assn. (Disting. Career Contbn. award 1979), Soc. Projective Techniques (past treas.), Phi Beta Kappa, Sigma Xi. Home: 12 Phinney Rd Lexington MA 02173-7717 Office: Harvard U 33 Kirkland St Cambridge MA 02138-2044

ROSENTHAL, ROBERT JON, newspaper editor, journalist; b. N.Y.C., Aug. 5, 1948; s. Irving and Ruth (Moss) R.; m. Inez Katherina von Sternenfels, Nov. 22, 1985; children: Adam, Benjamin. BA, U. Vt., 1970. Lectr. journalism N.Y. Times, N.Y.C., 1970-73; reporter Boston Globe, 1974-79; reporter Phila. Inquirer, 1979-82, Africa corr., Nairobi, Kenya, 1982-86, fgn. editor, Phila., 1986-91, city editor, 1991-93, asst. mng. editor, daily, 1993—. Recipient Third World Reporting award Nat. Assn. Black Journalists, 1983, Mag. award Overseas Press Club, 1985, Disting. Fgn. Corr. award Sigma Delta Chi, 1985, Mag. Writing award World Population Inst., 1986. Avocations: sports, painting, fishing, cooking. Office: Phila Inquirer 400 N Broad St Philadelphia PA 19130-4099

ROSENTHAL, ROBERT M., automotive sales executive; b. 1928. Pres. Rosenthal Chevrolet Co., Arlington, Va., 1954—; CEO Rosenthal Cos., Arlington, 1978—. Office: Rosenthal Cos Ste 700 1550 Wilson Blvd Arlington VA 22209

ROSENTHAL, SOL, lawyer; b. Balt., Oct. 17, 1934; s. Louis and Hattie (Getz) R.; m. Diane Myra Sackler, June 11, 1961; children: Karen Abby, Pamela Margaret, Robert Joel. AB, Princeton U., 1956; JD, Harvard U., 1959. Bar: Calif. 1961. Law clk. to chief judge U.S. Ct. Appeals, 4th cir., Balt., 1959-60; assoc. Kaplan, Livingston, Goodwin, Berkowitz & Selvin, Beverly Hills, Calif., 1960-66, ptnr., 1966-74; ptnr. Buchalter, Nemer, Fields & Younger, L.A., 1974—; bd. dirs. Playboy Enterprises, Inc., Chgo.; arbitrator Dirs. Guild Am., L.A., 1976—, Writers Guild Am., L.A., 1976—, Am. Film Mktg. Assn., 1989—; negotiator Writers Guild-Assn. Talent Agts., L.A., 1978—. Founder Camp Ronald McDonald for Good Times, L.A., 1985; charter founder Mus. Contemporary Art, L.A., 1988. Mem. ABA, Calif. Bar Assn., L.A. County Bar Assn. (trustee 1981-82), L.A. Copyright Soc. (pres. 1973-74), Acad. TV Arts and Scis. (bd. govs. 1990-92), Beverly Hills Bar Assn. (pres. 1982-83), Phi Beta Kappa. Office: Buchalter Nemer et al Ste 2400 1801 Century Park E Los Angeles CA 90067-2326

ROSENTHAL, SOL ROY, preventive medicine educator, researcher; b. Tyktin, Russia; naturalized; s. Harry and Sara E. (Kahn) R.; m. Dorothy Bobinsky, May 26, 1950 (div. 1972); children: Anthony J., Wendy Elizabeth; m. Lucy Donna Lough, Dec. 23, 1972 (div. 1984); children: Sara Lough, Sol Roy Jr. B.S., U. Ill.-Chgo., M.D., M.S., Ph.D. Diplomate Am. Bd. Pathology, Am. Bd. Clin. Pathology. Fellow Inst. Pasteur, France; fellow U. Freiburg, Germany; cons. USPHS, Chgo. Bd. Health; founder, dir. Research Found., Chgo.; dir. Inst. Tb Research, Chgo., Tice Lab., Chgo.; prof. preventive medicine U. Ill.-Chgo.; chmn. Internat. Com. BCG Vaccination Against Cancer and Leukemia. Author: BCG Vaccine: Cancer and Leukemia, 1980, Everybody Can't Be President: A Realistic Approach to Educating; contbr. articles to profl. jours. Originator Tuberculin Tine Test, Risk Exercise. Pres. People to People for Peace; founder, pres. Sr. for Jrs.; bd. dirs. Biennale de Paris; founder, chmn. Academia for the Arts. Mem. Am. Physiol. Soc., Soc. Exptl. Biology and Medicine, Am. Soc. Exptl. Pathology, Am. Thoracic Soc., Scripps Research Council, Sigma Xi, Alpha Omega Alpha. Club: Chicago Literary; Santa Fe Hunt (Rancho Santa Fe). Avocations: fox hunting, swimming, jogging, music.

ROSENTHAL, STANLEY LAWRENCE, meteorologist; b. Bklyn., Dec. 6, 1929; s. Louis and Fay (Pokorne) R.; m. Mildred Farlow, Aug. 8, 1953; children—Russell K., Sarah Lynn, David Scott. B.S., CCNY, 1951; M.S., Fla. State U., 1953, Ph.D., 1958. With NOAA, Dept. Commerce, 1960-93; chief theoretical studies group Nat. Hurricane Research Lab., Miami, Fla., 1960-75, chief modeling group, 1975-77, chief analytical and theoretical studies group, 1977-93, dir., 1980-93; dir. Nat. Hurricane and Exptl. Meterology Lab., 1977-80; dep. dir. Atlantic Oceanographic and Meteorol. Labs., 1981; sr. rsch. assoc. Coop. Inst. for Marine & Atmospheric Scis. U. Miami, 1993—; adj. prof. meteorology U. Miami, Coral Gables, Fla., 1964-84. Contbr. articles to profl. jours. Served with U.S. Army, 1953-55. Recipient Gold medal U.S. Dept. Commerce, 1970. Fellow Am. Meteorol. Soc. (council 1980-83), mem. com. on hurricanes and tropical meteorology 1981-85, past chmn. (Greater Miami br.), AAAS (past officer sect. W). Home: 13301 SW 99th Pl Miami FL 33176-6118 Office: Nat Hurrican Rsch Lab Hurricane Rsch Div 4301 Rickenbacker Cswy Miami FL 33149-1097

ROSENTHAL, STEVEN SIEGMUND, lawyer; b. Cleve., May 22, 1949; s. Fred Siegel and Natalie Josephine Rosenthal; m. Ilene Edwina Goldstein, Oct. 1, 1983. AB, Dartmouth Coll., 1971; JD, Harvard U., 1974. Bar: Fla. 1974, D.C. 1975, U.S. Supreme Ct. 1978, Calif. 1983. Law clk. U.S. Ct. Appeals (D.C. cir.), 1974-75; assoc. Covington & Burling, Washington, 1975-80; assoc. Morrison & Foerster, Washington, 1980-81, ptnr., 1981—; lawyer rep. Jud. Conf. D.C. Cir., 1981-83. Pres. Family and Child Services Washington, 1986-88, trustee, 1978—. Mem. ABA (chmn. banking, currency & treasury com. adminstrv. law sect. 1986-88), Am. Law Inst., Phi Beta Kappa. Republican. Office: Morrison & Foerster Ste 5500 2000 Pennsylvania Ave NW Washington DC 20006-1888

ROSENTHAL, STUART A., retail executive. Formerly sr. v.p. The Vons Cos. Inc., El Monte, Calif., now exec. v.p. mktg. Office: Vons Cos Inc PO Box 3338 Los Angeles CA 90051-1338

ROSENTHAL, TONY (BERNARD), sculptor; b. Highland Park, Ill., Aug. 9, 1914; s. Nathan H. and Bessie (Baumgarden) R.; m. Halina Kotlowicz, Apr. 2, 1946. AB, U. Mich., 1936; student, Art Inst. Chgo., Cranbrook Acad. Arts; hon. doctorate, Hofstra U., 1989. Exhbns. include Art Inst. Chgo., Met. Mus. Art, Mus. Modern Art, N.Y., Whitney Mus. Am. Art, N.Y.C., Pa. Acad. Fine Arts, Archtl. League, N.Y., Yale U., U. Ill., U. Nebr., 100 Biennale Exhbn., Sao Paulo, Brazil, Brussel's Fair, 1958, others; one man shows include San Francisco Mus, Western Mus. Assn. Travel Exhbn., Santa Barbara (Calif.) Mus., Long Beach (Calif.) Mus., Catherine Viviano Gallery N.Y., Kootz Gallery, N.Y.C., M. Knoedler & Co., Denise Rene Gallery, Paris, 1988, others; archtl. commn. include Temple Emanuel, Beverly Hills, Calif., 1955, IBM Bldg., 1958, Southland Ctr., Dallas, IBM Western Hdqrs., Los Angeles, Police Plaza, N.Y.C., Fullerton (Calif.) State Coll., Fin. Ctr. Pacific, Honolulu, Holocaust Meml., Buffalo, Metro-Rail Sta., Miami, S.E. Nat. Bank, Miami, Grove Isle, Miami, Met. Hosp., Phila., 1010 Lamar, Houston, Cranstrook Acad. Art, Bloomfield Hills, Mich., Steelpark 400 E. 80th St, N.Y.C., Alamo, Astor Pl., N.Y.C., Rondo, 111 E. 59th St., N.Y.C., U. Ind., Hofstra U., N.Y., others; works in permanent collections Milw. Art Ctr., Ill. State U., Los Angeles County Mus., Long Beach, Lincoln (Mass.) Mus., Ariz. State Coll., Mus. Modern Art, Whitney Mus. Art, Albright Knox Art Gallery, Buffalo, U. Ill., NYU, Yale U., Middelheim Mus., Antwerp, Belgium, Guggenheim Mus., N.Y.C., Hofstra U. Fashion Inst. Art, N.Y.C., others; pvt. collections. Served with AUS, 1942-46. Recipient awards, prizes San Francisco Mus., 1950, Los Angeles City Exhbn., 1951, 52, Audubon Artists, N.Y., 1953, Pa. Acad. Fine Arts, 1953, Los Angeles County Mus., 1950, 57, Santa Barbara Mus. Art, 1959, Art in Steel award Iron and Steel Inst., 1974-75, Disting. Alumni award U. Mich., 1977, Sculpture award Inst. Arts and Letters, N.Y.C., 1985. Address: 173 E 73rd St New York NY 10021-3510

ROSENTHAL, WILLIAM FORSHAW, advertising executive; b. St. Louis, Apr. 11, 1933; s. William Arthur and Elizabeth (Forshaw) R.; m. Carol Gage Johnson, Aug. 23, 1975. AB, Washington U., St. Louis, 1955. With Proctor & Gamble Co., 1957-59, D'Arcy-MacManus & Masius, 1960-85; sr. v.p., gen. mgr. Twin Cities office, Mpls., 1978-79; pres. D'Arcy-MacManus & Masius, N.Y.C., 1980-82, also dir., mem. worldwide planning group.; exec. v.p. D'Arcy-MacManus & Masius, World-wide, 1982-85; exec. v.p. Einson-Freeman, Paramus, N.J., 1985-90, also bd. dirs.; dir. bus. devel. Einson-Freeman, Paramus 1990—; sr. v.p. N.W. Ayer, N.Y.C., 1992—; exec. v.p. Dentsu divsn. Nova Promotion, 1993—, bd. dirs.; mem. compensation and long range planning coms. Einson-Freeman. Bd. dirs. Save African Endangered Wildlife. With AUS, 1955-57. Mem. Am. Assn. Advt. Agys. (mem. govt. affairs com., vice chmn. N.Y. council 1983, chmn. council 1984); Mem. Beta Theta Pi. Clubs: Tavern (Chgo.); Friars (N.Y.C.); Washington U. (St. Louis).

ROSENTHAL, WILLIAM J., lawyer; b. Balt., Nov. 4, 1920; s. Justin J. and Ray Marian (Stern) R.; m. Margaret Irwin Parker, July 4, 1956; children—Adriane Leigh, Jacqueline Rae, John Justin. AB, Johns Hopkins U., 1941; LL.B., U. Balt., 1950. Bar: Md. 1950. Adminstrv. asst. Office Price Adminstrn., Washington, 1941-42; assoc. firm Earle K. Shawe (name changed to Shawe & Rosenthal 1967), Balt., 1951-67; ptnr. Shawe & Rosenthal, Balt., 1967—; lectr. U. Balt., 1952-56; mem. regional adv. council NLRB; vets. rep. Md. Constrn. Adv. Council, 1946-49; lectr. NYU Conf. Labor Relations, Boston U. Labor Law Seminar, 1985; expert witness on labor law, legis. and congl. coms. Contbg. author: The Developing Labor Law; contbr. articles to profl. jours. Served to lt. USNR, 1942-46, ETO. Mem. ABA, Md. Bar Assn., Balt. Bar Assn., Spiked Shoe Soc., Omicron Delta Kappa, Pi Delta Epsilon. Club: Suburban of Baltimore County (bd. govs., pres.). Home: 8207 Cranwood Ct Baltimore MD 21208-1823 Office: Shawe & Rosenthal Sun Life Bldg Charles Center Baltimore MD 21201

ROSENWALD, E. JOHN, JR., brokerage house executive, investment banker; b. 1930. AB, Dartmouth Coll., 1952, MBA, 1953. With Bear Stearns Cos. Inc., N.Y.C., 1953—, past pres., vice-chmn., sr. mng. dir. Office: 245 Park Ave New York NY 10167-0001

ROSENWALD, WILLIAM, investment executive, philanthropist; b. Chgo., Aug. 19, 1903; s. Julius and Augusta (Nusbaum) R. B.S., Mass. Inst. Tech., 1924; student, Harvard Coll., 1924-25, London (Eng.) Sch. Econs. and Polit. Sci., 1925-27; hon. Dr. Hebrew Letters, Hebrew Union Coll., 1944; LL.D., Tuskegee Inst., 1964. Dir. Sears, Roebuck & Co., 1934-38; established W.R. Enterprises, 1936. Hon. v.p. Am. Jewish Joint Distbn. Com., Inc.; hon. pres. United Jewish Appeal-Fedn. Jewish Philanthropies N.Y. Inc.; life trustee, hon. nat. chmn. United Jewish Appeal, Inc.; life mem. bd. dirs. Coun. Jewish Fedns.; hon. v.p. Am. Jewish Com.; life mem., v.p. Hebrew Immigrant Aid Soc.; hon. trustee Tuskegee U.; hon. life trustee Mus. Sci. and Industry, Chgo.; gen. chmn. nat. United Jewish Appeal, 1954, 55, 56 Campaigns. Mem. Harmonie Club (N.Y.C.). Office: 122 E 42nd St New York NY 10168-0001

ROSENZWEIG, DAVID, newspaper editor; b. Jersey City, Feb. 17, 1940; s. Herbert and Ethel (Hinkes) Rosenzweig. B.A. in History, Rutgers U., 1961. Reporter Newark Star Ledger, N.J., 1962-63, Newark Evening News, N.J., 1963-64, AP, 1964-71; reporter L.A. Times, 1971-79, asst. met. editor, 1979-83, met. editor, 1983-89, asst. mng. editor, 1989—. Office: Los Angeles Times Times Mirror Sq Los Angeles CA 90012-3816

ROSENZWEIG, MARK RICHARD, psychology educator; b. Rochester, N.Y., Sept. 12, 1922; s. Jacob and Pearl (Grossman) R.; m. Janine S.A. Chappat, Aug. 1, 1947; children: Anne Janine, Suzanne Jacqueline, Philip Mark. B.A., U. Rochester, 1943, M.A., 1944; Ph.D., Harvard U., 1949; hon. doctorate, U. René Descartes, Sorbonne, 1980. Postdoctoral research fellow Harvard U., 1949-51; asst. prof. U. Calif., Berkeley, 1951-56; assoc. prof. U. Calif., 1956-60, prof. psychology, 1960-91, assoc. research prof., 1958-59, research prof., 1965-66, prof. emeritus, 1991—; vis. prof. biology Sorbonne, Paris, 1973-74; mem. exec. com. Internat. Union Psychol. Sci., 1972—, v.p. 1980-84, pres., 1988-92, past pres. 1992-96; mem. U.S. Nat. Com. for Internat. Union Psychol. Sci., NRC Nat. Acad. Sci., 1984—, chmn., 1984-88. Author: Biologie de la Mémoire, 1976, (with A.L. Leiman) Physiological Psychology, 1982, 2d edit., 1989, (with D. Sinha) La Recherche en Psychologie Scientifique, 1988; editor: (with P. Mussen) Psychology: An Introduction, 1973, 2d edit., 1977, (with E.L. Bennett) Neural Mechanisms of Learning and Memory, 1976, International Psychological Science: Progress, Problems, and Prospects, 1992; co-editor: (with L. Porter) Ann. Rev. of Psychology, 1968-94, (with M.J. Renner) Enriched and Impoverished Environments: Effects on Brain and Behavior, 1987; contbr. articles to profl. jours. Served with USN, 1944-46. Recipient Disting. Alumnus award U. Rochester; Fulbright research fellow; faculty research fellow Social Sci. Research Council, 1960-61; research grantee NSF, USPHS, Easter Seal Found., Nat. Inst. Drug Abuse. Fellow AAAS, APA (Disting. Sci. Contbn. award 1982), Am. Psychol. Soc.; mem. NAS, NAACP (life), Am. Physiol. Soc., Am. Psychol. Soc., Internat. Brain Rsch. Orgn., Soc. Exptl. Psychologists, Soc. for Neurosci., Société Française de Psychologie, Sierra Club (life), Common Cause, Fulbright Assn. (life), Phi Beta Kappa, Sigma Xi. Office: U Calif Dept Psychology 3210 Tolman Hall Berkeley CA 94720-1650

ROSENZWEIG, MARK RICHARD, economist, educator; b. N.Y.C., Apr. 19, 1947; s. Israel and Bertha (Resnick) R. BA, Columbia Coll., 1969; MA, Columbia U., 1971, PhD with distinction, 1973. Asst. prof. economics Yale U., New Haven, 1973-78, asst. dir. Econ. Growth Ctr., 1978-79, assoc. prof. economics, 1978-79; dir. rsch. Select Commn. on Immigration and Refugee Policy, Washington, 1979-80; vis. fellow Office of Population Rsch. Princeton (N.J.) U., 1976-77; assoc. prof. economics U. Minn., 1979-82, co-dir. Econ. Devel. Ctr., 1982-90, prof. economics, 1982-90; rsch. assoc. Population Studies Ctr. U. Pa., Phila., 1990—, prof. economics, 1990—; chair Behavioral Medicine Ad Hoc Rev. Panel, NIH, 1987, AIDS Rsch. Ad Hoc Rev. Panel, 1988; lectr. Dvid Horowitz Inst., Tel Aviv U., 1989, Upjohn Inst., We. Mich. U., 1992; Wei Lun vis. prof. Chinese U. Hong Kong, 1995. Author: Contractual Arrangements, Employment and Wages in Rural Labor Markets: A Critical Review, 1982, The New Chosen People: Immigrants in the United States, 1990; editor: The Theory and Experience of Economic Development: Essays in Honor of Sir W. Arthur Lewis, 1982, Contractual Arrangements, Employment and Wages in Rural Labor Markets in South Asia, 1984, Handbook of Population and Family Economics, 1995; contbr. numerous articles and papers to profl. publs. Recipient Herbert H. Lehman fellowship in Social Scis., 1969-73; Columbia U. Faculty fellowship, 1969-73, Woodrow Wilson Dissertation fellowship, 1971-72, NIH Rsch. Svc. award, 1976-77, Social Sci. Rsch. Coun. Rsch. Tng. fellowship, 1976-77; grantee Agy. for Internat. Devel., 1974-75, 76-78, 79-80, 79-82, 82-84, NIH, 1975-77, 78-85, 85-88, 86-88, 87-92, 90-94, 92-95, 93-97, NSF, 79-83, 93-97, Russell Sage Found., 1983-85, Rockefeller Found., 1985-86, 87-89, Ford Found., 1991-92. Fellow Econometric Soc. Office: U Pa Dept Econ 3718 Locust Walk Philadelphia PA 19104-6297

ROSENZWEIG, NORMAN, psychiatry educator; b. N.Y.C., Feb. 28, 1924; s. Jacob Arthur and Edna (Braman) R.; m. Carol Teneeves, Sept. 20, 1945; 1 child, Elizabeth Ann. MB, Chgo. Med. Sch., 1947, MD, 1948; MS, U. Mich., 1954. Diplomate Am. Bd. Psychiatry and Neurology. Asst. prof. psychiatry U. Mich., Ann Arbor, 1957-61, asst. prof., 1963-67, assoc. prof., 1967-73; prof. Wayne State U., Detroit, 1973—; chmn. dept. psychiat. Sch. Med. Wayne State U., Detroit, 1987-90, Sinai Hosp., Detroit, 1961-90; spl. cons., profl. advisor Oakland County Community Mental Health Services Bd., 1964-65; mem. protem med. adv. panel Herman Kiefer Hosp., Detroit, 1970, psychiat. task force N.W. Quadrangle Hosps., Detroit, 1971-78, planning com. mental health adv. council Dept. Mental Health State of Mich., Lansing, 1984-90, tech. adv.rsch. com., 1978-82; psychiat. bd. need task force Office Health and Med. Affairs State of Mich., 1980-84; bd. dirs. Alliance for Mental Health, Farmington Hills, Mich., 1986-94; speaker in field. Author: Community Mental Health Programs in England: An American View, 1975; co-editor: Psychopharmacology and Psychotherapy-Synthesis or Antithesis?, 1978, Sex Education for the Health Professional: A Curriculum Guide, 1978; contbr. articles to profl. jours. and chpts. to books. Mem. profl. adv. bd. The Orchards, Livonia, Mich., 1963. Served as capt. USAF, 1955-57. Recipient Appreciation and Merit cert. Mich. Soc. Psychiatry and Neurology, 1970-71, Career Svc. award Assn. Mental Health in Mich., 1994. Fellow Am. Coll. Mental Health Adminstrn., Am. Coll. Psychiatrists (hon. membership com., com. on regional ednl. programs, liaison officer to The Royal Australian and New Zealand Coll. Psychiatrists 1984-88), Am. Psychiat. Assn. (life fellow, coun. on internat. affairs 1979-79, chmn. 1973-76, assembly liaison to coun. on internat. affairs 1979-80, 82-84, reference com. 1973-76, nominating com. 1978-79, internat. affairs survey team 1973-74, assoc. representing Am. Psychiat. Assn. to Inter-Am. Coun. Psychiat. Assns 1973-75, treas. APA lifers 1991-94, v.p. 1994—, com. on sr. psychiatrists 1993—, others, Rush Gold Medal award 1974, cert. Commendation, 1973-76, 78-80, Warren Williams award 1986); mem. AAUP, AMA (Physician's Recognition award 1971, 74, 77, 80-81, 84, 87, 90, 92), Am. Assn. Dirs. Psychiat. Residency Tng. (nominating com. 1972-74, task force on core curriculum 1972-74), Am. Assn. Gen. Hosp. Psychiatry, Puerto Rico Med. Assn. (hon., presdl. award 1981), Am. Hosp. Assn. (governing coun. psychiat. svcs. sect. 1977-79, ad hoc com. on uniform mental health definitions, chmn. task force on psychiat. coverage under Nat. Health Ins. 1977-79, others), Brit. Soc. Clin. Psychiatrists (task force on gen. hosp. psychiatry 1969-74), Can. Psychiat. Assn., Mich. Assn. Professions, Mich. Hosp. Assn. (psychiat. and mental health svcs. com. 1979-81), Mich. Psychiat. Soc. (com. on ins. 1965-69, chmn. com. on community mental health svcs. 1967-68, chmn. com. on nominations of fellows 1972-73, mem. com. on budget 1973-74, task force on pornography 1973-74, chmn. commn. on health professions and groups 1974-75, pres. elect 1974-75, pres. 1975-76, chmn. com. on liaison with hosp. assns. 1979-81, chmn. subcom. on liaison with Am. Hosp. Assn. 1979-81, numerous others, Past Pres. plaque, 1978, cert. Recognition, 1980, Disting. Service award 1986), Mich. State Med. Soc. (vice chmn. sect. psychiatry 1972-73, chmn. sect. psychiatry 1974-75, mem. com. to improve membership 1977-78, alt. del for Mich. Psychiat. Soc. to Ho. of Dels. 1978-79, del. from Wayne County Med. Soc. to Mich. Med. Soc. Ho. of Dels. 1982-88), N.Y. Acad. Scis., Pan Am. Med. Assn., Wayne County Med. Soc. (com. on hosp. and prof. rels., 1983-84, com. on child health advocacy 1983-87, med. edn. com. 1983-87, mental health com. 1983-87), Royal Australian and New Zealand Coll. Psychiatrists (hon.), Indian Psychiat. Soc. (hon. corr.), World Psychiat. Assn., Sect. Gen. Hosp. Psychiat. Avocations:sic, films, reading. Home: 1234 Cedarholm Ln Bloomfield Hills MI 48302-0902 Office: 26211 Central Park Blvd Ste 60 Southfield MI 48076-4107

ROSENZWEIG, RICHARD STUART, publishing company executive; b. Appleton, Wis., Aug. 8, 1935; s. Walter J. and Rose (Bahcall) R. B.S., Northwestern U., 1957; Advanced Mgmt. Program, Harvard U., 1975. Credit rep. Dun & Bradstreet, Inc., 1958; with Playboy Enterprises, Inc., 1958—, exec. asst. to pres., 1963-73, sr. v.p., dir., 1973—, dir. mktg., 1974—, exec. v.p. publs. group, 1975-77, exec. v.p., head West Coast ops., 1977-80; exec. v.p. corp. affairs Playboy Enterprises, Inc., Los Angeles, 1980-82; exec. v.p., chmn. emeritus Playboy Enterprises, Inc., 1982—; pres. Playboy Jazz Festivals, 1989—; dir. I. Bahcall Industries, Appleton. Trustee L.A. Film Expn.; mem. 2d decade coun. Am. Film Inst.; bd. dirs. Mus. Contemporary Art, Chgo., Periodical and Book Assn. Am.; Internat. Inst. Kidney Diseases of UCLA, Children of Night, Maple Ctr. Beverly Hills; mem., chmn. bd. UCLA Legis. Network, Town Hall of Calif.; adv. bd. West Hollywood Mktg. Corp., 1985—; bd. dirs. So. Calif. ACLU, 1985—; mem. Los Angeles County Mus.; apptd. to blue ribbon com. project West Coast Gateway. With AUS, 1957. Recipient Do-ers award, 1988, Beverly Hills medal Beverly Hills City Coun., 1993. Mem. Am. Mktg. Aslsn., L.A. Pub. Affairs Officers Assn., UCLA Chancellor's Assocs., Pres.'s Cir., Beverly Hills C. of C. (bd. dirs., visitors' bur., v.p.), Beverly Hills Fine Art Commn. (chmn.), Beverly Hills Econ. Devel. Coun., Founders Circle of Music Ctr., Pub. Affairs Coun., Craft and Folk Art Mus., Pres.' Coun. and Contemporary ARts Coun. L.A. Mus. Contemporary Art, The Am. Cinematheque (groundbreaker), Variety Club So. Calif. (bd. dirs.). Office: Playboy Enterprises Inc 9242 Beverly Blvd Beverly Hills CA 90210

ROSENZWEIG, ROBERT MYRON, educational consultant; b. Detroit, Aug. 27, 1931; s. Louis and Gertrude (Lifsitz) R.; m. Adelle Ruth Rotman, Aug. 30, 1953; children—Kathryn Ann, David Michael. B.A., U. Mich., 1952, M.A., 1953; Ph.D., Yale U., 1956. Instr. polit. sci. Amherst Coll., 1955-57; with U.S. Office Edn., 1958-62, spl. asst. to commnr., 1961-62; assoc. dean Grad. Div., Stanford U., 1962-67, assoc. provost of univ., 1967-71, vice provost, adviser to pres., 1971-74, v.p. pub. affairs, 1974-83; pres. Assn. Am. Univs., Washington, 1983-93, pres. emeritus, 1993—; lectr. polit. sci. Grad. Div., Stanford U., 1963—; dir. Ctr. Rsch. Internat. Studies, 1967-68; chmn. steering com. Coalition for Advancement Fgn. Langs. and Internat. Studies, 1988-90. Author: (with H.D. Babbidge, Jr.) Federal Interest in Higher Education, 1962, The Research Universities and Their Patrons, 1982; also articles. Bd. dirs. CUNY Research Found., 1986—. Recipient Harvey Cushing Orator award Am. Assn. Neurol. Surgeons, 1984, Disting. Alumni award U. Mich., 1988. Mem. Assn. Ind. Calif. Colls. and Univs. (v.p. 1978-80, pres. 1980-82), Am. Polit. Sci. Assn. (coun. and adminstrv. com. 1987—), Coun. Fgn. Rels. Home and Office: 1462 Dana Ave Palo Alto CA 94301-3115

ROSENZWEIG, SAUL, psychologist, educator, administrator; b. Boston, Feb. 7, 1907; s. David and Etta (Tuttle) R.; m. Louise Ritterskamp, Mar. 21, 1941; children: Julia, Ann. A.B. summa cum laude, Harvard U., 1929, M.A., 1930, Ph.D., 1932. Research assoc. Harvard Psychol. Clinic, 1929-34, Worcester (Mass.) State Hosp., 1934-43; affiliate prof. Clark U., Worcester, 1938-43; chief psychologist Western State Psychiat. Ins. and Clinic, Pitts., 1943-48; lectr. psychology U. Pitts., 1943-48; assoc. prof. psychology and med. psychology Washington U., St. Louis, 1949-51; prof. Washington U., 1951-75, prof. emeritus, 1975—; chief psychologist Child Guidance Clinic, 1949-59; cons., mem. life scis. study sect. NIH, 1964-68; mng. dir. Found. for Idiodynamics and the Creative Process. Author: (with Kate L. Kogan) Psychodiagnosis, Grune and Stratton, 1949, Rosenzweig Picture-Frustration Study, 1948, Aggressive Behavior and the Rosenzweig Picture-Frustration Study, 1978, Freud and Experimental Psychology: The Emergence of Idiodynamics, 1986, Sally Beauchamp's Career, 1987, Freud, Jung, and Hall the King-Maker, 1992; assoc. editor: Jour. Abnormal and Social Psychology, 1950-56; cons. editor: Psychol. Monographs, 1948-57, Zeitschrift für Diagnostische Psychologie und Persönlichkeitsforschung, 1953-58, Diagnostica, 1959—; adv. editor: Cons. Psychology, 1959-64, Jour. Abnormal Psychology, 1965-67; mem. editorial bd. Aggressive Behavior, 1974—; contbr. articles to profl. jours. Fellow Am. Psychol. Assn. (rep. Internat. group for Coordination Psychiatry and Psychol. Methods 1955-61), Am. Psychopathol. Assn.; mem. Internat. Soc. for Research on Aggression (founding pres. 1972-73, archivist 1981-88), Soc. Prof. Emeriti Washington U. (founding pres. 1978), Sigma Xi, Phi Beta Kappa. Office: Washington U Box 1125 Saint Louis MO 63130

ROSETT, ANN DOYLE, librarian; b. Valdosta, Ga., Jan. 9, 1955; d. David Spencer Doyle and Lois Annette Gray; m. Robert Allen Richardson, Aug. 1, 1976 (div. June 1981); children: Caitlin Ann, Brendan Wesley; m. John David Rosett, Aug. 6, 1983. Student, Kenyon Coll., 1972-75, U. Dayton, 1974, U. Ala., Birmingham, 1978; BA, Shepherd Coll., 1982; MLS, U. Wash., 1988. Cert. profl. libr., Wash. College libr. Northwest Coll., Kirkland, Wash., 1988—. Mem. ALA, Assn. Christian Librs. (dir.-at-large 1992-93), Assn. Coll. and Rsch. Librs., Am. Theol. Lib. Assn., N.W. Assn. Christian Librs. (treas. 1989-91, pres. 1991-93). Democrat. Office: Northwest Coll DV Hurst Libr PO Box 579 5520 108th Ave NE Kirkland WA 98033-7523

ROSETT, ARTHUR IRWIN, lawyer, educator; b. N.Y.C., July 5, 1934; s. Milton B. and Bertha (Werner) R.; m. Rhonda K. Lawrence; children: David Benjamin, Martha Jean, Daniel Joseph. A.B., Columbia U., 1955, LL.B., 1959. Bar: Calif. 1968, N.Y. State 1960, U.S. Supreme Ct. 1963. Law clk. U.S. Supreme Ct., 1959-60; asst. U.S. atty. So. Dist. N.Y., 1960-63; practice law N.Y.C., 1963-65; assoc. dir. Pres.'s Commn. on Law Enforcement and Adminstrn. Justice, 1965-67; acting prof. law UCLA, 1967-70, prof., 1970—. Author: Contract Law and Its Application, 1971, 5th revised edit., 1994, (with D. Cressey) Justice by Consent, 1976, (with E. Dorff) A Living Tree, 1987. Served with USN, 1956-58. Mem. Am. Law Inst. Home: 641 S Saltair Ave Los Angeles CA 90049-4134 Office: UCLA Law Sch 405 Hilgard Ave Los Angeles CA 90024-1476

ROSETT, RICHARD NATHANIEL, economist, educator; b. Balt., Feb. 29, 1928; s. Walter and Essie (Stofberg) R.; m. Madelon Louise George, June 24, 1951; children: Claudia Anne, Martha Victoria, Joshua George, Sarah Elizabeth, Charles Richard. B.A., Columbia U., 1953; M.A., Yale U., 1954, Ph.D., 1957. Instr. Yale U., 1956-58; mem. faculty U. Rochester, 1958-74, chmn. dept. econs., 1966-74, prof. econs., 1967-74, prof. preventive medicine and community health, 1969-74; prof. bus. econs. Grad. Sch. Bus., U. Chgo., 1974-84, dean, 1974-83; dean Faculty Arts and Scis. Washington U., 1984-87, prof. econs., 1984-90; dean Coll. Bus. Rochester (N.Y.) Inst. Tech., 1990—; pres. U.S. Bus. Sch. in Prague, Inc., 1990—; bd. dirs. Hutchinson Techs., Inc., Lumbermans Mut. Ins. Co., Nat. Bur. Econ. Rsch., chmn., 1986-89, ORMEC; trustee Keuka Coll., 1992—. Editor: The Role of Health Insurance in the Health Services Sector, 1976; Contbr. articles to profl. jours. Bd. dirs. Nat. Bur. Econ. Rsch., 1986-89. With USNR, 1944-45. Mem. Am. Econ. Assn., Mont Pelerin Soc., Chgo. Club, Phi Beta Kappa, Beta Gamma Sigma. Home: 26 Whitestone Ln Rochester NY 14618-4118 Office: Rochester Inst Tech Office of Dean 107 Lomb Memorial Dr Rochester NY 14623-5608

ROSHON, GEORGE KENNETH, manufacturing company executive, b. Pottstown, Pa., July 30, 1942; s. George Washington III and Ellen Eleanor (Knopf) R.; B.S. in Elec. Engring., Pa. State U., 1964; M.S., Drexel U., Phila., 1974, postgrad., 1974-75; m. Ella Maye Barndt, Nov. 21, 1964; 1 child, Kirsten Renee. Sr. engr. Am. Electronics Labs., Inc., Colmar, Pa., 1966-69; v.p. engring. Acrodyne Industries, Inc., Montgomeryville, Pa., 1969-74; mgr. electric design W-J div. Hayes-Albion Corp., Norristown, Pa., 1974-78; mgr. quality assurance PSMBD, Gen. Electric Co., Phila., after 1978, mem. exec. com. electronics test council after 1980, mgr. advanced systems engring., 1983-84, mgr. communications engring., Malvern, Pa., 1984-86; v.p. quality assurance Hercules Aerospace Display Systems, Inc., Hatfield, Pa., 1986-88, v.p. engring., 1988-90; mgr. Electronics Group Westcode, Inc., Malvern, Pa., 1991-92; v.p. manufacturing Epitaxx Inc., West Trenton, N.J., 1992—. Patentee in field. Served to lt. USNR, 1964-66. Registered profl. engr., Pa. Mem. Nat. Soc. Profl. Engrs., Am. Soc. Quality Control (cert. quality engr.), Pa. Soc. Profl. Engrs., Gen. Electric Mgmt. Assn., Elfun Soc., Drexel U. Alumni Assn., Pa. State U. Alumni Assn., Tri-County Arabian Horse Assn. Home: 454 Eagle Ln Lansdale PA 19446-1547 Office: 7 Graphics Dr West Trenton NJ 08628-1547

ROSICA, GABRIEL ADAM, corporate executive, engineer; b. N.Y.C., Jan. 9, 1940; s. Gabriel J. and Elma (P.) R.; m. Bettina R. Nardozzi, Sept. 8,

1962; children: Gregory A., Julie Ann, Mark A. BA in Math. and Physics, Columbia U., 1962, BSEE, 1963; MSEE, Rensselaer Poly. Inst., 1966; MBA, Boston U., 1971. Registered profl. engr., Mass. Rsch. engr. United Aircraft Research Labs., East Hartford, Conn., 1963-67; mgr. electronic devel. The Foxboro (Mass.) Co., 1967-75, gen. mgr. U.S. div., 1975-77, v.p., 1977-80; pres., chief operating officer Modular Computer Systems, Inc., Ft. Lauderdale, Fla., 1980-82, pres., chmn., chief exec. officer, 1982-88; pvt. practice bus. cons. Boca Raton, Fla., 1988-91; sr. v.p. Elsag Bailey Corp., Pepper Pike, Ohio, 1991-92; exec. v.p. Bailey Controls Co., Wickliffe, Ohio, 1993-94; COO Bailey Control Co., Wickliffe, Ohio, 1994—; bd. dirs. Sturtevant Co., Dorchester, Mass., Keithley Instruments, Solon, Ohio; chmn. engring. adv. coun. U. Fla., Gainesville, 1987-90; chmn. hi tech adv. coun. Coll. Boca Raton, Fla., 1987-90. Mem. Pres.'s Coun. Fla. Atlantic U., Boca Raton, 1987-91; trustee Nova U., Ft. Lauderdale, Fla., 1987-94. Recipient Boston U. Chair, 1971, Outstanding Young Engr. of Year award Mass. Soc. Profl. Engrs., 1974. Mem. IEEE (sr. mem.), Am. Electronics Assn. (bd. dirs. 1987, chmn Fla. bd. dirs. 1987-88), Fla. High Tech. and Industry Coun. Home: 35640 Spicebush Ln Solon OH 44139 Office: Bailey Controls Co 29801 Euclid Ave Wickliffe OH 44092

ROSIN, WALTER L., religious organization administrator. Sec. Luth. Ch.-Mo. Synod, St. Louis. Office: The Lutheran Ch-Missouri Synod 1333 S Kirkwood Rd Saint Louis MO 63122-7226

ROSINSKI, EDWIN FRANCIS, health sciences educator; b. Buffalo, June 25, 1928; s. Theodore Joseph and Josephine M. (Wolski) R.; m. Jeanne C. Hueniger, Oct. 27, 1951; children: John T., Mary E., Sarah J. BS, SUNY, Buffalo, 1950; EdM, U. Buffalo, 1957, EdD, 1959. Prof. health scis. Med. Coll. Va., Richmond, 1959-66; dep. asst. sec. HEW, Washington, 1966-68; exec. vice chancellor U. Calif., San Francisco, 1968-72, prof., 1972-94; prof. emeritus medicine & pharmacy, 1994—; adv. Rockefeller Found., N.Y.C., 1962-67, WHO, Geneva, 1962-78, Imperial Com. Health, Tehran, Iran, 1974-77; cons. Stanford Research Inst., Menlo Park, Calif., 1975-79. Author: The Assistant Medical Officer, 1965; contbr. over 100 articles to profl. jours. Served with USAF, 1950-54. Recipient spl. citation HEW, 1968, Merrell Flair award, 1991; named disting. prof. Australian Vice Chancellors Office, 1974, disting. vis. prof. Tulane U., New Orleans, 1983. Fellow AAAS; mem. Assn. Am. Med. Colls. (Merrel Flair award), Am. Ednl. Research Assn., Soc. Health and Human Values (founding mem.), Calif. Pharmacists Assn. (hon.), Phi Delta Kappa. Roman Catholic. Avocation: physical fitness. Home: 80 Sotelo Ave San Francisco CA 94116-1423

ROSKAM, JAN, aerospace engineer; b. The Hague, The Netherlands, Feb. 22, 1930; came to U.S., 1957, naturalized, 1962; s. Kommer Jan and Agatha (Bosman) R.; m. Janice Louise Thomas-Barron, Dec. 21, 1994. M.A. in Aerospace Engring, Tech. U. Delft, 1954; Ph.D. in Aeros. and Astronautics, U. Wash., 1965. Asst. chief designer Aviolanda Aircraft Co., Netherlands, 1954-57; sr. aerodynamics engr. Cessna Aircraft Co., Wichita, Kans., 1957-59; sr. group engr. Boeing Co., Wichita and Seattle, 1959-67; Ackers disting. prof. aerospace engring. U. Kans., Lawrence, 1967—; pres. Roskam Aviation and Engring. Corp., 1972—, Design, Analysis and Rsch. Corp., 1991—; cons. to govt. and industry. Author: Airplane Flight Dynamics and Automatic Flight Controls, 2 vols, 1979; co-author: Airplane Aerodynamics and Performance, 1981, Airplane Design, Parts I-VIII, 1986. Served to 1st lt. Royal Netherlands Air Force, 1954-56. Fellow AIAA, Soc. Automotive Engrs.; mem. Air Force Assn., Am. Def. Preparedness Assn., Aircraft Owners and Pilots Assn., Royal Aero. Soc., Koninklijk Instituut van Ingenieurs, U.S. Chess Fedn., Exptl. Aircraft Assn., Internat. Wildlife Assn., Sigma Xi, Tau Beta Pi, Sigma Gamma Tau, Omicron Delta Kappa. Office: U Kans 2004 Lea Hall Lawrence KS 66045

ROSKAM, PETER JAMES, state legislator, lawyer; b. Hinsdale, Ill., Sept. 13, 1961; s. Verlyn Ronald and Martha (Jacobsen) R.; m. Elizabeth Andrea Gracey, June 18, 1988; children: Gracey, James (dec.), Frances, Stephen. BA, U. Ill., 1983; JD, Ill. Inst. Tech., 1989. Bar: Ill. 1989. Tchr. All Saints Sch., St. Thomas, V.I., 1984-85; legis. asst. to Congressman Tom Delay U.S. Ho. of Reps., Washington, 1985-86, legal asst. to Congressman Henry Hyde, 1986-87; exec. dir. Ednl. Assistance Ltd., Glen Ellyn, Ill., 1987-93; ptnr. Salvi & Roskam, Wheaton, Ill., 1994—; mem. Ill. Gen. Assembly, Springfield, 1993—. Republican. Mem. Evangelical Covenant Ch. Office: Salvi & Roskam 1755 S Naperville Rd Wheaton IL 60187

ROSKENS, RONALD WILLIAM, association administrator; b. Spencer, Iowa, Dec. 11, 1932; s. William E. and Delores A.L. (Beving) R.; m. Lois Grace Lister, Aug. 22, 1954; children: Elizabeth, Barbara, Brenda, William. BA, U. No. Iowa, 1953, MA, 1955, LHD (hon.), 1985; PhD, State U. Iowa, 1958; LLD (hon.), Creighton U., 1978, Huston-Tillotson Coll., 1981, Midland Luth. Coll., 1984, Hastings Coll., 1981; LittD (hon.), Nebr. Wesleyan U., 1981; PhD (hon.), Ataturk U. Turkey, 1987; LHD (hon.), U. Akron, 1987; DSc (hon.), Jayewardenepura U. Sri Lanka, 1991; LHD (hon.), Am. Coll. of Greece, Athens, 1994. Lic. min. United Ch. of Christ (Congl. and E&R). Tchr. Minburn (Iowa) High Sch., 1954, Woodward (Iowa) State Hosp., summer 1954; asst. counselor to men State U. Iowa, 1956-59; dean of men, asst. prof. spl. edn. Kent (Ohio) State U., 1959-63, assoc. prof., then prof., 1963-72, asst. to pres., 1963-66, dean for adminstrn., 1968-71, exec. v.p., prof. ednl. adminstrn., 1971-72; chancellor, prof. ednl. adminstrn. U. Nebr., Omaha, 1972-76; pres. U. Nebr. System, 1977-89, pres. emeritus, 1989; hon. prof. East China Normal U., Shanghai, 1985; adminstr. USAID, Washington, 1990-92; pres. Action Internat., Inc., Omaha, 1993—; bd. dirs. ConAgra Inc., 1992—, MFS Comms. Co. Inc., 1993—, Enron Corp., 1979-90, Art's Way Mfg. Co., 1981-90, Guarantee Mut. Life Ins. Co., 1979-90, Am. Charter Fed. Savs. and Loan Assn., 1986-90; mem. Bus.-Higher Edn. Forum, 1979-89, exec. com., 1984-87; mem. govtl. relations com. Am. Council Edn., 1979-83, bd. dirs., 1981-86, vice chair, 1984-85, chair, 1984-85; chmn. com. on financing higher edn. Nat. Assn. State Univs. and Land Grant Colls., 1978-83, vice chmn. com. on financing higher edn., 1983-84, chmn. com. on fed. student fin. assistance, 1981-87; mem. nat. adv. com. on accreditation and instl. eligibility U.S. Dept. Edn., 1983-86, chmn., bd. dirs., 1986; exec. bd. North Cen. Assn., 1979-84, chmn. exec. bd., 1982-84, pres., 1989-90; active Environ. Assn. Bd. 1991-92, Strategic Command Consultation Commn., 1993—, Nat. Exec. Res. Corps, Fed. Office Emergency Preparedness, 1968-88. Co-editor: Paradox, Process and Progress, 1968; contbr. articles profl. jours. Mem. Kent City Planning Commn., 1962-66; bd. dirs. United Ch. of Christ Bd. Homeland Ministries, 1968-74, Met. YMCA, Omaha, 1973-74; Mid-Am. council Boy Scouts Am., 1973-77, Midlands United Community Services, 1972-77, NCCJ, 1974-77, Omaha Rotary Club, 1974-77, Found. Study Presdl. and Congl. Terms, 1977-89, First Plymouth Congl. Ch., 1989-90, Midland Luth. Coll., 1993—; Coun. Aid to Edn., 1985-89; trustee Huston Tillotson Coll., Austin, Tex., 1968-81, chmn., 1976-78, Joslyn Art Mus., 1973-77, Nebr. Meth. Hosp., 1974-77, 1st Cntrl. Congregational Ch., Brownell-Talbott Sch., 1974-77, Harry S. Truman Inst., 1977-89, Willa Cather Pioneer Meml. and Ednl. Found., 1979-87; pres. Kent Area C. of C., 1966; active Met. Commn. Coll. Found., 1993—. Decorated comdr.'s cross Order of Merit (Germany); recipient Disting. Svc. award for community svc., Kent, Ohio, 1967, Brotherhood award NCCJ, 1977, Americanism citation B'nai B'rith, 1978, Legion of Honor, Order of DeMolay, 1980, gold medal Nat. Interfrat. Coun., 1987, Agri award Triumph Agr. Expn., Omaha, 1989; named Nat. 4-H Alumnus, 1967, Outstanding Alumnus, U. No. Iowa, 1974, Midlander of Yr., Omaha World Herald, 1977, King Ak-Sar-Ben LXXXVI, 1980; named to DeMolay Hall of Fame, 1993. Mem. AAAS, APA, AAUP, Am. Coll. Pers. Assn., Assn. Urban Univs. (pres. 1976-77), Am. Ednl. Rsch. Assn., Coun. on Fgn. Rels., Chief Execs. Orgn., Young Pres. Orgn., Lincoln C. of C. (bd. dirs. 1989-90), Masons (33 deg.), Rotary (bd. dirs. Omaha 1974-77), Phi Delta Kappa, Phi Eta Sigma, Sigma Tau Gamma (pres. grand coun. 1968-70, Disting. Achievement award 1980, Disting. scholar 1981), Omicron Delta Kappa (nat. pres. 1986-90, Found. pres. 1986—). Home: 1311 N 97th Plz Omaha NE 68114-2101

ROSKIN, LEWIS ROSS, broadcasting company executive; b. Moose Jaw, Sask., Can., July 16, 1920; s. Samuel and Molly (Ross) R.; m. Elizabeth Craig, Feb. 14, 1942; children: Fredrick, Robin, Craig, Deborah, Lance. Announcer Sta. CJOC, Lethbridge, Alta., Can., 1937-42; program mgr. Sta. CJOB, Winnipeg, Man., Can., 1944-46; program dir. Sta. CFRN, Edmonton, Alta., 1947-49; gen. mgr. Sta. CJDC, Dawson Creek, B.C., 1949-54, Sta. CFCN, Calgary, 1954-55; asst. mgr. Sta. CHED, Edmonton, 1955-

61; gen. mgr. Sta. CKLG, Vancouver, 1961-65; pres., gen. mgr. Sta. CHQT, Edmonton, 1965-90; v.p. corp. affairs CHQT, 1990—; pres. Roskin Comms. Inc., 1993—; dir. CHQT Broadcasting Ltd. Served with Can. Army, 1942-45. Mem. Can. Assn. Broadcasters, Western Assn. Broadcasters (past pres.), Broadcasters Assn. Alta. (past pres., dir.). Office: 4719 138th St, Edmonton, AB Canada T6H 3Y9

ROSKIND, E. ROBERT, real estate company executive; b. N.Y.C., Mar. 18, 1945; s. Edward R. and Harriet (Weinberg) R.; m. Diane L. Albert, Aug. 4, 1966; children: Dina Lee Walsh, Scott. BA, U. Pa., 1966; JD, Columbia U., 1969. Mng. ptnr. The LCP Group, N.Y.C., 1974—; chmn. CapStar Hotels, Washington, 1986—, Lexington Corp. Prop., N.Y.C., 1993—; dir. Berkshire Realty, Boston, Krupp Govt. Income Trust, Krupp Govt. Income Trust II. Chmn. Babies Heart Fund, N.Y.C., 1984—; mem. health & scis. adv. com. Columbia Presbyn. Hosp., N.Y.C., 1990—. Office: The LCP Group 355 Lexington Ave New York NY 10017

ROSKOSKI, ROBERT, JR., biochemist, educator, author; b. Elyria, Ohio, Dec. 10, 1939; s. Robert and Mary R.; m. Laura Martinsek, Aug. 27, 1974. B.S., Bowling Green State U., 1961; M.D., U. Chgo., 1964, Ph.D., 1968. Asst. prof. U. Iowa, Iowa City, 1972-75; assoc. prof. U. Iowa, 1975-79; prof., head dept. biochemistry and molecular biology Med. Center, La. State U., New Orleans, 1979—, Fred G. Brazda prof., 1991—; cons. biochemistry test com. Nat. Bd. Med. Examiners, merit rev. bd. for basic scis. Dept. Vet. Adminstrn. Affairs. Served with USAF, 1966-69. NIH postdoctoral fellow U. Chgo., 1964-66; NIH spl. fellow Rockefeller U., 1969-71. Mem. Am. Chem. Soc., Am. Soc. Neurochemistry, Soc. for Neurosci., Am. Soc. Biol. Chemists, Am. Soc. Pharmacology and Exptl. Therapeutics, Internat. Soc. Neurochemistry, Assn. Med. and Grad. Depts. Biochemistry (sec.). Condr. research enzymology. Home: 1206 Aline St New Orleans LA 70115-2421 Office: 1100 Florida Ave New Orleans LA 70119-2714

ROSKOTHEN, MICHAEL S., health care supply company executive; b. 1936. MA, U. Munich, Fed. Republic Germany, 1962. Exec. v.p. Kendall Co., Boston, 1981—; now exec. v.p. ops. Office: Kendall Co 15 Hampshire St Mansfield MA 02048-1113

ROSKY, BURTON SEYMOUR, lawyer; b. Chgo., May 28, 1927; s. David T. and Mary W. (Zelkin) R.; m. Leatrice J. Darrow, June 16, 1951; children: David Scott, Bruce Alan. Student, Ill. Inst. Tech., 1944-45; BS, UCLA, 1948; JD, Loyola U., L.A., 1953. Bar: Calif. 1954, U.S. Supreme Ct 1964, U.S. Tax Ct 1964; C.P.A.; Calif. Auditor City of L.A., 1948- 51; with Beidner, Temkin & Ziskin (C.P.A.s), L.A., 1951-52; supervising auditor Army Audit Agy., 1952-53; practiced law L.A., Beverly Hills 1954—; ptnr. Duskin & Rosky, 1972-82; s Rosky, Landau & Fox, 1982-93; ptnr. Rosky, Landau, Stahl & Sheehy, Beverly Hills, 1993-94; lectr. on tax and bus. problems; judge pro tem Beverly Hills Mcpl. Ct., L.A. Superior Ct.; mem. L.A. Mayor's Community Adv. Council. Contbr. profl. publs. Charter supporting mem. Los Angeles County Mus. Arts; contbg. mem. Assocs. of Smithsonian Instn.; charter mem. Air and Space Mus; mem. Am. Mus. Natural History, L.A. Zoo; supporting mem. L.A. Mus. Natural History; mem. exec. bd. So. Calif. coun. Nat. Fedn. Temple Brotherhoods, mem. nat. exec. bd. With USNR, 1945-46. Walter Henry Cook fellow Loyola Law Sch. Fellow Jewish Chautauqua Soc. (life mem.); mem. Am. Arbitration Assn. (nat. panel arbitrators), Am. Assn. Attys.-CPAs (charter mem. pres. 1968), Calif. Assn. Attys.-CPAs (charter mem., pres. 1963), Calif. Soc. CPAs, Calif., Beverly Hills, Century City, Los Angeles County bar assns., Am. Judicature Soc., Chancellors Assocs. UCLA, Tau Delta Phi, Phi Alpha Delta.; mem. B'nai B'rith. Jewish (mem. exec. bd., pres. temple, pres. brotherhood). Club: Mason. Office: Rosky Landau & Fox 8383 Wilshire Blvd Beverly Hills CA 90211-2410

ROSKY, THEODORE SAMUEL, insurance company executive; b. Chgo., Apr. 14, 1937; s. Theodore and Lora Marie (O'Connell) R.; m. Jacqueline Reed, Apr. 19, 1958; 1 child, Laura Marie. B.A., State U. Iowa, 1959. Various actuarial positions Conn. Gen. Life Ins. Co., Hartford, 1959-66; assoc. actuary Conn. Gen. Life Ins. Co., 1967-70, controller, 1970-73, 2d v.p., actuary, 1973, v.p., 1973-78; exec. v.p. Capital Holding Corp., 1978-84, exec. v.p., CFO, 1984-91, exec. v.p., 1991-92; bd. dirs. Legend Funds, 1993—; instr. State U. Iowa, 1958-59, U. Hartford, 1964-66, U. Conn., 1967-68. Bd. dirs. Hartford Coll. for Women, 1974-78, Macauley Theater, 1983-85, Louisville Fund for the Arts, 1980—, Louisville Luth. Home, 1983—, Louisville Orch., 1982-88, 89—, Ky. Opera Assn., 1992—, Lincoln Found., 1992—, Oak and Acorn, 1994—; mem. bd. pensions Evangl. Luth. Ch. Am., 1974-82, 84-87, 89—, Lincoln Found, 1992—. Recipient award Soc. Actuaries, 1958. Fellow Soc. Actuaries; mem. Am. Acad. Actuaries, Southeastern Actuaries Club. Republican. Lutheran. Club: Pendennis. Home: 2304 Speed Ave Louisville KY 40205-1642

ROS-LEHTINEN, ILEANA, congresswoman; b. Havana, Cuba, July 15, 1952; d. Enrique Emilio and Amanda (Adato) Ros; m. Dexter Lehtinen. AA, Miami (Fla.)-Dade C.C., 1972; BA, Fla. Internat. U., 1975, MS, 1987. Prin. Ea. Acad., from 1978; mem. Fla. Ho. of Reps., Tallahassee, 1982-86, Fla. Senate, 1986-89, 101st-104th Congresses from 18th Fla. Dist., 1989—; mem. govt. ops. com., subcom. employment, housing, commerce, consumer monetary affairs., govt. info., justice agrl., fgn. affairs. com. Roman Catholic. Office: 127 Cannon House Office Bldg Washington DC 20515-0918*

ROSLUND, CAROL L., lawyer; b. Ark., Sept. 5, 1943; d. Oliver Sidney and Lois (Stratton) R.; 1 child, Kari Ann Roslund-Mercurio. Student, Stockholm (Sweden) U., 1963-64; BA, Colo. Women's Coll., 1965; PhD, Syracuse (N.Y.) U., 1972; JD, Denver U., 1981. Bar: Colo. 1982. Dir. Pretrial Release Svcs., Arapahoe County, Colo., 1974-83; counsel, sr. project adminstr. U. Denver, 1983-84; div. counsel Honeywell Inc., Denver, 1984-88; assoc. counsel Olin Corp., East Alton, Ill., 1988-90; sr. counsel Olin Ordnance, St. Petersburg, Fla., 1990-95; sec. Olin Pantex Inc., Tex., 1990-93; bd. dirs. Nat. Assn. Pretrial Svc. Agys., Washington, 1973-85. Am. Scandinavian Found. fellow, 1971, Lithgow Osborne fellow, 1976. Mem. ABA, Am. Corp. Counsel Assn., Colo. Bar Assn. Avocations: skiing, golf. Office: 623 S Oneida Way Denver CO 80224

ROSNER, ANN See SEAMAN, BARBARA

ROSNER, FRED, physician, educator; b. Berlin, Oct. 3, 1935; came to U.S., 1949, naturalized, 1955; s. Sidney and Sara (Feingold) R.; m. Saranne Eskolsky, Feb. 24, 1959; children: Mitchel, Miriam, Aviva, Shalom. B.A. cum laude, Yeshiva Coll., 1955; M.D., Albert Einstein Coll., 1959. Diplomate: Am. Bd. Internal Medicine. Intern Maimonides Med. Center, Bklyn., 1959-60, resident in medicine, 1960-62, fellow in hematology, 1962-63, asst. dir. hematology, 1967-70; instr. medicine SUNY Downstate Med. Center, Bklyn., 1968-70; asst. prof. medicine SUNY Downstate Med. Center, 1970; asso. prof. SUNY, Stony Brook, 1970-78, prof. medicine, 1978-89; asst. dean, prof. medicine Albert Einstein Coll. Medicine, 1989-93; prof. medicine Mt. Sinai Sch. Medicine, N.Y.C., 1993—; dir. hematology Queens Hosp. Center, Jamaica, N.Y., 1970-78; dir. medicine Queens Hosp. Center, 1978—. Author: Modern Medicine and Jewish Law, 1972, Medicine in the Bible and Talmud, 1977, 2nd edit., 1995, Biblical and Talmudic Medicine, 1978, Jewish Bioethics, 1979, Modern Medicine and Jewish Ethics, 1986, 2d edit., 1991, Practical Medical Halachah, 1990, Medicine and Jewish Law vol. I, 1990, vol. II, 1993; translator, editor: several Moses Maimonides' works including Moses Maimonides' Treatise on Hemorrhoids and Responsa, 1969; Medical Aphorisms of Moses Maimonides, 1970, Sex Ethics in the Writings of Moses Maimonides, 1974, 94, Moses Maimonides' Introduction to the Mishnah, 1975, 95, Maimonides Glossary of Drug Names, 1979, Moses Maimonides' Commentary on Sanhedrin, 1981, Maimonides' Treatise on Resurrection, 1982, Medicine in the Mishneh Torah of Maimonides, 1984, Maimonides' Treatises on Poisons, Hemorrhoids and Cohabitation, 1984, Maimonides' Commentary on the Aphorisms of Hippocrates, 1987, Maimonides' Medical Aphorisms, 1990, The Existence and Unity of God: Three Treatises Attributed to Moses Maimonides, 1990, Moses Maimonides' Three Treatises on Health, 1990, Six Treatises Attributed to Maimonides, 1991, Maimonides: Physician, Philosopher and Scientist, 1993, Maimonides' Treatise on Asthma, 1994, Maimonides' Glossary of Drug Names, 1995; mem. editorial bd. Medica Judaica, 1970—; contbr. to: Ency. Bioethics; contbr. numerous articles to tech. lit. Served with USPHS, 1963-65. Recipient Maimonides award

Michael Reese Hosp., Chgo., 1969, Bernard Revel Meml. award Yeshiva U., 1971; Maimonides award of Wis., 1977. Fellow A.C.P., N.Y. Acad. Medicine; mem. AMA, Am. Assn. History Medicine, N.Y. Soc. Study of Blood, Am. Internat. socs. hematology, Am. Fedn. Clin. Research. Home: 750 Elvira Ave Far Rockaway NY 11691-5405 Office: Queens Hosp Ctr 82-68 164th St Jamaica NY 11432

ROSNER, JONATHAN LINCOLN, physicist, educator; b. N.Y.C., July 23, 1941; s. Albert Aaron and Elsie Augustine (Lincoln) R.; m. Joy Elaine Fox, June 13, 1965; children: Hannah, Benjamin. BA, Swarthmore Coll., 1962; MA, Princeton U., 1963, PhD, 1965. Research asst. prof. U. Wash., Seattle, 1965-67; vis. lectr. Tel Aviv U., Ramat Aviv, Israel, 1967-69; asst. prof. physics U. Minn., Mpls., 1969-71, assoc. prof., 1971-75, prof., 1975-82; prof. U. Chgo., 1982—. Contbr. numerous articles to profl. and scholarly jours. Alfred P. Sloan fellow, 1971-73. Fellow Am. Phys. Soc. Democrat. Jewish. Avocations: fishing, hiking, skiing, amateur radio. Office: U Chgo Enrico Fermi Inst 5640 S Ellis Ave Chicago IL 60637-1467

ROSNER, LYDIA S., sociology educator, author; b. N.Y.C., June 11, 1933; d. Abraham and Rose (Hutoryansky) Sokol; m. Jonathan Levi Rosner, Dec. 23, 1956; children: Beth, Marianne, Joshua. BA in Sociology, CUNY, 1955, MA in Sociology, 1961, PhD in Sociology, 1984. Coordinator criminal justice council Tng. Inst. of West County, N.Y., 1977-78; conf. coordinator, moderator, adj. prof. sociology and criminal justice Mercy Coll., Dobbs Ferry, N.Y., 1978-83; asst. dir. rsch. John Jay Coll. CUNY, N.Y.C., 1984-85, prof. sociology John Jay Coll., 1985—; freelance reporter N.Y. Times, N.Y.C., 1976-84; editor West County Youth Bur., White Plains, N.Y., 1974-76; cons. in field; participant various CIS related rsch. projects focusing on crime and entrepreneurship. Author: Soviet Way of Crime, 1986; contbr. articles to profl. jours, papers to profl. internat. socs. Commr. Greenburgh Housing Authority, White Plains, 1977—; liaison N.Y. State Div. for Youth, West Co., 1976. Mem. Ea. Sociol. Assn., Am. Soc. Criminology, Am. Correctional Assn., Nat. Assn. Housing and Redevel. Ofcls., N.Y. State Assn. Housing and Redevel. Ofcls., N.Y. Acad. Sci. Jewish. Avocations: swimming, boating, reading. Office: CUNY John Jay Coll 445 W 59th St New York NY 10019-1104

ROSNER, M. NORTON, business systems and financial services company executive; b. Camden, N.J., Aug. 17, 1931; s. Adolph and Anne (Cotler) R.; m. Patricia Eskin, Oct. 18, 1953; children—Robert, Susan, Jan. B.S. in Econs., U. Pa., 1953; M.B.A., U. Mich., 1965. From acct. to mgr. overhead standards RCA Corp., Camden, N.J., 1953-62; supr. methods and programs, then internal cons. forward model planning Ford Motor Co., Dearborn, Mich., 1962-66; asst. controller, then v.p. planning Singer Co., N.Y.C., 1966-70; treas., then v.p. fin. Popular Services, Passaic, N.J., 1970-72; dir. fin. planning, then asst. controller, then gen. mgr. GSD, then v.p. RE/GSD Xerox Corp., Rochester, N.Y., 1972-90; retired, 1990; bd. dirs., treas. Parcel Post Assn., N.Y.C., 1970-71; dir. Harbinger, Stamford, Conn.; chmn. Xerox Realty Corp., Stamford. Vice chmn. Compeer, Inc., Rochester, N.Y., 1981-87, chmn., 1987-89; chmn. DP2, Rochester, 1985-87; bd. dirs., treas. Rochester Blue Cross/Blue Shield, 1987-89; dir. Palm Beach County Mental Health Assn., 1992, treas., 1993, v.p., 1994-95; dir. JARC, 1992, v.p., 1993, pres., 1994. Recipient Nat. Vol. Action award Pres. U.S. Clubs: U. Mich.; U. Pa. Home: 17831 Heather Ridge Ln Boca Raton FL 33498-6423

ROSNER, ROBERT, astrophysicist; b. Garmisch-Partenkirchen, Bavaria, Germany, June 26, 1947; came to U.S., 1959; s. Heinz and Faina (Brodsky) R.; m. Marsha Ellen Rich, Nov. 8, 1950; children: Daniela Karin, Nicole Elise. BA, Brandeis U., 1969; PhD, Harvard U., 1975. Asst. prof. Harvard U., Cambridge, Mass., 1978-83, assoc. prof., 1983-86; astrophysicist Smithsonian Astrophys. Observatory, Cambridge, 1986-87; prof. U. Chgo., 1987—; trustee Adler Planetarium, Chgo., 1989—, chmn. dept. astronomy and astrophysics, 1991—. Contbr. over 100 articles to sci. jours. Woodrow Wilson fellow, 1969. Fellow Am. Phys. Soc.; mem. Am. Astron. Soc., Soc. Indsl. and Applied Math. Home: 4950 S Greenwood Ave Chicago IL 60615-2816 Office: U Chicago Astrophysics 5640 S Ellis Ave Chicago IL 60637-1433

ROSNER, T., insurance executive. V.p. Farmers Group Inc., L.A. Office: Farmers Ins Exch PO Box 2478 Terminal Annex Los Angeles CA 90051

ROSOFF, JEANNIE L, association administrator; b. Clamart, France, Nov. 8, 1924; came to U.S., 1948; d. Georges Auguste Marie and Suzenne (Philomene) Martin; m. Morton Rosoff, Dec. 8, 1945 (div. 1958); 1 child, Ann Susan. BA in Law cum laude, U. Paris, 1946. Cmty. organizer East Harlem Project, N.Y.C., 1953-56; assoc. dir. N.Y. Com. for Dem. Voters, N.Y.C., 1960-64; spl. projects coord. Planned Parenthood Fedn. Am., N.Y.C., 1964-74, assoc. dir., 1968-74, assoc. dir. Ctr. for Family Planning Program Devel., 1968-74; v.p. govt. affairs Planned Parenthood Fedn. Am., Washington, 1974-77, dir. Washington office, 1976-81; sr. v.p. Alan Guttmacher Inst., Washington, 1974-78, pres., 1978—; participant in UN Population Conf., Bucharest, 1974, UN Conf. on Internat. Women's Yr., Mexico City, 1975; ofcl. U.S. del. UN Conf. on Population and Devel., Cairo, 1994; del.-at-large Internat. Women's Yr. Conf., Houston, 1977. Author: Teenage Pregnancy in Industrialized Countries, 1986, Health Care Reform: A Unique Opportunity, 1993, (govt. pubs.) Family Planning: An Analysis of Laws, 1974, Family Planning: Contraception, 1979. Recipient merit award Nat. Family Planning and Repro. Health Assn., 1980, Ten for Ten award Ctr. for Population Options, 1990. Mem. APHA (dirs., chair population sect. 1976, Carl S. Schultz award 1980; maternal and child health sec. 1973-76), Nat. Health Lawyers Assn., Population Assn. Am., Nat. Inst. Child Health and Human Devel., Pathfinder Internat. (bd. dirs. 1993—). Office: Alan Guttmacher Inst 120 Wall St Fl 21 New York NY 10005-3901

ROSOFF, LEONARD, SR., retired surgeon, medical educator; b. Grand Forks, N.D., May 5, 1912; s. Albert and Sophie (Koblin) R.; m. Marie Louise Aronsfeld, June 1, 1935; 1 son, Leonard. BA, U. So. Calif., 1931; MD, U. Tex., 1935. Diplomate: Am. Bd. Surgery (dir. 1970-76). Intern, then resident gen. surgery Los Angeles County Hosp., 1935-40; from instr. to prof. surgery U. So. Calif. Sch. Medicine, 1946-80, emeritus, 1980—, chmn. dept., 1969-79; chief surg. services, dir. surgery Los Angeles County-U. So. Calif. Med. Center, 1955-77, sr. attending surgeon, 1977-80, ret., 1980; clin. prof. surgery U. Tex. Health Ctr., San Antonio, 1992—; hon. staff Hosp. Good Samaritan, Cedars-Sinai, Los Angeles Children's, Huntington Meml. hosps.; lectr. in field. Contbr. articles to med. jours., textbooks. Served with M.C., AUS, 1942-45. Recipient Outstanding Alumnus award U. Tex. Med. Br., 1971. Fellow ACS (bd. govs. 1975-81, 2d v.p. 1981), Tex. Surg. Soc. (hon.); mem. Am. Surg. Assn. (1st v.p. 1984), Western Surg. Assn. (2d v.p.), Pacific Coast Surg. Assn., L.A. Surg. Assn. (pres. 1970), Am. Assn. Endocrine Surgeons (bd. councilors 1980-87, pres. 1984), Am. Assn. Surgery Trauma, Soc. Surgery Alimentary Tract (pres. 1979-80), Internat. Soc. Surgery, L.A. Acad. Medicine, L.A. Athletic Club, Giraud Club (San Antonio). Research surgery parathyroids, thyroid gland and other endocrine systems, surgery peptic ulcer and other gastrointestinal diseases, studies in shock. Home: One Towers Park Ln # 1115 San Antonio TX 78209

ROSOFF, WILLIAM A., lawyer; b. Phila., June 21, 1943; s. Herbert and Estelle (Finkel) R.; m. Beverly Rae Rifkin, Feb. 7, 1970; children: Catherine D., Andrew M. BS with honors, Temple U., 1964; LLB magna cum laude, U. Pa., 1967. Bar: Pa. 1968, U.S. Dist. Ct. (ea. dist.) Pa. 1968. Law clk. U.S. Ct. Appeals (3d cir.), 1967-68; instr. U. Pa. Law Sch., Phila., 1968-69; assoc. Wolf, Block, Schorr & Solis-Cohen, Phila., 1969-75, ptnr., 1975—, chmn. exec. com., 1987-88; trustee RPS Realty Trust; guest lectr. confs. and seminars on tax law; mem. tax adv. bd. Commerce Clearing House, 1983-94; mem. legal activities policy bd. Tax Analysts, 1978—; mem. Little, Brown Tax Adv. Bd., 1994—. Editor U. Pa. Law Rev., 1965-67; mem. bd. contbg. editors and advisors Jour. Partnership Taxation, 1983—; author reports and papers on tax law. Bd. dirs., mem. com. on law and social action Phila. coun. Am. Jewish Congress. Fellow Am. Coll. Tax Counsel; mem. Am. Law Inst. (cons. taxation of partnerships, 1978-82, mem. adv. group on fed. income tax project 1982—), Locust Club (dir.), Order of Coif, Beta Gamma Sigma, Beta Alpha Psi. Office: Wolf Block Schorr Solis-Cohen Packard Bldg 12th Fl 15th & Chestnut Sts Philadelphia PA 19102

ROSOVSKY, HENRY, economist, educator; b. Danzig, Sept. 1, 1927; came to U.S., 1940, naturalized, 1949; s. Selig S. and Sophie (Rosovsky) R.; m. Nitza Brown, June 17, 1956; children—Leah, Judith, Michael. A.B. Coll. William and Mary, 1949; LL.D., 1976; A.M. (John E. Thayer scholar), Harvard U., 1953; Ph.D., 1959; L.H.D. (hon.), Yeshiva U., 1977, Hebrew Union Coll., 1978, Colgate U., 1979, Brandeis U., 1984; Ph.D. (hon.), Hebrew U. of Jerusalem, 1982; LL.D. (hon.), Queen's U., Ont., 1984, U. Hartford, 1984, CUNY, 1986, U. Mass., 1986; DHL (hon.), Hebrew Coll., Brookline, Mass., 1987, NYU, 1993; DL, St. Mary's Coll. Md., 1989. From asst. prof. to prof. econs. and history U. Calif., Berkeley, 1958-65; chmn. Center Japanese and Korean Studies, 1962-65; prof. econs. Harvard U., 1965—, Walter S. Barker prof. econs., 1975-84, Geyser univ. prof., 1984—, chmn. dept., 1969-72, dean Faculty Arts and Scis., 1973-84; assoc. dir. East Asia Research Center, 1967-69; mem. Harvard U. Corp., 1985—; vis. prof. Hitotsubashi U., Tokyo, 1957, Tokyo U., 1962, Hebrew U., Jerusalem, 1965; bd. dirs. Corning, Inc., Paine Webber Group, Japan Fund. Author: Capital Formation in Japan, 1868-1940, 1961, Quantitative Japanese Economic History, 1961, (with K. Ohkawa) Japanese Economic Growth, 1973, The University: An Owner's Manual, 1990; editor: Explorations in Entrepreneurial History, 1954-56, Industrialization in Two Systems, 1966, Discord in the Pacific, 1972, (with H. Patrick) Asia's New Giant, 1976, (with P. Higonnet, D. Landes) Favorites of Fortune, 1991, (with S. Kumon) The Political Economy of Japan, Vol. 3: Cultural and Social Dynamics, 1992. Chmn. bd. trustees Am. Jewish Congress, 1975-88. Served to 1st lt. AUS, 1946-47, 50-52. Jr. fellow Soc. Fellows, 1954-57; recipient Schumpeter prize Harvard, 1963, Clark Kerr medal U. Calif., Berkeley, 1992. Fellow Am. Acad. Arts and Scis., Am. Philos. Soc.; mem. Am. Econ. Assn., Econ. History Assn.; mem. Asian. Asian Studies, Chevalier, Legion of Honor, Order of Sacred Treasure, Star (Japan). Home: 37 Beechcroft Rd Newton MA 02158-2403 Office: Harvard Univ 218 Littauer Ctr Cambridge MA 02138

ROSOW, JEROME MORRIS, institute executive; b. Chgo., Dec. 2, 1919; s. Morris and Mary (Cornick) R.; m. Rosalyn Levin, Sept. 28, 1941; children: Michael, Joel. BA cum laude, U. Chgo., 1942. Position classification analyst Dept. Army, Washington, 1942-43; orgn. and methods examiner, asst. mgr. wage and salary div. Dept. Army, 1948-51; dir. compensation War Assets Adminstrn., Washington, 1946-48; dir. policy, salary stblzn. bd. Econ. Stblzn. Agy., 1952-53; with Creole Petroleum Corp. subs. Standard Oil N.J., Caracas, Venezuela, 1953-55; various exec. positions including coordinator of compensation, indsl. relations research Standard Oil N.J., N.Y.C., 1955-66; mgr. employee relations dept. ESSO Europe, Inc., London, 1966-69; asst. sec. labor for policy, evaluation and research Dept. Labor, 1969-71; planning mgr. pub. affairs dept. Exxon Corp., 1971-77; founder, pres. Work in Am. Inst., 1976—; cons. fed. pay plans U.S. Bur. Budget and U.S. CSC, 1964; mem. bus. adv. research com. Bur. Labor Stats., 1958-65; chmn. council of compensation Nat. Indsl. Conf. Bd., 1959-66; asso. seminar on labor, Columbia U., 1961—; dir. N.Y.C. Vocat. Adv. Service, 1961—, chmn. finance com., 1962-65; mem. White House Working Group on Welfare Reform, 1969-71; chmn. cabinet com. White House Conf. Children and Youth, 1970-71; chmn. subcabinet com. nat. growth policy; U.S. del OECD Ministers Conf., Paris, 1970, 74; vice-chmn. Nat. Productivity Commn., 1971; chmn. tech. experts multinat. indsl. relations OECD, Paris, 1972; chmn. subcom. manpower and social affairs; chmn. Pres.'s Adv. Com. Fed. Pay, 1971-82; adviser Pres. U.S.; chmn. Am. assembly The Changing World at Work. Editor: American Men in Government, 1949, The Worker and the Job: Coping with Change, 1974; Editor: (with Clark Kerr) Work in America: The Decade Ahead, 1979, Productivity: Prospects for Growth, 1981, Views from the Top, 1985, Teamwork: Joint Labor-Management Programs in America, 1986, Global Marketplace, 1988, Training-The Competitive Edge, 1988, Allies in Education Reform, 1988; contbr. articles on manpower, compensation, welfare reform, indsl. relations, orgn. transformation, labor mgmt. relations to profl. jours. Bd. dirs. Young Audiences; trustee Nat. Com. Employment of Youth; adviser Com. Econ. Devel., 1972—, Nat. Planning Assn., 1973—; mem. Nat. Commn. Productivity and Quality of Work, 1975; v.p. Population Edn. Inc., 1975—; mem. Study Group Work and Edn. in China, 1978; cons. comptroller gen. U.S., 1972—, Ford Found.; mem. Mayor's Commn. on Gainsharing, N.Y.C., 1993. With AUS, 1943-46. Recipient Comptroller Gen.'s Public Service award, 1980. Mem. Indsl. Relations Research Assn. (life, exec. bd. dirs., pres. 1979). Jewish. Home: 117 Fox Meadow Rd Scarsdale NY 10583-2301 Office: 700 White Plains Rd Scarsdale NY 10583-5013

ROSOW, STUART L, lawyer; b. N.Y.C., Mar. 28, 1950; s. Bernard and Lillian (Bonime) R.; m. Amy Berk Kuhn. AB cum laude, Yale U.; JD cum laude, Harvard U. Law clk. to presiding justice U.S. Ct. Appeals (7th cir.), Chgo., 1975-76; assoc. Paul, Weiss et al, N.Y.C., 1976-79; assoc. Kaye, Scholer, Fierman, Hays & Handler, N.Y.C., 1979-84, ptnr., 1985—. Mem. ABA, N.Y. State Bar Assn., assoc. Am. Bar of City of N.Y. Office: Kaye Scholer Fierman Hays & Handler 425 Park Ave New York NY 10022-3506

ROSOWSKI, ROBERT BERNARD, manufacturing company executive; b. Detroit, July 23, 1940; s. Bernard and Anna (Maciag) R.; m. Kathleen Patricia Bates, Aug. 26, 1961; children: John, Paul, Mary, Judith. BS, U. Detroit, 1962; MBA, Mich. State U., 1974. CPA, Mich. Auditor, staff supr. Coopers and Lybrand, Detroit, 1962-71; fin. analyst Masco Corp., Taylor, Mich., 1971-73, controller, 1973-85, v.p., controller, 1985—. Bd. dirs. Econ. Devel. Coun. of Taylor, 1983—; chmn. bd. dirs. Acctg. Aid Soc. Met. Detroit, 1987—, Oakwood Hosp. Found., 1990—. Mem. Am. Inst. CPA's, Mich. Assoc. CPA's. Avocations: golf, fishing, boating, photography. Office: Masco Corp 21001 Van Born Rd Taylor MI 48180-1340

ROSS, ADRIAN E., drilling manufacturing company executive; b. Clintonville, N.Y., Mar. 6, 1912; s. James A. and Bertha (Beardsley) R.; B.S. in Elec. Engring., M.I.T., 1934, M.S. in Elec. Engring., 1935; m. Ruth T. Hill, Mar. 2, 1934; children—James A., Daniel R. Materials engr. USN, 1935-37; devel. engr. Electrolux Corp., 1937-41; chief engr. and asst. to pres. Sprague & Henwood, Inc., Scranton, Pa., 1941-51, dir., 1951—, pres., 1953-74, chmn. bd., 1963—; pres. dir. Sprague & Henwood de Venezuela; dir. Hands Eng. Ltd., Scranton Lackawanna Indsl. Bldg. Co. (emeritus), N.E. Bank of Pa. (emeritus), profl. engrs. Past chmn. bd., dir. emeritus Keystone Jr. Coll.; pres., dir. Ross Family Found.; former chmn. bd., dir. emeritus Johnson Sch. Tech. Served from lt. to lt. col. Air Communication. USAAF, 1941-46. Registered profl. engr.; Pa. Mem. Diamond Core Drill Mfrs. Assn. (past pres.), AIME, ASCE, Soc. Profl Engrs., U.S. Nat. Council Soil Mechanics, Indsl. Diamond Assn. Am. (past pres.), C. of C. Presbyn. Clubs: Mining (N.Y.C.); Scranton, M.I.T. (Scranton, Pa.). Contbr. articles to Mining Congress Jour., Mining Engring., Engring. and Mining Jour., Diamond Drill Handbook. Home: 5 Overlook Rd Clarks Summit PA 18411-1121

ROSS, ALBERTA BARKLEY, chemist; b. Moores Hill, Ind., July 26, 1928; d. Lawrence Houston and Stella Olcott (Wright) Barkley; m. Joseph Hansbro Ross, June 2, 1956; children: Mary Angela, Joseph Hansboro Jr., Robert Barkley, Kathleen. BS, Purdue U., 1948, Wash. U., 1951; PhD, U. Md., 1957. Tech. libr. Monsanto Chem. Co., St. Louis, 1948-53; rsch. assoc. U. Mich., Ann Arbor, 1957-58; supr. Radiation Chemistry Data Ctr. U. Notre Dame (Ind.), 1964—. Mem. Am. Chem. Soc. (chmn. St. Joseph Valley chpt. 1977-78), Inter-Am. Photochem. Soc., European Photochem. Soc., Sigma Xi (chpt. pres. 1980-81), Iota Sigma Pi. Office: U Notre Dame Radiation Lab Radiation Chem Data Ctr Notre Dame IN 46556

ROSS, ALEXANDER DUNCAN, art librarian; b. N.Y.C., Aug. 3, 1941; s. Donald Duncan and Anita (Petersen) R.; m. Susan Dixon Getman, July 29, 1967 (div. 1977); m. Eleanore Saunders Stewart, June 22, 1985. B.A., Columbia U., 1966, M.S., 1968, M.A., 1971. Asst. art librarian Columbia U., N.Y.C., 1968-71; assoc. librarian Cleve. Mus. Art, 1971-75; head art librarian Stanford U., Calif., 1975—. Contbr. articles to profl. jours. Mem. Art Libraries Soc. N. Am. Home: 4175 Wilkie Way Palo Alto CA 94306-4159 Office: Stanford U Art & Arch Libr 102 Cummings Art Bldg Stanford CA 94305

ROSS, ALLAN ANDERSON, music educator, university official; b. Amesbury, Mass., Jan. 16, 1939; s. Frank Albert and Ruth Ethel (Anderson) R.; m. Barbara Kay Bedford, Apr. 15, 1962; children: Karen Elizabeth, Judith Carol, Donna Susan, Linda Beth, Jason Andrew. A.B., U. Rochester, 1961; MusM, Ind. U., 1962, MusD, 1968. Asst. dir. music U. Rochester, N.Y.,

1962-65; instr. music Ind. U., Bloomington, 1967-69, asst. prof. music, 1969-71, assoc. prof., dir. undergrad. studies, 1971-73, prof., 1977-79, asst. to dean, 1973-79; dean Shepherd Sch. Music, Rice U., Houston, 1979-81; prof. music U. Okla., Norman, 1981—, dir. music, 1981-92, devel. officer Coll. Fine Arts, 1992-93; condr. U. Okla. Symphony Orch., 1993—; dir. music Trinity Methodist Ch., Rochester, N.Y., 1963-65, First United Meth. Ch., Bloomington, Ind., 1969-79, 1st Christian Ch., Norman, Okla., 1981-91; bd. dirs. Riemenschneider Bach Inst.; bd. dirs., exec. bd. Okla. Summer Arts Inst. Guest condr. and adjudicator at music festivals throughout, U.S.; Author: Techniques for Beginning Conductors, 1976. Bd. dirs. United Way of Norman, Helpline of Norman, Okla. Arts Inst.; mem. gov.'s commn. for Okla. Symphony Orch. NDEA Title IV fellow, 1965. Mem. Music Educators Nat. Conf., Am. Choral Dirs. Assn., Coll. Music Soc., Nat. Assn. Schs. of Music (grad. commn., evaluator), Okla. Music Educators Assn., Phi Mu Alpha Sinfonia, Pi Kappa Lambda. Home: 1879 Rolling Hills St Norman OK 73072-6707 Office: U Okla Sch Music 560 Parrington Oval Norman OK 73019-0001

ROSS, ALLAN MICHAEL, physician, medical educator; b. N.Y.C., June 20, 1939; s. Irving and Rose (Jarin) R.; m. Loleta Saylors, Nov. 1, 1965; children—Jenifer, Aaron, Jed. B.A., Northwestern U., 1960; M.D., Chgo. Med. Sch., 1964. Diplomate Am. Bd. Internal Medicine. Fellow in cardiology Yale U., New Haven, 1971-72; instr. medicine Yale U., 1972-73, asst. prof. medicine, 1975-77, assoc. prof., 1977-78; dir. cardiol. cath. lab. West Haven VA Hosp., 1973-75; prof. medicine, dir. div. cardiology George Washington U., Washington, 1979-94; prof./assoc. chmn. dept. medicine, dir. cardiovascular rsch. George Washington U., 1994—. Inventor spl. function cardiac catheters; designer cadiologic diagnostic algorhythms. Served with M.C. U.S. Army, 1968-71. Am. Heart Lung and Blood Inst. prin. investigator, 1983. Fellow Am. Coll. Cardiology (gov. D.C. sect. 1982-85), Am. Coll. Cardiology, Am. Heart Assn. Coun. on Clin. Cardiology (D.C. counsellor 1983); mem. Am. Heart Assn. (dir. 1981). Office: George Washington U 2150 Pennsylvania Ave NW Washington DC 20037-2396

ROSS, ALLYNE R., federal judge; b. 1946. BA, Wellesley Coll., 1967; JD cum laude, Harvard Law Sch., 1970. Assoc. Paul, Weiss, Rifkind, Wharton & Garrison, 1971-76; asst. U.S. atty. U.S. Dist. Ct. (N.Y. ea. dist.), 2nd circuit, Brooklyn, 1976-83, chief, appeals div., 1983-86, magistrate judge, 1986-94, dist. judge, 1994—. Mem. Federal Bar Coun., New York City Bar Assn. Office: US District Court 225 Cadman Plz E Rm 619 Brooklyn NY 11201-1876

ROSS, AUSTIN, health care executive; b. Milw., Aug. 12, 1929; s. Austin and Elizabeth (Greene) R.; m. Annette Wolff, Dec. 28, 1950; children: Carol, Randall, Becky, Austin. BSBA, U. Calif., Berkeley, 1951, MPH, 1955. Adminstrn. intern Cowell Meml. Hosp., Berkeley, 1953-55; adminstrn. resident Virginia Mason Hosp., Seattle, 1955-56, assoc. adminstr., 1966-68, adminstr., 1968-77, v.p., exec. adminstr., 1977-90; asst. adminstr. The Mason Clinic, Seattle, 1956-66; prof. U. Wash., 1991—, chmn. external adv. com., 1983—; chmn. bd. dirs. Blue Cross Plan of Wash./Alaska, 1980-82, exec. com. mem., 1973-83; bd. dirs. Wash./Alaska Regional Med. Program, 1970-76, vice chmn. bd. trustees, 1976; cons. W.K. Kellogg Found., 1979-88, project co-dir. Health Svcs. Consortium Project, 1973-77; mem. Accrediting Commn. on Edn. for Health Svcs. Adminstrn., 1978-81; active numerous other local and nat. profl. orgns. Author: (with others) Ambulatory Care Organization and Management, 1984, Cornerstones of Leadership, 1992; co-editor: Integration of Clinical and Financial Information Systems, 1986; mem. editorial bd. Hosp. Health Svcs. Adminstrn. Jour., 1976-85, Jour. Ambulatory Health Care Mgmt., 1978—; contbr. articles, reports, book revs. to profl. publs. Bd. dirs. Downtown Seattle Devel. Assn., 1980-85, Alki Found., 1981-90, Bellevue Pk.-Episcopal Retirement Home Project, 1983-87; chmn. hosp. divsn. United Way, 1979, Pers. Commn. Episcopal Diocese of Olympia, 1983-85; sr. warden St. Thomas Episcopal Ch., 1979, 82; pres. bd. trustees St. Thomas Day Sch., 1978; adv. bd. Pike Market Community Clinic, 1986—. Lt. U.S. Army, 1950-53. Recipient Edgar Hayhow Article of Yr. award Am. Coll. Hosp. Adminstrs., 1982, Exec. Adminstr. of Yr. award Am. Group Practice Assn., 1987. Mem. Am. Coll. Healthcare Execs. (chmn. 1984-85, bd. govs. 1979-83, regent Wash./Alaska 1972-76, Gold medal 1989), Am. Coll. Med. Group Adminstrs. (bd. mem. 1973-74, Harry J. Harwick Disting. Svc. award 1983, Article of Yr. award 1982, 85), Am. Hosp. Assn. (chmn. ad hoc com. on physician involment 1989, mem. structure com. 1986-87, chmn. R & D coun. 1982-83, mem. adv. panel Ctr. Ambulatory Care 1979-80, coun. on manpower and edn. 1976-79), Assn. Western Hosps. (bd. mem. 1971-81, pres. 1976-77, Alfred Mafley Adminstr. on Campus award 1981), Med. Group Mgmt. Assn. (chmn. joint rsch. com. 1982-83, joint edn. com. 1980-81, pres. 1976-77), Seattle Area Hosp. Coun. (pres. 1968-70), Wash. State Hosp. Assn. (pres. 1971-72), Rainier Club. Republican. Office: Virginia Mason Med Ctr 1100 9th Ave Seattle WA 98101-2756

ROSS, BEATRICE BROOK, artist; b. N.Y.C., Mar. 31, 1927; d. Alexander and Ray (Tennenbaum) Brook; m. Alexander Ross, Dec. 23, 1945; children: Robert Alan, Kenneth Jay, Stefani Lynn. Student, Hunter Coll., 1943, CCNY, 1944, Bklyn. Mus. Art Sch., 1959-60, 64-65; pupil of, Ruben Tam, Wang Chi Yuan, Leo Manso. Owner, operator Jean Rosenthal Bea Ross Gallery, Jericho, 1961-64; represented by Gillary Gallery, Jericho, N.Y., Patrician Gallery, West Palm Beach, Fla.; founder Birchwood Art League, 1958-63; lectr. bd. edn., Ont., Can., 1972; mem. ad hoc com. with Lucy Lippard Women in Art, 1970-74. Exhbns. include Women in Art, Huntington, N.Y., 1972, C.W. Post Coll., 1972, 73-76, Guild Hall Mus., East Hampton, 1969-72, Lever House, Inc., 1969-72, J. Walter Thompson Loan Show, 1970, Whitehouse Gallery, 1970, Park Ave. Synagogue, 1970, Locust Valley Ann., 1970, Nat. Arts Club, 1970, Light Show, Loeb Student Ctr., NYU, 1969, Suffolk Mus., Stony Brook, N.Y., 1969, Lynn U., Boca Raton, 1992, 4-person show, Suffolk Mus., Stony Brook, N.Y., 1971, NAD, 1968, Audubon Artists, 1968, 70, Silvermine Guild, 1968, 71, Port Washington (N.Y.) Library, 1968, 70, 76, Light Environment Happening at Profl. Artists Guild L.I., 1968, Jericho (N.Y.) Gillary Gallery, 1968, Bklyn. Coll., 1968, Huntington Twp. Art League, Cold Spring Harbor, N.Y., 1967, 1-man show, Gillary Gallery, Jericho, 1966, 70, 72, 79, 83, Hecksher Mus., 1960, 63, 70, Ho. of Reps., 1965, Library of Congress, 1965, Award Winners Show, Merrick (N.Y.) Gallery, 1963, N. Shore Community Art Ctr. ann., Roslyn, N.Y., 1959, 62, 1-man show, Birchwood Art League, Jericho, N.Y., 1958, 61-62, Hofstra U., 1960, 1-man show, City Ctr., N.Y.C., 1960, Emily Lowe Gallery, 1960, Nassau Democratic County Com. ann., 1962, 1-person show, R.A.A. Gallery, N.Y.C., 1969-70, 77, 2-man show, Roosevelt Field Art Gallery, Garden City, N.Y., 1958, Boca Raton (Fla.) City Hall, 1991, 3-person family show Bryant Library, Roslyn, N.Y., 1973, 3-man show, Women's Interart Ctr., N.Y.C., 1974, Wantagh (N.Y.) Library, 1975, 4-person show, Port Washington Library, 1976, 1-person show, LIU, 1976, 2 person shows, N.Y. Tech., 1974, C.W. Post Coll. Schwartz Library, 1976, Wantagh (N.Y.) Libr., 1975, C.W. Post Coll., 1976, St. Johns U., 1976, Union Carbide, N.Y.C., 1977, 1-person show, Harley U. Ctr. Gallery, Adelphi U., 1976, 82, Lincoln Ctr., N.Y.C., 1978, 82, 1-person show, Gallery 84, N.Y.C., 1981; represented in pvt. collections, traveling shows in, France, Italy and Japan; mus. curated group show No. Trust Bank, Boca Mus., Fla., 1992. Recipient 1st prize oil Birchwood Art League, 1958; certificate award outstanding contbn. Mid Island Plaza Art League, Hicksville, N.Y., 1961, 2d prize oil, 1962; hon. mention oil Operation Democracy, Inc. ann., Locust Valley, 1967, 1st prize oil, 1970; Benjamin Altman landscape prize N.A.D., 1968; 2d prize Heckscher Mus., Huntington, N.Y., 1970; hon. mention Port Washington Ann., 1971, Benjamin Altman Landscape prize, Major Nat. award Nat. Acad. Design, N.Y.C., 1969, Solo Show award RAA Gallery, 1967-78, Harbor Gallery, Glen Cove, N.Y., 1983-85, Gillary Gallery Jericho, N.Y., 1984, others; named to Nat. Women's Hall of Fame; MacDowell fellow, 1975, 80; Sch. Chinese Brush Work scholar, 1973. Mem. Profl. Artists Guild L.I. (v.p. admissions 1971-74, exec. v.p. 1975-77, Judge's Recognition award at Boca Raton Mus. 1989, 2d prize for group show 1990), Profl. Artists Guild Fla., Easthampton Guild-Women in Arts, N.Y. Artists Equity, Nat. Mus. Women in Arts (charter), Gallery 84 (N.Y. chpt. 1979-85). Home and Studio: 5253 Bolero Ciir Delray Beach FL 33484

ROSS, BRIAN ELLIOTT, news correspondent; b. Chgo., Oct. 23, 1948; s. Kenneth Earl and Shirley Louise (Johnston) R. B.A., U. Iowa, 1971. Corr. KWWL-TV, Waterloo, Iowa, 1971, WCKT-TV, Miami, Fla., 1972-74; news corr. NBC News, Cleve. and N.Y.C., 1974—. Recipient Peabody award, 1974, 92, Columbia-DuPont award, 1975, 85, 86, Sigma Delta Chi award,

1976, Robert F. Kennedy award, 1979, Nat. Emmy award, 1980, 85, 88, 92, Nat. Headlines award, 1976, 77, 78, 87, Overseas Press Club award, 1988, 90, 92, George M. Polk award, 1989, 93, Sidney Hillman award, 1993. Office: NBC News 30 Rockefeller Plz New York NY 10112-0002

ROSS, CHARLES, artist; b. Phila., Dec. 17, 1937; s. Fred H. and Gertrude (Hill) R.; m. Elizabeth Ginsberg, 1977. A.B. in Math, U. Calif., Berkeley, 1960, M.A. in Sculpture, 1962. Exhibited in one-man shows: Dilexi Gallery, San Francisco, 1961, 65, 66, 68, Dwan Gallery, N.Y.C., 1968, 69, 71, Daytons Gallery 12, Mpls., 1968, John Weber Gallery, N.Y.C., 1972, 77, 79, 81, The Clocktower, N.Y.C., 1974, Utah Mus. Fine Arts, Salt Lake City, 1975, Mus. Contemporary Art, La Jolla, Calif., 1976, Chgo., 1976, Inst. Contemporary Art, Phila., 1977, Susan Caldwell Gallery, N.Y.C., 1977, MIT, 1977, Portland Center for Visual Arts, 1981, Sena Gallery, Santa Fe, 1991, Johnson Gallery U. N.Mex., 1992, Humphrey Gallery, N.Y.C., 1995; exhibited in group shows: Archtl. League of, New York, 1967, Albright Knox Art Gallery, Buffalo, 1967, Finch Coll., N.Y.C., 1967, Aldrich Mus., Ridgefield, Conn., 1967, Nelson Atkins Mus., Kansas City, 1968, Milw. Art Center, 1968, Whitney Mus., N.Y.C., 1969, Art Inst. Chgo., 1969, Art Gallery of Ont., Toronto, 1969, Galeries-pilotes, Lausanne, Switzerland, 1970, Mus. Fine Arts, Boston, 1971, Indpls. Mus. Art, 1974, Neuberger Mus., SUNY, Purchase, 1975, Stadtisches Mus., Leverkusen, Germany, 1975, Phila. Coll. Art, 1977, Hirshhorn Mus., Washington, 1977, Old Customs House, N.Y.C., 1977, Mus. Natural History, N.Y.C., 1977, Leo Castelli Gallery, N.Y.C., 1978, Yale U. Art Gallery, 1978, Dartmouth Coll. Gallery, 1978, Aspen (Colo.) Center for Visual Arts, 1980, Centre Georges Pompidou, Paris, 1980, Renwick Gallery, Smithsonian Instn., Washington, 1980, Mus. Contemporary Art, Chgo., 1981, MIT, Cambridge, 1981, Bard Coll., 1984, Light Gallery, N.Y.C., 1985, Venice Biennale, 1986, Differentes Natures la Defense, Paris, 1992; commn. include: prism and/or solar spectrum skylight sculpture for Fed. Bldg, Lincoln, Nebr., 1976, U. Pa., 1977, Dietrich Found., Phila., 1979, Spectrum Bldg, Denver, 1980, Grand Rapids Art Mus., Mich., 1982, Towson State U., Md., 1983, Cumberland Rapid Transit Sta., Chgo., 1983, Linay Corp., Kansas City, Mo., 1985, Plaza of the Americas, Dallas, 1985, Wells Fargo Bldg., San Diego, 1986, San Francisco Internat. Airport, 1987, Anchorage Internat. Airport, 1987, Naugatuck Higher Edn. Ctr., Conn., 1990, Harvard Bus. Sc. Chapel, 1992, French Ministry of Culture Chateau d'Oiron, 1993; represented in permanent collections Nelson Atkins Mus., Whitney Mus. Am. Art, Berkeley Art Mus., Indpls. Mus. Art, Butler Inst. Am. Art, Herbert F. Johnson Mus. Art Cornell U., GSA Art and Architecture Program, U. Pa., Dietrich Found., Grand Rapids Art Mus., Gen. Elec. Corp., City Chgo., Towson State U., Becton Dickinson Corp., Security Pacific Bank, Found. Ctr., N.Y.C., Wynne Jackson Inc., Albuquerque Mus., Linclay Corp., Witco Chem. Corp., City of San Diego, Walker Art Ctr., City of San Francisco, State of Alaska, Koll Co., Los Angeles County Mus. Art; works in progress include: Star Axis, monumental sculpture/observatory atop a mesa in N.Mex. Author: Sunlight Convergence Solar Burn (Am. Inst. Graphic Arts award 1976); films Sunlight Dispersion, 1972, Solar Eclipse, 1972. Recipient Art and Architecture Collaborations award Boston Soc. Architects, 1993. Office: Richard Humphrey Gallery PO Box 1358 Canal St Sta New York NY 10013-0377 *As I work to focus light and energy into material form, my work has shown me that it is possible for us to gain an intimacy with the stars.*

ROSS, CHARLES ROBERT, lawyer, consultant; b. Middlebury, Vt., Feb. 24, 1920; s. Jacob Johnson and Hannah Elizabeth (Holmes) R.; m. Charlotte Sells Hoyt, Aug 28, 1948; children—Jacqueline Hoyt, Peter Holmes, Charles Robert. A.B., U. Mich., 1941, M.B.A., 1948, LL.B., 1948. Bar: Ky. 1949, Vt. 1954, U.S. Supreme Ct. 1968. Instr. Oreg. State Coll., 1948-49; practice law Louisville and Burlington, Vt., 1949-59; chmn. Vt. Pub. Service Commn., 1959-61; commr. FPC, 1961-68; mem. U.S. sect. Internat. Joint Commn., 1962-81; mem. Nat. Consumers Energy Com., 1973-74; pub. mem. Adminstrv. Conf. U.S., 1971-74; adj. prof. econs. U. Vt., 1969-74. Served to capt. USAAF, 1941-46, PTO. Home: Hinesburg VT 05461 Office: PO Box 305 Hinesburg VT 05461-0305

ROSS, CHARLES WORTHINGTON, IV, metals company executive; b. Frederick, Md., Jan. 27, 1933; s. Charles Worthington and Priscilla Avis (Wilson) R., 3d; student U. Md., 1951-54; m. Betty Lou Waldvogel, May 26, 1956; children: Holly Theresa Ross-Hartung, Kristna Lynn Ross-Serpico, Amy Louise Ross-Drummond, Carol Ann. BA in Polit. Sci., Syracuse U., 1963; MA in Occupational Safety and Health, NYU, 1976. Commd. 2d lt. U.S. Air Force, 1954, safety officer, 1966-68; ret., 1968; gen. mgr. Mgmt. Recruiters, Inc., Norfolk, Va., 1968-71; regional safety mgr. Mobil Oil Corp., Scarsdale, N.Y., 1971-75; corp. safety mgr. Schering-Plough Corp. Kenilworth, N.J., 1975-79; corp. mgr. safety and health Westvaco Corp., N.Y.C., 1979-81; v.p. mktg., safety and health cons., dir. IHI-KEMRON, Huntington, N.Y., 1981-83, WAPORA, Inc., 1983-86, Essex Chem. Corp., Clifton, N.J., 1986-89; mgr. safety and loss control Handy & Harman, Rye, N.Y., 1989—; instr. safety mgmt. Kean Coll., Union, N.J., 1978-79. Recipient 2d place award for tech. paper Am. Soc. Safety Engrs./Vets. Safety, 1980. Registered profl. engr., Calif.; cert. safety profl., hazard control mgr. (masters level). Mem. Am. Soc. Safety Engrs. (profl. mem.), System Safety Soc., Nat. Safety Mgmt. Soc., Am. Indsl. Hygiene Assn., Safety Execs. N.Y. Democrat. Episcopalian. Author: Computer Systems for Safety and Health Management, 1984, 2d edit., 1991; contbr. articles to profl. jours. Home: 10 Ames Rd Morristown NJ 07960-2954 Office: 555 Theodore Fremd Ave Rye NY 10580-1437

ROSS, CHARLOTTE PACK, suicidologist; b. Oklahoma City, Oct. 21, 1932; d. Joseph and Rose P. (Traibich) Pack; m. Roland S. Ross, May 6, 1951 (div. July 1964); children: Beverly Jo, Sandra Gail; m. Stanley Fisher, Mar. 17, 1991. Student U. Okla., 1949-52, New Sch. Social Rsch., 1953. Cert. tchr. Exec. dir. Suicide Prevention and Crisis Ctr. San Mateo County, Burlingame, Calif., 1966-88; pres., exec. dir. Youth Suicide Nat. Ctr., Washington, 1985-93; exec. dir. Death with Dignity Edn. Ctr., San Mateo, Calif., 1994—; pres. Calif. Senate Adv. Com. Youth Suicide Prevention, 1982-84; speaker Menninger Found., 1983, 84; instr. San Francisco State U., 1981-83; conf. coord. U. Calif. San Francisco, 1971—; cons. univs. and health svcs. throughout world. Contbg. author: Group Counseling for Suicidal Adolescents, 1984, Teaching Children the Facts of Life and Death, 1985; mem. editorial bd. Suicide and Life Threatening Behavior, 1976-89. Mem. regional selection panel Pres.'s Commn. on White House Fellows, 1975-78; mem. CIRCLON Svc. Club, 1979—; Com. on Child Abuse, 1981-85; founding mem. Women for Responsible Govt., co-chmn., 1974-79. Recipient Outstanding Exec. award San Mateo County Coordinating Com., 1971, Koshland award San Francisco Found., 1984. Fellow Wash. Acad. Scis.; mem. Internat. Assn. Suicide Prevention (v.p. 1985—), Am. Assn. Suicidology (sec. 1972-74, svc. award 1990), bd. govs. 1976-78, accreditation com. 1975—, chair region IX, 1975-82), Assn. United Way Agy. Execs. (pres. 1974), Assn. County Contract Agys. (pres. 1982), Peninsula Press Club.

ROSS, CHRISTOPHER WADE STELYAN, diplomat; b. Quito, Ecuador, Mar. 3, 1943 (parents Am. citizens); s. Claude G. Anthony and Antigone Andrea (Peterson) R.; m. Carol Geraldine Canning, Nov. 30, 1968; 1 child, Anthony Gordon. AB summa cum laude, Princeton U., 1965; cert. Middle East Centre for Arab Studies, 1964; MA, Johns Hopkins U., 1967. Editorial asst. Middle East Jour., Washington, 1965-68; instr. Arabic lang. Columbia U., N.Y.C., 1966, Princeton U., 1967; pub. affairs trainee USIA, 1968-69; jr. officer trainee Am. Embassy, Tripoli, Libya, 1969-70; dir. Am. Cultural Ctr., Fez, Morocco, 1970-73; press attache Am. Embassy, Beirut, 1973-76; pub. affairs officer Am. Embassy, Algiers, Algeria, 1976-79, dep. chief mission and charge d'affaires, 1979-81; pub. affairs adviser Bur. Near Eastern and South Asian Affairs, Dept. State, Washington, 1981-82, spl. asst. to presdl. emissaries to Lebanon and Middle East, 1982-84, dir. regional affairs, 1984-85; exec. asst. to Under Sec. State for Polit. Affairs, Washington, 1985-88; amb. to Algeria, 1988-91; amb. to Syria, Damascus, 1991—; chmn. bd. trustees Am. Sch. Algiers, 1977-80; hon. chmn., bd. trustees Damascus Community Sch., 1991—. Contbr. articles to profl. jours. Recipient Superior Honor award U.S Info. Agy., 1976, 83, Dept. State, 1988, Presdl. Meritorious Svc. award, 1983, 85, 89, 93. Mem. Am. Fgn. Svc. Assn., Assn. for Diplomatic Studies, Middle East Inst., Middle East Studies Assn. of N.Am., Royal Soc. for Asian Affairs. Greek Orthodox. Club: Princeton (Washington). Avocations: classic cars; bicycling. Office: Damascus State Washington DC 20521 also: Am Embassy, 2 al-Mansur St Abu Rumaneh, Damascus Syria

ROSS, COLEMAN DEVANE, accountant, insurance company consultant; b. Greensboro, N.C., Mar. 18, 1943; s. Guy Matthews and Nancy McConnell (Coleman) R.; m. Carol Louise Morde, Aug. 26 1965; children: Coleman, Jonathan, Andrew. BS in Bus. Adminstrn., U. N.C., 1965; postgrad. Grad. Sch. of Banking of South, 1982-84, U. N.C. Advanced Mgmt. Program, 1994. CPA, CLU, ChFC; cert. bank auditor. With Price Waterhouse, Tampa, 1965-76, Toronto, 1970, Hartford, Conn., 1976-93, N.Y.C., 1993—, ptnr., 1977—, mng. ptnr. Nat. Ins. Svcs. Group, 1988-94. Mem. bd. dirs. N.E. Region Boy Scouts Am., 1988—, v.p., 1993—, pres. New Eng. area, 1988-91; mem. bd. dirs. Greater N.Y. Couns. Boy Scouts Am., 1994—, mem. exec. bd. Conn. Rivers coun., 1978—, pres. 1986-88; corporator Inst. Living, 1992—, vis. Nurses Assn. Health Care Greater Hartford, 1992—; div. campaign chmn. United Way of Capital Area, 1984; bd. dirs., treas. Family Svc. Soc. Greater Hartford, 1977-80; participant Leadership Greater Hartford, 1977. Recipient Silver Beaver award Boy Scouts Am., 1987, Silver Antelope award, 1991. Fellow Life Mgmt. Inst.; mem. AICPA (ins. cos. com. 1985-88, reins. auditing and acctg. task force 1979-85, rels. with actuaries com. 1982-85), N.Y. Soc. CPAs, N.C. Assn. CPAs, Conn. Soc. CPAs, Soc. Ins. Fin. Mgmt., Am. Soc. CLUs and ChFCs., N.Y.C. Soc. CLUs and ChFCs, Internat. Ins. Soc., Nat. Soc. Chartered Bank Auditors, Assn. Mut. Ins. Accts., Hartford Club (bd. govs. 1977-84). Home: 6 Wild Flower Ln West Simsbury CT 06092 Office: Price Waterhouse 1177 Ave of the Americas New York NY 10036

ROSS, DANIEL R., lawyer; b. Stamford, Conn., Oct. 20, 1941; s. Adrian E. and Ruth (Hill) R.; m. Faye Zerwekh, Aug. 15, 1965; children: Kevin S., Eric D., David W. SB, MIT, 1963; LLB, U. Pa., 1966. Atty. adviser to Hon. Theodore Tannenwald, Jr. U.S. Tax Ct., Washington, 1966-68; assoc. Drinker, Biddle & Reath, Phila., 1970-77, ptnr., 1977—. Presenter in field. Pres. bd. trustees First United Meth. Ch. Germantown, 1984—. Capt. U.S. Army, 1968-70, Vietnam. Mem. ABA (chair com. on income of estates and trusts 1985-87, com. on govt. subcoms. 1988-91, taxation sect.). Avocations: bicycling, skiing, tennis, computers. Office: Drinker Biddle & Reath 1100 PNB Bldg 1345 Chestnut St Philadelphia PA 19107

ROSS, DAVID A., art museum director; b. Malverne, N.Y., Apr. 26, 1949; s. Joshua and Grayce R.; m. Margaret Gronner; children—Lindsay, Emily. B.A., Syracuse U.; postgrad. Grad. Sch. Fine Arts, Syracuse. Curator video art Everson Mus. Art, Syracuse, N.Y., 1971-74; dep. dir. program devel. and TV Long Beach Mus. Art, Calif., 1974-77; chief curator Univ. Art Mus., Berkeley, Calif., 1977-82; dir. Inst. of Contemporary Art, Boston, 1982-91; dir., CEO Whitney Mus. Am. Art., 1991—. Active Fed. Adv. Com. on Internat. Exbns., 1990—. Contbr. articles to profl. jours. Mem. Am. Assn. Mus. Dirs. Office: Whitney Museum Am Art 945 Madison Ave New York NY 10021-2705*

ROSS, DAVID EDMOND, church official; b. Lewiston, Maine, Oct. 1, 1950; s. Rev. and Mrs. Lorne Arla Collins R.; m. Shirley Evelyn Godin, Aug. 19, 1972. BA in Theology cum laude, Berkshire Coll., 1973; MPA, U. Maine, 1989. Ordained to ministry Advent Christian Ch., 1975. Pastor State Road Advent Christian Ch., Presque Isle, Maine, 1973-91; exec. dir. Advent Christian Ch. Gen. Conf., Charlotte, N.C., 1991—; v.p. Maine State Conf. Advent Christian Chs., 1975-76, pres., 1976-81, 86-91; mem. exec. coun. Advent Christian Ch., 1981-90, long range strategy com., 1986—; seminar leader Am. Festival of Evangelism, Kansas City, 1981; dir. Northern Lights Youth Choir, 1974-90. Office: Advent Christian Church PO Box 23152 Charlotte NC 28227-0272

ROSS, DAVID LEE, lawyer; b. Chgo., Dec. 12, 1948; s. Herman Milton and Minnie (Devinatz) R.; m. Abby Lynn Kolber, June 20, 1971; children: Natalie, Jason, Blake. BS in Polit. Sci., Northwestern U., 1970; JD with honors, U. Chgo., 1973. Bar: Ga. 1973, U.S. Dist. Ct. (no. dist.) Ga. 1974, U.S. Ct. Appeals (5th cir.) 1974, Fla. 1979, U.S. Dist. Ct. (so. dist.) Fla. 1979, U.S. Dist. Ct. (mid. dist.) Fla., U.S. Ct. Appeals (11th cir.), U.S. Ct. Appeals (9th cir.). Assoc. Haas, Holland, Levison & Gilbert, Atlanta, 1973-77, ptnr., 1977-78; assoc. Greenberg, Traurig, Hoffman, Lipoff, Rosen & Quentel, P.A., Miami, Fla., 1978-80; shareholder Greenberg, Traurig, Hoffman, Lipoff, Rosen & Quentel, P.A., Miami, 1980—. Trustee Coconut Grove Playhouse, Miami, 1989-93. Mem. ABA (civil practice and procedure com. antitrust sect. 1991—), Fla. Bar (chmn. comml. litigation com. 1982-86, bus. law sect. 1987-88), Order of Coif. Home: 11915 SW 67th Ct Miami FL 33156-4755 Office: Greenberg Traurig Hoffman Lipoff Rosen & Quentel PA 1221 Brickell Ave Miami FL 33131

ROSS, DEBORAH LYNN (DEBBIE ROSS), reporter, photographer; b. Pitts., Mar. 29, 1961; d. David William and Joan Muriel (Reinhardt) R. BS in Journalism, Ball State U., 1984. Reporter, photographer High Country Ind. Press, Belgrade, Mont., 1986-87, Dillon (Mont.) Tribune-Examiner, 1987—. Recipient first prizes for best sports photo and best editorial page Mont. Newspaper Assn., 1987, third place award Nat. Newspaper Assn., 1988. Mem. Nat. Press Photographer's Assn. (best photo 1983, 1984), Mont. Press Assn. Democrat. Presbyterian. Avocations: photography, travel, sports, hiking, music. Home: PO Box 749 Dillon MT 59725-0749 Office: Dillon Tribune-Examiner Dillon MT 59725

ROSS, DELMER GERRARD, historian, educator; b. Los Banos, Calif., Nov. 5, 1942; s. Elmer G. and Orva Beth (Dickinson) R.; m. Karen Ann Gibson, June 17, 1977; children: Michelle, Richard. BA, Pacific Union Coll., 1965; MA, U. Calif., Santa Barbara, 1967, PhD, 1970. Instr. Pacific Union Coll., Angwin, Calif., 1969-68; from asst. to assoc. prof. Oakwood Coll., Huntsville, Ala., 1970-76; from assoc. prof. to prof. history Loma Linda U., Riverside, Calif., 1976-91, chmn. dept. history and polit. sci., 1986-90; prof. history and polit. sci. La Sierra U., Riverside, 1991—. Author: Visionaries and Swindlers, 1975, Rails Across Costa Rica, 1976, Rails in Paradise, 1991, Gold Road to La Paz, 1992; chmn. editorial bd. Adventist Heritage mag., 1987-90. Bd. dirs. Inst. for Research in Latin Am., Mobile, Ala., 1968-82. Mem. Am. Hist. Assn., Conf. Latin Am. History (Caribe-Centroamerica regional com. chmn. 1973-75), Assn. 7th Day Adventist Historians (sec.-treas. 1974-75, pres. 1981-82), Assn. Western Adventist Historians, Nat. Railway Hist. Soc., Colo. Railroad Hist. Found. Republican. Office: La Sierra U Dept of History Riverside CA 92515

ROSS, DIANA, singer, actress, entertainer, fashion designer; b. Detroit, Mar. 26, 1944; d. Fred and Ernestine R.; m. Robert Ellis Silberstein, Jan. 1971 (div. 1976); children: Rhonda, Tracee, Chudney; m. Arne Naess, Oct. 23, 1985; 1 son: Ross Arne. Grad. high sch. Pres. Diana Ross Enterprises, Inc., fashion and merchandising, Anaid Film Prodns., Inc., RTC Mgmt. Corp., artists mgmt., Chondee Inc., Rosstown, Rossville, music pub. Started in Detroit as mem. the Primettes; lead singer until 1969, Diana Ross and the Supremes; solo artist, 1969—; albums include Diana Ross, 1970, 76, Everything Is Everything, 1971, I'm Still Waiting, 1971, Lady Sings The Blues, 1972, Touch Me In The Morning, 1973, Original Soundtrack of Mahogany, 1975, Baby It's Me, 1977, The Wiz, 1978, Ross, 1978, The Boss, 1979, Diana, 1981, To Love Again, 1981, Why Do Fools Fall In Love?, 1981, Silk Electric, 1982, Swept Away, 1984, Eaten Alive, 1985, Chain Reaction, 1986, Diana's Duets, 1987, Workin' Overtime, 1989, Red Hot Rhythm and Blues, 1987, Surrender, 1989, Ain't No Mountain High Enough, 1989, The Force Behind the Power, 1991, Stolen Moment: The Lady Sings... Jazz & Blues, 1993, Musical Memories Forever, 1993, The Remixes, 1994; films include Lady Sings the Blues, 1972, Mahogany, 1975, The Wiz, 1978; NBC-TV spl., An Evening With Diana Ross, 1977, Diana, 1981, numerous others; TV movie Out of Darkness, 1994; album Endless Love, 1982; author: Secrets of a Sparrow, 1993. Recipient citation Vice Pres. Humphrey for efforts on behalf Pres. Johnson's Youth Opportunity Program, citation Mrs. Martin Luther King and Rev. Abernathy for contbn. to SCLC cause, awards Billboard, Cash Box and Record World as worlds outstanding singer, Grammy award, 1970, Female Entertainer of Year NAACP, 1970, Cue award as Entertainer of year, 1972, Golden Apple award, 1972, Gold medal award Photoplay, 1972, Antoinette Perry award, 1977, nominee as best actress of year for Lady Sings the Blues Motion Picture Acad. Arts and Scis., 1972, Golden Globe award, 1972; named to Rock and Roll Hall of Fame, 1988. Office: RTC Mgmt PO Box 1683 New York NY 10185-1683 also: care Shelly Berger 6255 W Sunset Blvd Los Angeles CA 90028-7403*

ROSS, DONALD, JR., English language educator, university administrator; b. N.Y.C., Oct. 18, 1941; s. Donald and Lea (Meyer) R.; m. Sylvia Berger

(div.); 1 child, Jessica; m. 2d, Diane Redfern, Aug. 27, 1971; children—Owen, Gillian. B.A., Lehigh U., 1963, M.A., 1964; Ph.D., U. Mich., 1967. Asst. prof. English U. Pa., Phila., 1967-70; prof. English U. Minn., Mpls., 1970—, dir. composition program, 1982-86, dir. Univ. Coll., 1984-89; ret., 1989. Co-author: Word Processor and Writing Process, 1984, Revising Mythologies: The Composition of Thoreau's Major Works, 1988; contbr. articles to profl. jours. Grantee Am. Coun. Learned Socs., 1976, 90, NSF, 1974, Fund for Improvement of Postsecondary Edn., 1982-85; recipient Disting. Teaching award U. Minn., 1992. Mem. Assn. for Computers and Humanities (exec. sec. 1978-88), MLA, Assn. for Lit. and Linguistic Computing. Office: U Minn Composition Program 209 Church St SE Minneapolis MN 55455-0152

ROSS, DONALD EDWARD, engineering company executive; b. N.Y.C., May 2, 1930; m. Jeanne Ellen McKessy, Apr. 4, 1954; children: Susan, Christopher, Carolyn. BA, Columbia U., 1952, BS in Mech. Engring., 1953; MBA, NYU, 1960. Registered profl. engr., N.Y., 14 other states. Engr. Carrier Corp., N.Y.C., 1955-70; v.p. Dynadata, 1970-71; with Jaros, Baum & Bolles, N.Y.C., 1971—, ptnr., 1977—. Vice chmn. adv. coun. Columbia U. Sch. Engring. and Applied Sci. Lt. (j.g.) USN, 1953-55. Fellow ASHRAE; mem. ASME, NSPE, Nat. Acad. Enrs. (mech. engring. peer com.), Am. Cons. Engrs. Coun., Nat. Bur. Engring. Registration, N.Y. Assn. Cons. Engrs. (pres. 1984-86), Coun. on Tall Bldgs. and Urban Habitat (vice chmn. N.Am., mem. steering group), Univ. Club (N.Y.C.), Nassau Country Club, Tau Beta Pi. Office: Jaros Baum & Bolles 345 Park Ave New York NY 10154-0002

ROSS, DONALD EDWARD, university administrator; b. Mineola, N.Y., June 29, 1939; s. Alexander Walker and Florence M. (Carville) R.; m. Helen Landgren, June 23, 1966; children: Ellen Ross Sarafian, Kevin McAndrew. BFA, N.Y. Inst. Tech., 1962, LLD (hon.), 1978; MS, Hofstra U., 1970. Dean of students N.Y. Inst. Tech., Old Westbury, 1962-68; pres. Wilmington (Del.) Coll., 1968-77; pres., CEO Lynn U. (formerly Coll. of Boca Raton), Fla., 1971—; chmn. adv. com. U.S. Army Command and Gen. Staff Coll. Bd. dirs. Fla. Endowment Fund, 1989—; trustee Boca Raton Community Hosp., 1990—; mem. governing bd. Philharmonic Orch. Fla., 1990—; mem. U.S. Mil. Screening Com. Named Industrialist of Yr., Greater Boca Raton C. of C., 1992, Man of the Yr., City of Hope; recipient Boy Scouts Am. Leadership Svc. award, Boca Raton award, 1991. Mem. Assn. Univ. Pres., Econ. Coun. of Palm Beach County, Royal Palm Yacht and Country, Loggerhead Club, Adirondack League Club, Old Forge Club, City (Boca Raton). Avocations: snowskiing, tennis, reading, travel. Home: 150 NE 5th Ave Boca Raton FL 33432 Office: Lynn Univ 3601 N Military Trail Boca Raton FL 33431

ROSS, DONALD HUGH, fraternal organization executive; b. Delta, Ohio, Aug. 19, 1949; s. Hugh Archbald and Margaret Baker (Harlton) R.; m. Mary Lynn Feuerborn, Dec. 21, 1974; children: Jon, Michael. BS, Miami U., Oxford, Ohio, 1971. Auditor Moose Internat., Mooseheart, Ill., 1971-76, dep. supreme sec., 1976-78, asst. comptroller, 1978-83; supreme sec. Supreme Lodge, Mooseheart, Ill., 1983—; sec. Mooseheart Bd. Govs., Moosehaven Bd. Govs., 1983—. Mem. editorial bd. Moose Action publ.; contbr. articles to newspapers and profl. jours. Republican. Club: Interact (Delta) (pres. 1966-67). Lodge: Moose (past gov. 1976, Pilgrim Degree of Merit 1983). Avocations: golf, bowling. Home: 1119 Woodland Ave Batavia IL 60510-3049 Office: Moose Internat Mooseheart IL 60539

ROSS, DONALD KEITH, retired insurance company executive; b. Rochester, N.Y., July 1, 1925; s. Alexander L. and Althea G. (Granger) R.; m. Mary F. Fyffe, June 4, 1949; children: Catherine (Mrs. Charles P. Lesher), Susan (Mrs. William Gardner Morris, Jr.), Donald Keith, Deborah Anne (Mrs. Michael Holt). B.E., Yale U., 1946; M.B.A., Harvard U., 1948. With N.Y. Life Ins. Co., N.Y.C., 1948—, exec. v.p., 1974-79, vice chmn., 1979-80, pres., 1980-81, chmn. bd., CEO, 1981-90, chmn. exec. com., 1990-93, also bd. dirs.; ret., 1993; trustee Consol. Edison of N.Y. Office: NY Life Ins Co 51 Madison Ave New York NY 10010-1603

ROSS, DONALD KENNETH, consulting engineering executive; b. St. Louis, Apr. 15, 1925; s. Maurice James and Babe Cyril (Grodsky) R.; m. Peggy Grosberg, July 1, 1951; 1 dau., Pamela Toder. BSEE, U. Minn., 1946; MS, MIT, 1948; ScD, Washington U., St. Louis, 1960. Rsch., teaching asst. MIT, 1946-48; electronics engr. Mo. Rsch., Inc., 1949-51; prin. Donald Ross & Assocs., St. Louis, 1953-61; pres. Ross & Baruzzini, Inc., St. Louis, 1961-91, chmn., 1991—; pres. Hanlon & Assocs., Inc., St. Louis, 1976-85; profl. assoc. Bldg. Rsch. and Adv. Bd., Nat. Acad. Scis.; lectr. Washington U. Patentee to 3 U.S. Patents. With USNR, 1943-46, 1951-53 Korea. Recipient Outstanding Achievement award IEEE Industry Applications Soc., 1989, Engring. Alumni Achievement award Washington U., 1993. Fellow Am. Cons. Engrs. Council, IEEE; mem. Assn. Profl. Material Handling Cons. (pres. 1976-77), Mo. Assn. Cons. Engrs. (past pres.), Sigma Xi, Tau Beta Pi, Eta Kappa Nu. Office: 1304 Baur Blvd Saint Louis MO 63132-1903

ROSS, DONALD ROE, federal judge; b. Orleans, Nebr., June 8, 1922; s. Roe M. and Leila H. (Reed) R.; m. Janice S. Cook, Aug. 29, 1943; children: Susan Jane, Sharon Kay, Rebecca Lynn, Joan Christine, Donald Dean. JD, U. Nebr., 1948, LLD (hon.), 1990. Bar: Nebr. bar 1948. Practice law Lexington, Nebr., 1948-53; mayor City of Lexington, 1953; assoc. Swarr, May, Royce, Smith, Andersen & Ross, 1956-70; U.S. atty. Dist. Nebr., 1953-56; gen. counsel Rep. party, Nebr. 1956-58; mem. Rep. Exec. Com. for Nebr., 1952-53; nat. com. mem. Rep. Nat. Com., 1958-70, vice chmn., 1965-70; sr. judge U.S. Ct. Appeals 8th cir., 1971—.

ROSS, DOROTHY, history educator; b. Milw. Aug. 13, 1936; m. Stanford G. Ross, June 9, 1958; children: John, Ellen. BA, Smith Coll., 1958; MA, Columbia U., 1959, PhD, 1965. Fellow in history and psychiatry Cornell U. Med. Coll/Payne Whitney Clinic, N.Y.C., 1965-67; spl. asst. com. on women historians Am. Hist. Assn., Washington, 1971-72; asst. prof. Princeton (N.J.) U., 1972-76; from assoc. prof. to prof. U. Va., Charlottesville, 1978-90; Arthur O. Lovejoy prof. history Johns Hopkins U., Balt., 1990—; mem. adv. com. on women HEW, Washington, 1978. Author: G. Stanley Hall, 1972, The Origins of American Social Science, 1991; editor: Modernist Impulses in the Human Sciences, 1870-1930, 1994; adv. editor Isis, 1979-86; bd. editors Jour. of the History of Ideas, 1993—; contbr. articles to profl. jours. USPHS grantee, 1965-68, NSF grantee, 1980-81. Fellow Ctr. for Advanced Study in Behavioral Scis. Soc. Am. Historians; mem. Am. Studies Assn., History of Sci. Soc., Am. Hist. Assn., Orgn. Am. Historians (exec. bd. 1987-89). Office: Johns Hopkins U Dept Of History Baltimore MD 21218

ROSS, DOUGLAS, lawyer; b. L.A., July 12, 1948; s. Mathew and Brenda Butler (Boynton) R.; m. Lynne Rose Maidman, June 14, 1970. AB cum laude, Tufts U., 1970; JD with honors, George Washington U., 1973. Bar: Ohio 1973, D.C. 1980, U.S. Supreme Ct. 1976. Asst. atty. gen., antitrust sect. Office of Ohio Atty. Gen., Columbus, 1973-74; spl. asst. U.S. atty. Ea. Dist. Va., Alexandria, 1977; trial atty. antitrust divsn. U.S. Dept. Justice, Washington, 1975-82; atty. advisor Office of Legis. Affairs, 1984-86; Office of Legal Policy, 1987-89; Office Policy Devel., 1989-92; Supreme Ct. counsel Nat. Assn. Attys. Gen., 1982-91; ran advocacy project for states to enhance their effectiveness before Supreme Ct., 1982-91, operated clearinghouse on state constl. law, 1987-91; civil divsn. Appellate Staff, 1992-94, Office of Consumer Litigation, 1994—. Recipient Meritorious award Dept. Justice, 1979, Spl. Achievement award, 1984. Mem. Supreme Ct. Hist. Soc., D.C. Bar Assn., Supreme Ct. Opinion Network (bd. dirs. 1989-91). Jewish. Home: 3153 19th St N Arlington VA 22201-5103 Office: US Dept Justice PO Box 386 Washington DC 20044-0386

ROSS, DOUGLAS TAYLOR, retired software company executive; b. Canton, Republic of China, Dec. 21, 1929; (parents Am. citizens); s. Robert Malcolm and Margaret (Taylor) R.; m. Patricia Mott, Jan. 24, 1951; children: Jean R. Yoos, Kathryn R. Chow, Margaret R. Thrasher. AB in Math. cum laude, Oberlin Coll., 1951; SM, MIT, 1954, postgrad. math., 1958. Head computer applications group elec. systems lab. MIT, Cambridge, 1952-69, lectr. dept. elec. engring. and computer sci., 1960-69, 83—, exec. com. MIT Enterprise Forum, 1984-89; pres. SofTech, Inc., Waltham, Mass., 1969-75, chmn. bd., 1975-89, 91-93, chmn. emeritus, 1989-91, 93-94, chmn. emeritus ret., 1994—. Mem. town meeting, Lexington, Mass., 1960-70; trustee, bd. dirs. Charles Babbage Inst., 1984—. Mem. United Ch. of Christ. Home and Office: 33 Dawes Rd Lexington MA 02173-5926

ROSS, E. DENNIS, retail executive; b. Springfield, Ohio, Dec. 20, 1941; s. Edward and Thelma (Burkepile) R.; m. Marian Ruth Dreyer; children: Christopher Dennis, Stephanie Dreyer. BCE, Ohio U., 1965, MCE, 1966. Mktg. rep. IBM Corp., Columbus, Ohio, 1966-71; dir. mktg. Applied Mgmt. Systems, Columbus, 1971-74, v.p., 1974-77; sr. cons. assoc. Mgmt. Horizons, Columbus, 1977-78, v.p., 1978-81, exec. v.p., 1981-83; v.p. The Home Depot, Atlanta, 1983-85, sr. v.p., 1985—; bd. dirs. Quality Stores Inc., North Muskegon, Mich.; speaker in field. Methodist. Avocations: golf, tennis. Office: Home Depot 2727 Paces Ferry Rd NW Atlanta GA 30339-4053

ROSS, EDWARD, cardiologist; b. Fairfield, Ala., Oct. 10, 1937; s. Horace and Carrie Lee (Griggs) R.; BS, Clark Coll., 1959; MD, Ind. U., 1963; m. Catherine I. Webster, Jan. 19, 1974; children: Edward, Ronald, Cheryl, Anthony. Intern, Marion County Gen. Hosp., Indpls., 1963; resident in internal medicine Ind. U., 1964-66, 68, cardiology rsch. fellowship, 1968-70, clin. asst. prof. medicine, 1970; cardiologist Capitol Med. Assn., Indpls., 1970-74; pvt. practice medicine, specializing in cardiology, Indpls., 1974—; staff cardiologist Winona Meml. Hosp., Indpls.; staff Meth. Hosp., Indpls., chmn. cardiovascular sect., chmn.; dir. cardiovascular ctr. Meth. Hosp., 1990-92; bd. dirs. Meth. Hosp. Heart-Lung Ctr., 1990—, med. dir. cardiovascular svcs., 1991—. Mem. Cen. Ind. Health Planning Coun., 1972-73; bd. dir. Ind. chpt. Am. Heart Assn., 1973-74, multiphasic screening East Side Clinic, Flanner House of Indpls., 1968-71; med. dir. Nat. Ctr. for Health Service Rsch. and Devel., HEW, 1970; consumer rep. radiologic device panel health, FDA, 1988-92; dir. hypertensive screening State of Ind., 1974; J.B. Johnson Cardiovascular lectr. Nat. Med. Assn., 1991. Assoc. editor Angiology, Jour. Vascular Disease. Capt., MC, USAF, 1966-68. Woodrow Wilson fellow, 1959; Nat. Found. Health scholar, 1955, Gorgas Found. scholar, 1955. Diplomate Am. Bd. Internal Medicine. Fellow Royal Soc. Promotion of Health (Eng.), Am. Coll. Angiology (v.p. fgn. affairs, sec. 1993—), Internat. Coll. of Angiology, Am. Coll. Cardiology, Assn. Black Cardiologists (mem. bd. dirs. 1990-94); mem. AMA, Am. Soc. Contemporary Medicine and Surgery, Nat. Med. Assn. (council sci. assembly 1985-89), Ind. Med. Soc., Marion County Med. Soc., Am. Soc. Internal Medicine, Am. Heart Assn., Ind. Soc. Internal Medicine (pres. 1987-89), Ind. State Med. Assn. (chmn. internal medicine sect. 1987-89), Aesculapean Med. Soc., Hoosier State Med. Assn. (pres. 1980-85, 90—), NAACP, Urban League, Ind. Med. Soc., Alpha Omega Alpha, Alpha Kappa Mu, Beta Kappa Chi, Omega Psi Phi. Baptist. Sr. editor Jour. Vascular Medicine, 1983—. Office: 3737 N Meridian St Ste 400 Indianapolis IN 46208-4348

ROSS, EDWARD JOSEPH, architect; b. Everett, Mass., Dec. 13, 1934; s. Miriam R.; m. Gail Tishler, Feb. 2, 1963; children: Linda Joy, Melissa Carol. Student Boston Archtl. Ctr., 1952-55, 61-62, USAF Surveying Sch., 1955-56, Boston Soc. Civil Engrs., 1956-57, Carl Bolivar Structural Engring., 1962-63. Registered architect, Mass., Calif., N.Y., Fla., N.H., Vt.; cert. Nat. Coun. Archtl. Registration Bds.; lic. constrn. supr., Mass.; expert witness. Draftsman, assoc. William W. Drummey, Architect, Boston, 1952-59; job capt., designer Drummey-Rosane-Anderson, Boston, 1959-64; projects architect Maginnis & Walsh & Kennedy, Boston, 1964-69; v.p. William Nelson Jacobs Assocs., Inc., Boston, 1969-73; staff architect Robert Charles Assocs., Inc., Architects, Boston, 1973-74; office mgr. Charles F. Jacobs Assocs., Inc., Cambridge, Mass., 1974-76; cons. architect Linenthal, Eisenberg & Anderson, Boston, 1976-77; staff architect Eisenberg Haven Assocs., Inc., Boston, 1977-78; chief architect, chief inspector Boston Housing Authority, 1978-83; prin. Edward J. Ross, AIA/FARA, Randolph, Mass., 1983-84; architect, sr. assoc., dir. constrn. administrn., Stull and Lee, Inc., Boston, 1984-91; practice architecture, Randolph, 1963—. Mem. Ancient and Honorable Arty. Co. of Mass. Staff sgt. USAF; lt. Mass. Def. Force. Fellow Soc. Am. Registered Architects; mem. Am. Arbitration Assn. (mem. nat. panel 1965—), AIA, Boston Soc. Architects (housing com. 1982-86), Mass. State Assn. Architects, Constrn. Specifications Inst., Air Force Assn. (pres. Boston chpt.), Ten of Us Club, Linderhof Golf Course Site One Assn. (pres. 1980-86), Elks, Knights of Pythias, Am. Legion. Office: 8 Eagle Rock Rd Randolph MA 02368-3516

ROSS, EDWARD W., diversified corporation executive; b. Chgo. Student, Ill. Inst. Tech., 1943. With Economy Chem. Industries, 1946—; pres. Jupiter Industries, Inc., Chgo., 1973—; exec. v.p. Jupiter Kenosha, Wis.; sr. v.p. Economy Plumbing and Heating Co.; former v.p. Kenosha Transport Corp.; chmn. Jupiter Transp. Co., Kenosha; vice chmn. bd. Jupiter Corp., 1973—; also bd. dirs.; dir. Lake Shore Bank. Office: Jupiter Industries Inc 919 N Michigan Ave Chicago IL 60611

ROSS, ELINOR, soprano; b. Tampa, Fla., Aug. 1, 1932; d. Joe D. and Lillian Rosenthal; m. Aaron M. Diamond; 1 son, Ross. Student, Syracuse U. Debuts include: Turandot, Met. Opera, N.Y.C., Il Trovatore, Cin. Opera, Cavalleria Rusticana, La Scala, Milan, Tosca, Bolshoi, Moscow; leading soprano roles with, Met. Opera, LaScala, Bolshoi, Chgo. Lyric Opera, San Francisco Opera, Tulsa Opera, Cin. Opera, Staatsoper, Vienna, LaFenice, Venice, Teatro Colon, Buenos Aires, Argentina, Arena de Verona, Massimo de Palermo; inaugurated Rossini Festival in Pesaro; televised concert tour in Peoples Republic of China, Taiwan; appeared in concerts, opera, symphony in Hong Kong, Japan, Thailand, Korea; appeared with symphony orchs. throughout world. Recipient medal of honor Novosibiresk, Siberia. Jewish. *

ROSS, EUNICE LATSHAW, judge; b. Bellevue, Pa., Oct. 13, 1923; d. Richard Kelly and Eunice (Weidner) Latshaw; m. John Anthony Ross, May 29, 1943 (dec. Jan. 1978); 1 child, Geraldine Ross Coleman. BS, U. Pitts., 1945, LLB, 1951. Bar: Pa. 1952. Atty., Pub. Health Law Research Project, Pitts., 1951-52; atty. judl. asst., law clk. St. Common Pleas, Pitts., 1952-70; adjunct law prof. U. Pitts., 1967-73; dir. family div. Ct. Common Pleas, Pitts., 1970-72; judge Ct. Common Pleas of Allegheny County, Pitts., 1972—; mem. Bd. Jud. Inquiry and Rev., Commonwealth of Pa., 1984-89, Gov's Justice Commn., 1972-78. Author: (with others) Survey of Pa. Public Health Laws, 1952. Co-author: Will Contests, 1992; contbr. articles to legal publs. Com. person for 14th ward, vice chmn. Democratic Com., Pitts., 1972; exec. com. bd. trustees U. Pitts., 1980-86, bd. visitors law sch., 1985—; bd. visitors sch. health, 1986—; adv. bd. Animal Friends, Pitts., 1973—; bd. mem. The Program, Pitts., 1983-87, Pitts. History and Landmarks FDTN., West Pa. Hist. Soc., West Pa. Conservancy. Recipient Disting. Amumna award U. Pitts., 1973, Medal of Recognition, 1987, Susan B. Anthony award Womens' Bar Assn. Western Pa., 1993, Probate and Trusts award, 1994; named Girl Scout Woman of Yr., Pitts. coun. Girl Scouts U.S., 1975; cert. of Achievement Pa. Fedn. Women's Clubs, 1975, 77. Mem. Scribes, Allegheny County Bar Assn. (vice chmn., exec. com. young lawyers sect. 1956-59), Pa. State Trial Judges Conf., Order of Coif. Home: 1204 Denniston Ave Pittsburgh PA 15217-1329 Office: Frick Bldg 3d Fl Pittsburgh PA 15219

ROSS, GEORGE MARTIN, investment banker; b. Phila., July 24, 1933; s. David L. and Beatrice (Rittenberg) Rosenkoff; m. Lyn Merry Goldberg, Nov. 26, 1959; children: Merry Beth, Michael John. BS, Drexel U., 1955. Mgmt. trainee Sears, Roebuck & Co., Phila., 1955-58; assoc. Goldman, Sachs & Co., Phila., 1959-68, v.p., 1968-70, gen. ptnr., 1971-90, ltd. ptnr., 1991—. Mem. Mayor's Cultural Adv. Coun., Phila., 1987-91, campaign steering com. Bus. Leadership Organized for Cath. Schs., 1983-89; campaign policy com. United Way Southeastern Pa., 1983-84, We the People 200 com., 1984-86, Gov.'s Pvt. Sector Initiatives Task Force, 1983-84, Gov.'s Commn. on Financing Higher Edn., 1983-84, Wills Eye Hosp. Adv. Coun., 1979-81, nat. bd. govs., exec. com., past pres., bd. dirs., past chmn. Phila chpt. Am. Jewish Com.; v.p., exec. com. Jewish Fedn. Greater Phila.; chmn. emeritus, bd. dirs., exec. com. Phila. Drama Guild; gov. Phila. Stock Exch., 1981-85; trustee Episcopal Acad., 1981-84; chmn. bd. trusts, mem. exec. com. Drexel U., Phila., 1981—; bd. dirs. Ave. of the Arts, 1994—, Phila. Orch. Assn. and Acad. Music Phila., 1985-91, Cystic Fibrosis Found., 1978-83, Nat. Found. Jewish Culture, 1986-91; mem. nat. bd., Phila. co-chmn. One to One; mem. investment com. U.S. Holocaust Mus. Mem. Urban Affairs Partnership (bd. dirs. 1978-83), Greater Phila. C. of C. (mem. exec. com. 1989—), Fin. Analysts Phila., Phila. Securities Assn., Bond Club Phila., Union League, Sunday Breakfast Club (Phila.), Locust Club, Phila. Club. Home: 1116 Barberry Rd Bryn Mawr PA 19010-1908 Office: Goldman Sachs & Co Mellon Bank Ctr Fl 26 Philadelphia PA 19103

ROSS, GEORGE WILLIAM, social scientist, educator; b. Cambridge, Mass., Aug. 18, 1940; s. Donald Reynolds and Mabel (Cumming) R.; m. Anne Gillain, Aug. 12, 1964 (div. 1967); m. Jane Jenson, Jan. 18, 1978; 1 child, Bridget Jenson. AB, Williams Coll., 1962; MSc in Econs., London Sch. Econs., 1964; PhD, Harvard U., 1972. Asst. prof. dept. sociology Brandeis U., Waltham, Mass., 1971-76, assoc. prof., 1976-82, prof. sociology, 1982—, Morris Hillquit prof. in labor and social thought, 1986—, chmn. dept. sociology, 1987-90; sr. assoc. Ctr. European Studies, Harvard U., Cambridge, 1983—. Author: Workers and Communists in France, 1982, (with others) Unions, Crisis and Change, 1982, The View from Inside, 1984; editor: The Mitterrand Experiment, 1987, Searching for the New France, 1991, Jacques Delors and European Integration, 1994; corp. editor Theory and Society, 1978—; co-editor French Politics and Society, 1982—. German Marshall Fund of U.S. fellow, 1978-79, 91-92, Fulbright fellow, 1984-85; Bellagio resident, Rockefeller Found., 1987. Mem. Am. Sociol. Assn., Am. Polit. Sci. Assn., Coun. European Studies (exec. com., chair coun.), Conf. Group French Politics and Soc. (exec. sec. 1985—). Avocations: music, hiking, skiing. Office: Brandeis Univ Dept Of Sociology Waltham MA 02154

ROSS, GERALD FRED, engineering executive, researcher; b. N.Y.C., Dec. 14, 1930; s. Samuel Henry and Jenny (Saltzman) Rozansky; m. Vivian Ida Turkish, Dec. 24, 1953; children: Jayne T. Ross Kaufman, Steven A., Helene B. Ross Joseph. BEE, CCNY, 1952; MEE, Poly. U., 1955, PhD, 1963. Registered profl. engr., N.Y., Mass. Rsch asst. U. Mich., Ann Arbor, 1952-53; sr. engr. W.L. Maxson Corp., N.Y.C., 1954-58; rsch. sect. head Sperry Gyroscope Co., Great Neck, L.I., N.Y., 1958-65; dept. mgr. Sperry Rsch. Ctr., Sudbury, Mass., 1965-81; pres. ANRO Engring., Inc., Sarasota, Fla., 1981—; pres., v.p., treas. Adams Pool Corp., Lexington, Mass., 1968-81. Capt. USAFR, 1953—. Contbg. author 3 books, 1986, 90, 93; contbr. numerous articles to profl. jours.; 55 patents in field. Fellow Polytechnic U. Fellow IEEE (K.C. Black Nerem Best Paper award 1974); mem. Electromagnetics Acad., Res. Officers Assn., Nat. Acad. Engring., Lexington Golf Club, Longboat Key Club, Sigma Xi (sr.), Tau Beta Pi, Eta Kappa Nu. Republican. Jewish. Avocations: golf, tennis. Office: ANRO Engring Inc Ste 878 1800 2d St Sarasota FL 34236

ROSS, GLORIA FRANKENTHALER, artist, consultant; b. N.Y.C., Sept. 5, 1923; d. Alfred and Martha (Lowenstein) Frankenthaler; m. John J. Bookman; children: Alfred Frankenthaler Ross, Beverly Ross, Clifford Ross. BA, Mt. Holyoke Coll., 1943. Owner, operator Gloria F. Ross Tapestries, N.Y.C., 1963—; lectr. Internat. Tapestry Symposium, Australian Bicentennial, Fashion Inst. Tech., N.Y., Harvard Club, Shared Horizons, Santa Fe. Exhibited in group shows at Rutgers Barclay Gallery, Santa Fe, N.Mex., Feigen Gallery, Chgo., Washington and N.Y., Pace Edits., N.Y., The Ringling Mus., Sarasota, Fla., Lausanne Biennale, Kauffman Gallery, Houston; represented in permanent collections at IBM, J.C. Penney Co., Tougaloo (Miss.) Coll. Art Mus., Kennedy Internat. Airport, N.Y., Bank of Tokyo, N.Y., Citibank, N.Y.; commd. tapestries for Westinghouse Broadcasting Co., Phila., Winters Bank, Dayton, Ohio, Fed. Courthouse, Portland, Oreg., Mazza Gallery Prudential Ins. Co., Washington; collaborator tapestries with various artists, including Avery Bearden, Stuart Davis, Hofmann Motherwell, Youngerman. Chmn. Child Devel. Ctr., N.Y.C., 1960's; trustee Mt. Holyoke Coll., South Hadley, Mass., 1986—; active numerous civic groups, N.Y.C. Mem. Am. Craft Council, ArtTable, Cooper Hewitt, Met. Mus. Modern Art, Mus. Natural History, Textile Mus., Mt. Holyoke Coll. Art Mus. Avocation: sports.

ROSS, GLYNN, opera administrator; b. Omaha, Dec. 15, 1914; s. Herman and Ida (Carlson) R.; m. Angelamaria Solimene, Nov. 15, 1946; children: Stephanie, Claudia, Melanie, Anthony. Student, Leland Powers Sch. Theater, Boston, 1937-39. bd. dirs. O.P.E.R.A. Am. Nat. Opera Inst., Sch. for Germanic Music Culture; founder, dir. Pacific N.W. Festival, 1975—. Opera stage dir., U.S., Can., 1939-63, debut, San Francisco Opera, 1948, gen. dir., Seattle Opera Assn., Inc., 1963-83, dir., Ariz. Opera, 1983—. Served to 1st lt. AUS, 1942-47. Office: Ariz Opera Assn 3501 N Mountain Ave Tucson AZ 85719-1925

ROSS, GUY MATTHEWS, JR., international leaf tobacco executive; b. Guilford County, N.C., May 5, 1933; s. Guy Matthews and Nancy McConnell (Coleman) R.; m. Patricia Jane Fields, Aug. 27, 1955; children: Charles Alan, Steven York. BSBA, U. N.C., Chapel Hill, 1955. With fin. mgmt. program, then supr. sales acctg. and billing, corp. audit staff, fin. analyst Gen. Electric Co., Ft. Wayne, Ind., Schenectady, Pittsfield, Mass., 1955-56, 58-66; chief acct., v.p. fin. and adminstrn. Imperial Group Ltd., Am. Leaf Orgn., Wilson, N.C., 1966-80; treas., sec. Std. Comml. Corp., Wilson, 1980-92, v.p., sec., 1992—; bd. dirs. Wachovia Bank and Trust Co., Wilson. Pres., heart fund chmn. Wilson div. N.C. Heart Assn., 1967-68; dir., exec. com. Wilson United Way; instl. rep. East Carolina council Boy Scouts Am., 1967-76, mem. administrv. bd. and fin. com., 1971-78; pres. Men's Fellowship Class, First United Methodist Ch., 1975-76. Served with U.S. Army, 1956-58. Mem. U. N.C. Alumni Assn. (life; mem. Ednl. Found.), Fin. Execs. Inst. (dir. N.C. chpt., pres. 1993-94), Nat. Investor Relations Inst., Kiwanis (life mem., disting lt. gov. 1978-79). Home: 1804 Chelsea Dr NW Wilson NC 27896-1412 Office: Standard Comml Corp 2201 Miller Rd S Wilson NC 27893-6860

ROSS, HENRY RAYMOND, advertising executive and legal counsel;; b. Toronto, Ont., Can., Nov. 9, 1919; S. Joseph and Mary (Rotenburg) R.; m. Ann Clarfield, Nov. 5, 1944; children: Ellen Louise, Janice Carol. Grad., Ont. Coll. Art, 1936. Pres. Ferris Theaters, Toronto, 1937-39, Ross Enterprises, Toronto, 1939-44; with F.H. Hayhurst Co. Ltd., Toronto, 1944—, sr. v.p., dir. creative svcs., 1957-73, sr. v.p. dir. industry, govt. and corp. affairs, 1973-79; dir., pres. Contemporary Paintings, Toronto, 1969—; sr. ptnr. H.M.S. Investments, Toronto, 1975—; pres. Henry R. Ross Cons. Inc., Toronto, 1979—; chmn. broadcast com. Assn. Can. Advertisers, Toronto, 1970—; chmn. talent negotiation com., bd. dirs. Can. Advt. Rsch. Found.; trustee Am. Fedn. Musicians; resource advisor Fed. and Provincial Govts. in devel. advt. bus. practices laws. Contbr. articles to jours. in field. Served with Can. Armed Forces, 1943-44. Fellow Inst. Can. Advt. (chmn. broadcast com. 1970—); mem. Art Dirs. Club Toronto, Broadcast Execs. Soc., Donalda Country Club. Home: 127 Munro Blvd, Willowdale, ON Canada M2P 1C7 Office: 55 Eglinton Ave E, Toronto, ON Canada M4P 1G9 *If only we would realize that we are indeed the masters of our own life's accomplishments. And so every deed and thought must be considered in that light, long before life passes us by.*

ROSS, HERBERT DAVID, film director; b. Bklyn., May 13, 1927; m. Nora Kaye, Aug. 21, 1959 (dec. 1987); m. Lee Radziwill, Sept., 1988. Dir. motion pictures Goodbye Mr. Chips, 1969, The Owl and The Pussycat, 1970, T. R. Baskin, 1971, Play It Again Sam, 1972, The Last of Sheila, 1973, Funny Lady, 1975, The Sunshine Boys, 1975, The Seven Percent Solution, 1976, The Goodbye Girl, 1977, The Turning Point, 1977, California Suite, 1978, Nijinsky, 1980, Pennies From Heaven, 1981, I Ought To Be in Pictures, 1982, Max Dugan Returns, 1983, Footloose, 1984, Protocol, 1984, The Secret of My Success, 1987, Dancers, 1987, Steel Magnolias, 1988, Undercover Blues, 1993; dir., producer: My Blue Heaven, 1989, True Colors, 1990, Boys On The Side, 1995; exec. prodr. Soapdish, 1991, choreographer: Spoleto (Italy) Festival, Berlin (Germany) Festival; active in numerous Broadway prodns., including Anyone Can Whistle; dir.: Broadway Chpt. Two, I Ought to Be in Pictures, 1980; opera dir. La Boheme, L.A. Music Ctr., 1993; recipient Golden Globe award 1978, award of distinction Dance mag. 1980. Office: care Rand Holsten CAA 9830 Wilshire Blvd Beverly Hills CA 90212-1804*

ROSS, HUGH COURTNEY, electrical engineer; b. Dec. 31, 1923; s. Clare W. and Jeanne F. Ross; m. Sarah A. Gordon (dec.); m. Patricia A. Malloy; children: John C., James G., Robert W. Student, Calif. Inst. Tech., 1942, San Jose State U., 1946-47; BSEE, Stanford U., 1950. Registered profl. elec. engr., Calif. Instr. San Benito (Calif.) High Sch. and Jr. Coll., 1950-51; chief engr. vacuum power switches Jennings Radio Mfg. Corp., San Jose, Calif., 1951-62; chief engr. ITT Jennings, San Jose, Calif., 1962-64; pres. Ross Engring. Corp., Campbell, Calif., 1964—. Contbr. articles to tech. jours.; patentee in field. Fellow IEEE (life) (chmn. Santa Clara Valley subsect. 1960-61); mem. Am. Vacuum Soc., Am. Soc. Metals. Avocations: electronics, electric autos, camping, ranching, solar power. Office: 540 Westchester Dr Campbell CA 95008-5012

ROSS, IAN MUNRO, electrical engineer; b. Southport, Eng., Aug. 15, 1927; came to U.S., 1952, naturalized, 1960; m. Christina Leinberg Ross, Aug. 24, 1955; children: Timothy Ian, Nancy Lynn, Stina Marguerite. BA, Gonville and Caius Coll., Cambridge U., 1948; MA in Elec. Engring, Cambridge U., 1952, PhD, 1952; DSc (hon.), N.J. Inst. Tech., 1983, Poly. U., 1988; D of Engring. (hon.), Stevens Inst. Tech., 1983; DSc (hon.), Polytech. U., 1988. With AT&T Bell Labs. (and affiliates), 1952—, exec. dir. network planning div., 1971-73, v.p. network planning and customer svcs., 1973-76; exec. v.p. systems engring. and devel. AT&T Bell Labs. (and affiliates), Holmdel, N.J., 1976-79, pres., 1979-91; pres. emeritus AT&T Bell Labs. Inc., Holmdel, 1991—; dir. Thomas & Betts Corp., B.F. Goodrich Co.; chmn. Nat. Adv. Commn. on Semicondrs. Patentee in field. Recipient NASA Pub. Svc. award, 1969, 75, medal Ind. Rsch. Inst., 1987. Fellow IEEE (Founders' medal 1988, Am. Acad. Arts and Scis.; mem. NAS, NAE, Nat. Sci. Bd. Home: 5 Black Point Rd Rumson NJ 07760-1500 Office: AT&T Bell Labs 101 Crawfords Corner Rd Holmdel NJ 07733-3030*

ROSS, JACK LEWIS, psychiatrist; b. Levelland, Tex., Sept. 3, 1932; s. Raymond T. and Mary Ann (Lewis) R.; m. Glenna M. Quillin, July 16, 1960; children: Sarah, Jennifer, Susan, Rebecca. BS, Texas Tech. Coll., 1952; MD, U. Tex., Dallas, 1956. Diplomate Am. Bd. Psychiatry and Neurology; cert. adult and child psychoanalyst. Staff psychiatrist Menninger Found., Topeka, 1962-92; tng. and supervising analyst Topeka Inst. Psychoanalysis, 1979—; dir. 1984-90. Contbr. articles to profl. jours. Served to capt. U.S. Army, 1960-62. Fellow Am. Psychiat. Assn., ACP; mem. Am Psychoanalytic Assn., Alpha Omega Alpha (life). Republican. Methodist. Home: 4841 SW Indian Hills Rd Topeka KS 66610-9660 Office: Ste A-1 211 E 8th St Lawrence KS 66044

ROSS, JAMES BARRETT, finance and insurance educator; b. Cleve., Apr. 25, 1930; s. James Barrett and Marjorie (Stutsman) R.; m. Ann Penney, July 1, 1950; children: James, Scott, Alison, Andrea, Alan, Dana, Ann Elizabeth, Brandon, Mary Ellen, Marjorie, Wendy. BA cum laude, Harvard U., 1951; MBA, U. R.I., 1988; PhD, U. Conn., 1992. CLU; CPCU; ChFC. With Conn. Gen. Life Ins. Co., 1951-62; pres., dir. Puritan Life Ins. Co., Providence, 1962-68; exec. v.p. mktg. Keystone Custodian Funds Inc., Boston, 1968-73; sr. v.p. Met. Life Ins. Co., N.Y.C., 1973-80; chmn., chief exec. officer INA Internat., 1980-83; pres. v.p. exec. v.p. Ins. Co. N.Am., 1980-83; pres. Continental Vision Fin. Svcs., 1983-86; vice chmn. Andersen & Walsh, 1986-91; assoc. prof. fin. and ins. Radford (Va.) U., 1992—. Fellow Soc. Actuaries, Life Mgmt. Inst.; mem. Am. Acad. Actuaries, Fin. Mgmt. Assn., Ea. Fin. Assn., Midwestern Fin. Assn., So. Fin. Assn., Acad. Fin. Svcs., Univ. Club (Kingston, R.I.), Tavern Hall Club (Kingston), Beta Gamma Sigma, Phi Kappa Phi. Congregationalist. Home: PO Box 7005 Radford VA 24142

ROSS, JAMES ELMER, economist, administrator; b. Danville, Ill., Jan. 15, 1931; s. Carl Henry and Lura Jane (Witherspoon) R.; m. Barbara Lou Becker, Dec. 24, 1958 (dec. Aug. 1982); 1 child, Candis Anne; m. Erin Elizabeth O'Shea, June 20, 1986. BS, U. Ill., 1953, MS, 1959, PhD, 1966. Agrl. counselor Am. Embassy, Caracas, Venezuela, 1976-78, Cairo, Egypt, 1978-81; asst. adminstr. Fgn. Agrl. Svc., Washington, 1981-83; mem. Sr. Exec. Seminar, Dept. State, 1983-84; alt. permanent rep. U.S. Mission to UN Agys., Rome, 1984-87; agrl. counselor U.S. Embassy, Seoul, Republic of Korea, 1987-88; dir. trade assistance and planning office Fgn. Agrl. Svc., Washington, 1988-92; adj. prof. U. Fla., 1992—; pres. J.E. Ross & Assocs., Inc., 1993—; cons. Govt. of Ecuador, 1971-72; mem. internat. programs U. Fla., Costa Rica, 1966-69, Ghana, 1969-70; assoc. dir., 1970-72; asst. dean Fla. Coop. Extension Svc., 1972-75; spl. asst. to undersecretary USDA, 1975-76. Author: Cooperative Rural Electrification, 1972; co-author: Rural Electrification and Development, 1978. Col. USAR, ret. Mem. Internat. Assn. Agrl. Economists, Am. Agrl. Econs. Assn., Assn. for Internat. Agriculture and Rural Devel., Assn. for the Study of the Cuban Economy, Internat. Agrl. Trade Rsch. Consortium, Internat. Agribus. Mgmt. Assn., Masons. Republican. Home: RR 1 Box 287-B18 Hawthorne FL 32640-8116

ROSS, JAMES FRANCIS, philosophy educator; b. Providence, Oct. 8, 1931; s. James Joseph and Teresa Marie (Sullivan) R.; m. Kathleen Marie Fallon, Dec. 1, 1956; children: Seamus, Ellen, Richard Fallon, Therese. A.B., Cath. U. Am., 1953, M.A. (Basselin Found. fellow), 1954; Ph.D., Brown U., 1958; J.D., U. Pa., 1974. Bar: Pa. bar 1975. Instr., then asst. prof. philosophy U. Mich., 1959-61; asst. prof. U. Pa., 1962-65, asso. prof., 1965-68, prof., 1968—; prof. philosophy and law, 1994—, chmn. philosophy dept. and grad. group in philosophy, 1966-70, 81-83; Rackham rsch. fellow U. Mich., 1960-61; NEH fellow, mem. Inst. Advanced Study, Princeton, 1975-76; vis. prof. Brown U., summer 1977; assoc. mem. Darwin Coll. Cambridge U. (Eng.), 1982-83. Author: Philosophical Theology, 1969, 2d edit., 1980, Introduction to Philosophy of Religion, 1970, Portraying Analogy, 1981; translator, editor: Suarez on Formal and Universal Unity, 1964; editor: Studies in Medieval Philosophy, 1971. Recipient Christian B. and Mary L. Linbach Found. award for Disting. Teaching, 1966; Disting. Scholarship award Cath. U. Am., 1971; Guggenheim fellow, 1982-83. Fellow Soc. Values in Higher Edn.; mem. Am. Philos. Assn., Am. Cath. Philos. Assn. (pres. 1987-89), Soc. for Medieval and Renaissance Philosophy, Am. Theol. Soc., Soc. Theol. Discussion. Roman Catholic. Home: Grange Ave Little Compton RI 02837 Office: U Pa 3440 Market St Fl 460 Philadelphia PA 19104-3338

ROSS, JAMES NEIL, JR., veterinary educator; b. Akron, Ohio, Dec. 18, 1940; s. James Neil and Ruth Evelyn (Gray) R.; m. Marcia Day Collins, June 27, 1964; children: Stephanie, Amy, Lisa. DVM, Ohio State U., 1965, MSc, 1967; PhD, Baylor Coll. Medicine, 1972. Diplomate in cardiology and internal medicine Am. Coll. Vet. Internal Medicine; diplomate Am. Coll. Vet. Emergency and Critical Care. Lectr., cardiologist Ohio State U. Vet. Sch., Columbus, 1965-67; asst. prof. surgery and physiology Baylor Coll. Medicine, Houston, 1967-74; assoc. prof. physiology Med. Coll. Ohio, Toledo, 1974-80; prof. and chmn. dept. medicine Tufts U. Sch. Vet. Medicine, North Grafton, Mass., 1981—; cons. Proctor & Gamble, Cin., 1976-84; mem. scientist rev. bds. of various jours. including Jour. of Investigative Surgery, Am. Jour. Vet. Rsch. 1983-86. Contbr. chpts. to books, articles to profl. jours. Named Veterinarian of the Yr. Animal Sci. Assn., 1972; grantee NIH, 1965-67; fellow NIH, 1969-71. Mem. AVMA (coun. on edn. 1989-95), Am. Bd. vet. spltys.), Am. Coll. Vet. Internat Medicine, Am. Heart Assn., Am. Animal Hosp. Assn., Vet. Emergency and Critical Care Soc. (pres. 1991-92), Phi Eta Sigma, Gamma Sigma Delta, Am. Coll. Vet. Emergency and Critical Care (treas. 1989—, recording sec. 1993—), Omega Tau Sigma, Phi Gamma Delta. Methodist. Achievements include research in cardiovascular disease in animals; assisted circulation. Office: Tufts U Sch Vet Medicine 200 Westboro Rd North Grafton MA 01536-1895

ROSS, JAMES ULRIC, lawyer, accountant, educator; b. Del Rio, Tex., Sept. 14, 1941; s. Stephen Mabrey and Beatrice Jessie (Hyslop) R.; m. Janet S. Calabro, Dec. 28, 1986; children: James Ulric Jr., Ashley Meredith. BA, U. Tex., 1963, JD, 1965. Bar: Tex. 1965, U.S. Tax Ct. 1969; CPA, Tex. Estate tax examiner IRS, Houston, 1965-66; tax acct. Holmes, Raquet, Harris & Shaw, San Antonio, 1966-67; pvt. practice law and acctg., Del Rio and San Antonio, 1968—; instr. St. Mary's U., San Antonio, 1973-75; assoc. prof. U. Tex., San Antonio, 1975—. Active Am. Cancer Soc., Residential Mgmt., Inc., Am. Heart Assn. Mem. ABA, Tex. Bar Assn., Tex. Soc. CPAs, San Antonio Bar Assn., San Antonio Estate Planners Coun. Contbr. articles on U.S. and Internat. Estate Planning and Taxation to legal and profl. jours. Home: 3047 Orchard Hill San Antonio TX 78230-3078 Office: 760 Tex Commerce Bank Bldg 7550 IH 10 W San Antonio TX 78229

ROSS, JEFFREY ALLAN, political scientist, organization executive, educator; b. N.Y.C., Dec. 24, 1947; s. Joseph and Pearl (Epstein) R.; B.A. in Polit. Sci. summa cum laude with high honors, SUNY, Binghamton, 1969; Ph.D. in Polit. Sci. (Ford Found. fellow, Ford Found. grantee), U. Minn., 1982; m. Marjorie Appelson, Aug. 30, 1970; children—Craig, Eric, Brian, Allison. N.Y. State Regents' fellow, teaching asst. U. Minn., Mpls., 1969-71, research asst., 1971-73, instr., 1973; instr. Kirkland Coll., Clinton, N.Y., 1973-78, Huber Found. faculty research grantee, 1973, 74, 77, Mellon Found. grantee, 1974, research prof., 1975-76; instr. govt. Hamilton Coll., Clinton, 1978-80, asst. prof., 1980-82; vis. prof. polit. sci. Syracuse U., 1984; adj. prof. polit. sci. Queens Coll., CUNY, 1987-88; dir. campus affairs dept. Anti-Defamation League of B'nai B'rith, 1984—; bd. dirs. Research Ctr. for Religion and Human Rights in Closed Socs.; exec. bd. Com. for Pub. Higher

Edn.; chmn., mem. various profl. panels; Mpls. Found., Frances E. Andrews Fund All-Univ. research fellow, surveyer Soviet Jewish emigrants, Israel, 1972. Precinct rep. Democratic Farm Labor Party, Mpls., 1972-73. Mem. Am. Polit. Sci. Assn., N.E. Polit. Sci. Assn. (exec. council), Internat. Polit. Sci. Assn., Internat. Studies Assn., Mongolia Soc., Can.-Mongolia Soc., Comparative Interdisciplinary Studies Soc. (exec. coun.), N.Y. State Polit. Sci. Assn. (v.p. 1982-83, pres. 1983-84), Sound Cyclists Bicycle Club (v.p. 1989-90, 94, pres. 1991-93), Norwalk Ski Club (v.p. 1992-93). Democrat. Author: (with Ann Cottrell) The Mobilization of Collective Identity: Comparative Perspectives, 1980, Pamyat: Hatred Under Glasnost, 1989; contbr. articles to profl. jours.; mem. editorial bd. Teaching Polit. Sci., 1971-81; editor Hamilton Social Sci. Rev., 1977-79; reviewer manuscripts for profl. jours., book pubs. Home: 20 Soundview Loop South Salem NY 10590 Office: Anti-Defamation League 823 United Nations Pla New York NY 10017

ROSS, JEFFREY KENNETH, lawyer. Student, Lehigh U., 1969-70; BS in Indsl. and Labor Rels., Cornell U., 1973, JD, 1976. Bar: Ill. 1976, U.S. Dist. Ct. (no. dist.) Ill. 1976, U.S. Ct. Appeals (4th cir.) 1981, U.S. Ct. Appeals (6th cir.) 1983, U.S. Ct. Appeals (7th cir.) 1986. Assoc. Seyfarth, Shaw, Fairweather & Geraldson, Chgo., 1976-83, ptnr., 1983—. Referral atty. Leadership Coun. for Met. Open Communities, 1977—. Mem. ABA (labor and employment law sect. and litigation sect.), Chgo. Bar Assn. Office: Seyfarth Shaw & Fairweather 55 E Monroe St Ste 4200 Chicago IL 60603-5803

ROSS, JIMMY DOUGLAS, army officer; b. Hosston, La., May 23, 1936; s. Horace Eugene and Lucile Marie (Pontious) R.; m. Patricia L. Cox., Dec. 18, 1955; children: Sabra, DiAnna, Tony. BS, Henderson State U., 1958; M.A. in Bus. Mgmt., Central Mich. U., 1975. Commd. 2d lt. U.S. Army, 1958, advanced through grades to 4 Star Gen., 1994, served comdr. co., bn., brigade levels; comdg. gen. 2d Support Command (Corps) VII Corps U.S. Army, Nellingen, W. Ger., 1980-82; dir. transp., energy and troop support Office Dep. Chief of Staff for Logistics, U.S. Army, Washington, 1982-84; chief staff U.S. Army Materiel Command, Alexandria, Va., 1984-86; comdr. U.S. Army Depot System Command, Chambersburg, Pa., 1986-87; dep. chief of staff for logistics U.S. Army, Washington, 1987-92; commdg. gen. U.S. Army Materiel Command, Alexandria, Va., 1992-94; retired, 1994; bd. dirs. VSE Engring.Co. Dist. commr. Alpine dist. Boy Scouts Am., 1980-82; sr. v.p. Biomed. Svcs., ARC Nat. Hdqrs., 1994—. Decorated D.S.M. with oak leaf cluster, Legion of Merit, Bronze Star, Air medal. Fellow Assn. United State Army (sr.); mem. Assn. U.S. Army, Am. Def. preparedness Assn., Nat. Def. Transp. Assn., Armed Forces Benefit Assn. (bd. dirs.). Methodist. Home: 9208 Cross Oaks Ct Fairfax Station VA 22039

ROSS, JOHN, physical chemist, educator; b. Vienna, Austria, Oct. 2, 1926; came to U.S., 1940; s. Mark and Anna (Krecmar) R.; m. Virginia Franklin (div.); children: Elizabeth A., Robert K.; m. Eva Madarasz. BS, Queens Coll., 1948; PhD, MIT, 1951; D (hon.), Weizmann Inst. Sci., Rehovot, Israel, 1984, Queens Coll., SUNY, 1987, U. Bordeaux, France, 1987. Prof. chemistry Brown U., Providence, 1953-66; prof. chemistry MIT, Cambridge, 1966-80, chmn. dept., 1966-71; chmn. faculty of Inst. MIT, 1975-77; prof. Stanford (Calif.) U., 1980—, chmn. dept., 1983-89; cons. to industries, 1979—; mem. bd. govs. Weizmann Inst., 1971—. Author: Physical Chemistry, 1980; editor Molecular Beams, 1966; contbr. articles to profl. jours. 2nd lt. U.S. Army, 1944-46. Recipient medal Coll. de France, Paris. Fellow AAAS, Am. Phys. Soc.; mem. NAS, Am. Acad. Arts and Scis., Am. Chem. Soc. (Irving Langmuir Chem. Physics prize 1992). Home: 738 Mayfield Ave Palo Alto CA 94305-1044 Office: Stanford U Dept Chemistry Stanford CA 94305

ROSS, JOHN, cultural organization administrator; b. Tahlequah, Okla., Feb. 16, 1955; s. John and Nancy (Augerhole) R.; m. Anita Faye Franklin, Jan. 1, 1976; children: Anthony John, Adam John. Student, U. Ark., 1976; degree, Nutrition and Diatetics Tng. Ctr., 1981; AA Health in Phys. Edn. and Recreation, Rogers State Health, 1982; cert. in food svc. mgmt., St. Louis, 1984; BA Social Sci., Northeastern State U., 1985. Cook Claremore Indian Hosp., Okla., 1979-86; asst. mgr. Horseshoe Bend Bingo, Sperry, Okla., 1986-87; owner/operator South Greasy Smokeshop, Stilwell, Okla., 1988; material handler Allied Signal, Tulsa, Okla., 1988-92; various elected and apptd. positions United Keetoowah Band of Cherokee Indians in Okla., 1985—, chief, 1992—. Office: United Keetoowah Cherokee Indians PO Box 746 Tahlequah OK 74465-0746

ROSS, JOHN J., petroleum products company executive. BA, U. Okla. 1951; LLB, U. Denver, 1958. Bar: Colo. 1958. Gen. tax counsel Chevron Corp., San Francisco. Office: Chevron Corp 555 Market St San Francisco CA 94105-2801

ROSS, JOHN MICHAEL, editor, magazine publisher; b. Bklyn., Oct. 17, 1919; s. Albert Henry and Dorothy Veronica (Murray) R.; m. Kathleen M. Courtney; children: Donna Patricia Ross Easterbrook, Maureen Courtney Ross Quick. Student pub. schs., N.Y.C. Sports writer Bklyn. Eagle, 1937-41, The Newspaper PM, 1946-47; editor Am. Law Tennis mag., 1947-50, Macfadden Pubis., 1950-51, 60-61; contbg. editor Am. Weekly, 1952-60; editor-in-chief Golf mag., 1961-67, Golf Bus. mag., 1963-65, Golfdom mag., 1965-67; v.p. Universal Pub. and Distbn. Corp., 1965-67; pres. Golf Promotions, Inc., 1967-70; pub. Golf Bus. Almanac, also Golf TV Guide, 1969; pub. relations dir. Profl. Golfers Assn. Golf Tour, 1970-71; editor-in-chief Golf mag., 1972-79, assoc. pub., 1979-84; publishing dir., v.p. The Golf Link, 1985-87; editorial dir. Am. Golf mag., 1990-94; sr. ptnr. J.M. Ross Assocs., Westport, Conn., 1994—; bd. dirs. World Golf Hall of Fame, 1974-83, mem. adv. bd. 1993—; chmn. Women's Golf Scholarship Fund, 1976-82; exec. dir. World Cup Golf Internat. Golf Assn., 1977-84. Co-author: Nothing But The Truth, 1960; editor: Encyclopedia of Golf, 1977; contbr. numerous articles to nat. publs. including Reader's Digest, Life, Sports Illustrated. Justice of peace, Newtown, Conn., 1960-64. Served with AUS, 1942-46. Recipient Christopher award for best mag. story, 1957; recipient Lincoln Werden award for golf journalism, 1991. Mem. U.S. Golf Assn. (nat. com. 1977—), Lawn Tennis Writers Assn. (sec. 1949-50), Golf Writers Assn. Am. (gov. 1966-67), Met. Golf Writers Assn. (pres. 1975-76), Assn. of Golf Writers (Great Britain), Am. Soc. Mag. Editors, Overseas Press Club (N.Y.C.), Patterson Club (Fairfield, Conn.). Roman Catholic. Home: 19 Riverfield Dr Weston CT 06883-2908 Office: J M Ross Assocs PO Box 774 Westport CT 06881-0774

ROSS, JOSEPH COMER, physician, educator, academic administrator; b. Tompkinsville, Ky., June 16, 1927; s. Joseph M. and Annie (Pinckley) R.; m. Isabelle Nevins, June 15, 1952; children: Laura Ann, Sharon Lynn, Jennifer Jo, Mary Martha, Jefferson Arthur. BS, U. Ky., 1950; MD, Vanderbilt U., 1954. Diplomate Am. Bd. Internal Medicine (bd. govs. 1975-81), Am. Bd. Pulmonary Disease. Intern Vanderbilt U. Hosp., Nashville, 1954-55; resident Duke U. Hosp., Durham, N.C., 1955-57, rsch. fellow, 1957-58; instr. medicine Ind. U. Sch. Medicine, Indpls., 1958-60, assoc. prof., 1960-62, assoc. prof., 1962-66, prof., 1966-70, chmn. dept. medicine Med. U. of S.C., Charleston, 1970-80; vis. prof. Vanderbilt U. Sch. Medicine, Nashville, 1979-80, prof. medicine, 1981—, assoc. vice chancellor for health affairs, 1982—; mem. cardiovascular study sect. NIH, 1966-70, program project com., 1971-75; mem. adv. coun. Nat. Heart, Lung and Blood Inst., 1982-86; mem. ad hoc coms. NAS, 1966, 67; mem. Pres.'s Nat. Adv. Panel on Heart Disease, 1972; mem. merit rev. bd. in respiration VA Rsch. Svc., 1972-76, chmn., 1974-76. Mem. editorial bd. Jour. Lab. and Clin. Medicine, 1964-70, Chest, 1968-73, Jour. Applied Physiology,1968-73, Archives of Internal Medicine, 1976-82, Heart and Lung, 1977-86; contbr. articles to profl. jours. With U.S. Army, 1945-47. Fellow ACP, Am. Coll. Chest Physicians (gov. S.C. 1970-76, vice chmn. bd. govs. 1974-75, chmn. bd. govs. 1975-76, exec. council 1974-80, pres.-elect 1976-77, pres. 1978-79, chmn. sci. program com. 1973), Am. Coll. Cardiology; mem. AMA (sect. on med. schs.), Am. Fedn. Clin. Rsch. (chmn. Midwest sect.), Am. Physiol. Soc., Am. Soc. Clin. Investigation, Assn. Am. Physicians, Assn. Profs. Medicine, Cen. Soc. Clin. Rsch., S.C. Med. Soc., Am. Thoracic Soc. (nat. councillor 1972-76), So. Soc. Clin. Rsch., S.C. Lung Assn. (v.p. 1974-75), Am. Soc. Internal Medicine, Phi Beta Kappa, Alpha Omega Alpha. Mem. Ch. of Christ (elder). Office: Vanderbilt University D 3300 Medical Ctr N Nashville TN 37232

ROSS, JOSEPH E., government official, lawyer; b. Bklyn., Jan. 12, 1923; s. Joseph John and Mary Elizabeth (Hurd) R.; m. Joan Marie Needham, Nov.

16, 1946; children—Richard, Patricia, John, Kenneth, Edward, Dennis, Chris, David. B.A., St. John's U., 1943, LL.B., 1948. Bar: N.Y., U.S. Supreme Ct. Assoc. Bain & Hoopes, Esquire, N.Y.C., 1948-51; commd. capt. U.S. Navy, 1965, various legal duties, 1951-66; dir. mil. justice U.S. Navy, Washington, 1966-69, ret., 1969; asst. chief legis. sect. Dept. Justice, Washington, 1969-72; chief Am. Law div. Congl. Research Service, Library of Congress, Washington, 1972-85, dir., 1986-93. Mem. Fed. Bar Assn. (pres. 1984-85), ABA, Aircraft Owners and Pilots Assn., Judge Advocates Assn. Roman Catholic. Club: Brent Soc. (Arlington, Va.).

ROSS, JOSEPH FOSTER, physician, educator; b. Azusa, Calif., Oct. 11, 1910; s. Verne Ralph and Isabel Mills (Bumgarner) R.; m. Eileen Sullivan, Dec. 19, 1942; children: Louisa, Elisabeth, Joseph, Jeanne, Marianne. AB with great distinction, Leland Stanford Jr. U., 1933; MD cum laude with spl. honors in Physiology, Harvard U., 1936. Diplomate Am. Bd. Internal Medicine (mem. 1973-83), Am. Bd. Nuclear Medicine (founding, sec. 1971-72, 79, chmn. 1973-77, pres., chief exec. officer 1980—). Asst. topographical anatomy Harvard U. Sch. Medicine, 1934-37, research fellow biochemistry, 1943-46; med. house officer Harvard cancer commn. Huntington Meml. Hosp., 1934-35; Palmer Meml., New Eng. Deaconess hosps., 1935-36; resident pathology Mallory Inst. Pathology, 1936-37; intern Harvard Med. Svc. Boston City Hosp., 1937-39; asst. pathology U. Rochester Sch. Medicine, 1939-40; resident pathology Strong Meml. Hosp., Rochester, N.Y., 1939-40; physician, dir. hematology and radioisotope divs. Mass. Meml. Hosp., 1940-54; instr., asst. prof., assoc. prof. medicine Boston U., 1940-54; dir. radioisotope unit Cushing VA, Boston VA hosps., 1948-54; prof. medicine UCLA, 1954—, prof. radiobiology, 1954-59, assoc. dean, 1954-58, chmn. dept. nuclear med. and radiation biology, 1958-60, dir. Lab. Nuclear Med. and Radiation Biology, 1958-65, prof., chmn. dept. biophysics and nuclear medicine, 1960-65, chief div. hematology, 1969-76; chief staff U. Calif. Hosp., Los Angeles, 1954-58; attending physician U. Calif. Hosp., 1954—; U.S. del. Internat. Conf. Peaceful Uses Atomic Energy, Geneva, 1955; mem. U.S. Atoms for Peace mission to Latin Am., 1956, U.S. AEC Life Scis. Mission to Greece, Turkey, 1961; mem. USA AEC sci. mission to USSR, 1966; mem. Calif. Adv. Council on Cancer, 1959-84, chmn., 1963-66, 74-77; mem. CENTO Sci. Mission Iran, Turkey, Pakistan, 1963; mem. nat. adv. cancer council Nat. Cancer Inst., 1956-60; Research preservation whole blood OSRD, World War II. Editorial bd.: Blood, Jour. Hematology, 1946-76, Annals Internal Medicine, 1960-70, Jour. Nuclear Medicine, 1968; med. book div., Little Brown Co., 1958-68, med. book series, U. Calif. Press, 1962-70; Contbr. articles to profl. jours. Recipient cert. of merit Pres. U.S., 1948, Van Meter award Am. Goiter Soc., 1953, Dorothy Kirsten French Meml. award for disting. contbn. to medicine French Found. for Alzheimer's Disease Rsch., 1994; Wilson medalist, lectr. Am. Clin. and Climatol. Assn., 1964; Disting. fellow Am. Coll. Nuclear Physicians, 1994. Fellow Am. Coll. Nuclear Medicine (Disting. fellow 1988); mem. ACP, AMA, Am. Soc. Exptl. Pathology, Am. Soc. Clin. Investigation, Assn. Am. Physicians, Am. Acad. Arts and Scis., Biophys. Soc., Radiation Research Soc. (council 1964-65), Internat. Soc. Hematology, Am. Soc. Hematology (pres. 1961-62), Western Assn. Physicians (pres. 1962-63), Am. Bd. Nuclear Medicine (co-founder 1972, sec. 1972-75, chmn., pres. 1975-78, exec. dir. 1978-79, pres. 1980—), Soc. Nuclear Med. (trustee 1962-72, pres. So. Calif. chpt. 1964-65, Nuclear Pioneer lectr. 1971, 77, Disting. Scientist award Western. sect. 1977, Disting. Svc. award 1984, Spl. Presdl. Recognition award 1991, Hevesy Nuc. Pioneer award and lectr., 1995), L.A. County Med. Assn. (dist. v.p. 1976-77, 78-79, del. to Calif. Med. Assn. 1978-79), Am. Bd. Med. Spltys. (exec. com. 1982-84), Council Med. Spltly. Socs. (sec. 1981-82, dir. 1980-82), World Fedn. Nuclear Medicine and Biology (chmn. statutes com. 1980-84), Phi Beta Kappa, Sigma Xi, Alpha Omega Alpha, Theta Xi, Nu Sigma Nu. Presbyterian (exec. com. Westminster Found. So. Calif. 1962-72, pres. 1968). Clubs: Harvard (Boston); Cosmos (Washington). Home: 11246 Cashmere St Los Angeles CA 90049-3503 Office: Am Bd Nuclear Med 900 Veteran Ave Rm 12-200 Los Angeles CA 90024

ROSS, JUNE ROSA PITT, biologist; b. Taree, May 2, 1931; came to U.S., 1957; d. Bernard and Adeline Phillips; m. Charles Alexander, June 27, 1959. BS with honors, U. Sydney, New S. Wales, Australia, 1953, PhD, 1959, DSc, 1974. Research assoc. Yale U., New Haven, 1959-60, U. Ill., Urbana, 1960-65; research assoc. Western Wash. U., Bellingham, 1965-67, assoc. prof., 1967-70, prof. biology, 1970—, chair dept. biology, 1989-90; pres. Western Wash. U. Faculty Senate, Bellingham, 1984-85; conf. host Internat. Bryozoology Assn., 1986. Author: (with others) A Textbook of Entomology, 1982, Geology of Coal, 1984; editor (assoc.) Palaios, 1985-89; contbr. articles to profl. jours. Grantee NSF; recipient Western Wash. U. Outstanding Educator award, 1973, Western Wash. U. Research award, 1986. Mem. Australian Marine Scis. Assn., The Paleontol. Soc. (councillor 1984-86, treas. 1987-93), U.K. Marine Biol. Assn. (life), Microscopy Soc. of Am., Internat. Bryozoology Assn. (pres. 1992-95). Avocations: hiking, classical music. Office: Western Wash U Dept Biology Bellingham WA 98255-9060

ROSS, KATHLEEN ANNE, college president; b. Palo Alto, Calif., July 1, 1941; d. William Andrew and Mary Alberta (Wilburn) R. BA, Ft. Wright Coll., 1964; MA, Georgetown U., 1971; PhD, Claremont Grad. Sch., 1979; BS with honors, Claremont Grad. Sch., 1979; LLD (hon.) Alverno Coll. Milw., 1990, Dartmouth Coll., 1991, Seattle U., 1992; LHD (hon.) Whitworth Coll., 1992, LLD (hon.) Pomona Coll., 1993. Cert. tchr., Wash. Secondary tchr. Holy Names Acad., Spokane, Wash., 1964-70; dir. rsch. and planning Province Holy Names, Wash. State, 1972-73; v.p. acads. Ft. Wright Coll., Spokane, 1973-81; rsch. asst. to dean Claremont Grad. Sch., Calif., 1977-78; assoc. faculty mem. Harvard U., Cambridge, Mass., 1981; pres. Heritage Coll., Toppenish, Wash., 1981—; cons. Wash. State Holy Names Schs., 1971-73; coll. accrediting assn. evaluator N.W. Assn. Schs. and Colls., Seattle, 1975—; dir. Holy Names Coll. Oakland, Calif., 1979—; cons. Yakima Indian Nation, Toppenish, 1975—; speaker, cons. in field. Author: (with others) Multicultural Pre-School Curriculum, 1977, A Crucial Agenda: Improving Minority Student Success, 1989; Cultural Factors in Success of American Indian Students in Higher Education, 1978. Chmn. Internat. 5-Yr. Convocation of Sisters of Holy Names, Montreal, Que., Can., 1981; TV Talk show host Spokane Council of Chs., 1974-76. Recipient E.K. and Lillian F. Bishop Founds. Youth Leader of Yr. award, 1986, Disting. Citizenship Alumna award Claremont Grad. Sch., 1986, Golden Aztec award Washington Human Devel., 1989, Harold W. McGraw Am. prize, 1989, John Carroll award Georgetown U., 1991, Holy Names medal Ft. Wright Coll., 1981, Pres. medal Eastern Washington U., 1994, State Wash. medal of Merit, 1995; named Yakima Herald Rep. Person of Yr. 1987, First Annual Leadership award Region VIII Coun. Advancement and Support Edn., 1993; Wash. State medal of Merit, 1995; numerous grants for projects in multicultural higher edn., 1974—. Mem. Nat. Assn. Ind. Colls. and Univs., Am. Assn. Higher Edn., Soc. Intercultural Edn., Tng. and Research, Sisters of Holy Names of Jesus and Mary. Roman Catholic. Office: Heritage Coll Office of Pres 3240 Fort Rd Toppenish WA 98948-9599

ROSS, LEONARD LESTER, anatomist; b. N.Y.C., Sept. 11, 1927; s. Aaron Theodore and Shirley (Smolen) R.; m. Marcella Gamel, June 23, 1951; children: Jane, Jill. A.B., NYU, 1946, Ph.D., 1954. Asst. prof. U. Ala. Med. Coll., 1954-57; assoc. prof. Cornell U. Med. Coll., 1957-69, prof., 1969-73; vis. prof. Cambridge U., 1967-68; prof., chmn. dept. anatomy Med. Coll. Pa., Phila., 1973-89; exec. v.p., Annenberg dean Med. Coll. Pa., 1989-93, pres. and Annenberg dean, 1993-94; provost Med. Coll. Pa., Hahnemann Univ., Phila., 1994—; exec. v.p. Allegheny Health, Edn. and Rsch. Found. Assoc. editor: Anat. Record, 1976. Served with M.C., U.S. Army, 1946-47. Recipient Lindback award for teaching, 1976; NIH sr. research fellow, 1967-68. Mem. Am. Assn. Anatomists (exec. com. 1984-88), Soc. Neurosci., Soc. Cell Biology, N.Y. Soc. Electron Microscopists (pres. 1975-76), Assn. Anatomy Chairmen (pres. 1983-84), AAUP (nat. council 1974-77), Sigma Xi. Office: Broad and Vine Philadelphia PA 19102-1192

ROSS, LEONARD Q. See ROSTEN, LEO CALVIN

ROSS, LOUIS ROBERT, automotive company executive; b. Detroit, Mar. 23, 1932; s. Louis Robert and Sadie Madge (Stobbe) R.; m. Carolyn Ann Lory, June 20, 1953; children: Stephen Charles, Philip Elliott. BME, Wayne State U., Detroit, 1954; MBA, Mich. State U., East Lansing, 1972. With Ford Motor Co., 1955—; v.p. Ford Brazil, Sao Paulo, 1973-75; appointed dir. Ford Motor Co., 1985; v.p., gen. mgr. tractor divsn. Ford Motor Co.,

Troy, Mich., 1975-77; exec. v.p. diversified products ops. Ford Motor Co., 1977-79, exec. v.p. car product devel. N.Am. automotive ops., 1979-83, exec. v.p. tech. staffs, from 1983-85, exec. v.p. ops., 1985-86, exec. v.p. internat. automotive ops., 1986—, vice chmn., 1993—; bd. dirs. Ford Motor Co., Ford Aerospace & Comm. Corp.. Recipient Outstanding Alumnus award Mich. State U., 1980, Corp. Leadership award Wayne State U., 1988. Mem. Soc. Automotive Engrs., Phi Kappa Phi, Beta Gamma Sigma. Club: Bloomfield Hills Country. Home: Bloomfield Hills MI 48302 Office: Ford Motor Co The American Rd Dearborn MI 48121-1899

ROSS, MADELYN ANN, newspaper editor; b. Pitts., June 26, 1949; d. Mario Charles and Rose Marie (Mangieri) R. B.A., Indiana U. of Pa., 1971; M.A., SUNY-Albany, 1972. Reporter Pitts. Press, 1972-78, asst. city editor, 1978-82, spl. assignment editor, 1982-83, mng. editor, 1983-93; mng. editor Pitts. Post-Gazette, 1993—; instr. Community Coll. Allegheny County, 1974-81; Pulitzer Prize juror, 1989, 90. Mem. Task Force Leadership Pitts., 1985-92; v.p. Old Newsboys Charity Fund; bd. dirs. Dapper Dan Charity. Mem. Associated Press Mng. Editors (bd. dirs.), Am. Soc. Newspaper Editors, Women's Press Club (bd. dirs.). Democrat. Roman Catholic. Avocations: tennis; piano; organ. Office: Pitts Post-Gazette 34 Blvd Of The Allies Pittsburgh PA 15222

ROSS, MALCOLM, mineralogist, crystallographer; b. Washington, Aug. 22, 1929; s. Clarence Samuel and Helen Hall (Frederick) R.; m. Daphne Dee Virginia Riska, Sept. 1, 1956; children: Christopher A., Alexander MacC. BS in Zoology, Utah State U., 1951; MS in Chemistry, U. Md., 1959; PhD in Geology, Harvard U., 1962. Rsch. mineralogist U.S. Geol. Survey, Washington, 1954-5, 61-74, Reston, Va., 1974—; prin. investigator lunar sci. program NASA, 1969-74. Author: Asbestos and Other Fibrous Minerals, 1988. First Lt. U.S. Army, 1952-54. Recipient Disting. Svc. award, U.S. Dept. Interior, 1986. Fellow Mineral. Soc. Am., Geol. Soc. Am., AAAS; mem. Am. Geophys. Union, Clay Minerals Soc., Mineral Soc. Am. (bd. dirs. treas. 1976-80, v.p. 1990, pres. 1991, Pub. Svc. award, 1990). Avocation: long distance bicycling. Home: 1608 44th St NW Washington DC 20007-2025 Office: US Geol Survey Ms # 959 Reston VA 22092

ROSS, MARION, actress; b. Albert Lea, Minn.; children: Jim, Ellen. Grad., San Diego State U. Performed with Globe Theatre, San Diego, LaJolla Summer Theater; Broadway debut in Edwin Booth; starred: in touring prodns. of Never Too Late, Barefoot in the Park, The Glass Menagerie, Long Days Journey Into Night, Love Letters; film debut in Forever Female, 1953; one woman show A Lovely Light, 1988—; TV series include Life with Father, 1953-55, Paradise Bay, 1965-66, Happy Days, 1974-84, Love Boat, 1985-86, Brooklyn Bridge, 1991-93 (Emmy nomination, Lead Actress - Comedy, 1992, 93). Office: Marion Ross Enterprises Inc 14159 Riverside Dr Apt 101 Sherman Oaks CA 91423-2346

ROSS, MARY O., religious organization administrator. Pres. Women's Auxiliary Convention of the Nat. Baptist Ch. USA, Detroit. Office: Women's Auxiliary Conv 584 Arden Pk Detroit MI 48202

ROSS, MICHAEL AARON, lawyer; b. Newark, Sept. 15, 1941; s. Alexander Ash and Matilda (Blumenthal) R.; m. Leslie Gordon, June 26, 1976; children—Christopher Gordon, Alan Gordon. B.A., Franklin and Marshall Coll., 1963; J.D., Columbia U., 1966; M.S. in Econs., U. London, 1967. Bar: N.Y. 1968. Assoc., then ptnr. Shearman & Sterling, N.Y.C., 1967-93; sr. v.p. Legal Affairs Citicorp, N.Y.C., 1993—. Mem. ABA, New York County Lawyers Assn., Bar City N.Y. Club: University. Office: Citicorp 399 Park Ave New York NY 10043

ROSS, MONTE, electrical engineer; b. Chgo., May 26, 1932; s. Jacob Henry and Mildred Amelia (Feller) R.; m. Harriet Jean Katz, Feb. 10, 1957; children—Karyn, Dianne, Ethan. B.S. in Elec. Engring., U. Ill., 1953; M.S., Northwestern U., 1962. Devel. engr. Chance Vought, Dallas, 1953-54; sr. electronics engr. Motorola, Chgo., 1955-56; project engr. Motorola, 1957-59, assoc. dir. research, 1960-63; dir. research Hallicrafters Co., Chgo., 1964-65; mgr. laser tech. McDonnell Douglas Astronautics Co., St. Louis, 1966-70, dir. laser communications; program mgr. Laser Space Communications, 1971-87; pres. Ultradata Sys., Inc. (formerly Laser Data Tech.), St. Louis, 1987—; mem. alumni bd. dept. elec. and computer engring. U. Ill., 1985-90; guest lectr. various univs.; cons. NSF. Author: Laser Receivers, 1966; tech. editor Laser Applications Series, vol. 1, 1971, vol. 2, 1974, vol. 3, 1977, vol. 4, 1980; patentee in field. McDonnell Douglas Corp. fellow, 1985. Fellow IEEE; mem. Internat. Laser Communications Soc. (pres. 1988-89), Sigma Xi. Home: 19 Beaver Dr Saint Louis MO 63141-7901 Office: Ultradata Sys Inc 9375 Dielman Industrial Dr Saint Louis MO 63132-2212

ROSS, MURRAY GEORGE, social science educator, university president emeritus; b. Sydney, N.S., Can., Apr. 12, 1910; s. George Robert and Catherine (MacKay) R.; m. Janet Kennedy Lang, May 10, 1940; children—Susan Janet, Robert Bruce. B.A., Acadia U., 1936, D.C.L., 1960; M.A., U. Toronto, 1938, LL.D., 1970; Ed.D., Columbia, 1948; D.Litt., York U., 1970; D.Un., U. York, Eng., 1973; LL.D., Laurentian U., 1977. Prof. U. Toronto, 1950-55, v.p., 1955-60; pres. York U., Downsview, Ont., 1960-70, prof. social sci., 1970—, pres. emeritus, 1972—; former dir. Continental Can Co., Can., McGraw Hill Ryerson, Ltd., Time Can., Capital Growth Fund Ltd., Walwyn, Que. and Toronto; mem. N.Am. adv. bd. Volvo Co. Author: Religious Beliefs of Youth, 1950, The Y.M.C.A. in Canada, 1951, (with C.E. Hendry) New Understanding of Leadership; A Survey and Application of Research, 1957, Case Histories in Community Organization, 1958, The New University, 1961, New Universities in the Modern World, 1965, Community Organization: Theory and Principles; and fgn. edits., 1955, 2d edit., 1965, The University: The Anatomy of Academe, 1976, Canadian Corporate Directors on the Firing Line, 1980, The WayMust Be Tried, 1992; editor: Towards Professional Maturity, 1948; contbr. articles to profl. jours. Past chmn. bd. trustees Hist. Series; trustee Sunnybrooke Hosp. Decorated officer Order of Can., Order of Ont.; recipient Book award Am. Coun. on Edn., 1976, Centennial medal, 1967, Queen's Jubilee medal, 1978, Commemorative medal 125th Anniversary of Can. Confedn. Fellow Am. Sociol. Soc. Home: 75 Highland Crescent, Willowdale, ON Canada M2L 1G7 Office: Glendon Coll, 2775 Bayview Ave, Toronto, ON Canada M4N 3M6

ROSS, MURRAY LOUIS, lawyer, business executive; b. Rochester, N.Y., Apr. 26, 1947; s. Charles Allen and Florence L. (Falk) R.; m. Linda Marie Wabschall, Dec. 26, 1970. AB in History, Lycoming Coll., 1969; JD, U. Toledo, 1972. Bar: Pa. 1976. Asst. to exec. v.p. Falk Machinery Inc., Rochester, 1972-74; asst. v.p. Phila. (Pa.) Stock Exch., 1975-78, dir. securities dept., 1978-79, dir. market surveillance, 1979-82, v.p., corp. sec., 1982—; corp. sec. Phila. (Pa.) Bd. Trade Inc., 1984—, Phila. (Pa.) Depository Trust Co., 1987—, Stock Clearing Corp. Phila., 1986—. Mem. ABA, Phila. Bar Assn., Secrities Assn., Phila. Securities Assn. Avocations: wine, golf, ice hockey. Home: 1126 Woodstock Ln West Chester PA 19382-7244 Office: Phila Stock Exchange Inc 1900 Market St Philadelphia PA 19103-3527

ROSS, NORMAN ALAN, publisher; b. Bklyn., Nov. 1, 1942; s. Robert E. and Bertha (Cohen) R.; m. Leslie Ann Sandler, Oct. 10, 1969; children: Caroline Beth, Juliet Michelle. B.B.A., CCNY, 1964, postgrad., 1967-74. Prodn. mgr. Thomas Pub. Co., 1964-67; systems analyst Reuben H. Donnelley Corp., 1968-70; project mgr. Holt Rinehart & Winston, 1971-73; pres. Clearwater Pub. Co., Inc., N.Y.C., 1973-88, Video Strategies USA Inc., N.Y.C., 1981-84, Broadside Ltd. pub. Broadside Mag., 1983-87, Norman Ross Pub. Inc. 1987—. Author: Index to the Decisions of the Indian Claims Commission, 1973, Index to the Expert Testimony Before the Indian Claims Commission, 1973, Guide to Architectural Trade Catalogs from the Avery Library, 1989, Guide to Yiddish Children's Books from the Yivo Inst., 1989. Mem. Assn. Info. Mgmt. Home: 392 Central Park W Apt 20-C New York NY 10025-5860 Office: Norman Ross Pub Inc 330 W 58th St New York NY 10019-1821

ROSS, NORMAN ALEXANDER, retired banker; b. Miami, Fla., Jan. 30, 1922; s. Norman DeMille and Beatrice (Dowsett) R.; children: Isabel, Diana. A.B., Stanford U., 1946; postgrad., Trinity Coll., Oxford U., Eng., 1953; D.H.L., Lincoln Coll., Ill., 1959, Fisk U., 1978, Roosevelt U., 1979; Litt.D., Lake Forest Coll., 1967. Airport mgr. Pan Am. Airways, 1943; asst. to producer Metro-Goldwyn-Mayer, 1943-44; ptnr. Norman Ross & Co.,

1947-50; owner Norman Ross Record Club, 1951-52; v.p. pub. affairs First Nat. Bank Chgo., 1968-79, sr. v.p. communications dept., 1979-81, sr. v.p. community affairs, 1981-86; pres. Ross-McElroy Prodns., Inc., 1962-68; sr. affairs commentator Sta. WLS-TV, Chgo., 1989—; radio-TV commentator NBC, ABC, Chgo., 1953-64, ABC, Stas. WGN and WBKB, Chgo., 1964-68; former columnist Chgo. Daily News. Served with inf. AUS, World War II. Decorated cavaliere Dell Ordine Repubblica Italiana, Knight 1st Class Republic of Austria, 1989; U.S. Army Outstanding Civilian Service medal; officier and cross of chevalier Legion of Honor France; recipient Peabody award for TV program Off the Cuff 1964. Mem. Phi Gamma Delta. Clubs: Chgo., Racquet, Oxford, Econ. (Chgo.), Wayfarers, Casino. Home: 1200 N Lake Shore Dr Apt 801 Chicago IL 60610-2347 Office: Pilot Knob Bed & Breakfast Inn PO Box 1280 Pilot Mountain NC 27041

ROSS, PERCY NATHAN, business executive, newspaper columnist; b. Laurium, Mich., Nov. 22, 1916; s. William and Ruth (Schuman) R.; m. Laurian Averbook, July 2, 1939; children—Steven, Larry. Grad., Calumet High Sch., Mich., 1934. Businessman, owner Ross Tire & Battery Service Laurium, Mich., 1933-36; with West End Iron and Metal Corp., 1936-41, Duluth Hide and Fur Co., 1936-41; owner United Hide and Fur Co., Alexandria, Minn., 1941-44; operator Percy's Fur House, Wadena, Minn., 1944-45; owner N.W. Fur Auction Co., Mpls., 1946-51, Ross & Ross Auctioneers, Inc., Mpls., 1951-58, Indian Head Plastics, Eau Claire, Wis., 1958-59, Poly-Tech Corp., Bloomington, Minn., 1959-69; investment entrepreneur, 1969—; chmn. B. F. Nelson Co., Edina, Minn.; numerous TV appearances including Cable Network News, CBS Morning News with Diane Sawyer, Late Night with David Letterman, profile on 20/20, Larry King Live, Joan Rivers, W-5, Can., Lifestyles of Rich and Famous, Gerardo. Author: Ask for the Moon and Get It, 1987; author nationally syndicated newspaper column Thanks a Million in over 600 newspapers, 1983—; host radio show Thanks a Million, 1990—. Recipient Mike Douglas Spl. People award, 1977, Swede of Yr. award Swedish Community Minn., 1978, Am. Hero award Big Bros./Big Sisters, 1991. Clubs: Decathalon, Oak Ridge Country (Mpls.). Lodge: Masons. Numerous philanthropic activities throughout U.S. and Can., Australia, India and the Orient, 1969—, including his now traditional silver dollar distribution to needy children. Home: 6566 France Ave S PH-04 Edina MN 55435 Office: Thanks A Million 5151 Edina Industrial Blvd Minneapolis MN 55439-3013

ROSS, PHILIP ROWLAND, library director; b. Indiana, Pa., Apr. 7, 1940; s. David Biddle and Miriam Elizabeth (Hill) R.; m. Elaine Lucille George, July 17, 1965; children: Mary Elizabeth, David Bruce. BA, Pa. State U., 1962; MSLS, U. Md., 1969. Postal fin. officer USAF, Tachikawa AFB Tokyo, 1963-65; chief data control and quality control Hdqrs. Air Force Systems Command, Andrews AFB, Md., 1965-68; asst. libr. acquisitions West Liberty (W.Va.) State Coll., 1969-86; dist. mgr. Wheeling (W.Va.) office First Investors Corp., 1986-89; divs. mgr. State of Ark. First Investors Corp., Little Rock, 1989-92; dir. Lonoke (Ark.) Prairie County Regional Libr. System, 1992—; founder, treas.-mgr. West Liberty (W.Va.) State Coll. Fed. Credit Union, 1977-82, chmn. bd., 1984-85; mem. Ark. On Line Network Adv. Com., Little Rock, 1993—, Libr. Devel. Dist. State Coun., Little Rock, 1993, 94, 95. Maj. USAF, 1962-68; maj. Res., 1968-84, ret. Decorated various USAF medals and decorations. Mem. Assn. Ark. Pub. Lib*rs.* (treas./sec. 1993, 94, v.p./pres. elect 1995), Ark. Libr. Assn. (mem. com. 1994-95), C. of C. (Lonoke, Ark.), Am. Legion, Lions Club. Republican. Methodist. Avocations: reading, gardening, refinishing antique furniture. Home: 691 Wayne Elmore Rd Lonoke AR 72086 Office: Lonoke/Prairie County Regional Libr System 303 Court St Lonoke AR 72086

ROSS, RHODA, artist; b. Boston, Dec. 24, 1941. Student, Skowhegan Sch. Painting; BFA, RISD, 1964; MFA, Yale U., 1966. tchr. NYU, 1994—, Chautaqua (N.Y.) Sch. Art, 1991; participant Art in Embassies Program Dept of State, Havana, Cuba, 1991-93. One-woman shows include Frick Gallery, Belfast, Maine, Yale U., New Haven, Convent of the Sacred Heart, Mcpl. Art Soc., L.I. U., Emma Willard Sch. Dietal Gallery, Marymount Manhattan Coll., N.Y.C., N.Y.C. Landmarks Preservation Commns. 25th Silver Anniversary, numerous others; permanent collections include The White House, Gracie Mansion, N.Y.C., The Juilliard Sch., N.Y.C., Bankers Trust, Mus. City of N.Y., Chem. Bank Nat. Hqrs., Lehman Coll., Waldorf Astoria Hotel, N.Y.C., Russian Tea Rm., Rose Assocs., Bklyn. Union Gas, numerous other pvt. and public collections; artwork appears on New Sch. Social Rsch. catalog cover, Gifts and Decorative Accessories Mag. cover, UNICEF greeting card. Treas. R.I. Sch. Design Alumni Exec. com., 1986-90. Fellow Va. Ctr. for Creative Arts. Mem. RISD Alumni Assn. (treas. 1986, mem. alumni exec. com.), Phi Tau Gamma. Home and Studio: 473 W End Ave New York NY 10024-4934

ROSS, RICHARD FRANCIS, veterinarian, microbiologist, educator; b. Washington, Iowa, Apr. 30, 1935; s. Milton Edward and Olive Marie (Berggren) R.; m. Karen Mae Paulsen, Sept. 1, 1957; children: Scott, Susan. D.V.M., Iowa State U., 1959, M.S., 1961, Ph.D., 1965. Rsch. assoc. Iowa State U., Ames, 1959-61, asst. prof., 1962-65, assoc. prof., 1966-72, prof., 1972—, assoc. dir., assoc. dean, 1990—, interim dean, 1992-93, dean, 1993—; oper. mgr. Vet. Lab. Inc., Remsen, Iowa, 1961-62; postdoctoral fellow Rocky Mountain Lab., NIAID, Hamilton, Mont., 1965-66; sr. U.S. scientist Alexander von Humboldt Found., Bonn, Fed. Republic Germany, 1975-76; chmn. Internat. Research Program on Comparative Mycoplasmology, 1982-86; pres. Iowa State U. Research Found., Ames, 1984-86; Howard Dunne meml. lectr. Am. Assn. Swine Practitioners, 1984. Contbr. numerous articles to profl. publs., 1963—. Named Disting. Prof. Iowa State U., 1982, Hon. Master Pork Producer, Iowa Pork Producers Assn., 1985; recipient faculty citation Iowa State U. Alumni Assn., 1984, Beecham award for research excellence, 1985, Howard Dunne Meml. award Am. Assn. Swine Practitioners, 1988. Mem. Am. Coll. Vet. Microbiologists (diplomate, vice chmn. 1974-75, sec.-treas. 1977-83), Am. Soc. Microbiology (chmn. div. 1985-86), Internat. Orgn. Mycoplasmology (chair 1990-92), AVMA, AAAS, Osborn Research Club, Conf. Rsch. Workers in Animal Diseases (coun. mem., pres. 1992). Republican. Lutheran. Avocations: fishing, gardening, walking. Home: 2003 Northwestern Ave Ames IA 50010-4522 Office: Iowa State U Coll Vet Medicine Ames IA 50011

ROSS, RICHARD STARR, medical school dean emeritus, physician, cardiologist; b. Richmond, Ind., Jan. 18, 1924; s. Louis Francisco and Margaret (Starr) R.; m. Elizabeth McCracken, July 1, 1950; children: Deborah Starr, Margaret Casad, Richard McCracken. Student, Harvard U., 1942-44, M.D. cum laude, 1947; Sc.D. (hon.), Ind. U. 1981; LHD (hon.), Johns Hopkins U., 1994. Diplomate: Nat. Bd. Med. Examiners, Am. Bd. Internal Medicine. (subsplty. bd. cardiovascular disease). Successively intern, asst. resident, chief resident Osler Med. Service, Johns Hopkins Hosp., 1947-54; research fellow physiology Harvard Med. Sch., 1952-53; instr. medicine Johns Hopkins Med. Sch., 1954-56, asst. prof. medicine, 1956-59, assoc. prof., 1959-65, assoc. prof. radiology, 1960-71, prof. medicine, 1965—, Clayton prof. cardiovascular disease, 1969-75; dir. Wellcome Research Lab., Johns Hopkins; physician Johns Hopkins Hosp.; dir. cardiovascular div. dept. medicine, adult cardiac clinic Johns Hopkins Sch. Medicine and Hosp., dir. myocardial infarction research unit, 1967-75; dean med. faculty, v.p. medicine Johns Hopkins U., 1975-90, dean. emeritus, 1990—; Sir Thomas Lewis lectr. Brit. Cardiac Soc., 1969; John Kent Lewis lectr. Stanford U., 1972; bd. dirs. emeritus Johns Hopkins Hosp., Francis Scott Key Med. Ctr.; mem. cardiovascular study sect. Nat. Heart and Lung Inst., 1965-69, chmn. cardiovascular study sect., 1966-69, mem. tng. grant com., 1971-73, chmn. heart panel, 1972-73, adv. coun., 1974-78; mem. Inst. of Medicine, 1976—; chmn. vis. com. Harvard Med. and Dental Sch., 1979-86; bd. overseers Harvard U., 1980-86. Editor Modern Concepts Cardiovascular Disease, 1961-65, The Principles and Practice of Medicine, 17th-22nd edits., 1968-88; mem. editorial bd. Circulation, 1968-74; mem. editorial com. Jour. Clin. Investigation, 1969-73; contbr. numerous articles on cardiovascular disease and physiology to profl. jours. Served as capt. M.C. AUS, 1949-51. Fellow Am. Coll. Cardiology; mem. ACP (master 1979), Boylston Med. Soc., Am. Fedn. Clin. Research, Am. Physiol. Soc., Assn. Am. Physicians, Am. Soc. Clin. Investigation (councilor 1967-69), Am. Clin. and Climatol. Assn. (pres. 1978-79, councilor 1979-83, Metzger lecture 1986), Assn. Univ. Cardiologists (councilor 1972-75), Am. Heart Assn. (chmn. sci. sessions program com. 1965-67, chmn. publs. com. 1970-73, pres. 1973-74, dir. 1974-77, Connor lectr. 1979, Gold Heart award 1964, James B. Herrick award 1982), Heart Assn. Md. (pres. 1967-68), Sigma Xi, Alpha Omega Alpha; corr. mem. Brit. Cardiac Soc., Sociedad Peruana de Cardiologie, Cardiac Soc. Australia

and New Zealand. Clubs: Peripatetic, Interurban (pres. 1978), Elkridge, 14 West Hamilton, Century Assn. (N.Y.), Blue Hill Country Club (Maine). Home: 901 Drohomer Pl Baltimore MD 21210-1342 Office: Johns Hopkins U 1830 E Monument St Baltimore MD 21205-2100

ROSS, ROBERT, health agency administrator. Exec. dir. Muscular Dystrophy Assn., Tucson. Office: Muscular Dystrophy Assn 3300 E Sunrise Dr Tucson AZ 85718*

ROSS, ROBERT JOSEPH, head professional football coach; b. Richmond, Va., Dec. 23, 1936; s. Leonard Aloysius and Martha Isabelle (MMiller) R.; m. Alice Louise Bucker, June 13, 1959; children: Chris, Mary Catherine, Teresa, Kevin, Robbie. BA, Va. Mil. Inst., 1959. Tchr., head football coach Benedictine High Sch., Richmond, 1959-60; tchr., coach Colonial Heights (Va.) High Sch., 1962-65; asst. football coach Va. Mil. Inst., Lexington, 1965-67, Coll. William and Mary, Williamsburg, Va., 1967-71, Rice U., Houston, 1971-72, U. Md., College Park, 1972-73; head football coach The Citadel, Charleston, S.C., 1973-77; head coach U. Md., College Park, 1982-87; head football coach Ga. Inst. Tech., Atlanta, 1987-91; asst. coach Kansas City (Mo.) Chiefs, 1978-82; head coach San Diego Chargers, 1992—. 1st lt. U.S. Army, 1960-62. Named Coach of Yr., Washington Touchdown Club, 1982, Kodak Coach of Yr., 1990, Bobby Dodd Coach of Yr., 1990, Bear Bryant Coach of Yr., 1990, Scripps-Howard Coach of Yr., 1990, Nat. Coach of Yr., CBS Sports, 1990, Coach of Yr., Walter Camp Football Found., 1990, NFL Coach of Yr. UPI, 1992, Pro Football Weekly, 1992, Pro Football Writers' Assn., 1992, Football News, 1992, Football Digest, 1992, Maxwell Football Club, 1992, AFC Coach of Yr. Kansas City 101 Banquet. Mem. Am. Football Coaches Assn., Coll. Football Assn. (coaching com. 1988-92). Roman Catholic. *

ROSS, ROBERT KING, retired educator; b. Manti, Utah, Jan. 27, 1927; s. Clarence King Ross and Annamae Plant Nielson; m. Patsy Ruth Tattu, Dec. 25, 1947 (dec. 1988); children: Scott, Barbara, Richard, Michael. BA in Secondary Edn., Ea. Wash. Coll. Edn., 1951. Cert. master tchr., Wash. Tchr. Reardon (Wash.) High Sch., 1951-52; microphotography specialist U.S. Atomic Energy Commn., Richland, Wash., 1952-54; mgr. St. Paul br. Dakota Microfilm Svc., 1954-61; system specialist 3M Co., Seattle, 1961-64; prin., tchr. U.S. Bur. Indian Affairs, Shungnak, Alaska, 1964-68; tchr. Port Angeles (Wash.) Sch. Dist., 1968-89; ret.; mem. Wash. State Newspaper in Edn. Com., Tacoma, 1970-92; instr. record ann. tchrs. seminars. Contbr. articles to profl. jours. With USMC, 1945-47. Recipient Cert. of Appreciation Seattle P.I. Newspaper, 1980. Fellow Elks; mem. DAV, VFW. Avocations: writing, photography, travel. Home: 324 E 11th St Port Angeles WA 98362-7932

ROSS, ROBERT THOMAS, neurologist, educator; b. Winnipeg, Man., Can., June 25, 1924; s. John L. and Alberta I. (Gray) R.; m. Margot Joan Ellacott, May 27, 1950; children: Gray T., John L., Mary E.; m. Angela Morrow Brady, Aug. 14, 1970; children: Diana Gray Salter, Drew Garland Salter. MD, U. Man., 1948. Intern Winnipeg Gen. Hosp., 1947-50; resident Nat. Hosp. Queen Sq., London, 1950-52; lectr. dept anatomy U. Man., Winnipeg, 1953-55, asst. prof. dept. medicine, 1955-59, assoc. prof., 1959-77, prof. medicine, 1977—, head sect. neurology, 1971-84. Editor., pub., founder: Can. Jour. Neurol. Scis., 1972-81; author: How to Examine the Nervous System, 1978, 2d edit., 1985; Syringobulbia-A Contribution to the Pathophysiology of the Brain Stem, 1986, Syncope, 1988. Trustee Man. Med. Svc., 1958-64; pres. United Health Found., Winnipeg, 1969-71; bd. dirs. Man. Med. Coll. Found., 1983-85; mem. senate U. Manitoba, 1988—. Recipient E.L. Drewry prize E.L. Drewry Found., 1948; recipient Can. Centennial Medal, 1967, Queen Elizabeth Jubilee Medal, 1977. Fellow Royal Coll. Physicians (Can. and London), Am. Acad. Neurology; mem. Can. Neurol. Soc. (pres. 1971), Coll. Physicians and Surgeons of Man (pres. 1971), Am. Neurol. Assn., Order of Can. Baptist. Home: 312 Park Blvd, Winnipeg, MB Canada R3P OG7 Office: Univ Man Sect Neurology, PE126 820 Sherbrook St, Winnipeg, MB Canada R3A 1R9

ROSS, ROBINETTE DAVIS, publisher; b. London, May 16, 1952; d. Raymond Lawrence and Pearl A. (Robinette) D.; m. William Bradford Ross III, Mar. 16, 1979; children: Nellie Tayloe, William Bradford IV. Student, Am. U., 1977-78. Asst. to editor The Chronicle of Higher Edn., Washington, 1978, advt. mgr., 1978-82, advt. dir., 1983-88, assoc. pub., 1988-94; assoc. pub. The Chronicle of Philanthropy, 1988-94; publ. The Chronicle of Higher Edn., Washington, 1994—; pub. The Chronicle of Philanthropy, Washington, 1994—. Mem. Newspaper Assn. Am., Am. News Women's Club, City Tavern Club. Episcopalian. Home: 3908 Virgilia St Chevy Chase MD 20815-5026 Office: The Chronicle of Higher Edn 1255 23rd St NW Washington DC 20037-1125

ROSS, RODERIC HENRY, insurance company executive; b. Jamestown, N.Y., July 14, 1930; s. Edwin A. and Mary (Dornberger) R.; m. Patricia Johnson, Aug. 6, 1955; children: Timothy, Amy, Jane, Christopher. BA, Hobart Coll., 1952, LLD (hon.), 1979. CLU, ChFC. Gen. agt. Phila. Life Ins. Co., 1957-70, sr. v.p. mktg., 1972-73, pres., 1973-83, vice chmn., 1983-84; chmn., pres. Keystone State Life Ins. Co., Phila., 1985—; bd. dirs. PNC Bank Corp., Pitts., Hunt Mfg. Corp., Phila., Resource Holdings Corp., Malvern, Pa., Key Home Capital Group, Louisville, Ky. Home Mut. Life Ins. Group, Louisville; past. chmn. Ins. Fedn. Pa. Rector's warden St. David's Ch., Radnor, Pa., 1989-90; trustee Hobart-William Smith Colls. Geneva, N.Y., 1972—, chmn. bd., 1983-88. Sgt. U.S. Army, 1952-54. Mem. Am. Soc. CLUs, Nat. Assn. Nat. Assn. Life Underwriters, Million Dollar Round Table (life), Union League (former dir.), Orpheus Club, St. David's Golf Club (Wayne, Pa.), Pine Valley Golf Club (Clementon, N.J.). Republican. Episcopalian. Avocations: golf, tennis. Home: 770 Pugh Rd Wayne PA 19087-2011 Office: Keystone State Life Ins Co 1401 Walnut St Philadelphia PA 19102

ROSS, RONALD JAY, radiologist; b. Cleve., Dec. 12, 1934; s. William and Dorothy (Abel) R.; m. Helen Deborah Manas, July 11, 1959; children: Heather Ross-Lowenstein, David Scott, Steven Michael. AB, Case Western Res. U., 1956; MD, Albert Einstein Coll. Medicine, 1960. Diplomate Am. Bd. Radiology. Resident in radiology Mt. Sinai Med. Ctr., Cleve., 1960-64; fellow in radiology Karolinska Hosp., Stockholm, 1964-65; radiologist Drs. Sachs, Ross & Assocs., Cleve., 1965-68, sr. radiologist, 1968-90; from clin. instr. to sr. clin. instr. radiology Case Western Res. U., Cleve., 1966-68, asst. clin. prof. radiology, 1968—; attending in radiology VA Hosp., Cleve., 1965-66; cons. radiology VA Hosp. 1966-80; chief dept. radiology, mem. med. exec. com. Community Hosp., Bedford, Ohio, 1970-90; chmn. med. exec. com. Community Hosp. Bedford, Ohio, 1977-79; pres. med. staff Community Hosp., Bedford, Ohio, 1977-79; dir. dept. radiology Meridia Hillcrest Hosp., Cleve., 1990—, mem. med. exec. com., 1990—; Mem. med. exec. com., 1969-73; chmn. Forest City Hosp., 1970-72, pres., 1970-72; vis. radiology cons. Cleve. Clinic, 1977-78; mem. cons. med staff Windsor Hosp., 1980-85; vol. cons. Free Med. Clinic Greater Cleve., 1984-90; cons. NIH, Nat. Cancer Inst., HHS, Bethesda, Md., 1985—; bd. dirs. Meridia Health Plan, Meridia Inst; bd. dirs Meridia Physicians Network, 1994-95; Founding Chmn. of the Bd. Meridia Health Found. 1995—. Bd. Trustees, Meridia Health System, 1995—. Author and co-author of 33 articles and chpts. in profl. jours.; abstractor, reviewer jours. in field. Trustee Cleve. Ctr. Contemporary Art, 1992-94. Recipient Study of Radiology award Govt. Sweden, 1964, Fulbright-Hays award U.S. Govt., 1964, Centre National de la Recherche Scientifique award France, 1982, Community Service award Office of Mayor of Bedford, 1982. Mem. Cleve. Radiol. Soc. (Otto Glasser award 1963), AMA (Physician Recognition in Continuing Med. Edn. award 1969-72, 73-76, 77-79, 80-82, 82-84, 84-86, 86-88, 88-90, 93-95), Cleve. Acad. Medicine, Albert Einstein Coll. Medicine Alumni Assn., Nat. Bd. Govs. 1973—(pres. Nat. Bd. Govs. 1973-75, Pres. award), Am. Roentgen Ray Soc., Ohio State Med. Assn. (Physician Recognition award 1977-81), Am. Coll. Nuclear Medicine (v.p. N.E. Ohio chpt. 1976-77, pres. N.E. Ohio chpt. 1977-78), Am. Coll. Radiology (Continuing Med. Ed. award 1979-81), Radiol. Soc. N.Am., Fulbright Assn. (bd. dirs., exec. com., v.p. 1994-95, treas. 1995—), Fulbright Alumni Assn. N.E Ohio (bd. dirs. 1989—, pres. 1992-94), Soc. MRI (exec. com. 1982-84, editorial bd. Jour. MRI, 1982-84); Medical Advisory Committee, Ohio State Boxing Commission, 1994—. Clubs: Cleve Racquet, Shorebeach Country. Avocations: tennis. Home: Fox Run Gates Mills OH 44040 Office: Meridia Hillcrest Hosp Dept Radiology 6780 Mayfield Rd Cleveland OH 44124-2203

ROSS, RUSSELL, pathologist, educator; b. St. Augustine, Fla., May 25, 1929; s. Samuel and Minnie (DuBoff) R.; m. Jean Long Teller, Feb. 22, 1956; children: Valerie Regina, Douglas Teller. A.B., Cornell U., 1951; D.D.S., Columbia U., 1955; Ph.D., U. Wash., 1962; DSc (hon.P, Med. Coll. of Pa., 1987. Intern Columbia-Presbyn. Med. Ctr., 1955-56, USPHS Hosp., Seattle, 1956-58; spl. research fellow pathology sch. medicine U. Wash., Seattle, 1958-62, asst. prof. pathology and oral biology sch. medicine and dentistry, 1962-65, assoc. prof. pathology Sch. Medicine, 1965-69, prof. Sch. Medicine, 1969—, adj. prof. biochemistry Sch. Medicine, 1978—, assoc. dean for sci. affairs sch. medicine, 1971-78, chmn. dept. pathology sch. medicine, 1982-94; dir. Ctr. for Vascular Biology, 1991—; vis. scientist Strangeways Rsch. Lab., Cambridge, Eng.; mem. rsch. com. Am. Heart Assn.; mem. adv. bd. Found. Cardiologique Princess Liliane, Brussels, Belgium; life fellow Clare Hall, Cambridge U.; mem. adv. coun. Nat. Heart, Lung and Blood Inst., NIH, 1978-81; vis. prof. Royal Soc. Medicine, U.K., 1987, 95. Editorial bd. Procs. Exptl. Biology and Medicine, 1971-86, Jours. Cell Biology, 1972-74, Exptl. Cell Rsch., 1982-92, Jour. Exptl. Medicine, Growth Factors, Am. Jours. Pathology, Internat. Cell Biology Jour., Circulation, Arteriosclerosis & Thrombosis, Growth Regulation; assoc. editor Arteriosclerosis, 1982-92, Jours. Cellular Physiology, Jours. Cellular Biochemistry; exec. editor Trends in Cariovascular Medicine; reviewing editorial bd. Sci. mag., 1987-90; contbr. articles to profl. jours. Trustee Seattle Symphony Orch. Recipient Birnberg Rsch. award Columbia U., 1975, Nat. Rsch. Achievement award Am. Heart Assn., 1990, Rous-Whipple award Am. Assn. Pathologists, 1992, Gordon Wilson medal Am. Clin. and Climatol. Assn., 1981; named to Inst. Medicine, Nat. Acad. Scis.; Japan Soc. Promotion of Sci. fellow, 1985, Guggenheim fellow, 1966-67. Fellow AAAS, Am. Acad. Arts and Scis.; mem. Am. Soc. Cell Biology, Tissue Culture Assn., Am. Assn. Pathologists (Rous-Whipple award 1992), Am. Soc. for Investigative Pathology (pres. 1994-95), Internat. Soc. Cell Biology, Electron Microscope Soc. Am., Am. Heart Assn. (fellow Coun. on Arteriosclerosis, Nat. Rsch. Achievement award 1990), Royal Micros. Soc., Harvey Soc. (hon.), Am. Soc. Biochemistry and Molecular Biology, Romanian Acad. Med. Scis. (hon.), Royal Belgian Acad. Scis. (fgn. corr. mem.). Sigma Xi. Home: 3812 48th Ave NE Seattle WA 98105 Office: U Wash Sch Medicine 1959 NE Pacific St Seattle WA 98195-0001

ROSS, RUSSELL MARION, political science educator; b. Washington, Iowa, June 2, 1921; s. Harold Ellis and Lucille Carrie (Dorris) R.; m. Jo Ellen Rude; children: Sheryl Ross, Julie. BA, U. Iowa, 1942; cert., Harvard U., 1945; MA, U.Iowa, 1946, PhD, 1948. Instr. dept. polit. sci. U. Iowa, Iowa City, 1946-48, asst. prof., 1948-52, assoc. prof., 1952-60, research prof., 1963-64, prof., 1965—, chmn. dept., 1970-91; prof. emeritus, 1991—; adminstrv. asst. to atty. gen., Iowa, 1960; exec. asst. to Gov. Iowa, 1961-62. Author: Iowa Government and Administration, 1958, State and Local Government and Administration, 1966, Gubernatorial Transitions, 1985, Political Science at the University of Iowa, 1990. Chmn. Regional Planning Commn., 1966-68; pres. Iowa City Community Sch. Bd., 1969-70; chmn. Iowa Campaign Finance Disclosure Commn., 1973-77; Mayor University Heights, 1954-60; Bd. dirs. Goodwill Industries S.E. Iowa. Served to lt. USNR, 1942-45. Mem. AAUP, Internat. City Mgrs. Assn. (hon.), Am. Pub. Adminstrn. Soc., Am. Polit. Sci. Assn., Mid-West Polit. Sci. Assn., Phi Beta Kappa, Phi Delta Kappa, Pi Sigma Alpha, Alpha Sigma Lambda. Club: Kiwanian. Home: 315 Highland Dr Iowa City IA 52246-1602

ROSS, SAMUEL D., JR., insurance company executive; b. 1933. Pres., ceo Medical Servives Assn of Pa., Camp Hill, 1970—. Office: Medical Services Assn of PA 1800 Center St Camp Hill PA 17011-1702

ROSS, SHELDON JULES, dentist; b. N.Y.C., June 17, 1924; s. Sam and Regina (Rosner) R.; 1 stepson, Nathan Sudnow; m. Carolyn L. M. Loesch, Apr. 26, 1946; children: Jane, Eric, Ellen, Lisa. D.D.S., NYU, 1949. Diplomate: Am. Bd. Periodontology, Am. Bd. Oral Medicine (examiner 1980-85). Pvt. practice periodontology N.Y.C., 1949—; prof. periodontics and oral medicine N.Y. U. Sch. Dentistry, 1949—; resident oral medicine Montefiore Hosp., N.Y.C., 1956-57; charge periodontics Montefiore Hosp., 1951-70, oral medicine, 1951-81, cons., 1981-95; attending charge oral medicine and periodontics Beth Abraham Hosp., Bronx, N.Y., 1961-81, cons., 1981-87; cons. in oral medicine Goldwater Meml. Hosp., N.Y.C., 1982—; former cons., lectr. periodontics and oral medicine Cabrini Hosp. and Med. Ctr., N.Y.C.; lectr. in field; honored lectr. Internat. Odontological Congress, Maringa, Brazil, 1972. Editor Jour. Oral Medicine, 1971-88, Annals of Dentistry, 1971-88; contbr. articles to dental jours., chpts. to textbooks. Served with AUS, 1942-43. Fellow Am. Coll. Dentists, N.Y. Acad. Dentistry (v.p. 1989-90, pres.-elect 1990-91, pres. 1991-92), Am. Acad. Oral Medicine (pres. 1980); mem. ADA, Am. Assn. Dental Editors, Am. Acad. Oral Medicine, Am. Acad. Oral Pathology, Am. Acad. Periodontology, N.E. Soc. Periodontists, Orgn. Tchrs. Oral Diagnosis, Am. Heart Assn., Omega Kappa Upsilon. Home and Office: 40 Twisting Ln Wantagh NY 11793-1947 *None admit to having any new ideals except loving redemption of some souls: Man expects rational and normal deliberation instead.*

ROSS, SHERMAN, psychologist, educator; b. N.Y.C., Jan. 1, 1919; s. Max R. and Rachel (Khoutman) R.; m. Jean Goodwin, Aug. 18, 1945; children: Norman Kimball, Claudia Lisbeth (Mrs. Overway), Michael Lachlan. B.S., CCNY, 1939; A.M., Columbia U., 1941, Ph.D., 1943. Asst. psychology, research psychologist Columbia U., 1941-44; asst., then assoc. prof. psychology Bucknell U., 1946-50; research fellow N.Y. Zool. Soc., 1948; guest investigator, sci. assoc. Jackson Lab., 1947-77; assoc. prof., then prof. psychology U. Md., 1950-60; spl. cons. Psychopharmacology Svc. Ctr. NIMH, 1956-63; assoc chief NIMH, 1956-57; exec. sec. and tng. bd., sci. affairs officer APA, 1960-68; prof. psychology Howard U., 1968-89, emeritus, 1989—; exec. sec., staff assoc., assembly of behavioral and social scis. Nat. Acad. Scis.-NRC, 1968-76; lectr. Himmelfarb Mobile U., 1994—; cons. VA, Human Ecology Fund, Stanford Research Inst., Office Naval Research, U.S. Sci. Exhibit, Am. U., HRB-Singer, Inc.; bd. dirs. Interdisciplinary Communications Assocs., Washington; adv. council Woodrow Wilson Rehab. Center Found.; mem. Med. Bd. Examiners Psychology, 1957-58, 84-89; chmn. bd. dirs. Inst. for Research, State Coll., Pa.; mem. Montgomery County Health Planning Commn.; mem. Md. Statewide Health Coordinating Coun., Met. Washington Area Council of Health Planning Agys., Emergency Med. Svcs. Adv. Council; commr. health emeritus Montgomery County, Md. Trustee Carver Research Found., Tuskegee U. Served to lt. (j.g.) USNR, 1944-46; capt. USNR (ret.). Fellow APA, Am. Coll. Neuropsychopharmacology, Royal Soc. Health, Washington Acad. Scis.; mem. Aerospace Med. Assn., Am. Soc. Zoologists, Ecol. Soc., Ergonomics Rsch. Soc., Md. Psychol. Assn. (pres. 1973-74), D.C. Psychol. Assn. (pres. 1982), Cosmos Club (Washington), Sigma Xi (pres. U. Md. 1957-58, pres. Howard U. 1983-84), Phi Kappa Phi, Psi Chi (nat. pres. 1964-68). Home: 382 Russell Ave Gaithersburg MD 20877-2863 also: Glen Mary Rd Bar Harbor ME 04609-1301

ROSS, STAN, accounting firm executive; b. 1939. With Kenneth Leventhal & Co., L.A., 1964—, now mng. ptnr. Office: Kenneth Leventhal & Co 2049 Century Park E Los Angeles CA 90067*

ROSS, STANFORD GORDON, lawyer, former government official; b. St. Louis, Oct. 9, 1931; m. Dorothy Rabin, June 9, 1956; children: John, Ellen. AB with honors, Washington U., 1953; JD magna cum laude, Harvard U., 1956. Bar: D.C. 1969, Calif. 1956, N.Y. 1959. Assoc. firm Irell & Manella, Los Angeles, 1956-57; teaching fellow, research asst. Harvard Law Sch., 1957-58; assoc. firm Dewey, Ballantine, Bushby, Palmer & Wood, N.Y.C., 1961-61; asst. tax legis. counsel U.S. Dept. Treasury, 1961-63; prof. law N.Y. U., 1963-67; White House staff asst. to Pres. Johnson, 1967-68; gen. counsel U.S. Dept. Transp., 1968-69; ptnr. Caplin & Drysdale, Washington, 1969-78; commr. Social Security Adminstrn., Washington, 1978-79; ptnr. Califano, Ross & Heineman, Washington, 1980-82, Arnold & Porter, Washington, 1983—; pub. trustee Social Security Trust Funds, Washington, 1990-95. Editor: Harvard Law Rev., 1954-56. Mem. ABA, Fed. Bar Assn., Internat. Fiscal Assn., Nat. Acad. Social Ins. (bd. dirs.). Office: Arnold & Porter 555 Twelfth St NW Washington DC 20004-1202

ROSS, STANLEY RALPH, writer, publisher, producer, software manufacturing executive; b. N.Y.C., July 22, 1940; s. Morris Harvey and Blanche (Turer) R.; m. Neila Hyman, Dec. 14, 1957; children: Andrew Steven, Lisa Michelle Turer, Nancy Ellen. Student, Pratt Inst.; DD, Universal Life Ch.,

Modesto, Calif., 1973; PhD in Lit., L.A. U., 1976. Self-employed photographer N.Y.C., 1956; copywriter Fuller, Smith & Ross, Los Angeles, 1956-60, Universal Pictures, Los Angeles, 1960-61; advt. exec. Universal Studios, Universal City, Calif., 1960-62; program exec. ABC-TV, Los Angeles, 1961-63; creative dir. Cole, Fischer & Rogow, Beverly Hills, Calif., 1963-65, Becker Adv., Long Beach, Calif., 1964-65; pres. freelance film and TV writer Neila, Inc., Los Angeles, 1965—; assoc. prof. U. So. Calif.; guest lectr. Calif. Luth. Coll., L.A. Coll., Sherwood Oaks U., others; tchr. writing, assoc. prof. U. So. Calif.; cons. in field; exec. v.p. bd. dirs. Crime Books, Wilmette, Ill., 1983—; bd. dirs. The Writers Group, L.A.; pres., CEO Comedy Software, Ltd., Disktop Pub., Inc.; new products cons. RJR Nabisco. Author: Games for Planes, 1974, Speak When You Hear the Beep, 1975, Swan Song, Any Port in a Storm, The Motion Picture Guide; writer TV programs All in the Family, The Monkees, Batman, The Man From UNCLE; developer programs Wonder Woman, The Electric Company, That's My Mama, The Kallikaks, The Monster Squad, The Challenge of the Sexes; Scriptwriter Banacek, Colombo, Kids, Inc., Tales From The Crypt, TV films Coffee, Tea or Me?, Gold of the Amazon Women, Murder at the Mardi Gras, The Town That Went on a Diet, Mrs. R, (films) The Answer, It Happened Tomorrow, Jojo, Rodeo Drive, Follow Me; editor, author: (with Jay Robert Nash) The Motion Picture Guide, feature film ency., 17 vols; actor appeared in (TV) Punky Brewster, The Facts of Life, Falcon Crest, Ellery Queen, Hart to Hart, Bill Cosby Show, Double Life of Henry Phyfe, Divorce Court, Superior Court, Family Medical Center, Superman, The Munsters Today (films) Sleeper, Romantic Comedy, John Goldfarb Please Come Home, Tony Rome, Sideout, numerous commls.; voice over cartoons, commls.; columnist Restaurant Row mag. Vol. The Thalians, Beverly Hills, 1972—; Nosotros, Los Angeles, 1985—; The Soc. of Singers. Recipient UNICEF award 1974, West Los Angeles Coll. Presdl. citation, 1974, Carson (Calif.) citation, 1973, Cert. Appreciation Personal Freedom Alliance, 1974, Inkpot award San Diego Comicon, 1977, Emmy award nomination Nat. Acad. TV Arts and Scis., 1970, 71, 72, Golden Eagle awards, Nat. Assn. Theater Owners awards, 3 Emmy nominations Nat. Acad. TV Arts and Scis.; named to Bklyn. Hall of Fame Celebrity Path, 1992. Mem. Writers Guild Am. West (award 1971, 72, 74, Family Film award 1990), Producers Guild, Dirs. Guild, Dramatists Guild, Screen Actors Guild, AFTRA, ASCAP, Hon. Order Ky. Cols, TV Acad., Beverly Hills C. of C. Republican. Mem. Universal Life Ch. Club: Saints and Sinners (Los Angeles). Avocations: composing, writing lyrics, baseball, oil painting. Home: 451 S Beverwil Dr Beverly Hills CA 90212-4209 Office: Neila Inc PO Box 3605 Beverly Hills CA 90212-0605 *My goal in life has been to have a good time and do only what I care to. I feel that I cannot do something that is alien to my nature and have so refused over the years until I discovered that writing was my true vocation. In the past three decades, I have enjoyed myself and had more success than in all my former work years due to this independence. The only other principle I espouse is the law of Karma. For every effect, there is a cause; and every good thing one does is noted in a grand book and the rewards for doing good are reaped here on earth.*

ROSS, STEPHEN BRUCE, public affairs consultant; b. Bklyn., May 23, 1944; s. Irving and Muriel (Friedman) R.; m. Linda Janine Holdredge, June 22, 1968 (div. Apr. 1986); children: Jason, David; m. Elizabeth Wallace, Nov. 29, 1992; children: Jill Wallace, Jaclyn. BA, Williams Coll., 1966; MPA, Syracuse U., 1968; postgrad., Johns Hopkins U., 1971. Sr. rapporteur U.S. Atomic Energy Commn., Washington, 1968-70, acting chief ops. br., 1971; v.p. Charles Yulish Assocs., N.Y.C., 1972-78; sr. v.p. Underwood Jordan Assocs., N.Y.C., 1978-80; pres. Holt & Ross, Inc., Clark, N.J., 1980—. Chmn. pub. rels. com. Bicentennial Commn., Williams Coll., Williamston, Mass., 1990-92. Avocations: racquetball, cooking, horseback riding. Office: Holt & Ross Inc Far Hills Ctr PO Box 127 Far Hills NJ 07931-0127

ROSS, STEVEN CARTER, entertainment executive; b. Indpls., Apr. 29, 1954; s. Glenn Elrick Sr. and Linda (Schnepal) R. BA, Ind. U., 1980. Account exec. Sta. WEFM, Chgo., 1980-81; pres. Bluebird Nightclub, Inc., Bloomington, Ind., 1981—; cons. Sta. WIVS, Bloomington, 1985-86; sec., treas. Vogue, Inc., Inpls., 1986—. Mem. Licensed Beverage Assn. (sec., treas. 1985—). Republican. Presbyterian. Club: Scuba (Bloomington). Avocations: sailing, video production, restoring classic cars. Home: 550 N Gettys Creek Rd Bloomington IN 47408-9401 Office: WSYW AM 8203 Indy Ct Indianapolis IN 46214

ROSS, STUART B., corporate financial executive; b. N.Y.C., Apr. 16, 1937; s. Bernard Theodore and Ruth R.; m. Stephanie Banks, Dec. 15, 1962; children: Jessica, Benjamin. BS, NYU, 1958; MBA, CCNY, 1966. Pub. acct. Harris, Kerr, Forster, N.Y.C., 1958-63; fin. analyst MacMillan Co., N.Y.C., 1963-69; with Xerox Corp., Stamford, Conn., 1966—, CFO, 1985—, exec. v.p., 1990—, also mem. pvt. sector coun., conf. bd.; chmn., CEO Xerox Fin. Svc., Stamford, 1990—; bd. dirs. ECKO Group, Inc. Mem. AICPA, Fin. Execs. Inst. Office: Xerox Corp PO Box 1600 800 Long Ridge Rd Stamford CT 06904

ROSS, SUE, entrepreneur, author, fundraising executive; b. Chgo., Feb. 2, 1948; d. Irving and Rose (Stein) R. BA in Secondary Edn., Western Mich. U., 1971; postgrad., Northwestern U., Chgo. State U., U. Ill., 1971-73. Dir. youth employment Ill. Youth Svcs. Bur., Maywood, Ill., 1978-79; exec. dir. Edn. Resource Ctr., Chgo., 1979-82; asst. dir. devel. Art Inst. Chgo., 1982-83, mgr. govt. affairs, 1983-84, dir. govt. affairs, 1984-85; v.p. devel. Spertus Coll. Judaica, Chgo., 1985-90; mgmt. and fundraising counsel Sue Ross Enterprises, San Francisco, 1990—; founder, pres. Kid Angels Internat., San Francisco, 1994—; lectr. Sch. Art Inst., Chgo., 1982-85, Episcopalian Archdiocese, Chgo., 1984, Nat. Soc. Fund Raising Execs. and Donor's Forum, Chgo., 1987; instr. DePaul U. Sch. for New Learning, 1987-88, Columbia Coll., Chgo., 1980-91. Resident counsel for devel. the Joffrey Ballet, 1990-91; adv. panelist Chgo. Office Fine Arts, 1981-82; mem. com. adv. bd. Lines Contemporary Ballet, 1995—; mem. adv. coun. Greater Chgo. Food Depository, 1984-85; exec. com. Chgo. Coalition Arts in Edn., 1981-82; mem. info. svcs. com. Donors' Forum Chgo., 1986-88, mem. internationally renowned Gospel Choir of Glide Meml., 1991-93, San Francisco City Chorus, 1994—; active Congregation Sherith Israel, San Francisco Angel Club, 1994—, Angel Collector's Club of Am., 1994—, Angels of World, 1994—; resident counsel for devel. The 1995 Children's World Peace Festival. Mem. Nat. Soc. Fund Raising Execs. (mem. svcs. com. Golden Gate chpt. 1993). Democrat. Jewish. Avocations: community service, singing. Home and Office: 1807 Octavia St San Francisco CA 94109-4328

ROSS, TERENCE WILLIAM, architect; b. Saginaw, Mich., Sept. 27, 1935; s. Oran Lewis and Drucilla (Chadman) R.; BArch, U. Mich., 1958; m. Patricia Ann Marshall, Sept. 27, 1974; children by previous marriage: Deborah, David. Designer, Roger W. Peters Constrn. Co., Fond du Lac, Wis., 1958-62; draftsman Kenneth Clark, Architect, Santa Fe, N.Mex., 1962-63, Holien & Buckley, Architects, Santa Fe, 1963-64; office mgr. Philippe Register, Architect, Santa Fe, 1964-68; prin. Register, Ross, & Brunet architects, engrs., Santa Fe, 1968-71, Luna-Ross & Assoc., 1971-77; staff CNWC Architects, Tucson, to 1981, ADP Architects, 1981-89; st. architect U. Calif., 1989—. Vice chmn. N.Mex. R.R. Authority, 1969-74, sec., 1970-72. Bd. dirs. Colo., N.Mex. Soc. Preservation of Narrow Gauge. Recipient award for hist. preservation N.Mex. Arts Commn., 1971, award for outstanding svcs.to community Santa Fe Press Club, 1972; named col. aide-decamp State of N.Mex., 1968, hon. mem. staff atty. gen. Mem. AIA (chpt. pres. 1970, dir.), Constrn. Specifications Inst., N.Mex. Soc. Architects (dir. 1972), Ariz. Soc. Architects, N.Mex. R.R. Authorities (chmn. joint exec. com. 1970-74), Sacramento Valley Garden Ry. Soc. (pres. 1993, dir. 1994), San Gabriel Hist. Soc. (hon.), Alpha Rho Chi, Sashay Rounders Sq. Dance Club (pres. 1974), Diamond Squares Sq. Dance Club, Railroad Club (pres. N.Mex. 1969, 70, dir.). Author: Track of the Cats. Home and Office: 2813 57th St Sacramento CA 95817-2403

ROSS, THOMAS BERNARD, federal government official; b. N.Y.C., Sept. 2, 1929; s. Henry M. and Evelyn (Timothy) R.; m. Gunilla Ekstrand, Nov. 2, 1963; children: Maria, Anne, Kristina. BA, Yale, 1951. Reporter I.N.S., 1955-58, UPI, 1958; mem. staff Chgo. Sun-Times, 1958-77, mem. staff Washington Bur., 1958-68; fgn. corr. Chgo. Sun-Times, Beirut and Paris, 1968-70; Washington bur. chief Chgo. Sun-Times, 1970-77; asst. sec. def. for pub. affairs, 1977-81; dir. corp. comm. Celanese Corp., 1981-82; sr. v.p. corp. affairs RCA Corp., 1982-86; sr. v.p. NBC News, 1986-90; sr. v.p., dir. media

rels. worldwide Hill and Knowlton, N.Y.C., 1990-94; spl. asst. to pres., sr. dir. pub. affairs NSC, 1994—; dep. pres. sec. for fgn. affairs White House, Washington, 1994—. Author: (with David Wise) The U-2 Affair, 1962, The Invisible Government, 1964, The Espionage Establishment, 1967. Lt. (j.g.) USNR, 1951-54. Nieman fellow Harvard U., 1964; recipient Marshall Field award, 1961, 71; decorated Def. Disting. Pub. Svc. medal. Mem. Coun. on Fgn. Rels., Elizabethan Club (New Haven), Gridiron Club (Washington), Century Club (N.Y.C.). Home: 1148 Fifth Ave New York NY 10128-0807 Office: The White House Washington DC 20506

ROSS, THOMAS MCCALLUM, association executive; b. Hamilton, Ont., Can., May 5, 1931; s. Laverne Robinson and Della Louise (McCallum) R.; m. Marguerite Hilda Ross, Aug. 14, 1954; children: Thomas Wayne, Gregory (dec.), Karyn. Mgr. Sutherland Pharmacy, Hamilton, 1955-60; assoc. sec. Can. Pharm. Assn., Toronto, Ont., 1960-63; mem. research staff Royal Commn. Health Services Govt. Can., Ottawa, Ont., 1963-64; exec. dir. Can. Retail Hardware Assn., Toronto, 1964—. Bd. dirs. People for Sunday Assn., pres. 1987-88. Founding fellow Hardware Mgmt. Inst.; mem. Internat. Fedn. Ironmongers Assn. (coun. 1970—), Can. Soc. Assn. Execs. (chmn. edn. com. 1986-88, bd. dirs. 1990-92, Pinnacle award 1989), Am. Soc. Assn. Execs., Can. C. of C. Home: 59 Walby Dr, Oakville, ON Canada Office: 6800 Campobello Rd, Mississauga, ON Canada

ROSS, VONIA PEARL, insurance agent, small business owner; b. Taylorville, Ill., Dec. 4, 1942; d. Alvin Clyde and Lois Eva (Weller) Brown; m. Wyatt Gene Ross, Nov. 11, 1962 (Div. Nov. 1986); children: Craig Allen Ross, Cayle Allen Ross. Student, So. Ill. U., 1962-64, Palomar Coll., 1986-88, San Diego State U., 1988-90. Real estate agt. Joe Foster Agy., Collinsville, Ill., 1964-69; ofice mgr. real estate Bank of St. Louis, 1969-73; real estate agt. Palmer-Stelman, San Diego, 1986-89; office mgr. real estate McMillin Realty, San Diego, 1989-90; mgr., ins. agt. Calif. Plus Ins., San Diego, 1990-93; prin. Vonia Ross Ins. Agy., 1993—; Bernardo Flooring, 1993—; mem. Calif. Assn. Real Estate, Sacramento, 1986—, San Diego Bd. Realtors, 1986—, Health Underwriters, 1991—. Mem. adv. com. Rancho Bernardo Libr. Campaign, 1994—; active NOW, San Diego, 1988; mem. activist Barbara Boxer Campaign, San Diego, 1992, Susan Golding Campaign, San Diego, 1992, Barbara Warden Campaign for San Diego City Councilwoman. Recipient Ill. State Assembly scholarship, 1962. Mem. Soroptimist Rancho Bernardo (pres. 1993-94), Rancho Bernardo C. of C. (v.p. bd. dirs. 1993—). Methodist. Avocations: walking, biking, mountain climbing, hiking, tennis, music, reading. Home: 18284 Fernando Way San Diego CA 92128-1213

ROSS, WALTER BEGHTOL, music educator, composer; b. Lincoln, Nebr., Oct. 3, 1936; s. Robert Thurber and Barbara Adeline (Ellis) R.; m. Marion Helen Wright, July 22, 1960; 1 child, Douglas Campbell. BA, U. Nebr., 1960, MusM, 1962; student, Inst. Torcuato Di Tella, Buenos Aires, 1965-66; D of Mus. Arts, Cornell U., 1966. Asst. prof. music CUNY, Cortland, 1966-67; prof. U. Va., Charlottesville, 1967—; mem. judging panel symphonic awards ASCAP, 1978, Internat. Biennial Composition Contest, P.R., 1981, Va. chpt. Coll. Band Dir.'s Nat. Assn. Nat. Band Composition Contest, 1982, 88; bass Blue Ridge Chamber Orch., Charlottesville, 1992—. Composer of 98 works including compositions for symphony orch., symphonic band, brass, chamber music, piano, voice, opera, theater and film; recordings include Concerto for Piano and Orch., Escher's Sketches, Concerto for Wind Quintet and String Orch., others. Nominee Pulitzer Prize, 1973; recipient ASCAP award, 1974—; 1st prize Internat. Trombone Assn., 1982; grantee Am. Music Ctr., 1983; fellow Presser Found., 1958, 59, Orgn. Am. States, 1965, NEA, 1975. Democrat. Avocations: chess, cooking, amateur astronomy. Office: U Va Music Dept Charlottesville VA 22903

ROSS, WENDY CLUCAS, newspaper editor, journalist; b. Balt., Apr. 15, 1942; d. Charles Max and Jean (Talbot) Clucas; m. David N. Ross, Sept. 5, 1964 (div. 1979). BA, Bradley U., 1964. Women's editor DeKalb (Ill.) Daily Chronicle, 1968-69; reporter Chgo. Tribune, 1969-70; copy editor, mag. editor Mpls. Tribune, 1970-72; copy editor Peoria (Ill.) Jour. Star, 1973-75, Miami (Fla.) Herald, 1975-77; asst. news editor Washington Post, 1977-83, dep. news editor, 1983-87, news editor, 1987-93; asst. mng. editor news desk, 1993—. Recipient award of excellence Soc. Newspaper Design, 1985, 87-91, Disting. Alumnae award Bradley U. Centurion Soc., 1994; Nieman fellow Harvard U., 1983-84. Avocations: skiing, sailing, reading, travel. Office: The Washington Post 1150 15th St NW Washington DC 20071-0002

ROSS, WILLIAM, financial planner; b. N.Y.C., Dec. 1, 1925; s. Robert Sidney and Celia (Gross) R.; m. Shirley Phillips, Aug. 28, 1955; children: Robyn Sue, Tina Dale Ross. BBA, Woodbury U., 1950. CPF; ChFC; registered fin. planner. Agy. gen. agt. Berkshire Life Ins. Co., Union, N.J., 1970-75; pres. William Ross & Assocs., Montvale, N.J., 1975-82; sr. fin. planner Shearson Am. Express, Paramus, N.J., 1982-84, Merril Lynch, N.Y.C., 1984-86; pres. The Fin. Planning Stores, Clifton, N.J., 1986-92; mng. ptnr. Xelan Corp., San Diego, Calif., 1990-91; chief fin. officer Trust Performance USA, Clifton, N.J., 1991-92; chief exec. officer Fin. Guidance Group Ltd., Paramus, N.J., 1992—; adj. instr. Coll. Fin. Planning, Denver. Contbr. articles to mags. Pres. bd. dirs. Vol. Counselling, N.Y. 1978-80. Sgt. U.S. Army, 1945-47. Mem. Assn. of CFP (program com. 1989-92), Nat. Assn. of Life Underwriters (bd. dirs. 1970-75). Mem. Assn. of CFP (program com. 1989-92), Nat. Assn. of Life Underwriters (bd. dirs.). Republican. Avocations: auto racing, karate-black belt, sculpture. Home: 55 Eastbourne Dr Chestnut Ridge NY 10977 Office: Fin Guidance Group Ltd One Woodland Ave Paramus NJ 07652

ROSS, WILLIAM H., accountant; b. Meridian, Miss., Aug. 19, 1946; s. Bertrand Grady and Mary (McDonald) R.; m. Kitty Wesley, June 7, 1969; children: Julie, Grady. BS, U. Ala., 1969; MBA, U. Ala., Birmingham, 1984. Acct. Ernst & Whinney, Birmingham, 1972-82, Cleve., 1982-86; ptnr. Ernst & Whinney, Los Angeles, 1986—. Capt. U.S. Army, 1969-72. Mem. Am. Inst. CPA's. Office: Ernst & Whinney 515 S Flower St Ste 2800 Los Angeles CA 90071-2291

ROSS, WILLIAM JARBOE, lawyer; b. Oklahoma City, May 9, 1930; s. Walter John and Bertha (Jarboe) R.; m. Mary Lillian Ryan, May 19, 1962; children: Rebecca Anne Roten, Robert Joseph, Molly Kathleen. B.B.A., U. Okla., 1952, LL.B., 1954. Bar: Okla. 1954. Since practiced in Oklahoma City; asst. municipal counselor Oklahoma City, 1955-60; mem. firm Rainey, Ross, Rice & Binns, 1960—, partner, 1965—; mem. admissions and grievences com. U.S. Dist. Ct. (we. dist) Okla.; bd. dirs. PetroUnited Terminals, Inc.; bd. dirs., mem. exec. com. Boatmen's First Nat. Bank of Okla. Past pres. bd. dirs. St. Anthony's Hosp. Found.; bd. dirs. Harn Homestead; trustee Ethics and Excellence in Journalism Found., Inasmuch Found. Mem. Okla. Bar Assn., Okla. Heritage Assn. (chmn. edn. com.), The Newcomen Soc., Phi Alpha Delta, Beta Theta Pi. Clubs: Oklahoma City Golf and Country, Econ. (Okla.). Lodges: Rotary, K.C. Home: 6923 Avondale Ct Oklahoma City OK 73116-5008 Office: Rainey Ross Rice & Binns 735 1st Nat Ctr W Oklahoma City OK 73102-7495

ROSS, WILLIAM WARFIELD, lawyer; b. Washington, Oct. 3, 1926; s. W. Warfield and Vera Elfleda (Payne) R.; m. Jennie Fitch, Jan. 30, 1963; children—James, Mary, Billy. A.B., St. John's Coll., Annapolis, Md., 1948; LL.B., Yale U., 1951. Bar: D.C. 1951. Legal asst. Exec. Office Pres. Harry S. Truman, 1952-53, Pres. Dwight D. Eisenhower, 1953; atty. appellate sect. civil div. Dept. Justice, Washington, 1954-57; asst. to solicitor FPC, Washington, 1957-59; ptnr. Wald, Harkrader & Ross, Washington, 1963-87, Pepper, Hamilton & Scheetz, Washington, 1987-91; adj. prof. Cornell U. Grad. Sch. Bus. and Pub. Adminstrn., 1977-80; chmn. D.C. Council Commn. on Bd. Appeals and Rev. of D.C. Govt., 1972. Chmn. Nat. Capital area ACLU, 1966-68; chmn. audit hearing panel Title I ESEA of 1965, 1976-80. Served with USN, 1945-46. Mem. ABA (chmn. sect. adminstrv. law 1978-79), Bar Assn. D.C. (chmn. adminstrv. law sect. 1968-69, gov. 1969-70), D.C. Bar, Fed. Bar Assn., Fed. Energy Bar Assn. (contbr. articles to jour.). Club: Metropolitan (Washington). Home: 4978 Sentinel Dr Apt 303 Bethesda MD 20816-3573

ROSSANO, AUGUST THOMAS, environmental engineering educator; b. N.Y.C., Feb. 1, 1916; s. August Thomas and Rosa (Cosenza) R.; m. Margie Chrisney, Dec. 6, 1944; children: August Thomas III, Marilyn, Pamela,

Jeannine, Renee, Christopher, Stephen, Teresa. B.S., M.I.T., 1938; M.S., Harvard U., 1941, S.D., 1954. Diplomate Am. Acad. Environ. Engrs., Am. Bd. Indsl. Hygiene. Commd. lt. (j.g.) USPHS, 1941, advanced through grades to capt., 1955; assigned Hdqrs. USPHS, 1941, 48, Taft Engring. Ctr., Cin., 1954-59; ret., 1963; prof. air resource engring. U. Wash., Seattle, 1963-81; prof. emeritus U. Wash., 1981—; pres. Rossano Inc., 1981—; vis. prof. Calif. Inst. Tech., 1960-63; Mem. expert adv. panel on air pollution WHO, Geneva, 1960—, Pan Am. Health Orgn., 1975—; cons. European office WHO, 1960—, U.S. Dept. HEW, 1962—, U.S. Dept. State, 1962—, U.S. Dept. Commerce, 1962—, State of Wash., 1963—, Puget Sound Air Pollution Control Agy., 1967—; cons. govts. U.S., Can., Greece, Czechoslovakia, Republic of China, Peoples Republic of China, Belgium, Netherlands, Mexico, Syria, Iran, Egypt, Brazil, Peru, Chile, Barbados, P.R., Philippines, Venezuela, Curacao, also; Smithsonian Instn. and World Bank, various other nat. and multi-nat. corps.; mem. subcom. on hydrogen sulfide NRC.; Bd. dirs. Environ. Resources Assos., Bellevue Montessori Sch., Environ. Sci. Service div. E.R.A., N.W. Environmental Scis. Ltd., Inst. Exec. Research, Nat. Air Conservation Commn.; lectr. applied physics and environment Bellevue Montessori Sch., WAsh., 1981—, Arbor Elem. Sch., Issaquah, Wash., 1993—; lectr. in field; co-founder Internat. Environ. Inst., 1988. Author: (with Hal Cooper) Source Testing for Air Pollution Control, 1971; Editor: Air Pollution Control, 1969; Contbr. 115 articles to tech. jours. Patentee pollution control device. Served with C.E. AUS. Recipient Spl. Svc. award USPHS, 1958, disting. achievement award Pacific NW-Internat. sect. Air Pollution Control Assn., Lyman A. Ripperton award Air and Waste Mgmt. Assn., 1993, Fulbright Travel Lectr. award to eight univs. and rsch. instns. Italy, 1987; HEW tng. grantee, 1964-70; EPA grantee, 1971—. Mem. Harvard Pub. Health Alumni Assn. (pres.), Sigma Xi, Delta Omega, Tau Beta Pi. Clubs: Bellevue Triangle Pool, Bellevue Athletic, Alderbrook (Wash.) Golf and Yacht, Wapato Point Resort, Elliott Bay Yacht, Columbia Towers. Home and Office: 10901 176th Cir NW Redmond WA 98052

ROSSANT, JAMES STEPHANE, architect, artist; b. N.Y.C., Aug. 17, 1928; s. Marcus and Anne (Orbach) R.; m. Colette Solange Palacci, Sept. 7, 1955; children—Marianne, Juliette, Cecile, Thomas. B.Arch., U. Fla., 1950; M.City and Regional Planning, Harvard U., 1953. Registered architect, N.Y., Calif., Fla. Architect Mayer & Whittlesey, N.Y.C., 1956-60; assoc. Whittlesey & Conklin, N.Y.C., 1961-65; ptnr. Whittlesey Conklin Rossant, N.Y.C., 1966-67, Conklin Rossant, N.Y.C., 1967-94; prin. James Rossant Architects, N.Y.C., 1994—; prof. Pratt Inst., Bklyn., 1958-61, Columbia U., N.Y.C., 1968, NYU, 1976-81, Harvard U., Cambridge, Mass., 1985-89; architect art commr. City of N.Y., 1979-83. Prin. works include design of Reston, Va., Dodoma, Tanzania, Butterfield House, Ramaz Sch. at N.Y.C.; one man shows include Galley Spaced, N.Y., 1976, John Nichols Gallery, 1990, Gallery Veda, Tokyo, 1991, Galeria Pecanins, Mexico City, 1993, Galerie Mantoux-Gignac, Paris, 1995. Fellow AIA (medal of honor N.Y. chpt. 1977). Democrat. Office: 114 Sullivan St New York NY 10012-3604

ROSSAVIK, IVAR KRISTIAN, obstetrician/gynecologist; b. Stavanger, Rogaland, Norway, Nov. 3, 1936; came to U.S., 1982; s. Andreas and Bergit (Berge) R.; divorced; children: Line, Anne Britt, Kirsten, Solveig; m. Claudia Lagos, May 23, 1987; children: Claudia Kristina, Eevar Benjamin. MD, U. Oslo, 1962, PhD, 1982. Pvt. practice, medicine Stavanger, 1974; asst. chief, acting chmn. U. Tromsoe, Norway, 1974-76; clin. fellow Nat. Hosp. of Norway, Oslo, 1976-81, Norwegian Radium Hosp./U. Oslo, 1981-82; pvt. practice Oslo, 1977-82; rsch. asst. prof. Baylor Coll. Medicine, Houston, 1983-86; assoc. prof. U. Okla., Oklahoma City, 1987-93, prof., 1993—; dir. Ultrasound Svcs., Dept. Ob/Gyn., U. Okla. Inventor Rossavik Growth Equation, 1980; author: (textbook) Practical Obstetrical Ultrasound: With and Without A Computer, 1991. Lt. Royal Norwegian Navy, 1964-65. Mem. AMA, Am. Fertility Soc., Am. Inst. Ultrasound in Medicine, Okla. State Med. Assn., Irish and Am. Paediatric Soc., Internat. Perinatal Doppler Soc., So. Med. Assn., AAAS. Lutheran. Avocations: ultrasonography technology, computer technology, fetal growth studies. Office: Univ Oklahoma Dept Ob/Gyn PO Box 26901 Oklahoma City OK 73126-0901

ROSSBACHER, LISA ANN, dean, geology educator, writer; b. Fredericksburg, Va., Oct. 10, 1952; d. Richard Irwin and Jean Mary (Dearing) R.; m. Dallas D. Rhodes, Aug. 4, 1978. BS, Dickinson Coll., 1975; MA, SUNY, Binghamton, 1978, Princeton U., 1979; PhD, Princeton U., 1983. Cons. Republic Geothermal, Santa Fe Springs, Calif., 1979-81; asst. prof. geology Whittier (Calif.) Coll., 1982-84; asst. prof. geology Calif. State Poly. U., Pomona, 1984-86, assoc. prof. geol. sci., 1986-91, assoc. v.p. acad. affairs, 1987-93, prof. geol. sci., 1991-93; v.p. acad. affairs, dean faculty Whittier (Calif.) Coll., 1993-95; dean of coll., prof. geology Dickinson Coll., Carlisle, Pa., 1995—; vis. researcher U. Uppsala, Sweden, 1984. Author: Career Opportunities in Geology and the Earth Sciences, 1983, Recent Revolutions in Geology, 1986; (with Rex Buchanan) Geomedia, 1988; columnist Geotimes, 1988—; contbr. articles to profl. jours. Recipient scholarship Ministry Edn. of Finland, Helsinki, 1984; grantee NASA, 1983-94. Mem. AAAS (geol. nominating com. 1984-87), Geol. Soc. Am., Sigma Xi (grantee 1976). Office: Dickinson Coll Dean of the Coll Carlisle PA 17013

ROSSBERG, ROBERT HOWARD, psychology educator, former university dean; b. Bklyn., Mar. 9, 1926; s. Benjamin William and Mollie (Linn) R.; m. Mary Jo Kogan, June 22, 1947; 1 child, Susan Lea. Student, U. Mich., 1943-44; B.S., CCNY, 1949; M.A., Columbia U., 1951; Ph.D., N.Y. U., 1956. Counselor, Fedn. of, 1950-51; staff psychologist N.Y. U. Med. Center, 1951-53; asst. chief psychologist, 1953-56; asst. prof. edn. and psychology SUNY, Buffalo, 1956-59; assoc. prof. SUNY, 1959-64, prof., 1964—; dir. grad. programs in counseling and ednl. psychology, 1959-65, assoc. dean, 1965-67; dean Faculty Ednl. Studies, 1978-80, v.p. for acad. affairs, 1980-84, dean faculty of health related profession, 1987-88, chair dept. psychology, 1988—; disting. svc. prof., 1990; cons. in field. Author: Youth: Myths and Realities, 1972; co-author: Counseling Psychology, Strategies and Services, 1989; co-author: Counseling: Theory and Practice, 1993; contbr. articles to profl. publs.; editorial assoc. Urban Edn., 1961-70. Served with USAAF, 1944-46. Rehab. Counseling grantee, 1956-60; NDEA grantee, 1959-60; Office Edn.; leadership tng. grantee, 1969-70. Mem. Am. Psychol. Assn., AAUP. Home: 105 Summerview Rd Buffalo NY 14221-1343 Office: SUNY Buffalo 562 Capen Hall Amherst NY 14260 *I am increasingly impressed by how much I owe to role models in my family, in schools, and in the work place. Values, ethics, and social priorities are learned through these important others.*

ROSSE, JAMES NELSON, economics educator, educational administrator; b. Sidney, Nebr., Nov. 4, 1931; s. James C. and Shirley F. (Nelson) R.; m. Janice Grimminger, 1952; children—Jay, Stuart, Anne. B.S. with high distinction in econs., U. Minn., 1961, M.A., 1963, Ph.D., 1966. Asst. prof. econs. Stanford U., Calif., 1965-71, assoc. prof., 1971-76, prof., 1976—, assoc. dean Humanities and Scis., 1978-82, dir. Ctr. Econ. Policy Research, 1982-84, v.p., provost, 1984—; prin. Rosse & Olszewski cons., Palo Alto, Calif., 1979—. Ford faculty fellow Stanford U., 1969; recipient Dean's award for Disting. Teaching, Stanford U., 1977. Mem. Am. Econ. Assn. (Dissertation award 1967), Econometric Soc., Phi Beta Kappa. Office: Stanford University Hoover Instn Rmiis 300 Pasteur Dr Stanford CA 94305-6011

ROSSE, WENDELL FRANKLYN, immunology educator; b. Sidney, Nebr., June 5, 1933; m. Simonne Vernier, July, 1959; children: Christopher, Stephanie, Philippe. Student, U. Chgo., 1949-52, MD with honors, 1958; BA, U. Omaha, 1953; student, U. Nebr. Sch. Medicine, 1953-55; M.S. in Physiology, Grad. Sch., 1956. Intern., resident Duke Hosp., Durham, N.C., 1958-60; sr. investigator Nat. Cancer Inst. NIH, Bethesda, Md., 1964-66; asst. prof. medicine Duke U. Med. Center, 1966-68, assoc. prof. medicine, 1968-72, assoc. prof. immunology, 1970-76, prof. medicine, 1972—, prof. immunology, 1976—, Florence McAllister prof. medicine, 1981—, chief sect. immunohematology, 1971-86, co-dir. blood bank, 1971-87, dir. hematology and transfusion svc., 1987-92, chief hematology-oncology, 1976-89; chief med. service Durham VA Hosp., 1973-76; vis. research prof. Institut de Pathologie Cellulaire, Paris, 1974; investigator Howard Hughes Med. Inst., 1976-81; bd. govs. Am. Bd. Internal Medicine, 1989-93. Contbr. numerous articles to med. publs. Mem. regional adv. com. ARC; mem. N.C. Gov's Council on Sickle Cell Syndrome. Recipient Career Devel. award, 1968, Golden Apple Student Teaching award Duke U. Med. Center, 1968, Thomas Kinney Meml. prize for teaching, 1980, Alumni Disting. Teaching award,

1991; Josiah Macy, Jr., scholar, 1974. Mem. Am. Soc. Hematology (Stratton lectr. 1976, pres. 1986-87), Assn. Am. Physicians, Am. Soc. Clin. Investigation, Am. Fedn. Clin. Research, Nat. Blood Club (pres. 1975), Red Cell Club, N.C. Assn. Blood Banks, N.C. Heart Assn., Alpha Omega Alpha. Home: 4605 Timberly Dr Durham NC 27707 Office: Duke U Medical Ctr PO Box 3934 Durham NC 27710

ROSSEELS, GUSTAVE ALOIS, music educator; b. Malines, Belgium, Jan. 19, 1911; came to U.S., 1946; s. Karel Hubert and Elisabeth (Rooms) R.; m. Jacqueline Crepin, Sept. 5, 1944; children: Marc, Elisabeth, Susanne. Grad. with highest distinction, Royal Conservatory Music, Brussels. Lectr. violin & chamber music U. Mich. Sch. Music, 1957, prof., 1962, prof. emeritus, 1978; instr. violin and chamber music Mills. Coll., Brigham Young U., Aspen (Colo.), Inst., All-State Program Nat. Music Camp, Interlochen, Mich., summers 1981, 82. Violinist, Pro Nova Quartet, Paganini Quartet, Stanley Quartet, Baroque Trio; condr. Jackson (Mich.) Symphony, 1960; author: (autobiography) A Remembering Journey, 1981. Avocations: swimming, golf, reading. Home: 3076 Bolgos Cir Ann Arbor MI 48105

ROSSELL, CHRISTINE HAMILTON, political science educator; b. Bklyn., Jan. 22, 1945; d. Robert Hamilton and Ann (Bezold) R.; m. Jens Christian Sorensen, Jan. 22, 1982; 1 child, Elise. AB, UCLA, 1967; MA, Calif. State U., Northridge, 1969; PhD, U. So. Calif., 1974. Asst. prof. Pitzer Coll., Claremont, Calif., 1973-74; rsch. assoc. U. Md., College Park, 1974-75; asst. prof. Boston U., 1975-82, assoc. prof., 1982-89, prof., 1989—, chair dept. polit. sci., 1992—; vis. asst. prof. Duke U., Durham, N.C., 1977-78, U. Calif., Berkeley, 1981; vis. lectr. Canberra (Australia) Coll., 1985. Author: Strategies for Effective Desegregation (with others), 1983, Carrot or Stick for School Desegregation, 1990; co-editor: Consequences of School Desegregation, 1983. Mem. Citywide Coord. Coun., Boston, 1976-77. Home: 44 High St Brookline MA 02146-7707 Office: Boston U Dept Polit Sci 232 Bay State Rd Boston MA 02215-1403

ROSSELLINI, ISABELLA, actress, model; b. Rome, June 18, 1952; d. Roberto Rossellini and Ingrid Bergman; m. Martin Scorsese, Sept. 1979 (div. Nov. 1982); m. Jonathan Wiedemann (div.); 1 child, Elettra Ingrid. Student, Finch Coll., 1972, New Sch. for Social Research, N.Y.C. Became model for Lancôme, 1982. Appeared in films A Matter of Time, 1976, Il Pap'occhio, 1980, The Meadow, 1982, White Nights, 1985, Blue Velvet, 1986, Siesta, 1987, Red Riding Hood, 1987, Tough Guys Don't Dance, 1987, Zelly and Me, 1988, Cousins, 1989, Wild at Heart, 1990, Les Dames Galantes, 1990, Death Becomes Her, 1992, The Pickle, 1992, Fearless, 1993, Wyatt Earp, 1994, Immortal Beloved, 1994, The Innocent, 1995; TV films: The Last Elephant, 1990, Lies of the Twins, 1991. also: Ford Modeling Agency 344 E 59th St New York NY 10022-1570*

ROSSELLÓ, PEDRO J., governor of Puerto Rico; b. San Juan, P.R., Apr. 5, 1944; m. Maga Nevares, Aug. 9, 1969; children: Juan Oscar, Luis, Ricardo. BS, U. Notre Dame, 1966; MD, Yale U., 1970; MPH, U. P.R., 1981. Intern straight surgery Beth Israel Hosp., Boston, 1970-71, resident gen. surgery, 1971-74; resident cardiac and burns Mass. Gen. Hosp., Boston, 1972; resident trauma San Francisco Gen. Hosp., 1973; sr. resident pediat. surgery Children's Hosp., Boston, 1974-75, chief resident, pediat. surgery-urology, 1975-76; instr. surgery Harvard Med. Sch., 1975-76; pvt. practice San Juan, 1976-92; asst. prof. surgery U. P.R., 1978-82, assoc. prof. surgery, 1982-92; dir. Dept. Health City of San Juan, 1985-87; chief surgery San Jorge Hosp., San Juan, 1989-92, med. dir., 1990; gov. Puerto Rico, 1993—; lead gov. So. Regional Project Infant Mortality; mem. exec. com. So. States Energy Bd.; mem. intergovtl. policy adv. com. U.S. Trade Rep. Contbr. articles to profl. jours. Mem. P.R. Olympic Com., 1982-84, 87-88; v.p. New Progressive Party, 1988-91, pres., 1991—; mem. steering com. Edn. Commn. States. Capt. USNG, 1970-76. Mem. Nat. Govs. Assn., So. Govs. Assn., Dem. Govs. Assn. (mem. exec. com.), P.R. Tennis Assn. (pres. 1982-84), Caribbean Tennis Assn. (pres. 1983-84), Alpha Omega Alpha. Avocations: jogging, tennis, ocean kayaking.

ROSSEN, JORDAN, lawyer; b. Detroit, June 13, 1934; s. Nathan Paul and Rebecca (Rizy) R.; m. Susan Friebert, Mar. 24, 1963 (div. June 1972); 1 child, Rebecca; m. M. Elizabeth Bunn, Jan. 3, 1981; children—N. Paul, Jordan David. B.A., U. Mich., 1956; J.D., Harvard U., 1959. Bar: Mich. 1960, U.S. Dist. Ct. (ea. dist.) Mich. 1960, U.S. Ct. Appeals (6th cir.) 1966, U.S. Ct. Appeals (7th cir.) 1974, U.S. Supreme Ct. 1966. Assoc. Sullivan, Elmer, Eames & Moody, Detroit, 1960-62; assoc. Sugar & Schwartz, Detroit, 1962-64; asst. gen. counsel UAW, Detroit, 1964-74, assoc. gen. counsel, 1974-83, gen. counsel, 1983—; vice pres. N.P. Rossen Agy., Inc., Detroit, 1960-83; gen. counsel Mich. Health & Social Security Research Inst., Inc., Detroit, 1965-83; dir. UAW Job Devel. & Tng. Corp., Detroit, 1984-90. Editor: Mich. Bar Labor Section Publication, 1961-64. Contbr. articles to profl. jours. Pres. Young Democrats, Mich., 1963-65; chmn. Americans for Democratic Action, Mich., 1966-68; chmn. Voter Registration Dem. Party, Mich., 1967. Recipient Human Rights award City of Detroit, 1978. Mem. ABA, Mich. Bar Assn., Nat. Bar Assn., Fed. Bar Assn., Wolverine Bar Assn., Women Lawyers Assn., Lawyers Guild. Jewish. Office: UAW Legal Dept 8000 E Jefferson Ave Detroit MI 48214-2699

ROSSER, ANNETTA HAMILTON, composer; b. Jasper, Fla., Aug. 28, 1913; d. Carlos Calvin and Jermai Reuben (Gilbert) Hamilton; m. John Barkley Rosser, Sept. 7, 1935 (dec. Sept. 1989); children: Edwenna Merryday, John Barkley Jr. BM, Fla. State U., 1932. Cert. tchr., Fla. Tchr. music Kirby-Smith Jr. High Sch., Jacksonville, Fla., 1932-35; 1st violinist Santa Monica (Calif.) Symphony, 1949-50; concertmaster Ithaca (N.Y.) Chamber Orch., 1948-56; concertmaster Cornell Univ. Orch., Ithaca, 1948-56, soloist, 1957; 1st violinist Princeton (N.J.) Symphony, 1959-61; concertmaster Madison (Wis.) Symphony Orch., 1963-66, 1st violinist, 1967-82. Composer of over 100 vocal and instrumental compositions including Meditations on Cross, song cycle for 2 voices, flute and piano, 1976, An Offering of Song, book of 48 songs, 1977, Songs of a Nomad Flute, song cycle for soprano, flute and piano, 1978, Six Songs of the T'ang Dynasty for soprano and violin, 1983, Nocturne for violin and piano, 1989, Trio for flute, violin and piano, 1991, Scherzo for flute ensemble, 1991. Bd. dirs. Madison Opera Guild, 1972-86, Madison Civic Music Assn., 1983-85; past pres. Madison Symphony Orch. League, Ithaca Federated Music Club, Ithaca Composers Club; trustee Madison Art Ctr., 1979-83, Madison Civics Club, 1976-79, Madison Woman of Distinction, 1980. Madison Woman of Distinction, 1980. Rotary Club, 1994. Mem. AAUW, Univ. League, Univ. League Bird Study Group, Madison Club, Madison Federated Music Club, PEO, Phi Kappa Phi, Pi Kappa Lambda, Sigma Alpha Iota. Republican. Presbyterian. Avocations: Chinese snuff bottles, English brass rubbings, birding. Home: 4209 Manitou Way Madison WI 53711-3703

ROSSER, EDWIN MICHAEL, mortgage company executive; b. Denver, Oct. 11, 1940; s. Edwin Michael and Anne (Ratliff) R.; m. Keren Call, July 17, 1969; children: Kevin, William. BS, Colo. State U., 1964; MA, U. No. Colo., 1974. Cert. mortgage banker. Mktg. officer United Bank Mortgage, Denver, 1968-74; dir. nat. accounts PMI Mortgage Ins. Co., Denver, 1974-85; v.p. Moore Mortgage Co., Denver, 1985-87, Pacific First Mortgage Corp., Englewood, Colo., 1987-89; 1st v.p. 1st Nat. Bank, San Francisco, 1990-93. Photographer represented in Denver Art Mus., The Buffalo in Winter, (1st place award 1981). Steering com. Blueprint for Colo., Govs. Unified Housing Task Force; mem. Colo. Housing Coun. (chmn. 1986-87); bd. dirs. Colo. State Found. Mem. Mortgage Bankers Assn. Am. (bd. dirs. 1986-90, state and local achievement award 1986, Ernest P. Schumacher award 1988), Colo. Mortgage Bankers Assn. (bd. dirs. 1979-88, pres. 1986, E.C. Spelman award 1978), Colo. Assn. Commerce and Industry, Denver Mus. Natural History, Denver C. of C., Colo. State U. Alumni Assn. (nat. pres. 1987, bd. dirs. 1969-87, mem. found. bd. 1987-91, 93—, Honor Alumnus 1984), City Club Denver, Commonwealth Club Calif. Republican. Roman Catholic. Avocations: competitive swimming, photography. Home: 12478 E Amherst Cir Aurora CO 80014-3306 Office: United Residential Ins Co 6312 So Fiddlers Greencircle Englewood CO 80111

ROSSER, JAMES MILTON, university president; b. East St. Louis, Ill., Apr. 16, 1939; s. William M. and Mary E. (Bass) R.; 1 son, Terrence. B.A., So. Ill. U., 1962, M.A., 1963, Ph.D., 1969. Diagnostic bacteriologist Holden Hosp., Carbondale, Ill., 1961-63; research bacteriologist Eli Lilly & Co., Indpls., 1963-66; coordinator Black Am. studies, instr. health edn. So. Ill. U.,

Carbondale, 1968-69; asst. prof. Black Am. studies dir. So. Ill. U., 1969-70, asst. to chancellor, 1970; asso. vice chancellor for acad. affairs U. Kans., Lawrence, 1970-74; assoc. prof. edn., pharmacology and toxicology U. Kans., 1971-74; vice chancellor dept. higher edn. State of N.J., Trenton, 1974-79; acting chancellor State of N.J., 1977; pres., prof. health care mgmt. Calif. State U., Los Angeles, 1979—; mem. tech. resource panel Ctr. for Research and Devel. in Higher Edn., U. Calif., Berkeley, 1974-76; mem. health maintenance orgn. com. Health Planning Coun., State of N.J., 1975-79; mem. standing com. on research and devel. bd. trustees Ednl. Testing Service, 1976-77; mem. steering com. and task force on retention of minorities in engring. Assembly of Engring. NRC, 1975-78; mem. Bd. Med. Examiners, State of N.J., 1978-79; vis. faculty mem. Inst. Mgmt. of Lifelong Edn., Grad. Sch. Edn., Harvard U., 1979; mem. Calif. State U. Trustees Spl. Long Range Fin. Planning Com., 1982-87; mem. Am. Coun. on Edn., 1979—, AFL/CIO Labor Higher Edn. Coun., 1983—, Nat. Commn. Higher Edn. Issues, 1981-82; mem. The Calif. Achievement Coun., 1983-89, strategic adv. counc. Coll. and Univs. Systems Exchange, 1988-91; bd. dirs. Am. Humanities Coun., So. Calif. Am. Humanics, Inc. Coun., Sanwa Bank Calif., 1993—, Edison, Fedco, Inc. Author: An Analysis of Health Care Delivery, 1977. Mem. exec. bd., chmn. varsity scouting program Los Angeles Area council Boy Scouts Am., 1980—; bd. dirs. Hispanic Urban Ctr., Los Angeles, 1979—, Los Angeles Urban League, 1982—, Community TV of So. Calif., Sta. KCET, 1980-89, United Way, Los Angeles, 1980-91, Orthopaedic Hosp., 1983-86; mem. Citizen's Adv. Council Congl. Caucus Sci. and Tech., 1983—; bd. dirs. Los Angeles Philharm. Assn., 1986—, Nat. Health Found., 1990; bd. trustees Woodrow Wilson Nat. Fellowship Found., 1993; mem. performing arts council/edn. council Music Ctr., 1984—; mem. minority bus. task force Pacific Bell, 1985-86; mem. bd. of govs Nat. ARC, 1986-91, Mayor's Blue Ribbon Task Force on Drugs City of L.A., 1988; Nat. Adv. Council on Aging, 1989-93. NSF fellow, 1961; NDEA fellow, 1967-68; recipient award of recognition in Edn. Involvement for Young Achievers, 1981, Pioneer of Black Hist. Achievement award Brotherhood Crusade, 1981, Alumni Achievement award So. Ill. U., 1982, Friend of Youth award Am. Humanics, Inc., 1985, Leadership award Dept of Higher Edn. Ednl. Equal Opportunity Fund Program, 1989; Medal of Excellence Golden State Minority Found., 1990, Take Charge of Learning Success award Inst. for the Redesign of Learning, 1995. Mem. Calif. C. of C. (bd. dirs. 1993—), Alhambra C. of C. (bd. dirs. 1979—), Los Angeles C. of C. (bd. dirs. 1989-93), Am. Assn. State Colls. and Univs., Kappa Delta Pi, Phi Kappa Phi. Roman Catholic. Office: Calif State Univ Office of the Pres 5151 State University Dr Los Angeles CA 90032-8500

ROSSER, RICHARD FRANKLIN, education consultant; b. Arcanum, Ohio, July 16, 1929; s. Harold Arm and Margaret (Whitacre) R.; m. Donna Eyssen., Mar. 21, 1951; children—Eric, Carl, Edward. B.A., Ohio Wesleyan U., 1951; M.P.A., Syracuse U., 1952, Ph.D., 1961. Joined U.S. Air Force, 1952, advanced through grades to col., 1968; prof. polit. sci. U.S. Air Force Acad., Colorado Springs, Colo., 1959-73; head dept. U.S. Air Force Acad., 1967-73, ret., 1973; prof. polit. sci., dean Albion (Mich.) Coll., 1973-77; pres. DePauw U., Greencastle, Ind., 1977-86, chancellor, 1986; pres. Nat. Assn. Ind. Colls. and Univs., Washington, 1986-93; cons. in higher edn. pvt. practice, Traverse City, Mich., 1993—. Author: An Introduction to Soviet Foreign Policy, 1969; Contbr. articles to profl. jours. Mem. univ. senate United Meth. Ch., 1980-84; mem. spl. commn. of Chief of Staff on Honor Code U.S. Mil. Acad., 1989; bd. visitors Air U., 1991-94; bd. trustees Ohio Wesleyan U., 1991—; mem. nat. adv. com. Instnl. Quality and Integrity, 1994—. Decorated Legion of Merit with oak leaf cluster. Mem. Am. Polit. Sci. Assn., Phi Beta Kappa, Omicron Delta Kappa. Presbyterian. Home and Office: 2161 Harbor Reach Dr Traverse City MI 49686

ROSSET, BARNET LEE, JR., publisher; b. Chgo., May 28, 1922; s. Barnet Lee and Mary (Tansey) R.; m. Joan Mitchell, 1950 (div. 1952); m. Hannelore Eckert, Aug. 1953 (div. 1957); 1 child, Peter; m. Cristine Agnini, Mar. 11, 1965 (div. 1979); children—Tansey, Beckett; m. Elisabeth Krug, 1980 (div. 1991; 1 child, Chantal. Ph.B., U. Chgo., 1947; B.A. New Sch. Social Research, N.Y.C., 1952. Pub. editor Grove Press, Inc., 1951-86, Evergreen Rev., Rosset and Co., Inc., 1957-73, Blue Moon Books, Inc., N.Y.C., 1987—. Served to 1st lt. Signal Corps AUS, 1942-46. Recipient Ninth Pub. citation PEN Am. Ctr., 1988. Mem. PEN Club.; mem. Overseas Press. Office: 61 4th Ave New York NY 10003-5202

ROSSET, LISA KRUG, editor; b. N.Y.C., Nov. 11, 1952; d. George William and Rita (Earle) Krug; m. Barney Rosset, Nov. 5, 1980 (div. Dec. 1990); 1 child, Chantal. B.A. magna cum laude, Smith Coll., 1974; M.A., Columbia U., 1976. Editor Latin Am. Series, N.Y.C., 1976-86; gen. editor Grove Press, N.Y.C., 1976-86; mng. editor Aperture, N.Y.C., 1987-90; pvt. practice N.Y.C., 1990—; cons. editor UNICEF, N.Y.C., 1995—. Author: James Baldwin, 1989, Thurgood Marshall, 1993. Mem. Phi Beta Kappa. Office: 106 Perry St New York NY 10014

ROSSETTI, JOSEPH PAUL, trucking industry executive; b. Weymouth, Mass., Nov. 24, 1938; s. Joseph W. and Louise (Petrucelli) R.; m. Shiela U. Natale, May 8, 1965; children: Brenda, Donna. BS in Mktg., U. Richmond, 1960. Sales rep. P. Ballantine & Sons., Newark, 1964; with Mack Trucks, Inc., Providence, 1964-72; mgr. Mack Trucks, Inc., Syracuse, N.Y., 1972-74; dist. mgr. Mack Trucks, Inc., Maspeth, N.Y., 1974-75; mgr. western mktg. div. Mack Trucks, Inc., Hayward, Calif., 1975-76; v.p. western product div. Mack Trucks, Inc., 1976-77; v.p. mktg. distbn. Mack Trucks, Inc., Allentown, Pa., 1977-81, sr. v.p. sales, from 1981, now exec. v.p. mktg. Served with U.S. Army, 1962-64. Mem. Allentown-Lehigh County C. of C. (gov. 1981—). Roman Catholic. Office: Mack Trucks Inc 2100 Mack Blvd Allentown PA 18103-5622

ROSSEY, PAUL WILLIAM, school superintendent, university president; b. Richmond, Ind., July 7, 1926; s. Chris C. and Lela (Longman) R.; m. Adelaide Elizabeth Finnegan; 1 dau., Joanne Rossey Szczubelek. B.S., Jersey City State Coll., 1952, Litt. D., 1971; M.A., NYU, 1953, Ed.D. (Kellogg Found. fellow 1955), 1958. Head jr. sch. Peddie Sch., Hightstown, N.J., 1952-53; cons., elem. sch. instr. West Hempstead, N.Y., 1953-55; prin. elem. sch. Dobbs Ferry, N.Y., 1955-58; supt. schs. Litchfield, Conn., 1958-60, Scotch Plains-Fanwood, N.J., 1960-67; dist supt. schs. Nassau County, N.Y., 1967-69; pres. West Chester (Pa.) State U., 1969-74; supt. schs. Millburn-Short Hills, N.J., 1974-92; ret.; lectr. NYU, 1954-67. Contbr. articles to profl. jours. County dir. Boy Scouts Am.; v.p. YMCA; bd. dirs Garbe Found., Community Fund; trustee NYU, 1970-74, The Peddie Sch., 1974-92; mem. exec. com. N.J. Coun. Edn., 1977-83. With USNR, 1944-46, USMCR, 1972-86; ret. Named Outstanding Alumnus, Jersey City State Coll., 1962; recipient NYU medallion, 1966, Ernest O. Melby award human relations, 1970. Mem. Am. Assn. Sch. Administrs. (chmn. N.J. 1965-67), Am. Council Edn., Aircraft Owners and Pilots Assn., N.J. Assn. Sch. Administrs. (exec. com. 1964-67, 81-85), Horace Mann League U.S. (nat. pres. 1977-78), Kappa Delta Pi, Phi Delta Kappa. Republican. Presbyn. Clubs: Exchange (dir.), N.J. Schoolmasters. Home: 219 Summit Ave Summit NJ 07901-2213

ROSS-FLANIGAN, NANCY, reporter. Sci. reporter The Detroit Free Press. Office: Detroit Free Press Inc 321 W Lafayette Blvd Detroit MI 48226

ROSSI, ALICE S., sociology educator, author; b. N.Y.C., Sept. 24, 1922; d. William A. and Emma (Winkler) Schaerr; m. Max Kitt, Dec. 1941 (div. Sept. 1951); m. Peter H. Rossi, Sept. 29, 1951; children: Peter Eric, Kristin Alice, Nina Alexis. BA, Bklyn. Coll., 1947; PhD, Columbia U., 1957; 9 hon. degrees. Rsch. assoc. Cornell U. Ithaca, N.Y., 1951-52, Harvard U., Cambridge, Mass., 1952-55; resident assoc. U. Chgo., 1961-67, Johns Hopkins U. Balt., 1967-69; prof. sociology Goucher Coll., Balt., 1969-74; prof. sociology U. Mass., Amherst 1974-91, prof. emerita, 1991—. Author/editor: 11 books; contbr. numerous articles to profl. jours. Founder, bd. mem. NOW, 1966-70; pres. Sociologists for Women in Soc., 1971-72. Career grantee NIMH, 1965-69, rsch. grantee Rockefeller Found., Ford Found., NIH, NSF, others; CommonWealth Disting. Scholarship award, 1988. Mem. Am. Sociol. Assn. (pres. 1983-84), Ea. Sociol. Soc. (pres. 1973-74). Avocations: design, sewing, gardening, creative writing. Home: 34 Stagecoach Rd Amherst MA 01002-3527

ROSSI, ANTHONY GERALD, lawyer; b. Warren, Ohio, July 20, 1935; s. Anthony Gerald and Lena (Guarnieri) R.; m. Marilyn J. Fuller, June 22, 1957; children: Diana L., Maribeth, Anthony Gerald III. BS, John Carroll U., 1957; JD, Cath. U. Am., 1961. Bar: Ohio 1961. Ptnr. Guarnieri & Secrest, Warren, 1961—; former acting judge Warren Municipal Ct. Mem. Mahoning-Shenango Estate Planning Coun., 1968—, past sec.; past pres. Warren Olympic Club; past bd. govs. Cath. U. Am. Law Sch. Coun.; past trustee Trumbull Golf Guild, Warren Civic Music Assn. Capt. Transp. Corps, AUS, 1957-65. Mem. ABA, Ohio Bar Assn., Trumbull County Bar Assn. (exec. com., pres. 1976-77), Am. Arbitration Assn., Ohio Motorist Assn. (corp. mem., trustee 1980-86, 92—), Wolf's Club, KC, Elks. Home: 2500 Hidden Lakes Dr NE Warren OH 44484-4165 Office: 151 E Market St Warren OH 44481-1102

ROSSI, DOMINICK F., JR., advertising agency executive; b. 1941. BA, Boston Coll., 1962. Market analyst Beech Nut Inc., 1965-67; with N.W. Ayer Inc., N.Y.C., 1967—, v.p., 1972-73, sr. v.p., 1973-80, exec. v.p., 1980—, also bd. dirs.; pres. N.Y. office Ayer, Inc., N.Y.C., 1989—; now pres. Ayer U.S.A., N.Y.C. Lt. USN, 1962-65. Office: N W Ayer Inc Worldwide Plz 825 8th Ave New York NY 10019-7416

ROSSI, FAUST F., lawyer, educator; b. 1932. BA, U. Toronto, 1953; JD, Cornell U., 1960. Bar: N.Y. 1960. Tax trial atty., Dept. Justice, Washington, 1960-61; sole practice, Rochester, N.Y., 1961-66; assoc. prof. Cornell U., Ithaca, N.Y., 1966-69, prof. 1970—, assoc. dean, 1973-75, Samuel S. Leibowitz prof. trial techniques, 1982—; vis. fellow Wadham Coll., Oxford, 1987-88; vis. prof. Emory U., 1990; cons. report of fed. class actions Am. Coll. of Trial Lawyers, 1971-72; cons. com. on proposed fed. rules of evidence N.Y. Trial Lawyers Assn., 1970; cons., instr. annual seminar N.Y. State Trial Judges, 1970-78; cons., instr. Nat. Inst. for Trial Advocacy, 1974-75, 80-84, 88; cons. N.Y. Law Revision Commn. Project for N.Y. Code of Evidence, 1978-80. Lt. j.g. USN. Recipient Jacobsen prize for teaching trial advocacy, 1992. Mem. Order of Coif. Author: Study of the Proposed Federal Rules of Evidence, 1979, Report on Rule 23 Class Actions, 1972, The Federal Rules of Evidence, 1970, Expert Witnesses, 1991; contbr. articles to profl. jours. Office: Cornell U Law Sch Myron Taylor Hall Ithaca NY 14853

ROSSI, HARALD HERMANN, retired radiation biophysicist, educator, administrator; b. Vienna, Austria, Sept. 3, 1917; came to U.S., 1939; s. Oswald J. and Hedwig E. (Braun) R.; m. Ruth Gregg, June 22, 1946; children: Gerald, Gwendolyn Gladstone, Harriet Furey. Student, U. Vienna, 1935-39, U. Bristol, Eng., 1939; Ph.D., Johns Hopkins U., 1942. Cert. in radiol. physics Am. Bd. Radiology. Instr. Johns Hopkins U., Balt., 1940-45; research physicist Nat. Bur. Standards, Washington, 1945; physicist and radiation protection officer Presbyn. Hosp., N.Y.C., 1954-60; rsch. scientist radiol. rsch. lab. Columbia U., N.Y.C., 1946-60, asst. prof. radiology, 1949-53, assoc. prof., 1953-60, prof. radiology and physics, dir. radiol. rsch. lab., 1960-84, prof. radiation oncology, 1984-87, prof. emeritus, 1988—; cons., 1988—; cons. NIH, NRC, Dept. Energy, FAA; chmn. tech. com. Recommn. to Health Commr. of N.Y.C., 1978-82; mem. Internat. Com. on Radiation Units and Measurements, Main Coun., Washington, 1959—, Nat. Coun. on Radiation Protection, Main Coun., 1954-83, hon. mem., 1983—. Co-author: Advances in Biological and Medical Physics, 1967, Radiation Dosimetry, 1968, Cancer: A Comprehensive Treatise, 1982. Trustee, pres. Upper Nyack sch. Bd., N.Y., 1957-60; trustee Rockland County Day Sch., 1961-63. Recipient Shonka Meml. Found. award, 1972, Gray medal Internat. Commn. on Radiation Units and Measurements, 1985, Disting. Scientific Achievement award Health Physics Soc., 1987. Fellow Am. Coll. Radiology; mem. AAAS, Radiation Research Soc. (pres. 1974-75), Am. Coll. Radiology, Radiol. Soc. N.Am., Sigma Xi. Office: 105 Larchdale Ave Nyack NY 10960-1003

ROSSI, MARIO ALEXANDER, architect; b. Chgo., Apr. 9, 1931; s. Gastone J. and Irma (Giorgi) R.; m. Jo Ann Therese Kneip, Apr. 12, 1958; children: John Vincent, Lyn Ann, Paul Alexander, Mara Ann. BArch, Ill. Inst. Tech., 1955. Architect Omnimetrics, L.A., 1967-78; pvt. practice Seal Beach, Calif., 1975—. Prin. works include fin. models for Calif. Fed. Bank, L.A., First Nat. City Bank, N.Y.C., Glendale (Calif.) Fed. Bank, Wailea, Alexander and Baldwin, Hawaii. Lt. (j.g.) USN, 1955-58. Research computerized techniques in architecture and economic feasibility land development. Home and Office: 1721 Catalina Ave Seal Beach CA 90740-5710

ROSSI, PETER HENRY, sociology educator; b. N.Y.C., Dec. 27, 1921; s. Peter Maxim and Elizabeth (Porcelli) R.; m. Alice Schaerr, Sept. 29, 1951; children: Peter Eric, Kristin Alice, Nina Alexis. B.S., CCNY, 1943; Ph.D., Columbia, 1951. Research asso. Bur. Applied Social Research, Columbia U., 1947- 51; asst. prof. Harvard U., 1951-55; prof. dept. sociology U. Chgo., 1955-67; dir. Nat. Opinion Research Center, 1960-67; prof. dept. social relations Johns Hopkins, 1967-74, chmn. dept., 1967-70; dir. research Center for Met. Planning and Research, 1972-74; prof. sociology, dir. Social and Demographic Research Inst., U. Mass., Amherst, 1974-92; Stuart A. Rice prof. sociology, dir. Social and Demographic Research Inst., U. Mass., 1984-92, prof. emeritus, 1992—. Author: Why Families Move, 1956, The Politics of Urban Renewal, 1962, The Education of Catholic Americans, 1966, New Media and Education, 1967, Ghetto Revolts, 1970, Cities Under Siege, 1971, Evaluating Social Programs, 1972, Roots of Urban Discontent, 1974, Reforming Public Welfare, 1976, Prison Reform and State Elites, 1977, Evaluation: A Systematic Approach, 1979, Money, Work & Crime, 1980, After the Clean-up, 1980, Social Science and Natural Hazards, 1981, Measuring Social Judgements, 1982, Natural Hazards and Public Choice, 1982, Under the Gun, 1983, Applied Sociology, 1983, Without Shelter, 1989, Down and Out in America, 1989, Of Human Bonding, 1990; editor: Am. Jour. Sociology, 1957-58; assoc. editor: Social. Rev, 1957-60, Am. Sociologist, 1964-66; editor: Social Sci. Research, 1972-89; contbr. articles to profl. and popular jours. Served with AUS, 1942-45. Recipient Alvah and Gunnar Myrdal award for contbns. to evaluation research, 1981; Commonwealth award for contbns. to sociology, 1985; faculty research grantee Social Sci. Research Council, 1959; Carnegie sr. fellow, 1965. Fellow Am. Acad. Arts and Scis.; mem. Am. Sociol. Assn. (sec. 1968-72, pres.-elect 1979-80, pres. 1980-81), Am. Evaluation Assn.

ROSSI, RALPH L., tobacco company executive; b. 1928; married. BBA, Pace Coll., 1952. From salesman to div. mgr. to dir. sales U.S. Tobacco Co., Greenwich, Conn., 1955-73, v.p. sales, 1973-77, exec. v.p. ops., 1977-81, exec. v.p. adminstrn., 1981-85, vice-chmn., 1985—, also bd. dirs., 1973—. Office: UST 100 W Putnam Ave Greenwich CT 06830-5314

ROSSI, STEVEN B., newspaper publishing executive. Grad., Ursinus Coll., 1971; MBA, U. Pa., 1974. With UI Internat. Corp., Phila., 1974-78, UGI Corp., Phila., 1978-87, with Phila. Newspapers, 1987—, exec. v.p., gen. mgr. Office: Phila Newspapers Inc 400 N Broad St Philadelphia PA 19130*

ROSSIDES, EUGENE TELEMACHUS, lawyer, writer; b. N.Y.C., Oct. 23, 1927; s. Telemachus and Anna (Maravel) R.; m. Elinor Burcham (div.); 1 child, Gale; m. Aphrodite Macotsin, Dec. 30, 1961; children: Michael, Alexander, Eleni. AB, Columbia U., 1949, JD, 1952. Criminal law investigator Office of Dist. Atty., N.Y.C., 1952; assoc. Rogers & Wells, N.Y.C., 1954-56, 61-66, ptnr., 1966-69, 73-92, sr. counsel, 1993—; asst. atty. gen. State of N.Y., N.Y.C., 1958-61; asst. sec., 1969-73; bd. dirs Sterling Nat. Bank, N.Y.C. Author: U.S. Import Trade Regulation, 2d edit., 1986, Foreign Unfair Competition, 3d edit., 1991, United States Import Trade Law, 1992, also articles; chief import editor Internat. Trade Reporter, Bur. Nat. Affairs, 1980—; editor: Doing Business in Greece, 1993. Mem. Grace Commn., Washington, 1981-82; chmn. nationalities div. Reagan Bush Com., Washington, 1980; campaign mgr. N.Y.C. Nixon for Pres. Com., 1968, Keating for Senator Com, N.Y. State, 1964; bd. dirs. Eisenhower World Affairs Inst., Washington, Am. Hellenic Inst. Inc. Capt. USAF, 1952-60. Recipient Medal for Excellence, Columbia U., 1972, Young Lawyer's award Columbia Law Sch. Alumni Assn., 1972, Silver Anniversary award NCAA, 1974, John Jay Award Columbia Coll. Alumni Assn., 1994. Mem. ABA, N.Y. State Bar Assn., Fed. Bar Assn. Republican. Greek Orthodox. Avocations: tennis, photography. Home: 3666 Upton St NW Washington DC 20008-3125 Office: Rogers & Wells 607 14th St NW Washington DC 20005-2011

ROSSIE, CARLOS ENRIQUE, computer school administrator, consultant; b. Havana, Cuba, Oct. 7, 1948; s. Dionisio M. and Edelmira (Blanco) R.; came to U.S., 1966; m. Claudia V. Velilla, Mar. 24, 1972; children—Cynthia Patricia, Claudette Marie, Carlos Fernando. Assoc. in Sci., Miami Dade Jr. Coll., 1970; postgrad., Fla. Internat. U., 1978—; B in Computers, Internat. Coll. of Cayman Islands, 1988; MBA, Internat. Coll., 1990; EdD, Nova Southeastern U., 1994. Dir., owner Programar Computer Sch., Colombia, 1972-78; computer system and procedures analyst, dir. programmers and analysts tng. Burger King Corp., Miami, Fla., 1978-79; asst. v.p. computer dept. Flagler Fed. Savs. and Loans, Miami, 1979-81; dir., owner Fla. Programming Computer Sch., Miami, 1981—; pres. READ (Rossie Ednl. Advisors), Miami, 1994—; computer cons. for Cuban-Am. Orgn. program, Dade County (Fla.), 1981—; computer presentations Dade County High Schs. Author: Cobol Computer Language, 1974 (Best Cobol Book award Columbia, S.Am.), How to Design and Implement a Recruitment Program for International Students, 1994; 3 other computer books and intro. to data processing computer book. Cons. econ. com. Colombian Conservative Party. Roman Catholic. Office: 10415 SW 145 Ave Miami FL 33186

ROSSIN, HERBERT YALE, television broadcaster; b. Phila., May 15, 1936; s. Jack Rossin and Edna Wolinsky; m. Meryl Ann Barsky, Nov. 15, 1965; children: Abby Rae, Shane J.P. Student, Spring Garden Inst., Phila., 1956, Temple U., 1958. Gen. mgr. KIKU TV/13, Honolulu, 1968-70; br. mgr. Columbia Pictures, Las Vegas, 1970-74; ptnr. Internat. TV Concepts, Las Vegas, 1974-78; sta. mgr. KUAM AM/FM/TV, Agana, Guam, 1978-80; v.p. Tag Mktg. and Advt., Cherry Hill, N.J., 1981-83; gen. mgr. WLXI-TV/61, Greensboro, N.C., 1983-85; v.p., gen. mgr. WHLL-TV/27, Boston, 1986-87; v.p. Home Shopping Network, L.A., 1987-88; owner A.S.A.P. Multi-Corp., Las Vegas, 1988—; broadcast cons. Fashion Channel-Video Mall, L.A., 1987-88; scriptwriter Four Star Pictures, L.A., 1988-89; network cons. Las Vegas TV Network, 1992; pres. Video Music TV Stas. Am., 1984-88, named Broadcaster of Yr., 1985. Producer motion picture Miss Conduct, 1957; creator TV show New Millionaires; editor Israel Mag., 1960. Producer telethon Heart Fund Am., Las Vegas, 1972, Albert Einstein Sch., Las Vegas, 1974. With U.S. Air N.G., 1954-58. Recipient Edn. award Albert Einstein Hebrew Acad., 1974, People Law Sch. award Nev. Trial Lawyers, 1992 Citizenship award Govt. of Guam, 1979, others. Mem. Nat. Assn. TV Program Execs. Avocations: collecting classic cars, softball. Home and Office: ASAP Multi Corp 7704 Musical Ln Las Vegas NV 89128

ROSSING, THOMAS D., physics educator; b. Madison, S.D., Mar. 27, 1929; s. Torstein H. and Luella E. Rossing; children: Karen, Barbara, Erik, Jane, Mary. BA, Luther Coll., 1950; MS, Iowa State U., 1952, PhD, 1954. Rsch. physicist Univac div. Sperry Rand, 1954-57; prof. physics St. Olaf Coll., 1957-71, chmn. physics dept., 1963-69; prof. physics No. Ill. U., DeKalb, 1971—, Disting. Rsch. prof., chmn. dept., 1971-73; rschr. Microwave Lab., Stanford (Calif.) U., 1961-62, Lincoln Lab., MIT, Cambridge, Mass., summer 1963, Clarendon Lab., Oxford (Eng.) U., 1966-67, physics dept. MIT, 1976-77; rsch. assoc. Argonne (Ill.) Nat Lab., 1974-76, scientist-in-residence, 1990—; vis. lectr. U. New Eng., Armidale, Australia, 1980-81; vis. exch. scholar People's Republic of China, 1988; guest rschr. Royal Inst. Tech., Stockholm, 1983, 84, 85, Inst. Perception Rsch., Eindhoven, The Netherlands, 1984, 85, Physikalisch-Technische Bundesanstalt, Braunschweig, Germany, 1988-89. Author 10 books in field; contbr. more than 200 articles to profl. publs. Fellow AAAS, Acoustical Soc. Am. (Silver medal in mus. acoustics 1992); mem. IEEE, Am. Phys. Soc., Am. Assn. Physics Tchrs. (pres. 1991), Catgut Acoustical Soc., Percussive Arts Soc., Guild Am. Luthiers, Sigma Xi (nat. lectr. 1984-87), Sigma Pi Sigma. Achievements include research in musical acoustics, psychoacoustics, speech and singing, vibration analysis, magnetic levitation, environmental noise control, surface effects in fusion reactors, spin waves in metals, physics education; 9 U.S. and 11 foreign patents in field. Office: No Ill U Physics Dept De Kalb IL 60115

ROSSINGTON, DAVID RALPH, physical chemistry educator; b. London, July 13, 1932; s. George Leonard and Clara Fanny (Simmons) R.; children: Andrew, Carolyn, Nicholas, Philip. BSc with honors, U. Bristol, Eng., 1953, PhD, 1956. Postdoctoral research fellow N.Y. State Coll. Ceramics at Alfred (N.Y.) U., 1956-58; tech. officer Imperial Chem. Industries Ltd., Eng., 1958-60; asst. prof. physics Alfred U., 1960-63, assoc. prof., 1963-69, prof., 1969—, head div. ceramic engring., 1976-79, 82-84, dean sch. engring., 1984-91. Editor: Advances in Materials Characterization, 1983; contbr. numerous articles to profl. jours. Town Justice, Alfred, 1976-84. Fulbright scholar, 1956, 58. Mem. Am. Ceramic Soc.; mem. Am. Chem. Soc., Ceramic Edn. Coun., Materials Rsch. Soc., Am. Soc. Engring. Edn., Tau Beta Pi, Phi Kappa Phi. Democrat. Episcopalian. Office: Alfred U Sch Of Engring Alfred NY 14802

ROSSINI, JOSEPH, contracting and development corporate executive; b. New Rochelle, N.Y., Nov. 25, 1939; m. Antonia Rossini; children: Katherine, Anthony, Andrew. Student, Fordham U., 1965-66, Iona Coll., 1972. Pres. Rossini Contracting Corp., New Rochelle, 1963—; prin. Rossini Devel. Co., Monticello, N.Y., 1965—; bd. dirs. Circuit Realty Corp., New Rochelle, 1970-71. Mem. planning bd. City of New Rochelle, 1986-92, mem. bldg. dept. adv. com., 1985; vol. instr. N.Y. State Dept. Environ. Conservation, Albany, 1968—; vice chmn. New Rochelle Conservative Party, 1984—; county committeeman Westchester County Conservative Party; trustee Beechwoods Cemetery, New Rochelle; dir. New Rochelle Neighborhood Revitalization Corp. With USN, 1959-61. Mem. NRA, Gen. Contractors Assn. N.Y., Constrn. Industry Coun. Westchester and Hudson Valley, Bldg. Trades Employers Assn., Soc. Explosives Engrs., Deep Founds. Inst., Young Ams. for Freedom, Am. Lauretana Assn., Mensa, Assoc. Gen. Contractors Am. Roman Catholic. Office: Rossini Contracting Corp 113 Edison Ave Mount Vernon NY 10550-5005

ROSSITER, ALEXANDER, JR., news service executive, editor; b. Elmira, N.Y., Mar. 2, 1936; s. Alexander H. and Eleanor (Howell) R.; m. Sylvia Lee Vanlandingham, June 11, 1960; children: Alexander H. III, Jill Jarrell. BA, Rutgers U., 1958; postgrad., Emory U., 1959. With UPI, 1959-92; newsman Atlanta, 1959-61, Richmond, Va., 1961-63; bur. mgr. Cape Canaveral, Fla., 1963-73; sci. editor Washington, 1973-87, exec. editor, 1987-88, exec. editor, sr. v.p., 1988-91, editor, exec. v.p., 1991-92; asst. v.p., dir. news svc. Duke U., Durham, N.C., 1992—; mem. nat. adv. bd. Knight Ctr. for Specialized Journalism, Colleg Pk., Md., 1988-92. Recipient Grady-Stack medal Am. Chem. Soc., 1987, other journalism awards. Mem. Nat. Assn. Sci. Writers, Edn. Writers Assn. Office: Duke U 615 Chapel Dr Durham NC 27706-2500

ROSSITER, BRYANT WILLIAM, chemistry consultant; b. Ogden, Utah, Mar. 10, 1931; s. Bryant B. and Christine (Peterson) R.; m. Betty Jean Anderson, Apr. 16, 1951; children: Bryant, Mark, Diane, Steven, Linda, Karen, Matthew, Gregory. BA, U. Utah, 1954, PhD, 1957. Researcher Eastman-Kodak Co., Rochester, N.Y., 1957-63, head color phys. chem. lab., 1963-70, dir. chemistry div., 1970-84, dir. sci. tech. devel., 1984-86; pres. Viratek Inc., Costa Mesa, Calif., 1986-89; sr. v.p. ICN Pharms., Costa Mesa, 1989-90; ret., 1990; pres., chief exec. officer Wrecon Corp., cons., Laguna Hills, Calif., 1991—; sr. editor John Wiley & Sons, N.Y.C., 1970—; chmn. bd. Nucleic Acid Rsch. Inst., Costa Mesa, 1987-88; trustee Eastman Dental Ctr., Rochester, 1973-93 (bd. pres. 1982-85); bd. dirs. Verax & Corp. Editor: (chem. treatises) Physical Methods of Chemistry (11 vols.), 1970-76, Physical Methods, (12 vols.), 1986—, Chemical Experimentation Under Extreme Conditions, 1979. Mem. rsch. adv. com. U.S. Agy. for Internat. Devel., Washington, chmn. rsch. adv. com., 1989-92; mem. panel on biosci. Pres.' Coun. Advisors on Sci. and Tech., 1991; mem. adv com. Cornell Internat. Inst. for Food, Agr. and Devel., 1991; presiding officer Ch. Jesus Christ Latter Day Saints, Ea. U.S. and Can., 1959-86. 1st lt. USAFR, 1951-58. Named Hon. Alumni Brigham Young U., Provo, Utah, 1982. Fellow AAAS, Am. Inst. Chemists (lectr., Fellows award 1988, Will Judy award Juanita Coll. 1978); mem. Internat. Union Pure and Applied Chemistry (chmn. U.S. nat. com., originator, chmn. Chemical Rsch. Applied to World Needs com. 1975-87, chmn. Chemical Rsch. Applied to World Needs II The Internat. Conf. on Chemistry and World Food Supplies, 1982), Am. Chem. Soc. (chmn. internat. activities). Avocations: horseback riding, reading, fishing. Home and Office: 25662 Dillon Rd Laguna Hills CA 92653

ROSSITER, MARGARET WALSH, history of science educator; b. Malden, Mass., July 8, 1944; d. Charles Aston and Mary Julia (Madden) R. AB, Radcliffe Coll., 1966; MS, U. Wis., 1967; MPhil, Yale U., 1969, PhD, 1971. Acting asst. prof., lectr. dept. history U. Calif., Berkeley, 1973-74, 75-76, rsch. assoc. Office for History of Sci. and Tech., 1976-82; rsch. assoc. Am. Acad. Arts and Scis., Cambridge, Mass., 1977-86; program dir. history and philosophy of sci. program NSF, Washington, 1982-83; vis. lectr., vis. scholar dept. history of sci. Harvard U., Cambridge, Mass., 1983-86; NSF vis. prof. history sci., dept. history Cornell U., Ithaca, N.Y., 1986-88, prof. history sci., 1988-91, prof. dept. sci. and tech. studies, 1991—; mem. adv. com. NSF, 1981-82, 83-84; Kreeger-Wolf Disting. vis. prof. Northwestern U., 1985; Regents lectr. U. Calif., Riverside, 1986. Author: The Emergence of Agricultural Science: Justus Liebig and the Americans, 1975, Women Scientists in America: Struggles and Strategies to 1940, 1982, paperback, 1984; co-editor: (with Sally Gregory Kohlstedt) Historical Writing on American Science, 1986; compiler Bibliography of the History of the Agricultural Sciences, 1980; assoc. editor Am. Nat. Biography, 1989—; mem. editorial bd. Tech. and Culture, 1978-84, Osiris, 1983-90, Isis, 1989—; editor Osiris, 1993—; reviewer sci. books; contbr. articles to jours. Recipient Silver medal Justus-Liebig U., Giessen, Germany, 1979, Berkshire prize for best book in field of history by Am. woman, 1983, Wilbur Cross medal Yale U. Grad. Sch., 1984, Hoopes Teaching award Harvard U., 1984, Rsch. prize Justus-Liebig U., 1985; Rockefeller fellow; Guggheim fellow; MacArthur Found. fellow. Mem. AAUP (com. A. acad. freedom and tenure 1989-92), AAAS (Sarton lectr. 1990), History of Sci. Soc. (numerous coms.), Internat. Commn. on History of Women in Scis., Tech. and Medicine (pres. 1981-89), Forum for the History of Am. Sci. (coun. 1989-92, keynote speaker 1989), Agrl. History Soc. (exec. com. 1979-82), Soc. for History Tech. (numerous coms. 1979-84). Roman Catholic. Office: Cornell U Dept Sci and Tech Studies 726 University Ave #201 Ithaca NY 14850

ROSSITER, ROBERT E., diversified corporation executive; b. 1946. With Lear Siegler Inc., 1971-87, former pres. seating div.; pres., chief oper. officer Lear Seating Corp., Southfield, Mich., 1987—; also bd. dirs. Office: Lear Seating Corp 21557 Telegraph Rd Southfield MI 48034-6817

ROSSKAMM, ALAN, retail company executive; b. 1950. With Fabri-Ctrs. of Am., Inc., 1978—, v.p., from 1980, now pres., chief exec. officer. Office: Fabri-Ctrs Am Inc 5555 Darrow Rd Hudson OH 44236-4054

ROSSKAMM, MARTIN, fabric manufacturing company executive; b. 1915. With Fabri-Ctrs. of Am., Inc., Cleve., 1953—, first pres., chief exec. officer, now chmn. bd. dirs. Served with AUS, 1941-45. Office: Fabri-Ctrs Am Inc PO Box 2550 5555 Darrow Rd Hudson OH 44236-4011

ROSSLER, WILLIS KENNETH, JR., petroleum company executive; b. Houston, Nov. 17, 1946; s. Willis Kenneth and Fay Lee (Olle) R.; BS in Indsl. Engring., Tex. Tech. U., 1969; postgrad. in bus. Stanford U.; children: Nancy Kay, Deborah Anne, Ryan Konrad, Eric George. Dist. mgr. Tex.-La. ops. Continental Pipe Line Co., Lake Charles, La., 1974-75, mgr. engring., Houston, 1976-77; asst. mgr. corp. planning and devel. Conoco, Inc., Houston, 1977-78; v.p. project devel. PetroUnited, Inc., Houston, 1978-80, pres., 1981-86, also dir. Pres., Village Pl. Community Assn., Houston, 1978, v.p., gen. mgr., Pilko and Assoc., Inc., Houston, 1986-90; pres., CEO Houston Fuel Oil Terminal Co., 1990—; bd. dirs. Pilko and Assocs., Naylor Industries, Inc., Clean Channel Assn., Greater Houston Port Bur., Grace Presbyn. Sch. Mem. Am. Inst. Indsl. Engrs., Am. Petroleum Inst., Houston Mgmt. Council, Intensive Mgmt. Devel. Inst. (adv. dir. 1983-84), Ind. Liquid Terminals Assn. (vice chmn. 1986, chmn.-elect 1987), Am. Mgmt. Assn., Planning Forum (pres. chpt. 1985), Petroleum Club of Houston, Lakeside Country Club. Office: Houston Fuel Oil Terminal Co 16642 Jacintoport Blvd Houston TX 77015-6541

ROSSMAN, JANET KAY, architectural interior designer; b. Lansing, Mich., Feb. 13, 1954; d. Elmer Chris and Jean Elizabeth (Schell) R.; m. Farzad Moazed; children: Alexander, Christina. BA with High Honors, Mich. State U., 1976. Designer Tilton & Lewis Assocs., Inc., Chgo., 1977-79, Swanke Hayden Connell & Ptnrs., N.Y.C., 1979-81, Bonsignore Brignati & Mazzotta Architects, N.Y.C., 1982-84; dir. design, assoc. SPGA Group, Inc., N.Y.C., 1984—; instr. Design Edn. Ctr., Lansing, 1975-76. Fellow Mus. Modern Art, N.Y.C., 1977—. Mem. Am. Soc. of Interior Designers (chair. 1973-76, editor Collage 1973-76), Inst. Bus. Designers, Nat. Assn. for Female Execs., Omicron Nu. Republican. Club: Atrium, Landmark. Avocations: photography, equestrian activities, travel. Home: 367 W Hill Rd Stamford CT 06902

ROSSMAN, RICHARD ALAN, lawyer; b. Albany, N.Y., June 16, 1939; s. Kenneth Fisher and Edith Bell (Wheeler) R.; m. Patricia Margaret Booth, Jan. 2, 1965; children: Lisa, Jeffrey. AB, U. Mich., 1961, JD, 1964. Asst. pros. atty. Oakland County, Pontiac, Mich., 1965-67, 70-71; chief dep. fed. defender, Detroit, 1972-75, sole practice, 1975-77; chief asst. U.S. Atty. Ea. Dist. Mich., Detroit, 1977-80, U.S. atty., 1980-81; ptnr. Butzel, Long, Gust, Klein & Van Zile, Detroit, 1981-86, Pepper, Hamilton & Scheetz, Detroit, 1986—. Mem. ABA, Fed. Bar Assn. (pres. Detroit chpt. 1982-83), Mich. Bar Assn. (rep. assembly 1980-82), Oakland County Bar Assn., Detroit Bar Assn. (trustee found. 1984-86). Office: Pepper Hamilton & Scheetz 100 Renaissance Ctr Ste 3600 Detroit MI 48243

ROSSMAN, RUTH SCHARFF, artist, educator; b. Bklyn.; d. Joseph and Elsie (Frankel) Scharff; m. Phillip Rossman; 1 dau., Joanne. Grad., Cleve. Inst. Art, 1934; BS, Case Western Res. U., 1934; postgrad., Kahn Inst. Art, 1947-50, UCLA, 1960. Art instr. Canton (Ohio) public schs., 1934-39, Canton Art Inst., 1937-45, Rustic Canyon Art Center, Los Angeles, 1978-81. One-woman shows at Heritage Gallery, L.A., 1963, 66, Canton (Ohio) Community Ctr., 1967, Marymount Coll., U. Judaism, 1980, L.A. Fedn. Bldg., 1981, 89, Platt Gallery, 1986, 93, others; exhibited in group shows Mus. Modern Art, N.Y.C., Butler Mus., Washington and Jefferson Coll., Denver Mus., Space Mus., Mt. St. Mary's Coll., L.A., M.H. de Young Mus., San Francisco Mus. Art, Venice Art Walk, ann. 1981-94, Univ. Judaism, 1986, 93, Brand Art Gallery, 1987, others; represented in permanent collections Pa. Acad. Fine Arts, Phila., Brandeis-Bardin Inst., U. Redlands, Calif., Nat. Watercolor Soc., Ahmanson Collection, Rocky Mt. Nat., others; paintings included in book The California Romantics: Harbingers of Watercolor, 1987. Chair selection com. for Platt Gallery, U. Judaism, L.A., 1986—. Recipient purchase-cash awards Los Angeles All-City Art Exhbn. Mem. Nat. Watercolor Soc. (pres. 1974-75), Artists for Econ. Action.

ROSSMAN, STUART T., lawyer; b. Bklyn., Jan. 7, 1954; s. Marvin Warren and Phyllis (Berenbaum) R.; m. Rochelle S. Sorkin, May 18, 1975; children: Jessie Joanne, Rachel Joy. BA, U. Mich., 1975; JD, Harvard U., 1978. Bar: Mass. 1978, U.S. Dist. Ct. Mass. 1979, U.S. Ct. Appeals (1st cir.) 1979, U.S. Claims Ct. 1984, U.S. Supreme Ct. 1984. Assoc. Gaston & Snow, Boston, 1978-87, ptnr., 1987—. Editor: (handbook) Homeless Not Helpless, 1988, Social Change, 1986, Boston Bar Jour. Exec. bd. mem. United Jewish Appeal Young Leadership Cabinet, N.Y.C., 1983—; Coun. Jewish Federations Leadership Devel. Com., N.Y.C., 1986—; trustee Combined Jewish Philanthropies, Boston, 1987—; bd. dirs. Vol. Lawyers Project, Boston, 1984—; curriculum com. Mass. Continuing Legal Edn., Boston, 1984-87. Mem. ABA, Mass. BAr Assn., Boston Bar Assn. (chmn. young lawyers sect. 1983-86). Democrat. Office: Gaston & Snow 1 Federal St Boston MA 02110-2003

ROSSMAN, TOBY GALE, genetic toxicology educator, researcher; b. Weehawken, N.J., June 3, 1942; d. Norman N. and Sylvia Betty (May) Natowitz; m. Neil I. Rossman, Sept. 16, 1962 (div. Sept. 1980); m. Gordon Rauer, Aug. 19, 1990. AB, NYU, 1964, PhD, 1968; postgrad., Brandeis U., 1964-65. Instr. Polytech. Inst. of N.Y., N.Y.C., 1968-69; postdoctoral dept. pathology NYU, N.Y.C., 1969-71; from asst. to assoc. prof. Inst. for Environ. Medicine Nelson Inst. of Environ. Medicine, N.Y.C., 1974-85; prof. Inst. for Environ. Medicine, 1985—. Mem. editorial bd. Molecular Toxicology, 1989-91, Teratogenesis, Carcinogenesis, Mutagenesis, 1990-91, Environmental and Molecular Mutagenesis, 1994—, Mutation Research, 1994—; contbr. numerous articles to profl. jours. EPA grantee, NIH grantee. Mem. AAAS, Assn. for Women in Sci., Am. Assn. for Cancer Rsch., Am. Soc. for Microbiology, Environ. Mutagen Soc. (councilor 1990-93). Office: NYU Inst Environ Medicine Long Meadow Rd Tuxedo Park NY 10987

ROSSMANN, JACK EUGENE, psychology educator; b. Walnut, Iowa, Dec. 4, 1936; s. Wilbert C. Rossmann and Claire L. (Mickel) Walter; m. Marilyn Martin, June 14, 1958; children: Ann, Charles, Sarah. BS, Iowa State U., 1958, MS, 1960; PhD, U. Minn., 1963. Lic. cons. psychologist, Minn. Asst. prof. Macalester Coll., St. Paul, 1964-68, assoc. prof., 1968-73, prof., 1973—, v.p. acad. affairs, 1978-86; chair dept. psychology Macalester Coll., 1990—; cons. Pers. Decisions Inc., Mpls., 1989—. Author: (with others) Open Admissions at CUNY, 1975; contbr. articles to profl. jours. Bd. dirs. Twin City Inst. for Talented Youth, St. Paul, 1978-91, United Theol. Sem., New Brighton, Minn., 1984—. 2d lt. U.S. Army, 1959. Mem. APA, Am. Psychol. Soc., Assn. for Instl. Rsch., Am. Assn. for Higher Edn., AAUP. Home: 99 Cambridge St Saint Paul MN 55105-1947 Office: Macalester Coll Saint Paul MN 55105

ROSSMANN, MICHAEL GEORGE, biochemist, educator; b. Frankfurt, Germany, July 30, 1930; s. Alexander and Nelly (Schwabacher) R.; m. Audrey Pearson, July 24, 1954; children—Martin, Alice, Heather. B.Sc. with honors, Polytechnic, London, 1951, M.Sc. in Physics, 1953; Ph.D. in Chemistry, U. Glasgow, 1956. Fulbright scholar U. Minn., 1956-58; research scientist MRC Lab. Molecular Biology, Cambridge, Eng., 1958-64; asso. prof. biol. scis. Purdue U., West Lafayette, Ind., 1964-67; prof. Purdue U., 1967-78, Hanley Disting. prof. biol. scis., 1978—, prof. biochemistry, 1975—. Editor: The Molecular Replacement Method, 1972; mem. editl. bd. Jour. Biol. Chemistry, 1975-80; contbr. over 300 articles to profl. jours. NIH grantee; NSF grantee; recipient Fankuchen award Am. Crystallographic Assn., 1986, Horwitz prize Columbia U., 1990. Mem. Am. Soc. Biol. Chemists, Am. Chem. Soc., Biophys. Soc., Am. Crystallographic Assn., Brit. Biophys. Soc., Inst. Physics, Chem. Soc. (U.K.), Am. Acad. Arts and Sci., Nat. Acad. Sci. Democrat. Club: Lafayette Sailing. Home: 1208 Wiley Dr West Lafayette IN 47906-2434 Office: Dept Biol Scis Purdue Univ West Lafayette IN 47907-1392

ROSSMILLER, GEORGE EDDIE, agricultural economist; b. Gt. Falls, Mont., June 8, 1935; s. Albert E and Romaine (Hennford) R.; m. Betty Ann Rinio, Dec. 20, 1955 (dec. Mar. 1990); children: David W., Diane J.; m. Norma Lee Adams, Apr. 18, 1992. B.S., Mont. State U., 1956, M.S., 1962; Ph.D., Mich. State U., 1965. Rsch. assoc. Mich. State U., East Lansing, 1965-66, asst. prof., 1967-71, assoc. prof., 1972-76, prof. agrl. econs., 1977-80; agrl. attache to OECD, Fgn. Agrl. Service, USDA, Paris, 1978-79; asst. adminstr. internat. trade policy Fgn. Agrl. Svc., USDA, Washington, 1979-81, dir planing and analysis, 1981-85; sr. fellow and dir. Nat. Ctr. Food and Agr. Policy, Resources for the Future, 1986-92; also exec. dir. Internat. Policy Council on Agr. and Trade, 1988-92; chief situation and policy studies svc. Food and Agr. Orgn. of UN, Rome, 1992—. Author: The Grain-Livestock Economy of West Germany with Projections to 1970 and 1975, 1968, (with others) Korean Agricultural Sector Analysis and Recommended Development Strategies, 1971-1985, 1972; editor: (with others) Agricultural Sector Planning: A General System Simulation Approach, 1978. Served with U.S. Army, 1956-59. Recipient service citation Korean Ministry of Agrl. and Fisheries, 1973, service citation Office of Prime Minister of Korea, 1977, Superior Service award U.S. Dept. Agr., 1983, Fgn. Agrl. Service merit award, 1984. Mem. Am. Agrl. Econs. Assn. (Disting. Policy Contbn. award 1992), Internat. Assn. Agrl. Economists. Presbyterian. Home: Interno 20, Via dell, Accademia Albertina 38, 00147 Rome Italy Office: Food and Agrl Orgn UN, viale delle Terme di Caracalla, 00100 Rome Italy

ROSSNER, JUDITH, novelist; b. N.Y.C., Mar. 31, 1935; d. Joseph George and Dorothy (Shapiro) Perelman; m. Robert Rossner (div.); children: Jean, Daniel; m. Mort Persky (div.). Student, City Coll. N.Y., 1952-55. Author: novels To the Precipice, 1966, Nine Months in the Life of an Old Maid, 1969, Any Minute I Can Split, 1972, Looking for Mr. Goodbar, 1975, Attachments, 1977, Emmeline, 1980, August, 1983, His Little Women, 1990, Olivia, or the Weight of the Past, 1994; also short stories. Address: care Wendy Weil Agency 232 Madison Ave New York NY 10016

ROSSO, LOUIS T., scientific instrument manufacturing company executive; b. San Francisco, 1933; married. A.B., San Francisco State Coll., 1955; M.B.A., U. Santa Clara, 1967. Product specialist Spinco div. Beckman Instruments, Fullerton, Calif., 1959-63, mktg. mgr., 1963-69, mgr. Spinco div., 1969-70, mgr. clin. instruments div., 1970-74, corp. v.p., mgr. analytical instruments group, 1974-80, corp. sr. v.p., 1980-83, pres., 1983—, now also chmn., chief exec. officer; also bd. dirs. Beckman Instruments, Inc.; v.p. SmithKline Beckman Corp., Phila. Office: Beckman Instruments Inc 2500 N Harbor Blvd Fullerton CA 92634

ROSSON, GLENN RICHARD, building products and furniture company executive; b. Galveston, Tex., Aug. 17, 1937; s. John Raymond and Elsie Lee (Reece) R.; m. Edwina Lucille Hart, June 2, 1956; children—Darrell Richard, Alex Mark. B.B.A., Tex. Tech U., 1959. C.P.A., Tex. Supr., accountant Axelson div. U.S. Industries Inc., Longview, Tex., 1960-67; controller U.S. Industries Inc., 1968; group financial v.p. U.S. Industries Inc., Dallas, 1969; group chmn. U.S. Industries Inc., 1969-72, v.p., 1973-74, sr. v.p., 1974, exec. v.p., 1974-80, also dir.; pres. Rosson Investment Co., 1980—; chmn. bd. Yorktowne Inc., 1988—. Mem. Am. Inst. C.P.A.s, Tex. Soc. C.P.A.s, Nat. Assn. Accts. (past nat. dir., past pres. Tex. chpt.), Assn. for Corp. Growth (past pres.). Club: Dallas Athletic, TBARM Raquet. Home: 11367 Drummond Dr Dallas TX 75228-1946 Office: 5910 N Central Expy # 1000 Dallas TX 75206-5106

ROSSOTTI, BARBARA JILL MARGULIES, lawyer; b. Englewood, N.J., Feb. 28, 1940; d. Albert and Loretta (Jill) Margulies; m. Charles Ossola Rossotti; children: Allegra Jill, Edward Charles. BA magna cum laude, Mount Holyoke Coll., 1961; LLB, Harvard U., 1964. Bar: D.C. 1966. Assoc. Nutter McClennen & Fish, Boston, 1964-65, Covington & Burling, Washington, 1965-72; assoc. Shaw, Pittman, Potts & Trowbridge, Washington, 1972-73, ptnr., 1973—. Trustee Mt. Holyoke Coll., South Hadley, Mass., 1984, vice chmn., 1989-94, chmn., 1994—; chmn. exec. com. Campaign for Mt. Holyoke Coll., 1986-91; trustee Legal Aid Soc., D.C., 1979-92, pres. 1985-89. mem. pres. coun., 1992—; trustee Choral Arts Soc., Washington, 1989—, chair, 1993—, bd. dirs. Washington Home, 1989—. Fellow Am. Bar Found.; mem. ABA (sect. on taxation 1978—), Am. Soc. Internat. Law, Internat. Law Assn., D.C. Bar Assn., 1925 F Street Club. Office: Shaw Pittman Potts & Trowbridge 2300 N St NW Washington DC 20037-1122

ROSSOTTI, CHARLES OSSOLA, computer consulting company executive; b. N.Y.C., Jan. 17, 1941; s. Charles C. and V. Elizabeth (Ossola) R.; m. Barbara Jill Margulies, June 9, 1963; children: Allegra Jill, Edward Charles. AB magna cum laude, Georgetown U., 1962; MBA with high distinction, Harvard U., 1974. Mgmt. cons. Boston Cons. Group, 1964-65; prin. dep. asst. sec. Office of Systems Analysis, Dept. Def., Washington, 1965-70; prin. dep. asst. sec. of Def. Office of Systems Analysis, Dept. Def., 1969-70; pres. Am. Mgmt. Systems, Inc., Arlington, Va., 1970—, chief exec. officer, 1981—, chmn. bd., 1989—; bd. dirs. Cateratr Internat., Nations Bank of Va. Bd. dirs. Georgetown U., 1969-77, 92—; trustee Woodstock Theol. Ctr., 1990—; chmn. Corp. Against Drug Abuse, 1993—. Mem. Coun. Fgn. Rels. Office: Am Mgmt Systems Inc 1777 N Kent St Arlington VA 22209-2100

ROSSOWSKA, MAGDALENA JOANNA, physiology educator, research scientist; b. Warsaw, Poland, Feb. 24, 1938; came to U.S. 1981; d. Czeslaw Taracha and Anna Szulakowska-Taracha; m. Wojciech Joseph Rossowski, July 8, 1965; 1 child, Thomas Maciej. MS in Biology, U. Warsaw, 1961; postgrad., Polish Acad. of Sci., Warsaw, 1962-66; PhD in Biochemistry, Inst. of Biochemistry and Biophysics, Warsaw, 1966. Postdoctoral fellow, instr. Med. Rsch. Ctr., Polish Acad. Sci., Warsaw, 1966-70, asst. prof. dept. neurochemistry, 1970-81; rsch. assoc. dept. biochemistry La. State U., New Orleans, 1982-83, rsch. assoc. Eye Ctr., 1984-89, rsch. assoc. dept. physiology, 1989-91, instr. dept. physiology, 1991-92, asst. prof., 1992—. Contbr. articles to profl. jours. Mem. Solidarity, Polish Acad. Sci., 1980-81, Polish-Am. Assn. of La., New Orleans, 1985—. Avocation: music. Office: La State U Med Ctr 23 Theresa Ave New Orleans LA 70119

ROSSTON, EDWARD WILLIAM, lawyer; b. San Francisco, Nov. 14, 1918; s. Ernest William and Goldah Ray (Charmak) R.; m. Maxine Goldmark Aaron, June 28, 1947; children—Edward William, Richard Mark,

Ellen Maxine Rosston Neft, Jean Frances. A.B., U. Calif.-Berkeley, 1939, JD, 1947; LL.M., Columbia U., 1948. Bar: Calif. 1947. Assoc. Heller Ehrman White & McAuliff, San Francisco, 1948-58; ptnr. Heller Ehrman White & McAuliff, 1958—; instr. Hastings Coll. Law, U. Calif., San Francisco, 1949-51; bd. dirs. Consumer Credit Counsellors, San Francisco; sec. MPC Ins. Ltd., 1986-93. Nat. trustee Lawyers Com. for Civil Rights, 1977—; co-chmn., mem. exec. com. San Francisco Lawyers Com. for Urban Affairs, 1972-83; trustee The Mechanics Inst. and Chessroom, 1991—, 2d v.p., 1993-94. Lt. USNR, 1941-46, PTO. Mem. ABA, State Bar Calif., Bar Assn. San Francisco (bd. dirs., com. chmn. 1959-65), Am. Arbitration Assn. (arbitrator and mediator, adv. coun. North Calif. chpt. 1988—), Boalt Hall Alumni Assn. (trustee 1977-79). Democrat. Jewish. Club: Commonwealth (San Francisco). Office: Heller Ehrman White & McAuliffe 333 Bush St San Francisco CA 94104-2806

ROSSUM, RALPH ARTHUR, political science educator; b. Alexandria, Minn., Dec. 17, 1946; s. Floyd Arthur and June Marion (Carlson) R.; m. Constance Mary Brazina, Aug. 19, 1972; children: Kristin, Brent, Pierce. BA summa cum laude, Concordia Coll., 1968; MA, U. Chgo., 1971, PhD, 1973. Instr. Grinnell (Iowa) Coll., 1972-73; asst. prof. Memphis State U., 1973-77, assoc. prof., 1977-80; assoc. prof. Loyola U., Chgo., 1980-83, assoc. dean grad. sch., 1981-82; dep. dir. bur. justice stats. U.S. Dept. Justice, Washington, 1983-84; Alice Tweed Tuohy prof. govt. Claremont (Calif.) McKenna Coll., 1984-88, v.p. and dean of faculty, 1988-91; pres. Hampden-Sydney (Va.) Coll., 1991-92; Salvatori Vis. prof. Claremont (Calif.) McKenna Coll., 1992-93, Salvatori prof. Am. Constitutionalism, 1994—; Fletcher Jones Prof. of Am. Politics U. Redlands, Redlands, Calif., 1993-94; mem. adv. bd. Nat. Inst. Corrections, U.S. Dept. Justice, 1988-91; mem. Robert Presley Inst. Corrections Rsch. and Tng., State of Calif., 1988-91. Author: Reverse Discrimination, 1980, others; co-author: The American Founding, 1981, American Constitutional Law, 1983, 4th edit., 1995, others; sr. editor Benchmark, 1983-86, book rev. editor, 1986—; contbr. 50 articles to profl. jours. and chpts. to books. Trustee Episcopal Theol. Sch., Claremont, 1987-91. Ford Found. fellow, 1968-72. Mem. Am. Polit. Sci. Assn. Episcopalian. Office: Claremont McKenna Coll Dept of Government 850 Columbia Claremont CA 91711

ROST, THOMAS LOWELL, plant biology educator; b. St. Paul, Dec. 28, 1941; s. Lowell Henry Rost and Agnes Marie (Wojtowicz) Jurek; m. Ann Marie Ruhland, Aug. 31, 1963; children: Christopher, Timothy, Jacquelyn. BS, St. John's U., Collegeville, Minn., 1963; MA, Mankato State U., 1965; PhD, Iowa State U., 1970. Postdoctoral fellow Brookhaven Nat. Lab., Upton, N.Y., 1970-72; prof. plant biology and interim chmn. U. Calif., Davis, 1972—; cons. faculty of agronomy U. Uruguay, 1979, 89; vis. fellow Rsch. Soc. Biol. Sci., Canberra, Australia, 1979-80; vis. prof. U. Wroclaw, Poland, 1987, U. Exeter, Eng., 1993. Co-author: Botany: A Brief Introduction to Plant Biology, 1979, Botany: An Introduction on Plant Biology, 1982; co-editor: Mechanisms and Control of Cell Division, 1977; also numerous articles to profl. jours. Served to capt. U.S. Army, 1965-67. Fellow Japan Soc. Promotion of Sci.; mem. Bot. Soc. Am., Soc. Exptl. Biology, Am. Inst. Biol. Sci. Democrat. Roman Catholic. Avocations: horseback riding, community theatre, reading. Office: U Calif Sect Plant Biology Davis CA 95616-8537

ROST, WILLIAM JOSEPH, chemist; b. Fargo, N.D., Dec. 8, 1926; s. William Melvin and Christine Ruth (Hamerlik) R.; m. Rita Cincoski, Sept. 15, 1951; children—Kathryn, Patricia, Carol. B.S., U. Minn., 1948, Ph.D., 1952. From asst. prof. to prof. pharm. chemistry Sch. Pharmacy U. Kansas City, Mo., 1952-63; prof. pharm. chemistry Sch. Pharmacy U. Mo., Kansas City, 1963—. Co-author: Principles of Medicinal Chemistry, 1974, 3d rev edit., 1988; contbr. articles profl. jours. Mem. Am. Pharm. Assn., Am. Chem. Soc., Sigma Xi, Sigma Psi, Rho Chi, Phi Lambda Upsilon. Home: 709 W 115th Ter Kansas City MO 64114-5597 Office: U Mo Sch of Pharmacy Kansas City MO 64110

ROSTAD, KENNETH LEIF, provincial government official; b. Yorkton, Sask., Can., Sept. 7, 1941; s. Leif and Mary Katherine (McLennan) R.; m. Shirley Gail Tien, May 19, 1979; children: Kyle, Kelsy, Karsten. B Commerce, U. Saskatoon, Sask., 1967, LLB, 1979. With Royal Bank Can., 1959-60, Shell Can. Ltd., 1967-69, Sears Can. Inc., 1969-76; ptnr. Gaede Fielding Rostad & Syed, Camrose, Alta., Can., 1979-86; solicitor gen. Govt. Alta., Edmonton, 1986-88, min. responsible for housing, 1987-89, min. responsible for native affairs, 1987-91, atty. gen., 1988-92, apptd. min. justice and atty. gen., 1993-94; min. responsible for govt. reorganization secretariat Govt. Alta., 1993—; apptd. min. fed. and intergovernmental affairs Govt. Alta., Edmonton, 1994—. Alderman City of Camrose, 1985-86; mem. legis. assembly Province Alta., 1986—. Mem. Law Soc. Alta. (hon. bencher), Can. Bar Assn., Lions Internat. (pres.). Progressive Conservative. Lutheran. Avocations: golf, skiing, hiking, reading, music. Office: Min Fed & Intergovernmental, Legislature Bldg Rm 404, Edmonton, AB Canada T5K 2B6

ROSTAGNO, DERRICK, professional tennis player; b. Los Angeles, Calif., Oct. 25, 1965; s. Juan and Helga R. Student, Stanford U. Mem. U.S. Olympic Team, 1984; 6th in U.S. Tennis Assn. rankings, 13th in world ranking, 1991, ranked 14th in U.S. Tennis Assn., 1993. Office: care US Tennis Assn 1212 Avenue of the Americas New York NY 10036-1601*

ROSTEN, IRWIN, writer, producer, director. Mgr. news and pub. affairs Du Mont TV Network, N.Y.C., 1950-54; writer-producer news, pub. affairs Sta. KNXT-CBS, Los Angeles, 1954-60; dir. news, pub. affairs Sta. KTLA, Los Angeles, 1960-63; writer-producer, dir. Wolper Prodns., Inc., Los Angeles, 1963-67; chief documentary dept. MGM Studios, Culver City, Calif., 1967-72; pres. Ronox Prodns., Inc., Los Angeles, 1970-87. Writer-producer-dir. Nat. Geog. Soc. spls.: Splendid Stones, Elephant, Great Moments with National Geographic, The Thames, Mysteries of the Mind, Gold!, The Legacy of L.S.B. Leakey, The Volga, The Incredible Machine, Grizzly!, The Eerie World of Jacques-Yves Cousteau; National Parks: Playground or Paradise?, numerous other shows including Unsolved Mysteries, The Wold Men, Pitley's Believe It or Not, Sprots Illustrated, Trial by Wilderness, Hollywood: The Dream Factory, Kifaru: The Black Rhinoceros, Birds Do It, Bees Do It, Indestructible People, Journey into Life, One Men's Noise: Stories of An Adventursome Oceanography, World of Discovery; video producer opening ceremonies 1984 Olympic Games, L.A., Interactive Multimedia: Columbus, Evolution/Revolution. Recipient Emmy award Acad. TV Arts and Scis.; recipient Writers Guild Am. award, Peabody award, Am. Med. Writers Assn. award, Christophers award, Ohio State U. award, Saturday Rev. award, CINE Golden Eagle award. Mem. Writers Guild Am., Dirs. Guild Am., Acad. TV Arts and Scis., Internat. Documentary Assn. Office: 2217 Chelan Dr Los Angeles CA 90068-2620

ROSTEN, LEO CALVIN (LEONARD Q. ROSS), author, political scientist; b. Lodz, Poland, Apr. 11, 1908; came to U.S., 1911; s. Samuel C. and Ida (Freundlich) R.; m. Priscilla Mead, Mar. 30, 1935 (dec.); children: Philip, Madeline, Margaret; m. Gertrude Zimmerman, Jan. 5, 1960. Ph.B. U. Chgo. 1930, PhD, 1937; postgrad., London (Eng.) Sch. Econs. and Polit. Sci., 1934; travel, study, Europe, 1928, 34, 45, 51, 53; LHD (hon.), U. Rochester, 1973, Hebrew Union Coll., 1980. Instr. English U. Chgo., 1932-34, rsch. asst. polit. sci. dept., 1934-35; pub. lectr., 1932-35; fellow Social Sci. Rsch. Council, 1935-36; mem. rsch. staff Pres.'s Com. Adminstrv. Mgmt., 1936; dir. Motion Picture Rsch. Project, 1939-41; spl. cons. Nat. Defense Commn., 1939-40; cons. expert to Nat. Def. Adv. Commn. and Office for Emergency Mgmt. (Exec. Office Pres.), 1941; chief motion pictures div. Office Facts and Figures, 1942; dep. dir. OWI, 1942-44; expert cons. Sec. of War's Office, War Dept., 1945, sent to France, Germany, Eng. on spl. mission; sr. staff RAND Corp., 1947-49; lectr. NYU, Stanford, New Sch. Social Rsch., UCLA, Yale, others; faculty assoc. Columbia; Ford vis. prof. polit. sci. U. Calif., 1960-61; cons. Pres.'s Commn. on Nat. Goals, 1960; spl. editorial advisor Look mag., N.Y.C., 1950-74. Writer for motion pictures, 1937; author: The Washington Correspondents, 1937, The Education of Hyman Kaplan, 1937, The Strangest Places, 1939, Dateline: Europe, 1939, Adventure in Washington, 1940, Hollywood: The Movie Colony, the Movie Makers, 1941, The Dark Corner, 1945, 112 Gripes About the French, 1945, Sleep, My Love, 1946, The Return of Hyman Kaplan, 1959, Captain Newman, M.D. 1961, The Story Behind the Painting, 1961, The Many Worlds of Leo Rosten, 1964, A Most Private Intrigue, 1967, The Joys of Yiddish, 1968, A Trumpet for

Reason, 1970, People I Have Loved, Known, or Admired, 1970, Rome Wasn't Burned In a Day: The Mischief of Language, 1972, Leo Rosten's Treasury of Jewish Quotations, 1972, Dear Herm, 1974, The 3:10 to Anywhere, 1976, O Kaplan! My Kaplan!, 1976, The Power of Positive Nonsense, 1977, Passions and Prejudices: or, Some of My Best Friends Are People, 1978, Silky!: A Detective Story, 1979, King Silky!, 1980, Hooray for Yiddish: A Book about English, 1982, Leo Rosten's Giant Book of Laughter, 1985, The Joys of Yinglish, 1989, Leo Rosten's Carnival of Wit: From Aristotle to Groucho Marx, 1994; editor: A Guide to the Religions of America, 1955, The Look Book, 1975, Infinite Riches: Gems from a Lifetime of Reading, 1979; screenwriter: All Through the Night, 1942, The Conspirators, 1944, Lured, 1947, Sleep, My Love, 1947, The Velvet Touch, 1948, Where Danger Lives, 1950, Double Dynamite, 1952, Walk East on Beacon, 1952; contbr. to nat. mags. Recipient George Polk Meml. award, 1955, Freedom Found. award, 1955, Profl. Achievement Alumni award U. Chgo., 1969; hon. fellow London Sch. Econs. and Polit. Sci. Mem. Am. Acad. Polit. and Social Sci., Am. Polit. Sci. Assn., AAAS, Authors League Am. (bd.), Authors' Guild Am., Roundtable, Phi Beta Kappa. Home and Office: 36 Sutton Pl S New York NY 10022-4166 *From Captain Newman, M.D.: " Most men debase the pursuit of happiness by transforming it into a narcotic pursuit of 'fun'. But there are those sublimely cursed by discontent, and to them happiness comes only when they push their brains and hearts to the farthest reaches of which they are capable. Nothing is more rewarding than the effort a man makes to matter-to count, to stand for something, to have it make some difference that he lived at all.".*

ROSTENKOWSKI, DAN, congressman; b. Chicago, Ill., Jan. 2, 1928; s. Joseph P. and Priscilla (Dombrowski) R.; m. LaVerne Pirkins, May 12, 1951; children: Dawn, Kristie, Gayle, Stacy. Student, St. John's Mil. Acad., 1942-46, Loyola U., 1948- 51. Mem. Ill. Gen. Assembly, 1952; mem. Ill. senate, 1954, 56, 86th-103rd Congresses from 8th (now 5th) Dist. Ill., 1959—; chmn. Democratic caucus 90th-91st Congresses; chief dep. majority whip 95th-96th Congresses; former chmn. com. on ways and means, joint com. on taxation. Del. Dem. Nat. Conv., 1960, 64, 68, 72, 76, 80, 84, 88, 92. Office: 2148 N Damen Ave Chicago IL 60647

ROSTER, MICHAEL, lawyer; b. Chgo., May 7, 1945. AB, Stanford U., 1967, JD, 1973. Bar: Calif. 1973, D.C. 1980. Reporter UPI, Chgo., 1965; writer Time-Life, San Francisco, 1966-67; ptnr. McKenna, Conner & Cuneo, L.A. and Washington, 1973-87, Morrison & Foerster, L.A. and Washington, 1987-93; gen. counsel Stanford (Calif.) U., 1993—; bd. dirs. Silicon Valley Bancshares, 1994—. Contbr. articles to profl. jours. Chmn. Cityscape Panel of Strategic Planning Commn., Pasadena, Calif., 1985-86; bd. dirs. Pasadena Heritage, 1988-91. Lt. (j.g.) USN, 1969-71. Mem. ABA (chmn. com. on savs. insts. 1985-89, fin. svcs. com. 1981—, banking com. 1989—), Calif. Bar Assn. (chmn. banking com. 1978-79), Stanford U. Alumni Assn. (chmn. 1992), Univ. Club (Washington), L.A. Athletic Club. Office: Stanford U Gen Counsel Box N Stanford CA 94309

ROSTKY, GEORGE HAROLD, editor; b. N.Y.C., Feb. 28, 1926; s. Morris and Mary (Wyloge) R.; m. Rhoda Thelma Bornstein, June 29, 1950; children: Mark, Lisa. B.E.E., CCNY, 1957. Assoc. editor Electronic Design, N.Y.C., 1957-61; editor-in-chief Electronic Design, Rochelle Park, N.J., 1971-78; editorial dir./assoc. pub. Electronic Engring. Times, Manhasset, N.Y., 1978-85; cons., 1985—; founder George Rostky Assocs., Focus Rsch., Great Neck, N.Y.; securities analyst McDonnell & Co., N.Y.C., 1961-62; editorial dir. Mactier Pub. Co., N.Y.C., 1962-71; U.S. Dept. Commerce industry tech. rep. to U.S. Electronics Catalog Exhbn., India, 1980. Served with AUS, 1942-45. Recipient Indsl. Mktg. award for editorial excellence, 1964, Neal awards, 1967, 74, 75, 77. Home: 39 Cumberland Ave Great Neck NY 11020-1422 Office: 600 Community Dr Manhasset NY 11030-3847

ROSTOKER, GORDON, physicist, educator; b. Toronto, Ont., Can., July 15, 1940; s. Louis and Fanny (Silbert) R.; m. Gillian Patricia Farr, June 29, 1966; children: Gary David, Susan Birgitta, Daniel Mark. BSc in Physics, U. Toronto, 1962, MA in Physics, 1963; PhD in Geophysics, U. B.C., June 25, 1966. Postdoctoral fellow Royal Inst. Tech., Stockholm, 1966-68; asst. prof. physics U. Alta., B.C., 1968-73, assoc. prof., 1973-79, prof., 1979—, McCalla Rsch. Prof., 1983-84, ann. Killam Prof., 1991-92, dir. Inst. Earth and Planetary Physics, 1985-91; assoc. chmn. dept. physics U. Alta., 1976-79, univ. rep. to bd. dirs. Can. Network for Space Rsch., 1992-94, mem. univ. rsch. policy com., 1987-91; cons. TRW Sys. Group, 1973, Dome Petroleum Ltd., 1981, U. Western Ont., 1983, Tovk U., 1986; contract rschr. Energy, Mines and Resources, Can., Hydro-Québec; mem. assoc. com. space rsch. Nat. Rsch. Coun. Can., 1975-80, mem. com. on internat. sci. exchanges, 1977-79, others; mem. physics and astronomy com. Natural Scis. and Engring. Rsch. Coun., 1979-82, mem. spl. ad hoc com. on physics and astronomy, 1987-91, mem. grant selection com. for sci. publs., 1988-92; prin. investigator CANOPUS, 1989—; chmn. divsn. III Internat. Assn. Geomagnetism and Aeronomy, 1979-83; chmn. working group on data analysis phase of Internat. Magnetospheric Study Sci. Com. on Solar Terrestrial Physics of Internat. Coun. Sci. Unions, 1980-86, co-chmn. steering com. for Solar-Terrestrial Energy Program, 1987-89, chmn., 1989—. Editor Can. Jour. Physics, 1980-86, mem. editorial adv. bd., 1986—; contbr. over 250 articles to profl. publs. Mem. pub. adv. com. Govtl. Environ. Conservation Authority of Province of Alta., Edmonton, 1973-74. Recipient Steacie prize EWR Steacie Meml. Fund, 1979, Geophys. Centenary medal Acad. Scis. USSR, 1984. Mem. Am. Geophys. Union (assoc. editor Jour. Geophys. Rsch., 1976-79, 92-94, Jour. Geomagnetism and Geoelectricity 1993—), Can. Assn. Physicists (sec.-treas. Can. Geophys. Union 1973-74, chmn. divsn. aeronomy and space physics 1977-78, publs. com. 1980-86). Achievements include use of ground magnetometer arrays to document stepwise evolution of electric current systems which flow in the ionosphere and magnetosphere during episodes of strong auroral disturbance. Office: U Alta, Dept Physics, Edmonton, AB Canada T6G 2J1

ROSTOKER, MICHAEL DAVID, micro-electronics executive, lawyer; b. Quincy, Mass., Mar. 15, 1958; s. David and E. Louise (Berleue) R. Student, Carnegie-Mellon U., 1976-78; BS in Indsl. Engring., U. Pitts., 1980; JD, Franklin Pierce Law Ctr., 1984; PhD in Indsl. Engring., City U., L.A., 1992. Bar: U.S. Patent and Trademark Office 1983, N.H. 1984, U.S. Dist. Ct. N.H. 1984, Mass. 1985, Pa. 1985, U.S. Dist. Ct. D.C. 1985, U.S. Ct. Appeals (D.C. cir.) 1985. Lectr. in computer sci. Point Park Coll., Pitts., 1979-80; sys. analyst GE, Fitchburg, Mass., 1980-81; patent atty. Rines and Rines, Boston and Concord, N.H., 1983-85; patent counsel Schlumberger Well Svcs., Houston, 1985-87; sr. counsel intellectual property Intel Corp., Santa Clara, Calif., 1987-88; v.p. strategic alliances LSI Logic Corp., Milpitas, Calif., 1988—; dir. Nat. Inventors Coun., Concord, 1984-85; cons. on computers, Concord, 1981-85; mem. faculty computer sci. and math. Franklin Pierce Coll., Rindge, N.H., 1981-85; mem. adj. faculty law Franklin Pierce Law Ctr., Concord, 1983-85; mem. editl. bd. Software Protection Reporter, 1984-94; lectr. various seminars. Author: Computer Jurisprudence: Legal Responses to the Information Revolution, 1985, Technology Management: Licensing and Protection for Computers in the World Market, 1993; contbr. articles to profl. jours.; patentee in field. Mem. ABA (patents, sci. and tech., litigation sects.), Am. Trial Lawyers Assn., Am. Intellectual Property Assn. Republican. Jewish. Avocations: volleyball, racquetball, weightlifting, theater, music. Home: 108 McPherson Ct Boulder Creek CA 95006-9203 Office: LSI Logic Corp 1525 Mccarthy Blvd Milpitas CA 95035-7424

ROSTON, ARNOLD, information specialist, educator, advertising executive, artist, editor; b. Racine, Wis., June 29, 1923; s. Felix and Hannah (Epstein) R.; m. Evelyn Eisen, June 16, 1944 (dec.); children: Karen Laurie, Susan Joyce. Student, CCNY, New Sch., 1942, Harvard Grad. Sch., 1975. Info. specialist Exec. Office of the Pres. Office of Emergency Mgmt., 1942, Joint (U.S.) Army Navy Intelligence Svc.-BSC, 1943; asst. to adminstrv. v.p., co-dir., advt. and promotion, creative dir. MBS-RKO, 1944-59; creative group head Grey Advt. Agy., 1959-60; dir. creative services Van Brunt & Co., 1961-64; pres. Roston & Co., 1965-76, 1979—; pres. Van Brunt/ Roston Corp. Communications, 1977-78; exec. editor Budget Decorating Mag., 1973-76; dean Ctr. for Understanding Media of The New Sch., 1975; organizer, exec. sec. The Election Process and The New Media Workshop Conf., N.Y.C. 1975; dir. program devel. art therapy deg. program & accreditation Sch. Visual Arts, N.Y.C., 1976-77; cultural affairs corr. Broadcasting Co. of the Carolinas Inc., 1976-88; instr. Cooper Union, 1947-53, Bklyn. Mus. Art Sch., 1949-51, Pratt Inst. Grad. Seminar, 1954-55, CUNY,

1973; designer 29th Art Dirs. ann., 1949-50; instr. workshop in advt. design Am. Inst. Graphic Arts, 1951; chmn. Great Neck Com. Art and Design, N.Y., 1967-77; chmn. 36th Ann. Nat. Exhbn. Art and Design, 1956-57; founder, pres., dir. Art Dirs. Scholarship Fund, Inc., 1961—; chmn. U.S.A. Vatican-Verona Fathers Sudan Commn., 1968-72; sec., dir. Art Dirs. Club, 1971-73, also mem. bd., chmn. coms.; mem. Pres.'s adv. bd. N.Y.C. C.C., 1972-75; mem. adv. commn. N.Y. H.S. of Art and Design, 1974—; organizer N.Y.C. of Edn. "Expo '74" in Times Sq. and Radio City. Exhbns. include Met. Mus. Art, Mus. Modern Art, Pa. Acad. Fine Arts, N.Y. World"s Fair, Bklyn. Mus., Heckscher Mus., Montclair Art Mus., N.Y. Mcpl. Art Galleries, Lever House, Cooper Hewitt Mus., others; represented in permanent collections: Met. Mus. Art, Mus. Modern Art, Libr. of Congress, N.Y. Pub. Libr., Aldridge Mus., Ridgefield, Conn., The Vatican; mural Great Neck Pub. Libr.; contbr. articles on design, advt., scholarship to profl. jours. Trustee, sec. Sch. Art League Bd. Edn., N.Y.C., 1969-79; chmn. Landmarks Preservation Commn. Inc., Village of Great Neck, 1979-84; bd. dirs. Canterbury Crossing, 1984-85. George Foster Peabody-Yaddo Found. resident fellow; recipient awards including Suydam Silver medal NAD, Nat. Exhbn. Advt. and Editorial Art and Design awards, Certs. of Excellence and Gold medals Art Dirs. ann. nat. exhibts; Mus. Modern Art nat. hemispherical poster awards, 1940, 41, Certs. of Excellence Am. Inst. Graphic Arts, Ptnr. in Edn. award N.Y.C. Bd. Edn., 1979, Gt. Trademarks of World catalog, Milan, Italy, others. Mem. Princeton Club of N.Y., Art Dirs. Club. Studio: PO Box 717 Shrub Oak NY 10588-0717

ROSTON, DAVID C., lawyer; b. Evanston, Ill., Oct. 15, 1943. BA cum laude, Brandeis U., 1964; JD cum laude, Harvard U., 1967. Bar: Ill. 1967. Ptnr. Altheimer & Gray, Chgo. Mem. ABA, Ill. State Bar Assn., Chgo. Bar Assn., Chgo. Coun. Lawyers. Office: Altheimer & Gray 10 S Wacker Dr Ste 4000 Chicago IL 60606-7407

ROSTOVICH, SHARON RENEA, airport executive; b. Temple, Tex., Mar. 12, 1957; d. David Allen and Wanda Jean (Brown) Houston; m. Larry Christopher Michael Rostovich, Feb. 7, 1978; 1 child, Allen Wesley. AA, Temple Jr. Coll., 1978; postgrad., U. Mary Hardin-Baylor, 1979-86. Sec. City of Temple Airport, 1986-87, ops. coord., 1987-93, airport coord., 1993—. City campaign coord. United Way of Ctrl. Tex., Temple, 1993. Mem. Tex. Assn. Airport Execs., Temple Jaycees (sec. 1989-90, project chmn. 1991, Jaycee of Yr. 1990, state Community Project award 1991), Pi Gamma Mu. Avocations: pets, gardening, cooking, outdoor activities. Home: 1705 Lavendusky Dr Temple TX 76501 Office: Draughon-Miller Mcpl Airport 7720 Airport Rd Temple TX 76501

ROSTOW, CHARLES NICHOLAS, lawyer, educator; b. Geneva, Switzerland, Mar. 3, 1950; s. Eugene Victor and Edna (Greenberg) R.; m. Heyden White, Oct. 31, 1987; children: Theodore Isaac, Celia A. BA, Yale U., 1972, PhD, 1979, JD, 1982. Assoc. Shearman & Sterling, N.Y.C., 1982-85; spl. asst. to legal adviser U.S. Dept. State, Washington, 1985-87; dep. legal adviser Nat. Security Coun., Washington, 1987, spl. asst. to Pres., legal adviser, 1987-93; assoc. prof. Coll. of Law U. Taulsa, Tulsa, 1993—; exec. dir. Mass. Office Internat. Trade and Investment, 1995—. Author: Anglo-French Relations 1934-36, 1984; editor: Akten zur deutschen auswaertigen Politik: 1918-1945, vols. XIV-XXI, 1980-83; contbr. articles to prof. jours. Bd. dirs. John Goodwin Tower Ctr. for Polit. Studies, So. Meth. U.; nat. adv. bd. Am. Jewish Com. Mem. Royal Inst. Internat. Affairs, Coun. Fgn. Rels., Assn. of Bar of City of N.Y., Phi Beta Kappa, Cosmos Club, Yale Club (N.Y.C.), Elizabethan Club (New Haven). Jewish. Office: c/o Internat Trade Ste 1302 100 Cambridge St Boston MA 02202

ROSTOW, ELSPETH DAVIES, political science educator; b. N.Y.C.; d. Milton Judson and Harriet Elspeth (Vaughan) Davies; m. Walt Whitman Rostow, June 26, 1947; children: Peter Vaughan, Ann Larner. AB, Barnard Coll., 1938; AM, Radcliffe Coll., 1939; MA, Cambridge (Eng.) U., 1949; LHD (hon.), Lebanon Valley Coll.; LLD (hon.), Austin Coll., 1982, Southwestern U., 1988. Mem. faculty various instns. Barnard Coll., N.Y.C. and MIT, Boston, 1939-69; mem. faculty U. Tex., Austin, 1969—, dean div. gen. and comparative studies, 1975-77, prof. govt., 1976—; dean Lyndon B. Johnson Sch. Pub. Affairs, 1977-83, Stiles prof. Am. studies, 1985-88, Stiles prof. emerita, 1988—; mem. Pres.'s Adv. Com. for Trade Negotiations, 1978-82, Pres.'s Commn. for a Nat. Agenda for the Eighties, 1979-81; rsch. assoc. OSS, Washington, 1943-45; Geneva corr. London Economist, 1947-49; lectr. Air War Coll., 1963-81, Army War Coll., 1965, 68, 69, 78, 79, 81, Nat. War Coll., 1962, 68, 74, 75, Indsl. Coll. Armed Forces, 1961-65, Naval War Coll., 1971, Fgn. Svc. Inst., 1974-77, Dept. of State, Europe, 1973; bd. dirs. U.S. Inst. of Peace, vice chmn., 1991, chmn. 1991-92; co-founder The Austin Project, 1991; mem. Gov.'s Task Force on Revenue, Tex., 1991. Author: Europe's Economy After the War, 1948, (with others) American Now, 1968, The Coattailless Landslide, 1974; editor (with Barbara Jordan) The Great Society: A Twenty-Year Critique, 1986; columnist Austin Am. Statesman, 1985-92; contbr. articles to revs., poems to scholarly jours., newspapers, and mags. Trustee Sarah Lawrence Coll., 1952-59, Nat. Acad. Pub. Adminstrn., 1989—, So. Ctr. for Internat. Studies, 1990—; bd. visitors and govs. St. John's Coll., 1986-89; bd. dirs. Barnard Coll., 1962-66, Lyndon Baines Johnson Found., 1977-83, Salzburg Seminar, 1981-89; vis. scholar Phi Beta Kappa, 1984-85. Recipient award Air U.; Fulbright lectr., USIA participant, 1983-84, 90. Mem. Tex. Philos. Soc. (trustee 1989—), Phi Beta Kappa, Phi Nu Epsilon (hon.), Mortar Bd. (hon.), Omicron Delta Kappa. Club: Headliners (Austin). Home: One Wild Wind Point Austin TX 78746 Office: U Tex Drawer Y Univ Station Austin TX 78713

ROSTOW, EUGENE VICTOR, lawyer, educator, economist; b. Bklyn., Aug. 25, 1913; s. Victor A. and Lillian (Helman) R.; m. Edna Berman Greenberg; children: Victor A. D., Jessica, Charles Nicholas. AB, Yale U., 1933, LLB, 1937, AM, 1944; postgrad., King's Coll., Cambridge (Eng.) U., 1933-34; M.A., Cambridge U., 1959, LL.D., 1962; LL.D., Boston U., 1976, U. New Haven, 1981, N.Y. Law Sch., 1984. Bar: N.Y. 1938. Practice in N.Y.C., 1937-38; mem. faculty Law Sch. Yale, 1938—, prof. law, 1944-84, prof. emeritus, sr. research scholar, 1984—, dean, 1955-65, Sterling prof. law and pub. affairs, 1984-84; master Trumbull Coll., 1966; dir. ACDA, 1981-83; Disting. vis. research prof. law and diplomacy Nat. Def. U., 1984-90, 92—; under-sec. state for polit. affairs, 1966-69; pres. Atlantic Treaty Assn., 1973-76; vis. prof. U. Chgo., 1941; Pitt prof. Am. history and instns., professorial fellow King's Coll., Cambridge U., 1959-60; William W. Cook lectr. Mich. U., 1958; John R. Coen lectr. U. Colo., 1961; Leary lectr. U. Utah, 1965; Brandeis lectr. Brandeis U., 1965; Rosenthal lectr. Northwestern U., 1965; George Eastman vis. prof., fellow Balliol Coll., Oxford (Eng.) U., 1970-71; Adviser Dept. State, 1942-44; asst. exec. sec. Econ. Commn. for Europe, UN, 1949-50; mem. Jud. Council of Conn., 1955-66, Atty. Gen.'s Nat. Com. Study Antitrust Laws, 1954-55; chmn. exec. com. Com. on the Present Danger, 1976-81, 86-92. Author: Planning for Freedom, 1959, The Sovereign Prerogative, 1962, Law, Power and the Pursuit of Peace, 1968, Peace in the Balance, 1972, The Ideal in Law, 1978, Toward Managed Peace, 1993, A Breakfast for Bonaparte, 1994; editor: Is Law Dead?, 1971. Decorated Chevalier Legion d'Honneur (France), Grand Cross Order of Crown (Belgium); recipient Disting. Civilian Svc. award U.S. Army, 1990; Guggenheim fellow, 1959-60, Randolph fellow U.S. Inst. Peace, 1990-92, hon. fellow Hebrew U. of Jerusalem, 1992—. Fellow Am. Acad. Arts and Scis.; mem. Am. Law Inst., Phi Beta Kappa, Alpha Delta Phi, Elizabethan Yale Club, Century Assn. N.Y.C. Club, Cosmos Club Washington. Democrat. Jewish. Home: 1315 4th St SW Washington DC 20014-2201 Office: Nat Def U Washington DC 20319-6000 also: Yale U Sch Law New Haven CT 06520

ROSTOW, WALT WHITMAN, economist, educator; b. N.Y.C., Oct. 7, 1916; s. Victor Aaron and Lillian (Helman) R.; m. Elspeth Vaughan Davies, June 26, 1947; children: Peter Vaughan, Ann Larner. BA, Yale U., 1936, PhD, 1940. Instr. econs. Columbia U., 1940-41; asst. chief German-Austrian econ. div. Dept. State, 1945-46; Harmsworth prof. Am. history Oxford (Eng.) U., 1946-47; asst. to exec. sec. Econ. Commn. for Europe, 1947-49; Pitt. prof. Am. history Cambridge (Eng.) U., 1949-50; prof. econ. history MIT, 1950-60; staff mem. Center Internat. Studies, 1951-60; dep. spl. asst. to Pres. for nat. security affairs, 1961; counselor, chmn. policy planning council Dept. State, 1961-66; spl. asst. to Pres., 1966-69; U.S. rep., ambassador Inter-Am. com. Alliance for Progress, 1964-66; now Rex G. Baker Jr. prof. polit. economy, depts. econs. and history U. Tex., Austin, prof. emeritus; mem. Bd. Fgn. Scholarships, 1969-72; chmn. bd., task force dir. Austin Project, 1982—. Author: The American Diplomatic Revolution, 1947, Essays on the British Economy of the Nineteenth Century, 1948, The Process of Economic Growth, 1953, 2d edit., 1960, (with A.D. Gayer, A.J. Schwartz) The Growth and Fluctuation of the British Economy, 1790-1850, 1953, 2d edit., 1975, (with A. Levin, others) The Dynamics of Soviet Society, 1953, (with others) The Prospects for Communist China, 1954, (with R.W. Hatch) An American Policy in Asia, 1955, (with M.F. Millikan) A Proposal: Key to an Effective Foreign Policy, 1957, The United States in the World Arena, 1960, The Stages of Economic Growth, 1960, 2d edit., 1971, 3d edit., 1990, A View from the Seventh Floor, 1964, A Design for Asian Development, 1965, (with William E. Griffith) East-West Relations: Is Detente Possible?, 1969, Politics and the Stages of Growth, 1971, The Diffusion of Power, 1972, How It All Began, 1975, The World Economy: History and Prospect, 1978, Getting From Here to There, 1978, Why the Poor Get Richer and the Rich Slow Down, 1980, Pre-Invasion Bombing Strategy: General Eisenhower's Decision of March 25, 1944, 1981, British Trade Fluctuations, 1868-1896: A Chronicle and a Commentary, 1981, The Division of Europe After World War II: 1946, 1981, Europe After Stalin: Eisenhower's Three Decisions of March 11, 1953, 1982, Open Skies: Eisenhower's Proposal of July 21, 1955, 1982, The Barbaric Counter-Revolution: Cause and Cure, 1983, Eisenhower, Kennedy, and Foreign Aid, 1985, The United States and the Regional Organization of Asia and the Pacific: 1965-1985, 1986, Rich Countries and Poor Countries, 1987, Essays on a Half Century: Ideas, Policies and Action, 1988, History, Policy, and Economic Theory, 1989, Theorists of Economic Growth From David Hume to the Present with a Perspective on the Next Century, 1990; editor: The Economics of Take-Off Into Sustained Growth, 1963. Maj. OSS, AUS, 1942-45. Decorated Legion of Merit, Hon. Order Brit. Empire (mil.); recipient Presdl. Medal of Freedom with distinction; Rhodes scholar Balliol Coll., 1936-38, Outstanding Work in Social Scis. award Assn. Am. Pubs., 1990. Mem. Am. Acad. Arts and Scis., Am. Philos. Soc., Mass. Hist. Soc., Tex. Philos. Soc., Cosmos Club, Elizabethan Club. Clubs: Cosmos (Washington); Elizabethan (New Haven). Home: 1 Wildwind Pt Austin TX 78746-2434

ROSTROPOVICH, MSTISLAV LEOPOLDOVICH, musician; b. Baku, USSR, Mar. 27, 1927; s. Leopold and Sofia (Fedotova) R.; m. Galina Pavlovna Vishnevskaya; children: Olga, Elena. Grad., Moscow Conservatory 1948; numerous hon. doctorate degrees. Faculty mem. Moscow Conservatory, 1953, prof., 1960; head cello and double-bass dept., formerly prof. Leningrad Conservatory; music dir., conductor Nat. Symphony Orch., Washington, 1977-94; hon. prof. Cuban Nat. Conservatory, 1960-78; pres. Evian Internat. Music Festival. Debut as violoncellist, 1935; performer world concert tours, Moscow Philharm. Orch.; recordings include (with various artists) Mstislav Rostropovich Melodiya Recordings, 1949-56, 48-59, The Young Rostropovich: Rare Recordings for the 1950-52 Years. Decorated Hon. Knight of the Brit. Empire, 1987; Commdr. French Legion of Honor, 1987; Officer's Cross of Merit, Fed. Republic Germany, 1987; recipient Stalin prize, 1951, 53, Lenin prize, 1963, Life in Music prize, 1984, Albert Schweitzer Music award, 1985, Grammy awards, 1970, 77, 80, 84, Presdl. Medal Freedom, 1987, Ditson Condr.'s award, Columbia U., 1990, Four Freedoms award Franklin and Eleanor Roosevelt Inst., 1992; named Musician of Yr., Mus. Am. 1987. Mem. Am. Acad. Arts and Scis., Union Soviet Composers, Brit. Royal Acad. Music (hon.), Acad. Arts of French Inst.-Forty Immortals. Office: c/o Columbia Artists Mgmt 165 W 57th St New York NY 10019 also: Melodiya (Russia) c/o Melodiya Am Distrs Inc 265 Great Neck Rd Great Neck NY 11021 also: CAMI 165 W 57th St New York NY 10019*

ROSZKOWSKI, STANLEY JULIAN, federal judge; b. Booneville, N.Y., Jan. 27, 1923; s. Joseph and Anna (Christkowski) R.; m. Catherine Mary Claeys, June 19, 1948; children: Mark, Gregory, Dan, John. BS, U. Ill., 1949, JD, 1954. Bar: Ill. 1954. Sales mgr. Warren Petroleum Co., Rockford, Ill., 1954; ptnr. Roszkowski, Paddock, McGreevy & Johnson, Rockford, 1955-77; judge U.S. Dist. Ct. (we. dist.), Rockford, Ill., 1977—; pres. First State Bank, Rockford, 1963-75; chmn. bd. First State Bank, 1977—. Chmn. Fire and Police Commn., Rockford, 1967-74, commr., 1974—; chmn. Paul Simon Com., 1972; active Adlai Stevenson III campaign, 1968-71, Winnebago County Citizens for John F. Kennedy, 1962, Winnebago County Dem. Cen. Com., 1962-64; bd. dirs. Sch. of Hope, 1960—; mem. Ill. Capital Devel. Bd., 1974—. With USAAF, 1943-45. Decorated Air medal with 2 oak leaf clusters; recipient Pulaski Nat. Heritage award Polish Am. Congress, Chgo., 1982. Mem. ABA, Ill. Bar Assn., Fla. Bar Assn., Winnebago County Bar Assn., Am. Coll. Trial Lawyers, Am. Judicature Soc., Assn. Trial Lawyers Am., Ill. Trial Lawyers Assns., Am. Arbitration Assn. (arbitrator), Fed. Judges Assn. (bd. dirs. 1988—), Forest Hills Country Club (Rockford). Office: US Dist Ct 260 US Courthouse Rockford IL 61101-1201

ROTA, GIAN-CARLO, mathematician, educator; b. Vigevano, Italy, Apr. 27, 1932; came to U.S., 1950, naturalized, 1961; s. Giovanni and Gina (Facoetti) R.; m. Teresa Rondón-Tarchetti, June 23, 1956 (div. 1979). BA summa cum laude, Princeton U., 1953; MA, Yale U., 1954, PhD, 1956; D honoris causa, U. Strasbourg, France, 1984, U. L'Aquila, Abruzzi, Italy, 1990. Vis. fellow Courant Inst. Math. Scis., NYU, 1956-57; B. Pierce instr. Harvard U., 1957-59; asst. prof., then assoc. prof. math. MIT, 1959-65, prof. math., 1967-74, prof. applied math. and philosophy, 1975—; prof. math. Rockefeller U., 1965-67; vis. prof. Courant Inst. Math. Scis., 1964, U. Ill., 1963, Ind. U., 1963, U. Paris, 1972, U. Mex., 1973, Scuola Normale Superiore, 1975, 86, 90, U. Buenos Aires, 1975, U. Strasbourg, 1976, 78, 87, U. So. Calif., 1985-92; Taft lectr. U. Cin., 1971; spl. vis. prof. U. Colo., 1969-82; Andre' Aisenstadt vis. prof. U. Montreal, 1971; Hardy lectr. London Math. Soc., 1973; professore linceo, Rome, 1979, U. Cagliari, 1989, U. Milan, 1989, I.H.E.S., France, 1989; lezioni lincee, Pisa, Italy, 1986; lezioni Volterra, Rome U., 1990; cons. Rand Corp., 1965-71; Sigma Xi nat. lectr., 1980-81; fellow Los Alamos Sci. Lab., 1966—; cons. Brookhaven Nat. Lab., 1971-79. Author: (with G. Birkhoff) Ordinary Differential Equations, 1962, (with H. Crapo) Combinatorial Geometries, 1970, Finite Operator Calculus, 1975, MAA Survey in Combinatorics, 1978; (with M. Kac and J.T. Schwartz) Discrete Thoughts, 1986, (with K. Baclawski and M. Cerasoli) Introduzione alla probabilità, 1986, also articles combinatorial theory, differential equations, probability, philosophy, Phenomenology; founding editor Jour. Combinatorial Theory, 1966—, Advances in Applied Math., 1980—; editor Jour. Math. and Mechanics, 1965-71, Jour. Math. Analysis, 1966—, Utilitas Mathematica, 1973—; assoc. editor Am. Math. Monthly, 1966-73, Proceedings of Royal Soc. Edinburgh, 1976-85; founding editor, editor-in-chief Advances in Math., 1967—; editor Bull. Am. Math. Soc. 1967-73, Ency. of Math, 1974—, Mathematicians of our Time, 1982—. Sloan fellow, 1962-64. Fellow NAS, AAAS (chair math. sect. 1988), Am. Acad. Arts and Scis., Academia Argentina de Ciencias, Inst. Math. Statistics; mem. Am. Math. Assn. (Hedrick lectr. 1967), Am. Math Soc. (council 1967-72, 83-86, Steele prize 1988), London Math. Soc., Heidegger Circle, Husserl Circle, Soc. Indsl. and Applied Math. (v.p. 1975), Am. Philos. Assn., Soc. Phenomenology and Existential Philosophy, AAUP, Unione Matematica Italiana, Unión Matemática Argentina (life), Phi Beta Kappa (pres. chpt. 1978-80). Roman Catholic. Address: MIT 2-351 77 Massachusetts Ave Cambridge MA 02139-3594 Home: 1105 Massachusetts Ave Apt 8F Cambridge MA 02138-5216

ROTAN, WALTER, sculptor; b. Balt., Mar. 29, 1912. Grad., Md. Inst., Pa. Acad. Fine Arts. Head art dept. Taft Sch., Watertown, Conn., 1938-53. Exhibited in group shows Met. Mus., Pa. Mus., Phila. Art Alliance, Carnegie Inst., Cin. Mus. Art, Pa. Acad. Fine Arts, NAD, Art Inst. Chgo., Corcoran Gallery, Arts Club Chgo., Springfield Art League, Conn. Acad. Fine Arts, Ferargil Gallery, N.Y. World's Fair, Archtl. League N.Y., Audubon Artists, Sculpture Ctr., Milch Gallery, also others; represented in permanent collections Brookgreen Gardens Mus., Georgetown, S.C., Pa. Acad. Fine Arts, also pvt. collections. Recipient Barnett prize NAD, Watrous gold medal, Speyer Meml. prize, Proctor prize; hon. mention Springfield Art League, fellowship prize Pa. Acad. Ann. Exhbn.; Cresson European fellow Pa. Acad. Fine Arts, 1933, fellow Tiffany Found. Fellow Nat. Sculpture Soc., Pa. Acad. Fine Arts; mem. Audubon Artists. Home and Studio: 45 Christopher St Apt 17G New York NY 10014-3587

ROTBERG, EUGENE HARVEY, investment banker, lawyer; b. Phila., Jan. 19, 1930; s. Irving Bernard and Blanche Grace (Levick) R.; m. Iris Sybil Comens, Aug. 29, 1954; children—Diana Golda, Pamela Lynn. B.S., Temple U., 1951; LL.B., U. Pa., 1954; PhD (hon.), Salem-Teikyo U., 1992. Chief counsel Office Policy Research Securities and Exchange Commn., Washington, 1963-66; v.p., treas. World Bank, Washington, 1969-87; exec.

v.p. Merrill Lynch & Co., N.Y.C., 1987-90. Served with U.S. Army, 1954-55. Decorated King Leopold II medal (Belgium); recipient Disting. Svc. award Securities and Exch. Commn., 1968; named Alumnus of Yr., Temple U., 1969. Home: 7211 Brickyard Rd Potomac MD 20854 Office: Washington Harbour 3050 K St NW Washington DC 20007

ROTBERG, IRIS COMENS, social scientist; b. Phila., Dec. 16, 1932; d. Samuel Nathaniel and Golda (Shuman) Comens; m. Eugene H. Rotberg, Aug. 29, 1954; children: Diana Golda, Pamela Lynn. BA, U. Pa., 1954, MA, 1955; PhD, Johns Hopkins U., Balt., 1958. Research psychologist Pres.'s Commn. on Income Maintenance Programs, Washington, 1968-69, Office Planning, Research and Evaluation, Office Econ. Opportunity, Washington, 1970-73; dep. dir. compensatory edn. study Nat. Inst. Edn., Washington, 1974-77, dir. Office Planning and Program Devel., 1978-82; program dir. NSF, Arlington, Va., 1985-87, 89-91, 1993—; tech. policy fellow Com. on Sci., Space and Tech., U.S. Ho. of Reps., Washington, 1987-89; sr. social scientist RAND, Washington, 1991-93. NSF fellow, 1956-58. Home: 7211 Brickyard Rd Potomac MD 20854

ROTCH, WILLIAM, business administration educator; b. Cambridge, Mass., Nov. 19, 1929; s. Charles Morgan and Helen Aldis (Bradley) R.; m. Jane Coolidge Whitehill, Dec. 20, 1952; children: Jane Revere, William Jr., Sarah Aldis. AB, Harvard U., 1951, MBA, 1956, DBA, 1959. Asst. auditor Ga. R.R. Bank, Augusta, 1953-54; rsch. assoc. Harvard Bus. Sch., Boston, 1956-57; mem. faculty Colgate Darden Grad. Sch. Bus. Adminstrn. U. Va., Charlottesville, 1959—, now Johnson and Higgins prof. bus. adminstrn.; vis. assoc. prof. Amos Tuck Sch., Dartmouth Coll., 1966-67; vis. prof. IMEDE Mgmt. Devel. Inst., Lausanne, Switzerland, 1973-75. Co-author: Executives Guide to Management Accounting and Control, 5th edit., 1993, Cases in Management Accounting and Control Systems, 3d edit., 1995. Vestryman St. Paul's Meml. Ch., Charlottesville, 1962-89; trustee World Learning, Brattleboro, Vt., 1957—, chmn. bd., 1988—. 2d lt. Signal Corps, U.S. Army, 1951-53. Recipient Experiment citation Experiment in International Living, 1986. Mem. Am. Acctg. Assn. (mem. various coms.), Inst. Mgmt. Accts., Somerset Club (Boston), Harvard Club (N.Y.). Avocations: sailing, photography. Home: 808 Fendall Ter Charlottesville VA 22903-1653 Office: U Va Darden Grad Bus Sch Arlington Blvd Charlottesville VA 22906

ROTELL, THOMAS M., publishing executive. Dir. U of Penn. Press, Phila.; now dir. Texas A & M Press. Office: Texas A&M Press Lindsey Bldg Drawer C College Station TX 77843

ROTEMBERG, JULIO JACOBO, economist, educator, consultant; b. Buenos Aires, Argentina, Sept. 26, 1953; came to U.S., 1972; s. Salomon and Ellen (Wolf) R.; m. Analisa Lattes, Nov. 8, 1982; childrenL Veronica M., Martin S. BA, U. Calif., Berkeley, 1975; PhD, Princeton U., 1981. Researcher Banco Cen. De La Republica Argentina, Buenos Aires, 1976; from asst. prof. to assoc. prof. econs. Sloan Sch. Mgmt. MIT, Cambridge, 1980-89, prof., 1989—; rsch. assoc. Nat. Bureau of Econ. Rsch., Cambridge, 1986—; vis. prof., bus. adminstrn. Harvard Bus. Sch., Boston, 1994-95. Mem. bd. editors Rev. Econ. Studies, 1985-88, Econometrica, 1987—, Quarterly Jour. Econs., 1989—; contbr. articles to profl. jours. Fellow Econometric Soc.; mem. Am. Econ. Assn. Avocations: skiing, bicycling. Office: MIT Sloan Sch Mgmt Cambridge MA 02139

ROTENBERG, MANUEL, physics educator; b. Toronto, Ont., Can., Mar. 12, 1930; came to U.S., 1946; s. Peter and Rose (Plonzker) R.; m. Paula Weissbrod, June 23, 1952; children: Joel, Victor. BS, MIT, 1952, PhD, 1956. Mem. staff Los Alamos (N.Mex.) Nat. Lab., 1955-58; instr. physics Princeton (N.J.) U., 1958-59; asst. prof. U. Chgo., 1959-61; prof. applied physics U. Calif., San Diego, 1961—, dean grad. studies and research, 1975-84, chair dept. elect. engring. and computer engring., 1988-93. Author: The 3-j and 6-j Symbols, 1959; founding editor: Methods of Computational Physics, 1963, Jour. of Computational Physics, 1962; editor: Biomathematics and Cell Kinetics, 1981. Fellow Am. Phys. Soc.; mem. AAAS, Sigma Xi. Office: U Calif San Diego La Jolla CA 92093-0407

ROTENBERG, SHELDON, violinist; b. Attleboro, Mass., Apr. 11, 1917; s. Joseph and Jennie (Almer) R.; m. Hilde Sussmann, Jan. 29, 1950; children: David, Steffi. A.B., Tufts U., 1939, grad. student, 1939-40; violin pupil of, Felix Winternitz, Georges Enesco, Maurice Hewitt. Tchr. violin, 1947—; music adviser, cons. pub. schs., Brookline, Mass.; archivist, cons. Boston Symphony Orch., 1992-93. Concertized extensively with the Boston String Quartet sponsored by Elizabeth Sprague Collidge, including concerts and rec. at the Libr. of Congress, 1948-52, occupies endowed Kasdon-Paley chair, 1st violin sect., Boston Symphony Orch., 1948-91, solo performances with Boston Pops Orch., 1939-41; Boston Symphony rep. as soloist, tchr., mem. orch. in State Dept. cultural exchange program with Japan Philharm., Tokyo, 1968-69; mem. faculty Boston U. Tanglewood Inst., 1979—. Served to capt. AUS, 1942-46. Mem. Tufts U. Alumni Assn. Home: 60 Browne St Brookline MA 02146-3441 Office: care Boston Symphony Orch Symphony Hall Boston MA 02115

ROTENIZER, R. EUGENE, financial planner, consultant and advisor; b. Hillsville, Va., Oct. 31, 1937; s. William Ray and Ava Marie (Robinson) R.; children: David E., Jeffrey W. BS in Bus., Nat. Coll., 1956. CFP, CLU, ChFC; registered investment advisor, registered prin. Fin. advisor and planner, money mgr., owner Countrywide Fin. Group, Mt. Airy, N.C., 1973—; E.F. Hutton & Co., Blackburg, Va. and Winston-Salem, N.C., 1980-84; owner So. Conn Exion, Mt. Airy, 1981—; pvt. practice fin. cons.; cons., bus. advisor Mount Airy, 1981—. Author: Financial Independence Can Be Yours! How to - For All Ages, 1994; contbr. articles to profl. jours. With U.S. Army, 1957-62. Mem. Nat. Assn. CLUs and ChFCs, Nat. Assn. Realtors, Internat. Assn. Registered Fin. Consultants, Internat. Assn. CFPs. Republican. Baptist. Avocations: sports enthusiast, politics, theology. Office: 1253 W Lebanon Dr Mount Airy NC 27030

ROTENSTREICH, JON W., insurance company executive; b. 1943. Ptnr. Salomon Bros., N.Y.C., 1972-82; v.p., treas. Internat. Bus. Machines Corp., 1982-86; pres., chief investment officer, dir. Torchmark Corp., Birmingham, Ala., 1986-91; pres., CEO, dir. United Investors Mgmt. Corp. subs. Torchmark Corp., 1986-91; pres. Jon Rotenstreich Consultants, 1991-93; chmn., CEO TIG Holdings, Inc., N.Y.C., Calif., 1993—. Office: TIG Holdings Inc 126 E 56th St New York NY 10022

ROTH, ALAN J., lawyer, congressional aide; b. Bklyn., Feb. 18, 1955; s. Benjamin and Naomi (Wisler) R. BA, Am. U., 1976; JD, N.Y.U., 1979. Bar: Conn. 1979, U.S. Dist. Ct. Conn. 1979, D.C. 1980, U.S. Ct. Appeals (D.C. cir.) 1980, U.S. Ct. Appeals (2d cir.) 1982, U.S. Supreme Ct. 1983. Law clk. to Hon. M. Joseph Blumenfeld U.S. Dist. Ct., Hartford, Conn., 1979-80; assoc. Tyler, Cooper & Alcorn, New Haven, Conn., 1980-84; counsel com. energy and commerce U.S. Ho. of Reps., Washington, 1985-92, chief counsel com. energy and commerce, 1992, staff dir., chief counsel, 1993-95, minority staff dir., chief coun. com. on commerce, 1995—; adj. professorial lectr. sch. pub. affairs Am. U., Washington, 1989-92. Democrat. Jewish. Office: Commerce Com US Ho of Reps Washington DC 20515

ROTH, ALLAN ROBERT, lawyer, educator; b. Newark, June 7, 1931; s. Michael H. and Belle F. (Rosenberg) R.; m. Deborah R. Comerford, Feb. 29, 1976; children: Joseph (dec.), Alexander, Charles (dec.), Sarah. AB, Rutgers U., 1953; LLB, Harvard U., 1956. Bar: D.C. 1956, N.J. 1959, N.Y. 1965. Assoc. Toner, Crowley, Woelper & Vanderbilt, Newark, 1956-61; staff atty. for Gen. Counsel, SEC, Washington, 1962-64; dir. legal and govt. affairs dept. Am. Stock Exch., N.Y.C., 1964-68; prof. grad. sch. mgmt. Rutgers U., Newark, 1969—; dir. Internat. Bus. Inst., 1969-87; coord. Rutgers U. program with Dalian U. of China, 1993—; mem. legal adv. coun. Mid-Atlantic Legal Found., 1978-81; cons. IFC, 1972, Asian Devel. Bank, 1990, 91, 93, AID, 1965, 67, 71, 72, 94, World Bank, 1994; cons. to fgn. govts., 1965—; resident UN advisor to Pakistan, 1968-69; Fulbright prof. scholar to Thailand, 1988; mem. adv. bd. BNA Direct Investment in N.Am., 1988—; mem. book rev. panel Am. Jour. Internat. Law, 1978. Mem. editorial bd.: Jour. Internat. Bus. Studies, 1975-85, adv. bd. BNA Direct Investment in N.Am. 1988—; contrib. editor: Corp. Law Rev., 1977-86; mem. book rev. panel: Am. Jour. Internat. Law, 1978; Contbr. chpts. to books; contbr. articles to profl. jours. With U.S. Army, 1956-58. Mem.

ABA (staff dir. study of regulation of fgn. investment in U.S. 1975-79, 87—), Soviet-Am. Securities Law Working Group, Am. Soc. Internat. Law, Am. Law Inst., Phi Beta Kappa. Home: 630 Prospect St Maplewood NJ 07040-2724 Office: Rutgers U Grad Sch Mgmt 180 University Ave Newark NJ 07102-1803

ROTH, ALVIN ELIOT, economics educator; b. N.Y.C., Dec. 18, 1951; s. Ernest and Lillian (Caesar) R.; m. Emilie Matarasso May 22, 1977; children: Aaron Leon, Benjamin Nathaniel. B.S., Columbia U., 1971; M.S., Stanford U., 1973, Ph.D., 1974. Asst. prof. dept. bus. adminstrn and dept. econs. U. Ill., Urbana, 1974-77, assoc. prof., 1977-79, prof., 1979-82; A.W. Mellon prof. econs. U. Pitts., 1982—. Author: Axiomatic Models of Bargaining, 1979, Game-Theoretic Models of Bargaining, 1985, Laboratory Experimentation in Economics, 1987, The Shapley Value, 1988; (with M. Sotomayor) Two-Sided Matching: A Study in Game Theoretic Modeling and Analysis, 1990; (with J. Kagel) Handbook of Experimental Economics, 1995. Recipient Founders' prize Tex. Instruments Found., 1980; Guggenheim fellow, 1983; A.P. Sloan research fellow, 1984; 10 Outstanding Young Ams. award, 1984; Lanchester prize Ops. Rsch. Soc. Am., 1991. Fellow Econometric Soc.; mem. AAAS, Am. Econ. Assn., Inst. Mgmt. Scis. Jewish. Home: 2061 Beechwood Blvd Pittsburgh PA 15217-1705 Office: U Pitts Dept Econs Pittsburgh PA 15260

ROTH, ANN, costume designer. Student, Carnegie-Mellon U. costume designer Am. Conservatory Theatre, San Francisco, McCarter Theatre Co., Princeton, Am. Ballet Theatre, Am. Shakespeare Festival, Stratford, Kennedy Ctr. for Performing Arts, Minneapolis Opera, San Francisco Opera, Hartman Theatre Co., Stanford, Long Wharf Theatre, New Haven. Costume designer: (theatre) Maybe Tuesday, 1958, Make a Million, 1958, The Disenchanted, 1958, Edward II, 1958, A Desert Incident, 1959, The Cool World, 1960, Gay Divorcee, 1960, Ernest in Love, 1960, Face of a Hero, 1960, The Pleasure of His Company, 1960-61, A Far Country, 1961, Purlie Victorious, 1961, Look: We've Come Through, 1961, This Side of Paradise, 1962, Isle of Children, 1962, Venus at Large, 1962, A Portrait of the Artist as a Young Man, 1962, The Barroom Monks, 1962, We Comrades Three, 1962, Natural Affection, 1963, Hey You, Light Man!, 1963, Children from Their Games, 1963, A Case of Libel, 1963, The Last Analysis, 1964, Slow Dance on the Killing Ground, 1964, I Had a Ball, 1964, In the Summer House, 1964, The Odd Couple, 1965, 85, Mrs. Dally, 1965, The Impossible Years, 1965, Romeo and Juliet, 1965, The Wayward Stork, 1966, The Star-Spangled Girl, 1966, The Beard, 1967, Something Different, 1967, The Deer Park, 1967, Happiness Is Just a Little Thing Called a Rolls Royce, 1968, Play It Again, Sam, 1969, My Daughter, Your Son, 1969, Tiny Alice, 1969, The Three Sisters, 1969, Gantry, 1970, Purlie, 1970, What the Butler Saw, 1970, The Engagement Baby, 1970, Father's Day, 1971, Prettybelle, 1971, Fun City, 1972, Rosebloom, 1972, Twelfth Night, 1972, Children! Children!, 1972, 6 Rms Riv Vu, 1972, Enemies, 1972, The Merchant of Venice, 1973, Seesaw, 1973, The Women, 1973, The Royal Family, 1975, 85 (Tony award nomination best costume design 1985), The Heiress, 1976, The Importance of Being Earnest, 1977, Do You Turn Somersaults?, 1978, The Best Little Whorehouse in Texas, 1978, The Crucifer of Blood, 1978 (Tony award nomination best costume design 1979), First Monday in October, 1978, They're Playing Our Song, 1979, Strangers, 1979, Lunch Hour, 1980, Gardenia, 1982, Kaufman at Large, 1982, Present Laughter, 1982, The Misanthrope, 1983, Yankee Wives, 1983, Open Admissions, 1984, Hurlyburly, 1984, Design for Living, 1984, Biloxi Blues, 1984, 85, Arms and the Man, 1985, Juno's Swans, 1985, Singin' in the Rain, 1985, Social Security, 1986, The House of Blue Leaves, 1986-87 (Tony award nomination best costume design 1987), Light Up the Sky, 1986, Woman in Mind, 1988, O Pioneers!, 1989-90, Elliot Loves, 1990, Square One, 1990, Road to Nirvana, 1991, Any Given Day, 1993, (films) The World of Henry Orient, 1964, A Fine Madness, 1966, Up the Down Staircase, 1967, Pretty Poison, 1968, Sweet November, 1968, Midnight Cowboy, 1969, The Owl and the Pussycat, 1970, Jenny, 1970, The People Next Door, 1970, Klute, 1971, The Pursuit of Happiness, 1971, They Might Be Giants, 1971, The Valachi Papers, 1972, Law and Disorder, 1974, The Day of the Locust, 1975, The Happy Hooker, 1975, Mandingo, 1975, Murder by Death, 1976, Burnt Offerings, 1976, Independence, 1976, The Goodbye Girl, 1977, California Suite, 1978, Coming Home, 1978, Nunzio, 1979, Promises in the Dark, 1979, Hair, 1979, The Island, 1980, Dressed to Kill, 1980, Nine to Five, 1980, Honky Tonk Freeway, 1981, Only When I Laugh, 1981, Rollover, 1981, Blow Out, 1981, The World According to Garp, 1982, The Man Who Loved Women, 1983, Silkwood, 1983, The Survivors, 1983, Places in the Heart, 1984 (Academy Award nomination best costume design 1984), Sweet Dreams, 1985, The Slugger's Wife, 1985, Maxie, 1985, Jagged Edge, 1985, Heartburn, 1986, The Morning After, 1986, Biloxi Blues, 1988, Funny Farm, 1988, The Unbearable Lightness of Being, 1988, Stars and Bars, 1988, Working Girl, 1988, The January Man, 1989, Her Alibi, 1989, Family Business, 1989, Everybody Wins, 1990, Q & A, 1990, Pacific Heights, 1990, Postcards from the Edge, 1990, The Bonfire of the Vanities, 1990, Regarding Henry, 1991, Consenting Adults, 1992, The Mambo Kings, 1992, School Ties, 1992, A Stranger Among Us, 1992, Dennis the Menace, 1993, Dave, 1993, Guarding Tess, 1993, Wolf, 1994, (TV movies) The Silence, 1975, The Rivalry, 1975, Strangers: The Story of a Mother and Daughter, 1979, A Good Sport, 1984, (TV spls.) The House of Blue Leaves, PBS, 1987, O Pioneers!, PBS, 1991; costume design cons.: (TV spl.) Roanoak, 1986 (Emmy award nomination outstanding costume design 1986). Office: care United Scenic Artists 575 Fifth Ave New York NY 10018*

ROTH, BERNARD, mechanical engineering educator, researcher; b. N.Y.C., May 28, 1933; s. Morris Michael and Sara (Goldfarb) R.; m. Ruth Ochs, June 24, 1954; children: Steven Howard, Elliot Marc. BS, CCNY, 1956; MS, Columbia U., 1958, PhD, 1962. Engr. Ford Instrument Co. L.I., N.Y., 1955, Lockheed Aircraft Co., Van Nuys, Calif., 1956, Atlantic Design Co., Newark, 1958; lectr. CCNY, 1956-59; rsch. asst. Columbia U., N.Y.C., 1959-62; prof. Stanford (Calif.) U., 1962—; guest prof. U. Paris, 1988-90; expert, team leader UN Devel. Orgn., Vienna, Austria, 1986-88; mem. tech. adv. bd. Adept Tech., Inc., San Jose, Calif., 1988—; mem. adv. bd. Ctr. for Econ. Conversion, Mountain View, Calif., 1988—; bd. dirs. Peace Rev. Jour., Palo Alto, Calif., 1988-93. Co-author: Theoretical Kinematics, 1979, 2d edit., 1990; contbr. numerous articles on kinematics, robotics and design to profl. jours. Recipient Joseph F. Engelberger award Robotics Industries Assn., 1986. Fellow ASME (Melville medal 1967, Best Papers award mechanism conf. 1978, 80, 82, 92, 94, Mechanisms Coms. award 1982, Machine Design award 1984, chair design engring. divsn. 1981-82), Japanese Soc. for Promotion Sci.; mem. IEEE, Internat. Fedn. for Theory of Machines and Mechanisms (pres. 1980-83, hon. chmn. 7th World Congress 1987). Office: Stanford U Dept Mech Engring Stanford CA 94305

ROTH, DANIEL BENJAMIN, lawyer, business executive; b. Youngstown, Ohio, Sept. 17, 1929; s. Benjamin F. and Marion (Benjamin) R.; m. Joann M. Roth; children: William M., Jennifer A., Rochelle. BS in Fin., Miami U., Oxford, Ohio, 1951; JD, Case-Western Res. U., 1956. Bar: Ohio 1956, D.C. 1983. Pres. Roth, Stephens, Blair, Roberts & Co., Youngstown, 1959—; cofounder, vice chmn. Nat. Data Processing Corp., Cin., 1961-69, Torent, Inc., Youngstown, 1971—; vice chmn. Morrison Metalweld Process Corp., 1979—, McDonald Steel Corp., 1980—, Torent Oil & Gas Co., 1979—, Vaughn Indsl. Car & Equipment Co., 1988—, DTS Explosive Hardening Co., 1988—; bd. dirs., exec. com. Mahoning Nat. Bank, Gasser Chair Co., Jarret Corp. Profl. singer: appearances including Steve Allen Show, 1952. Bd. dirs. Youngstown Symphony, Youngstown Speech and Hearing Ctr.; bd. dirs. Youngstown Playhouse, 1971—; pres. Rodef Sholom Temple, Youngstown, 1982-84. 1st lt. USAF, 1951-53, lt. col. Res., ret. Recipient Mgr. of Yr. award Mahoning Valley Mgmt. Assn., 1989. Mem. ABA, D.C. Bar Assn., Ohio Bar Assn., Mahoning County Bar Assn., Lawyer-Pilots Bar Assn., Nat. Assn. Corp. Dirs., Soc. Benchers of Case Western Res. U. Law Sch., Youngstown Club, Squaw Creek Country Club, Pelican Isle Yacht Club (Naples, Fla.), Zeta Beta Tau (nat. v.p. 1964-66), Omicron Delta Kappa, Phi Eta Sigma, Tau Epsilon Rho. Jewish. Home: PO Box 959 Canfield OH 44406 Office: Bank One Bldg Youngstown OH 44503

ROTH, EDWIN MORTON, manufacturing executive; b. Cleve., Oct. 15, 1927; s. Bernath and Lottie (Klafter) R.; m. Sarah Kennedy; children: Causley Jan Roth, Alden Hope Guren, Corey Bruce, Cullen Andrew. Student, Ohio State U., 1946-47; B.B.A., Case Western Res. U., 1949. With Weather-Proof Co., Cleve., 1949-50; pres. E.M. Roth & Assocs., Cleve., 1950-52; sales mgr. Garland Co., Cleve., 1952-54, PlastiKote, Inc., Cleve., 1954-56; v.p. ITT

Consumer Services, Cleve., 1967-75; pres., dir. ITT Service Industries, Cleve., 1970-75, Yellow Cab Co., Kansas City, Mo., 1968-75; v.p., dir. Abbey Casualty Ins. Co., Washington, 1968-75; chmn., chief exec. officer APCOA, Inc., 1975-87; pres. APCOA B.V. Amsterdam, 1979-87; chmn.; pres. Momentum, Inc., Cleve., 1982-92; chmn., CEO Splty. Chem. Resources Inc., 1992—; bd. dirs. Working Walls Inc. Trustee Cleve. Am. Jewish Com.; chmn. bd. dirs. Mt. Sinai Hosp., Cleve., 1979-82; bd. dirs. Menorah Park Home for Aged, No. Ohio coun. Camp Fire Girls, Cleve. Ballet, United Way of Cleve., Playhouse Sq. Found.; bd. overseers Case Western Res. U.; trustee, exec. com. Jewish Community Fedn.; bd. dirs. Bellefaire Children's Home, pres., 1975-78; trustee Cleve. Mus. Art, 1994—, mem. joint distbn. com., 1993—. With USNR, 1945-46. Mem. Nat. Parking Assn. (pres. 1976-78, chmn. 1978-80), Musical Arts Assn. Cleve., No. Ohio Tennis Assn. Jewish (trustee, v.p. synagogue). Clubs: Union, Oakwood Country (Cleve.), Palm Beach Country. Home: 1050 N Lake Way Palm Beach FL 33480-3252 Office: Splty Chem Resources Inc 9100 Valley View Rd Macedonia OH 44056

ROTH, ERIC, screenwriter. screenplays include: The Nickel Ride, 1975, The Concorde - Airport '79, 1979, Suspect, 1987, Memories of Me, 1988 (with Billy Crystal), Mr. Jones, 1993, Forrest Gump, 1994 (Acad. award Best Adapted Screenplay). Office: care CAA 9830 Wilshire Blvd Beverly Hills CA 90212*

ROTH, GEORGE STANLEY, research biochemist, physiologist; b. Honolulu, Aug. 5, 1946; s. George Frederick and Laura Ann (Zembrzuski) R.; m. Mary Jane Fletcher, Mar. 11, 1972; children: Susan Marie, George William. BS, Villanova U., 1968; PhD, Temple U., 1971. Postdoctoral fellow Fels Rsch. Inst., Phila. 1971-72; staff fellow Gerontology Rsch. Ctr. NIH, Balt., 1972-76. rsch. chemist, 1976—, chief molecular physiology and genetics sect., 1984—; vis. prof. Meharry Med. Coll., Nashville, 1983; Alpha Omega Alpha prof. U. P.R. Med. Sch., San Juan, 1986; chmn. Gordon Rsch. Conf. on Biology of Aging, Oxnard, Calif., 1985; rsch. cons. George Washington U., 1977-82; lectr. Md. Sci. Ctr. Student Sci. Program, 1980, Sandoz lectr. gerontology, Basel, Switzerland, 1984, 86, also various other nat. and internat. meetings and workshops including Gordon confs., NATO workshops, internat. congresses, etc. Contbr. numerous articles and papers to profl. publs.; editor Exptl. Gerontology, Exptl. Aging Rsch., Proc. Soc. Exptl. Biology and Medicine; co-editor Chem. Rubber Co. Press Series in Aging, 1981—; assoc. editor The Ency. of Aging, 1987—. V.p. Community Coalition Harford County, Bel Air, Md., 1988-90, bd. dirs., 1990-92; co-dir. Ea. Harford County Civic Assn., Bel Air, 1981—. Recipient Ann. Rsch. award Am. Aging Assn., 1981, Sandoz prize for gerontol. rsch. Sandoz Ltd., Basel, 1989, Third Age award Internat. Assn. Gerontology, 1989, Spl. award Balt. Longitudinal Study on Aging, 1991; Sigma Chi scholar in residence Miami U., Oxford, Ohio, 1989. Fellow Gerontol. Soc. Am. (chair indsl. scis. sect. 1975-76, chair rsch. com. 1978-79, chair fellowship com. 1986-87); mem. Soc. Exptl. Biology and Medicine. Republican. Roman Catholic. Avocations: basketball, fishing, hiking, canoeing. Office: Gerontology Rsch Ctr Molecular Physiology & Gen Hopkins Bayview Campus Baltimore MD 21224

ROTH, HADDEN WING, lawyer; b. Oakland, Calif., Feb. 10, 1930; s. Mark and Jane (Haley) R.; m. Alice Becker, Aug., 1987; 1 child, Elizabeth Wing. AA, Coll. Marin, 1949; BA, U. Calif., Berkeley, 1951; JD, U. Calif., San Francisco, 1957. Bar: Calif. 1958, U.S. Dist. Ct. (no. dist.) Calif. 1958, U.S. Ct. Appeals (9th cir.) 1958, U.S. Supreme Ct. 1966. Pvt. practice San Rafael, 1970—; hearing officer Dist. Hosps., 1981—; dep. city atty. City of San Rafael, 1958-60, City of Sausalito and Mill Valley, Calif., 1964-66; dep. dist. atty. County of Marin, 1960-63; judge Marin County Mcpl. Ct., 1966-70; spl. cons. Marin Muni Water Dist., Corte Madera, Calif., County of Marin; atty. Bolinas Pub. Utility Dist., Ross Valley Fire Svc., Ross Valley Paramedics, Town of Ross and San Anselmo, Calif.; hearing officer dist. hosps., 1981—; lectr. law Golden Gate Coll. Law, San Francisco, 1971-73. Chmn. Marin County prison task force, 1973; bd. dirs. Marin Gen. Hosp., 1964-66. Cpl. U.S. Army, 1952-54. Named Outstanding Citizen of Yr., Coll. Marin, 1972. Mem. ABA, Calif. and Marin County Bar Assns. Avocations: Running, racquetball, reading. Home: 343 Fairhills Dr San Rafael CA 94901-1110 Office: 1050 Northgate Dr San Rafael CA 94903-2544

ROTH, HAROLD, architect; b. St. Louis, June 30, 1934; s. Samuel and Dorothy (Yawitz) R.; m. Dvora Pappo, Dec. 6, 1959; children: Elizabeth, David. AB, Washington U., 1956; MArch, Yale U., 1957. Designer Warner Burns Toan & Lunde, N.Y.C., 1957; sr. designer Eero Saarinen & Assocs., Roche Dinkeloo & Assocs., Hamden, Conn., 1959-65; ptnr. Harold Roth - Edward Saad, Hamden, Conn., 1965-72; sr. ptnr. Roth & Moore Architects, New Haven, 1973—; critic archtl. design Yale U. Sch. Architecture, New Haven, 1964—; pres., trustee Perspecta, Yale Archtl. Jour. Trustee Long Wharf Theatre, New Haven, 1972—, Conn. Trust for Hist. Preservation, 1983-90; pres. bd. trustees Conn. Architecture Found., 1990-93. Officer U.S. Army, 1957-59, Korea. Recipient Design award Nat. Coun. Religious Arch., 1970, Design award New Haven Preservation Trust, 1978, 88, Tucker award Bldg. Stone Inst., 1983, 88, Honor award Concrete Reinforcing Steel Inst., 1983, Design award Portland Cement Assn., 1984, Design award Archtl. Record, 1970, 80, Design award AIA/ALA, 1983, Faculty Design award Assn. Collegiate Schs. of Arch., 1988, Healthcare Facilities Design award Boston Soc. Archs., 1992; fellow Pierson Coll., Yale U., 1978—. Fellow AIA (chmn. nat. com. on design 1990, bd. dirs. 1992-94, mem. Conn. chpt., bd. dirs. Conn. chpt. 1982-85, Design award Conn. chpt. 1974, 78, 83, 86, 88, 90, 92, 93, Design award New Eng. chpt. 1968, 84, 92)); mem. Elihu Club, Yale Club N.Y. Home: 37 Autumn St New Haven CT 06511-2220 Office: Roth & Moore Architects 108 Audubon St New Haven CT 06510-1206

ROTH, HAROLD PHILMORE, physician; b. Cleve., Aug. 2, 1915; s. Abraham J. and Ida (Harris) R.; m. Kelly Cecile Rabinovitch, Dec. 9, 1952; children: Anita Alix, Edward Harris. B.A., Western Res. U., Cleve., 1936, M.D., 1939; M.S. in Hygiene, Harvard U., 1967. Diplomate Am. Bd. Internal Medicine. Intern Cin. Gen. Hosp., 1939-40; house officer Boston City Hosp., 1940-42; asst. resident in medicine Barnes Hosp., St. Louis, 1942-43; clin. instr. Western Res. U., Cleve., 1949-52; sr. clin. instr. Western Res. U., 1953-55, asst. prof., 1955-63, assoc. prof., 1963—; assoc. prof. dept. community health Case Western Res. U., 1971-74; chief gastroenterology service VA Hosp., Cleve., 1947-74; dir. gastroenterology tng. program Univ. Hosps. and VA Hosp., 1963-74; assoc. physician Univ. Hosps. of Cleve., 1969-74; cons.; asst. physician Highland View Hosp.; vis. physician in gastroenterology dept. medicine Cleve. Met. Gen. Hosp.; assoc. dir. for Digestive Diseases and Nutrition Nat. Inst. Arthritis, Diabetes, Digestive and Kidney Disease, NIH, Bethesda, Md., 1974-85, dir. div. Digestive Disease and Nutrition, 1983-85, epidemiology and data systems program dir., div. digestive diseases and nutrition, 1985-91, sr. gastroenterologist emeritus, 1991—; mem. Nat. Commn. on Digestive Diseases, Nat. Digestive Diseases Adv. Bd. Contbr. articles to med. jours. Served with AUS, 1943-46. USPHS fellow, 1966-67. Mem. Am. Gastroenterol. Assn., Am. Assn. Study of Liver Disease, Central Soc. Clin. Rsch., ACP, Soc. Clin. Trials (pres. 1978-80), Phi Beta Kappa. Home: 10319 Gary Rd Potomac MD 20854-4102 Office: NIH 9000 Rockville Pike Rm 9A47 Bethesda MD 20892-0001 *Fifty years ago when I graduated from medical school, the practice of medicine was primarily an art. The physician had a limited number of useful diagnostic tests and procedures and an even more limited number of effective treatments. Since then new diagnostic tests and procedures have been developed that make diagnosis more precise, and new treatments such as the antibiotics still seem miraculous. I was fortunate to have an opportunity to become involved in some of these developments in medicine.*

ROTH, HARVEY PAUL, publisher; b. N.Y.C., Feb. 20, 1933; s. Lewis Theodore and Harriet (Wallow) R.; m. Tanya Cohen; children by previous marriage: Andrea, Matthew Jay; stepchildren: Laura Meryl, Matthew Robert. A.B., Bklyn. Coll., 1954; LL.B., N.Y. U., 1957. Bar: N.Y. bar 1959. Editor West Pub. Co., N.Y.C., 1959-61; pres. BFL Communications, Inc., Plainview, N.Y., 1961-76, Roth Pub., Inc., Great Neck, N.Y., 1976—; chmn. Alcove Press, London 1970-75, Nash Pub. Corp., Los Angeles, 1971-75. Served with U.S. Army, 1957-58. Office: Roth Pub Inc 185 Great Neck Rd Great Neck NY 11021-3312

ROTH, HENRY, writer; b. Tysmenica, Galicia, Austria-Hungary, Feb. 8, 1906; s. Herman and Leah (Farb) R.; m. Muriel Parker, Oct. 7, 1939; children: Jeremy, Hugh. BA, CCNY, 1928; LittD (hon.), U. N.Mex., 1994, Hebrew Union Coll. of Cin. 1994. With Works Progress Adminstrn., 1939; substitute high sch. tchr. Bronx, N.Y., 1939-41; precision metal grinder N.Y.C., 1941-45, Boston and Providence, R.I., 1945-46; tchr. Maine, 1947-48; attendant Augusta (Maine) State Hosp., 1949-53; water fowl farmer, 1953-63, tutor math and latin, 1956-65. Author: Call t Sleep, 1934, Nature's First Green, 1979, Shifting Landscape: A Composite, 1925-87, 1987, A Star Shines Over Mount Morris Park, 1994, Mercy of a Rude Stream, vol. I, 1994, A Diving Rock on the Hudson Vol. II Mercy of a Rude Stream, 1995; contbr. Best American Short Stories 1967, 1967. Recipient Townsend Harris medal CCNY, 1965; Nat. Inst. Arts & Letters grantee, 1965, D.H. Lawrence fellow, 1968. Office: Roslyn Targ Literary Agy 105 W 13th St New York NY 10011

ROTH, HERBERT, JR., corporate executive; b. South Bend, Ind., Oct. 7, 1928; s. Gilbert and Vita (Augustienovicz) Shoemaker; m. Dolores Maloney, June 5, 1951; children: Christine, Diane, Carla. B.S., U.S. Mil. Acad., 1951; M.S., Newark Coll. Engring., 1959. Sr. product planner EDP div. RCA, 1956-61; v.p. Nuclear Corp. Am., Phoenix, 1961-62, GCA Corp., Bedford, Mass., 1962-66; pres., chief exec. officer Annex Corp., Boston, 1966-67; dir., chmn. exec. com. Mohawk Data Scis., Corp., Boston, 1967-68; pres., chief exec. officer, dir. LFE Corp., Clinton, Mass., 1968-85; chrm., dir. Key Energy Group, Inc.; dir. Boston Edison Co., Key Energy Group, Inc., Landauer Inc., Tech/OpsSevcon Inc., Phoenix Mut. Life Ins. Co., Mark IV Ind. and Phoenix Series Funds. Served with U.S. Army, 1951-55. Mem. Boston C. of C. (pres. 1980-81). Office: Key Energy Group Inc 257 Livingstone Ave New Brunswick NJ 08901

ROTH, JACK JOSEPH, historian, educator; b. Dec. 17, 1920; s. Max and Dinah (Kraus) R.; m. Sheilagh Goldstone. B.A., U. Chgo., 1942, Ph.D., 1955; postgrad., Inst. d'Études Politiques, Paris, 1949-50. Mem. faculty Roosevelt U., 1951-68, prof. history, chmn. dept., 1960-68; prof. history Case Western Res. U., Cleve., 1968—; mem. dept. Case Western Res. U., 1968-73; vis. asso. prof. history U. Chgo., 1962, professorial lectr. history, 1968; vis. prof. history U. Wis., 1964-65. Project dir.: The Persistence of Surrealism, Nat. Endowment for Humanities, festival, 1979, film, 1982; Translator: (Georges Sorel) Reflections on Violence, 1951, Sorel und die Totalitären Systeme, 1958, Revolution and Morale in Modern French Thought: Sorel and the Sorelians, 1963, The First World War: A Turning Point in Modern History, 1967, The Roots of Italian Fascism, 1967, Georges Sorel: on Lenin and Mussolini, 1977, The Revolution of the Mind: The Politics of Surrealism Reconsidered, 1977, The Cult of Violence: Sorel and the Sorelians, 1980; Contbr. articles to profl. jours., chpts. to books. Served with AUS, 1942-46. Recipient Penrose Fund award Am. Philos. Soc., 1964. Home: 24301 Bryden Rd Beachwood OH 44122-4038 Office: Dept History Case Western Res U Cleveland OH 44106

ROTH, JAMES FRANK, manufacturing company executive, chemist; b. Rahway, N.J., Dec. 7, 1925; s. Louis and Eleanor R.; m. Sharon E. Mattes, June 20, 1969; children by previous marriage: Lawrence, Edward, Sandra. B.A. in Chemistry, U. W.Va., 1947; Ph.D. in Phys. Chemistry, U. Md., 1951. Research chemist Franklin Inst., Phila., 1951-53, mgr. chemistry lab., 1958-60; chief chemist Lehigh Paints & Chems. Co., Allentown, Pa., 1953-55; research chemist GAF Corp., Easton, Pa., 1955-58; with Monsanto Co., St. Louis, 1960-80, dir. catalysis research, 1973-77, dir. process sci. research, 1977-80; corp. chief scientist Air Products and Chems., Inc., Allentown, 1980-91; indsl. cons., 1991—. Contbr. articles to profl. jours.; editorial bd.: Jour. Catalysis, 1976-85, Catalysis Revs, 1973-93; editorial bd. Applied Catalysis, 1981-85, editor for Ams., 1985-88, assoc. editor, 1988—. With USN, 1943-46. Recipient Richard J. Kokes award Johns Hopkins U., 1977, Chem. Pioneer award Am. Inst. Chemists, 1986, Perkin medal Soc. Chem. Industry, 1988. Mem. NAE, Am. Chem. Soc. (St. Louis sect. St. Louis award 1975, E.V. Murphree nat. award 1976, Indsl. Chemistry award 1991), Catalysis Soc. N.Am. (E.J. Houdry award 1991), Catalysis Club of Phila. (award 1981). Inventor process biodegradable detergents, for acetic acid; U.S., fgn. patents in field. Home: 4436 Calle Serena Sarasota FL 34238-5641

ROTH, JANE RICHARDS, federal judge; b. Philadelphia, Pa., June 16, 1935; d. Robert Henry Jr. and Harriett (Kellond) Richards; m. William V. Roth Jr., Oct. 9, 1965; children: William V. III, Katharine K. BA, Smith Coll., 1956; LLB, Harvard U., 1965; LLD (hon.), Widener U., 1986, U. Del., 1994. Bar: Del. 1965, U.S. Dist. Ct. Del. 1966, U.S. Ct. Appeals (3d cir.) 1974. Adminstrv. asst. various fgn. service posts U.S. State Dept., 1956-62; assoc. Richards, Layton & Finger, Wilmington, Del., 1965-73, ptnr., 1973-85; judge U.S. Dist. Ct. Del., Wilmington, 1985-91, U.S. Ct. Appeals (3d cir.), Wilmington, 1991—; adj. faculty Villanova U. Sch. Law. Mem. Chesapeake Bay coun. Girl Scouts U.S.; hon. chmn. Del. chpt. Arthritis Found., Wilmington; bd. overseers Widener U. Sch. Law; trustee Hist. Soc. Del. Recipient Nat. Vol. Service citation Arthritis Found., 1982. Mem. Fed. Judges Assn., Del. State Bar Assn. Republican. Episcopalian. Office: US Ct House J Caleb Boggs Fed Bldg 844 King St Rm 5100 Wilmington DE 19801-3519

ROTH, JOE, motion picture company executive; b. 1948. Prodn. assistant various commls. and feature films, San Francisco; also lighting dir. Pitchel Players, San Francisco; then producer Pitchel Players, L.A.; co-founder Morgan Creek Prodns., L.A., 1987-89; chmn. 20th Century Fox Film Corp., L.A., 1989-92; founder Caravan Pictures, L.A., 1992-94; chmn. Walt Disney Motion Pictures Group, Burbank, 1994—. Prodr. numerous films including Tunnelvision, Cracking Up, Americathon, Our Winning Season, The Final Terror, The Stone Boy, Where the River Runs Black, Bachelor Party, Off Beat, Streets of Gold (dir. debut), Revenge of the Nerds II (also dir.); exec. prodr. Young Guns, Dead Ringers, Skin Deep, Major League, Renegades, Coupe de Ville (also dir.), Enemies A Love Story: Caravan Pictures releases include Walt Disney's The Three Musketeers, Angie, Angels in the Outfield, I Love Trouble, A Low Down Dirty Shame, Houseguest, The Jerky Boys, Heavyweights, Tall Tale, While You Were Sleeping. Office: Walt Disney Studio 500 S Buena Vista St Burbank CA 91521-1060

ROTH, JOHN KING, philosopher, educator; b. Grand Haven, Mich., Sept. 3, 1940; s. Josiah V. and Doris Irene (King) R.; m. Evelyn Lillian Austin, June 25, 1964; children: Andrew Lee, Sarah Austin. BA, Pomona Coll., 1962; student, Yale U. Div. Sch., 1962-63; MA, Yale U., 1965, PhD, 1966; LHD, Ind. U., 1990. Asst. prof. philosophy Claremont McKenna Coll., Calif., 1966-71, assoc. prof., 1971-76, Russell K. Pitzer prof. philosophy, 1976—; vis. prof. philosophy Franklin Coll., Lugano, Switzerland, 1973; Fulbright lectr. Am. studies U. Innsbruck, Austria, 1973-74; vis. prof. philosophy Doshisha U., Kyoto, Japan, 1981-82; vis. prof. Holocaust studies U. Haifa, Israel, 1982; Fulbright lectr. in Am. studies Royal Norwegian Ministry of Edn. Oslo, Norway, 1995—. Author: Freedom and the Moral Life, 1969, Problems of the Philosophy of Religion, 1971, American Dreams, 1976, A Consuming Fire, 1979, (with Richard L. Rubenstein) Approaches to Auschwitz, 1987, (with Frederick Sontag) The American Religious Experience, 1972, (with Frederick Sontag) The Questions of Philosophy, 1988, (with Robert H. Fossum) The American Dream, 1981, (with Fossum) American Ground, 1988, (with Rubenstein) The Politics of Latin American Liberation Theology, 1988, (with Michael Berenbaum) Holocaust: Religious and Philosophical Implications, 1989, Ethics, 1991, (with Carol Rittner) Memory Offended, 1991, (with Creighton Peden) Rights, Justice, and Community, 1992, (with Carol Rittner) Different Voices, 1993, American Diversity, American Identity, 1995. Spl. advisor U.S. Holocaust Meml. Coun., Washington, 1980-85, mem., 1995—. Danforth grad. fellow, 1962-66; Graves fellow, 1970-71; NEH fellow, 1976-77; Faculty Amering grantee Japan-U.S. Friendship Commn., 1981-83; named U.S. Prof. of Yr. Coun. Advancement and Support of Edn. and Carnegie Found. Advancement of Tchg., 1988. Mem Am. Philos. Assn., Am. Acad. Religion, Am. Studies Assn., Calif. Coun. for Humanities, Phi Beta Kappa. Presbyterian. Home: 1648 N Kenyon Pl Claremont CA 91711-2905 Office: Claremont McKenna Coll 850 Columbia Ave Claremont CA 91711

ROTH, J(OHN) REECE, electrical engineer, educator, researcher, consultant; b. Washington, Pa., Sept. 19, 1937; s. John Meyer and Ruth Evangeline (Iams) R.; m. Helen Marie DeCrane, Jan. 14, 1972; children: Nancy Ann, John Alexander. S.B. in Physics, MIT, 1959; Ph.D., Cornell U., 1963. Engring. aide Aerojet-Gen. Corp., Azusa, Calif., 1957, 58; aerospace engr. N.Am. Aviation, Canoga Park, Calif., 1959; prin. investigator NASA Lewis Research Ctr., Cleve., 1963-78; prof. elec. engring. U. Tenn., Knoxville, 1978—; N.Am. Philips prof. elec. engring. U. Tenn., 1986-91; hon. prof. U. Electronic Sci. and Tech. of China, Chengdu, 1992—; prin. investigator Office Naval Rsch., Washington, 1980-89, Air Force Office Sci. Rsch., Washington, 1981-95, Army Rsch. Office, 1988-93; cons. TVA, Chattanooga, 1982-84, BDM Corp., 1987-88, Tenn. Eastman, 1989-90; speaker at profl. meetings; mem. NAS-NRC Com. on Aneutronic Fusion, 1986-87. Author: Industrial Plasma Engineering, Introduction to Fusion Energy; contbr. articles to profl. jours. Sloan scholar, 1955-59; Ford fellow, 1961-62. Fellow IEEE, AIAA (assoc.); mem. Am. Phys. Soc., Am. Nuclear Soc. (exec. com. No. Ohio sect. 1975-78), Nuclear and Plasma Scis. Soc., Am. Soc. Engring. Edn., Knoxville Art Gallery, East Tenn. Soc. of Archaeol. Inst. Am., Sigma Xi (pres. U. Tenn. Knoxville chpt. 1985-86). Club: U. Tenn. Faculty (Knoxville). Home: 4301 Hiawatha Dr Knoxville TN 37919-6605 Office: U Tenn Dept Elec and Computer Engring Knoxville TN 37996-2100

ROTH, JOHN ROGER, geneticist, biology educator; b. Winona, Minn., Mar. 14, 1939; s. Frederick Daniel and Louise Mae (Wirt) R.; m. Uta Goetz (div.); children: Katherine Louise, Frederick Phillip; m. Sherylynne Harris, Jan. 4, 1986. BA, Harvard U., 1961; PhD, John Hopkins U., 1965. From asst. prof. molecular biology to prof. molecular biology U. Calif., Berkeley, 1967-76; prof. biology U. Utah, Salt Lake City, 1976—. Recipient Disting. Prof. award, 1990, Rosenblatt award, 1990. Mem. NAS, Am. Soc. for Microbiology, Genetics Soc. Am. Office: U Utah Dept Biology Salt Lake City UT 84112

ROTH, JUDITH SHULMAN, lawyer; b. N.Y.C., Apr. 25, 1952; d. Mark Alan and Margaret Ann (Podell) Shulman; m. William Hartley Roth, May 30, 1976; children: Andrew Henry, Caroline Shulman. AB, Cornell U., 1974; JD, Columbia U., 1977. Bar: N.Y. 1978, U.S. Dist. Ct. (ea. dist.) N.Y. 1978, U.S. Dist. Ct. (so. dist.) N.Y. 1993, U.S. Ct. Appeals (2d cir.) 1993. Assoc. Phillips Nizer Benjamin Krim & Ballon, N.Y.C., 1978-87, ptnr., 1988—; lectr. CLE Fordham Law Sch., N.Y.C., 1990. Mem. Cosmopolitan Club. Jewish. Avocations: reading, tennis, golf, art, gardening. Office: Phillips Nizer Benjamin Krim & Ballon 31 W 52nd St New York NY 10019

ROTH, LAURA MAURER, physics educator, researcher; b. Flushing, N.Y., Oct. 11, 1930; d. Keith Langden and Ruth (Oliphint) Maurer; m. Willard Dale Roth, June 6, 1952; children: Andrew Eric, Karen Elsa. AB, Swarthmore Coll., 1952; AM, Radcliffe Coll., 1953, PhD, 1957. Staff physicist Lincoln Lab., MIT, Lexington, Mass., 1956-63; lectr. Harvard U., Cambridge, Mass., summer 1959; assoc. prof., prof. physics Tufts U., Medford, Mass., 1963-67; physicist GE R & D Ctr., Schenectady, N.Y., 1967-72; lectr. Inst. for Theoretical Physics, U. Colo., Boulder, Colo., summer 1969; Abbey Rockefeller Mauze vis. prof. physics MIT, Cambridge, Mass., 1972-73; rsch. physicist SUNY, Albany, 1973-77, prof. physics, 1977—; cons. Lincoln Lab., MIT, Lexington, Mass., 1963,. Co-author: Women in Physics, 1975; co-editor: Fundamental Questions in Quantum Mechanics, 1984; editor: Dharma Paths, 1993; contbr. 80 articles to physics jours., 1956—. Dir. Karma Thegsum Choling Buddhist Ctr., Albany, N.Y., 1979—; program dir. for publs. Karma Kagyu Inst., Woodstock, N.Y., 1988—. Recipient medal Radcliffe Grad. Soc., 1962; grantee Sloan Found., Tufts U., 1963-65, NSF, SUNY, Albany, 1976-81. Democrat. Buddhist. Home: 1270 Ruffner Rd Niskayuna NY 12309-4601 Office: SUNY Albany Dept Physics 1400 Washington Ave Albany NY 12222-0001

ROTH, LAWRENCE MAX, pathologist, educator; b. McAlester, Okla., June 25, 1936; s. Herman Moe and Blanche (Brown) R.; m. Anna Berit Katarina Sundstrom, Apr. 3, 1965; children—Karen Esther, David Josef. BA., Vanderbilt U., 1957; M.D., Harvard U., 1960. Diplomate Am. Bd. Pathology. Rotating intern U. Ill. Research and Ednl. Hosps., Chgo., 1960-61; resident in anat. pathology Washington U. Sch. Medicine, St. Louis, 1961-64; resident in clin. pathology U. Calif. Med. Ctr., San Francisco, 1967-68; asst. prof. pathology Tulane U. Sch. Medicine, New Orleans, 1968-71; assoc. prof. pathology Ind. U. Sch. Medicine, Indpls., 1971-75, prof., 1975—; dir. div. surg. pathology. Series editor: Contemporary Issues in Surgical Pathology; mem. editorial bd. Am. Jour. Surg. Pathology, Human Pathology, Seminars in Diagnostic Pathology, Internat. Jour. Gynecol. Pathology, Endocrine Pathology; contbr. articles to med. jours. Served to capt. U.S. Army, 1965-67. Mem. Am. Assn. Investigative, Pathologists, U.S. and Can. Acad. Pathology, Am. Soc. Clin. Pathologists, Internat. Soc. Gynecol. Pathologists, Arthur Purdy Stout Soc. Surg. Pathologists, Assn. Dirs. Anatomic and Surg. Pathology. Home: 7898 Ridge Rd Indianapolis IN 46240-2538 Office: 550 N University Blvd Indianapolis IN 46202

ROTH, LEE BRITTON, lawyer; b. Perth Amboy, N.J., May 8, 1937; s. Alton James and Katherine (Crouse) R.; m. Nancy Hanawalt, Aug. 10, 1960; children: Barbara, Jon. BA, Oberlin Coll., 1959; JD, Cornell U., 1962. Bar: N.J. 1962, U.S. Dist. Ct. N.J. 1963. Assoc. Wharton, Stewart, Davis, Somerville, N.J., 1962-65; pvt. practice Flemington, N.J., 1965; sr. ptnr. Roth & Beeman and predecessor firm, Flemington, 1978—; bd. dirs. Princeton Bank & Trust Co., Morristown, N.J.; chmn. Yeaton & Yeaton Real Estate, Flemington. Author: Negotiating Residential Real Estate Contract, Resolving Disputes in Real Transactions. Fund drive chmn. Hunterdon Dr. Am. Cancer Soc., Flemington; pres. Raritan Twp. Rep. Club. Mem. N.J. State Bar Assn. (trustee, chmn. real property probate trust sect.), Hunterdon County Bar Assn. (pres. 1979-80), N.Y. State Bar Assn. (trustee), Lyons Club. Avocations: photography, LaCrosse, tennis. Home: 10 Birch St Flemington NJ 08822-4525 Office: Roth & Beeman 8 Main St Flemington NJ 08822-1468

ROTH, LOREN, psychiatrist; b. May 9, 1939; m. Ellen A. Roth; children: Jonathan, Alexandra, Elizabeth. BA in Philosophy, Cornell U., 1961; MD cum laude, Harvard U., 1966, MPH, 1972; postgrad., Am. U., 1972-73. Diplomate Am. Bd. Psychiatry and Neurology; lic. physician, Conn., Md., Mass., Pa. Med. intern Univ. Hosps., Western Res. U., Cleve., 1966-67; resident psychiatry Yale U., New Haven, 1969-70, Mass. Gen. Hosp., Boston, 1970-72; staff psychiatrist Ctr. for Studies Crime and Delinquency, NIMH, Rockville, Md., 1972-74; co-dir., dir. law and psychiatry program Western Psychiat. Inst. and Clinic/U. Pitts., 1974—; chief adult clin. svcs., 1983-87, 88-89, chief clin. svcs., 1989—; vice-chmn. dept. psychiatry U. Pitts., 1988—; asst. prof., 1974-78, assoc. prof., 1978-82, prof., 1982—; v.p. for Managed Care U. Pitt. Med. Ctr., 1993—; med. staff Presbyn.-Univ. Hosp., Pitts., 1983—; gen. med. officer Fed. Penitentiary, Lewisburg, Pa., 1967-69; William E. Schumacher disting. lectr. Maine Dept. Mental Health and Mental Retardation, Portland, 1982; mem. commn. on mentally disabled ABA, Washington, 1987; cons. law and psychiatry Dept. Welfare, Commonwealth Pa., 1974—; cons. reviewer, site visitor crime and delinquency sect. NIMH, 1977—; examiner Am. Bd. Psychiatry and Neurology, 1977—. Author: (with others) Informed Consent: A Study of Decisionmaking in Psychiatry, 1984; editor: (with others) Psychiatry, Social, Epidemiologic and Legal Psychiatry, Vol. 5, 1986; contbr. articles to profl. jours., chpts. to books; editorial bd. Criminology, 1974-78, Law and Human Behavior, 1980-85, Internat. Jour. Law and Psychiatry, 1980-88, Behavioral Scis. and the Law, 1987—; assoc. editor Am. Jour. Psychiatry, 1980-90; cons. editor Criminal Justice and Behavior, 1982-85. Lt. comdr. USPHS Res., 1967—. Recipient Steve Allen award United Mental Health, Inc., 1990; grantee NIMH, 1979, 80-81, 89, Founds. Fund for Rsch. in Psychiatry, 1980-82. Fellow Am. Psychiat. Assn. (Isaac Ray award 1988), Am. Coll. Utilization Rev. Physicians, Am. Coll. Psychiatrists; mem. AMA, Am. Acad. Psychiatry and Law (pres. 1983-84), Group for Advancement Psychiatry (com. on psychiatry and law 1979-80, chmn. 1981-84), Am. Soc. Criminology, Am. Soc. Law and Medicine (bd. dirs. 1982-85), Internat. Acad. Law and Mental Health (bd. dirs.), Am. Psychopath. Assn., Phi Beta Kappa, Phi Kappa Phi. Home: 6820 Edgerton Ave Pittsburgh PA 15208-2803 Office: Western Psychiat Inst 3811 Ohara St Pittsburgh PA 15213-2593

ROTH, SISTER M. AUGUSTINE, nun, educator; b. Mpls., Jan. 16, 1926; d. J.A., and Anne A. (Boies) R. BA, U. Minn., 1947, MA, 1948; PhD, Cath. U. Am., 1961. Joined Sisters of Mercy, Roman Catholic Ch., 1949. Faculty Mt. Mercy Coll., Cedar Rapids, Iowa, 1948—, prof. dept. English; v.p. bd. dirs. Mercy Med. Ctr. Endowment Found., exec. dir., 1987—, chmn. bd. trustees of med. ctr., 1987—. Author: Written in His Hands, 1976; With

Mercy Toward All, 1979; Courage and Change, 1980, One Life, 1987. Home: 1125 Prairie Dr NE Cedar Rapids IA 52402-4730

ROTH, MICHAEL, lawyer; b. N.Y.C., July 22, 1931; s. Philip Arthur and Mollie (Breitenbach) R.; m. Jeanny Macoir, Nov. 24, 1957; 3 children. B.A., Yale Coll., 1953; J.D., Columbia U., 1956, M. Internat. Affairs, 1964. Bar: N.Y. 1956. Law assoc. Stroock & Stroock & Lavan, N.Y.C., 1956-63; ptnr. Roth, Carlson, Kwit & Spengler, N.Y.C., 1964-74; chmn. N.Y. State Liquor Authority, N.Y.C., 1974-77; ptnr. Shea & Gould, N.Y.C., 1979-89; of counsel Rosenman & Colin, N.Y.C., 1989—. Mem. U.S. del. to UN Population Commn., 1969; Rep.-Conservative candidate for N.Y. State atty. gen., 1978; mem. Pres.' Task Force on Internat. Pvt. Enterprise, 1983-84, Pres.' Commn. on Mgmt. AID Programs, 1991-92. Mem. ABA, N.Y. State Bar Assn., Assn. of Bar of City of N.Y. Republican. Clubs: Yale (N.Y.C.); Sunningdale Country (Scarsdale, N.Y.).

ROTH, MICHAEL I., lawyer, financial executive; b. Bklyn., Nov. 22, 1945; s. Harry A. and Sally (Kutin) R.; m. Carole A. Snofsky, Aug. 10, 1968; children—Barrie, Marc, Andrew. BS, CCNY, 1967; JD, Boston U., 1971; LL.M., NYU, 1973. Bar: N.Y. 1971. CPA: N.Y. 1973, Conn. 1973. With Coopers & Lybrand, N.Y.C., 1969-76; ptnr. Stamford, Conn., 1976-82; exec. v.p. corp. fin., tax and adminstrn. Primerica Corp. (formerly Am. Can Co.), Greenwich, Conn., 1982-87, exec. v.p., 1987, chief fin. officer, 1987-88; exec. v.p., chief fin. officer MONY Fin. Svcs., N.Y.C., 1989-91; pres., COO, MONY-Mut. Ins. Co., N.Y.C., 1991-94, also bd. dirs., chmn. bd. dirs., CEO, 1994—; bd. dirs. Mut. of N.Y. Bd. dirs. Child Guidance Ctr., Stamford, 1984-85; trustee Temple BethEl, Stamford, 1984-85. Mem. Am. Inst. CPA's, Conn. Soc. CPA's, Stamford Tax Assn. (pres. 1981-82). Office: MONY Fin Svcs 1740 Broadway New York NY 10019-4315*

ROTH, PAUL NORMAN, lawyer; b. N.Y.C., May 4, 1939; s. Sol and Florence (Glassman) R.; m. Ellen Joan Lipp, May 24, 1964; children: Stefanie H., Jessica A. AB, Harvard U., 1961, LLB, 1964. Bar: N.Y. 1966, U.S. Ct. Appeals (2d cir.) 1966, U.S. Dist. Ct. (so. and ea. dists.) N.Y. 1967, U.S. Supreme Ct. 1975. Assoc. Cleary, Gottlieb, Steen & Hamilton, N.Y.C., 1965-69; ptnr. Schulte Roth & Zabel, N.Y., 1969-. Trustee Ctrl. Synagogue, N.Y.C., 1987-95. Fulbright fellow, Netherlands, 1965. Mem. ABA, N.Y. State Bar Assn., Assn. of Bar of City of N.Y. (com. on securities regulation 1982-85, chmn. 1989-92), Harvard Law Sch. Assn. N.Y. (trustee 1987-90, v.p. 1992-93), Century Country Club. Office: Schulte Roth & Zabel 900 3rd Ave New York NY 10022-4728

ROTH, PHILIP, writer; b. Newark, Mar. 19, 1933; s. Herman and Bess (Finkel) R.; m. Margaret Martinson, Feb. 22, 1959 (dec. 1968); m. Claire Bloom, Apr. 29, 1990. Student, Newark Coll. of Rutgers U., 1950-51; AB, Bucknell U., 1954; MA, U. Chgo., 1955. Tchr. English U. Chgo., 1956-58; faculty Iowa Writers Workshop, 1960-62; writer in residence Princeton U., 1962-64; adj. prof. U. Pa., 1967-77; disting. prof. Hunter Coll. CUNY, 1989-92. Short story writer, novelist; works pub. in Harper's, New Yorker, Epoch, Commentary, others; reprints in Best Am. Short Stories of 1956, 59, 60, O'Henry Prize Stories of 1960; author: Goodbye, Columbus, 1959 (Nat. Book award), Letting Go, 1962, When She Was Good, 1967, Portnoy's Complaint, 1969, Our Gang, 1971, The Breast, 1972, The Great American Novel, 1973, My Life as a Man, 1974, Reading Myself and Others, 1975, The Professor of Desire, 1977, The Ghost Writer, 1979, A Philip Roth Reader, 1980, Zuckerman Unbound, 1981, The Anatomy Lesson, 1983, The Prague Orgy, 1985, Zuckerman Bound, 1985, The Counterlife, 1987 (Nat. Book Critics Circle award for fiction, 1988), The Facts, 1988, Deception, 1990, Patrimony, 1991 (Nat. Book Critics Circle award for biography/autobiography 1992), Operation Shylock, 1993 (PEN-Faulkner award for fiction 1993), Sabbath's Theater, 1995. Recipient prize for fiction Paris Rev., 1958, Nat. Inst. Arts and Letters award, 1960, Daroff award Jewish book Coun. Am., 1960, Medal of Honor for Lit., Nat. Arts Club, 1991, Karel Capek prize Czech Republic, 1994; Guggenheim fellow, 1959-60, Rockefeller fellow, 1966. Office: Wylie Aitken & Stone 250 W 57th St New York NY 10107

ROTH, PHILLIP JOSEPH, judge; b. Portland, Oreg., Feb. 29, 1920; s. Harry William and Minnie Alice (Segel) R.; m. Ida Lorraine Thomas, Feb. 22, 1957 (div. 1977); children: Phillip J. Jr., David William; m. Allison Blake Ramsey, Feb. 14, 1978 (div. 1994). BA cum laude, U. Portland, 1943; JD, Lewis and Clark Coll., 1948. Bar: Oreg. 1948, U.S. Dist. Ct. Oreg. 1949, U.S. Ct. Appeals (9th cir.) 1959, U.S. Supreme Ct. 1962. Dep. atty. City of Portland, 1948-50; dep. dist. atty. Multnomah County, Portland, 1950-52; sole practice Portland, 1952-64; cir. judge Multnomah County State of Oreg., Portland, 1964—, presiding cir. judge, 1970-71, 76-78; adj. prof. Lewis & Clark U. Law Sch., Portland, 1978-80, mem. standing com., 1972-90; mem. exec. com. Nat. Conf. State Trial Judges, 1980-91. Author: Sentencing: A View From the Bench, 1973; co-author: The Judicial Immunity Doctrine Today: Between the Bench and a Hard Place, 1984, The Brief Hour; The Dangerous Erosion of Judicial Immunity, 1989. Rep. Oreg. Legislature, 1952-54; Rep. nominee for Congress, 1956; chmn. Oreg. Rep. Cen. Com., 1962-64; mem. adv. bd. Portland Salvation Army, 1976—; bd. overseers Lewis & Clark Coll., 1972—. Named Alumnus of Yr. U. Portland, 1963; named Alumnus of Yr. Lewis & Clark Law Sch., 1973. Fellow ABA (chmn. jud. immunity com. jud. adminstrn. divsn. 1982-90, mem. commn. on standards of jud. adminstrn. divsn. 1973-77, chmn. conf. of state trial judges 1990-91, vice-chair jud. adminstrn. divsn. 1992-93, chair 1993-94); mem. Oreg. Bar Assn. (mem. bd. govs. 1961-64), Multnomah County Bar Assn. (pres 1959), Am. Judicature Soc., Oreg. Cir. Judges Assn. (pres. 1988-89), U. Portland Alumni Assn. (pres. 1976), Lewis and Clark Coll. Alumni Assn. (pres. 1974-76, bd. dirs.), Multnomah Law Libr. Assn. (bd. dirs.), Portland Rotary, City Club, Univ. Club, Masons, Shriners, B'nai B'rith, Delta Theta Phi. Jewish. Home: 1335 SW 66th Ave Portland OR 97225-6024

ROTH, RICHARD, JR., architect; b. N.Y.C., Feb. 20, 1933; s. Richard and Edith Roth; m. Alene Biales, Dec. 20, 1954; children—Robyn Roth Moise, Richard Lee. B.Arch., Miami U., Oxford, Ohio, 1957. Draftsman, designer Emery Roth & Sons, N.Y.C., 1957-63, sr. designer, 1963-66, dir. of design, 1967-74, pres., 1975-88, chmn., 1988—. Fellow AIA (del. internat. engring and constrn. industries council 1984—); mem. N.Y. State Assn. Architects (bd. dirs. 1984—), Nat. Council Archtl. Registration Bds., Royal Inst. Brit. Architects. Avocations: travel; photography. Office: Emery Roth & Sons PC 560 Lexington Ave New York NY 10022-6828

ROTH, RICHARD J., marketing and advertising consulant; b. N.Y.C., Feb. 11, 1936; s. Aaron and Eleanor (Oppenheim) R.; m. Leslie B. Roth, Sept. 27, 1970; children: Erik, Gregory, Nickolas. BS, Dartmouth Coll., 1958; MBA, Amos Tuck Sch. Bus., 1959. With Burlington Industries, 1959-60, Gen. Foods., 1960-64, Grey Advt., 1964-74; exec. v.p. Scali McCabe Sloves, Inc., N.Y.C., 1974-85; pres. Richard Roth Assocs., Chappaqua, N.Y., 1987—.

ROTH, ROBERT AUGUST, university administrator; b. Cleve., Jan. 26, 1943; s. August Joseph and Carmel Maria (Narducci) R.; children: Rob Eugene, Todd Jason, Tracy Lynn. BA, Hiram Coll., 1964; MEd, Pa. State U., 1967; PhD, Kent State U., 1970; postgrad., Rutgers U., 1972-73. Cert. tchr. Tchr., coach Kirtland (Ohio) Schs., 1965-67, Cuyahoga Heights High Sch., Cleve., 1968-69; mem. edn. faculty, dir. performance project State of N.J. Rutgers U., New Brunswick, N.J., 1971-73; state supr. State of Mich. Dept. Edn. Certification, Lansing, 1974-79, state dir., 1979-83; dir. Ctr. for Rsch. on Teaching and Human Resources Devel. U. So. Fla., Tampa, 1985-86; dir., chmn., edn. tchr. Calif. State U., Long Beach, 1987—. Contbr. over 150 books and articles to profl. jours. recipient Resolution of Tribute Mich. Legislature, 1983, Resolution of Recognition of Leadership Mich. State Bd. Edn., 1982, 84; named Disting. Leader in Tchr. Edn. in U.S., 1990, Univ. Disting. Faculty scholar, Calif. State U. at Long Beach, 1990. Mem. Assn. Tchr. Educators of Mich. (Leadership award 1979, past pres.), Nat. Assn. State Dirs. of Edn. (past nat. pres., Disting. Leadership award 1984), Assn. Tchr. Educators (past nat. pres., Leadership award 1985, Disting. mem. 1988, Disting. Tchr. Educator State of Calif. 1992), Phi Delta Kappa. Avocations: photography, sports. Office: Calif State U Coll Edu 1250 N Bellflower Blvd Long Beach CA 90840-2201

ROTH, ROBERT EARL, environmental educator; b. Wauseon, Ohio, Mar. 30, 1937; s. Earl Jonas and Florence Lena (Mahler) R.; m. Carol Sue Yackee, Aug. 8, 1959; children: Robin Earl, Bruce Robert. BSc, Ohio State U.,

Columbus, 1959, BSc in Secondary Sci. Edn., 1960, MSc in Conservation Edn., 1960; PhD in Environ. Edn., U. Wis., Madison, 1969. Supr. conservation edn. Ethical Culture Schs., N.Y.C., 1961-63; naturalist, sci. tchr. Lakeside Sch., Spring Valley, N.Y., 1963-65; instr. No. Ill. U.-Oregon, 1965-67; asst. prof. Ohio State U., Columbus, 1969-73, assoc. prof., 1973-78, prof. environ. edn. and sci. edn., 1978—, chmn. div., 1973-84, coord. Office of Internat. Affairs, 1985-89, asst. dir., sch. sec., Sch. Natural Resources Coop. Extension Svc. 1989-93, acting dir. Sch. Natural Resources, 1993-94, assoc. dir., 1994—, state extension specialist Environ. Edn., 1993—; R&D assoc. Moseley & Assocs., Columbus, 1986-89; project cons. NARMA project, U.S. Agy. Internat. Devel., Santo Domingo, Dominican Rep., 1982-87; cons. Richard Trott and Assocs., 1988-90, Kinzelman and Kline, 1990-93; workshop leader Carribean Conservation Assn., Bridgetown, Barbados, 1981-83; vis. scholar Indonesian Second U. Devel. project, Jakarta, 1988; vis. scholar Uganda Makerere U., 1989, Pacific Cultural Found., Taipei, Taiwan, 1989; AID lectr., Thesolonika, Greece, 1992. Exec. editor Jour. Environ. Edn., 1974-91, Pub.'s prize 1970; contbr. article to profl. jours. Committeeman Boy Scouts Am., 1983-86; adv. council McKeever Environ. Learning Ctr., Pa., 1977-83. Recipient Pomerene Teaching Enhancement award, Ohio State U., 1986, Environ. Edn. award Ohio Alliance for the Environ., 1992. Mem. N. Am. Assn. Environ. Edn. (life mem., bd. dirs. 1972-82, pres. 1977-78, Walt Jeske award 1988), Nat. Sci. Tchrs. Assn. (life), Sch. Nat., Resource Alumni Assn. (inducted hon. 100), Agrl. Faculty Coun. (elect-pres. 1989, pres. 1990), TBDBITL Alumni Club, Phi Beta Delta, Gamma Sigma Delta (treas. 1987-88, sec. 1988-89, pres.-elect. 1989-90, pres. 1990-91). Avocations: swimming, canoeing, camping, fishing, travel. Home: 570 Morning St Columbus OH 43085-3775 Office: Ohio State U Environ Edn Sch Natural Resources Columbus OH 43210

ROTH, SANFORD IRWIN, pathologist, educator; b. McAlester, Okla., Oct. 14, 1932; s. Herman Moe and Blanche (Brown) R.; m. Kathryn Ann Corliss, Sept. 3, 1961; children: Jeffrey Franklin, Elisabeth Francyne, Gregory James, Suzannah Joan. Student, Vanderbilt U., 1949-52; MD, Harvard U., 1956. Intern Mass. Gen. Hosp., Boston, 1956-57; resident in pathology Mass. Gen. Hosp., 1957-60, pathologist, 1962-75; pathologist Armed Forces Inst. Pathology, 1960-62; asst. prof. Med. Sch. Harvard U., 1962-69, assoc. prof. Med. Sch., 1969-75; pathologist, prof., chmn. dept. Coll. Medicine U. Ark., Little Rock, 1975-81; prof. Med. Sch. Northwestern U., Chgo., 1981—; chief lab. svc. VA Lakeside Med. Ctr., Chgo., 1981-86; attending pathologist Northwestern U. Hosp., 1981—. With M.C. U.S. Army, 1960-62. Mem. AMA, AAAS, Internat. Acad. Pathologists, Am. Assn. Pathologists, Am. Soc. Cell Biology, Coll. Am. Pathology. Home: 920 Forest Glen Dr W Winnetka IL 60093-1430 Office: 303 E Chicago Ave Chicago IL 60611-3008

ROTH, SOL, rabbi; b. Rzeszow, Poland, Mar. 8, 1927; came to U.S., 1934, naturalized, 1939; s. Joseph and Miriam (Lamm) R.; m. Debra H. Stitskin, Nov. 26, 1957; children: Steven, Michael, Sharon. B.A., Yeshiva U., 1948, D.D. (hon.), 1977; M.A., Columbia U., 1953, Ph.D., 1966; Rabbi, Yeshiva U. Theol. Sem., 1950. Ordained rabbi Orthodox Jewish Congregations, 1950; pres. Rabbinical Council Am., 1980-82, N.Y. Bd. Rabbis, 1976-79; chmn. Israel Commn. Rabbinical Council Am., 1976-78; dean Chaplaincy Sch., N.Y. Bd. Rabbis, 1976-79; Samson R. Hirsch prof. philosophy Yeshiva U., N.Y.C.; rabbi Jewish Ctr. Atlantic Beach, N.Y., 1956-86; Fifth Ave Synagogue, 1986—; pres. Religious Zionists Am., 1991-94. Author: Science and Religion, 1967, The Jewish Idea of Community, 1977, Halakhah and Politics: The Jewish Idea of a State, 1988 (Samuel Belkin Meml. Lit. award 1989); editor: Morasha. Recipient award Synagogue Adv. Council United Jewish Appeal, 1975. Mem. Am. Philos. Assn. The Rabbi Dr. Sol Roth Chair in Talmud and Contemporary Halakha established at Yeshiva U., 1989. Home: 30 East 62 St New York NY 10021 Office: Yeshiva U Dept Philosophy 500 W 185th St New York NY 10033-3201

ROTH, STEPHEN EVANS, lawyer; b. Ames, Iowa, Dec. 12, 1960; s. L. Evans and Nancy Elizabeth (Lewis) R. BA, U. Tenn., 1982, JD, 1986. Bar: Tenn. 1986. Assoc. Heiskell, Donelson, Bearman, Adams, Williams & Kirsch, Knoxville, Tenn., 1986—. Mem. Knox County Home Rule Charter Commn., Knoxville, 1988, Future Knox Commn., 1989-90, Knox County Rep. Exec. Com., 1980—. Mem. ABA (young lawyers div., litigation com., debtor-creditor com., exec. com. 1991—), Tenn. Bar Assn., Knoxville Bar Assn., Tenn. Young Lawyers Conf. (exec. bd. 1989—), Order of Coif, Phi Beta Kappa, Phi Kappa Phi. Presbyterian. Avocation: reading. Home: 600 Lookout Ct Knoxville TN 37920-5920 Office: Heiskell Donelson Et Al 600 Plaza Tower 800 S Gay St Knoxville TN 37929

ROTH, THOMAS, marketing executive. Grad., Western Mich. U. With Tarkenton and Co., Atlanta; with Wilson Learning Corp., Eden Prairie, Minn., v.p. product mgmt. in global R & D, 1992-94, v.p. product mgmt. and tng. group, 1994—; founder Nat. Edn. Tng. Group, 1988-92; cons. IBM, AT&T, Ford Motor Co., Gen. Motors, E.I. DuPont, Am Express, Dow Chem., Hughes Aircraft, Eli Lily, Colgate-Palmolive, Honeywell, others; spkr. in field. Co-author: Creating the High Performance Team, 1987. Office: Wilson Learning Corp 7500 Flying Cloud Dr Eden Prairie MN 55344*

ROTH, TIM, actor; b. London, 1961. With Glasgow Citizen's Theatre, The Oval House, The Royal Ct. Appeared in play Metamorphosis; films include The Hit, 1985, A World Apart, 1988, The Cook, the Thief, His Wife and Her Lover, 1990, Vincent and Theo, 1990, Rosencrantz and Guildenstern Are Dead, 1991, Jumpin' at the Boneyard, 1992, Reservoir Dogs, 1992, Backsliding, 1993, Bodies, Rest and Motion, 1993, Pulp Fiction, 1994, Rob Roy, 1995, Little Odessa, 1995; TV movies include Meantime, Made in Britain, Metamorphosis, Knuckle, Yellow Backs, King of the Ghetto, The Common Pursuit, Murder in the Heartland, 1993. Office: care UTA 9560 Wilshire Blvd Beverly Hills CA 90212*

ROTH, TOBY, congressman; b. Strasburg, N.D., Oct. 10, 1938; s. Kasper and Julia (Roehrich) R.; m. Barbara Fischer, Nov. 28, 1964; children: Toby Jr., Vicky, Barbie. B.A., Marquette U., 1961. Mem. 96th-103rd Congresses from 8th Wis. dist., Washington, D.C., 1979—; mem. Banking and Fin. Svcs. Com.; mem. Subcom. Internat. Econ. Policy and Trade. Served to 1st lt. USAR, 1962-69. Named Wis. Legislator of Yr. Wis. Towns Assn., 1978. Republican. Clubs: VFW (hon.), Optimists (hon.), Kiwanis (hon.). *

ROTH, WILLIAM GEORGE, manufacturing company executive; b. Lamberton, Minn., Oct. 3, 1938; s. Euclair Ford and Kathryn (Kluegel) R.; m. Patricia Elizabeth Gibson, Aug. 27, 1960; children: William, David. B.S.M.E., U. Notre Dame, 1960; MS in Indsl. Adminstrn., Purdue U., 1961. With The Trane Co., LaCrosse, Wis., 1961-85, v.p., gen. mgr., 1973-77, dep. chmn., 1977-78, chmn., chief exec. officer, 1978-85; pres. Am. Standard, Inc., N.Y.C., 1985-87; pres., chief exec. officer Dravo Corp., Pitts., 1987-89, chmn. bd., 1990—; bd. dirs. Amcast Indsl., Dayton, Cimflex Teknowledge, Pitts. Mem. NAM (bd. dirs. 1978-87). Republican. Roman Catholic. Office: Dravo Corp 1 Oliver Plz Pittsburgh PA 15222-2602

ROTH, WILLIAM MATSON, former corporate executive; b. San Francisco, Sept. 3, 1916; s. William Philip and Lurline Berenice (Matson) R.; m. Joan Osborn, Apr. 13, 1946; children: Jessica, Margaret, Anna. A.B., Yale U., 1939. With Barber Oil Corp., 1947; with Honolulu Oil Corp., 1948-50, also past dir.; chmn. bd. Pacific Nat. Life Assurance Co., 1960-63; v.p. fin., dir. Matson Nav. Co. (and subs.'s), San Francisco, 1952-61; dep. spl. rep. for trade negotiations, 1963-66, White House spl. rep. for trade negotiations with rank of ambassador, 1967-69; fellow Kennedy Center for Sch. Govt., Harvard U., 1969—; dir. McClatchy Newspapers, Sacramento. Hon. trustee Com. for Econ. Devel. Clubs: Pacific Union, Bohemian, Century. Address: 5073 Province Line Rd Princeton NJ 08540

ROTH, WILLIAM V., JR., senator; b. Great Falls, Mont., July 22, 1921; m. Jane K. Richards; children: William V. III, Katharine Kellond. BA, U. Oreg., 1944; MBA, Harvard U., 1947, LLB, 1949. Bar: Del., U.S. Supreme Ct., Calif. Mem. 90th-91st congresses at large from, Del., 1967-71; senator State of Del., 1971—; mem. fin., govt. affairs coms.; mem. joint econ. com., com. on banking, housing and urban affairs; chmn. Del. Rep. State Com., 1961-64; mem. Rep. Nat. Com., 1961-64. Served to capt. AUS, 1943-46. Decorated Bronze Star medal. Mem. ABA, Del. Bar Assn. Episcopalian. Office: US Senate 104 Hart Senate Bldg Washington DC 20510

ROTHBAUM, IRA, advertising and marketing executive; b. Phila.; s. Samuel and Charlotte (Gross) R.; m. Eileen Glickfeld, Dec. 26, 1972; children: Stephen Ira, Peggy Ann, John E. A.B. in Journalism, U. N.C., 1947; student, Columbia U., 1944. Copywriter RCA Victor, 1947-49, advt. and sales promotion mgr., 1949-50; divisional sales mgr. RCA Service Co., 1953; instr. Tulane U., 1952; copywriter N.W. Ayer, Phila., 1953-56; account exec., account supr. N.W. Ayer, Detroit, 1956-63; v.p., sr. v.p., mgmt. supr. N.W. Ayer, N.Y.C., 1963-71; sr. v.p., mgmt. supr. SSC & B, 1971-77; asst. to pres. W.B. Doner & Co., Southfield, Mich., 1977-80; pres. Wingfoot Mktg. Co., Boynton Beach, Fla., 1980-83; sr. broker Alan Bush Brokerage Co., Delray Beach, Fla.; v.p. investments Gruntal & Co. Inc., Boca Raton, Fla.; v.p. J.W. Charles Securities, Boca Raton, 1989-94; v.p. investments Stock Depot Inc., Delray Beach, Fla., 1994—; adj. prof. Fla. Atlantic U., Boca Raton. Served with USNR, 1943-46, 50-52. Home: 6109 Old Court Rd Boca Raton FL 33433-7844

ROTHBERG, ABRAHAM, author, educator, editor; b. N.Y.C., Jan. 14, 1922; s. Louis and Lottie (Drimmer) R.; m. Esther Conwell, Sept. 30, 1945; 1 son, Lewis Josiah. A.B., Bklyn. Coll., 1942; M.A., U. Iowa, 1947; Ph.D., Columbia U., 1952. Chmn. editorial bd. Stateside (mag.), N.Y.C., 1947-49; instr. English, creative writing Columbia U., N.Y.C., 1948; instr. English, humanities Hofstra Coll., Hempstead, N. Y., 1947-51; prof. English St. John Fisher Coll., 1973-83, chmn. dept. English, 1981-82; disting. writer-in-residence, vis. prof. Wichita State U., 1985; Ford Found. fellow, N.Y.C., 1951-52; editor-in-chief Free Europe Press, N.Y.C., 1952-59; mng. editor George Braziller, Inc., N.Y.C., 1959, New Leader (mag.), N.Y.C., 1960-61; cons. editor New Jewish Ency., 1960-62; writer, editorial cons.; European corr. Nat. Observer, Washington, Manchester (Eng.) Guardian, 1962-63; sr. editor Bantam Books, Inc., N.Y.C., 1966-67; Cons. editor The New Union Prayer Book, N.Y.C., 1975. (Recipient John H. McGinnis Meml. award for short story 1970, John H. McGinnis Meml. award for essay 1973-74, Lit. award Friends of Rochester Library 1980); Author: Abraham, Eyewitness History of World War II, 1962, The Thousand Doors, 1965, The Heirs of Cain, 1966, The Song of David Freed, 1968, The Other Man's Shoes, 1969, The Boy and the Dolphin, 1969, The Sword of the Golem, 1971, Aleksandr Solzhenitsyn: The Major Novels, 1971, The Heirs of Stalin: Dissidence and the Soviet Regime, 1953-1970, 1972, The Stalking Horse, 1972, The Great Waltz, 1978, The Four Corners of the House, 1981; Editor: U.S. Stories, 1949, Flashes in the Night, 1958, Anatomy of a Moral, 1959, A Bar-Mitzvah Companion, 1959, Great Adventure Stories of Jack London, 1967; Contbr. articles, essays, stories, poems to various pubs., anthologies, collections. Served with AUS, 1943-45. Home: 340 Pelham Rd Rochester NY 14610-3355

ROTHBERG, GERALD, editor, publisher; b. Bklyn., Oct. 29, 1937; s. Abraham and Pauline Rothberg; m. Glenda Fay Morris, June 18, 1970 (div. 1988); children: Laura, Abigail. B.A., Bklyn. Coll., 1960; postgrad., Dickinson Law Sch., 1962. Spl. projects editor Esquire (mag.), 1963-66; owner, editor, pub., founder Circus (mag.), N.Y.C., 1966—; owner, founder, editor Sci. and Living Tomorrow, 1980—, Who's In, 1981; founder, editor Sports Mirror mag., 1983—, MGF mag., 1985—; Country Mirror mag., 1994—. Author: (novels) Composition 36, 1993, The Six-Hour Song, 1994, Redeeming Esau, 1995. Mem. Periodical and Book Assn. Am. (pres.). Office: Circus Mag 6 W 18th St New York NY 10011

ROTHBERG, JUNE SIMMONDS, nursing educator emerita, psychotherapist, psychoanalyst; b. Phila., Sept. 4, 1923; d. David and Rose (Protzel) Simmonds; m. Jacob Rothberg, Sept. 7, 1952; children: Robert, Alan. Diploma in nursing, Lenox Hill Hosp., 1944; BS, N.Y. U., 1950, MA, 1959, PhD (NIH fellow), 1965; Diploma in Psychotherapy and Psychoanalysis, Adelphi U., Inst. for Advanced Psychol. Studies, 1987. USPHS traineeship N.Y. U., 1957-59; sr. public health nurse Bklyn. Vis. Nurse Assn., 1951-53; prin. investigator in nursing, homestead study project Goldwater Hosp. and N.Y. U., 1959-61; instr. N.Y. U., 1964-65, asst. prof., 1965-68, assoc. prof., 1968-69, project dir. grad. program rehab. nursing, 1964-69, prof., 1969-87, prof. emeritus, 1987—; dean Adelphi U., Garden City, N.Y., 1969-85; v.p. acad. adminstrn. Adelphi U., 1985-86; pvt. practice West Hempstead, N.Y., 1993—; pres. David Simmonds Co. Inc., Med. Supply Co., 1982-89; dir., chmn. compensation com. Quality Care, Inc.; cons. to various ednl. and svc. instns.; cons. region 2 Bur. Health Resources Devel., HHS.; speaker on radio and TV; bd. dirs. mem. audit com. Ipco Corp. (formerly Sterling Optical Corp.), 1991. Contbr. articles to profl. jours. Mem. pres's coun. N.Y. U. Sch. Edn., 1973-75; treas. Nurses for Polit. Action, 1971-73; trustee Nurses Coalition for Action in Politics, 1974-76; bd. visitors Duke Med. Ctr., 1970-74; mem. governing bd. Nassau-Suffolk Health Systems Agy., 1976-79; leader People-to-People Internat. med. rehab. del. to People's Republic of China, 1981; mem. com. for the study pain disability and chronic illness behavior Inst. Medicine, 1985-86, com. on ethics in rehab. Hastings Ctr., 1985-87; trustee Paget's Disease Found., 1987-89. Recipient Disting. Alumna award NYU, 1974, recognition award Am. Assn. Colls. Nursing, 1976, Achievers award Ctr. for Bus. and Profl. Women, 1980. Fellow Am. Acad. Nursing (governing coun. 1980-82); mem. Nat. League Nursing (exec. com. coun. of baccalaureate and higher degree programs 1969-73), Am. Nurses Assn. (joint liaison com. 1970-72), Commn. Accreditation of Rehab. Facilities, Am. Congress Rehab. Medicine (pres. 1977-78, chmn. continuing edn. com. 1979-86, 34th Ann. John Stanley Coulter Meml. lectr. 1984, Gold Key award 1984, Edward W. Lowman award 1990), Am. Assn. Colls. Nursing (pres. 1974-76), L.I. Women's Network (pres. 1980-81), Kappa Delta Pi, Sigma Theta Tau, Pi Lambda Theta. June S. Rothberg collection in Nursing Archives, Mugar Meml. Library, Boston U. Home and Office: 305 Elm St West Hempstead NY 11552-3224

ROTHBLATT, DONALD NOAH, urban and regional planner, educator; b. N.Y.C., Apr. 28, 1935; s. Harry and Sophie (Chernofsky) R.; m. Ann S. Vogel, June 16, 1957; children: Joel Michael, Steven Saul. BCE, CUNY, 1957; MS in Urban Planning, Columbia U., 1963; Diploma in Comprehensive Planning, Inst. Social Studies, The Hague, 1964; PhD in City and Regional Planning, Harvard U., 1969. Registered profl. engr. N.Y. Planner N.Y.C. Planning Commn., 1960-62, N.Y. Housing and Redevel. Bd., 1963-66; research fellow Ctr. for Environ. Design Studies, Harvard U., Cambridge, Mass., 1965-71; teaching fellow, instr., then asst. prof. city and regional planning Harvard U., 1967-71; prof. urban and regional planning, chmn. dept. San Jose State U., Calif., 1971—; Lady Davis vis. prof. urban and regional planning Hebrew U., Jerusalem and Tel Aviv U., 1978; vis. scholar Indian Inst. ARchitects, 1979; vis. scholar, rsch. assoc. Inst. Govtl. Studies, U. Calif., Berkeley, 1980—; cons. to pvt. industry and govt. agys. Author: Human Needs and Public Housing, 1969, Thailand's Northeast, 1969, Regional Planning: The Appalachian Experience, 1971, Allocation of Resources for Regional Planning, 1972, The Suburban Environment and Women, 1979, Regional-Local Development Policy Making, 1981, Planning the Metropolis: The Multiple Advocacy Approach, 1982, Comparative Suburban Data, 1983, Suburbia: An International Assessment, 1986, Metropolitan Dispute Resolution in Silicon Valley, 1989, Good Practices for the Congestion Management Program, 1994; editor: National policy for Urban and Regional Development, 1974, Regional Advocacy Planning: Expanding Air Transport Facilities for the San Jose Metropolitan Area, 1975, Metropolitan-wide Advocacy Planning: Dispersion of Low and Moderate Cost Housing in the San Jose Metropolitan Area, 1976, Multiple Advocacy Planning: Public Surface Transportation in the San Jose Metropolitan Area, 1977, A Multiple Advocacy Approach to Regional Planning: Open Space and Recreational Facilities for the San Jose Metropolitan Area, 1979, Regional Transpotation Planning for the San Jose Metropolitan Area, 1981, Planning for Open Space and Recreational Facilities in the San Jose Metropolitan Area, 1982, Regional Economic Development Planning for the San Jose Metropolitan Area, 1984, Planning for Surface Transportation in the San Jose Metropolitan Area, 1986, Expansion of Air Transportation Facilities in the San Jose Metropolitan Area, 1987, Provision of Economic Development in the San Jose Met. Area, 1988, Metropolitan Governance: American/Canadian Intergovernmental Perspectives, 1993; contbr. numerous articles to profl. jours.; dir.: Pub. TV series Sta. KTEH, 1976. Served to 1st lt. U.S. Army Corps of Engrs., 1957-59. Rsch. fellow John F. Kennedy Sch. Govt. Harvard U., 1967-69; William F. Milton rsch. fellow, 1970-71; faculty rsch. grantee, NSF, 1972-82; Calif. State U. 1977-88; grantee Nat. Inst. Dispute Resolution, 1987-88, Can. Studies Enrichment Program, 1989-90, Can. Studies Rsch. Program, 1992-93, Univ. Rsch. and Tng. Program grantee Calif. Dept. Transp., 1993-95; recipient Innovative Teaching award Calif. State U. and Coll., 1975-79; co-recipient Best of West award Western Ednl.

Soc. for Tele-communication, 1976; recipient award Internat. Festival of Films on Architecture and Planning, 1983, Meritorious Performance award San Jose State U., 1986, 88, 90. Mem. Assn. Collegiate Schs. of Planning (pres. 1975-76), Am. Inst. Cert. Planners, Am. Planning Assn., Planners for Equal Opportunity, Internat. Fedn. Housing and Planning, AAUP, Calif. Edn. Com. on Architecture and Landscape, Architecture and Urban and Regional Planning (chmn. 1973-75). Office: Urban and Regional Planning Dept San Jose State U San Jose CA 95192 *My basic view is that we should try to develop ourselves fully and help others do the same, so that we will be able to live in harmony with, and contribute to, our world community.*

ROTHCHILD, HOWARD LESLIE, advertising executive; b. Burlington, Vt., June 14, 1929; s. Daniel and Florence (Agel) R.; m. Sheila Segelman, June 3, 1973; children—Staci, Erik, Jessica. B.S., U. Vt., 1951; M.Litt., U. Pitts., 1952. Account exec. Lando Advt., Inc., Pitts., 1957-64; v.p. Goldman, Shoop & Rothchild, Inc., Pitts., 1964-67, Marc & Co., Inc., Pitts., 1967-72; chmn. bd. Rafshoon Shivers Tolpin, Inc., Atlanta, 1972-81; exec. v.p. Garber, Goodman & Rothchild Advt., Inc., Miami, Fla., 1981-87; pres. The Rothchild Group, Inc., Miami, 1987-89; chmn., pres., chief exec. officer The Rothchild Cos., Inc., Miami, 1989-93; dir. account devel. Gold Coast Advt. Assoc. Inc., Miami, 1994—; instr. U. Pitts. Grad. Sch. Bus., 1964-71. Bd. dirs. Big Bros. Am., Pitts., 1967-71, Lucky Acorns, Miami, 1991—. Served with AUS, 1952-54. Recipient Top Radio Comml. of Yr. award Nat. Retail Mchts. Assn. Mem. Am. Mktg. Assn., Bus./Profl. Advt. Assn., Advt. Fedn. Miami, Fla. Advt. Golf Assn. (founding dir.). Office: Gold Coast Advt Assoc Inc 3625 NW 82nd Ave Miami FL 33166-6633

ROTHCHILD, LOREN, toy manufacturing executive; b. 1940. V. chmn. bd. Franklin Mint Inc., Media, Pa., 1985—. Office: Franklin Mint Inc Baltimore Pike Media PA 19064

ROTHENBERG, ALAN I., professional sports association executive, lawyer; b. Detroit, Apr. 10, 1939; m. Georgina Rothenberg; 3 children. B.A., U. Mich., 1960, J.D., 1963. Bar: Calif. 1964. Assoc. O'Melveny & Myers, Los Angeles, 1963-66; ptnr. Manatt Phelps Rothenberg & Phillips, Los Angeles, 1968-90, Latham & Watkins, Los Angeles, 1990—; instr. sports law U. So. Calif., 1969, 76, 84, Whittier Coll. Law, 1980, 84; pres., gen. counsel L.A. Clippers Basketball Team, 1982-89; pres. U.S. Soccer Fedn., Chgo., 1990—. Mem. soccer commn. 1984 Olympic Games, Equal Edn. Opportunities Commn. State Calif. Bd. Edn., 1972-75; chmn., pres., chief exec. officer 1994 World Cup organizing com., 1990—. Mem. ABA, State Bar of Calif. (pres. 1989-90), local and county bar assns., Nat. Basketball Assn. (bd. govs. 1971-79, 82—, N.Am. Soccer League (bd. govs. 1977-80), Constitutional Rights Found. (dir., pres. 1987-90), Order of Coif. Office: Latham & Watkins 633 W 5th St Ste 4000 Los Angeles CA 90071

ROTHENBERG, ALBERT, psychiatrist, educator; b. N.Y.C., June 2, 1930; s. Gabriel and Rose (Goldberg) R.; m. Julia C. Johnson, June 28, 1970; children: Michael, Mora, Rina. A.B., Harvard U., 1952; M.D., Tufts U., 1956. Diplomate: Am. Bd. Psychiatry and Neurology. Intern Pa. Hosp., Phila., 1956-57; resident in psychiatry Yale U., West Haven (conn.) VA Hosp., 1957-58, Grace-New Haven Hosp., 1958-59; resident in psychiatry Yale Psychiat. Inst., New Haven, 1959-60, chief resident, 1960-61; practice medicine specializing in psychiatry New Haven, 1960-61, 1963-75; chief neuropsychiatry Rodriguez U.S. Army Hosp., San Juan, P.R., 1961-63; practice medicine specializing in psychiatry Farmington, Conn., 1975-79, Stockbridge, Mass., 1979-94, Chatham, N.Y., 1994—, Great Barrington, Mass., 1994—; dir. rsch. Austen Riggs Center, Stockbridge, Mass., 1979-94; asst. dir. Yale Psychiat. Inst., 1963-64, sr. staff mem., 1964-83; mem. staff Yale-New Haven Med. Ctr., West Haven VA Hosp., U. Conn. Health Ctr., Farmington; cons., mem. editorial bd. various jours. in psychiatry and psychology; instr. dept. psychiatry Yale U. Sch. Medicine, 1960-63, 64, asst. prof., 1964-68, assoc. prof., 1968-74, clin. prof., 1974-84; prof. psychiatry U. Conn. Sch. Medicine, Farmington, 1975-79, dir. residency tng., 1976-78, dir. clin. svcs., 1975-78; prin. investigator Studies in the Creative Process, 1964—; vis. prof. Pa. State U., 1971, adj. prof., 1971-78; vis. prof. dept. Am. studies Yale U., 1974-76; lectr. dept. psychiatry Harvard U. Med. Sch., 1982-86, clin. prof., 1986—; researcher in psychotherapy. Author: (with B. Greenberg) Index of Scientific Writings on Creativity: Creative Men and Women, 1974, Index of Scientific Writings on Creativity: General 1566-1974, 1976; (with C.R. Hausman) The Creativity Question, 1976; The Emerging Goddess: The Creative Process in Art, Science and Other Fields, 1979; The Creative Process of Psychotherapy, 1988; Adolescence: Psychopathology, Normality, and Creativity, 1990; Creativity and Madness: New Findings and Old Stereotypes, 1990; contbr. numerous articles on the creative process, schizophrenia, anorexia nervosa, and psychotherapy to profl. and popular jours. Researcher on creativity in the arts, sci. and tech. Served with M.C. U.S. Army, 1961-63. Recipient Tufts Med. Alumni award 1956, Rsch. Scientist Career Devel. award NIMH 1964, 69, Golestan Found. award 1991, 92; Guggenheim Meml. fellow 1974-75, Ctr. Adv. Study in Behavioral Studies fellow 1986-87, Netherlands Inst. for Adv. Study in Humanities and Social Scis. fellow, 1992-93. Fellow Am. Psychiat. Assn. (life), Royal Soc. Health, Am. Coll. Psychoanalysts; mem. AAAS, Am. Psychiat. Soc., Am. Soc. Aesthetics, Sigma Xi. Democrat. Home: Box 236 4 Pine Ridge Rd Canaan NY 12029

ROTHENBERG, ELLIOT CALVIN, lawyer, writer; b. Mpls., Nov. 12, 1939; s. Sam S. and Claire Sylvia (Feller) R.; m. Sally Smayling; children: Sarah, Rebecca, Sam. BA summa cum laude, U. Minn., 1961; JD, Harvard U. (Fulbright fellow), 1964. Bar: Minn. 1966, U.S. Dist. Ct. Minn. 1966, D.C. 1968, U.S. Supreme Ct. 1972, N.Y. 1974, U.S. Ct. Appeals (2d cir.) 1974, U.S. Ct. Appeals (8th cir.) 1975. Assoc. project dir. Brookings Inst., Washington, 1966-67; fgn. svc. officer, legal advisor U.S. Dept. State, Washington, 1968-73; Am. Embassy, Saigon; U.S. Mission to the UN; nat. law dir. Anti-Defamation League, N.Y.C., 1973-74; legal dir. Minn. Pub. Interest Rsch. Group, Mpls., 1974-77; pvt. practice law, Mpls., 1977—; adj. prof. William Mitchell Coll. Law, St. Paul, 1983—; faculty mem. several nat. communications law and First Amendment seminars. State bd. dirs. YMCA Youth in Govt. Program, 1981-84; v.p. Twin Cities chpt. Am. Jewish Com., 1980-84; mem. Minn. House of Reps., 1978-82, asst. floor leader (whip), 1981-82; pres., dir. North Star Legal Found., 1983—; Legal affairs editor Pub. Rsch. Syndicated, 1986—; briefs and oral arguments contained in Landmark Briefs and Arguments of the Supreme Court of the U.S., 1992; Mem. citizens adv. com. Voyageurs Nat. Park, 1979-81. Fulbright fellow, 1964-65; recipient Legis. Evaluation Assembly Legis. Excellence award, 1980, Vietnam Civilian Service medal U.S Dept. State, 1970, North Star award, U. Minn., 1961. Mem. Am. Bar Assn., Harvard Law Sch. Assn., Minn. Bar Assn., Am. Legion, Mensa, Phi Beta Kappa. Jewish. Contbr. articles to profl. and scholarly jours. and books, newspapers, popular magazines; author: (with Zelman Cowen) Sir John Latham and Other Papers, 1965. Avocations: long distance running, classical music, baseball. Home and Office: 3901 W 25th St Saint Louis Park MN 55416-3803

ROTHENBERG, GUNTHER ERICH, history educator; b. Berlin, July 11, 1923; came to U.S., 1949, naturalized, 1952; s. Erich and Lotte Rothenberg; m. Ruth Gillah Smith, June 19, 1969 (dec. Dec. 1992); children: Judith, Laura, Georgia. B.A., U. Ill., 1954, Ph.D., 1958; M.A., U. Chgo., 1956. Asst. prof. history So. Ill. U., 1958-63; assoc. prof. U. N.Mex., 1963-69, prof., 1969-73; prof. mil. history Purdue U., 1973—; lectr. U.S. Army Command and Gen. Staff Coll., U.S. Army War Coll., USAF Acad., USAF War Coll., U.S. Mil. Acad., USMC Command and Gen. Staff Coll., disting. chair mil. affairs 1992—. Author: The Military Border in Croatia, 1740-1882, 1960, The Austrian Military Border in Croatia, 1522-1747, 1966, The Army of Francis Joseph, 1976, The Art of Warfare in the Age of Napoleon, 1978, The Anatomy of the Israeli Army, 1979, Napoleon's Great Adversaries, 1981; also others. With Brit. Army, 1941-48. Guggenheim fellow, 1962-63; Fullbright fellow, vis. prof. Royal Mil. Coll., Duntroon, Australia, 1985. Jewish. Home: 210 E Lutz Ave West Lafayette IN 47906-3015 Office: Purdue U Dept History West Lafayette IN 47907

ROTHENBERG, JEROME, author; b. N.Y.C., Dec. 11, 1931; s. Morris and Estelle (Lichtenstein) R.; m. Diane Brodatz, Dec. 25, 1952; 1 son, Matthew. B.A., CCNY, 1952; M.A., U. Mich., 1953. With Mannes Coll. Music, N.Y.C., 1961-70; vis. prof. U. Calif., San Diego, 1971, 77-84, U. Wis.-Milw., 1974-75, San Diego State U., 1976-77, U. Calif., Riverside, 1980, U. Okla., Norman, 1984; vis. Aerol Arnold prof. English U. So. Calif., 1983;

vis. writer in residence SUNY, Albany, 1986, prof. English SUNY, Binghamton, 1986-88; prof. visual arts and lit. U. Calif., San Diego, 1989—, chmn. visual arts, 1990-93; head, creative writing, 1994—. Poet, freelance writer, 1956—; author numerous books of poetry and prose including Between, 1967, Technicians of the Sacred, 1968, Poems for the Game of Silence, 1971, Shaking the Pumpkin, 1972, America a Prophecy, 1973, Revolution of the Word, 1974, Poland/1931, 1974, A Big Jewish Book, 1978, A Seneca Journal, 1978, Vienna Blood, 1980, Pre-Faces, 1981, Symposium of the Whole, 1983, That Dada Strain, 1983, New Selected Poems, 1986, Khurbn, 1989, Exiled in the Word, 1989, The Lorca Variations I-VIII, 1990, Après le jeu du silence, 1991, Gematria, 1994, The Lorca Variations (Complete), 1993, An Oracle for the Deaf, 1995, Poems for the Millennium, 1995; editor, pub. Hawk's Well Press, N.Y.C., 1958-65, Some/Thing mag., 1966-69, Alcheringa: Ethnopoetics,1970-76, New Wilderness Letter, 1976-86. U.S. amb. to Spain, 1993—. Served with AUS, 1953-55. Recipient award in poetry Longview Found., 1960, Am. Book award, 1982, PEN Ctr. USA West award, 1994, PEN Oakland Josephine Miles award, 1994; Wenner-Gren Found. grantee-in-aide for rsch. in Am. Indian poetry, 1968; Guggenheim fellow in creative writing, 1974; NEA poetry grantee, 1976. Mem. P.E.N. Am. Center, New Wilderness Found. Office: c/o New Directions 80 8th Ave New York NY 10011-5126

ROTHENBERG, JOSEPH HOWARD, federal agency administrator; b. N.Y.C., Dec. 23, 1940; s. Abe Arthur and Nevia Theresa (Vuotto) R.; m. Frances Bernice Albano, Feb. 1, 1964; children: Edward, Joyce, Annette. BS Engring. Sci., SUNY, Farmingdale, 1964; MS Mgmt. Engring., C.W. Post Coll., 1973, MS, 1977. Project engr. Grumman Aerospace, Bethpage, N.Y., 1964-78, mgr. solar Max Mission Ops., 1978-81; mgr. ops. and test projects Computer Tech., Assocs., Englewood, Colo., 1981-83; space telescope ops. mgr. NASA, Goddard Space Flight Ctr., Greenbelt, Md., 1983-87, chief, mission ops. div., 1987-89; dep. dir. mission ops. and data systems directorate, 1989-90, assoc. dir. flight projects Hubble Space Telescope, 1990—. With USN, 1957-62. Recipient Laurel Award, Space/Missiles, Aviation Week & Space Tech., 1993. Mem. AIAA (Robert H. Goddard Astronautics award 1994), Instrument Soc. Am. (pres. I.I. sect. 1968-69). Avocations: sailing, skiing, music. Office: NASA Goddard Space Flight Code # 440 Greenbelt MD 20771

ROTHENBERG, LESLIE STEVEN, lawyer, ethicist; b. Wheeling, W.Va., June 22, 1941; s. Emil and Lucie (Kern) R.; m. Rose-Emily Horkheimer, Dec. 22, 1963; children—Joshua Samuel. B.S., Northwestern U., 1963; M.A., Stanford U., 1964; J.D., UCLA, 1968. Bar: Calif. 1969, U.S. Supreme Ct. 1972. Spl. asst. to pres. U. Calif. and to chancellor UCLA, 1968-69; exec. sec. Los Angeles County Employee Relations Commn., 1969; assoc. firm Kaplan, Livingston, Goodwin, Berkowitz & Selvin, Beverly Hills, Calif., 1969-71; dep. dir. Los Angeles Legal Aid Found., 1971-73; acting prof. law Loyola U., Los Angeles, 1973-77; vis. prof. law U. Calif., Berkeley, 1977-78; pvt. practice, L.A., 1978-84; pres. Leslie Steven Rothenberg A.P.C., Pacific Palisades, Calif., 1984—; adj. asst. prof. medicine UCLA Med. Sch., 1980-87, adj. assoc. prof. medicine, 1987-91, assoc. prof. clin. medicine, 1991—; dir. program in med. ethics UCLA Med. Ctr., 1984—; cons. ethics, 1979—; fellow The Hastings Ctr., Briarcliff Manor, N.Y. Author: The Draft and You, 1968; contbr. articles to profl. jours. Bd. govs. U. Judaism, Los Angeles, 1980-88. Woodrow Wilson fellow, 1963-64. Mem. AAAS, ABA, Los Angeles County Bar Assn. (trustee 1979-80), Bar Assn. San Francisco, State Bar Calif., Am. Soc. Human Genetics, European Soc. Human Genetics, Assn. Jewish Studies, Soc. Christian Ethics, Soc. Values in Higher Edn., Soc. Health and Human Values, N.Y. Acad. Scis., Internat. Soc. Technology Assessment in Health Care, Can. Bioethics Soc., Soc. Bioethics Consultation, Assn. Practical and Profl. Ethics, Soc. for Bus. Ethics, European Bus. Ethics Network. Jewish. Office: 16751 Edgar St Pacific Palisades CA 90272-3226

ROTHENBERG, MARC, historian; b. Phila., Oct. 13, 1949; s. William David and Marcinda (Paul) R.; m. Ivy S. Baer, June 23, 1985; children: Sara, Leslie. BA, Villanova U., 1970; PhD, Bryn Mawr Coll., 1974. Rsch. assoc. Acad. Natural Scis., Phila., 1974-75; cons. Am. Mus. Natural History, N.Y., 1975-77; asst. editor Joseph Henry Papers Smithsonian Inst., Washington, 1975-82, assoc. editor Joseph Henry Papers, 1982-85, editor Joseph Henry Papers, 1985—; gen. editor Garland Encyclopedias in the History of Sci. Garland Publishing, Inc., N.Y., 1992—. Author: (book) The Science and Technology in the United States: A Critical and Selective Bibliography, 1993. Mem. Forum History Sci. Am. (co-founder, editor 1988—), Interest Group History of Astronomy (co-organizer, mem. coun. 1993-94), Hist. Sci. Soc. (mem. coun. 1994—). Home: 8533 Milford Ave Silver Spring MD 20910 Office: Joseph Henry Papers Smithsonian Inst MRC 429 900 Jefferson Dr SW Washington DC 20560

ROTHENBERG, PETER JAY, lawyer; b. N.Y.C., Apr. 3, 1941; s. Max and Judith (Berkowitz) R.; m. Laraine H. Silver, Aug. 29, 1970; children: Daniel, Jason. AB, Harvard U., 1961, LLB, 1964. Bar: N.Y. 1965, U.S. Tax Ct. 1969. Dep. counsel judiciary sub. com. on jud. machinery U.S. Senate Com., Washington, 1965-66; assoc. Paul, Weiss, Rifkind, Wharton & Garrison, N.Y.C., 1969-73, ptnr., 1974—. Capt. U.S. Army, 1966-69. Mem. N.Y. State Bar Assn. (exec. com. tax sect 1979-87), Assn. Bar City N.Y. (tax com. 1977-79, com. on taxation of internat. transactions 1990-93), Internat. Fiscal Assn. Democrat. Jewish. Home: 895 Park Ave New York NY 10021-0327 Office: Paul Weiss Rifkind Wharton & Garrison 1285 Avenue Of The Americas New York NY 10019-6028

ROTHENBERG, ROBERT EDWARD, physician, surgeon, author; b. Bklyn., Sept. 27, 1908; s. Simon and Caroline A. (Baer) R.; m. Lillian Lustig, 1933 (dec. 1977); m. Eileen Fein, 1977 (dec. 1987); children: Robert Philip, Lynn Barbara Rothenberg Kay; m. Florence Richman, 1989. A.B., Cornell U., 1929, M.D. 1932. Diplomate: Am. Bd. Surgery. Intern Jewish Hosp., Bklyn., 1932-34; attending surgeon Jewish Hosp., 1955-82; postgrad. study Royal Infirmary, Edinburgh, 1934-35; civilian cons. U.S. Army Hosp., Ft. Jay, N.Y., 1960-66; attending surgeon French Polyclinic Med. Sch. and Health Center, N.Y.C., 1964-76; pres., 1973-76, trustee, 1972-76; attending surgeon Cabrini Health Care Center, 1976-86; cons. surgeon Cabrini Med. Ctr., 1986—; dir. surg. research, 1981—; clin. asst. prof. environ. medicine and community health State U. Coll. Medicine, N.Y.C., 1950-60; clin. prof. surgery N.Y. Med. Coll., 1981-86, prof. emeritus, 1986—; pvt. practice, 1935-86; chmn. Med. Group Coun. Health Ins. Plan of Greater N.Y., 1947-64; cons. Office and Profl. Employees Internat. Union (Local 153) Health Plan, 1960-82, United Automobile Workers (Local 259) Health Plan, 1960-86, Sanitationmen's Security Benefit Fund, 1964-83; dir. Surgery Internat. Ladies Garment Workers Union, 1970-85; med. adv. bd. Hotel Assn. and Hotel Workers Health Plan, 1950-60, Hosp. Workers Health Plan, 1970-76; past bd. dirs. Health Ins. Plan of Greater N.Y. Author and/or editor: Group Medicine and Health Insurance in Action, 1949, Understanding Surgery, 1955, New Illustrated Med. Ency., 4 vols., 1959, New Am. Med. Dictionary and Health Manual, 1962, Reoperative Surgery, 1964, Health in Later Years, 1964, Child Care Ency., 12 vols., 1966, Doctor's Premarital Medical Adviser, 1969, The Fast Diet Book, 1970, The Unabridged Medical Encyclopedia, 20 vols., 1973, Our Family Medical Record Book, 1973, The Complete Surgical Guide, 1973, What Every Patient Wants to Know, 1975, The Complete Book of Breast Care, 1975, Disney's Growing Up Healthy, 4 vols., 1975, First Aid—What to Do in an Emergency, 1976, The Plain Language Law Dictionary, 1980; contbr. articles to med. jours. Served to lt. col. M.C., AUS, 1942- 45. Recipient Cabrini Gold medal, 1986. Fellow ACS; mem. AMA, Bklyn. Surg. Assn., N.Y. Surg. Soc., Alpha Omega Alpha. Home: 35 Sutton Pl New York NY 10022-2464 also: Monterosso, Camaiore Italy *Truly great ideas are had by a large number of people. Success, however, is limited to the very few who have the ability to carry them out.*

ROTHENBERG, ROBERT PHILIP, public relations counselor; b. N.Y.C., June 5, 1936; s. Robert Edward and Lillian Babette (Lustig) R. BA, Cornell U., 1956; MS, Boston U., 1958. With publicity dept. Columbia Pictures Corp., N.Y.C., 1959-60; asst. to pres., pub. rels. dir. Harry N. Abrams Pub. Co., N.Y.C., 1960-62; press sec. to gubernatorial candidate William R. Anderson Tenn., 1962; with Rowland Co., N.Y.C., 1963-70, v.p., 1965-67, sr. v.p., 1967-70; ptnr., exec. v.p. Robert Marston and Assocs., N.Y.C., 1970-88, sr. exec. v.p. 1978-88, also bd. dirs.; pres. Marston and Rothenberg Pub. Affairs, Inc., N.Y.C. and Washington, 1977-88, Rothenberg Pub. Rels. Comms. Counsel, N.Y.C., 1988—. Trustee Mus. of Holography, N.Y.C.;

bd. dirs. Found. to Save African Endangered Wildlife; assoc. Nat. Park Found.; counselor Am. Bus. Cancer Rsch. Found., Southport, Conn.; bd. dirs. World Rehab. Fund, N.Y.C.; fellow Met. Mus. of Art, 1990—; pres., chmn., bd. trustees St. Bartholomew's Preservation Found., 1992-95; mem. Blue Hill Troupe, Ltd. With USAFR, 1959-65. Mem. Pride and Alarm Soc. Unitarian. Home and Office: Ste 29B 400 E 54th St New York NY 10022

ROTHENBERG, SUSAN, artist; b. Buffalo, Jan. 20, 1945; d. Leonard M. and Adele (Cohen) R.; m. George Trakas, May 1, 1971-1976; 1 dau., Maggie. B.F.A., Cornell U., 1966. One-woman shows of paintings include Willard Gallery, N.Y.C., 1976, 77, 79, 81, 83, Univ. Art Mus., Berkeley, Calif., 1978, Walker Art Center, Mpls., 1978, Greenberg Gallery, St. Louis, 1978, Mayor Gallery, London, 1980, Akron (Ohio) Art Mus., 1981-82, Stedelijk Mus., Amsterdam, 1982, Los Angeles County Mus., 1983, San Francisco Mus. Art, 1983, Carnegie Inst. Mus. Art, Pitts., 1984, Baltimore Museum of Art, 1988, Albright-Knox, Buffalo, N.Y. 1992-94; numerous group shows, 1974—, including Mus. of Modern Art, N.Y.C., 1980, Padiglione d'Arte Contemporanea di Milano, Italy, 1980, Clarke-Benton Gallery, Santa-Fe, 1980, Indpls. Mus. Art, 1980, Yarlow/Salzman Gallery, Toronto, 1980, Tex. Gallery, Houston, 1981, Young Hoffman Gallery, Chgo., 1981, Inst. Contemporary Art, Richmond, Va., 1981, Kunsthalle, Basel (Switzerland), 1981, Willard Gallery, N.Y., 1983, Los Angeles County Mus. Art, 1983, Inst. Contemporary Art, Boston, 1983, Barbara Krakow Gallery, Boston, 1984, Des Moines Art Ctr., 1985, A.P. Giannini Gallery, San Francisco; group exhbns. include A.M. Sachs Gallery, N.Y.C., 1974, Willard Gallery, 1975, 76, Inst. for Art and Urban Resources, Long Island City, N.Y., 1977, Mus. Modern Art, N.Y., 1977, Cleve. Mus. Art, 1978, Inst. Contemporary Art, Philadelphia, 1991-92, Museum of Modern Art, NY, 1992. N.Y., 1978, Whitney Mus. Am. Art, 1979, Renaissance Soc. of U. Chgo., 1979, Clarke-Benton Gallery, Santa Fe, 1980, Audrey Stohl Gallery 1980, Tex. Gallery, Houston, 1981, Univ. Art Mus., Santa Barbara, 1981, Akron Art Mus., 1981, Art Inst. Chgo., 1982, Sidney Janis Gallery, 1982,Paula Cooper Gallery, N.Y., 1983, Fogg Art Mus., Harvard U., 1984, CDS Gallery, 1984, N.Y. Pub. Library, 1985, Seattle Art Mus., 1985, Daniel Weinberg Gallery 1985,Barbara Mathes Gallery, 1986, Butlre Inst. Am. Art, Youngstown, Ohio, 1986, 1st Bank of Mpls., 1986-87, Mus. Fine Arts, Boston, 1986-87; represented in permanent collections, Mus. Modern Art, N.Y.C., Mus. Fine Arts, Houston, Whitney Mus. Am. Art, N.Y.C., Albright-Knox Art Gallery, Buffalo, Walker Art Center, Des Moines, Iowa., Akron Art Mus., Stedelijk Mus., Carnegie Inst. Mus. Art, Dallas Mus. Fine Art. Guggenheim fellow, 1980. mem. Am. Acad and Inst. of Arts and Letters, 1990. Office: care Sperone Westwater 142 Greene St New York NY 10012-3236*

ROTHER, JOHN CHARLES, association executive, lawyer; b. Springfield, Mo., Apr. 18, 1947; s. Charles C. and Eleanor J. (Morrison) R. BA with honors, Oberlin Coll., 1969; JD with honors, U. Pa., 1975. Bar: Pa. 1975, D.C. 1977. Appellate litigator NLRB, Washington, 1975-77; counsel Senator Jacob Javits U.S. Senate labor & human resources commn., Washington, 1977-81; staff dir., chief counsel spl. commn. on aging U.S. Senate, Washington, 1981-84; dir. legislation and pub. policy Am. Assn. Retired Persons, Washington, 1984—; mem. Commonwealth Fund Commn. on Elderly Persons Living Alone, N.Y.C., 1986-90, FDA Adv. Commn. Sec. Sullivan, Edward Commn., 1990-91; co-chmn. Generations United; founder Long-Term Care Campaign; founding mem. Nat. Acad. Social Ins. Bd. dirs. Corp. for Nat. and Comty. Svc. Named One of 150 Who Make A Difference, Nat. Jour., Washington, 1986. Mem. D.C. Bar, Nat. Council on Aging, Gerontol. Soc. Am., Am. Soc. on Aging. Office: Am Assn of Retired Persons 601 E St NW Washington DC 20049-0001

ROTHERHAM, LARRY CHARLES, insurance executive; b. Council Bluffs, Iowa, Oct. 22, 1940; s. Charles Sylvester and Edna Mary (Sylvanus) R.; m. Florene F. Black, May 29, 1965; children: Christopher Charles, Phillip Larry, Kathleen Florene. Student, Creighton U., 1959-61; BSBA, U. Nebr., 1965; postgrad. Am. Coll., Bryn Mawr, Pa., 1985, 87. CPCU, CLU, ARM. Claims rep. and underwriter Safeco Ins. Co., Albuquerque, New Mex., 1965-69; br. mgr. Ohio Casualty Group, Albuquerque, 1969—; assoc. in risk mgmt. Ins. Inst. Am., 1976—. Mem. PTA Collet Park Elem. Sch., Albuquerque, 1963-82, Freedom H.S., Albuquerque, 1982-86; bd. chmn. N.M. Property Ins. Program. Mem. New Mex. Soc. Chartered Property & Casualty Underwriters (charter mem., pres. 1975-77), New Mex. Soc. Chartered Life Underwriters, New Mex. Ins. Assn. Democrat. Roman Catholic. Avocations: race walker, swimming, taxidermist, hiking, camping. Home: 2112 Gretta St NE Albuquerque NM 87112 Office: Ohio Casualty Group 10400 Academy Rd NE Ste 200 Albuquerque NM 87111

ROTHERMEL, DANIEL KROTT, lawyer, holding company executive; b. West Reading, Pa., Mar. 21, 1938; s. Daniel Grim and Ruth Elizabeth (Krott) R.; m. Sarah Finch, July 9, 1960; children: Anne, Daniel F., K. Melissa. BS, Pa. State U., 1960; JD, Am. U., 1966. Bar: D.C. 1967. Acct. Lukens Steel Co., Coatesville, Pa., 1960-61; pvt. practice Reading, Pa., 1966-68; atty. Carpenter Tech. Corp., Reading, 1968-70, resident counsel, 1970-78, asst. sec., 1972-73, sec., 1973-88, v.p., gen. counsel, sec., 1978-88; pres., chief exec. officer Cumru Assocs. Inc., Reading, Pa., 1989—; bd. dirs. Sovereign Bank, Sovereign Bancorp, Inc. Mem. Inst. Cmty. Affairs, Pa. State U., 1974-78; bd. dirs. Berks County chpt. ARC, 1983-86; mem., chmn. adv. bd. Berks campus Pa. State U., 1982—; ch. lay leader. Lt. USNR, 1961-66. Mem. ABA, D.C. Bar Assn., Am. Soc. Corp. Secs., U.S. C. of C., Pa. C. of C., Reading-Berks C. of C., Rotary. Republican. Lutheran. Home: 20 Glenbrook Dr Reading PA 19607 Office: Cumru Assocs Inc PO Box 6573 Reading PA 19610-0573

ROTHFELD, MICHAEL B., investment banker; b. N.Y.C., May 19, 1947; m. Ella Foshay, May 21, 1970; 2 children. BA, Columbia U., 1969, MS, 1971, MBA, 1971. Assoc. editor Fortune Time Inc., N.Y.C., 1971-74, asst. to chmn. bd. dirs., 1974-76; assoc. Salomon Bros., N.Y.C., 1976-79, v.p., 1979-83; v.p. First Boston Corp., N.Y.C., 1983-85, mng. dir., from 1985. Office: First Boston Corp Pk Ave Pla 55 E 52nd St New York NY 10055-0186

ROTHFIELD, LAWRENCE I., microbiology educator; b. N.Y.C., Dec. 30, 1927; s. Joseph and Henrietta (Brown) R.; m. Naomi Fox, Sept. 18, 1953; children: Susan Anne, Lawrence, Jane, John. BA, Cornell U., 1947; MD, NYU, 1951. Intern, then resident Bellevue, Presbyn. hosps., N.Y.C., 1951-53, 55-57; successively instr., clin. asst. prof., asst. prof. NYU Sch. Medicine, 1957-64; from asst. prof. to assoc. prof. Albert Einstein Coll. Medicine, N.Y.C., 1964-68; prof. U. Conn. Sch. Medicine, Farmington, 1968—, chmn. dept. microbiology, 1968-80; mem. molecular biology rev. panel NIH, 1970-75, microbiology and immunology adv. com. Pres.'s Biomed. Rsch. Panel, 1975, molecular biology rev. panel NSF, 1979-83; mem. microbial physiology and genetics rev. panel NIH, 1990-94, chairperson, 1991-93. Author: Structure and Function of Biological Membranes, 1972; mem. editorial bd. Jour. Membrane Biology, 1969-83, Jour. Biol. Chemistry, 1974-80. With M.C. U.S. Army, 1953-55. Mem. Am. Soc. Biol. Chemists, Am. Soc. Microbiology (chmn. microbial physiology div. 1975). Home: 540 Deercliff Rd Avon CT 06001-2859 Office: U Conn Health Center Farmington CT 06032

ROTHFIELD, NAOMI FOX, physician; b. Bklyn., Apr. 5, 1929; d. Morris and Violet (Bloomgarden) Fox; m. Lawrence Rothfield, Sept. 18, 1954; children—Susan, Lawrence, John, Jane. B.A., Bard Coll., 1950; M.D., N.Y. U., 1955. Intern Lenox Hill Hosp., N.Y.C., 1955-56; instr. N.Y. U. Sch. Medicine, 1956-62, asst. prof., 1962-68; assoc. prof. U. Conn. Sch. Medicine, Farmington, 1968-72; prof., chief div. rheumatic diseases U. Conn. Sch. Medicine, 1972—. Contbr. chpts. to books; contbr. articles to med. jours. Mem. Am. Soc. Clin. Investigation, Am. Rheumatism Assn., Assn. Am. Physics. Home: 540 Deercliff Rd Avon CT 06001-2859 Office: U Conn Sch Medicine Div of Rheumatic Diseases Farmington CT 06030

ROTHFUS, JOHN ARDEN, chemist; b. Des Moines, Dec. 25, 1932; s. Truman Clinton and Beatrice (Keeney) R.; m. Paula Kay Harris, Sept. 26, 1959; children: Lee Ellen, David Merrill. B.A., Drake U., 1955; Ph.D., U. Ill., 1960. Asst. biochemistry U. Ill., Urbana, 1955-59; instr. U. Utah Coll. Medicine, Salt Lake City, 1961-63; asst. prof. U. Calif. Med. Sch., Los Angeles, 1963-65; prin. research chemist U.S Dept. Agr., Peoria, Ill., 1965-70, investigations head, 1970-74, research leader 1974-90, lead scientist, 1990—. Proctor & Gamble Co. fellow, 1957-58; USPHS postdoctoral fellow, 1959-61. Mem. Am. Chem. Soc., AAAS, N.Y. Acad. Scis., Am. Oil

Chemists Soc., Am. Soc. Plant Physiologists, Jojoba Soc., Phi Beta Kappa, Sigma Xi, Phi Lambda Upsilon, Omicron Delta Kappa, Alpha Chi Sigma. Home: 5615 N Sherwood Ave Peoria IL 61614-4148 Office: 1815 N University St Peoria IL 61604-3999 *Science and technology are stewardships passed to each generation. To preserve and nurture the spirit of inquiry and innovation that is their foundation while extending human opportunity and perspective, even incrementally, is to pass these stewardships successfully.*

ROTHHOLZ, PETER LUTZ, public relations executive; b. Berlin, June 23, 1929; came to U.S., 1945, naturalized, 1947; s. Alfred and Bertha (Isner) R.; m. Paula Trachtman, Sept. 16, 1951; 1 dau., Amy Elisabeth (dec.); m. Barbara Peters Margules, July 4, 1971; stepchildren: David, Thomas. B.A., Queens Coll., 1950; postgrad., N.Y. U., 1956-60; certificates, U. London, 1949, McGill U., 1950. With Lissone-Lindeman U.S., Inc., N.Y.C., 1953-56, KLM Royal Dutch Airlines, N.Y.C., 1956-61; exec. v.p. Simmons Tours, Inc., N.Y.C., 1961-62; pres., prin. Peter Rothholz Assocs., Inc., N.Y.C., 1962—; mem. faculty div. bus. mgmt. Sch. Continuing Edn. N.Y. U., 1969-70; mem. faculty Queens Coll., 1992—; mem. exec. com. Pacific Asia Travel Assn., Caribbean Tourism Orgn. Contbr. articles to various pubs. Bd. dirs. Queens Coll. Found., 1973-94, Nat. Coun. on Aging. With U.S. Army, 1951-52. Fellow Inst. Certified Travel Agts; mem. Pub. Relations Soc. Am., Soc. Am. Travel Writers, Queens Mus. (pres. 1977-78, chmn. 1978-80), Queens Coll. Alumni Assn. (pres. 1973-75), Phi Alpha Theta. Club: N.Y. Publicity (past v.p., dir.) Home: 55 Squaw Rd East Hampton NY 11937-4510 Office: Peter Rothholz Assocs Inc 380 Lexington Ave New York NY 10168-3297

ROTHING, FRANK JOHN, government official; b. Chgo., July 4, 1924; s. Frank Joseph and Eva A. (Buhl) R.; m. Carita Reiss Corbett, June 16, 1951; children: Frank John, Reginald, Peter, James, Richard, Joseph, Thomas, Carita Ann. B.S., U. Notre Dame, 1948. C.P.A., U. Ill., 1954. Pub. accountant Arthur Young & Co., Chgo., 1948-55; v.p. Midwest Stock Exchange, 1955-60, v.p., treas., 1960-66, sr. v.p., 1966-71; exec. v.p., sec., dir. Ill. Co., 1971-74; v.p. 1st Nat. Bank Chgo., 1974-75; exec. v.p. Front St. Securities, Inc., 1975-78; mem. Chgo. Office SEC, 1978, ret., 1989; chmn. bd. Chgo. Bd. Options Exchange Clearing Corp.; mem. Chgo. Bd. Trade. Adviser Jr. Achievement Chgo.; bd. dirs. St. Elizabeth's Hosp., Chgo.; mem. citizens bd. U. Chgo.; Bd. dirs., mem. exec. bd. North Shore Area Boy Scouts Am.; chmn. bd. trustees St. Mary of Woods Coll., Terre Haute, Ind. Served to 1st lt. USAAF, 1943-45. Decorated D.F.C., Air medal. Mem. Am. Inst. Accountants, Ill. Soc. C.P.A.s, Am. Accounting Assn., Newcomen Soc., Navy League U.S. Clubs: Michigan Shores; Bond of Chicago (dir.), Economic, Chgo. Athletic, Notre Dame (dir.), Attic (Chgo.)

ROTHKOPF, DAVID JOCHANAN, federal official; b. Urbana, Ill., Dec. 24, 1955; s. Ernst Zacharias and Carol Louise (Zeman) R.; m. Jane Octavia Prelinger, Dec. 14, 1985; children: Joanna Susan, Laura Madeleine. BA, Columbia U., 1977, postgrad., 1977-78. Press sec. Office of Congressman Stephen J. Solarz, Washington, 1979-80; sr. v.p. Tilley, Marlieb & Alan, Inc., N.Y.C., 1980-82; coord. prodr. TV Series-Omni: The New Frontier, N.Y.C., 1980-82; exec. prodr. PBS Series-Flashpoint, Newark, 1984; v.p. Fin. World Mag., N.Y.C., 1984-85; v.p., pub. spl. pubs. Instnl. Investor, Inc., N.Y.C., 1985-87; chmn., CEO Internat. Media Ptnrs., Inc., 1987-93; dep. under sec. commerce for internat. trade policy devel. U.S. Dept. Commerce, Washington, 1993—; CEO, chmn. The CEO Insts., N.Y.C., 1987-93. Author: The Common Market, 1978; editor Global Money Mgmt. Forum, 1986-87, Global Capital Markets Forum, 1986-87; editor-in-chief CEO/Internat. Strategies Mag., 1989-93, Emerging Markets Newspapers, 1987-93, World Market Outlook, 1991-93, Nat. Conv. News, 1992. Mem. Coun. Fgn. Rels. Democrat. Jewish. Home: 1228 30th St NW Washington DC 20007 Office: US Dept Commerce 14th & Constitution Ave NW Washington DC 20230

ROTHMAN, BERNARD, lawyer; b. N.Y.C., Aug. 11, 1932; s. Harry and Rebecca (Fritz) R.; m. Barbara Joan Schaeffer, Aug. 1953; children: Brian, Adam, Helene. BA cum laude, CCNY, 1953; LLB, NYU, 1959. Bar: N.Y. 1959, U.S Dist. Ct. (ea. and so. dists.) N.Y. 1962, U.S. Ct. Apls. (2d cir.) 1965, U.S. Supreme Ct. 1966, U.S. Tax Ct. 1971. Assoc. Held, Telchin & Held, 1961-62; asst. U.S. atty. U.S. Dept. Justice, 1962-66; assoc. Edward Gettinger & Peter Gettinger, 1966-68; ptnr. Schwartz, Rothman & Abrams, P.C., 1968-78; ptnr. Finkelstein, Bruckman, Wohl, Most & Rothman, N.Y.C., 1978—; acting judge Village of Larchmont, 1982-88, dep. Village atty., 1974-81, former arbitrator Civil Ct. N.Y.C., family disputes panel Am. Arbitration Assn., guest lectr. domestic rels. and family law on radio and TV, also numerous legal and mental health orgns. Author: Loving and Leaving-Winning at the Business of Divorce, 1991; co-author: Family Law Sect. Syracuse Law Rev., 1992, Leaving From Family Law Review, 1987; contbr. articles to profl. jours. Mem. exec. bd., past v.p. Westchester Putnam coun. Boy Scouts Am., 1975—; past mem. nat. coun., 1977-81; mem. N.Y. State PEACE Adv. Commn., 1991—. Recipient Silver Beaver award Boy Scouts Am., Wood Badge award; mem. Congregation B'nai Israel, 1961-63, B'nai Brith, Larchmont chpt., 1981-83. Fellow Am. Acad. Matrimonial Lawyers (bd. govs. N.Y. chpt. 1986-87, 91-93), Interdisciplinary Forum on Mental Health and Family Law (co-chair 1986—); mem. ABA (family law sect.), N.Y. State Bar Assn. (exec. com. family law sect. 1982—, co-chmn. com. on mediation and arbitration 1982-88, 93—, com. on legis. 1978-88, com. on child custody 1985-88, com. alternative dispute resolution, peace adv. com.), Assn. of Bar of City of N.Y., N.Y. State Magistrate Assn., Westchestr Magistrate Assn., N.Y. Road Runners Club, Limousine 6 Track Club. Democrat. Jewish. Office: Finkelstein Bruckman Wohl Most & Rothman 575 Lexington Ave New York NY 10022-6102

ROTHMAN, CLAIRE LYNDA, entertainment executive; b. Phila., Aug. 8, 1928; d. Paul and Anna (Schwartz) Polakoff; div.; children: Barry S., Karen Rothman Weinryt. Grad. high sch., Phila. Bus. mgr. The Spectrum, Phila., 1967-71; v.p. Wild Kingdom, Orlando, Fla., 1971-73; gen. mgr. Richfield (Ohio) Coliseum, 1973-75; dir. booking Calif. Sports, Inglewood, 1975-78, v.p., 1979-88; pres., gen. mgr. Calif. Forum, Inglewood, 1988-95; v.p., gen. mgr. we. region, sr. v.p. cmty. affairs Ticketmaster, L.A., 1995—; bd. dirs. Music Ctr. Operating Co. Bd. dirs. Am. Collegiate Talent Showcase, 1985-88, L.A. Sports Coun., Beckman Rsch. Inst., Women's Trusteeship/Internat. Women's Forum, mem., 1984, pres., 1993—, City of Hope, Duarte, Calif., Women Yr. Benefactor's award, 1986, mem. resources bd., former mem. conv. cabinet; mem. adv. bd. Centinela Hosp., Inglewood, 1980-91; active Women in Bus.; speaker numerous civic orgns.; commr. L.A. Conv. Ctr., 1993—, pres. commn., 1994—. Named Facility Mgr. Yr. Billboard mag., 1976, 79-82, One of Ten Women of the Decade Women in Bus., 1984; recipient Diamond Superwoman award Harper's Bazaar mag., 1980, Portfolio award Bullock's 1985, Sports and the Law award Constitutional Rights Found. 1988, Silver Achievement award YMCA, 1990, Outstanding Bus. Woman award Am. Bus. Women's Assn., 1991. Mem. Internat. Assn. Auditorium Mgrs. (past bd. dirs., speaker). Office: Ticketmaster 3701 Wilshire Blvd Inglewood CA 90016

ROTHMAN, DAVID J., history and medical educator; b. N.Y.C., Apr. 30, 1937; s. Murray and Anne (Beier) R.; m. Sheila Miller, June 26, 1960; children: Matthew, Micol. B.A., Columbia U., 1958; M.A., Harvard U., 1959, Ph.D., 1964. Asst. prof. history Columbia U., N.Y.C., 1964-67; assoc. prof. Columbia U., 1967-71, prof., 1971—; Bernard Schoenberg prof. social medicine, dir. Ctr. for Study of Society and Medicine; Fulbright-Hayes prof. Hebrew U., Jerusalem, 1968-69, India, 1982; vis. Pinkerton Prof. Sch. Criminal Justice, State U. N.Y., at Albany, 1973-74; Samuel Paley lectr. Hebrew U. Jerusalem, 1977; Mem. Com. for Study of Incarceration, 1971-74; co-dir. Project on Community Alternatives, 1978-82; chmn. adv. bd. on criminal justice Clark Found., 1978-82. Author: Politics and Power, 1966, The Discovery of the Asylum, 1971; co-author: Doing Good, 1978, Conscience and Convenience: The Asylum and its Alternatives in Progressive America, 1980, (with Sheila M. Rothman), The Willowbrook Wars, 1984, Strangers at the Bedside, 1991; Editor: The World of the Adams Chronicles, 1976, (with Sheila M. Rothman) On Their Own: The Poor in Modern America, 1972, The Sources of American Social Tradition, 1975, (with Stanton Wheeler) Social History and Social Policy, 1981. Bd. dirs. Mental Health Law Project, 1973-80, 82—. Recipient Albert J. Beveridge prize Am. Hist. Assn., 1971; NIMH fellow, 1974-75, 78-81; Law Enforcement Assistance Adminstrn. fellow, 1975-76. Mem. Am. Hist. Assn., Orgn. Am. Historians, N.Y. State Acad. Medicine, Phi Beta Kappa. Office: Columbia U

Coll Physicians and Surgeons Ctr Study Soc and Medicine 630 W 168th St New York NY 10032-3702

ROTHMAN, FRANK, lawyer, motion picture company executive; b. Los Angeles, Dec. 24, 1926; s. Leon and Rose (Gendel) R.; m. Mariana Richardson, Aug. 7, 1985; children: Steven, Robin, Susan. B.A., U. So. Calif., 1949, LL.B., 1951. Bar: Calif. 1952, D.C., U.S. Dist. Ct. (cen. dist.) Calif. 1951. Dep. city atty. City of Los Angeles, 1951-55; mem. law firm Wyman, Bautzer, Rothman, Kuchel & Silbert, Los Angeles, 1956-82; chmn. bd., chief exec. officer MGM-UA Entertainment Co., Culver City, Calif., 1982-86; ptnr. Skadden Arps Slate, L.A., 1986—. Bd. editors U. So. Calif. Law Rev., 1948. Served with USAAF, 1945-46. Fellow Am. Coll. Trial Lawyers; mem. L.A. Bar Assn., Calif. Bar Assn., Univ. Club. Democrat. Home: 10555 Rocca Pl Los Angeles CA 90077-2904 Office: Skadden Arps Slate 300 S Grand Ave Bldg 3400 Los Angeles CA 90071-3144

ROTHMAN, FRANK GEORGE, biology educator, biochemical genetics researcher; b. Budapest, Hungary, Feb. 2, 1930; came to U.S., 1938; s. Stephen and Irene Elizabeth (Manheim) R.; m. Joan Therese Kiernan, Aug.22, 1953; children: Michael, Jean, Stephen, Maria. BA, U. Chgo., 1948, MS, 1951; PhD, Harvard U., 1955. Postdoctoral fellow NSF, U. Wis., MIT, 1956-58, Am. Cancer Soc., MIT, Cambridge, 1958-59; postdoctoral assoc. MIT, Cambridge, 1957-61; asst. prof. Brown U., Providence, 1961-65, assoc. prof., 1965-70, prof., 1970—, dean of biology, 1984-90, provost, 1990-95. Contbr. articles to profl. jours. Served with U.S. Army, 1954-56. Spl. fellow USPHS, U. Sussex, Eng., 1967-68; NSF grantee, 1961-84. Fellow AAAS; mem. Genetics Soc. Am. Office: Brown U Box G Providence RI 02912

ROTHMAN, HENRY ISAAC, lawyer; b. Rochester, N.Y., Mar. 29, 1943; s. Maurice M. and Golde (Nusbaum) R.; m. Golda R. Shatz, July 3, 1966; children: Alan, Miriam, Cheryl, Suri. BA, Yeshiva U., 1964; JD, Cornell U. 1967. Bar: N.Y. 1967. Trial atty. SEC, N.Y.C., 1967-69; ptnr. Booth, Lipton & Lipton, N.Y.C., 1969-87, Parker, Chapin, Flattau & Klimpl, N.Y.C., 1987—. Bd. dirs. Camp Morasha, Lake Como, Pa., 1982—, vice chmn., 1992—; bd. dirs. Assn. of Jewish Sponsored Camps, Inc., 1986—; bd. dirs. Yeshiva U. High Schs., N.Y.C., 1984—, vice chmn. bd. 1990-91, chmn. bd., 1992—; v.p. Manhattan Day Sch., N.Y.C., 1985—; assoc. v.p. Orthodox Union, N.Y.C., 1990—. Mem. ABA (com. on fed. regulation of securities), N.Y. State Bar Assn., assn. of Bar of City of N.Y., Nat. Assn. Hebrew Day Schs., Yeshiva U. Alumni Assn. (pres. 1986-88, hon. pres. 1988-90). Office: Parker Chapin Flattau & Klimpl 1211 Avenue Of The Americas New York NY 10036-8701

ROTHMAN, HOWARD JOEL, lawyer; b. N.Y.C., July 10, 1945; s. Samuel and Avy (Avrutin) R.; m. Joan Andrea Solomon, July 2, 1967; children: Samantha, Rodney. BA, CCNY, 1967; JD, Bklyn. Law Sch., 1971; LLM, NYU, 1972. Bar: N.Y. 1972. From assoc. to ptnr. Marshall, Bratter, Greene, Allison & Tucker, N.Y.C., 1972-82; ptnr. Rosenman & Colin, N.Y.C., 1982—; mem. adv. panel Commr. Fin. of City of N.Y., 1981-83. Author profl. books and articles. Mem. ABA (corp. tax. com. 1977-87, income from real property com. 1980—), Internat. Bar Assn., N.Y. State Bar Assn. (corps. com. 1979-97, partnerships com. 1979—, N.Y.C. tax matters com. 1967—, income from real property com. 1987—), Bur. Nat. Affairs (real estate jour. 1984—, tax mgmt. adv. bd. 1979—), Alliance Resident Theatres N.Y. (bd. dirs. 1989—), Alliance for Young Artists and Writers (bd. dirs. 1994—). Office: Rosenman & Colin 575 Madison Ave New York NY 10022-2511

ROTHMAN, JAMES EDWARD, cell biologist, educator; b. Haverhill, Mass., Nov. 3, 1950. BA, Yale U., 1971; PhD in Biochemistry, Harvard U., 1976. Fellow MIT, Cambridge, 1976-78, asst. prof., 1978-81, assoc. prof., 1981-84; prof. Stanford (Calif.) U., 1978-88; prof. dept. molecular biology Princeton (N.J.) U., 1988-91; Paul Marks chair, chmn. program in cellular biochemistry and biophysics Sloan-Kettering Inst., N.Y.C., 1991—. Office: Meml Sloan Kettering Cancer Ctr Rockefeller Rsch Lab 1275 York Ave Box 251 New York NY 10021-6007

ROTHMAN, JULIUS LAWRENCE, retired English language educator; b. N.Y.C., Sept. 22, 1920; s. Samuel and Bessie (Kantor) R.; m. Stella Lambert, June 23, 1948. BSS, CCNY, 1941; MA, Columbia U., 1947, PhD, 1954. Lectr. Hunter Coll., N.Y.C., 1947-50, Rutgers U., New Brunswick, N.J., 1950-53; tech. writer Olympic Radio & TV, L.I. City, N.Y., 1951-61; prof. English Nassau Community Coll., Garden City, N.Y., 1962-86, prof. emeritus, 1986—; broadcaster, talk show host weekly program Sta. WHPC, 1974-82; deputy dir. gen. Internat. Biographical Ctr., Cambridge, England, 1992—. Editor, contbg. author The Cabellian, 1968-72; contbr. sects. to books on folklore and legend; contbr. articles to profl. jours. Mem. Nat. Com. to Preserve Social Security and Medicare, Arthritis Found.; mem. adv. bd. 9th Senatorial Dist. N.Y., 1984-88; seat sponsor Ariz. State U. Sundome Performing Arts Assn. Named Internat. Man of Year 1991-92, Internat. Biographical Ctr., Cambridge. Mem. Cabell Soc. (founder 1967, exec. v.p 1968-72), Ret. Pub. Employees Assn., Nat. Wildlife Fedn., Nat. Ret. Tchrs. Assn., Columbia U. Alumni Assn. Methodist. *Personal philosophy: Nothing is fully known. I expect more trouble than I bargained for.*

ROTHMAN, MARTHA L., architectural firm executive. Bachelor's degree, Sarah Lawrence Coll.; MArch, Harvard U. Registered profl. arch. speaker in field Am. Hosp. Assn.'s Internat. Conf. on Health Facility Planning, Design and Constrn., Nat. Symposium on Healthcare Design. Prin. works include Beth Israel Hosp., Mass. Gen. Hosp., Boston, Mass. Eye and Ear Infirmary, Boston, Beverly (Mass.) Hosp., The Cooley Dickinson Hosp., Northampton, Mass., The VA Med. Ctr., Togus, Maine, Maine Med. Ctr., Portland; published in profl. jours. including Hospitals, Healthcare Strategic Mgmt., Contract Design. Recipient numerous design awards. Fellow AIA. Office: Rothman Rothman Heineman Arch 711 Atlantic Ave Boston MA 02111-2809

ROTHMAN, MELVIN L., judge; b. Montreal, Que., Can., Apr. 6, 1930; s. Charles and Nellie (Rosen) R.; m. Joan Elizabeth Presant, Aug. 4, 1954; children: Ann Elizabeth, Claire Presant, Margot Sneyd. B.A., McGill U., 1951, B.C.L., 1954. Bar: Que. 1954. Practice law Montreal, 1954-71; mem. Phillips, Vineberg, Goodman, Phillips & Rothman; judge Superior Ct., Dist. of Montreal, 1971-83, Ct. Appeal of Que., 1983—. Mem. Jr. Bar of Montreal (pres. 1963-64), Bar of Montreal (council 1964-65), Institut Philippe Pinel (sec., dir. 1965-70). Home: 487 Argyle Ave, Westmount, PQ Canada H3Y 3B3 Office: Que Ct of Appeal, Court House, 10 St Antoine St E, Montreal, PQ Canada

ROTHMAN-DENES, LUCIA BEATRIZ, biology educator; b. Buenos Aires, Feb. 17, 1943; came to U.S., 1967; d. Boris and Carmen (Couto) Rothman; m. Pablo Denes, May 24, 1968; children: Christian Andrew, Anne Elizabeth. Lic. in Chemistry, Sch. Scis., U. Buenos Aires, 1964, PhD in Biochemistry, 1967. Vis. fellow NIH, Bethesda, Md., 1967-70; postdoctoral fellow biophysics U. Chgo., 1970-73, rsch. assoc., 1973-74, asst. prof., 1974-79, assoc. prof., 1980-83, prof. molecular genetics and cell biology, 1983—; mem. microbial genetics study sect. NIH, 1980-83, 93—, chair, 1994—, genetic basis of disease study sect., 1985-89; mem. Damon Runyon and Walter Winchell Sci. Adv. Com., N.Y.C., 1989-93; mem. biochemistry panel NSF, 1990-92. Contbr. numerous articles to profl. pubs. Fellow Am. Acad. Microbiology; mem. AAAS, Am. Soc. Microbiology (divsn. chair 1985, divsn. group II rep. 1990-92, vice chair GMPC 1995—), Am. Soc. Virology (councilor 1987-90), Am. Soc. Biochemistry and Molecular Biology. Office: Univ Chgo 920 E 58th St Chicago IL 60637-1432

ROTHMAN, STEVEN GEORGE, merchant banker, investment manager; b. Mankato, Minn., Oct. 4, 1946; s. Edwin George and Alice Joan (Johnson) R. BBA, U. Notre Dame, 1968; MBA, U. Chgo., 1972. Corp. fin. analyst Northwest Airlines, Inc., St. Paul, 1973, mgr. econ. analysis, 1973-78, dir. econ. planning, 1978, v.p. fin., treas., 1978-82, exec. v.p., treas., dir., 1982-83, exec. v.p. fin. and adminstrn., treas., dir., 1983, pres., chief operating officer, 1984, pres., chief exec. officer, 1985-86, chmn., chief exec. officer, 1986-89, also bd. dirs.; pres. IAI Capital Group, Mpls., 1989-93; chmn., CEO Great No. Capital, St. Paul, 1993—; bd. dirs. Honeywell Inc., Precision Castparts, E.W. Blanch Holdings Inc., Dept. 56 Inc. Chmn. St. Agnes Found., Channel 53 Cath. TV Minn. Decorated Bronze Star.

Republican. Roman Catholic. Clubs: Mpls.; Minn. Office: Great Northern Capital 332 Minnesota Dr Ste W 1295 Saint Paul MN 55121 *Success is not an accident; it is a habit. Success is the result of desire, dedication, sacrifice, mental toughness, hard work—and prayer. And you are not successful until you can share your success with others.*

ROTHSCHILD, ALAN FRIEND, lawyer; b. Columbus, Ga., Aug. 15, 1925; s. Irwin Bernard and Aleen (Samuels) R.; m. Eva Garrett Pound, Sept. 21, 1957; children: Alan Friend, William Garrett, Elizabeth Pound. B.S. in Commerce, U. Va., 1945, LL.B., 1947. Bar: Ga. bar 1948. Partner Rosenstrauch & Rothschild, Columbus, 1948-51; assoc. Hatcher, Stubbs, Land, Hollis & Rothschild (and predecessor), Columbus, 1951-57; ptnr. Hatcher, Stubbs, Land, Hollis & Rothschild (and predecessor), 1957—; bd. dirs. First Union Nat. Bank Columbus. Mem. Gov.'s Commn. on Revision Appellate Cts. Ga., 1976-80; mem. Ga. Bd. Bar Examiners, 1980-84, chmn., 1984; mem. bd. commrs. Med. Center, 1958-74, chmn., 1973-74; pres. Community Counseling Center, 1960-62; local co-chmn. NCCJ, 1958; active Boys Club, Jr. Achievement; trustee Springer Theatre, St. Francis Hosp., chmn., 1979-90; past trustee Three Arts League, Brookstone Sch.; life trustee, Columbus Mus.; bd. dirs. Walter Alan Richards Found., Anne Elizabeth Shepherd Home; pres. Columbus Legal Aid Soc., 1971-73. Fellow Am. Coll. Trusts and Estates Counsel, Am. Bar Found., Ga. Bar Found.; mem. ABA, Ga. Bar Assn., Columbus Lawyers Club (pres. 1967), Ga. Hosp. Assn. (trustee). Jewish. Home: 2328 Fairway Ave Columbus GA 31906-1018 Office: 500 Corporate Center Columbus GA 31902

ROTHSCHILD, AMALIE ROSENFELD, artist; b. Balt., Jan. 1, 1916; d. Eugene Isaac and Addye (Goldsmith) Rosenfeld; m. Randolph S. Rothschild, Aug. 3, 1936; children: Amalie R., Adrien R. Diploma, Md. Inst. Coll. Art, 1934; student, N.Y. Sch. Fine and Applied Art, 1934. Instr. painting Met. Sch. Art, Balt., 1956-59; lectr. fine arts Goucher Coll., 1960-68. One-woman shows include Balt. Mus. Art, 1971, NAS, Washington, 1975, Kornblatt Galery, Balt., 1978, 80, travelling retrospective exhbn., 1984, C. Grimaldi's Gallery, Balt., 1985, 88, 91, Md. Inst. Coll. Art, 1985, Franz Bader Gallery, Washington, 1989, 91, Artist's Pavillion, Tel Aviv, 1990, Gomez Gallery, Balt., 1993, 95, Art Rsch. and Tech., Lancaster, Pa., 1993; group shows include Jewish Mus., N.Y.C., 1952, Corcoran Gallery Art, Washington, 1958, 59, Pub. Art Trust, Washington, 1985, Elements of Style, Md. Inst. Coll. Art, 1986, Internat. Sculpture Ctr. Conf. Exhbn. of Sculptors Inc., Phila., 1992, N.Y. Sculptor's Guild, 1994, 95; represented in permanent collections Corcoran Gallery Art, Phillips Collection, Washington, Peale Mus. Balt., Balt. Mus. Art, Honolulu Acad. Arts, Fed. Res. Bank, Richmond, Va.; also corp. and univ. collections; commns. include archtl. panels Martin Luther King, Jr. Elem. Sch., Balt., 1969, wall hanging, Walters Art Gallery, Balt., 1974, plexiglass windos, Forest Park H.S., Balt. 1981. Chmn. artists com. Balt. Mus. Art, 1956-58, trustee, 1977-83, mem. accessions com., 1980-83; trustee Md. Inst. Coll. Art., 1991—. Recipient Disting. Alumni award Md. Inst. Coll. Art, 1985. Mem. Artists Equity Assn. (bd. dirs. Md. chpt. 1977-83), Sculptors Inc., Internat. Sculpture Ctr., New York Sculptor's Guild. Democrat. Jewish. Address: 2909 Woodvalley Dr Baltimore MD 21208-1915 *The definition of talent as power of mind and body committed to one for use and improvement describes my purpose in life. Late intellectual motivation followed early practical preparation for commercial art. Continuing self-education through multi-disciplinary reading, directing of energy into daily art-related endeavor, expecting integrity of performance in myself and others—these are my criteria for pursuit of excellence and fulfillment.*

ROTHSCHILD, CAROLYN ANITA, art dealer; b. Mineola, N.Y., Apr. 3, 1939; d. Edwin Ephraim and Mildred Marie (Hausel) Kohl; m. John David Rothschild, Nov. 26, 1966. BS, SUNY, Potsdam, 1961; MS, So. Ill. U., 1963; postgrad., NYU, 1963-65, Internat. U. Santander, Spain, 1965. Copywriter various advt. agys., N.Y.C., 1965-76; pres., owner Rothschild Fine Arts Inc., N.Y.C., 1976—.

ROTHSCHILD, DIANE, advertising agency executive; b. Apr. 11, 1943; d. Morton Royce and Marjorie Jay (Simon) R.; 1 child, Alexandra Rothschild Spencer. B.A., Aldephi U., 1965. Copywriter Doyle Dane Bernbach Advt., Inc., N.Y.C., 1967-73, v.p., 1973-79, sr. v.p., assoc. creative dir., 1979-85, exec. v.p., creative dir., 1985-86; pres. Grace and Rothschild, N.Y.C., 1986—. Recipient maj. advt. awards. Mem. YWCA Acad. Women Achievers. Office: Grace & Rothschild 114 Fifth Ave New York NY 10011

ROTHSCHILD, GEORGE WILLIAM, judge, lawyer; b. Chgo., Mar. 21, 1917; s. Edwin and Hannah (Loeb) R.; m. Valerie Jane Myers, Mar. 16, 1946; children: Jane Rothschild Jacobsen, John Steven. A.B. cum laude, Harvard U., 1939; J.D. cum laude, U. Chgo., 1942. Bar: Ill. 1942, N.Y. 1947. Assoc. Root, Ballantine, Harlan, Bushby & Palmer, N.Y.C., summer 1942, 46-49; atty., asst. and assoc. gen. counsel ECA (and successor aggys.), Washington, 1949-55; atty. GATX (formerly Gen. Am. Transp. Corp.), Chgo., 1955-61, gen. counsel, 1961-69, v.p., gen. counsel, 1969-78, sec., dir., 1972-78; spl. counsel Steel Project Program, Econ. Devel. Adminstrn., Dept. Commerce, 1979; counsel Coin, Crowley & Nord, Chgo., 1979-82; assoc. judge Circuit Ct. of Cook County, Chgo., 1983—. Trustee Hull House Assn. Lt. USNR, 1942-46. Mem. ABA, Ill. Bar Assn., Chgo. Bar Assn. (com. chmn. 1968, 71, 72), Chgo. Council Lawyers, Order of Coif, Cliff Dwellers (Chgo.), Columbia Yacht Club (Chgo.), Harvard Club (Chgo., N.Y.C.), Midland Shores (Wilmette, Ill.). Home: 321 Hamilton St Evanston IL 60202-1304 Office: Cir Ct Cook County 2102 Daley Ctr Chicago IL 60602

ROTHSCHILD, JOSEPH, political science educator; b. Fulda, Germany, Apr. 5, 1931; came to U.S., 1940, naturalized, 1945; s. Meinhold and Henriette (Loewenstein) R.; m. Ruth Deborah Nachmansohn, July 19, 1959; children: Nina, Gerson. A.B. summa cum laude, Columbia U., 1951, A.M., 1952, D.Phil. (Euretta J. Kellett fellow), Oxford U., 1955. Instr. dept. polit. sci. Columbia, N.Y.C., 1955-58; asst. prof. Columbia, 1958-62, asso. prof., 1962-68, prof., 1968—, Class of 1919 endowed prof., 1978—, chmn. dept., 1971-75, 81-82, 89-91; Vice chmn., mem. exec. com. Am. Profs. for Peace in Mid. East, 1975-90. Author: The Communist Party of Bulgaria, 1959, Introduction to Contemporary Civilization in the West, 3d edit, 1960, Chapters in Western Civilization, 3d edit, 1962, Communist Eastern Europe, 1964, Pilsudski's Coup d'Etat, 1966, East Central Europe Between the Two World Wars, 1974, Ethnopolitics: A Conceptual Framework, 1981 (transl. into Italian 1984, Japanese 1989), Return to Diversity: A Political History of East Central Europe Since World War II, 1989; contbr. articles to profl. jours. Recipient Mark Van Doren Great Tchr. award Columbia Coll., 1991; Social Sci. Rsch. Coun. 1963-64, J.S. Guggenheim fellow, 1967-68, Am. Coun. Learned Socs. fellow, 1971-72, Chamberlain sr. fellow, 1974, Ford rsch. fellow, summer 1976, NEH fellow, 1978-79, Lehrman Inst. fellow, 1979-80, Ford Found.-Am. Coun. Learned Socs. rsch. fellow, 1985-87, Woodrow Wilson fellow, 1994. Mem. Polit. Sci. Acad., Am. Assn. for Advancement Slavic Studies, Polish Inst. Arts and Scis., Am., Phi Beta Kappa. Home: 445 Riverside Dr New York NY 10027-6842

ROTHSCHILD, MICHAEL, economics educator; b. Chgo., Aug. 2, 1942; s. Edwin Alfred and Ann (Meyer) R.; m. Linda Preiss, Sept. 7, 1969 (div. 1991); m. Lynn Kay Greenberg, May 1, 1994; children: David, Daniel. B.A., Reed Coll., 1963; M.A., Yale U., 1965; Ph.D., MIT, 1969. Asst. prof. econs. Harvard U., 1969-73; lectr. Princeton U., 1972-74, assoc. prof., 1974-75, prof., 1975-76; then prof. U. Wis., Madison, 1976-83; prof. U. Calif.-San Diego, 1983-95, divisional dean social scis., 1985-95; dean Woodrow Wilson Sch. Pub./Internat. Affairs, Princeton U., 1995—. Editor: (with Peter Diamond) Uncertainty in Economics, 1978, (with Charles T. Clotfelder) Studies of Supply and Demand in Higher Education, 1993. Guggenheim fellow, 1978-79. Fellow Am. Acad. Arts and Scis, Econometric Soc.; mem. Am. Econ. Assn. Office: Woodrow Wilson Sch Econs Dept Princeton U Princeton NJ 08544-1013

ROTHSCHILD, STEVEN JAMES, lawyer; b. Worcester, Mass., Mar. 23, 1944; s. Alfred and Ilse (Blumenfeld) R. B.A., U. Vt., 1965; J.D., Georgetown U., 1968. Bar: D.C. 1968, Del. 1969, N.Y. 1992. Ptnr. Skadden Arps Slate Meagher & Flom, Wilmington; mem. Del. Bd. Bar Examiners, 1979-83; chmn. Del. Citizens Conf. on Adminstrn. of Justice, 1982; mem. Del. Bd. on Profl. Responsibility, 1992—, vice chmn., 1993, chmn., 1994—; vice chmn. rules com. Del. Supreme Ct., 1991-94; chmn. Del. Gov.'s

Commn. on Major Comml. Litigation Reform, 1993-94. Bd. dirs. United Way Del., 1978-85, 93—; v.p., 1981-84, chmn., 1994—; bd. dirs. Milton and Hattie Kutz Home, 1972—, pres., 1982-84; bd. dirs. Del. region NCCJ, 1981-92, Hebrew Immigrant Aid Soc., 1986-91, Jewish Fedn. Del., 1988-91; trustee Del. Art Mus., 1986-92, pres., 1990-92. Mem. ABA, Bar Assn. D.C., Assn. of Bar of City of N.Y., Del. Bar Assn. Office: Skadden Arps Slate Meagher & Flom One Rodney Sq PO Box 636 Wilmington DE 19899

ROTHSTEIN, ANNE LOUISE, education educator, college official; b. Bklyn., Feb. 15, 1943; d. William and Rose Mary (Smith) R. BS, Bklyn. Coll., 1963; MA, Tchrs. Coll. Columbia, N.Y.C., 1965, EdD, 1970. Tchr. Erasmus Hall High Sch., Bklyn., 1963-64, Fort Hamilton High Sch., Bklyn., 1964-64; lectr. Hunter Coll. in the Bronx, N.Y., 1965-68; instr., prof. Lehman Coll., Bronx, 1968—, dept. chair, 1980-83, assoc. dean, 1983-93, assoc. provost for sponsored program devel., 1993—; dir. Lehman Ctr. for Sch./Coll. Collaboratives, Bronx, 1988—. Editor, pub. (jour.) Motor Skills: Theory into Practice, 1976-87; chair editorial bd. (jour.) Strategies, 1986-92; author: Research and Statistics, 1985, Motor Learning: Basic Stuff, 1987. Fellow Rsch. Consortium Am. Alliance, Am. Alliance for Health, Physical Edn., Recreation and Dance; mem. Nat. Assn. for Sport and Physical Edn., Nat. Assn. for Girls and Women in Sport, Assn. for Supervision and Curriculum Devel., Am. Ednl. Rsch. Assn. Avocations: computers, golf. Home: PO Box 3007 Newtown CT 06470-3007 Office: Lehman Coll Bedford Park Blvd W Bronx NY 10468

ROTHSTEIN, ASER, radiation biology educator; b. Vancouver, B.C., Can., Apr. 29, 1918; emigrated to U.S., 1940, naturalized, 1955; s. Samuel and Etta (Wiseman) R.; m. Evelyn Paperny, Aug. 18, 1940; children: Sharon Leslie, David Michael, Steven Jay. B.A. in Zoology, U.B.C., 1938; student, U. Calif. at Berkeley, 1938-40; Ph.D., U. Rochester, 1943, D.Sc. (hon.), 1983. With atomic energy project U. Rochester, 1948—, co-dir., 1965—; mem. faculty U. Rochester (Med. Sch.), 1946—, prof. radiation biology, 1959—, co-chmn. dept., 1965—; dir. Rsch. Inst. Hosp. for Sick Children, Toronto, Ont., 1971-87, dir. emeritus, 1987—; prof. med. biophysics U. Toronto Med. Sch., 1972-87, prof. emeritus, 1987—, Univ. prof., 1980; vis. prof. Eidgenossische Technische Hochschule, Zurich, 1977; U.S. del. UNESCO Conf., Paris, France, 1957; NSF sr. postdoctoral fellow U. Bern, Switzerland, 1959-60. Recipient Wightman award Gairdner Found., 1986. Fellow AAAS, Royal Soc. Can. Home: 33 Harbour Sq #2018, Toronto, ON Canada M5J 2G2

ROTHSTEIN, BARBARA JACOBS, federal judge; b. Bklyn., Feb. 3, 1939; d. Solomon and Pauline Jacobs; m. Ted L. Rothstein, Dec. 28, 1968; 1 child, Daniel. B.A., Cornell U., 1960; LL.B., Harvard U., 1966. Bar: Mass. 1966, Wash. 1969, U.S. Ct. Appeals (9th cir.) 1977, U.S. Dist. Ct. (we. dist.) Wash. 1971, U.S. Supreme Ct. 1975. Pvt. practice law Boston, 1966-68; asst. atty. gen. State of Wash., 1968-77; judge Superior Ct., Seattle, 1977-80; judge Fed. Dist. Ct. Western Wash., Seattle, 1980—, chief judge, 1987-94; faculty Law Sch. U. Wash., 1975-77, Hastings Inst. Trial Advocacy, 1977, N.W. Inst. Trial Advocacy, 1979—; mem. state-fed. com. U.S. Jud. Conf., chair subcom. on health reform. Recipient Matrix Table Women of Yr. award Women in Comm., Judge of Yr. award Fed. Bar Assn., 1989, Wash. Women Lawyers Vanguard Hon. award, 1995. Mem. ABA (jud. sect.), Am. Judicature Soc., Nat. Assn. Women Judges, Fellows of the Am. Bar, Wash. State Bar Assn., U.S. Jud. Conf. (state-fed. com., health reform subcom.), Phi Beta Kappa, Phi Kappa Phi. Office: US Dist Ct 705 US Courthouse 1010 5th Ave Seattle WA 98104-1130

ROTHSTEIN, ERIC, English educator; b. Bklyn., Mar. 12, 1936; s. Emil and Charlotte (Spielberger) R.; m. Marian Grunwald, June 20, 1965 (div. Nov. 1985). AB summa cum laude, Harvard U., 1957; PhD, Princeton U., 1962. Instr. U. Wis., Madison, 1961-63, asst. prof. English, 1963-66, assoc. prof., 1966-70, prof., 1970-82, Edgar W. Lacy prof. English, 1982—. Author: Restoration Tragedy: Form and the Process of Change, 1967, George Farquhar, 1967, Systems of Order and Inquiry in Later Eighteenth-Century Fiction, 1975, Restoration and Eighteenth-Century Poetry, 1660-1780, 1981; co-author: (with F.M. Kavenik) Designs of Carolean Comedy, 1988, (with Jay Clayton) Influence and Intertextuality in Literary History, 1991; editor: George Farquhar: The Beaux' Strategem, 1967, The Augustan Milieu: Essays Presented to Louis A. Landa, 1970; co-editor: Literary Monoliths, 1967—. Named Univ. Houses professorship U. Wis., 1982; fellow Am. Council of Learned Socs., 1973; NEH fellow, summer 1980; fellow Inst. Research in The Humanities, 1985. Home: 417 Ridge St Madison WI 53705-3625 Office: U Wis 7187 Helen White Hall 600 N Park St Madison WI 53706*

ROTHSTEIN, FRED H., clothing executive; b. Berlin; came to U.S., 1941; s. Max M. and Margo (Kronheim) R.; children from a previous marriage: Paul M., Randi E.; m. Anita E. Gallo. Student, UCLA. Mdse. mgr. McGregor Sportswear, N.Y.C., 1955-59, Manhattan Shirts, N.Y.C., 1956-63; gen. mdse. mgr. Manhattan Internat., N.Y.C., 1963-66, v.p., 1966-69, pres., 1969—. Mem. YMA, N.Y.C., 1965—. With U.S. Army, 1950-52. Republican. Jewish. Office: Manhattan International 1114 Avenue Of The Americas New York NY 10036-7701

ROTHSTEIN, GERALD ALAN, investment company executive; b. Bklyn., Oct. 18, 1941; s. Manuel and Gertrude (Buxbaum) R.; m. Cynthia Bea Pincus, June 11, 1967; children: Michael Neil, Lori Pamela, Meryl Patricia. BBA, City Coll. N.Y., 1962; MBA, U. Pa., 1965. 1st v.p. Shearson Hammill & Co., N.Y.C., 1964-74, Shearson Hayden Stone, N.Y.C., 1974-75; v.p. William D. Witter, Inc., N.Y.C., 1975-76; v.p. Oppenheimer & Co., N.Y.C., 1976-79, sr. v.p., 1979-83, mng. dir., 1983—; dir. internat. rsch., 1991—; bd. dirs. Midway Guaranty S.A. Mem. N.Y. Soc. Security Analysts, Inst. Chartered Fin. Analysts, Coun. of the Americas, Internat. Soc. Fin. Analysts. Office: Oppenheimer & Co Inc Oppenheimer Tower World Fin Ctr New York NY 10281

ROTHSTEIN, MORTON, historian, retired educator; b. Omaha, Jan. 8, 1926; s. Joseph Isadore and Rose (Lindman) R.; m. Frances Irene Lustig, Nov. 18, 1950; children: Laurence, Eric, David. Student, Bklyn. Coll., 1952-54; Ph.D., Cornell U., 1960; postgrad., London Sch. Econs., 1956-57. Instr. U. Del., 1958-61; asst. prof. U. Wis.-Madison 1961-65, assoc. prof., 1965-69, prof. history and agrl. econs., 1969-84, chmn. history dept., 1969-72; prof. history U. Calif., Davis, 1984-94; emeritus prof. U. Calif., Davis, 1994—; vis. prof. London Sch. Econs., 1977; mem. acad. adv. bd. Eleutherian Mills-Hagley Found., 1970-74; mem. Wis. Humanities Coun., 1978-84, chmn., 1980-82, Calif. Coun. Humanities, 1985-90, chmn. 1988-90. Editor: Explorations in Economic History, 1970-73, Agricultural History, 1984-94; co-editor: Outstanding In His Field: Essays in Honor of Wayne D. Rasmussen, 1993, Quantification in Agrarian History: Essays by American and Soviet Historians, 1994; contbr. articles to profl. jours. Social Sci. Research Council fellow, 1956-57, 67-68; NEH fellow, 1976-77, 83. Mem. Orgn. Am. Historians, Agrl. History Soc. (pres. 1975-76), Bus. History Conf. (pres. 1985-86), Econ. History Assn., Econ. History Soc. (U.K.), So. History Assn., We. History Assn., Calif. Hist. Soc. (trustee 1989-90). Jewish. Home: 3417 Seabright Ave Davis CA 95616-5641 Office: U Calif Dept History Davis CA 95616 *The example of teachers who were thoroughly engaged in research, and generated excitement from it, has informed my own efforts at writing and in the classroom. A professor must have something to profess. Openness and generosity has benefited me, and taught me never to count other people's money, or to fear doing someone a favor.*

ROTHSTEIN, PAUL FREDERICK, lawyer, educator; b. Chgo., June 6, 1938. B.S., Northwestern U., 1958, LL.B., 1961. Bar: Ill. 1962, D.C. 1967, U.S. Supreme Ct. 1975. Instr. U. Mich. Law Sch., 1963; assoc. prof. law U. Tex., 1964-67; mem. Surrey, Karasik, Gould & Greene, Washington, 1967-70; prof. Georgetown U. Law Ctr., Washington, 1970—ABA (chmn. rules of evidence and criminal procedure com., criminal justice sect. 1984—), univs.; spl. counsel U.S. Senate Jud. Com. Subcom. on Criminal Laws and Procedures, 1975-77, U.S. Ho. of Reps. Jud. Com. Subcom. on Criminal Law, 1980; cons. Treasury, 1967-74, HEW, 1970, Commrs. on Uniform State Laws, 1969-75, Nat. Acad. Scis., 1976-77, D.C. Law Revision Commn., 1976-78; speaker, coordinator numerous legal edn. seminars for judges and lawyers, 1970—. Recipient U. Iowa Legal Edn. award 1974, Disting. Pub. Service award Crime Victims Compensation Bd., 1978; other civic and profl. awards; Fulbright scholar, Oxford, Eng., 1962-63. Mem. Fed. Bar Assn.

(chmn. fed. rules of evidence com. 1974-77, Disting. Service award 1975 nat. council 1976—, chmn. continuing legal edn. com. 1980), D.C. Bar (continuing legal edn. bd. 1980—), ABA (chmn. rules of evidence and criminal procedure com., criminal justice sect. 1984—), Assn. Am. Law Schs. (sec. evidence sect. 1976, chmn. 1977), Nat. Assn. Criminal Injuries Compensations Bds. (sec. 1977—), Internat. Assn. Criminal Injuries Compensation Bds. Author: Evidence in a Nutshell, 1970, 2d edit., 1981; Understanding the New Federal Rules of Evidence, 1973, 74, 75; Federal Rules of Evidence with Practice Comments and Annotations, 1978, 2d edit., 1981; Cases, Materials and Problems in Evidence, 1986; contbr. articles on evidence and trial to profl. jours.; editor-in-chief Northwestern U. Law Rev., 1960-61. Office: Georgetown U Law Ctr 600 New Jersey Ave NW Washington DC 20001-2075

ROTHSTEIN, RICHARD, public relations executive; b. N.Y., Oct. 22, 1948. BA in Hist., Montclaire State Coll., 1970. Assoc. editor Lebhar-Friedman, 1971-72; editor Harcourt Brace Jovanovitch, 1972-76; sr. editor Med. Econs. Co., 1977-80; A/S Daniel J. Edelman, 1981-83, v.p., 1983-84, sr. v.p., 1984-85, exec. v.p., 1986-87; R & R, mng. dir. Med. Commns., 1987; pres. Ruder Finn & Rotman Med. Mktg. Unit, 1987; pres. Edelman Med. Communications Edelman PR Worldwide, 1991—. Recipient Jesse H. Neal award in Journalism, 1973. Office: Edelman PR Worldwide 1500 Broadway New York NY 10035

ROTHSTEIN, RONALD, professional basketball coach; b. Bronxville, NY, Dec. 27, 1942; m. Olivia Pierorazio; children: David, Dana. Grad., U. R.I., 1964; M degree, CCNY. Asst. coach Upsala Coll., 1974-75; high sch. coach, 1976-79; northeastern regional scout Atlanta Hawks, 1979-82, asst. coach, 1983-86; asst. coach Detroit Pistons, 1986-88, head coach, 1992-93; head coach Miami Heat, 1988-91; scout N.Y. Knicks, 1982-83; asst. coach Cleveland Cavaliers, 1993—. Office: care Cleveland Cavaliers 1 Center Court Cleveland OH 44115-4001*

ROTHSTEIN, RUTH M., hospital adminstrator. Dir. Cook County Hosp., Chgo.; chief Cook County Bur. of Health Svcs. Mailing: Cook County Hosp 1835 W Harrison St Chicago IL 60612

ROTHSTEIN, SAMUEL, librarian, educator; b. Moscow, Jan. 12, 1921; arrived in Can., 1922, naturalized, 1929; s. Louis Israel and Rose (Checov) R.; m. Miriam Ruth Teitelbaum, Aug. 26, 1951; children: Linda Rose, Sharon Lee. BA, U. B.C., 1939, MA, 1940; student, U. Calif., Berkeley, 1941-42, BLS, 1947; student, U. Wash., 1942-43; PhD (Carnegie Corp. fellow 1951-54), U. Ill., 1954; DLitt, York U., 1971. Teaching fellow U. Wash., 1942-43; prin. libr. asst. U. Calif., Berkeley, 1947; mem. staff U. B.C. Libr., Vancouver, Can., 1946-51, 54-62; acting univ. libr. U. B.C., Vancouver, Can., 1961-62, prof. libr. sci., 1961-86, prof. emeritus, 1986—, dir. Sch. Librarianship, 1961-70; vis. prof. U. Hawaii, 1969, U. Toronto, 1970, 79, Hebrew U., Jerusalem, 1973; mem. Common. Nat. Plan Libr. Edn., 1963—; mem. assoc. com. sci. info. Nat. Rsch. Coun. Can., 1962—; councillor B.C. Med. Libr. Svc., 1971; mem. exec. com. Pacific divsn. Can. Jewish Congress, 1962-69, Internat. House Assn. B.C., 1959-60; mem. Can. Adv. Bd. Sci. and Tech. Inof.l; mem. cabinet Combined Jewish Appeal of Greater Vancouver, 1992—; pres. Vancouver Pub. Libr. Trust, 1987-88. Author: The Development of Reference Services, 1955, (with others) Training Professional Librarians for Western Canada, 1957, The University-The Library, 1972, Rothstein on Reference..., 1989; also articles.; co-editor: As We Remember It, 1970. Life mem. bd. dirs. Jewish Cmty. Ctr. of Greater Vancouver, pres., 1972-74; bd. dirs. Jewish Fedn. of Greater Vancouver, 1993—. Recipient Helen Gordon Stewart award, 1970, ALISE award Am. Library Info. Sci. Edn., 1987, Beta Phi Mu award ALA, 1988. Mem. Can. Libr. Assn. (hon. life), Assn. Am. Libr. Schs. (pres. 1968-69), Can. Assn. Libr. Schs. (hon. life, pres. 1982-84), ALA (coun. 1963-69, Beta Phi Mu award 1988), B.C. Libr. Assn. (hon. life, pres. 1959-60), Pacific N.W. Libr. Assn. (pres. 1963-64, hon. life), Can. Libr. Assn. (hon. life, coun. 1958-60, Outstanding Svc. to Librarianship award 1986), Bibliog. Soc. Can. (coun. 1959-63), Can. Assn. Univ. Tchrs. Home: 1416 W 40th Ave, Vancouver, BC Canada

ROTHWELL, ALBERT FALCON, retired lawyer, retired natural resource company executive; b. N.Y.C., Sept. 2, 1926; s. Albert Cyril and Finita Maria (Falcon) R.; m. Jane Thomas, June 4, 1949 (dec. Dec. 1994); children: Susan, Peter, Anne James. AB, Princeton U., 1948; LLB, Columbia U., 1951, postgrad., 1956-58. Bar: N.Y. Assoc. Sullivan & Cromwell, N.Y.C., 1951-56; chief exec. officer Nat. Potash Co., N.Y.C., 1972-75; v.p. Freeport Minerals Co., N.Y.C., 1975-81; sr. v.p., treas. Freeport-McMoRan Inc., N.Y.C., 1981-86, ret., 1986. Pres. Quioque Assn., Westhampton Beach, N.Y., 1982-83; Citizens for Good Schs., Glen Ridge, N.J., 1973-74; vice chmn. civic conf. com., Glen Ridge, 1970-71. Served with USN, 1944-46. Mem. Quantuck Yacht Club (commodore 1969-70), Quantuck Beach Club (Westhampton Beach, N.y., pres. 1989-92). Avocations: fishing, photography.

ROTHWELL, ROBERT CLARK, agricultural products executive; b. St. Louis, Dec. 7, 1939; s. Fountain and Frances Marie (Bickell) R.; m. Virginia Warren Hubbard, Apr. 18, 1961; children: Sharon Lee, James Clark, Janice Lynn, David Matthews. BSBA, U. Mo., 1967. CPA, Mo. Staff auditor Arthur Andersen & Co., Kansas City, Mo., 1967-71; internal auditor MFA, Inc., Columbia, Mo., 1971-75, mgr. auditing, 1975-79, contr., 1979-81, v.p. fin., 1981-88, treas., 1987—, sr. v.p. fin., 1988—; treas. Agmo Corp., Columbia; mem. investment com. MFA Found., Columbia, MFA Employees Retirement Plan, Columbia; advisor U. Mo. Sch. Accountancy, Columbia, 1987-91. Author various presentations on fin. mgmt. Instr. Mo. Inst. Cooperation, Columbia, 1987-91; bd. dirs. Coop. Buyers Assn., Stuttgart, Ark., Inst. Coop. Fin. Officers, Mo. Coun. on Econ. Edn., Mid-Mo. Alzheimer's Assn., 1995—. Mem. AICPA, Mo. Soc. CPAs, Fin. Execs. Inst., Nat. Assn. Accts. for Coops., Nat. Coun. Farmer Coops. Republican. Office: MFA Inc 615 Locust St Columbia MO 65201-4891

ROTHWELL, TIMOTHY GORDON, pharmaceutical company executive; b. London, Jan. 8, 1951; came to us., 1965; s. Kenneth Gordon Rothwell and Jean Mary (Stedman) Davey; m. Joanne Claire Fleming; children: Tiffany, Heather. BA, Drew U., 1972; JD, Seton Hall U., 1976; LLM, NYU, 1979, MBA, 1983. With Sandoz Pharms., East Hanover, N.J., 1972—, patent atty., 1974-77, patent and trademark counsel, 1980-82, mng. ops. planning and adminstrn., 1982-84, dir. mktg. ops., 1984-85, exec. dir. field ops., 1985-86, v.p. field ops., 1986-87, pres. profl. bus. ops., 1987-88, corp. v.p., chief oper. officer, 1988-89; sr. v.p. sales Squibb Pharm. Group, Princeton, N.J., 1989—. Patentee in field. Mem. N.J. State Bar Assn., N.Y. State Bar Assn., Am. Soc. for Pharmacy Law, Nat. Health Care Quality Coun., Am. Found. for Pharm. Exec. (bd. dirs.), N.J. Patent Law Assn. (pres. 1986). Republican. Episcopalian. Avocations: philately, coaching youth soccer, golf, tennis. Office: Sandoz Pharm Corp 59 State Route 10 East Hanover NJ 07936

ROTMAN, CARLOTTA J. H., physician; b. Chgo., Apr. 8, 1948; d. Clarence Kenneth and Vlasta (Cizek) Hayes; m. Chester James Hill III, June 10, 1967 (div. 1974); m. Carlos Alberto Rotman, July 31, 1980; children: Robin Mercedes. BA magna cum laude, Knox Coll., 1969; MD with honors, U. Ill., 1973. Diplomate Nat. Bd. Med. Examiners, 1974, Am. Bd. Dermatology, 1978. Intern Mayo Sch. Medicine, Rochester, N.Y., 1973-74; resident U. Ill. Chgo., 1975-78, asst. prof. clin. dermatology Coll. Medicine, 1978-93, assoc. prof. clin. dermatology Coll. Medicine, 1993—; sen. U. Ill. Senate, Chgo., 1986-91; councilor Chgo. Med. Soc., 1990—. Contbr. articles to profl. jours. mem. bd. dirs. Summerfest St. James Cathedral, Chgo., 1986-91; master gardner Chgo. Botanic Garden, Glencoe, Ill., 1994. Recipient Janet Glascow award Am. Women's Med. Assn., 1973. Mem. AMA, Am. Acad. Dermatology, Herb Soc. Am., Ill. State Med. Assn., Ill. State Dermatologic Soc., Chgo. Med. Soc., Chgo. Dermatologic Soc., Phi Beta Kappa, Alpha Omega Alpha. Episcopalian. Avocations: travel, cooking, gardening, reading. Office: Dept Dermatology 808 S Wood Chicago IL 60612

ROTMAN, MORRIS BERNARD, public relations consultant; b. Chgo., June 6, 1918; s. Louis and Etta (Harris) R.; m. Sylvia Sugar, Mar. 1, 1944; children: Betty Ruth, Jesse, Richard. Student, Wright Jr. Coll., 1936-37, Northwestern U., 1937-39. Editor Times Neighborhood publs., Chgo., 1938-40; asst. editor City News Bur., 1940-42; mng. editor Scott Field Broad-

caster, USAAF, 1942-43; publicity dir. Community and War Fund of Met. Chgo., 1943-45; v.p. William R. Harshe Assocs., 1945-49, pres., 1949-66; chmn. bd., chief exec. officer (name changed to Harshe-Rotman & Druck, Inc.), 1966-81; pres. Ruder Finn & Rotman, Inc. (merger of Harshe-Rotman & Druck and Ruder & Finn), 1982, ret.; founder Morris B. Rotman & Assocs., Chgo., 1989—; adj. prof. Coll. of Desert, Palm Desert, Calif. Chmn. solicitations pub. rels. div. Community Fund Chgo., 1948-49, spl. events chmn., 1953; chmn. communications div. Jewish Fedn. Chgo., 1965, Combined Jewish Appeal,1 966; life dir. Rehab. Inst. Chgo.; U.S. dir. The Shakespeare Globe Centre (N.Am.) Inc.; trustee Roosevelt U. (emeritus). Recipient Prime Minister Israel medal, 1969. Mem. Pub. Rels. Soc. Am. (past dir.), Chgo. Presidents' Orgn. (pres. 1970-71), Acad. Motion Picture Arts and Scis. (assoc.), Chief Execs. Orgn., Chgo. Press Vets. Assn., Mid-Am. Club, Standard Club, Publicity Club, Bryn Mawr Country Club, Tamarisk Country Club (Palm Springs), Headline Club, Desert Rats (Palm Springs; chair), Sigma Delta Chi. Home (winter): 3 Columbia Dr Rancho Mirage CA 92270-3149 Home (summer): 2650 N Lake View # 1701 Chicago IL 60614

ROTT, NICHOLAS, fluid mechanics educator; b. Budapest, Hungary, Oct. 6, 1917; came to U.S. 1951; s. Alexander and Margaret (Pollak) R.; m. Rosanna Saredi, Sept. 30, 1944; children: Paul, Kathy. Diploma in Mechanical engring., Swiss Fed. Inst. Tech., Zurich, 1940; PhD, ETH, Zurich, 1944. Rsch. asst., pvt. dozent Aerodynamics Inst., Zurich, 1944-51; prof. Grad. Sch. Aeronautical Engring. Cornell U., Ithaca, N.Y., 1951-60; prof. UCLA, 1960-67, ETH, Zurich, 1967-83; vis. prof. Stanford (Calif.) U., 1983—. Fellow AIAA, Am. Phys. Soc.; mem. NAE, Acoustical Soc. Am. Home: 1865 Bryant St Palo Alto CA 94301 Office: Stanford U Aero Astro Dept Stanford CA 94305

ROTTER, PAUL TALBOTT, retired insurance executive; b. Parsons, Kans., Feb. 21, 1918; s. J. and LaNora (Talbott) R.; m. Virginia Sutherlin Barksdale, July 17, 1943; children—Carolyn Sutherlin, Diane Talbott. B.S. summa cum laude, Harvard U., 1937. Asst. mathematician Prudential Ins. Co. of Am., Newark, 1938-46; with Mut. Benefit Life Ins. Co., Newark, 1946—; successively asst. mathematician, asso. mathematician, mathematician Mut. Benefit Life Ins. Co., 1946-59, v.p., 1959-69, exec. v.p., 1969-80, ret., 1980. Mem. Madison Bd. Edn., 1958-64, pres., 1959-64; Trustee, mem. budget com. United Campaign of Madison, 1951-55; mem. bd., chmn. advancement com. Robert Treat council Boy Scouts Am., 1959-64. Fellow Soc. Actuaries (bd. govs. 1965-68, gen. chmn. edn. and exam. com. 1963-66, chmn. adv. com. edn. and exam. 1969-72); mem. Brit. Inst. Actuaries (asso.), Am. Acad. Actuaries (v.p. 1968-70, bd. dirs., chmn. edn. and exam. com. 1965-66, chmn. rev. and evaluation com. 1968-74), Asso. Harvard Alumni (regional dir. 1965-69), Actuaries Club N.Y. (pres. 1967-68), Harvard Alumni Assn. (v.p. 1964-66); Am. Lawn Bowls Assn. (pres. SW div.), Phi Beta Kappa Assos., Phi Beta Kappa. Clubs: Harvard N.J. (pres. 1956-57); Harvard (N.Y.C.); Morris County Golf (Convent, N.J.); Joslyn-Lake Hodges Lawn Bowling (pres. 1989-90). Home: 18278 Canfield Pl San Diego CA 92128-1002

ROTTER, STEPHEN A., film editor. Editor: (films) Night Moves, 1975, (with Dede Allen and Jerry Greenberg) The Missouri Breaks, 1976, (with Ronald Roose) The World According to Garp, 1982, (with Glenn Farr, Lisa Fruchtman, Douglas Stewart, and Tom Rolf) The Right Stuff, 1983 (Academy award best film editing 1983), (with Richard P. Cirincone) Target, 1985, Heaven Help Us, 1985, (with Cirincone and William Reynolds) Ishtar, 1987, (with William Scharf) Dirty Rotten Scoundrels, 1988, (with Vivien Hollgrove Gilliam and B.J. Sears) The Unbearable Lightness of Being, 1988, (with Scharf) An Innocent Man, 1989, My Blue Heaven, 1990, (with Robert Reitano) True Colors, 1991, Prelude to a Kiss, 1992, (with Scharf) Rising Sun, 1993, (with Scharf) Cops and Robbersons, 1994. Office: care Motion Picture Editors 7715 Sunset Blvd #220 Los Angeles CA 90046*

ROTTER, STEVE, advertising executive; b. N.Y.C., May 4, 1950; s. Milton and Cecilia (Bloch) R.; m. Karyn, Aug. 26, 1973; children: Gabriel, Emily, Julie. BS, Ohio U., 1973. Media asst., media supr. Helfgott, Towne, Silverstin, N.Y.C., 1973-74; asst. acct. exec. 1974, acct. exec., 1975, acct. supr., 1976-77, v.p. acct. svcs., 1978, sr. v.p. acct. svcs., 1979-81; exec. v.p. ptnr. Towne, Silverstein, Rotter, N.Y.C., 1981-85, pres., 1985-91, chmn., 1992—. Fundraiser Cancer Soc. N.Y. Marathon, 1991. Office: Towne Silverstein Rotter Inc 411 Lafayette St Fl 3 New York NY 10003-7032

ROTTMAN, ELLIS, public information officer; b. Balt., Apr. 5, 1930; s. Abraham Isaac and Sadie (Harris) R.; m. Carol Parker Donovan, May 30, 1965; children—Marcus, Lisa, Jason, Adam. B.S., U. Md., 1952. Assoc. editor Army Times Pub. Co., Washington, 1956-59; editor, dir. pub. relations Am. Fedn. Govt. Employees, AFL-CIO, 1959-65; pub. info. officer U.S. Post Office Dept., 1966-69; editor Manpower mag. Dept. Labor, 1969-75; editor, publs. dir. FDA, Rockville, Md., 1975-78; public info. dir. Labor-Mgmt. Services Adminstrn. Dept. Labor, 1978-84; public info. officer Office Sec. of Labor, 1984—. Served with AUS, 1952-54. Recipient Journalism award Internat. Labor Press Assn., AFL-CIO, 1959, 60, 61, 62, 64; award merit Fed. Editors Assn., 1974, 75, 77, 78. Jewish. Home: 901 N Belgrade Rd Silver Spring MD 20902-3247 Office: 2nd St and Constitution Ave NW Washington DC 20210

ROTUNDA, RONALD DANIEL, law educator, consultant; b. Blue Island, Ill., Feb. 14, 1945; s. Nicholas and Frances (Manna) R.; m. Marcia Ann Mainland, June 21, 1969; children—Nora, Mark. AB. magna cum laude, Harvard U., 1967, J.D. magna cum laude, 1970. Bar: N.Y. 1971, U.S. Ct. Appeals (2d cir.) 1971, U.S. Ct. Appeals (D.C. cir.) 1971, U.S. Ct. Appeals (7th cir.) 1990, U.S. Supreme Ct. 1974, Ill. 1975. Law clk. U.S. Ct. Appeals (2d cir.), 1970-71; assoc. Wilmer, Cutler & Pickering, Washington, 1971-73; asst. majority counsel Watergate Com., U.S. Senate, Washington, 1973-74; asst. prof. U. Ill. Coll. Law, Champaign, 1974-77, assoc. prof., 1977-80, prof., 1980-93, Albert E. Jenner, Jr. prof. of law, 1993—; vis. prof. law European U. Inst., Florence, Italy, 1981; mem. profl. responsibility exam. com. Nat. Conf. Bar Examiners, 1980-87; constnl. advisor Supreme Nat. Coun. Cambodia, 1993. Author: (with Morgan) Problems and Materials of Professional Responsibility, 1976; (with Nowak and Young) Constitutional Law, 1978, 2d edit., 1983, 3rd edit., 1986, 4th edit., 1991; (with Nowak) Modern Constitutional Law: Cases and Materials, 1981, 5th edit., 1995; (with Morgan) Problems and Materials o. Fulbright research scholar, Italy, 1981, Venezuela, 1986. Fellow Am. Bar Found. (life), Ill. Bar Found. (life); mem. Am. Law Inst. Roman Catholic. Office: U Ill Coll Law Rm 216 504 E Pennsylvania Ave Champaign IL 61820

ROTUNNO, GIUSEPPE, cinematographer; b. Rome, Italy, Mar. 19, 1923. Camera operator: (films) Senso, 1954; cinematographer: (films) Pane amore e..., 1955, Tosca, 1956, The Monte Carlo Story, 1957, Le notti bianche, 1957, Anna of Brooklyn, 1958, La Maja desnuda, 1958, La ragazza del palio, 1959, (with Daniel Fapp) On the Beach, 1959, (with Robert Gerardi) La grande guerra, 1959, The Angel Wore Red, 1960, Five Branded Women, 1960, Rocco e i suoi fratelli, 1960, The Best of Enemies, 1962, Boccaccio '70 ("The Job"), 1962, Cronaca familiare, 1962, Le guepard, 1963, I compagni, 1963, Ieri, oggi e domani, 1963, The Bible...In the Beginning, 1966, Lo straniero, 1967, Le streghe, 1967, Anzio, 1968, (with Aldo Graziata and Robert Krasker) Senso, 1968, Candy, 1968, Fellini Satyricon, 1969, The Secret of Santa Vittoria, 1969, Histoires extraordinaires ("Never Bet the Devil Your Head"), 1968, Sunflower, 1969, Carnal Knowledge, 1971, Man of La Mancha, 1972, Roma, 1972, Film d'amore e d'anarchia, 1973, Amarcord, 1974, Il bestione, 1974, Tutto a posto e niente in ordine, 1974, Il Casanova di Federico Fellini, 1976, Sturmtruppen, 1976, Divina Creatura, 1976, The End of the World in Our Usual Bed in a Night Full of Rain, 1978, Prova d'orchestra, 1978, All That Jazz, 1979 (Academy award nomination best cinematography 1979), La Citta delle donne, 1980, Popeye, 1980, (with William Garroni) Rollover, 1981, Bello mio bellezza mia, 1982, Five Days One Summer, 1982, E la nave va, 1983, American Dreamer, 1984, Non ci resta che piangere, 1984, Desiderio, 1984, The Assisi Underground, 1985, Red Sonja, 1985, Hotel Colonial, 1986, Julia and Julia, 1987, Rent-a-Cop, 1988, Haunted Summer, 1988, The Adventures of Baron Munchausen, 1989, Rebus, 1989, Regarding Henry, 1991, Once Upon a Crime, 1992, Wolf, 1994, (TV movies) The Scarlet and the Black, 1983. Office: The Gersh Agency 232 N Canon Dr Beverly Hills CA 90210*

ROTUNNO, JOSEPH ROCCO, construction company executive; b. Chgo. Sept. 1, 1928; s. Rocco and Kathleen C. (O'Brien) R.; m. Marilyn Lahey, Oct. 17, 1953; children: J. Dennis, John, Gerard, Mary Pat, Marguerite, Thomas. BS in Civil Engring., Marquette U., 1951. With W.E. O'Neil Constrn. Co., Chgo., 1951—, pres., 1972-80, chmn., 1980—; chmn. O'Neil Industries, Chgo., 1981—; bd. dirs. Chgo. Bldg. Congress, 1972—; pres. Chgo. Bldg. Congress, 1984-86. Mem. Chgo. Athletic Assn., Westmoreland Country Club (Wilmette, Ill.). Roman Catholic. Avocations: golf, gardening, travel. Office: O'Neil Industries Inc 2751 N Clybourn Ave Chicago IL 60614-1005

ROTZOLL, KIM BREWER, advertising and communications educator; b. Altoona, Pa., Aug. 21, 1935; s. Fredrick Charles and Anna (Brewer) R.; m. Nancy Benson, Aug. 26, 1961; children: Keith, Kristine, Amanda, Jason. BA in Advt., Pa. State U., 1957, MA in Journalism, 1965, PhD in Sociology, 1971. Account exec. Ketchum, Macleod and Grove, Pitts., 1957-61; instr. advt. Pa. State U., University Park, 1961-71; asst. prof. advt. U. Ill, Urbana, 1971-72, assoc. prof., 1972-78, prof., 1978—; rsch. prof., head advt. dept., 1983-92; dean Coll. Commns., 1992—; lectr. in People's Republic of China, Bahrain. Author, co-author, editor: Is There Any Hope for Advertising, 1986, Advertising in Contemporary Society, 1990, Media Ethics, 1995, The Book of Gossage, 1995. Named Disting. Advt. Educator of Yr. by Am. Advt. Fedn., 1992. Mem. Am. Acad. Advt. (pres. 1991), Am. Advt. Found., Nat. Advt. Rev. Bd., Alpha Kappa Delta, Phi Kappa Phi. Democrat. Presbyterian. Avocations: reading, films, cycling. Office: U Ill 119 Gregory Hall 810 S Wright St Urbana IL 61801-3611

ROUB, BRYAN R(OGER), financial executive; b. Berea, Ohio, May 1, 1941; s. Bernard Augustus and Pearl Irene (Koeblitz) R.; m. Judith Elaine Penman, June 19, 1965; children: Paul, Bradley, Michael. Student, Ohio Wesleyan U., 1959-62; BS, Ohio State U., 1966; MBA, U. Pa., 1978. Mem. audit staff Ernst & Ernst, Cleve., 1966-70; asst. contr. Midland-Ross, Cleve., 1970-73, contr., 1973-81, v.p., 1977-81, sr. v.p., 1981-82, exec. v.p fin., 1982-84; sr. v.p. fin. Harris Corp., Melbourne, Fla., 1984-93, sr. v.p., CFO, 1993—; mem. fin. coun. II Machinery and Allied Products Inst., Washington, 1978-84, coun. I, 1984—, vice chmn., 1994, mem. conf. bd. coun. of CFO's, 1993—. Mem. adv. coun. Coll. Adminstrv. Scis., Ohio State U., 1978-81; mem. citizen's adv. coun. Westlake (Ohio) Schs., 1981-83; trustee Alcoholism Svcs. Cleve., 1982-84; mem. devel. bd. St. John's Hosp., 1983-84; pres. Westridge Homeowners' Assn., 1977; dir., treas. Tortoise Island Homeowners' Assn., 1988-90; bd. dirs. Easter Seal Soc. of Brevard County, 1993—. Mem. AICPA, Ohio Soc. CPAs, Fin. Execs. Inst. (treas. N.E. Ohio chpt. 1976-78, bd. dirs. 1980-81, 83-84, v.p. 1981-82, pres. 1982-83, bd. dirs. Orlando chpt. 1984—, v.p. 1985-86, pres. 1986-87, nat. bd. dirs. 1987-90, area v.p. 1990-91, chmn. budget and fin. com. 1988-89), Fin. Execs. Rsch. Found. (trustee 1994—), Westwood Country Club, Eau Gallie Yacht Club (mem. bd. govs., treas. 1990-92). Home: 556 Lanternback Island Dr Satellite Beach FL 32937-4712 Office: Harris Corp 1025 W Nasa Blvd Melbourne FL 32919-0001

ROUBOS, GARY LYNN, diversified manufacturing company executive; b. Denver, Nov. 7, 1936; s. Dorr and Lillian Margaret (Coover) R.; m. Terie Joan Anderson, Feb. 20, 1960; children: Lyndel, Leslie. BSChemE with high honors, U. Colo., 1959; MBA with distinction, Harvard U., 1963. With Boise Cascade Corp., 1963-71, Dieterich Standard Corp., Boulder, Colo., 1971-76; exec. v.p., then pres. Dieterich Standard Corp. (co. acquired by Dover Corp. 1975), 1975-76; exec. v.p. Dover Corp., N.Y.C., 1976, pres., 1977-93, chief exec. officer, 1981-94, chmn., 1989—; bd. dirs. Omnicom Inc., N.Y.C., Bell & Howell Co., Skokie, Ill., Dovatron Internat., Inc., Boulder, Colo., Scott Paper Co., Phila., Gabelli-O'Connor Treas. Fund, Darien, Conn.; mem. adv. bd. U. Colo. Engring. Devel. Coun., 1990—. Mem. Colo. Engring. Devel. Coun., 1990—. Served to 1st Lt. C.E., U.S. Army, 1959-61. Mem. North River Yacht Club, Sky Club, Winged Foot Golf Club, Boulder Country Club, Dover Golf Club, Econ. Club of N.Y. Office: Dover Corp 280 Park Ave New York NY 10017-1216*

ROUDYBUSH, ALEXANDRA, novelist; b. Hyres, Cote d'Azur, France, Mar. 14, 1911; d. Constantine and Ethel (Wheeler) Brown; m. Franklin Roudybush, 1942. Student, St. Paul's Sch. for Girls, London, London Sch. Econs., 1930. Journalist London Eve. Standard, 1931, Time mag., 1933, French News Agy., 1935, CBS, 1936, MBS, 1940; White House corr. MBC Radio, 1940-48. Author: Before the Ball Was Over, 1965; Death of a Moral Person, 1967; Capital Crime, 1969; House of the Cat, 1970; A Sybaritic Death, 1972; Suddenly in Paris, 1975; The Female of the Species, 1977; Blood Ties, 1981. Mem. Crime Writers Am. and Brit., Am. Woman's Club (Paris), Miramar Golf Club (Porto, Portugal). Democrat. Episcopalian.

ROUDYBUSH, FRANKLIN, diplomat, educator; b. Washington, Sept. 17, 1906; s. Rumsey Franklin and Frances (Mahon) R.; student U. Vienna, 1925, Ecole National des Langues Orintales Vivantes, Paris, 1926, U. Paris, 1926-28, U. Madrid, 1928, Academie Julian, Paris, 1967; B.Fgn. Svc., Georgetown U., 1930; postgrad. Harvard U., 1931; MA, George Washington U., 1944; PhD, U. Strasbourg (France), 1953; m. Alexandra Brown, May 22, 1941. Dean Roudybush Fgn. Svc. Schs., Washington, L.A., Phila., N.Y.C., 1932—. Prof. internat. econ. rels. Southeastern U., Washington, 1938-42; dir. Pan Am. Inst., Washington, 1934, London Econ. Conf., 1934, Internat. Textile Conf., Washington, 1935; editor Affairs, 1934-42; v.p France Libre, Washington; censor Diplomatic Pouch World War II; commodity economist, statistician Dept. State, 1945; with Fgn. Svc. Inst., Dept. State, 1945-48, Council of Europe, Strasbourg and the Saar, Germany, 1948-54, Am. Embassy, Paris, 1954, Pakistan, 1955, Dublin, 1956; consular Acad. Vienna, 1925; mem. Punjab U., Lahore, Pakistan, 1954. Recipient prize Julian painting, Paris. Mem. Am. Soc. Internat. Law, Brit. Inst. Internat. and Comparative Law (London), Delta Phi Epsilon. Clubs: Assns. des Amis du Salon d'Automne (Paris); France Amerique; English Speaking Union (London); Nat. Press (Washington); Harvard (Paris), Royal Aberdeen Golf; Miramar Golf (Oporto, Portugal); Yacht (Angiers, France); Pormarnock Golf (Dublin); Les Societe des Artistes Independants Grand Palais (Paris). Author: The Twentieth Century; The Battle of Cultures; Diplomatic Language; Twentieth Century Diplomacy; The Present State of Western Capitalism, 1959; Diplomacy and Art, French Educational System, 1971; The Techniques of International Negotiation, 1979; The Diplomacy of the Cardinal, Duke de Richilieu, 1980, From Calcutta to Chungking, 1982, The Mysteries of Marsailles, 1983, Tea for Two, 1984, The Fromme Family, 1985, Casino Protocol, 1987, Talleyrand - The Diplomat, 1989, The French Government Political Science School, 1989, History of a Family During the XXth Century, 1990, The Flying Dutchman, 1990, Monsieur Fedeaux, 1990, Death in Darjeeling, 1991, The Alsatians, 1991, The Oriental Express to Constantinople and On To Teheran, 1992, The Elegant Facade of Macaó, 1992, Café Royal, 1993, The Roman Holiday, 1992, The Burlington Sisters, 1993, The Strange Fate of Madame Tarleton, 1980, Rendezvous in Basle, 1989, From Naples to Buenos Aires, 1977, Drawn Blinds, 1972. Home: Villa St Honoré, Moledo do Minho, Minho Portugal Office: 15 Ave du Pres Wilson, Paris 16, France Home: Sauveterre de Rouerque, 12800 Aveyron France

ROUECHE, JOHN EDWARD, II, education educator, leadership program director; b. Statesville, N.C., Sept. 3, 1938; s. John Edward and Mary (Harris) R.; m. Suanne Davis; 1 stepchild, Robin Sue Maca; children by previous marriage: Michelle Renee, John Edward III. BA, Lenoir Rhyne Coll., Hickory, N.C., 1960; MA, Appalachian Coll., Boone, N.C., 1961; PhD, Fla. State U., 1964. Dean Gaston Coll., Gastonia, N.C., 1964-67; assoc. rsch. educator U. Calif., L.A., 1967-69; dir. jr. coll. div. Nat. Lab. Higher Edn., 1968-71, also assoc. prof. edn. Duke U.; prof. edn., dir. c.c. leadership program U. Tex., Austin, 1971—; Sid W. Richardson regents chair, 1987—; mem. chancellor's coun. U. Tex. System, 1990—, U. Tex. Littlefield Soc., 1992—; lectr. Earl Pullias lectr. U. So. Calif., 1992, Coll. Bd. Disting. Lectr. U. Calif., 1993, Frances Crain Cook Disting. Lectr. U. Tex., 1994; chmn. nat. ednl. adv. bd. Great Am. Res. Ins. Co., 1991—; bd. dirs. Acordia Collegiate Benefits, Inc.; co-chair, Nat. Adv. Bd. for Community Colls., Invest Learning Corp., 1993—. Community coll. editor Jossey-Bass Pubs., 1971-82; editor Creative Teaching Series, Media Systems Corp., 1980-85; mem. editorial bd. Community Coll. Times, Community Coll. Jour., 1990—; others; author 33 books, including Profiles of Excellence in America's Schools, 1986, Access With Excellence, 1987, Shared Vision, 1989, Teaching As Leading, 1990, Under-representation: A Question of Diversity, 1991,

Between a Rock and a Hard Place, 1993, The Company We Keep, 1995, Stranger in Their Own Land: Part Time Faculty, 1995, over 100 articles and monographs. Chmn. nat. community coll. adv. bd. Invest Learning Corp.; pres. Doss Sch. PTA, 1974-75; chmn. bd. N.W. Hills United Meth. Ch., 1973-76. Recipient Disting. Svc. award A.M.E. Ch., 1971, Disting. Rsch. award Nat. Coun. Univs. and Colls., 1990,Disting. Rsch. Publ. award, 1990, Outstanding Alumnus award Appalachian State U., 1979, Disting. Grad. award Fla. State U., 1981, Teaching Excellence award U. Tex., 1982, Outstanding Researcher award, 1985, Excellence award for outstanding learned article U.S. Edn. Press Assn., 1983, Disting. Rsch. award Nat. Assn. Devel. Edn., 1984, 86, Disting. Rsch. Publ. award Nat. Coun. Student Devel., 1987, Disting. Rsch. award Nat. Coun. Staff, Program, and Orgn. Devel., B. Lamar Johnson Nat. Leadership award, 1988, Disting. Svc. & Leadership award, CCP, INC., 1993—; Disting Faculty award U. Texas, 1994; named lifetime ambassador for N.C., 1978; Kellogg fellow, 1962-64. Mem. Am. Assn. Community and Jr. Colls. (bd. dirs. 1989—, Nat. Leadership award 1986, 1994, Disting. Rsch. award coun. univs. 1990), Am. Assn. Higher Edn., Coun. Univs. and Colls. (past pres., bd. dirs.), Phi Beta Kappa, Phi Delta Kappa. Home: 6804 Edgefield Dr Austin TX 78731-2906 Office: U Tex Austin Coll Education Ste 348 Austin TX 78712

ROUGH, DAVID S., marketing professional, consultant; b. Lake Placid, N.Y., Dec. 20, 1933; s. Jack and Veva Lillian (Bickford) R.; m. Patricia Anne Healy, June 10, 1962 (div. Sept. 1974); children: Robert Scott, Patricia Anne, Jonathan Lee; m. Gay Louise Vance, Apr. 9, 1988. BA, U. Conn., 1954; MA, U. Miami, 1963, PhD, 1966. Exec. v.p. Internat. Apparel, Miami, Fla., 1966-69; pres. Outlet Holding Corp., Atlanta, 1969-74; exec. dir. Marco Group, San Bernardino, Calif., 1975-82; exec. v.p., cons. Chroma Concepts, Inc., Irvine, Calif., 1986-91; exec. v.p. Holographics, Inc., Irvine, 1991—; pres. Worldwide Systems, Inc., Laguna, Calif., 1987—; cons. Maxines, Encido, Calif., 1982—, Bobbies, San Diego, 1982—. Served with USAF, 1955-58. Republican. Baptist. Avocations: sports, backgammon, tennis, golf. Office: Worldwide Systems Inc 5 Whitewood Way Irvine CA 92715

ROUGH, HERBERT LOUIS, insurance company executive; b. N.Y.C., Jan. 19, 1935; s. Albert and Jean (Bendeth) R.; m. Fern Sadkin Schultz; children: Lee Michael, Lisa Joi. BS, NYU, 1956. CLU. From agt. to dist. mgr. Equitable Life Assurance Soc., N.Y.C., 1961-69; brokerage mgr. Bernard Bergen Cos. Inc., N.Y.C., 1969-73; pres., gen. agt. Rough Agy. Inc., Great Neck, N.Y., 1973—, Comprehensive Planning Group Ltd., Port Washington, N.Y., 1988—, Rough Agy. Inc. of Fla., Ft. Lauderdale, 1991—; pres., mem. field adv. coun. Am. Gen. Life Ins. Co. of N.Y., Syracuse, 1978-83, Madison Life Ins. Co., N.Y.C., 1974-77; guest speaker in field. Treasurer Gray Wig Repertory Theatre, Hofstra U., Uniondale, N.Y., 1981-84; pres. Heart Assn. of Great Neck, 1977. Capt. USAF, 1956-59. Mem. Life Underwriters Assn., Gold Coast Assn. of Health Underwriters (exec. bd. dirs.), Nat. Assn. Ind. Life Brokerage Agys., CLU Assn., Knickerbocker Yacht Club, Kiwanis (pres. Great Neck chpt. 1977—). Democrat. Jewish. Avocations: racquetball, tennis, singing. Office: Comprehensive Planning Group Ltd 22 Sintsink Dr E Port Washington NY 11050-2014

ROUGHSEDGE, CAROLYN DUNN, advertising agency executive; b. Rocky Ford, Colo., June 9, 1944; d. Joseph Michael and Frances (Barnes) Dunn.; m. Robert Roughsedge, Nov. 29, 1968 (div. Nov. 1978); 1 son, Michael Caine. BA, Manhattanville Coll., 1966. Casting sec. Grey Advt., N.Y.C., 1966-67; TV producer Savage Friedman, N.Y.C., 1967-68; v.p., owner Steppingstone Prodns., N.Y.C., 1968-77; TV producer CBS Records, N.Y.C., 1977-78; v.p., dir. broadcast prodn. Needham, Harper & Steers, L.A., 1978-83; v.p., dir. broadcast prodn. Needham, Harper & Steers, N.Y.C., from 1983, to sr. v.p.; sr. v.p., dir. broadcast prodn. Saatchi & Saatchi Advt. Inc., N.Y.C., from 1983, to sr. v.p., dir. broadcast ops., 1988—. Office: Saatchi & Saatchi Advt Inc 375 Hudson St New York NY 10014-3658

ROUGIER-CHAPMAN, ALWYN SPENCER DOUGLAS, furniture manufacturing company executive; b. Ostende, Belgium, Feb. 19, 1939; came to U.S., 1970; s. Douglas Alwyn and Simone (Stiernet) Rougier-C.; m. Christine Hayes, Mar. 14, 1964; children—Andrew Douglas, Duncan Peter. Chartered Acct., City of London Coll., 1963. Chartered acct., Eng. and Wales; C.P.A., Mich. Articled clk. Spain Bros., London, 1958-64; mgr. Deloitte & Co., Brussels, 1964-70; ptnr. Seidman & Seidman, Grand Rapids, Mich., 1970-81; v.p. planning Steelcase Inc., Grand Rapids, Mich., 1981-83, sr. v.p. fin., 1983—; dir. Meijer, Inc. Pres. French Soc., Grand Rapids, Mich., 1974-75; treas., vice chmn. Opera Grand Rapids, 1981-86, pres., 1987-89; treas. Grand Rapids Symphony, 1991—; bd. trustees Blodgett Meml. Hosp., 1989—; bd. dirs. Fin. Execs. Inst., Western Mich., 1988—, pres., 1991-92. Fellow Inst. Chartered Accts. Eng. and Wales; mem. Am. Inst. C.P.A.s (computer exec. com. 1977-81), Mich. Assn. C.P.A.s (auditing standards com. 1973-78). Roman Catholic. Clubs: Cascade Country, Peninsular (Grand Rapids). Avocations: golf; tennis; squash; travel; music (symphony and opera). Home: 2018 San Lu Rae Dr SE Grand Rapids MI 49506-3473 Office: 901 44th St SE Grand Rapids MI 49508-7575

ROUKEMA, MARGARET SCAFATI, congresswoman; b. Newark, N.J., Sept. 19, 1929; d. Claude Thomas and Margaret (D'Alessio) Scafati; m. Richard W. Roukema, Aug. 23, 1951; children—Margaret, Todd (dec.), Gregory. B.A. with honors in History and Poli. Sci, Montclair State Coll., 1951, postgrad. in history and guidance, 1951-53; postgrad. program in city and regional planning, Rutgers U., 1975. Tchr. history, govt., public schs. Livingston and Ridgewood, N.J., 1951-55; mem. 97th-103rd Congresses from 5th N.J. dist., Washington, D.C., 1981—; mem. Banking, Fin. Urban Affairs com., subcom. Housing, Community devel., Internat. devel., Fin., Trade, Monetary Policy, Econ. Growth on; mem. Credit formation, Edn. Labor com., subcom. labor mgmt. rels., elementary, sec., vocat. edn., postsecondary edn. tng.; vice pres. Ridgewood Bd. Edn., 1970-73; bd. dirs., cofounder Ridgewood Sr. Citizens Housing Corp.; chairwoman Fin. Inst. and Consumer Credit Sub. Com. U.S. Congress; sponcer Family Med. Leave U.S. Congress. Trustee Spring House, Paramus, N.J.; trustee Leukemia Soc. No. N.J., Family Counseling Service for Ridgewood and Vicinity; mem. Bergen County (N.J.) Republican Com.; NW Bergen County campaign mgr. for gubernatorial candidate Tom Kean, 1977. Mem. Bus. and Profl. Women's Orgn. Clubs: Coll. of Ridgewood, Ridgewood Rep. Office: US Ho of Reps 2244 Rayburn Washington DC 20515 *I have served in several roles in my life. Wife, mother, teacher, public servant. All are personally rewarding; each affords the opportunity to help others in need and to enrich the lives of those around you. As a member of Congress, I find the most rewards are in the knowledge that I can truly make a difference and improve the lives of thousands of people. The challenges are frequently insurmountable, but the rewards are incalculable.*

ROULAC, STEPHEN E., real estate consultant; b. San Francisco, Aug. 15, 1945; s. Phil Williams and Elizabeth (Young) R.; children: Arthur, Fiona. BA, Pomona Coll., 1967; MBA with distinction, Harvard Grad. Sch. Bus. Administrv., 1970; JD, U. Calif., Berkeley, 1976; PhD, Stanford U., 1978. CPA, Hawaii. Asst. constrn. supt., foreman, adminstr. Roulac Constrn. Co., Pasadena, Calif., 1963-66; rsch. asst. Econs. Rsch. Assocs., L.A., 1966-67; assoc. economist Urbanomics Rsch. Assocs., Claremont, Calif., 1967; acquisition auditor Litton Industries Inc., Chgo., Beverly Hills, 1967-68; tax cons. Lybrand, Ross Bros. and Montgomery, L.A., 1968; cons. to constrn. group and corp. planning dept. Owens-Corning Fiberglas Corp., Toledo, 1969-70; CEO Questor Assocs., San Francisco, 1972-83; chmn. nat. mgmt. adv. svcs. Kenneth Leventhal & Co., 1983-84; pres. Stephen E. Roulac & Co., 1985-86; mng. ptnr. Roulac Group of Deloitte Haskins & Sells (Deloitte & Touche), 1987-91; CEO The Roulac Group, Larkspur, Calif., 1992—; strategic and fin. econ. cons.; expert witness, preparer econ. analyses for legal matters including civil trial of Irvine Co., Jewell et. al. vs. Bank of Am., Tchrs. vs. Olympia & York, Calif. Legis., Calif. Corps. Dept., Midwest Securities Commrs. Assn., Nat. Assn. Securities Dealers, SEC, Dept. of Labor, HUD; advisor to investment arm of Asian country, Calif. Pub. Employees Retirement System, U.S. Dept. Labor, numerous others; adj. prof. Tex. A&M U., 1986, U. Chgo., 1985, UCLA, 1983-84, Stanford Grad. Sch. Bus., 1970-79, Pacific Coast Banking Sch., 1978, Hastings Coll. Law, 1977-78, U. Calif., Berkeley, 1972-77, Calif. State U., 1970-71, Northeastern U., 1969-70; keynote speaker, instr. continuing edn. sessions, program chmn., corps., orgns. Author: Real Estate Syndications: Principles and Ap-

plications, 1972, Case Studies in Property Development, 1973, Syndication Landmarks, 1974, Tax Shelter Sale-Leaseback Financing: The Economic Realities, 1976, Modern Real Estate Investment: An Institutional Approach, 1976, (with Sherman Maisel) Real Estate Investment and Finance, 1976 (1976 Bus. Book of Yr. The Libr. Jour.); editor-in-chief, pub. Calif. Bicyclist, 1988—, Tex. Bicyclist, 1989—, Roulac's Strategic Real Estate, 1979-89; columnist Forbes, 1983, 84, 87, 92, 93; mem. editorial adv. bd. Am. Real Estate and Urban Econs. Assn. Jour., 1977-81, Housing Devel. Reporter, 1978-80, Fin. Edn. Jour., 1976-70; contbg. editor Real Estate Law Jour., 1973-78, Real Estate Rev., 1973-75; spl. issue editor Calif. Mgmt. Rev., 1976; editor: Real Estate Syndication Digest, 1971-72, Notable Syndications Sourcebook, 1972, Real Estate Securities and Syndication: A Workbook, 1973, Due Diligence in Real Estate Transactions, 1974, Real Estate Venture Analysis, 1974, Real Estate Securities Regulation Sourcebook, 1975, Questor Real Estate Investment Manager Profiles, 1982, Questor Real Estate Securities Yearbook, 1980-85, Retail Giants and Real Estate, 1986, Roulac's Top Real Estate Brokers, 1984-88; contbr. articles to profl. jours., newspapers; cassettes; frequent appearer on TV shows including MacNeil/Lehrer Newshour, 1986, Cable News Network, 1987, ABC TV, 1987, KCBS Radio, 1986, WABC Radio, Dallas, 1986. Mem. real estate adv. com. to Calif. Commr. Corps., 1973, Calif. Corp. Commr.'s Blue Ribbon Com. on Projections and Track Records, 1973-74; mem. adv. bd. Nat. Bicycle Month, League of Am. Wheelmen, Ctr. for Real Estate Rsch. Kellogg Grad. Sch. Mgmt., Northwestern U. Named Highest Instr. Student Teaching Evaluations, Schs. Bus. Adminstrv., U. Calif., Berkeley, 1975-76; named to Pomona Coll. Athletic Hall of Fame, 1981; W.T. Grant fellow Harvard U., 1969-70.; George F. Baker scholar Harvard Grad. Sch. Bus. Adminstrn., 1970; Stanford U. Grad. Sch. Bus. fellow, 1970-71. Mem. Strategic Mgmt. Soc., Acad. Mgmt., Am. Real Estate and Urban Econs. Assn., Intuition Network, World Future Soc. (exec. com. and adv. bd. World 2000), Am. Econ. Assn., Am. Real Estate Soc. (pr), Noetic Soc., Nat. Bur. Real Estate Rsch. (founder, bd. dirs.), Harvard Club N.Y., L.A. Adventures Club. Avocations: arts, antiquarian books, reading, bicycle racing (U.S. team 1990), outdoor activities. Office: The Roulac Group Ste 125 900 Larkspur Landing Ctr Larkspur CA 94939

ROULEAU, REYNALD, bishop; b. St.-Jean-de-Dieu, Que., Can., Nov. 30, 1935. Ordained priest, 1963, bishop, 1987. Bishop Churchill-Hudson Bay, 1987—. Office: Diocese of Churchill-Baie D'Hudson, C P 10, Churchill, MB Canada R0B 0E0

ROULSTON, THOMAS HENRY, investment adviser; b. N.Y.C., Apr. 6, 1933; s. Henry Davies and Marjorie (Heather) R.; m. Lois Mueller, July 31, 1954; children: Scott Davies, Thomas Henry III, Heather Ettinger. BA, Dartmouth, 1955. Vice pres. Gunn, Carey & Roulston (stockbrokers), Cleve., 1960-63; pres. Roulston & Co., Inc., Cleve., 1963-90, chmn., 1990—; vice chmn. Bank Roulston Ltd., Zurich, Switzerland, 1972-76; pres., chmn. Investment Guidance Fund, 1967-80; chmn., dir. Womens Fed. Savs. Bank, 1983-93; chmn. bd. dirs. MJM Industries, 1990—, Defiance Inc., 1990—, Continental Pharmacy, 1994, Ramwear, 1994—, Roulston Investment Capital Corp., Roulston Capital Ltd.; chmn. oulston Investment Trust; bd. dirs. City Life Inc. Mem. Ohio Criminal Justice Supervisory Commn., 1970-73; chmn. Adminstrn. of Justice Com., 1968-70; past trustee Soc. for Crippled Children, Hill House, Health Hill Hosp., Cleve. Coun. World Affairs, Choate Rosemary Hall, Lakeview Cemetery Assn.; trustee, mem. exec. com. Univ. Circle, Inc.; trustee, pres. Bluecoats Inc.; trustee, chmn. State Troopers; vice chmn. Midtown Corridor, 1981-84; past trustee Cleve. State U. Devel. Found. Capt. USAF, 1955-58. Mem. World Bus. Coun., Chief Execs. Orgn., Union Club, Country Club, Pepper Pike Club, Univ. Club (chmn.), Country Club of the Rockies. Home: 2627 Fairmount Blvd Cleveland Heights OH 44106-3601 Office: 4000 Chester Ave Cleveland OH 44103-3612

ROUMAN, JOHN CHRIST, classics educator; b. Tomahawk, Wis., May 1, 1926; s. Christ and Soteria (Dedes) R. BA in Greek, Carleton Coll., 1950; MA in Greek, Columbia U., 1951; student, Rutgers U., 1951-53, U. Kiel, Germany, 1956-57, U. Minn., Mpls., 1959-60; PhD in Classics, U. Wis., 1965. German tchr. Seton Hall Preparatory Sch., South Orange, N.J., 1954-56; ancient history tchr. Malverne (N.Y.) High Sch., 1957-59; tchg. asst. in ancient history U. Wis., Madison, 1960-61, rsch. asst. in ancient history, 1961-65; rsch. asst. in Greek epigraphy Inst. Advanced Study, Princeton, N.J., 1962-63; asst. prof. Classics U. N.H., Durham, 1965-71, assoc. prof., 1971-91, prof., 1991—; examiner N.H. State Bd. Edn. in Latin and Greek, 1979-80; judge Warren H. Held Jr. Exam-Contests in Latin and Mythology, 1988—; cons. Nat. Classical Greek Examination, 1980; presenter, lectr. in field. Active Colovos Rd. Com., 1981-82. With USN, 1944-46. Fulbright scholar U. Kiel, 1956-57; recipient Disting. Tchg. award U. N.H. Alumni Assn., 1985, Pericles award Am. Hellenic Ednl. Progressive Assn. and Daus. of Penelope, 1993. Mem. Am. Classical League (rep. to TCNE at ann. meeting 1978, mem. fin. com. 1981-82, treas. 1982-83), Am. Philol. Assn. (Nat. Excellence in Teaching Classics award, 1991), Archaeol. Inst. Am., Classical Assn. Can., Classical Assn. New Eng. (mem. exec. com. at-large 1981-84, mem. nominating com. 1983-84, 86-87, pres. 1987-88, Barlow-Beach award 1991, mem. ad hoc com. on elections and appointments), Medieval Acad. Am., Modern Greek Studies Assn., Nat. Assn. Advisors for Health Professions, N.H. Classical Assn. (mem. exec. com. 1965—, chair nominating com. 1986—), Strafford County Greco-Roman Found. (pres. 1978—), Vergilian Soc. Am., Phi Kappa Theta (faculty advisor, 1982—, chmn. nat. bd., 1993—). Office: U NH Dept Spanish and Classics 209G Murkland Hall Durham NH 03824-3596

ROUND, ALICE FAYE BRUCE, school psychologist; b. Ironton, Ohio, July 19, 1934; d. Wade Hamilton and Martha Matilda (Toops) Bruce; m. Leonard Paul Round, June 21, 1958; children: Leonard Bruce, Christopher Frederick. BA, Asbury Coll., 1956; MS in Sch. Psychology, Miami U., Oxford, Ohio, 1975. Cert. tchr., sch. psychologist, supr., Ohio; cert. tchr., Calif. Tchr. Madison County (Ohio) Schs., 1956-58, Columbus (Ohio) Pub. Schs., 1958, San Diego Pub. Schs., 1958-60, Poway (Calif.) Unified Sch. Dist., 1960-64; substitute tchr. Princeton City Schs., Cin., 1969-75; sch. psychologist, intern Greenhills/Forest Park City Schs., Cin., 1975-76; sch. psychologist Fulton County Schs., Wauseon, Ohio, 1976-77, Sandusky (Ohio) pub. and Cath. schs., 1977—; tchr. art cmty. group and pvt. lessons, Sandusky, 1962, Springdale, Ohio, 1962-69; mem. Youth Svcs. Bd., Sandusky, 1978-88; bd. dirs., cons. Sandusky Sch. Practical Nursing, 1983-91; presenter suicide prevention seminars for mental health orgns.; speaker at ch., civic and youth orgns., local radio and TV programs; cons. on teen pregnancy to various schs., health depts. Mem. Huron (Ohio) Boosters Club, 1978-92, Vols. in Action, Sandusky, 1987—. Mem. NAACP, NEA, Nat. Sch. Psychologist Assn., Ohio Sch. Psychologist Assn., Maumee Valley Sch. Psychologist Assn., Coun. Exceptional Children, Ohio Edn. Assn., Sandusky Edn. Assn., Phi Delta Kappa (historian 1984-88, Most Innovative Preservation of History award 1988). Home: 821 Seneca Ave Huron OH 44839-1842 Office: Sandusky Bd Edn 407 Decatur St Sandusky OH 44870-2442

ROUNDELL, HENRY J., banker; b. London, Oct. 24, 1947; came to U.S. 1975; s. Henry Richard Martin and Louise Roundell; m. Hilke Lietzmann, Aug. 30, 1975; 1 child, Cristiana. Student, Winchester Coll., London, 1960-66; B.A. in Econs., Cambridge U., 1970. With Morgan Guaranty, London, 1970-75; staff Morgan Guaranty, N.Y.C., 1975-84, sr. v.p., 1984—; head of equity arbitrage J.P. Morgan, N.Y.C., 1990—. Club: Met. Opera. Avocations: sailing.

ROUNDS, DONALD EDWIN, cell biologist; b. Maywood, Ill., Jan. 17, 1926; s. Howard Gilmore and Dorothy May (Stucker) R.; m. Helen Lorraine Cann, Mar. 16, 1951 (dec. Mar. 1986); children: Robin Anne, Wendy Jeanne; m. Janice Mary Price, Oct. 17, 1987. BA, Occidental Coll., 1951; PhD, UCLA, 1958. Research assoc. med. br. U. Tex., Galveston, 1958-59; dir. dept. cell biology Pasadena Found. for Med. Research, Calif., 1959-65; research coordinator Pasadena Found. for Med. Research, 1965-72, sr. research investigator, dir. carcinogenesis lab., 1972-82; dir. cell biology and laser labs. Huntington Med. Research Insts., 1982-90, chief scientist Advanced Med. Diagnostics Ltd., 1990—; prof. Loma Linda Med. Sch., 1974—; adj. prof. U. So. Calif. Med. Sch. Contbr. numerous articles to profl. jours., also chpts. books.; Reviewing editor: In Vitro, 1970-83. Served with U.S. Army, 1945-47. Mem. AAAS, Am. Soc. Zoologists, Tissue Culture Assn., Am. Soc. Cell

Biologists, Am. Film Assn., Am. Inst. Biol. Scis., Sigma Xi. Democrat. Home: 1261 Sonoma Dr Altadena CA 91001-3151 Office: 36 S Chester Ave Pasadena CA 91106-3105

ROUNDS, DONALD MICHAEL, public relations executive; b. Centralia, Ill., May 9, 1941; s. Donald Merritt and Alice Josephine (Soulsby) R.; m. Alma Genevieve Beyer, Dec. 13, 1975. BS in History, Polit. Sci., Colo. State U., 1963. Police reporter, night city editor The Rocky Mountain News, Denver, 1960-70; mgr. Don M. Rounds Co., Denver, 1970-75; sr. editor Western Oil Reporter, Denver, 1975-80; energy writer The Rocky Mountain News, Denver, 1980-87; sr. media rels. advisor Cyprus Minerals Co., Englewood, Colo., 1987-92, media and community rels. mgr., 1992-93; media and community rels. mgr. Cyprus Amax Minerals Co., Englewood, 1994-95, dir. coms., 1995—; adv. bd Colo. State Minerals, Energy, and Geology (appointed by gov.), 1992—. Contbr. articles to mags. and newspapers. Sec. covenant mem. Ken Caryl Ranch Master Assn., Littleton, Colo., 1980-84. Recipient 1st place spl. news series AP, 1987, 1st place news sweepstakes, 1987, Margolin award U. Denver Coll. Bus., 1986, Betty McWhorter Commendation of Honor Desk & Derrick Club of Denver, 1987, Journalism award Rocky Mountain Assn. Geologists, 1985, Citizen Svc. award Denver Police Dept., 1969, Pub. Svc. award Englewood Police Dept., 1967. Mem. Nat. Mining Assn. (pub. rels. com.), Soc. Profl. Journalists, Sigma Delta Chi, Denver Press Club (bd. dirs. 1987). Republican. Methodist. Avocations: scuba diving, skiing, hiking, photography. Home: 8220 S San Juan Range Rd Littleton CO 80127-4011 Office: Cyprus Amax Minerals Co 9100 E Mineral Circle Englewood CO 80112

ROUNDS, JOHN SCOVILLE, JR., publishing executive; b. Phila., Apr. 12, 1954; s. John Scoville R. and Suzanne Elizabeth (Braman) McClenahan; m. Mary Jo Rhodes, Aug. 7, 1982; children: Jeremy Rhodes, Timothy Morgan. BA magna cum laude, Wilmington Coll., 1975. Prodn. editor The Berkley Publ. Group, N.Y.C., 1982-88; mng. editor St. Martin's Press, N.Y.C., 1988-93, assoc. publisher, mng. editor, 1993—.

ROUNDS, PHILARD LEON, SR., fundraiser; b. Des Moines, Jan. 9, 1928; s. Clarence Leaon and Alice Rudella (Eitel) R.; m. Shirley Anne Rounds, 1946; children: Rose Ann Rounds Farabough, Philard L. BA, Fla. So. Coll., Lakeland; diploma in Bible, Open Bible Coll., Des Moines. Missionary to Japan, 1950-67; Oral Roberts U., Tulsa, 1967-87, David Livingston Missionary Assn., 1988-89, First United Meth. Ch., 1989—; regional rep. Oral Roberts U., Tulsa, 1967-87; sr. v.p. planned giving David Livingstone Assn., Tulsa, 1987-88; min. planned giving First United Meth. Ch., tulsa, 1989—. Author: Planned Giving Manual, 1989. Fundraising exec. Nat. Soc. Fundraising, Tulsa, 1988—; active alumnus Nat. Planned Giving Inst., Memphis, 1988. With U.S. Army, 1946-49. Mem. Nat. Inst. Planned Giving, Nat. Soc. Fundraising Execs. (pres. ca. Okla. chpt. 1994), Fla. Acad. Scis., Pi Gamma Mu. Republican. Methodist. Home: 6443 S Sandusky Ave Tulsa OK 74136-1626 Office: First United Methodist Ch 1115 S Boulder Ave Tulsa OK 78411-2418

ROUNICK, JACK A., lawyer, company executive; b. Phila., June 5, 1935; s. Philip and Nettie (Brownstein) R.; BBA, U. Mich., 1956; JD, U. Pa., 1959; m. Noreen A. Garrigan, Sept. 4, 1970; children: Ellen, Eric, Amy, Michelle. Bar: Pa. 1960, U.S. Dist. Ct. (ea. dist.) Pa., 1960. Spl. asst. atty. gen., 1963-71; ptnr. Israelit & Rounick, 1960-67, Moss & Rounick, 1968-69, Moss, Rounick & Hurowitz, Norristown, Pa., 1969-72, Moss & Rounick, Norristown, 1972-73; ptnr. Pechner, Dorfman, Wolffe, Rounick and Cabot, Norristown, 1973-87; pres., CEO Think Big!, Inc., 1992—; v.p., gen. counsel Martin Lawrence Ltd. Edits., Inc., 1987-93; dir. Martin Lawrence Ltd. Edits., Inc., 1984—, Deb Shops, Inc., 1974—. Fin. chmn. Pa. Young Rep., 1964-66, treas., 1966-68, chmn., 1968-70; fellow Mus. Modern Art, Phila. Mus. Art; mem. Nat. Mus. Am. Jewish History; supporting assoc. Solomon R. Guggenheim Foun.; friend Phila. Mus. Art; friend Whitney Mus. Am. Art. Recipient Boss of Yr. award Montgomery County Legal Secs. Assn., 1970, Cert. of appreciation Pa. Bar Inst., 1980. Fellow Am. Acad. Matrimonial Lawyers (pres. Pa. chpt. 1982-84, gov. 1983-85, v.p. 1985-87); mem. ABA (coun. family law sect. 1982-87), Pa. Bar Assn. (past chmn. family law sect., Spl. Achievement award 1979-80), Montgomery Bar Assn., Am. Friends of the Hebrew U. (v.p. 1990-91, bd. dirs. 1987-93, Nat. Coun. Trustees 1987-93, pres. Phila. chpt. 1988-91). Republican. Jewish. Author: Pennsylvania Matrimonial Practice, 5 vols., 1982; editor Pa. Family Lawyer, 1980-87. Office: Think Big Inc 960 Brook Rd Conshohocken PA 19428

ROUNTREE, ASA, lawyer; b. Birmingham, Ala., Aug. 9, 1927; s. John Asa and Cherokee Jemison (Van de Graaff) R.; m. Elizabeth Rhodes Blue, Aug. 11, 1951; children—Robert B., John A. A.B., U. Ala., 1949; LL.B., Harvard U., 1954. Bar: Ala. 1954, U.S. Dist. Ct. (no. dist.) Ala. 1954, U.S. Ct. Appeals (5th cir.) 1955, N.Y. 1962, U.S. Dist. Ct. (so. dist.) N.Y. 1963, U.S. Ct. Appeals (2d cir.) 1963, U.S. Supreme Ct. 1972. Assoc. Cabaniss & Johnston, Birmingham, Ala., 1954-60, ptnr., 1960-62; assoc. Debevoise & Plimpton, N.Y.C., 1962-63, ptnr., 1963-91; mem. Maynard, Cooper & Gale, P.C., Birmingham, 1991—. Bd. dirs. U. Ala. Law Sch. Found. Served with U.S. Army, 1945-46, to lt., 1951-53. Mem. ABA (chmn. litigation sect. 1980-81), Ala. Bar Assn., N.Y. State Bar Assn., Assn. Bar City N.Y., Am. Law Inst., Am. Coll. Trial Lawyers, Am. Bar Found. Episcopalian. Clubs: River (N.Y.C.); Mountain Brook (Birmingham). Office: Maynard Cooper Gale PC 2400 AmSouth/Harbert Plz 1901 6th Ave N Birmingham AL 35203-2602

ROUNTREE, GEORGE DENTON, health services management consultant; b. Houston, Mar. 14, 1937; s. George Washington and Verda Mae (Wagnon) R. B.S., Lamar U., 1960; M.H.A., Washington U., St. Louis, 1963; postgrad. Grad. Sch. Bus. and Public Health, Harvard U., 1976. Vice pres. Methodist Hosp., Houston, 1963-75; pres. Quadrus Internat. Inc. Tex., Houston, 1977—. Adj. asst. prof. Washington U. Med. Sch., St. Louis, 1978-85; adj. prof. U. Istanbul, Turkey; guest lectr. U. Tex. Health Sci. Ctr., Houston, 1983. Contbr. articles to profl. jours. Mem. profl. adv. com. Mental Health Assn. Houston and Harris County; adv. and instl. rep. Boy Scouts Am. Served with USNR, 1956-63. Fellow Am. Coll. Hosp. Adminstrs.; mem. Houston C. of C. (chmn. art com. Ronald McDonald House), Am. Assn. Hosp. Planning, Greater Houston Hosp. Council, Nat. Council Internat. Health, Assn. Univ. Programs in Health Adminstrn. Club: Rotary. Home: Ste 9B 1101 North Post Oak Blvd Houston TX 77056-3101 Office: Am Hosp Istanbul, Guzelbahce Sokak Nisantasi, 80220 Istanbul Turkey

ROUNTREE, JANET CARYL, astrophysicist; b. Chgo., Aug. 14, 1937; d. Ernest Alonzo and Frances Careta (Vogel) R.; m. J. Harold Lesh, Apr. 19, 1960 (div. 1971); 1 child, Kathryn Frances; m. Marshall A. Aizenman, June 24, 1977. A.B., Cornell U., 1958; postgrad., U. Paris, 1958-60; Ph.D., U. Chgo., 1967. Sci. officer Leiden (Netherlands) Obs., 1968-70; astronomer adjoint Meudon (France) Obs., 1970-71; vis. fellow U. Colo., 1971-72; research astronomer, lectr. astronomy U. Denver, 1972-77, dir. obs. ops., 1974-77; rsch. prof. of elec. and computer engring. U. Ariz., 1994—; NASA-NRC sr. resident research assoc. Goddard Space Flight Center, 1977-79; phys. scientist Dept. Air Force, 1979-93; cons., sr. scientist Sci. Applications Internat. Corp., 1993—. English lang. editor, translator: Astronomy and Astrophysics: A European Jour, 1969-71; Contbr. numerous articles to profl. publs.; translator books from French, numerous articles from French and German. Fulbright fellow, 1958-60. Mem. Internat. Astron. Union (commn. mem.), Am. Astron. Soc., Royal Astron. Soc., Fulbright Alumni Assn. (dir. 1978-83, nat. capital area, treas. 1991-93), Phi Beta Kappa, Sigma Xi, Phi Kappa Phi. Achievements include visible and ultraviolet classification systems for early-type stars. Office: PO Box 65285 Tucson AZ 85728-5285

ROUNTREE, NEVA DIXON, public relations executive; b. Jacksonville, Fla., Dec. 13, 1943; d. Jarma E. and Helen (McIlvaine) Dixon; m. Don C. Rountree, Mar. 23, 1941; 1 child, Don C. III. AB in Journalism, U. Ga., 1964, MA, 1979. Press sec. Underwood for US Senate, Atlanta, 1979-80; account exec. Cohn & Wolfe, Atlanta, 1980-81; v.p Carl Byoir & Assocs., Atlanta, 1981-84; pres. Rountree Group, Inc., Atlanta, 1985—. Co-chmn. Leadership Sandy Springs, Ga., 1985-86, trustee, 1986—; adv. bd. Northside Found., 1994—; comm. com. Atlanta Com. for Olympic Games, 1990-92. Recipient 1 of 3 Best Run Agys. award Atlanta Bus. Chronicle, 1988, 89; named 25 Hot Smaller Pub. Rels. Agys. by Inside Pub. Rels., 1992, named

Best Mktg. Driven Pub. Rels. by Atlanta Bus. Chronicle, 1991, 92. Mem. Pub. Rels. Soc. Am. (Counselors Acad., pres. Ga. chpt. 1994—, George Goodwin award 1992), Pub. Rels. Exch. (bd. dirs. 1987—), U. Ga. Journalism Alumni Assn. (v.p., pres. 1986-89).

ROURKE, MICKEY (PHILIP ANDRE ROURKE, JR.), actor; b. Miami, Fla., 1956; m. Debra Feuer (div.); m. Carre Otis. Appearences include (films) including 1941, 1979, Heaven's Gate, 1980, Fade to Black, 1980, Body Heat, 1981, Diner, 1982, Rumblefish, 1983, The Pope of Greenwich Village, 1984, Year of the Dragon, 1985, Eureka, 1985, 9 1/2 Weeks, 1985, Angel Heart, 1987, A Prayer for the Dying, 1987, Barfly, 1987, Homeboy (also screenwriter), 1988, Johnny Handsome, 1989, Wild Orchid, 1990, The Desperate Hours, 1990, Harley Davidson and the Marlboro Man, 1991, White Sands, 1992, (TV movies) Act of Love, 1980, City in Fear, 1980, Rape and Marriage: The Rideout Case, 1980. *

ROUS, STEPHEN NORMAN, urologist, educator; b. N.Y.C., Nov. 1, 1931; s. David H. and Luba (Margulies) R.; m. Margot Woolfolk, Nov. 12, 1966; children: Benjamin, David. A.B., Amherst Coll., 1952; M.D., N.Y. Med. Coll., 1956; M.S., U. Minn., 1963. Diplomate: Am. Bd. Urology. Intern Phila. Gen. Hosp., 1956-57, resident, 1959-60; resident Flower-Fifth Ave. and Met. Hosp., N.Y.C., 1957-59; Mayo Clinic, Rochester, Minn., 1960-63; practice medicine specializing in urology San Francisco, 1963-68; assoc. prof. urology N.Y. Med. Coll., N.Y.C., 1968-72; assoc. dean N.Y. Med. Coll., 1970-72; prof. surgery, chief div. urology Mich. State U., East Lansing, 1972-75; prof., chmn. dept. urology Med. U. S.C., Charleston, 1975-88; urologist-in-chief Med. U. S.C. and County hosps., Charleston, 1975-88; editorial dir. Norton Med. Books div. W.W. Norton and Co., 1988-94, editorial cons. 1994—; clin. prof. surgery Uniformed Svcs. U. of Health Scis., Bethesda, Md., 1992—; adj. prof. urology Med. U. S.C., 1988—, adj. prof. surgery Dartmouth Med. Sch., 1988-91, prof. surgery (urology), 1991—; staff urologist Dartmouth-Hitchcock Med. Ctr., 1991—; cons. urologist Saginaw VA Hosp., 1971-75, Charleston VA Hosp., 1975-88; hon. cons. St. Peter's Hosp., London, 1981-82; sr. vis. fellow Inst. Urology, London, 1981-82; mil. cons. in urology USAF Surgeon Gen., 1982-85; chmn. alumni devel. com. Mayo Clinic, 1979-82; hon. staff The Exeter Hosp., N.H., 1988—; mem. nat. bd. visitors N.Y. Med. Coll., 1988—; chief urology VA Med. Ctr., White River Junction, Vt., 1991—. Author: Understanding Urology, 1973, Urology in Primary Care, 1976, Spanish edit., 1978, Russian edit., 1979, Urology: A Core Textbook, 1985, The Prostate Book, 1988, latest rev. edit., 1995, (with Judge Hiller B. Zobel) Doctors and the Law: Defendants and Expert Witnesses, 1993; editor Urology Ann., 1987—, Stone Disease: Diagnosis and Management, 1987; mem., editl. bd. Mil. Medicine, 1984-94; contbr. articles to med. jours. Mem. East Lansing Planning Commn., 1974-75; vestryman, jr. warden All Saints Episcopal Ch., E. Lansing, Mich., 1973-75, lay reader; mem. diocesan com. on continuing edn., 1975-86; vestryman St. Michael's Episc. Ch., 1979-82, Charleston, S.C., chmn. every mem. canvas, 1979-80, chmn. lay readers, 1983-86; mem. fin. com., lay reader Christ Episc. Ch., Exeter, N.H., 1989-91; lector St. Thomas Episc. Ch., Hanover, N.H., 1991—, vestryman, 1992—, stewardship chmn., 1992-94, jr. warden, 1994—; mem. selectman's alt. Hampton Falls Planning Bd., 1989-91. Col. USAFR, 1981-85; col. USAR, 1985—. Recipient "A" designator in urology, U.S. Army Surgeon Gen., 1986. Fellow ACS, Am. Acad. Pediatrics; mem. AMA, Soc. Univ. Urologists, Internat. Soc. Urology, Am. Urol. Assn., Nat. Urologic Forum, Soc. Pediatric Urology, Brit. Assn. Urol. Surgeons, German Urol. Assn. (hon.), Mayo Alumni Assn. (v.p. 1979-81, pres. 1983-85), Army and Navy Club (Washington), Lotos Club (N.Y.C.), Sigma Xi, Alpha Omega Alpha (hon.). Republican. Home: Main St Box 296 Norwich VT 05055 Office: Dartmouth Hitchcock Med Ctr Sect Urology Lebanon NH 03756

ROUSAKIS, JOHN PAUL, former mayor; b. Savannah, Ga., Jan. 14, 1929; s. Paul V. and Antigone (Alexopoulos) R.; m. Elizabeth Lattimore, Oct. 24, 1987; children: Rhonda, Paul, Thea, Tina. B.B.A., U. Ga., 1952. Commr. Chatham County, Ga., 1965-69; vice chmn. Chatham County, 1969-70; mayor of Savannah, 1970-92; ins. broker Savannah, 1956—. Past pres. Nat. League Cities. With AUS, 1953-56. Named Outstanding Young Man of Savannah, Outstanding Young Man of Ga., 1962, Archon Greek Orthodox Ch., 1988, Outstanding City Ofcl., State of Ga.; recipient Tree of Life award Jewish Nat. Fund, 1983, Pres.'s award Nat. League of Cities, 1991. Mem. Ga. Mcpl. Assn. (past pres.), Am. Legion, Ahepa, Masons, (Shriner, Knight Comdr. 32d deg.). Office: 24 E Liberty St Savannah GA 31401-3953

ROUSE, ANDREW MILES, management consultant; b. Newark, Sept. 11, 1928; m. Matthew and Lillian (Steele) R. BA cum laude, Franklin & Marshall Coll., 1949; LLB, Columbia U., 1952; MBA with distinction, Harvard U., 1959. Sr. assoc. Arthur D. Little, Inc., Boston, 1959-67; exec. dir. Pres.'s Adv. Council on Exec. Orgn., Washington, 1968-71; spl. asst. for domestic affairs to Pres. U.S., 1971; spl. assignment Arthur D. Little, Inc., Boston, 1971-72; exec. v.p. INA Corp., Phila., 1972-82, CIGNA Corp., 1982-86; pres. Pa. Ballet, 1987-89; ptnr. Drotter, McKinnon, Inc., 1989—; program dir. The Mahler Co., Fairlawn, N.J.; bd. dirs. Westco Fin., Ramsey, N.J., Phila. Fund for Edn. Bd. trustees Franklin & Marshall Coll., Lancaster, Pa., 1978—; bd. dirs. Phila. Singers, Pa. Ballet; treas./trustee Phila. Mus. Art, 1979—. Home: 1929 Panama St Philadelphia PA 19103-6609 also: Rapp Hollow Farm Ottsville PA Office: 1811 Chestnut St Philadelphia PA 19103-3721

ROUSE, CHRISTOPHER CHAPMAN, III, composer; b. Balt., Feb. 15, 1949; s. Christopher Chapman Jr. and Margery (Harper) R.; m. Ann Jensen, Aug. 28, 1983; children: Jillian, Alexandra, Adrian; 1 stepchild, Angela. MusB, Oberlin Conservatory, 1971; MFA, DMA, Cornell U., 1977. Asst. prof. composition U. Mich., Ann Arbor, 1978-81; asst. prof. composition Eastman Sch. Music, Rochester, N.Y., 1981-85, assoc. prof. composition, 1985-91, prof. composition, 1991—; composer-in-residence Balt. Symphony Orch., 1986-89; writer numerous musical subjects; historian rock music. Composer for numerous soloist and ensembles including Yo-Yo Ma, Charles Castleman, James VanDemark, Jan de Gaetani, Leslie Guinn, Carol Wincenc, Cho-Liang Lin, William Albright, Soc. New Music, Blackearth Percussion Group; commd. composer Atlanta Symphony, Phila. Orch., N.Y. Philharm., L.A. Philharm., Balt. Symphony, Houston Symphony, Detroit Symphony, St. Louis Symphony, Rochester Philharmonic, Cleve. Quartet, Boston Musica Viva, Aspen Music Festival, N.Y. Internat. Festival of Arts, Chamber Music Am., New England Conservatory, Nonesuch Records; orchestral works programmed by Berlin, Stockholm, N.Y.C., Buffalo, L.A., Rochester Philharmonics, Orchestre Nat. de France, also Philharmonia Chgo., Boston, St. Louis, Detroit, Balt., Nat. Pitts., Houston, Denver, Milw., Cleve., Minn., Phila., Oakland, Cin., Atlanta, Indpls., Memphis, San Francisco, Dallas Symphony Orchs. Recipient awards from Guggenheim Found., League Composers/ISCM, NEA, Rockefeller Found., Am. Music Ctr., Warner Bros. Record Co., BMI and Pitney Bowes, Friedheim 1st prize Kennedy Ctr., 1988, Pulitzer prize for music, 1993, Acad. award Am. Acad. Arts and Letters, 1993. Home: 162 Selborne Chase Fairport NY 14450 Office: Eastman Sch Music 26 Gibbs St Rochester NY 14604-2599

ROUSE, DORIS JANE, physiologist, research administrator; b. Greensboro, N.C., Oct. 3, 1948; d. Welby Corbett and Nadia Elizabeth (Grainger) R.; m. Blake Shaw Wilson, Jan. 6, 1974; children: Nadia Jacqueline, Blair Elizabeth. B.A. in Chemistry, Duke U., 1970, Ph.D. in Physiology and Pharmacology, 1980. Tchr. sci. Peace Corps, Tugbake, Liberia, 1970-71; research scientist Burroughs Wellcome Co., Research Triangle Park, N.C., 1971-76; sr. physiologist Rsch. Triangle Inst., 1976-83, ctr. dir., 1980—, also dir. NASA tech. application team, 1980—, administr. ANSI Tech. Adv. Group for Wheelchairs, N.Y.C., 1982-86; adj. asst. prof. Sch. Medicine U. N.C., 1983—; chair Instl. Rev. Bd., Profl. Devel. Award Com., Rsch. Triangle Inst. Mem. adv. bd. Assns. Retarded Citizens, Arlington (Tex.), 1981-88, Western Gerontology Soc., San Francisco, 1982-85; bd. dirs. Simon Found., Chgo. 1983—; mem. spl. rev. com. small bus. applications; Nat. Forum on Tech. and Aging. Recipient Group Achievement award NASA, 1979. Mem. Rehab. Engring. Soc. N.Am. (chm. wheelchair com. 1981-86), Am. Soc. on Aging, Rehab. Engring. Soc. N.Am., Tech. Transfer Soc., Nat. Space Soc. Club: Triangle Dive. Home: 2410 Wrightwood Ave Durham NC 27705-5802 Office: Research Triangle Inst PO Box 12194 Durham NC 27709-2194

ROUSE, IRVING, anthropologist, emeritus educator; b. Rochester, N.Y., Aug. 29, 1913; s. Benjamin Irving and Louise Gillespie (Bohachek) R.; m. Mary Uta Mikami, June 24, 1939; children: Peter, David. BS, Yale U., 1934, PhD, 1938; D in Philosophy and Letters (hon.), Centro de Estudios Avanzados de Puerto Rico y el Caribe, 1990. Asst. anthropology Yale Peabody Museum, 1934-38, asst. curator, 1938-47, assoc. curator, 1947-54, research assoc., 1954-62, curator, 1977-85, emeritus curator, 1985—; instr. anthropology Yale U., 1939-43, asst. prof., 1943-48; assoc. prof. Yale, 1948-54; prof. Yale U., 1954-69, Charles J. MacCurdy prof. anthropology, 1969-84, prof. emeritus, 1984—. Author monographs on archaeology of Fla., Cuba, Haiti, P.R., Venezuela. Recipient Medalla Commemorativa del Vuelo Panamericano pro Faro de Colon Govt. Cuba, 1945, A. Cressy Morrison prize in natural sci. N.Y. Acad. Sci., 1951, Viking fund medal Wenner-Gren Found., 1960, Wilbur Cross medal Yale U., 1992; Guggenheim fellow, 1963-64. Mem. Am. Anthrop. Assn. (pres. 1967-68), Eastern States Archeol. Fedn. (pres. 1946-50), Assn. Field Archaeology (pres. 1977-78), Soc. Am. Archaeology (editor 1946-50, pres. 1952-53), Nat. Acad. Scis., Am. Acad. Arts and Scis., Soc. Antiquaries (London). Office: Box 208277 Yale Sta New Haven CT 06520-8277

ROUSE, JEFF, Olympic athlete, swimmer. Olympic swimmer Barcelona, Spain, 1992. Recipient 100m Backstroke Silver medal Olympics, Barcelona, 1992, 4*100 Medley Relay Gold Medal Olympics, Barcelona, 1992. World record holder 100m backstroke long course and short course, 1992. Office: US Olympic Com 1750 E Boulder St Colorado Springs CO 80909-5746*

ROUSE, JOHN WILSON, JR., research institute administrator; b. Kansas City, Mo., Dec. 7, 1937; s. John Wilson and Gail Agnes (Palmer) R.; m. Susan Jane Davis, May 3, 1981; 1 son, Jeffrey Scott. A.S., Kansas City Jr. Coll., 1957; B.S., Purdue U., 1959; M.S., U. Kans., 1965, Ph.D., 1968. Registered profl. engr., Mo., Tex. Engr. Bendix Corp., Kansas City, Mo., 1959-64; rsch. coord. Ctr. for Rsch., U. Kans., Lawrence, 1964-68; prof. elec. engring., dir. remote sensing ctr. Tex. A&M U., College Station, 1968-78; Logan prof. engr., chmn. dept. elec. engring. U. Mo., Columbia, 1978-81; dean engring. U. Tex., Arlington, 1981-87; pres. So. Rsch. Inst., Birmingham, Ala., 1987—; mgr. microwave program NASA Hdqrs., Washington, 1975-77; bd. dirs. Protective Life Corp., Ala. Power Co.; chmn. bd. So. Rsch. Techs. Inc. Contbr. articles to profl. jours. Recipient Outstanding Tchr. award Tex. A&M U., 1971; Outstanding Prof. award U. Mo., 1980; Engr. of Yr. Tex. Soc. Profl. Engrs., 1983. Mem. IEEE, Nat. Soc. Profl. Engrs., Am. Soc. Engring. Edn., Internat. Bus. Fellows, Internat. Union Radio Sci., Sigma Xi, Eta Kappa Nu, Tau Beta Pi. Home: 2004 Bridgelake Dr Birmingham AL 35244-1421 Office: Southern Research Institute PO Box 55305 2000 9th Ave S Birmingham AL 35205-2708

ROUSE, RICHARD HUNTER, historian, educator; b. Boston, Aug. 14, 1933; s. Hunter and Dorothee (Hüsmert) R.; m. Mary L. Ames, Sept. 7, 1959; children: Thomas, Andrew, Jonathan. B.A., State U. Iowa, 1955; M.A., U. Chgo., 1957; Ph.D., Cornell U., 1963. Mem. faculty UCLA, 1963—, prof. history, 1975—; assoc. dir. Ctr. Medieval and Renaissance Studies, 1966-67, acting dir., 1967-68; dir. Summer Inst. in Paleography, 1978, chair grad. coun., 1989-90; adv. bd. Hill Monastic Microfilm Libr., St. John's U., Collegeville, Minn., Ambrosiana Microfilm Library, Notre Dame (Ind.) U., Corpus of Brit. Medieval Libr. Catalogues, Brit. Acad. Author: Serial Bibliographies for Medieval Studies, 1969, (with M.A. Rouse) Preachers, Florilegia and Sermons: Studies on the Manipulus Florum of Thomas of Ireland, 1979; (with others) Texts and Transmission, 1983; (with C.W. Dutschke) Medieval and Renaissance Manuscripts in the Claremont Libraries, 1986; (with M.A. Rouse) Cartolai, Illuminators and Printers in Fifteenth-Century Italy, 1988; (with L. Bataillon and B. Guyot) La Production du livre universitaire au moyen age, exemplar et pecia, 1988, (with others) Guide to Medieval and Renaissance Manuscripts in the Huntington Library, 1989, (with M. Ferrari) Medieval and Renaissance Manuscripts at the University of California, Los Angeles, 1991, (with M.A. Rouse and R.A.B. Mynors) Registrum de libris doctorum et auctorum veterum, 1991, (with M.A. Rouse) Authentic Witnesses: Approaches to Medieval Texts and Manuscripts, 1991; co-editor: Viator: Medieval and Renaissance Studies, 1970—; mem. editorial bd. Medieval and renaissance manuscripts in Calif. libraries, Medieval Texts, Toronto; Medieval Texts, Binghamton, Library Quar., 1984-88, Speculum, 1981-85, Revue d'histoire des Textes, 1986—, Cambridge Studies in Paleography and Codicology, 1990—, Catalogue of Medieval and Renaissance Manuscripts in the Beinecke Rare Book and Manuscript Library Yale University, 1984—. Am. Coun. Learned Socs. fellow, 1972-73, fellow All Souls Coll., Oxford, 1978-79, Guggenheim Found., 1975-76, Rosenbach fellow in bibliography U. Pa., 1976, NEH fellow, 1981-82, 84-85, 94-96, Inst. for Advanced Studies fellow Jerusalem, 1991; J.R. Lyell reader in bibliography U. Oxford, 1991-92; vis. fellow Pembroke Coll., U. Oxford, 1992. Fellow Royal Hist. Soc., Medieval Acad. Am.; mem. Medieval Assn. Pacific (councillor 1965-68, pres. 1968-70), Medieval Acad. Am. (councillor 1977-80), Comité international de paléographie (treas. 1985-90), Comité international du vocabulaire des institutions et de la communication intellectuelles au moyen age, 1987—, Societa internazionale per lo studio del medioevo latino, 1988—. Home: 11444 Berwick St Los Angeles CA 90049-3416 Office: Univ Calif Dept History Los Angeles CA 90024

ROUSE, ROBERT MOOREFIELD, mathematician, educator; b. Auburn, N.Y., Aug. 1, 1936; s. Lester Mallory and Margaret (Moore) R.; m. Mary Josephine Sellers, Aug. 3, 1968; 1 child, Meredeth Elizabeth. BEE, Clarkson U., 1958, M in Engring. Sci., 1972; MS, Syracuse U., 1962. Registered profl. engr., N.Y. Envr. Gulf Oil Corp., Phila, Port Arthur, Tex., 1958-61; prof. SUNY, Morrisville, 1964—. 1st. lt. U.S. Army, 1962-63. Mem. IEEE, ASCE, Am. Soc. for Engring. Edn. Republican. Presbyterian. Home: Hart Rd PO Box 159 Morrisville NY 13408-0159 Office: SUNY Morrisville NY 13408

ROUSE, ROBERT SUMNER, former college official; b. Northampton, Mass., Sept. 2, 1930; s. Charles Edward and Laura Elisabeth (Rowbotham) R.; m. children: R. Daniel, Roland, James, Katherine; m. Mary Ellen Morgan, Dec. 5, 1992; children: Morgan, Laura; stepchildren: Matthew, James, Joseph. B.S., Yale U., 1951, M.S., 1953, Ph.D. in Chemistry, 1957. Lab. asst., then asst. in instrn. Yale, 1951-56; asst. prof. chemistry Lehigh U., 1956-62; group leader, plastics div. Allied Chems. Corp., 1962-66, tech. supr., 1966-67; prof. chemistry Monmouth Coll., West Long Branch, N.J., 1967—; chmn. chemistry dept. Monmouth Coll., 1967-73, asso. dean faculty, 1968-73, dean faculty, v.p. acad. affairs, 1973-80, provost and v.p. acad. affairs, 1980-81, chmn. faculty coun., 1990-93; mem. licensure adv. and approval bd. N.J. Dept. Higher Edn., 1973-82, chmn., 1980-81; bd. dirs. Assn. Ind. Colls. and Univs. N.J., 1978-81. Author: (with Robert O. Smith) Energy: Resource, Slave, Pollutant-A Physical Science Text, 1975. Recipient Disting. Tchr. award Monmouth Coll., 1991. Fellow N.Y. Acad. Scis.; mem. Am. Chem. Soc. AAUP, Sigma Xi. Home: 482 Cedar Ave West Long Branch NJ 07764-1806

ROUSE, ROSCOE, JR., librarian, educator; b. Valdosta, Ga., Nov. 26, 1919; s. Roscoe and Minnie Estelle (Corbett) R.; m. Charlie Lou Miller, June 23, 1945; children: Charles Richard, Robin Lou. BA, U. Okla., 1948, MA, 1952; MALS, U. Mich., 1958, PhD, 1962; student (Grolier Soc. scholar), Rutgers U., 1956. Bookkeeper C & S Nat. Bank, Valdosta, Ga., 1937-41; draftsman R.K. Rouse Co. (heating engrs.), Greenville, S.C., 1941-42; student asst. U. Okla. and Rice U., 1947-48; asst. librarian Northeastern State Coll., Tahlequah, Okla., 1948-49; acting librarian, instr. library sci. Northeastern State Coll., 1949-51; circulation librarian Baylor U., 1952-53, acting univ. librarian, 1953-54, univ. librarian, prof., 1954-63, chmn. dept. library sci., 1956-63; dir. libraries State U. N.Y. at Stony Brook, L.I., 1963-67; dean libr. svcs., prof. Okla. State U., Stillwater, 1967-87, univ. libr. historian, 1987-92, chmn. dept. libr. edn. Okla. State U., 1967-74; Vis. prof. U. Okla. Sch. Library Sci., summer 1962, N. Tex. State U., summer 1965; acad. library cons.; mem. AIA-Am. Library Assn. Library Bldg. Awards Jury, 1976; bd. dirs. Fellowship Christian Libr. and Info. Specialists. Author: A History of the Baylor University Library, 1845-1919, 1962; editor: Okla. Librarian, 1951-52; co-author: Organization Charts of Selected Libraries, 1973; A History of the Okla. State U. Library, 1992; contbr. articles, book revs., chpts. to publs. in field. Bd. dirs. Okla. Dept. Librs. articles, book revs., chpts. to publs. in field. Bd. dirs. Okla. Dept. Librs., 1989-92, chmn., 1990-92. 1st lt. USAAF, 1942-45. Decorated Air medal with 4 oak leaf clusters; recipient citation Okla. State Senate, 1987; named in

150 Prominent Individuals in Baylor's History, 1994. Mem. ALA (life, mem. coun. 1971-72, 76-80, 83-84, 84-88, chmn. libr. orgn. and mgmt. sect. 1973-75, planning and budget assembly 1978-79, coun. com. on coms. 1979-80, bldgs. and equipment sect. exec. bd. 1979-80, chmn. bldgs. for coll. and univ. librs. com. 1983-85, chmn. nominating com. libr. history roundtable 1993-94), Okla. Libr. Assn. (life, pres. 1971-72, ALA coun. rep. 1976-80, 83-84, OLA Disting. Svc. award 1979, Spl. Merit award 1987), S.W. Libr. Assn. (chmn. coll. and univ. div. 1958-60, chmn. scholarship com. 1968-70), Internat. Fedn. Libr. Assns. (standing com. on libr. bldgs. and equipment 1976-88), Assn. Coll. and Rsch. Librs. (chmn. univ. librs. sect. 1969-70, mem. exec. bd. and rep. to ALA Coun. 1971-72), U. Mich. Sch. Libr. Sci. Alumni Soc. (pres. 1979-80, Alumni Recognition award 1988), mem. Alumni Found. Com., 1992—, Payne County Ret. Educators Assn. (v.p., pres. elect 1991-92, pres. 1992-93), Okla. Hist. Soc. (com. on Okla. Higher Edn. mus. 1985—), Beta Phi Mu. Baptist (chmn. bd. deacons 1973). Clubs: Archons of Colophon, Stillwater Rotary (dir. 1978-82, pres. 1980-81). *It is sometimes a hidden influence in our lives which drives us toward a set goal. We ourselves may not recognize the real source of that urge to fulfill a dream. Only after many years was I able to look back and discern the factors in my youth that pushed me toward my goal of attaining a good education. They grew out of the influence that the Great Depression had on my early life. Because of that experience the preparation for a career became my first goal in life, yet the ways and means for achieving it were virtually nonexistent. It was to be, however, and I was fortunate to realize that goal. It causes me to think now that perhaps the degree of determination and endurance one possesses is paced more by adverse condition than by times of comfort and ease.*

ROUSE, ROY DENNIS, retired university dean; b. Andersonville, Ga., Sept. 20, 1920; s. Joseph B. and Janie (Wicker) R.; m. Madge Mathis, Mar. 6, 1946; children—David Benjamin, Sharon. Student, Ga. Southwestern Coll., 1937-39; B.S. in Agr, U. Ga., 1942, M.S., 1947; Ph.D., Purdue U., 1949. Asst. prof. agronomy and soils Auburn (Ala.) U., 1949-50, assoc. prof., 1950-56, prof., 1956-66, assoc. dir., asst. dean Sch. Agr. and Agrl. Expt. Sta., 1966-72, dean, dir., 1972-81, emeritus, 1981—; mem. Com. of Nine, Dept. Agr., 1970-74. Contbr. articles to profl. jours. Pres. Auburn Beautification Coun., 1987-88. Capt. USN, 1942-46, PTO; USNR, 1946-67, ret. Recipient Leadership award Farm-City Com. Ala., 1975, Disting. Svcs. award Catfish Farmers Am., 1976, Disting. Svcs. award Ala. Voc.-Agrl. Tchrs. Assn., 1976, Man of Yr. in Agr. award Progressive Farmer, 1977, Aeolian award Ga. Southwestern Coll., 1981, Charles W. Summerour award Ala. Soil Fertility Soc., 1987, Conservation medal Nat. Soc. DAR, 1993; named Hon. State Farmer Future Farmers Am., 1976, Man of Yr. Crop Improvement Assn., 1981, Hon. County Agt., 1981; named to Ala. Agrl. Hall of Honor, 1985; R. Dennis Rouse Life Sciences Bldg. named in honor Auburn U., 1993. Fellow Am. Soc. Agronomy, Soil Sci. Soc. Am., Am. Rhododendron Soc. (pres. Chattahoochee chpt. 1993); mem. Am. Assn. Ret. Persons (pres. Lee County chpt. 1989-91), So. Assn. Agrl. Scientists (pres. 1976), Assn. So. Agrl. Expt. Sta. Dirs. (chmn. 1974), Assn. Univs. and Land-Grant Colls (chmn. expt. sta. com. on orgn. and policy 1977), Men's Camellia Club (pres. 1965-66, 82-83), Outing Club, Lions (pres. Auburn 1993-94, Melvin Jones fellow 1994), Sigma Xi, Alpha Zeta, Phi Kappa Phi, Xi Phi Xi. Presbyterian. Home: 827 Salmon St Auburn AL 36830-5930

ROUSE, WILLIAM BRADFORD, systems engineering executive, researcher, educator; b. Fall River, Mass., Jan. 20, 1947; s. Gaylor Louis Rouse and Barbara (Peirce) Rouse Sherman; m. Sandra Howard Kane, Sept. 8, 1968; children: Rebecca Kane, William Howard. B.S.M.E., U. R. I., 1969; S.M., MIT, 1970, Ph.D., 1972. Postdoctoral research assoc. MIT, Cambridge, 1972; asst. prof. Tufts U., Medford, Mass., 1973; prof. U. Ill., Urbana, 1974-81; adj. prof. indsl. and systems engring. Ga. Inst. Tech., Atlanta, 1981—; CEO Search Tech., Inc., Norcross, Ga., 1980—. Author/ editor 16 books including: Best Laid Plans, 1994; also numerous chpts., articles. Recipient O. Hugo Schuck award Am. Automatic Control Council, 1979. Fellow IEEE (Centennial medal 1984), Human Factors Soc.; mem. NAE, Systems, Man and Cybernetics Soc. of IEEE (pres. 1982-83, Norbert Wiener award 1986), Am. Inst. Indsl. Engrs. (sr.), Unitarian-Universalist Assn. Home: 2389 Little Brooke Dr Atlanta GA 30338-3187 Office: Search Tech Inc 4898 S Old Peachtree Rd Norcross GA 30071

ROUSEFF, RUSSELL LEE, food chemistry educator, researcher; b. Chgo., Nov. 20, 1944; s. Walter and Evelyn Alice Rouseff; m. June Mary-Faye Duren, Aug. 19, 1967; children: Rebecca, Christopher. BS in Chemistry, Wheaton Coll., 1966; MS in Analytic Chemistry, Southern Ill. U., 1968; PhD in Analytic Chemistry, U. Ga., 1972. Chemist Sherwin-Williams Chem. Co. Rsch. Ctr., summers 1964-66; prof. chemistry Polk C.C., Winter Haven, Fla., 1971-74; chemist III sci. asst. Fla. Dept. Citrus, 1974-77; rsch. scientist I, 1977-81, rsch. scientist II, 1981-85, rsch. scientist III, 1985-87; rsch. prof. food sci. and human nutrition dept. Citrus Rsch. and Edn. Ctr., U. Fla., Lake Alfred, 1987—; Mem. editorial adv. bd. Jour. Agrl. and Food Chemistry, 1982-86, 93—. Co-author: Citrus Fruits and Their Products, 1986; editor: Bitterness in Foods and Beverages, Developments in Food Science Series, 1990; contbr. articles to profl. publs., chpts. to books. Soccer referee U.S. Soccer Fedn., 1990-95. USDA grantee, 1989-92, 92—. Fellow Am. Chem. Soc. (chmn. local sect., sec./treas. 1974-77, state analytical topic group chmn. 1974-77, nat. membership chmn. agrl. and food divsn. 1979-83, chmn., program chmn., sec./treas. flavor subdivsn. 1981-86, councilor 1990-93); mem. Inst. Food Technologists (citrus products divsn. sec./treas. 1987-89, sensory divsn., state chmn., program chair 1989-90, exec. com. 1986-88, councilor 1991—). Avocations: tennis, painting, stained glass, underwater photography. Office: U Fla Citrus Rsch and Edn Ctr 700 Experiment Station Rd Lake Alfred FL 33850

ROUSH, G. JON, organization administrator. PhD in English, U. Calif., Berkeley, 1965. Pres. The Wilderness Soc., Washington, 1994—; asst. prof. lit. and humanities Reed Coll.; program officer Carnegie Corp., N.Y.; pres. Canyon Consulting, 1988-94. Contbr. articles to profl. jours., chpts. to books. Past chmn. bd. dirs., exec. v.p. Nature Conservancy; bd. dirs. Conservation Fund, No. Rockies Action Group, No. Lights Inst., Mont. Land Reliance. Office: The Wilderness Soc 900 17th St NW Washington DC 20006*

ROUSH, WILLIAM R., chemistry educator. BS in Chemistry, UCLA, 1974; PhD in Chemistry, Harvard U., 1977. Prof. chemistry dept. Ind. U., Bloomington. Recipient Arthur C. Cope Scholar award Am. Chem. Soc., 1994, Alan R. Day award Phila. Organic Chemist's Club, 1992. Office: Indiana U Dept Chemistry Bloomington IN 47405-4000*

ROUSS, RUTH, lawyer; b. Des Moines, May 21, 1914; d. Simon Jacob and Dora (Goldin) R.; m. Dennis O'Rourke, Jan. 21, 1940; children: Susan Jerene, Kathleen Frances, Brian Jay, Dennis Robert, Ruth Elizabeth, Dolores Ann. B.A., Drake U., 1934, J.D., 1937. Bar: Iowa bar 1937, U.S. Supreme Ct. bar 1945, Colo. bar 1946, D.C. bar 1971. Legal counsel to Jay N. Darling, Des Moines, 1937-38; atty. Office of Solicitor, Dept. Agr., 1938-45, asst. to solicitor, 1940-45; practice law Colorado Springs, Colo., 1946—; mem. firm Williams & Rouss, 1946-50, individual practice law, 1950-69; of counsel firm Sutton, Shull & O'Rourke, Colorado Springs and Washington, 1969-72; mem. firm Rouss & O'Rourke, Colorado Springs and Washington, 1972—; dir., sec.-treas. ManExec., Inc. Mem. cast chorus, Colo. Opera Festival, 1976, 78; mem., Colorado Springs Chorale, 1976—. Bd. dirs. Human Relations Commn. City Colorado Springs, 1968-73, chmn., 1971-72; bd. dirs., sec. Colorado Springs Community Planning and Research Council, 1972-78; bd. dirs. Logos, Inc., Colorado Springs, 1972-78, sec., 1976-77, v.p., 1977-78; bd. dirs. Colorado Springs Opera Festival, Colorado Springs World Affairs Council, Urban League of Pikes Peak Region; mem. com. protection human rights Penrose Hosp., adv. council Am. Lung Assn. of Colo., Pikes Peak region; dir. Joseph Henry Edmondson Found.; adv. bd. Care Castle Divsn. Pikes Peak Seniors,El Paso County, Colo. Mem. El Paso County (Colo.) Bar Assn., Colo. Bar Assn., D.C. Bar Assn., Am. Law Inst. (life), Internat. Fedn. Women Lawyers, Women's Forum Colo., Phi Beta Kappa. Home: 8 Heather Dr Colorado Springs CO 80906-3114 Office: Rouss & O'Rourke Box 572 231 E Vermijo Ave Colorado Springs CO 80901 also: 1614 20th St Washington DC 20009

ROUSSEAU, EUGENE ELLSWORTH, musician, music educator, consultant; b. Blue Island, Ill., Aug. 23, 1932; s. Joseph E. and Laura M. (Schindler) R.; m. Norma J. Rigel, Aug. 15, 1959; children—Lisa-Marie,

Joseph. B of Mus Edn., Chgo. Mus. Coll., 1953; MusM, Northwestern U., 1954; student, Conservatoire National de Musique, 1960-61; PhD, U. Iowa, 1962. Instr. Luther Coll., 1956-59; asst. prof. Cen. Mo. State Coll., 1962-64; prof. music Ind. U., Bloomington, 1964-88, disting. prof. music, 1988—; guest prof. U. Iowa, 1964, Hochschule fur Musik, Vienna, Austria, 1981-82, Ariz. State U., 1984, Prague Conservatory Music, 1985; tchr. U. Wis.-Ext., 1969—; chief adviser for design and mfg. saxophones Yamaha, 1972—; music arranger; svc. on numerous acad. coms.; tchr. 1st course in saxophone Mozarteum in Salzburg, Austria, 1991—; mem. jury Munich Internat. competitions, 1987, 90-92; first saxophonist to perform on Prague Spring Festival, 1993; mem. jury Can. Nat. Music Competition, 1994. Worldwide concert saxophonist; Carnegie Hall debut, 1965; author: Marcel Mule: His Life and the Saxophone, 1982, Saxophone High Tones, 1978, Method for Saxophone (2 vols.), 1975; performer 1st solo saxophone recitals, several European cities, 1st Am. solo saxophone performance in Japan, 1984; 1st to record concert saxophone on compact disc (Delos); radio broadcasts in Berlin, Bremen, London, Montreal, Ostrava, Paris, Prague, Toronto, Vienna; saxophone recs. for Deutsche Gramophon, Golden Crest, Coronet, Delos, Liscio, ALM and McGill. Instr., asst. band leader 25th Infantry Div. U.S. Army, 1954-56. Fulbright grantee, 1960-61, Research and Exchanges Bd. grantee, 1983, Internat. Research and Exchanges Bd., 1985, NEA grantee, 1986; named hon. prof. music Prague Conservatory, 1993—. Mem. N.Am. Saxophone Alliance (pres. 1978-80), Comite Internat. de Saxophone (pres. 1982-85), Coll. Music Soc., Clarinet and Saxophone Soc. (U.K.), Music Tchrs. Nat. Assn. (Tchr. of Yr. award for Ind. 1993), Fulbright Assn. (life). Office: Indiana U Sch Music Bloomington IN 47405

ROUSSEAU, EVA RICE, principal; b. Washington, Sept. 29, 1944; d. Edward and Ione Chrystalia (Niles) Rice; 1 child, Richard. BA, Bennett Coll., 1966; MA in Edn., George Washington U., 1971; EdD in Edn., Nova U., 1992. Cert. principal. Tchr. Browne Jr. High Sch., Washington, 1966-71; tchr. Dunbar Sr. High Sch., Washington, 1972-75, administrv. intern, 1976-77; asst. prin. Eastern Sr. High Sch., Washington, 1977-83; prin. Dunbar Sr. High Sch., Washington, 1984—; guest speaker for Fulbright tchr. orientation Georgetown U., Washington, 1987-89; workshop presenter Nat. Coun. of States on In-Svc. Edn., New Orleans, 1986; prin.'s rep. Coordinating Coun. on Sch. Improvement, Washington, 1987-88; guest lectr. George Washington U., 1990; lead prin. 24 schs. in Cluster IV. Author: Improving Supervisory Relationship, 1989. Mem. Howard U. Community Rels. Bd., Washington, 1985, Male Youth Enhancement Adv. Couns., Washington, 1987-88, Pub./ Pvt. Partnership Steering Com., Washington, 1989—, Sch. Partners of N.Am. Program Rev. Com.; bd. dirs. Ctr. for Ednl. Change, D.C. Ctr. for Citizen Edn. in Law, Ward 5 Community Corp. Devel. Coun. Rockefeller Found. fellow D.C. Schs., 1976, IBM Edn. Exec. fellow D.C. Schs., 1984, Danforth Found. fellow D.C. Schs., 1986, Vanderbilt Found. fellow D.C. Schs., 1988, Harvard Principals' Ctr. fellow D.C. Schs., 1990, Yale Comer Child Study Ctr. fellow D.C. Schs., 1992; recipient U.S. Dept. Def. Employer Support award, Outstanding Prin.'s award Save Our Youth Am. Inc., Outstanding Prin.'s award for Support of Sch. Libr./Media Svcs., Burger King's Outstanding Prin. of the Year award Nat. Assn. Secondary Sch. Prins., 1992, Washington Post Disting.Ednl. Leadership award, 1992, Grace Basinger Child Advocacy award, 1992, Phobe Apperson Hearst award Nat. PTA, Outstanding Prin.'s award Children's Day com. United House of Prayer, Outstanding Role Model award Mt. Lebanon Ch.; named Outstanding Participant, DCPS Mgmt. Inst.; George Washington U. honoree, 1993. Mem. Prin.'s Ctr. (bd. dirs.), Middle State Assn. for Schs. and Colls. (state adv. bd.), Am. Assn. Sch. Adminstrs., Nat. Assn. Secondary Sch. Prins., Assn. for Supervision and Curriculum Devel., Nat. Staff Devel. Coun., Alpha Kappa Alpha (Advanced Profl. Achievement award), Phi Delta Kappa (honoree 1993). Avocation: playing the piano. Office: Dunbar SHS 1301 New Jersey Ave NW Washington DC 20001-1294

ROUSSEAU, GEORGE SEBASTIAN, eighteenth century studies educator, chamber musician; b. N.Y.C., Feb. 23, 1941; s. Hyman Victoire and Esther (Zacuto) R. B.A., Amherst Coll., 1962; diploma, Am. Sch. Classical Studies, Athens, 1963; M.A., Princeton U., 1964, Ph.D., 1966. Instr. English Harvard U., Cambridge, Mass., 1966-68; asst. prof. UCLA, 1968-70, prof. English, 1970-79, prof. 18th Century studies, 1980-94; Regius prof. English U. Aberdeen, Scotland, 1994—; dir. Sir Thomas Reid Inst. Rsch. in Humanities, Scis., Medicine, 1994—; vis. fellow Magdalen Coll., Oxford, 1993-94; Fulbright vis. prof. U. Lausanne, 1994. Author: (with Marjorie Hope Nicolson) This Long Disease, My Life: Alexander Pope and the Sciences, 1968, The Rape of the Lock: Twentieth-Century Interpretations, 1969, The Augustan Milieu: Essays Presented to Louis A. Landa, 1970, (with Neil Rudenstine) English Poetic Satire: Wyatt to Byron, 1972, (with P.G. Boucé) Tobias Smollett: Bicentennial Essays Presented to L.M. Knapp, 1971, Organic Form: The Life of an Idea, 1972, Goldsmith: The Critical Heritage, 1974, (with Roy Porter) The Ferment of Knowledge: Studies in the Historiography of Science, 1980, The Letters and Papers of Sir John Hill, 1982, Tobias Smollett: Essays of Two Decades, 1982, (with Roy Porter) Sexual Underworlds of the Enlightenment, 1987, Exoticism in the Enlightenment, 1989, The Languages of Psyche: Mind and Body in Enlightenment Thought, 1990, Enlightenment Crossings, Perilous Enlightenment, Enlightenment Borders: Pre- and Post-Modern Discourses, 3 vols., 1991 (with others) Hysteria Beyond Freud, 1993; mem. editorial bd. The Eighteenth Century, 1974—, Eighteenth-Century Life, 1980—, Literature and Medicine, 1983—, History of Psychiatry, 1990—; contbr. The Crisis in Modernism: Bergson and the Vitalist Tradition, 1992. Osgood fellow in lit. Princeton U., 1965-66; Am. Council Learned Socs. fellow, 1970; vis. fellow commoner Trinity Coll., Cambridge U., 1982; sr. Fulbright research prof. Sir Thomas Browne Inst., Leiden, Netherlands, 1983; Clark Library prof. U. Calif., 1985-86; sr. research fellow NEH, 1986-87. Mem. Am. Soc. 18th-Century Studies, MLA, History of Sci. Soc., Am. Hist. Assn. (1972), Am. Assn. History of Medicine, Royal Soc. Arts, Royal Soc. Medicine. Home and Office: Taylor Bldg, Univ Aberdeen, Aberdeen AB9 2UB, Scotland

ROUSSEAU, IRENE VICTORIA, artist, sculptor; m. Denis Lawrence Rousseau; children: Douglas, Scott. BA, Hunter Coll., N.Y.C.; MFA, Claremont (Calif.) Grad. Sch., 1969; PhD, N.Y.U., 1977. Tenured prof. William Paterson Coll., Wayne, N.J., 1970-74; invited speaker CAA-WCA Conf., L.A., 1985, N.J. Ctr. for Visual Arts, Summit, N.J., 1985, Noyes Mus., 1994, Mus. African Art, 1994. Exhbns. include Betty Parsons Gallery, N.Y.C., Claremonte Colls., State Mus. Sci. and Industry, L.A., Morris Mus. Arts and Scis., Morristown, N.J., The Bronx Mus. of Art, Galleri Sci. Agnes, Copenhagen/Roskilde, Denmark, Sculptors 5, Madison, N.J., Edmund Scientific Co. Barrington, N.J., AT&T World Headquarters, Basking Ridge, N.J., N.J. Ctr. for Visual Arts, The Brotherhood Synagogue Holocaust Meml. Gramercy Pk. (mosaic), N.Y.C., 1986, 1st Internat. Art Biennale, Malta, 1995, painted aluminum wall releifs Capital Sports Inc., headquarters Sprots in Action, Stamford, Conn., 1989, Mosaic mural Spiraling Light, Overlook Hosp., Summit, N.J., 1993, Nayes Mus., N.J., 1994; represented in permanent collections Brit. Mus., Met. Mus., Guggenheim Mus., Walker Art Ctr., Nat. Mus. Am. Art, Smithsonian Instn. Recipient seven 1st prize awards for creative work in N.J., ER Squibb and Sons Sculpture award. Mem. AIA (profl. affiliate N.J., N.Y., chmn. architecture dialogue com.), Internat. Sculptors Assn., Am. Abstract Artists (exhbn. chmn. 1978-79, pres. 1979-82), Fine Arts Fedn. (bd. dirs.), Coll. Art Assn., Women's Caucus on Art (conf. speaker), Phi Delta Kappa. Home: 41 Sunset Dr Summit NJ 07901-2322

ROUSSEAU, RONALD WILLIAM, chemical engineering educator, researcher; b. Bogalusa, La., Sept. 28, 1943; s. Ivy John and Dorothy Dean (Talley) R.; m. Tess Marie McKinney, Aug. 5, 1963 (div. June 1978); children: Ronald William Jr., David Patrick, Brett Charles; m. Sandra Barbara Geller, Sept. 2, 1978. BS, La. State U., 1966, MS, 1968, PhD, 1969. Registered profl. engr., N.C. Prof. N.C. State U., Raleigh, 1969-86; prof., dir. Sch. Chem. Engring. Ga. Inst. Tech., Atlanta, 1987—; vis. prof. Princeton U., 1983-84; cons. numerous chem. cos., 1969—. Co-author: Elementary Principles of Chemical Processes, 1978, 2d edit., 1986; editor: Handbook of Separation Process Technology, 1987; contbr. over 120 articles to profl. publs. Mem. AIChE (bd. dirs. 1990-92, Outstanding Chem. Engr. award Ga. N.C. sect. 1986), Am. Chem. Soc., Coun. Chem. Rsch. (bd. govs. 1994-97, 2d vice-chmn. 1995). Democrat. Roman Catholic. Home: 4288 Conway Valley Ct NW Atlanta GA 30327-3602 Office: Sch Chem Engring Ga Inst Tech Atlanta GA 30332

ROUSSEL, LEE DENNISON, diplomat; b. N.Y.C., May 15, 1944; d. Ethan Allen and Frances Isabel (Ferry) Dennison; m. Andre Homo Roussel, Sept. 6, 1980; children: Cecilia Frances, Stephanie Anne. AB, Wellesley Coll., 1966; MA, Northeastern U., 1973. Mgmt. intern U.S. Dept. HEW, 1966-68; with Planning Office Commonwealth of Mass., 1968-70; exec. dir. Gov.'s Commn. Citizen Participation, Boston, 1973; with Boston Area Office U.S. Dept. HUD, 1970-78; fgn. svc. officer USAID, 1978—; with Housing and Urban Devel. Office USAID, Washington and Tunis, 1978-82; chief Housing and Urban Devel. Office for C.Am. USAID, Honduras, 1982-87; asst. dir. Office Housing and Urban Programs USAID, Washington, 1987-91; country rep. for Czech and Slovak Fed. Rep. USAID, 1991-92, country rep. for Czech Rep., 1993-94; min. counselor, U.S. rep. to Devel. Assistance Com. OECD, Paris, 1994—. Episcopalian. Office: USOECD, 19 rue de Franqueville, 75016 Paris France also: OECD PSC 116 APO AE 09777

ROUSSELOT, PETER FRESE, lawyer; b. N.Y.C., Jan. 7, 1942; s. Louis Marcel and Evelyn Valdez (Hastrup) R.; m. Mary Dumesnil, Cobb, Nov. 22, 1975; children: Laura Andren, Richard Frese, Anne Stewart, Louise Dierks. BA summa cum laude, Yale U., 1963; LLB, Harvard U., 1966. Bar: U.S. Dist. Ct. D.C. 1967, U.S. Ct. Appeals (D.C. cir.) 1967, U.S. Ct. Appeals (3d cir.) 1993, U.S. Supreme Ct. 1970. Assoc. Hogan & Hartson, Washington, 1966-74, ptnr., 1975—, mem. exec. com., 1986-88. Asst. to nat. co-chmn. Citizens for Robert F. Kennedy, Washington, 1968; vol. Kerrey for Pres., 1992. Mem. City Club Washington, Yale Club Washington, Phi Beta Kappa. Democrat. Episcopalian. Avocations: tennis, hiking, photography. Office: Hogan & Hartson 555 13th St NW Washington DC 20004-1109

ROUSSELOT, PHILIPPE, cinematographer; b. Meurthe et Moselle, France, 1945. Attended, Vaugirard Film Sch., Paris. Camera asst. (to Nestor Almendros): My Night at Maud's, Claire's Knee, Love in the Afternoon; cinematographer: (films) Absences Repetees, 1972, Il pleut toujours ou c'est mouille, 1974, Pour Clemence, 1977, Pauline et l'Ordinateur, 1977, Paradiso, 1977, Diabolo Menthe, 1977, Adom ou le sang d'abel, 1977, Le Couple Temoin, 1977, Peppermint Soda, 1977, La Drolesse, 1979, Cocktail Molotov, 1980, La Provinciale, 1980, Diva, 1980 (Cesar award Nat. Soc. of Film Critics 1980, Moscow award 1980), The Roads of Exile, 1981, La Gueule du Loup, 1981, Gut de Maupassant, 1982, Nemo, 1983, The Girl from Lorraine, 1983, Thieves after Dark, 1983, The Moon in the Gutter, 1983, Dream One, 1984, Les voleurs de la nuit, 1984, La nuit magique, 1985, The Emerald Forest, 1985, Night Music, 1985, Therese, 1986 (Cesar award Nat. Soc. of Film Critics 1986), (with John Harris) Hope and Glory, 1987 (Academy award nomination best cinematography 1987), Dangerous Liaisons, 1988, The Bear, 1989 (Outstanding Achievement award Am. Soc. of Cinematographers 1990), Too Beautiful for You, 1989, We're No Angels, 1989, Henry and June, 1990 (Academy award nomination best cinematography 1990), The Miracle, 1991, Merci, la vie, 1991, A River Runs Through It, 1992 (Academy award best cinematography 1992), Sommersby, 1993, Flesh and Bone, 1993, Interview with the Vampire, 1994, (TV miniseries) Les Chemins de l'exil, ou les dernieres de Jean Jacques Rousseau, 1978. Office: The Gersh Agency 232 N Canon Dr Beverly Hills CA 90210*

ROUSSEY, ROBERT STANLEY, accountant, educator; b. N.Y.C., July 20, 1935; s. George Albert and Estelle (Smegelski) R.; m. Jeanne Archer, May 8, 1965; children: Robert Scott, John Stephen. BS, Fordham U., 1957. CPA, N.Y., Japan. Staff acct. Arthur Andersen & Co., N.Y.C., 1957-63; mgr. Arthur Andersen & Co., N.Y.C. and Tokyo, 1964-69; ptnr. Arthur Andersen & Co., N.Y.C. and Chgo., 1969-92, dir. auditing procedures, 1977-92; prof. acctg. U. So Calif., L.A., 1992—; adj. prof. acctg. Northwestern U. Kellogg Grad. Sch. Mgmt., 1990, 91. Edit. cons. Handbook of Corporate Finance, 1986, Handbook of Financial Markets and Institutions, 1987; mem. edit. bd. Advances in Accounting, 1987—, Jour. Internat. Acctg. Auditing and Taxation, 1991—, Auditing: A Journal of Theory and Practice, 1994—; contbr. articles to profl. jours. Treas., bd. dirs. Kenilworth (Ill.) Community House, 1979-81, Troop 13 Boy Scouts Am., Kenilworth, 1978-80, St. Joseph's Ch. Men's Club, Bronxville, N.Y., 1971-73. With U.S. Army, 1958, 61-62. Mem. AICPAs (chmn. EDP auditing standards com. 1978-81, auditing standards bd. 1986-90, MAS practice standards and adminstrn. com. 1990-93), Am. Acctg. Assn. (v.p. auditing sect. 1987-90, pubs. com. 1993—), EDP Auditors Found. (standards bd. 1986—), Ill. State Soc. CPAs, N.Y. State Soc. CPAs, Inst. Internal Auditors (bd. rsch. advisors 1986—), Internat. Fedn. Accts. (internat. auditing practices com. 1990-95, chmn. 1995—, EDP audit com. 1980-88), Met. Club (gov. 1977-78), Tokyo-Am. Club (life), Union League Club, Beta Alpha Psi, Beta Gamma Sigma. Republican. Roman Catholic. Avocations: skiing, sailing, tennis, karate. Office: U So Calif Dept Acctg Los Angeles CA 90089-1421

ROUSUCK, J. WYNN, theater critic; b. Cleve., Mar. 19, 1951; d. Morton I. and Irene Zelda (Winograd) R.; m. James William Cox, Jr., May 8, 1983. BA with honors, Wellesley Coll., 1972; MS, Columbia U., 1974. Assoc. editor, program guide, Sta. WCLV-FM, Cleve., 1972-73; theater and film reviewer Cleve. Press, 1973; gen. assignment arts reporter Balt. Sun, 1974-84, theater critic, 1984—; instr. English Goucher Coll., Towson, Md., 1981; master critic Nat. Critics Inst., Waterford, Conn., 1990—; theater critic Md. Pub. TV., 1986; spkr. in field. Recipient Dog Writers Assn. Am. awards 1977, 79, Md. chpt. 1st Place Arts Reporting award Soc. Profl. Journalists, 1993; NEH journalism fellow U. Mich., 1979-80; Durant scholar Wellesley Coll., 1972. Fellow Nat. Critics Inst.; mem. Balt. Bibliophiles (bd. dirs. 1982-83), Octavo Plus, Walters Art Gallery, Balt. Wellesley Club (pres. 1978-79). Jewish. Avocations: rare books, art, dogs. Office: The Baltimore Sun 501 N Calvert St Baltimore MD 21278

ROUT, NANCY LOUISE, health facility administrator; b. Vincennes, Ind.; d. Melvin Milton and Clara Louise Miller; m. H. Wayne Rout; children: Annecia, David, Timothy. AD, Vincennas U., 1965; BS, U. Phoenix, 1984; MBA, Ball State U., 1991. Profl. nurse, adminstrv. supr. Bloomington (Ind.) Hosp., 1966-73; asst. adminstr. Harvard (Ill.) Community Meml. Hosp., 1978-83, Mesa (Ariz.) Gen. Hosp., 1983-85; asst. DON Deaconess Hosp., Evansville, Ind., 1986-88; asst. adminstr. Sun Towers Hosp., El Paso, Tex., 1988—; mem. adv. bd. dirs. continuing edn. El Paso Community Coll., 1990—; mem. adv. bd. dirs. U. Tex. at El Paso, 1991-92; adv. Tex. Peer Assistance Program for Nurses, Austin, 1990—; bd. dirs. TONE, Austin, 1990-91. Active Am. Cancer Soc., El Paso, 1991-92. Mem. ANA (dist. 1), Nat. League for Nursing, Tex. Orgn. Nurse Execs., El Paso Coun. of Nurse Execs. (pres. 1989-91). Avocations: geneology, sewing, reading, sports. Home: 360 Rio Estancia Dr El Paso TX 79932-2327 Office: Sun Towers Hosp-EPHS 1801 N Oregon St El Paso TX 79902-3524

ROUTH, DONALD K(ENT), psychology educator; b. Oklahoma City, Mar. 3, 1937; s. Ross Holland and Fay (Campbell) R.; m. Marion Starbird Wendler, Sept. 10, 1960; children—Rebecca Ann (dec.), Laura Diane. B.A., U. Okla., 1962; Ph.D., U. Pitts., 1967. Diplomate Am. Bd. Profl. Psychology; lic. psychologist, Fla. Asst. prof. psychology and pediatrics U. Iowa, Iowa City, 1967-70; prof. U. Iowa, 1977-85; assoc. prof. psychology Bowling Green State U., Ohio, 1970-71; assoc. prof. U. N.C., Chapel Hill, 1971-77; prof. psychology and pediatrics U. Miami, Coral Gables, Fla., 1985—; Chmn. behavioral medicine study sect. NIH, 1983-85. Editor Jour. Pediatric Psychology, 1976-82, Jour. Clin. Child Psychology, 1987-91, Jour. of Abnormal Child Psychology, 1992—; contbr. numerous articles to profl. jours., books. Pres. Eno River Unitarian Universalist Fellowship, 1970-71. Recipient award for disting. contbn. Soc. Pediatric Psychology, 1981, Presidential award, 1988; Fla. Psychol. Assn. Research Psychologist of Yr. award, 1987. Mem. APA (pres. div. child, youth and family services 1984, pres. div. on mental retardation 1987), Disting. Profl. Contbns. to Clin. Psychology (sect. on clin. child psychology 1989, div. clin. psychology, 1992). Democrat. Home: 9394 SW 77th Ave Apt F-7 Miami FL 33156-7959 Office: Dept Psychology Univ Miami PO Box 248185 Miami FL 33124-8185

ROUTIEN, JOHN BRODERICK, mycologist; b. Mt. Vernon, Ind., Jan. 23, 1913; s. William Evert and Frances Lolita (Broderick) R.; m. Helen Harrison Boyd, Mar. 11, 1944 (dec. 1965); m. Constance C. Connolly, Feb. 22, 1967. B.A., DePauw U., 1934; M.A., Northwestern U., 1936; Ph.D., Mich. State Coll., 1939. Instr. botany U. Mo., 1939-42; mycologist Pfizer, Inc., N.Y.C., 1946-77; research adviser Pfizer, Inc., 1974-77. Editorial bd.: Applied Microbiology, 1964-71, Antimicrobial Agts. and Chemotherapy, 1974-77. Recipient Comml. Solvents award in antibiotics, 1950. Mem.

Mycol. Soc. Am., Bot. Soc. Am., Soc. Am. Bacteriologists, Soc. Indsl. Microbiology. Research on molds producing new antibiotics, strain improvement of cultures, identification of fungi. Home: 318 Grassy Hill Rd Old Lyme CT 06371-3312 Office: Pfizer Inc Groton CT 06340

ROUVELAS, EMANUEL LARRY, lawyer; b. Seattle, Sept. 10, 1944; s. Larry E. and Mary (Derezes) R.; m. Marilyn S. Edmunds, Jan. 23, 1967; children: Eleftherios, Mary. BA, U. Wash., 1965; JD, Harvard U., 1968. Bar: Ill. 1968, D.C. 1973. Assoc. Kirkland & Ellis, Chgo., 1968-69; counsel U.S. Senate Com. on Commerce, Washington, 1969-73; chief counsel U.S. Senate Mcht. Marine and Fgn. Commerce Subcoms., Washington, 1969-73, Preston, Gates, Ellis, Rouvelas & Meeds, Washington, 1974—; advisor to two presdl. transitions and bi-partisan congl. caucus. Dir. OMI Corp, 1989—; trustee Am. Coll. of Greece, 1993—. Office: Preston Gates Ellis & 1735 New York Ave NW Washington DC 20006-5209

ROUX, AMBROISE MARIE CASIMIR, business executive; b. Piscop, France, June 26, 1921; s. Andre and Cecile (Marchilhacy) R.; m. Françoise Marion, June 17, 1946; children: Christian, Véronique. Student, Coll. Stanislas, Paris, Ecole Polytechnique, 1940, Ecole des Ponts & Chaussées, 1944, Ecole Supérieure d'Electricité, 1945. Engr. Dept. Civil Engring., France, 1944-51; exec. dir. Office Sec. States for Industry and Commerce, 1952-55; sr. v.p. Compagnie Générale d'Electricité, Paris, 1955-63, pres., 1963-69, chmn. bd., 1970-82, hon. chmn., 1982—; dir. Compagnie Générale d'Electricité (Alcatel-Alsthom), Paris, 1986—; also hon. chmn. Pétrofigaz, Afnor; chmn. AGREF, 1976-82, Association Française des entreprises Privées, 1983—; chmn. Compagnie Industrielle des Télécommunications (CIT-Alcatel), 1966-82, hon. chmn., 1982—; chmn. Compagnie Electro-Financière, 1969-82, hon. chmn., 1982—; vice chmn. Sté. des Plantations des Terres Rouges; dir. Barclays Bank, 1983-85, vice chmn., 1985-91; chmn. Conseil Surveillance, 1991—; vice chmn. Compagnie Generale des Eaux, 1992—; bd. dirs. Cie. Financiére Paribas, 1972-82, 86-90, mem. Conseil Surveillance, 1990—; bd. dirs. CEP-Communication, Schneider, 1991—; Miles Kali Ste Thérèse, 1986—; dir. Banque du Louvre, 1991, vice chmn., 1993—; dir. Banque du Touvre, 1991-93, vice-chmn., 1993—; dir. Sté du Louvre; mem. Conseil de Surveillance Printemps, 1991-92; chmn. Counseil de Surveillance, 1992—, Pinault-Printemps-Redoute; dir. La Radiotechnique, 1967-92, FNAC, 1994—, Sté d'investissement IENA, 1994—; hon. dir., 1993. Author: La Science et les Pouvoirs Psychiques de l'Homme. Decorated grand officer Légion d'Honneur, comdr. Mérite Comml., comdr. Instrn. Publique. Mem. the N.Y. Acad. of Scis., mem. Fedn. French Industries (vice chmn. 1966-75, 1st vice chmn. 1975-82, hon. 1st vice chmn. 1982—). Home: 17 place des Etats-Unis, 75116 Paris France Office: 8 bis rue Margueritte, 75017 Paris France

ROVELSTAD, MATHILDE VERNER, library science educator; b. Kempten, Germany, Aug. 12, 1920; came to U.S., 1951, naturalized, 1953; d. George and Therese (Hohl) Hotter; m. Howard Rovelstad, Nov. 23, 1970. Ph.D., U. Tubingen, 1953; M.S. in L.S, Catholic U. Am., 1960. Cataloger Mt. St. Mary's Coll., Los Angeles, 1953; sch. librarian Yoyogi Elem. Sch., Tokyo, 1954-56; mem. faculty Cath. U. Am., 1960-90, prof. library sci., 1975-90, prof. emeritus, 1990—; vis. prof. U. Montreal, 1969. Author: Bibliotheken in den Vereinigten Staaten, 1974; translator Bibliographia, an Inquiry into its Definition and Designations (R. Blum), 1980, Bibliotheken in den Vereinigten Staaten von Amerika und in Kanada, 1988; contbr. articles to profl. jours. Research grantee German Acad. Exch. Svc., 1969, Herzog August Bibliothek Wolfenbüttel, Germany, 1995. Mem. ALA (internat. relations com. 1977-80), Internat. Fedn. Library Assns. and Instns. (standing adv. com. on library schs. 1975-81), Assn. for Library and Info. Sci. Edn. Home: PO Box 111 Gibson Island MD 21056 Office: Cath U Am Sch Libr & Info Sci Washington DC 20064

ROVER, EDWARD FRANK, lawyer; b. N.Y.C., Oct. 4, 1938; s. Frederick James and Wanda (Charkowski) R.; m. Maureen Wyer, June 15, 1968; children: Elizabeth, Emily, William. AB, Fordham U., 1961; JD, Harvard U., 1964. Bar: N.Y. 1964, U.S. Tax Ct. 1968, U.S. Dist. Ct. (so. dist.) N.Y. 1975, U.S. Supreme Ct. 1994. Assoc. White & Case, N.Y.C., 1964-71, ptnr., 1972—; bd. dirs. Cranshaw Corp., N.Y.C., The Brearley Sch., N.Y.C., Harvard-Mahoney Neuroscience Inst., Boston, Waterford Sch., Sandy, Utah, E.N. Dana Inst., N.Y.C., Norton Simon Art Mus., L.A., Rumsey-Carter Found., Geneva, Charles A. Dana Found. Mem. ABA, N.Y. Bar Assn., N.Y. County Lawyers Assn., Assn. Bar City N.Y, Century Assn., Scarsdale Golf Club, Harvard Club. Avocations: sailing, skiing. Home: 1111 Park Ave New York NY 10128-1234 Office: White & Case 1155 Avenue of Americas New York NY 10036-2711

ROVERA, GIOVANNI AURELIO, medical educator, scientist; b. Cocconato, Italy, Sept. 23, 1940; came to U.S., naturalized, 1984.; Student, Liceo Classico Valsalice, Torino, Italy, 1955-58; MD summa cum laude, U. Torino, 1964, postgrad., 1965-68. Diplomate Am. Bd. Anatomic Pathology; lic. physician, Italy, Pa. Postdoctoral fellow Fels Rsch. Inst. Temple U. Sch. of Medicine, Phila., 1968-70, resident in anatomic pathology, 1970-72, chief resident in pathology, 1972; asst. prof. pathology Sch. Medicine Temple U., Phila., 1972-75; assoc. prof. Wistar Inst., Phila., 1975-78, prof., 1979—, assoc. dir., 1988-91, dir., 1991—; Wistar Inst. prof. pathology and lab. medicine Sch. Medicine U. Pa., Phila., 1984—; mem. promotion coms. U. Pa. Sch. of Medicine, The Wistar Inst., 1979—; chmn. grad. tng. program The Wistar Inst., 1981-91; mem. sci. adv. com. Leukemia Soc. Am., 1983-88, Am. Cancer Soc., 1986-90; mem. ad hoc sci. adv. com. Nat. Cancer Inst., 1985—. Editor: (with H. Koprowski) Current Opinion in Immunology: Cancer and Immunology, 1990; assoc. editor Proceedings Soc. Exptl. Biol. Medicine, 1975-78, Jour. Cellular Physiology, 1978—, Leukemia, 1988—, Haematologica Pathology, 1990—; mem. editorial adv. bd. Haematologica, 1989—, Fellow EURATOM, 1965-66, Ministero della Publica Istruzione, 1966-67; scholar Leukemia Soc., 1974-79. Achievements include development of techniques of monitoring the extent of residual leukemia in B and T lineage malignancies. Home: 933 Wooton Rd Bryn Mawr PA 19010-2227 Office: Wistar Inst 3601 Spruce St Philadelphia PA 19104-4265

ROVERUD, ELEANOR, pathologist, neuropathologist; b. Spring Grove, Minn., Oct. 24, 1912; d. Henry S. and Sigrid (Bakken) R.; m. Stuart Henry Nam (dec. Nov. 1986); children: Sue, Kay, Becky, Howard, Signe, Sonia, Tom, Ted, Kurt. Diploma, Kahler Sch. Nursing, Rochester, Minn., 1934; BS in Nursing Edn., U. Minn., 1940; MD, Med. Coll. Pa., 1947. Intern Swedish Hosp., Mpls., 1947-48; resident in pathology, resident instr. Sch. of Tropical Medicine U. P.R., San Juan, 1949-52; fellow in Neuropathology Columbia U., Presbyn. Hosp., N.Y.C., 1952-54; neuropathologist Wayne County Gen. Hosp., Eloise, Mich., 1954-59; assoc. prof. Woman's Med. Coll./Med. Coll. Pa., Phila., 1959-61; pathologist Women's Hosp., Phila., 1961-62, St. Anthony Regional Hosp., Carroll, Iowa, 1962-77; cons. in pathology Carroll, Iowa, 1977-87, Spring Grove, 1987—; expert witness forensic cases Carroll County, Iowa, 1962-77. Chmn., v.p., sec. Carroll chpt. ARC, 1968-75. Mem. AMA, Am. Assn. Neuropathologists, Iowa Med. Soc. (life), Carroll County Med. Assn. (sec. 1968-74), Am. Med. Women's Assn., Zumbro Valley Med. Soc., Minn. Med. Assn. Democrat. Lutheran. Office: PO Box 706 Spring Grove MN 55974-0706

ROVETO, CONNIE IDA, financial services executive; b. Montreal, Que., Can.; d. Charles and Angela (Difruscia) R. BA in English Lang. & Lit., U. Toronto, Ont., Can., 1972, BEd, 1973. Cert. officer/dir. Investment Dealers Assn. Can. Mgr. human resources Can. Permanent Trust, Toronto, 1980-81, mgr. orgn. planning, 1981-82, mgr. trust bus. systems, 1982-84, project dir., 1984-85; asst. v.p. Can. Trust, Toronto, 1986; v.p. Cen. Guaranty Trust, Toronto, 1988, Cen. Capital Mgmt. Inc., Toronto, 1986-89; exec. v.p. United Fin. Mgmt. Ltd., Toronto, 1989-93; pres., CEO United Fin. Mgmt. Ltd., 1993; also bd. dirs.; bd. dirs. Ont. Film Devel. Corp. Mem. senate U. St. Michael's Coll., Toronto, 1989—; mem. acad. planning com., 1991—; mem. capital campaign com., 1987—; mem. ocean health care planning Archdiocese Toronto, 1986-90; bd. dirs. Queen Elizabeth Hosp. Found. Mem. Can. Club of Toronto (bd. dirs. 1994). Investment Funds Inst. Can. Avocations: films, reading, tennis, fitness.

ROVINE, ARTHUR WILLIAM, lawyer; b. Phila., Apr. 29, 1937; s. George Isaac and Rosanna (Lipsitz) R.; m. Phyllis Ellen Hamburger, Apr. 7, 1963; children: Joshua, Deborah. AB, U. Pa., 1958; LLB, Harvard U., 1961; PhD,

Columbia U., 1966. Bar: D.C. 1964, N.Y. 1984. Assoc. Curtis, Mallet-Prevost, Colt & Mosle, N.Y.C., 1964-66; asst. prof. Cornell U., Ithaca, N.Y., 1966-72; editor Digest of U.S. Practice in International Law U.S. Dept. State, Washington, 1972-75, asst. legal adviser, 1975-81; agt. U.S. Govt. to Iran-U.S. Claims Tribunal U.S. Dept. State, The Hague, Netherlands, 1981-83; of counsel Baker & McKenzie, N.Y.C., 1983-85, ptnr., 1985—; adj. prof. law Georgetown U., Washington, 1977-81. Author: The First Fifty Years: The Secretary-General in World Politics, 1920-1970, 1970; editor: Digest of U.S. Practice in International Law, 1973, 74; co-editor: The Case Law of the International Court of Justice, 1968, 1972, 1974, 1976; bd. editors Am. Jour. Internat. Law, 1977-87; also articles on internat. law. Mem. panel on settlement of transnat. bus. disputes, N.Y. panel Ctr. for Pub. Resources; chmn. law subcom. of internat. adv. coun. on profl. edn. Coun. on Internat. Ednl. Exch.; mem. Coun. on Fgn. Rels. Mem. ABA (chmn. internat. law sect. 1985-86, del. to Ho. of Dels. 1988-90), Am. Soc. Internat. Law (cert. of merit 1974, exec. coun. 1975-77), U.S. Coun. for Internat. Bus. (arbitration com.), Am. Arbitration Assn. (panel of arbitrators), Assn. Bar City of N.Y. (coun. on internat. affairs). Home: 150 E 61st St New York NY 10021 Office: Baker & McKenzie 805 3rd Ave New York NY 10022-7513

ROVINSKY, JOSEPH JUDAH, obstetrician, gynecologist; b. Phila., Sept. 4, 1927; s. Israel and Sarah (Blackman) R.; m. Judith S. Levin, June 24, 1964; children: Audrey, John, Jill, Michael, Paul, David. B.A., U. Pa., 1948, M.D., 1952. Diplomate Am. Bd. Ob-Gyn. Intern U. Pa. Hosp., Phila., 1952-53; resident in ob-gyn Mt. Sinai Hosp., N.Y.C., 1953-58; practice medicine specializing in ob-gyn, 1958—; chmn. dept. ob-gyn City Hosp. Center, Elmhurst, N.Y., 1964-74; prof. ob-gyn Mt. Sinai Sch. Medicine, N.Y.C., 1969-74; prof., chmn. dept. ob-gyn Sch. Medicine Health Scis. Center, SUNY, Stony Brook, 1975-79, prof., 1979-85; chmn. dept. ob-gyn L.I. Jewish Med. Center, 1973-92; prof. ob-gyn. Albert Einstein Coll. Medicine, 1989—; dir. dept. ob-gyn. New Rochelle (N.Y.) Hosp. Med. Ctr., 1992—; mem. obstetric adv. com. N.Y.C. Dept. Health, 1964—. Author: Medical, Surgical and Gynecological Complications of Pregnancy, 1961, 2d edit., 1965; editor: Davis' Gynecology and Obstetrics, 1968-73. Served to capt., M.C. USAF, 1964-66. Mem. Am. Coll. Obstetricians and Gynecologists, ACS, Am. Fertility Soc., Am. Uro-Gynecologic Soc., N.Y. Acad. Medicine, N.Y. Obstetrical Soc., N.Y. Gynecol. Assn., Med. Soc. State N.Y. Jewish. Office: New Rochell Hosp Med Ctr 16 Guion Pl New Rochelle NY 10802

ROVIRA, LUIS DARIO, state supreme court justice; b. San Juan, P.R., Sept. 8, 1923; s. Peter S. and Mae (Morris) R.; m. Luis Ann Thau, June 25, 1966; children—Douglas, Merilyn. B.A., U. Colo., 1948, LL.B., 1950. Bar: Colo. 1950. Now chief justice Colo. Supreme Ct., Denver.; mem. Pres.'s Com. on Mental Retardation, 1970-71; chmn. State Health Facilities Council, 1967-76. Bd. dirs YMCA, 1969-78, Children's Hosp.; trustee Temple Buell Found. With AUS, 1943-46. Mem. ABA, Colo. Bar Assn., Denver Bar Assn. (pres. 1970-71), Colo. Assn. Retarded Children (pres. 1968-70), Alpha Tau Omega, Phi Alpha Delta. Clubs: Athletic (Denver), Country (Denver). Home: 4810 E 6th Ave Denver CO 80220-5137 Office: Colo Supreme Ct 2 E 14th Ave Denver CO 80203-2116

ROVNER, DAVID RICHARD, endocrinology educator; b. Phila., Sept. 20, 1930; s. Arthur and Rae Theresa (Lieb) R.; m. Margaret McCann, Jan. 15, 1987; children: Arthur, Daniel, Gregory, Robert, Paul, Jessica. AB in Chemistry with distinction, Temple U., 1951, MD, 1955. Diplomate Am. Bd. Internal Medicine. Resident, fellow in internal medicine U. Mich., Ann Arbor, 1956-61, from instr. to assoc. prof. endocrinology and metabolism, 1961-71, prof., 1971; prof. medicine, chief endocrinology and metabolism Mich. State U., East Lansing, 1971—, assoc. chmn. dept. medicine, 1975-77, acting chmn., 1976-77; chmn. dept. medicine Ingham Med. Ctr., Lansing, Mich., 1984-86. Contbr. articles to profl. jours. Pres. PTO, Ann Arbor, 1966-71; pilot Civil Air Patrol, Lansing, 1975-87. Served to capt. USAFR, 1960-70. Fellow ACP (sec., treas., various coms.); mem. Mich. State Med. Soc. (chmn. continuing edn. com.), Am. Diabetes Assn. (pres. Mich. affiliate 1990-92), Am. Heart Assn., Alpha Omega Alpha. Avocations: electronics, computers. Office: Mich State Univ Dept of Medicine East Lansing MI 48824

ROVNER, ILANA KARA DIAMOND, federal judge; b. Aug. 21, 1938; came to U.S., 1939; d. Stanley and Ronny (Medalje) Diamond; m. Richard Nyles Rovner, Mar. 9, 1963; 1 child, Maxwell Rabson. AB, Bryn Mawr Coll., 1960; postgrad. U. London King's Coll., 1961, Georgetown U., 1961-63; JD, Ill. Inst. Tech., 1966; LittD (hon.), Rosary Coll., 1989, Mundelein Coll., 1989; DHL (hon.), Spertus Coll. of Judaica, 1992. Bar: Ill. 1972, U.S. Dist. Ct. (no. dist) Ill. 1972, U.S. Ct. Appeals (7th cir.) 1977, U.S. Supreme Ct. 1981, Fed. Trial Bar (no. dist.) Ill. 1982. Jud. clk. U.S. Dist. Ct. (no. dist.) Ill., Chgo., 1972-73; asst. U.S. atty. U.S. Atty.'s Office, Chgo., 1973-77; dep. chief of pub. protection, 1975-76, chief pub. protection, 1976-77; dep. gov., legal counsel Gov. James R. Thompson, Chgo., 1977-84; dist. judge U.S. Dist. Ct. (no. dist.) Ill., Chgo., 1984-92; cir. judge U.S. Ct. Appeals (7th cir.), Chgo., 1992—. Trustee Bryn Mawr Coll., Pa., 1983-89; mem. bd. overseers Ill. Inst. Tech./Kent Coll. of Law, 1983—; trustee Ill. Inst. Tech., 1989—; adv. coun. Rush Ctr. for Sports Medicine, Chgo., 1991—; civil justice reform act adv. com. for the 7th cir., Chgo., 1991-92; bd. visitors No. Ill. U. Coll. of Law, 1992-94; vis. com. Northwestern U. Sch. of Law, 1993—; vis. com. U. Chgo. Law Sch., 1993—. Recipient Spl. Commendation award U.S. Dept. of Justice, 1975, Spl. Achievement award 1976, Ann. Nat. Law and Social Justice Leadership award League to Improve the Community, 1975, Ann. Guardian Police award, 1977, Profl. Achievement award Ill. Inst. Tech., 1986, Louis Dembitz Brandeis medal for Disting. Legal Svc., Brandeis U., 1993, First Woman award Valparaiso U. Sch. of Law, 1993, ORT Women's Am. Community Svc. award, 1987-88, Judaica Svc. award Spertus Coll., 1987, Ann. award Chgo. Found. for Women, 1990; named Today's Chgo. Woman of Yr., 1985, Woman of Achievement Chgo. Women's Club, 1986, more. Mem. ABA, Ill. Bar Assn., Chgo. Bar Assn. (commendation def. of prisoners com. 1987), Women's Bar Assn. Ill. (sec. 1988 and 1989, 1st Myra Bradwell Woman of Achievement award 1994), Fed. Bar Assn. (jud. selection com. Chgo. chpt. 1977-80, treas. 1978-79, sec. 1979-80, 2d v.p. 1980-81, 1st v.p. 1981-82, pres. 1982-83, 2d v.p. 7th cir. 1983-84, v.p. 7th cir. 1984-85), Fed. Judges Assn., Nat. Assn. Women Judges, Chgo. Coun. Lawyers, Decalogue Soc. (citation of honor 1991), Kappa Beta Pi, Phi Alpha Delta (hon.). Republican. Jewish. Office: 219 S Dearborn St Rm 2774 Chicago IL 60604-1803

ROVNER, JACK ALAN, lawyer; b. Boston, May 6, 1946; s. Abraham George and Sarah Rebecca (Miller) R.; m. Sheila Marie Boyle, June 24, 1979; children—Joseph Conahan, Edward Witty, Benjamin Flanagan. B.A., Brandeis U., 1968; J.D. cum laude, Boston U., 1976. Bar: Ill. 1976, U.S. Dist. Ct. (no. dist.) Ill. 1976, U.S. Ct. Appeals (7th and 9th cir.) 1979, U.S. Supreme Ct. 1979. Admin. asst. U.S. EPA, Boston, 1971-73; assoc. Kirkland & Ellis, Chgo., 1976-81, ptnr. 1982-93; pvt. practice, Naperville, Ill., 1993—. Served to lt. jr. grade USCG, 1968-71. Article editor Boston U. Law Rev., 1974-76. Mem. ABA (litigation sect., antitrust sect.), Nat. Health Lawyers Assns., Ill. State Bar Assn., DuPage County Bar Assn., Ill. Assn. Hosp. Attys. Club: Mid-Am., White Eagle Golf Club. Office: 535 S Washington St Naperville IL 60540-6662

ROW, PETER L., musician, educator. BM, MM, DM, Prayag Sangit Samiti, Allahabad, India; student, Rabindra Bharati U., Calcutta. Formerly rsch. assoc. Grad. Sch. Edn. Harvard U., Cambridge, Mass.; educator, provost New Eng. Conservatory Music; lectr. on Indian music nationwide; cons. on Asian music Smithsonian Instn. Performed as sitarist throughout U.S., India; appeared on TV, radio show numerous times. Mem. Soc. Ethnomusicology (former pres. N.E. chpt.). Office: New Eng Conservatory 290 Huntington Ave Boston MA 02115-5000

ROWAN, CARL THOMAS, columnist; b. Ravenscroft, Tenn., Aug. 11, 1925; s. Thomas David and Johnnie (Bradford) R.; m. Vivien Louise Murphy, Aug. 2, 1950; children: Barbara, Carl Thomas, Geoffrey. Student, Tenn. State U., 1942-43, Washburn U., 1943-44; A.B. in Math, Oberlin Coll., 1947, D.Litt., 1962; M.A. in Journalism, U. Minn., 1948; D.Litt., Simpson Coll., 1957, Hamline U., 1958, Coll. Wooster, 1968, Drexel Inst. Tech., 1969; L.H.D., Washburn U., 1964, Talladega Coll., 1965, St. Olaf Coll., 1966, Knoxville Coll., 1966, R.I. Coll., 1970, U. Maine, 1971, Am. U., 1980; LL.D., Howard U., 1964, Alfred U., 1964, Temple U., 1964, Atlanta U.,

1965, Allegheny Coll., 1966, Colby Coll., 1968, Clark U., 1971; D. Pub. Adminstrn., Morgan State Coll., 1964. Copywriter Mpls. Tribune, 1948-50, staff writer, 1950-61; dep. asst. sec. State for pub. affairs Dept. of State, 1961-63; U.S. ambassador to Finland Helsinki, 1963-64; dir. USIA, Washington, 1964-65; syndicated columnist News Am. Syndicate (formerly Field Syndicate); now panelist Inside Washington, Washington, D.C.; now syndicated columnist King Features, N.Y. Author: South of Freedom, 1953 (named to A.L.A. ann. list best books), The Pitiful and the Proud, 1956 (A.L.A. ann. list best books), Go South to Sorrow, 1957, Wait Till Next Year, 1960, Just Between Us Blacks, 1974, Breaking Barriers: A Memoir, 1991, Dream Makers, Dream Breakers: The World of Justice Thurgood Marshall, 1993. Recipient Sidney Hillman award for best newspaper reporting, 1952; selected one of 10 outstanding young mem of Am. U.S. Jr. C of C., 1954; award for best gen. reporting on segregation cases pending before U.S. Supreme Ct. Sigma Delta Chi, 1954; fgn. corr. medallion for articles on India, 1955; fgn. corr. medallion for articles on S.E. Asia, coverage of Bandung Conf., 1956; Distinguished Achievement award Regents; Distinguished Achievement award U. Minn., 1961; Communications award in Human Relations Anti- Defamation League B'nai B'rith, 1964; Contbns. to Am. Democracy award Roosevelt U., 1964; Nat. Brotherhood award Nat. Conf. Christians and Jews, 1964; Liberty Bell award Howard U., 1965; George Foster Peabody award for TV spl. Race War in Rhodesia, 1978. Address: 3251-C Sutton Pl NW Washington DC 20016 also: King Features Inc 235 E 45th St New York NY 10017

ROWAN, GERALD BURDETTE, insurance company executive, lawyer; b. Powersville, Mo., Feb. 9, 1916; s. M. C. and Blanch (Spidle) R.; m. Mary Elizabeth Turner, Dec. 24, 1939; children: Sandra Josephine, Roger Turner. A.B., N.W. Mo. State Coll., 1937; LL.B., Mo. U., 1940. Bar: Mo. bar 1940. Practice in Marble Hill, 1940-49, Cape Girardeau, 1949-59, Kansas City, 1959-81, Eagle Rock, Mo., 1981—; mem. firm Frye & Rowan, 1940-42, 46-49, Oliver & Oliver, 1949-59; with legal dept. Kansas City Life Ins. Co., 1959-76, sr. v.p. tech. services, 1976-81, also dir.; pros. atty., Bollinger County, 1946-49; city atty., Cape Girardeau, 1954-59. Pres. Jackson County unit Am. Cancer Soc., 1963-65, 70-73; chmn. Mo. div. Am. Cancer Soc., 1974-76; mem. Mo. Park Bd., 1965-77. Served with F.A. AUS, 1943-45, MTO. Mem. Mo. Bar Assn. (com. chmn.), World Assn. Lawyers, Assn. Life Ins. Counsel, State City Attys. Assn. (past pres.), Mo. Law Sch. Alumni Assn. (past pres.), Order of Coif, Sigma Tau Gamma. Republican. Methodist. Home: PO Box 135 Eagle Rock MO 65641-0135

ROWAN, JOHN ROBERT, medical center director; b. Joliet, Ill., Aug. 19, 1919; s. Hugh Hamilton and Elizabeth Margaret (Maloney) R.; m. Ruth Elaine Boyle, June 17, 1944; 1 child, Robert J. Student, Butler U., 1952-53, Ind. U., 1953-54. Personnel specialist VA Br. Office 7, Chgo., 1946; personnel officer VA Hosp., Ft. Benjamin Harrison, Ind., 1946-51, Indpls., 1951-56; asst. dir. VA Hosp., 1960-67; asst. mgr. VA Hosp., Iron Mountain, Mich., 1956-60; hosp. adminstrn. specialist VA Central Office, Washington, 1967-69; dir. VA Hosp., Manchester, N.H., 1969-71, Buffalo, 1971-72; dir. VA Med. Center, Lexington, Ky., 1972-88, Montgomery, Ala., 1988—, VA Med. Dist. 11, 1975-86. Bd. dirs. Marion County (Ind.) unit Am. Cancer Soc., 1960-67, pres., 1964-66, bd. dirs. Ind. div., 1966-67; bd. dirs. Western N.Y. Regional Med. Program, 1971-72, Eastern Ky. Health Systems Agy., 1976-79, United Way of Bluegrass, 1976-79, 82-85; mem. regional advisory council Ohio Valley Regional Med. Program, 1972-76; mem. State Health Planning Bd., 1982-88; bd. dirs. Hosp. Hospitality House of Lexington, 1981; mem. adv. coun. Cen. Ala. Aging Consortium, 1991; chmn. Montgomery Area Combined Fed. Campaign, 1991. Served in USAAF, 1942-46. Decorated Bronze Star; recipient Meritorious Svc. citations Ind. dept. DAV, 1964, Meritorious Svc. citations Ky. dept. Am. Legion, 1975, Meritorious Svc. citations Ky. dept. VFW, 1976, Meritorious Svc. citations Eastern Ky. U., 1974, Meritorious Svc. citations Ky. dept. DAV 1978, Spl. Recognition award VFW, 1982, cert. of Merit, DAV, 1982; recipient Dedicated Svc. to Vets. award DAV, 1984, Meritorious Svc. to Vets. award, Am. Legion, 1985, Meritorious Svc. award, Chpt. I, Ky. DAV, 1988, VA Performance award, 1990, Joint Fed. Campaign Meritorious Svc. award, 1990, Dedicated Svc. award DAV, 1992, McClusky award Ala. State Nurses Assn., 1993. Fellow Am. Coll. Healthcare Execs.; mem. Am. Hosp. Assn., Ala. Hosp. Assn. (profl. standards and quality assurance com. 1991—), Ctrl. Ala. Hosp. Coun., Ala. Assn. Hosp. Execs., Assn. Mil. Surgeons U.S., Fed. Hosp. Inst. Alumni Assn. Roman Catholic. Home: 2213 Walbash Dr Montgomery AL 36116-2220 Office: Va Med Ctr 215 Perry Hill Rd Montgomery AL 36109-3725

ROWAN, RICHARD LAMAR, business management educator; b. Guntersville, Ala., July 10, 1931; s. Leon Virgle and Mae (Williamson) R.; m. Marilyn Walker, Aug. 3, 1963; children: John Richard, Jennifer Walker. A.B., Birmingham-So. Coll., 1953; postgrad., Auburn U., 1956-57; Ph.D., U. N.C., 1961. Instr. Auburn (Ala.) U., 1956-57, U. N.C., Chapel Hill, 1958-59, 60-61; lectr. U. Pa., Phila., 1961-62, asst. prof., 1962-66, asso. prof. industry, 1966-73, prof. industry, 1973—; dir. indsl. research unit, 1989-91; co-dir. Ctr. for Human Resources, 1991—; visitor to Faculty Econs. and Politics Cambridge (Eng.) U., 1972; pvt. sector advisor U.S. State Dept. Com. on Internat. Investment and Multinational Enterprises, OECD, 1982-89; chmn. Labor Relations Council, 1985—. Author: (with H.R. Northrup) The Negro and Employment Opportunity, 1965, Readings in Labor Economics and Labor Relations, 5th edit., 1984, The Negro in the Steel Industry, 1969, The Negro in the Textile Industry, 1970, (with others) Studies of Negro Employment, 1970, Educating the Employed Disadvantaged for Upgrading, 1972, Collective Bargaining: Survival in the 1970's, 1972, Opening the Skilled Construction Trades to Blacks, 1972, The Impact of Government Manpower Programs, 1975, International Enforcement of Union Standards in Ocean Transport, 1977, The Impact of OSHA, 1978, Multinational Bargaining Attempts: The Record, the Cases, and the Prospects, 1980; (with H.R. Northrup) Employee Relations and Regulations in the 80s, 1982; (with others) Multinational Union Organizations in the Manufacturing Industries, (with D.C. Campbell) The Multinational Enterprises and the OECD Industrial Relations Guidelines, 1984, Trade Union Clout Erodes, But For How Long?, 1985, Employee Relations Trends and Practices in the Textile Industry, 1986; contbr. articles to profl. jours. Mem. personnel com. Del. Valley Settlement Alliance, 1966-68. Served with Transp. Corps U.S. Army, 1953-56. Mem. Indsl. Rels. Rsch. Assn. (sec. Phila. 1964-65), Acad. Internat. Bus., The Penn Club. Democrat. Episcopalian. Home: 113 Blackthorn Rd Wallingford PA 19086-6046 Office: U Pa Wharton Sch Labor Rels Coun Vance Hall 3733 Spruce St Philadelphia PA 19104-6358

ROWARK, MAUREEN, fine arts photographer; b. Edinburgh, Midlothian, Scotland, Feb. 28, 1933; came to U.S., 1960, naturalized, 1970; d. Alexander Pennycook and Margaret (Gorman) Prezdpelski; m. Robert Rowark, May 3, 1952 (div. July 1965). 1 child, Mark Steven. Student, Warmington Bus. Coll., Royal Leamington Spa, Eng., 1950-51, Royal Leamington Spa Art Sch.; diploma, Speedwriting Inst., N.Y.C., 1961; AS in Edn., St. Clair County Community Coll., Port Huron, Mich., 1977, AA, 1978. Supr. proof reading Nevin D. Hirst Advt., Ltd., Leeds, Eng., 1952-55; publicity asst. Alvis Aero Engines, Ltd., Coventry, Eng., 1955-57; adminstrv. asst. Port Huron Motor Inn, 1964-66; adminstrv. asst. pub. rels. dept. Geophysics and Computer Svcs., Inc., New Orleans, 1966-68; sales mgr. Holiday Inn, Port Huron, 1968-70; adminstrv. asst. Howard Corp., Port Huron, 1971-73; sales and systems coord. Am. Wood Products, Ann Arbor, Mich., 1973-74; systems coord. Daniels & Zermack Architects, Ann Arbor, 1974; systems coord., cataloger fine arts dept. St. Clair County Community Coll., Port Huron, 1976-79; freelance fine arts photographer Port Huron, 1978—; photographer Patterns mag. front cover, 1978, Erie Sq. Gazette, 1979, Bluewater Area Tourism Bur. brochure, 1989, Port Huron, Can. Legion, Wyo., Ont. Br., 1987, 88—, Grace Episcopal Ch. Mariner's Day, Port Huron, 1987, 92, 93, 94, 95, Homes mag. 1989. Exhibited in internat. shows at Ann. Ea. Mich. Internat. Exhbn., 1982, 83, 84 (awards of excellence 1982, 83), St. Clair County C.C., 1983, 86 (award of excellence), Sarnia (Ont.) Gallery, 1983-92, 94, Bluewater Bridge Exhibit, 1988, Kaskilaaksontie exhibit, Finland, 1991 (Par Excellence award), others; contbr. short stories to mags. Cons., buyer interior decor Grace Episcopal Ch., 1994; active Mus. of Arts and History, Port Huron, 1965—. Recipient Hon. Mention award Sarnia Art Gallery, 1981; named Best Photographer, Sarnia Art Gallery, 1988; winner 2d and 3d Pl. awards Times Herald Newspapers Art Show. Mem. St. Clair County C.C. Alumni Assn., Camaraderie Club, Phi Theta Kappa, Lambda Mu. Democrat. Episcopalian. Avocations: costumes and interior design, travel, theater, ballroom dancing, gardening. Home and Office: 2005 Riverside Dr #15 Port Huron MI 48060-2677

ROWDEN, MARCUS AUBREY, lawyer, former government official; b. Detroit, Mar. 13, 1928; s. Louis and Gertrude (Lifsitz) Rosenzweig; m. Justine Leslie Bessman, July 21, 1950; children: Gwen, Stephanie. B.A. in Econs, U. Mich., Ann Arbor, 1950, J.D. with distinction, 1953. Bar: Mich. 1953, D.C. 1978. Trial atty. Dept. Justice, 1953-58; legal advisor U.S. Mission to European Communities, 1959-62; solicitor, assoc. gen. counsel, gen. counsel AEC, 1965-74; commr., chmn. U.S. NRC, Washington, 1975-77; 2tnr. Fried, Frank, Harris, Shriver and Jacobson, Washington, 1977—. Served with AUS, 1946-47. Decorated officer Order Legion of Honor Republic of France; Recipient Disting. Service award AEC, 1972. Mem. Am., Fed., Mich., D.C. bar assns., Internat. Nuclear Law Assn., Order of Coif. Home: 7937 Deepwell Dr Bethesda MD 20817-1927 Office: Fried Frank Harris Shriver and Jacobson 1001 Pennsylvania Ave NW Washington DC 20004-2505

ROWDEN, WILLIAM HENRY, naval officer; b. Woodsville, N.H., May 12, 1930; s. Henry Thomas and Kathleen M. (Gochey) R.; m. Sarah Sumner, Apr. 14, 1956; children: Sarah Jane, Thomas Sumner, John William. B.S., U.S. Naval Acad., 1952, U.S. Naval Postgrad. Sch., 1963. Commd. ensign U.S. Navy, 1952, advanced through grades to vice adm., 1980; comdr. cruiser-destroyer group 3 U.S. Navy, San Diego, 1977-79; staff chief naval ops. U.S. Navy, Washington, 1979-81; comdr. 6th Fleet U.S. Navy, 1981-83, comdr. Mil. Sealift Command, 1983-85; comdr. Naval Sea Systems Command U.S. Navy, Washington, 1985-88, ret., 1988; Disting. fellow Ctr. for Naval Analyses, Alexandria, Va., 1988—. Decorated D.S.M., Legion of Merit, Bronze Star. Mem. Naval Inst. Presbyterian. Avocations: walking, sailing. Home: Rt 1 Box 818 Lancaster VA 22503 Office: Ctr for Naval Analyses Alexandria VA 22302

ROWDER, WILLIAM LOUIS, lawyer; b. Chgo., Aug. 21, 1937; s. John Joseph and Theresa Veronica (Major) R.; m. Josephine M. Laurino, Apr. 20, 1940; children: Lauren, Lisa, Jessica, William. Ba, DePaul U., 1961, JD, 1965. Bar: Ill. 1965, U.S. Dist. Ct. (no. dist.) Ill. 1967. Atty. Kirkland & Ellis, Chgo., 1965-76; sr. ptnr. estate planning dept. Kirkland & Ellis, 1979-87; mem. Pope, Ballard, Shephard & Fowle, 1976-79; sr. ptnr. estate planning dept. Coffield, Ungaretti, Harris & Slavin, Chgo., 1987—; of counsel Coffield, Ungaretti & Harris, Chgo.; dir. Forest Park Nat. Bank; adj. prof. law DePaul U. Contbr. articles to profl. jours. Village trustee Village of River Forest, 1975-76. Fellow Am. Coll. Trust & Estate Counsel; mem. ABA, Ill. Bar Assn., Chgo. Bar Assn., Chgo. Athletic Club, The Law Club, Oak Park Country Club. Office: Coffield Ungaretti & Harris 3500 Three 1st National Plz Chicago IL 60602

ROWE, ALLAN DUNCAN, food products executive; b. Corner Brook, Nfld., Can., Feb. 23, 1951. B in Commerce, Dalhousie U., 1974; MBA, U. Western Ont., 1978. V.p. fin. B.F. Goodrich Can. Inc., Kitchener, Ont., 1978-87; chief fin. officer Sobeys Inc., Stellarton, N.S., Can., 1987—. Mem. Fin. Execs. Inst. Office: Sobeys Inc, 115 King St, Stellarton, NS Canada B0K 1S0

ROWE, ARTHUR EDGAR, manufacturing company executive; b. Marlborough, Mass., Sept. 11, 1929; arrived in Scotland, 1987; s. Arthur Percy and Bearice (Bond) R.; m. Shirley Ann Watts; children: Robert, Heather. B.Engring., U. Mass., Amherst, 1955. Mng. dir. Terex Equipment Ltd., Motherwelle, Scotland, 1987—; pres. Terex, Hudson, Ohio, 1986—; pres., chief exec. officer Fruehauf Trailer Corp., Southfield, Mich., 1990—. Office: Fruehauf Trailer Corp 26999 Central Park Blvd Southfield MI 48076-4174

ROWE, CHARLES ALFRED, artist, designer, educator; b. Great Falls, Mont., Feb. 7, 1934; s. Alfred Lewis and Alice Lillian (Ledbetter) R.; m. Eugenia Dean, July 5, 1958; children: Allison Rene, Jon Garner, Dorian Leigh. Student, Mont. State U., 1952-53, So. Meth. U., 1956-57, U. Chgo., 1959-60; BFA, Sch. Art Inst., Chgo., 1960; MFA, Tyler Sch. Art, 1968. Prin. Charles Rowe Advt., Chgo., 1957-60; graphic designer Am. Can Co., Bellwood, Ill., 1960-62, Abrams-Bannister Engraving, Inc., Greenville, S.C., 1962-64; prof. art U. Del., Newark, 1964—. One-man shows include C.M. Russell Mus., Gt. Falls, 1972-73, 81, 92, Mickelson Gallery, Washington, 1970, 74, Pleiades Gallery, N.Y.C., 1977, 81, Vision of La Herradura, Almuñecar, Spain, 1988, USAF exhbn. Soc. Illustrators, N.Y.C., 1989, 91, West Chester (Pa.) U., 1992, Soc. Illustrators, N.Y.C., 1993; exhibited in group shows at C.M. Russell Mus., 1974, 76, 78, 80, 82-83, Am. Painters in Paris, 1976, Monac-Western Art Exhbt., Spokane, Wash., 1977-78, Easton (Md.) Waterfowl Festival, 1981-82, USAF Nat. Collection, 1989, 91; represented in permanent collections U. Del., Mont. State Collection, Del. State Collection, Gt. Falls Pub. Schs., Michael Landon Prodns., Calif., Collection Knissel, Austria, Archives Victoria and Albert Mus., London; artist USAF Nat. Collection, Washington, 1989, 91, NASA Space Mus., 1992; fabric designer Galleon Fabrics, Inc., N.Y.C., Jones of N.Y., Saks Fifth Ave.; designed graphics Mont. State Arts Coun. With inf. U.S. Army, 1954-56. Ctr. for Advanced Study fellow, 1981-82; grantee U. Del., 1964-79, Nat. Endowment for Arts and Humanities, 1972-73, U. Del. Bicentennial, 1976. Mem. AAUP. Home: Chapel Hill 133 Aronimink Dr Newark DE 19711-3802 Office: U Delaware Dept Art Newark DE 19711 In my paintings and other artforms I strive for perfection, uniqueness, and a special inner beauty, but more than that, I try to create art that has a universal quality. This universality makes an artform communicate beyond a specific locale, continent or a limited time reference. All great works of art have this special element regardless of when they were created.

ROWE, CHARLES SPURGEON, newspaper publishing and broadcasting executive; b. Fredericksburg, Va., May 28, 1925; s. Josiah Pollard and Genevieve Sinclair (Bailey) R.; divorced; children: Ashley K. Rowe Gould, Charles Spurgeon, Timothy D.; stepchildren: Laura Huntsman, Kathleen H. Huntsman. A.B., Washington and Lee U., 1947, postgrad. Law Sch., 1947-49. Editor, co-pub. Free Lance-Star, Fredericksburg, 1949—, mng. editor, 1949-76; pres. Free Lance-Star Pub. Co. (newpaper and radio stas. WFLS AM-FM), Fredericksburg, 1949—; dir. AP, 1976-85, vice chmn., 1983-85, dir. Fredericksburg Savs. & Loan Assn.; trustee Washington and Lee U., 1984-94; former mem. bar news media rels. com. Va. State Bar, 1969-85, co-chmn., 1981-85. Chmn. bd. trustees Cen. Rappahannock Regional Libr., 1969-75; Pulitzer Prize juror, 1982-83, 92-93. Lt. (j.g.) USNR, 1943-46, now capt. Res. ret. Recipient George Mason award, 1974; named Outstanding Young Man of 1958 Fredericksburg Jaycees; named to Va. Communication Hall of Fame, 1989. Mem. A.P. Mng. Editors Assn. (pres. 1969, chmn. regents 1973-75); Am. Soc. Newspaper Editors (dir. 1971-72, 79-84), Newspaper Assn. Am. (dir. 1985-93, chmn. found. 1991-92), So. Newspaper Pubs. Assn. (dir. 1984-87), Va. Press Assn. (dir. 1977-83), Soc. Profl. Journalists, Phi Beta Kappa, Omicron Delta Kappa, Phi Delta Phi, Delta Tau Delta. Episcopalian. Clubs: Nat. Press, Fredericksburg Country, Dominion, John's Island. Home: PO Box 754 Fredericksburg VA 22404-0754 Office: The Free Lance-Star 616 Amelia St Fredericksburg VA 22401-3848

ROWE, CLARENCE JOHN, psychiatrist; b. St. Paul, May 24, 1916; s. Clarence John and Sayde E. (Mabin) R.; m. Patricia A. McNulty, Jan. 15, 1945; children: Padraic, Rory, Kelly Michael. B.A., Coll. St. Thomas, 1938; M.B., U. Minn., 1942, M.D., 1943; M.D. fellow in psychiatry, 1946-49. Intern St. Joseph's Hosp., St. Paul, 1942-43; resident VA Hosp., Mpls.-U. Minn. Hosps., Mpls., 1946-49; instr., asst. prof. U. Minn., 1949-54; dir. Hamm Meml. Psychiat. Clinic, St. Paul, 1954-57; pvt. practice psychiatry St. Paul, 1957—; from clin. asst. prof. to clin. assoc. prof. U. Minn. 1954-64; cons. 3M Co., 1957-72, Ramsey County Municipal Ct., 1958-80, Constance Bultman Wilson Center, Faribault, Minn., 1973—; clin. prof. psychiatry U. Minn. Med. Sch., 1964—; adj. faculty mem. Antioch Coll., 1974-86; cons. St. Thomas Acad., 1979—; chmn. Minn. Mental Health Planning Council, 1963-69. Author: An Outline of Psychiatry, 10th edit., 1993, The Mentally Ill Employee, 1965; editor: (with A.W. Richard Sipe) Psychiatry, Ministry and Pastoral Counseling, 1984. Mem. Mayor's Council on Drug Use and Abuse, 1969-71; mem. Gov.'s Council on Employment of Handicapped, 1954-65; mem. adv. bur. hearing and appeals Social Security Adminstrn., 1965—; trustee St. Thomas Acad., 1970-76; bd. dirs. St. Johns U. Inst. Mental Health, Collegeville, Minn., 1954-78. Served with M.C., U.S. Army, 1943-46.

Mem. AMA (chmn. mental health in industry com. 1965-71), Group for Advancement Psychiatry (com. on psychiatry in industry), Am. Psychiat. Assn. (com. on occup. psychiatry 1959-65), Minn. Psychiat. Soc. (pres. 1973-75), Minn. Soc. Adolescent Psychiatry (pres. 1978-79), St. Paul Soc. Psychiatry and Neurology (pres. 1977-79), Town and Country Club. Roman Catholic. Home: 1770 Colvin Ave Saint Paul MN 55116-2709

ROWE, DAVID JOHN, physics educator; b. Totnes, Devonshire, Eng., Feb. 4, 1936; came to Can., 1968; s. Herbert Tyack and Marguerite Ella (Whitehead) R.; m. Una Mary Dawson, Oct. 4, 1959; children: Mark Jørgen Dawson, Jacqueline Amanda. BA, Cambridge (Eng.) U., 1959; MA, DPhil, Oxford (Eng.) U., 1959-62. Research assoc. U. Rochester, N.Y., 1966-68; assoc. prof. U. Toronto, Ont., Can., 1968-74, prof., 1974—. Author: Nuclear Collective Motion, 1970; editor: Dynamic Properties of Nuclear States, 1972; mem. editorial bd. (jour.) Phys. Rev., 1983-86, Jour. Phys. G., 1988-92, assoc. editor, 1992; contbr. articles to profl. jours. Dir. Mont Tremblant Internat. Summer Sch., 1971. Served to cpl. RAF, 1954-56. Ford Found. fellow, 1962-63, U.K. Atomic Energy Authority fellow, 1963-66, Sloan Found. fellow, 1972-74, Isaac Walton Killam rsch. fellow, 1990-92. Fellow Royal Soc. Can. (Rutherford Meml. medal and prize 1983); mem. Can. Assn. Physicists (chmn. theoretical physics div. 1970-710. Avocations: piano, woodworking, skiing. Office: U Toronto Physics Dept, Toronto, ON Canada M5S 1A7

ROWE, EDWARD LAWRENCE, JR., graphic designer; b. Bridgeport, Conn., Nov. 5, 1940; s. Edward L. Sr. and Elvera Rowe; m. Elayne Bassler, Oct. 24, 1964; children: Heather, Jonathan David. Assoc., U. Bridgeport, 1960, BS, 1963. Graphic designer Lester Beall, Brookfield, Conn., 1965-69; graphic design cons. Stead Young & Rowe, New Milford, Conn., 1969-87, Rowe & Ballantine, Brookfield, Conn., 1987—; design cons. Atlas Corp., Allied Signal, Borden, Caterpillar Tractor Co., Com. for Econ. Devel., Internat. Paper, Martin Marietta, N.Y. Clearing House, Otis Elevator. Design cons. Literacy Vols. N.Y., N.Y.C., 1990, Harlem R.B.I. (Returning Baseball to Inner Cities), N.Y.C., 1993. With U.S. Army, 1963-65. Recipient award Jour. Am. Inst. Graphic Arts, 1967, 68, Indsl. Design mag., 1969, Packaging Design mag., 1969, 74, Fin. World Merit award, 1978, Design Excellence award, 1991, Mohawk Paper Merit award, 1993. Mem. Conn. Art Dirs. Club, Inc. Avocations: photography, architecture, jazz music. Office: Rowe & Ballantine 8 Galloping Hl Brookfield CT 06804-3611

ROWE, EDWARD THOMAS, university administrator, educator; b. Plymouth, Mich., May 14, 1937; s. Milton Sterling and Ruth Elizabeth (Leonard) R.; m. Mary Jane Price, Sept. 15, 1956 (div. Mar. 1985); children: Rebecca, Jennifer. BA, U. Mich., 1959; MA, U. Calif., Berkeley, 1961, PhD, 1966. Instr., asst. prof. U. Conn., Storrs, 1963-90; asst. prof. Va. Poly. Inst. and State U., Blacksburg, 1970-74; assoc. prof. U. Denver, 1974—, dean Grad. Sch. of Internat. Studies, 1987—; vis. prof. U. Tübingen, 1988; mem. nat. policy and planning bd. Pub. Policy and Internat. Affairs Program, Washington, 1994—; exec. bd. dirs. Denver Com. on Fgn. Rel.; project dir. Nat. Resource Ctr. in Internat. Studies, U.S. Dept. Edn., 1991—. Author: Strengthening the United Nations, 1975; co-author: (report) International Disaster Response, 1976; contbr. articles to profl. publs. including Relaciones Internacionales, Internat. Orgn., Jour. Conflic Resolution, Internat. Studies Quar. Grantee U.S. Inst. Peace, Ford Found., Pew Charitable Trusts, Woodrow Wilson Found., U.S. Info. Agy., U.S. Agy. for Internat. Devel., U.S. State Dept., others, 1970—. Mem. Internat. Studies Assn., Am. Polit. Sci. Assn., Colo. Coun. on Internat. Orgns. (exec. bd. dirs. 1994—), Assn. Profl. Schs. in Internat. Affairs (chmn. minority affairs task force 1991—). Home: 5651 E Cornell Ave Denver CO 80222 Office: U of Denver Social Sci Found Univ Park Campus Grad Sch of Internat Studies Univ Of Denver CO 80208

ROWE, ERNEST RAS, education educator, academic administrator; b. Hot Springs, Ark., July 19, 1933; s. Stephen Paul and Emma Leathia (Martin) R. BS with distinction, Ariz. State U., 1955, MEd, 1962, EdD, 1965; postgrad., Gonzaga U., 1975, Dublin City U., Ireland, 1989. Tchr. Madison Sch. Dist., Phoenix, 1960-61, Garden Grove (Calif.) Unified Sch. Dist., 1964-66; cons. spl. edn. Ariz. Dept. Pub. Instrn., Phoenix, 1966-67; asst. prof. Idaho State U, Pocatello, 1967-70, assoc. prof., 1970-74, prof. edn., 1974-95, interim chmn. dept. edn., summer 1992; adminstrv. intern Ctrl. Administrn., 1994-95; vis. prof. edn. Calif. State U., Long Beach, 1965; adv. mem. Idaho Task Force on Higher Edn., 1982-83; gov. apptd. Idaho commr. to Edn. Commn. of the States, 1979-93, rep. to steering com., 1989-93; elected chmn. Idaho State U. Faculty Senate, 1969, 70, 71-72, 86-87. Contbr. articles to profl. jours. Bd. dirs. Bannock Meml. Hosp., 1975-78; mem. Idaho Bd. Medicine pre-litigation panel for malpractice hearings, 1980-95. 1st lt. U.S. Army, 1955-57. Mem. AAUP, Nat. Soc. Study Edn., Am. Inst. Parliamentarians (univ. parlimentarian, gov. N.W. region 1992-94), Rotary (pres. 1981-82), Mason, Phi Delta Kappa, Phi Kappa Phi (pres. 1972-73, 87-88). Avocations: reading, photography, golf. Office: Idaho State U PO Box 8137 Pocatello ID 83209-8137

ROWE, GEORGE GILES, cardiologist, educator; b. Vulcan, Alta., Can., May 17, 1921; came to U.S., 1923, naturalized, 1929; s. James Giles and Cora (Blotz) R.; m. Patsy Barnett, Sept. 12, 1947; children—George Lee, James Andrew, Jane Ellen. B.A., U. Wis., Madison, 1943, M.D., 1945. Diplomate: Am. Bd. Internal Medicine. Intern Phila. Gen. Hosp., 1945-46; resident U. Wis., 1950-52; instr. in anatomy Washington U., St. Louis, 1948-50; Am. Heart Assn. rsch. fellow cardiovascular rsch. lab. U. Wis., 1952-54, rsch. assoc. in medicine, 1954-55, asst. prof. medicine, 1957-59, assoc. prof., 1959-64, prof., 1964-89; prof. emeritus, 1989—; lab. dir., 1969-76, Markle scholar in med. sci. dept. medicine, 1955-60; vol. research asso. Hamersmith Hosp., London, 1956-57. Contbr. numerous articles on congenital and acquired heart disease to profl. publs.; co-editor: Cardiovascular Nursing, 1968-71. Served with M.C. U.S. Army, 1946-48. Mem. Wis. Heart Assn. (pres. 1969-70), Am. Heart Assn., Assn. Univ. Cardiologists (pres. 1974-75), Central Clin. Research Club (pres. 1968-69), Am. Physiol. Soc., Am. Soc. Pharmacology, and Exptl. Therapeutics. Home: 5 Walworth Ct Madison WI 53705-4805 Office: 600 Highland Ave Madison WI 53792-0001

ROWE, GILBERT THOMAS, oceanography educator; b. Ames, Iowa, Feb. 7, 1942; s. Charles Gilbert and Catherine (Corkery) R.; m. Judith Lee Ingram, Nov. 27, 1962; 1 child, Atticus Ingram. BS in Zoology, Texas A&M U., 1964, MS in Oceanography, 1966; PhD in Zoology, Duke U., 1968. From asst. to assoc. scientist Woods Hole (Mass.) Oceanographic Inst., 1968-79; oceanographer Brookhaven Nat. Lab., Upton, N.Y., 1979-87; prof., head dept. oceanography Tex. A&M U., College Station, 1987-93. Editor: (books) The Sea, 1983, Deep-Sea Food Chains, 1992; U.S. editor: Jour. Marine Systems. Fellow AAAS. Office: Texas A&M U Dept Oceanography College Station TX 77843

ROWE, HERBERT JOSEPH, retired trade association executive; b. Granite City, Ill., Mar. 25, 1924; s. Herbert Bernard and Maude (Klein) R.; m. Ann Muter, Dec. 2, 1950; children: Douglas H., Stephen F., James D., Edith L. Student, U. Tex., 1942-43, Purdue U., 1943-44; BS in Mgmt.; BS in Mktg., U. Ill., 1948; LittD (hon.), London Inst. for Applied Research, 1975. With Edward Valves, Inc. (subs. Rockwell Mfg. Co.), Chgo. 1948-50; with Muter Co., Chgo., 1952-71, v.p., 1957-64, pres., 1964-71, treas., 1964-67, chmn. bd., 1965-71, also dir., 1957-71; pres., treas., dir. Wescoil Co., 1964-66, Tri-Axial Corp., 1966-67; v.p., treas. Gen. Magnetic Corp., 1965-67, chmn. bd., 1967-70, dir., 1964-70; chmn. bd., dir; Pemcor, Inc., Westchester, Ill., 1971-75; assoc. adminstr. external affairs NASA, 1975-78; sr. v.p. Electronic Industries Assn., 1978-89; chmn. Famro Corp., 1989-90; pres. Internat. Electronics Fed., 1989-90; sec.-treas. Englewood Elec. Supply Wis., Inc., 1972-75, Rahr's Inc., 1972-75; pres. Enclave of Naples, Inc., 1992-94, treas., 1994—; bd. dirs. Aerovox Corp.; pres. Rowe Corp., 1994—; treas. Quality Wholesale Foods of S.W. Fla., 1954—. Pres. Pokagon Trails coun. Boy Scouts Am., 1964-66, pres. Calumet coun., 1966-68, region 7 exec. com., 1966-72, vice chmn., 1971-72, bd. dirs. East Central region, 1972-75, mem. nat. program com., 1970-78, 90-94, nat. Cub Scout com., 1970-80, chmn., 1990-94, SE regional exec. com., 1978-90. So. regional exec. bd., 1993—; bd. dirs. Nat. Capital Area coun. Boy Scouts Am., 1978-90, adv. bd., 1990-94, mem. exec. bd. SW Fla. Coun. Boy Scouts Am., 1992—, mem. nat. exec. com. and exec. bd., 1990—; membership chmn. Nat. Eagle Scouts Assn., 1976-80; corp. campaign chmn. Chgo. Met. Crusade Mercy, 1964-68; chmn. Bd. Edn. Caucus, Flossmoor, Ill., 1962; Mem. bd. Flossmoor United Party,

1963-68; Mem. U. Ill. Found., 1967—; mem. advisory com. U. Ill. Coll. Commerce and Bus. Adminstrn., 1968-78; bd. dirs. Electronic Industries Found., 1974-94; mem. advisory bd. Air and Space Mus., Smithsonian Instn., 1975-78; active Moorings Presbyn. Ch., Naples, Fla. With USMCR, 1942-46, 50-52. Recipient Silver Beaver award Boy Scouts Am., 1966, Silver Antelope award, 1969, Silver Buffalo award, 1994; NASA team award Bicentennial Expo on Sci. and Tech., Exceptional Svc. medal, 1978, Baden-Powell fellow World Scout Found., 1992. Mem. AIAA, AAAS, Electronic Industries Assn. (hon., bd. dirs. 1967-69, bd. govs. 1969-75, exec. com. parts div. 1966-75, vice chmn. parts div. 1970-74, 74-75, bd. dirs. consumer electronics div. 1972-75, chmn. world trade com. 1968-70, vice chmn. 1970-73, chmn. membership and scope com. 1972-74, Disting. Svc. award 1989), Am. Loudspeaker Mfrs. Assn. (v.p., dir. 1967-68, pres., bd. dirs. 1968-70), Greater Washington Soc. Assn. Execs., Assn. Electronic Mfrs. (bd. dirs. 1970-73), Nat. Space Club, Nat. Space Inst., Am. Acad. Polit. Social Sci., Am. Soc. Assn. Execs. (vice chmn. internat. sect. 1986-87, chmn. 1988), U.S. Naval Inst., Field Mus. Natural History, European Soc. of Assn. Execs., Chgo. Art Inst., Beta Gamma Sigma, Alpha Phi Omega, Sigma Chi (dir. Kappa Kappa corp. 1954-75, sec. 1971-73, pres. 1973-75, Charles J. Kiler award 1975, Grand Consul's citation 1976), Am. Legion, Chaîne des Rôtisseurs Order Mondial. Home: 4601 Gulf Shore Blvd N # 12 Naples FL 33940

ROWE, JACK FIELD, retired electric utility executive; b. Minn., May 10, 1927; s. William F. and Anna (Stenborg) R.; m. Mary E. Moen, Mar. 26, 1955; 1 dau., Lizette Ann. B.E.E., U. Minn., 1950. Registered profl. engr., Minn., Wis. With Minn. Power and Light Co., Duluth, 1950-89; asst. to pres. Minn. Power and Light Co., 1966-67, v.p., 1967-68, exec. v.p., 1969-74, pres., 1974-84, chief exec. officer, 1978-89, chmn., 1969-93, bd. dirs.; chmn. bd., CEO FiberCore, Inc., Minn. Paper, Inc., So. States Utilities, Universal Telephone, Inc., Topeka Group, Inc., NorLight, Inc.; mem. exec. bd. Nat. Electric Reliability Coun., 1970-73; vice chmn. Mid-Continent Area Reliability Coun., 1970-71, chmn.; 1972-73; mem. bus. and econs. adv. bd. U. Minn., Duluth, 1980; bd. dirs. Na Tec, Inc., Houston. Past bd. dirs., v.p. Duluth Jr. C. of C.; mem. exec. bd. Lake Superior coun. Boy Scouts Am., 1967-75, chmn. Explorers, 1968-72; comml. chmn. Duluth United Fund, 1960-61; vice chmn. Duluth United Way, 1975, chmn., 1976, U.S. Savs. Bond chmn., St. Lois County, Minn., 1974-77; chmn. St. Louis County Heritage and Arts Ctr., 1979-81; pres. NE Minn. Devel./Assn., 1981-83; mem. Minn. Bus. Partnership, 1979-88; bd. dirs. Minn. Safety Coun., 1979-85, pres., 1983-84, chmn., 1984-85; bd. dirs. Duluth Downtown Devel. Corp., 1979-81, Duluth Growth Co., 1984-85, Greysolon Mall Corp., 1980-86, Duluth Superior Area Cmty. Found., 1984-86, Duluth Clin. Edn. and Rsch. Found., 1985-86, Benedictine Health Sys., 1985-88; mem. adv. bd. exec. program U. Minn., 1979; adv. coun. Inst. Tech., 1979; mem. Minn. High Tech. Coun., 1982-87. With USNR, 1945-46. Recipient Distinguished Service award Duluth Jr. C. of C., 1960, Outstanding Leadership award in energy conversion scis. N.Y.C. sect. ASME, 1980, Outstanding Achievement award U. Minn. Alumni Assn., 1986, Bronze Chief Exec. Officer of Decade award Fin. World Mag., 1989; named Chief Exec. Officer of Yr., Fin. World mag., 1986, 89; Jack F. Rowe Chair of Engring. named in his honor U. Minn., Duluth, 1986. Mem. NAM (dir. 1975-78), IEEE, Electric Info. Coun. (pres. 1978-82), North Cen. Electric Assn., Duluth C. of C. (pres. 1972-73, exec. com., bd. dirs.), Mpls. Club, Engrs. Club (Duluth), Northland Country Club (Duluth), Quail Creek County Club (Naples), Naples Yacht Club, Kitchi Gammi (Duluth) (dir. 1979-87, pres. 1985-87), Rotary Club (Duluth) (pres. 1974-75), Masons, Shriners, Jesters, Kappa Eta Kappa. Lutheran. Home: 4735 Villa Mare Ln Naples FL 33940-3473

ROWE, JAMES W., food chain executive; b. Chattanooga, Dec. 28, 1923; s. John Howard and Anne Lou (Borders) R.; m. Doris Eileen Carlton, Feb. 19, 1946; children: Carlton, Leigh Anne. Student advanced mgmt, Northeastern U., 1976. Vice pres., sec. Colonial Stores, Atlanta, 1970-77, sr. v.p. adminstrn., 1978, pres., 1979-80; sr. v.p., asst. to chief exec. officer Grand Union Co., Elmwood Park, N.J., 1979; exec. v.p., asst. chief exec. officer Gt. Atlantic & Pacific Tea Co., Inc., Montvale, N.J., 1980-82, vice chmn., chief adminstrn. officer, asst. chief exec. officer, 1982-88; vice chmn. bd. and exec. com. Gt. Atlantic and Pacific Tea Co., Inc., Montvale, N.J., 1988—; bd. dirs. Colonial Stores, Grand Union Co., Gt. Atlantic and Pacific Tea Co. Served with AUS, 1942-45. Republican. Home: 4070 Ridgehurst Dr Smyrna GA 30080-3107 Office: Great Atlantic & Pacific Tea Co Box 418 2 Paragon Dr Montvale NJ 07645

ROWE, JAY E., JR., research and development director; b. Tacoma, Wash., Jan. 10, 1947; s. Jay E. and Betty V. Rowe; m. Lisha L. Mohn, Aug. 5, 1991; children: Coby, Kistin, Felicity, Robbi, Daniel, Emery. BS in Chemistry, Bucknell U., 1968; PhD in Organic Chemistry, Lehigh U., 1973; MBA, St. Joseph's U., Phila., 1987. Rsch. chemist Crompton and Knowles Corp., Reading, Pa., 1974-79, group leader, 1979-91, dir. R & D, 1991—. Office: Crompton & Knowles Corp Dyes & Chemicals Div PO Box 341 Reading PA 19603-0341

ROWE, JOHN HOWLAND, anthropologist, educator; b. Sorrento, Maine, June 10, 1918; s. Louis Earle and Margaret Talbot (Jackson) R.; m. Barbara Bent Burnett, June 6, 1942; children: Ann Pollard, Lucy Burnett; m. Patricia Jean Lyon, Apr. 24, 1970. A.B., Brown U., 1939, L.H.D. (hon.), 1969; M.A. in Anthropology, Harvard U., 1941, Ph.D. in Latin Am. History and Anthropology, 1947; Litt.D. (hon.), U. Nacional del Cuzco, Peru, 1954; student, U. Paris, France, 1945-46. Field supr. So. Peru, Inst. Andean Research, 1941-42; prof. archaeology dir. Sect. Archaeology U. Nacional del Cuzco, 1942-43; rep. in Colombia, Inst. Social Anthropology, Smithsonian Instn., also tchr. U. del Cauca, Popayán, 1946-48; mem. faculty U. Calif., Berkeley, 1948—, prof. anthropology, 1956-88, prof. emeritus, 1988—, chmn. dept., 1963-67; curator S. Am. archaeology Mus. Anthropology, 1949—; cons. UNESCO, Cuzco, Peru, 1975; sr. fellow Dumbarton Oaks, 1984-90; field rsch. in Maine, 1938, 40, Mass., 1939-41, Fla., 1940, Guambia and Popayan, Colombia, 1946-48, Peru, 1939, 41-43, 46, 54, 58, 59, 61-78, 80-90, 92-94; hon. prof. del Cauca, 1947; rsch. prof. Mil. Inst. Basic Rsch. Sci., U. Calif., Berkeley, 1964-65. Author: An Introduction to the Archaeology of Cuzco, 1944, Max Uhle, 1954, Chavin Art, 1962, (with Menzel and Dawson) The Paracas Pottery of Ica, 1964; Editor: (with Patricia Lyon) Nawpa Pacha, 1963—. Served with AUS, 1944-46, ETO. Recipient Diploma de Honor Soc. Cientifica del Cuzco, 1954, Prémio de Honor Concejo Provincial de Ica, Peru, 1958; ofcl. Orden El Sol del Peru, 1968; Diploma de Honor Concejo Provincial del Cuzco, Peru, 1974; Gran Cruz Orden Al Merito por Servicios Distinguidos, Peru, 1981, Medalla de la Ciudad, Municipalidad del Qosqo, Peru, 1993; Guggenheim fellow, 1958. Mem. Archaeol. Inst. Am., Soc. Am. Archaeology, Soc. des Americanistes de Paris, Soc. Antiquaries London, Am. Anthrop. Assn., Acad. National de la Historia (Peru), Soc. History Tech., Inst. Andean Studies (pres. 1960—). Home: 1029 Cragmont Ave Berkeley CA 94708-1411

ROWE, JOHN WALLIS, academic administrator, hospital administrator; b. Jersey City, June 20, 1944; s. Albert Wallis and Elizabeth (Lynch) R.; m. Valerie Ann DelTufo, Aug. 10, 1968; children: Meredith, Abigail, Rebecca. BS with honors, Canisius Coll., 1966; MD with distinction, U. Rochester, 1970. Diplomate: Am. Bd. Internal Medicine, Am. Bd. Nephrology. Resident in internal medicine Harvard Med. Sch., Beth Israel Hosp., Boston, 1970-72; clin. assoc. Nat. Inst. Child Health and Human Devel., Balt., 1972-74; rsch., clin. fellow Harvard Med. Sch., Mass. Gen. Hosp., Boston, 1974-75; from instr. to prof. Harvard Med. Sch., Boston, 1976-88; pres. Mount Sinai Sch. Medicine, Mount Sinai Hosp., N.Y.C., 1988—, prof. geriatrics and medicine, 1988—; trustee N.Y. Acad. Medicine, 1989—, Buck Ctr. for Rsch. in Aging, Marin, Calif., 1989—. Editor: Health and Disease in Old Age, 1982, Geriatric Medicine, 1988, Handbook of the Biology of Aging, 1990, Geriatric Neurology, 1991; contbr. articles to jours. in field. Lt. comdr. USPHS, 1972-74. MacArthur Found. grantee, 1985—. Mem. NAS Inst. Med., Gerontol. Soc. Am. (pres. 1988), Am. Fedn. for Aging Rsch. (pres. 1988), N.Y. Yacht Club, Century Assn. Roman Catholic. Avocation: sailing. Home: 300 Central Park W New York NY 10024-1513 Office: Mt Sinai Med Ctr Fifth Ave & 100th St New York NY 10029

ROWE, JOHN WESTEL, retired organic chemist; b. Forest Hills, N.Y., Sept. 3, 1924; s. John Edward and laura Robinson (Willoughby) R.; m. Mary Dorothy Lowens, June 26, 1949; children: Peter Willoughby, William Westel,

Michael Delano. B.S., MIT, 1948; M.S., U. Colo., 1952; Sc.D., Swiss Fedn. Inst. Tech., Zurich, 1956. With Forest Products Lab. Forest Service, USDA, 1957-89; project leader Forest Products Lab., Forest Service, USDA, Madison, Wis., 1966-84; also supervisory research chemist Forest Products Lab., Forest Service, USDA; lectr. U. Wis. Editor: Natural Products of Wood Planets, 1980; contbr. articles on wood and natural products chemistry to profl. jours. Active Boy Scouts Am., 1962-74. Served with USN, 1942-44. Recipient Wood Salutes award Wood & Wood Products, 1975. Fellow Internat. Acad. Wood Sci., AAAS, Am. Inst. Chemists; mem. Soc. Econ. Botany, Phytochem. Assn. N.Am., Am. Chem. Soc. (chmn. Wis. sect. 1968, 69, alt. counselor 1976-78), Am. Soc. Pharmacology, Forest Products Research Soc., Internat. Assn. for Biomass Utilization, TAPPI,. Republican. Unitarian. Home: 1001 Tumalo Trl Madison WI 53711-3024

ROWE, JOHN WILLIAM, utility executive; b. Dodgeville, Wis., May 18, 1945; s. William J. and Lola (Rule) R.; m. Jeanne M.; 1 son, William John. BS, U. Wis., 1967, JD, 1970. Bar: Wis. 1970, Ill. 1970, U.S. Supreme Ct. 1979, Pa. 1982. Assoc. Isham, Lincoln & Beale, Chgo., 1970-77, ptnr., 1978-80; counsel to trustee Chgo. Milw. St. Paul & Pacific R.R., Chgo., 1979-80; v.p. law Consol. Rail Corp., Phila., 1980-82, sr. v.p. law, 1982-84; pres., chief exec. officer Cen. Maine Power Co., Augusta, 1984-89; pres., chief exec. officer New Eng. Elec. System, Westboro, Mass., 1989—, also bd. dirs.; bd. dirs. UNUM Corp., Bank of Boston Corp. Trustee Pa. Ballet, 1982-84, Bryant Coll.; chmn. Ft. Western Endowment Fund, 1987-88; co-chmn. Maine Aspirations Compact, 1988; bd. dirs. USS Constitution Mus., Jobs for Mass., Electric Power Rsch. Inst., Dana Farber Cancer Inst. Mem. Mass. Bus. Roundtable (chmn.), R.I. Commodores, Order of Coif, Chgo. Club, Worcester Club, Framingham Country Club, Phi Beta Kappa. Home and Office: New England Electric System 25 Research Dr Westborough MA 01582-0001

ROWE, JOSEPH EVERETT, electrical engineering educator, administrator; b. Highland Park, Mich., June 4, 1927; s. Joseph and Lillian May (Osbourne) R.; m. Margaret Anne Prine, Sept. 1, 1950; children: Jonathan Dale, Carol Kay. BS in Engring., U. Mich., 1951, BS Engring. in Math., 1951, MS in Engring., 1952, PhD, 1955. Mem. faculty U. Mich., Ann Arbor, 1953-74; prof. elec. engring. U. Mich., 1960-74, dir. electron physics lab., 1958-68, chmn. deptl. elec. and computer engring., 1968-74; vice provost, dean engring. Case Western Res. U., Cleve., 1974-76; provost Case Inst. Tech., 1976-78; v.p. tech. Harris Corp., Melbourne, Fla., 1978-81; v.p., gen. mgr. Controls divsn. Harris Corp., 1981-82; exec. v.p. rsch. and def. Gould Inc., 1982, vice chmn., chief tech. officer, 1983-87; sr. v.p., chief technologist Inst. Rsch., Ill. Inst. Tech., Chgo., 1987; v.p. and chief scientist PPG Industries, Inc., Pitts., 1987-92; v.p., dir. Rsch. Inst., U. Dayton, Ohio, 1992—; cons. to industry; mem. adv. group electron devices Dept. Def., 1966-78, 93—; bd. govs. Rsch. inst. of Ill. Inst. Tech.; chmn. Coalition for Advancement of Indsl. Tech., U. Ill.; mem. indsl. adv. bd. U. Ill. at Chgo.; mem. Army Sci. Bd., 1985-91, 93—. Author: Nonlinear Electron-Wave Interaction Phenomena, 1965, also articles. Fellow AAAS, IEEE (chmn. administrv. com. group electron devices 1968-69, editor procs. 1971-73); mem. NAE, Am. Phys. Soc., Am. Soc. Engring. Edn. (Curtis McGraw rsch. award 1964), Am. Mgmt. Assn. (R & D), Sigma Xi, Phi Kappa Phi, Tau Beta Pi, Eta Kappa Nu. Office: U Dayton 300 College Pk Dayton OH 45469-0101

ROWE, KEVIN S., banker; b. Seldom come bye, Nfld., Can., Feb. 14, 1938; m. Valma Jean Rowe, Aug. 28, 1958; children: Todd, Michelle, Natalie, Scott. Student, Curtis Acad., St. Johns, Nfld. With The Bank of N.S., various locations, Can., U.S. and abroad, 1955-70; agt. N.Y.C., 1970-73; area mgr. V.I. and P.R., 1973-77; v.p., gen. mgr Pacific Regional Office Manila, 1977-83; exec. v.p., gen. mgr. internat. Bank of N.S., Toronto, Ont., Can., 1983-86, exec. v.p. Pacific Region, 1987—; bd. dirs. BNS Internat. (Hong Kong) Ltd., The Bank of Nova Scotia Asia Ltd., The Bank of Nova Scotia Berhad, Solidbank Corp., Poonpipat Fin. & Securities Co. Ltd. Office: Bank of NS, United Centre 25th Fl, 95 Queensway, Hong Kong Hong Kong

ROWE, MARJORIE DOUGLAS, retired social services administrator; b. Bklyn., July 29, 1912; d. Herbert Lynn and Mary Manson (Hall) Douglas; m. Richard Daniel Rowe, July 29, 1937; 1 child, Richard Douglas. AB cum laude, Whitman Coll., 1933; MS in Social Administrn., Case Western Res. U., 1936. Caseworker Children's Svcs., Cleve., 1933-36, supr., 1937-39; dir. Adoption Svc. Bur., Cleve., 1940-41; social work supr., psychiat. social work cons. Ea. State Hosp., Medical Lake, Wash., 1962-67; dir. social svcs. Interlake Sch.for Developmentally Disabled, Medical Lake, 1967-74, supt., 1975-82. Pres. chpt. R.P.E.O., Spokane, Wash., 1949, Spokane Alumnae chpt. Delta Delta Delta, 1955-57; chpt. mem. ARC, Orofino, Idaho, 1941-45, Orofino chpt. chmn., 1945-46; sec. Idaho state chpt. AAUW, 1945-46. Mem. Am. Assn. for Mental Deficiency (region I chmn. 1976-77, social work chmn. 1971-73), NASW (gold card mem.), P.E.O. (pres. Spokane Reciprocity 1950), Acad. Cert. Social Workers, Spokane Women of Rotary (pres. 1960-61), Phi Beta Kappa, Delta Sigma Rho, Mortar Bd. Episcopalian. Avocations: local museum volunteer, traveling, antiques, lake cabin activities. Home: 946 E Thurston Ave Spokane WA 99203-2948

ROWE, MARY P., university official, educator; b. Chgo., Feb. 18, 1936; married; children: Katherine, Susannah, Timothy. BA in History, Swarthmore Coll., 1957; PhD in Econs., Columbia U., 1971; LLD (hon.), Regis Coll., 1975. With World Council of Chs./Office of UN High Commr. for Refugees, Salzburg and Vienna, Austria, 1957-58; research asst. Nat. Bur. Econ. Research, N.Y.C., 1961; economist planning bd. Office of Gov., V.I., 1962-63; free-lance cons. Nigeria, 1963-66, Boston, 1967-69; cons., sr. economist with Ctr. for Ednl. Policy Research, Harvard U. Harvard U., Cambridge, Mass., 1970, cons., sr. economist with Abt Assocs., 1970; tech. dir. early edn. project Harvard U., 1971-72, cons. economist with Abt Assocs., 1971; dir. Carnegie Corp. Grant Radcliffe Inst., Cambridge, 1972; spl. asst. to pres. MIT, Cambridge, 1973—, adj. prof. Sloan Sch. Mgmt., 1985—. Mem. editorial bd. Negotiation Jour., 1985—, Alternative Dispute Resolution Report, 1987—; contbr. articles to profl. jours. Trustee Cambridge Friends Sch., 1969-75; mem. bd. advisors Brookline Children's Ctr., 1971-76; mem. Cambridge Friends Meeting and Com. on Clearness, 1971-78, New Eng. Concerns Com., 1973—, Mass. Policy Adv. Com. on Child Abuse/ Neglect, 1977-79, Mass. State Youth Council, 1978-83; mem. Mass. State Employment and Tng. Council, 1975-83, chair, 1980-83; mem. nat. adv. Com. Black Women's Ednl. Policy and Research Network Project/Wellesley Coll. Ctr. for Research on Women, 1980-83; bd. dirs. Bay State Skills Commn., 1980-81, Wellesley Women's Research Ctr., 1984-87; sec. bd. dirs. Bay State Skills Corp., 1981-90; mem. panel on employment disputes Ctr. for Pub. Resources, 1986—. Recipient Meritorious Civilian Svc. award Dept. of Navy, 1993. Mem. Am. Econs. Assn., Soc. Profls. in Dispute Resolution (chair com. on ombudspersons 1982—), Calif. Caucus Coll. and Univ. Ombudsmen, Univ. and Coll. Ombudsman Assn., Corp. Ombudsman Assn. (pres. 1987-8, Disting. Neutral Ctr. for Pub. Resources 1990). Office: MIT 10-213 77 Massachusetts Ave Cambridge MA 02139

ROWE, MAX L., lawyer, corporate executive, management consultant, judge; b. Dallas City, Ill. Aug. 14, 1921; s. Samuel Guy and Nellie (Moyes) R.; m. Maxine Marilyn Gladson, May 23, 1944; children: Melody Ann (Mrs. Gunn), Susan Elaine, Joyce Lynn, Andrew Blair. Student, Knox Coll., Galesburg, Ill., 1939-40; A.B., U. Ill., 1943, J.D., 1946; M.B.A., U. Chgo., 1952. Bar: Ill. 1947, Ind. 1954, also U.S. Supreme Ct. 1964. Pvt. practice in Aurora and Urbana, 1947; asst. to sec., asst. treas. Elgin Nat. Watch Co., 1948-50; gen. atty., asst. to pres.-treas. Rival Packing Co., 1950- 51; gen. counsel, asst. sec.-treas. Victor Mfg. & Gasket Co., Chgo., 1951-54; sec. Mead Johnson & Co., Evansville, Ind., 1954-55; assoc. counsel Caterpillar Tractor Co., 1955-62; assoc. gen. counsel, sec., asst. treas. Thomas J. Lipton, Inc. and subs., 1962-68; v.p., treas. Seeburg Corp., Chgo. 1968-69; v.p. fin., law and adminstrn. Nightingale Conant Corp., Chgo., 1970-71; pvt. legal practice, also mgmt. cons., 1968—; v.p. law, sec. Ward Foods, Inc. Wilmette, Ill., 1972-76; mem. firm Kirkland & Ellis, Chgo. 1978-87; atty. Ill. Dept. Profl. Regulation, Chgo. and Springfield, 1987-92; adminstrv. law judge State of Ill., 1993—; dir. Ward-Johnston, Inc., Ward Internat., Inc.; Superior Potato Chips, Inc., Quinlan Pretzel Co., Horian-Philippines, Inc.; instr. extension div. U. Ill., 1960-61, eve. div. Fairleigh Dickinson U., 1966- 68; leader Am. Mgmt. Assn., other corp. seminars, 1966-87. actor various TV, radio and print commercials, 1992—. Treas. Peoria County (Ill.) Republican Central Com., 1958-62, Rep. precinct committeeman, Peoria

County, 1958-62, Bergen County, N.J., 1966-68, del., Rep. Nat. Conv., 1980; elder Presbyterian Ch., 1975—; mem. nat. adv. council SBA, 1976-78; chmn., mem. adv. bd. Ill. Dept. Personnel, 1979-82; mem. Ill. Compensation Rev. Bd., 1984-87; mem. Pres. Reagan's Nat. Commn. for Employment Policy, 1984-88; mem. U. Ill. Found. and Pres.'s Council, 1979—, bd. visitors Coll. of Law, 1993—; dir. mem. exec. com., chmn. Outreach and Devel., World Heritage Mus., 1992—; mem. bd. dirs. Oak Ridge Cemetary, 1994—. Served to 2d lt. AUS, 1943-45. Named Alumni of Month, U. Ill. Coll. Law, 1982. Mem. Am. Mgmt. Assn., Conf. Bd., Am., Ill, Chgo. bar assns., Am. Soc. Corp. Secs., Phi Gamma Delta. Republican. Clubs: Union League (Chgo.), Execs. (Chgo.). Office: 49 Inverness Rd Springfield IL 62704

ROWE, PETER A., newspaper columnist; b. Walnut Creek, Calif., Sept. 7, 1955; s. Raymond Alan and Marian (Green) R.; m. Lynn Hanson, Aug. 13, 1977; children: Kyle, Reid, Alec. BA in History, U. Calif., Berkeley, 1977, BA in Journalism, 1977; MSJ, Northwestern U., 1981. Reporter Argus, Fremont, Calif., 1977-80, Va.-Pilot, Norfolk, 1981-84; reporter San Diego Union, 1984-87, asst. features editor, 1987-88, features editor, 1988-92; columnist San Diego Union-Tribune, 1992—. Bd. dirs., mem. adv. bd. St. Didacus Sch., San Diego, 1992-95; coach Mid-City Little League, San Diego, 1993—. Recipient 1st pl. series award Va. Press Assn., 1984, 1st pl. feature story award Copley Newspapers, 1987, 1st place columns award Soc. Profl. Journalists, 1992; Gannett fellow Northwestern U., 1980-81. Roman Catholic. Office: San Diego Union Tribune PO Box 191 San Diego CA 92112-4106

ROWE, PETER GRIMMOND, architecture educator, researcher; b. Wellington, New Zealand, June 28, 1945; came to U.S., 1969; s. Leslie Grimmond and Dorothy Olive (Perkins) R.; m. Lauretta Vinciarelli, Oct. 18, 1993; 1 child, Anthony. BArch, Melbourne (Australia) U., 1969; MArch in Urban Design, Rice U., 1971; AM (hon.), Harvard U., 1986. Asst. prof. architecture Rice U., Houston, 1973-78, assoc. prof., 1978-85, dir. Sch. Architecture, 1981-85; Raymond Garbe prof. architecture and urban design Grad. Sch. Design, Harvard U., Cambridge, Mass., 1985—, chmn. dept. urban planning and design, 1989-92, dean Grad. Sch. Design, 1992—; program dir. S.W. Ctr. Urban Rsch., Houston, 1974-78; rsch. dir. Rice Ctr., Houston, 1978-81, v.p., 1979-81; prin. Environ. Planning and Design, Houston, 1980-86. Author: Principles for Environmental Management, 1978, Design Thinking, 1987, Making a Middle Landscape, 1991, Modernity and Housing, 1993. Mem. Boston Soc. Architects (hon.). Office: Harvard U Grad Sch Design 48 Quincy St Cambridge MA 02138-6502

ROWE, RICHARD HOLMES, lawyer; b. Waltham, Mass., Jan. 2, 1937; s. Robert C. Rowe and Roberta (Holmes) Hayes; m. Sylvia C. Barrow, Aug. 23, 1963; children: Elizabeth C., Dorothy H., Christopher H. AB, Bates Coll., 1957; JD, Harvard U., 1964. Bar: D.C. 1965, N.Y. 1980. Atty., exec. SEC, Washington, 1964-69, 70-79; v.p. Shareholders Mgmt. Co., L.A., 1969-70; ptnr. Proskauer Rose Goetz & Mendelsohn, Washington, 1979—. 1st lt. USMCR, 1957-60. Mem. ABA, Fed. Bar Assn., D.C. Bar Assn., Assn. of Bar of City of N.Y. Democrat. Office: Proskauer Rose et al 1233 20th St NW Ste 800 Washington DC 20036-2304

ROWE, RICHARD LLOYD, aviation executive, management consultant; b. N.Y.C., Sept. 21, 1926; m. Mercedes L. Walker; children: Delena, Patricia, Richard Jr. BBA in Indsl. Mgmt., CCNY, 1961, MBA, 1963. Asst. mgr., operating personnel dept. Port Authority of N.Y. and N.J., N.Y.C., 1968-70, mgr. equal opportunity programs, 1970-72, mgr. operating personnel, 1972-76, mgr. employee relations, 1976-78, asst. dir. aviation, 1978-83, gen. mgr. J.F. Kennedy Internat. Airport, 1983—. Office: JFK Internat Airport Bldg 141 Jamaica NY 11430

ROWE, RICHARD R., on-line information and management services company executive; b. Burlington, Iowa, Apr. 14, 1933; s. Charles Ronald and Elva Margaret (Gilliland) R.; children: Katherine, Susannah, Timothy, Christopher, Jonathan. B.A. in Psychology, UCLA, 1955; S.T.B. in Psychology of Religion, Boston U., 1958; Ph.D. in Psychology, Columbia U., 1963. Cert. and lic. psychologist, Mass. Dir. test devel. and research West African Exams. Council, 1963-67; assoc. dean Grad. Sch. Edn., Harvard U., Cambridge, Mass., 1967-73; dir. program in clin. psychology and pub. practice Harvard U., 1967-73; v.p. Am. Inst. for Research, Cambridge, 1973-79; pres., chief exec. officer The Faxon Co., Westwood, Mass., 1979-93; pres., CEO Rosewood KM, Inc., 1994—; chmn. Serials Industry Systems Adv. Com.; mem. State Bd. Edn., Mass., 1990—; chmn., Mass. Edn. Reform Implementation Task Force, 1993—. Pres. Statewide Adv. Council to Office for Children, Mass., 1980-87, chmn., 1983-87; mem. K-12 computer literacy com. Mass. High Tech Council, 1983-84; spl. advisor Mass. Legis. Com. on Ednl. Excellence, 1983-84; mem. Mass. Legis. Commn. Early Edn., 1988—. Mem. Am. Psychol. Assn., ALA, Library and Info. Tech. Assn. Club: Harvard (N.Y.C.). Home: 37 Goden St Belmont MA 02178-3002 Office: Faxon Co Inc Rosewood KM Inc 37 Goden St Belmont MA 02178-3002

ROWE, SANDRA MIMS, newspaper editor; b. Charlotte, N.C., May 26, 1948; d. David Lathan and Shirley (Stovall) Mims; m. Gerard Paul Rowe, June 5, 1971; children—Mims Elizabeth, Sarah Stovall. BA, East Carolina U., Greenville, N.C., 1970; postgrad., Harvard U., 1991. Reporter to asst. mng. editor The Ledger-Star, Norfolk, Va., 1971-80, mng. editor, 1980-82; mng. editor The Virginian-Pilot and The Ledger Star, Norfolk, Va., 1982-84, exec. editor, 1984-86, v.p., exec. editor, 1986-93; editor The Oregonian, Portland, 1993, 1994—; mem. nominating jury for Pulitzer Prize in Journalism, 1986, 87, mem. Pulitzer Prize Bd., 1994—. Bd. visitors James Madison U., Harrisonburg, Va., 1991—. Named Woman of Yr. Outstanding Profl. Women of Hampton Rds., 1987. Mem. Am. Soc. Newspaper Editors (bd. dirs. 1992—, pres. 1995), Va. Press Assn. (bd. dirs. 1985-93). Episcopalian. Office: The Oregonian 1320 SW Broadway Portland OR 97201-3469

ROWE, THOMAS DUDLEY, JR., law educator; b. Richmond, Va., Feb. 26, 1942; s. Thomas Dudley and Georgia Rosamond (Stripp) R. B.A., Yale U., 1964; M.Phil., Oxford U., Eng., 1967; J.D., Harvard U., 1970. Bar: D.C. 1971, N.C. 1976. Law clk. to assoc. justice Potter Stewart U.S. Supreme Ct., 1970-71; asst. counsel adminstrv. practice subcom. U.S. Senate, 1971-73; assoc. Miller, Cassidy, Larroca & Lewin, Washington, 1973-75; assoc. prof. Duke U. Sch. Law, Durham, N.C., 1975-79, prof., 1979—, assoc. dean for rsch., 1981-84, sr. assoc. dean acad. affairs, 1995—; vis. prof. Georgetown U. Law Ctr., Washington, 1979-80, U. Mich. Law Sch. Ann Arbor, fall 1985, U. Va. Law Sch., Charlottesville, fall 1991; pres. Ctr. for computer Assisted Legal Instrn., 1988-91; atty. Munger, Tolles & Olson, 1991; mem. adv. com. on rules of civil procedure U.S. Jud. Conf., 1993—; chmn. adv. com. on rules and procedures U.S. Ct. Appeals (4th cir.), 1994—. Author: (with M. Gerhardt) Constitutional Theory: Arguments and Perspectives, 1993; contbr. articles to profl. jours. Fellow U.S. Dept. Justice, Washington, 1967-70; Rhodes scholar, 1964-67; recipient Disting. Teaching award Duke Bar Assn., 1985. Mem. ABA, Am. Law Inst. (adviser study complex litigation 1985- 93). Democrat. Office: Duke U Sch Law Durham NC 27708-0360

ROWE, WILLIAM DAVIS, financial services company executive; b. Hibbing, Minn., June 5, 1937; s. Richard Lawrence and Alicia (Davis) R.; m. Bobbie Grace Childress, Apr. 20, 1963; children—Lisa, William. BA in Psychology, U. Minn, 1959, postgrad. in indsl. relations and bus. adminstrn., 1960; grad. exec. devel. program, Northeastern U., 1975; grad. Advanced Mgmt. Program, Harvard U., 1980. Dir. personnel, adminstrn. EDP Control Data Corp., Mpls., 1964-70; with Comml. Credit Co. subs. Control Data Corp, 1971-84, 85—; sr. v.p. consumer group Balt., 1975-81, sr. v.p. consumer realty services, 1981-83, sr. v.p. consumer banking services, 1983-84; v.p. market devel. Computer Service Co., Control Data Corp., Mpls., 1984; sr. v.p., chief adminstrv. officer Comml. Credit Co., Balt., 1985-87, officer, 1985-87; pres. Enterprise Bank Network Banc Svcs. Co., Atlanta, 1988-91; exec. mng. dir., vice chmn. Foster Ptnrs. Inc., Peat Marwick Alliance Co., 1991—; lectr. in field. Mem. Mayor's Vol. Council of Equal Opportunity, Balt.; trustee St. Paul's Sch. for Girls, Brooklandville, Md., 1981—; bd. dirs. Boy Scouts Am. Served to capt. USMC, 1960-63. Mem. Am. Fin. Services Assn. (bd. dirs. and mem. exec. com. 1980-84, consumer banking adv. com. 1983-84), Am. Mgmt. Assn. (pres.'s roundtable 1976). Republican. Avocations: hunting, skiing, cattle ranching.

ROWE, WILLIAM JOHN, newspaper publishing executive; b. Detroit, Jan. 11, 1936; s. Howard Tiederman and Thelma Irene (Fox) R.; m. Ellen

McCabe, Nov. 28, 1959; children: Peter William, Susan Victoria. BA in Journalism and Advt., Mich. State U., 1958. With Chgo. Tribune, 1958-79; pres., gen. mgr. area publs. Suburban Trib., 1977-79; pres., gen. mgr. Merrill Printing Co., Chgo., 1977-79; pres., CEO Peninsula Times Tribune, Palo Alto, Calif., 1979-84; exec. v.p., COO Times Mirror Nat. Mktg., N.Y.C., 1984-85, pres., CEO, 1985-86; pres., pub., CEO Adv. and Greenwich Time, Stamford, Conn., 1986—. Bd. dirs. United Way, Greenwich, Conn., Conn. Bus. for Edn. Coalition. 2d lt., inf. USAR, 1959. Mem. Newspaper Assn. Am., New England Newspaper Assn. (bd. dirs.), Indian Harbor Yacht Club (bd. dirs.), Landmark Club (bd. dirs.). Office: Advocate So Conn Newspapers Box 9307 75 Tresser Blvd Stamford CT 06901-3300

ROWELL, CHARLES FREDERICK, chemistry educator; b. Lowville, N.Y., May 29, 1935; s. Erwin Charles and Winifred Jane (Manning) R.; m. JoAnn Cowling, June 19, 1955; children: Mark Edward, Jan Ellen. BS, Syracuse U., 1956; MS, Iowa State U., 1959; PhD, Oreg. State U., 1963. From. asst. to assoc. prof. U.S. Naval Postgrad. Sch., Monterey, Calif., 1962- 75; field scientist Office Naval Research, Chgo., 1975-76; prof. U.S. Naval Acad., Annapolis, Md., 1976—, chmn. dept. chemistry, 1984-88; scientist Forensic Techs. Internat., Annapolis, 1980—. Mem. AAAS, Am. Chem. Soc. (counselor 1980—, sect. chair 1982-83, nat. sec. membership affairs com. 1988-90, chmn. admissions com. 1989-91, chmn. constitution and bylaws com. 1994—), Royal Soc. Chemistry, Sigma Xi (sec. chpt. 1972-73, v.p. 1973-74). Presbyterian. Home: 900 Randell Rd Severna Park MD 21146- 4726 Office: US Naval Acad Dept Of Chemistry Annapolis MD 21402

ROWELL, EDWARD MORGAN, retired foreign service officer, lecturer; b. Oakland, Calif., Oct. 13, 1931; s. Edward Joseph and Mary Helen (Mohler) R.; m. Lenora Mary Wood, Aug. 23, 1957; children: Edward Oliver, Karen Elizabeth Schuler, Christopher Douglas. B.A. in Internat. Relations, Yale U., 1953; postgrad., Stanford U., 1964-65, Stanford Bus. Sch., 1970-71. Fgn. service insp. U.S. Govt., Washington, 1971-74; dep. dir., econ. officer Office Iberian Affairs, Washington, 1974-75; dep. dir. Office West European Affairs, Washington, 1975-76, dir., 1977-78; minister-counselor U.S. Embassy, Lisbon, Portugal, 1978-83; dep. asst. sec. Bur. Consular Affairs, Washington, 1983-85; U.S. amb. to Bolivia La Paz, 1985-88; U.S. amb. to Portugal Lisbon, 1988-90; U.S. amb. to Luxemburg, 1990-94. Treas. Cleveland Park Congl. Ch., Washington, 1984-85; bd. dirs. Luso-Am. Devel. Found., 1988- 90. Served to cpl. U.S. Army, 1953-55. Recipient Bolivian Condor of the Andes, Grand Cross, 1988, Luxembourg Oaken Crown, Grand Cross, 1994, Superior Honor award, 1983, Presdl. Honor award, 1988; scholar Yale U., 1949, 50, 51, 52; U. Calif. fellow, 1953; Una Chapman Cox Found. grantee, 1984. Mem. Am. Fgn. Service Assn., Stanford U. Alumni Assn., Yale U. Alumni Assn., Arena Stage Assocs., Friends of Kennedy Ctr. Avocations: photography; tennis. Home: 5414 Newington Rd Bethesda MD 20816

ROWELL, HARRY BROWN, JR., technology company executive; b. Roberta, Ga., Sept. 21, 1941; s. Harry Brown Sr. and Essie Jewel (Sloan) R.; m. Mary Jeanette Hancock, Sept. 18, 1961; children: Harry Brown III, T. Scott. BBA, U. Ga., 1963, MA, 1964. Dir. cosmic U. Ga., Athens, 1964-69; dir. ops. Carnegie Mellon U., Pitts., 1969-74; v.p., treas. U. Bridgeport, Conn., 1974-79; v.p. corp. planning and devel., group v.p. Hubbell, Inc., Orange, Conn., 1985—; also exec. v.p. Hubbell, Inc., Orange, 1988—; bd. dirs. The Bank Mart, Bridgeport. Bd. dirs. Goodwill Industries, Bridgeport, 1976-87. Mem. Fin. Execs. Inst., Assn. for Corp. Growth. Club: Brokklawn Country (Fairfield, Conn.). Office: Hubbell Inc 584 Derby Milford Rd Orange CT 06477-2204

ROWELL, LESTER JOHN, JR., insurance company executive; b. Cleve., Apr. 2, 1932; s. Lester John and Francis Laureen (Corbett) R.; m. Patricia Ann Loesch, Jan. 16, 1953 (div. Sept. 1970); children: Deborah, Cynthia, Gregory, Maureen, Diane; m. Carol Ann Jankowski, Sept. 26, 1970. BS, Pa. State U., 1955; grad. Advanced Mgmt. Program, Harvard U. Bus. Sch., 1971. CLU. Second v.p., field mgmt. Mut. Life Ins. Co. N.Y., N.Y.C., 1969-70, v.p. agys., 1970-72, v.p. sales, 1972-78, sr. v.p., 1978-80; exec. v.p. Provident Mut. Life Ins. Co., Phila., 1980-84, pres., 1984-86, pres., chief oper. officer, 1987, pres., chief exec. officer, 1991-93, chmn., pres., chief exec. officer, 1993—; bd. dirs. Provident Mut. Life Ins. Co., Provident Mut. Life and Annuity Co. Am., Sigma Am. Corp. Chmn. advt. book campaign and bd. dirs. Southeastern Pa. chpt. ARC, 1989; bd. dirs., Paoli Meml. Hosp., Phila. Drama Guild, Internat. Ins. Soc., Inc., Pa. State U. Am. Coun. Life Ins., Ins. Fedn. of Pa., The PMA Group. Cpat. USMC, 1953-62. Recipient Alumni award Pa. State U., 1972, Disting. Alumni award Pa. State U., 1988; Alumni Fellow Pa. State U., 1987. Mem. Life Ins. Mktg. and Rsch. Assn. (dir. 1980-83, mem. strategic mktg. issues com. 1987—), NALU, Agy. Officers Round Table (chmn. 1980-81), Life Underwriters Tng. Coun. (past trustee), Greater Phila. C. of C. (bd. dirs.). Republican. Office: Provident Mut Life Ins Co 1600 Market St Philadelphia PA 19103-7240*

ROWEN, DANIEL, architect; b. Washington, DC, Oct. 10, 1953; s. Hobart Quentin and Alice Brooks (Stadler) R.; m. Coco Myers, June 26, 1993. BA magna cum laude, Brown U., 1975; MArch, Yale U., 1981. Prin. Daniel Rowen Architects, N.Y.C. Prin. works include Lipschutz/Jones Apt., N.Y.C., 1990, 91, Soho townhouse, N.Y.C., 1990, Lowe & Ptnrs. screening rooms, 1991. Recipient citation N.Y. State Assn. Architects, 1991. Mem. AIA, (citation N.Y.C. chpt. 1990, 91, award 1991), Archtl. League N.Y. Office: 448 West 37th St 12 B New York NY 10018

ROWEN, HARVEY ALLEN, investment company executive; b. Chgo., Sept. 21, 1943. BS in Acctg., UCLA, 1964; JD, U. Calif., Berkeley, 1967; MBA in Mktg. & Fin., NYU, 1981. Bar: Calif., D.C., N.Y. Pvt. practice Beverly Hills, Calif., 1967-68; counsel Securities & Exch. Commn., Washington, 1968-71, Com. Energy & Commerce, US Congress, Washington, 1971-75; sr. cons. SRI Internat. (formerly Stanford Rsch. Inst.), Palo Alto, 1975-77; asst. to pres. Merrill Lynch, Pierce, Fenner & Smith, Inc., N.Y.C., 1977-80, v.p. corp. planning, 1980-81; v.p. corp. planning Merrill Lynch & Co., Inc., N.Y.C., 1981-83, v.p. banking devel., banking divsn., 1983-84; exec. v.p. Merrill Lynch Bank & Trust Co., N.Y.C., 1984-85, pres., 1985-88; chmn. trust com. Merrill Lynch Trust Co., N.Y.C., 1987-90; prin. Harvey Rowen & Assocs., Newport Beach, Calif., 1990-91; pres., CEO The Charles Schwab Trust Co., S.F., 1992—; sr. v.p. Schwab Instl. Svcs. to Corps. Charles Schwab & Co., Inc., 1992—; mem. dean's adv. bd. Haas Sch. Bus., U. Calif., Berkeley; lectr. in field. Author: The Securities Acts Amendments of 1975, 1975, The Securities Acts Amendments of 1975: A Legislative History, 1976, The Emerging Financial Services Industry, 1983; author: (with others) The Deregulation of the Banking and Securities Industries 305, 1979; mem. editorial adv. bd. Banking Expansion Reporter. Mem. ABA (bus. sect., banking com., fed. regulation securities com., chmn. product and svc. devels. subcom. of com. devels. in investment svcs. 1985-87), Am. Bankers Assn., Calif. Bankers Assn., Calif. Bar Assn. Office: The Charles Schwab Trust Co 1 Montgomery St 7th Flr San Francisco CA 94104

ROWEN, HENRY STANISLAUS, economics educator; b. Boston, Oct. 11, 1925; s. Henry S. and Margaret Isabelle (Maher) R.; m. Beverly Camille Griffiths, Apr. 18, 1951; children: Hilary, Michael, Christopher, Sheila Jennifer, Diana Louise, Nicholas. BS, MIT, 1949; M in Philosophy, Oxford (Eng.) U., 1955. Economist Rand Corp., Santa Monica, Calif., 1950-61, pres., 1967-72; dep. asst. sec. internat. security affairs Dept. Def., Washington, 1961-64; asst. dir. Bur. Budget, Washington, 1965-66; prof. pub. policy Stanford (Calif.) U., 1972—, dir. pub. policy program, 1972-75; sr. fellow Hoover Inst., Stanford, Calif., 1983—; Edwin B. Rust prof. pub. policy Stanford (Calif.) U., 1986—; asst. sec. internat. security affairs Dept. Def., Washington, 1989-91; chmn. nat. intelligence coun. CIA, Washington, 1981-83. Author: (with R. Imai) Nuclear Energy and Nuclear Proliferation, 1980; (with C. Wolf Jr.) The Future of the Soviet Empire, 1987; editor: Options for U.S. Energy Policy, 1977, (with C. Wolf Jr.) The Impoverished Super power, 1990; contbr. numerous articles to profl. jours. Chmn. chief naval ops. exec. panel USN, Washington, 1972-81, mem., 1983-89, 91-93; mem. def. sci. bd. Dept. Def., Washington, 1983-89, chmn. Def. Policy Bd., 1991-94. With USN, 1943-46, PTO. Mem. Internat. Inst. Strategic Studies. Republican. Roman Catholic. Office: Stanford U Grad Sch Bus 350 Memorial Way Stanford CA 94305-5015

ROWEN, MARSHALL, radiologist; b. Chgo.; s. Harry and Dorothy (Kasnow) R.; m. Helen Lee Friedman, Apr. 5, 1952; children: Eric, Scott, Mark. AB in Chemistry with highest honors, U. Ill., Urbana, 1951; MD with honors, U. Ill., Chgo., 1954, MS in Internal Medicine, 1954. Diplomate Am. Bd. Radiology. Intern Long Beach (Calif.) VA Hosp., 1955; resident in radiology Los Angeles VA Hosp., 1955-58; practice medicine specializing in radiology Orange, Calif., 1960—; chmn. bd. dirs. Moran, Rowen and Dorsey, Inc., Radiologists, 1969—; asst. radiologist L.A. Children's Hosp., 1958; assoc. radiologist Valley Presbyn. Hosp., Van Nuys, Calif., 1960; dir. dept. radiology St. Joseph Hosp., Orange, 1961—, v.p. staff, 1972; dir. dept. radiology Children's Hosp. Orange County, 1964—, chief staff, 1977-78, v.p., 1978-83; asst. clin. prof. radiology U. Calif., Irvine, 1967-70, assoc. clin. prof., 1979-72, clin. prof. radiology and pediatrics, 1976-95, pres. clin faculty assn., 1980-81, v.p., trustee Children's Hosp. Orange County, 1990-91, 1992-95; trustee Choc. Padrinos; sec. Choco Health Svcs., 1987-89, v.p., 1990-93, trustee, 1995—; trustee Found. Med. Care Orange County, 1972-76, Calif. Commn. Adminstrn. Svcs. Hosp., 1975-79, Profl. Practice Systems, 1990-92, Med. Specialty Mgrs., 1990-95, St. Joseph Med. Corp., 1993-95; v.p. Found Med. Care Children's Hosp., 1988-89; v.p., bd. dirs. St. Joseph Med. Corp. IPA; bd. dirs Orange Coast Managed Care Svcs., 1995, Paragon Med. Imaging, 1993-95, Calif. Med. Imaging, 1994-95. Mem. editorial bd. Western Jour. Medicine; contbr. articles to med. jours. Founder Orange County Performing Arts Ctr., mem. Laguna Art Mus., Laguna Festival of Arts, Opera Pacific, S. Coast Repertory, Am. Ballet Theater, World Affairs Council. Served to capt. M.C., U.S. Army, 1958-60. Recipient Rea sr. med. prize U. Ill, 1953; William Cook scholar U. Ill., 1951. Fellow Am. Coll. Radiology; mem. AMA, Am. Heart Assn., Soc. Nuclear Medicine (trustee 1961-62), Orange County Radiol. Soc. (pres. 1968-69), Calif. Radiol. Soc. (pres. 1978-79), Radiol. Soc. So. Calif. (pres. 1976), Pacific Coast Pediatric Radiologists Assn. (pres. 1971), Soc. Pediatric Radiology, Calif. Med. Assn. (chmn. sect. on radiology 1978-79), Orange County Med. Assn. (chmn. UCI liason com. 1976-78), Cardioradiology Soc. So. Calif., Radiol. Soc. N.Am., Am. Roentgen Ray Soc., Am. Coll. Physician Execs., Soc. Chmn. Radiologists Children Hosp., Rams Booster Club, Center Club, Sequoia Athletic Club, Phi Beta Kappa, Phi Eta Sigma, Omega Beta Phi, Alpha Omega Alpha. Office: 1201 W La Veta Ave Orange CA 92668-4213

ROWEN, ROBERT G., savings and loan executive. Pres., CEO Bell Bancorp. Office: Bell Bancorp Inc 79 W Monroe St Chicago IL 60603

ROWEN, RUTH HALLE, musicologist, educator; b. N.Y.C., Apr. 5, 1918; d. Louis and Ethel (Fried) Halle; m. Seymour M. Rowen, Oct. 13, 1940; children: Mary Helen Rowen, Louis Halle Rowen. B.A., Barnard Coll., 1939; M.A., Columbia U., 1941, Ph.D., 1948. Mgmt. ednl. dept. Carl Fischer, Inc., N.Y.C., 1954-63; assoc. prof. musicology CUNY, 1967-72, prof., 1972—, mem. doctoral faculty in musicology, 1967—. Author: Early Chamber Music, 1948, reprinted, 1974; (with Adele T. Katz) Hearing-Gateway to Music, 1959, (with William Simon) Jolly Come Sing and Play, 1956, Music Through Sources and Documents, 1979, (with Mary Rowen) Instant Piano, 1979, 80, 83; contbr. articles to profl. jours. Mem. ASCAP, Am. Musicol. Soc., Music Library Assn., Coll. Music Soc., Nat. Fedn. Music Clubs (nat. musicianship chmn. 1962-74, nat. young artist auditions com. 1964-74, N.Y. state chmn. Young Artist Auditions 1981, dist. coord. 1983, nat. bd. dirs. 1989—, rep. UN 1991—), N.Y. Fedn. Music Clubs (pres.), Phi Beta Kappa. Home: 115 Central Park W New York NY 10023-4153 *Opportunity grows with each constructive thought.*

ROWLAND, ARTHUR RAY, librarian; b. Hampton, Ga., Jan. 6, 1930; s. Arthur and Jennie (Goodman) R.; m. Jane Thomas, July 1, 1955; children: Dell Ruth, Anna Jane. A.B., Mercer U., Macon, Ga., 1951; M. Librarianship, Emory U., 1952. Circulation asst. Ga. State Coll. Library, 1952, circulation librarian, 1952-53; librarian Armstrong Coll., Savannah, Ga., 1954-56; head circulation dept. Auburn U. Library, 1956-58; librarian, assoc. prof. library sci. Jacksonville U., 1958-61; librarian, asso. prof. library sci. Augusta Coll., 1961-76, prof., libr., 1976-91, libr. emeritus, 1991—; lectr. libr. edn. U. Ga., 1962-66; trustee Augusta-Richmond County Pub. Libr., 1980-93, pres. bd. trustees, 1983-85, v.p. bd., 1988-91; trustee Augusta Regional Libr., chmn., 1984-85; trustee East Cen. Ga. Regional Libr., 1987-93, chmn., 1988-91; chmn. Gov.'s Conf. on Ga. Librs. and Info. Sci., 1977; del. White House Conf. on Librs. and Info. Sci., 1979; cons. on libr. mgmt. to Govt. of Indonesia, 1986. Author: Bibliography of the Writings of Georgia History, 1966, A Guide to the Study of Augusta and Richmond County, Georgia, 1967, (with Helen Callahan) Yesterday's Augusta, 1976, (with James E. Dorsey) A Bibliography of the Writings on Georgia History 1900-1970, rev. edit., 1978, (with Marguerite F. Fogleman) Reese Library Genealogical Resources, 1988, supplement, 1990, Goodman Cousins, 1988, Rowland Cousins, 1990, New Guide to the Study of Augusta, 1990, Index to City Directory of Augusta, Georgia, 1841-1879, 1991, More Goodman Cousins, 1993, My Fair Grandmother: The Huguenots, Connecting DeVeaux, Fair, Bessent and Rowland Families, 1994, Distant Cousing, The Huguenots Connecting Rowland, Bulloch, de Bourdeaux, DeVeaux and Roosevelt Families of S.C., N.C. and Ga., 1995, The Bessent Family of Georgia, 1995; editor: Reference Services, 1964, Historical Markers of Richmond County, Georgia, rev. edit., 1971, The Catalog and Cataloging, 1969, The Librarian and Reference Service, 1977, Reminiscences of Joseph B. Cumming, 1893-1983, an Oral History, 1983, Reminiscences of Augusta Marines, 1985; supervising editor (with Heard Robertson) Jour. Archibald Campbell, 1981; contbr. to profl. jours. V.p. Ga. Libr. Assn. Trustees and Friends, 1989-91. With USN, 1948-49. Recipient Nix-Jones award for disting. service Ga. Library Assn., 1981, Town and Gown award Augusta Coll. Alumni Assn., 1985. Mem. ALA, Am. Assn. State and Local History, Bibliog. Soc. Am., Southeastern Libr. Assn. (hon. life, exec. bd. 1971-72), Ga. Libr. Assn. (hon. life, 2d v.p. 1965-67, 71-73, 1st v.p., pres.-elect 1973-75, pres. 1975-77, chmn. budget com. 1977-79, adv. to pres. 1979-83, 85-92), Ctrl. Savannah River Area Libr. Assn. (past pres., editor union list of serials 1967), Duval County Libr. Assn. (past v.p.), Nat. Geneal. Soc., Ga. Geneal. Soc., N.C. Geneal. Soc., Va. Geneal. Soc., Augusta Geneal. Soc., Richmond County Hist. Soc. (curator 1964-91, pres. 1967-69, founder, editor Richmond County History), Ga. Hist. Soc. (curator emeritus), Ga. Bapt. Hist. Soc., Nat., Young Men's Libr. Assn. (v.p. 1988-91), Ga. Trusts for Hist. Preservation, Hist. Augusta (trustee emeritus), Soc. Ga. Archivists, Kappa Phi Kappa. Baptist. Address: One Seventh St Ste 603 Augusta GA 30901

ROWLAND, DAVID JACK, college chancellor; b. Columbus, Ohio, June 17, 1921; s. David Henry and Ethel (Ryan) R.; m. Mary Ellen Stinson, Apr. 8, 1944; children: David Allen, Ryan Stinson, Sue Ellen Rowland Summers. BS, Ohio U., 1949; MA, Ala., 1951; LittD (hon.), Athens State Coll., 1967; LLD (hon.), Jacksonville State U., 1969. Pres. Walker Coll., Jasper, Ala., 1956-88, chancellor, 1988—; bd. dirs. First Nat. Bank, Jasper, first Comml. Bancshares, Birmingham, Ala.; chmn. Ala. ACT Bd., Tuscaloosa, 1968—; real estate developer. Chmn. Jasper Indsl. Bd., 1987—; commr. Ala. Mining Commn., Jasper, 1976—; mem. Ala. Employer Guard Res. Commn., Birmingham, 1988—; trustee Walker Coll.; mem. adv. bd. Jasper Salvation Army. Col. U.S. Army, 1942-46, ATO. Decorated Legion of Merit; recipient Silver Beaver award Boy Scouts Am., 1972. Mem. Res. Officers Assn. (pres. Jasper chpt.), Summit Club, Met. Dinner Club, Rotary (pres. Jasper 1967-68, Paul Harris fellow), Masons. Avocations: tree farmer, growing Christmas trees, wildfowl carver. Home: 1005 Valley Rd Jasper AL 35501-4964 Office: Walker Coll Office of Chancellor Jasper AL 35501

ROWLAND, DOYLE ALFRED, federal judge; b. Northville, Mich., May 22, 1938; s. Doyle Vernal and Georgiana (Britcher) R.; m. Carol Ann Fritz, July 26, 1964; children: Doyle Andrew, Matthew Mark. BS, Ea. Mich. U., 1965; JD, Detroit Coll., 1967. Bar: Mich. 1968, U.S. Dist. Ct. (ea. dist.) Mich. 1968, U.S. Dist. Ct. (we. dist.) Mich. 1984. Asst. city atty. City of Midland, Mich., 1967-69; friend of the ct. Midland County, Mich., 1969-72; ptnr. Whittaker & Rowland, Midland, 1969-77; pros. atty. Midland County, 1977-81; pvt. practice Midland, 1981-84; U.S. magistrate judge Western Dist. Mich., Kalamazoo, 1984—. Mem. Midland County Bar Assn. (pres. 1978-79), Kalamazoo County Bar Assn. Office: US Dist Ct We Dist Mich 410 W Michigan Ave Kalamazoo MI 49007-3746

ROWLAND, ESTHER E(DELMAN), college dean; b. N.Y.C., Apr. 12, 1926; d. Abraham Simon and Ida Sarah (Shifrin) Edelman; m. Lewis P. Rowland, Aug. 31, 1952; children: Andrew, Steven, Judith. B.A., U. Wis., 1946; M.A., Columbia U., 1948, M.Phil., 1984. Instr. in polit. sci. CCNY, 1947-51. Mt. Holyoke Coll., South Hadley, Mass., 1948-49; dir. health professions adv. bd. U. Pa., Phila., 1971-73; adviser to pre-profl. students Barnard Coll., N.Y.C., 1974-79, dean for pre-profl. students, 1980-93, assoc.

dean studies, 1989—. Mem. exec. com. Nat. Emergency Civil Liberties Com., N.Y.C., 1975-90; mem. exec. com. Women's Counseling Project, 1981-86. Mem. N.E. Assn. Health Professions Advisers (exec. com. 1973-74), N.E. Assn. Pre Law Advisors (exec. com. 1981-83, 85-86), Neurol. Inst. Aux. Home: 404 Riverside Dr New York NY 10025-1861 Office: Barnard Coll New York NY 10027

ROWLAND, FRANK SHERWOOD, chemistry educator; b. Delaware, Ohio, June 28, 1927; m. Joan Lundberg, 1952; children: Ingrid Drake, Jeffrey Sherwood. AB, Ohio Wesleyan U., 1948; MS, U. Chgo., 1951, PhD, 1952, DSc (hon.), 1989; DSc (hon.), Duke U., 1989, Whittier Coll., 1989, Princeton U., 1990, Haverford Coll., 1992; LLD (hon.), Ohio Wesleyan U., 1989, Simon Fraser U., 1991. Instr. chemistry Princeton (N.J.) U., 1952-56; asst. prof. chemistry U. Kans., 1956-58, assoc. prof. chemistry, 1958-63, prof. chemistry, 1963-64; prof. chemistry U. Calif., Irvine, 1964—, dept. chmn., 1964-70, Aldrich prof. chemistry, 1985-89, Bren prof. chemistry, 1989-94, Bren rsch. prof., 1994—; Humboldt sr. scientist, Fed. Republic of Germany, 1981; chmn. Dahlem (Fed. Republic of Germany) Conf. on Changing Atmosphere, 1987; vis. scientist Japan Soc. for Promotion Sci., 1980; co-dir. western region Nat. Inst. Global Environ. Changes, 1989-93; del. Internat. Coun. Sci. Unions, 1993—; fgn. sec. NAS, 1994—; lectr., cons. in field. Contbr. numerous articles to profl. jours. Mem. ozone commn. Internat. Assn. Meteorology and Atmospheric Physics, 1980-88, mem. commn. on atmospheric chemistry and global pollution, 1979-91; mem. acid rain peer rev. panel U.S. Office of Sci. and Tech., Exec. Office of White House, 1982-84; mem. vis. com. Max Planck Insts., Heidelberg and Mainz, Fed. Republic Germany, 1982—; ozone trends panel mem. NASA, 1986-88; chmn. Gordon Conf. Environ. Scis.-Air, 1987; mem. Calif. Coun. Sci. Tech., 1989—, Exec. Com. Tyler Prize, 1992—. Recipient numerous awards including John Wiley Jones award Rochester Inst. of Tech., 1975, Disting. Faculty Rsch. award U. Calif., Irvine, 1976, Profl. Achievement award U. Chgo., 1977, Billard award N.Y. Acad. Sci., 1977, Tyler World Prize in Environment Achievement, 1983, Global 500 Roll of Honor for Environ. Achievement UN Environment Program, 1988, Dana award for Pioneering Achievements in Health, 1987, Silver medal Royal Inst. Chemistry, U.K., 1989, Wadsworth award N.Y. State Dept. Health, 1989, medal U. Calif., Irvine, 1989, Japan prize in Environ. Sci., 1989, Dickson prize Carnegie-Mellon U., 1991; Guggenheim fellow, 1962, 74, Albert Einstein prize of World Cultural Coun., 1994. Fellow AAAS (pres. elect 1991, pres. 1992, chmn. bd. dirs. 1993), Am. Phys. Soc. (Leo Szilard award for Physics in Pub. Interest 1979), Am. Geophys. Union (Roger Revelle medal 1994); mem. NAS (bd. environ. studies and toxicology 1986-91, com. on atmospheric chemistry 1987-89, com. atmospheric scis., solar-terrestrial com. 1979-83, co-DATA com. 1977-82, sci. com. on problems environment 1986-89, Infinite Voyage film com. 1988-92, Robertson Meml. lectr. 1993, chmn. com. on internat. orgns. and programs 1993—), Am. Acad. Arts and Scis. (chmn. office of internat. affairs 1994—), Am. Chem. Soc. (chmn. div. nuclear sci. and tech. 1973-74, chmn. div. phys. chemistry 1974-75, Tolman medal 1976, Zimmermann award 1980, E.F. Smith lectureship 1980, Environ. Sci. and Tech. award 1983, Esselen award 1987, Peter Debye Physical Chem. award 1993), German Am. Acad. Coun. Home: 4807 Dorchester Rd Corona Del Mar CA 92625-2718 Office: U Calif Irvine Dept of Chemistry 571 PS1 Irvine CA 92717

ROWLAND, HERBERT LESLIE, public relations executive; b. N.Y.C., Dec. 4, 1925; s. I. Martin and Matilda (Appelbaum) R.; m. Joan Feldman, Apr. 9, 1949 (div. 1970); children: Russell Lloyd, Daryl Verne, Julie Anne; m. Patricia Dickson George, Nov. 9, 1985. BS, CCNY, 1948; MA, Columbia U., 1951. Corr. N.Y. Times, 1949-50; editor Where mag., also TV Week mag., 1951-53; gen. mgr. Roger Brown, Inc., N.Y.C., 1954-56; ptnr. Brown & Rowland, N.Y.C., 1957-60; pres. Rowland Co., N.Y.C., 1961-88; chmn., chief exec. officer Rowland Worldwide, Inc., N.Y.C., 1988—. With USAAF, 1944-46. Mem. Pub. Rels. Soc. Am. Home: 1080 5th Ave New York NY 10128-0102 Office: Rowland Worldwide 200 E 33rd St Apt 21J New York NY 10016-4830

ROWLAND, HOWARD RAY, mass communications educator; b. Eddy County, N.Mex., Sept. 9, 1929; s. Lewis Marion and Ursula Lorene (Hunt) R.; m. Meredith June Lee, Apr. 19, 1951; children: Runay Ilene Smith, Rhonda Lee Fisher. B in Journalism, U. Mo., 1950; MS in Journalism, So. Ill. U., 1959; PhD, Mich. State U., 1969. Feature writer Springfield (Mo.) Newspapers, Inc., 1954; newspaper editor Monett (Mo.) Times, 1954-55; editorial writer So. Ill. U., Carbondale, 1955-59; pub. rels. dir. St. Cloud (Minn.) State U., 1959-86, asst. dean, 1986-87, 88-90; dir. Ctr. for British Studies, Alnwick, Eng., 1987-88, 90-91; adj. prof. Mass Comms., St. Cloud State U., 1986—; cons. Conf. of Campus Ombudsmen, Berkeley, 1971; recorder Seminar on Fund Raising, Washington, 1985; bibliographer Higher Edn. Bibliography Yearbook, 1987. Author: American Students in Alnwick Castle, 1990, St. Cloud State University--125 Years, 1994; editor: Effective Community Relations, 1980; sect. editor: Handbook of Institutional Advancement, 1986; author book revs. Chair All-Am. City Com., St. Cloud, 1973-74. With U.S. Army, 1951-53. NDEA doctoral fellowship Mich. State U., 1967-69; recipient Appreciation award Mayor of St. Cloud, 1974, Disting Svc. award Coun. for Advancement and Support of Edn., 1985. Mem. Soc. of Profl. Journalists (Minn. chpt. pres. 1963-64, dep. dir. 1965-67), Coun. for Advancement and Support of Edn. (dist. 5 chair 1977-79, Leadership award 1979), Rotary Internat., Phi Delta Kappa (Mich. State U. chpt. pres. 1968-69, St. Cloud State Univ. chpt. pres. 1978-79). Presbyterian. Avocations: writing, fishing, travel, photography, antiques. Home: 29467 Kraemer Lake Rd Saint Joseph MN 56374

ROWLAND, JAMES RICHARD, electrical engineering educator; b. Muldrow, Okla., Jan. 24, 1940; s. Richard Cleveland and Imogene Beatrice (Angel) R.; m. Joan Il Condren, Aug. 24, 1963 (dec. May 1991); children: Jennifer Lynn, Angela Janel; m. Mary Anderson, Jan. 2, 1995. BSEE, Okla. State U., 1962; MSEE, Purdue U., 1964, PhD in Elec. Engring., 1966. Registered profl. engr., Okla. Instr. Purdue U., West Lafayette, Ind., 1964-65; from asst. to assoc. prof. Ga. Inst. Tech., Atlanta, 1966-71; from assoc. to full prof. Okla. State U., Stillwater, 1971-85; prof., chmn. dept. elec. and computer engring. U. Kans., Lawrence, 1985-89, prof., 1985—; cons. Lockheed-Ga. Co., Marietta, 1966-71, U.S. Army Missile Command, Huntsville, Ala., 1969-79, Sandia Nat. Labs., Albuquerque, 1979, Puritan-Bennett, Lenexa, Kans., 1992. Author: Linear Control Systems, 1986; mem. editorial adv. bd. Computer and Elec. Engring., 1971—; co-contbr. 50 articles to profl. jours. Fellow IEEE (edn. soc. pres. 1982-83, Centennial medal 1984, edn. soc. Achievement award 1986, edn. conf. award 1988), Am. Soc. Engring. Edn. (dir. grad. div. 1987-89), Eta Kappa Nu (dir. 1989-910. Republican. Methodist. Lodge: Kiwanis. Avocations: golf, gardening. Home: 2424 Free State Ct Lawrence KS 66047-2831 Office: U Kans Dept Elec Engring & Computer Sci 1013 Learned Hall Lawrence KS 66045-2228

ROWLAND, JAN BROWNSTEIN, marketing statistician; m. James R. Rowland. BS in Math., Psychology, U. Pitts., 1980, PhD in Epidemiology, 1984; postgrad. in mktg., NYU, 1989. Biostatistician Revlon Health Care Group, Tarrytown, N.Y., 1984-85; policy analyst Empire Blue Cross and Blue Shield, N.Y.C., 1985-86; v.p. mktg. statistics Citibank, N.A., N.Y.C., 1986-90; v.p. quantitative svcs. AIG Mktg. Systems, N.Y.C., 1990-91; dir. analytic svcs. Dun & Bradstreet Info. Svcs., Parsippany, N.J., 1991—; appointed cons. U.S. Congress task force studying impact of office automation on quality of work life, 1984. NSF grantee, 1981-84. Mem. Am. Statis. Assn., Am. Mktg. Assn. Office: Dun & Bradstreet 3 Sylvan Way Parsippany NJ 07054-3805

ROWLAND, JOHN ARTHUR, lawyer; b. Joliet, Ill., Mar. 6, 1943; s. John Fornof and Grace Ada (Baskerville) R.; m. Lana D. Lee, Sept. 8, 1984; children: Sean B., Keira L. B.A., U. Notre Dame, 1965; J.D., U. San Francisco, 1968. Bar: Calif. 1969, U.S. Dist. Ct. 1982. U.S. Dist. asst. dist. atty. San Francisco Dist. Atty.'s Office, 1971-82; assoc. Ropers, Majeski, Kohn and Bentley, San Francisco, 1982—, ptnr., 1985—. Pres., South of Market Boys, San Francisco, 1981; bd. dirs. Former San Francisco Asst. Dist. Attys., 1984. Served to capt. U.S. Army, 1969-71, Korea. Recipient Commendation San Francisco Bd. Suprs., 1981, Merit award Mayor of San Francisco, 1982. Roman Catholic. Office: 670 Howard St San Francisco CA 94105-3916

ROWLAND, JOHN G., governor, former congressman; b. Waterbury, Conn., May 24, 1957; s. Sherwood L. and Florence (Jackson) R.; m.

Deborah Nabhan; children: Kirsten Elizabeth, Robert John, Julianne Marie. B.S. in Bus. Adminstrn., Villanova U., 1979. Former mem. Conn. Ho. of Reps.; mem. 99th-101st Congress from 5th Conn. dist., 1985-91; governor Conn., 1995—; pres. Rowland Assocs. Ambassador, St. Mary's Hosp., Waterbury; bd. dirs. Am. Cancer Soc., Waterbury. Recipient Disting. Service award VFW, Holy Cross Alumni Assn. Republican. Home: 654 South St Middlebury CT 06762-3505 Office: US Ho of Reps 654 South St House Office Bldg Middlebury CT 06762

ROWLAND, LANDON HILL, diversified holding company executive; b. Fuquay Springs, N.C., May 20, 1937; s. Walter Elton and Elizabeth Carr (Williams) R.; m. Sarah Fidler, Dec. 29, 1959; children: Sarah Elizabeth, Matthew Hill, Joshua Carr. B.A., Dartmouth Coll., 1959; LL.B., Harvard U., 1962. Bar: Mo. Assoc. Watson, Ess, Marshall & Enggas, Kansas City, Mo., 1962-70; ptnr. Watson, Ess, Marshall & Enggas, 1970-80; v.p. Kansas City So. Industries, Inc., 1980-83, pres., chief oper. officer, 1983-86, pres., chief exec. officer, 1987—, also bd. dirs.; exec. officer Kansas City So. Ry. Co., 1990-91, chmn., 1990—; lectr. antitrust law U. Mo. Kansas City; chmn. DST Systems, 1983—. Co-author West's Mo. Practice Series. Trustee Midwest Rsch. Inst., Kansas City, Mo.; chmn. bd. dirs. Swope Ridge Health Care Ctr.; bd. dirs. Lyric Opera of Kansas City, Am. Royal, Jacob L. & Ella C. Loose Found.; chmn. Met. Performing Arts Fund. Mem. ABA, Mo. Bar Assn., Phi Beta Kappa. Clubs: Kansas City Country, Kansas City, River. Home: Ever Glades Farm 12717 NE Mt Olivet Rd Kansas City MO 64166-1236 Office: Kans City So Industries Inc 114 W 11th St Kansas City MO 64105-1804*

ROWLAND, LEWIS PHILLIP, neurologist, medical editor, educator; b. Bklyn., Aug. 3, 1925; s. Henry Alexander and Cecile (Coles) R.; m. Esther Edelman, Aug. 31, 1952; children: Andrew Simon, Steven Samuel, Joy Rosenthal. B.S., Yale U., 1945, M.D., 1948; hon. doctorate, U. Aix-Marseilles, France, 1986. Diplomate: Am. Bd. Psychiatry and Neurology. Intern New Haven Hosp., 1949-50; asst. resident N.Y. Neurol. Inst., 1950-52, fellow, 1953; clin. assoc. NIH, Bethesda, Md., 1953-54; practice research medicine, specializing in neurology N.Y.C., 1954-67, Phila., 1967-73, N.Y.C., 1973—; asst. neurologist Montefiore Hosp., N.Y.C., 1954-57; vis. fellow Nat. Inst. Med. Research, London, 1956; from asst. prof. to prof. neurology Columbia Coll. Physicians and Surgeons, 1957-67, prof., chmn. dept. neurology, 1973—; prof., chmn. dept. neurology U. Pa., Med. Sch., 1967-73; from asst. neurologist to attending neurologist Presbyn. Hosp., 1957-67; co-dir. Neurol. Clin. Research Center, 1961-67, dir. neurology service, 1973—, pres. med. bd., 1991-94; cons. Harlem Hosp., 1973—; mem. med. adv. bd. Myasthenia Gravis Found., pres., 1971-73; med. adv. bd. Muscular Dystrophy Assocs., Nat. Multiple Sclerosis Soc., Com. to Combat Huntington's Disease; pres. Parkinson's Disease Found., 1979—; mem. tng. grants com. Nat. Inst. Neurol. Diseases and Stroke, NIH, 1971-73, bd. sci. counselors, 1978-83, chmn., 1981-83, nat. adv. council, 1986-90. Editorial bd.: Archives of Neurology, 1968-76, Advances in Neurology, 1969—, Italian Jour. Neurol. Sci., 1979—, Handbook of Clin. Neurology, 1982—, New England Jour. Medicine, 1990—, Medical Letter, 1990—, Jour. Neurol. Sci., 1991—, Jour. Neuromuscular Disorders, 1991—; editor-in-chief: Neurology, 1977-87. Served with USNR, 1942-44; with USPHS, 1953-54. Mem. Am. Neurol. Assn. (pres. 1980, hon. mem. 1989—), Am. Acad. Neurology (pres.-elect 1987-89, pres. 1989-91), Phila. Neurol. Soc. (pres. 1972), Assn. Research Nervous Mental Disease (mem. pres. trustee 1976—, v.p. 1980, chmn. bd. trustees 1992—), Assn. Univ. Profs. Neurology (sec. 1971-74, pres. 1978), Eastern Pa. Multiple Sclerosis Soc. (chmn. med. adv. bd. 1969-73); hon. mem. Neurol. Socs. France, Poland, Can., Europe, Italy, Gt. Britain, Spain, Japan; mem. N.Y.C. Multiple Sclerosis Soc. (chmn. med. adv. bd. 1977-92). Home: 404 Riverside Dr New York NY 10025-1861 Office: Columbia-Presbyn Med Ctr Neurological Inst 710 W 168th St New York NY 10032-2699

ROWLAND, RALPH THOMAS, architect; b. Elizabeth, N.J., Oct. 10, 1920; s. Thomas Aloysius and Anna Frances (McQuaid) R.; m. Bernice Barbara Cannizzo, Sept. 7, 1946; children: Glenn Thomas, Mark Louis, Roy Joseph, Lisa Mary. Student, Manhattan Coll., 1937-38, Columbia U., 1945-49. Archtl. field supr., specifier Voorhees Walker Foley & Smith, N.Y.C., 1945-50; specifier, project mgr. Sargent Webster Crenshaw & Folley, Watertown, N.Y., 1951-53; individual archtl. practice Hamden, Conn., 1958-65; field supr. Fletcher Thompson, Inc., Bridgeport, Conn., 1954-56; project mgr. Fletcher Thompson, Inc., 1957, 65-73, asso., 1969-73, v.p., 1973-81, dir. archtl. research, 1981-85, also dir., 1973-93; cons. Cheshire, Conn., 1981—; chmn. Conn. Bldg. Code Standards Com., 1978-82; vice chmn. Conn. State Codes and Standards Com., 1982-86. Editorial chmn.: Conn. Architect Mag., 1966-74; project mgr. design, St. Vincents Med. Center, Bridgeport. Mem. Cheshire Planning Commn., 1966-72, chmn., 1967-68; pres. Hamden C. of C., 1964, New Eng. Bldg. Code Com., 1989; mem. Cen. Naugatuck Valley Regional Planning Agy., 1966-74, chmn., 1969; mem. Cheshire Democratic Town Com., 1960-70, treas., 1963-69; mem. Conn. Archtl. Sch. Task Force, 1987-88. With USN, 1942-45. Fellow AIA; mem. AIA Conn. (past pres.), AARP (pres. Cheshire chpt. 1995), Bridgeport Assn. Architects (past sec.), Bldg. Ofcls. and Code Adminstrs. Internat., Conn. Bldg. Ofcls. Assn., Cheshire C. of C. Roman Catholic. Home and Office: 201 N Rolling Acres Rd Cheshire CT 06410-2119

ROWLAND, ROBERT E., secondary school principal. Prin. Danville (Ky.) High Sch. Recipient Blue Ribbon award U.S. Dept. Edn., 1990-91. Office: Danville High Sch 203 E Lexington Ave Danville KY 40422

ROWLAND, RONALD LEE, lawyer; b. Columbus, Ohio, Nov. 15, 1947; s. Charles Lossie and Beatrice Gertrude (Lachell) R.; m. Barbara Ann Baird, Mar. 21, 1970; children: Tracy Michelle, Andrew Tyler, Jennifer Kay. B.A., Wittenberg U., 1969; J.D., Ohio State U., 1972; LL.M. in Taxation, U. Fla., 1976. Bar: Ohio 1972, Fla. 1973. Atty., ptnr. Vorys, Sater, Seymour & Pease, Columbus, 1976—; adj. prof. Capital U. Law Sch., Columbus, 1981, 82, 87-90, Grad. Tax Program, 1985-86; chmn. tax com. Ohio Oil and Gas Assn., 1985-93; mem. exec. com. Ohio Small Bus. and Entrepreneurship Coun., 1991—; chmn. Columbus Investment Interest Group, 1993—; trustee, sec. Indsl. and Tech. Coun., 1993—. Contbr. papers to confs. Past pres. devel. bd. Children's Hosp., Columbus, 1983-84; trustee Worthington Hills Civic Assn., Ohio, 1983-85. Lt. JAGC, USN, 1972-75. Mem. ABA (partnership taxation com. tax sect.), Fla. Bar, Ohio State Bar Assn., Columbus Bar Assn. (chmn. tax com. 1981-83, chmn. Columbus tax conf. 1983-84), Ind. Petroleum Assn. Am. (tax com.), Worthington Hills Country Club, Athletic Club of Columbus. Roman Catholic. Home: 821 Old Woods Rd West Worthington OH 43235-1248 Office: Vorys Sater Seymour & Pease PO Box 1008 52 E Gay St Columbus OH 43215-3161

ROWLAND, (JAMES) ROY, congressman; b. Wrightsville, GA, Feb. 3, 1926; s. J. Roy and Jerradine Z.; m. Luella Price, July 28, 1924; children: Lou Rowland Neal, Jane, Jim. Student, Emory U., 1943, South Ga. Coll., 1946, U. Ga., 1946-48; M.D. Med. Coll. Ga., 1952. Intern Macon Hosp., Ga., 1952-53, resident in family practice, 1953-54; practice medicine specializing in family practice Dublin, Ga., 1954-82; state rep. Ga. Ho. of Reps., Atlanta, 1976-82; mem. 98th-103rd Congresses from 8th Ga. Dist., 1983—; mem. Energy, Commerce com., subcom. Health and Environ., veteran's affairs com., subcom. hosp. and health care, oversight and investigations, house Dem. steering and policy com. Served with U.S. Army, 1944-46, ETO. Decorated Bronze Star. Democrat. Methodist. Office: Ste 950 1455 Pennsylvania Ave NW Washington DC 20004

ROWLAND, THEODORE JUSTIN, physicist, educator; b. Cleve., May 15, 1927; s. Thurston Justin and Lillian (Nesser) R.; m. Janet Claire Millar, June 28, 1952 (div. 1967); children: Theodore Justin, Dawson Ann, Claire Miliar; m. Patsy Marie Beard, Aug. 21, 1968. BS, Western Res. U., 1948; MA, Harvard U., 1949, PhD, 1954. Rsch. physicist Union Carbide Metals Co., Niagara Falls, N.Y., 1954-61; prof. phys. metallurgy U. Ill., 1961-92, asst. dean Coll. Engring., acting assoc. dean Grad. Coll., 1990-91, prof. emeritus, 1992—; cons. dir. Materials Cons., Inc.; cons. physicist, 1961—; cons. metallurgist, 1976—. Editor 2 books; author monograph; contbr. articles to profl. jours. Fellow Am. Phys. Soc.; mem. AIME, AAAS, AAUP (pres. U. Ill. chpt.), Phi Beta Kappa, Sigma Xi. Achievements include initial verification of charge density waves in dilute alloys; original contributions to theory and experiment in nuclear magnetic resonance in metals. Home: 805

Park Lane Dr Champaign IL 61820-7613 Office: U Ill Dept Materials Sci and Engring 1304 W Green St Urbana IL 61801-2920

ROWLAND, THOMAS WILLIAM, lawyer, sugar company executive; b. Berkeley, Calif., Dec. 6, 1948; s. Thomas Hunter and Anna Caroline (Rasmussen) R.; m. Carolyn Clark, August 19, 1972; children: Heather, Melissa, Jennifer. AB, U. Calif., Berkeley, 1971; JD, Columbia U., 1975. Bar: Calif. 1975. Assoc. McCutchen, Doyle, Brown & Enersen, San Francisco, 1975-78; atty. Calif. and Hawaiian Sugar Co., San Francisco, 1978-82, asst. gen. counsel, 1982-85, v.p., sec., gen. counsel, 1985-90, sr. v.p., sec., gen. counsel, 1990, sr. v.p. adminstrn., gen. counsel, 1990—; bd. dirs. MLM Corp., San Francisco; corp. sec. Hawaiian Sugar Transp. Co., San Francisco and Aiea, Hawaii, 1985-90. Office: First Brands Corp Box 1911 83 Wooster Hts Danbury CT 06810-7548

ROWLANDS, DAVID THOMAS, pathology educator; b. Wilkes-Barre, Pa., Mar. 22, 1930; s. David Thomas and Anna Jule (Morgan) R.; m. Gwendolyn Marie York, Mar. 1, 1958; children: Julie Marie, Carolyn Jane. M.D., U. Pa., 1955. Diplomate: Am. Bd. Pathology, Am. Bd. Allergy and Immunology. Intern Pa. Hosp., Phila., 1955-56; resident Cin. Gen. Hosp., 1956-60; asst. prof. U. Colo., 1962-64, Rockefeller U., 1964-66; assoc. prof. Duke U., Durham, N.C., 1966-70; prof. pathology U Pa., Phila., 1970-82; chmn. dept. pathology U. Pa., 1973-78, prof. medicine, 1979-82; prof., chmn. dept. pathology U. So. Fla., Tampa, 1982-91; assoc. dean U. So. Fla., 1983-84, prof. pediatrics, 1986-91; med. dir. Lifelink Tissue Bank, 1991-93. Mem. editorial bd.: Am. Jour. Pathology, 1971-81, Developmental and Comparative Immunology, 1977-79. Served with USNR, 1960-62. Recipient Lederle Med. Faculty award U. Colo., 1964, Jacob Ehrenzeller award Pa. Hosp., 1976. Mem. Am. Assn. Pathologists, Internat. Acad. Pathology, Am. Soc. Clin. Pathology, Am. Assn. Immunologists, Coll. Am. Pathologists, Arthur Purdy Stout Soc. Presbyterian. Home: 13804 Cypress Village Cir Tampa FL 33624-4406

ROWLANDS, GENA, actress; b. Cambria, Wis., June 19, 1936; d. Edwin Merwin and Mary Allen (Neal) R.; m. John Cassavetes (dec.); children: Nicholas, Alexandra, Zoe. Student, U. Wis., Am. Acad. Dramatic Art, N.Y.C. Theatrical appearance include The Middle of the Night, 1956; films include The High Cost of Loving, 1958, Lonely Are The Brave, 1962, A Child is Waiting, 1962, Spiral Road, 1962, Faces, 1968, At Any Price, 1970, Minnie and Moscowitz, 1971, Woman Under the Influence, 1973, Two Minute Warning, 1976, Opening Night, 1977, The Brinks Job, 1978, One Summer Night, 1979, Gloria, 1980, Tempest, 1982, Love Streams, 1983, Light of Day, 1987, Another Woman, 1988, Once Around, 1990, Ted and Venus, 1991, Night on Earth, 1992; TV movies A Question of Love, 1978, Strangers, 1979, Thurday's Child, 1983, Early Frost, 1986, The Betty Ford Story, 1987, Montana, Face of a Stranger, 1991 (Emmy award, Leading Actress in a Mini-Series or Special, 1992), Parallel Lives, 1994; numerous other TV appearances. Mem. Actors Equity Assn., Screen Actors Guild, AFTRA, Am. Guild Variety Artists. •

ROWLANDS, MARVIN LLOYD, JR., publishing and communications consultant; b. Wellington, Kans., Apr. 30, 1926; s. Marvin Lloyd and Opal Mary (Pilant) R. BS in Journalism, U. Kans., 1950. Wire editor Manhattan (Kans.) Mercury, 1950-51; reporter Leavenworth (Kans.) Times, 1951-56, Topeka (Kans.) Daily Capital, 1956-57, Cin. Times-Star, 1957-58; assoc. editor The Am. Med. News, Chgo., 1958-61, mng. editor, 1961-65, editor, 1965-75; editor-in-chief Modern Healthcare, Chgo., 1975-76; editor Contemporary Surgery and Contemporary Ob/Gyn, N.Y.C., 1976-77; dir. devel. McGraw-Hill Publs. Co., N.Y.C., 1978-84, dir. planning, 1984-85, v.p. planning, 1985-86, v.p. editorial, planning and devel., 1986-88; v.p. editorial McGraw-Hill Fin. Services Co., N.Y.C., 1988-89; sr. v.p. comm. McGraw-Hill Fin. Svcs. Co., N.Y.C., 1989-90; pub., communications cons., N.Y.C., 1990-92, North Chatham, Mass., 1992—. Mem., chmn. bd. dirs. Rush Dance, A Found., Inc., N.Y.C., 1980—. Served with USNR, 1944-46. Mem. Omicron Delta Kappa. Baptist. Home and Office: PO Box 757 52 Spring Hill Rd North Chatham MA 02650

ROWLANDS, ROBERT EDWARD, engineer, educator; b. Trail, B.C., Can., July 7, 1936; s. Edward and Eda May (Randell) R.; m. Mary Roma Ranaghan, Nov. 14, 1959; children: Robert Philip, Edward Hugh. BA. Sc., U. B.C., Vancouver, 1959; MS, U. Ill., 1964, PhD, 1967. Engr. mechanics MacMillan & Bloedel, Powell River, B.C., 1959, Ill. Inst. Tech. Rsch. Inst., Chgo., 1967-74; asst. prof., engring. U. Wis., 1974-76, assoc. prof. engring., 1976-79, prof. engring., 1979—; dir. structural and materials testing lab., 1983-90; vis. scholar People's Republic China, 1983; Clark C. Heritage vis. scientist USDA Forest Products Lab., 1987; vis. scholar Gadjah Mada U., Yogyakarta, Indonesia, 1991; lectr. in field; cons. to rsch. insts., engring. orgns., instrument mfrs., ins. cos., auto, farm-implement, food processing, paper products, forestry, composite, plastics, petroleum and mining industries; expert witness law firms; internat. tech. travel, Scandanavia, Europe, U.K., Japan, Spain, Portugal, Australia, China, and former USSR. Registered profl. engr., Wis. Fellow ASME; mem. Soc. Exptl. Mechanics (mem. papers rev. com. 1967—, mem. editorial com. 1976—, book rev. editor 1976—, chmn. composite com. 1977-79, tech. chmn. 1975, also chmn. various tech. sessions, Hetényi award 1970, 76, fellow 1982, Frocht award 1989), Am. Acad. Mechanics. Author chpt. Handbook of Composite Materials, Handbook of Experimental Mechanics; contbr. over 130 articles to profl. jours. Home: 5401 Russett Rd Madison WI 53711-3564 Office: Dept Mechanical Engring U Wisc 1415 Johnson Dr Madison WI 53706-1691

ROWLANDS, T. DEWI, aerospace executive; b. North Wales, U.K., Apr. 11, 1939; came to U.S., 1970; m. Yolande Noella Stevens, Dec. 5, 1961 (dec. 1978); m. Sophia Zezanis, July 29, 1979; children—Francine A., Michael W., Carys M., Kathleen, A.S. ONC, Filton Coll. Tech, Eng., 1961; HNC, Bristol Coll. Tech., Eng., 1963. Apprentice engr. Bristol Aeroplane Co., Eng., 1956; regional sales mgr. Hawker-Siddeley, Eng., 1968-70; sales mgr., dir. com. AC Sales Brit. Aircraft Corp. U.S.A., Inc., 1970-77, v.p. ops., 1977-80, sr. v.p. 1980-81; exec. v.p. Brit. Aerospace Inc., Washington, 1981—. Vol. firefighter Vol. Firedepartment Co. 14, Fairfax County, Va., 1971-73, Co. 11, Loudoun County, Va., 1973-78, also pres., 1975, Vol. Rescue Squad Co. 15, Loudoun County, 1978-81; pres. Sterling Safety Ctr., Loudoun County, 1977-79. Named Outstanding Rescue Person Loudoun Co. WAGE Radio, 1979. Mem. Wings Club, Royal Aero. Soc. AIAA. Methodist. Home: Rte 3 Box 137 Leesburg VA 22075 Office: Brit Aerospace Inc PO Box 17414 Washington DC 20041-0414

ROWLENSON, RICHARD CHARLES, lawyer; b. Camden, N.J., Dec. 27, 1949; s. Alton Joseph and Margaret (Mietzelfeld) R.; m. Frances Ambury, July 28, 1979; children: Mary, Anne. BS, Georgetown U., 1971, JD, 1975. Bar: D.C. 1975, U.S.C. App. Appeals (D.C. cir.) 1975, U.S. Supreme Ct. 1979. Atty. Hennessey, Stambler & Siebert, Washington, 1975-87; sr. v.p., gen. counsel Vanguard Cellular Systems Inc., Greensboro, N.C., 1987—. Mem. ABA, Bar Assn. D.C., Greensboro Bar Assn., Fed. Communications Bar Assn., Sherwood Swim and Racquet Club (Greensboro). Office: Vanguard Cellular Systems 2002 Pisgah Church Rd Ste 300 Greensboro NC 27455-3314

ROWLETT, RALPH MORGAN, archaeologist, educator; b. Richmond, Ky., Sept. 11, 1934; s. Robert Kenny and Daisy (Mullikin) R.; m. Elsebet Sander-Jorgensen, Aug. 25, 1963 (div. Jan. 1986); children: Rolf Arvid, Erik Kenneth; m. Elizabeth Helen Dinan, Apr. 21, 1989; 1 child, Helen Holly. Student, U. Ky., 1952-53; BA summa cum laude, Marshall U., 1956; postgrad., U. London, 1962-63; PhD, Harvard U., 1968. Instr. anthropology U. Mo., Columbia, 1965-67, asst. prof., 1967-69, assoc. prof., 1969-75, prof., 1975—; postdoctoral fellow Ghent U., 1969. Co-author: Neolithic Levels on the Titelberg. Luxembourg, 1981; anthropology editor Random House Unabridged Dictionary of English, 1980—; editor Horizons and Styles, 1993, Horizons and Styles in West Eurasiatic Archaeology; developer thermoluminescence dating of flint, 1972; co-developer electron spin resonance dating of flint, 1981. 1st lt. arty., U.S. Army, 1956-58. Decorated officer Legion of Merit (Luxembourg); named Ky. col., 1976; grantee NSF, 1973-75, 76-79, 82-83; vis. Archeologique de Neuchatel, 1989, British Coun., 1993. Fellow Am. Anthrop. Assn.; mem. AAAS, Archaeol. Inst. Am., Soc. Am. Archaeology, Prehistory Soc., Societe Prehistorique de Luxembourg, Societe Archeologique Champenoise, English Heritage, Palomino Horse Breeders Assn. Democrat. Mem. Christian Ch. (Disciples of Christ). Home:

Hollywell Hill 1197 State Rd WW Fulton MO 65251-9805 Office: Univ Mo Dept Anthropology Columbia MO 65211

ROWLEY, BEVERLEY DAVIES, medical sociologist; b. Antioch, Calif., July 28, 1941; d. George M. and Eloise (DeWhitt) Davies; m. Richard B. Rowley, Apr. 1, 1966 (div. 1983). BS, Colo. State U., 1963; MA, U. Nev., 1975; PhD, Union Inst., 1983. Social worker Nev. Dept. Pub. Welfare, Reno, 1963-65, Santa Clara County Dept. Welfare, San Jose, Calif., 1965-66; field dir. Sierra Sage Council Camp Fire Girls, Sparks, Nev., 1966-70; program coord. div. health scis. sch. medicine U. Nev., 1976-78, program coord., health analyst office rural health, 1978-84, acting dir. office rural health, 1982-84; exec. asst. to pres. Med. Coll. of Hampton Rds., Norfolk, Va., 1984-87; rsch. mgr. Office Med. Edn. Info. AMA, Chgo., 1987-88, dir. dept. data systems, 1988-91; dir. med. edn. Maricopa Med. Ctr., Phoenix, 1992—; v.p. Med. Edn. and Rsch. Assocs., Inc., Phoenix, Chgo., 1992—; various positions as adj. prof. and lectr. in health scis. U. Nev. Sch. of Medicine, 1972-75; lectr. Dept. of Family and Community Medicine, U Nev., 1978-84, asst. dir., evaluator Health Careers for Am. Indians Programs, 1978-84; cons. Nev. Statewide Health Survey, 1979-84; interim dir. Health Max, 1985-86; asst. prof. dept. of family and community medicine Med. Coll. of Hampton Rds., Norfolk, Va., 1985-87; v.p., treas. Systems Devel. Assocs., Reno, 1981-84. Editor of five books; contbr. numerous articles to profl. jours; developer three computer systems including AMA-FREIDA. Mem. Am. Sociol. Assn., Nat. Rural Health Assn. (bd. dirs. 1986-88), Assn. Behavioral Sci. and Med. Edn. (pres. 1986), Assn. Am. Med. Colls. (exec. coun. 1993—), Coun. of Acad. Scis. (adminstrv. bd. 1992—), Delta Delta Delta. Avocations: hiking, skiing, gardening, sewing, ceramics. Office: Maricopa Med Ctr Dept Acad Affairs 2601 E Roosevelt St Phoenix AZ 85008-4973

ROWLEY, FRANK SELBY, JR., artist; b. N.Y.C., Aug. 2, 1913; s. Frank Selby and Caroline Estelle (Bremmer) R.; m. Dorothy Folger, June 30, 1942. Student, Art Students League, N.Y.C., 1934, Nassau Inst. of Art, Hempstead, N.Y., 1935-38, U. Richmond, Va., 1952. Designer, illustrator Nina Robinson Studio, Hempstead, 1938-41; designer, muralist, 1946-49; tchr. comml. art John Marshall High Sch., Richmond, 1949-57; lectr. various art orgns. 1957—; judge art exhbns., 1957—. Exhibited in group shows at Portraits Inc., N.Y.C., 1959-87, Gallery Mayo, Richmond, Va., 1975—, Va. Mus. of Fine Arts; represented in permanent collections Va. Mus. of Fine Arts, State of Va., City of Richmond, Richmond Meml. Hosp., Va. Fedn. Womens Clubs and numerous pvt. collections. Founder Richmond Concert Band, 1970; music dir., conductor Richmond Pops Band, 1977—; pres., chmn. bd. Richmond Band Assn., 1977—; vol. art tchr. Va. Home, 1989—. Sgt. U.S. Army, 1941-45. Mem. Lions. Avocations: water color painting, music. Home: 8909 Elm Rd Richmond VA 23235-1427

ROWLEY, JANET DAVISON, physician; b. N.Y.C., Apr. 5, 1925; d. Hurford Henry and Ethel Mary (Ballantyne) Davison; m. Donald A. Rowley, Dec. 18, 1948; children: Donald, David, Robert, Roger. PhB, U. Chgo., 1944, BS, 1946, MD, 1948; DSc (hon.), U. Ariz., 1989, U. Pa., 1989, Knox Coll., 1991, U. So. Calif., 1992. Cert. Am. Bd. Med. Genetics. Rsch. asst. U. Chgo., 1949-50; intern Marine Hosp., USPHS, Chgo., 1950-51; attending physician Infant Welfare and Prenatal Clinics Dept. Pub. Health, Montgomery County, Md., 1953-54; rsch. fellow Levinson Found., Cook County Hosp., Chgo., 1955-61; clin. instr. neurology U. Ill., Chgo., 1957-61; USPHS spl. trainee Radiobiology Lab. The Churchill Hosp., Oxford, Eng., 1961-62; rsch. assoc. dept. medicine and Argonne Cancer Rsch. Hosp. U. Chgo., 1962-69, assoc. prof. dept. medicine and Argonne Cancer Rsch. Hosp., 1969-77, prof. dept. medicine and Franklin McLean Meml. Rsch. Inst., 1977-84, Blum-Riese Disting. Svc. prof., dept. medicine and dept. molecular genetics and cell biology, Franklin McLean Meml. Rsch. Inst., 1984—; mem. Nat. Cancer Adv. Bd., 1979-84; bd. scientific counsellors Nat. Ctr. for Human Genome Rsch. NIH, 1994—, chmn., 1994—; mem. scientific adv. bd. Dana Farber Cancer Ctr., 1994—. Co-founder, co-editor Genes, Chromosomes and Cancer; mem. editl. bds. Oncology Rsch., Cancer Genetics and Cytogenetics, Internat. Jour. Hematology, Genomics, Internat. Jour. Cancer, Leukemia; past mem. editorial bd. Blood, Cancer Rsch., Hematol. Oncology, Leukemia Rsch.; contbr. chpts. to books., articles to profl. jours. Mem. Bd. Sci. Counsellors, Nat. Inst. Dental Rsch., NIH, 1972-76, chmn. 1974-76, Nat. Cancer Adv. Bd. Nat. Cancer Inst., 1979-84, Frederick Cancer Rsch. Facility adv.com., 1983-85, med. adv. bd. Leukemia Soc. Am., 1979-84, MIT Corp. vis. com., Dept. Applied Biol. Scis., 1983-86, selection com., scholar awards in Biomed. Sci., Lucille P. Markey Charitable Trust, 1984-87; trustee Adler Planetarium, Chgo., 1978—; bd. dirs. Am. Bd. Med. Genetics, 1982-83, Am. Bd. Human Genetics, 1985-88; bd. sci. cons. Meml. Sloan-Kettering Cancer Ctr., 1988-90; nat. adv. com. McDonnell Found. Program for Molecular Medicine in Cancer Rsch. 1988—; adv. com. Ency. Britannica, U. Chgo., 1988—; med. adv. bd. Howard Hughes Med. Inst., 1989—. Served with USPHS, 1950-51. Recipient First Kuwait Cancer prize, 1984, Esther Langer award Ann Langer Cancer Rsch. Found., 1983, A. Cressy Morrison award in natural scis. N.Y. Acad. Scis., 1985, Past State Pres.' award Tex. Fedn. Bus. and Profl. Women's Clubs, 1986, Karnofsky award and lecture Am. Soc. Clin. Oncology, 1987, prix Antoine Lacassagne Lique Nationale Francaise Contre le Cancer, 1987, King Faisal Internat. prize in medicine (co-recipient), 1988, Katherine Berkan Judd award Meml. Sloan-Kettering Cancer Ctr., 1989, (co-recipient) Charles Mott Prize Gen. Motors Cancer Rsch. Found., 1989, Steven C. Beering award U. Ind. Med. Sch., 1992, Robert de Villiers award Leukemia Soc. Am., 1993. Mem. NAS, Am. Acad. Arts and Scis., Am. Philos. Soc., Am. Soc. Human Genetics (pres.-elect 1992, pres. 1993, Allen award and lectr. 1991), Genetical Soc. (Gt. Britain), Am. Soc. Hematology (Presdl. Symposium 1982, Dameshek prize 1982), Am. Assn. Cancer Rsch. (G.H.A. Clowes Meml. award 1989), Inst. Medicine (coun. 1988-90), Sigma Xi (William Proctor prize for sci. achievement 1989). Episcopalian. Home: 5310 S University Ave Chicago IL 60615-5106 Office: U Chgo 5841 Maryland Ave NC 2115 Chicago NM 60637-1470

ROWLEY, JOHN F., manufacturing executive. Former v.p. Fort Howard Corp., Green Bay, Wis., now exec. v.p. Office: Ft Howard Corp PO Box 19130 1919 S Broadway Green Bay WI 54304-4905

ROWLEY, PETER TEMPLETON, physician, educator; b. Greenville, Pa., Apr. 29, 1929; s. George Hardy and Susan Mossman (Templeton) R.; m. Carol Stone, Mar. 19, 1967; children: Derek Stone, Jason Templeton. AB magna cum laude, Harvard U., 1951; MD, Columbia U., 1955. Diplomate: Am. Bd. Internal Medicine. Intern med. service N.Y. Hosp.-Cornell Med. Center, 1955-56; clin. assoc. Nat. Inst. Neurol. Disease and Blindness, NIH, 1956-58; asst. resident, then resident Harvard Med. Service, Boston City Hosp.; asst. in medicine Harvard U. Med. Sch. and researcher Thorndike Meml. Lab., 1958-60; hon. research asst. dept. eugenics, biometry and genetics Univ. Coll., U. London, 1960-61; postdoctoral fellow dept. microbiology NYU Sch. Medicine, 1961-63; asst. prof. medicine Stanford U., 1963-70; assoc. prof. medicine pediatrics and genetics U. Rochester, 1970-75, prof. medicine, pediatrics, genetics and microbiology, 1975—, prof. oncology, 1991—, chmn. div. genetics, 1990—; physician, pediatrician Strong Meml. Hosp., 1970—; mem. N.Y. State Exec. and Adv. Coms. on Genetic Disease, 1979—; WHO vis. scholar Inst. Biol. Chemistry, U. Ferrara, Italy, 1970. Editor: (with M. Lipkin Jr.) Genetic Responsibility: On Choosing Our Children's Genes, 1974. With USPHS, 1956-58. Recipient Excellence in Teaching award U. Rochester Class of 1976, 1973; NRC fellow, 1960-63; Buswell research fellow, 1970-71, 71-72. Fellow ACP, Am. Coll. Genetics; mem. Am. Fedn. Clin. Rsch., Am. Soc. Hematology, Am. Soc. Human Genetics (social issues com 1980-89, program com. 1993—). Office: U Rochester Med Sch Div Genetics PO Box 641 601 Elmwood Ave Rochester NY 14642

ROWLEY, ROBERT DEANE, JR., bishop; b. Cumberland, Md., July 6, 1941; s. Robert Deane Sr. and Alice Marquerite (Wilson) W.; m. Nancy Ann Roland, June 27, 1964; children: Karen Gordon Rowley Butler, Robert Deane III. BA, U. Pitts., 1963, LLB, 1965; LLM, George Washington U., 1970; MDiv, Episcopal Sem. of S.W., 1977, DD (hon.), 1989. Ordained deacon Episcopal Ch., 1977; priest, 1978; bishop, 1989. Bar: Pa. 1965, U.S. Supreme Ct. 1970. Dean of students St. Andrew's Priory Sch., Honolulu, 1977-80; canon St. Andrew's Cathedral, Honolulu, 1979-81; rector St. Timothy's Episcopal Ch., Aiea, Hawaii, 1981-83; canon to bishop Diocese of Bethlehem (Pa.), 1983-89; bishop Diocese of Northwestern Pa., Erie, 1989—;

pres. 3rd prov., 1993—. Capt. USN, 1966-92. Mem. Erie County Bar Assn., Erie Club, Lake Shore Country Club. Home: 810 Huntington Dr Erie PA 16505-1087 Office: Diocese of Northwestern Pa 145 W 6th St Erie PA 16501-1099

ROWLEY, WILLIAM ROBERT, surgeon; b. Omaha, June 7, 1943; s. Robert Kuhlmeyer and Dorothy Eleanor (Larson) R.; m. Eileen Ruth Murray, Aug. 11, 1968; children: Bill II, Jeff, Jill. BA in Psychology, U. Minn., 1966, MD, 1970. Diplomate Am. Bd. Surgery. Commd. lt. USN, 1972, advanced through grades to rear admiral, 1994; intern U. Calif., San Diego, 1970-71, gen. surgery resident, 1971-72; gen. surgery resident Naval Regional Med. Ctr., Phila., 1973-76; peripheral vascular surgery fellow Naval Regional Med. Ctr., San Diego, 1977-78; staff surgeon Naval Regional Med. Ctr., Phila., 1977; staff vascular surgeon Naval Regional Med. Ctr., San Diego, 1978-85, chmn. dept. surgery, 1985-88, dir. surg. svcs., 1987-88; asst. chief of staff for plans and ops. Naval Med. Command S.W. Region, San Diego, 1988-89; dep. comdr. Nat. Naval Med. Ctr., Bethesda, Md., 1989-91; comdg. officer Naval Hospital, Camp Pendleton, Calif., 1991-93; dep. asst. chief for health care ops. Navy Bur. of Medicine and Surgery, Washington, 1993-94, asst. chief for plans, analysis and evaluation, 1994—; program dir. vascular surgery fellowship Naval Hosp., San Diego, 1980-85, gen. surgery residency, 1985-89; assoc. prof. surgery Uniformed Svcs. U. for Health Scis., Bethesda, 1985—. Fellow ACS; mem. AMA, Am. Coll. Physician Execs., Internat. Soc. Cardiovascular Surgery. Avocations: backpacking, water skiing, sailing. Home: 6202 Kirby Rd Bethesda MD 20817-6640 Office: Asst Chief Plans Analysis & Evaluation Bur Med-Surgery 2300 E St NW Washington DC 20372-5300

ROWLINGSON, JOHN CLYDE, anesthesiologist, educator, physician; b. Syracuse, N.Y., Aug. 3, 1948; s. John Winthrop and Genevieve Estelle (Mahan) R.; m. Rosemary Colette Laney, Oct. 26, 1974 (div.); children: Kristen, Andrew. BS, Allegheny Coll., 1970; MD, SUNY, Buffalo, 1974. Intern Millard Fillmore Hosp., Buffalo, 1974-75; resident in anesthesiology U. Va., Charlottesville, 1975-77; fellow in anesthesia pain mgmt. U. Va. Med. Ctr., 1977-78; asst. prof. anesthesiology U. Va. Sch. Medicine, Charlottesville, 1978-82, assoc. prof., 1982-86, prof., 1986—; assoc. dir. Pain Mgmt. Ctr., U. Va. Health Sci. Ctr., 1978-79, dir., 1980—. Author: Regional Anesthesia, 1984; co-editor: Handbook of Critical Care Pain Management, 1993. Nat. Inst. Handicapped Rsch. fellow, 1983-87, Pain fellow 1977-78. Fellow Am. Coll. Anesthesiology; mem. Am. Soc. Anesthesiologists, Am. Soc. Regional Anesthesia (rsch. grantee 1977, pres.-elect 1995—), Am. Pain Soc., Internat. Assn. Study of Pain, Am. Acad. Pain Medicine. Methodist. Avocations: running, tennis, skiing, biking. Home: 1255 Hunters Ridge Ln Earlysville VA 22936-9571 Office: U Va Health Sci Ctr Anesthesiology PO Box 238 Charlottesville VA 22902-0238

ROWND, ROBERT HARVEY, biochemistry and molecular biology educator; b. Chgo., July 4, 1937; s. Walter Lemuel and Marie Francis (Joyce) R.; m. Rosalie Anne Lowery, June 13, 1959; children: Jennifer Rose, Robert Harvey, David Matthew. BS in Chemistry, St. Louis U., 1959; MA in Med. Scis, Harvard U., 1961, PhD in Biophysics, 1963. Postdoctoral fellow Med. Rsch. Coun., NIH, Cambridge, Eng., 1963-65; postdoctoral fellow Nat. Acad. Scis.-NRC, Institut Pasteur, Paris, 1965-66; prof., chmn. molecular biology and biochemistry U. Wis., Madison, 1966-81; John G. Searle prof., chmn. molecular biology and biochemistry Med. and Dental Schs., Northwestern U., Chgo., 1981-90; leader cancer molecular biology program Cancer Ctr.Northwestern U., Chgo., 1982-89; prof. biochemistry, dir. Ctr. for Molecular Biology Wayne State U., Detroit, 1990-94, interim chair dept. molecular biology and genetics, 1993-94, dir., prof. Ctr. Molecular Medicine and Genetics, prof. internalmedicine, 1994—; vice chmn. Gordon Rsch. Conf. Extrachromosomal Elements, 1984, chmn., 1986; hon. rsch. prof. Biotech. Rsch. Ctr., Chines Acad. Agrl. Scis., Beijing, 1987—. Contbr. numerous articles to sci. jours. and books; mem. editorial bd. Jour. of Bacteriology, 1975-81, editor, 1981-90; assoc. editor Plasmid, 1977-87. Mem. troop coms., treas. Four Lakes coun. Boy Scouts Am., Madison, 1973-77, mem. People to People Program del. of microbiologists to China, 1983; mem. Nat. Acad. Scis./Nat/ Rsch. Coun. Com. on Human Health Effects of Subtherapeutic Antibiotic Use in Animal Feeds, 1979-81; sr. tech. adv. recruitment cons. United Nations Devel. Program in China, 1987. NSF fellow, NIH fellow, 1959-66, rsch. grantee, 1966—; tng. grantee, 1970-79, 83-91; USPHS Rsch. Career Devel. awardee, 1968-73; recipient Alumni Merit award St. Louis U., 1984. Mem. NIH (microbial genetics study sect. 1978-82, dir. med. scientist tng. program 1982-90, adv. panel Nat. Rsch. Coun. 1974-77, chmn. 1976-77, adv. panel for devel. biology 1968-71), Am. Soc. Microbiology, Am. Harvard Chemists, Am. Soc. Biol. Chemists, Am. Acad. Microbiology, N.Y. Acad. Scis. Home: 14010 Harbor Place Dr Saint Clair Shores MI 48080-1528

ROWSEY, MICHAEL, printing company executive; b. 1954. BS in Zoology, Marshall U., 1975; grad. Advanced Exec. Program, Kellogg Grad. Sch. Mgmt., 1988. Sales rep. Carnation Co., 1975-79; dealer sales rep. Boise Cascade Office Products, W.Va., 1979-84; sales mgr. Boise Cascade Office Products, Cin., 1984-86, gen. mgr., 1986-87; sales mgr. Boise Cascade Office Products, Columbus, Ohio, 1987-89, Columbus and Cleve., 1989-90; north regional mgr. Assoc. Stationers, Inc., Itasca, Ill., 1990, now pres. Office: Associated Stationers Inc 1075 W Hawthorn Dr Itasca IL 60143-2075

ROWSON, RICHARD CAVANAGH, publisher; b. Hollywood, Calif., Apr. 7, 1926; s. Louis Cavanagh and Mable Louise (Montney) R.; m. Elena Louisa Costabile, Nov. 22, 1952; children: Peter Cavanagh, John Cummings. A.B., U. Calif., Berkeley, 1946; certificate, Sorbonne, 1949; M.I.A., Columbia U., 1950. Trainee Fgn. Policy Assn., 1950; dir. World Affairs Council R.I., 1951-52; with Fgn. Policy Assn., 1951-62, dir. finance and devel., 1960-62; with Radio Free Europe, 1962-69, dir. policy and planning, 1964-69; dir. spl. studies Praeger Pubs., Inc., N.Y., 1969-77; pres. Praeger Pubs., Inc., 1975-77, Pergamon Press, 1977-80, R.R. Bowker, 1980; info. and pub. cons., 1981; dir. Duke U. Press, 1981-90, sr. cons. editor, 1990-91; dir. Am. U. Press, 1989-91, cons. acquisitions, 1992-94, cons. pub., 1994—; dir.; pub. Woodrow Wilson Ctr. Press, 1992-93; lectr., condr. workshops in field. Contbr. articles to profl. jours. Served to lt. (j.g.) USNR, 1944-47. Mem. Am. Assn. Advancement Slavic Studies, N.Y. Acad. Scis., Soc. for Scholarly Pub., U. Calif. Alumni Assn., Columbia U. Pomona Alumni Assn. Democrat. Clubs: Century Assn., Overseas Press (N.Y.C.). Home: 4701 Connecticut Ave NW Washington DC 20008 also: Am U Press 350 McKinley 4400 Massachusetts Ave Washington DC 20016

ROXIN, EMILIO OSCAR, mathematics educator; b. Buenos Aires, Apr. 6, 1922; came to U.S., 1960; s. Emil Karl and Ullranda Hildegard (Loebel) R.; m. Gudrun D. Kappus, 1962 (div. 1983); children: Ursula R., Walter E. Diploma in engring., U. Buenos Aires, 1947, PhD in Math., 1958. Mem. faculty U. Buenos Aires, 1947-62; researcher Rsch. Inst. Advanced Study, Balt., 1960-64; prof. math. U. R.I., Kingston, 1960-92, prof. emeritus, 1992—; researcher, AEC of Argentina, Buenos Aires, 1956-59. Author: Differential Equations, 1972; contbr. to sci. publs. Mem. Am. Math. Soc., Math. Assn. Am., Soc. Indsl. and Applied Math., Union Math. Argentina, AAAS. Home: 31 Nichols Rd Kingston RI 02881-1803 Office: U RI Dept Math Kingston RI 02881

ROY, AMIT H., agricultural executive. Pres.,ceo Internat. Fertilizer Devel. Ctr., Sheffield, Ala. Office: Internat Fertilizer Develop Ct PO Box 2040 Muscle Shoals AL 35662

ROY, CATHERINE ELIZABETH, physical therapist; b. Tucson, Jan. 16, 1948; d. Francis Albert and Dorothy Orme (Thomas) R.; m. Richard M. Johnson, Aug. 31, 1968 (div. 1978); children: Kimberly Anne, Troy Michael. BA in Social Sci. magna cum laude, San Diego State U., 1980; MS in Phys. Therapy, U. So. Calif., 1984. Staff therapist Sharp Meml. Hosp., San Diego, 1984-85, chairperson patient and family edn. com., 1986-87, chairperson sex edn. and counselling com., 1987-89; chairperson adv. bd. for phys. therapy, asst. for edn. program, 1987-89; mgr. rehab. phys. therapy San Diego Rehab. Inst., Alvarado Hosp., 1989-91; dir. therapeutic svcs. VA Med. Ctr., San Diego, 1991—; lectr. patient edn., family edn., peer edn.; mem. curriculum rev. com. U. So. Calif. Phys. Therapy Dept., 1982; bd. dirs. Ctr. for Edn. in Health; writer, reviewer licensure examination items for phys. therapy Profl. Examination Services.. Tennis coach at clinics Rancho Penasquitos Swim and Tennis Club, San Diego, 1980-81; active Polit. Activities Network, 1985; counselor EEO, 1992-95. Mem. Am. Phys. Therapy Assn. (rsch. presenter nat. conf. 1985, del. nat. conf. 1986-94, rep. state conf. 1987-89, 92-94, Mary McMillan student award 1984, mem. exec. bd. San Diego dist. 1985-88, 92-94), AAUW, NAFE, Am. Congress Rehab. Medicine, Phi Beta Kappa, Phi Kappa Phi, Chi Omega. Avocations: tennis, reading, piano, travel, puzzles. Home: 5067 Park West Ave San Diego CA 92117-1048 Office: San Diego VA Med Ctr Spinal Cord Injury Svc 3350 La Jolla Village Dr San Diego CA 92161

ROY, CHUNILAL, psychiatrist; b. Digboi, India, Jan. 1, 1935; came to Can., 1967, naturalized, 1975; s. Atikay Bandhu and Nirupama (Devi) R.; m. Elizabeth Ainscow, Apr. 15, 1967; children: Nicholas, Phillip, Charles. MB, BS, Calcutta Med. Coll., India, 1959; diploma in psychol. medicine, Kings Coll., Newcastle-upon-Tyne, Eng., 1963. Intern Middlesborough Gen. Hosp., Eng., 1960-61; jr. hosp. officer St. Luke's Hosp., Middlesborough, Eng., 1961-64, sr. registrar, 1964; sr. hosp. med. officer Parkside Hosp., Macclesfield, Eng., 1964-66; sr. registrar Moorehaven Hosp., Ivybridge, Eng., 1966; reader, head dept. psychiatry Maulana Azad Med. Coll., New Delhi, 1966; sr. med. officer Republic of Ireland, County Louth, 1966; sr. psychiatrist Sask. Dept. Psychiat. Services, Can., 1967-68; regional dir. Swift Current, Can., 1968-71; practice medicine specializing in psychiatry Regina, Sask., Can., 1971-72; founding dir., med. dir. Regional Psychiat. Ctr., Abbotsford, B.C., Can., 1972-82; with dept. psychiatry Vancouver Gen. Hosp., 1987—; cons. to prison adminstrs.; hon. lectr. psychology and clin. prof. dept. psychiatry U. B.C.; ex-officio mem. Nat. Adv. Com. on Health Care of Prisoners in Can.; cons. psychiatrist Vancouver Hosp.; advisor Asian chpt. Psychosomatic Medicine, World Congress of Law and Medicine, New Delhi, 1985. Author: (with D.J. West and F.L. Nichols) Understanding Sexual Attacks, 1978; co-author: Oath of Athens, 1979; mem. editorial rev. bd. Evaluation, 1977—; assoc. editor Internat. Jour. Offender Therapy and Comparative Criminology, 1978—; mem. Bd. Internat. Law Medicine, 1979—; field editor Jour. of Medicine and Law; contbr. articles to profl. jours. Recipient merit award Dept. Health, Republic of Ireland, 1966, merit award Can. Penitentiary Svc., 1974, merit award Correcitonal Svcs. Can., 1983, citation by pres. U. B.C., 1983; knighted by Order of St. John Ecumenical Found., 1993. Fellow Royal Coll. Psychiatry (Can.), Royal Coll. Psychiatry (Eng.), Pacific Rim Coll. Psychiatrists (founder); mem. World Psychiat. Assn. (sec., vice chmn. forensic psychiatry 1983), World Fedn. Mental Health, Internat. Coun. Prison Med. Svcs. (founding sec.-gen. 1977), Can. Med. Assn., Can. Psychiat. Assn., Internat. Acad. Legal Medicine and Social Medicine, Indian Psychiat. Assn. (life), Can. Assn. Profl. Treatment Offenders (founding dir. 1975), Assn. Physicians & Surgeons Who Work in Can. Prisons (founding pres. 1974), Internat. Found. for Tng. in Penitentiary Medicine and Forensic Psychiatry (founding pres. 1980, vice-chmn., sec.), World Psychiatry Assn., Asutralian Acad. Forensic Sci. (corr.), Can. Physicians Interested in South Asia (v.p. 1989, pres. 1990), Itnernat. Coll. Psychosomatic Med. (adv. Asian Chapt.), Internat. Conf. on Health, Culture, & Contemporary Soc. (chief advisor Bombay, India 1989, v.p. 1989, pres. 1990), Internat. Coun. Peniteniary Medicine (founding sec. bd. dirs.), World Psychiat. Assn. (vice chmn., forensic psychiat. sect. 1989), Order of St. John (knight 1992—), Vancouver Multi Cultural Soc. (bd. dirs. 1992-93), B.C. Psychiat. Assn. (pres. elect 1994). Home: 2439 Trinity St, Vancouver, BC Canada V5K 1C9 Office: 1417-750 W Broadway, Vancouver, BC Canada V5Z 1J4

ROY, CLARENCE LESLIE, landscape architect; b. Ironwood, Mich., Mar. 6, 1927; s. Theodore Gideon and Myrtle May (Mathews) R.; m. Ruth Serou, Nov. 11, 1959. B.S. in Landscape Architecture, U. Mich., 1951. Landscape architect Lambert Assoc. Cos., Dallas, 1951-59; assoc. Eichstedt-Johnson Assoc., Grosse Pointe, Mich., 1960; prin. Johnson Johnson & Roy/inc., Ann Arbor, Mich., 1961-81, Dallas, 1982-92, ret.; dir. The Smith Group, Detroit, 1979-82. Founder Old West Assn., Ann Arbor, 1966, pres., 1968-73; pres. Ann Arbor Tomorrow, 1978-79. Served with USN, 1945-46. Fellow Am. Soc. Landscape Architects; mem. Am. Planners Assn., U. Mich. Alumni Assn. (bd. dirs. 1976-79), Tau Sigma Delta, Alpha Rho Chi. Home: 4039 Travis St Dallas TX 75204-7514

ROY, DAVID TOD, Chinese literature educator; b. Nanking, China, Apr. 5, 1933; s. Andrew Tod and Margaret (Crutchfield) R.; m. Barbara Jean Chew, Feb. 4, 1967. AB, Harvard U., 1958, AM, 1960, PhD, 1965. Asst. prof. Princeton U., 1963-67; assoc. prof. U. Chgo., 1967-73, prof., 1973—, chmn. com. on Far Eastern Studies, 1968-70, chmn. dept. Far Eastern Langs. and Civilizations, 1972-75. Author: Kuo Mo-jo: The Early Years, 1971; contbr.: How to Read the Chinese Novel, 1990; co-editor: Ancient China: Studies in Early Civilization, 1978; translator: The Plum in the Golden Vase or Chin P'ing Mei, 1993. Served with U.S. Army, 1954-56. Ford Found. fellow, 1958-60, Jr. fellow Harvard Soc. Fellows, 1960-63, fellow Fulbright-Hays Commn., 1967, Chgo. Humanities Inst. fellow, 1994-95; grantee Am. Council Learned Socs., 1976-77, NEH, 1983-86, 95—. Mem. Am. Lit. Translators Assn., Am. Oriental Soc., Assn. for Asian Studies, Chinese Lang. Tchrs. Assn. Democrat. Club: Quadrangle (Chgo.). Home: 5443 S Cornell Ave Chicago IL 60615-5612 Office: U Chgo 1050 E 59th St Chicago IL 60637-1512

ROY, ELSIJANE TRIMBLE, federal judge; b. Lonoke, Ark., Apr. 2, 1916; d. Thomas Clark and Elsie Jane (Walls) Trimble; m. James M. Roy, Nov. 23, 1943; 1 son, James Morrison. JD, U. Ark., Fayetteville, 1939; LLD (hon.), U. Ark., Little Rock, 1978. Bar: Ark. 1939. Atty. Rose, Loughborough, Dobyns & House, Little Rock, 1940-41, Ark. Revenue Dept., Little Rock, 1941-42; mem. firm Reid, Evrard & Roy, Blytheville, Ark., 1945-54, Roy & Roy, Blytheville, 1954-63; law clk. Ark. Supreme Ct., Little Rock, 1963-65; assoc. justice Ark. Supreme Ct., 1975-77; U.S. dist. judge then sr. judge Ea. and We. Dists. Ark., Little Rock, 1977—; judge Pulaski County (Ark.) Cir. Ct., Little Rock, 1966; asst. atty. gen. Ark., Little Rock, 1967; sr. law clk. U.S. Dist. Ct., Little Rock and Ft. Smith, 1967-75; Mem. med. adv. com. U. Ark. Med. Center, 1952-54; Committeewoman Democratic Party 16th Jud. Dist., 1940-42; vice chmn. Ark. Dem. State Com., 1946-48; mem. chmn. com. Ark. Constnl. Commn., 1967-68. Recipient disting. alumnae citation U. Ark., 1978, Gayle Pettus Pontz award, 1986, Brooks Hays Meml. Christian Citizenship award, 1994; named Ark. woman of yr., Bus. and Profl. Women's Club, 1969, 76, outstanding appellate judge, Ark. Trial Lawyers Assn., 1976-77, Delta Theta Phi mem. of yr. 1989; named among top 100 women in Ark. bus., 1995; Paul Harris fellow Rotary Club Little Rock, 1992. Recipient disting. alumnae citation U. Ark., 1978, Gayle Pettus Pontz award, 1986, Brooks Hays Meml. Christian Citizenship award, 1994; named Ark. Woman of Yr., Bus. and Profl. Women's Club, 1969, 76, Outstanding Appellate Judge, Ark. Trial Lawyers Assn., 1976-77, Mem. of Yr., Delta Theta Phi, 1989; named among top 100 women in Ark. bus., 1995, Ark. Bus. Top 100 Women in Ark., 1995; Paul Harris fellow Rotary Little Rock, 1992. Office: US Dist Ct 600 West Capitol Rm 423 Little Rock AR 72201-3325

ROY, J(AMES) STAPLETON, ambassador; b. Nanking, China, June 16, 1935; s. Andrew Tod and Margaret (Crutchfield) R.; m. Elissandra Nicole Fiore, Jan. 27, 1968; children—Andrew, David, Anthony. B.A. magna cum laude, Princeton U., 1956; postgrad., U. Wash., 1964-65, Nat. War Coll., 1974-75. Dep. dir. Office of Soviet Union Affairs Dept. of State, Washington, 1972-74, dep. dir. Office of Chinese Affairs, 1975-78; minister counselor U.S. Embassy, Beijing, Peoples Republic of China, 1978-81, Bangkok, Thailand, 1981-84; U.S. amb. to Singapore, 1984-86; dep. asst. sec. Bur. East Asian and Pacific Affairs Dept. of State, 1986-89, spl. asst. to sec. and exec. sec., 1989-91; U.S. amb. to People's Republic of China Beijing, 1991—. Recipient Presdl. Meritorious Service award Pres. of U.S., 1983, 88, 90, Superior Honor award Dept. State, 1977, 80. Mem. Assn. Asian Studies, Am. Fgn. Service Assn., Phi Beta Kappa. Avocations: swimming; jogging; chess; computers. Office: US Embassy, Xiu Shui Bei Jie 3, Beijing 100600, China

ROY, KENNETH RUSSELL, educator; b. Hartford, Conn., Mar. 29, 1946; s. Russell George and Irene Mary (Birkosh) R.; BS, Central Conn. State Coll., New Britain, 1968, MS, 1974; 6th yr. degree in profl. edn. U. Conn., 1981, Ph.D., 1985; m. Marisa Anne Russo, Jan. 27, 1968; children: Lisa Marie, Louise Irene. Tchr. sci. Rocky Hill (Conn.) High Sch., 1968-73, N.W. Cath. High Sch., West Hartford, Conn., 1973-74; sci. and math. coord. Bolton (Conn.) High Sch., 1974-78; chmn. scis. Bacon Acad., Colchester, Conn., 1978-81; K-12 dir. sci. Glastonbury (Conn.) Pub. Schs., 1981—;

mem. adj. faculty Manchester C.C., 1976—, Tunxis C.C., 1975—; instr. U. Conn. Coop. Program, 1974-78; cons./adv. Project Rise, 1978-81; lectr., sci. curriculum cons. various Conn. sch. dists.; nat. dir. Nat. Sci. Suprs. Assn., 1989-91, exec. dir. Leadership Inst. Cen. Conn. State U., New Britain, 1989-91; exec. dir. Nat. Sci. Suprs. Assn., 1992—. Co-editor Conn. Jour. Sci. Edn., 1984-88; editor Sci. Leadership Trend Notes, 1989-91; contbr. articles to profl. jours. Mem. St. Christopher Sch. Bd., 1982-83. Recipient Disting. Educator's and Conn. Educator's awards Milken Family Found., 1989; named Tchr. of Yr., Colchester, 1980; NSF grantee, 1968, staff devel. grantee, 1979, 80, Nat. Sci. Supr. Leadership Conf. grantee, 1980. Mem. ASCD, AAAS, Nat. Sci. Tchrs. Assn., Nat. Sci. Suprs. Assn. (pres.-elect 1986-87, pres 1987-88), Conn. Sci. Tchrs. Assn., Conn. Sci. Suprs. Assn. (pres. 1985-86), Conn. Assn. Profl. Devel., Conn. Assn. Supervision and Curriculum Devel., Glastonbury Adminstrs. and Suprs. Assn., Nat. Ctr. Improvement Sci. Teaching and Learning (mem. adv. bd. 1988-91), Internat. Council Assns. Sci. Edn. (nat. rep. 1987-88, N.Am. region rep. and exec. com. mem. 1989—), Phi Delta Kappa. Roman Catholic. Office: Glastonbury Pub Schs Glastonbury CT 06033

ROY, MELINDA, dancer; b. Lafayette, La.. Student, Sch. Am. Ballet. Mem. corps de ballet N.Y.C. Ballet, 1978—, soloist, 1984, prin., 1989—. Dancer in ballets including The Nutcracker, Symphont in C (third movement), Symphony in Three Movements, Apollo (polyhymnia), Brahms-Schoenberg Quartet (first movement), Who Cares, the rubies sect. of Jewels, Divertimento no. 15, Serenade, Western Symphony (first movement), Chaconne (fast pas de deux), Tschaikovsky suite no. 3 (Scherzo), Stars and Stripes, Tschaikovsky pas de Deux, Walpurgisnacht ballet, Golberg Variations, The Concert, Gershwin Concerto, Fanfare, Interplay, The Four Seasons (spring), The Unanswered Questions, Behind the China Dogs, The Waltz Project, Seven by Five, N.Y.C. Ballet's Balanchine Celebration, 1993; performed in Spain, Italy, Denmark, Eng., France, Germany, China, Japan. Office: NYC Ballet Inc NY State Theater Lincoln Ctr Plz New York NY 10023*

ROY, NORMAN E., construction company executive; b. Central Falls, R.I., Dec. 2, 1926; s. Ernest and Melanie (Morin) R.; m. Jeannette Martel, Oct. 30, 1948; children—Norman E., Jr., Richard R., Jean Roy McGarry, Paul, Deborah Roy Edwards, Ronald, John. B.S. in Acctg., Bryant Coll., 1948; postgrad., Providence Coll., U. R.I. Various positions Gilbane Bldg. Co., Providence, 1949-69; v.p., controller Gilbane Bldg. Co., 1969-79, v.p. fin., 1979-83, sr. v.p. fin., 1983-91, sr. v.p., treas., 1991—. Mem. Nat. Assn. Accts., Fin. Execs. Inst., Assoc. Gen. Contractors Am. (mem. ins. info. and surety assn. of Am. coms., 1983—), Adminstrv. Mgmt. Soc., Bryant Coll. Alumni Assn. (mem. exec. bd. 1986-87). Office: Gilbane Bldg Co 7 Jackson Walkway Providence RI 02903-3623

ROY, P. NORMAN, manufacturing company executive; b. Fitchburg, Mass., Nov. 25, 1934; s. Joseph and Della (Lavoie) R.; m. Mary Elizabeth Duggan, May 30, 1959; children: Mary Eileen, Ann Elizabeth, Kathleen Theresa, Michele Ann, Ellen Marie, Paul Norman. B.S.B.A. in Acctg. with honors, Boston Coll., 1956; M.B.A., Babson Inst., 1967. C.P.A., Mass. With Gen. Electric Co., Pittsfield, Mass., 1956-62; auditor Arthur Andersen & Co., Boston, 1962-65; ops. analyst Barry Wright Corp., Newton Lower Falls, Mass., 1965-68, mgr. internal audit, 1968-70, asst. to pres., 1970, treas., 1971-73, v.p. fin., treas., 1973-75, v.p. fin. and adminstrn., 1975-76, dir., 1973—; exec. v.p. fin. and adminstrn., 1976-80, exec. v.p., 1980—; bd. dirs., chmn. examining com., mem. exec. com. Baybanks Middlesex, Burlington, Mass., 1982—; dir. mem. exec. com., mem. Loan rev. com. Mass. Bus. Devel. Corp., Boston, 1982—; dir. mem. exec. com., mem. nominating com., mem. budget com., asst. treas. Assoc. Industries of Mass., Boston, 1984—; dir., chmn. audit com. Kronos Inc., Waltham, Mass., 1984—; dir. Mass. Indsl. Devel. and Employment Commn., Boston;. Trustee, bd. govs. Newton Wellesley Hosp., Boston, 1978-83, overseer, 1983-84; trustee Emmanuel Coll., Boston, 1976-78, overseer, 1983—; dir. adv. bd. Nat. Com. on Fraudulent Fin. Reporting, Washington, 1984—; trustee, mem. adminstrn. and Fin. Com., St. Elizabeth's Hosp. of Boston, 1988—. Served to 1st lt. U.S. Army, 1956-58. Recipient Knight award Equestrian Order Holy Sepulchre Jerusalem, 1984. Fellow Am. Inst. C.P.A.s; mem. Fin. Execs. Inst. (chmn. 1984-85, nat. dir. 1980-87), Mass. Soc. C.P.A.s, Machinery and Allied Products Inst. (fin. council), Watertown C. of C. (v.p., dir. 1978-81), Am. Mgmt. Assn., Nat. Assn. Mfrs. (steering com.). Republican. Roman Catholic. Clubs: Brae Burn Country (Newton); Ancient Order Beefeaters (N.Y.C.); Treas., Hundred (Boston). Avocations: golf, travel, country skiing, woodcrafts, bicycling, fishing.

ROY, PATRICK, professional hockey player; b. Quebec City, Que., Can., Oct. 5, 1965. Goaltender Montreal Canadiens, 1984—. Recipient Conn Smythe trophy as playoff MVP, 1986, William M. Jennings trophy 1986-89, 91-92, Trico Goaltender award, 1988-89, 89-90, Georges Vezina trophy, 1988-89, 89-90, 91-92; named to NHL All-Rookie Team, 1985-86, NHL All-Star Second Team, 1987-88, 90-91, NHL All-Star First Team, 1988-89, 89-90, 91-92., Sporting News All-Star Team, 1988-89, 89-90, 91-92. Played in Stanley Cup Championships, 1986, 93. Office: Montreal Canadiens, 2313 St Catherine St W, Montreal, PQ Canada H3H 1N2*

ROY, PAUL EMILE, JR., county official; b. Sumter, S.C., Dec. 18, 1942; s. Paul Emile and Harriette Orvilla (Sorenson) R.; m. Patricia Jane Stariha, July 2, 1977; 1 child, Jennifer Jo. AA, Grand Rapids Jr. Coll., 1963; student, Universidad de las Americas, Mexico City, 1963-64, Instituto Mexicano-Norteamericano de Relaciones Culturales, Mexico City, 1964-65; BA, Aquinas Coll., Grand Rapids, 1967; MA, U. Americas Escuela de Graduados, Mexico City, 1968; postgrad., U. Mich., 1977-79; MBA, Calif. Coast U., 1994. Asst. prin., instr. Spanish Muskegon (Mich.) Cath. Cen. High Sch., 1971-75; govt. offcl. County of Muskegon, 1975—, dir. employment and tng. Muskegon/Oceana Consortium, 1975-87, dir. employment and tng., 1988—, dir. employment and tng. and facilities mgmt., 1995—; mem. Mich. Com. for Devel. of Romance Lang. Performance Objectives; adult edn. adv. com. Muskegon Pub. Schs.; appointee Mich. Youth Employment Coun.; v.p. regional adv. coun. U.S. Dept. Labor, 1981; mem. City of Muskegon Local Devel. Funding Authority, 1988—, Downtown Devel. Authority, 1988—, City of Whitehall (Mich.) Local Devel. Funding Authority, 1988—, Muskegon Econ. Growth Alliance Edn. Com.; cons. U.S. Dept. Labor, Washington, Mich. Dept. Labor, Lansing, Gov.'s Office Manpower, Ind., U. Mich., Ann Arbor, various pvt. cos., non-profit orgns. Campaign chmn. Muskegon County United Way, 1986-88, Pacesetter award, 1987. Mem. Am. Assn. Tchrs. Spanish and Portuguese, Mich. Assn. Tchrs. English as Second Lang., Mich. Assn. Employment and Tng. Dirs. (pres. 1980-81), Mich. Employment and Tng. Inst. (founding bd. dirs. 1980-81), Nat. Assn. Counties (employment steering com.), Nat. Assn. County Employment and Tng. Adminstrs. (nat. bd. dirs. 1979-80, nat. chmn. organizational resources com. 1981). Avocations: golf, travel, reading, theater. Office: Muskegon County Dept Employment & Tng 20 W Muskegon Ave Muskegon MI 49440-1317

ROY, RAYMOND, bishop; b. Man., Can., May 3, 1919; s. Charles-Borromée and Zephirina (Milette) R. B.A. in Philosophy and Theology, U. Man., 1942; student, Philos. Sem., Montreal, 1942-43, Major Sem., Montreal, 1943-46, Major Sem. St. Boniface, 1946-47. Ordained priest Roman Catholic Ch. 1947. Asst. pastor, then pastor chs. in Man., 1947-50, 53-66; chaplain St. Boniface (Man.) Hosp., 1950-53; superior Minor Sem., St. Boniface, 1966-69; pastor Cathedral Parish, St. Boniface, 1969-72; ordained bishop, 1972; bishop of St. Paul, Alta., Can., 1972—. Club: K.C. Address: 4410 51st Ave Box 339, Saint Paul, AB Canada T0A 3A0

ROY, RICHARD E., lawyer; b. Portland, Oreg., July 7, 1939; s. Leighton Eugene and Dorris Mary (Scott) R.; m. Jeanne Beverly Hawley, June 9, 1962; children: Bradley Scott, Jeffrey Alan, Melinda Louise. BS in Engring., Oreg. State U., 1961; MS in Engring., Stanford State U., 1966; JD, Harvard U., 1970. Bar: Oreg. 1970, U.S. Dist. Ct. Oreg. 1970. Assoc. Stoel, Rives, Boley, Fraser & Wyse, Portland, 1970-76; ptnr. Stoel, Rives, Boley, Jones & Grey, Portland, 1976-94; exec. dir. N.W. Earth Inst., 1993—; mem. corp. commrs. task force corp. law, chmn. 1985; mem. model bus. corp. Act Task Force, 1986-88. Editor: Advising Oregon Businesses, 5 vols., 1984-93. Chmn. Oreg. Water Policy Rev. Bd., Salem, 1975-77; mem. Oreg. Bd. of Forestry, Salem, 1987—; pres., bd. dirs. Oreg. Scholastic Chess Found., Portland, 1983—. Served to lt. USN, 1961-65. Mem. Oreg. State Bar Assn.

(chmn. bus. and corp. sect. 1982-83), Profl. Engrs. Soc. of Oreg. Democrat. Club: City (Portland). Avocations: music, backpacking. Home: 2420 SW Boundary St Portland OR 97201-2025 Office: Stoel Rives Boley Jones & Grey 900 SW 5th Ave Portland OR 97204-1235

ROY, ROB J., biomedical engineer, anesthesiologist; b. Bklyn., Jan. 2, 1933; m. Carole Ann Roy, Aug. 1, 1959; children: Robert Bruce, David John, Bruce Glenn. BSEE, Cooper Union, N.Y.C., 1954; MSEE, Columbia U., 1956; DEngSc, Rensselaer Poly. Inst., 1962; MD, Albany (N.Y.) Med. Coll., 1976. Profl. engr., N.Y.; diplomate Am. Bd. Anesthesiology. Prof. elec. engrin. dept. Rensselaer Poly. Inst., Troy, N.Y., 1962—, prof. biomed. engring. dept., 1980—, head biomed. engring. dept., 1986—; cons. numerous cos. Author: State Variables for Engineers, 1965; author 150 papers in field. Sr. mem. IEEE; mem. Am. Soc. Anesthesiologists, Sigma Xi. Home: 10 Sevilla Dr Clifton Park NY 12065-5013 Office: Rensselaer Polytech Inst Dept Biomedical Engring Jonsson Engring Ctr Troy NY 12180-3590

ROY, RUSTUM, interdisciplinary materials researcher, educator; b. Ranchi, India, July 3, 1924; came to U.S., 1945, naturalized, 1961; s. Narendra Kumar and Rajkumari (Mukherjee) R.; m. Della M. Martin, June 8, 1948; children: Neill, Ronnen, Jeremy. BS, Patna (India) U., 1942; MS, Patna (India) U., India, 1944; Ph.D., Pa. State U., 1948; DSc (hon.), Tokyo Inst. Tech., 1987, Alfred U, 1993. Research asst. Pa. State U., 1948-49, mem. faculty, 1950—, prof. geochemistry, 1957—, prof. solid state, 1968—, chmn. solid state tech. program, 1960-67, chmn. sci. tech. and soc. program, 1977-84, dir., 1984—, dir. materials research lab., 1962-85, Evan Pugh prof., 1981—; sr. sci. officer Nat. Ceramic Lab., India, 1950; mem. com. mineral sci. tech. Nat. Acad. Scis., 1967-69, com. survey materials sci. tech., 1970-74; exec. com. chem. div. NRC, 1967-70, nat. materials adv. bd., 1970-77, mem. com. radioactive waste mgmt., 1974-80, chmn. panel waste solidification, 1976-80; chmn. com. NRC, USSR and Eastern Europe, 1976-81; mem. com. material sci. and engring. NRC, 1986-89; mem. Pa. Gov.'s Sci. Adv. Com.; chmn. materials adv. panel Gov.'s Sci. Adv. Com., 1965; mem. adv. com. on engring. NSF, 1968-72, adv. com. to ethical and human value implications sci. and tech., 1974-76, adv. com. div. materials rsch., 1974-77; Hibbert lectr. U. London, 1979; bd. dirs. Kirkridge, Inc., Bangor, Pa.; cons. to industry; mem. adv. com. Coll. Engring., Stanford U., 1984-86. Author: Honest Sex, 1968, Crystal Chemistry of Non-metallic Materials, 1974, Experimenting with Truth, 1981, Radioactive Waste Disposal, Vol. 1, the Waste Package, 1983, Lost at the Frontier, 1985; also articles.; editor-in-chief: Materials Research Bull, 1966—, Bull. Sci. Tech. and Soc, 1981—. Chmn. bd. Dag Hammarskjold Coll., 1973-75; chmn. ad hoc com. sci., tech. and ch. Nat. Council Chs., 1966-68. Sci. policy fellow Brookings Instn., 1982-83. Fellow Indian Acad. Scis. (hon.); mem. AAAS (chmn. chemistry sect. 1985), NAE, Nat. Rsch. Coun. (internat. sci. lectr. 1991-92), Royal Swedish Acad. Engring. Scis. (fgn.), Indian Nat. Acad. Sci. (fgn.), Engring. Acad. Japan, Fedn. Materials Socs. (Nat. Materials Advancement award 1991), Ceramic Soc. Japan (Centennial award 1991, hon. mem. 1991), Mineral Soc. Am. (award 1957), Fine Ceramics Assn. Japan (Internat. award), Am. Chem. Soc. (Petroleum Rsch. Fund award 1960, Dupont award for Chem. of Materials 1993), Acad. Natural Scis. (chem. sect., elected fgn. mem. 1995), Am. Ceramic Soc. (Sosman lectr. 1975, Orton lectr. 1984, disting. life mem. 1993, Educator of Yr. 1993), Am. Soc. Engring. Educators (Centennial medal 1993, named to Hall of Fame 1993), Materials Rsch. Soc. (founder, pres. 1976). Home: 528 S Pugh St State College PA 16801-5312 Office: 102 Materials Rsch Lab University Park PA 16802 *Integration of the insights of science (and the vehicle of art) and the highest religious value systems is the urgent need of our time. Having started from a Christian background I seek to join others of many religious convictions, in increasing our own and society's commitment to proclaiming the centrality of other-centered love, and educating and training all citizens in a new macro-ecumenical synthesis including a radically redirected commitment to technology and science.*

ROYAL, DARRELL K., university administrator; b. Hollis, Okla., July 6, 1924; s. Burley Ray and Katy Elizabeth (Harmon) R.; m. Edith Marie Thomason, July 26, 1944; children: Marian (Mrs. Abraham Kazen III) (dec.), Mack, David (dec.). B.S. in Bus, U. Okla., 1950. Former head football coach, then dir. athletics U. Tex., now asst. to univ. pres. Author: Darrell Royal Talks Football, 1963. Named Football Coaches Assn. Coach of Yr., 1963, 70, Tex. Sports Writers' Coach of Yr., 1961, 63, 69, 70, Southwesterner of Yr., 1961, 62, 63; named to U. Tex. Longhorn Hall Fame, 1976; Tex. Sports Hall Fame, 1976; Jim Thorpe Okla. Hall of Fame, 1977; Nat. Football Hall of Fame, 1983; selected as Coach of the Decade for the 1960's by ABC. Mem. Delta Upsilon. Presbyterian.

ROYAL, WILLIAM HENRY, real estate developer, architect; b. Jackson, Tenn., Dec. 16, 1924; s. Joe Henry and Millie Earline (Anderson) R.; m. Odell Peebles, June 16, 1943; children: William H. Jr., Frederick E., Diana, Carolyn M., Wanda H. Diploma, Chicago Tech. Coll., 1959; student, MIT, 1969, '73, U. Neb., 1971-76, U. Minn., 1974-76. Reg. architect, Ill., Mo. Architect, engr. U.S. Army Engr. Dist., Detroit, 1957-61; gen. architect U.S. Army Engr. Dist., St. Paul, Minn., 1959-62; supr. architect U.S. Army Engr. Dist., Chgo., 1962-70; gen. architect U.S. Army Engr. Dist., Omaha, Neb., 1970-73; architect, job captain Ellerbe & Co., St Paul, 1962; cons. FREBO, U.S. Postal Svc., St. Paul, 1973-77; constr. mgr. H.Q. U.S. Postal Svc., Washington, 1977-80; pres. William H. Royal & Assoc., Inc., Lake St. Louis, Mo., 1987—, St. Louis Airport Devel. Corp., 1988-89; v.p. Steelgrade Corp., Clayton, Mo., 1991-93; sec.-treas. Am. Community Telecomms. System, Inc., Ferguson, Mo., 1992—. Author: (tng. manual) Architect Engineer Contracts, 1970; editor: Master Planning, Kinloch Redevelopment, 1987. Steward, United Meth. Ch., Omaha, 1970-73; urban cons. United Meth. Ministries, Omaha, 1970-73, Youth Coord., United Meth. Ch., Omaha, 1971-73; mem. Douglas County Parole Bd., Omaha, 1971-72. Recipient Commendation U.S. Postal Svc., Washington, 1976, Svc. award, 1980, letter of Appreciation, 1982; nominee Rockefeller Pub. Svc. award, U.S. Postal Svc., St. Paul, 1976. Avocations: computer programming, fishing, travel. Home: 1 Berry Ct Lake Saint Louis MO 63367-1921 Office: William H Royal & Assocs 1 Berry Ct Lake Saint Louis MO 63367-1921

ROYALL, ROBERT VENNING, JR., banker; b. Mt. Pleasant, S.C., Dec. 11, 1934; s. Robert Venning and Eleanor (Williams) R.; m. Edith Gregorie Frampton, July 30, 1955; children: Eleanor, Margaret, Edith. AB, U. S.C., 1956; postgrad., Stonier Grad. Sch. Banking, Rutgers U., 1969; grad. advanced mgmt. program, Harvard U., 1975. Chmn., CEO NBSC Corp. and Nat. Bank S.C., Columbia, 1991—; sec. commerce State of S.C.; bd. dirs. Blue Cross-Blue Shield S.C. Trustee Sch. Bus. U. S.C., U. S.C. Bus. Partnership Founjd., S.C. Ednl. Comms. Inc.; mem. bd. visitors Coll. Charleston; chmn. S.C. Coord. Coun. for Econ. Devel. Capt. USMCR, 1956-59. Mem. Young Man of Yr. Jr. C. of C., 1961, 65, Outstanding Man of Yr., 1968, 1 of 3 Outstanding Young Men in S.C., 1968, Outstanding Young Banker S.C., 1971, Amb. of Yr. Columbia C. of C., 1986, S.C. Bus. Man of Yr. S.c. State C. of C., 1992. Mem. S.C. Bankers Assn. (state legis. com., pres. 1985-86). Episcopalian (past trustee diocese S.C., vestryman). Home: 4632 Perry Ct Columbia SC 29206-4516 Office: Nat Bank of SC PO Box 1457 Columbia SC 29202-1457

ROYALTY, KENNETH MARVIN, lawyer; b. Cin., Nov. 1, 1940; s. Maurice K. and Frances G. (Budd) R.; div. 1991; children by previous marriages: Ted, Sara. BA, Ohio State U., 1962, JD summa cum laude, 1970. Bar: Ohio 1970. From assoc. to ptnr. Vorys, Sater, Seymour & Pease, Columbus, Ohio, 1970-77, 81—; assoc. regional counsel Prudential Ins. Co. Am., Cin., 1977-81; spl. counsel Ohio Divsn. Securities, Columbus, 1973. Contbr. articles to profl. jours.; presenter in field. Lt. USN, 1962-67, Vietnam. Mem. ABA, Ohio State Bar Assn., Columbus Bar Assn. Office: Vorys Sater Seymour & Pease PO Box 1008 52 E Gay St Columbus OH 43215-3161

ROYBAL-ALLARD, LUCILLE, congresswoman; b. Boyle Heights, Calif., June 12, 1941; d. Edward Roybal; m. Edward T. Allard; 4 children. BA, Calif. State U., L.A. Former mem. Calif. State Assembly; mem. 103rd Congress from 33rd Calif. dist., 1993—; mem. Banking and Fin. Svcs., Budget Com. Office: Ho of Reps 324 Cannon Washington DC 20515*

ROYCE, BARRIE SAUNDERS HART, physicist; b. Eng., Jan. 10, 1933; came to U.S., 1957, naturalized, 1978; s. Vincent Pateman Hart and Kathlene (Saunders) R.; m. Dominique J.M. Vallee, May 7, 1964; children:

Vincent Rene Hart, Marc Edward Hart. B.Sc. in Physics, King's Coll., U. London, 1954; Ph.D., U. London, 1957. Research assoc. Carnegie Inst. Tech., 1957-60; research assoc. Princeton U., 1960-61, mem. faculty, 1961—, prof. applied physics and materials scis., 1978—; master of Dean Mathey Coll. Dean Mathey Coll., 1986-94. Editorial adv. bd.: Jour. Photoacoustics, to 1984, Crystal Lattice Defects. Mem. Princeton Borough Zoning Bd. Adjustment, 1980-93, chair, 1993—. Grantee NSF; Grantee Air Force Office Sci. and Research; Grantee Army Research Office. Mem. Am. Phys. Soc., Sigma Xi. Office: Princeton U D416 Duffield Hall (EQ) Princeton NJ 08544

ROYCE, EDWARD R. (ED ROYCE), congressman; b. Los Angeles, Oct. 12, 1951; m. Marie Porter. BA, Calif. State U., Fullerton. Tax mgr. Southwestern Portland Cement Co.; mem. Calif. Senate, 1983-93, 103rd Congress from 39th dist. Calif., 1993—; vice chmn. Public Employment and Retirement Com.; mem. Bus. and Profs. com., Indsl. Rels. com.; legis. author, campaign co-chmn. Proposition 15 Crime Victims/Speedy Trial Initiative; author nation's 1st felony stalking law, bill creating Foster Family Home Ins. Fund, legis. creating foster parent recruitment and tng. program; mem. Banking and Fin. Svcs. Com., Internat. Rels. Com. Named Legis. of Yr. Orange County Rep. Com., 1986, Child Adv. of Yr. Calif. Assn. Svc. for Children, 1987. Mem. Anaheim C. of C. Republican. Office: US Ho of Reps 1113 Longworth Ho Office Bldg Washington DC 20515-0539*

ROYCE, PAUL CHADWICK, medical administrator; b. Mpls., July 2, 1928. BA, U. Minn., 1948, MD, 1952; PhD, Case Western Res. U., 1959. Diplomate Am. Bd. of Internal Medicine. Intern U. Chgo. Clinics, 1952-53; fellow NSF Case Western Res. U., Cleve., 1953-54, 56-58, Upjohn fellow, 1958-59; resident internal medicine Bronx Mcpl. Hosp., N.Y., 1959-61; asst. prof. of medicine Albert Einstein Coll. of Med., N.Y.C., 1961-69; sr. staff endocrinologist Guthrie Clinic, Sayre, Pa., 1970-81; assoc. prof. of medicine Hahnemann Med. Sch., Phila., 1973-81; dean and prof. clin. sci. and physiology Sch. Medicine U. Minn., Duluth, 1981-87; sr. v.p., clin. dir. Monmouth Med. Ctr., Long Branch, N.J., 1987-94; prin. Royce Assocs., Atlantic Highlands, N.J., 1995—; bd. dirs. Frank & Louise Groff Found., Red Bank, N.J., 1987—. Producer, host TV prgram Doctors on Call, 1983-87 (Nat. Friends of Pub. Broadcasting Hill award 1987). Lt. USNR, 1954-56. Mem. Harvey Soc., Am. Physiol. Soc., Fedn. Am. Scientists, Physicians for Social Responsibility, Am. Coll. Physician Execs., Sigma Xi, Alpha Omega Alpha. Avocations: skiing, cycling, canoeing. Office: Royce Associates 9 Prospect Rd Atlantic Highlands NJ 07716-1721

ROYCE, RAYMOND WATSON, lawyer, rancher, citrus grower; b. West Palm Beach, Fla., Mar. 5, 1936; s. Wilbur E. and Veda (Watson) R.; m. Catherine L. Setzer, Apr. 21, 1979; children: Raymond, Steven, Nancy, Kathryn, Ryan. BCE, U. Fla., 1958, JD, 1961. Bar: Fla. 1961, U.S. Dist. Ct. (so. dist.) Fla. 1961, U.S. Ct. Appeals (5th cir.) 1961, U.S. Ct. Appeals (11th cir.) 1981. Assoc. William W. Blakeslee, Palm Beach, Fla., 1961-62; with Scott, Royce, Harris & Bryan P.A., Palm Beach, Fla., 1962-94; pres. Scott, Royce, Harris, Bryan, Barra and Jorgensen, P.A., Palm Beach Gardens, Fla., 1982—. Bd. supvrs. Palm Beach County Water Control Dist. Mem. Fla. Bar (bd. govs. 1974-78), Fla. Citrus Mut., Fla. Cattleman's Assn., Internat. Brangus Breeders Assn., Fla. Blue Key, Phi Delta Phi. Democrat. Presbyterian. Home: 5550 Whirlaway Rd West Palm Beach FL 33418-7735 Office: Scott Royce Harris Bryan Barra and Jorgensen PA 4400 P G A Blvd Ste 800 West Palm Beach FL 33410-6562

ROYCHOUDHURI, CHANDRASEKHAR, physicist; b. Barisal, Bengal, India, Apr. 7, 1942; s. Hiralal and Amiyabala (Sengupta) R.; children: Asim, Onnesha. BS in Physics, Jadavpur U., India, 1963; MS in Physics, Jadavpur U., 1965; PhD, U. Rochester, 1973. Asst. prof. U. Kalyani, West Bengal, India, 1965-68; sr. scientist Nat. Inst. Astrophysics, Puebla, Mex., 1974-78; sr. staff scientist TRW Inc., Redondo Beach, 1978-86; mgr. laser systems Perkin-Elmer, Danbury, Conn., 1986-89; chief scientist Optics & Applied Tech. Lab. United Technologies Optical Systems, West Palm Beach, Fla., 1990-91; dir. Photonics Rsch. Ctr. U. Conn., Storrs, 1991—. Author: chpt. Optical Shoptesting, 1978; contbr. articles to profl. jours. Fulbright scholar U. Vt., 1968. Mem. IEEE, Optical Soc. Am., Soc. Photo-optical Instrumentation, Am. Phys. Soc. (life). Avocations: hiking, spl. edn. programs for children.

ROYCROFT, HOWARD FRANCIS, lawyer; b. Balt., Sept. 9, 1930; s. Howard F. and Bessie (Weaver) R.; B.A., U. Md., 1953; LL.B., Georgetown U., 1958; m. Barbara Lee Seal, Mar. 20, 1954; children: Suzanne Carol Roycroft Soderberg, Nancy Lee Roycroft Branigan. Admitted to D.C. bar, 1958, since practiced in Washington; mem. firm Hogan & Hartson, 1958, ptnr., 1965-87, mem. exec. com., 1970-73, counsel, 1987—; dir. United TV, Inc., 1982—; U TV San Francisco, Inc., 1983; mng. ptnr., dir. WIJY, Inc., Hilton Head, S.C.; lectr. Howard U. Sch. Law, 1971-73; mem. U. Tex., 1980; mem. Met. Washington Bd. Trade. Bd. dirs. YMCA Met. Washington, 1974-76. Served to 1st lt. USMC, 1953-55. Mem. ABA, Va. Bar Assn., Fed. Communications Bar Assn., Bar Assn. D.C., Nat. Broadcasters Club, Barristers, Aircraft Owners and Pilots Assn., Nat. Acad. TV Arts and Scis., Broadcast Pioneers, Kappa Alpha, Beta Kappa, Delta Theta Phi. Republican. Methodist. Clubs: Bryce Mountain Ski and Country (dir., pres. 1974-87, 82-87), Mt. Vernon Country, Old Dominion Boat, Washington Tennis Patrons, Army-Navy, Chaine des Rotisseurs Gastronome, Skull Creek Yacht Club. Office: Hogan & Hartson 555 13th St NW Washington DC 20004-1109 also: WIJY 2 Park Ln Hilton Head SC 29938

ROYDEN, HALSEY LAWRENCE, mathematics educator; b. Phoenix, Sept. 26, 1928; s. Halsey Lawrence and June (Slavens) R.; m. Virginia Voegeli, June 15, 1948; children: Leigh Handy, Halsey Lawrence, Constance Slavens. B.S. Stanford U., 1948, M.S., 1949; Ph.D., Harvard U., 1951. Mem. faculty Stanford U., 1951—, prof. math., 1958—, acting exec. head dept., 1957-58; assoc. dean Sch. Humanities and Scis. Stanford, 1962-65; acting dean Sch. Humanities and Sci. Stanford U., 1968-69, dean Sch. Humanities and Sci., 1973-81; vis. prof. Orta Dogu Teknik Universitesi, Ankara, 1966; Mem. math. scis. div. NRC, 1971-75; mem. adv. com. for research NSF, 1975-77, mem. adv. council, 1978-81; sr. postdoctoral fellow NSF, Swiss Fed. Inst. Tech., Zürich, 1958-59; mem. Inst. for Advanced Study, Princeton, 1969, 82-83, Forschungsinstitut für Mathematik, Zürich, 1979. Author: Real Analysis, 1963; editor: Pacific Jour. Mathematics, 1955-58, 67-69. Recipient Silver medal U. Helsinki, 1970; Guggenheim fellow, 1974. Fellow AAAS; mem. Am. Math. Soc., Math. Assn. Am., Finnish Math. Soc., Am. Inst. Archeology, Phi Beta Kappa, Sigma Xi. Club: Cosmos (Washington). Home: 13466 Three Forks Ln Los Altos CA 94022-2404 Office: Mathematics Dept Stanford U Stanford CA 94305

ROYER, DONALD E., lawyer; b. 1949. Grad., Ariz. State U.; JD, Western State U., 1976. V.p. Am. Savs. and Loan Assn., Irvine, Calif., 1983-85, exec. v.p., acting gen. counsel, 1985, sr. exec. v.p., gen. counsel, 1985—; v.p., asst. gen. counsel Fin. Corp. of Am. (parent), Irvine, Calif., 1983-84, sr. v.p., acting gen. counsel, 1984-85; exec. v.p., gen. counsel Fin. Corp. of Am. (parent), Irvine, 1985-88, Am. Savs. Bank, Irvine, 1988-91; pvt. practice law Irvine, 1991—.

ROYER, KATHLEEN ROSE, pilot; b. Pitts., Nov. 4, 1949; d. Victor Cedric and Lisetta Emma (Smith) Salway; m. Michael Lee Royer, June 6, 1971 (div. Aug. 1975). Student, Newbold Coll., 1968-69; BS, Columbia Union Coll., 1971; MEd, Shippensburg U., 1974; student, Lehigh U., 1974-75. Cert. tchr. Pa. Music tchr. Harrisburg (Pa.) Sch. Dist., 1971-77; flight instr. Penn-Air, Inc., Altoona, Pa., 1977; capt., asst. chief pilot Air Atlantic Airlines, Centre Hall, Pa., 1977-80; capt., chief pilot Lycoming Air Svc., Williamsport, Pa., 1980-81; govs. pilot Commonwealth of Pa, Harrisburg, 1981-87; flight engnr. Pan-Am, N.Y.C., 1987-91; pilot, 1st officer B737 United Airlines, Chgo., 1992—; first woman pilot/engr. crew mem. on 747, 1989-91, chief pilot, cons. Mem. Internat. Soc. Women Airline Pilots, Flight Engrs. Internat. Assn. (scheduling rep. 1989, scheduling dir. 1990, 1st vice chmn., mem. bd. adjustments 1989, rp. dir. scheduling, 1991-92), UAL-Airline Pilots Assn., 99's (coord. critical incident response program, 1994—, local chair Con Pa. chpt. 1987-92), Whirley-Girls (Washington), Hershey Country Club. Republican. Avocations: skiing, computers, golf. Home: 2047 Raleigh Rd Apt D Hummelstown PA 17036-8709 Office: United Airlines PO Box 66140 O'Hare Internat Airport Chicago IL 60666

ROYER, RAYMOND, transportation equipment manufacturing company executive. Pres., COO Bombardier Inc., Montreal, PQ. Office: Bombardier Inc, 800 René-Lévesque Blvd O, Montreal, PQ Canada H3B 1Y8

ROYER, RICHARD ADRIAN, hospital administrator; b. Akron, Ohio, July 31, 1951; s. Richard William and Jacqueline Ethel (Nelan) R.; m. Linda Louise Collins, Apr. 15, 1977; 1 child, Keith. BS, U. Akron, 1973; MBA, Cleve. State U., 1983. Staff auditor Ernst & Ernst, Akron, Ohio, 1972-74; asst. mgr., acct. Arnold Graphic Industries, Uniontown, Ohio, 1974-75; asst. controller Akron (Ohio) Gen. Med. Ctr., 1975-80; v.p. fin. Cuyahoga Falls (Ohio) Gen. Hosp., 1980-82, pres., 1982-88; exec. dir. Columbia (Mo.) Regional Hosp., 1988—. Dir. Community Improvement Corp., Cuyahoga Falls, 1987-88; v.p. Cuyahoga Falls C. of C., 1988; dir. Columbia United Way, 1989-90; dir. Mo. Symphony Soc. Mem. Am. Coll. Health Exec., Healthcare Fin. Mgmt. Assn., Coll. Osteopathic Healthcare Exec. (trustee 1988). Roman Catholic. Avocations: golf, music, reading, photography.

ROYER, ROBERT LEWIS, retired utility company executive; b. Louisville, Jan. 2, 1928; s. Carl Brown and Martha Helen (Garrett) R.; m. Carol Jean Pierce, June 24, 1950; children: Jenifer Lea, Todd Pierce, Robert Douglas. BS in Elec. Engring., Rose Hulman Inst. Tech., 1949. Registered profl. engr., Ky. With Louisville Gas and Electric Co., 1949-91, asst. v.p. ops., 1962-63, asst. v.p., asst. gen. supt., 1963-64, v.p., gen. supt., 1964-69, v.p. ops., 1969-78, exec. v.p, 1978, pres., chief exec. officer, 1978-89; chmn., 1989-91; dir. Louisville Gas and Electric Co., 1972-91, chmn. emeritus, 1991—; dir. LG&E Energy Corp., 1990-91; mem. exec. bd. East Cen. Area Reliability Coun., 1978-89; mem. Ky. Energy Resources Commn., 1974-79; mem. energy task force Gov.'s Econ. Devel. Commn., 1976-79; mem. Ky. Energy Rsch. Bd., 1978-88; v.p. Ind.-Ky. Electric Corp., 1979-89; dir. Ohio Valley Transmission Corp., 1978-90, Ohio Valley Electric Corp., 1979-89, Citizens Fidelity Corp. & Citizens Fidelity Bank and Trust Co., 1976-90. Mem. exec. bd. Old Ky. Home Coun. Boy Scouts Am., v.p. dist. ops., 1970-75, 79-80, 1st v.p., 1981-82, pres., 1982-84, commr., 1975-79, rep. to nat. coun., 1975-84, 95—, mem. regional bd., 1985—, S.E. region area pres., 1988-93; bd. dirs. East End Boys Club, 1975-78, Louisville Indsl. Found., 1980-86, Ky. Coun. Sci. and Tech., 1987-92; trustee Spirit of Louisville Found., 1978-90, J. Graham, Brown Found., 1980—; bd. mgrs. Rose Hulman Inst. Tech., 1979—; bd. dirs. Ky. Derby Mus., 1991-93, Leadership Louisville Found., 1985-91, Alliant Health Sys., 1989-94; mem. Louisville Devel. Com., 1979-83. Served with U.S. Army, 1955. Recipient Silver Beaver award Boy Scouts Am., 1975, Disting. Eagle award, 1989, Silver Antelope award, 1990. Mem. IEEE, Execs. Club Louisville (dir. 1980-83), Louisville Automobile Club (dir. 1974—, treas. 1977-79, v.p 1979-81, pres 1981-83, nat. adv. coun. 1982-86), Louisville Area C. of C. (dir. 1978-80), Hurstbourne Country Club, Pendennis Club, Rotary. Methodist. Home and Office: 4014 Norbourne Blvd Louisville KY 40207-3806

ROYESTESS, ROY, aerospace science administrator. Dir. John C. Stennis Space Ctr., Stennis Space Center, Miss. Office: John C. Stennis Space Ctr Bldg 1100 Stennis Space Center MS 39529*

ROYHAB, RONALD, journalist, newspaper editor; b. Lorain, Ohio, Oct. 6, 1942; s. Halim Farah and Elizabeth Della (Naiser) R.; m. Roberta Lee Libb, Apr. 20, 1969; children: David Libb, Aaron Nicholas. Student, Lorain County (Ohio) Coll., Kent State U.; postgrad., Am. U., Washington. Reporter Lorain Jour., 1966-69; state ho. correspondent Ohio Scripps Howard Bur., Columbus, 1969-70; reporter spl. assignment Scripps Howard Cle. Post, 1971-72; investigative reporter Scripps Howard Cleve. Press, 1972-75; chief bur. Scripps Howard Ohio Hur., Columbus, 1975-78; asst. mng. editor Scripps Howard News Svc., Washington, 1978-81; mng. editor Scripps Howard El Paso (Tex.) Herald Post, 1981-83; asst. mng. editor Scripps Howard Pitts. Press, 1983-92; assoc. editor Pitts. Post Gazette, 1992-93; mng. editor Toledo Blade, 1993—; bd. dirs. Toledo Blade Co. Bd. dirs. Am. Lebanese Congress. With USAR, 1964-70. Recipient 7 awards for Excellence Cleve. Newspaper Guild, 1972-75, spl. Sect. awards Pa. Newspaper Pubs. Assn., 1985, 86, 88; fellow Am. Polit. Sci. Assn., 1970-71. Mem. AP Mng. Editors Assn., AP Soc. Ohio. Eastern Orthodox. Avocations: physical fitness, music, outdoor activities. Home: 27262 Fort Meigs Rd Perrysburg OH 43551 Office: Toledo Blade 541 N Superior St Toledo OH 43660

ROYKO, MIKE, newspaper columnist; b. Chgo., Sept. 19, 1932; s. Michael and Helen (Zak) R.; m. Carol Joyce Duckman, Nov. 7, 1954 (dec. Sept. 1979); children: M. David, Robert F.; m. Judith Arndt, May 21, 1985; children: Samuel, Katherine. Student, Wright Jr. Coll., 1951-52. Reporter Chgo. North Side Newspapers, 1956; reporter, asst. city editor Chgo. City News Bur., 1956-59; reporter, columnist Chgo. Daily News, 1959-78, assoc. editor, 1977-78; reporter, columnist Chgo. Sun-Times, 1978-84; columnist Chgo. Tribune, 1984—. Author: Up Against It, 1967, I May Be Wrong But I Doubt It, 1968, Boss-Richard J. Daley of Chicago, 1971, Slats Grobnik and Some Other Friends, 1973, Sez Who? Sez Me, 1982, Like I Was Sayin', 1984, Dr. Kookie, You're Right!, 1989. Served with USAF, 1952-56. Recipient Heywood Broun award, 1968, Pulitzer prize for commentary, 1972, H.L. Mencken award, 1981, Ernie Pyle award, 1982; medal for svc. to journalism U. Mo. Sch. Journalism, 1979, Lifetime Achievement award Nat. Press Club, 1990; named Best Newspaper Columnist in Am., Washington Journalism Rev., 1985, 87, 88, 90; named to Chgo. Press Club Journalism Hall of Fame, 1980. Club: LaSalle St. Rod and Gun. Office: Chgo Tribune Co 435 N Michigan Ave Chicago IL 60611-4001

ROYSTER, VERMONT (CONNECTICUT), journalist; b. Raleigh, N.C., Apr. 30, 1914; s. Wilbur High and Olivette (Broadway) R.; m. Frances Claypoole, June 5, 1937; children: Frances Claypoole, Sara Eleanor. Grad. Webb Sch., Bellbuckle, Tenn., 1931; A.B., U. N.C., 1935, LL.D., 1959; Litt.D., Temple U., 1964, Williams Coll., 1979; L.H.D., Elon Coll., 1968; LL.D., Colby Coll., 1976. Reporter N.Y.C. News Bur., 1936; reporter Wall St. Jour., 1936, Washington corr., 1936-41, 45-46, chief Washington corr., 1946-48, editorial writer and columnist, 1946-48, assoc. editor, 1948-51, sr. assoc. editor, 1951-58, editor, 1958-71, contbg. editor, columnist, 1971—, editor emeritus, 1993—; sr. v.p. Dow Jones & Co., Inc., 1960-71; William Rand Kenan prof. journalism and pub. affairs U. N.C., Chapel Hill, 1971-86; regular commentator pub. affairs CBS Radio and TV, 1972-77; appears on pub. affairs programs on TV and radio.; sr. fellow Inst. Policy Scis., Duke, 1973-85; mem. adv. com. Pulitzer prizes Columbia, 1967-76; mem. Nat. Commn. Hist. Publs., 1974-76. Author: (with others) Main Street and Beyond, 1959, Journey Through the Soviet Union, 1962, A Pride of Prejudices, 1967, (memoirs) My Own, My Country's Time, 1983, The Essential Royster (ed. Edmund Fuller), 1985 contbr. numerous articles on financial and econ. subjects to periodicals. Bd. dirs. Newspaper Fund, Inc.; trustee St. Augustine Coll., Raleigh, N.C. Commd. ensign USNR, 1940; active duty 1941-46, Atlantic, Caribbean, Pacific theaters; exec. officer USS LaPrade comdg. officer USS Jack Miller, USS PC-1262 lt. comdr. Res. Recipient Pulitzer prize for editorial writing, 1953, Pulitzer prize for commentary, 1984; medal for distinguished service in journalism Sigma Delta Chi, 1958; William Allan White award for distinguished service to journalism, 1971; Loeb Meml. award for contbn. to econ. journalism UCLA, 1975; Elijah Lovejoy award Colby Coll., 1976; Fourth Estate award Nat. Press Club, Washington, 1978; Presdl. Medal of Freedom, 1986; named to N.C. Journalism Hall of Fame, 1980. Mem. Am. Soc. Newspaper Editors (pres. 1965-66), Nat. Conf. Editorial Writers (chmn. 1957), Phi Beta Kappa Assos., Phi Beta Kappa. Episcopalian. Clubs: University (N.Y.C.); Nat. Press (Washington). Home: 3450 Springmoor Cir Raleigh NC 27615 *Although mankind forgets old lessons to its pain, just as young people do those of their fathers, it always relearns them. It's comforting to remember that the Dark Ages lasted only 500 years.*

ROZEBOOM, JOHN A., religious organization administrator. Dir. Christian Ref. Home Missions. Office: Christian Ref Ch in N Am 2850 Kalamazoo Ave Grand Rapids MI 49560

ROZEL, SAMUEL JOSEPH, lawyer; b. Louisville, Apr. 22, 1935; s. Sam and Anna (Sessmer) R.; m. Jeanne Frances Foulkes, July 3, 1965; children: Brooke Jane, John Samuel. BSL, U. Louisville, 1955, LLB, 1957; grad., Advanced Mgmt. Program, Harvard U., 1979. Bar: Ky. 1958, D.C. 1962, Minn. 1968, Ind. 1970, N.Y. 1983. Atty. FTC, Washington, 1962-67; antitrust counsel Honeywell, Inc., Mpls., 1967-69; atty. Magnavox Corp., Ft. Wayne, Ind., 1969-71, gen. counsel, 1971, v.p., 1972-75, sec., 1973-75; v.p.

U.S. Philips Corp., N.Y.C., 1975-77, sr. v.p., 1977—; assoc. gen. counsel Philips Electronics N.Am. Corp., N.Y.C., sec. exec. mgmt. com., 1980—; v.p., sec., gen. counsel, dir. Phillips Electronics N.Am. Corp., N.Y.C., 1987-91, sr. v.p., sec., gen. counsel, mem. exec. com. bd. dirs., 1991—; bd. dirs. Philips Electronics N.Am. Corp., Std. Communications Corp. Served to capt. JAGC, AUS, 1957-62. Mem. ABA, Fed. Bar Assn., Ky. Bar Assn., Ind. Bar Assn., N.Y. Bar Assn., Harvard Club (N.Y.C.), Met. Club (Washington). Home: 215 S Bald Hill Rd New Canaan CT 06840-2908 Office: Philips Electronics N Am 125 Park Ave New York NY 10017-5613

ROZELLE, LEE THEODORE, physical chemist; b. Rhinelander, Wis., Mar. 9, 1933; s. Theodore and Alice (Omholt) R.; m. Barbara J. Ingli, June 21, 1955; children—David, Steven, Carolyn, Ann, Kenneth. B.S., U. Wis., 1955, Ph.D., 1960. Rsch. chemist DuPont Corp., Circleville, Ohio, 1960-63; prin. scientist-tech. coord. Honeywell Corp., Mpls., 1963-67; dir. chemistry div. North Star Rsch. Inst., Mpls., 1967-74; v.p. R&D USCI div. C.R. Bard, Billerica, Mass., 1974-77; dir. engring. tech. div. Mellon Inst., Pitts., 1977-78; dir. rsch. and devel. Permutit Co., Monmouth Junction, N.J., 1978-80; v.p. rsch. and devel. Gelman Scis., Inc., Ann Arbor, Mich., 1980-82; v.p. sci. and tech. Culligan Internat. Co., Northbrook, Ill., 1982-87; assoc. dir. rsch. Olin Chems. Rsch. div. Olin Corp., Cheshire, Conn., 1987-92; cons. in water treatment tech., mktg. and mgmt., 1992—; cons. in field; mem. Nat. Drinking Water Adv. Council EPA, 1987-90. Contbr. chpts. to books, numerous articles to profl. jours. Bd. dirs. Unitarian Ch., Andover, Mass., 1974-77. NIH fellow, 1958-60; recipient Spl. Hominum award Nat. Sanitation Found., 1988. Fellow Am. Inst. Chemists; mem. AAAS, Am. Chem. Soc., Am. Soc. Artificial Internal Organs, Health Industry Mfrs. Assn. (chmn. spl. activities com.), Water Pollution Control Fedn., Water Quality Assn. (chmn. sci. adv. com., Award of Merit 1989), Am. Water Works Assn., Assn. Met. Water Agencies, Filtration Soc., Pacific Water Quality Assn. (bd. dirs. 1987-90, Robert Gans award 1988), Am. Soc. Agrl. Engring., Internat. Water Supply Assn., European Membrane Soc., N.Am. Membrane Soc., Sigma Xi, Eta Alpha, Phi Lambda Upsilon. Home and Office: 626 N 23rd St La Crosse WI 54601-3825

ROZELLE, PETE (ALVIN RAY ROZELLE), former commissioner athletic league; b. South Gate, Calif., Mar. 1, 1926; s. Raymond Foster and Hazel Viola (Healey) R.; 1 dau., Ann Marie. B.A., U. San Francisco, 1950. Athletic news dir. U. San Francisco, 1948-50, asst. athletic dir., 1950-52; pub. relations dir. Los Angeles Rams Football Club, 1952-55; partner Internat. Bus. Relations (pub. relations), San Francisco, 1955-57; gen. mgr. Los Angeles Rams Football Club, 1957-60; commr. NFL, N.Y.C., 1960-89. Served with USNR, 1944-46. Mem. Pro Football Hall of Fame. Office: care Commr's Office NFL 410 Park Ave New York NY 10022-4407

ROZEN, JEROME GEORGE, JR., research entomologist, museum curator and research administrator; b. Evanston, Ill., Mar. 19, 1928; s. Jerome George and Della (Kretchmar) R.; m. Barbara L. Lindner, Dec. 18, 1948; children—Steven George, Kenneth Charles, James Robert. Student, U. Pa., 1946-48; B.A., U. Kans., 1950; Ph.D., U. Calif.-Berkeley, 1955. Entomologist in taxonomy U.S. Dept. Agr., 1956-58; asst. prof. entomology Ohio State U., 1958-60; assoc. curator hymenoptera, dept. entomology Am. Mus. Natural History, N.Y.C., 1960-65, curator hymenoptera, 1965—, chmn. dept. entomology, 1960-71, dep. dir. research, 1972-86; field expdns. in U.S., Europe, Mex., Trinidad, Argentina, Chile, Brazil, Venezuela, Morocco, Pakistan, Republic of South Africa, Namibia, Egypt; adj. prof. CUNY, 1968—. Contbr. numerous sci. articles on bees (Apoidea) and beetles (Coleoptera). Fellow AAAS; mem. Am. Inst. Biol. Scis., Entomol. Soc. Am. (editor misc. publs. 1959-60), Soc. Study of Evolution, Soc. Systematic Biology, N.Y. Entomol Soc. (pres. 1964-65), Washington Entomol. Soc., Pacific Coast Entomol. Soc., Kans. Entomol. Soc., Organ. Biol. Field Stas. (pres. 1990), Internat. Soc. Hymenopterists. Home: 55 Haring St Closter NJ 07624-1709 Office: Am Mus Natural History Central Park West New York NY 10024-5192

ROZENDALE, DAVID S., engineering and construction firm executive; b. Murphy, N.C., Mar. 18, 1934; s. Gerardus and Mary (Swan) R.; m. Helen Wallace McDaniel, Sept. 12, 1959; children: Kathy, Louise, Beth, Dirk. BS in Civil Engring., Clemson (S.C.) U., 1957. Registered profl. engr., Ala., Okla. Engr. U.S. Steel, Birmingham, Ala., 1960-62; with Rust Engring. Co., Birmingham, 1962-81, project mgr., 1972-75, v.p. constrn. dept., 1979-81; v.p. engring. and constrn. Rust Internat., Birmingham, 1981-83, pres., 1986—; pres. Kellogg Rust, Houston, 1983-85; chmn. adv. bd. Coll. Engring. Clemson U., 1984-88. Mem. exec. bd. Boy Scouts Am., Birmingham, 1986—, ARC, Birmingham, YWCA, Birmingham, Jr. Achievement, Birmingham. Capt. U.S. Army, 1954-66. Fellow ASCE; mem. TAPPI, AACB, ASME, Shoal Croer. Office: Rust Internat Corp Del 100 Corporate Pky Birmingham AL 35242-2928

ROZIN, PAUL, psychology educator; b. Bklyn., Aug. 3, 1936. BA, U. Chgo., 1956; AM, Harvard U., 1959, PhD, 1961. NIH fellow Harvard Sch. Pub. Health, Cambridge, Mass., 1961-63; asst. prof. psychology U. Pa., Phila., 1963-67, assoc. prof., 1967-70, prof., 1970—, chmn. dept. psychology, 1978-81; dir. honors programs U. Pa., 1974-76; mem. adv. bd. Children's TV Workshop, 1971-76; advisor psychology W.W. Norton & Co., Pubs., N.Y.C., 1974—. Editor Appetite, 1983—; mem. editorial bd. Jour. of Gastronomy, 1986—. Fellow Ctr. Adv. Studies, Stanford, Calif., 1985. Fellow AAAS; mem. Sigma Xi (nat. lectr.). Home and Office: U Pa Dept Psychology 3815 Walnut St Philadelphia PA 19104-3604

ROZMAN, GILBERT FRIEDEL, sociologist, educator; b. Mpls., Feb. 18, 1943; s. David and Celia (Friedell) R.; m. Masha Dwosh, Jan. 25, 1945; children: Thea Dwosh, Noah Dwosh. B.A., Carleton Coll., Northfield, Minn., 1965; Ph.D. (Woodrow Wilson fellow 1965-66), Princeton U., 1971. Mem. faculty Princeton U., 1970—, prof. sociology, 1979—, Musgrave prof. sociology, 1992—, dir. Internat. Studies Program, 1993—; dir. Coun. on Regional Studies, 1993—; mem. com. studies Chinese civilization Am. Council Learned Socs., 1975-80; mem. U.S.-USSR Bi-Nat. Commn. Humanities and Social Scis., 1978-86. Author: Urban Networks in Ch'ing China and Tokugawa Japan, 1973, Urban Networks in Russia, 1750-1800, and Premodern Periodization, 1976, Population and Marketing Settlements in Ch'ing China, 1982, A Mirror for Socialism: Soviet Criticisms of China, 1985, The Chinese Debate About Soviet Socialism 1978-85, 1987, Japan's Response to the Gorbachev Era, 1985-1991: A Rising Superpower Views a Declining One, 1992; co-author: The Modernization of Japan and Russia, 1975; editor: The Modernization of China, 1981, Soviet Studies of Premodern China: Assessments of Recent Scholarship, 1984, Japan in Transition: From Tokugawa to Meiji, 1986, The East Asian Region: Confucian Heritage and Its Modern Adaptation, 1991, Dismantling Communism: Common Causes and Regional Variations, 1992. Guggenheim fellow, 1979-80; grantee NSF, NEH, Social Sci. Research Council, Nat. Council for Soviet and E. European Studies. Mem. Assn. Asian Studies, Am. Sociol. Assn., Am. Assn. Advancement Slavic Studies, Am. Polit. Sci. Assn. Home: 20 Springwood Dr Trenton NJ 08648-1048 Office: Princeton U 2-N-2 Green Hall Princeton NJ 08544

ROZOF, PHYLLIS CLAIRE, lawyer; b. Flint, Mich., Aug. 3, 1948; d. Eugene Robert and Loveta Lucille Greenwood; m. Robert James Rozof, July 17, 1970; children: Nathan, Zachary. AB with high distinction, U. Mich., 1970, JD magna cum laude, 1977. Bar: Mich. 1977, Fla. 1978. Assoc. Honigman Miller Schwartz and Cohn, Detroit, 1977-81, ptnr., 1982—. Mem. Comml. Real Estate Women Detroit (pres. 1992-93). Office: Honigman Miller Schwartz & Cohn 2290 1st National Bldg Detroit MI 48226

ROZZELL, SCOTT ELLIS, lawyer; b. Texarkana, Tex., Apr. 12, 1949; s. George M. and Dora Mae (Boyett) R.; m. Mary Elizabeth McVicker, Dec. 16, 1972; children: Stacey Elizabeth, Kimberly Marie. BA, So. Meth. U., 1971; JD, U. Tex., 1975. Bar: Tex. 1975, U.S. Dist. Ct. (so. dist.) Tex. 1975, U.S. Ct. Appeals (5th and D.C. cirs.) 1976. Assoc. Baker & Botts, Houston, 1975-82; ptnr. Baker & Botts, 1983—. Bd. dirs. Houston Vol. Lawyers, 1984-86, 91-93; vice chair Cancer Counseling Inc., Houston, 1991-92; mem. devel. bd. U. Tex. Houston Health Sci. Ctr., 1994—. Mem. State Bar Found. (life sustaining), Houston Bar Found. (life, bd. dirs. 1991-93, chair bd. dirs. 1993), Am. Bar Found.; mem. ABA, Houston Bar Assn. (pres. elect

1995, bd. dirs. 1991-95), Fed. Energy Bar Assn., Ghost Squadron Confederate Air Force, Exptl. Aircraft Assn., Warbirds Am. Republican. Presbyterian. Avocation: flying old airplanes. Home: 5 Long Timbers Ln Houston TX 77024-5445 Office: Baker & Botts 3000 One Shell Plz 910 Louisiana St Houston TX 77002

ROZZI, SANTA CAPUTO, county official; b. Brklyn., Aug. 4, 1950; d. Frank Vincent and Mary (LaCava) Caputo; m. Samuel J. Rozzi, Mar. 7, 1981 (dec. July 1992). BA, Marymount Coll., N.Y., 1971; JD, St. John U. Law Sch, Jamaica, N.Y., 1981. Admission Bar of N.Y., 1982. Sec. Office of Town Atty., Town of Oyster Bay, N.Y., 1972-73, Office of County Comptroller, County Nassau, Mineola, N.Y., 1973-81; insp. Office of Compt. County of Nassau, Mineola, N.Y., 1981-82, dep. county atty., 1982-84, deputy county treas., 1984-86, bur. chief BREI, Office of County Atty., 1986-88, deputy county exec., 1988-93, treas., 1993—. Mem. Bar Assn. of Nassau County, Columbian Lawyers Assn. of N.C. Republican. Roman Catholic. Office: Office County Treas 240 Old Country Rd Mineola NY 11501

RUA, MILTON FRANCISCO, lawyer; b. San German, P.R., Dec. 8, 1919; s. Urbano F. and Josefa A. (Gonzalez-Ferrer) R.; B.A. cum laude, U. P.R., 1941, LL.B., 1943; m. Barbara Ann Becher (dec. Nov. 1989); children by previous marriage: Milton J., Jaime L. Admitted to P.R. bar, 1943; legal counsel Dept. Finance of P.R., 1943-46; sr. partner Rivera-Zayas, Rivera-Cestero & Rua, San Juan, P.R., 1950-73; founder Milton F. Rua Law Offices, San Juan, P.R., 1973-86; founder, counsellor Banco Mercantil de P.R., Rio Piedras, 1966—, chmn. bd. dirs., 1975—; founder Assn. Ins. Agencies, Inc., San Juan, 1972, Fajardo Fed. Savs. & Loan Assn., 1972—. Mem. bar exam. com. Supreme Ct. P.R., 1955-56; spl. counsel com. natural resources and beautification P.R. Ho. of Reps., 1967-68; mem. citizens com. nuclear plants Environ. Quality Bd. of P.R., 1972; chmn. Electoral Reform Commn., 1973-74; mem. organizing com. First Latin Am. Biennal Graphic Arts, P.R., 1970; bd. dirs. Casa el Libro, chmn., 1960-70; bd. dirs. Inst. of Culture of P.R., 1968-79, Students Art League of San Juan, Mus. P.R., P.R. Found. for Humanities, 1981-84; trustee Advance Ctr. for Studies P.R. and Caribbean, 1986—. Mem. Found. Bar Assn. P.R. (hon. pres. 1976-78), Bar Assn. P.R., Am., Inter-Am. bar assns., Iberoamerican Inst. Aero. Law. Clubs: Bankers, Union League (N.Y.C.), Elks. Address: Calle Candina # 10 Candina 10 San Juan PR 00907

RUAN, JOHN, transportation executive; b. Beacon, Iowa, Feb. 11, 1914; s. John Arthur and Rachel Anthony (Llewellyn) R.; m. Rose Duffy, July 10, 1941 (dec. May 1943); 1 child, John III; m. Elizabeth J. Adams, Sept. 6, 1946; children: Elizabeth Jayne Ruan Fletcher, Thomas Heyliger. Student, Iowa State U., 1931-32. Pres. The Ruan Cos., Des Moines, 1932-86, chmn., 1986—; chmn. Ruan Transp. Corp., Ruan Leasing Co., Ruan Aviation Corp., Ruan Fin. Corp., Ruan Ctr. Corp.; pres. and treas. City Ctr. Corp.; chmn. bd. dirs. and chmn. exec. com. Bankers Trust Co.; bd. dirs. Heritage Communications, Inc., Northwestern States Portland Cement Co. Mem. Des Moines Devel. Corp.; past pres. Greater Des Moines Com., Iowa State Engring. Coll. Adv. Council; fin. chmn., exec. com. Northwestern U. Transp. Ctr.; bd. govs. Iowa State U. Found.; bd. dirs. Des Moines Area Council on Alcoholism, Living History Farms; trustee Hoover Presidential Library Assns., Inc. Named Des Moines Citizen Yr., Des Moines City Council, 1981; elected to Iowa Bus. Hall of Fame, 1982; recipient Disting. Iowa Citizen award Mid-Iowa Council Boy Scouts Am., 1985, Humanitarian award Variety Club of Iowa, 1986, People With Vision award Iowa Soc. Prevent Blindness, 1986. Mem. Am. Trucking Assns., Inc. (treas., exec. com., chmn. fin. com.), Am. Trucking Assns. Found. (trustee), Iowa Assn. Bus. and Industry (bd. dirs.), Des Moines C. of C. (bd. dirs.). Republican. Methodist. Clubs: Wakonda, Des Moines; Lost Tree, Old Port Yacht (North Palm Beach, Fla.); Rancho LaCosta (Carlsbad, Calif.). Avocations: golf, mushroom hunting. Home: 23 34th St Davenport IA 52806 Office: Ruan Fin Corp 666 Grand Ave Des Moines IA 50309 Office: Ruan Cos 3200 Ruan Ctr Des Moines IA 50309-2535

RUANE, MAUREEN MURIEL, labor union official; b. Oceanside, N.Y., June 8, 1945; d. Joseph William and Muriel Helen (Bennett) Murphy; m. Martin Conrad Ruane, July 15, 1967 (div. May 1992). Grad. high sch., Valley Stream, L.I., N.Y. Sec. Local 854 IBT, H&W Benefits Plan, Valley Stream, N.Y., 1971-81; fund mgr. Local 854 Pension Fund Health & Welfare Benefits Plan, Valley Stream, N.Y., 1981-89; bus. agt. Local 854 I.B. of T., Valley Stream, N.Y., 1989, pres., 1990—; dir. Labor Edn. and Community Svc. Agy. Inc., Westbury, N.Y., 1988—; trustee Local 854 Health and Welfare and Pension Fund, Valley Stream, 1990—; del. Eastern Conf. Teamsters, Bethesda, Md., 1990—, Joint Coun. #16, N.Y.C., 1990—, indsl. trade divsn. Internat. Brotherhood of Teamsters, 1992—; area v.p. Internat. Teamsters' Women's Caucus, 1992—; adv. bd. Nat. Conf. Unions and Employees Benefit Funds, 1992—; commr. Teamsters Human Rights Com. and Joint Coun. 16 (rep. women's issues). Mem. Internat. Found. of Employee Benefits Plans, Assn. Benefit Adminstrs., N.Y. Inst. Technol., Indsl. Rels. Rsch. Assn., Ednl. Conf. Health and Welfare and Pension Plans. Lutheran. Avocations: exercise, sewing, decorating & modeling.

RUANO ANGULO, LUIS CARLOS, secretary of Mexican navy; b. Veracruz, Mexico, Aug. 29, 1927; s. Luis and Olga Joaquina (Angulo) Ruano; m. Clementina Beltran Ruano, Oct. 23, 1975; children: Olga Maria, Clementina, Luisa Fernanda, Beatriz Elena, Flor Herendira Ruano Beltran; m. Mrtha Elba Maldonado Ruano, Sept. 13, 1976; 1 child, Mariana Paola Ruano Maldonado. Grad. high sch., Mexico City. Commd. midshipman Mexican Navy, 1948, advanced through grades to admiral, 1986, naval attache Mexican Embassy in U.K. and France, commanding officer 6th Naval Zone, comdr. in chief Pacific-Alert 84 Operation, gen. inspector, commanding officer 1st Naval Zone, pres. Admirals Counsel, naval attache Mexican Embassy in Peru; Sec. of Navy Washington; prof. Superior War Coll. Roman Catholic. Avocations: naval modelism, saber fencing. Office: Escuela Naval 861, Eje 2 Oriente Tramo H, 04830 Mexico City Mexico

RUB, LOUIS JOHN, savings and loan executive; b. Bklyn., Oct. 2, 1915; s. Louis C. and Paula K. (Knoll) R.; m. Marguerite Gustafson, Sept. 5, 1942; children: Christopher L., Peter M., Timothy F., Marguerite L. B.S. in accounting; M.B.A., N.Y. U. Asst. sec. East River Savs. Bank, N.Y.C., 1946-49; asst. v.p. East River Bank, 1949-57; exec. v.p. First Fed. Savs. & Loan Assn., Shreveport, La., 1957-58; v.p. Fed. Home Loan Bank N.Y., N.Y.C., 1958-68; exec. v.p. Fed. Home Loan Bank N.Y., 1968-72; pres. Fed. Home Loan Bank of Pitts., 1973-80; chmn. bd. dirs. Suffolk County Fed. Savs. & Loan Assn., Centereach, N.Y., 1982-83; dir. First Fed. Savs. & Loan Assn. Pitts., 1981-85, U.S Mortgage Ins. Co., Blue Bell, Pa., 1981-86; mem. faculty N.Y. U., 1946-57, 59-63. Club: Duquesne (Pitts.).

RUBANYI, GABOR MICHAEL, medical research company executive; b. Budapest, Hungary, Jan. 7, 1947; arrived in U.S., 1982; s. Paul and Agnes (Hofmann) R.; m. Edith Linda Zoltan, May 5, 1973; children: Thomas and Dora. MD, Semmelweis Med. Sch., Budapest, 1971; PhD, Nat. Acad. Scis., Budapest, 1980. Med. diplomate. Asst. prof. dept. physiology Semmelweis Med. U., Budapest, 1971-76, assoc. prof. dept. physiology, 1976-82; vis. prof. dept. physiology U. Cin., 1982-83; assoc. com. dept. physiology Mayo Clinic, Rochester, Minn., 1983-86; dir. dept. pharmacology Berlex Labs., Cedar Knolls, N.J., 1986-90; head inst. Schering AG, Berlin, 1990-92; dir. vascular rsch. Berlex Bioscis., Richmond, Calif., 1992—. Editor: EDRF and EDCF, 1989, Cardiovascular Significance of Endothelium-Derived Vasoactive Factors, 1990, Endothelin, 1991, others; founder and editor-in-chief Endothelium, 1993—. Grantee NIH, 1988, AHA, 1989. Avocations: tennis, classical music, books, bridge, traveling. Home: 2426 Heritage Oaks Dr Alamo CA 94507-1445 Office: Berlex Bioscis 15049 San Pablo Ave Richmond CA 94806-1834

RUBARDT, PETER CRAIG, conductor, educator; b. Oakland, Calif., Aug. 7, 1958; s. Kenneth and Betty (Maspero) R.; m. Hedi Salanki; 1 child, Daniel. BA, U. Calif., Berkeley, 1981; M of Music, SUNY, Stony Brook, 1984; student, Hochschule fur Musik, Vienna, 1984-86; D Mus. Arts, Julliard Sch., 1989. Prof., conductor SUNY, Purchase, 1989-90, Rutgers U., New Brunswick, N.J., 1991—; resident conductor N.J. Symphony, Newark, 1990-93; assoc. conductor Syracuse (N.Y.) Symphony, 1993—; guest conductor various orchs. Condr. rec. Bach Concerti, 1988. Fullbright fellow USIA, 1984-86; Bruno Walter scholar, Julliard Sch., 1986-88. Mem. Am.

Symphony Orch. League, Condrs. Guild. Democrat. Office: Syracuse Symphony Orch 411 Montgomery St Syracuse NY 13202

RUBBERT, PAUL EDWARD, engineering executive; b. Mpls., Feb. 18, 1937; s. Adolf Christian and Esther Ruth Rubbert; m. Mary Parpart, Oct. 6, 1958 (div. 1985); children: Mark, David, Stephen; m. Rita Monica Saiia, Oct. 7, 1989. BS with high distinction, U. Minn., 1958, MS in Aero. Engring., 1960; PhD in Aerodyn., MIT, 1965. Rsch. engr. The Boeing Co., Seattle, 1960-62, 65-72, unit chief aerodyns rsch., comml. airplane group, 1972—; cons. NASA, 1989—, aeronautics adv. com., aerospace rsch. and tech. subcoms.; corp. vis. com. MIT, 1990—; served on various coms. Nat. Rsch. Coun. Panel; aerodyns. cons. GM; speaker in field. Contbr. articles to profl. jours. Recipient Arch T. Colwell Merit award Soc. Automotive Engrs., 1968. Fellow AIAA (Outstanding Tech. Mgmt. award Pacific N.W. sect., disting. lectr., assoc. editor jour., past mem. fellow selection com., dir., chmn. various workshops and coms.); mem. NAE. Achievements include three patents in field. Office: Boeing Comml Airplane Group MS 67-KE PO Box 3707 Seattle WA 98124-2207

RUBEL, ARTHUR JOSEPH, anthropologist, educator; b. Shanghai, China, Aug. 29, 1924; came to U.S., 1924; s. Arthur John and Marcella (Crohn) R.; m. Phyllis Lavern Howard, Apr. 22, 1954 (dec.); 1 child, Laura; m. Carole H. Browner, Jan. 1, 1986. B.A., Mexico City Coll., 1949; M.A., U. Chgo., 1958; Ph.D., U. N.C., Chapel Hill, 1962. Behavioral scientist behavioral sci. br. USPHS, 1962-63; asst. prof. U. N.C., Greensboro, 1963-64, U. Tex., Austin, 1964-66; asso. prof. U. Notre Dame, Ind., 1966-68; prof. U. Notre Dame, 1968-73; population program adv. Ford Found., Mexico City, Mex., 1969; prof. anthropology Mich. State U., East Lansing, 1973-83; behavioral sci. coordinator Mich. State U. (Coll. Human Medicine), 1975-77; prof. anthropology U. Calif.-Irvine, 1983—, rsch. prof., 1994—; cons. Ford Found.; reviewer social sci. rev. panel NIMH; Disting. vis. prof. Instituto de Investigación Antropológica, Nat. U. Mex., 1980-81; alt. U.S. del. Pan Am. Inst. Geography and History, 1980-83. Author: Across the Tracks: Mexican-Americans in a Texas City, 1966, (with others) Susto, a Folk Illness, 1984; contbr. articles to profl. jours. Served with USNR, 1942-46. NIMH fellow, 1962-63; grantee, 1969-71; NSF grantee, 1994-95. Fellow Am. Anthrop. Assn., Soc. Applied Anthropology, Soc. Med. Anthropology (pres. 1976), Latin Am. Studies Assn. Office: U Calif Dept Family Medicine Irvine CA 92717

RUBELI, PAUL E., gaming company executive; b. 1943; married. BS, U. Notre Dame; MBA, Columbia U., 1967. Assoc. A.T. Kearney Inc., Chgo., 1969-73; v.p., gen. mgr. Bunker-Ramo Corp., 1973-76; group v.p. Baker Industries, Parsippany, N.J., 1976-79; exec. v.p. and pres. Ramada Inns Inc., Phoenix, 1979-89; pres., CEO Aztar Corp., Phoenix, 1989—; chmn. Aztar Corp., 1991—. Served to 1st lt. AUS, 1967-69. Office: Aztar Corp 2390 E Camelback Rd Ste 400 Phoenix AZ 85016-3452

RUBELLO, DAVID JEROME, artist; b. Detroit, Sept. 3, 1935; s. Ludovico and Girolama (Trupiano) R.; m. Mary Anne Keithan, Oct. 14, 1978. BFA, Am. Acad. Art, Rome, 1961; MFA, U. Mich., 1972; cert., Accad. Fine Art Copenhagen, 1966. Lect. art U. Mich., Ann Arbor, 1973-74; assist. prof. art Pa. State U., University Park, 1974-80; assoc. prof. art Towson (Md.) State U., 1980-81; assoc. prof. U. Mich., Ann Arbor, 1988-90. One man shows include Cade Gallery, Royal Oak, Mich., 1987; exhibited in group shows at Detroit Inst. Art, 1987, GMB Gallery Internat., Bloomfield Hills, Mich., 1991, Kresge Art Inst., 1989, Kalamazoo Art Inst., 1990, 91, Photo Nat. 2, Ella Sharp Mus., Jackson, Mich., BBAA, Birmingham, Mich., Arts Coun., Traverse City, Mich.; also exhibited Null Dimension, Fulda, Germany, 1988, Systematica Constructive Art, Madrid, 1989, B4 Pub. Invitational, London, 1990, Konkrete Miniatures Invitational, Amsterdam, 1991.

RUBEN, ALAN MILES, lawyer, educator; b. Phila., May 13, 1931; s. Maurice Robert and Ruth (Blatt) R.; m. Betty Jane Willis, May 23, 1965. A.B., U. Pa., 1953, M.A., 1956, J.D., 1956. Bar: Pa. 1957, Ohio 1972. Law clk. Supreme Ct. Pa., 1956-58; prvt. practice Phila., 1958-65; assoc. counsel Aetna Life & Casualty Co., Hartford, Conn., 1965-69; corp. counsel Lubrizol Corp., Cleve., 1969-70; prof. Cleve.-Marshall Coll. Law, Cleve. State U., 1970—; adv. prof. law Fudan U., Shanghai, People's Republic of China, 1993—; dep. to city solicitor Phila., 1958-61; dep. atty. gen. State of Pa., 1961-65; spl. counsel to U.S. Senate Subcom. on Nat. Stockpile, 1962; commentator Higher Edn. Issues Sta. WCLV-FM, Cleve., 1975-87; mem. nat. panel labor arbitrators Nat. Acad. Arbitrators, Fed. Mediation and Conciliation Svc. and Am. Arbitration Assn., Ohio State Employment Rels. Bd.; lectr. law U. Conn. Law Sch., 1968; vis. prof. law FuDan U., Shanghai, Peoples Republic of China, 1988-89; cons. Shanghai Law Office for Fgn. Economy and Trade, Peoples Republic of China, 1991—. Author: The Constitutionality of Basic Protection for the Automobile Accident Victim, 1968, Unauthorized Insurance: The Regulation of the Unregulated, 1968, Arbitration in Public Employee Labor Disputes: Myth, Shibboleth and Reality, 1971, Illicit Sex of Campus: Federal Remedies for Employment Discrimination, 1971, Model Public Employees Labor Relations Act, 1972, Sentencing the Corporate Criminal, 1972, Modern Corporation Law, supp. edit., 1978, An American Lawyer's Observations on the Inauguration of the Shanghai Stock Exchange, 1989, Ohio Limited Partnership Law, 1992—, Practice Guides, Ohio Limited Liability Company, Law, 1995—; contbr.: With an Eye to Tomorrow: The Future Outlook of the Life Insurance Industry, 1968, The Urban Transportation Crisis: The Philadelphia Plan, 1961, Philadelphia's Union Shop Contract, 1961, The Administrative Agency Law: Reform of Adjudicative Procedure and the Revised Model Act, 1963, The Computer in Court: Computer Simulation and the robinson Patman Act, 1964, State Ltd. Partnership Laws, 1993. Bd. dirs. U.S. Olympic Com., 1968-73; chmn. U.S. Olympic Fencing Sport Com., 1969-73; pres. U.S. Fencing Assn., 1968-73; capt. U.S. Pan-Am. Fencing Team, 1971, U.S. Olympic Fencing Team, 1972; bd. dirs. Legal Aid Soc. Cleve., 1973-77. Winner Internat. Inst. Edn. Internat. Debate Championship, 1953; recipient Harrison Tweed Bowl and Am. Law Inst. prizes Nat. Moot Ct. Competition, 1955; named Guggenheim scholar, 1949-53, Fulbright scholar FuDan U., Shanghai, 1993-94. Mem. ABA, Phila. Bar Assn., Ohio Bar Assn. (corp. law and profl. responsibility com.), Cleve. Bar Assn. (Securities Law Inst.), Assn. Am. Law Schs. (chmn. sect. law and edn. 1976-78), Internat. Indsl. Rels. Rsch. Assn., Internat. Soc. Labor Law, AAUP (pres. Ohio conf. 1974-75), Phi Beta Kappa, Pi Gamma Mu. Home: 9925 Lake Shore Blvd Bratenahl OH 44108-1052 Office: Cleve State U 18th St And Euclid Ave Cleveland OH 44115

RUBEN, BRENT DAVID, communication educator; b. Cedar Rapids, Iowa, Oct. 17, 1944; s. Nate and Ruth (Subotnik) R. m. Jann M., Oct. 3, 1967; children, Robbi Lynn, Marc David. BA in Psychology and Advt., U. Iowa, 1966, MA in Mass Communication Rsch., 1968, PhD in Communication, 1970. Instr. to asst. prof. mass communication U. Iowa, 1969-71; asst. to assoc. prof. communication Rutgers U., New Brunswick, N.J., 1971-80, chmn. dept., 1980-84, prof., 1980-87, mem. exec. com. faculty profl. studies, 1981-82, mem. exec. com. PhD program in info. and libr. studies, 1981-83; fellow Rutgers Coll., New Brunswick, N.J., 1982—; dir. PhD program Sch. Communication, Inf. and Libr. Studies Rutgers U., New Brunswick, N.J., 1984-93, mem. Inst. for Health, Health Policy and Aging Rsch., 1986—, 1986—, Disting. prof. communication, 1987—; co-project dir. adv. bd. Nat. Survey Pub. Perceptions of Digestive Health and Disease and Louis Harris & Assocs., 1982-84; chmn. steering com. nat. digestive disease edn. program, NIH, 1983-84; sr. cons. grants Fund for Improvement Post-Secondary Edn., 1984-86; mem. nat. digestive diseases adv. bd. HHS, 1982-84; spl. cons. Can. Royal Commn. on Conditions Fgn. Svc., 1980-81; mem. Malcolm Baldrige Nat. Quality Awards Examination Com. 1994—; invited lectr. Yale U., W.Va. U. Med. Sch., Pitts. U., Duquesne U., Drake U., James Madison U., Columbia-Free State Health System, NIH, others; cons. Johnson & Johnson, Humana Hosp.-Sunrise, N.J. Bell, Bell Can., AT&T, Can. Agy. Internat. Devel., U.S. AID, Merck Sharpe & Dohme, Morristown Meml. Hosp., Cathedral Health Care Systems, York Rehab. Hosp. Chilton Meml. Hosp. Author: (with Richard W.Budd) Human Communication Handbook: Simulations and Games, Vol. 1, 1975, (with John Y. Kim) General Systems and Human Communication Theory, 1975, Human Communication Handbook: Simulations and Games, Vol. 2, 1978, (with Budd) Beyond Media: New Approaches to Mass Communication, 1979, Vol. 2, 2d rev. edit., 1988, Communication and Human Behavior, 1984, 2d rev. edit., 1988, 3d rev. edit., 1992, Non-Verbal Codes: Appearance, Action, Space and Time, 1985

(Japanese adaptation 1984), The Bottom Line: A Patient Relations Training Program, 1985, 2d rev. edit, 1988, (with Hunt) Mass Communication: Producers and Consumers, 1993, Communicating with Patients, 1992, (with Nurit Guttman) Caregiver-Patient Communication: Readings, 1993; author, editor: (with Budd) Approaches to Human Communication, 1972; (with John Kim) General Systems Theory and Human Communication, 1975; Communication Yearbook 1, 1977 (also founding editor), Communication Yearbook 2, 1978, Interdisciplinary Approaches to Human Communication, 1979, Information and Behavior, Vol. 1, 1985, Vol. 2, 1988, (with Leah Lievrouw) Vol. 3, 1990, Vol. 4 (with Jorge Schement), 1993, Quality in Higher Education, 1995; cons. editor: Hayden Communication and Human Behavior Series, 1978-78; Ablex, Communication: The Human Context Series, 1986—; mem. editl. bd. Internat. and Intercultural Communication Annual, 1980-86, Jour. Communication Therapy, 1982-86, Society, 1983-86, Communication Quar., 1979—; rev. editor Behavioral Sci., 1974-77; cons. editor Internat. Jour. Intercultural Rels., 1983—; reviewer Jour. Am. Soc. Info. Sci.; contbr. numerous articles, book revs., essays, conf. papers to profl. jours., chpts. to books. Mem. Franklin County, (N.J.) Twp. Human Rels. Commn., 1973-75; spl. cons. Ctr. for Disease Control, N.J. Collegiate Consortium for Health in Edn., 1981-82, chair Univ. Community Affairs and Outreach Com., 1992-93, Univ. Sen. Com. Rutgers and the Pub., 1992-93. Recipient Disting. Svc. award Coalition Digestive Disease Orgns., 1984; grantee , project co-dir. Nat. Assn. Broadcasters, 1970, U.S. Office Edn., 1970, Rutgers U., 1973-74, 74-75. Mem. Internat. Communication Assn. (chair pubs. com., conf. site selection com.), Ea. Communication Assn. (pubs. com., adv. bd.), Speech Communication Assn., Am. Soc. Info. Sci., Am. Hosp. Assn., Am. Soc. Patiesentation and Consumer Affairs, Am. Soc. Health Edn. and Tng., Assn. Libr. and Info. Sci Educators (rsch. com. 1988-89), Kappa Tau Alpha, Alpha Kappa Psi. Office: Rutgers U Sch Communication Info and Libr Studies 4 Huntington St New Brunswick NJ 08901-1071

RUBEN, GARY A., marketing and communications consultant; b. Cochem, Germany, Jan. 1, 1924; came to U.S., 1939, naturalized, 1943; s. Jules and Erna (Hirsch) R.; m. Irene Jehle, Aug. 12, 1962; 1 child, Monique L. Student, Acad. Comml. Art, Indpls., 1940-41. With advt. dept. Indpls. News, 1940-41; advt. mgr. Greater Indpls. Amusement Corp., 1941-42; pres. Ruben Advt. Agy., Indpls., 1948-68; chmn. bd. Ruben, Montgomery & Assos., 1968-76; pres. Prestige Program Sales Inc., 1973-76, Gary A. Ruben Inc. (advt. and mktg. cons.), Indpls., 1976—; past lectr. advt. Northwood Inst.; past pres. Nat. Fedn. Advt. Agys., 1971; bd. dirs. Connor Prairie Settlement, Noblesville, Ind., Acordia Sr. Benefits Corp. Hon. trustee Indpls. Children's Mus. With Combat Engrs. AUS, 1943-46. Home: 11812 Forest Dr Carmel IN 46033-4345 Office: 8900 Keystone Xing Indianapolis IN 46240-2146 *It was years ago, in the late 30's in Vienna, that the cry "Lebensraum" echoed across yet another land. And, a family, judged comfortable by most standards, scattered to the four winds, leaving behind all things material, but salvaging the will to survive and to commence once again in a new land. To a boy in his teens and still dressed in European-style short pants upon arrival in this country, the emotion, the sights, the sounds, and the smells were overwhelming and exciting to say the least. . .so began another chapter in my life. In the ensuing years, I learned the true meaning of individual freedom. And while the echoes of Vienna have become dim, that dim sound will continue to remind me that all worthwhile things in life are earned—not given, and even in adversity, there is opportunity.*

RUBEN, IDA GASS, state senator; b. Washington, Jan. 7, 1929; d. Sol and Sonia E. (Darman) Gass; m. L. Leonard Ruben, Aug. 29, 1948; children: Garry, Michael, Scott, Stephen. Del. Md. Ho. of Dels., Annapolis, 1974-86; mem. Md. Senate, Annapolis, 1986—, majority whip, 1995—; chair Montgomery County House Delegation, 1981-86, Montgomery County Senate Delegation, 1987—; mem. house econ. matters com., 1974-85, house ways and means com., 1985-86, legis. policy com., 1991—, senate budget and taxation com., joint budget and audit com., 1991—, exec. nominations com., 1991—, joint protocol com., 1991—, chair subcom. on pub. safety, transp., econ. devel. and natural resources, 1995—, mem. joint com. on spending affordability, 1995—, mem. capital budget subcom., 1995—; mem. Gov's. Motor Carrier Task Force, 1989—; conv. chair Nat. Order Women Legislators, 1980. Chair Women Legislators Caucus Md., 1982-84; trustee Washington Adventist Hosp., Takoma Park, Md.; bd. dirs. Ctrs. for Handicapped, Silver Spring, Md.; former internat. v.p. B'nai Brith Women. Recipient Cert. of Appreciation Ctrs. for Handicapped, 1987, Meritorious Svc. award Safety and Survival, 1989, Cover Those Trucks award AAA Potomac, 1989, Leadership Laurel award Safety First Club Md., 1989, Woman of Valor award B'nai B'rith Women, 1991, Pub. Affairs award Planned Parenthood Md., 1992, ESOL support recognition Montgomery County Pub. Schs., 1992, Appreciation award Fraternal Order Police, 1992, John Dewey award Montgomery County Fedn. Tchrs., 1992, Appreciation award ARC of Md., 1992, Safety Leader award Advocates for Hwy. and Auto Safety, 1993, Disting. Svc. award Gov.'s Commn. Employment of People with Disabilities, 1993, award Faculty Guild U. Md. for support of faculty and univ., 1993, Sincere Appreciation award for commitment to Md.'s youth Md. Underage Drinking Prevention Coalition, 1994, Faithful Svc. to citizens of Montgomery County award Montgomery County Assn. of Realtors, 1994; named Most Effective Pub. Ofcl. by residents of Silver Spring, 1990, One of 100 Most Powerful Women in Washington Metro Area by Washingtonian Mag., 1994. Mem. Coun. State Govts. (com. on suggested legislation), Hadassah. Democrat. Jewish. Home: 11 Schindler Ct Silver Spring MD 20903-1329 Office: Md State Senate 204 James Senate Off Bldg 110 College Ave Annapolis MD 21401-1676

RUBEN, LAWRENCE, real estate developer, building company executive, lawyer; b. Bklyn., Sept. 28, 1926; s. Irving and Minnie (Sruelif) R.; m. Selma Belfer. Dec. 20, 1952; children: Richard Gordon, Lenore Denise, Rochelle Gail Ruben Kivell. BA, NYU, 1949; LLB, Bklyn. Law Sch., 1951. Bar: N.Y. 1952. Gen. practice law N.Y.C., 1952-53; pres. Ru-Min Constrn. Co., N.Y.C., 1953-54; exec. v.p. Belco Petroleum Corp., N.Y.C., 1954-64, dir., 1954-85; v.p. Fundamental Bldg. Corp., 1952—; pres. Randall Devel. Co., Aragon Devel. Corp., Lawrence Ruben Co., Inc.; ptnr. Lexington Madison Co., Tower Plaza Assocs., Devonshire Assocs., Boylston Ptnrs., Devonshire Constrn. Co. Inc., Lawrence Assocs.; pres. Washington Mgmt. Corp.; mem. adv. bd. NYU Real Estate Inst. Chmn. N.Y. Builders and Realtors Fellowship Fund; trustee Nat. Jewish Ctr. for Immunology and Respiratory Medicine, Denver; patron Albert Einstein Coll. Medicine; sponsor Grad. Sch. Sci.; bd. dirs. Cardoza Sch. Law at Yeshiva U.; chmn. United Jewish Appeal, Scarsdale, N.Y., 1974-75. With AUS, 1945-46. Mem. ABA. Clubs: Fenway Golf, Boca Rio Golf. Office: 600 Madison Ave New York NY 10022-1615

RUBEN, LEONARD, retired art educator; b. St. Paul, June 3, 1921; s. Theodore and Elizabeth (Hauchman) R.; m. Sue Levey; children: James M., Elizabeth A., Nancy L., Thomas C. Diploma with hon., Pratt Inst., 1948, BFA, 1952; MA, Columbia Tchrs. Coll., 1961; PhD, NYU, 1970. Designer L.W. Frolich, N.Y.C., 1949-52; art dir. Young & Rubicam, N.Y.C., 1952-60; art group head North Advt., N.Y.C., 1960-62; instr. Columbia U. Tchrs. Coll., N.Y.C., 1962-63; assoc. creative dir. Compton Advt., N.Y.C., 1962-64; v.p. assoc. creative dir. J.M. Mathes, N.Y.C., 1964-68; exec. creative dir. Lake Spiro Shurman, Memphis, 1968-69; asst. prof. art Northeast La. U., Monroe, 1969-71; asst. prof. art U. Tex., Austin, 1971-74, assoc. prof., 1974-79, prof. art, 1979-82, F.J. Heyne Centennial Prof. in Communication, 1983-87; design cons. B.B. Martin Pub. Co., Austin, 1978; creative dir. Heart Assn., Austin, 1973. Precinct chmn. Dems., Lake Travis, Tex., 1979; chmn. advt. com. Austin Community Coll., 1980-84. 1st lt. U.S. Army, 1940-46, ETO, PTO. Decorated Bronze Arrowhead, Presdl. Unit emblem; recipient numerous awards including Advt. Appreciation award City of Houston, 1980, Thomas McCartin Tchg. Excellence award, 1983, Founders Day award NYU, 1971; Leo Burnet Creative Excellence Endowment, 1986, Frank Rizzo Meml. Creative grant Tracy-Locke, 1986. Mem. 27th Infantry Div. Assn., 105th (226th) Field Arty Assn., Dallas Soc. Visual Communication. Jewish. Home: 1102A Locust Ave Charlottesville VA 22901-4034

RUBEN, ROBERT JOEL, physician, educator; b. N.Y.C., Aug. 2, 1933; s. Julian Carl and Sadie (Weiss) R.; children—Emily, Karin, Arthur. A.B., Princeton U., 1955; M.D., Johns Hopkins U., 1959. Intern Johns Hopkins Hosp., Balt., 1959-60; resident Johns Hopkins Hosp., 1960-64, dir. neurophysiology lab., div. otolaryngology, 1958-64; practice specializing in pediatric otorhinolaryngology N.Y.C., 1964—; asst. prof. otorhinolaryngology N.Y. U. Sch. Medicine, 1966-68; mem. staff hosps. Montefiore Med. Ctr., Bronx Med. Hosp. Ctr., N. Cen. Bronx Hosp., Montefiore Med.; prof. Montefiore Med. Ctr., Bronx Mcpl. Hosp. Ctr., N. Cen. Bronx Hosp., N.Y., 1979—; prof. pediatrics Albert Einstein Coll. Medicine, Bronx, 1983—; assoc. prof. otorhinolaryngology Albert Einstein Coll. Medicine, N.Y.C., 1968-70, prof., chmn. dept. otolaryngology, 1970—; prof. pediatrics Albert Einstein Coll. Medicine and Montefiore Med. Ctr., 1983—; chmn. Nat. Com. for Research and Neurol. and Communicative Disorders, pres., 1982-84. Editor-in-chief: Internat. Jour. Pediatric Otorhinolaryngology, 1979—. Bd. dirs. N.Y. League Hard of Hearing, 1969-75, 76-85. Served to surgeon USPHS, 1964-66. Recipient Rsch. award Am. Acad. Ophthalmology and Otolaryngology, 1962, Edmund Prince Fowler award Am. Rhinological-Laryngological-Otological Assn., 1973, Gold medal Best Didactic Film, IX World Congress Otorhinolaryngology, 1977, Pres.'s award Am. Acad. Otolaryngology-Head and Neck Surgery, 1992, Johns Hopkins U. Soc. of Scholars, 1993. Fellow ACS, N.Y. Acad. Medicine; mem. AMA, Am. Assn. Anatomists, Audiology Study Group N.Y. (pres. 1964-66), Acoustical Soc. Am., Am. Acad. Ophthalmology and Otolaryngology, Soc. Univ. Otolaryngologists, Am. Otol. Soc. (sec.-treas. rsch. fund 1979—), Soc. for Ear, Nose and Throat Advances in Children (pres. 1973), Assn. for Rsch. in Otolaryngology (pres. 1985-86), Am. Acad. Pediatrics (chmn. otol. bronchoesphology 1983-85), Am. Soc. Pediatric Otolaryngology (historian 1986—), Am. Soc. Ped. Otolaryngologists (historian 1986-93, pres.-elect 1993-94, pres. 1994—), Nat. Inst. Deafness and other Comm. Disorders. Home: 1025 Fifth Ave Apt 12C S New York NY 10028-0134 Office: Montefiore Med Ctr 111 E 210th St # Vca-4 Bronx NY 10467-2401

RUBEN, ROBERT JOSEPH, lawyer; b. N.Y.C., Apr. 9, 1923; s. Ira Herbert and Kathleen Marie (Murphy) R.; m. Audrey H. Zweig, Nov. 20, 1949; children: Pamela Joan, James Bradford. B.S., Columbia U., 1943; M.A., Harvard U., 1948; LL.B., Fordham U., 1953. Bar: N.Y. 1954. Exec. trainee Chase Nat. Bank, N.Y.C., 1948-49; economist, 1949-53; assoc. Milbank, Tweed, Hope & Hadley, N.Y.C., 1953-55; assoc., then ptnr. Shea & Gould, N.Y.C., 1955-90; sec. Gen. Battery Corp., Reading, Pa., 1963-73, Fiat Metal Mfg. Co., Inc., Plainview, N.Y., 1961-64, Filtors, Inc., East Northport, N.Y., 1961-64, Trans-Industries, Inc. 1969—; asst. sec. Elgin Nat. Industries, 1975-88; asst. judge City Ct., Rye, N.Y., 1977-90; arbitrator Nat. Assn. Securities Dealers, 1990—, Pacific Stock Exch., 1992—, Am. Arbitration Assn., 1990—. Trustee Rye Hist. Soc.; bd. dirs. Carver Center, Port Chester, N.Y., 1972-90. Served with AUS, 1943-46. Decorated Combat Inf. medal. Mem. ABA, N.Y. State Bar Assn., Assn. Bar of City of N.Y., Am. Arbitration Assn., Harvard Club (N.Y.C.), Harvard-Radcliffe Club So. Calif., Columbia U. Club So. Calif., Beta Gamma Sigma, Zeta Beta Tau. Home: 21285 Amora Mission Viejo CA 92692

RUBEN, WILLIAM SAMUEL, marketing consultant; b. N.Y.C., June 23, 1927; s. Nathaniel Benjamin and Bertha Teresa (Stein) R.; children: Michaele, Marc. B.B.A., Syracuse U., 1950. Exec. trainee, buyer Dey Bros., Syracuse, N.Y., 1950-54; staff asst.-sr. v.p. Allied Stores Corp., N.Y.C., 1954-58; with Jordan Marsch-Fla., Miami, 1958—; gen. mdse. mgr. Jordan Marsch-Fla., 1962-64, mng. dir., 1964-66, pres., 1966-79, chmn. bd., 1979-83; pres. Bonwit Teller, N.Y.C., 1983-89, William Ruben, Inc., N.Y.C., 1989—; bd. dirs. Carnival Cruise Lines Inc. Pres. United Way of Dade County, 1979; mem. stategic planning com. United Way Am.; chmn. Dade County Co-ordinating Council, 1979—; mem. Gov.'s Revitalization Bd., 1980—; bd. dirs. Fla. Philharm., 1980-81; bd. overseers Parsons Sch. of Design, 1986—; chmn. Nat. Found. for Advancement in the Arts, 1983-88; bd. dirs. Theatre for a New Audience, Concordia Chamber Symphony. Served with USMCR, 1945-46. Recipient Silver medallion NCCJ, 1978, Humanitarian award Nat. B'nai B'rith, 1980, Outstanding Citizen award Dade County B'nai B'rith, 1979, Parsons Fashion award, 1983. Mem. Fla. Retail Feds., Greater Miami C. of C. (v.p. 1979—). Jewish. Clubs: Standard, Sky, Jockey, New World Center. Office: William Ruben Inc 40 E 88th St New York NY 10128-1176

RUBENFELD, STANLEY IRWIN, lawyer; b. N.Y.C., Dec. 7, 1930; s. George and Mildred (Rose) R.; m. Caryl P. Ellner, June 8, 1952; children: Leslie Ann, Lise Susan, Kenneth Michael. B.A., Columbia U., 1952, J.D. 1956. Bar: N.Y. 1956. Practice law N.Y.C., 1956-65, 68—, 1965-68; assoc. Shearman & Sterling, 1956-65; ptnr. Shearman & Sterling Paris, 1965-68; ptnr. Shearman & Sterling, N.Y.C., 1968-93, of counsel, 1994—crw; mediator U.S. Fed. Ct. Editor-in-chief Columbia Law Rev., 1955-56; contbr. articles to profl. jours. Bd. dirs., past pres. Port Washington (N.Y.) Community Chest, Levi Strauss Leukemia Found.; former bd. dirs. Residents for a More Beautiful Port Washington; advisor Columbia Law Sch. Lt. (j.g.) USNR, 1952-54. Stone scholar, 1951-52, 54-55, 55-56; Rockefeller Found. grantee, 1955. Mem. ABA, N.Y. State Bar Assn. (exec. com. tax sect., past chmn. fgn. activities com., reorgn. corp.), Assn. of Bar of City of N.Y. (tax com., past chmn. com. on recruitment lawyers), Nat. Assn. Law Placement (past bd. dirs., exec. com.), Columbia U. Law Sch. Alumni Assn. (bd. visitors, past bd. dirs.), Columbia Coll. Alumni Assn., Tax Club (past chmn.), Phi Delta Phi, Tau Epsilon Phi (past pres.). Home: 41 Longview Rd Port Washington NY 11050-3039 Office: Citicorp Ctr 153 E 53rd St New York NY 10022-4611

RUBENS, PHILIP, communications educator, technical writer; b. Washington, Jan. 13, 1943; s. Maurice and Anna Mae (Kindilien) R.; m. Brenda Knowles, May 4, 1969; children: Theresa Marie Norman, Alesia Lauree Chavez. BA, U. Tex., Arlington, 1970; MA, U. Tex., 1972; PhD, No. Ill. U., 1976. Instr. Braniff Airways, Santiago, Chile, 1966-67; teaching asst. U. Tex. at Arlington, 1970-71, No. Ill. U., DeKalb, 1972-74; asst. prof. William Rainey Harper Coll., Chgo., 1975-76; assoc. prof. Mich. Tech. U., Houghton, 1976-80; prof. visual & tech. comm. Rensselaer Poly. Inst., Troy, N.Y., 1980—; tech. writer Washington Gas Light Co.; dir. comm. Braniff Airways, LTV Aerospace, Gas Dynamics Lab., City of Arlington; sr. rsch. assoc. TechWriting Affiliates, Inc.; cons. in field including Software Group, 1984, N.Y. Edn. Assns., 1981-84, IBM Corp., 1984, 85, 87, TechWriting Affiliates Inc., 1985, 86, 88—, Short Bros., Inc., Belfast, Ireland, 1985, Indsn. Assocs., 1985, DuPont Corp., 1985, Bell Labs., 1985, U. Leeds, 1986, High Tech., Inc., Tokyo, 1987. Editor: (book) Science and Technical Writing: A Manual of Style, 1993; mem. editorial bd. Mohawk Monitor, 1980—, Roxbury Press, 1986, Iowa Jour. Bus. and Tech. Comm., 1987—, Computers and Composition, 1987—, MIT Press, 1988—. Mem. Smithsonian Inst., Washington, 1976—; faculty advisor Keweenaw Chpt. Soc. for Tech. Comm., 1976-80; mem. Sierra Club, 1980—; dept. rep. Hudson-Mohawk Consortium, 1980-81; sustaining mem. No. Ill. U. Exec. Alumni Assn., 1980—; chair, membership com. Mohawk Chpt. Soc. for Tech. Comm., 1980-81, vice chair, 1981-82; exec. alumni U. Tex. at Arlington, 1981—; mem. Saratoga Sailing Club, 1981—, Saratoga Performing Arts Ctr., 1981—; mem. Westport (Conn.) Hist. Soc., 1985—. Recipient Chgo. Poetry Soc. Award for Outstanding Religious Poetry, Award for Outstanding Children's Poetry, Award for Most Outstanding Poem for Yr., 1975, Writer's Key for Outstanding Writing Ability, Sigma Tau Delta, 1976, Chpt. Achievement award Soc. for Tech. Comm., 1979, Outstanding Article award, 1982, Tchr. of Excellence award N.Y. State English Coun., 1984, Award of Merit for Softbridge Online Tutorial, 1986; MIT Sloan Sch. Mgmt. Rsch. fellow, 1990, Soc. for Tech. Comm. fellow, 1992. Mem. AAAS (edn. com. 1982—), MLA, Am. Bus. Comm. Assn. (chair undergrad. studies com. 1977), Coun. for Programs in Tech. and Sci. Comm. (charter mem., judge CPTSC Logo Competition 1982), IEEE Profl. Comm. Soc. (edn. com. 1986, co-program chair of 1989 conf.), Midwest MLA, Nat. Coun. Tchrs. English (mem. tech. writing com. 1976—), Popular Culture Assn., Sci. Fiction Rsch. Assn., Sci. Writing Educators Group, Soc. for Tech. Comm. (judge internat. audiovisual competition 1985— and others. Home: 303 Bebington Dr Cary NC 27513 Office: Rensselaer Poly Inst Sage Labs Troy NY 12180

RUBENS, SIDNEY MICHEL, physicist, technical advisor; b. Spokane, Wash., Mar. 21, 1910; s. Max Zvoln and Jennie Golda (Rubinovich) R.; m. Julienne Rose Fridner, May 11, 1944; 1 dau., Deborah Janet. BS, U. Wash., 1934, PhD, 1939. Instr. U. So. Calif., 1939-40; research assoc. UCLA, 1940-41; physicist Naval Ordnance Lab., Washington, 1941-46; physicist Engring. Research Assocs., St. Paul, 1946-52; mgr. physics Univac div. Sperry Rand, St. Paul, 1958-61, dir. research, 1961-66, staff scientist, 1969-71, dir. spl. projects, 1971-75; cons., 1975-81; technical advisor Vertimag Systems Corp., 1981—, Advanced Research Corp., 1986—; lectr. U. Pa., 1960-61; mem. adv. subcom. on instrumentation and data processing NASA, 1967-69, panel on computer tech. Nat. Acad. Sci., 1969. Hon. fellow U. Minn., 1977— Fellow IEEE (magnetic soc. info. storage award 1987); mem. AAAS, N.Y. Acad.

Sci., Am. Phys. Soc., Am. Geophys. Union, Acad. Applied Sci., Minn. Acad. Sci., Am. Optical Soc., Phi Beta Kappa, Sigma Xi, Pi Mu Epsilon. Patentee in magnetic material and devices. Author: Amplifier and Memory Devices, 1965. Contbr. articles to profl. jours. Home: 1077 Sibley Hwy Apt 506 Saint Paul MN 55118-3616 Office: Advanced Rsch Corp 815 14th Ave SE Minneapolis MN 55414-1515

RUBENSTEIN, ALBERT HAROLD, industrial engineering and management sciences educator; b. Phila., Nov. 11, 1923; s. Leo and Jean (Kaplan) R.; m. Hildette Grossman, Sept. 11, 1949; children—Michael Stephen, Lisa Joan. B.S. magna cum lauda in Indsl. Engring. (Sr. prize econs.), Lehigh U., 1949; M.S. in Indsl. Engring, Columbia, 1950, Ph.D. in Indsl. Engring. and Mgmt, 1954; DEng (hon.), Lehigh U., 1993. Asst. to pres. Perry Equipment Corp., 1940-43; research assoc. Columbia U., 1950-53; asst. prof. indsl. mgmt. MIT, 1954-59; prof. indsl. engring. and mgmt. scis. Northwestern U., 1959—, Walter P. Murphy prof., 1986—, dir. Ctr. for Info. Tech., 1986—; pres. Internat. Applied Sci. and Tech. Assos., 1977—; vis. prof. U. Calif., Berkeley; cons. to govt. and industry. Dir. Narragansett Capital Corp. Author books and articles in field. Served with inf. AUS, World War II. Decorated Purple Heart, Combat Inf. badge.; Recipient Lincoln Arc Welding Found. prize paper, 1948, Pioneer in Innovation Mgmt. award Ctr. Innovation Mgmt., 1992; Omicron Delta Kappa annual fellow, 1949-50; Fulbright research fellow, 1955. Fellow IEEE (editor trans. 1959—, Engring. Mgr. of Yr. award 1992), Soc. Applied Anthropology; mem. Inst. Mgmt. Scis. (dir. studies for coll. on research and devel. 1960—, v.p. research and edn. 1966-68). Home: 2348 Ridge Ave Evanston IL 60201-2600

RUBENSTEIN, ARTHUR HAROLD, physician, educator; b. Johannesburg, South Africa, Dec. 28, 1937; came to U.S., 1967; s. Montague and Isabel (Nathanson) R.; m. Denise Hack, Aug. 19, 1962; children: Jeffrey Lawrence, Errol Charles. MB, BChir, U. Witwatersrand, 1960. Diplomate Am. Bd. Internal Medicine. Intern, then resident Johannesburg Gen. Hosp., 1961, 63-65, 66-67; fellow in endocrinology Postgrad. Med. Sch., London, 1965-66; fellow in medicine U. Chgo., 1967-68, asst. prof., 1968-70, assoc. prof., 1970-74, prof., 1974—, Lowell T. Coggeshall prof. med. sci., 1981—, assoc. chmn. dept. medicine, 1975-81, chmn., 1981—, dir. Diabetes Rsch. and Tng. Ctr., 1986-91; attending physician Mitchell Hosp., U. Chgo., 1968—; mem. study sect. NIH, 1973-77, Hadassah Med. Adv. Bd., 1986—, adv. council Nat. Inst. Arthritis, Metabolism and Digestive Diseases, 1978-80; chmn. Nat. Diabetes Adv. Bd., 1982, mem., 1981-83. Mem. editorial bd. Diabetes, 1973-77, Endocrinology, 1973-77, Jour. Clin. Investigation, 1976-81, Am. Jour. Medicine, 1978-81, Diabetologia, 1982-86, Diabetes Medicine, 1987-91, Annals of Internal Medicine, 1991—, Medicine, 1992—; contbr. articles to profl. jours. Mem. Gov's Sci. Adv. Coun. State of Ill., 1989—. Recipient David Rumbough Meml. award Juvenile Diabetes Found., 1978. Master ACP (John Phillips Meml. award 1995); fellow South African Coll. Physicians, Royal Coll. Physicians London; mem. Am. Soc. Clin. Investigation, Am. Diabetes Assn. (Eli Lilly award 1973, Banting medal 1983, Solomon Berson Meml. lectr. 1985), Brit. Diabetes Assn. (Banting lectr. 1987), Endocrine Soc., Am. Fedn. Clin. Rsch., Ctrl. Soc. Clin. Rsch. (v.p. 1988, pres. 1989), Assn. Am. Physicians (treas. 1984-89, councillor 1989-94, v.p. 1994—), Am. Diabetes Assn. (mem. bd. govs. 1985-93, mem. exec. com. 1990-93, chmn. 1992-93, mem. residency rev. com. 1994—), Am. Acad. Arts and Scis., Inst. Medicine (mem. coun. 1991—), Assn. Profs. of Medicine (councillor 1991-94, v.p. 1994—). Home: 5517 S Kimbark Ave Chicago IL 60637-1618 Office: U Chgo Dept of Medicine 5841 S Maryland Ave Chicago IL 60637-1463

RUBENSTEIN, BERNARD, orchestra conductor; b. Springfield, Mo., Oct. 30, 1937; s. Milton and Evelyn Marion (Friedman) R.; m. Ann Warren Little, Aug. 28, 1961; children: Tanya, Stefan Alexei. B.Mus. with distinction, Eastman Sch. Music, U. Rochester, 1958; M.Mus., Yale U., 1961. Assoc. prof. conducting, dir. orch. orgns. Northwestern U., Evanston, Ill., 1968-80. Asst. condr. R.I. Philharm. Orch., 1961-62; condr. music dir. Santa Fe Symphony Orch., 1962-64; condr. Greenwood Chamber Orch., Cummington, Mass., 1968-79; asst. condr. Stuttgart Opera, 1966-68; condr., music dir. Music for Youth, Milw., 1970-80; assoc. condr. Cin. Symphony Orch., 1980-86; music dir. Tulsa Philharm., 1984—; guest condr. numerous orchs. including, Milw. Symphony Orch., St. Paul Chamber Orch., Guadalajara Symphony Orch., Berlin Radio Orch., Frankfurt Radio Orch., Grant Park Orch., Chgo., die reihe, Vienna, Austrian Radio Orch., Eastman Philharm., Halle Symphony Orch., E. Ger., Warsaw Philharm., St. Louis Little Symphony, W. German Radio Orch., Palazzo Pitti Orch. Florence, Italy, Frankfurt Opera, Tonkuenstler Orch., Vienna., Southwest German Radio Orch., Baden-Baden, Jerusalem Symphony, Anchorage, Hamilton, Ont., Hartford, Conn., Am. Composers Orch., N.Y.C. Winner internat. conducting competition Serate Musicale Fiorentine, 1965; Fulbright scholar, 1964-66; recipient Charles Ditson award Yale U., 1961, Martha Baird Rockefeller award, 1966-68. Mem. Am. Symphony Orch. League. Office: Tulsa Philharmonic 2901 S Harvard Ave Tulsa OK 74114-6100

RUBENSTEIN, EDWARD, physician, educator; b. Cin., Dec. 5, 1924; s. Louis and Nettie R.; m. Nancy Ellen Millman, June 20, 1954; children: John, William, James. MD, U. Cin., 1947. House staff Cin. Gen. Hosp., 1947-50; fellow May Inst., Cin., 1950; sr. asst. resident Ward Med. Service, Barnes Hosp., St. Louis, 1953-54; chief of medicine San Mateo County Hosp., Calif., 1960-70; assoc. dean postgrad. med. edn., prof. medicine Stanford (Calif.) U., 1971—, emeritus, active; mem. teaching faculty mem. Stanford Photon Research Lab.; affiliated faculty mem. Stanford Synchrotron Radiation Lab., 1971—; mem. maj. materials facilities com. Nat. Research Council, 1984-85, Nat. Steering Com. 6 GeV Electron Storage Ring, 1986—. Author: (textbook) Intensive Medical Care; editor-in-chief: (textbook) Sci. Am. Medicine, 1978-94; editor: Synchrotron Radiation Handbook, 1988, vol. 4, 1991; editor Synchrotron Radiation in the Biosciences, Molecular Medicine; mem. editorial adv. bd. Sci. Am., Inc., 1991-94. Served with USAF, 1950-52. Recipient Kaiser award for outstanding and innovative contbns. to med. edn., 1989, Albion Walter Hewlett award, 1993. Fellow AAAS, Royal Soc. Medicine; mem. APS, ACP (master), Inst. Medicine, Calif. Acad. Medicine, Western Assn. Physicians, Soc. Photo-Optical Engrs., Am. Clin. and Climatol. Assn., Alpha Omega Alpha. Research on synchrotron radiation medicine. Office: Stanford Medical Center Dept of Medicine Stanford CA 94305

RUBENSTEIN, HOWARD JOSEPH, public relations executive; b. N.Y.C., Feb. 3, 1932; s. Samuel and Ada (Sall) R.; m. Amy Forman, Dec. 17, 1959; children: Roni, Richard, Steven. A.B., U. Pa., 1953; student law, Harvard, 1953; LL.B. (Dean's degree), St. Johns Sch. Law, 1959, LLD (hon.), 1990. Bar: N.Y. State bar 1960. Pres. Rubenstein Assocs., Inc. pub. rels. cons., N.Y.C., 1954—; asst. counsel judiciary com. U.S. Ho. of Reps., 1960; cons. U.S. Fgn. Claims Commn., 1961-62; cons. joint legis. com. child care needs N.Y., 1965-66; adviser SBA, 1965-66. Mem. Gov.'s Com. on Sale of World Trade Center, 1981, Mayor's Com. on Holocaust Commemoration, 1981—, N.Y. State Task Force on Energy Conservation, Dept. Housing, 1981-83, Mayor's Coun. Econ. Advisors, N.Y.C., 1974-77, Mayor's Com. Pub. Interest, 1975-77, Mayor's Coun. Econ. Advisors, 1991-93; co-chmn. Holocaust Commn., 1993—; v.p. Jewish Community Rels. Coun., 1988-94; past dir. Brownsville Boys Club; bd. dirs. Provide Addict Care Today, Police Athletic League, N.Y. chpt. March of Dimes; mem. U.S. Internat. Coun., 1977-81, Commn. on Status of Women, 1982-89, N.Y.C. Commn. Operation Welcome Home, 1992-97; trustee Cen. Park Conservancy. Mem. Assn. Better N.Y. (mem. exec. com. 1972—), Phi Beta Kappa, Beta Sigma Rho. Jewish (dir. congregation). Home: 993 Fifth Ave New York NY 10028-0105 Office: Rubenstein Assoc Inc 1345 Ave Of The Americas New York NY 10105-0109

RUBENSTEIN, JEROME MAX, lawyer; b. St. Louis, Feb. 16, 1927; s. Jacob J. and Anne (Frankel) R.; m. Judith Hope Grand, July 31, 1954; children—Edward J., Emily Rubenstein Muslin, Daniel H. A.B., Harvard U., 1950, LL.B., 1955. Bar: Mo. 1956, U.S. Dist. Ct. (ea. dist.) Mo. 1956, U.S. Ct. Appeals (8th cir.) 1956. Mem. English lit. faculty U. So. Philippines, Cebu, 1950-51; law clk U.S Dist. Ct., St. Louis, 1955-56; assoc. Lewis, Rice, Tucker, Allen & Chubb, St. Louis, 1956-64; assoc. Grand, Peper & Martin, St. Louis, 1964-65, ptnr., 1965-66; jr. ptnr. Bryan, Cave, McPheeters & McRoberts, St. Louis, 1966-67, sr. ptnr., 1968—; dir. Commerce Bank of St. Louis, N.A. Bd. dirs. Independence Ctr., St. Louis, 1985-88, The Arts and Edn. Coun. Greater St. Louis, 1991—. Served with USN, 1945-46. Bd. dirs. Independence Ctr., St. Louis, 1985. Served with USN, 1945-46. Mem.

ABA, Mo. Bar Assn., St. Louis Bar Assn. Jewish. Clubs: Mo. Athletic, Harvard of St. Louis (pres. 1982-83, bd. dirs. 1983—). Avocations: jogging; tennis. Home: 7394 Westmoreland Dr Saint Louis MO 63130-4240 Office: Bryan Cave 1 Metropolitan Sq Saint Louis MO 63102-2750

RUBENSTEIN, JOSHUA SETH, lawyer; b. Bklyn., Aug. 5, 1954; s. Seth and Elaine (Freedman) R.; m. Marta Johnson; children: Mary-Jane, Kenan, Rebecca. BA magna cum laude, Columbia U., 1976, JD, 1979. Bar: N.Y. 1980, N.J. 1980, U.S. Dist. Ct. (ea. dist.) N.Y. 1980, U.S. Dist. Ct. (so. dist.) N.Y. 1980, U.S. Dist. Ct. N.J. 1980, U.S. Tax Ct. 1986. Assoc. Fried, Frank, Harris, Shriver & Jacobson, N.Y.C., 1979-82; assoc. Rosenman & Colin, N.Y.C., 1982-88, ptnr., 1988—; mgmt. com. Rosenman & Colin, N.Y.C., 1994—, chmn. trusts & Estates dept., 1995—; adv. bd. TE/DEC Systems, Inc., Jour. N.Y. Taxation; lectr. in field. Contbr. articles to legal publs. Pres. Brasch Farms Civic Assn., Middletown, N.J., 1982-84, 340 E. 74th St. Owners Corp., 1990-91; dir., sec. Irvington Inst. Med. Rsch., 1991, treas., 1991-92, sec., 1992-93, co-pres., 1993-94, pres., 1994—; chmn. estates and trust splty. group task force, mem. exec. com. lawyers divsn. United Jewish Appeal-Fedns., 1989—, mem. legis. com., devel. com., bd. governance com., Madeleine Borg com., chmn., mem. exec. com., 1994—; trustee Jewish Bd. Family and Children's Svcs., 1991—. Recipient James H. Fogelson award Lawyers divsn. United Jewish Appeal-Fedns., 1993; named to Best Lawyers in Am. list, N.Y. Mag., Best Lawyers in N.Y. list, N.Y. Mag. Fellow Am. Coll. Trusts and Estate Counsel (state laws com.), N.Y. State Bar Found.; mem. Practising Law Inst. (estate adv. com., Hadassah estate planning seminar faculty and adv. bd. 1993—), ABA (real property and probate sect.), N.Y. State Bar Assn. (trust and estate law sect., lectr. 1984—, vice chmn. legis. com. 1988, chmn. 1989-91, Pres.'s Pro Bono Svc. award 1991, exec. com. award 1992, co-chmn. ad hoc com. to rev. proposals of EPTL adv. com. of N.Y. State 1991—, mem.-at-large exec. com. 1992—, exec. com. award 1992), N.J. Bar Assn. (adv. com. rels. with legis. and exec. brs., real property and probate sect.), Assn. of Bar of City of N.Y., Practising Law Inst. (lectr. 1984—), Phi Beta Kappa. Democrat. Jewish. Office: Rosenman & Colin 575 Madison Ave New York NY 10022-2585

RUBENSTEIN, MICHAEL ALAN, architect; b. St. Louis, July 18, 1944; s. Melvin Paul and Miriam (Schwartz) R. BArch, Wash. U., 1966, MArch, 1968. Registered architect, Calif. Designer Skidmore, Owings, Merrill, N.Y.C., 1967-68, Helmuth, Obata, Kassabaum, St. Louis, 1968-69, Peckham/Guyton Assocs., St. Louis, 1969-70, B.A. Berkus, L.A., 1970-71, Gruen Assocs., L.A., 1971-72; design cons. Gruen Assocs., N.Y.C., 1971, Studio Works, N.Y.C., 1972; design cons., mem. staff Experiments in Art and Tech., L.A., 1972-73; pvt. practice architecture Healdsburg, 1975-86; ptnr. Anderson & Rubenstein, Santa Rosa, 1986-87; prin. Rubenstein Architects, AIA, Santa Rosa, 1987—. Exhibited Eugenia Butler Gallery, Los Angeles, 1970, Calif. 101, Monterey Design Conf., 1980, Cultural Arts Council Sonoma County, 1986. Mem. Design Rev. Com., Healdsburg, Calif., 1978-80, chmn. 1980-83; mem. Steering Com., Healdsburg, 1981-83; coordinator Regional Urban Design Assistance Team, Healdsburg, 1982; chmn. Cultural Resource Survey Rev. Com., Healdsburg, 1982-83. Recipient Gold Nugget award Pacific Coast Builders Conf., 1989, Western Red Cedar Lumber Assn. Merit award, Quivira Vineyards Winery, 1990. Mem. AIA (bd. dirs. Redwood Empire chpt., v.p. pres. elect Redwood Empire chpt. 1986, pres. 1987, past pres., bd. dirs. 1988, Honor award 1984, Design awards, Plaza St. Cafe Merit award 1984, 86), Metal Constrn. Assn. (Honor award 1988), Quivira Winery.

RUBENSTEIN, RICHARD LOWELL, theologian, educator; b. N.Y.C., Jan. 8, 1924; s. Jesse George and Sara (Fine) R.; m. Betty Rogers Alschuler, Aug. 21, 1966; children by previous marriage: Aaron, Nathaniel (dec.), Hannah Rachel, Jeremy. Student, Hebrew Union Coll., Cin., 1942-45; AB, U. Cin., 1946; MHL rabbi, Jewish Theol. Sem., N.Y.C., 1952; DHL (honoris causa), Jewish Theol. Sem., 1987; STM, Harvard U., 1955, PhD, 1960. Rabbi in Brockton, Mass., 1952-54, Natick, Mass., 1954-56; chaplain to Jewish students Harvard U., 1956-68; univ. chaplain to Jewish students U. Pitts. and Carnegie Inst. Tech., 1958-70; adj. prof. humanities U. Pitts., 1969-70; prof. religion Fla. State U., Tallahassee, 1970-77; Disting. prof. religion Fla. State U., 1977-81, Robert O. Lawton Disting. prof. religion, 1981—; dir. So. Center for Study of Religion and Culture, 1973-82; co-dir. Inst. for Humanities, 1980—; pres. Washington Inst. for Values in Pub. Policy, 1982—; disting. vis. prof. Calif. State U., Chico, 1979; Edgar M. Bronfman vis. prof. U. Va., 1985; adv. bd. Washington Times, 1982-91, chmn. editorial adv. bd., 1991—; exec. adv. bd. The World and I mag., 1986—; exec. com. Internat. Jour. of the Unity of Scis., 1987—; adv. bd. Inst. for Study of Am. Wars, 1989-92; mem. presiding coun. Internat. Religious Fedn. for World Peace, 1991—; chmn. bd. trustees U. Bridgeport, 1994—; bd. dirs. Nostalgia TV Network, 1994—. Author: After Auschwitz: Radical Theology and Contemporary Judaism, 1966, The Religious Imagination, 1968 (Portico d'Ottavia lit. prize for Italian transl. 1977), Morality and Eros, 1970, My Brother Paul, 1972, Power Struggle: An Autobiographical Confession, 1974, The Cunning of History, 1975, The Age of Triage, 1983, (with John K. Roth) Approaches to Auschwitz, 1986, After Auschwitz: History, Theology and Contemporary Judaism, Johns Hopkins U. Press, 1992; editor: Modernization: The Humanist Response to Its Promise and Problems, 1982, Spirit Matters: The Worlwide Impact of Religion on Contemporary Politics, 1987, The Dissolving Alliance: The United States and the Future of the NATO Alliance, 1987, In Depth: A Journal of Values in Public Policy, 1991—; regular columnist Sekai Nippo, Tokyo, 1987—. Recipient Portico d' Ottavia lit. prize Rome, 1977; John Phillips fellow Phillips Exeter Acad., 1970; postdoctoral fellow Soc. Religion in Higher Edn.; Nat. Humanities Inst. fellow Yale U., 1976-77; Rockefeller Found. fellow Aspen Inst. for Humanistic Studies, 1979. Mem. Rabbinical Assembly Am., Am. Acad. Religion, Soc. Sci. Study Religion, Profs. World Peace Acad. (exec. com. 1980—, pres. 1981-82), Internat. House of Japan, Harvard Club at Nat. Press Club, Cosmos Club. Home: 751 N Lakeshore Dr Tallahassee FL 32312-1457 Office: Fla State U Tallahassee FL 32306

RUBENSTEIN, STANLEY ELLIS, public relations consultant; b. Balt., July 25, 1930; s. Albert B. and Lee (Goodman) R.; m. Ruth Anne Zinder, Feb. 8, 1953; children: Deborah C., Steven M., Michael L., Kenneth J., Andrew L. BA, U. Md., 1953. Writer, researcher Bozell & Jacobs, Inc., N.Y.C., 1953-54; reporter Jour. of Commerce, N.Y.C., 1954-56; writer, account exec. Ruder & Finn, Inc., N.Y.C., 1956-60; founder, pres. Rubenstein, Wolfson & Co., Inc., N.Y.C., 1960-91; pub. rels. cons. S. E. Rubenstein, N.Y.C., 1991—. Mem. Bd. Edn. Gt. Neck (N.Y.) Pub. Sch., 1968-74, pres. 3 yrs. Served with USN, 1948-49. Mem. Pub. Relations Soc. Am., N.Y. Fin. Writers Assn. (assoc.). Jewish. Clubs: Nat. Press; World Trade (N.Y.C.). Avocations: photography, travel, boating. Home: 51 Colgate Rd Great Neck NY 11023-1519 Office: 420 Lexington Ave Ste 300 New York NY 10170-0001

RUBENSTEIN, STEVEN PAUL, newspaper columnist; b. L.A., Oct. 31, 1951; s. Victor Gerald and Florence (Fox) R.; m. Caroline Moira Grannan, Jan. 1, 1989; children: William Laurence, Anna Katherine. BA, U. Calif., Berkeley, 1977. Reporter L.A. Herald Examiner, 1974-76; reporter San Francisco Chronicle, 1976-81, columnist, 1981—. Office: San Francisco Chronicle 901 Mission St San Francisco CA 94103-2905

RUBEO, BRUNO, production designer. Art dir.: (films) Spring Fever, 1983; prodn. designer: (films) Platoon, 1986, Salvador, 1986, Walker, 1987, Talk Radio, 1988, Blood Red, 1988, Born on the Fourth of July, 1989, Driving Miss Daisy, 1989 (Academy award nomination best art direction 1989), (with Stuart Wurtzel) Old Gringo, 1989, Kindergarten Cop, 1990, Sommersby, 1992, (with Marek Dobrowolski) Blood In Blood Out, 1993, The Client, 1994, Dolores Claiborne, 1995. Office: Sandra Marsh Mgt 9150 Wilshire Blvd Ste 220 Beverly Hills CA 90210*

RUBERG, ROBERT LIONEL, surgery educator; b. Phila., July 22, 1941; s. Norman and Yetta (Wolfman) R.; m. Cynthia Lief, June 26, 1966; children: Frederick, Mark, Joshua. BA, Haverford (Pa.) Coll., 1963; MD, Harvard U., 1967. Diplomate Am. Bd. Surgery, Am. Bd. Plastic Surgery. Instr. surgery U. Pa., Phila., 1972-75; asst. prof. Ohio State U., Columbus, 1975-81, assoc. prof., 1981-88, prof., 1988—; bd. dirs. Am. Bd. Plastic Surgery; chmn. curriculum com. Coll. Medicine, Ohio State U., 1984—; chief plastic surgery Ohio State U. Hosps., 1985—. Plastic Surgery Ednl. Found. research grantee, 1976, 78. Fellow ACS; mem. Am. Assn. Plastic Surgeons,

Assn. Acad. Chairmen of Plastic Surgery (sec.-treas. 1990-93, pres. elect 1993-94, pres. 1994—). Avocations: basketball, bicycling. Home: 100 Walnut Woods Ct Gahanna OH 43230-6200 Office: Ohio State U Hosps 410 W 10th Ave N-809 Columbus OH 43210-1236

RUBIN, A. LOUIS, advertising executive; b. Paterson, N.J., Jan. 15, 1954; m. Jeanne Stark, Jan. 21, 1978; 1 child, Matthew. BA, Clark U., 1976; MEd, Harvard U., 1977. Project dir. Benton & Bowles, N.Y.C., 1977-79; account exec. Dancer Fitzgerald Sample, N.Y.C., 1979-81; product mgr. Gen. Foods, White Plains, N.Y., 1981-84; account supr. Scali McCabe Sloves, N.Y.C., 1984-85; v.p., mgmt. dir. FCB/Leberkatz Ptnrs., N.Y.C., 1985-88; sr. v.p., mgmt. dir. Scali McCabe Sloves, N.Y.C., 1988-92; exec. v.p. Y & R Inc., LD & P, N.Y.C., 1992—. Home: 15 Whig Rd Scarsdale NY 10583-3013

RUBIN, ALAN A., pharmaceutical and biotechnology consultant; b. N.Y.C., July 10, 1926; s. Harry and Gertrude R.; m. Helen M. Feinstein; children: Jeffrey, Ronald, Howard. BS, NYU, 1950, M.S., 1953, Ph.D., 1959. Pharmacologist Schering Corp., Bloomfield, N.J., 1954-64; dir. pharmacology Endo Labs., Garden City, N.Y., 1964-70, v.p. research, 1970-74; dir. research DuPont Pharms., Wilmington, Del., 1974-82, dir. sci. info. and tech., 1982-87; dir. licensing tech. DuPont Merck Pharms., Wilmington, Del., 1987-91; cons. ARA Assoc., Rockland, Del., 1991—. Editor: Search for New Drugs, 1972, New Drugs: Discovery and Development, 1978; contbr. articles to profl. jours. Served with U.S. Army, 1944-46. Mem. AAAS, Am. Soc. Pharmacology and Exptl. Therapeutics, Soc. Exptl. and Biol. Medicine, Am. Heart Assn. Home: 207 Hitching Post Dr Wilmington DE 19803-1914 Office: ARA Assoc PO Box 244 Rockland DE 19732-0244

RUBIN, ALAN J., environmental engineer, chemist; b. Yonkers, N.Y., Mar. 20, 1934; s. Jerome and Lydia R.; m. Ann Kopyt, June 17, 1962; 1 dau., Sara. B.S in Civil Engring. U. Miami (Fla.), 1959; M.S. in San. Engring. U. N.C., Chapel Hill, 1962, Ph.D. in Environ. Chemistry, 1966. Civil engr. FAA, Ft. Worth, 1959-60; asst. prof. U. Cin., 1965-68; prof. civil engring. Ohio State U., Columbus, 1968-91, prof. emeritus, 1991—; with U.S. Geol. Survey, Columbus, 1991-93; vis. prof. Technion, Haifa, 1984. Editor 4 books on environ. chemistry; contbr. articles profl. jours. Served with AUS, 1953-55. Mem. Am. Chem. Soc., Am. Water Works Assn., Water Pollution Control Fedn., Internat. Assn. Water Pollution Research. Achievements include research on giardia cysts, metal ion chemistry, flotation techniques, disinfection, flocculation, coagulation, adsorption, and other physical-chemical treatment processes. Home: 1438 Sherbrooke Pl Columbus OH 43209-3113 Office: Ohio State U Civil Engring 590 Woody Hayes Dr Columbus OH 43210-1057

RUBIN, ALBERT L., physician, educator; b. Memphis, May 9, 1927; m. Carolyn Diehl; 1 child, Marc. BS, MIT, 1945; MD, Cornell U., 1950. Diplomate Am. Bd. Internal Medicine. Intern Bellevue Hosp., N.Y.C., 1950-51, resident internal medicine, 1951-54, fellow nephrology, 1954-55; dir. Rogosin Labs., Cornell U. Med. Coll., N.Y.C., 1963—, The Rogosin Kidney Ctr., N.Y.C., 1971—; The Rogosin Inst., N.Y.C., 1983—; prof. biochemistry, surgery, medicine Cornell U. Med. Coll., N.Y.C., 1969—; surgeon The N.Y. Hosp., N.Y.C., 1969—; mem. com. on sci. and tech. aspects of processing materials in space Nat. Rsch. Coun., N.Y.C. Cons. med. editor Time mag., 1983—. Mem. N.Y. Soc. of Nephrology (pres.). Office: Cornell U Med Ctr 1300 York Ave New York NY 10021-4805*

RUBIN, ALLAN MAIER, physician, surgeon; b. Bavaria, Germany, Aug. 4, 1947; s. Benjamin Rubin and Ida Spiegle; children: Alanna T., Marissa D., Sarina D.; m. Jean Tellander, Mar. 5, 1989. BS, McGill U., Montreal, Que., Can., 1968, MS, 1970; PhD, MD, U. Toronto, Ont., Can., 1979. Diplomate Am. Bd. Otolaryngology. Demonstrator neuroanatomy U. Toronto, 1971-73, resident, 1979-84; investigator Toronto Gen. Hosp., 1976-78; fellow otolaryngology Toronto East Gen. Hosp., 1985; asst. prof. dept. otolaryngology Creighton U., Omaha, 1986-87; assoc. prof. dept. surgery Med. Coll. Ohio, Toledo, 1987-88, chmn., prof. dept. otolaryngology, 1988—; mem. subcom. on equilibrium Am. Acad. Otolaryngology-Head & Neck Surgery, Washington, 1988-94; resident edn. com. Soc. Univ. Otolaryngologists, 1992—; Blue Cross N.W. Ohio, Toledo, 1992-93, HMO/Toledo Health Plan, 1989-93; pres. Acad. Senate Med. Coll. Ohio, Toledo, 1991-92; chmn. search for urology chair Med. Coll. Ohio, Toledo, 1991-92, presdl. search com., 1991-93. Mem. internat. editorial adv. bd. Jour. Otolaryngology, 1991—; contbr. articles to profl. jours. Rsch. grantee Biomed. Rsch. Support Grant, 1984, NIH, 1986, 87. Fellow ACS, Royal Soc. Medicine, Am. Neurotology Soc., Am. Acad. Otolaryngology, Am. Acad. Otolaryngology-Head and Neck Surgery (subcom. on equilibrium 1988—); mem. Soc. Univ. Otolaryngologists (resident edn. com. 1992—), elected AOA, 1994. Achievements include management and treatment of vestibular dysfunction and dizziness in children; correlation and transcranial doppler (TCD) and brain single photon emission computed tomography (SPECT) in patients with dizziness. Office: Med Coll Ohio 3000 Arlington Ave Toledo OH 43614

RUBIN, ARNOLD JESSE, aeronautical engineer; b. Bklyn., Sept. 30, 1924; s. Jack and Birdie (Reiss) R.; B. Aero. Engring., N.Y.U., 1949; postgrad., U. Va., 1950. Poly. Inst. Bklyn., 1960-62; m. Gloria Form, June 19, 1949; children—Jacquelin Sue, Mitchell Myles. Aero. research scientist Langley Research Center, NASA, Hampton, Va., 1949-51; with Fairchild Republic Co., Fairchild Industries, Inc., Farmingdale, N.Y., 1951-87, prin. aerodyn. engr., 1979-82, chief aerodyns., T-46A, 1982-87. Served with USAAF, 1943-45. Fellow AIAA (asso.); mem. Soc. Flight Test Engrs., N.Y.U. Alumni Assn. Club: Huron. Home: 106 Sprucewood Dr Levittown NY 11756-3837

RUBIN, BARRY MITCHEL, foreign policy analyst, writer; b. Washington, Jan. 28, 1950; s. David and Helen Victoria (Segal) R.; m. Judith Colp; 1 child, Gavriella. BA, Richmond Coll., 1972; MA, Rutgers U., 1974; PhD, Georgetown U., 1978. Sr. fellow CSIS, Washington, 1978-85, Washington Inst. Near East Policy, Washington, 1988-91; congl. fellow Coun. Fgn. Rels., Washington, 1985-86; fellow Johns Hopkins SAIS, Washington, 1986-93, prof., 1986-93; sr. fellow Hebrew U. Harry S. Truman Inst., 1989—, U. Haifa Jewish-Arab Ctr., 1993—, Bar-Ilan U. BESA Ctr., 1994—; adj. prof. Johns Hopkins SAIS, Washington, 1986-93, dir. SAIS project public study terrorism; mem. fgn. policy staff U.S. Senate, 1985-86; prof. Hebrew U., 1994—. Author: Paved with Good Intentions, 1980, The Arab States and the Palestine Conflict, 1982, Secrets of State, 1985, Modern Dictators, 1987, Istanbul Intrigues, 1989, Islamic Fundamentalists in Egyptian Politics, 1991, Cauldron of Turmoil, 1992, Resolution Until Victory?: The Politics of the PLO, 1994, Assimilation and its Discontents, 1995; editor: (with others) The Human Rights Reader, 1979, The Israel-Arab Reader, 1984, 95, Central American Crisis Reader, 1987, The Politics of Terrorism, 3 vols., Iraq's Road to War, 1994. Internat. affairs fellow Coun. on Fgn. Rels. 1984-85, Fulbright fellow, 1990-91; grantee U.S. Inst. of Peace, 1989-91, Davis Inst., 1994; Harry Guggenheim fellow, 1990. Mem. Assn. Israel Studies (v.p. 1984-89). Address: Haim ve-Elisha 16, Tel Aviv Israel 64288

RUBIN, BONNIE MILLER, journalist; b. Chgo., Aug. 17, 1951; d. George and Florence Ila (Rubin) Miller; m. David Rubin, June 30, 1974; children: Michael, Alyssa. BA, Drake U., 1973. Sports reporter Quad City Times, Davenport, Iowa, 1973-75; community rels. asst. dir. Metropolitan Med. Ctr., Minn., 1975-77; reporter Minneapolis Star Tribune, 1977-85; features editor Post Tribune, Gary, Ind., 1985-90; home editor Chgo. Tribune, 1990-93, met. reporter, 1993—. Author Time Out, 1987, Great Escapes from Chicago, 1992. Mem. Am. Assn. Sunday and Feature Editors. Office: Chgo Tribune Co 435 N Michigan Ave Chicago IL 60611-4001

RUBIN, BRUCE ALAN, lawyer; b. Pitts., Sept. 12, 1951; s. Stanley and Elaine (Roth) R.; m. Suzanne Kay Boss, Aug. 23, 1975; children: Daniel, Jay. BA, Yale U., 1973; JD, Stanford U., 1976. Bar: Oreg. 1976, U.S. Dist. Ct. Oreg. 1976, U.S. Ct. Appeals (9th cir.) 1976. Atty. Miller, Nash, Wiener, Hager & Carlsen, Portland, 1976—; bd. dirs. Classroom Law Project, Portland, 1990-94. Author Wrongful Discharge in Oregon, 1988. Mem. Oreg. State Bar (disciplinary coun. 1990—), Jewish Community Ctr. Avocation: competitive long distance running. Office: Miller Nash Wiener Hager & Carlsen 111 SW 5th Ave Portland OR 97204-3604

RUBIN, BRUCE JOEL, screenwriter, director, producer; b. Detroit, Mar. 10, 1943; s. Jim and Sondra R.; m. Blanche Mallins; children: Joshua, Ari. Student, Wayne State U., 1960-62; grad. film sch., NYU, 1965. Former asst. film editor NBC News; mem. film dept. Whitney Mus., assoc. curator. Screenwriter: (with Robert Statzel and Phillip Frank Messina) Brainstorm, 1983, Deadly Friend, 1986, Ghost, 1990 (Academy award best original screenplay 1990), Jacob's Ladder, 1990; writer, dir., prodr. My Life, 1993. Office: care Geoffrey Sanford 1015 Gayley Ave Fl 3 Los Angeles CA 90024-3424

RUBIN, BRUCE S., public relations executive; b. Miami, Fla., June 28, 1947; s. Earl Myrona and Claire (Malbin) R.; m. Cheryl Joy Cunningham, Aug. 1, 1980. BA in Journalism, U. Miami, 1969. Reporter The Miami News, 1969; v.p. Ronald Levitt Assocs., Inc., Coral Gables, Fla., 1970-75; pres. Bruce Rubin & Assocs., Miami, 1975-94; chmn. bd. Rubin Barney & Birger, Inc., Miami, 1994—; (pres. Counselors Acad., 1987. Recipient Exec. Achievement in Pub. Rels. award O'Dwyer's Directory of Pub. Rels. Execs., 1991, 94. Mem. Pub. Rels. Soc. Am. (accredited, pres. Miami chpt., counselor of pub. rels. 1978). Home: 8065 SW 86 Ter Miami FL 33143 Office: 255 Alhambra Circle #500 Miami FL 33134-7404

RUBIN, CARL BERNARD, federal judge; b. Cin., Mar. 27, 1920; s. John I. and Ethel (Friedman) R.; m. Gloria Weiland, Sept. 23, 1945; children: Marc W., C. Barry, Pam G., Robert S. BA, U. Cin., 1942, JD, 1944, LLD (hon.), 1988. Bar: Ohio 1944. Practiced in Cin., 1944-71; asst. pros. atty. Hamilton County (Ohio), Cin., 1950-60; judge U.S. Dist. Ct. So. Dist. Ohio, 1971—, chief judge, 1979-90; instr. criminal law Chase Coll. Law, Cin., 1965-67, adj. prof. law, 1987-88; adj. prof. law U. Dayton Coll. Law, 1976; mem. com. on ct. adminstrn. fed. cts. U.S. Jud. Conf., 1975-83; mem. Jud. Coun. 6th Cir., 1985-88. Contbr. articles to legal publs. Mem. 6th Cir. Dist. Judges Assn. (pres. 1977-78). Office: US Dist Ct 801 US Courthouse & PO Bldg 5th & Walnut Sts Cincinnati OH 45202

RUBIN, CHARLES ELLIOTT, lawyer, sports agent; b. Kansas City, Mo., May 28, 1947; s. Irving C. and Anna Lee (Strauss) R.; m. Linda Jean Nichols, Aug. 6, 1973; children: Aaron Mathew, Joanne Michelle. BSBA, U. Mo., 1969, JD, 1972. Bar: Mo. 1973, U.S. Dist. Ct. (we. dist.) Mo. 1973, U.S. Tax Ct. 1974, U.S. Ct. Appeals (8th cir.) 1974, U.S. Supreme Ct. 1976. Ptnr. Jackson & Sherman, Kansas City, 1973-76, Barker, Rubin & Pummill, Kansas City, 1976—; chmn. Assured Mgmt. Co., Westwood, Kans., 1990—. Mem. Kansas City Bd. Zoning Adjustment, 1981-84; bd. dirs. New Reform Temple, Kansas City, 1985—, Menorah Med. Ctr., Kansas City, 1987—, Children's Mercy Hosp., Kansas City, 1988—. Mem. ABA, Kansas City Bar Assn., Am. Judicature Assn., Oakwood Country Club (bd. dirs.), Shadow Glen Club. Avocations: outdoors activities, golf, scuba diving. Office: Assured Mgmt Co 1901 W 47th Pl Ste 200 Shawnee Mission KS 66205-1834

RUBIN, DAVID LEE, French literature educator, critic, editor, publisher; b. Indpls., Sept. 30, 1939; s. Ira Bertram and Jeanne Iva (Gamso) R.; m. Carolyn Dettman, June 12, 1965; 1 child, Timothy Craig. BA, U. Tenn., 1962; cert., U. Paris, 1963; MA, U. Ill., 1964, PhD, 1967. Instr. French U. Ill., Urbana, 1966-67; asst. prof. U. Chgo., 1967-69; asst. prof. U. Va., Charlottesville, 1969-74, assoc. prof., 1974-82, prof. French, 1982—; seminar dir. Folger Inst., 1989; founder Rookwood Press, 1992—; cons. Can. Coun., Etudes littéraires françaises, NEH, numerous univ. presses; lectr., spkr. in field. Author: Higher Hidden Order, 1972, The Knot of Artifice, 1981, A Pact with Silence, 1991; editor: The Selected Poetry and Prose of John T. Napier, 1972, La poesie française du siecle, 1986, Sun King, 1991; co-editor: La Coherence interieure, 1977, Convergences, 1989, The Ladder of High Designs, 1991, The Fulbright Difference, 1993; founding editor Continuum, 1989-93, EMF Studies in Early Modern France, 1994—, EMF Monographs, 1994—; mem. editl. bd. Purdue Monographs, 1975—, Oeuvres et Critiques, 1976—, Cahiers du, 1986—, French rev., 1986-94; Am. corr. Cahiers Maynard, 1973—, Cahiers Tristan L'Hermite, 1989—; contbr. chpts. to books, articles to profl. jours. U.S. State Dept. Fulbright fellow, 1962-63, Woodrow Wilson Found. fellow, 1963-64, Guggenheim Found. fellow, 1980-81. Mem. MLA, ACLU, Farmington Club, Boar's Head Club, Phi Beta Kappa. Avocations: reading, travel, fitness. Home: 520 Rookwood Pl Charlottesville VA 22903-4734 Office: U Va French Dept 302 Cabell Hall Charlottesville VA 22903

RUBIN, DAVID ROBERT, corporate executive; b. Bklyn., Aug. 3, 1933; s. Benjamin and Ruth M. (Shapiro) R.; m. Roberta Jean Hattis, July 4, 1959; children: Julia Anne, Martha Beth, Laura Rachel, John Andrew. B.A. cum laude, Harvard Coll., 1955; M.B.A. with distinction, U. Mich., 1959. C.P.A., Ill. Mgmt. cons. Arthur Young & Co., Chgo., 1959-68; sr. v.p. Midwest Stock Exchange, Chgo., 1968-70, exec. v.p., 1972-79; pres. Midwest Stock Exchange Service Corp., Chgo., 1970-72; chmn., dir. GRI Corp., 1979-89; CEO Odesta Corp., Northbrook, Ill., 1989-94, also bd. dirs.; dir. The Hollins Group, Chgo., 1994—; bd. dirs. Direct Mktg. Assn., Midwest Securities Trust Co., Mortgage Backed Securities Clearing Corp., Geo. T. Schmidt & Co., Buckingham Fin. Svcs., Allnet Comm. Svcs., Inc., Options Clearing Corp., ATC & Assocs. Inc.; adj. prof. DePaul U. Grad. Sch. Bus., Lake Forest Grad. Sch. Mgmt. Trustee Glencoe (Ill.) Village Caucus, 1970-72, 76-88, Glencoe Sch. Bd. Caucus, 1970-72; trustee Village of Glencoe, 1980-87, treas., 1989—; chief crusader Crusade of Mercy, Chgo., 1972—; class agt. Harvard Coll.; bd. dirs. Columbia Coll., Chgo., 1987—; Ill. Facility Fund, 1992—. Served with U.S. Army, 1955-57. Mem. AICPAs, Ill. Soc. CPAs, Standard Club, Castle Park Club. Home: 415 Kelling Ln Glencoe IL 60022-1112 Office: ATC & Assocs Inc 415 Kelling Ln Glencoe IL 60022-1112

RUBIN, DONALD BRUCE, statistician, educator, research company executive; b. Washington, D.C., Dec. 22, 1943; s. Allan A. and Harriet (Schainis) R.; m. Kathryn M. Kazarow; children: Scott Wilk, Paul Stuart. AB magna cum laude, Princeton U., 1965; MS, Harvard U., 1966, PhD, 1970. Rsch. statistician Ednl. Testing Svc., Princeton, N.J., 1971-75, chmn. stats., 1975-79; sr. statis. advisor, 1979-81; pres. Datamatrics Rsch. Inc., Waban, Mass., 1981—; chmn. stats., 1985-94. Author: Handling Nonresponse in Sample Surveys by Multiple Imputation, 1980, Multiple Imputation for Nonresponse in Surveys, 1987; author: (with others) Incomplete Data in Sample Surveys (Vol. 2): Theory and Bibliography, 1983; co-author: (with R.J.A. Little) Statistical Analysis With Missing Data, 1987, (with A. Gelman, J. Cavlin. H. Steven) Bayasian Data Analysis, 1995; co-editor: (with P.W. Holland) Test Equating, 1982; contbr. over 200 articles to profl. jours. Woodrow Wilson Grad. fellow Woodrow Wilson Soc., 1965, NSF Grad. fellow, 1965, 68, John Simon Guggenheim fellow, 1977-78. Fellow AAAS (stats. 1992), Am. Acad. Arts and Scis., Am. Statis Assn. (editor jour. 1980-82), Inst. Math. Stats. (coun. mem. 1990-92); mem. NAS (mem. com. on nat. stats. 1989-92, mem. panel on confidentiality data 1989-92, mem. panel bilingual edn. 1990-92, mem. working group on statis. analysis of com. on basic rsch. in behavioral and social scis., 1985-86, mem. panel stats. in 21st century, 1995, mem. other coms.), N.Y. Acad. of Sci., Biometric Soc., Internat. Assn. Survey Statisticians, Internat. Statis. Inst., Psychometric Soc., Royal Statis Soc. Office: Harvard U Dept Statistics Cambridge MA 02138

RUBIN, EDWARD STEPHEN, engineering educator, mechanical engineer; b. N.Y.C., Sept. 19, 1941; s. Hyman Rubin and Esther Pinto; m. Maria Carmen Seligra, Dec. 20, 1966; children: Denise, Lisa. B.E. cum laude in Mech. Engring., CCNY, 1964; M.S. in Mech. Engring., Stanford U., 1965, Ph.D., 1969. Asst. prof. mech. engring. Carnegie-Mellon U., Pitts., 1969-72, asst. prof. mech. engring. and pub. affairs, 1972-74, assoc. prof. mech. engring.-engring. and pub. policy, 1974-79, prof. mech. engring.-engring. and pub. policy, 1979—; dir. Ctr. for Energy and Environ Studies-Carnegie Mellon U., Pitts., 1978—; alumni prof. environ. engring. and sci., 1989—; dir. Environ. Inst. Carnegie Mellon U., Pitts., 1991-93; vis. mech. engr. Brookhaven Nat. Lab., Upton, N.Y., 1975, 77; vis. prof. dept. physics, vis. fellow Churchill Coll.-U. Cambridge (Eng.), 1979-80; mem. com. on advanced fossil energy tech. NAE, 1983-84, mem. com. on engring. research priorities, 1984-86; mem. com. on clean coal tech. Energy Adv. Bd. Dept. Energy, 1984-85; mem. nat. air pollution control tech. adv. com. EPA, 1985-89 ; mem. com. on innovative clean coal tech. deployment, Nat. Coal Coun., 1988 (adv. to Sec. of Energy, Dept. Energy); mem. mitigation panel on policy implications of greenhouse warming NAS, 1989-91; mem. com. on Nat. Energy Modeling System, NRC, 1990-92, vice chmn. panel on strategic planning for DOE Coal Rsch., 1993-94; mem. Dept. of Energy rev. panel fuel cycle externalities, 1992-93; cons. to energy-environ. problems govt. agy., pvt. orgns. Contbr. numerous articles on air pollution control, coal utilization, and modelling of energy, econ. and environ. impacts to profl. publs. Mem. Allegheny County Air Pollution Control Adv. Bd., 1973-80; mem. Pa. Gov.'s Energy Council Task Force on Energy Mgmt., 1974-76, Pa. Air and Water Quality Tech. Adv. Com., 1977-79. Recipient Ralph R. Teetor Ednl. award Soc. Automotive Engrs., 1972; trainee NSF, 1964-68. Fellow ASME (exec. com. Pitts. sect. 1970-74, exec. com. Air Pollution Control div. 1980-85, chmn. Air Pollution Control div. 1983-84); mem. AAAS, Air Pollution Control Assn., Sigma Xi, Tau Beta Pi, Pi Tau Sigma. Office: Carnegie-Mellon U Schenley Park Pittsburgh PA 15213

RUBIN, EDWIN MANNING, advertising executive; b. Charleston, S.C., May 18, 1927; s. Louis Decimus and Janet (Weinstein) R.; m. Jane Leslie Goldman, Apr. 20, 1969; children: Edward M., James E., Joshua D. BA in History and English, U. Richmond, 1950; MA in Writing, Speech and Drama, Johns Hopkins, 1951. Trainee Lennen & Mitchell Advt., N.Y.C., 1952-53; dir. radio-TV Cargill, Wilson & Acree, Inc., Richmond, Va., 1953-60; TV producer Benton & Bowles, Inc., N.Y.C., 1960-62; producer TV Grey Advt., Inc., N.Y.C., 1962-64, sr. v.p. dir. radio-TV, 1964-69; sr. v.p., creative dir. Grey Advt., Inc., 1969-80; pres. Creative Alliance, Inc., 1980-84; sr. v.p., group creative dir. J. Walter Thompson, Inc., 1984-89, NTC, Inc., N.Y.C., 1989-90; group creative dir. J. Walter Thompson, Paris; sr. v.p. internat. creative dir. J. Walter Thompson, N.Y.C., 1990—; chmn. TV comml. prodn. com. Am. Assn. Advt. Agys., 1967—; chmn. audio-visual com., mem. nat. commn. and exec. com. Anti-Defamation League. Author: 60 Ways to Relieve Stress in 60 Seconds, 1993. Served with AUS, 1944-47. Recipient Sam Dalsimer Human Relations award Anti-Defamation League B'nai B'rith, 1976; also numerous awards for creative work. Mem. Internat. Radio-TV Soc., Nat. Acad. TV Arts and Scis., Council Motion Pictures-E. Coast, Phi Beta Kappa. Home: 970 Park Ave New York NY 10028-0324 Office: J Walter Thompson Inc 466 Lexington Ave New York NY 10017-3140 Three rules I have lived by in business: 1. Never take for granted that what you asked to be done is being done (check on it). 2. Never assume anything (find out first). 3. Never make the same mistake twice (once is o.k.).

RUBIN, EMANUEL, pathologist, educator; b. N.Y.C., Dec. 5, 1928; s. Jacob and Sophie R.; m. Barbara Kurn, Mar. 27, 1955 (div. 1985); children: Raphael, Jonathan, Daniel, Rebecca; m. Linda A. Haegele, Oct. 13, 1985; children: Ariel, Ethan. B.S., Villanova U., 1950; M.D., Harvard U., 1954. Intern Boston City Hosp., 1954-55; resident Children's Hosp. of Phila., 1957-58; research fellow in pathology Mt. Sinai Hosp., N.Y.C., 1958-62, asst. attending pathologist, 1962-64, assoc. attending pathologist, 1964-68; attending pathologist-in-chief, 1972-76; dir. labs. Hahnemann Hosp., Phila., 1977-86; physician-in-chief pathology Thomas Jefferson U. Hosp., 1986—; prof. pathology Mt. Sinai Sch. Medicine, CUNY, 1966-72, Irene Heinz and John LaPorte Given prof. pathology, chmn. dept., 1972-76; prof., chmn. dept. pathology and lab. medicine Hahnemann U. Sch. Medicine, Phila., 1977-86; Gonzalo Aponte prof. pathology, chmn. dept. pathology and cell biology Thomas Jefferson U. Coll. Medicine, Phila., 1986-94, chmn. dept. anatomy, pathology and cell biology, 1994—; adj. prof. biochemistry and biophysics U. Pa. Sch. Medicine, Phila., 1977-88 . Author: (with J.L. Farber) Pathology, 1988, 94; (with K.W. Miller and S.H. Roth) Cellular and Molecular Mechanisms of Alcohol and Anesthetics, 1991; editor-in-chief Lab. Investigation, 1982—; pathology editor: Fedn. Proc., 1982-86, J. Stud Alc, 1982—. Served with USN, 1955-57. Mem. ACP, Am. Soc. Investigative Pathology, Internat. Acad. Pathology, U.S.-Can. Acad. Pathology, Am. Soc. Biol. Chemists and Molecular Biology, Am. Assn. Study of Liver Diseases, Am. Gastroent. Assn., Internat. Assn. Study of the Liver, Am. Coll. Toxicology. Home: 1505 Monk Rd Gladwyne PA 19035-1390 Office: 1020 Locust St Philadelphia PA 19107-6799

RUBIN, E(RWIN) LEONARD, lawyer; b. Chgo., Jan. 11, 1933; s. Samuel and Frances Birdie (Rabin) R.; m. Stephanie Siegel, Mar. 4, 1961 (div. Dec. 1981); children: Matthew, Suzanne; m. Audrey Gay Holzer, May 8, 1983; children: Margot, Bette. Student, U. Ill., Urbana, 1948-51; AB, U. Miami, 1956, JD, 1959. s. N.Y. 1960, Ill. 1962, U.S. Dist. Ct. (no. dist.) Ill. 1962, U.S. Ct. Appeals (7th cir.) 1990. Assoc. Hays, St. John A&H, N.Y.C., 1960-62, Devoe, Shadur, Mikva & P., Chgo., 1962-65; gen. counsel Playboy Enterprises, Inc., Chgo., 1965-78; ptnr. E. Leonard Rubin Law Offices, Chgo., 1978-81, Epton, Mullin & Druth Ltd., Chgo., 1981-86, Willian, Brinks, Hofer, Gilson & Lione, Chgo., 1986—. Pres. Lawyers for Creative Arts, Chgo., 1983-85; chmn. bd. dirs. Mus. Holography; bd. dirs. Wisdom Bridge Theatre, Chgo., 1983-85. Cpl. U.S. Army, 1953-5, ETO. Mem. ABA, Ill. Bar Assn., Chgo. Bar Assn. (bd. mgrs. 1983-85, chmn. various coms., dir. Christmas Spirits Satire Show 1965—), Union Internat. Des Avocats (v.p. intellectual property commn.), Copyright Soc. Am. (trustee, pres. Midwest chpt.). Jewish. Home: 270 Sunset Dr Northfield IL 60093-1047 Office: Willian Brinks Hofer Gilson & Lione 455 N Cityfront Plaza Dr Chicago IL 60611-5503

RUBIN, GUSTAV, orthopedic surgeon, consultant, researcher; b. N.Y.C., May 19, 1913; s. William and Rose (Strongin) R.; m. Mildred Synthia Holtzer, July 4, 1946 (dec. Dec. 1964); m. Esther Rosenberg Partnow, July 23, 1965; 1 stepchild, Michael Partnow. B.S., NYU, 1934; M.D., SUNY-Downstate Med. Ctr., 1939. Diplomate Am. Bd. Orthopedic Surgery. Intern Maimonides Hosp., Bklyn., 1939-41; resident in orthopedics Hosp. for Joint Diseases, N.Y.C., 1941-42, 1946; practice medicine specializing in orthopedics Bklyn., 1947-56; from orthopedic surgeon to dir. clinic VA Clinic, Bklyn., 1956-70; chief Spl. Prosthetic Clinic VA Prosthetics Ctr., N.Y.C., 1970-85, dir. spl. team for amputations, mobility, prosthetics/orthotics, 1985-87, mem. chief med. dir. adv. group on prosthetics services, rehab. research and devel., 1985-87, orthopedic cons., 1970-87, ret., 1987; pvt. practice N.Y.C., 1987—; med. advisor prosthetic rsch. com. N.Y. State DAV, 1990—; lectr. prosthetics NYU, 1972-89; clin. prof. orthopedics N.Y. Coll. Podiatric Medicine, 1980—. Contbr. book chpts., articles to profl. jours. Capt. U.S. Army, 1943-46. Recipient Nat. Comdrs. award DAV, 1968, Amvets award for outstanding service, 1969, award for Service to Veterans Allied Veterans Memnl. Com., 1970, Eastern Paralyzed Veterans Assn. award, 1977, award for Service to Israeli Wounded Israeli Govt. Dept. Rehab., 1981, Cert. of Merit, Nat. Amputation Found., 1972, Olin E. Teague award VA, 1984, Physician of Yr. award Pres.'s Commn. on Employment of People with Disabilities, 1984. Fellow Am. Acad. Orthopedic Surgeons, ACS, Am. Acad. Neurol. and Orthopedic Surgeons; mem. Alumni Assn. Hosp. Joint Disease, Sigma Xi. Jewish. Avocations: sculpting; oil painting. Home: PO Box 572 15 Circle Dr Moorestown NJ 08057 Office: 41 E 29th St New York NY 10016-9101

RUBIN, HARRIS B., psychology educator; b. Jersey City, May 12, 1932; s. Eli L. and Doris R.; m. Angela Battaglia, June 11, 1960; children: Amy L., Chad A., Thea F., Garth A. B.A. in Psychology, So. Ill. U., 1959; Ph.D., U. Chgo., 1965. Research scientist behavior research lab. Anna State Hosp., Ill., 1965-72; asst. prof. rehab. inst. So. Ill. U., Carbondale, 1966-71, assoc. prof. behavioral sci. Sch. Medicine and Rehab. Insti., 1972-78, prof., 1978—; interim asst. dean student affairs, 1994—; cons. Ill. Dept. Corrections, Ill. Dept. Mental Health. Bd. editors Jour. Applied Behavior Analysis, 1972-75, Jour. Exptl. Analysis of Behavior, 1973-75, The Behavior Analyst, 1990-96; adv. editor various jours.; contbr. articles to profl. jours. Mem. Carbondale Human Relations Com., 1973-85, chmn., 1969-72. Served with U.S. Army, 1952-54. Fellow APA, Am. Psychol. Soc., Am. Assn. Applied and Preventive Psychology; mem. Assn. Behavior Analysis, Midwest Psychol. Assn., Behavior Analysis Soc. Ill. (pres. 1989-90). Office: So Ill U Sch Medicine Carbondale IL 62901

RUBIN, HARRY MEYER, entertainment industry executive; b. N.Y.C., Dec. 21, 1952; s. Martin J. and Helen Rubin; children: Gabriella, James. B.A., Stanford U., 1974; M.B.A., Harvard U., 1976. Investment banker Wertheim & Co., Inc., N.Y.C., 1976-77; fin. mgr. Am. Airlines, Inc., N.Y.C., 1977-79; dir. fin. planning-entertainment, electronics groups RCA Corp., N.Y.C., 1979-81, chief fin. officer RCA Videodiscs, 1981-82, chief fin. officer RCA video and cable ops., 1982-86, group fin. exec. RCA entertainment ops., 1984-86, v.p. strategic planning and video ops., 1983-87; gen.

mgr. Home Video Gen. Electric Co., 1986-87; v.p., gen. mgr. home video ops. NBC, Inc., 1988-93; exec. v.p. GT Interactive Software Corp., 1994—; dir., co-head exec. com. RCA/Columbia Pictures Home Video and Internat. Video; dir. Genisco Tech. corp.; founding ptnr. Samuel Adams Beer; dir. Arts & Entertainment Network. Mem. Phi Beta Kappa, 22 Club. Avocations: travel, foreign languages. Home: 118 W 79th St New York NY 10024-6445

RUBIN, HENRI, electronics executive. Exec. v.p., chief oper. officer Commodore Internat. Ltd., West Chester, Pa. Office: Commodore Internat Ltd 1200 Wilson Dr West Chester PA 19380-4231

RUBIN, HERBERT, lawyer; b. Lisbon, Conn., June 4, 1918; s. Simon and Rose (Berko) R.; m. Rose Luttan, July 6, 1941; children: Barbara, Caroline, Donald. AB, CCNY, 1938; JD, NYU, 1942. Bar: N.Y. 1942, U.S. Dist. Ct. (so. and ea. dists.) N.Y. 1951, U.S. Supreme Ct. 1956, U.S. Ct. Appeals (2d, 3d, 4th, 6th, 9th, 10th, D.C. cirs.). Assoc., Newman & Bisco, 1942; mem. faculty U. Law Sch., 1946-50, 57-62; prof. creditors' rightsRutgers U. Law Sch., 1949-57; pvt. practice, 1946-47, 50-56; ptnr. Atkin & Rubin, 1948-50; ptnr. Sereni, Herzfeld & Rubin, and successor, Herzfeld & Rubin, N.Y.C., 1956—, sr. ptnr., 1968—; instr. mil. law, 1944-46; prof. constl. law LIU, 1963-68. Editor-in chief NYU Law Rev., 1940-41; bd. editors N.Y. Law Jour., 1971—. Contbr. articles to profl. jours. Mem. N.Y. State Banking Bd., 1975-85, N.Y. State Jud. Selection Com., 1975-83, Sen. Moynihan's Jud. Selection Com., 1977—; Mayor's Jud. Selection Com., 1982—. Served to 1st lt. Signal Corps, AUS, 1942-46. Recipient awards NCCJ, 1967, United Jewish Appeal, 1968, Israel Bonds, 1973, NYU Law Assn. award, 1987, Judge Weinfeld award, 1992. Fellow Am. Bar Found.; mem. ABA (mem. coun. N.Y. State), N.Y. State Bar Assn., Queens County Bar Assn. (pres. 1970), Assn. Bar City of N.Y., Fed. Bar Council, ABA. Mem. Liberal Party. Jewish. Clubs: City Downtown, World Trade Ctr., Woodmere (N.Y.C.). 53 jours. Office: Herzfeld & Rubin 40 Wall St New York NY 10005-1303

RUBIN, IRVING, editor; b. N.Y.C., Apr. 7, 1916; s. Julius and Sadie (Seidman) R.; m. Florence Podolsky, Mar. 12, 1949; children: Joanne, Saul Robert. PhG, Bklyn. Coll. Pharmacy, 1936; BA, Bklyn. Evening Coll., 1948; PharmD (hon.), Mass. Coll. Pharmacy, 1973; DSc (hon.), Union U., 1986; DHL (l.on.), L.I. U., 1986; DSc (hon.), St. John's U., 1989. With retail pharmacies N.Y.C., 1933-38; assoc. editor, then mng. editor Pharmacy, Am. Druggist mag.; editorial dir. Blue Price Book, 1938-60; editor, v.p., publ. dir. Pharmacy Times (and predecessors), Port Washington, N.Y., 1960-86; pub. Pharmacy Times (and predecessors), Port Washington, 1984, editor-in-chief, pub., 1987, editor-at-large, 1988-93; pharmacy cons. Resident and Staff Physician mag., 1978—; mem. consumer interest/health edn. panel U.S. Pharmacopeial Conv., Inc., 1991—; mem. dean's adv. bd. steering com. Coll. Pharmacy and Allied Health Professions St. John's U. Author: The Pharmacy Graduate's Career Guide, 1970; editor Wellcome Trends in Pharmacy, 1990-93; editor-in-chief emeritus Pharmacy Times, 1994—. Trustee Arnold and Marie Schwartz Coll. Pharmacy, Bklyn.; del. leader People to People Internat., People's Republic China, 1988, USSR, 1990, Great Britain and Ireland, 1992; also addressed about 150 mems. of the Supreme Soviet in the Kremlin about the Chernobyl disaster, 1990. With AUS, 1941-46, ETO. Decorated Bronze Star; recipient Alumni Achievement award Alumni Assn. Bklyn. Coll. Pharmacy, 1963, Editorial Achievement award Alpha Zeta Omega, 1968, Am. Cancer Soc., 1964, Gold medal Nicholas S. Gesoalde Pharm. Econ. Research Found., 1972, J. Leon Lascoff award Am. Coll. Apothecaries, 1977, Presdl. citation ADA, 1982, Disting. Journalism award Pharm. Soc. State N.Y., 1984, Citation Merit, Nat. Assn. Chain Drug Stores, 1986, Spl. Journalism award Nat. Assn. Chain Drug Stores, 1987; named Man of Yr. Pharmacy, B'nai B'rith, 1973, Man of Yr., Empire State Pharm. Soc., 1985; established Irving Rubin scholarship Arnold and Marie Schwartz Coll. of Pharmacy and Health Scis., L.I. U., 1988. Fellow N.Y. Acad. Pharmacy; mem. Am. Coll. Pharmacists (hon. life), Am. Inst. History Pharmacy (coun. 1982-88), Nat. Assn. Retail Druggists (award 1987), Am. Pharm. Assn. (pres. N.Y. chpt. 1955-56, ho. dels., Remington Honor medal 1986), Am. Soc. Hosp. Pharmacists, Am. Found. for Pharm. Edn. (exec. com., bd. dirs. 1988—), Okla. Pharm. Assn. (hon.), Alumni Assn. Bklyn. Coll. Pharmacy (pres. 1946-48), Alpha Zeta Omega, Rho Pi Phi, Delta Sigma Theta, Rho Chi, Kappa Psi, Phi Delta Chi (hon.), Phi Lambda Sigma (hon., Nat. Leadership award 1993). Jewish. Achievements include leadership of national drive for U.S. postage stamp to honor pharmacy, national effort to implement one symbol for pharmacy in U.S, to administr. pharmacist's oath to pharmacy students at graduation, national drive to get pharmacist in U.S. Capitol's pharmacy. Home: 39 Ruxton Rd Great Neck NY 11023-1514 Office: Irv Rubin Assocs 39 Ruxton Rd Great Neck NY 11023-1514

RUBIN, JACOB CARL, mechanical research engineer; b. N.Y.C., Nov. 22, 1926; s. Abraham and Bessie (Tockman) R.; m. Nancy Jean Weinstein, Aug. 2, 1952; children: Sara Lee, Jeffrey Daniel. BSME, CUNY, 1945; MMechE, NYU, 1947; MS of Applied Statistics, Rochester (N.Y.) Inst. Tech., 1969, MSEE, 1971, MS in Imaging Sci., 1975. Registered profl. engr., N.Y., D.C. Design group leader MacDonnell Aircraft Corp., St. Louis, 1955-56; mem. research staff U. Mich., Ann Arbor, 1956-57; staff engr. IBM, Vestal, N.Y., 1957-58; engr. advance design GE, Johnson City, N.Y., 1958-60; program engr. GE, Phila., 1960-62; mgr. standards engring. Martin-Marietta Corp., Balt., 1962-63; mgr. product design dept. Am. Car & Foundry Co., Rockville, Md., 1963-64; cons. reliability NASA, Greenbelt, Md., 1964-65; project engr. Eastman Kodak Co., Rochester, 1965-75, sr. rsch assoc., 1975-90; staff mech. engr. Med. Lab. Automation, Inc., Pleasantville, N.Y., 1990-91; prin. engr. instrument div. Dresser Industries, Stratford, Conn., 1992; sr. mech. engr. Materials Rsch. Corp., Congers, N.Y., 1993; sr. mech design engr. Electronic Retailing Systems Internat., Inc., Wilton, Conn., 1993-94; mfg. engr. Contact Systems Inc., Danbury, Conn., 1995—; course dir. Ctr. Profl. Advancement, East Brunswick, N.J., 1975—; adj. faculty Rochester Inst. Tech., 1965-90; assoc. prof. mech. engring. Bridgeport Engring. Inst., 1991-94; assoc. prof. mech. engring. Fairfield U., 1994—. Patentee artificial kidney, piezo-electric generator. Pres. Grove Place Neighborhood Assn., Rochester, 1984. Mem. NSPE (life), N.Y. State Soc. Profl. Engrs. Republican. Jewish. Avocations: teaching Sunday sch., music appreciation, theater, travel. Home: 161B Heritage Village Southbury CT 06488 Office: Contact Systems Inc Miry Brook Rd Danbury CT 06810

RUBIN, JANE LOCKHART GREGORY, lawyer; b. Richmond, Va., May 27, 1944; d. Phillip Henry and Jane Ball (Lockhart) Gregory; m. Reed Rubin, Jan. 22, 1966; children: Lara Ross, Maia Ayers, Peter Lyon. BA, Vassar Coll., 1965; JD, Columbia U., 1975; LLM in Taxation, NYU, 1984. Bar: N.Y. 1976. Of counsel Lankenau Kovner and Kurtz, N.Y.C., 1985-95; bd. dirs., treas. Reed Found., N.Y.C., 1985—; adv. bd. Vt. Studio Ctr., 1985—; mem. Mcpl. Archives Reference and Rsch. Adv. Bd., 1991-94, N.Y.C. Commn. for Cultural Affairs, 1991-94; dir. InterAmericas, 1992—. Author: intro. and catalog for exhibit Temple of Justice: The Appellate Division Court House; (with others) The Art World and the Law, 1987. Bd. dirs., vice chair Vol. Lawyers for the Arts; mem. profl. advisors coun. Lincoln Ctr. for the Performing Arts, 1994—; bd. vis. Columbia U. Sch. of Law, 1994—. Harlan Fiske Stone scholar Columbia U. Sch. Law. Mem. ABA (sect. real property and probate law, sect. internat. law and practice), N.Y. Bar Assn., Union Internat. des Avocats, Assn. of the Bar of the City of N.Y. (mem. com. on non-profit orgns., 1984—), Copyright Soc. of the U.S.A. Office: 135 Cen Park W New York NY 10023

RUBIN, JEAN ESTELLE, mathematics educator; b. Bklyn., Oct. 29, 1926; d. Leonard Lewis and Phyllis Irma (Mann) Hirsh; m. Herman Rubin, Mar. 23, 1952; children: Arthur Leonard, Leonore Anne Rubin Findsen. B.S., Queens Coll., 1948; M.A., Columbia U., 1949; Ph.D., Stanford U., 1955. Instr. Queens Coll., 1949-51, Stanford U., 1953-55; lectr. U. Oreg., 1955-59; asst. prof. Mich. State U., 1960-67; asso. prof. math. Purdue U., West Lafayette, Ind., 1968-75; prof. Purdue U., 1975—. Author: Set Theory for the Mathematician, 1967, Mathematical Logic: Applications and Theory, 1990; co-author: (with H. Rubin) Equivalents of the Axiom of Choice, 1963, Equivalents of the Axiom of Choice II, 1985. Vol. West Lafayette Libr., 1981—; bd. dirs. Lafayette Symphony Orch., Inc., 1987-93, Friends of West Lafayette Libr., 1993—. Mem. Am. Math. Soc., Assn. Symbolic Logic, Math. Assn. Am. (vis. lectr. 1976-86), Purdue Staff Aero Club Inc. (bd. dirs. 1975-90). Home: 1214 Sunset Ln West Lafayette IN 47906-2429 Office: Purdue U Math Dept Lafayette IN 47907-1395

RUBIN, JEFFREY ZACHARY, psychologist, educator; b. N.Y.C., Jan. 21, 1941; s. Zoltan and Frances Evelyn (Sternberg) R.; m. Carol Milligan, May 27, 1972; children: David, Sally, Noah. BA, Antioch Coll., 1963; PhD, Columbia U., 1968. Asst. prof. psychology Tufts U., Medford, Mass., 1969-75, assoc. prof. psychology, 1975-81, prof. psychology, 1981—, prof. diplomacy, 1989—; dir. ctr. for study decision making Tufts, 1980-84; assoc. dir. program on negotiation Harvard U. Law Sch., Cambridge, Mass., 1985-89, 91-92, exec. dir. program on negotiation, 1987-91; sr. lectr. Fulbright Fellowship Tel Aviv U., 1984-85, sr. fellow program on negotiation, 1992—. Co-author: Social Psychology of Bargaining and Negotiation, 1975, Social Psychology, 1983, Social Conflict: Escalation, Stalemate and Settlement, 1986, 2nd edit., 1993, When Families Fight: How to Handle Conflict with Those You Love, 1989, Culture and Negotiation, 1993; editor: Dynamics of Third Party Intervention: Kissinger in the Middle East, 1981; co-editor: Leadership and Negotiation in the Middle East, 1988, Negotiation Theory and Practice, 1991, Mediation in International Relations; editor Negotiation Jour., 1983—. Guggenheim fellow, 1977-78, U. Canterbury Vis. fellow, 1986. Fellow Am. Psychol. Assn., Am. Psychol. Soc.; mem. Soc. for the Psychol. Study Social Issues (pres. 1987-88). Office: Harvard U Law Sch Program on Negotation Pound 500 Cambridge MA 02138

RUBIN, JEROME SANFORD, publishing company executive, lawyer; b. Bklyn., Mar. 9, 1925; s. Abraham and Dora R.; m. Ida Elizabeth Ely, Mar. 1, 1957; children: Richard Ely, Alicia Mirella. S.B., Harvard U., 1944, LL.B., 1949. Bar: N.Y. 1949, U.S. Supreme Ct. 1958. Assoc. Root, Ballantine, Harlan, Bushby & Palmer, N.Y.C., 1949-55; trial counsel Waterfront Commn. N.Y. Harbor, 1955-57; ptnr. Schur, Rubin & Montgomery, N.Y.C., 1957-70; exec. v.p. Mead Data Central, Inc., N.Y.C., 1970-71, pres., 1971-81; group v.p. Times Mirror, N.Y.C., 1983-90; group chmn. Times Mirror Co., N.Y.C., 1990-92; chmn. News in the Future Program, MIT Media Lab., 1992—, Info Soft Internat., 1994—; bd. dirs. Rsch. Librs. Group, SatelLife, Magnascreen Corp. Policy rev. bd. Pub. Agenda Found., 1981—; trustee Inst. Philos. Research, 1981—; co-chmn. Bus. and Profl. Men for Kennedy, 1960; trustee Argentine-Am. Found., 1967-70, Found. Environ. Art, 1966-68; mem. vis. com. univ. libr. Harvard U., 1988—, vis. com. Harvard Sch. Pub. Health, 1988—; bd. dirs Starkoff Inst. Ethics, 1988—; mem. internat. adv. bd. LOGOS, 1989—. Served to lt (j.g.) USN, 1943-45, PTO. Mem. ABA, AAAS, Assn. Bar of City of N.Y., N.Y. State Bar Assn., Info. Industry Assn. (dir. 1980-82, Hall of Fame award 1985), Assn. of Am. Pubs. (bd. dirs. 1985-87, 88-92, exec. com. 1985-87, 88-92, vice chmn. 1989-90, chmn. 1990-92), Internat. Pub. Assn. (bd. dirs. internat. com. 1988-92, exec. com. 1991-92). Democrat. Clubs: Harvard, Century Assn. (N.Y.C.). Office: MIT Media Lab 20 Ames St Cambridge MA 02139

RUBIN, JOEL EDWARD, consulting company executive; b. Cleve., Sept. 5, 1928; s. Morris and Pearl (Jacobs) R.; m. Lucille Schutmaat, Dec. 18, 1953; children: Brian G., Jennifer L., Rebecca R. BS, Case Inst. of Tech., 1949; MFA, Yale U., 1951; PhD, Stanford U., 1960. Exec. v.p. Kliegl Bros. Lighting, N.Y.C., 1954-85; prin. cons. Joel E. Rubin & Assocs., N.Y.C., 1985—; sr. advisor theater planning Artec Cons., Inc., N.Y.C., 1993—. Co-author: Theatrical Lighting Practice 1954; author: Technological Development of Stage Lighting 1960. Member Coll. of Fellows of Am. Theatre, John F. Kennedy Ctr. for the Performing Arts, Washington. Recipient Golden Triaga, Prague Quadrennial, 1987, Zlatou medal, 1991, 1st time award Bus. Com. for the Arts, Forbes Mag., 1987, Founders' award U.S. Inst. for Theatre Tech., 1972, 79, U.S. Inst. Tech. Nat. award, 1990. Fellow Am. Theatre Assn. (v.p. 1961-63), U.S. Inst. of Theatre Technology (pres. 1963-64); mem. Am. Nat. Theatre Acad. (bd. dirs. 1971-75), Internat. Theatre Inst. of the U.S. (bd. dirs. 1975-79), Nat. Coun. of Arts and Gov't (bd. dirs. 1975-79), Internat. Org. Theatre Architects and Scenographers (U.S. chmn., rep. 1968—, pres. 1971-79), Illuminating Engring. Soc. Avocations: collecting books, stage design, Lincolniana. Home: 24 Edgewood Ave Hastings On Hudson NY 10706-2024 Office: Joel E Rubin & Assocs 119 W 57th St Ste # 820 New York NY 10019-2303

RUBIN, KENNETH ALLEN, lawyer; b. Rockville Centre, N.Y., Nov. 24, 1947; s. Albert Alton and Marion (Osterweis) R.; m. Susan Kurman, Sept. 14, 1980; children: Jennifer, Kelly. BS, Cornell U., 1969, MS, 1971, JD, 1973. Bar: D.C. 1974, N.Y. 1974, U.S. Ct. Appeals (D.C. crct.) 1974, U.S. Ct. Appeals (5th crct. 1975, U.S. Ct. Appeals (4th, 9th and 10th crct.) 1976, U.S. Ct. Appeals (3d, 8th and 11th crcts.) 1986, U.S. Supreme Ct. 1992. Trial atty. Dept. Justice, Washington, 1973-74; ptnr. Morgan, Lewis & Bockius, Washington, 1974—; adj. prof. USDA Grad. Sch., Washington, 1977-85, U. Ala., Huntsville, 1978-91, Antioch U., Washington, 1978; lectr. Cornell U., Ithaca, N.Y., 1979—. Author: What the Business Executive Needs To Know about U.S. Environmental Laws and Liabilities, 1991. Mem. adv. com. Cornell Ctr. for Environment. Mem. ABA, Am. Water Works Assn., Swiss Club Washington, Cornell Club Washington. Office: Morgan Lewis & Bockius 1800 M St NW Washington DC 20036-5869

RUBIN, LARRY BRUCE, writer, reporter; b. Chgo., Apr. 5, 1958; s. Philip and Helen (Orlove) R. BA in Journalism, Roosevelt U., 1983; postgrad., Northwestern U., 1985-86. Intern Chgo. Pub. Libr., 1982; freelance writer Chgo., 1983—; freelance investigative reporter, 1983—; poet World of Poetry, Sacramento, Calif., 1988—; prepared own civil lawsuit up to The U.S. Supreme Ct. Author: The Silence of Success, also numerous poems. Recipient Golden Poet award World Poetry, 1988. Mem. Pi Delta Epsilon (scrolls and crolls com. 1983). Jewish.

RUBIN, LAWRENCE GILBERT, physicist, laboratory manager; b. Bklyn., Sept. 17, 1925; s. Harry E. and Ruth (Feirberg) R.; m. Florence Ruth Kagan, Feb. 11, 1951; children: Michael G., Richard D., Jeffrey N. Student, Cooper Union, N.Y.C., 1943, 46-47; B.S. in Physics, U. Chgo., 1949; M.A. in Physics, Columbia U., 1950. Staff mem., physicist research div. Raytheon Co., Waltham, Mass., 1950-64; group leader Nat. Magnet Lab., MIT, Cambridge, Mass., 1964-78, divsn. head high magnetic field facility, 1978-93; advisor to high magnetic field facility, 1994—; mem. NAS adv. panel Nat. Bur. Standards, 1976-82, 85-90; bd. dirs. Lake Shore Cryotronics, Inc., Columbus, Ohio; gen. chmn. 6th Internat. Temperature Symposium, Washington, 1982, 7th Internat. Temperature Symposium, Toronto, Ont., Can., 1992; chmn. adv. com. Physics Today Buyers' Guide; part time staff Am. Physical Soc. Tutorial program. Mem. editorial bd. Rev. Sci. Instruments, 1968-70, 79-81; assoc. editor Ency. Scientific Instrumentation, 1992; contbr. articles to physics jours. With U.S. Army, 1943-46, ETO. Fellow IEEE (life), Am. Phys. Soc. (organizer and 1st chmn. new instrument and measurement sci. group 1985); mem. Instrument Soc. Am. (sr.), Am. Vacuum Soc. Jewish. Home: 1504 Centre St Newton MA 02159-2447 Office: Nat Magnet Lab MIT 170 Albany St Bldg Cambridge MA 02139-4294

RUBIN, LOUIS DECIMUS, JR., English language and literature educator, writer, publisher; b. Charleston, S.C., Nov. 19, 1923; s. Louis Decimus and Janet (Weinstein) R.; m. Eva M. Redfield, June 2, 1951; children: Robert Alden, William Louis. Student, Coll. of Charleston, 1940-42, LittD (hon.), 1989; AB, U. Richmond, 1946, LittD (hon.), 1972; MA, Johns Hopkins U., 1949, PhD, 1954; LittD (hon.), Clemson U., 1986, U. of the South, 1991; U. N.C. at Asheville, 1993, U.N.C., Chapel Hill, 1995. Instr. Johns Hopkins U.; editor Hopkins Rev., 1950-54; fellow criticism Sewanee Rev., 1953-54; exec. sec. Am. Studies Assn., asst. prof. Am. civilization U. Pa., 1954-56; assoc. editor Richmond (Va.) News Leader, 1956-57; assoc. prof. English Hollins Coll., 1957-60, prof., chmn. dept., 1960-67; prof. English U. N.C., 1967-73, Univ. Disting. prof., 1973-89, prof. emeritus 1989—; editor Hollins Critic, 1963-68; vis. prof. history La. State U., 1957; Fulbright lectr. U. Aix-Marseille, 1960; lectr. Breadloaf Writer's Conf., 1961; vis. prof. U. N.C., 1965, Harvard U., 1969; lectr. Am. studies seminars Kyoto (Japan) U., 1979; pub., editl. dir. Algonquin Books Chapel Hill, 1982-91. Author: Thomas Wolfe: The Weather of His Youth, 1955, No Place on Earth, 1959, The Golden Weather, 1961, The Faraway Country, 1963, The Teller in the Tale, 1967, The Curious Death of the Novel, 1967, George W. Cable, 1969, The Writer in the South, 1972, William Elliott Shoots A Bear, 1975, Virginia: A History, 1977, The Wary Fugitives, 1978, Surfaces of a Diamond, 1981, A Gallery of Southerners, 1982, The Even-Tempered Angler, 1983, The Edge of the Swamp, 1989, The Algonquin Literary Quiz Book, 1990, The Mockingbird in the Gum Tree, 1991, Small Craft Advisory, 1991; editor: Southern Renaissance, 1953, The Lasting South, 1957, Teach the Freeman: R.B. Hayes and the Slater Fund for Negro Education, 1959, The Idea of an American

Novel, 1961, South: Modern Southern Literature in Its Cultural Setting, 1961, Bibliographical Guide to the Study of Southern Literature, 1969, The Comic Imagination in American Literature, 1973, The Literary South, 1978, The American South, 1980, The History of Southern Literature, 1985, An Apple for My Teacher, 1987; co-editor: So. Lit. Jour, 1968-89; contbr. articles to periodicals. Served with AUS, 1943-46. Guggenheim fellow, 1958-59, fellow Am. Coun. Learned Socs., 1964. Fellow So. Writers (chancellor 1991-93); mem. Soc. Study So. Lit. (pres. 1975-76), Phi Beta Kappa. Address: 702 Gimghoul Rd Chapel Hill NC 27514

RUBIN, MEL, advertising executive; b. Bklyn., Sept. 6, 1922; s. Henry Meyer and Ida (Posner) R.; m. Isabelle C., Jan. 6, 1946; children: Nina Joan, Jason Seth, Emily Laura. BS, CCNY, 1943; postgrad., U.S. Naval Acad., 1944. Copy chief D.H. Ahrend Co., N.Y.C., 1946-50; chmn. Shaller-Rubin Co., Inc., N.Y.C., 1950-86; pres. Rubin Reid Noto & Ehrenthal, N.Y.C., 1987—. Creative dir. Pearl Drop & Topol (CLIO 1969); acct. supr. Stock Vermooth Radio, 1975 (CLIO). Lt. USNR, 1943-46. Mem. Nat. Acad. TV Arts & Sciences, Pharm. Advt. Council, Lucullus Circle, B.I.C. Tennis & Racquet. Avocations: tennis, river kayaking, birdwatching. Home: 7 Old Colony Ln Great Neck NY 11023-1623 Office: Rubin Reid Noto & Ehrenthal 100 6th Ave # 8 New York NY 10013-1605

RUBIN, MELVIN LYNNE, ophthalmologist, educator; b. San Francisco, May 10, 1932; s. Morris and May (Gelman) R.; m. Lorna Isen, June 21, 1953; children: Gabrielle, Daniel, Michael. A.A., U. Calif., Berkeley, 1951, B.S., 1953; M.D., U. Calif., San Francisco, 1957; M.S., State U. Iowa, 1961. Diplomate Am. Bd. Ophthalmology (bd. dirs. 1977-83, chmn. 1984). Intern U. Calif. Hosp., San Francisco, 1957-58; resident in ophthalmology State U. Iowa, 1958-61; attending surgeon Georgetown U., Washington, 1961-63; asst. prof. surgery U. Fla. Med. Sch., Gainesville, 1963-66; assoc. prof. ophthalmology U. Fla. Med. Sch., 1966-67, prof. ophthalmology, 1967—, chmn. dept. ophthalmology, 1978-95; eminent scholar U. Fla. Med. Sch., Gainesville, 1989; research cons. Dawson Corp.; ophthalmology cons. VA Hosp., Gainesville. Author: Studies in Physiological Optics, 1965, Fundamentals of Visual Science, 1969, Optics for Clinicians, 1971, 2d edit., 1974, The Fine Art of Prescribing Glasses, 1978, 2d edit., 1991; editor: Dictionary of Eye Terminology, 1984, 2d edit., 1990, Eye Care Notes, 1989; mem. editorial bd. Survey Ophthalmology; contbr. over 100 articles to med. jours. Cofounder Gainesville Assn. Creative Arts, Citizens for Pub. Schs., Inc., ProArteMusica of Gainesville, Inc., 1969, pres., 1971-73; mem. Thomas Ctr. Adv. Bd. for the Arts, 1978-84, nat. sci. adv. bd. Helen Keller Eye Rsch. Found., 1989—; bd. dirs. Hippodrome State Theater, 1981-87; bd. trustees Friends of Photographer Ansel Adams Ctr., 1991—. Served with USPHS, 1961-63. Recipient Best Med. Book for 1978 award Am. Med. Writers Assn., 1979; M.L. Rubin Ann. Lectureship established in his honor by Fla. Soc. Ophthalmology, 1993. Fellow ACS, Am. Acad. Ophthalmology (sec., dir. 1978-92, pres. 1988, Sr. Honor award 1987. Guest of Honor 1992), Found. Am. Acad. Ophthalmology (bd. trustees, 1988-95, chmn., 1992-94), Joint Commn. on Allied Health Pers. in Ophthalmology (Statesman of Yr. award 1987); mem. Assn. Rsch. in Vision and Ophthalmology (trustee 1973-78, pres. 1979), Retina Soc., Macula Soc., Club Jules Gonin, N.Y. Acad. Sci., Fla. Soc. Ophthalmology, Am. Ophthal. Soc., Pan Am. Soc. Ophthalmology, Ophthalmic Photographers Soc., Alachua County Med. Soc., Fla. Med. Assn., AMA (editorial bd. Archives of Ophthalmology 1975-85), Sigma Xi, Alpha Omega Alpha, Phi Kappa Phi. Office: U Fla Med Ctr Box 100284 Gainesville FL 32610

RUBIN, MICHAEL, lawyer; b. Boston, July 19, 1952; m. Andrea L. Peterson, May 29, 1983; children: Peter, Eric, Emily. AB, Brandeis U., 1973; JD, Georgetown U., 1977. Bar: Calif. 1978, U.S. Dist. Ct. (no. dist.) Calif. 1978, U.S. Ct. Appeals (9th cir.) 1978, U.S. Ct. Appeals (5th, 7th, 10th cirs.) 1982, U.S. Supreme Ct. 1984, U.S. Ct. Appeals (D.C. cir.) 1984, U.S. Ct. Appeals (11th cir.) 1987. Teaching fellow Law Sch. Stanford (Calif.) U., 1977-78; law clerk to Hon. Charles B. Renfrew U.S. Dist. Ct. (no. dist.) Calif., San Francisco, 1978-79; law clerk to Hon. James R. Browning U.S. Ct. Appeals (9th cir.), San Francisco, 1979-80; law clerk to Hon. William J. Brennan, Jr. U.S. Supreme Ct., Washington, 1980-81; assoc. Altshuler & Berzon, San Francisco, 1981-85, ptnr., 1985-89; ptnr. Altshuler, Berzon, Nussbaum, Berzon & Rubin, San Francisco, 1989—. Office: Altshuler Berzon Nussbaum Berzon & Rubin 177 Post St Ste 300 San Francisco CA 94108-4700

RUBIN, NORMAN JULIUS, columnist; b. New Haven, May 22, 1923; s. Louis and Ida (Levine) R. BA, Yale U., 1948. City health-police reporter Meriden (Conn.) Record, 1948-50; assoc. editor Meriden Jour., 1950-53; reporter news bur. Yale U., 1953-55, asst. dir. news bur., 1955-58; dir. pub. rels. New York Tuberculosis Health Assn., N.Y.C., 1958-61; pub. affairs assoc. Western Electric Co., N.Y.C., 1961-64, asst. mgr., pub. affairs, 1964-80; asst. mgr. community rels., 1980-86; asst. to exec. Western Electric Fund, N.Y.C., 1974-80; mgr., com. rels. Western Electric Co., N.Y.C., 1980-86; columnist N.Y. Newsday, N.Y.C., 1986—. With Infantry U.S. Army, 1943-46, ETO. Recipient Humanitarian award for oustanding community svc. Jobs for Youth, 1989; cited for successfully promoting N.Y.C.'s non-profit sector by Nonprofit Coord. Com. N.Y., 1992. Mem. Pub. Rels. Soc. Am. (accredited mem.), Yale Club, Grads. Club. Avocations: squash tennis, ballet. Home: 115 E 9th St Apt 14E New York NY 10003-5429 Office: NY Newsday Two Park Ave New York NY 10016

RUBIN, RICHARD ALLAN, lawyer; b. N.Y.C., June 19, 1942; s. Louis Max and Ruth Ann (Goldman) R.; m. Susan Deborah Levitt, June 18, 1966; children: Karen, Jill. BS, Queens Coll., 1964; JD, Bklyn. Law Sch., 1967; LLM, NYU, 1968. Bar: N.Y. 1967. Assoc. Schwartz and Frank, N.Y.C., 1968-69, Javits and Javits, N.Y.C., 1969-71; ptnr. Wolf Haldenstein Adler Freeman Herz & Frank, N.Y.C., 1972-76, Parker Chapin Flattau & Klimpl, N.Y.C., 1977—; lectr. Am. Mgmt. Assn., N.Y. Bar Assn. Mem. ABA. Office: Parker Chapin Flattau & Klimpl 1211 Avenue Of The Americas New York NY 10036-8701

RUBIN, RICK, record producer; b. Long Beach, N.Y., Mar. 10, 1963; s. Mickey and Linda (Tomberg) R. Mikey Linda, 1985. Owner, founding pres. DEF JAM Recordings, N.Y.C., 1984-88, Am. (formerly DEF Am.) Recordings, L.A., 1988—; producer recordings including: L.L. Cool J Radio, 1985 (Gold), Beastie Boys License to Kill, 1986 (4x Platinum), Run DMC Raising Hell, 1986 (4x Platinum), The Cult Electric, 1987 (Gold), sound track Less Than Zero, 1988 (Gold), Andrew Dice Clay, 1989 (Gold), Red Hot Chili Peppers Blood Sugar Sex Magic; exec. producer recordings Public Enemy It Take A Nation, 1988 (Platinum); dir., co-producer movie Tougher than Leather, 1987. Named Hot Producer of Yr. Rolling Stone Mag., 1988; recipient Joel Weber award New Music Seminar, 1990.

RUBIN, ROBERT EDWARD, U.S. secretary of the treasury; b. N.Y.C., Aug. 29, 1938; s. Alexander and Sylvia (Seiderman) R.; m. Judith Leah Oxenberg, Mar. 27, 1963; children: James Samuel, Philip Matthew. AB summa cum laude, Harvard U., 1960; postgrad., London Sch. Econs., 1960-61; LLB, Yale U., 1964. Bar: N.Y. 1965. Assoc. Cleary, Gottlieb, Steen & Hamilton, N.Y.C., 1964-66; assoc. Goldman Sachs & Co., N.Y.C., 1966-70, ptnr., 1971-92, mem. mgmt. com., 1980-92, vice chmn., co-chief oper. officer, 1987-90, co-sr. ptnr., co-chmn., 1990-92; asst. to Pres. Clinton for econ. policy The White House, Washington, 1993-95; sec. U.S. Dept. Treasury, 1995—; ptnr., bd. dirs. N.Y.C. Partnership, Inc., 1991-92; bd. dirs. Chgo. Bd. Options Exch., Inc., 1972-76, N.Y. Futures Exch., N.Y.C., 1979-85, N.Y. Stock Exchange, Inc., 1991-92, Harvard Mgmt. Co., Inc., 1990-92; mem. Pres.'s Adv. Com. for Trade Negotiations, Washington, 1980-82, mem. adv. com. on tender offers SEC, Washington, 1983, Gov.'s Commn. on Trade Competitiveness, 1987-92, regulatory adv. com. N.Y. Stock Exch., 1988-90, adv. com. internat. capital markets Fed. Res. Bank N.Y., 1989-92; mem. Securities and Exch. Commn. Market Oversight and Fin. Svcs. Adv. Com., 1991-92; Gov.'s Adv. Panel on Fin. Svcs., 1988-89; trustee Mt. Sinai Hosp., Mt. Sinai Med., 1977, vice chmn.; bd. dirs. Ctr. for Nat. Policy, 1982-92, vice chmn., 1984; trustee Sta. WNET-TV, 1985-92; mem., trustee Carnegie Corp. of N.Y., 1990—; mem. Mayor's Coun. Econ. Advisors, 1990-92, Gov.'s Coun. on Fiscal and Econ. Priorities, 1990-92. Trustee Am. Ballet Theatre Found., Inc., N.Y.C., 1969-92, Collegiate Sch., 1978-84; mem. bd. overseers' com. to visit econs. dept. Harvard U., 1981-87, com. on un'v. resources, 1987-92; mem. fin. com. N.Y. campaign Mondale for Pres., 1983-84; mem. investment adv. coun. N.Y.C. Pension Fund, 1980-89; chmn. Dem.

Congl. Dinner, Washington, 1982; Dems. for the 80s, 1985-89, Dems. for the 90s, 1989-90; chmn. N.Y.C. host com. 1992 Dem. Conv., 1989-92; mem. Commn. Nat. Elections. Recipient award NCCJ, N.Y.C., 1977. Mem. Phi Beta Kappa. Jewish. Clubs: Harvard (N.Y.C.); Century Country (Purchase, N.Y.). Home: 911 Park Ave New York NY 10021-0337 Office: Dept of Treasury Office of the Secretary 15th & Pennsylvania Ave NW Washington DC 20220

RUBIN, ROBERT J., lawyer; b. Chgo., Apr. 13, 1947. BA, U. Wis., 1969, JD, 1972. Bar: Wis. 1972, Ill. 1974. Ptnr. Altheimer & Gray, Chgo.; instr. law Ind. U., 1972-73. Ford fellow, 1971. Mem. ABA, Ill. State Bar Assn., Chgo. Bar Assn., State Bar Wis. Office: Altheimer & Gray 10 S Wacker Dr Ste 4000 Chicago IL 60606-7407

RUBIN, ROBERT JOSEPH, physician, health care consultant; b. Bklyn., Feb. 7, 1946; s. B. Norman and Suzanne (Fried) R.; m. Fran Auerbach, June 14, 1970; children: Elyse Beth, David Jon. AB, Williams Coll., 1966; MD, Cornell U., 1970. Diplomate Am. Bd. Internal Medicine. Intern New England Med. Ctr. Hosps., Boston, 1970-71, resident, 1971-72, 74-76; epidemic intelligence officer, respiratory disease and spl. pathogens, divsn. viral diseases Ctr. for Disease Control, 1972-74; asst. dean govt. affairs Tufts U., 1979-84, assoc. prof. medicine, 1981-84; chief renal divsn. Lemuel Shattuck Hosp., Boston, 1979-81; asst. sec. planning and evaluation U.S. HHS, Washington, 1981-84; clin. assoc. prof. Georgetown U., Washington, 1984-95, clin. prof., 1995—; exec. v.p. ICF, Inc., 1984-88; pres. Health and Scis. Internat., 1988-92, Lewin ICF Inc., 1992, Lewin-VHI, Inc., 1992—. Contbr. articles to profl. jours. With USPHS, 1972-74. Robert Wood Johnson Health Policy fellow, 1977. Mem. ACP, AMA, Am. Soc. Nephrology, Internat. Soc. Nephrology, Am. Fedn. Clin. Rsch., Mass. Med. Soc., Kenwood Club, Potomac Club, Williams Club, Maugus Club, Phi Beta Kappa. Republican. Jewish. Office: 9302 Lee Hwy Ste 500 Fairfax VA 22031-1214

RUBIN, ROBERT SAMUEL, investment banker; b. Boston, Sept. 22, 1931; s. Jesse Abraham and Rose (Solomon) R.; m. Martha Lucy Adams, Dec. 15, 1956; children: Rebecca, David, James, Nathaniel. BA, Yale U., 1953; MBA, Harvard Coll., 1955. With Lehman Bros., 1958-70, ptnr., 1967-70; mng. dir., bd. dirs. Lehman Bros. Kuhn Loeb, Inc., N.Y.C., 1970-84; mng. dir. Smith Barney, Inc., N.Y.C., 1989—. Trustee Bklyn. Hosp.; chmn. Bklyn. Mus.; treas. N.Y. Mcpl. Arts Soc.; bd. dirs. St. Ann's Sch. 2nd lt. AUS, 1955-58. Home: 218 Columbia Hts Brooklyn NY 11201-2105 Office: Smith Barney Inc 390 Greenwich St New York NY 10013

RUBIN, SAMUEL HAROLD, physician, consultant; b. N.Y.C., July 24, 1916; s. Joseph and Esther (Goldfarb) R.; m. Audrey Arndt, Nov. 20, 1943; children: James E., David A. A.B., Brown U., 1938; M.D., St. Louis U., 1943; M.S., U. Chgo., 1957. Diplomate: Am. Bd. Internal Medicine. Intern Jewish Hosp. St. Louis, 1943-44; resident St. Louis U. Group Hosp., 1944-45, St. Mary's Hosp., Kansas City, Mo., 1945-46; practice medicine Asbury Park, N.J., 1948-61; vol. faculty mem. N.Y. Med. Coll., 1948-61, assoc. prof. dept. medicine, 1962-65, prof., 1965—; dir. Inst. Human Values in Med. Ethics, 1984-86; chief med. service N.Y. Med. Coll.-Met. Hosp. Center, 1966-71, assoc. dean, 1971-72, exec. dean, 1972-74, dean, v.p. acad. affairs, 1975, provost, dean, 1977-83, provost, dean emeritus, 1983—, cons., 1983—; cons. medicine Jersey Shore Med. Ctr., 1962—; mem. bd. trustees St. Clares' Hosp., 1975—, N.Y. Med. Coll., 1988-94. Contbr. articles to med. jours. With M.C. AUS, 1946-48. NIH program dir. grantee, 1966-71. Fellow A.C.P.; mem. N.Y. Acad. Sci. Home: 425E Heritage Hills Dr Somers NY 10589-1912

RUBIN, SANDRA MENDELSOHN, artist; b. Santa Monica, Calif., Nov. 7, 1947; d. Murry and Freda (Atliss) Mendelsohn; m. Stephen Edward Rubin, Aug. 6, 1966. BA, UCLA, 1976, MFA, 1979. Instr. Art Ctr. Coll. Design, Pasadena, Calif., 1980, UCLA, 1981. One-woman exhbns. include L.A. County Mus. Art, 1985, Fischer Fine Arts, London, 1985, Claude Bernard Gallery, N.Y.C., 1987, L.A. Louver Gallery, L.A., 1992; group exhbns. include L.A. County Mus. Artm 1977, 82, 83, L.A. Mcpl. Art Gallery, 1977, 83, 93, L.A. Contemporary Exhbns., 1978, L.A. Inst. Contemporary Arts, 1978, Newport Harbor Art Mus., Newport Beach, Calif., 1981, Odyssia Gallery, N.Y.C., 1981, Nagoya (Japan) City Mus., 1982, Long Beach (Calif.) Mus. Art, 1982, Brooke Alexander Gallery, N.Y.C., 1982, Laguna Beach (Calif.) Mus. Art, 1982, Jan Baum Gallery, L.A., 1984, San Francisco Mus. Art, 1986, Claude Bernard Gallery, 1986, Struve Gallery, Chgo., 1987, Boise (Idaho) Mus., 1988, Judy Youen's Gallery, London, 1988, Tatistscheff Gallery, Inc., Santa Monica, Calif., 1989, Tortue Gallery, Santa Monica, 1990, Contemporary Arts Forum, Santa Barbara, Calif., 1990, San Diego Mus. Art, 1991, Fresno (Calif.) Met. Mus., 1992, Jack Rutberg Fine Arts, L.A., 1993. Recipient Young Talent Purchase award L.A. County Mus. Art, 1980; Artist's Fellowship grant NEA, 1981, 91. Avocations: gardening, exercise, reading, singing.

RUBIN, SEYMOUR JEFFREY, lawyer, educator; b. Chgo., Apr. 6, 1914; s. Sol and Sadie (Bloom) R.; m. Janet Beck, Mar. 26, 1943. BA, U. Mich. 1935; LLB magna cum laude, Harvard U., 1938, LLM, 1939. Bar: Ill. 1939, D.C. 1941. Mem. U.S. Reparations Del., 1945, Inter-Am. Conf. on Problems of War and Peace, 1945; chief U.S. Delegation on Post-War Problems, Portugal, Spain, Sweden, 1946; asst. legal adviser econ. affairs Dept. State, 1946-48; legal adviser U.S. dels. to organizing confs. GATT, 1947-48; practiced law Washington, 1948-61; mem. Spl. Presdl. Mission to Bolivia, 1961; personal rep. Pres. to Bolivia wih rank of spl. ambassador, 1962; gen. counsel ICA and AID, 1961-62; U.S. rep. Devel. Assistance Com., 1962-64; U.S. rep. to spl. com. UN Security Council, 1964-65; counsel Surrey, Karasik & Morse, 1964-75; U.S. rep. UN Commn. on Internat. Trade Law, 1967-69; prof. law sch. Am. U., Washington, 1973-85, prof. emeritus, 1985—; exec. v.p. Am. Soc. Internat. Law, 1975-85; mem. Inter Am. Juridical Commn., 1974-94, chmn., 1988; U.S. rep. UN Commn. on Transnat. Corps., 1975-87; mem. U.S. del. UNCTAD Tech. Transfer Conf. 1978; mem. panel of conciliators Internat. Centre for Settlement of Investment Disputes, 1981—; cons. U.S. Dept. State, Brookings Instn., 1948-49; chief US del negotiating Marshall Plan Agreements, 1951-52; dep. administr. Mut. Def. Assistance Control Act, 1952-53; pub. mem. Commn. on Internat. Rules Jud. Procedure, 1961-62; adj. prof. Georgetown U. Law Ctr., Washington, 1964-72; lectr. Sloan Sch. Bus. Adminstrn., MIT, Cambridge, 1969; pres. InterAm. Legal Services Assn., 1980-82; sr. cons. Am. Soc. Internat. Law; lectr. in field at various univs. worldwide, 1949—; chmn. Bellagio Trade Conf., 1985, Symposium on U.S.-European Community trade issues, Boston, 1987; chmn. U.S. Govt. Constitution Com. on Dem. Instns., 1987—; cons. legal issues of trade and investment. Author: Private Foreign Investment, 1956, The Conscience of the Rich Nations - The Common Aid Effort and the Development Assistance Committee, 1966, (with others) The International Corporation, 1970, Global Companies, 1975, Emerging Standards for Internat. Trade and Investment, 1983, Managing Trade Relations in the 1980s, 1984; editor, contbr.: Foreign Development Lending—Legal Aspects, 1971, Environment and Trade, 1981; editor: Avoidance and Settlement of International Trade Disputes, 1986; contbr. (with others) articles in field to profl. jours. Mem. bd. Inst. Internat. Law, Consumers for World Trade. Recipient Sesquicentennial award U. Mich., 1967, Grand Silver medal Austria, 1967, Cert. of Honor from U.S. Dept. State, 1994. Mem. Am. Soc. Internat. Law (sr. advisor), Internat. Law Assn., Washington Inst. Fgn. Affairs, ABA, Coun. Fgn. Affairs, Am. Law Inst., Am. Judicature Soc., InterAm. Bar Assn. (trustee), Soc. Internat. Devel., Washington Fgn. Law Soc. (bd. dirs.). Democrat. Home: 1675 35th St NW Washington DC 20007-2335 Office: 2223 Massachusetts Ave NW Washington DC 20008-2864

RUBIN, STANLEY CREAMER, producer; b. N.Y.C., Oct. 8, 1917; s. Michael Isaac and Anne (Creamer) R.; m. Elizabeth Margaret von Gerkan (actress Kathleen Hughes), July 25, 1954; children: John, Chris, Angela, Michael. Student, UCLA, 1933-37. Writer Universal Studios, Universal City, Calif., 1940-42, Columbia Pictures, Los Angeles, 1946-47; writer, producer NBC-TV, Burbank, Calif., 1948-49; theatrical film producer various studios, 1949-55, Rastar Prodns., Columbia Pictures, 1988-91; TV producer CBS-TV, Los Angeles, 1956-59, Universal Studios, Universal City, 1960-63, 20th Century-Fox, Los Angeles, 1967-71, MGM Studios, Culver City, Calif., 1972-77; pres. TBA Prodns., Los Angeles, 1978—. Producer theatrical films including The Narrow Margin, 1950, My Pal Gus, 1950, Destination Gobi,

1951, River of No Return, 1952, Promise Her Anything, 1966, The President's Analyst, 1967, Revenge, 1989; co-producer White Hunter, Black Heart, 1990; TV prodns. include G.E. Theatre, 1959-63, Ghost and Mrs. Muir, 1968-69, Bracken's World, 1969-71; writer, producer TV film The Diamond Necklace, 1948 (Emmy award 1949); producer TV films including Babe, 1975 (Hollywood Fgn. Press Golden Globe award, Christopher medal), And Your Name is Jonah, 1978 (Christopher medal 1979), The Story of Satchel Paige, 1980 (Image award 1981); exec. producer TV prodn. Escape from Iran: The Canadian Caper, 1981. Producer spl. programming Dem. Nat. Conv., San Francisco, 1984, Columbia Pictures and Rastar Prodns., 1988-91. 1st lt. USAAF, 1942-46. Mem. Writers Guild Am. (dir. 1941-42), Producers Guild Am. (bd. dirs. 1968-74, pres. 1974-79, v.p. 1987-94, bd. dirs. 1994—), Acad. Motion Picture Arts and Scis., Acad. TV Arts and Scis. (bd. govs. 1971, 73), Phi Beta Kappa. Home and Office: 8818 Rising Glen Pl Los Angeles CA 90069

RUBIN, STANLEY GERALD, aerospace engineering educator; b. Bklyn., May 11, 1938; s. Harry Jack and Cele (Sake) R.; m. Carol Ruth Kalvin, Sept. 29, 1963; children—Stephany, Elizabeth, Barbara. B.Ac.E., Poly Inst. Bklyn., 1959; Ph.D., Cornell U., 1963. Asst. prof. to prof. dept. aerospace engring. Poly. Inst. N.Y., Farmingdale, 1964-79, Assoc. dir. aerodynamic labs., 1977-79; prof. aerospace engring. and engring. mechanics U. Cin., 1979—, head dept., 1979-89, dir. NASA Univ. Space Engring. Ctr. on Health Monitoring Space Propulsion Systems, U. Cin., 1988-91; cons. Aerospace Corp., NASA, Allison (GM), others; mem. adv. com. Inst. for Computational Methods in Propulsion, NASA; speaker 9th Internat. Conf. Numerical Methods in Fluid Mechanics, Saclay, France. Chief editor Internat. Jour. Computers and Fluids, 1978—; contbr. articles to profl. jours. and Ann. Rev. Fluid Mechanics, 1992. NSF fellow, 1963-64; grantee Office Naval Research, 1978-88, AFOSR 1968-92, NASA, 1973—, others. Fellow AIAA (assoc.); mem. ASME, Soc. Indsl. and Applied Math., Am. Soc. Engring. Edn., Sigma Xi, Sigma Gamma Tau, Tau Beta Pi. Home: U Cin PO Box 210070 761 Baldwin Hall Cincinnati OH 45221-0070 Office: U Cin ML 070 761 Baldwin Hall Cincinnati OH 45221

RUBIN, STEPHEN EDWARD, editor, journalist; b. N.Y.C., Nov. 10, 1941; s. Irving and Evelyn (Halprin) R. B.A., NYU, 1965; M.S., Boston U., 1966. Editor UPI, N.Y.C., 1966-69; freelance writer N.Y.C., 1969-82; founder, dir. Writers Bloc, N.Y.C., 1976-82; editor Vanity Fair Mag., N.Y.C., 1982-83; exec. editor Bantam Books, N.Y.C., 1984-85, v.p., editorial dir., 1985-88, sr. v.p., editor-in-chief adult fiction and non-fiction, 1987-88, sr. v.p., pub., editor-in-chief adult fiction and non-fiction, 1988-90; pres., pub. Doubleday divsn. Bantam Doubleday Dell Pub. Group, N.Y.C., 1990-95; chmn., CEO Bantam Doubleday Dell Internat. Divsn., N.Y.C., 1995—. Author: The New Met in Profile, 1974. Avocations: listening to musical performances, collecting records, tapes and cds, reading, exercising. Office: Doubleday 1540 Broadway New York NY 10036

RUBIN, STEPHEN WAYNE, lawyer; b. N.Y.C., Mar. 29, 1951; s. Oscar R. and Irene J. (Widelok) R.; m. Eileen Grossman, Sept. 23, 1978; children: Ashley G., Camner G. BS, Cornell U., 1973; JD, Columbia U., 1976. Bar: N.Y. 1977, U.S. Dist. Ct. (so. dist.) N.Y. 1977. Assoc. Gordon, Hurwitz & Butowsky, N.Y.C., 1976-79; assoc. Feit & Ahrens, N.Y.C., 1979-84, ptnr., 1984-88; ptnr. Proskauer Rose Goetz & Mendelsohn, N.Y.C., 1989—; lectr. grad. sch. bus., NYU, 1985-92. Co-conflbr. law articles to profl. jours. Nat. pres., sec. Friends of Israel Def. Forces, N.Y.C., 1985—. Mem. ABA, N.Y. State Bar Assn., Assn. of Bar of City of N.Y. Office: Proskauer Rose Goetz Mendelsohn 1585 Broadway New York NY 10036-8200

RUBIN, THEODORE ISAAC, psychiatrist; b. Bklyn., Apr. 11, 1923; s. Nathan and Esther (Marcus) R.; m. Eleanor Katz, June 16, 1946; children: Jeffrey, Trudy, Eugene. B.A., Bklyn. Coll., 1946; M.D., U. Lausanne, Switzerland, 1951; grad., Am. Inst. Psychoanalysis, 1964. Resident psychiatrist Los Angeles VA Hosp., 1953, Rockland (N.Y.) State Hosp., 1954, Bklyn. State Hosp., 1955, Kings County (N.Y.) Hosp., 1956; chief psychiatrist Women's House of Detention, N.Y.C., 1957; mem. faculty Downstate Med. Sch., N.Y. State U., 1957-59; pvt. practice N.Y.C., 1956—; tng. and supervising psychoanalyst Am. Inst. for Psychoanalysis of Karen Horney Clinic and Ctr.; mem. faculty Am. Inst. Psychoanalytic Psychoanalysis, 1962—; pres. emeritus bd. trustees Am. Inst. Psychoanalysis. Author: Jordi, 1960, Lisa and David, 1961, Sweet Daddy, 1963, In The Life, 1964, Platzo and the Mexican Pony Rider, 1965, The Thin Book by a Formerly Fat Psychiatrist, 1966, The 29th Summer, 1966, Cat, 1966, Coming Out, 1967, The Winner's Note Book, 1967, The Angry Book, 1969, Forever Thin, 1970, Emergency Room Diary, 1972, Doctor Rubin Please Make Me Happy, 1974, Shrink, 1974, Compassion and Self-Hate, An Alternative to Despair, 1975, Love Me, Love My Fool, 1976, Reflections in a Goldfish Tank, 1977, Alive and Fat and Thinning in America, 1978, Reconciliations, 1980, Through My Own Eyes, 1982, One to One, Understanding Personal Relationships, 1983, Not to Worry, The American Family Book of Mental Health, 1984, Overcoming Indecisiveness, 1985, Lisa and David, The Story Continues, 1986, Miracle at Bellevue, 1986, Real Love, 1990, Child Potential, 1990, Anti-Semitism: A Disease of the Mind, 1990; mem. editorial bd. Am. Jour. Psychoanalysis; also articles, columns. Served as officer USNR, World War II. Recipient Adolf Meyer award Assn. Improvement Mental Health, 1963. Fellow Am. Acad. Psychoanalysis; mem. N.Y. County Med. Soc., Am. Psychiat. Assn., Assn. Advancement Psychoanalysis, Authors Guild. Office: 219 E 62nd St New York NY 10021-7685

RUBIN, VERA COOPER, research astronomer; b. Phila., July 23, 1928; d. Philip and Rose (Applebaum) Cooper; m. Robert J. Rubin, June 25, 1948; children: David M., Judith S. Young, Karl C., Allan M. BA, Vassar Coll., 1948; MA, Cornell U., 1951; PhD, Georgetown U., 1954; DSc (hon.), Creighton U., 1978, Harvard U., 1988, Yale U., 1990, Williams Coll., 1993. Research assoc. to asst. prof. Georgetown U., Washington, 1955-65; physicist U. Calif.-LaJolla, 1963-64; astronomer Carnegie Inst., Washington, 1965—; Chancellor's Disting. prof. U. Calif., Berkeley, 1981; vis. com. Harvard Coll. Obs., Cambridge, Mass., 1976-82, 92—, Space Telescope Sci. Inst., 1990-92; Beatrice Tinsley vis. prof. U. Tex., 1988; Commonwealth lectr. U. Mass., 1991, Yunker lectr. Oreg. State U., 1991, Bernhard vis. fellow Williams Coll., 1993, Oort vis. prof. U. Leiden, The Netherlands, 1995; lectr. in field, U.S., Chile, Russia, Armenia, India, Japan, China, Europe; trustee Associated Univs., Inc., 1993—. Assoc. editor Astrophys. Jour. Letters, 1977-82; editorial bd.: Sci. Mag., 1979-87; contbr. numerous articles sci. jours.; assoc. editor: Astron. Jour., 1972-77. Pres.'s Disting. Visitor, Vassar Coll., 1987. Mem. Smithsonian Instn. Coun., 1979-85; recipient Pres.'s Nat. Medal of Sci., 1993, Dickson prize in sci. Carnegie-Mellon U., 1994. Mem. NAS (Space Sci. Bd. 1977-74, chmn. sect. on astronomy 1992-95), Am. Astron. Soc. (coun. 1977-80, Russell prize lectr. 1994), Internat. Astron. Union (pres. Commn. on Galaxies 1982-85), Assn. Univ. Rsch. in Astronomy (divs. 1973-76, 94—), Am. Acad. Arts and Scis., Phi Beta Kappa (scholar 1982-83). Democrat. Jewish. *As an observational astronomer, it is my aim to obtain data of highest quality in order to answer questions concerning the universe in which we live. In spite of our enormous ignorance, each day offers exciting opportunities to learn a little more. This is the real joy of doing science.*

RUBIN, WILLIAM, editor; b. N.Y.C., Jan. 10, 1928; s. Herman and Molly (Goodman) R.; m. Claire Levine, Aug. 30, 1953; children: Deborah E., Joan S., Howard I. BA, Bklyn. Coll., 1953. Tech. editor Drug Trade News, N.Y.C., 1952-63; dir. pub. info. Nat. Vitamin Found., N.Y.C., 1958-61; editorial dir. FDC Reports & Drug Rsch. Reports, Washington, 1963-64; proprietor Sci. Reports and Projects, Bethesda, MD., 1964-67; editor Internat. Med. News Group, Rockville, Md., 1967-91; editorial coms., 1992—. Editor Clin. Psychiatry News, Family Practice News, Internal Medicine News, Ob-Gyn. News, Pediatric News, Skin & Allergy News, Internat. Med. News Group. Adminstr. Washington chpt. Am. Suicide Found.; mem. Md. State Adv. Coun. on Arthritis and Related Diseases. With USAAF, 1946-47. Mem. Nat. Assn. Sci. Writers (life), Am. Med. Writers Assn., N.Y. Acad. Scis., Nat. Press Club. Avocations: book accumulating, reading history, woodworking. Office: 6808 Greyswood Rd Bethesda MD 20817-1541

RUBIN, ZICK, psychology educator, lawyer, writer; b. N.Y.C., Apr. 29, 1944; s. Eli and Adena (Jaglofsky) R.; m. Carol Moses, June 21, 1969; children—Elihu James, Noam Moses. BA, Yale U., 1965; PhD, U. Mich., 1969; JD, Harvard U., 1988. Bar: Mass., 1988. Asst. to assoc. prof.

Harvard U., Cambridge, Mass., 1969-76; Louis and Frances Salvage prof. social psychology Brandeis U., Waltham, Mass., 1976-89, adj. prof. psychology, 1989—; law clk. chief judge U.S. Ct. Appeals (1st cir.), 1988-89; assoc. Palmer & Dodge, Boston, 1990-93, counsel, 1994—; chmn. com. behavioral scis. Yale U. Coun., New Haven, 1981-86; mem. adv. bd. Palmer & Dodge Agy., 1994—. Author: Liking and Loving, 1973, Children's Friendships, 1980; co-author: Psychology, 1993; editor: Doing Unto Others, 1974, Relationships and Development, 1986; contbg. editor: Psychology Today, 1980-85; editorial bd.: Harvard Law Rev., 1986-88. Recipient Socio-Psychol. prize AAAS, 1969, Nat. Media award Am. Psychol. Found., 1980; grantee NSF, NIMH, Ford Found., Social Sci. Research Council, Found. Child Devel. Fellow APA; mem. ABA, Boston Bar Assn., Am. Psychology-Law Soc., Authors Guild, Text and Academic Authors Assn. (mem. coun. 1994—), Soc. Exptl. Social Psychology, Phi Beta Kappa. Jewish. Club: Elihu (New Haven).

RUBINFELD, DANIEL LEE, law educator, consultant; b. Newark, May 3, 1945; s. William A. and Ann (Weinstein) R.; m. Gail N. Soon, Aug. 25, 1973; children: Sarah, Rachel. BA in Math. magna cum laude, Princeton U., 1967; MS in Econs., MIT, 1968, PhD, 1972. Instr. Suffolk U., Boston, 1968-70, Wellesley (Mass.) Coll., 1970-71; asst. prof. U. Mich., Ann Arbor, 1972-77, assoc. prof., 1977-82, prof. econs. and law, 1982-83; prof. econs. and law U. Calif., Berkeley, 1983—, chmn. Jurisprudence and Social Policy program, 1987—; cons. MIT/Harvard, 1972, Urban Inst., 1973, Nat. Acad. Sciences, 1974, 85—, U.S. Treasury, 1984-85; economist Staff of Pres. Council Econ. Advisors, 1969; mem. adv. panel NSF program law and social sci., 1982-84. Author: Statistical Analysis of Economic and Financial Data, rev. ed., 1974, Essays on the Law and Economics of Local Governments, 1979, Econometric Models and Economic Forecasts, 2d ed., 1981, Microeconomics, 1989; co-editor: American Domestic Priorities: An Economic Appraisal, 1985, Internat. Review of Law and Economics, 1977—; editorial bd. Pub. Fin. Quarterly, 1980—, Law and Soc. Rev., 1982-86, Evaluation Rev., 1985-87; also articles. Mem. Ann Arbor Rent Control Study Commn. 1973, faculty adv. bd. U. Calif. Ctr. Real Estate and Urban Econs., Berkeley, 1983. NSF grantee; Woodrow Wilson fellow, 1967, NSF fellow, 1968-69, Nat. Bur. Econ. Research fellow, 1975-76. Mem. Am. Econ. Assn., Nat. Tax Assn., Econometric Soc., Law and Soc. Assn., Phi Beta Kappa. Office: U Calif Berkeley Sch Law 360 Boalt Hall Berkeley CA 94720

RUBINFIEN, LEO H., photographer, filmmaker; b. Chgo., Aug. 16, 1953. Student, Reed Coll.; BFA, Calif. Inst. Arts, 1974; MFA, Yale U., 1976. Instr. in photography Swarthmore Coll., 1977, Sch. Visual Arts, N.Y.C., 1978-87; assoc. prof. art Fordham U., 1981-87; represented by Robert Mann Gallery, N.Y.C.; vis. lectr. Cooper Union, 1982. One man shows include Gastelli Gallery, N.Y., 1981, Fraenkel Gallery, San Francisco, 1982, 86, Robert Mann Gallery, N.Y., Met. Mus. Art, N.Y.C., 1992, Seibu Art Forum, Tokyo, 1993, Cleve. Mus. Art, 1994, Seattle Art Mus., 1994, Robert Mann Gallery, N.Y.C.; exhibited in group shows at Internat. Ctr. Photography, N.Y., 1981, Inst. Contemporary Arts, London, 1981, San Francisco Mus. Modern Art, 1981, George Eastman House, Rochester, N.Y., 1981, Corcoran Gallery, Washington, 1981, Mus. Modern Art, N.Y., 1984; dir., co-author (film) The Money Juggler, 1988, My Bed in the Leaves, 1990; author: (books) A Map of the East, 1992, 10 Takeoffs 5 Landings, 1994, (essays) A Love-Hate Relations, Artforum, 1978. Fellow Guggenheim Found., 1982-83, Asian Cult Coun., 1984. Home: 1 Furnace Dock Rd Croton On Hudson NY 10520

RUBINO, VICTOR JOSEPH, law institute executive; b. N.Y.C., Dec. 25, 1940; s. Joseph V. and Olympia (Gayda) R.; m. Shawna Gargone, June 20, 1971; 1 child, Victor Gayda. BA in Govt., Cornell U., 1962, LLB, 1965. Bar: N.Y. 1965, U.S. Dist. Ct. (so. dist.) N.Y. 1969. Staff atty. Westchester Legal Svcs., White Plains, N.Y., 1968-71; assoc. Squadron Ellenoff Plesent & Lehrer, N.Y.C., 1971; treas., program officer Council on Legal Edn., N.Y.C., 1971-79; assoc. dir. Practising Law Inst., N.Y.C., 1979-83, exec. dir., 1983—. Democratic candidate for N.Y. State Assembly, 1970; chmn. Rye (N.Y.) Human Rights Commn., 1975-76. Served to capt. U.S. Army, 1966-68. Mem. ABA, Assn. Bar City N.Y. Office: Practising Law Inst 810 7th Ave New York NY 10019

RUBINOFF, IRA, biologist, research administrator, conservationist; b. N.Y.C., Dec. 21, 1938; s. Jacob and Bessie (Rose) R.; m. Roberta Wolff, Mar. 19, 1961; 1 son, Jason; m. Anabella Guardia, Feb. 10, 1978; children: Andres, Ana. B.S., Queens Coll., 1959; A.M., Harvard U., 1960, Ph.D., 1963. Biologist, asst. dir. marine biology Smithsonian Tropical Research Inst., Balboa, Republic of Panama, 1964-70; asst. dir. sci. Smithsonian Tropical Research Inst., 1970-73, dir., 1973—; assoc. in ichthyology Harvard U., 1965—; courtesy prof. Fla. State U., Tallahassee, 1976—; mem. sci. adv. bd. Gorgas Meml. Inst., 1964-88; trustee Rare Animal Relief Effort, 1976-85; bd. dirs. Charles Darwin Found. for Galapagos Islands, 1977—; chmn. bd. fellowships and grants Smithsonian Instn., 1978-79; vis. fellow Wolfson Coll., Oxford (Eng.) U., 1980-81; vis. scientist Mus. Comparative Biology-Harvard U., 1987-88. Author Strategy for Preservation of Moist Tropical Forests; contbr. articles to profl. jours. Vice chmn. bd. dirs. Panama Canal Coll., 1989-93; bd. dirs. Internat. Sch. Panama, 1983-85, 90-93, Fundacion Natura, sec., bd. dirs. 1991—; hon. dir. Instituto Latino Americano de Estudios Avanzados. Awarded Order of Vasco Nunez de Balboa of Republic of Panama. Fellow Linnean Soc. (London), AAAS; mem. Am. Soc. Naturalists, Soc. Study of Evolution, N.Y. Acad. Scis., Ancon Panama (bd. dirs.). Club: Cosmos (Washington). Home: Box 2072, Balboa Panama Office: Smithsonian Tropical Rsch Unit 0948 APO AA 34002-0948

RUBINOFF, ROBERTA WOLFF, government administrator; b. N.Y.C., Aug. 26, 1939; d. Leon and Leah (Landauer) W.; m. Ira Rubinoff, 1961 (div. 1975); 1 child, Jason. BS, Queens Coll., 1959; Masters of Environ. Mgmt., Duke U., 1981. Biologist Smithsonian Tropical Rsch. Inst., Balboa, Canal Zone, 1966-75, marine sci. coord., 1975-79; asst. dir. Office Fellowships and Grants Smithsonian Instn., Washington, 1980-84, acting dir. Office Fellowships and Grants, 1984-85, dir. Office Fellowships and Grants, 1985—. Mem. AAAS, Am. Soc. Zoologists, Am. Inst. Biol. Sci. Office: Smithsonian Instn Office Fellowships & Grants 955 L'Enfant Plz Ste 7000 Washington DC 20560

RUBINOVITZ, SAMUEL, diversified manufacturing company executive; b. Boston, Dec. 26, 1929; s. Benjamin Ephraim and Pauline (Kaufman) R.; m. Phyllis Ann Silverstein; children: David Jay, Robert Neal. BS, MIT, 1951, MS, 1952. Sales engr. Clevite Transistor Products, Waltham, Mass., 1954-63; sales mgr. EG&G Inc., Wellesley, Mass., 1963-72, div. mgr., 1972-79, v.p., 1979-86, sr. v.p., 1986-89, exec. v.p., 1989-94; ret.; bd. dirs. KLA Instruments, Inc., Santa Clara, Calif., Richardson Electronics Ltd., Chgo., Kronos Inc., Waltham, Temptronic Corp., Newton, Mass., EG&G Inc., Wellesley, Mass., LTX Corp., Westwood, Mass. Served to 1st lt. USAF, 1952-54. Democrat. Jewish. Office: EG & G Inc 45 William St Wellesley MA 02181-4004

RUBINOWITZ, LEONARD S., lawyer, educator; b. 1943. BA, U. Wis.-Madison, 1965; LLB, Yale U., 1968. Bar: Conn. 1968. Spl. asst. to adminstr. HUD, Chgo., 1969-72; rsch. assoc. Ctr. for Urban Affairs, Northwestern U., Chgo., 1972-75, assoc. prof. law and urban affairs, 1975-80; prof., 1980—; Field assoc. Brookings Inst., 1975—. Author: Low Income Housing: Suburban Strategies, 1974. Office: Northwestern U Sch Law 357 E Chicago Ave Chicago IL 60611-3069

RUBINROIT, HOWARD J., lawyer; b. Newark, Apr. 23, 1944. BA, Rutgers U., 1966; LLB, U. Pa., 1969. Bar: N.J. 1969, Calif. 1971. Law clk. to hon. Nathan Jacobs N.J. Supreme Ct., 1969-70; ptnr. Sidley & Austin, L.A. Mem. Beverly Hills Bar Assn. (bd. govs. 1977-78, bd. govs. barristers 1975-79), Assn. Bus. Trial Lawyers. Office: Sidley & Austin 555 W 5th St 40th Fl Los Angeles CA 90013-1010

RUBINSTEIN, AARON, lawyer; b. N.Y.C., Nov. 15, 1950; s. Jacob and Golda Rubinstein; m. Carri Sue Zogan, Mar. 3, 1974; children: David Michael, Jennifer Lauren. BA magna cum laude, Cornell U., 1972; JD, NYU, 1975. Bar: N.Y. 1976, U.S. Dist. Ct. (so. and ea. dists.) 1976, U.S. Supreme Ct. 1986. Assoc. Kaye, Scholer, Fierman, Hays & Handler, N.Y.C., 1975-84, ptnr., 1985—. Mem. ABA, N.Y. State Bar Assn., Assn. of Bar of City of N.Y., Order of Coif. Office: Kaye Scholer Fierman et al 425

Park Ave New York NY 10022-3506 also: KPMG Peat Marwick 365 Park Ave New York NY 10154

RUBINSTEIN, ALVIN ZACHARY, political science educator; author; b. Bklyn., Apr. 23, 1927; s. Max and Sylvia (Stone) R.; m. Frankie Kimmelman, Nov. 12, 1960. B.B.A., CCNY, 1949; M.A., U. Pa., 1950, Ph.D., 1954. Mem. faculty U. Pa., 1957—; prof. polit. sci., 1966—; vis. lectr. Queen Coll., 1959, vis. prof. U. Calif. at Santa Barbara, summer, 1968, Am. U., Cairo, 1971, Lehigh U., spring, 1973, U. Va., spring 1977, 80; chmn. grad. program internat. relations U. Pa., 1966-70; dir. Anspach Inst. Diplomacy and Fgn. Affairs, 1968-70; cons. Inst. Def. Analysis, 1966-70, Inst. for Fgn. Policy Analysis, 1976-81; vis. assoc. Russian Research Center, Harvard, 1956-57. Author: Communist Political Systems, 1966, (with P. Berton) Soviet Writings on S.E. Asia, 1968, The Soviets in International Organizations, 1964, The Foreign Policy of the Soviet Union, 3d edit, 1972, Yugoslavia and the Nonaligned World, 1970; Co-editor: Soviet and American Policies in the United Nations: A Twenty Five Year Perspective, 1971; editor: Soviet and Chinese Influence in the Third World, 1975, Red Star on the Nile: The Soviet-Egyptian Influence Relationship Since the June War, 1977, The Great Game: Rivalry in the Persian Gulf and South Asia, 1983; The Arab-Israeli Conflict: Perspectives, 2d edit., 1991, Moscow's Third World Strategy, 1988 (Marshall Shulman prize Am. Assn. Slavic Studies, 1989); co-editor: Soviet Foreign Policy Toward Western Europe, 1978, Soviet Foreign Policy Since World War II: Imperial and Global, 4th edit., 1992, Soviet Policy Toward Turkey, Iran and Afghanistan, 1982, Anti-Americanism in the Third World, 1985, Perestroika at the Crossroads, 1991, Russia and America: From Rivalry to Reconciliation, 1993, America's National Interest in a Post Cold War World, 1994; book rev. editor Current History, 1959-69, bd. editors, 1968—; mem. editorial bd. Studies in Comparative Communism, 1973-89, ORBIS, 1974, Soviet Union, 1974-80. Mem. bd. advisers Naval War Coll., 1983-85. Served to lt. USNR, 1954-56. Ford Found. fellow, 1956-57; Rockefeller Found. grantee, 1961-62; Guggenheim fellow, 1965-66; grantee Am. Philos. Soc., 1958, 59, 68, 73; NSF travel grant, 1970-71; Barra Found. research grant, 1970-71; resident scholar Bellagio Study and Conf. Center, Rockefeller Found., Italy, 1974; Earhart Found. research grantee, 1974; Joint Com. on Soviet Studies of Am. Council Learned Socs. and Social Sci. Research Council grantee, 1975; vis. fellow Clare Hall, Cambridge (Eng.) U., 1974-75; NATO research fellow, 1977; Earhart Found. research grantee, 1979, 81; sr. fellow Fgn. Policy Research Inst., 1981—; sr. assoc. St. Anthony's Coll., Oxford U., spring 1985. Home: The Mermont Apt 503 Bryn Mawr PA 19010

RUBINSTEIN, ARTHUR B., composer. Scores include (films) The Great Bank Hoax, 1978, On the Right Track, 1981, Whose Life Is It Anyway?, 1981, Fake Out, 1982, Deal of the Century, 1983, Blue Thunder, 1983, Wargames, 1983, Lost in America, 1985, Hyper Sapien, 1986, The Best of Times, 1986, Stakeout, 1987, Defense Play, 1988, The Hard Way, 1991, Another Stakeout, 1993, (TV movies) The Prince of Central Park, 1977, Portrait of a Stripper, 1979, Aunt Mary, 1979, The Great American Traffic Jam, 1980, Portrait of a Rebel: Margaret Sanger, 1980, The Phoenix, 1981, Rivkin, Bounty Hunter, 1981, Not Just Another Affair, 1982, Skeezer, 1982, It Came Upon the Midnight Clear, 1984, Sins of the Past, 1984, The Parade, 1984, The Cartier Affair, 1984, Murder in Space, 1985, Doubletake, 1985, Doing Life, 1986, Love Among Thieves, 1987, Roses Are for the Rich, 1987, The Betty Ford Story, 1987, Once Upon a Texas Train, 1988, Inherit the Wind, 1988, Internal Affairs, 1988, Where the Hell's That Gold?!!, 1988, Nightmare at Bitter Creek, 1988, Indiscreet, 1988, Agatha Christie's The Man in the Brown Suit, 1989, Unconquered, 1989, Gideon Oliver: Sleep Well, Professor Oliver, 1989, Baywatch: Panic at Malibu Pier, 1989, Guts and Glory: The Rise and Fall of Oliver North, 1989, Line of Fire: The Morris Dees Story, 1991, Crazy From the Heart, 1991, Fatal Friendship, 1991, Danielle Steel's Secrets, 1992, When No One Would Listen, 1992, Deep Trouble, 1993, Caught in the Act, 1993, Hart to Hart Returns, 1993, Hart to Hart: Crimes of the Hart, 1994. Office: Gorfaine Schwartz Agency 3301 Barham Blvd Ste 201 Los Angeles CA 90068*

RUBINSTEIN, EVA (ANNA), photographer; b. Buenos Aires, Argentina, 1933; d. Arthur and Aniela (Mlynarska) R.; m. William Sloane Coffin Jr., 1956 (div. 1968); children: Amy, Alexander (dec.), David. Ballet tng., Paris, N.Y.C., Calif., 1938-53; student, Scripps Coll., 1950-51, UCLA, 1952-53; student in photography, Lisette Model, 1969, Jim Hughes, 1971, Ken Heyman, 1970, Diane Arbus, 1971. lectr. numerous workshops, seminars, confs.; photo seminars Lodz Film Sch., Poland, 1986, 86-87. Dancer, actress: off-Broadway and Broadway, including original prodn. The Diary of Anne Frank, 1955-56; European dance tour, 1955; one-person shows of photographs include Underground Gallery, N.Y.C., 1972, Dayton Art Inst., Ohio, 1973, Arles Festival, France, 1975, Canon Photo Gallery, Amsterdam, 1975, Neikrug Gallery, N.Y.C., 1975, 79, 81, 82, 85, La Photogalerie, Paris, 1975, Friends of Photography, Carmel, Calif., 1975, Galerie 5.6, Ghent, Belgium, 1976, Gallery Trochenpresse, Berlin, 1977, Frumkin Gallery, Chgo., 1977, Galeria Sinisca, Rome, 1979, Hermitage Found. Mus., Norfolk, Va., 1982, Photographers Gallery, London, 1983, Galerie Forum Labo, Arles, France, 1983, Galerie Nicephore, Lyon, France, 1983, Image Gallery, Madrid, 1984, Muzeum Sztuki, Lodz, Poland, 1984, Il Diaframma/Canon Gallery, Milan, 1984, A.R.P.A. Gallery, Bordeaux, 1984, Chateau d'Eau, Toulouse, France, 1985, Galerie Demi-Teinte, Paris, 1985, Associated Artist Photographers galleries in Warsaw, Krakow, Lodz, Katowice and Gdansk, Poland, 1985-86, Foto/Medium/Art Gallery, Wroclaw, Poland, 1986, Visions Gallery, San Francisco, 1986, Canon Galerie, Paris, 1986, Salone Internat. SICOF, Milan, 1987, St. Krzysztof Gallery, Lodz, 1987, L'Image Fixe, Lyon, 1988, Artotheque, Grenoble, 1988, Neikrug Gallery, N.Y.C., 1988-89, Neikrug Photographica Elegies, N.Y.C., 1984-88, Heuser Art Ctr. Gallery, Bradley U., Peoria, Ill., 1989, 3-os Encontros da Imagem, Braga, Portugal, 1989, Bibliotheque Nat. Galerie Colbert, Paris, 1989, Galerie Picto-Bastille, Paris, 1989-90, Portfolio Gallery, London, 1990, Vaison-La-Romaine, France, 1990, Hist. Mus. of City of Lodz, 1990, Galerie Artem, Quimper, France, 1993, Galerie F.N.A.C. Etoile, Paris, 1994, other F.N.A.C. galleries (France, Belgium, Spain), 1994—, Galerie Augustus, Berlin, 1995, L'Imagerie, Lannion, France, 1995; group shows include. Internat. Salon, Krakow, Poland, 1971, Delgado Mus., New Orleans, 1972, Neikrug Gallery, 1972, 73, 75, Salone Internationale, Milan, Italy, 1973, Photo-OVO, Montreal, Que., Can., 1974, Nat. Portrait Gallery, London, 1976, Hera Gallery, R.I., 1977, Musee National d'Art Moderne Georges Pompidou, Paris, 1977, Centre Culturel de l'ouest Aquitain, Bordeaux, France, 1978, Fotografiska Museet, Stockholm, 1978, Nat. Arts Club, N.Y.C., 1979, Chrysler Mus., Norfolk, 1979, Maine Photog. Gallery, 1981, Floating Found. Photography, N.Y.C., 1970, 71, 72, 73, 79, 82, Ffoto Gallery, Cardiff, Wales, 1983, Musée d'Art Moderne de la Ville de Paris, 1987-88, Boca Raton (Fla.) Mus., 1989, Galerie PICTO Bastille, Paris, 1989, Galerie Arena, Arles, 1989-90, Settimana della Fotografia, Palermo, 1990, Festival de l'Image, Le Mans, France, 1993; represented: in permanent collections Library of Congress, Washington, Met. Mus. Art, N.Y.C., Bibliotheque Nationale, Paris, Musee Reattu, Arles, France, Kalamazoo Inst. Arts, Israel Mus., Jerusalem, Fotografiska Museet, Stockholm, Muzeum Sztuki, Lodz, Poland, Histo Mus. of City of Lodz, others; author 2 monographs, 2 ltd. edit. portfolios with introductions by John Vachon and André Kertész; contbr. photographs in various books, mags., profl. jours. *Making photographs is my way of exploring the questions that keep me alive by ever leading to further questions.*

RUBINSTEIN, FREDERIC ARMAND, lawyer; b. Antwerp, Belgium, Apr. 20, 1931; came to U.S., 1942; s. Samuel N. and Steffa (Warrenreich) R.; m. Susan August, Dec. 24, 1968; 1 child, Nicolas Eric August Rubinstein. BA, Cornell U., 1953, JD, 1955. Bar: N.Y. 1955. Assoc. Law Offices of I. Robert Feinberg, N.Y.C., 1955-60; assoc. Guggenheimer & Untermyer, N.Y.C., 1960-65, ptnr., 1965-85; ptnr. Kelley Drye & Warren, N.Y.C., 1985—, Vice chmn. zoning & planning com. Local Community Bd. # 6, N.Y.C., 1980-86. Mem. ABA (bus. law sect., emerging growth ventures subcom., chmn 1988—), Cornell Club of N.Y. Office: Kelley Drye & Warren 101 Park Ave New York NY 10178-0062

RUBINSTEIN, LAURENCE HENRY, university administrator, fund raiser; b. N.Y.C., Mar. 1, 1940; s. Benjamin and Irene (Schwartz) R.; m. Robin Mae Spero, June 16, 1963; children: Mara Kocahvi, Eve Miri. AB, Columbia U., 1960; BHL, Hebrew Union Coll., 1963, MAHL, 1965, DD, 1990. Asst. Rabbi Temple Israel, Omaha, 1965-68; assoc. Rabbi Keneseth Israel, Elkins Park, Pa., 1968-72; Rabbi Temple Shalom, Levittown, Pa., 1972-78; dir. UJA-Young Leadership, N.Y.C., 1978-82; campaign dir. Fedn.

Jewish Agys., Phila., 1982-87; sr. v.p. Brandeis U., Waltham, Mass., 1987-89, Jewish Theol. Sem. of Am., N.Y.C., 1989-93; exec. v.p. Yivo Inst. for Jewish Rsch., N.Y.C., 1993—; chmn., campaign dir. Council of Jewish Fedns., N.Y.C., 1985-87; chmn. Rabbinical Cabinet United Jewish Appeal, N.Y.C., 1976-78; bd. dirs. Sunrise Lake Camp, N.Y.C., 1990—. Contbr. articles to profl. jours. Recipient U. medal Columbia U., 1985, Deans award Columbia Coll., 1980, Lion award Columbia Alumni Assn., 1977, David ben Gurion award Israel Bonds, 1975. Mem. Cen. Conf. Am. Rabbis, Assn. Jewish Community Profls., Columbia Coll. Alumni Assn. (pres. 1982-84). Republican. Jewish. Avocations: oenology, music. Home: 333 W End Ave Apt 3C New York NY 10023-8129 Office: Yivo Inst for Jewish Rsch 555 W 57th St New York NY 10019

RUBINSTEIN, MOSHE FAJWEL, engineering educator; b. Miechow, Poland, Aug. 13, 1930; came to U.S., 1950, naturalized, 1965; s. Shlomo and Sarah (Rosen) R.; m. Zafrira Gorstein, Feb. 3, 1953; children—Iris, Dorit. B.S., UCLA, 1954, M.S., 1957, Ph.D., 1961. Designer Murray Erick Assos. (engrs. and architects), Los Angeles, 1954-56; structural designer Victor Gruen Assos., Los Angeles, 1956-61; asst. prof. U. Calif. at Los Angeles, 1961-64, asso. prof. dept. engring., 1964-69, prof., 1969—, chmn. engring. systems dept., 1970-75, program dir. modern engring. for execs. program, 1965-70; cons. Pacific Power & Light Co., Portland, Oreg., Northrop Corp., U.S. Army, NASA Research Center, Langley, Tex. Instruments Co., Hughes Space System Div., U.S. Army Sci. Adv. Com., Kaiser Aluminum and Chem. Corp., IBM Corp., TRW. Author: (with W.C. Hurty) Dynamics of Structures, 1964 (Yugoslavian trans. 1973), Matrix Computer Analysis of Structures, 1966 (Japanese transl. 1974), Structural Systems, Statics Dynamics and Stability, 1970 (Japanese transl. 1979), Patterns of Problem Solving, 1975, (with K. Pfeiffer) Concepts in Problem Solving, 1980, Tools for Thinking and Problem Solving, 1986; IEEE Press Videotapes: Models for People Driven Quality, 1991, Quality Through Innovation, 1991, Creativity for Ongoing Total Quality, 1993, Relentless Improvement, 1993, (with I.R. Firstenberg) Patterns of Problem Solving, 2nd edit., 1994. Recipient Disting. Teaching award Acad. Senate, UCLA, 1964, Western Electric Fund award Am. Soc. Engring. Edn., 1965, Disting. Tchr. trophy Engring. Student Soc., UCLA, 1966; Sussmann chair for Disting. Visitor Technion Israel Inst. Tech., 1967-68; Fulbright-Hays fellow Yugoslovia and Eng., 1975-76; named Outstanding Faculty Mem., UCLA Engring. Alumni award, 1979, Outstanding UCLA CE Alumni award, 1990, Outstanding Faculty Mem., State Calif. Command Coll., 1987, 88, 89, 94. Mem. ASCE, Am. Soc. Engring. Edn., Seismol. Soc. Am., Sigma Xi, Tau Beta Phi. Research in use of computers in structural systems, analysis and synthesis; problem solving and decision theory. Home: 10488 Charing Cross Rd Los Angeles CA 90024-2646 Office: UCLA Sch Engring and Applied Sci Los Angeles CA 90024

RUBINSTEIN, PHYLLIS M., lawyer. BA in English, Pa. State U., 1966; JD, Temple U., 1977. Bar: Pa. 1977, D.C. 1980, Va. 1982. English tchr. Abington (Pa.) High Sch., 1967-70; paralegal Schnader, Harrison, Segal & Lewis, Phila., 1970-73; jud. clk. to Hon. Israel Packel Phila. Supreme Ct., 1977-78; with Samuel B. Hornstein & Assocs., Doylestown, Pa., 1978-79; adj. instr. Inst. Paralegal Tng., Phila., 1979; counsel Hunton & Williams, Richmond, Va., 1981—; speaker in field. Mem. condominium adv. bd. Commonwealth of Va.; mem. exec. bd. Comml. Real Estate Women; bd. dirs. B'Nai B'rith Youth Orgn. Mem. ABA (chair com. pub. edn., task force on Applying Fed. Legis. to Congress, coun. Real Property, Probate and Trust Law Section, mem. spl. study sect. com., mem. standing com. on membership of real property, probate and trust law sect., former vice chair com. on significant decisions of real property, probate and trust law sect.), former mem. real estate fin. com.), Va. Bar Assn., Va. State Bar, Met. Richmond Women's Bar Assn. Home: 1905 Oakway Dr Richmond VA 23233-3513

RUBINSTEIN, ROBERT LAWRENCE, anthropologist, gerontologist; b. Bklyn., Jan. 3, 1951; s. Jack Rubinstein and Enid Farley; m. Susan Hersker, Feb. 13, 1980; children: Lily, Gabriel. BA, Case Western Res. U., 1972; MA, Bryn Mawr Coll., 1974, PhD, 1978. Rsch. anthropologist Polisher Rsch. Inst. of the Phila. Geriatric Ctr., 1981-89, asst. dir. rsch., 1989-91, assoc. dir. rsch., 1991-92, dir. rsch., 1992—. Author: Singular Paths: Old Men Living Alone, 1986, Elders Living Alone, 1992. NIH grantee. Fellow Gerontol. Soc. Am.; mem. Am. Anthrop. Assn. Achievments include research on old age and aging, older men, childless elders, home environments of older people. Office: Polisher Rsch Inst Phila Geriatric Ctr 5301 Old York Rd Philadelphia PA 19141

RUBINSTEIN, SIDNEY JACOB, orthopaedic technologist; b. Boston, July 1, 1936; s. Harry and Shirley (Block) R.; m. Sheila Ruby Goldstein, Sept. 4, 1955 (div. 1974); children: Ronda, Barry, Terry, Debra, Neysa; m. Margaret Catherine Burns, Nov. 19, 1976; 1 stepchild, Jerry Hiltonen. Cert., Dimock Ctr., Boston, 1971. Cert. Nat. Bd. of Orthopaedic Technologists. Chief orthopaedic technologist Beverly (Mass.) Hosp., 1971-82; orthopaedic technologist Beverly Orthopaedic Assoc., 1982—; owner Orthotics Lab., Danvers Mass., 1993—. Mem. Nat. Assn. Orthopaedic Technologists (pres. 1992—), Can. Soc. Orthopaedic Technologists, Venezuela Soc. Orthopaedic Technologists, New Eng. Soc. Orthopaedic Technologists (pres. 1988-92). Democrat. Jewish. Avocations: music, traveling, theater, literature. Office: Orthotic Lab 74 Elm St Danvers MA 01923

RUBIO, SUZANNE SARAH, ballet dancer; b. Montreal, Que.. Grad., Nat. Ballet Sch., Toronto, 1981, 1983. Mem. corps de ballet Royal Winnipeg Ballet, Man., 1985-90, soloist, 1990-94, prin. dancer 1994—; invited guest artist Dance in Canada Gala, Calgary, Alta., 1989. Stage appearances include (musicals) Kismet, 1984, Mame, 1985, (film) The Big Top, Flamenco at 5:15; prin. roles in The Nutcracker, Rodeo, Swan Lake, The Dream, The Sleeping Beauty, Romeo and Juliet, Tarantella, Ballo Della Regina, Allegro Brillante, Piano Variations III, 5 Tangos, Four Last Songs, others. Recipient Can. Coun. Arts grant, 1984, 2nd prize Helsinki Internat. Ballet Competition, 1991. Mem. Can. Actors Equity Assn., Alliance Can. Cinema, TV & Radio Artists. Office: Royal Winnipeg Ballet, 380 Graham Ave, Winnipeg, MB Canada R3C 4K2

RUBLE, DUANE RUSSELL, retail drug store executive; b. Lewistown, Pa., Apr. 27, 1943; s. Russell Leroy and Jane (Suloff) R.; m. Paula Mae, June 1, 1974; children—Cynthia Jane, Chad Russell, Matthew Ryan. B.S., Juniata Coll., 1965. With Sears Roebuck & Co., Harrisburg, PA., 1965-68; sr. v.p. Rite Aid Corp, Harrisburg, PA., 1968-88; owner Cumberland Truck Equipment Co., 1988—. Served with U.S. Army, 1967-73. Home: 1576 W Lisburn Rd Mechanicsburg PA 17055-9766 Office: Cumberland Truck Equipment Co 25 Roadway Dr Carlisle PA 17013-8811

RUBLE, RANDALL TUCKER, theologian, educator, academic administrator; b. Greenville, Va., Apr. 15, 1932; s. William Cecil and Carrie Mae (Connor) R.; m. Martha L. Grant, Sept. 6, 1958; children: John, Jeffrey, Ellen. A.B., Erskine Coll., 1958, B.D., 1961; Th.M., Princeton Theol. Sem., 1962; Ph.D., U. Edinburgh, 1964. Prof. Hebrew and Old Testament Erskine Sem., Due West, S.C., 1965—, v.p., dean, 1976—; supply pastor Abbeville (S.C.) Assoc. Ref. Presbyn. Ch., 1967—; chmn. N.Am. and Carribean area World Alliance of Reformed Chs., 1979-80. Author: The Ten Commandments For Our Day, 1971; contbr. articles to jours., mags. Mem. Town Council, Due West, 1972-75; chmn. Christian Prison Ministries, 1987—. Served with USAF, 1951-55. Mem. Soc. Bibl. Lit., Brit. Old Testament Soc., Nat. Assn. Profs. of Hebrew, S.C. Acad. Religion, S.C. Juvenile Parole Bd., Atlanta Theol. Assn. (pres. 1990—). Presbyterian. Home and Office: PO Box 172 Due West SC 29639-0172

RUBOTTOM, DONALD JULIAN, management consultant; b. Tulsa, Sept. 29, 1926; s. George William and Nellie Dorcas (Core) R.; m. Wanda Mae Stockton, Apr. 29, 1951; children: Rinda Louise, Joy Lynn, Donald Jay, Jill Anna. BS in Fin., Okla. State U., 1951; postgrad., Tulsa U. Chartered fin. analyst; cert. mgmt. cons. V.p., trust officer 1st Nat. Bank & Trust Co., Tulsa, 1955-56; exec. v.p., trust officer, then v.p. F&M Bank & Trust Co., Tulsa, 1966-68; pres. Rubottom, Dudash & Assocs., Tulsa, 1968—; tchr. Boston Ave. United Meth. Ch., Tulsa, 1962—. With U.S. Army, 1945-46. Mem. Inst. Mgmt. Cons., Nat. Assn. Bus. Economists, CFA Inst., Okla. Soc. Fin. Analysts, S.W. Regional Assn., Small Bus. Investments Cos. (pres. 1979), Tulsa Knife and Fork Club (pres. 1985-86), Tulsa So. Tennis Club, Rotary

(pres. 1988-89, dist. gov. 1993-94). Avocations: tennis, skiing, gardening. Home: 2450 E 47th Pl Tulsa OK 74105-5112 Office: Rubottom Dudash & Assocs Inc 4870 S Lewis Ave Ste 180 Tulsa OK 74105-5172

RUBOTTOM, ROY RICHARD, JR., retired diplomat and educator, consultant; b. Brownwood, Tex., Feb. 13, 1912; s. Roy Richard and Jennie Eleanor (Watkins) R.; m. Billy Ruth Young, Dec. 23, 1938; children: Eleanor Ann Rubottom Odden, Frank, John. BS, So. Meth. U., 1932, MA, 1933; postgrad., U. Tex.; LLD, Southwestern Coll., Winfield, Kans., 1968, Cen. Meth. Coll., Fayette, Mo., 1985. Asst. dean student life U. Tex., 1937-41; apptd. fgn. service officer, 1947; sec. of embassy and consul Bogota, Colombia, 1947-49; officer-in-charge Mex. affairs State Dept., 1950, dep. dir. Middle Am. Affairs, 1951, dir.; 1952-53; 1st sec. embassy Madrid, 1953, counselor of embassy, 1954, dir. U.S. Ops. Mission, 1954-56; asst. sec. of state for inter-Am. affairs, 1957-60, U.S. Ambassador to Argentina, 1960-62; advisor Naval War Coll., Newport, R.I., 1962-64; v.p. So. Meth. U., Dallas, 1964-71, prof. polit. sci. emeritus, 1975—; dir. Ctr. of Ibero-Am. Civilization, 1975-77; pres. U. Americas, Puebla, Mex., 1971-73; dir. Office Internat. Affairs, Dallas, 1985-87. Co-author: Spain and the U.S. Since W.W. II, 1984. Active Scouting U.S.A. Served with USNR, 1941-46. Recipient Silver Beaver award Boy Scouts Am., 1975, Inter-Am. award Boy Scouts Am., Silver Buffalo, 1993. Mem. Lambda Chi Alpha, Pi Sigma Alpha. Methodist. Lodge: Rotary. Office: 3429 University Blvd Dallas TX 75205-1833

RUBOW, W. STEVEN, food company executive; b. Chgo., July 15, 1941; s. Walter Franklin and Lorna (Neeley) R.; m. Sharon Jean Matheson, Nov. 22, 1961; children: Steven, Tamara, Brian, Starley, Jennifer, Adam, Neeley, Jonathan, Angela, Mary. BA, Brigham Young U., 1963; MS, Lake Forest Coll., 1973. V.p. merchandising Jewel Food Stores, Chgo., 1972-82; v.p. mktg. Star Market, Boston, 1982-87; v.p. perishables Topco Assocs., Inc., Skokie, Ill., 1987-90, sr. v.p. perishables, 1990, exec. v.p., 1991, pres., CEO, 1992—, also bd. dirs. Bishop L.D.S. Ch., 1984-87, counselor stake presidency, 1988—. Mem. Midwest Frozen Food Assn. (pres. 1972-73). Republican. Avocations: reading, genealogy. Office: Topco Assocs Inc 7711 Gross Point Rd Skokie IL 60077-2615*

RUBRIGHT, JAMES ALFRED, natural resources company executive; b. Phila., Dec. 17, 1946; s. James Alfred and Helen Lucille (Evans) R.; children: Noah Michael, Benjamin James, Jaime Anne, Nathaniel Drew, James McCurdy; m. Mary Elizabeth Angelich, Dec. 30, 1988. BA, Yale U., 1969; JD, U. Va., 1972. Bar: Ga. 1972. Ptnr. King & Spalding, Atlanta, 1972-94; sr. v.p., gen. counsel Sonat Inc., Birmingham, 1994—. Mem. ABA, Ga. Bar Assn., Atlanta Bar Assn. Office: Sonat Inc 1900 5th Ave N Birmingham AL 35203 Office: Sonat Inc PO Box 2563 Birmingham AL 35202

RUBRIGHT, ROYAL CUSHING, lawyer; b. Denver, Nov. 27, 1909; s. John Compton and Marie (Popovich) R.; m. Dorothy Kelley, Jan. 4, 1985; 1 child, Lynnell. BA, LLB, U. Colo., 1932, LLM, 1933. Bar: Colo. 1933. Pvt. practice law Denver, 1933-40; ptnr. Fairfield & Woods, P.C., Denver, 1940-90; ret., 1990; part-time instr. law U. Denver; spl. lectr. law U. Colo. Recipient William Lee Knous award U. Colo. Law Sch. Mem. ABA, Colo. Bar Assn. (mem. award deserving sect.), Denver Bar Assn. (pres., award of merit), City Club, Rotary, Masons, Pi Kappa Alpha. Home: 7877 E Mississippi Ave Apt 601 Denver CO 80231-2035

RUBY, BURTON BENNETT, men's apparel manufacturer; b. Chgo., Oct. 27, 1919; s. Jacob M. and Fay S. (Silver) R.; m. June Stinnett Zylstra, Sept. 13, 1975; children: Thomas M., Patricia Ruby Sinervo, Roger J., Pamela J. Karger, Kirk D. Zylstra, Julie B. Zylstra, John A. Zylstra. B.S., U. Wis., 1941; LLD (hon.), Purdue U., 1987. With Jaymar-Ruby, Inc., Michigan City, Ind., 1940—; plant supt., then v.p. Jaymar-Ruby, Inc., 1946-54, exec. v.p., 1954-57, pres., chief exec. officer, 1957-81, chmn., 1981—, chief exec. officer, 1981-85; bd. dirs. Hartmarx Inc., Horizon Bankcorp, Ruby Chevrolet Inc., Nixon Newspapers, Inc.; past adv. bd. Fashion Inst. Tech., midwest Liberty Mut.; chancellor's adv. bd. Purdue NC. Chmn. bd. Meml. Hosp. of Michigan City Found., 1962; bd. dirs. Michigan City YMCA, pres., 1952. Served with AUS, 1943-45. Decorated Bronze Star; recipient Brotherhood award NCCJ, 1979, Disting. Service award Michigan City Jaycees, 1949, Sagamor of Wabash, 1985. Mem. Men's Fashion Assn. (adv. bd. dirs.), Am. Apparel Mfrs. Assn. (dir., sec.chmn. 1987), Trouser Inst. Am. (pres. 1954), World Bus. Council (sec., dir.), Chgo. Presidents Orgn., Am. Legion. Clubs: Standard, Chicago Yacht; Pottawattomie Country (Michigan City), Michigan City Yacht (Michigan City); B'nai B'rith (pres. 1949, lodge Humanitarian of Year award 1980). Lodges: Rotary (Paul Harris fellow 1978); Elks. Patentee garment constrn. Office: Jaymar-Ruby Inc 5000 Ohio St Michigan City IN 46360-7700

RUBY, LEONARD KENNETH, hand surgeon, orthopaedic surgeon, educator; b. San Francisco, Mar. 12, 1942; s. Maurice and Mildred M. (Kaplan) R.; m. Margaret Ellen Farrer, Mar. 5, 1969; children: Brian, Rebecca, Abigail. BS, U. Calif., Berkeley, 1962; MD, U. Calif., San Francisco, 1966. Diplomate Am. Bd. Orthopaedic Surgery. Intern in surgery U. Calif. San Francisco Med. Ctr., 1966-67; resident in surgery Beth Israel Hosp., Boston, 1967-68; resident in orthopaedics Tufts Combined Orthopaedics, Boston, 1970-72; chief resident orthopaedic surgery Boston City Hosp./N.E. Med. Ctr., 1973; fellow hand surgery Samuel Merritt Hosp., Oakland, Calif., 1974; instr. orthopaedic surgery Tufts U. Sch. Medicine, Boston, 1974-75, asst. prof., 1975-81, assoc. prof., 1981-87, prof., 1987—; co-dir. Tufts Combined Hand Surg. Fellowship Program, Tufts U., mem. exec. com. dept. orthopaedic surgery; presenter in field; vis. prof. numerous hosps. and univs., U.S., Italy, Israel. Author chpts. in books; reviewer Mayo Clinic Proceedings, 1988; cons. editor Jour. Bone and Joint Surgery, 1993—, Yearbook of Hand Surgery, 1995—; contbr. over 60 articles to profl. jours. Pres. Internat. Sunfish Class Assn., 1992-94; mem. Temple Emeth Brotherhood. Served to lt. comdr. USN, 1968-70, Vietnam. Recipient award Lifetime Calif. Scholarship Fedn., 1959. Fellow Am. Acad. Orthopaedic Surgeons, Am. Coll. Surgeons; mem. Am. Soc. for Surgery of the Hand (assoc., hand fellowship dir. com. 1984—, hand surg. forward planning 1992-94, hand surg. update com. 1993-84), Hand Study Soc. (pres. 1994), Am. Orthopaedic Assn., Am. Acad. Orthopaedic Surgeons, Mass. Med. Soc., Am. Rheumatism Assn., Boston Hand Club, Boston Orthopedic Club, Mass. Med. Soc., New Eng. Hand Soc., Ea. Orthopedic Assn. Republican. Jewish. Avocations: sailing, windsurfing. Office: NE Med Ctr Dept Orthopaedic 750 Washington St # 26 Boston MA 02111

RUBY, MICHAEL, magazine executive. Editor U.S. News and World Report, Washington. Office: US News & World Report 2400 N St NW Washington DC 20037-1177

RUBY, RALPH, JR., vocational business educator; b. Newburgh, N.Y., Apr. 11, 1944; m. Dorothy Nelle Privette; children: Laconya Dannet, Ralph III, Vanessa Rae. AAS, Orange County C.C., 1968; BS, U. Tenn. Knoxville, 1969, MS in Bus. Edn., 1972; EdD, U. Mo., Columbia, 1975. Cert. tchr., adminstr., N.Y. Tchr. keyboarding, bus. law Valley Cen. High Sch., Montgomery, N.Y., 1969-76, chair bus. dept., 1974-75; asst. prof. vocat. bus. edn. U. Ark., Fayetteville, 1976-79; from asst. prof. to prof. bus. edn., coord. vocat. bus. edn. Ark. State U., State University, 1979—; mem. ednl. adv. com. 26th Congl. Dist., N.Y.; vis. prof. McGill U., Montreal, Que., Can., 1977; acctg. author Gregg divsn. McGraw-Hill Book Co., 1978—; presenter workshops, tng. programs. Author: Rough Draft Typing Practice, 1980, Target Type!: Improving Speed and Accuracy, 1987, Word Processing and Editing Techniques, 1988, Real Life Keyboarding Applications: (Word Processor, Data Base, Spreadsheet), 1990, Top Row Target Type, 1991, Starship Speller, 1991, Number Pad Tutor, 1991, Lotus in Your Classroom, 1991, WordPerfect in Your Classroom, 1992, Microsoft Works in Your Classroom, 1993, The Big Board Stock Market (simulation), 1993, PageMaker in Your Classroom, 1993, MS-DOS Made Easy, 1993, WordPerfect for Desktop Publications, 1993, Microsoft Windows in your Classroom, 1994, Mystery at Laser Age Hardware, 1994, The Class Works, 1994, WordPerfect in your Classroom Using the MacIntosh, 1994; editor Jour. of Edn. for Bus. 1980—, others. Mem. Am. Vocat. Assn. (life), Nat. Bus. Edn. Assn., So. Bus. Edn. Assn., Nat. Assn. Tchr. Edn. for Bus. and Office Edn. (life), Delta Pi Epsilon, Kappa Delta Pi, Phi Delta Kappa (life). Office: Ark State U Coll Bus State University AR 72467

RUBY, RUSSELL (GLENN), lawyer; b. Albany, Mo., Nov. 19, 1911; s. Gordon Romeo and Minnie (Hazelrigg) R.; m. Elizabeth Bradford Popkin, Feb. 11, 1939 (dec. Aug. 1967); children: Michael Gordon, Adrienne Elizabeth, Glenn Russell; m. Dorothea King, 1972 (dec. Dec. 1991). Student, Palmer Coll., 1929-31; B.J., U. Mo., 1933; LL.B., Tulsa U., 1939. Bar: Okla. 1939, U.S. Dist. Ct. (ea. dist.) Okla. 1941, U.S. Supreme Ct. 1957. Pvt. practice, Muskogee, 1939—; spl. agt. FBI, 1942-47; pres. Mandire Corp., 1974—. Mem. Okla. Ho. of Reps., 1955-66; mem. Muskogee City Coun., 1968-72, 76-88, vice mayor, 1968-72, dep. mayor, 1976-83, 84-88, mayor, 1983-84; chmn. Muskogee City-County Port Authority, 1974-76; mem. Muskogee Met. Planning Commn., 1968-72, 76-88, chmn., 1978-79; mem. small cities adv. com. Nat. League Cities, 1980-84; trustee Okla. Mcpl. Pension Fund, 1980-84; bd. dirs. Muskogee Community Concert Assn., Kate Frank Manor, Family Guidance Center; chmn. bd. trustees Muskogee Pub. Libr., 1986-88. Named Outstanding Older Oklahoman Eastern Okla. Devel. Dist., 1984. Mem. ABA, Okla. Bar Assn. (50 Yr. plaque 1989), Muskogee Bar Assn. (past pres., 50 Yr. plaque 1989), Assn. Fed. Attys., Soc. Former Agts. FBI, SAR, Masons, Shriners (potentate 1970), Jesters, Elks. Democrat. Episcopalian. Address: 4500 Girard St Muskogee OK 74401-1543

RUCCI, ANTHONY JOSEPH, health care products and services executive; b. Youngstown, Ohio, Sept. 19, 1950. BS, Bowling Green State U., 1972, MA, 1976, PhD in Inds I and Organizational Psychology, 1978. Asst. dir., pers. adminstr. Mahoning County Mental Health and Retardation Bd., Youngstown, Ohio, 1972-74; cons., grad. student Bowling Green (Ohio) State U., 1974-78; cons. LWFW Inc., Dallas, 1978-79; pers. planning specialist Baxter Internat. Inc., Deerfield, Ill., 1979-80, mgr. pers. planing, 1980-85; v.p. orgn. and human resource planning Am. Hospital Supply Corp. Am. Hosp. Supply Corp., 1985-86; sr. v.p. human resources Baxter Internat. Inc., Deerfield, Ill., 1986-92; instr. Bowling Green State U., 1974-78, Davis Jr. Coll., 1975-77, U. Tex. at Dallas, 1979, U. Ill., Chgo. Cir., 1981, Lake Forest Grad. Sch. Mgmt., 1983; invited speaker confs., socs., forums, seminars; mem. White House Fellows Regional Selections Panel, Chgo., 1988, 89. Cons. editor, mem. editorial bd. Jour. Applied Psychology, 1982-86; assoc. editor Human Resource Planning Jour., 1989; editorial reviewer Jossey-Bass Pub. Co., 1991; contbr. articles to profl. jours. Mem. Chancellor's Exec. Adv. Bd., U. Ill. at Chgo.; bd. dirs. Lake Forest Grad. Sch. Mgmt., 1984-87; mem. Human Resource Mgmt. Adv. Bd. U. Mich. Sch. Bus. Adminstrn. Mem. APA, The Bus. Roundtable (bd. dirs., employee rels. com.), Adv. Coun. on Human Resources Mgmt. of the Conf. Bd. (bd. dirs.), Coun. on Orgn. and Mgmt. of the Conf. Bd. (bd. dirs.), Soc. Indsl./Organizational Psychology, Human Resource Planning Soc. (bd. dirs. 1986-90), Human Resource Mgmt. Assn. Chgo. (bd. dirs. 1986-89), Antaean Soc., Sigma Xi, Omicron Delta Kappa. Office: Baxter Internat Inc 1 Baxter Pky Deerfield IL 60015-4625

RUCH, CHARLES P., university official; b. Longbranch, N.J., Mar. 25, 1938; s. Claud C. and Marcella (Pierce) R.; m. Sally Joan Brandenburg, June 18, 1960; children: Cheryl, Charles, Christopher, Cathleen. BA, Coll. of Wooster, 1959; MA, Northwestern U., 1960, PhD, 1966. Counselor, tchr. Evanston (Ill.) Twp. High Sch., 1960-66; asst. prof. U. Pitts., 1966-70, assoc. prof., dept. chmn., 1970-74; assoc. dean sch. edn. Va. Commonwealth U., Richmond, 1974-76, dean sch. edn., 1976-85, interim provost, v.p., 1985-86, provost, v.p., 1986-93; pres. Boise (Idaho) State U., 1993—; cons. various univs., govtl. agys., ednl. founds. Author or co-author over 50 articles, revs., tech. reports. Mem. Am. Psychol. Assn., Am. Ednl. Research Assn., Phi Delta Kappa. Office: Boise State U 1910 University Dr Boise ID 83725-0001

RUCH, PAUL EDWARD, banker; b. Buffalo, Aug. 19, 1927; s. Edward James and Virginia Marie (Makely) R.; m. Joan Esther Swannie, Sept. 14, 1957; children: Martha E., David E. Grad., Rugters U. Stonier Grad. Sch. Banking, 1966. Exec. v.p. Marine Midland Bank, Buffalo, 1956-83; pres., chief operating officer, dir. Goldome FSB, Buffalo, 1983—; bd. dirs. Savs. Bank Life Ins. Trustee U. Buffalo Found., 1980, Buffalo Gen. Hosp.; bd. dirs. U. at Buffalo Found. Served with USN, 1945-46. Club: The Buffalo (bd. dirs.), Country of Buffalo. Home: 12 Hampton Hill Dr Buffalo NY 14221-5840 Office: Goldome Fed Savs Bank 546 Windermere Blvd Buffalo NY 14226-2863

RUCH, RICHARD HURLEY, manufacturing company executive; b. Plymouth, Ind., Apr. 15, 1930; s. Dallas Claude and Mabel (Hurley) R.; m. Patricia Lou Overbeek, June 27, 1931; children: Richard, Michael, Christine, Douglas. BA, Mich. State U., 1952. Stores acctg. supr. Kroger Inc., Grand Rapids, Mich., 1954-55; chief acct. Herman Miller Inc., Zeeland, Mich., 1955-58, controller, 1958-63, dir. mfg., 1963-67, v.p. mfg., 1967-77, v.p. adminstrn., 1978, v.p. corp. resources, 1979-85, chief fin. officer, sr. v.p., 1985-87, chief exec. officer, 1988-92, pres, chief exec. officer, 1990-92, also vice chair bd. dirs.; bd. dirs. Milcare, Zeeland. Active Hope Coll., Twentieth Century Club, Holland, Mich.; formerly active Holland C. of C., Zeeland Planning Com. Mem. Scanlon Plan Assocs. (bd. dirs., past pres.). Avocations: tennis, running. Office: Herman Miller Inc 855 E Main Ave Zeeland MI 49464-0302

RUCH, WILLIAM VAUGHN, writer, educator, consultant; b. Allentown, Pa., Sept. 29, 1937; s. Weston H. and Dorothy D. (Daubert) R. BA, Moravian Coll., 1959; MA in Communication, Syracuse U., 1969; MBA, Fairleigh Dickinson U., 1972; PhD, Rensselaer Poly. Inst.; 1980; JD, Western State U. Coll. Law, 1983. Reporter Call-Chronicle Newspapers, Allentown, Pa., 1959-60; tchr. English conversation Jonan Sr. High Sch., Matsuyama, Japan, 1960-62; asst. editor Dixie News, Am. Can Co., Easton, Pa., 1964-65; fin. editor Pa. Power & Light Co., Allentown, 1967-69, advt. asst., 1966-67, sales promotion writer, 1965-66; tech. writer, editor Space Tech. Ctr., GE Co., King of Prussia, Pa., 1969; asst. editor Bell System Tech. Jour., Bell Telephone Labs., Murray Hill, N.J., 1969-71; field rep. N.W. Ayer & Son, Inc., N.Y.C., 1972-73; asst. prof. bus. communication Fairleigh Dickinson U., Madison, N.J., 1974-75, Bloomsburg (Pa.) State Coll., 1975-76; lectr. Sch. Bus. and Pub. Adminstrn., Calif. State U., Sacramento, 1977-79; asst. prof. bus. communication Coll. Bus. Adminstrn., San Diego (Calif.) State U., 1979-84; lectr. European div. U. Md., 1984-85; prof. mgmt. Monmouth Coll., West Long Br., N.J., 1985-88; cons. Corp. Communication, 1988-91; pres., owner WVR Assocs., 1991—; founder, exec. dir. Internat. Inst. of Corp. Communication, 1992—; adj. prof. orgnl. commn., N.Y.U., 1993—. Author: Corporate Communications: A Comparison of Japanese and American Practices, 1984, Business Reports: Written and Oral, 1988, International Handbook of Corporate Communication, 1990, The Manager's Complete Handbook of Communication, 1992, Business Reporting in the Information Age, 1994, Effective Business Reports, 1995, (novel) Infinity/Affinity, 1994. Named Outstanding Prof. of Yr. San Diego State U., 1983. Mem. Acad. Mgmt., Assn. for Bus. Communication, Internat. Assn. Bus. Communicators, Internat. Platform Assn. Republican. Mem. United Ch. of Christ. Home: PO Box 517 Rockaway NJ 07866-0517

RUCHELMAN, LEONARD ISADORE, urban studies and public administration educator; b. Bklyn., June 28, 1933; s. Jacob and Sarah (Rosenblum) R.; m. Diana G. Hoffberger, Feb.11, 1961; children: Lauren, Charles. BA, Bklyn. Coll., 1954; PhD in Polit. Sci., Columbia U., 1965. Vis. asst. prof. dept. polit. sci. W.Va. U., Morgantown, 1962-64; assoc. prof., chair polit. sci. Alfred (N.Y.) U., 1964-69; assoc. prof., dir. urban studies Lehigh U., Bethlehem, Pa., 1969-75; prof., chmn. dept. urban studies and pub. adminstrn. Old Dominion U., Norfolk, Va., 1975-92, dir. Ctr. for Regional Studies, 1986-90; mem. editorial com. on socio-polit. influences Coun. on Tall Bldgs. and Urban Habitat, Bethlehem, 1975—. Author: Big City Mayors, 1969, Police Politics, 1974, The World Trade Center, 1977, A Workbook in Program Design for Public Managers, 1983, A Workbook in Redesigning Public Services, 1989. With U.S. Army, 1954-56. Mem. AAUP, Am. Soc. Pub. Adminstrn. (pres. Tidewater chpt. 1977-78), Urban Affairs Assn., Am. Polit. Sci. Assn.

RUCKELSHAUS, WILLIAM DOYLE, waste disposal services company executive; b. Indpls., July 24, 1932; s. John K. and Marion (Doyle) R.; m. Jill Elizabeth Strickland, May 11, 1962; children: Catherine Kiley, Mary Hughes, Jennifer Lea, William Justice, Robin Elizabeth. B.A. cum laude, Princeton U., 1957; LL.B., Harvard U., 1960. Bar: Ind. 1960. Atty. Ruckelshaus, Bobbitt & O'Connor, Indpls., 1960-68; dep. atty.-gen. Ind., 1960-65, chief counsel office atty.-gen. Ind., 1963-65; minority atty. Ind. Senate, 1965-

67; mem. Ind. Ho. of Reps., 1967-69, majority leader, 1967-69; asst. atty.-gen. charge civil div. Dept. Justice, 1969-70; adminstr. EPA, Washington, 1970-73; acting dir. FBI, 1973; dep. atty. gen. U.S., 1973; mem. firm Ruckelshaus, Beveridge, Fairbanks & Diamond, Washington, 1974-76; sr. v.p. law and corp. affairs Weyerhaeuser Co., Tacoma, 1975-85; adminstr. EPA, Washington, 1983-85; pres. William D. Ruckelshaus Assocs., 1985-88; mem. firm Perkins Coie, Seattle, 1985-88; chmn. bd., CEO Browning-Ferris Industries, Inc., Houston, 1988—; bd. dirs. Cummins Engine Co., Monsanto Co., Nordstrom, Inc., Tex. Commerce Bancshares, Inc., Weyerhaeuser Co. Inc.; chmn., chief exec. officer Browning-Ferris Industries, Houston. Rep. nominee for U.S. Senate, Ind., 1968. With AUS, 1953-55. Mem. Fed. Bar Assn., Ind. Bar Assn., D.C. Bar Assn., Indpls. Bar Assn. Office: Browning-Ferris Ind Inc 757 N Eldridge Pky Houston TX 77079-4435

RUCKENSTEIN, ELI, chemical engineering educator; b. Botosani, Romania, Aug. 13, 1925; came to U.S., 1969; m. Velina Rothstein, May 15, 1948; children: Andrei, Lelia. BSChemE, Poly. Inst., Bucharest, Romania, 1949, PhD in Chem. Engring., 1967; doctor honoris causa, Tech. U. Bucharest, 1993. Prof. Poly. Inst., Bucharest, 1949-69; vis. prof. U. London, 1969; NSF sr. scientist Clarkson Coll. Tech., Potsdam, N.Y., 1969-70; prof. U. Del., Newark, 1970-73; prof. SUNY, Buffalo, 1973-81, disting. prof., 1981—; vis. Humbolt prof. Bayreuth U., Fed. Republic Germany, 1986; Gulf vis. prof. Carnegie Mellon U., Pitts., 1988-89; disting. lectr. U. Waterloo, 1985, U. Mo., 1983; Fair Meml. lectr. U. Okla., 1987, Colburn Symposium lectr. U. Del., 1988, Van Winkle lectr. U. Tex., 1989. Contbr. articles, papers to profl. jours. Recipient Nat. award Romanian Dept. Edn., 1958, 64, Teaching award, 1961, George Spacu award Romanian Acad. Sci., 1963, Sr. Humbolt award Alexander von Humbolt Found., 1985, Creativity award NSF, 1985. Mem. NAE, Am. Inst. Chem. Engrs. (Alpha Chi Sigma award 1977, Walker award 1988), Am. Chem. Soc. (Kendall award 1986, Jacob F. Schoellkopf medal 1991, Langmuir Disting. Lectr. award 1994). Office: SUNY Dept Chem Engring Buffalo NY 14260

RUCKER, CHARLES THOMAS, science facility administrator; b. Augusta, Ga., June 30, 1931; s. Julius Thornton and Ida (Johnson) R.; m. Mary Laura Underwood, June 20, 1959; children: Julie Ann, Patricia Lynn. BEE, Ga. Inst. Tech., 1957. Mem. engring. staff Sperry Rand Corp., Clearwater, Fla., 1957-71, cons. Sperry Microwave Electronics Electron Tube div., Gainesville, Fla., 1971-73; prin. rsch. engr. Ga. Inst. Tech., Atlanta, 1973-88, assoc. dir. Microelectronics Rsch. Ctr., 1988-95; prin. rsch. engr., 1995; cons. USAF, 1987-89; univ. rep. Coun. on Rsch. and Tech., Washington, 1989. Patentee in field. With USN, 1950-54, Korea. Fellow IEEE (Centennial medal 1985); mem. IEEE Microwave Theory and Techniques Soc. (pres. 1983, Disting. Svc. award 1991). Baptist. Avocations: woodworking, mechanical repair, tennis, boating.

RUCKERT, ANN JOHNS, musician, singer; b. N.Y.C., Mar. 12, 1945; d. G. Wallace and Elizabeth (Johns) R. Student, Julliard Sch., 1961-69, NYU, 1969-70, Royal Acad. Music, London, 1972; studies in composition with Nadia Boulanger, Paris, 1972-73; studies with Helen Hobbs Jordon, N.Y.C., 1973-75; studies with David Sorin Collyer, 1975-78. Profl. musician over 3,000 commercially released records, 1960—; owner, pres. Ann Ruckert Music, N.Y.C. and Los Angeles, 1980—; cons., speaker Platinum Record Industry seminars; chairperson N.Y. Jazz Mus., N.Y.C., 1977-79; bd. dirs. Jazzmobile, N.Y.C., 1983-89, 92—; TV com. Grammy awards, 1985-87; creative staff Lifetime Achievement awards show, 1987; adv. Universal Jazz Coalition, N.Y.C., 1979-87; cons. rec. industry. Musician, singer: (recs.) Strawbs, Greatest Hits (Gold Record award, 1975); music contractor: (film) Housesitter, 1993, Boys on the Side, 1994; performed at Hudson Theatre, 1994, Shea Stadium, 1994, Lincoln Ct., 1994. Commr. Deed, N.Y., 1986—; Schomberg Collection N.Y.C. Pub. Library; mem. county com. Westside Manhattan, 1980-89. Mem. NARAS (Named Most Valuable Player 1982, 89, trustee, gov., v.p. N.Y. chpt., bd. trustees 1989—, bd. dirs. World Hunger Yr.), Soc. Singers (bd. dirs. N.Y.C. chpt.), Songwriters Guild Am. (bd. dirs.). Democrat. Episcopalian. Avocations: arts, music, visual arts. Home and Office: 119 W 71st St New York NY 10023-3876

RUCKERT, EDWARD M., lawyer; b. N.Y.C., Aug. 26, 1950. BA, Georgetown U., 1972; JD, U. Toledo, 1975. Bar: N.Y. 1976, D.C. 1982. Trial atty. Office Gen. Counsel USDA, Washington, 1976-81; ptnr. McDermott, Will & Emery, Washington. Mem. ABA (chmn. agrl. com., mem. adminstrv. law sect. 1983-85), Fed. Bar Assn., D.C. Bar Assn. Office: McDermott Will & Emery 1850 K St NW Washington DC 20006-2296

RUDAWSKI, JOSEPH GEORGE, educational administrator; b. Nanticoke, Pa., Feb. 22, 1942; s. Nicholas Rudawski and Pauline Zelek; m. Regina Marie Jamiolkowski, Aug. 19, 1967; children: Joseph, Tamra, Valerie, Jeanne. BA, King's Coll., Wilkes-Barre, Pa., 1963; MS in Counseling Psychology, U. Scranton, 1967; postgrad., East Stroudsburg State Coll., summer 1981, Pa. State U., summer 1988. Cert. tchr. math. and English, Pa.; instrnl. II cert. secondary sch. guidance counselor, Pa. Counselor, caseworker Kis-Lyn Indsl. Sch. for Boys, Drums, Pa., 1963-64, adminstrv. caseworker, 1964; math. and psychology instr. MMI Prep. Sch., Freeland, Pa., 1964-67, math. and psychology instr., guidance dir., 1967-71, psychology instr., guidance dir., dean students and faculty, 1971-73, guidance dir., pres., 1973—; guidance counselor Luzerne Intermediate Unit, Kingston, Pa., 1974-84; rep. Bd. of Coll. Bd., 1976—, Bd. Coll. Scholarship Svc., Pa. Assn. Ind. Schs., 1973—; rep. Nat. Assn. Ind. Schs., 1982—, pres., 1986; rep. Mid. States Assn. Colls. and Secondary Schs., 1970—, vice-chmn. evaluating com., 1991. Dir. Freeland YMCA, 1973—, pres. bd. dirs. 1981-83, chmn. budget com., mem. bldg. com., 1984—, svc. award 1983; bd. dirs. United Way, 1975-86; bd. v.p., chmn. coms. Hazleton-St. Joseph Med. Ctr., 1984-92, chmn. nuclear task force com., 1992; comml. div. chmn. United Way Campaign, Hazleton, 1985-86; facilitator edn. program Leadership Hazleton, 1986—; mem. Freeland Indsl. Corp., 1981—; vice-chmn. Sophia G. Coxe Charitable Trust, 1987—; mem. adv. bd. WOLF-TV, 1988—; bd. mem. Luth. Welfare Svc., 1991-93, chmn. resource devel. com., 1992—; bd. dirs. Luth. Welfare Svc. Found., 1993—. Recipient Appreciation award Arthritis Found., Ea. Pa. chpt., Hazleton, 1983, Svc. award YMCA, Freeland, 1983, Community award VFW, Freeland, 1988, Declaration of Achievement Pa. Senate, Harrisburg, 1988. Mem. Pers. and Guidance Assn., Pa. Sch. Counselors Assn., Luzerne County Counselors Assn. (pres. 1975-76, Outstanding Svc. award 1976), Freeland Rotary Club (pres. 1976-77). Office: MMI Prep Sch 154 Centre St Freeland PA 18224-2117

RUDBACH, JON ANTHONY, biotechnical company executive; b. Long Beach, Calif., Sept. 23, 1937; s. John Alexander and Lola (Whitcomb) R.; m. Inge Clye Steincke, July 4, 1959; children: Lucy Trine, Karl Kristian. BA, U. Calif., Berkeley, 1959; MS, U. Mich., 1961, PhD, 1964; MBA, Lake Forest Coll., 1986. Rsch. scientist Rocky Mountain Lab., Hamilton, Mont., 1964-70; prof. microbiology U. Mont., Missoula, 1970-77; mgr. exploratory rsch. Abbott Labs., North Chicago, Ill., 1977-79; dir. Stella Duncan Meml. Rsch. Inst., Missoula, 1979-82; head infectious disease rsch. Abbott Labs., Missoula, 1982-85; v.p. rsch. and devel. Ribi Immunochem Rsch., Inc., Hamilton, 1985—. Contbr. articles to profl. jours.; author 2 books; patentee in field. Mem. Bitterroot Community Bd., Hamilton, 1988—. USPHS grantee, 1970-79, fellow, 1964-66. Mem. Am. Assn. Immunologists, Am. Soc. Microbiology, Soc. for Exptl. Biology and Medicine, Soc. for Biol. Therapy, Lions (local pres. 1993-94, bd. dirs. 1987—). Republican. Congregationalist. Avocations: skiing, fishing, hunting, hiking, band. Home: 243 Hilltop Dr Hamilton MT 59840-9317 Office: Ribi ImmunoChem Rsch 553 Old Corvallis Rd Hamilton MT 59840-1409

RUDBERG, JOE ARTHUR, lawyer; b. Dallas, Jan. 1, 1947; s. Max I. and Doris M. (Argovitz) R.; children: Rachelle Leigh, Max Evan; m. Helene Susan Cohen, May 1, 1982; children: Devon Alissa, Sloan Benjamin. BA in Acctg., Duke U., 1968; JD (with honors), U. Tex., 1971. Bar: Tex. Law clk. U.S. Ct. Appeals (9th cir.), L.A., 1971-72; from assoc. to sr. ptnr. Thompson & Knight, Dallas, 1972—; adj. prof. U.S.Taxation of Fgn. Investment So. Meth. U., Dallas, 1988-89. Trustee Linda Blotcky Scholarship Fund, Dallas, 1987—; bd. dirs. Congregation Shearith Israel, Dallas, 1989—. Mem. ABA (internat., tax, bus. sects.), Internat. Fiscal Assn., Internat. Tax Assn., Internat. Bar Assn., Tex. Bar Assn., Dallas Bar Assn., Asociacion Nacional de Abogados de Empresa (Nuevo Leon Sect., first fgn. mem., guest lectr.), U.S.-Mex. C. of C., Phi Kappa Phi. Office: Thompson & Knight 3300 First City Ctr 1700 Pacific Ave Dallas TX 75201-4617

RUDCZYNSKI, ANDREW B., academic administrator, medical researcher; b. Nottingham, England, Sept. 7, 1947; came to U.S., 1951; s. Richard B. and Krystyna Z. (Stachlewska) R.; m. Andrea Skalny, Oct. 16, 1976 (div. Oct. 1990); children: Christina, Thomas. BSc in Biology/Biochemistry, McGill U., 1969; PhD in Immunology, Syracuse U., 1974; MBA in Adminstrn., So. Ill. U., 1984. Prin. investigator scrub typhus project divsn. Rickettsiology U.S. Army Med. Rsch. Infectious Diseases, Ft. Detrick, Md., 1974-76; rsch. assoc. dept. Biology Mich. Cancer Found., Detroit, 1976-77, rsch. scientist dept. Immunology, unit chief immunology unit Breast Cancer Prognostic Study, 1977-80; asst. dir. Office Rsch. and Grants U. Md. Ea. Shore, Princess Anne, 1980-83; extramural assoc. Office Extramural Rsch. and Tng., Office of Dir. NIH, 1981-82; asst. dir. Office Rsch. & Sponsored Programs Rutgers U., Piscataway, N.J., 1983-84, dir., 1984—, asst. v.p. rsch. adminstrn., 1985-93, assoc. v.p. rsch. policy and adminstrn., 1993—; field reader strengthening devel. instns. program U.S. Dept. Edn., 1990; mem. Chancellor's task force instrn. and rsch. infrastructure support N.J. Dept. Higher Edn., 1992. Contbr. articles, abstracts to profl. jours. Capt. U.S. Army Med. Svc. Corps, 1974-76. Recipient traineeship award NSF, 1969-71; predoctoral fellow NIH, 1973-74. Mem. AAAS, Nat. Coun. Univ. Rsch. Adminstrs. (profl. devel. com. 1988-90, region II program com. 1989-90, chmn. region II 1990-92, nat. program com. 1994-95), Coun. Govtl. Rels. (fed. mgmt. devel. com. 1989-90), Soc. Rsch. Adminstrs., Assn. Univ. Tech. Mgrs., Beta Gamma Sigma, Sigma Xi. Roman Catholic. Home: 2 Carina Dr Milltown NJ 08850 Office: Rutgers U Office Rsch/Sponsored Programs Adminstrv Svcs Bldg 123 Annex II PO Box 1179 Piscataway NJ 08855-1179

RUDD, DALE FREDERICK, retired chemical engineer; b. Mpls., Mar. 2, 1935; s. Henry G. and Emmy E. (Grip) R.; m. Sandra Coryell, Aug. 1, 1964; children—Karen, David. Ph.D., U. Minn., 1959. Prof. chem. engring. U. Wis., Madison, 1961-94, ret., 1994. Author: (with Watson) Strategy of Process Engineering, 1968, (with Powers and Siirola) Process Synthesis, 1973, (with Berthouex) Strategy of Pollution Control, 1977, (with Fathi-Afshar, Treviño and Stadtherr) Petrochemical Technology Assessment, 1981, (with Dumesic, Aparicio, Rekoske and Trevino) Microkinetics of Heterogeneous Catalysis, 1992. Guggenheim fellow, 1971-72. Mem. Nat. Acad. Engring. Office: U Wis Dept Chem Engring Madison WI 53706

RUDD, ELDON, retired congressman; b. Camp Verde, Ariz.; m. Ann Merritt. B.A., Ariz. State U., 1947; J.D., U. Ariz., 1950. Bar: Ariz. 1949, U.S. Supreme Ct. 1953. Pvt. practice Tucson, 1950; spl. agt.-diplomatic assignment principally Latin Am. FBI, 1950-70; mem. Maricopa County (Ariz.) Bd. Suprs., 1972-76; bd. dirs. Ariz.-Mex. Commn., 1972-92; with U.S.-Mex. Interplalamentary Com., 1976-84; mem. 95th-99th Congresses from 4th Dist. Ariz., 1976-87; of counsel Shimmel, Hill, Bishop & Gruender, P.C., Phoenix, 1987-93; pres. Eldon Rudd Consultancy, Scottsdale, Ariz., 1993—; bd. dirs. So. Pacific Transp. Co., 1987-88, Salt River Project, 1988—. Author: World Communism-Threat to Freedom, 1987. Mem. numerous pub. svc. orgns., including energy and water, mil. and internat. affairs. Fighter pilot USMCR, 1942-46. Mem. Fed. Bar Assn. (chpt. pres. 1976), Ariz. Bar Assn., Maricopa County Bar Assn., Scottsdale Bar Assn., Paradise Valley Country Club (bd. dirs. 1989-92), Phi Delta Phi, Blue Key. Republican. Roman Catholic. Home: PO Box 873 Scottsdale AZ 85252-0873 Office: 6909 E Main St Scottsdale AZ 85251-4311

RUDD, GERALD RAY, retail food and drug company executive; b. Kinsley, Kans., Oct. 6, 1929; s. Linford L. and Bertha Viola (Workman) R.; m. Nicole Cardoso-Ayres, Oct. 4, 1930; children: Christian, Derek. BA, George Washington U., 1958; grad. Program for Mgmt. Devel., Harvard U., 1968. Mgmt. intern AEC, Washington, 1958-59; labor relations mgr. Albertsons, Inc., Boise, Idaho, 1959-62, dir. indsl. relations, 1962-70, v.p. personnel and indsl. relations, 1970-74, sr. v.p. human resources, 1974—. Served to lt. USN, 1951-55. Mem. Am. Soc. Personnel Adminstrn. (Profl. of Yr. awards Boise chpt. 1984, nat. soc. 1986). Republican. Mormon. Club: Hillcrest Country (Boise). Avocations: tennis. skiing, woodworking. Home: 1101 S Owyhee St Boise ID 83705-2208 Office: Albertson's Inc 250 E Parkcenter Blvd Boise ID 83706-3940

RUDD, LEO SLATON, psychology educator, minister; b. Hereford, Tex., Feb. 20, 1924; s. Charles Ival and Susan Leola (Horton) R.; m. Virginia Mae Daniel, Nov. 17, 1943; children: Virginia Kaye, Leo Jr., Bobbie Ann. BA, William Jewell Coll., Liberty, Mo., 1947; MRE, Cen. Bapt. Sem., Kansas City, Kans., 1948; MS, E. Tex. State U., Commerce, 1957; PhD, N. Tex. State U., Denton, 1959. Ordained to ministry, Southern Bapt. Conv., 1936. Bapt. student dir./instr. Smith County Bapt., Tyler, Tex.; psychology instr. Tyler (Tex.) Jr. Coll.; dir. missions Linn County, Mo. Author: Syllabus for New Testament Studies, Syllabus for Old Testament Studies. With U.S. Army, 1942-43. Named Tchr. of the Yr., Tyler Jr. Coll., 1987, 1986 Best Tchr. Alumni award. Mem. Tex. Jr. Coll. Tchrs. Assn., Southwestern Bible Tchrs. Assn., East Tex. Counselors Assn., Internat. Platform Assn., DAV. Home: 1913 E 5th St Tyler TX 75701-3593 *The slight of our yesterdays are so soon forgotten in the tomorrow of God's grace and love. Nothing can out do or surpass His goodness to us.*

RUDD, NICHOLAS, marketing communications company executive; b. N.Y.C., Mar. 18, 1943; s. Emmanuel and Lucie Lia (Weinberg) R.; children: Alexis Henry, Kenneth Charles. B.A., Columbia U., 1964, M.B.A., 1967. Mem. pub. relations staff Ford Motor Co., N.Y.C., 1964-65; account mgr. Young & Rubicam Inc., N.Y.C., 1968-75, v.p., mgmt. supr., 1975-80, sr. v.p. mgmt. svcs., 1980-90, chief info. officer, 1990—; cons. Nat. Neurofibromatosis Found., Inc., 1981—; bd. dirs. Vol. Cons. Group, Inc., N.Y.C., 1987. Bd. dirs. Nat. Choral Coun., chmn., 1993-95. Mem. Soc. for Info. Mgmt., Am. Assn. Advt. Agys. (chair info. tech. com. 1993-94), Beta Gamma Sigma. Office: Young & Rubicam Inc 285 Madison Ave New York NY 10017-6486

RUDDELL, GARY RONALD, publisher; b. Washington, Feb. 15, 1948; s. Paul Alexander and Jessie Pauline (Barker) R.; m. Mary Lee Receveur, Jan. 25, 1969; children: Mary Elizabeth, Aimee Suzanne, Paul Alexander II. B.S., U. Md., 1973. Pres. Expert Lawn Service, Hyattsville, Md., 1964-68, Manor House Press, Inc., Riverdale, Md., 1969-71, Hobby House Press, Inc., Cumberland, Md., 1971-93; pub. Grantsville, Md., 1993—, Hobby House Press, Ind. Curator, Western Md. Sta. Ctr. Mus., 1984-87, bd. dirs. Western Md. Hospitality Bur., 1988-92; pres. Zeitgeist Publishing, Inc.; German Life Mag.; mem. bus. adv. bd. First United Nat. Bank and Trust, Cumberland, 1992—, Bank Strategic Planning Com., 1993—; dir. Md. State Appalachian Regional Commn., 1995—; founder, chmn. bd. Internat. Doll Acad., 1985-92; pres. Dolls of Yr., 1985-92; pres. Crafted Heirlooms, Inc., Cumberland, 1983-93. Mem. bus. adv. curriculum com . Allegany Community Coll., Cumberland, 1987-92. Mem. United Fedn. Doll Clubs (treas. 1978-79), Allegany County Hist. Soc. (curator 1983-86, trustee 1983, 87-89); bd. dirs. Potomac Coun. Boy Scouts Am. Mem. Western Md. Small Bus. Adv. Commn., Allegany County C. of C. (bd. dirs. 1988-89, chmn. tourism commn 1987-88). Republican. Methodist. Club: Civitan (sec., treas. 1977-79, civitan of yr. 1979) (Hyattsville). Lodge: Rotary (bd. dirs. 1981-83, pres. 1985-86). Office: Hobby House Press Inc 1 Corporate Dr Grantsville MD 21536

RUDDER, CATHERINE ESTELLE, political science association administrator; b. Atlanta, Dec. 16; d. James M. and Virginia Rudder. BA, Emory U., 1969; MA, Ohio State U., 1972, PhD, 1973. Asst. prof. U. Ga., Athens, 1973-77; chief staff to Rep. W. Fowler, Jr. U.S. House Reps., Washington, 1978-81, assoc. dir., 1983-87; exec. dir. Am. Polit. Sci. Assn., Washington, 1987—. Office: Am Polit Scis Assn 1527 New Hampshire Ave NW Washington DC 20036-1206

RUDDER, PAUL R., transportation executive; b. 1932; married. BSCE, U. Tenn., 1955. V.p. So. Railway Co., 1955-87; v.p. Norfolk So. Corp., 1987-89, sr. v.p. ops., 1989-90, pres. 1990—; v.p. Norfolk So. Railway Corp.; v.p. ops. Norfolk and Western Railway Co., 1982—; pres. Ctrl. of Ga. Railway Co., Cin. New Orleans Tex. Railway, Norfolk, Va. With USAF, 1956-57. Office: Cincinatti New Orleans Texas Railway 3 Commercial Pl Norfolk VA 23510-2108

RUDDLE, FRANCIS HUGH, genetics educator; b. West New York, N.J., Aug. 19, 1929; s. Thomas Hugh and Mary Henley (Rodda) R.; m. Nancy Marion Hartman, Aug. 1, 1964; children: Kathlyn Gabrielle, Amy

Elizabeth. BA, Wayne State U., 1953, MS, 1956, hon. degree, 1990; PhD, U. Calif.-Berkeley, 1960; hon. degree, Lawrence U., 1982, Weizmann Inst., Israel, 1983. Asst. prof. Yale U., New Haven, 1961-67, assoc. prof., 1967-72, prof. biology and human genetics, 1972—, Ross Granville Harrison prof. biology, 1983-88, Sterling prof. biology, 1988—, chmn. dept. biology, 1977-83, 88—; adv. com. Am. Type Culture Collection, 1963-71; planning com. 1st Internat. Congress on Cell Biology, 1975; mem. cell study sect. NIH, 1965-70, chmn. mutant cell lines com., 1972-77; R.E. Dyer lectr., 1978; Merck lectr. Montreal Cancer Inst., 1979; Condon lectr. U. Oreg. 1981; co-chmn. 10th Internat. Workshop on Human Gene Mapping, 1989. Editor Genomics, 1986—; editor-in-chief Jour. Exptl. Zoology, 1985—; editorial bd. Exptl. Cell Research, 1975—, Genetics, 1973—, In Vitro, 1970—, Somatic Cell Genetics, 1975—, Am. Jour. Cell Biology, Biochemistry. Served with USAAF, 1946-49. Recipient Dickson prize in medicine U. Pitts., 1981, Disting. Alumni award Wayne State U., 1981, Herman Beerman award Soc. for Investigative Dermatology, 1982, Bertner Meml. award U. Tex., 1987, Katherine Berkan Judd award Meml. Sloan-Kettering Cancer Ctr., 1988; NIH postdoctoral fellow U. Glasgow, Scotland, 1960-61. Fellow N.Y. Acad. Scis. (award 1987); mem. NAS, Inst. of Medicine of NAS, Am. Acad. Arts and Scis., Conn. Acad. Sci. and Engring., Harvey Soc., Soc. Devel. Biology (pres. 1971-72, trustee 1970-73), AAAS, Am. Soc. Cell Biology (pres. 1987), Am. Soc. Human Genetics (dir. 1972-75, pres. 1984-85, 85-86, Allan award 1983), Am. Soc. Naturalists, Am. Soc. Zoologists, Genetics Soc. Am., Am. Soc. Biochemistry, Pattern Recognition Soc., Tissue Culture Assn. (dir.), Am. Cancer Soc., Sigma Xi (pres. Yale U. chpt. 1985). Office: Yale U Dept Of Biology New Haven CT 06511

RUDDLE, NANCY HARTMAN, microbiology educator; b. St. Louis, Apr. 3, 1940; d. David Eugene and Josephine (Odell) Hartman; m. Francis Hugh Ruddle, Aug. 1, 1964; children: Kathlyn, Amy. BA, Mt. Holyoke Coll., 1962; PhD, Yale U., 1968. Rsch. assoc. Yale U., New Haven, 1968-71, postdoctoral fellow, 1971-74, rsch. assoc., 1974-75, asst. prof., 1975-80, assoc. prof., 1980-91, prof. microbiology, 1991—, head microbiology div., 1990—; panel mem. Am. Cancer Soc., 1987-91; study sect. mem. NIH, 1991—. Contbr. over 100 articles to profl. jurs. Am. Cancer Soc. postdoctoral fellow, Damon Runyon postdoctoral fellow; recipient Am. Cancer Soc. Faculty Rsch. award; NIH grantee, Am. Cancer Soc. grantee, others. Office: Yale Univ Sch Medicine 60 College St New Haven CT 06510-3210

RUDDON, RAYMOND WALTER, JR., pharmacology educator; b. Detroit, Dec. 23, 1936; married, 1961; three children. BS, U. Detroit, 1958; PhD in Pharmacology, U. Mich., 1964, MD, 1967. Teaching fellow in chemistry U. Detroit, 1958-59; from instr. to prof. pharmacology U. Mich., Ann Arbor, 1964-76; dir. biol. marker program Nat. Cancer Inst., Frederick, Md., 1976-81; Maurice H. Seevers prof., chmn. dept. pharmacology U. Mich. Med. Sch., Ann Arbor, 1981-90; dir. Eppley Inst. for Rsch. in Cancer and Allied Diseases U. Nebr. Med. Ctr., Omaha, 1990—; Eppley prof. oncology U. Nebr. Med. Ctr. NIH predoctoral fellow, 1959-64; Am. Cancer Soc. scholar, 1964-67. Mem. AAAS, Am. Soc. Pharmacology and Exptl. Therapeutics, Am. Assn. Cancer Rsch., Am. Soc. Biochemistry and Molecular Biology, Endocrine Soc. Research in field of biol. markers of neoplasia; glycoprotein hormones; protein folding. Office: U Nebr Med Ctr Eppley Inst Rsch in Cancer & Allied Dise 600 S 42nd St Omaha NE 68198-0001*

RUDDY, FRANK S., lawyer, former ambassador; b. N.Y.C., Sept. 15, 1937; s. Francis Stephen and Teresa (O'Neil) R.; m. Kateri Mary O'Neill, Aug. 29, 1964; children—Neil, David, Stephen. A.B., Holy Cross Coll., 1959; M.A., NYU, 1962, LL.M., 1967; LL.B., Loyola U., New Orleans, 1965; Ph.D., Cambridge U., Eng., 1969. Bar: D.C., N.Y., Tex., U.S. Supreme Ct. Faculty Cambridge U., 1967-69; asst. gen. counsel USIA, Washington, 1969-72, 73-74; sr. atty. Office of Telecommunication Policy, White House, Washington, 1972-73; counsel Exxon Corp., Houston, 1974-81; asst. adminstr. AID (with rank asst. sec. state) Dept. State, Washington, 1981-84; U.S. ambassador to Equatorial Guinea, 1984-88; gen. counsel U.S. Dept. Energy, Washington, 1988-89; v.p. Sierra Blanc Devel. Corp., Washington, 1989-92; prin. Law Offices of Frank Ruddy, Washington, 1992—; vis. scholar Johns Hopkins Sch. Advanced Internat. Studies, 1990—; dep. chmn. UN Referendum for Western Sahara, 1994—. Author: International Law in the Enlightenment, 1975; editor: American International Law Cases (series), 1972—; editor in chief Internat. Lawyer, 1978-83; contbr. articles to legal jours. Bd. dirs. African Devel. Found., Washington, 1983-84. Served with USMCR, 1956-61. Mem. ABA (chmn. treaty compliance sect. 1991—), Am. Soc. Internat. Law, Internat. Law Assn., Hague Acad. Internat. Law Alumni Assn., Oxford and Cambridge Club (London), Conservative Club, Internat. Club, Dacor House. Republican. Roman Catholic. Home: 5600 Western Ave Chevy Chase MD 20815-3406 Office: 6 E St SE Washington DC 20003

RUDDY, JAMES W., lawyer; b. 1949. AB, U. Mich., 1971; JD, Wayne State U., 1973. Bar: Wash. 1974, Mich. 1974. Assoc. gen. counsel Safeco Corp., 1984-89, v.p., gen. counsel, 1989—. Office: Safeco Corp Safeco Plz Seattle WA 98185*

RUDE, BRIAN DAVID, state legislator; b. Viroqua, Wis., Aug. 25, 1955; s. Raymond and Conelee (Johnson) R.; m. Karen Thulin; children: Erik, Nels. BA magna cum laude, Luther Coll., 1977; MA, U. Wis., Madison, 1994. Mem. Wis. Assembly, Madison, 1982-84; mem. Wis. Senate, Madison, 1984—, asst. minority leader, 1989-93; pres. Wis. State Sen., 1993—; with corp. communications The Trane Co., La Crosse, Wis., 1981-85. Bd. advisers Nat. Trust Historic Preservation, 1990—. Mem. Lions, Sons of Norway, Norwegian-Am. Hist. Assn. (trustee). Republican. Lutheran. Avocations: reading, gardening, traveling, fishing. Home: 307 Babcock St PO Box 367 Coon Valley WI 54623-0367 Office: Wis State Senate State Capitol Rm 239-S PO Box 7882 Madison WI 53703

RUDEE, MERVYN LEA, engineering educator, researcher; b. Palo Alto, Calif., Oct. 4, 1935; s. Mervyn C. and Hannah (Mathews) R.; m. Elizabeth Eager, June 20, 1958; children: Elizabeth Diane, David Benjamin. BS, Stanford U., 1958, MS, 1962, PhD, 1965. Asst. prof. materials sci. Rice U., Houston, 1964-68, assoc. prof., 1968-72, prof. materials sci., 1972-74; prof. U. Calif., San Diego, 1974—; founding provost U. Calif., San Diego, La Jolla, 1974-82, founding dean Sch. Engring., 1982-93; coord. grad. program on materials sci. U. Calif., San Diego, 1994—; vis. scholar Corpus Christi Coll., Cambridge, Eng., 1971-72; CFO, prin. Univ. Planning Assocs., Inc.; vis. scientist IBM Thomas J. Watson Rsch. Ctr., Yorktown Heights, N.Y., 1987. Pres., bd. trustees Mus. Photographic Art, San Deigo, 1995—. Lt. (j.g.) USN, 1958-61. Guggenheim fellow, 1971-72. Mem. Electron Microscope Soc. Am., Materials Rsch. Soc., Am. Physics Soc., Tex. Soc. Electron Microscopy (hon.), Sigma Xi, Tau Beta Pi. Home: 1745 Kearsarge Rd La Jolla CA 92037-3829 Office: Univ Calif San Diego Dept Elec & Cptr Engring La Jolla CA 92093-0407

RUDEL, JULIUS, conductor; b. Vienna, Austria, Mar. 6, 1921; came to U.S., 1938, naturalized, 1944; s. Jakob and Josephine (Sonnenblum) R.; m. Rita Gillis, June 24, 1942 (dec. May 1984); children: Joan, Madeleine, Anthony Jason. Student, Acad. Music, Vienna; diploma in conducting, Mannes Coll. Music, 1942; diploma hon. doctorates, U. Vt., 1961, U. Mich., 1971; doctorates hon. causa, Pace Coll., Manhattan Coll., 1994, Mannes Coll. Music, 1994, Manhattanville Coll., 1994. With, N.Y. City Opera, 1943-79, debut, 1944; gen. dir., 1957-79, Third St. Music Sch. Settlement, 1945-52, mus. dir., Chautauqua Opera Assn., 1958-59, Caramoor Festival, Katonah, N.Y., 1964-76, Lar May Festival, 1971-72, Kennedy Center Performing Arts, 1971-75, music adviser, Wolf Trap Farm Park, 1971, condr., Spoleto (Italy) Festival, 1962-63, music adv., Phila. Opera, 1978-81, music dir., Buffalo Philharmonic Orch., 1979-85, debut as condr., Met. Opera, 1978, San Francisco Opera, 1979, Vienna State Opera, 1976, Royal Opera, Covent Garden, 1984, Rome Opera, 1987, Opera de la Bastille, 1992, Teatro Colon, Buenos Aires, Argentina, 1992, Royal Danish Opera, Copenhagen, 1993; dir. prodn.: Kiss Me Kate, Vienna Volksoper Opera, 1956; guest condr., Chgo. Symphony, Phila. Orch., N.Y. Philharm., Boston Symphony, Detroit Symphony, Israel Philharmonic, Paris Opera, Munich Opera, Hamburg State Opera, Vienna State Opera, other symphonic, operatic orgns. in, U.S. and Europe. Decorated Croix du Chevalier in arts and letters France; recipient gold medal Nat. Arts Club, 1958, citation Nat. Assn. Am. Composers and Conductors, 1958, citation Nat. Fedn. Music Clubs, 1959, Ditson award Columbia, 1959, Page One award in music Newspaper Guild,

1959, hon. insignia for arts and sci. Govt. of Austria, 1961, Handel medal for music City N.Y., 1965, citation Nat. Assn. Negro Musicians, 1965, citation Nat. Opera Assn., 1971, comdr.'s Cross German Order Merit, 1967, hon. lt. Israeli Army, 1969, Julius Rudel award for young condrs., Pan Am./Pan African award for humanism, 1981, Peabody award, 1985. Office: c/o Shuman Assocs 120 W 58th St Apt 8D New York NY 10019

RUDELIUS, WILLIAM, marketing educator; b. Rockford, Ill., Sept. 2, 1931; s. Carl William and Clarissa Euclid (Davis) R.; m. Jacqueline Urch Dunham, July 3, 1954; children: Robert, Jeanne, Katherine, Kristi. B.S. in Mech. Engring., U. Wis., 1953; M.B.A., U. Pa., 1959, Ph.D. in Econs., 1964. Program engr., missile and space vehicle dept. Gen. Electric Co., Phila., 1956-57, 59-61; sr. research economist North Star Research Inst., Mpls., 1964-66; lectr. U. Minn., Mpls., 1961-64; asst. prof. mktg. Coll. Bus. Adminstrn. U. Minn., 1964, assoc. prof., 1966-72, prof., 1972—. Co-author: (with W. Bruce Erickson) An Introduction to Contemporary Business, 1973, rev. 4th edit., 1985, (with Eric N. Berkowitz, Roger A. Kerin and Steven W. Hartley) Marketing, 1986, rev. 4th edit., 1994, (with Krzysztof Przybytowski, Roger A. Kerin and Steven W. Hartley) Marketing na Przykładach, 1994; contbr. articles to profl. jours. Served with USAF, 1954-55. Home: 1425 Alpine Pass Minneapolis MN 55416-3560 Office: Carlson Sch Mgmt U Minn 271 19th Ave S Minneapolis MN 55455-0430

RUDELL, MILTON WESLEY, aerospace engineer; b. Rice Lake, Wis., July 9, 1920; s. George C. and Edna (Bjoraa) R.; m. Doris Lorraine Shella, Nov. 30, 1941; children: Helen, Geoffrey, Lynn, Deborah, Leah, Andrea, Kessea, Eric, Erin. B in Aerospace Engring., U. Minn., 1946. Registered profl. engr. Chief tool engr. Boeing Aircraft Corp., Wichita, Kans. and Seattle, 1941-43, stateside and overseas field engr., 1943-45; chief fueling systems engr. N.W. Airlines, Mpls., 1946-50; pres. Rumoco Co., Frederic, Wis., 1950-68; registrar ECPI-Nat. IBM computer sch., Mpls., 1968-69; pres. Life Engring. Co., Milw. and Frederic, Wis., 1969—. Designer original med. surg. suture tape, 1951; designer 1st match-book cover with strike plate on rear side for safety, 1942; pioneered high-speed underwing fueling systems for comml. aircraft and 1st hydrant ground fueling systems for comml. aircraft; co-author Ops. & Maintenance Manual for B-29 aircraft, 1943. Founder Frederic Found. for Advanced Edn. Recipient WWII Aeronautical Engring. Citation from Pres. Eisenhower, 1944. Mem. Exptl. Aircraft Assn., Wis. Aviation Hall of Fame, Northwestern Wis. Mycol. Soc. (charter). Lutheran. Home and Office: 501 Wisconsin Ave N Frederic WI 54837-0400 *We shall pass through this world but once. Any good therefore that we can do or any kindness that we can show to any human being, let us do it now. Let us not defer nor neglect it, for we shall not pass this way again.*

RUDENSTINE, NEIL LEON, academic administrator, educator; b. Ossining, N.Y., Jan. 21, 1935; s. Harry and Mae (Esperito) R.; m. Angelica Zander, Aug. 27, 1960; children: Antonia Margaret, Nicholas David, Sonya. B.A., Princeton U., 1956; B.A. (Rhodes Scholar), Oxford U., 1959, M.A., 1963; Ph.D., Harvard U., 1964. Instr. dept. English Harvard U., Cambridge, Mass., 1964-66; asst. prof. Harvard U., 1966-68; assoc. prof. English Princeton (N.J.) U., 1968-73, prof. English, 1973-88, dean of students, 1968-72, dean of Coll., 1972-77, provost, 1977-88; exec. v.p. Andrew W. Mellon Found., N.Y.C., 1988-91; pres. Harvard U., Cambridge, Mass., 1991—, prof. English, 1991—. Author: Sidney's Poetic Development, 1967, (with George Rousseau) English Poetic Satire, 1972, (with William Bowen) In Pursuit of the PhD, 1992. Served to 1st lt. arty. AUS, 1959-60. Hon. fellow New Coll., Oxford U. Mem. Am. Philos. Soc., Coun. on Fgn. Rels., Com. for Econ. Devel.; fellow Am. Acad. Arts and Scis. Office: Harvard U Office of Pres Massachusetts Hall Cambridge MA 02138

RUDER, DAVID STURTEVANT, lawyer, educator, government official; b. Wausau, Wis., May 25, 1929; s. George Louis and Josephine (Sturtevant) R.; m. Susan M. Small; children: Victoria Chesley, Julia Larson, David Sturtevant II, John Coulter; m stepchildren: Elizabeth Frankel, Rebecca Wilkinson. BA cum laude, Williams Coll., 1951; JD with honors, U. Wis., 1957. Bar: Wis. 1957, Ill. 1962. Of counsel Schiff Hardin & Waite, Chgo., 1957-61; assoc. Quarles & Brady, Milw., 1957-61; asst. prof. law Northwestern U., Chgo., 1961-63, assoc. prof., 1963-65, prof., 1965—, assoc. dean Law Sch., 1965-66, dean Law Sch., 1977-85; chmn. Securities and Exch. Commn., Washington, 1987-89; ptnr. Baker & McKenzie, Chgo., 1990-94, sr. counsel, 1994—; cons. Am. Law Inst. Fed. Securities Code; planning dir. Corp. Counsel Inst., 1962-66, 76-77, com. mem., 1962-87, 90—; cons. Ray Garrett Jr. Corp. and Securities Law Inst., 1980-87, 90—; vis. lectr. U. de Liege, 1967; vis. prof. law U. Pa., Phila., 1971; faculty Salzburg Seminar, 1976; mem. legal adv. com. bd. dirs. N.Y. Stock Exch., 1978-82; mem. com. profl. responsibility Ill. Supreme Ct., 1978-87; adv. bd. Securities Regulation Inst., 1978—, (chmn. 1994—); bd. govs. Nat. Assn. Securities Dealers, 1990-93, chmn. Legal Adv. bd., 1993—; Policy Task Force, 1994—. Editor-in-chief: Williams Coll. Record, 1950-51, U. Wis. Law Rev, 1957; editor: Proc. Corp. Counsel Inst, 1962-66; contbr. articles to legal periodicals. 1st lt. AUS, 1951-54. Fellow Am. Bar Found. (bd. dirs. 1984-86), Ill. Bar Found.; mem. ABA (coun. sect. corp. banking and bus. law 1970-74, com. chmn.), Chgo. Bar Assn. (com. chmn.), Wis. Bar Assn., Am. Law Inst., Order of Coif, Comml. Club of Chgo., Econ. Club of Chgo., Law Club of Chgo., Legal Club of Chgo., Gargoyle Soc., Phi Beta Kappa, Phi Delta Phi, Zeta Psi. Home: 325 Orchard Ln Highland Park IL 60035-1939 Office: Northwestern U Sch Law 357 E Chicago Ave Chicago IL 60611-3069 also: Baker & McKenzie One Prudential Pla 130 E Randolph Dr Chicago IL 60601

RUDER, MELVIN HARVEY, retired newspaper editor; b. Manning, N.D., Jan. 19, 1915; s. Moris M. and Rebecca (Friedman) R.; m. Ruth Bergan, Feb. 10, 1950; 1 dau., Patricia E. Morton. B.A., U. N.D., 1937, M.A., 1941; grad. student, Northwestern U., 1940. Asst. prof. journalism U. N.D., 1940; indsl. relations specialist Westinghouse Electric Co., Sharon, Pa., 1940-41; pub. relations with Am. Machine & Foundry Co., N.Y.C., 1946; founder, editor Hungry Horse News, Columbia Falls, Mont., 1946-78; editor emeritus Hungry Horse News, 1978—. Chmn. adv. coun. Flathead Nat. Forest, Dist. 6 Sch. Bd., 1967-70. Served to lt. (s.g.) USNR, 1942-45. Recipient Pulitzer prize for gen. local reporting, 1965. Mem. Mont. Press Assn. (pres. 1957), Flathead Associated C. of C. (pres. 1971), Glacier Natural History Assn. (pres. 1983). Home: Buffalo Hill Terr 40 Claremont Kalispell MT 59901

RUDER, WILLIAM, public relations executive; b. N.Y.C., Oct. 17, 1921; s. Jacob L. and Rose (Rosenberg) R.; m. Betty Cott, May 23, 1980; children—Robin Ann, Abby, Brian, Michal Ellen, Eric. B.S.S., City Coll., N.Y., 1942. With Samuel Goldwyn Prodns., 1946-48; pres. Ruder & Finn, Inc., N.Y.C., 1948-80, William Ruder Inc., 1981—; asst. sec. commerce, 1961-62; Tobe lectr. Harvard Grad. Sch. Bus., 1962; mem. grad. adv. bd. City Coll. N.Y., Baruch Sch. Bus., N.Y.C.; cons. State Dept.; bd. dirs. W.P. Carey & Co., Inc. Author: The Businessman's Guide to Washington. Bd. dirs. Bus. Com. for Arts, Jewish Bd. Guardians, Chamber Music Soc. Lincoln Ctr., Fund for Peace, Project Return Found.; exec. com. United Way Am.; trustee, chmn. Manhattanville Coll., Purchase, N.Y., 1974-75; bd. overseers Wharton Sch. U. Pa.; mem. pres.'s coun. Meml. Sloan-Kettering Cancer Ctr.; chmn. bd. ACCESS. Capt. USAAF, 1941-45. Mem. UN Assn. U.S.A. (nat. policy panel dir.). Home: 430 E 86th St New York NY 10028-6476 Office: Ruder Finn Inc 301 E 57th St New York NY 10022

RUDERMAN, ARMAND PETER, health economics educator, consultant, volunteer; b. N.Y.C., Nov. 19, 1923; s. Louis and Lillian (Prigohzy) R.; m. Alice Helen Holton, June 17, 1948; children: Ann, Mary, William, John. S.B., Harvard U., 1943; M.A., 1946, Ph.D., 1947; M.B.A., U. Chgo., 1944. Instr. econs. various U.S. univs., 1946-50; statistician, economist ILO, Pan-Am. Health Orgn., WHO, 1950-67; chmn. sci. working group on social and econ. aspects of tropical disease research WHO/TDR, 1979-83; prof. health adminstrn. U. Toronto, Ont., Can., 1967-75, adj. prof., 1989—; founding dean adminstrv. studies Dalhousie U., Can., 1975-80, prof. health adminstrn., 1981-89; prof. emeritus Dalhousie U., N.S., Can., 1989—; vis. prof. Nat. U. Singapore, 1982-83; cons. in field. Contbr. articles to profl. jours. and books. Bd. dirs. Northwood Home Care, 1987-89, Northwestern Gen. Hosp. Toronto, 1991—; mem. Etobicoke Bd. Health, 1991—; mem. cmty. adv. com. Toronto Hosp., 1992—; mem. region 3 exec. com. Ont. Hosp. Assn., 1994—. Mem. Can. Pub. Health Assn., Royal Econ. Soc.

RUDHART, ALEXANDER H., modern European history educator; b. Vienna, Austria, May 24, 1930; came to U.S., 1953; s. Hugo Alexander and Leopoldine (Grüner) R.; m. Kate Blake, Aug. 19, 1963; 1 child, Alex Joseph. JD Utriusque, U. Vienna, 1952, PhD in Philosophy, 1962. Prof. Villanova (Pa.) U., 1954—. Author: 20th Century Euope I, 1975, 20th Century Europe II, 1986. With Volkssturm Army 1945. Mem. AHA. Republican. Roman Catholic. Avocations: painting, sculpture, shooting, cabinet making, flying. Home: 200 Hilldale Rd Villanova PA 19085-1506 Office: Villanova U Lancaster Pike Villanova PA 19085

RUDIN, ALFRED, chemistry educator emeritus; b. Alta., Can., Feb. 5, 1924; m. Pearl Rudin; children: Jonathan, Jeremy, Joel. BSc, U. Alta., 1949; PhD, Northwestern U., 1952. Profl. engr. Ont. Rsch. chemist CIL Cen. Rsch. Lab., 1952-60, rsch. group leader, 1960-64; lab. mgr. CIL Plastics, 1964-67; assoc. prof. chemistry U. Waterloo, Ont., 1967-69, prof. chemistry, 1969-73, prof. chemistry & chem. engring., 1973-89, disting. prof. emeritus, 1990—; vis. prof. chem. engring. Technion, Israel, 1975-76, 81; vis. scientist IBM, San Jose, Calif., 1980; dir. Inst. for Polymer Rsch., Waterloo, 1990-94. Author: Elements of Polymer Science & Engineering, 1982; contbr. over 250 articles to profl. jours. Served with Royal Canadian Signals, 1942-45. Recipient Polysar Lecture award Chem. Soc. Can., 1989, Protective Coatings award, 1983. Fellow Royal Soc. of Can., Chem. Inst. of Can. Achievements include 19 patents. Office: U Waterloo, Dept of Chemistry, Waterloo, ON Canada N2L 3G1

RUDIN, ANNE NOTO, former mayor, nurse; b. Passaic, N.J., Jan. 27, 1924; m. Edward Rudin, June 6, 1948; 4 children. BS in Edn., Temple U., 1945, RN, 1946; MPA, U. So. Calif., 1983; LLD (hon.), Golden Gate U., 1990. RN, Calif. Mem. faculty Temple U. Sch. Nursing, Phila., 1946-48; mem. nursing faculty Mt. Zion Hosp., San Francisco, 1948-49; mem. Sacramento City Council, 1971-83; mayor City of Sacramento, 1983-92. Prse. LWV, Riverside, 1957, Sacramento, 1961, Calif. Elected Women's Assn., 1973—; mem. Calif. bd. dirs. Common Cause; bd. trustees Golden Gate U.; mem. adv. bd. U. So. Calif., Army Depot Reuse Commn.; bd. dirs. Sacramento Theatre Co., Sacramento Symphony. Recipient Women in Govt. award U.S. Jaycee Women, 1984, Woman of Distinction award Sacramento Area Soroptimist Clubs, 1985, Civic Contbn. award LWV Sacramento, 1989, Woman of Courage award Sacramento History Ctr., 1989, Peacemaker of Yr. award Sacramento Mediation Ctr., 1992, Regional Pride award Sacramento Mag., 1993, Humanitarian award Japanese Am. Citizen's League, 1993, Outstanding Pub. Svc. award Am. Soc. Pub. Adminstrn., 1994; named Girl Scouts Am. Role model, 1989.

RUDIN, SCOTT, film and theatre producer; b. N.Y.C., July 14, 1958. Prodn. asst., asst. to theatre prodrs. Kermit Bloomgarden and Robert Whitehead; casting dir. motion pictures and theatre, prodr. with Edgar Scherick, exec. v.p. prodn. 20th Century Fox, 1984-86, pres. prodn., 1986-87; founder Scott Rudin Prodns., 1990—. Prodr.: (films) He Makes Me Feel Like Dancing, 1982 (Outstanding Children's Program Emmy award 1982, Feature Documentary Acad. award 1982), Mrs. Soffel, 1984, Flatliners, 1990, Pacific Heights, 1990, Regarding Henry, 1991, Little Man Tate, 1991, The Addams Family, 1991, White Sands, 1992, Sister Act, 1992, Jennifer Eight, 1992, Life With Mikey, 1993, The Firm, 1993, Searching for Bobby Fischer, 1993, Sister Act 2, 1993, Addams Family Values, 1993, I.Q., 1994, Nobody's Fool, 1994; (theatre) Passion, 1994 (Best Musical Tony award 1994). Office: Paramount Pictures DeMille 200 5555 Melrose Ave Hollywood CA 90038-3197

RUDING, HERMAN ONNO, banker, former Dutch government official; b. Aug. 15, 1939; m. Renee V.M. Hekking; 2 children. MA in Econs., Netherlands Sch. Econs. (Erasmus U.), 1964, PhD in Econs. cum laude, 1969. Head div. internat. monetary affairs Treas. Gen. of Ministry of Fin., The Hague, Netherlands. 1965-70; joint gen. mgr. Amsterdam-Rotterdam Bank N.V., Amsterdam, 1971-76; exec. dir. IMF, Washington, 1977-80; bd. mng. dirs. Amsterdam-Rotterdam Bank N.V., 1981-82; minister of fin. Netherlands, The Hague, 1982-89; chmn. Netherlands Christian Fedn. Employers, The Hague, 1990-92; vice chmn., bd. dirs. Citicorp, N.Y.C., 1992—. Contbr. articles to profl. jours. Bd. dirs. Foster Parents Plan Internat., 1981-82, Mt. Sinai Hosp., N.Y.C. Mem. Christian Democratic Alliance, Com. Monetary Union of Europe, Trilateral Commn. Office: Citibank 399 Park Ave New York NY 10043

RUDINS, LEONIDS (LEE RUDINS), retired chemical company executive, financial executive; b. Linava, Latvia, Dec. 15, 1928; came to U.S., 1949; s. Leonids and Aleksandra (Zimins) R.; m. Galina Zakidalski, July 24, 1960; 1 child, Andrew. BS in Commerce, Rider Coll., 1953; MBA, Seton Hall U., 1967, cert. of internat. bus., 1968. Acct. Johnson & Johnson, New Brunswick, N.J., 1957-58; mgr. budget and cost LePage's, Johnson & Johnson, Gloucester, Mass., 1958-60; plant contr. Permacel, Johnson & Johnson, Decatur, Ill., 1960-62; asst. contr. Permacel, Johnson & Johnson, New Brunswick, 1962-63, treas., contr., 1963-70; div. contr. Titanium Pigments, NL Industries, Inc., Sayreville, N.J., 1970-71, group contr., 1971-76; dir. fin. and adminstrn. NL Pigments-U.S., NL Industries, Inc., Sayreville, N.J., 1976-77; dir. fin. and planning NL Pigments-Worldwide, NL Industries, Inc., Sayreville, N.J., 1977-79; v.p. fin., chief fin. officer NL Chemicals, Inc., Hightstown, N.J., 1979-89; pres. Internat. Bus. Mgmt. Assocs., Inc., Princeton, 1990-91; bd. dirs. Robertson-CECO Corp., Benton Chemie GmbH, Nordenham, Federal Rep. Germany, Abbey Chems., Ltd., Livingston, Eng., Enenco, Inc., Memphis. Solicitor, budget com. mem., United Fund, New Brunswick, 1962-69; bd. dirs. St. Vladimir Russian Cath. Soc., 1992—. With U.S. Army, 1953-56, Korea. Mem. Nat. Assn. Accts., Fin. Exec. Inst., Forsgate Club, Battleground Club. Republican. Greek/Russian Orthodox. Avocations: golf, stamp collecting, hiking. Home: 28 Tamarack Dr Englishtown NJ 07726-2734

RUDLIN, DAVID ALAN, lawyer; b. Richmond, Va., Nov. 4, 1947; s. Herbert and Dorothy Jean (Durham) R.; m. Judith Bond Faulkner, Oct. 4, 1975; 1 child, Sara Elizabeth. BA with high distinction, U. Va., 1969, JD with honors, 1973. Bar: Va. 1973, U.S. Dist. Ct. (ea. dist.) Va. 1975, U.S. Ct. Appeals (4th cir.) 1975, U.S. Ct. Appeals (10th cir.) 1980, U.S. Ct. Appeals (2d cir.) 1983, U.S. Supreme Ct. 1979. Assoc. gen. counsel U.S. Commn. on Orgn. of Govt. for Conduct of Fgn. Policy, Washington, 1973-75; assoc. Hunton & Williams, Richmond, 1975-82, ptnr., 1982—; adj. faculty William and Mary Coll., Marshall-Wythe Sch. Law, Williamsburg, Va., 1982—, U. Richmond, 1993—; faculty mem. Boulder and S.E. Regional programs Nat. Inst. Trial Advocacy; vis. lectr. U. Va. Sch. Law, Charlottesville, 1980—; mem. dispute resolution svcs. adv. coun. Supreme Ct. Va. Bd. dirs., ex officio mem. Cystic Fibrosis Found., Richmond; alumni Metro Leadership Richmond, 1988-89; mem. bd. editorial advisors The Environmental Counselor, Chesterland, Ohio, 1989—, The Toxics Law Reporter, Washington, 1988—; bd. dirs., apt. special adv., adv. com. Richmond Juvenile and Domestic Rels. Ct., 1990-94. Author: (book chpts.) Toxic Torts: Litigation Of Hazardous Substances Cases, 1983, 2nd edit., 1992, Federal Litigation Guide, 1989, Corporate Counselor's Guide To Environmental Law, 1989, Sanctions: Rule 11 and Other Powers, 1992; contbr. articles to profl. jours. and mags. chpts. to books. Mem. ABA (chmn. litigation sect. environ. litigation com. 1985-88, co-chmn. litigation sect. liaison with jud. com. 1988-91, vice-chmn. toxic and hazardous substances and environ. law com. tort and ins. practice sect., 1988-91, co-liaison to standing com. on environ. law from environ. litigation com. litigation section, 1988-92, dir. divsn. IV litigation sect. 1991—, litigation sect. co-chair programs subcom. first amendment & media litigation com. 1993—, mem. litigation sect. task force on specialization 1994—, mem. litigation sect. task force on justice sys. 1994—, litigation sect. liaison to ABA jud. adminstrn. divsn. task force on reduction of litigation cost and delay 1995—), Va. Bar Assn. (chair joint com. on alternative dispute resolution with Va. State Bar 1991—), Va. Trial Lawyers Assn. Richmond Bar Assn. (chmn. membership com. 1988-91, mem. judiciary com. 1991-94, mem. continuing legal edn. com. 1994—), Am. Assn. Def. Attys., Ctr. Pub. Resources (products liability com. 1988—, judge Ann. Awards in Alternative Dispute Resolution 1994—). Office: Hunton & Williams Riverfront Pla E Tower 951 E Byrd St Richmond VA 23219-4040

RUDMAN, HERBERT CHARLES, education educator; b. N.Y.C., July 29, 1923; s. Abraham and Celia (Factor) R.; m. Florence Bromberg, Dec. 22, 1923; 1 child, Jane Ann (Mrs. Robert Schumacher). B.S., Bradley U., 1947; M.S., U. Ill., 1950, Ed.D., 1954. Tchr., asst. to prin. Peoria (Ill.) Bd. Edn.,

1946-51; instr. U. Ill., 1951-53; chmn. dept. elementary edn. U.S.C., 1954-56; prof. adminstrn. and higher edn. Mich. State U., East Lansing, 1956-83, prof. ednl. measurement, evaluation and research design, 1983-93, prof. emeritus, 1993—; admissions testing cons. Nat. U. Sci. and Tech., Pakistan, 1992; chmn. tchr. testing tech. adv. coun. State of Mich., 1989-91. Author: (with Truman Kelly, Richard Madden and Eric Gardner) Stanford Achievement Tests, 1964, (with Richard Featherstone) Urban Schooling, 1968, (with Donald J. Leu) Preparation Programs for School Administrators, 1968, (with Frederick King, Herbert Epperly) Concepts in Social Science, 1970, School and State in the USSR, 1967, (with others) Stanford Achievement Tests, 1973, (with Frederick King) Understanding People, 1977, Understanding Communities, 1977, Understanding Regions, 1978, Understanding Our Country, 1979, Understanding Our World, 1979, tests for At Your Best, 1977, Toward Your Future, 1977, Balance In Your Life, 1977; (with others): Stanford Achievement Tests, 1982; editor: Measurement in Education, 1979-82; guest editor: Bull. Nat. Secondary Sch. Prins., 1986; contbr. articles to profl. jours. Assoc. bd. trustees Bradley U., 1992—. With USAAF, 1942-46. Recipient Outstanding Leadership award Mich. Assn. Elem. Prins., 1972; resolution for contbns. to ednl. measurement Mich. Senate; 1980; named Outstanding Prof. of Yr. Mich. State U. Alumni Assn., 1980; Ford Found. fellow USSR, 1958; head U.S. deg. to USSR for U.S. State Dept., 1963-64; Disting. Alumnus award Bradley U., 1988. Office: Mich State U Coll Edn 463 Erickson Hall East Lansing MI 48824-1034 *I have, all of my life, valued integrity and truth above all else. Without these two values all relationships—professional and personal—mean little. While I have valued excellence in professional conduct and commitment to professional goals, I have rarely lost perspective concerning my commitment to family and community. While honors, such as this one, are appreciated and valued by me, the greatest honor is that of watching my daughter grow into a fine young woman who, in turn, has developed many of the same values in her professional and personal life, and who now passes them on to her son and daughter.*

RUDMAN, JOAN ELEANOR, artist, educator; b. Owensburg, Ind., Oct. 7, 1927; d. William Hobart and Elizabeth Joaquin (Edington) Combs; m. William Rudman, June 9, 1951; children: Mary Beth, Pamela Ann. BA, Mich. State U., 1949, MA, 1951. tchr. Arlington Jr. and High Sch., Poughkeepsie, N.Y., Rippowam High Sch., Stamford, Conn., North Branch Club, West Dover, Vt., Greenwich (Conn.) Art Soc.; lectr., demonstrator Round Hill Community House, Greenwich; artist-in-residence So. Vt. Art Ctr., Manchester; arts reporter to 42 newspapers, N.Y., N.J. and Conn.; jurist of selection Hudson Valley Art Assn., 1971—; selection and awards jurist 2d Bergen County Mus. Open Mems. Juried Awards-Allied Artist, N.Y.; dir. Watercolor Workshops, Greenwich; liaison to Metro. Mus. Catharine Lorillard Wolfe Art Club; watercolor lectr. and demonstrator tri-state area. One-woman shows include Burning Tree Country Club, Greenwich, Town and Country Club, Hartford, Conn., U. Conn., Stamford, Conn. Valley Art Gallery, New Milford, So. Vt. Art Ctr., Manchester, The Nathaniel Witherall Gallery, Greenwich, Burke Rehab. Ctr., White Plains, N.Y.; exhibited in group shows at Wadsworth Antheneum, 1970, Mus. of Am. Art, New Britain, Conn., So. Vt. Art Ctr., Manchester, 1980-81, Nature Ctr. Westport, Conn., 1979-80, Mus. Fine Arts, Springfield, Mass., 1977, Wadsworth Antheneum, 1970, Mus. Am. Art, New Britain, Conn., Nat. Arts Club Open Show, 1969, 78, 79, 81, 82, Salmagundi Club, N.Y.C., 1978, 79, 80, 82, Am. Watercolor Soc., N.Y.C., 1974, 77, 82, Nat. Acad. Design, 1986, 94; represented in permanent collection Kresge Mus., East Lansing, Mich., numerous others; contbr. chpts. to books. Active North Stamford Congl. Ch. Recipient Nat. Art League awards, 1969, 71, 72, 73, Art Soc. Old Greenwich award, 1989, 94, Windsor Newton award, 1982, YWCA Greenwich Contemporary Women's Art Exhibit award, 1985, Best in Show award Art Soc. Old Greenwich, 1991, 1st Prize Graphics award Art Soc. Old Greenwich, 1994, 2nd Prize award Watercolor. Mem. Am. Watercolor Soc. (bd. dirs., asst. editor newsletter), Acad. Artists, Inc., Hoosier Salon (awards 1975, 76), Am. Artists Profl. League (50th Nat. Exhbn. award 1978), Hudson Valley Art Assn. (bd. dirs., publ. rels. editor, awards 1970, 80-90), Conn. Watercolor Soc. (award 1978), Conn. Artists 33, Whiskey Painters Am. (award 1978), Conn. Women Artists, Catharine Lorillard Wolfe Art Club (awards 1989, 90, chmn. 1989-90, co-chair 1994), Pen and Brush (award 1977-78), Nat. League Am. Pen Women (awards 1967, 69, 76-87), Nat. Press Club, Round Hill Community Guild (art dir.), New Canaan - Am. Assn. Univ. Women, Columbia U. Alumni Club (hon.), Nat. Soc. Daus. Am. Revolution (mem. Stamford chpt., historian), Mich. State Alumni Club, Delta Phi Delta (hon.), Phi Kappa Phi (hon.), Alpha Xi Delta. Republican. Home: 274 Quarry Rd Stamford CT 06903-5004

RUDMAN, MARK, poet, educator; b. N.Y.C., Dec. 11, 1948; s. Charles Kenneth and Marjorie Louise (Levy) R.; m. Madelaine Bates, Dec. 28, 1977; 1 child, Samuel. BA, New Sch. Social Rsch., 1971; MFA, Columbia U., 1974. With Tchrs. and Writers Collaborative, 1971-72, Poetry in the Schs. Program, 1974-80; adj. lectr. Queens Coll., CUNY, Flushing, 1980-81; poet-in-residence, assoc. prof. York Coll., CUNY, Jamaica, 1984-88; adj. prof., asst. dir. grad. creative writing program NYU, 1986—; adj. prof. creative writing sch. gen. studies Columbia U., 1988—, adj. prof. sch. of the arts, 1992; writer-in-residence U. Hawaii, Manoa, 1978, Wabash Coll., 1979, SUNY, Buffalo, 1979; lectr. Parsons Sch. Design, 1983; poet in residence SUNY, Purchase, 1991; lectr. in field. Author: Robert Lowell: An Introduction to Poetry, 1983, The Mystery in the Garden, 1985, The Ruin Revived, 1986, Literature and the Visual Arts, 1990, Diverse Voices: Essays on Poetry, 1993, Rider, 1994 (Cir. award Nat. Book Critics 1995), Realm of Unknowing: Meditations on Art, Suicide, Uncertainty, and Other Transformations, 1995 (poems) IN the Neighboring Cell, 1982, By Contraries and Other Poems: 1970-84, Selected and New, The Nowhere Steps, 1990; translator (with Bohdan Boychuk) Square of Angels: The Selected Poems of Bohdan Antonych, 1977, Orchard Lamps (Ivan Drach), 1978, My Sister—Life (Boris Pasternak), 1983, rev. edit., 1993, The Sublime Malady (Boris Pasternak), 1983; editor and co-translator: Memories of Love: The Selected Poems of Bohdan Boychuk, 1981; editor: Secret Destinations: Writers on Travel, 1986; poetry and criticism editor Pequod, 1975—, editor-in-chief, 1984—; contbr. poems, transls. of poems and essays to anthologies and profl. jours. Recipient Acad. Am. Poets award, 1971, Hackney award Birmingham Arts Festival, 1972, Max Hayward award Columbia U. Translation Ctr., 1985, Editor's award N.Y. Coun. Arts, 1986; Internat. P.E.N. fellow, 1976-77, Yaddo fellow, 1977, 83, Coordinating Coun. for Literary Mags. fellow, 1981-82, Ingram Merrill fellow, 1983-84, N.Y. Found. Arts fellow, 1988, fellow in poetry NEA, 1994. Mem. Internat. P.E.N., Poetry Soc. Am. (mem. bd. govs. 1984-88), Nat. Book Critics Circle. Office: 817 West End Ave New York NY 10025 also: New York Univ Dept of English New York NY 10003*

RUDMAN, MICHAEL P., publishing executive; b. N.Y.C., 1950. Grad., U. Mich., 1972, NYU, 1975. Pres., chief exec. officer Nat. Learning Corp., Syosset, N.Y., also dir.; pres., chief exec. officer, dir., Delaney Books Inc., Frank Merriwell, Inc. Mem. Assn. Am. Pubs., Nat. Assn. Corp. Dirs., Nat. Assn. Coll. Stores. Office: Nat Learning Corp 212 Michael Dr Syosset NY 11791-5305

RUDMAN, SOLOMON KAL, magazine publisher; b. Phila., Mar. 6, 1930; s. Benjamin and Lena (Holtzman) R.; m. Lucille Steinhauer, June 29, 1958; 1 child, Mitchell. BS in Edn., U. Pa., 1951; MS in Edn., Temple U., 1957. Chmn. dept. spl. edn. Franklin D. Roosevelt Sch., Bristol Twp., Pa., 1960-68; pub. premier record/radio trade Fri. Morning Quarterback, Cherry Hill, Pa., 1968—; bd. dirs. Variety Club, NARAS; co-host Merv Griffin TV Show, 1981-82; music expert Today Show, 1981-82, Tomorrow Show, 1981-82, Tom Snyder TV Show; creator-sponsor Jazz Piano Competition Pub. Parochial, Pvt. Schs. Name given to new wing Cen. High Sch., Phila., 1994. Mem. Phila. Music Alliance (bd. dirs.), Nat. Arthritis Found. (bd. dirs.), Nat. Acad. Arts and Sci. (bd. dirs.), Masons. Office: Friday Morning Quarterback 1930 Marlton Pike E Cherry Hill NJ 08003-2150

RUDMAN, WARREN BRUCE, former senator, lawyer; b. Boston, May 18, 1930; s. Edward G. and Theresa (Levenson) R.; m. Shirley Wahl, July 9, 1952; children: Laura, Alan, Debra. B.S., Syracuse (N.Y.) U., 1952; LL.B. Boston Coll., 1960. Bar: N.H. 1960, D.C. Mem. firm Rudman & Gormley, Nashua, N.H., 1960-69; counsel to Gov. Walter Peterson, Concord, N.H., 1970; atty. gen. State of N.H., Concord, 1970-76; mem. firm. Sheehan Phinney Bass & Green, 1976-80; U.S. Senator from N.H., 1980-92; cofounder Concord Coalition, 1992—; ptnr. Paul, Weiss, Rifkind, Wharton & Garrison, N.Y.C., Washington, 1993—; deputy chmn. Fed. Reserve Bank of

Boston. 1993, mem. bd. dirs. Chubb Corp., 1993—, Raytheon Corp., 1993—, Dreyfus Corp., 1993—. Founder, chmn. bd. trustees Daniel Webster Jr. Coll., 1965—, trustees Boston Coll., Aspen Inst., Valley Forge, Mil Acad.; chmn., founder New Eng. Aero. Inst., v. chmn. Pres. Fgn. Intelligence adv. bd.; sr. adv. com. Inst. of Politics John F. Kennedy Sch. Capt. AUS, 1952-54, Korea. Decorated Bronze Star, Combat Inf. Badge. Mem. Am. Legion. Republican. Office: Paul Weiss Rifkind Wharton & Garrison 1615 L St NW Ste 1300 Washington DC 20036-5694*

RUDMANN, SALLY VANDER LINDEN, medical technology educator; b. Rochester, N.Y., Sept. 10, 1942; d. Egbert W. and Mildred M. (Schrader) Vander Linden; m. Ronald J. Rudmann, June 4, 1964 (div.); children: Daniel G., Stephen M.; m. James G. Barlow, Mar. 31, 1980. BA, Russell Sage Coll., 1964; MS, Wright State U., 1980; PhD, Ohio State U., 1986. Lic. med. technologist, Calif.; registered med. technologist and specialist in blood banking Am. Soc. Clin. Pathologists. Intern in med. tech. South bay Hosp., Redondo Beach, Calif., 1965-66; med. technologist Green Meml. Hosp., Xenia, Ohio, 1968-72; med. technologist Community Blood Ctr., Dayton, Ohio, 1974-75, intern, 1975-76; tech. supr. Greene Meml. Hosp., Xenia, 1976-78; tech. dir. Brown Labs., Columbus, Ohio, 1979-82; med. technologist Drs. Hosp. North, Columbus, Ohio, 1982-84; instr med. tech. Ohio State U., Columbus, Ohio, 1984-87, from asst. prof. to assoc. prof. med. tech., 1987—; dir. med. tech., 1987—; lect. and cons. in field. Editor: Textbook of Blood Banking and Transfusion, 1994; cons. MacMillan Pub. Co., 1984; editl. assoc. procs., editl. rev. Modern Blood Banking and Transfusion Practice, 1987, 88; cons. editor Clin. Lab. Sci., 1987—, editor-in-chief, 1988; profl. adv. panel Med. Lab. Observer, 1989-90; contbr. numerous articles to profl. jours. Mem. Am. Assn. Blood Banks (abstract rev. com., inspector inspection and accreditation program, sci. and tech. workshops com.), Am. Soc. Clin. Lab. Sci. (planning com. region IV 1985), Am. Soc. Clin. Pathologists (R&D com., cons.), Am. Soc. Allied Health Professions, Ohio Soc. Allied Health Professions, Ohio Soc. Med. Tech., Ohio Assn. Blood Banks (chairperson awards com. 1990-92, mem. award com. 1992—), Dayton Area Blood Bankers (pres. 1976), Phi Kappa Phi. Avocations: hiking, fitness, photography. Office: Ohio State U Med Tech Divsn 1583 Perry St Columbus OH 43210-1234

RUDNER, SARA, dancer, choreographer; b. Bklyn., Feb. 16, 1944; d. Henry Nathaniel and Jeannette (Smolensky) R.; m. Edward C. Marschner; 1 child, Edward Eli. A.B. in Russian Studies, Barnard Coll., 1964. Dancer Sansardo Dance Co., N.Y.C., 1964-65, Am. Dance Co. at Lincoln Ctr., N.Y.C., 1965, Shakespeare Festival Touring Children's Show, N.Y.C., 1966; featured dancer Twyla Tharp Dance Found., N.Y.C., 1966-85; artistic dir., dancer 18th St. Dance Found., N.Y.C., 1977—; guest dancer Joffrey Ballet, N.Y.C., 1973, Pilobolus Dance Theatre, N.Y.C., 1975, Lar Lubovitch Dance Co., N.Y.C., 1975-76; guest lectr., choreographer grad. dance dept. UCLA, 1975; tchr. master workshop NYU Theater Program, 1988, 89, 90. Choreographer: Palm Trees and Flamingoes, 1980, Dancing for an Hour or So, 1981, Minute by Minute, 1982, Eight Solos, 1991, Heartbeats, Inside Out, 1993 (with Jennifer Tipton and Dana Reitz) Necessary Weather, 1994. Grantee Creative Artists Pub. Svc. Program, N.Y., 1975-76, N.Y. State Coun. on Arts, 1975-78, Nat. Endowment for Arts, 1979-81, 91-92, 94-97; Guggenheim fellow, 1981-82; recipient N.Y. Dance and Performance award, 1984.

RUDNEY, HARRY, biochemist, educator; b. Toronto, Ont., Can., Apr. 14, 1918; came to U.S., 1948, naturalized, 1956; s. Joshua and Dina (Gorback) R.; m. Bernice Dina Snider, June 25, 1946; children—Joel David, Paul Robert. B.A., U. Toronto, 1947, M.A., 1948; Ph.D., Western Res. U., 1952. Faculty Western Res. U., Cleve., 1952-67; prof. biochemistry Western Res. U., 1965-67; prof., dir. dept. biochemistry and molecular biology U. Cin. Coll. Medicine, 1967-89, Andrew Carnegie Found. prof. biol. chemistry, 1967-89, prof. emeritus, 1989—; vis. prof. Case Inst. Tech., Cleve., 1965-66; mem. rsch. adv. panel N.E. Ohio Heart Assn., 1966-67; mem. panel metabolic biology NSF, 1968-71; rsch. career award com. NIH, 1969-73; mem. biochemistry test com. Nat. Bd. Med. Examiners, 1974-77; co-chair Instnl. Rev. Bd., U. Cinn. Med. Ctr., 1994—, interim chair dept. pharmecology, 1994—. Mem. editorial bd. Archives of Biochemistry and Biophysics, 1965-89, Jour. Biol. Chemistry, 1975-80; contbr. articles profl. jours. Recipient USPHS Research Career award, 1963-67; Am. Cancer Soc. scholar, 1954-56; NSF Sr. Research fellow U. Amsterdam, Netherlands, 1957. Mem. Am. Soc. Biol. Chemists, Am. Chem. Soc., Am. Soc. Microbiology, Biochem. Soc. (Eng.), Sigma Xi. Home: 4040 Winding Way Cincinnati OH 45229-1919

RUDNICK, ELLEN AVA, health care executive; b. New Haven; d. Harold and C. Vivian (Soybel) R.; children from previous marriage: Sarah, Noah; m. Paul W. Earle. BA, Vassar Coll., 1972; MBA, U. Chgo., 1973. Sr. fin. analyst Quaker Oats, Chgo., 1973-75; various positions Baxter Internat., Deerfield, Ill., 1975-80, dir. planning, 1980-83, corp. v.p., 1985-1990; pres. Baxter Mgmt. Svcs., Deerfield, 1983-1990, HCIA, Northbrook, Ill., 1990-92, CEO Advs., Northbrook, Ill., 1992—; prin. BioQuant, Northbrook, 1993—. Chief crusader Met. Chgo. United Way, 1982-85; pres. coun. Nat. Coll. Edn., Evanston, Ill., 1983—; circle of friends Chgo. YWCA, 1985-89; bd. dirs Highland Park Hosp., 1990—. Mem. Chgo. Network, Econs. Club Chgo. (officer, bd. dirs.). Office: CEO Advs 255 Revere Dr Ste 111 Northbrook IL 60062-1595

RUDNICK, IRENE KRUGMAN, lawyer, state legislator, educator; b. Columbia, S.C., Dec. 27, 1929; d. Jack and Jean (Getter) Krugman; AB cum laude, U. S.C., 1949, JD, 1952; m. Harold Rudnick, Nov. 7, 1954; children: Morris, Helen Gail. Admitted to S.C. bar, 1952; individual practice law, Aiken, S.C., 1952—, now ptnr. Rudnick & Rudnick; instr. bus. law, criminal law U. S.C., Aiken, 1962—; tchr. Warrenville Elem. Sch., 1965-70; supt. edn. Aiken County, 1970-72; mem. S.C. Ho. of Reps., 1972-78, 80-84, 86-94; pres. Adath Yeshurun Synagogue; active Aiken County Dem. Party, S.C. Dem. Party, Network Aiken; hon. mem. Aiken Able-Disabled. Recipient Citizen of Yr. award, 1976-77, Bus. and Profl. Women's Career Woman of Yr., 1978, 94, Aiken County Friend of Edn. award, 1985, 93, Outstanding Legis. award Disabled Vets., 1991, Citizen of the Yr. award Planned Parenthood, 1994. Mem. NEA, S.C. Tchrs. Assn., Aiken County Tchrs. Assn., Am. Bar Assn., Aiken County Bar Assn., Nat. Order Women Legislators, AAUW, Network Aiken, Aiken Able-Disabled (hon.), Alpha Delta Kappa. Clubs: Order Eastern Star, Hadassah, Am. Legion Aux. Office: PO Box 544 135 Pendleton NW Aiken SC 29802

RUDNICK, MARVIN JACK, lawyer; b. St. Joseph, Mich., Mar. 9, 1948; s. Milton P. and Edna O.R.; m. Cynthia Jane Vanhooser, Sept. 4, 1982; children: Matthew, Andrew. BA, Middlebury Coll., 1970; JD, Syracuse U., 1973. Bar: N.Y. 1973. Corp. atty. Oneida Ltd., N.Y., 1973-76, assoc. counsel, 1976-84, asst. gen. counsel, 1985-86, v.p., sec., gen. counsel, 1986—; mem. adj. faculty Utica Coll., Syracuse U., Utica, N.Y., 1982-84; bd. dirs. Oneida Silversmith's Div. Pres. Sherrill-Kenwood Community Chest, Sherrill, N.Y., 1979-81. With U.S. Army, lt. Res. Mem. ABA, N.Y. State Bar Assn., Madison County Bar Assn., Justinian Soc. Republican. Office: Oneida Ltd Kenwood Station Adminstrn Bldg Oneida NY 13421

RUDNICK, PAUL, playwright, screenwriter; b. Piscataway, N.J., 1957. Attended, Yale U. Author: (novels) Social Disease, 1986, I'll Take It, 1989; (plays) Poor Little Lambs, 1982 (Outer Critics Cirle award 1983), Cosmetic Surgery, 1983, I Hate Hamlet, 1991, Jeffrey, 1993 (Obie award for outstanding playwriting 1994, Outer Drama Critics Cirle award 1994, John Gassner Playwriting award 1994), The Naked Truth, 1994; (screenplays) (with others as Joseph Howard) Sister Act, 1992, Addams Family Values, 1993; columnist: (as Libby Gelman-Waxer) "If You Ask Me", Premiere mag., 1989—. Office: CAA 9830 Wilshire Blvd Beverly Hills CA 90212-1804*

RUDNICK, PAUL DAVID, lawyer; b. Chgo., May 15, 1940; s. Harry Louis and Cele (Gordon) R.; m. Hope Korshak, June 13, 1963; children: William A., Carolyn. BS, Tulane U., 1962; JD cum laude, Northwestern U., 1965. Bar: Ill. 1965, U.S. Dist. Ct. (no. dist.) Ill. 1965. Assoc. Schiff, Hardin & Waite, Chgo., 1965-66; ptnr. Rudnick & Wolfe, Chgo., 1966—. Editor Northwestern U. Law Rev., 1964-65; co-editor, author: Illinois Real Estate Forms, 1989. Mem. ABA, Am. Coll. Real Estate Lawyers, Internat. Found. Em-

ployee Benefits, Tavern Club, Order of Coif. Avocations: skiing, music. Office: Rudnick & Wolfe 203 N La Salle St Ste 1800 Chicago IL 60601-1210

RUDNICK, ROBERT ALAN, lawyer; b. N.Y.C., Jan. 2, 1948; s. Carl J. and Lillian (Zweibon) R.; m. Nancy Ann Spokes (div.); m. Jana Clayton Orth; children: Elena Ann, Lucas Edward. BA, Colby Coll., Waterville, Maine, 1969; JD, Cornell U., 1972. Bar: N.Y. State 1973; U.S. Dist. Ct. (so. dist.) N.Y. 1973); U.S. Tax Ct. Assoc. Cadwalader, Wickersham & Taft, N.Y.C. and Washington, 1972-81; ptnr. Cadwalader, Wickersham & Taft, Washington, 1981—. Contbr. numerous articles to Boston Coll. Law Rev. Lt. USAR, 1972-79. Mem. N.Y. State Bar Assn. Office: Cadwalader Wickersham et al 1333 New Hampshire Ave NW Washington DC 20036-1500

RUDNICKI, JOHN WALTER, engineering educator; b. Huntington, W.Va., Aug. 12, 1951; s. John Walter Francis and Helen (Nadenichek) R.; m. Joan Weston, June 11, 1977; children: Ellen (dec.), Jean, Stephen, Christopher. BS, Brown U., 1973, MS, 1974, PhD, 1977. Rsch. fellow Seismological Lab. Calif. Inst. Tech., Pasadena, 1977-78; asst. prof. dept. theoretical and applied mechanics U. Ill., Urbana, 1978-81; assoc. prof. dept. civil engring. Northwestern U., Evanston, Ill., 1981-90, prof. dept. civil engring., mech. engring. and geological sci., 1990-91, prof. dept. mech. engring. and dept. geol. sci., 1991—; cons. Sandia Nat. Labs., Albuquerque, 1982-92, SAIC, 1990-91; mem. U.S. Nat. Com. on Rock Mechanics; adv. bd. mechanics of cohesive frictional material and structure An Internat. Jour. on Experiments, Modelling and Computation. Contbr. articles to Jour. Geophysics Rsch., Jour. Applied Mechanics, Pure and Applied Geophysics, Ann. Rev. Earth and Planetary Sci., Jour. Applied Mechanics, 1988-94. Recipient Outstanding Rsch. in Rock Mechanics award U.S. Nat. Com. on Rock Mechanics, 1977. Mem. AAAS, ASME, Am. Geophys. Union, Seismological Soc. Am., Soc. Engring. Sci., Sigma Xi. Achievements include discovery of solutions for cracks and dislocations in porous elastic solids and application of same to the study of faults in the Earth's crust. Office: Northwestern U 2145 Sheridan Rd Evanston IL 60208-3109

RUDO, MILTON, retired manufacturing company executive, consultant; b. Balt., Jan. 17, 1919; s. Saul E. and Bertha (Berkowitz) R.m. Roslind Mandel, Mar. 27, 1943; children: Stephanie Ellen, Neil Dennis. Ba, Johns Hopkins U., 1940; AMP, Harvard U., 1964. With Brunswick Corp., Skokie, Ill., 1940-84, beginning as sales rep., Balt., successively br. mgr., Pitts., billiard mdse. mgr., Chgo., bowling and billiard products mdse. mgr., Chgo., sales v.p. Ea. region, Harrisburg, Pa., div. sales v.p., gen. sales mgr., Chgo., mktg. v.p., Chgo., pres. Bowling div., corp. v.p., Chgo., pres. Bowling div., Chgo., 1940-74, group v.p. recreation bus., 1974-84, ret., 1984, cons. to chief exec. officer, 1984-87; dir., cons. to chief exec., Donlen Leasing Corp, Skokie, Ill., 1986-90. Pres. Nat. Bowling Hall of Fame and Mus., 1979. Capt. AUS, 1942-45, ETO. Recipient ann. award N.Y. Mktg. Club, 1960, Industry Service award, 1973; named to Bowling Hall of Fame, 1984. Mem. Nat. Bowling Council (pres. 1972), Briarwood Country Club, Hamlet Country Club (Delray Beach, Fla.). Office: 1777 Balsam Rd Highland Park IL 60035-4343

RUDOFF, SHELDON, lawyer, former religious organization executive; b. Bklyn., May 29, 1933; s. Raphael and Goldie (Gorelick) R.; m. Hedda Muller, Nov. 22, 1964; children: Shaindy, Sara, Simone. BA cum laude, Yeshiva Coll., 1954; JSD cum laude, NYU, 1958; ordination, RIETS, 1957. Bar: N.Y. 1958, U.S. Dist. Ct. (so. and ea. dists.) N.Y. 1958, U.S. Supreme Ct. 1978. Ptnr. Shatzkin, Cooper & Rudoff, N.Y.C., 1970-84, Goodkind, Labaton, Rudoff & Sucharow, N.Y.C., 1984—; hon. pres. Union Orthodox Jewish Congregation Am., 1990-94. Vice-pres. Yeshiva Coll. Alumni, N.Y.C., 1962-64; pres. Young Israel West Side, N.Y., 1969-72; sec. Orthodox Union, 1972-76, v.p., 1976-78, sr. v.p., 1978-84, chmn. bd., 1984-90, pres. 1990—; mem. exec. com. World Zionist Orgn.; bd. dirs. Am. Zionist Movement; trustee United Israel Appeal, Fedn. Jewish Philanthropies, 1980-91, United Jewish Appeal, Ctrl. Claims Conf., Am. Zionist Youth Fedn. Recipient Pres.'s award Orthodox Union, N.Y.C., 1972, Nat. Leadership award Nat. Conf. Synagogue Youth, N.Y.C., 1974, Kesser Shem Tov award Ortohdox Union, 1995. Mem. ABA, N.Y. State Bar Assn., N.Y. City Bar Assn. (transp. com. 1976—). Home: 110 Riverside Dr New York NY 10024 Office: Goodkind Labaton Rudoff & Sucharow 100 Park Ave New York NY 10017-5516 also: Union Orthodox Jewish Congs 333 7th Ave New York NY 10001-5004

RUDOLF, MAX, symphony and opera conductor; b. Frankfurt-Am-Main, Germany, June 15, 1902; came to U.S., 1940, naturalized, 1946; student Goethe-Gymnasium, Frankfurt, Hoch Conservatory Music, Frankfurt U.; pvt. mus. instrn.; D.Mus. (hon.), Cin. Conservatory Music; L.H.D. (hon.), U. Cin., 1960, Miami U., 1963, Curtis Inst. Music, 1972; D.Mus., Baldwin-Wallace Coll., 1973, Temple U., 1975; m. Liese Ederheimer, Aug. 4, 1927; children: Wilhelmine. Asst. condr. Freiburg (Germany) Municipal Opera, 1922-23; condr. State Opera of Hesse, Darmstadt, Germany, 1923-29, German Opera, Prague, 1929-35; guest condr. Gothenburg (Sweden) Orch. Soc., also choral dir. radio concerts Swedish Broadcasting Corp., 1935-40; mem. faculty Central YMCA Coll., Chgo., 1941-43; condr. New Opera Co., N.Y.C., 1944; mem. mus. staff Met. Opera Assn., N.Y.C., 1945-58, artistic adminstr., 1950-58; adminstr. Kathryn Long opera courses Met. Opera, N.Y.C., 1949-58; mus. dir. Cin. May Festival, 1963-70; music dir., condr. Cin. Symphony Orch., 1958-70, world-wide concert tour, 1966; condr. Met. Opera Assn., N.Y.C., 1973-75; mem. faculty Curtis Inst. Music, Phila., 1970-73, 83—; tchr. conducting Ford Found. project, Balt., 1962-64, Tanglewood, 1964; Distinguished Service award, Balt., 1966-68; condr. Columbia Records, Book of Month Club Music Appreciation Series, Cetra (Italy), Decca; guest condr. symphony orchs. throughout U.S., Italy; panel mem. Nat. Endowment for Arts, Washington, 1970-73; artistic adviser Dallas Symphony Orch., 1973, N.J. Symphony Orch., 1976-77, Detroit Symphony Orch., 1983, Exxon/Art Endowment Condrs. Program, 1977—. Recipient Alice M. Diston award, 1964; 1st recipient of Theodore Thomas award Conductors' Guild, 1988. Author: The Grammar of Conducting, 1950, 3d edit., 1993. Home: 220 W Rittenhouse Sq Philadelphia PA 19103-5709 *LIFE. In this confusing make-believe world we preserve our mental health by assuming an attitude which combines realism with friendly skepticism. EDUCATION. Education cannot make anything of anybody, but can serve to open the minds, to advance from cocksure ignorance to thoughtful uncertainty. PERFORMING ARTS. Aren't we lucky, we performers. We are not only permitted to escape from reality in pursuing our daily work, we are even being paid for doing so.*

RUDOLPH, ABRAHAM MORRIS, physician, educator; b. Johannesburg, Republic of South Africa, Feb. 3, 1924; s. Chone and Sarah (Feinstein) R.; m. Rhona Sax, Nov. 2, 1949; children: Linda, Colin, Jeffrey. M.B.B.Ch. summa cum laude, U. Witwatersrand, Johannesburg, 1946, M.D., 1951. Instr. Harvard Med. Sch., 1955-57, assoc. pediatrics, 1957-60; assoc. cardiologist in charge cardiopulmonal lab. Children's Hosp., Boston, 1955-60; dir. pediatric cardiology Albert Einstein Coll. Medicine, 1960-66; prof. pediatrics, assoc. prof. physiology Albert Einstein Coll. Medicine, N.Y.C., 1962-66; vis. pediatrician Bronx Mcpl. Hosp. Ctr., N.Y.C., 1960-66; prof. pediatrics U. Calif., San Francisco, 1966—, prof. physiology, 1974-88, Neider prof. pediatric cardiology, prof. ob-gyn and reproductive scis., 1974—, chmn. dept. pediatrics, 1987-91; practice medicine, specializing in pediatric cardiology San Francisco; mem. cardiovascular study sect. NIH, 1961-65, mem. nat. adv. heart council, 1968-72; established investigator Am. Heart Assn., 1958-62; career scientist Health Research Council, City N.Y., 1962-66; Harvey lectr., Oxford, Eng., 1984; inaugural lectr. 1st Nat. Congress Italian Soc. Perinatal Medicine, 1985. Mem. editorial bd. Pediatrics, 1964-70; assoc. editor Circulation Research, 1965-70; mem. editorial bd. Circulation, 1966-74, 83—; Am. Assoc. editor Pediatric Research, 1970-77; contbr. articles profl. jours. Recipient Merit award Nat. Heart, Lung and Blood Inst., 1986, Arvo Yllpo medal Helsinki U., Finland, 1987, Jonxis medal Children's Hosp. Groningen, 1993. Fellow Royal Coll. Physicians (Edinburgh), Royal Coll. Physicians (London); mem. NAS Inst. Medicine, Am. Acad. Pediatrics (E. Mead Johnson award for research in pediatrics 1964, Borden award 1979, past chmn. sect. on cardiology, Lifetime Med. Edn. award 1992, Joseph St. Geme leadership award Pediatrics 1993), Am. Phys. Soc., Soc. for Clin. Investigation, Soc. for Pediatric Research (coun. 1961-64), Am. Pediatric Soc. (coun. 1985-92, v.p. 1992-93, pres. 1993-94), Am. Heart Assn. (Rsch.

Achievement award 1991). Office: U Calif Cardiovascular Rsch Inst Calif Rm 1403 Hse San Francisco CA 94143

RUDOLPH, ALAN, film director; b. Los Angeles, Dec. 18, 1943; s. Oscar Rudolph. asst. dir.: The Long Goodbye, 1973, California Split, 1974, Nashville, 1975; co-writer: Buffalo Bill and the Indians, 1976; dir., screenwriter: Premonition, 1972, Welcome to L.A., 1977, Remember My Name, 1979, Endangered Species, 1982, Choose Me, 1984, The Moderns, 1988, Love at Large, 1990, Equinox, 1993, Mrs. Parker and the Vicious Circle, 1994; dir., story: Roadie, 1980; dir.: Return Engagement, 1983 (film documentary), Songwriter, 1984, Made in Heaven, 1987, Mortal Thoughts, 1991; actor: The Rocket Man, 1954, The Player, 1992. Mem. Dirs. Guild Am. Office: William Morris Agency Inc 151 S El Camino Dr Beverly Hills CA 90212-2775*

RUDOLPH, ARNOLD JACK, pediatrician, neonatologist, medical educator; b. Johannesburg, South Africa, Mar. 28, 1918; came to U.S., 1956, naturalized, 1978; s. Chone and Sarah R.; m. Myrna Eunice Marks, Feb. 6, 1951; children: Arlene, Jennifer, Susan, Clifford. M.B. B.Ch., U. Witwatersrand, 1940; postgrad. in neonatology, Harvard U. Med. Sch., Boston, 1956-59. Diplomate Am. Bd. Pediatrics, Am. Bd. Neonatal-Perinatal Medicine. Residency tng. Transvaal Meml. Hosp. for Children, Johannesburg, 1941-46; pvt. practice Johannesburg, 1947-56; asst. prof. pediatrics Baylor Coll. Medicine, Houston, 1961-66, assoc. prof. pediatrics, 1966-70, prof. pediatrics, 1970—, head neonatology sect., dept. pediatrics, 1971-86, prof. pediatrics dept. ob-gyn., 1973—, mem. neonatology sect., 1987—. Contbr. chpts. to books in field; articles to profl. publs. Fellow Am. Acad. Pediatrics, Philippines Pediatric Soc (hon.); mem. AMA, Brit. Med. Assn., Tex. Med. Assn., Harris County Med. Soc., Am. Pediatric Soc., Tex. Pediatric Soc., So. Soc. Pediatric Research, Tex. Perinatal Assn., Houston Pediatric Soc., Nat. Perinatal Assn., Alpha Omega Alpha (hon.). Jewish. Home: 5239 Birdwood Rd Houston TX 77096-2503 Office: Baylor Coll Medicine One Baylor Plz Houston TX 77030

RUDOLPH, CHARLES HERMAN, retired computer software development executive; b. Balt., Mar. 14, 1953; s. Charles Henry and Margaret Theresa (McCarron) R.; m. Terri Gay; 1 child, Kristin Margaret. B.S. summa cum laude, King's Coll., 1975. Asst. mgr. product mktg. Datapoint Corp., San Antonio, 1977-78, mgr. systems planning, 1978-79, mgr. software devel., 1979-82, dir. software devel., 1982-84; sr. dir. Custom Systems, San Antonio, 1984-85; dir. engring. Digital Communications Assocs., Atlanta, 1985-88; v.p. mktg. Crosstalk Communications, Roswell, Ga., 1988-89, pres., 1989-90; pres. Pacific Data Producers, San Diego, 1990-93; v.p. Peregrine Sys. Inc., Carlsbad, Calif., 1994—. Republican. Lutheran. Home: 13814 Lake Poway Rd Poway CA 92064-2278 Office: Peregrine Sys Inc 1959 Palomar Oaks Way Carlsbad CA 92009

RUDOLPH, FREDERICK, history educator; b. Balt., June 19, 1920; s. Charles Frederick and Jennie Hill (Swope) R.; m. Dorothy Dannenbaum, June 18, 1949; children: Marta R. MacDonald, Lisa R. Cushman. B.A., Williams Coll., 1942, Litt.D., 1985; M.A., Yale U., 1949, Ph.D., 1953; LHD, U. Rochester, 1994. Instr. history Williams Coll., 1944-47; asst. instr. Yale, 1949-50; mem. faculty Williams Coll., 1951—, prof., 1961—, Mark Hopkins prof. history, 1964-82, emeritus, 1982—, chmn. Am. civilization program, 1971-80; Williams Coll. marshal, 1978-87; vis. lectr. history and edn. Harvard U., 1960, 61; vis. prof. Sch. Edn., U. Calif.-Berkeley, 1983; mem. commn. plans and objectives Am. Council Edn., 1963-66; mem. study group on postsecondary edn. Nat. Inst. Edn., 1980-83; mem. com. on baccalaureate degrees Assn. Am. Colls., 1981-85; vis. assoc. Ctr. Studies in Higher Edn., U. Calif.-Berkeley, 1983. Author: Mark Hopkins and the Log, 1956, The American College and University: A History, 1962, rev. edit., 1990, Curriculum: A History of the American Undergraduate Course of Study Since 1636, 1977, rev. edit., 1993; editor: Essays on Education in the Early Republic, 1965, Perspectives: A Williams Anthology, 1983; exec. editor: Change, 1980-84, cons. editor, 1985-92. Founding mem. Berkshire County Hist. Soc., 1962, v.p., 1962-66, pres., 1966-68, bd. dirs., 1974-76; trustee Hancock-Shaker Community Inc., 1974-91, Wyoming Sem., 1976-79, Bennington Mus., 1985—; bd. dirs. Armand Hammer United World Coll. Am. West, 1993—. Served to capt. AUS, 1942-46. Guggenheim fellow, 1958-59, 68-69; recipient Frederic W. Ness award Assn. Am. Colls., 1980, Rogerson cup Williams Coll., 1982, Disting. Svc. award Wyo. Seminary, 1986. Mem. Nat. Acad. Edn., Mass. Hist. Soc., Am. Hist. Assn., Am. Studies Assn., Orgn. Am. Historians, AAUP, Phi Beta Kappa. Democrat. Home: 234 Ide Rd Williamstown MA 01267-2800

RUDOLPH, FREDERICK BYRON, biochemistry educator; b. St. Joseph, Mo., Oct. 17, 1944; s. John Max and Maxine Leah (Wood) R.; m. Glenda M. Myers, June 18, 1971; children: Anna Dorine, William K. BS in Chemistry, U. Mo., Rolla, 1966; PhD in Biochemistry, Iowa State U., 1971. Prof. biochemistry Rice U., Houston, 1972—, dir. Lab. for Biochem. and Genetic Engring., 1986—, exec. dir. Inst. Bioscience and Bioengineering; cons. World Book, Chgo., 1972—; mem. biochemistry study sect. NIH, Bethesda, Md., 1983-87; bd. dirs. S.W. Assn. Biotech. Cos., Houston, 1990-93. Contbr. over 160 articles to profl. jours. including Jour. Biol. Chemistry, Biochemistry, Transplantation, Exptl. Hematology, Jour. Parenteral and Enteral Nutrition, Jour. Molecular Biology, Applied and Environ. Microbiology, Life Scis., Archives Biochem. Biophysics, Critical Care Medicine, Archives Surgery, Sci.; also chpts. to books. Recipient Disting. Alumnus award Iowa State U., 1980. Mem. Am. Chem. Soc., Am. Soc. for Biochemistry and Molecular Biology. Achievements include research on dietary requirements for immune function, new techniques for protein purification, new methods for kinetic analysis of enzymes, structure and function of various enzymes. Office: Rice U Dept Biochemistry PO Box 1892 Houston TX 77251-1892

RUDOLPH, FREDERICK WILLIAM, contractor; b. Wood County, Ohio, July 10, 1929; s. John William and Verna Sophia (Libbe) R.; m. Marilyn Louise Early, Jan. 31, 1954; children—Gail Susan, William David, Frederick John, John Douglas. B.S., Bowling Green State U., 1951. Constrn. supt. V. N. Holderman, Columbus, Ohio, 1951-54, United Constrn., Winona, Minn., 1954-55; pres. Rudolph-Libbe Inc., Walbridge, Ohio, 1955—; dir. Trustcorp Bank, Ohio; dir. N.W. Ohio Bank, 1978-81. Named Concrete Man of Yr., Concrete Improvement Assn., 1977. Mem. Young Pres.'s Orgn., World Bus. Council, Associated Gen. Contractors (chpt. pres. 1975). Republican. Lutheran. Clubs: Belmont Country, Sigma Alpha Epsilon. Home: 6486 Latcha Rd Walbridge OH 43465-9738 Office: Rudolph/Libbe Inc 6494 Latcha Rd Walbridge OH 43465-9788

RUDOLPH, GILBERT LAWRENCE, lawyer; b. L.A., Aug. 23, 1946; s. Martin Muttel and Marion (Perlman) R.; Susan Ilene Fellenbaum, Sept. 18, 1983; children: Samara Lisa, Felicia Beth. BA, Ariz. State U., 1967; postgrad., Am. U., Washington, 1967-69; JD, U. Cin., 1973. Bar: D.C. 1973, U.S. Dist. Ct. D.C. 1974, U.S. Ct. Appeals (D.C. cir.) 1974, Ariz. 1975, U.S. Dist. Ct. Ariz. 1975, Calif. 1979. Assoc. Streich, Lang, Weeks & Cardon, P.A., Phoenix, 1975-78; ptnr. Gilbert L. Rudolph, P.C., Phoenix, 1978-87; sr. mem. O'Connor, Cavanagh, Anderson, Killingsworth & Beshears, P.A., Phoenix, 1987—. Bd. dirs. Make-A-Wish Found. of Am., 1984-89, Aid to Adoption of Spl. Kids, Ariz., 1995—. Mem. ABA (com. on consumer fin. svcs. bus. law sect. 1981—, com. on comml. fin. svcs. 1989—, mem. com. on uniform comml. code, 1992—), Conf. on Consumer Fin. Law (governing com. 1986—). Republican. Jewish. Office: O'Connor Cavanagh Anderson Westover Killingsworth & Beshears PA 1 E Camelback Rd Ste 1100 Phoenix AZ 85012-1656

RUDOLPH, JEFFREY N., museum director. Exec. dir. California Museum of Science and Industry, Los Angeles, Calif. Office: Calif Mus Sci & Industry 700 State Dr Los Angeles CA 90037-1210*

RUDOLPH, JOHN W., architectural firm executive. Student, Universita Internacional Del Arte, Florence, Italy, 1972; BArch cum laude, Pa. State U., 1973. Registered architect, N.J., N.H., Mass.; cert. Nat. Coun. Archtl. Registration Bds. Prin. PMR Architects, P.C., 1978—. Prin. works include Milford (N.H.) Med. Ctr., Nashua (N.H.) Brookside Hosp., Hollis (N.H.) Village Marketplace, Digital Equipment Corp., Nashua, Birch Pond Office Pk., Nashua, Greenridge Office Pk., Nashua, Gottesman and Hollis Law Offices, Nashua, City Plz., Prolman & Stabile, Nashua, Fox Hollow Con-

dominium, Hudson, N.H., 1st Bapt. Ch. Nashua (Award for Excellence in Architecture N.H. chpt. AIA 1983), Londonderry (N.H.) Sq., NFS Savs. Bank, Londonderry, Royal Ridge Mall, Nashua, Ledgewood Hills Condominiums, Nashua (2 Gold awards Builder's Choice Awards 1987), Gottesman Residence (Best in Am. Living Merit award Profl. Builder Mag. 1988, Honor award N.H. chpt. AIA 1989), 221 Main St. Office Bldg. (Merit award N.H. chpt. AIA 1986). Mem. Nashua Fire Code Bd. Appeals, 1985-91, Nashua Hist. Dist. Commn., 1986-92, Nashua Bldg. Code Bd. Appeals, 1988-92; bd. dirs. Adult Learning Ctr. Mem. AIA (dir. N.H. chpt. 1982-83, sec. 1983-84, v.p. 1984-85, pres. 1985-86), Nat. Trust Hist. Preservation, Rotary (treas. Nashua West 1989-89, 92, Paul Harris fellow), Pa. State U. Alumni Assn. Office: PMR Architects 9A East Pearl St Nashua NH 03060

RUDOLPH, LAVERE CHRISTIAN, library director; b. Jasper, Ind., Dec. 24, 1921; s. Joseph Frank and Rose (Stradtner) R. A.B., DePauw U., 1948; B.D., Louisville Presbyn. Sem., 1951; Ph.D., Yale, 1958; student, U. Zurich, Switzerland, 1960; M.L.S., Ind. U., 1968. Ordained to Ministry Presbyn. Ch., 1950; pastor in Ind. and Conn., 1950-54; mem. faculty Louisville Presbyn. Sem., 1954-69, prof. ch. history, 1960-69; lectr. history U. Louisville, 1965-69; rare books bibliographer Van Pelt Library U. Pa.; head tech. services Lilly Library, Ind. U., 1970-78, curator of books, 1978-86, librarian emeritus, 1987—. Author: Hoosier Zion, 1963 (Thomas Kuch award; Ind. U. Writers Conf. 1964), Story of the Church, 1966, Francis Asbury, 1966, Indiana Letters, 1979, Religion in Indiana, 1986. Served to capt. USAAF, 1940-46. Mem. Am. Soc. Ch. History, ALA, Assn. Coll. and Research Libraries, Presbyn. Hist. Soc., Phi Beta Kappa. Democrat. Home: 1509 E Dunstan Dr Bloomington IN 47401-8775 Office: Ind U Library Bloomington IN 47405

RUDOLPH, LLOYD IRVING, political science educator; b. Chgo., Nov. 1, 1927; s. Charles N. and Bertha (Margolin) R.; m. Susanne Hoeber, July 19, 1952; children: Jenny W., Amelia C., Matthew C.J. Cadet, U.S. Mil. Acad., 1945-46; A.B. magna cum laude, Harvard U., 1948, M.P.A., 1950, Ph.D., 1956. Adminstrv. asst. Office Territories, Dept. Interior, Washington, 1948; research officer Council Econ. Advisers, Washington, 1949; mem. faculty Harvard U., Cambridge, Mass., 1951-64, asst. prof. govt., Allston Burr sr. tutor Dunster House, 1960-64; assoc. prof. polit. sci. U. Chgo., 1964-72, prof. polit. sci. and social scis., 1972—, chmn. Coll. Polit. Sci. program, 1968-70, chmn. divisional master's program social scis., 1973-75, chmn. pub. affairs program, 1980-83, chmn. com. on internat. relations, 1985-87, 94-95; contbr., participant Commn. on Orgn. Govt. for Conduct Fgn. Policy, 1974-75, 1980's Project of Council on Fgn. Relations, 1976-80, report of the Carnegie Task Force on non-proliferation and South Asian security, 1986-88; Bd. overseers com. to visit dept. govt. Harvard, 1978-81. Author: (with Susanne H. Rudolph) The Modernity of Tradition: Political Development in India, 1967, Education and Politics in India: Studies in Organization, Society and Policy, 1972, The Coordination of Complexity in South Asia, 1975, The Regional Imperative, 1980, Gandhi: The Traditional Roots of Charisma, 1983, Essays on Rajputana, 1984; editor: Cultural Policy in India, 1984, In Pursuit of Lakshmi; The Political Economy of the Indian State, 1987; co-editor: The Idea of Rajasthan, 2 vols., 1993; also articles. Served with AUS, 1954-56. Ford Found. fgn. area tng. fellow India, 1956-57, sr. fellow Fulbright Program, India, 1962-63, faculty fellow Am. Inst. Indian Studies, India, 1966-67, 87-88, Am. Inst. Indian Studies and Guggenheim fellow, 1975-76; Fulbright prof. India, 1970-71, 91-92; grantee NSF, 1973-75, NSF and Am. Inst. Indian Studies, 1979-80, Smithsonian Instn., India, 1983-84, MacArthur Found., 1992-93. Mem. Am. Polit. Sci. Assn., Am. Soc. Pub. Adminstrv., Assn. Asian Studies, Council Fgn. Relations (N.Y.), Chgo. Council Fgn. Relations (Chgo. com.). Home: 5555 Everett Ave #11-F Chicago IL 60637 Office: Pick 422 5828 S Univ Ave Chicago IL 60637

RUDOLPH, MALCOLM ROME, investment banker; b. Balt., Sept. 22, 1924; s. Louis and Sara E. (Rome) R.; m. Zita Herzmark, July 1, 1956 (div. 1979); children: Madelon R. II, Margot R.; m. Barbara J. Girson, 1979. AB, Harvard U., 1947; postgrad., Grenoble U., France, 1948, Hayden Stone Mgmt. Sch., 1965. With div. internat. confs. U.S. Dept. State, Paris, 1949; registered rep. trainee Orvis Bros. & Co., N.Y.C., 1949, rep., asst. mgr., acting mgr.,-1950-64; mgr. Hayden Stone Inc., Washington, 1964-68, ptnr., 1968-69; chmn. bd. Donatelli, Rudolph & Schoen Inc., Washington, 1970-74; chmn. bd. Multi-Nat. Fin. Group, Inc., Washington, 1974-79, pres., 1979-86; chmn. Multi-Nat. Precious Metals Corp., 1974-75; chmn. bd. Multi-Nat. Money Mgmt. Co. Inc., 1974-79, pres., 1979—; pres. Rudolph & Schoen Inc., 1975-85; sr. v.p. Laidlaw Adams & Peck Inc., 1975-79; pres. Laidlaw Resources Inc., 1976—, Sutton Energy, Inc., 1976—, DeRand Resources Corp., 1979-88; sr. v.p. dir. DeRand Corp. Am., 1979-88; chmn. bd. Arlington Energy Corp., 1980-88; mem. Phila.-Balt.-Washington Stock Exch., 1972-75; pres. Rome Resources Corp., 1982—, Investment Bankers and Cons.; assoc. mem. Pitts., Boston, Montreal stock exchs., 1972-75; allied mem. N.Y. Stock Exch., 1975-79. Mem. Presdl. Inaugural Com., 1960, 64; mem. select com. Palm Beach County Coop Ext. Svc., 1993, U. Fla. Inst. Food and Agrl. Scis. ext. 2000 Select Com.; treas. and dir. Friends of the Mounts Bot. Garden, West Palm Beach, 1994; v.p., dir. Hort. Soc. South Fla., 1994. Mem. Assn. Investment Brokers Met. Washington (v.p. 1965-66, pres. 1967), Bond Club Wahsington, Ohio Oil and Gas Assn., Ind. Oil and Gas Assn., W.Va., Indl. Petroleum Assn. Am., Southeastern Ohio Oil and Gas Assn., Washington Met. Bd. Trade, Itnertnat. Assn. Fin. Planners, Internat. Club of Washington, Hasy-Pudding Inst. 1770, Harvard Club of Washington (asst. treas. 1957-60, treas. 1960-64, exec. com. 1957-67), Harvard Club Palm Beaches, Nat. Aviation Club, Club Colette (Palm Beach), Palm Beach Yacht Club. Home: 1333 N Lake Way Palm Beach FL 33480-3109

RUDOLPH, SUSANNE HOEBER, political and social science educator; b. Mannheim, Fed. Republic of Germany, Germany, Apr. 3, 1930; (parents Am. citizens); d. Johannes and Elfriede (Fischer) H.; m. Lloyd I. Rudolph, July 19, 1952; children: Jenny W., Amelia C., Matthew C. J. AB, Sarah Lawrence Coll., 1951; MA, Radcliffe Coll., 1953; PhD in Polit. Sci., Harvard U., 1955. Instr., asst. prof. Harvard U., Cambridge, Mass., 1957-64; assoc. prof. polit. and social scis. U. Chgo., 1964-72, prof., 1972—; master social scis. collegiate div., 1973-75, chair dept. polit. sci., 1976-79, 89, dir. South Asia Ctr., 1980—; bd. dir. Rockefeller Residency Inst., 1990-94; lectr. Phi Beta Kappa, 1977-79, 86-90; mem. Bd. Fgn. Scholarships, 1979-82; chmn. com. on problems and policy, Social Sci. Coun., 1987-89. Author: (with Lloyd I. Rudolph) The Modernity of Tradition: Political Development in India, 1967, Education and Politics in India, 1972, The Regional Imperative: Foreign Policy in South Asia, 1980, Gandhi, 1983, Essays on Rajputana, 1984, In Pursuit of Lakshmi, 1987. Bd. dirs. Sarah Lawrence Coll., 1984-90, Kodaikanal-Woodstock Found., 1988—. Ford Found. fgn. area tng. fellow, India, 1956-57, Fulbright sr. fellow, India, 1962-63, 87-88, Am. Inst. Indian Studies faculty fellow, India, 1966-67, 83-84, 91-92, Guggenheim fellow, 1970-71; grantee NSF, 1973-75, NEH, 1977-79, 95. Mem. Am. Polit. Sci. Assn. (v.p 1973-74), Assn. Asian Studies (bd. dirs. 1973-75, v.p. 1985-86, pres. 1986-87), Asia Soc. (bd. dirs. 1991—). Office: U Chgo Dept Polit Sci 5828 S University Ave Chicago IL 60637-1515

RUDOLPH, WALLACE MORTON, legal educator; b. Chgo., Sept. 11, 1930; s. Norman Charles and Bertha (Margolin) R.; m. Janet L. Gordon, Feb. 14, 1964; children: Alexey, Rebecca, Sarah. B.A., U. Chgo., 1950, J.D. 1953. Bar: Ill. 1953, U.S. Ct. Mil. Appeals 1954, U.S. Supreme Ct. 1954, Nebr. 1962, Wash. 1978, also others. Research assoc. Ford Found., 1953-54, Ford Found. (Project in Law and Behavior Sci.), 1954-55; instr. U. Chgo. Law Sch., 1959; assoc. firm Antonow & Fink, Chgo., 1960-61; asst. prof. law U. Nebr., Lincoln, 1961-63; assoc. prof. U. Nebr., 1963-64, prof., 1965-76; prof. U. Puget Sound Sch. Law, 1976-94, dean, 1976-80; prof. Sch. of Law Seattle U., 1994—; vis. prof. law U. Wis., 1980-81, U. Ill. 1984; chair excellence in law Memphis State U. Law Sch., 1991; mem. Commrs. Uniform State Law, 1973-77; judge pro tem. (Indsl. Rels., Nebr.), 1975-77; mem. Wash. Jud. Coun. and COm. II, 1976-80, Pub. Employment Rels. Commn., Wash., 1977—. Author: Handbook for Correctional Law; contbr. articles to profl. jours.; author: Model Criminal Procedure Code, 1975, Model Sentencing and Corrections Act, 1978, Amicus Curiae Brief, Wash. State Supreme Ct, 1979. Bd. dirs. LIMIT, 1992-94, Nebr. chpt. ACLU, 1965-72; mem. Nebr. Dem. Contact Com., 1973-74, 75-76; chmn. Firt Congl. Dist. Dem. Party, 1975-76; mem. exec. com. Unitarian Ch., Lincoln, 1965-67. Served with JAGC, U.S. Army, 1954-57. Mem. AAUP, Soc. Criminology, ABA Am. Law Inst., Am. Arbitration Assn. Office: Seattle U Sch Law 950 Broadway Tacoma WA 98402-4405

RUDSTEIN, DAVID STEWART, law educator; b. Leeds, Eng., Sept. 27, 1946. B.S., U. Ill., 1968, LL.M., 1975; J.D., Northwestern U., 1971. Bar: Ill. 1971, U.S. Supreme Ct. 1977. Teaching asst. U. Ill. Coll. Law, 1971-72; law clk. to Justice Walter V. Schaefer Supreme Ct. Ill., Chgo., 1972-73; asst. prof. law Ill. Inst. Tech.-Chgo. Kent Coll., 1973-76, assoc. prof., 1976-79, prof., 1979—, assoc. dean, 1983-87. Mem. ABA, Chgo. Council Lawyers, Order of Coif. Office: Ill Inst Tech-Chgo 565 W Adams St Chicago IL 60661-3636

RU DUSKY, BASIL MICHAEL, cardiologist; b. Wilkes-Barre, Pa., July 27, 1933; s. Michael and Anne RuD.; B.A., Va. Mil. Inst., 1955; M.D., U. Pitts., 1959; m. Bernadine RuDusky, 1957; children: Daryl, Bryan. Intern, Martin Army Hosp., Ft. Benning, Ga., 1959-60; resident Youngstown (Ohio) Hosp. Assn., 1962-63, Temple U. Hosp., 1963-66; practice medicine specializing in internal medicine and cardiovascular disease, Wilkes-Barre, Pa., 1966—; mem. staff Mercy Hosp., 1966—, chief of medicine, 1966-70, dir. ICU AND CCU, 1966-70, dir. phonocardiography lab., 1966-70; dir. N.E. Cardiovascular Clinic and Research Inst.; mem. staff Wilkes-Barre Gen. Hosp.; cons. cardiology Armed Forces Examining Service; sr. cons. Social Security Adminstrn., HEW; sr. cons. physician Met. Ins. Co. Am., Liberty Mut. Ins. Co., Aetna Ins. Co.; cons. internal medicine and cardiology Retreat State Hosp.; dir. Northeast Cardiovascular Clinic and Research Inst.; clin. instr. medicine Temple U., 1966-70. Served to capt. M.C., U.S. Army, 1959-62. Diplomate Am. Bd. Internal Medicine, Am. Bd. Forensic Examiners (fellow). Fellow ACP, Am. Coll. Angiology (bd. govs. Eastern Pa.), Am. Coll. Chest Physicians, Am. Coll. Cardiology; mem. Am. Soc. Internal Medicine, AMA, Am. Coll. Occupl. and Environ. Medicine, Nat. Rehab. Assn., N.Y. Acad. Scis., Am. Geriatrics Soc., Assn. Mil. Surgeons U.S., Ferrari Club Am., Maserati Owners Club, Lamborghini Owners Club, Amateur Fencers League Am. Home: 7 Pinetree Rd Wilkes Barre PA 18707 Office: Bicentennial Bldg 15 Public Sq Wilkes Barre PA 18701-1702

RUDY, DAVID ROBERT, physician, educator; b. Columbus, Ohio, Oct. 19, 1934; s. Robert Sale and Lois May (Arthur) R.; m. Rose Mary Sims; children by previous marriage: Douglas D., Steven W., Katharine L., Hunter A. Elam. BSc, Ohio State U., 1956, MD, 1960, MPH Med. Coll. Wis., 1995. Intern, Northwestern Meml. Hosp., Chgo., 1960-61; resident in internal medicine Ohio State U. Hosp., 1963-64; resident in pediatrics Children's Hosp., Columbus, Ohio, 1964; practice medicine specializing in family practice, Columbus, 1964-75; dir. Family Practice Center and residency program Riverside Meth. Hosp., Columbus, 1975-85; dir. Family Practice Ctr. and residency Monsour Med. Ctr., Jeannette, Pa., 1985-88; dir. Family Practice Ctr. and residency Bon Secours Hosp., Grosse Pointe, Mich., 1988-91; prof., dept. chmn. Finch U. Health Scis., Chgo. Med. Sch., 1991—; former clin. assoc. prof. Ohio State U., Penn. State U., Wayne State U. Dept. Family Medicine. Contbr. articles to profl. jours. Served as capt., flight surgeon, M.C., USAF, 1961-63; 1t. col. USAFR. Recipient USAF Commendation medal. Diplomate Am. Bd. Family Practice (charter). Fellow Am. Acad. Family Physicians; mem. AMA, Ill. State Med. Assn., Central Ohio Acad. Family Practice (pres. 1979), Pa. Acad. Family Physicians (bd. dirs. 1985-88, treas. 1988), Columbus Maennerchor, Chgo. Coun. on Fgn. Rels. Republican. Office: Finch Univ Health Scis Chgo Med Sch 3333 Green Bay Rd North Chicago IL 60064-3095

RUDY, LESTER HOWARD, psychiatrist; b. Chgo., Mar. 6, 1918; s. Sol and Mildred (Weinzimmer) R.; m. Ruth Jean Schmidt, Nov. 25, 1950; 1 dau., Sharon Ruth. B.S., U. Ill., 1939, M.D., 1941; M.S. in Hosp. Adminstrn, Northwestern U., 1957. Diplomate: Am. Bd. Psychiatry and Neurology (exec. dir. 1972-86). Intern Cedars of Lebanon Hosp., Los Angeles, 1941-42; resident in psychiatry VA Hosp., Downey, Ill., 1946-48; staff psychiatrist VA Hosp., 1948-52, chief service, 1952-54; supt. Galesburg (Ill.) State Research Hosp., 1954-58; practice medicine specializing in psychiatry Chgo.; supt. Ill. State Psychiat. Inst., Chgo., 1958-61; dir. Ill. State Psychiat. Inst., 1961—, Ill. Mental Health Insts., Chgo., 1967-75; prof. psychiatry U. Ill. Coll. Medicine, 1971-88, emeritus, 1988—, head dept. psychiatry, 1975-88, pres. hosp. staff, 1979-80; dir. U. Ill. Hosp., 1981-82; sr. med. dir. Health Care Compare, 1988—; Chmn. research rev. com. mental health services NIMH, 1972-73; AMA commr. Joint Commn. on Accreditation of Hosps., 1967-75; sr. cons. VA; cons. adv. bd. Chgo., Police Dept.; lectr. dept. psychiatry and neurology Loyola U., 1968-75; mem. Ill. Gov.'s Com. Competency to Stand Trial, 1968. Contbr. articles to profl. jours. Served to col. AUS, 1942-46. Decorated Bronze Star with two oak leaf clusters. Fellow Am. Psychiat. Assn. (chmn. ethics com. 1963, Simon Bolivar award 1985), Am. Coll. Psychiatrists (charter, Bowis award 1979); mem. Am. Acad. Psychoanalysis (sci. asso.), Ill. Psychiat. Soc. (pres. 1962-63), U. Ill. Med. Alumni Assn. (ann. outstanding achievement award 1980). Home: 6343 Collingswood Ct Rockford IL 61103-8961 Office: 912 S Wood St Chicago IL 60612-7325

RUDY, RAYMOND BRUCE, JR., retired food company executive; b. L.A., Apr. 24, 1931; s. Raymond Bruce and Wrena Margaret (Higgins) R.; m. Kathleen Vermeulen; children: Bruce Calvin, Alice R. Wingert, Barbara R. Frith. BS, UCLA, 1953; MBA, Xavier U., Cin., 1960. Brand mgr. Procter & Gamble, Cin., 1956-62; product mgr. Hunt-Wesson Foods, Fullerton, Calif., 1962-63; group v.p. Gen. Foods Corp., White Plains, N.Y., 1963-79; pres. Oroweat Foods Co. subs. Continental Grain Co., N.Y.C., 1979-83; chmn., pres. Arnold Foods Co., Inc., Greenwich, Conn., 1984-86; pres. Affiliates of Best Foods subs. CPC Internat., Englewood Cliffs, N.J., 1987-89; ret., 1989; chmn., CEO, New Hampton, Inc., 1993-94; dep. chmn. Snapple Natural Beverages, Inc., 1992-94; oper. ptnr. J.W. Childs Assn., 1995—; bd. dirs. Select Beverages, Inc.; advisor Desai Capital Mgmt. Inc., Kirshenbaum Bond & Ptnrs., Advt. With U.S. Army, 1954-56. Mem. Greenwich Country Club, Dorset Field Club. Congregational.

RUDY, RUTH CORMAN, state legislator; b. Millheim, Pa., Jan. 3, 1938; d. Orvis E. and Mabel Jan (Stover) Corman; m. C. Guy Rudy, Nov. 21, 1956; children: Douglas G., Donita Rudy Koval, Dianna F. Degree in x-ray tech. Carnegie Inst., 1956; student Pa. State U.,1968-71. Clk. of cts. County of Centre (Pa.), Bellefonte, 1976-82; rep. Pa. Gen.Assembly, Harrisburg, 1982—. Mem. Dem. Nat. Com., 1980—, chair women's caucus,1989-91; past pres. Pa. Fedn. Dem. Women, Harrisburg; pres. Nat. Fedn. Dem. Women, 1987-89; mem. exec. com. Dem. Nat. Com., 1987-89, chmn. women's caucus, 1989-91. Named Woman of Yr., Pa. Fedn. Dem. Women, 1982. Methodist. Granted U.S. Patent on hair spray face shield 1995. Office: Pa Ho Reps PO Box 115 Harrisburg PA 17108-0115

RUDY, WILLIS, historian; b. N.Y.C., Jan. 25, 1920; s. Philip and Rose (Handman) R; B.S.S., CCNY, 1939; M.A., Columbia U., 1940, Ph.D., 1948; m. Dorothy L. Richardson, Jan. 31, 1948; children: Dee Dee, Willis Philip, Willa. Instr. City N.Y., 1939-49; instr., lectr. Harvard U., 1949-53, 57-58; prof. Mass. State Coll., Worcester, 1953-63; prof. history Fairleigh Dickinson U., Teaneck, N.J., 1963-82, prof. emeritus, 1982—; mem. editorial bd. Fairleigh Dickinson U. Press, 1966-77. Mem. Orgn. Am. Historians, Phi Beta Kappa. Author: The College of the City of New York, A History, 1847-1947, 1949, 1976; The American Liberal Arts College Curriculum, 1960; Higher Education in Transition, 1958, 68, 76; Schools in an Age of Mass Culture, 1965; The Universities of Europe: a History, 1984; Total War and Twentieth Century Higher Learning, 1991, The Campus and a Nation in Crisis: From the Revolution to Vietnam, 1995. Home: 161 W Clinton Ave Tenafly NJ 07670-1916 Office: Fairleigh Dickinson U Dept Of Hist Teaneck NJ 07666

RUDZKI, EUGENIUSZ MACIEJ, chemical engineer, consultant; b. Warsaw, Poland, Feb. 24, 1914; came to U.S., 1955.; s. Aleksander and Wanda (Łukasiewicz) R.; m. Fiorina Maria Di Vito, Feb. 23, 1952; children: Robert Alexander, Marcella Wanda Rudzki Meddick. Diploma with honors, Warsaw (Poland) Poly. Inst., 1937; Chem. Engr., The Polish U. Coll., London, 1951. Project devel. and head engr. Chance Bros. Ltd., Eng., 1951-54; head instr. chem. engring. dept. U. Toronto, Can., 1954-55; rsch. engr. T.C. Wheaton Co., N.J., 1955-56; plant engr. Bethlehem (Pa.) Steel Corp., 1956-61, supr. rsch. dept., 1961-82, ret., 1982; cons. Am. Flame Rsch. com., 1982—. Patentee in field, U.S., Eng., Can., Belgium; contbr. articles to profl. jours. Active The Polish Inst. Arts and Scis., N.Y.C., 1975, The Kosciuszko Found., N.Y.C., 1977; polit. prisoner Gulag Abis forced labor camp, Peczora, USSR, 1940-41. Maj. 2d Polish Army Corp. Gen. Anders, 1942-46. Decorated the Virtuti Militari Order, The Cross of Valor with Bar,

The Silver Order of Merit with Swords. Fellow Inst. Energy London, Coun. Engring. Insts. London (chartered engr.); mem. AIME, AIChE, Combustion Inst., Polish Vets. WWII, Assn. Vets. of 2nd Polish Army Corp. Roman Catholic. Avocations: gardening, reading, travel.

RUEB, RICHARD V., SR., information systems management consultant; b. Tulsa, Sept. 26, 1939; s. Thurston Aaron and Thelma (Wells) R.; m. Denise Ann Rueb, Jan. 1, 1991; children: Richard V. Jr., Beckee K. BSBA, U. Denver, 1970. Cert. internal auditor, info. systems auditor. Enlisted USAF, 1956, commd., 1970, advanced through grades to capt., 1974, info. systems audit mgr., 1971-81, ret., 1981; mgr. info. sys. audit Anderson Clayton, Houston, 1980-81; disruption recovery advisor Litton Computer Svcs., 1981-82; pres. The Concorde Group, Inc., Newport Beach, Calif., 1982-87; exec. dir. Info. Systems Security Assn., Newport Beach, 1987-92; prin. Balboa Pacific Co., Newport Beach, Calif.; founder and pres. Balboa Park Mortgage, Newport Beach, 1994—. Co-author: IBM Personal Computer Handbook; pub., creator Access Mag. Mem. Info. Sys. Security Assn. (Orange county chpt. sec. 1993—, past pres. Houston chpt.), Info. Control and Audit Assn., Internat. Auditors Assn. Republican. Home and Office: PO Box 7367 Newport Beach CA 92658

RUEBHAUSEN, OSCAR MELICK, lawyer; b. N.Y.C., Aug. 28, 1912; s. Oscar and Eleonora J. (Melick) R.; m. Zelia Krumbhaar Peet, Oct. 31, 1942. AB summa cum laude, Dartmouth Coll., 1934; LLB cum laude, Yale U., 1937. Bar: N.Y. 1938, U.S. Supreme Ct., 1945. Assoc. Debevoise, Stevenson, Plimpton & Page, N.Y.C., 1937-42, Lend-Lease Adminstrn., Washington, 1942-44; gen. counsel Office Sci. Rsch. and Devel., Washington, 1944-46; ptnr. Debevoise and Plimpton, 1946-84, presiding ptnr., 1972-81, of counsel, 1984-87; counselor to ednl. instn., 1988—. Editor: Pension and Retirement Policies in Colleges and Universities, 1990; contbr. articles to profl. jours. Chmn. Commn. on Coll. Retirement, 1984-93; spl. adviser atomic energy to gov. N.Y. State, 1959; vice chmn. N.Y. State adv. com. on atomic energy, 1959-62; chmn. N.Y. State Gov.'s Task Force on protection from radioactive fallout, 1959; mem. Pres.'s Task Force on Sci. Policy, 1969-70, Pres.'s Sci. Adv. Com. Panel on Chems. and Health, 1970-72, Commn. on Critical Choices for Am., 1973-77, adv. com. Carnegie Commn. on Sci. Tech. and Govt., 1988-93; chmn. UN Day, N.Y. State, 1962, chmn. Spl. N.Y. Com. on Ins. Holding Cos., 1967-68; mem. U.S. govt. panel on Privacy and Behavioral Rsch., 1965-66; mem. presdl. panel Chronic Renal Disease, 1966-67; sec., dir. Fund Peaceful Atomic Devel., Inc., 1954-72; dir. Carrie Chapman Catt Meml. Fund, 1948-58; chmn. bd. Bennington Coll., 1957-61, 62-67; trustee Hudson Inst., Inc., 1961-71; trustee Russell Sage Found., chmn. bd., 1965-80; vice-chmn. N.Y.C. Univ. Constrn. Fund, 1966-69; mem. Coun. on Fgn. Rels., nat. com on U.S.-China rels., Rockefeller U. Coun.; bd. dirs. Greenwall Found., 1956—, chmn., 1982-91, Scripps Clinic and Rsch. Found, 1983-89. Recipient U.S. Presdl. Cert. of Merit, 1948. Mem. ABA, N.Y. State Bar Assn., Yale Law Sch. Assn. (exec. com. and pres. 1960-62, chmn. 1962-64), Assn. of Bar of City of N.Y. (pres. 1980-82, pres. and bd. dirs. fund 1980-82), Order of Coif, Phi Beta Kappa, Sigma Phi Epsilon, Sigma Xi (hon.). Clubs: Century (N.Y.C.), River (N.Y.C.), Rancho Santa Fe Assn. (Calif.); Rockefeller Ctr. (N.Y.C.). Home: 450 E 52d St New York NY 10022 Office: 875 3rd Ave New York NY 10022-6225

RUECK, JON MICHAEL, manufacturing executive; b. Riley, Kans., Oct. 23, 1940; s. G.M. Karl and Esther Margaret (Jones) R.; m. Connie Lee Dick Rueck, Apr. 14, 1962; children: Michael Jon, Robin Renee. BS in Nuclear Engring., Kans. State U., 1964, MS in Mech. Engring., 1971. Registered profl. engr., KS, Ohio. Radiation safety trainee Argonne Nat. Lab., Lemont, Ill., 1962; tech. sales trainee Owens-Corning Fiberglas Corp., Granville, Ohio, 1964-65; tech. sales Owens-Corning Fiberglas Corp., Mpls., 1965-66; customer svc. engr. Owens-Corning Fiberglas Corp., Granville, Ohio, 1966-67; environ. engr. Owens-Corning Fiberglas Corp., Toledo, 1971-75; dir. plant ops. Leila Y. Post Montgomery Hosp., Battle Creek, Mich., 1975; environ. engr. Thompson Dehydrating Co., Topeka, 1976, Kans. Dept. Health Environ., Topeka, 1976-77; v.p. Hosp. Instrument Svc. Co., Silver Lake, Kans., 1977-80; supr. air pollution source monitoring Kans. Dept. of Health and Environ., 1979-85; chmn. Rueck Assocs., Silver Lake, Kans., 1985—; cons. to Nat. Coun. Examiners for Engring. and Surveying, 1991-. Inventor: Invention (Patent) Air Pollution Control Device, 1977. Res. police officer St. Mary's (Kans.) Police Dept., 1981-86; cert. lay speaker Kans. East Conf., United Meth. Ch., 1979—, vol. coord. Topeka dist. disaster response, 1993, coord., 1994—; merit badge counselor Boy Scouts Am., Silver Lake, 1988—; del. candidate for Robertson for Pres., Shawnee County, Kans., 1988; coord. Kans. Interfaith Disaster Recovery, 1993. Mem. Am. Acad. Environ. Engrs. (diplomate, chmn. admissions com. Annapolis, Md. 1986-90, state rep. Kans. 1990—), Midwest Air and Waste Mgmt. Assn. (officer 1987-90), Kaw Valley Bicycle Touring Club (Topeka), Lions. Republican. United Methodist. Avocations: bicycling, vocalist, amateur radio, computers. Home: 617 Walnut Silver Lake KS 66539 Office: Rueck Assocs 617 Walnut Silver Lake KS 66539-9461

RUECKERT, ROLAND RUDYARD, virologist, educator; b. Rhinelander, Wis., Nov. 24, 1931; s. George Leonard and Monica Amelia (Seiberlich) R.; m. Ruth Helen Ullrich, Sept. 5, 1959; 1 child, Wanda Lynne. BS in Chemistry, U. Wis., 1953, PhD in Oncology, 1960. Fellow Max Planck Inst. for Biochemistry, Munich, 1960-61, Tübingen, Fed. Republic Germany, 1961-62; asst. rsch. virologist virus lab. U. Calif. Berkeley, 1962-65; asst. prof. biophysics lab. U. Wis., Madison, 1965-69; assoc. prof. biophysics lab. U. Wis., 1969-73; prof. Inst. for Molecular Virology, Madison, 1973-85; dist. rsch. prof. Inst. for Molecular Virology, 1985—. Mem. virology study sect. NIH, Bethesda, Md., 1981-85; pres. Am. Soc. Virology, 1989-90. With U.S. Army, 1953-55. Recipient William D. Stovall award U. Wis., 1953, Marie Christine Kohler award U. Wis., 1959, Rsch. Career Devel. award, 1966, Faculty rsch. award Am. Cancer Soc., 1972; named Hilldale Disting. prof. 1988. Achievements include research in dodecahedral model for picornavirus structure and assembly, molecular biology of picornaviruses (polio 8 common cold), structure 8 biology of small insect viruses, mechanism of neutralization by antibodies and antivirals. Home: 2234 W Lawn Ave Madison WI 53711-1952 Office: U Wis Inst Molecular Biology 1525 Linden Dr Madison WI 53706-1596

RUEDENBERG, KLAUS, theoretical chemist, educator; b. Bielefeld, Germany, Aug. 25, 1920; came to U.S., 1948, naturalized, 1955; s. Otto and Meta (Wertheimer) R.; m. Veronika Kutter, Apr. 8, 1948; children: Lucia Meta, Ursula Hedwig, Annette Veronika, Emanuel Klaus. Student, Montana Coll., Zugerberg, Switzerland, 1938-39; licence es Scis., U. Fribourg, Switzerland, 1944; postgrad., U. Chgo., 1948-50; PhD, U. Zurich, Switzerland, 1950; PhD (hon.), U. Basel, Switzerland, 1975, U. Bielefeld, Germany, 1991, U. Siegen, Germany, 1994. Research assoc. physics U. Chgo., 1950-55; asst. prof. chemistry, physics Iowa State U., Ames, 1955-60; assoc. prof. Iowa State U., 1960-62, prof., 1964-78, disting. prof. in sci. and humanities, 1978-91, disting. prof. emeritus, 1991—, sr. chemist Ames Lab., U.S. Dept. Energy, 1964-91, assoc., 1991—; prof. chemistry Johns Hopkins, Balt., 1962-64; vis. prof. U. Naples, Italy, 1961, Fed. Inst. Tech., Zurich, 1966-67, Wash. State U. at Pullman, 1970, U. Calif. at Santa Cruz, 1973, U. Bonn., Germany, 1974, Monash U. and CSIRO, Clayton, Victoria, Australia, 1982, U. Kaiserslautern, Fed. Republic Germany, 1987; lectr. univs., rsch. instns. and sci. symposia, 1953—. Author articles in field; assoc. editor: Jour. Chem. Physics, 1964-67, Internat. Jour. Quantum Chemistry; Chem. Physics Letters, 1967-81, Lecture Notes in Chemistry, 1976—; Advances in Quantum Chemistry, 1987—; editor-in-chief Theoretica Chimica Acta, 1985—. Co-founder Octagon Center for the Arts, Ames, 1966, treas., 1966-71, also bd. dirs. Guggenheim fellow, 1966-67; Fulbright sr. scholar, 1982. Fellow AAAS, Am. Phys. Soc., Am. Inst. Chemists, Internat. Acad. for Quantum Molecular Scis.; mem. AAUP, Am. Chem. Soc. (Midwest award 1982), Sigma Xi, Phi Lambda Upsilon. Home: 2834 Ross Rd Ames IA 50014-4030 Office: Dept Chemistry Iowa State Univ Ames IA 50011

RUEGER, LAUREN JOHN, physicist; b. Archbold, Ohio, Dec. 30, 1921; s. Edwin Z. and Hazel Lulu (Fisher) R.; m. Florence Marian Scott, July 30, 1944; children: Carol, Beth, Lauren A., Mary. BS in Engring. Physics, Ohio State U., 1943, MS in Physics, 1947. Advanced tech. planner Johns Hopkins U. Applied Physics Lab., Laurel, Md., 1953-88; project leader Nat. Bur. Standards, Washington, 1948-52; research assoc. Battelle Meml. Inst., Columbus, Ohio, 1946-48; staff MIT Radiation Lab., 1943-45; U.S. del. Internat. Radio Cons. Com., Geneva, 1978, 80, 81, 83, 85, 88; tech. program

com. Frequency Control Symposium, Phila., 1976-78, 84-88; com. co-chmn. Internat. Time and Frequency Symposium, Helsinki, Finland, 1978; exec. com. Conf. on Precision Electromagnetic Measurements, Delft, Holland, 1984, Braunschweig, Fed. Republic of Germany, 1980, Tsukuba, Japan, 1988. Patentee in field. Fellow IEEE; mem. Am. Phys. Soc., Photog. Soc. Am. Avocation: photography. Home: 1415 Glenallan Ave Silver Spring MD 20902-1360

RUEGG, DONALD GEORGE, retired railway company executive; b. LaJunta, Colo., Sept. 11, 1924; s. George Albert and Cecilia Corrine (Decker) R.; m. Ruth Carson, June 27, 1946 (dec. 1963); m. Mary Ann Eichelberger, June 24, 1964. B.A., Dartmouth Coll., 1947; M.B.A., U. Chgo., 1972. Stenographer Atchison, Topeka & Santa Fe Ry. Co., Pueblo, Colo., 1942-51; supr., trainmaster Atchison, Topeka & Santa Fe Ry. Co., various locations, 1951-68; asst. to v.p. info. systems Atchison, Topeka & Santa Fe Ry. Co., Topeka, 1968-69; asst. to v.p. ops. Atchison Topeka & Santa Fe Ry. Co., Chgo., 1969-72; gen. mgr. Atchison Topeka & Santa Fe Ry. Co., Los Angeles, 1972-73; asst. v.p. ops. Atchison, Topeka & Santa Fe Ry. Co., Chgo., 1973-78, v.p. ops., 1978-83, exec. v.p., 1983-86. Served with USN, 1943-46. Republican. Roman Catholic.

RUEGGER, PHILIP THEOPHIL, III, lawyer; b. Plainfield, N.J., Oct. 14, 1949; s. Philip T. Jr. and Gloria Marie (McLaughlin) R.; m. Rebecca Lee Huffman, Aug. 3, 1974; children: Sarah, Brittain, Michael. AB, Dartmouth Coll., 1971; JD, U. Va., 1974. Bar: N.Y. 1975. Assoc. Simpson Thacher & Bartlett, N.Y.C., 1974-81, ptnr., 1981—. Chmn. Rye Edn. Fund, Inc.; bd. dirs. Port Chester Carver Ctr. Mem. Assn. of Bar City N.Y., Phi Beta Kappa. Presbyterian. Clubs: Manursing Island (Rye, N.Y.), Apawamis (Rye). Avocation: sports. Home: 275 Grace Church St Rye NY 10580-4201 Office: Simpson Thacher & Bartlett 425 Lexington Ave New York NY 10017-3903

RUEHL, MERCEDES, actress; b. Queens, N.Y.. BA in English, Coll. of New Rochelle; studied acting with Uta Hagen, Tad Danielewski. Appearances include (theatre) Vanities, 1977-78, Billy Irish, 1980, Much Ado About Nothing, Misalliance, Androcles and the Lion, Tartuffe, Medea, 1980-82, Three Sisters, 1982-83, The Day They Shot John Lennon, 1982-83, Flirtation, 1983, June Moon, 1983-84, Monday After the Miracle, 1983-84, Coming of Age in Soho, 1985, The Marriage of Bette and Boo, 1985, I'm Not Rappaport, 1985 (Obie Award), American Notes, 1988, Other People's Money, 1989, Lost in Yonkers, 1991 (Tony award, 1991, Drama Desk award, 1991, Outer Critics Circle award 1991), The Shadow Box, 1994 (Tony nominee - Featured actress in a Play, 1995), The Rose Tattoo, 1995, (film) The Warriors, 1979, Four Friends, 1981, Heartburn, 1986, 84 Charing Cross Road, 1987, Leader of the Band, 1987, The Secret of My Success, 1987, Radio Days, 1987, Big, 1988, Married to the Mob, 1988, Slaves of New York, 1989, Crazy People, 1990, Another You, 1991, The Fisher King, 1991 (Academy award Best Supporting Actress 1991), Lost in Yonkers, 1993, Last Action Hero, 1993, (TV movie) Indictment, 1995. Recipient Nat. Film Critics Circle award, 1988, Clarence Derwent award, 1989. Office: UTA 9560 Wilshire Blvd 5th Fl Beverly Hills CA 90212*

RUEHLE, DIANNE MARIE, elementary education educator; b. Detroit, Aug. 14, 1943; d. Richard Francis and Luella Mary (Kopp) R. BS, Ea. Mich. U., 1966, MA, 1971, adminstrv. cert., 1990, renewed adminstrv. cert., 1995. Cert. tchr., adminstr., Mich. Tchr. Cherry Hill Sch. Dist., Inkster, Mich., 1966-85; tchr. elem. sch. Wayne-Westland (Mich.) Community Schs., 1985—; dist. com. Pub. Act 25 for State of Mich., Westland, 1990-93, chair bldg., 1991-95. Improvement Instrn. grantee Wayne Westland Found., 1992-94. Mem. ASCD, NEA, Mich. Edn. Assn., Wayne-Westland Edn. Assn. Avocations: reading, golf, photography, travel. Home: 26117 LaSalle Ct Roseville MI 48066 Office: David Hicks Elem Sch 100 Helen St Inkster MI 48141

RUELLAN, ANDREE, artist; b. N.Y.C., Apr. 6, 1905; d. André and Louise (Lambert) R.; m. John W. Taylor, May 28, 1929. Student, Art Students League, 1920-22; art schs., France and Italy. guest instr. Pa. State Coll., summer 1957. One-man shows include Paris, 1925, Weyhe Galleries, N.Y.C., 1928, 31, Maynard Walker Galleries, 1937, 40, Kraushaar Galleries, 1945, 52, 56, 63, 80-81, Phila. Art Alliance, 1955, S.I. Mus., 1958, nat. exhbns., Carnegie Inst., Whitney Mus., Art Inst. Chgo., Corcoran Gallery, Internat. Expn., San Francisco, Artists for Victory Exhbn., N.Y.C. other cities U.S.; retrospective exhbns., Storm King Art Ctr., Mountainville, N.Y., 1966, Lehigh U., 1965, Woodstock Artists Assn., 1977, Ga. Mus. of Art, 1993, Hyde Collection, Glens Falls, N.Y., 1993, Gibbs Mus. of Art, Charleston, S.C., 1993, Prints Gallery at Parkbest, Kingston, N.Y., 1995; drawing retrospective Kaushaar Galleries, 1990, 93, Ga. Mus. Art, Athens, 1993, The Hyde Collection, Glen Falls, N.Y., 1993, Gibbs Mus. Art, Charleston, S.C., 1993; executed murals in Emporia, Va., Lawrenceville, Ga.; represented in permanent collections, Met. Mus. Art, Whitney Mus. Am. Art, N.Y.C., Fogg Mus., Harvard U., Phila. Mus., Storm King Art Ctr., William Rockhill Nelson Mus., Kansas City, Mo., Duncan Phillips Gallery, Washington, Springfield Mus., Norton Gallery, Art Mus., New Britain, Conn., Library of Congress, Ency. Brit., IBM Collections, Art Inst., Zanesville, Ohio, U. Ga., S.I. Mus., Butler Inst., Pa. State U., Lehigh U., Columbia (S.C.) Mus. Art, The Whatcom Mus., Washington, Springville (Utah) Mus. Art, S.C. State Mus., Wichita Art Mus., also numerous pvt. collections. Recipient 3d prize for painting Charleston Worcester Mus. Biennial, Jan. 1938; 1,000 grant in arts Am. Acad. and Inst. Arts and Letters, 1945 Pennell medal Pa. Acad., 1945; medal of Honor and purchase Pepsi-Cola Paintings of Year, 1948; Dawson Meml. medal Pa. Acad., 1950; Purchase award N.Y. State Fair, 1951; Drawing award Ball State Tchrs. Coll.; Guggenheim fellow, 1950-51; recipient Kuniyoshi award, 1994. Mem. Woodstock Artists Assn. (Sally Jacobs award 1981), Art Students League (life), Nat. Mus. Women in Arts. Home: RR 2 Box 154 Shady NY 12409-9510

RUELLO, SAMUEL ANGUS, management consultant; b. Atlantic City, Apr. 26, 1931; s. John and Catherine (Buchanan) R.; B.A., Bklyn. Coll., 1954; M.B.A., Temple U., 1961; m. Brenda Tausend, May 2, 1976; children—Nicole, Jeffrey. Chief indsl. engr. Philco Ford Lansale div. (Pa.), 1959-63; pres. Par Technology and sr. v.p. Booz-Allen & Hamilton, N.Y.C., 1963-73; exec. v.p Bradford Nat. Corp., N.Y.C., 1973-77; mng. partner Coopers & Lybrand, N.Y.C., 1977—; now CEO Meritus Cons. Svc., N.Y.C.; speaker; sr. v.p., mem. exec. com. N.Y. Bd. Trade, 1979—. Served in U.S. Army, 1954-56; Korea. Registered profl. engr., Calif. Mem. N.Am. Soc. Corp. Planning, Am. Inst. Indsl. Engring. Home: 165 E 66th St New York NY 10021-6132 Office: Meritus Cons Svc 1251 Ave of the Americas New York NY 10020

RUESCH, JANET CAROL, federal magistrate judge; b. New Brunswick, N.J., May 9, 1943. AB in Polit. Sci., Gettysburg Coll., 1965; JD, Ind. U. 1970. Bar: Tex. 1971, U.S. Dist. Ct. (we. dist.) Tex. 1973, U.S. Ct. Appeals (5th cir.) 1975, U.S. Dist. Ct. (so. dist.) Tex. 1977, U.S. Supreme Ct. 1979. Law clk. Malcolm McGregor and Mark Howell, El Paso, Tex., 1970-71; ptnr. Malcolm McGregor, Inc., El Paso, 1971-78; substitute mcpl. ct. judge City of El Paso, 1977-78; asst. U.S atty. Western Dist. Tex., El Paso, 1978-79; U.S. magistrate judge El Paso divsn. U.S. Dist. Ct. (we dist.) Tex., 1979—. Bd. dirs. El Paso County Gen. Assistance Agy., 1977-79; past mem. profl. adv. bd. El Paso Mental Health Assn.; v.p. El Paso Women's Pol. Caucus, 1977, program chair, 1976, pub. chair, 1975. Mem. Tex. Bar Assn., El Paso Bar Assn. (pres. 1984), El Paso Women's Bar Assn. (pres. 1975). Office: 206 US Courthouse 511 E San Antonio El Paso TX 79901

RUESCHEMEYER, DIETRICH, sociology educator; b. Berlin, Aug. 28, 1930; came to U.S., 1966; s. Philipp and Eufemia (Ross) R.; m. Marilyn R. Schattner, June 14, 1962; children: Julia Yael, Simone Margalit. Degree, U. Cologne, 1953, PhD in Sociology, 1958; postgrad., Columbia U., U. Chgo., U. Calif. Berkeley, 1960-61. Postdoctoral fellow Rockefeller Found., 1960-61; asst. prof. Dartmouth Coll., Hanover, N.H., 1962-63; from asst. prof. to assoc. prof. U. Toronto, 1963-66; assoc. prof. Brown U., Providence, R.I., 1966-71, prof. sociology, 1971—; Asa Messer Prof., 1995—; vis. assoc. prof. Hebrew U. of Jerusalem, 1969, vis. fellow, 1990; dir. Ctr. Comparative Study of Devel., Brown U., 1989—; mem. selection com. Berlin program for Advanced German and European Studies, 1986-91; mem. rsch. planning com. on states and social structures Social Sci. Rsch. Coun., N.Y., 1983-90, now Working Group on States and Social Structures, Russell Sage Found.,

1990—; acad. vis. Nuffield Coll., Oxford, 1979, Wolfson Coll., Oxford, 1982. Author: Lawyers and Their Society, 1973, German edit., 1976, Power and the Division of Labour, 1986, (with others) Capitalist Development and Democracy (Outstanding Book award Am. Sociological Assn. 1991-92); editor, co-editor: Das Interview: Formen, Technik, Auswertung, 2d edit., 1957, Beitrage zur soziologischen Theorie, 1964, Bringing the State Back In, 1985, States Vs. Markets in the World System, 1985, State and Market in Development: Synergy or Rivalry?, 1992; cons. editor Am. Jour. Sociology, 1977-79, Geschichte und Gesellschaft: Zeitschrift fuer historische Sozialwissenschaft, 1975—; assoc. editor Sociological Forum, 1985-92; mem. editorial bd. Am. Bar Found. Rsch. Jour., 1987, now Law and Social Inquiry, 1991-94, Sociological Theory, 1980-83; editor Working Papers on Comparative Development, 1983—; contbr. articles to profl. jours., book chpts.; presenter papers in field; speaker in field. Rsch. fellow Can. Coun., 1966; Faculty fellow Ford Found., 1968-69; Inst. Advanced Study Berlin fellow, 1987-88, Swedish Collegium for Advanced Study in the Social Scis. fellow Uppsala, 1992; recipient Torgny T. Segerstedt Professorship of Swedish Coun. for Studies in Higher Edn., 1992, Fgn. Franqui Chair of Belgium Free U. Brussels, 1987. Mem. Am. Sociol. Assn., Internat. Sociol. Assn., Polit. Svc. Assn. Home: 60 Oriole Ave Providence RI 02906 Office: Brown U Dept Sociology 79 Waterman St Brown Sta Providence RI 02912

RUESINK, ALBERT WILLIAM, biologist, plant sciences educator; b. Adrian, Mich., Apr. 16, 1940; s. Lloyd William and Alberta May (Foltz) R.; m. Kathleen Joy Cramer, June 8, 1963; children: Jennifer Li, Adriana Eleanor. B.A., U. Mich., 1962; M.A., Harvard U., 1965, Ph.D., 1966. Postdoctoral fellow Swiss Fed. Inst. Tech., Zurich, 1966-67; prof. biology Ind. U., Bloomington, 1967—. Recipient Amoco Teaching award Ind. U., 1980. Mem. AAUP (pres. chpt. 1978-79, 90-91), Am. Soc. Plant Physiologists, Bot. Soc. Am. Democrat. Mem. United Ch. of Christ. Home: 2605 E 5th St Bloomington IN 47408-4286 Office: Ind U Dept Biology Bloomington IN 47405

RUETTGERS, MICHAEL CADET, electronics executive; b. Muskogee, Okla., Dec. 11, 1942; s. John J. and Florence J. (Nunn) R.; m. Maureen Lee Sanders, July 12, 1969; children: Polly K., Christopher M., Abigail G. BBA, Idaho State U., 1964; MBA, Harvard U., 1967. Engring. planner LTV Aerospace Co., Detroit, 1964-68; bus. area mgr. Raytheon Co., Lexington, Mass., 1968-81; sr. v.p., gen. mgr. Keane Inc., Boston, 1981-86; chief oper. officer TFS Inc., Chelmsford, Mass., 1987-88; pres., chief oper. officer EMC Corp., Hopkinton, Mass., 1988—; bd. dirs. Keane Inc., TFS Inc. Republican. Roman Catholic. Avocations: hunting, fishing. Home: 453 Bedford Rd Carlisle MA 01741-1815 Office: EMC Corp 171 South St Hopkinton MA 01748-2208

RUF, JOHN FREDERIC, banker; b. Madison, Wis., May 9, 1937. BS, Lawrence U., 1959; JD, U. Wis., 1964. Bar: Wis. 1964. Asst. cashier Continental Ill. Bank, Chgo., 1964-68; v.p. M&I Marshall & Ilsley, Milw., 1968-81; pres. RBP Chem. Corp., Milw., 1981-84, First Interstate Bank of Wis., Milw., 1984-90; chair A.C. Battery, 1990—; mem. legis. council Wis. Bankers Assn., Madison, 1974-81, 88-90; bd. dirs., pres. TYME Corp., Milw., 1974-90. Sec.-treas Inland Lake Yachting Assn., Lake Geneva, Wis.; trustee Lawrence U., Appleton, Wis. Mem. Lawrence U. Alumni Assn. (pres.). Clubs: Kettle Moraine Curling (Hartland, Wis.) (pres.); Pewaukee Yacht (Wis.) (commodore). Home: 2772531 NW Rocky Rd Pewaukee WI 53072 Office: Future Resources LTD 1441 N Mayfair Rd Milwaukee WI 53226-3253

RUFA, ROBERT HENRY, writer, editor, photographer, artist; b. Bklyn., Jan. 11, 1943; s. Joseph Simon and Alma (Weintrecht) R.; m. Barbara LeeJohnson, June 25, 1971 (div. Oct. 1980); 1 child, Eric; m. Donnita Butler Dicus, June 27, 1990 (div. Aug. 1994). Grad. high sch. Tech. editor Tele-Signal Corp., Woodbury, N.Y., 1968; assoc. editor Tobacco Leaf mag., Rockville Centre, N.Y., 1969; mem. staff Travel mag., Floral Park, N.Y., 1969-76; mng. editor Travel mag., 1973-74, editor, 1975-76; artist, writer, photographer, 1976—; mng. editor The Pinehurst Outlook, 1977-78, 88; columnist Moore County Citizen News-Record, 1987-88; columnist The Pilot, 1988—, feature writer, 1990-93; feature writer Stringer News and Observer, Raleigh, 1990-91; dir. publs. Asheville-Buncombe Discovery, Asheville, N.C., 1991-92; arts & features editor Green Line/Mountain Xpress, Asheville, N.C., 1992-95. With USAF, 1961-65. Home: 59 Watauga St # 8 Asheville NC 28801

RUFEH, FIROOZ, energy research firm administrator; b. Isfahan, Iran, Feb. 15, 1937; s. Eberhim and Marian R. Rufeh; m. Heide Marie Haseruck, June 12, 1965; children: Bejan Renard, Jiela Mariam. BS in Chemistry, Cornell U., 1959; MS in Nuclear Engring., U. Calif., Berkeley, 1963. Rsch. scientist Thermo Electron Corp., Waltham, Mass., 1963-67, mgr. rsch. dept., 1967-75, dir. energy conservation and rsch., 1975-79, pres. R & D, new bus. div., 1979-84, group exec., 1984-86, v.p., 1986—; bd. dirs. Thermedics Inc., Tecogen Inc., Thermo Cardiosystems, Inc. Office: Thermo Electron Corp 101 1st Ave PO Box 9046 Waltham MA 02254-9046

RUFENACHT, ROGER ALLEN, accounting educator; b. Waldron, Mich., Dec. 17, 1933; s. Alphus Leroy and Frieda (Aschliman) R.; m. Carol Carnahan, June 13, 1965; children: Jeffrey, Jonathan. BS, Mich. State U., 1959, MS, 1965. Cert. tchr., Fla. Tchr. Madison High Sch., Adrian, Mich., 1959-61; bus. edn. instr. Charlotte High Sch., Rochester, N.Y., 1961-62; bus. edn. instr. Edgewater High Sch., Orlando, Fla., 1962-68, chmn. bus. dept., 1965-68; instr. in acctg. Orlando Vo Tech. Ctr. (formerly Orlando Vocat. Sch.), 1968-94, chmn. bus. dept., 1980-85; ret., 1994. Bd. dirs., v.p. Winter Park Jaycees, 1963-68; asst. coach, scorekeeper N.W. Little League; chmn. adv. com. local PTA, 1973-83; pres. Bandboosters 1985-86; cub scout den leader, com. chmn., mem. dist. com., mem. coms. Boy Scouts Am.; adminstrv. bd. local Meth. Ch., 1965—. Recipient Scouters Tng. award, Ten Yr. Vet. award Boy Scouts Am., 1991. Mem. NEA, Am. Vocat. Assn., Fla. Vocat. Assn. (registration com. ann. conf., pres.'s reception planning com.), Orange County Classroom Tchrs. Assn. (bd. dirs., bldg. rep.), Orange County Credit Union (rep.), Orange County Vocat. Assn. (bd. dirs., Pres.'s award 1988-89, Outstanding Vocat. Educator Bus. Edn. award 1988-89), Fla. Bus. Edn. Assn. (chmn. mem. various coms.), Orange County Bus. Edn. Assn. (pres. 1968, 76, chmn. mem. various coms.). Republican. Avocations: reading, golf. Home: 9510 Bear Lake Rd Apopka FL 32703-1917

RUFF, LARRY, geology educator; b. Riverside, Calif., Oct. 1, 1952; s. Jack J and Patricia H. Ruff. BS, U. Calif., Riverside, 1975; MS, Calif. Inst. Tech., 1978, PhD, 1982. Asst. prof U. Mich., Ann Arbor, assoc. prof. Editor: Subduction Zones, 1989; contbr. articles to profl. jours. Recipient Presdl. Young Investigator award NSF, 1985; Lilley Teaching fellow Lilley Found., 1983, Shell Faculity fellow Shell Found., 1986. Mem. Am. Geophysical Union, Seismological Soc. Am. Office: U Mich Dept Geol Scis Seismological Observat Ann Arbor MI 48109

RUFFER, DAVID GRAY, museum director, former college president; b. Archbold, Ohio, Aug. 25, 1937; s. Lawrence A. and Florence A. (Newcomer) R.; m. Marilyn Elaine Taylor, Aug. 23, 1958; children: Rochelle Lynne, Robyn Lynne, David Geoffrey. B.S., Defiance Coll., 1959; M.A., Bowling Green State U., 1960; Ph.D., U. Okla., 1964. Spl. instr. U. Okla., 1963-64; asst. prof. biology Defiance Coll., 1964-68, assoc. prof. 1968-73, faculty dean, 1969-73; provost Elmira (N.Y.) Coll., 1973-78; pres. Albright Coll., Reading, Pa., 1978-91, U. Tampa, Fla., 1991-94; exec. dir. Dayton (Ohio) Soc. Natural History, 1995—. Author: Exploring and Understanding Mammals, 1971; contbr. articles to profl. jours. NSF grantee, 1965, 67; Ohio Biol. Survey grantee, 1968-69. Fellow AAAS; mem. Am. Assn. Higher Edn., Animal Behavior Soc., Am. Soc. Mammalogists. Methodist. Club: Rotary. Home: 3700 Wales Dr Dayton OH 45405 Office: Dayton Mus Natural History 2600 DeWeese Pkwy Dayton OH 45414

RUFFER, MICHAEL R., hotel company executive. Exec. v.p., gen. mgr. Residence Inn, by Marriott Inc., Washington. Office: Residence Inn By Marriott Inc 1 Marriott Dr Washington DC 20058-0001

RUFFING, ANNE ELIZABETH, artist; b. Bklyn.; d. John Paul and Ruth Elizabeth (Price) Frampton; m. George W. Ruffing, Mar. 29, 1967; 1 dau., Elizabeth Anne. B.S., Cornell U., 1964; postgrad., Drexel Inst. Tech., 1966.

One-woman exhbns. include, IBM, 1966, Hall of Fame, Goshen, N.Y., 1971, group exhbns. include, Internat. Women's Arts Festival, World Trade Center, N.Y.C., 1975-76, Berkshire Mus., Pittsfield, Mass., 1965, 76, Cooperstown (N.Y.) Mus., 1969; represented in permanent collections, Met. Mus. Art, Bklyn. Mus., Library of Congress, Harvard U., Smithsonian Instn., N.Y. Hist. Soc. Johnston Hist. Mus., Atwater Kent Mus., Albany Inst. History and Art, Whitney Mus. Am. Art, Boston Public Library. Recipient 1st place Eric Sloane award, 1974; Internat. Women's Year award Internat. Women's Art Festival, 1976. Address: PO Box 125 Bloomington NY 12411-0125

RUFFLE, JOHN FREDERICK, banker; b. Toledo, Mar. 28, 1937; s. Matthew Frederick and Hazel Ruth (Johnson) R.; m. Eleanor Grace Loock, Nov. 19, 1960; children: Donald Alan, William Charles, John Garrett. B.A., Johns Hopkins, 1958; M.B.A., Rutgers, 1963. C.P.A., N.J. With Price Waterhouse & Co., N.Y.C., 1958-65; sr. accountant Price Waterhouse & Co., 1962-65; asst. treas. Internat. Paper Co., N.Y.C., 1965-70; comptroller Morgan Guaranty Trust Co. N.Y., N.Y.C., 1970-80; exec. v.p. Morgan Guaranty Trust Co. N.Y., 1980-85, vice chmn. bd., 1985-93, ret., 1993; cons. J.P. Morgan & Co., Inc., N.Y.C., 1993—; dir. Bethlehem Steel Corp., Student Loan Mktg. Assn.; bd. dirs. Trident Corp., JPM Advisor Funds. Trustee Johns Hopkins U., Balt., 1990—. With AUS, 1959-60. Mem. AICPA, Fin. Execs. Inst. (chmn. bd. 1983-84), N.J. Soc. CPAs, Fin. Acctg. Found. (trustee 1984-90, pres. 1989-90). Office: 23 Wall St New York NY 10260-0023

RUFFNER, FREDERICK G., JR., book publisher; b. Akron, Ohio, Aug. 6, 1926; s. Frederick G. and Olive Mae (Taylor) R.; m. Mary Ann Evans, Oct. 8, 1954; children: Frederic G. III, Peter Evans. B.S., Ohio State U., 1950. Advt. mgr. Jim Robbins Co., Royal Oak, Mich., 1950-52; research mgr. Gen. Detroit Corp., 1953-54; pres. Gale Research Co., Detroit, 1954-87, Omnigraphics, Inc., 1987—. Editor: Ency. of Assns, 1956-68, Code Names Dictionary, 1963, Acronyms and Initialisms Dictionary, 1965, Allusions Dictionary, 1985; pub. Gold Coast Mag., 1992—; patentee in field. Bd. dirs. Friends of Detroit Pub. Libr., pres., 1975-76; mem. exec. bd. Detroit coun. Boy Scouts Am., 1974—, v.p., 1976-82; pres. Coun. for Fla. Librs., 1979—; trustee Bon Secours Hosp., Grosse Pointe, Mich., 1980-81, Etruscan Found., Florence, Italy, 1980—; pres. Mich. Ctr. for the Book, 1990, Literary Landmarks Assn., Gold Coast Jazz Soc., Ft. Lauderdale, 1992—; bd. dirs. Ohio State U. Found., Bonnet House, Ft. Lauderdale, 1992. 1st lt. AUS, 1944-46. Decorated Bronze Star; recipient Centennial award Ohio State U., 1970, Benjamin Creativity award Assn. Am. Pubs., 1985, Career medal Ohioana Libr. Assn., 1988, Lifetime Achievment award Am. Libr. Trustees Assn., 1992. Mem. Am. Antiquarian Soc., ALA (hon. life), Am. Mgmt. Assn., Am. Assn. Mus., Detroit Hist. Soc., Am. Hist. Print Collectors Soc., Bibliog. Soc. Am., Sierra Club, Pres. Assn., Audubon Soc., Am. Name Soc., Early Am. Industries Assn., Ephemera Soc. (pres.), Johnny Appleseed Soc., Navy League, Newcomen Soc., Cen. Bus. Dist. Assn. Detroit (vice-chmn. 1985-87), Jazz Forum (Grosse Pointe Farms, Mich., pres. 1989—), Nat. Trust Hist. Preservation, Fairfield Heritage Soc., Archives Am. Art, Pvt. Librs. Assn., Friend Ft. Lauderdale Pub. Libr. (pres. 1974-78), Phileas Soc. (pres. 1985—), Ohio State U. Club (pres. Detroit club 1958, nat. chmn. Ohio State U. campaighn, 1985-88), Masons, Shriners, Book Club, Detroit Athletic Club, Lauderdale Yacht Club, Princeton Club, Salmagundi Club, Grolier Club, Century Assn., Marco Polo Club, Faculty Club Ohio State U., Old Club, Tau Kappa Epsilon. Republican. Methodist. Home: 221 Lewiston Rd Grosse Pointe MI 48236-3519 also: 1000 Riviera Dr Fort Lauderdale FL 33301-2670 also: 100 E 50th St New York NY 10022-6805 Office: Omnigraphics Inc 2500 Penobscot Bldg Detroit MI 48226 also: 901 E Las Olas Blvd Fort Lauderdale FL 33301-2320

RUFFNER, JAY STURGIS, lawyer; b. Washington, Pa., June 22, 1941; s. Hugh Lewis And Eleanore (Burchinal) R.; m. Mary Eleanor Glass, Oct. 3, 1966; children: Jay S. Jr., Megan L., Stephanie B. BA, Hobart Coll., 1963; JD, U. Pitts., 1966; LLM, NYU, 1972. Ptnr. Lewis and Roca Law Firm, Phoenix, 1972-93; mem. Meyer, Hendricks, Victor, Osborn & Maledon, Phoenix, 1993—. Bd. dirs. The Flinn Found., Phoenix, 1979—, Phoenix Art Mus., 1991—, Blood Sys., Inc., 1995—. Mem. ABA, Am. Soc. Corp. Secs. (former chmn. membership com., corp. practices com., audit com., former bd. dirs., chmn. budget com., fin com., securities industry com.), Stockholder Rels. Soc. N.Y. (past pres. and dir.). Westchester Clubmen (pres.), Phi Delta Phi, Sigma Pi Phi, Alpha Phi Alpha. Office: Meyer Hendricks Victor Osborn & Maledon 2929 N Central Ave Ste 2100 Phoenix AZ 85012

RUFLIN, PAUL LEROY, accountant, consultant; b. Canton, Ohio, Jan. 4, 1954; s. Edward and Mary (Frank) R.; m. Susan M. Steigerwald, Aug. 14, 1976; children: Justin, Michael, Paul J. BA in Acctg., Walsh Coll., 1976; MBA, Bowling Green State U., 1977. CPA, Ohio. Ptnr. Ernst & Whinney, Cleve., 1977—. Contbr. articles to profl. jours. Mem. Healthcare Fin. Mgmt. Assn., Ohio Soc. CPA's. Office: Ernst & Whinney 1300 Huntington Bldg Cleveland OH 44115

RUGABER, WALTER FEUCHT, JR., newspaper executive; b. Macon, Ga., Nov. 29, 1938; s. Walter Feucht and Edith Almeda (Maynard) R.; m. Sally Sanford, Oct. 6, 1962; children—Leslie, Christopher, Mark. B.S., Northwestern U., 1960. Corr., editor N.Y. Times, 1965-78; v.p., exec. editor Greensboro Daily News & Record, N.C., 1978-82; pres., pub. Roanoke Times & World News, Va., 1982—; mem. Pulitzer Prize Bd. Bd. dirs. United Way of Roanoke Valley, 1982-88, Roanoke Symphony Soc., 1985—, pres., 1986-88; trustee Hollins Coll. Mem. Am. Newspaper Pubs. Assn., Am. Soc. Newspaper Editors, So. Newspaper Pubs. Assn. Office: Times World Corp PO Box 2491 201-209 W Campbell Ave Roanoke VA 24010

RUGE, DANIEL AUGUST, retired neurosurgeon, educator; b. Murdock, Nebr., May 13, 1917; s. August Daniel and Mary Louise R.; m. Greta Piper, June 12, 1942; children: Charlotte, Thomas. B.A., N. Central Coll., Naperville, Ill., 1939, Sc.D., 1971; M.D., Northwestern U., 1945, Ph.D., 1961. Intern Wesley Meml. Hosp., Chgo., 1945-46; resident Wesley Meml. Hosp., 1949-50, Passavant Meml. Hosp., Chgo., 1946-49, VA Hosp., Hines, Ill., 1950-52; practice medicine specializing in neurosurgery Chgo., 1952-76; prof. surgery Northwestern U., Chgo., 1973-76; professorial lectr. George Washington U., Washington, 1976-86, ret., 1986; dep. dir. spinal cord injury service VA Central Office, Washington, 1976-80; dir. VA Central Office, 1980-81, 85-86, ret., 1986; physician to pres. U.S., White House, 1981-85. Author: Spinal Cord Injuries, 1969, Spinal Disorders: Diagnosis and Treatment, 1977; editor: Jour. Am. Paraplegia Soc., 1976-88. Trustee North Cen. Coll., 1960—, chmn. bd., 1974-77. Lt comdr. USN, 1954-56. Recipient Service award Northwestern U., 1966, Merit award Northwestern U., 1983, Outstanding Alumnus award N. Central Coll., 1978, Meritorious Service award VA, 1986. Fellow A.C.S.; mem. AMA, Am. Assn. Neurol. Surgeons, Central Surg. Assn., James IV Assn. Surgeons. Republican. Presbyterian. Home: 240 S High St Denver CO 80209-2628

RUGE, NEIL MARSHALL, retired law educator; b. Washington, Dec. 28, 1913; s. Oscar Gustave and Ruth (Jones) R.; m. Madeleine Filhol, Jan. 1942 (dec. May 1944); m. Helga Maria Kley, July 23, 1949; children: Carl, Madeleine. Student, Calif. Inst. Tech., 1931-33; A.B., Stanford U., 1935; J.D., U. Calif. at Berkeley, 1938; postgrad., Harvard U. Grad. Sch. Bus. Adminstrn., 1946-47. Bar: Calif. 1938, U.S. Supreme Ct. 1962. Practiced law in Tulare, Calif., until 1941; joined U.S. fgn. service, 1947; assigned to Palermo, Italy, 1947-49, Casablanca, 1950-55, London, 1956, Cardiff, 1956-58; security and personnel officer State Dept., 1958-62; dep. polit. officer Munich, 1962-68; 1st sec. Am. embassy Guatemala, 1968-69; prof. law Calif. State U., Chico, 1969-80. Contbr. articles to profl. jours. Served to maj. AUS, 1941-46; colonel res. Mem. Sierra Club, Phi Beta Kappa. Home: 936 Bryant Ave Chico CA 95926-2818

RUGER, WILLIAM BATTERMAN, firearms manufacturing company executive; b. Bklyn., June 21, 1916; s. Adolph and May R.; m. Mary Thompson, Aug. 26, 1938 (dec.); children: William Batterman, Carolyn Amalie Ruger Vogel, James Thompson (dec.). Student, U. N.C. Firearms design engr. U.S. Armory, Springfield, Mass., 1939-40; machine gun designer Auto Ordnance Corp., Hartford, Conn., World War II; founder, pres. Ruger

Corp. (hand tool mfrs.), Southport, Conn., 1946-48; co-founder, 1948; since pres., chmn. bd., treas. Sturm, Ruger & Co., Inc., Southport; v.p. Sporting Arms and Ammunition Inst., 1978—; past bd. dirs. Nat. Shooting Sports Found. Author, editor; patentee in field. Trustee Salisbury (Conn.) Sch., 1970-73, Naval War Coll. Found.; Buffalo Bill Hist. Ctr. Recipient Nat. Leadership award Hunting Hall of Fame, 1979; named Handgunner of Year Am. Handgunner Found., 1975. Mem. NRA (past bd. dirs.), Blue Mountain Forest Assn., Vintage Sports Car Club Am., Auburn-Cord-Duesenberg, Rolls Royce Owners Club, Rolls Royce Silver Ghost Assn., Am. Bugatti Club, Bugatti Owners' Club, Vet. Motor Club, Stutz Club, Ferrari Club Am., Campfire Club, Pequot Yacht Club, N.Y. Yacht Club, Boone and Crockett Club, Cat Cay Club, Clambake Club, Delta Kappa Epsilon. Lutheran. Office: Sturm Ruger & Co 1 Lacey Pl Southport CT 06490-1241

RUGERONI, IAN, aluminum company executive. Pres. Alcan Enterprises; pres. Can. & U.S.A. div. Alcan Aluminum Ltd., Can. & U.S.A. Office: Alcan Enterprises, 1188 Sherbrooke St W, Montreal, PQ Canada H3A 3G2

RUGGE, HENRY FERDINAND, medical products executive; b. South San Francisco, Oct. 28, 1936; s. Hugo Heinrich and Marie Mathilde (Breiholz) R.; m. Sue Callow, Dec. 29, 1967. BS in Physics, U. Calif., Berkeley, 1958, PhD in Physics, 1963. Sr. physicist Physics Internat. Co., San Leandro, 1963-68; dir. adminstrn. and fin. Arkon Sci. Labs., Berkeley, Calif., 1969-71; v.p. Norse Systems, Inc., Hayward, Calif., 1972-74; v.p. Rasor Assocs., Inc., Sunnyvale, Calif., 1974-81, v.p., gen. mgr., 1983-87, exec. v.p. fin., 1988-89, pres., chief exec. officer, 1990—; pres., CEO UltraVision, Inc., Calgary, Alta., Can., 1993—, also bd. dirs., 1993—; pres. Berlinscan, Inc., Sunnyvale, 1981-82; cons. The Rugge Group, Berkeley, 1987-90; bd. dirs. Rasor Assocs., Inc., Space Power Inc., Analatom, Inc. Patentee in area med. devices. U. Calif. scholar, 1954-58. Mem. Am. Heart Assn., Berkeley Bicycle (treas. 1983-84), Phi Beta Kappa. Avocations: bicycle racing, wine, food. Home: 46 Hiller Dr Oakland CA 94618-2302 Office: Rasor Assocs Inc 253 Humboldt Ct Sunnyvale CA 94089-1100

RUGGE, HUGO ROBERT, physicist; b. South San Francisco, Calif., Nov. 7, 1935; s. Hugo Heinrich and Marie (Breiholz) R.; m. Coral Loy Irish, Dec. 28, 1969; children—Leslie Anne, Robert David. A.B., U. Calif.-Berkeley, 1957, Ph.D., 1962. Research physicist Lawrence Berkeley Lab., 1961-62; mem. tech. staff Aerospace Corp., Los Angeles, 1962-68, dept. head, 1968-79, prin. dir., 1979-81, lab. dir., 1981-89, v.p. lab. ops., 1989-91, v.p. tech. ops., 1991—. mem. mission systems panel AGARD/NATO. Contbr. numerous articles on space sci. and astrophysics to profl. jours. Fellow Am. Phys. Soc.; mem. Am. Astron. Soc., Am. Geophys. Union, Internat. Astron. Union, Phi Beta Kappa, Sigma Xi.

RUGGERI, RICCARDO, automotive sales executive. Chmn. bd., CEO Ford New Holland (Pa.), Inc.; COO N.H. Geotech N.V., London. Office: New Holland Ford Inc 500 Diller Ave New Holland PA 17557

RUGGIERO, LAURENCE JOSEPH, museum director; b. Paterson, N.J., Mar. 25, 1948; s. Salvatore Joseph and Grace Marie (Williams) R.; m. Virginia Frances Fornaci, Mar. 7, 1970; 1 child, John Laurence. BA, U. Pa., 1969, MA, 1973, PhD, 1975; MBA, Boston U., 1978. Asst. prof. history of architecture U. Ill., Chgo., 1973-77; fin. analyst Met. Mus. Art, N.Y.C., 1978-79, asst. to pres., 1979-81; exec. dir. Oakland (Calif.) Mus. Assocs., 1981-85; dir. John and Mable Ringling Mus., Sarasota, Fla., 1985-92; assoc. dir. Charles Hosner Morse Mus. Am. Art, Winter Park, Fla., 1992—; adj. prof. Ringling Sch. Art and Design, Sarasota, 1986-92. Kress Found. fellow, 1972. Mem. Fla. Art Mus. Dirs. Assn. (treas. 1987-92), Coll. Art Assn. Am., Am. Assn. Mus., Il Cenacolo (San Francisco). Office: Charles Hosner Morse Mus Am Art 151 E Welbourne Ave Winter Park FL 32789-4337

RUGGIERO, MATTHEW JOHN, bassoonist; b. Phila., Sept. 18, 1932; s. Pompeo and Theresa (Ciampa) R.; m. Nancy Cirillo, Apr. 2, 1961; children: Eleanor, Claudia, Lisa. Diploma, Curtis Inst. Music, 1957; AA, Harvard U., 1982, BA cum laude, 1984, MA, 1987; PhD, Boston U., 1993. Second bassoonist Nat. Symphony Orch., Washington, 1957-60; asst. prin. bassoonist Boston Symphony Orch., 1961-89; prin. bassoonist Boston Pops Orch., 1974-89; ret., 1989; mem. faculty Boston U., 1963—, New Eng. Conservatory Music, 1963—. Served with U.S. Army, 1954-57. Boston U. Profs. Program scholar and fellow, 1989.

RUGGIERO, THOMAS WILLIAM, lawyer; b. Glen Cove, N.Y., Dec. 2, 1946; s. Philip P. and Virginia M. Ruggiero; m. Patricia Williams, Aug. 7, 1971; 2 children. AB in Hist., St. Michael's Coll., 1968; JD, Boston Coll., 1971. Bar: N.Y. 1972. Ptnr. LeBoeuf, Lamb, Greene and MacRae, N.Y.C., 1983—. Office: LeBoeuf Lamb Greene & MacRae 125 W 55th St New York NY 10019-4513

RUGGLES, BARBARA ANN, elementary education educator; b. Chgo., Mar. 19, 1943; d. Ernest Leonard and Nigel Marie (Roser) Hvale; 1 child, David M. BS in Edn., Kans. U., 1965; MA in Social Scis., Gov.'s State U., 1984. Tchr. Sch. Dist. 163, Park Forest, Ill.; bd. dirs. Employee's Fed. Credit Union, legis. Adv. Coun. State Ill. 80th House Dist. Mem. ASCD, Devel. Am. Women in Sci., Nat. Women's History Project, Ednl. Svc. Ctr. #7 (governing bd. mem.), Am. Fedn. Tchrs. Local 604 (v.p.), Tchrs. Fedn. Park Forest (pres.), Am. Fedn. Tchrs. Edn. Rsch. and Dissemination (local site coord.). Home: 21426 Hillside Rd Frankfort IL 60423-9195

RUGH, WILLIAM ARTHUR, diplomat; b. N.Y.C., May 10, 1936; s. Roberts and Harriette (Sheldon) R.; m. Andrea Scott Bear, July 12, 1958; children—David William, Douglas Edward, Nicholas Alexander. Student, Hamburg U., Germany, 1958-59; B.A., Oberlin Coll., 1958; M.A., Johns Hopkins U., 1961; Ph.D., Columbia U., 1967. Near East policy dir. USIA, Washington, 1971-72, dep. asst. dir., 1973-76; pub. affairs counsellor U.S. Embassy, Cairo, 1976-81; dep. chief of mission U.S. Embassy, Damascus, Syria, 1981-84; amb. U.S. Embassy, Sanaa, Yemen, 1984-87; diplomat in residence Fletcher Sch. Tufts U., Medford, Mass., 1987-89; dir. Near East, North Africa, South Asia divs. USIA, Washington, 1989-92; U.S. amb. to United Arab Emirates, Abu Dhabi, 1992—. Author: Riyadh, a History, 1969; The Arab Press; 1979, 87; also contbr. articles and chpts. to books. Coun. on Fgn. Rels. fellow, 1972-73; recipient Presdl. award U.S. Pres., 1983. Mem. Middle East Inst., Middle East Studies Assn. Home: 10113 Montrose Ave Garrett Park MD 20896-0315 Office: Am Embassy Abu Dhabi Dept State Washington DC 20521-6010

RUGH, WILSON JOHN, II, electrical engineering educator; b. Tarentum, Pa., Jan. 16, 1941; s. Wilson John and Florence (Saul) R.; m. Theresa M. Winter, June 26, 1976; children: David, Karen. B.S., Pa. State U., 1965; M.S., Northwestern U., 1967, Ph.D., 1969. Asst. prof. Johns Hopkins U., Balt., 1969-74, assoc. prof., 1974-79, prof. elec. engring., 1979—, chmn. dept. elec. engring. and computer sci., 1980-83. Author: Mathematical Description of Linear Systems, 1975, Nonlinear System Theory, 1981; contbr. articles to profl. jours. Mem. IEEE, Soc. Indsl. and Applied Math. Home: 3906 Juniper Rd Baltimore MD 21218-1850 Office: Charles and 34th Sts Johns Hopkins U Baltimore MD 21218

RUHFUS, JÜRGEN, ambassador; b. Bochum, Fed. Republic of Germany, Aug. 4, 1930; s. Heinz and Grete (Rose) R.; m. Karin Engel, 1958; children: Andrea, Maren, Antje. Student, U. Munich, U. Denver; PhD in Law, U. Münster, Fed. Republic of Germany, 1965. Entered Fgn. Service, Bonn, Fed. Republic of Germany, 1955-57; assigned to consulates Geneva, Dakar, Senegal, Athens, Greece, 1957-63; from dep. spokesman to spokesman Fgn. Service, Bonn, 1964-70; ambassador to Kenya Nairobi, 1970-73; head UN directorate Fgn. Service, Bonn, 1973-74, head polit. directorate for W. Hemisphere, 1974-75; advisor on fgn. affairs and security matters Fed. Chancellery, Bonn, 1976-79; ambassador to U.K. and No. Ireland London, 1980-83; head of polit. directorate-gen. for third world countries Fgn. Service, Bonn, 1983-84, state sec., 1984-87; ambassador to U.S. Washington, 1987—. Fulbright scholar U. Denver, 1952-53. Home: 2500 Foxhall Rd NW Washington DC 20007-1123 Office: German Embassy 4645 Reservoir Rd NW Washington DC 20007-1998

RUHLMAN, TERRELL LOUIS, business executive; b. Warren, Pa., Nov. 13, 1926; s. Ross L. and Gertrude R.; m. Phyllis E., Jan. 15, 1951; chil-

dren—Robyn Ruhlman Dempsey, Randall L., Heather Ruhlman Martin, Mark A. BS, Pa. State U., 1949; JD, George Washington U., 1954; postgrad., Duquesne U. Grad. Bus. Sch., 1966-68. Bar: D.C. bar. Patent counsel Joy Mfg. Co., Pitts., 1954-59; gen. counsel Joy Mfg. Co., 1959-62, asst. to pres., 1962-69; v.p. oilfield ops. Joy Mfg. Co., Houston, 1969-73; gen. mgr. Reed Tool Co., Houston, 1973-74; pres., chief operating officer Reed Tool Co., 1974-76, dir., 1975-76; v.p., dir. Baker Internat. Corp., 1975-76, pres. mining group, 1976; pres., chief exec. officer, dir. Ansul Co., Marinette, Wis., 1976-80; pres. Wormald Americas, Inc., Scottsdale, Ariz., 1980-88; chmn., chief exec. officer Cade Industries, Inc., Scottsdale, 1988—, also bd. dirs.; bd. dirs. Environ. Engring. Concepts Inc. With USAF. Served with USAF. Home: 9710 E La Posada Cir Scottsdale AZ 85255-3716 Office: # 114 8711 E Pinnacle Peak Rd Scottsdale AZ 85255

RUHRUP, CLIFTON BROWN, sales executive; b. Jacksonville, Fla., Nov. 9, 1916; s. Ernest Alfred and Elizabeth L. (Garrett) R. Student, U. Okla., 1934-35, Oklahoma City U., 1946-48; cert. sales mgmt., U. Okla., 1962. From intern trainee to asst. sales mgr. Dolese Bros. Co., Oklahoma City, 1950-54, gen. sales mgr. aggregate div., 1955-61, gen. sales mgr. aggregate and prestress div., 1966—, asst. sec., 1971—. Chmn. bd. dirs. Cen. YMCA, Oklahoma City, 1973-78, named Outstanding Vol. of Yr., 1978, fellow mem., 1978—; bd. dirs. Better Bus. Bur., 1992—; mem. assoc. bd. Associated Bd. Contractors Okla. S/Sgt. USAAF, 1943-46, PTO. Mem. Oklahoma City C. of C., Toastmasters (pres. 1968), Rotary (editor newspaper 1972-76, contbg. editor 1988—, Paul Harris fellow), Phi Eta Sigma. Republican. Mem. First Christian Ch. Avocations: photography, fishing, travel, real estate. Office: Dolese Bros Co 20 NW 13th St Oklahoma City OK 73103-4806

RUIBAL, CHARLES ADRIAN, chemical company executive; b. Habana, Cuba, Mar. 5, 1947; came to U.S., 1961; s. Evelino Arsenio and Maria Gloria (de Puzo) R.; m. Geraldine Catherine McNabb, Aug. 31, 1968; children: Gloria Lynne, Michael Charles. BSChemE, Villanova U., 1968. With Am. Cyanamid Co., 1968—; process engr. indsl. chems. div. Am. Cyanamid Co., Linden, N.J., 1968-69; tech. sales rep. paper chems. dept. Am. Cyanamid Co., Pittsfield, Mass., 1969-72, Montgomery, Ala., 1972-74; asst. to mktg. mgr. paper chems. dept. Am. Cyanamid Co., Wayne, N.J., 1974-75; dist. sales mgr. paper chems. dept. Am. Cyanamid Co., Ft. Washington, Pa., 1975-77; nat. sales mgr. paper chems. dept. Am. Cyanamid Co., Wayne, N.J., 1977-78, mktg. mgr. paper chems. dept., 1978-80, mktg. mgr. water treating chems. dept., 1980-81, dept. mgr. specialty polymers dept., 1981-83, dept. mgr. crop protection chems. dept., 1983-84, v.p. agrl. div., 1984, pres. indsl. products div., 1984-89, pres. indsl. and performance products div., 1990-92; group v.p. Cytec Industries (bus. unit of Am. Cyanamid Co.), West Paterson, N.J., 1992-93; exec. v.p. Cytec Industries Inc., West Paterson, 1994—; bd. dirs. Am. Indsl. Health Coun., 1987-92, vice chmn. bd. dirs., 1990, chmn., 1991; bd. dirs. Mitsui Cyanamid, Ltd. Chmn. bd. dirs. United Way Passaic Valley; bd. dirs. N.C. State U. Pulp and Paper Found. Mem. Soc. Chem. Industry, Paper Industry Mgmt. Assn. Republican. Roman Catholic. Office: Cytec Industries Inc 5 Garret Mountain Plz West Paterson NJ 07424-3360

RUINA, JACK PHILIP, electrical engineer, educator; b. Rypin, Poland, Aug. 19, 1923; came to U.S., 1927; naturalized, 1932; s. Michael and Nechuma (Warshaw) R.; m. Edith Elster, Oct. 26, 1947; children: Ellen, Andrew, Rachel. BEE, CCNY, 1944; MEE, Poly. Inst. Bklyn., 1949, DEE, 1951. Rsch. fellow Microwave Rsch. Inst., Poly. Inst. Bklyn., 1948-50; from instr. to assoc. prof. elec. engring. Brown U., 1950-54; rsch. assoc. prof. coordinated sci. lab. U. Ill., 1954-59, rsch. prof., prof. elec. engring., 1959-63; prof. elec. engring. MIT, 1963—, v.p. for spl. labs., 1966-70; U.S. observer Antarctica, 1964; on leave to U.S. Govt., 1959-63, pres. Inst. Def. Analysis, 1964-66; dep. for rsch. to asst. sec. air force, 1959-60; asst. dir. for def. rsch. and engring. Office Sec. Def., 1960-61; dir. Advanced Rsch. Projects Agy., Dept. Def., 1961-63; mem. panel Presdl. Sci. Adv. Commn., 1963-72, sci. adv. bd. USAF, 1964-67, adv. bd. and panels for Dept. Def., HEW, Dept. Transp., ACDA, Office Tech. Assessment, NSF, NSC, 1963—; mem. gen. advisory com. ACDA, 1969-74; sr. cons. Office Sci. and Tech. Policy, The White House, 1977-80; chmn. com. on environ. decision making NAS, 1974-77; bd. dirs. Mitre Corp., Gen. Rsch. Corp. Recipient Fleming award, 1962, Disting. Alumnus award Poly. Inst. Bklyn., 1970, One Hundred and Twenty Fifth Anniversary medal CCNY, 1973. Fellow IEEE, AAAS, Am. Acad. Arts and Scis.; mem. Inst. Strategic Studies, Coun. on Fgn. Rels., Internat. Sci. Radio Union, Sigma Xi. Home: 130 Mt Auburn St Apt 409 Cambridge MA 02138 Office: MIT Dept Elec Engring 292 Main St Cambridge MA 02139

RUIZ, JOSE RAFAEL, podiatric surgeon; b. Santurce, P.R., Jan. 15, 1965; s. Jose A. and Elzira (Cabre) R.; m. Irene E. Diaz, Dec. 14, 1985. BS in Gen. Scis., U. P.R., Rio Piedras, 1988; D Podiatric Medicine, Pa. Coll. Podiatric Medicine, 1994. Resident foot and ankle surgery Springfield (Pa.) Hosp., 1994—; rsch. asst. Dr. R.A. Christman, Phila., 1992—; extern USPHS-GWLHDC, Carville, La., 1994. Capt. USAR, 1988—. Mem. Am. Podiatric Med. Assn. IEEE; Soc. Indsl. and Applied Math. (William J. Stickel Silver award 1993). Avocations: jogging, golf, antiques. Office: Springfield Hosp Dept Podiatric Surgery 190 W Sproul Rd Springfield PA 19064-2027

RUIZ, OTHON, financial executive; b. Monterrey, Mexico, July 25, 1943; s. Othon and Clara (Montemayor) R.; m. Elizabeth Najera, May 3, 1969; children: Othon, Maria Fernanda, Eugenia. BA in Adminstrn., Inst. Tech. Estudios Superiore de Monterrey, 1965. Auditor Visa Group, Monterrey, 1965-68, asst. to pres., 1968-74, fin. dir., 1974-85, chief operating officer, 1985—; fin. dir. Inst. Tech. de Monterrey, Hosp. San Jose, 1977. Pres. Charolais Herd Book Assn., Monterrey, Centro Ecuestre Dan Pedro, Monterrey, 1988; sec. bd. dirs. Simmental Assn., Monterrey, Union Ganadera de Nuevo Leon, Monterrey. Mem. Inst. Mexicano Ejectivos de Finanzas, Inst. de Contadores Publicos de Nuevo Leon, Club de Cazadores Mty., Club Cinegetico Monterrey, Casino Monterrey, Club Campestre Monterrey, Monterrey C. of C. (bd. dirs. 1979-80), Chamber of Industry (pres. 1989-91). Roman Catholic. Avocations: horseback riding, golf, hunting. Office: Grupo Visa SA de CV, Ave Alfonso Reyes 2202 Nte, 64000 Monterrey Mexico

RUIZ, RAMON EDUARDO, history educator; b. La Jolla, Calif., Sept. 9, 1921; s. Ramon and Dolores (Urueta) R.; m. Natalia Marrujo, Oct. 14, 1944; children—Olivia, Maura. B.A., San Diego State Coll., 1947; M.A., Claremont Grad. Sch., 1948; Ph.D., U. Calif.-Berkeley, 1954. Asst. prof. U. Oreg., Eugene, 1955-57; So. Meth. U., Dallas, 1957-58; prof. Smith Coll., Northampton, Mass., 1958-69; prof. Lat. Am. history U. Calif. at San Diego, 1969-91; prof. emeritus, 1991—; chmn. dept. history U. Calif. at San Diego, 1971-76, div. humanities, 1972-74; mem. project grant com. NEH, 1972-73, 75-77, dir. public programs div., 1979-80; vis. prof. Facultad de Economia, Univ. de Nuevo Leon, Mexico, 1965-66, Coll. de Sonora, Mexico, summer 1983, Pomona Coll., 1983-84, Coll. de Michoacan, Mexico, summer 1986, 87, Univ. Nacional Autonoma de Mexico, fall 1992; scholar-in-residence Colegio de la Frontero Norte, Mexico, 1994—; mem. project grant com. Ford Found. Author: Cuba: The Making of A Revolution, 1968 (One of Best History Books, Book World of Washington Post 1968), Mexico: The Challenge of Poverty and Illiteracy, 1963, An American in Maximillians's Mexico, 1865-1866, 1959, (with James D. Atwater) Out From Under; Benito Juarez and Mexico's Struggle for Independence, 1969, (with John Tebbel) South by Southwest; The Mexican-American and his Heritage, 1969, Interpreting Latin American History, 1970, Labor and the Ambivalent Revolutionaries: Mexico, 1911-23, 1975, The Mexican War: Was It Manifest Destiny?, 1963, The Great Rebellion: Mexico, 1905-1924, 1980 (Hubert C. Herring prize), The People of Sonora and Yanqui Capitalists, 1988, Triumphs and Tragedy: A History of the Mexican People, 1992 (named One of Five Best History Books 1991-92, L.A. Times, Gold Medal award Commonwealth Club San Francisco 1993). Served to lt. USAAF, 1943-46. William Harrison Mills traveling fellow in internat. relations, 1950; John Hay Whitney Found. fellow, 1950; Fulbright fellow Mex., 1965-66; fellow Ctr. for Advanced Study in Behavioral Scis., 1984-85, Ena H. Thompson lectureship, Pomona Coll., 1959; recipient Am. Philos. Soc. grant in aid, 1959. Mem. Am. Hist. Assn., Conf. Latin Am. History, Chicano-Latino Faculty Assn. U. Calif. (pres. 1989-91), Phi Beta Kappa, Sigma Delta Pi. Home: PO Box 1775 Rancho Santa Fe CA 92067-1775 Office: Univ Calif San Diego Dept History La Jolla CA 92093

RUIZ, VANESSA, lawyer; b. San Jaun, PR, Mar. 22, 1950; D. Fernando and Irma (Bosch) Ruiz-Suria; m. Eduardo Elejalde, Feb. 11, 1972 (div. Jan. 1982); children: Natalia, Alexia; m. David E. Birenbaum, Oct. 22, 1983; stepchildren: Tracy, Matthew. BA, Wellesley Coll., 1972; JD, Georgetown U., 1975. Bar: D.C. 1972, U.S. Supreme Ct. 1981. Assoc. Fried, Frank, Harris, Shrives & Kampelman, Washington, 1975-83; sr. mgr., counsel Sears World Trade Inc., Washington, 1983—; speaker in field. Mem. ABA, Inter-Am. Bar Assn. Office: Sears World Trade Inc 633 Pennsylvania Ave NW Washington DC 20004-2605 also: Pepper Hamilton & Scheetz 1300 19th St NW Washington DC 20036

RUIZ, VICKI LYNN, history educator; b. Atlanta, May 21, 1955; d. Robert Paul and Erminia Pablita (Ruiz) Mercer; m. Jerry Joseph Ruiz, Sept. 1, 1979 (div. Jan. 1990); children: Miguel, Daniel; m. Victor Becerra, Aug. 14, 1992. AS in Social Studies, Gulf Coast Community Coll., 1975; BA in Social Sci., Fla. State, 1977; MA in History, Stanford U., 1978, PhD in History, 1982. Asst. prof. U. Tex., El Paso, 1982-85; asst. prof. U. Calif., Davis, 1985-87, assoc. prof., 1987-92; Andrew W. Mellon prof. Claremont (Calif.) Grad. Sch., 1992-95, chmn. history dept., 1993-95; prof. Ariz. State U., Tempe, 1995—; dir. Inst. of Oral History, U. Tex., El Paso 1983-85, minority undergrad. rsch. program U. Calif., Davis, 1988—. Author: Cannery Women, Cannery Lives, 1987; co-editor: Women on U.S.-Mexican Border, 1988, Unequal Sisters, 1990, 2d edit., 1994. Mem. Calif. Coun. for Humanities, 1990-94, vice chmn., 1991-93. Fellow Univ. Calif. Davis Humanities Inst., 1990-91, Am. Coun. of Learned Socs., 1986, Danforth Found., 1977. Mem. Orgn. Am. Historians (chmn. com. on status of minority history 1989-91, nominating com. 1987-88, exec. bd. 1995—), Immigration History Soc. (exec. bd. 1989-91), Am. States Assn. (nominating bd. 1992-94), Phi Beta Kappa. Democrat. Roman Catholic. Avocations: walking, needlework. Office: Ariz State U Women's Studies Tempe AZ 85287

RUIZ-DE-CONDE, JUSTINA, retired foreign language educator; b. Madrid, Spain, Nov. 30, 1909; came to U.S., 1939, naturalized, 1945; d. Andres Ruiz de la Peña and Prudencia Malaxechevarria. Bachiller, Inst. Cardenal Cisneros, Madrid, 1926; Licenciada en Derecho, Univ. Central, Madrid, 1931; M.A., Radcliffe Coll., 1943, Ph.D. 1945. Tchr. Inst. Nacional de Segunda Ensenañza, Valdepeñas, Madrid and Barcelona, 1933-38; practice law Madrid, 1931-38; instr. Abbott Acad., Andover, Mass., also Middlebury (Vt.) Coll., summers 1939-41; mem. faculty Wellesley Coll., 1941-75, prof. Spanish, 1958-75, Helen J. Sanborn prof., 1973-75, emeritus, 1975—, chmn. dept., 1946-52, 54-58, 61-62, 64-69. Author: El Amor y el Matrimonio Secreto en los Libros de Caballerias, 1948, Un Pueblo Mexicano, 1949, Antonio Machado y Guiomar, 1964, El cantico americano de Jorge Guillén, 1973; editor: (with Ada M. Coe) Estudios Hispánicos, Homenaje a Archer M. Huntigton, 1952, (with others) Homenaje a Jorge Guillén, 1978, Academic Women in Retirement, 1987. Mem. New Eng. Assn. Tchrs. Spanish and Portuguese (sec. 1956-57), MLA (group sec. 1949-51), AAUW, Phi Beta Kappa; corr. mem. Hispanic Soc. Home: 85 Grove St Apt 310 Wellesley MA 02181-7843

RUKEYSER, LOUIS RICHARD, economic commentator; b. N.Y.C., Jan. 30, 1933; s. Merryle Stanley and Berenice Helene (Simon) R.; m. Alexandra Gill, Mar. 3, 1962; children: Beverley Jane, Susan Athena, Stacy Alexandra. AB, Princeton U., 1954; LittD (hon.), N.H. Coll., 1975; LLD (hon.), Moravian Coll., 1978, Mercy Coll., 1984, Am. U., 1991; DBA (hon.), Southeastern Mass. U., 1979; LHD (hon.), Loyola Coll., 1982, Johns Hopkins U., 1986, Western Md. Coll., 1992. Reporter Balt. Sun newspapers, 1954-65; chief polit. corr. Evening Sun, 1957-59; chief London bur. The Sun, 1959-63, chief Asian corr., 1963-65; sr. corr., commentator ABC News, 1965-73, Paris corr., 1965-66, chief London bur., 1966-68, econ. editor, commentator, 1968-73; host Wall St. Week With Louis Rukeyser PBS-TV, 1970—; nationally syndicated econ. columnist McNaught Syndicate, 1976-86, Tribune Media Services, 1986-93; frequent lectr. Author: How to Make Money in Wall Street, 1974, 2d edit., 1976 (Literary Guild selection 1974, 76), What's Ahead for the Economy: The Challenge and the Chance, 1983, 2d edit., 1985 (Literary Guild selection 1984), Louis Rukeyser's Business Almanac, 1988, 2d edit., 1991; editor-in-chief monthly newsletters, Louis Rukeyser's Wall Street, 1992—, Louis Rukeyser's Mutual Funds, 1994—. With U.S. Army, 1954-56. Recipient Overseas Press Club award, 1963, Overseas Press Club citation, 1964, G.M. Loeb award U. Conn., 1972, Janus award for excellence in fin. news programming, 1975, George Washington Honor medal Freedoms Found., 1972, 78, N.Y. Fin. Writers Assn. award, 1980, Free Enterprise Man of the Yr. award Tex. A&M U. Ctr. for Edn. and Research in Free Enterprise, 1987, Women's Econ. Round Table award, 1990. Office: 586 Round Hill Rd Greenwich CT 06831-2724

RUKEYSER, M. S., JR., television consultant, writer; b. N.Y.C., Apr. 15, 1931; s. Merryle Stanley and Berenice (Simon) R.; m. Phyllis L. Kasha, May 16, 1975; children: Jill Victoria, Patricia Bern. Student, U. Va., 1948-52. Reporter Albany (N.Y.) Times-Union, 1949, Internat. News Service, N.Y.C., 1951; TV publicist Young & Rubicam, Inc., N.Y.C., 1952-57; with NBC, 1958-80, 81-88; dir. news info. NBC, Washington, 1962; v.p. press and publicity NBC, N.Y.C., 1963-72; v.p. corp. info. NBC, 1972-74, v.p. pub. info., 1974-77, exec. v.p. pub. info., 1977-80, 81-84, exec. v.p. corp. communications, 1984-88; v.p. comm. Newsweek Inc., 1980-81; sr. v.p. GTE Entertainment, N.Y.C., 1988-90; pres. Rukeyser Communications, N.Y.C., 1990—; sr. fellow Freedom Forum Media Ctr., 1991-92. Author: (with Grant Tinker) Tinker in Television: From General Sarnoff to General Electric, 1994. Mem. adv. coun. Ctr. for Media in the Pub. Interest. Served with U.S. Army, 1953-54. Home and Office: 2434 NW 59th St # 1404 Boca Raton FL 33496 also: RR 1 Box 1036 Waymart PA 18472

RUKEYSER, ROBERT JAMES, manufacturing executive; b. New Rochelle, N.Y., June 26, 1942; s. Merryle Stanley and Berenice Helene (Simon) R.; m. Leah A. Spiro, July 26, 1964; children: David Bern, Peter Lloyd. BA, Cornell U., 1964; MBA with distinction, N.Y.U., 1969. Mgr. services analyst Dun & Bradstreet, N.Y.C., 1964-65; bond analyst Standard & Poors, N.Y.C., 1965-66; mktg. rep. data processing div. IBM, N.Y.C., 1967-72, regional mktg. staff, 1973-74, mktg. mgr., 1974-76; corp. mgr. internal communications IBM, Armonk, N.Y., 1976-79; mgr. communication ops. IBM, Franklin Lakes, N.J., 1979-81; pub. affairs dir., asst. to chmn. Am. Brands Inc., N.Y.C., 1981-83, v.p. pub. affairs, asst. to chmn., 1983-85; v.p. office products Am. Brands, Inc., Old Greenwich, Conn., 1986-87, v.p. ops., 1987-89, sr. v.p. corp. affairs, 1990—; bd. dirs. Am. Brands Internat. Co., Jim Beam Brands Co., Am. Franklin Co., Acushnet co., MasterBrand Industries, Acco World Corp. Mem. communications com. Boy Scouts Am., 1982-86; personal solicitation chair Cornell U., 1985-87; bd. dirs., mem. fin. and devel. com. The Hole in the Wall Gang Camp.; bd. dirs. Stamford Ctr. for Arts. Mem. Nat. Office Products Assn. Office: Am Brands Inc 1700 E Putnam Ave Old Greenwich CT 06870-1300

RUKEYSER, WILLIAM SIMON, journalist, business executive; b. N.Y.C., June 8, 1939; s. Merryle Stanley and Berenice (Simon) R.; m. Elisabeth Mary Garnett, Nov. 21, 1963; children: Lisa Rukeyser Burn, James William. A.B., Princeton U., 1961; student, Christ's Coll., Cambridge (Eng.) U., 1962-63. Copyreader Wall St. Jour., 1961-62; staff reporter Wall St. Jour., Europe, 1963-67; assoc. editor Fortune mag., 1967-71, mem. bd. editors, 1971-72; mng. editor Money mag., N.Y.C. 1972-80, Fortune mag., 1980-86; dir. internat. bus. devel. Time Inc., 1986-88; editor in chief, exec. v.p. Whittle Communications, Knoxville, Tenn., 1988-91; chmn., chief exec. officer Whittle Books, Knoxville, 1991-94; CEO Uptime Interactive, Inc., 1995—; commentator Good Morning America, ABC-TV, 1978-85, CBS Radio Stas. News Service, 1979-86; bd. dirs. Computational Svcs., Inc. Mem. jud. com. Union County (N.J.) Med. Soc., 1977-80; co-chair capital campaign Nat. Mental Health Assn., 1984-85; dir., mem. exec. com. Knoxville Mus. Art, Knoxville Symphony Orch.; mem. liaison com. U. Tenn. Med. Ctr.; mem. adv. coun. U. Tenn. Coll. Bus. Adminstrn.; dir. Bijou Theatre Ctr. Knoxville; v.p. East Tenn. Hist. Soc. Home: 1509 Rudder Ln Knoxville TN 37919

RULAND, MIDLRED ARDELIA, retail executive, retail buyer; b. Draketown, Ga., Aug. 11, 1918; m. Harry Morse Ruland, Aug. 19, 1947; children: Hal Morse, Judy Lee Ruland Rigas. BS, West Ga. Coll., 1966. Elem. tchr. New London, Conn., 1947-48, Atlanta, 1948-51, Rome, Ga., 1951-81; mgr. McBrayer Bros. Furniture Co., Rome, 1981—. Rosenwald

Found. scholar, 1941-42. Mem. NEA, Nat. Fedn. Ind. Bus. (corr. sec. 1975—), Ga. Edn. Assn. (del. 1964-74), Ga. Home Furnishings Assn., Twickham Garden Club, Rome Pride Assn., Rome C. of C., Alfa Delta Kappa. Republican. Baptist. Avocations: dancing, swimming, bowling, hiking, singing.

RULAND, RICHARD EUGENE, English and American literature educator, critic, literary historian; b. Detroit, May 1, 1932; s. Eugene John and Irene (Janette) R.; m. Mary Ann Monaghan; children: Joseph, Michael, Paul, Susan; m. Birgit Noll. BA, Assumption Coll. U. Western Ont., Can., 1953; MA, U. Detroit, 1955; PhD, U. Mich., 1960. Instr., then asst. prof. English and Am. studies Yale U., New Haven, 1960-67, Morse rsch. fellow, 1966-67; prof. English and Am. lit. Washington U., St. Louis, 1967—, chmn. dept. English, 1969-74; chmn. comparative lit. program, 1993-94; vis. Bruern prof. Am. lit. Leeds (Eng.) U., 1964-65; vis. Fulbright prof. U. Groningen, The Netherlands, 1975, Sch. of English and Am. Studies U. East Anglia, Eng., 1978-79; vis. disting. prof. Am. lit. Coll. of William and Mary, 1980-81. Author: The Rediscovery of American Literature: Premises of Critical Taste, 1900-1940, 1967, America in Modern European Literature: From Image to Metaphor, 1976, (with Malcolm Bradbury) From Puritanism to Postmodernism: A History of American Literature, 1991 (paperback, 1992); editor: Walden: A Collection of Critical Essays, 1967, The Native Muse: Theories of American Literature, Vol. I, 1972, 76, A Storied Land: Theories of American Literature, Vol. II, 1976; contbr. articles to jours. in field. Guggenheim Rsch. fellow, 1982-83. Mem. Assn. Depts. English (pres. 1974). Avocation: jazz musician. Office: Washington U Dept English Saint Louis MO 63130

RULAU, RUSSELL, numismatic consultant; b. Chgo., Sept. 21, 1926; s. Alphonse and Ruth (Thorsen) R.; student U. Wis., 1946-48; m. Hazel Darlene Grizzell, Feb. 1, 1968; children by previous marriage: Lance Eric, Carla Rae, Russell A.W., Marsha June, Scott Quentin, Roberta Ann, Kyle Christopher, Yvonne Marie; 1 step-dau., Sharon Maria Kenowski. With U.S. Army, 1944-1950, master sgt. USAF, 1950-62; resigned active duty, 1962; asst. editor Coin World newspaper, Sidney, Ohio, 1962-74, editor World Coins mag., 1964-74, Numis. Scrapbook mag., 1968-74; editorial coordinator How to Order Fgn. Coins guidebook, 1966-74; editor in chief World Coin News newspaper, 1974-84, Bank Note Reporter, 1983-84; fgn. editor Numis. News newspaper, 1974-77; cons. editor Standard Catalog of World Paper Money, 1975-83; contbg. editor Standard Catalog of World Coins, 1974-81; pres. House of Rulau, 1984—, Alpha Enterprises Inc., 1989—; v.p. Keogh-Rulau Galleries, Dallas, 1984-85, Pobjoy Mint Ltd., Iola, Wis., 1985-94; U.S. agent Christie's Pty. Ltd., 1992-95. Recipient Clemy Literary award 1993, Smedley Lifetime Achievement award, 1994. Mem. U.S. Assay Commn., 1973. Sec., Numismatic Terms Standardization Com., 1966-74; vice-chmn. Waupaca County Republican party, 1977-79, 1988-89, chmn., 1979-82; chmn. county chairmen, 3d vice chmn. Wis. Rep. Party, 1981-83; del. Rep. Nat. Conv., 1980; exec. com. 6th Wis. Dist. Rep. Com., 1984-87 . Fellow Royal Numis. Soc., Am. Numis. Soc. (asso.); mem. Token and Medal Soc. (editor 1962-63), Am. Numis. Assn. Medal of Merit 1994), Canadian, S. African numis. assns., Mont. Hist. Soc., Am. Vecturist Assn., Numis. Lit. Guild (dir. 1974-78, editor 1984-86), VFW (post commdr. 1985-89), Am. Legion. Lutheran. Author: (with George Fuld) Spiel Marken, 1962-65, American Game Counters, 1972: World Mint Marks, 1966; Modern World Mint Marks, 1970; (with J. U. Rixen and Frovin Sieg) Seddelkatalog Slesvig Plebiscit Zone I og II, 1970; Numismatics of Old Alabama, 1971-73; Hard Times Tokens, 1980; Early American Tokens, 1981; U.S. Merchant Tokens 1845-1860, 1982; U.S. Trade Tokens 1866-1889, 1983, Tokens of the Gay Nineties, 1987, Discovering America: The Coin Collecting Connection, 1989, Latin American Tokens, 1992; (with George Fuld) Medallic Portraits of Washington, 1985, Standard Catalog of U.S. Tokens 1700-1900, 1994; contbr. numis. articles to profl. jours. Home: N7747 County J Iola WI 54945 Office: Pobjoy Mint USA Ltd PO Box 153 Iola WI 54945-0153

RULE, CHARLES FREDERICK (RICK RULE), lawyer; b. Nashville, Apr. 28, 1955; s. Frederick Charles and Mary Elizabeth (Malone) R.; m. Ellen Friedland, May 13, 1976. BA, Vanderbilt U., 1978; JD, U. Chgo., 1981. Bar: U.S. Ct. Appeals. (D.C. cir.) 1983. Law clk. U.S. Ct. Appeals (fed. cir.), Washington, 1981-82; spl. asst. to asst. atty. gen. Antitrust div. Dept. Justice, Washington, 1982-83, dep. asst. atty. gen. policy planning, 1984-85, acting asst. atty. gen., then dep. asst. atty. gen. regulatory affairs, 1985-86, asst. atty. gen., 1986-89; ptnr. Covington & Burling, Washington, 1989—; legal, econ. analyst Lexecon, Inc., Chgo., 1979-80. Mem. Bar of D.C. Ct. Appeals, Phi Beta Kappa, Phi Eta Sigma. Republican. Presbyterian. Office: Covington & Burling PO Box 7566 Rm 915B 1200 Pennsylvania Ave NW Washington DC 20004-2411

RULE, DANIEL RHODES, opera company executive; b. L.A., Aug. 25, 1940; s. Rhodes Elmore and Maud Justice (Edwards) R. BA, Occidental Coll., 1962. Asst. music adminstr. N.Y.C. Opera, 1965-70, assoc. mng. dir., 1970-79, mng. dir., 1980-83; gen. mgr. Central City Opera, Denver, 1984—; cons. Ohio State Arts Coun., Columbus, 1984, 86. Bd. dirs. Colo. Children's Chorale, Denver, Colo. Lawyers for Arts. Ford Found. fellow, N.Y., 1966-68. Mem. Am. Guild Mus. Artists (employer chmn. pension and health fund), Denver Athletic Club. Republican. Mem. Christian Ch. (Disciples of Christ). Avocations: travel, violin. Office: Central City Opera House Assn 621 17th St Ste 1601 Denver CO 80293-1601*

RULE, DONALD, research physicist. Rsch. scientist Naval Surface Warfare Ctr., Silver Spring, Md. Recipient Faraday Cup Bergoz, Inc., 1993. Office: Naval Surface Warfare Ctr 10901 New Hampshire Ave Silver Spring MD 20903-5000*

RULE, JOHN CORWIN, history educator; b. Evanston, Ill., Mar. 2, 1929; s. Corwin V. and Elaine (Simons) R. A.B., Stanford U., 1951, M.A., 1952; M.A., Harvard U., 1955, Ph.D., 1958. Tutor and fellow Harvard U., Cambridge, Mass., 1956-58; instr. Northeastern U., Boston, 1955-56; from instr. to prof. history Ohio State U., Columbus, 1958—; vis. asst. prof. Western Res. U., Cleve., 1961; vis. prof. Johns Hopkins U., Balt., 1968. Editor and contbg. author: Louis XIV and the Craft of Kingship, 1970; editor: Louis XIV, 1974, Letters from the Hague and Utrecht, 1711-1712, 1979, The Reign of Louis XIV, 1990. Folger Shakespeare Library fellow, 1968, 1970; Huntington Library fellow, 1978; Am. Council Learned Socs. fellow, 1981. Fellow Royal Hist. Soc. (London); mem. Soc. for French Hist. Studies (sec. 1963-70, assoc. editor jour. 1975-86, co-pres. 1989-91), Signet Soc., Crichton Club. Democrat. Home: 118 E Beck St Columbus OH 43206-1110 Office: Dept History Ohio State U 230 W 17th Ave Columbus OH 43210-1367

RULIFSON, JOHNS FREDERICK, computer company executive, computer scientist; b. Bellefontaine, Ohio, Aug. 20, 1941; s. Erwin Charles and Virginia Helen (Johns) R.; m. Janet Irving, June 8, 1963; children: Eric Johns, Ingrid Catharine. BS in Math., U. Wash., 1966; PhD in Computer Sci., Stanford U., 1973. Mathematician SRI, Internat., Menlo Park, Calif., 1966-73; scientist Xerox Rsch., Palo Alto, Calif., 1973-80; mgr. ROLM, Santa Clara, Calif., 1980-85; scientist Syntelligence, Sunnyvale, Calif., 1985-87; exec. Sun Microsystems, Mountain View, Calif., 1987—. Fellow Assn. for Computing Machinery (System Software award 1990); mem. IEEE. Avocation: photography. Home: 3785 El Centro Ave Palo Alto CA 94306-2642 Office: Sun Microsystems 2550 Garcia Ave Mountain View CA 94043

RULIS, RAYMOND JOSEPH, manufacturing company executive, consultant; b. New Britain, Conn., June 2, 1924; s. James Alexander and Eva (Ragauskas) R.; m. Thelma Pelchat, June 16, 1949; children: Elaine, Jeffery, Catherine, Elizabeth, Amy, Daniel, Jean. BSME, U. Conn., 1949; postgrad., U. Conn., Ohio State U. Northeastern U., 1949-58; student, Fed. Exec. Inst., Charlottesville, Va., 1976. Devel. engr. Hamilton Standard, U.T.C., Windsorlocks, Conn., 1951-55; mgr. fuel controls Lycoming Textron, Stratford, Conn., 1955-59; mgr. controls and accessories GE, Lynn, Mass., 1959-62; successively program mgr. sert spacecraft, chief spacecraft engr., chief launch vehicle engr., chief engring design, program mgr. QCSEE program NASA Lewis Rsch. Ctr., Cleve., 1962-81; v.p. rsch. and devel. Textron Turbocomponents Group, Walled Lake, Mich., 1981-92; cons., 1992—; cons. Joint FAA/NASA Civil Aero Rsch. Document Study, 1972, Cruise Missile PRogram, 1977-78, C-17 Aircraft Source Selection Bd., 1978, Tri-Svcs. Propulsion Group, 1976-78; chmn. Conf. on Short Haul Systems, NASA, 1976; mem. exec. coun. Aerospace Industries Tech. Coun., 1988-89.

Contbr. articles to profl. jours.; patentee in field. Chmn. Boy Scouts Am. Fund Drives, Cleve., 1976-78; mem. Coun. on World Affairs, Cleve., 1976-81. Mem. Am. Helicopter Soc. (chmn. tech. session 1970), AIAA (chmn. tech. session 1965), Detroit Engring Soc., KC. Roman Catholic. Avocation: golf. Office: RJR Cons 9 Outpost Ln Hilton Head Island SC 29928

RULON, RICHARD R., lawyer; b. Phila. 1943. BA, Brown U., 1964; JD, U. Pa., 1967. Bar: Pa. 1967. Ptnr. Dechert Price & Rhoads, Phila. Office: Dechert Price & Rhoads 4000 Bell Atlantic Tower 1717 Arch St Philadelphia PA 19103-2713

RUMBAUGH, CHARLES EARL, lawyer, corporate executive; b. San Bernardino, Calif., Mar. 11, 1943; s. Max Elden and Gertrude Maude (Gulker) R.; m. Christina Carol Pinder, Mar. 2, 1968; children: Eckwood, Cynthia, Aaron, Heather. BS, UCLA, 1966; JD, Calif. Western Sch. Law, 1971; cert. in Advanced Mgmt., U. So. Calif., 1993. Bar: Calif. 1972, U.S. Dist. Ct. (cen. dist.) Calif. 1972, U.S. Ct. Appeals (9th cir.) 1972. Engr. Westinghouse Electric Corp., Balt., 1966-68; legal counsel Calif. Dept. of Corps., L.A., 1971-77; legal counsel Hughes Aircraft Co., L.A., 1977-84, asst. to corp. dir. contracts, 1984-89, asst. to corp. v.p. contracts, 1989—; arbitrator comml., franchise, real estate and constrn. panels Am. Arbitration Assn., L.A., 1989—; mem. arbitration and mediation panels Franchise Arbitration and Mediation, Inc., 1994—, Ctr. for Conflict Resolution, L.A., 1990—, L.A. County Superior Ct., 1993—; speaker to profl. and trade assn. Contbr. articles to profl. jours. Counselor Boy Scouts Am., L.A., 1976—; mem. City of Palos Verdes Estates (Calif.) Stables Planning Com., 1986-90; judge pro tem Los Angeles County Superior Ct., L.A., 1991—. Fellow Nat. Contract Mgmt. Assn. (cert. profl. contracts mgr., nat. v.p. southwestern region 1993-95, nat. dir. 1992-93, pres. L.A./South Bay chpt. 1991-92, Outstanding Fellows award 1994); mem. ABA (forum on constrn. industry, forum on franchising), Nat. Security Indsl. Assn. (vice chmn. west coast legal subcom. 1994—), Fed. Bar Assn. (pres. Beverly Hills chpt. 1992-93), State Bar Calif. (franchise law com. 1992-95, Willey W. Manual award 1992), Los Angeles County Bar Assn., South Bay Bar Assn., Soc. Profls. in Dispute Resolution, Aerospace Industries Assn. (chmn. procurement techniques com. 1987-88, 1993-94), Christian Legal Soc. Avocations: camping, skiing, jogging, equestrian. Home: PO Box 2636 Rolling Hills Estates CA 90274

RUMBAUGH, MAX ELDEN, JR., professional society administrator; b. Ada, Okla., Dec. 11, 1937; s. Max E. and Gertrude (Gulker) R.; m. Joan E. Brockway; children: Maria Rumbaugh Gross, Max E. III. BS in Engring., U.S. Mil. Acad., 1960; MS in Engring. Scis., Purdue U., 1965, MBA, 1972. Instr. Purdue U., West Lafayette, Ind., 1964-65; corp. officer Midwest Applied Sci. Corp., West Lafayette, 1965-72; chief engr. advanced tech. Schwitzer div. Wallace-Murray Corp., Indpls., 1972-77, dir. research, 1977-81; mgr. engring. activities div. Soc. Automotive Engrs., Warrendale, Pa., 1981-84, v.p., asst. gen. mgr., 1984-86, exec. v.p., 1986—; pres. Performance Rev. Inst., 1991—; pres. Soc. Rsch. Adminstrs. Internat., 1973-74; chmn. Ind. sect. Soc. Automotive Engrs., 1978-79; bd. dirs., exec. com. Am. Nat. Standards Inst., N.Y.C., 1986—; bd. dirs. Intelligent Transp. Soc. of Am., 1992—. Author mag. column Focus, 1986—. Bd. dirs. Jr. Achievement Western Pa., Pitts., 1986-95, YMCA, North Hills, Pitts., 1985-94. 1st lt. U.S. Army, 1960-63. Mem. ASME, Coun. Engring. and Sci. Soc. Execs. (bd. dirs. 1990—, sec. 1993-94, v.p. 1994—), Rotary (bd. dirs. 1982-84, 93—, v.p. 1994-95). Avocations: skiing, photography. Home: 2274 Wood Acre Ct Pittsburgh PA 15237-1524 Office: Soc of Automotive Engrs Inc 400 Commonwealth Dr Warrendale PA 15086-7511

RUMBAUGH, MELVIN DALE, geneticist, agronomist; b. Pella, Iowa, Sept. 13, 1929; s. Herbert Robert and Lena (Schakel) R.; m. Annabelle Eis, July 5, 1953; children: Alan Lee, Rosemary Ann, David James, Steven Thomas. BS, Cen. Coll., Pella, 1951; MS, U. Nebr., 1953, PhD, 1958. Prof. agronomy Colo. State U., Ft. Collins, 1958; prof. plant sci. S.D. State U., Brookings, 1959-77; rsch. scientist USDA-Agrl. Rsch. Svc., Logan, Utah, 1977-92; pvt. cons. Humboldt, Nebr., 1993—; participant plant germplasm collection Can., China, Bolivia, Peru, Ecuador, USSR, Morocco, Pakistan, Spain, Romania; exchange scientist People's Republic China, 1987, 90, 91. Contbr. 250 articles to profl. jours., chpts. to books, sci. papers; inventor superior methods to genetically improve rangeland plant species; authority plant growth on saline soils. Cpl. U.S. Army, 1953-55. Fellow Am. Soc. Agronomy, Crop Sci. Soc. Am.; mem. Soc. Range Mgmt. Republican. Avocations: genealogy, history, fishing. Home: RR 3 Box 125 Humboldt NE 68376-9352

RUMBOUGH, STANLEY MADDOX, JR., industrialist; b. N.Y.C., Apr. 25, 1920; s. Stanley Maddox and Elizabeth (Colgate) R.; m. Nedenia Hutton, Mar. 23, 1946 (div. 1966); children: Stanley H., David P. (dec.), Nedenia Colgate; m. Margaretha Wagstrom, Dec. 21, 1967 (div. 1990); m. Janna Herlow, Mar. 8, 1990. A.B., Yale U., 1942; postgrad. in bus. adminstrn., NYU, 1947-51. Vice pres., dir. Willis Air Service, Teterboro, N.J., 1946-47; v.p., dir. White Metal Mfg. Co., Hoboken, N.J., 1945-61; pres. White Metal Mfg. Co., 1960-61; pres., dir. Metal Container Corp., 1950-59, Am. Totalisator, Balt., 1956-58; chmn. bd. Extrusion Devel. Corp., 1959-61; co-founder, chmn. bd. Elec. Engring. Ltd., 1960-69; chmn. bd. Wallace Clark & Co., 1962-69; co-founder, dir. Trinidad Flour Mills, 1961-72, Jamaica Flour Mills, 1963-66, Telemedia Inc., 1980-89; bd. dirs. Internat. Flavors and Fragrances, CUC Internat., Inc., ABT Family of Funds Inc.; spl. asst. to sec. Dept. Commerce, 1953; spl. asst. White House charge exec. bd. liaison, 1953-55. Chmn. U.S. Com. for UN, 1957-58; co-founder Citizens for Eisenhower, 1951; vice chmn. Citizens for Eisenhower-Nixon Com., 1952; trustee Young Pres. Found., 1957-70, pres., 1962-65; bd. dirs. N.Y. World's Fair Corp., 1961-70, Nat. Conf. on Citizenship, 1973—; trustee Libr. for Presdl. Papers, 1966-70, Internat. House, 1959—, Fgn. Policy Assn., 1961-70, Am. Health Found., 1972-76; bd. dirs. Population Resource Ctr., 1978-92, Planned Parenthood of Palm Beach Area, 1979-95, Planned Parenthood Fedn. Am., 1981-84. Served as capt. USMCR, 1942-46. Decorated Air medal (8), D.F.C. (2). Mem. Chief Execs. Orgn., World Pres.'s Orgn., Def. Orientation Conf. Assn., Racquet and Tennis Club, Internat. Lawn Tennis Club, Maidstone Club, Seminole Club, Bath and Tennis Club, Beach Club, Everglades Club, Nat. Golf Links Am. Club, Zeta Psi. Republican. Home: 114 Clarke Ave Palm Beach FL 33480-6121 Office: 280 Sunset Ave Palm Beach FL 33480-3815

RUMER, RALPH RAYMOND, JR., civil engineer, educator; b. Ocean City, N.J., June 22, 1931; s. Ralph Raymond and Anna (Hibbard) R.; m. Shirley Louise Haynes, Nov. 30, 1953; children: Sherri, Sue, Sandra, Sarah. BS in Civil Engring. Duke U., 1953; M.S., Rutgers U., 1959; Sc.D. (ASCE research fellow), M.I.T., 1962. Lic. prof. engr., N.Y. With Lukens Steel Co., Coatesville, Pa., 1953-54; instr. dept. civil engring. Rutgers U., New Brunswick, N.J., 1956-59; civil engr. U.S. Dept. Agr., New Brunswick, summer 1957-59; research asst. Hydrodynamics lab. M.I.T., Boston, 1961-62; asst. prof. dept. civil engring. M.I.T., 1962-63; assoc. prof. dept. civil engring. SUNY, Buffalo, 1963-69; prof. SUNY, 1969-76, 78—, acting head, 1966-67, chmn. 1967-73, 84-87; dir. SUNY (Gt. Lakes Program), 1986-90, acting provost engring. and applied scis., 1974-75; prof., chmn. dept. civil engring. U. Del., Newark, 1976-78; dir. N.Y. Ctr. Hazardous Waste Mgmt., 1987—; tech. cons. to govt. and industry in hydraulics, water resources and environ. engring.; mem. water resources rsch. com. Nat. Acad. Sci., 1985-86; mem. water mgmt. adv. com. N.Y. State Dept. Environ. Conservation, 1988-93; chmn. sci. adv. com. EPA regions 1 & 2 Hazardous Substance Rsch. Ctr., N.J. Inst. Tech., 1989—; mem. sci. adv. com. Gulf Coast States Hazardous Substance Rsch. Ctr., Lamar U., Tex., 1991—. Contbr. research articles in field to profl. jours. Served with U.S. Army, 1954-56. Recipient Educator of Yr. award Erie-Niagara chpt. N.Y. State Soc. Profl. Engrs., 1989, Excellence award N.Y. State/United Univ. Professions, 1990; Ford fellow, 1962-63; sr. rsch. fellow Calif. Inst. Tech., 1970-71. Mem. ASCE (dir. Buffalo sect., pres. Buffalo sect. 1984-85), Internat. Assn., Hydraulic Research, Am. Geophys. Union, Internat. Assn. Gt. Lakes Research, Sigma Xi, Tau Beta Pi, Chi Epsilon. Home: 821 Eggert Rd Buffalo NY 14226-4135

RUMFORD, LEWIS, III, retail company executive; b. Balt., Dec. 21, 1947; s. Lewis and Rose (Clymer) r.; m. Frances Rosenfeld; children: Julia, Grace, William. BA, Wesleyan U., 1972; MBA, Harvard U., 1977. Asst. v.p. The Rouse Co., Columbia, Md., 1972-75; ptnr. The JBG Cos., Washington, 1977—. Office: The JBG Cos Ste 500 1250 Connecticut Ave NW Washington DC 20036-2603

RUMLER, ROBERT HOKE, agricultural consultant, retired association executive; b. Chambersburg, Pa., Apr. 4, 1915; s. Daniel Webster and Jennie (Sellers) R.; m. Frances Jeannette Montgomery, June 7, 1939 (dec. 1983); children: Craig M., Karen A. Loden; m. Hazel Miller-Karper, Aug. 23, 1986. B.S., Pa. State U., 1936. Asst. county agt. U. Mo., 1936-37; county agrl. agt. Pa. State U., 1937-45; asst. mgr., editor agrl. promotion div. E. I. duPont de Nemours & Co., Inc., Wilmington, Del., 1945-48; asst. exec. sec. Holstein-Friesian Assn. Am., 1948-53, 53-75, exec. sec., chief exec. officer, 1975-81, exec. chmn., 1981-82, chmn. emeritus, 1982—; pres. Holstein-Friesian Svcs., Inc., 1968-81; agribus. cons., 1982—; hom. mem. Holstein-Friesian de Mex. (C.A.); bd. dirs., chmn. Vt. Nat. Bank, Vt. Fin. Svcs., Inc., 1957-88; mem. U.S./USSR Joint Com. Agrl. Cooperation; past chmn. U.S. Agrl. Export Devel. Coun., FAS-USDA; mem. coordinating group Nat. Coop. Dairy Herd Improvement program USDA, 1964-80; mem. agrl. policy adv. com. USTR/USDA Multilateral Trade Negotiations, 1973-87, mem. agrl. tech. adv. com., 1987—. Contbg. editorial writer Holstein World. Trustee Ea. States Expn., trustee emeritus, 1993—; trustee Assoc. Industries Vt.; past bd. dirs. Internat. Stockmans Ednl. Found.; chmn. adv. bd. Pa. State U., Mont Alto, 1990-94; bd. advisors Pa. State U., Harrisburg. Recipient Disting. award Nat. Dairy Herd Improvement Assn., 1974, Disting. Service award Nat. Agrl. Mktg. Orgn., 1977, Disting. Service award Holstein Assn. 1985; named Disting. Alumnus Pa. State U., 1978, Dairy Industry Man of Yr., 1979; named to Internat. Livestock Hall of Fame, 1987; Robert H. Rumler scholar. Fellow Agr. Adventures; mem. Purebred Dairy Cattle Assn. (dir., exec. com.), Nat. Soc. Livestock Record Assns. (past pres., dir., Disting. Svcs. award 1981), Am. Dairy Sci. Assn. (Disting. Svc. award 1977), Agri-Bus. Found. (All-Time Gt. award 1981), Nat. Dairy Shrine (Dairy Hall of Fame 1976), N.E. Master Farmers Assn. (hon. master farmer), U.S. Animal Health Assn., Kiwanis, Masons, Elks, Alpha Zeta, Gamma Sigma Delta. Mem. United Ch. of Christ. Home: 937 Wallace Ave Chambersburg PA 17201-3884 Office: PO Box 945 Chambersburg PA 17201-0945

RUMMAN, WADI (SALIBA RUMMAN), civil engineer; b. Beit-Jala, Palestine, Sept. 7, 1926; came to U.S., 1948, naturalized, 1959; s. Saliba Y. and Miladeh (Nasrallah) R.; m. Doris E. Reed, Sept. 6, 1955; children—Mary Elaine, Linda Jean. B.S.E., U. Mich., 1949, M.S.E., 1953, Ph.D., 1959. Field engr. Finkbeiner Pettis and Strout, Toledo, 1949; structural engr. Vogt, Ivers, Seaman and Assos., Cin., 1950-51, Giffels and Vallet, Inc., Detroit, 1951-52; instr. U. Mich., 1952-59, asst. prof. civil engring., 1959-64, assoc. prof., 1964-75, prof., 1975-88, prof. emeritus, 1988—; cons. on design of reinforced concrete chimneys and other tower structures to industry and other agys. Author: Engineering, 1974, 3d edit., 1991. Fellow Am. Concrete Inst.; mem. ASCE (life), Am. Soc. Engring. (life), Internat. Assn. Bridge and Structural Engring., Sigma Xi, Chi Epsilon, Phi Kappa Phi. Home: 709 Woodhill Dr Saline MI 48176-1708 Office: U Mich Dept Civil Engring Ann Arbor MI 48109

RUMMEL, HAROLD EDWIN, real estate developing executive; b. Youngstown, Ohio, Oct. 4, 1940; s. Harold Edward and Florence Louise (Hill) R.; children: Timothy B., Jonathan S., Briana. BS, U. Fla., 1963. Writer, editor various newspapers, Fla., 1958-70; polit. campaign mgr. various state campaigns, Tallahassee, Fla., 1971-79; sr. v.p. Fla. Fed. Sav. Bank, St. Petersburg, 1979-86; pres., chief exec. officer Rummel Cos., St. Petersburg, 1986—. Active in civic and polit. orgns. Democrat. Home: 1682 Ocean View Dr Tierra Verde FL 33715 Office: Rummel Cos 5401 Central Ave Saint Petersburg FL 33710-8049

RUMMEL, ROBERT WILAND, aeronautical engineer, author; b. Dakota, Ill., Aug. 4, 1915; s. William Howard and Dora (Ely) R.; m. Marjorie B. Cox, Sept. 30, 1939; children—Linda Kay, Sharon Lee, Marjorie Susan, Robert Wiland, Diana Beth. Diploma aeronautical engring., Curtiss Wright Tech. Inst. Aeros., 1935. Stress analyst Hughes Aircraft Co., Burbank, Calif., 1935-36, Lockheed Aircraft Corp., Burbank, 1936; draftsman Aero Engring. Corp., Long Beach, Calif., 1936; Nat. Aircraft Co., Alhambra, Calif., 1936-37; chief engr. Rearwin A/C & Engines, Inc., Kansas City, Kans., 1937-42; chief design engr. Commonwealth A/C, Inc., Kansas City, Kans., 1942-43; v.p. engring. Trans World Airlines, Inc., Kansas City, Mo., 1943-59; v.p. planning and research Trans World Airlines, Inc., 1959-69, v.p. tech. devel., 1969-78; pres. Robert W. Rummel Assos., Inc., Mesa, Ariz., 1978-87; aerospace cons., 1987—; commnr. Presdl. Commn. Space Shuttle Challenger Accident, 1986; chmn. nat. rsch. coun. Aero Space Engring. Bd. Fellow Inst. Aero. Scis., Soc. Automotive Engrs.; mem. NAE, Masons (32 deg.), Shriners. Home and Office: PO Box 7330 Mesa AZ 85216-7330

RUMMERFIELD, BENJAMIN FRANKLIN, geophysicist; b. Denver, May 25, 1917; s. Lawrence L. and Helen A. (Roper) R.; Engr. Geology, Colo. Sch. Mines, 1940; grad. Harvard U. Advanced Mgmt. Program, 1947, Aspen Inst. Humanistic Studies, 1958, Indsl. Coll. Armed Forces, 1963; m. Mary Merchant, Feb. 16, 1979; children: Ann S., Michael J., Benjamin F., Mary Susan, Sonya, Karim. Asst. mgr. Seismograph Service Corp., Mexico City, 1947-50, Venezuela and Colombia, 1945-47; exec. v.p. U.S. and Can. ops. Century Geophys. Corp., Tulsa, 1950-60, also dir.; pres. GeoData Corp., Tulsa, 1960—, Gulf Coast GeoData, Houston, 1962—; dir. Permian Exploration, Custom Data Services; cons. Petróleos Mexicanos. Bd. dirs. YMCA, Tulsa, 1955—, pres., 1956-59. Recipient Outstanding Service award YMCA, Tulsa, 1958, 63, Disting. Achievement medal Colo. Sch. Mines, 1978, hon. mention for painting Philbrook Art Mus., 1961. Mem. Tulsa Geol. Soc., Colo. Sch. Mines Alumni Assn. (pres. 1953), Asociación Mexicana de Geólogos Petróleos, Am. Assn. Petroleum Geologists, Soc. Exploration Geophysicists (life, nat. v.p. 1958), Sigma Gamma Epsilon. Clubs: Tulsa, Harvard (Tulsa). Contbr. numerous articles to profl. jours. Home: 6787 Timberlane Rd Tulsa OK 74136-4518 Office: care GeoData Corp 211 S Cheyenne Ave Tulsa OK 74103-3009

RUMMERY, TERRANCE EDWARD, nuclear engineering executive, researcher; b. Brockville, Ont., Can., 1937; s. Albert Edward and Evelyn Maud (Hayter) R.; m. Margaret Dianne Walker, Mar. 1967; children: Tara, Marcus. BSc with honours Engring. Chem., Queen's Univ., Kingston, PhD Phys. Chem., DS (hon., 1993; student, Nat. Defence Coll., Can., 1984-85. Engr. Brockville Chems.; rsch. scientist Ont. Rsch. Found., Am. Labs. Airco Speer Carbon and Graphite with Rsch. Chemistry br. Whiteshell Labs., Pinawa, Man., Can., 1971; head Rsch Chemistry br. Whiteshell Labs., Pinawa, Manitoba, Can., 1976; dir. Nuclear Fuel Waste Mgmt. divsn. Atomic Energy Can. Ltd., Pinawa, Manitoba, Can., 1979-84; team leader reactor mktg. activities Atomic Energy Can. Ltd., The Netherlands, Yugoslavia, 1986-88; mgr. marine propulsion unit Atomic Energy Can. Ltd., Ottawa, Ont., 1988, acting pres., 1990, pres. rsch., 1993; acting pres., CEO, Atomic Energy Can. Ltd., Ottawa, 1993, 94, sci. adviser, 1995—; past mem. Queen's Univ. adv. coun. Engring.; adv. bd. U. Toronto Centre Nuclear Engring., Environ. Engring. Contbr. numerous publications to profl. jours. Recipient W.B. Lewis medal Can. Nuclear Assn., 1994. Fellow Chem. Inst. Can., Can. Nuclear Soc.; mem. Assn. Profl. Engrs. Ont., Canadian Nuclear Soc., Am. Nuclear Soc. Office: Atomic Energy Can Ltd, 344 Slater St, Ottawa, ON Canada K1A 0S4

RUMP, ERWIN ELMER, state agency administrator; b. Dillsboro, Ind., Nov. 18, 1928; s. Edward H. and Emilie R. (Schulenburg) R.; m. Donna Jean Folkening Rump, June 22, 1957; children: Kendall E., Amy L., David C., Jonathan E. BA, Valparaiso U., 1957; MS, Ind. U., 1959. Tchr. Valparaiso (Ind.) H.S., 1957-60; administry. asst. Huntington County Schs., Huntington, Ind., 1970-74; bus. dir. Met. Sch. Dist. Washington Twp., Indpls., 1961-70, asst. supr., 1975-88; Stephen min. Carmel (Ind.) Luth. Ch., 1988-90; tr. officer Ind. Dept. Edn., Indpls., 1991—. Served to cpl. U.S. Army, 1950-52, Korea. Lutheran. Avocations: camping, golf, gardening. Home: 6929 N Butler Ave Indianapolis IN 46220 Office: Ind Dept Edn 229 State House Indianapolis IN 46204

RUMPF, JOHN LOUIS, university official, civil engineer, educator; b. Phila., Feb. 21, 1921; s. Harry L. and Emma S. R.; m. Grace Willis, Apr. 1, 1944 (dec.); children—Jonathan, Christopher; m. Patricia E. Burkitt, June 20, 1970. B.S.C.E., Drexel U., 1943; M.S.C.E., U. Pa., 1954; Ph.D. in Civil Engring. (NSF fellow), Lehigh U., 1960. Structural engr. Belmont Iron Works, Phila., 1946; instr. Drexel U., 1947-50, asst. prof. civil engring., 1950-54, assoc. prof., 1954-56, prof., head dept. civil engring., 1960-69; research instr. Fritz Engring. Lab., Lehigh U., 1956-60; dean Coll. Engring. and Architecture Temple U., Phila., 1969-76; v.p. acad. affairs Temple U., 1976-82, exec. v.p., 1982-84, prof. civil engring., 1984-86; cons. engr. for bldg. and bridge design and investigations, 1947—. Author: Plastic Design of Braced Multistory Steel Frames, 1968; contbg. author Structural Steel Design, 1974. Mem. Lower Moreland Twp. (Pa.) Zoning Bd., 1953-56; mem. Lower Moreland Twp. Sch. Dist. Authority, 1962-70; bd. dirs. Abington Meml. Hosp. (Pa.), 1982-88. Served to capt. C.E. U.S. Army, 1943-46. Decorated Army Commendation medal; Named Engr. of Yr. Tech. Socs. of Delaware Valley, 1975. Fellow ASCE; mem. Am. Soc. Engring. Edn., Nat. Soc. Profl. Engrs., Research Council for Structural Connections, Am. Concrete Inst., Sigma Xi, Tau Beta Pi, Phi Kappa Phi, Chi Epsilon. Club: Engrs. of Phila. (George Washington medal 1979). Research, publs. on structural connections and members, 1956-69. Home: 1213 Red Rambler Rd Jenkintown PA 19046-2916 Office: Temple U Coll Engring & Architecture Philadelphia PA 19122

RUMSEY, VICTOR HENRY, electrical engineering educator emeritus; b. Devizes, Eng., Nov. 22, 1919; s. Albert Victor and Susan Mary (Norman) R.; m. Doris Herring, Apr. 2, 1942; children: John David, Peter Alan, Catherine Anne. B.A., Cambridge U., 1941, D.Sc. in Physics, 1972; D.Eng., Tohoku U., Japan, 1962. With U.K. Sci. Civil Service, 1941-48; asst. to asso. prof. Ohio State U., 1948-54; prof. U. Ill., 1954-57, U. Calif., Berkeley, 1957-66; prof. elec. engring. and computer scis. U. Calif., San Diego, 1966-87, prof. emeritus, 1987—; dept. chmn. U. Calif., 1977-81. Author 1 book in field; contbr. articles to profl. jours. Guggenheim fellow; recipient George Sinclair award Ohio State U., 1982. Fellow IEEE (Morris Liebman prize), Union Radio Scientifique Internationale, Internat. Astron. Union; mem. Nat. Acad. Engring. Patentee in field. Home: PO Box 400 Occidental CA 95465-0400

RUMSFELD, DONALD HENRY, former government official, corporate executive; b. Chgo., July 9, 1932; s. George Donald and Jeannette (Husted) R.; m. Joyce Pierson, Dec. 27, 1954; 3 children. A.B., Princeton U., 1954; hon. degree, De Paul U. Coll. Commerce, Ill. Coll., Lake Forest Coll., Park Coll., Tuskegee Inst., Nat. Coll. Edn., Bryant Coll., Claremont (Calif.) Grad. Sch., Ill. Wesleyan U., Rand Grad. Sch. Adminstrv. asst. U.S. Ho. of Reps., 1958-59; with A.G. Becker & Co., Chgo., 1960-62; mem. 88th-91st Congresses from 13th Ill. dist., Pres.'s Richard Nixon's Cabinet, 1969-73; dir. OEO, asst. to pres., 1969-70; counsellor to Pres., dir. econ. stabilization program, 1971-72; U.S. ambassador and permanent rep. to NATO, 1973-74; White House chief of staff for Pres. Gerald Ford, 1974-75; sec. Dept. Def., 1975-77; pres., chief exec. officer, then chmn. G.D. Searle & Co., Skokie, Ill., 1977-85; spl. envoy of Pres. Ronald Reagan to Mid. East, 1983-84; sr. advisor William Blair & Co., Chgo., 1985-90; chmn., chief exec. officer General Instrument Corp., Chgo., 1990-93; bd. dirs. Allstate Corp., Metricom, Kellogg Co., Tribune Co., Gilead Scis., Inc., Amylin Pharms., Inc., Sears, Roebuck and Co.; chmn. bd. trustees RAND Corp. Naval Aviator USN, 1954-57. Recipient Presdl. Medal of Freedom, George Catlett Marshall award, Woodrow Wilson award, Dwight David Eisenhower medal. Office: 400 N Michigan Ave Ste 405 Chicago IL 60611-4102

RUND, DOUGLAS ANDREW, emergency physician; b. Columbus, Ohio, July 20, 1945; s. Carl Andrew and Caroline Amelia (Row) R.; m. Sue E, Padavana, 1980; children: Carie, Emily, Ashley. BA, Yale U., 1967; MD, Stanford U., 1971. Lic. physician, Ohio; Diplomate Nat. Bd. Med. Examiners, Am. Bd. Family Practice, Am. Bd. Emergency Medicine (pres., 1995—). Intern in medicine U. Calif., San Francisco-Moffett Hosp., 1971-72; resident in gen. surgery Stanford U., 1972-74; Robert Wood Johnson Found. clin. scholar in medicine Stanford U., 1974-76; med. dir. Mid-Peninsula Health Svc., Palo Alto, Calif., 1975-76; clin. instr. dept. medicine and preventive medicine Stanford U. Med. Sch., 1975-76; assoc. prof., dir. div. emergency medicine Ohio State Coll. Medicine, 1982-87; dir. emergency medicine residency program, assoc. prof. dept. family medicine, 1976-87, prof., chmn. dept. preventive medicine, 1988-90, prof., chmn. dept. emergency medicine, 1990—, prof., interim chmn. dept. family medicine, 1994-95; attending staff Ohio State U. Hosps., 1976—; med. dir. CSCC, Emergency Med. Svcs. Dept.; pres. Internat. Rsch. Inst. Emergency Medicine; med. dir. Internat. Soc. for Emergency Med. Svcs.; sr. rsch. fellow NATO: Health and Med. Aspects of Disaster Preparedness, 1985-87; bd. dirs. ABEM, 1988—, sr. editor in tng. exam., 1989—; on profl. leave epidemiology and injury control, U. Edinburgh, Scotland, 1987. Fellow Am. Coll. Emergency Physicians (task force on substance abuse and injury control); Mem. Nat. Inst. on Alcohol Abuse and Alcoholism, IAAA, Assn. Acad. Chairs Emergency Medicine (pres. 1992-93), Soc. Acad. Emergency Medicine (chmn. internat. com. 1991—), Columbus Medical Forum (pres. 1993), Alpha Omega Alpha. Author: Triage, 1981; Essentials of Emergency Medicine, 1982, 2nd edit., 1986; Emergency Radiology, 1982; Emergency Psychiatry, 1983; Environmental Emergencies, 1985; editor: Emergency Medicine Ann., 1983, 84; Emergency Medicine Survey, Annals of Emergency Medicine; editor-in-chief Ohio State Series on Emergency Medicine, Emergency Medicine Observer, 1986-87; guest editor Annals of Emergency Medicine Symposium, 1986; mem. editorial bd. Physician, Sports Medicine, Emergency Med. Svcs.; contbr. chpt. to Family Medicine Principles and Practice, 1978, 2d edit., 1983; contbr. articles to profl. jours. Office: Ohio State U 005 Upham Hall 473 W 12th Ave Columbus OH 43210-1228 also: Ohio State U B0902B Univ Hosps Clinic 456 W 10th St Columbus OH 43210-1228

RUNDELL, THOMAS GARDNER, lawyer; b. Wichita Falls, Tex., Nov. 14, 1945; s. William Kennard and Margaret (Shanklin) R.; m. Charlotte McWhorter; children: Thomas Gardner Jr., John R. BA cum laude, Midwestern U., 1967; JD, So. Meth. U., 1970. Bar: Tex. 1970, U.S. Dist. Ct. (no. dist.) Tex. Ptnr. Strasburger & Price, Dallas, 1970—. Mem. ABA, Tex. Assn. Bank Counsel (dir. 1985-88), State Bar Tex. Office: Strasburger & Price 901 Main St Ste 4300 Dallas TX 75202-3794

RUNDGREN, TODD, musician, record producer; b. Upper Darby, Pa., June 22, 1948; 3 children. Solo artist, 1970—; mem. mus. groups Nazz, 1967-69, Utopia, 1973—; record producer for numerous mus. groups including Badfinger, Paul Butterfield, Grand Funk, Hall & Oates, New York Dolls, The Band, Patti Smith, The Tubes, The Pursuit of Happiness, XTC; numerous recs. and compositions including Can We Still be Friends, Hello It's Me, Up Against It, 1989; albums include Another Life, 1975, (with The Nazz) Nazz, 1968, Nazz Nazz, 1969, Nazz III, 1970, (with Utopia) Todd Rundgren's Utopia, 1974, Oops! Wrong Planet, 1987, Adventures in Utopia, 1980, Deface the Music, 1980, Swing to the Right, 1982, Utopia, 1982, Anthology, 1989; solo albums include Runt, 1970, Something/Anything, 1972, Initiation, 1975, Faithful, 1976, Hermit of the Mink Hollow, 1978, Back to the Bars, 1978, Healing, 1981, A Capella, 1985, Nearly Human, 1989, -2nd Wind, 1991, No World Order, 1993, The Best of Todd Rundgren, 1994; composer TV mus. scores Crime Story, Pee-wee's Playhouse, theatre musical score Up Against It, 1990. Office: care Bearsville Warner Bros Record 3300 Warner Blvd Burbank CA 91505-4632*

RUNDIO, LOUIS MICHAEL, JR., lawyer; b. Chgo., Sept. 13, 1943; s. Louis Michael Sr. and Germaine Matilda (Pasternack) R.; m. Ann Marie Bartlett, July 10, 1971; children: Matthew, Melissa. BS in Physics, Loyola U., Chgo., 1965, JD, 1972. Bar: Ill. 1972, U.S. Dist. Ct. (no. dist.) Ill. 1972, U.S. Ct. Appeals (7th cir.) 1974, U.S. Dist. Ct. (ea. dist.) Mich. 1983. Assoc. McDermott, Will & Emery, Chgo., 1972-77, ptnr., 1978—. Served to 1st lt. U.S. Army, 1965-68, Vietnam. Mem. ABA, Chgo. Bar Assn. Home: 676 Skye Ln Barrington IL 60010-5506 Office: McDermott Will & Emery 227 W Monroe St Chicago IL 60606-5016

RUNDQUIST, HOWARD IRVING, investment banker; b. Winona, Minn., Mar. 21, 1929; s. Howard Wadsworth and Delilah Jeanette (Erickson) R.; m. Nancy Evelyn Hood, July 30, 1980; children: Sarah Louise, Beth Anne, Peter Hood, Susan Jenniffer, Rebecca Jane. AB, Gustavus Adolphus Coll., 1951; MBA, Harvard U., 1958. Mem. staff MIT Lincoln Lab., Lexington, Mass., 1954-56, 58-60; sr. v.p. Aubrey G. Lanston Co. Inc., N.Y.C., 1960-92; ret., 1992. Investment advisor bd. pensions Evang. Luth. Ch. in Am., 1992—. Lt. USNR, 1951-54. Mem. Webhanet Golf Club, Edgecomb Tennis Club (Kennebunk, Maine). Republican. Lutheran.

RUNG, RICHARD ALLEN, lawyer, retired air force officer, retired educator; b. Rome, N.Y., Dec. 16, 1929; s. George Stuart and Ruth Marie (Henderberg) R.; m. Yolande Moalli, June 15, 1957; children: Michael, Bruce, Colette. B.A. summa cum laude, St. Michael's Coll., 1957; J.D., Syracuse U., 1960. Bar: N.Y. 1961. Law partner Lawler & Rung, DeWitt, N.Y., 1960-61; law assoc. J. F. Ferlo Law Office, Rome, N.Y., 1961-63; commd. 2d lt. USAF, 1952, advanced through grades to col., 1979; USAF fighter pilot, 1952-55; USAF fighter pilot and flight comdr. La., Spain, Vietnam, N.Y., 1963-74; USAF flight safety evaluator and cons. Norton AFB, Calif., 1974-79; prof. aerospace studies, Air Force ROTC detachment comdr. U. Ill. Champaign-Urbana, 1979-82; commandant AFJROTC Pompano Beach High Sch., (Fla.), 1982-85, Northeast High Sch., (Fla.) 1985-92. Decorated Legion of Merit, DFC, Air medal with 7 oak leaf clusters; recipient award Aerospace Safety Hall Fame, 1979, Disting. Svc. award Am. Vets., 1980, Citation Am. Legion, 1984, Citizenship medal SAR, 1989, Citation Air Force Assn. Fla., 1990. Mem. Delta Epsilon Sigma, Sigma Nu, Phi Delta Phi. Roman Catholic. Home: 2672 Emerald Way N Deerfield Beach FL 33442-8640 *The human being, a magnificent creation, remains obscure if the element of motivation lies dormant. The human will is the key to personal achievement.*

RUNGE, DE LYLE PAUL, retired library director, consultant; b. Madison, Wis., Feb. 3, 1918; s. Charles Delial and Josephine Ida Clara (Niebuhr) R.; m. Ethelyn Fay Green, Sept. 26, 1943; children: Richard Rene, Willa Dee, Robert Roy. BA in Commerce, U. Wis., 1940, BSLS, 1943. Dir. pub. rels., coord. ref. svcs. Grand Rapids (Mich.) Pub. Libr., 1946-53; libr. dir. St. Petersburg (Fla.) Pub. Libr., 1953-82; cons. on libr. bldgs., 1964—; mem. Fla. State Libr. Adv. Coun., 1973-82. With AUS, 1943-46, ETO, lt. col. USAR. Mem. ALA, Fla. Libr. Assn. (pres. 1968-69, exec. bd. 1969-70), Southeastern Libr. Assn., ASPA, Am. Philatelic Soc., St. Petersburg Stamp Club, Kiwanis, Beta Phi Mu. Home: 4520 Cortez Way S Saint Petersburg FL 33712-4029

RUNGE, DONALD EDWARD, food wholesale company executive; b. Milw., Mar. 20, 1938; s. Adam and Helen Teresa (Voss) R.; divorced; children: Roland, Richard, Lori. Grad., Spencerian Coll., Milw., 1960. Fin. v.p. Milw. Cheese Co., Waukesha, Wis., 1962-69; dir. Farm House Foods Corp., Milw., 1966-89, pres., 1966-89, chief exec. officer, treas., 1984-89, chmn., pres., 1985-89; chmn., chief exec. officer Retailing Corp. Am., Milw., 1982-89; chief exec. officer, treas. Drug Systems Inc., Milw., 1984-89; chmn. Drug Systems Inc. (now Retailing Corp. of Am.), Milw., 1985-89; pres. TDC, 1987-89; chmn., pres. Runge Industries, Gen. Growth, Inc., 1989—; bd. dirs. Convenient Food Mart, CasaBlanca Industries, Inc., City of Industry, Calif.; sec. The Diana Corp., Milw., 1985-86, treas. 1986—, pres. 1987—; chmn. Economy Dry Goods Co. Inc.; treas. Fairbanks Farms Inc. Adventist. *I believe there is very little in life that cannot be accomplished if a person truly wants to attain the goal.*

RUNGE, KAY KRETSCHMAR, library director; b. Davenport, Iowa, Dec. 9, 1946; d. Alfred Edwin and Ina (Paul) Kretschmar; m. Peter S. Runge Sr., Aug. 17, 1968; children: Peter Jr., Katherine. BS in History Edn., Iowa State U., 1969; MLS, U. Iowa, 1970. Pub. service librarian Anoka County Library, Blaine, Minn., 1971-72; cataloger Augustana Coll., Rock Island, Ill., 1972-74; dir. Scott County Library System, Eldridge, Iowa, 1974-85, Davenport (Iowa) Pub. Libr., 1985—. Bd. dirs. River Ctr. for Performing Arts, Davenport, 1983—, Am. Inst. Commerce, 1989—, Quad-Cities Conv. and Visitors Bur., 1991—, Quad-Cities Grad. Study Ctr., 1992—, Downtown Davenport Devel. Corp., 1992—, Hall of Honor Bd. Davenport Ctrl. High Sch., 1992—; mem. steering com. Quad-Cities Visions for the Future, 1987-91; bd. govs. Iowa State U. Found., 1991—. Recipient Svc. Key award Iowa State U. Alumni Assn., 1979. Mem. ALA (chmn. library adminstrs. and mgrs. div., fundraising section 1988), Iowa Library Assn. (pres. 1983), Pub. Library Assn. (bd. dirs. 1990—), Iowa Edn. Media Assn. (Intellectual Freedom award 1984), Alpha Delta Pi (alumni state pres. 1978). Lutheran. Office: Davenport Pub Libr 321 N Main St Davenport IA 52801-1409

RUNGE, PAUL EDWARD, baseball umpire, realtor; b. St. Catherine's, Ont., Can., Oct. 20, 1940; came to U.S. 1947; s. Edward Paul and Viola Irene (Meek) R.; m. Anastasia Mouzas, Oct. 17, 1965; children: Brian Edward, Reneé Dyann. Student, San Diego City Coll., 1959-61; BA in Edn. and Bus., Ariz. State U., 1964. Lic. real estate broker. Umpire Nat. League of Profl. Baseball. Mem. Helenic Cultural Soc. Baseball scholar Ariz. State U., 1961; named Umpire of Yr. by Harry Wendelsted Sch. of Umpiring, 1993; inducted Hall of Fame San Diego H.S., 1991. Mem. Major League Umpires Assn. Union (pres., v.p., bd. dirs.), San Diego Bd. Realtors, Ariz. State U. Alumni Assn., Phi Delta Theta. Republican. Mem. New Apostolic Ch. Umpire All-Star games, San Diego, Houston, Pitts., 1978, 86, 94, Championship Series, 1977, 81, 82, 85, 88, 90, World Series, 1979, 84, 93. Home: 649 Called de la Sienna El Cajon CA 92019 Office: RBL & Abra Realtors 99 O Campo Rd Spring Valley CA 92077*

RUNKLE, MARTIN DAVEY, library director; b. Cin., Oct. 18, 1937; s. Newton and Ilo (Neal) R.; m. Nancy Force, Aug. 7, 1965; children: Seth, Elizabeth. BA, Muskingum Coll., 1959; MA, U. Pitts., 1964, U. Chgo., 1973. Library systems analyst U. Chgo., 1970-75, head cataloging librarian, 1975-79, asst. dir. tech. services, 1979-80, dir. library, 1980—; sr. lectr. grad. library sch. U. Chgo., 1977-90. Fulbright grantee, 1965. Mem. ALA, Univ. Club Chgo. Office: U Chgo 1100 E 57th St Chicago IL 60637-1596

RUNNALLS, (OLIVER) JOHN (CLYVE), nuclear engineering educator; b. Barrie Island, Ont., Can., June 26, 1924; s. John Lawrence and Ethel May (Arnold) R.; m. Vivian Constance Stowe, Sept. 13, 1947; children: David John, Catherine Ruth. B.A.Sc., U. Toronto, 1948, M.A.Sc., 1949, Ph.D. 1951. Registered profl. engr., Ont. Research and devel. scientist Atomic Energy of Can., Ltd., Chalk River, Ont. and Paris, 1951-71; sr. adviser uranium and nuclear energy Energy, Mines and Resources Can., Ottawa, Ont., 1971-79; dir. energy studies U. Toronto 1979-89, chmn. Ctr. Nuclear Engring., 1983-89; prof. emeritus nuclear engring. and energy studies, 1989—; chmn. bd. Inst. Hydrogen Systems, 1983-89; mem. internat. adv. com. and tech. adv. com. Concord-Nuexco, Denver; pres. O.J.C. Runnalls & Assocs. Ltd.; bd. dirs. Ont. Hydro, Rio Narcea Gold Mines Ltd., Toronto. Contbr. articles to profl. jours.; patentee in field. Decorated Queen's Silver Jubilee medal, 1977; recipient B.T.A. Bell Commemorative medal Can. Mining Jour., 1979, Ian F. McRae award Can. Nuclear Assn., 1980. Fellow Royal Soc. Can.; mem. Assn. Profl. Engrs., Can. Nuclear Assn. (bd. dirs., past chmn.), Can. Nuclear Soc. Home and Office: 170 Lytton Blvd, Toronto, ON Canada M4R 1L4

RUNNELLS, DONALD DEMAR, geochemist, consultant; b. Eureka, Utah, Dec. 30, 1936; s. Raymond DeMar and Cleo Cecil (Beckstead) R.; m. Erika Anna Bahe, Sept. 3, 1958; children: Timothy, Suzanne. BS with high honors, U. Utah, 1958; MA, Harvard U., 1960, PhD, 1963. Rsch. geochemist Shell Devel. Co., Houston and Miami, 1963-67; asst. prof. U. Calif.-Santa Barbara, 1967-69; assoc. prof. geochemistry U. Colo., Boulder, 1969-75, prof., 1975-92, chair dept. geol. sci., 1990-92; pres. Shepherd Miller, Inc., Ft. Collins, Colo., 1993—. cons. geochemistry to cos., and govt. agys. Mem. water sci. and tech. bd. NRC/NAS, 1989-92. Contbr. articles to profl. publs. NSF fellow, 1958-62. Fellow Geol. Soc. Am.; mem. Am. Chem. Soc., Assn. Exploration Geologists (pres. 1990-91), Geochemical Soc., Assn. Ground-water Scientists and Engrs., Phi Kappa Phi. Home: 8032 Allott Ave Fort Collins CO 80525-4269 Office: Shepherd Miller Inc 1600 Specht Point Dr Ste F Fort Collins CO 80525-4311

RUNNICLES, DONALD, conductor; b. Edinburgh, Scotland, Nov. 16, 1954. Student, Edinburgh U., Cambridge U., London Opera Ctr. Repetiteur Mannheim, Germany, Nat. theater, from 1980, Kapellmeister, from 1984; prin. condr. Hanover, from 1987; numerous appearances with Hamburg Staatsoper; former gen. music dir. Stadtische Buhnen, Freiburg/Breisgau; mus. dir. San Francisco Opera, 1992—; appearances with Met. Opera include Lulu, 1988, The Flying Dutchman, 1990, The Magic Flute; condr. Vienna Staatsoper, 1990-91; debut at Glyndebourne with Don Giovanni, 1991; condr. London Symphony Orch., Orch. de Paris, Israel Philharm., Rotterdam Philharm., Seattle Symphony, Pitts. Symphony, Chgo. Symphony; rec. Hansel und Gretel (Humperdinck); also numerous symphonic engagements. Office: San Francisco Opera War Meml Opera House San Francisco CA 94102 also: Stadtische Buhnen, Bertoldstr 46, W-7800 Freiburg/Breisgau Germany*

RUNNING, NELS, career officer; b. Missoula, Mont.. BS, USAF Acad., 1964; postgrad., George Washington U., 1978-79. Commn. 2d lt. USAF, 1964, advanced through grades to maj. gen., 1992; pilot F4E, left wing position, ops. officer USAF Thunderbirds, 1973-74; comdr. 26th tactical fighter aggressor squadron USAF, Clark AB, The Philippines, 1980-81; dep. comdr. ops., vice comdr. 8th tactical fighter wing USAF, Kunsan AB, Korea, 1981-82; chief ho. liaison officer Office of Sec. USAF, Washington, 1982-84; dir. inspection, hdqs. Pacific Air Forces USAF, Hickam AFB, Hawaii, 1984-85; comdr. 8th tactical fighter wing USAF, Kunsan AB, Korea, 1985-86; dep. dir. internat. programs, hdqs. USAF, Washington, 1986-88, dep. dir. internat. negotiations The Joint Staff, 1988-90; dir. plans, policy, doctrine, simulations and analysis U.S Spl. Ops. Command, MacDill AFB, Fla., 1990-92; dep. chief of staff UN Command, Seoul, Korea, 1992—. Mem. Korea coun. USO. Mem. Air Force Assn., Air Force Acad. Alumni Assn. (bd. dirs. 1971-75), Korean Am. Friendship Assn. (dir. 1994—). Avocations: racquetball, skiing, running, hunting, golf. Office: UN Command APO AP 96205

RUNNION, HOWARD J., JR., banker; b. Hot Spring, N.C., May 23, 1930; s. Howard Jackson and Blanche Mae (Elam) R.; m. Betty Ann Bishop, June 30, 1951; children—Debra Joy Sizemore, Jill Marie Glenn. B.S., U. N.C. 1952. Various postions Wachovia Bank and Trust Co.-Wachovia Corp., Winston-Salem, N.C., 1952—; ret. vice chmn., dir. Depository Trust Co., N.Y.C.; chmn. bd. PSA Treasury Com, 1984-85; ret. exec. v.p. First Wachovia Corp.; bd. dirs. Cardinal Bancshares, Lexington, Ky. Chmn. bd. trustees Coll. Found. Raleigh, 1978—. Mem. Res. City Bankers Assn., Pub. Securities Assn. (dir. 1976-79, 84-85). Republican. Presbyterian. Clubs: Forsyth Country, Roaring Gap. Lodge: Elk. Avocation: golf. Home: 3521 York Rd Winston Salem NC 27104-1346 Office: 1st Wachovia Corp PO Box 3099 Winston Salem NC 27150-3099

RUNQUIST, LISA A., lawyer; b. Mpls., Sept. 22, 1952; d. Ralf E. and Violet R. BA, Hamline U., 1973; JD, U. Minn., 1976. Bar: Minn. 1977, Calif. 1978, U.S. Dist. Ct. (cen. dist.) Calif. 1985, U.S. Supreme Ct. 1995. Assoc. Caldwell & Toms, L.A., 1978-82; ptnr. Runquist & Flagg, L.A., 1982-85; pvt. practice Runquist & Assocs., L.A., 1985—; mem. adv. bd. dirs. The Exempt Orgn. Tax Rev., 1990—. Contbr. articles to profl. jours. Mem. ABA (bus. law sect., counselor 1995, com. on nonprofit corps., 1986—, chair 1991-95, subcom. current devels. in nonprofit corp. law 1989—, chair 1989-91, subcom. rel. orgns. 1989—, chair 1987-91, subcom. legal guidebook for dirs. 1986—, subcom. model nonprofit corp. act, partnerships and unincorp. bus. orgns. com. 1987—, state regulation of securities com. 1988—; tax law sect., exempt orgns. com. 1987—, subcom. rel. orgns. 1989—, co-chair 1995), Calif. Bar Assn. (bus. law sect., nonprofit and unincorp. orgns. com. 1985-92, 93—, chair 1989-91), Christian Legal Soc., Ctr. Law and Rel. Freedom, Christian Mgmt. Assn. (dir. 1983-89). Office: 10821 Huston St North Hollywood CA 91601-4613

RUNSTAD, JUDITH MANVILLE, lawyer; b. Ontario, Oreg., July 15, 1944; d. Gerry Wright and Jean (Thurston) Manville; m. H. Jon Runstad, Dec. 3, 1977. BS, U. Idaho, 1966, MS, 1967; JD, U. Wash. 1974. Bar: Wash. 1974. Tchr. Shorecrest High Sch., Seattle, 1967-71; assoc. Foster, Pepper & Riviera, Seattle, 1974-79, 1979-88; ptnr. Foster, Pepper & Shefelman, Seattle, 1988—; bd. dirs. Safeco Mut. Funds, Seattle. Exec. editor U. Wash. Law Rev. Trustee Downtown Seattle Assn., 1982—, v.p. 1985-86, pres., 1986-87; trustee Seattle Art Mus., 1984-92, Seattle Repertory Theatre, 1985-93; bd. dirs. ACT Theater, Seattle, 1979-84; gen. chmn. United Way Campaign for Seattle-King County, 1988. Mem. ABA, Wash. State Bar Assn. (bd. dirs. land use sect.), Urban Land Inst., Seattle C. of C. (gen. counsel 1985-86), Lamda Alpha, Phi Beta Kappa. Clubs: Seattle Tennis, Seattle Yacht, Wash. Athletic. Office: Foster Pepper & Shefelman 1111 3rd Ave Seattle WA 98101-3207

RUNTE, ROSEANN, academic administrator; b. Kingston, N.Y., Jan. 31, 1948; arrived in Can., 1971, naturalized, 1983; d. Robert B. and Anna Loretta (Schorkopf) O'Reilly; m. Hans-Rainer Runte, Aug. 9, 1969. BA summa cum laude, SUNY-New Paltz, 1968; MA, U. Kans., 1969, PhD, 1974, DLitt (hon.), Acadia U., 1989, Meml. U., 1990. Lectr. Bethany Coll., W.Va., 1970-71; lectr. adult studies St. Mary's U., Halifax, N.S., Can., 1971-72; from lectr. to assoc. prof. Dalhousie U., Halifax, 1972-83, asst. dean, 1980-82, chmn. dept. French, 1980-83; pres. Universite Sainte-Anne, Pointe-de-l'Eglise, N.S., Can., 1983-88; prin. Glendon Coll., Toronto, 1988-94; pres., vice chancellor Victoria U., 1994—. Author: Brumes bleues, 1982; Faux-Soleils, 1984, Birmanie Blues, 1993; editor: Studies in 18th Century Culture, vols. VII, VIII, IX, 1977, 78, 79; co-editor: Man and Nature, 1982, Le Développement régional, 1986, 87, From Orality to Literature/de L'Oralite la littérature, 1991, Lectures canadiennes, 1993, Visions of Beauty, 1994; rev. editor French Rev., 1988-94; co-translator Local Development, 1987. Bd. dirs. Assn. Med. Svcs., 1989-92; adv. bd. Nat. Libr., 1984-91; v.p. Can. Commn. for UNESCO, 1991-92, pres., 1992—; vice chair exec. bd. Found. for Internat. Tng., 1994—; chair Gottschalk Prize Com., 1994; chairwoman publs. com. Hannah Found, 1989-92; internat. adv. bd. Expo 2000, 1995—. Decorated Ordre du Mérite; recipient Prix Fr. Coppée French Acad., 1989; regents scholar SUNY-New Paltz, 1965; NDEA Title IV grantee U. Kans., Lawrence, 1968; Acad. Palmes, 1986. Mem. Internat. Soc. 18th Century Studies (assoc. treas. 1983-87), Internat. Assn. of Comparative Lit. (treas. 1985-91, sec. 1991-94), Can. Fedn. Humanities (pres. 1982-84), Atlantic Soc. 18th Century Studies (pres. 1972-76), Canadian Soc. 18th Century Studies (pres. 1975-76), Soc. for Study Higher Edn. (bd. dirs. 1988-90), Found. Internat. Tng. (bd. dirs. 1992), Knights of Malta (grande dame 1991—), Delta Kappa Gamma, Phi Delta Kappa, Club of Rome. Home: 44 Charles St W # 3803, Toronto, ON Canada M4Y 1R8 Office: 73 Queen's Park Crescent, Toronto, ON Canada M5S 1K7

RUNYAN, JOHN WILLIAM, JR., medical educator; b. Memphis, Jan. 23, 1924; s. John William and Lottie (Roberts) R.; m. Barbara Ruth Zerbe, July 16, 1949; children: John William III, Scott Baylor, Keith Roberts. A.B., Washington and Lee U., 1945; M.D., Johns Hopkins, 1947. Diplomate: Am. Bd. Internal Medicine (examiner 1967-72). Intern Johns Hopkins Hosp., 1947-48; asst. to chief resident internist Albany (N.Y.) Hosp., 1948-50; research fellow Harvard Med. Sch., 1950-53, also Thorndike Meml. Lab., Boston City Hosp.; instr., then assoc. prof. medicine Albany Med. Coll., 1953-60; mem. faculty U. Tenn. Med. Sch., 1960—, prof. medicine, 1964—, chief sect. endocrinology, 1963-72, dir. div. health care scis., chmn. dept. community medicine, 1972-87, prof., chmn. preventive medicine, 1987-94, Univ. Disting. prof., 1980—; chief med. svc. John Gaston Hosp., Memphis, 1965-72; cons. endocrinology Memphisa VA Hosp., 1962-70; chmn. Nat. Heart, Blood, Lung Inst. com. on Diabetes and Hypertension, 1985-87; chmn. Generalist and Curriculum Reform Task Force U. of Tenn., 1992-94. Author: Primary Care Guide, 1975, Problem Oriented Primary Care, 1982. Served with AUS, 1951-53. Commonwealth Fund fellow, 1950; recipient John D. Rockefeller III Public Service award in health, 1977; Upjohn award, 1981. Fellow ACP (Rosenthal award 1980, Laureate award Tenn. chpt. 1991, named master 1993); mem. AMA, Am. Fedn. Clin. Rsch., Am. Diabetes Assn. (Outstanding Physician Educator in Diabetes 1981), Tenn. Med. Soc., Memphis Med. Soc., Tenn. Diabetes Soc. (pres. 1968-69). Home: 5496 S Angela Ln Memphis TN 38120-2208

RUNYAN, TIMOTHY JACK, historian, educator; b. Gary, Ind., Aug. 9, 1941; s. Jack Elmore and Mavis Lydia (Lewis) R.; m. Laurie Ann Blackmore, July 25, 1964; children: Christopher T., Michael A. BS, Capital U., 1963; MA, U. Md., 1965; postgrad., U. Md. fellow, U. London, 1967-69; PhD, U. Md., 1972. Instr. U. Md., College Park, 1969; instr. Cleve. State U., 1969-71, asst. prof., 1971-74, assoc. prof., 1974-87, prof. dept. history, 1987—, asst. dean Coll. Arts and Scis., 1976-79, dir. classical and medieval studies, 1978-86, chmn. dept. art, 1981-82, chmn. dept. modern langs., 1982-86; chmn. dept. history, 1991—; vis. prof. Oberlin (Ohio) Coll., 1989; editor Am. Neptune, Jour. of Maritime History, Peabody Mus.. Salem, Mass.. 1990—. Author: European Naval and Maritime History, 300-1500, 1985; editor: Ships, Seafaring and Society, 1987 (John Lyman Book award 1988); contbr. articles to scholarly publs. Mgr. Cleve. Commn. on Higher Edn., 1976-79; pres. Gt. Lakes Mus. Sci., Tech. and Environment, Cleve., 1987-91, vice chair bd. trustees, 1991—; gov.'s appointee to Ohio 1992 Commn., Columbus, 1989-92. Grantee Am. Philos. Soc., 1973, 76; recipient Award of Achievement for Mus. N. Ohio Live, 1991. Fellow Royal Hist. Soc. (London); mem. Internat. Commn. Maritime History (exec. coun. 1985—)

treas. 1990—), N.Am. Soc. Oceanic History (pres. 1980-84), Nat. Maritime Alliance Bd., Nat. Maritime Hist. Soc. (adv bd. 1989—), Gt. Lakes Hist. Soc. (pres. 1985—), Medieval Acad. Am. (nominating com. 1985-87, chair 1990-91), Midwest Medieval Hist. Conf. (pres. 1981-82), Assn. Gt. Lakes Maritime History (v.p. 1984-87). Episcopalian. Avocations: sports, travel. Home: 2597 Dartmoor Rd Cleveland OH 44118-4233 Office: Cleve State U E 22d and Euclid Ave Cleveland OH 44115

RUNYON, KEITH LESLIE, lawyer, newspaper editor; b. Louisville, Oct. 3, 1950; s. Leslie Thomas and Marjorie Fillmore (Fisher) R.; M. Amelia Payne Sweets, Dec. 29, 1979; children: Amelia Brown Payne, Keith Leslie Jr. Student, U. London, 1971; BA cum laude, U. Louisville, 1972, JD, 1982. Staff writer Courier-Jour., Louisville, 1972-77, staff atty., 1984-86; staff atty., assoc. editor Louisville Times and Courier Jour., 1977-86, forum editor, 1986-80; editorial page editor, 1990-92, editor opinion pages, 1992—. Nat. bd. dirs. English-Speaking Union U.S., N.Y., 1996-79, pres. Ky. br., Louisville, 1986-87, U. Louisville Alumni Assn., 1987-93; mem. exec. com. Louisville com. on fgn. rels., 1985-87, Leadership Louisville, 1993-97; clk. Session Calvin Presbyn. Ch., Louisville, 1986-88. Recipient William E. Leidt award The Episc. Ch. of U.S., 1975, Roy Howard award (shared) Scripps Howard Journalists Nat. for Pub. Svc., 1976; named Alumnus of Yr., U. Louisville, 1991. Mem. ABA, Ky. Bar Assn., Louisville Bar Assn., Nat. Conf. Edit. Writers (editor The Masthead, 1994—), Soc. Profl Jours. (Outstanding Editorial Writing award, 1983, 84, 85). Home: Nitta Yuma Harrods Creek KY 40027 Office: Courier-Jour and Louisville Times Co 525 W Broadway St Louisville KY 40202-2137

RUNYON, MARVIN TRAVIS, postmaster general; b. Ft. Worth, Sept. 16, 1924; s. Marvin T. and Lora Lee (Whittington) R.; children: Marvin, Elizabeth Anne, Paul, James. BS in Mgmt. Engring., Tex. A&M U., 1948. Staff mem. mfg. engring. areas assembly plants Ford Motor Co., 1943-60, asst., plant mgr. various assembly plants, 1960-70; mgr. assembly engring. automotive assembly div. gen. office Ford Motor Co., Dearborn, Mich., 1970-72; gen. mgr. automotive assembly div. Ford Motor Co., 1972-73, v.p. body and assembly ops., 1973-77, v.p. powertrain and chassis ops., 1977-78, v.p. body and assembly ops., 1979-80; pres., chief exec. officer Nissan Motor Mfg. Corp. U.S.A., Smyrna, Tenn., 1980-87; chmn. bd. TVA, Knoxville, Tenn., 1988-92; postmaster gen. U.S. Postal Svc., Washington, 1992—; mem. at large Nuclear Power Oversight Com., 1991-92. Bd. dirs. United Way Knoxville, 1988-92, mem. campaign adv. com. 1990; bd. dirs. Downtown Orgn., Knoxville, 1988-92, Tenn. Tech. Found., 1982, NCCJ, 1985-88, Nashville-Davidson County unit Am. Cancer Soc., 1986-88, United Way Rutherford County, 1986-89, Cumberland Mus., Nashville, 1986; participant Leadership Nashville Assn., 1982—, pres., 1986, Leadership Knoxville, 1989, Leadership Memphis, 1990-91; hon. chmn. Clinic Bowl, Nashville, 1986; mem. devel. adv. bd. Ctr. for Internat. Bus. Studies Tex. A&M U., 1987, mem. coll. bus. administrv. devel. coun., 1984-87; mem. outreach com. Knoxville Bicentennial '91 Coord. Coun.; mem. adv. bd. Inroads/Nashville, Inc., 1983—; mem. devel. adv. bd. Nashville State Tech. Inst., 1987; chmn. corp. adv. com. Middle Tenn. Regional Minority Purchasing Coun., 1982-83; mem. gov.'s adv. bd. to S.E./U.S. Japan Assn., 1981; gen. campaign chmn. United Way Nashville and Middle Tenn., 1985-86, trustee, 1984-86; trustee Automotive Hall of Fame, 1985—; chmn. Tenn. Minority Bus. Opportunity Fair, 1987-89, 1992 Trade Fair, Midsouth Minority Purchasing Coun., 1991-92; Sr. Ptnrs. Bd. for May 1992 World Congress of Indsl. Devel. Rsch. Coun., 1991-92; bd. dir. Memphis in May Internat. Festival Inc., 1991-92, Met. Nashville Pub. Edn. Found., 1991-92; mem. U. Tenn. Devel. Coun., 1990—, Nucleus Fund Com. and Internat. Programs Resource Devel. Com., Tex. A&M U. Named Outstanding Man of Year Soc. Advanced Mgmt., 1968, Pres. slot on 1985 Model Yr. Automotive News All-Star Team, Automotive News; recipient Mgr. of Yr. award Avco Aerostructures chpt. Nat. Mgmt. Assn., 1985, CEO of Yr., Advantage mag., 1985, Disting. Service citation Automotive Hall of Fame, 1986, Salesman of Yr., Nashville chpt. Sales and Mktg. Exec. Club, 1985, award Tenn.-Japan Friends in Commerce, 1989; hon. gen. com. Internat. Automotive Engring. Socs. 1988 Congress; recipient Human Rels. award NCCJ Nashville chpt., 1990, Spl. Recognition award Minority Bus. Devel. Agy., 1990, Gold Knight of Mgmt. award Nat. Mgmt. Assn., 1992, Exec. of Yr. award Nat. Mgmt. Assn., 1992, Adv. Mail Mktg. Assns. J. Edward Day award, 1993. Mem. Soc. Automotive Engrs., Engring. Soc. Detroit, Nashville Area C. of C. (bd. govs. 1983-85), Knoxville C. of C. (bd. dirs. 1988-92), Memphis C. of C. (bd. dirs. 1990-92), Tenn. Assn. Bus. (bd. dirs.), Soc. Internat. Bus Fellows, Belle Meade Country Club (Nashville). Episcopalian. Office: US Postal Svc Office of Postmaster Gen 475 L'Enfant Pla West SW Washington DC 20260-0010

RUOFF, ANDREW CHRISTIAN, III, orthopedic surgeon, educator, consultant; b. Jersey City, Apr. 7, 1919. Ba, Dartmouth Coll., 1939; MD, Jefferson Med. Coll., 1943. Diplomate: Am. Bd. Orthopedic Surgery. Intern Mountainside Hosp., Montclair, N.J., 1943; resident in orthopedic surgery Halloran Gen. Hosp., S.I., N.Y., 1945-46, N.J. Orthopedic Hosp., Orange, N.J., 1946-47, Jersey City Med. Ctr., 1947-48; practice medicine specializing in orthopedic surgery Pompton Plains and Paterson, N.J., 1948-67; assoc. clin. prof. Seton Hall Coll. Medicine, 1961-67; asst. prof. surgery U. Utah, Salt Lake City, 1967-70, assoc. prof., 1970-80, asst. dean admissions, 1970-72; pres. med. staff U. Utah Med. Ctr., Salt Lake City, 1971, 73; chief orthopedic surgery Salt Lake VA Med. Ctr., Salt Lake City, 1967-80; prof. orthopedic surgery Ind. U., Indpls., 1980-83, asst. dean Sch. Medicine, 1980-83; chief of staff VA Med. Ctr., Indpls., 1980-83, prof. surgery, 1983-87; prof. surgery Uniformed Svcs., U. Health Scis., Bethesda, Md., 1983-87, clin. prof. surgery, 1987—; clin. prof. surgery U. Utah Coll. Medicine, 1987-91, clin. prof. emeritus, 1991—; mem. Nat. Acad. Sci./NRC Task Force to Determine Feasibility of Nat. Research Ctr. on Emergency and Disaster Svcs., 1965-66; active CARE/MEDICO, 1973-82, mem. medico adv. bd., 1976-82, mem. exec. com., 1980—; dir. emergency mgmt. and resource sharing VA, Washington, 1983-85; dep. asst. chief med. dir. prosthetics and rehab. rsch. VA, 1985-87, acting dir. rehab., 1985-87; staff physician VA Med. Ctr., Salt Lake City, 1987-88; oral examiner Am. Bd. Orthopedic Surgery, 1968-82, mem. residency rev. com., 1980-81; orthopaedic cons. VA Med. Ctr., Miami, 1994—. Contbr. articles, chpts. to med. publs. Med. adviser Multiple Sclerosis Soc., Utah, 1967-80; mem. Utah Gov.'s Emergency Med. Services Council, 1973-80, chmn., 1973-75; mem. Intermountain Regional Med. Program Regional Adv. Council, 1973-76, Greater Salt Lake Health Planning Council, 1974-76, Utah Health Planning Adv. Com., 1978-79; treas. Park Ave. Assn., Park City, Utah, 1979-80, pres., 1980-81. Served with USAR, 1956-69. Mem. AMA (adv. com. current procedural terminology 1987—), ACS (com. on pubs. for com. on trauma 1972-80, vice chmn. com. on trauma 1975-79, VA chmn. com. on trauma 1980-86, chmn. com. on applicants 1976-80), Am. Assn. Surgery Trauma (bd. govs. 1973-75, v.p. 1979-80), Orthopedic Rsch. and Edn. Found. (founder mem., Utah 1967-70), Am. Acad. Orthopedic Surgeons, Internat. Soc. Orthopedics and Trauma, Orthopedics Overseas, Inc. (founder mem., chmn. 1981), Am. Trauma Soc. (founder mem., chmn. ho. of dels. 1974, bd. dirs. 1974-79, emeritus cons. 1979—, program chmn. 1995—), Rocky Mountain Traumatol. Soc., Soc. Mil. Orthopedic Surgeons, Soc. Med. Cons. to Armed Forces (sec.-treas. 1981-84, v.p. 1984-85, pres. 1985-86, alt. del. to AMA 1988-91, del. to AMA 1991—), Ret. Officers Assn. (pres. intermountain chpt. 1989-90, Jefferson Orthopedic Soc., Egyptian Orthopedic Assn. (hon.), Internat. Coll. Surgeons, Jefferson Alumni Assn. (Utah state v.p. 1976-80), World Orthopedic Concern (founding mem., hon., bd. dirs., Am. Legion, Mil. Order of World Wars (comdr. Indpls. 1983). Address: 8814 SE Riverfront Ter Tequesta FL 33469

RUOFF, ARTHUR LOUIS, physicist, educator; b. Ft. Wayne, Ind., Sept. 17, 1930; s. Louis A. and Wilma (Rall) R.; m. Enid Frances Seaton, Jan. 24, 1954; children—William Louis, Stephen Arthur, Rodney Scott, Jeffrey Kevin, Kenneth James. B.S., Purdue U., 1952; Ph.D., U. Utah, 1955. Asst. prof. materials sci. and engring. Cornell U., 1955-58, assoc. prof., 1958-65, prof., 1965—, Class of 1912 prof. engring., 1978—, chmn. dept. materials sci. and engring., 1978-88, dir. Cornell ceramics program, 1987—. Author: Introduction to Materials Science, 1972, Materials Science, 1973, Introductory Materials Science, 1973, Concepts of Packaged Courses, 1973. Pres. Ithaca (N.Y.) Youth Hockey, 1972-73. Named Engr. of Distinction Engrs. Joint Coun., 1970; recipient Bridgman award Internat. Assn. Advancement of High Pressure Sci. and Tech., 1993. Fellow Am. Phys. Soc., Böhmlische Physicalische Soc.; mem. N.Y. Acad. Scis. Office: Materials Sci and Engring Bard Hall Cornell U Ithaca NY 14853

RUOFF, CYNTHIA OSOWIEC, foreign language educator; b. Chgo., Mar. 1, 1943; d. Stephen R. and Estelle (Wozniak) O.; m. Gary Edward Ruoff, June 5, 1965; children: Gary S., Laura A. AB, Loyola U., 1965; MA, Western Mich. U., 1973; PhD in French Lang. and Lit., Mich. State U., 1992. Tchr. Kalamazoo (Mic.) Pub. Schs., 1965-68; instr. Western Mich. U., Kalamazoo, 1980—; nat. and internat. spkr. in field. Contbr. articles to profl. jours. Mem. MLA, N.Am. Soc. Seventeenth-Century French Lit., Am. Assn. Tchrs. of French, Mich. Fgn. Lang. Assn., Internat. Soc. Phenomenology and Lit., L'Alliance Française, Southeast Am. Soc. French Seventeenth-Century Studies, Phi Sigma Iota, Pi Delta Phi. Avocations: piano, skiing. Office: Dept Fgn Langs & Lit Western Mich Univ Kalamazoo MI 49008

RUPERT, DONALD WILLIAM, lawyer; b. Clearfield, Pa., Oct. 15, 1946; s. Donald Lee and Dorothy Mae (Bonsall) R.; m. Patricia A. Rupert, June 21, 1969. BS in Chemistry, Miami U., Ohio, 1968; JD, Washburn U., Topeka, 1976. Bar: Tex. 1976, Ill. 1978, U.S. Ct. Appeals (Fed. cir.) 1978, U.S. Dist. Ct. (so. dist.) Tex. 1977, U.S. Ct. Appeals (7th cir.) 1981, U.S. Dist. Ct. (no. dist.) Ill. 1979, U.S. Supreme Ct., 1992. Assoc. Arnold, White & Durkee, Houston, 1976-78, Kirkland & Ellis, Chgo., 1978-83, ptnr., 1983-86; ptnr. Neuman, Williams, Anderson & Olson, Chgo., 1986-90; founding ptnr. Roper & Quigg, 1990-93; ptnr. Keck, Mahin & Cate, Chgo., 1993—; cons. USAF, Dayton, Ohio, 1974-81. Contbr. articles to profl. jours. Served to capt. USAF, 1968-74. Miami U. Undergrad. Rsch. fellow, 1967, Grad. Rsch. fellow, 1968. Mem. ABA, Am. Intellectual Property Law Assn., Tex. Bar Assn., Ill. Bar Assn., Phi Kappa Phi. Democrat. Presbyterian. Home: 2519 Park Pl Evanston IL 60201-1315 Office: Keck Mahin & Cate 77 W Wacker Dr Ste 4900 Chicago IL 60601-1693

RUPERT, ELIZABETH ANASTASIA, retired university dean; b. Emlenton, Pa., July 12, 1918; d. John Hamilton and Eva Blanche (Elliott) R. Diploma, Altoona Sch. Commerce, 1936; BS in Edn., Clarion State Coll., 1959; MSLS, Syracuse U., 1962; PhD, U. Pitts., 1970. Sec. Quaker State Oil Refining Corp., 1939-56; tchr., libr. Oil City Area Schs., 1959-61; libr. Venango campus Clarion (Pa.) U., 1961-62; prof. Coll. Libr. Sci. Clarion (Pa.) U., Clarion, 1962-70; dean Sch. Libr. Sci., Coll. Libr. Sci. Clarion (Pa.) U., 1971-85; prof. emeritus, 1994; interim pres. Clarion U., spring 1977; acct. William Rupert Mortuary, Inc., 1948-88. Author: Pennsylvania Practicum Program for School Librarians: An Appraisal, 1970; mem. ad hoc edit. com. Pa. Media Guidelines, Pa. Dept. Edn., 1976, author (with others) Encyclopedia of Library and Information Science, 1984. Bd. dirs. Knox Pub. Libr.; mem. Abscurf Sec. Ch. Orgns.; active Knox Civic Club. Recipient Disting. Faculty award Clarion U. Alumni Assn., 1976, Disting. Alumni award, 1987. Mem. ALA, Zonta Internat. (Women of Achievement award 1987), Beta Phi Mu, Pi Gamma Mu. Republican. Home: PO Box H Knox PA 16232

RUPERT, (LYNN) HOOVER, minister; b. Madison, N.J., Nov. 3, 1917; s. Lynn Hoover and Hazel L. (Linabary) R.; m. Hazel Pearl Senti, June 22, 1941; children—Susan (Mrs. Max Unland), Elizabeth (Mrs. Warren W. Wright). A.B., Baker U., 1938; A.M., Boston U., 1940, M.Div. cum laude, 1941; student (summers), Garrett Bibl. Inst. and Northwestern U., 1942, Union Theol. Sem., 1943; D.D., Adrian Coll., 1952, Baker U., 1966; L.H.D., Milliken U., 1974. Ordained to ministry Methodist Ch., 1940; asst. pastor First Meth. Ch., Baldwin, Kans., 1936-38, St. Mark's Meth. Ch., Brookline, Mass., 1938-41; pastor Thayer-St. Paul, Kans., 1941-43, First Ch., Olathe, Kans., 1943-45; dir. youth dept. Gen. Bd. Edn. Meth. Ch., Nashville, 1945-50; pastor 1st Meth. Ch., Jackson, Mich., 1950-59; pastor 1st United Meth. Ch., Ann Arbor, Mich., 1959-72, Kalamazoo, 1972-83; faculty dept. religion Fla. So. Coll., Lakeland, 1983-89; adj. faculty Wesley Theol. Sem., Washington, 1989-93; dean Mich. Meth. Pastors Sch., 1955-65; mem. Jud. Council United Meth. Ch., 1968-88 , sec., 1976-88, sec. emeritus, 1988. Author: Prayer Poems on the Prayer Perfect, 1943, Christ Above All (editor), 1948, Youth and Evangelism, 1948, Youth and Stewardship, rev. 1960, Your Life Counts (editor), 1950, What Methodists Believe, rev. 1959, John Wesley and People Called Methodists, 1953, I Belong, 1954, And Jesus Said, 1960, Enjoy Your Teen-Ager, 1962, A Sense of What is Vital, 1964, The Church in Renewal, 1965, My People are Your People, 1968, Where is thy Sting?, Christian Perspectives on Death, 1969, What's Good about God?, 1975, God Will See You Through, 1976, An Instrument of Thy Peace, 1982, The High Cost of Being Human, 1986, Why Didn't Noah Swat Both Mosquitoes, 1993; writer, syndicated weekly mag. column Accent on Living; newspaper series Prayer for Today; newspaper feature Talking to Teens; other publs., periodicals and newspapers. Trustee Bronson Hosp., 1972-83, Adrian Coll.; pres. bd. dirs. Youth For Understanding, 1970-83, Ann Arbor United Fund, YMCA-YWCA. Recipient Distinguished Alumnus award Boston U., 1969; Lucinda Bidwell Beebe fellow Boston U., 1941. Mem. World Meth. Council, Nat. Council Chs., Mark Twain Soc., Nat. Forensic League, Pi Kappa Delta, Alpha Psi Omega. Lodges: Mason, Rotary (Paul Harris fellow 1983). Home: 403 Russell Ave Gaithersburg MD 20877-2811

RUPERT, JOHN EDWARD, retired savings and loan executive, business and civic affairs consultant; b. Cleve., Oct. 19, 1927; s. Edward J. and Emma (Levegood) R.; m. Virginia Carlson, Oct. 27, 1951; children: Kristen, Karen Rupert Keating, David. B.A., Cornell U., 1949, LL.B., 1951; certificate Grad. Sch. Savs. & Loan, Ind. U., 1958. With Broadview Savs. & Loan Co., Cleve., 1953-86; v.p. Broadview Savs. & Loan Co., 1964-74, mng. officer, 1965-86, pres., chief exec. officer, 1974-86, chmn., 1979-86. Mem. Cleve. Real Estate Bd., 1955-86; mem. Lakewood (Ohio) Bd. Edn., 1971-77, pres., 1975-77; v.p., trustee Lakewood Hosp., 1966-71; trustee exec. com. of Cleve. Zool. Soc., pres. 1982-83; chmn., 1992—; trustee Cleve. Orch., WVIZ Ednl. TV; bd. dirs. West Side YMCA; mem. Greater Cleve. Literacy Coalition, 1991—; mem. Cornell U. Coun., 1971—, pres., 1977; trustee Med. Ctr. Corp., 1987—, chair, 1990—; trustee Internat. Ctr. for Preservation of Wild Animals, 1991—. With USAF, 1951-53. Mem. Cleve. Interfaith Housing Corp. (pres. 1971—), Inst. Fin. Edn. (pres. 1970), Cleve. Real Property Inventory (pres. 1976—), Ohio Motorists Assn., Delta Kappa Epsilon, Phi Delta Phi, Sphinx Head Soc. Clubs: Cleve. Yachting, Cornell (Cleve.) (trustee); Cornell (N.Y.C.). Home and Office: 18129 W Clifton Rd Cleveland OH 44107-1037

RUPLEY, THEODORE J., insurance company executive; b. Sacramento, Apr. 28, 1939; s. Charles Jerrett and Amelia Mea (Oswald) R.; m. Geraldine Annette Wilson, Aug. 14, 1960 (div. Jan. 8, 1977); children: Theodore, Joseph, Elizabeth; m. Candace Joy Newman, Jan. 8, 1979; 1 child, Mea. B.S. in Econs., U. Nev., 1962. With Allstate Ins., Sacramento, 1964-67; research analyst, underwriter, pricer Allstate Research Ctr., Menlo Park, Calif., 1967-69; field rev. mgr. Allstate Research Ctr., Chgo., 1969; mgr. underwriting Allstate Ins. Co., Houston and New England, 1970-73; territorial underwriting mgr. Allstate Ins. Co., Atlanta, 1973-75; regional v.p. Allstate Ins. Co., Indpls., 1975-77, Hartford, Conn., 1977-79; v.p. underwriting Allstate Ins. Co., Northbrook, Ill., 1979-81, sr. v.p., 1984-85; exec. v.p. Allstate Ins. Co., Cupertino, Calif. 1982-86; dir. Allstate Ins. Co.; pres., chief exec. officer Met. Property & Liability Ins. Co., Warwick, R.I., 1986—; bd. dirs. Ins. Info. Inst., Alliance Am. Insurers; trustee Ins. Inst. Am. Bd. dirs. Neighborhood Housing Services Am., Oakland, Calif., 1979-82; trustee Republican Leadership Council, Assn. Calif. Ins. Cos., Sacramento. Served to capt. C.E., U.S. Army, 1962-64. Lutheran. Avocations: boating, golf, skiing, fishing, hunting. Office: Met Property & Liability Ins Co 700 Quaker Ln Warwick RI 02886-6681

RUPP, FRANK A., III, association executive; b. Syracuse, N.Y., Sept. 29, 1947; s. Frank A. Jr. and Marilyn June (Mammerle) R.; m. Cynthia Marie Montague, Oct. 8, 1993; twins: Peter and Colin; children from previous marriage: Frank A. IV, Jason W. BS, Rutgers U., 1970, postgrad., 1970-72. Environ. engr. City of Raleigh, N.C., 1972-75, State of Ill., Chgo, 1975-85; mng. dir. Chgo. (Ill.) Historic Panel, 1985-87; pres. Sportscare Vintage Racing Assn., Charleston, S.C., 1988-89, 91—, Racing Ventures, Charleston, 1989-90. Avocations: vintage car racing, wooden boats, electronics. Office: Sportscar Vintage Racing PO Box 489 N Atlantic Whorf Charleston SC 29401

RUPP, GEORGE ERIK, university president; b. Summit, N.J., Sept. 22, 1942; s. Gustav Wilhelm and Erika (Braunoehler) R.; m. Nancy Katherine Farrar, Aug. 22, 1964; children: Katherine Heather, Stephanie Karin. Student, Ludwig Maximilians U., Munich, Germany, 1962-63; A.B.,

Princeton U., 1964; B.D., Yale U., 1967; postgrad., U. Sri Lanka, Peradeniya, 1969-70; PhD, Harvard U., 1972. Ordained to ministry Presbyn. Ch. U.S.A., 1971; faculty fellow in religion, vice chancellor Johnston College, U. Redlands, Redlands, Calif., 1971-74; asst. prof. Harvard Divinity School, Harvard U., Cambridge, Mass., 1974-76, assoc. prof., 1976-77, prof., dean, 1979-85; prof., dean acad. affairs U. Wis., Green Bay, 1977-79; prof., pres. Rice U., Houston, Tex., 1985-93; Columbia U., N.Y.C., 1993—; bd. dirs. Panhandle Ea. Corp. Author: Christologies and Cultures: Toward a Typology of Religious Worldviews, 1974, Culture Protestantism: German Liberal Theology at the Turn of the Twentieth Century, 1977, Beyond Existentialism and Zen: Religion in a Pluralistic World, 1979, Commitment and Community, 1989; contbr. articles to profl. jours. Bd. dirs. Amigos de las Americas, Consortium on Financing Higher Edn., Martel Found., Inc.. Danforth Grad. fellow, 1964-71. Mem. AAAS, Soc. for Values in Higher Edn., Am. Acad. Religion. Office: Columbia Univ 202 Law Libr New York NY 10027*

RUPP, GLENN N., sporting goods executive; b. Washington, Sept. 27, 1944; s. Glenn N. and Verda Mae (McCullough) R.; m. Judith Carpenter, Dec. 28, 1968; children: Kerry, Edward. BS, Duke U., 1966; MBA, Harvard U., 1968. Pres. N.Am. Van Lines Can., Toronto, Ont., 1971-75; v.p., gen. mgr. N.Am. Van Lines, Ft. Wayne, Ind., 1975-79; v.p. internat. PepsiCo Inc., Purchase, N.Y., 1979, 82, Frankfurt, Fed. Republic Germany, 1980-82; v.p., gen. mgr. internat. Wilson Sporting Goods Co., River Grove, Ill., 1983-85, pres., chief ops. officer, 1985-87, pres., chief exec. officer, 1987—; also bd. dirs.; bd. dirs. Nat. Golf Found., Jupiter, Fla., 1986—. Mem. Sporting Goods Mfgs. Assn., Caribbean, Cen. Am. Action Com., Lake Forest Club, Knollwood Club, Harvard Club (N.Y.C.). Office: Wilson Sporting Goods Co 2233 N West St River Grove IL 60171-1895

RUPP, JOHN NORRIS, lawyer; b. Seattle, Mar. 18, 1913; s. Otto Burton and Edith Cornelia (Norris) R.; m. Elizabeth Milner McElroy, Aug. 31, 1937; children: Joanne (Mrs. George Crispin), William John, Elizabeth (Mrs. Brian Fulwiler), James McElroy. A.B., U. Wash., 1934, J.D., 1937. Bar: Wash. 1937. Law clk. to chief justice Wash. State Supreme Ct., Olympia, 1937-38; atty. McMicken, Rupp & Schweppe, Seattle, 1939-62; v.p., gen. counsel Pacific N.W. Bell Telephone Co., 1962-75; of counsel Schweppe, Krug & Tausend, Seattle, 1975-90, Preston Gates and Ellis, Seattle, 1990—. Mem. Wash. State Bd Edn., 1957-67; mem. Seattle Transit Commn., 1957-62, Wash. State Hwy. Commn., 1967-73. Served from ensign to lt. (j.g.) USNR, 1944-46. Decorated Bronze Star. Mem. ABA (ho. dels. 1964-68), Wash. Bar Assn. (pres. 1966-67), Seattle Bar Assn. (pres. 1956-57), Seattle C. of C. (gen. counsel 1960-62), Mcpl. League of Seattle (pres. 1948-50), Seattle Hist. Soc. (pres. 1978-79), Order of Coif, Phi Gamma Delta, Phi Delta Phi. Clubs: Rainier, Monday, Harbor, Seattle Yacht. Home: 6403 Sand Point Way NE Seattle WA 98115-7915 Office: 5000 Columbia Seafirst Ctr 701 5th Ave Seattle WA 98104-7016

RUPP, MARK EDMUND, medical educator. BSChemE, U. Tex., 1981; MD, Baylor Coll. Medicine, 1984. Diplomate Am. Bd. Internal Medicine, Am. Bd. Infectious Diseases. Postdoctoral fellow dept. microbiology and immunology Baylor Coll. Medicine, Houston, 1985; intern in internal medicine Med. Coll. Va./Va. Commonwealth U., Richmond, 1985-86, resident in internal medicine, 1986-88, infectious disease fellow, 1988-91, instr. internal medicine, 1991-92; asst. prof. dept. medicine and med. microbiology Sch. Medicine Creighton U., Omaha, 1992—; asst. prof. dept. internal medicine U. Nebr. Med. Ctr., Omaha, 1992—, asst. prof. dept. pathology and microbiology, 1993—; attending physician McGuire Vets Affairs Med. Ctr., Richmond, 1991-92, St. Joseph's Hosp., Omaha, 1992—, Omaha Vets Affairs Med. Ctr.; spkr. in field; instr. physical diagnosis Med. Coll. Va., Va. Commonwealth U., 1991, U. Nebr. Med. Ctr., 1993; guest, invited lectr. univs., confs., med. socs., med. schs. Contbr. book chpts., abstracts, articles to profl. jours.; patentee. Recipient Young Investigators award Nat. Found. Infectious Diseases, 1993, Nat. Rsch. Svc. award NIH, 1991; Am. Heart Assn. grantee, 1993, Rsch. Project grantee Soc. Med. Assn., 1991, Collaborative Rsch. grantee NATO, 1993. Fellow ACP; mem. Infectious Diseases Soc. Am., Am. Soc. Microbiology, Soc. Hosp. Epidemiology of Am. Office: U Nebraska Med Ctr Dept Internal Med 600 S 42nd St Omaha NE 68198-5400

RUPP, RALPH RUSSELL, audiologist, educator, author; b. Saginaw, Mich., Apr. 12, 1929; s. Martin Carl and Veronica Marie (Riethmeier) R. B.A., U. Mich., 1951, M.A., 1952; Ph.D., Wayne State U., 1964. Speech and hearing cons. Detroit Pub. Schs., 1955-60; exec. dir. Detroit Hearing and Speech Center, 1960-62; assoc. in audiology Henry Ford Hosp., Detroit, 1962-65; prof. audiology U. Mich., Ann Arbor, 1965-89; coordinator audiology Eastern Mich. U., 1985-93; cons. St. Joseph Mercy Hosp., Ann Arbor, Ann Arbor VA Hosp., Mott Children's Health Center, Flint, Mich., Pontiac (Mich.) Gen. Hosp.; pres. Detroit Hearing Center, 1966. Author: (with James Maurer) Hearing and Aging: Tactics for Intervention, 1979, (with Kenneth Stockdell) Speech Protocols in Audiology, 1980; contbr. articles to profl. jours. Served with Med. Service Corps, U.S. Army, 1953-55. Named Disting. Alumnus, Saginaw High Sch., 1981, Outstanding Grad., Wayne State U. Fellow Am. Speech, Lang. and Hearing Assn. (Editor's award); mem. Acad. Rehab. Audiology (past editor Jour.), Mich. Speech and Hearing Assn. (pres. 1954, Disting. Service award, past editor Jour, honor award). Home: 1395 Laurel View Dr Ann Arbor MI 48105

RUPP, SHERON ADELINE, photographer, educator; b. Mansfield, Ohio, Jan. 14, 1943; d. Warren Edmund Rupp and Frances Adeline (Hanson) Christian. BA in Sociology and Psychology, Denison U., 1965; MFA in Photography, U. Mass., 1982. Teaching asst. in photography Hampshire Coll., Amherst, Mass., 1981; instr. photography Northfield (Mass.) Mt. Hermon Sch., 1982-83, U. Mass., 1984, Holyoke (Mass.) Community Coll., 1986, 87-88; vis. asst. prof. photography Hampshire Coll., 1985, 87; vis. lectr. photography Amherst (Mass.) Coll., 1994; guest artist, lectr. Boston Mus. Sch., Portland (Maine) Sch. Art, NYU, U. Mass., Deerfield (Mass.) Acad., Hartford Sch. Art/U. Hartford-Conn., Springfield Mus. Fine Arts, Mass., Bard Coll, N.Y., Mass. Coll. Art, Boston, others. Exhibited in one-person shows at Tisch Sch. Arts, NYU, 1987, Portland Sch. Art, 1989, Hart Gallery, Northampton, Mass., 1992, O.K. Harris Gallery, N.Y.C., 1992; exhibited in group shows at Zone Art Ctr., N.Y.C., 1987, Mus. of Modern Art, N.Y.C., 1991, Springfield Mus. Fine Art, 1993, U. Mass., Amherst, 1993, Dirs. Guild, L.A., 1994, Manchester (N.H.) Inst. Arts and Scis., 1995; represented in collections at Mus. Modern Art, N.Y.C., Fogg Art Mus. at Harvard U., Rose Art Mus. at Brandeis U., Smith Coll. Mus. Art, U. Mass., Mead Art Mus., Amherst Coll., Boston Mus. Fine Arts, Springfield Mus. Fine Arts, Danforth Mus. Fine Arts, Framingham, Mass; contbr. photographs and articles to jours. Bd. dirs., mem. artistic com. Zone Art Ctr., 1987-94. Recipient Mass. Fellowship award in photography Artist Found., 1984, 87; visual arts fellow Nat. Endowment for the Arts, 1986; Guggenheim fellow, 1990, visual artist fellowship Nat. Endowment for Arts, 1994. Avocations: gardening, bicycling, writing. Home and Office: 100 Chestnut St Northampton MA 01060-1407

RUPP, WILLIAM JOHN, architect; b. Phila., Aug. 25, 1927; s. Frank Julius and Sara Viola (Hibbs) R.; m. Gwendolyn O'Rourke, May 10, 1956; children: Susan Hibbs, Molly O'Rourke, Jason Franz. B.Arch., U. Fla., 1953. Draftsman Paul Rudolph, Architect, Sarasota, Fla., 1953-55; pvt. practice architecture Sarasota and Naples, Fla., 1956-67; assoc. Morris Ketchum, Jr. & Assos., Architects, N.Y.C., 1968-72; mem. firm Callister, Payne & Bischoff (architects and community planners), Amherst, Mass., 1972-75; pvt. practice architecture and planning, 1975—; vis. lectr. U. Mass., 1976-78, asst. prof., 1978-84, assoc. prof., 1984-91, prof., 1991—. Author: (with A.W. Friedmann) Construction Materials for Interior Designers, 1989; contbr. articles to jours. With AUS, 1945-46, 2d lt., 1952. Recipient Archtl. Record award for Housing Design, 1960; Progressive Architecture Design award, 1961. Corp. mem. AIA (N.Y. chpt. 1st award for House Design 1964). Home: 128 Dry Hill Rd Montague MA 01351-9555 Office: U of Mass Fine Arts Center Amherst MA 01003

RUPPE, LORET MILLER, former ambassador; b. Milw., Jan. 3, 1936; d. Frederick C. Miller and Adele (Kanaley) O'Shaughnessy; m. Philip E. Ruppe, Nov. 30, 1957; children: Antoinette B., Adele E., Loret M., Katherine T., Mary Speed. D Pub. Svc. (hon.), No. Mich. U., 1981; LHD (hon.), Marymount Coll., 1981, Luther Coll., 1990; HHD (hon.), Wheeling Coll., 1982, Loyola U., 1987; DCL (hon.), Marquette U., 1983, Marquette

U., 1986; hon. degree, Nebr. Wesleyan U., Augustana Coll., Concordia Coll., 1994, St. Bonaventure, 1994, Pace U., Concordia Coll.. St. Bonaventure U. Chair Bush Campaign Com., Mich., 1980; co-chair Reagan-Bush Com., Mich., 1980; dir. Peace Corps, Washington, 1981-89; amb. to Norway U.S. Embassy, Oslo, 1989-93. Chair Vice Presdl. Inaugural Reception, 1981; trustee U. Notre Dame, 1988—; bd. dirs. Nat. Peace Garden, Save the Children, The Hewlett Found., Winrock Internat. Decorated Grand Cross Royal Norwegian Order of Merit, Dame of Sovereign Mil. Order Malta. Mem. LWV, Internat. Neighbor's Club IV, Overseas Edn. Fund (hon.), Coun. Am. Ambs., The Explorer's Club, Sons of Norway. Roman Catholic. Avocations: reading, tennis. Office: 1 Darby Ct Bethesda MD 20817-2910

RUPPEL, EDWARD THOMPSON, geologist; b. Ft. Morgan, Colo., Oct. 26, 1925; s. Henry George and Gladys Myrtle (Thompson) R.; m. Phyllis Beale Tanner, June 17, 1956; children: Lisa, David, Douglas, Kristin. BA, U. Mont., 1948; MA, U. Wyo., 1950; PhD, Yale U., 1958. Cert. profl. geologist. Geologist U.S. Geol. Survey, Washington and Denver, 1948-86; chief cen. regional br. U.S. Geol. Survey, Denver, 1971-75, geologist, 1975-86; dir., state geologist Mont. Bur. Mines and Geology, Butte, 1986-94; geol. cons., 1994—. Contbr. about 40 articles to profl. jours. With USNR, 1943-46. Fellow Geol. Soc. Am., Soc. Econ. Geologists; mem. Am. Inst. Profl. Geologists, Mont. Geol. Soc., Tobacco Root Geol. Soc., Rotary. Office: PO Drawer K 326 S Main St Twin Bridges MT 59754

RUPPEL, GEORGE ROBERT, accountant; b. N.Y.C., Jan. 6, 1911; s. George W. and Cornelia (Klein) R.; m. Eleanor Holton, Apr. 4, 1941; children—Sandra, Shirley, Lorraine. Grad., St. John's U., 1933. C.P.A. N.Y. State. Chief accountant Am. Agrl. Chem. Co., 1930-36; financial supr. Am. Water Works & Electric Co., 1936-44; v.p., treas., dir. MBS, Inc., 1944-57; v.p., treas. RKO Gen., Inc., 1957-60; treas. Visual Drama, Inc., 1957-60; v.p. finance, dir. Hwy. Trailer Industries, Inc.; v.p., treas. Clinton Engines Corp., 1960-63; pres. Tomahawk Enterprises, Inc., 1963—, Gehar Co., 1963—; financial cons. Treas. RKO Teleradio Found., 1957-60. Mem. Tax Execs. Inst. (past pres., dir. N.Y. chpt.), Fin. Execs. Inst., N.Y. State Soc. CPAs, Inst. of Mgmt. Accts., Nat. Tax Assn. Address: Pound Ridge Rd Bedford NY 10506

RUPPEL, HOWARD JAMES, JR., sociologist, sexologist, educator; b. Orange, N.J., July 22, 1941; s. Howard J. and Lillian M. (Wordley) R.; m. Barbara Margaret Wiedemann, June 3, 1967. BA, St. Joseph's Coll., Ind., 1963; MA, No. Ill. U., 1968; postgrad. U. Iowa, 1968-76; EdD Inst. for Advanced Study of Human Sexualty, San Francisco, Ca., 1993; PhD 1994. Diplomate Am. Bd. Sexology. Instr. social sci. St. Francis High Sch., Wheaton, Ill., 1963-65, debate coach, 1963-65; instr. sociology St. Dominic Coll., St. Charles, Ill., 1966-67; instr. sociology Cornell Coll., Mt. Vernon, Iowa, 1969-70, asst. prof., 1970-72, lectr., 1972-73; rsch. dir. Social Sci. Rsch. Assos., Cedar Rapids, Iowa, 1973-80; founder, co-dir. Center for Sexual Growth and Devel., Mt. Vernon, 1980—; instr. Sch. Social Work, U. Iowa, 1976-78, adj. asst. prof., 1979-81, adj. assoc. prof., 1981—; exec. dir. Soc. for Sci. Study of Sex, 1988—, Found. for the Sci. Study of Sexuality, 1989—; cons. Iowa Dept. Social Svcs., Families Inc., West Branch; bd. dirs. The Human Outreach and Achievement Inst., Boston, 1988-90—; Found. for the Sci. Study of Sexuality, 1988—; profl. adv. bd. The Sinclair Inst. NSF fellow, 1968. Cert. sexologist Am. Coll. Sexologists. Mem. Am. Sociol. Assn., Nat. Coun. Family Rels., Iowa Coun. Family Rels. (sec. 1983-84, treas. 1985), Changing Family Conf. (bd. dirs. 1983-87), Soc. Sci. Study of Sex Inc. (bd. dirs. 1983-88, pres. Midcontinent Region, 1984-85, treas. 1986-88, chmn. membership com. 1983-85, chmn. exhibits com. 1983-88, ann. meeting chmn. 1986), Am. Assn. Sex Educators, Counselors and Therapists, Soc. Sex Therapy and Research (research mem.), Harry Benjamin Internat. Gender Dysphoria Assn., Coun. Assns. for Sexual Sci., Health and Edn. (del.), Nat. Forensic League, No. Ill. U. Alumni Assn., Alpha Kappa Delta, Alpha Sigma Lambda (hon.). Democrat. Co-editor: Sexuality and the Family Life Span, 1983, Annual Review of Sex Research, 1992, 93, 94, 95; contbr. articles on complex orgns., marriage and the family, sexual attitudes and behavior, childhood and preadolescent sexuality, methodology and child care theory to profl. publs. Home: 608 5th Ave N Mount Vernon IA 52314-1107 Office: SSSS PO Box 208 Mount Vernon IA 52314-0208

RUPPERT, JOHN LAWRENCE, lawyer; b. Chgo., Oct. 7, 1953; s. Merle Arvin and Loretta Marie (Ford) R.; m. Katharine Marie Tarbox, June 5, 1976. BA, Northwestern U., 1975; JD, U. Denver, 1978; LLM in Taxation, NYU, 1979. Bar: Colo. 1978, U.S. Dist. Ct. Colo. 1978, Ill. 1979, U.S. Tax Ct. 1981. Assoc. Kirkland & Ellis, Denver, 1979-84, ptnr., 1984-88; ptnr. Ballard, Spahr, Andrews & Ingersoll, Denver, 1988—; lectr. U. Denver Coll. Law, fall, 1984-92, adj. prof. law grad. tax program, 1993—. Contbr. articles to profl. jours. Mem. ABA, Colo. Bar Assn. (exec. coun. tax sect. 1985-89), Denver Bar Assn., Equipment Leasing Assn. Am. Office: Ballard Spahr Andrews & Ingersoll 1225 17th St Ste 2300 Denver CO 80202-5596

RUPPRECHT, CAROL SCHREIER, comparative literature educator, dream researcher; b. Stafford Springs, Conn., June 30, 1939; d. William Joseph and Caroline Brown (Comstock) Schreier; divorced; children: Jody Francine, Whitney Glenn; m. Richard P. Suttmeier, May 8, 1987. BS, U. Va., 1962; MA, Yale U., 1963, M in Philosophy, 1973, PhD, 1977. Teaching fellow Yale U., 1973; asst. prof. Kirkland Coll., Clinton, N.Y., 1974-78; asst. prof. Hamilton Coll., Clinton, 1978-81, assoc. dean, 1981-82, assoc. prof. comparative lit., 1982-89; prof., 1989—, chmn. dept., 1984-89; lectr. Switzerland, Israel, The Netherlands, Ireland, People's Republic China, Eng., Japan. Author, editor: The Dream and the Text: Essays on Literature and Language, 1993; co-editor and author: Feminist Archetypal Theory, 1985; cons. editor Dreaming; contbr. articles to profl. jours., chpts. to books. NEH fellow Dartmouth Dante Inst., 1986. Founding mem. Assn. for Study Dreams, 1983, Conn. Assn. Jungian Psychology, 1981. Merrill fellow Bunting Inst., 1970-72. Mem. MLA, Am. Comparative Lit. Assn., Shakespeare Soc., Assn. Study of Dreams (pres., v.p. bd. dirs., mem. editorial bd.), Conn. Assn. for Jungian Psychology (bd. dirs.). Avocations: sports; wilderness activities. Office: Hamilton Coll Clinton NY 13323

RUSAW, SALLY ELLEN, librarian; b. Potsdam, N.Y., Apr. 24, 1939; d. Ralph Clinton and Marion Ellen (Jenack) R. BS in Edn., Potsdam Coll., 1964; MLS, SUNY, Albany, 1975. Cert. libr. media specialist, pub. libr., permanent libr. N-6, N.Y. Tchr. grade 7th-9th Diocese of Ogdensburg, N.Y., 1960-74, cons. office edn., 1975-78; assoc. libr. Mater Dei Coll., Ogdensburg, 1974-89, head libr., 1989—. Vol. Ogdensburg Correctional Facility, 1982, Riverview Correctional Facility, Ogdensburg 1987—; lectr. Eucharistic min., Rite for Christian Initiation of Adults catechist St. Mary's Cathedral; vol. Ogdensburg Cath. Ctrl. Sch. Named Vol. of Yr. Ogdensburg Correctional Facility, 1985, Outstanding Vol. Riverview Correctional Facility, 1991; Nat. Def. Edn. Act grantee, 1965. Mem. ALA, N.Y. Libr. Assn., North Country 3Rs Coun., North Country Ref. and Rsch. Resources Coun. (trustee 1994—). Roman Catholic. Avocations: music, reading, berrying, outdoor activities, swimming. Office: Mater Dei Coll Augsbury Meml Libr Ogdensburg NY 13669-9669

RUSCH, THOMAS WILLIAM, manufacturing executive; b. Alliance, Nebr., Oct. 3, 1946; s. Oscar William and Gwen Falerne (Middleswart) R.; m. Gloria Ann Sutton, June 20, 1968 (div. Oct. 1979); children: Alicia Catherine, Colin William; m. Lynn Biebighauser, Jan. 17, 1981. BEE, U. of Minn., 1968, MSEE, 1970, PhD, 1973; MS in Mgmt. of Tech., U. Minn., 1993. Sr. physicist cen. rsch. 3M Co., St. Paul, 1973-77, rsch. specialist cen. rsch., 1977-79; project scientist phys. electronics div. Perkin Elmer Corp., Eden Prairie, Minn., 1979-83, sr. project scientist phys. electronics div., 1983-85, lab mgr. phys. electronics div., 1985-87, product mgr. phys. electronics div., 1987-88, sr. product mgr. phys. electronics div., 1988-93; v.p. product devel. Chorus Corp., St. Paul, 1993-94; pres. Creekside Techs. Corp., Eden Prairie, Minn., time.— Editor: X-rays in Materials Analysis, 1986; co-author: Oscillatory Ion Yields, 1977; patentee in field. Recipient IR100 award for transfer vessel Rsch. and Devel. mag., 1981, IR100 award for energy analyser, 1985. Democrat. Methodist. Office: Creekside Techs Corp 7685 Corporate Way Eden Prairie MN 55344

RUSCH, WILLIAM GRAHAM, religious organization administrator; b. Buffalo, Dec. 23, 1937; s. William Godfrey and Hope (French) R.; m. Thora Joan Ellefsen, Sept. 2, 1967. BA, SUNY, Buffalo, 1959, MA in Classical Langs., 1960; MDiv, Luth. Theol. Sem., Phila., 1963; PhD, Oxford (Eng.)

U., 1965; DD (hon.), Yale U., 1995. Ordained to ministry Evang. Luth. Ch., 1966. Assoc. pastor Evang. Luth. Ch. of the Holy Trinity, N.Y.C., 1966-68; asst. prof., chmn. dept. classical langs. Augsburg Coll., Mpls., 1968-71; assoc. exec. dir. div. Theol. Studies Luth. Coun. in the USA, 1971-78; adj. prof. The Gen. Theol. Sem., N.Y.C., 1978-82, 95; exec. dir., asst. to Bishop Evang. Luth. Ch. in Am., Chgo., 1987—; vis. lectr. Waterloo Luth. Theol. Sem., 1969; adj. prof. theology Fordham U., N.Y.C., 1984-86; mem. cen. com. World Coun. Chs., 1991—, mem. standing com. faith and order commn., 1991—. Author: The Trinitarian Controversy, Ecumenism: A Movement Toward Church Unity; contbr. articles to profl. jours. Samuel Trexler fellow of N.Y. Synod Luth. Ch. in Am., 1964, 65. Mem. Am. Acad. Religion, Am. Soc. Christian Ethics, Am. Soc. Ch. History, Internat. Assn. Coptic Studies, Gen. Bd. Nat. Coun. Chs. Avocations: book collecting, chess, tennis. Office: Evang Luth Ch in Am 8765 W Higgins Rd Chicago IL 60631-4101

RUSCHA, EDWARD, artist; b. Omaha, Dec. 16, 1937; m. Danna Knego, 1967; children: Edward Joseph. Studied at Chouinard Art Inst., Los Angeles, 1956-60. Numerous vis. artist positions including UCLA, 1969-70. Author: Twentysix Gasoline Stations, 1962, Various Small Fires, 1964, Some Los Angeles Apartments, 1965, The Sunset Strip, 1966, Thirtyfour Parking Lots, 1967, Royal Road Test, 1967, Business Cards, 1968, Nine Swimming Pools, 1968, Crackers, 1969, Real Estate Opportunities, 1970, Records, 1971, A Few Palm Trees, 1971, Colored People, 1972, Hard Light, 1978; noted for numerous graphite, gunpowder and pastel drawings, over 200 limited-edit. prints; producer, dir.: films Premium, 1970, Miracle, 1974; works include (paintings) Standard Station, Amarillo, Tex., 1963; Annie, 1963, Smash, 1963, Electric, 1964, (mural) Miami-Dade Pub. Library, Fla., 1985; one-man exhbns. include Minn. Inst. Arts, 1972, Nigel Greenwood Ltd., London, 1970, 73, 80, Leo Castelli Gallery, N.Y.C., (10 shows) 1973—, Albright-Knox Art Gallery, Buffalo, 1976, Stedelijk Mus., Amsterdam, 1976, Ft. Worth Art Mus., 1977, San Francisco Mus. Modern Art, 1982, Whitney Mus. Am. Art, 1982, Vancouver Art Gallery, 1982, Contemporary Arts Mus., Houston, 1983, Los Angeles County Mus. Art, 1983, James Corcoran Gallery, Los Angeles, 1985, also others; exhibited in group shows at 64th Whitney Biennial, 1987, Centre Pompidou, Paris, 1989, Mus. Boymans—van Beuningen, Rotterdam, The Netherlands, 1990, Ghislaine Hussenot, Paris, 1990, Fundacio Caixa, Barcelona, Spain, 1990, Serpentine Gallery, London, 1990, Mus. Contemporary Art, L.A., 1990-91, Robert Miller Gallery, N.Y.C., 1992, Thaddaeus Ropac, Salzburg, Austria, 1992; represented in permanent collections including Mus. Modern Art, Los Angeles County Mus. Art, Whitney Mus., Hirshhorn, Washington, Miami-Dade Pub. Libr., Denver Pub. Libr., also others. Guggenheim fellow; Nat. Endowment Arts grantee. Office: care Leo Castelli 420 W Broadway New York NY 10012-3764

RUSCHE, BENARD C., engineering executive; b. Yazoo City, Miss., Feb. 18, 1931; s. Bernard Clements and Naomi (Young) R.; m. Eunice Middleton, Apr. 5, 1953; children: Grace, Mark, Kevin. BS in Physics, Tenn. Tech. U., 1953; postgrad., Ga. Inst. Tech., 1958-59. Dir. environ. scis. DuPont, Savannah River, Aiken, S.C., 1953-75; dir. nuclear regulation NRC, Washington, 1975-77; dir. health, safety DuPont Co., Wilmington, Del., 1977-78; exec. dir. S.C. Energy Rsch. Inst., Columbia, 1978-81; spl. asst. to sec. Dept. of Energy, Washington, 1981-82; v.p. exec. svcs. Mgmt. Analysis Co., San Diego, 1982-84; pres. Mgmt. and Tech. Resources, Columbia, 1983-84; dir. office civil radioactive waste mgmt. Dept. Energy, Washington, 1984-87; sr. v.p. Law Cos. Group, Inc., Atlanta, 1987—; trustee Furman U., Greenville, S.C., 1964-75. Mem., chmn. Aiken County Sch. Bd., 1970-75. Mem. Assn. Gov. Bds. of U. and Colls. (bd. dirs., exec. com. 1971-75), Am. Nuclear Soc., Kappa Mu Epsilon, Tau Beta Pi. Republican. Baptist. Avocations: tennis, flying, music. Office: Law Environmetal Inc 114 Town PArk Dr Kennesaw GA 30144

RUSCO, GENE EARL, radio broadcasting executive; b. Stockton, Calif., Mar. 4, 1949; s. Forrest Albert and Mildred Lea (Overholser) R.; m. Linda S. Collins, Mar. 4, 1989. News dir. KDON AM-FM, Salinas, Calif., 1971, KIDD Radio, Monteray, Calif., 1971-76, Aptos/Capitola, Aptos Capitola, Calif., 1976-81; reporter, anchor KGO/ABC Radio, San Francisco, 1981-83, bur. chief South Bay, 1983—. Writer, author documentary Dying for a Drink, 1986 (St. Francis Media award 1986), writer anchor news series Alcoholism, 1986 (Best Series award 1986); reporter spot news Crash of Airlines, 1987 (Best Coverage award 1987). Recipient Best Individual Achievement award UPI, 1990. Mem. Radio and TV News Dirs., Peninsula Press Club, Alpha Epsilon Rho, Alpha Omega (past pres.). Avocations: backpacking, hiking, traveling. Office: KGO Radio 900 Front St San Francisco CA 94111-1450

RUSE, STEVEN DOUGLAS, lawyer; b. Wichita, Kans., Mar. 8, 1950; B.A., U. Kans., 1972; J.D., Creighton U., 1975. Bar: Mo. 1975, U.S. Dist. Ct. (we. dist.) Mo. 1975, Kans. 1982, U.S. Dist. Ct. Kans. 1982. Law clk. to dist. justice U.S. Dist. Ct. Mo., Kansas City, 1975-77; assoc. Shughart, Thomson & Kilroy, Kansas City, 1977-81, ptnr., 1981—. Mem. ABA, Mo. Bar Assn., Kans. Bar Assn. Office: Shughart Thomson & Kilroy 9225 Indian Creek Pky Overland Park KS 66210-2009

RUSH, ANDREW WILSON, artist; b. Detroit, Sept. 24, 1931; s. Harvey Ditman and Mary Louise (Slater) R.; m. Jean Cochran, Apr., 1957; children: Benjamin, Samuel, Joseph, Margaret; m. Ann Woodin, Oct., 1978. B.F.A. with honors, U. Ill., 1953; M.F.A., U. Iowa, 1958. Asso. prof. art U. Ariz., 1959-69; co-dir. Rockefeller Found. Indian Arts Project, 1960-64; vis. artist, artist-in-residence Ohio State U., 1970, U. Ark., 1972, Colo. Coll., 1973-74; resident mem. Rancho Linda Vista, Community of the Arts, Oracle, Ariz., 1969—. One-man shows include Carlin Galleries, Ft. Worth, 1973, Graphics Gallery, Tucson, 1972, 75, Tucson Art Inst., 1984; exhibited in group shows at World's Fair, N.Y.C., 1964, USIS exhbns., Europe, Latin Am., 1960-65; represented in permanent collections Libr. of Congress, Uffizzi Mus., Dallas Mus., Ft. Worth Mus., Seattle Mus., Free Libr., Phila.; illustrator: Andrew Rush on Oliver Wendell Holmes, 1973, Rule of Two (Ann Woodin), 1984, Voice Crying in the Wilderness (Edward Abbey), 1990, Ask Marilyn, 1992. Served with USMC, 1953-55. Fulbright grantee, 1958-59. Address: Rancho Linda Vista O M Star Rte 2360 Oracle AZ 85623

RUSH, BOBBY L., congressman; b. Ga., Nov. 23, 1946; m. Carolyn Rush; 5 children. BA in Polit. Sci., Roosevelt U., 1974; MA in Polit. Sci., U. Ill., 1992. Fin. planner Sanmar Fin. Planning Corp.; assoc. dean Daniel Hale Williams U.; ins. agent Prudential Ins. Co.; city alderman Chgo., 1984-93; democratic committeeman Chgo. 2nd ward, 1984, 88, Central Ill., 1990; dep. chmn. Ill. Democratic Party, 1990; mem. 103d Congress from 1st Ill. Dist., 1993—; chmn. Environ. Protection, Energy and Pub. Utilities com., Budget and Govt. Operations com., Capitol Devel. com., Hist. Landmark Preservation Com.; mem. Commerce com. Former mem. Student Non-Violent Coordinating com.; founder Ill. Black Panther Party; past coord. Free Breakfast for Children, Free Med. Clinic. With US Army, 1963-68. Recipient Ill. Enterprise Zone award Dept. Commerce and Community, Operation PUSH Outstanding Young Man award, Henry Booth House Outstanding Community Svc. award, Outstanding Bus. and Profl. Achievement award South End Jaycees, Chgo. Black United Communities Disting. Polit. Leadership award. Office: US Ho of Reps 131 Cannon Ho Office Bldg Washington DC 20515-1301*

RUSH, DAVID, medical investigator, epidemiologist; b. N.Y.C., May 3, 1934; s. Samuel Hersh and Fannie (Dubin) R.; m. Catharine Ireland Dawson, June 24, 1957; children: Naomi Rush Olson, Hannah M., Leah D. BA cum laude, Harvard U., 1955, MD, 1959. Diplomate Am. Bd. Pediatrics. Resident in medicine U. Ill. Hosp., Chgo., 1959-61; resident in pediatrics Children's Hosp., Boston, 1963-65; registrar in pediatrics St. Mary's Hosp. Med. Sch. London, 1964-65; rsch. fellow, Harvard U. Med. Sch., Boston, 1965-66; asst. prof. preventive medicine and pediatrics, U. Rochester (N.Y.), 1967-69; asst. prof. pub. health (epidemiology) and pediatrics Columbia U., N.Y.C., also dir. prenatal project, 1969-76, assoc. prof., 1976-82; prof. pediatrics, social medicine and ob-gyn Albert Einstein Coll. Medicine, Bronx, N.Y., 1983-88; dir. epidemiology program USDA, Human Nutrition Research Ctr. on Aging, prof. nutrition, community health, pediatrics Tufts U., Boston, 1988—; mem. human devel. and aging study sect. NIH, USPHS, 1982-86; prin. investigator nat. evaluation of spl. supplemental food program for women, infants and children U.S. Dept. Agr., 1981-

86. Author: Diet in Pregnancy, 1980, Dead Reckoning, 1992; assoc. editor Medicine and Global Survival; mem. editorial bd. Am. Jour. Pub. Health; contbr. articles to profl. jours. Trustee, chmn. health services com. Children's Aid Soc., N.Y.C., 1971-86. Served as surgeon USPHS, 1961-63; capt. Res. Recipient career investigator award N.Y.C. Health Research Council, 1977; sr. internat. fellow Fogarty Ctr., NIH, USPHS, U. Bristol, Eng., 1977-78, U. Paris, 1984-85; research grantee Nat. Inst. Child and Human Devel., NIH, 1979-86. Fellow Am. Pub. Health Assn. (governing council 1976-79); mem. Soc. for Epidemiologic Research (pres. 1980-81), Soc. for Pediatric Research, Internat. Epidemiologic. Assn., Am. Epidemiol. Soc., Am. Pediatric Soc., Perinatal Research Soc., Am. Inst. of Nutrition, Am. Soc. Clin. Nutrition, Am. Coll. of Epidemiology. Office: Human Nutrition Rsch Ctr 711 Washington St Boston MA 02111-1524

RUSH, FLETCHER GREY, JR., lawyer; b. Orlando, Fla., Dec. 28, 1917; s. Fletcher Grey and Elizabeth (Knox) R.; m. Lena Mae Willis, June 6, 1942; children: Patricia Rush White, Richard Fletcher. BSBA, JD with honors, U. Fla., 1942; LLD (hon.), Fla. So. Coll., 1975. Bar: Fla. 1942. Practice in Orlando, 1946—; pres. firm Rush, Marshall, Reber & Jones P.A., 1957-91, of counsel, 1991—; Trustee Lawyers Title Guaranty Fund, 1953-65, chmn. bd., 1962-63, gen. counsel, 1968-90; v.p., dir., gen. counsel Orlando Fed. Savs. & Loan Assn., 1955-75; dir. Trust Co. Fla., 1974-82; mem. jud. nominating council Supreme Ct. Fla., 1972-73, jud. nominating commn., 1983-87. Contbr. articles to legal jours. Mem. Orlando Municipal Planning Bd., 1961-63; mem. Orlando Loch Haven Park Bd., 1973-81, vice chmn., 1978-81; bd. regents State Fla. Colls. and Univs., 1965; trustee Coll. Orlando, 1960-71, Fla. House, Inc., Washington, 1974-76, Fla. Supreme Ct. Hist. Soc., 1988-91; mem. president's council U. Fla., 1970—, v.p., exec. com. U. Fla. Found., 1973-75, bd. dirs., 1971-75; bd. dirs. Inst. for Study of Trial, Central Fla. U., 1978-80; mem. president's council Nat. Meth. Found., 1977-82. Served as officer F.A. AUS, 1942-46, ETO. Recipient Distinguished Service award Stetson U., 1967; Outstanding Alumnus award John Marshall Bar Assn. U. Fla. Coll. Law, 1971; Distinguished Alumnus award U. Fla., 1976. Fellow Am. Coll. Trust and Estate Counsel, Am. Bar Found., Fla. Bar Found.; mem. ABA (ho. of dels. 1967-85, adv. bd. jour. 1968-71, chmn. standing com. on legislation 1973-75 on lawyers title guaranty funds 1979-83), Orange County (Fla.) Bar Assn. (pres. 1960-61), Fla. Bar (bd. govs. 1959-67, pres. 1966-67), Am. Judicature Soc. (dir. 1968—, exec. com. 1972, treas. 1973-75, v.p. 1975-77, pres. 1977-79), U. Fla. Law Center Assn. (trustee, exec. com., chmn. bd. trustees 1973-75), Blue Key (pres. Fla. 1941), Phi Kappa Phi, Alpha Tau Omega, Phi Delta Phi. Republican. Methodist (chmn. ch. adminstrv. bd. 1961-63, 75-76, trustee 1968-74, 77-80, trustee Fla. Conf., 1973-76). Clubs: Country, Univ. (Orlando) Orange County Old Timers (pres. 1986-87). Lodge: Kiwanis (pres. North Orlando club 1954). Home: 1105 Edgewater Dr Orlando FL 32804-6311 Office: Rush Marshall Reber & Jones PA 109 E Church St Orlando FL 32801-3318

RUSH, HERMAN E., television executive; b. Phila., June 20, 1929; s. Eugene and Bella (Sacks) R.; m. Joan Silberman, Mar. 18, 1951; children: James Harrison, Mandie Susan. BBA, Temple U., 1950. With Ofcl. Films, 1951-57; owner Flamingo Films, 1957-60; with Creative Mgmt. Assos., N.Y.C., 1960-71; pres. TV div. Creative Mgmt. Assos., 1964-71, exec. v.p. parent co., dir., 1964-71; ind. producer, 1971-75; producer Wolper Orgn., 1975-76; pres. Herman Rush Assos., Inc. (Rush-Flaherty Agy. subs.), 1977-78, Marble Arch TV, Los Angeles, 1979-80, Columbia Pictures TV, Burbank, Calif., 1980-87; chmn., chief exec. officer Coca-Cola Telecommunications, 1987-88, Rush Assocs., Inc., Burbank, 1988—, Katz/Rush Entertainment, Beverly Hills, Calif., 1990—; mem. Entertainment Industries Council. Trustee Sugar Ray Robinson Youth Found., 1967-75; pres. Retarded Infant Services, N.Y.C., 1957-63; bd. dirs. U.S. Marshall's Service Found., Just Say No Found.; conferee White House Conf. for a Drug Free America, 1987, 88. Mem. Acad. TV Arts and Scis., Hollywood Radio and TV Soc., Producers Caucus. Clubs: Friars, Filmex. Office: Katz/Rush Entertainment 345 N Maple Dr Ste 205 Beverly Hills CA 90210-3857

RUSH, KENNETH G., lawyer; b. Springfield, Ohio, July 7, 1930; s. Kenneth Leon and Hazel Joy (Fisher) R.; m. Mary Margaret Jackson, May 28, 1953. BS, U. Wis., 1952; JD, Harvard U., 1957. Ptnr. Lagos, Lagos, & Rush, Springfield, 1957—. Served to 1st lt. U.S. Army, 1952-54. Mem. ABA (coun. gen. practice sect. 1980-84, spl. com. on prepaid legal ins. 1985-91), Ohio State Bar Assn. (chmn. gen. practice sect. 1980-82). Democrat. Lutheran. Avocations: skiing, tennis, archaeology. Office: 1 S Limestone St Ste 1000 Springfield OH 45502-1243

RUSH, NORMAN, author; b. San Francisco, Oct. 24, 1933; s. Roger and Leslie (Chessé) R.; m. Elsa Scheidt, July 10, 1955; children: Jason, Liza. BA, Swarthmore Coll., 1956. Dealer antiquarian books, 1960-78; instr. English, history Rockland C.C. Suffern, N.Y., 1973-78; co-dir. Peace Corps, Botswana, 1978-83; freelance writer, 1983—. Autor: Whites, 1986, Mating, 1991 (Nat. Book award for fiction 1991, Internat. Fiction prize Irish Times and Aer Lingus 1992). Mem. lit. com. War Resisters League, N.Y.C., 1985—; bd. dirs. A.J. Muste Inst., N.Y.C., 1988-92; sec. Rockland County, N.Y. chpt. Amnesty Internat., 1990—. Recipient Rosenthal award Nat. Acad. and Inst. Arts and Letters, 1987, Nat. Book award for fiction, 1991, internat. fiction prize Aer Lingus/Irish Times, 1992; fellow Nat. Endowment for Arts, 1986, Guggenheim fellow, 1987, Bellagio residency fellow Rockeller Found., 1990. Mem. PEN Am. Ctr.

RUSH, RICHARD HENRY, financier, writer, lecturer; b. N.Y.C., Mar. 6, 1915; s. Henry Frederick and Bessie (Vreeland) R.; m. Julia Ann Halloran, Aug. 15, 1946; 1 dau., Sallie Haywood. B.A. summa cum laude, Dartmouth Coll., 1937, M.C.S., 1938; M.B.A., Harvard U., 1941, D.C.S. (Littauer fellow), 1942. Dir. aviation U.S. Bur. Fgn. and Domestic Commerce, 1945-46; chief economist, chmn. planning com. All Am. Aviation (U.S. Air), 1943-45; dir. aircraft div. Nat. Security Resources Bd., 1948-51; Washington rep. to J. Paul Getty, 1951-52; partner Rush & Halloran (finance and ins.), 1953-58; pres., chmn. bd. N.Am. Acceptance Corp., Atlanta, also Washington, 1956-59; owner Richard H. Rush Enterprises, Greenwich, Conn., also Washington, 1953-73; prof., chmn. dept. finance and investments Sch. Bus. Adminstrn., Am. U., Washington, 1967-70, 77-79. Author: 12 books, including Art as an Investment, 1961, A Strategy of Investing for Higher Return, 1962, The Techniques of Becoming Wealthy, 1963, Antiques as an Investment, 1968, The Wrecking Operation: Phase One, 1972, Investments You Can Live With and Enjoy, 1976, Techniques of Becoming Wealthy, 1977, Automobiles as an Investment, 1982, Selling Collectibles, 1982, Collecting Classic Cars for Profit and Capital Gain, 1984; contbr. over 700 articles to newspapers, mags. and profl. jours.; editor series of books on starting businesses for U.S. Dept. Commerce; contbg. editor Wall St. Transcript, 1971—, Art/Antiques Investment Report, 1972—. Trustee, mem. exec. com. Finch Coll., 1968-72. Mem. Am. Mktg. Assn. (chmn. nat. com.), Am. Econ. Assn., Am. Statis. Assn., Internat. Platform Assn., AAUP, Harvard Club (N.Y.C.), BocaWest Club (Boca Raton), Royal Palm Yacht Club (Ft. Myers), Phi Beta Kappa, Phi Kappa Phi, Omicron Delta Kappa. Episcopalian. *Strive to your best, get the best education you can and the world will open up to you. Three graduate degrees opened the door to success for me, but to get the top education, all else must be put aside. Also know the reality and strength of good and keep your thought on positive goals.*

RUSH, RICHARD R., university administrator. Pres. Mankato (Minn.) U. Office: Mankato State U South Rd And Ellis Ave Mankato MN 56001

RUSH, WILLIAM JOHN, newspaper executive; b. Alliance, Ohio, Nov. 11, 1936; s. Serle Emmons and Doris Esther (Crider) R.; BA in Journalism, Ohio State U., 1958; m. Ruth Ann Lee, Feb. 29, 1972; children—Kayci, Wendy, Nathan, Jenny, Molly. Mgr., The Madison Press, London, Ohio, 1960-62; adv. mgr. Times Pub. Co., New Milford, Conn., 1966-25; asst. to pub. N.Adams (Mass.) Transcript, 1965-69; asst. to pub. Horvitz Newspapers, 1969-70; gen. mgr. Lake City (Ohio) News-Herald, 1970-72; v.p./gen. mgr. Times Record, Troy, N.Y., 1972-82; assoc. pub., v.p. Times Record and News Jour., Mansfield, Ohio, 1982-86; pub. Warren (Ohio) Tribune-Chronicle, 1986-89, Lorain (Ohio) Morning Jour., 1989-90; pub., chief exec. New Haven (Conn.) Register, 1990—. Bd. dirs. Long Wharf Theater, Conn. Policy and Econ. Coun., Inc., Regional Leadership Coun., United Way. Mem. Nat. Co. Mil. Historians, Gateway C. C. Found., Habitat for Humanity, Pine Orchard Yacht and Country Club, Quinnipiac Club, Ohio

State U. Alumni Assn., Hon. Order of Ky. Cols., Masons, Shriners, Elks, Theta Chi. Episcopalian. Office: New Haven Register Inc Long Wharf 40 Sargent Dr New Haven CT 06511-5918

RUSHER, WILLIAM ALLEN, writer, commentator; b. Chgo., July 19, 1923; s. Evan Singleton and Verna (Self) R. AB, Princeton, 1943; DLit (hon.), Harvard, 1948, Nathaniel Hawthorne Coll., 1973. Bar: N.Y. bar 1949. Assoc. Shearman & Sterling & Wright, N.Y.C., 1948-56; spl. counsel fin com. N.Y. Senate, 1955; assoc. counsel internal security subcom. U.S. Senate, 1956-57; pub., v.p. Nat. Review mag., N.Y.C., 1957-88, also bd. dirs.; Disting. fellow The Claremont Inst, 1989—; mem. Adv. Task Force on Civil Disorders, 1972. Author: Special Counsel, 1968 (with Mark Hatfield and Arlie Schardt) Amnesty?, 1973, The Making of the New Majority Party, 1975, How to Win Arguments, 1981, The Rise of the Right, 1984, The Coming Battle for the Media, 1988; editor: The Ambiguous Legacy of the Enlightment, 1995; columnist Univesal Press Syndicate, 1973-82, Newspaper Enterprise Assn., 1982—; played role of Advocate in TV program The Advocates, 1970-73. Bd. dirs. Media Rsch. Ctr., Washington; chmn. bd. advisors Ashbrook Ctr., Ashland, Ohio; past vice chmn. Am. Conservative Union; past trustee Pacific Legal Found., Sacramento; trustee, treas. Wilbur Found., Santa Barbara. Recipient Disting. Citizen award NYU Sch. Law, 1973. Mem. ABA, U. Club (N.Y.C. and San Francisco), Met. Club (Washington). Anglican. Home and Office: 850 Powell St San Francisco CA 94108-2051

RUSHFORTH, CRAIG K., electrical engineering educator, researcher; b. Ogden, Utah, Sept. 4, 1937; s. Knewel H. and June (Nelson) R.; m. Martha Hollist, June 19, 1958; children—Kevin, Kim, Alan, Rebecca, Brett. B.S. in E.E., Stanford U., 1958, M.S., 1960, Ph.D, 1962. Asst. prof. elec. engring. Utah State U., Logan, 1962-66; staff mem. Inst. for Def. Analyses, Arlington, Va., 1967-68; prof. Mont. State U. Bozeman, 1966-73; prof., chmn. elec. engring. U. Utah, Salt Lake City, 1974—; cons. Sperry Corp., Salt Lake City. Contbr. articles to profl. jours. Bell Labs. fellow, 1960-61, NSF fellow, 1961-62. Mem. IEEE (sr.), Phi Beta Kappa, Tau Beta Pi. Democrat. Mormon. Home: 1152 Sherwood Dr Kaysville UT 84037-1349 Office: Univ Utah Ctr Comm Rsch Merrill Engring Bldg Salt Lake City UT 84112

RUSHING, BYRON DOUGLAS, state legislator; b. N.Y.C., July 29, 1942; s. William and Linda (Turpin) R.; (div. 1972); 1 child: Osula Evadne. AA (hon.), Roxbury (Mass.) Community Coll, 1989; DD (hon.), Episcopal Divinity Sch., 1994. Pres. Mus. Afro Am. History, Boston, 1972-85; state rep. Commonwealth of Mass., Boston, 1983—; chair pub. svc. com., vice chair redistricting com., 1993—; former chair Com. on Local Affiars, Com. on Counties; mem. Congl. Redistricting com.; mem. Martin Luther King, Jr. Holiday Commn., Commonwealth of Mass. Active St. John's St. Jame's Parish, Roxbury, Mass.; past pres. Episc. Urban Caucus, Episc. City Mission; mem. standing com. Diocese of Mass.; lay dep. to gen. conf. Episc. Ch., 1973—; chaplain House of Deputies, 1994; mem. program, budget and fin. com., com. on status of women Episco. Div. Sch., Cambridge, Mass.; lectr. in studies in contemporary soc. Mem. ACLU of Mass. (bd. dirs.), Roxbury Hist. Soc. (pres. 1969–), Roxbury Heritage State Park Adv. Bd. (vice chmn.). Episcopalian. Office: Mass House Reps State House Boston MA 02133

RUSHING, JANE GILMORE, writer; b. Pyron, Tex., Nov. 15, 1925; d. Clyde Preston and Mabel Irene (Adams) Gilmore; m. James Arthur Rushing, Nov. 29, 1956; 1 son, James Arthur. BA, Tex. Tech U., 1944, MA, 1945, PhD, 1957. Reporter Abilene (Tex.) Reporter-News, 1946-47; tchr. Tex. high schs., 1947-54; instr. U. Tenn., 1957-59; instr. to asst. prof. Tex. Tech U., intermittently, 1959-68. Author: Walnut Grove, 1964, against the Moon, 1968, Tamzen, 1972, Mary Dove, 1974, The Raincrow, 1977, Covenant of Grace, 1982, Winds of Blame, 1983, Starting from Pyron, 1992; co-author (with Kline A. Nall) Evolution of a University, Texas Tech's First Fifty Years, 1975. Vassie James Hill fellow of AAUW, 1956-57; recipient Emily Clark Balch prize, 1961; LeBaron R. Barker, Jr., Fiction award, 1975; Tex. Lit. award for fiction, 1984. Mem. Tex. Inst. Letters. Methodist. Home: 3809 39th St Lubbock TX 79413-2521

RUSHMORE, STEPHEN, hotel consulting and appraisal specialist; b. Glen Cove, N.Y., Mar. 18, 1945; s. Leon A. and Caroline (Jackson) R.; m. Judith Ruth Kellner, June 10, 1967; children: Cynthia Ruth, Stephen Jr. BA, Cornell U., 1967; MBA, U. Buffalo, 1971. Lic. real estate broker; cert. gen. appraiser. Active real estate Hinksley-Spear Hospitality Svcs., Inc., N.Y.C., 1971-74, 77-80; appraiser, active hotel operations, mortgage banking James E. Gibbons Assocs., Garden City, N.Y., 1974-77; hotel/motel valuations and investment counselor Hospitality Valuation Svcs. (divsn. Hotel Appraisals, Inc.), Mineola, N.Y., 1980—; appraiser, evaluator hotels and motels throughout U.S. and world; affiliated ownership interest includes Hospitality Valuation Svcs., San Francisco, Miami, Fla., Vancouver, Can., London, Hospitality Equity Investors, Inc., Trumbull Marriott Hotel, Princeton (N.J.) Hotel Assocs., Seaview Golf Resort Assocs., Abescon, N.J., Shelton (Conn.) Hotel Assocs., Danbury (Conn.) Hotel Assocs., Prudential-Hei Joint Venture, Atlanta, Delaware Hotel Assocs., Wilmington, Del., Hospitality Valuation Software, Inc., HVS Eco Svcs., HVS Exec. Search; adj. asst. prof. real estate NYU; hon. faculty Mich. State U.; lectr. in field. Author: (textbooks) The Valuation of Hotels and Motels, 1978, Hotels, Motels and Restaurants: Valuations and Market Studies, 1983, How to Perform an Economic Feasibility Study of a Proposed Hotel/Motel, 1986, Hotel Investments: A Guide for Owners and Lender, 1990, supplement, 1992, 93, The Computerized Income Approach to Hotel Market Studies and Valuations, 1990, Hotels and Motels: A Guide to Market Analysis and Investment Analysis and Valuations, 1992; author manuals and chpts. to books; contbr. articles to profl. jours. Mem. adv. bd. NYU Master's in Hospitality Mgmt. Mem. Am. Soc. Real Estate Counselors (bd. govs.), Am. Hotel and Motel Assn. (mem. industry real estate financing adv. coun., cert. hotel adminstr.), Am. Arbitration Assn. (mem. nat. real estate valuation coun.), Appraisal Inst. (devel., instr. hotel investment and valuation seminar, hotel computer valuation seminar), Internat. Soc. Hospitality Cons., Foodservice Cons. Soc. Internat., Cornell Soc. Hotelmen, Beta Gamma Sigma. Avocations: comml. pilot, instrument, multi-engine; sailing, skiing. Office: Hospitality Valuation Services 372 Willis Ave Mineola NY 11501-1818

RUSHNELL, SQUIRE DERRICK, television executive; b. Adams Center, N.Y., Oct. 31, 1938; s. Reginald Grant and Erica Mifanwy Redwood Sedgemore (Squire) R.; m. Jinny Schreckinger, Feb. 29, 1980; 1 child, Squire Grant Sedgemore; children by previous marriage: Robin Tracy, Hilary Adair. Ed., Syracuse U., 1956-60. Disc jockey Stas. WOLF, WHEN and WFBL, Syracuse, N.Y., 1958-61, Sta. WTRL, Bradenton, B, 1961-62; exec. prodr. Sta. WBZ AM-TV, Boston, 1962-67; program dir. KYW News-Radio, Phila., 1968; exec. prodr. Kennedy & Co. Sta. WLS-TV, Chgo., 1969-71, program dir. 1971-73; v.p. programs ABC-owned TV stas., N.Y.C., 1973-74; v.p. children's TV ABC Entertainment Network, N.Y.C., 1974-78; v.p. Good Morning Am. and children's programs ABC-TV Network, N.Y.C., 1978-81, v.p. long range planning and children's TV, 1981-87; v.p. late night and children's TV ABC Entertainment, N.Y.C., 1987-89; pres. Rushnell Co., 1990-92, Rushnell Comm. & Pub., Inc., 1993—. Author: The Kingdom Chums Greatest Stories, 1986, Read to Me, Sing to Me Stories, 1993; co-author: Broadcast Programming, 1981, Broadcast/Cable Programming, 1985, rev. edit., 1989, 93. Recipient Emmy awards, 1975-88, TV Critics Circle award, 1976, all for outstanding children's TV programming, Am. Children's TV Festival award, 1985, 87. Mem. NATAS, Nat. Acad. Arts and Scis., Internat. Radio and TV Soc., Action for Children's TV (award for outstanding children's TV programming). Office: Rushnell Comm & Pub Inc 640 Fifth Ave 5th FL New York NY 10019-6102

RUSHTON, BRIAN MANDEL, chemical company executive; b. Sale, Cheshire, Eng., Nov. 16, 1933; came to U.S., 1957; s. Ronald Henry and Edith (Slater) Riley; m. Jean Wrigley, Apr. 1, 1958; children: Jacqueline, Lisa, Amy. A.R.I.C. in Chemistry, U. Salford, Eng., 1957; M.S. in Phys. Organic Chemistry, U. Minn., 1959; Ph.D in Phys. Organic Chemistry, U. Leicester, Eng., 1963; postgrad. Sr. Exec. program, MIT, 1972. Prodn. mgr. trainee 3M Co. U.K., 1959-60; sr. research chemist Petrolite Corp., 1963-65, group leader, 1965-66; sect. mgr. Ashland Chem. Co., 1966-69; corp. research mgr. Hooker Chem. Corp. subs. Occidental Petroleum, 1969-72, dir. polymer and plastics research and devel., 1972-74, v.p. research and devel.

chem. and plastics div., 1974-75; pres. Celanese Research Corp., 1975-80; corp. v.p. tech. Celanese Corp.; also pres. Celanese Research Corp., 1980-81; v.p. research and devel. Air Products & Chem., Inc., Allentown, Pa., 1981-92, sr. v.p. rsch. and devel., 1992-94; pres., mem. exec. com., bd. dirs. Indsl. Rsch. Inst., 1990-94, chmn. plans and policies com., 1988-90; bd. dirs. Mich. Molecular Inst., 1991-94, Mallinckrodt Inc., 1994—; mem. chem. vis. com. Lehigh U., 1992—; mem. exec. master sci. in engring. adv. coun. U. Pa., 1992-94. Contbr. articles to profl. jours.; patentee in field. Mem. life scis. vis. com. Lehigh U., chmn. surface sci. vis. com., 1983-86; bd. dirs. WLVT Channel 39, Bethlehem, Pa., 1992—; trustee Summit YMCA, N.J., 1976-79; mem. nat. materials bd. NRC, 1980-84. Mem. Coun. Chem. Rsch. (dir. treas.), Am. Chem. Soc. (pres.-elect 1994, pres. 1995), Soc. Chem. Industry, Am. Mgmt. Assn., Saucon Valley Country Club. Episcopalian. Home: 3366 Bingen Rd Bethlehem PA 18015-5715

RUSHTON, WILLIAM JAMES, III, insurance company executive; b. Birmingham, Ala., Apr. 23, 1929; s. William James and Elizabeth (Perry) R.; m. LaVona Price, Aug. 19, 1955; children: William James IV, Deakins Ford, Tunstall Perry. B.A. magna cum laude, Princeton U., 1951; LL.D. (hon.), Birmingham So. Coll., 1981. Asso. actuary Protective Life Ins. Co., Birmingham, Ala., 1954-59; dir. Protective Life Ins. Co., 1956—, agt.; 1959-62, v.p., 1962-63, agy. v.p., 1963-67, pres., from 1967, pres., chief exec. officer, 1969-82, chmn., 1982—; pres. Protective Life Corp., Birmingham, 1981-82, CEO, chmn., 1982-92, chmn., 1992—; dir. Ala. Power Co., The Southern Co., Amsouth Bank N.A., Amsouth Bancorp. Trustee So. Rsch. Inst., Children's Hosp., Birmingham So. Coll., Highland Day Sch.; mem. deacon 1 st Presbyn. Ch., Birmingham, chmn. bd. deacons, 1960—; chmn. United Way campaign, 1977, pres., 1986, life mem., 1993; chmn. Leadership Birmingham, United Appeal, Indsl. Health Coun.; mem. adv. com. Meyer Found., Greater Birmingham Found. Capt. arty., U.S. Army, Korea. Decorated Bronze Star; named to Ala. Acad. of Honors, 1979; recipient Disting. Eagle Scout award Boy Scouts Am., 1980, Brotherhood award NCCJ, 1990. Fellow Soc. Actuaries; mem. Am. Council Life Ins. (dir.), Am. Life Conv. (state v.p. 1975), Am. Life Ins. Assn. (Ala. v.p. 1975), Health Ins. Assn. Am. (dir. from 1982), Million Dollar Round Table, Birmingham C. of C. (dir.). Clubs: Rotary (bd. dirs. 1973-74, treas. 1978-79, pres. 1988-89), Mountain Brook Country, Summit, Birmingham Country, The Club, Redstone. Office: Protective Life Corp 2801 Hwy 280 S Birmingham AL 35223-2488

RUSIN, EDWARD A., bank executive; b. Fenton, Mich., June 10, 1922; s. Andrew Stephen and Anna Maria (Kostka) R.; m. Virginia Ruth Ware, May 14, 1953; children: Gregory, Stephen, Valerie, Lisa, Tracey. Student, Ohio Wesleyan U. and Carroll Coll., 1942; BA, Mich. State U., 1948, MA, 1955. With Citizens Comml. Bank and Trust, Flint, Mich., 1953-55; examiner Fed. Res. Bank of Chgo., 1955-60; rev. examiner Fed. Res. Bd. Govs., Washington, 1961-62; pres., chmn Mich. Nat. Bank-North Metro, Troy, 1962-87; chmn Mich. Nat. Bank-Sterling, Sterling Heights, Mich., 1980-87, Mich. Nat. Bank-Macomb, Warren, Mich., 1985-87; sr. v.p. Mich. Nat. Corp., Farmington Hills, 1987-88. Mem. Troy Master Plan Commn., 1963; pres., founder Troy C. of C., 1964-65; chmn. Troy Comml./Indsl. Devel. Commn., 1963-65; bd. dirs. Oakland County Traffic Safety Com., Pontiac, Mich., 1975-86, P.I.M.E. Missionaries, Detroit, 1968-95. Served with U.S. Naval Air Corps, 1942-45, PTO. Recipient Toppers award Detroit area Boy Scouts Am., 1964, Troy Sesquicentennial Commn. award, 1971, Outstanding Svc. award Troy C. of C., 1984; named Outstanding Citizen of Troy, 1993. Mem. Red Run Golf club (Royal Oak, Mich.), Stoneybrook Golf and Country Club (Sarasota, Fla.). Republican. Roman Catholic. Avocations: golf, collecting classic golf clubs, fishing, swimming. Home (summer): 912 Robinhood Rd Bloomfield Hills MI 48304-3760 also (winter): Villas of Deer Creek 4420 Deer Trail Blvd Sarasota FL 34238

RUSINKO, FRANK, JR., fuels and materials scientist; b. Nanticoke, Pa., Oct. 12, 1930; s. Frank Sr. and Eva (Ruduski) R.; m. Lucy Geryak, June 1, 1957; children: Nancy, Lawrence. BS, Pa. State U., 1952, MS, 1954, PhD, 1958. Vice-pres., tech. dir. Airco Carbon, St. Mary's, Pa., 1959-76; pres. Electrotools Inc., Broadview, Ill., 1976-89, Intech EDM Electrotools, Broadview, Ill., 1989-91; sr. scientist, dir. Carbon Rsch. Ctr. Pa. State U. University Park, 1991—; dir. Anthracite Inst., dir. coop. program in coal rsch. Carbon Rsch. Ctr., Pa. State U., University Park, 1991—; bd. dirs, bd. chmn. Transor Filter USA, Park Ridge, Ill., C-Cor Electronics, State College Pa. Contbr. articles to profl. jours. Mem. Hinsdale (Ill.) Plan Commn., 1986; mem. Region Campaign Pa. State U., 1989; pres. Sch. Bd. Edn., St. Marys, Pa., 1965-76. Fellow Pa. State Alumni Assn.; mem. Am. Chem. Soc., Am. Carbon Soc., N.Y. Acad. Sci., Sigma Xi. Orthodox. Home: 2392 Pine Hurst Dr State College PA 16803-3385 Office: Pa State U Carbon Rsch Ctr C204 Coal Utilization Lab State College PA 16802-2323

RUSKAI, MARY BETH, mathematics researcher, educator; b. Cleve., Feb. 26, 1944; d. Michael J. and Evelyn (Gortz) R. BS, Notre Dame Coll., Cleve., 1965; MA, PhD, U. Wis., 1969. Battelle fellow in theoretical physics U. Geneva, 1969-71; rsch. assoc. in math. MIT, Cambridge, Mass., 1971-72; rsch. assoc. in physics U. Alta., Edmonton, Can., 1972-73; asst. prof. math. U. Oreg., Eugene, 1973-76; asst. prof. U. Lowell, Mass., 1977-82, assoc. prof., 1982-86, prof. dept. math., 1986—, pres. faculty senate, 1990-91; sci. scholar Bunting Inst., Cambridge, Mass., 1983-85; vis. prof. Rockefeller U., N.Y.C., 1980-81, U. Vienna, Austria, 1981, Rome, 1988; faculty rsch. assoc. Naval Surface Warfare Ctr., Silver Springs, Md., 1986; vis. prof. math. U. Mich., Ann Arbor, 1991-92; vis. mem. Courant Inst. Math. Sci., NYU, 1988-89; cons. Bell Labs., Murray Hill, N.J., 1972, 83, 88-89; conf. dir. NSF/CBMS Conf. on Wavelets, 1990; Flora Stone Mather vis. prof. Case Western Res. U., Cleve., 1995. Editor-in-chief Wavelets Wavelets and Their Applications, 1990-92; mem. editl. bd. Notices of AMS, 1994—; contbr. articles to profl. jours. NSF predoctoral fellow, 1965-69; recipient NSF Career Advancement award, 1988-89. Fellow AAAS (symposium organizer, 1991, nominating com. math. sect. 1991-94); mem. Internat. Assn. Math. Physicists, Am. Math. Soc. (reviewer, session chmn. 1987—, com. chmn.), Math. Assn. Am. (com.), Am. Phys. Soc. (reviewer), Assn. Women in math., Assn. Women in Sci. (pres. New Eng. chpt. 1986-87), Appalachian Mountain Club (Boston, winter leader 1979—), Sigma Xi. Club: Appalachian Mountain (Boston, winter leader 1979—). Office: U Lowell Dept Math 1 University Ave Lowell MA 01854-2881

RUSKIN, JOSEPH RICHARD, actor, director; b. Haverhill, Mass., Apr. 14, 1924; s. Ely and Betty Edith (Chaimson) Schlafman; m. Barbara Greene; 1 child, Alicia. Grad., Carnegie Inst. Tech., 1949. Founder Rochester (N.Y.) Arena Theatre, 1949-52. Actor N.Y. stage plays, 1952-58, Theatre Group, UCLA, Mark Taper Forum, 1959—, (films) Fall of Legs Diamond, 1959, Magnificent Seven, 1960, Escape from Zahrein, 1963, Robin and the Seven Hoods, 1965, Prizzi's Honor, 1985, Longshot, 1987, regular appearances various TV programs, 1952—; dir. Houston Alley, 1965-69; freelance dir., 1969—. Served with USNR, 1943-46. Mem. AFTRA, SAG (nat. bd. dirs.), Actors Equity Assn. (nat. coun.). Home: 1326 Devon Ave Los Angeles CA 90024-5346

RUSMISEL, STEPHEN R., lawyer; b. N.Y.C., Jan. 27, 1946; s. R. Raymond and Esther Florence (Kutz) R.; m. Beirne Donaldson, Sept. 6, 1980 (div. Jan. 1984); 1 child, Margo Alexander; m. Melissa J. MacLeod, Aug. 24, 1985; children: Benjamin William, Eric Scot Kunze, Erin Lea Kunze. AB, Yale U., 1968; JD, U. Va., 1971. Bar: N.Y. 1972, U.S. Ct. Appeals (2d cir.) 1974, U.S. Dist. Ct. (so. dist.) N.Y. 1975. Assoc. Winthrop, Stimson, Putnam & Roberts, N.Y.C., 1971-80, ptnr., 1980—. Aux. officer Bedminster Twp. (N.J.) Police, 1976—. Mem. Practicing Law Inst., Am. Arbitration Assn. (arbitrator 1976—), Phi Delta Phi. Republican. Clubs: Far Hills Polo (Annandale, N.J.); India House (N.Y.C.); Ausable (St. Huberts, N.Y.). Avocations: polo, flying, carpentry, gardening, poetry. Home: Shadowline Farm Bedminster NJ 07921 Office: Winthrop Stimson Putnam & Roberts One Battery Park Plz New York NY 10004-1490

RUSNAK, MICHAEL, bishop; b. Beaverdale, Pa., Aug. 21, 1921; arrived in Can., 1951; s. Andrew and Maria (Sotak) R. Student, Slovak U. Bratislava, Oberiste. Ordained priest Slovak Cath. Byzantine Rite Ch., 1949, joined Redemptorist Fathers, 1949. Founder Maria publ., 1953; dean Slovak parishes Byzantine Rite, Ukrainian Eparchy Toronto, Can., 1957; apptd. titular bishop Diocese of Cernik, 1964; apptd. apostolic visitator for Slovak Caths. of Byzantine Rite in Can., 1964, consecrated bishop, 1965; named eparch

Diocese of Sts. Cyril and Methodius, Slovak Byzantine Cath. Eparchy in N.Am., Can., 1980. Address: Slovak Cath Ch in Can, 223 Carlton Rd, Unionville, ON Canada L3R 2L8

RUSNELL, JOANNE D., brewery, entertainment business executive; b. Stouffville, Ont., Can., Dec. 24, 1954; s. W. Bruce Rusnell and Doreen M. (McKay) Cunningham. BA, U. Toronto, 1975, LLB, 1978. Bar: Ont. 1980. Lawyer McElwain & Assocs., Toronto, 1980-87; corp. solicitor John Labatt Ltd., London, Ont., 1987-90; corp. sec., asst. gen. counsel John Labatt Ltd., 1990-94; corp. sec. John Labatt Ltd. Subs., including Labatt Brewing Co., London, 1990-94; dir. projects and asst. gen. counsel John Labatt Ltd., 1995—. Mem. Law Soc. Upper Can., South-Western Ont. Corp. Counsel Assn. (pres. 1991-92), Middlesex Law Assn. (trustee 1992). Office: John Labatt Ltd Labatt House, BCE Pl 181 Bay St Ste 200, Toronto, ON Canada M5J 2T3

RUSS, CHARLES PAUL, III, lawyer, corporate executive; b. N.Y.C., Aug. 24, 1944; s. Charles Paul Jr. and Dorothea (von Frieling) R.; m. Dianne P. McLaughlin, June 24, 1969; children: Alexander Peter, Andrew William. B.A., Amherst Coll., 1966; J.D., Columbia U., 1969. Bar: N.Y. 1970, Ga. 1973. Assoc. Sullivan & Cromwell, N.Y.C., 1969-72; assoc. Gambrell & Mobley, Atlanta, 1972-74, ptnr., 1974; sr. atty. Stauffer Chem. Co., Westport, Conn., 1975-78; asst. gen. counsel Geo Internat. Corp., Stamford, Conn., 1978-80, v.p., gen. counsel, 1980-84; v.p., sec., gen. counsel NCR Corp., Dayton, Ohio, 1984-92; exec. v.p., sec., gen. counsel U.S. West, Inc., Englewood, CO, 1992—. Harlan Fiske Stone scholar Columbia U., 1969. Mem. ABA, Am. Corp. Counsel Assn., Ohio State Bar Assn., Assn. Gen. Counsel. Clubs: Dayton Country, Miami Valley Hunt and Polo, NCR Country, Seabrook Island Ocean. Home: 88 Glenmoor Pl Englewood CO 80110-7122 Office: US West Inc 7800 E Orchard Rd Ste 480 Englewood CO 80111-2533*

RUSS, JOANNA, writer, English language educator; b. N.Y.C., Feb. 22, 1937; d. Evarett and Bertha (Zinner) R. B.A. in English with high honors, Cornell, U., 1957; M.F.A. in Playwriting and Dramatic Lit, Yale U., 1960. Lectr. in English Cornell U., 1967-70, asst. prof., 1970-72; asst. prof. English, Harpur Coll., State U. N.Y. at Binghamton, 1972-75, U. Colo., 1975-77; asso. prof. English, U. Wash., 1977-90, prof., 1984-90. Author: Picnic on Paradise, 1968, And Chaos Died, 1970, The Female Man, 1975, We Who Are About To, 1977, Kittatinny: A Tale of Magic, 1978, The Two of Them, 1978, On Strike Against God, 1980, The Adventures of Alyx, 1983, The Zanzibar Cat, 1983, How To Suppress Women's Writing, 1983, Extra (Ordinary) People, 1984, Magic Mommas, Trembling Sisters, Puritans and Perverts: Feminist Essays, 1985, The Hidden Side of the Moon, 1987; also numerous short stories. Mem. Sci. Fiction Writers Am. (Nebula award for best short story 1972, Hugo award for best novella 1983). Address: 8961 E Lester St Tucson AZ 85715-5568

RUSSELL, ALLAN DAVID, lawyer; b. Cleve., May 6, 1924; s. Allan MacGillivray and Marvel (Zinner) R.; m. Lois Anne Robinson, June 12, 1947; children: Lisa Anne, Robinson David, Martha Leslie. B.A., Yale U., 1945, LL.B., 1951. Bar: N.Y. 1952, Conn. 1956, Mass. 1969, U.S. Supreme Ct. 1977. Atty. Sylvania Electric Products, Inc., N.Y.C., 1951-56; div. counsel Sylvania Electric Products, Inc., Batavia, N.Y., 1956-65; sr. counsel Sylvania Electric Products, Inc., 1965-71; sec., sr. counsel GTE Sylvania Inc., Stamford, Conn., 1971-76; asst. gen. counsel GTE Service Corp., 1976-80, v.p., assoc. gen. counsel staff, 1980-83; sole practice law Redding, Conn., 1983—; sec., dir. mktg. subs. Sylvania Entertainment Products Corp., 1961-67; sec. Wilbur B. Driver Co. Dist. leader Rep. Party, New Canaan, Conn., 1955-56; sec. bd. dirs. Youth Found., Inc., 19812-83, bd. dirs., 1985—; mem. planning commn., Redding, Conn., 1987-89; mem. Redding Bd. Ethics, 1990—, chmn., 1992—; warden Christ Ch. Parish, Redding, 1987-89; bd. dirs. Mark Twain Libr., 1988-94, v.p., 1988-89, pres., 1990-92. With USAAF, 1943-46. Mem. SAR, Assn. of Bar of City of N.Y., Conn. Bar Assn. (exec. com. corp. counsel sect. 1986-90), Am. Soc. Corp. Secs., St. Nicholas Soc., Collie Club Am. Found., Inc. (v.p., dir. 1986-90, mem. 1989-90), Soc. Colonial Wars, Yale Alumni Assn. (sec. local chpt. 1953-56), Yale Club of Danbury (pres. 1990—), Phi Delta Phi. Home: 9 Little River Ln Redding CT 06896-2018

RUSSELL, ALLEN STEVENSON, retired aluminum company executive; b. Bedford, Pa., May 27, 1915; s. Arthur Stainton and Ruth (Stevenson) R.; m. Judith Pauline Sexauer, Apr. 5, 1941. B.S., Pa. State U., 1936, M.S., 1937, Ph.D., 1942. With Aluminum Co. Am., 1940-82, assoc. dir. research, 1973-74; v.p. Alcoa, Pa., 1974-78; v.p. sci. and tech. affairs, 1978-81, v.p., chief scientist, 1981-82; adj. prof. U. Pitts., 1981-86. Contbr. articles to profl. jours. Named IR-100 Scientist of Yr., 1979; Pa. State U. alumni fellow, 1980; K.J. Bayer medalist, 1981; recipient chem. Pioneer award Am. Inst. Chemists, 1983. Fellow Am. Soc. Metals (Gold medal 1982), AIME (James Douglas gold medal 1987), Am. Inst. Chemists; mem. NAE (coun. 1978-84), Am. Chem. Soc., Sigma Xi. Republican. Presbyterian. Patentee in field. Home: 9 N Calibogue Cay Rd Sea Pines Plantation Hilton Head Island SC 29928

RUSSELL, ANDREW GEORGE ALEXANDER, author, naturalist; b. Lethbridge, Alta., Can., Dec. 8, 1915; s. Harold George and Lorenda Scarlett (McTavish) R.; m. Anna Kathleen Riggall, Nov. 1, 1936; children: Richard, Charles, John, Gordon, Anne. Grad. high sch., Lethbridge; LLD (hon.), U. Lethbridge, 1978, U. Calgary, Alta., 1978. Rocky Mountain guide, author, photographer, cinematographer, Alta., 1936—; rancher, lectr., 1936—. Author: Grizzy Country, 1964, Trails of a Wilderness Wanderer, 1971, Horns in the High Country, 1973, The High West, 1974, The Rockies, 1975, Wild Animals, 1977, Men of the Saddle, 1978, Alpine Canada, 1979, Memoirs of a Mountain Man, 1984, Life of a River, 1987, The Canadian Cowboy, 1993; contbr. articles to mags.; columnist; prodr. 3 feature films; writer radio scripts. Liberal candidate for Parliament, 1972. Decorated Order of Can.; recipient commemorative medal Confedn. of Can., 1992. Mem. Explorers Club. Avocations: fly fishing, target shooting, corresponding. Office: Box 68, Waterton Lakes Park, AB Canada T0K 2M0

RUSSELL, ANDREW MILO, music educator; b. Fredericksburg, Tex., July 16, 1948; s. Daniel Louden and Evelyn Sarah (Allen) R.; m. Sharon Anne Shelburne, June 2, 1968 (div. June 1994); children: Emily Christine, Andrea Layne, Dana Leslie. MusB, U. Houston, 1974; performance cert., Ind. U., 1974; MusM, Ind. U., Bloomington, 1975. Asst. prof. Baylor U., Waco, Tex., 1975-79; assoc. prof. U. Tex., Arlington, 1979—; cons. Tex. Commn. on Arts, Austin, 1985—. Performer numerous concerts, recitals nationwide, 1968—. E-5 with U.S. Army, 1971-74. Mem. Internat. Trombone Assn., Am. Fedn. Music, Chicago Chamber Brass. Democrat. Baptist. Home: 1213 Scott Dr Hurst TX 76053-4223 Office: U Tex PO Box 19105 Arlington TX 76019

RUSSELL, ANGELA VETA, state legislator, social worker; b. Crow Agency, Mont., Aug. 25, 1943; d. William A. and Josephine (Pease) R. BA, U. Mont., 1965; MSW, Tulane U., 1974. Lic. social worker, Mont. Field rep. United Scholar Svc., Denver, 1965-67; child welfare worker Yellowstone County Pub. Welfare, Billings, Mont., 1968-72; counselor Rocky Mt. Coll., Billings, Mont., 1972-73; com. organizer Crow Tribe Office of Coal Rsch., Crow Agency, Mont., 1975-76; cons. pvt. practice, Lodge Grass, Mont., 1976-77; project dir. Denver U. Social Rsch., 1977-78; med. social worker USPHS, Crow Agy., Brow Agency, 1978-85; psychotherapist, cons. pvt. practice, Billings, 1985—; bd. mem. Rocky Mountain Coll., Billings. Editor Hist. Crow Calender, 1978—. State adv. com. U.S. Civil Rights Commn. Rocky Mt. Region, Denver, 1976-83; trustee Lodge Grass Schs., 1981-84; rep. Mont. Ho. of Reps., Helena, 1987-94; chmn. Mt. Rhodes Scholar Com. Missoula, Mont., 1990-94, Nat. Assn. Native Am. Legis., Denver, 1991-94; mem. adv. bd. Mont. Initiative for Abatement of Mortality in Infants, Helena, Mont., 1991—; cmty. organizer Crow Healthy Mothers/Healthy Babies, Apsaalooke Com. for the Arts. Named to Salute to Women, YWCA, Billings, 1990; named Mont. Social Worker of Yr., 1993. Mem. NASW, Nat. Assn. Indian Social Workers (treas. 1986-88), Indian Law Resource Ctr. (bd. dirs. 1992—). Democrat. Baptist. Avocations: walking, reading, sewing, beading. Home: PO Box 333 Lodge Grass MT 59050-0333 Office: 1236 N 28th #103 Billings MT 59101

RUSSELL, ATTIE YVONNE, academic administrator, dean, pediatrics educator; b. Washington, Aug. 10, 1923; d. George and Kathleen L. (Milliner) Werner; m. Rex Hillier, Apr. 19, 1954 (dec.); m. Henry J. Russell, 1960 (div. 1971); children: Richard Russell, Margaret Jane Russell-Harde; m. Harry F. Camper, Sept. 2, 1984. BS, Am. U., 1944; PhD, State U. Iowa, 1952; MD, U. Chgo., 1958. Intern Phila. Gen. Hosp., 1958-59; resident in pediatrics Bronx (N.Y.) Mcpl. Hosp., 1960-61, Del. Hosp., Wilmington, 1962-63; dir. maternal and child health, crippled children's svcs. Del. State Bd. Health, Dover, 1963-68; asst. dean community health affairs, assoc. prof. pediatrics U. Cin. Coll. Medicine, 1968-71; clin. assoc. prof. pediatrics Med. Coll. Pa., Phila., 1966-68, 71-74; dep. dir. div. pub. health State of Del., Dover, 1971-74; dir. Santa Clara Valley Med. Ctr., San Jose, Calif., 1974-79; assoc. dean, clin. prof. pediatrics, family medicine Stanford (Calif.) U. Sch. Medicine, 1974-79; dir. USPHS Hosp., Boston, 1979-81, Balt. City Hosps., 1981-82; asst. v.p. community affairs, prof. pediatrics U. Tex. Med. Br., Galveston, 1982-87, asst. v.p. student affairs, dean students, prof. pediatrics, 1987-92, clin. prof. pediatrics, 1992—; reviewer Coun. for Internat. Exchange of Scholars, Washington, 1987-94; dir. III Symposium on Health and Human Svcs. in the U.S.-Mex., Brownsville, 1988; mem. sci. coun. Am. Fedn. for Aging Rsch., Inc., 1983-86. Contbr. articles and abstracts to profl. jours. Mem. budget com. United Way, Galveston, 1982-84; mem. Mayor's Adv. Com. for Sr. Citizens and Handicapped Persons for the City of Galveston, 1983-85; bd. dirs Galveston County Coordinated Community Clinics, 1983-87; bd. advisors Galveston Hist. Found., 1983-88; mem. Com. for Coop. Action Planning, 1983-88, Houston-Galveston Health Promotion Consortium, 1983-88, Injury Control Prevention (Houston), 1984-89, aging programs adv. com. Houston-Galveston Area Coun., 1985-92. Recipient Disting. Alumni award Am. U., 1984. Fellow Am. Acad. Pediatrics, Am. Pub. Health Assn.; mem. AMA, Am. Coll. Preventive Medicine, Soc. for Adolescent Medicine, Am. Physiol. Soc., Am. Fedn. for Aging Rsch., Am. Geriatrics Soc., Mass. State Med. Soc., Galveston Med. Soc., Tex. Med. Assn., Tex. Pediatric Soc., Galveston C. of C. (legis. com. 1988), Order of Eastern Star, Sigma Xi, Alpha Omega Alpha. Office: U Tex Med Branch Ashbel Smith Rm 1.208 Galveston TX 77550

RUSSELL, BILL, former professional basketball team executive, former professional basketball player; b. Monroe, La., Feb. 12, 1934. Grad., San Francisco State Coll., 1956. Player, NBA Boston Celtics Profl. Basketball Club, 1956-69, coach, 1966-69; sportscaster ABC-TV, 1969-80, CBS-TV, 1980-83; coach NBA Seattle Supersonics, 1973-77; coach NBA Sacramento Kings, 1987-88, v.p. basketball ops., then exec. v.p., 1988-89; mem. U.S. Olympic Basketball Team (Gold medal), 1956. Appeared in: TV series Cowboy in Africa; also commls.; co-host: The Superstars, ABC-TV, 1978-79; Author: Second Wind: Memoirs of an Opinionated Man, 1979. Inducted into Basketball Hall of Fame, 1974; mem. 11 NBA championship teams. Office: Sacramento Kings 1 Sports Pky Sacramento CA 95834-2301*

RUSSELL, CAROL ANN, personnel service company executive; b. Detroit, Dec. 14, 1943; d. Billy and Iris (Driver) Koud; m. Victor Rojas (div.). BA in English, Hunter Coll., 1993. Registered employment cons. Various positions in temp. help cos. N.Y.C., 1964-74; v.p. Wollborg-Michelson, San Francisco, 1974-82; co-owner, pres. Russell Staffing Resources, Inc., San Francisco and Sonoma, 1983—; media guest, spkr., workshop and seminar leader in field; host/cmty. prodr. Job Net program for Viacom Cable T.V.; pres. bd. Russell Ctr. for Career Skills. Pub. Checkpoint Newsletter; contbr. articles to profl. pubs. Named to the Inc. 500, 1989, 90. Mem. Soc. to Preserve and Encourage Radio Drama Variety and Comedy, Internat. Platform Assn.. No. Calif. Human Resources Coun., Soc. Human Resource Mgmt., Calif. Assn. Pers. Cons. (pres. Golden State chpt. 1984-85), Calif. Assn. Temp. Svcs., Bay Area Pers. Assn. (pres. 1983-84), Pers. Assn. Sonoma County. Office: Russell Pers Svcs Inc 120 Montgomery St San Francisco CA 94104-4303

RUSSELL, CHARLES, film director, producer. films include: (dir.): Nightmare on Elm Street III, 1987 (also co-writer), The Blob, 1988 (also co-writer), The Mask, 1994 (also exec. prodr.); (prodr.): Cheerleaders' Wild Weekend, 1979, Hell Night, 1981, The Seduction, 1982, Body Rock, 1984, Dreamscape, 1984 (also co-writer), Girls Just Want to Have Fun, 1985, Back To School, 1986. Office: UTA 9560 Wilshire Blvd Beverly Hills CA 90212*

RUSSELL, CHARLES F., newspaper publishing executive. V.p. technology The Wall Street Journal, N.Y.C. Office: Wall Street Journal 200 Liberty St New York NY 10281*

RUSSELL, CHARLES ROBERTS, chemical engineer; b. Spokane, Wash., July 13, 1914; s. Marvin Alvin and Dessie Corselia (Price) R.; m. Dolores Kopriva, May 17, 1943; children—Ann E., John C., David F., Thomas R. B.S. in Chem. Engring, Wash. State U., 1936; Ph.D. in Chem. Engring. (Procter and Gamble Co. fellow 1940-41), U. Wis., 1941. Egr. div. reactor devel. AEC, Washington, 1950-56; engr. Gen. Motors Tech. Center, Warren, Mich. and Santa Barbara, Calif., 1956-68; assoc. dean engring. Calif. Poly. State U., San Luis Obispo, 1968-73; prof. mech. engring. Calif. Poly. State U., 1973-80; mem. nuclear standards bd. Am. Nat. Standards Inst., 1956-78; cons., 1980—; sec. adv. com. reactor safeguards AEC, 1950-55. Author: Reactor Safeguards, 1962, Elements of Energy Conversion, 1967, Energy Sources, Ency. Britannica. Served with USNR, 1944-46. Mem. Am. Chem. Soc. Republican. Roman Catholic. Club: Channel City (Santa Barbara). Home and Office: 3071 Marilyn Way Santa Barbara CA 93105-2040

RUSSELL, CHARLES T., bank executive; b. 1930. With Wachovia Bank & Trust, Winston-Salem, N.C. to 1970, Visa USA, Inc., 1970—; with Visa Internat. Svc. Assn., San Mateo, Calif., 1974—, now pres., CEO. Office: Visa International Svc Assn 707 Leahy St # 300-a Redwood City CA 94061-3959

RUSSELL, CHARLOTTE SANANES, biochemistry educator, researcher; b. N.Y.C., Jan. 4, 1927; d. Joseph and Marguerite (Saltiel) Sananes; m. Joseph Brooke Russell, Dec. 20, 1947; children: James Robert, Joshua Sananes. BA, Bklyn. Coll., 1946; MA, Columbia U., 1947, PhD, 1951. Asst. prof. biochemistry CCNY, N.Y.C., 1958-68, assoc. prof., 1968-72, prof., 1972—; peer reviewer NSF, NIH; ad hoc reviewer sci. jours. including Jour. Bacteriology, Biochemistry. Contbr. articles to profl. jours. Mem. AAAS, AAUP, AAUW (internat. fellowship panel 1986-89), Am. Soc. Biochemistry and Molecular Biology, Am. Chem. Soc., Amnesty Internat., Urgent Action Network, Sigma Xi. Office: CCNY Dept Chemistry 138th St & Convent Ave New York NY 10031

RUSSELL, CLIFFORD SPRINGER, economics and public policy educator; b. Holyoke, Mass., Feb. 11, 1938; s. Kenneth Clifford and Helen Alwilda (Springer) R.; m. Louise Pancoast Bennett, Feb. 3, 1965 (div. June 1985); m. Susan Vanston Reid, Sept. 7, 1985; stepchildren: Timothy Taylor Greene, Elizabeth Claussen Greene. BA, Dartmouth Coll., 1960; PhD, Harvard U., 1968. Sr. rsch. assoc. Resources for the Future, Washington, 1968-70, fellow, 1970-73, sr. fellow, 1973-85, div. dir., 1981-85; prof. econs. and pub. policy Vanderbilt U., Nashville, 1986—; dir. Vanderbilt Inst. for Pub. Policy Studies, 1986—. Author: Drought and Water Supply: Implications of the Massachusetts Experience for Municipal Planning, 1970, Residuals Management in Industry: A Case Study of Petroleum Refining, 1973, Steel Production: Processes, Products and Residuals, 1976, Environment Quality Management: An Application to the Lower Delaware Valley, 1976, Freshwater Recreational Fishing: The National Benefits of Water Pollution Control, 1982, Enforcing Pollution Control Laws, 1986; contbr. articles to profl. jours. Trustee, treas. Environ. Def. Fund, N.Y.C. and Washington, 1973-85; mem. Tenn. Gov.'s Energy Adv. Bd., Nashville, 1989-94; trustee Tenn. Environ. Coun., Nashville, 1989—, pres. 1992-95. Lt. USN, 1960-63. Mem. Assn. Environ. and Resource Econs. Office: Vanderbilt Inst Pub Policy Studies 1207 18th Ave S Nashville TN 37212-2892

RUSSELL, DAN M., JR., federal judge; b. Magee, Miss., Mar. 15, 1913; s. Dan M. and Beulah (Watkins) R.; m. Dorothy Tudury, Dec. 27, 1942; children—Truett Daniel, Dorothy Dale, Richard Brian. B.A., U. Miss., 1935, LL.B., 1937. Bar: Miss. bar 1937. Practice in Gulfport and Bay St. Louis, Miss.; U.S. judge So. Dist. Miss., 1965—; now sr. judge; dir.

Savs. & Loan Assn., Gulfport, Miss. Chmn. Hancock (Miss.) Civic Action Assn., 1964—; Democratic presdl. elector, 1964; chmn. Hancock County Election Commn., 1959-64. Served to lt. comdr. USNR, 1941-45. Mem. Miss. Bar Assn., Hancock County Bar Assn. (v.p. 1964-65), Hancock County C. of C. (pres. 1946), Tau Kappa Alpha, Scribblers. Club: Rotarian (pres. Bay St. Louis, Miss. 1946). Office: US Dist Ct PO Box 1930 Gulfport MS 39502-1930

RUSSELL, DANIEL FRANCIS, hospital administrator; b. Tiskilwa, Ill., Oct. 8, 1940; married. BA, U. Miami, 1963; MA, Washington U., 1966. Adminstrv. intern James M. Jackson Meml. Hosp., Miami, Fla., 1963-64; adminstrv. resident Rush Presbyn. St. Luke's Med. Ctr., Chgo., 1965-66, adminstrv. asst., 1966-68; asst. adminstr. St. Joseph's Hosp. & Med. Ctr., Phoenix, 1968-70, assoc. adminstr., 1970-74; pres. St. Joseph Hosp. & Med. Ctr., Tacoma, 1974-86, Ea. Mercy Health System, Radnor, Pa., 1986—. Mem. Am. Hosp. Assn., Washington Hosp. Assn. (bd. dirs.). Office: Ea Mercy Health System 100 Matsonford Rd Radnor PA 19087-4527

RUSSELL, DAVID ALLISON, aeronautical engineering educator; b. Saint John, N.B., Can., Apr. 25, 1935; came to U.S., 1954, naturalized, 1967; s. James Vener and Helen Ringen (Allison) R.; m. Hazel Anne Garnett, Mar. 22, 1957; children: Karen, Kristen, Kathryn. Student, U. N.B., Fredericton, 1950-54; B.Mech.Engring., U. So. Calif., 1956; M.Sc. in Aeros, Calif. Inst. Tech., 1957, Ph.D. in Aeros. and Physics, 1961. Sr. scientist Jet Propulsion Lab., Pasadena, Calif., 1961-67; research asso. prof. aeros. and astronautics U. Wash., 1967-70, asso. prof., 1970-74, prof., 1974—, chmn. dept. aeros. and astronautics, 1977-92; cons. in field. Contbr. articles on fluid mechanics and gas physics to profl. jours., especially on shock processes, laser fluid dynamics and aerodynamics. Mem. Kirkland (Wash.) Planning Commn., 1971-79, chmn., 1977-79; chmn. Kirkland Land Use Policy Plan, 1977-79; mem. Kirkland City Coun., 1984—, mayor, 1992—. NASA grantee, 1969-78, 84-87; Dept. Def. grantee, 1969-71, 73-81. Fellow Am. Phys. Soc., AIAA (Pacific N.W. Coun. 1974-76, 86-88, Pacific N.W. award for contbns. to aerospace tech. 1972, nat. plasmadynamics and lasers com. 1970-72, 86-92); mem. Sierra Club, Nature Conservancy, Sigma Xi, Tau Beta Pi, Pi Tau Sigma. Home: 4507 105th Ave NE Kirkland WA 98033-7637 Office: 312 Guggenheim Hall U Wash FS-10 Seattle WA 98195

RUSSELL, DAVID E., federal judge; b. Chicago Heights, Ill., Mar. 19, 1935; s. Robert W. and Nellie (Petkus) R.; m. Denise A. Hurst, Apr. 1, 1968 (div. 1978); children: Dirk, Kent, Laura, Rachel; m. Sandra M. Niemeyer, Oct. 31, 1982; children: Jeff Ahrens, Penny, Stacy. BS in Acctg., U. Calif., Berkeley, 1957, LLB, 1960. Bar: Calif. 1961, U.S. Dist. Ct. (no. dist.) Calif. 1961, U.S. Tax Ct. 1967; CPA, Calif. Staff acct. Lybrand, Ross Bros. & Montgomery, San Francisco, 1960-64; assoc. Robert C. Burnstein, Esquire, Oakland, Calif., 1964-65; ptnr. Russell & Humphreys, Sacramento, 1965; ptnr. Russell, Humphreys & Estabrook, Sacramento, 1966-70, prin., 1971-73; shareholder Russell, Jarvis, Estabrook & Dashiell, Sacramento, 1974-86; bankruptcy judge U.S. Dist. Ct. for Ea. Dist. Calif., Sacramento, 1986—. Office: US Bankruptcy Ct 650 Capitol Mall Rm 8038 Sacramento CA 95814-4792

RUSSELL, DAVID EMERSON, consulting mechanical engineer; b. Jacksonville, Fla., Dec. 20, 1922; s. David Herbert and Wilhelmina (Ash) R.; B.Mech. Engring., U. Fla., 1948; postgrad. Oxford (Eng.) U. Mech. engr. United Fruit Co., Jacksonville, 1948-50, U.S. Army C.E., Jacksonville, 1950-54, Aramco, Saudi Arabia, 1954-55; v.p. Beiswenger Hoch and Assocs., Inc., Jacksonville, 1955-57; owner, operator David E. Russell and Assocs., cons. engrs., Jacksonville, 1957—. Chmn. Jacksonville Water Quality Control Bd., 1969-73; bd. dirs. Jacksonville Hist. Soc., 1981-82; mem. Jacksonville Bicentennial Commn., 1973-79. Served to 2d lt. AUS, 1943-46. Recipient Outstanding Service award City of Jacksonville, 1974. Registered profl. engr., Fla., Ga. Mem. ASME (chmn. N.E. Fla. 1967-68), Nat. Soc. Profl. Engrs., ASHRAE, Fla. Engring. Soc. Episcopalian. Club: University (Jacksonville). Contbr. articles to profl. jours.; holder of 5 U.S. patents. Avocations: world travel, boating. Home: 4720 Timuquana Rd Jacksonville FL 32210-8231 Office: 110 Riverside Ave Jacksonville FL 32202-4906

RUSSELL, DAVID L., federal judge; b. Sapulpa, Okla., July 7, 1942; s. Lynn and Florence E. (Brown) R.; m. Dana J. Wilson, Apr. 16, 1971; 1 child, Sarah Elizabeth. BS, Okla. Bapt. U., 1963; J.D., Okla. U., 1965. Bar: Okla. 1965. Asst. atty. gen. State of Okla., Oklahoma City, 1968-69, legal adviser to gov., 1969-70; legal adviser Senator Dewey Bartlett, Washington, 1973-75; U.S. atty. for Western dist. Okla. Dept. Justice, 1975-77, 81-82; ptnr. Benefield & Russell, Oklahoma City, 1977-81; chief judge U.S. Dist. Ct. (we. dist.) Okla., Oklahoma City, 1982—. Lt. comdr. JAGC, USN, 1965-68. Selected Outstanding Fed. Ct. Trial judge Okla. Trial Lawyers Assn., 1988. Mem. Okla. Bar Assn., Fed. Bar Assn. (pres. Oklahoma City chpt. 1981). Republican. Methodist. Office: US Dist Ct 3321 US Courthouse 200 NW 4th St Oklahoma City OK 73102-3003

RUSSELL, DAVID LAWSON, psychology educator; b. Apr. 1, 1921; m. Jean Williams; children: David W., Nancy K. B.A. in Psychology with honors, Wesleyan U., 1942; postgrad., Columbia U., summers 1942, 46; Ph.D. in Psychology, U. Minn., 1953. Lic. psychologist, Ohio. Adminstrv. fellow Office Dean of Students, U. Minn., Mpls., 1947; teaching asst. dept. psychology U. Minn., 1947-48; clin. fellow Student Counseling Bur., 1948-50; dir. student counseling Bowdoin Coll., Brunswick, Maine, 1950-59; instr. Bowdoin Coll., 1950-54, asst. prof. psychology, 1954-59; assoc. prof. Ohio U., 1959-67, prof., 1967-91, asst. chmn. dept. psychology, 1968, chmn., 1969-72, prof. emeritus, 1991—; vis. prof. U. N.H., summer 1958; mem. faculty NDEA Counseling and Guidance Inst. at Ohio U., 1961, 63, 65, 1966-67; pres. Maine Psychol. Assn., 1956-57; chmn. Maine Bd. Examiners Psychologists, 1959; cons. Div. Undergrad. Edn. in Sci., NSF, 1965, 70, 71; sec. Nat. Coun. Chmns. Grad. Depts. Psychology, 1971-72. Author: (with others) Applied Psychology, 1966; contbr. articles to profl. pubs. Mem. Superintending Sch. Com., Topsham, Maine, 1953-59, chmn., 1953-54, 56-57, mem. sch. bldg. com., 1953-55, com. chmn., 1953-55; sec. Joint-Com. Maine Sch. Union 46, 1953-59; mem. Topsham Zoning Com., 1956-57; bd. dirs. United Srs. of Athens County, 1987-91; mem. adv. bd. Athens County Dept. Human Services, 1987-94, pres. 1993-94; mem. Buckeye Hills—Hocking Valley Regional Devel. Dist. area agy. on aging, adv. coun. on aging, 1988-94; mem. Athens County Coun. on Aging, 1988-94, pres., 1990-93. Lt. USCGR, 1943-52. Mem. AAUP, VFW, Am. Psychol. Assn., Midwestern Psychol. Assn., Am. Ednl. Rsch. Assn., Mass. Audubon Soc., Hocking Valley Audubon Soc., Buckeye Trail Assn., Vergilian Soc., Athens League of Women Voters, Athens County Humane Soc., Columbus Urban League, Orleans Hist. Soc., Ohio U. Soc. Alumni Friends of Coll. Arts and Scis. (exec. sec. 1985-90), Athens County Hist. Soc., Sierra Club, Appalachian Mountain Club, Psi Chi, Sigma Phi Omega. Home: 41 Elmwood Pl Athens OH 45701-1905 Home (summer): PO Box 727 Orleans MA 02653-0727

RUSSELL, DONALD STUART, federal judge; b. Lafayette Springs, Miss., Feb. 22, 1906; s. Jesse and Lula (Russell) R.; m. Virginia Utsey, June 15, 1929; children: Donald, Mildred, Scott, John. AB, U. S.C., 1925, LLB, 1928; postgrad., U. Mich., 1929; LLD (hon.), Wofford Coll., Lander Coll., The Citadel, U.S.C., Emory U., Clemson U., C.W. Post Coll. Bar: S.C. 1928. Pvt. practice law Spartanburg 1930-42, 1938-42, 47-51, 57-63; with Nicholls, Wyche & Byrnes, Nicholls, Wyche & Russell, and Nicholls & Russell, 1930-42; mem. Price Adjustment Bd., War Dept., Washington, 1942; asst. to dir. econ. stabilization, 1942, asst. to dir. war mobilization, 1943; dep. dir. Office War Mobilization Reconversion, 1945; asst. sec. state, 1945-47; pres. U. S.C., 1951-57; gov. S.C., 1963-65; mem. U.S. Senate from S.C., 1965-66, U.S. Dist. Ct. judge, 1966-71; judge U.S. Ct. Appeals, Spartanburg, S.C., 1971—. Mem. Wriston Com. on Reorgn. Fgn. Service, 1954; trustee emeritus Emory U., Atlanta, Converse Coll., Spartanburg, S.C., Benedict Coll., Columbia, S.C. Served as maj. AUS, 1944, SHAEF, France. Mem. ABA, Am. Law Inst., S.C. Bar Assn., Spartanburg County Bar Assn., Phi Beta Kappa. Methodist. Office: US Ct Appeals 4th Ct PO Box 1985 Spartanburg SC 29301*

RUSSELL, ELBERT WINSLOW, neuropsychologist; b. Las Vegas, N.Mex., June 4, 1929; s. Josiah Cox and Ruth Annice (Winslow) R.; children from previous marriage: Gwendolyn Marie Harvey, Franklin Winslow, Kirsten Nash, Jonathan Nash; m. Sally Lynn Kolitz, Apr. 2, 1989. BA,

Earlham Coll., Richmond, Ind., 1951; MA, U. Ill., 1953; MS, Pa. State U., 1958; PhD, U. Kans., 1968. Clin. psychologist Warnersville (Pa.) State Hosp., 1959-61; clin. neuropsychology VA Med. Ctr., Cin., 1968-71; dir. neuropsychology lab. VA Med. Ctr., Miami, Fla., 1971-89, rsch. psychologist, 1989—; adj. prof. Nova U., Ft. Lauderdale, 1980-87, U. Miami Med. Sch., 1980-94, U. Miami, 1979—. Author: (with C. Neuringer and G. Goldstein) Assessment of Brain Damage, 1970, (with R. Starkey) Halstead Russell Neuropsychological Evaluation System, 1993; contbr. articles to profl. jours. Fellow Am. Psychol. Assn., Am. Psychol. Soc.; mem. Nat. Acad. Neuropsychology, Sigma Xi. Democrat. Soc. of Friends. Home: 6091 SW 79th St Miami FL 33143-5030 Office: VA Med Ctr 1201 NW 16th St Miami FL 33125-1624

RUSSELL, FRANCIA, ballet director, educator; b. Los Angeles, Jan. 10, 1938; d. W. Frank and Marion (Whitney) R.; m. Kent Stowell, Nov. 19, 1965; children: Christopher, Darren, Ethan. Studies with, George Balanchine, Vera Volkova, Felia Doubrouska, Antonina Tumkovsky, Benjamin Harkarvy; student, NYU, Columbia U. Dancer, soloist N.Y.C Ballet, 1956-62, ballet mistress, 1965-70; dancer Ballets USA/Jerome Robbins, N.Y.C., 1962; tchr. ballet Sch. Am. Ballet, N.Y.C., 1963-64; co-dir. Frankfurt (Fed. Republic Germany) Opera Ballet, 1976-77; dir., co-artistic dir. Pacific N.W. Ballet, Seattle, 1977—; affiliate prof. of dance U. Wash. Dir. staging over 100 George Balanchine ballet prodns. throughout world, including the Soviet Union and People's Republic of China, 1964—. Named Woman of Achievement, Matrix Table, Women in Communications, Seattle, 1987, Gov.'s Arts award, 1989. Mem. Internat. Women's Forum. Home: 2833 Broadway E Seattle WA 98102-3935 Office: Pacific NW Ballet 301 Mercer St Seattle WA 98109

RUSSELL, FRANK ELI, newspaper publishing executive; b. Kokomo, Ind., Dec. 6, 1920; s. Frank E. and Maude (Wiggins) R.; children: Linda Carole Russell Atkins, Richard Lee, Frank E. III, Rita Jane Russell Eagle, Julie Beth Russell Smith; m. Nancy M. Shover, Oct. 5, 1991. AB, Evansville Coll., 1942; JD, Ind. U., 1951; LLD (hon.), U. Evansville, 1985; HHD (hon.), Franklin Coll., 1989. Bar: Ind. 1951; CPA, Ind. Ptnr. George S. Olive & Co., Indpls., 1947-53; exec. v.p. Spickelmier Industries, Inc., Indpls., 1953-59; bus. mgr. Indpls. Star & News, 1959-77; v.p., gen. mgr. New Ctrl. Newspapers, Inc., Indpls., 1977-79, pres., 1979—, also bd. dirs.; pres. Ctrl. Newsprint, also bd. dirs.; pres. Bradley Paper Co., also bd. dirs.; sec.-treas., bd. dirs. Phoenix Newspapers Inc., Indpls., Newspapers, Inc., Muncie Newspapers, Inc., Ctrl. Newspapers Found., Indpls.; past chmn. adv. bd. Met. Indpls. TV Assn., Inc.; trustee retirement trust Ctrl. Newspapers, Inc.; bd. dirs. Newspaper Advt. Bur.; chmn. retirement com. Hoosier State Press. Bd. dirs. Ariz. Cmty. Found., 1992—, Eiteljorg Mus., 1994—. Recipient Life Salvation award Salvation Army, 1989, Disting. Alumni award Ind. U. Sch. Law, 1989, Life Trustee award U. Evansville, 1991. Mem. ABA, AICPA, Ind. Bar Assn., Indpls. Bar Assn. (past bd. dirs., past treas.), Ind. Assn. CPAs (past dir.), Tax Execs. Inst. (past pres.), Ind. Assn. Credit Mgmt. (dir., v.p.), Inst. Newspaper Controllers and Fin. Officers (dir., past pres.), Ind. Acad. Ind. Assn. Colls., Midwest Pension Conf. (Ind. chpt.), Newspaper Advt. Bur. (bd. dirs.), Salvation Army (life mem. award), Order of Coif, Phi Delta Phi, Sigma Alpha Epsilon. Methodist. Clubs: Indpls. Athletic, Columbia, Meridian Hills Country, Skyline. Lodges: Masons, Shriners. Office: Cen Newspapers Inc Ste 1200 1st Indiana Plaza 135 N Pennsylvania St Indianapolis IN 46204

RUSSELL, FRED MCFERRIN, journalist, author, lawyer; b. Nashville, Aug. 27, 1906; s. John E. and Mabel Lee (McFerrin) R.; m. Katherine Wyche Early, Nov. 2, 1933; children: Katherine (Mrs. Earl Beasley), Ellen (Mrs. Robert Sadler), Lee (Mrs. John Brown, Carolyn Russell. Student, Vanderbilt U., 1923-27. Bar: Tenn. 1928. Atty. Real Estate Title Co., 1928; reporter Nashville Banner, 1929, sports editor, 1930-69, sports dir., 1969-87, v.p., 1955—; chmn. honors ct. Nat. Football Found. and Hall of Fame, 1967-92; So. chmn. Heisman Trophy Com., 1946-92. Author: 50 Years of Vanderbilt Football, 1938, I'll Go Quietly, 1944, I'll Try Anything Twice, 1945, Funny Thing About Sport, 1948, Bury Me in an Old Press Box, 1957, Big Bowl Football, 1963; contbr. to mags. including Saturday Evening Post, 1939-63. A founder Harpeth Hall Sch., 1951, trustee, 1951-55; nat. pres. Vanderbilt Alumni Assn., 1960-61; dir. Children's Regional Med. Center, 1970-72. Recipient Nat. Headliners award, 1936; Grantland Rice award for sports writing, 1955; Jake Wade award, 1966; Coll. Football Centennial award, 1969; writing award Golf Writers Assn. Am., 1972; award for disting. journalism U.S. Olympic Com., 1976; Disting. Am. award Nat. Football Found. and Hall of Fame, 1980; Amos Alonzo Stagg award Am. Football Coaches Assn., 1981; award Nat. Turf Writers Assn., 1983; Red Smith award AP Sports Editors, 1984; named to Tenn. Sports Hall of Fame, 1974, Nat. Sportscasters and Sportswriters Hall of Fame, 1988. Mem. Football Writers Assn. Am. (pres. 1960-61), Sigma Delta Chi, Kappa Sigma (nat. man of yr. 1983), Omicron Delta Kappa. Methodist. Clubs: Belle Meade Country, Univ. Lodges: Masons (33 degree), Shriners. Office: Nashville Banner 1100 Broad St Nashville TN 37203 *There is a close affinity between sport and humor, and a sportswriter can provide a good measure of entertainment just by putting into print some of the humor he sees and hears along the way.*

RUSSELL, FREDERICK WILLIAM, Canadian provincial official; b. St. John's, Nfld., Can., Sept. 10, 1923; s. Herbert J. and Jean (Campbell) R.; m. Margaret M. Cross, June 15, 1946; children: Douglas, Janice, James, Peter. Student, Prince of Wales Coll., St. John's, Dalhousie U., Halifax, N.S., Can.; LLD (hon.), Meml. U. Nfld., St. John's, 1976. Pres. Blue Peter Steamships, St. John's, 1949-72, Terra Nova Motors Ltd., St. John's, 1962-79, Gen. Industries, St. John's, 1980-88, Delta Holdings Ltd., St. John's, 1980-88, Fremar Investments Ltd., St. John's, 1980-91; lt. gov. Province of Nfld., St. John's, 1991—; mem. Royal Trust Adv. Bd., St. John's, 1980-91. Mem. Nfld. Labour Rels. Bd., St. John's 1953-89; chmn. United Ch. Sch. Bd., St. John's, 1958-67; chmn. bd. regents Meml. U. Nfld., 1974-82; bd. dirs. Atlantic Can. Opportunities Agy., Moncton, N.B., Can., 1986-91. Decorated Order of Can.; knight of justice Order of St. John; recipient Order of Red Cross, Can. Red Cross Soc., 1992. Mem. Rotary (bd. dirs. St. John's). Mem. United Ch. of Canada. Avocations: skiing, boating, salmon fishing. Home and office: Govt House, Military Rd PO Box 5517, Saint John's, NF Canada A1C 5W4

RUSSELL, GARY, broadcast executive; b. Winnepeg, Man., Can., Dec. 17, 1948; s. Raymond Anthony Wakefield and Florence Margret (Willson) Vidler; m. Deborah Kim Finnson, Oct. 10, 1984; children: Amanda, Charles. Grad., Kelvin High Sch., Winnepeg, 1967. Radio announcer Sta. CHLO, St. Thomas, Ont., 1967, Sta. CKOM, Saskatoon, Sask., 1968-69, Sta. CJME, Regina, Sask., 1969, Sta. CKLW, Windsor, Ont., 1970; radio announcer Sta. CKLG, Vancouver, B.C., 1970-73, program dir., 1975-85; program dir. Sta. CKY, Winnepeg, 1975-86; nat. program dir. Moffat Comm., Winnepeg, 1986-89; v.p., gen. mgr. 54 Rock, Ottawa, 1990-92, Sta. CJAY, Calgary, Alta., 1992—. Avocations: camping, boating. Office: Standard Radio Inc, Box 2750 Station M, Calgary, AB Canada TZP 4P8

RUSSELL, GEORGE ALBERT, university president; b. Bertrand, Mo., July 12, 1921; s. George Albert and Martha (Cramer) R.; m. Ruth Ann Ashby, Nov. 11, 1944; children: George Albert, Frank Ashby, Ruth Ann, Cramer Anderson. B.S. in Elec. Engring. Mass. Inst. Tech., 1947; M.S., U. Ill., 1952, Ph.D. in Physics, 1955. Assoc. prof. So. Ill. U. 1960-62; faculty U. Ill., Urbana, 1962-72, prof. physics, 1963-72, assoc. dir. Materials Research Lab., 1963-68, assoc. head physics dept., 1968-70, assoc. dean Grad. Coll., 1970-72, vice chancellor research, dean Grad. Coll., 1972-77; chancellor U Mo.-Kansas City, 1977-91; pres. U Mo. system admin., Columbia, Mo., 1991—; cons. Office Naval Research, 1961-76; dir. Microthermal Applications Inc. dir. Kansas City Power and Light Co.; mem. adv. bd. dirs. Boatman's First Nat. Bank Kansas City; mem. acad. adv. panel Com. on Exchanges. Vice chmn. Illini Union Bd., 1970; pres. Levis Faculty Center, 1972; chmn. bd. trustees AUA, 1977; mem. Mo. Sci. and Tech. Corp.; trustee Midwest Research Inst.; bd. dirs. Edgar Snow Meml. Fund, Inc. Served with USN, World War II. Mem. Am. Assn. Physics Tchrs., Am. Phys. Soc. Clubs: Champaign Country (pres. 1972), Mission Hills Country, Rockhill Tennis. Home: 1900 S Providence Rd Columbia MO 65203-3544 Office: U of Mo 321 University Hall Columbia MO 65211

RUSSELL, GEORGE ALLEN, composer, musicologist; b. Cin., June 23, 1923; s. Joseph and Bessie (Sledge) R.; 1 son, Jock Millgardh; m. Alice Norbury, Aug. 4, 1981. Student, Wilberforce U. High Sch., 1940-43; pupil composition, Stephan Volpe, 1949. Pvt. tchr. concept N.Y.C., 1953-68, also confs. and festivals; apptd. mem. faculty New Eng. Conservatory Music, 1969; also tchr. in Sweden, Norway and Finland; Mem. panel Nat. Endowment of Arts, 1975-76. Published concept, 1953, composer (with Dizzy Gillespie); 1st composition featuring jazz and Latin influences Cubana-Be, Cubana Bop; presented Carnegie Hall, 1947; performed John F. Kennedy's People to People Music Festival, Washington, 1962, Philharmonic Hall, Lincoln Center, 1963, tours of Europe with Newport Jazz Festival, 1964, jazz orchestras 1970—; performed original compostions with large and small European ensembles for radio, TV and new music socs., in Scandinavia, Italy, Sweden, W.Ger., also other parts Europe, 1964-70; condr. seminars on Lydian Chromatic concept, N.Y.C., 1975, Carnegie Hall performance, 1975; participant 1st White House Jazz Festival, 1978; recs. for RCA Records, Decca, Prestige, Capitol, Atlantic, Columbia, Contemporary, Blue Note, Soul Note, numerous others.; commd. composer maj. jazz work, Brandeis U., 1957, Norwegian TV; other commns. include original music for ballet Othello, 1967, Norwegian Cultural Fund, 1st choral work Listen to the Silence, 1971, Columbia Recs., Living Time for big band featuring Bill Evans, 1975, Swedish Radio for orch., 1977, 81, 83, Mass. Council on the Arts, 1983, Boston Musica Viva, 1987, work for orch. New Eng. Presentors, 1988, work for Relache New Music Ensemble, 1989; Composer jazz and electronic music; author papers on Lydian Chromatic concept tonal orgn.; sponsor Am. Music Week, 1985, 86; artist-in-residence Glasgow Internat. Festival, 1990, Ezz-thetics with Don Ellis, Dave Baker, et al, N.Y. Big Band, New York, N.Y., Electronic Sonata for Souls Loved By Nature, The Essence of George Russell, Listen to the Silence with Bjornar Andresen et al, 1994. Recipient Outstanding Composer award Metronome mag., 1958, New Star Composer award Downbeat mag., 1961, Nat. Endowment of the Arts award, 1969, 76, 80, 81, Jazz Masters fellow, 1989; recipient Nat. Music award Am. Music Conf. 1976, numerous awards for recs.; Guggenheim fellow, 1969, 72; Nat. Endowment for Arts grantee, 1979; MacArthur Found. fellow, 1989. Mem. Internat. Soc. Contemporary Music, Norwegian Soc. New Music, Am. Fedn. Musicians. Formed principles of Lydian Chromatic concept of tonal orgn., 1945-46. Address: care Concept 1770 Massachusetts Ave Ste 182 Cambridge MA 02140-2808*

RUSSELL, GERALD EDWARD, social worker, retired army officer; b. Monticello, Miss., Apr. 7, 1933; s. Jessie Edward and Lavert Virdew (Franklin) R.; m. Nina Merle Holmes, Dec. 17, 1955; children: Tina, Aprile, Glen, Eric. MSW, Tulane U., 1962. Cert. social worker, La.; diplomate Am. Bd. Examiners in Clin. Social Work. With Dept. Pub. Welfare, Jackson, Miss., 1958-64, supr. child welfare, 1962-64; commd. 1st lt. U.S. Army, 1964, advanced through grades to lt.col., 1979; ret., 1982; chief social work U.S Army Hosp., Ft. Jackson, S.C., 1964-66; mem. child fellowship program Walter Reed Hosp., Washington, 1966-68; asst. chief social work Brooke Gen. Hosp., Ft. Sam Houston, Tex., 1968-72; chief social work U.S. Army Hosp., Ft. Polk, La., 1972-82, supr. child protection, 1982—. Mem. NASW (cert.). Acad. Cert. Social Workers, La. Assn. Substance Abuse, La. Conf. Social Welfare, La. Soc. Clin. Social Workers. Home: 136 Russell Cir Leesville LA 71446-9011

RUSSELL, GLEN ALLAN, chemist, educator; b. Johnsonville, N.Y., Aug. 23, 1925; s. John Allen and Marion (Cottrell) R.; m. Martha Ellen Havill, June 6, 1953; children: Susan Ann, June Ellen. B.S., Rensselaer Poly Inst., 1947, M.S., 1948; Ph.D., Purdue U., 1951. Research assoc. Gen. Electric Research Lab., Schenectady, 1951-58; assoc. prof. Iowa State U., Ames, 1958-61, prof., 1961—; disting. prof. scis. and humanities, 1972—; vis. prof. Chemistry Rsch. Promotion Ctr., Taiwan, 1994, Korean Soc. Advanced Sci., 1993, U. Grenoble, France, 1985; mem. adv. panel Petroleum Research Fund, 1964-67; vis. prof. U. Würzburg, Fed. Republic Germany, 1966; Reilly lectr. U. Notre Dame, 1966. Edit. adv. bd. Jour. Organic Chem., 1985-89. Recipient Iowa Gov.'s medal for sci. achievement, 1988; Guggenheim fellow Centre d'Etude Nucleaires de Grenoble, France, 1972; Alfred P. Sloan Found. fellow, 1959-63; Fulbright-Hayes lectr., 1966. Fellow AAAS, Japan Soc. for Promotion of Sci.; mem. Am. Chem. Soc. (award in petroleum chemistry 1965, Iowa medal 1971, Midwest award 1974, James Flack Norris award 1983, mem. editorial adv. bd. Jour. Am. Chem. Soc. 1966-76), AAUP, Chem. Soc. (London). Research, numerous publs. on directive effects in aliphatic substitutions occurring via free radicals, photochlorination, oxidation, bromination, solvent effects, application of E.S.R. spectroscopy to problems of structure and conformation, mechanism of autoxidation of organic substances in basic solution. Home: 1014 Murray Dr Ames IA 50010-5151 Office: Iowa State U Dept Chemistry Ames IA 50011

RUSSELL, H. DIANE, museum curator, educator; b. Kansas City, Mo., Apr. 8, 1936; d. Harry Fay Russell and Georgia Mae (Canfield) Haeberle. AB, Vassar Coll., 1958; PhD, Johns Hopkins U., 1970; postgrad., Inst. for Advanced Study, Princeton, N.J., 1980-81. Mus. curator Nat. Gallery Art, Washington, 1964-90, curator of Old Master Prints, 1990—; professorial lectr. The Am. U., Washington, 1966-82, adj. prof. Art History, 1982—. Author: Rare Etchings of G.B. and G.D. Tiepolo, 1972, Jacques Callot, 1975, Claude Lorrain, 1982 (Barr award 1984), EVA/AVE: Woman in Renaissance and Baroque Prints, 1990. Woodrow Wilson Foun. fellow, 1958-59; Univ. fellow, Johns Hopkins U., 1961-63; Kress Found. fellow, 1973; Nat. Endowment for Arts fellow, 1980-81. Mem. Coll. Art Assn., Renaissance Soc. Am., Print Coun. Am., Vassar Club. Avocations: gardening, walking, poodles. Office: Nat Gallery Art 4th & Constitution Ave NW Washington DC 20565-0001

RUSSELL, HAROLD LEROY, accountant; b. Devon, Kans., Apr. 4, 1934; s. Ernest Maxwell and Emma Corrine (Wiley) R.; m. Laural Joniel Foster, Aug. 12, 1963; children: David Allen, Sondra Kathryn. BSBA, Pitts. (Kans.) State U., 1955; MBA, Ind. U., 1959; AMP, Columbia U., 1970. CPA, Okla. Mem. audit staff Arthur Young & Co., Tulsa, 1959-64, audit mgr., 1964-68, audit prin., 1968-69, audit ptnr., 1969-74; mng. ptnr. Arthur Young & Co., Oklahoma City, 1974-84, Coopers & Lybrand, Oklahoma City, 1984—; cons. Homeland Stores, Inc., Oklahoma City, 1990—. Editor: (book) AICPA Bank Audit Guide, 1979. Pres. Okla. Symphony Orch., Oklahoma City, 1985-86; trustee St. Anthony Hosp., Oklahoma City, Oklahoma City Art Mus.; bd. dirs. Coms. of 100, Oklahoma City. 1st lt. U.S. Army, 1955-57. Named Outstanding Expert Witness, Woodward/White Inc., 1990. Mem. AICPAs (com. chmn.), Okla. Soc. CPAs (bd. dirs. 1965-68), Downtown Rotary Club, Men's Dinner Club (bd. dirs. 1983-85), Petroleum Club (bd. dirs. 1983-84), Oklahoma City Golf and Country Club, Econs. Club of Oklahoma City (bd. dirs. 1982-85). Methodist. Avocations: painting, golf, reading. Home: 1609 W Wilshire Blvd Oklahoma City OK 73116-5006 Office: Coopers & Lybrand 3300 Liberty Bank Tower Oklahoma City OK 73102

RUSSELL, HAROLD LOUIS, lawyer; b. Abingdon, Va., July 1, 1916; s. Harold L. and Bess N. (Kinzel) R.; m. Katherine C. (Thompson) May 19, 1939; 1 child, Katherine T. Russell Prophet; m. Mildred Baggett Roach, Sept. 5, 1970. AB, Hendrix Coll., 1937; JD, Columbia U., 1940. Bar: N.Y. 1941, Ga. 1942, U.S. Ct. Appeals (1st, 2d, 3d, 5th, 11th and D.C. cirs.), U.S. Supreme Ct. 1950, D.C. 1972. Assoc. Gambrell & Russell and predecessors, Atlanta and N.Y.C., 1941-47, ptnr., 1947-84; ptnr. Smith, Gambrell & Russell, 1984—. Bd. dirs. Atlanta Fed. Defender Program, 1973-80, pres. 1978-79; bd. visitors, Columbia Law Sch., 1959—; mem. council Adminstrv. Conf. of U.S., 1968-76; bd. legal advisers Southeastern Legal Found., 1976—. Recipient Alumni Fedn. medal Columbia U., 1965; Disting. Alumnus award, Hendrix Coll., 1969. Fellow Am. Coll. Trial Lawyers, Am. Bar Found.; mem. ABA (past chmn. pub. utilities law sect., past chmn. spl. com. on legal service procedure, past chmn. adminstrv. law sect., ho. of dels. 1983—), D.C. Bar Assn., Fed. Bar Assn., Atlanta Bar Assn., Atlanta Lawyers Club, Assn. Bar City of N.Y., Columbia Law Sch. Assn. (nat. pres. 1973-75), Atlanta C. of C., Phi Delta Phi. Democrat. Clubs: Capital City, Piedmont Driving. Home: 3999 Parian Ridge Rd NW Atlanta GA 30327-3029 Office: Smith Gambrell & Russell 3100 Promenade II 1230 Peachtree St NE Atlanta GA 30309

RUSSELL, HENRY GEORGE, structural engineer; b. Tewkesbury, Eng., June 12, 1941; came to U.S. 1968. BE, Sheffield U., Eng., 1962, PhD, 1965. Registered structural engr., Ill.; registered profl. engr., Wash., Minn. Rsch.

fellow Bldg. Rsch., Eng., 1965-68; structural engr. Constrn. Tech. Labs., Inc. (formerly Portland Cement Assn.), Skokie, Ill., 1968-74, mgr., 1974-79, dir., 1979-88, pres., 1989-91, v.p. 1991-94; v.p. Henry G. Russell, Inc., Glenview, Ill., 1994-95. Contbr. articles to profl. jours. Named one Those Who Made Marks in 1992, Engring. News Record. Fellow Am. Concrete Inst. (Delmar L. Bloem award 1986, Wason medal 1992, Anderson award 1994); mem. Prestressed Concrete Inst. (Martin P. Korn award 1980). Office: 720 Coronet Rd Glenview IL 60025-4457

RUSSELL, HERMAN JEROME, business executive; b. Atlanta, Dec. 23, 1930; s. Rogers and Maggie (Goodson) R.; m. Otelia Hankey, Aug. 18, 1956; children: Donata C., Jerome, Michael. Student, Tuskegee Inst., 1949-53. Chmn. bd., chief exec. officer H.J. Russell & Co., Atlanta, 1952—; Concessions Internat. Inc., Los Angeles, 1959—, Ga. Southeastern Land Co. Inc., Atlanta, 1959—, H.J. Russell Plastering Co., Atlanta, 1959—, H.J. Russell Constrn. Co., Atlanta, 1962—, Interstate Constrn. Co. Inc., Atlanta, 1981—, Wet and Dry Walls Inc., Atlanta, 1983—, Russell Program Mgmt. (formerly Diversified Mgmt. Inc.), Atlanta, 1984—, Gibraltar Land Inc., Atlanta, 1985—, Russell-Rowe Communications Inc., Atlanta, 1985—; bd. dirs. Citizens Trust Co. Bank, Atlanta (chmn.), Ga. Power Co., Ga. Cable TV, Inc., WACHOVIA Bank of Ga. Bd. dirs. Butler St. YMCA, Tuskegee U., Martin Luther King Jr. Ctr. for Nonviolent Social Change (Salute to Greatness award 1985); trustee Morris Brown Coll., Atlanta.; mem. nat. adv. bd. Ga. Inst. Tech., Ga. State U., Coll. Bus. Adminstrn. Ga. State U. Recipient Meritorious Alumni award Tuskegee Inst. Alumni Assn., 1967, Black Enterprise mag. ann. achievement award, 1978, Top Hat award New Pittsburg Courier, 1980, award for outstanding achievement in breaking new ground on road to democracy in housing Nat. Assn. Real Estate Brokers, 1980, Disting. Humanitarian award Nat. Jewish Ctr. for Immunology and Respiratory Medicine, 1986, Chief Exec. Officer of Yr. award Atlanta Bus. League, 1986, Tree of Life award Jewish Nat. Fund, 1985, Bus. and Youth award Jr. Achievement, 1979, Nat. Alumni award Tuskegee U., 1968, Equal Opportunity Day award Atlanta Urban League, 1972; Drum Major for Justice award in Bus. Ga. State U. Coll. Bus. Adminstrn., 1982; named to Pres.'s Club, Morehouse Sch. Medicine, 1986, Nat. Black Coll. Alumni Hall of Fame, 1986, Bus. Hall of Fame, Ga. State U. Coll. of Bus. Adminstrn., 1985, Entrepreneurs Hall of Fame, Atlanta U. Sch. Bus., 1982, Dow Jones Entrepreneurial Excellence award Dow Jones & Co. Inc. and Wall Street Journal, 1992, Atlanta Bus. Hall of Fame award Junior Achievement, 1992, Horatio Alger award, Horatio Alger Assn. Am., Entrepreneur of Yr. award Nat. Black and Ga. MBA assn., 1991. Mem. Atlanta C. of C. (bd. dirs., past pres. 1981), U.S. C. of C., NAACP (life), Cen. Atlanta Progress, Atlanta Commerce Club, Atlanta Action Forum, Phi Beta Sigma. Mem. African Meth. Episcopal Ch. Office: H J Russell & Co Inc 3 Ravinia Dr Ste 1470 Atlanta GA 30346-2131

RUSSELL, JAMES ALVIN, JR., college administrator; b. Lawrenceville, Va., Dec. 25, 1917; s. Dr. James Alvin and Nellie M. (Pratt) R.; m. Lottye J. Washington, Dec. 25, 1943; children: Charlotte Justyne, James Alvin III. BA, Oberlin Coll., 1940; BS, Bradley U., 1941, MS, 1950, spl. insts.; EdD, U. Md., 1967; spl. insts., Wayne U., U. Mich., U. Ill., NSF. Prof., dir. div. engring., also prof. edn. div. grad. studies Hampton Inst., 1950-71; pres. St. Paul's Coll., Lawrenceville, 1971-81; dir. instructional programs and student services Va. C.C. System, 1981-82; chmn. div. profl. studies W.Va. State Coll., 1982-86, acting pres., 1986-87, exec. asst. to pres., 1987-88; pres. So. W.Va. C.C., 1988-89, ret., 1989. Pres. Peninsula Council Human Relations, 1961-65. United Negro Coll. Fund fellow, 1966-67. Mem. IEEE, Am. Soc. Engring. Edn., Am. Assn. Univ. Adminstrs., Am. Vocat. Assn., Am. Tech. Edn. Assn., Nat. Assn. Indsl. Tech., Am. Assn. for Higher Edn., Nat. Assn. for Equal Opportunity in Edn., Brunswick C. of C., Sigma Pi Phi, Alpha Kappa Mu, Iota Lambda Sigma, Omega Psi Phi. Home: 811 Grandview Dr Dunbar WV 25064-1175

RUSSELL, JAMES DONALD MURRAY, hospital administrator; b. Madison, Wis., Feb. 6, 1934; s. Roger Bridgford and Margaret (Murray) R.; m. Charlotte Russell. BS, U. Wis., 1956; MA, State U. Iowa, 1961. Asst. adminstr. Luther Hosp., Eau Claire, Wis., 1960-70, adminstr., 1970-77; adminstr. St. Mary's Hosp., Pierre, S.D., 1978—; chief exec. officer St. Mary's Hosp., Maryhouse Nursing Home and Parkwood Apts., Pierre, 1990—. Bd. dirs. S.D. Delta Dental Plan, 1990—, Pierre Econ. Devel. Corp., S.D. and Western Iowa Blue Cross, 1980-87; sec. bd. dirs. Capital U. Ctr., Pierre. Fellow Am. Coll. Healthcare Execs.; mem. Am. Hosp. Assn., S.D. Hosp. Assn. (chmn. 1985-86, bd. dirs. 1981-87, 90-92). Office: St Marys Healthcare Ctr 800 E Dakota Ave Pierre SD 57501-3313

RUSSELL, JAMES FRANKLIN, lawyer; b. Memphis, Mar. 21, 1945; s. Frank Hall and Helen (Brunson) R.; m. Marilyn Land, June 1, 1968 (div. May 1976); children: Mary Helen, Myles Edward; m. Linda Hatcher, July 9, 1977; 1 child, Maggie Abele. BA, Rhodes Coll., 1967; JD, Memphis State U., 1970. Bar: Tenn. 1971, U.S. Dist. Ct. (we. dist.) Tenn. 1971, U.S. Ct. Appeals (6th cir.) 1971, U.S. Dist. Ct. (so. dist.) Miss. 1976, U.S. Ct. Appeals (5th cir.) 1977, U.S. Ct. Appeals (8th cir.) 1987. Assoc. Nelson, Norvell, Wilson, McRae, Ivy & Sevier, Memphis, 1971-75; ptnr. Stanton, Russell & Challen, Memphis, 1975-78, Russell, Price, Weatherford & Warlick, Memphis, 1978-82, Price, Vance & Criss, Memphis, 1982-85, Apperson, Crump, Duzane & Maxwell, Memphis, 1985—. V.p. mid-south chpt. Am. Red Cross, Memphis, 1992-94; treas. Epilepsy Found. West Tenn., Memphis, 1992-94. Mem. ABA, Nat. Assn. R.R. Trial Counsel, Internat. Assn. Def. Counsel, Tenn. Bar Assn., Tenn. Def. Lawyers Assn., Memphis Bar Assn. (pres. 1992). Episcopalian. Avocations: golf, snow skiing. Home: 1792 Autumn Ave Memphis TN 38112 Office: Apperson Crump Duzane and Maxwell 2110 One Commerce Sq Memphis TN 38103

RUSSELL, JAMES H., lawyer; b. Oak Park, Ill., Aug. 22, 1943. BA, Ohio Wesleyan U., 1965; JD, Ohio State U., 1969. Bar: Ill. 1970, Fla. 1982, Ohio 1985. Ptnr. Winston & Strawn, Chgo. Contbr. articles to profl. jours. Mem. ABA, Ohio State Bar Assn., The Fla. Bar, Chgo. Bar Assn. Office: Winston & Strawn 35 W Wacker Dr Chicago IL 60601-1614

RUSSELL, JAMES SARGENT, retired naval officer; b. Tacoma, Mar. 22, 1903; s. Ambrose J. and Loella Janet (Sargent) R.; m. Dorothy Irene Johnson, Apr. 13, 1929 (dec. Apr. 1965); children: Donald Johnson, Kenneth McDonald (dec. 1993); m. 2d, Geraldine Haus Rahn, July 12, 1966. BS, U.S. Naval Acad., 1926; MS, Calif. Inst. Tech., 1935. Served with U.S. Mcht. Marine, 1918-22; commd. ensign U.S. Navy, 1926, advanced through grades to adm., 1958; naval aviator, 1929-65; comdg. officer aircraft sqdn. VP 42, Aleutians and Alaska, 1941-42; chief of staff to comdr. Carrier Div. Two, Pacific campaigns of Palau, P.I., Iwo Jima, Okinawa, 1944-45; bombing survey, Japan, 1945; comdg. officer U.S.S. Bairoko, 1946-47, U.S.S. Coral Sea, 1951-52; with aircraft carrier desk Bur. Aero., 1939-41, dir. mil. requirements, 1943-44; dept. dir. mil. application AEC, 1947-51; dir. air warfare div. Office Chief Naval Ops., 1952-54; comdr. carrier div. 17 & 5, Pacific Fleet, 1954-55, chief Bur. of Aero., 1955-57; dep. comdr. Atlantic Fleet, 1957-58, vice chief Naval Ops., 1958-61; comdr. NATO forces in So. Europe, 1962-65, ret., 1965; recalled to active duty, 1967, 68, Vietnam; mem. various Navy adv. bds.; cons. Boeing Co., 1965-79. Decorated D.S.M. with oak leaf cluster, Legion of Merit with two oak leaf clusters, D.F.C., Air medal (U.S.); grand cross Royal Order King George I (Greece); Grand Ofcl. Order Republic of Italy; comdr. Legion of Honor (France); Gt. Cross Peruvian Cross of Naval Merit; Grand Officer Order of Naval Merit (Brazil); recipient Collier-Trophy, 1956, Russell Trophy Order of Daedalians; named to Nat. Mus. of Naval Aviation Hall of Honor, 1990. Fellow AIAA. Home: 7734 Walnut Ave SW Tacoma WA 98498-5223

RUSSELL, JAMES WEBSTER, JR., newspaper editor, columnist; b. Shreveport, La., Nov. 30, 1921; s. James Webster and Aline (Faulk) R.; m. Jean Buck, June 29, 1949; children: Nancy Russell Dearr, Eileen Russell Goure. B.A., La. State U., 1942. Fla. mgr. Internat. News Service, 1946-51; bur. chief UPI, Tallahassee, 1951-52; regional editor U.P.I., Atlanta, 1953-57; asst. city editor Miami (Fla.) Herald, 1957-58, bus.-fin. editor, 1958—; guest lectr. U. Miami, Fla. Internat. U., Miami-Dade Community Coll., La. State U. Contbr. articles to: Fla. Trend, Times of London, N.Y. Times, Gentlemen's Quar. Trustee Fla. So. Coll. Served with USAAF, 1942-45. Recipient Eagle award Invest-in-Am. Nat. Council, 1976; Decorated Air medal with eleven oak leaf clusters. Mem. Soc. Am. Bus. Writers, Lambda Chi Alpha, Sigma Delta Chi. Republican. Methodist (chmn. ch. council on ministries 1971-72). Home: 4800 SW 64th Ct Miami FL 33155-6133 Office: 1 Herald Plz Miami FL 33132-1609

RUSSELL, JEFFREY BURTON, historian, educator; b. Fresno, Calif., Aug. 1, 1934; s. Lewis Henry and Ieda Velma (Ogborn) R.; m. Diana Emily Mansfield, June 30, 1956; children: Jennifer, Mark, William, Penelope. A.B., U. Calif., Berkeley, 1955, A.M., 1957; Ph.D., Emory U., 1960. Asst. prof. U. N.Mex., Albuquerque, 1960-61; jr. fellow Soc. of Fellows, Harvard U., Cambridge, Mass., 1961-62; mem. faculty U. Calif., Riverside, 1962-75; prof. dept. history U. Calif., 1969-75, assoc. dean grad. div., 1967-72; dir. Medieval Inst.; Michael P. Grace prof. medieval studies U. Notre Dame, South Bend, Ind., 1975-77; dean grad. studies Calif. State U., Sacramento, 1977-79; prof. history U. Calif., Santa Barbara, 1979—, prof. religious studies, 1994—. Author: Dissent and Reform in the Early Middle Ages, 1965, Medieval Civilization, 1968, A History of Medieval Christianity: Prophecy and Order, 1968, Religious Dissent in the Middle Ages, 1971, Witchcraft in the Middle Ages, 1972, The Devil: Perceptions of Evil from Antiquity to Primitive Christianity, 1977, A History of Witchcraft: Sorcerers, Heretics, and Pagans, 1980, Medieval Heresies: a Bibliography, 1981, Satan: The Early Christian Tradition, 1981, Lucifer: The Devil in the Middle Ages, 1984, Mephistopheles: The Devil in the Modern World, 1986, The Prince of Darkness, 1988, Ruga in Aevis, 1990, Inventing the Flat Earth: Columbus and the Historians, 1991, Dissent and Order in the Middle Ages, 1992; contbr. articles in field to profl. jours. Fulbright fellow, 1959-60; Am. Council Learned Socs. grantee, 1965, 70; Social Sci. Research Council grantee, 1968; Guggenheim fellow, 1968-69; Nat. Endowment for Humanities sr. fellow, 1972-73. Fellow Medieval Acad. Am.; mem. Medieval Assn. of Pacific, Am. Soc. Ch. History, Am. Acad. Religion, Sierra Club. Home: 4796 Calle Camarada Santa Barbara CA 93110-2053 Office: U Calif Dept History Santa Barbara CA 93106

RUSSELL, JOHN DAVID, English literature educator; b. Chgo., Dec. 12, 1928; s. John David and Charlotte Rita (Graf) R.; m. Mary Elizabeth Need, Aug. 20, 1954; 1 child, Ryan. AB, Colgate U., 1951; MA, U. Wash., Seattle, 1956; PhD, Rutgers U., 1959. Prof. English U. S.C., 1958-69, U. Md., College Park, 1969—. Author: Henry Green, 1960, Anthony Powell, 1970, Style in Modern British Fiction, 1978, Honey Russell: Between Games, Between Halves, 1986. Served to lt. USNR, 1952-55. Recipient award for criticism, Explicator Mag., 1961, Russell Research award, U.S.C., 1962; Fulbright grantee Brazil, 1966, Portugal, 1984. Home: 3112 Landfall Ln Annapolis MD 21403-4312 Office: Dept English Univ of Maryland College Park MD 20742

RUSSELL, JOHN LYNN, JR., physicist; b. Woodsborough, Tex., Aug. 5, 1930; s. John Lynn and Ethna Nora (Nester) R.; m. Patricia Ann Parker, Sept. 5, 1950; children: Teri Lynn, Audrey Lee, Patricia Renee. BS in Elect. Engring., U. Tex., 1951; MS in Physics, Rice U., Houston, 1954, PhD in Physics, 1956. Mgr. exptl. physics Gen. Electric Co., San Jose, Calif., 1956-62; mgr. spl. projects Gen. Atomic Co., San Diego, 1962-78; prof. nuclear engring. Ga. Inst. Tech., Atlanta, 1978-83; pres., chmn. Theraganics Corp., Atlanta, 1983—. Patentee in well-logging, solar energy, thermal water spliting, plastics and cancer therapeutics; contbr. articles to profl. jours. Mem. Am. Nuclear Soc. Republican. Methodist.

RUSSELL, JOHN ST. CLAIR, JR., lawyer; b. Albany, N.Y., Mar. 21, 1917; s. John St. Clair and Hazel (Barbiers) R.; m. Betty Kixmiller, Sept. 12, 1941; children—Patricia Russell, John St. Clair III (dec.), David K. A.B. cum laude, Dartmouth Coll., 1938; LL.B., Yale U., 1941. Bar: N.Y. 1942, D.C. 1965. Mem. Hale Russell & Gray (and predecessors), N.Y.C., 1948-85; mem. Winthrop, Stimson, Putnam & Roberts, N.Y.C., 1985-90, sr. counsel, ret. ptnr., 1991—. Mem. Irvington (N.Y.) Zoning Bd. Appeals, 1955-89; chmn. Raoul Wallenberg Com. of U.S., 1985-90; exec. trustee Am.-Scandinavian Found. Maj. USMCR, OSS, 1942-46. Decorated Order of Vasa Sweden; recipient medal of merit Swedish Red Cross. Mem. ABA, Assn. of Bar of City of N.Y., Dartmouth Club, Downtown Assn. (N.Y.C.), Phi Beta Kappa, Phi Gamma Delta. Office: Winthrop Stimson Putnam and Roberts One Battery Park Pla New York NY 10004-1490

RUSSELL, JOSIAH COX, historian, educator; b. Richmond, Ind., Sept. 3, 1900; s. Elbert and Lieuetta (Cox) R.; m. Ruth Winslow, Sept. 15, 1924; children: Elbert Winslow, Walter Howard, Joan (dec.). A.B., Earlham Coll., 1922; M.A., Harvard U., 1923, Ph.D., 1926. Asst. in history Radcliffe Coll., 1923-24, Harvard U., 1924-26; asst. prof. Colo. Coll., 1927-29; prof. history and head social sci. dept. N.Mex. Highlands U., 1929-31; instr. to assoc. prof. U. N.C., 1931-46; chmn. history dept. U. N.Mex., 1946-53, prof., 1946-65; prof. emeritus U. N. Mex., 1965—; prof. Tex. A & I U., 1965-71, Piper prof. (hon.), 1971. Author: Dictionary of Writers of Thirteenth Century England, 1936, British Medieval Population, 1948, Late Ancient and Medieval Population, 1958, Medieval Regions and Their Cities, 1972, Twelfth Century Studies, 1978, Control of Late Ancient and Medieval Population, 1985, Medieval Demography, 1987; contbr. chpt. to Fontana Economic History of Europe, Historia Universal, Salvat, vol. IV; author: (with others) Ever Since Eve: Archaeology, 1994; contbr. numerous articles to profl. jours. Chmn. Orange Dist. com. Boy Scouts Am., 1945-46. Fulbright lectr. Univ. Coll., Wales, 1952-53; research grantee Guggenheim Found., 1930-31, Am. Council Learned Socs., summers 1933, 34, Social Sci. Research Council, summers 1938, 49, 51, Am. Philos. Soc., 1938-39, 61; fellow Islamic Seminar Princeton, summer 1935; cons. Fulbright Brit. Empire Prof. Selection, 1955. Fellow Mediaeval Acad. Am.; mem. Am. Hist. Assn. (mem. Pacific Coast council 1964-65), Soc. of Friends, AAUP (state chmn. 1951-52, nat. council 1953-56), Phi Alpha Theta. Address: 116 South Wind Cir Saint Augustine FL 32084

RUSSELL, JOYCE ANNE ROGERS, librarian; b. Chgo. Nov. 6, 1920; d. Truman Allen and Mary Louise (Hoelzle) Rogers; m. John VanCleve Russell, Dec. 24, 1942; children: Malcolm David, John VanCleve. Student, Adelphi Coll., 1937; B.S. in Chemistry, U. Ky., 1942; M.L.S., Rosary Coll., 1967; postgrad., Rutgers U., 1970-71. Research chemist Sherwin Williams Paint Co., Chgo., 1942-45; reference librarian Chicago Heights (Ill.) Pub. Library, 1959-61; librarian Victor Chem. Works, Chicago Heights, 1961-62; lit. chemist Velsicol Chem. Corp., Chgo., 1964-67; chemistry librarian U. Fla., Gainesville, 1967-69; interim assoc. prof. U. Fla., 1967-69; librarian Thiokol Chem. Corp., Trenton, N.J., 1969-73; supr. library operations E.R. Squibb Co., Princeton, N.J., 1973-80, sr. research info scientist, 1980-91; mem. library adv. commn. Mercer Community Coll., 1979—; adv. asso. Rutgers U. Grad. Sch. Library and Info. Scis., 1978—. Editor: Bibliofile, 1967-69; contbr. articles to profl. jours. Mem. PTA, 1950-66; den mother Cub Scouts, 1952-59. Mem. Spl. Libraries Assn. (sec., dir., v.p., pres. Princeton-Trenton 1971, 75-80), Am. Chem. Soc. (bus. mgr. sec., dir. Trenton sect. 1969-78), AAUW, Mortar Board, Beta Phi Mu, Sigma Pi Sigma, Chi Delta Phi, Pi Sigma Alpha. Home: 1189 Parkside Ave Trenton NJ 08618-2625

RUSSELL, JOYCE M., lawyer, apparel executive; b. Green County, Ky., Oct. 23, 1946; d. Woodson and Sybil (Milby) R.; m. Arnold H. Haberkorn, Apr. 7, 1977. BA, Western Ky., 1968; JD, U. Ky., 1972. Bar: Ky. Supreme Ct. 1972. Assoc. Harlin, Parker, Lucas and English, Bowling Green, Ky., 1972-74; ptnr. Cole, Harned & Broderick, Bowling Green, 1974-75; corp. counsel Fruit of the Loom, Bowling Green, 1975-80, v.p., gen. counsel, 1980-93, sr. v.p., gen. counsel, 1993—. Mem. ABA, Am. Corp. Counsel, Internat. Trademark Assn., Ky. Bar Assn., Bowling Green Bar Assn. Republican. Avocations: reading, gardening. Office: Fruit of the Loom PO Box 90015 1 Fruit of the Loom Dr Bowling Green KY 42102

RUSSELL, KEN (HENRY KENNETH ALFRED RUSSELL), film and theatre director; b. Southampton, Eng., July 3, 1927; s. Henry and Ethel (Smith) R.; m. Shirley Kingdom, Feb. 3, 1957 (div.); 5 children; m. Vivian Jolly, June 10, 1984; children: Molly, Rupert. Student, Walthamstow Art Sch., Internat. Ballet Sch. Formerly dancer, actor, still photographer, BBC documentary film maker; feature film dir.; feature films include French Dressing, 1964, Billion Dollar Brain, 1967,Women in Love, 1970, The Music Lovers, 1970, The Boy Friend, 1971, The Devils, 1971, Savage Messiah, 1972, Mahler, 1975, Tommy, 1975, Lizstomania, 1975, Altered States, 1980, Crimes of Passion, 1984, Gothic, 1986, Salome's Last Dance, 1986, Aria, 1987, The Lair of the White Worm, 1988, The Rainbow, 1989, Whore, 1991, Lady Chatterly, 1993; dir., writer: film Valentino, 1977; actor, The Russia

House, 1990; dir.: operas Rakes Progres, 1982, Die Soldaten, 1983, Madame Butterfly, Spoleto and Melbourne; La Boheme, Macenata; Faust, Vienna; Mephisto, Rhodes and Genoa. Served with Mcht. Navy, 1945; Served with also RAF. Recipient Screen writers Guild award for TV films Elgar, Debussy, Isadora, Dante's Inferno; Delius award (Merit Scroll); award Guild TV Producers and Dirs., 1966; Desmond Davis award, 1968. Office: care Peter Rawley Internat Creative Mgmt 8942 Wilshire Blvd Beverly Hills CA 90211 Office: 16 Salisbury Pl, London W1H 1FH, England*

RUSSELL, KENNETH CALVIN, metallurgical engineer, educator; b. Greeley, Colo., Feb. 4, 1936; s. Doyle James and Jennie Frances (Smith) R.; m. Charlotte Louise Wolf, Apr. 13, 1963 (div. 1978); children: David Allan, Doyle John. Met.E., Colo. Sch. Mines, 1959; Ph.D., Carnegie Inst. Tec., 1963. Engr. Westinghouse Research and Devel. Center, 1959-61; NSF postdoctoral fellow Physics Inst., U. Oslo, 1963-64; asst. prof. metallurgy M.I.T., Cambridge, 1964-69; assoc. prof. M.I.T., 1969-78, prof. metallurgy, 1978—, prof. nuclear engring., 1979—. Contbr. articles to profl. publs. Served as 2d lt. U.S. Army, 1959-60. DuPont fellow, 1961-62; NSF grad. fellow, 1962-63. Mem. AIME, Am. Phys. Soc., Am. Soc. for Metals. Office: MIT Rm 8-411 Cambridge MA 02139

RUSSELL, KENT, hospital administrator. With Arthur Andersen Accounting Firm, L.A., 1968-1972, AMI, Beverly Hills, Calif., 1972-1976, St. Joseph Hospital, Tacoma, Wa., 1976-1986; exec. v.p., cfo Eastern Mercy Health System, Wayne, Pa., 1986—. Office: Eastern Mercy Health System 100 Matsonford Rd Wayne PA 19087-4527

RUSSELL, KURT VON VOGEL, actor; b. Springfield, Mass., Mar. 17, 1951; s. Bing Oliver and Louise Julia (Crone) R.; m. Season Hubley, Mar. 17, 1979 (div.), 1 son, Boston; 1 son (with Goldie Hawn), Wyatt Russell. Student, pub. schs. Profl. baseball player, 1971-73. Actor in numerous films including The Absent Minded Professor, 1961, It Happened at the World's Fair, 1963, Follow Me Boys, 1966, The One and Only Genuine Original Family Band, 1968, The Horse in the Grey Flannel Suit, 1968, The Computer Wore Tennis Shoes, 1970, The Barefoot Executive, 1971, Fools' Parade, 1971, Now You See Him Now You Don't, 1972, Charley and the Angel, 1972, Superdad, 1974, The Strongest Man in the World, 1975, Used Cars, 1980, Escape from New York, 1981, The Thing, 1982, Silkwood, 1983, Swing Shift, 1984, The Mean Season, 1985, The Best of Times, 1986, Big Trouble in Little China, 1986, Overboard, 1987, The Winter People, 1988, Tequila Sunrise, 1988, Winter People, 1989, Tango and Cash, 1989, Backdraft, 1991, Unlawful Entry, 1992, Captain Ron, 1992, Tombstone, 1993, Stargate, 1994; TV series include Travels with Jamie McPheeters, 1963-64, The New Land, 1974, The Quest, 1976; TV movies include Search for the Gods, 1975, The Deadly Tower, The Quest (pilot), 1975, Christmas Miracle in Caulfield USA, 1977, Elvis, 1979, Amber Waves, 1988; TV guest appearences include The Fugitive, Daniel Boone, Gilligan's Island, Lost in Space, The FBI, Love American Style, Gunsmoke, Hawaii Five-O. Served with Calif. Air N.G. Recipient numerous auto racing trophies, 10 baseball awards, 5 acting awards, 1 golf championship. Mem. Profl. Baseball Players Assn., Stuntman's Assn. World championship Class Modified Stock, 1959 Race of Champions, Las Vegas. Office: Creative Artists Agy 9830 Wilshire Blvd Beverly Hills CA 90212*

RUSSELL, LIANE BRAUCH, geneticist; b. Vienna, Austria, Aug. 27, 1923; came to U.S., 1941; d. Arthur and Clara (Starer) B.; m. William Lawson Russell, Sept. 23, 1947; children: David Lawson, Evelyn Ruth. AB, Hunter Coll., 1945; PhD, U. Chgo., 1949. Fellow U. Chgo., 1945-46, teaching asst., 1946-47; research asst. Jackson Lab., Bar Harbor, Maine, 1945, 46; research staff mem. Oak Ridge (Tenn.) Nat. Lab., 1947-75, sect. head., 1975—, disting. research staff mem. 1983—; sci. advisor U.S. Del. at 1st Atoms for Peace Conf., Geneva, Switzerland, 1955; mem. numerous sci. bds. including Nat. Research Council com. on energy and environment, 1975-77, com. on biol. effects of ionizing radiation, 1977-80, bd. on environ. studies and toxicology, 1981-90, Nat. Council on Radiation Protection and Measurement Task Group, Washington, 1975-77, Genetox Program EPA, Washington, 1979—, Internat. Com. for Protection Against Environ. Mutagens and Carcinogens, Lausanne, Switzerland, 1977-83, Internat. com. on standardized genetic nomenclature for mice, 1977-91, office of tech. assessment, scientific adv. panel, 1985-86; mem. task group Internat. Agy. for Research on Cancer, Hanover, Fed. Republic of Germany, 1979, EPA review panel on mutagenicity guidelines, 1985-86. Assoc. editor: Mutation Research, 1976—; Environ. Mutagenesis, 1980-83; editor: TCWP Newsletter, 1966—; editor: (book) Genetic Mosaics and Chimeras, 1979; contbr. over 125 articles in field to profl. jours. Founder Tenn. Citizens for Wilderness Planning, Oak Ridge, 1966, pres. 1967-70, 86-87; active numerous environ. groups. Corp. fellow Union Carbide, 1983; corp. fellow Martin Marietta, 1985, sr. corp. fellow, 1988; recipient Merit award Mademoiselle, 1955, Roentgen medal City of Remscheid-Lennep, 1973, Disting. Assoc. award U.S. Dept. Energy, 1987; named to Hall of Fame Hunter Coll., 1979, Sol Feinstone Environ. Achievement award, N.Y., 1987, Tenn. Environ. Coun. Lifetime Achievement award, 1990, Oak Ridge Rotary Club Vocational Svc. award, 1992, Marjorie Stoneman Douglas award Nat. Parks & Conservation Assn., 1993, Enrico Fermi award U.S. Dept. Energy, 1994. Fellow AAAS, Environ. Health Inst.; mem. Nat. Acad. Scis. (elected 1986), Environ. Mutagen Soc. (EMs award 1993, pres. 1984-85), Genetics Soc. Am. (presdl. nominee 1979). Avocation: environ. acitivism. Office: Oak Ridge Nat Lab Biol Div PO Box 2009 Oak Ridge TN 37831-2009*

RUSSELL, LILLIAN, medical, surgical nurse; b. N.Y.C., Feb. 21, 1942; d. Joserelle Russell; 1 child, Evan Gregory. AAS, N.Y.C. Community Coll., 1973; BS, St. Xavier Coll., Chgo., 1986; MS, Spertus Coll. of Judaica, Chgo., 1989. RN, Ill. Staff/charge nurse Beth Israel Med. Ctr., N.Y.C., 1973-76; charge nurse Roosevelt Hosp., N.Y.C., 1977-78; staff/charge nurse U. Ill. Hosp., Chgo., 1979—; asst. adminstrv. coord. Bethany Hosp., Chgo., 1990-91; adminstrv. nurse I Mile Square Health Ctr., Chgo., 1991—; mem. instnl. rev. com. Bethany Hosp., 1987—. Maj. USAR, 1981—. Mem. ANA, Ill. Nurses Assn., Res. Officers Assn. Home: 1342 N Oakley Blvd Chicago IL 60622-3048

RUSSELL, LOUISE BENNETT, economist, educator; b. Exeter, N.H., May 12, 1942; d. Frederick Dewey and Esther (Smith) B.; m. Robert Hardy Cosgriff, May 3, 1987; 1 child, Benjamin Smith. BA, U. Mich., 1964; PhD, Harvard U., 1971. Economist Social Security Adminstrn., Washington, 1968-71, Nat. Commn. on State Workmen's Compensation Laws, Washington, 1971-72, Dept. Labor, Washington, 1972-73; sr. economist Nat. Planning Assn., Washington, 1973-75; sr. fellow Brookings Instn., Washington, 1975-87; prin. rsch. fellow Inst. for Health, Health Care Policy and Aging Rsch. Rutgers U., New Brunswick, N.J., 1987—, rsch. assoc., 1987—; chmn. health care policy divsn. Rutgers U., 1988—; mem. tech. bd. Milbank Fund, 1993—. Author: Technology in Hospitals, 1979, The Baby Boom Generation and the Economy, 1982, Is Prevention Better Than Cure, 1986, Evaluating Preventive Care: Report on a Workshop, 1987, Medicare's New Hospital Payment System: Is It Working, 1989, Educated Guesses: Making Policy About Medical Screening Tests, 1994; also numerous articles. Mem. U.S. Preventive Svcs. Task Force, 1984-88; co-chair Panel on Cost Effectiveness in Health and Medicine DHHS, ODPHP, 1993—. Mem. Inst. Medicine of NAS (com. to study future pub. health 1986-87, bd. on health scis. policy 1989-91, com. on clin. practice guidelines 1990-91, com. on setting priorities for practice guidelines 1994—). Office: Rutgers U Inst for Health Care Policy 30 College Ave New Brunswick NJ 08901-1245

RUSSELL, LYNN DARNELL, mechanical engineer, educator; b. Pontotoc, Miss., Nov. 1, 1937; s. Clyde Austin and Clytee Lora (Faulkner) R.; m. Elaine Lowery, June 16, 1963; children—Kathy, Brent, Mark, Jeffrey. B.S., Miss. State U., 1960, M.S., 1961; Ph.D., Rice U., 1966. Profl. engr. Ala., Miss., Tenn. Engr. NASA Marshall Space Flight Ctr., Johnson Spacecraft Ctr., 1961-64; research scientist Lockheed, Huntsville, Ala., 1966-67; mem. tech. staff TRW, Huntsville, 1967-69; dean engring U. Tenn.-Chattanooga, 1969-79; prof. mech. engring. Miss. State U., 1979-87, dean Coll. Engring., U. Ala., Huntsville, 1987—; energy cons. Recipient numerous fellowships and grants. Mem. Chattanooga Engrs. Club (pres. 1975); pres. Tenn. Soc. Profl. Engrs. 1978-79. Mem. ASME, Nat. Soc. Profl. Engrs., Ala. Soc. Profl. Engrs., Am. Soc. Engring. Edn., Internat. Solar Energy Soc., Sigma Xi, Pi Tau Sigma (past pres. Miss. chpt.). Contbr. articles to profl. jours. Office: U Ala 300 Sparkman Dr NW Huntsville AL 35805-1912

RUSSELL, MARJORIE ROSE, manufacturing company executive; b. Welcome, Minn., Sept. 3, 1925; d. Emil Frederick and Ella Magdalene (Sothman) Wohlenhaus; m. Kenneth Kollmann Russell, Sept. 15, 1947 (div. May 1973); children: Jennie Rose, Richard Lowell, Laura Eloise, James Wesley. Student, Northwestern Sch., Mpls., 1944-45, St. Paul Bible Inst., 1946-47. Cook U. Minn., Mpls., 1943-45; maintenance person U. Farm Campus/N.W. Schs., St. Paul, 1945-46; clk. Kresge Corp., Mpls., 1945; cook, waitress, mgr. Union City Mission Bible Camp, Mpls., 1944-47; caterer for v.p. Gt. No. R.R., St. Paul, 1947; custodian Old Soldiers Home, St. Paul, 1946; nurse Sister Elizabeth Kenney Polio Hosp., St. Paul, 1946; seamstress Hirsch, Weis, White Stag, Pendleton, Mayfair, Portland, Oreg., 1960-72; owner, operator, contract mgr., creative designer The Brass Needle, Portland, 1972—; contractor Forrester's Sanderson Safety, Scotsco, Nero & Assocs., Gara Gear, Portland, 1972—, Columbia Sportswear; tchr. Indo Chinese Cultural Ctr., Portland, 1982; mfr. of protective chaps and vests for the Pacific Northwest hogging industry. Designer, producer Kisn Bridal Fair, 1969; composer: He Liveth in Me, 1968; prodr. Safety Chaps for Loggers. Sec. Model Cities Com., Portland, 1969; com. mem. Neighborhood Black Christmas Parade, Portland, 1970; custume designer Local Miss Jr. Black Beauty Contest, Portland, 1973; nominating com. Nat. Contract Mgmt. Assn., Portland, 1978; mem. nominating com. Multi-Cultural Sr. Adv. Com., 1988-91. Mem. NAFE, Urban League, Urban League Guild (historian 1991-92), Am. Assn. Ret. Persons, Nat. Contract Mgmt. Assn. Democrat. Mem. United Ch. of Christ. Avocations: music, swimming, painting, gardening, arts. Home and Office: The Brass Needle 2809 NE 12th Ave Portland OR 97212

RUSSELL, MARK, comedian; b. Buffalo, Aug. 23, 1932; s. Marcus Joseph and Marie Elizabeth (Perry) Ruslander; m. Alison Kaplan, Dec. 17, 1978; children: Monica, John, Matthew. Student, George Washington U., 1952; LittD, Union Coll., 1987; LHD, Canisius Coll., 1988; LHD (hon.), Goucher Coll., 1990. lectr., public speaker. Polit. comedian, featured performer Shoreham Hotel, Washington, 1961-81; prin.: Mark Russell Comedy Spls., Public Broadcasting Service, 1975—; host: Mark Russell's England, PBS-TV, 1988, Mark Russell's Irish Fling, 1993, Mark Russell's Great Alaska Trek, 1994, Mark Russell's Tour de France, 1995; co-host: NBC's Real People, 1979-84; regular contbr.: Good Morning, America, ABC-TV; author: Presenting Mark Russell, 1980; syndicated columnist via Los Angeles Times Syndicate, 1975. Served with USMC, 1953-56. Recipient Mark Twain award Internat. Platform Assn., 1980, 86, 4th Ann. Lucy award Shea's Buffalo, 1992, Nat. Humor Treasure award, 1995. Mem. AFTRA, Am. Fedn. Musicians. Office: 2800 Wisconsin Ave NW Washington DC 20007-4703

RUSSELL, MICHAEL JAMES, lawyer; b. Northampton, Mass., May 19, 1958; s. John Michael and Celia (Jaskolka) R. Cert. in German, U. Vienna, 1979; BA summa cum laude, Gettysburg Coll., 1980; MA, JD, Vanderbilt U., 1984. Bar: Pa. 1984, D.C. 1985. Rsch. asst. Vanderbilt U., Nashville, 1982-84; legal intern U.S. State Dept., Washington, 1982; law clk. Stewart, Estes & Donnell, Nashville, 1983; atty. U.S. Dept. Agr., Washington, 1984-85; majority counsel subcom. on juvenile justice senate judiciary com. U.S. Senate, Washington, 1985-86, minority gen. counsel subcom. on constn., 1987, legislative dir. to Sen. Arlen Specter, 1987-90, chief of staff, 1988; senate staff mem. Congrl. Crime Caucus, 1987-90; dep. dir. Nat. Inst. Justice U.S. Dept. Justice, Washington, 1990-93, acting dir., 1993-94; pres. Russell & Assocs., Washington, 1994—. Editorial staff Vanderbilt Jour. Transnat. Law, Nashville, 1982-83, contbr., 1983, rsch. editor, 1983-84 (editor award 1984). Mem. senate staff club, 1985-90, Bush/Quayle Campaign's Crime Adv. Com., 1988, Friends of the Nat. Parks at Gettysburg, Pa., 1989—; bd. fellows Gettysburg Coll., 1990—; vol. Nat. Constrn. Ctr., Phila., 1990; mem. Bush/Quayle Adminstrn. S.E.S. Assn., 1990-92; Eisenhower Leadership Prize Dinner Com., Eisenhower World Affairs Inst., 1992, 93, mem. com. to celebrate bicentennial of constn., Northampton, Mass., 1987; mem. Bush/Quayle Alumni Assn., 1993—. Recipient Voluntary Svc. award VA, Northampton, 1978, Trustees award Forbes Libr., Northampton, 1989, cert. of appreciation Correctional Edn. Assn., 1991, Phi Alpha Delta, 1989, Fed. Bur. Alcohol, Tobacco and Firearms, 1989, Gettysburg Coll. Career Svcs. Office, 1992, Young Alumni Achievement award Gettysburg Coll., 1992. Mem. ABA, Am. Soc. Internat. Law, Pa. Soc. of Washington, Phi Beta Kappa, Psi Chi (jr. award 1979). Avocations: racquetball, politics, community svc. Office: Russell & Assocs 3509 Connecticut Ave NW Ste 110 Washington DC 20008-2402

RUSSELL, NEDRA JOAN BIBBY, secondary school educator; b. May, Tex., Mar. 19, 1942; d. Samuel Ross Bibby and Velva (Osburn) Bibby Bowden; m. James L. Russell, Aug. 27, 1960; children: Pettye Russell Arrington, Jamie Len Russell Trammell, Joan Lee Russell Dela Rosa. BS, Howard Payne U., 1967; postgrad., Hardin Simmons U., summer 1968; MA in Teaching, Angelo State U., 1976; vocat. office cert., North Tex. State U., 1986. Cert. tchr. secondary gen., bus., provisional lang./learning disabilities, Tex. Tchr. bus. and vocat. courses to at-risk students Coleman (Tex.) Ind. Sch. Dist. Alternative H.S., 1967—; instr. keyboarding technique Brain Damaged Children Conf., Angelo State U. and San Angelo Sch. System; participant profl. workshops and confs. including State Vocat. Office Conf., 1985-92, Trade and Indsl. Arts State Conf., 1990, Tex. Commn. on Ednl. Tech. Conf., North Tex. State U., summer 1992, others. Named Bus. Tchr. of Yr. for Dist. XV, 1993. Mem. NEA, ASCD, Tex. Bus. Edn. Assn. (dist. chmn. 1977, state historian 1980-81, mem. ednl. adv. com. to dist. 17 rep.), Tex. State Tchrs. Assn. (treas. Coleman County unit, dist. del., membership chairperson), Nat. Bus. Edn. Assn., Vocat. Office Edn. Assn., Tex. Computer Edn. Assn., Mountain-Plains Bus. Edn. Assn. Home: RR 2 Box 199 Coleman TX 76834-9518 Office: CAP High Sch RR 1 Box 43 Talpa TX 76882-9608

RUSSELL, NEWTON REQUA, state senator; b. L.A., June 25, 1927; s. John Henry and Amy (Requa) R.; m. Diane Henderson, Feb. 12, 1953; children: Stephen, Sharon, Julia. BS, U. So. Calif., 1951; postgrad. UCLA, Georgetown U. Spl. agt. Northwestern Mut. Life Ins. Co., Calif., 1954-64; mem. Calif. State Assembly, 1964-74, Calif. Senate, 1974—; vice-chmn. com. on energy, utilities and comm., mem. com. on local govt., vice chmn. com. on fin. and investment, internat. trade, mem. com. on transp., com. ins., joint com. on rules, com. on Pub. Employment and Retirement, select com. on Calif.'s wine industry, mem. Com. on Legis. Ethics, Joint Oversight Com. on Lowering the Cost of Electric Svcs, senate select com. modernization. Mem. Rep. State Central Com. Served with USN, 1945-46. Recipient Outstanding Legislator award Calif. Rep. Assembly, 1968, 76, 81, Mayor's commendation City of Burbank, 1978, Disting. Service award County Suprs. Assn. Calif., 1980, Nat. Rep. Legislator of Yr., 1981, Legislator of Yr. award Los Angeles County Fedn. Rep. Women, 1982, Legislator of Yr. award Calif. Credit Union League, 1983, Paul Harris Fellow award Rotary Found. Rotary Internat., numerous honors from cmty. orgns. and instns. Mem. Rotary Internat., Am. Legion, Delta Tau Delta, Alpha Kappa Phi. Mem. Church on the Way. Office: Office of State Senate 401 N Brand Blvd Ste 424 Glendale CA 91203-2307

RUSSELL, PAUL EDGAR, electrical engineering educator; b. Roswell, N.Mex., Oct. 10, 1924; s. Rueben Matthias and Mary (Parsons) R.; m. Lorna Margaret Clayshulte, Aug. 29, 1943; children: Carol Potter, Janice Russell Cook, Gregory. BSEE, N.Mex. State U., 1946, BSME, 1947; MSEE, U. Wis., 1950, PhDEE, 1951. Registered elec. engr., Ariz., Minn., S.C. From instr. to asst. prof. elec. engring. U. Wis., Madison, 1947-52; sr. engr., design specialist Gen. Dynamics Corp., San Diego, 1952-54; from prof. to chmn. elec. engring. dept. U. Ariz., Tucson, 1954-63; dean engring. Kans. State U., Manhattan, 1963-67; prof. Ariz. State U., Tempe, 1967-90; dir. engring. Ariz. State U. West, Phoenix, 1985-88; dir. Sch. Constrn. and Tech. Ariz. State U., Tempe, 1988-90; cons. in field, 1954—; programs evaluator, mem. engring. commn. Accreditation Bd. for Engring. and Tech., N.Y.C., 1968-81. Contbr. articles to jours. and chpts. to books. Served as sgt. U.S. Army, 1944-46. Recipient Disting. Service award N.Mex. State U., 1965. Fellow IEEE (life, chmn. Ariz. sect. 1960), Accreditation Bd. Engring. and Tech.; mem. Am. Soc. Engring. Educators. Home: 5902 E Caballo Ln Paradise Valley AZ 85253

RUSSELL, PAUL FREDERICK, lawyer; b. Kansas City, Mo., Feb. 3, 1948; s. Walter Edward and Dorothy Marie (Sickels) R.; m. Kerry Diann Anderson, June 2, 1973; children: Philip, Erin, Shannon, Kelsey, Scott. BA,

Northwestern, 1970; JD, U. Mich., 1973. Bar: Ill. 1973, U.S. Dist. Ct. (no. dist.) Ill. 1973. Assoc. Vedder, Price, Kaufman & Kammholz, Chgo., 1973-79, ptnr., 1980—. Mem. ABA, Chgo. Bar Assn., Ill. State Bar Assn., Midwest Benefits Coun., University Club (Chgo.), Mich. Shores Club. Office: Vedder Price Kaufman & Kammholz 222 N La Salle St Chicago IL 60601-1003

RUSSELL, PAUL SNOWDEN, surgeon, educator; b. Chgo., Jan. 22, 1925; s. Paul Snowden and Carroll (Mason) R.; m. Allene Lummis, Sept. 24, 1952; children—Katherine Swift, Paul Snowden, Allene, Laura Rice. Student, Groton (Mass.) Sch., 1939-41; Ph.B., U. Chgo., 1944, B.S., 1945, M.D., 1947; M.A. (hon.), Harvard U., 1962. Diplomate: Am. Bd. Surgery, Am. Bd. Thoracic Surgery. From surg. intern, to resident Mass. Gen. Hosp., 1948-56, asst. surgery, 1957-60, chief gen. surg. services, 1962-69, vis. surgeon, 1969—, chief transplantation unit, 1969-90, chmn. com. on research, 1973-76; postdoctoral fellow USPHS, 1954-55; successively teaching fellow, instr., clin. asso. surgery Harvard Med. Sch., 1956-60, John Homans prof. surgery, 1962—; asso. prof. surgery Columbia Coll. Phys. and Surg., 1960-62; asso. attending surgeon Presbyn. Hosp., N.Y.C., 1960-62; asso. vis. surgeon Francis Delafield Hosp., N.Y.C., 1960-62, 74; bd. dirs. Warner Lambert Co.; mem. com. tissue transplantation NRC-Nat. Acad. Scis., 1963-71, com. trauma, 1963-68; ad hoc com. to study clin. investigation and edn. in USN, 1971-73; allergy and immunology study sect. USPHS, 1963-65, chmn. allergy and immunology study sect. B, 1965-67; mem. transplantation and immunology com. Nat. Inst. Allergy and Infectious Diseases, 1967-69, chmn., 1970; mem. com. on cancer immunotherapy Nat. Cancer Inst., 1974-79. Contbr. papers in field.; Editorial bd.: Archives Surgery, 1963-72, Surgery, 1963-71, Transplantation, 1965-79, Annals of Surgery, 1966—, Transplantation Procs, 1966—, Jour. Immunology, 1977-80. Trustee Pine Manor Coll., Chestnut Hill, Mass., 1963-76, Groton Sch., 1964-79; bd. dirs. Boston Fulbright Com., 1968, pres., 1980; bd. governing trustees Jackson Lab.; bd. trustees Worcester Found. for Biomed. Rsch. With USAF, 1951-53. Fellow ACS, Royal Soc. Medicine; mem. AAAS, Am. Acad. Arts and Scis., Assn. Immunologists, N.Y. Acad. Scis., Mass. Med. Soc., New Eng. Surg. Soc., Boston Surg. Soc. (pres. 1994), Soc. Univ. Surgeons, Soc. Exptl. Biology and Medicine, Halsted Soc., Whipple Soc., Internat. Soc. Surgery, Am. Surg. Assn., Transplantation Soc. (pres. 1970), Polish Acad. Sci. (fgn.), Sigma Xi. Home: 32 Lawrence Rd Chestnut Hill MA 02167-1230 Office: Dept Surgery Mass Gen Hosp Boston MA 02114

RUSSELL, PEGGY TAYLOR, soprano, educator; b. Newton, N.C., Apr. 5, 1927; d. William G. and Sue B. (Cordell) Taylor; Mus.B. in Voice, Salem Coll., 1948; Mus.M., Columbia U., 1950; postgrad. U. N.C., Greensboro, 1977; student Am. Inst. Mus. Studies, Austria, 1972, 78; student of Clifford Bair, Nell Starr, Salem Coll., Winston-Salem, N.C., Edgar Schofield, Chloe Owen, N.Y.C.; student opera-dramatics Boris Goldovsky, Southwestern Opera Inst., Ande Andersen, Max Lehner, Graz, Austria; m. John B. Russell, Feb. 23, 1952; children: John Spotswood, Susan Bryce. Mem. faculty dept. voice Guilford Coll., Greensboro, 1952-53, Greensboro Coll., 1971-72; pvt. tchr. voice, Greensboro, 1963—; co-founder, v.p. sales, mktg. Russell Textiles, Inc., 1988; vis. instr. in voice U. N.C., Chapel Hill, 1973-77; founding artistic dir., gen. mgr. Young Artists Opera Theatre, Greensboro, 1983; staged and produced 18 operatic prodns., 1983-91; guest lectr. opera workshop U. N.C. Greensboro, 1990-91; lectr. opera Friends of Weymouth, So. Pines, N.C., 1994; lectr. on music history and opera, High Point, N.C., Center for Creative Leadership, Greensboro, 1979-80, First Presbyn. Ch., 1982; debut in light opera as Gretchen in The Red Mill, Winston-Salem Opera Assn., 1947; debuts include: Rosalinda in Die Fledermaus, Piedmont Festival Opera Assn., 1949, Lola in Cavalleria Rusticana, Greensboro Opera Assn., 1951, Violetta in La Traviata, Greensboro Opera Assn., 1953, Fiordiligi in Cosi fan tutte, Piedmont Opera Co., 1956; appeared as Marguerite in Faust, Brevard Music Center Resident Opera Co., 1967, First Lady in The Magic Flute, Am. Inst. Mus. Studies, Graz, Austria, 1972; mem. Greensboro Oratorio Soc., 1955-59, soprano soloist in The Messiah, 1952, 58, The Creation, 1955, Solomon, 1958; soprano soloist Presbyterian Ch. of the Covenant, Greensboro, 1958-71; guest appearances Sta. WFMY-TV, Greensboro, 1958-62; soprano soloist with Greensboro Symphony Orch., 1964, 80, Eastern Music Festival Orch. 1965, Greensboro Civic Orch., 1980; soloist in numerous recitals including: Wesleyan Coll., 1964, Roanoke Symphony Guild, 1967, Am. Inst. Mus. Studies, Austria, 1972, 78, U. N.C. Chapel Hill, 1974, 75, 76, 77, N.C. Mus. of Art, 1978; recital, masterclass Mars Hill Coll., 1981. Bd. dirs. Music Theater Assocs., Greensboro Friends of Music, N.C. Lyric Opera; judge Charlotte Opera Guild Auditions, 1994. Mem. Friendship Force of Guilford County, Holland, 1985, No. Germany, 1987. scholarship grantee N.C. Arts Council and Nat. Endowment for the Arts, 1991. Mem. Nat. Opera Assn. (chmn. regional opera cos. com. 1985-91, judge vocal competition auditions 1991, 92, 94, chmn. trustees Cofield Endowment 1991), Central Opera Service, Nat. Assn. Tchrs. of Singing (state gov. 1976-82, coordinator Regional Artist Contest 1982-84), N.C. Fedn. Music Clubs (dir. 1956-58), Music Educators Nat. Conf., Greensboro Music Tchrs. Assn. (pres. 1966-67), Symphony Guild (dir. 1977-78), Broadway Theater League (chmn. 1961-63), Atlanta Opera Guild, Civic Music Assn. (chmn. 1963-64), English Speaking Union (bd. dirs. Greensboro chpt., chmn. Shakespeare competition 1995), N.C. Symphony Soc., Piedmont Triad Coun. Internat. Vis. (Appreciation award Nat. Coun. Internat. Visitors 1994), Greensboro Preservation Soc., Guilford County Planning/Devel. Assn. (forecast 2015 com.). Presbyterian. Clubs: Sherwood Swim and Racquet, The Greensboro City. Home: 3012 W Cornwallis Dr Greensboro NC 27408-6730

RUSSELL, RALPH ERNEST, librarian, educator; b. Bradenton, Fla., Jan. 25, 1938; s. Wilbur Lee and Beatrice (Parrish) R.; m. Linda Dee Sherman, June 16, 1962; 1 child, Lauren Susan Russell Fallon. BA in English, Fla. State U., 1960, MLS, 1961, PhD in Libr. Sci., 1973; MA in English, NYU, 1962. Br. reference libr. Queens Borough Pub. Libr., N.Y.C., 1961-62; asst. circulation libr., asst. acquisitions libr. U. So. Calif., L.A., 1964-66; head libr. Fla. Jr. Coll., Jacksonville, 1966-68; sci. libr. U. Ga., Athens, 1968-71; dir. libr. svcs. East Carolina U., Greenville, N.C., 1973-75; libr. Ga. State U., Atlanta, 1975—; coun. Xavier U., 1990, U. Wis.-Oshkosh, 1991, S.C. Commn. Higher Edn., 1992; bd. dirs. Southeastern Libr. Network, chmn. bd. dirs., nominating com., 1977, chair, 1982; bd. trustees OCLC, 1988-94, audit com. 1989, personnel and compensation com. 1990; chair Regents' Acad. Com., 1988-89; adv. coun. State of Ga. Libr. Svcs. and Constrn. Act., 1981-83; mem. exec. bd. dirs. Friends of the Atlanta-Fulton Pub. Libr., 1981-85, chair exec. bd. dirs., 1985-87; mem. libr. coun. U. Ctr. in Ga., Inc. Contbr. articles to profl. jours. Mem. presdl. inaugural commn. Ga. State U., 1993, chair com. on inaugural pub. events and ceremonies; program chair Ga. Gov.'s Conf. on Librs. and Info. Svcs., 1990; elected Ga. del. to 1991 White House Conf. on Libbrs. and Info. Svcs. With USN, 1962-64. Coun. on Libr. Resources grantee, 1977-78, NEH grantee, 1990-94. Mem. ALA (coun.), Southeastern Libr. Assn. (chair coll. and u. sect. 1978-80, hdqrs. com. 1983-85, chair program com. 1986), Ga. Libr. Assn. (2nd v.p. 1986-87), Met. Atlanta Libr. Assn. (v.p. 1976-77, pres. 1977-78), Omicron Delta Kappa, Beta Phi Mu, Phi Kappa Phi. Republican. Presbyterian. Avocations: running, swimming, piano, trashy fiction. Home: 96 Spring Lake Pl NW Atlanta GA 30318-1646 Office: Ga State U U Libr 100 Decatur St SE Atlanta GA 30303-3202

RUSSELL, RAY, author; b. Chgo., Sept. 4, 1924; s. William James and Margaret (Otto) R.; m. Ada Beth Stevens, Sept. 5, 1950; children: Marc Antony, Amanda. Student, Chgo. Conservatory, 1947-48, Goodman Meml. Theater, Chgo., 1949-51. Asso. editor Playboy mag., Chgo., 1954-55; exec. editor Playboy mag., 1955-60, contbg. editor, 1968-75; Guest lectr. Pasadena City Coll., 1963. Author and screenplay writer, Beverly Hills, Calif., 1961—; author: Sardonicus and Other Stories, 1961, The Case Against Satan, 1962 (Catholic Book Club Eng. selection 1963), The Little Lexicon of Love, 1966, Unholy Trinity, 1967, The Colony, 1969, Sagittarius, 1971, Prince of Darkness, 1971, Incubus, 1976, Holy Horatio, 1976, Princess Pamela, 1979 (Lit. Guild, Doubleday Book Club selection 1980), The Devil's Mirror, 1980, The Book of Hell, 1980, The Bishop's Daughter, 1981, Haunted Castles, 1985, (poetry) The Night Sound, 1987, Dirty Money, 1988, Absolute Power, 1992; screenplays: Mr. Sardonicus, Zotz, Columbia, 1961, The Soft Sell, 1961, The Other Place, 1966, Murder in Paradise, 1975, Universal, X- The Man With X-Ray Eyes, The Premature Burial, Genghis Khan, A.I.P., 1962-64, The Florentine Ring, Dominion, 1963, Chamber of Horrors, Warner, 1964, The Horror of It All, 20th Century Fox, 1964, Peer Gynt, Galaxy, 1965, Odd John, Rip Van Winkle, Metro-Goldwyn-Mayer, 1965-66; contbr. short stories, essays, satire, poetry to Paris Rev., Midatlantic Rev., Verbatim, Odyssey, Playboy, Theology Today, others; works transl. into French, German, Spanish, Dutch, Italian, Portuguese, Danish, Swedish, Polish, Japanese, Norwegian. Editor: Playboy's Ribald Classics, 1957, The Permanent Playboy, 1959. Served with USAAF, 1943-46. Recipient Silver Globe award for film X Festival Internat. Film Fantascienza, Trieste, Italy, 1963, winner Writers Digest Poetry competition, 1976, Sri Chinmoy Poetry award, 1977, World Fantasy Life Achievement award, 1991, Bram Stoker award Horror Writers of Am., 1993. Chaucer said it for all of us: " The life so short, the craft so long to learn.".

RUSSELL, RICHARD, religious organization adminstrator. Moderator North Am. Baptist Conf., Villa Park, Il. Office: North American Baptist Conf 1 S 210 Summit Ave Villa Park IL 60181

RUSSELL, RICHARD DONCASTER, geophysicist, educator, geoscientist; b. Toronto, Ont., Can., Feb. 27, 1929; s. Richard Douglas and Ada Gwennola (Doncaster) R.; m. Virginia Ann Reid Clippingdale, Aug. 11, 1951; children: Linda Jean, Morna Ann, Mary Joyce. BA, U. Toronto, 1951, MA, 1952, PhD, 1954. Asst. prof. physics U. Toronto, 1956-58, prof., 1962-63; asso. prof. physics U. B.C., Vancouver, 1958-62; prof. geophysics U. B.C., 1963-91, prof. emeritus, 1991—, head dept. geophysics, 1968-72, head dept. geophysics and astronomy, 1972-79, bd. govs., 1978-81, assoc. dean sci., 1980-83, assoc. v.p. acad., 1983-86; sec.-gen. Inter-Union Commn. on Geodynamics, 1976-80; profl. geoscientist. Author textbooks.; Contbr. articles to profl. jours. Fellow Royal Soc. Can.; mem. Am. Geophys. Union, Can. Geophys. Union (J. Tuzo Wilson medal 1992), Can. Soc. Exploration Geophysics. Home: 226-4955 River Rd, Delta, BC Canada V4K 4V9 Office: Dept Geophysics and Astronomy, U BC, Vancouver, BC Canada V6T 1Z4

RUSSELL, RICHARD L., van line executive; b. Evansville, Ind., Mar. 10, 1946; s. Frank E. and Dorothy (Armstrong) R.; m. Jan C. Russell, Sept. 1, 1963; children—Roderick, Mark, Brian, Amanda. B.S. in Transp., Ind. U., 1968. Comml. account salesman Mayflower Agy., Chgo., 1968-69; comml. account salesman Mayflower Agy., Indpls., 1969-70, office mgr., 1970-71, v.p., gen. mgr., 1971-72; v.p., gen. mgr. Mayflower Agy., Detroit, 1972-73; v.p. wholesale div. Aero Mayflower Transit Co., Indpls., 1973-74, v.p., 1977-78, exec. v.p., chief operating officer, 1978-79, pres., chief operating officer, 1980-82, pres., chief exec. officer, 1982—, also dir.; exec. v.p. Mayflower Group, Indpls., 1979—; chmn. bd. Household Goods Carriers Bur. Officer Indpls. 500 Festival; bd. dirs. Indpls Conv. and Visitors Bur. Mem. Am. Movers Conf. (bd. dirs. 1982-86), Am. Trucking Assn. (conf. v.p.), Young Pres.' Orgn., Am. Bus. Club. Republican. Presbyterian. Clubs: Crooked Stick Golf (Carmel, Ind.); Meridian Hills Country (Indpls.). Office: Mayflower Transit Inc 9998 N Michigan Rd Carmel IN 46032-8713 also: Mayflower Group Inc 9998 N Michigan Rd Carmel IN 46032

RUSSELL, RICHARD OLNEY, JR., cardiologist, educator; b. Birmingham, Ala., July 9, 1932; s. Richard Olney and Louise (Taylor) R.; m. Phyllis Hutchinson, June 15, 1963; children: Scott Richard, Katherine Hutchinson, Meredith Cooper, Stephen Wilbon. A.B., Vanderbilt U., 1953, M.D., 1956. Diplomate Am. Bd. Internal Medicine, Am. Bd. Cardiovascular Disease. Intern Peter Bent Brigham Hosp., Boston, 1956-57; resident Peter Bent Brigham Hosp., 1959-60, 63-64; fellow in cardiology Med. Coll. Ala., Birmingham, 1960-62; instr. Med. Coll. Ala., 1962-63; instr. medicine U. Ala., Birmingham, 1964-65; asst. prof. U. Ala., 1965-70, assoc. prof., 1970-73, prof., 1973-81, clin. prof., 1981—; practice medicine specializing in cardiology Birmingham, 1981—; Mem. Jefferson County Bd. Health, 1977-81, chmn., 1979. Author: (with Charles Edward Rackley) Hemodynamic Monitoring in a Coronary Intensive Care Unit, 1974, 2d rev. and enlarged edit., 1981, Coronary Artery Disease: Recognition and Management, 1979, (with others) Radiographic Anatomy of the Coronary Arteries: An Atlas, 1976, Acute Ischemic Syndromes in American College of Cardiology Self Assessment Program, 1993; mem. editorial bd. Circulation, 1976-80, Am. Jour. Cardiology, 1977-82, Heart and Lung, 1978-83, Chest, 1978-83, Ala. Jour. Med. Scis, 1977-80, Jour. Am. Coll. Cardiology, 1987-90; contbr. articles to profl. jours. Distbn. com. greater Birmingham Found., 1984-90; exec. bd. Birmingham area coun. Boy Scouts Am., 1987—, v.p., 1990—, vice chmn. Vulcan dist., 1988-89, chmn., 1989-91, bd. dirs. S.E. region, 1990-92, bd. dirs. so. region, 1992—; bd. dirs. Ctrl. Ala. United Way, 1988-92; mem. Necomen Soc., 1988—; chmn. exec. com. Birmingham Bapt. Med. Ctr., Montclair, 1995. Decorated Commendation medal; recipient Dist. Award of Merit, Boy Scouts Am., 1991, Silver Beaver award, 1990; NIH rsch. fellow, 1966-67. Fellow ACP, Am. Coll. Cardiology (bd. govs. 1979-81, trustee 1984-85, 89-94, ann. sci. session program chmn. 1994); mem. Am. Heart Assn. (pres. Ala. affiliate 1975-76, v.p. so. region 1986-87), Am. Coll. Chest Physicians (bd. regents 1985-91), Am. Fedn. Clin. Rsch., Am. Bd. Cardiovascular Disease, So. Soc. Clin. Investigation, Jefferson County Med. Soc. (v.p. 1982, pres. 1984), Birmingham Cardiovascular Soc. (pres. 1981), Med. Assn. State Ala. (speaker house counselors dels. 1989-94), Leadership Birmingham, Kiwanis (Birmingham sec. 1984-85, pres. 1994-95), Phi Beta Kappa, Alpha Omega Alpha, Omicron Delta Kappa. Home: 4408 Kennesaw Dr Birmingham AL 35213-1826 Office: Ala Heart Inst 880 Montclair Rd 1st Fl Birmingham AL 35213

RUSSELL, ROBERT GILMORE, lawyer; b. Detroit, May 22, 1928; s. William Gilmore and Esther Marion (Redmond) R.; m. Martha Jones, July 9, 1955; children: Robin Russell Millstein, Julie Russell Smith. AB, U. Mich., 1951, JD, 1953. Bar: Mich. 1954. Atty. Kerr Russell & Weber (and predecessors), Detroit, 1953—; ptnr. Kerr, Russell & Weber (and predecessors), 1959-93, of counsel, 1994—; instr. Wayne State U. Law Sch., 1954-60. Assoc. editor Mich. Law Rev., 1952-53. Fellow Am. Coll. Trial Lawyers, Am. Bar Found. (sustaining life), Mich. Bar Found.(charter); mem. ABA, Mich. Bar Assn. (chair negligence council 1988-89), Detroit Bar Assn. (dir. 1977—, pres. 1981-82), Am. Judicature Soc., Am. Arbitration Assn., Internat. Assn. Def. Counsel, Assn. Def. Trial Counsel Detroit (pres. 1973-74), U.S. Supreme Ct. Hist. Soc., Mich. Supreme Ct. Hist. Soc. (mem. lawyers com.), Nat. Conf. State Trial Cts., Def. Rsch. Inst., Am. Bd. Trial Attys. (advocate, charter mem. Mich. chpt.), Barristers, Order of Coif, Mimes, Theta Xi, Phi Delta Phi, Phi Eta Sigma. Club: Thomas Cooley. Home: 879 Sunningdale Dr Grosse Pointe MI 48236-1629 Office: Kerr Russell & Weber 500 Woodward Ave Detroit MI 48226-3407

RUSSELL, ROBERT HILTON, Romance languages and literature educator; b. Oak Park, Ill., Dec. 26, 1927; s. Melvin Alvord and Gladys (Hilton) R.; m. June Adele Thayer, Oct. 27, 1956. A.B., Knox Coll., 1949; A.M., Harvard U., 1950, Ph.D., 1963; A.M., Dartmouth Coll., 1968. Instr. Romance langs. and lits. Dartmouth Coll., 1957-61, asst. prof., 1961-63, assoc. prof., 1963-67, prof. 1967-91, prof. emeritus, 1991—; vis. prof. Spanish, U. San Diego, 1989, 90, 91, Knox Coll., 1993; guest lectr. Trinity Coll., Dublin, 1967, U. Salamanca, 1977, U. Leeds, 1978, Oxford U., 1978, U. P.R., 1987. Author: The Christ Figure in Misericordia, 1968; translator: Our Friend Manso, 1987. Corporate mem. United Ch. Bd. Homeland Ministries, 1963-69; N.H. del. Gen. Synod, United Ch. Christ, 1973, 75; corporator Internat. Inst. in Spain. Mem. MLA, Asociación Internacional de Hispanistas, Asociación Internacional de Galdosistas, Phi Beta Kappa. Democrat. Home: 14 Allen St Hanover NH 03755-2005 Office: 6072 Dartmouth Hall Hanover NH 03755

RUSSELL, STANLEY G., JR., accountant. Formerly dep. mng. ptnr. Deloitte and Touche, Wilton, Conn.; mng. ptnr. Deloitte and Touche, Pitts., 1992—. Office: Deloitte and Touche 2500 One PPG Pl Pittsburgh PA 15222

RUSSELL, TED MCKINNIES, electronics technician; b. Marion, Va., Feb. 25, 1943; s. Frank and Virginia (Pollit) R.; m. Patricia Ann Gilroy, Feb. 25, 1979. B in Elec. Tech., Grantham Sch. Electronics, 1966. Sr. electronic technician DPL Svcs., 1965-76; ind. gen. contractor, 1976-78; electronics technician Teltronic Instl. Systems, Silver Spring, 1978-80, Washington Met. Transit Authority, 1980—; pres. TMR Design, 1989—. Recipient Cert. Achievement Motorola Communications and Electronics, 1978. Home: 1414 17th St NW Apt 814 Washington DC 20036-6415 Office: Washington Met Transit Authority 600 5th St NW Washington DC 20001-2651

RUSSELL, THEODORE EMERY, diplomat; b. Madras, India, Nov. 21, 1936; s. Paul Farr and Phyllis Hope (Additon) R.; m. Sara Mather (Stedman) Russell, Sept. 3, 1960; children: Douglas Richmond Russell, Richard Mather Russell. BA, Yale U., 1958; MA, Fletcher Sch. Law & Diplomacy, 1960, MALD, 1961; sr. tng., Nat. War Coll., 1980-81. Fgn. svc. officer Dept. State, Italy, Czechoslovakia, Washington, 1963-80; dep. office dir. (EUR/RPE) Dept. State, Washington, 1981-83; dep. chief mission Dept. State, Copenhagen, 1983-87, Prague, Czechoslovakia, 1988-91; ambassador to Slovak Republic Dept. State, Bratislava, Slovakia, 1993—; dep. asst. adminstr. for internat. activities EPA, Washington, 1992-93. Sch. bd. chmn.Internat. Sch. of Prague, Czechoslovakia, 1988-91; pres. Dept Chief of Mission Club, Prague, Czechoslovakia. 1990-91. Councillor Atlantic Coun.; mem. Army-Navy Club, Fgn. Svc. Assn., Nat. War Coll. Alumni Assn. Avocations: hiking, fishing, history, numismatics, philaterlics. Home and Office: Am Embassy Bratislava Dept State Washington DC 20521

RUSSELL, THERESA LYNN, actress; b. San Diego, Mar. 20, 1957; d. Jerry Russell Paup and Carole (Mall) Platt; m. Nicholas Jack Roeg, Feb. 12, 1986; children: Statten Jack, Maximilian Nicolas Sextus. Appeared in films including The Last Tycoon, 1976, Straight Time, 1977, Blind Ambition, 1978, Bad Timing, 1980, Eureka, 1981, Razor's Edge, 1983, Insignificance, 1984, Aria, 1984, Black Widow, 1985 (Nat. Assn. Theater Owners award 1985), Track 29, 1986 (Newcomer of Yr. award), Physical Evidence, 1987, Impulse, 1988, Cold Heaven, 1989 (Best Actress award Viareggio Film Festival 1991), Whore, 1990, Kafka, 1990, Thicker Than Water, 1992, Flight of the Dove, 1994, The Trade Off, 1994, (narrator) Being Human, 1994, Grotesque, 1995; TV movies Blind Ambition, 1979, Women's Guide to Adultery, 1993; BBC radio play Double Indemnity, 1993.

RUSSELL, THOMAS WILLIAM FRASER, chemical engineering educator; b. Moose Jaw, Saskatchewan, Can., Aug. 5, 1934; s. Thomas D. and Evelyn May (Fraser) R.; m. Shirley A. Aldrich, Aug. 1956; children: Bruce, Brian, Carey. BS, U. Alberta, Edmonton, Can., 1956, MS, 1958; PhD, U. Del., 1964. Registered profl. engr., Del. Asst. prof. U. Del., 1964-67, assoc. prof., 1967-70, prof., 1970-81, assoc. dean, 1974-77, acting dean, 1978-79, dir. Inst. of Energy Conversion, 1979—, Allan P. Colburn prof., 1981—, chmn. chem. engring. dept., 1986-91; cons. E.I. duPont de Nemours & Co., Inc., Wilmington, Del., 1968—. Author 2 books; contbr. articles to profl. jours., patentee in field. Mem. NAE, Am. Inst. Chem. Engring. (Thomas H. Chilton award 1988, Chem. Engring. Practice award 1987), Am. Chem. Soc., Am. Soc. Engring. Edn. (3M Lecture award chem. engring. divsn. 1984). Avocations: wind surfing, hiking, skiing. Home: 46 Darien Rd Newark DE 19711-2024 Office: U Del Inst Energy Conversion Wyoming Rd Newark DE 19716-0001

RUSSELL, THOMAS WRIGHT, JR., retired manufacturing executive; b. Hartford, Conn., July 19, 1916; s. Thomas Wright and Dorothy (Mason) R.; m. Mary Ferguson, Feb. 16, 1946; children: Thomas Wright 3d, Jennifer, Sarah. B.A., Yale U., 1939; student, Advanced Mgmt. Program, Harvard U., 1955. With Am. Brake Shoe Co. (now Abex Corp.), 1945-70, dir., 1966-70, pres., 1968-70, chmn., chief exec. officer, 1970, cons., dir., 1971-90. Bd. dirs. Met. Opera Assn. Served from pvt. to capt. AUS, 1941-45, PTO. Mem. Yale Assn. Class Officers (pres. 1955-57), Council Fgn. Relations, Delta Kappa Epsilon. Republican. Presbyterian (elder, trustee). Clubs: Yale, Century Assn.; Hay Harbor (Fishers Island). Home: L-4 Heritage Cove 85 River Rd Essex CT 06426

RUSSELL, VALERIE EILEEN, social service executive; b. Winchester, Mass., Apr. 28, 1941; d. John Randolph Russell and Carrie Belle (Finley) Jones. BA in Sociology, Suffolk U., 1967; postgrad., Columbia U.; D in Theology (hon.), LaFayette Coll., 1985. Program dir. Blue Hill Christian Ctr., Roxbury, Mass., 1965-67; racial justicestaff mem. Bd. YWCA, N.Y.C., 1967-72; cons. Riverside Ch., N.Y.C., 1972-73; nat. conf. organizer, 1980-81; asst. to pres. United Ch. of Christ, N.Y.C., 1973-79; pres., exec. dir. City Mission Soc., Boston, 1981-90; adj. prof. Union Theol. Sch., N.Y.C., 1976, Harvard U. Div. Sch., Cambridge, Mass., 1983—; bd. dirs. Ctr. Ministry of the Laity, Newton, Mass. Author: Laity in the Church, 1987; inventor simulation game on pluralism, 1973; regular panelist weekly TV program A Show of Faith, Boston; lectr. in field. Bd. dirs. United Way Mass. Bay, Boston 1984-88, Women and Poverty Network, Boston, 1984—; co-founder Christians for Justice Action, United Ch. of Christ, 1980—. Named Outstanding Young Women in N.Y., 1969; Recipient Outstanding Alumni award Suffolk U., 1981, Outstanding Social Work award The Girl Friends, Boston, 1985, Outstanding Human Services award Delta Sigma Phi, Boston, 1986. Uniter Ch. of Christ. Avocation: writing. Office: Office for Ch in Soc United Ch of Christ 700 Prospect Ave Cleveland OH 44115

RUSSELL, WILLIAM FLETCHER, III, opera company director; b. Denver, Aug. 31, 1950; S. William Fletcher Jr. and Ruth Talcott (Kenyon) R. MusB, U. Colo., 1973; MBA, UCLA, 1981. Singer various opera cos. including N.Y. Met. Opera, 1956-78; asst. bus. mgr. San Francisco Opera Co., 1980-84; mng. dir. The Washington Opera, 1984-87, L.A. Music Ctr. Opera, 1987-88; gen. dir. Anchorage Opera Co., 1988-92, Opera/Columbus, Ohio, 1991—; cons. NEA, Washington, 1984—; dramatic coach Anchorage Opera Co., 1988-92. Actor: (TV film) Disappearance of Aimee, 1976, (film) Duchess and Dirtwater Fox, 1977; assoc. prodr.: (TV operas) La Gioconda, 1979, Samson et Dalila, 1982, Pavarotti in Concert, 1983 (Emmy award 1983), Aida, 1984; prodr.: (TV opera) Goya, 1986 (Emmy award 1987). Mem. Anchorage East Rotary. Avocation: ski jouring. Home: 1779 N Galena Rd Sunbury OH 43074-9588 Office: Opera/Columbus 177 Naghten Columbus OH 43215*

RUSSELL, WILLIAM JOSEPH, association executive; b. Boston, Sept. 23, 1941; s. Stanley Whiteside and Helen Rita R.; m. Frances Marie Chapdelaine, June 25, 1967; 1 son, Scott David. B.S., Boston Coll., 1963; M.Ed., Northeastern U., 1966; Ph.D., U. Calif., Berkeley, 1971. Head math. dept. Oceana, Pacifica, Calif., 1966-71; asst. for fed. and profl. affairs Am. Ednl. Research Assn., Washington, 1971-73; dep. exec. officer Am. Ednl. Research Assn., 1973-74, exec. officer, 1974—; adv. bd. Edn. Resource Info. Center Ednl. Testing Center, Princeton, N.J. 1975-87; exec. officer Nat. Council on Measurement in Edn., Internat. Assn. Computing in Edn., 1987-89. Editor: Ednl. Researcher, 1979-90. Mem. Am. Ednl. Research Assn., Phi Delta Kappa. Roman Catholic. Home: 1443 Creekside Ct Vienna VA 22182-1701 Office: AERA 1230 17th St NW Washington DC 20036-3003

RUSSELL, WILLIAM STEVEN, finance executive; b. Evanston, Ill., Aug. 5, 1948; s. John W. and Lillian H. Russell; m. Susan M. Hanson, Aug. 20, 1972. BS, So. Ill. U., 1970. CPA, Ill. Sr. staff auditor Arthur Andersen & Co., Chgo., 1972-76; acctg. mgr., controller, asst. sec. and treas. Lawter Internat., Inc., Northbrook, Ill., 1976-86, treas., sec., 1986-87, v.p. fin., treas. and sec., 1987—. Served with U.S. Army, 1970-72. Mem. Am. Inst. CPA's, Beta Alpha Psi, Beta Gamma Sigma. Roman Catholic. Home: 2690 Edgewood Ct Deerfield IL 60015-1906 Office: Lawter Internat Inc 990 Skokie Blvd Northbrook IL 60062-4096

RUSSELL, WILLIAM T., government executive, nuclear engineer; b. Seattle, Dec. 2, 1944; s. T.J. Radcliff and Betty Marie (Heiges) R.; stepfather Donald George Russell; m. Harriet Ann Leigh, June 10, 1967; children: Karen Leigh Combs, William Randolph. BS in Math. and Systems Engring., U.S. Naval Acad., 1967; MS in Nuclear Engring., Cath. U., 1978. Commd. ensign U.S. Navy, 1967; nuclear submarine officer U.S. Navy, East Coast, 1967-75; resigned U.S. Navy, 1975; group mgr. ARINC Rsch. Corp., Annapolis, Md., 1975-76; with U.S. NRC/NRR, Washington, 1976—; div. dir. U.S. NRC/Nuclear Reactor Regulation (NRR), Washington, 1985-87, assoc. dir., 1990-94, dir. NRR, 1994—. Served with USNR, 1976-90, Capt. USNR, 1988. Recipient Presdl. Meritorious Rank, Ronald Reagan, 1988. Presbyterian. Avocation: sailing. Home: 354 Kingsberry Dr Annapolis MD 21401

RUSSELL-HUNTER, W(ILLIAM) D(EVIGNE), zoology educator, research biologist, writer; b. Rutherglen, Scotland, May 3, 1926; came to U.S., 1963, naturalized, 1968; s. Robert R. and Gwladys (Dew) R-H.; m. Myra Porter Chapman, Mar. 22, 1951 (dec. 1989); 1 child, Peregrine D. BSc with honors, U. Glasgow, 1946, PhD, 1953, DSc, 1961. Sci. officer Bisra, Brit. Admiralty, Millport, Scotland, 1946-48; asst. lectr. U Glasgow, Scotland, 1948-51, univ. lectr. in zoology, 1951-63; examiner in biology Pharm. Soc. Gt. Britain, Edinburgh, 1957-63; chmn. dept. invertebrate zoology Marine Biol. Lab., Woods Hole, Mass., 1964-68, trustee, 1967-75, 77-87, trustee emeritus, 1989—; prof. zoology Syracuse (N.Y.) U., 1963-90, emeritus prof., 1990—; continuing rsch. fellow in biology Syracuse (N.Y.) U., N.Y., 1990—; cons. editor McGraw-Hill Encys., 1977—; bd. dirs. Upstate Freshwater Inst., Syracuse, 1981—. Author: Biology of Lower Invertebrates, 1967, Biology of Higher Invertebrates, 1968, Aquatic Productivity, 1970, A Life of Invertebrates, 1979, The Mollusca: Ecology, 1983; mng. editor: Biol. Bull. Woods Hole, Mass., 1968-80; contbr. over 120 articles to sci. jours. William Wasserstrom award Syracuse U., 1988; Carnegie and Brown fellow, 1954; rsch. grantee NIH, 1964-70, NSF, 1971-81, U.S. Army C.E., 1985-87; confirmed Scottish armiger, 1967. Fellow Linnean Soc. London, Royal Soc. Edinburgh, Inst. Biology U.K., AAAS; mem. Ecol. Soc. Am., Soc. Internat. Limnology, Am. Malacological Union, Malacological Soc. London, Soc. Sys. Biol. Avocations: book collecting, small boat sailing, model railroading, painting (oils and acrylics). Home: 711 Howard St Easton MD 21601-3934 Office: Syracuse U 026C Lyman Hall Syracuse NY 13244 *Having a sufficiency of books around one results in more than mere contentment. Many of us who come from a more literate pre-electronic civilization cannot imagine - if we exclude only the countercharging transports of sex - any bliss superior to that of living surrounded by books.*

RUSSELL-WOOD, ANTHONY JOHN R., history educator; b. Corbridge-on-Tyne, Northumberland, Eng., Oct. 11, 1939; came to U.S., 1971; s. James and Ethel Kate (Roberts) R.-W; m. Hannelore Elisabeth Schmidt, May 19, 1972; children: Christopher James Owen, Karsten Anthony Alexander. Diploma in Portuguese studies, Lisbon U., Portugal, 1960; BA with honors, Oxford (Eng.) U., 1963, MA, DPhil., 1967. Lectr. Portuguese lang. and lit. Oxford U., 1963-64; rsch. fellow St Antony's Coll., Oxford, 1967-70; vis. assoc. prof. Johns Hopkins U., Balt., 1971-72, assoc. prof., 1972-76, prof., 1976—, chmn. dept. history, 1984-90; chmn. Albert Beveridge award and the Dunning prize coms., 1986-87; mem. U.S. Commn. Maritime History, 1977—. Author: Manuel Francisco Lisboa: A Craftsman of the Golden Age of Brazil, 1968, Fidalgos and Philanthropists: The Santa Casa da Misericordia of Bahia, 1550-1755, 1968, The Black Man in Slavery and Freedom in Colonial Brazil, 1982; Society and Government in Colonial Brazil, 1500-1822, 1992; A World on the Move: The Portuguese in Africa, Asia and America 1415-1808, 1992; co-author: From Colony to Nation: Essays on the Independence of Brazil, 1975; general editor: An Expanding World: The European Impact on World History, 1450-1800, 1995—; mem. editorial com. L.Am. Studies, Tsukuba, Japan, 1989—. Chmn. CLAH Columbus Quincentennial Com., 1987-90, Md. State Humanities Coun., 1980-82; mem. Md. Heritage Com., 1982-85, Balt. County Commn. Arts and Scis., 1982-84. Recipient Bolton Meml. prize Conf. Latin Am. Hist., 1969, Whitaker prize Middle-Atlantic Coun. Latin Am. Studies, 1983, Dom João de Castro prize Portuguese Nat. Commn. for Commemoration of Discoveries, 1993. Fellow Royal Geog. Soc. (life), Istituto Historico e Georgrafico da Bahia (corr.); mem. Brazilian Studies Assn., Forum on European Expansion and Global Interaction, Latin Am. Studies Assn., Conf. on Latin Am. History, European Acad. of Scis. and Arts (Vienna, elected mem.). Avocations: squash, hiking, cycling. Home: 113 Belmore Rd Lutherville Timonium MD 21093-6111 Office: Johns Hopkins Univ Dept Of History Baltimore MD 21218

RUSSERT, TIMOTHY JOHN, broadcast journalist, executive; b. Buffalo, N.Y., May 7, 1950; m. Maureen Orth; 1 child, Luke. BA, John Carroll U., 1972; JD, Cleve. State U., 1976; LHD (hon.), Canisius Coll., Marist Coll., D'Youville Coll.; LLD (hon.), Albany Law Sch. Bar: N.Y., D.C. Spl. counsel, then chief of staff U.S. Senator Daniel Patrick Moynihan, 1977-82; counselor N.Y. Gov. Mario M. Cuomo, 1983-84; with NBC News, 1984—; moderator Meet the Press, 1991—; anchor The Tim Russert Show CNBC, 1994—; sr. v.p., Washington bureau chief NBC News; nat. polit. analyst Today program and NBC Nightly News with Tom Brokaw; supr. NBC News Today program live broadcasts from Rome, 1985; oversser prodn. prime time spl. A Day in the Life of President Bush, 1990, A Day in the Life of President Clinton, 1993; has covered 8 U.S./Russian Summits, Geneva, Malta, Washington, Moscow, Vancouver; lectr. at more than 30 univs. Recipient Alumni Spl. Achievement award Cleve.-Marshall Coll. Law, Pres.'s medal Trocaire Coll., Dean's award Cleve.-Marshall Coll. Law, John Peter Zenger award N.Y. State Bar Assn., 1992, Disting. Grad. award Nat. Cath. Educator's Assn., 1995, Spl. Achievement Alumni medal John Carroll U. Fellow Common European Communities. Office: NBC News Meet the Press 4001 Nebraska Ave NW Washington DC 20016-2733

RUSSETT, BRUCE MARTIN, political science educator; b. North Adams, Mass., Jan. 26, 1935; s. Raymond Edgar and Ruth Marian (Martin) R.; m. Cynthia Margaret Eagle, June 18, 1960; children: Margaret Ellen, Mark David, Lucia Elizabeth, Daniel Alden. BA magna cum laude, Williams Coll., 1956; diploma in econs., Cambridge (Eng.) U., 1957; MA, Yale U., 1958, PhD, 1961. Instr. MIT, Cambridge, 1961-62; asst. prof., then assoc. prof. Yale U., New Haven, 1964-68, prof., 1968—; Dean Acheson prof. internat. rels. and polit. sci., 1985—, chair dept. polit. sci., 1990—; vis. prof. Columbia U., 1965, U. Mich., 1965-66, U. Libre de Bruxelles, 1969-70, U. N.C., 1979-80, Richardson Inst., London, 1973-74, Netherlands Inst. Advanced Study, 1984, Tel Aviv U., 1989; prin. cons. pastoral letter on peace Nat. Conf. Cath. Bishops, Washington, 1981-83; co-dir., scientist ind. working group Future of the U.N., 1993—. Author: World Handbook of Political and Social Indicators, 1964, What Price Vigilance?, 1970 (Kammerer award Amn. Polit. Sci. Assn. 1971), Interest and Ideology (with E. Hanson), 1975, Controlling the Sword, 1990, Grasping the Democratic Peace, 1993, others; editor: Jour. Conflict Resolution, 1972—; contbr. articles to profl. jours. Grantee NSF, 1964, 65, 69, 77, 79, 85, 88, 89, 90, 95, Ford Found., 1993, 94, John and Catherine MacArthur Found., 1988; Fulbright-Hays fellow, Belgium and Israel, 1969, 89; John Simon Guggenheim Found fellow, 1969, 77; German Marshall Fund fellow, 1977. Mem. AAUP, Am. Acad. Arts & Scis., Am. Polit. Sci. Assn. (coun. 1984-86), Internat. Studies Assn. (pres. 1983-84), Peace Sci. Soc. Internat. (pres. 1977-79), Internat. Polit. Sci. Assn. (chair N.Am. adv. coun. 1977-80), Fedn. Am. Scientists. Avocations: tennis, classical music, hiking. Home: 70 Martin Ter Hamden CT 06517-2333 Office: Yale U Dept Polit Sci PO Box 208301 New Haven CT 06520-8301

RUSSI, JOHN JOSEPH, priest, educational administrator; b. San Francisco, Oct. 27, 1939; s. Frank John and Catherine Mary (Carroll) R. BA, Chaminade U., 1962; STL, U. Fribourg, Switzerland, 1967; MA, U. San Francisco, 1978; PhD, Kennedy We. U., 1993. Cert. secondary tchr., jr. coll. tchr.; marriage, family, and child counselor, Calif. Tchr. St. Louis Sch., Honolulu, 1961-62, pres., 1988—; tchr. Riordan High Sch., San Francisco, 1962-63; tchr., counselor, prin., pres. Archbishop Mitty High Sch., San Jose, Calif., 1967-88; regent Archbishop Mitty High Sch., 1990—, Chaminade U., Honolulu, 1988—; bd. dirs. St. Anthony Sch., Wailuku, Hawaii, 1989—. Bd. dirs. Kukui Gardens, Honolulu, 1988. Mem. Waialae Country Club. Democrat. Roman Catholic. Home: 3140 Waialae Ave Honolulu HI 96816 Office: St Louis Sch 3142 Waialae Ave Honolulu HI 96816

RUSSIANO, JOHN See MILES, JACK

RUSSIN, JONATHAN, lawyer, consultant; b. Wilkes-Barre, Pa., Oct. 30, 1937; s. Jacob S. and Anne (Wartella) R.; m. Antoinette Stackpole, Oct. 6, 1962; children: Alexander, Andrew, Benjamin, Jacob. BA, Yale U., 1959, LLB., 1963. Bar: D.C. 1963. Guide interpreter Am. Nat. Exhibit, Moscow, 1959; rsch. asst. Law Faculty, U. East Africa, Dar es Salaam, Tanganyika, 1961-62; regional legal adviser for Caribbean, AID, 1967-69; ptnr. Kirkwood, Kaplan, Russin & Vecchi, Santo Domingo, Dominican Republic, 1969-74, Washington, 1974-78; ptnr. Kaplan Russin & Vecchi, Madrid, 1978-81, Washington, 1981-92; ptnr. Russin & Vecchi, 1992—; cons. on financing worker's housing in less developed countries of Latin Am., 1991; Washington rep. for Moscow Patriarchate of Russian Orthodox Ch.; convener adv. coun. Inst. for European, Russian and Eurasian Studies, George Washington U.; mem. adv. bd. Caribbean Am. Directory; trustee St. Nicholas Cathedral, Washington, St. Vladimir's Orthodox Theol. Sem., Crestwood, N.Y., 1985-93; legal adviser Orthodox Ch. in Am.; bd. dirs. Delphi Rsch. Assocs., Washington; Dominican Am. Cultural Inst., Santo Domingo, Dominican Republic, 1988-92, Nat. Coun. Internat. Visitors, Washington, 1987-93, Fund for Democracy and Devel., Washington, 1993—. Recipient Order of St. Vladimir, Moscow Patriarchate, Russian Orthodox Ch., 1991. Mem. Latin Am. Studies Assn., Caribbean Studies Assn., ABA, Inter-Am. Bar Assn. Republican. Clubs: Yale of N.Y., Yale of Washington. Contbr. articles to profl. jours. Office: 1140 Connecticut Ave NW Ste 250 Washington DC 20036

RUSSIN, ROBERT ISAIAH, sculptor, educator; b. N.Y.C., Aug. 26, 1914; s. Uriel and Olga (Winnett) R.; m. Adele Mutchnick, May 21, 1937; children: Joseph Mark, Lincoln David, Uriel Robin. BA, CCNY, 1933, MS, 1935; postgrad. (Inst. fellow), Beaux Arts Inst. Design, 1935-36. Tchr. sculpture Copper Union Art Inst., N.Y.C., 1944-47; prof. art U. Wyo., Laramie, 1947-86; prof., artist-in-residence U. Wyo., 1976-85, Disting. prof. emeritus, 1985—. One-man shows Tucson Fine Arts Ctr., 1966, Colorado Springs (Colo.) Fine Arts Ctr., 1967, Palm Springs (Calif.) Desert Mus., Chas. G. Bowers Meml. Mus., Judah L. Magnes Meml. Mus., Berkeley, Calif.; retrospective one-man exhbn. Nat. Gallery Mexican Art, Santo Domingo, Dominican Republic, 1976, Tubac Ctr. of the Arts, Ariz., 1987, Riggins Gallery, Scottsdale, Ariz., 1989, Fine Arts Mus., U. Wyo., 1991; sculpture commns. include 2 8-foot metal figures, Evanston (Ill.) Post Office, 1939, three life-size carved figures, Conshohocken (Pa.) Post Office, 1940, Benjamin Franklin Monument, U. Wyo., 1957, Bust of Lincoln, Lincoln Mus., Washington, (now in Gettysburg Mus.), 1959, Lincoln Monument atop summit Lincoln Hwy., (now U.S. Interstate 80), Wyo, 1959, monumental bas-relief bronze (Wyo.) Fed. Bldg, 1966, two carved wood walls, Denver Fed. Bldg., 1966, monumental fountain, City of Hope Med. Ctr., Los Angeles, 1966-67, statue, Brookhaven (N.Y.) Nat. Lab. 1968, life-size bronze sculpture fountain, Pomona Coll., 1969, monumental bronze sculpture Prometheus Natrona County (Wyo.) Pub. Library, 1974, Man and Energy, Casper (Wyo.) C. of C., 1974, 12-foot marble carving Menorah Med. Ctr., Kansas City, Mo., 1975, Einstein and Gershwin medals Magnes Meml. Mus, Berkeley, Nat. Mus. Art, Santo Domingo, Dominican Republic, 1975, monumental fountain, Galleria d'Arte Moderna, Santo Domingo, 1977, Duarte Monument, Santo Domingo, 1977, 30 foot steel and water fountain monument City Hall, Casper, 1980, marble and bronze monument, Lincoln Centre, Dallas, 1982, acrylic steel and bronze monument, Herschler State Office Bldg., Cheyenne, 1984, marble monument, U. Wyo., Laramie, 1985, portrait head Charles Bluhdorn, chmn. Gulf & Western, 1975, portrait bust Pres. J. Balaguer of Dominican Republic, 1975, portrait head G. Wilson Knight, Shakespearean actor and scholar, 1975, 2 12-foot bronze figures The Greeting and the Gift for Bicentennial Commn., Cheyenne, 1976, monumental marble head of Juan Pablo Duarte liberator Dominican Republic, Santo Domingo, 1976, marble sculpture Trio, U. Wyo., 1985, Isaac B. Singer medal for Magnes Mus., 1983, monumental Holocaust Figure Tucson Jewish Community Ctr., 1989, granite monument Chthonodynamis, Dept. Energy Bldg., Washington, 1992, bust Hon. Milward Simpson, 1993, bust James Forest U. Wyo., 1993, bronze statue Univ. Med. Ctr., Tuscon, 1995; contbr. articles to profl. jours. Recipient awards sec. fine arts U.S. Treasury, 1939, 40, Lincoln medal U.S. Congress, 1959, Alfred G.B. Steel award Pa. Acad. Fine Arts, 1961, medal of Order of Duarte Sanchez y Mella, Dominican Republic, 1977; Ford Found. fellow, 1953. Mem. Nat. Sculpture Conf. (exec. bd.), Sculptors Guild, Nat. Sculpture Soc., AIA, AAUP, Coll. Art Internat. Inst. Arts and Letters, Phi Beta Kappa (hon.). Home: 61 N Frk Rd Centennial WY 82055 also: 1160 Placita Salubre Green Valley AZ 85614

RUSSMAN, THOMAS ANTHONY, philosophy educator; b. Pitts., June 20, 1944; s. Joseph Anthony and Mary Virginia (LaGuardia) R. BA, St. Fidelis Coll., 1967; MA in Philosophy, Cath. U. of Am., 1971; M of Theology, Capuchin Coll., 1971; PhD, Princeton U., 1976. Asst. prof. Cath. U. Am., Washington, 1976-83; assoc. prof. U. St. Thomas, Houston, 1983-90, dept. chmn., dir. PhD and MA programs, 1987—, dir. Ctr. for Thomistic Studies, 1987—, prof., 1990—; fin. cons., portfolio mgr. St. Augustine Province of Capuchin Order, Pitts., 1986—. Author: Prospectus for Triumph of Realism, 1987; editor: Thomistic Papers V, 1990, Thomistic Papers VI, 1994; contbr. articles to profl. jours. Mem. Am. Philos. Assn., Am. Cath. Philos. Assn. (treas. 1977-83), Metaphys. Soc. Avocations: performing arts, hiking, canoeing, Bridge, trail riding. Office: U St Thomas 3800 Montrose Blvd Houston TX 77006-4626

RUSSO, ALEXANDER PETER, artist, educator; b. Atlantic City, June 11, 1922; s. Peter Joseph and Lillian Mary (Soma) R.; 1 child, Eugenie. Student, Pratt Inst., 1940-42, Swarthmore Coll., 1946-47; S.S., Bard Coll., 1947; B.F.A. (Breevort-Eickenmeyer fellow), Columbia U., 1952; postgrad., Acad. Fine Arts, Rome, 1952-54; Inst. Advanced Fine Arts, 1977-79. Instr. New Orleans Acad. Art, 1948-49; asst. prof. art U. Buffalo, 1955-58; instr. in graphic design Parsons Sch. Design, 1958-60; chmn. dept. drawing and painting Corcoran Sch. Art. 1961-70, chmn. faculty, acting dean, 1966-70; lectr., thesis adv. George Washington U., 1961-70; prof. Hood Coll., Frederick, Md., 1970-90, prof. emeritus, 1990—, chmn. dept. art, 1970-87; vis. guest prof. art Instituto Allende, San Miguel de Allende, Mexico, 1993-94; panelist Md. State Coun. Arts, Balt., 1981-82; reviewer art programs Md. State Bd. Edn., 1981—; guest art critic Southampton Press, N.Y., 1989, 91; cons. in field. One-man shows include Corcoran Gallery Art, Washington, 1946, 64, Chiurazzi Gallery, Rome, 1953, Cavallino Gallery, Venice, Italy, 1954, U. So. Ill., 1955, Frank Rehn Gallery, N.Y.C., periodic exhbns., 1954-74, Phoenix II Gallery, Washington, 1983, Ingber Gallery, N.Y.C., 1983, Washington Gallery Art, 1963, Franz Bader Gallery, Washington, 1967, Internat. Monetary Fund, Washington, 1968, 79, Agra Gallery, Washington, 1971, Benson Gallery, Bridgehampton, L.I., 1976, Phoenix Fine Arts, Frederick, 1981, Benton Gallery, Southampton, N.Y., 1985, 86, 88, 90, 91, Arlene Bujese Gallery, East Hampton, N.Y., 1994, Hood Coll., Frederick, Md., 1991, Western Md. Coll., Westminster, 1991, Bell Gallery, Seattle, 1991, 92, Gettysburg (Pa.) Coll., 1989; group exhbns. include Salon de la Marne, Paris, 1945, Met. Mus. Art, N.Y.C., 1948, Bordighera Internat., Italy, 1953-54 (hon. mention), Mus. Modern Art, Madrid, 1953, Sala di Esposizione delle Biblioteca Americano, Rome, 1953, Whitney Mus. Am. Art, N.Y.C., 1960, Mus. Modern Art, N.Y.C., 1969, Guild Hall, East Hampton, N.Y., 1976, East Hampton Avant-Garde, A Salute to the Signa Gallery, 1990, NAS, Washington, 1984, Bell Gallery, Seattle, 1990, Illustrator's Club, N.Y.C., 1991, Armory Exhbn., N.Y.C., 1991, Instituto Allende, San Niguel de Allende, Mex., 1994, Josh Kligerman Gallery, San Miguel de Allende, Mex., 1994; represented in permanent collections Albright-Know Gallery, Buffalo, Columbia U., N.Y.C., Delgado Mus. Art, New Orleans, Corcoran Gallery Art, Fiat Automobile Co., Rome, Nat. Collection Smithsonian Inst., Washington, Fed. Ins. Deposit Corp., Washington, Gettysburg Coll. of Pa.; author: Profiles on Women Artists, 1985, The Challenge of Drawing, 1986. Served with USNR, 1942-46. Fellow Guggenheim Found., 1947-48, 49-50,Edward McDowell Found., 1956, Hood Coll. Hodson teaching fellow, 1983; Fulbright grantee for painting and research, Rome, 1952-54, U.S.-Indo Subcommn. on Edn. and Culture grantee, India, 1984. Office: PO Box 1377 Wainscott NY 11975-1377 also: Benton Gallery Southampton NY 11968 *Success is an equivocal matter. "Outward success", no doubt, is meaningful and necessary to most people in terms of fulfilling goals or for some similar reason. "Interior success" is more difficult to achieve, for it means the labor of a developing soul, and, more often than not, the relinquishing of what most would consider to be "material success". Whatever I have achieved in the way of outward or material success, therefore, is but a minute reflection of that which I would wish to achieve on the spiritual level. There is a long way to go.*

RUSSO, ANTHONY JOSEPH, public relations professional; b. N.Y.C., Oct. 23, 1953; s. Lucio and Tina (Iarossi) R. BA cum laude, Alfred U., 1974; MA, Columbia U., 1975; PhD, Claremont Grad. Sch., 1982. Asst. to chmn. Mocatta Metals, N.Y.C., 1982-83; account exec. Gavin Anderson and Co., N.Y.C., 1983-85; sr. account exec. Adams and Reinhart, N.Y.C., 1985; dir. corp. rels. Geto and DeMilly, N.Y.C., 1985-86; v.p. Cameron Assocs., N.Y.C., 1986-88; chief exec. officer, chmn. Noonan/Russo Communications, N.Y.C., 1988—. Mem. Am. Psychol. Assn., Pub. Rels. Soc. Am., Psi Chi. Democrat. Home: 10 W 15th St Apt 1914 New York NY 10011-6829 Office: Noonan/Russo Group Comm 220 5th Ave New York NY 10001-7708 Also: Noonan/Russo Ltd, 3 Olaf St, London 411 4BE, England

RUSSO, D(OROTHY) CHRISTINE FIORELLA, elementary education and university educator; b. N.Y.C., July 24, 1931; d. Anthony Joseph and Assunta Mary (Moroni) Fiorella; m. Victor Donald Russo, Jr., Apr. 30, 1960. BA, Marymount Manhattan Coll.; MS, Fordham U., 1959; diploma in reading, Hofstra U., 1978, PhD, 1987, postgrad., 1987—; cert. in litigation, Adelphi U. and Nat. Ctr. for Paralegal Tng., 1980. Cert. elem. and secondary English tchr., N.Y., reading specialist, N.Y. Tchr. St. Margaret's Sch., Bronx, N.Y., 1955-56, Sacred Heart, Manhattan, N.Y., 1956-57, Bd. Edn., N.Y.C., 1957-60, Harborfields Dist. 6, L.I., 1960—; English instr. Marymount Manhattan Coll., N.Y. Bd. dirs. Marymount Alumnae Adv. Coun., N.Y., 1985—; Fordham U. Pres.'s Coun., Bronx, 1985-87, Fordham

U. Recruitment Program, Bronx, 1983-87; campaign worker Dem. Party, N.Y.C., 1990, 92; Marymount rep. N.Y. State Bundy/Affairs Fund, 1982-83; L.I. rep. Marymount Recruitment Program, 1992; chmn. Ft. Salonga Assn., L.I., 1979-83; campaign worker Dem. Party, N.Y.C. 1990, 92, 94; vol. St. John's Hosp., L.I.; co-dir. Just Say No Thomas J. Lahey Sch.; mem. adv. coun. alumni bd. dirs. Fordham U. Sch. Edn. Recipient Tchr.-Student Participation award Suffolk Reading Coun., 1991-95, Tchr.-Student Participation award 3d and 4th ann. N.Y. Senate Earth Day Competition, 1994, 95. Mem. APA, Guilford Internat. Soc. Intelligence Res. (v.p. 1991—, bd. dirs. 1990—), N.Y. Acad. Scis., N.Y. Orton Dyslexia Soc., Nat. Dyslexia Rsch. Found., Coun. for Exceptional Children, World Coun. for Gifted and Talented Children, Am. Assn. Higher Edn., Marymount Manhattan Coll. (1st v.p. 1995), Fordham U. Alumni Assn. (bd. dirs. adv. coun. 1995), Children and Adults With Attention Deficit Disorders. Roman Catholic. Home: 7 Bonnie Dr Northport NY 11768-1448

RUSSO, GREGORY THOMAS, lawyer; b. Bellerose, N.Y., Dec. 19, 1949; s. Albert Thomas and Geraldine Ann (Norton) R.; m. Helen Mary Shannon, Dec. 29, 1973; children: Deirdre Leslie, Nicholas Shannon, Barbara Celeste. AB, Georgetown U., 1971; JD, Cath. U. Am., 1974. Bar: N.Y. 1975, D.C. 1977, U.S. Supreme Ct. 1979. Sr. counsel, v.p. corp. staff, corp. sec. Merrill Lynch & Co., Inc., N.Y.C., 1974—. Capt. USAR, 1975. Mem. ABA. Republican. Roman Catholic. Avocation: golf. Office: Merrill Lynch & Co Inc 100 Church St New York NY 10007-2601

RUSSO, IRMA HAYDEE ALVAREZ DE, pathologist; b. San Rafael, Mendoza, Argentina, Feb. 28, 1942; came to U.S. 1972; d. Jose Maria and Maria Carmen (Martinez) de Alvarez; m. Jose Russo, Feb. 8, 1969; 1 child, Patricia Alexandra. BA, Escuela Normal MTSM de Balcarce, 1959; MD, U. Nat. of Cuyo, Mendoza, 1970. Diplomate Am. Bd. Pathology. Intern Sch. of Medicine Hosps., Argentina, 1969-70; resident in pathology Wayne State U. Sch. Medicine, Detroit, 1976-80; rsch. asst. and instr. Inst. of Histology and Embryology Sch. Medicine U. Nat. of Cuyo, 1963-71, assoc. prof. histology Faculty of Phys., Chem. and Math. Scis., 1970-72; rsch. assoc. Inst. for Molecular and Cellular Evolution, U. Miami, Fla., 1972-73; rsch. assoc. exptl. pathology lab. div. biol. scis., Mich. Cancer Found., Detroit, 1973-75, rsch. scientist, 1975-76, vis. rsch. scientist, 1976-82, asst. mem., pathologist, 1982-89, assoc. rsch. mem., 1989-91, co-dir. pathology reference lab., 1982-86, chief exptl. pathology lab., 1989-91; co-dir. Mich. Cancer Found. Lab. Svcs., 1986-91; mem. Dept. Pathology Fox Chase Cancer Ctr., 1991—, dir. anatomic pathology 1991-92; dir. Lab. Svcs., 1992—; mem. dept. pathology Fox Chase Cancer Ctr., Phila., 1992—; chief resident physician dept. pathology Wayne State U. Sch. Medicine, 1978-80, asst. prof., 1980-82; mem. staff Harper-Grace Hosps., Detroit, 1980-82; adj. prof. Pathology and Cell Biology Jefferson Sch. of Medicine/Thomas Jefferson Univ., 1992—. Rockefeller grantee, 1972-73; Nat. Cancer Inst. grantee, 1978-81, 84-87, 1994—; Am. Cancer Soc. grantee 1988-89, 91—; Recipient Shannon award Nat. Cancer Inst./NHHSS, 1992-94. guest lectr. dept. obstetrics Sch. Medicine U. Nat. of Cuyo, 1965-71. Mem. AAAS, Nat. Cancer Inst. (breast cancer working group, breast cancer program 1984-88), Nat. Alliance Breast Cancer Orgns. (med. adv. bd. N.Y.C. chpt. 1986—), Eastern Coop. Oncology Group, 1992—, Coll. Am. Pathologists, Am. Soc. Clin. Pathologists, Am. Assn. for Cancer Research, Mich. Soc. Pathologists, Am. Assn. Clin. Chemistry, Electron Microscopy Soc. Am., The Endocrine Soc, Internat. Assn. Against Cancer, Mich. Electron Microscopy Forum, Sigma Xi. Roman Catholic. Contbr. numerous articles on pathology to profl. jours. Office: Fox Chase Cancer Ctr 7701 Burholme Ave Philadelphia PA 19111-2497 also: PO Box 549 Abington PA 19001-0549

RUSSO, JOSE, pathologist; b. Mendoza, Argentina, Mar. 24, 1942; came to U.S., 1971; s. Felipe and Teresa (Pagano) R.; m. Irma Haydee, Feb. 8, 1969; 1 child, Patricia Alexandra. BS, Agustin Alvarez Nat. Coll., 1959; MD, U. Nat. Cuyo, 1967. Instr. Inst. Gen. and Exptl. Pathology Med. Sch., Mendoza, 1961-66; assoc. prof. Inst. Histology and Embryology, 1967-71; Rockefeller Found. postdoctoral fellow Inst. Molecular and Cellular Evolution U. Miami, 1971-73; chief exptl. pathology lab. Mich. Cancer Found., Detroit, 1973-81; assoc. clin. prof. pathology Wayne State U., Detroit, 1979-91, chmn. dept. pathology, 1981-91; chmn. dept. pathology, sr. mem. Fox Chase Cancer Ctr., Phila., 1991-94, sr. mem., dir. Breast Cancer Rsch. Lab., 1994—; mem. Mich. Cancer Found., 1982-91; adj. prof. pathology Jefferson Sch. Medicine, Univ. Penn. Sch. Medicine, Phila. Author: Tumor Diagnosis by Electron Microscopy, vol. 1, 1986, vol. 2, 1988, vol. 3, 1990, Immunocytochemistry in Tumor Diagnosis, 1985; contbr. over 200 articles to profl. jours. USPHS grantee, 1978, 80, 84, 88, 90, 93, 94, 95, grantee Am. Cancer Soc., 1982; NRC Argentina fellow, 1967-71. Mem. Am. Assn. Cancer Rsch., Am. Soc. Cell Biology, Soc. Exptl. Biology and Medicine, Tissue Culture Assn., Am. Soc. Clin. Pathology, Internat. Acad. Pathology, Am. Coll. Pathology, Sigma Xi. Roman Catholic.

RUSSO, JOSEPH FRANK, former college president; b. Pitts., Jan. 11, 1924; s. Joseph and E. Carmella (Sanseverino) R.; m. Jean Montierth, Mar. 26, 1947; children: Joseph Gary, Nancy Louise Russo Cook. BA, U. Ariz., 1953; MA, Ariz. State U., 1961, EdD, 1969. Tchr.-coach to prin. Prescott (Ariz.) High Sch., 1953-68; asst. supt. schs. Prescott, 1968; dean student personnel services, then dean instrn. Yavapai Coll., Prescott, 1968-74; pres. Yavapai Coll., 1974-84, pres. emeritus, 1984—; faculty assoc. Ariz. State U., 1960-63, No. Ariz. U., 1972, 73, 78; mem. Ariz. Commn. Post-Secondary Edn., 1972-83; interim pres. Burlington County Coll., Pemberton, N.J., 1986; adj. prof. history Embry-Riddle Aero. U., Prescott, Ariz., acting chancellor acads., 1985-86. Contbr. articles to profl. jours. Mem. Prescott Charter Rev. Com., 1975; bd. dirs. Prescott Salvation Army, 1970-73. With U.S. Army, 1944-46. Far Eastern Studies scholar Harvard U., 1955; recipient Builder Greater Ariz. award Ariz. Savs. and Loan Assn.-Sta. KTAR, Phoenix, 1967. Mem. Community Colls. of Ariz. (bd. dirs.), Phi Delta Kappa. Republican. Roman Catholic. Home: 628 Cypress Dr Prescott AZ 86303-4905 Office: 1100 E Sheldon St Prescott AZ 86301-3220

RUSSO, KATHLEEN MARIE, art educator; b. Worcester, Mass., Jan. 14, 1947; d. Cornelius Joseph and Miriam Nancy (Bradford) Lucey; m. Don Albert Russo, Apr. 12, 1969 (div. Apr. 1988). BA, U. Miami, Coral Gables, Fla., 1968, MA, 1971; PhD, Fla. State U., 1976. Prof. art history Fla. Atlantic U., Boca Raton, 1976—, chair art dept., 1988—. Co-author: International Dictionary of Art and Artists, 1990, Eros in the Minds Eye, 1985, Encyclopedia of Architects, 1982, The Symbolism of Vanitas in the Arts, Literature and Music, 1992. Summer fellow Nat. Endowment for the Humanities, 1979, 83. Mem. Am. Soc. Archtl. Historians, S.E. Soc. Archtl. Historians (Fla. rep. 1985-92), Coll. Art Assn., Am. Soc. 18th Century Studies, Am. Assn. Italian Studies, Phi Kappa Phi. Home: 925 Iris Dr Delray Beach FL 33483-4810 Office: Fla Atlantic U Art Dept Boca Raton FL 33431

RUSSO, PEGGY ANNE, English language educator; b. Sturgis, Mich., Sept. 7, 1941; d. Dale Miller and Virginia (Rifenburg) B.; m. Jerry Russo (dec.); children: Daniel Carleton, Christopher Sanford. AA with honors, Jackson C.C., 1967; BA in English Lang. and Lit., U. Mich., 1972, MA in English Lang. and Lit., 1979, PhD in English Lang. and Lit., 1988. Teaching asst. English dept. U. Mich., Ann Arbor, 1979-83; lectr. Pa. State U., University Park, 1985-88; asst. prof. English Pa. State U., Mont Alto, 1988—; part-time instr. Jackson (Mich.) C.C., 1979; adj. instr. Wayne C.C., Detroit, 1979-83; adj. lectr. U. Mich., 1984-85; participant workshops in field; presenter in field. Sr. editor: The Adelphi Theater Calendar, Part II, 1993; asst. editor RaJah, 1981-83; contbr. articles to profl. jours. Roy W. Cowden Meml. scholar U. Mich., 1983; Rackham Thesis grantee U. Mich., 1982; Cranbrook Writer's Conf. scholar Cranbook Acad., 1979, 80, Dorothy Guies McGuigan scholar U. Mich., 1983; recipient Avery Hopwood award in Drama, 1979. Mem. MLA, Am. Soc. Theatre Rsch., Internat. Fedn. Theatre Rsch., Pa. Coll. English Assn., Shakespeare Assn. Am. Office: Pa State U Dept English Mont Alto PA 17237

RUSSO, PETER FRANCIS, financial executive, accountant; b. Brockton, Mass., May 24, 1932; s. Frank George and Mary Alice (Maxwell) R.; m. Joan Theresea Dollfuss, June 6, 1959; children: Frank John, Paul Robert, Laura Jean. B.S. in Acctg. and Fin, Bryant Coll., Provo, R.I., 1957. C.P.A., Mass. Corp. auditor Am. Standard Inc., N.Y.C., 1957-59; supr. Spark Mann & Co. (C.P.A.'s.), Boston, 1959-66; asst. treas. Stevens Linen Assos., Webster, Mass., 1966-67; dir. corp. acctg. and fin. Rustcraft Greeting

Cards, Inc., Dedham, Mass., 1967-70; sr. v.p. fin., treas., chief fin. officer Multibank Fin. Corp., Quincy, Mass., 1971—; dir. Multibank Service Corp., Multibank Internat. Co. Bd. dirs. Meml. Battleship Mass., 1974-79, Old Colony Coun. Cath. Charities, 1974-78, chmn., 1982-91; trustee Cath. Charities Archdioceses Boston, 1987-91. With USN, 1950-54. Mem. Am. Inst. C.P.A.'s, Nat. Assn. Accountants, Tax Execs. Inst., Bank Adminstrn. Inst., Nat. Assn. Controllers, Mass. Soc. C.P.A.'s. Home: 86 Tilton Ave Brockton MA 02401-3030 Office: Multibank Fin Corp 100 Rustcraft Rd Dedham MA 02026

RUSSO, PETER ROBERT, JR., data instrument company executive; b. Passaic, N.J., Sept. 8, 1952; s. Peter Robert and Louise Jean (Savino) R.; m. Darsan Majury, June 8, 1974; children—Andrea, Bethany. B.S., Montclair State Coll., 1974; M.B.A., Harvard U., 1980. C.P.A., Mass., N.J. Sr. acct. Deloitte, Haskins & Sells, Morristown, N.J., 1974-78; controller Data Instruments Inc., Lexington, Mass., 1980, v.p. fin., 1980-83, pres., chief operating officer, 1983—. Bd. dirs. Amego Sch., Quincy, Mass., 1981—. Alpha Kappa Psi scholar Montclair State Coll., 1974; Baker scholar Harvard U., 1980. Mem. Am. Electronics Assn., Mass. Soc. C.P.A.'s, N.J. Soc. C.P.A.'s (J.H. Cohn award 1974), Am. Mgmt. Assn., Japan Am. Soc., Mass. Hi-Tech. Council. Office: Data Instruments Inc 100 Discovery Way Acton MA 01720-3648

RUSSO, ROY LAWRENCE, electronic design automation engineer, retired; b. Kelayres, Pa., Nov. 6, 1935; s. Peter John and Mary (Fudge) R.; m. Elizabeth Jean Tautkus, Dec. 26, 1959; children: Mark, Keith, Aileen, Linda. B.S.E.E., Pa. State U., 1957, M.S.E.E., 1959, Ph.D.E.E., 1964. Asst. prof. elec. engring. Pa. State U., University Park, 1964-65; mgr., staff mem. IBM Research, Yorktown Heights, N.Y., 1965-77, mem. research staff, 1983-85; mgr. design automation lab. IBM Research, 1985—; sr. engr. Gen. Tech. div. IBM, Hopewell Junction, 1977-81; mgr. strategy Gen. Tech. div. IBM, 1981-82; cons. prof. elec. engring Stanford U., 1982-83; retired, 1993. Editor-in-chief IEEE Computer Soc., 1983-85; co-inventor ink jet printer correction system. Treas. St. Patrick's Ch., Yorktown Heights, 1975-77. Recipient Invention Achievement award IBM, 1978, Outstanding Contbn. award IBM, 1968, 89, Outstanding Writing award Pa. State U., 1967. Fellow IEEE (dir. computer divsn. 1989); mem. IEEE Computer Soc. (pres. 1986-87, Svc. award, Centennial medal 1984, Richard E. Merwin award 1992), Sigma Xi, Eta Kappa Nu.

RUSSO, THOMAS ANTHONY, lawyer; b. N.Y.C., Nov. 6, 1943; s. Lucio F. and Tina (Iarossi) R.; m. Nancy Felipe, June 18, 1966 (div. 1974); m. Janice Davis, June 10, 1977 (div. 1979); m. Marcy C. Appelbaum, June 16, 1985; children: Morgan Danielle and Alexa Anne (twins). BA, Fordham U., 1965; MBA, Cornell U., 1969, JD, 1969. Bar: N.Y., 1970, U.S. Ct. Appeals (2d cir.) 1971, U.S. Dist. Ct. (so. and ea. dists.) N.Y. 1971, U.S. Ct. Appeals (7th cir.) 1982. Staff atty. SEC, Washington, 1969-71; assoc. Cadwalader, Wickersham & Taft, N.Y.C., 1971-75; dir. div. trading and markets Commodity Futures Trading Commn., Washington, 1975-77; ptnr. Cadwalader, Wickersham & Taft, N.Y.C., 1977-92; mgmt. com., 1984-92; mng. dir., mem. op. com. Lehman Bros., N.Y.C., 1993—; bd. dirs. Futures Industry Inst., Rev. Securities and Commodities Regulation, N.Y.C., Futures Internat. Law Letter, N.Y.C. Author: Regulation of the Commodities Futures and Options Markets; co-author: Regulation of Brokers, Dealers and Securities Markets, Supplement Markets; editorial bd. mem. Jour. Fin. Regulation and Compliance; practitioner bd. advisors Stanford Jour. of Law. Mem. ABA (com. futures regulations, exec. coun., adv. com. on fed. regulation of securities, past co-chmn. derivative instruments subcom. of com. on fed. regulation), Assn. of Bar of City of N.Y. (chmn. internat. law sub com. of the com. on commodities regulation 1984-85, chmn. com. commodities regulations 1981-82), D.C. Bar Assn. Office: Lehman Brothers Inc 10th Fl 200 Vesey St Fl 10 New York NY 10285-1000

RUSSO, THOMAS JOSEPH, hospitality and consumer durables industry executive; b. Stamford, Conn., Sept. 15, 1941; s. Thomas and Ann (Petrozzi) R.; m. Wendy Fenwick, May 2, 1964; children: Michelle, Matthew. BS, Fordham U., 1963; postgrad., Chewton Pl., Bristol, Eng., 1980; D of Bus. Adminstrn. in Hospitality Mgmt. honoris causa, Johnson and Wales U., 1990. Div. gen. mgr. Howard Johnson Co., Wilmington, Del., 1974-76; v.p. Howard Johnson Co., Braintree, Mass., 1976-78, group v.p., 1978-80, sr. v.p., 1980-82, exec. v.p., 1982-83, pres., 1983-85; pres., chief exec. officer Ponderosa Steakhouse div., 1984-87; group chmn., CEO Hanson Industries Housewares Group, Framingham, Mass., 1987-94; chmn., CEO, pres. Miami Subs Corp., Ft. Lauderdale, Fla., 1994—; bd. dirs. Summit Family Restaunts, Inc., The Ground Round Inc., Legal Sea Foods, Inc. Trustee Framingham Union Hosp., 1981—. Mem. Nat. Restaurant Assn. (bd. dirs. 1982-83), Mass. Restaurant Assn., Del. Restaurant Assn. (bd. dirs. 1974-76), Rotary. Roman Catholic. Home: 2650 Edgewater Dr Fort Lauderdale FL 33332 Office: Miami Subs Corp 6300 NW 31st Ave Fort Lauderdale FL 33309-1633

RUSSO, WILLIAM, composer, educator; b. Chgo., Ill., June 25, 1928; s. William Joseph and Evelyn Viola (Guarno) R.; m. Shelby Davis, Mar. 13, 1947 (div. 1953); 1 child, Camille; m. Jeremy Warburg Feb. 6, 1960 (div. 1973); children: Condee Nast, Alexander William; m. Carol Loverde, Aug. 23, 1982 (div. 1992). B.A., Roosevelt U., Chgo., 1955. Composer, trombonist Stan Kenton Orch., Los Angeles, 1950-54; composer, dir. The Russo Orch., N.Y.C., 1958-60, The London Jazz Orch., 1962-65; dir. Ctr. for New Music, Chgo., Ill., 1965-75; composer in residence City and County of San Francisco, 1975-76; dir. Contemporary Am. Music program Columbia Coll., Chgo., Ill., 1976—; guest condr. Minn. Orch., Kansas City Philharm., New Am. Orch., Chgo. Chamber Orch.; condr., dir. Chgo. Jazz Ensemble, 1965—. Composer (operas) John Hooton, 1963, The Island, 1963, Land of Milk and Honey, 1964, Talking to the Sun, 1989, The Sacrifice, 1990, The General Opera, 1976, The Shepherds' Christmas, 1979, Sonata for Violin and Piano, 1986, Dubrovsky, 1988, Women, 1990, The Seasons, 1991, (film score) Everybody Rides the Carousel, 1976, (chamber pieces) The Carousel Suite, 1974, The English Concerto, 1963, Memphis, 1988, (mus. story) The Golden Bird, 1984, (cantata) Touro Cantata, 1988 (symphonic pieces) Street Music, 1975, Three Pieces for Blues Band and Orch., 1968, Urban Trilogy, 1981, numerous pieces for jazz orch. including America, 1966, The New Age Suite, 1984, The World of Alcina, 1954, 62, author: The Chicago Suite No. 1, 1995, (symphony) Symphony # 2 in C (Koussevitzky award), Jazz Composition and Orchestration, 1968, 74, Composing for the Jazz Orchestra, 1961, 73, Composing Music, A New Approach, 1988; composed for films: Everybody Rides the Carousel, Wrapped in Steel, Five Short films by Faith Hubley; record albums with own orch.: The English Concerto, Stonehenge, The Seven Deadly Sins, The School of Rebellion, Jump for Joy, with Cannonball Adderly, An Image, with Lee Konitz, The World of Alcina, An Experiment in Jazz. Recipient 25th Anniversary award Roosevelt Alumni Assn., 1970, Golden Eagle award, 1975-76, Grand Prix du Disc award, 1978, Italia, BBC submission, 1963, ASCAP Spl. award, 1961—, NARAS Lifetime Achievement award, 1990, Collaborative Artists of the Yr., 1991; inducted into 1st Navy Pier Hall of Fame, 1981. Mem. Am. Soc. Composers and Pubs., Ctr. for Black Music Resch. (nat. adv. bd.), Arts Club (Chgo.). Home: 824 S Laflin St Chicago IL 60607-4026 Office: Columbia Coll 600 S Michigan Ave Chicago IL 60605 *I have been guided in my music by Plato and Socrates, who taught that art is intended to maintain the just and good society, that art not only reflects the world but seeks to influence it and to maintain in it the honorable and decent and fair.*

RUST, EDWARD BARRY, JR., insurance company executive, lawyer; b. Chgo., Aug. 3, 1950; s. Edward Barry Sr. and Harriett B. (Fuller) R.; m. Sally Buckler, Feb. 28, 1976; 1 child, Edward Barry III. Student, Lawrence U., 1968-69; BS, Ill. Wesleyan U., 1972; JD, MBA, So. Meth. U., 1975. Bar: Tex. 1975, Ill. 1976. Mgmt. trainee State Farm Ins. Cos., Dallas, 1975-76; atty. State Farm Ins. Cos., Bloomington, 1976, sr. atty., 1976-78, asst. v.p., 1978-81, v.p., 1981-83, exec. v.p., 1983-85, chmn., 1987—; pres., CEO State Farm Life Ins. Cos., Bloomington, 1985—; now also pres., CEO, chmn. State Farm Mutual Auto Ins. Co.; pres. and bd. dirs. State Farm Investment Mgmt. Corp.; State Farm Internat. Services, Inc., State Farm Cos. Found.; chmn. State Farm Mut. Automobile Ins. Co., 1987; bd. dirs. exec. and investment coms State Farm Annuity and Life Ins. Co., State Farm Mut. Automobile Ins. Co., State Farm Life Ins. Co., State Farm Fire and Casualty, State Farm Gen. Trustee Ill. Wesleyan U., 1985—; mem. adv. coun. Grad. Sch. Bus. Stanford U.; mem. bus. adv. coun. Coll. Commerce and Bus.

Adminstrn. U. Ill. Mem. ABA, Am. Enterprise Inst., Bus. Roundtable, Tex. State Bar Assn., Ill. Bar Assn., Am. Inst. Property and Liability Underwriters (trustee 1986—), Ins. Inst. Am. (trustee 1986—). Office: State Farm Ins Cos 1 State Farm Plz Bloomington IL 61701

RUST, FRANCES O'CONNELL, education educator; b. Laguna Beach, Calif., Oct. 10, 1944; d. Walter Francis and Pauline Peyton (Forney) O'Connell; m. Langbourne Williams Rust, June 4, 1966; children: Edgar Forney Rust, Susanne Lancaster Rust. BA in English Lit., Manhattanville Coll., 1966, MA in Teaching, 1970; MEd, Columbia U., 1982, EdD, 1984. Asst. tchr. Bede Sch., Englewood, N.J., 1966-67; tchr., trainer, supr. Am. Montessori Soc., Fairleigh Dickinson U., Tenafly, N.J., 1967-68; tchr. Acorn Sch., N.Y.C., 1967-68; lectr. in edn. Briarcliff Coll., Briarcliff, N.Y., 1968-70; founder, dir., head tchr. Hudson Community Sch., Briarcliff, 1970-71; dir., head tchr. Woodland Sch., Chappaqua, N.Y., 1975-81; assoc. dir., asst. prof. preservice program Tchr.'s Coll. Columbia U., N.Y.C., 1983-85; assoc. prof., dir. dept. edn. Manhattanville Coll., Purchase, N.Y., 1985-89; assoc. prof., chair dept. of curriculum and teaching Hofstra U., Hempstead, N.Y., 1989-91; assoc. prof., coord. undergraduate early childhood/elem. edn. NYU, 1991—; mem. editorial bd. Ency. of Early Childhood, 1988-92; mem. adv. bd. Great Potential Westchester, Purchase, 1989; cons. on early childhood Metro Ctr. of NYU, N.Y.C., 1986—, New Rochelle (N.Y.) Pub. Schs., 1989-90. Author: Changing Teaching; Changing Schools: Bringing Early Childhood into Public Education, 1993; editor: Care & Education of Young Children, 1989. Chair Region 2 Resource Team of Episcopal Diocese of N.Y., Westchester County, 1980-88; bd. dirs. alumni coun. Columbia U. Tchr.'s Coll., N.Y.C., 1987—; pres., 1994-96; bd. dirs. Westchester County Jr. Achievement, 1988-89. Mem. Am. Ednl. Rsch. Assn., Nat. Soc. for Study of Edn., Assn. for Supervision and Curriculum Devel., Nat. Assn. for Edn. of Young Children, Soc. for Rsch. in Child Devel. Democrat. Episcopalian. Avocations: sailing, running. Home: 96 Round Hill Dr Briarcliff Manor NY 10510 Office: NYU Dept of Teaching and Learning 239 Greene St New York NY 10003

RUST, JOHN LAURENCE, manufacturing company executive; b. Normal, Ill., June 23, 1925; married. Student, Ill. Wesleyan U., 1943; BA, U.S. Mil. Acad., West Point, N.Y., 1949. Enlisted U.S. Army, 1943; resigned from active duty Ill. Army N.G., 1954; owner, mgr. Chevrolet dealership, Bloomington, Ill., 1954-60; pres. Rust Tractor Co., Albuquerque, 1960—; chmn. Rust Equipment Co., Albuquerque, 1967—; bd. dirs. Sunwest Bank Albuquerque, Mountain States Mut. Casualty Co., Fed. Home Loan Bank Dallas. Campaign chmn. United Community Fund, Albuquerque, 1965, pres., 1967-68; bd. regents N.Mex. Mil. Inst., Roswell, 1962-74; vice chmn. Presbyn. Healthcare Services, Albuquerque, 1968-82, chmn., trustee, 1982-83; pres. U. N.Mex. Found., Inc., 1980-84, bd. dirs. 1980—; vice chmn. Southwest Community Health Services, Albuquerque, 1981-83, chmn., 1983—. Served to col. USAR, ret. Home: 3550 Tucson Ct NW Albuquerque NM 87120-1124 Office: Rust Tractor Co 4000 Osuna Rd NE Albuquerque NM 87109-4423

RUST, WILLIAM JAMES, retired steel company executive; b. Newark, Mar. 21, 1929; s. William G. and Anna (Glavin) R.; m. Adele M. Laubner, July 29, 1950; 1 dau., Rita Marie. B.S. in Math. magna cum laude, Boston Coll., 1953; M.B.A. with high distinction, Harvard, 1955. With Nat. Cash Register Co., 1955-68, dir. distbn. and material, 1964-68; v.p., treas. Indian Head, Inc., 1968-72, v.p. planning and fin., 1972-77; v.p. fin. Nat. Steel Co., Pitts., 1977-84, ret., 1984. Pres. Social Health Agy., Dayton, Ohio, 1966-68; chmn. United Fund campaigns Dayton, 1962-68; bd. dirs. Good Samaritan Hosp., 1965-68. Served with USAAF, 1946-49. Mem. Nat. Assn. Accountants (bd. dirs. Dayton 1960-63), Fin. Execs. Inst. Clubs: Duquesne, Fox Chapel Golf. Home: 117 Haverford Rd Pittsburgh PA 15238-1639

RUSTHOVEN, PETER JAMES, lawyer; b. Indpls., Aug. 12, 1951; s. Richard and Henrietta (Iwema) R.; children from previous marriage: Julia Faith, David James; m. Linda C. Bennett, Dec. 28, 1987; children: Mark Bennett, Matthew Boyd. A.B. magna cum laude, Harvard U., 1973, J.D. magna cum laude, 1976. Bar: Ind., 1976. Assoc. Barnes, Hickam, Pantzer & Boyd, Indpls., 1976-81; assoc. counsel to Pres. of U.S. White House, Washington, 1981-85; of counsel Barnes & Thornburg, Indpls., 1985-86, ptnr., 1987—; counsel Presdl. Commn. on Space Shuttle Challenger Accident, 1986; spl. cons. U.S. Atty. Gen.'s Adv. Bd. on Missing Children, 1988; adj. fellow Hudson Inst., 1989-91, adj. sr. fellow, 1991—; sr. fellow Ind. Policy Rev. Found., 1991—; bd. advisors Indpls. Lawyers Chpt., Federalist Soc., 1993—. Contbr. monthly column The Am. Spectator mag., 1973-79; mem. bd. editors Harvard Law Rev., 1974-76, case editor, 1975-76; contbr. articles to nat. mags. Bd. dirs. Ednl. Choice Charitable Trust, 1994—, Legal Svcs. Orgn. Indpls., 1977-79; precinct committeeman Marion County Rep. Ctrl. Com., Indpls., 1978-81; state media dir. Ind. Reagan for Pres. Com., 1979-80, Ind. Reagan-Bush Com., 1980; speechwriter nat. Reagan for Pres. Campaign, 1980; mem. legal policy adv. bd. Washington Legal Found., 1989—. Grantee Inst. Politics, Harvard U., 1972. Mem. ABA, Ind. Bar Assn., Indpls. Bar Assn., Phi Beta Kappa. Roman Catholic. Avocations: golf; contract bridge; baseball memorabilia. Office: Barnes & Thornburg 1313 Merchants Bank Bldg 11 S Meridian St Indianapolis IN 46204-3506

RUSZKIEWICZ, CAROLYN MAE, newspaper editor; b. Tucson, Nov. 10, 1946; d. Robert Frank and Charlotte Ruth (Hadley) Knapton; m. Joseph Charles Ruszkiewicz, July 11, 1969. BA, Calif. State U., Long Beach, 1971, MA, 1973. Reporter Long Beach (Calif.) Press-Telegram, 1968-85, consumer editor, 1985-86, lifestyle editor, 1986-89, regional news editor, 1989-91, city editor, 1991-95, asst. mng. editor, 1995—. Avocations: swimming, walking, reading. Office: Long Beach Press-Telegram 604 Pine Ave Long Beach CA 90844-0003

RUTAN, ELBERT L. (BURT RUTAN), aircraft designer; b. 1943; s. George and Irene R.; m. BS in Aero. Engring., Calif. State Polytech. U., 1965. Flight test project engr. Air Force Flight Test Ctr., Edwards AFB, Calif., 1965-72; dir. Bede Test Ctr., Kans., 1972-74; pres. Rutan Aircraft Factory, Mojave, Calif., 1974—; founder Scaled Composites, Mojave, Calif., 1982—; v.p. Beech Aircraft, 1985—. Designer more than 100 aircraft including VariViggen, Solitaire, Defiant, and other kits; designer Voyager aircraft, first to fly around-the-world without stopping, refueling. Recip. Spirit of St. Louis Medal, Am. Soc. Mech. Engrs., 1987, Best Design Award, Exptl. Aircraft Assn.; Air medal, 1970, Stan Szik design contbn. trophy, 1972, EAA Outstanding New Design, 1975-76, 78; Dr. August Raspet Meml. award, 1976, ABC World News Tonight Person of the Week, 1986, Presdl. Citizens medal, 1986, FAI gold medal for Voyager Constrn., 1987, medal for the City of Paris, 1987, NASA langley Rsch. Ctr. dirs. award, 1987, Soc. of NASA Flight Surgeons, W. Randolph Lovelace award 1987, Collier trophy for ingenious design and devel., 1987, medal of Outstanding Achievement and disting. leadership, 1987, Soc. of exptl. test pilots, 1987, Aviation Man of the Yr, 1987, Lindbergh Eagle award, 1987, USAF 40th anniversary award, 1987, The City of Genoa, Italy, Christopher Columbus Internat. Communications medal, 1987, British gold medal, 1987, Outstanding Engring. achievement awards, 1988, Franklin medal, 1987, Disting. inventor award 1988, Meritorious Svc. award, 1988, Internat. Aerospace Hall of Fame Honoree, 1988, medal of achievement, 1989, Crystal Eagle award, 1989, Meritorious Civilian Svc. medal, 1989, Leroy Randle Grumman medal, 1989, Structures, Structural Dynamics and Materials award AIAA, 1991. Mem. NAE. Office: Scaled Composites Inc Mojave Airport Hangar 78 Mojave CA 93501

RUTENBERG-ROSENBERG, SHARON LESLIE, journalist; b. Chgo., May 23, 1951; d. Arthur and Bernice (Berman) Rutenberg; m. Michael J. Rosenberg, Feb. 3, 1980; children: David Kaifel and Jonathan Reuben (twins), Emily Mara. Student, Harvard U., 1972; B.A., Northwestern U., 1973, M.S.J., 1975; cert. student pilot. Reporter-photographer Lerner Home Newspapers, Chgo. 1973-74; corr. Medill News Service, Washington, 1975; reporter-newsperson, sci. writer UPI, Chgo., 1975-84. Interviewer: exclusives White House chief of staff, nation's only mother and son on dead week; others. Vol. Chgo.-Read Mental Health Ctr. Recipient Peter Lisagor award for exemplary journalism in features category, 1980, 81; Golden Key Nat. Adv. Bd. of Children's Oncology Service Inc., 1981; Media awards for wire service feature stories, 1983, 84, wire service news stories, 1983, 84, all from Chgo. Hosp. Pub. Relations Soc. Mem. Profl. Assn. Diving Instrs., Nat. Assn. Underwater Instrs., Hon. Order Ky. Cols., Hadassah, Sigma Delta

Chi, Sigma Delta Tau. Home: 745 Marion Ave Highland Park IL 60035-5123

RUTES, WALTER ALAN, architect; b. N.Y.C., Sept. 21, 1928; s. Jack and Sarah (Ogur) R.; m. Helene Darville, Apr. 2, 1952; children: Daniel J., Linda Lee. B.Arch. (Sands Meml. medal 1950), Cornell U., 1950; fellow city planning, MIT, 1951; postgrad., Harvard U. Grad. Sch. Design, 1978. Cert. Nat. Council Archtl. Registration Bds. Assoc. ptnr. Skidmore, Owings & Merrill, N.Y.C., 1951-72; v.p. John Carl Warnecke & Assocs., N.Y.C., 1972-74; staff v.p. Intercontinental Hotels Corp., N.Y.C., 1974-80; dir. architecture Holiday Inns, Inc., Memphis, 1980-83; dir. design The Sheraton Corp., Boston, 1983-85; chmn 9 Tek Ltd. Hotel Cons., 1985—; chmn. adv. bd. Hult Fellowships for Constrn. Industry, 1968-75, Architects and Engrs. Com. New Bldg. Code, 1968; mem. zoning adv. com. N.Y.C. Planning Commn., 1970; lectr. in field, 1968—; mem. steering com. UNESCO Council Tall Bldgs. and Urban Habitat, 1980—; vis. prof. Cornell-Essec Grad. Program; vis. prof. Nova U. Author: Hotel Planning and Design, New Trends in Resort Design and Development; (software system) SHAPE, Megatrends and Marketecture; contbr. articles to profl. jours.; prin. works include Lincoln Center Library for Performing Arts, N.Y.C., 1967, Am. Republic Ins. Co. Nat. Hdqrs., Des Moines, 1967, HUD Apts., Jersey City, 1972, Merrill Lynch Bldg., N.Y.C., 1973, Tour Fiat, Paris, 1974, Aid Assn. for Luths. Nat. Hdqrs., Appleton, Wis., 1976, Semiramis Intercontinental Hotel, Cairo, 1985, Intercontinental, Jeddah, 1983, Embassy Suites Internat., 1985, Universal City Hotel Complex, L.A., 1986, TechWorld Conv. Hotel, Washington, 1986, Sheraton Fairplex Conv. Ctr., L.A., 1992, Orlando Conv. Ctr. Hotel, 1993, Winter Olympiad Media Complex, Norway, 1993, Ephesus Resort Complex, Turkey, 1986, Royal Christiania Hotel, Oslo, Norway, 1991, EuroFrance Leisure Park Complex, Cannes, 1993, Kuna Hills Multi Resort, Guam, 1994. Recipient Platinum Circle award Hotel Design Industry, 1988. Fellow AIA; mem. Ethical Culture Soc. Office: 8501 N 84th Pl Scottsdale AZ 85258-2419 also: 25 Richbell Rd White Plains NY 10605-4110

RUTFORD, ROBERT HOXIE, university educator; b. Duluth, Minn., Jan. 26, 1933; s. Skuli and Ruth (Hoxie) R.; m. Marjorie Ann, June 19, 1954; children: Gregory, Kristian, Barbara. B.A., U. Minn., 1954, M.A., 1963, Ph.D., 1969; DSc (hon.), St Petersburg State Tech U., Russia, 1994. Football and track coach Hamline U., 1958-62; research fellow U. Minn., 1963-66; asst. prof. geology U.S.D., 1967-70, assoc. prof., 1970-72, chmn. dept. geology, 1968-72, chmn. dept. physics, 1971-72; dir. Ross Ice Shelf Project U. Nebr., Lincoln, 1972-75; vice chancellor for research and grad. studies, prof. geology U. Nebr., 1977-82, interim chancellor, 1980-81; U. Tex., Dallas, 1992-94, Excellence in Edn. Found. prof. of geoscis., 1994—; U.S. del. to Scientific Com. on Antarctic Rsch., 1986—; dir. div. of Polar Programs, NSF, Washington, 1975-77; chmn. NRC Polar Rsch. Bd., 1991-95; mem. editl. bd. Issues In Science and Technology, 1991-94. Trustee Baylor Coll. Dentistry, 1989—. 1st lt. U.S. Army, 1954-56. Recipient Antarctic Service medal, 1964, Distinguished Service award NSF, 1977, Ernie Gunderson award for service to amateur athletics S.D. AAU, 1972, Outstanding Achievement award U. Minn., 1993. Fellow Geol. Soc. Am.; mem. Antarctican Soc. (pres. 1988-90), Arctic Inst. N.Am., Explorers Club, Am. Polar Soc., Philos. Soc. Tex., St. Petersburg Acad. Engring. (Russia), Cosmos Club, Sigma Xi. Lutheran. Home: 1882 Quail Ln Richardson TX 75080-3456 Office: Univ Tex Dallas Geosciences Program Richardson TX 75083-0688

RUTGERS, KATHARINE PHILLIPS (MRS. FREDERIK LODEWIJK RUTGERS), dancer; b. Butler, Pa., Sept. 2, 1910; d. Thomas Wharton and Alma (Sherman) Phillips; m. Frederik Lodewijk Rutgers, Feb. 2, 1942; children: Alma, Corinne Tolles. Diploma Briarcliff Coll., 1928; student L'Hermiage, Versailles, France, 1929-30; pupil ballet Vera Trefilova, Paris, Carl Raimund, Vienna, Varga Troyanoff, Budapest; pupil modern dance with Iris Barbura, Bucharest Ballet, Vincenzo Celli, N.Y.C., Igor Schwezoff, N.Y.C., Jean Yazvinsky, N.Y.C. Performed dance concerts Bucharest, 1937-40, U.S., 1941—; repertoire includes patriotic, dramatic, poetical dances, religious interpretations; dance therapist St. Barnabas Hosp., N.Y.C., 1965-70; author numerous pamphlets on dance, verses for choreographies. Chmn. ethnol. dance dept. Bruce Mus. Assocs., Greenwich, Conn., 1970—. Bd. dirs. Bruce Mus. Recipient citation for promoting culture with dance programs Nat. Fedn. Music Clubs, 1973. Mem. DAR, Conn. Fedn. Music Clubs (chmn. dance dept. 1965-66), Nat. League Am. Pen Women (local pres. 1973-78), Alliance Francaise, Mayflower Soc., Colonial Dames Am., Federated Music Club N.Y.C. (dir., dance chmn.), Met. Farm and Garden Club (dir.), Indian Harbor Club. Home: 9 Riversville Rd Greenwich CT 06831-3666

RUTH, ALPHEUS LANDIS, dairy farmer; b. Souderton, Pa., Sept. 6, 1915; s. Henry M. and Mary (Landis) R.; m. Miriam D. Rittenhouse, Sept. 26, 1936; children: Esther R., Mary Ellen, Samuel, Joseph, Pheobe. Student, pub. schs. Sunday sch. supt. Oley Mennonite Sunday Sch., Fleetwood, Pa., 1954-64; dir. Lehigh Valley Coop., Allentown, Pa., 1969—; lay minister Oley Mennonite Ch., 1977—; dir. Berks Lehigh Fed. Land Bank Bd., 1960—; diary farmer; treas. Hope Christian Ctr., South Bronx, N.Y., 1975—; pres. Lehigh Valley Farmers, Lansdale, Pa., 1978—; chmn. bd. Atlantic Processing, Inc., Allentown, Pa., 1978—; sales exec. Prudential Rittenhouse Realty Group, Harleysville, Pa.; mem. North Penn. Bd. of Realtors, 1992—. Active N.E. Dairy Coord. Com., 1985—, Berks County Farm Land Preservation Task Force, 1986-92; pres. Dock Woods Residence Coun. Named to Pa. Holstein Hall of Fame, 1989. Mem. Nat. Holsten Club, Pa. Holstein Club, Nat. Holstein Assn., Berks County Soil Conservation, Pa. Farmer Assn. Republican. Office: Prudential Rittenhouse 418 Main St Harleysville PA 19438-2350

RUTH, BETTY MUSE, college administrator; b. Florence, Ala., Oct. 24, 1943; d. Paul and Mary Lucille (Gresham) Muse; m. Thomas Gary Ruth, Dec. 17, 1965 (div. Sept. 1979); 1 child, Thomas Paul; m. Charles Larry Oliver, Jr., Mar. 10, 1990. BSBA, Athens State Coll., 1982; MBA, U. N.Ala., 1986. Sec., bookkeeper Anderson News Co., Florence, 1963-65; acct. receivable bookkeeper McConnell AFB, Wichita, Kans., 1967-68; legal sec. Reynolds Law Firm, Selmer, Tenn., 1973-74; subs. tchr. Athens (Ala.) City Schs., 1974-78, dir. RSVP, 1978—. Active United Way, Athens, 1990-94; sec. Gov.'s Commn. Nat. and Comty. Svc., Ala, 1994; vice chair Tenn. Valley Exhibit Commn., Ala., 1984—; past pres. Athens-Limstone County Beautification Bd., 1991-94; People-to-People internat. del. to People's Republic of China, 1994. Named outstanding project dir. Action, Atlanta, 1985, outstanding woman of Ala., 1989. Mem. Nat. Assn. RSVP Dirs. (v.p., del. 1985-93, svc. award 1993), Region IV Assn. RSVP Dirs. (pres., v.p., treas. 1979—, svc. award 1989), Ala. Assn. RSVP Dirs. (v.p., sec., treas. 1978—, citizens award 1991), Ala. Assn. Nat. Edn. Assn., Athens State Coll. Alumni Assn. (bd. dirs. 1993-94). Mem. Ch. of Christ. Avocations: reading, traveling, volunteerism. Home: 15705 Kings Dr Athens AL 35611

RUTH, CAROL A., public relations executive; b. N.Y.C., June 19, 1942; d. Edward McDonald and Dorothea (Beauman) Smith. BBA, CUNY, 1979. Sr. v.p. Hill and Knowlton, Inc., N.Y.C., 1968-86; pres., chief exec. officer Dewe Rogerson Inc., N.Y.C., 1986—, also bd. dirs.; Dewe Rogerson Group, London; exec. dir. Dewe Rogerson Asia. Recipient Woman Achievers award YWCA of N.Y. 1985, bd. dirs. 1991—. Mem. Nat. Investors Rels. Inst. (bd. dirs. 1981-85, chmn. bd. 1984-85). Office: Dewe Rogerson Inc 850 3rd Ave New York NY 10022-6222

RUTH, CRAIG, business executive; b. July 18, 1930; s. Clarence Miller and Kathryn Dorothy (Buch) R.; m. Marion Nelson, Apr. 19, 1958; children: Robert Nelson, Lee Kathryn, William Walter, Ann Alva. BA, Muskingum Coll., 1952; postgrad., Northwestern U., 1956. Tchr., coach N.Y.C. and Chgo., 1955-66; dir. mktg. Great Lakes Carbon Co., Los Angeles, 1966-68; exec. v.p. Ketchum, Peck & Tooley, Los Angeles, 1968-75; pres. Tooley & Co., Los Angeles, 1975—; mgr. Two Rodeo Dr., Beverly Hills; bd. dirs. Los Angeles Internat. Bus. Corp.; council mem. Urban Land Inst., 1982—. Bd. dirs. Bldg. Owner & Mgrs. Assn.; chmn. Elgin Baylor & Jerry West Nights Los Angeles Lakers, Ed Sherman Night, Muskingum Coll., Los Angeles, Muskingum Coll. Reunion Com.; vice chmn. USMC Scholarship Ball. Capt. USMC, 1953-55. Named one of Outstanding Men of Am. C. of C., 1965; recipient Humanitarian award Nat. Conf. Christians and Jews, 1988.

Mem. Internat. Assn. Corp. Real Estate Execs., Spinal Cord Soc., 3rd Marine Divsn. (life), Japan Am. Cultural Coun., Beverly Hills Econ. Devel. Coun., Bus. Devel. Coun. (beverly Hills chpt.), Big Ten Club. Republican. Presbyterian. Avocations: tennis, playing trumpet, skiing, flying, boating. Home: 4045 Miraleste Dr Rncho Pls Vrd CA 90274-6574 Office: Tooley & Co 11150 Santa Monica Blvd Ste 20 Los Angeles CA 90025-3379

RUTH, DANIEL JOHN, journalist; b. Akron, Ohio, Sept. 16, 1949; s. John Edgar and Ruth (Motz) R.; m. Barbara Verde, July 10, 1980 (div. June 1988); m. Angela Pecoulas, July 31, 1992. BA in Polit. Sci., Gannon U., 1972. Reporter, critic Tampa (Fla.) Tribune, 1973-81; v.p., pub. Group W Satellite Com., Stamford, Conn., 1981-84; reporter, critic, columnist Chgo. Sun-Times, 1984-91; editor The Big Guava Mag., Tampa, Fla., 1991-92; columnist Tampa (Fla.) Tribune, 1992—; critic Sta. WMAQ, Chgo., 1988-91; tchr. Columbia Coll., Chgo., 1988-90. Pres. Hillsborough County (Fla.) Suicide and Crisis Ctr., Tampa, 1979-80. Recipient 1st place in commentary Fla. chpt. Sigma Delta Chi, 1980, Peter Lisagor award Chgo. chpt., 1985. Roman Catholic. Home: 10706 N Rome Tampa FL 33612

RUTH, JAMES PERRY, financial planning executive; b. Washington, Feb. 27, 1946; s. Robert Walker and Virginia Null Ruth; m. Kathleen McHugh, Aug. 10, 1968; children: Heather Lynn, Michael James. BS in Bus. and Public Adminstrn., U. Md., 1970; postgrad. Am. Coll., Bryn Mawr, Pa., 1971-83; CLU, CFP, chartered fin. cons. agt., Northwestern Mutual Life Ins. Co., Washington, 1967-74; gen. agt. Indpls. Life, Rockville, Md., 1974-82; partner Fox, Ruth & Middledorf, Rockville, 1975-82; mgr. Mfrs. Fin. Svcs., Rosslyn, Va., 1982-84; pres. Potomac Fin. Group, 1984—. Past pres. Jelleff Boys' Club; past pres. Montgomery County Police Boys' and Girls' Club; bd. dirs. Boys' Clubs Greater Washington. Named Outstanding Young Man Am., U.S. Jaycees, 1979. Mem. Nat. Assn. Life Underwriters, Nat. Assn. Securities Dealers, Suburban Md. Life Underwriters assn. (past pres.; H.L. Meyer Meml. award 1980), Internat. Assn. Fin. Planning, Suburban Md. Estate Planning Coun. (past pres.), Million Dollar Round Table, Md. State Life Underwriters Assn. (pres. 1995—). Lutheran. Contbr. articles to profl. publs; quoted in N.Y. Times, U.S. News and World Report, USA Today, others. Home: 7920 Warfield Rd Gaithersburg MD 20882-4409 Office: Ste 420 18310 Montgomery Village Ave Gaithersburg MD 20879

RUTH, MARTHA CRUZ, senator; b. Agana, Guam, July 19, 1948; d. Augusto Pangelinan and Dolores Leon Guerrero (Sablan) Cruz; m. H. Mark Ruth, Oct. 11, 1969. Bus. editor Pacific Daily News, Agana, 1970-76; assoc. news dir. KUAM AM-FM-TV, Agana, 1977; info. officer speaker Guam Legislature, Agana, 1978-79; sales/mktg. mgr. South Pacific Island Airways, Agana, 1980-84; mktg. cons. Air France, Agana, 1985—; senator 21st Guam Legislature, Agana, 1986—; minority whip 21st Legislature, Agana, 1991—; mem. gov.'s debt adv. coun. Govt. of Guam, Agana 1986-87; mem. com. on ethics and standards 20th Legislature, Agana, 1989-90; mem. territorial planning coun. Govt. Guam, Agana, 1990—. Mem. Guam Meml. Hosp. Vols. Assn., Agana, 1986—; del. Rep. Party Nat. Conv., New Orleans, 1987, Houston, 1992. Mem. SKAL Club. Roman Catholic. Office: 21st Guam Legislature 155 Hessler Pl Agana GU 96910-5004

RUTH, THOMAS GRISWOLD, history educator; b. Benton Harbor, Mich., Nov. 7, 1940; s. John Griswold and Ruth Margery (Hopkins) R. BA, U. Mich., 1963; MA, U. Tex., 1968. Instr. Am.-Nicaraguan Sch., Managua, 1965-67; instr. history (Ind. Found. Teaching Endowment) The Hill Sch., Pottstown, Pa., 1968—. Mem. Assn. Am. Historians, Sloan Club (London). Avocations: travel, coin collecting, ancient map collecting. Home and Office: The Hill Sch Pottstown PA 19464

RUTHCHILD, GERALDINE QUIETLAKE, training and development consultant, writer, poet; d. Nathan and Ruth (Feldman) Stein; m. Neil Wolinsky, Dec. 31, 1993. BA summa cum laude, Queens Coll., 1977; MA in Am. Lit., Johns Hopkins U., 1980, PhD in Am. Lit., 1983. Asst. prof. Albion (Mich.) Coll., 1982-84; assoc. Investor Access Corp., N.Y.C., 1984-85; program dir. Exec. Enterprises, Inc., N.Y.C., 1985-86; pres. Ruthchild Assocs., N.Y.C., 1987-90; Exemplar, N.Y.C., 1991—; cons. J.P. Morgan & Co., Inc., Bankers Trust Co., Chase Manhattan Bank N.A., Merill Lynch, Nat. Westminster Bank, U.S.A., Citibank N.A., Robert Morris Assocs., Goldman, Sachs & Co., Dean Witter Reynolds, Inc., also others, 1987—. Contbr. articles, poems to profl. and lit. jours. Vol. handicapped children N.Y. Foundling Hosp., N.Y.C., 1988-90, Fgn. Visitors Desk, Met. Mus. Art, N.Y.C., 1989—. Hopkins fellow Johns Hopkins U., 1979-80, Andrew Mellon Found. fellow, 1980-81, 81-82. Mem. ASTD, Assn. Bank Trainers and Cons., Internat. Soc. Philos. Enquiry, Phi Beta Kappa. Avocations: foreign languages, needlework, house plants. Office: Exemplar 501 E 87th St Fl 12 New York NY 10128-7601

RUTHERFORD, JOHN SHERMAN, III (JOHNNY RUTHERFORD), professional race car driver; b. Coffeyville, Kans., Mar. 12, 1938; s. John Sherman and Mary Henrietta (Brooks) R.; m. Betty Rose Hoyer, July 7, 1963; children: John Sherman, Angela Ann. Student, Tex. Christian U., 1956. Profl. race car driver, 1959-94, ret., 1994, driver super-modified race cars, sprint cars, stock cars, midgets, sports cars, Indy cars, Trans-Am cars and formula 5000; mem. Indy Car Racing Inc.; lectr. in field. Host: TV show The Racers; race commentator TV show, NBC, ESPN, CBS, ABC; appeared in numerous TV commercials; art work included in traveling exhbn. Art and Athletes; TV and radio pub. services messages for Nat. Safety Council, Calif. Hwy. Patrol, U.S. Marines, Muscular Dystrophy Assn., Cystic Fibrosis Assn., Boy Scouts, Camp Fire, Shriner's Hosp., Tex. Soc. to Prevent Blindness, Air N.G. Hon. state chmn. Am. Cancer Soc., Tex., Tarrant County Soc. to Prevent Blindness, Emergency Medicine Found., Ft. Worth Kidney Assn., Ft. Worth Burn Ctr.; lit. chmn. Am. Heart Assn. Named Fort Worth Newsmaker of Yr., 1974; Driver of Yr. Sport Mag., 1976; Driver of Yr. Auto Race Writers and Broadcasters Am., 1974, 80; Corvette Challenge's Sportsman of Yr., 1988; recipient Jim Clark award, 1969, Extra Mile award, 1973, Jim Malloy award, 1974, Eddie Sachs award, 1975, Louie Meyer award, 1992; chosen for Internat. Race of Champions, 1974, 76, 77, 78, 79, 84; chosen Fast Masters, 1993; named Olsonite Driver of Yr., 1980, Motorsports amb., 1993; elected to Tex. Sports Hall of Fame, 1981, Indy 500 Hall of Fame, 1987, Boys Clubs Am.'s Celebrity Hall of Fame, 1987; voted to Ft. Worth Sports Hall of Honor, 1987; Tex. Auto Racing Hall of Fame, 1988. Mem. Fedn. Internat. Automobile, Internat. Motors Sports Assn., Exptl. Aircraft Assn., Warbirds of Am., Confederate Air Force, Internat. Aerobatic Club, League Auto Racing (sec., bd. dirs.), Championship Drivers Assn. (bd. dirs.), Nat. Rifle Assn., Air Force Assn., Air Power Coun., Blue Angels Assn., Ft. Worth Boat Club, Shady Oaks Country Club, Lions. Winner 27 championship car races; winner Indianapolis 500, 1974, 76, 80, second place, 1975; set new world's record for stock cars, Daytona Beach, Fla., 1963; set record at Indpls. 500, 1973; at Mich. Internat. Raceway, 1984; U.S. Auto Club Nat. Sprint Car champion, 1965; Nat. Driving champion USAC and CART, 1980; oldest driver (48) to win a 500 mile Indy Car Race, 1986. *I am a firm believer in the fact that a person can do anything in this world he or she wants to as long as you have desire. People have to set goals, things to achieve. No one ever remembers who finished second. Luck is where preparation meets opportunity.*

RUTHERFORD, PAUL HARDING, physicist; b. Shipley, Yorkshire, Eng., Jan. 22, 1938; came to U.S., 1965, naturalized, 1976; s. Joseph William and Annie (Harding) R.; m. Audrey Jones Irvine, Oct. 31, 1959; children—Andrea Christine, Julia Irvine. B.A., Cambridge (Eng.) U., 1959, M.A., 1963, Ph.D., 1963. Research asso. Princeton (N.J.) U. Plasma Physics Lab., 1962-63, mem. research staff, 1965-68, research physicist, 1968-71, sr. research physicist, 1971—, head theoretical div., 1972-80, dep. asso. dir. for research, 1978-80, asso. dir. research, 1980—; chair tech. adv. com. Internat. Thermonuclear Exptl. Reactor, 1992—; research asso U.K Atomic Energy Authority Culham (Berkshire, Eng.) Lab., 1963-65; lectr. astrophys. scis. Princeton U. Mem. bd. asso. editors: Physics of Fluids, 1973-75; mem. editorial bd.: Nuclear Fusion, 1980—. Recipient E.O. Lawrence award U.S. Dept. Energy, 1983. Fellow Am. Phys. Soc. Home: 192 Bertrand Dr Princeton NJ 08540-2904 Office: Plasma Physics Lab PO Box 451 Princeton NJ 08544-0999

RUTHERFORD, ROBERT BARRY, surgeon; b. Edmonton, Alta., Can., July 29, 1931; s. Robert Lyon and Kathleen Emily (Gunn) R.; m. Beulah Kay Folk, Aug. 20, 1955; children: Robert Scott, Lori Jayne, Holly Anne,

---

Trudy Kaye, Jay Wilson. BA in Biology, Johns Hopkins U., 1952, MD, 1956. Surgeon U. Colo. Health Sci. Ctr., Denver; cons. EndoVascular Techs., Menlo Park, Calif., 1989; mem. adv. bd. Med. Edn. Collaborative, Lakewood, Colo., 1989; bd. dirs. Am. Bd. Surgery. Editor: (texts) Management of Trauma, 1968, 4 edits., Vascular Surgery, 1978, 4 edits.; editor quar. rev. Seminars in Vascular Surgery. Mem. Internat. Soc. for Cardiovascular Surgery (pres. N.Am. chpt.), Phi Beta Kappa, Alpha Omega Alpha. Republican. Unitarian. Avocations: skiing, biking, wind surfing, sailing. Office: U Colo Dept Vascular Surgery 4200 E 9th Ave # C-312 Denver CO 80220-3706

RUTHERFORD, ROBERT L., career military officer. Gen. USAF; formerly vice comdr. in chief Pacific Air Forces, comdr., 1993-94; comdr.-in-chief U.S. Transp. Command, Scott AFB, Ill., 1994—; comdr. Air Mobility Command, Scott AFB, 1994—. Office: USAF Hickam AF Base Honolulu HI 96853-5420

RUTHERFORD, THOMAS TRUXTUN, II, state senator, lawyer; b. Columbus, Ohio, Mar. 3, 1947; s. James William and Elizabeth Whiting (Colby) R.; m. Linda Sue Rogers, Aug. 28, 1965 (div.). 1 child, Jeremy Todd. Mag., U N.Mex., 1970, JD, 1982. Page, reading clk. N.Mex. State Legislature, 1960-65; mem. N.Mex. Atty. Gen. Environ. Adv. Commn., 1972; radio broadcaster Sta. KOB Radio and TV, 1963-72; mem. N.Mex. Senate, Albuquerque, 1972—, majority whip, 1978-88, chmn. rules com., 1988—, chmn. econ. devel. and new tech. interim com., mem. sci. and new tech. oversight com.; pres. Rutherford & Assocs., Albuquerque, 1978-83; pvt. practice, Albuquerque, 1983—; former bd. dirs. Union Savs. Bank, Albuquerque; past chmn. Albuquerque Cable TV adv. bd.; mem. Southwest Regional Energy Council, N.Mex. Gov.'s Commn. on Public Broadcasting; bd. dirs., v.p. Rocky Mountain Corp. for Pub. Broadcasting; mem. Am. Council Young Polit. Leaders, del. mission to Hungary, Austria, Greece, 1983; mem. Fgn. Trade Adv. Com. Bd. Econ. Devel. and Tourism; trade del. to People's Republic of China, 1985. N.Mex. Broadcasting Assn. scholar, 1970. Home: 4719 Marquette Ave NE Albuquerque NM 87108-1267 also: PO Box 1610 Albuquerque NM 87103

RUTHERFORD, WILLIAM DRAKE, investment executive, lawyer; b. Marshalltown, Iowa, Jan. 14, 1939; s. William Donald and Lois Esther (Drake) R.; m. Janice W. Rutherford, Feb. 4, 1965 (div. Mar. 1982); children: Wayne Donald, Melissa Drake; m. Karen Anderegg, Jan. 2, 1994. B.S., U. Oreg., 1961; LL.B., Harvard U., 1964. Bar: Oreg. 1964, U.S. Dist. Ct. Oreg. 1966. Assoc. Maguire, Kester & Cosgrave, Portland, Oreg., 1966-69; house counsel May & Co., Portland, 1969-70, pvt. practice, 1970-71; pvt. practice McMinnville, Oreg., 1971-84; mem. Oreg. Ho. of Reps., Salem, 1977-84; state treas. State of Oreg., Salem, 1984-87; chmn. Oreg. Investment Coun., Salem, 1986-87; exec. v.p.; dir. U.S. and Australia ops. ABD Internat. Mgmt. Corp., N.Y.C., 1987-88, pres., chief exec. officer, bd. dirs., 1988-89; pres., bd. dirs. Societé Gen. Touche Remnant, 1990-93; dir. spl. projects Metallgesellschaft Corp., N.Y.C., 1994—. 1st lt. U.S. Army, 1964-66. Recipient Contbn. to Individual Freedom award ACLU, 1981. Mem. Nat. Assn. State Treas. (exec. v.p. 1985, 86, pres. western region 1985, 86), Nat. Assn. State Auditors, Comptr. and Treas. (exec. com. 1987). Republican. Home: 6978 SW Foxfield Ct Portland OR 97225

RUTHERGLEN, GEORGE A., law educator; b. Portland, Oreg., Sept. 12, 1949; s. John Alfred and Helen Kathleen (Bero) R.; m. Jessica Rosalind Feldman, Apr. 25, 1975; children: Susannah Kathleen, Michael Francis. AB, U. Calif., 1971, JD, 1974. Bar: Va. 1979, U.S. Dist. Ct. (we. dist.) Va. 1980, U.S. Ct. Appeals (4th cir.) 1980, U.S. Supreme Ct. 1988. Law clk. to judge J. Clifford San Diego, 1974-75; law clk. to justices William O. Douglas, John Paul Stevens Washington, 1975-76; prof. law U. Va., Charlottesville, 1976—; supervising atty. Post-Conviction Assistance Project, 1980—; cons. standing com. on fed. jud. improvements ABA, Chgo., 1988-89. Author: Major Issues in the 1983 Federal Law of Employment Discrimination, 1988. Mem., chair adv. com. 4th Cir. Rules, Richmond, Va., 1988—. Mem. Order of Coif, Phi Beta Kappa. Democrat. Home: 1698 Rugby Ave Charlottesville VA 22903-5141 Office: U Va Sch Law 580 Massie Rd Charlottesville VA 22903-1738

RUTHVEN, DOUGLAS MORRIS, chemical engineering educator; b. Ernakulam, India, Oct. 9, 1938; arrived in Can., 1966; s. Joseph Morris and Beryl (Mackay) R.; m. Patricia Evelyn Goodwin, July 20, 1968; 1 child, Fiona Beryl. BA, U. Cambridge, Eng., 1960, MA, 1963, PhD, 1966, ScD, 1988. Design engr. Davy Power Gas Corp., Stockton-on-Tees, Eng., 1961-63; asst. prof. dept. chem. engring. U. N.B., Fredericton, Can., 1966-72, assoc. prof., 1973-74, prof., 1975—. Author: Principles of Adsorption and Adsorption Processes, 1984; co-author: Diffusion in Zeolites, 1991, Pressure Swing Adsorption, 1993; contbr. numerous articles to profl. jours. Recipient Max Planck rsch. prize, 1993. Fellow Royal Soc. Can.; mem. Am. Inst. Chem. Engrs. Avocation: Scottish country dancing. Home: RR # 1, Mouth of Keswick, NB Canada E0H 1N0 Office: Univ NB Dept Chem Engring, PO Box 4400, Fredericton, NB Canada E3B 5A3

RUTIGLIANO, LOUIS J., telecommunications industry executive; b. 1938. BSEE, Marquette U., 1960, MSEE, 1965. With Wis. Bell, 1965—; with Ameritech Corp., exec. v.p. corp. strategy, 1989, now vice chmn. bd. Office: Ameritech Corp 30 S Wacker Dr Chicago IL 60606-7402*

RUTKIN, SEYMOUR, architect; b. Weehawken, N.J., Oct. 22, 1927; s. Herman Irving and Dora (Oltarsh) R. B.S. in Architecture, Ill. Inst. Tech., 1949; certificate arts and architecture, Cooper Union. Apprentice with R.M. Schindler (architect), L.A. Contbr. articles to profl. jours.; one-man show projected designs, Peter Cooper Gallery, N.Y.C., 1957; presented new shell designs and theories, World Conf., San Francisco, 1962, Internat. Congress IASS, Mexico City, 1967, Internat. Colloquim, Madrid, 1969; group juried art show, East Islip (N.Y.) Arts Council, 1984, exhibited, 1985-90 (honorable mention water colors); two-person architecture show of new designs, Storefront for Art and Architecture Gallery, N.Y.C., 1985; prin. works include schs., hotels, 42 story office bldg., hosp., shell bldg. design, dormitories, residential, and interiors; patentee in field. Schweinburg scholar Cooper Union; recipient Art in Architecture New Talent USA award, 1959. Address: 445 E 65th St New York NY 10021

RUTKOFF, ALAN STUART, lawyer; b. Chgo., May 31, 1952; s. Roy and Harriet (Ruskin) R.; m. Mally Zolterman, Dec. 22, 1974; children: Aaron Samuel, Jordana Michal, Robert Nathaniel. BA with high distinction, U. Mich., 1973; JD magna cum laude, Northwestern U., 1976. Bar: Ill. 1976, U.S. Dist. Ct. (no. dist.) Ill. 1976, U.S. Ct. Appeals (7th cir.) 1977, U.S. Ct. Appeals (3d cir.) 1978, U.S. Supreme Ct. 1981, U.S. Ct. Appeals (5th cir.) 1983, U.S. Ct. Appeals (8th cir.) 1990. Assoc. Altheimer & Gray, Chgo., 1976-80; ptnr. Kastel & Rutkoff, Chgo., 1980-83, Holleb & Coff Ltd., Chgo., 1983-84, McDermott, Will & Emery, Chgo., 1984—. Mem. ABA, Chgo. Bar Assn., Order of Coif. Home: 801 Timberhill Rd Highland Park IL 60035-5148 Office: McDermott Will & Emery 227 W Monroe St Chicago IL 60606-5016

RUTKOWSKI, JAMES ANTHONY, state legislator; b. Milw., Apr. 6, 1942. BS in Bus., Marquette U., 1964, JD, 1966. Instr. Marquette U., Milw.; asst. instr. U. Wis., Milw.; state legis. State of Wis., Madison, 1970. With USAR, 1966-72. Recipient Clean 16 award, 1982, 88, 90, 94, Wis. Man of Achievement award, 1976. Mem. KC, Greendale Jaycee Roosters. Home: 4550 S 117th St Greenfield WI 53228-2451 Office: State Capitol 216 North PO Box 8953 Madison WI 53708

RUTLAND, GEORGE PATRICK, banker; b. Tifton, Ga., Sept. 4, 1932; s. George Patrick Sr. and Peggy (Roberts) R.; m. Dawn Mary O'Neill, Jan. 2, 1954; children: Michael, Kathleen, Dawn Kelly, Mary Linderman. BBA, Pace Coll. N.Y., 1961; postgrad. Rutgers U., 1962-64. With Citicorp, N.Y.C., 1954-75; sr. v.p. corp. svcs. Citicorp, 1970-73; exec. v.p. Citicorp (Advance Mortgage subs), 1973-75; exec. v.p., cashier Crocker Nat. Bank, San Francisco, 1975-81, sr. exec. v.p. ops, 1981-82; exec. v.p. Calif. Fed. Savs. and Loan Assn., L.A., 1982-83, pres., chief exec. officer, 1983-84, vice chmn., 1984-88; pres., chief exec. officer CalFed Inc., L.A., 1985-88, also bd. dirs.; chmn., pres., chief exec. officer N.E. Savs., Hartford, 1988—, also bd. dirs. Trustee Pace U. With USN, 1950-53. Mem. Town Hall of Calif., The

---

Hartford Club, Golf Club of Avon, (Conn.), St. James (London.). Republican. Roman Catholic. Home: 83 Stagecoach Rd Avon CT 06001-4038

RUTLEDGE, BRIAN AARON, zoo director; b. Greenville, S.C., Oct. 7, 1951; s. Aaron Leslie and Stella Star (Woodard) R.; married; children: Laura, Gregory, Caleb, Aaron. B.A., Oakland U., 1973. Youth sepcialst W.J. Maxey Boy's Tng., State of Mich., 1973-74; social worker Dept. Social Services, State Mich., 1974-77; ind. farmer Pickford, Mich., 1977-79; edn. coordinator Okla. City Zoo, Oklahoma City, 1980-81; dir. Balt. Zoo, 1981—. Named Student of Distinction Oakland U., 1973. Fellow Am. Assn. Zool. Parks and Aquariums. Home: 15705 Woodbine Morgan Rd Woodbine MD 21797-8711 Office: Balt Zoo Druid Hill Park Baltimore MD 21217-4599

RUTLEDGE, CHARLES OZWIN, pharmacology educator; b. Topeka, Oct. 1, 1937; s. Charles Ozwin and Alta (Seaman) R.; m. Jane Ellen Crow, Aug. 13, 1961; children: David Ozwin, Susan Harriett, Elizabeth Jane, Karen Ann. BS in Pharmacy, U. Kans., 1959, MS in Pharmacology, 1961; PhD in Pharmacology, Harvard U., 1966. NATO postdoctoral fellow Gothenborg U., Sweden, 1966-67; asst. prof. U. Colo. Med. Ctr., Denver, 1967-74, assoc. prof., 1974-75; prof., chmn. dept. pharmacology U. Kans., Lawrence, 1975-87; dean, prof. pharmacology Purdue U., West Lafayette, Ind., 1987—; mem. rev. com. NIGMS, Bethesda, Md., 1992—. Contbr. articles on neuropharmacology to profl. jours. Grantee: NIH, 1970, Kans. Heart Assn., 1978. Mem. Am. Soc. Pharmacology and Exptl. Therapeutics (councillor 1982-84, sec.-treas. 1990-93), Am. Assn. Coll. Pharmacy (chmn. biol. scis. sect. 1983-84, chmn. council of faculties 1986-87, chmn. coun. deans, 1993-94, commn. implement change pharm. edn. 1989-92), Soc. for Neurosci., Am. Pharm. Assn. AAAS. Avocations: gardening; skiing. Home: 40 Brynteg Est West Lafayette IN 47906-5643 Office: Purdue U Office of Dean Sch Pharmacy 1330 R Heine Pharm Bldg West Lafayette IN 47907-1330

RUTLEDGE, ELLIOTT MOYE, soil scientist, educator; b. Gallatin, Tenn., Mar. 26, 1935; s. Elliott Moye and Emma Sugg (McKoin) R.; m. Barbara Bolton Green, Sept. 14, 1957; children: Malinda Sugg Rutledge Kirchner, Elliott Moye III. BS, Tenn. Tech., 1958; MS, U. Ark., 1963; PhD, Ohio State U., 1969. Soil sci.-trainee Soil Conservation Svc., Summerville, Tenn., 1957, Cookville, Tenn., 1958; rsch. asst. U. Ark., Fayetteville, 1958-62, asst. prof. agronomy, 1968-73, assoc. prof., 1973-77, prof., 1977—; asst. agronomy Ohio State U., Columbus, 1962-68. Tour leader Friends of Pleistocene, 1990. Fellow Am. Soc. Agronomy (bd. dirs. 1992-95), Soil Sci. Am. (divsn. chmn. 1984-85, bd. dirs. 1992-95); mem. Soil and Water Conservation Soc., Internat. Soil Sci. Soc., Ark. Soc. Profl. Soil Classifiers, Rotary. Democrat. Presbyterian. Avocations: travel, history, riding, current events. Home: 1507 Rolling Hills Dr Fayetteville AR 72703-3625 Office: U Ark at Fayetteville Agronomy Dept Plant Sci 115 Fayetteville AR 72701

RUTLEDGE, IVAN CATE, retired legal educator, arbitrator; b. White Pine, Tenn., Dec. 24, 1915; s. Wiley Blount and Tamsey (Cate) R.; children: Ann, Thomas Carroll. BA, Carson-Newman Coll., 1934; MA, Duke U., 1940, LLB, 1946; LLM, Columbia U., 1952. Bar: Ga. 1946, Wash. 1951, Ohio 1966. asst. prof. law Mercer U., Macon, Ga., 1946-47; from asst. prof. to prof. law U. Wash., Seattle, 1947-54; prof. law Ind. U., Bloomington, 1954-63; prof. law Ohio State U., Columbus, 1963-79, dean, 1965-70; Walter F. George prof. law Mercer U., Macon, 1979—, prof. emeritus, 1986—. Home: 3188 Vista Cir Macon GA 31204-1960

RUTLEDGE, JACKIE JOE, genetics educator; b. Woodward, Okla., Dec. 20, 1941; s. Thomas Henry and Tena Bertha (Croisant) R.; m. Mary Lorraine Leibfried, Aug. 8, 1984. BS, Okla. State U., 1968; MS, N.C. State U., 1970, PhD, 1972. Prof. genetics, prof. and chmn. meat and animal sci. U. Wis., Madison, 1975—. Office: U Wis Dept Meat Animal Sci 1675 Observatory Dr Madison WI 53706-1284

RUTLEDGE, JOHN WILLIAM, former watch company executive; b. Eureka, Calif., Mar. 12, 1923; s. William Eugene and Ellen Agnes (Jordan) R.; m. Mary Jo McKinley, Nov. 23, 1951; children: Ellen, John William, Amy. B.S., Northwestern U., 1943; M.B.A., Harvard U., 1947; MA. in Archaeology, Yale U., 1985. Tchr. Charlestown State Penitentiary, Boston, 1946-47; salesman Lahey Fargo & Co., 1947-48; asst. controller Lehigh Coal & Navigation Co., 1948-54; sr. v.p., dir. Xerox Corp., Stamford, Conn., 1954-71; sr. v.p. home furnishings group, dir. Magnavox Co., N.Y.C., 1971-73; pres., dir. Bulova Watch Co., N.Y.C., 1973-79; dir. Nat. Telecommunications and Controls, Nat. Aviation & Tech. Corp., Orion Capital Corp. Served to lt. USNR. Mem. Sigma Alpha Epsilon. Clubs: Harvard (N.Y.C.), N.Y. Athletic (N.Y.C.). Home: 127 Dunning Rd New Canaan CT 06840-4011 also: 893 S County Rd Palm Beach FL 33480

RUTLEDGE, KENNETH DEAN, food company executive; b. Fayette, Ala., Nov. 29, 1946; s. Murray Frederick and Lula Vaudine (Sawyer) R.; m. Brenda Catherine Lanman, July 19, 1969; children: Scott Christopher, John Andrew. BS, Ind. State U., 1969. Elem. tchr. Franklin (Ind.) Sch. Corp., 1969-70; middle sch. tchr. No. Harrison Schs., Ramsey, Ind., 1970-73; procurement mgr. Swift and Co., Jasper, Ind., 1973-76; adminstrv. asst. Swift and Co., Chgo., 1976-77; asst. mgr. Swift and Co., Jasper, Ind., 1977-78; comlpex mgr. Swift and Co., Jasper, 1978-80; prodn., procurement mgr. Swift and Co., Chgo., 1980-82; complex mgr. Marshall, Minn., 1982-83; dir. proc. and processing Chgo., 1983; dir. ops. Norbest, Inc., Salt Lake City, 1983-86, exec. v.p., 1986-87, pres., gen. mgr., 1988—; mem. sec. of agriculture's USDA Com. on Meat and Poultry Inspection; bd. dirs., exec. com. Nat. Turkey Fedn., Reston, Va., 1984-88; bd. dirs. Pacific Egg and Poultry Assn., Modesto, Calif., 1985-88. Republican. Methodist. Avocations: tennis, golf, boating. Office: Norbest Inc 6925 Union Park Ctr Midvale UT 84047-4142

RUTLEDGE, PAUL E., III, insurance company executive; b. 1953. Grad., Duke U. With Torch Cos., Birmingham, Ala., 1975-91, pres., COO, 1991—; pres. Life Ins. Co. of Va., Richmond. Office: Life Ins Co of Va 6610 W Broad Sr Richmond VA 23230-1702

RUTLEDGE, WILLIAM P., manufacturing company executive; b. 1942. BS, Lafayette Coll., 1963; MS, George Washington U., 1967. With Bethlehem Steel Corp., 1963-68, foreman; with Stamco Sales Co., 1968-71, sales engr.; successively bus. planner, works mgr., dir. planning, div. mgr. FMC Corp., 1971-86; with Teledyne Inc., 1986—, group exec., v.p. 1987-88, sr. v.p. 1988-90, pres., 1990-91, pres., CEO, 1991—, now also chmn., bd. dirs. Office: Teledyne Inc 1901 Avenue Of The Stars Los Angeles CA 90067*

RUTMAN, MARK CHARLES, public relations executive; b. N.Y.C., Sept. 3, 1930; s. Nathan and Sarah Barbara (Korman) R.; m. Geraldine N. Leitner, Jan. 31, 1954; children: Lee, Lisa, Neil. B.A., NYU, 1952; M.S. in Journalism, Columbia U., 1953. Account exec., then v.p., gen. mgr. Affiliated Public Relations Agy., N.Y.C., 1956-60; pres., owner Nat. Public Relations Counsel, N.Y.C., 1960-78; exec. v.p. Grey & Davis Inc., N.Y.C., 1978; pres. Grey & Davis Inc., 1979-84; chmn. Grey Com Inc., 1984-85; sr. assoc. Fred Rosen Assocs., Inc., 1985-90; mng. dir. LH&H Pub. Rels., N.Y.C., 1990—. Served with Ordnance Corps AUS, 1953-55. Recipient Freedoms Found. medal, 1955. Jewish. Club: Overseas Press (N.Y.C.). Home: 9 Crossway Scarsdale NY 10583-7136 Office: 866 Third Ave New York NY 10022

RUTMAN, ROBERT JESSE, biochemist, educator; b. Kingston, N.Y., June 23, 1919; s. Leon and Anne (Porringer) R.; B.S., Pa. State U., 1940; postgrad. U. Idaho, 1942, U. Calif., Berkeley, Ph.D., 1950; M.S., U. Pa., 1975; m. Geraldine Burwell, Jan. 1971; children—Rose, Randy, Steven, Brian, David, Ellen. Mem. teaching rsch. staffs Jefferson U., Phila., 1950-53; rsch. assoc. chemistry dept. U. Pa., 1954-60, assoc. prof., 1961-68, prof. biochemistry and molecular biology Sch. Vet. Medicine, 1968-87, prof. emeritus, 1987—; chmn. dept. biochemistry, 1976-80; vis. prof. U. Ibadan (Nigeria); coord. U. Pa.-U. Ibadan Exch. Agreement; expert witness on carcinogenesis; cons. on environ. contamination. Mem. nat. steering com. Am. Found. Negro Affairs, also co-chmn. sci. and tech. div.; pres. C.W. Henry Home and Sch. Assn., 1960; pres. Phila. Citizens Com. on Pub. Edn., 1963; campaign fin. mgr. Mayoralty Campaign, Phila., 1978; bd. dirs. S.E. Pa. region Leukemia Soc., Southeastern Pa. Anti-Drug Symposium; chmn. bd.

Ile-Ife Ctr. for Humanities, Parkside Human Svcs., Inc. (corp. sec.); v.p. Phila. region Martin Luther King Jr. Ctr., Pa. State Commn. Martin Luther King Celebration, Earth Regeneration Soc. (adv. bd. dirs.), Univ. Conversion Project; chmn. bd. dir. WACI-TV Channel 62, Atlantic City, N.J., bd. dirs. Del. Valley Rain Forest Action Group. Served to capt. C.E., AUS, 1944-48, PTO. USPHS grantee, 1960-82. Mem. AAAS, AAUP, Am. Soc. Biol. Chemistry, Am. Chem. Soc., Am. Assn. Cancer Rsch., Phila. Cancer Club, Vet. Oncology Soc., Am. Assn. Vet. Educators, Phila. Biochemists Club (pres.), U.S. Fedn. Sci. Scholars (exec. bd.), World Fedn. Sci. Workers (exec. com.). Office: 3900 Ford Rd Apt PH-P Philadelphia PA 19131

RUTSALA, VERN A., poet, English language educator, writer; b. Feb. 5, 1934; s. Ray Edwin and Virginia Mae (Brady) R.; m. Joan Merle Colby, Apr. 6, 1957; children: Matthew, David, Kirsten. BA, Reed Coll., 1956; MFA, U. Iowa, 1960. Instr. Lewis and Clark Coll., Portland, 1961-64, asst. prof., 1964-69, assoc. prof., 1969-76, prof., 1976—; vis. prof. U. Minn., Mpls., 1968-69, Bowling Green (Ohio) State U., 1970; writer-in-residence U. Idaho, Moscow, 1988, Redlands (Calif.) U., 1979; chair English dept. Lewis and Clark, Portland, 1986-89. Author: The Window, 1964, Laments, 1975, The Journey Begins, 1976, Paragraphs, 1978, Walking Home from the Icehouse, 1981, Backtracking, 1985, Ruined Cities, 1987, Selected Poems, 1991, Little-Known Sports, 1994. With U.S. Army, 1956-58. GUggenheim Found. fellow, 1982-83, NEA fellow, 1975, 79, Masters fellow Oreg. Arts Commn., 1990; recipient Carolyn Kizer prize Western Oreg. State Coll., 1988, N.W. Poets prize N.W. Rev., 1975, Hazel Hall award Oreg. Inst. Lit. Arts, 1992, Juniper prize U. Mass. Press, 1993, Duncan Lawrie prize Arvon Found., 1994. Mem. AAUP, AWP, PEN, Poetry Soc. Am. Avocations: drawing, painting, watching the ocean, sports. Office: Lewis and Clark Coll Dept English Portland OR 97212

RUTSTEIN, STANLEY HAROLD, apparel retailing company executive; b. Wilkes-Barre, Pa., July 1, 1941; s. Sydney D. and Bessie H. (Cohen) R.; m. Jo Ella Rutstein; children—Wendy Sue, Michael Scott, Lynne Elizabeth. Student, Wilkes Coll., 1959-61; grad., Advanced Mgmt. Program, Harvard U., 1975. Buyer Barbara Lynn Stores, Inc., N.Y.C., 1961-63; buyer, then mdsg. mgr. Casual Corner div. U.S. Shoe Corp., Enfield, Conn., 1963-71; pres. Casual Corner div. U.S. Shoe Corp., 1971-76; pres., cons., dir. U.S. Shoe Corp., Cin., 1976-79; pres. Commonwealth Trading, Inc., Stoughton, Mass., 1979-85, Chadwick's of Boston Ltd., 1983-85; cons. Commonwealth Trading, Inc., 1985—; pres. Trim Trends, Inc., Boston, 1986-87, chmn., 1987-91; chmn., chief exec. officer, pres. Narragansett Clothing Co., Tiverton, R.I., 1987-90, also bd. dirs.; bd. dirs. Reynolds Bros. Inc., 1989-95; pres., chief exec. officer S/J Designs Inc.; 1989—; pres., chief exec. officer DBA, Northeast Knitters; bd. dirs. The Icing, Inc., Sycamore Shops, Inc. Bd. dirs. Ptnrs. for Disabled Youth, 1992. Mem. Young Pres. Orgn. Home: 18 Charles River Sq Boston MA 02114-3266 Office: 560 Harrison Ave Boston MA 02118-2436

RUTTAN, VERNON WESLEY, agricultural economist; b. Alden, Mich., Aug. 16, 1924; s. Ward W. and Marjorie Ann (Chaney) R.; m. Marilyn M. Barone, July 30, 1945; children: Lia Marie, Christopher, Alison Elaine, Lore Megan. BA, Yale U., 1948; MA, U. Chgo., 1950, PhD, 1952; LLD (hon.), Rutgers U., 1978; D Agrl. Sci. (hon.), U. Kiel, Germany, 1986, Purdue U., 1991. Economist TVA, 1951-54; prof. agrl. econs. Purdue U., 1954-63; staff economist President's Council Econ. Advisers, 1961-63; economist Rockefeller Found., 1963-65; head dept. agrl. econs. U. Minn., St. Paul, 1965-70, Regent's prof., 1986—; pres. Agrl. Devel. Council, N.Y.C., 1973-77. Author: (with Y. Hayami) Agricultural Development: An International Perspective, 1971, 85, Agricultural Research Policy, 1982, Aid and Development, 1989, Agriculture, Environment and Health, 1994, U.S. Devel. Alliance Policy, 1995. Recipient Alexander von Humboldt award, 1985. Fellow AAAS, Am. Acad. Arts and Scis.; mem. Agrl. Econs. Assn. (pres. 1971-72, Publ. award 1956, 57, 62, 66, 67, 71, 79, 85); mem. NAS. Home: 2381 Commonwealth Ave Saint Paul MN 55108-1605 Office: U Minn Saint Paul MN 55108

RUTTENBERG, CHARLES BYRON, lawyer; b. Reading, Pa., Nov. 16, 1922; s. Abraham David and Mollie Belle (Rabinowitz) R.; m. Arden Honore Suk, July 29, 1955; children—Victoria Arden, Valerie Honore, Alexandra Anne. B.A., U. Va., 1946; LL.B., U. Pa., 1949. Bar: D.C. With Covington & Burling, Washington, 1949-69; gen. counsel NSF, Washington, Nat. Found. Arts and Humanities, Washington, 1949-69; ptnr. Arent, Fox, Kintner, Plotkin & Kahn, Washington, 1969—; chmn. Legis. Bur., mem. exec. com., bd. dirs., gen. counsel Greater Washington Bd. of Trade, 1983-92. Co-chmn. U. Pa. Law Sch. Alumni Fund, Washington, 1983-91, chmn. lawyers com. D.C. Commn. on Arts, 1972-75; gen. counsel People to People Music Program, Washington, 1970-91; trustee, gen. counsel Wolf Trap Found. Performing Arts, Vienna, Va., 1981-91, Nat. Inst. Music Theatre, Washington, 1969-90; bd. dirs. Washington Area Lawyers for Arts, 1984-95, Greater Washington Rsch. Ctr., Washington, 1980-95. With USAAF, 1942-46, capt. USAFR, 1946-55. Recipient Outstanding Service awards U.S. Govt., 1967, 68. Mem. ABA, U. Pa. Law Alumni Assn. (pres. 1967-71, bd. dirs. 1967-78), Arts Internat. (gen. counsel), Phi Beta Kappa. Clubs: Cosmos, St. Alban's, Mitchell Lane, Washington Athletic (bd. govs. 1969-74). Home: 4735 Butterworth Pl NW Washington DC 20016-4459 Office: Arent Fox Kintner Plotkin & Kahn 1050 Connecticut Ave NW Washington DC 20036-5303

RUTTENBERG, HAROLD JOSEPH, manufacturing executive; b. St. Paul, May 22, 1914; s. Charles H. and Fannie R. (Weinstein) R.; m. Katherine Monori, Sept. 23, 1936; children: Charles L. (dec.), James E., Edward F., Ellen Ruttenberg Rabin. B.A., U. Pitts., 1935. Research dir. United Steelworkers Am., 1936-46; asst. dir. steel div. WPB, 1942-44; exec. v.p. Portsmouth Steel Co., Ohio, 1946-49; pres. Harkit Corp., Pitts., 1949-51; pres., chmn. bd. Stardrill-Keystone Co., Beaver Falls, Pa., 1951-59; mng. dir. Humanation Assos., Pitts., 1959-64; chmn. bd. dirs. United Steel & Wire Co., Battle Creek, Mich., 1964-68; chmn. Rehovoth Instruments Co., Israel, 1968-78; chmn. bd., pres. AVM Corp. (name changed to Am. Locker Group Inc. 1985), Pitts., from 1973, now chmn. bd., chief exec. officer, treas.; chmn., treas. Rollform of Jamestown (N.Y.), Inc. Author: (with C.S. Golden) Dynamics of Industrial Democracy, 1942, Self-Developing America, 1960. Democrat. Jewish. Home: 307 S Dithridge St Apt 814 Pittsburgh PA 15213-3519 Office: 300 S Craig St Pittsburgh PA 15213-3707

RUTTENBERG, STANLEY HARVEY, economist; b. St. Paul, Mar. 19, 1917; s. Charles and Fannie (Weinstein) R.; m. Gertrude Bernstein, Nov. 28, 1940; children: Joel, Ruth, Charles. Student, Massanutten Mil. Acad., Woodstock, Va., 1929-33; B.S., U. Pitts., 1937. Asst. to dir. Hull House, Chgo., 1938-39; with CIO, 1937-55; organizer and field rep. in Ohio Valley CIO, Cin., 1937-38; assoc. dir. research CIO, Washington, 1939-48; dir. dept. edn. and research CIO, 1948-55; dir. dept. research AFL-CIO, 1955-62; spl. asst. to sec. of labor, 1963-65, manpower administr., 1965-69, asst. sec. labor, manpower administr., 1966-69; pres. Stanley H. Ruttenberg Assos. Inc., 1969-82; chmn. bd. RFK & A, Inc., 1982—; bd. dirs. Nat. Planning Assn.; dir. Nat. Bur. Econ. Res., 1940-41, 48-62; exec. com. Nat. Planning Assn. UNESCO, 1948-53, vice chmn., 1952; spl. adviser to (Am. del. 4th and 5th Internat. Confs.), 1949, 50; del. to Internat. Labor Orgn. Conf., Geneva, 1952; dir. Resources for the Future, Inc., 1952-79; pub. mem. Fgn. Service Selection Bd., 1950; mem. Presdl. Price Adv. Com., 1979-80. Author: (with Jocelyn Gutchess) Manpower Challenge of the 1970s: Institutions and Social Change, 1970, The Federal-State Employment Service: A Critique, 1970. Served as 1st lt. AUS, 1943-46, PTO. Mem. Am. Econ. Assn., Am. Statis. Assn., Indsl. Relations Research Assn. (exec. bd. 1953). Home: 6310 Maiden Ln Bethesda MD 20817-5610 Office: 1211 Connecticut Ave NW Washington DC 20036-2701

RUTTER, DEBORAH FRANCES, orchestra administrator; b. Pottstown, Pa., Sept. 30, 1956; d. Marshall Anthony and Winifred (Hitz) R. BA, Stanford U., 1978; MBA, U. So. Calif., 1985. Orch. mgr. L.A. Philharm., 1978-86; exec. dir. L.A. Chamber Orch., 1986-92, Seattle Symphony, 1992—. Bd. dirs. AIDS project L.A., 1985-92; active Jr. League L.A. 1982-92. Mem. Am. Symphony Orch. League, Assn. Calif. Symphony Orchs. (pres. 1988-91), Assn. N.W. Symphony Orchs. (bd. dirs. 1993—), Chamber Music Soc. L.A. (bd. dirs. 1987-92), Ojai Festival (pres.'s coun.). Democrat. Episcopalian. Avocations: skiing, tennis, gardening, reading. Office: Seattle Symphony Ctr House 305 Harrison St Fl 4 Seattle WA 98109-4645

RUTTER, FRANCES TOMPSON, publisher; b. Arlington, Mass., Apr. 12, 1920; d. Harold F. and Mildred F. (Wheeler) Tompson; m. John H. Ottemiller, Mar. 24, 1943; children: Joan Tompson, John Tompson; m. William D. Rutter, Oct. 26, 1970. AB magna cum laude, Pembroke Coll., Brown U., 1941; postgrad., Mt. Holyoke Coll., 1942-43. Res. book librarian Brown U. 1941-42; annotator ship's papers John Carter Brown Library, Providence, 1943-44; librarian Sci. Service, Washington, 1944-45; ptnr. Shoe String Press, Hamden, Conn., 1952-58; sec., treas. Shoe String Press, Inc., 1958-68, pres., treas., 1968-80, also bd. dirs.; sec.-treas., dir. Tompson-Malone, Inc. book mfrs., 1967-80; pres., treas., dir. Tompson & Rutter, Inc., 1980-89. Vice pres. class 1941 Pembroke Coll., 1967-73, 76—, pres., 1973-76, head class agt., 1979-85, bequests and trust chmn., 1979-90, 40th runion gift com., 1980, cho-chair 50th reunion gift com., 1990-91; spl. projects adv. panel N.H. Commn. on Arts, 1980-84; mem. natural resources com. Grantham, 1980; mem. Grantham Planning Bd., 1981-87, sec., 1981-83, chmn., 1985-87; chmn. Grantham Recycling Com., 1988-89, Grantham Hist. Soc., 1992—, Habitat for Humanity-Kearsarge/Sunapee chpt., 1989-94; mem. Diocesan Altar Guild Bd., 1990-93, sec., 1991-92; vol. Mary Hitchcock Meml. Hosp. Aux., 1991—. Mem. Friends of Fernald Libr. of Colby-Sawyer Coll., ACLU (life), LWV (editor newsletter 1987-89), Assoc. Alumni Brown U. (bd. dirs. 1981-83), Nicholas Brown Soc., Pembroke Ctr. Assocs. (coun. 1984-86), Soc. for Preservation N.H. Forests, Episcopal Peace Fellowship, River City Arts Club, Assocs. of Holy Cross, Phi Beta Kappa. Episcopalian. Home: 19 The Gardens White River Junction VT 05001-3344

RUTTER, JEREMY BENTHAM, archaeologist, educator; b. Boston, Mass., June 23, 1946; s. Peter and Nancy Kendall (Comstock) R.; m. Sarah Robbins Henderson, Jan. 31, 1970; children: Benjamin Ryerson, Nicholas Kendall. BA Classics with honors, Haverford Coll., 1967; PhD Classical Archaeology, U. Pa., 1974; MA, Dartmouth Coll., 1993. Vis. asst. prof. dept. classics U. Calif., L.A., 1975-76, from asst. prof. to prof. dept. classics, 1976—, also chmn. dept. classics, 1992—; participant excavations West Germany, 1966, Italy, 1968-69, Greece, 1972, 73-74, 75, 77, 78, 80-81, 84-86, 88-89, 91—. Publ. com. Am. Sch. Classical Studies at Athens; contbr. numerous articles, reviews to profl. jours. With U.S. Army, 1969-71, vietnam. Woodrow Wilson fellow, 1967-68; NDEA fellow U. Pa., 1968-69, 71-73; Olivia James Traveling fellow Archeol. Inst. Am., 1974-75; NEH rsch. grantee, 1979-81; travel grantee Am. Coun. Learned Socs., 1982; sr. faculty grantee, 1985-86, 91-92. Mem. Archaeol. Inst. Am. (numerous coms.), Classical Assn. New England, Phi Beta Kappa. Home: 47 Eagle Ridge Dr Lebanon NH 03766-1900 Office: Dept Classics Dartmouth College Hanover NH 03755

RUTTER, NATHANIEL WESTLUND, geologist, educator; b. Omaha, Nov. 22, 1932; s. John Elliot and Karleen (Ludden) R.; m. Mary Marie Munson, Sept. 11, 1961; children: Todd, Christopher. B.S., Tufts U., 1955; M.S., U. Alaska, 1962; Ph.D., U. Alta., 1965. Geologist Venezuelan Atlantic Refining Co., 1955-58; research scientist Geol. Survey Can., Calgary, Alta., 1965-74; head urban projects sect Geol. Survey Can., Ottawa, Ont., 1974; environ. advisor Nat. Energy Bd., Ottawa, 1974-75; assoc. prof. dept. geology U. Alta., Edmonton, 1975-77, 77-80, prof., chmn. dept., 1980-89, 77—; mem. Can. nat. com. Internat. Geol. Correlation Program, UNESCO, 1986—; pres. Internat. Union Quaternary Rsch. Congress, 1982-87; mem. Internat. Geosphere-Biosphere Program: A Study of Global Change; mem. rsch. com. Can. Global Change Program, 1992-94; mem. global change com. INUQA, 1991—; hon. prof. Chinese Acad. Sci., Beijing, 1994—; nat. lectr. Sigma Xi, 1995—. Contbr. numerous articles to profl. jours.; assoc. editor Arctic, Geosci. Can. Quaternary Rsch.; mem. editorial bd. Quaternary Sci. Revs.; editor in chief Quaternary Internat. Grantee Natural Scis. and Engring. Research Council of Can.; grantee Energy, Mines and Resources. Fellow Royal Soc. Can.; mem. Assn. Profl. Engrs., Geologists and Geophysicists of Alta., Internat. Union Quaternary Research (v.p. 1982-87, pres. 1987-91), Can. Quaternary Assn. (v.p. 1981-82), Geol. Soc. Am. (mgmt. bd. dirs. quaternary geol. and geomorphology div. 1982-84). Clubs: Explorer's, Cosmos. Home: Rural Route 3, Stony Plain, AB Canada T7Z 1X3 Office: Dept Geology U Alta, Edmonton, AB Canada T6G 2E3

RUTTER, WILLIAM J., biochemist, educator; b. Malad City, Idaho, Aug. 28, 1928; s. William H. and Cecilia (Dredge) R.; m. Jacqueline Waddoups, Aug. 31, 1951 (div. Nov. 1969); children: William Henry II, Cynthia Susan; m. Virginia Alice Bourke, 1972 (div. 1978). BA, Harvard U., 1949; MA, U. Utah, 1950; PhD, U. Ill., 1952. USPHS postdoctoral fellow U. Wis., Madison, 1952-54, Nobel Inst., Stockholm, 1954-55; from asst. prof. to prof. biochemistry, dept. chemistry U. Ill., 1955-65; prof. biochemistry U. Wash., 1965-69; Hertzstein prof. biochemistry U. Calif., San Francisco, chmn. dept. biochemistry and biophysics, 1969-82, dir. Hormone Research Inst., 1983-89; chmn. bd. dirs. Chiron Corp., 1981—; mem. USPHS Biochemistry and Nutrition Fellowship Panel, 1963-66; cons. physiol. chemistry study sect. NIH, 1967-71; mem. basic sci. adv. exec. com. Nat. Cystic Fibrosis Research Found., 1969-74, chmn., 1972-74, pres.'s adv. council, 1974-75; exec. com. div. biology and agr. NRC, 1969-72; mem. developmental biology panel NSF, 1971-73; mem. biomed. com. Los Alamos Sci. Lab., 1972-75; pres. Pacific Slope Biochem. Conf., 1972-73; mem. bd. sci. counselors Nat. Inst. Environ. Health Scis., 1976—; mem. adv. com. biology div. Oak Ridge Nat. Lab., 1976-80; adv. bd. Oak Ridge Nat. Lab. and Martin-Marietta Energy Systems, 1984-87; basic research adv. com. Nat. Found., 1976—; bd. dirs. Keystone Life Sci. Study Ctr., Meridian Instruments, 1982-88, Hana Biologies, 1980-83; sci. adv. bd. German Ctr. Molecular Biology, U. Heidelberg, 1983—, AMGEN, 1979-81; panel sci. advisors Internat. Ctr. Genetic Engring. and Biotechnology, 1984—; mem. bd. overseers Harvard U., 1992-96, special commn. NSF, 1992, sci. adv. bd. FDA, 1993. Asso. editor: Jour. Exptl. Zoology, 1968-72; editor: PAABS Revista, 1971-76, Jour. Cell Biology, 1976-78, Archives Biochemistry and Biophysics, 1978—, Developmental Genetics, 1979—; editorial bd. various jours. Served with USNR, 1945. Guggenheim fellow, 1962-63. Mem. Am. Soc. Biol. Chemists (treas. 1970-76, mem. editorial bd. jour. 1970-75), Am. Soc. Cell Biology, Am. Chem. Soc. (Pfizer award enzyme chemistry 1967), Am. Soc. Developmental Biology (pres. 1975-76), Nat. Acad. Scis. Home: 111 Telegraph Hill Blvd San Francisco CA 94133 Office: Univ Calif Hormone Rsch Inst San Francisco CA 94143-0534 also: Chiron Corp 4560 Horton St Emeryville CA 94608*

RUTTINGER, GEORGE DAVID, lawyer; b. Detroit, Jan. 17, 1948; s. George Jacob and Margaret Mary (Smith) R.; m. Camille Ann Larson, Oct. 4, 1975; children: Jacob Charles, David Hayes, Philip George. AB with high distinction and honors, U. Mich., 1970, JD magna cum laude, 1973. Bar: Calif. 1975, D.C. 1975, U.S. Dist. Ct. D.C. 1975, U.S. Dist. Ct. Md. 1987, U.S. Ct. Appeals (D.C. and 4th cirs.) 1984, U.S. Ct. Appeals (1st cir.) 1988, U.S. Supreme Ct. 1984. Law clk. to Hon. Malcolm R. Wilkey U.S. Ct. Appeals, Washington, 1973-74; assoc. Latham & Watkins, L.A., 1974; assoc. Crowell & Moring (formerly Jones, Day, Reavis & Pogue), Washington, 1975-79, ptnr., 1980—. Author: (with others) Containing Legal Costs: ADR Strategies for Corporations, Law Firms and Government, 1988; contbr. articles to profl. jours. Office: Crowell & Moring 1001 Pennsylvania Ave NW Washington DC 20004-2505

RUTZ, RICHARD FREDERICK, physicist, researcher; b. Alton, Ill., Feb. 9, 1919; s. Erwin William and Esther Norma (Brooks) R.; m. Mary Lamsom Lambert, June 10, 1945; children—Frederick R., Carl R., William L. BA, Shurtleff Coll., Alton, Ill., 1941; MS, State U. Iowa, 1947. Staff mem. Sandia Corp., Albuquerque, 1948-51; mem. staff, mgr. IBM T.J. Watson Sr. Rsch. Ctr., Yorktown Heights, N.Y., 1951-87. Contbr. articles to profl. jours.; patentee numerous semicond. devices. With U.S. Maritime Svc., 1941-42, USAAF, 1942-46. Fellow IEEE; mem. Am. Phys. Soc. Home: 9 Burgundy Ct Grand Junction CO 81503

RUTZICK, MARK CHARLES, lawyer; b. St. Paul, Sept. 6, 1948; s. Max Arthur and Bertha (Ward) R.; childrenfrom a previous marriage: Elizabeth Leslie, Karen Deborah; m. Cynthia Lombardi Jan. 16, 1994. B.A., U. Mich., 1970; J.D., Harvard U. 1973. Bar: N.Y. 1974, U.S. Supreme Ct. 1977, U.S. Ct. Appeals (9th cir.) 1982, Oreg. 1984, Wash. 1987. Spl. asst. corp. counsel N.Y.C. Housing Administrn. 1973-75; assoc. Alexander Hammond P.C., N.Y.C., 1975-76; asst. atty. gen. N.Y. State Atty. Gen., N.Y.C., 1976-78; atty. Dept. Justice, Washington, 1978-82, spl. litigation counsel, 1982-83, atty.-in-charge field office, Portland, Oreg., 1983-86; counsel Preston, Thorgrimson, Shidler, Gates & Ellis, Portland, 1986-87,

ptnr. 1988-94; shareholder Mark C. Rutzick Law Firm, P.C., 1994—. Mem. ABA, Oreg. State Bar Assn., Wash. State Bar Assn. Home: 3450 SW Downsview Ter Portland OR 97221 Office: 500 Pioneer Tower 888 5th Ave Portland OR 97204-2089

RUUD, CLAYTON OLAF, engineering educator; b. Glassgow, Mont., July 31, 1934; s. Asle and Myrtle (Bleken) R.; children: Kelley Astrid, Kirsten Anne; m. Paula Kay Mannino, Feb. 24, 1990. BS in Metallurgy, Wash. State U., 1957; MS in Matl. Sci., San Jose State U., 1967; PhD in Materials Sci., U. Denver, 1970. Registered profl. engr., Calif., Colo. Asst. remelt metallurgist Kaiser Aluminum & Chem. Corp., Trentwood, Wash., 1957-58; devel. engr. Boeing Airplane Co., Seattle, 1958-60; mfg. rsch. engr. Lockheed Missiles & Space Corp., Sunnyvale, Calif., 1960-63; rsch. engr. FMC Corp., San Jose, 1963-67; sr. rsch. scientist U. Denver, 1967-79; prof. indsl. engring. Pa. State U., University Park, 1979—; cons. in field; bd. dirs. Denver X-Ray Inst. Inc., Altoona, Pa. Editor series of books: Advances in X-Ray Analysis, Vol. 12-22, 1970-80, Nondestructive Character of Materials, Vol. 1-6, 1983—; editl. com. X-Ray Spectrometry, 1975-87; editl. adv. com. Nondestructive Testing and Evaluation, 1991—; contbr. more than 100 sci. papers to profl. jours. Mem., chmn. Nat. Acad. Sci. Safe Drinking Water Com., Washington, 1976-78. Recipient IR 100 award, 1983, Gov.'s New Product Award, Pa. Soc. Profl. Engrs., 1988. Mem. ASM (interna. chmn. Resid. Stress Conf. 1989-91), Internat. Ctr. for Diffraction Data, Soc. Mfg. Engrs., Metall. Soc. of AIME. Achievements include patent on Method for Determining Internal Stresses in Polycrystalline Solids; patent on Stress-Unstressed Standard for X-Ray Stress Analysis; invention of a Fiber Optic Based Position Sensitive Scintillation X-Ray Detector; invention of an instrument for simultaneous stress and phase composition measurement; development of an X-ray diffraction instrument for manufacturing process quality control. Office: Pa State U 207 Hammond Bldg University Park PA 16802

RUUD, MILLARD HARRINGTON, former legal association administrator, retired educator; b. Ostrander, Minn., Jan. 7, 1917; s. Mentor L. and Helma M. (Olson) R.; m. Barbara W. Dailey, Aug. 28, 1943; children: Stephen D., Christopher O., Michael L. B.S. in Law, U. Minn., 1942, LL.B., 1947; LL.D., Georgetown U., 1980, U. Pacific, 1981, New Eng. Sch. Law, 1981, Southwestern U., 1983, Widener U., 1987, John Marshall Law Sch., 1987. Bar: Minn. 1947, Tex. 1956. Asst. prof. law U. Kans., Lawrence, 1947-48; assoc. prof. U. Tex., Austin, 1948-52, prof., 1952-78, 80-83, prof. emeritus, 1983—; asst. exec. dir. Tex. Legis. Council, 1950-52; exec. dir. Assn. Am. Law Schs., Washington, 1973-80, 83-87; mem. Tex. Commn. Uniform State Laws, 1967—; cons. legal edn. Am. Bar Assn., 1968-73; chmn. Law Sch. Admission Council, 1966-69, Council on Legal Edn. Opportunity, 1968. Bd. vis. U. Miami, 1980-94, McGeorge Sch. Law, 1985—. Recipient Disting. Grad. award U. Minn., 1980. Mem. ABA (Robert J. Kutak award for disting. svc. to legal edn. and profession 1988), Tex. Bar Assn., Am. Law Inst., Order of Coif (nat. sec.-treas. 1981-83). Club: Cosmos. Home: 3416 Foothill Ter Austin TX 78731-5836 Office: U Tex Sch Law 727 E 26th St Austin TX 78705-3224

RUVANE, JOHN AUSTIN, pharmaceutical industry consultant; b. Jersey City, N.J., Nov. 27, 1935; s. Joseph Jerome and Anne Agnes (Sullivan) R.; m. Anne Patricia Beebe, Apr. 13, 1957; children: Anne Julie, Kathleen Kearney Vrabel, Molly Vaughn Kamensky, Alice Regan, John Austin, Susan Sullivan D'Avanzo. A.B. in Econs., Princeton U., 1957; postgrad., NYU, 1958-60. Salesman Ayerst Co., N.Y.C., 1960-65; asst. to v.p. McCann-Erickson Co., N.Y.C., 1965-70; pres., chief exec. officer J.R. Druid-Ruvane-Leverte, N.Y.C., 1970-83; chmn., bd. dirs. Bozell & Jacobs Co., N.Y.C., 1983-85; pres. JARCOM Inc., N.Y.C., 1985—; bd. dirs. Pharm. Advt. Coun., N.Y.C., 1974-86, pres., 1983; mem. adv. coun. Health Care Expo, N.Y.C., 1984-88. Contbr. articles to profl. jours., newsletter. mem. fin. coun. St. Rose of Lima Parish Coun., Short Hills, N.J., 1974-76; chmn., interviewer Princeton Schs. & Scholarship Commn., Short Hills; jazz pianist, choral singer Univ. Glee Club N.Y.C.; pres., bd. dirs. Buck Hill Lot and Cottage Assn., Buck Hills Falls, Pa., 1988-94. Recipient numerous advt. awards. Mem. Pharm. Advt. Council (pres. 1983), Med. Advt. Agy. Assn. Republican. Roman Catholic. Clubs: Princeton (N.Y.C.); Canoe Brook Country (committeeman 1980-87, Summit, N.J.), Buck Hill Golf Club. Avocations: music; golf. Home: PO Box 275 64 Hemlock Ln Buck Hill Falls PA 18323 Office: Jarcom Inc 304 Park Ave S New York NY 10010-5312

RUVELSON, ALAN KENNETH, investment company executive; b. St. Paul, Sept. 5, 1915; s. Philip Godfrey and Eva (Lumpkin) R.; m. Ethel Newberg, 1938 (dec. 1965); children—Judith, Alan, Jr., Mary Ellen, Richard; m. Louise Loidolt, Dec. 26, 1966. Student Coll. St. Thomas., St. Paul, 1932-34; B.B.A., U. Minn., 1936. Diamond importer and wholesale jewelry salesman Phil G. Ruvelson Inc., Mpls., 1936-66; pres. First Midwest Corp., Mpls., 1959-86; pres. First Midwest Ventures, Inc. 1986—; dir. Dicomed Corp., Mpls., HEI, Inc., Victoria, Minn. Mem. exec. com. Regional Export Expansion Council, 1964-67; trustee St. Thomas Mil. Acad. Alumni Assn., 1965-68; founding mem. Gov. John Sargent Pillsbury Fellowship, U. Minn., 1966; past mem. Gov.'s Adv. Commn. on Econ. Devel. for State of Minn.; trustee Coll. St. Benedict, St. Joseph, Minn., 1967-71, St. Thomas Acad., 1976-82, Convent of Visitation Sch., 1976-78, St. Catherine's Coll., 1980-83; chmn. adv. council Nat. Small Bus. Investment Co., 1969-70; chmn. lay adv. bd. St. Mary's Hosp., Mpls., 1970-71; mem. exec. com. Lawyers Profl. Responsibility Bd., 1978-81; bd. dirs. Found. Minn. Progress, 1978-79; mem. adv. council Coll. St. Thomas Small Bus. Devel. Ctr., 1979—; mem. all univ. honors com. U. Minn., 1980—; Bus.-Industry Polit. Action Com. Minn., 1980-81. Recipient Hames Meml. Alumni award St. Thomas Acad., 1979, Cross of Merit with Silver Star of Holy Sepulchre Jerusalem, 1983, SBA Silver Anniversary award, 1983; named to Minn. Bus. Hall of Fame, 1980. Mem. Nat. Assn. Small Bus. Investment Cos. (pres. 1961-62), Minn. C. of C. (pres. 1973-74), U. Minn. Alumni Assn. (nat. pres., bd. dirs. 1978-79), Am. Arbitration Assn. (bd. dirs. Minn. chpt. 1975-78, vice chmn. 1981-82), Minn. State Bar Assn. (com. on task force on principles of professionalism 1984-85), Midwest Regional Assn. Small Bus. Investment Cos. (pres. 1964-65). Clubs: Minneapolis, Minn. (St. Paul), Town and Country; U. of Minn. Alumni (Mpls.). Home: 1293 Pinehurst Ave Saint Paul MN 55116-2216 Office: First Midwest Ventures Inc 914 Plymouth Bldg 12 S 6th St Minneapolis MN 55402-1508

RUWART, DAVID PETER, lawyer; b. Balt.; s. William M. and Inez W. (Wilder) R.; m. Susan J. Collins, Oct. 15, 1960; children: Carole, Sharon, Peter, Denise. B.A., Xavier U., Cin., 1954; J.D., U. Detroit, 1956; LL.M. in Taxation, NYU, 1957. Bar: Mich. 1956, U.S. Dist. Ct. (ea. dist.) Mich. 1957. Sole practice, Detroit, 1957-81; prin. in charge bus. law sect. Plunkett & Cooney P.C. and predecessor firms, Detroit, 1982—; mem. faculty U. Detroit Law Sch., 1969-74, Wayne State U., 1966-69, U. Mich., 1964-66. Mem. ABA, Mich. State Bar Assn., Detroit Bar Assn., Fed. Bar Assn., Am. Judicature Soc., Assn. For Corp. Growth (bd. dirs. 1986—, Detroit chpt. pres. 1990-92, intergrowth chmn. 1995), Internat. Assn. Fin. Planners (bd. dirs. 1982-86), Am. Law Firm Assn. (chmn. 1987-89). Roman Catholic. Home: 43 Deming Ln Grosse Pointe MI 48236-3742 Office: Plunkett & Cooney 243 W Congress St Detroit MI 48226

RUWE, ROBERT P., federal judge; b. 1941. Grad., Xavier U., 1963; JD, No. Ky. U., 1970. With Office of chief counsel IRS Dept. Treasury, 1970-87; judge U.S. Tax Ct., Washington, 1987—. Office: US Tax Ct 400 2nd St NW Washington DC 20217

RUXIN, PAUL THEODORE, lawyer; b. Cleve., Apr. 14, 1943; s. Charles and Olyn Judith (Koller) R.; m. Joanne Camy, May 25, 1965; children: Marc J., Sarah. BA, Amherst Coll., 1965; LLB, U. Va., 1968. Bar: Ill. 1968, Ohio 1977, U.S. Dist. Ct. (no. dist.) Ill. 1968, U.S. Ct. Appeals D.C. 1972. Assoc. Isham, Lincoln & Beale, Chgo., 1968-73, ptnr., 1974-77; ptnr., chmn. energy utilities sect. Jones, Day, Reavis & Pogue, Cleve., 1977—. Mem. Hudson Archtl. and Hist. Bd. Rev., 1981-91; exec. bd. Greater Cleve. Boy Scouts Am., 1978-90; bd. dirs. ARC Cleveland Chpt., 1991—. Mem. ABA, Ohio State Bar Assn. (pub. utilities sect.), Bar Assn. Greater Cleve., Fed. Energy Bar Assn. (com. chmn. 1981), Western Res. Hist. Soc. (collections com. Cleve. chpt.), Club at Soc. Ctr., Rowfant Club. Home: 40 Wellgate Dr Hudson OH 44236-3143 Office: Jones Day Reavis & Pogue 901 Lakeside Ave E Cleveland OH 44114-1116

RUYAK, ROBERT FRANCIS, lawyer; b. Columbus, Ohio, July 9, 1949; s. Robert and Rosemarie (Shuster) R.; m. Elizabeth Fletcher Mueller, 1974; children: Robert J., Kathleen E., Eric C., Christopher M. BA in Polit. Sci., Gannon U., 1971; JD, Georgetown U., 1974. Bar: Pa. 1974, D.C. 1976. Law clk. Hon. John J. Sirica U.S. Dist. Ct., Washington, 1974-76; assoc. Howrey & Simon, Washington, 1976-81, ptnr., 1981—; mgmt. com., 1985. Pres., bd. trustees Mater Dei Sch., Bethesda, Md.; bd. dirs. Archdiocesan Legal Network. Mem. ABA. Democrat. Roman Catholic. Clubs: Army Navy (Washington); Congl. Country (Bethesda, Md.), City Club (Washington). Office: Howrey & Simon 1299 Pennsylvania Ave NW Washington DC 20004-2400

RUYTER, NANCY LEE CHALFA, dance educator; b. Phila., May 23, 1933; d. Andrew Benedict Chalfa and Lois Elizabeth (Strode) McClary; m. Ralph Markson (div.); m. Hans C. Ruyter, Dec. 7, 1968. BA in History, U. Calif., Riverside, 1964; PhD in History, Claremont Grad. Sch., 1970. Tchr. theater dept. Pomona Coll., 1965-72; instr. dance program U. Calif., Riverside, 1972-76, acting chair dance program, 1974-75; instr. dance dept. UCLA, 1976; instr. phys. edn. dept. Orange Coast Coll., 1976-77; asst. prof. dept. phys. edn. and dance Tufts U., 1977-78; asst. prof. phys. edn. dept. Calif. State U. Northridge, 1978-82; asst. prof., then assoc. prof. dance dept. U. Calif., Irvine, 1982—, assoc. dean Sch. Fine Arts, 1984-88, chair dept. dance, 1989-91; presenter in field. Appeared with Jasna Planina Folk Ensemble, 1972-77, 78-79, Di Falco and Co., 1955-57; choreographer, dir. numerous coll. dance prodns.; contbr. articles, revs. to profl. publs.; author: Reformers and Visionaries: The Americanization of the Art of Dance, 1979. Mem. Am. Soc. Theatre Rsch., Bulgarian Studies Assn., Congress on Rsch. in Dance (bd. dirs. 1977-80, pres. 1981-85), Folk Dance Fedn., Internat. Fedn. Theatre Rsch., Soc. Dance Rsch., Soc. Ethnomusicology, Soc. Dance History Scholars (steering com. 1980-81), Spanish Dance Soc., Theatre Libr. Assn. Office: U Calif-Irvine Dept Dance Irvine CA 92717

RUZIC, NEIL PIERCE, author, publisher, scientist; b. Chgo., May 12, 1930; s. Joseph Francis and Ida (Pierce) R.; m. Carol W. Kalsbeek, Apr. 14, 1950; 1 child, David Neil. BS in Journalism, Psychology and Sci., Northwestern U., 1950. Corr. Costa Rica, 1949; reporter Michigan City (Ind.) News-Dispatch, 1950-52; dir. mags. IIT Research Inst., Chgo., 1954-58; founder Indsl. Research, Inc., Beverly Shores, Ind., 1958; pres., editor, pub. Indsl. Research, Inc., 1958-73; founder Rsch. & Devel., Inc. (formerly Indsl. Rsch.), 1959, and Oceanology mag., 1966; acquired Electro-Tech. mag., 1968; founder Neil Ruzic & Co., Chgo., 1973—; cons. to NASA, 1973-78; founder Island for Sci. Inc., Little Stirrup Cay Ltd., Bahamas, 1976—. Author: There's Adventure in Civil Engineering, 1958, There's Adventure in Meteorology, 1959, Stimulus, 1960, The Case for Going to the Moon, 1965, Where the Winds Sleep, 1970 (Lit. Guild selection), Spinoff, 1976, Blueprint for an Island for Science, Part 1, 1976, Part 2, 1977, Open-Ocean Polyculture, 1979, Emerging Technologies, 1984; (novel) The Shallow Sea, 1993. Served with AUS, 1952-54. Mem. IEEE (sr.), Nat. Space Soc. (founder, bd. govs.), Am. Vacuum Soc., Sigma Delta Chi. Inventor mag. inquiry system, tongue-and-grooved cement block, mobile lunar water mill, lunar cryostat, patentee device for use on moon, Ruzic Water Tower Lodge, self-contained bldg. for remote locations (1986-88). Office: Little Stirrup Cay Ltd PO Box 527 Beverly Shores IN 46301-0527 also: Little Stirrup Cay, Berry Islands Bahamas *Every major invention advances human life more significantly than treaties between countries. And yet modern invention is anything but profound: it is primarily the combining of existing knowledge with off-the-shelf components.*

RYALL, A(LBERT) LLOYD, horticulturist, refrigeration engineer; b. Phoenix, June 25, 1904; s. Lloyd Oliver and Kate Florence (Southam) R.; m. Mary Elizabeth Newton, Dec. 26, 1928; children: Patricia June, Philip Lloyd, Pamela Kate, Peter Newton. BS, N.D. Agrl. Coll., 1926; MS, Oreg. Agrl. Coll., 1928. Jr. pomologist USDA, Yakima, Wash., 1928-41; assoc. horticulturist USDA, Harlingen, Tex., 1942-49; horticulturist USDA, Fresno, Calif., 1949-57; sr. horticulturist USDA, Beltsville, Md., 1957-62; prin. horticulturist, br. chief USDA, Washington, 1962-69; asst. prof. N.Mex. State U., Las Cruces, 1971-75; hort. cons. various produce and transp. cos., 1970-82. Author: (with others) Handling, Transportation and Storage, Vol. 1, Vegetables and Melons, 1981, Handling, Transporation and Storage, Vol. 2, Fruits and Tree Nuts, 1983; contbr. over 90 articles to profl. jours. Fellow AAAS, Am. Soc. Hort. Sci. (chmn. Pacific chpt. 1956); mem. ASHRAE, Am. Inst. Biol. Sci., Alpha Zeta, Phi Kappa Phi, Lambda Kappa Delta. Achievements include development of advanced applications in precooling, special storage requirements, packaging and transportation services for fresh fruits and vegetables. Home: 6101 Camelot Dr Harlingen TX 78550

RYALL, JO-ELLYN M., psychiatrist; b. Newark, May 25, 1949; d. Joseph P. and Tekla (Paraszczuk) R.; BA in Chemistry with gen. honors, Douglass Coll., Rutgers U., 1971; MD, Washington U., St. Louis, 1975. Diplomate Am. Bd. Psychiatry and Neurology. Resident in psychiatry Washington U., 1975-78, psychiatrist Student Health, 1980-84, clin. instr. psychiatry, 1978-83, clin. asst. prof. psychiatry, 1983—; inpatient supr. Malcolm Bliss Mental Health Center, St. Louis, 1978-80, psychiatrist outpatient clinic, 1980-82; pvt. practice medicine specializing in psychiatry, St. Louis, 1980—. Bd. dirs. Women's Self Help Ctr., St. Louis 1980-83. Fellow APA, Soc. (pres. Ea. Mo. Dist. Br. 1983-85, sect. coun. Am. Med. Assn. 1986—); mem. AMA (alt. del. Mo. 1988-90, 93-94, del. 1995—), Am. Med. Women's Assn. (pres. St. Louis Dist. br. 1981-82, 92, regional gov. VIII 1986-89, spkr. house of dels., 1993—), St. Louis Met. Med. Soc. (del. to state conv. 1981-86, 93—, councilor 1985-87, v.p. 1989), Mo. State Med. Assn. (vice speaker ho. of dels. 1986-89, speaker 1989-92), Manic Depressive Assn. St. Louis (chmn. bd. dirs. 1985-89), Washington U. Faculty Club. Office: 9216 Clayton Rd Saint Louis MO 63124-1560

RYALS, CLYDE DE LOACHE, humanities educator; b. Atlanta, Dec. 19, 1928; s. Chester A. and Ruth C. (de Loache) R.; m. Hildegard Thun Scheffey Ellerkmann, Sept. 4, 1971. A.B. Emory U., 1947, M.A., 1949; Ph.D., U. Pa., 1957. Instr. U. Md., 1956-57; instr. U. Pa., Phila., 1957-60; asst. prof. U. Pa., 1960-64, assoc. prof., 1964-69, prof. English, 1969-73, grad. chmn. dept. English, 1969-72; prof. English Duke U., Durham, N.C., 1973—, chmn. dept., 1977-82; exec. dir. Carlyle Letters Project, 1980—; mem. Christian Gauss Award Com., 1989-91. Author: Theme and Symbol in Tennyson's Poetry to 1850, 1964, From the Great Deep, 1967, Browning's Later Poetry, 1871-1889, 1975, Becoming Browning: The Poems and Plays of Robert Browning, 1833-46, 1983, A World of Possibilities: Romantic Irony in Victorian Literature, 1990, The Life of Robert Browning: A Critical Biography, 1993; editor: Tennyson's Poems, Chiefly Lyrical, 1966, Mrs. Humphry Ward's Robert Elsmere, 1967, Nineteenth-Century Literary Perspectives, 1974, The Collected Letters of Thomas and Jane Welsh Carlyle, 1980—; mem. editorial bd.: Victorian Poetry, 1964—, South Atlantic Quar., 1975-87, Nineteenth Century Lit., 1986—, Studies in Browning and His Circle, 1987—, Jour. Narrative Lit., 1986-90, South Atlantic Rev. 1988-90, The Carlyle Ann., 1989—, Victorian Literature and Culture, 1991—; contbr. articles to profl. jours. Guggenheim fellow, 1972-73; fellow Beinecke Libr., Yale U., 1994. Mem. MLA, Am. Soc. for Aesthetics, Century Assn. N.Y. Chi Phi. Democrat. Episcopalian. Home: 1620 University Dr Durham NC 27707-1629

RYALS, CONNIE, state government department administrator; b. Nampa, Idaho, June 6, 1952; d. Samuel Wesley and Elaine Louise (Pace) Beeson; m. Steven Elden Ryals, April 20, 1969. Audit clerk Albertson's Inc., Boise, Idaho, 1970-73, adminstrv. sec., 1973-75, staff acct., 1975, coord. accts. payable, 1975-78, acctg. supr. pvt. label, 1978-82, mgr. sales audit dept., 1982-87; adminstr. internal ops. Idaho Dept. Adminstrn., Boise, Idaho, 1987-91; dir. Idaho Dept. of Employment, Boise, Idaho, 1991—; mem. bd. dirs. Idaho Total Quality Inst., 1993— Interstate Conf. of Employment Security Admnstrs., Washington, 1993—; mem. strategic planning com. Boise State U., 1993; mem. steering com. State Employee Compensation Com., Boise, 1993—. Chmn. Govt. Adminv./Robert Redford Fund Raiser, Boise, 1989. Mem. Idaho Total Quality Inst. (dir. 1991—). Avocations: bicycling, hiking, danicing, world travel, reading. Home: 2773 Haven Dr Eagle ID 83616 Office: Employment Dept 317 Main St Boise ID 83735

RYAN, ALLAN ANDREW, JR., lawyer, author, lecturer; b. Cambridge, Mass., July 3, 1945; s. Allan Andrew and Anne (Conway) R.; m. Nancy

Foote, June 30, 1978; children: Elisabeth, Andrew. AB, Dartmouth Coll., 1966; JD magna cum laude, U. Minn., 1970. Bar: D.C. 1972, Mass. 1985. Law clk. to assoc. justice Byron R. White U.S. Supreme Ct., 1970-71; assoc. Williams, Connolly & Califano, Washington, 1974-77; asst. to Solicitor Gen. U.S., Washington, 1977-80; dir. office of spl. investigations, Dept. Justice, Washington, 1980-83, spl. asst. to atty. gen., 1983; pvt. practice law, 1983-85; with office of gen. counsel, Harvard U., 1985—; presenting counsel Internat. Commn. Inquiry on Kurt Waldheim, London, 1988; adj. prof. Law Sch., Boston Coll., 1989—. Author: Quiet Neighbors: Prosecuting Nazi War Criminals in America, 1984. pres., editor-in-chief: Minn. Law Rev., 1969-70. Mem. adv. bd. holocaust and human rights rsch. project Boston Coll. Law Sch., 1984—; bd. dirs. Facing History and Ourselves Nat. Found., 1985-92; mem. exec. com. New Eng. region Anti-Defamation League, 1990—. Capt. USMC, 1971-74. Recipient Internat. Human Rights award B'nai B'rith, 1986. Mem. ABA, Boston Bar Assn. Office: Harvard U Office Gen Counsel 1350 Massachusetts Ave Ste 980 Cambridge MA 02138-3800

RYAN, ARTHUR FREDERICK, insurance company executive; b. Bklyn., Sept. 14, 1942; s. Arthur Vincent and Gertrude (Wingert) R.; m. Patricia Elizabeth Kelly; children: Arthur, Kelly Ann, Kevin, Kathleen. BA in Math., Providence Coll., 1963. Area mgr. Data Corp., Washington, 1965-72; project mgr. Chase Manhattan Corp. and Bank, N.Y.C., 1972-73, 2d v.p., 1973-74, v.p., 1974-75, from 1978, former ops. exec., from 1978, former exec. v.p., from 1982, former vice-chmn., then pres., chief operating officer, 1990-94; chmn., CEO Prudential Ins. Co. Am., Newark, N.J., 1994—; mem. policy and planning com.; bd. dirs. chmn. audit com. Depository Trust Co.; past mem. exec. com., Cedel (European Depository); past chmn. steering com., program mgr. CHIPS Same Day Settlement, N.Y. Clearing House. Past bd. dirs. Urban Acad. N.Y.C. Lt. U.S. Army, 1963-65. Mem. Am. Bankers Assn. (vice chmn. ops. and automation div. and govt. rels. coun., past chmn. internat. ops. com.). Home: 144 The Helm East Islip NY 11730 Office: Prudential Ins Co Am 213 Washington St Newark NJ 07101*

RYAN, BARBARA ANN, church official; b. East Saint Louis, Mo., Nov. 1, 1951; d. Paul Charles and Blanche Vernie (Hamblin) Becker; divorced; children: Nicole, McKenzie C. AS in Bus. Adminstrn., Belleville Jr. Coll., 1989; postgrad., Webster U. Officer, congl. sec. Luth. Ch.-Mo. Synod, 1992, 93, lay del. SID conv., 1994, dir. human resources. Mem. Concordia Mut. Life Assn. (bd. dirs., vice chair 1991—). Office: Luth Ch-Mo Synod 1333 S Kirkwood Rd Saint Louis MO 63122

RYAN, BUDDY (JAMES RYAN), professional football coach; b. Frederick, Okla., Feb. 17, 1931; m. Doris Ward, children: Jim, Rex, Rob, (div. 1966); m. Joanie Clark. Ed., Okla. State U. Football coach, athletic dir. Gainesville, H.S., Gainesville, Okla., 1959-60; defensive coordinator U. Buffalo, 1961-65, Vanderbilt U., Nashville, 1965-66, U. of Pacific, Stockton, Calif., 1966-67; mem. defensive staff N.Y. Jets, 1968-75; defensive line coach Minn. Vikings, 1976-77; defensive coordinator Chgo. Bears, 1978-86; head coach Phila. Eagles, 1986-91; defensive coordinator Houston Oilers, 1993-94; head coach, gen. manager Arizona Cardinals, 1994—; horse breeder Lawrenceburg, Ky., 1977—. Master Sergeant, US Army, Korean War. former Baptist, now Roman Catholic. Coached in Super Bowls III (1969) and XX (1986). Office: Arizona Cardinals PO Box 888 Phoenix AZ 85001-0888*

RYAN, CARL RAY, electrical engineer; b. Gateway, Ark., Mar. 3, 1938; s. Clarence and Stella (Schnitzer) R.; m. Arline Walker; children: Carline, Julie. BSEE, U. Ark., 1962; MSEE, Iowa State U., 1963; PhD in Elec. Engring., U. Mo.-Rolla, 1969, profl. degree Elec. Engring., 1994. Instr. U. Mo.-Rolla, 1968-69; sr. engr. Govt. Electronics Group, Motorola Inc., Scottsdale, Ariz., 1969-72, mem. tech. staff, 1972-76, sr. mem. tech. staff, chief engr., 1979-89, v.p. tech. staff, 1989-90, dir. communication systems tech., 1990—; prof. Mich. Tech. U., 1976-79; adj. prof. Ariz. State U., Tempe, 1980-89; panel mem. Internat. Solid States Circuits Conf., Phila., 1977; session chmn. Future Space Communications Tech. Workshop, Pasadena, Calif., 1980; external advisor Mich. Technol. U. Contbr. articles to profl. jours.; patentee in field. Assoc. Motorola Sci. Adv. Bd. Served with USAF, 1956-60. Fellow IEEE (communications tech., solid state circuits, accreditation com., Dan Nobel fellow, chmn. Phoenix chpt. 1981-82, program chmn. 1989, gen. chmn. Phoenix Conf. on computers and communication 1988).

RYAN, CHARLES EDWARD, public relations executive, advertising executive; b. Cumberland, Md., Feb. 28, 1940; s. William Donaldson and Mabel Thestle (Miner) R.; children: Elizabeth Shandon, Margaret Amy. AA, Potomac State Coll., Keyser, 1960; BS in Journalism, W.Va. U., Morgantown, 1962. Announcer, disc jockey Sta. WKYR Radio, Keyser, 1957-60; announcer, newsman Sta. WCLG Radio, Morgantown, 1960; news dir., newsman Sta. WAJR Radio, Morgantown, 1960-62; reporter Sta. WSAZ-TV, Charleston, W.Va., 1962-65, 66-67; news editor Sta. WSAZ-TV, Charleston, 1968-69; state broadcast editor AP, Charleston, 1965-66; news reporter Sta. KTVI-TV, St. Louis, 1967-68; news dir. Sta. WCHS-TV, Charleston, 1969-74; pres. Charles Ryan Assocs., Inc., Charleston, 1974—; prin. Ryan-McGinn pub. rels. firm, Arlington, Va., Ryan-McGinn-Samples rsch. firm, Charleston and Arlington; lectr. in field. Bd. dirs. YMCA, Charleston, 1983-86, Charleston Symphony, 1983-86, State Spl. Olympics, Parkersburg, W.Va., 1984-86, Faculty Merit Found., Charleston, 1985—, W.Va. State Coll. Found., 1991—. Recipient Alumni Achievement award Potomac State Coll., 1985, Profl. Achievement award Perley Isaac Reed Sch. Journalism Alumni Assn., 1989. Mem. Nat. Fed. Am. (accredited, bd. dirs. 1986—), W.Va. State Pub. Rels. Soc. Am. (honoree 1983), Nat. Counselors Acad., W.Va. C. of C. (bd. dirs. 1985—), Advt. Club, Edgewood Country Club (bd. dirs. 1993), Rotary (bd. dirs. 1987—). Democrat. Methodist. Avocations: squash, tennis, golf, running. Office: Charles Ryan Assocs Inc 1012 Kanawha Blvd E Charleston WV 25301-2809

RYAN, CHRISTOPHER RICHARD, construction company executive; b. Ft. Dix, N.J., Jan. 18, 1948; s. Albert John and Pamela Joan (Hudson) R.; m. Mary Lasky, Sept. 8, 1979; children: Patrick Hudson, Peter Dacey, Katelyn Christine. BS Civil Engring., MIT, 1969, MS Civil Engring., 1972. Registered profl. engr., Pa. Project mgr. Engineered Construction Internat., Pitts., 1972-79; pres. Geo-Con, Monroeville, Pa., 1979—; spkr. in field. Contbr. articles to profl. jours. Bd. dirs. Three Rivers Rowing Assn., Pitts., 1989-93. Named Entrepreneur of Yr. Arthur Anderson, Western Pa., 1988. Mem. Am. Soc. Civil Engrs., Am. Inst. Entrepreneurs, Young Pres. Orgn., Moles, Longue Vue Country Club. Republican. Presbyterian. Avocations: rowing, skiing, golf. Office: Geo-Con Inc 4075 Monroeville Blvd Monroeville PA 15146-2529

RYAN, CLARENCE AUGUSTINE, JR., biochemistry educator; b. Butte, Mont., Sept. 29, 1931; s. Clarence A. Sr. and Agnes L. (Duckham) R.; m. Patricia Louise Meunier, Feb. 8, 1936; children: Jamie Arlette, Steven Michael (dec.), Janice Marie, Joseph Patrick (dec.). BA in Chemistry, Carroll Coll., 1953; MS in Chemistry, Mont. State U., 1956, PhD in Chemistry, 1959. Postdoctoral fellow in biochemistry Oreg. State U., Corvallis, 1959-61, U.S. Western Regional Lab., Albany, Calif., 1961-63; chemist U.S. Western Regional Lab., Berkeley, Calif., 1963-64; asst. prof. biochemistry Wash. State U., Pullman, 1964-68, assoc. prof., 1968-72, prof., 1972—, Charlotte Y. Martin disting. prof., 1991—, chmn. dept. agrl. chemistry, 1977-80, fellow Inst. Biol. Chemistry, 1980—; faculty athletics rep. to PAC-10 & NCAA Wash. State U., 1991-94; vis. scientist dept. biochemistry U. Wash., 1981, Harvard U. Med. Sch., 1982; cons. Kemin Industries, Des Moines, 1981—, Plant Genetics, Davis, Calif., 1987-89; research adv. bd. Frito-Lay, Inc., Dallas, 1982, Plant Genetic Engring. Lab., N.M. State U., Las Cruces, 1986-89; mem. NRC rev. bd. Plant Gene Exptl. Ctr., Albany, Calif., 1990-93; mgr. biol. stress program USDA Competitive Grants Program, Washington, 1983-84; former mem. adv. panels for H. McKnight Found., Internat. Potato Ctr., Lima, Peru, Internat. Ctr. Genetic Engring. and Biotech., New Delhi, Internat. Ctr. Tropical Agr., Cali, Columbia, Internat. Tropical Agr., Ibandan, Africa; mem. grant rev. panels NSF, USDA, DOE, NIH; co-organizer Internat. Telecommunications Symposium on Plant Biotech. Mem. edit. bd. several biochem. and plant physiology jours.; contbr. articles to profl. publs. chpts. to books; co-editor 2 books. Grantee USDA, NSF, NIH, Rockefeller Found., McKnight Found.; recipient Merck award for grad. rsch. Mont. State U., 1959, career devel. awards NIH, 1964-74, Alumni Achievement award Carroll Coll., 1986, Pres.'s Faculty Excellence award in rsch. Wash.

State U., 1986; named to Carroll Coll. Alumni Hall of Fame, 1981, Carroll Coll. Basketball Hall of Fame, 1982. Mem. AAAS, Nat. Acad. Scis. (elected 1986), Am. Chem. Soc. (Kenneth A. Spencer award 1992), Am. Soc. Plant Physiologists (Steven Hales Prize 1992), Am. Soc. Exptl.Biology, Biochem. Soc., Internat. Soc. Chem. Ecology, Internat. Soc. Plant Molecular Biology (bd. dirs.), Phytochem. Soc. N.Am., Nat. U. Continuing Assn. (Creative Programming award 1991), Phi Kappa Phi (Recognition award 1976, selected 1 of 100 centennial disting. alumni Mont. State U. 1993). Avocations: fishing, basketball, golf. Office: Wash State Univ Inst Biol Chemistry Pullman WA 99164

RYAN, CORNELIUS O'BRIEN, lawyer; b. Abilene, Tex., Oct. 15, 1917; s. William Cornelius and Joanna Genevieve (Morris) R.; m. Mary Anne Kelley, Mar. 24, 1942; children: Elisabeth Ryan Goldstein, Robert C., Carl E., William E., Joseph W., Mary Louise Ryan Ray. BA, Rice U., 1937; LLB, So. Meth. U., 1940. Bar: Tex. 1940. Mem. firm Kelley & Ryan, Houston, 1951—; v.p., gen. counsel Tex. United Corp., 1982-88. Bd. dirs. Am. Irish Found., 1977-90, hon. life trustee, 1990—. Lt. USNR, 1942-46. Decorated knight grand order Order Holy Sepulchre Knight of Malta. Mem. Am. Houston bar assns., Tex. State Bar, Am. Judicature Soc., Phi Beta Kappa, Phi Delta Theta, Phi Alpha Delta. Republican. Roman Catholic. Clubs: Houston (Houston), Serra (Houston). Home: 3107 Newcastle Dr Houston TX 77027-5507 Office: Kelley & Ryan 5847 San Felipe St Ste 4295 Houston TX 77057-3011

RYAN, DANIEL LEO, bishop; b. Mankato, Minn., Sept. 28, 1930; s. Leonard Bennett and Irene Ruth (Larson) R. BA, Ill. Benedictine Coll., 1952; JCL, Pontificia Università Lateranense, Rome, 1960. Ordained priest Roman Cath. Ch., 1956, consecrated bishop, 1981. Parish priest Roman Cath. Diocese, Joliet, Ill., 1956-82, chancellor, 1965-78, vicar gen., 1977-79, aux. bishop, 1981-84; bishop Roman Cath. Diocese, Springfield, Ill., 1984—. Office: Diocese of Springfield PO Box 3187 1615 W Washington Springfield IL 62708-3187

RYAN, DAVID THOMAS, lawyer; b. Torrington, Conn., Apr. 18, 1939; s. Edward John and Margaret (Murphy) R.; m. Dale Anderson, Aug. 21, 1965; children: Rachael Anderson, Conor Anne. BS, U. Md., 1961; LLB, Georgetown U., 1965. Bar: Conn. 1966, U.S. Dist. Ct. Conn. 1967, U.S. Ct. Appeals (2d cir.) 1969, U.S. Ct. Appeals (fed. cir.) 1982, U.S. Claims Ct. 1983, U.S. Supreme Ct. 1992. Ptnr. Cooney, Scully & Dowling, Hartford, Conn., 1966-77, Robinson & Cole, Hartford, 1977—. Fellow Am. Coll. Trial Lawyers; mem. Am. Bd. Trial Advs. Home: 126 Westerly Ter Hartford CT 06105-1117 Office: Robinson & Cole 1 Commercial Plz Hartford CT 06103-3599

RYAN, DESMOND, film critic; b. London, May 30, 1943; came to U.S., 1967; s. Christopher and Evelyn (Daley) R.; m. Patricia Mazer, Jan. 27, 1967; 1 child, Christopher. B.A. with honors, New Coll., Oxford U. Eng., 1965, M.A., 1968. Reporter Phila. Inquirer, 1969-74, film critic, 1974—; columnist mag.; 1975-82. Author: (novels) Helix, 1979, Deadlines, 1984 (Athanaeum award 1984); (video capsule revs.) Guide to 3000 Movies, 1985. Office: Phila Inquirer 400 N Broad St Philadelphia PA 19130-4099

RYAN, EARL M., public affairs analyst; b. Detroit, Oct. 23, 1942; s. Thomas M. and Margaret L. (Halsey) R.; m. Jo Ellen Junod, July 3, 1965; children: Andrew M., Jeffrey A. BA in Polit. Sci., U. Mich., 1964; MA in Polit. Sci., Wayne State U., 1968. Dir. rsch. Detroit Urban League, 1965-67; resch. assoc. Citizens Rsch. Coun. Mich., Lansing, 1967-70; budget analyst Dept. Social Svcs., Lansing, 1970-71; dir. rsch. Health Impact Project, Lansing, 1971, Office of Program Effectiveness Rev., Lansing 1971-74, Legis. Program Effectiveness Rev., Lansing, 1974-77, Citizens Rch. Coun. Mich., Detroit, 1977-84; pres. Pub. Affairs Rsch. Coun. La., Baton Rouge, 1984-87, Ind. Fiscal Policy Inst., Indpls., 1987-94; exec. dir. Citizens Rsch. Coun. of Mich., 1994—; polit. analyst Sta. WWL-TV, New Orleans, 1986; mem. blue ribbon panel Indpls. Bus. Jour., 1992—. Recipient Disting. Achievement award grad. program pub. adminstrn. Wayne State U., Detroit, 1991, Disting. Achievement award Sagamore of the Wabash, 1994. Mem. Govtl. Rsch. Assn. (pres. 1985-86, Disting. rsch. award 1977), Govtl. Fin. Officers Assn. Avocations: photography, Anthony Trollope novels. Home: 40292 Woodside Dr N Northville MI 48167 Office: Citizens Rsch Coun Mich Ste 1B 625 Shelby St Detroit MI 48226

RYAN, EDWARD W., economics educator; b. Plainfield, N.J., Aug. 23, 1932; s. Edward A. and Helen R. (Shannon) R.; m. Georgian Hurley, Dec. 17, 1966; children: Sarah, Jennifer. BS, U. Pa., 1955; MA, Duke U., 1957. Lectr. Fordham U., N.Y.C., 1956-57; instr. Iona Coll., New Rochelle, N.Y., 1958-60; prof. econs. Manhattanville Coll., Purchase, N.Y., 1958—; dir. Econ. Freedom Inst. Author: In the Words of Adam Smith: The First Consumer Advocate, 1990. Mem. Am. Econ. Assn., Indsl. Rels. Rsch. Assn., Pub. Choice Assn., Econ. History Assn. Roman Catholic. Home: 25 Jefferson Rd Scarsdale NY 10583-6411 Office: Manhattanville College 2900 Purchase St Purchase NY 10577-2628

RYAN, ELLEN BOUCHARD, psychology educator, gerontologist; b. Holyoke, Mass., Jan. 11, 1947; emigrated to Can. 1982; d. Raoul Rosario and Etiennette Marie (Morin) Bouchard; m. Patrick J. Ryan, July 12, 1969; children: Lorraine Yvette, Dennis Patrick, Kevin Myles. B.A., M.A., Brown U., 1968; Ph.D., U. Mich., 1970. Asst. prof. psychology U. Notre Dame, 1970-76, assoc. prof., 1976-81, prof., 1981-82, chmn. dept., 1978-82; prof. psychiatry McMaster U., Hamilton, Ont., Can., 1982—; dir. Office Gerontol. Studies McMaster U., 1985—. Editor: Attitudes Toward Language Variation, 1982, Language Communication and The Elderly, 1986, Intergenerationl Communication, 1994, Language Attitudes, 1994. Grantee NICHD, 1972-75, NSF, 1976-79, Nat. Inst. Edn., 1979-82, Natural Scis. and Engring. Rsch., 1983-89, Gerontol. Rsch. Coun. of Ont., 1983-85, Ont. Ministry Health, 1986-89, Soc. Sci. and Humanities Rsch. Coun., 1986—. Fellow APA, Gerontol. Soc. Am., Can. Psychol. Assn.; mem. Internat. Comm. Assn., Can. Assn. Gerontology. Roman Catholic. Home: 346 Brookview Ct, Ancaster, ON Canada L9G 4C2 Office: McMaster U Dept Psychiatry, 1200 Main St W, Hamilton, ON Canada L8N 3Z5

RYAN, FREDERICK JOSEPH, JR., lawyer, public official; b. Tampa, Fla., Apr. 12, 1955; s. Frederick Joseph and Cordelia Beth (Hartman) R.; m. Genevieve Ann McSweeney, Dec. 28, 1985; children: Genevieve Madeline, Madeline Elizabeth. BA, U. So. Calif., 1977, JD, 1980. Bar: Calif. 1980, D.C. 1986. Assoc. Hill, Farrer and Burrill, Los Angeles, 1980-82; dep. dir. then dir. presdl. appointments and scheduling The White House, Washington, 1982-87; dir. pvt. sector initiatives, 1985-87, asst. to the Pres., 1987-89; chief of staff Office of Ronald Reagan, L.A., 1989-95; vice chmn. Allbritton Comm. Co., Washington, 1995—; mem. staff Reagan-Bush Campaign, Los Angeles, 1980; dir. Internat. Conf. on Pvt. Sector Initiatives, Paris, 1986, Italian-Am. Conf. on Pvt. Sector Initiatives, 1987, Brit.-Am. Conf. on Pvt. Sector Initiatives, 1988. Author (column) Legal Briefs, 1980-82. Chmn. Monterey Park (Calif.) Community Rels. Commn., 1977-78; bd. dirs. Fordi Theater, Washington, Town Hall of Calif., L.A., Nancy Reagan Found.; trustee Ronald reagan Presdl. Found. Recipient Presdl. Commendation for pvt. sector initiatives Pres. Ronald Reagan, 1986, Medal of Arts and Letters, Govt. of France, 1986, Golden Ambrosiana medal of Milan, Italy, 1987, The Lion of Venice medal, Italy, 1987, Comdr. of the Order of Merit of Republic of Italy, 1992. Mem. ABA, Jonathan Club (L.A.). Presbyterian. Avocations: karate, running, skiing. Office: Allbritton Comm Co 800 17th St NW Washington DC 20006

RYAN, GEORGE H., secretary of state, pharmacist; b. Maquoketa, Iowa, Feb. 24, 1934; s. Thomas J. and Jeanette (Bowman) R.; m. Lura Lynn Lowe, June 10, 1956; children: Nancy, Lynda, Julie, Joanne, Jeanette, George. BS in Pharmacy, Ferris State Coll., Big Rapids, Mich. Mem. Ill. Ho. of Reps., 1973-82, minority leader, 1977-80, speaker, 1981-82; lt. gov. State of Ill., 1983-91, sec. of state, 1991—. Mem. Kankakee County Bd., 1966-72, chmn., 1971-72; chmn. Ill. Literacy Coun., 1991—. With U.S. Army, Korea. Recipient Humphrey award Am. Pharm. Assn., 1980, "E" award Pres. of U.S., 1989, Top award Ill. chpt. DARE, 1989. Mem. Am. Pharm. Assn., Ill. Pharm. Assn., One Hundred Club, Masons (33d degree). Republican. Methodist. Lodges: Elks, Moose, Shriners.

RYAN, GEORGE WILLIAM, manufacturing executive; b. Sinking Springs, Ohio, Oct. 13, 1939; s. Winson Mark and Mary Edith (Smalley) R.; 1 child: Gina Kristin. Student, Wilmington Coll., 1962. Process engr. B.F. Goodrich Co., Marietta, Ohio, 1962-66; product dev. mgr. Chrysler Corp., Sandusky, Ohio, 1966-70; asst. tech. mgr. Inmont Corp., Toledo, Ohio, 1970-72; tech. mgr. Occidental Petroleum, Burlington, N.J., 1973; owner Ryan Devel. Corp., Peebles, 1973-88; prin. Straight Fork Valley Ranch, Ohio, 1986—; cons. Hooker Chem. Corp., Burlington, N.J., 1973. Bd. dirs., pres. Missionary Evang. Ch. of Christ. Mem. Soc. Plastic Engrs., Senatorial Trust (Washington), Peebles Ind. Inc. (sec., treas., bd. dirs., 1984-88). Republican.

RYAN, GERALD ANTHONY, financial adviser, venture capitalist; b. Milw., Oct. 24, 1935; s. Gerald Edward and Frances (Dierksmeier) R.; m. Carole Lesley Schuster, May 19, 1956; children: Karen P., Kevin M., Kimberly F., Kendra A., Keith A. B.S.M.E., MIT, 1957. Engr., Johnson Controls, Buffalo, 1958-61; mgr. Johnson Controls, Erie, Pa., 1961-73; pres. TEI Corp., Erie, 1973-75; chmn., CEO Erie Bus. Mgmt. Corp., 1975—; chmn., CEO Skinner Engine Co., 1986—; pres. Ryco Holding Ltd., 1986—; chmn. bd. Automated Indsl. Sys., Fairview, Pa., 1981—; Spectrum Control, Inc., Erie, Personal Svc. Corp., 1974-82, Rent-Way, Inc., 1981—. Mem. Kahkwa Club. Republican. Roman Catholic. Home: 10 Peninsula Dr Erie PA 16505 Office: EBMC PO Box 6242 Erie PA 16512-6242

RYAN, GERARD SPENCER, inn executive; b. N.Y.C., June 10, 1926; s. Gerard Aloysius and Helen (Kirwan) R.; m. Barbara Battle, May 3, 1952; children—Jerry, Catherine, Janet, Mary Ellen, Barbara, Elizabeth, David, Peter. B.A., Georgetown U., 1950. Dir. fund raising Georgetown U., 1950-51; sales rep. McGraw Hill Pub. Co., Chgo., 1951-53; mgr. Pitts. Chem. Engring. Dist., 1953-68; sales mgr. Power Mag., N.Y.C., 1968-73; SLS mgr. Elec. Constrn. and Maintenance and Elec. Wholesaling mags., N.Y.C., 1973-74; pub. Elec. Constrn. and Maintenance and Elec. Wholesaling mags., 1974-85; propr. Arrowhead Inn, Durham, N.C., 1985—. Pres. South Hills Assn. Racial Equality, Pitts., 1966-68, Debra, Montclair, N.J., 1981-83. Served with USN, 1944-46. Mem. N.C. Bed and Breakfast Assn. (past pres.). Democrat. Roman Catholic. Home and Office: Arrowhead Inn 106 Mason Rd Durham NC 27712-9201

RYAN, HALFORD ROSS, speech educator; b. Anderson, Ind., Dec. 29, 1943. AB, Wabash Coll., 1966; MA, U. Ill., 1968, PhD, 1972. Prof. Washington and Lee U., Lexington, Va., 1970—. Author: FDR's Rhetorical Presidency, 1988, Harry Emerson Fosdick, 1989, Henry Ward Beecher, 1990, Classical Communication for the Contemporary Communicator, 1992, Harry S. Truman, 1993; editor: Oratorical Encounters, 1988, Inaugural Addresses of Twentieth-Century American Presidents, 1993; also articles. Recipient awards Eleanor Roosevelt Inst., 1979, Herbert Hoover Inst., 1986, Maurice Mednick Found., 1991; Rockefeller Theol. fellow, 1967. Mem. Speech Communication Assn. Office: Washington and Lee U Robinson Hall Lexington VA 24450

RYAN, HOWARD CHRIS, retired state supreme court justice; b. Tonica, Ill., June 17, 1916; s. John F. and Sarah (Egger) R.; m. Helen Cizek, Oct. 16, 1943; children: John F., Elizabeth Ellen, Howard Chris. B.A., U. Ill., 1940, LL.B., J.D., 1942; LL.D. (hon.), John Marshall Law Sch., 1978. Bar: Ill. 1942. Practice in Decatur, 1946-47, Peru, 1947-57; asst. state's atty. LaSalle County, 1952-54, county judge, 1954-57, circuit judge, 1957-68; chief judge, 1964-68; judge appellate ct. 3d Jud. Dist. Ill., 1968-70; justice Ill. Supreme Ct., 1970-90, chief justice, 1981-84; of counsel Peterson & Ross, Chgo., 1990-93. Served with USAAF, 1942-45. Mem. ABA, Ill. Bar Assn., LaSalle County Bar Assn., Am. Legion, Masons, Elks, Odd Fellows, Phi Kappa Delta. Republican. Methodist. Home: PO Box 397 Tonica IL 61370-0397

RYAN, IONE JEAN ALOHILANI, retired educator, counselor; b. Honolulu, Oct. 18, 1926; d. William Alexander and Lilia (Nainoa) Rathburn; m. Edward Parsons Ryan, June 23, 1948 (dec.); children: Ralph M., Lilia K. BEd, U. Hawaii, 1948; MS in Pub. Health, U. Minn., 1950; EdD, Stanford U., 1960. Lic. marital and family therapist, N.C. Tchr. W.R. Farrington High Sch., Honolulu, 1948; instr. to asst. prof. U. Hawaii, Honolulu, 1950-66; assoc. prof. to prof. East Carolina U., Greenville, 1966-90; prof. emerita East Carolina U., Greenville, N.C., 1990—; adv. com. Eastern Regional Tng. Program, Greenville, N.C., 1975-80; cons. Title III Grant, Lenoir Community Coll., Kinston, N.C., 1981; adult svcs. adv. com. Pitt County Mental Health, Greenville, N.C., 1976-78. Contbr. articles to profl. publs. Recipient first scholarship Honolulu C. of C., 1948-50. Mem. APA.

RYAN, J. BRUCE, financial consulting company; b. Southbridge, Mass., Mar. 28, 1944; s. Charles J. and Doris (Olney) R.; m. Sarah E. Pattison, Aug. 16, 1993. BSBA in Fin., U. Mass., 1972, MSBA, 1974; MA in Econs., U. Wash., 1976. Regional v.p. Amherst Assocs. Inc., Atlanta, 1976-85; exec. v.p. Jennings Ryan & Kolb, Inc., Atlanta, 1985—. Contbr. articles to profl. jours. With U.S. Army, 1968-70. Mem. Healthcare Fin. Mgmt. Assn. (Helen M. Yerger/L. Van Seawell best article award 1990), Soc. for Healthcare Planning & Mktg., Fin. Mgmt. Assn., Am. Assn. Physician-Hosp. Orgns. Avocation: sailing. Home: 1060 Kentucky Ave NE Atlanta GA 30306-3534 Office: Jennings Ryan & Kolb Inc 17 Executive Park Dr NE # 300 Atlanta GA 30329-2222

RYAN, J. PATRICK, fund raising consulting company executive; b. Sandusky, Ohio, Nov. 2, 1940; s. James E. and Dorothy G. (McNeil) R.; m. Mary Anne Moore, Dec. 27, 1968 (div. 1986); children: J. Michael, McNeil T., Mark M., J. Matthew; m. Bari Rose Ryan, Feb. 1, 1989. BA in Philosophy, U. Ky., 1963; postgrad. in bus., U. So. Calif., 1966. Asst. dean U. So. Calif., L.A., 1966-68; alumni dir. Lambda Chi Alpha Frat., Indpls., 1969-70; cons., ptnr. Marts & Lundy, Inc., N.Y.C., 1971-75; devel. dir. Archdiocese of Cin., 1976-77; sr. ptnr. Staley-Robeson-Ryan-St. Lawrence, Inc., Cin., 1978-85, pres., 1985—; joint mng. dir. Downes/Ryan Group, Cin., 1988—. Chmn. Mt. Lookout Civic Assn., Cin., 1982. Mem. Nat. Soc. Fund Raising Execs. (chmn. Found. 1987-89, bd. dirs., Fund Raising Exec. of Yr. award Cin. 1985), Camargo Hunt Club, Bankers Club Cin. (life), World Fundraising Coun. (hon. sec.). Republican. Roman Catholic. Home: 2943 Mt Pisgah Rd New Richmond OH 45157-9731 Office: Staley Robeson Ryan & St Lawrence Inc 635 W 7th St Cincinnati OH 45203-1513

RYAN, J. RICHARD, lawyer; b. N.Y.C., Oct. 23, 1929; s. Peter Leon and Mary Martha (Franklin) R.; m. Diana Louise Gambarelli, Nov. 6, 1954 (dec. Feb. 1988); children: Christopher, Claudia; m. Joan Revelle, Jan. 21, 1995. BA, Georgetown U., 1951, JD, Fordham U., 1954. Bar: N.Y. 1956, U.S. Dist. Ct. (so. dist.) N.Y., 1957, U.S. Supreme Ct., 1987. Assoc. Engel, Judge, Miller, Sterling & Reddy, N.Y.C., 1956-63, ptnr., 1963-66; ptnr. Kantor, Shaw & Ryan, N.Y.C., 1966-71; ptnr. Ryan & Silberberg, N.Y.C., 1971-84, Ryan & Fogerty, 1984-88, Ryan, Botway, Reddy and Mesrop, 1988-90; sole practice, 1990—. Bd. dirs. Guiding Eyes for the Blind, Inc., pres., 1973-77, Am. Health Capital Ins. Co.; trustee Cooper Inst. for Advanced Studies in Medicine and Humanities. Mem. Bar Assn. City N.Y. (Young Lawyers Com. 1957-60), N.Y. State Bar Assn., ABA, The Soc. of the Friendly Sons of St. Patrick, Copyright Soc. Candidate for mayor, Pelham, N.Y., 1963. Served with AUS, 1954-56. Clubs: Pelham Country (past pres.), Union League, Winged Foot Golf Club. Office: 516 Fifth Ave New York NY 10036

RYAN, JAMES, insurance company executive; b. Pittsburgh, Pa., Jan. 21, 1937; s. Martin Charles and Lucy Elizabeth (Misklow) r.; m. Marlene Sullivan Ryan, Jan. 27, 1973. BA, U. Pitts., U. Louisville. Cert. ins. wholesaler. Chmn. Market Finders Ins. Corp., Louisville, 1972—; com. chmn. Am. Assn. Mng. Gen. Agts., 1988-89; pres. Ky. Lloyd's Agts. Assn., 1985—; bd. dirs. Nat. Assn. Profl. Surplus Lines Office, Inc., 1983-86; pres. Ky. Surplus Lines Assn., Louisville, 1988-89; mem. adv. coun. Essex Ins. Co., 1991-93. Mem. Ky. Thoroughbred Owners & Breeders, Inc., Hon. Order of Blue Goose internat., Kosair Shrine Temple, Hon. Order of Ky. Col. Named Adv. Coun. Colony Ins. Co., Glen Allen, Va., 1991-93, Hamilton Ins. Co., 1993, Cardinal Ins. Co., 1990-91. Mem. Profl. Ins. Agts., Ind. Ins. Agts. Assn., Am. Assn. Mng. Gen Agts. (cert., chmn. adv. com. 1991-92, bd. dirs. 1994-96, v.p. zone 3 1995-96), Nat. Assn. Profl. Surplus Lines Offices (chmn. legis. com. 1988-89). Republican. Roman Catholic. Avocations: breeding and racing Thoroughbred horses, golf.

RYAN, JAMES See RYAN, BUDDY

RYAN, JAMES E., attorney general; married; 6 children. BA in Polit. Sci., Ill. Benedictine Coll., 1968; JD, Ill. Inst. Tech., 1971. Bar: Ill. 1971. Asst. state's atty. criminal divsn. DuPage County State's Atty.'s Office, 1971-74, 1st. asst. state's atty., 1974-76; founder Ryan & Darrah; state's atty. DuPage County State's Atty.'s Office, 1984-94; atty. gen. State of Ill., 1994—. Recipient numerous awards from various orgns. including Nat. Assn. Counties, Alliance Against Intoxicated Motorists. Republican. Office: State of Ill Ctr 100 W Randolph St Chicago IL 60601*

RYAN, JAMES EDWIN, industrial arts educator; b. Pittsburg, Kans., Oct. 21, 1919; s. James Joseph and Eva May (Bates) R.; m. Carol Floella Nowell, June 15, 1941; 1 child, Carol Jean. B.S., Kans. State Coll., 1940; M.A., Calif. State Coll., Long Beach, 1954; Ed.D., UCLA, 1964. High sch. tchr. Mo. and Kans., 1940-43; journeyman printer Long Beach (Calif.) Ind. Press-Telegram, 1947-54; mem. faculty Calif. State U., Long Beach, 1954-83; prof. indsl. arts Calif. State U., 1964-83, prof. emeritus, 1983—, chmn. acad. senate, 1976-78; mem. acad. senate Calif. State Univs. and Colls., 1979-83; mem. graphic arts adv. com. Downey (Calif.) City Schs., 1964-83, Golden West Coll., 1970-83; mem. visitation team accreditation council Calif. Assn. Schs. Cosmetology, 1965-83; judge tech. exhibits Gt. Western Exposition, Los Angeles, 1962-83; cons. in field. Contbr. articles to profl. jours. Served with AUS, 1943-46. Mem. Soc. History Tech., Am. Indsl. Arts Assn., Assn. Calif. State Univ. Profs. (past officer), Am. Coun. Indsl. Arts Tchr. Educators, Calif. Indsl. Edn. Assn. (life), Congress Faculty Assn. (v.p. 1976-79, treas. 1979-81), Calif. Colls. Univ. Faculty Assn. (chpt. pres. 1977-79), Calif. State U. Long Beach Emeritus and Ret. Faculty Assn. (mem. 1988-89, 92-93), Calif. State U. Emeritus and Ret. Faculty Assn. (v.p. 1992—), Epsilon Pi Tau (Laureate citation 1960), Phi Kappa Phi, Phi Delta Kappa. Home: 13952 Falmouth Walk Westminster CA 92683-3432

RYAN, JAMES FRANKLIN, oil company executive; b. London, Ont., Can., July 21, 1948; s. Patrick and Helen Anne (Wenechuk) R.; m. Dora Lee Ballan, Mar. 17, 1979; children: Christine, Carol. BS, U. Western Ont., London, 1970; MBA, York U., Toronto, Ont., 1972. Various mgmt. positions Shell Can. Ltd., Toronto, 1972-84; mgr. retail Shell Can. Ltd. Calgary, 1984-85; dir. mktg. svcs. Petro-Can., Inc., Toronto, 1985-86; pres. Pyne Mgmt., Inc., Toronto, 1986-88, Can. Tire Petroleum, Toronto, 1988-92; sr. v.p. dealer rels. Can. Tire Corp., Toronto, 1992—. Avocation: tennis. Home: 9 Ferndell Circle, Unionville, ON Canada L3R 3Y7 Office: Can Tire Corp, 2180 Yonge St, Toronto, ON Canada M4S 2B9

RYAN, JAMES LEO, federal judge; b. Detroit, Mich., Nov. 19, 1932; s. Leo Francis and Irene Agnes R.; m. Mary Elizabeth Rogers, Oct. 12, 1957; children: Daniel P., James R., Colleen M. Hansen, Kathleen A. LL.B., U. Detroit, 1956, BA, 1992; LL.D. (hon.), Madonna Coll., 1976, Detroit Coll. Law, 1978, Thomas M. Cooley Law Sch., Lansing, Mich., 1986, U. Detroit Sch. Law, 1986. Justice of the peace Redford Twp., Mich., 1963-66; cir. judge 3d Jud. Circuit Mich., 1966-75; justice Mich. Supreme Ct., 1975-86; judge U.S. Ct. Appeals (6th cir.), 1986—; faculty U. Detroit Sch. Law, Nat. Jud. Coll., Reno, Am. Acad. Jud. Edn., Washington, Thos M.Cooley Law Sch. Contbr. article to legal jour. Served with JAGC, USNR, 1957-60; to capt. JAGC, mil. judge Res., 1960-92, ret., 1992. Mem. Am. Judicature Soc., Naval Res. Lawyers Assn., nat. Conf. Appellate Ct. Judges, Fed. Judges Assn., State Bar Mich., Fed. Bar Assn., KC. Office: US Ct Appeals 611 US Courthouse Detroit MI 48226

RYAN, JAMES WALTER, physician, medical researcher; b. Amarillo, Tex., June 8, 1935; s. Lee W. and Emma E. (Haddox) R.; children: James P.A., Alexandra L.E., Amy J.S. A.B. in Polit. Sci., Dartmouth Coll., 1957; M.D., Cornell U., 1961; D.Phil., Oxford U. (Eng.), 1967. Diplomate: Nat. Bd. Med. Examiners. Intern, Montreal (Que.) Gen. Hosp., McGill U. Can., 1961-62; asst. resident in medicine Montreal (Que.) Gen. Hosp., McGill U., 1962-63; USPHS research asso. NIMH, NIH, 1963-65; guest investigator Rockefeller U., N.Y.C., 1967-68; asst. prof. biochemistry Rockefeller U., 1968; asso. prof. medicine U. Miami (Fla.) Sch. Medicine, 1968-79, prof. medicine, 1979-95; prof. anesthesiology, pharmacology and toxicology Med. Coll. Ga., Augusta, 1995—; sr. scientist Papanicolaou Cancer Rsch. Inst., Miami, 1972-77; hon. med. officer to Regius prof. medicine Oxford U., 1965-67; vis. prof. Clin. Rsch. Inst. Montreal, 1974; mem. vis hospice thoracic disease divsn., dept. internal medicine Mayo Clinic, 1974; cons. Hycor, Inc., Chugai Pharm. Co., Ltd., Tokyo, Apotex, Inc., Toronto. Contbr. numerous articles on biochem. research and pathology to sci. jours.; patentee in field. Rockefeller Found. travel awardee, 1962; William Waldorf Astor travelling fellow, 1966; USPHS spl. fellow, 1967-68; Pfizer travelling fellow, 1972; recipient Louis and Artur Luciano award for research of circulatory diseases McGill U., 1984-85. Fellow Am. Inst. Chemists; mem. Am. Chem. Soc., Biochem. Soc., Am. Soc. Biol. Chemists, Am. Heart Assn. (mem. council cardiopulmonary diseases 1972—, Council for High Blood Pressure Research 1976—), Microcirculatory Soc., So. Soc. Clin. Investigation, AAAS, N.Y. Acad. Scis., Sigma Xi. Baptist. Club: United Oxford and Cambridge U. (London). Home: 3047 Lake Forest Dr Augusta GA 30909 Office: Med Coll Ga Vascular Biology Ctr Augusta GA 30912

RYAN, JERRY WILLIAM, lawyer; b. Highland Park, Mich., Mar. 18, 1928; s. Jeremiah Ryan and Irene (Evans) R. BA, U. Mich., 1949, JD, 1952; postgrad., Inst. Universitaire des Hautes Etudes Internat., Geneva, Switzerland, 1954, 55. Bar: Mich. 1952, N.Y. 1958, D.C. 1966. Field atty. VA, Detroit, 1953-54; sr. atty. Pan Am. World Airways Inc., N.Y.C., 1956-66; ptnr. Pogue & Neal, Washington, 1966-67, Jones, Day, Reavis & Pogue and predecessor firm Reavis, Pogue, Neal & Rose, Washington, 1967-79, Crowell & Moring, Washington, 1979—; arbitrator U.S. and internat. arbitrations; speaker Inst. Continuing Edn., U. Mich., 1989-90. Capt. USAF, 1952-53. Mem. ABA (speaker 1985), Assn. of Bar of City of N.Y., Sky Club (N.Y.C.), Metropolitan Club (washington). Office: Crowell & Moring 1001 Pennsylvania Ave NW Washington DC 20004-2505

RYAN, JOAN, sportswriter; b. Sept. 20, 1959; m. Barry Tompkins; 1 child. BS in Journalism with honors, U. Fla., 1981. Copy editor Orlando (Fla.) Sentinel, 1981-82, copy editor sports, 1982-83, sports writer, 1983-85; sports columnist San Francisco Examiner, 1985—. Recipient Fla. Sports Columnist of Yr. award, 1984, numerous AP Sports Editors awards, AP 1st place enterprise reporting award, 1993, Nat. Headliner award sports writing, 1990, Women's Sports Found. Journalism award, 1992. Office: San Francisco Examiner PO Box 7260 110 5th Ave San Francisco CA 94120

RYAN, JOHN DUNCAN, lawyer; b. Portland, Oreg., Dec. 20, 1920; s. Thomas Gough and Virgian Abigail (Hadley) R.; m. Florence A. Ryan, Jan. 30, 1970 (dec. 1987). BS, Fordham U., 1943; JD, Lewis & Clark Coll., Portland, 1950. Bar: Oreg. 1950. Private practice Portland, 1950—; adj. instr. Northwestern Sch. Law Lewis & Clark Coll., 1953-70. Author: (poems) Expressions, 1993. Sgt. Air Corps, U.S. Army, 1942-46, ETO. Mem. ABA (Oreg. delegate 1985-93, chmn. spl. com. on law & literacy 1991-93), Am. Coll. Trial Lawyers, Am. Trial Lawyers Assn., Oreg. State Bar (bd. govs. 1963-67), Oreg. Trial Lawyers Assn. (Trial Lawyer of Yr. 1993), Multnomah Bar Assn., Washington County Bar Assn. Home and Office: 1760 SW 90th Ave Portland OR 97225

RYAN, JOHN EDWARD, federal judge; b. Boston, Jan. 22, 1941; s. Howard Frederick and Mary (Burke) R.; m. Terri Reynolds; children: Valerie, Jennifer, Keely. BSEE, U.S. Naval Acad., 1963; LLB, Georgetown U., 1972; MS, Pacific Christian U., 1979. Assoc. Hale and Dorr, Boston, 1972-76, C.F. Braun, Alhambra, Calif., 1976-77; gen. counsel Altec Corp., Anaheim, Calif., 1977-79; v.p., sr. atty. Oak Industries, San Diego, 1979-82; sr. v.p. Oak Media, San Diego, 1982-84; ptnr. Dale and Lloyd, La Jolla, Calif., 1984-85, Jennings, Engstrand and Henrikson, San Diego, 1985-86; bankruptcy judge U.S. Bankruptcy Ct., Santa Ana, Calif., 1986—; ex officio dir. Orange County Bankruptcy Forum; exec. com. 9th Cir. conf. With USN, 1963-69. Mem. Mass. Bar Assn., Calif. Bar Assn., Orange County Bar Assn., Bankruptcy Judges Assn. Republican. Roman Catholic. Avocations: tennis, camping, basketball. Home: 3155 Summit Dr Escondido CA 92025-7529 Office: US Bankruptcy Ct PO Box 12600 Santa Ana CA 92712-2600

RYAN, JOHN FRANKLIN, multinational company executive; b. Huntington, W.Va., Apr. 10, 1925; s. Oscar F. and Marie J. (Tyler) R.; m. Renee B. Bourn, June 17, 1948; children—Carolyn, Linda, Elizabeth. Student, Emory and Henry Coll., 1943-44; B.S., Marshall U., 1948. Data processing sales mgr. IBM, Phila., 1958-60; dir. worldwide integrated data systems ITT, Washington, 1960-62, dept. dir., 1962-72, dir. corp. relations, 1972-87, v.p., 1981-87; cons., 1987—. Mem. Bus.-Govt. Relations Council, pres. 1978; bd. dirs. Pub. Affairs Council. Served with USNR, 1943-45. Clubs: Carlton (pres. 1982), Burning Tree. Home: 8447 Portland Pl Mc Lean VA 22102-1707

RYAN, JOHN MICHAEL, landscape architect; b. Chgo., Sept. 27, 1946; s. Terrance Joseph and Norma (Morris) R.; m. Victoria Jean Wheetley, June 26, 1986; children: Micheline Giannasi, Andrew Morris Jennings, Melissa Constance Victoria. B.A. in Landscape Architecture, U. Ill., 1969. Registered landscape architect, Ill., Mich., Ariz.; cert. CLARB. Assoc. landscape architect Carl Garnder & Assocs., Inc., Chgo., 1969-71; v.p. landscape architect Collaborative Rsch. & Planning, Chgo., 1971-73; v.p. Michael L. Ives & Assocs., Inc., Downers Grove, Ill., 1973-84; pres. Ives/Ryan Group, Inc., Downers Grove, 1984—. Prin. works include renovation of Old Orchard Shopping Ctr., Skokie, Ill., Lake Katherine Nature Preserve, Palos Heights, Ill., Crystal Tree Residential Golf Course Cmty., Orland Park, Ill., Corporetum Office Campus, Lisle, Ill. Crew chief search and rescue USCG Aux., 1980—. Recipient Nat. Landscape award Am. Assn. Nurserymen, 1988, 92, Key award in landscape arch. Home Bldrs. Assn. Greater Chgo., 1981, 84, 90. Mem. Am. Assn. Landscape Architects (Merit award 1991, 94), Ill. Landscape Contractors Assn. (Gold award 1991, Silver award 1986, 90, 93, Merit award 1988, 91), Chgo. Hort. Soc., Perennial Plant Assn. (Nat. Honor award 1993), Morton Arboretum. Avocations: competitive volleyball, golf, gardening, travel. Office: Ives/Ryan Group Inc 4932 Main St Downers Grove IL 60515

RYAN, JOHN THOMAS, JR., business executive; b. Pitts., Mar. 1, 1912; s. John Thomas and Julia (Brown) R.; m. Irene O'Brien, Aug. 1, 1939; children: John, III, Irene (Mrs. L. Edward Shaw, Jr.), Michael, Denise, Julia (Mrs. Robert F. Parker), William. B.S., Pa. State Coll., 1934; M.B.A., Harvard U., 1936; D.Sc. (hon.), Duquesne U.; LL.D., U. Notre Dame, 1973. Engr. with Mine Safety Appliances Co., 1936-38, asst. gen. mgr., 1938-40, gen. mgr., 1940-48, exec. v.p. and dir., 1948-53, pres., dir., 1953-63, chmn. bd., 1963-90, chmn. exec. com., 1990—. Mem. exec. com. Allegheny Conf. Community Devel.; trustee emeritus U. Notre Dame; trustee Thomas A. Edison Found.; life dir. Pitts. Symphony Soc. Mem. NAS (pres.' circle 1989), ASME, AIME, NSPE, Am. Chem. Soc., Am. Soc. Safety Engrs., Vets. of Safety, Coun. Fgn. Rels., Phi Delta Theta, Tau Beta Pi, Pitts. Athletic Assn. Roman Catholic. Clubs: Pitts. Golf, University, Duquesne; N.Y. Yacht, Union League (N.Y.C.); Chicago; Metropolitan (Washington); Fox Chapel (Pa.); Rolling Rock (Ligonier, Pa.), Allegheny (Laurel Valley). Lodge: Knights of Malta. Home: W Woodland Rd Pittsburgh PA 15232 Office: Mine Safety Appliances Co PO Box 426 Pittsburgh PA 15230-0426

RYAN, JOHN THOMAS, III, safety equipment company executive; b. Pitts., Aug. 6, 1943; s. John Thomas and Mary Irene (O'Brien) R.; m. Catharine Marie Murray, Nov. 18, 1946; children: Mary Catharine, Maureen Emily, John Thomas IV. AB, U. Notre Dame, 1965; MBA, Harvard U., 1969. Mgmt. trainee Mine Safety Appliances Co., Pitts., 1969-70, asst. to dir. of product planning, 1970-74, mgr. S.Am., 1974-78, v.p. internat., 1978-82, v.p., 1982-86, exec. v.p., 1986-90, pres., chmn. and chief exec. officer, 1991—, also dir.; dir. Auergesellschaft, Berlin; dir. Pitts. br. Fed. Reserve Bank Cleve., 1995—, Regional Indsl. Devel. Corp. Southwestern Pa., 1995—. Trustee Penn's S.W. Assn., 1991—; mem. adv. council Coll. Bus. Adminstrn., U. Notre Dame, Ind., 1978—; mem. exec. com. Allegheny Conf. on Community Devel., 1992—. Served to lt. U.S. Army, 1967-69. Mem. N.Y.C. Council on Fgn. Relations, Am. Mining Congress (gov. mfrs. div. 1988—, chmn. export com.). Republican. Roman Catholic. Home: 5708 Lynne Haven Rd Pittsburgh PA 15217 Office: Mine Safety Appliances Co PO Box 426 Pittsburgh PA 15230-0426

RYAN, JOHN WILLIAM, retired university president; b. Chgo., Aug. 12, 1929; s. Leonard John and Maxine (Mitchell) R.; m. D. Patricia Goodday, Mar. 20, 1949; children: Kathleen Elynne Ryan Acker, Kevin Dennis Mitchell, Kerrick Charles Casey. BA, U. Utah, 1951; MA, Ind. U., 1958, PhD, 1959, LLD (hon.), 1988; LLD (hon.), U. Notre Dame, 1978, Oakland City Coll., 1981, St. Joseph Coll., 1981, Hanover Coll., 1982, DePauw U., 1983, U. Ma., 1983, Manchester Coll., 1983, U. Evansville, 1985, Wabash Coll., 1986, Ind. U., 1988; DLitt (hon.), U. St. Thomas, 1977; D Pub. Adminstrn., Nat. Inst. Devel. Adminstrn., Thailand, 1991; LLD (hon.), U. Md., 1994. Rsch. analyst Ky. Dept. Revenue, Frankfort, 1954-55; vis. rsch. prof. U. Thammasat, Bangkok, Thailand, 1955-57; asst. dir. Inst. Tng. for Pub. Svc. Ind. U., 1957-58; successively asst. prof., assoc. prof. polit. sci., assoc. dir., Bur. Govt. U. Wis., 1958-62; exec. asst. to pres., sec. of univ. U. Mass., chancellor U. Mass., Boston, 1965-68; v.p. acad. affairs Ariz. State U., 1963-65; v.p., chancellor U. Mass., Boston, 1965-68; v.p. acad. and environ. affairs, 1981-95, prof. emeritus, 1995—; cons. AID, 1991-92; cons. AID, 1991-92; interim pres. Fla. Atlantic U., 1989, U. Md., Balt., 1994; bd. dirs. Ind. U. Found., chmn. 1972-87; chmn. Nat. Adv. Bd. on Internat. Edn. Programs, 1985-89. Contbr. articles to profl. jours. Bd. govs. Pub. Broadcasting Svc., 1973-82; bd. visitors Air U., 1974-81; chmn. Air Force Inst. Tech Subcom., 1976-81; mem. univ. adv. com. Am. Coun. Life Ins.; bd. dirs. Corp. Community Coun., 1976; mem. nat. adv. coun. Pan Am. Games, 1985; mem. adv. bd. Assocs. for Religious and Intellectual Life, 1984—; active United Way Ind. Centennial Commn. Mem. Am. Soc. Pub. Adminstrn. (pres. Ind. chpt. 1969-70, nat. chpt. 1972-73, nat. coun. from 1970, Ind. Soc. Chgo. (non-resident v.p. from 1976, Am. Polit. Sci. Assn. Assn. Asian Studies, Am. Coun. Edn., Am. Judicature Soc., Assn. Am. Univs. (exec. com. from 1978, chmn. com. on cons. 1984, health edn. com. from 1978, chmn. 1981-82), Ind. Soc. N.Y.C. Ind. Soc. Washington, Nat. Acad. Public Adminstrn., Ind. Acad., Explorers Club, Adelphia (hon.), Circumnavigators Club (N.Y.C.), Columbia Club (Indpls.), Skyline Club, Cosmos Club (Washington), St. Botolph (Boston), K.C. Elks, Phi Kappa Phi, Phi Alpha Theta, Pi Sigma Alpha, Beta Gamma Sigma, Kappa Sigma (worthy grand master 1985-87). Office: Ind U Spea # 316 Bloomington IN 47405

RYAN, JOHN WILLIAM, association executive; b. Manchester, N.H., Sept. 16, 1937; s. William Charles and Mary Ann (Marcoux) R.; m. Carol Jean Battaglia, Sept. 17, 1960; children: James, Kathleen, John, Michael. A.B., St. Anselm Coll., 1959; M.A., Niagara U., 1960; Ph.D., St. John's U., 1965. Asst. prof. history Gannon U., Erie, Pa., 1965-66; edn. specialist, div. grad. programs U.S. Office Edn., Washington, 1966-68; regional coordinator, grad. acad. programs U.S. Office Edn., 1968-70; dir. univ. programs Univ. Assos., Inc., Washington, 1970-72; asst. to pres., sec. Council of Grad. Schs. in U.S., Washington, 1972-80; exec. v.p. Renewables Research Inst., Annandale, Va., 1980-81; exec. dir. Worcester (Mass.) Consortium Higher Edn., 1981-89, N.H. Coll. and Univ. Coun., Manchester, 1989-93; cons. Contbr. articles to profl. jours. Mem. Am. Soc. Assn. Execs.

RYAN, JOHN WILLIAM, JR., construction-related consulting company executive; b. N.Y.C., Feb. 6, 1940; s. John William and Josephine E.; m. Cathy D. Kurtz, July 10, 1976; children—John William III, Kerry Elizabeth, Casey Andrew, Neil Alexander. B.S.E., Villanova U., 1962. With John W. Ryan Constr. Co. Inc., N.Y.C., 1962-88, chief exec. officer, 1972-88; chmn. bd. RBI Cons. Inc., N.Y.C., 1990—. Past pres. bd. dirs. Lincoln Hall Sch., Lincolndale, N.Y. Served with Air N.G., 1962-68. Named Gen. Contractor of Yr., N.J. Contractors Assn., 1978. Mem. Am. Arbitration Assn. Republican. Roman Catholic. Clubs: Union League, Sleepy Hollow Country.

RYAN, JOSEPH, lawyer; b. Seattle, Feb. 11, 1942; s. John Joseph and Jane (Wing) R.; m. Mary Katherine Gavin, Aug. 10, 1963; children: Michael Gavin, Kathleen Ann, Jennifer Jo. BA, U. Washington, 1964; JD, Columbia U., 1967. Bar: Calif. 1968, N.Y. 1983, D.C. 1983. Ptnr. O'Melveny & Myers, Los Angeles, 1967-94; exec. v.p., gen. counsel Marriott Internat., Inc., Washington, 1994—; teacher, lecturer N.Y. Law Jour. Author: Stating Your Case—How To Interview for a Job as a Lawyer, 1982, Take or Pay Contracts: Alive and Well in California, vol. 192, 1987, Current Investment Banking Activities in the United States, vol. 2, #15 M&A Report, 1988; co-author (with Lorin Fife) The Urban Lawyer, 1987; contbr. articles to law publs. Bd. dirs. Pasadena Playhouse, L.A., 1981-92, Planetary Soc., Pasadena, 1981, Westridge Sch., L.A., 1982-91, Natural History Mus. Los Angeles County, 1988-93. Capt. U.S. Army, 1968-70. Mem. ABA, N.Y. Bar Assn., D.C. Bar Assn., Calif. Bar Assn., Nat. Assn. Bond Lawyers (legis. com.), Bond Club L.A., Practicing Law Inst. (tchr., lectr.), CEB (tchr., lectr.). Pub. Securities Assn. (treas. regional com.), Nat. Assn. Rehab. and Housing Ofcls., N.Am. Securities Adminstrn. Assn., Calif. Club, Valley Hunt Club, Pacific Union Club, Columbia Tower Club. Republican. Roman Catholic. Avocations: running, biking, camping, hunting and fishing, boating. Home: 10836 Alloway Dr Potomac MD 20854 Office: Marriott Internat Inc Dept 52/923 The Marriott Dr Washington DC 20058

RYAN, JOSEPH W., JR., lawyer; b. Phila., June 24, 1948; s. Joseph W. Sr. and Marie R. (Hilgrube) R.; m. Mary Pat Law, Sept. 11, 1971; children: Caitlin, Joseph W. III. BA, St. Joseph's U., Phila., 1970; MA, Villanova U., 1971; JD, U. Va., 1978. Bar: Ohio 1978, U.S. Supreme Ct. 1982. Ptnr. Porter, Wright, Morris & Arthur, Columbus, Ohio, 1978—; lectr. Sch. Dentistry Ohio State U., Columbus, 1982-89, Continuing Legal Edn. Inst. 1984—. Author: Use of Demonstrative Evidence, 1985; assoc. editor Litigation News, 1986—. Trustee Columbus Zool. Assn., 1980-90; dir. Columbus Speech & Hearing Ctr., 1988—. Mem. ABA, Ohio State Bar Assn., Columbus Bar Assn., Internat. Assn. Def. Counsel, Am. Arbitration Assn. (panel of arbitrators). Republican. Roman Catholic. Office: Porter Wright Morris & Arthur 41 S High St Fl 30 Columbus OH 43215-6101

RYAN, JUDITH ANDRE, health care executive, hospital administrator, nurse; b. Vermillion, S.D., Sept. 11, 1936; d. Hugo Carl and Nelle Marie (Schultz) Andre; m. Darrell Richard Yates, Sept. 13, 1958 (div. June 1975); m. Gerald Odin Ryan, Dec. 22, 1982; children: Allison Marie, Matthew Andre. BSN, St. Olaf Coll., 1958; PhD in Hosp. and Health Care Adminstrn., U. Minn., 1983. Registered nurse, Minn. Staff nurse Mower County Pub. Health Nursing Services, Family Nursing Service, St. Paul, 1958-62; asst. exec. dir. govtl. and pub. relations Minn. Nurses Assn., Mpls., 1964-68; instr. St. Mary's Jr. Coll., Mpls., 1975-76; dir. nursing edn. Rochester Meth. Hosp., Minn., 1976-80; dep. exec. dir. Am. Nurses' Assn., Kansas City, Mo., 1980-81, exec. dir., 1982-89; v.p. Luth. Gen. Health Care System, Park Ridge, Ill., 1989-91, sr. v.p., 1991—; bd. govs. EcuMed, N.Y.C.; bd. dirs. The Kendall Co.; cons. in field. Author: Moving and Lifting Patients, 1970; assoc. editor Minn. Nursing Accent, 1964-68; contbr. articles to profl. jours., chpts. to books. Mem. exec. com. Minn. Comprehensive Health Planning Adv. Coun., 1968-76; trustee St. Olaf Coll. Bush Leadership fellow, 1978-79; recipient Disting. Alumnae award St. Olaf Coll., 1984. Mem. Am. Acad. Nurses, Am. Soc. Assn. Execs., Nat. League for Nursing, Nat. Commn. on Nursing, Sigma Theta Tau. Republican. Lutheran. Office: Luth Gen Health Sys 1775 Dempster St Park Ridge IL 60068-1173

RYAN, JUDITH LYNDAL, German language and literature educator; b. Sydney, Australia, Apr. 6, 1943; came to U.S., 1967; d. William Matthew and Kathleen (Ferris) O'Neil; m. Lawrence Ryan, Feb. 24, 1964 (div. 1985); children: Antony Lawrence, Vanessa Lyndal. B.A. with honors, U. Sydney, 1964; Dr. Phil., U. Munster, Westfalia, W. Ger., 1970. Research student U. Sydney, 1965; instr., asst. prof. then assoc. prof. German Smith Coll., Northampton, Mass., 1967-79; prof. German German Smith Coll., 1979—, Doris Silbert prof. humanities, 1982-85; prof. German and comparative lit. Harvard U., Cambridge, 1985—; vis. assoc. prof. Brown U., Providence, 1978-79. Author: Umschlag und Verwandlung, 1972, The Uncompleted Past, 1983 (Basilius award 1983); mem. editorial bd. German Quar., 1983—; mem. adv. bd. German Studies Rev., 1983—, PMLA, 1984—. NEH fellow, 1978; Humboldt-Stiftung grantee, 1970-71. Mem. MLA (del. 1973-75, 1977-79, programs com. 1980-83), AAUP (exec. Smith Coll. 1982-83). Office: Harvard U Dept German Cambridge MA 02138

RYAN, JUDITH W., geriatrics nurse, adult nurse practitioner, educator, researcher; b. Waterbury, Conn., Dec. 8, 1943; d. James Patrick Ryan and Edna (Swanson) Billings. BS, U. Conn., 1965; MS, Boston U., 1967; PhD, U. Md., 1984. RN, Md., Conn.; cert. adult nurse practitioner ANA. Instr. U. Conn., Storrs, 1967-69; asst. prof. Ind. U., Purdue U., Indpls., 1969-73; asst. prof. U. Md., Balt., 1973-82, dir. nursing and health care dept. family medicine, supportive care project, 1985-87, asst. prof. sch. nursing, 1987—; asst. prof. Coll. Notre Dame, Balt., 1982-83; dir. primary care adult nurse practitioner cert. program U. Md., 1976-82; arbitrator Health Claims Arbitration Program, Md., 1976—; mem. Md. Bd. Nursing, Balt., 1991—; bd. trustees Md. Nurses Assn. Polit. Action Com., Balt., treas., 1989-91. Contbr. articles to profl. jours. Named Distinguished Practitioner Nursing, Nat. Acad. Practice, 1984—. Mem. Md. Nurses Assn. (2d v.p. 1986-88, 92-93, nat. del. 1990-92), Md. Gerontological Assn., Sigma Theta Tau, Phi Kappa Phi. Home: 622 Lucia Ave Baltimore MD 21229 Office: U Md Sch Nursing Parsons Hall # 336 622 W Lombard St Baltimore MD 21201

RYAN, KENNETH JOHN, physician, educator; b. N.Y.C., Aug. 26, 1926; s. Joseph M. R.; m. Marion Elizabeth Kinney, June 8, 1948; children: Alison Leigh, Kenneth John, Christopher Elliot. Student, Northwestern U., 1946-48; M.D., Harvard U., 1952. Diplomate: Am. Bd. Obstetrics and Gynecology. Intern, then resident internal medicine Mass. Gen. Hosp., Boston, also Columbia-Presbyn. Med. Center, N.Y.C., 1952-54, 56-57; resident obstetrics and gynecology Boston Lying-in Hosp., also Free Hosp. for Women, Brookline, Mass., 1957-60; instr. obstetrics and gynecology Harvard U.; also dir. Harvard (Fearing Research Lab.), 1960-61; prof. obstetrics and gynecology, dir. dept. Western Res. U. Med. Sch., 1961-70; prof. reproductive biology, dept. obstetrics and gynecology U. Calif.-San Diego, La Jolla, 1970-73; Kate Macy Ladd prof., chmn. dept. obstetrics and gynecology Harvard U. Med. Sch., 1973-93, dir. Lab. Human Reprodn. and Reproductive Biology, 1974-93, Disting. prof., 1993—; chief staff Boston Hosp. for Women, 1973-80; chmn. dept. ob-gyn. Brigham Women's Hosp., Boston, 1980-93. Chmn. Nat. Commn. for Protection Human Subjects Biomed. and Behavioral Research, 1974-78. Recipient Schering award Harvard Med. Sch., 1951, Soma Weis award, 1952, Bordon award, 1952; Ernst Oppenheimer award, 1964; Max Weinstein award, 1970; fellow Mass. Gen. Hosp., 1954-56. Fellow Am. Cancer Soc.; mem. Am. Coll. Obstetricians and Gynecologists, Am. Soc. Biol. Chemists, Endocrine Soc., Soc. Gynecol. Investigation, Mass. Med. Soc., Am. Soc. Clin. Investigation, Am. Gynecol. Soc., Alpha Omega Alpha. Office: Brigham & Woman's Hosp 75 Francis St Boston MA 02115-6195

RYAN, KEVIN WILLIAM, research virologist, educator; b. Fort Dodge, Iowa, Dec. 8, 1952; s. Joseph Michael Ryan and Etoile Evelyn Werth; m. Mary Ellen Lyman, June 1, 1974; children: Matthew Lyman, Mark Joseph. BS, U. Iowa, 1978; PhD, U. Mich., 1984. Staff fellow Nat. Inst. of Allergy and Infectious Diseases/NIH, Bethesda, Md., 1984-86; rsch. asst. dept. virology and molecular biology St. Jude Children's Rsch. Hosp., Memphis, 1986-89, asst. mem., 1989—; asst. prof. pathology U. Tenn. Coll. Medicine, Memphis, 1994—. Contbr. articles to profl. jours. and tech. manuals. Predoctoral fellow Mich. Cancer Rsch. Inst., U. Mich., Ann Arbor, 1982. Mem. AAAS, Am. Soc. for Virology, Am. Soc. Microbiology, Soc. Gen. Microbiology, Radiol. Soc. N.Am., Sigma Xi. Roman Catholic. Avocations: golf, chess. Office: St Jude Childrens Rsch Hosp 332 N Lauderdale Memphis TN 38101

RYAN, LEHAN JEROME, lawyer; b. Des Moines, July 30, 1935; s. Lehan T. and Hannah (Cody) R.; m. Carol F. Crawford, Feb. 22, 1958; children: Dennis M., David L. BS, U. Iowa, 1957, JD, 1964. Bar: Minn. 1964, U.S. Dist. Ct. Minn. 1964, U.S. Ct. Appeals (8th cir.) 1964. Assoc. Oppenheimer, Wolff & Donnelly, St. Paul, 1964-68, ptnr., 1969—. Pres. St. Paul Jaycees, 1970; v.p. St. Paul Winter Carnival, 1974; bd. trustees U. Iowa Law Sch. Found., 1990—, U. Minn. Med. Found. 1991—. 1st lt. USAF, 1958-61. Recipient Ted Christian award St. Paul Jaycees, 1982. Fellow Am. Coll. Trust and Estate Counsel (Minn. state chmn. 1986-91); mem. Minn. Bar Assn. (chmn. legal edn. com. 1980, chmn. probate and trust law com. 1982-83, bd. govs. 1988-90), Ramsey County Bar Assn. (pres. 1987-88), St. Paul Area C. of C. (bd. dirs. 1987, 89, sec. 1989), Gyro Club (bd. dirs., treas. 1985-88), St. Paul Alea YMCA (bd. dirs. 1993—). Democrat. Office: Oppenheimer Wolff & Donnelly 1700 1st Bank Bldg Saint Paul MN 55101

RYAN, LEO VINCENT, business educator; b. Waukon, Iowa, Apr. 6, 1927; s. John Joseph and Mary Irene (O'Brien) R. BS, Marquette U., 1949; MBA, DePaul U., 1954; PhD, St. Louis U., 1958; postgrad., Catholic U. Am., 1951-52, Bradley U., 1952-54, Northwestern U., 1950; LLD, Seton Hall U., 1988. Joined Order Clerics of St. Viator, Roman Cath. Ch., 1950. Mem. faculty Marquette U., Milw., 1957-65; dir. continuing edn. summer sessions, coord. evening divs. Marquette U., 1959-65, prof. indsl. mgmt., 1964; prof. and chmn. dept. mgmt. Loyola U., Chgo., 1965-66; adj. prof. mgmt. Loyola U., 1967-69; dep. dir. Peace Corps, Lagos, Nigeria, 1966-67; dir. Western Nigeria Peace Corps, Ibadan, 1967-68; asst. superior gen. and treas. gen. Clerics of St. Viator, Rome, 1968-69; dir. edn. Am. province Clerics of St. Viator, Arlington Heights, Ill., 1969-74; pres. St. Viator High Sch., 1972-74; dean, prof. mgmt. Coll. Bus. Adminstrn. U. Notre Dame, Ind., 1975-80; dean Coll. Commerce DePaul U., 1980-88, prof. mgmt. Coll. Commerce, 1980—, Wicklander prof. profl. ethics, 1993—; dir. Peace Corps. tng. programs Marquette U., 1962-65; adj. prof. human devel. St. Mary's Coll. Winona, Minn., 1972-74; mem. nat. bd. Archdiocese Chgo., 1972-75, vice chmn., 1973-75; mem. nat. edn. com. U.S. Cath. Conf., 1971-75, mem. exec. com., 1973-75; mem. nat. adv. bd. Benedictine Sisters of Nauvoo, 1973-83; mem. nat. adv. coun. SBA, 1982-85, vice chmn. minority bus., 1982-85; exec. com. Chgo. chpt., 1982-84; vis. prof. U. Ife, Ibadan, 1967-68; mem. adv. bd. 1st Bank-Milw., 1991-93, chmn. trust audit com., 1980-85, chmn. audit and examination com., 1985-90, mem. bus. adv. coun., 1991-93; bd. dirs. Vilter Mfg. Co., external dir. Vilter ESOP, Filbert Corp., Vilter Internat. (name now Vilter Export Corp.), Henricksen & Co., Inc., Gebhardt Refrigeration Co., DePaul Bus. Ethics Inst., Cath. Theol. Union U. Chgo., 1992—, Ctr. for Enterprise Devel., 1993—; mem. fin. commn. Clerics of St. Viator, 1978—, mem. provincial chpt., 1985—; cons. Pontifical Commn. on Justice and Peace, 1968-70; vis. prof. Helsinki Sch. Econs., Mikkeli, Finland, 1990, 91, 94, Poznan (Poland) Sch. Mgmt., 1991, 92, 93; coord. Polish Am. summer program in econs. Acad. Econs., Poznan, 1991; Fulbright prof. Adam Mickiewicz U., Poland, 1993, 94, 95; co-chair bus. and profl. com. Archdiocese of Chgo. Sesquetennial Com. Out Reach Divsn. Ctrl. Planning Group, 1993-94. Mem. editl. bd. The Internat. Trade Jour., Internat. Jour. Value Based Mgmt., European Bus. Jour., Bus. Ethics Quar. Mem. Pres.'s Com. on Employment Handicapped, 1959-65, Wis. Gov.'s Com. on Employment Handicapped, 1959-65, Wis. Gov.'s Com. on UN, 1961-64, Burnham Park Planning Commn., 1982-88; bd. dirs. Ctr. Pastoral Liturgy U. Notre Dame, 1976-79, Lake Forest Grad. Sch. Mgmt., 1989-91; trustee St. Mary of Woods Coll., 1978-81; regent Seton Hall U., 1981-87, mem. acad. affairs com., 1981-87, chmn., 1983-87; trustee Cath. Theol. Union U. Chgo., 1992—; dir. Ctr. for Enterprise Devel., 1992—; fellow St. Edmunds Coll. Cambridge U., 1992; mem. Caht. Commn. Intellectual and Cultural Affairs, 1992. Recipient Freedom award Berlin Commn., 1961; chieftaincy title Asoju Atoaja of Oshogbo Oba Adenle I, Yorubaland, Nigeria, 1967; Brother Leo V. Ryan award created in his honor Cath. Bus. Edn. Assn., 1962; Ryan Scholars in Mgmt. established in his honor DePaul U., 1989, Outstanding Svc. award, 1991, 93; named Man of Year Jr. C. of C. Milw., 1959, Marquette U. Bus. Adminstrn. Alumni Man of Year, 1974, Tchr. of Yr. U. Notre Dame, 1980; recipient B'nai Brith Interfaith award Milw., 1963, Disting. Alumnus award DePaul U., 1976, Tchr. of Yr. award Beta Alpha Psi, Notre Dame U., 1980, Centennial Alumni Achievement award Marquette U., 1981, Boland Meml. Disting. Alumni award St. Louis U., 1989, Disting. Alumni and Bicentennial awards Jesuit Bus. Schs., 1989, Pres.' award St. Viator High Sch., 1992; Milw. Bd. Realtors travelling fellow, 1964, Nat. Assn. Purchasing Agts. faculty 1958, German Am. Acad. Exchange Coun. fellow, summer 1983, Presdl. fellow Am. Grad. Sch. of Internat. Mgmt., 1989, vis. scholar, 1995, Malone fellow in Islamic studies, 1990, fellow Kosciuszko Found. Adam Mickiewicz U., Poznan, Poland, 1990; scholar-in-residence Mgmt. Sch., Imperial Coll. Sci. and Tech., U. London, 1988, vis. scholar U. Calif., Berkeley, Spring, 1989; USIA Acad. Specialists grantee (3), Poland, 1991, 92, 93; fellow St. Edmund's Coll. Cambridge U., 1992; named vis. rsch. fellow Von Hugel Inst., St. Edmund's Coll., 1992-93. Mem. Cath. Bus. Edn. Assn. (nat. pres. 1960-62, nat. exec. bd. 1960-64), Assn. Sch. Bus. Ofcls. (nat. com. chmn. 1965-67), Am. Assembly Collegiate Schs. Bus. (com. internat. affairs 1977-84, chmn. 1981-84, bd. dirs. 1981-87, program chmn. 1979-80, exec. com., chmn. projects/svc. mgmt. com. 1984-86), Am. Fgn. Svc. Assn., Allamakee County Hist. Soc. (charter life), Acad. Internat. Bus., Acad. Mgmt. (social issues div., chmn. membership com. 1990-91), Nat. Returned Peace Corps Assn., Atomic Vets. Assn., August Derleth Soc., Chgo. Area Return Peace Corps Vols., Econ. Club Chgo., Chgo. Coun. Fgn. Rels., Coun. Fgn. Rels. (Chgo. com.), European Found. Mgmt. Edn., European Bus. Ethics Network, Soc. Bus. Ethics (mem. exec. com 1991—, pres. 1993-94), Dubuque County Hist. Soc., Iowa Hist. Soc., Fulbright Assn. (life), Internat. Assn. for Bus. and Soc. (founder), Internat. Soc. for Bus., Econs. and Ethics (charter), Internat. Trade and Fin. Assn. (founder, bd. dirs. 1989-92, v.p. membership 1991-92), Internat. Assn. Environ. Ethics, Internat. Learned Soc. Praxiology, Milw. Press Club (hon.), USS Mt. McKinley Reunion Assn. (hon. chaplain AGC-7 1989-93, Disting. Svc. award 1991), Alpha Sigma Nu, Alpha Kappa Psi (bd. dirs. found. 1985-91, vice chmn. 1987-91, chmn. scholarship com. 1987-91, chmn. devel. com. 1987, mem. exec. com. 1990-91, Bronze Disting. Svc. award 1949, Silver Disting. Svc. award 1958), Beta Alpha Psi, Beta Gamma Sigma (co-chair 75th Anniversary com. 1991-, faculty advisor DePaul chpt. 1986-92), Delta Mu Delta, Pi Gamma Mu, Tau Kappa Epsilon. Office: De Paul U Dept Mgmt 7016 1 E Jackson Blvd Chicago IL 60604-2287

RYAN, LEONARD EAMES, administrative law judge; b. Albion, N.Y., July 8, 1930; s. Bernard and Harriet Earle (Fitts) R.; m. Ann Allen, June 18, 1973; 1 child, Thomas Eames Allen-Ryan. Grad., Kent Sch., 1948; AB, U. Pa., 1954; JD, NYU, 1962. Bar: D.C. 1963, N.Y. 1963, U.S. Ct. Appeals (D.C. cir.) 1963, U.S. Dist. Ct. (so. and ea. dists.) N.Y. 1965, U.S. Ct. Appeals (2nd cir.) 1966, U.S. Supreme Ct. 1967. Reporter Upper Darby (Pa.) News, 1954; newsman AP, Pitts., Phila., Harrisburg, N.Y.C., 1955-62; reporter, spl. writer on law N.Y. Times, 1962-63; info. adviser corp. hqdrs. IBM, N.Y.C., 1963; trial atty. firm Perrell, Nielsen & Stephens, N.Y.C., 1964-66; trial atty. civil rights div. Dept. Justice, Washington, 1966-68; asst. to dir. bus. affairs CBS News, N.Y.C., 1968; program officer Office Govt. and Law, Ford Found., N.Y.C., 1968-74; pvt. practice law, cons. pub. affairs N.Y.C., 1974-91; v.p., sec. W. P. Carey & Co., Inc., Investment Bankers, N.Y.C., 1976-81; hearing examiner Family Ct. of State of N.Y., 1981-82; adminstrv. law judge N.Y. State Div. Human Rights, 1976-91, N.Y. State Dept. Health, 1982-91; adminstrv. law judge Office of Hearings and Appeals, San Rafael, Calif., 1991-93, Phila., 1993-94, N.Y.C., 1994—; impartial hearing officer Edn. for All Handicapped Children Act of 1975, 1976-91; hearing officer N.Y. State Dept. Agr. and Markets, 1987-91, N.Y. State Office Mental Retardation and Devel. Disabilities, 1989-91; arbitrator Small Claims Ct., N.Y.C., 1974-84; bd. dirs. Community Action for Legal Svcs. Inc., N.Y.C., 1971-77, vice-chmn., 1975-77; co-chmn. Citizens Com. to Save Legal Svcs., N.Y.C., 1975-76; bd. dirs. Lower East Side Svc. Ctr., N.Y.C., 1977-89. Author: (with Bernard Ryan Jr.) So You Want to Go Into Journalism, 1963; contbr. articles to profl. jours. Served with USAR, 1950-57. Mem. Am. Judicature Soc., Assn. of Bar of City of N.Y., N.Y. State Bar Assn., St. Elmo Club (Phila.), Heights Casino (Bklyn.). Home: 32 Orange St Brooklyn NY 11201

RYAN, LOUIS FARTHING, lawyer; b. Richmond, Va., Mar. 18, 1947; s. Louis Anthony and Catherine Louise (Farthing) R.; m. Prudence Elwell Hartshorn, Sept. 5, 1970. BSE, Princeton U., 1969; JD, U. Va., 1973. Bar: Va. 1973. Mgmt. cons. Arthur Andersen & Co., Boston, 1969-70; assoc. firm Kaufman and Canoles, Norfolk, Va., 1973-77; sec. Landmark Communications, Inc., Norfolk, 1977-85, v.p., gen. counsel, 1985-88, exec. v.p., gen. counsel, 1988—; sec. TeleCable Corp., Norfolk, 1984-85, v.p., gen. counsel, 1985-88., exec. v.p., gen. counsel, 1988-95. Bd. dirs. Feldman Chamber Music Soc., 1975-77, Jr. Achievement Tidewater, 1979-81, adv. coun., 1986—; bd. dirs., exec. v.p. Va. Symphony 1979-89, pres., 1983-84; vol. United Way, 1975-88, chmn. campaign Norfolk divsn., 1988; mem. Norfolk Harborfest Com., 1979; mem. allocation com. Bus. Consortium for Arts Support, South Hampton Roads, 1987—; chmn. auction Sta. WHRO-Pub. TV, 1987; bd. dirs., exec. com. Planning Coun., Norfolk, Va., 1988-93; bd. dirs. Leadership Hampton Rds., 1990—, chmn. budget com., 1993, bd. dirs.—; mem. exec. adv. coun. Coll. Bus. & Pub. Adminstrn., Old Dominion U., 1990—; mem. exec. steering com. Hampton Rds. Black Achiever Program, 1990-92, mem. Forward Hampton Roads, 1990-91; mem. memberships com. Chrysler Mus., 1991, com. 101 of Future of Hampton Roads, Inc., 1992—; bd. dirs. Norfolk Acad. Alumni, 1991—, Norfolk Festevents, 1994—. Mem. ABA, Va. Bar Assn., Va. State Bar (chmn. bus. law sect. 1980-81), Norfolk-Portsmouth Bar Assn., Am. Newspaper Pubs. Assn.

(legal affairs com. 1986—), Hampton Rds. C. of C. (bd. dirs. 1989—, Norfolk divsn. 1990—, treas. 1994), Town Point Club, Norfolk Yacht and Country Club, Country Club Va. Episcopalian. Office: Landmark Communications Inc 150 W Brambleton Ave Norfolk VA 23510-2018

RYAN, MARLEIGH GRAYER, Japanese language educator; b. N.Y.C., May 1, 1930; d. Harry and Betty (Hurwick) Grayer; m. Edward Ryan, June 4, 1950; 1 child, David Patrick. B.A., NYU, 1951; M.A., Columbia U., 1956, Ph.D., 1965; Cert., East Asian Inst., 1956; postgrad., Kyoto U., 1958-59. Research assoc. Columbia U., N.Y.C., 1960-61, lectr. Japanese, 1961-65, asst. prof., 1965-70, assoc. prof., 1970-72; vis. asst. prof. Yale U ., New Haven, 1966-67; assoc. prof. U. Iowa, Iowa City, 1972-75, prof., 1975-81, chmn. dept., 1972-81; prof. Japanese SUNY, New Paltz, 1981—, dean liberal arts and scis., 1981-90; vice chmn. seminar on modern Japan, Columbia U., 1984-85, chmn., 1985-86; co-chmn. N.Y. State Conf. on Asian Studies, 1986, editor, 1993—, mem. exec. com., 1993-96, sec., 1993—. Co-author: (with Herschel Webb) Research in Japanese Sources, 1965; author: Japan's First Modern Novel, 1967, The Development of Realism in the Fiction of Tsubouchi Shoyo, 1975; assoc. editor: Jour. Assn. Tchrs. Japanese, 1962-71, editor, 1971-75. East Asian Inst. fellow Columbia U., 1955; Ford Found. fellow, 1958-60; Japan Found. fellow, 1973, Woodrow Wilson Ctr. Internat. Scholars fellow, 1988-89; recipient Van. Am. Disting. Book award Columbia, 1968. Mem. MLA (sec. com. on teaching Japanese Lang. 1962-68, mem. del. assembly 1979-87, mem. exec. com. div. Asian lit. 1981-86), Assn. Tchrs. Japanese (exec. com. 1969-72, 74-77), Assn. Asian Studies (bd. dirs. 1975-78, coun. of confs., 1993—), Midwest Conf. Asian Studies (pres. 1980-81). Office: SUNY Ft # 414 New Paltz NY 12561 Studying the most difficult language in the world has taught me patience and tact. One learns what it is to sit completely still at the Japanese No theatre and absorb wondrous sights and sounds in an atmosphere of absolute peace. Discovering the stillness in movement is perhaps the most important lesson we in the West can derive from our Asian experience.

RYAN, MARY A., diplomat; b. New York, N.Y., Oct. 1, 1940. B.A., St. John's Univ., 1963, M.A., 1965. With Foreign Service, Dept. of State, 1966—; consular and adminstrv. officer Naples, Italy, 1966-69; personnel officer Am. Embassy, Tegucigalpa, Honduras, 1970-71; consular officer Am. Consulate Gen., Monterrey, Mexico, 1971-73; adminstrv. officer Bur. of African Affairs, Dept. of State, Washington, 1973-75, post mgmt. officer, 1975-77; career devel. officer Bur. of Personnel, Dept. of State, 1977-80; adminstrv. counselor Abidjan, Ivory Coast, 1980-81, Khartoum, Sudan, 1981-82; inspector, Office of Insp. Gen. Dept. of State, Washington, 1982-83, exec. dir. Bur. of European and Can. Affairs, 1983-85, exec. asst. to Under Sec. of State for Mgmt., 1985-88; ambassador to Swaziland, 1988-90; dep. asst. sec. Bur. of Consular Affairs, Washington, 1990; dir. Kuwait task force, 1990-91, ops. dir. UN spl. commn. on elimination of Iraqi weapons, 1991; dep. asst. sec. Bur. European & Can. Affairs, Washington, 1991-93; asst. sec. Bur. of Consular Affairs, Washington, 1993—. Office: Dept State Bureau of Consular Affairs 2201 C St NW Washington DC 20520

RYAN, MARY CATHERINE, pediatrician; b. N.Y.C., Mar. 22, 1938; d. Thomas Michael and Catherine (Scullin) McLaughlin; m. Enda Kieran Ryan, Feb. 8, 1969; children: Denise Marie, Kathleen May. BS in Chemistry, St. John's U., Bklyn., 1959; MD, NYU, 1963. Diplomate Am. Bd. Pediatrics. Cons. Hampton health dept. Va. State Dept. Health, 1969-71; med. coord. N.Y.C. Bur. Handicapped, 1971-72; asst. prof. pediatrics L.I. Hosp., Bklyn., 1972-73; pub. health clinician Fairfax County Health Dept., Fairfax, Va. 1973—; pvt. contractor pediatrics PHP Healthcare Corp., Fairfax, 1987-93. Tchr. religious edn. St. Thomas al Becket Ch., Reston, Va., 1978-81. Maj. M.C., U.S. Army, 1969. Fellow Am. Acad. Pediatrics; mem. AMA, Med. Soc. Va., No. Va. Pediatric Soc., Fairfax County Med. Soc., Soc. Devel. Pediatrics. Avocation: gardening. Home: 1423 Aldenbam Ln Reston VA 22090 Office: Fairfax County Health Dept 1850 Cameron Glen Dr Ste 100 Reston VA 22090

RYAN, MARY HEADD, nursing educator, administrator; b. Syracuse, N.Y., Mar. 18, 1951; d. Harry A. Headd and Anne E. Burke; m. Patrick H. Ryan, Sept. 30, 1989; 1 child, Paul. Diploma, St. Joseph's Hosp. Sch. Nursing, Syracuse, 1972; BSN magna cum laude, Boston Coll. Sch. Nursing, Chestnut Hill, Mass., 1974; MS, Syracuse U., 1977. RN, N.Y.; cert. nurse adminstr. Camp health dir. Clover Patch Camp, Glenville, N.Y., 1979-90; staff nurse New Eng. Deaconess Hosp., Brookline, Mass., 1972-73; head nurse, supr., instr. St. Joseph's Hosp. Health Ctr., Syracuse, 1974-85, 92—; assoc. adminstr. nursing Auburn (N.Y.) Meml. Hosp., 1985-92. Mem. Sigma Theta Tau.

RYAN, MEG, actress; b. Fairfield, Conn., Nov. 19, 1961; m. Dennis Quaid, 1991; 1 child, Jack Henry. Student, NYU. Appearances include (TV) One of the Boys, 1982, As The World Turns, 1982-84, Wild Side, 1985, (films) Rich and Famous, 1981, Amityville 3-D, 1983, Top Gun, 1986, Armed and Dangerous, 1986, Innerspace, 1987, Promised Land, 1987, D.O.A., 1988, The Presidio, 1988, When Harry Met Sally, 1989, Joe Versus the Volcano, 1990, The Doors, 1991, Prelude to a Kiss, 1992, Sleepless in Seattle, 1993, Flesh and Bone, 1993, When a Man Loves a Woman, 1994, Restoration, 1994, I.Q., 1994, French Kiss, 1995. Recipient Golden Apple award Hollywood Women's Press Club, 1989. Office: care ICM 8942 Wilshire Blvd Beverly Hills CA 90211*

RYAN, MICHAEL BEECHER, lawyer, former government official; b. Chgo., Aug. 20, 1936; s. Walter Joseph and Mary Agnes (Beecher) R.; m. Maria Chantal Wiesman, June 1, 1963; children—Mary, Catherine, Matthew. B.S. in Labor Relations, Manhattan Coll., 1957; J.D., U. Notre Dame, 1964. Bar: N.Y. 1964, Ill. 1991. With NLRB, 1964-91; sr. trial atty. NLRB, Peoria, Ill. region, 1968-74, dep. officer in charge, 1974-78, regional atty., 1978-91; exec. v.p. NLRB Union, 1968-69, pres., 1969-71; mem. Peoria Planning Commn., 1977-89, chmn., 1979-89; sole practice Peoria; adj. prof. labor relations Bradley U., 1972-74. Mem. Tri-County Land Use Adv. Com., 1978-82; Pres. Catholic Interracial Council Peoria, 1971-72, North Sterling Homeowners Assn., 1973-77. Served with AUS, 1958-61, Korea. Mem. Regional Attys. Guild (chmn. 1982-88), Wedgewood Country Club. Roman Catholic. Home: 3438 W Villa Rdg Apt A Peoria IL 61604-1739 also: E-9 Plantation Hale Kapaa Kapaa, Kauai HI 96746

RYAN, MICHAEL CLIFFORD, lawyer; b. N.Y.C., June 21, 1948; s. Cyril R. and Margaret (Glennon) R.; m. Patricia Dolan, Sept. 4, 1971; children: Bonnie, Cliff. AB, Boston Coll., 1970; JD, Harvard U., 1974. Bar: N.Y. 1975, U.S. Dist. Ct. (so. dist.) N.Y. 1975, U.S. Ct. Appeals (2d cir.) 1975. Assoc. Cadwalader Wickersham & Taft, N.Y.C., 1974-83, ptnr., 1983—; bd. dirs. Nat. Ctr. for Health Edn. Avocations: skiing, tennis, theater. Office: Cadwalader Wickersham & Taft 100 Maiden Ln New York NY 10038-4818

RYAN, MICHAEL LEE, lawyer; b. N.Y.C., Feb. 23, 1951; s. William Francis and Helen (Lee) R.; m. Julia A. Smith, Dec. 1, 1979; children: Matthew, Rachel. BA, Harvard U., 1973; JD, NYU, 1978. Bar: N.Y. 1979, Mass. 1980. Sr. editor E.P Dutton, N.Y.C., 1974-77; assoc. Cleary, Gottlieb, Steen & Hamilton, N.Y.C., 1978-80, 83-86, ptnr., 1986—; assoc. Ropes & Gray, Boston, 1980-82. Articles editor NYU Law Rev., 1977-78. Dir. Pub. Interest Law Found. NYU. Named Urban Fellow Office of Mayor, N.Y.C. 1973. Mem. Order of Coif. Office: 1 Liberty Plz New York NY 10006-1401

RYAN, NOEL, librarian, consultant; b. St. John, N.B., Canada, May 27, 1925; s. Fergus James and Evelyn Grace (Hayes) R.; m. Doreen Lillian Allison, Dec. 19, 1950; children: Colin Allison, Karen Jennifer. B.A., Sir George Williams U., Montreal, 1964; M.L.S., McGill U., 1967; M.B.A., Northland U., Toronto, 1963. Vice-pres. Temco Electric Mfg. Co., Montreal, 1949-57; owner, operator photo finishing co. Local Photo, Montreal, 1957-67; chief librarian Dorval (Que.) Pub. Library, 1967-69, Brampton (Ont.) Pub. Library, 1969-71; chief librarian Mississauga (Ont.) Library System, 1971-87, bldg. projects mgr., 1987-89. Joint author: Juxtapoised, 1974. Served with Can. Army, 1944-46, ETO. Mem. Toronto Black Watch Assn. Avocations: painting, making pots, writing poetry. Home and Office: 55 Falconer Dr Apt 35, Mississauga, ON Canada L5N 1B3

RYAN, NOLAN, former professional baseball player; b. Refugio, Tex., Jan. 31, 1947; s. Lynn Nolan and Martha (Hancock) R.; m. Ruth Elsie Holdruff,

June 26, 1967. Student, Alvin (Tex.) Jr. Coll., 1966-69. Pitcher N.Y. Mets, N.Y.C., 1966-71, Calif. Angels, 1972-79, Houston Astros, 1980-88, Texas Rangers, 1989-93; mem. Am. League All-Star Team, 1972, 73, 75, 79, Nat. League All-Star Team, 1981, 85. Author: (with Steve Jacobson) Nolan Ryan: Strike-Out King, 1975, (with Bill Libby) Nolan Ryan: The Other Game, 1977, (with Joe Torre) Pitching and Hitting, 1977, (with Harvey Frommer) Throwing Heat: The Autobiography of Nolan Ryan, 1988, (with Tom House) Nolan Ryan's Pitcher's Bible, 1991, (with Jerry Jenkins) Miracle Man: Nolan Ryan, The Autobiography, 1992, (with others) Kings of Hill, 1992. Served with AUS, 1967. Named Sporting News AL pitcher of yr., 1977. Holds over 50 Major League records including most seasons pitched (27), most strikeouts (5,714) and most no-hit games (7). Address: care Texas Rangers Arlington Stadium PO Box 1111 Arlington TX 76004*

RYAN, PATRICK G., insurance company executive; b. Milw., May 15, 1937; m. Shirley Welsh, Apr. 16, 1966; children—Patrick III, Robert J., Corbett M. BS, Northwestern U., 1959. Sales agt. Penn Mut., 1959-64; Pat Ryan & Assocs. Penn Mut., Chgo., 1964-71; chmn., pres. Ryan Ins. Group Inc., Chgo., 1971-82; pres., chief exec. officer Combined Internat. Corp. (now Aon Corp.), Northbrook, Ill., 1982—; bd. dirs., 1982—; chmn., pres., chief exec. officer Aon Corp., Chgo., 1990—; bd. dirs. Commonwealth Edison, Chgo., First Chgo. Corp., First Nat. Bank, Chgo., Gould Inc., Rolling Meadows, Ill. Past pres. Chgo. Boys Clubs; trustee Rush-Presbyterian-St. Luke's Med. Ctr., Chgo., Northwestern U., Field Mus. Natural History, Chgo. Recipient Disting. Mgr. award, Lake Forest Coll., Ill., 1983. Roman Catholic. Office: Aon Corp 123 N Wacker Dr #27 Chicago IL 60606-1700*

RYAN, PATRICK J., electric utility company executive; b. Chgo., July 31, 1938; s. Phillip W. and Estelle F. Ryan; m. Grace M. Marelo, Sept. 5, 1959; children: Rachel, Nicole. BS in Elect. Engring., U. Okla. 1961; hon. degree in mgmt. Edison Electric Inst., 1976. Registered profl. engr., Okla Western div. service mgr. Okla. Gas and Electric, Oklahoma City, 1971-73, chief environ. affairs, 1973-76, asst. v.p., 1976-78, treas., 1978-80, v.p. and treas., 1980-81, sr. v.p. and treas., 1981-84, exec. v.p. fin. and adminstrn., 1984-86, exec. v.p. and chief oper. officer, 1986-94, vice chmn. 1994—; bd. dirs. St. Anthony Hosp. Found., Inc., ARC, Oklahoma City, 1981-91, Last Frontier coun. Boy Scouts Am., 1985-91, United Way Cen. Okla., Blue Cross and Blue Shield Okla.; bd. visitors Coll. Engring. U. Okla.; bd. dirs. Funds IV, Witicha, Kans. Served with U.S. Army, 1962. Mem. U. Okla. Assocs., Okla. Soc. Profl. Engrs., NSPE, Okla. City C. of C. (bd. dirs.). Republican. Episcopalian. Clubs: Oklahoma City Golf and Country, Petroleum. Office: Okla Gas & Electric Co 101 N Robinson Ave Oklahoma City OK 73102-5501

RYAN, PATRICK JOHN, mining company executive; b. Krugersdorp, Transvaal, Republic of South Africa, Feb. 11, 1937; came to U.S., 1984; s. Maurice and Nora (Knapp) R.; m. Dorothy Barclay, Mar. 30, 1963; children: Jennifer, Jacqueline, Richard, Rosemary, Catherine. BSc in Mining/Geology, U. Witwatersrand, Johannesburg, South Africa, 1960, MSc in Geology, 1963, PhD in Geology, 1967. Sr. v.p. Phelps Dodge Corp., Phoenix, 1984—. Capt. South African Army, 1962. Mem. AIME, South Africa Inst. Mining and Metallurgy, South Africa Geol. Soc. Home: 5481 E Lupine Ave Scottsdale AZ 85254-5716 Office: Phelps Dodge Corp 2600 N Central Ave Phoenix AZ 85004-3050

RYAN, PATRICK MICHAEL, lawyer; b. Chgo., May 26, 1944; s. Edward Michael and Kathleen Teresa (Crimmins) R.; m. Holly Ann Daleske, Aug. 31, 1968; children: Rebecca Eileen, Brendan Patrick, Abigail Christine, Lucas Christopher. BA, St. Mary's Coll., Winona, Minn., 1966; JD, Marquette U., 1969. Bar: Wis. 1969. Law clk. Wis. Supreme Ct., Madison, 1969-70; ptnr. Quarles & Brady, Milw., 1970—; dir. and officer several pvt. bus. corps. Mem. ABA, Wis. Bar Assn., Milw. Bar Assn., University Club. Avocations: reading, sports. Home: 363 Huntington Dr Cedarburg WI 53012-9507 Office: Quarles & Brady 411 E Wisconsin Ave Milwaukee WI 53202-4409

RYAN, PHILIP BROWNE, investment banker; b. Holyoke, Mass., Dec. 11, 1942; s. Philip Francis and Claire Marie (Browne) R.; m. Judith Lee Biron, Aug. 24, 1968; children: Philip, Katherine. BS in Civil Engring., Worcester (Mass.) Poly. Inst., 1965; MBA, Harvard U., 1970. Salesman Exxon, Boston, 1965-68; v.p. The Bigelow Co., Inc., Boston, 1970—; bd. dirs. Health NE, Manchester, N.H., Elkin Coffee Inc., Concord, N.H., Pub. Svc. N.H., Manchester, Adage, Inc., West Chester, Pa., Amoskeag Bank Shares, Manchester. Vice chmn. Derryfield Sch., Manchester. Republican. Roman Catholic. Avocations: skiing, golf, music, reading. Home: 31 Oak Dr Bedford NH 03110-6032 Office: The Bigelow Co Inc 102 Bay St Manchester NH 03104-3008

RYAN, RANDEL EDWARD, JR., airline pilot; b. N.Y.C., Jan. 11, 1940; s. Randel Edward and Ann Augusta (Horwath) R.; m. Pamela Michael Wiley, May 12, 1962; children: Katherine, Gregory. BS in Sci., Trinity Coll., 1961. Quality control supr. Ideal Toy Corp., Jamaica, N.Y., 1961-62; airline pilot United Airlines, San Francisco, 1967—. Editor: The Lowdown, 1980-83. Pres., Highlands Community Assn., San Mateo, Calif., 1975; chmn. Com. to Re-elect County Supr., San Mateo, 1976; mediator San Mateo County, 1986—; arbitrator Better Bus. Bureau, 1988—; rep. Highlands Community Assn., San Mateo, 1970-86; coach Little League and Babe Ruth Baseball, San Mateo, 1979-83. Served to capt. USAF, 1962-68. Recipient Vandor award San Mateo PTA, 1976, awards of merit United Airlines, San Francisco, 1975, 79. Mem. Air Line Pilots Assn. (chmn. speakers panel 1983-86, community rels com. 1983-86, bd. dirs. 1986-89, 91-93, chmn. coun. 34 1991-93, vice-chmn. 1986-89, editor newspaper The Bayliner 1984-86, mem. contract study com. 1984-86, vice-chmn. MEC grievance com. 1989-91, chmn. MEC grievance rev. 1993—, mem. nat. hearing bd. 1994—).Democrat. Club: Highland Tennis (San Mateo). Home: 1768 Lexington Ave San Mateo CA 94402-4025 Office: United Airlines San Francisco Internat Airport San Francisco CA 94128

RYAN, RAY DARL, JR., academic administrator; b. Joliet, Ill., Dec. 2, 1945; s. Ray D. and Oral Ada (Smiley) R.; m. Marianne Ryan, Aug. 28, 1965; children: Kimberley, Kristin, Matthew. BS, U. Wis., Menomonie, 1970, MEd, U. Mo., 1973, EdD, 1975. Cert. vocat./tech. tchr., adminstr., chief sch. officer. Dep. supt. pub. instrn. New. Dept. Edn., Carson City; dep. supt. spl. programs Ariz. Dept. Edn., Phoenix, state dir., vocat. educator; exec. dir. Ctr. Edn. and Tng. for Employment Ohio State U., Columbus, assoc. dean rsch., internat. affairs; vice-chair Coun. Ednl. Devel. and Rsch., bd. dirs.; bd. advisors Marquis Who's Who, New Providence, N.J., rep. at large. Mem. OTT, Am. Vocat. Assoc., ASTD, Omicron Tau Theta. Home: 1080 Kirk Ave Columbus OH 43085-2925 Office: Ohio State U Ctr Edn and Tng Employment 1900 Kenny Rd Columbus OH 43210-1016

RYAN, RAYMOND D., retired steel company executive, insurance and marketing firm executive; b. Big Timber, Mont., Feb. 7, 1922; s. Robert Allen and Elsie (Beery) R.; m. Eunice Dale Burnett, Jan. 17, 1943; children: Raymond Brant, Brenda Ruth, Ronald Dale. BA, Mont. State U., 1948, JD (hon.), 1970; LLM, NYU, 1949. Bar: Mont. 1948. Tax acct. Geneva Steel, Provo, Utah, 1949-50; tax supr., asst. compt. Orinoco Mining Co., Puerto Ordaz, Venezuela, 1950-58; compt. Oliver Iron Mining Co. div. U.S. Steel, Duluth, Minn., 1958-61; v.p. U.S. Steel, Pitts., 1968-74; v.p. U.S. Steel, Caracas, 1974-75, v.p., treas., 1975-83; pres. The Evergreen Group Inc., Stamford, Conn., 1984-94, chmn., 1995—. With mil. police AUS, 1943-45, ETO. Mem. ABA, Duquesne Club (Pitts.), Allegheny Country Club (Sewickley), Metropolitan Club, Phi Sigma Kappa, Phi Delta Phi. Office: 300 Atlantic St Ste 301 Stamford CT 06901-3522 *Although luck and ambition are the basis of many apparently successful careers, true success comes from hard work, ethical relationships, dedication, and a willingness to accept responsibility.*

RYAN, READE HAINES, JR., lawyer; b. Plainfield, N.J., Jan. 4, 1937; s. Reade Haines and Anne Mary (Moment) R.; m. Joan Louise Larson, June 16, 1966; children: Reade Haines III, Rebecca Marie. AB, Princeton U., 1959; LLB, Harvard U., 1965. Bar: N.Y. 1966, Calif. 1985. Assoc. Shearman & Sterling, N.Y.C., 1965-73; ptnr. Shearman & Sterling, 1973—; lectr. Practicing Law Inst., 1977-88, Am. Law Inst.-ABA, 1979-94, Calif. Continuing Edn. of the Bar, 1995. Lt. USN, 1959-62. Mem. ABA, Internat. Bar Assn., Calif. State Bar Assn. (fin. instns. com.), N.Y. State Bar Assn., Assn. of Bar of City of N.Y., L.A. County Bar Assn., Beverly Hills Bar

---

Assn., L.A. County Bar Found. (trustee), Fin. Lawyers Conf. (trustee), The Calif. Club. Republican. Home: 201 Homewood Rd Los Angeles CA 90049-2709 Office: 725 S Figueroa St Fl 21 Los Angeles CA 90017-5524 also: 599 Lexington Ave New York NY 10022-6030

RYAN, REGINA CLAIRE (MRS. PAUL DEUTSCHMAN), editor, book packager, literary agent; b. N.Y.C., June 19, 1938; d. Edward F.X. and Kathryn Regina (Gallagher) R.; m. Paul Deutschman, Apr. 11, 1970. B.A., Trinity Coll., 1960; postgrad., New Sch. for Social Research, 1960-61, N.Y. U. Film Sch., 1961, N.Y. U. Grad. Sch. English, 1962-63. Copywriter trainee, sec. J. Walter Thompson Co., N.Y.C., 1960-64; asst. to mng. editor Alfred A. Knopf, Inc., N.Y.C., 1964-67; editor Alfred A. Knopf, Inc., 1967-75; editor-in-chief, v.p. Gen. Books div. Macmillan Pub. Co., N.Y.C., 1975-76; pres. Regina Ryan Pub. Enterprises, Inc., N.Y.C., 1976—. Co-author: Janice LaRouche's Strategies for Women at Work, 1984, 1987. Active Larchmont-Mamaroneck (Westchester) Young Republicans, 1960-64; campaign worker, speech writer mayoralty campaign, Larchmont, 1962, 64; mem. Manhattan Women's Polit. Caucus, 1972-74; mem. com. Jimmy Carter Presdl. Campaign.; mem., chmn. Sherman Democratic Town Com., 1985-86; elected Justice of the Peace, Sherman Ct., 1986—. Mem. PEN Am. Ctr., Women's Forum (bd. dirs. 1976-77, co-chair issues com. 1990-92), Am. Book Prodrs.' Assn. (pres. 1985-86, dir. 1985-88, 93-95), Women's Media Group, Nat. Women's Health Network, Nat. Abortion Rights Action League, Internat. Women's Com. on Human Rights, Planned Parenthood of Conn., The Mad Gardeners. Democrat. Office: 251 Central Park W New York NY 10024-4134 also: 3 Coburn Rd W Sherman CT 06784-2218

RYAN, ROBERT COLLINS, lawyer; b. Evanston, Ill., Sept. 15, 1953; s. Donald Thomas and Patricia J. (Collins) R.; m. Joanne Kay Holatta, Nov. 5, 1983. BA in Econs., BSIE with high honors, U. Ill., 1976; JD, Northwestern U., 1979. Bar: Ill. 1979, U.S. Dist. Ct. (no. dist.) Ill. 1980, U.S. Ct. Appeals (Fed. cir.) 1982, U.S. Supreme Ct. 1984. Assoc., Allegretti, Newitt, Witcoff & McAndrews, Ltd., Chgo., 1979-83, ptnr. 1983-88; founding ptnr. McAndrews, Held & Malloy, Ltd., Chgo., 1988—; lectr. engring. law Northwestern U. Tech. Inst., Evanston, Ill., 1981-85, adj. prof. engring. law, 1985-90; lectr. patent law & appellate practice John Marshall Law Sch., 1991-93, adj. prof. patent law, 1993—. Exec. editor Northwestern Jour. Internat. Law & Bus., 1978-79. Contbr. articles to profl. jours. James scholar U. Ill., 1976. Mem. ABA, Fed. Cir. Bar Assn., Intellectual Property Law Assn. Chgo., Licensing Execs. Soc., Tau Beta Pi, Phi Eta Sigma, Alpha Pi Mu, Phi Kappa Phi. Home: 61 Hawkins Cir Wheaton IL 60187-8464 Office: McAndrews Held & Malloy Ltd Atrium Ctr 34th Fl 500 W Madison St Chicago IL 60661-2511

RYAN, ROBERT JOHN, JR., agricultural cooperative executive; b. Boston, July 31, 1944; s. Robert John and Marjorie MacFarland (Collins) R.; m. Linda Marie Villa, Dec. 28, 1968; children—Robert, Melissa. BS in Mech. Engring., U. Vt., 1966; M.B.A., Cornell U., 1971. Asst. treas. Agway, Inc., Syracuse, N.Y., 1971-79, treas., 1979-82, v.p., treas., 1982—; dir. Curtice Burns, Inc., Rochester, N.Y., Blue Cross, Syracuse; adv. bd. Marine Midland Bank, Syracuse, 1980—. Pres. Syracuse Boys Club, 1983—. Served to lt. USN, 1967-70, Vietnam. Mem. Fin. Mgmt. Assn. Democrat. Roman Catholic. Avocations: skiing; golf.

RYAN, ROBERT SEIBERT, consulting company executive; b. Columbus, Ohio, July 25, 1922; s. Howard L. and Jannie Gertrude (McComis) R.; m. Esther Lee Moore, Mar. 15, 1947; children: Phillip Craig, Lynda Joyce, Lois Jean. BS in Indsl. Engring. Ohio State U., 1947. Registered profl. engr., Ohio, Ind. Maintenance foreman Internat. Harvester Co., Richmond, Ind., 1947-52; prin. welding engr. Battelle Meml. Inst., Columbus, 1952-55; dir. engring. Columbia Gas System, Columbus, 1955-67; sr. v.p. Columbia Gas System, Pitts., 1967-73; sr. v.p., dir. Columbia Gas Cos. in, Pa., W.Va., Md., N.Y., 1973-75; dir. Columbia Gas Distbn. Cos., N.Y., Md., Ky., Ohio, W.Va., Va., Ohio Energy and Resource Devel. Agy., 1975-76, Ohio Dept. Energy, 1977-80; mem. Gov.'s Cabinet; pres. Robert S. Ryan & Assocs., 1981—; chmn. bd. dirs. Resource Gen. Corp., 1995—. Contbr. articles profl. jours. Served to capt. U.S. Army, 1943-46, Japan. Recipient Disting. Alumnus award Ohio State U. Coll. Engring., 1970. Mem. NSPE, Am. Gas Assn., Pa. Gas Assn. (pres. 1974), Duquesne Club (Pitts), Capital Club (Columbus). Republican. Methodist. Avocation: golf. Home: 6566 Plesenton Dr S Columbus OH 43085-2931 Office: Robert S Ryan & Assocs 6566 Plesenton Dr S Columbus OH 43085-2931

RYAN, STEPHEN COLLISTER, funeral director; b. Salina, Kans. Jan. 10, 1942; s. Kenneth Richard and Janys (Collister) R.; m. Lynne Katheryn Slease, June 18, 1966; children: Scott Richard, Carrie Anne. BS in Bus. Adminstrn., U. Kans., 1964; Cert. in Mortuary Sci., Kans. U. Med. Ctr., 1965. Diplomate Acad. of Profl. Funeral Svc. Practice. Sec.-treas. Ryan Mortuary, Inc., Salina, 1969-80, pres., COO, 1980—. Contbr. articles to profl. jours. Mem., chmn. City Planning Commn., Salina, 1981-85; mem. Salina City Commn., 1985-93, mayor, 1987-88, 91-92; chmn. Govt. Bldg. Authority, Salina, 1990-91, 92-93. Capt. USAF, 1965-69. Mem. Nat. Selected Morticians (bd. dirs. 1993—), Nat. Funeral Dirs. Assn. (Spl. Recognition award 1991), Kans. Funeral Dirs. Assn. (bd. dirs. 1984-92, pres. 1990-91), Morticians of the S.W. (Kans. Funeral Dir. of Yr. 1991), Salina Area C. of C. (vice chair 1984-85, sec.-treas. 1994-95), Lions, Masons (Knight comdrs. ct. of honor, 32 KCCH), Shriners, Phi Gamma Delta. Republican. Lutheran. Avocations: golf, nautilus exercise. Home: 2313 Melrose Ln Salina KS 67401-3546 Office: Ryan Mortuary Inc 137 N 8th St Salina KS 67401-2605

RYAN, STEPHEN JOSEPH, JR., ophthalmology educator, university dean; b. Honolulu, Mar. 20, 1940; s. S.J. and Mildred Elizabeth (Farrer) F.; m. Anne Christine Mullady, Sept. 25, 1965; 1 dau., Patricia Anne. A.B., Providence Coll., 1961; M.D., Johns Hopkins U., 1965. Intern Bellevue Hosp., N.Y.C., 1965-66; resident Wilmer Inst. Ophthalmology, Johns Hopkins Hosp., Balt., 1966-69, chief resident, 1969-70; fellow Armed Force Inst. Pathology, Washington, 1970-71; instr. ophthalmology Johns Hopkins U., Balt., 1970-71, asst. prof., 1971-72, assoc. prof., 1972-74; prof., chmn. dept. ophthalmology Los Angeles County-U. So. Calif. Med. Ctr., L.A., 1974-95; acting head ophthalmology div., dept. surgery Children's Hosp., L.A., 1975-77; med. dir. Doheny Eye Inst. (formerly Estelle Doheny Eye Found.), L.A., 1977-86; chief of staff Doheny Eye Hosp., L.A., 1985-88; dean U. So. Calif. Sch. Medicine, L.A., 1991—; mem. advisory panel Calif. Med. Assn., 1975—. Editor: (with M.D. Andrews) A Survey of Ophthalmology--Manual for Medical Students, 1970, (with R.E. Smith) Selected Topics on the Eye in Systemic Disease, 1974, (with Dawson and Little) Retinal Diseases, 1985, (with others) Retina, 1989; assoc. editor: Ophthalmol. Surgery, 1974-85; mem. editorial bd. Am. Jour. Ophthalmology, 1981—, Internat. Ophthalmology, 1982—, Retina, 1983—, Graefes Archives, 1984—; contbr. articles to med. jours. Recipient cert. of merit AMA, 1971; Louis B. Mayer Scholar award Research to Prevent Blindness, 1973; Rear Adm. William Campbell Chambliss USN award, 1982. Mem. Wilmer Ophthal. Inst. Residents Assn., Am. Acad. Ophthalmology and Otolaryngology (award of Merit 1975), Am. Ophthal. Soc., Pan-Am. Assn. Ophthalmology, Assn. Univ. Profs. of Ophthalmology, L.A. Soc. Ophthalmology, AMA, Calif. Med. Assn., Los Angeles County Med. Assn., Pacific Coast Oto-Ophthal. Soc., L.A. Acad. Medicine, Pan Am. Assn. Microsurgery, Macula Soc, Retina Soc., Nat. Eye Care Project, Rsch. Study Club, Jules Gonin Club, Soc. Scholars of Johns Hopkins U. (life). Office: U So Calif Sch of Medicine 1975 Zonal Ave Los Angeles CA 90033

RYAN, SUZANNE IRENE, nursing educator; b. Yonkers, N.Y., Mar. 13, 1939; d. Edward Vincent and Winifred E. (Goemann) R. BA in Biology, Mt. St. Agnes Coll., Balt., 1962; BSN, Columbia U., 1967, MA in Nursing Svc., 1973, MEd in Nursing Edn., 1975; MS in Oncology, San Jose (Calif.) State Coll. U., 1982. RN, N.Y.; cert. AIDS educator, N.Y. Prof. nursing Molloy Coll., Rockville Centre, N.Y., 1971—, co-dir. health svcs., dir. ednl. programs, 1987-94, dir. health svcs., 1994—, health educator, 1992—, co-dir. mobile health van, administr. health edn., 1992—; pres., CEO SIR Enterprises, Inc., 1982—; photographer Molloy Coll. Pubs., 1991—; photographic dir. Bale Art, N.H., 1992—; mem. N.Y. State AIDS Coun., 1987—, L.I. Alcohol Consortium, 1987—; educator Nassau County Dept. Sr. Citizens Health, 1991—; photographer-in-residence Molloy Coll., 1992—; lectr. on landscape, wildlife and flower photography, L.I., N.H., Can., 1993—. Represented in permanent collections in photographic galleries in Carmel, Calif., Laconia, Wolfboro and Moultonboro, N.H., 1963—; photographer 4

---

books on Monterey Peninulsa, New Eng. and N.H.; writer, editor Health News Letter Molloy Coll., 1990—. Health educator Nassau County Dept. of Sr. Citizens Outreach Program, Molloy Coll., AIDS educator, 1991—; adminstr., chief AIDS counselor Interaction AIDS Counseling, Babylon, N.Y., 1992. USPHS fellow, 1962, Nat. Cancer Inst. fellow, 1981-82. Mem. AAUP, AAUW, Nat. Congress Oncology Nurses, N.Y. State Fedn. Health Educators, Inc., Nurses Assn. Counties L.I. Dist. 14, N.Y. State Nurses Assn., World Wildlife Orgn., Audubon Soc., Internat. Ctr. Photography, Nature Conservancy, Sierra Club, Sigma Theta Tau (Epsilon Kappa chpt., rsch. grantee 1985, 87). Roman Catholic. Avocation: writing, photography. Home: 16 Walker St Malverne NY 11565-1829

RYAN, SYLVESTER D., bishop; b. Catalina Island, Calif., Sept. 3, 1930. Grad., St. John's Sem., Camarillo, Calif. Ordained priest Roman Cath. Ch., 1957, titular bishop of Remesiana. Aux. bishop L.A., 1990-92; bishop Monterey, Calif., 1992—. Office: Chancery Office PO Box 2048 580 Fremont St Monterey CA 93940-3216*

RYAN, THERESE EILEEN, nursing administrator; b. Chgo., Mar. 22, 1952; d. William B. and Catherine T. (Fennell) R. BSN, Coll. of St. Theresa, Winona, Minn., 1974; MSN, Loyola U., 1979. RN, N.Y., Ill. Asst. head nurse Rush-Presbyn. St. Luke's Med. Ctr., Chgo., 1974-76; staff nurse Northwestern U. Hosp., Chgo., 1976-77; mem. faculty Wesley Passavant Sch. Nursing, Chgo., 1977-79; clin. nurse specialist U. Chgo. Med. Ctr., 1979-83; asst. dir. nursing Chgo. Lakeshore Hosp., 1983-87; assoc. adminstr. of nursing Hillside Hosp. L.I. Jewish Med. Ctr., Glen Oaks, N.Y., 1987—. Mem. Am. Psychiat. Nurses Assn., Nat. League Nursing. Democrat. Roman Catholic. Office: Hillside Hosp 75-59 263rd St Glen Oaks NY 11004

RYAN, THOMAS A., school system administrator. Supt. schs. Diocese of Grand Island, Nebr. Office: Office Schs Supt 311 W 17th PO Box 996 Grand Island NE 68802-0996

RYAN, THOMAS D., naval officer; b. Buffalo, July 4, 1939; s. Thomas Leo and Virginia Marguerita (Stoffel) R.; m. Jane Ann Gleixner, Aug. 25, 1962; children: Thomas, Timothy, Jennifer, Jeanette, Joanne. BSChemE, U. Notre Dame, 1961; MS in Nuclear Engring., U. Mich., 1964, PhD in Nuclear Engring., 1974. Commd. It. (j.g.) USN, 1961, advanced through grades to rear adm.; exec. officer USS Simon Bolivar (SSBN 641), Charleston, S.C., 1974-77; comdr. officer USS Batfish (SSN 681), Charleston, 1978-82; dep. comdr. Submarine Squadron 4, Charleston, 1982-83; sr. mem. nuclear propulsion Comdr.-in-Chief Pacific Fleet, Pearl Harbor, Hawaii, 1983-85; comdr. submarine devel. Squadron 12, New London, Conn., 1985-87; sr. fellow strategic study group U.S. Naval War Coll., Newport, R.I., 1987-88; dep. insp. gen. Dept. Def., Washington, 1988-90; comdr. Submarine Group 8, Naples, Italy, 1990—. Pres. coun. USO, Naples, 1990—. Decorated Legion of Merit. Mem. U.S. Naval Inst., U.S. Submarine League. Roman Catholic. Home: #87 Via Vecchia Delle Vigne, Pozzuoli Naples Italy Office: Submarine Group Eight PSC 810, Box 16 FPO AE 09619-3000

RYAN, THOMAS F., lawyer; b. Detroit, Nov. 4, 1943. BS, Ferris State U., 1965; JD magna cum laude, Wayne State U., 1971. Bar: Ill. 1972, U.S. Supreme Ct. 1978. Ptnr. Sidley & Austin, Chgo.; mem. adv. com. cir. rules 7th Fed Ct. Appeals. 1st lt. U.S. Army, 1966-68. Mem. Chgo. Bar Assn. (mem. jud. evaluation com.), 7th Cir. Bar Assn. (bd. govs. 1986-89, 2nd v.p. 1990-91, pres. 1991-92). Office: Sidley & Austin 1 First Nat Plz Chicago IL 60603

RYAN, THOMAS GRADY, lawyer; b. Evanston, Ill., Oct. 12, 1949; s. Jack T. and Betty Jane (Pokorney) R.; m. Caroline Gregory, Nov. 5, 1977; children: Maureen, Erin, Caroline, Emma. BA, Amherst Coll., 1972; JD, UCLA, 1975. Bar: Ill. 1975, U.S. Dist. Ct. (no. dist.) Ill. 1976, U.S. Ct. Appeals (7th crct.) 1976, U.S. Ct. Appeals (10th crct.) 1977, Wis. 1979, U.S. Dist. Ct. (ea., we. dists.) Wis. 1979, Ariz. 1986, U.S. Dist. Ct. Ariz. 1986, U.S. Ct. Appeals (9th crct.) 1993. Assoc. Isham, Lincoln & Beale, Chgo., 1975-79; ptnr. Minahan & Peterson, Milw., 1979-86, Lewis & Roca, Phoenix, 1986—. Contbr. articles to profl. jours. Mem. ABA, Ill. State Bar Assn., Wis. State Bar Assn. (Authorship award 1984), Ariz. State Bar Assn., Maricopa County Bar Assn. Roman Catholic. Avocations: reading, running, tennis. Home: 3651 E Denton Ln Paradise Valley AZ 85253-7508 Office: Lewis & Roca 40 N Central Ave Phoenix AZ 85004

RYAN, THOMAS JOSEPH, lawyer; b. Waltham, Mass., Sept. 10, 1945; s. Joseph H. and Mary (Murphy) R.; m. Margaret Atkins, June 21, 1969. BA, St. Lawrence U., 1968; JD with honors, Suffolk U., 1974; LLM in Trade Regulation, NYU, 1977; PMD, Harvard U. , 1982. Bar: Mass. 1974, N.Y. 1975, Wis. 1984. Sales rep. Gen. Foods Corp., New Haven, 1969-71, atty., White Plains, N.Y., 1974-76, sr. atty., 1976-77, counsel, 1977-80, sr. counsel, 1980-83; dir. legal svcs. Oscar Mayer Foods Corp., Madison, Wis., 1983-84, v.p., chief legal counsel, 1984—; bd. dirs. Oscar Mayer Found., Madison, 1984-86; mem. allocations com. Dane County United Way, 1984-88, cochair, 1987-88, bd. dirs. 1991—; chmn. legal com. Pet Food Inst., 1978-80; chmn. legal com. Am. Meat Inst., 1987-90. Trustee law alumni Suffolk U., 1982-85; alumni rep. admissions office St. Lawrence U., Canton, N.Y., 1983—; bd. dirs. Red Cross Dane County, 1991—, Ronald McDonald House, 1992—. Mem. ABA (anti-trust and corp. sects., corp. counseling com., Robinson-Parman com.), Wis. State Bar, Madison Repertory Theater (v.p. exec. com. bd. dirs. 1989—), Sigma Chi (chpt. trustee 1970-83). Clubs: Maple Bluff Country (mem. ho. com. 1985-89), Harvard Club of N.Y.C., Madison Club. Lodge: Kiwanis (chmn. maj. emphasis com. Madison 1986-90), Rotary. Office: Oscar Mayer Foods Corp PO Box 7188 Madison WI 53707-7188

RYAN, THOMAS TIMOTHY, JR., banker, lawyer, government official; b. Washington, June 13, 1945; s. Thomas Timothy and Elizabeth (Ockershausen) R.; m. Judith Rush, June 13, 1970; children: Kathryn, Michael. A.B., Villanova (Pa.) U., 1967; J.D., Am. U., 1973. Bar: D.C. 1973. Atty. NLRB, Washington, 1973-74, Balt. and Washington, 1974-75, 76-80; dep. gen. counsel Pres. Ford Com., 1975-76; solicitor of labor U.S. Dept. Labor, 1981-83; assoc., ptnr. Reed, Smith, Shaw & McClay and predecessor Pierson, Ball & Dowd, Washington, 1978-81, 83-90; dir. Office Thrift Supervision Dept. Treasury, Washington, 1990-93; mng. dir. J.P. Morgan Securities Inc., N.Y.C., 1993—; adj. prof. Georgetown U. Law Sch., 1979-83; mem. bd. overseas Pvt. Investment Corp., 1981-83; mem. bd. Program for Advancement of Tech. in India, 1985-90; bd. dirs. FDIC, RTC, Neighborhood Re-investment Corp., 1990-93. 1st lt. USAR, 1967-70. 1st lt. USAR, 1967-70. Mem. ABA, D.C. Bar Assn., Am. Coun. Young Polit. Leaders (bd. dirs. 1983-89, pres. 1985-88), Congl. Country Club, Army and Navy Club. Republican. Roman Catholic. Office: JP Morgan Securities 60 Wall St New York NY 10005-2807

RYAN, THOMAS W., treasurer manufacturing company; b. Detroit, Jan. 28, 1947; m. Barbara L. Schembri, Sept. 6, 1968; children: Thomas III, Kristie, Kelly, Stephanie, Michael. BSBA, Wayne State U., 1969. Contr. Leader Internat. Industries, 1973; contr. Kenosha mfg. complex Am. Motors Corp., Wis., 1974-78; contr. mktg. Am. Motors Corp., 1978-80, dir. fin. planning, 1981-82; dir. internat. operations Am. Motors Corp., Southfield, Mich., 1982-85; v.p. A.O. Smith Corp., Milw., 1985—, treas., 1987—; treas., contr., 1990—. Trustee Wis. Nat. Multiple Sclerosis Soc., Milw., 1986; mem. Zoning Bd. of Appeals, Whitefish Bay, Wis., 1987; bd. dirs., treas. A.O. Smith Found., 1987. Mem. Fin. Exec. Inst., Nat. Assn. Accts. Office: A O Smith Corp 11270 W Park Pl 1 Park Pla Milwaukee WI 53224

RYAN, TOM KREUSCH, cartoonist; b. Anderson, Ind., June 6, 1926; s. Francis Gavin and Mary Katherine (Kreusch) Ryan Smith; m. Joanne Faulkner, Dec. 19, 1947; children—Linda, Tim, Dan, Diane. Student, U. Notre Dame, 1945, U. Cin., 1946-47. Artist Del. Engraving Co., Muncie, Ind., 1950-54, Robinson Agy., Muncie, 1954-60; free-lance artist, 1960-65. Author: Best of Tumbleweeds, 1993; syndicated cartoonist Tumbleweeds, Lew Little Syndicate, 1965—; pub. 20 paperback book compilations of strips, 1970-87; created Tumbleweeds Candy, a sect. MGM Grand Theme Park, Las Vegas. Named Hon. 'Old Master Purdue U., 1978. Mem. Nat. Cartoonists Soc. (Outstanding Cartoonist cert. 1970, 80), Graphic Artists Guild. Roman Catholic.

RYAN, TULA FLESHMAN, health service consultant and nursing facility administrator; b. Rich Creek, Va., Feb. 5, 1927; d. John Elijah and Ophelia Kline (Cooper) Fleshman; m. James Joseph Ryan, May 1, 1948 (div. June 1973); children: John Keith (dec.), James Kenneth. Diploma in gen. nursing, Passaic (N.J.) Gen. Hosp., 1947; BS in Nursing, Ariz. State U., 1963; MA in Nursing Adminstrn., Columbia U., 1970; cert. in advanced nursing adminstrn., 1983, 88. Pub. health nurse City Health Dept, Newark, 1947-53; supr. nursing Vincent Pallotti Hosp., Morgantown, W.Va., 1953-55; instr. nursing Lewis-Gale Hosp., Roanoke, Va., 1955-60, Good Samaritan Hosp., Phoenix, 1963-67; asst. adminstr., dir. nursing services John C. Lincoln Hosp., Phoenix, 1970-76; adminstr. nursing Whittaker Corp. and Hosp. Corp. Internat., Jidah, Tabuk, Riyadh, Al-Ain, Abu Dhabi, 1976-83; cons. Al-Mutabighani Health Svc., Jubail Industrial City, Saudi Arabia, 1984—; adminstr. Portamedic, Phoenix, 1985; nursing adminstrn. cons. Thunderbird Health Care Ctr. and Phoenix Jewish Care Ctr., Phoenix, 1986-87; cons. nursing svcs. Manzanita Manor, Payson, Ariz., 1987; cons. patient svcs. and nursing adminstrn. Hinduja Nat. Hosp., Bombay, India, 1987-88; cons., health supr. Ariz. Cactus-Pine Girl Scout Coun., 1989-94. Vol. cmty. first aid instr., HIV/AIDS edn. spkrs. bur. Ctrl. Ariz. Chpt., ARC, 1992—; USPHS scholar, 1963. Mem. ANA (del. 1965), Ariz. Nurses Assn. (sec. 1963-64), Ariz. State Alumni Assn., Tchrs. Coll. Columbia U. Alumni Assn. Internat. of Camelback (life), Soroptomist. Avocations: gardening, hiking, quilting, reading the classics. Home and Office: 518 E Boca Raton Rd Phoenix AZ 85022-4716

RYAN, WILLIAM B. F., geologist; b. Troy, N.Y., Sept. 1, 1939; married, 1962; 2 children. BA, Williams Coll., 1961; PhD in Geology, Columbia U., 1971. Rsch. asst. oceanography Woods Hole Oceanographal Inst., 1961-62; rsch. asst. geologist Lamont-Doherty Geol. Observatory Columbia U., 1962-74, sr. rsch. assoc. geologist, 1974—. Co-editor: Deep Drilling Results in the Atlantic Ocean: Continental Margins & Paleoenvironment, 1979. Recipient Francis P. Shepard medal, Soc. Sedimentary Geology, 1993. Am. Geophysics Union, Sigma Xi. Achievements include research in marine geology and geophysics. Home: 12 Clinton Ave Nyack NY 10960 Office: Columbia U Dept Geology Lamont-Doherty Geological Obs Palisades NY 10964*

RYAN, WILLIAM FRANCIS, priest; b. Renfrew, Ont., Can., Apr. 4, 1925; s. William Patrick Ryan and Helen Mary Doneg. BA, Montreal U., 1951; MA in Labor Rels., St. Louis U., 1953; postgrad., Heythrop Coll., Oxon, Eng.; STL, St. Albert Coll., Louvain, 1958; PhD in Econs., Harvard U., 1964. Ordained priest Roman Catholic Ch., 1957. Asst. prof. econs. Loyola Coll., Montreal, Que., Can., 1963-65; nat. dir. Social Justice Office Can. Conf. Cath. Bishops, Ottawa, Ont., 1964-70, gen. sec., 1984-90; founding dir. Ctr. of Concern, Washington, 1970-78; nat. supr. Jesuit Order, Toronto, Ont., Can., 1978-84; chancellor Sch. Theology Regis Coll., Toronto, 1978-84; vis. sr. rsch. fellow Can. Inst. for Internat. Peace and Security, Ottawa, 1990-91; chair on Cath. social thought St. Paul U., Ottawa, 1991-92; dir. Jesuit Project on Ethics in Politics, Ottawa, 1992—; exec. sec. Inter-religious Peace Colloquium, Washington, 1975-78; bd. dirs. Roncalli Internat. Found., Montreal, 1979-83; North/South Inst., Ottawa, 1979-91; spl. advisor to Internat. Devel. Rsch. Ctr., Ottawa, 1993—; lectr. in field. Author: The Clergy and Economic Growth in Quebec, 1966; co-author: Religious as Contemplatives in the 80's, 1984; translator: The Primacy of Charity in Moral Theology, 1961; contbr. articles to profl. jours. Mem. Am. Econs. Assn. Avocations: hiking; skiing. Office: 169 Sunnyside Ave, Ottawa, ON Canada K1S 0R2

RYAN, WILLIAM FRANK, management consultant; b. Inkster, Mich., May 6, 1924; s. William Henry and Gertrude Mary (Kling) R.; m. Loke Waiau Akoni, Oct. 5, 1963; children: Ilima, Lokelani, Eugene. Student Georgetown U., 1948-49, Columbia U., 1951-52, U. Padua (Italy), 1950-51; B.A., U. Mich., 1948. Diplomatic assignments in Russia, Italy and Japan, 1949-53; investment broker N.Y.C., Detroit and Honolulu, 1953-63; mgmt. cons. Bus. Mgmt. Internat., Honolulu, 1963-68; officer, dir. numerous corps.; ins. and risk mgr. U. Mich., Ann Arbor, 1969-88; mem. Nat. Univ. Property Pool Ins. Study Group, 1969-70; chmn. ins. com. Mich. Council State Coll. Pres., 1971-73; mem. Nat. Task Force on Instl. Liability, 1974-76; exec. cons. William Ryan Risk Mgmt. Assocs., 1984-89; v.p. Higher Edn. Liability Mut. Ins. Co., 1988; chmn. adv. com. Assoc. Degree program in health care risk mgmt. Oakland Community Coll., 1984-88; pres. Veritas Ins. Corp, 1986-88; pres. Risk Mgmt. Internat. Ltd., 1986-90. Trustee Assn. Ind. Colls. and Univs. Mich. Workers Compensation Self-Ins. Fund; mem. Bishop Mus., Honolulu, Friends of Iolani Palace, Honolulu. Served to lt. (j.g.) USN, 1943-46. Recipient Instl. Risk Mgr. of Yr. award Bus. Ins. mag., 1981, Disting. Service award Assn. Ind. Colls. and Univs. of Mich., 1986. Mem. Am. Soc. Hosp. Risk Mgmt. (bd. dirs. 1981-84, pres. 1983), Univ. Risk Mgmt. and Ins. Assn. (dir.), Mich. Coll. and Univ. Risk Mgmt. Officers Assn. (chmn. 1973-75), Midwest Univ. Risk and Ins. Mgmt. Assn. (chmn. 1977-78), Hist. Soc. Mich., Nat. Trust for Hist. Preservation, Irish Georgian Soc., Am. Conf. for Irish Studies, Royal O'Connor Clan Assn. Democrat. Roman Catholic. Avocations: world travel, historical rsch. Home: 801 Center Dr Ann Arbor MI 48103-2851

RYAN, WILLIAM J., bank executive; b. 1943. With All Allstate, White Plains, N.Y., 1964-72, Essex Bank, Peabody, Mass., 1973-82, Bank New Eng. Corp., 1982-89; with People's Heritage Bank, Portland, Maine, 1989-90, pres., CEO, 1990—. Office: Peoples Heritage Fin Group 1 Portland Sq Portland ME 04101-4057

RYAN, WILLIAM JOSEPH, communications company executive; b. Nyack, N.Y., Apr. 14, 1932; s. William Joseph and Elizabeth (Langley) R.; m. Jane Householder, June 27, 1970; children: Ashley Allison, William Joseph, III. BA, U. Notre Dame, 1954. TV producer Jules Power Prodn., Chgo., 1954-56; pres., gen. mgr. Radio Naples, Naples, Fla., 1956-70; gen. mgr. Radio Naples (Fla.) div. Palmer Broadcasting, 1970-73; v.p., cable-radio Palmer Broadcasting, Fla. and Calif., 1973-80; v.p. cable Palmer Communications, Naples, 1980-82; pres. Palmer Communications, Inc., Des Moines, 1982-84, pres., chief exec. officer, 1984—; bd. dirs. Norwest Bank, Des Moines, C&S Bank, Ft. Myers., Fla., N. Collier Hosp. State committeeman Rep. Com., Collier County, Fla., 1970-72; pres. Navy League, Naples, local chpt. Am. Cancer Soc.; chmn. Collier County Econ. Devel. Coun.; bd. dirs. Philharm. Ctr. Arts, Naples Philharm., N. Collier Hosp. Recipient Walter Kaitz award Nat. Cable TV Assn. Mem. Cable Advt. Bur. (founding chmn., bd. dirs.), Econ. Develop. Coun. (chmn.), So. Cable Assn. (pres.), Fla. Cable Assn. (pres.), Fla. Assn. Broadcasters (pres.), Cable TV Pioneers, Broadcast Pioneers, Cable TV Adminstrn. and Mktg. Soc. (Grand Tammy award 1981), Cellular Telephone Industry Assn. (bd. dirs.), Naples C. of C. (pres.), Royal Poinciana Club, Rotary, KC (grand knight). Office: Palmer Comm Inc 12800 University Dr Ste 500 Fort Myers FL 33907-5337

RYAN, WILLIAM MATTHEW, lineman, state legislator; b. Great Falls, Mont., June 28, 1955; s. William Duncan and Jeanette Rosette (Merrill) R.; m. Elaine Louise Brastrup, Jan. 19, 1974; children: Jennifer, Kelli, Katie. Grad., Great Falls. Cert. journeyman, lineman. Meter reader Mont. Power Co., Great Falls, 1973, head meter reader, 1974, dispatcher, 1975, groundman, 1976-79, apprentice, 1979-82, lineman, 1982—; mem. Ho. of Reps. Mont. State Legislature, Helena, 1993—; instr. Mont. Power Apprentice Program, 1982—. Mem. NAACP, Internat. Brotherhood Elec. Workers (local 44, unit v.p. 1984—, officer exam bd. 1988—, sec. Joint Apprenticeship Tng. Com. 1988—), Rocky Mountain Coord. Assn., Russell Country Sportsman, Walleyes Unlimited. Democrat. Roman Catholic. Avocations: rose gardening, fishing, hunting, youth coach. Home: 8 18th Ave S Great Falls MT 59405-4113 Office: Mont Power Co 100 1st St SW Great Falls MT 59404-2880

RYAN-JOHNSON, DEBORAH, principal. Prin. West Ridge Elem. Sch., Greece, N.Y. Office: West Ridge Elem Sch 200 Alcott Rd Greece NY 14626-2424

RYANS, YVONNE, principal. Prin. Richland High Sch., Wash., 1994—. Office: Richland High Sch 930 Long Ave Richland WA 99352

RYBCZYNSKI, WITOLD MARIAN, architect, educator, writer; b. Edinburgh, Scotland, Mar. 1, 1943; emigrated to Can., 1953; s. Witold Kasimir and Anna Jadwiga (Hofman) R.; m. Shirley Hallam, Nov. 15, 1974. Diploma, Loyola Coll., Montreal, 1960; B.Arch., McGill U., 1966,

M.Arch., 1972. Pvt. practice architecture Montreal, 1970-82; research assoc. McGill U., Montreal, 1972-75, asst. prof. architecture, 1975-80, assoc. prof., 1980-86, prof., 1986-93; Meyerson prof. of Urbanism U. Pa., 1994—; cons. UN, Manila, 1976, Internat. Devel. Research Ctr., Ottawa, 1977, Banco de Mex., 1979-80. Author: Paper Heroes: A Review of Appropriate Technology, 1980, Taming the Tiger: The Struggle to Control Technology, 1983, Home: A Short History of an Idea, 1986, The Most Beautiful House in the World, 1989, Waiting for the Weekend, 1991, Looking Around: A Journey Through Architecture, 1992, A Place for Art, 1993; contbg. editor Saturday Night, 1990—; adv. bd. Encyclopedia Americana. Recipient QSPELL lit. prize for nonfiction, 1988, 89, Prix Paul-Henri Lapointe, 1988, Progressive Architecture Design award, 1991, Alfred Jurzykowski Found. award, 1993; Ballard Real Estate scholar, 1994-95. Fellow AIA (hon.); mem. Authors Guild. Home: 230 Rex Ave Philadelphia PA 19118 Office: Grad Sch Fine Arts U Pa 215 Meyerson Hall Philadelphia PA 19104

RYBURN, SAMUEL MCCHESNEY, marketing executive; b. Morristown, Tenn., Oct. 25, 1914; s. Samuel McChesney and Mary Belle (Whittaker) R.; m. Margaret Beverly Huse, June 5, 1943; children: John Huse, Marie DuPlessis. B.S., U. Ala., 1936; postgrad., U. Vienna, Austria, 1937-38; M.B.A., Boston Coll., 1962. Vice pres. Boston Capital Corp., 1960-72; v.p. Urban Nat. Corp., Boston, 1972-73, Am. Research and Devel. Co., Boston, 1973-77; pres. Textron Adv. Group Inc., Providence, 1977-80; advisor Egypt-Sudan Integration Fund, Cairo, 1985; advisor FocoInsa S.A., Guadalajara, Mexico, 1982, Consomado S.A. Panama, 1984, Mohammad Ali Habib Group, Karachi, Pakistan, 1986, Capital Markets Authority Govt. of Egypt, 1987, agy. for investment and free zones Govt. of Egypt, 1988, Phatra Thanakit Co. Ltd., Bangkok, 1988-89, Kenya Capital Corp., 1989, Adv. Jamaica Capital Corp., 1992. Pres. bd. trustees Charles River Sch., Dover, Mass., 1961-64; trustee Hale Reservation, Boston, 1963-69; v.p. Dover Found., 1965-67, Nat. Inst. Campus Ministries, Boston, 1980-81. Lt. comdr. USN, 1941-45, PTO. Recipient Gamma Sigma Epsilon award, Internat. Scholarship award. Mem. Am. Chem. Soc., Nat. Venture Capital Assn., Am. Rock Garden Soc. (chmn. New Eng. chpt.), Phi Gamma Delta. Roman Catholic. Clubs: Dedham Country and Polo, Marshall St. Hist. Home: 33 Wilsondale St Dover MA 02030-2260

RYCE, DONALD THEODORE, lawyer; b. New Orleans, Dec. 15, 1943; s. Donald Theodore and Martha (Herndon) R.; m. Claudine Dianne Walker, July 8, 1984; children: Ted, Martha, Jimmy. BA, U. Fla., 1966, JD, 1968. Bar: Fla. 1968, U.S. Dist. Ct. (so. dist.) Fla. 1972, U.S. Ct. Appeals (5th and 11th cirs.) 1973; approved arbitrator Broward County Sheriff's Office. Jud. law clk. Fla. Dist. Ct. Appeals (4th cir.), West Palm Beach, 1968-70; ptnr. Hogg, Allen, Ryce, Norton & Blue, Miami, Fla., 1970-89; pvt. practice Miami, 1989—; co-chmn. liaison com. labor and employment sect. NLRB, Fla., 1990—, mem. publs. com., 1990—, exec. coun. labor and employment sect. Mem. Fla. Police Chiefs Edn. Rsch. Found. (Leadership award 1993). Mem. ABA, Miami Rotary Club, Microcomputer Edn. for Employment of the Disabled (bus. adv. coun.), Winter Haven C. of C. (Cmty. Leadership award 1994). Episcopalian. Avocations: tennis, gourmet cooking. Home: 23700 SW 162nd Ave Homestead FL 33031-1310 Office: Internat Pl 100 SE 2d St Ste 2600 Miami FL 33131

RYCHECK, JAYNE BOGUS (MRS. ROY RICHARD RYCHECK), retired educational administrator; b. Schenectady; d. Peter and Sylvia (Cywinski) Bogus; M.A., N.Y. U., 1953; B.S., State U. N.Y., Albany, 1941; postgrad. Syracuse U., 1957-66; m. R. Richard Rycheck, July 26, 1942. Tchr. various schs., 1935-43; elementary sch. tchr. Schenectady (N.Y.) City Schs., 1943-51, leadership intern, 1951-52, elementary sch. prin., 1952-61, dir. spl. edn., 1961-72. Instr. Russell Sage Coll., 1955-58, State U. N.Y., Oneonta, 1956; cons. bur. handicapped children N.Y. Edn. Dept., 1966-76, mem. commrs. and hoc coms., 1964-72, State Planning Com. Insts. for In-Service Edn., 1964-67; rep. to Community Welfare Council Schenectady County, 1961-62; adv. council N.Y. State Joint Legislative Com. Mental and Phys. Handicapped, 1970-72; mem. adv. com. Schenectady County Office for Aging, 1976-81, vice chmn., 1977-78, chmn., 1978-81; advisory com. Older Ams. Act program N.Y. State Office of Aging, 1977-80. Trustee, chmn. edn. Schenectady Mus., 1974-77; mem. human services adv. com. Schenectady County Community Coll., 1977-92; rec. sec. Ladies of Charity, 1992-94, Schenectady-Albany diocese Cath. Daus. Ct. 128, 1992, Our Lady of Fatima Ch. Rosary Soc., 1981—; chair, coord sr. club activities Our Lady of Fatima Ch., 1981-92. Recipient Humanitarian service awards United Cerebral Palsy Schenectady County, 1966, 67, Capital dist. Assn. for Brain-Injured Children, 1967, Today's Woman award Schenectady YWCA, 1987, various citations from N.Y. State Sen. and Assembly, Am. Assn. Ret. People, AAUW, Schenectady County Legis., N.Y. State Legis., 1986, and others; named Sr. Citizen of Yr. Schenectady County, 1986; recipient Meritorious Alumni award State U. N.Y. Coll. at Oneonta, 1972; Capitol Dist. Speech and Hearing award, 1972, Distinguished Service award N.Y. Fedn. chpts. Council for Exceptional Children, 1972, Joseph P. Kennedy, Jr. Found. award for outstanding activity for the mentally retarded, 1972, Achievement award for contbns. to quality of life for sr. citizens N.Y. State Legislature, 1979, Disting. Service award Council Adminstrs. Spl. Edn., 1980, N.Y. State Achievement award by Senate Com. on Aging and Assembly Standing Com. on Aging for outstanding dedication to task improving quality on N.Y. State sr. citizen, 1986, Schenectady YWCA Recognition award for Today's Women, 1987; cert. of appreciation for community service by the City of Schenectady Coun. and Mayor Karen B. Johnson, 1986; cert. of merit for outstanding com. service N.Y. State Senator Hugh T. Farley, 1986, cert. in recognition of valuable pub. service Schenectady County Bd. of Reps., 1986, citation N.Y. State Assembly, 1986. Mem. N.Y. State (sec. 1967-68), Nat. councils adminstrs. spl. edn., Assn. Childhood Edn. (state sec. 1952-55, state exec. bd. 1951-59), Council Exceptional Children (mem. chpt. regional and state bds. 1966-78, state regional dir. 1966-68, state adv. bd. 1966-72, v.p. 1968-69, state pres. 1970), Schenectady County Assn. Childhood Edn. (treas. and v.p. 1952), N.Y. State Assn. Childhood Edn. Internat. (sec., v.p. 1962-65), Am. Assn. Mental Deficiency, N.Y. State Assn. Brain-Injured Children (state adv. bd. 1963-67, state adv. bd. 1966-72), Nat. Soc. Autistic Children, Assn. Retarded Children (adv. bd.), Gifted Children Soc. (adv. com.), Schenectady C. of C. (edn. com.), Schenectady County Ret. Tchrs. Assn. (v.p. 1973, pres. 1974-76), AARP (program com. chpt. #490 1973-76, legis. chmn., dir. 1981-84, cert. of appreciation for dedicated service 1986, 87), AAUW (topic chmn. 1977-79, chpt. Name Grant honoree 1981), N.Y. Assn. Elementary Prins. (hon. life), N.Y. State Ret. Tchrs. Assn. (county dir. Eastern zone, del. state conv. 1974-76), Schenectady County Hist. Soc. (rec. sec. 1982-84, 92—, dir. exec. bd. 1982-84, 1st v.p. 1986-87), Delta Kappa Gamma (chmn. chpt. profl. affairs com. 1972-76, del. state legis. forum 1974-79, mem. state com. profl. affairs 1974-75). Contbr. articles to publs. Home: 1537 Kingston Ave Schenectady NY 12308-17

RYCHLAK, JOSEPH FRANK, psychology educator, theoretician; b. Cudahy, Wis., Dec. 17, 1928; s. Joseph Walter and Helen Mary (Bieniek) R.; m. Lenora Pearl Smith, June 16, 1956; children: Ronald, Stephanie. B.S., U. Wis., 1953; M.A., Ohio State U., 1954, Ph.D., 1957. Diplomate Am. Bd. Examiners in Profl. Psychology. Asst. prof. psychology Fla. State U., Tallahassee, 1957-58, Washington State U., Pullman, 1958-61; assoc. prof., then prof. psychology St. Louis U., 1961-69; prof. psychology Purdue U., West Lafayette, Ind., 1969-83, interim dept. head, 1979-80; prof. Loyola U. Chgo., 1983—, Maude C. Clarke prof. humanistic psychology, 1983—; dir. Human Relations Ctr., Pullman, Wash., 1958-61; research cons. AT&T, 1957-82. Author: The Psychology of Rigorous Humanism, 1977, 2d edit., 1988, Discovering Free Will and Personal Responsibility, 1979, A Philosophy of Science for Personality Theory, 2d edit., 1981, Personality and Life Style of Young Male Managers, 1982, (with N. Cameron) Personality Development and Psychopathology, 2d edit., 1985, Artificial Intelligence and Human Reason: A Teleological Critique, 1991; assoc. editor Psychotherapy: Theory, Research and Practice, 1965-76, Jour. Mind and Behavior, 1985-94, Logical Learning Theory: A Human Teleology and Its Empirical Support, 1994. With USAF, 1946-49. Named Outstanding Contbr. to Human Understanding, Internat. Assn. Social Psychiatry, 1971. Fellow Am. Psychol. Assn. (div. 24 pres. 1977-78, 86-87), Am. Psychol. Soc.; mem. Soc. Personality Assessment, Phi Beta Kappa. Roman Catholic. Home: 916 Michigan Ave Apt 2 Evanston IL 60202-1463 Office: Loyola U Chgo Dept Psychology 6525 N Sheridan Rd Chicago IL 60626-5311 *From my father I learned to have a sense of purpose, work hard, and assume responsibility. From my mother I learned not to take myself too seriously, and to realize that my achievements are never entirely up to me.*

RYCKMAN, DEVERE WELLINGTON, consulting environmental engineer; b. South Boardman, Mich., May 27, 1924; s. Seymour Willard and LaVerne Eliza (Jenkins) R.; m. Betty Jane Rendall, May 28, 1949; children—Mark, Jill, Stewart. Student, U. Maine at Orono, 1941-43; B.S. in Civil Engring, Rensselaer Poly. Inst., 1944; M.S. in Civil Engring, Mich. State U., 1949; Sc.D., Mass. Inst. Tech., 1956. Diplomate: Am. Acad. Environ. Engrs. Cons. san. engr. Frank R. Theroux & Assos., East Lansing, Mich., 1946-53; environ. engr., research asst. Mass. Inst. Tech., 1953-56; A.P. Greensfelder prof. environ. engring. Washington U., St. Louis, 1956-69; founder, pres. Ryckman/Edgerley/Tomlinson & Assos., St. Louis, 1956-75; pres., dir. Reta/Nolte & Assos., San Francisco, 1974-76; founder, mem. bd. dirs. D.W. Ryckman & Assos., St. Louis, 1975—; also Ryckman's Emergency Action and Cons. Team (REACT); asst. prof. Mich. State U., 1946-53; vis. prof. U. Hawaii, Honolulu, 1962-63; pres., dir. Environ. Triple S Co., St. Louis, 1969-75. Contbr. articles to profl. jours. Mem., dir. Mo. Gov.'s Sci. Adv. Bd., 1959-66; mem. Washington Architect and Engrs. Pub. Affairs Conf., 1969-75; founder grad. program environ. engring. Washington U.; mem. adv. bd. Salvation Army, 1987—; bd. dirs. Ctr. for Biology, Washington U., 1964-70, Arts and Edn. Fund, St. Louis, 1970-75; chmn. Salvation Army Bequest & Endowment Fund, 1991—. Served with USNR, 1944-46. Mem. ASCE (Profl. Recognition award 1991), MIT Alumni (dir. leadership fund 1970-74), Am. Water Works Assn. (Man of Yr. 1965), Engrs. Club St Louis (award of merit 1970, Hon. Mem. award 1993), Cons. Engring. Coun. U.S. (Grand Conceptor award for excellence in design 1969), Cons. Engrs. Coun. Mo. (dir. 1971-75, pres. 1973-75), Nat. Soc. Profl. Engrs., Air Pollution Control Assn., Water Environment Fedn., Assn. Environ. Engring. Profls., Sigma Xi, Tau Beta Pi, Chi Epsilon, Lambda Chi Alpha. Republican. Congregationalist (chmn. exec. com., bd. deacons, bd. Christian edn. 1960-72, chmn. stewardship campaign 1992-93). Clubs: Washington U. Century, Masons, Shriners, Rotary (mem. program and membership coms.). Patentee in field. Address: 1733 S Vandeventer Saint Louis MO 63110

RYCROFT, DONALD CAHILL, insurance executive; b. Chgo., Jan. 3, 1938; s. Ernest C. and Helen C. (Cahill) R.; m. Sabina Bielawski; children—Deborah, Laura, Taylor, Elliot. B.S., Northwestern U., 1960. Chartered financial analyst. Sales rep. Penn Mut. Life Ins. Co., Chgo., 1960-62; investment analyst Continental Assurance Co., Chgo., 1962-67; asst. treas. Continental Assurance Co., 1967-70, treas., 1970-75, v.p., dir. investments, 1973—; also chmn. com. for separate account B; asst. treas. Continental Casualty Co., 1967—; v.p., dir. in investments, 1973—; treas. Valley Forge Life Ins. Co., 1970-75; pres., dir. CNA Income Shares Inc.; sr. v.p., treas. Continental Assurance and Continental Casualty Co., Chgo., 1993—. Alumni adviser Phi Delta Theta, Northwestern U., 1965-70. Served with U.S. Army, 1961. Mem. Transp. Securities Club of Chgo. (past pres.), Investment Analysts Soc. Chgo., Sunset Ridge Country Club (Winnetka, Ill.). Home: 1133 Taylorsport Ln Winnetka IL 60093-2015 Office: Continental Assurance Co CNA Pla Chicago IL 60685

RYCUS, MITCHELL JULIAN, urban planning educator, urban security and energy planning consultant; b. Detroit, June 20, 1932; s. Samuel Israel and Esther (Mitnick) R.; m. Carole Ann Lepofsky, Aug. 31, 1958; children: Lisa Karen Rycus Mikalonis, Peter Todd. BS in Math., U. Mich., 1958, MS in Math., 1961, MS in Physics, 1965, PhD in Urban and Regional Planning, 1976. Asst. rsch. scientist radiation lab. U. Mich., Ann Arbor, 1958-61, pvt. cons. extension gaming svc., 1972-77, rsch. assoc. Mental Health Rsch. Inst., 1977-80; asst. prof. Coll. Architecture and Urban Planning, Ann Arbor, 1980-83; assoc. prof. U. Mich., Ann Arbor, 1983-86; chmn. Coll. Architecture and Urban Planning, Ann Arbor, 1986-92; prof. Coll. Architecture and Urban Planning, 1989—; co-dir. Studies in Urban Security Group U. Mich., Ann Arbor, 1985—; mathematician Bendix Corp. & Rocketdyne, Ann Arbor, 1961-62; group scientist Conductron Corp., Ann Arbor, 1962-70; project assoc. Mich. State C. of C., Lansing, 1970-72; cons. Community Systems Found., Ann Arbor, 1985—. Contbr. rsch. reports, articles. Advisor assessment com. United Way of Washtenaw County, Ann Arbor, 1988-89. With USN, 1950-54. Recipient Faculty Recognition award U. Mich., 1982-83. Mem. AAAS, Am. Planning Assn. Democrat. Jewish. Avocation: computer applications to planning. Office: U Mich Coll Architecture & Urban Planning Ann Arbor MI 48109-2069

RYDELL, AMNELL ROY, artist, landscape architect; b. Mpls., Sept. 17, 1915; s. John S. and Josephine Henrietta (King) R.; m. Frances Cooksey, Jan. 24, 1942. BFA, U. So. Calif., 1937; postgrad., Atelier 17, Paris, 1938, U. Calif., Berkeley, 1939-40, U. Calif., Santa Cruz, 1988. Instr. engring. Douglas Aircraft, El Segundo, Calif., 1940-46; ind. artist, designer San Francisco, 1946-48; ind. artist, designer Santa Cruz, 1948—, ind. landscape architect, 1958-91. Author: cons.: Low Maintenance Gardening, 1974. Pres. Santa Cruz Hist. Soc., 1978-79, Rural Bonny Doon Assn., 1955-56, Santa Cruz Orgn. for Progress and Euthenics, 1977-78; mem. vision bd. City of Santa Cruz, 1991-92; mem. task force Ctr. for Art and History, 1986-94; bd. dirs. Santa Cruz Hist. Trust, 1978-94, Art Mus. Santa Cruz County, 1982-94; donor advisor Roy and Frances Rydell Visual Arts Fund, Greater Santa Cruz County Cmty. Found.; archivist pers. hist. archives, spl. collections Libr. U. Calif., Santa Cruz. Mem. Am. Soc. Landscape Architects (emeritus), William James Assn. (vice chair bd. 1979—), Art Forum (chair 1983-90), Art League. Avocation: gardening. Home: 201 Pine Flat Rd Santa Cruz CA 95060-9708

RYDELL, MARK, film director, producer, actor; b. N.Y.C., Mar. 23; s. Sidney and Evelyn R.; children: Christopher, Amy. Student, NYU, The Julliard Sch. Bd. dirs. Actors Studio. Actor TV series As the World Turns, play Seagulls Over Sorrento, films Crime in the Streets, The Long Goodbye; dir. motion pictures The Fox, 1968, The Reivers, 1970; producer, dir.: motion pictures The Cowboys, 1972, Cinderella Liberty, 1974; dir. motion pictures Harry and Walter Go to N.Y., 1976, The Rose, 1979, On Golden Pond, 1980 (nominated for Acad. award for best dir.), The River, 1984, For the Boys, 1991, Intersection, 1993; producer: The Man in the Moon, 1991. Mem. Dirs. Guild Am. Office: Concourse Prodns Formosa Bldg 1041 N Formosa Ave Los Angeles CA 90046 also: ICM 8942 Wilshire Blvd Beverly Hills CA 90211*

RYDEN, JOHN GRAHAM, publishing executive; b. N.Y.C., Dec. 19, 1939; s. Albert Graham and Margaret Keating (Bastable) R.; m. Barbara Dee Kelly, June 19, 1962; children: Linda, Patricia. A.B., Harvard U. 1961. Sales rep. McGraw-Hill Book Co., 1965-68; editor coll. dept. Harper & Row, 1968-71, editor in chief coll. dept., 1971-74; editor in chief, asst. dir. U. Chgo. Press, 1974-78, assoc. dir., 1978-79; dir. Yale U. Press, New Haven, 1979—; chmn. bd. trustees Yale Univ. Press, London, 1981—; mem. adminstr. bd. The Papers of Benjamin Franklin, 1979—; chmn. adv. bd. Beacon Press, 1983—. Mem. editorial bd. Public Historian, 1980-86, Scholarly Publishing, 1992—; adv. bd. The Yale Review, 1992—. Trustee Orch, New Eng., 1980—, pres. 1983-86; bd. dirs. Fund for Free Expression, 1990—; mem. Helsinki Watch Com., 1992—. With USNR, 1962-65. Berkeley Coll. fellow Yale U. Mem. Assn. Am. Publs. (bd. dirs. 1990-94), Assn. Am. U. Presses (bd. dirs. 1980-83, 87-90, pres. 1988-89), Conn. Acad. Arts and Scis., Internat. Assn. Scholarly Pubs., Grads. Club, Hasty Pudding Club (Cambridge, Mass.), Yale Club (N.Y.C.), Century Assn. (N.Y.C.). Office: Yale Univ Press PO Box 209040 New Haven CT 06520-9040 also: Yale U Press 302 Temple St New Haven CT 06511

RYDEN, KATHERINE, publishing executive, human resources executive; b. N.Y.C., Aug. 2, 1947; d. Albert Graham and Margaret (Bastable) Ryden; m. Paul Nickolatos, Nov. 22, 1974. BA, NYU, 1969; postgrad., Harvard U., 1983. News editor Life mag. Time Inc., N.Y.C., employment counsellor, 1976-80, dir. affirmative action, 1980-83, dir. labor rels., 1984-86; v.p. human resources Scholastic Inc., N.Y.C., 1986—; bd. dirs. Dome Project edn. program for disadvantaged youth, N.Y.C., 1991—. Fellow Counterparts. Avocations: travel, art collecting, gardening, theatre, tennis. Office: Scholastic Inc 730 Broadway New York NY 10003-9511

RYDER, DAVID R., lawyer; b. Hinsdale, Ill., Oct. 8, 1946. BA, DePauw U., 1968; JD, U. Mich., 1971. Bar: Ill. 1971, Fla. 1977. Ptnr. McDermott, Will & Emery, Chgo. Mem. Ill. State Bar Assn., Fla. Bar. Office: McDermott Will & Emery 227 W Monroe St Chicago IL 60606-5096

RYDER, GENE ED, retired United States Air Force training administrator; b. Canyon, Tex., Sept. 19, 1932; s. Johnny Allen and Rilda (New) R.; m. Mary Louise Wilson, Feb. 16, 1958; children: Carlyn, Katherine, Anita, Valerie. BA in Govt. cum laude, St. Mary's U., 1965; MEd, Our Lady of the Lake U., 1968; PhD in Adminstrn., The Union Inst., 1979. Instr. USAF, Scott, Keesler & Lackland AFB, 1958-65; tng. specialist USAF, Lackland AFB, Tex., 1965-69, tng. evaluator, 1969-72, curriculum coord., 1972-75, supr. curriculum devel., 1975-78, supr. tng. evaluation, 1978-83, tng. advisor, 1983-92; chief tng. policy USAF, Randolph AFB, Tex., 1992-95; ret., 1995; chmn. affiliated schs. adv. panel C.C. of Air Force, Maxwell AFB, Ala. 1984-88; co-chmn. USAF Tng. and Instrnl. Sys. Career Program, Randolph AFB, 1992—. Author: Basics of Sunday School Leadership: A Guide for Lay Leaders, 1982. Dir. edn Calvary Hills Bapt. Ch., San Antonio, 1981—; coord. state scripture Gideons Internat., Nashville, 1991—; elected mem. Tex. State Rep. Exec. Com., 1994—. With USAF, 1953-56. Mem. Am. Soc. Quality Control, Am. Tech. Edn. Assn., Air Force Assn., Phi Delta Kappa. Home: 1502 Copperfield Rd San Antonio TX 78251-3324 Office: USAF Hdqs Air Edn & Tng Command Ste 2 244 F St E Randolph A F B TX 78150

RYDER, GEORGIA ATKINS, university dean, educator; b. Newport News, Va., Jan. 30, 1924; d. Benjamin Franklin and Mary Lou (Carter) Atkins; m. Noah Francis Ryder, Sept. 16, 1947; children: Olive Diana, Malcolm Eliot, Aleta Renee. B.S., Hampton (Va.) Inst., 1944; Mus.M., U. Mich., 1946; Ph.D., NYU, 1970. Resource music tchr., Alexandria, Va., 1944-48; faculty music dept. Norfolk State U., 1948—, prof., 1970—, head dept., 1969-79, dean Sch. Arts and Letters, 1979-86. Contbr. articles to profl. jours, contbr. chpts. to books. Trustee Va. Symphony, Va. Wesleyan Coll.; bd. dirs. Black Music Rsch. Ctr., Columbia Coll., Chgo., Nat. Assn. Negro Musicians, Southeastern Va. Arts Assn.; mem. advisory com. Norfolk chpt. Young Audiences, Va. Coalition for Mus. Edn., Gordon Inst. Music Learning, Temple U. Grantee So. Fellowship Fund, 1967-69, Consortium Rsch. Tng., 1973; recipient Norfolk Com. Improvement Edn. award, 1974, People's Acad. of Arts award, 1985, City of Norfolk award, 1989, Nat. Assn. Negro Musicians award, 1989, Nat. Conf. Christians and Jews award, 1990, Va. Laureate in Music award, 1992, Cultural Alliance award Greater Hampton Roads, 1992, Disting Alumni award Hampton U., 1993, Norfolk State U. Alumni. award, 1994. Mem. Music Educators Nat. Conf., Coll. Music Soc., Intercoll. Music Assn., Va. Music Educators Assn., Delta Sigma Theta.

RYDER, HARL EDGAR, economist, educator; b. Mt. Vernon, Ill., July 11, 1938; s. Harl Edgar and Pearl (Kirkpatrick) R.; m. Mary Irene Kingsolver, June 30, 1970; children—Jonathan Harl, David Eugene, Benjamin James. A.A., Mt. Vernon Community Coll., 1958; B.A., U. Ill., 1960, M.S., 1961; Ph.D., Stanford U., 1967. Asst. prof. econs. Brown U., Providence, 1965-69; assoc. prof. Brown U., 1969-73, prof., 1973—, chmn. dept. econs., 1974-81. Mem. Am. Econ. Assn., Econometric Soc. Office: Brown Univ Dept Econs 79 Waterman St Providence RI 02912-9079

RYDER, HENRY C(LAY), lawyer; b. Lafayette, Ind., Feb. 18, 1928; s. Raymond Robert and Mina Elizabeth (Arnold) R.; m. Ann Sater Clay, Nov. 29, 1952 (dec.); children: David C., Sarah Paige Hugon, Anne M.; m. Velma Iris Dean, Aug. 27, 1976. BS, Purdue U., 1948; LLB, U. Mich., 1951. Bar: Mich. 1951, Ind. 1952, U.S. Dist. Ct. (so. dist.) Ind. 1953, U.S. Ct. Appeals (7th cir.) 1957, U.S. Supreme Ct. 1981. Assoc. Buschmann, Krieg, DeVault & Alexander, Indpls., 1953-57, ptnr., 1957-60; ptnr. Roberts & Ryder and successor firms, Indpls., 1960-86, Barnes & Thornburg (merger), Indpls., 1987—; bd. dirs. Peoples Bank and Trust Co., Indpls., 1985—. Pres. Ind. State Symphony Soc. Inc., 1979-82, bd. dirs., 1972-91, trustee, 1991—; chmn. United Way of Greater Indpls., 1984; vice chmn. Greater Indpls. Progress Com., 1978-86, chmn., 1987-89; trustee Purdue U., 1983-89, Hanover Coll., 1979, chmn., 1988—; bd. dirs. Hist. Landmark Found. of Ind., 1987—, chmn., 1992-95; bd. dirs. Purdue Rsch. Found., 1992—; hon. v.p. Ind. Soc. Chgo. Lt. U.S. Army, 1951-53. Recipient Jefferson award Indpls. Star, 1984, Civic Leadership award Hanover Coll., 1994; named Man of Yr. B'nai B'rith Soc., 1984. Fellow Am. Bar Found., Ind. Bar Found.; mem. ABA, Ind. Bar Assn., Indpls. Bar Assn., Purdue U. Alumni Assn (pres. 1975-77, Alumni Svc. award 1982, Citizenship award 1989), Ind. C. of C. (bd. dirs. 1991-94), Ind. Acad., Lawyers Club (pres. Indpls. 1966), U.S. Automobile Club (sec., bd. dirs., President's award 1989, U.S. Automobile Club Properties (sec., bd. dirs.), Columbia Club (bd. dirs. 1987-90, sec. 1988, pres. Found. 1990-95, Benjamin Harrison award 1983), Kiwanis (pres. Indpls. 1983, civil award 1981). Republican. Presbyterian. Office: Barnes & Thornburg 1313 Merchants Bank Bldg 11 S Meridian St Indianapolis IN 46204-3506

RYDER, JACK MCBRIDE, educational consultant; b. Newport, Ky., Dec. 2, 1928; s. Amon McBride Ryder and Esther Mabel (Harris) Ryder Rachford; m. Roberta Joyce Hayward, Mar. 17, 1951 (div. 1964); children: Joyce Ann (dec.), Constance Lynn, Judith Louise, John McBride; m. Lila Joan Baker, Oct. 2, 1964; 1 child, Suzanne Carol. BS in Biology, Mich State U., East Lansing, 1952; MA in Sch. Adminstrn., Mich State U., 1955, PhD in Ednl. Adminstrn., 1962; LLD (hon.), Saginaw Valley State U., 1992. Tchr. Anglo-Am. Schs., Athens, Greece, 1952-54; supt. of schs. Brady Community Schs., Oakley, Mich., 1955-57, Cassopolis (Mich.) Pub. Schs., 1957-61; assoc. instr. Coll. Edn. Mich. State U., East Lansing, 1961-62; asst. to dean univ. extension adminstrn. Purdue U., W. Lafayette, Ind., 1962-63; interim dir. (on loan) Ind. Vocat. Tech. Coll., Indpls., 1964-65; dir., dean and dir. Purdue U., Indpls., 1963-69; vice chancellor, dean for adminstrv. affairs Indiana U. and Purdue U., Indpls., 1969-74; prof. edn., pres. Saginaw Valley State U., University Center, Mich., 1974-89, prof. edn., 1989-92; pres. J&L Assoc. Internat Ednl. Cons., 1992—; bd. dirs. Saginaw, Second Nat. Bank, Saginaw; chmn. Valley Libr. Consortium, Saginaw, 1981-89, Saginaw Valley R&D Corp., Univ. Ctr., 1982-89; vis. prof., cons. Fedn. Universitaire ET PolyTechnique, De Lille, France, 1989. Mem. Saginaw Area Growth Alliance, 1989; bd. dirs. Saginaw Future, 1989, St. Luke's Healthcare Assn., Saginaw, 1981-89; mem. Leadership Bay County, Bay City, Mich., 1988; bd. dirs., 1st vice chmn. Saginaw Valley State U. Found., 1974-89; pres. emeritus Saginaw Valley State U. Bd. Control, 1992. Recipient Albert Community Svc. award Saginaw Area C. of C., 1989, Disting. Contbr. of Svc. award Delta Coll., Bay City, 1989, Leadership and Svc. award Saginaw Valley State U., 1989, Saginaw Valley State U. Found., 1989; Ryder Ctr. for Health and Phys. Edn. named in honor of him and his wife Saginaw Valley State U.; Paul Harris fellow Rotary Internat., 1988. Mem. Am. Assn. State Colls. and Univs. (Disting. Leadership award 1988), President's Coun. State Univs. (chmn. 1984-86, Leadership and Svc. award 1989), Internat. Torch Club (bd. dirs. Chgo. 1988-89), Phi Delta Kappa. Avocations: fishing, spectator sports, gardening, walking, tennis.

RYDER, KENNETH GILMORE, university chancellor; b. Brockton, Mass., Apr. 30, 1924; s. Russell Gilmore and Etta Coffin (Carr) R.; m. Virginia Patricia Gagnon, June 29, 1944 (div. July 1975); children: Anne, Jeanne, Bruce; m. C. Teresa Ryan, Aug. 9, 1975; children: Amy, Julie. A.B. (Augustus Howe Buck fellow 1941-46), Boston U., 1946; A.M. (A.H. Buck fellow 1946-48), Harvard U., 1947; L.H.D., Nasson Coll., 1972; Litt.D., Northeastern U., 1983; L.H.D., U. Mass., 1985; LHD, Boston Coll., 1988. Instr. history Cambridge Jr. Coll., 1948; instr. history and govt. Northeastern U., Boston, 1949-53; asst. prof. Northeastern U., 1953-57, assoc. prof. history, from 1957, dean of adminstrn., 1958-67, v.p., dean of univ. adminstrn., 1967-71, exec. v.p., 1971-75, pres., 1975-89; chancellor Northeastern U., Boston, 1989—; bd. dirs. Stone & Webster, Inc., The Ford Hall Forum. Contbg. author: Handbook of College and University Administration, 1970, Global Stakes, 1982, Cooperative Education in a New Era, 1987. Past pres. Friends of the Libr. of Boston U.; past trustee Cambridge Jr. Coll., Forsyth Dental Ctr., Nat. Commn. for Coop. Edn.; trustee Mass. Horticultural Soc., Thayer Acad., Northeastern U. Lt. (j.g.) USNR, WWII. Mem. Phi Beta Kappa, Phi Alpha Theta, Phi Kappa Phi, Kappa Delta Pi, Beta Gamma Sigma. Episcopalian. Office: Northeastern U Office of Chancellor 716 Columbus Ave Boston MA 02115-5096

RYDER, THOMAS MICHAEL, newspaper editor; b. East Chicago, Ind., May 17, 1934; s. Thomas Henry and Margaret (Lauber) R.; m. George-Anne Richmond, Sept. 22, 1962. B.S. in Journalism, Marquette U., 1956. Reporter Daily Dispatch, Moline, Ill., 1956-60; reporter The Press, Evansville, Ind., 1960-62, Tri-state editor, 1962-64, city editor, 1969-83; editor The Sunday Courier & Press, Evansville, 1983-86; asst. mng. editor Evansville

Courier, 1986—; adj. prof. Ind. State U., Evansville, 1984. Contbr. articles to mags. Served with U.S. Army, 1967-69. Mem. Soc. Profl. Journalists, Stamp Club (pres. 1966). Roman Catholic. Club: Meml. Patrons (pres. 1983). Office: The Courier 300 E Walnut St Evansville IN 47713-1938

RYDER, THOMAS O., magazine publishing executive; b. Varnville, S.C., July 19, 1944; s. Floie Fritz and Helen Ryder; m. Darlene Wood, May 4, 1963; children: Shannon, Robert Ashley, Alyson. BA, La. State U., 1966. Subscription mgr. Life Mag., N.Y.C.; group pub. edn. periodicals Xerox Pub., Conn.; founder Edn. Today, Palo Alto, Calif., Learning Today, Palo Alto; sr. v.p. CBS Mags., N.Y.C.; pres. Am. Express Pub. and Direct Mktg. Group, N.Y.C.; faculty mem. Stanford (Calif.) Pub. Course. Contbr. articles to mags. Named to Sch. Journalism Hall of Fame, La. State U., 1987. Mem. Mag. Pubs. Am. (vice chmn.), Young Pres. Orgn. (Gotham chpt.). Office: Am Express Pub Dir Mktg Group 1120 Avenue Of The Americas New York NY 10036-6700

RYDER, WINONA (WINONA LAURA HOROWITZ), actress; b. Winona, Minn., Oct. 29, 1971; d. Michael and Cynthia (Ista) Horowitz. Films include: Lucas, 1986, Square Dance, 1987, 1969, 1988, Beetlejuice, 1988, Great Balls of Fire, 1989, Heathers, 1989, Edward Scissorhands, 1990, Mermaids, 1990, Welcome Home, Roxy Carmichael, 1990, Night On Earth, 1992, Bram Stoker's Dracula, 1992, Age of Innocence, 1993 (Golden Globe for Best Supporting Actress, 1994, Academy award nominee, Best Supporting Actress, 1993), The House of the Spirits, 1994, Reality Bites, 1994, Little Women, 1994 (Acad. Awd. nom., Best Actress), Boys, 1995, How to Make An American Quilt, 1995. Office: CAA 9830 Wilshire Blvd Beverly Hills CA 90212*

RYDHOLM, RALPH WILLIAMS, advertising agency executive; b. Chgo., June 1, 1937; s. Thor Gabriel and Vivian Constance (Williams) R.; m. Jo Anne Beechler, Oct. 5, 1963; children: Kristin, Erik, Julia. B.A., Northwestern U., 1958, postgrad. in bus. adminstrn, 1958-59; postgrad. Advanced Mgmt. Program, Harvard U., 1982. Acct. trainee, copywriter Young & Rubicam Advt., Chgo., 1960-63; copywriter Post-Keyes-Gardner Advt., Chgo., 1963, E. H. Weiss Advt., Chgo., 1963-65; copy group head BBDO Advt., Chgo., 1965-66; with J. Walter Thompson Advt., Chgo., 1966-86; creative dir. J. Walter Thompson Advt., 1969-76, exec. creative dir., 1976-86, sr. v.p., 1972-80, exec. v.p., dir., 1980-86; exec. v.p., chief creative officer, dir. Ted Bates Worldwide, N.Y.C., 1986-87; mng. ptnr., chmn. mgmt. com., chief creative officer, chmn., CEO Tatham EURO RSCG Advt., Chgo., 1987—; bd. dirs., ops. com., chmn. 4A's creative com.; guest spkr. Ad Age Workshop, 1969, 77, 86, Adweek Seminar, 1993; keynote spkr. Stephen B. Kelly Awards, 1993. Mem. assoc. bd. Newberry Libr. Assn.; bd. dirs. Mus. of Broadcasting. With USAFR, 1959-65. Recipient Clio award, Internat. Broadcast award Hollywood Radio and TV Soc., award Cannes Film Festival, Addy award Women's Ad Clubs; named one of Top 100 Creative Ad People Ad Daily, 1972, Advt. Exec. of Yr. Adweek, 1991, Best Man in Advt. McCalls and Adweek, 1992, Creative Leader Wall St. Jour., 1994. Mem. ASCAP, Chgo. Advt. Fedn., Saddle and Cycle Club, Econ. Club Chgo., Northwestern Club Chgo., Harvard Club Chgo., Exec.'s Club Chgo., Tavern Club, Carlton Club, Chikaming Country Club (Mich.), Dunes Club (Mich.), Phi Delta Theta. Office: Tatham EURO RSCG 980 N Michigan Ave Chicago IL 60611-4501

RYDSTROM, CARLTON LIONEL, chemist, paint and coating consultant; b. Indpls., Dec. 4, 1928; s. Carlton Lionel and Sara Ann (McNeese) R.; m. Kathleen O'Leary, Oct. 21, 1954 (dec.); children: Carlton L. III, Michael, Mary (dec.), Leslie, Patricia, Timothy, Molly; m. Mary L. Murphy, June 13, 1992. BS in Polymer Chemistry, N.D. State U., 1951; MS in Phys. Chemistry, U. Puerto Rico, Rio, Piedras, 1953. Chemist Am. Marietta Co., Kankakee, Ill., 1951-52; chemist, plant mgr. Chinamel Paints, Hato Rey, Puerto Rico, 1952-53; tech. mgr. Midwest Synthetics (Valspar), Rockford, Ill., 1953-55; mng. ptnr. Norcote Co., St. Petersburg, Fla., 1955-71; pres. C.M. Industries, Inc., St. Petersburg, 1971-74, Tuf-top/Norcote Coatings, Inc., St. Petersburg, 1974-80; owner Rydstrom Lab., Inc., St. Petersburg, 1980—; bd. dirs. Stacote Finishes, Ltd., W.I.; cons. Sch. Bds. State of Fla., 1981—, paint and adhesive industries. Pres. parish coun. St. Jude Catholic Cathedral Parish, 1977-78, 78-79, St. Vincent de Paul Pinellas Dist., St. Petersburg, 1988-91; nat. secretariat Cursillo Movement, Roman Cath. Ch., Dallas, 1985-88; dir. St, Vincent de Paul Food Ctr., St. Petersburg, 1988—; chmn. Waterfront Planning Com., St. Petersburg, 1959; mem. bd. dirs. St. Petersburg Catholic H.S., 1977-80. Fellow N.Y. Acad. Sci.; mem. Nat. Assn. Corrosion Engrs., Soc. Coatings Tech. (chmn./pres. 1958-59, Disting. Svc. award 1975), Fla. Paint and Coating Assn. (treas., dir. 1959-75), St. Vincent dePaul Soc. (Top Hat award 1991), Jr. C. of C. (DSA 1960). Republican. Roman Catholic. Avocations: golf, gardening, travel, public speaking, working with needy. Home and Office: 6300 25th Ave N Saint Petersburg FL 33710-4128

RYDZ, JOHN S., manufacturing executive; b. Milw., May 7, 1925; s. John M. and Victoria A. (Kosse) R.; m. Clare L. Steinke, May 18, 1946; children: John A., Karen E. BS in Physics, MIT, 1952; MS in Physics, U. Pa., 1956; postgrad., Case Western Res. U., 1965-70. Mem. staff of sr. exec. v.p RCA, N.Y.C., 1952-61; exec. v.p. Nuclear Corp. Am. (NUCOR), Phoenix, 1961-63; dir. research Adressograph/Multigraph, Cleve., 1963-65; v.p. Diebold Inc., Canton, Ohio, 1965-70; v.p., chief tech. officer The Singer Co., N.Y.C., 1970-80; corp. v.p. Emhart Corp., Farmington, Conn., 1980-89; pres. Music Memories Inc., Avon, Conn., 1989—; vis. prof. U. Conn., 1988—; mem. engring. adv. com. NSF, Washington, 1986—. Author: Managing Innovation and Common Sense Manufacturing Management, 1986; contbr. articles to profl. jours.; patentee in field. Mem. MIT Lab. for Mfg. and Productivity, Cambridge, Mass., 1975—, U. Hartford Engring. Exec. Council, West Hartford, Conn., 1982—, Worcester (Mass.) Poly. Inst. Mech. Engring. Adv. Com., 1980—; chmn. engring adv. com. U. Conn., Storrs, 1986—. Served with USN, 1943-46, WWII. Mem. Soc. Mfg. Engrs., IEEE, Indsl. Research Inst. Avocations: astronomy, swimming.

RYDZEL, JAMES A., lawyer; b. Worcester, Mass., Nov. 13, 1946; s. Joseph S. and Shirley F. Rydzel; m. Mary C. Chandler; 1 child, Molly. BA, St. Louis U., 1968; JD, Duke U. 1971. Bar: Ohio, 1972, Fla. 1975, U.S. Dist. Ct. (no. dist.) Ohio, U.S. Dist. Ct. (ea. dist.) Mich., U.S. Ct. Appeals (2d, 3d, 4th and 6th cirs.). Ptnr. Jones, Day, Reavis & Pogue, Cleve., 1972—; adj. prof. law Case Western Res. U. Bd. dirs. New Orgn. Visual Arts, 1990, Greater Cleve. Growth Assn., Citizens League. Mem. ABA (litigation labor and employment law com.), Ohio State Bar Assn., Fla. Bar Assn., Def. Rsch. Inst. Office: Jones Day Reavis & Pogue 901 Lakeside Ave E Cleveland OH 44114-1190

RYERSON, PAUL SOMMER, lawyer; b. Newark, Oct. 2, 1946; s. Robert Paul and Audrey Mae (Sommer) R.; m. Susan Jean Duckrow, Aug. 7, 1971; children: James Sommer, Jill Carin. BA, Wesleyan U., 1968; JD, Columbia U., 1971. Bar: N.Y. 1972, D.C. 1972, U.S. Ct. Appeals (D.C. cir.) 1973, U.S. Dist. Ct. D.C. 1973, U.S. Supreme Ct. 1976, U.S. Ct. Appeals (5th cir.) 1979, U.S. Ct. Appeals (4th cir.) 1980. Law clk. to judge Jack B. Weinstein U.S. Dist. Ct. ea. dist. N.Y., 1971-72; assoc. Arnold & Porter, Washington, 1972-79, ptnr., 1980-89; ptnr. Jones, Day, Reavis & Pogue, Washington, 1989—. Contbr. articles to profl. publs. Mem. ABA, D.C. Bar Assn. Home: 408 A St SE Washington DC 20003-3807 Office: Jones Day Reavis & Pogue 1450 G St NW Washington DC 20005-2088

RYERSON, WILLIAM EDWIN, diplomat; b. Pompton Lakes, N.J., Dec. 10, 1936; s. J. Delbert and Marian (Wheeler) R.; m. Suzanne Somes Williams, June 25, 1962; children: Nina, Thomas, Marten, Nicholas. BA, Cornell U., 1960. With coord. divsn. Visa office U.S. Dept. State, Washington, 1976-78, with pub. and diplomatic svcs. Visa Office, 1980-81, dep. dir. Visa office, 1990-91, Berlin desk officer, 1978-80, lang. trainee, 1985-86; consular officer Am. Embassy, Vienna, Austria, 1973-76; consul gen. Am. Embassy, Bonn, Germany, 1981-85, Belgrade, Yugoslavia, 1986-90; amb. Am. Embassy, Tirana, Albania, 1991—. Episcopalian. Avocations: reading, biking. Office: US Embassy Psc 59 Box 100 A APO AE 09624-5009

RYKER, CHARLES EDWIN, former aerospace company executive; b. Baxter Springs, Kans., Mar. 17, 1920; s. Herbert Earl and Nellie (Sims) R.; m. Evelyn Maude Fairchild, July 28, 1943; children: Patricia Evelyn, Charles Franklyn. Student, San Diego State Coll., 1937-38; B.S. cum laude, U. So.

Calif., 1947. C.P.A., Calif. Sr. accountant Arthur Andersen & Co., Los Angeles, 1947-49; auditor Airquipment Co., Burbank, Calif., 1949-50; accounting mgr. Hughes Aircraft Co., Culver City, Calif., 1950-52; with N.Am. Aviation, Inc., Los Angeles, 1952-67; v.p., controller Los Angeles airplane div. N.Am. Aviation, Inc., 1959-62, asst. corp. controller, asst. corp. treas., 1962-67; controller Rockwell Internat. Corp. (merger N.Am. Aviation, Inc. and Rockwell-Standard Corp.), 1967-73, staff v.p. controller's office Western region, 1973-75, v.p., controller, 1975-81, v.p., corp. fin.-major programs, 1981-84; fin. cons., 1984-86. Served to lt. USNR, 1941-45, PTO. Mem. Fin. Execs. Inst., Am. Inst. C.P.A.'s, Calif. Soc. C.P.A.'s, Nat. Assn. Accountants, Beta Gamma Sigma, Beta Alpha Psi, Phi Kappa Phi, Chi Phi. Home: 248 Rocky Point Rd Palos Verdes Peninsula CA 90274-2622

RYKER, NORMAN J., JR., retired manufacturing company executive; b. Tacoma, Dec. 25, 1926; s. Norman Jenkins and Adelia Gustine (Macomber) R.; m. Kathleen Marie Crawford, June 20, 1947 (div. 1983); children: Jeanne Ryker Flores, Christina, Vickie Ryker Risley, Norman Jenkins, Kathy; m. Judith Kay Schneider, Dec. 18, 1983. B.S., U. Calif.-Berkeley, 1949, M.S., 1951; postgrad. Advanced Mgmt. Program, Harvard U., 1973. Asst. chief engr. space divsn. Rockwell Internat., Downey, Calif., 1962-68, v.p. rsch. engring. and testing, 1968-70, v.p. rsch. and engring. graphic systems group, 1970-74, v.p., v.p. gen. mgr. Webb divsn., 1974, v.p., gen mgr. transp. and equipment divsn., 1974-76; pres. Rocketdyne divsn. Rockwell Internat., Canoga Park, Calif., 1976-83; sr. v.p. aerospace and indsl. group Pneumo Corp., Boston, 1983-84, exec. v.p., COO, 1984-85; pres., CEO Pneumo Corp. subs. IC Industries, 1985-86, Pneumo Abex Corp., 1986-88; vice chmn., CEO Cross & Trecker Corp., 1989-91; lectr. in field. Contbr. articles to profl. jours. Served with U.S. Army, 1944-46. Recipient cert. of appreciation NASA, 1969, merit award, 1979, Disting. Pub. Svc. medal, 1981, Silver Knight award Nat. Mgmt. Assn., 1979, Tech. Mgmt. award Calif. Soc. Profl. Engrs., 1979. Fellow Inst. Advancement Engring., AIAA; mem. ASCE, Am. Astronautical Soc., Nat. Mgmt. Assn., Instn. Prodn. Engrs. (elected companion). Republican. Address: 15233 Jarrettsville Pike Monkton MD 21111-2402

RYKHUS, DAVID ANTHONY, healthcare executive; b. Tracy, Minn., BS, S.D. State U., 1960; MA in Hosp. and Healthcare Adminstrn., U. Iowa, 1962. Adminstr. Green County Hosp., Jefferson, Iowa, 1962-67; exec. dir. St. Joseph Hosp., Mitchell, S.D., 1968-85; v.p. Ctr. for Rural Health Svcs. Sioux Valley Hosp., 1985—; pres. Sioux Valley Svc. Corp.; founder Sioux Valley Hosp. Outreach Program, Hosp. Lease, Mngt. and Affiliate Program. Del. Am. Hosp. Assn. Fellow Am. Coll. Healthcare Execs. (past state regent), S.D. Hosp. Assn. (past pres.). Office: Sioux Valley Hospital PO Box 5039 Sioux Falls SD 57117-5039

RYKWERT, JOSEPH, architecture and art history educator; b. Warsaw, Poland, Apr. 5, 1926; arrived in Eng., 1939; s. Szymon Mieczyslaw and Elizabeth (Melup) R.; m. Anne-Marie Sandersley, Feb. 14, 1972; 1 child from previous marriage, Simon Sebastian; 1 stepchild, Marina Joanna Engel. Student, Archtl. Assn., London, 1944-47; MA, U. Cambridge, London; PhD, Royal Coll. Art, London, 1970; MA (hon.), U. Pa., 1988; DSc (hon.), U. Edinburgh, Scotland, 1995. Libr., tutor Royal Coll. Art, 1960-67; prof. art, chmn. dept. U. Essex, Colchester, Eng., 1967-81; Slade prof. fine arts U. Cambridge, 1980, reader in architecture, 1981-87; Paul Philippe Cret prof. architecture, prof. art history U. Pa., Phila., 1988—, also chmn. PhD program in architecture; Andrew Mellon prof. Cooper Union, N.Y.C., 1977; George Lurcy prof. Columbia U., N.Y.C., 1986; commr. Venice (Italy) Biennale, 1974-77; mem. jury Parc de la Villette Competition, Paris, 1982, Wolf Found. Prize, Jerusalem, 1983; trustee Cubitt Trust, London, 1986—; sr. scholar Getty Ctr. for History Art and Humanities, 1992, 93; co-editor catalogue, curator Alberti Exhbn., Mantua, Italy, 1994. Author: The Golden House, 1947, The Idea of a Town, 1963, 76, 88, Church Building, 1966, On Adam's House in Paradise, 1972, 82, The First Moderns, 1980, 84, The Necessity of Artifice, 1982, (with Anne-Marie Rykwert), The Brothers Adam, 1985; editor transl.: On the Art of Building (L.B. Alberti), 1989, 91; editor Res jour., Peabody Mus., Cambridge, Mass., 1979—. Mem. steering com. UNESCO Conf. on Urbanism, 1989—. Decorated Chevalier des Arts et des Lettres, Govt. of France, 1985; recipient Alfred Jurzykowski Found. award, 1990, Accademia di San Luca, 1993. Mem. Coll. Art Assn., Comite Internat. des Critiques d'Architecture, Savile Club (London). Office: U Pa Dept Architecture 210 S 34th St 102 Meyerson Hall Philadelphia PA 19104-6311

RYLAND, DAVID RONALD, lawyer; b. Ashland, Ohio, Mar. 22, 1945; s. Willis A. and Lois Eleanor (Landis) R.; m. Rita Ann Cooney, Jan. 20, 1973. BA, Coll. of Wooster, 1967; JD, Columbia U., 1970. Bar: Calif. 1970. Assoc. U. of Calif., Berkeley, 1970-71; from assoc. to ptnr. Severson, Werson, Berke & Melchior, San Francisco, 1971-82; ptnr. Sheppard, Mullin, Richter & Hampton, San Francisco, 1982—. Home: 3 Edgewater Rd Belvedere CA 94920-2315 Office: Sheppard Mullin Richter & Hampton Ste 1700 4 Embarcadero Ctr San Francisco CA 94111-4158

RYLAND, G(REANER) NEAL, financial executive; b. Richmond, Va., June 26, 1941; s. William Bradford and Elizabeth (Neal) R.; m. Marjorie Kane Gerry II, Aug. 18, 1978; children: Averell, Elizabeth, Bradford; children from previous marriage: Alexandra, Nelson. BA, Harvard U., 1963; MBA, NYU, 1967. With Bank of N.Y., N.Y.C., 1964-67; treas. Ea. Gas & Fuel Assn., Boston, 1967-78; sr. v.p., chief fin. officer Courier Corp., Lowell, Mass., 1979-85, Kenner Parker Toys Inc., Beverly, Mass., 1985-88; exec. v.p., CFO The Boston Co., Boston, 1988-93, New Eng. Investment Cos., L.P., Boston, 1993—. Editor: The American Business Corporation, 1972. Pres. bd. trustees Shore Country Day Sch., Beverly, 1987; trustee Trustees of Reservation; chmn. fin. com., trustee Mass. Gen. Hosp.

RYLANDER, HENRY GRADY, JR., mechanical engineering educator; b. Pearsall, Tex., Aug. 23, 1921; married; 4 children. B.S., U. Tex., 1943, M.S., 1952; Ph.D. in Mech. Engring., Ga. Inst. Tech., 1965. Design engr. Steam Div., Aviation Gas Turbine Div., Westinghouse Elec. Corp., 1943-47; from asst. to assoc. prof. mech. engring. U. Tex., Austin, 1947-68, research scientist, 1950, prof. mech. engring., 1968—, Joe J. King prof. engring., 1980—; cons. engr. TRACOR, Inc., 1964-69; founding dir. Ctr. for Electromechanics, U. Tex., 1977-85, chmn., mech. engring. dept., 1976-86. Named Disting. Grad. Coll. Engring., U. Tex., Austin, 1989. Fellow ASME (Leonardo da Vinci award 1985); mem. ASME. Office: U Tex Coll Engring Austin TX 78712

RYLANT, CYNTHIA, author; b. Hopewell, Va., June 6, 1954; d. John Tune and Leatrel (Rylant) Smith; 1 child, Nathaniel. BA, Morris Harvey Coll., 1975; MA, Marshall U., 1976; MLS, Kent State U., 1982. English instr. Marshall U., Huntington, W.Va., 1979-80, U. Akron, Ohio, 1983-84; children's libr. Akron (Ohio) Pub. Libr., 1983; part-time lectr. Northeast Ohio Univs. Coll. Medicine, Rootstown, Ohio, 1991—. Author: (picture books) When I Was Young in the Mountains, 1982 (Caldecott Honor book 1983, English Speaking Union Book-Across-the-Sea Amb. of Honor award 1984, Am. Book award nomination 1983), Miss Maggie, 1983, This Year's Garden, 1984, The Relatives Came, 1985 (Horn Book Honor book 1985, Children's Book of Yr. Child Study Assn. Am. 1985, Caldecott Honor Book 1986), Night in the Country, 1986, Birthday Presents, 1987, All I See, 1988, Mr. Grigg's Work, 1989, An Angel for Solomon Singer, 1992, The Everyday Town, 1992, The Everyday School, 1993, The Everyday House, 1993, The Everyday Garden, 1993, The Everyday Children, 1993, The Everyday Pets, 1993, Mr. Putter and Tabby Pour the Tea, 1994, Mr. Putter and Tabby Walk the Dog, 1994, The Old Woman Who Named Things, 1994, The Blue Hill Meadows and the Much Loved Dog, 1994, Gooseberry Park, 1995; (Henry and Mudge series) Henry and Mudge: The First Book of Their Adventures, 1987, Henry and Mudge in Puddle Trouble, 1987, Henry and Mudge in the Green Time, 1987, Henry and Mudge Under the Yellow Moon, 1987, Henry and Mudge in the Sparkle Days, 1988, Henry and Mudge and the Forever Sea, 1989, Henry and Mudge Get the Cold Shivers, 1989, Henry and Mudge and the Happy Cat, 1990, Henry and Mudge and the Bedtime Thumps, 1991, Henry and Mudge Take the Big Test, 1991, Henry and Mudge and the Long Weekend, 1992, Henry and Mudge and the Wild Wind, 1993, Henry and Mudge and the Careful Cousin, 1994, Henry and Mudge and the Best Day Ever, 1995; (poetry) Waiting to Waltz ... a Childhood, 1984 (Nat. Coun. for Social Studies Best Book 1984), Soda Jerk, 1990, Something Permanent, 1994; (novels) A Blue-Eyed Daisy, 1985 (Children's Book of Yr. Child Study Assn. Am. 1985), A Fine White Dust, 1986 (Newbery Honor Book 1987), A Kindness, 1988; (stories) Every Living Thing, 1985, Children of Christmas: Stories for the Season, 1987, A Couple of Kooks: And Other Stories About Love, 1990; (autobiography) But I'll Be Back Again: An Album, 1989, Best Wishes, 1992; (other) Appalachia: The Voices of Sleeping Birds, 1991 (Boston Globe/Horn Book Honor book for nonfiction 1991), Missing May, 1992 (John Newbery medal 1992), I Have Seen Castles, 1993, The Dreamer, 1993. Office: PO Box 368 Kent OH 44240*

RYLE, JOSEPH DONALD, public relations executive; b. Stamford, Conn., Aug. 19, 1910; s. Joseph P. and Vivian (Sander) R. B.S., NYU, 1933. With pub. relations dept. Joseph D. Ryle, N.Y.C., 1933-41; dir. pub. relations Am. Overseas Airlines, London, 1946-50, Am. Airlines, N.Y.C., 1950-52; exec. v.p. Fedn. Ry. Progress, 1953-55, vice chmn., 1955—; pres. Nat. Transit Ads., 1955-57; exec. v.p. pub. relations Thomas J. Deegan Jr., Inc., now dir.; pub. relations cons. N.Y.C; promotion cons. Met. Mus. Art. Exec. dir. Gov's Com. for the Centennial of Thoroughbred Racing at Saratoga; v.p., bd. dirs. East Side Settlement House; adv. com. Am. Folk Art Mus.; chmn. emeritus Winter Antiques Show; trustee Hancock (Mass.) Shaker Village; bd. dirs. Isabel O'Neil Sch., N.Y.C. Served with USAAF, 1942-45; dep. to Gen. H. H. Arnold, pub. relations. Decorated Legion of Merit. Mem. Air Transport Assn. (past chmn. pub. relations com.), Newcomen Soc., Irish Georgian Soc. (bd. dirs.). Clubs: Nat. Press (Washington), Army Navy (Washington), Overseas Press (N.Y.C.), Wings (N.Y.C.); Squadron A; Reading Room (Saratoga, N.Y.). Home: 455 E 51st St New York NY 10022-6474 also: The Academy Remsenburg NY 11960

RYLES, GERALD FAY, private investor, business executive; b. Walla Walla, Wash., Apr. 3, 1936; s. L. F. and Janie Geraldine (Bassett) R.; m. Ann Jane Birkenmeyer, June 12, 1959; children—Grant, Mark, Kelly. B.A., U. Wash., 1958; M.B.A., Harvard U., 1962. With Gen. Foods Corp., White Plains, N.Y., 1962-65, Purex Corp., Ltd., Lakewood, Calif., 1966-68; cons. McKinsey & Co., Inc., Los Angeles, 1968-71; with Fibreboard Corp., San Francisco, 1971-79, v.p., 1973-75, group v.p., 1975-79; with Consol. Fibres, Inc., San Francisco, 1979-88, exec. v.p., 1979-81, pres., dir., 1981-86, chief exec. officer, 1986-88; cons. Orinda, Calif., 1988-90; with Interchecks Inc., 1990-92, pres., CEO, 1990-92; bus. exec., pvt. investor, 1992-94; chmn. bd., CEO Microserv, Inc., Kirkland, Wash., 1994—; bd. dirs. Morning Sun, Inc., Tacoma, Wash. Mem. adv. com. entrepreneur and innovation program U. Wash. Bus. Sch. Served to capt. U.S. Army, 1958-66. Mem. Harvard Bus. Sch. Assn., Univ. Wash. Alumni Assn., World Trade Club (San Francisco), Orinda Country Club, Wash. Athletic Club. Republican. Episcopalian. Home: 2625 90th Ave NE Bellevue WA 98004-1601

RYMAN, ROBERT TRACY, artist; b. Nashville, May 30, 1930; s. William Tracy and Nora (Broom) R.; m. Lucy Lippard, 1961 (div. 1966); children: Ethan, Ryman; m. Merrill Wagner, Jan. 31, 1969; children: William Tracy, George Corydon. Exhibited one man shows: Paul Bianchini Gallery, 1967, Solomon R. Guggenheim Mus., N.Y.C., 1972, Kunsthalle, Basel, Switzerland, 1975, Palais des Beaus-Arts, Brussels, 1974, Stedelijk Mus., Amsterdam, Netherlands, 1974, Whitechapel Gallery, London, 1977, Centre Pompidou, Paris, 1981, Sidney Janis Gallery, N.Y.C., 1981, Kunsthalle, Dusseldorf, Germay, 1982, Bonnier Gallery, N.Y.C., 1983, Daniel Weinberg Gallery, L.A., 1983, Galerie Maeght LeLong, Paris, 1984, Rhona Hoffman Gallery, Chgo., 1985, Leo Castelli Gallery, N.Y.C., 1986, Galerie Maeght LeLong, N.Y.C., 1986, Pace Gallery, N.Y.C., 1990, DIA Art Found., N.Y.C., 1988-89, Konrad Fischer Gallery, Dusseldorf, Fed. Republic Germany, 1987, Pace Gallery, N.Y., Tate Gallery, London, MMA, N.Y., San Francisco Mus. Modern Art, Walker Arts Ctr., Mpls.; group shows: Biennal Whitney Mus. Am. Art, N.Y.C., 1977, Stedelijk Mus., Amsterdam, 1978, Art of the 70's, Venice Bernnale, Italy, 1980, Haus der Kunst, Munich, 1981, Stedelijk Mus., Amsterdam, 1983, Whitney Mus. Am. Art, 1983, Skowhegan Sch. of Painting and Sculpture Medal, 1987, Whitney Biennal Exhbn, 1987; Mus. Modern Art, N.Y.C., 1985, Carnegie International, 1985; represented permanent collections: Mus. Modern Art, N.Y.C., Milw. Art Center, Stedelijk Mus., Amsterdam, Whitney Mus. Am. Art, pvt. collections; apptd. commr. City of N.Y. Art Commn. Mem. AAAL, Mcpl. Art Soc. N.Y. (bd. dirs. 1991—). Home: 17 W 16th St New York NY 10011-6301 Studio: 637 Greenwich St New York NY 10014 *There is never a question of what to paint, but only how to paint. The "how" of painting is the image, the end product.*

RYMER, PAMELA ANN, federal judge; b. Knoxville, Tenn., Jan. 6, 1941. AB, Vassar Coll., 1961; LLB, Stanford U., 1964; LLD (hon.), Pepperdine U., 1988. Bar: Calif. 1966, U.S. Ct. Appeals (9th cir.) 1966, U.S. Ct. Appeals (10th cir.), U.S. Supreme Ct. V.p. Rus Walton & Assoc., Los Altos, Calif., 1965-66; Assoc. Lillick McHose & Charles, L.A., 1966-72, ptnr., 1973-75; ptnr. Toy and Rymer, L.A., 1973-83; judge U.S. Dist. Ct. (cen. dist.) Calif., L.A., 1983-89, U.S. Ct. Appeals (9th cir.), L.A., 1989—; faculty The Nat. Jud. Coll., 1986-88; mem. com. summer ednl. programs Fed. Jud. Ctr., 1987-88; chair exec. com. 9th Cir. Jud. Conf., 1990; mem. com. criminal law Jud. Conf. U.S., 1988-93, Ad Hoc com. gender-based violence, 1991-94, fed.-state jurisdiction com., 1993—. Mem. editorial bd. The Judges' jour., 1989-91; contbr. articles to profl. jours. and newsletters. Mem. Calif. Postsecondary Edn. Commn., 1974-84, chmn., 1980-84; mem. L.A. Olympic Citizens Adv. Commn.; bd. visitors Stanford U. Law Sch., 1986—, chair, 1993—, exec. com.; bd. visitors Pepperdine U. Law Sch., 1987—; mem. Edn. Commn. of States Task Force on State Policy and Ind. Higher Edn., 1987-89; bd. dirs. Constnl. Rights Found., 1985; Jud. Conf. U.S. Com. Fed.-Sttae Jurisdiction, 1993, Com. Criminal Law, 1988-93, ad hoc com. gender based violence, 1991-94; chair exec. com. 9th Cir. jud. conf., 1990-94. Recipient Outstanding Trial Jurist award L.A. County Bar Assn., 1988. Mem. ABA (task force on civil justice reform 1991—), State Bar Calif. (antitrust and trade regulation sect., exec. com. 1990-92), L.A. County Bar Assn. (chmn. antitrust sect. 1981-82), Assn. of Bus. Trial Lawyers (bd. govs. 1990-92), Stanford Alumni Assn., Stanford Law Soc. Soc. Calif., Vassar Club So. Calif. (past pres.). Office: US Ct Appeals 9th Cir Ste 600 125 S Grand Ave Pasadena CA 91105-1652

RYMER, S. BRADFORD, JR., retired appliance manufacturing company executive; b. Cleveland, Tenn., May 30, 1915; s. S. Bradford and Clara Ladosky (Gee) R.; m. Anne Roddye Caudle, Nov. 7, 1942; children: Anita Elise, S. Bradford III. Grad., Fishburne Mil. Sch., 1933; BS in Indsl. Mgmt, Ga. Inst. Tech., 1937; D of Bus. Adminstration (hon.), Tenn. Wesleyan Coll. Indsl. engr. Dixie Foundry Co., Inc., Cleveland, Tenn., 1937-40, sec.-treas., dir. prodn., 1940-50; pres. Dixie Foundry Co., Inc. (name changed to Magic Chef Inc. 1961), Cleveland, Tenn., 1950-61; pres., chmn. Magic Chef Inc., Cleveland, 1961-87; chmn. Magic Chef Inc. div. Maytag Corp., Cleveland, 1986-87, ret., 1987; past chmn. Dixie-Narco, Inc., Ranson, W. Va.; forum dir. Munford Co.; former dir. Provident Life and Accident Ins. Co., Citizens & So. Nat. Bank, Atlanta. Past pres. Cleveland Asso. Industries; past trustee Tenn. Wesleyan Coll., Ga. Tech. Found.; past bd. dirs. Bradley County Meml. Hosp., Allied Arts of Chattanooga; past nat. dir. Jr. Achievement; trustee Fishburne Mil. Sch.; trustee Hiwassee Coll., John Templeton Found., 1993—. Civilian flight instr. World War II. Recipient Palm Beach Atlantic Colleges Am. Free Enterprise medal. Mem. Am. Gas Assn. (past exec. com. dir.), NAM (past dir.), Chief Execs. Orgn. (pres. 1971, dir.), Gas Appliance Mfrs. Assn. (pres. 1965), Young Pres. Orgn. (past dir., area v.p., chmn. Rebel chpt.), Ga. Tech. Nat. Alumni Assn. (past trustee), Toastmasters (bd. dirs. 1992—), Phi Gamma Delta. Republican (chmn. bd. trustees). Home: 28 Stonedge 100 Scenic Hwy Lookout Mountain TN 37350-1267 also: 1326 Lake Worth Ln Lost Tree Village North Palm Beach FL 33408 *No man is a success unto himself; for his success has been wrought with the help and talents of many associates.*

RYMER, WILLIAM ZEV, research scientist, administrator; b. Melbourne, Victoria, Australia, June 3, 1939; came to U.S., 1971; s. Jacob and Luba Rymer; m. Helena Bardas, Apr. 10, 1961 (div. 1975); children: Michael Morris, Melissa Anne; m. Linda Marie Faller, Sept. 5, 1977; 1 child, Daniel Jacob. MBBS, Melbourne U., 1962; PhD, Monash U., Victoria, 1971. Resident med. officer dept. medicine Monash U., Victoria, 1964-66; Fogarty internat. fellow NIH, Bethesda, Md., 1971-74; rsch. assoc. Johns Hopkins U. Med. Sch., Balt., 1975-76; asst. prof. SUNY, Syracuse, 1976-78; asst. prof. Northwestern U., Chgo., 1978-81, assoc. prof., 1981-87, prof., 1987—; rsch. dir. Rehab. Inst. Chgo., 1989—. Contbr. articles to profl. jours. Grantee

NIH, VA, Dept. of Def., Nat. Inst. Disability Rehab. Rsch., pvt. founds. Fellow Royal Australian Coll. Physicians; mem. Soc. Neurosci., Am. Soc. Biomechanics. Democrat. Avocations: tennis, racquetball. Office: Rehab Inst Chgo 345 E Superior St Chicago IL 60611-3015

RYN, CLAES GÖSTA, political science educator, author, research institute administrator; b. Norrköping, Sweden, June 12, 1943; permanent resident of U.S., 1979; s. Gösta Karl and Cecilia Edit (Blom) R.; m. Marianne Carin Tedhagen, Aug. 30, 1969; children: Charlotte, Viveka, Elisabet. Fil.kand. (MA), Uppsala (Sweden) U., 1967, postgrad., 1969-71; postgrad., Syracuse U., 1968-69; PhD, La. State U., 1974. Asst. prof. politics Cath. U. Am., Washington, 1974-78, assoc. prof. politics, 1978-82, prof. politics, 1982—; asst. dean Sch. Arts and Scis., Catholic U. Am., Washington, 1977-79; chmn. dept. politics Catholic U. Am., Washington, 1979-85; vis. assoc. prof. U. Va., Charlottesville, 1981; co-founder, chmn. Nat. Humanities Inst., Washington, 1984—; referee, evaluator NEH, Dept. Edn., USIA, others; dir. several scholarly confs. and lecture series; mem. Richard M. Weaver fellowship selection com., 1980—; faculty sponsor Earhart Found., 1989—; mem. awards com. Ingersoll Prizes, 1990; mem. Salvatori doctoral fellowship selection com. Intercollegiate Studies Inst., 1990—. Author: (with Bertil Häggman) Nykonservatismen i USA, 1971, Democracy and the Ethical Life, 1978, 2nd expanded edit., 1990, Will, Imagination and Reason, 1986, Individualism och Gemenskap, 1986, The New Jacobinism, 1991; editor: Humanitas, 1992—; co-editor (with George Panichas), author (with others): Irving Babbitt in Our Time, 1986; editor, author introduction for other volumes; contbr. numerous articles to profl. jours. and collective vols.; mem. editorial adv. bd. Modern Age, 1981—; editorial advisor Marknadsekonomisk Tidskrift, Sweden, 1986-92; mem. editorial bd. This World, 1992—. Mem. vestry St. Francis Episcopal Ch., Potomac, Md., 1986-88. Served with Swedish Army, Royal Life Company, 1963, Signal Corps, 1967-68. Rsch. fellow various orgns., including Earhart Found., 1980-81, 87-88, Wilbur Found., 1980-81, 90, 93-94; recipient award King of Sweden, 1983; named Outstanding Grad. Prof., Cath. U. Am., 1992. Episcopalian. Home: 10008 Crestleigh Ln Potomac MD 20854-1820 Office: Cath Univ Am Dept Politics Washington DC 20064

RYNEARSON, W. JOHN, association executive; b. Grosse Point, Mich., Oct. 10, 1948; s. William J. and Anna Lee (Hutto) R.; m. Justine M. Pointer, Aug. 28, 1971; children: Jill, Amy, Julie. Cert. in French, Sorbonne U., Paris, 1967; BA in Mktg., Jacksonville U., 1970, MA in Teaching, 1973. Instr. Duval County Schs., Jacksonville, Fla., 1970-73, Fla. Jr. Coll., Jacksonville, 1973-74; territory mgr. Burroughs Corp., Jacksonville, 1974-76; Mideast, Far East sales administr. Coleman Co., Wichita, Kans., 1976-77; Asia sales mgr. Coleman Co., Wichita, 1977-79, Asia, Europe mktg. mgr., 1979-82; v.p. mktg. O'Brien Co. div. Coleman Co., Seattle, 1982-84; pres., gen. mgr. Knight Internat., Seattle, 1984-85; exec. v.p., found. sec., bd. dirs. Civitan Internat., Birmingham, 1985—; com. chmn. Shoreline Community Coll. Internat. Studies, Seattle, 1984-85. Author: Yankee Traveler, 1986. Sunday sch. tchr., dir. youth program Emmanual Bapt. Ch., Jacksonville, 1975-76; bd. dirs., missions bd. Faith Chapel, Wichita, 1976-82, bd. mgr., 1976-82, Redmond (Redmond) Assembly of God, 1982-85. Mem. Am. Soc. Assn. Execs. (cert. assn. exec. 1991), Am. Mktg. Assn. Republican. Pentacostal. Lodges: Civitan. Avocations: sailing, snow skiing. Home: 3404 Field Stone Ln Birmingham AL 35242-3936 Office: Civitan Internat 1 Civitan Pl Birmingham AL 35213-1983

RYNKIEWICZ, STEPHEN MICHAEL, journalist; b. Sheboygan, Wis., Oct. 20, 1955; s. Walter Paul and Ruth Catherine (Van Hercke) R.; m. Brenda Gail Russell, Sept. 27, 1986. BA, U. Wis., 1976. Various staff assignments Chgo. Sun-Times, 1979—, real estate editor, 1990—; pres. Ill. Freedom of Info. Coun., 1991-93; regional dir. Soc. Profl. Journalists, 1992—; exec. com. 1995—. Office: Chicago Sun-Times 401 N Wabash Ave Chicago IL 60611

RYNN, NATHAN, physics educator, consultant; b. N.Y.C., Dec. 2, 1923; s. Meyer and Rose (Wolkerwiczer) Rynkowsky; m. Glenda Brown, June 24, 1989; children by previous marriage: Jonathan, Margaret, David. BSEE, CCNY, 1944; MS, U. Ill., 1947; PhD, Stanford U., 1956. Rsch. engr., RCA Labs., Princeton, 1947-52; rsch. asst. Stanford U., 1952-56, rsch. assoc., 1958; mem. tech. staff Ramo-Woolridge, L.A., 1956-57; supr. Huggins Labs., Menlo Park, Calif., 1957-58; rsch. staff physicist Princeton U., 1958-65; prof. physics U. Calif., Irvine, 1965-94, prof. physics emeritus, rsch. prof. physics, 1994—; vis. prof. Ecole Polytechnique Fed. of Lausanne, Switzerland, 1984-90, Ecole Polytechnique, Paris, and other European univs. and labs., 1973-80; indsl. sci. advisor/cons., 1964—; com. mem. Plasma Sci. Com. Nat. Rsch. Coun. Contbr. articles and revs. to profl. jours. Founder and leader plasma physics research facility. With USN, 1944-46. Grantee NSF, U.S. Dept. Energy, Air Force Geophys. Lab.; Fulbright sr. fellow, 1978. Fellow Am. Phys. Soc., IEEE, AAAS. Office: U Calif Dept Physics Irvine CA 92717-4575

RYNO, RONALD PAT, business executive, chemical engineer; b. Childress, Tex., Oct. 20, 1942; s. Leroy K. and Paulene (Bland) R.; div.; 1 child, Melanie; m. Andrea Jeane Denault, July 1, 1977; children: Heather, Erin. BS in Chem. Engring., Tex. Tech U., 1965; MBA, So. Meth. U., 1971. Engr. Dow Chem. Co., Freeport, Tex., 1965-66, Tex. Instruments, Dallas, 1966-72; pres., chief exec. officer Cuplex Inc., Garland, Tex., 1973—. Mem. Corp. Council, Garland, 1988—; mem. Garland Community Relations Council, 1988—. Mem. Inst. for Interconnecting and Packaging Electronic Circuits, Garland C. of C., Sigma Chi. Republican. Avocations: travel, collecting Southwestern art, reading. Office: Cuplex Inc 1500 Hwy 66 Garland TX 75040-6799

RYPIEN, MARK ROBERT, professional football player; b. Calgary, Alta., Can., Oct. 2, 1962. Student, Wash. State U. With Washington Redskins, 1987-94, Cleve. Browns, 1994—. Named to Pro Bowl team, 1989, 91; recipient Most Valuable Player award Superbowl, 1992. Office: Cleve Browns 80 1st Ave Berea OH 44017*

RYSANEK, LEONIE, soprano; b. Vienna, Austria, Nov. 14, 1926; d. Peter and Josefine (Hoeberth) R.; m. Ernst-Ludwig Gausmann, Dec. 23, 1968. Student, Vienna Conservatory, 1947-49. First singing engagements include, Bayreuth, (Sieglinde-Die Walkure), 1951, San Francisco Opera, (Senta-Der Fliegende Hollaender), 1956, Metropolitan Opera, (Lady Macbeth), 1959; now appears in world's foremost opera houses, N.Y.C., Vienna, Milano, San Francisco, London, Paris, (Chrysothemis-Elektra, 1973, Berlin, (Gioconda, 1974, Munich, Hamburg, Budapest, Moscow, (Parsifal, 1975; and festivals of, Salzburg, (Kaiserin-Die Frau Ohne Schatten, 1974, Bayreuth, Orange, (Salome, 1974, Sieglinde-Die Walkuere, 1975, Aix en Provence, Athens, (Medea, 1973, Edinburgh, recordings, RCA Victor, Deutsche Grammophon, London Records, EMI and Philips, Kundry, Parsifal (Stuttgart 1978), Kammersangerin of Austria and Bavaria, Kostelnicka, Jenufa, australian Opera, 1985, Vienna, 1986, San Francisco, 1986, N.Y. Carnegie Hall, 1988; debut Spain, Sieglinde in Die Walküre, N.Y. Met., 1988, Kostelnicka in Jenufa, Carnegie Hall, 1988, Liceo, Barcelona, 1989, Kabanicha in Katya Kabanova, Paris and L.A., 1988, Klytaemnesha in Elektra, Marseille, France, 1989, Orange, 1991, Met. Opera, N.Y.C., 1992, Old Countess, Queen of Spades, Barcelona, 1992. Recipient Chappel Gold medal of singing London; Silver Rose Vienna Philharmonic; Austrian Gold Cross 1st class for arts and scis.; San Francisco medal. Hon. mem. Vienna Staatsoper. Office: Merle Hubbard Mgmt 133 W 71st St Ste 8A New York NY 10023*

RYSCAVAGE, RICHARD JOSEPH, Jesuit priest, social services administrator; b. Pa., Mar. 25, 1945; s. Edward Thomas and Kathleen (Loftus) R. AB, Assumption Coll., 1967; MA, Boston Coll., 1972; M in Intercultural Adminstrn., Sch. Internat. Tng., Brattleboro, Vt., 1973; MDiv, Weston Sch. Theology, Cambridge, Mass., 1977; M of Law & Diplomacy, Tufts U., 1977. Ordained Jesuit priest, 1977, Md. Pres. Cath. Legal Immigration Network, Inc., Washington; exec. dir. migration and refugee svcs. U.S. Cath. Conf., Washington, 1990-94; Arrupe tutor, Oxford rsch. assoc. Refugee Studies Program Oxford U., Eng., 1995—; v.p. Internat. Cath. Migration Commn., Geneva, 1993—; chmn. com. on migration and refugee affairs, Interaction, Washington, 1993—; bd. dirs. Ctr. for Migration Studies, N.Y.C., Nat. Forum, Washington, Nat. Coalition for Haitian Refugees, N.Y.C.; mem. adv. bd. Refugee Policy Group, Washington, 1991—. Home: Oxford U, Campion

Hall, Oxford OX1 1QS, England Office: Refugee Studies Program, Queen Elizabeth Ho 21 St Giles, Oxford OX1 3LA, England

RYSKAMP, BRUCE E., publishing executive; b. Grand Rapids, Mich., 1941. AB, Calvin Coll., 1962; MBA, Mich. State U., 1964. With R. H. Donnelly Corp., 1964-82; with Zondervan Pub. House Zondervan Corp., Grand Rapids, 1983—, v.p. book and bible pub. Zondervan Pub. House, 1986—. Office: Zondervan Pub House 5300 Patterson SE Grand Rapids MI 49530

RYSKAMP, CHARLES ANDREW, museum executive, educator; b. East Grand Rapids, Mich., Oct. 21, 1928; s. Henry Jacob and Flora (DeGraaf) R. A.B., Calvin Coll. 1950; M.A., Yale U., 1951, Ph.D., 1956; postgrad., Pembroke Coll., Cambridge U., 1953-54; Litt.D., Trinity Coll., Hartford, 1975; L.H.D., Union Coll., 1977. Nathan Hale fellow Yale U., 1954-55; instr. English Princeton U., 1955-59, asst. prof., 1959-63, assoc. prof., 1963-69; curator English and Am. lit. Univ. Library, 1967-69, prof., 1969—; Procter & Gamble faculty fellow, 1958-59; jr. fellow Council of Humanities, 1960-61, John E. Annan preceptor, 1961-64; dir. Pierpont Morgan Library, N.Y.C., 1969-87, Frick Collection, N.Y.C., 1987—; mem. adv. bd. Skowhegan Sch. Painting and Sculpture, Private Papers of James Boswell, Yale U. Author: William Cowper of the Inner Temple, Esq, 1959, William Blake, Engraver, 1969; editor: (with F.A. Pottle) Boswell: The Ominous Years, 1963, The Cast-Away, 1963, Wilde and the Nineties, 1966, William Blake: The Pickering Manuscript, 1972, (with J. King) The Letters and Prose Writings of William Cowper, vol. I, 1979, vol. II, 1981, vol. III, 1982, Vol. IV, 1984, Vol. V, 1986, (with R. Wendorf) The Works of William Collins, 1979, (with J. Baird) The Poetical Works of William Cowper, vol. I, 1980, vols. II-III, 1995, (with J. King) William Cowper: Selected Letters, 1989, Report to the Fellows of the Pierpont Morgan Library, vols. 16-21, 1969-89. Trustee, mem. exec. com. Mus. Broadcasting, 1977-87; trustee Andrew W. Mellon Found., John Simon Guggenheim Meml. Found., Corning Mus. Glass, Amon Carter Mus.; mem. adv. coun. art mus. Princeton U.; vis. com. dept. paintings, conservation Met. Mus. Art; patron William Blake Trust; bd. mgrs. Lewis Walpole Libr. yale U.; bd. dirs., v.p. Gerard B. Lambert Found.; v.p. Frederick R. Koch Found.; v.p. Giannalisa Feltrinelli Found. Decorated Order St. John of Jerusalem, comdr. Order Orange Nassau, The Netherlands, officer Order Leopold II, Belgium, comdr. Order of Falcon, Iceland; recipient Peter Stuyvesant award Dutch Am. West-India Co., 1987, Gold medal Holland Soc., 1991. Mem. Am. Acad. Arts and Scis., Am. Philosphical Soc., Museums Coun. N.Y.C. (past v.p.), Royal Soc. Arts London, Keats-Shelley Assn. Am. (past v.p.), Master Drawings Assn. (pres.), Met. Opera Assn. (bd. advisors), Drawing Soc. (nat. com.), Bibliog. Soc. Am., Acad. Am. Poets, Am. Antiquarian Soc., Assn. Art Mus. Dirs. (past pres.), N.Y. Geneal. and Biog. Soc. (spl. corr.), Cowper Soc., Assn. Internationale de Bibliophilie (com. of Honor), Found. French Mus. (adv. bd.), Royal Soc. Arts (London), Wordsworth Rydel Mount Trust, Pilgrims, Grolier Club, Century Assn., Lotos Club (N.Y.C.), Elizabethan Club (New Haven), Roxburghe Club (London). Office: The Frick Collection 1 E 70th St New York NY 10021-4994

RYSKAMP, KENNETH LEE, federal judge; b. 1932; m. Karyl Sonja Ryskamp; 1 child, Cara Leigh. AB, Calvin Coll., 1955; JD, U. Miami, 1956. Bar: Fla. 1956, Mich. 1957, U.S. Supreme Ct. 1970. Law clk. to presiding judge Fla. Ct. Appeals 3d Dist., 1957-59; pvt. practice law Miami, Fla., 1959-61; ptnr. Goodwin, Ryskamp, Welcher & Carrier, Miami, 1961-84; mng. ptnr. Squire, Sanders & Dempsey, Miami, 1984-86; judge U.S. Dist. Ct. (so. dist.) Fla., Miami, 1986—. Office: US Dist Ct 701 Clematis St 4th Fl West Palm Beach FL 33401

SA, JULIE, mayor, restaurant chain owner; b. Korea, Dec. 15, 1950; came to US, 1970; married;. Degree in Polit. Sci., Dong-A U., Korea. Owner restaurant chain; councilwoman City of Fullerton, Calif., 1992-94, mayor, 1994—; rep. bd. Orange County Sanitation Dists. Mem. Fullerton C. of C., Orange County Korean C. of C., Orange County Chinese C. of C. Office: Office of the Mayor 303 W Commonwealth Ave Fullerton CA 92632*

SA, LUIZ AUGUSTO DISCHER, physicist; b. Lages, Brazil, Sept. 28, 1944; came to U.S., 1983; s. Catulo J.C. and Maria (Discher) S. MSc in Physics, Carnegie Mellon U., 1969; PhD in Elec. Engring., Stanford U., 1989. Asst. prof. Cath. U. of Rio, Rio de Janeiro, 1969-72, Fed. U. of Rio, Rio de Janeiro, 1973-83; post-doctoral scholar Stanford (Calif.) U., 1990-91, rsch. scientist, 1991—; rsch. scientist for MDI instrument to be flown in SOHO spacecraft, NASA, 1992—. Contbr. articles to Jour. of Applied Physics, Jour. Geophys. Rsch., Proc. of 4th SOHO Workshop on Helioseismology, ESA, 1995. Recipient of Recognition award NASA, 1994. Mem. Am. Astronomical Soc., Am. Geophysical Union, Sigma Xi. Roman Catholic. Achievements include research in non-linear plasma physics, naturally occurring plasmas, large scale flows on the sun. Office: CSSA ERL 328 Stanford CA 94305

SAAD, MOHAMMED FATHY, medical educator; b. Kom Hamada, Behaira, Egypt, Jan. 23, 1952; came to the U.S., 1981; s. Hassaneen Hilmy and Faiza S. (Younis) S. MBBCh with honors, U. Alexandria, Egypt, 1975, M of Medicine, 1979, MD, 1986; MS in Biomedical Scis., U. Tex., Houston, 1984. Intern Alexandria U. Hosp., 1976-77, resident dept. medicine, 1977-80; asst. lectr. Alexandria U., 1980-81, instr., 1984-86, asst. prof. medicine and endocrinology, 1986-87; fellow sect. endocrinology, dept. medicine U. Tex., Anderson Hosp. and Tumor Inst., Houston, 1981-84; staff physician Sacaton (Ariz.) Indian Hosp., 1987-91, Phoenix Indian Med. Ctr., 1988-91; attending physician dept. medicine Rancho Los Amigos Med. Ctr., L.A., 1991—; attending physician dept. medicine U. So. Calif.-Los Angeles County Med. Ctr., L.A., 1991—, assoc. prof. medicine, 1991—; vis. assoc. Phoenix epidemiology and clin. rsch. br. Nat. Inst. Diabetes and Digestive and Kidney Diseases, NIH, 1987-91; vis. endocrinologist Maricopa Med. Ctr., Phoenix, 1988-91. Author: (with others) Fundamentals of Surgical Oncology, 1986; subeditor sect. endocrine tumors Year Book Cancer, 1985-88; reviewer Am. Jour. Physiology, Diabetes, Diabetes Care, European Jour. Clin. Investigations, Jour. Lipid Rsch., Obesity Rsch., Ethnicity & Disease; contbr. articles to profl. jours. Recipient Egyptian State prize and medal of honor Nat. Acad. Sci., 1985; grantee Ariz. Kidney Found., 1989-90, Nat. Heart, Lung and Blood Inst., 1991—, Genentech, Inc., 1992-93, 94—. Mem. Am. Diabetes Assn. (grantee 1989-90, 93—), Am. Fedn. Clin. Rsch., Royal Coll. Physicians U.K., Am. Heart Assn. (mem. high blood pressure coun.), Egyptian Med. Assn., European Assn. Study Diabetes, Endocrine Soc. Office: U So Calif Med Sch Divsn Endocrinology 1200 N State St Rm 8250 Los Angeles CA 90033-4525

SAAD, THEODORE SHAFICK, retired microwave company executive; b. Boston, Sept. 13, 1920; s. Wadie Assad and Mary (Shalhoub) S.; m. Afeefi Abdelnour, May 5, 1943; children: Karen Jeanne, Janet Elaine. BSEE, MIT, 1941. Engr. Sylvania Electric Products, Danvers, Mass., 1941-42; rsch. assoc. radiation lab. Radiation Lab. MIT, Cambridge, 1942-45; sr. engr. Submarine Signal Co., Boston, 1945-49, v.p., chief engr. Microwave Devel. Labs., Waltham, Mass., 1949-53; engring. specialist Sylvania Electric Products, Woburn, Mass., 1953-55; pres., chmn. Sage Labs. Inc., Natick, Mass., 1955-93; ret., 1993; cons. Horizon House Microwave, Norwood, Mass., 1958—. Editor: Microwave Engineers Handbook, 1971, Historical Perspectives of Microwave Technology, 1984; patentee in microwavetech. and passive components fields. Fellow IEEE (life), AAAS; mem. Microwave Soc. of IEEE (hon. life, nat. lectr. 1972, Disting. Svc. award 1983, Centennial medal 1984, Career award 1992). Avocations: photography, reading, travel, music. Home: 52 Doublet Hill Rd Weston MA 02193-2331

SAADA, ADEL SELIM, civil engineer, educator; b. Heliopolis, Egypt, Oct. 24, 1934; came to U.S., 1959, naturalized, 1965; s. Selim N. and Marie (Chahyne) S.; m. Nancy Helen Hernan, June 5, 1960; children: Christine Mona, Richard Adel. Ingénieur des Arts et Manufactures, École Centrale, Paris, 1958; M.S., U. Grenoble, France, 1959; Ph.D. in Civil Engring., Princeton U., 1961. Registered profl. engr., Ohio. Engr. Société Dumez, Paris, 1959; research assoc. dept. civil engring. Princeton (N.J.) U., 1961-62; asst. prof. civil engring. Case Western Reserve U., Cleve., 1962-67; assoc. prof. Case Western Reserve U., 1967-72, prof., 1973—, chmn. dept. civil engring., 1978—, Frank H. Neff prof. civil engring., chmn. dept., 1987; R.J. Carroll Meml. lectr. Johns Hopkins U., 1990; cons., lectr. soil testing and properties Waterways Expt. Sta. (C.E.), Vicksburg, Miss., 1974-79; cons. to various firms, 1962—. Author: Elasticity Theory and Applications, 1974, 2d edit., 1993; contbr. numerous articles on soil mechanics and foundation engring. to profl. jours. Fellow ASCE (Civil Engr. of Yr. Cleve. sect. 1992); mem. Internat. Soc. Soil Mechanics, ASTM, One Two One Athletic Club. Inventor pneumatic analog computer and loading frame. Home: 3342 Braemar Rd Cleveland OH 44120-3332 Office: Case Western Res U Dept Civil Engring Case Sch Engring Cleveland OH 44106

SAAFELD, FRED ERICH, naval researcher, officer; b. Joplin, Mo., Apr. 9, 1935; s. Eric Arthur and Milla (Kessler) S.; m. Elizabeth Renner, Nov. 22, 1958; 1 child, Fred E. Jr. (dec.). BS cum laude, So. East Mo. State U., 1957; MS in Chemistry, Iowa State U., 1959, PhD in Physical Chem., 1961. Instructor Iowa State U., Ames, 1961-62; chemist Naval Rsch. Lab, Washington, 1962-63, head mass spectrometry sect., 1963-74, head physical chm. br., 1974-76, supt. chem. divsn., 1976-82; chief scientist Office Naval Rsch., London, 1979-80; dir. rsch. Office Naval Rsch., Arlington, Va., 1982-87, dir., 1987-93, dep. chief naval rsch., tech. dir., 1993—. Author more than 500 publications, reports, presentations on applications of mass spectrometry to fields of combustion, laser, environ. analysis. Recipient Disting. Rank award Pres., Washington, 1989, Meritorious Rank award Pres., Washington, 1986, Robert Conrad award Sec. U.S. Navy, Washington, 1988; named Fed. Exec. of Yr. Fed. Exec. Inst., Washington, 1991. Fellow AAAS; mem. Am. Chem. Soc. (councilor 1973-89), Am. Soc. Mass Spectrometry (sec. 1970-74), Combustion Inst., Chem. Soc. Washington (pres. 1972). Avocations: history, woodworking, sports. Office: Office of Naval Research 800 N Quincy St Arlington VA 22217

SAAL, HUBERT DANIEL, journalist; b. Bklyn., Feb. 23, 1924; s. Theodore Henry and Mary Rebecca (Valins) S.; m. Rollene Waterman (div.); children—Theodora Mathilde, Matthew Adlai, Drusilla Mary. Student, U. Fla., 1941-43; A.B.; Yale, 1948; postgrad., Sorbonne, Paris, France, 1948-50, 53-54, Columbia, 1950-51. Free-lance writer Europe, 1948-50, 53-55, N.Y.C., 1955-60; asso. editor Town & Country, 1950-53; instr. U. Miami, Fla., 1960-64; sr. writer Newsweek Mag., 1964-84. Author: The Say-Hey Kid. Served with USAAF, 1943-45. Recipient Deems Taylor award, 1974; Fulbright fellow Paris, 1952-53. Jewish. Home: 35 W 81st St New York NY 10024-6045

SAALMAN, HOWARD, architectural historian, educator; b. Stettin, Germany, Feb. 17, 1928; s. Walter Guenter and Gertrude (Robert) S.; m. Jeanne Eloise Farr, July 27, 1954; 1 dau., Daphne Lydia. A.B., CCNY, 1949; M.A., NYU, 1955, Ph.D., 1960. Prof. archtl. history Carnegie-Mellon U., Pitts., 1958-70, Andrew Mellon prof. architecture, 1970-93; emeritus, 1993; vis. prof. U. Calif., Berkeley, 1968, Harvard U., 1969, univs., Berlin, 1973, Bonn, 1979; vis. prof. U. Calif.-Berkeley, Vienna, 1982, Jerusalem, 1987, Heidelberg, 1988, Villa I Tatti, Florence, Italy, 1991. Author: Medieval Architecture, 1962, Medieval Cities, 1968, Haussman: Paris Transformed, 1971, Filippo Brunelleschi: The Cupola of S. Maria del Fiore, 1980, Filippo Brunelleschi: The Buildings, 1993, others. Fellow Am. Coun. Learned Socs., 1963, Kress Found., 1964, NEH, 1974, 91—, Guggenheim Found., 1984; grantee Am. Philos. Soc., 1966-67, 84-85, 91; recipient Alexander von Humboldt prize, 1992. Mem. Coll. Art Assn. Am., Accademia Nazionale Virgiliana di Scienze Lettere el Arti (corr.), Soc. Archtl. Historians. Democrat. Jewish. Office: Carnegie-Mellon U Pittsburgh PA 15213

SAAR, BETYE (IRENE SAAR), artist; b. L.A., July 30, 1926; d. Jefferson Maze and Beatrice Lillian (Parson) Brown; m. Richard W. Saar, Sept. 16, 1952 (div. 1968); children: Lesley Irene, Alison Marie, Tracye Ann. BA, UCLA, 1949. Instr. art Calif. State U., Hayward, 1971, Northridge, 1973-74; instr. art Otis Art Inst., L.A., 1976-83; lectr., free-lance designer for films, 1970-75—; costume designer Inner City Cultural Ctr., Napa Valley Theatre Co., 1968-73. One-woman exhbns. include Monique Knowlton, N.Y.C., 1976, 81, Calif. State U. Gallery, L.A., 1972, Whitney Mus. Art, N.Y.C., 1975, Jan Baum, L.A., 1977, 79, 81, Maneville Art Gallery, U. Calif., San Diego, 1979, Quay Gallery, San Francisco, 1982, Mus. Contemporary Art, L.A., 1984, Pa. Acad. Art, Phila., 1987, MIT, Cambridge, Mass., 1987, Calif. State U., Fullerton, 1988, also galleries in Manila, Kuala Lumpur, Malaysia, Taichung, Taiwan, 1988, Aukland and Wellington, New Zealand, 1988, 89, Montgomery Art Gallery Pomona Coll., 1991, U. Hartford (Conn.) Art Gallery, 1992, Fresno (Calif.) Art Mus., 1993, U. Ctrl. Fla. Art Gallery, Orlando, 1994, Santa Monica (Calif.) Mus. Art, 1994; two-woman exhbns. San Francisco Mus. Modern Art, 1977, Wight Gallery, UCLA, 1990; group exhbns. include Small Environments, Univ. Galleries, So. Ill. U., 1972, 20th Century Black Am. Art, San Jose (Calif.) Mus., 1976, San Francisco Mus. Modern Art, 1977, Smithsonian Instn.; touring exhbn. with daughter Alison Saar, 1990—, Netherlands Textile Mus., Tilburg, 1993, Mus. Applied Arts, Helsinki, Finland, 1993, Ctr. for Arts at Yerba Buena Gardens, San Francisco, 1993, Mus. Modern Art, Sao Paulo, 1994, Wilfredo Law Ctr., Havana, Cuba, 1994. NEA grantee, 1974, 84, James Van Der Zee grantee, 1992; J. Paul Getty fellow, 1990, Guggenheim Found. fellow, 1991. Mem. L.A. Inst. Contemporary Art. Democrat.

SAARI, DONALD GENE, mathematician; b. Ironwood, Mich., Mar. 9, 1940; s. Gene August and Martha Mary (Jackson) S.; m. Lillian Joy Kalinen, June 11, 1966; children: Katri, Anneli. BS, Mich. Tech. U., 1962; PhD, Purdue U., 1967, DSc (hon.), 1989. Research astronomer Yale U., New Haven, 1967-68; prof. dept. math. Northwestern U., Evanston, Ill., 1968—, prof. econs., 1988—, chmn. dept., 1981-84; cons. Nat. Bur. Standards, Gaithersburg, Md., 1979-86, Commn. 9, Internat. Astron. Union, 1985-91. Assoc. editor Jour. Econ. Behavior and Organ., 1988-94, Celestial Mechanics and Dynamical Astronomy. 1989-95, Econ. Theory, 1990—. Recipient Duncan Black award, Pub. Choice Soc., 1991; Guggenheim fellow, 1988-89. Mem. Am. Math. Soc., Math. Assn. Am. (Chauvenet prize 1995), Am. Astron. Soc., Soc. Indsl. and Applied Math. (editor jour. 1981-88), Econometric Soc. Office: Dept Math Northwestern U Evanston IL 60208-2730

SAARI, JOHN WILLIAM, JR., lawyer; b. Jersey City, Oct. 12, 1937; s. John William Sr. and Ina Marie (Bain) S.; m. Susan Jo Olson, Aug. 27, 1967 (div. June 1971); m. Marjorie Ann Palm, Nov. 16, 1973. Student, Duke U., 1955-58, U. N.C., 1962-63; JD with honors, Ill. Inst. Tech., Chgo., 1972. Bar: Ill. 1972, Wis. 1980, U.S. Ct. Appeals (7th cir.) 1972, Wis. 1980, U.S. Dist. Ct. (no. dist.) Ill. (ea. and we. dists.) Wis. 1980. Assoc. Yates, Goff, Gustafson & Been, Chgo., 1972-76, Hubbard, Hubbard, O'Brien & Hall, Chgo., 1976-78; atty. Ill. Bell Telephone Co., Chgo., 1978-79; assoc. Cirilli Law Office, Rhinelander, Wis., 1979-83; pvt. practice Rhinelander, 1983-90; ptnr. Rodd, Mouw & Saari, Rhinelander, 1990—. With U.S. Army, 1958-61, ETO. Mem. ABA, Ill. State Bar Assn., Wis. State Bar Assn., Oneida-Vilas-Forest Bar Assn. (treas. 1994-95), Sugarcamp Lions Club (pres. 1983-84). Avocations: hunting, fishing, baseball, reading, golf. Home: 7279 Arbutus Dr Eagle River WI 54521-9249 Office: Rodd Mouw & Saari 8A W Davenport St Rhinelander WI 54501-0757

SAARI, LEONARD MATHEW, paper company executive, lawyer; b. Los Angeles, Jan. 19, 1938; s. Mathew A. and Esther E. (Rantanen) S.; m. Yanna F. Asch, Oct. 18, 1968; children: Allison, Karina. BA in English, Lehigh U., 1960; JD, U. Mich., 1963. Bar: N.Y. 1964, Pa. 1971, Conn. 1974. V.p., sec., asst. gen. counsel Bowater Inc., Darien, Conn., 1975—. Office: Bowater Inc 1 Parklands Dr Box 4012 Darien CT 06820

SAATCHI, MAURICE, communications and marketing company executive; b. June 21, 1946; s. Nathan and Daisy Saatchi; m. Josephine Hart, 1984; 1 son, 1 stepson. BS in Econs., London Sch. Econs. and Polit. Sci., 1967. Co-founder Saatchi & Saatchi Co., 1970; chmn. Saatchi & Saatchi Co., plc, 1984-94; founder, chmn. The New Saatchi Agy., 1995—. Avocations: gardens, plays. Office: 35 Davies St, London WIY 1FN, England

SABALA, JAMES ANTHONY, mining company executive; b. Aug. 5, 1954; s. Tony Joe and Dorthy Molly (Kirkpatrick) S.; m. Janice Rae Oman, Aug. 14, 1976; children: Dominick James, Toni Marie. BS in Bus., U. Idaho, 1978. Acct. Price Waterhouse and Co., Seattle, 1978-81; asst. treas. Coeur d'Alene Mines Corp., Coeur d'Alene, Idaho, 1981, controller, 1981-82, treas., 1982-86, sec., treas., 1986-87, v.p. fin., 1987—. Bd. dirs. Excell Edn. Found., Coeur d'Alene, 1986—, North Idaho Coll. Pvt. Founs.; treas Statler for Sheriff, 1987—. Recipient Elijah Watt Sells award AICPA, 1978. Mem. Hayden Lake Country Club. Republican. Roman Catholic. Office: Coeur

d'Alene Mines Corp 505 E Front Ave Ste 400 Coeur D Alene ID 83814-2753

SABAROFF, ROSE EPSTEIN, retired education educator; b. Cleve., Sept. 4, 1918; d. Hyman Israel and Bertha (Glaser) Epstein; m. Bernard Joseph Sabaroff, Dec. 28, 1940; children: Ronald Asher, Katya Nina. B.A., U. Ariz., 1941; M.A., San Francisco State U., 1954; Ed.D., Stanford U., 1957. Tchr. Presidio Hill Elem. Sch., San Francisco, 1951-55; asst. prof. edn. Oreg. State U., Corvallis, 1958-61; asst. dir., then dir. elem. edn. Harvard Grad. Sch. Edn., Cambridge, Mass., 1961-66; prof. edn., head elem. edn., head reading program Va. Poly. Inst. and State U., Blacksburg, 1967-82; dir. Grad. Edn. Ctr. Calif. Luth. Coll., North Hollywood, 1982-84; reading specialist How to Learn, Inc., West Los Angeles, Calif., 1983-88. Author: (with Hanna, Davies, Farrar) Geography in the Teaching of Social Studies, 1966, (with Mary Ann Hanna) The Open Classroom, 1974, Teaching Reading with a Linguistic Approach, 1980, Developing Linguistic Awareness, 1981; contbr. articles to profl. jours. Recipient Disting. Research award Va. Edn. Research Assn., 1977; Phi Delta Kappa grantee, 1980. Mem. AAUP, Internat. Reading Assn., NEA, Va. Edn. Assn., Va. Coll. Reading Educators (pres. 1976-77), Va. Reading Assn., Phi Delta Kappa, Pi Lambda Theta, Gamma Theta Upsilon. Democrat. Jewish. Conducted 15 month study abroad comparing ednl. systems in 4 European countries with differing social-econ. systems. Home: 23826 Villena Mission Viejo CA 92692

SABAT, RICHARD J., lawyer; b. Nov. 24, 1947. BA, SUNY Binghamton, 1970; JD, Syracuse U., 1973. Bar: Pa. 1973. Ptnr. Morgan, Lewis & Bockius, Phila. Office: Morgan Lewis & Bockius 2000 One Logan Sq Philadelphia PA 19103

SABATH, LEON DAVID, internist, educator; b. Savannah, Ga., July 24, 1930; s. Sholom and Sarah (Cherkas) S.; children—Natasha, Joanna, Rachel. A.B. magna cum laude, Harvard U., 1952, M.D., 1956. Diplomat Am. Bd. Internal Medicine, Am. Bd. Infectious Disease. Intern Peter Bent Brigham Hosp., Boston, 1956-57; sr. resident in medicine Peter Bent Brigham Hosp., 1962-63; jr. resident in medicine Bellevue Hosp., N.Y.C., 1959-60; fellow in infectious disease Harvard U. and Thorndike Meml. Lab., Boston City Hosp., 1960-62; fellow in antibiotic resistance Sir William Dunn Sch. Pathology, Oxford U., Eng., 1963-65; mem. faculty dept. medicine Harvard U., also; staff physician Boston City Hosp., 1965-74; asst. Harvard Med. Sch., 1965-67, asst. prof., 1967-70, asso. prof., 1970-74; head sect. infectious diseases U. Minn., Mpls., 1974-83; prof. medicine U. Minn., 1974—; chmn. coms. U. Minn. Hosps.; adj. faculty Rockefeller U., 1990-91. Editor: Pseudomonas aeruginosa, 1980, Antibiotic Action in Patients, 1982; editorial bd.: Clin. Pharmacology and Theapeutics, 1978-80; contbr. articles on antibiotics and their use, bacterial resistance to antibiotics and chlamydia to profl. jours. Trustee E.P.A. Cephalosporin Fund, Oxford U., 1970—. Capt. M.C. AUS, 1957-59. NIH spl. fellow, 1963-65; recipient Career Devel. award NIH, 1968-72. Fellow ACP, Infectious Disease Soc. Am.; mem. Am. Soc. Clin. Investigation, Am. Soc. Microbiology (vice chmn. div. antimicrobial chemotherapy 1976-77, chmn. 1977-78), Am. Soc. Clin. Pharmacology and Theapeutics, Central Soc. Clin. Research, Am. Fedn. Clin. Research, Soc. Gen. Microbiology, Mass. Med. Soc., Soc. Exptl. Biology and Medicine, Brit. Soc. Antimicrobial Chemotherapy, Sigma Xi. Home: 2504 Washburn Ave S Minneapolis MN 55416-4351 Office: Phillip Wangensteen Bldg 14-168A University ofMinn Hospitals Minneapolis MN 55455

SABATINI, GABRIELA, tennis player; b. Buenos Aires, May 16, 1970; d. Osvaldo and Beatriz S. Winner French Jr. Open, 1984, Italian Jr. Open, 1984, Japan Open, 1985, Tokyo Open, 1987, Brighton Open, 1987, Italian Open, 1988, 1989, 1991, 1992, Virginia Slims Championship, 1988, 94, U.S. Open, 1990; Silver medalist in Tennis, 1988 Summer Olympics. Office: care Womens Tennis Assn 500 Ave Of The Champions Palm Beach Gardens FL 33410*

SABATINI, LAWRENCE, bishop; b. Chgo., May 15, 1930; s. Dominic and Ada (Piloi) S. Ph.L., Gregorian U., Rome, 1953, S.T.L., 1957, J.C.D., 1960; M.S. in Edn., Iona Coll., 1968. Ordained priest, Roman Catholic Ch., 1957, bishop, 1978. Prof. canon law St. Charles Sem., S.I., N.Y., 1960-71; pastor St. Stephen's Parish, North Vancouver, B.C., Canada, 1970-78; provincial superior Missionaries of St. Charles, Oak Park, Ill., 1978; aux. bishop Archdiocese Vancouver, B.C., Can., 1978-82; bishop Diocese Kamloops, B.C., Can., 1982—; procurator, adviser Matrimonial Tribunal, N.Y.C., 1964-71; founder, dir. RAP Youth Counseling Service, S.I., N.Y., 1969-71; vice ofcl. Regional Matrimonial tribunal of Diocese Kamloops, 1978-82; chmn. Kamloops Cath. Pub. Schs., 1982—. Named Man of Yr. Confratellanza Italo-Canadese, 1979. Mem. Can. Canon Law Soc., Canon Law Soc. Am., Can. Conf. Cath. Bishops. Office: Diocese of Kamloops, 635A Tranquile Rd, Kamloops, BC Canada V2B 3H5

SABATINI, NELSON JOHN, government official; b. Rochester, N.Y., Jan. 20, 1940; s. John R. and Ida M. (Ceconi) S.; m. Marilyn Jean Gromala, Jan. 19, 1963; children—John Nelson, Michael Christopher. Student, Lewis Coll., Lockport, Ill., 1958-62; B.A. in Psychology, George Washington U., 1971, postgrad. Claims rep. Social Security Adminstrn., Chgo., 1962-65; various positions Social Security Adminstrn., Balt., 1965-79, dep. dir. disability programs, 1979-81, exec. asst. to commr., 1981-82, assoc. commr., 1982—, dep. commr., 1983-88; dep. sec. health and mental hygiene State of Md., 1988, sec. health and mental hygiene, 1991—; v.p. U. Md. Med. System, 1995—. Named Disting. Marylander of Yr. 1993; recipient Sec.'s cert. HHS, 1975; Commr.'s citation Social Security Adminstrn., 1977, 81; Presdl. Merit Rank award Pres. of U.S., 1984. Roman Catholic. Avocations: sailing; tennis.

SABATINI, VINCENT FERNANDO, lawyer; b. Providence, Apr. 16, 1942; s. Vincent M. and Esther (Izzo) S.; m. Joyce Budney, Aug. 16, 1969; children: Jamie, Joanna, Joshua. BS, U. R.I., 1964; JD, Suffolk U., 1969. Bar: Conn. 1969, U.S. Dist. Ct. Conn. 1969, U.S. Ct. Appeals (2d cir.) 1969, U.S. Supreme Ct. 1983. Assoc. Riscassi & Davis, Hartford, Conn., 1969-72; ptnr. Clark, Sabatini, Mayo & Kuckro, Hartford, 1972-75, Sabatini & Budney, Newington, Conn., 1975-91; prin. Sabatini and Assocs., Newington, 1991—; mem. adv. bd. Conn. Bank & Trust, Newington, 1976—; atty. trial referee Conn. Supreme Ct., 1986—; spl. master Superior Ct. Hartford County. Mem. coun. Town of Wethersfield, Conn., 1973-79, dep. mayor, 1977-79, atty., 1981-89. Mem. ABA, Conn. Trial Lawyers Assn., Conn. Bar Assn. (mem. fee arbitration panel), Conn. Trial Lawyers Assn., Hartford County Bar Assn. (pres. 1993-94, bd. dirs. 1987—). Democrat. Roman Catholic. Avocations: tennis, boating, skiing, reading. Office: Sabatini and Assocs One Market Sq Newington CT 06111

SABATINI, WILLIAM QUINN, architect; b. Pitts.; s. William L. and Lydia M. (Contento) S.; m. Carol Anne Christoffel, Feb. 26, 1972; children: Quinn, Jay, Jillian. BA, Franklin & Marshall Coll., 1971; MArch, U. N.Mex., 1978. Registered arch., N.Mex., Nev.; cert. Nat. Coun. Archtl. Registration Bds. Intern Jess Holmes, Arch., Albuquerque, 1974-78; project mgr. Jack Miller & Assocs., Las Vegas, 1978-81; sr. design arch. HNTB, Kansas City, Mo., 1981-84; prin. Holmes Sabatini Assocs. Arch., Albuquerque, 1984—. Prin. works include Ctrl. Campus Bookstore U. N.Mex. (Merit award N.Mex. Soc. Archs. 1977), Luna County Courthouse, Deming, N.Mex. (Honor award AIA 1981, Honor award Nev. Soc. Arch. 1981), Reno Conv. Ctr. (Merit award Nev. Soc. Archs. 1983), Corp. Hdqs. Nev. Power Co., Las Vegas (Honor award Nev. Soc. Archs. 1983), YMCA, Las Vegas (Honor award Nev. Soc. Archs. 1983) Sanctuary Remodel St. Johns United Meth. Ch., Albuquerque (Best Interiors award N.Mex. Bus. Jour. 1986), The Presidio Office Bldg., Albuquerque (Best Bldgs. award and Best Interiors award N.Mex. Bus. Jour. 1987, Project of Yr. award Assoc. Gen. Contractors N.Mex. 1987) Suarez Residence, Albuquerque (Merit award N.Mex. Soc. Am. 1988), Fire Sta. Number 13 and Fire Marshall's Office, Albuquerque (Merit award Albuquerque Conservation Soc. 1987, Best Bldgs. award N.Mex. Bus. Jour. 1988), Santa Fe Imaging Ctr. (Citation of Excellence, Modern Health Care Mag., AIA com. on healthcare 1989, Best Bldgs. award N.Mex. Bus. Jour. 1989), Health Scis. Bldg. U. N.Mex. (Best Bldgs. award N.Mex. Bus. Jour. 1989), U.S. Port of Entry, Columbus, N.Mex. (Best Bldgs. award N.Mex. Bus. Jour. 1989, Honor award N.Mex. Soc. Archs. 1990, GSA Design award U.S. Gen. Svcs.

Adminstrn. 1990), Student Svcs. Bldg., Albuquerque TVI (Best Bldgs. award N.Mex. Bus. Jour. 1989, Merit award Albuquerque Conservation Soc. 1990), Expansion and Renovation Albuquerque Conv. Ctr. (Best Bldgs. award N.Mex. Bus. Jour. 1990), Lovelace Multi-Specialty Clinic Facility, Albuquerque (Merit award N.Mex. Soc. Archs. 1991), Pete's Playground U. N.Mex. Hosp. (Honor award N.Mex. Soc. Archs. 1992, Best Bldgs. Spl. award N.Mex. Bus. Jour. 1993), Nursing Unit Remodel U. N.Mex. Hosp. (Excellence award Am. Soc. Interior Designers 1992), 3.5 Meter Telescope Kirtland AFB, N.Mex. (Honor award AIA 1993). Bd. dirs. Albuquerque Chamber Orch., 1988, Hospice Rio Grande, 1992—; mem. adv. bd. Balloon Mus., 1989—; v.p. mem. adv. bd. St. Pius High Sch., 1993—. With USAR, 1971-78. Mem. AIA (bd. dirs. Albuquerque chpt. 1986-87). Roman Catholic. Office: Holmes Sabatini Assocs Archs West Courtyard 202 Central Ave SE Albuquerque NM 87102-3428

SABATO, LARRY JOSEPH, political science educator; b. Norfolk, Va., Aug. 7, 1952; s. N.J. and Margaret F. (Simmons) S. BA, U. Va., 1974; postgrad. Princeton U., 1974-75; DPhil, Oxford U., 1977. Lectr. politics New Coll., Oxford U., 1977-78; Robert Kent prof. Govt. and Foreign Affairs, U. Va., Charlottesville, 1978—; guest scholar Brookings Instn., 1980; Thomas Jefferson vis. prof. Downing Coll., Cambridge U., 1982; Danforth fellow, 1975; Kellogg fellow, 1983; Rhodes scholar. Mem. Am. Polit. Sci. Assn., Phi Beta Kappa. Author: The Rise of Political Consultants: New Ways of Winning Elections, 1981, Goodbye to Goodtime Charlie: The American Governorship Transformed, 1983, PAC Power: Inside the World of Political Action Committees, 1984, The Party's Just Begun: Shaping Political Parties for America's Future, 1988, Feeding Frenzy: How Attack Journalism Has Transformed American Politics, 1991, American Government: Roots and Reform, 1992, Corrupt Campaigning: The Dirty Little Secrets of American Politics, 1995. Office: U Va Dept Govt 232 Cabell Charlottesville VA 22901

SABAT-RIVERS, GEORGINA, Latin American literature educator; b. Santiago, Oriente, Cuba; came to U.S., 1962; d. José and Balbina (Mercadé) Sabat; m. Armando A. Guernica (div.); children: Armando A., Antonio J., Rodolfo M., Georgina M.; m. Elias L. Rivers, Sept. 19, 1969. MA in Romance Langs., Johns Hopkins U., 1967, PhD in Romance Langs., 1969. Instr. U. Oriente, Santiago de Cuba, 1956-61; asst. prof. Georgetown Visitation Coll., Washington, 1962-63; asst. prof. Western Md. Coll., Westminster, 1963-69, assoc. prof., 1969-73, prof., 1973-78, chair dept., 1974-78; assoc. prof. SUNY, Stony Brook, 1978-86, prof., 1986—, chair dept., 1981-84; vis. prof. U. Calif., Irvine, 1989, U. Iowa, Iowa City, 1994. Author: El Sueño de Sor Juana Inés de la Cruz tradiciones literarias y originalidad, 1976, Sor Juana Inés de la Cruz Inundación castálida, 1982, Literatura Femenina conventual: Sor Marcela de San Félix, hija de Lope..., 1992; also others; mem. editl. bd. Colonial L.Am. Rev., 1990—; contbr. articles to profl. jours. Fellow NEH, 1984-85, Fulbright, 1987; Soviet Union Internat. Rsch. and Exch. Bd. grantee, 1986, Summer seminar grantee NEH, 1995. Fellow Am. Philos. Soc.; mem. MLA (del. 1988-93), AAUW, Assn. Internat. hispanistas, Assn. Internat. Siglo de Oro, Assn. Internat. Cervantes, Inst. Internat. Lit. (editl. bd. 1987-90). Democrat. Roman Catholic. Avocations: interior decorating, gardening.

SABEL, BRADLEY KENT, lawyer; b. Charleston, Ill., Oct. 6, 1948; s. Walter Bernard and Charlotte (Ahlstrom) S.; m. Nancy Jean Parker, Apr. 4, 1984. B.A., Vanderbilt U., 1970; J.D., Cornell U., 1975; M.S. in Bus. Policy, Columbia U., 1983. Bar: N.Y. 1976. Atty. Fed. Reserve Bank of N.Y., N.Y.C., 1975-80; asst. counsel Fed. Reserve Bank of N.Y., 1980, sec., asst. counsel, 1981-85, assoc. counsel, 1985-87, counsel, 1988-93, counsel, v.p., 1993-94; counsel Shearman & Sterling, N.Y.C., 1994—. Contbr. numerous articles to profl. jours. Bd. dirs., treas. N.Y. Chamber Orch., N.Y.C., 1985-87; Served with U.S. Army, 1970-72. Home: 2 Midland Gdns Apt 4E Bronxville NY 10708-4729 Office: Shearman & Sterling 599 Lexington Ave New York NY 10022-6069

SABERHAGEN, BRET WILLIAM, professional baseball player; b. Chicago Heights, Ill., Apr. 13, 1964; s. Bob Saberhagen; m. Janeane Saberhagen; children—Drew, William. Pitcher Kansas City Royals, 1982-91, N.Y. Mets, 1991—. Recipient Cy Young award Baseball Writers' Assn. Am., 1985, 89, Gold Glove award, 1989; named Am. League Pitcher of the Year Sporting News, 1985, 89; pitched no-hit game, 1991; mem. All-Star team, 1987, 90, named AL Comeback Player of the Year, 1987; named to The Sporting News Am. League All-Star Team, 1985, 89. Office: NY Mets Shea Stadium Roosevelt Ave and 126th St Flushing NY 11368*

SABERS, RICHARD WAYNE, state supreme court justice; b. Salem, S.D., Feb. 12, 1938; s. Emil William and Elrena Veronica (Godfrey) S.; m. Colleen D. Kelley, Aug. 28, 1965; children: Steven Richard, Susan Michelle, Michael Kelley. BA in English, St. John's U., Collegeville, Minn., 1960; JD, U. S.D., 1966. Bar: S.D. 1966, U.S. Dist. Ct. S.D. 1966, U.S. Ct. Appeals (8th cir.) 1983. From assoc. to ptnr. Moore, Rasmussen, Sabers & Kading, Sioux Falls, S.D., 1966-86; justice Supreme Ct. S.D., Pierre and Sioux Falls, 1986—. Mem. editorial bd. U. S.D. Law Rev., 1965-66. State rep. March of Dimes, Bismarck, N.D., 1963; bd. dirs. St. Joseph Cathedral, Sioux Falls 1971-86; trustee, bd. dirs. O'Gorman Found., Sioux Falls, 1978-86; active sch. bd. O'Gorman High Sch., Sioux Falls, 1985-86. Lt. U.S. Army, 1960-63. Named Outstanding Young Religious Leader, Jaycees, Sioux Falls, 1971. Mem. ABA, S.D. Bar Assn., Inst. Jud. Adminstrn., St. John's Alumni Assn. (pres. Sioux Falls chpt. 1975-91). Republican. Roman Catholic. Avocations: tennis, skiing, sailing, sports. Home: 1409 Cedar Ln Sioux Falls SD 57103 Office: SD Supreme Ct 500 E Capitol Ave Pierre SD 57501-5070

SABERSKY, ROLF HEINRICH, mechanical engineer; b. Berlin, Germany, Oct. 20, 1920; came to U.S., 1938, naturalized, 1944; s. Fritz and Berta (Eisner) S.; m. Bettina Sofie Schuster, June 16, 1946; children—Carol, Sandra. B.S., Calif. Inst. Tech., 1942, M.S., 1943, Ph.D., 1949. Devel. engr. Aerojet Gen. Co., 1943-46, regular cons., 1949-70; asst. prof. Calif. Inst. Tech., Pasadena, 1949-55, assoc. prof., 1955-61, prof. mech. engring., 1961-88, prof. emeritus, 1988—; cons. various indsl. orgns. Author: Engineering Thermodynamics, 1957, Fluid Flow, 3d edit., 1989; contbr. articles to profl. jours. Fellow ASME (Heat Transfer Meml. award 1977, 50th anniversary award Heat Transfer Div 1988); mem. Sigma Xi, Tau Beta Pi. Home: 1060 Fallen Leaf Rd Arcadia CA 91006-1903 Office: Div Engring and Applied Sci Calif Inst Tech Pasadena CA 91125

SABEY, J(OHN) WAYNE, academic administrator, consultant; b. Murray, Utah, Dec. 10, 1939; s. Alfred John and Bertha (Lind) S.; m. Marie Bringhurst, Sept. 10, 1964; children: Clark Wayne, Colleen, Carolyn, Natasha Lynne. BA in Asian Studies, Brigham Young U., 1964, MA in Asian History, 1965; PhD in East Asian History, U. Mich., 1972. Teaching asst. Brigham Young U., Provo, 1964-65; rsch. asst., 1965, adj. prof. history, 1988-89; rsch. assist. U. Mich., Ann Arbor, 1966; from instr. to asst. prof. history U. Utah, Salt Lake City, 1970-80; v.p. Western Am. Lang. Inst., Salt Lake City, 1980-84, dir., 1984-86, pres., 1986—; exec. v.p. Pacific Rim Bus. Coords., Salt Lake City, 1993—, also bd. dirs., 1993—; assoc. dir. exch. program between U. Utah and Nagoya Broadcasting Network of Japan, 1973-79; lectr. in field. Superior award in extemporaneous speaking, 1956. Author essay, contbr. articles to ency. Consult. bd. trustees Western Am. Lang. Inst., 1986—, sec. to bd. trustees, 1980-86; chmn. bd. trustees Found. for Internat. Understanding, 1982—; mem. internat. adv. coun. Salt Lake C.C., 1988-94; mem. bd. advisors Consortium for Internat. Edn., 1972-77. Horace H. Rackham Sch. grad. studies fellow, 1969-70, Fulbright-Hays rsch. fellow (Japan), 1968-69, U.S. Nat. Def. fgn. lang. fellow, 1965-68. Mem. Assn. for Asian Studies (gen. chairperson, chairperson local arrangements western conf. 1970-72), Phi Kappa Phi. Avocations: piano, hiking, basketball, stamp collecting, tennis. Home: 8710 Oakwood Park Cir Sandy UT 84094

SABHARWAL, RANJIT SINGH, mathematician; b. Dhudial, India, Dec. 11, 1925; came to U.S., 1958, naturalized, 1981; s. Krishan Ch and Devti (An) S.; m. Pritam Kaur Chadha, Mar. 5, 1948; children—Rajinderpal, Amarjit, Jasbir. B.A. with honors, Punjab U., 1944, M.A., 1948; M.A., U. Calif., Berkeley, 1962; Ph.D., Wash. State U., 1966. Lectr. math. Khalsa Coll., Bombay, India, 1951-58; teaching asst. U. Calif., Berkeley, 1958-62; instr. math. Portland (Oreg.) State U., 1962-62; Wash. State U., 1963-66; asst. prof. Kans. State U., 1966-68; mem. faculty Calif. State Hayward, 1968—, prof. math., 1974—. Author papers on non-Desarguesian planes.

Mem. Am. Math. Soc., Math. Assn. Am., Sigma Xi. Address: 27892 Adobe Ct Hayward CA 94542-2102

SABIN, JAMES THOMAS, publisher; b. Toledo, June 23, 1943; s. Siegfried S. and Pauline R. (Lewis) S.; m. Anna Helen Greenhut, Oct. 1, 1971; children: David Michael, Karla Karen. BS, Georgetown U., 1965; MA (cert. in African studies), Columbia U., 1967, PhD, 1974. Writer, cons. Funk & Wagnalls Inc., N.Y.C., 1967-83; asst. editor Macmillan Inc., N.Y.C., 1969-70; social sci. editor Am. Book co., N.Y.C., 1971-73; sr. editor Greenwood Press Inc., Westport, Conn., 1973-74, exec. editor, 1974-75, v.p., editorial, 1975-84, exec. v.p., 1984—; cons. NAS; cons./referee NEH; cons./del. People to People Book Publ. Del. to Peoples Republic of China, 1987. Contbr. more than 200 articles to books and encys. Alumni admissions interviewer Georgetown U., Washington, 1988—; mem. nat. adv. bd. Ctr. for Black Music Rsch., Columbia Coll., Chgo., 1988—. African Inst. fellow Columbia U., 1965-67, Nat. Def. Fgn. Lang. fellow (Hausa) Columbia U., 1965-69. Democrat. Avocations: travel, music. Home: 459 Barrack Hill Rd Ridgefield CT 06877-2301 Office: Greenwood Publ Group Inc 88 Post Rd W Westport CT 06881-5007

SABIN, JOAN MARY, nursing executive, nurse; b. Cleve., Feb. 2, 1947; d. Paul James and Esther (Bolger) Hritz; m. Robert Phillip Sabin, June 14, 1969; 1 child, Robert Phillip Jr. Diploma, St. John's Hosp. Sch. Nursing, Cleve., 1968; BSN, Coll. of. Mt. St. Joseph, Cin., 1981; MBA, Xavier U., 1987. Staff nurse St. John's Hosp., Cleve., 1968-69; staff nurse Good Samaritan Hosp., Cin., 1969-75, various positions to dir. of nursing, 1985-88, acting asst. v.p., 1988-89, asst. v.p., 1989-91; asst. v.p. nursing dept. The Jewish Hosp., Cin., 1991-93; dir. patient care svcs. Franciscan Sys. of Cin., 1994—. Nurse ARC, Cin., 1981—. Mem. AACN, Nat. League for Nursing, Ohio Citizens League for Nursing (bd. dirs. 1988-92, mem. nominating com. 1992), Greater Cin. Nurse Execs. (sec., treas. 1989, pres. 1991—, sec. 1995), Ohio State Nurse Execs., Ohio League for Nursing (chairperson Cin. chpt. Ohio River Valley coun. 1982-83, vice chairperson 1983-84), Sigma Theta Tau (treas. Beta Iota chpt. 1995-96). Roman Catholic. Home: 831 Dunore Rd Cincinnati OH 45220-1416 Office: St Francis St George Hosp 3131 Queen City Ave Cincinnati OH 45238

SABIN, WILLIAM ALBERT, editor; b. Paterson, N.J., May 29, 1931; s. David and Esther (Goodman) S.; m. Marie Frances Noonan, May 31, 1958; children—Margaret, John, Katherine, Christopher, James. B.A. in English, Yale Coll., 1952; M.A. in English, Yale U., 1956. Pub. bus. and office edn. McGraw Hill Book Co., N.Y.C., 1973-78, editor in chief bus. books, 1979-86, pub. bus. books, 1987-90. Author: The Gregg Reference Manual, 8th edit., 1995; co-author: College English: Grammar and Style, 1967. Served as cpl. U.S. Army, 1952-54, ETO. Home: 38 Afterglow Way Montclair NJ 07042-1712

SABINE, GORDON ARTHUR, educator, writer; b. Brockton, Mass., Feb. 10, 1917; s. Charles Arthur and Esther (Carey) S.; m. Lois Eleanor Freiburg, June 26, 1941 (div. 1973); children: Ellen Jean, Gordon Arthur, Robert Allan, Roger Malcolm; m. Patricia Lundblade Williams, May 15, 1980; children: Patricia Glyn Williams Rhodes, John Paul, Nina Lynn Williams Keenan, Janet Anne Williams Maxim. A.B., U. Wis., 1939, M.A., 1941; Ph.D., U. Minn., 1949. Reporter, Lynchburg (Va.) News, 1931-35; reporter, copy editor Wis. State Jour., 1939-42; corr. UP, 1946-47; grad. asst. journalism U. Wis., 1939-41; instr., later asst. prof. journalism U. Kans., 1945-47; lectr. journalism U. Minn., 1947-48; asst. prof. U. Oreg., 1948-50, assoc. prof., 1950-52, prof. journalism, 1952-55, dean Sch. Journalism, 1950-55; prof. communication arts, dean Coll. Communication Arts, Mich. State U., East Lansing, 1955-60; prof. Coll. Communication Arts, Mich. State U., 1955-72, v.p. spl. projects, 1960-71; spl. asst. to pres. Ill. State U., 1971-72; dir. Sch. Communication, U. Iowa, 1972-75; prof. journalism Va. Poly. Inst. and State U., 1975-84; prof. journalism Ariz. State U., 1985, spl. asst. to univ. libr. dean, 1986-93; dir. Nat. Project in Agrl. Communication, 1960-62, GI Project MEMO, 1969-70; prof.-in-residence Time, Inc., 1951; Bd. dirs. Oregon Newspaper Pubs. Assn., 1950-55. Contbr. articles to nat. mags. and newspapers, 1938—; writer syndicated newspaper column Youthpoll America, 1976-77, Books That Made The Difference project Center for the Book, Library of Congress, 1980-81; author: When You Listen, This Is What You Can Hear, 1971, How Students Rate Their Schools and Teachers, 1971, Teachers Tell It Like It Is, Like It Should Be, 1972, The Folks in the Newsroom, 1977, Broadcasting in Virginia: Benchmark '79, 1980, (with Patricia L. Sabine) Books That Made the Difference: What People Told Us, 1983, (with Monsignor Robert Donohoe) Monsignor Donohoe, 1988, (with Donald Riggs) Libraries in the '90s: What the Leaders Expect, 1988, (with Tom Chauncey) The Memoir of Tom Chauncey, A Memoir, 1989, (with Albert Plotkin) Rabbi Plotkin, A Memoir, 1992, G. Homer, A Biography of Arizona State University President G. Homer Durham, 1992, Culver Bill Nelson, 1992, Phyllis B. Steckler and the Oryx Press, 1993, ". . . a damn beautiful butterfly": The Memoir of the Rev. William Lee Burkhardt, 1993, Nan Pyle: Payson's Unhappy Millionaire, 1993, Father Jack: Physician to the Soul, 1993, The Memoir of a Book: The Norton Reader of Expository Prose, 1995. Mem. Gov.'s Commn. on Employment of Handicapped, 1958-59; mem. research com. Am. Council Edn. for Journalism, 1951-53. Served to 1st lt. AUS, 1942-45, Iceland. Carnegie Corp. fellow, 1953; FAE-NAEB scholar TV, 1954; sr. postdoctoral research fellow Am. Coll. Testing Program, 1970-71. Mem. Assn. Edn. in Journalism, Assn. Accredited Schs. and Depts. Journalism (pres. 1954-55), Am. Polit. Sci. Assn., Sigma Delta Chi (nat. research com. 1949-51), Omicron Delta Kappa. Home: 2625 E Southern Ave C-102 Tempe AZ 85282

SABINSON, HARVEY BARNETT, cultural organization administrator; b. N.Y.C., Oct. 24, 1924; s. Samuel and Sarah Sabinson; m. Sarah S. Sabinson, Aug. 15, 1944; children: Eric, Allen. BS, Queens Coll., 1947. Freelance publicist N.Y., 1946-73; dir. spl. projects League Am. Theatres & Producers, N.Y.C., 1976-82, exec. dir., 1982—; vis. prof. theatre adminstrn. Yale U. Sch. of Drama, New Haven, 1966-70. Author: Darling, You Were Wonderful, 1977. Recipient Lifetime Achievement award United Jewish Appeal Fedn., 1990; Lifetime Achievement Tony award, 1995. Mem. Actor's Fund of Am. (trustee 1990—), Broadway Assn. (bd. dirs. 1977), Theatre Devel. Fund (bd. dirs. 1992—), Broadway Hall of Fame (bd. dirs. 1992—), Times Square Bus. Improvement Dist. (bd. dirs. 1994—), Mayor's Midtown Citizens Com. Avocation: theatre. Office: League Am Theatres & Producers 226 W 47th St New York NY 10036-1413

SABINSON, MARA BETH, theatre educator, director, actress; b. N.Y.C., Mar. 1, 1946; d. Lee S. and Belle M. (Lindenauer) S.; m. John David Bergman, Sept. 6, 1987. BA, U. Calif., Berkeley, 1968; postgrad., Dartmouth Coll.; acting studies with Joseph Chaikin, Herbert Berghoff, Carl Weber, directing studies with Aaron Frankel, Jan Kott, Augusto Boal, voice and singing studies with Kristin Linklater and Mark Zeller. Mem. faculty Dell'Arte Sch. of Mime and Comedy, Blue Lake, Calif., 1978-81; acting coach N.Y.C., 1983—; assoc. prof. drama & film studies Dartmouth Coll., Hanover, N.H., 1984—; tchr. numerous workshops and programs including Mark Taper Forum, L.A., Stanford U., U. Calif.-Berkeley, Santa Cruz & Irvine, San Jose State U., Calif. State U. at Hayward, San Francisco State U., Laney Coll., San Francisco, Orange Coast Coll., Weed Coll., Chico State U., Columbia Jr. Coll., Coll. of the Siskiyous, Studiejamfrandet, Stockholm, Humboldt State U., Geese Theatre Co., Berkshire Theatre Festival; vis. faculty Calif. State Coll. of the Redwoods, 1980, Dell'Arte Sch. Phys. Theatre, 1990; extensive adminstrn. & prodn. experience. Co-author: (plays) Profiles in Porridge, 1972, Clowns, 1973, Ever Since Felix Moved to New Zealand, 1974, Phenoxy Follies, 1979, Intrigue at Ah-Pah, 1979, Whiteman Meets Bigfoot, 1980, The Gump Show, 1985, The Fall and Rise of Roger Gump, 1987; dir. plays including Orestes, 1967, Clowns, 1974, Jim Doodle Dandy, 1976, Space Bondage, 1979, Italian Detectives, 1981, We Are Not From Here, 1982, Judy's Floating Head, 1984-85, Female Transport, 1987, Cruel and Unusual Couples, 1988, Finale, 1988, Lone Star, 1989, The Taming of the Shrew, 1989, Cloud 9, 1990, numerous others; stage appearances include The Fool of the World, 1972, Human Rites, 1975, And Still I Rise, 1976, Music for Homemades, 1983, Canaries and Sitting Ducks, 1984, Heartbreak House, 1985, A Streetcar Named Desire, 1989, In the Jungle of Cities, 1991, God, 1991, numerous others; TV appearances on Sid Caesar's Show of Shows, 1956, The Immigrants, 1979, September Song: An American Autumn, 1987; film appearances include The Projectionist, 1975, History Book: Part I, 1975, Family Plot, 1976, The Killer Elite, 1976, The

Reunion, 1976, Shaping Things, 1977, The Great Weirton Steel, 1984; also radio appearances, commls., theatrical adaptations, interviews, play readings; editorial contbr. various publs.; contbr. photographs and articles to numerous jours. and publs. Grantee Nat. Endowment for the Arts, Calif. State Arts Coun., Berkeley City Arts Coun., Rosenberg Found.; recipient Bay Area Critics' Circle award, Critic's Choice/Best Bets citations, Lila Wallace/Reader's Digest Found. Arts Ptnrs. award, 1990. Home: RR 2 Box 312 Cornish NH 03745-9720 Office: Dartmouth Coll Dept Drama Hanover NH 03755

SABISTON, DAVID COSTON, JR., surgeon, educator; b. Onslow County, N.C., Oct. 4, 1924; s. David Coston and Marie (Jackson) S.; m. Agnes Foy Barden, Sept. 24, 1955; children: Anne Sabiston Leggett, Agnes Sabiston Butler, Sarah Coston. BS, U. N.C., 1944; MD, Johns Hopkins U., 1947; DSc (hon.), U. Madrid. Diplomate: Am. Bd. Surgery (chmn. 1971-72). Successively intern, asst. resident, chief resident surgery Johns Hopkins Hosp., 1947-53; successively asst. prof., assoc. prof., prof. surgery Johns Hopkins Med. Sch., 1955-64, Howard Hughes investigator, 1955-61; Fulbright research scholar U. Oxford, Eng., 1960; research assoc. Hosp. Sick Children, U. London, Eng., 1961; James B. Duke prof. surgery, chmn. dept. Duke Med. Sch., 1964-94; chief of staff Duke U. Med. Ctr., 1994—; chmn. Accreditation Council for Grad. Med. Edn., 1985-86. Editor: Textbook of Surgery, Essentials of Surgery, Atlas of General Surgery, Atlas of Cardiothoracic Surgery, A Review of Surgery; co-editor: Gibbon's Surgery of the Chest, Companion Handbook to Textbook of Surgery; chmn. editl. bd. Annals of Surgery; mem. editl. bd. Annals Clin. Rsch., ISI Atlas of Sci.: The Classics of Surgery Libr., Surgery, Gynecology and Obstetrics, Jour. Applied Cardiology, Jour. Cardiac Surgery, World Jour. Surgery, Jour. Served to capt., M.C. AUS, 1953-55. Recipient Career Rsch. award NIH, 1962-64, N.C. award in Sci., 1978, Disting. Achievement award Am. Heart Assn. Sci. Coun., 1983 Michael E. DeBakey award for Outstanding Achievement, 1984, Significant Sigma Chi award, 1987, Coll. medalist Am. Coll. Chest Physicians, 1987, Disting. Tchr. award Alpha Omega Alpha, 1992; named Disting. Physician, U.S. VA, 1995. Mem. ACS (chmn. bd. govs. 1974-75, regent 1975-82, chmn. bd. regents 1982-84, pres. 1985-86), NAS Inst. Medicine, Am. Surg. Assn. (pres. 1977-78), So. Surg. Assn. (sec. 1969-73, pres. 1973-74), Am. Assn. Thoracic Surgery (pres. 1984-85), Soc. Clin. Surgery, Internat. Soc. Cardiovascular Surgery, Soc. Vascular Surgery (v.p. 1967-68), Soc. Univ. Surgeons (pres. 1968-69), Halsted Soc., Surg. Biology Club II, Soc. Thoracic Surgery, Soc. Surgery Alimentary Tract, Johns Hopkins U. Soc. Scholars, Soc. Surg. Chairmen (pres. 1974-76), Soc. Thoracic Surgeons Great Britain and Ireland, Soc. Internat. De Chirurgie, James IV Assn. Surgeons (bd. dirs. U.S. chpt.), III. Surg. Soc. (hon.), Phila. Acad. Surgery (hon.), Royal Coll. Surgeons Edinburgh (hon., editl. bd. jour.), Royal Coll. Surgeons Eng. (hon.), Asociación de Cirugía del Litoral (Argentina) (hon.), Royal Coll. Physicians and Surgeons Can. (hon.), Royal Coll. Surgeons Ireland (hon.), Royal Australasian Coll. Surgeons (hon.), German Surgical Soc. (hon.), Colombian Surg. Soc. (hon.), Brazilian Coll. Surgeons (hon.), Japanese Coll. Surgeons (hon.), French Surg. Assn. (hon.), Surg. Congress Assn. Espanola de Cirujanos (hon.), Philippine Coll. Surgeons (hon.), Phi Beta Kappa, Alpha Omega Alpha. Clubs: Cosmos (Washington), Hope Valley Country Club (Durham), Treyburn City Club (Durham). Home: 1528 Pinecrest Rd Durham NC 27705-5817 Office: Duke U Med Ctr PO Box 2600 MSRD Durham NC 27710

SABL, JOHN J., lawyer; b. L.A., June 16, 1951. AB with distinction, Stanford U., 1973, JD, 1976. Bar: Calif. 1976, Ill. 1977. Ptnr. Sidley & Austin, Chgo. editorial bd. Stanford U. Law Review, 1974-75, assoc. mng. editor, 1975-76. Mem. Chgo. Bar Assn. (chmn. securities law com. 1985-86), Legal Club Chgo. Office: Sidley & Austin 1 First National Plz Chicago IL 60603-0001

SABLE, BARBARA KINSEY, former music educator; b. Astoria, L.I., N.Y., Oct. 6, 1927; d. Albert and Verna Rowe Kinsey; B.A., Coll. Wooster, 1949; M.A., Tchrs. Coll. Columbia U., N.Y.C., 1950; D.Mus., U. Ind., 1966; m. Arthur J. Sable, Nov. 3, 1973. Office mgr., music dir. sta. WCAX, Burlington, Vt., 1954; instr. Cottey Coll., 1959-60; asst. prof. N.E. Mo. State U., Kirksville, 1962-64; asst. prof. U. Calif., Santa Barbara, 1964-69; prof. music U. Colo., Boulder, 1969—. Author: The Vocal Sound, 1982; contbr. poetry to literary jours. Mem. Nat. Assn. Tchrs. Singing (past state gov., asso. editor bull.), AAUP, Colo. State Music Tchrs. Assn. Democrat. Avocation: poetry. Home: 3430 Ash Ave Boulder CO 80303-3432 Office: U Colo Coll Music Campus Box 301 Boulder CO 80309

SABLOFF, JEREMY ARAC, archaeologist; b. N.Y.C., Apr. 16, 1944; s. Louis and Helen (Arac) S.; m. Paula Lynne Weinberg, May 26, 1968; children: Joshua, Saralinda. A.B., U. Pa., 1964; M.A., Ph.D., Harvard U., 1969. Asst. prof., assoc. prof. Harvard U., Cambridge, Mass., 1969-76; asso. prof. anthropology U. Utah, Salt Lake City, 1976-77; curator anthropology Utah Mus. Natural History, Salt Lake City, 1976-77; prof. anthropology U. N.Mex., Albuquerque, 1978-86; chmn. dept. U. N.Mex., 1980-83; Univ. prof. anthropology and the history and philosphy of sci. U. Pitts., 1986-94, chmn. dept. anthropology, 1990-92; Charles K. Williams II dir. U. Mus., U. Mus. Term prof. anthropology, curator Mesoamerican archaeology U. Pa., Phila. 1994—; sr. fellow for Pre-Columbian Studies, Dumbarton Oaks, 1986-92, chmn. 1989-92. Author: (with G.R. Willey) A History of American Archaeology, 1974, 2d edit., 1980, 3d edit., 1993, Excavations at Seibal: Ceramics, 1975, (with C.C. Lamberg-Karlovsky) Ancient Civilizations: The Near East and Mesoamerica, 1979, 2nd edit., 1995, (with D. A. Freidel) Cozumel: Late Maya Settlement Patterns, 1984, The Cities of Ancient Mexico, 1989, The New Archaeology and the Ancient Maya, 1990, (with G. Tourtellot) The Ancient Maya City of Sayil: The Mapping of a Puuc Region Center, 1991; editor(with C.C. Lamberg-Karlovsky) The Rise and Fall of Civilizations, 1974, Ancient Civilization and Trade, 1975, (with W.L. Rathje) A Study of Changing Pre-Columbian Commercial Systems, 1975, American Antiquity, 1977-81, (with G.R. Willey) Scientific American Readings in Pre-Columbian Archaeology, 1980, Simulations in Archaeology, 1981, Supplement to the Handbook of Middle American Indians: Archaeology, 1981, Archaeology: Myth and Reality: A Scientific American Reader, 1982, Analyses of Fine Paste Ceramics, 1982, (with D. Meltzer and D. Fowler) American Archaeology: Past and Future, 1986, (with E.W. Andrews V) Late Lowland Maya Civilization: Classic to Postclassic, 1986, (with J.S. Henderson) Lowland Maya Civilization in the Eighth Century A.D., 1993. Nat. Geog. Soc. grantee, 1972-74; NSF grantee, 1983-88; NEH grantee, 1990-91. Fellow Am. Anthrop. Assn., AAAS (sec. H, chair 1994-95), Royal Anthrop. Inst., Soc. Antiquaries London; mem. Nat. Acad. Sci., Soc. Am. Archaeology (pres. 1989-91), Prehist. Soc., Internat. Soc. Comparative Study of Civilizations, Sigma Xi. Office: U Pa Mus Archaeology and Anthropology 33d and Spruce Sts Philadelphia PA 19104-6324

SABO, MARTIN OLAV, congressman; b. Crosby, N.D., Feb. 28, 1938; s. Bjorn O. and Klara (Haga) S.; m. Sylvia Ann Lee, June 30, 1963; children: Karin, Julie. BA cum laude, Augsburg Coll., Mpls., 1959; postgrad., U. Minn., 1961-62. Mem. Minn. Ho. of Reps. from 57B Dist., 1960-78, democratic-farmer-labor party minority leader, 1969-72, speaker, 1973-78; mem. 96th to 103rd congresses from 5th Minn. Dist., 1979—; chmn. Dem. Study Group 96th to 101st Congresses from 5th Minn. Dist.; Dep. Majority Whip 96th to 103rd Congresses from 5th Minn Dist., mem. Appropriations Com.; mem. permanent select com. on intelligence 102nd Congress from 5th Minn. Dist.; chmn. Ho. Budget Com. 103rd Congress from 5th Minn. Dist.; mem. 104th Congress from 5th Minn Dist.; former mem. Nat. Adv. Commn. on Intergovtl. Rels.; past pres. Nat. Legis. Conf.; bd. regents Augsburg Coll.; ranking minority mem. Appropriations subcom. on transp., Budget Com. Recipient Disting. Alumni citation Augsburg Coll., Arms Control Leadership award Employees Union, Local 113, SEIU, AFL-CIO; named One of 200 Rising Young Leaders in Am. Time mag., 1974; Man of Yr. Mpls. Jr. C of C., 1973-74, One of Ten Outstanding Young Men of Yr. Minn. Jr. C. of C., 1974. Mem. Nat. Conf. State Legis. Leaders (past pres.). Office: 2336 Rayburn House Office B Washington DC 20515*

SABO, RICHARD STEVEN, electrical company executive; b. Walkertown, Pa., Jan. 1, 1934; s. Alex S. and Elizabeth (Haluska) S.; m. Gail P. Digon, Feb. 15, 1954; children: Gailyn J., Richard A., Kerry S., Dale A. BS in Edn., California (Pa.) U., 1955; MS in Edn., Edinboro (Pa.) U., 1965. Tchr. Northwestern Sch. Dist., Albion, Pa., 1955-65; prodn. technician The Lincoln Electric Co., Cleve., 1965-66, staff asst. mktg., 1966-70, mgr. pub.

rels., 1971-86, asst. to chmn., 1986—, dir. cop. comms. and investor rels.; also exec. dir. James F. Lincoln Arc Welding Found. Editor: The Procedure Handbook of Arc Welding, 1994, 10 other books on arc welding; contbr. numerous articles to profl. jours. Chmn. Area Recreation Bd., Chesterland, Ohio, 1970, West Geauga Boosters, Chesterland, 1973-77; mem., bd. dirs. Profit Sharing Coun. Am., 1991—. Recipient Svc. award Future Farmers Am., 1970—, Svc. award U.S Skill Olympics, 1980, Lakeland Community Coll. award, 1990, Ohio State U. Hon. Welding Engring. Alumni award, 1990, Calif. U. (Pa.) medallion of Distinction, 1990. Mem. Am. Welding Soc. (vice chmn. edn. and fin. com., mem. fin. com. 1988—, speaker, various awards, Plummer lectr. 1992), Am. Soc. for Engring. Edn., Am. Inst. Steel Cons. (mem. edn. com. 1986—), Steel Plate Fabricators Assn. (past chmn. promotions com., mem. bd. dirs.s profit sharing coun. 1991—), California U. Alumni Assn. (trustee 1983—). Republican. Presbyterian. Lodge: Masons. Avocations: golf, hunting, fishing, classical music. Office: The Lincoln Electric Co 22801 Saint Clair Ave Cleveland OH 44117-2524

SABOSIK, PATRICIA ELIZABETH, publisher, editor; b. Newark, Aug. 25, 1949; d. George Aloysius and Elizabeth Ann (Simko) S.; m. Kenneth Donald Gursky, Apr. 21, 1972 (div. 1980). BA in English, Kean Coll. N.J., 1976; MBA in Mktg., Seton Hall U., 1984; cert. advanced study in fin., Fairfield U., 1989. Proofreader Baker & Taylor, Somerville, N.J., 1969-71, database coordinator, 1971-74, prodn. editor, 1974-77, publs. mgr., editor, 1977-82; dir. mktg. services H.W. Wilson Pub. Co., Bronx, N.Y., 1982-84; editor, pub. Choice mag. Am. Library Assn., Middletown, Conn., 1984-94; project dir. Books for Coll. Librs. Am. Library Assn., Middletown, 1985-88, project dir. Guide to Ref. Books, 1988-94; v.p. electronic text Booklink Technologies, Wilmington, Mass., 1994; v.p. Linked Media, Navi Soft Divsn. Am. Online, Inc., Needham, Mass., 1994—; membership chmn. Serials Industry Systems Adv. Com., 1983-89, vice chmn., 1985-86, newsletter editor, 1986-87. Contbr. articles to profl. jours. Party rep. Twp. Com. Cranford, N.J., 1977-79; hon. bd. advisors U. Conn. Women's Ctr., 1989-91; mem. Conn. Women's Edn. and Legal Fund; nat. bd. dirs. Literacy Vols. of Am., 1992-94, also chair pub. and mktg. com. Mem. ALA (coms., editorial bd. Choice), AAUW, Assn. Coll. and Rsch. Librs. (publs. com.), Soc. for Scholarly Pub. (membership com., editor newsletter 1988-91, budget and fin. com. 1990-92, sec.-treas. 1994—, bd. dirs. 1994—), Appalachian Mountain Club, Women's Outdoors Club (newsletter editor 1984-86, regional rep. 1986-87). Republican. Roman Catholic. Office: Navi Soft Inc An Am Online Co 75 2d Ave Ste # 710 Needham MA 02194

SABSAY, DAVID, library consultant; b. Waltham, Mass., Sept. 12, 1931; s. Wiegard Isaac and Ruth (Weinstein) S.; m. Helen Glenna Tolliver, Sept. 24,1 966. AB, Harvard U., 1953; BLS, U. Calif., Berkeley, 1955. Circulation dept. supr. Pomona (Calif.) Pub. Library, 1955-56; librarian Santa Rosa (Calif.) Pub. Library, 1956-65; dir. Sonoma County Library, Santa Rosa, 1965-92; libr. cons., 1992—; coordinator North Bay Coop. Library System, Santa Rosa, 1960-64; cons. in field, Sebastopol, Calif., 1968—. Contbr. articles to profl. jours. Commendation, Calif. Assn. Library Trustees and Commrs., 1984. Mem. Calif. Library Assn. (pres. 1971, cert. appreciation 1971, 80), ALA. Club: Harvard (San Francisco). Home and Office: 667 Montgomery Rd Sebastopol CA 95472-3020

SABSHIN, MELVIN, psychiatrist, educator, medical association administrator; b. N.Y.C., Oct. 28, 1925; s. Zalman and Sonia (Barnhard) S.; m. Edith Goldfarb, June 12, 1955; 1 child, James K. B.S., U. Fla., Gainesville, 1944; M.D., Tulane U., New Orleans, 1948. Diplomate Am. Bd. Psychiatry and Neurology. Assoc. dir. Michael Reese Hosp. Psychosomatic and Psychiat. Inst., Chgo., 1953-61; prof., head dept. psychiatry U. Ill. Coll. Medicine, Chgo., 1961-74; med. dir. Am. Psychiat. Assn., Washington, 1974—. Author Depression, 1960, Psychiatric Ideology, 1961; Normality, 1978; Normality and Life Cycle, 1984. Served with U.S. Army, 1944. Recipient Bowen award Am. Coll. Psychiatrists, 1978, Disting. Psychiatrist award, 1985. Mem. Am. Coll. Psychiatrists (pres. 1974-75). Home: 2801 New Mexico Ave NW Washington DC 20007-3921 Office: Am Psychiat Assn 1400 K St NW Washington DC 20005-2403

SABY, JOHN SANFORD, physicist; b. Ithaca, N.Y., Mar. 21, 1921; s. Rasmus S. and Maude Emily (Sanford) S.; m. Mary Elizabeth Long, June 9, 1945; children: Arthur D., Thomas S., Joseph A., Jean E. B.A., Gettysburg (Pa.) Coll., 1942, Sc.D. (hon.), 1969; M.S., Pa. State U., 1944, Ph.D., 1947. Lab. instr. Gettysburg Coll., 1940-42; instr. Cornell U., 1947-50; with Gen. Electric Co., 1951-82; mgr. semicondr./solid state Gen. Electric Co., Syracuse, N.Y., 1954-56; mgr. lamp phenomena research Gen. Electric Co., Cleve., 1956-82; cons., 1982—; mem. vis. com. biol. and phys. scis. Case Western Res. U., chmn., 1969. Co-author: Principles of Transistor Circuits, 1953. Fellow IEEE (past com. officer); mem. Am. Phys. Soc., Cleve. Assn. Research Dirs. (1963-64), Am. Watchmakers Inst., Nat. Assn. Watch and Clock Collectors, Phi Beta Kappa, Sigma Xi, Phi Kappa Phi, Phi Sigma Kappa. Patentee in field. Home: 8 Tamarac Ter Hendersonville NC 28739-9770

SACCHET, EDWARD M., foreign service officer; b. Bklyn., Sept. 28, 1936; m. Elizabeth Priore. BA in Internat. Affairs, George Washington U., 1958; postgrad., Sch. Advanced Internat. Studies, Johns Hopkins U., Bologna, Italy, 1958-59; MA in Internat. Affairs, Sch. Advanced Internat. Studies, Johns Hopkins U., 1960; postgrad., U. Oslo, Norway, 1959. Labor economist U.S. Dept. of Labor, Washington, 1961-63; mem. U.S. Fgn. Service-Dept. of State, Washington, 1963—; internat. economist White House Office of Spl. Trade Rep., Washington and Geneva, 1964-67; sec., econ. comml. officer Am. Embassy, Tananarive, Madagascar, 1967-69; consul, econ. comml. officer Am. Consulate Gen., Naples, Italy, 1969-72; 1st sec., fin. economist Am. Embassy, Rome, Italy, 1972-75; congl. fellow U.S. State Dept.-U.S. Congress, 1975-76; econ. officer Bur. Econ. and Bus. Affairs-U.S. Dept. State, 1976-78; career devel. and assignments officer Bur. of Personnel-U.S. Dept. State, 1978-80; consul gen. Am. Consulate Gen., Marseille, France, 1980-84; Pearson fellow, spl. advisor to Gov. of Fla. for Internat. Issues Tallahassee, 1984-85; fgn. service inspector-office Inspector Gen. Fgn. Service-U.S. Dept. State, Washington, 1985-87; U.S. consul gen. Am. Consulate Gen., Martinique, French W. Indies, 1987-88; spl. asst. Office Exec. Dir., Bur. Econ. and Bus. Affairs-Dept. State, 1987; acting ambassador U.S. Embassy, Antigua, W.I., 1988; cons. Bur. Adminstrn., info. mgmt. system and diplomatic security U.S. Dept. State, 1989—; lectr. in field. George Washington U. scholar, 1954-58, Johns Hopkins Sch. Internat. Studies scholar, Washington and Bologna, Italy, 1958-60; State Dept. fellow, 1980, Pearson fellow Office of Gov. Fla., 1984, Congl. fellow Am. Polit. Sci. Assn., 1980. Mem. Am. Fgn. Svc. Assn., Johns Hopkins U. Alumni Assn., Army-Navy Club of Washington. Home: 118 Monroe St # 907 Rockville MD 20850-2513 also: 13167 La Lique Ct Palm Bch Gdns FL 33410-1417

SACCO, FRANK VINCENT, hospital administrator; b. Akron, Ohio, June 28, 1947; married. BA, U. Miami, 1970; MA, Fla. Internat. U., 1978. Various positions Meml. Hosp., Hollywood, Fla., 1973-78, adminstrv. asst., 1978-79, asst. adminstr., 1979-84, sr. assoc. adminstr., 1984-85, sr. assoc. adminstr., COO, 1985-87, adminstr., CEO, 1987—; adj. educator in field. Home: 3120 Peachtree Cir Fort Lauderdale FL 33328-6705 Office: Meml Hosp 3501 Johnson St Hollywood FL 33021-5487

SACCO, ROBERT ANTHONY, financial executive; b. N.Y.C., Oct. 24, 1944; s. Amerigo and Margaret (McCarthy) S.; children—Stephanie, Robert. Student U. Miami, 1962-64; B.S., Monmouth Coll., 1966; M.B.A., NYU, 1968. C.P.A., N.Y. Staff acct. J.H. Cohn & Co., Newark, 1969; supr. Rudolf, Cinamon & Calafato, Ocean, N.J., 1969-78; mgr. M. Sternlieb & Co., Hackensack, N.J., 1978-79; chief fin. officer Conf. Environs. Corp., N.Y.C., 1979—; dir., officer Cox Hotel Corp., Long Branch, N.J., Twin Gardens Condo Assn., Long Branch; mng. dir. East Beach Ocean Front, N.Y., 1983—; prof. acctg. Monmouth Coll., 1974-79; treas. dir. Horizon Hotels, Ltd., N.Y.C. Mem. N.J. Soc. C.P.A.s, Am. Inst. C.P.A.s, NYU Alumni Assn. Roman Catholic. Address: Horizon Hotels Ltd PO Box 3277 147 Brighton Ave Long Branch NJ 07740*

SACERDOTE, MANUEL RICARDO, banker; b. Buenos Aires, Feb. 20, 1943; s. Ricardo Edmundo and Ana Maria (Devoto) S.; m. Nora Alejandrina Mascarenhas, Aug. 24, 1966; children: Juan Martín, Diego Raul, Andrea María, Matías. E.E., U. Buenos Aires, 1966; M.B.A., Harvard U., 1968. Treas., Chrysler Argentina, Buenos Aires, 1969-71; gen. mgr. Sasin S.A.,

Buenos Aires, 1971-74; pres. Banco de Boston, Buenos Aires, 1974—; pres. Bank of Boston Found., Buenos Aires; dir. La Continental Ins. Co., Buenos Aires, Pfizer S.A., Buenos Aires, Swift Armour S.A., Buenos Aires. Mem. Argentine Bankers Assn. (bd. dirs. 1976—, vice chmn. 1989—, chmn. 1987-89), Argentine Bus. Coun., Latin Am. Found. Econ. Research (bd. dirs. 1983—). Clubs: Martindale, Belgrano Athletic, Harvard of Argentina (pres. 1979-80). Avocations: tennis, swimming, reading. Office: First Nat Bank of Boston, Florida 99, Buenos Aires 1005, Argentina

SACERDOTE, PETER M., investment banker; b. Turin, Italy, Oct. 15, 1937; came to U.S., 1940; s. Giorgio S. and Luciana (Levi) S.; m. Bonnie Lee Johnson, June '18, 1967; children: Alisa, Alexander, Laurence. B.E.E., Cornell U., 1960; M.B.A., Harvard U., 1964. Assoc. investment banking div. Goldman, Sachs & Co., N.Y.C., 1964-69, v.p. investment banking div., 1969-73, gen. ptnr., 1973-90, ltd. ptnr., 1990—; bd. dirs. Weis Markets, Inc., Sunbury, Pa., Qualcomm, Inc., San Diego, Franklin Resource, San Mateo, Calif.; in charge Pvt. Fin. Dept., 1974-80, The Corp. Fin. Dept., 1980-87, Merch Bank, 1987-90; chmn. Committments, Credit and Investment Cons., 1987-90, GS Capital Partnership; adj. prof. Columbia Grad. Sch. Bus., 1984-86; nat. chmn. HBSFD, Milton (Mass.) Acad. Trustee Day Sch., N.Y.C., 1980—; chmn. Alumni Bd. Harvard Bus. Sch., 1990; bd. visitors Fuqua Sch. Duke U., 1990; bd. overseers Cornell Med. Coll. Served to lt. (j.g.) USNR, 1960-62. Mem. Harvard Club N.Y.C., River Club N.Y.C., Downtown Assn., Nantucket Yacht Club, Stanwich Golf Club, Country Club of the Rockies, Sankaty Head Golf Club (Siasconset, Mass.). Office: Goldman Sachs & Co 85 Broad St New York NY 10004-2434

SACHA, ROBERT FRANK, osteopathic physician, allergist; b. East Chicago, Ind., Nov. 29, 1946; b. S. Frank John and Ann Theresa Sacha; m. Linda T. Le Page, 1988; children: Joshua Jude, Josiah Gerard, Anastasia Levon, Jonah Bradley. BS, Purdue U., 1969; DO, Chgo. Coll. Osteo. Medicine, 1975. Diplomate Am. Bd. Pediatrics, Am. Bd. Allergy and Immunology. Pharmacist, asst. mgr. Walgreens Drug Store East Chicago, Ind., 1969-75; intern David Grant Med. Ctr., San Francisco, 1975-76, resident in pediatrics, 1976-78; fellow in allergy and immunology Wilford Hall Med. Ctr., 1978-80; staff pediatrician, allergist Scott AFB (Ill.) 1980-83; practice medicine specializing in allergy and immunology Cape Girardeau, Mo., 1983—; assoc. clin. instr. St. Louis U., 1980—; clin. instr. Purdue U., 1971-72, Pepperdine U., 1975-76, U. Tex.-San Antonio, 1978-80, assoc. clin. instr. So. Ill. U. Pres., Parent Tchrs. League. Maj. M.C., USAF, 1975-83, comdr., USNR. Fellow Am. Coll. Allergy, Am. Coll. Chest Physicians, Am. Acad. Pediatrics, Am. Acad. Allergy-Immunology, Am. Assn. Cert. Allergists; mem. AMA, Am. Acad. Allergy, Assn. Mil. Allergists, ACP, Am. Coll. Emergency Physicians, Mil. Surgeons and Physicians. Republican. Lutheran.

SACHAR, DAVID BERNARD, gastroenterologist, medical educator; b. Urbana, Ill., Mar. 2, 1940; s. Abram Leon and Thelma (Horwitz) S.; m. Joanna Maud Belford Silver, Aug. 29,1 961; children: Mark Benson, Kenneth Hulbert Belford. AB magna cum laude, Harvard U., 1959, MD cum laude, 1963. Diplomate Bd. Gastroenterology Am. Bd. Internal Medicine. Intern medicine Beth Israel Hosp., Boston, 1963-65, resident, 1967-68; asst. chief clin. rsch. Pakistan-SEATO Cholera Rsch. Lab., Dhaka, Bangladesh, 1965-67; resident in gastroenterology Mt. Sinai Hosp., N.Y.C., 1968-70; from instr. to prof. medicine Mt. Sinai Sch. Medicine, CUNY, N.Y.C., 1970-92, 1st Burrill B. Crohn prof. medicine, 1992—; dir. div. gastroenterology Mt. Sinai Hosp., N.Y.C., 1983—, vice chmn. dept. medicine, 1992—; co-chmn. work group on inflammatory bowel disease NIH, 1973-75; expert adv. panel on gastroenterology and nutrition U.S Pharmacopeial Conv., 1980-85; chmn. rsch. devel. com. Nat. Found. for Ileitis and Colitis, 1984-89; co-founder, sec.-treas. Burrill B. Crohn Rsch. Foun., N.Y.C., 1984—; K.H. Koster meml. lectr. Danish Soc. of Gastroenterology, 1992; Internat. State of the Art lectr. Brit. Soc. Gastroenterology, 1995; mem. Gastroenterology Leadership Coun. Task Force on Fellowship Curriculum, 1994. Author over 130 articles and chpts. on natural history and treatment of inflammatory bowel disease; editor 7 books and monographs on gastroenterology. Trustee Bangladesh Coun. of the Asia Soc., N.Y.C., 1972-75, Bd. Edn., Englewood Cliffs, N.J., 1973-75. Sr. surgeon, comdr. USPHS,1965-67. Recipient Jacobi medallion for Disting. Achievement Mt. Sinai Alumni Assn., 1994. Fellow ACP, Am. Coll. Gastroenterology (program dirs. com. 1991—, Henry Baker Presdl. lectr. 1989); mem. Am. Gastroent. Assn. (chmn. subcom. on cert. 1987, 1st chmn. clin. teaching project 1984-90, mem. nominating com. Immunology-Microbiology-Inflammatory Disorders sect. 1993, chmn. nominating com. 1995), Crohn's and Colitis Found. Am. (grants rev. com. and coun. 1990-94, chmn. clin. rsch. subcom.Disease Classification and Measurement 1994, Disting. Svc. award 1991, N.Y. Govs. medal 1992), Internat. Orgn. for Study of Inflammatory Bowel Disease (1st Am. elected chmn. 1989-92), Phi Beta Kappa, Alpha Omega Alpha. Achievements include co-development of oral rehydration therapy for diarrhea; development of resources and standards for clinical teaching in gastroenterology. Office: Mt Sinai Med Ctr One Gustave L Levy Pl New York NY 10029

SACHAR, HOWARD MORLEY, history educator; b. St. Louis, Feb. 10, 1928; s. Abram Leon and Thelma (Horwitz) S.; m. Eliana Steimatzky, July 23, 1964; children: Sharon, Michele, Daniel. B.A., Swarthmore Coll., 1947; M.A., Harvard U., 1950, Ph.D., 1953. Instr. history U. Mass., 1953-54; dir; Hillel Found. UCLA, 1954-57; dir. Hillel Found., Stanford (Calif.) U., 1959-61, Hiatt Inst. in Israel, 1961-64; assoc. prof. history George Washington U., Washington, 1964-66; prof. George Washington U., 1966—. Author: The Course of Modern Jewish History, 1958, Aliyah, 1961, From the Ends of the Earth, 1964, The Emergence of the Middle East, 1969, Europe Leaves the Middle East, 1972, A History of Israel, 1976, The Man on the Camel, 1980, Egypt and Israel, 1981, Diaspora, 1985, A History of Israel Vol. II, 1987; gen. editor Rise of Israel: A Documentary History, 1988, A History of the Jews in America, 1992, Farewell España, 1994; contbr. articles to N.Y. Times, Washington Post, Commentary, others. Charles Brown fellow, 1957-58; NEH fellow, 1970-71; recipient Nat. Jewish Book award, 1976, 81. Mem. Am. Hist. Assn., Am. Jewish Hist. Soc., Phi Beta Kappa. Democrat. Jewish. Home: 9807 Hillridge Dr Kensington MD 20895-3228 Office: Dept History George Washington U Washington DC 20052

SACHDEV, MOHINDAR SINGH, engineering educator; b. Amritsar, Punjab, India, Apr. 1, 1928; naturalized Can. citizen; s. Khushal Singh and Kishen Kour (Chawla) S.; m. Joginder Kour, Feb. 4, 1951; children—Narinder P., Mandhir, Sukhbir, Sukhvinder. B.Sc., Benares Hindu U., Varanasi, India, 1950; M.Sc., Panjab U., Chandigarh, India, 1965, U. Sask., 1967; Ph.D., U. Sask., 1969; DSc, U. Sask, 1994. Registered profl. engr., Sask.; chartered engr. U.K. Asst. engr. Pub. Works Dept., Amritsar, India, 1950-59; exec. engr. Pub. Works Dept., Nangal, 1960-61; assoc. prof. Punjab Engring. Coll., Chandigarh, India, 1961-65; supt. engr. State Electricity Bd., Patiala, India, 1968-69; asst. to assoc. prof. U. Sask., Saskatoon, 1969-76; prof. U. Sask., 1976—, head elec. engring. dept., 1988-93; cons., lectr. in field; mem. Can. subcom. Internat. Electrotech. Commn.; mem. grant selection com. NSERC, 1991-94, chmn., 1993-94. Coordinator/author: (IEEE Course text) Computer Relaying, 1979, Microprocessor Relays and Protection Systems, 1988. Instr. def. driving courses Can. Safety Council, Ottawa, Ont., 1973-84; bd. dirs. Sask. Safety Council, 1976-81, chmn. traffic div., 1979-80. Recipient Cert. of Appreciation, Punjab State Electricity Bd., India, 1962; Sci. Research Council sr. vis. fellow, U.K, 1980. Fellow IEEE (chmn. western Can. coun. 1984-86, awards com. 1989-91, Outstanding Engring. Educator award IEEE Can. 1994), Instn. Engrs. India, Instn. Elec. Engrs. (U.K.), Engring. Inst. Can.; mem. Can. Elec. Assn. (vice chmn. power sys. planning and operation sect. 1989-92, chmn. 1993—). Sikh. Office: Univ Sask, Saskatoon, SK Canada S7N 0W0

SACHDEV, VED PARKASH, neurosurgeon; b. Mitranwali, India, Feb. 22, 1932; came to the U.S., 1969; s. Girdhari Lal and Amar Kaur Sachdev; m. Ranjit Kaur Sachdev, Apr. 17, 1970; children: Ulka, Rivka. MB BS, Govt. Med. Coll., Amritsar, Panjab, India, 1955. Diplomate Am. Bd. Neurosurgery. Asst. prof. neurosurgery Med. Inst., Chandigarh, India, 1964-69; intern St. Josephs Hosp., Lorain, Ohio, 1969-70; resident in neurosurgery Mt. Sinai Med. Ctr., N.Y.C., 1970-73, from asst. to assoc. clin. prof. dept. neurosurgery, 1974-88, clin. prof. dept. neurosurgery, 1988—; vice chmn. dept. neurosurgery Mt. Sinai Med. Ctr., N.Y.C., 1988-92. Author chpts. in 7 med. books. Surgeon lt, Indian Navy, 1957-60. Fellow ACS, Royal Coll. Surgeons Eng. (diplomate laryngology and otology). Avocation:

music. Home: 128 Moorland Dr Scarsdale NY 10583-1937 Office: Mt Sinai Med Ctr Dept Neurosurgery 1148 5th Ave New York NY 10128-0807

SACHEDINA, ABDULAZIZ, religious studies educator; b. Lindi, Tanzania, May 12, 1942; came to U.S., 1976; s. Abdulhussein and Hamida (Shariff) S.; m. Fatima Akbar Takim, Aug. 14, 1967; children: Alireza, Muhammadreza. BA, Aligarh (India) Muslim U., 1966; BA in Persian Lang. and Literature, U. Mashad, Iran, 1971; MA in Islamic Studies, U. Toronto, Can., 1972, PhD, 1976. Instr. English Jorjani Nursing Sch., Mashhad, Iran, 1968-71; rsch. asst. dept. Mid. East and Islamic studies U. Toronto, 1971-72; asst. prof. dept. history, asst. prof. dept. French and gen. linguistics U. Va., 1977-78, asst. prof. dept. religious studies, oriental langs., 1978-82, assoc. prof., 1982-88, prof., 1988—; vis. lectr. dept. religious studies U. Waterloo, Ont., Can., 1975, dept. religion and culture Wilfrid Laurier U., Waterloo U., 1975-76; vis. asst. prof. dept. religious studies U. Va., 1976-77; vis. prof. Faculty Shari'a U. Jordan, Amman, 1986; Margaret Gest vis. prof. religion Haverford (Pa.) Coll., 1987-88; adj. prof. dept. religion Temple U., Phila., 1987-88; vis. scholar U. Jordan, Amman, 1990-91; mem. editorial bd. Ency. Modern World Islam Oxford U. Press Project, Al-Mizan Translation Project Mostazafan Found. N.Y.; mem. adv. bd. Ctr. for Islamic-Jewish Studies U. Denver, joint program on conflict resolution Inst. for Victims Trauma, McLean, Va.; bd. dirs. Am. Coun. Study of Islamic Socs.; lectr. in field. Author: Islamic Messianism: The Idea of the Mahdi in Twelver Shi'ism, 1980, The Just Ruler in Twelver Shi'ism: The Comprehensive Authority of the Jurist in Imamite Jurisprudence, 1988; author: (with others) Human Rights and the Conflict of Cultures: Western and Islamic Perspectives on Religious Religion Liberty, 1988; contbr. articles to profl. jours., chpts. to books; contbr. articles to reference books. Religious scholar East African Fedn. of Shia Ithnashery Jamaats, 1963-66, Cultural scholar Govt. Iran, 1967-71; Grad. fellow Province of Ont., 1972-73, Open fellow U. Toronto, 1973-75, Rsch. fellow Ferdowsi U., 1973-74, Rsch. fellow Muhammedi Trust, 1978-79, Rsch. fellow Sesquicentennial, 1983; Summer Rsch. grantee U. Va., 1978, 80, 81, 83, Rsch. in Iran grantee, 1982-83. Mem. Am. Acad. Religion, Am. Oriental Soc., Mid. East Studies Assn., Iranian Studies Assn. Home: 698 Highland Ave Charlottesville VA 22903 Office: U Va Dept Religious Studies Charlottesville VA 22903

SACHER, BARTON STUART, lawyer; b. Birmingham, Ala., Apr. 9, 1948; s. Martin R. and Inez (Zuckerman) S.; 1 child, Joseph Alan; m. Susan Angela Anton, Sept. 30, 1976. BBA, U. Ala., 1970, JD, 1973. Law clk. to judge J. Pointer U.S. Dist. Ct., Birmingham, 1973-74; assoc. Berkkowitz, Lefkowitz & Patrick, Birmingham, 1974-77; atty. investigations, trial counsel SEC, Washington, 1977-79; chief of investigations and enforcement SEC, Atlanta Region, 1979-85; ptnr. Tew, Jorden, Schulte & Beasley, Miami, 1986-90; pres., dir., ptnr. Hornsby, Sacher, Zelman & Stanton, P.A., Miami, 1990—. Vice chmn. bd. dirs. Atlanta Fantasy Fair Inc., 1982—; v.p., trustee Temple Israel of Greater Miami, Inc.; v.p., dir. Alex Maus H.S.; Israel; regional dir. ADL, Nat. Fin. Com., Dem. Party, Dem. Leadership Coun. Mem. ABA, Fed. Bar Assn., Fla. Bar Assn., D.C. Bar Assn., Ala. State Bar Assn., Greater Miami C. of C. (trustee), Grove Isle Club, Brickell Club. Jewish. Office: Hornsby Sacher Zelman & Stanton PA 1110 Brickell Ave Penthouse Miami FL 33131

SACHER, STEVEN JAY, lawyer; b. Cleve., Jan. 28, 1942; s. Albert N. and Cecil P. (Chessin) S.; m. Colleen Marie Gibbons, Nov. 28, 1970; children—Alexander Jerome, Barry Elizabeth, William Paul. B.S., U. Wis., 1964; J.D., U. Chgo., 1967. Bar: D.C. 1968. Assoc. solicitor Employee Retirement Income Security Act U.S. Dept. Labor, Washington, 1974-77; spl. counsel com. on labor and human resources U.S. Senate, Washington, 1977-79, gen. counsel, 1980-81; ptnr. Pepper, Hamilton & Scheetz, Washington, 1982-88; shareholder Johnson & Wortley, Washington, 1988-94; ptnr. Kilpatrick & Cody, Washington, 1994—; adj. prof. law Georgetown U. Law Ctr., 1977; co-chair sr. editors Employee Benefits Law and Annual Supplements, Bur. Nat. Affairs, Washington, 1991—. Mem. adv. bd. BNA Pension and Benefits Reporter; mem. editorial bd. Benefits Law Jour., Jour. Pension Planning and Compliance, Jour. Taxation of Employee Benefits. Founding mem. ERISA Roundtable, Washington. Mem. ABA (mgmt. co-chmn. com. on employee benefits, sect. on labor and employment law 1988-91, chmn. prohibited trans. subcom., com. on employee benefits, sect. on taxation 1986-91), Fed. Bar Assn., D.C. Bar Assn. Office: Kilpatrick & Cody Ste 800 700 13th St NW Washington DC 20005

SACHS, ALAN ARTHUR, lawyer, corporate executive; b. Bklyn., Feb. 7, 1947; s. Herman and Clara Ethel (Treinkman) S.; m. Marilyn Neda Mushlin, May 19, 1974; children: David Henry, Stephen Edward. B.A., Columbia U., 1967; J.D., Harvard U., 1970. Bar: N.Y. 1971, U.S. Dist. Ct. (ea. and so. dists.) N.Y. 1972, U.S. Ct. Appeals (2d cir.) 1973, U.S. Dist. Ct. (no. dist.) N.Y. 1977, Wis. 1983, Mo. 1989. Law clk. to judge U.S. Dist. Ct. (ea. dist.) N.Y., 1970-71; assoc. Cleary, Gottlieb, Steen & Hamilton, N.Y.C., 1971-79, Paskus, Gordon & Hyman, N.Y.C., 1979-81; sec., gen. counsel The Trane Co., LaCrosse, Wis., 1981-85; exec. v.p., gen. counsel, sec. Edison Bros. Stores Inc., St. Louis, 1985—, also bd. dirs. Mem. ABA, Am. Soc. Corp. Secs. Office: Edison Bros Stores Inc 501 N Broadway Saint Louis MO 63102-2102

SACHS, DAVID, lawyer; b. N.Y.C., Aug. 4, 1933; s. Morris and Fannie R. (Kaplan) S.; m. Frumet P. Lome, July 7, 1957; children: Diane R., Daniel L., Francine E. BS, U. Pa., 1954; JD, Harvard U., 1957. Bar: N.Y. 1958, U.S. Tax Ct. 1959, U.S. Ct. Fed. Claims 1960, U.S. Ct. Appeals (2d cir.) 1960, U.S. Supreme Ct. 1967. Assoc. White & Case, N.Y.C., 1957-68, ptnr., 1968-88, ret. ptnr., 1988—. Fellow Am. Coll. Tax Counsel, N.Y. Bar Found.; mem. ABA, N.Y. Bar Assn. (chmn. tax sect. 1980), N.Y.C. Bar Assn. (chmn. com. on taxation 1986-89, mem. coun. on taxation 1990-95). Office: White & Case 1155 Avenue Of The Americas New York NY 10036-2711

SACHS, HOWARD F(REDERIC), federal judge; b. Kansas City, Mo., Sept. 13, 1925; s. Alex F. and Rose (Lyon) S.; m. Susanne Milson, 1960; children: Alex Wilson, Adam Phinney. B.A. summa cum laude, Williams Coll., 1947; J.D., Harvard U., 1950. Bar: Mo. 1950. Law clk. U.S. Dist. Ct., Kansas City, Mo., 1950-51; pvt. practice law Phineas Rosenberg, Kansas City, 1951-56; with Spencer, Fane, Britt & Browne, 1956-79; U.S dist. judge Western Dist. Mo., Kansas City, 1979—, chief dist. judge, 1990-92, now sr. judge. Contbr. articles to various publs.; contbr. chpt. to Mid-America's Promise, 1982. Mem. Kansas City Commn. Human Rels., 1967-73; chmn. Jewish Community Rels. Bur., 1968-71, Kansas City chpt. Am. Jewish Com., 1963-65; mem. exec. com. Nat. Jewish Community Rels. Adv. Coun., 1968-71; pres. Urban League Kansas City, 1957-58, Kansas City chpt. Am. Jewish Congress, 1974-77; co-chmn. Kansas City chpt. NCCJ, 1958-60; mem. Kansas City Sch. Dist. Desegregation Task Force, 1976-77; pres. Jackson County Young Democrats, 1959-60; trtes. Kennedy-Johnson Club, Jackson County, 1960. Served with USNR, 1944-46. Mem. ABA, Mo. Bar, Kansas City Bar Assn., Am. Judicature Soc., Lawyers Assn. Kansas City, Dist. Judges Assn. (8th cir., pres. 1992-94), Phi Beta Kappa. Office: US Dist Ct US Courthouse 811 Grand Ave Rm 716 Kansas City MO 64106-1909

SACHS, JERRY, professional basketball team executive; b. Balt.; m. Joyce; children: Gene, Barbara. Pub. rels. asst. Balt Orioles, 1959-62, pub. rels. dir., 1962-65; dir. advt. mktg. and pub. rels. Atlanta Braves, 1965-70; gen. mgr. Balt. Bullets, 1970-73; former exec. v.p., now vice chmn. Washington Bullets NBA; pres. Capital Centre, 1979—. Office: Washington Bullets USAir Arena Landover MD 20785*

SACHS, JOHN PETER, carbon company executive; b. Duesseldorf, Germany, 1926; married. BAChemE, Ill. Inst. Tech., 1948, MAChemE, 1950, PhDChemE, 1952. Various mgmt. positions in research and devel., engring. and ops. Union Carbide Corp., 1951-66; v.p. ops. then group v.p. Great Lakes Carbon Corp., N.Y.C., 1966-78; pres., chief exec. officer St. Lakes Carbon Corp., N.Y.C., 1978-86, now bd. dirs.; chmn. bd., dir. Gen. Refractories Co., 1978-85; ptnr. J.P. Sachs Assocs., Mgmt. Cons., New Canaan, Conn., 1987—. Trustee Fairfield U., 1978-92; bd. dirs. Kneissl-Dachstein 1992—, Peridot, 1989—. Mem. Am. Inst. Chem. Engrs. (pres. 1985). Home and office: JP Sachs Assocs 67 Dunning Rd New Canaan CT 06840-4009

SACHS, LLOYD ROBERT, entertainment critic, writer; b. Flushing, N.Y., Dec. 3, 1950; s. Sidney Howard Sachs and Eleanor Sachs Brown. BA in English, Marietta Coll., 1972; MSJ, Northwestern U., 1974. Reporter, critic Variety, Chgo., 1975-76; pop culture columnist The Reader, Chgo., 1976-80; pop music reviewer USA Today, Washington, 1983-84; entertainment critic Chgo. Sun-Times, 1984—; vis. lectr. in journalism U. Ill., Chgo., 1983. Trustee The Ragdale Found., Lake Forest, Ill., 1985—; vol. The Peace Mus., Chgo., 1984—. Grantee Ill. Arts Coun., Chgo., 1985. Democrat. Jewish. Office: Chgo Sun-Times Inc 401 N Wabash Ave Chicago IL 60611-3532

SACHS, MARILYN STICKLE, author, lecturer, editor; b. N.Y.C., Dec. 18, 1927; d. Samuel and Anna (Smith) Stickle; m. Morris Sachs, Jan. 26, 1947; children: Anne, Paul. BA, Hunter Coll., 1949; MSLS, Columbia U., 1953. Children's libr. Bklyn. Pub. Libr., 1949-60, San Francisco Pub. Libr., 1961-67. Author: Amy Moves In, 1964, Laura's Luck, 1965, Amy and Laura, 1966, Veronica Ganz, 1968, Peter and Veronica, 1969, Marv, 1970, The Bears' House, 1971 (Austrian Children's Book prize 1977, Recognition of Merit award George C. Stone Ctr. for Children's Books 1989), The Truth About Mary Rose, 1973 (Silver Slate Pencil award 1974), A Pocket Full of Seeds, 1973 (Jane Addams Children's Book Honor award 1974), Matt's Mitt, 1975, Dorrie's Book, 1975 (Silver State Pencil award 1977, Garden State Children's Book award 1978), A December Tale, 1976, A Secret Friends, 1978, A Summer's Lease, 1979, Bus Ride, 1980, Class Pictures, 1980, Fleet Footed Florence, 1981, Hello...Wrong Number, 1981, Call Me Ruth, 1982 (Assn. Jewish Librs. award 1983), Beach Towels, 1982, Fourteen, 1983, The Fat Girl, 1984, Thunderbird, 1985, Underdog, 1985 (Christopher 1986), Baby Sister 1986, Almost Fifteen, 1987, Fran Ellen's House, 1987 (award Bay Area Book Reviewers Assn. 1988, Recognition of Merit award George C. Stone Ctr. for Children's Books 1989), Just Like A Friend, 1989, At the Sound of the Beep, 1990, Circles, 1991, What My Sister Remembered, 1992, Thirteen, 1993, Ghosts in the Family, 1995; co-editor: (with Ann Durell) Big Book for Peace, 1990 (Calif. Children's Book award 1991, Jane Addams Children's Book prize 1991); reviewer books N.Y. Times, San Francisco Chronicle, 1970—. Mem. PEN, ACLU, SANE-Freeze, Sierra Club, Authors' Guild, Soc. Children's Bookwriters. Democrat. Jewish. Avocations: reading, hiking, baseball. Home: 733 31st Ave San Francisco CA 94121-3523

SACHS, ROBERT GREEN, physicist, educator, laboratory administrator; b. Hagerstown, Md., May 4, 1916; s. Harry Maurice and Anna (Green) S.; m. Selma Solomon, Aug. 28, 1941; m. Jean K. Woolf, Dec. 17, 1950; children: Rebecca, Jennifer, Jeffrey, Judith, Joel; m. Carolyn L. Wolf, Aug. 21, 1968; stepchildren: Thomas Wolf, Jacqueline Wolf, Katherine Wolf. Ph.D., Johns Hopkins U., 1939; D.Sc. (hon.), Purdue U., 1967, U. Ill., 1977, Elmhurst Coll., 1987. Research fellow George Washington U., 1939-41; instr. physics Purdue U., 1941-43; on leave as lectr., research fellow U. Calif. at Berkeley, 1941; sect. chief Ballistic Rsch. Lab., Aberdeen Proving Ground, Md., 1943-46; dir. theoretical physics divsn. Argonne (Ill.) Nat. Lab., Ill., 1946-47; asso. prof. physics U. Wis., 1947-48, prof., 1948-64; assoc. dir. Argonne Nat. Lab., 1964-68, dir., 1973-79; prof. physics U. Chgo., 1964-86, prof. emeritus, 1986—; dir. Enrico Fermi Inst., 1968-73, 83-86; Higgins vis. prof. Princeton U., 1955-56; vis. prof. U. Paris, 1959-60, Tohoku U., Japan, 1974; cons. Ballistic Research Labs., 1945-59, Argonne Nat. Lab., 1947-50, 60-64; cons. radiation lab. U. Calif. at Berkeley, 1955-59; adv. panel physics NSF, 1958-61; mem. physics survey com., chmn. elem. particle physics panel Nat. Acad. Scis., 1969-72; high energy physics adv. panel div. research AEC, 1966-69; mem. steering com. (Sci. and Tech., A Five Year Outlook), 1979; mem. DOE task force on energy rsch. priorities, 1991-93. Author: Nuclear Theory, 1953, The Physics of Time Reversal, 1987; chief editor: High Energy Nuclear Physics, 1957; editor: National Energy Issues: How Do We Decide, 1980, The Nuclear Chain Reaction--Forty Years Later, 1984. Recipient Disting. Svc. to Engring. citation U. Wis., 1977; Guggenheim fellow, 1959-60. Fellow Am. Phys. Soc. (coun. 1968-71, regional sec. Cen. States 1964-69), Am. Acad. Arts and Scis. (v.p. Midwest Ctr. 1980-83); mem. NAS (chmn. physics sect. 1977-80, chmn. Class I Math. and Phys. Scis. 1980-83), AAAS (v.p., chmn. physics sect. 1970-71), Am. Inst. Physics (mem. gov. bd. 1969-71), Phi Beta Kappa, Sigma Xi. Achievements include reseach in theoretical particle, nuclear and solid state physics, terminal ballistics, nuclear power reactors. Office: U Chicago Enrico Fermi Inst 5630 Ellis Ave Chicago IL 60637

SACHS, SAMUEL, II, museum director; b. N.Y.C., Nov. 30, 1935; s. James Henry and Margery (Fay) S.; m. Susan McAllen (div.); children: Katherine, Eleanor; m. Jerre S. Hollander (div.); 1 child, Alexander; m. Elizabeth M. Gordon; 1 child, Hadley Elizabeth. BA cum laude, Harvard U., 1957; MA, NYU Inst. Fine Arts, 1962. Asst. in charge prints and drawings Mpls. Inst. Arts, 1958-60; asst. dir. U. Mich. Mus. of Art, Ann Arbor, 1963-64; chief curator Mpls. Inst. Arts, 1964-73, dir., 1973-85; dir. Detroit Inst. Arts, 1985—. Bd. dirs. Ctr. for Creative Studies, Detroit. Decorated knight 1st class Order North Star (Sweden); Order of Dannebrog (Denmark). Mem. Am. Assn. Museums, Coll. Art Assn., Assn. Art Mus. Dirs. Clubs: Detroit, Century Assn, Harvard, Grosse Pointe. Home: 19344 Cumberland Way Detroit MI 48203-1456 Office: Detroit Inst Arts 5200 Woodward Ave Detroit MI 48202-4094

SACHS, STEPHEN HOWARD, lawyer; b. Balt., Jan. 31, 1934; s. Leon and Shirley (Blum) S.; m. Sheila Kleinman, Sept. 4, 1960; children: Elisabeth Leon. BA, Haverford Coll., 1954; postgrad., New Coll., Oxford, Eng., 1954-55; LLB, Yale U., 1957. Bar: Md. 1960, D.C. 1988, U.S. Supreme Ct. 1965. Law clk. U.S. Ct. Appeals, Washington, 1960-61; asst. U.S. atty. Dist. of Md., 1961-64, U.S. atty., 1967-70; pvt. practice law Balt., 1970-78; atty. gen. State of Md., Balt., 1979-87; with firm Wilmer, Cutler & Pickering, Washington, 1987—. Served with U.S. Army, 1955-57. Fulbright scholar, 1954-55. Fellow Am. Coll. Trial Lawyers; mem. ABA, Md. Bar Assn., Balt. Bar Assn., Fed. Bar Assn., Nat. Urban Coalition and Lawyers Com. for Civil Rights Under the Law. Democrat. Jewish. Home: 5 Roland Mews Baltimore MD 21210 Office: Wilmer Cutler & Pickering 2445 M St NW Washington DC 20037

SACHS, SUSAN F., publishing executive; b. Harvey, Ill.; d. John P. and Mary K. (Sims) S. BS in Fin., Lehigh U., 1977; MS in Fin., Columbia U., 1987. Bus. office analyst Time-Life Books, Alexandria, Va., 1977-81; asst. v.p. fin. Time-Life Books (Europe), London, 1981-84; mgr. corp. fin. Time Inc., N.Y.C., 1984-86, bus. mgr. Picture Week, 1986-87, bus. mgr. Money Mag., 1987-89, bus. mgr. Time Mag., 1989-90; internat. advt. sales dir. Time Internat., N.Y.C., 1990-91; pub. Sports Illustrated for Kids Time, Inc., N.Y.C., 1991-92, assoc. pub. Internat. Fortune Mag., 1992—. Mem. Bus. Mktg. Assn., Advt. Women of N.Y., Women's Sports Found. (corp.), Columbia Alumni Career Counseling. Office: Fortune Mag 1271 Avenue Of The Americas New York NY 10020-1300

SACHTLER, WOLFGANG MAX HUGO, chemistry educator; b. Delitzsch, Germany, Nov. 8, 1924; came to U.S., 1983; s. Gottfried Hugo and Johanna Elisabeth (Bollmann) S.; m. Anne-Lore Luise Adrian, Dec. 9, 1953; children: Johann Wolfgang Adrian, Heike Kathleen Julia, Yvonne Rhea Valeska. Diplomchemiker. Tech. U., Braunschweig, Ger., 1949; Dr.rer.nat. (Ph.D), 1952. Research chemist Kon-Shell Lab., Amsterdam, Netherlands, 1952-71, dept. head, 1972-83; extraordinary prof. chemistry U. Leiden, Netherlands, 1963-83; V.N. Ipatieff prof. Northwestern U., Evanston, Ill., 1983—; chmn. Gordon Research Conf. Catalysis, N.H., 1985; Rideal lectr. Faraday div. Royal Soc. Chemistry, 1981; F. Gault lectr., 1991. Mem. editorial bd. Jour. Catalysis, 1976-88, Applied Catalysis, 1983-87, Catalysis Letters, 1987—, Advances in Catalysis, 1987—; contbr. more than 280 articles to sci. jours. Recipient German Deutshe Gesellschaft Mineralöl und Kohle Kolleg award, 1991. Fellow AAAS; mem. Royal Netherlands Acad. Scis., Internat. Congress Catalysis (pres. coun.), Royal Dutch Chem. Soc., Am. Chem. Soc. (E.V. Murphree award 1987, petroleum chemistry award 1992), Catalysis Soc. N.Am. (hon. Catalsis divsn., Robert L. Burwell award 1985, E. Houdry award 1993). Home: 2141 Ridge Ave Apt 2D Evanston IL 60201-2788 Office: Northwestern U Sheridan Rd Evanston IL 60208-0002

SACK, BURTON MARSHALL, restaurant company executive; b. Melrose, Mass., Dec. 13, 1937; s. Samuel and Bertha (Gersin) S.; m. Susan Lightbown, June 9, 1963 (dec.); children: Brian, David, Scott; m. Gail Summerfield, June 17, 1990. B.S., Cornell U., 1961; P.M.D., Harvard Bus. Sch., 1967. With Howard Johnson's, 1951-83, successively dishwasher, counter-man, cook, and asst. mgr., to 1955, advt. asst., 1961, asst. dir. mktg., 1961-62, dir. public relations, 1962-67, gen. mgr. fast food service div., 1967-70; gen. mgr. Ground Round Restaurant div., 1970-73, v.p. splty. restaurants, 1973-76, group v.p. corp. devel., 1976-81, sr. v.p. corp. devel., 1981-83; pres. Exeter Hospitality Group, Boston, 1983-87, Pub Ventures of New Eng., Braintree, Mass., 1984-94; exec. v.p. Applebees Internat., Inc., 1994—; lectr. Cornell U., Wharton Sch. Bus. U. Pa., Cape Cod C.C., Babson Coll.; mem. Marshfield (Mass.) Indsl. and Devel. Commn., 1972-73; bd. dirs. Bay Street Restaurants; mem. bd. advisors Restaurant Assocs. Chmn. fund raising Greater Boston Assn. Retarded Citizens. With USMC, 1955-58. Mem. Nat. Restaurant Assn. (past chpt. pres.), Nat. Assn. Corp. Real Estate Execs., Broadcasting Execs. New Eng. (past dir.), Mass. Restaurant Assn. (1st v.p., mem. bd. dirs.), Greater Boston Assn., Cornell Soc. Hotelmen (past pres. New Eng. chpt., past nat. pres.). Home: 136 Rockport Rd Weston MA 02193-1470 Office: Applebees Internat Inc Ste 200 13 Riverside Office Pk Weston MA 02193

SACK, EDGAR ALBERT, electronics company executive; b. Pitts., Jan. 31, 1930; s. Edgar Albert and Margaret Valentine (Engelmohr) S.; m. Eugenia Ferris, June 7, 1952; children: Elaine Kimberley, Richard Warren. B.S., Carnegie-Mellon U., 1951, M.S., 1952, Ph.D., 1954. Dept. mgr. Westinghouse Research Lab., Pitts., 1960-63; engring. mgr. Westinghouse Microelectronics, Balt., 1963-65; operations mgr. Westinghouse Microelectronics, 1965-67, div. mgr., 1967-69; div. v.p. Gen. Instrument Corp., Hicksville, N.Y., 1969-73; group v.p. Gen. Instrument Corp., 1973-77, sr. v.p., 1977-84; pres., chief exec. officer Zilog Inc., Campbell, Calif., 1984—, also chmn. bd. dirs.; vis. com. elec. engring. dept. Carnegie-Mellon U., 1969-74; bd. dirs. Catalyst Semiconductor, Inc.; mem. indsl. adv. council SUNY, Stony Brook, 1979-83; mem. Adv. Com. on Solid State Electronics for Poly. Inst. Tech., 1981-83. Author: Forward Controllership Business Management System, 1989, 2nd edit., 1993. Mem. Action Com. Long Island, 1982-84. Fellow IEEE, Poly. Inst. Tech.; mem. Semicondr. Industry Assn. (dir. 1982-85); mem. Carnegie Mellon Alumni Assn. (Merit award 1981), Eta Kappa Nu (Outstanding Young Elec. Engr. 1959), Huntington Yacht Club (vice comdr. 1977), Tau Beta Pi (finalist San Francisco Entrepreneur of Yr. award 1991), Phi Kappa Phi. Patentee in field. Home: 21412 Sarahills Ct Saratoga CA 95070-4814 Office: Zilog Inc 210 E Hacienda Ave Campbell CA 95008-6617

SACK, JAMES MCDONALD, JR., radio and television producer, marketing executive; b. London, Ky., Oct. 11, 1948; s. James McDonald and Ruth Elmore (Bryant) S.; m. Cheryl S. Gremaux, July 13, 1969 (div. June 1974); 1 child, Graehm McDonald. BA in History, Ind. U., 1975, MS in Telecommunications, 1976. Coordinator Latin Am. Ednl. Ctr., Ft. Wayne, Ind., 1979-81, Mayor's Office, Ft. Wayne, 1981-83; producer WMEE-WQHK Radio, Ft. Wayne, 1983-85; owner, operator Festival Mgmt. and Devel., Ft. Wayne, 1984—; ptnr. Lily Co., Fort Wayne, 1991—, v.p. communications, mktg. United Way of Allen County, Ft. Wayne, Ind., 1989—; owner The Sack Co., 1992; owner The Lily Co.; pub. affairs prodr. WBYR, Ft. Wayne; dir. Cable Access, Inc. Producer radio documentary, 1985 (First Place award Ind. Broadcasters Assn. 1985), producer WFWA-PBS Eye on the Arts, 1987-89. Founder, pres. Germanfest of Ft. Wayne, 1981-92; pres. cable TV program adv. coun. City of Ft. Wayne; founder Ft. Wayne-Gera (Germany) Sister City Affiliation; commr. Ind. Hoosier Celebration, 1988; dir. Ind. Highland Games, 1992, cons., 1993—. Named Ky. Col. 1991. Mem. German Heritage Soc. (founder, bd. dirs. 1986—), Ind. German Heritage Soc. (founder, bd. dirs. 1986-92, Gov.'s Commendation award 1983), N.Am. Sängerbund (sec. 1985-86), Männerchor Club (Ft. Wayne), Ft. Wayne Sport Club (sec. 1985-86, trustee 1987-89). Lutheran. Avocations: fencing, canoeing, flying, politics, linguistics. Home: 2502 S Harrison Fort Wayne IN 46802 Office: United Way of Allen County 227 E Washington Blvd Fort Wayne IN 46802-3199

SACK, ROBERT DAVID, lawyer; b. Phila., Oct. 4, 1939; s. Eugene J. and Sylvia I. (Rivlin) S.; div.; children: Deborah Gail, Suzanne Michelle, David Rivlin; m. Anne K. Hilker, 1989. B.A., U. Rochester, 1960; LL.B., Columbia U., 1963. Bar: N.Y. 1963. Law clk. to judge Fed. Dist. Ct., Dist. of N.J., 1963-64; assoc. Patterson, Belknap & Webb, N.Y.C., 1964-70; ptnr. Patterson, Belknap, Webb & Tyler, N.Y.C., 1970-74, 74-86, Gibson, Dunn & Crutcher, N.Y.C., 1986—; sr. assoc. spl. counsel U.S. Ho. of Reps. Impeachment Inquiry, 1974; lectr. Practising Law Inst., 1973—; mem. adv. bd. Media Law Reporter. Author: Libel, Slander and Related Problems, 1980, 2nd edit., 1994, CD-Rom edit., 1995, N.Y.C. Commission on Public Information and Communication, 1995; mem. adv. bd. Media Law Reporter BNA; contbr. articles to legal jours. Chmn. bd. dirs. Nat. Council on Crime and Delinquency, 1982-83; trustee Columbia seminars on media and society Columbia U. Sch. Journalism, 1985-92; v.p., dir. William F. Kerby and Robert S. Potter Fund. Mem. ABA (bd. govs. forum com. on communications law 1980-88), N.Y. State Bar Assn., assn. Bar City N.Y. (chmn. communications law com. 1986-89). Office: Gibson Dunn & Crutcher 200 Park Ave 47th Fl New York NY 10166-0193

SACK, SYLVAN HANAN, lawyer; b. Phila., Dec. 26, 1932; s. Isidore F. and Mollye (Bellmore) S.; m. Ellen L. Foreman, Aug. 13, 1972; children: Reuben H., Sara I. M.S. in Bus. Adminstrn, Pa. State U., 1956; J.D., U. Balt., 1964. Bar: Md. 1964, U.S. Tax Ct. 1967, U.S. Supreme Ct. 1970; C.P.A., Md. Pvt. practice Balt., 1967—; assoc. counsel Safety First Club of Md., 1975-78, spl. counsel, 1979—; gov. Md. chpt. Retinitis Pigmentosa Found., 1974-75. Contbr. articles to profl. jours. Chmn. Indsl. Toxicology NIOSH Function, 1977, Occupational Disease Forum, 1979, OSHA and Diseases in Workplace Seminar, 1981. Mem. Fed. Bar Assn. (gov. chpt. 1968—, chmn. bd. govs. 1969-70, chmn. environ. law program 1984), ABA (chmn. subcom. sect. taxation 1972-75), Md. Bar Assn., Assn. Trial Lawyers Am.; mem. Md. Trial Lawyers Assn. (lectr. toxic torts 1983 conv.). Home: 27 Brightside Ave Baltimore MD 21208-4802 Office: 2404 St Paul St Baltimore MD 21218-5118

SACKEIM, HAROLD, psychologist; b. Hackensack, N.J., July 13, 1951; s. Alexander and Ruth (Frymer) S.; m. Donna Zucchi, Oct. 9, 1977. BA, Columbia U., 1972; BA, MA, Oxford (Eng.) U., 1974; PhD, U. Pa., 1977. Asst. prof. psychology Columbia U., N.Y.C., 1977-79, lectr. psychiatry Coll. Physicians and Surgeons, 1980-87; asst. prof. psychology N.Y.U., N.Y.C., 1979-81, assoc. prof., 1981-87; assoc. prof. dept. psychiatry Columbia U., N.Y.C., 1987-90, prof. dept. psychiatry, 1990—, chief dept. biol. psychiatry, 1991—; assoc. attending psychologist N.Y. State Psychiat. Inst., N.Y.C., 1980—, rsch. sci. and dep. chief dept. biol., 1980-91, chief dept. biol. psychiatry, 1991—; cons. WNET, 1978, 85; pvt. practice psychology, N.Y.C., 1977—. NIMH grantee, 1981—, NYU Rsch. Challenge Fund grantee, 1981-82, McGraw-Hill grantee, 1979-80, NIA grantee, 1985—. Fellow Am. Psychiat. Assn. (hon.); mem. AAAS, APA, Am. Coll. Neuropsychopharmacology (Joel Elkes Internat. award 1994), Am. Psychopathol. Assn., Internat. Neuropsychol. Soc., Soc. Biol. Psychiatry. Assoc. editor Jour. Social and Clin. Psychology, 1982-87; cons. editor jour. Imagination, Cognition and Personality, 1981—, Convulsive Therapy, 1985—, Neuropsychiatry, Neuropsychol. and Behavior Neurology, 1987—; contbr. numerous articles to profl. jours. Office: Columbia U Dept Psychiatry 722 W 168th St # 72 New York NY 10032-2603

SACKELLARES, JAMES CHRIS, neurology educator; b. Savannah, Ga., July 30, 1948; s. James and Doris Evelyn (Parks) S.; m. Dalma Kalogjera, Dec. 14, 1991; children: Stephanie, Chiara. BS in Chemistry, U. Ga., 1970; MD, Med. Coll. Ga., 1973. Cert. neurology, clin. neurophysiology. Intern in internal medicine U. Louisville, Ky., 1973-74; resident in neurology Med. Coll. Ga., Augusta, 1974-77; fellow in epilepsy U. Va., Charlottesville, 1977-79, rsch. asst. prof., 1979; asst. prof. neurology U. Mich., Ann Arbor, 1979-84, assoc. prof. neurology, 1984-91, prof. neurology, 1991-93; prof. neurology U. Fla., Gainesville, 1993-95, affiliate prof. neurosci., 1995—; chief neurology svcs. VA Med. Ctr., Gainesville; dir. epilepsy program U. Mich., Ann Arbor, 1979—; cons. neurologist Ann Arbor (Mich.) VA, 1982-93; dir. Clin. Neurophysiology Labs., U. Mich., Ann Arbor, 1984-87. Contbr. chpts. to books and articles to profl. jours. Mem. adv. bd. Epilepsy Found. Am., 1981-84; mem. anticonvulsant drug use com. Mich. Dept. Mental Health, 1991-92. Fellow Am. Acad. Neurology, Am. Electroencephalographic Soc.; mem. AAAS, Am. Epilepsy Soc., Am. Neurol. Assn., N.Y. Acad. Scis., Royal Soc. Medicine. Avocations: sailing, piano, tropical fish, photography.

SACKETT, ROSS DEFOREST, publisher; b. Chgo., Mar. 26, 1930; s. DeForest and Margaret (Ross) S.; m. Marvyda Wild, Sept. 1, 1951; children: David, Scott, Cynthia, Amy, Stuart. BA, Lawrence Coll., 1951. Editor in chief Charles Merrill Books, Inc., Columbus, Ohio, 1959-61; gen. mgr., v.p., exec. v.p., dir. Holt, Rinehart & Winston, N.Y.C., 1961-67, pres., dir., 1967-70, chmn. bd., 1970-72; pres. CBS Edn. Pub. Group, 1970-72, Ency. Brit. Ednl. Corp., 1972-76; chmn. Crescent Park Press, Angeles Toy Corp., Childs/Play, Inc.; chmn. bd. Big Toys Inc.; pres., chmn. bd. Kompan Holdings; dir. Ency. Brit. Corp., Kompan, Inc.; former dir. CBS. Trustee Highscope Ednl. Rsch. Found. Mem. Am. Assn. Pubs. (chmn.), Civil War Round Table, Delta Tau Delta, Eta Sigma Phi. Episcopalian. Office: PO Box 448 Eureka Springs AR 72632-0448

SACKETT, SUSAN DEANNA, film and television production associate, writer; b. N.Y.C., Dec. 18, 1943; adopted d. Maxwell and Gertrude Selma (Kugel) S. BA, U. Miami, Fla., 1966-68, L.A. City Schs., 1968-69; asst. publicist, comml. coordinator NBC-TV, Burbank, Calif., 1970-73; asst. to creator of Star Trek Gene Roddenberry, 1974-91; prodn. assoc. Star Trek: The Next Generation TV Series, 1987-91; writer Star Trek: The Next Generation, 1990-92; lectr. and guest speaker STAR TREK convs. in U.S., Eng., Australia, 1974-93. Author and editor: Letters to Star Trek, 1977; co-author: Star Trek Speaks, 1979; The Making of Star Trek-The Motion Picture, 1979; You Can Be a Game Show Contestant and Win, 1982, Say Goodnight Gracie, 1986; author: The Hollywood Reporter Book of Box Office Hits, 1990, Prime Time Hits, 1993, Hollywood Sings, 1995. Mem. ACLU, Writers Guild Am., Am. Humanist Assn., Mensa, Sierra Club. Democrat. Address: PO Box 3372 Carefree AZ 85377

SACKHEIM, ROBERT LEWIS, aerospace engineer, educator; b. N.Y.C., N.Y., May 16, 1937; s. A Frederick and Lillian L. (Emmer) S.; m. Babette Freund, Jan. 12, 1964; children: Karen Holly, Andrew Frederick. B-SChemE, U. Va., 1959; MSChemE, Columbia U., 1961; postgrad., UCLA, 1966-72. Project engr. Comsat Corp., El Segundo, Calif., 1969-72; project mgr. TRW, Redondo Beach, Calif., 1964-69, sect. head, 1972-76, dept. mgr., 1976-81, mgr. new bus., 1981-86, lab. mgr., 1986-90, dep. ctr. dir., 1990-93, ctr. dir., 1993—; instr. UCLA engring. ext., 1986; mem. adv. bds. NASA, Washington, 1989—; mem. peer rev. bd. various univs. and govtl. agys., 1990—; mem. Nat. Rsch. Coun./Aeronautics and Space Engring. Bd., 1994—; guest lectr. various univs. and AIAA short courses. Author: Space Mission Analysis and Design, 1991, Space Propulsion Analysis and Design, 1995; contbr. over 70 papers to profl. jours., confs. Mem. adv. bd. L.A. Bd. Edn., 1990-92; fund raiser March of Dimes, L.A., 1970-90, YMCA, San Pedro, Calif., 1974-86. Capt. USAF, 1960-63. Recipient Group Achievement award NASA, 1970, 78, 86. Fellow AIAA (chmn. com. 1980-83, J.H. Wyld Propulsion award 1992, Shuttle Flag award 1984). Achievements include 4 patents for spacecraft propulsion systems, devices and components. Office: TRW Space & Elects Group Bldg 01/RM 2010 1 Space Park Redondo Beach CA 90278

SACKLER, ARTHUR BRIAN, lawyer; b. Utica, N.Y., June 9, 1950; s. Joseph Leon and Leonore (Guttman) S.; m. Linda J. Cimarusti, May 27, 1979; children: Joshua Michael, Jenna Rachel. BA, Syracuse U., 1970, J.D., 1973; LL.M., Georgetown U., 1979. Bar: N.Y. 1974, D.C. 1975, U.S. Dist. Ct. D.C. 1979, U.S. Supreme Ct. 1979, U.S. Ct. Appeals (D.C. cir.) 1981. Appeals examiner U.S. Civil Service Commn., Washington, 1973-75, atty. advisor, 1975-76, trial atty., 1976-79; gen. counsel Nat. Newspaper Assn., Washington, 1979-82; dir. pub. policy devel. Time Warner, Washington, 1982-92, v.p. law and pub. policy, 1992—; mng. dir. Mailers Coun., 1990—; mem. Joint Washington Media Com., 1979—, Am. Copyright Council, Washington, 1984-86; faculty communications law Practicing Law Inst., 1980, forum com. on communications law seminar, 1980; instr. Am. Press Inst., 1980-82. Editor and contbr.: Federal Laws Affecting Newspapers, 1981; founder, editor newsletter News Media Update, 1979-82; contbr. articles to profl. jours., newspapers. Pres. Birnam Wood Community Assn., Potomac, Md., 1983-84; sec., treas. Potomac Springs Community Assn., Potomac, Md., 1986-87. Mem. ABA (chmn. postal matters com., adminstrv. law sect.), D.C. Bar Assn., Fed. Communications Bar Assn., Fed. Bar Assn. Mag. Pubs. Am. (govt. rels. coun. N.Y.C. 1982-85, 92—), Am. Advt. Fedn. (govt. relations com. Washington 1984—), Direct Mktg. Assn. (govt. relations com. 1986—), Am. Tort Reform Assn. (bd. dirs. 1987-88, corp. steering com. 1986-88), Assn. Am. Pubs. (postal com. N.Y.C. 1983—). Jewish. Clubs: Nat. Press, Bethesda Country. Office: Time Warner Inc 800 Connecticut Ave NW Ste 800 Washington DC 20006-2718

SACKLOW, STEWART IRWIN, advertising executive; b. Albany, N.Y., July 29, 1942; s. Jacob David and Freda Ruth (Pearlman) S.; A.A.S., N.Y.C. Community Coll., 1962; B.S., Western Mich. U., 1965; m. Harriette Lynn Cooperman, July 2, 1967; 1 son, Ian Marc. Asst. dist. office Humble Oil & Refining Co., Inc., Albany, 1963-65; dir. advt. and sales promotion Albany Pub. Markets div. Weiss Foods, 1965-68; Golub Corp., v.p. and dir. advt. Price Chopper Discount Foods, Schenectady, 1968-78; pres., creative dir. Wolkcas Advt., Inc., 1978-93, pres., CEO, 1993—; dir. Ski the Catskills, 1982-84; pres. Broadcast Creations, 1985—; pres. Testimonials, Inc., 1991-93. Mem. Dist. Atty.'s readiness team; active Albany County Cerebral Palsy Telethons, 1966-68; mem. fund drive com. Sta. WMHT-TV ednl. TV, 1967-74; bd. dirs. N.E. Cystic Fibrosis Found., Video Spirit; bd. dirs., mem. exec. com. Upstate Leukemia Assn.; mem. bd. Gov. Clinton council Boy Scouts Am., leader, Voorheesville, N.Y.; N.Y. State Arbor Day Com., 1988-93; pres Takundewide Home Owners Assn., 1991-92; key market coord. Partnership Drug Free Am.; coord. Drug Free N.Y. State. Recipient certificate merit Nat. Research Bur., 1966, Freedoms Found., 1966, Amsterdam Recorder, 1968, Retail Advt. Conf., 1969, 70, Woman's Day Mag., 1971, 72, 73, 74, 75, 76; Grand Nat. award Am. Dairy Assn., 1969, Hunt Wesson Foods, 1970; recipient 4 1st place awards Am. Advt. Fedn., 1972, Crystal Prism award, 1973; Effie award Am. Mgmt. Assn., 1972; Silver medal award Am. Advt. Fed., 1973, Addy award, 1973, 74, 75; award excellence Retail Advt. Conf., 1971; Best 15 Internat. Ads award Internat. Newspaper Advt. Execs., 1972, Gold Leaf award Interant. Arborist Soc., 1993. Mem. N.Y. Art Dirs. Club, Ad Club N.Y. (bd. dirs. 1974-79, 93-94, pres. 1976-77), Am. Advt. Fedn. (bd. govs. 1975), Profl. Pub. Rels. Coun. Albany Execs. Assn. Mem. B'nai B'rith (bd. dir. housing 1992-93), N.Y. Art Dirs. Club, Capital Dist. Creative Club, Mohawk Antique Auto Club, Albany Yacht Club, Schenectady Racquet Club, KP. Home: 716 St Marks Ln Niskayuna NY 12309-4843 Office: 435 New Karner Rd Albany NY 12205-3833

SACKNER, MARVIN ARTHUR, physician; b. Phila., Feb. 16, 1932; s. Albert B. and Goldie Mildred (Haber) S.; m. Ruth Karsch, June 24, 1956; children: Sara, Deborah, Jonathan. BS, Temple U., 1953; MD, Jefferson Med. Coll., 1957. Diplomate Am. Bd. Internal Medicine. Intern Phila. Gen. Hosp., 1957-58, med. resident, 1958-61; ACP rsch. fellow U. Pa., Phila., 1961-64; chief pulmonary disease Mt. Sinai Hosp., Miami Beach, Fla., 1964-74, dir. med. svcs., 1974-91; dir. med. svcs. emeritus Mt. Sinai Hosp., Fla., 1992—; prof. medicine U. Miami, Fla., 1973—; gov., chmn. pulmonary disease exam. bd. Am. Bd. Internal Medicine, 1977-80; chief exec. officer Non-Invasive Monitoring Systems, Inc., Miami Beach, Fla., 1986—. Author: Scleroderma, 1966; editor: Diagnostic Techniques in Pulmonary Disease, Parts I and II, 1980; mem. editorial bd. Fla. Med. Assn., 1974, Am. Rev. Respiratory Physiology, 1976-80, Jour. Applied Physiology, 1976-80, Annals Internal Medicine, 1979; patentee in field; contbr. articles to profl. jours. Pres. Art in Pub. Places, Inc., 1975-78; co-dir. Ruth and Marvin Sackner Archive of Concrete and Visual Poetry, 1979—; bd. dirs. Ctr. for Book Art, N.Y.C., 1987-93; mem. libr. com. Mus. Modern Art, N.Y.C., 1990—. NEA grantee, 1977-78, Nat. Heart, Lung and Blood Inst. grantee, 1966—, others. Fellow ACP, Am. Coll. Chest Physicians; mem. Am. Thoracic Soc. (pres.1980), Am. Physiol. Soc., Grolier Club N.Y.C. Jewish. Office: 1840 West Ave Miami FL 33139

SACKS, DAVID ARNOLD, lawyer; b. Balt., Feb. 14, 1940; s. Jerome and Jennie (Lieben) S.; m. Lois Resnick, June 29, 1963; children: Darrin, Jill. JD, Georgetown U., 1967. Bar: Md. 1967, D.C. 1968. Ptnr. Foley & Lardner, Washington. Office: Foley & Lardner Washington Harbour Ste 500 3000 K St NW Washington DC 20007-5109

SACKS, DAVID G., retired distilling company executive, lawyer; b. N.Y.C., Jan. 6, 1924; s. Irving and Jeannette (Greenhoot) S.; m. Naomi Gostin, Oct.

12, 1947; children: Jonathan E., Deborah A., Judith A., Joshua M. A.B. Columbia U., 1944, LL.B., 1948. Ptnr. Simpson Thacher & Bartlett, N.Y.C. 1961-67, sr. ptnr., 1967-76, counsel, 1981-83; chief adminstrv. officer Lehman Bros., Inc., N.Y.C., 1976-81; exec. v.p. fin. adminstrn. The Seagram Co. Ltd., Montreal, Que., Can., 1983-86, pres., chief operating officer, 1986-89, also bd. dirs.; exec. v.p. fin. adminstrn. Joseph E. Seagram & Sons, N.Y.C. 1983-86, pres., chief operating officer, 1986-89; vice chmn. The Seagram Co. Ltd. and Joseph E. Seagram & Sons, Inc., Montreal and N.Y.C., 1989-91, now bd. dirs. Pres. United Jewish Appeal, Fedn. Jewish Philanthropies, N.Y.C., 1989-92. Cpl. USAAF, 1943-46. Club: Beach Point (Mamaroneck, N.Y.). Office: Joseph E Seagram & Sons 375 Park Ave New York NY 10152-0002

SACKS, HERBERT SIMEON, psychiatrist, educator, consultant; b. N.Y.C., Nov. 29, 1926; s. Maxwell Lawrence and Anne (Edelstein) S.; m. Helen Margery Levin, Dec. 26, 1948; children—Eric Livingston, Katharine Bird, Douglas Lowell, Russell Avery. A.B. magna cum laude, Dickinson Coll., 1948; M.D. Cornell U., 1952. Diplomate Am. Bd. Psychiatry and Neurology and subspecialty Child and Adolescent Psychiatry. Clin. assoc. Western New Eng. Psychoanalytic Inst., New Haven, 1955-63; intern in pediatrics Yale-New Haven Med. Ctr., 1952-53; jr. asst. resident in psychiatry Yale Psychiat. Inst., 1953-54; sr. asst. resident in psychiatry, USPHS fellow Yale-New Haven Med. Ctr., psychiat. out patient dept., 1954-55; USPHS fellow in child psychiatry Yale U. Child Study Ctr., 1955-57; clin. dir. Mid-Fairfield Child Guidance Ctr., Norwalk, Conn., 1957-59; cons. Expt. in Internat. Living, Putney, Vt., 1962-69; sr. cons. U.S. Peace Corps, Washington, 1962-69; cons. AID, U.S. Dept. State, Office of Sahel, West Africa, 1974-84, Neurosci. Consultation Group, Grosse Point Farms, Mich., 1984-94; clin. prof. child and adolescent psychiatry Child Study Ctr., Yale U. Sch. Medicine, New Haven; co-investigator, co-dir. Senegal River pilot health research program, New Haven and West Africa, 1976-78, co-investigator, co-dir. health sector, design team Senegal River integrated devel. project, 1981-83; vis. lectr. Yale Coll., 1969-71; mem. com. reviewers Dept. Commerce Nat. Bur. Standards, Inst. for Computer Scis. and Tech., Washington, 1975-77; mem. exec. com. Nat. Commn. on Confidentiality of Health Records, 1975-80. Author: Hurdles: The Admissions Dilemma in American Higher Education, 1978; contbg. author chpts. in books, articles on confidentiality, juvenile justice, higher edn., issues of youth in transition, other topics; author monographs. Mem. Conn. Juvenile Justice Commn., Hartford, 1975-80; bd. advisors Dickinson Coll., Carlisle, Pa., 1980-85. Served to lt. (j.g.) U.S. Navy, 1944-46; PTO. Fellow AMA, ACPO, Am. Psychiat. Assn. (trustee 1988-94, v.p. 1994—), Am. Acad. Child and Adolescent Psychiatry, Am. Orthopsychiat. Assn., Am. Coll. Psychiatrists; mem. Conn. Psychiat. Soc. (pres. 1976-77), Conn. Coun. Child and Adolescent Psychiatrists (pres. 1972-73), World Fedn. for Mental Health, Phi Beta Kappa. Avocations: farming, photography, fishing, lawn bowling. Home: 110 Laurel Rd New Haven CT 06515-2426 Office: 260 Riverside Ave Westport CT 06880-4804 also: Yale U Child Study Ctr PO Box 207900 New Haven CT 06520

SACKS, IRA STEPHEN, lawyer; b. N.Y.C., Dec. 6, 1948; s. Marvin Leonard and Mildred (Finkelstein) S.; children: Jennifer, Allison, Gillian. BS, MIT, 1970; JD, Georgetown U., 1974. Bar: N.Y. 1975, U.S. Dist. Ct. (so. and ea. dists.) N.Y. 1975, U.S. Ct. Appeals (2d cir.) 1975, U.S. Ct. Appeals (3d cir.) 1984, U.S. Supreme Ct. 1985, U.S. Ct. Appeals (9th cir.) 1986, U.S. Ct. Appeals (11th cir.) 1987, U.S. Ct. Appeals (D.C. and fed. cirs.) 1993. Assoc. Kaye, Scholer, Fierman, Hays & Handler, N.Y.C., 1974-82, ptnr., 1983-87; ptnr. Fried, Frank, Harris, Shriver & Jacobson, N.Y.C., 1988—. Contbr. articles to profl. jours. NSF fellow, 1970. Mem. ABA (com. on pvt. antitrust litigation antitrust sect.), N.Y. State Bar Assn., Assn. of Bar of City of N.Y., Supreme Ct Hist. Soc. Democrat. Jewish. Avocations: tennis, skiing, softball. Home: 333 Rector Pl New York NY 10280 Office: Fried Frank Harris Shriver & Jacobson 1 New York Pla New York NY 10004

SACKS, OLIVER WOLF, neurologist, writer; b. London, July 9, 1933; Came to U.S., 1960; s. Samuel and Muriel Elsie (Landau) S. BA, U. Oxford, 1954; MA, BM, BCh, Middlesex Hosp., London, 1958; DHL (hon.), Georgetown U., 1990, Coll. Staten Island, CUNY, 1991; DS (hon.), Tufts U., 1991, N.Y. Med. Coll., 1991. Intern in medicine, surgery and neurology Middlesex Hosp., 1958-60; rotating intern Mt. Zion Hosp., San Francisco, 1961-62; resident in neurology UCLA, 1962-65; I.D. fellow in neuropathology and neurochemistry Albert Einstein Coll. Medicine, N.Y.C., 1965-66, instr. neurology, 1966-75, asst. prof., 1975-78, assoc. prof., 1978-85, clin. prof. neurology, 1985—; cons., speaker, lectr. in field; hon. lectureships in field. Author: Migraine, 1970, Awakenings, 1973, rev. paperback edit., 1990 (Hawthornden prize 1975), A Leg To Stand On, 1984, The Man Who Mistook His Wife for a Hat, 1985, Seeing Voices: A Journey into the World of the Deaf, 1989, An Anthropologist on Mars, 1995. Recipient Felix Martlbanez book award MD mag., 1987, Oskar Pfister award APA, 1988, Harold D. Vursell Meml. award Am. Acad. and Inst. Arts and Letters, 1989, Odd Fellows book award, 1990, Scriptor award U. So. Calif., 1991, profl. support award Nat. Headache Found., 1991; open scholar in biology Queen's Coll., Oxford U., 1950, Theodoe Williams scholar in anatomy, 1953, med. rsch. scholar, 1954; Guggenheim fellow, 1989. Mem. Am. Acad. Neurology (presdl. citation 1991), N.Y. State Med. Soc., N.Y. Inst for the Humanities, Alpha Omega Alpha. Office: 299 W 12th St # 14C New York NY 10014-1832

SACKS, PATRICIA ANN, librarian, consultant; b. Allentown, Pa., Nov. 6, 1939; d. Lloyd Alva and Dorothy Estelle (Stoneback) Stahl; m. Kenneth LeRoy Sacks, June 27, 1959. A.B., Cedar Crest Coll., 1959; M.S. in L.S., Drexel U., 1965. News reporter Call-Chronicle, Allentown, 1956-59, 1961-63; reference librarian Cedar Crest Coll., Allentown, 1964-66, head librarian, 1966-73; dir. libraries Muhlenberg and Cedar Crest Colls., Allentown, 1973-94; dir. libr. svcs. Cedar Crest Coll., 1994; sr. fellow Lehigh Valley Assn. Ind. Colls., 1994— del. On Line Computer Library Ctr. Users Council, Columbus, Ohio, 1977-84; cons. colls./health care orgns., libr. bldgs. 1981-84. Author: (with Whildin Sara Lou) Preparing for Accreditation: A Handbook for Academic Librarians, 1993; mem. editorial bd. Jour. Acad. Librarianship, 1982-84, Coll. and Undergrad. Libr., 1993—. Trustee Cedar Crest Coll., 1985-89. Mem. United Way Lehigh Valley Coms., 1993—; bd. dirs. John and Dorothy Morgan Cancer Ctr., 1994—. Named Outstanding Acad. Woman, Lehigh Valley Assn. for Acad. Women, 1984, Muhlenberg Coll. Outstanding Adminstr., 1987, Alumni Tricorn award Muhlenberg Coll., 1989, Alumnae Achievement award Cedar Crest Coll., 1994. Mem. ALA (chmn. copyright com. 1985-87), Assn. Coll. and Research Libraries (chmn. standards and accreditation com. 1976-78, 81-84), Lehigh Valley Assn. Ind. Colls. (chmn. librarians sect. 1967-81, 88-92), AAUW, LWV, Lehigh Valley Conservancy, Appalachian Mountain Club, Phi Alpha Theta, Phi Kappa Phi, Beta Phi Mu. Democrat. Home: 2997 Fairfield Dr Allentown PA 18103-5413 Office: Lehigh Valley Assn Ind Colls 119 W Greenwich St Bethlehem PA 18018

SACKS, TEMI J., public relations executive; b. Phila.; d. Jule and Adeline (Levin) S. BA, Temple U. Pubs. editor Del. Valley Regional Planning Commn., Phila.; communications assoc. Fedn. Jewish Agys., Phila.; pres. T. J. Sacks Pub. Relations, Phila.; exec. v.p., mng. dir. healthcare div. Lobsenz-Stevens Inc., Phila.; guest lectr. Temple U. Sch. Communications. Mem. Healthcare Businesswomen's Assn., Pharm. Advt. Coun., Women Execs. in Pub. Rels. Avocations: skiing, Americana antiques, jewelry design. Home: 142 West End Ave New York NY 10023-6103 Office: Lobsenz-Stevens Inc 460 Park Ave S New York NY 10016-7315

SACKSTEDER, FREDERICK HENRY, former foreign service officer; b. N.Y.C., July 12, 1924; s. Frederick H. and Denise (Dorin) S.; m. Evelyn M. Blickensderfer, Oct. 14, 1977; children by previous marriage: Frederick Henry, III, Timothy W. B.A., Amherst Coll., 1947; postgrad., Sch. Advanced Internat. Studies, Washington, 1947. Asst. to exec. v.p. Internat. Standard Electric Corp., N.Y.C., 1948-49; joined U.S. Fgn. Service, 1950; Kreis resident officer U.S. High Commn. for Germany, 1950-52; vice consul, consul, sec. Am. embassy, Lyon, France, 1952-55, Madrid, 1959-61, Barcelona, Spain, 1962-65, Tunis, Tunisia, 1967-69; internat. relations officer Dept. State, 1955-59; 65-67; mem. U.S. Mission to UN, 1969-72, Internat. Boundary and Water Commn.; El Paso, Tex., 1972-75; mem. U.S. Delegation UN Gen. Assembly, N.Y.C., 1969-71; consul gen. Hermosillo, Sonora, Mexico, 1975-79; bd. examiners Fgn. Service, Dept. State, 1979-81, expert cons. Bur. Personnel, 1981-86; mem. U.S. del. to UN Gen. Assembly,

N.Y.C., 1969-71. Mem. UN Trusteeship Coun., 1970-71, U.S. rep., 1971; pres. El Paso chpt. UN Assn., 1973-75. Lt. (j.g.) USNR, 1943-46. Mem. Fgn. Service Assn., Diplomatic and Consular Officers Ret., Council Fgn. Relations (chmn. Charlottesville com.). Lodge: Rotary (local club pres. 1988-89). Home: The Westchester 4000 Cathedral Ave NW # 344-b Washington DC 20016-5249

SACKTON, FRANK JOSEPH, university official, lecturer, retired army officer; b. Chgo., Aug. 11, 1912; m. June Dorothy Raymond, Sept. 21, 1940. Student, Northwestern U., 1936, Yale, 1946, U. Md., 1951-52; B.S., U. Md., 1970; grad., Army Inf. Sch., 1941, Command and Gen. Staff Coll., 1942, Armed Forces Staff Coll., 1949, Nat. War Coll., 1954; M.Pub. Adminstrn., Ariz. State U., 1976. Mem. 131st Inf. Regt., Ill. N.G., 1929-40; commd. 2d lt. U.S. Army, 1934, advanced through grades to lt. gen., 1967; brigade plans and ops. officer (33d Inf. Div.), 1941, PTO, 1943-45; div. signal officer, 1942-43, div. intelligence officer, 1944, div. plans and ops. officer, 1945; sec. to gen. staff for Gen. MacArthur Tokyo, 1947-48; bn. comdr. 30th Inf. Regt., 1949-50; mem. spl. staff Dept. Army, 1951; plans and ops. officer Joint Task Force 132, PTO, 1952; comdr. Joint Task Force 7, Marshall Islands, 1953; mem. gen. staff Dept. Army, 1954-55; with Office Sec. Def., 1956; comdr. 18th Inf. Regt., 1957-58; chief staff 1st Inf. Div., 1959; chief army Mil. Mission to Turkey, 1960-62; comdr. XIV Army Corps, 1963; dep. dir. plans Joint Chiefs Staff, 1964-66; army general staff mil. ops., 1966-67, comptroller of the army, 1967-70, ret., 1970; spl. asst. for fed./state relations Gov. Ariz., 1971-75; chmn. Ariz. Programming and Coordinating Com. for Fed. Programs, 1971-75; lectr. Am. Grad. Sch. Internat. Mgmt., 1973-77; vis. asst. prof., lectr. public affairs Ariz. State U., Tempe, 1976-78; founding dean Ariz. State U. Coll. Public Programs, 1979-80; prof. public affairs Ariz. State U., 1980—, finance educator, v.p. bus. affairs, 1981-83, dep. dir. intercollegiate athletics, 1984-85, dir. strategic planning, 1987-88. Contbr. articles to public affairs and mil. jours. Mem. Ariz. Steering Com. for Restoration of the State Capitol, 1974-75, Ariz. State Personnel Bd., 1978-83, Ariz. Regulatory Coun., 1981-93. Decorated D.S.M., Silver Star, also Legion of Merit with 4 oak leaf clusters, Bronze Star with 2 oak leaf clusters, Air medal, Army Commendation medal with 1 oak leaf cluster, Combat Inf. badge. Mem. Ariz. Acad. Public Adminstrn., Pi Alpha Alpha (pres. chpt. 1976-82). Politics: Army-Navy (Washington); Arizona (Phoenix). Home: 12000 N 90th St Apt 2071 Scottsdale AZ 85260-8604 Office: Sch Pub Affairs Ariz State U Tempe AZ 85287

SADA, FEDERICO G., glass manufacturing executive. Chmn. bd. dirs., CEO Anchor Glass Container Corp., 1993—. Office: Anchor Glass Container Corp 4343 Anchor Plaza Pky Tampa FL 33634-7537

SADAO, SHOJI, architect; b. Los Angeles, Jan. 2, 1927; s. Riichi and Otatsu (Kodama) S.; m. Tsuneko Sawada, Apr. 8, 1972. B.Arch., Cornell U., 1954; Fulbright scholar, Waseda U., Tokyo, 1956-57. Designer Geodesics, Inc., Raleigh, N.C., 1954-56; job capt. Edison Price, Inc., N.Y.C., 1959-64; v.p. Fuller & Sadao (P.C.), Long Island City, N.Y., 1965—; assoc. prof. archtl. design Sch. Architecture and Environ. Design, SUNY, Buffalo, 1976-77. Works include Dymaxion World Map, 1954; co-designer works include, U.S. Pavilion at Montreal Expo 67. Trustee and exec. dir. Isamu Noguchi Found., Long Island City, N.Y., 1989—. With AUS, 1945-49. Mem. AIA, Japan Soc., Yamashita Sekkei Architecs and Engrs. (U.S. rep. 1989—). Address: Fuller & Sadao 32-37 Vernon Blvd Long Island City NY 11106-4926

SADD, WILLIAM WHEELER, trade association executive; b. Evergreen Park, Ill., May 7, 1935; s. Sumner Harry and Louise (Beardsley) S.; m. Linnea Paulson, Sept. 10, 1960; children: Juliet, Karen. B.S., Denison U., 1957; J.D., U. Chgo., 1960. Assoc. Fuller & Henry, Toledo, 1960-74; pres., gen. mgr. Glass Packaging Inst., McLean, Va., 1974-86; exec. v.p. Nat. Spa and Pool Inst., Alexandria, Va., 1986-92; retired, 1992; trustee Food Processors Inst., Washington, 1979-86. Pres. Mid-Atlantic Band Festival, Herndon, Va., 1984. Republican. Episcopalian. Club: Loudoun Country (Purcellville, Va.). Home: 35385 Carnoustie Cir Round Hill VA 22141-2509

SADDLEMYER, ANN (ELEANOR SADDLEMYER), educator, critic, theater historian; b. Prince Albert, Sask., Can., Nov. 28, 1932; d. Orrin Angus and Elsie Sarah (Ellis) S. BA, U. Sask., 1953, DLitt, 1991; MA, Queen's U., 1956, LLD (hon.), 1977; PhD, U. London, 1961; DLitt (hon.), U. Victoria, 1989, McGill U., 1989, Windsor U., 1990. Lectr. Victoria (B.C.) Coll., 1956-57, instr., 1960-62, asst. prof., 1962-65; assoc. prof. U. Victoria, 1965-68, prof. English, 1968-71; prof. English Victoria Coll. U. Toronto, 1971-95; prof., dir. grad. ctr. for study of drama Grad. Ctr. Study of Drama, U. Toronto, 1972-77, 85-86; sr. fellow Massey Coll., 1975-88, master, 1988-95; Berg prof. NYU, 1975. Dir. Theatre Plus, 1972-84; dir. Colin Smythe Pubs.; author: The World of W.B. Yeats, 1965, In Defence of Lady Gregory, Playwright, 1966, Synge and Modern Comedy, 1968, J.M. Synge Plays Books One and Two, 1968, Lady Gregory Plays, 4 vols, 1970, Letters to Molly: Synge to Maire O'Neill, 1971, Letters from Synge to W.B. Yeats and Lady Gregory, 1971, Collected Letters of John Millington Synge, Vol. 1, 1983, vol. II, 1984, Theatre Business, The Correspondence of the First Abbey Theatre Directors, 1982, (with Colin Smythe) Lady Gregory Fifty Years After, 1987, Early Stages: Theatre in Ontario, 1800-1914, 1990; co-editor Theatre History in Canada, 1980-86; editorial bds. Modern Drama, 1972-82, English Studies in Can., 1973-83, Themes in Drama, 1974—, Shaw Rev, 1977—, Research in the Humanities, 1976-90; Irish Univ. Rev, 1970—, Yeats Ann., 1982-86, Studies in Contemporary Irish Lit., 1986—; contbr. articles to profl. jours. Recipient Brit. Acad. Rose Mary Crawshay award, 1986, Disting. Svc. award Province of Ont., 1985, U. Toronto Alumni award of excellence, 1991; named Disting. Dau. of Pa., 1992, Women of Distinction in Letters, Toronto, YWCA, 1994; Can. Coun. scholar, 1958-59, fellow, 1968, Guggenheim fellow, 1968, 77, sr. rsch. fellow Connaught, 1985. Fellow Royal Soc. Can.; Royal Soc. Arts; mem. Internat. Assn. Study Anglo-Irish Lit. (chmn. 1973-76), Assn. Can. Theatre History (pres. 1976-77), Can. Assn. Irish Studies, Assn. Can. Univ. Tchrs. English, Can. Assn. Univ. Tchrs., Assn. Can. and Que. Lit. Home: 100 Lakeshore Rd E Apt 803, Oakville, ON Canada L6J 6M9 Office: Massey Coll, 4 Devonshire Pl, Toronto, ON Canada M5S 2E1

SADDLER, DONALD EDWARD, choreographer, dancer; b. Van Nuys, Calif., Jan. 24, 1920; s. Elmer Edward and Mary Elizabeth (Roberts) S. Student, Los Angeles City Coll., 1939; dance pupil of, Carmalita Maracci, Anton Dolin, Anthony Tudor, Madame Anderson Ivantzova. Mem. Ballet Theatre, N.Y.C., 1940-43, 46-47; asst. dir., then artistic dir. Harkness Ballet, N.Y.C., 1964-70; exec. v.p. Rebekah Harkness Found., 1967-69; mem. exec. bd. Internat. Ballet Corp., 1979; prodr. N.Y. Dance Festival, Delacorte Theatre; guest artist Valerie Bettis Co. Stage appearances include Grand Canyon Suite, 1937, High Button Shoes, 1947, Dance Me A Song, 1950, Bless You All, 1950, The Song of Norway, 1951, Winesburg, Ohio, 1958, The Golden Round, 1960, The Castle Period, 1961, Happy Birthday, Mr. Abbot!, 1987, (with the Ballet Theatre, N.Y.C.) Bluebeard, Billy the Kid, Swan Lake, Aurora's Wedding, Les patineurs, Lilac Garden, Gala Performance, Romeo and Juliet, Peter and the Wolf, (television) Holiday Hotel, 1950; choreographer: (theatre) Blue Mountain Ballads, 1948, Wish Your Were Here, 1952, Wonderful Town, 1952 (Tony award for choreography 1953), 55, John Murray Anderson's Almanac, 1953, Tobia la Candida Spia, 1954 (Maschera d'Argento 1954), La patrona di raddio di luna, 1955, Shangri-La, 1956, Buona notte Bettina, 1956, L'adorabile Giulio, 1957, Winesburg, Ohio, 1958, This Property is Condemned, 1958, Un trapezio per Lisistrata, 1958, When in Rome, 1959, Un manderino per Teo, 1959, Dreams of Glory, 1961, Milk and Honey, 1961, Sophie, 1963, Morning Sun, 1963, To Broadway, With Love, 1964, No, No, Nanette, 1971 (Tony award for choreography 1971, Drama Desk award for choreography 1971), 73, Much Ado About Nothing, 1972 (Tony award nomination for choreography 1973), Fanfare Gala, 1973, Good News, 1973, Tricks, 1973, The Merry Wives of Windsor, 1974, Miss Moffat, 1974, A Midsummer Night's Dream, 1975, A Doll's House, 1975, A Gala Tribute to Joshua Logan, 1975, Rodgers and Hart, 1975, The Robber Bridegroom, 1975, 1976, Koshare, 1976, Vaudeville, 1976, Dear Friends and Gentle Hearts, 1976, Icedancing, 1978, The Grand Tour, 1979, A Long Way to Boston, 1979, Happy New Year, 1980, Hey Look Me Over!, 1981, Pardon, Monsieur Moliere, 1982, On Your Toes, 1983 (Tony award nomination for choreography 1983), The Loves of Anatol, 1985, The Golden Land, 1985, Broadway, 1987, The Student Prince, 1987, Teddy and Alice, 1987, My Fair Lady, 1993, The Boys

from Syracuse, Aida, La Perichole, The Merry Widow, Tropicana, (tours) We Take This Town, 1962, Knickerbocker Holiday, 1971, No, No, Nanette, 1971-73, Good News, 1973-74, Hellzapoppin', 1976-77, On Your Toes, 1984, (films) April in Paris, 1952, By the Light of the Silvery Moon, 1953, Young at Heart, 1954, The Main Attraction, 1963, The Happy Hooker, 1975, Radio Days, 1987, (television) Holiday Hotel, 1950, The Perry Como Show, 1950, Canozionissima, 1959-60, Bell Telephone Hour, 1961-64, Much Ado About Nothing, 1973, Tony award broadcasts, 1973, 75-78, 83, Verna: U.S.O. Girl, 1978; dir., choreographer: (theatre) Wonderful Town, 1955, (tour) Oh, Kay!, 1978, A Celebration for Sir Anton Dolin, 1984, 100 Years of Performing Arts at the Metropolitan, 1984, Kiss Me Kate, 1989, American Ballet Theatre's Fortieth Anniversary, Tribute to Lucille Lortel, Tribute to Richard Rodgers, Merman-Martin Gala, Tribute to Cy Coleman, An Evening with Kurt Weill, Jo Sullivan in Concert, Tribute to George Abbott, Tribute to Lerner and Loewe, Stratford Shakespeare Festival Gala, American Guild of Musical Artists 100th Anniversary Gala, (operas) Bitter Sweet, Weiner Blut, Abduction from the Seraglio, Washington Opera Follies; dir.: (theatre) Berlin to Broadway with Kurt Weill, 1972, George Abbott...A Celebration, 1976, Life with Father, 1982, I Hear Music...of Frank Loesser and Friends, 1984, State Fair Music Hall, Dallas, 1957, 59, Carousel Theatre, Framingham, Mass., 1958, Stratford Shakespeare Festival, 1979; prodr.: (theatre) The Sol Hurok Birthday Gala, 1973, The 30th Anniversary of City Center Theatre, 1975, (with Martin Feinstein) The Pre-Inaugural Ballet-Opera Gala, 1981, The Dance Collection Gala, 1972, The 35th Anniversary of the American Ballet Theatre, 1975, The Cynthia Gregory Gala. Recipient Dance Mag. award, 1984. Office: care Coleman-Rosenberg Agy 210 E 58th St New York NY 10022-2037*

SADE (HELEN FOLASADE ADU), singer, songwriter; b. Ibadan, Nigeria, 1959; d. Adebisi Adu and Anne. BA, St. Martin's Coll. of Art, London, 1979. Mem. band Sade; recording artist Epic, A Division of Sony Music, N.Y.C. Albums include Diamond Life, 1984, Promise, 1985, Stronger Than Pride, 1988, Love Deluxe, 1992; singles include Smooth Operator, 1984. Recipient Grammy award Best New Artist, 1986, Best R&B duo or group performance for "No Ordinary Love", 1994. Office: Epic Records 666 Fifth Ave New York NY 10103*

SADE, DONALD STONE, anthropology educator; b. Charleston, W.Va., July 17, 1937; s. Samuel and Charlotte Tracy (Stone) S.; m. Bonita Diane Chepko, Dec. 24, 1971 (div. Feb. 1994); children: Irony Cuervo del Norte, Omen Ondatra; m. Kerry L. Knox, Nov. 24, 1994. Grad., N.Y. State Ranger Sch., 1957; student, Hamilton Coll., 1957-60; A.B., U. Calif., Berkeley, 1963, Ph.D., 1966. Instr. anthropology Northwestern U., Evanston, Ill., 1965-66; asst. prof. Northwestern U., 1966-70, asso. prof., 1970-75, prof., 1975—; scientist-in-charge Cayo Santiago, U. P.R., 1970-77; founder, pres. North Country Inst. for Natural Philosophy, Inc., Mexico, N.Y., 1980—. Sr. author: Basic Demographic Observations on Free-Ranging Rhesus Monkeys, 3 vols., 1985; editor: The North Country Naturalist, Vol. 1, 1987. NSF grantee, 1967—. Mem. AAAS, Am. Assn. Phys. Anthropologists, Am. Soc. Mammalogists, Animal Behavior Soc. Office: North Country Inst for Natural Philosophy Inc Emery Rd RR 3 Box 53 Mexico NY 13114 *I have never given undue heed to the opinions of others regarding my work or character.*

SADEGH, ALI M., mechanical engineering educator, researcher, consultant; b. Tehran, Iran, Sept. 1, 1950; came to U.S., 1974; s. Saleh S. Mir-Mohamad-Sadegh and Asam Lotfi; m. Guita Miremadi, July 10, 1980; children: Mietra, Cameron, Mona, Jasmin, David. BS in Mech. Engring., Arya-Mehr U. Tech., Tehran, 1972; MS in Mech. Engring., Mich. State U., 1975, PhD in Mechanics, 1978; postgrad., U. Mich., 1979. Registered profl. engr., Mich.; cert. mfg. engr. Design engr. Nat. Radio engring. sect., Tehran, 1972-74; rsch. and teaching asst. Mich. State U., East Lansing, 1975-78; postdoctoral scholar U. Mich., Ann Arbor, 1978-79; asst. prof. Arya-Mehr U. Tech., 1979-81; vis. asst. prof. Mich. State U., 1981-82; asst. prof. CUNY, N.Y.C., 1982-87, assoc. prof., 1987-91, prof., 1991—, chmn. dept. mech. engring., 1992—; cons. Devel. Iranian Heavy Industries, Tehran, 1979-81; tech. cons. AC Rochester Gen. Motors Co., 1986-92; cons. to industry, 1988—; expert witness, 1990—. Contbr. 80 articles to profl. jours.; patentee (2) in field. Recipient 22 rsch. awards NSF, AT&T Found., PSC-CUNY, many others. Mem. ASME (Best Paper award; Melville medal), Am. Acad. Mechanics, Soc. Mfg. Engrs. (chmn. chpt. 320), Sigma Xi. Avocations: tennis, swimming. Home: 33 Greenway Ct Closter NJ 07624-2201 Office: CUNY 140th St and Convent Ave New York NY 10031

SADER, CAROL HOPE, former state legislator; b. Bklyn., July 19, 1935; d. Nathan and Mollie (Farkas) Shimkin; m. Harold M. Sader, June 9, 1957; children: Neil, Randi Sader Friedlander, Elisa. BA, Barnard Coll., Columbia U., 1957. Sch. tchr. Bd. Edn., Morris, Conn., 1957-58; legal editor W. H. Anderson Co., Cin., 1974-78; freelance legal editor Shawnee Mission, Kans., 1978-87; mem. Kans. Ho. of Reps., 1987-94; chair Ho. Pub. Health and Welfare Com., 1991-92; chair Joint Ho. and Senate Com. on Health Care Decisions for the 90's, 1992; vice chair Ho. Econ. Devel. Com., 1991-92; policy chair Ho. Dem. Caucus, 1993-94. Dem. candidate for Kans. Lt. Gov., 1994; chmn. bd. trustees Johns County C.C., Overland Park, Kans., 1984-86, trustee, 1981-86; pres. LWV, Johnson County, 1983-85; bd. dirs. United Cmty. Svcs. of Johnson County Shawnee Mission, 1984-92, Jewish Vocat. Svc. Bd., 1983-92; chmn. Kans. State Holocaust Commn., 1991-94, John. Recipient Trustee award Assn. of Women in Jr. and C.C., 1985, awards Kans. Pub. Transit Assn., 1990, AARP, 1992, Assn. Kans. Theater, 1992, Nat. Coun. Jewish Women, 1992, Kans. Assn. Osteo. Medicine, 1992, Kans. Chiropractic Assn., 1992, United Com. Svcs. Johnson County, 1992, Disting. Pub. Svcs. award Johnson County, 1993, Hallpac Kans. Pub. Svc. award Hallmark Cards, Inc., 1993. Mem. Coun. Women Legislators, LWV (pres. Johnson County chpt. 1983-85, mem. state bd. 1986-87), Phi Delta Kappa. Democrat. Avocations: lakehouse, theatre, travel. Home: 8612 Linden Dr Shawnee Mission KS 66207-1807

SADIK, MARVIN SHERWOOD, art consultant, former museum director; b. Springfield, Mass., June 27, 1932; s. Harry Benjamin and Florence (Askins) S. A.B. magna cum laude, Harvard U., 1954, A.M., 1960; D.F.A. (hon.), Bowdoin Coll., Brunswick, Maine, 1978. Curatorial asst. Worcester (Mass.) Art Mus., 1955-57; curator Mus. Art Bowdoin Coll., 1961-64, dir., 1964-67; dir. Mus. Art U. Conn. at Storrs, 1967-69, Nat. Portrait Gallery, Washington, 1969-81; cons. Am. and European art, 1981—; mem. Pres.'s com. on Arts and the Humanities, 1990—; bd. visitors Edmund S. Muskie Inst. of Pub. Affairs, U. So. Maine, bd. dirs. The Osher Map Libr. U. So. Maine. Author: Colonial and Federal Portraits at Bowdoin College, 1966, The Drawings of Hyman Bloom, 1968, The Paintings of Charles Hawthorne, 1968, Christian Gullager: Portrait Painter to Federal America, 1976; co-author: American Portrait Drawings, 1980. Decorated knight Order Dannebrog Denmark; recipient Maine State Art award, 1975, gold medal for exceptional svc. Smithsonian Instn., 1981; Harris fellow, 1957-61; Barr fellow, 1957-61. Fellow Pierpont Morgan Library; mem. Am. Antiquarian Soc., Colonial Soc. Mass. (corr.). Clubs: Century Assn, Grolier. Home: PO Box 6039 Falmouth ME 04105-6039

SADLER, DAVID GARY, financial institution crisis management consultant; b. Iowa City, Mar. 14, 1939; s. Edward Anthony and Elsie June (Sherman) S.; m. Karen Sadler. Student, St. Ambrose Coll., 1957-59; BS in Indsl. Adminstrn. and Prodn., Kent State U., 1961. Various mgmt. positions Ford Motor Co., Lorain, Ohio, 1962-67, Sperry-New Holland, Lebanon, Ohio, 1967-71; mgr. mfg. Allis Chalmer, Springfield, Ill., 1971-72; dir. mfg. Purolator, Inc., Fayetteville, N.C., 1972-73; v.p. mfg. farm equipment and ops. truck div. White Motor Co., Eastlake, Ohio and Chgo., 1973-78; corp. v.p. mfg. Massey Ferguson Ltd., Toronto, Ont., Can., 1978-80; corp. v.p. mfg. Internat. Harvester, Chgo., 1980-81, sr. v.p. ops. staff, 1981-82, v.p. bus. devel., 1982, pres. diversified group, 1982-83, pres. internat. group, 1983-85; pres. AMI, Inc., Chgo., 1985-86; vice chmn., chief exec. officer Savin Corp., Stamford, Conn., 1986, chmn., chief exec. officer, 1986-89, also bd. dirs.; bd. dirs. Gulfstream Housing Corp. Bd. dirs. greater Chgo. Safety Coun., 1981-84; mem. adb. bd. Hellmond Assocs. Opportunity Fund II. Roman Catholic. Home and office: 318 Greens Farms Rd Westport CT 06880-6329

SADLER, ERIC, recording industry executive; b. Hempstead, N.Y., Sept. 18, 1960; s. Donald Joseph and Lygia Ann (Wilson) S.; m. Karen Ann

Francis Douglas, Nov. 10, 1990; 1 child, Karis Leigh. Student, Hempstead (N.Y.) High, 1978. Composer, assoc. Cassad Studios, Hempstead, 1981-87; producer, assoc. Greene St. Recording Inc., N.Y.C., 1987-89; pres. Street Element Inc., N.Y.C., 1989—. Grantee NEA, 1990; recipient 3 platinum, 5 gold albums CBS Records, 1988-90, 1 platinum, 1 gold album, MCA, Virgin & Priority Records, 1990; grammy nominee Nat. Acad Recording Arts and Scis., 1990.

SADLER, GRAHAM HYDRICK, library administrator; b. Sikeston, Mo., Aug. 17, 1931; s. Philip Landis and Montie Pearl (Hydrick) S.; m. Betty A. Grugett, Nov. 22, 1950; children—Graham Hydrick, Lee, Susan, Harrison. B.S., S.E. Mo. State Coll., 1952; M.L.S., Emory U., 1957. Asst. libr. S.E. Mo. State Coll., Cape Girardeau, 1954-61; adminstrv. libr. Kinderhook Regional Libr., Lebanon, Mo., 1961-66; dir. Fort Lewis Coll. Libr., Durango, Colo., 1966-67; assoc. prof. librarianship Kans. State Tchrs. Coll., Emporia, 1967-69; asst. libr., dir. community svc. Denver Pub. Libr., 1970-77; dir. County of Henrico Pub. Libr., Richmond, Va., 1978-94, ret., 1994; mem. adv. com. Office of Library Service to Disadvantaged, 1978-91. Mem. ALA (membership com. 1989-92), Southeastern Libr. Assn., Va. Libr. Assn.

SADLER, LUTHER FULLER, JR., lawyer; b. Jacksonville, Fla., Apr. 10, 1942; s. Luther Fuller and Jane Grey (Lloyd) S.; children: Catherine Winchester, Anna Stephenson Lloyd. BA, Yale U., 1964, LLB, 1967. Bar: Fla. 1967. Ptnr. Mahoney, Hadlow, Chambers & Adams, Jacksonville, 1967-81, Commander, Legler, Werber, Dawes, Sadler & Howell, Jacksonville, 1982-91, Foley & Lardner, Jacksonville, 1991—; gen. counsel Jacksonville C. of C., 1987. Trustee Jacksonville Art Mus., 1984-95, Episcopal Child Care and Devel. Ctrs., Inc., 1990-94. Lt. USNR, 1967-73. Mem. ABA, Fla. Bar Assn. (chmn. corp. banking and bus. law sect. 1979-80), Timuquana Country Club. Episcopalian. Office: Foley & Lardner PO Box 240 200 N Laura St Jacksonville FL 32202-3528

SADLER, M. WHITSON, petroleum company executive. Pres., chief exec. officer Soltex Polymer Corp., Houston. Office: Soltex Polymer Corp 3333 Richmond Ave Houston TX 77098-3007

SADLER, ROBERT LIVINGSTON, banker; b. Beloit, Kans., Dec. 19, 1935; s. D.M. and Retha (Livingston) S.; m. E. Ellen Lewis, July 14, 1957; children: Diane, Julia. AB, Baker U., 1958; MBA, Ind. U., 1959; student, Stonier Grad. Sch. Banking, Rutgers U., 1970. Dir. alumni relations Baker U., Baldwin, Kans., 1957-58; indsl. engr. Colgate-Palmolive Co., N.Y.C., 1958-60, pers. mgr., 1961-64, product mgr., 1964-65; v.p. pers. and adminstrv. svcs. Old Kent Bank & Trust Co., Grand Rapids, Mich., 1965-72, exec. v.p., 1972-86; exec. v.p. Old Kent Fin. Corp., Grand Rapids, 1972-89, vice chmn., 1989—; pres. Old Kent Bank, Grand Rapids, 1995—. Pres. Grand Rapids Jr. Achievement, 1976; pres. United Way Kent County, 1982; chmn. Grand Rapids Found., 1987; Davenport Coll. Bus., Grand Rapids. Mem. Am. Bankers Assn. (chmn. communications council 1980—, dir. 1982-83), Sigma Iota Epsilon, Delta Mu Delta. Republican. Methodist. Clubs: Cascade Country (dir. 1978-80); University (Grand Rapids). Office: Old Kent Fin Corp 1 Vandenberg Ctr Grand Rapids MI 49503

SADLER, THEODORE R., JR., thoracic and cardiovascular surgeon; b. St. Louis, Mar. 26, 1930; s. Theodore R. and Nellie R. (Guffey) S.; m. Roberta Cary Moody, Nov. 26, 1953; children: Michael, Patrick, Susan, Daniel, Shelley. AB, U. Mo., 1951, BS in Medicine, 1954; MD, Washington U., 1956. Diplomate Am. Bd. Thoracic and Cardiovascular Surgery. Commd. U.S. Army, 1956, advanced through grades to brig. gen., 1990; chief of surgery Noble Army Hosp., Ft. McClellans, Ala., 1964-66; comdr. 3d Surgery Hosp., Vietnam, 1966-67; chief thoracic surgery Fitzsimmons Army Hosp., Denver, 1968-71; resigned U.S. Army, 1971, with Res., 1971-82; comdr. 181st Thoracic Detachment, 1971-73, 5502d U.S. Army Hosp. Augmentation Fitzsimmons Army Hosp., Denver, 1974-77; brig. gen. 2d Hosp. Ctr., Hamilton AFB, Calif., 1977-81; ret. Res. U.S. Army, 1990; rotating intern Walter Reed Hosp., Washington, 1956-57; resident in gen. surgery Brooke Gen. Hosp., San Antonio, 1958-61, resident thoracic and cardiovascular surgery, 1964-66; practice medicine specializing in thoracic and cardiovascular surgery St. Joseph's Hosp. and Presbyn. Hosp., Denver, 1971-88; comdr. 147th U.S. Army Hosp. Colo. N.G., 1987-90; mem. staff St. Mary' Hosp., Grand Junction, 1988—, Community Hosp., Hilltop Rehab. Hosp., 1989—; ret.; cons. to surgeon gen. Fitzsimmons Army Hosp., 1983—, VA Hosp., Grand Junction, 1989—; past pres. bd. dirs. St. Joseph's Hosp. Contbr. articles to profl. jours. Vice chmn. Bd. of Health and Hosps., 1982-88; mem. Commn. Mental Health, Denver, 1985-88. Fellow ACS, Am. Coll. Chest Physicians; mem. Soc. Thoracic Surgeons, Western Thoracic Assn., AMA, Colo. Med. Soc. (pres.-elect 1986, bd. dirs., house speaker, pres. 1987-88), Denver Med. Soc. (bd. dirs., past pres.), Mesa County Med. Soc. (bd. dirs. 1989—), Rocky Mounty Individual Physicians Assn. (bd. dirs. 1990—). Republican. Presbyterian. Clubs: Denver Athletic, Bookcliff Country, Metropolitan. Avocations: golf, sports, stamp collecting. Home: 2680 Kimberly Dr Grand Junction CO 81506-1850 Office: 425 Patterson # 506 Grand Junction CO 81506-1935

SADOCK, BENJAMIN JAMES, psychiatrist, educator; b. N.Y.C., Dec. 22, 1933; s. Samuel William and Gertrude S.; m. Virginia Alcott, Oct. 20, 1963; children: James William, Victoria Anne. A.B., Union Coll., 1955; M.D., N.Y. Med. Coll., 1959. Rotating intern Albany (N.Y.) Hosp., 1959-60; resident Bellevue Psychiat. Hosp., N.Y.C., 1960-63; instr. psychiatry Southwestern Med. Sch., Dallas, 1964-65, N.Y. Med. Coll., N.Y.C., 1965-67; asst. prof. N.Y. Med. Coll., 1967-71, assoc. prof., 1972-74, prof., 1975-80, dir. student health psychiatry, 1980—; prof. psychiatry NYU Sch Medicine, 1981—, vice chmn. dept. psychiatry, 1984—; attending psychiatrist Tisch Univ. Hosp. of NYU Med. Ctr., Bellevue Hosp.; cons. psychiatrist Franklin Delano Roosevelt VA Hosp., 1970-78, U.S. Dept. State, 1980-81, P.R. Inst. Psychiatry, 1976-80; examiner Am. Bd. Psychiatry and Neurology, 1970—; mem. conf. on recert. Am. Bd. Med. Spltys.-Am. Psychiat. Assn., 1974; mem. Commn. on Continuing Edn. in Psychiatry, NIMH-Am. Psychiat. Assn., 1974-75. Co-author: Synopsis of Psychiatry, 1972, 4th edit., 1985, 5th edit., 1989, 6th edit., 1991, 7th edit., 1994, Comprehensive Textbook of Psychiatry, 5th edit., 1988, 6th edit., 1995, The Sexual Experience, 1976, Comprehensive Group Psychotherapy, 1971, 3d edit., 1993, Study Guide Modern Synopsis of Psychiatry, 1983, 2d edit., 1985, 3d edit., 1989, 4th edit., 1991, 5th edit., 1994, Pocket Handbook of Clinical Psychiatry, 1991, Comprehensive Glossary of Psychiatry and Psychology, 1991, Pocket Handbook of Drug Treatment in Psychiatry, 1992, Pocket Handbook of Psychiatric Emergency Medicine, 1993; contbr. articles on psychiat. edn., individual and group psychotherapy, diagnosis and treatment psychiat. and sexual disorders to med. jours.; contbr. to: Ency. Americana. Fellow Am. Psychiat. Assn. (treas. N.Y. County dist. br. 1973-76, mem. conf. on psychiatry and med. edn. 1967), N.Y. Acad. Medicine, A.C.P.; mem. AMA, Med. Soc. County and State N.Y., N.Y. Acad. Scis., AAAS, Am. Group Psychotherapy Assn., World Psychiat. Assn., Am. Public Health Assn., Royal Soc. Medicine (London), Psychiat. Soc. N.Y. Med. Coll. (founder, pres. 1975-79), N.Y. Med. Coll. Alumni Assn. (gov. 1965-90), NYU-Bellevue Psychiat. Soc. (pres. 1981—), Alpha Omega Alpha. Office: 4 E 89th St New York NY 10128-0636 also: NYU Med Ctr 550 1st Ave New York NY 10016

SADOFF, ROBERT LESLIE, psychiatrist; b. Mpls., Feb. 8, 1936; s. Max and Rose C. (Karroll) S.; m. Joan A. Handleman, June 21, 1959; children—Debra, David, Julie, Sherry. B.A. U. Minn., 1956, B.S., 1957, M.D., 1959; M.S., UCLA, 1963. Intern Los Angeles VA Hosp., 1959-60; resident UCLA, 1960-63; asst. prof. psychiatry Temple U., Phila., 1966-72; clin. prof. psychiatry U. Pa., Phila., 1972—; lectr. in law Villanova U., 1972-85. Author: (with Marvin Lewis) Psychic Injuries, 1975; Forensic Psychiatry, 1975, 2d edit., 1988; Legal Issues in the Care of Psychiatric Patients, 1982, Violence and Responsibility, 1988; (with Robert I. Simon) Psychiatric Malpractice, 1992; editor: Psychiatric Clinics of North America, 1984. Bd. dirs. Joseph T. Peters Inst., Phila., 1980—. Served to capt. U.S. Army, 1963-65. Recipient Earl Bond award U. Pa., 1979, VIIth Annual Nathaniel Winkelman award Phila. Psychiat. Ctr., 1988, Manfred Guttmacher award Am. Psychiat. Assn., 1992. Fellow Am. Psychiat. Assn., Am. Coll. Psychiatrists, Am. Coll. Legal Medicine; mem. AMA, Am. Acad. Psychiatry and Law (pres. 1971-73), Internat. Soc. for Politics. Enquiry (mentor 1987—), Am. Red Magen David for Israel (nat. pres. 1987—), Internat. Acad. Law and Mental Health (bd. dirs. 1989—, Pinel award 1995). Avocation: collecting antique books in law and medicine. Office: Benjamin Fox Pavilion Ste 326 Jenkintown PA 19046

SADOULET, BERNARD, astrophysicist, educator; b. Nice, France, Apr. 23, 1944; s. Maurice and Genevieve (Berard) S.; m. Elisabeth M.L. Chaine, Apr. 27, 1967; children: Loic, Helene, Samuel. Lic. in Physics., U. Paris, 1965; diploma, Ecole Polytechnique, Paris, 1965; Diploma in Theoretical Physics, U. Orsay, France, 1966, PhD in Phys. Scis., 1971. Fellow CERN, Berkeley, Calif., 1966-73; physicist, then sr. physicist CERN, France, 1976-84; postdoctoral fellow Lawrence Berkeley (Calif.) Lab., 1973-76; mem. faculty U. Calif., Berkeley, 1984—, prof. physics, 1985—, dir. Ctr. Particle Astrophysics, 1988—; mem. commn. astrophysics Internat. Union Pure and Applied Physics, 1991—; vis. com. Max Planck Inst., Heidelberg, Germany, 1991—, Fermilab, 1992—, Lawrence Livermore Nat. Lab., 1992—; mem. program initiation com. NAS, 1992; internat. adv. com. various profl. confs. Contbr. to Sky and Telescope, The Early Universe Observable from Diffuse Backgrounds, other profl. publs. Fellow Am. Phys. Soc., U.S. Nat. Res. Coun. (com. on astronomy & astrophysics 1992) Achievements include work on the problem of the dark matter which constitutes more than 90% of the mass of the universe; devel. of a high-pressure gas scintillation drift chamber; search for WIMPs using cryogenic detectors of phonons and ionization. Office: Univ Calif Berkeley Ctr Particle Astrophysics 301 Le Conte Hall Berkeley CA 94720

SADOVE, STEPHEN IRVING, consumer products company executive; b. Washington, July 25, 1951; s. A. Robert and Harriet (Tenenbaum) S.; m. Sandra Rozenberg, Feb. 24, 1982; children: Stacy, David, Laurie. BA, Hamilton Coll., 1973; MBA, Harvard U., 1975. Asst. product mgr. Gen. Foods Corp.-Desserts Div., White Plains, N.Y., 1975-76; assoc. product mgr. Gen. Foods Corp.-Desserts Div., White Plains, 1976-77, product mgr., 1977-80, group product mgr., 1980-82, category mgr., 1982-84; mktg. mgr. Gen. Foods Corp.-Meals Div., White Plains, 1984-86, bus. unit mgr., 1986-88, v.p., gen. mgr., 1988-89; exec. v.p., gen. mgr. Gen. Foods Corp.-Desserts Div., White Plains, 1989-91; pres. Clairol, Inc., 1991—; alumni coun. Hamilton Coll., Clinton, N.Y. Bd. trustees, exec. com. Coun. for Arts in Westchester, White Plains, 1990—; bd. trustees Caramoor, Hazeldon. Avocations: tennis, golf, reading, arts. Home: 6 Crest Ct Armonk NY 10504-2901 Office: Clairol Inc 345 Park Ave New York NY 10154

SADOW, HARVEY S., health care company executive; b. N.Y.C., Oct. 6, 1922; s. Nat and Frances Donna (Saveth) S.; m. Sylvia June Riber, Dec. 22, 1944 (div. 1966); children: Harvey Jr., Suzanne Gail, Todd Forrest, Gay Summer; m. Jacqueline Lucille Clavel, Jan. 24, 1969 (div. 1993); 1 adopted child, Daniel Jean Marie. BS, Va. Mil. Inst., Lexington, 1947; MS, U. Kans., 1949; PhD, U. Conn., 1953. Intelligence officer CIA, Washington, 1951-53; assoc. dir. rsch. Lakeside Labs., Inc., Milw., 1953-56; med. rsch. cons. Milw., 1956; dir. clin. rsch. U.S. Vitamin & Pharm. Corp., N.Y., 1957-64, v.p. rsch. and devel., 1964-68; sr. v.p. scientific affairs USV Pharm./Revlon Corp., N.Y.C., 1969-71; pres., CEO Boehringer Ingelheim, Ltd. (named changed to Boehringer Ingelheim Pharms., Inc. 1984), Ridgefield, Conn., 1971-88; pres., CEO Boehringer Ingelheim Corp., Ridgefield, 1984-88, chmn. bd., 1988-90; chmn. bd. Roxane Labs., Inc., Columbus, Ohio, 1981-88, Boehringer Ingelheim Animal Health, Inc., St. Joseph, Mo., 1981-88, Henley Co., N.Y.C., 1986-88, U. Conn. Rsch. and Devel. Corp., Storrs, 1984-87; bd. dirs. Cortex Pharms., Inc., Irvine, Calif., 1989—, chmn. bd., 1991—; bd. dirs. Triton Biosciences, Inc., Alameda, Calif., 1989, Telios Pharms., Inc., La Jolla, Calif., Penederm Corp., Foster City, Calif., TargeTech, Inc., Meriden, Conn., 1992, Microgenesys Corp., Meriden, Conn., 1994, Delta Health Products Devel. Corp., Mill Valley, Calif., Conn. Innovations Inc., Rocky Hill, Neocrin Corp., Irvine, Houghten Pharms, Inc., San Diego, Cytel Corp., San Diego; bd. dirs. Cholestech Corp., Hayward, Calif., chmn. bd., 1992—; bd. dirs. Cytel Corp., San Diego; mem. adv. bd. Salk Inst. Biotechnology/Indsl. Assocs., Inc., La Jolla, 1988-90. Co-author: Oral Treatment of Diabetes, 1967; author, co-author 23 papers on intermediary metabolism, diabetes, obesity and cardiovascular disease., 1963-72. Mem. Conn. Comm. on Bus. Opportunity, Def. Diversification and Indsl. Policy, 1992-93; chmn. Pharm. Mfrs. Assn. Found., 1988-90; bd. dirs. Conn. Bd. Higher Edn., Hartford, 1977-83, Govs. Tech. Adv. Bd., Hartford, 1984-87, Pharm. Mfrs. Assn., 1983-90; mem. bd. visitors Va. Mil. Inst., Lexington, 1987—; bd. dirs. pres., 1991-95; chmn. bd. Conn. Law Enforcement Found., Hartford, 1981-86, 92—, U. Conn. Found., Storrs, 1984-87; chmn., pres.' coun. Am. Lung Assn., N.Y.C., 1986-87, York Sch., Monterey, Calif., 1988-89; trustee Conn. Coll., Groton, 1991—, Aldrich Mus. Contemporary Art, Ridgefield, Conn., 1991—. Capt. U.S. Army, 1943-53, ETO, Korea. Decorated Disting. Svc. Cross, Fed. Republic of Germany, 1987; recipient Univ. medal U. Conn., 1987, Recognition award Nat. Hypertension Assn., 1990, Humanitarian award Am. Lung Assn. Conn., 1993. Mem. Am. Soc. for Clin. Pharmacology and Therapeutics, Am. Fedn. for Clin. Rsch., Am. Diabetes Assn., Danbury C. of C. (Abraham Ribicoff Community Svc. award City of Danbury 1987, bd. dirs. 1978-81), Union League (N.Y.C.), Landmark Club (Stamford, Conn.), Masons, Sigma Xi, Sigma Pi Sigma, Phi Lambda Upsilon. Avocations: art collecting, photography, music, writing, golfing. Home and Office: 120-36 Prospect St Ridgefield CT 06877-4648

SADOWAY, DONALD ROBERT, materials science educator; b. Toronto, Mar. 7, 1950; came to U.S., 1977; s. Donald Anthony and Irene Mary (Romanko) S.; m. Sandra Lynn Mary Babij, Sept. 8, 1973; children: Steven, Laryssa, Andrew. BASc, U. Toronto, 1972, MASc, 1973, PhD, 1977. Cert. in chem. metallurgy. Asst. prof. materials engring. MIT, Cambridge, 1978-82, assoc. prof., 1982-92, prof. materials chemistry, 1992—; MacVicar faculty fellow MIT, 1995—. Contbr. over 65 articles on electro and phys. chemistry to profl. jours.; patentee in field, U.S., Can., and Europe. Recipient Grad. Student Coun. Teaching award MIT, 1982, 84, 87, 88, 93, Prof. T.B. King Meml. award dept. materials sci. and engring. undergrad. students MIT, 1986; NATO postdoctoral fellow Nat. Rsch. Coun. Can., 1977. Mem. AAAS, Minerals, Metals and Materials Soc., Electrochem. Soc. Internat. Soc. Electrochemistry. Ukrainian Orthodox. Avocation: choral music. Home: 53 Vernon Rd Belmont MA 02178-1031 Office: MIT # 8-109 77 Massachusetts Ave Cambridge MA 02139-4307

SADOWSKI, ANTHONY JAMES, chemical company executive, physical chemist; b. Chgo., July 2, 1938; s. Anthony Joseph and Vera (Norwich) S.; m. Valerie DiMuro, July 8, 1962; children: Cherie Ann, Carey Scott. BS in Chemistry, De Paul U., Chgo., 1960; MS in Chemistry, Ill. Inst. Tech., 1964, PhD in Chemistry, 1967; MBA, U. Chgo., 1980. Chemist Nalco Chem. Co., Naperville, Ill., 1967-69, group leader pulp paper, 1969-72, tech. dir., mining, pollution control, 1972-77, dir. corp. rsch., 1977-80, account. mgr., sales, 1980-81, dist. mgr., sales, 1981-82, div. v.p., rsch. process and petroleum chems. div., 1982-87, v.p. environ. health and safety, 1988—; mem. sci. adv. com. 13th Cong. Dist., Ill., 1986—. Patentee in field. Trustee Ill Math. and Sci. Acad., Aurora, 1985-87; campaign chmn. Naperville United Way, 1985; bd. dirs. Am. Ind. Health Coun., 1991-94. Mem. AIME, Naperville C. of C. (pres. 1986). Republican. Roman Catholic. Avocations: music, gardening, baseball, cooking. Home: 510 Delkir Ct Naperville IL 60565-4166 Office: Nalco Chem Co One Nalco Ctr Naperville IL 60566

SADOWSKI, CAROL JOHNSON, fine artist, painter; b. Chgo., Mar. 20, 1929; d. Carl Valdamar Johnson and Elizabeth Hilma (Booth) Johnson-Chellberg; m. Edmund Sadowski, July 9, 1949; children: Lynn Carol Mahoney, Christie Sadowski Cortez. AAS, Wright-Ill. Coll., 1949. Tchr. art Malverne (N.Y.) High Sch., 1968-69; artist Valley Stream, N.Y., 1968-76, Hollywood, Fla., 1976—; guest speaker Mus. Art Ft. Lauderdale, Fla., 1991, Oakland Park (Fla.) Libr. League Lit. Luncheon, 1985. One-person shows include Hist. Mus. Hollywood, Fla., 1985, 87, Elliott Mus., Stuart, Fla., 1987, Mus. Fla. History, Tallahassee, 1984, 85, 87, Hemingway Home and Mus., Key West, Fla., 1986, Alliance Francaise de Miami, 1995; commd. paintings St. Augustine, Fla., 1985, Atlantic Bank, Bonnet House, Ft. Lauderdale, Fla., 1987. Recipient Hemingway medal Ernest Hemingway Mus., Cuba, 1990. Mem. Broward Art Guild, Fla. Hist. Assn., Ernest Hemingway Soc., Chopin Found., Am. Inst. for Polish Culture, Alliance Francaise de Miami. Avocations: travel, hiking, biking, swimming, reading. Home and Office: Apt B-17 1480 Sheridan St Hollywood FL 33020

SADWITH, JAMES STEVEN, screenwriter, director; b. New Brunswick, N.J., Oct. 20, 1952; s. Howard Marvin and Elizabeth Sadwith; m. Kathleen Tyler, May 21, 1983; children: Ryan Tyler, Hannah Leigh. Student, Harvard Coll., 1971-73; VMD, U. Pa., 1977; MA in Cinema, U. So. Calif., 1981. Directed numerous TV movies, miniseries and pilots, including In Broad Daylight, 1991, Deadly Intentions...Again, 1991, Sinatra, 1992, Angels' Attic, 1994; writer/dir. Baby M., 1988, Bluffing It, 1987, Monsters in My Room and The Odds Tales from the Darkside, 1985; writer/producer Two of a Kind, 1982, Who Is Julia, 1986, Crossroads, 1992. Recipient Emmy award for best directing, 1993, Golden Globe award for best miniseries, 1993. Mem. Writers Guild Am. West, Dirs. Guild Am. Office: Internat Creative Mgmt 8942 Wilshire Blvd Beverly Hills CA 90211-1908

SAEGER, DIXIE FORESTER, dietitian; b. Cullowhee, N.C., Oct. 16, 1940; d. James Fred and Thelma (Phillips) Forester; m. Henry E. Saeger, Aug. 6, 1962; 1 child, Jeffrey Alan. BS in Home Econs., Tenn. Tech. U., 1962; MS in Nutrition, U. Tenn., 1978. Registered dietitian. Clin. instr. dietetics U. Tenn., Knoxville, 1980-81; instr. U. Tenn., Chattanooga, 1976-88; clin. dietitian North Park Hosp., Chattanooga, 1979-87; dir. dietetic svcs. Parkwood Health Care Ctr., Chattanooga, 1987-89; clin. dietitian Meml. Hosp., Chattanooga, 1989—. Mem. Am. Dietetic Assn. (practice groups dietitians in nutrition support, dietitians in clin. nutrition mgmt.), Tenn. Dietetic Assn. (chmn. quality assurance 1987-88, chmn. coun. practice divsn. mgmt. 1989-91), Chattanooga Dist. Dietetic Assn. (sec. 1980-82, chmn. ednl. program devel. 1981-82, pres. 1983-84, coun. on practice 1984-89, administr. coord. lic. com. 1986, chmn. long range planning com. 1987-88, chmn. coun. practice 1988-89, nominating com. 1992-93, chmn. long range planning 1993-94). Home: 2807 St Johns Ln Chattanooga TN 37421

SAEKS, ALLEN IRVING, lawyer; b. Bemidji, Minn., July 14, 1932; m. Linda J. Levin; 1 child, Adam Charles. BS in Law, U. Minn., 1954, JD, 1956. Bar: Minn. 1956, U.S. Dist. Ct. Minn. 1956, U.S. Ct. Appeals (8th cir.) 1957, U.S. Ct. Appeals (fed. cir.) 1959, U.S. Supreme Ct. 1959; cert. civil trial specialist. Asst. atty. Dept. Justice, St. Paul, 1956-57; assoc. Leonard Street & Deinard, Mpls., 1960-63, ptnr., 1964—; adj. prof. law U. Minn. Law Sch., 1960-65; chmn. Lawyer Trust Account Bd., Interest on Lawyers Trust Accounts., 1984-87. Chmn. Property Tax Com., 1986-87; bd. dirs. Citizens League, Mpls., 1984-87; pres. Jewish Cmty. Rels. Coun. of Minn. and the Dakotas, 1994—. Served to 1st lt. JAGC, U.S. Army, 1957-60. Fellow Am. Bar Found.; mem. Hennepin County Bar Assn. (pres. 1983-84), ABA (commn. on interest on lawyers trust accts. 1990-93), Minn. State Bar Assn. (cert. trial specialist 1988), Order of Coif, Phi Delta Phi. Office: Leonard Street and Deinard 150 S 5th St # 2300 Minneapolis MN 55402-4238

SAEKS, RICHARD EPHRAIM, electrical engineer; b. Chgo., Nov. 30, 1941; s. Morris G. and Elsie E. S. B.S., Northwestern U., 1964; M.S., Colo. State U., 1965; Ph.D., Cornell U., 1967. Elec. engr. Warwick Mfg. Co., Niles, Ill., 1961-63; asst. prof. dept. elec. engring. U. Notre Dame, 1967-71, asso. prof., 1971-73; assoc. prof. dept. elec. engring., math. Tex. Tech U., Lubbock, 1973-77; prof. Tex. Tech U., 1977-79, Paul Whitfield Horn prof. elec. engring., math., computer sci., 1979-82; prof., chmn. elec. engring. Ariz. State U., 1983-88; dean Armour Coll. Engring. Ill. Inst. Tech., 1988-91, Motorola prof., 1991-92; v.p. engring. Accurate Automation Corp., 1992—; cons. Research Triangle Inst., 1977-80, Marcel Dekker Inc., 1978-80. Author: Generalized Networks, 1972, Resolution Space Operators and Systems, 1973, Interconnected Dynamical Systems, 1981, System Theory: A Hilbert Space Approach, 1982; contbr. articles to profl. jours.; Editor: Large-Scale Dynamical Systems, 1976, Rational Fault Analysis, 1977, The World of Large Scale Systems, 1982. Recipient Disting. Faculty Research award Tex. Tech U., 1978. Fellow IEEE.

SAENGER, EUGENE LANGE, radiology educator, laboratory director; b. Cin., Mar. 5, 1917; s. Eugene and Therese (Lange) S.; m. Sue Reis, June 18, 1941; children: Katherine Saenger Soodek (dec.), Eugene Lange. A.B., Harvard U., 1938; M.D., U. Cin., 1942. Diplomate: Am. Bd. Radiology, Am. Bd. Nuclear Medicine. Intern Cin. Gen. Hosp., 1942-43, resident in radiology, 1943-46; asst. prof., then assoc. prof. radiology U. Cin. Med. Ctr., 1949-62, prof., vice chmn. dept., 1962-87, prof. radiology emeritus, 1987—; radiation therapist Children's Hosp., Cin., 1947-87; dir. E.L. Saenger Radioisotope Lab., U. Cin., 1950-87; cons. AEC and NRC, 1962-88, to med. liaison EPA, 1968—; dir. Nat. Coun. Radiation Protection, 1967—; mem. Internat. Com. on Radiation Protection, 1977-84. Author: Medical Aspects of Radiation Accidents: A Handbook for Physicians, Health Physicists and Industrial Hygienists, 1963. Trustee Cin. Community Chest and Council, 1964-70. Served to maj. M.C. U.S. Army, 1953-55. Mem. Soc. Med. Decision Making (pres., co-founder 1979-80), Nat. Coun. Radiation Protection (hon. mem.), Queen City Club, Literary Club (Cin.), Cosmos Club (Washington), Optimists Club. Jewish. Home: 9160 Given Rd Cincinnati OH 45243-1148 Office: Eugene L Saenger Radioisotope Lab U Cin Hosp ML 569 Cincinnati OH 45267-0569

SAENZ, MICHAEL, college president; b. Laredo, Tex., Oct. 25, 1925; s. C. A. and Pola R. Saenz; B.S. with honors in Accounting, Tex. Christian U., 1949, M.Ed., 1952; Ph.D. in Econs., U. Pa., 1961; m. Nancy Elizabeth King; children—Michael King, Cynthia Elizabeth. Dep. collector IRS, Ft. Worth, Dallas, 1949-52; administr. United Christian Missionary Soc., Bayamon, P.R., 1954-57, 59-65, exec. sec., Indpls., 1965-71; acad. dean Laredo Jr. Coll., 1971-74; pres. N.W. campus Tarrant County Jr. Coll., 1975—; founder Nat. Comm. Coll. Hispanic coun., 1985, bd. dirs. 1985— (pres. 1989-91); founder, co-chr. Nat. Hispanic Leadership Inst., 1989—; trustee Tex. Christian U., Brite Div. Sch., 1973—. Bd. dirs. Civic Ballet of Laredo (Tex.), Ft. Worth chpt. NCCJ, Juliette Fowler Homes, Dallas; chmn. Aztec Dist., dir. Gulf Coast council Boy Scouts Am., 1971-75; gov. Career Devel. Center, Arlington, Tex.; chmn. Laredo's Bicentennial Com., 1973-76; trustee, bd. dirs. United Way Ft. Worth, 1979—; mem., vice moderator gen. bd. Christian Ch. (Disciples of Christ), 1991-93. Mem. Am. Assn. Cmty. Colls.(bd. dirs., 1991-94), Community Internat. Edn. Am. Coun. Edn., Tex. Jr. Coll. Tchrs. Assn., Tex. Assn. Jr. Coll. Instructional Adminstrs., Am. Acad. Polit. and Social Scis., Urban Ministries in Higher Edn, Civic Music Assn. Laredo, N. Ft. Worth C. of C. (dir. 1978—). Lodge: Rotary (North Ft. Worth). Home: 4427 Tamworth Rd Fort Worth TX 76116-8127 Office: Tarrant County Jr Coll 1500 Houston St Fort Worth TX 76102-6524

SAETA, PHILIP MAX, judge; b. L.A., Feb. 21, 1931; s. Maurice and Elizabeth (Jacobs) S.; m. Joanne Edith Hixson, Aug. 28, 1954; children: David, Peter, Sandra. AB, Stanford U., 1953, LLB, 1957. Bar: Calif. 1958, U.S. Dist. Ct. (cen. dist.) Calif. Assoc., ptnr. Beardsley, Hufstedler & Kemble, L.A., 1964-75; judge Mcpl. Ct., L.A., 1964-75; judge L.A. County Superior Ct., L.A. 1975-91, ret., 1991. With U.S. Army, 1953-55. Mem. ABA, Calif. Judges Assn. (Jefferson award 1987), L.A. County Bar Assn. Democrat. Jewish. Avocation: music. Home and Office: 2036 Oak St South Pasadena CA 91030-4954

SAFAN, CRAIG ALAN, film composer; b. L.A., Dec. 17, 1948; s. Eugene Leroy and Betty Lou (Torchin) S.; m. Linda Sue McClelland, Aug. 27, 1978; children: Alec, Kira. BA, Brandeis U., 1970. Film composer, 1973—. Composer film scores The Great Texas Dynamite Chase, 1976, The Bad News Bears in Breaking Training, 1977, Corvette Summer, 1978, Good Guys Wear Black, 1978, The Great Smokey Roadblock, 1978, Roller Boogie, 1979, Fade to Black, 1980, Die Laughing, 1980, T.A.G.: The Assassination Game, 1982, Nightmares, 1983, Angel, 1984, The Last Starfighter, 1984, The Legend of Billie Jean, 1985, Remo Williams: The Adventure Begins, 1985, Warning Sign, 1985, Lady Beware, 1987, The Stranger, 1987, Stand and Deliver, 1988, A Nightmare on Elm Street IV: The Dream Master, 1988, Money for Nothing, 1993, Major Payne, 1995, Mr. Wrong, 1995, TV scores Cheers, 1983-94, Life Goes On, 1990-94, Hope and Gloria, 1995. Fellow Watson Found., 1970-71. Mem. NARAS, ASCAP (award for Cheers 1987-93), Acad. Motion Picture Arts and Scis. (exec. music com. 1987-95). Avocation: collecting American sheet music. Office: MSK Agy 4146 Lankershim Blvd Ste 401 North Hollywood CA 91602

SAFAR, MICHAEL, information scientist. BA in English-History, Butler U., 1972; MLS in Info. Sci., Rosary Coll., 1982. Credit reporter Dun & Bradstreet, Indpls., 1972-73; supr. svc., 1974-75; supr. telephone order dept. Dun & Bradstreet, Chgo., 1976, sales rep. 1977, adminstrv. asst., 1978; supr. Chgo. Blue Cross and Blue Shield, 1979-81; asst. libr. East-West U., Chgo., 1983-85; mgr. rsch. mfg. dept. IIT Rsch. Inst., Chgo., 1985—, info. specialist

mfg. tech. info. analysis ctr., 1985-87, tech. coordinator, 1987-90, dir., 1990—. Mng. editor Mfg. Competitiveness Frontiers. Mem. ALA, Am. Soc. Info. Sci., Am. Def. Preparedness Assn. (treas. Chgo. chpt.), Nat. Contract Mgmt. Assn., Ill. Librs. Assn., Spl. Librs. Assn. Office: IIT Rsch Inst Mfg Productivity Ctr 3350 S Federal St Chicago IL 60616-3703

SAFAR, PETER, emergency health care facility administrator, educator; b. Vienna, Austria, Apr. 12, 1924; came to U.S. 1949; s. Karl and Vinca (Landauer) S.; m. Eva Kyzivat, July 6, 1950; children: Elizabeth, Philip, Paul. MD, U. Vienna, 1948; Dr. Hon. Causa, Gutenberg U., Mainz, Fed. Republic Germany, 1972. Resident in surgery U. Vienna and Yale U., 1948-50; resident in anesthesiology U. Pa., Phila., 1950-52; chief anesthesiologist Nat. Cancer Hosp., Lima, Peru, 1953, Balt. City Hosp., 1955-61; anesthesiologist Johns Hopkins Hosp., Balt., 1954; asst. prof. anesthesiology Johns Hopkins U., Balt., 1955-61; prof., chmn. dept. anesthesiology/CCM U. Pitts. Med. Ctr., 1961-78; dir. Internat. Resuscitation Rsch. Ctr. U. Pitts., 1978—; disting. svc. prof. resuscitation medicine, 1978—; co-initiator cardiopulmonary-cerebral resuscitation; researcher in field; mem. emergency med. svcs. and resuscitation coms. NRC/NAS, Washington, 1950-70; mem. Emergency Med. Svcs. Interagy. Com., Washington, 1974-76. Co-author nat. and internat. guidelines for modern resuscitation. Considered Father of Modern Resuscitation. Mem. Soc. Critical Care Medicine (pres., co-initiator 1972-73), Am. Coll. Emergency Physicians (hon.), Nat. Assn. Emergency Med. Svcs. Physicians (hon.), Univ. Assn. Emergency Medicine (hon.), German Acad. Natural Scis. Leopoldina (hon., corr.), Am. Acad. Scis. (hon., corr.), Czechoslovak Med. Soc. J.E. Purkinje (hon., corr.). Avocations: snow skiing, mountaineering, water sports, music, piano. Office: U Pitts Internat Resuscitation Rsch 3434 5th Ave Pittsburgh PA 15213-3235

SAFARIAN, ASHOT ANDRANIKI, Armenian government official; b. Yerevan, Armenia, Sept. 20, 1954; s. Safarian Andranik Hovhannesi and Safarian Parandzem (Stepanian) Enoki; m. Shogakat Nahapeti Mikaelian; children: Andranik, Gevork. Cand. tech. scis., Polytech. Inst., Yerevan, 1976; postgrad., All-Union Sci. Rsch. Inst. Electromechanics, Moscow, 1977-80. Cert. elec. engr. Asst. prof., sr. engr., sr. scientist, dept. mgr. Polytech. Inst., Yerevan, 1980-90; dep. pres. State Com. Economy, Yerevan, 1990-91; min. Ministry of Industry, Yerevan, 1991—. Author 59 sci. works; inventor. Mem. Tennis Fedn. (pres.). Office: Embassy of Republic of Armenia 1660 L St NW Ste 210 Washington DC 20036

SAFARS, BERTA See FISZER-SZAFARZ, BERTA

SAFDIE, MOSHE, architect; b. Haifa, Israel, July 14, 1938; s. Leon S.; m. Nina Nusynowicz, Sept. 6, 1959 (div. 1981); children: Taal, Oren; m. Michal Ronnen, June 7, 1981; children: Carmelle, Yasmin. B.Arch, McGill U., 1961; LL.D. (hon.), 1982; DSc (hon.), Laval U., 1988; D.F.A. (hon.), U. Victoria, 1989. With H.P.D. Van Ginkel (architect), Montreal, Can., 1961-62, then Louis I. Kahn, Phila., 1962-63; assoc. David, Barrott and Boulva, Montreal, 1964; pvt. practice Boston, 1964—; with br. in, Toronto, Can., Jerusalem; prof. architecture and urban design, dir. urban design program Harvard U. Grad. Sch. Design, 1978-84, Ian Woodner Studio prof. architecture and urban design, 1984-89. Recipient Massey medal in architecture, Lt. Gov. Can. gold medal, urban design concept award HUD, 1980, internat. design award in urban design Am. Soc. Interior Designers, 1980, Prix d'Excellence in architecture Que. Order Architects, 1988, Gov. Gen.'s medal for architecture, 1992, Richard J. Neutra award, 1993. Recipient Massey medal in architecture, Lt. Gov. Can. gold medal, urban design concept award HUD, 1980, internat. design award in urban design Am. Soc. Interior Designers, 1980, Prix d'Excellence in architecture Que. Order Architects, 1988, Gov. Gen.'s medal for architecture, 1992, Richard J. Neutra award, 1993. Fellow Royal Inst. Architects Can., Order of Can.; mem. AIA, Order Architects Province Que., Ont. Assn. Architects. Office: 100 Properzi Way Somerville MA 02143 also: 165 Avenue Rd Ste 501, Toronto, ON Canada M5R 2H7 also: 4 Ha'emek St, Jerusalem Israel 94106

SAFER, JAY GERALD, lawyer; b. Jacksonville, Fla., Oct. 11, 1946; s. Moe B. and Rubye (Lipsitz) S.; m. Annette Fashing, Nov. 26, 1970; children: Michelle Laurie, Ellie Renee. BA, Vanderbilt U., 1968; JD, Columbia U. 1971. Bar: N.Y. 1972, U.S. Dist. Ct. (so. and ea. dists.) N.Y. 1973, U.S. Dist. Ct. Conn. 1984, U.S. Ct. Appeals (2d cir.) 1974, U.S. Supreme Ct. 1992. Assoc. Paul, Weiss, Rifkind, Wharton & Garrison, N.Y.C., 1971-75, Hardee, Barovick, Konecky & Braun, N.Y.C., 1975, LeBoeuf, Lamb, Leiby & MacRae, N.Y.C., 1975-80; ptnr. LeBoeuf, Lamb, Greene & MacRae, N.Y.C., 1980—. Contbr. articles to profl. jours. Served to capt. U.S. Army, 1972. Harlan Fiske Stone scholar, Columbia U. 1971. Mem. ABA, N.Y. State Bar Assn., Assn. Bar City N.Y. Office: LeBoeuf Lamb Greene MacRae 125 W 55th St New York NY 10019-5389

SAFER, JOHN, artist, lecturer; b. Washington, Sept. 6, 1922; s. John M. and Rebecca (Herzmark) S.; m. Joy Scott; children: Janine Whitney, Thomas. AB, George Washington U., 1947; LLB, Harvard, 1949. chmn. NationsBank/D.C., 1980-92; chmn. exec. com. Fin. Gen. Bankshares, 1977-80. Represented in permanent collections at Balt. Mus. Art, Corcoran Gallery Art, Nat. Air and Space Mus., Washington Tennis Ctr., Washington, High Mus. Art, Atlanta, Milw. Mus. Art, Harvard Law Sch., Harvard Bus. Sch., Phila. Mus. Art, San Francisco Mus. Art, Georgetown U., George Washington U., Williams Coll., Mus. Fine Arts, Caracas, Venezuela, Royal Collection Madrid, Am. Hosp., Paris, Embassy of U.S., London, Beijing; pub. sculpture includes World Series of Golf Trophy, Timepiece (World's largest clock - Guiness Book of Records), Christa McAuliffe Meml., Bowie, Md. Served as 1st lt. USAAF, 1942-46. Clubs: Cosmos, Burning Tree, Harvard, Woodmont (Washington); Harvard (N.Y.); Lyford Cay (Nassau); Mid-Ocean (Bermuda); Linville Ridge (N.C.). Office: PO Box 30163 Bethesda MD 20814

SAFER, MORLEY, journalist; b. Toronto, Ont., Can., Nov. 8, 1931; came to U.S., 1964; s. Max and Anna (Cohn) S. Student, U. Western Ont., 1952. With Reuters, London, Eng., 1955; corr., producer Canadian Broadcasting Corp., 1955-60, writer, London corr., 1961-64; corr., producer BBC, 1961; Vietnam corr. CBS, 1964-71; co-host 60 Minutes news program CBS-TV, 1971—; writer-corr. news documentary The Second Battle of Britain, 1976. Author: Flashbacks: On Returning to Vietnam, 1990. Recipient Polk award L.I.U., 1965, Overseas Press Club award, 1965, 66, Sigma Delta Chi award, 1965, Peabody award, 1965, Paul White award Radio and TV, News Dirs. Assn., 1966, 4 Emmy awards, 1981, 82, 3 Emmy awards, 1985, George Foster Peabody award, 1983, 3 prestigious awards, George Foster Peabody, Alfred I. duPont-Columbia U., Emmy for "Lenell Geter's in Jail", 60 Min. broadcast, 1984. Fellow Royal Coll. Bloviation (Edinburgh). Office: care CBS News 60 Minutes 555 West 57th St New York NY 10019

SAFERITE, LINDA LEE, library director; b. Santa Barbara, Calif., Mar. 25, 1947; d. Elwyn C. and Polly (Frazer) S.; m. Andre Doyon, July 16, 1985. BA, Calif. State U., Chico, 1969; MS in Library Sci., U. So. Calif., 1970; cert. in Indsl. Relations, UCLA, 1976; MBA, Pepperdine U., 1979. Librarian-in-charge, reference librarian Los Angeles County Pub. Libr. System, 1970-73, regional reference librarian, 1973-75, sr. librarian-in-charge, 1975-78, regional adminstr., 1978-80; libr. dir. Scottsdale (Ariz.) Pub. Libr. System, 1980-93, Fort Collins (Colo.) Pub. Libr., 1993—; task force del. White House Conf. on Libr. and Info. Svcs., 1992—, regional, Region V, 1982-94. Bd. dirs. Scottsdale-Paradise Valley YMCA, 1981-86, Ariz. Libr. Friends, 1990-92; bd. dirs. AMIGOS, 1990, chmn., 1992-93; mem. Class 5, Scottsdale Leavership, 1991. Recipient Cert. Recognition for efforts in civil rights Ariz. Atty. Gen.'s Office, 1985, Libr. award Ariz. Libr. Friends, 1988, Women of Distinction award for Edn., 1989; named State Libr. of Yr., 1990. Mem. ALA, Ariz. State Libr. Assn. (pres. 1987-88), Ariz. Women's Town Hall AlumniAssn., Met. Bus. and Profl. Women (Scottsdale, pres. 1986-87), Soroptimist (pres. 1981-83). Republican. Avocations: mountain jaunts, reading, ballroom dancing, photography. Office: Fort Collins Pub Libr 201 Peterson St Fort Collins CO 80524

SAFF, DONALD JAY, artist, educator; b. Bklyn., Dec. 12, 1937; s. Irving H. and Rose (Koslow) S.; m. Ruth E. Simon, 1960; children: Stephen M., Jeffrey M. B.A., Queens Coll., 1959; M.A., Columbia U., 1960; M.F.A., Pratt Inst., 1962; Ed.D, Tchrs. Coll., Columbia U., 1964; postgrad., Istituto Statale di Belle Arti, Italy, 1965. Lectr. Queens Coll., City U. N.Y., 1960-64; asst. prof. SUNY, New Paltz, 1964; instr. printmaking and design Columbia

U. Tchrs. Coll., N.Y.C., summers 1965, 66; assoc. prof. U. South Fla., Tampa, 1965-67; chmn. dept. visual arts U. South Fla., 1967-71, prof. dept. visual arts, 1967-82; assoc. dean U. South Fla. (Coll. Fine Arts), 1971, dean Coll. Fine Arts, 1971-77, dir. graphic studio, 1968-76, 85—, disting. prof., 1982; dir., curator Rauschenberg Overseas Culture Interchange, 1984—; guest lectr. history of the print Lowe Mus., Fla., 1972, Washington U., St. Louis, 1972, U. Alaska, 1974, Northwestern U., 1981; mem. Pennell com. Library of Congress, 1978—. Author: Printmaking: History and Technique, 1976, (with Deli Sacilotto) Screen Printing: History and Technique, 1979; one-man shows of prints, 1960—, including, Trend House Gallery, Tampa, Fla., 1974, Getler/Pall Gallery, N.Y.C., 1979, 80, Texann Ivy Gallery, Orlando, Fla., 1979, Russell Sage Coll., N.Y.C., 1979, Tom Lutrell Gallery, San Francisco, 1980, Edison Community Coll., Ft. Myers, Fla., 1980, Galleria D'Arte Moderna, Udine, Italy, 1981, numerous groups shows, including, Fla. Gulf Coast Art Center, Clearwater, 1974, Bklyn. Mus., 1976, Dartmouth Coll., N.H., 1980, Cramer Gallery, Washington, 1980, Alex Rosenberg Gallery, N.Y.C., 1980, Leo Castelli Gallery, N.Y.C., 1981; represented in permanent collections, Library of Congress, Washington, Bklyn. Mus., Mus. Fine Arts, Boston, Met. Mus. of Art, N.Y.C., Mus. Modern Art, N.Y.C., Fogg Mus., Harvard U., Boston, Nat. Gallery of Art, Washington, Phila. Mus. Art, So. Ill. U., Carbondale, N.Y. U., N.Y.C., Nelson Rockefeller Collection, N.Y.C. Recipient Patrick Gavin Meml. prize award Boston Printmaking Assn., 1966; Fulbright grantee Italy, 1964-65; U. South Fla. grantee, 1969-70; Fla. Endowment for the Arts grantee, 1980. Mem. Nat. Council Art Adminstrs. (founder, dir. 1973-75). Jewish. Office: M. Knoedler & Co 19 E 70th St New York NY 10021

SAFF, EDWARD BARRY, mathematics educator; b. N.Y.C., Jan. 2, 1944; s. Irving H. and Rose (Koslow) S.; m. Loretta Singer, July 3, 1966; children: Lisa Jill, Tracy Karen, Alison Michelle. BS with highest honors, Ga. Inst. Tech., 1964; PhD, U. Md., 1968. Asst. prof. U. Md., 1968; post-doctoral researcher Imperial Coll., London, 1968-69; asst. prof. math. U. South Fla., 1969-71, assoc. prof., 1971-76, prof., 1976-86, disting. rsch. prof., 1986—, dir. Ctr. for Math. Svcs., 1978-83, dir. Inst. for Constructive Math., 1985—; sr. vis. fellow Oxford U., 1978. Author: (with A.D. Snider) Fundamentals of Complex Analysis, 1976, (with A.W. Goodman) Calculus, Concepts and Calculations, 1981, (with A. Edrei and R.S. Varga) Zeros of Sections of Power Series; editor (with R.S. Varga) Pade and Rational Approximation: Theory and Applications, 1977, (with R.K. Nagle) Fundamentals of Differential Equations, (with R.K. Nagle) Fundamentals of Differential Equations and Boundary Value Problems, 1993, (with D.S. Lubinsky) Strong Asymptotics for Extremal Polynomials Associated with Weights on R., 1988; editor-in-chief Constructive Approximation Jour., 1983—; editor Jour. Approximation Theory, 1990—; Cambridge Univ. Press, 1995—. Fulbright fellow, 1968-69, Guggenheim fellow, 1978; NSF grantee, 1970-72, 80—; Hon. prof. Zhejiang Normal U. Mem. Am. Math. Soc., Math. Assn. Am., Sigma Xi. Home: 11738 Lipsey Rd Tampa FL 33618-3620 Office: U South Fla Dept Math Tampa FL 33620

SAFFELS, DALE EMERSON, federal judge; b. Moline, Kans., Aug. 13, 1921; s. Edwin Clayton and Lillian May (Cook) S.; m. Margaret Elaine Nieman, Apr. 2, 1976; children by previous marriage: Suzanne Saffels Gravitt, Deborah Saffels Godowns, James B.; stepchildren: Lynda Cowger Harris, Christopher Cowger. AB, Emporia State U., 1947; JD cum laude, LLB cum laude, Washburn U., 1949. Bar: Kans. 1949. Pvt. practice law Garden City, Kans., 1949-71, Topeka, 1971-75, Wichita, Kans., 1975-79; U.S. dist. judge Dist. of Kans., Topeka, 1979—; county atty. Finney County, Kans., 1951-55; chmn. bd. Fed. Home Loan Bank Topeka, 1978-79; mem. Jud. Conf. Com. on Fin. Disclosure, 1993—. Bd. govs. Washburn U. Sch. Law, 1973-85; pres. Kans. Dem. Club, 1957; Dem. nominee for gov. of Kans., 1962; mem. Kans. Ho. of Reps., 1955-63, minority leader, 1961-63; mem. Kans. Corp. Commn., 1967-75, chmn., 1968-75; mem. Kans. Legis. Coun., 1957-63; Kans. rep. Interstate Oil Compact Commn., 1967-75, 1st vice chmn., 1971-72, Midwest Assn. Regulatory Commns., 1972-73, Midwest Assn. R.R. and Utilities Commrs., 1972-73; trustee Emporia State U. Endowment Assn.; bd. dirs. Nat. Assn. Regulatory Utility Commrs., 1972-75. Maj. Signal Corps, U.S. Army, 1942-46. Fellow Am. Bar Found., Kans. Bar Found.; mem. ABA, Kans. Bar Assn., Wichita Bar Assn., Am. Judicature Soc., Jud. Conf. Com. on Fin. Disclosure, Delta Theta Phi. Lutheran. Home: 2832 SW Plass Ave Topeka KS 66611-1630 Office: US Dist Ct 420 Federal Bldg 444 SE Quincy St Topeka KS 66683-3582

SAFFER, ALFRED, retired chemical company executive; b. N.Y.C., Dec. 3, 1918; s. Louis and Ruth (Mirkis) S.; m. Ruth Lillian Rudow, Jan. 31, 1942 (dec. Dec. 1983); children: Anita Carolyn Horowitz, Martin Kenneth; m. Doris Barbara Graubard, June 18, 1985. AB in Chemistry, NYU, 1939, MS in Chemistry, 1941, PhD, 1943. Research chemist Princeton (N.J.) U., 1943-46; sr. research assoc. Firestone Tire and Rubber Co., Akron, Ohio, 1946-48; dir. research Sci. Design Co., Inc., N.Y.C., 1948-57, v.p. mfg.; pres. Catalyst Devel. Corp., Little Ferry, N.J., 1957-69; exec. v.p. Halcon Internat., Inc., N.Y.C., 1963-69; vice chmn. ret. Halcon SD Group, Inc., N.Y.C., 1978-81; exec. v.p. Oxirane Corp, Princeton, 1969-76; pres. Oxirane Internat., Princeton, 1976-78; bd. dirs. Norwood Venture Co., N.Y.C. Contbr. articles to profl. jours.; patentee in field. Trustee Internat. Ctr. for Disabled, N.Y.C., 1978—; assoc. trustee North Shore U. Hosp., Manhasset, N.Y., 1981—; active instl. rev. bd. Boca Raton (Fla.) Community Hosp., 1992—. Fellow Am. Inst. Chemists (Chem. Pioneer award, 1982); mem. Nat. Acad. Engring., Am. Chem. Soc., Soc. Chem. Industry. Clubs: Glen Oaks (Old Westbury, N.Y.); Delaire Country (Delray Beach, Fla.). Avocation: golf. Home: 16629 Ironwood Dr Delray Beach FL 33445-7050

SAFFERMAN, ROBERT SAMUEL, microbiologist; b. Bronx, N.Y., Dec. 19, 1932; s. Irving and Rose (Schuler) S.; m. Jewel S. Reisman, June 7, 1958; children—Karen M., Sharon L., Steven I. B.S., Bklyn. Coll., 1955; Ph.D., Rutgers U., 1960. With USPHS, Cin., 1959-64; with Dept. Interior, Cin., 1964-70; with EPA, Cin., 1970—, chief virology sect. Environ. Monitoring and Support Lab., 1974-88, chief virology br. Environ. Monitoring Systems Lab., 1988-94, chief virology and parasitology br. Environ. Monitoring Systems Lab., 1994—; mem. Internat. Com. on Taxonomy of Viruses. Recipient Spl. Service award San. Engring. Ctr., USPHS, 1963; Gans medal Soc. Water Treatment and Examination, Eng., 1970; named Fed. Employee of Yr., Cin., 1974. Fellow Am. Acad. Microbiology; mem. AAAS, ASTM, Am. Soc. Microbiology, Phycological Soc. Am., Sigma Xi. Home: 1669 Locksley Dr Cincinnati OH 45230-2220 Office: 26 Martin Luther King Dr W Cincinnati OH 45268

SAFFIOTTI, UMBERTO, pathologist; b. Milan, Jan. 22, 1928; came to U.S., 1960, naturalized, 1966; s. Francesco Umberto and Maddalena (Valenzano) S.; m. Paola Amman, June 21, 1958; children: Luisa M., Maria Francesca. MD cum laude, U. Milan, 1951, splty. diploma occupational medicine cum laude, 1957. Intern Inst. Pathol. Anatomy U. Milan, 1951-52, asst. to chmn. occupational medicine, chief lab. pathology, Inst. Occupational Medicine, 1956-60, fellow Inst. Gen. Pathology, 1957-60; rsch. asst. oncology, rsch. assoc. Chgo. Med. Sch., 1952-55, from asst. prof. to prof. oncology, 1960-68; mem. staff Nat. Cancer Inst., NIH, Bethesda, Md., 1968—, assoc. dir. carcinogenesis, 1968-76, chief lab. exptl. pathology, 1974—, acting head Registry of Exptl. Cancers, 1988—; mem. pathology B study sect., NIH, 1964-68; mem. various adv. coms. govt. agys.; mem. cancer prevention com. Internat. Union Against Cancer, 1959-66, panel on carcinogenicity, 1963-66; chmn. ad hoc com. evaluation low levels environ. carcinogens HEW, 1969-70. Co-editor books; contbr. articles to profl. jours. Bd. dirs. Rachel Carson Trust, 1976-79. Recipient Career Devel. award NIH, 1965-68, Superior Svc. Honor award HEW, 1971, Pub. Interest Sci. award Environ. Def. Fund, 1977, Spl. Recognition award USPHS, 1980. Fellow NYAS; mem. AAAS, Am. Assn. Cancer Rsch. (pres. Chgo. chpt. 1966-67), Am. Soc. Investigative Pathology, Internat. Commn. Occupational Health, Soc. Occupational and Environ. Health (councillor 1972-76, v.p. 1976-78, pres. 1978-82), Soc. Toxicology, Sigma Xi. Democrat. Home: 5114 Wissioming Rd Bethesda MD 20816-2259 Office: NIH Nat Cancer Inst Lab Exptl Pathology Bldg 41 Bethesda MD 20892-0041

SAFFIR, HERBERT SEYMOUR, structural engineer, consultant; b. N.Y.C., Mar. 29, 1917; s. A.L. and Gertrude (Samuels) S.; m. Sarah Young, May 9, 1941; children: Richard Young, Barbara Joan. BS in Civil Engring. cum laude, Ga. Inst. Tech., 1940. Registered profl. engr., Fla., N.Y., Tex., P.R., Miss. Civil engr. TVA, Chattanooga, 1940, NACA, Langley Field,

Va., 1940-41; structural engr. Ebasco Services, N.Y.C., 1941-43, York & Sawyer & Fred Severud, N.Y.C., 1945; engr. Waddell & Hardesty, Cons. Engrs., N.Y.C., 1945-47; asst. county engr. Dade County, Miami, Fla., 1947-59; cons. engr. Herbert S. Saffir, Coral Gables, Fla., 1959—; adj. lectr. civil engring. Coll. Engring., U. Miami, 1964—; adviser civil engring. Fla. Internat. U., 1975-80; cons. on bldg. codes Govt. Bahamas; cons. on engring. in housing to UN; mem., chmn. Met. Dade County Unsafe Structures Bd., 1977-92; mem. Bldg. Code Evaluation Task Force after Hurricane Andrew; mem. Am. Nat. Stds. Inst. Commn. Bldg. Design Loads, Nat. Adv. Group on Glass Design, Dade County Bldg. Code Com. 1993—; mem. U. Miami/ Coral Gables Community Rels. Com., 1993—; cons. to govt. and industry, condr. seminars, Australia; reviewer for NSF; mem. bd. adjustment Coral Gables, 1994—. Author: Housing Construction in Hurricane Prone Areas, 1971, Nature and Extent of Damage by Hurricane Camille, 1972, Evaluation of Structural Damage Caused by Hurricanes, 1993; contbg. author: Wind Effects on Structures, 1976; editor: Wind Engr., 1986-92; contbr. articles to profl. jours.; designer Saffir/Simpson hurricane scale. With N.Y. Guard, 1942-43, AUS, 1943-44. Recipient Outstanding Service award Fla. Profl. Engrs., 1954, Pub. Service award Nat. Weather Service, 1975, Disting. Service award Nat. Hurricane Conf., 1987; named Miami Engr. of Year, 1978, 94, Gov.'s Design award, 1986, Gov. Gilchrist award for Profl. Excellence, 1988, Albert H. Friedman Community Svc. award, 1992. Fellow ASCE (past pres., sec., aerodynamics com. 1983—, mem. mitigation of wind damage com. 1985—, chmn. com. on damage investigation 1989—, mem. com. A7 on design loads for bldgs. 1972—), Fla. Engring. Soc. (award for outstanding tech. achievement 1973, Cmty. Svc. award 1980); mem. Soc. Am. Mil. Engrs., Am. Concrete Inst., ASTM (mem. com. performance bldg. constrn.), Prestressed Concrete Inst., Internat. Assn. for Bridge and Structural Engring., Colegio de Ingenieros P.R., Am. Meterol. Soc., Am. Arbitration Assn., Wind Engring. Rsch. Coun. (past bd. dirs., Svc. award 1990), Coral Gables C. of C. (bd. dirs., past pres., past chmn.), Tau Beta Pi, Chi Epsilon (hon.). Club: Country of Coral Gables. Home: 4818 Alhambra Cir Coral Gables FL 33146-1615 Office: 255 University Dr Ste 211 Coral Gables FL 33134-6733

SAFFIR, LEONARD, public relations executive; b. N.Y.C., Apr. 19, 1930; s. Abraham and Gertrude (Samuels) S.; m. Patricia Roemer (div. 1980); children: Andrew, Michelle; m. Wendy McConaughy (div. 1992); 1 child, Samantha. Student, Syracuse U., 1948-51. Editor, bur. chief Internat. News Service, Dallas, Tokyo, 1953-58; producer Eng., Australia, Asia, 1958-60; ptnr. Haft, Saffir, Siegel Polit. Pub. Relations & Advt., N.Y.C., 1960-64; cons. Ferdinand Marcos, 1964; pub. Latin Am. Times, N.Y.C., 1965; exec. v.p. Franchises Internat., N.Y.C.; chief of staff to Senator James Buckley U.S. Senate, Washington, 1970-76; pub., editor The Trib, N.Y.C., 1977-78, The Sun, Bridgehampton, N.Y., 1978-84; exec. v.p. Porter/Novelli, N.Y.C., 1984-90; pres. Jay DeBow & Ptnrs., 1990—. Chmn. Marchi for Mayor, N.Y.C., 1973, Buckley for Senator, N.Y., 1976. Served as sgt. USMC, 1951-53. Recipient Silver Anvil and Big Apple awards Pub. Rels. Soc. Am., Mayor's award City of N.Y., others. Mem. Overseas Press Club (pres. 1988-89).

SAFFMAN, PHILIP G., mathematician; b. Leeds, Eng., Mar. 19, 1931; s. Sam Ralph and Sarah (Rebecca) S.; m. Ruth Arion, Sept. 2, 1954; children—Louise J., Mark E., Emma E. B.A., Trinity Coll., Cambridge U., 1953; M.A., Cambridge U., 1956, Ph.D., 1956. Asst. lectr. applied math. Cambridge U., 1958-60; reader in applied math. Kings Coll., London U., 1960-64; prof. fluid mechanics Calif. Inst. Tech., Pasadena, 1964-69; prof. applied math. Calif. Inst. Tech., 1969-95, Theodore von Kármán prof. applied math. and aeros., 1995—. Contbr. articles to profl. jours. Trinity Coll. fellow, 1955-59. Fellow Am. Acad. Arts and Scis., Royal Soc. London. Office: 217-50 Firestone Calif Inst Tech Pasadena CA 91125

SAFFRAN, BERNARD, economist, educator; b. Bklyn., May 13, 1936; s. Isidore and Goldie (Bleeker) S.; m. Eleanor Meyerowitz, Aug. 24, 1959; children: Jenny, Linnea (dec.). B.A., CCNY, 1956; Ph.D., U. Minn., 1963. Asst. prof. econs. U. Calif.-Berkeley, 1961-67; assoc. prof. Swarthmore Coll., Pa., 1967-73, prof., 1973—, Franklin and Betty Barr prof. econs., 1989, chmn. dept. econs., 1976-83; sr. staff economist Coun. Econ. Advisors, Washington, 1971-72; vis. lectr. London Sch. Econs., 1979-80, CED Rsch. adv. bd., 1992—. Assoc. editor Jour. Econ. Perspectives, 1987—. Home: 201 Garrett Ave Swarthmore PA 19081-1433 Office: Swarthmore Coll Dept Econs Swarthmore PA 19081

SAFFRAN, KALMAN, engineering consulting company executive, entrepreneur; b. Boston, Dec. 28, 1947; s. Max and Marion (Patick) S. B.A., Northeastern U., 1971; postgrad. MIT, 1971-72. Lic. real estate broker, Mass. Mgr. systems MIT, 1972-76; corp. cons. United Brands Co., Boston, 1977-78; chief exec. officer Monitrex Corp., Boston, 1977-82; pres. Kalman Saffran Assocs., Inc., Newton, Mass., 1978—; bd. advisors Blackstone Bank and Trust Col, Boston; mem. network implementation panel U.S. Energy Research and Devel. Adminstrn., Washington, 1975-76; mem. computer com. MIT Lab. for Nuclear Sci., 1975-76. Mem. Data Processing Mgmt. Assn., Assn. Computing Machinery, Soc. for Info. Mgmt., IEEE, Mensa. Republican. Jewish. Home: 1564 Commonwealth Ave W Newton MA 02165-2806 Office: Kalman Saffran Assocs Inc 1841 Commonwealth Ave Newton MA 02166-2725

SAFFRAN, MURRAY, biochemist; b. Montreal, Oct. 30, 1924; s. Isidore Irving and Rebecca Reva (Elimelech) S.; m. Judith Cohen, June 8, 1947; children—Michael David, Wilma Anne, Arthur Martin, Richard Eli. B.Sc., McGill U., 1945, M.Sc., 1946, Ph.D., 1949. Mem. faculty depts. psychiatry and biochemistry McGill U., Montreal, 1948-69; prof. McGill U., 1966-69; prof. biochemistry Med. Coll. Ohio, Toledo, 1969—, chmn. dept., 1969-80, asst. dean Med. Edn., 1992—; Dozor vis. prof. biochemistry Ben Gurion U., Israel, 1981; vis. prof. Inst. Biochemistry, Armenian Acad. Scis., Yerevan, 1988, U. Autonom. Guadalajara, 1991—. Book rev. editor Trends in Endocrinology and Metabolism; mem. editl. bd. Biochem. Edn., Med. Biochemistry Question Bank, Drug Delivery, articles to profl. jours. Recipient Ayerst-Squibb award Endocrine Soc., 1968. Fellow AAAS, Ohio Acad. Sci.; mem. Am. Soc. Biochemistry and Molecular Biology, Endocrine Soc., Internat. Brain Rsch. Orgn., Alpha Omega Alpha. Home: 2331 Hempstead Rd Toledo OH 43606-2447 Office: Med Coll Ohio PO Box 10008 Toledo OH 43699-0008

SAFIAN, GAIL ROBYN, public relations executive; b. Bklyn., Dec. 12, 1947; d. Jack I. and Harriet S.; m. Jay Mark Eisenberg, Jan. 6, 1979; children: Julia, Eric. BA, SUNY, Albany, 1968; MBA, NYU, 1982. Reporter Albany (N.Y.)-Knickerbocker News/Times-Union, 1969, Athens (Ohio) Messenger, 1969-71; pub. relations asst. Mountainside Hosp., Montclair, N.J., 1971-74; dir. pub. relations Riverside Hosp., Boonton, N.J., 1974-78; consumer affairs coordinator Johnson & Johnson Personal Products Div., Milltown, N.J., 1978-79; v.p., group mgr. Harshe Rotman & Druck, N.Y.C., 1979-82; exec. v.p., dir. Health Care Div. Ruder Finn & Rotman, N.Y.C., 1982-84; v.p., mgr. client services Burson-Marsteller, N.Y.C., 1984-86; v.p., group mgr. health care Cohn & Wolfe, N.Y.C., 1986-90; exec. v.p., gen. mgr. MCS, Summit, N.J., 1990-94; pres. Safian Comm. Inc., Maplewood, N.J., 1994—. Mem. devel. com. Cancer Care, N.Y.C., 1985—. Recipient MacEachern award Am. Hosp. Assn., 1974, Communications Award Internat. Assn. Bus. Communicators, 1976, Creativity in Pub. Rels. award Inside PR, 1992, 93. Mem. N.Y. Acad. Scis., Drug Info. Assn., Women in Communications (Clarion award 1974), Healthcare Businesswomen's Assn. (mem. bd. dirs.). Jewish. Home: 31 Hickory Dr Maplewood NJ 07040-2107 Office: Safian Comm Inc 31 Hickory Dr Maplewood NJ 07040

SAFIAN, KEITH FRANKLIN, hospital administrator; b. Bklyn., June 22, 1950; s. Jack I. and Harriet S. (Cohen) S.; m. Ellen Rita Babat, May 18, 1974; children: Elizabeth Anne, Alexander William. BS in EE and Indsl. Engring., SUNY, Buffalo, 1972; MBA, U. Pa., 1974. Asst. dir. Kings County Hosp. Ctr., Bklyn., 1974-76; asst. adminstr. NYU Med. Ctr., N.Y.C., 1977-94, assoc. adminstr., 1981-84, sr. assoc. adminstr., 1984-85; adminstr. St. John's Episcopal Hosp., Far Rockaway, N.Y., 1985-89; pres., CEO Phelps Meml. Hosp. Ctr., North Tarrytown, N.Y., 1989—. Bd. dirs. Addabbo Family Health Ctr., Arverne, N.Y., 1987-89, Rockaway Devel. and Revitalization Corp., Far Rockaway, 1988-89, The ExcelCare Sys., Bronxville, N.Y., 1993—; vice chmn. No. Met. Hosp. Assn., Newburgh, N.Y., 1995—. Fellow Am. Coll. Healthcare Execs.; mem. Hosp. Adminstrs.

Club of N.Y. Home: 16 Brokaw Ln Great Neck NY 11023 Office: Phelps Memorial Hosp 701 N Broadway Tarrytown NY 10591

SAFIOL, GEORGE E., electronics company executive; b. Bklyn., Apr. 23, 1932; s. Charles and Effie (Patika) S.; m. Demetra Karambelas, July 12, 1958; children: Olympia Safiol Twomey, Peter, Christina. BS in Engring., NYU, 1954; postgrad. Sch. Engring., Columbia U., 1954-55. V.p., gen. mgr. No. Am. Telecom, ITT, Memphis, 1957-69; exec. v.p., chief operating officer Sycor, Inc., Ann Arbor, Mich., 1969-70; v.p. investments Heizer Co., Chgo., 1970-71; sr. v.p. Gen. Instrument Corp., Chicopee, Mass., 1971-77; pres., chief exec. officer Am. Biltrite, Framingham, Mass., 1977-83; various sr. exec. positions Gen. Instrument Corp., N.Y.C., 1984-87, chief operating offficer, pres., 1987—, also dir.; pvt. practice mgmt. cons., 1983-84. Served to 1st lt. U.S. Army, 1955-57. Mem. Alpha Omega. Republican. Greek Orthodox. Club: Metropolitan (N.Y.C.). Avocations: racquetball, golf, reading. Home: 64 Juniper Rd Weston MA 02193-1358 Office: Gen Instrument Corp 767 Fifth Ave New York NY 10153-0002

SAFIR, HOWARD, fire commissioner; b. N.Y.C., Feb. 24, 1942; s. George and Rose (Weiner) S.; m. Carol Ferrara, Nov. 21, 1965; children: Jennifer, Adam. BA in History and Polit. Sci., Hofstra U., 1963; postgrad., Bklyn. Law Sch., 1963-65; cert., Harvard U., 1988, 89. Spl. agent Fed. Bur. Narcotics; dep. chief spl. projects Bur. Narcotics and Dangerous Drugs, 1970-72; asst. regional dir. Drug Enforcement Administrn., 1972-74, spl. asst. for organized crime, 1974-75, chief spl. enforcement programs, 1975-76, dep. regional dir., 1976-77, asst. dir., 1977-79; chief witness security divsn. U.S. Marshals Svc., 1979-81, asst. dir. ops., 1979-84, assoc. dir. ops., 1984-90; pres. Safir Assocs. Ltd., 1990—; fire commr. N.Y.C. Fire Dept., 1994—; del. Interpol Gen. Assembly, 1981-88, Nat. Drug Policy Bd., 1986-88, Nat. Office Drug Policy; directed Warrant Apprehension Narcotic Team Program, 1989; dir. security Pres. Task Force on Victims of Crime, 1982; protected dir. security force fgn. delegations UN Gen. Assembly, 1979-89; nat. coord. Spl. Op. Mex. Nat. Heroin Interdiction Program, 1975, Spl. Op. SE Asia Interdiction Program, 1971; rep. Pres. Law Enforcement Com. Domestic Coun. Drug Abuse Task Force, 1975; mem. steering com. Nat. Conf. Organized Crime, 1975; dir. spl. investigations. Served USMCR, 1960-66. Mem. Internat. Assn. Chiefs of Police (chmn. N.Am. subcom., chmn. internat. adv. com. 1988-90 , Internat. Assn. Intelligence Analysts, Am. Soc. Indsl. Security, Pi Delta Epsilon. Office: Fire Dept 250 Livingston St Brooklyn NY 11201

SAFIRE, WILLIAM, journalist, author; b. N.Y.C., Dec. 17, 1929; s. Oliver C. and Ida (Panish) S.; m. Helene Belmar Julius, Dec. 16, 1962; children: Mark Lindsey, Annabel Victoria. Student, Syracuse U., 1947-49. Reporter N.Y. Herald Tribune Syndicate, 1949-51; corr. WNBC-WNBT, Europe and Middle East, 1951; radio-TV producer WNBC, N.Y.C., 1954-55; v.p. Tex McCrary, Inc., 1955-60; pres. Safire Pub. Relations, Inc., 1960-68; spl. asst. to Pres. Nixon, Washington, 1969-73; columnist N.Y. Times, Washington, 1973—. Author: The Relations Explosion, 1963, Plunging into Politics, 1964, Safire's Political Dictionary, 1968, rev. edit., 1972-78, Before the Fall, 1975, Full Disclosure, 1977, Safire's Washington, 1980, On Language, 1980, What's the Good Word?, 1982, (with Leonard Safir) Good Advice on Writing, 1982, I Stand Corrected, 1984, Take My Word for It, 1986, Freedom, 1987, You Could Look It Up, 1988, Words of Wisdom, 1989, (with Leonard Safir) Leadership, 1990, Language Maven Strikes Again, 1990, Fumblerules, 1990, Coming to Terms, 1991, The First Dissident, 1992, Lend Me Your Ears, 1992, Good Advice on Writing, 1992, Quoth the Maven, 1993, Safire's New Political Dictionary, 1993, In Love with Norma Loquendi, 1994. Served with AUS, 1952-54. Recipient Pulitzer prize for Disting. Commentary, 1978. Republican. Office: NY Times 1627 I St NW Washington DC 20006-4085

SAFLEY, JAMES ROBERT, lawyer; b. Cedar Rapids, Iowa, Sept. 19, 1943; s. Robert Starr and Jean (Engelman) S.; m. Dianne Lee McInnis; children: Anne Michele, Jamie Leigh. BA, U. Iowa, 1965; JD, Duke U., 1968. Bar: Minn. 1968, U.S. Ct. Appeals (4th, 6th, 8th and 9th cirs.), U.S. Supreme Ct. Law clk. U.S. Dist. Ct. Minn., Mpls., 1968-69; assoc. Robins, Kaplan, Miller & Ciresi, Mpls., 1969-74, ptnr., 1974—. Mem. adv. coun. Women's Intercollegiate Athletics, U. Minn., 1988-94. Mem. ABA, Minn. State Bar Assn. (antitrust sect. chmn. 1985-87), Hennepin County Bar Assn., Phi Beta Kappa. Office: Robins Kaplan Miller & Ciresi 2800 LaSalle Pla 800 Lasalle Ave Minneapolis MN 55402-2013

SAFONOV, MICHAEL GEORGE, electrical engineering educator, consultant; b. Pasadena, Calif., Nov. 1, 1948; s. George Michael and Ruth Garnet (Ware) S.; m. Nancy Kelshaw Schorn, Aug. 31, 1968 (div. Oct. 1983); 1 child, Alexander; m. Janet Sunderland, Feb. 25, 1985; 1 child, Peter. BSEE, MSEE, MIT, 1971, EE, 1976, PhDEE, 1977. Electronic engr. Air Force Cambridge Rsch. Lab., Hanscom AFB, Mass., 1968-71; rsch. asst. MIT, Cambridge, 1975-77; prof. elec. engring. U. So. Calif., L.A., 1977—, assoc. chmn. dept., 1989-93; vis. scholar Cambridge (Eng.) U., 1983-84, Imperial Coll., London, 1987, Calif. Inst. Tech., Pasadena, 1990-91; cons. Honeywell Systems and Rsch. Ctr., Mpls., 1978-83, Space Systems div. TRW, Redondo Beach, Calif., 1984, Northrop Aircraft, Hawthorne, Calif., 1985-91, also numerous others. Author: Stability and Robustness of Multivariable Feedback Systems (hon. mention Phi Beta Kappa 1981); co-author (book and software) Robust-Control Toolbox, 1988; assoc. editor IEEE Trans. on Automatic Control, 1985-87, Internat. Jour. Robust and Nonlinear Control, 1989-93. Lt. (j.g.) USNR, 1972-75. Rsch. grantee Air Force Office Sci. Rsch., 1978—, NSF, 1982-84. Fellow IEEE; mem. AIAA (sr.), Common Cause. Democrat. Office: U So Calif Dept EE-Systems MC-2563 3740 McClintock Ave EEB 310 Los Angeles CA 90089-2563 Consider first only the very simplest problem--but strive for a representation of the simplest problem that generalizes easily.

SAFRAN, CLAIRE, writer, editor; b. N.Y.C.; d. Simon and Flora (R) S.; m. John Milton Williams, June 8, 1958; 1 son, Scott Edward. B.A. in English cum laude, Bklyn. Coll., 1951. News editor Photo Dealer mag., 1951-53; assoc. editor TV Radio Mirror, 1954-58; mng. editor Photoplay mag., 1958-61; editor TV Radio Mirror, 1961-65, IN mag., 1965-67; assoc. editor Family Weekly mag., 1967-68; editor Coronet mag., 1968-71; contbg. editor Redbook, 1974-77; exec. editor, 1977-78, contbg. editor, 1979-81; roving editor Reader's Digest, 1983-88; contbg. editor Woman's Day, 1988-91. Author: New Ways to Lower Your Blood Pressure, 1984, Secret Exodus, 1987; contbr. to maj. nat. mags., 1972—. Recipient Media award Am. Psychol. Found., 1977; finalist Penney-Missouri Mag. Awards, 1977; Merit award in Journalism Religious Public Relations Council, 1978; honorable mention journalism awards Am. Acad. Pediatrics, 1979; 1st pl. nat. editorials Odyssey Inst. Media Awards, 1979, 80, 86; Matrix award Women in Communication, 1982, 83, 84; William Harvey award, 1984, 91; Journalism award Am. Acad. Family Physicians, 1984; Investigative Journalism citation Deadline Club, 1993. Mem. Am. Soc. Journalists and Authors (Outstanding Mag. Article award 1984). Home: 53 Evergreen Ave Westport CT 06880-2563

SAFRAN, EDWARD MYRON, financial service company executive; b. Boston, Oct. 9, 1937; s. Morris and Sophie (Radin) S.; m. Harriet Reva Podolsky, Jan. 15, 1966; children: Steven, Rebecca. BS in Math., MIT, 1959; MBA, Harvard U., 1961. Pres. Suncrest Corp., Worcester, Mass., 1962-65; exec. asst. Am. Metal Climax, N.Y.C., 1965; sr. auditor Gen. Electric Co., Lynn, Mass., 1966-68; fin. analyst Polaroid Corp., Cambridge, Mass., 1968-70; mgr. banking and investments, 1970-84, asst. treas., 1984-87; pres. Merganser Capital Mgmt. Corp., Cambridge, 1984—; chmn. Direct Fed. Credit Union, Needham, Mass., 1986—. Gleason Works fellow Harvard U., 1959-60. Mem. Fin. Execs. Inst., Bond Analysts Soc. of Boston. Home: 37 Barney Hill Rd Wayland MA 01778-3601 Office: Merganser Capital Mgmt Corp One Cambridge Ctr Cambridge MA 02142

SAGALKIN, SANFORD, lawyer; b. N.Y.C., June 24, 1942; s. Nathan and Blanche (Hoffner) S.; m. Monda E. Fifield, Aug. 25, 1969; children: Nicholas, Amy. BA, Queens Coll., 1964; LLB, Columbia U., 1967. Bar: N.Y. 1967, Alaska 1969, D.C. 1980, Md., 1986. Staff atty. N.Y. Mental Health Info. Service, N.Y.C., 1967-69; mem. firm Faulkner, Banfield, Doogan, Gross and Holmes, Juneau, Alaska, 1969-74; firm Ely, Guess & Rudd, Juneau, 1974-75; asst. atty. gen. Atty. Gen.'s Office, State of Alaska, 1975-77; dep. asst. atty. gen. Dept. Justice, Washington, 1977-80; mem. firm Ely, Guess & Rudd, Washington, 1980-82; pvt. practice Sharpsburg, Md.,

1982-86; assoc. gen. counsel CIA, Washington, 1986—. Mem. Juneau Parks and Recreation Com., 1972-74; bd. dirs. Defenders of Wildlife, 1986-90. Mem. Alaska Bar Assn., D.C. Bar Assn., Md. Bar Assn. Democrat. Jewish. Office: Cia Washington DC 20001

SAGAMI, KIM, dancer; b. Inglewood, Calif.. Scholarship student, The Joffrey Ballet Sch. Dancer Am. Ballet Theatre II, N.Y.C., 1981-82, Garden State Ballet, 1982, The Joffrey Ballet, N.Y.C., 1983—. Office: The Joffrey Ballet 130 W 56th St New York NY 10019-3818*

SAGAN, CARL EDWARD, astronomer, educator, author; b. N.Y.C., Nov. 9, 1934; s. Samuel and Rachel (Gruber) S.; m. Ann Druyan; children: Alexandra, Samuel; children by previous marriages: Dorion, Jeremy, Nicholas. AB with gen. and spl. honors, U. Chgo., 1954, BS, 1955, MS, 1956, PhD, 1960; ScD (hon.), Rensselaer Poly. Inst., 1975, Denison U., 1976, Clarkson Coll. Tech., 1977, Whittier Coll., 1978, Clark U., 1978, U. S.C., 1984, Hofstra U., 1985, L.I. U., 1987, Tuskegee U., 1988, Lehigh U., 1990, Wheaton Coll., 1993, SUNY, Albany, 1994; DHL (hon.), Skidmore Coll., 1976, Lewis and Clark Coll., 1980, Bklyn. Coll., CUNY, 1982; LLD (hon.), U. Wyo., 1978, Drexel U., 1986, Queens U., 1993; DScL (hon.), U. Ill., 1990; LHD (hon.), U. Hartford, 1991. Miller research fellow U. Calif.-Berkeley, 1960-62; vis. asst. prof. genetics Stanford Med. Sch., 1962-63; astrophysicist Smithsonian Astrophys. Obs., Cambridge, Mass., 1962-68; asst. prof. Harvard U., 1962-67; mem. faculty Cornell U., 1968—, prof. astronomy and space scis., 1970—, David Duncan prof., 1976—, dir. Lab. Planetary Studies, 1968—, assoc. dir. Center for Radiophysics and Space Research, 1972-81, Johnson Disting. lectr. Johnson Grad. Sch. Mgmt., 1985; pres. Carl Sagan Prodns. (Cosmos TV series), 1977—; nonresident fellow Robotics Inst., Carnegie-Mellon U., 1982—; NSF-Am. Astron. Soc. vis. prof. various colls., 1963-67, Condon lectr., Oreg., 1967-68; Holiday lectr. AAAS, 1970; Vanuxem lectr. Princeton U., 1973; Smith lectr. Dartmouth Coll., 1974, 77; Wagner lectr. U. Pa., 1975; Bronowski lectr. U. Toronto, 1975; Philips lectr. Haverford Coll., 1975; Disting. scholar Am. U., 1976; Danz lectr. U. Wash., 1976; Clark Meml. lectr. U. Tex., 1976; Stahl lectr. Bowdoin Coll., 1977; Christmas lectr. Royal Instn., London, 1977; Menninger Meml. lectr. Am. Psychiat. Assn., 1978, Adolf Meyer lectr., 1984; Carver Meml. lectr. Tuskegee Inst., 1981; Feinstone lectr. U.S. Mil. Acad., 1981; Pal lectr. Motion Picture Acad. Arts and Scis., 1982; Dodge lectr. U. Ariz., 1982; Disting. lectr. USAF Acad., 1983; Lowell lectr. Harvard U., 1984; Poynter fellow, Schultz lectr. Yale U., 1984; Disting. lectr. Fla. State U., 1984; Jack Disting. Am. lectr., Ind. U., Pa., 1984; Keystone lectr. Nat. War Coll., Nat. Def. U., Washington, 1984-86; Marshall lectr. Nat. Resources Def. Coun., Washington, 1985; Gifford lectr. in natural theology U. Glasgow, 1985; Lilenthal lectr. Calif. Acad. Sci., 1986; Dolan lectr. Am. Pub. Health Assn., 1986; von Braun lectr. U. Ala., Huntsville, 1987; Gilbert Grosvenor Centennial lectr. Nat. Geog. Soc., Washington, 1988; Murata lectr., Kyoto, Japan, 1989; Bart Bok Centennial lectr. Astron. Soc. of the Pacific, 1989, James R. Thompson Leadership lectr. Ill. Math. and Sci. Acad., 1991, Nehru Meml. lectr. New Delhi, 1991, Boyer lectr. Stanford U., 1993, Robert Resnick lectr. in physics Rensselaer Poly. Inst., 1993; other lectureships; mem. various adv. groups NASA and Nat. Acad. Scis., 1959—; mem. council Smithsonian Instn., 1975-80; vice chmn. working group moon and planets, space orgn. Internat. Council Sci. Unions, 1968-74; lectr. Apollo flight crews NASA, 1969-72; chmn. U.S. del. joint conf. U.S. Nat. and Soviet Acads. Sci. on Communication with Extraterrestrial Intelligence, 1971; responsible for Pioneer 10 and 11 and Voyager 1 and 2 interstellar messages; judge Nat. Book Awards, 1975; mem. fellowship panel Guggenheim Found., 1976—; disting. vis. scientist Jet Propulsion Lab., Calif. Inst. Tech., 1986—; researcher physics and chemistry of planetary atmospheres and surfaces, origin of life, exobiology, Mariner, Viking, Voyager amd Galileo spacecraft observations of planets, long-term consequences nuclear war. Author: Atmospheres of Mars and Venus, 1961, Planets, 1966, Intelligent Life in the Universe, 1966, Planetary Exploration, 1970, Mars and the Mind of Man, 1973, The Cosmic Connection, 1973, Other Worlds, 1975, The Dragons of Eden, 1977, Murmurs of Earth: The Voyager Interstellar Record, 1978, Broca's Brain, 1979, Cosmos, 1980, (novel) Contact, 1985, (with Ann Druyan) Comet, 1985, (with Richard Turco) Path Where No Man Thought: Nuclear Winter and the End of the Arms Race, (with Ann Druyan) Shadows of Forgotten Ancestors: A Search for Who We Are, 1993, Pale Blue Dot, 1994; also numerous articles; editor: Icarus: Internat. Jour. Solar System Studies, 1968-79, Planetary Atmospheres, 1971, Space Research, 1971, UFOs: A Scientific Debate, 1972, Communication with Extraterrestrial Intelligence, 1973; editorial bd.: Origins of Life, 1974-84, Icarus, 1962—, Climatic Change, 1976-90, Science 80, 1979-82. Mem. bd. advisors Children's Health Fund, N.Y.C., 1988—. Recipient Smith prize Harvard U., 1964, NASA medal for exceptional sci. achievement, 1972, Prix Galabert, 1973, John W. Campbell Meml. award, 1974, Klumpke-Roberts prize, 1974, Priestley award, 1975, NASA medal for disting. pub. service, 1977, 81, Pulitzer prize for lit., 1978, Washburn medal, 1978, Rittenhouse medal, 1980, Peabody award, 1981, Hugo award, 1981, Sakanaga prize, 1981, Roe medal, 1981, Environment Programme medal UN, 1984, SANE Nat. Peace award, 1984, Regents medal Bd. Regents Univ. of State N.Y., 1984, Ann. award Physicians for Social Responsibility, 1985, Disting. Svc. award World Peace Film Festival, 1985, Honda prize Honda Found., 1985, Nahum Goldmann medal World Jewish Congress, 1986, Ann. award of merit Am. Cons. Engrs. Coun., 1986, Maurice Eisendrath award Cen. Conf. Am. Rabbis and Union Am. Hebrew Congregations, 1987, In Praise of Reason award Com. for Sci. Investigation of Claims of the Paranormal, 1987, Konstantin Tsiolkovsky medal Soviet Cosmonautics Fedn., 1987, George F. Kennan Peace award SANE/Freeze, 1988, Roger Baldwin award Mass. Civil Liberties Union, 1989, Oersted medal Am. Assn. Physics Tchrs., 1990, Ann. award for Outstanding TV Script Writers Guild Am., 1991, UCLA medal UCLA, 1991, Disting. Leadership award Nuclear Age Peace Found., 1993, 1st Carl Sagan Pub. Understanding of Sci. award Coun. Sci. Soc. Pres., 1993, 1st Isaac Asimov award Com. Sci. Investigation of Claims of Paranormal, 1994, Public Welfare medal NAS, 1994; named Humanist of Yr. by Am. Humanist Assn., 1981; NSF fellow, 1955-60, Sloan research fellow, 1963-67. Fellow AAAS (chmn. astronomy sect. 1975, John Wesley Powell Meml. lectr. Tucson, 1992), AIAA, Am. Geophys. Union (pres. planetology sect. 1980-82), Am. Astronautical Soc. (council 1976-81, Kennedy award 1983), Brit. Interplanetary Soc., Explorers Club (75th Anniversary award 1980); hon. mem. NAS, mem. Am. Phys. Soc. (Leo Szilard award 1985), Am. Astron. Soc. (councillor, chmn. div. for planetary scis. 1975-76, Mazursky award 1991, Annenberg Found. prize 1993), Fedn. Am. Scientists (council 1977-81, bd. sponsors 1988—, Ann. award 1985), Am. Com. on East-West Accord, Soc. Study of Evolution, Genetics Soc. Am., Internat. Astron. Union, Internat. Acad. Astronautics, Internat. Soc. Study Origin of Life (council 1980—), Planetary Soc. (pres. 1979—), Authors Guild, Astron. Soc. of th ePacific, Asahi Shinbun, Coun. Fgn. Rels., Coun. Econ. Priorities, Am. Com. on U.S.-Soviet Rels., Phi Beta Kappa, Sigma Xi. Office: Cornell U Space Sci Bldg 302 CRSR Ithaca NY 14853

SAGAN, HANS, mathematician, educator, author; b. Vienna, Austria, Feb. 15, 1928; came to U.S., 1954, naturalized, 1960; s. Hans and Josefa (Seif) S.; m. Ingeborg Ulbrich, Mar. 20, 1954; 1 child, Ingrid. Ph.D. in Math., U. Vienna, 1950. Asst. prof. U. Tech., Vienna, 1950-54; asst. prof. Mont. State U., Bozeman, 1954-57; assoc. prof. U. Idaho, Moscow, 1957-61, prof., head dept., 1961-63; prof. N.C. State U., Raleigh, 1963-94, prof. emeritus, 1994—; vis. prof. U. Tech., Munich, 1964, U. Vienna, 1972, 95; vis. lectr. Math. Assn. Am., 1963-73, 77—; assoc. editor Math. Mag., 1963-73; mem. sci. adv. bd. Monatshefte für Mathematik, 1994—. Co-author: Die Laplace Transformation and Ihre Anwendung, 1953; author: Boundary and Eigenvalue Problems in Mathematical Physics, 1961, Integral and Differential Calculus-an Intuitive Approach, 1962, Introduction to the Calculus of Variations, 1969, Advanced Calculus, 1974, Beat the Odds, 1980, Calculus-Accompanied on the Apple, 1984, Space-Filling Curves, 1994; co-author: Ten Easy Pieces, 1980; also articles in field. Recipient Outstanding Faculty award U. Idaho, 1959-60; Poteat award N.C. Acad. Sci., 1966. Mem. Math. Assn. Am., AAUP, Oesterreichische Mathematische Gesellschaft, Sigma Xi. Avocations: swimming; sailing; horseback riding; fishing.

SAGAN, JOHN, former automobile company executive; b. Youngstown, Ohio, Mar. 9, 1921; s. John and Mary (Jubinsky) S.; m. Margaret Pickett, July 24, 1948; children: John, Linda, Scott. B.A. in Econs, Ohio Wesleyan U., 1948; M.A., U. Ill., 1949, Ph.D., 1951; Fellow, Ohio Wesleyan U., 1946-48; scholar, fellow research, U. Ill., 1948-51. Various positions Ford Motor Co., Dearborn, Mich., 1951-66; v.p.; treas. Ford Motor Co., 1966-86; pres.

John Sagan Assocs., Dearborn, 1986—; bd. dirs. Telident Corp., Chartwell Corp., Lemna Corp., SBCM Derivatives Products, Ltd. Trustee Ohio Wesleyan U., 1964—, Com. Econ. Devel. U.S.A., Oakwood Hosp., Dearborn, Mich., YMCA Found. Detroit Fund for Henry Ford Hosp. Served with USNR, 1943-46. Mem. Am. Econ. Assn., Phi Beta Kappa, Phi Kappa Phi, Delta Sigma Rho. Home and Office: 22149 Long Blvd Dearborn MI 48124-1104

SAGANSKY, JEFF, broadcast executive. BA, Harvard U., MBA. Fin. analyst CBS-TV, 1976-77; mgr. film programs NBC-TV, 1977, dir. dramatic devel. entertainment div., 1978, sr. v.p. series programming, 1983-85; v.p. devel. David Gerber Co., 1979-83; pres. prodn., then pres. Tri-Star Pictures Inc., 1985-90; pres. CBS Entertainment Divsn., 1990-94; exec. v.p. Sony U.S., 1994—. Office: Sony Corp of USA 10202 W Washington Blvd Culver City CA 90232*

SAGAWA, SHIRLEY SACHI, lawyer; b. Rochester, N.Y., Aug. 25, 1961; d. Hidetaka H. and Patricia (Ford) S.; m. Gregory A. Baer; children: Jackson Ford Baer, Matthew Sagawa Baer. AB, Smith Coll., 1983; MSc, London Sch. Econs., 1984; JD, Harvard U., 1987. Bar: Md. 1988. Chief counsel youth policy, labor and human resources com. U.S. Senate, Washington, 1987-91; sr. counsel and dir. family and youth policy Nat. Women's Law Ctr., Washington, 1991-93; spl. asst. to Pres. Clinton for domestic policy, 1993; exec. dir., mng. dir., exec. v.p. Corp. for Nat. and Cmty. Svc., Alexandria, 1993—. Mem. exec. bd. Orgn. for Pan-Asian Am. Women, Washington, 1987-89; mem. Women of Color Leadership Coun., 1991-92; vice chair, bd. dirs. Nat. Community Svc. Commn., 1991-93. Recipient Philip V. McGance award Coun. for Advancement of Citizenship, 1991, cert. of recognition Nat. Coun. Jewish Women, 1989; Harry S Truman scholar, 1981; Smith Coll. Alumnae Assn. fellow, 1983; AAUW fellow, 1986. Mem. Md. Bar Assn. Democrat. Episcopalian. Office: Corp for Nat and Community Svc 1201 New York Ave NW Washington DC 20525-0001

SAGAWA, YONEO, horticulturist, educator; b. Olaa, Hawaii, Oct. 11, 1926; s. Chikatada and Mume (Kuno) S.; m. Masayo Yamamoto, May 24, 1962 (dec. Apr. 1988); children: Penelope Toshiko, Irene Teruko. AB, Washington U., St. Louis, 1950, MS, 1952; PhD, U. Conn., 1956. Postdoctoral research assoc. biology Brookhaven Nat. Lab., Upton, N.Y., 1955-57; guest in biology Brookhaven Nat. Lab., 1958; asst. prof., then assoc. prof. U. Fla., 1957-64; dir. undergrad. sci. ednl. research participation program NSF, 1964; cons. biosatellite project NASA, 1966-67; prof. horticulture U. Hawaii, 1964—; dir. Lyon Arboretum, 1967-91; assoc. dir. Hawaiian Sci. Fair, 1966-67, dir., 1967-68; research assoc. in biology U. Calif., Berkeley, 1970-71; rsch. assoc. Bishop Mus., Honolulu, 1992—, Botanical Rsch. Inst. of Tex., 1993—; external assessor U. Pertanian, Malaysia, 1994—; mem. Internat. Orchid Commn. on Classification, Nomenclature and Registration; fellow Inst. voor Toepassing van Atoomengerie in de Landbouw, U. Agr., Wageningen, The Netherlands, 1979-80; mem. sci. adv. bd. Nat. Tropical Bot. Garden, 1975—; councilor Las Cruces Bot. Garden, Costa Rica; cons. FAO, Singapore, 1971, U.S. AID-ASAP, 1993, VOCA, 1993, 94, UNDP-UNISTAR, 1993; dir. Hawaii Tropical Bot. Garden. Editor: Lindleyana 1995—, Hawaii Orchid Jour., 1972—, Pacific Orchid Soc. Bull, 1966-71; editorial bd.; Allertonia, 1976; contbr. numerous articles to profl. jours. Trustee Friends of Foster Garden, 1973—. With AUS, 1945-47. Recipient Disting. Svc. award South Fla. Orchid Soc., 1968; grantee Am. Orchid Soc., AEC, NIH, HEW, IMS, Stanley Smith Hort. Trust, Honolulu Orchid Soc. Fellow Am. Orchid Soc. (hon. life); mem. AAAS, Internat. Assn. Hort. Sci., Am. Assn. Hort. Sci., Am. Inst. for Biol. Scis., Bot. Soc. Am., Hawn Bot. Soc. (past v.p.), Internat. Plant Tissue Culture, Internat. Palm Soc., Am. Anthurium Soc. (hon., life), Pacific Orchid Soc. (trustee 1994), Kaimuki Orchid Soc. (hon., life), Honolulu Orchid Soc. (hon., life), Lyon Arboretum Assn. (trustee 1974-91), Garden Club Honolulu (hon., life), Aloha Bonsai Club, Sigma Xi, Gamma Sigma Delta, Phi Kappa Phi (past pres., v.p., councillor Va. chpt.). Democrat. Office: U Hawaii Horticulture Rm 102 3190 Maile Way Honolulu HI 96822-2232

SAGE, ANDREW GREGG CURTIN, II, corporate investor, manager; b. Bryn Mawr, Pa., Mar. 11, 1926; s. Henry W. and Eleanor (Purviance) S.; m. Sara Wakefield, Sept. 29, 1956; children: Andrew Gregg Curtin III, Sally. Mem. staff DeCoppet & Doremus (odd lot stock house), N.Y.C., 1946-47, Sage & Co., N.Y. Stock Exchange Specialists, N.Y.C., 1947-48; assoc. Lehman Bros., N.Y.C., 1948-60; gen. partner Lehman Bros., 1960-68, pres., 1970-73, vice chmn., 1973-77, mng. dir., 1977-82; mng. dir. Lehman Bros. Kuhn Loeb, Inc., 1977-82; mng. dir. Shearson Lehman Bros., Inc., 1982-87, sr. cons., 1987-90; pres., dir. Robertson CECO Corp., Boston, 1992-93, chmn. bd. dirs., 1994—; bd. dirs. Fluid Conditioning Products, Lititz, Pa., Pettibone Corp., Heico, Inc., Tom's Foods, Computervision Corp.; pres., treas. Sage Land Devel. Co.; pres., dir. Sage Capital Corp. Served with USAAF, 1944-46. Home: PO Box 455 Wilson WY 83014

SAGE, ANDREW PATRICK, JR., systems information and software engineering educator; b. Charleston, S.C., Aug. 27, 1933; s. Andrew Patrick and Pearl Louise (Britt) S.; m. LaVerne Galhouse, Mar. 3, 1962; children: Theresa Annette, Karen Margaret, Philip Andrew. BS in Elec. Engring. The Citadel, 1955; SM, MIT, 1956; PhD, Purdue U., 1960; DEng (hon.), U. Waterloo, Can., 1987. Registered profl. engr. Tex. Instr. elec. engring. Purdue U., 1956-60; assoc. prof. U. Ariz., 1960-63; mem. tech. staff Aerospace Corp., Los Angeles, 1963-64; prof. elec. engring. and nuclear engring. scis. U. Fla., 1964-67; prof., dir. Info. and Control Scis. Center, So. Methodist U., Dallas, 1967-74; head elec. engring. dept. So. Meth. U., 1973-74; Quarles prof. engring. sci. and systems U. Va., Charlottesville, 1974-84; chmn. dept. chem. engring. U. Va., 1974-75, chmn. dept. engring. sci. and systems, 1977-84, assoc. dean, 1974-80; First Am. Bank prof. info. tech. George Mason U., Fairfax, Va., 1984—, assoc. v.p. for acad. affairs, 1984-85; dean Sch. Info. Tech. and Engring. George Mason U., 1985—; cons. Martin Marietta, Collins Radio, Atlantic Richfield, Tex. Instruments, LTV Aerospace, Battelle Meml. Inst., TRW Sys., NSF, Inst. Def. Analyses, Planning Rsch. Corp., MITRE, Engring. Rsch. Assocs., Software Productivity Consortium; gen. chmn. Internat. Conf. on Sys., Man and Cybernetics, 1974, 87; mem. spl. program panel on sys. sci. NATO, 1981-82; trustee, cons. Ctr. Naval Analysis, 1990-94. Author: Optimum Systems Control, 1968, 2d edit., 1977, Estimation Theory with Applications to Communications and Control, 1971, System Identification, 1971, An Introduction to Probability and Stochastic Processes, 1973, Methodology for Large Scale Systems, 1977, Systems Engineering: Methodology and Applications, 1977, Linear Systems Control, 1978, Economic Systems Analysis, 1983, System Design for Human Interaction, 1987, Information Processing in Systems and Organizations, 1990, Introduction to Computer Systems Analysis, Design, and Applications, 1989, Software Systems Engineering, 1990, Decision Support Systems Engineering, 1991, Systems Engineering, 1992, Systems Management for Information Technology and Software Engineering, 1995; assoc. editor IEEE Transactions on Systems Sci. and Cybernetics, 1968-72; editor: IEEE Transactions on Systems, Man and Cybernetics, 1972—; assoc. editor: Automatica, 1968-81; editor, 1981—; mem. editl. bd. Systems Engring. 1968-72, IEEE Spectrum, 1972-73, Computers and Elec. Engring., 1972-94, Jour. Interdisciplinary Modeling and Simulation, 1976-80, Internat. Jour. Intelligent Sys., 1986—, Orgn. Sci.-94, 1990; editor Elsevier North Holland textbook series in sys. sci. and engring., 1970-88, John Wiley textbook series on sys. engring., 1989—; co-editor-in-chief Jour. Large Scale Sys.: Theory and Applications, 1978-88, Info. and Decision Technologies, 1988-94, Info. and Sys. Engring., 1995—; contbr. articles on computer sci. and sys. engring. to profl. jours. Recipient Norbert Wiener award, 1980, Joseph G. Wohl career award, 1991, Superior Pub. svc. award Sec. of Navy, 1994; Case Centennial scholar, 1980. Fellow IEEE (M. Barry Carlton award 1970, Centennial medal 1984, Outstanding Contbn. award 1986, Donald G. Fink prize 1994), AAAS (chmn. sect. M 1990), IEEE Sys. Soc.; mem. Man and Cybernetics Soc. (pres. 1984-85, Inst. Mgmt. Scis., Internat. Fedn. Automatic Control (Outstanding Svc. award), Am. Soc. Engring. Edn. (Frederick Emmonds Terman award 1970, Centennial cert. for exceptional contbn. 1993), Ops. Rsch. Soc. Am., Sigma Xi, Eta Kappa Nu, Tau Beta Pi. Home: 8011 Woodland Hills Ln Fairfax VA 22039-2433 Office: George Mason U Sch Info Tech Fairfax VA 22030-4444

SAGE, GORDON, metal products executive. With Indal. Inc., Norcross, Ga., 1992—. Office: Indal Inc 4350 Peachtree Industrial Blvd Norcross GA 30071-1647

SAGE, LOUIS E., environmental science executive. BA, U. Vt., 1964, MA in Limnology, 1969; PhD in Marine Ecology, Lehigh U., 1974. Instr. comparative vertebrate anatomy Cedar Crest Coll., Allentown, Pa., 1971-72; dir. Benedict (Md.) Estuarine Rsch. Lab., 1973-81; rsch. curator Acad. Natural Scis. Phila., 1972-81, v.p., dir. divsn. environ. rsch., 1981—; adj. asst. prof. marine ecology Temple U., Phila., 1978-79; mem. exec. com. Md. Coastal Zone Adv. Com., 1977-83; chmn. Environ. Comm., Calvert County, Md., 1978-81, vice chmn., 1977-78, active, 1976-81, Muddy Run Wildlife Mgmt. Com., 1983-84; mem. adv. com. and subcoms. Chesapeake Bay Sci. and Tech. Adv. Com., 1984—; active Patuxent River Tech. Adv. Group, 1978-81, Chesapeake Bay Monitoring Adv. Commn., 1983-88. Contbr. articles to profl. jours. Bd. dirs. Alliance for Chesapeake Bay, 1992—, also pres., v.p. for Pa., Darby Creek Watershed Assn., 1987—; Water Resources Assn. of Del. River Basin, 1984—; active Earth Day 20 Com., 1988—. Mem. AAAS, ASTM, Am. Soc. Limnology and Oceanography, Atlantic Estuarine Rsch. Soc., Water Pollution Control Fedn., Sigma Xi. Office: Acad of Natural Scis 1900 Benjamin Franklin Pky Philadelphia PA 19103-1195*

SAGER, CAROLE BAYER, lyricist, singer; b. N.Y.C., Mar. 8, 1947; d. Elias and Anita (Nathan) Bayer; m. Burt Bacharach, 1982 (div.); 1 son, Cristopher Elton. B.S. in Speech and Dramatic Art, N.Y. U., 1967. Lyricist numerous songs including Midnight Blue, A Groovy Kind of Love, Don't Cry Out Loud, You're Moving Out Today, Nobody Does It Better, When I Need You, Come In From the Rain, I'm Coming Home Again, I'd Rather Leave While I'm In Love, Heartbreaker, You're the Only One, If You Remember Me, 1979, It's My Turn, 1981, Arthur's Theme (Best that You Can Do) (Academy award 1982) That's What Friends Are For, 1986 (Grammy award 1987; recorded by Dionne Warwick, Elton John, Stevie Wonder, Gladys Knight), On My Own (Patti La Belle and Michael Mac Donald), Love Power, (Dionne Warwick and Jeffrey Osborne), Heartlight (Neil Diamond); Love is My Decision (Chris De Burgh), The Day I Fall in Love (from Beethoven's 2nd, 1993, Academy award nominee, Best Original Song, 1993); lyricist in collaboration with Marvin Hamlisch (Broadway play) They're Playing Our Song, 1979, Dancin', 1978; also movies The Spy Who Loved Me, 1977, Ice Castles, 1979, Arthur, 1981, Continental Divide, 1981, The Devil and Max Devlin, 1981, I Ought to Be in Pictures, 1982, Night Shift, 1982, Making Love, 1983, Tough Guys, 1986, Baby Boom, 1987, Three Men and A Baby, 1987, Arthur 2: On the Rocks, 1988; rec. artist, 1977—; albums include: Carole Bayer Sager, 1977, Carole Bayer Sager, Too, 1979, Carole Bayer Sager/Sometimes Late at Night, 1981 (Voted Best New Artist in France and Germany, German Record Acad. 1977); collaborated with numerous composers including Peter Allen, Marvin Hamlisch, Alice Cooper, Mike MacDonald, Melissa Manchester, Bette Midler, Bruce Roberts, Neil Sedaka, Burt Bacharach; author: (novel) Extravagant Gestures, 1986. Recipient Academy award for best song (Arthur's Theme), 1982; Acad. award nom. Best Original Song ("Look What Love Has Done" from Junior, 1994); Grammy award for song of the yr., (That's What Friends Are For), 1986. Office: care Guttman & Pam 118 S Beverly Dr Ste 201 Beverly Hills CA 90212-3016*

SAGER, CLIFFORD J(ULIUS), psychiatrist, educator; b. N.Y.C.; s. Max and Lena (Lipman) S.; m. Anne Scheinman; children by previous marriage: Barbara L., Philip T., Rebecca J., Anthony F. B.S., Pa. State U., 1937; M.D., N.Y. U., 1941; cert. in psychoanalysis, N.Y. Med. Coll., 1949. Diplomate: Am. Bd. Psychiatry and Neurology. Rotating intern Montefiore Hosp., N.Y.C., 1941-42; resident fellow Bellevue Hosp., N.Y.C., 1942, 46-48; practice medicine specializing in psychiatry N.Y.C., 1946—; dir. therapeutic services, assoc. dean Postgrad. Ctr. Mental Health, 1948-60; vis. psychiatrist, med. bd. Flower and Fifth Ave Hosp., 1960-71, Met. Hosp., 1960-71; dir. psychiat. tng. and edn. N.Y. Med. Coll., 1960-61; attending psychiatrist Bird S. Coler Hosp., 1960-71; clin. dir. N.Y. Med. Coll., 1960-63, assoc. prof. psychiatry, 1960-65, prof., 1966-71, dir. partial hosp. programs and family treatment and study unit, 1964-71; clin. prof. psychiatry Mt. Sinai Sch. Medicine, 1971-80; assoc. dir. psychiatry Beth Israel Hosp. for Family and Mental Therapy; chief of psychiatry Gov.'s Hosp., 1970-74; dir. family therapy Mt. Sinai Sch. Medicine, 1974-80; clin. prof. psychiatry N.Y. Hosp.-Cornell Univ. Med. Ctr., 1980—; attending psychiatrist N.Y. Hosp.-Payne Whitney Clinic, 1980—; dir. marital and family clinic N.Y. Hosp., 1991—; attending psychiatrist Mt. Sinai Hosp., 1971-80; chief behavioral scis. Gouvernour Hosp.; chief family treatment unit Beth Israel Med Ctr., 1970-74, assoc. dir. psychiatry family and group therapy, 1971-74; psychiat. dir. Jewish Family Svc., 1974-77; dir. family psychiatry Jewish Bd. Family and Children's Svcs., 1978-90; dir. Remarried Consultation Svc., 1976-90; dir. Tng. and Sex Therapy Clinic, 1974-90; founder The Relationship Inst., N.Y.C., 1990—; psychiat. dir. Employee Consultation and Corp. Health Programs, JBFCS, 1980—; faculty, supr. Contemporary Ctr. Advanced Psychoanalytic Studies, 1990—; chief neuropsychiatry 42d and 312th Gen. Hosp. Author: Marriage Contracts and Couple Therapy, 1976, Intimate Partners, 1979, Treating the Remarried Family, 1983; 4 other books; mem. editorial bd. Am. Jour. Orthopsychiatry, 1960-69, Internat. Jour. Group Psychotherapy, 1968—, Family Process, 1969-92, Divorce and Remarriage, 1977—, Comprehensive Rev. Jour. Family and Marriage, 1978—; cons. Sexual Medicine, 1974-82; co-editor, founder Jour. Sex and Marital Therapy, 1974—; mem. editorial bd.: Jour. Marriage and Family Counseling, 1977—, Internat. Jour. Family Counseling, 1977—; author or contbr. over 88 sci. articles to jours. Capt. M.C. AUS, 1942-46, chief neuropsychiatry 42d and 312th Gen. Hosp. Recipient Am. Family Therapy Assn. award for Outstanding Contribution to Family Therapy 1983, Marriage and Family Therapists award for Outstanding Contributions to the field of Marital and Family Therapy, 1984. Fellow Am. Psychiat. Assn. (life), Am. Orthopsychiat. Assn. (life), Acad. Psychoanalysis (charter), Am. Group Psychotherapy Assn. (pres. 1968-70, dir. 1962-74), Soc. Med. Psychoanalysts (pres. 1960-61, dir. 1958-62), Am. Assn. Marital and Family Therapists; mem. AMA, Am. Soc. Advancement of Psychotherapy (dir. 1954-67), N.Y. Soc. Clin. Psychiatry, Soc. for Sex Therapy and Rsch. (N.Y.C. pres. 1976-77, bd. dirs. 1953-58), PAIRS Found. (bd. dirs. 1985—). Office: 65 E 76th St New York NY 10021-1844 also: 33 Breeze Hill Rd East Hampton NY 11937-4505

SAGER, DONALD JACK, publisher, former librarian; b. Milw., Mar. 3, 1938; s. Alfred Herman and Sophia (Sagan) S.; m. Sarah Ann Long, May 23, 1987; children: Geoffrey, Andrew. B.S., U. Wis., Milw., 1963; M.S. in L.S, U. Wis., Madison, 1964. Sr. documentalist AC Electronics divsn. GM, Milw., 1958-63; teaching asst. U. Wis., Madison, 1963-64; dir. Kingston (N.Y.) Pub. Libr., 1964-66, Elyria (Ohio) Pub. Libr., 1966-71, Mobile Pub. Libr., 1971-75, Pub. Libr. Columbus and Franklin County, Ohio, 1975-78; commr. Chgo. Pub. Libr., 1978-81; dir. Elmhurst Pub. Libr., Ill., 1982-83, Milw. Pub. Libr., 1983-91; pub. Highsmith Press, Ft. Atkinson, Wis., 1991—; sec. Online Computer Libr. Ctr., 1977-78, disting. vis. scholar, 1982; chmn. feasibility com. PLA Pub. Libr. Mus., 1989-91, mem. investment com., 1985-89, mem. PLA nat. conf. com., 1986-88; bd. dirs. Coun. Wis. Librs., 1982-91; bd. dirs. Urban Librs. Coun., 1985-93, sec., 1991-93; adj. faculty U. Wis.-Milw., 1984-91; cons. in field. Author: Reference: A Programmed Instruction, 1970, Binders, Books and Budgets, 1971, Participatory Management, 1981, The American Public Library, 1982, Public Library Administrators Planning Guide to Automation, 1983, Managing the Public Library, 1984, 2d rev. edit., 1989, Small Libraries, 1992; co-editor: Urban Library Management Trends, 1989; contbg. editor: Public Libraries, 1990—; contbr. articles to profls. publs. Bd. dirs. Goethe House, 1985-91; pres. Milw. Civic Alliance, 1990-91; chmn. Milw. United Way Campaign, 1984; pres. Milw. Westown Assn., 1987-90. With inf. AUS, 1956-58. Mem. ALA, Pub. Libr. Assn. (dir., v.p., pres.-elect, pres. 1982-83), Chgo. Libr. Club, Libr. Info. and Tech. Assn., Libr. Administrn. and Mgmt. Assn., Wis. Libr. Assn., Wis. Libr. Assn. Found. (chmn. 1986-88), Libr. Administrn. Assn. of Wis. (chmn. 1987-88), Early Music Soc. (treas. 1987-88), Ench. Club of Milw. (pres. 1988-89). Home: 1050 Brookside Ln Deerfield IL 60015-4206 Office: Highsmith Press 5527W Highway 106 Fort Atkinson WI 53538

SAGER, JOHN WILLIAM, lawyer; b. N.Y.C., Aug. 27, 1946; s. Edward Leroy and Germaine (Smith) S.; m. Gail Ann Hill, June 9, 1988; children: Michelle, James, Jennifer. BA, Beloit Coll., 1968; JD, Syracuse U., 1971.

Bar: Ohio 1971. Ptnr. Jones, Day, Reavis & Pogue, Cleve., 1971—. Office: Jones Days Reavis & Pogue 901 Lakeside Ave E Cleveland OH 44114-1116

SAGER, LAWRENCE GENE, law educator; b. 1941. AB, Pomona Coll., 1963; LLB, Columbia Coll., 1966. Bar: Calif. 1967. From asst. prof. to prof. law NYU, N.Y.C., 1966—; vis. prof. law and social planning Woodrow Wilson Sch., Princeton, 1974-76; vis. prof. Harvard U., spring 1981, Boston U., 1986-89. Mem. N.Y. CLU. Office: NYU Sch Law 40 Washington Sq S New York NY 10012-1099

SAGER, RODERICK COOPER, retired life insurance company executive; b. Washington, May 25, 1923; s. Theron Parker and Rebecca (Ward) S.; m. Ruth Regina Ross, Sept. 2, 1947; children: Lawrence Cooper, Jonathan Ward, Timothy Charles. A.B., Syracuse U., 1948, J.D., 1950. Bar: N.Y. 1951, U.S. Supreme Ct. 1958; C.L.U., 1969; chartered fin. cons. Assoc. Mackenzie, Smith, Lewis, Michell and Hughes, Syracuse, 1950-62; gen. counsel Farmers and Traders Life Ins. Co., Syracuse, 1962-66, v.p., gen. counsel, 1966-69, sr. v.p., gen. counsel, 1969-74, exec. v.p., gen. counsel, 1974-79, pres., chief exec. officer, 1979-89, also bd. dirs., ret., 1989; chmn. Life Ins. Council, N.Y., 1984. Trustee Jamesville-DeWitt Cen. Sch. Dist., 1956-69, Onondaga Community Coll., 1971-75; bd. dirs. N.Y. State Tchrs. Retirement System, 1977-92, Onondaga Indsl. Devel. Corp., 1984-89, Lit. Vols. of Greater Syracuse, Inc., 1990-91; trustee Rescue Mission Alliance, Syracuse, 1980—, pres., 1985-86. 1st lt. U.S. Army, 1943-46, 51-52. Mem. Onondaga County Bar Assn., Assn. Life Ins. Counsel, CLU Central N.Y. (pres. 1974-75). Clubs: Century (Syracuse); Onondaga Golf and Country (Fayetteville, N.Y.). Lodge: Rotary. Home: 3 Wynnridge Rd Fayetteville NY 13066-2532

SAGER, RUTH, geneticist; b. Chgo., Feb. 7, 1918; married, 1973. BS, U. Chgo., 1938; MS, Rutgers U., 1944; PhD, Columbia U., 1948. Merck fellow Nat. Research Council, 1949-51; asst. in biochemistry Rockefeller Inst., 1951-55; research assoc. in zoology Columbia U., N.Y.C., 1955-60, sr. research assoc. in zoology, 1961-65; prof. biology Hunter Coll., CUNY, 1966-75; prof. cellular genetics Harvard Med. Sch., 1975-88, prof. emeritus, 1988—; chief cancer genetics div. Dana-Farber Cancer Inst., from 1975; mem. sci. adv. bd. Friedrich Miescher Inst., Basle, 1990—; mem. coun. Nat. Inst. Aging NIH, 1993—. Author: (with F.J. Ryan) Cell Heredity, 1961, Cytoplasmic Genes and Organelles, 1972. Recipient Gilbert Morgan Smith medal Nat. Acad. Scis., 1988, Alumni medal U. Chgo. Alumni Assn., 1994; Guggenheim fellow, 1972-73. Fellow AAAS; mem. Am. Acad. Arts and Sci., Nat. Acad. Scis., Inst. of Medicine, Am. Soc. Cell Biologists, Genetics Soc. Am., Am. Assn. Cancer Rsch., Am. Soc. Biol. Chem., Sigma Xi, Phi Beta Kappa. Office: Dana-Farber Cancer Inst 44 Binney St Boston MA 02115-6084

SAGER, WILLIAM F., retired chemistry educator; b. Glencoe, Ill., Jan. 22, 1918; s. Fred Anson and Alta (Stansbury) S.; m. Marilyn Olga Williams, Dec. 26, 1941; children: Karen Louise Sager Dickinson, Judith Lynn SagerPeyton, Kathryn Gwen Sager Potts. B.S. in Chemistry, George Washington U., 1939, M.A. in Organic Chemistry, 1941; Ph.D. in Organic Chemistry, Harvard U., 1948. Research chemist The Texas Co., 1941-45; prof. chemistry George Washington U., 1948-60; prof. chemistry U. Ill.-Chgo., 1965-86, prof. emeritus, 1986—, chmn., 1965-80; cons. to govt. and industry, 1952—. Recipient Disting. Service award U. Ill. Alumni Assn.; Guggenheim fellow, 1954-55. Mem. Am. Chem. Soc., Sigma Xi, Alpha Chi Sigma. Home: 1552 John Anderson Dr Ormond Beach FL 32176-3567 Office: Dept Chemistry U Ill-Chicago Chicago IL 60680

SAGERHOLM, JAMES ALVIN, retired naval officer; b. Uniontown, Pa., Dec. 23, 1927; s. Frithiof Norris and Margaret Blocher S.; m. Margaret Ann Herrlich, June 7, 1952; children—Lisa Marie, Ann Denise, Jeannine Louise, Mark Christian. B.S., U.S. Naval Acad., 1952. Commd. ensign U.S. Navy, 1952, advanced through grades to vice admiral, navigator USS Seadragon, 1965, exec. officer blue crew USS Mariano G. Vallejo, 1966-67, commanding officer gold crew USS Kamehameha, 1968-71, head gen. purpose warfare forces group Office of Chief Naval Ops., 1971, dep. exec. dir. Chief Naval Ops. Exec. Panel, 1972, exec. sec. Chief Naval Ops. Exec. Bd., 1973; comdr. Naval Intelligence Support Ctr. U.S. Navy, Washington, 1974-75; dep. dir. naval intelligence Chief Naval Ops. U.S. Navy, 1975-76, comdr. South Atlantic Force, U.S. Atlantic Fleet, 1976-78, dir. Office of Program Appraisal, Office of Sec. Navy, 1978-81; chief naval edn. and tng. U.S. Navy, Pensacola, Fla., 1983-85; exec. dir. Pres. Fgn. Intelligence Adv. Bd. White House, Washington, 1981-85, ret., 1985; chmn. bd. dirs. Piedmont Environ. Coun., 1987-89; v.p. for nat. affairs Gen. George C. Marshall Home Found., 1990-91. Decorated D.S.M., Legion of Merit, Meritorious Service medal. Mem. Naval Submarine League, U.S. Naval Inst., Civil War Soc., K.C. Roman Catholic. Avocations: golf; tennis; Civil War enthusiast. Home: 414 Rockfleet Rd Unit 102 Mays Chapel MD 21093-7458

SAGET, BOB, actor, comedian. Grad. film studies, Temple U., 1978. Stand-up comedian clubs around country; has performed at Carnegie Hall, also Las Vegas, Lake Tahoe, Atlantic City; did stand-up at The Comedy Store, The Improv, Calif.; actor (film) Critical Condition, 1986, (series) Full House, ABC-TV, 1986-94; co-host The Morning Program, CBS-TV, 1986; host, writer: America's Funniest HomeVideos, ABC-TV, 1989—; dir., writer: HBO Comedy Hour: In The Dream State. Address: care Vin Di Bona Prodns 4151 Prospect Ave Los Angeles CA 90027-4524*

SAGETT, JAN JEFFREY, lawyer, former government official; b. Chgo., Dec. 12, 1943; s. Leonard Henry and Carolyn (Zilberman) S.; BS with honors, U. Ill.-Urbana, 1965; JD, U. Chgo., 1968. Bar: Ill. 1969, D.C. 1969, U.S. Supreme Ct. 1972; CPA, Ill. Assoc., McDermott, Will, and Emery, Chgo., 1968-69; spl. asst. to dir. Office of Minority Bus. Enterprise, Washington, 1969; spl. counsel, asst. gen. counsel Office Econ. Opportunity, Washington, 1969-73; legis. counsel Small Bus. Adminstrn., Washington, 1973-74; dep. assoc. commr., legal counsel Social Security Adminstrn., Washington, 1974-81; asst. assoc. counsel, asst. treas. Edison Electric Inst., Washington, 1981-94; v.p. First Nat. Bank Md., Balt., 1995—; treas., mem. exec. com., bd. dirs., chmn. audit com. U.S. Energy Assn., 1991-93; mem. bd. dirs Dreyfus Edison Electric Index Fund, 1992-94, mem. industry adv. bd., 1991-94. Contbg. author: Federal Regulatory Process: Agency Practices and Procedures, 1981-84. Ill. State scholar, 1961-65; selected for Sr. Mgrs. in Govt. program Harvard U., 1978. Mem. ABA (taxation sect., employee benefits com., regulated pub. utilities com., legis. and regulations subcom.), Washington Met. Area Corp. Counsel Assn., Am. Corp. Counsel Assn., Beta Gamma Sigma, Phi Eta Sigma, Pi Lambda Phi (exec. council 1963-64), Phi Kappa Phi, Beta Alpha Psi. Jewish. Office: First Nat Bank Md 25 S Charles St Baltimore MD 21201

SAGHIR, ADEL JAMIL, artist, painter, sculptor; b. Beirut, Lebanon, May 27, 1930; came to U.S., 1973; s. Jamil Khalil and Aisha Rachid (Mirii) S.; m. Jindriska Antonin Moucka, Aug. 24, 1968; children: Jamil, Ryan. BA, Am. U., Beirut, 1968, diploma in tchg., 1973; MFA, Pratt Inst., 1975; postgrad., NYU, 1976-79. Asst. prof. Fine Arts Inst., Lebanese U., Beirut, 1963-73; lectr. Am. Beirut U. Coll., 1972-73; adj. prof. Western Conn. State U., Danbury, 1988—; instr., sculpture Silvermine Sch. Art, New Canaan, Conn., 1989—. Artist various murals and tapestries. Recipient 4th prize Alexandria Biennale, Egyptian Govt., 1963, 1st prize silk tapestries Nat. Contest Lebanon, 1965, 1st prize major sculpture monuments, 1966, 1st prize City Ctr. Sculpture Contest, 1969; Fine Arts scholar, Germany, Munic Acad., 1958-60; Fulbright-Hayes fellow NYU, N.Y.C., 1973-79. Mem. Internat. Soc. Advancement of Living Traditions in Art, Washington Pl. Artists Assn. (pres. 1977-80), Lebanese Artists Assn. (v.p. 1964-73). Avocations: gardening, fishing, upland hunting. Home: 20 Newfane Rd New Fairfield CT 06812-4721 Office: Western Conn State U 181 White St Danbury CT 06810-6845

SAGLE, ROBERT FRANKLIN, lawyer; b. Hagerstown, Md., Dec. 8, 1930; s. Quay Jabez and Hattie (Shank) S.; m. Elizabeth Louise Blanchard, Nov. 5, 1960; children—Philip Robert, Leslie Elizabeth. B.A., George Washington U., 1951, J.D. with honors, 1953. Bar: D.C. 1953. Page, clk. U.S. Congress, Washington, 1947-53; asst. to dep. atty. gen. U.S. Dept. Justice, Washington, 1956-58, 60; asst. U.S. atty. for D.C., 1958; spl. atty. 1st U.S. Dept. of Justice Task Force on Organized Crime, N.Y.C. and Washington, 1958-60; counsel Schenley Industries Inc. (distiller), N.Y.C., 1960-62; assoc. firm

---

Cooke & Beneman, 1962-68, ptnr., 1968-70; ptnr. Harrison, Lucey & Sagle, Washington, 1970-78, McDermott, Will & Emery, Chgo., Washington, Boston, L.A., N.Y.C., Paris and Miami, Fla., 1978—; counsel Bourbon Inst., N.Y.C., 1965-73, Assn. Am. Vintners. Bd. editors: George Washington Law Rev, 1952-53. Mem. task force for ballot security Republican Nat. Com., 1968, 72, co-chmn., 1976; chmn. laws and regulations com. Distilled Spirits Council U.S., 1978-80. Served as 1st lt., JAGC USAF, 1953-56, Germany. Mem. D.C. Bar, Assn. Bar City N.Y., Bar Assn. D.C., Fed., Am. bar assns., Am. Legion, Phi Delta Phi, Sigma Chi. Episcopalian. Club: Kenwood Country (Bethesda, Md.). Home: 5207 Bradley Blvd Bethesda MD 20814-1209 Office: McDermott Will & Emery 1850 K St NW Washington DC 20006-2213

SAGMEISTER, EDWARD FRANK, small business owner, career officer, consultant; b. N.Y.C., Dec. 10, 1939; s. Frank and Anna (Unger) S.; m. Anne Marie Ducker, Aug. 18, 1962; children: Cynthia Anne, Laura Marie, Cheryl Suzanne, Eric Edward. BS, U. San Francisco, 1962; MBA, Syracuse U., 1968; postgrad., Air Command and Staff Coll., 1977, Air War Coll., 1981. Commd. 2d lt. USAF, 1963, advanced through grades to lt. col., pers. officer, 1963, aide-de-camp, 1965; dir. pers. systems Alaska Air Command, USAF, 1968; hdqs. Pentagon sys. design, program analysis officer USAF, The Pentagon, 1971; spl. asst. sec. Air Force Pers. Coun., USAF, 1975; hdqs. Europe dir. pers. assignments USAF, 1979, dir. personnel assignments, 1982, ret., 1984; dir. devel. Am. Cancer Soc., Riverside, Calif., 1984-87; cons. Redlands, Calif., 1987-92; chmn. of bd., pres., CEO Hospitality Pub and Grub, Inc., San Bernardino, Calif., 1992—; program dir. Am. Radio Network, L.A., 1987; instr. Am. Internat. U., L.A., 1987; bd. dirs. Crafton Hills Coll. Found., Yucaipa, Calif., 1988; ptnr., owner Midway Med. Ctr., San Bernardino, 1990-91. Foreman pro tem San Bernardino County Grand Jury, 1990-91; active with Redlands 2000 Com., 1988, (v.-chmn., charter mem.) Redlands Human Rels. Commn., 1994—, San Bernardino County Dept. Probation, 1985-88, Redlands Cmty. Chorus, Redlands Youth Accountability Bd., San Bernardino County, 1994—; campaign cabinet mem. Arrowhead United Way, San Bernardino, 1986-87, loan exec. 1985. Mem. San Bernardino C. of C., Redlands C. of C., Ret. Officers Assn., Nat. Soc. Fundraising Execs., (dir. charter mem. Inland Empire chpt. 1987-88), Empire Singers (v.p. 1987). Republican. Roman Catholic. Avocations: travel, music, singing, tennis, reading. Home: 503 Sunnyside Ave Redlands CA 92373-5629 Office: Hospitality Pub and Grub Inc 1987 Diners Ct San Bernardino CA 92408-3330

SAGNESS, RICHARD LEE, education educator, former academic dean; b. Rock Rapids, Iowa, Jan. 9, 1937; s. David Harold and Joyce Morrow (Carlson) S.; m. Donna Jayne Lanxon, Feb. 18, 1956; children: Debbi Van Vooren, Becky Hardy, Beth Sagness Higbee. BA, U. No. Iowa, 1961; MS, Emporia State U., 1965; PhD, Ohio State U., 1970; grad. Inst. for Higher Edn. Mgmt., Harvard Coll., 1977. Tchr. biology Cen. High Sch., Sioux City, Iowa, 1961-66; lectr. biology Emporia (Kans.) State U., 1966-67; info. analyst Ohio State U., 1967-70; asst. prof. sci. edn. U. S.D., Vermillion, 1970-72, assoc. prof., 1972-75, coord. sci. edn., 1970-75; prof. sci. edn., assoc. dean Sch. Edn. U. S.D., Vermillion, 1975-79; prof. edn. Coll. Edn. Idaho State U., Pocatello, 1979—, dean Coll. Edn., 1979-89, dir. student acad. svcs. Coll. Edn., 1993—; mem. Idaho Profl. Stds. Commn.; faculty rep. to bd. dirs. Idaho State U. Found., 1992—; mem. Idaho Sch.-to-Work Collaborative Team, 1994—. Contbr. articles to profl. jours. Bd. dirs. Vermillion Devel. Corp., 1974-78, pres., 1976-77; bd. dirs. Pocatello United Fund, 1976-79, 82-83, v.p., 1982-83, pres., 1985-86. With U.S. Army, 1955-57. Mem. Idaho Assn. Colls. Tchr. Edn. (pres. 1984-88), Am. Assn. Colls. of Tchr. Edn. (rep., chairperson govtl. rels. com. 1988-89, bd. dirs. 1988-92), Pocatello C. of C. (bd. dirs. 1983-89, pres. 1987-88), Tchr. Edn. Coun. State Colls. and Univs. (exec. coun. 1988-90), Rotary (bd. dirs. local club 1988-89, team leader study exch. team to Sweden 1991), Masons, Order Eastern Star, Phi Delta Kappa. Office: Idaho State Univ PO Box 8059 Pocatello ID 83209-8059

SAGO, ANTHONY E.W., financial service executive; b. Toronto, Ont., Can., Sept. 15, 1946; s. Antonio and Julie (Zawacki) S.; m. Judith Hamilton, May 31, 1949; children: Heather, Gregory. B in Bus. Adminstrn. with honours, York U., Toronto, 1975. Cert. mgmt. acct. Acct. Gray Coach Lines, Toronto, 1967-68; sr. analyst Borden Co., Toronto, 1968-72; contr. beaver homes Beaver Lumber Molson Group, Winnepeg, Man., Can., 1973-77, mgr. fin. planning Willson Off Spec, 1977-78; sr. contr. Qualico Devels., Winnepeg, 1978-80; single family divsn. mgr. Qualico Devels., Edmonton, Alta., Can., 1980-85; v.p. Jostens Can., Winnepeg, 1985-89; pres. Jostens Can., Mississauga, Ont., 1989—. Home: 403 Winston Blvd, Cambridge, ON Canada Office: Jostens Canada Ltd, 7145 W Credit Ave, Mississauga, ON Canada L5N 6J7

SAGO, PAUL EDWARD, college administrator; b. Mo., July 5, 1931; s. John and Mabel S.; m. Donna; children: Bruce, Brad. Student, Mineral Area Coll., 1949-51; BS, Findlay Coll., 1953; postgrad., Winebrenner Theol. Sem., 1953-55; MS, St. Francis Coll., 1964; PhD, Walden U., 1976. Dir. devel. Findlay (Ohio) Coll., 1964-67, Hiram (Ohio) Coll., 1967-68; v.p. fin. affairs, treas. Anderson (Ind.) Coll., 1968-76; pres. Azusa Pacific U., Azusa, Calif., 1976-90, Woodbury U., Burbank, Calif., 1990—; participant seminars and insts. Trustee Findlay Coll., 1958-64; mem. Ind. adv. council SBA, 1972-76. Mem. assn. Governing Bds. (pres.'s coun.), Internat. Platform Assn., Coun. for Advancement and Support Edn., Nat. Assn. Ind. Colls. and Univs., Assn. Ind. Calif. Colls. and Univs., Rotary. Office: Woodbury U 7500 N Glenoaks Blvd Burbank CA 91504-1052

SAGOFF, MARK, philosopher, educator, academic administrator; b. Boston, Nov. 29, 1941; s. Maurice and Hazel Sagoff; m. Kendra Heymann, Oct. 14, 1984; children: Jared, Amelia. AB, Harvard U., 1963; PhD, U. Rochester, 1968. Lectr. dept. philosophy Princeton (N.J.) U., 1968-69; asst. prof. dept. philosophy U. Pa., Phila., 1969-75; vis. asst. prof. dept. philosophy U. Wis., Madison, 1975-76; asst. prof. sci., tech. and soc. program Cornell U., Ithaca, N.Y., 1976-79; rsch. scholar Inst. for Philosophy and Pub. Policy U. Md., College Park, 1979-86, sr. rsch. scholar, dir. Inst. for Philosophy and Pub. Policy, 1986—; mem. pub. advisor panel Chem. Mfrs. Assn., Washington, 1989-91; mem. adv. bd. biotech. U.S. EPA, Washington, 1992-95; speaker in field. Author: The Economy of the Earth, 1988; contbr. articles to profl. jours. Pew scholar, 1991-94; NSF grantee, 1981—. Mem. Internat. Soc. Environ. Ethics (pres. 1994—). Democrat. Jewish. Avocations: his children. Home: 6801 Carlynn Ct Bethesda MD 20817-4302 Office: University of Maryland Inst for Philosophy Pu College Park MD 20742

SAHAI, HARDEO, medical statistics educator; b. Bahraich, India, Jan. 10, 1942; m. Lillian Sahai, Dec. 28, 1973; 3 children. BS in Math., Stats. and Physics, Lucknow U., India, 1962; MS in Math., Banaras U., Varanasi, India, 1964; MS in Math. Stats., U. Chgo., 1968; PhD in Stats., U. Ky., 1971. Lectr. in math. and stats. Banaras U., Varanasi, India, 1964-65; asst. stats. officer Durgapur Steel Plant, Durgapur West Bengal, India, 1965; statistician Rsch. and Planning div. Blue Cross Assn., Chgo., 1966; statis. programmer Cleft Palate Ctr., U. Ill., 1967, Chgo. Health Rsch. Found., 1968; mgmt. scientist Mgmt. Systems Devel. Dept. Burroughs Corp., Detroit, 1971-72; from asst. prof. to prof. dept. math. U.P.R., Mayaguez, 1972-82; vis. research prof. Dept. Stats. and Applied Math. Fed. U. of Ceara, Brazil, 1978-79; sr. research statistician Travenol Labs., Inc., Round Lake, Ill., 1982-83; chief statistician U.S. Army Hqrs., Ft. Sheridan, Ill., 1983-84; sr. math. statistician U.S. Bur. of Census Dept. of Commerce, Washington, 1984-85; sr. ops. rsch. analyst Def. Logistics Agy. Dept. Def., Chgo., 1985-86; prof. Dept. Biostats. and Epidemiology U.P.R. Med. Scis., San Juan, 1986—; cons. P.R. Univ Cons., P.R. Driving Safety Evaluation Project, Water Resources Rsch. Inst., Travenol Labs., Campo Rico, P.R., U.S. Bur. Census, Washington, Lawrence Livermore Nat. Lab. Calif., others; vis. prof. U. Granada, Spain, U. Veracruzana, Mex. U. Nacional de Colombia; vis. prof. U. Nacional de Trujillo, Peru, 1993-94, hon. rof. dept. stats., 1994—; adj. prof. dept. math. U. P.R. Natural Scis. Faculty, 1995—. Author: Statistics and Probability: Learning Module, 1984; author: (with Jose Berrios) A Dictionary of Statistical Scientific and Technical Terms: English-Spanish and Spanish-English, 1981, (with Anwer Khurshid) Statistical in Epidemiology: Methods, Techniques and Applications, 1995, (with Wilfredo Martinez) Statisical Tables and Formulas for the Social, Physical and Biological Sciences, 1995, (with Satish C. Misra and Michael Graham) Quota-

---

tions On Probability and Statistics with Illustrations, 1995; mem. editorial bd. Sociedad Colombiana de Matematicas, P.R. Health Scis Jour.; contbg. editor Current Index to Stats; reviewer: Collegiate Microcomputer, Communications in Statistics, Indian Jour. Statistics, Jour. Royal Statistical Soc. (series D, The Statistician), The New Zealand Statistician, Biometrics, Canadian Jour. of Statistics, Technometrics, Problems, Resources and Issues in Mathematics Undergraduate Studies; contbr. more than 100 articles and papers to profl. and sci. jours., numerous articles to tech. mags. Active Dept. Consumer Affairs Svcs. Commonwealth of P.R., San Juan, Dept. Anti-Addiction Svcs., Commonwealth of P.R., San Juan., Inst. of AIDS, Municipality of San Juan, VA Med. Ctr. of San Juan. Recipient Dept. Army Cert. Achievement award, 1984, U. Ky. Outstanding Alumnus award, 1993, medal of honor U. Granada, 1994, plaque of honor U. Nacional de Trujillo, 1994; fellow Coun. Sci. and Indsl. Rsch., 1964-65, U. Chgo., 1965-68, Harvard U., 1979, Fulbright Found., 1982; U.P. Bd. Merit scholar, 1957-59, Govt. India Merit scholar, 1949-64; grantee NSF, 1974-77, NIMH, 1987-90, 91—, NIDA, 1991—. Fellow AAAS, Inst. Statisticians (charter statistician), Inst. Math. and Its Applications (charter mathematician), N.Y. Acad. Scis., Royal Statis. Soc.; mem. Internat. Statis. inst., Internat. Assn. Teaching Stats., Soc. Epidemiol. Rsch., Inst. Math. Stats., Bernouilli Soc. for Math. Stats. and Probability, Internat. Biometric Soc., Am. Soc. for Quality Control, Am. Stats. Assn., Japan Statis. Soc., Can. Statis. Soc., Inter-Am. Statis. Inst., Internat. Assn. Statis. Computing, Sci. Sci. and Math. Assn., Sigma Xi. Avocations: religious studies, philosophy, reading, gardening. Home: Street Dr Gaudier Texidor K-5-B Terrace Mayaguez PR 00680-9998 Office: U PR Grad Sch Pub Health Med Scis Campus Dept Biostats & Epidemiology PO Box 365067 San Juan PR 00067

SAHAI, YOGESHWAR, engineering educator; b. Moradabad, India, Feb. 26, 1945; came to U.S., 1982; s. Someshwar and Shakuntla Sahai; m. Usha Saxena, June 2, 1971; children: Smita, Vivek. BE, U. Roorkee, India, 1968; ME, U. Roorkee, 1973; PhD and DIC, U. London, 1979. Lecturer U. Roorkee, Roorkee, India, 1968-75; researcher U. London, London, Eng., 1975-79; rsch. assoc. McGill U., Montreal, Can., 1979-82; asst. prof. Ohio State U., Columbus, Ohio, 1983-86; assoc. prof. Ohio State U., Columbus, 1986-88; I.S.S. prof. Iron and Steel Soc. prof., Columbus, 1988—; cons. various metal and materials cos., 1982—. Author over 100 tech. papers, 3 tech. books. Recipient P.T.D. award, Iron and Steel Soc., 1988, 90, Mars G. Fontana award, Ohio State U., 1986, extractive metallurgy sci. award, Metallurgical Soc. of AIME, 1984; Stanley Elmore fellow, Inst. Mining and Metallurgy, Eng., 1975-78; Thomson Meml. gold medal, U. Roorkee, 1968. Home: 877 Highview Dr Columbus OH 43235-1232 Office: Ohio State U Dept MSE 2041 N College Rd Columbus OH 43210-1124

SAHANEK, TATANA, librarian, editor; b. Prague, Czechoslovakia, Nov. 2, 1922; d. Emanuel and Frances (Blovsky) S.; naturalized, 1969; JUDr., Masaryk U., Brno, Czechoslovakia, 1947; BLS, U. Toronto, Ont., Can., 1953; PhD (Higher Edn. Act fellow), U. Tex., Austin, 1973. Cataloger, Toronto Pub. Libr., 1953-55; law libr., gen. reference libr. Ont. Legis. Libr., Toronto, 1956-61; head catalog and classification divsn. Harvard Law Sch. Libr., Cambridge, Mass., 1962-65; head catalog dept. Law Libr., U. Mich., Ann Arbor, 1965-66; translator, interpreter Dow Chem. Internat., Midland, Mich., 1967-68; libr.-translator Dow Chem. Co., Tex. div., Freeport, 1968-70; asst. libr. Antioch Sch. Law, Washington, 1972-74; editor Index to Legal Priodicals, H.W. Wilson Co., Bronx, N.Y., 1974-78; coordinator Saginaw (Mich.) Med. Ctr., 1978-79; acquisitions libr. Exec. Office of Pres. Info. Ctr., Washington, 1980—. Recipient award U. Tex. Grad. Sch. Subvention Fund, 1972. Mem. ALA, Assn. Am. Law Librs., Spl. Librs. Assn., Can. Libr. Assn., Ont. Libr. Assn., Czechoslovak Soc. Arts and Scis. Club: Worldwide Sportmen's. Author: Entries for Provincial Publications, Province of Ontario, 1867-1960, 1960; editor Index to Legal Periodicals, 1973-79. Home: 205 S Yoakum Pky Apt 1602 Alexandria VA 22304-3840 Office: New Exec Office Bldg Washington DC 20503

SAHID, JOSEPH ROBERT, lawyer; b. Paterson, N.J., Feb. 14, 1944; s. Joseph James and Helen (Vitale) S.; m. Annunziata Carol Aiello, May 16, 1981 (div.); children: Annuziata, Joe. BS, Rutgers U., 1965; LLB, U. Va., 1968. Bar: N.Y. 1973, U.S. Dist. Ct. (so. dist.) N.Y., U.S. Ct. Appeals (2d and 3d cirs.), U.S. Supreme Ct. Staff mem. Nat. Commn. on Causes and Prevention of Violence, Washington, 1968-69; cons. Pres.'s Commn. on Campus Unrest, Washington, 1970; assoc. Cravath, Swaine & Moore, N.Y.C., 1972-77, ptnr., 1977-93; ptnr. Barrack, Rodos & Bacine, N.Y.C., 1994—. Author: Rights in Concord, 1969; co-author: Law and Order Reconsidered, 1969; contbr. articles to profl. jours. Lt. USCG, 1968-72. Office: Barrack Rodos & Bacine 575 Madison Ave 6th Fl New York NY 10022

SAHLEM, JAMES ROBERT, law librarian; b. Buffalo, Feb. 21, 1948; s. Lee M. and Mildred A. (Hibschweiler) S.; m. Susan Mary Schifferli, Aug. 9, 1969; children: Steven, Andrea, Gregory. BS in Mgmt., Canisius Coll., 1970; MLS, SUNY, Buffalo, 1971, ASC, 1985; MS in Edn., Canisius Coll., 1995. Cert. pub. libr. profl., N.Y. State Edn. Dept. Libr. trainee Bus. Labor Dept. Buffalo-Erie County Pub. Libr., Buffalo, 1970-71; libr. I Mobile Librs. Buffalo-Erie County Pub. Libr., Buffalo, 1971-74; libr. II Amherst Pub. Librs., Williamsville, N.Y., 1974-78; libr. III, dir. North Park Crane Brs., Buffalo, 1978-81; prin. law libr. Supreme Ct. Libr., Buffalo, 1981—; cons. Lippes, Silverstein et al, Buffalo, 1985—. Co-author: (with Jo Ann M. Wahl and Kevin Bauer) Powers of the New York Court of Appeals 1952-1993 Supplement, 1994. Mem. exec. bd., sec. Western N.Y. Libr. Resources Coun., 1994—. Mem. Am. Assn. Law Librs., Buffalo Curling Club (officer 1985-89). Avocations: curling, gardening. Office: Supreme Ct Libr Buffalo 92 Franklin St Buffalo NY 14202

SAHLI, NANCY ANN, government agency administrator; b. Beaver Falls, Pa., Jan. 4, 1946; d. John Rankin and Betty Melville (McClane) S. AB, Vassar Coll., 1967; MA, U. Pa., 1971, PhD, 1974. Research asst. Drexel U., Phila., 1969-74; archivist Nat. Hist. Publs. and Records Commn., Washington, 1975-81, 83-84, archives cons., 1981-84, archives specialist, 1984-87, dir. records program, 1987-95, program dir., 1991—, acting exec. dir., 1994—; cons. Princeton Theol. Sem., N.J., 1981-82, Vassar Coll., Poughkeepsie, N.Y., 1981-82, Smithsonian Instn., Washington, 1983. Author: Elizabeth Blackwell, 1982, Women and Sexuality, 1984, MARC for Archives and Manuscripts, 1985 (Coker prize 1986); editor Directory of Archives and Mss. Repos., 1978. AAUW fellow, 1973-74; NEH grantee, 1981-83; recipient Commendable Svc. award GSA, 1978, GSA citation, 1979, 81, Archivists' Achievement award, 1994. Fellow Soc. Am. Archivists (cons. 1983-84); mem. Am. Assn. State and Local Hist., Assn. Document Editing, Nat. Assn. Govt. Archives and Records Adminstrs., Orgn. Am. Historians (life), Sierra Club (life), Appalachian Trail Conf. Democrat. Buddhist. Avocations: gardening, hiking, traveling. Home: 9 Indian Spring Dr Silver Spring MD 20901-3016 Office: Nat Hist Publs & Records Commn Nat Archives Washington DC 20408

SAHLSTROM, E(LMER) B(ERNARD), lawyer; b. Seattle, Feb. 25, 1918; s. August Waldimer and Alma Carolyn (Ostrom) S.; m. Phyllis May Horstman, June 18, 1946; children: Gary Bernard, Cheryl Linn Sahlstrom Monohan, Gregory Lane. B.S., U. Oreg., 1945, J.D., 1947. Bar: Oreg. 1947, U.S. Dist. Ct. Oreg. 1948, U.S. Dist. Ct. Hawaii, 1961, U.S. Ct. Appeals (9th cir.), 1950, U.S. Supreme Ct. 1977; CPA, Oreg. Acct. Haskins & Sells, N.Y.C., 1941-44; mem. Thompson & Sahlstrom, Eugene, Oreg., 1947-57, Sahlstrom, Lombard, Starr & Vinson, and predecessor, Eugene, 1957-76, Sahlstrom & Lombard, Eugene, 1976-78; sole practice Eugene, 1978-80; ptnr. Sahlstrom & Dugdale, Eugene, 1980—. Bd. visitors U. Oreg. Law Sch., 1977-79, 92—. Mem. Oreg. State Bar, ABA, Assn. Trial Lawyers Am. (1st v.p. western regional conf. 1954, 4th v.p. conf. 1956, dir. 1955-56, v.p. Oreg. chpt. 1970-71, pres. So. Oreg. chpt. 1972-74), Am. Judicature Soc., Assn. Attys. and CPA's, Oreg. State Bar (com. taxations, unauthorized practice of law, procedure and practice, continuing legal edn., council on ct. procedures), U. Oreg. Sch. Law Alumni Assn. (bd. dirs., pres.), Phi Alpha Delta, Beta Alpha Psi. Clubs: Country, Town (dir. 1970-71, pres. 1978) (Eugene). Lodge: Elks. Home: 715 Fairoaks Dr Eugene OR 97401-2392 Office: Sahlstrom & Dugdale 915 Oak St Eugene OR 97401-3142

SAHS, MAJORIE JANE, art educator; b. Altadena, Calif., Aug. 27, 1926; d. Grayson Michael and Janie Belle (Aaron) McCarty. m. Eugene Otto Sahs, July 21, 1949; children: Victoria, Stephen, Jeffry. Student, Emerson Coll.,

Boston, 1945; BA, Sacramento State U., 1970; MA in Art Edn., Calif. State U., Sacramento, 1972, postgrad., 1973-79. Cert. secondary tchr., Calif. Tchr. art Sacramento County Schs., 1971-80; cons. Whole Brain Learning Modes, Sacramento, 1980-84; tng. specialist Art Media, Sacramento, Calif., 1983—; instr. Found. for Continuing Med. Edn., Calif., 1985; presenter Nat. Art Edn. Conf., Chgo., 1992, 93, Asian Pacific Conf. on Arts Edn., Franklin, Australia, Internat. Conf., Montreal, Can., 1993; cons. and lectr. in field; judge U.S. Treas., 1994, 95, Dept. of Calif. Student Art. Prodr., writer guide and video Gesture Painting Through T'ai Chi, 1992; editor, pub. Calif.'s state newspaper for art edn., 1987-90; editor: Crocker Museum Docent Guide, 1990; mem. editl. bd. Jour. for Nat. Art Edn. Assn., 1990—; editor (newsletter) U.S. Soc. for Edn. Through Art, 1994; designer of ltd. edits. scarves and cards for Nat. Breast Cancer Rsch. Fund, Exploration Inspiration '95. Del. Calif. Arts Leadership Symposium for Arts Edn., 1979, Legis. Coalition Through The Arts, Calif., 1989; judge Calif. State Fair Art Show, 1989, Fed. Treasury Poster Contest, 1994, 95; organizer and host art show and fundraiser for women candidates, 1992. Recipient State award of Merit. Mem. Internat. Assn. Edn. through Art, U.S. Soc. Edn. through Art (editor newsletter 1994-96), Nat. Art Edn. Assn. (mem. editl. bd. jour. 1990—, Nat. Outstanding Newspaper Editor award 1988, 89), Calif. Art Edn. Assn. (mem. state coun., mem. area coun., editor state paper, State Award of Merit), Calif. Children's Homes Soc. (pres. Camellia chpt. 1990-91), Asian Pacific Arts Educators Assn., Art Ctr. L.A. Alumni. Avocations: creating art pieces, textile clothing design, writing, designing jewelry, designing greeting cards. Home and Office: 1836 Walnut Ave Carmichael CA 95608

SAIA, LOUIS P., III, transportation executive; b. 1956. With Saia Motor Freight Line, Inc., Houma, La., 1977—, pres., 1986—. Office: Saia Motor Freight Line Inc 104 Woodlawn Ranch Rd Houma LA 70363

SAIBLE, STEPHANIE, magazine editor; b. Mobile, Ala., Sept. 11, 1954; d. Lewis J. Slaff and Phoebe-Jane (Berse) Deats; m. Mark Saible, May 31, 1981 (div. 1983). Student, Va. Commonwealth U., 1972-75. Editorial asst. Woman's World Magazine, Englewood, N.J., 1980-81, service copywriter, 1981-83, assoc. articles editor, 1983-84, articles editor, 1984-85, sr. editor features dept., 1985-86, sr. editor services dept., 1986, now editor-in-chief. Contbr. articles to Woman's World, Modern Bride, New Body, Celebrity Beauty, Trim & Fit. Named Wonder Woman of the Yr., Bus. Jour. N.J., 1986. Mem. Women in Communications. Office: Woman's World Mag 270 Sylvan Ave Englewood Cliffs NJ 07632*

SAID, EDWARD W., English language and literature educator; b. Jerusalem, Palestine, Nov. 1, 1935; s. Wadie A. and Hilda (Musa) S.; m. Mariam Cortas, Dec. 15, 1970; children: Wadie, Najla. A.B., Princeton U., 1957; A.M., Harvard U., 1960, Ph.D., 1964. Tutor history and lit. Harvard U., 1961-63; instr. Columbia U., 1963-65, asst. prof. English, 1965-67, assoc. prof., 1968-70, prof., 1970-77, Parr prof. English and comparative lit., 1977-89, Old Dominion Found. prof. humanities, 1989—; univ. prof., 1992—; vis. prof. Harvard U., 1974, Johns Hopkins, spring 1979, Yale U., fall 1985; fellow Ctr. for Advanced Study in Behavioral Scis., Palo Alto, Calif., 1975-76; Christian Gauss lectr. in criticism Princeton U., spring 1977, T.S. Eliot lectr. U. Kent, Canterbury, U.K., 1985, Messenger lectr. Cornell U., 1986, Little lectr. Princeton U., 1988, Raymond Williams Meml. lectr., London, 1989, Wilson lectr. Wellesley Coll., 1991, Amnesty lectr. Oxford U., 1992, Lord Northcliffe lectr., U. Coll., London, 1993, Reith lectr. BBC, London, 1993, others; Carpenter prof. U. Chgo., 1983; Northrop Frye chair U. Toronto, fall 1986. Author: Joseph Conrad and the Fiction of autobiography, 1966, Beginnings: Intention and Method, 1975, Orientalism, 1978, The Question of Palestine, 1979; editor: Literature and Society, 1979, Covering Islam, 1981, The World, the Text, and the Critic, 1983, After the Last Sky, 1986, Blaming the Victims, 1988, Musical Elaborations, 1991, Culture and Imperialism, 1993, Representations of the Intellecual, 1994, Politics of Dispossession, 1994, Ghazzah-Arihah: Salam Amriki, 1994. Social Sci. Research fellow, 1975; Guggenheim fellow, 1972-73; Recipient Lionel Trilling award Columbia U., 1976, 94. Mem. AAAS, MLA, Assn. Arab Am. U. Grads. (past v.p.), N.Y. Coun. Fgn. Rels., Am. Comparative Lit. Assn. (René Wellek award 1985), PEN (exec. bd. 1989—), Am. Acad. Arts and Scis. Office: Columbia U Dept English 602 Philosophy Hall New York NY 10027

SAID, KAMAL E., accounting educator; b. Cairo, Egypt, May 26, 1937; came to U.S., 1965; s. Mohamed A. and Ehsan (Yasin) S.; m. Sally Sneed, Dec. 22, 1967 (div. 1979); children: Jamal E., Karim E.; m. Maria A. Gruner, Aug. 11, 1984; 1 child, Noelle Rianne. B in Comm., Ain-Shams U., Cairo, 1957; MBA, U. Tex., 1967, PhD, 1971. CPA, Tex., La. Asst. prof. U. Houston, 1971-75, assoc. prof., 1975-76, assoc. prof. acctg., 1978-83; Fulbright prof. U. Khartoum, Sudan, 1976-78; chmn. acctg. dept. King Saud U., Saudi Arabia, 1984-88; prof. acctg. U. Southwestern La., Lafayette, 1988-92; prof. Coll. of Indsl. Mgmt., U. Petroleum & Minerals, Dhahran, Saudi Arabia, 1992—; cons. Nat. Coun. Higher Edn., Khartoum, 1976-78, European Econ. Community, Khartoum, 1977; external examiner U. Calcutta, India, 1978-79. Author: Auditing: Theory and Practice, 1989, Modern Advanced Accounting, 1989, Accounting Information Systems, 1988, Intermediate Accounting, I and II, 1987, The Voice of Music, Inc. Practice Set, 1986, Naggie and Sons, Inc. Practice Set, 1986, Gasseem Sporting Goods, Inc. Practice Set, 1986, Cost Accounting I and II, 1985, Managerial Accounting, 1984, Implementation of Long-Range Plans Through Current Operating Budgets, 1978, A Budgeting Model for Institutions of Higher Education, 1974, others. U. Houston grantee, 1974, 75, 78. Mem. Am. Acctg. Assn. (grad. rsch. 1973-75), Inst. Internal Auditors, Phi Beta Delta, Delta Sigma Pi, Beta Gamma Sigma, Beta Alpha Psi. Avocations: Arabian horse shows, horse-back riding, swimming, racquetball.

SAIDMAN, GARY K., lawyer; b. Washington, July 29, 1952; s. Harry and Rose K. (Kruger) S.; m. Suzan R. Kinbar, Mar. 25, 1984; children: Benjamin A., David M. BS, SUNY, Stony Brook, 1974; JD, Emory U., 1978. Bar: Ga. 1978, D.C. 1983, U.S. Dist. Ct. (no. dist.) Ga. 1978, U.S. Ct. Appeals (5th cir.) 1978, U.S. Ct. Appeals (11th cir.) 1981. Assoc. Seward & Kissel, Atlanta, 1978-80; assoc. Kilpatrick & Cody, Atlanta, 1980-86, ptnr., 1986—. Mem. Lawyers Club Atlanta, Ga. State Bar Assn. (chmn. Computer Law Section 1987-88). Office: Kilpatrick & Cody 1100 Peachtree St Ste 2800 Atlanta GA 30309

SAIDMAN, LAWRENCE JAY, anesthesiologist; b. Detroit, 1936. MD, U. Mich., 1961. Diplomate Am. Bd. Anesthesiology (v.p. 1992-93, pres. 1993-94). Intern Sinai Hosp., Detroit, 1961-62; resident in anesthesiology U. Calif., San Francisco, 1962-65; fellow Cardiology Rsch. Inst., San Francisco, 1963-64; anesthesiologist U. Calif. Med. Ctr., San Diego; prof. U. Calif., San Diego. Editor-in-chief Anesthesiology, 1985—. Mem. Am. Bd. Anesthesiology (bd. dirs.). Office: U Calif at San Diego Sch Medicine T-015 San Diego CA 92110*

SAIER, MILTON H, JR., biology educator; b. Palo Alto, Calif., July 30, 1941; s. Milton H. and Lucelia (Bates) S.; m. Jeanne K. Woodhams; children: Hans H., Anila J., Amanda L. BS, U. Calif., Berkeley, 1964, PhD, 1968. Prof. biology U. Calif., Berkeley, 1959-68, Johns Hopkins U., Balt., 1968-72, U. Calif., San Diego, 1972—; cons. Merck, Eli Lilly. Author 4 books; contbr. 200 sci. articles to profl. jours. U.S. Pub. Health Svc. grantee NIH. Mem. Am. Soc. Microbiology, Am. Soc. Biochemistry and Molecular Biology. Avocations: music, tennis, ping pong, swimming, hiking. Home: 666 Quail Gardens Dr Encinitas CA 92024 Office: U Calif San Diego Dept Bio 0116 La Jolla CA 92093-0116

SAIFER, MARK GARY PIERCE, pharmaceutical executive; b. Phila., Sept. 16, 1938; s. Albert and Sylvia (Jolles) S.; m. Phyllis Lynne Trommer, Jan. 28, 1961 (dec.); children: Scott David, Alandria Gail; m. Merry R. Sherman, June 26, 1994. AB, U. Pa., 1960; PhD, U. Calif., Berkeley, 1966. Acting asst. prof. zoology U. Calif., Berkeley, 1966, postdoctoral fellow, 1967-68; sr. cancer research scientist Roswell Park Meml. Inst., Buffalo, 1968-70; lab. dir. Diagnostic Data Inc., Palo Alto, Calif., 1970-78; v.p. DDI Pharms., Inc., Mountain View, Calif., 1978-94, Oxis Internat., Inc., 1994—. Patentee in field. Mem. AAAS (life), Am. Assn. Pharm. Scientists, Parenteral Drug Assn. Office: Oxis Internat Inc 518 Logue Ave Mountain View CA 94043-4096

SAIGO, ROY H., chancellor; b. Aug. 6, 1945. BA, U. Calif., Davis, 1962; PhD, Oreg. State U., 1969. Intern acad. affairs U. Wis. Sys., Madison, 1976-77, dir. speech projects, summer 1976; asst. to dean Coll. Arts and Scis. U. Wis., Eau Claire, 1976-80, 81-84; dean Coll. Natural Scis. U. No. Iowa, Cedar Falls, 1984-90; provost, vice chancellor acad. and student affairs Southeastern La. U., Hammond, 1990-94; chancellor Auburn U., Montgomery, Ala., 1994—; mem. bd. Colonial Bank. Recipient Charles E. Bessey award Bot. Soc. Am., Svc. and Contbn. award Am. Inst. Biol. Scis., Disting. Alumni award U. Calif., Davis, 1994. Fellow AAAS; mem. Am. Assn. Higher Edn., C. of C., Phi Delta Kappa. Office: Auburn U 7300 University Dr Montgomery AL 36117

SAIKI, PATRICIA (MRS. STANLEY MITSUO SAIKI), former federal agency administrator, former congresswoman; b. Hilo, Hawaii, May 28, 1930; d. Kazuo and Shizue (Inoue) Fukuda; m. Stanley Mitsuo Saiki, June 19, 1954; children: Stanley Mitsuo, Sandra Saiki Williams, Margaret C., Stuart K., Laura H. BA, U. Hawaii, 1952. Tchr. U.S. history Punahou Sch., Kaimuki Intermediate Sch., Kalani High Sch., Honolulu, 1952-64; sec. Rep. Party Hawaii, Honolulu, 1964-66, vice chmn., 1966-68, 82-83, chmn., 1983-85; rsch. asst. Hawaii State Senate, 1966-68; mem. Hawaii Ho. of Reps., 1968-74, Hawaii State Senate, 1974-82, 100th-101st Congresses from 1st Hawaii dist., Washington, 1987-91; adminstr. SBA, Washington, 1991-93; mem. Pres.'s Adv. Coun. on Status of Women, 1969-76; mem. Nat. Commn. Internat. Women's Yr., 1969-70; commr. We. Interstate Commn. on Higher Edn.; fellow Eagleton Inst., Rutgers U., 1970; fellow Inst. of Politics, Kennedy Sch. Govt., Harvard U., 1993; bd. dirs. Bank of Am.-Hawaii, Landmark Systems Corp., Internat. Asset Recovery Corp. Mem. Kapiolani Hosp. Aux.; sec. Hawaii Rep. Com., 1964-66, vice chmn., 1966-68, chmn., 1983-85; del. Hawaii Constl. Conv., 1968; alt. del. Rep. Nat. Conv., 1968, del., 1984; Rep. nominee for lt. gov. Hawaii, 1982; mem. Fedn. Rep. Women.; trustee Hawaii Pacific Coll.; past bd. govs. Boys and Girls Clubs Hawaii; mem. adv. coun. ARC; bd. dirs. Nat. Fund for Improvement of Post-Secondary Edn., 1982-85 ; past bd. dirs. Straub Med. Rsch. Found., Honolulu, Hawaii's Visitors Bur., Honolulu, Edn. Commn. of States, Honolulu, Hawaii Visitors Bur., 1983-85; trustee U. Hawaii Found., 1984-86, Hawaii Pacific Coll., Honolulu; Rep. nominee for Gov. of Hawaii, 1994. Episcopalian. Avocation: golf. Home: 784 Elepaio St Honolulu HI 96816-4710

SAIMAN, MARTIN S., lawyer; b. N.Y.C., Jan. 27, 1932; s. Adolph and Mary (Kaplan) S.; m. Rita C. Chernick, Apr. 10, 1955; children: Lisa, Richard, Gwen. A.B., Columbia Coll., 1953; LL.B., Columbia U., 1955. Bar: N.Y. 1956. Ptnr. Kaye, Scholer, Fierman Hays and Handler, 1971-94; spl. counsel firm Kaye, Scholer, Fierman, Hays & Handler, N.Y.C., 1995—; adv. bd. dirs. Ticor Title Guarantee Co., N.Y.C. Bd. dirs. Smalley Found., 1966—. Mem. ABA, Assn. Bar City of N.Y., City Athletic Club. Office: Kaye Scholer Fierman Hays & Handler 425 Park Ave New York NY 10022-3506

SAIN, MICHAEL KENT, electrical engineering educator; b. St. Louis, Mar. 22, 1937; s. Charles George and Marie Estelle (Ritch) S.; m. Frances Elizabeth Bettin, Aug. 24, 1963; children: Patrick, Mary, John, Barbara, Elizabeth. BSEE, St. Louis U., 1959, MSEE, 1962; PhD, U. Ill., 1965. Engr. Sandia Corp., Albuquerque, 1958-61, Vickers Electric Corp., St. Louis, 1962; instr. U. Ill., Urbana, 1962-63; asst. prof. U. Notre Dame (Ind.), 1965-68, assoc. prof., 1968-72, prof., 1972-82, Frank M. Freimann prof. elec. engring., 1982—; vis. scientist U. Toronto, Ont., Can., 1972-73; disting. vis. prof. Ohio State U., Columbus, 1987; cons. Allied-Bendix Aerospace, South Bend, Ind., 1976—, Deere & Co., Moline, Ill., 1981, 82, Garrett Corp., Phoenix, 1984, GM, Warren, Mich., 1984-94; plenary spkr. IEEE Conf. on Decision and Control, 1990. Author: Introduction to Algebraic System Theory, 1981; editor: Alternatives for Linear Multivariable Control, 1978; hon. editor: Ency. of Systems and Control, 1987; editor jour. IEEE Trans. on Automatic Control, 1979-83; contbr. 260 articles to profl. jours., books and refereed proc. Grantee Army Rsch. Office, NSF, Ames Rsch. Ctr., Lewis Rsch. Ctr. NASA, Office Naval Rsch., Air Force Office Sci. Rsch., Law Enforcement Assistance Adminstrn., Clark-Hurth Components. Fellow IEEE (mem. prize papers com. 1992-95, chair IEEE Trans. awards bd. 1994-95); mem. Control Systems Soc. of IEEE (bd. govs. 1978-84, Disting. Mem. award 1983, Centennial medal 1984, Axelby prize chair 1991-95, awards com. chair 1993-95), Circuits and Systems Soc. of IEEE (co-chair internat. symposium on circuits and sys. 1990, newsletter editor 1990-95, v.p. adminstrn. 1992-93, v.p. tech. activities 1994), Soc. Indsl. and Applied Math. Republican. Roman Catholic. Avocations: photography, swimming, jogging. Office: U Notre Dame Dept Elec Engring 275 Fitzpatrick Heights Notre Dame IN 46556-5637

SAINE, BETTY BOSTON, elementary school educator; b. Newton, N.C., Dec. 1, 1932; d. Glenn and Carrie Queen Boston; m. Thomas Paul Saine, Aug. 3, 1968; 1 child, Carrie Ann. BA, Lenoir Rhyne Coll., 1956. Tchr. grade 4 High Point (N.C.) City Schs., 1956-59, Charlotte City Schs./Charlotte-Mecklenburg Schs., 1959-66; art tchr. grades 1-8 Newton-Conover City Schs., 1966-67; tchr. grade 4 Charlotte-Mecklenburg Schs., 1967-68; tchr. grade 6 Lincolnton (N.C.) City Schs., 1968-70; tchr. grades 5 and 6 Lincolnton City Schs./Lincoln County Schs., 1972-90; ret. Historian, publicity chair beautification com. Sunflower Garden Club, Lincolnton, 1976-87. Mem. Alpha Delta Kappa (various offices and coms.). Methodist. Avocations: painting, creative embroidery, horticulture, calligraphy, children's books. Home: 2492 Pickwick Pl Lincolnton NC 28092-7748

SAINE, CARROLL LEE, banker; b. Lincolnton, N.C., Sept. 14, 1934; s. Henry Greer and Velma Prue (Hallman) S.; m. Wanda Mauney Boring, June 24, 1956; children: Mark, Martha. BA, Lenoir-Rhyne Coll., Hickory, N.C., 1954; MS in Bus. Adminstrn. U. Richmond, Va., 1965. With Cen. Fidelity Bank (N.A.), Richmond, 1957—; dir. Cen Fidelity Bank (N.A.), 1975—, exec. v.p., 1973-76, pres., chief exec. officer, 1976, also dir., chmn., chief exec. officer, 1981—. With USAR, 1954-56. Lutheran. Clubs: Commonwealth (Richmond), Country of Va. (Richmond). Office: Cen Fidelity Banks Inc 1021 E Cary St Richmond VA 23219-4023

SAINER, ARTHUR, writer, theater educator; b. N.Y.C., Sept. 12, 1924; s. Louis and Sadie (Roth) S.; m. Maryjane Treloar, Apr. 18, 1981; children: Douglas M., Stephanie M., Jane M., Ross M. B.A., Washington Sq. Coll., N.Y.C., 1946; M.A., Columbia U., 1948. Tchr. Bennington Coll., Vt., 1967-69, Adelphi U., Garden City, N.Y., 1974-75, S.I. Community Coll., 1974-75; faculty Wesleyan U., Middletown, Conn., 1977-80, Hunter Coll., N.Y.C., 1980-81; assoc. prof. theatre Middlebury Coll., Vt., 1981-83; theater faculty New Sch. for Social Rsch., N.Y.C., 1985—, Sarah Lawrence Coll., Bronxville, N.Y., 1989—; play dir. Boat Sun Cavern Middlebury Coll., Vt., 1983; drama critic Village Voice, N.Y.C., 1961—; play dir. Lord Tom Goldsmith at Theatre for New City, N.Y.C., 1979, Witnesses at Open Space, N.Y.C., 1977, Poor Man Rich Man, Theatre for the New City, 1992. Editor: Village Voice, 1962; author: (plays) The Celebration Reclaimed, 1993-95, Images of the Coming Dead, 1980, After the Baal-Shem Tov, 1979, Carol in Winter Sunlight, 1977, The Children's Army Is Late, 1974, The Burning Out of '82, 1983, Cruising Angel, 1984, Sunday Childhood Journeys to Nobody at Home (Berman award), 1984, Jews and Christians in the End Zone, 1987, (criticism) The Radical Theatre Notebook, 1975, The Sleepwalker and the Assassin, 1964; reporter: Nat. Endowment for Arts, Washington, 1979-82. Panelist Vt. Council on the Arts, Montpelier, 1982, 83; panelist N.Y. State Council on the Arts, 1976-78. Ford Found. grantee, 1979, 80; recipient grant Office for Advanced Drama Research, U. Minn., 1967, award for Grab Your Hat John Golden Found., 1946. Address: 565 W End Ave New York NY 10024-2751 *From a work of mine in progress: Francis: But finally, who is going to do my work? No one is going to do it. Lev: Each will do his work. But in the end only God's work amounts to anything. Francis: And does that make you happy? Lev: It makes me useful.*

SAINSBURY OF PRESTON CANDOVER, LORD (BARON JOHN DAVAN SAINSBURY), entrepreneur; b. Nov. 2, 1927; m. Anya Linden, 1963. Student, Oxford U.; fellow (hon.), 1982; DSC in Econs. (hon.), Worcester Coll., Oxford, 1985. Vice chmn. J Sainsbury PLC, 1967-69, chmn., 1969-92; pres. J. Sainsbury plc, 1992—; also bd. dirs. J Sainsbury PLC. Bd. dirs. Royal Opera House, Covent Garden, Eng., 1969-85, chmn., 1987—; bd. dirs. Royal Opera House Trust, 1974-84, The Economist, 1972-80, chmn. Coun. Friends of Covent Garden, 1969-81, Benesh Inst. Chore-

ology, 1986-87; gov. Royal Ballet Sch., 1965-76; joint hon. treas. European Movement, 1972-75, pres., 1975-89; trustee Nat. Gallery, 1976-83, Westminster Abbey Trust, 1977-83, Tate Gallery, 1982-83, Rhodes Trust, 1984—; active Nat. Com. for Electoral Reform, 1976-85. Named Hon. Bencher Inner Temple, 1985. Fellow Inst. Grocery Distbrs.; mem. Coun. Retail Consortium, Garrick Club, Contemporary Arts Soc. (v.p. 1984—). Office: J Sainsbury PLC, care Stamford House Stamford St, SE1 9LL London England Office: J Sainsbury U S A Inc 140 Laurel St East Bridgewater MA 02333-1764

SAINT, CROSBIE EDGERTON, retired army officer; b. West Point, N.Y., Sept. 29, 1936; s. Frederick Gilman and Jean (Crosbie) Saint Malevich; m. Virginia Fisher Carnahan, Aug. 3, 1961; children: Frederick Gilman II, Mary Elizabeth. B.S., U.S. Mil. Acad., 1958; M.A., Am. U., 1973. Commd. 2d lt. U.S. Army, 1958, advanced through grades to gen.; comdr. 1st Squadron, 1st Cav., Vietnam, 1970; exec. to chief of staff U.S. Army, Washington; comdr. 11th Armored Cav. Regt., Fulda, Germany, 1978-78, 7th Army Tng. Command, Grafenwohr, Germany, from 1979; dept. comdt. Command and Gen. Staff Coll., Ft. Leavenworth, Kans., 1981-83; comdr. 1st Armored Div., Ansbach, Germany, 1983-85; comdr. 3d Corps and Ft. Hood Tex., 1985-88; comdr. in chief U.S. Army Europe, Heidelberg, Germany, 1988-92; ret. U.S. Army, 1992; v.p. Europe MPRI; cons. Decorated D.D.S.M. with two oak leaf clusters, Silver Star, Legion of Merit with two oak leaf clusters, D.F.C., Air medal with V device, Legion of Honor (France), German Armed Forces Gt. Cross of Merit with star. Mem. Assn. U.S. Army, Armor Assn. Address: 1116 N Pitt St Alexandria VA 22314-1455

SAINT, EVA MARIE, actress; b. Newark, July 4, 1924; d. John Merle and Eva Marie (Rice) S.; m. Jeffrey Hayden, Oct. 28, 1951; children: Darrell, Laurette. BA, DFA, Bowling Green State U., 1946; student, Actors Studio, after 1950. Appeared in various radio and TV dramatic shows, N.Y.C., 1947—; theater roles include The Trip to Bountiful, 1953 (Outer Circle Critics award, N.Y. Drama Critics award, 1953), The Rainmaker, 1953, Winesburg, Ohio, 1970, The Lincoln Mask, 1972, Summer and Smoke, 1973, Desire Under the Elms, 1974, The Fatal Weakness, 1976, Candida, 1977, Mr. Roberts, First Monday in October, 1979, Duet for One, 1982-83, The Country Girl, 1986 (L.A. Dramalogue award 1986), Death of a Salesman, 1994, Love Letters, 1994; appeared in films On the Waterfront, 1954 (Acad. Award for best supporting actress, 1955), Raintree County, 1957, That Certain Feeling, 1956, A Hatful of Rain, 1957, North by Northwest, 1959, Exodus, 1961, All Fall Down, 1962, 36 Hours, 1963, The Sandpiper, 1964, The Russians Are Coming, The Russians Are Coming!, 1965, Grand Prix, 1966, The Stalking Moon, 1969, Loving, 1970, Cancel My Reservation, 1972, Nothing in Common, 1986; TV dramas The Macahans, 1976 (Emmy nom.), The Fatal Weakness, 1976, Taxi!!, 1978 (Emmy nom.), A Christmas to Remember, 1978, When Hell Was in Session, 1980, The Curse of King Tut's Tomb, The Best Little Girl in the World, 1981, Splendor in the Grass, 1981, Love Leads the Way, 1983, Jane Doe, 1983, Fatal Vision, 1984, The Last Days of Patton, 1986, A Year in the Life, 1986, Breaking Home Ties, 1987, I'll Be Home for Christmas, 1988, Voyage of Terror: The Achille Lauro Affair, 1990, People Like Us, 1990 (Emmy award, 1990), Palomino, 1991, Kiss of the Killer, ABC, 1992, documentary Primary Colors: The Story of Corita, 1991, My Antonia, 1994; also appeared in TV series Moonlighting, 1986-89.

ST. AMAND, PIERRE, geophysicist; b. Tacoma, Wash., Feb. 4, 1920; s. Cyrias Z. and Mable (Berg) St. A.; m. Marie Pöss, Dec. 5, 1945; children: Gene, Barbara, Denali, David. BS in Physics, U. Alaska, 1948; MS in Geophysics, Calif. Inst. Tech., 1951, PhD in Geophysics and Geology, 1953; Dr. honoris causa, U. De Los Altos, Tepatitlan, Mex., 1992. Asst. dir. Geophys. Lab., U. Alaska, also head ionospheric and seismologic investigations, 1946-49; physicist U.S. Naval Ordnance Test Sta., China Lake, Calif., 1950-54; head optics br. U.S. Ordnance Test Sta., 1955-58, head earth and planetary sci. div., 1961-88, now cons. to tech. dir., head spl. projects office; fgn. service with ICA as prof. geol. and geophys. Sch. Earth Scis., U. Chile, 1958-60; originator theory rotational displacement Pacific Ocean Basin; pres. Saint-Amand Sci. Services; adj. prof. McKay Sch. Mines, U. Nev., U. N.D.; v.p., dir. Covillea Corp.; v.p., dir. tech. Muetal Corp.; cons. World Bank, Calif. Div. Water Resources, Am. Potash & Chem. Co., OAS; mem. U.S. Army airways communications system, Alaska and Can., 1942-46; cons. Mexican, Chilean, Argentine, Philipines, Can. govts.; mem. Calif. Gov.'s Com. Geol. Hazards; mem. com. magnetic instruments Internat. Union Geodesy and Geophys., 1954-59, Disaster Preparation Commn. for Los Angeles; charter mem. Sr. Exec. Service. Adv. bd. GeoScience News; contbr. 100 articles to scientific jours. Chmn. bd. dirs. Ridgecrest Community Hosp.; chmn. bd. dirs. Indian Wells Valley Airport Dist.; v.p. bd. dirs. Kern County Acad. Decathlon. Decorated knight Mark Twain, Mark Twain Jour.; recipient cert. of merit OSRD, 1945, cert. of merit USAAF, 1946, letter of commendation USAAF, 1948, Spl. award Philippine Air Force, 1969, Diploma de Honor Sociedad Geologica de Chile, Disting. Civilian Svc. medal USN, 1968, L.T.E. Thompson medal, 1973, Thunderbird award Weather Modification Assn., 1974, Disting. Pub. Svc. award Fed. Exec. Inst., 1976, Meritorious Svc. medal USN, 1988, Disting. Alumnus award U. Alaska, 1990; Fulbright rsch. fellow France, 1954-55. Fellow AAAS, Geol. Soc. Am., Eathquake Engr. Rsch. Inst.; mem. Am. Geophys. Union, Weather Modification Assn., Am. Seismol. Soc., Sister Cities (Ridgecrest-Tepatitlan) Assn. (pres.), Rotary (past pres., Paul Harris fellow), Footprinters Internat. (mem. grand bd., pres.), Sigma Xi. Achievements include patents in photometric instrument, weather and ordnance devices. Home: 1748 W Las Flores Ave Ridgecrest CA 93555-9672

SAINT-AMAND, PIERRE NEMOURS, humanities educator; b. Port-Au-Prince, Haiti, Feb. 22, 1957; came to U.S., 1978; s. Nemours and Carmen (Clerveaux) Saint-A. BA, U. Montreal, 1978; MA, Johns Hopkins U., 1980, PhD, 1981. Asst. prof. Yale U., New Haven, 1981-82, Stanford (Calif.) U., 1982-86; assoc. prof. Brown U., Providence, 1986-90, prof., 1990—; vis. prof. Harvard U., Cambridge, Mass., 1992. Author: Diderot, Le Labyrinthe de La Relation, 1984, Seduire Ou La Passion des Lumieres, 1986, Les Lois de L'Hostilite, 1992, The Libertine's Progress, 1994. Fellow Stanford Humanities Ctr., 1985-86, John Simon Guggenheim Meml. Found., 1989. Office: Brown U Box 1961/French Providence RI 02912

ST. ANTOINE, THEODORE JOSEPH, legal educator, arbitrator; b. St. Albans, Vt., May 29, 1929; s. Arthur Joseph and Mary Beatrice (Callery) S.; m. Elizabeth Lloyd Frier, Jan. 2, 1960; children: Arthur, Claire, Paul, Sara. AB, Fordham Coll., 1951; JD U. Mich., 1954; postgrad. (Fulbright grantee), U. London (Eng.), 1957-58. Bar: Mich. 1954, Ohio 1954, D.C. 1959. Assoc., U. London (Eng.), 1957-58. Bar: Mich. 1954, Ohio 1954, D.C. 1959. Assoc. Squire, Sanders & Dempsey, Cleve., 1954; assoc., ptnr. Woll, Mayer & St. Antoine, Washington, D.C., 1958-65; assoc. prof. law U. Mich. Law Sch., Ann Arbor, 1965-69, prof. 1969—; Degan prof. 1981—; dean, 1971-78; pres. Nat. Resource Ctr. for Consumers of Legal Svcs., 1974-78; mem. Pub. Rev. Bd., UAW, 1973—; chmn. UAW-GM Legal Svcs. Plan, 1983—; Mich. Gov.'s spl. counselor on workers' compensation, 1983-85; reporter Uniform Law Commrs., 1987-92. Ist lt. JAGC, U.S. Army, 1955-57. Mem. ABA (past sec. labor law sect., coun. 1984-92), Am. Bar Found., State Bar Mich. (past chmn. labor rels. law sect.), Nat. Acad. Arbitrators (bd. govs. 1985-88, v.p. 1994—), Internat. Soc. Labor Law and Social Security (U.S. br. vice chmn. 1989—), Indsl. Rels. Rsch. Assn., Order of Coif. Democrat. Roman Catholic. Author (with R. Smith, L. Merrifield and C. Craver) Labor Relations Law: Cases and Materials, 4th edit., 1968, 9th edit., 1994; contbr. numerous articles to various profl. jours. Home: 1421 Roxbury Rd Ann Arbor MI 48104-4047 Office: U Mich Law Sch 625 S State St Ann Arbor MI 48109-1215

ST. ARNOLD, DALE S., hospital administrator. Attended, Mich. Tech. U., 1974; BS in Bus. Adminstrn., Pa. State U., 1976; MHA, Washington U., 1986, MBA, 1986. Staff acct. Francis L. Killer & Co., Pub. Accts., Rapid City, S.D., 1976-77; staff acct. Andrew Meeter, Inc. CPA, Tulsa, 1977, comptroller, adminstrv. mgr., 1978, fin. svcs. mgr., 1979; owner, gen. mgr. Fin. and Acctg. Svcs. of Tulsa, 1980-84; adminstrv. fellow Holy Cross Health System, South Bend, Ind. 1986-87; v.p. ops. St. Benedict's Hosp., Ogden, Utah, 1987-89, pres., chief oper. officer, 1989-91; exec. v.p. Mt. Carmel Health, Columbus, Ohio, 1991; chief oper. officer Mt. Carmel East Hosp., Columbus, 1991; interim pres., chief exec. officer Mt. Carmel Health, 1991-92, pres., chief exec. officer, 1992—; bd. dirs. St. Benedict's Hosp., mem. all bd. coms.; gen. ptnr. mgmt. responsibility Medico Home Health,

Ltd., 1987-90. Home: 953 Avir Ct Gahanna OH 43230 Office: Mt Carmel Health 793 W State St Columbus OH 43222

ST. AUBIN, J. ARTHUR, Canadian federal agency executive; b. Paris, July 2, 1930; m. Doreen Spence Flett, Mar. 10, 1956; children: Robert, Marc, Catherine, Richard. BA, U. Montreal, 1951. Exec. dir. tng. programs Govt. of Can., Ottawa, Ont., 1980-88; asst. commr. corp. mgmt. Correctional Svc. Can., Ottawa, Ont., 1988-90; CEO, pres. Can. Ctr. Occupational Health and Safety, Hamilton, Ont., 1990—. Maj. Gen. Can. Army, 1950-80, Viet Nam, Middle East, Europe. Recipient Centennial medal, Jubilee medal Can. Armed Forces, Order Military Merit. Avocation: fitness tng. Office: Can Ctr for Occupational H & S, 250 Main St East, Hamilton, ON Canada L8N 1H6

ST. CLAIR, CARL, conductor, music director. Music dir. Pacific Symphony Orch., Santa Ana, Calif., 1990—. Office: Pacific Symphony Orch 1231 E Dyer Rd Santa Ana CA 92705-5606*

ST. CLAIR, DONALD DAVID, lawyer; b. Hammond, Ind., Dec. 30, 1932; s. Victor Peter and Wanda (Rubinska) Small; m. Sergine Anne Oliver, June 6, 1970 (dec. June 1974); m. Beverly Joyce Tipton, Dec. 28, 1987. BS, Ind. U., 1955, MS, 1963, EdD, 1967; JD, U. Toledo, 1992. Bar: Ohio 1992, U.S. Dist. Ct. (no. dist.) Ohio 1993. Assoc. prof. Coll. Edn. Western Ky. U., Bowling Green, 1967-68; assoc. prof. U. Toledo, 1968-77, prof., 1977-92; atty., ptnr. Garand, Bollinger, Saggese & St. Clair, Oregon, Ohio, 1992—; bd. dirs. Toledo Mental Health Ctr., 1977-79; mem. Ohio Coun. Mental Health Ctrs., Columbus, 1978-79; dir. honors programs U. Toledo. Author: (poetry) Daymarks and Beacons, 1983; contbr. numerous articles to profl. jours. Organizer Students Toledo Organized for Peace, 1970-71; mem. Lucas County Dem. Party, 1990—. With U.S. Army, 1955-57. Mem. ABA, AAU (exec. com. 1973-74), Ohio Bar Assn., Toledo Bar Assn., Ohio Acad. Trial Lawyers, Toledo Power Squadron (commdg. officer 1981), Bay View Yacht Club, Masons (32 degree), Shriners, Ancient Order Friars, Phi Alpha Delta Law Soc. Home: 3353 Christie Blvd Toledo OH 43606-2862 Office: Garand Bollinger Saggese & St Clair 445 Earlwood Ave Oregon OH 43616-2744

ST. CLAIR, HAL KAY, electrical engineer; b. Los Angeles, Oct. 11, 1925; s. Millard T. and Ruth (McGrew) S. C.; m. Jane Creely, June 24, 1949; children: Gregory, Russell, Elizabeth. Student, U. So. Calif., 1943-44; BS, U. Calif.-Berkeley, 1946, MS, 1948. Research engr. Marchant Calculators, Emeryville, Calif., 1948-52; project engr. RCA, Camden, N.J., 1953-54; program mgr. IBM, San Jose, Calif., 1954-69; tech. staff IBM, Boca Raton, Fla., 1969-72; mgr. input/output devel., 1972-75, mgr. gen. lab. devel., 1975-81, mgr. small comml. systems engring., 1981-83; ergonomics adviser div. hdqrs. staff IBM, White Plains, N.Y., 1983-85, devel. engr., 1986-88, ret., 1988; instr. U. Calif. Extension Div., 1951-52; tech. adv. U.S. Nat. Com. Internat. Electrotechnical Commn., 1967-69. Mem. Republican Central Com. of Calif., 1962-66. Served to lt. (j.g.) USNR, 1943-46. Mem. IEEE, SAR, Mensa, Phi Beta Kappa, Sigma Xi, Tau Beta Pi, Eta Kappa Nu. Home: 17137 Bernardo Oaks Dr San Diego CA 92128-2104

ST. CLAIR, JAMES DRAPER, lawyer; b. Akron, Ohio, Apr. 14, 1920; s. Clinton Draper and Margaret Joanna (Glenn) St. C.; m. Asenath Nestle, Nov. 25, 1944; children: Margaret Nestle, David Scott, Thomas Bruce. Student, Augustana Coll., 1938-39; AB, U. Ill., 1941; LLB, Harvard U., 1947; LLD, Gettysburg Coll., 1975, New Eng. Sch. Law, 1975, Emerson Coll., 1993. Bar: Mass. Assoc. Hale & Dorr, Boston, 1947-52; jr. ptnr. Hale & Dorr, 1952-56, sr. ptnr., 1956-95; spl. counsel to Pres. Richard Nixon, 1974; lectr. Harvard Law Sch.; asst. counsel to Army, Army-McCarthy Hearings, 1954; co-mng. trustee Amelia Peabody Found., 1985—. Author: (with others) Assignments in Trial Practice, 1960. Mem. Town Meeting, Wellesley, Mass., 1963-73; gen. counsel United Fund, 1966; mem. Town of Wellesley Adv. Com., 1966-69; mem. steering com. Lawyers Com. for Civil Rights Under Law, 1968-73; mem. adv. com. Mass. Jud. Conf. Com. on Criminal Rules Project, 1972-73; Trustee, bd. dirs. Walker Home for Children, 1951-73, 75—; pres. Horizons for Youth, 1981-94, chmn. bd., 1994—; bd. dirs. The Met in Boston, The Boston Opera Assn.; mem. New Eng. Bapt. Health Care Corp., 1991—; chair mgmt. rev. com. Boston Police Dept., 1991-92; mem. Corporation Mass. Gen. Hosp., 1992—. Served to lt. USNR, 1942-45. Mem. ABA (council of litigation sect. 1974—), Boston Bar Assn. (council), Am. Law Inst., Am. Coll. Trial Lawyers, Practising Law Inst. (nat. adv. council 1967-73), New Eng. Law Inst. (adv. council 1970-71), Order of Coif. Republican. Conglist. Clubs: Brae Burn Country, Eastward Ho Country. Office: Hale & Dorr 60 State St Boston MA 02109-1816

ST. CLAIR, JAMES WILLIAM, lawyer; b. Charleston, W.Va., Apr. 1, 1935; s. James William and Daisy Catherine (Litz) St. C.; m. Doria Diana Arrington, Aug. 10, 1956; children: Patricia A. St. Clair Deford, Laura J. St. Clair Johnson, J. William, Samual A. AB in History, U. Va., 1957, LLB, 1960. Bar: Va. 1960, W.Va. 1960, U.S. Dist. Ct. (no. and so. dists.) W.Va. 1960, U.S. Ct. Appeals 1965, U.S. Supreme Ct. 1970. Ptnr. Marshall Harghbarer & St. Clair, Huntington, W.Va., 1960-70, Marshall & St. Clair, Huntington, 1970-80, Marshall, St. Clair & Levine, Huntington, 1980-89, St. Clair & Levine, Huntington, 1989—; bd. dirs. 1st Huntington Nat. Bank; dir., officer Huntington Realty Corp.; Gen. Allied Oil and Gas Corp., Frankfurt, Germany, Town and Country Shopping Ctr., Inc., Huntington. Pres., bd. mem. Cabell Wayne Hist. Soc., Huntington, 1970—, Greater Huntington Pk. Bd., 1971—. 1st lt. U.S. Army, 1957-62. Mem. ABA (law practice mgmt. sect., bd. mem. 1985-91). Democrat. Presbyn. Avocations: lawn and gardening. Home: 1805 Mccoy Rd Huntington WV 25701-4823 Office: St Clair & Levine 717 6th Ave Huntington WV 25701-2105

ST. CLAIR, JANE ELIZABETH, management executive; b. Concord, Mass., Aug. 15, 1944; d. James F. and Mary E. (Clyne) Connell. BA, Salem State Coll., 1969; MPH, Columbia U., N.Y.C., 1990. Field rep., safety program Am. Red Cross of Greater N.Y., 1971-72; program dir. Bronx Community Coll., N.Y., 1973-75; dir. edn. Council N.Y.C., Inc., 1975-77, asst. exec. dir., 1978; exec. dir. Regional Emergency Med. Services, N.Y., 1979-91; dir. Peace Corps, Kenya, 1991-94; adjunct asst. prof., Hunter Coll. N.Y., 1973-91. Contbr. articles to profl. jours. Mem. Emergency Cardic Care Com. N.Y., Heart Assn., Am. Soc. Safety Engrs., Profl. Edn. Com., Am. Red Cross, First Aid Com. Address: 1749 Highland Ave Apt 12A Clearwater FL 34616

ST. CLAIR, JESSE WALTON, JR., retired savings and loan executive; b. Phila., Jan. 15, 1930; s. Jesse Walton and Susan Elizabeth (Leath) St. C.; m. Elizabeth Anne Bartlett, Oct. 6, 1951; children: Jesse Walton III, Susan Elizabeth, Bruce Bartlett, Anne Leath. BA, Coll. of William and Mary, 1951; MBA, U. Pa., 1958; postgrad., Harvard U., 1968. Trainee Fed. Res. Bank, Phila., 1955-57; with Girard Trust Bank, Phila., 1957-78; asst. treas. Girard Trust Bank, 1960-64, asst. v.p., 1964-67, v.p., 1967-70, sr. v.p., 1970-75, exec. v.p., 1976-78; pres., chief exec. officer First Nat. Bank of Allentown (Pa.), 1978-82; chmn., chief exec. officer Wilmington Savs. Fund Soc., 1982-90, ret., 1990. Trustee emeritus endowment fund Coll. William and Mary; dir. Del. Mut. Ins. Co.; mem. exec. bd., v.p. fin. Delmarva coun. Boy Scouts Am.; trustee Wesley Coll.; bd. dirs. Ingleside Homes Inc. With USN, 1951-55. Mem. Wilmington Country Club, Theta Delta Chi. Republican. Methodist. Home: 4011 Springfield Ln Greenville Wilmington DE 19807

ST. CLAIR, MICHAEL, art dealer; b. Bradford, Pa., May 28, 1912. Student, Kans. City Art Inst., Colo. Springs Fine Arts Ctr. Instr. Okla. Art Ctr. Sch., Oklahoma City; dir. Babcock Galleries, N.Y.C., 1959—. Named Vanderslice scholar Kansas City Art Inst. Mem. Art Dealers Assn. Am. (founding mem. 1962), Architecture & Am. Art Drawing Soc. Office: Babcock Galleries 724 5th Ave New York NY 10019-4106

ST. CLAIR, ROBERT NEAL, English language and linguistics educator; b. Honolulu, Apr. 24, 1934; divorced; 1 child, Tiffany Neal. BA, U. Hawaii, 1964; MA, U. Wash., 1966, U. Calif., La Jolla, 1970; PhD, U. Kans., 1973. Asst. prof. Calif. State U., L.A., 1966-67; asst. prof. English and linguistics U. Louisville, 1974-75, assoc. prof., 1975-76, prof., 1978—; chmn. Forum for Interdisciplinary Rsch., Cancun, Mex., 1976, Curacao, Antilles, 1978; disting. vis. prof. N.Mex. State U., Las Cruces, 1978, Internat. Christian U., Tokyo, 1979. Author: Language and Social Psychology, 1976, Social Metaphors, 1990, Languages of the World, 1990, numerous others; editor

Lektos, 1974-78; contbr. over 400 articles and revs. to profl. jours. Sgt. U.S. Army, 1957-60. Grantee Philips Found., 1974, NEH, 1975-77, U.S. Office Edn., 1977-79. Mem. MLA, Nat. Coun. Tchrs. English, Coll. Composition Comm. Conf. Office: 9431 Westport Rd Ste 343 Louisville KY 40241-2225

ST. CLAIR, THOMAS MCBRYAR, mining and manufacturing company executive; b. Wilkinsburg, Pa., Sept. 26, 1935; s. Fred C. and Dorothy (Renner) St. C.; m. Sarah K. Stewart, Aug. 1, 1959; children—Janet, Susan, Carol. AB, Allegheny Coll., 1957; MS, MIT, 1958; grad. advanced mgmt. program, Harvard U. With Koppers Co., Inc., Pitts., 1958-88, asst. to gen. mgr. engring. and constrn. div., 1966-69, comptroller, asst. treas., 1969-78, pres. Engineered Metal Products Group, 1978-83, v.p., asst. to chmn., 1983-84, v.p., treas., chief fin. officer, 1984-88; sr. v.p., chief fin. officer Phelps Dodge Corp., Phoenix, 1989—; bd. dirs. Nortrust of Ariz. Bd. dirs., treas. Herberger Theater Ctr., Phoenix; trustee Allegheny Coll. Mem. Fin. Execs. Inst., Duquesne Club (Pitts.), Univ. Club (Pitts. and Phoenix). Presbyterian. Office: Phelps Dodge Corp 2600 N Central Ave Phoenix AZ 85004-3050

ST. CLAIRE, FRANK ARTHUR, lawyer; b. Charlotte, N.C., June 16, 1949. BS, MIT, 1972; JD, NYU, 1975. Bar: Tex. 1975, U.S. Dist. Ct. (no. dist.) Tex. 1985. Assoc. James H. Wallenstein, Dallas, 1975-78; v.p. Wallenstein & St. Claire, Dallas, 1978-81; pres. Frank A. St. Claire, P.C., Dallas, 1981-84; ptnr. St. Claire & Case, P.C., Dallas, 1984-88, pres., 1988—; chmn. bd. Sunbelt Empire Title Co., Dallas, 1983-88; pres. St. Claire & Assocs., Dallas, 1993—; chmn. real estate section Godwin & Carlton, P.C., Dallas, 1994—. Author: Texas Condominium Law, 1986; contbr. articles to profl. jours. Ofcl. del. Dallas to Baltic Legal Conf., Riga, Latvia, 1990. Mem. ABA, Tex. Bar Assn. (study of uniform condominium act com., legis. liaison com. 1981-85, vice chmn. 1981-82, chmn. 1982-85, chmn. condominium and coop. housing com. 1985-89, title ins. com., mem. coun. real estate, probate & trust coun. 1991—), Dallas Bar Assn., Community Assn. Inst. (bd. dirs. Dallas-Ft. Worth chpt. 1984-85, 87-89, pres.-elect 1989-90), Real Estate Fin. Exec. Assn., Am. Coll. Real Estate Lawyers (planning com. 1990—, chmn. practice tech. com. 1993—, mem. common interest ownership com. 1986—, alternative dispute resolution com. 1993—), Tex. Coll. Real Estate Attys. (chmn. projects com. 1991-92, bd. dirs. 1994—). Episcopalian. Office: NationsBank Plz 901 Main St Ste 3300 Dallas TX 75202

ST. CYR, ROGER JOSEPH, banker; b. Burlington, Vt., July 13, 1946; s. Alfred Joseph and Ursula (Paquin) St. Cyr.; m. Sandra Rose Flanagan, June 14, 1975; children: Molly, Maureen, Emelie. ABS, Champlain Coll., Burlington, Vt., 1966; student, U. Md., Heidelburg, Germany, 1966-68; BS Double Major, U. Dayton, Ohio, 1972; MBA, Capital U., Columbus, Ohio, 1980. Data processing mgr. Third Nat. Bank, Dayton, Ohio, 1971-74, Park One, Columbus, Ohio, 1974-75, Blue Shield, Columbus, 1975-76; data processing mgr. BancOhio Nat. Bank, Columbus, 1976-80, sales mgr., cash mgmt., 1980-84; v.p. nat. accounts BancOhio Nat. Bank, 1984-87; v.p. & mgr. nat. accts. Nat. City Trust, Columbus, 1987-91, v.p., sales mgr. institutional trust, 1991—. Author: Thesis-Cash Management, 1985, Thesis-Psychological Study on How Acquisition Targets React to and Adapt to Culture Change, 1991. Chair Sta. WOSU (PBS) Fundraiser - Auction Columbus; Bd. Mem. Friends of Sta. WOSU (PBS) Columbus. With U.S. Army 1966-69, Fed. Rep. Germany. Mem. Athletic Club of Columbus, Muirfield Country Club. Office: Nat City Trust 155 E Broad St Columbus OH 43251-0050

ST. FLORIAN, FRIEDRICH GARTLER, architect, educator, university dean; b. Graz, Austria, Dec. 21, 1932; came to U.S., 1967, naturalized, 1973; s. Friedrich and Anna Maria (Prassl) G.; m. Livia Campanella, Jan. 12, 1967; children: Alisia, Ilaria. Diploma in architecture, U. Graz, 1958; M.S. in Architecture, Columbia U., 1962. Instr. architecture Columbia U., N.Y.C., 1962-63; asst. prof. R.I. Sch. Design, Providence, 1963-70; assoc. prof. R.I Sch. Design, 1974-77, prof. architecture, 1980—, chmn. div. archtl. studies, 1977-78, dean of architecture, 1978-88; chief critic European Honors Program R.I. Sch. Design, Rome, 1991-93; vis. assoc. prof. MIT, Cambridge, 1970-71, 74-75; prin. St. Florian Assos., architects, Providence, 1978—. Works exhibited Nat. Inst. Architects, Rome, 1967, 14th Triennale, Milan, 1968, Moderna Museet, Stockholm, 1969, Hayden Gallery, MIT, 1973, Mus. Modern Art, N.Y.C., 1975, Drawing Ctr., N.Y.C., 1979, Walker Art Ctr., Mpls., 1980, George Pompidou Ctr., Paris, 1994. Recipient Nat. Endowment for Arts award, 1972-73, 76-77, 79, 26th ann. Progressive Architecture Mag. award, 1979; Ctr. for Advanced Visual Studies fellow MIT, 1970-77, Rome Prize fellow, fellow Am. Acad. in Rome, 1985. Mem. AIA. Address: RI Sch Design Providence RI 02903

ST. GEORGE, JUDITH ALEXANDER, author; b. Westfield, N.J., Feb. 26, 1931; d. John Heald and Edna (Perkins) Alexander; m. David St. George, June 5, 1954; children: Peter, James, Philip, Sarah Anne. BA, Smith Coll., 1952. Author: Turncoat Winter, Rebel Spring, 1970, The Girl with Spunk, 1975, By George, Bloomers!, 1976, The Chinese Puzzle of Shag Island, 1976, The Shad Are Running, 1977, The Shadow of the Shaman, 1977, The Halo Wind, 1978, The Halloween Pumpkin Smasher, 1978, Mystery at St. Martin's, 1979, The Amazing Voyage of the New Orleans, 1980, Haunted, 1980, Call Me Margo, 1981, The Mysterious Girl in the Garden, 1981, The Brooklyn Bridge: They Said It Couldn't Be Built, 1982 (Am. Book award), Do You See What I See?, 1982, In The Shadow of the Bear, 1983, What's Happening to My Junior Year?, 1983, Who's Scared? Not Me!, 1984, The Mount Rushmore, 1985 (Christopher award), Panama Canal: Gateway to the World, 1989 (Golden Kite award), The White House, 1990, Mason and Dixon's Line of Fire, 1991, Dear Dr. Bell...Your Friend Helen Keller, 1992, Crazy Horse, 1994; (from filmscript) A View to a Kill, 1985; (from screenscript) Tales of the Gold Monkey, 1983. Mem. adv. coun. on children's lit. Rutgers U., 1977—; chmn. ednl. com. Bklyn. Bridge Centennial Commn., 1981-83. Mem. Soc. Children's Book Writers, Author's Guild. Episcopalian. Avocations: tennis, hiking, travel. Home: 8 Binney Rd Old Lyme CT 06371

ST. GEORGE, NICHOLAS JAMES, lawyer, manufactured housing company executive; b. Waltham, Mass., Feb. 11, 1939; s. Louis and Rose (Argonti) St. G.; B.A. in Econs., Coll. William and Mary, 1960, J.D., 1965; children: Blane Stephen, Nicholas John; m. Eugenia Metzger, July 25, 1987. Trainee, Gen. Electric Co., Schenectady, 1960; admitted to Va. bar, 1965; trust rep. Va. Nat. Bank, Norfolk, 1965-66; group v.p.-in-charge investment banking dept. Ferguson Enterprises, Newport News, Va., 1977-78; pres., chief exec. officer Oakwood Homes Corp., Greensboro, N.C., 1979—, also dir.; dir. Am. Bankers Ins. Group, First Union Nat. Bank Greensboro, Legg Mason, Inc.; dir. Manufactured Housing Inst.; trustee Marshall-Wythe Sch. Law Coll. William and Mary. 1st lt. U.S. Army, 1960-62. Mem. ABA, Va. Bar Assn., Am. Mgmt. Assn. Republican. Roman Catholic. Office: Oakwood Homes Corp 2225 S Holden Rd Greensboro NC 27407-4605

ST. GEORGE, WILLIAM ROSS, lawyer, retired naval officer, consultant; b. Southport, N.C., Nov. 19, 1924; s. William B. and Ila (Ross) St. G.; m. Emma Louise Bridger, June 10, 1950; children—Victoria Butler, William Ross, Susan Bridger. B.S., U.S. Naval Acad., 1946; J.D., George Washington U., 1953. Bar: D.C. 1953, U.S. Supreme Ct. 1964, Calif. 1980. Commd. ensign U.S. Navy, 1946, advanced through grades to vice adm., 1973; comdg. officer U.S.S. Josephus Daniels, 1969-70; comdr. Cruiser-Destroyer Flotilla 11, also comdr. Cruiser-Destroyer Flotilla 3, 1973; dep. and chief staff to comdr.-in-chief U.S. Pacific Fleet, 1973-76; comdr. Naval Surface Force, U.S. Pacific Fleet, 1976-79; ret., 1979; sole practice San Diego, 1980—. Decorated D.S.M. with oak leaf cluster, Legion of Merit, Bronze Star. Republican. Home: 862 San Antonio Pl San Diego CA 92106-3057 Office: 1110 Rosecrans St Fl 2D San Diego CA 92106-2630

ST. GERMAIN, FERNAND JOSEPH, congressman; b. Blackstone, Mass.; s. Albert Joseph and Pearl (Talaby) St Germain; m. Rachel O'Neill, Aug. 20, 1953; children: Laurene, Lisette. Ph.B in Social Sci, Providence Coll., 1948, LL.D., 1965; LL.B., Boston U., 1955; J.S.D. (hon.), Suffolk U., 1976; D.C.L. (hon.), Our Lady of Providence Sem., 1968; D.B.A. (hon.), Bryant Coll., 1981; D.Public Service (hon.), Roger Williams Coll., 1981; LL.B., Brown U., 1985. Bar: R.I. 1956, Fed. 1957, U.S. Supreme Ct. 1983. Mem. R.I. Ho. of Reps., 1952-60; mem. 87th to 100th Congresses from 1st R.I. Dist., 1961-1989, chmn. house com. on banking fin. and urban affairs, 1980-88. Served with AUS, 1949-52. Recipient Silver Shingle award for disting. public service Boston U. Sch. Law Alumni Assn., 1981, Alumni award

disting. pub. service Boston U. Sch. Law, 1982. Mem. ABA, R.I., Bar Assn. Fed. Bar Assn., alumni assns. Our Lady of Providence Sem., Providence Coll., Boston U. Law Sch., Am. Legion. Office: 7601 Lewinsville Rd Ste 205 Mc Lean VA 22102

ST GERMAIN, GEORGE, retail executive. With Applebaums Food Markets Inc., Saint Paul, Minn., 1958-78; with Jerry's Enterprises Inc, Mpls., 1978—, now v.p. grocery ops. Office: Jerry's Enterprises Inc 5101 Vernon Ave S Minneapolis MN 55436*

ST. GOAR, HERBERT, food corporation executive; b. Hamburg, Germany, Apr. 7, 1916; came to U.S., 1938, naturalized, 1943; s. Otto and Thekla St.G.; m. Maria Karsch, Sept. 3, 1954; children: Edward, Elisabeth. Student schs., Hamburg, Germany; LL.B., Chattanooga Coll. Law, 1943. With Internat. Harvester Co., Hamburg, Germany, 1936-38; with Dixie Saving Stores, Inc., Chattanooga, 1938—; pres. Dixie Saving Stores, Inc., 1969—, chief exec. officer, 1969—. Bd. dirs. Chattanooga Opera Assn., Jr. C. of C., 1945-54; mem. Hamilton County Juvenile Ct. Commn. Served with Intelligence Sect., U.S. Army, World War II. Decorated Bronze Star, Legion of Merit.; Named Disting. Citizen Chattanooga, 1979. Mem. Southeastern Food Coop. Assn. (past pres.), Tenn. Wholesale Grocers Assn. (bd. dirs. 1988-91), Retailer-Owned Food Distrbrs. Assn. (bd. dirs. 1988—), NGA Retailer-Owned Exec. Coun., Asparagus Club. Home: 1502 Hixson Pike Chattanooga TN 37405-2431 Office: PO Box 1637 Chattanooga TN 37401-1637

SAINT-JACQUES, BERNARD, linguistics educator; b. Montreal, Que., Can., Apr. 26, 1928; s. Albert and Germaine (Lefebvre) Saint-J.; m. Marguerite Fauquenoy. M.A., Sophia U., Tokyo, 1962; M.S., Georgetown U., 1964; Doctorat es Lettres and Scis. Humaines, Paris U., 1975. Asst. prof. linguistics U. B.C., Vancouver, 1967-69; assoc. prof. U. B.C., 1969-78, prof., 1978-90, prof. emeritus, 1991—; prof. Aichi U. Japan, 1990—; mem. U.S. Citizen Amb. Program. Author: Structural Analysis of Modern Japanese, 1971, Aspects sociolinguistiques du bilinguisme canadien, 1976, Language and Ethnic Relations, 1979, Japanese Studies in Canada, 1985, Studies in Language and Culture, 1995. Leave fellow Can. Council, 1974; profl. fellow Japan Found., 1981; research fellow French Govt., 1982, Ohira Programme, Japan, 1983. Fellow Royal Soc. Can. Acad.; mem. Sociolinguistic Assn. (co-editor); Linguistic Soc. Am., Can. Soc. Asian Studies, Can. Linguistics Assn. Office: U BC, Dept Linguistics, Vancouver, BC Canada V6T 1Z1 also: Aichi ShuKutoKu U., Katahira NagaKute, NagaKute-cho Aichi-gun Aichi 480-11, Japan

SAINT-JACQUES VALLÉE, MADELEINE, advertising agency executive; b. Montreal, Can., June 27, 1935; d. Henri and Marie-Jeanne (Ostiguy) S.J. BA, U. Montreal, 1972. Writer, producer Young & Rubicam, Montreal, 1955-70, creative dir., 1970-77, exec. v.p., mng. dir., 1977-90, pres., 1990-94, chmn. bd. dirs., 1995; bd. dirs. Télé Métropole Inc., Ultramar Corp., Premier Choix: TVEC Inc.; bd. govs. Inno-Centre Québec; v.p. Soc. d'édition de la revue Forces, La Corp. des Célébrations du 350e anniversaire de Montréal, 1989-93; adv. bd. Guarant Trust, 1979-84. Bd. dirs. Internat. Mag. Mgmt., 1980-92. 1st v.p. Children's Broadcast Inst., 1972-77; grievance com. L'Union des Artistes, 1976-78; gen. v.p. comm. divsn. Centraide campaign, 1980, v.p. bd. dirs 1983-87; v.p. Coun. Arts Montreal Urban Community, 1979-89; co-pres. Com. Econ. Promotion Montreal, 1981-82; bd. govs. McGill U. 1986-90; bd. dirs. Terry Fox Humanitarian Award Program, St. Mary's Hosp. Found., Can. Mental Health Assn., 1975-79, Soc. Devel. Industries and Culture of Comm. (SDICC), 1979-82, Via Rail Can. Inc., 1977-82, Soc. Devel. Montreal, 1982-88, Found. Films of World Festival, Montreal, 1990-92. Recipient advt. award Assn. Can. Advertisers, 1975, 76, Gold award, 1977, award distinction Faculty commerce and adminstrn. Concordia U., 1992, mgmt. achievement award Mgmt. Undergrad. Soc. McGill U., 1993. Mem. Can. Club Montréal (bd. dirs., pres. 1993—, pres. centennial yr. 1987), Club St.-Denis, Forest and Stream, Publicité Club Montreal (pres. 1972-73). Roman Catholic. Avocations: skiing, tennis, golf. Office: Young & Rubicam 12th Fl, 1600 René Lévesque Blvd W, Montreal, PQ Canada H3H 1P9

ST. JAMES, LYN, business owner, professional race car driver; b. Cleve., Mar. 13, 1947; d. Alfred W. and Maxine W. (Rawson) Cornwall; m. John Raymond Carusso, Dec. 7, 1970 (div. 1979); m. Roger Lessman, Feb. 27, 1993; 1 stepchild, Lindsay. Cert. in piano, St. Louis Inst. Music, 1967. Sec. Cleve. dist. sales office U.S. Steel Corp., 1967-69, Mike Roth Sales Corp., Euclid, Ohio, 1969-70; co-owner, v.p. Dynasales Fla., Hollywood, 1970-79; owner, pres. Autodyne, Ft. Lauderdale, Fla., 1974—; Creative Images, Inc., 1979—; professional race car driver, 1979—; ranked 11th Indpls. 500, 1992; race car driver Ford Motor Co., Dearborn, Mich., 1981—, spokesperson, cons., 1981—; media spokesperson 3M Co., Mpls., 1987. Author: Lyn St. James Car Owner's Manual, 1989; contbg. editor automotive articles Seventeen mag., 1987—, Cosmopolitan mag., 1989-90. Bd. trustees Women's Sports Found., N.Y.C., 1988—. Recipient Rookie of the Year, AutoWeek Magazine, 1984, Woman of Yr. award McCalls mag., 1986, Leadership award Girl Scouts U.S., 1988, Rookie of the Year at the Victory Banquet, 1992; first woman since Janet Evans to qualify for the Indpls. 500. Mem. Internat. Motorsports Assn., Sports Car Club of Am. Republican. Avocation: tennis.Only woman winner in the Internat. Motor Sports Assn.'s Camel GTO series; holder of 21 auto racing speed records; first woman to win a professional road race driving solo; first woman to drive over 200 mph on an oval track. Office: U.S. Auto Club PO Box 660460 Dallas TX 75266-0460

ST. JEAN, ANDRE, paper executive; b. 1947. With Donahue CO., Quebec City, Can., 1966-90; with Noranda Forest USA, Inc., Madawaska, Maine, 1990—, now CFO. Office: Noranda Forest USA Inc Bridge St Madawaska ME 04756*

ST. JEAN, GARRY, professional basketball coach; m. Mary Jane St. Jean; children: Emily, Gregory. B in Phys. Edn., Springfield (Mass.) Coll., 1973, M in Phys. Edn., postgrad. cert. Head coach Chicopee (Mass.) High Sch., 1973-80; coll. scout, asst. bench coach, asst. dir. player pers. Milw. Bucks, 1980-86; asst. coach, asst. player pers. dir. N.J. Nets, 1986-88; asst. coach Golden State Warriors, 1988-92; head coach Sacramento Kings, 1992—. Office: Sacramento Kings One Sports Pkwy Sacramento CA 95834*

ST. JEAN, GUY, electric power industry executive; b. Montreal, Que., Can., Oct. 8, 1941; s. Jean-Paul and Marie Marthe (Vandemeulebroecke) St. J. BSc in Math. and Physics, Sir George Williams U., Montreal, 1964; MSc in Physics, U. Que., Varennes, 1977; postgrad., Internat. Mgmt. Inst., Geneva. Analyst spl. tests Hydro-Que. Montreal, 1965-67, analyst self-synchronization large generators, 1967-69; researcher Electricité de France, Paris, 1969-70; researcher Hydro-Que., Varennes, 1970-83, program mgr., 1975-83, mgr. switchgear rsch., 1983-86, mgr. power apparatus rsch., 1986—; lectr. grad. course Ecole Poly. Montreal, 1977-84, thesis dir., 1978-88; mem. Can. com. Internat. Electrotech. commn., Ottawa, Ont., Can., 1985—, chmn. coms. 17 and 37, 1985—; Can. rep. Internat. Commn. Electric Rsch., 1982—; mem. Conf. Bd. Can. 1991—. Author: Power System Recovery Voltages, 1987; also over 50 articles; patentee synthetic test cir., cir. for protecting device, surge arrester, U.S. Recipient prize paper award IEEE Power Engring. Soc., 1986, 87, R&D 100 award R&D mag., 1990. Fellow IEEE (technol. editor Can. Rev. 1988-91); mem. Can. Standard Assn. (chmn. 1985—). Avocations: skiing, windsurfing, sailing and officiating regattas. Home: 560 St-Laurent Apt 122, Longueuil, PQ Canada J4H 3X3 Office: Hydro-Quebec, Apparatus Rsch Dept PO Box 1000, Varennes, PQ Canada J0L 2P0 *The pursuit of truth will set you free, even if you never catch up to it*

ST. JEAN, JOSEPH, JR., micropaleontologist, educator; b. Tacoma, July 24, 1923; s. Joseph Leger and Ruby Pearl (Burg) St. J.; m. Elena Mikhailovna Melnik, Sept. 22, 1951. B.S., Coll. Puget Sound, 1949; M.A., Ind. U., 1953, Ph.D., 1956. Field asst., party chief Ind. Geol. Survey, summers 1950-53; instr. Kans. State U., Manhattan, 1951-52; instr., asst. prof. Trinity Coll., Hartford, Conn., 1955-57; faculty U. N.C., Chapel Hill, 1957-90; prof. geology U. N.C., 1966-90, gen. coll. advisor, 1979-90, ret., 1990; peer reviewer NSF, 1966—; profl. jours., 1960—. 2d violinist, Durham (N.C.) Symphony Orch., 1977-84; contbr. sects. to McGraw-Hill Ency. Sci. and Tech; papers to paleontol., biol. jours. Served as Q.M. USNR, 1942-45. Grantee Geol. Soc. Am., 1956-58; Grantee AEC, 1958-60; Grantee NSF,

1960-62; Grantee U. N.C. Faculty Research Council, 1960-62; Grantee Soc. Sigma Xi, 1954-56. Mem. Paleontol. Soc., Soc. Econ. Paleontologists and Mineralogists, Carolina Geol. Soc., Paleontol. Rsch. Instn., N.C. Acad. Scis., Paleontol. Assn. London, Sigma Xi. Home: 1212 Hillsborough Rd Chapel Hill NC 27516-8712 Office: U NC Dept Geology CB #3315 Mitchell Hall Chapel Hill NC 27599-3315

ST. JOHN, ADRIAN, II, retired army officer; b. Ft. Leavenworth, Kans., Nov. 16, 1921; s. Adrian and Marie (McMahon) St John; m. Petronella Elizabeth Durham, Jan. 19, 1943; children: Adrian III, Brian. BS, U.S. Mil. Acad., 1943; MA, U. Va., 1951; MPA, Am. U., 1981; postgrad., Army War Coll., 1960, U. Hawaii, 1963, Am. U., 1977-82. Commd. 2d lt. U.S. Army, 1943, advanced through grades to maj. gen., 1969; co. comdg. officer 15th Cav., 1943-45; intelligence staff officer Berlin, 1945-47; bn. comdg. officer 3d Bn., 31st Inf. Regt., Korea, 1954; comdr. 73d Tank Bn., Korea, 1955; mem. faculty Command and Gen. Staff Coll., Ft. Leavenworth, 1956-59; faculty adviser Iranian Def. Coll., 1959; S.E. Asia plans officer G3, U.S. Army-Pacific, 1960-64; long range plans br. Strategic Div., Orgn. Joint Chiefs of Staff, Washington, 1964-66; chief Surface P & O Div. J3, USMACV, Vietnam, 1966-67; comdg. officer 14th Armored Cav. Regt., Europe, 1967-69; asst. div. comdr. 4th Armored Div., Europe, 1969-70; chief Strategic Plans and Policy Div. J5, Orgn. Joint Chiefs of Staff, Washington, 1970-71; dir. plans Army Gen. Staff, Washington, 1971-72; comdg. gen. 1st Armored Div., Europe, 1972-74; vice dir. joint staff Joint Chiefs of Staff, 1974-76; ret., 1976; mem. adv. council on internat. security affairs Republican Nat. Com., 1977-80; del. Va. State Rep. Conv., 1980, 81; sr. mil. adv. U.S. Negotiating Del. Mut. Balanced Force Reductions, Vienna, 1982-88; Joint Chiefs of Staff rep. U.S. Del. Conventional Stability Talks, Vienna, 1987-88, negotiations on Conventional Armed Forces, Europe Brussels, Europe, 1989-92; del.; presenter Congress Arms Control Mid. East, Delphi, Greece, 1994; U.S. del. World Helicopter Championships, Moscow, 1994; chmn. operational working group internat. conf. on arms control in Middle East, Jordan, 1994. Co-chmn. orchestral benefit ball Austrian Embassy, 1993, 94; mem. pres. club Heritage Found. Decorated D.S.M. with oak leaf cluster, Silver Star, Legion of Merit with 3 oak leaf clusters, Bronze Star with V device, Joint Svc. Commendation medal, Army Commendation medal with oak leaf cluster, Joint Meritorious Unit award, French Croix de Guerre with silver star, Vietnamese Gallantry Cross with palm; recipient European Comdr. in Chief's Individual Project partnership award, 1968, Presdl. award Disting. Citizen, 1993, Dept. State Superior honor award, 1989, 91, Dept. of Def. medal for disting. pub. svc., 1992. Mem. Am. Security Coun., Am. Fgn. Affairs Coun., Pres. Club Heritage Found., World Affairs Coun., Pacific-Sierra Rsch. Corp. (cons.). Roman Catholic. Home: #118 9110 Belvoir Woods Pkwy Ft Belvoir VA 22060-2717 Office: Pentagon Bldg Washington DC 20301 *There are no limits to the heights man can reach so long as he cares not who gets the credit.*

ST. JOHN, ANTHONY PAUL, automotive executive; b. Washington, Jan. 13, 1937; s. Sterling and Beulah (Marston) St. J.; m. Myra Grace Cornfeld, Oct. 30, 1959; children: James Sterling, Ivy Kemp, Mary Marston. LLB, U. Va., 1960; cert. Advanced Mgmt., Harvard U., 1979. Bar: Md. 1961. Various positions Bethlehem (Pa.) Steel Corp., 1960-78, asst. v.p. indsl. relations, 1978-83, asst. v.p., asst. gen. counsel, 1983, v.p. union relations, 1984-86; v.p. human resources Chrysler Corp., Detroit, 1986—; chmn. litigation com. Bus. Roundtable, Washington, N.Y.C., 1974-77; bd. dirs. Labor Policy Assn., Washington, 1988—; chmn. indsl. rels. com. Motor Vehicle Mfrs. Assn. Vice-chmn. Moravian Acad. Bd. Trustees, Bethlehem, 1982-85; vice chmn. Greater Detroit Alliance of Bus., 1987-89, chmn., 1989-90; bd. dirs. ARC Southeastern Mich., Detroit, 1986-90, Henry Ford Hosp. Northeastern Group, 1991. 1st lt. U.S. Army, 1960-61. Mem. ABA, Detroit C. of C. (bd. dirs.), Orchard Lake Country Club, Saucon Valley country Club (Bethlehem), Lehigh Country Club (Allentown, Pa.). Republican. Avocation: golf. Home: 3701 Lakecrest Dr Bloomfield Hills MI 48304-3038 Office: Chrysler Corp 12000 Chrysler Dr Detroit MI 48288-1899

ST. JOHN, BILL DEAN, diversified equipment and services company executive; b. Wewoka, Okla., 1931. BBA, So. Meth. U., 1952. Asst. treas. Seaboard Oil Co., 1954-58; auditor Alford Merony & Co., 1958-60; v.p. fin. Can. Refractories Ltd., 1968; with Dresser Industries Inc., Dallas, 1960—; treas. Ideco div. Dresser Industries, Dallas, 1961-63; fin. contr. Dresser Industries Inc., Dallas, 1970-73, staff v.p. fin. svcs., 1975-76, v.p. acctg., 1976-80; exec. v.p. adminstrn. Dresser Industries Inc., Dallas, 1980-92, vice chmn., 1992—, CFO, 1993—. With U.S. Army, 1952-54. Mem. AICPA, Mfrs.' Alliance for Productivity and Innovation (fin. coun.), The Conf. Bd. (chief administrs. officers coun.). Office: Dresser Industries Inc PO Box 718 2001 Ross Ave Dallas TX 75221-0718

ST. JOHN, BOB, journalist, columnist, author; b. Canton, Okla., Jan. 10, 1937. Sportswriter, columnist, until 1978; gen. columnist Dallas Morning News, 1978—. Author: Tex, On Down the Road, 1977, Landry: The Man Inside, The Landry Legend, 1990, Sketches, While The Music Lasts, 1989, South Padre: The Island and its People, Heart of a Lion, 1991, others; over 150 radio, TV interviews. Recipient Disting. Alumni award U. North Tex., 1986, two 1st place awards Pro Football Writers Assn. Am., over 40 awards for newspaper writing. Office: The Dallas Morning News Communications Ctr PO Box 655237 Dallas TX 75265-5237

ST. JOHN, DAVID MARSHALL, poet, English educator; b. Fresno, Calif., July 24, 1949; s. Dean and Phyllis (Fries) St. J.; m. Bonnie Gail Bedford, Dec. 8, 1968 (div. 1974); 1 child, David Wyle. B.A. in English, Calif. State U., Fresno, 1972; M.F.A. in English and Creative Writing, U. Iowa, Iowa City, 1974. Asst. prof. Oberlin Coll., Ohio, 1975-77; asst. prof. Johns Hopkins U., Balt., 1977-81, assoc. prof., 1981—. Assoc. editor Field mag., Oberlin, 1975-77; poetry editor The Antioch Rev., 1982—. Author: (poetry vols.) Hush, 1976 (Great Lakes Coll. Assn. New Writers award for best first book of poetry 1976); The Shore, 1980 (James D. Phelan award San Francisco Found. 1980); No Heaven, 1985. Nat. Endowment Arts fellow in poetry, 1976, 83; John S. Guggenheim Meml. fellow in poetry, 1977; Am. Acad. and Inst. Arts and Letters Rome fellow in lit., 1984. Democrat. Avocation: tennis. Office: The Writing Seminars Johns Hopkins U Charles & 34th Baltimore MD 21218

ST. JOHN, HOWARD CHAMBERS, lawyer, bank executive; s. Howard R. and Christine St. John; m. Phyllis Ertrel, Sept. 29, 1946; children: Ellen, Victoria St. John Gilligan, Kent Ertel. LL.B, Albany Law Sch., 1948. Sr. ptnr. Howard C. St. John and Assocs., 1948—; former dist. attorney Ulster County, N.Y.; with Ulster Savs. Bank, Kingston, N.Y., 1965—, chmn. bd. dirs., CEO, 1988—; bd. dirs. Mid-Hudson Pattern Inc.; bd. dirs. Cen. Hudson Corp., vice-chmn., 1987—; chmn. com. on fin. Cen. Hudson Corp., 1986—; chmn. Stavo Industries, Kingston; former assoc. gen. counsel N.Y. Joint Legis. Com. on Reapportionment. U.S. del. to Switzerland, Spain, China, 1978; appointed by Gov. Cuomo to N.Y. State Banking Bd., 1986; former mem. Ulster County Community Coll. Adv. Coun. New Devel. Ctr. for Bus.; trustee Kingston YMCA, Albany Law Sch. With USAF, 1943-45. Mem. Savs. Bank Assn. N.Y. State, Nat. Coun. Savs. Insts., N.Y. State Bar Assn., ABA, Justinian Soc., Kiwanis. Office: Cen Hudson Gas & Electric 284 South Ave Poughkeepsie NY 12601-4823

ST. JOHN, JOHN, food company executive; b. Battle Creek, Mich., Aug. 8, 1921; s. Raymond Martin and Hazel (Eastman) St. J.; m. Lorraine Margaret McCarthy, Feb. 27, 1943; 1 dau., Shannon Elaine. B.A., Mich. State U., 1943. With Minute Maid Co. (and predecessors), 1949—, fin. v.p., 1963-65, pres., 1965-69; v.p. finance and ops. Citrus Central, Inc., Orlando, Fla., 1969-71; exec. v.p. Citrus Central, Inc., 1971-87, mgmt. cons., 1987—; dir., chmn. Farm Credit Capital Corp., Kansas City, Mo., 1985-87; bd. dirs. Treasure Coast Citrus, Inc., Ft. Pierce, Fla., 1989—. Past pres., bd. dirs. Central Fla. unit Am. Cancer Soc. Served with USAAF, 1943-46. Mem. Country Club of Orlando, Racquet Club (Winter Park, Fla.), Univ. Club (Lansing, Mich.). Episcopalian. Home: 910 Pace Ave Maitland FL 32751-5768 Office: 2251 Lucien Way Ste 220 Maitland FL 32751-7027

ST. JOHN, KATHERINE IVA, artistic director, dance educator; b. St. Paul, Nov. 18, 1948; d. Arthur E. and Lillian Faye (Teetsell) Tester; m. Curtis St. John (div.). BA, U. Utah, 1989; MA, Brigham Young U., 1994, U. Utah, 1994. Instr. U. Utah, Salt Lake City, 1989-94; dir. Ea. Arts, Salt Lake City, 1988—; artistic dir. Internat. Dance Theatre, Salt Lake City,

1993—. Author, choreographer: Radif E Raos; contbr. articles to profl. publs. Vol. Salt Lake Ethnic Arts Coun.; bd. chair Assn. Students Univ. Utah, 1992; speaker Utah Humanities Coun. Grantee Utah Arts Coun., Salt Lake City Arts Coun. Mem. Internat. Orgn. of Folk Arts, Mid. East Studies Assn., Soc. Ethnomusicology, Congress on Rsch. in Dance, Dance and the Child Internat., Phi Kappa Phi. Home: PO Box 526362 Salt Lake City UT 84152 Office: Eastern Arts Ethnic Dance Co PO Box 526362 Salt Lake City UT 84152

ST. JOHN, RICHARD See HARRIS, RICHARD

ST. LAURENT, DAVID FRANCIS, insurance company executive. With Electric Mut. Liability Ins. Co., Beverly, Mass., 1989—, pres. Office: Electric Mut Liability Ins Co 152 Conant St Beverly MA 01915*

SAINT LAURENT, YVES (HENRI DONAT MATHIEU), couturier; b. Oran, Algeria, Aug. 1, 1936; s. Charles Mathieu and Lucinne-Andree (Wilbaux) Saint L. Student, Lycée d'Oran. Worked with Christian Dior, 1954-57, successor, 1957-60; adminstr. Société Yves Saint Laurent, 1962—. Costume designer (ballets) Cyrano de Bergerac, 1959, Adage et Variations, Notre-Dame de Paris, 1965, Delicate Balance, 1967, Sheherezade, 1973, (films) The Pink Panther, 1962, Belle de Jour, 1967, La Chamade, 1968, La Sirène du Mississippi, 1969, L'Affaire Stavisky, 1974; stage sets and costumes Spectacle Zizi Jeanmaire, 1961, 63, 68, Les Chants de Maldoror, 1962; costume designer for Mariage de Figaro, 1964; illus. La Vilaine Lulu, 1967; exhbns. include Met. Mus. Art, N.Y., 1983, Beijing Mus. Fine Arts, 1985, Musée des Arts de la Mode, Paris, 1986, Ho. Painters USSR, 1986, Hermitage Mus., St. Petersburg, 1987, Art Gallery NSW, Sydney, 1987, Sezon Mus., Tokyo, 1990. Recipient Neiman-Marcus award for fashions, 1958; Oscar from Harper's Bazaar, 1966, Internat. award Coun. Fashion Designers Am., 1982, Best Fashion Designer Oscar, 1985; named Chevalier Légion d'honneu. Office: 5 ave Marceau, 75116 Paris France

ST.MARIE, SATENIG, writer; b. Brockton, Mass., June 2, 1927; d. Harry and Mary K. Sahjian; m. Gerald L. St. Marie, Dec. 26, 1959. B.S., Simmons Coll., Boston, 1949; M.A., Columbia U., 1959; LL.D. (hon.), N.D. State U., 1976. Extension home economist U. Mass. Extension Service, 1949-52, U. Conn. Extension Service, 1953-56; with J.C. Penney Co., Inc., 1959-87, mgr. endl. and consumer relations, 1967-73, dir. consumer affairs, 1973-87, div. v.p., 1974-87; dir. Nat. Reins. Co.; mem. U.S. Metric Bd. Author: Homes Are For People, 1973, Romantic Victorian Weddings: Then and Now, 1992; pub. J.C. Penney Consumer Edn. Services, 1981-87; lifestyles editor: Victorian Homes Mag., 1987—. Mem. Am. Home Econs. Assn. (past pres.), Antiques Dealers Assn. Am. (exec. dir. 1987—). Office: PO Box 335 Greens Farms CT 06436

ST. MARY, EDWARD SYLVESTER, direct mail marketing company executive; b. Campbellsport, Wis., May 31, 1941; s. Raymond O. and Freida (Beisbier) St. Mary; m. Patricia Dyer, Aug. 5, 1961; children—Todd M., Brian D. B.S. in Bus. Adminstrn, Drake U., Des Moines, 1963. CPA, Wis., Minn. With Gen. Electric Co., 1963-72, mgr. sales analysis and planning, 1972; asst. contr., then contr. and treas. Fingerhut Corp., Minnetonka, 1972, 1972-75; v.p. fin. Fingerhut Corp., Minnetonka, Minn., 1975-80, sr. v.p. adminstrn., CFO, 1981-87; CFO, Hanover (Pa.) House, 1988-90; prin. SEC Cons. Group, Maple Grove, Minn., 1991—; bd. dirs. HomServ Co. Mem. AICPA, Nat. Acctg. Assn., Minn. Soc. CPA's. Roman Catholic. Home and Office: 13831 TonBridge Ct Bonita Springs FL 33923

ST-ONGE, DENIS ALDERIC, geologist, research scientist; b. Ste-Agathe, Man., Can., May 11, 1929; s. Adolphe and Jeanne M. (Ritchot) St-O.; m. Jeanne Marie Behaegel, Jan. 7, 1955; children—Marc R, Nicole J.M. B.A., Coll. St-Boniface, 1951; Lic. Sci., U. Louvain, Belgium, 1957, D.Sc., 1962; D.Sc. honoris causa, U. Man., 1990. Research scientist Geol. Survey, Ottawa, Ont., Can., 1958-68, sect. head, 1982-85; chief sub. div. Quaternary Geology, 1985-87, dir. terrain scis. div., 1987-91, sci. advisor Polar Continental Shelf Project, 1991—; prof. geography U. Ottawa, 1968-82, chmn. geography, 1974-77, vice dean grad. studies, 1977-80. Author: Geomorphologie Ellef-Ringnes Island, 1965, Quaternary Geology, Inman River Region, N.W.T. Canada, 1995; contbr. articles to profl. jours. Pres. Ont. Francophone PTA, 1967-69. Recipient medal Queen Elizabeth II, Gov. Gen. Can., 1979, medal of honor U. Liege, Belgium, 1980, medal A. Cailleux, 1991, medal Can. 125, 1992, medal Royal Scottish Geog. Soc., 1994. Fellow Geol. Assn. Can. (coun. 1978-86), Roya, Can. Georg. Soc. (bd. dirs. 1980-92, pres. 1992—), Arctic Inst. N.Am.; mem. Can. Assn. Geographers, Can. Quaternary Assn., Assn. Quebecoise pour l'etude du Quaternaire (hon.), Internat. Union Quaternary Rsch. (hon. life). Avocations: swimming; skiing; photography. Home: 1115 Sherman Dr, Ottawa, ON Canada K2C 2M3 Office: Polar Continental Shelf Project, 344 Wellington St, Ottawa, ON Canada K1A 0E4

ST. ONGE, VINCENT A., electronics executive. Exec. v.p. of precision materials and components Osram Sylvania Inc., Danvers, Mass. Office: Osram Sylvania Inc 56 Holton St Woburn MA 01801-5297

ST. PE, GERALD J., manufacturing company executive. Student, Loyola U. With Litton Industries Inc., Beverly Hills, Calif., 1961—, various mgmt. positions, 1961-85; pres. Ingalls Shipbldg. Div., Pascagoula, Miss., 1985—, sr. v.p. parent co., 1985—. Office: Ingalls Shipbuilding PO Box 149 Pascagoula MS 39568-0149 also: Litton Industries 360 N Crescent Dr Beverly Hills CA 90210-4867

ST. PIERRE, GEORGE ROLAND, JR., materials science and engineering administrator, educator; b. Cambridge, Mass., June 2, 1930; s. George Rol and Rose Ann (Levesque) St. P.; m. Roberta Ann Hansen, July 20, 1956; children: Anne Renee, Jeanne Louise, John David, Thomas George; m. Mary Elizabeth Adams, Dec. 11, 1976. BS, MIT, 1951, ScD, 1954. Rsch. metallurgist Inland Steel Co., 1954-56; mem. faculty Ohio State U., 1956—, prof. metall. engring., 1957-88, assoc. dean Grad. Sch., 1964-66, chmn. Metall. Engring., 1983-88, chmn. mining engring., 1985-92; dir. Ohio Mineral Rsch. Inst., 1984—, prof., chmn. material sci. and engring., 1988-92, Presdl. prof., 1988—, chmn., presdl. prof. emeritus, 1992—; chief scientist, materials directorate Wright Patterson AFB, 1995—; vis. prof. U. Newcastle, NSW, Australia, 1975; mem. adv. com. materials sci. MIT, 1990—; mem. adv. bd. Argonne Nat. Lab., 1994—. Editor: Physical Chemistry of Process Metallurgy, Vols. 7 and 8, 1961, Advances in Transport Processes in Metallurgical Systems, 1992, Transactions Iron and Steel Society, 1994—; contbr. articles to profl. jours. Bd. dirs. Edward Orton Jr. Ceramic Found., 1989-92. With USAF, 1956-57. Recipient Milton (Mass.) Sci. prize, 1947; MacQuigg award, 1971; Alumni Disting. Tchr. award, 1978; named Disting. scholar Ohio State U., 1988, Presdl. prof. Ohio State U., 1988. Fellow Metall. Soc. AIME (bd. dirs. 1988-91, 93—), Am. Soc. Materials Internat. (Bradley Stoughton Outstanding Tchr. award 1961, Gold medal 1987); mem. Am. Inst. Mining Metall. and Petroleum Engrs. (Mineral Industry Educator award 1987), Iron and Steel Soc. (Elliott lectr. 1994), Am. Contract Bridge League (silver life master), Faculty Club (pres. 1990-92), Sigma Xi. Home: 1250 E Cooke Rd Columbus OH 43224-2058 Office: Ohio State U Dept Materials Sci/Engring 2041 N College Rd Columbus OH 43210-1124

SAINT-PIERRE, GUY, engineering executive; b. Windsor Mills, Que., Can., Aug. 3, 1934; s. Arm and Alice (Perra) Saint-P.; m. Francine Garneau, May 4, 1957; children—Marc, Guylaine, Nathalie. B in Applied Sci. in Civil Engring, Laval U., 1957; diploma, Imperial Coll., London, 1958; MSc, U. London, 1959; LLD (hon.), Concordia U., 1992; hon. degree, le Coll. militaire Royal de Saint-Jean, 1993; DSc (hon.), Laval U. 1992; hon. degree Applied Sci., Sherbrooke, 1994. Registrar, Corp. Engrs. Que., 1964-66. Dir. Irnes Inc., 1966-67; v.p. Acres Que., 1967-70; minister of edn. Govt. Que. 1970-72, of industry and commerce, 1972-76; asst. to pres. John Labatt Ltd., Montreal, 1977-80; sr. v.p. John Labatt Ltd.; pres., chief operating officer Ogilvie Mills Ltd., Montreal, 1977-80; pres., chief exec. officer, bd. dirs The SNC-Lavalin Group Inc., 1989—; dir. GM of Can., Royal Bank, BCE Inc., Purolator Cour., Alcan Aluminum; chmn. Bus. Coun. Nat. Issues, 1995—. Bd. dirs. Clin. Rsch. Inst., Montreal; gov. Conseil de Patronat de Que.; me. British-N.Am. Com. Served as officer C.E. Can. Army, 1959-64. Decorated officer Order of Can. Mem. Montreal Bd. Trade, Engring. Inst. Can., Can. Mfrs. Assn. (chmn. bd., pres. 1987), Order Engrs. Que., Council Can. Unity

(v.p.), Mil. and Hospitalier Order St. Lazarus Jerusalem, Met. Montreal C. of C., Can. Club Montreal (adv. com.). Liberal. Roman Catholic. Clubs: Mt. Royal, St. Denis, Mt. Bruno, Forest and Streams, Hermitage. Office: SNC-Lavalin Group Inc, 455 Boul René-Lèvesque O, Montreal, PQ Canada H2Z 1Z3

SAINT-PIERRE, JACQUES, statistics educator, consultant; b. Trois Rivières, Que., Can., Aug. 30, 1920; s. Oscar and Lucie (Landreville) St. P.; m. Marguerite Lachaine, July 15, 1947; children: Marc, Guy, Andre, Louis, Francois, Mireille. B.S., U. Montreal, 1948, M.S., 1951; Ph.D., U. N.C. 1954. Mem. faculty U. Montreal, 1947—, prof. stats., 1960-83, prof. emeritus, 1983—, dir. computing center, 1964-71, v.p. planning, 1971-82; cons. statistician, 1954—. Contbr. articles to profl. jours. Mem. Canadian Assn. Univ. Tchrs. (pres. 1965-66). Home: 4949 Earnscliffe, Montreal, PQ Canada H3X 2P4 Office: U Montreal, Box 6128, Montreal, PQ Canada H3C 3J7

ST. PIERRE, RONALD LESLIE, anatomy educator, university administrator; b. Dayton, Ohio, Feb. 2, 1938; s. Leslie Frank and Ruth Eleanor (Rhoten) St.P.; m. Joyce A. Guilford, Apr. 1, 1961; children: Michele Christine, David Bryan. B.S., Ohio U., 1961; M.Sc., Ohio State U., 1962, Ph.D., 1965. Instr. anatomy Ohio State U., Columbus, 1965-67; asst. prof. Ohio State U., 1967-69, assoc. prof., 1969-72, prof., 1972—, chmn. dept. anatomy, 1972-81, assoc. v.p. health scis., 1981-83, assoc. v.p. health services and acad. affairs, 1983—, assoc. dean coll. medicine, 1987—; assoc. dir. Cancer Research Center, 1974-78; vis. research asso. Duke U., 1966-67; cons. Battelle Meml. Inst., Columbus. Contbr. articles to profl. jours. Chmn. Ohio Gov.'s Com. on Employment of Handicapped, 1970-78; mem. state exec. com. Presdl. Commn. Employment of Handicapped, 1970-78, chmn., 1971-72; mem. planning and adv. council White House Conf. on Handicapped Individuals, 1975-78; mem. Columbus Mayor's Com. on Internat. Yr. of Disabled. Recipient Lederle Med. Faculty award, 1968-71; prize for basic research South Atlantic Assn. Obstetricians and Gynecologists, 1968; Outstanding Individual award Ohio Rehab. Assn., 1969; Gov.'s award for community service, 1973. Mem. Am. Assn. Anatomists, Am. Assn. Immunologists, Soc. Exptl. Biology and Medicine, Sigma Xi (pres. Ohio State chpt. 1979-80). Republican. Presbyterian. Home: 290 Bryant Ave Columbus OH 43085-3009 Office: Ohio State U 218 Meiling Hall 370 W 9th Ave Columbus OH 43210-1238

SAINTY, GUY STAIR, art dealer; b. Cuckfield, Sussex, Eng., Dec. 12, 1950; came to U.S., 1979; s. Christopher Lawrence and Virginia Cade (Stair) S.; children: Charles Henry Alastair, Clementine Virginia, Constance Della. LLB, Coll. of Law, London, 1975. Dir. M. Newman Ltd., London, 1976-79; cons. Stair & Co., N.Y.C., 1979-82; pres. Stair Sainty Matthiesen, N.Y.C., 1982—. Author: The Sacred Military Constantinian Order of Saint George, 1976, The Orders of Chivalry and Merit of the Bourbon Two Sicilies Dynasty, 1989, Eighty Years of French Painting, 1991, The Orders of Saint John, 1991; co-author: (exhbn. catalog) The Macchiaioli, 1984, First Painters of the King, 1985, Francois Boucher, His Circle and Influence, 1987. Vice grand chancellor Sacred Mil. Constantinian Order of St. George, Madrid, 1989—; historiographer Most Venerable Order St. John of Jerusalem Am. Soc., N.Y.C., 1990—. Decorated knight of justice Most Venerable Order St. John of Jerusalem, comdr. with star Papal Order St. Gregory the Gt., grand cross of justice Constantinian Order of St. George, knight Order St. Januarius, comdr. Order of Sts. Maurice and Lazarus. Mem. Art Dealers Assn. Am., Syndicat Nat. des Antiquaires, Royal Acad. Heraldry and Genealogy (academician), Madrid Pvt. Art Dealers Assn. (v.p.), Nat. Assn. Papal Knights and Dames in U.S. (pres.), Turf Club. Roman Catholic. Home: 38 Hudson St Kinderhook NY 12106 Office: Stair Sainty Matthiesen 22 E 80th St New York NY 10021-0158

ST-YVES, ANGÈLE, agricultural engineer; b. Charette, Que., Can., Apr. 30, 1940; d. Léonard St. Yves and Lucille Déziel; m. Denis Désilets, July 1, 1961; children: Luc, Marie-Christine, Valérie. BA in Teaching, Laval U., Ste.-Foy, Que., 1973, BS in Agrl. Engring., 1977, MS in Agrl. Engring., 1983. Tchr. Commn. Scolaire Shawinigan-Sud, Que., 1958-61, pvt. practice, Que., N.S. and Mich., 1961-70; corr. Farmer's Union, Que., 1970-72; engr. SNC, Morocco, 1977, Roche & Assocs., Que., 1979, Commn. de Protection des Terres Agricoles, Que., 1979-82; engr. Ministère de l'Environment du Que., 1982-85, chief divsn. mgmt. of agrl. nonpoint source pollution, 1985-89, chief divsn. agrl. sector, 1989-90, dir. agrl. sector and pesticide mgmt., 1990-91; dir. rsch. station Agriculture Can., Que., 1991—; sci. coord. for R & D on Sludge Utilization in Agriculture Consortium; mem. selection bds. for employment of profls. and mgrs.; assessor sci. papers; expert in agrl. vs. environ. issues; lectr. on vision of future, soil and water, environment, recycling residue or tech., rsch. and devel. issues in agriculture. Co-author: La Recherche du Matrimoine, 1991 (Laura Jamieson award 1992); contbr. numerous tech. papers to profl. jours. and confs. V.p. fundraising campaign Laval U., Ste.-Foy, 1991-92. Recipient Comdr. of Order of Agrl. Merit award Que. Govt., 1989, Spl. Merit award Environment Que, 1990; named Personality of Week, La Presse Montreal, 1989, named Woman of Yr. in Agriculture, Salon de la Femme de Montreal, 1990. Mem. Am. Soc. Agrl. Engrs. (NABEC disting. lectr. 1990), Que. Order of Agronomists (bd. dirs. 1986-91, exec. com. 1986-91, v.p. 1987-89, pres. 1989-91, keynote speaker 1993), Que. Order Engrs. (examinor's com. 1986—, named one of Personalities of Yr. 1989), Que. Soc. of Agrl. Engrs. (pres. 1985-87), Can. Soc. Agrl. Engring. (in charge of environ. engring. 1992—), Agrl. Inst. Can. (land utilization com. 1987-8), Soil Conservation Soc. Am., Que. Soc. Water Works. Home: Agriculture Canada Research Stn, 1291 rue de la Visitation, Sainte-Foy, PQ Canada G1W 3K5 Office: Agri & Agri Food Can Rsch Station, 2560 Blvd Hochelaga, Quebec, PQ Canada G1V 2J3*

SAISSELIN, REMY GILBERT, fine arts educator; b. Moutier, Bern, Switzerland, Aug. 17, 1925; came to U.S., 1938, naturalized, 1944; s. Paul A. and Jeanne (Nydegger) S.; m. Nicole M. Fischer, May 31, 1955; children: Anne, Juliet, Peter. B.A., Queens Coll., 1951; M.A., U. Wis-Madison, 1952; M.A. in French, U. Wis.-Madison, 1953, Ph.D, 1957. Asst. prof. French Western Res. U., Cleve., 1956-59; asst. curator publs. Cleve. Mus. Art, 1959-65; prof. French lit. U. Rochester (N.Y.), 1965-70, prof. fine arts, 1970-87; prof. humanities Hobart & William Smith Coll., 1987-90. Asst. editor: Jour. Aesthetics and Art Criticism, 1959-62; author: Taste in Eighteenth Centruy France, 1965, Rule of Reason and Ruses of the Heart, 1970, Literary Enterprise in XVIII Century France, 1979, The Bourgeois and the Bibelot, 1984, The Enlightenment Against the Baroque, 1992. Served with U.S. Army, 1944-46. Guggenheim fellow, 1972-73. Mem. Phi Beta Kappa. Home: 117 Westland Ave Rochester NY 14618-1044

SAITO, KIYOMI, investment banking executive; b. Tokyo, Japan, Dec. 1, 1950; d. Genichiro and Kimiko Saito; m. Tsuguo Tadakawa, Aug. 20, 1974 (div. Aug. 1975); m. Kenji Takei, Dec. 3, 1994. BA, Keio U., Tokyo, 1973; MBA, Harvard Bus. Sch., 1981. Staff Nihon Econ. Jour., Tokyo, 1973-74; asst. Sony Corp., Tokyo, 1977-79; account officer, product specialist Bank of Am., Tokyo, 1981-82; mktg. mgr. Elizabeth Arden, Tokyo, 1982-84; v.p. Morgan Stanley Internat., Tokyo, 1984-88, N.Y.C., 1988-89, Morgan Stanley Realty, 1989-91; prin. Rep. Office Morgan Stanley Realty Inc., Tokyo, 1991-92; pres. Port du Gard Co. Ltd., 1992—. Author: A Woman's New Start, 1984, Women's Era, 1986, Kiyomi's Challenge, 1994. Home: 4-35-13 Nishiogi-Kita, Suginamiku Tokyo 167, Japan

SAITO, PAUL MAKOTO, landscape architect; b. Los Angeles, Oct. 2, 1936; s. William Taketora and Mabel Hiro (Ono) S.; m. Gloria Katsuko Takehashi, June 1, 1963; 1 child, Naomi Kikuko. A.A., Pierce Coll.; B.S., Calif. Poly. Inst. Landscape architect asst. Recreation and Parks Dept., Los Angeles, 1959-64; landscape architect asst. Anaheim Recreation and Parks Dept., Calif., 1964-72; pres. Recreation Land Planners Inc., Placentia, Calif., 1972-76, Saito-Sullivan Assocs., Brea, Calif. 1976-80, Saito Assocs., Fresno, Calif., 1980—. Served with Air N.G., 1968-74. Recipient Daisy award Calif. Landscape Contractors Assn., 1975; Cert. Recognition, Calif. Poly. Alumni Assn., 1981; award of Merit, Calif. Garden Club, 1985. Fellow Am. Soc. Landscape Architects, Am. Inst. Landscape Architects (internat. pres. 1971-73), Council Landscape Architects (pres. 1985), State Bd. Landscape Architects (pres. 1984—). Democrat. Baptist. Avocation: attending football and baseball games. Office: Saito Assocs 2904 N Blackstone Ave Ste C Fresno CA 93703-1014

SAITO, SHUZO, electrical engineering educator; b. Nagoya, Aichi, Japan, Jan. 12, 1924; s. Sukesaburo and Masa Saito; m. Yoko Nakane, Mar. 26, 1953; children: Jun'ichiro, Ken'jiro. BSEE, Nagoya U., 1948, MSEE, 1953, PhD, 1962. Mem. tech. staff Elec. Com. Lab. NT&T, Tokyo, 1953-64, chief rsch. sect., 1964-75, dir. rsch. dept., 1975-79; prof. speech sci. U. Tokyo, 1979-84; prof. elec. engring. Kogakuin U., 1984-92; prof. info. sci. Hokkaido Info. U., 1992—; mem. tech. staff Japanese Patent Agy., Tokyo, 1963; tech. specialist Japanese Ministry Transp., Tokyo, 1982. Author: Fundamental Speech Signal Processing, 1979; contbr. articles to profl. publs.; inventor PARCOR speech synthesis. Recipient promotion award Asahi Newspaper Co., 1981. Fellow IEEE (chmn. acoustics, speech and signal processing Tokyo chpt. 1986-88, chmn. tech. program com. internat. conf. on acoustics, speech and signal processing 1986), Acoustical Soc. Am.; mem. Audio and Visual Rsch. Group (hon., pres. 1985-88), Inst. Elec. and Comm. Engrs. Japan (adviser speech com. and pattern recognition com. 1983, paper award 1970, 79, achievement award 1973), Acoustical Soc. Japan (exec. coun. 1969-83, Sato paper award 1972, meritorious award 1994). Avocations: golf, photography. Home: 1-1-3-38-704 Atsubetsu Chuo, Atsubetsu-ku, Sapporo 004, Japan Office: Hokkaido Info U, Nishinopporo 59-2, Ebetsu, Hokkaido 069, Japan

SAITOH, TAMOTSU, pharmacology educator; b. Tokyo, May 29, 1938; s. Jiro and Tayo Saitoh; m. Masako Hayashida, June 4, 1967. PhD, U. Tokyo, 1969. Postdoctoral fellow chemistry dept. UCLA, 1969-71; instr. U. Tokyo, 1968-76; asst. prof. Showa U., Tokyo, 1976-78; prof. Teikyo U., Tokyo, 1978—. Author: Natural Products Chemistry, Vol. 2, 1975, Pharmacognosy, 1983. Avocations: travel, photography, computer programming, painting. Home: 7-13-19 Tsukimino, Yamato 242, Japan Office: Teikyo U, Sagamiko-machi, Tsukui Kanagawa 199-01, Japan

SAJAK, PAT, television game show host; b. Chgo., Oct. 26, 1947; m. Lesly Brown, Dec. 31, 1990. Newscaster WEDC-Radio, Chicago, IL; disk jockey WNBS-Radio, Murray, KY; staff announcer, public affairs program host, weatherman WSM-TV, Nashville, TN; weatherman, host The Sunday Show, 1977-81; host Wheel of Fortune, 1981—, The Pat Sajak Show, 1989-90. film appearances include: Airplane II: The Sequel, 1982, Jack Paar is Alive and Well, 1987; NBC television specials, host The Thanksgiving Day Parade, The Rose Parade. Served with U.S. Army, Vietnam. *

SAKAGUCHI, GENJI, food microbiologist, educator; b. Kobe, Hyogo, Japan, Sept. 17, 1927; s. Kazumasa and Yuko (Fujita) S.; m. Sumiko Igarashi, Nov. 25, 1951; children: Akiko, Ei, Fumiko, Hide, Kei. BSc, Hokkaido U., 1950, PhD, 1960; postgrad., U. Chgo., 1956. Tech. ofcl. Nat. Inst. Health, Tokyo, 1950-70, chief investigator, 1965-70; prof. U. Osaka Prefecture, Sakai, Japan, 1970-91; prof. emeritus U. Osaka, Sakai, Japan, 1991—; sci. adviser Japan Food Rsch. Labs., Suita, Osaka, 1991—; cons. WHO, Geneva, 1967-86, Chiba Serum Inst., 1970—; advisor Ministry of Health and Welfare, Tokyo, 1974—. Editor Internat. Jour. Food Microbiology, 1990—, assoc. editor-in-chief, 1993—; author books and articles in field. Grantee USPHS, 1962-67, WHO, 1967-70, Fulbright Found., 1955-56. Mem. Japanese Soc. Bacteriology (bd. dirs. 1991-94, Sakakawa-sho award 1988), Soc. Antibacterial and Antifungal Agts. (bd. dirs. 1991—), Japanese Soc. Food Microbiology (pres. 1990-93, Purple Ribbon award 1993). Avocations: photography, classical music, driving, swimming, cooking. Home: 7-22-404 Koda 3-chome, Tondabayashi Osaka 584, Japan Office: Japan Food Rsch Labs, 3-1 Toyotsu-cho, Suita-shi Osaka 564, Japan

SAKAI, SHINJI, finance company executive. With Toyota Motor Corp., Japan, 1985-1992; pres. and dir. Toyota Motor Sales, USA, Inc., Torrance, Calif., 1992—; pres. Toyota Motor Credit Corp., Torrance, Calif., 1992—. Office: Toyota Motor Credit Corp 19300 Gramercy Pl Torrance CA 90501-1131

SAKAI, YOSHIRO, chemistry educator; b. Nagasaki, Japan, Dec. 28, 1935; s. Tsuyoshi and Rei (Ikeno) S.; m. Mutsuko Abe, Oct. 18, 1964; children: Hideaki, Masako. BS, Kyushu U., Fukuoka, Japan, 1958, ScD, 1970. Research fellow Govt. Indsl. Research Inst., Nagoya, Japan, 1958-68; assoc. prof. Ehime U., Matsuyama, Japan, 1968-74, prof. chemistry, 1974—. Mem. Chem. Soc. Japan, Soc. Polymer Sci., Electrochem. Soc. Japan, Japan Assn. Chem. Sensors (pres. 1995—). Avocations: traveling, reading. Home: 225-4 Shin-ishite, Matsuyama 790, Ehime Japan Office: Ehime Univ, Bunkyo-cho Matsuyama, Ehime Japan

SAKAINO, KOZO, automobile company executive; b. 1938. Student Keio U., Tokyo; with Am. Isuzu Motors Inc., 1987—, pres.

SAKAMOTO, RYUICHI, composer. Score include (fillms) Merry Christmas, Mr. Lawrence, 1983, (with David Byrne and Cong Su) The Last Emperor, 1987 (Academy award best original score 1987), The Handmaid's Tale, 1990, The Sheltering Sky, 1990, Tacones Lejanos, 1991, Emily Bronte's Wuthering Heights, 1992, Little Buddha, 1993, (TV miniseries) Wild Palms, 1993. Office: Creative Artists Agency 9830 Wilshire Blvd Beverly Hills CA 90210*

SAKHUJA, RAVINDER KUMAR, electronics executive; b. Nagpur, India, Oct. 17, 1944; s. Krishan Lal Sakhuja and Kaushlya (Rani) Batra; m. Rohini Sakhuja, Sept. 6, 1969; children: Rohit, Rahul. BS, Indian Inst. Tech., Kanpur, India, 1966; MS, MIT, 1968, ScD, 1970. V.p. Thermal Product div. Thermo Electronics, Waltham, Mass., 1982-84, pres., 1984-85; pres., chief exec. officer Tecogen, Inc., Waltham, 1985—; co-chair Promotion and Advancement of Cogeneration Tech. Inventor thermal storage system, rotary combustor; contbr. articles to profl. jours. Mem. ASHRAE, ASME, Internat. Cogeneration Soc., Cogeneration Inst., Sigma Xi. Home: 50 Turning Ml Rd Cuttyhunk MA 02713 Office: Thermo Power Corp 81 Wyman St Waltham MA 02154

SAKITA, BUNJI, physicist, educator; b. Inami, Toyama-ken, Japan, June 6, 1930; came to U.S., 1956; s. Eiichi and Fumi (Morimatsu) S.; children—Mariko, Taro. B.S., Kanazawa U., 1953; M.S., Nagoya U., 1956; Ph.D., U. Rochester, 1959. Research asso. U. Wis., Madison, 1959-62; asst. prof. U. Wis., 1963-64, prof., 1966-70; assoc. physicist Argonne (Ill.) Nat. Lab., 1964-66; distinguished prof. City Coll. CUNY, 1970—; vis. prof. IHES, Bures-sur-Yvette, France, 1970-71, Ecole Normale Superieur, Paris, 1979-80, 88, U. Tokyo, 1987. Guggenheim fellow, 1970-71; Japan Soc. Promotion Sci. fellow, 1975, 80, 87; recipient Nishina prize, 1974. Fellow Am. Phys. Soc. Home: 5 Horizon Rd Apt 2406 Fort Lee NJ 07024-6646 Office: City College CUNY Convent Ave at 138th St New York NY 10031

SAKOWITZ, ROBERT TOBIAS, investor; b. Houston, Oct. 13, 1938; s. Bernard and Ann (Baum) S.; m. Laura Howell, 1984; children: Robert Tobias Jr., Alexandra Noelle, Brittany Ann, Laura Alexis. BA in History and Econs. cum laude, Harvard U., 1960. Exec. trainee Bloomingdales, N.Y.C., 1959-62; Macy's, N.Y.C., 1961-62, Galleries Lafayette, Paris, 1960; buyer Sakowitz, Inc., Houston, 1962-65, exec. v.p. gen. mdse. mgr., 1965-71, pres., 1971-74; pres. Sakowitz, Inc., Ariz., 1974-75; pres., CEO Sakowitz, Inc., 1975-90, chmn., 1981-87; chmn., CEO Sakowitz Ventures, 1990—; chmn. Clean fuels Inc., 1991—; chmn., CEO Hazak Corp., 1986—, Robosak Corp., 1983—; co-mgr. Thunderbird Ranch, 1993—; Bd. dirs. Continental Air Lines, Inc.; dir. Morse Shoe, 1974-87, Tex. Am. Bank-Galleria, 1972-83, Fed. Reserve Bank, Houston br., 1983-85, chmn., 1985—, Societe Viticole, S.A. (Lux.), 1983-87. Mem. exec. com., nat. bd. dirs. Am. Council for Arts, N.Y.C., 1970-83; bd. dirs. Found. for Joffrey Ballet, Houston Internat. Festival, Houston Symphony Soc., NCCJ, Greater Houston Conv. and Visitors Bur., chmn. 1990-92; Houston Econ. Devel. Council, Houston Indsl. Devel. Corp.; co-chmn. Tex. Conf. on Small Bus., 1981; chmn. S.E. del. White House Conf. on Small Bus., 1980; mem. Houston Mcpl. Art Commn., 1965-83, vice chmn., 1972-73, chmn., 1974-75; chmn. Sesquicentennial Commn. State of Tex., Houston and Harris County, 1984-86, Greater Houston Ptnrship.; mem. bd. selectors Am. Inst. for Public Service, Washington; mem. pres. coun. and pub. policy coun. U. Houston; bd. dirs. host com. Rep. Nat. Conv., 1991-92; bd. advisors Edna Gladney Home. Served with USAF, 1961-66. Decorated knight Nat. Order of Merit (France, 1976) (Italy, 1983); recipient Epingle d'Or, French Fashion Fedn. 1972; Am. Acad. Achievement award, 1973; Gt. Texan Award Nat. Ileitis and Colitis Found., 1975; Display award Nat. Assn. Display Industries,

1976; Ten Outstanding Nat. Bus. Leaders award Northwood Inst., 1981; named to Internat. Best Dressed List, 1970, 71, 72, 73, 74, 75; named to Hall of Fame, 1975. Mem. Nat. Retail Mchts. Assn. (dir., mem. exec. com., internat. com.), Houston C. of C. (dir., mem. downtown com. 1980-81, chmn. small bus. task force 1978-79, chmn. cultural affairs com. 1971-73), German Am. C. of C. (dir.), German Wine Soc. (chmn. S.W. chpt.), Confrerie des Chevaliers du Tastevin, Brotherhood of Knights of Vine, Confrerie de la Chaine des Rotisseurs, Commanderie de Bordeaux du Texas. Clubs: Houston, Houstonian; Fly (Cambridge, Mass.); Knickerbocker (N.Y.C.). Avocations: skiing, tennis, art, oenology. Office: 3050 Post Oak Blvd Ste 640 Houston TX 77056-6525

SAKS, ARNOLD, graphic designer; b. N.Y.C., Dec. 21, 1931; s. Alfred and Esther (Barnett) S.; m. Joanna Ernst, Sept. 23, 1959. B.F.A., Syracuse U., 1953; postgrad., Yale U., 1953-54. Exhbn. designer Mus. Natural History, N.Y.C., 1956-57; art dir. Interiors Mag., N.Y.C., 1957-58; ptnr. Ward & Saks, N.Y.C., 1958-68; prin. Arnold Saks, Assocs., N.Y.C., 1968—. Served with U.S. Army, 1954-56. Mem. Alliance Graphique Internationale, Am. Inst. Graphic Arts, Century Assn. Office: Arnold Saks Assocs 350 E 81st St New York NY 10028-3931

SAKS, GENE, theater director, actor; b. N.Y.C. Began career as an actor off-Broadway at Provincetown Playhouse and the Cherry Lane Theatre; played in: Auden's Dog Beneath the Skin, E.E. Cummings' Him, Molière's The Bourgeois Gentilhomme; appeared on Broadway in Mr. Roberts, South Pacific, Middle of the Night, The Tenth Man, A Shot in the Dark, Love and Libel, A Thousand Clowns; debut as dir. on Broadway in Enter Laughing, 1963; dir. stage plays Nobody Loves an Albatross, Half a Sixpence, Generation, Mame, Same Time, Next Year, California Suite, I Love My Wife (best dir. of Musical award Drama Desk, Tony), Brighton Beach Memoirs (best dir. award, Tony), Biloxi Blues (best dir. of play award, Tony, 1985), The Odd Couple, 1985, Broadway Bound, 1986, A Month of Sundays, 1987, Rumors, 1988, Lost in Yonkers, 1991, Jake's Women, 1992; dir. films Barefoot in the Park, The Odd Couple, Cactus Flower, Last of the Red Hot Lovers, Mame, Brighton Beach Memoirs, A Fine Romance; appeared in films including A Thousand Clowns, Prisoner of Second Avenue, Lovesick, The One and Only, The Goodbye People, 1986, Nobody's Fool, 1994, DQ, 1994. Recipient George Abbott award for lifetime achievement in the theatre, 1990; elected to Theatre Hall of Fame, 1991.

SAKS, MICHAEL JAY, law educator; b. Phila., Mar. 8, 1947; s. Harold and Bella (Pall) S.; m. Roselle Wissler, May 18, 1986. BS in Psychology, BA in English, Pa. State U., 1969; MA in Social Psychology, Ohio State U., 1972, PhD in Social Psychology, 1975; MSL in Law, Yale U., 1983. Prof. psychology Boston Coll., Chestnut Hill, Mass., 1975-88; sr. staff assoc. Nat. Ctr. for State Cts., Williamsburg, Va., 1978-80; vis. prof. law Georgetown U. Law Ctr., Washington, 1985-86; prof. law U. Iowa, Iowa City, 1986—; disting. vis. prof. law Ohio State U., Columbus, 1991; vis. prof. law grad. program for judges U. Va., Charlottesville, 1981, 83, 85, 87, 89; cons. Office of Tech. Assessment, U.S. Congress, Washington, numerous law firms. Editor-in-chief Law & Human Behavior, 1985-87; mem. editorial bd. Jour. Personality and Social Psychology, Law & Society Rev., Law & Human Behavior, Law & Policy, Applied Social Psychology Annual, Social Behaviour: An Internat. Jour. Applied Social Psychology, Ethics and Behavior; contbr. articles to profl. jours. Chair bd. Cen. Ohio chpt. Ohio Civil Liberties Union, Columbus, 1972-73; bd. dirs. Civil Liberties Union Mass., Boston, 1984-86; mem. subcom. on organ and tissue transplants Mass. Legis., Boston, 1975. U. Iowa Faculty scholar, 1990-93. Fellow Am. Psychol. Assn. (Disting. Contbn. award 1987), Am. Psychology Law Soc. (pres. 1988-89), Soc. for the Psychol. Study of Social Issues (bd. dirs.); mem. Law & Soc. Assn. Office: U Iowa Coll Law Iowa City IA 52242

SAKS, STEPHEN HOWARD, accountant; b. Phila., May 16, 1941; s. Samuel and Edythe (Edelman) S.; m. Ruth Workman, Dec. 22, 1963; children: Amy Meryl, Brian Eric, Joshua Marc. BS in Econs., U. Pa., 1962. CPA, Pa. Staff acct. to ptnr. Peat, Marwick, Mitchell & Co., Phila., 1962-78; ptnr. Laventhol & Horwath, Phila., 1978-91; chief fin. officer Northeastern Health Sys., Phila., 1991—. Bd. dirs. Jewish Family and Children's Agy, Phila., 1979-88; treas. Jewish Employment and Vocat. Svc., Phila. 1984-88; chmn. bd. overseers Gratz Coll., Melrose Pk., Pa., 1987-90; pres. Beth Sholom Men's Club, Elkins Pk., Pa., 1987-90. Mem. AICPA, Pa. Inst. CPAs, Healthcare Fin. Mgmt. Assn. (advanced). Democrat. Avocations: community activities, travel. Home: 1110 Gypsy Ln Oreland PA 19075-2508 Office: Northeastern Health System 2346 E Allegheny Ave Philadelphia PA 19134-4434

SAKS, WILLIAM JOSEPH, JR., osteopathic physician, educator; b. Allentown, Pa., Feb. 3, 1943; s. William J. and Josephine (Sorrentino) S.; m. Valerie E. Nacinovich, June 17, 1967; children: William, Stephen, Damian, Jessica, Benjamin. BS in Biology, King's Coll., Wilkes-Barre, Pa., 1964; postgrad., Cath. U. Am., 1964-65; DO, Phila. Coll. Osteo. Medicine, 1969. Intern Brentwood Hosp., Warrensville Heights, Ohio, 1969-70; resident in gen. surgery and ob-gyn. Brentwood Hosp., Warrensville Heights, Ohio, 1970-72; resident in ob-gyn. surgery Allentown Osteo. Med. Ctr., 1972-74; mem. staff, 1972-90, chmn. ob-gyn. dept., 1979-80, 85-90, vice chmn., 1982-85; pvt. practice, Wescosville, Pa., 1974-90, Montour Falls, N.Y., 1990-92; pvt. practice Guthrie Clinic, Inc., Watkins Glen, N.Y., 1992—; asst. clin. prof. Phila. Coll. Osteo. Medicine, 1980—; chmn. ob-gyn. dept. Schuyler Hosp., Montour Falls, 1990—. Bd. dirs. CONFRONT, drug and alcohol rehab. ctr., past mem. adv. bd.; mem. med. adv. bd. Allentown-Bethlehem Midwifery Ctr., 1983—; former lectr. pre-marriage confs. and religious ednl. program on natural family planning Dioceses of Allentown and Rochester, Roman Cath. Ch. Fellow Am. Coll. Osteo. Obstetricians and Gynecologists (diplomate); mem. Am. Osteo. Assn. (bd. dirs. internl. and residency tng. programs), Pa. Osteo. Med. Assn. (bd. dirs. dist. III 1984-90, chmn. com. on ob-gyn., com. on constn. and bylaws, com. on orgn. policy, com. on pubils., com. on property), Lehigh Valley Osteo. Soc. (treas. 1975-80, chmn. 1982-90). Avocations: music, hunting, fishing, boating, archery. Office: One 1st St Watkins Glen NY 14891

SALA, LUIS FRANCISCO, surgeon, educator; b. N.Y.C., Dec. 13, 1919; s. Luis and Josefina (Goenaga) S.; m. Judith Colon, June 5, 1943; children: Luis E., Francisco A., Jorge P., Jose M. B.S. cum laude, Georgetown U., 1939, M.D., 1943; M.Sc. in Surgery, U. Pa., 1951. Diplomate: Am. Bd. Surgery. Intern, resident Presbyn. Hosp., San Juan, P.R., 1943-45; resident Presbyn. Hosp., 1944-45; chief resident Grad. Hosp. U. Pa., 1947-51, instr. surgery, 1950-51; clin. asst. surgery Med. Coll. Pa.; practice medicine, specializing in surgery Ponce, P.R., 1951-91; chmn. dept. surgery Damas Hosp., Ponce, 1955-88; prof. surgery U. P.R. Sch. Medicine, 1968-88; pres., dean, prof. surgery Ponce Sch. of Medicine, 1988-94; del. P.R. Med. Assn., 1960-93, pres., 1965-66. Author: Consideracions Basicas para la Acreditacion de Hospitales, 1978; contbr. chpts. to books, articles to profl. jours. Active Boy Scouts Am., 1955-74; pres. adv. com. to pres. Cath. U. P.R., 1963-72; bd. dirs. Boys Home of Ponce, 1966-76; bd. regents Amigos Museo de Arte de Ponce, 1968-73, Cath. U., 1972-89; pres. bd. regents Ponce Med. Sch. Found., 1980-92. Served with M.C. U.S. Army, 1945-47. Recipient Silver Beaver award, 1965; named It. P.R. Equestrian Order of Holy Sepulchre of Jerusalem, 1982—. Fellow ACS (gov. for P.R. 1965-74, Disting. Svc. award 1989), Internat. Soc. Surgery, C. of C. (Profl. of Yr. award 1990), P.R. Med. Assn. (so. dist., Dr. Pila medal for Disting. Svcs. 1991), Indsl. Med. Coun. of SIF (apptd. pres. by Gov. of P.R. 1993), P.R. Mfrs. Assn. (Profl. of Yr. in Area of Svcs. 1994). Republican. Roman Catholic. Home: 6 Almena Alhambra Ponce PR 00731 Office: 43 Calle Concordia Ponce PR 00731-4984

SALAAM, RASHAAN, professional football player; b. San Diego, Oct. 24, 1974; s. Teddy Washington and Dolores Shelly Salaam. Attended, U. Colo., 1992-94. With Chgo. Bears, 1995—; mem. Aloha Bowl, 1992. Recipient Heisman trophy, 1994, Doak Walker award, 1994, Walter Camp Player of Yr. trophy, 1994; named to AP All-Am. Team, 1994. Avocations: rap music, sega. Office: Chgo Bears Halas Hall 250 N Washington Rd Lake Forest IL 60045*

SALABOUNIS, MANUEL, computer information scientist, mathematician; b. Salonica, Greece, Apr. 15, 1935; came to U.S., 1954; s. Anastasios and Matrowa (Paraskeuaidou) Tsalabounis; children from previous marriage:

Stacy, Mary E., John; m. Baerbel Thekla Steinbach-Ruschford, July 2, 1988. Cert., Anatolia Coll., Salonica, Greece, 1954; student, Morris Harvey Coll., 1954-56; BS in Engring. Sci., Cleve. State U., 1960; MS in Math., Akron U., 1964. Master Univ. Sch., Shaker Heights, Ohio, 1960-62; mathematician Babcock and Wilcox, Alliance, Ohio, 1962-66; dir. computer ctr. John Carroll U., University Heights, Ohio, 1966-68; pres. Electronic Service Assocs. Corp., Euclid, Ohio, 1968-73; v.p. North Am. Co., Chgo., 1974-79; sr. project leader Hibernia Bank, New Orleans, 1979-83; project mgr. Compuware Corp., Farmington Hills, Mich., 1984—; mgr. spl. projects, 1990-91, MIS planning mgr., 1991—. Accomplishments include work in internat. banking applications, 3 dim. thermostress analysis, generic tool definitions and design, law office info. systems, software delivery system, and other. Vol. Sts. Constantine and Helen Ch., Cleve., 1960-74, St. Nicholas, Detroit, 1986-92, Annunciations Ch., Detroit, 1992—. Avocations: classical music, opera, golf, fishing, cooking. Home: 28691 Bristol Ct Farmington MI 48334-2914 Office: Compuware Corp 31440 Northwestern Hwy Farmington MI 48334-2564

SALACUSE, JESWALD WILLIAM, lawyer, educator; b. Niagara Falls, N.Y., Jan. 28, 1938; s. William L. and Bessie B. (Buzzelli) S.; m. Donna Booth, Oct. 1, 1966; children: William, Maria. Diploma U. Paris, 1959; AB, Hamilton Coll., 1960; JD, Harvard U., 1963. Bar: N.Y. 1965, Tex. 1980. Lectr. in law Ahmadu Bello U., Nigeria, 1963-65; assoc. Conboy, Hewitt, O'Brien & Boardman, N.Y.C., 1965-67; assoc. dir. African Law Ctr., Columbia U., 1967-68; prof., dir. Research Ctr., Nat. Sch. Adminstrn., Zaire, 1968-71; Middle East regional advisor on law and devel. Ford Found., Beirut, 1971-74, rep. in Sudan, 1974-77; vis. prof. U. Khartoum (Sudan), 1974-77; vis. scholar Harvard Law Sch., 1977-78; prof. law So. Meth U., Dallas, 1978-80, dean, prof. law, 1980-86; dean, prof. internat. law The Fletcher Sch. Law and Diplomacy Tufts U., Medford, Mass., 1986-94; Henry J. Braker prof. comml. law Fletcher Sch. Law and Diplomacy Tufts U., 1994—; fellow Inst. Advanced Legal Studies, U. London, 1995—; vis. prof. Ecole Nat. des Ponts et Chaussées, Paris, 1990—; cons. Ford Found., 1978-82, 93, U.S. Dept. State, 1978-80, U.N. Ctr. on Transnat. Corps., 1988—, Harvard Inst. Internat. Devel., 1990—, Asia Found., 1992, Harvard Law Sch./World Bank Laos Project, 1991-93; with Sri Lanka fin. sector project ISTI/USAID, 1993-94; lectr. Georgetown U. Internat. Law Inst., 1978-94, Universidad Panamericana, Mexico City, 1981; chmn. com. on Middle Eastern law Social Sci. Research Council, 1978-84; chmn. Council for Internat. Exchange of Scholars, 1987-91; bd. dirs. Boston World Affairs Coun., Emerging Markets Income Funds. I & II, Inc., Global Ptnrs. Income Fund, Inc., Salomon Brothers Worldwide Income Fund, Inc., The Asia Tigers Fund, Inc., The India Fund. Inc., Emerging Markets Floating Rate Fund, Inc., Mcpl. Advantage Fund, Inc.; trustee Southwestern Legal Found., 1992—; Am. U. of Paris, 1993; pres. Internat. Third World Legal Studies Assn., 1987-91; chmn. Inst. Transnat. Arbitration, 1988—; pres. Assn. Profl. Schs. Internat. Affairs, 1988-89. Author: (with Kasunmu) Nigerian Family Law, 1966, An Introduction to Law in French-Speaking Africa, vol. I, 1969, vol. II, 1976, (with Steng) International Business Planning, 1982; Making Global Deals-Negotiating in the International Marketplace, 1991, The Art of Advice, 1994; contbr. articles to profl. jours. Mem. ABA, Dallas Bar Found. (trustee 1983-86), Coun. on Fgn. Rels., Am. Law Inst., Am. Soc. Internat. Law, Cosmos Club (Washington). Home: 220 Stone Root Ln Concord MA 01742-4708 Office: Tufts U Fletcher Sch Law & Diplomacy Office of Dean Medford MA 02155

SALADINO, JOHN F., architect, interior decorator, furniture designer; b. Kansas City, Mo., 1939. BFA, U. Notre Dame, 1960; MFA, Yale U., 1963; pvt. studies with, Piero Sartago, Rome, 1968-69. Prin., architect, decorator, furniture designer John F. Saladino Inc., N.Y.C., 1972—; bd. dirs. Formica Corp. Bd. dirs. Parsons Sch. Design. Recipient 2 Awards of Excellence, Illuminating Engring. Soc., 1976, 2 Best Show awards Daphne, 1981, Design Excellence award Daphne, 1981, 1st Ann. award Chgo. Design Sources Com., 1982, Euster Mdse. Mart award, 1982, Award for Excellence, Chgo. Design Fest, 1983; named Designer of Yr., Interiors Mag., 1980. Mem. Am. Soc. Interior Designers (Designer Disting. 1982). Office: 305 E 63rd St New York NY 10021-7772

SALAH, JOSEPH ELIAS, research scientist, educator; b. Jerusalem, Feb. 27, 1944; came to U.S., 1961; s. Elias and Souraya (Nesnas) S.; m. Marie Shintani, Jan. 30, 1965; 1 child. Anthony. BSEE, U. Ill., 1965, MSEE, 1966; PhD, MIT, 1972. Staff mem. Lincoln Lab., MIT, Lexington, 1966-76, group leader, 1977-83; sr. lectr. dept. earth, atmospheric and planetary scis. MIT, Cambridge, 1983—, prin. rsch. scientist, 1983—; dir. Haystack Obs. MIT, Westford, 1983—; mem. adv. com. for astron. scis. NSF, Washington, 1985-88, mem. steering com. Coupling, Energetics and Dynamics of Atmospheric Regions, 1987-90; mem. com. on solar terrestrial rsch. NRC-NAS, Washington, 1986-89. Contbr. articles on physics of earth's upper atmosphere and ionosphere to sci. jours. Mem. Am. Geophys. Union, Am. Astron. Soc., Am. Meteorol. Soc., Internat. Union Radio and Sci., Internat. Assn. for Geomagnetism and Aeronomy. Office: MIT Haystack Obs RR 40 Westford MA 01886

SALAMA, C. ANDRE TEWFIK, electrical engineering educator; b. Heliopolis, Egypt, Sept. 27, 1938; arrived in Can., 1957; s. Tewfik and Sarine (Bigio) S.; m. Rhoda R. Kurtz, Dec. 19, 1974. BASc with honours, U. B.C., Vancouver, Can., 1961, MASc, 1963, PhD, 1966. Registered profl. engr., Ont. Mem. sci. staff Bell No. Rsch., Ottawa, Ont., Can., 1966-67; asst. prof. elec. engring. U. Toronto, Ont., 1967-70, assoc. prof., 1970-77, prof., 1977-92, univ. prof., 1992—; chmn., bd. dirs. Can. Microelectronics Corp., Kingston, Ont., 1984—; program leader, bd. dirs. Micronet, Toronto, 1990—. Mem. editorial bd. Solid State Electronics, 1982—; contbr. over 200 articles to sci. jours. Recipient Izaak Walton Killam Meml. prize, 1994; Info. Tech. Assn. Can. and Natural Scis. and Engring. Rsch. Coun. fellow U. Toronto, 1989-90. Fellow IEEE (assoc. editor Trans. on Cirs. and Systems 1987-89); mem. Electrochem. Soc., Assn. Profl. Engrs. Ont. Avocations: swimming, sailing, scuba diving, horseback riding, reading. Office: U Toronto, Dept Elec Engring, Toronto, ON Canada M5S 1A4

SALAMAN, MAUREEN KENNEDY, nutritionist; b. Glendale, Calif., Apr. 4, 1936; d. Ted and Elena (Peters) Kennedy; 1 child, Sean. West Coast Report, Sta. WMCA-AM, N.Y.C., 1980—; hostess Maureen Salaman's Accent on Health Sta. KFCB, Concord, Calif.; pres. Nat. Health Fedn., Monrovia, Calif., 1982—; cons., lectr., rschr. on cancer rsch. and metabolic medicine, nutrition; freedom of choice lobbyist. Author: Foods That Heal, Nutrition: The Cancer Answer, 1983, The Diet Bible, The Light at the End of the Refrigerator, Health Freedom News, 1982-85. Contbr. articles to profl. jours.; hostess TV show Maureen Salaman's Maximize Your Life. Developer nutrition programs for radio and TV. Office: Nat Health Fedn PO Box 688 Monrovia CA 91017-0688 Office: Maureen Kennedy Salaman Inc 1259 El Camino Real Ste 1500 Menlo Park CA 94025-4227

SALAMANCA, MERLINA ESPIRITU, secondary education educator; b. Abra, Philippines, Feb. 6, 1940; came to U.S., 1970; d. Santiago and Luisa (Panday) Espiritu; m. Manuel Valdez Salamanca; children: Merilyn Elaine, Michael Edward. LLB, Manuel L. Quezon U., Manila, 1963; BA, Columbus (Ga.) Coll., 1980, MEd, 1987; EdS, Troy State U., 1992. Legal researcher Paredes & Poblador Law Offices, Manila, 1965-69; title searcher Lawyer Title Ins., Inc., Ohio, 1970-72; acct. clk. St. Vincent Charity Hosp., Cleve., 1975-77; title searcher St. Patrick Sch., Phenix City, Ala., 1983-84, Adult Edn. Urban League, Columbus, Ga., 1984-85; tchr., behavior disorder therapist Woodall Psychoendl. Program, Columbus, 1985—. Contbr. articles to various publs. Mem. AAUW (pres. 1989—). Avocations: reading, cooking. Office: Woodall Psychoednl Program 4312 Harrison Ave Columbus GA 31904-6634

SALAMON, LESTER MILTON, political science educator; b. Pitts., Jan. 11, 1943; s. Victor William Salamon and Helen (Sanders) Weiss; m. Lynda Anne Brown, June 27, 1965; children: Noah, Matthew. BA in Econs. and Pub. Policy, Princeton U., 1964; PhD in Govt., Harvard U., 1971. Instr. dept. polit. sci. Tougaloo (Miss.) Coll., 1966-67; asst. prof. Vanderbilt U., Nashville, 1970-73; assoc. prof. policy scis. and polit. sci. Duke U., Durham, N.C., 1973-80, dir. Ctr. for Urban and Regional Devel., 1977-80; dep. assoc. dir. U.S. Office Mgmt. and Budget, Washington, 1977-79; dir. Ctr. for Governance and Mgmt. Rsch., Urban Inst., Washington, 1980-86; profl. Am. Inst. for Policy Studies, Johns Hopkins U., Balt., 1987—. Author: America's

Nonprofit Sector: A Primer, 1992, The Emerging Sector: Nonprofit Organizations in Comparative Perspective, 1994, Partners in Public Service: Government Nonprofit Relations in the Modern Welfare State, 1995; editor: The Tools of Government Action, 1989, Human Capital and America's Future, 1991; mem. editl. bd. Adminstrn. and Soc., 1985—, Voluntas, 1988—, Nonprofit and Voluntary Sector Quar., 1990—. Mem. Balt. City Planning Commn., 1987—. Recipient Laverne Burchfield award Am. Soc. Pub. Adminstrn., 1977. Mem. Internat. Soc. Third Sector Rsch. (vice chmn. 1991—), Nat. Acad. Pub. Adminstrn. Avocations: tennis, swimming, carpentry. Home: 2410 W Rogers Ave Baltimore MD 21209-4322 Office: Johns Hopkins U Inst Policy Studies 3400 N Charles St Baltimore MD 21218

SALAMON, LINDA BRADLEY, university dean, English literature educator; b. Elmira, N.Y., Nov. 20, 1941; d. Grant Ellsworth and Evelyn E. (Ward) Bradley; divorced; children: Michael Lawrence, Timothy Martin. B.A., Radcliffe Coll., 1963; M.A., Bryn Mawr Coll., 1964, Ph.D., 1971; Advanced Mgmt. Cert., Harvard U. Bus. Sch., 1978; D.H.L., St. Louis Coll. Pharmacy, 1993. Lectr., adj. asst. prof. Eng. Dartmouth Coll., Hanover, N.H., 1967-72; mem. faculty lit. Bennington Coll., Vt., 1974-75; dean students Wells Coll., Aurora, N.Y., 1975-77; exec. asst. to pres. U. Pa., Phila., 1977-79; assoc. prof. English Washington U., St. Louis, 1979-88, prof., 1988-92, dean Coll. Arts and Scis., 1979-92; prof. English, dean Columbia Sch. Arts and Scis. George Washington U., Washington, 1992-95, interim v.p. academic affairs, 1995—; mem. faculty Bryn Mawr Summer Inst. for Women, 1979—. Author, co-editor: Nicholas Hilliard's Art of Limning, 1983; co-author: Integrity in the College Curriculum, 1985; contbr. numerous articles to literary and ednl. jours. Bd. dirs. Assn. Am. Colls., vice chmn., 1985, chmn., 1986; bd. dirs. Greater St. Louis council Girl Scouts U.S.A.; trustee Coll. Bd., St. Louis Coll. Pharmacy. Fellow Radcliffe Coll. Bunting Inst., 1973-74; Am. Philos. Soc. Penrose grantee, 1974; fellow Folger Shakespeare Library, 1986, NEH Montaigne Inst., 1988. Mem. MLA, Renaissance Soc., Cosmos Club, Phi Beta Kappa. Office: George Washington U Washington DC 20052

SALAMON, MIKLOS DEZSO GYORGY, mining educator; b. Balkany, Hungary, May 20, 1933; came to U.S., 1986; s. Miklos and Sarolta (Obetko) S.; m. Agota Maria Meszaros, July 11, 1953; children: Miklos, Gabor. Diploma in Engring., Polytech U., Sopron, Hungary, 1956; PhD, U. Durham, Newcastle, England, 1962; doctorem honoris causa, U. Miskolc, Hungary, 1990. Research asst. dept. mining engring. U. Durham, 1959-63; dir. research Coal Mining Research Controlling Council, Johannesburg, South Africa, 1963-66; dir. collieries research lab Chamber of Mines of South Africa, Johannesburg, 1966-74; dir. gen. research org., 1974-86; disting. prof.; dir. Ctr. for Advanced Mining Sys. Colo. Sch. Mines, Golden, 1986-94, head dept. mining engring., 1986-90; dir. Colo. Mining and Mineral Resources Rsch. Inst., 1990-94; 22d Sir Julius Wernher Meml. lectr., 1988; hon. prof. U. Witwatersrand, Johannesburg, 1979-86; vis. prof. U. Minn., Mpls., 1981, U. Tex., Austin, 1982, U. NSW, Sydney, Australia, 1990, 91—; mem. Presdl. Commn. of Inquiry into Safety and Health in South African Mining Industry, 1994-95. Co-author: Rock Mechanics Applied to the Study of Rockbursts, 1966, Rock Mechanics in Coal Mining, 1976; contbr. articles to profl. jours. Mem. Pres.'s Sci. Adv. Council, Cape Town, South Africa, 1984-86; Nat. Sci. Priorities Com., Pretoria, South Africa, 1984-86. Recipient Nat. award Assn. Scis. and Tech. Socs., South Africa, 1971. Fellow South African Inst. Mining and Metallurgy (hon. life, v.p. 1974-76, pres. 1976-77, gold medal 1964, 85, Stokes award 1986, silver medal 1991), Inst. Mining and Metallurgy (London); mem. AIME, Internat. Soc. Rock Mechanics. Roman Catholic. Office: Colo Sch of Mines Dept Of Mining Engring Golden CO 80401

SALAMON, MYRON BEN, physicist, educator; b. Pitts., June 4, 1939; s. Victor William and Helen (Sanders) S.; m. Sonya Maxine Blank, June 12, 1960; children—David, Aaron. B.S., Carnegie-Mellon U., 1961; Ph.D., U. Calif., Berkeley, 1966. Asst. prof. physics U. Ill., Urbana, 1966-72, assoc. prof., 1972-74, prof., 1974—; program dir. materials research lab., 1984-91; vis. scientist U. Tokyo, 1966, 71, Tech. U. Munich, Fed. Republic Germany, 1974-75; cons. NSF. Editor: Physics of Superionic Conductors, 1979; co-editor: Modulated Structures, 1979; divisional assoc. editor: Phys. Rev. Letters, 1992—; contbr. sci. papers to profl. jours. Recipient Alexander von Humboldt Sr. U.S. Scientist award, 1974-75; NSF coop. fellow, 1964-66; postdoctoral fellow, 1966; A.P. Sloan fellow, 1972-73; Berndt Matthias scholar Los Alamos Nat. Lab., 1995—; visiting scientist CNRS and Inst. Laue-Langevin Grenoble, France, 1981-82. Fellow Am. Phys. Soc. Office: Dept of Physics U Ill 1110 W Green St Urbana IL 61801-3003

SALAMONE, GARY P. (PIKE SALAMONE), newspaper editor-in-chief, cartoonist; b. Rochester, N.Y., Aug. 26, 1950. BA, St. John Fisher Coll., 1972; MA, San Diego State U., 1979. Editor, pub. Inkslinger's Review, San Diego, 1981—; founder, news dir. Continental News Svc., San Diego, 1985—; pub., columnist Continental Newstime, San Diego, 1987—; founder, editor-in-chief Continental Features/Continental News Svc., San Diego and Washington, 1988—; pub., cartoonist Kids' Newstime, San Diego, 1992—. Author: An Examination of Alexander Hamilton's Views on Civil Liberty, 1979. Vol. radio announcer, reader Nat. Pub. Radio Affiliate Sta. KPBS, San Diego, 1976-81; founder Fisher Recycling, Rochester, N.Y., 1971; pres. Young People's Conservation Com., Webster-Penfield, N.Y., 1971; high sch. coord. Ecology Centre, San Diego, 1976; vol. pub. info. asst. Cleve. Nat. Forest, San Diego. Mem. Phi Alpha Theta, Pi Sigma Alpha. Democrat. Office: Continental Features Continental News Svc 341 W Broadway Ste 265 San Diego CA 92101

SALAMONE, JOSEPH CHARLES, polymer chemistry educator; b. Bklyn., Dec. 27, 1939; s. Joseph John and Angela (Barbagallo) S.; children: Robert, Alicia, Christopher. BS in Chemistry, Hofstra U., 1961; PhD in Chemistry, Poly. Inst. N.Y., 1967. NIH postdoctoral fellow U. Liverpool, Eng., 1966-67; rsch. assoc., Horace H. Rackham postdoctoral fellow U. Mich., Ann Arbor, 1967-70, adminstrv. sec., 1968-70; asst. prof., then assoc. prof. chemistry U. Mass., Lowell, 1970-76, prof., 1976-90, prof. emeritus, 1990—, dean Coll Sci., 1978-84, Disting. Rsch. fellow, 1984-90, chmn. dept. chemistry, 1975-78; pres. Optimers Inc., Lowell, 1985—; bd. dirs. Rochal Industries, Inc., Boca Raton, Fla.; cons. editor CRC Press, Inc., Boca Raton, 1992—. Mem. editl. bd. Polymer, 1976-94, Jour. Macromolecular Sci.-Chemistry, 1985—, Progress of Polymer Sci., 1987—, ChemTech, 1995—; adv. bd. Jour. Polymer Sci., 1974—; editor-in-chief Polymeric Materials Ency., 1993—; contbr. more than 155 articles to profl. jours. Recipient Disting Alumnus award, Poly. Inst. N.Y., 1984. Mem. Am. Chem. Soc. (chmn. div. polymer chemistry 1982), Soc. Plastics Engrs., Polymer Sci., Am. Acad. Ophthalmology (assoc.), Pacific Polymer Fedn. (sec., treas. 1988-90, dep. v.p. 1991-92, v.p., 1993, pres. 1994-95). Office: U Mass Dept Chemistry 1 University Ave Lowell MA 01854-2891

SALAMY, FARRIS NAJEEB, lawyer; b. Amarillo, Tex., Oct. 29, 1929; s. Najeeb Farris and Anna Helen (Elkouri) S.; children: Derek, Mark, Scott, Suzanne. BA in Econs., U. Calif., Berkeley, 1952, JD, 1955. Bar: Calif. Dep. dist. atty. Sacramento County Dist. Atty.'s Office, Sacramento, 1956-59; chief asst. pub. defender Sacramento County Pub. Defender's Office, Sacramento, 1959-89, pub. defender, 1989—; judge pro tempore Sacramento Mcpl. Ct., Sacramento County Superior Ct.; v.p., pres. Sacramento Legal Aid Soc. Mem. allottment bd. United Crusade, Sacramento, 1970-71, chair, 1975-76; cub troop leader Sacramento area Boy Scouts Am.; chmn. bd. dirs. Regional Area Planning Com., Sacramento. Mem. Calif. State Bar, Sacramento County Bar, Calif. Pub. Defenders Assn. (past. sec.-treas., v.p., pres.). Democrat. Avocations: golf, home care, automobile care. Office: Sacramento County Pub Defender 700 H St Ste 0270 Sacramento CA 95814-1215

SALAND, LINDA CAROL, anatomy educator, researcher; b. N.Y.C., Oct. 24, 1942; d. Charles and Esther (Weingarten) Gewirtz; m. Joel S. Saland, Aug. 16, 1964; children—Kenneth, Jeffrey. B.S., CCNY, 1963, Ph.D. in Biology, 1968; M.A. in Zoology, Columbia U., 1965. Research assoc. dept. anatomy Columbia U. Coll. Physicians and Surgeons, N.Y.C., 1968-69; sr. research assoc. dept. anatomy Sch. Medicine, U. NMex., Albuquerque, 1971-78, asst. prof., 1978-83, assoc. prof., 1983-89, prof., 1989—. Mem. editorial bd. Anat. Record, 1980—; contbr. articles to profl. jours. Predoctoral fellow NDEA, 1966-68; research grantee Nat. Inst. on Drug Abuse, 1979-83, NIH Minority Biomed. Research Support Program, 1980—;

NIH research grantee, 1986—. Mem. AAAS, Am. Assn. Anatomists, Soc. for Neurosci., Women in Neuroscience (chair steering comm. 1991-93), Am. Soc. Cell Biology, Sigma Xi. Office: U NMex Sch Medicine Dept Anatomy Basic Med Sci Bldg Albuquerque NM 87131

SALANS, CARL FREDRIC, lawyer; b. Chicago Heights, Ill., Mar. 13, 1933; s. Leon and Jean (Rudnick) S.; m. Edith Motel, Sept. 26, 1956; children: Eric Lee, Marc Robert, Christopher John. A.B., Harvard, 1954; B.A., Trinity Coll., Cambridge (Eng.) U., 1956, LL.B., 1958, M.A., 1962; J.D., U. Chgo., 1957. Bar: Ill. 1958, D.C. 1973, U.S. Supreme Ct. 1972, admitted in France as avocat, 1972. With State Dept., 1959-72, dep. legal adviser, 1966-72; practice law Paris, 1972—; legal adviser U.S. del. Vietnam Peace Talks, Paris, 1968-71; assoc. prof. law George Washington U., 1965-66; lectr. on internat. comml. arbitration Inst. Internat. Bus. Law and Practice, Internat. C. of C., Paris, France; arbitrator internat. cases; arbitrator U.S.-Iran Claims Tribunal, The Hague. Mem. ABA (chmn. com. East-West trade and investment 1975-82), Am. Soc. Internat. Law, Am. Arbitration Assn. (panel arbitrators), Am. C. of C. in France (bd. dirs. 1977-87, chmn. laws and pub. affairs com. 1980-85). Home: 18 Ave Raphael, 75016 Paris France Office: Salans Hertzfeld & Heilbronn, 9 Rue Boissy d'Anglas, 75008 Paris France

SALANS, LESTER BARRY, physician, scientist, educator; b. Chicago Heights, Ill., Jan. 25, 1936; s. Leon K. and Jean (Rudnick) S.; m. Lois Audrey Kapp, Dec. 21, 1958; children: Laurence Eliot, Andrea Eileen. B.A., U. Mich., 1957; M.D. with honors, U. Ill., 1961. Internal medicine intern Stanford U. Med. Ctr., 1961, resident, 1962-64; USPHS postdoctoral and spl. fellow Rockefeller U., 1964-67, asst. prof., 1967-68, adj. prof., 1984—; asst. prof. medicine Dartmouth Coll., 1968-70, assoc. prof., 1970-77, adj. prof., 1978-79; assoc. dir. diabetes, endocrinology, metabolism, also chief lab. cellular metabolism and obesity Nat. Inst. Arthritis, Metabolism and Digestive Diseases, NIH, Bethesda, 1976-81; dir. Nat. Inst. Arthritis, Diabetes, Digestive and Kidney Diseases, NIH, 1981-84; v.p., head preclin. rsch. Sandoz Rsch. Inst., 1985-92, v.p. scientific and acad. affairs, 1993—; dean Mt. Sinai Sch. Medicine, 1984, prof. internal medicine, 1984-85, clin. prof. medicine, 1987—; adj. prof. Rockefeller U., 1985—; vis. prof. U. Geneva, Switzerland, 1974-75. Contbr. articles on insulin, diabetes mellitus, obesity to profl. jours., textbooks. Recipient NIH Research Career Devel. award, 1972-76, NIH Dirs. award, 1980, Juvenile Diabetes Fedn Pub. Service award, 1979. Fellow ACP; mem. AAAS, Am. Soc. Clin. Investigation, Am. Fed. Clin. Research, Am. Diabetes Soc., Am. Diabetes Assn. (Charles H. Best award 1985), Endocrine Soc., Assn. Am. Physicians, Harvey Soc., Am. Soc. Clin. Nutrution. Office: Sandoz Rsch Inst RR 10 Hanover NJ 07936

SALANT, NATHAN NATHANIEL, athletic conference executive; b. Bronx, N.Y., June 25, 1955; s. Benjamin B. and Marilyn (Balterman) S. BA cum laude, SUNY, Albany, 1976; JD, Boston U., 1979. Bar: N.J. 1981. Asst. athletic dir. SUNY, Albany, 1979-80, St. Francis Coll., Bklyn., 1981-85; spl. asst. athletic dir. Adelphi U., Garden City, N.Y., 1985-88; commr. Mid. Atlantic States Collegiate Athletic Conf., Chester, Pa., 1988-92; adj. prof. English Widener U., Chester, 1988-92; commr. Gulf South Conf., Birmingham, Ala., 1992—; mem. Men's Com. on Comms., NCAA, 1993—. Author: This Date in New York Yankees History, 1979, 81, 83, Superstars, Stars and Just Plain Heroes, 1982. Head coach Rockland (N.Y.) OTB Pirates Am. Legion Baseball Team, 1974-76, 77—. Named Coach of Yr. Rockland County Big League, 1979-81, 83, 85-86, 87, 89, N.Y. State Am. Legion, 1987, 89-94. Mem. ABA. Avocations: collecting sports memorabilia, stamps and coins, writing. Home: 174 Woodmere Creek Ln Birmingham AL 35226-3561 Office: Gulf South Conf 4 Office Park Cir Ste 218 Birmingham AL 35223-2538

SALANT, WALTER S., economist; b. N.Y.C., Oct. 24, 1911; s. Aaron Bennett and Josephine Adele (Scheider) S.; m. Edna Goldstein, Jan. 25, 1939; children—Michael Alan, Stephen Walter. B.S., Harvard, 1933; A.M., Grad. Sch. Pub. Adminstrn., 1937-38, Ph.D., 1962; postgrad., Cambridge U., Eng., 1933-34. Research, statistics Treasury Dept., 1934-36; research Wall St. firm, 1936; asst. econs. Harvard, 1938; research SEC, 1938-39; mem. sr. staff indsl. econ. div. Office of Sec. Dept. Commerce, 1939-40; head economist research div. OPA (and predecessor agencies), 1940-45; econ. adviser to Econ. Stbhzn. Dir., 1945-46, Price Decontrol Bd., 1946; economist Council Econ. Advisers, Exec. Office Pres., 1946-52; cons. econ. and finance div. NATO, 1952-53; vis. prof. Stanford, 1954, 69; sr. fellow Brookings Instn., 1954-76, emeritus, 1977—; cons. to sec. of treasury, 1961—, mem. U.S. econ. survey team to Indonesia, 1961; cons. AID, 1963-66. Author: (with B.N. Vaccara) Import Liberalization and Employment, 1961, (with others) Indonesia: Perspectives and Proposals for U.S. Economic Aid, 1963, The U.S. Balance of Payments in 1968, 1963, International Monetary Arrangements: The Problem of Choice, 1967, Maintaining and Restoring Balance in International Payments, 1966, International Mobility and Movement of Capital, 1972, European Monetary Unification and Its Meaning for the United States, 1973, Worldwide Inflation: Theory and Recent Experience, 1977, also The Effects of Increases in Imports on Domestic Employment: A Clarification of Concepts, 1978; bd. editors: (with others) Am. Econ. Rev., 1956-58; contbr. (with others) articles to econs. jours. Mem. Univ.-Nat. Bur. Com. Econ. Research, 1956—, mem. exec. com., 1962-74, vice chmn., 1967-74. Mem. Am. Econ. Assn., Royal Econ. Soc., Phi Beta Kappa. Clubs: Cosmos (Washington), Harvard (Washington). Home: 2101 Connecticut Ave NW Washington DC 20008-1700

SALATHE, JOHN, JR., manufacturing company executive; b. Montreal, Que., Can., Sept. 25, 1928; s. John and Ida (Schenk) S.; m. Harriet Edith Styles; children: Linda Paul, Craig. BSME, San Jose State U., 1950. Gen. mgr. Indsl. Steel Tank & Body Co., Berkeley, Calif., 1958-62; project mgr. Pacific Foundry div. PACCAR Inc., Renton, Wash., 1962-66, prodn. mgr., 1966-70, asst. gen. mgr., 1970-71, gen. mgr., 1971-79; asst. v.p. PACCAR Inc., Bellevue, Wash., 1979-81, v.p., 1981-90; ret., 1991. Bd. dirs. Jr. Achievement, Seattle, 1979-85; mem. adv. bd. Seattle Pacific U., 1985—. Sloan fellow Stanford U., 1970. Mem. Soc. Mfg. Engrs. (sr.), Am. Soc. Quality Control (sr.). Avocations: gardening, boating, reading.

SALATKA, CHARLES ALEXANDER, archbishop; b. Grand Rapids, Mich., Feb. 26, 1918; s. Charles and Mary (Balun) S. Student, St. Joseph's Sem., Grand Rapids, 1932-38; M.A., Cath. U. Am., 1941; J.C.L., Inst. Civil and Canon Law, Rome, 1948. Instr. St. Joseph's Sem., Grand Rapids, Mich., 1945; ordained priest Roman Catholic Ch., 1945; assigned chancery office Diocese of Grand Rapids, 1948-54, vice chancellor, 1954-61; aux. bishop, 1961, vicar gen., 1961, consecrated bishop, 1962; pastor St. James Parish, Grand Rapids, 1962-68; titular bishop of Cariana and aux. bishop of Grand Rapids, 1962-68; bishop of Marquette, 1968-77; archbishop of Okla. City, 1977-92; ret., 1992. Mem. Canon Law Soc. Am.

SALAY, CAROLYN JEANNE, advertising agency executive; b. Birmingham, Ala.; d. Augustus Alexander and Mary Elizabeth (White) S. BA, Birmingham So. Coll., 1966; postgrad., U. Ala., Tuscaloosa, 1966-68. Client liaison Unigrafix, Birmingham, 1970-71; traffic mgr. Luckie & Forney Advt., Inc., Birmingham, 1972-76; creative dir. Perry-Hoyle Advt., Inc., Birmingham, 1976-77; freelance copywriter Birmingham, 1977; copywriter Bentley Huggins Smith & Whittington, Inc., Birmingham, 1977-78, Bear Britton Black Advt., Montgomery, Ala., 1978-82; creative dir. Bear Advt., Montgomery, 1982-88, Salay St. Advt., Montgomery, 1988-90, Salay Advt., Montgomery, 1990—. Copywriter Bank Marketing Assn. (Best of Print Pub. award 1982); contbr. articles to advt. jours. Charter mem. Montgomery Mus.; active various local charities; campaign staff Folmar for Gov., Montgomery, 1982. Recipient Class of '86 award Ala. Bus. Rev., Montgomery, 1986; Best of Show award Huntsville (Ala.) Advt. Fedn., 1988, numerous Gold and Silver Addy awards. Mme. NAFE, Montgomery Advt. Fedn. (bd. dirs. 1979-80, pres. 1986-87, vice chmn. Pres.'s coun. 1986-87, 1st chmn. pres.'s coun., Copywriter of Yr. 1979, 84, 86, Best of Show 1982, 86, 88), Am. Advt. Fedn. (7th dist. club: vice-chmn. pres.'s coun. 1986-87, Advt. for Advt. award 1986-87; mem. nat. club achievement and awards com. 1987-89, nat. pub. svc. com. 1989—, Ad Club Pres. of Yr. 1986-87, Saatchi & Saatchi Compton Edn. award 1986-87), Community Rels. Soc. for Advancement of Mgmt. (v.p. Montgomery chpt. 1988-90), Capital City Club (bus. com. 1989—). Episcopalian. Office: Salay Advt PO Box 230399 Montgomery AL 36123-0399

SALAZAR, ALBERTO, Olympic professional runner; b. Havana, Cuba, Aug. 7, 1958; s. Jose and Marta Galbis (Rigal) S.; m. Molly Morton, Dec. 21, 1981; 1 son, Antonio Roberto. B.A., U. Oreg., 1981. Mem. U.S. Olympic Team, 1980, 1984; cons. Nike Co., 1981—. Record holder N.Y. Marathon, Oct. 25, 1980, winner, 1980-82; winner Boston Marathon, 1982. Mem. Assn. Bd. Racing Athletes. Office: Internat Mgmt Group 1 Erieview Plz Ste 1300 Cleveland OH 44114-1715*

SALAZAR, RAMIRO S., library administrator; b. Del Rio, Tex., Mar. 3, 1954; s. Jesus and Juanita (Suarez) S.; m. Cynthia Castillo, Dec. 19, 1976 (div. 1990); children: Ramiro Orlando, Selinda Yvette. BA, Tex. A&I U., 1978; MLS, Tex. Woman's U., 1979. Asst. libr. dir. Val Verde County Libr., Del Rio, Tex., 1975-76; libr. Robert J. Kleberg Libr., Kingsville, Tex., 1977-78; libr. dir. Eagle Pass Pub. Libr. (Tex.), 1980-84; dir. Main Libr. San Antonio Pub. Lib., 1984-90; dir. librs. El Paso Pub. Libr., 1991-93, Dallas Pub. Libr., 1993—; chmn. Tex. State Libr. Planning Task Force, 1991-92; active Tex. Women's U. Sch. Libr. and Info. Studies Adv. Bd., 1993—, Alliance for Higher Edn. Libr. Dirs. Coun., 1993—; bd. advs. U. N. Tex. Sch. Lib. and Info. Scis., 1993. Chair customer svc. steering com. City of Dallas, 1993—. Mem. ALA (cultural diversity com. 1995—), Libr. Adminstrn. and Mgmt. Assn. (bldg. and equipment sect., arch for pub. lib. com. 1993-95, cultural diversity com. 1995—), Tex. Mcpl. Libr. Dirs. Assn., Tex. Libr. Assn. (legis. com. 1993-95), Pub. Libr. Adminstrs. North Tex., Reforma (exec. bd. dirs. 1993—), Tex. Lib. Assn. (chmn. pubs. com. 1992-93, ad hoc com. value of public libs. 1995—, awards com. 1995—), Jaycees. Democrat. Roman Catholic. Home: PO Box 15031 Dallas TX 75201 Office: Dallas Pub Libr 1515 Young St Dallas TX 75201-5499

SALAZAR-CARRILLO, JORGE, economics educator; b. Havana, Cuba, Jan. 17, 1938; came to U.S., 1960; s. Jose Salazar and Ana Maria Carrillo; m. Maria Eugenia Winthrop, Aug. 30, 1959; children: Jorge, Manning, Mario, Maria Eugenia. BBA, U. Miami, 1958; MA in Econs., U. Calif., Berkeley, 1964, cert. in econ. planning, 1964, PhD in Econs. 1967. Sr. fellow, nonresident staff mem. Brookings Instn., Washington, 1973—; dir. mission chief UN, Rio de Janeiro, Brazil, 1974-80; prof. econs. Fla. Internat. U., Miami, 1980—, chmn. dept. econs., 1980-89; dir. Ctr. Econ. Rsch. & Edn.; mem. coun. econ. advisors State of Fla.; advisor U.S. Info. Agy., advisor, contbg. editor Library of Congress, Washington, 1972—; chmn. program com. Hispanic Profs. of Econs. and Bus.; cons. econs. Agy. for Internat. Devel., Washington, 1979—; council mem. Internat. Assn. Housing, Vienna, 1981—; exec. bd. Cuban Am. Nat. Council, Miami, 1982—; bd. dirs., pres. Fla. chpt. Insts. of Econ. and Social Rsch. of Caribbean Basin, Dominican Republic and Costa Rica, 1983—, U.S.-Chile Council, Miami, 1984—, Fla.-Brazil Inst. Co-author: Trade, Debt and Growth in Latin America, 1984; Prices for Estimation in Cuba, 1985; The Foreign Debt and Latin America, 1983; External Debt and Strategy of Development in Latin America, 1985; The Brazilian Economy in the Eighties, 1987, Foreign Investment, Debt and Growth in Latin America, 1988; World Comparisons of Incomes, Prices, and Product, 1988, Comparisons of Prices and Real Products in Latin America, 1990, The Latin American Debt, 1992; author: Wage Structure in Latin America, 1982. Fellow Brit. Council, London, 1960, Georgetown U., Washington, 1961-62, OAS, Washington, 1962-64, Brookings Instn., Washington, 1964-65. Mem. Am. Econ. Assn., Internat. Assn. Research in Income and Wealth, Econometric Soc. Latin Am., N.Am. Econs. and Fin. Assn., Nat. Assn. Cuban Am. Educators (treas. exec. com.), Internat. Assn. Energy Economists (pres. Fla. chpt.), Nat. Assn. Forensic Economists, Assn. for Study Cuban Economy (exec. com.), Latin Am. Studies Assn., Knights of Malta. Roman Catholic. Home: 5335 Orduna Dr Miami FL 33146 Office: Fla Internat U Tamiami Campus DM 347 Miami FL 33199

SALBAING, PIERRE ALCEE, retired chemical company executive; b. Lectoure, France, May 8, 1914; emigrated to Can., 1946, naturalized, 1968; s. Jean and Sylvia (LaForgue) S.; m. Genevieve Nehlil, July 18, 1942; children: Michel, Christian, Francois, Patrick. B.A., Caen (France) U., 1931; Engring. Degree, Ecole Polytechnique, Paris, 1937; Naval Architecture Degree, Ecole Genie Maritime, Paris, 1939. With N.Am. dept. Air Liquide, Montreal, Que., Can., 1946-91, asst. gen. mgr., 1957-58, gen. mgr., 1958-60; exec. v.p. Canadian Liquid Air Ltd., Montreal, 1960-62, pres., 1962-82, chmn. bd., 1982-91; vice chmn. bd. Liquid Air Corp N.Am., San Francisco, 1984-91. Served to lt. comdr. French Navy, 1939-44. Decorated Legion of Honour., Nat. Order of Merit. Clubs: Mt. Royal, Montreal Amateur Athletic Assn.

SALBERG, MELVIN, lawyer; b. N.Y.C., Jan. 16, 1926; s. Max and Esther (Cukierman) S.; m. Rita Cecile Kahn, Sept. 19, 1948 (dec. 1985); children: Michael, Robert, Barbara, Lawrence; m. Anita Marie Gessler, Jan. 24, 1987. BA, NYU, 1949, JD, 1951. Bar: N.Y., 1951. Ptnr. Lipkowitz, Plaut, Salberg & Harris, N.Y.C., 1957-85; Graubard, Mollen, Horowitz, Pomeranz & Shapiro, N.Y.C., 1985-92, Anderson, Kill, Olick & Oshinsky, N.Y.C., 1992—; pres. British Controlled Oilfields, Ltd., Montreal, Can., 1970—. Nat. chmn. Anti-Defamation League B'nai B'rith, N.Y.C. Served with U.S. Maritime Svc., 1943-45. Mem. ABA, N.Y. State Bar Assn., N.Y. County Bar Assn., B'nai B'rith Internat. (bd. govs. 1992—). Office: Anderson Kill 1251 Ave of the Americas New York NY 10020-1182

SALCH, STEVEN CHARLES, lawyer; b. Palm Beach, Fla., Oct. 25, 1943; s. Charles Henry and Helen Louise (Alverson) S.; m. Mary Ann Prim, Oct. 7, 1967; children—Susan Elizabeth, Stuart Trenton. B.B.A., So. Meth. U., 1965, J.D., 1968. Bar: Tex. 1968, U.S. Tax Ct. 1969, U.S. Dist. Ct. (so. dist.) Tex. 1969, U.S. Dist. Ct. (ea. dist.) Tex. 1972, U.S. Ct. Appeals (5th cir.) 1969, U.S. Ct. Appeals (fed. cir.) 1982, U.S. Ct. Fed. Claims, 1982. Assoc. Fulbright & Jaworski, Houston, 1968-71, participating assoc., 1971-75, ptnr., 1975—. Co-author: Tax Practice Before the IRS, 1994; contbr. articles to legal jours. Pres. Tealwood Owners Assn., 1982-83, Meml. High Sch. PTA, 1985-86; mem. Tex. PTA (Hon. Life Member award 1986). Mem. ABA (coun. dir. 1985-88, vice chmn. tax sect. 1988-91, chair-elect tax sect. 1995—), State Bar Tex., Houston Bar Assn., Am. Law Inst., Nat. Tex Assn., Am. Coll. Tax Counsel, Internat. Fiscal Assn., Harris County Heritage Soc., Galveston Hist. Found., Smithsonian Assocs., Colonial Williamsburg Found., Am. Bar Found., Southwestern Legal Found., Houston Bar Found., Beta Alpha Psi, Phi Eta Sigma, Order of Coif, Phi Delta Phi. Presbyterian. Clubs: Houston, Cotillion, Lakeside Country, Houston Center, Governor's, Galveston Country, Yacht, Pelican of Galveston, Galveston Artillery. Home: 342 Tamerlaine Dr Houston TX 77024-6147 Office: Fulbright & Jaworski 51st Fl 1301 Mckinney St Houston TX 77010-3049

SALCUDEAN, MARTHA EVA, mechanical engineer, educator; b. Cluj, Romania, Feb. 26, 1934; emigrated to Can., 1976, naturalized, 1979; d. Edmund and Sarolta (Hirsch) Abel. B.Eng., U. Cluj, 1956; postgrad., 1962; PhD, U. Brasov (Romania), 1969; PhD (hon.), U. Ottawa, 1993; m. George Salcudean, May 28, 1955; 1 child, Septimiu E. (Tim). Mech. engr. Armatura, Cluj, 1956-63; sr. rsch. officer Nat. Rsch. Inst. Metallurgy, Bucharest, 1963-75; part-time lectr. Inst. Poly., Bucharest, 1967-75; sessional lectr. U. Ottawa (Ont., Can.), 1976-77, asst. prof., 1977-79, assoc. prof., 1979-81, prof., 1981-85; prof., head dept. mech. engring. U. B.C., 1985—, assoc. v.p. rsch., 1993—; mem. grant selection com. for mech. engring. Natural Scis. and Engring. Rsch. Coun. Can.; mem. Nat. Adv. Panel to Min. Sci. and Tech. on advanced indsl. materials, Can., 1990; mem. governing coun. Nat. Rsch. Coun. Recipient Gold medal B.C. Sci. Coun., Killam Rsch. prize U. B.C. Rsch. Coun. Can. grantee, 1978—, Commemorative Medal 125th anniversary Can. Confederation, 1993, Julian C. Smith medal Engring. Inst. Can., 1994-95. Fellow Can. Acad. Engring., Royal Soc. Can.; mem. ASME, Assn. Profl. Engrs. Ont. Contbr. numerous articles to profl. jours. Home: 1938 Western Pkwy, Vancouver, BC Canada V6T 1W5

SALDICH, ROBERT JOSEPH, electronics company executive; b. N.Y.C., June 7, 1933; s. Alexander and Bertha (Kasakove) S.; m. Anne Rawley, July 21, 1963 (div. Nov. 1979); 1 child, Alan; m. Virginia Vaughan, Sept. 4, 1983; stepchildren: Tad Thomas, Stan Thomas, Melinda Thomas, Margaret Thomas. BSChemE, Rice U., 1956; MBA, Harvard U., 1961. Mfg. mgr. Procter & Gamble Mfg. Co., Dallas, Kansas City, Kans., 1956-59; rsch. asst. Harvard Bus. Sch., Boston, 1961-62; asst. to pres. Kaiser Aluminum & Chem. Corp., Oakland, Calif., 1962-64; mgr. fin. and pers., then gen. mgr. various divs. Raychem Corp., Menlo Park, Calif., 1964-83, with office of pres., 1983-87, sr. v.p. telecommunications and tech., 1988-90, pres., CEO, 1990—; pres. Raynet Corp. subs. Raychem Corp., 1987-88. Chair mfg. com.

adv. bd. Leavy Sch. Bus. and Administrn., Santa Clara U. Mem. Calif. Roundtable (dir. Bay Area Coun.), San Francisco Com. on Fgn. Rels. Jewish. Avocations: sailing, skiing. Office: Raychem Corp Mailstop 120/7815 300 Constitution Dr Menlo Park CA 94025-1164

SALE, JAMES PROWANT, JR., lawyer; b. Cin., Sept. 29, 1947; s. James Sr. and Betty Louise (Tourtellotte) S.; m. Rhani Leatherwood, May 21, 1977 (div. Nov. 1985); 1 child, James Wiley. BS, Okla. State U., 1969; JD, U. Houston, 1972. Bar: Tex. 1972, U.S. Supreme Ct. 1978, U.S. Ct. Appeals (5th cir.) 1974, U.S. Ct. Appeals (11th cir.) 1981. Assoc. Black, Hebinck, Hargrove & Clark, Houston, 1973-74; atty. United Gas Pipeline, Houston, 1974-79; sr. atty. United Energy Resources, Inc., Houston, 1979-85; v.p. legal dept. United Tex. Transmission Co., Houston, 1985-86; asst. gen. counsel Mid Con Corp., Houston, 1986—. Served to 1st lt. U.S. Army, 1969-73. Mem. ABA, Houston Bar Assn., Fed. Energy Bar Assn., Tex. Utility Lawyer's Assn., Am. Gas Assn. Clubs: Kingwood (Tex.) Country, Deerwood (Kingwood). Home: 2511 Spruce Pine Kingwood TX 77345

SALE, (JOHN) KIRKPATRICK, writer; b. Ithaca, N.Y., June 27, 1937; s. William M. Jr. and Helen (Stearns) S.; m. Faith Apfelbaum Sale, June 21, 1962; children: Rebekah Zoe, Kalista Jennings. BA, Cornell U., 1958. Editor The New Leader, N.Y.C., 1959-61; corr. Chgo. Tribune, San Francisco Chronicle, 1961-62; lectr. U. Ghana, Accra, 1963-65; editor N.Y. Times mag., N.Y.C., 1965-68, The Nation, N.Y.C., 1981-82; ind. scholar and writer, 1968—; bd. dirs. PEN Am. Ctr. N.Y.C., The Learning Alliance, N.Y.C. Author: The Land and People of Ghana, 1963, SDS: The Rise of the Students for a Democratic Society..., 1973, Power Shift: The Rise of the Southern Rim and Its Challenge to the Eastern Establishment, 1975, Human Scale, 1980, Dwellers in the Land: The Bioregional Vision, 1985, The Conquest of Paradise: Christopher Columbus and the Columbian Legacy, 1990, The Green Revolution: The American Environmental Movement, 1962-92, 1993, Rebels Against the Future: The Luddites and Their War on the Industrial Recolution: Lessons for the Computer Age, 1995; contbg. editor The Nation; contbr. articles to profl. jours. Bd. dirs. EF Schumacher Soc., Great Barrington, Mass., 1981—; co-dir. Hudson Bioregional Coun., N.Y.C., 1985—; co-founder N.Y. Greens, N.Y. Green Party, 1985, 1989. Home: 113 W 11th St New York NY 10011-8325 Office: Joy Harris Agy 156 5th Ave New York NY 10010-7002

SALE, LLEWELLYN, III, lawyer; b. St. Louis, May 19, 1942; s. Llewellyn Jr. and Kathleen (Rice) S.; m. Cynthia Jean Bricker, Aug. 17, 1968 (dec. Apr. 26, 1995); children: Allyson J., Erin E. AB cum laude, Yale U., 1964; LLB cum laude, Harvard U., 1967. Bar: Mo. 1967, U.S. Dist. Ct. (ea. dist.) Mo. 1967, U.S. Tax Ct. 1982, U.S. Ct. Claims 1985. From assoc. to ptnr. to mng. ptnr. Husch & Eppenberger, St. Louis, 1967-88; ptnr. Bryan Cave, St. Louis, 1988—. Bd. dirs. Washington U. Child Guidance Clinic, St. Louis, 1978-80, Mental Health Assn. St. Louis, 1988-89. Mem. ABA, Bar Assn. Met. St. Louis (chmn. law econs. subcom. 1982), Media Club, Noonday Club. Avocations: spectator sports, jogging. Office: Bryan Cave 211 N Broadway Ste 3600 Saint Louis MO 63102-2733

SALE, TOM S., III, economist, educator; b. Haynesville, La., July 27, 1942; s. Thomas and Mary Belle (Fagg) S.; divorced; children: Jennifer Elizabeth, Sarah Elaine. BA, Tulane U., 1964; MA, Duke U., 1965; PhD, La. State U., 1972. Mem. faculty La. Tech. U., Ruston, 1965—, prof. econs., 1975—, head dept. econs. and fin., 1974-86, 90—, dir. grad. studies Coll. Adminstrn and Bus., 1988-89. Chartered fin. analyst. Mem. Am. Econs. Assn., So. Econs. Assns., Southwestern Fin. Assn. (pres. 1985-86), Am. Fin. Assn., Inst. Chartered Fin. Analysts (exam. com. 1983-92, curriculum com. 1993—), SW Fedn. Adminstrv. Disciplines (v.p. 1988-89, pres. 1989-90), Dallas Assn. Fin. Analysts, Omicron Delta Kappa, Omicron Delta Epsilon. Episcopalian. Contbr. articles to profl. jours. Home: PO Box 1365 Ruston LA 71273-1365 Office: La Tech U Ruston LA 71272

SALE, WILLIAM MERRITT, classicist, comparatist, educator; b. New Haven, Nov. 27, 1929; s. William Merritt and Helen (Stearns) S.; m. Marilyn Mills, June 13, 1953 (div. Oct. 1967); children: Elizabeth, David; m. Anne Perkins, May 18, 1991. B.A., Cornell U., 1951, M.A., 1954, Ph.D., 1958. Engr. U.S. Metals Co., Carteret, N.J., 1951-52; instr. in classics Yale U., New Haven, 1957-58; asst. prof., assoc. prof. Washington U., St. Louis, 1958-75, chmn. classics dept., 1961-69, prof. classics and comparative lit., 1975—, chmn. comparative lit. dept., 1981-90. Author: Sophocles' Electra: Commentary with Introduction and Translation, 1970, Existentialism and Euripides, 1977, Homer and the Roland, 1993, The Government of Troy, 1995. Recipient Founder's Day award for Excellence in Teaching Washington U., 1978. Mem. Am. Philol. Assn., London Inst. for Classical Studies. Home: 2342 Albion Pl Saint Louis MO 63104-2524 Office: Washington U Dept Comparative Lit Saint Louis MO 63130

SALEH, BAHAA E. A., electrical engineering educator; b. Cairo, Sept. 30, 1944; came to U.S., 1977.; BS, Cairo U., 1966; PhD, Johns Hopkins U., 1971. Lectr. Johns Hopkins U., Balt., 1969-71; asst. prof. U. Santa Catarina, Brazil, 1971-74; rsch. assoc. Max Planck Inst., Göttingen, Fed. Republic Germany, 1974-76; asst. prof. elec. engring. U. Wis., Madison, 1977-79, assoc. prof., 1979-81, prof., 1981-94, chmn. dept. elec. and computer engring., 1990-94; prof., chmn. dept. elec. computer and systems engring Boston Univ., Boston, 1994—. Author: Photoelectron Statistics, 1978, Fundamentals of Photonics, 1991; also over 150 articles on optics and image processing. Romnes faculty fellow U. Wis., 1981, Guggenheim fellow, 1984. Fellow IEEE, Optical Soc. Am.; Jour Optical Soc. of Am. A., editor-in-chief; mem. Phi Beta Kappa, Sigma Xi. Office: 44 Cummington St Boston MA 02215

SALEM, ELI, chemical engineer; b. Jan. 21, 1936. BSChemE, CCNY, 1957; MSChemE, Poly. Inst., 1967; MBA in Fin., NYU, 1977. Chem. engr. water div. Graver Co., Union, N.J., 1957—, v.p. tech. dept., 1978— Author papers in field. Mem. ASTM, ASME, Am. Inst. Chem. Engrs., Am. Water Works Assn., Water Pollution Control Fedn. Achievements include over 13 patents in the water treatment field. Office: Graver Co Aqualytics 7 Powderhorn Dr Warren NJ 07059

SALEM, GEORGE RICHARD, lawyer; b. Jacksonville, Fla., Dec. 24, 1953; s. Kamel Abraham and Margaret Virginia (Bateh) S.; m. Rhonda M. Ziadeh, June 28, 1980; children: James George, Jihan Camille, Laila Suad. BA, Emory U., 1975, JD, 1977; LLM, Georgetown U., 1984. Bar: Ga. 1978, Fla. 1979, D.C. 1981. Ptnr. Thompson, Mann & Hutson, Washington, 1977-85; dep. solicitor U.S. Dept. Labor, Washington, 1985-86, solicitor of labor, 1986-89; ptnr. Akin, Gump Strauss, Hauer & Feld, Washington, 1990—; bd. dirs. Overseas Pvt. Investment Corp. Contbr. articles to profl. jours. Nat. exec. dir. ethnic voters div. Reagan Bus '84; bd. dirs. United Palestinian Appeal, Inc., 1981-85, 86—, Arab Am. Inst., Jan.-Mar., 1985, Dec. 1986—; chmn. Arab Am. Leadership Coun., 1990—; mem. Am. Arab Anti-Discrimination Com., Interagy. Coordinating Coun.; chmn. Arab-Ams. for Bush-Quayle '88, '92. Recipient Ellis Island Medal of Honor, 1992. Mem. ABA (labor and employment law sect.), Ga. Bar Assn. (labor rels. div.), fla. Bar Assn. (labor rels. div.), D.C. Bar Assn. (labor rels. div.), Nat. Assn. Arab Ams. (bd. dirs. 1987, pres. 1992—), Am. Ramallah Club (pres. D.C. chpt. 1984, Wash. rep. 1982-84), Am. Ramallah Fedn. (chmn. human rights com., Washington rep 1982-84) Arab Am. Rep. Fedn. (chmn 1985), Assn. Am. Arab Univ. Grads., Century Club Nat. Rep. Heritage Groups Coun., Delta Theta Phi, Omicron Delta Kappa. Mem. Eastern Orthodox Christian Ch. Office: Akin Gump Hauer & Feld 1333 New Hampshire Ave NW #210 Washington DC 20036-1564

SALEMBIER, VALERIE BIRNBAUM, publishing executive; b. Teaneck, N.J., July 2, 1945; d. Jack and Sara (Gordon) Birnbaum; m. David J. Salembier, June 23, 1968 (div. 1980); m. Paul J. Block, Dec. 9, 1990. B.A., Coll. of New Rochelle, 1973. Merchandising mgr. Life Internat., Time, Inc., N.Y.C., 1964-69; merchandising copywriter Newsweek, Inc. N.Y.C., 1970; promotion prodn. mgr. Newsweek, Inc. 1971, adv. sales rep., 1972-76; advt. dir. Ms. Mag., N.Y.C., 1976-79, assoc. pub., 1979-81; pub. Inside Sports Mag., N.Y.C., 1982; v.p., pub. 13-30 Corp, N.Y.C., 1983; sr. v.p. advt. USA Today, 1983-88; pub. TV Guide, Radnor, PA, 1988-89; pres. N.Y. Post, N.Y.C., 1989-90; pub. Family Circle Mag., N.Y.C., 1991-93; v.p. advt. The N.Y. Times, 1993—; lectr. in field. Trustee Coll. New Rochelle; trustee,

exec. com. N.Y.C. Police Found.; mem. exec. com. Women of Distinction, United Jewish Appeal; pres., bd. dirs. Nat. Alliance Breast Cancer Orgns., N.Y. Road Runners Club, BOX (Beneficial Orgn. to Aid Ex-Fighters). Mem. C200, Women in Commn., Womens Forum, Nat. Coun. Jewish Women (bd. dirs.), N.Y. Rd. Runners Club. Home: 1075 Park Ave New York NY 10128-1003 Office: The NY Times 229 W 43rd St New York NY 10036-3913

SALEM-MURDOCK, MUNEERA, anthropologist; b. Amman, Jordan, May 15, 1947; d. Yahya Salem and Zahra (Shapsugh) Abzach; m. Paul Irving Murdock, Apr. 14, 1973 (div. Apr. 1983); 1 child, Tamara. MA in English Lit., Ill. State U., 1973; MA in Anthropology, SUNY, Binghamton, 1977, PhD in Anthropology, 1984. Mem. Pakistan Forestry Planning and Devel. Project, 1983; project mgr. Evaluation of Potable Water Projects in Rural Tunisia, 1983; dir. Liberia: Social Institutional Profile of Agrl. Sector, 1984; dir. rsch. devel. Ctrl. Tunisia Devel. Authority, 1985-87, 86-88; co-dir. African River Basin Devel. Project, 1984-85, 85-89; dir. Regional Range Mgmt. Project, UN Food and Agriculture Orgn., 1986-88; dir. long term rsch. Senegal River Basin Monitoring Activity I, 1988-90, Senegal River Basin Monitoring Activity II, 1990—; socioeconomist Maroc/MIAC Dryland Rsch. Ctr.: Socioeconomic Monitoring and Evalution USAID/Rabat and U. Nebr., 1989, Island of Socotra, People's Dem. Republic of Yemen, 1989; environ. and resettlement expert The World Bank, 1987; sr. rschr. USAID/Tunis and Tunisian Govt., 1985; community devel. specialist Rural Community Deve. Project, 1984; rschr. Socio-institutional Profile of Niger, 1982-83, rschr. numerous other projects; conference presenter. Contbr. numerous articles to profl. jours. Scholarship Ministry of Edn., Govt. of Jordan, 1965-69, Am. Friends of the Middle East, 1971-73, Lang. scholarship Goethe Inst., 1969; grad. rsch. fellowship SUNY, Binghamton, 1975-80, 82, Inst. for Devel. Anthropology, 1979-80; grantee Social Sci. Rsch. Coun., 1982, Wenner-Gren Found. for Anthropol. Rsch., 1981. Democrat. Islam. Avocations: travel, theatre, tennis. Home: 15 Beethoven St Binghamton NY 13905-4245 Office: PO Box 2207 Binghamton NY 13902-2207

SALENGER, LUCY LEE, producer, consultant; b. St. Louis, Sept. 12, 1938; d. Leo and Lucille (Mier) Berner; m. Marvin Zonis, Jan. 4, 1976; children: Laura, Nadia, Leah. BA with honors, UCLA, 1961. Press asst. Kennedy for Pres., L.A., 1968; field producer, reporter, researcher 60 Minutes, CBS News, L.A., 1970-72; reporter, producer Sta. WLS-TV, Chgo., 1972-74; field producer CBS News, Chgo., 1974-75; dir. Ill. Film Office, Chgo., 1975-83; gen. ptnr. The Odeon Group, Chgo., 1986—; sr. cons. Harpo Studios, Chgo., 1988-89; assoc. prodr. Brewster Place, Chgo., 1989-90; cons. to gov. on culture State of Ill., Chgo., 1988; v.p. Marvin Qonis and Assoc., Internat. Cons., 1990—; bd. dirs. Radio Sta. WBEZ. Bd. advisors Ill. State Fair, Chgo., 1980-83; bd. dirs. Chgo. Film Festival, 1978-82, Rehab. Inst. Chgo., 1981-83, Mus. Broadcasting, Chgo., 1984-89, Chgo. Coalition, 1980-83. Recipient 1st achievement award Facets Multimedia, 1980, ann. award Chgo. Coalition, 1983, Woman of Yr. award Sta. WBBM, Chgo., 1985, 1st ann. achievement award Women in Film 1987; urban fellow Northeastern U., 1985. Mem. Chgo. Network (bd. dirs. 1989—), Women in Film (Chgo. adv. bd. 1990), Nat. Assn. Film Communicators (bd. dirs. 1984—). Jewish. Avocations: international travel, exercise, designing gardens. Home: 4942 S Ellis Ave Chicago IL 60615-2708

SALENTINE, THOMAS JAMES, pharmaceutical company executive; b. Milw., Aug. 8, 1939; s. James Edward and Loretta Marie (Burg) S.; m. Susan Anne Sisk, Apr. 16, 1966; children: Anne Elizabeth, Thomas James Jr. BS in Acctg., Marquette U., Milw., 1961. CPA, Ind., Wis. Sr. audit mgr. Price Waterhouse, Milw., 1961-74; dir. corp. acctg. Ward Foods Inc., Wilmette, Ill., 1974-78; corp. contr. Johnson Controls Inc., Milw., 1984-85; v.p., contr. Stokely Van Camp Inc., Indpls., 1978-87; exec. v.p., chief fin. officer Bindley Western Industries Inc., Indpls., 1987—, also bd. dirs. Chmn. com. United Way, Indpls., 1989-90; lt. USN, 1962-65. Mem. AICPA, Fin. Execs. Inst. Republican. Roman Catholic. Home: 13540 Brentwood Ln Carmel IN 46033-9488 Office: Bindley Western Industries Inc 4212 W 71st St Indianapolis IN 46268-2259

SALERNO-SONNENBERG, NADJA, violinist; b. Rome, Jan. 10, 1961; came to U.S., 1969; d. Josephine Salerno-Sonnenberg. Grad., Curtis Inst. Music, 1975, Juilliard Sch., 1982. Profl. debut Phila. Orch., Phila., 1971; appearances include Am. Symphony Orch., Balt. Symphony, Chgo. Symphony, Cin. Symphony, Cleve. Orch., Detroit Symphony, Houston Symphony, Indpls. Symphony, Los Angeles Chamber Orch., Milw. Symphony, Montreal Symphony, New Orleans Philharm., N.J. Symphony, N.Y. Philharm., Phila. Orch., Pitts. Symphony, L.A. Philharmonic, Minn. Orch.; guest appearances include Mostly Mozart Festival, Ravinia, Blossom, Meadow Brook, Great Woods, Caramoor, Aspen, Hollywood Bowl; internat. appearances in Vienna, Munich, Stuttgart, Frankfurt, Geneva, Rotterdam, Lisbon, Tokyo; featured on CBS' 60 Minutes, CBS Sunday Morning, NBC Nat. News, PBS' Live From Lincoln Ctr., Charlie Rose Show; numerous appearances on The Tonight Show with Johnny Carson; rec. artist Angel, 1987. Recipient 1st prize Naumburg Violin Competition, N.Y.C., 1981; Avery Fisher Career grantee., N.Y.C. 1983. Mem. AFTRA, Screen Actors Guild. Office: care M L Falcone Pub Rels 155 W 68th St New York NY 10023-5808

SALES, A. R., financial executive; b. Holguin, Oriente, Cuba, Sept. 20, 1948; came to U.S., 1961; s. Angel Alberto and Adeina Rosa (Paneque) S.; m. Barbara Cornell Felix, Aug. 26, 1972; children: Ashley Lynden, Alison Lane. BS, Ind. U., 1972, MBA, 1977. Mgmt. trainee Lincoln Nat. Bank, Ft. Wayne, Ind., 1972-73; asst. v.p. Am. Fletcher Nat. Bank, Indpls., 1973-77; treasury mgr. The Upjohn Co., Kalamazoo, 1977-82, v.p., treas., 1985-90; asst. treas. Midland-Ross Corp., Cleve., 1982-85; treas. Arvin Industries, Inc., Columbus, Ind., 1990—. Bd. dirs. C. Brown Speech and Hearing Ctr., Kalamazoo, 1987-90, treas., 1989; bd. dirs. Columbus Pro Musica Orch., Bartholomew Co. United Way; adv. bd. Ind. U.-Purdue U., Columbus. Mem. Fin. Execs. Inst., Nat. Assn. Corp. Treas., Beta Gamma Sigma. United Methodist. Avocations: tennis, golf, art. Office: Arvin Industries PO Box 3000 Columbus IN 47202-3000

SALES, EUGENIO DE ARAUJO CARDINAL, archbishop; b. Acari, Brazil, Nov. 8, 1920; d. Celso Dantas and Josefa de A. Sales; student Seminary Fortaleza City. Ordained priest Roman Cath. Ch., 1943, consecrated bishop, 1954, elevated to cardinal, 1969; Sede Plena apostolic adminstr., Natal, 1962, Salvador, 1964; archbishop, Salvador, 1968-71, Rio de Janeiro, 1971—. Mem. Congregations Bishops, for Divine Cult, clergy, Evangelization, Oriental Chs., Cath. Edn., Couns. for Social Communication. Editor: The Pastors Voice. Address: Gloria 446, 20241-150 Rio de Janeiro Brazil

SALES, JAMES BOHUS, lawyer; b. Weimar, Tex., Aug. 24, 1934; s. Henry B. and Agnes Mary (Pesek) S.; m. Beuna M. Vornsand, June 3, 1956; children: Mark Keith, Debra Lynn, Travis James. BS, U. Tex., 1956, LLB with honors, 1960. Bar: Tex. 1960. Practiced in Houston, 1960—; sr. ptnr. firm and head litigation dept. Fulbright & Jaworski, 1960—; advocate Am. Bd. Trial Advocates; pres. State Bar of Tex., 1988-89. Author: Products Liability in Texas, 1985; co-author: Texas Torts and Remedies, 5 vols., 1986; contbr. articles to legal publs. Trustee South Tex. Coll. Law, 1982-88, 90—, A.A. White Dispute Resolution Ctr. 1991-94; bd. dirs. Tex. Resource Ctr., 1990—, Tex. Bar Hist. Found., 1990-93. 1st lt. USMCR, 1956-58. Fellow Internat. Acad. Trial Lawyers, Am. Coll. Trial Lawyers (state chair 1994—), Am. Bar Found. (sustaining life, state chmn. 1993—), Tex. Bar Found. (trustee 1991-95, vice chmn. 1992—, chmn. 1993-94, sustaining life mem.), Houston Bar Found. (sustaining life, chmn. bd. 1982-83); mem. Internat. Assn. Def. Counsel, ABA (ho. of dels. 1984—), Nat. Def. Res. Counsel. 1989-92), So. Conf. Bar Pres., Def. Rsch. Inst., So. Tex. Coll. Trial Advocacy (dir. 1983—), Fed. Bar Assn., State Bar Tex. (pres. 1988-89, bd. dirs. 1983-87, chmn. bd. 1985-86), Tex. Assn. Def. Counsel (v.p. 1977-79, 83-84), Houston Bar Assn. (pres. 1980-81), Gulf Coast Legal Found. (bd. dirs. 1982-85), Bar Assn. 5th Fed. Cir., The Forum. Roman Catholic. Clubs: Westlake (bd. govs. 1985-88), Inns of Ct., Ramada. Home: 10803 Oak Creek St Houston TX 77024-3016 Office: Fulbright & Jaworski 1301 Mckinney St Houston TX 77010-3029

SALES, ROBERT JULIAN, newspaper editor; b. N.Y.C., Jan. 1, 1936; m. Naomi Simon, Oct. 11, 1958; children: Jonathan, Marian. B.A., L.I. U., 1957. Reporter Newsday, Garden City, N.Y., 1960-63; N.Y. Herald

Tribune, N.Y.C., 1963-66, Boston Globe, 1966-78; editor Boston Phoenix, 1978-79; mng. editor Boston Herald Am., 1979-81; exec. editor Boston Herald, 1981-83, Toledo Blade, Ohio, 1983; met. editor N.Y. Newsday, N.Y.C., 1984-86; sports editor Boston Herald, 1986—. Urban Journalism fellow Northwestern U., Evanston, Ill., 1973. Club: Univ. Club (Boston). Office: Boston Herald One Herald Sq Boston MA 02106*

SALESKI, VERNA MAE, nursing educator; b. Taylor, Pa., Oct. 10, 1945; d. Dominick N. and Jennie (Biscontini) S.; m. John Charles Saleski, Sept. 18, 1971; children: John Vincent, Cheryl Lynn. BS in Nursing, U. Pa., 1968; Student sch. of nursing, Community Med. Ctr., Scranton, Pa., 1966; MS in Counselor Edn., U. Scranton, 1981; MS in Family Nursing, SUNY, Binghamton, 1985. Cert. nurse, Pa. Staff nurse Community Med. Ctr., Scranton, 1966; instr. Sch. of Nursing Community Med. Ctr., 1969-88, dir. Sch. of Nursing, 1988—; staff nurse U. Pa. Hosp., Phila. 1966-68; coord., instr. nursing Worthington campus ADN program Pa. State U., 1992—; part-time family nurse practitioner in maternal family health svcs. Wilkes-Barre, Pa. Fed. traineeship, U. Pa., 1967-68. Mem. ANA (cert. CRNP), Nat. League for Nursing, Community Med. Ctr. Alumnae Assn., Sigma Theta Tau. Republican. Roman Catholic. Avocations: crocheting, gourmet cooking. Home: RR 1 Box 1375 Gouldsboro PA 18424-9440 Office: Pa State U Sch Nursing Worthington Campus Scranton PA 18510

SALESSES, JOHN JOSEPH, university administrator; b. Providence, Feb. 13, 1933; s. William Edward and Alice Marie (McConnell) S.; m. Dolores Ann Serbst, Nov. 27, 1954; children: John J., Robert G., Gregory M., Beth Ann. AB, Providence Coll., 1954; MA, U. R.I., 1960, PhD, 1979. Instr. Coll. Steubenville, Ohio, 1960-62; asst. prof. English R.I. Coll., Providence, 1962-79, assoc. prof. English, 1979—, chmn. dept. English, 1976-79, asst. v.p., dean, 1979-90, v.p., 1990—; adj. faculty U.S. Naval War Coll., Newport, R.I., 1963-73; mem. Dept. Def. Res. Forces Policy Bd., Washington, 1985-88. Mem. R.I. Postsecondary Commn. Maj. gen. USMCR, 1954-88. Decorated Disting. Svc. medal; recipient Disting. Svc. award R.I. Coll., 1985; fellow U. R.I., 1958-60. Mem. N.E. MLA, Soc. for Eighteenth Century Studies, Res. Officers Assn., Marine Corps Res. Officers Assn., Renaissance Soc. Am., Barrington Yacht Club (R.I.), Newport Arty. Co. (master gunner) Waneumetonomy Golf Club (R.I.). Roman Catholic. Avocations: running, golf, sailing. Home: 89 Peleg Rd Portsmouth RI 02871-3831 Office: RI Coll 600 Mt Pleasant Ave Providence RI 02908-1924

SALGADO, LISSETTE, dancer; b. Hialeah, Fla.. Dancer Miami (Fla.) Dance Theater Co., 1980-86, Joffrey II Dancers, N.Y.C., 1986-88, The Joffrey Ballet, N.Y.C., 1988—. Office: The Joffrey Ballet 130 W 56th St New York NY 10019-3818*

SALGIA, TANSUKH JAWAHARLAL, academic administrator; b. Partabgarh, India, Oct. 5, 1937; came to U.S., 1966; s. Jawaharlal Rupchand and Sarekuwar (Govadia) S.; m. Bharati T. Ghia, Jan. 4, 1970; children: Anupdev, Amar Deep. B in Commerce, VIKRAM U., Ujjain, India, 1961; MBA, Atlanta U., 1967; d in Bus. Adminstrn., Columbia Pacific U., 1979; D of Commil. Sci., The London Inst. Applied Rsch., 1973. Bus. mgr., dir. budgets Knoxville (Tenn.) Coll., 1967-72; controller, chief fin. officer, treas. Lewis U., Romeoville, Ill., 1972-77; v.p. bus. affairs, treas. Dyke Coll., Cleve., 1977-89; v.p. fin., treas. Quincy (Ill.) Coll., 1989-93; chief fiscal officer Ohio Student Aid Commn., Columbus, 1993—; mem. Inter Faith Commn., Cleve., 1987-89, Greater Cleve. Round Table, 1987-89; trustee The Nationality Svcs. Ctr., Cleve., 1987-89; dir. Quincy chpt. Credit Union, 1991—. Editor: Jainism-Past & Present, 1984, My Prayer, 1985, Jainism-Non-Violence, 1987. State co-chmn. Asian, Indian Bush-Quayle for Pres., Cleve., 1988; state co-chmn. coalition div. Voinovich for Gov. Ohio, Cleve., 1990; mem. Rep. Presidential Task Force, Washington, 1988, Mayor's Asian Adv. Coun., Cleve., 1989-90; trustee Nationalities Svcs. Ctr. of Greater Cleve.; mem. cultural heritage adv. com. Cuyahoga Community Coll., Cleve.; dir., treas. Quincy Chpt. Credit Union. Recipient Citizen awards Bishop of Cleve., 1987, the White House, 1987, Gov. of Ohio, 1987, also awards from Mayor of City of Cleve., City Coun. of Cleve., Nat. Fedn. Asian Indians in N.Am., Fedn. of Jain Assns. in N.Am., Ohio Ho. of Reps., Congresswoman Mary Rose Oakar, Congressman Louis Stokes, Fedn. India Community Assns. in N.E. Ohio, Asian/Pacific Am. Fedn. Mem. Nat. Assn. Colls. & Univ. Bus. Officers, Cen. Assn. Coll. & Univ. Bus. Officers. Republican. Jain. Avocations: reading, traveling, community svc. Home: 1884 Dorsetshire Rd Columbus OH 43229 Office: Ohio Student Aid Commn 309 S 4th St Columbus OH 43215

SALHANY, LUCILLE S., broadcast executive. Formerly with Paramount Pictures; pres. Paramount Domestic Television, from 1985; chmn. Twentieth Television, a unit of Fox Inc., 1991-92, Fox Broadcasting Co., Beverly Hills, Calif., 1993-94; pres. United ParamountNetwork, 1994—.

SALIBA, JACOB, manufacturing executive; b. East Broughton, Que., Can., June 10, 1913; s. Said and Nazira (David) S.; m. Adla Mudarri, May 31, 1942; children: John, Thomas, Barbara. BS, Boston U., 1941. Sr. supervising engr. Thompson and Lichtner Co., Boston, 1944-49; pres. Kingston Dress Co., Boston, 1949-51, Indsl. & Mgmt. Assocs., Inc., Boston, 1951-54, Maine Dress Co., Cornish, 1948-61; exec. v.p., mem. exec. com. Cortland Corp., Inc. (formerly Brockway Motor Co., Inc.), N.Y.C., 1954-59; exec. v.p. Sawyer-Tower, Inc., Boston, 1955-56, pres., 1956-59; v.p. Farrington Mfg. Co.; exec. v.p. Farrington Packaging Corp., 1959-61, Farrington Instruments Corp.; pres. N.E. Industries, Inc., from 1961, also bd. dirs.; pres. Fanny Farmer Candy Shops, Inc., 1963-66, W.F. Schrafft & Sons Corp., 1967-68; pres. frozen foods div. W.R. Grace & Co., 1966-68; pres. Katy Industries, Inc., Elgin, Ill., 1969-88, chmn., CEO, 1988-94; bd. dirs. Schon & Cie, Emerging Germany Fund, NYSE, Syratech Corp., NYSE, Katy Industries, NYSE; spl. cons. Air Material Commmand, USAF, Dayton, Ohio, 1942-43; cons. to chief air staff USAF, 1952-54; co-chmn. Air Force Spare Study Group, 1953. Mem. corp. Mass. Gen. Hosp., Mus. Sci. Mem. Union League Club, Bridgton Club, Highlands Country Club, Palm Beach Yacht Club. Methodist. Office: Katy Industries Inc 853 Dundee Ave Elgin IL 60120-3036

SALIBA, PHILIP E., archbishop; b. Abou-Mizan, Lebanon, 1931; came to U.S., 1956, naturalized, 1961; s. Elias Abdallah and Salema (Saliba) S. B.A., Wayne State U., 1959; M.Div., D.D., St. Vladimir's Sem., N.Y., 1964; DHL, Wayne State U., 1986. Became sub-deacon Antiochian Orthodox Christian Ch. N.Am., 1945-49, ordained deacon, 1949-59, priest, 1959-66, consecrated archbishop, 1966, now primate; chmn. Standing Conf. Am.-Middle Eastern Christian and Moslem Leaders; chmn. Orthodox Christian Edn. Commn.; vice chmn. Standing Conf. Canonical Orthodox Bishops in Ams. Vice-chmn. St. Vladimir's Orthodox Theol. Sem. Address: 358 Mountain Rd Englewood NJ 07631-3727

SALIGMAN, HARVEY, consumer products and services company executive; b. Phila., July 18, 1938; s. Martin and Lillian (Zitin) S.; m. Linda Powell, Nov. 25, 1979; children: Martin, Lilli Ann, Todd Michael, Adam Andrew, Brian Matthew. BS, Phila. Coll. Textiles and Sci., 1960. With Queen Casuals, Inc., Phila., 1960-88; v.p. Queen Casuals, Inc., 1966-68, pres., chief exec. officer, 1968-81, chmn., 1981-88; pres., chief operating officer Interco Inc., St. Louis, 1981-83, chief exec. officer, 1983-85; chief exec. officer Interco Inc., 1985-89, chmn., 1989-90; bd. dirs. Merc. Bank, Union Electric. Trustee Jewish Hosp. Mem. St. Louis Club, Masons. Office: 10 S Brentwood Blvd Ste 408 Saint Louis MO 63105-1694

SALIH, HALIL IBRAHIM, political science educator; b. Kyrenia, Cyprus, Feb. 26, 1939; came to U.S. 1959; s. Hasan Kaya and Sabire (Ismail) S.; m. Sharon Kettlewell, Jan. 20, 1964 (div. 1989); children: David Kerim, Julie Shermin; m. Elizabeth Scott, Oct. 28, 1989. BA, U. Pacific, Stockton, Calif., 1963; MA, Am. U., 1965, PhD, 1967. Asst. prof. polit. sci. Tex. Wesleyan Coll., Ft. Worth, 1966-71; chmn. dept. polit. sci. Tex. Wesleyan Coll., 1973, prof. polit. sci., 1981—, dir. Mexican prog., 1977-86; prof. faculty coun. Tex. Wesleyan U., 1989-90; lectr. in field. Author: Cyprus: The Impact of Diverse Nationalism on a State, 1978; contbr. articles to profl. jours. Bd. dirs. Mothers Against Drunk Driving, Tarrant County, 1990. Recipient Tex. Wesleyan Faculty Recognition award, 1981, 94, Wesleyan Flame award, 1988; Hall of Nations scholar Am. U., 1965; Malone fellow, 1994. Fellow Danforth Assn.; mem. Phi Alpha Theta, Pi Gamma Mu, Pi Sigma Alpha, Alpha Phi Omega. Democrat. Muslim. Avocations: reading, swimming, photography, travel, hunting. Home: 6508 Spring River Ln Fort Worth TX 76180-8056 Office: Tex Wesleyan U PO Box 50010 Fort Worth TX 76105-0010

SALINAS, CARLOS FRANCISCO, dentist educator; b. Iquique, Chile, Apr. 9, 1941; came to U.S., 1972; s. Carlos F. and Victoria (Cerda) S.; m. Maria Asunción Córdova, 1963; children: Carlos Miguel, Claudio Andres, Maria Asunción. BS, U. Chile, Santiago, 1958; DDS, U. Chile, 1963; DMD, Med. U. S.C., 1985. Cert. Chile, 1982, Tenn., 1982, S.C., 1985. Dentist Nat. Health Svc., Viña del Mar, Chile, 1963-65; pvt. practice Viña del Mar, 1963-72; fellow in medicine/genetics Johns Hopkins U., Balt., 1972-74; faculty mem. Med. Univ. S.C., Charleston, 1974-88, assoc. prof., 1988-94, prof. and dir. divsn. craniofacial genetics, 1994—; faculty mem. U. Chile, Valparaiso, 1965-74; dentist Dental Ctrl. Clinic for Chilean Navy, Valparaiso, 1964-66; vis. scientist U. Montreal, 1974; internat. cons. Interamerican Coll. Physicians and Surgeons, Ptnrs. of Ams., WHO/Pan Am. Health Orgn. Editor: Genetica Craniofacial, 1979, Craniofacial Anomalies: New Perspectives, 1982, (with R.J. Jorgenson) Dentistry in the Interdisciplinary Treatment of Genetic Diseases, 1980, (with K.S. Brown) Craniofacial Mesenchyme In Morphogensis and Malformations, 1984, (with J.M. Opitz) Recent Advances in Ectodermal Dysplasias, 1988; contbr. articles to profl. jours. Bd. dirs. Ptnrs. Ams. (award 1992), East Cooper Cmty. Outreach, S.C. World Trade Ctr., Charleston; chmn. bd. S.C. Hispanic Coalition, 1994—; pres. Circulo Hispanoamericano de Charleston; hon. Consul of Chile, 1978—. Grantee NIH, 1972-74, HEW, 1979-80, 80-81, 81-82, 82-83, 83-84, Dept. Health and Human Svcs., 1983-84, 84-85, March of Dimes Birth Defects Found., 1984-85, S.C. State Health and Human Svcs. Fin. Commn., 1989—. Mem. AAAS, Soc. Craniofacial Genetics (pres. 1985, 92, chmn. membership com. 1993-94), Iberoam. Soc. Human Genetics of N.Am. (v.p. 1992-94, pres. 1994—), Am. Assn. Dental Schs., Am. Soc. Human Genetics, Am. Cleft Palate and Craniofacial Anomalies Assn., Interam. Assn. for Dental Rsch., Am. Assn. for Dental Rsch., Interam. Coll. Physicians and Surgeons (bd. dirs. chpt. faculty and rschrs. 1994—), Med. Assn. P.R. (hon.), Peruvian Soc. Human Genetics (hon.), Med. Soc. Western Dist. P.R. (hon.). Home: 948 Equestrian Dr Mount Pleasant SC 29464-3608 Office: Med Univ SC 171 Ashley Ave Charleston SC 29425-2601

SALINAS DE GORTARI, CARLOS, former president of Mexico; b. Mexico City, Mex., Apr. 3, 1948; s. Raul Salinas Lozano and Margarita de Gortari Carvajal; m. Yolanda Cecilia Occeli Gonzalez; children: Cecilia, Emiliano, Juan Cristobal. Grad. in econs., Nat. U. Mex., 1971; MPA, Harvard U., 1973, MA in Polit. Economy, 1976, PhD in Polit. Economy and Govt., 1978. Asst. prof. stats. Nat. U. Mex., 1970; asst. dir. pub. fin. Ministry of Fin., Mex., 1971-74, head of econ. studies, 1974-76, asst. dir. fin. planning, 1978, dir. gen., 1978-79; dir. gen. econ. and social policy Ministry of Programming and Budget, 1979-81; dir. gen. Inst. Polit., Social and Econ. Studies, 1981-82; minister of planning and fed. budget, 1982-87, pres. of Mexico, 1988-94; tchr. pub. fin. and fiscal policy, Mex., 1976, 78; rsch. asst. Harvard U., 1974. Author numerous articles and essays. Mem. Partido Revolucionario Institucional (PRI).

SALINE, LINDON EDGAR, industrial company executive; b. Mpls., Mar. 16, 1924; s. Emil and Anna (Hinz) S.; m. Jane Sprenger, Oct. 14, 1950; children: Sandra, Susan, Jeffrey, Bradley. B.E.E., Marquette U., 1945; M.S. in Elec. Engring., U. Wis., 1948, Ph.D. in Elec. Engring., 1950, Sc.D. hon., 1973. Registered profl. engr., Ariz., Fla., Md., N.Y. With Cutler-Hammer, Milw., 1946-47; with Gen. Electric Co., Fairfield, Conn., 1948-84, tech. and mgmt. positions in power systems, computers, aerospace and def., human resources and health care mgmt.; bd. dirs. St. Francis Med. Ctr., Franciscan Health System, LaCrosse Found., Chileda Habilitation Inst.; adv. com. on sci. edn. NSF; lectr. in field. Contbr. tech. papers and articles to profl. jours. Leader nat. minority engring. effort, chmn. State of Conn. Task Force on Mgmt. Human Resources, 1977-78; exec. dir. Bus. Roundtable on Health Initiatives, 1982-84. Served with USN, 1942-46. Recipient Disting. Service Citation U. Wis., 1973; named Disting. Engring. Alumnus Marquette U., 1981. Fellow IEEE, Am. Soc. Engring. Edn.; mem. AAAS, ASME, Sigma Xi, Tau Beta Pi, Eta Kappa Nu, Pi Mu Epsilon. Republican. Presbyterian. Club: La Crosse Country. Lodge: Rotary. Home: 1874 Mulder Ct Dresbach MN 55947-3013 *Balancing the spiritual, intellectual, and physical aspects of my life has given me the energy, freedom and desire to pursue a wide variety of interests. I am most grateful that somehow, somewhere I "learned how to learn", which gives me the confidence to enjoy and cope with a rapidly changing society.*

SALINGER, JEROME DAVID, author; b. N.Y.C., Jan. 1, 1919; s. Sol and Miriam (Jillich) S.; m. Claire Douglas, 1953 (div. 1967); children: Margaret Ann, Matthew. Student, Valley Forge Mil. Acad., Columbia U. Author: Catcher in the Rye, 1951, Nine Stories, 1953, Franny and Zooey, 1961, Raise High the Roof Beam, Carpenters; and Seymour: An Introduction, 1963; contbr. stories to New Yorker mag. Sgt. AUS, 1942-46. Address: care Harold Ober Assocs 425 Madison Ave New York NY 10017-1110*

SALINGER, PIERRE EMIL GEORGE, journalist; b. San Francisco, June 14, 1925; s. Herbert and Jehanne (Bietry) S.; m. Renee Laboure, Jan. 1, 1947; children: Marc (dec.), Suzanne, Stephen; m. Nancy Brook Joy, June 28, 1957; m. Nicole Helene Gillmann, June 18, 1965 (div. June 1988); 1 son, Gregory; m. Nicole Beauvillain de Menthon, June 17, 1989. BS, U. San Francisco, 1947. Reporter, night city editor San Francisco Chronicle, 1944-55; guest lectr. journalism Mills Coll., 1950-55; West Coast editor, contbg. editor Collier's mag., 1955-56; investigator select com. to investigate improper activities in labor or mgmt. field U.S. Senate, 1957-59; press sec. U.S. Senator Kennedy, 1959-60, Pres. Kennedy, 1961-63, Pres. Johnson, 1963-64; U.S. Senator from Calif., 1964; v.p. Nat. Gen. Corp., 1965; v.p. internat. affairs Continental Airlines, Inc. and Continental Air Services, Inc. (subsidiary), 1965-68; pres. Gramco Devel. Corp., 1968—; dep. chmn. Gramco (U.K.) Ltd., 1970-71; sr. v.p. AMROP Inc., 1969; L'Express, Paris, 1973-78; contbg. corr. ABC for Europe, 1977—; Paris bur. chief, 1979-87, sr. editor, 1988-90; sr. editor ABC News, 1988-93; vice chmn. Burson Marstellar, Washington, 1993—. Author: With Kennedy, 1966, On Instructions of My Government; editor: A Tribute to John F. Kennedy, 1964, A Tribute to Robert F. Kennedy, 1968, Je Suis un Americain, 1975, La France et le Nouveau Monde, 1976, America Held Hostage-The Secret Negotiations, 1981, The Dossier, 1984, Mortal Games, 1988, Secret Dossier—The Hidden Agenda Behind the Gulf Crisis, 1991. Press officer Calif. Stevenson for Pres. Campaign, 1952, Richard Graves for Gov. Calif. Campaign, 1954; trustee Robert F. Kennedy Meml. Found.; chmn. bd. trustees Am. U. in Paris, 1978-88, hon. chmn., 1988—. With USNR, World War II. Decorated officer Legion of Honor (France); recipient Ellis Island Medal of Honor, 1992. Mem. Nat. Press Club. Office: Burson Marstellar 1850 M St NW Washington DC 20036

SALISBURY, ALICIA LAING, state senator; b. N.Y.C., Sept. 20, 1939; d. Herbert Farnsworth and Augusta Belle (Marshall) Laing; m. John Eagan Salisbury, June 23, 1962; children: John Eagan Jr., Margaret Salisbury La Rue. Student Sweet Briar Coll., 1957-60; BA, Kans. U. 1961. Mem. Kans. Senate, 1985—, chmn. commerce com., telecomm. strategic planning com.; vice chmn. ways and means com., mem. legis. post audit com., mem. joint com. on econ. devel.(mem. orgn. and calendar rules comm.). Elected mem. State Bd. Edn., Topeka, 1981-85, Kans.; past pres. Jr. League of Topeka; trustee Leadership Kans., 1982-89; bd. dirs. Topeka Community Found., 1983—, Topeka Pub. Sch. Found., 1985-89, Capitol Area Pla. Authority, 1989—, Mid-Am. Mfg. Tech. Ctr., mem. workers' compensation fund oversight com., mem. Kids Count steering com., mem. Stormont-Vail Hosp. Aux.; mem. adv. commn. Juvenile Offenders Program, Kans., 1985—; mem. adv. bd. Topeka State Hosp., Kans. Action for Children, 1982—; Kans. Ins. Edn. Found., 1984—; Youth Center at Topeka, 1987-95; steering com. One Stop Career Ctr., Interstate Cooperation Com. Coun. State Govts.; mem. Nat. Fedn. Rep. Women; past bd. mem. United Way Greater Topeka, ARC, Family Service and Guidance, Topeka, Shawnee County Mental Health Assn., Florence Crittenton Services, Topeka, Topeka City Commn. Govtl. Adv. Com. Mem. Nat. Conf. State Legislators (chmn. blue ribbon adv. panel on workers' compensation, vice chmn. assembly on fed. issues), Nat. Rep. Legislators' Assn. (Nat. Rep. Legislator of Yr. 1993), Bus. Guardian award 1990, Outstanding Individual Legis. Achievement award 1989), Nat. Fedn. Ind. Bus., Shawnee County Rep. Women, Kappa Kappa Gamma. Epis-

copalian. Avocations: tennis; downhill skiing; water sports; horseback riding; gardening. Office: Kans State Senate State Capital Topeka KS 66612

SALISBURY, CHARLES A. (LEX), zoo director, educator; b. Fairbanks, Alaska, July 22, 1958; s. Lee Harvey Salisbury and Lesley (Hampton) Vo392te; m. Julie Amanda Tanner, Jan. 27, 1977 (div. May 1984); m. Lisa C. West, Apr. 5, 1986; 1 child, Alexander Lee. BA, U. Sydney, Australia, 1981; M in Philosophy, Griffith U., Brisbane, Australia, 1991. Wildlife officer Currumbin Sanctuary, Queensland, Australia, 1981-82; owner Portage Bay Constrn. Co., Bainbridge Island, Wash., 1985-86; gen. curator, dep. dir. Lowry Park Zool. Soc., Tampa, Fla., 1987-94, exec. dir., 1994—; adj. lectr. dept. psychology U. South Fla., Tampa, 1994—. Avocations: orchidist, lic. falconer, traveling. Home: 1105 W Patterson St Tampa FL 33604 Office: Lowry Park Zool Garden 7530 North Blvd Tampa FL 33604-4756

SALISBURY, EUGENE W., lawyer, justice; b. Blasdell, N.Y., Mar. 20, 1933; s. W. Dean and Mary I. (Burns) S.; m. Joanne M. Salisbury, July 14, 1950; children: Mark, Ellen, Susan, David, Scott. BA in History and Govt. cum laude, U. Buffalo, 1959, JD cum laude, 1968. Bar: N.Y. 1960, D.C. 1973, U.S. Dist. Ct. (we. and no. dists.) 1961, U.S. Ct. Appeals (2d cir.) 1970, U.S. Dist. Ct. Appeals (D.C. cir.) 1973, U.S. Supreme Ct. 1973. Ptnr. Lipsitz, Green, Fahringer, Roll, Salisbury and Cambria, Buffalo, 1960—; justice Village of Blasdell, 1961—; lectr. N.Y. Office Ct. Adminstrn., N.Y.C., 1961—; mem. N.Y. State Commn. on Jud. Conduct, 1989—. Author: Manual for N.Y. Courts, 1973, Forms for N.Y. Courts, 1977. Capt. U.S. Army, 1948-54, Korea. Decorated Bronze Star, Purple Heart. Mem. ABA (del. spl. ct. sect. 1988—), D.C. Bar Assn., Erie County Bar Assn., N.Y. State Bar Assn., World Judges Assn., N.Y. State Magistrates Assn. (pres. 1973, Man of Yr. 1974), N.Y. State Jud. Conf. Office: Lipsitz Green Fahringer Roll Salisbury and Cambria 42 Delaware Ave Ste 300 Buffalo NY 14202-3857

SALISBURY, FRANK BOYER, plant physiologist, educator; b. Provo, Utah, Aug. 3, 1926; s. Frank M. and Catherine (Boyer) S.; m. Lois Marilyn Olson, Sept. 1, 1949; children: Frank Clark, Steven Scott, Michael James, Cynthia Kay, Phillip Boyer (dec.), Rebecca Lynn, Blake Charles; m. Mary Thorpe Robinson, June 28, 1991. BS, U. Utah, 1951, MA, 1952; PhD, Calif. Inst. Tech., 1955. Asst. prof. botany Pomona Coll., Claremont, Calif., 1954-55; faculty Colo. State U., Ft. Collins, 1955-66; prof. plant physiology Colo. State U., 1961-66; plant physiologist Expt. Sta., 1961-66; prof. plant physiology Utah State U., Logan, 1966—, disting. prof. Apr., 1987—, head dept. plant sci., 1966-70; tech. rep. plant physiology AEC, Germantown, Md., 1973-74; vis. prof. U. Innsbruck, Austria; Lady Davis fellow Hebrew U. Jerusalem, 1983; mem. aerospace medicine adv. com. NASA, 1988-93, life scis. adv. com., 1986-88, chmn. NASA Controlled Ecol. Life Support System Discipline Working Group, 1989—. Author: The Flowering Process, 1963, Truth by Reason and by Revelation, 1965, The Biology of Flowering, 1971, The Utah UFO Display, 1974, The Creation, 1976; co-author: (with R.V. Parke) Vascular Plants, Form and Function, 2d edit., 1970, (with C. Ross) Plant Physiology, 1969, 4th edit. 1992, (with W. Jensen) Botany: An Ecological Approach, 1972, Botany, 2d edit., 1984, (with others) Biology, 1977; editor Jour. Plant Physiology, Ams. and the Pacific Rim, 1989—. Trustee Colo. State U. Rsch. Found., 1959-62; leader People to People bot. del. to Republic South Africa, 1984, Peoples Republic China, 1988, Soviet Union, 1990. NSF sr. postdoctoral fellow Germany and Austria, 1962-63. Fellow AAAS; mem. Am. Soc. for Gravitational and Space Biology (Founders award 1994), Am. Soc. Plant Physiologists (editl. bd. 1967-92), Ecol. Soc. Am., Utah Acad. Sci., Arts and Letters, Am. Inst. Biol. Scis. (governing bd. 1976-79), Bot. Soc. Am. (Merit award), Sigma Xi, Phi Kappa Phi. Mem. LDS Ch. Home: 2020 North 1250 East North Logan UT 84347-2077 Office: Utah State U Dept Plants Soils and Biometeorology Logan UT 84322-4820 *This is an extremely exciting time to live! Science has provided marvelous insight into the cosmos, the earth, and the nature of life. The fact that mankind exists and can contemplate it all cries out that it has purpose and direction. My life is full to overflowing because God's revelation of Himself adds the final capstone to this beautiful structure.*

SALISBURY, FRANKLIN CARY, foundation executive, lawyer; b. Cleve., Sept. 29, 1910. B.A., Yale U., 1932; J.D., Case Western Res. U., 1937; LL.D. (hon.), U. Wales, 1985. Bar: Ohio 1937, D.C. 1947. Adminstrv. asst. to commr. FCC, 1939-40; chief legal div. ammunition br. Office Chief Ordnance, U.S. Army, 1941-45; chief clearance div. WPB, Army Service Forces, 1945; dir. legal div. Office Fgn. Liquidation Commn., Rio de Janeiro, Brazil, 1945-46; asst. solicitor Indian legal activities Dept. Interior, 1956-61; gen. counsel Ams. United for Separation Ch. and State, 1963-72; pres., chief exec. officer Nat. Found. Cancer Research, Bethesda, Md., 1973—; hon. pres., hon. dir. Assn. for Internat. Cancer Research, St. Andrews, Scotland, 1973-95; chmn. Krebsforschung Internat., Dusseldorf, Federal Republic Germany; trustee, counsel Latin Am. Inst., 1943-75; sec., dir. Atlantic Research Corp., 1949-64, Dryomatic Corp., 1950-59; chmn. bd., sec., dir. Orbit Industries, Inc., 1960-68; co-founder, dir. Internat. Soc. Law (now George Mason Law Sch.), 1975-77. Named Pro Universitate Med. U. Debrecen, 1982; recipient Quantum Biology award Internat. Soc. Quantum Biology, 1983, Medal of Merit U. Turin, Italy, 1984; decorated Order of Leopold II (Belgium). Mem. Fed. Bar Assn.; associated fgn. mem. Institut de Biologie Physico-Chimique (Fondation Edmond de Rothschild). Office: NFCR 7315 Wisconsin Ave Rm 500W Bethesda MD 20814-3202

SALISBURY, JOHN FRANCIS, distillery and chemical company executive, corporate lawyer; b. Limon, Costa Rica, Dec. 15, 1930; s. Edward I. and Kathleen (O'Sullivan) S.; m. Nancy Furlong, Aug. 20, 1960; children: Adrienne, Philippa, Anne, Eugenia. A.B. Villanova U., 1952; J.D., U. Pa., 1958. Bar: N.Y. 1959. Assoc. firm Breed, Abbott & Morgan, N.Y.C., 1958-66; sec. Quantum Chem. Corp. (formerly Nat. Distillers & Chem. Corp.), N.Y.C., 1966-74, v.p., sec., gen. counsel, 1974-94; sr. ptnr. Garland, Salisbur & Van Assn., 1994—; pres. Trafalgar Products, Ltd., 1993—. Chmn. bd. Am. Found. for Tropical Medicine, Liberian Inst. Tropical Medicine; bd. dirs. Brazilian Am. C. of C., Brazilian Cultural Found.; trustee Pop Warner Found. Served with USN, 1952-55. Decorated Rhee Battle Commendation medal Korean, U.S. Commendation medal. Mem. N.Y. Bar Assn., Union League, Sky Club, Naval and Mil. Club (London). Home: 484 Old Long Ridge Rd Stamford CT 06903-1113 Office: 2701 Summer St Stamford CT 06905-4304

SALISBURY, JUDITH MURIEL, marketing consultant; b. Plainfield, N.J., Aug. 5, 1940; d. James Donald and Gladys Maybelle (Scull) S.; m. Leonard Gordon Hartsoe, July 9, 1966 (div. 1982); 1 child, Allison Lynn Hartsoe. BA in English, Vassar Coll., 1962; MA, Ind. U., Pa., 1972. Cert. paralegal; lic. real estate broker, Pa.; cert. secondary sch. tchr., N.J., Pa. Tchr. Greater Johnstown (Pa.) Pub. Schs., 1967-68, Altoona (Pa.) Area Pub. Schs., 1968-71; instr. Pa. State U., Altoona, 1970-72, C.C. Allegheny County, Pitts., 1973-84; realtor Greater Pitts. Bd. Realtors, 1973-91; instr. La Roche Coll., Pitts., 1974-75; cons. Salisbury Mktg. Assocs., Evans City, Pa., 1991—; mktg. mgr. TRI-V, Inc., 1994—; staff writer Butler (Pa.) Eagle, 1993-94; sales rep. Future Electronics Corp., Westborough, Mass., 1984-87. Vol. Peace Corps, Sierra Leone, West Africa, 1962-64; Butler County Literacy, 1991-94; Neighborhood Legal Svc., Butler, 1993, Butler County Hospice, 1990-94; telephone bank coord. Campaign for State Rep., Butler County, 1992; active pub. rels. LWV, Butler County, 1990-91, AAUW, Pa., 1990-91. Recipient Andron Epiphanon award Greater Pitts. Bd. Realtors, 1975-77, Pa. Gov.'s award Pennserve, 1991; named Top 25 Realtors North Suburban Multi-List, 1974. Mem. Internat. Toastmasters (v.p. pub. rels. 1993-94), West. Pa. Press Club, Returned Peace Corps Vols. Episcopalian. Avocations: genealogy research, history, needlework, poetry. Office: 121 Needle Point Rd Evans City PA 16033-7625

SALISBURY, NANCY, convent director. Head Convent of Sacred Heart, N.Y.C. Office: Convent of the Sacred Heart 1 E 93rd St New York NY 10128-0613

SALISBURY, ROBERT CAMERON, financial executive; b. N.Y.C., NY, Nov. 7, 1943; s. Robert Elmore and Grace Louise (Rowe) S.; m. Linda C. Lindefield, Jan. 4, 1965; children: Dianne, Brenda. BS in Fin., Fla. State U., 1965, MBA, 1974. Asst. v.p. First Union Nat. Bank, Charlotte, NC, 1972-74; cash adminstr., mgr. cash mgmt., group mgr. cash and planning. The Upjohn Co., Kalamazoo, MI, 1974; dir. internat. fin. Upjohn Internat., Inc.,

Kalamazoo, 1981-82, dir. corp. fin., 1982-87; sr. v.p. fin., chief fin. officer Upjohn Co., Kalamazoo, 1988-93, exec. v.p., CFO, 1994—; bd. dirs. Allendale Ins. Co., R.I., First of Am. Bank, Mich. Bd. dirs. Kalamazoo Inst. Arts, Greater Kalamazoo United Way. Capt. USAF, 1965-71, lt. col. Res., ret. Mem. Fin. Execs. Inst. Republican. Avocations: golf, skiing, soaring. Office: Upjohn Co 7000 Portage Rd Kalamazoo MI 49001

SALISBURY, ROBERT HOLT, political science educator; b. Elmhurst, Ill., Apr. 29, 1930; s. Robert Holt and Beulah (Hammer) S.; m. Rose Marie Cipriani, June 19, 1953; children: Susan Marie, Robert Holt, Matthew Gary. A.B., Washington and Lee U., 1951; M.A., U. Ill., 1952, Ph.D., 1955. Mem. faculty Washington U., St. Louis, 1955—; prof. Washington U., 1965—, chmn. dept. polit. sci., 1966-73, 86-92, dir. Center for Study Pub. Affairs, 1974-77, Sidney W. Souers prof. govt., 1982—; vis. prof. State U. N.Y. at Buffalo, 1965, So. Ill. U., Edwardsville, 1975; affiliated scholar Am. Bar Found., 1981—; cons. U.S. Conf. Mayors, 1965, Hartford (Conn.) C. of C., 1964, NSF, 1973. Author: Interest Groups Politics in America, 1970, Governing America, 1973, Citizen Participation in the Public Schools, 1980, Interests and Institutions, 1992, The Hollow Core, 1993; contbr. articles to profl. jours. Mem. St. Louis County Charter Commn., 1967, Gov.'s Commn. on Local Govt., 1968-69. Guggenheim fellow, 1990; Rockefeller Ctr. scholar, 1990. Mem. Mo. Polit. Sci. Assn. (pres. 1964-65), Am. Polit. Sci. Assn. (exec. council 1969-71, v.p. 1980-81), Midwest Polit. Sci. Assn. (pres. 1977-78), Pi Sigma Alpha. Democrat. Methodist. Home: 337 Westgate Ave Saint Louis MO 63130-4710 Office: Washington U Dept Polit Sci Saint Louis MO 63130

SALISBURY, TAMARA PAULA, foundation executive; b. N.Y.C., Dec. 14, 1927; d. Paul Terrance and Nadine (Korolkova) Voloshin; m. Franklin Cary Salisbury, Jan. 22, 1955; children: Franklin Jr., John, Elizabeth, Elaine, Claire. BA, Coll. Notre Dame, 1948; postgrad., Am. U., George Washington U. Chemist depts. pathology and chemotherapy NIH Cancer Inst., Bethesda, Md., 1946-52; asst. to chief of Chemistry Br. Office of Naval Rsch., Bethesda, 1953-55; v.p., COO Nat. Found. Cancer Rsch., Bethesda, 1973—. Mem. Krebsforschung Internat., Assn. Internat. Cancer Rsch. Decorated d'Officier De L'Ordre De Leopold II; outstanding contbns. award Internat. Soc. Quantum Biology, 1983, award of appreciation Beth Israel Hosp., Harvard Med. Sch., Brigham & Women's Hosp., 1993. Mem. AAAS, Am. Chem. Soc., N.Y. Acad. Scis., Inst. Phys. and Chem. Biology (fgn.), Assn. Internat. Cancer Rsch., Krebsforschung Internat., Nat. Liberal Club. Home: 10811 Alloway Dr Potomac MD 20854 Office: Nat Found Cancer Rsch 7315 Wisconsin Ave Ste 500W Bethesda MD 20814-3206

SALITERMAN, RICHARD ARLEN, lawyer, educator; b. Mpls., Aug. 3, 1946; s. Leonard Slitz and Dorothy (Sloan) S.; m. Laura Shrager, June 15, 1975; 1 child, Robert Warren. BA summa cum laude, U. Minn., 1968; JD, Columbia U., 1971; LLM, NYU, 1974. Bar: Minn. 1972, D.C. 1974. Mem. legal staff U.S. Senate Subcom. on Antitrust and Monopoly, 1971-72; acting dir., dep. dir. Compliance and Enforcement div. Fed. Energy Office, N.Y.C., 1974; mil. atty. Presdl. Clemency Bd., White House, Washington, 1975; sr. ptnr. Saliterman & Siefferman, Mpls., 1975—; adj. prof. law Hamline U., 1976-81. Chmn. Hennepin County Bar Jour., 1985-87. Bd. dirs. Mpls. Urban League, 1987—; pres. Am. Jewish Com. Mpls. St. Paul chpt., 1988-90; v.p., trustee W. Harry Davis Found, 1989—; treas. bd. dirs. Pavek Mus. Broadcasting. With USN, 1972-75. Mem. ABA, Minn. State Bar Assn., Hennepin County Bar Assn. (governing council 1987-89), Oakridge Country Club (Hopkins, Minn.), Mpls. Club, Wayzata Yacht Club.

SALIZZONI, FRANK LOUIS, financial executive; b. Bridgeville, Pa., July 21, 1938; s. Augustine and Alice (Berteotti) S.; m. Sarah B. Russel, June 27, 1964; children—Susan, Laura, John. B.S.I.E., Pa. State U., 1960; M.E.A., George Washington U., 1964. Vice-pres., treas. TWA, N.Y.C., 1971-76, sr. v.p. fin., treas., 1976-78; also dir. Trans World Airlines, N.Y.C.; sr. v.p. fin. Transworld Corp. (name changed to TW Svcs. Inc. 1987), N.Y.C., 1979-81, sr. v.p. fin. and real estate, 1981-82, sr. v.p. fin. and adminstrn., 1982-84, vice-chmn., chief fin. officer, from 1984, now chmn., chief exec. officer, also dir.; instr. Fairleigh Dickinson U., Rutherford, N.J., 1966-68. Home: 707 Somerset St Franklin Lakes NJ 07417-1034 Office: TW Svcs Inc Mark Centre IV 61 S Paramus Rd Paramus NJ 07652-1236

SALK, JONAS EDWARD, physician, scientist; b. N.Y.C., Oct. 28, 1914; s. Daniel B. and Dora (Press) S.; m. Donna Lindsay, June 8, 1939; children: Peter Lindsay, Darrell John, Jonathan Daniel; m. Francoise Gilot, June 29, 1970. BS, CCNY, 1934, LLD (hon.), 1955; MD, NYU, 1939, ScD (hon.), 1955; LLD (hon.), U. Pitts., 1955; PhD (hon.), Hebrew U., 1959; LLD (hon.), Roosevelt U., 1955; ScD (hon.), Turin U., 1957. U. Leeds, 1959, Hahnemann Med. Coll., 1959, Franklin and Marshall U., 1960; DHL (hon.), Yeshiva U., 1959; LLD (hon.), Tuskegee Inst., 1964. Fellow in chemistry NYU, 1935-37, fellow in exptl. surgery, 1937-38, fellow in bacteriology, 1939-40; Intern Mt. Sinai Hosp., N.Y.C., 1940-42; NRC fellow Sch. Pub. Health, U. Mich., 1942-43, research fellow epidemiology, 1943-44, research asso., 1944-46, asst. prof. epidemiology, 1946-47; asso. research prof. bacteriology Sch. Medicine, U. Pitts., 1947-49, dir. virus research lab., 1947-63, research prof. bacteriology, 1949-55, Commonwealth prof. preventive medicine, 1955-57, Commonwealth prof. exptl. medicine, 1957-63; dir. Salk Inst. Biol. Studies, 1963-75, resident fellow, 1963-84, founding dir., 1976—, disting. prof. internat. health scis., 1984—; developed vaccine, preventive of poliomyelitis, 1955, cons. epidemic diseases sec. war, 1944-47, sec. army, 1947-54; mem. commn. on influenza Army Epidemiol. Bd., 1944-54, acting dir. commn. on influenza, 1944; mem. expert adv. panel on virus diseases WHO; adj. prof. health scis. depts. psychiatry, community medicine and medicine U. Calif., San Diego, 1970—. Author: Man Unfolding, 1972, The Survival of the Wisest, 1973, (with Jonathan Salk) World Population and Human Values: A New Reality, 1981, Anatomy of Reality, 1983; Contbr. sci. articles to jours. Decorated chevalier Legion of Honor France, 1955, officer, 1976; recipient Criss award, 1955, Lasker award, 1956, Gold medal of Congress and presdl. citation, 1955, Howard Ricketts award, 1957, Robert Koch medal, 1963, Mellon Inst. award, 1969, Presdl. medal of Freedom, 1977, Jawaharlal Nehru award for internat. understanding, 1976. Fellow AAAS, Am. Pub. Health Assn., Am. Acad. Pediatrics (hon., assoc.); mem. Am. Coll. Preventive Medicine, Am. Acad. Neurology, Assn. Am. Physicians., Soc. Exptl. Biology and Medicine, Inst. Medicine (sr.), Phi Beta Kappa, Alpha Omega Alpha, Delta Omega. Office: Salk Inst Biol Studies PO Box 85800 San Diego CA 92186-5800

SALKIN, PATRICIA E., law educator; b. Suffern, N.Y., Aug. 18, 1964; d. Stuart David and Sheila Diane (Gustin) S.; m. Howard F. Gross, Aug. 17, 1986. BA, SUNY, Albany, 1985; JD, Albany Law Sch., 1988. Bar: N.J. 1988, N.Y. 1989. Asst. counsel N.Y. State Office of Rural Affairs, Albany, 1988-90; asst. dir. Govt. Law Ctr., Albany Law Sch., 1990-91, acting dir., 1992, dir., 1992—; mem. adj. faculty Rensselaer Poly. Inst., Troy, N.Y., 1990-93, Albany Law Sch., 1992—, SUNY, Albany, 1993—. Editor: Everything You Wanted to Know About Zoning, 2d edit. 1993; contbr. articles to profl. jours, chpts. to books. Active Albany Civic Forum, 1992—, community devel. coun. Ctr. for Econ. Growth, 1992—; bd. dirs. Albany-Tula Alliance, 1992-94, Homeless and Travelers Aid Soc. of Capital Dist., 1992—. Recipient Pres.'s award for Outstanding Alumni Svc., SUNY, Albany, 1990, Tribute to Women award YMCA, Albany, 1994. Mem. ABA (co-chair state adminstrv. law com. 1993—, chair govt. ops. com. 1992—), Am. Planning Assn. (reporter Land Use Law & Zoning Digest 1992—), N.Y. State Bar Assn. (mem. exec. com municipal law sect. 1993—), Capital Dist. Women's Bar Assn., SUNY Albany Alumni Assn. (bd. dirs. v.p. 1994). Office: Albany Law Sch Govt Law Ctr 80 New Scotland Ave Albany NY 12208-3494

SALKIND, ALVIN J., electrochemical engineer, educator; b. N.Y.C., June 12, 1927; s. Samuel M. and Florence (Zins) S.; m. Marion Ruth Koenig, Nov. 7, 1965; children: Susanne, James. B.Ch.E., Poly. Inst. N.Y., 1949, M.Ch.E., 1952, D.Ch.E., 1958; postgrad. and mgmt. courses, Pa. State U., 1965, Harvard U., 1976. Registered profl. engr., N.Y., N.J. Chem. engr. U.S. Electric Mfg. Co., N.Y.C., 1952-54; sr. scientist Sonotone Corp., Elmsford, N.Y., 1954-56; research assoc. Poly. Inst. N.Y., 1956-58, adj. prof. chem. engring., 1960-70; with ESB-Ray OVAC Co., Yardley, Pa., 1958-79; dir. tech. ESB-Ray OVAC Co., 1971-72, v.p. tech., 1972-79; pres. ESB Tech. Co., 1978-79; prof., chief bioengring. div., dept. surgery UMDNJ-Robert Wood Johnson Med. Sch., Piscataway, N.J., 1970—; vis. prof. chem. engring., 1979-85; prof. biomed. engring. and chem. and biochem. engring Rutgers U., Piscataway, 1985—, dir. Bur. Engring. Rsch., assoc. dean Coll. Engring., 1989—; vis. prof. and exec. officer Case Ctr. for Electrochem. Sci., 1981-82; bd. dirs., cons. various cos., rsch. instns. and govt. orgns. Author: (with S.U. Falk) Alkaline Storage Batteries, 1969, (with Herbert T. Silverman and Irving F. Miller) Electrochemical Bioscience and Bioengineering, 1973; editor: (with E. Yeager) Techniques of Electrochemistry, 1971, vol. 2, 1973, vol. 3, 1978, History of Battery Technology, 1987; contbr. articles to profl. jours. Served with USNR, 1945-46. Recipient Alumnus citation Poly. Inst. N.Y., 1975, award Internat. Tech. Exch. Soc., 1992; Case Centennial scholar Case-Western Res. U., 1980. Fellow Acad. Medicine of N.J., Am. Coll. Cardiology, AAAS; mem. Electrochem. Soc. (past chmn. new tech. com., past chmn. battery div.), Assn. Advancement Med. Instrumentation, Indsl. Research Inst. (emeritus 1979), Internat. Soc. Electrochemistry, N.Y. Acad. Scis., Sigma Xi, Phi Lambda Upsilon. Home: 51 Adams Dr Princeton NJ 08540-5401 Office: Rutgers U Bur Engring Rsch Busch Campus PO Box 909 Piscataway NJ 08855

SALKIND, MICHAEL JAY, metallurgical engineer, academic administrator; b. N.Y.C., Oct. 1, 1938; s. Milton and Esther (Jaffe) S.; m. Miriam E. Schwartz, Aug. 16, 1959 (div. 1979); children: Michael Jay, Elizabeth Jane, Jonathan Hillson, Joshua Isaac; m. Carol T. Gill, Dec. 23, 1990. B in Metall. Engring., Rensselaer Polytech. Inst., 1959, PhD, 1962. Chief advanced metallurgy United Techs. Rsch. Labs., East Hartford, 1964-68; chief structures and materials Sikorsky Aircraft div. United Techs. Corp., 1968-75; dir. product devel. Avco Systems div., 1975-76; mgr. structures NASA, 1976-80; dir. aerospace scis. Air Force Office of Sci. Rsch., 1980-89; pres. Ohio Aerospace Inst., 1990—; adj. faculty metallurgy Trinity Coll., Hartford; adj. faculty aerospace U. Md., 1982-85; adj. faculty materials Johns Hopkins U., 1985-89. Cons. editor Internat. Jour. Fibre Sci. and Tech.; editor Applications Composite Materials, 1973; contbr. to profl. jours. and textbooks. Evaluator Accreditation Bd. Engring. and Tech., 1989—; mem. Daniel Guggenheim Medal Bd. Awards, 1984-90; mem. Spirit of St. Louis Medal Bd., 1984-89. Capt. AUS, 1962-64. Fellow AAAS, AIAA (assoc.); mem. ASME (Disting. lectr. 1989-93), ASTM (chmn. com. D-30 on high modulous fibers and their composites 1968-74), Am. Helicopter Soc., Am. Int. Mining Metall. and Petroleum Engrs., Am. Soc. Metals, Brit. Inst. Metals, Rsch. Soc. Am., Plansee Soc., Cosmos Club, Union Club, Leadership Cleve., Sigma Xi, Alpha Sigma Mu. Office: Ohio Aerospace Inst 22800 Cedar Point Rd Cleveland OH 44142-1099

SALLE, DAVID, artist; b. Norman, Okla., Sept. 28, 1952; s. Alvin S. and Tillie Dean (Brown) S. B.F.A., Calif. Inst. Arts, 1973, M.F.A., 1975; student, Wichita Art Assn. One-man shows include Project Inc., Cambridge, Mass., 1975, Found. Corps de Garde, Groningen, Holland, 1976, 78, Artists Space, N.Y.C., 1976, Found. de Appel, Amsterdam, 1977, The Kitchen, N.Y.C., 1977, 79, Mary Boone Gallery, N.Y.C., 1981, 82, 83, 85, 87, 88, Lucio Amelio Gallery, Naples, Italy, 1981, Mario Diacono, Rome, 1982, Anthony D'offay Gallery, London, 1982, Akira Ikeda Gallery, Tokyo, 1983, Castelli Graphics, N.Y.C., 1983, Gagosian Gallery, Los Angeles, 1984, Castelli Gallery, N.Y.C., 1984, Tel Aviv Mus. Art, 1989, Maria Diacono Gallery, Boston, 1990, Castelli Graphics, N.Y.C., 1990, Gagosian Gallery, N.Y.C., 1991; retrospective exhibition, Mus. Contemporary Art, Chgo., 1987; group shows include Calif. State Coll., Los Angeles, 1974, Long Beach Mus. Art, Calif., 1975, The Kitchen, 1975, Auction 393, N.Y.C., 1976, Serial Gallerie, Amsterdam, 1977, Studio Cannaviello, Milan, 1979, Mary Boone N.Y.C., 1980, 83, Grand Palais, Paris, 1980, Musee d'Art et d'Industrie et Maison de la Culture, St. Etienne, France, 1980, Nigel Greenwood Gallery, London, 1981, Kunsthallen, Goteborg, Sweden, 1981, Josef Gallery, N.Y.C., 1982, N.Y. Pub. Library, N.Y.C., 1982, Whitney Mus. Am. Art, N.Y.C., 1982, 83, Walker Art Ctr., Mpls., 1982, Mus. Contemporary Art, La Jolla, Calif., 1982, Rennaissance Soc., Chgo., 1982, Mura Aureliane, Rome, 1982, Chgo. Art Inst., 1982, Kassel, Fed. Rep. Germany, 1982, Venice, 1982, Stiftelsen Karlsvik, 10, Stockholm, 1983, Hirshhorn Mus., Washington, 1983, Castelli Gallery, 1983, Chrystal Palace, Madrid, 1983, Sao Paulo Biennale, Brazil, 1983, Tate Gallery, London, 1983, Pace Gallery, 1983, Sara Hilden Art Mus., Finland, 1988, Parish Art Mus., Southhampton, N.Y., 1988, Museo de Arte Contemporaneo de Monterrey, Mex., 1991. Guggenheim fellow, 1986. Office: care Leo Castelli Gallery 420 W Broadway New York NY 10012-3764 Address: Mary Boone Gallery 420 W Broadway New York NY 10012-3764

SALLER, RICHARD PAUL, classics educator; b. Ft. Bragg, N.C., Oct. 18, 1952; s. George E. and Arthea E. (North) S.; m. Carol Joann Fisher, Jan. 12, 1974; children: John E., Benjamin T. BA in Greek and History, U. Ill., 1974; PHD in Classics, U. Cambridge, Eng., 1978. Asst. prof. Swarthmore (Pa.) Coll., 1979-84; assoc. prof. U. Chgo., 1984-89, prof., 1990—; dean of social scis., 1994—. Author: Personal Patronage, 1982, Patriarchy, Property and Death in the Roman Family, 1994; co-editor: Economy and Society in Ancient Greece, 1981; co-author: Roman Empire, 1987; editor Classical Philology, 1991-93. Rsch. fellow Jesus Coll., U. Cambridge, 1978-79; Ctr. for Adv. Study fellow, Stanford U., 1986-87; Trinity Coll., U. Cambridge fellow commoner, 1991. Mem. Am. Philol. Assn., Am. Hist. Assn. Office: U Chgo Dept History 1126 E 59th St Chicago IL 60637-1539

SALLEY, JOHN JONES, university administrator, oral pathologist; b. Richmond, Va., Oct. 29, 1926; s. Thomas Raysor and Kathryn (Josey) S.; m. Jean Gordon Cunningham, Dec. 21, 1950; children: Katharine Gordon, John Jones, Martha Cunningham. DDS, Med. Coll. Va., 1951; PhD, U. Rochester, 1954; DSc, Boston U., 1975. Research fellow U. Rochester, 1951-54; from instr. to prof., chmn. dept. oral pathology Med. Coll. Va., 1954-63, prof. emeritus, 1991—; prof. pathology, dean Sch. Dentistry U. Md., 1963-74, dean emeritus Sch. Dentistry 1977—, ret., 1991; v.p. research and grad. affairs Va. Commonwealth U., Richmond, 1974-85; acting pres. Va. Ctr. for Innovative Tech., 1985, v.p., 1985-87; cons. div. research grants NIH, 1962-66; cons. U.S. Naval Dental Sch., Bethesda, Md., 1966-75; spl. cons. Nat. Inst. Dental Research, NIH, 1957-64; cons. USPHS Hosp., Balt., 1963-74, U.S. Naval Hosp., Portsmouth, Va., VA Hosp., Balt., 1964-74; dental health div. USPHS; mem. Md. Adv. Council Comprehensive Health Planning, 1968-74, Nat. Health Council, 1970-71; mem. Am. Assn. Dental Schs., 1971-72, Conf. So. Grad. Schs., 1983-84; sr. program cons. Robert Wood Johnson Found., 1978-84; mem. career devel. rev. com. VA, 1974-78; mem. com. health care resources in VA, NRC, 1974-77; cons. WHO, 1969-75; mem. Va. Gov.'s Task Force Sci. and Tech., 1982-83, sci. advisor to Gov. of Va., 1984-86; mem. research com. Va. State Council Higher Edn., 1974-84; chmn. task force Council Grad. Schs. in U.S., 1979-82. Contbr. articles in field; editorial rev. bd.: Jour. Dental Edn., 1974-78. Bd. dirs. Md. divns., Am. Cancer Soc., 1963-70, Am. Fund Dental Health, Nat. Found. Dentistry for the Handicapped, 1986, pres., 1992-94; mem. adv. bd. Va. Inst. for Devel. Disabilities, 1987-91; bd. trustees Middlesex County Pub. Libr., 1994—. With USAAF, 1945-46. Recipient Outstanding Civilian Service medal Dept. Army, 1961, Disting. Citizenship award State Md., 1974. Fellow AAAS, Am. Coll. Dentists; mem. ADA, Nat. Conf. Univ. Research Adminstrs., Am. Acad. Oral Pathology, Internat. Assn. Dental Research (Novice award 1953), Internat. Med. Informatics Assn. (chmn. working group 1989-92), Sigma Xi, Sigma Zeta, Omicron Kappa Upsilon. Episcopalian (vestryman). Home and Office: PO Box 838 Urbanna VA 23175-0838

SALLUS, MARC LEONARD, lawyer; b. Washington, Sept. 14, 1954; s. Gerald M. and Bette R. (Rosenthal) S. BA, Claremont Men's Coll., 1976; JD, U. Calif., Hastings, 1979. Bar: Calif. 1979, U.S. Dist. Ct. (no., cen., so. and ea. dists.) Calif. 1980, U.S. Ct. Appeals (9th cir.) 1980. Assoc. Long & Levit, Los Angeles, 1979-80, Overton, Lyman & Prince, Los Angeles, 1980-87, Brobeck, Phleger & Harrison, Los Angeles, 1987-88, Weinstock, Marion, Reisman, Shore & Neumann, L.A., 1989—. Chmn. adv. bd. Nat. Resource Ctr. for Child Advocacy and Protection, Washington, 1985-86, 88-89; bd. dirs. Pub. Counsel. Mem. ABA (chmn. com. for child advocacy and protection young lawyers sect. 1985-86, 88-89, vice chmn. com. awards of achievement 1987-88, parliamentarian of the assembly 1987-91, ho. dels. 1990-91), Los Angeles County Bar Assn. (bd. trustees 1986-88, exec. com. 1986-88, asst. v.p. 1986-88, litigation sect. exec. com. 1987-89, co-chmn. minority employment com. 1986-87, chmn. ABA rels. com. 1990-92, 93—), Los Angeles County Barristers (pres. 1987-88, pres.-elect 1986-87, v.p. 1985-86, exec. com., 1984-88, chmn. child abuse com. 1983-85), Thurston Soc., Calif. CEB (probate and estate planning adv. com. 1985—), Order of the Coif. Democrat. Jewish.

SALMANS, CHARLES GARDINER, banker; b. Washington, Apr. 23, 1945; s. Marion K. and Agnes A. (Gardiner) S.; m. Robin Elizabeth Wakeman, June 8, 1986; children: Jonathan, Peter, Charles II. BS, Northwestern U., 1967; MBA in Fin., Columbia U., 1970. Account supr. Burson-Marsteller, N.Y.C., 1970-74; v.p. Bankers Trust Co. N.Y.C., 1974-84; sr. v.p., div. head Chem. Bank, N.Y.C., 1984—; mem. editl. adv. bd. Grad. Sch. of Bus. Columbia U. N.Y.C., 1984—; mem. bus. adv. com. Guggenheim Mus., N.Y.C., 1994—. Home: 6 Red Rose Cir Darien CT 06820-4928 Office: Chemical Bank 270 Park Ave New York NY 10017-2014

SALMELA, DAVID DANIEL, architect; b. Wadena, Minn., Mar. 28, 1945; s. Laurie Fredrich and Lempi Christin (Matti) S.; m. Gladys Elaine Hanka, June 23, 1967; children: Cory, Chad, Tia, Kai, Brit. Grad. high sch., Sebeka, Minn. Registered profl. architect, Minn. Draftsman McKenzie Hague & Gilles, Mpls., 1965-66, A.G. McKee, Hibbing, Minn., 1966, ABI Contracting, Virginia, Minn., 1966-69, Archtl. Resources, Hibbing, 1969-70; designer, arch. Damberg Scott Peck & Booker, Virginia, 1970-89; arch. Mulfinger Susanka, Duluth, Minn., 1989-90; prin. Salmela Fospick Ltd., Duluth, 1990-94, Salmela, Arch., Duluth, 1994—. Recipient Minn. Masonry Inst. award, 1987, citation Am. Wood Coun., 1994. Mem. AIA (Honor award Minn. br. 1985, 87, 90, 92, 93, 94, Honor award Western Rek Cedar Coun./AIA 1994). Office: Architect 852 Grandview Ave Duluth MN 55812

SALMOIRAGHI, GIAN CARLO, physiologist, educator; b. Gorla Minore, Italy, Sept. 19, 1924; came to U.S., 1952, naturalized, 1958; s. Giuseppe Carlo and Dina (Rinetti) S.; m. Eva Tchoukourlieva, Dec. 5, 1970; 1 child, George Charles. M.D., U. Rome, 1948; Ph.D., McGill U., 1959. Sr. med. officer Internat. Refugee Orgn., Naples, Italy, 1949-52; research fellow Cleve. Clinic Found., 1952-55; lectr. dept. physiology McGill U., Montreal, Que., Can., 1956-58; from neurophysiologist to dir., div. spl. mental health research NIMH, Washington, 1959-73; assoc. commr. research N.Y. State Dept. Mental Hygiene, Albany, 1973-77; assoc. dir. for research Nat. Inst. Alcohol Abuse, HHS, Bethesda, Md., 1977-84; prof. neurology and physiology Hahnemann U., Phila., 1984-85, vice provost for research affairs, 1984-85, chmn. dept. physiology, asst. v.p sci. affairs, 1986-94; clin. prof. psychiatry George Washington U., 1966-73. Contbr. articles to profl. jours. Recipient Superior Service award HEW, 1970. Fellow Am. Coll. Neuropsychopharmacology; mem. AAAS, Am. Physiol. Soc., Am. Soc. Pharmacology and Exptl. Therapeutics, Internat. Brain Research Orgn., Internat. Soc. Psychoneuroendocrinology, Am. Psychiat. Assn., Soc. Neurosci., Royal Soc. Medicine, Soc. Biol. Psychiat., Assn. Research Neurol. and Mental Disease, Research Soc. Alcoholism, Assn. Chmn. Dept. Physiology, Sci. Research Soc., Sigma Xi. Club: Cosmos (Washington). Home: 8216 Hamilton Spring Ct Bethesda MD 20817

SALMON, CHARLES B., JR., diplomat; b. N.Y.C., Jan. 3, 1938; s. Charles B. and Regina C. (McCarthy) S. AB, Fordham U., 1959; MA, Columbia U., 1960; diploma, Nat. War Coll., 1978. Dir. Office Human Rights U.S. Dept. State, Washington, 1978-80; dep. chief mission U.S. Embassy, Wellington, New Zealand, 1980-83, Rangoon, Burma, 1983-85; dir. Thailand and Burma affairs U.S. Dept. State, Washington, 1985-86, dir. Philippine affairs, 1986-89; charge d'affaires to Lao People's Dem. Republic U.S. Dept. State, Vientiane, Laos, 1989-92; U.S. amb. to Laos U.S. Dept. State, Vientiane, 1992-93; fgn. policy adviser to the commander-in-chief U.S. Pacific Fleet, Honolulu, 1993—. Capt. U.S. Army, 1960-62. Recipient Presdl. Meritorious award, 1990. Mem. Metropolitan Club. Roman Catholic. Avocations: tennis, reading. Office: US Pacific Fleet Honolulu HI 96860-7000

SALMON, EDWARD LLOYD, JR., bishop; b. Jan. 30, 1934; s. Edward Lloyd Sr. and Helen Bernice (Burley) S.; m. Louise Hack, 1972; children: Catherine, Edward III. BA, U. of the South, 1956; BD, Va. Theol. Seminary, 1960. Ordained to deaconate Episc. Ch., 1960, to priesthood, 1961. Vicar St. Andrew's Ch., Rogers, Ark.; rector St. Andrew's Ch., Rogers, 1963-68; vicar St. James Ch., Eureka Springs, Ark., St. Thomas Ch., Springdale, Grace Ch., Siloam Springs; assoc. St. Paul's Ch., Fayetteville, 1968, rector, 1968-78; rector Ch. St. Michael and St. George, St. Louis, 1978-90; elected bishop Diocese S.C., 1990—; chmn. bd. dirs. Speak, Inc., The Anglican Digest. Pres. Episc.-Presbyn. Found. Office: PO Box 20127 Charleston SC 29413-0127

SALMON, JOHN HEARSEY MCMILLAN, historian, educator; b. Thames, New Zealand, Dec. 2, 1925; came to U.S., 1969; s. John Hearsey and Elizabeth (McMillan) S. M.A., U. New Zealand, 1951; M.Litt., Cambridge (Eng.) U., 1957; Litt.D., Victoria U., 1970. Prof. history U. New S. Wales, Sydney, Australia, 1960-65; prof. history, dean humanities U. Waikato, New Zealand, 1965-69; Marjorie Walter Goodhart prof. history Bryn Mawr Coll., 1969-91, prof. emeritus, 1991—. Author: The French Religious Wars in English Political Thought, 1959, A History of Goldmining in New Zealand, 1963, Cardinal de Retz, 1969, Society in Crisis - France in The 16th Century, 1975, Renaissance and Revolt: Essays in the Intellectual and Social History of Early Modern France, 1987; editor: The French Wars of Religion, 1967; co-editor: Francogallia by François Hotman, 1972; contbr. to hist. jours. Fellow Royal Hist. Soc. Home: 1853 County Line Rd Villanova PA 19085-1729 Office: Bryn Mawr Coll Bryn Mawr PA 19010

SALMON, JOSEPH THADDEUS, lawyer; b. Auburn, Ala., Nov. 13, 1927; s. William Davis and Helen (Bowman) S.; m. Mabel Marie Groves, July 7, 1951; children: Joseph Thaddeus Jr., Bruce Groves. B.S., Auburn U. 1949; J.D., U. Ala., 1951. Bar: Ala. 1951. Practice in Montgomery, 1953-93; sec., gen. counsel Alfa Mut. Ins. Co., Alfa Mut. Fire Ins. Co., Alfa Mut. Gen. Ins. Co., Alfa Corp., Alfa Ins. Corp., Alfa Gen. Ins. Corp., Alfa Life Ins. Co.; ret., 1993. Served with USNR, 1946-47; to 1st lt. USAF, 1951-53. Mem. Internat. Assn. Def. Counsel, Ala. Def. Lawyers Assn., Phi Alpha Delta, Kappa Sigma. Episcopalian. Home: 2731 Lansdowne Dr Montgomery AL 36111-1741

SALMON, KATHLEEN A., insurance company executive; b. 1945. With Commonwealth of Penn., Harrisburg, 1967-79, Penn. Blue Shield, Camp Hill, Penn., 1979-83; sr. v.p.-adminstrn. Capital Blue Cross, Harrisburg, Penn., 1983—. Office: Capital Blue Cross 2500 Elmerton Ave Harrisburg PA 17110

SALMON, MATT, congressman; b. Salt Lake City, Jan. 21, 1958; s. Robert James and Gloria (Aagard) S.; m. Nancy Huish, June, 1979; children: Lara, Jacob, Katie, Matthew. BA in English Lit., Ariz. State U., 1981; MA in Pub. Adminstrn., Brigham Young U., 1986. Mgr. pub. affairs U.S. West, Phoenix, 1988—; mem. Ariz. Senate, Mesa, 1990-94, 104th Congress, Washington, 1995—; congressman, Ariz. U.S. House of Reps., Washington, D.C., 1995—. Bd. dirs. Mesa United Way, 1990—, Ariz. Sci. Mus., 1992—. Recipient Outstanding Svc. award Ariz. Citizens with Disabilities, 1991, Excellence in Govt. award Tempe Ctr. for Handicapped, 1992; named Outstanding Young Phoenician, Phelps Dodge/Phoenix Jaycees, 1990, Outstanding Legislator, Mesa United Way, 1991. Republican. Mormon. Avocations: tennis, racquetball, cycling. Office: 104th Congress Cannon 115 House Office Bldg Washington DC 20515

SALMON, RUSSELL OWEN, II, Latin American studies educator, administrator; b. Port Jervis, N.Y., Dec. 10, 1933; s. Fred Dunning and Helen (De Woody) S.; m. Cynthia Mae March, June 17, 1956 (div. Oct. 1982); children: Russell C., Scott D., Sarah D. Jones; m. Catherine C. Wenzel, Aug. 9, 1984. BA, Williams Coll., 1956; MA, Middlebury Coll., 1962; PhD, Columbia U., 1969. Tchr. Kilmarnock (N.H.) Sch., 1956-62; prof. dept. Spanish and Portuguese Ind. U., Bloomington, 1967—; dir. Latin Am. Consortium, Bloomington/Notre Dame, 1988—, Ctr. Latin Am. and Caribbean Studies Ind. U. Editor: Homenaje a Andres Iduarte, 1976, Gaucho Literature, 1990, Golden UFOs, 1992. Chair bd. Bloomington Sister Cities Internat. Inc., 1990-91; mem. PASO and NOC rels. com. PAX/I, Indpls., 1985-87. NDFL Title 6 grantee Dept. Edn., 1962-65; Fgn. Lang. fellow Ford Found., Santiago, Chile, 1965-67; Internat. grantee Ford Foundn., Santiago, 1970. Mem. AAUP, MLA, Midwest MLA, Am. Assn. Tchrs. Spanish and Portuguese, Ind. Fgn. Lang. Tchrs. Assn., Latin Am. Studies Assn., Midwest Assn. Latin Am. Studies. Democrat. Presbyterian. Avocations: swimming, canoeing. Office: Dept Spanish and Portuguese Ballantine 858/Ind U Bloomington IN 47405

SALMON, VINCENT, acoustical consultant; b. Kingston, Jamaica, Jan. 21, 1912; came to U.S., 1914; s. Albert James and Ethlin (Baruch) S.; m. Madeline L. Giuffra, June 11, 1937 (dec. 1977); children—Margaret Elizabeth, Jean Louise. B.A., Temple U., 1934, M.A., 1936; Ph.D., MIT, 1938. Registered profl. engr., Calif. Physicist research and devel. Jensen Mfg. Co. Chgo., 1939-49; mgr. sonics sect. Stanford Research Inst., Menlo Park, Calif., 1949-65; staff scientist SRI Internat., Menlo Park, Calif., 1965-94; acoustical cons., Chgo., 1946-49, Menlo Park, 1949-71, 76—; dir. Acoustical Services, v.p.; sec. Indsl. Health, Inc., 1971-76; cons. prof. dept. aeronautics and astronautics Stanford U., Calif., 1977—. Contbr. articles to profl. jours.; inventor new family of horns, 1942, 46. Pres. Palo Alto Sr. Housing Project, Calif., 1966; v.p. Stebbins Found. for Community Facilities, San Francisco, 1966; pres. Planned Parenthood Assn. of Santa Clara County, 1967, Sr. Coordinating Council of Palo Alto, 1971. Recipient Disting. Alumnus award Temple U., Phila., 1964. Fellow Acoustical Soc. Am. (pres. 1970-71, Biennial award 1946, Silver Medal in engring. acoustics 84), Audio Engring. Soc. (life charter, western v.p. 1958-59); mem. Chgo. Audio and Acoustical Group (founder, pres. 1948), Inst. Noise Control Engring. (pres. 1974-75), Nat. Council of Acoustical Cons. (pres. 1969-71). Democrat. Unitarian. Club: Stanford Faculty. Avocations: chamber music; photography; automobile technology. Home: 765 Hobart St Menlo Park CA 94025-5705

SALMON, WILLIAM COOPER, mechanical engineer, engineering academy executive; b. N.Y.C., Sept. 3, 1935; s. Chenery and Mary (Cooper) S.; m. Josephine Stone, Sept. 16, 1967; children—William Cooper, Mary Bradford, Pauline Alexandra. S.B. in Mech. Engring., MIT, 1957, S.M. in Mech. Engring., 1958, Mech. Engr., 1959, S.M. in Mgmt. Sci., 1969. Registered profl. engr., Mass. Research and teaching asst. MIT, Cambridge, 1957-59; sr. engr. Microtech, Cambridge, 1959-60; 1st lt. U.S. Army Ord. C., Aberdeen, Md., 1960; asst. sci. advisor U.S. Dept. State, Washington, 1961-74, sr. advisor for sci. and tech., 1978-86; counselor for sci. and tech. Am. embassy, Paris, 1974-78; exec. officer Nat. Acad. Engring., Washington, 1986—. Recipient Superior Honor award Dept. State, 1964; Meritorious Service award Pres. U.S., 1984; Sloan fellow MIT, 1968. Mem. ASME, Nat. Soc. Prof. Engrs., Am. Soc. Engring. Edn., Cosmos Club, Masons. Episcopalian. Office: Nat Acad Engring 2101 Constitution Ave NW Washington DC 20418-0007

SALMONS, JOANNA, health facility administrator; b. Smiths Grove, Ky., Nov. 7, 1931; d. Walter Scott and Birdie Wilma (Jackson) Parker; m. William L. Salmons, June 6, 1970; children by previous marriage: Robert B. Morrow, Scott Alan Morrow. RN, Fla. Hosp. Sch. Nursing, 1954; student, So. Missionary Coll., 1979; cert. in health systems mgmt. Harvard U., 1980, Yale U., 1985, Cornell, 1993; BS in Nursing, SUNY, 1987; postgrad., Trinity Coll. Dir. nursing Larkin Gen. Hosp., Miami, Fla., 1969-74; adminstr., Ft. Walton Beach (Fla.) Hosp., 1974-75; dir. surg. nursing Fla. Hosp., Orlando, 1976-78; v.p. profl. stds. Adventist Health Systems/Sunbelt Corp., Orlando, 1978-79; bd. dirs. 1986—; bd. dirs. Adventist Health Systems, Sunbelt, Health Mgmt., Inc., Princeton Profls., Inc., Fla. Hosp. and Healthcare Systems, Inc., Health Mgmt. Group, Waterman Hosp., Eustis, Fla., Quest, Inc.; sr. v.p. Fla Hosp. Med. Ctr., Orlando, 1979—; dir. Health Care Mgmt. Corp.; cons. in field. Mem. A Thousand Plus com. Am. Cancer Soc.; bd. dirs. Fla. Coll. Allied Health, 1991—. Recipient Outstanding Achievement award, Larkin Gen. Hosp., Miami, 1969, excellence in leadership award F.H. 1993. Mem. NAFE, AAUW, Fla. Nurses Assn. (bd. dirs. 1980-81, 83-84, Nurse of Yr. award dist. 8 1988, for Fla., 1988, Nursing Adminstr. of Yr. 1988), Am. Heart Assn., Retarded Children's Assn. Orange County, Fla. Hosp. Assn., Am. Nurses Assn. (cert. nurse adminstr.), Fla. Orgn. Nursing Execs., Am. Orgn. Nursing Execs., Assn. Seventh-Day Adventist Nursing Execs. (bd. dirs.), Adventist Health Care Execs. (bd. dirs. 1986-87), Am. Health Care Execs. Assn., Ventura Lakes Golf and Tennis Club, Summer Island Racquet Club, Rotary. Home: 1212 Waverly Way Longwood FL 32750-6243 Office: Fla Hosp Med Ctr 601 E Rollins St Orlando FL 32803-1248

SALO, HARRY A., health care executive; b. Rahway, N.J., Jan. 27, 1944; s. E. Arthur and Nina (Hill) S.; m. Karen Waugh, Sept. 7, 1964 (div. 1972); 1 child, Jannine; m. Carol Ann Vath, Mar. 17, 1973; children: Jessica, Adam. BA, Cornell U., 1967; MA, Fairfield U., 1974; postgrad., Columbia U., 1974, NYU, 1974-75. Tchr. Miami (Fla.) Country Day Sch., 1967-69; tchr. Fairfield (Conn.) Country Day Sch., 1968-74, dir. admissions, 1972-74; adminstr. Med. Pers. Pool, Cin., 1975-77; v.p. Salo Inc., Cin., 1977-79; v.p.; founder T.S.O. Mgmt. Corp., Media, Pa., 1979-84, pres., 1984-90, chmn., 1990—; chmn. bd. dirs. Ind. Franchise Assn., San Francisco; mem. Owners Adv. Coun., Ft. Lauderdale, Fla., 1981-82, chmn., 1993—. Bd. dirs. Women Against Rape, Delaware County, Pa., 1985-88; mem. leadership group Amnesty Internat., N.Y.C., 1989—; fundraiser Berkshire Sch., Sheffield, Mass., 1990; vol. Oxfam Am., N.Y.C., 1991—. Recipient L.E. Dettman Founders award Pers. Pool Am., 1981, Raymond Herrighes Mgmt. award, 1986. Office: TSO Mgmt Corp 113 N Olive Media PA 19063

SALOMON, DARRELL JOSEPH, lawyer; b. San Francisco, Feb. 16, 1939; s. Joseph and Rosalie Rita (Pool) S.; m. Christine Mariscal, Apr. 25, 1992; 1 child, Camilla Lind. Student Georgetown U., 1957-59; BS, U. San Francisco, 1964, JD, 1966. Bar: Calif. 1970, U.S. Dist. Ct. (ctrl. and no. dists.) Calif. 1970, U.S. Supreme Ct. 1971. Assoc., Offices of Joseph L. Alioto, San Francisco, 1970, 73, Demanes & Sanders, Burlingame, Calif., 1972; dep. city atty. City of San Francisco, 1972; with Salomon & Costello, 1981; ptnr. Hill, Farrer & Burrill, L.A., 1984-87, Arter & Hadden, L.A., 1987-94, Keck, Mahin & Cate, San Francisco, 1994—; lectr. law Santa Clara U. Contbr. articles to profl. jours. Mem. Human Rights Commn. City and County of San Francisco, 1975, mem., past pres. Civil Svc. Commn., San Francisco, 1976-84; trustee San Francisco War Meml. and Performing Arts Ctr., 1984-88; bd. dirs. L.A. Symphony Master Chorale, 1985-87. D'alton-Power scholar Georgetown U., 1957; recipient Disting. Svc. citation United Negro Coll. Fund, 1975. Mem. ABA, L.A. Bar Assn., Calif. Trial Lawyers Assn. (bd. govs. 1977), Svc. Employees Internat. Union (hon. life), Soc. Calif. Pioneers, Chit Chat Club, Univ. Club L.A., San Francisco Lawyers Club. Office: Keck Mahin & Cate 1 Maritime Plz 23d fl San Francisco CA 94111-2496

SALOMON, JANET LYNN NOWICKI See LYNN, JANET

SALOMON, LEON EDWARD, career officer; b. Chgo., Apr. 27, 1936; s. Milton and Marcella (Johnson) S.; m. Shirley Fredberg, Feb. 6, 1960; children: Jeffery, Gregory, Kristen. BS, U. Fla., 1958; MS in Mgmt. Logistics, USAF Inst. Tech., 1971. Commd. 2d lt. U.S. Army, 1958, advanced through grades to gen., 1994; various assignments U.S. Army, U.S., Europe, Vietnam, 1961-76; asst. chief staff G-4 Logistics 3d Armored Div., Europe, 1976-77; student Indsl. Coll. Armed Forces, Ft. Lesley J. McNair, 1977-78; staff officer logistics, later chief commd. indsl. type activity team, Mgmt. Directorate Office of Chief of Staff, Washington, 1978-80; dir. combat svc. support systems U.S. Army Tng. and Doctrine Command, Ft. Monroe, Va., 1980-82; comdr. div. support command 1st Cav. Div., Ft.Hood, Tex., 1982-84; spl. asst. to commdg. gen. 21st Support Command U.S. Army Europe, 7th Army, 1984, mem. dep. commdg. gen. 21st Support Command, 1984-86; commdg. gen., chief of ordnance U.S. Army Ordnance Ctr. and Sch., Aberdeen Proving Ground, Md., 1986-88; dep. chief of staff for readiness U.S. Army Materiel Command, Alexandria, Va., 1988-89; commdg. gen. U.S. Army Combined Arms Support Command and Ft. Lee, Ft. Lee, Va., 1989-92; dep. chief of staff for logistics Washington, 1992-94; commanding gen. Army Material Command, 1994—. Decorated D.S.M. with oak leaf cluster, Legion of Merit, Bronze Star, Meritorious Svc. medal with two oak leaf clusters, Air medals, Army Commendation medal with two oak leaf clusters, Expert Infantryman badge, Army Gen. Staff Identification badge. Mem. Assn. U.S. Army, Am. Def. Preparedness Assn. Roman Catholic. Office: US Army Materiel Command Commdg Gen 5001 Eisenhower One Alexandria VA 22333-0001

SALOMON, MIKAEL, cinematographer, director; b. Copenhagen, Denmark, Feb. 24, 1945. Cinematographer, Zelly and Me, 1988, Torch Song Trilogy, 1988, The Abyss, 1989 (Oscar nomination), Always, 1989, Stealing Heaven, 1989, Arachnophobia, 1990, Backdraft, 1991, Far and Away, 1992; TV, The Man Who Broke 1,000 Chaines, 1987 (ACE award); dir.: (films) A Far Off Place, 1993, (television) Space Rangers, 1993.. Office: Am Soc Cinematographers N Orange Dr Hollywood CA 90028 also: care

Spyros Skouras Sanford Skouras Gross & Assocs 1015 Gayley Ave 3rd Fl Los Angeles CA 90024-3424

SALOMON, RICHARD, investor; b. N.Y.C., Jan. 9, 1912; s. Emanuel and Mignon (Eckstein) S.; m. Edna Barnes, Nov. 20, 1939; children: Richard E., Robert B., Ralph B. Ph.B., Brown U., 1932, LL.D., 1972. Chief exec. officer Lanvin-Charles of the Ritz (merged into Squibb Corp. 1971), 1936-71; bd. dirs., mem. exec. com. Squibb Corp., 1971—; mng. ptnr. Riverbank Assocs., N.Y.C.; chancellor Brown U., Providence, 1979-88, chancellor emeritus, 1988—; also vice-chmn. Spears Benzak Salomon Farrell, N.Y.C. Past chmn. bd. N.Y. Pub. Libr.; now chmn. emeritus and vice chmn., nominating com. mem., exec. com. mem.; trustee Lincoln Ctr. Served with Signal Corps U.S. Army, 1942-46. Decorated Bronze Star. Mem. Nat. Acad. Arts and Sci., Century Assn. (N.Y.C.), Century Country Club (Purchase, N.Y.), Hope Club (Providence). Democrat. Office: Spears Benzak Salomon Farrell 45 Rockefeller Plz New York NY 10111

SALOMON, RICHARD ADLEY, business executive, lawyer; b. Chgo., Nov. 3, 1953; s. Bernard Salomon and Marian (Schwarz) Elkan; m. Jacqueline B. Cohen, Jan. 9, 1988; children: Mark Bernard, Eve Michelle. Student, U. Chgo., 1973-74; BA magna cum laude, Carleton Coll., 1975; JD, Harvard U., 1979. Bar: Ill. 1980, U.S. Dist. Ct. (no. dist.) Ill. 1980, U.S. Ct. Appeals (7th cir.) 1983, U.S. Dist. Ct. (no. dist.) Ga. 1986, U.S. Dist. Ct. (so. dist.) N.Y. 1986. Assoc. Jones, Day, Reavis & Pogue, Cleve., 1979; law clk. U.S. Dist. Ct. (no. dist.) Ill., Chgo., 1980; assoc. Mayer, Brown & Platt, Chgo., 1981-86, ptnr., 1986-94; CEO Vantage Point Cons., 1994—; asst. atty. gen. State of Ill., Chgo., 1981-83; cons. spl. commn. to Study Cook County Cts., Chgo., 1985-88; program chmn. Columbia U. media and soc. seminars, 1986-93; chief counsel Spl. Commn. on Adminstrn. of Justice, Ill. Supreme Ct., 1992-94; lectr. on litigation abuse, ethics, white collar crime and racketeering litigation, 1984-94. Author: Analysis of Executive Impoundment Reports, 1975, (with Timothy W. Joranko) A Primer on Civil Racketeering Issues, 1988, Professional Responsibility, 1988; contbg. author: Dombroff on Unfair Litigation Tactics, 1985, Civil RICO Practice: Materials and Comments, 1991, Corporate Counsel's Guide to Litigation Management, 1992, mem. adv. bd., 1994—; co-author: Managing the Corporate Legal Function, 1995; legal ethics editor Ill. Inst. Continuing Edn., 1988-93; also numerous tech. and newspaper articles. Alumni rep., speaker Carleton Coll., 1980—; legal adv. LaRabida Children's Hosp., Chgo., 1983-93; chief counsel Ill. Supreme Ct. Commn. on the Adminstrn. of Justice, 1992-94; mem. sch. bd. Glencoe (Ill.) Jr. Kindergarten, 1992—. Am. Legion scholar 1967; Thomas J. Watson fellow 1975-76; recipient Harold Goettler Pol. Insts. Prize 1974. Mem. ABA (spl. asst. to chmn. commn. on professionalism 1985-86), Am. Law Inst. (adv. coun. restatement of law 3d, the law governing lawyers and consultative group to complex litigation project 1988-93, consultative group on product liability project 1985-93), Lawyers Alliance for Nuclear Arms Control, Aspen Inst. for Humanistic Studies (seminar on justice and soc.), Jewish United Fund (chair legal edn. program 1992-94), Chgo. Coun. on Fgn. Rels. (fgn. affairs com.). Jewish. Avocations: philately, tennis, photography, piano, Fed., State, and Legis. civil litigation. Office: Vantage Point Cons 5 Revere Dr Ste 200 Northbrook IL 60062

SALOMON, ROBERT S., JR., portfolio manager. Chmn., CEO Salomon Bros. Asset Mgmt., Inc.; portfolio mgr. Salomon Bros. Capital Fund, Inc. Office: Salomon Bros Inc 1 New York Plz New York NY 10004-1902 Office: 7 World Trade Ctr Fl 38 New York NY 10048-1100

SALOMON, ROGER BLAINE, English language educator; b. Providence, Feb. 26, 1928; s. Henry and Lucia Angell (Capewell) S.; m. Elizabeth Helen Lowenstein, June 14, 1950; children—Pamela, Wendy. B.A., Harvard, 1950; M.A., U. Calif. at Berkeley, 1951, Ph.D., 1957. Instr. Mills Coll., Oakland, Calif., 1955-57; instr., then asst. prof. Yale U., New Haven, 1957-66; mem. faculty Case Western Res. U., Cleve., 1966—, prof. English, 1969—, Oviatt prof. English, 1990, chmn. dept., 1974-80; Mem. adv. screening com. Am. lit. Sr. Fulbright-Hays Program, 1973-76, chmn., 1975; mem. grants-in-aid selection com. Am. Council Learned Socs., 1976-78. Author: Twain and the Image of History, 1961, Desperate Storytelling: Post-Romantic Elaborations of the Mock-Heroic Mode, 1987. Served to 1st lt. USAF, 1952-53. Morse fellow, 1960-61; Guggenheim fellow, 1972-73. Mem. AAUP, MLA. Home: 2830 Coventry Rd Cleveland OH 44120-2231 Office: Case Western Res U Dept English Cleveland OH 44106

SALONEN, ESA-PEKKA, conductor; b. Helsinki, Finland, June 30, 1958. Student, Sibelius Acad., Helsinki; studies with, Rautavaara and Panula. Condr. Finnish Radio Symphony, 1979; guest condr. orchs., London, Berlin, Paris, L.A., Phila., Minn.; prin. condr. Swedish Radio Symphony Orch., 1985—; prin guest condr. Philharmonia Orch., London, 1985-94, Oslo Philharm. Orch., 1985-90; artistic advisor Stockholm Chamber Orch., 1986—; music dir. L.A. Philharm. Orch., 1992—. Office: Van Walsum Mgmt, 26 Wadham Rd, London SW15 2LR, England also: Los Angeles Philharm Orch 135 N Grand Ave Los Angeles CA 90012-3013 also: Swedish Radio Symphony, Sveriges Radio, S-105 10 Stockholm Sweden

SALONEN, HEIKKI OLAVI, corporate executive; b. Joroinen, Finland, May 12, 1933; s. Viljo Ilmari and Vieno (Valimaa) S.; m. Kirsti-Liisa Koskinen, June 20, 1958; children: Marju, Jyri. BS in Econs., Helsinki (Finland) U., 1958, MS in Econs., 1962. Pres. Finnish Export Inst., Helsinki, 1962-67; exec. v.p. Saastamoinen-Yhtyma oy Teollisuus, Kuopio, Finland, 1968, pres., 1969-72; pres., chief exec. officer Amer Group, Ltd., Helsinki, 1972-86, chmn., chief exec. officer, 1986—; chmn. bd. Am. Cultural Found., 1978-85, Wilson Sporting Goods Co., USA, Amer Holding Co., USA, numerous others; mem. supervisory bd. Pohjola Group, 1983—, MTV Oy, 1975—, Kansallis-Osake-Pankki, 1986—; mem. adv. bd. Med. Rsch. Found., 1978—; alt. mem. adv. bd. Finnish Export Inst., 1976—; bd. dirs. Found. for Econ. Edn., Mgmt. Study Group. Mem. adv. bd. Helsinki Sch. Econs. and Bus. Adminstrn., 1979—; Scout Found., 1980—; Mannerheim League for Child Welfare, 1979—; Voluntary Def. Promotion, 1979—; vice chmn. bd. Helsinki Rsch. Inst. for Bus. Econs., 1976-78, chmn. bd., 1978-85, bd. dirs., 1985—; bd. trustees World Wildlife Fund of Finland, 1980—; v.p. delegation Valamo Found., 1988—; bd. dirs. Finnish Employers Gen. Group, 1982—, Confederation of Finnish Industries, 1984—; mem. del. Europe Inst., 1988—. Mem. Confederation Finnish Industries (vice mem. bd. 1984—), Employer's Assn. Food Industries (bd. dirs. 1985—), Finnish Heart Assn. (bd. dirs. 1983—). Lutheran. Avocations: literature, fishing. Office: Amer Group Ltd, Makelankatu 91, 00610 Helsinki Finland also: Wilson Sporting Goods Co 2233 West St River Grove IL 60171

SALONER, GARTH, management educator; b. Johannesburg, South Africa, Jan. 18, 1955; came to U.S. 1978; s. Max and Rachel (Aronowitz) S.; m. Marlene Shoolman, Dec. 26, 1978; children: Amber, Romy, Kim. BCom, U. Witwatersrand, S. Africa, 1976; MBA, U. Witwatersrand, 1977; MS in Statistics, Stanford U., 1981, MA in Econs., PhD, 1982. Asst. lectr. U. Witwatersrand, 1977-78; asst. prof. econs. MIT, Cambridge, 1982-86, assoc. prof. econs. and mgmt., 1986-89, prof., 1990; vis. assoc. prof. bus. adminstrn. Harvard Bus. Sch., Boston, 1989-90; vis. asst. prof. Stanford (Calif.) U., 1986-87, prof. strategic mgmt. and econs. Grad. Sch. Bus., 1990—, Robert A Magowan prof., 1993—, dir. rsch. and curriculum devel., 1993—; assoc. dean for acad. affairs, 1994—; rsch. assoc. Nat. Bur. Econ. Rsch., 1991—; bd. dirs. Quick Response Svcs. Inc., 1993—. Contbr. articles to profl. jours.; assoc. editor Rand Jour. Econs., 1986-88, co-editor, 1988—; assoc. editor Internat. Jour. Indsl. Orgn., 1988—, Econs. of Innovation & New Tech., 1988—, Strategic Mgmt. Jour., 1991-94. Nat. fellow, Hoover Inst., 1986-87, Sloan fellow, 1987-89; grantee, NSF, 1982, 85, 88. em. Am. Econ. Assn., Econometric Soc., Acad. Mgmt. Jewish. Avocations: bicycling, photography. Home: 4151 Amaranta Ave Palo Alto CA 94306-3903 Office: GSB Stanford U Stanford CA 94305

SALONGA, LEA, actress, singer; b. Manila, Feb. 22, 1971; d. Feliciano Genuino and Maria Ligaya (Imutan) S. Attended, Ateneo De Manila U., 1988-89. Actress, singer The King and I, Manila, 1978, Annie, Manila, 1980, The Rose Tattoo, Manila, 1980, The Bad Seed, Manila, 1981, The Goodbye Girl, Manila, 1982, Paper Moon, Manila, 1983, The Fantasticks, Manila, 1988, Miss Saigon, London, 1989-90 (Outstanding Performance by Actress in Musical Olivier award 1990), Broadway, 1991-92 (Best Actress in Musical Tony award 1991, Best Actress in Musical Drama Desk award 1991, Best Actress in Musical Outer Critics Circle award 1991, Outstanding Debut

Theatre World award 1991), Les Miserables, Broadway, 1993, My Fair Lady, Manila, 1994, Into the Woods, Singapore, 1994, also The Sound of Music, Manila, Fiddler on the Roof, Manila, Cat on a Hot Tin Roof; Philippine films include Bakit Labis Kitang Mahal?, Dear Diary, Pik Pak Boom, Captain Barbell, Ninja Kids, Like Father, Like Son, Tropang Bulilit; Philippine TV: (host) Kulit Bulilit, Love Lea, Naku, Ha!, Sunday Special, Iba Ito!, That's Entertainment!, This is It!, (co-host) Patok Na Patok!; opening act for Stevie Wonder, Menudo; concerts: The Filipinos of Miss Saigon, A Miss Called Lea, Lea Salonga in Concert, L.A., San Francisco; recs. include Small Voice, 1981 (gold record), Lea, Happy Children's Club, Christmas Album, We are the World, (debut album) Lea Salonga, 1993, Miss Saigon original London cast rec. (gold record), The King and I, Aladdin, 1992 (singing voice Princess Jasmine, motion picture soundtrack), The Little Tramp; TV films include: Redwood Curtain, 1995. Recipient AWIT award outstanding svc. Philippings Recording Industry, 1993, ASEAN Industry award performing arts, 1992, Ten Outstanding Young Men award outstanding debut, 1991, AWIT award outstanding performer, 1990, Presdl. Award of Merit Pres. Aquino, 1990, Laurence Olivier award best actress musical, 1990, Cecil award best recording by a child, 1984, Tining award one of 10 outstanding singers, 1983, 94, 92, ALIW award best child performer, 1980, 81, 82; named Outstanding Manilan by Govt. City of Manila, 1990. Mem. AFTRA, Actor's Equity Assn. Roman Catholic. Avocations: music, reading, collecting raised-trunk elephants, collecting swatches, working on computers. Office: C Winston Simone Mgmt 1790 Broadway Fl 10 New York NY 10019-1412•

SALOOM, JOSEPH A., III, diplomat; b. Urbana, Ill., Apr. 8, 1948; s. Joseph A. and Barbara (Bombard) S.; m. Anne Elizabeth Mayer, Jan. 22, 1972; children: Elizabeth, Shahin, Ilyas. BA in Econs., Georgetown U., 1970; MS, MIT, 1973. Joined Fgn. Svc.; comml. officer U.S. Consulate Gen., Dusseldorf, Germany, 1974-76; econ. officer Am. Embassy, Rabat, Morocco, 1976-78; fin. economist Am. Embassy, Jidda, Saudi Arabia, 1978-80; econ. counselor Am. Embassy, Kinshasa, Zaire, 1983-87; dep. chief mission Am. Embassy, Niamey, Niger, 1987-90; U.S. amb. to Guinea Am. Embassy, Conakry, Guinea, 1993—; transp. economist Dept. State, Washington, 1980-83, dir. office monetary affairs, 1990-91, dep. asst. sec., 1991-93. Office: Am Embassy, BP 603, Conakry Guinea

SALOP, STEVEN CHARLES, economics educator; b. Reading, Pa., Dec. 23, 1946; s. Saul Harold and Byrd (Kalish) S.; m. Judith Rebecca Gelman, Mar. 14, 1982; children: Aviva, Ezra, Joshua. BA summa cum laude, U. Pa., 1968; M Phil, Yale U., 1971, PhD, 1972. Economist Fed. Res. Bd., Washington, 1972-77, CAB, Washington, 1977-78; economist FTC, Washington, 1978-79, asst. dir., 1979-80, assoc. dir., 1980-81; prof. econs. and law Georgetown U. Law Ctr., Washington, 1981—; spl. cons. Charles River Assocs. Boston, 1987—; bd. dirs.; bd. dirs. Lowell Sch. Editor: Strategic Competition, 1982. Mem. Am. Econ. Assn., Phi Beta Kappa. Jewish. Office: Georgetown U Law Ctr 600 New Jersey Ave NW Washington DC 20002

SALPETER, ALAN N., lawyer; b. Phila., Oct. 7, 1947. BA with honors, Am. U., 1969; JD, Villanova U., 1972. Bar: Ill. 1972. Ptnr. Mayer, Brown & Platt, Chgo.; lectr. and author in field. Mem. ABA, Chgo. Bar Assn., Chgo. Coun. Lawyers. Office: Mayer Brown & Platt 190 S La Salle St Chicago IL 60603-3441

SALPETER, EDWIN ERNEST, physical sciences educator; b. Vienna, Austria, Dec. 3, 1924; came to U.S., 1949, naturalized, 1953; s. Jakob L. and Frieder (Horn) S.; m. Miriam Mark, June 11, 1950; children—Judy Gail, Shelley Ruth. M.S., Sydney U., 1946; Ph.D., Birmingham (Eng.) U., 1948; DSc, U. Chgo., 1969, Case-Western Reserve U., 1970, U. Sydney, 1994. Research fellow Birmingham U., 1948-49; faculty Cornell U., Ithaca, N.Y., 1949—; now J.G. White prof. phys. scis. Cornell U.; mem. U.S. Nat. Sci. Bd., 1979-85. Author: Quantum Mechanics, 1957, 77; mem. editorial bd. Astrophys. Jour, 1966-69; assoc. editor Rev. Modern Physics, 1971—; contbr. articles to profl. jours. Mem. AURA bd., 1970-72. Recipient Gold medal Royal Astron. Soc., 1973, J.R. Oppenheimer Meml. prize U. Miami, 1974, C. Bruce medal Astron. Soc. Pacific, 1987, A. Devaucouleurs medal, 1992. Mem. NAS, Am. Astron. Soc. (v.p. 1971-73), Am. Philos. Soc., Am. Acad. Arts and Scis., The Royal Soc. (fgn.), Australian Acad. Sci., Deutsche Akademie Leopoldina. Home: 116 Westbourne Ln Ithaca NY 14850-2414 Office: Cornell U Newman Lab Ithaca NY 14853

SALSBERG, ARTHUR PHILIP, publishing company executive; b. Bklyn., Aug. 28, 1929; s. Solomon William and Rae (Miller) S.; m. Rhoda Gelb, Sept. 11, 1960; children—Charles Martin, Solomon William. B.B.A. CCNY, 1951. Mng. editor Ojibway Press, N.Y.C., 1957-64; advt. and promotion mgr. RCA Corp., Harrison, N.J., 1965-67; editor N.Am. Pub. Co., Phila., 1967-70; v.p., gen. mgr. Lawyers World, Inc., Phila., 1970-72; editorial dir. Ziff-Davis Pub. Co., N.Y.C., 1973-83; editor, assoc. pub. CQ Communications, Inc., Hicksville, N.Y., 1984—; Mag. and newsletter pub. cons.; electronics instr.; local campaign publicist, speech writer for town mayor, town council, library bd., sch. bd. Author: Complete Book of CB Radios, 1976, Complete Book of Video Games, 1977, Collier's Ency. Yearbook, 1977, 78, 79, 80, 81, 82, First Book of Modern Electronics Fun Projects, 1986, Second Book of Modern Electronics Fun Projects, 1986; editor: Audio Mag, 1967-70, Lawyers World, 1970-72, Popular Electronics, 1973-83, Communications Handbook, 1973-83, Electronic Experimenters Handbook, 1973-83, Stereo Directory, 1973-83, Tape Recorder Directory, 1973-83, Citizens Band Handbook, 1976-83, Invitation to Electronics, 1972-83, Modern Electronics, 1984-91, Computer Craft, 1992-93, MicroComputer Jour., 1994—; assoc. pub.: Amateur Radio Equipment Buyers Guide, 1988, 89, 90, 91, 92, Amateur Radio Antenna Buyers Guide, 1989, 90, 91-92. Publicity chmn. Nassau council Boy Scouts Am., 1975; Adv. com. Bramson OR Tech. Inst., 1975. Served with AUS, 1951-53, Korea. Recipient Indsl. Mktg. Mag. award, 1959. Home: 7844A Lexington Club Blvd Delray Beach FL 33446 Office: 76 N Broadway Hicksville NY 11801-2909

SALSBURY, STEPHEN MATTHEW, historian, educator; b. Oakland, Calif., Oct. 12, 1931; s. Ralph Thomas and Roma Enola (Connor) S. A.B., Occidental Coll., 1953; A.M., Harvard U., 1957, Ph.D., 1964. Research assoc. Harvard Sch. Bus. Adminstrn., 1961-62; asst. prof. history U. Del., Newark, 1963-68; assoc. prof. U. Del., 1968-70, prof., 1970-77, chmn. history dept., 1974-77; prof. econ. history U. Sydney, Australia, 1977—; also head dept., dean Faculty Econs. U. Sydney, 1980-88, prof. dean Faculty Econs., 1989-90—; vis. asst. prof. Johns Hopkins, 1967-68; vis. scholar La Trobe U., Melbourne, Australia, 1974; Hunter Baillie fellow St. Andrew's Coll., Sydney; vis. prof. history U. Calif., Berkeley, 1987-88; hon. curator Harvard U. Libr., 1989—. Author: The State, The Investor and the Railroad, 1967, (with Alfred D. Chandler, Jr.) Pierre S. duPont and the Making of the Modern Corporation, 1971, Essays on the History of the American West, 1975, No Way to Run a Railroad: The Untold Story of the Penn Central Crisis, 1982, (with Kay Sweeney) The Bull, The Bear and the Kangaroo: The History of the Sydney Stock Exchange, 1988, (with Kay Sweeney) Sydney Stockbrokers: Biographies of the Members of the Sydney Stock Exchange 1871-1987, 1992; assoc. editor: American National Biography, 1992—. Mem. adv. bd. Eleutherian-Mills-Hagley Found., 1975-78, Bus. History Rev., 1981-85. Served with USAF, 1955-57, 62-63. Mem. Am. Hist. Assn., Econ. History Assn. (chmn. com. research 1976-77), Econ. History Assn. Australia and N.Z., Am. Historians, Agrl. History Soc., Hist. Soc. Del., AAUP, Assn. Evolutionary Econs., Phi Beta Kappa, Alpha Tau Omega. Congregationalist. Club: Am. Nat. (Sydney), Rotary (Sydney), Union Club (Sydney). Home: 28 Wahroonga Ave, Wahroonga NSW, Australia Office: U Sydney, Dean Faculty Econs, Sydney NSW 2006, Australia

SALTARELLI, EUGENE A., retired engineering and construction company executive, consultant; b. Buffalo, Feb. 22, 1923; s. Joseph A. and Mary (Cataldo) S.; m. Jean Marie Cray, Nov. 25, 1950; children—Margaret, Joseph, Thomas, Paul, Mary, John. B.Mech. Engring., U. Detroit, 1949; M.S. in Mech. Engring., Northwestern U., 1951. Registered profl. engr., Calif., Md., Mich., N.Y., Pa., Tex., W.Va., Ariz., Ga. Design engr. Bell Aircraft Corp., Buffalo, 1950-56; sr. mgr. Bettis Atomic Power Lab., Pitts., 1956-67; group v.p. NUS Corp., Gaithersburg, Md., 1967-80; sr. v.p., chief engr. Brown & Root, U.S.A., Inc., Houston, 1980-88; now pvt. cons.; expert witness in power plant engring. and constrn. litigation. Contbr. articles to profl. jours.; patentee in field. Served to 1st lt. USAAF, 1942-46.

Mem. ASME (George Westinghouse Gold medal 1985), Atomic Indsl. Forum, Am. Nuclear Soc. (exec. com. power div. 1975), Nat. Soc. Profl. Engrs. Roman Catholic. Club: Montgomery Country Club, Laytonsville, Md. Avocations: woodworking; piano and organ; golf.

SALTEN, DAVID GEORGE, university administrator, educator; b. N.Y.C., Aug. 23, 1913; s. Max Elias and Gertrude (Brauer) S.; m. Frances Claire Brown (div. 1983); children—Phoebe, Cynthia, Melissa; m. Adrienne O'Brien, 1989. ScB, Washington Sq. Coll., N.Y.C., 1933; AM, Columbia U., 1939; PhD, NYU, 1944; LLD (hon.), Lynn U., 1976; L.H.D., Nova U., Ft. Lauderdale, Fla., 1983; Sc.D. (hon.), N.Y. Inst. Tech., 1984. Registered psychologist, N.Y. Chemist Almay Cosmetics, 1934-35, City of New York, 1938-40; tchr., chmn. dept., high sch. prin. N.Y.C. Bd. Edn., 1940-50; assoc. prof. Hunter Coll. Grad. Program, 1947-63; supt. of schs. City of Long Beach, N.Y., 1950-62, City of New Rochelle, N.Y., 1962-65; exec. v.p. Fedn. of Jewish Philanthropies, N.Y.C., 1965-69; exec. v.p., provost N.Y. Inst. Tech., Old Westbury, 1969-90; chmn. Nassau County Indsl. Devel. Agy., Mineola, N.Y., 1985—; exec. dir. Nassau County Tax Relief Commn., 1990-93; mem. White House Conf. on Edn., 1955, White House Conf. on Youth, 1960; U.S. resource person on edn. World Mental Health Congress, Paris, 1961; mem. Bd. Edn., Hawthorne, Cedar Knolls, N.Y., 1963-65; mem. adv. council Columbia U. Sch. of Social Work, 1967-69; chmn. adv. council NYU Sch. Edn., 1963-65; chmn. adv. council to Select Com. on Higher Edn. N.Y. Legislature, 1971-73. Author: Mathematics: A Basic Course, 1957. Editor instructional software. Contbr. articles on edn. and ednl. adminstrn. to profl. publs. Vice chmn. N.Y. State Mental Health Council, Albany, 1965-72; pres. N.Y. State Citizens Council, 1957, Nat. Council on Aging, Washington, 1975-77; chmn. Nassau County Local Devel. Agy., 1982—; Nassau County Local Devel. Corp., N.Y., 1982—, pres., 1992—; chmn. Nassau County Cultural Devel. Bd., 1980—; bd. dirs. NAACP Legal Def. Fund, 1964-74; chmn. bd. trustees The Hewlett Sch., 1991—. Recipient citation U.S. Navy, 1947, Mental Health Assn., Nassau County, N.Y., 1955, Long Beach Edn. Assn., N.Y., 1962, Council of City of New Rochelle, N.Y., 1965, Council of Town of Islip, N.Y., 1982. Fellow AAAS, Am. Orthopsychiat. Assn.; mem. Princeton Club (N.Y.C.), Capitol Hill Club (Washington), Masons (32d degree). Clubs: Princeton (N.Y.C.); Capitol Hill (Washington). Lodge: Mason (32d degree). Avocations: opera; ballet; international travel; photography. Office: Nassau County Indsl Devel Agy 400 County Seat Dr Mineola NY 11501-4825

SALTER, EDWIN CARROLL, physician; b. Oklahoma City, Jan. 19, 1927; s. Leslie Ernest and Maud (Carroll) S.; m. Ellen Gertrude Malone, June 30, 1962; children—Mary Susanna, David Patrick. B.A., DePauw U., 1947; M.D., Northwestern U., 1951. Intern Cook County Hosp., Chgo., 1951-53; resident in pediatrics Children's Meml. Hosp., Chgo., 1956-58, Cook County Hosp., Chgo., 1956-58; practice medicine specializing in pediatrics Lake Forest, Ill., 1958—; attending physician Lake Forest Hosp., 1958—, pres. med. staff, 1981-82; attending physician Children's Meml. Hosp., Chgo.; clin. faculty mem. dept. pediatrics Northwestern U. Med. Sch. Served to capt. M.C., U.S. Army, 1954-56. Mem. AMA, Ill. State Med. Soc., Lake County Med. Soc. (pres. 1984), Phi Beta Kappa. Republican. Methodist. Home: 19 N Maywood Rd Lake Forest IL 60045-3233 Office: 900 N Westmoreland Rd No 110 Lake Forest IL 60045-1671

SALTER, KEVIN THORNTON, lawyer; b. N.Y.C., Oct. 21, 1947; s. Hershel Fletcher and Elizabeth (Thornton) S.; m. Eleanor Raftery, Aug. 28, 1982. BA, Iona Coll., 1973; JD, St. John's U., 1977. Bar: N.Y. 1978, U.S. Dist. Ct. (so. and ea. dists.) N.Y., 1978. Atty. Nat. Coun. on Compensation Ins., N.Y.C., 1978-80; coun. James G. Barron, N.Y.C., 1980-81; assoc. St. Regis Paper Co./ Champion Internat., N.Y.C. and Stamford, Conn., 1981-88; sr. ptnr. Kroll & Tract, N.Y.C., 1988-94; ptnr. Peterson & Ross, N.Y.C., 1994—; bd. dirs. Alliance Assurance Co. Am. Inc., N.Y.C., Sea Ins. Co. Am. Inc., N.Y.C., Sun Ins. Office Am. Inc., N.Y.C., Merc. and Gen. Reins. Co. Am., Morristown, N.J., Fortress Ins. Co. Am., N.Y.C. With U.S. Army, 1967-69. Mem. ABA, N.Y. State Bar Assn., Brit. Ins. Law Assn. Office: Peterson & Ross 805 Third Ave 6th Fl New York NY 10022

SALTER, LESTER HERBERT, lawyer; b. Waterbury, Conn., Apr. 26, 1918; s. Nathan M. and Eva G. (Levy) S.; m. Nina F. Scheftel, Sept. 15, 1951; 1 child, Ellen Lee. BS in Econs, U. Pa., 1940, LL.B., 1948. Bar: R.I. bar 1948. Trial atty. Office of Chief Counsel, IRS, Newark and Boston, 1949-53; individual practice law Providence, 1953-57; partner firm Salter & McGowan, Providence, 1957-70, Salter, McGowan, Arcaro & Swartz, 1970-74; pres. firm Salter, McGowan, Swartz & Holden, Inc., Providence, 1974—; lectr. Northeastern U., 1955-56; chmn. U. R.I. Fed. Tax Inst., 1972-77; chmn. disciplinary bd. Supreme Ct., R.I., 1975-81; mem. R.I. Adv. Commn. Jud. Appts., 1978-82, ethics adv. panel Supreme Ct., R.I., 1987-92. Assoc. editor: R.I. Bar Jour, 1961-68. Served with F.A. AUS, 1941-46. Decorated Bronze Star. Mem. ABA (Ho. of Dels. 1987—), R.I. Bar Assn. (pres. 1986-87), Am. Judicature Soc., Am. Law Inst. Home: 75 Blackstone Blvd Providence RI 02906-5413 Office: 321 S Main St Providence RI 02903-7108

SALTER, MARY JO, poet; b. Grand Rapids, Aug. 15, 1954; d. Albert Gregory and Lormina (Paradise) S.; m. Brad Leithauser, 1980; 1 child, Emily Salter. BA cum laude, Harvard U., 1976. Instr. Harvard U., 1978-79; instr. English conversation Japan, 1980-83; lectr. English Mount Holyoke Coll., S. Hadley, 1984-85; staff editor Atlantic Monthly, 1978-80; poet-in-residence Robert Frost Place, 1981; vis. artist Am. Acad., Rome, 1985. Author: Henry Purcell in Japan, 1985, Unfinished Painting, 1988 (Lamont prize in poetry 1988), The Moon Comes Home, 1989, Sunday Skaters: Poems, 1994 (Nat. Book Critics Circle award nomination 1994); contbr. to periodicals including New Yorker, New Republic, Kenyon Rev. Recipient Discovery prize Nation, 1983; Nat. Endowment for Arts fellow, 1983-84. Mem. Internat. P.E.N. Office: 9 Stanton Ave South Hadley MA 01075•

SALTER, ROBERT MUNDHENK, JR., physicist, consultant; b. Morgantown, W. Va., Apr. 24, 1920; s. Robert Mundhenk and Sara Opal (Godfrey) S.; m. Darlene Jeanette Oliva, Jan. 21, 1977; children by previous marriage: Robert Mundhenk III, Wendy Lou Salter Reynolds, Gary Coddington. BME, Ohio State U., 1941; MA, UCLA, 1957, PhD, 1965. Research engr. Gen. Motors Research Labs., Detroit, 1941-42; research engr. Aerophysics Lab. N.Am. Aviation, Los Angeles, 1946-48; project dir. USAF satellite devel. Rand Corp., Santa Monica, Calif., 1948-54, phys. scientist, 1965-82; project dir. USAF WS-117L satellite devel. Lockheed Aircraft, Palo Alto, Calif., 1954-59; founder, pres. Quantatron, Inc., Santa Monica, 1960-62; sci. cons. to various industries, 1962—; chief exec. officer Xerad, Inc., Santa Monica, 1973—. Patentee in field. Founding dir. U.S. chpt. Elsa Wild Animal Appeal, 1968. Lt. USN, 1942-46. Recipient Space Pioneer medal Dept. Def., 1985. Mem. Sigma Xi, Sigma Pi Sigma, Tau Beta Pi. Republican. Presbyterian. Club: Riviera Country. Achievements include design and constrn. of Giga-bit optical CD/rom; and an invention of variable-geometry, moving spike diffuser. Home and Office: 767 Paseo Miramar Pacific Palisades CA 90272-3026 *My professional goal has been to apply and focus knowledge of new and emerging technologies in the development of large and complex systems to benefit both U.S. defense and the public sector. An example is the early Air Force "Spy" satellite program-a forerunner to NASA. Another is Planatran, a future ultra high speed subway system magnetically levitated and propelled in evacuated tubeways.*

SALTER, SALLY, reporter. Comml. real estate reporter The Atlanta Jour. Constn., Atlanta. Office: Atlanta Journal & Constitution 72 Marietta St NW Atlanta GA 30302

SALTON, GERARD, computer science educator; b. Nuremberg, Germany, Mar. 8, 1927; s. Rudolf and Elisabeth (Tuchmann) S.; m. Mary Birnbaum, Aug. 31, 1950; children: Mariann, Peter. B.A. magna cum laude, Bklyn. Coll., 1950, M.A., 1952; Ph.D., Harvard U., 1958. Mem. staff computation lab. Harvard U., 1952-58, instr., then asst. prof. applied math., 1958-65; prof. computer sci. Cornell U., 1965—, chmn. dept., 1971-77; cons. to industry. Author: Automatic Information Organization and Retrieval, 1968, The Smart System-Experiments in Automatic Document Processing, 1971, Dynamic Information and Library Processing, 1975, Introduction to Modern Information Retrieval, 1983, Automatic Text Processing, 1989; editor-in-chief ACM Comms., 1966-68, ACM Jour., 1969-72; editor ACM Transactions on Info. Systems. Guggenheim fellow, 1963; recipient Alexander von Humboldt Sr. Scientist award, 1988. Fellow AAAS, Assn. Computing

Machinery (coun. 1972-78, Outstanding Contbn. award 1983); mem. Am. Soc. for Info. Sci. (award of merit 1989), Phi Beta Kappa. Home: 221 Valley Rd Ithaca NY 14850-6152 Office: Upson Hall Cornell U Ithaca NY 14853

SALTONSTALL, CECILIA DRINKER, musician; b. Phila., Jan. 16, 1917; d. Henry Sandwith and Sophie Lewis (Hutchinson) D.; m. Henry Saltinstall, July 27, 1940; children: Kent S., Henry Jr., Caroline S., Ellen S. BA in Music, Bennington Coll. dir. Amateur Chamber Music Players, N.Y.C. 1985—, chmn., 1991-94. Co-author: A Catalogue of Music for Small Orchestra, 1978. Avocations: instrumentalist, botany. Home: 7 Riverwoods Dr F119 Exeter NH 03833-4370

SALTOUN, ANDRE MEIR, lawyer; b. Baghdad, Iraq, Jan. 21, 1929; came to U.S., 1947; s. Meir and Synthia (Noury) S.; m. Beverly Melnik, 1947 (div. 1959); children: Myra, Cynthia, Julie; m. Francine Klein, Aug. 17, 1960; children: Diane, Josiane, Carol. BA, U. N.C., 1950; JD, U. Wis., 1960. Bar: Ill. 1960, Wis., U.S. Dist. Ct. (no. dist.) Ill. 1960, Calif. 1978, U.S. Ct. Claims 1978, U.S. Tax Ct. 1978, U.S. Ct. Appeals (6th, 7th and 10th cirs.) 1978, U.S. Supreme Ct. 1978. Ptnr. Baker & McKenzie, Chgo. and Palo Alto, 1964—. Contbr. articles to profl. jours. Mem. ABA, Ill. Bar Assn., Calif. Bar Assn., Wis. Bar Assn., Chgo. Bar Assn., Chgo. Assn. Commerce and Industry (exec. com. of bd. dirs.), Plaza Club. Office: Baker & McKenzie PO Box 60309 660 Hanson Way Palo Alto CA 94304

SALTZ, HOWARD JOEL, newspaper editor; b. Bronx, N.Y., Apr. 11, 1960; s. Fred Raymond and Sheila Lois (Goldberg) S. BA in Liberal Arts, SUNY, Stony Brook, 1983. Reporter Greenwich Time So. Conn. Newspapers, divsn. Times Mirror, 1983-85; with Garden State Newspapers, divsn. MediaNews Group, 1985—; with N.J. Advance, Garden State Newspapers div. MediaNews Group, Dover, 1985-87, editor, 1987-88; editor Hamilton (Ohio) Jour.-News Garden State Newspapers div. MediaNews Group, 1988-89, editor Fremont (Calif.) Argus, 1989-91, editor Johnstown (Pa.) Tribune-Democrat, 1991—; mem. adv. com. dept. journalism Ohlone Coll., Fremont, Calif., 1990-91. Bd. dirs. YMCA of Fremont-Newark, Calif., 1990-91, Johnstown Area Heritage Assn., 1991-93. Mem. Greater Johnstown C. of C. (bd. dirs. 1991—), Soc. Profl. Journalists (bd. dirs. Northern Calif. chpt. 1990-91). Avocations: skiing, travel. Home: 43 Venango St Johnstown PA 15905 Office: The Tribune Democrat 425 Locust St Johnstown PA 15907

SALTZ, RALPH, corporate lawyer; b. May 31, 1948; s. Peter and Eve (Bass) S.; m. Linda Bergman, Mar. 15, 1970; children: Erica, Alan. BA, Queens Coll., 1969; JD, St. John's U., 1972. Bar: N.Y. 1973, N.J. 1975. Atty. The Port Authority of N.Y. and N.J., N.Y.C., 1972-76, The Great Atlantic and Pacific Tea Co., Montvale, N.J., 1976-77; asst. real estate counsel Supermarkets Gen. Corp., Woodbridge, N.J., 1977-82, Toys 'R' Us, Inc., Rochelle Park, N.J., 1982-84; v.p., house counsel, sec. Jamesway Corp., Secaucus, N.J., 1984-94; v.p., gen. counsel Rickel Home Ctrs., Inc., South Plainfield, N.J., 1994—. Mem. ABA. Democrat. Office: Rickel Home Ctrs Inc 200 Helen St South Plainfield NJ 07080

SALTZBURG, STEPHEN ALLAN, law educator, consultant; b. Phila., Sept. 10, 1945; s. Jack Leonard and Mildrid (Osgood) S.; m. Susan Lee; children: Mark Winston, Lisa Marie, Diane Elizabeth, David Lee Mussehl. AB, Dickinson Coll., 1967; JD, U. Pa., 1970. Bar: Calif. 1971, D.C. 1972, Va. 1976. Law clk. U.S. Dist. Ct. (no. dist.) Calif., San Francisco, 1970-71, U.S. Supreme Ct., 1971-72; asst. prof. law sch. U. Va., Charlottesville, 1972-74, assoc. prof., 1974-77, prof., 1977-82, Class of 1962 chairholder, 1987-90; Howrey prof. trial advocacy, litigation and profl. responsibility George Washington U. Nat. Law Ctr., Washington, 1990—; reporter Alaska Rules of Evidence, 1976-77, Alaska Civil Jury Instrns., 1979-81, Adv. Com. on Rules of Criminal Procedure, 1984-89, Virginia Rules of Evidence, 1984-85; dep. asst. atty. gen. criminal divsn. U.S. Dept. Justice, 1988-89; mem. adv. com. on Fed. Rules of Criminal Procedure, 1989—; reporter Civil Justice Reform Act Adv. Group, U.S. Dist. Ct. D.C., 1992-93, chair, 1994—; liaison mem. adv. com. Fed. Rules of Evidence, 1993—; project dir. Tax Refund Fraud Task Force, U.S. Dept. Treasury, 1994-95. Author: American Criminal Procedure, 4th edit., 1992, Criminal Law: Cases and Materials, 1994, Federal Rules of Evidence Manual, 6th edit., 1994, A Modern Approach to Evidence, 2d edit., 1982, Federal Criminal Jury Instructions, 2d edit., 1991, Evidence in America, 1987, Military Rules of Evidence Manual, 3d edit., 1991, Basic Criminal Procedure, 1994, Military Evidentiary Foundations, 1994. Mem. ABA, Am. Law Inst. Office: George Washington U Nat Law Ctr 720 20th St NW Washington DC 20052-0001

SALTZER, JEROME HOWARD, computer science educator; b. Nampa, Idaho, Oct. 9, 1939; s. Joseph and Helene (Scheuermann) S.; m. Marlys Anne Hughes, June 16, 1961; children—Rebecca, Sarah, Mark. B.S., MIT, 1961, M.S., 1963, Sc.D., 1966. Faculty dept. elec. engring. and computer sci. MIT, Cambridge, Mass., 1966—, now prof., tech. dir. project Athena, 1984-88; cons. Chem. Abstracts Svc., 1968-88, IBM Corp., 1970-84. Mem. Mayor's Cable Adv. Bd., Newton, Mass., 1984—. Fellow AAAS, IEEE; mem. NRC (computer sci. and telecom. bd. 1991-93), Assn. for Computing Machinery (mem. com. on computers and pub. policy 1984—), Eta Kappa Nu, Tau Beta Pi. Home: 54 Gammons Rd Newton MA 02168-1216 Office: MIT Lab Computer Sci 545 Technology Sq Cambridge MA 02139-3594

SALTZMAN, BARRY, meteorologist, educator; b. N.Y.C., Feb. 26, 1931; s. Benjamin and Bertha (Burmil) S.; m. Sheila Eisenberg, June 10, 1962; children—Matthew David, Jennifer Ann. B.S., CCNY, 1952; S.M., Mass. Inst. Tech., 1954, Ph.D., 1957; M.A. (hon.), Yale, 1968. Research staff meteorologist MIT, 1957-61; sr. research scientist Travelers Research Center, Inc., Hartford, Conn., 1961-66, research fellow, 1966-68; prof. geophysics Yale U., 1968—, chmn. dept. geology and geophysics, 1988-91. Editor: Selected Papers on the Theory of Thermal Convection, 1962, Advances in Geophysics, 1977—; asso. editor Jour. Geophys. Research, 1971-74; mem. editorial bd. Climate Dynamics, 1986—, ATMOSFERA, 1987—; co-editor Milankovitch and Climate, 1984; contbr. articles to profl. publs. Fellow AAAS, Am. Meteorol. Soc.; mem. Conn. Acad. Sci. and Engring., Am. Geophys. Union, Acad. Scis. Lisbon (hon. fgn.), European Geophys. Soc., Phi Beta Kappa, Sigma Xi. Home: 9 Forest Glen Dr Woodbridge CT 06525-1420 Office: Yale U Dept Geology and Geophysics PO Box 208109 New Haven CT 06520-8109

SALTZMAN, BENJAMIN NATHAN, retired state health administrator, physician; b. Ansonia, Conn., Apr. 24, 1914; s. Joseph N. and Frances (Levine) S.; m. Ruth Elizabeth Bohan, Dec. 19, 1941 (dec. May 1994); children: Sue Ann, John Joseph, Mark Stephen. B.A., U. Oreg., 1935, M.A., 1936, M.D., 1940; D.Sc., U. Ark., 1989. Diplomate Am. Bd. Family Practice. Intern, then resident Gorgas Hosp., Ancon, Panama, 1940-42; gen. practice medicine Saltzman Clinic, Mountain Home, Ark., Panama Canal Zone, 1946-74; prof. family and community medicine U. Ark. for Med. Scis., Little Rock, 1974-81; prof. emeritus U. Ark. for Med. Scis., 1981—; dir. Ark. Dept. Health, Little Rock, 1981-87; med. dir. Pulaski County unit Ark Dept. Health, Little Rock, 1987-91. Mem. editorial bd. Jour. Ark. Med. Soc., 1989—; contbr. articles to profl. publs. Alderman Mountain Home City Coun., 1947-55; pres. Ark. Brotherhood NCCJ, 1986-88; sr. bd. dirs. Florence Crittendon Home Svcs., Ark., 1986-89; v.p. Ark. 4H Found., 1988-89, pres., 1989—. Capt. AUS, 1942-46, lt. col. USAFR, ret. 1973. Recipient Ark. Man of Yr. award Ala. Democrat, 1975, Will Ross award Am. Lung Assn., 1979; Tom T. Ross award Ark. Pub. Health Assn., 1975, Outstanding Achievement award 1975; Ark. Human Rels. award NCCJ, Ark., 1980, Disting. Leadership award Am. Rural Health Assn., 1985; named Arkansan of Yr., Ark. Gerontol. Soc., 1987. Fellow Am. Acad. Family Physicians (chmn. rural health and mental health com. 1956-71), Am. Coll. Preventive Medicine, AMA (chmn. council on rural health 1966-69, 50 yr. club); mem. Ark. Acad. Family Physicians (life mem., pres. 1955-56), Ark. Med. Soc. (life, pres. 1974-75, 50 yr. club), Gerontologic Soc. (life, Arkansan of the Yr. 1987), Mountain Home C. of C. (pres. 1955-68), Am. Lung Assn. (Ark. rep. to bd. 1964-75, pres. bd. Ark. div. 1957-63, hon. life mem. 1991), Am. Cancer Soc. (pres. bd. Ark. div. 1983, hon. life mem. 1991), Sigma Xi. Lodges: Rotary Internat. (bd. dirs. 1961-63, trustee Rotary Internat. Found. 1965-67, bd. dirs. internat. chpt., Rotary Found Citation for Meritorious Svc. 1982-83, Disting. Svc. award 1988-89), Masons (33 degree), Elks (state pres. 1956-59). Avocation: lapidary work. Home: PO Box 823 Mountain Home AR 72653-0823

SALTZMAN, GLENN ALAN, behavioral sciences educator; b. Findlay, Ohio, Sept. 10, 1935; s. Andrew Frank and Lois Elizabeth (Stahl) S.; m. Ruth Elinor Weaver, June 9, 1957; children—Jeff Alan, Jay Aaron, Jill Lynn. B.S., Ohio State U., 1957, M.A., 1962, Ph.D., 1966. Tchr., counselor Lakota Pub. Schs., Fremont, Ohio, 1960-62; asst. state supr. guidance Ohio Dept. Edn., Columbus, 1962-66; prof., chmn. counseling Kent (Ohio) State U., 1966-76; prof. behavioral scis. Northeastern Ohio Univs. Coll. Medicine, Rootstown, 1976—, chmn. behavioral scis., 1976-83, dir. div. basic med-scis., 1982-95. Author: Career Education (6 vols.), 1978, Midshipman Counseling, 1978, Is Anybody Listening?, 1987; contbr. articles to profl. jours. Bd. dirs. Am. Cancer Soc., 1974-78; v.p. Am. Heart Assn., 1981-82, pres., 1982-84; lay leader Kent United Meth. Ch., 1974-78. Served with USN, 1957-60; capt. USNR, ret. Recipient Provost's award Northeastern Ohio U. Coll. Medicine, 1988; Paul Harris fellow, 1981. Mem. APA, Assn. Behavioral Scis. in Med. Edn., Am. Pers. and Guidance Assn., Am. Sch. Counselors Assn., Assn. Counselor Edn. and Supervision, Ohio Pers. and Guidance Assn., Ohio Sch. Counselors Assn., Ohio Assn. Counselor Edn. and Supervision, Rotary (pres. 1980-81, pres. Kent club 1985-91, A.Z. Baker Leadership award dist. 663 1981). Office: Northeastern Ohio Univs Coll Medicine PO Box 95 Rootstown OH 44272-0095

SALTZMAN, JOSEPH, journalist, producer, educator; b. L.A., Oct. 28, 1939; s. Morris and Ruth (Weiss) S.; m. Barbara Dale Epstein, July 1, 1962; children: Michael Stephen Ulysses, David Charles Laertes. BA, U. So. Calif., 1961; MS, Columbia U., 1962. Freelance writer, reporter, producer, 1960—; reporter Valley Times Today, Los Angeles, CA, 1962-64; editor Pacific Palisades Palisadian Post, 1964; sr. writer-producer CBS-KNXT TV, Los Angeles, 1964-74; freelance broadcast cons. Los Angeles, 1974—; sr. producer investigative unit Entertainment Tonight, 1983; supervising producer Feeling Fine Prodns., Los Angeles, 1984-92; prof. journalism U. So. Calif., Los Angeles, 1974—. Documentaries include Black on Black, 1968, The Unhappy Hunting Ground, 1971, The Junior High School, 1971, The Very Personal Death of Elizabeth Schell-Holt-Hartford, 1972, Rape, 1972, Why Me?, 1974; spl. producer: Entertainment Tonight, 1983; supervising producer med. films, video, audio, 1984-93; assoc. mass media editor, columnist USA Today, 1983; syndicated columnist King Features Syndicate, 1983-92; contbg. editor Emmy Mag., 1986—, Roberts Reviewing Service, 1994—; others. Recipient AP certificates of excellence and merit, 1968, 72, 73, 74, 75, Edward R. Murrow awards for distinguished achievements in broadcast journalism, 1969, 72, Alfred I. duPont-Columbia U. award in broadcast journalism, 1973-74, Silver Gavel award Am. Bar Assn., 1973, Ohio State award Am. Exhbn. Ednl. Radio-Television Programs and Inst. for Edn. by Radio-Television Telecommunications Center, 1974, Broadcast Media awards San Francisco State U., 1974, 75; Media award for excellence in communications Am. Cancer Soc., 1976; awards for teaching excellence U. So. Calif., 1977, 88, 90; Disting. Alumni award U. So. Calif., 1992; Seymour Berkson fellow, 1961; Robert E. Sherwood fellow, 1962; alt. Pulitzer traveling fellow, 1962-63. Mem. Radio-Television News Assn. (Golden Mike awards 1969, 71, 73, 75), Nat. Acad. Television Arts and Scis. (regional Emmy awards 1965, 68, 74, 75), Writers Guild Am., Greater Los Angeles Press Club (awards 1968, 74, 75), Columbia U., U. So. Calif. alumni assns., Skull and Dagger, Blue Key, Phi Beta Kappa, Sigma Delta Chi, Pi Sigma Alpha, Alpha Epsilon Rho. Home: 2116 Via Estudillo Palos Verdes Peninsula CA 90274-4931 Office: U So Calif Sch Journalism Univ Park Los Angeles CA 90007

SALTZMAN, PHILIP, television writer, producer; b. Sonora, Mexico, Sept. 19, 1928; came to U.S., 1929, naturalized, 1948; s. Louis and Vanya (Liberman) S.; m. Caroline Veiller, Jan. 24, 1960; children: Jennifer, Daniel Anthony. B.A., UCLA, 1951, M.A., 1953. Free lance writer, 1958-68; pres. Woodruff Prodns., Inc. Writer: TV shows Alcoa Goodyear Theater, 1959, Richard Diamond, 1959, Rifleman, 1961, Perry Mason, 1964, Dr. Kildare, 1964, Fugitive, 1964, Twelve O'Clock High, 1966; producer, writer: TV shows Felony Squad, 1966-69, F.B.I, 1969-73, Barnaby Jones, 1973-77; producer, writer, creator Intertect, 1973; producer: TV movie The FBI vs. Alvin Karpis, 1974, Attack on Terror: The FBI vs. the KKK in Mississippi, 1975, Brinks: The Great Robbery, 1976; co-writer: feature film The Swiss Conspiracy, 1975; creator-writer-producer TV movie Crossfire, 1975; exec. producer: TV shows Barnaby Jones, 1978-80, Escapade, 1978, Colorado C-I, 1978, A Man Called Sloane, 1979, The Aliens Are Coming, 1979, Freebie and the Bean, 1980; producer: TV shows Bare Essence, 1982; supervising producer-writer Partners in Crime, 1984; producer-writer Crazy Like a Fox, 1985; producer, co-writer TV movie That Secret Sunday, 1986; exec. supervising producer The New Perry Mason movies, 1987-88; exec. supervising producer, writer Jake and The Fatman, 1987-88; supervising producer Columbo, 1989-90; creator-writer The Caller, 1991. Mem. dean's coun. Coll. Letters and Sci., UCLA, Friends of English, UCLA. Mem. Writers Guild Am., West, Caucus for Writers, Producers, Dirs., Acad. TV Arts and Scis., PEN Ctr. USA West.

SALTZMAN, ROBERT PAUL, insurance company executive; b. Chgo., Oct. 25, 1942; s. Al and Viola (Grossman) S.; m. Diane Maureen Schulman, Apr. 10, 1964; children: Amy, Adam, Suzanne. BA in Math., Northwestern U., 1964. Mgr. Continental Casualty Co., Chgo., 1964-69; sr. v.p. Colonial Penn Group, Phila., 1969-83; pres., CEO Sun Life Ins. of Am. and Anchor Nat. Life Ins. Co., 1985-93; exec. v.p. mktg. Kaufman & Broad (now Broad, Inc.), L.A., 1987-93; pres., CEO Jackson Nat. Life Ins. Co., Lansing, Mich., 1994—. Office: Jackson Nat Life Ins Co 5901 Executive Dr Lansing MI 48911

SALTZMAN, SIDNEY, city and regional planning educator; b. N.Y.C., Jan. 26, 1926; s. Morris Joseph and Fannie (Grossbaum) S.; m. Dolores S. Lehrman, Nov. 23, 1950; children—Matthew Joseph, Nancy Gail. Student, Worcester Poly. Inst., 1943-44; B.S.M.E., Purdue U., 1946; M.S.I.E., Columbia U., 1951; Ph.D., Cornell U., 1963. Engr. Combustion Engring., Inc., N.Y.C., 1946-48; asst. to v.p. prodn. Atlas-Ansonia Co., North Haven, Conn., 1948-49; prodn. planner Renwal Mfg. Co., Mineola, N.Y., 1949-51; ops. research and systems analyst Royal McBee Corp., Hartford, Conn. and Port Chester, N.Y., 1953-58; instr. Cornell U., 1958-63, asst. prof. ops. research and indsl. engring., 1963-68, assoc. prof. city and regional planning, 1968-71, prof., 1971—, asst. dir. office computer services, 1966-68, chmn. dept. policy planning and regional analysis, 1974-75, chmn. dept. city and regional planning, 1975-83; Fulbright-Hays scholar Technion-Israel Inst. Tech., 1965-66, Albert Alberman vis. lectr., 1987; sr. fellow Mathematica Policy Research, Washington, 1980-81; cons. public, pvt. sectors, internat. devel. Editor: (with others) The Future of Electrical Energy: A Regional Perspective of an Industry in Transition, 1986; contbr. articles on mgmt. sci., planning, regional econs., energy and edn. to profl. jours. Trustee Tompkins Cortland Community Coll., Dryden, N.Y. Served with USN, 1943-46, 51-53. NSF sci. faculty fellow, 1969-70; NATO sci. faculty fellow, 1974; NSF grantee, 1967-68, 73-75. Mem. AAUP, Inst. Mgmt. Scis., Regional Sci. Assn., Peace Sci. Soc., Sigma Xi, Phi Kappa Phi. Office: 215 W Sibley Hall Cornell U Ithaca NY 14853

SALTZMAN, WILLIAM, painter, sculptor, designer; b. Mpls., July 9, 1916. B.A., U. Minn. Asst. dir. U. Minn. Art Gallery, 1946-48; resident artist, also dir. Rochester (Minn.) Art Ctr., 1948-64; vis. prof. U. Nebr., Lincoln, Minn.; vis. prof. art Macalester Coll., St. Paul, 1967-68, assoc. prof. art, 1969-74, prof. art, 1974-83, emeritus, 1983—. Exhbns. include Calif. Palace Legion of Honor, 1945, Mpls. Inst. Art. 1936-41, 59, St. Paul Art Gallery, 1946, 54, 57, U. Minn., 1939, San Francisco Mus. Art, 1948, Whitney Mus., 1951, Corcoran Gallery Art, 1950, Walker Art Ctr. traveling exhbn., 1950-52, Chgo., 1952, Carnegie Inst., 1952, Chgo. Art Inst., 1947, numerous others; one man exhbns. include Little Gallery, Madison, Wis., Waterloo (Iowa) Art Center, Women's City Club, St. Paul, Luther Coll., Decorah, Iowa, St. Paul Art Center, St. Olaf Coll., Minn., Rochester Art Center, 1948-58, 63, 80, Kilbridge-Bradley Art Gallery, Mpls., U. Nebr., 1950, Stephens Coll., 1950, Carlton Coll., 1951, Dayton (Ohio) Art Inst., 1952, Little Studio, N.Y.C., 1960-61, Walker Art Ctr., 1960, Central Luth. Ch., Mpls., 1983, Philbrook Art Ctr., Tulsa, Macalester Coll., 1982, retrospective, Tweed Gallery, U. Minn., 1966, Steensland Gallery; spl. invitational showing nat. conf. Stained Glass Assn. Am., 1980, Artbanque Gallery, Mpls., 1989, S.K. Gallery, Mpls., 1990; major watercolor show Premier Gallery, Mpls., 1991-92, Am. Contemporary Artist Premier Gallery, Mpls., 1992; major works include mural Mayo Clinic Bldg., Rochester, Minn., 1953, stained glass windows Temple of Aaron Sanctuary, 1956, mural Northwestern Nat. Bank, Rochester, 1957, stained glass Midwest Fed. Bldg.,

1968, copper relief Plymouth Congl. Ch., Lincoln, Nebr., 1968, stained glass Holiday Inn Central, Mpls., 1962, Meditation Chapel at U. Minn., 1965, St. Edward's Parish Ch., Austin, Minn., 1965, Vinje Luth. Ch., Willmar, Minn., 1980, Central Luth. Ch., Mpls., 1982, New Univ. Hosp., Mpls., 1986, New Univ. Music Bldg., Mpls., 1986, chapel at Mpls.-Midwest Fed. Bank Bldg., 1968, Mt. Zion Temple, St. Paul, 1973, brick mural YMCA-YWCA, Rochester, Minn., 1964, copper sculpture B'nai Abraham Synogogue, St. Louis Park, Minn., 1965, Coast to Coast Stores Hdqrs. Bldg., Edina, Minn., 1978, Temple of Israel, Mpls., 1981, sculpture in lobby Lincoln Gen. Hosp., 1967, copper relief sculpture U. Nebr., glass mobile 1st Bank, Crystal, Minn., 1986, New Law Sch. Bldg., 1975, 1st Nat. Bank, Sioux Falls, S.D., 1976, Twin Cities Fed. Bank Bldg., Mpls., 1978, Title Ins. Co., Mpls., 1978, Farm Credit Ctr., Lincoln, Nebr., 1982, copper relief Nationality Cultural Ctr., Internat. Inst., St. Paul, chapel doors United Hosps., St. Paul, glass mobile sculptures Wayzata (Minn.) Bank & Trust Co., Crystal Bank, New Univ. Hosp. Mpls., mixed relief sculpture Bryan Meml. Hosp., Lincoln, Nebr., brass sculpture Federated Ins. Co., Owatonna, Minn., stained glass relief sculpture of cross hanging over pulpit St. Mark's Luth. Ch., N. St. Paul, walnut sculpture Pen Corp., St. Paul, 1989, 91, atrium glass mobile (peace theme), St. Olaf Residence, Mpls., 1995, Valley Cmty. Presbyn. Ch., Robinsdale, Minn., 1993, sheet copper sculpture Eternal Light, Sholom Nursing Home, St. Paul, 1993, painting Luth. Brotherhood exec. dining room, Mpls., other sculptures and stained glass in various corps. and chs., pvt. residence, 1994; designer sets and costumes Minn. Opera prodn. The Abduction from the Seraglio (Mozart), 1979. Recipient awards from Mpls. Inst. Art, 1936, Minn. State Fair, 1937, 40, Walker Art Ctr. 1949, 51, Guild for Religious Architecture, 1973, AIA, 1973; honor award for stained glass Interfaith Forum on Religion, Art, and Architecture, 1981, 92; Ford Found. grantee. Mem. Nat. Soc. Mural Painters. Home and Studio: 5916 Walnut Ave Edina MN 55436

SALVADO, AUGUST J., think-tank executive. Dir., comdt. Water Reed Army Inst. of Rsch., Wash., D.C. Office: Walter Reed Army Inst Rsch Washington DC 20307-5100

SALVADORI, MARIO, mathematical engineer; b. Rome, Italy, Mar. 19, 1907; came to U.S., 1939; s. Riccardo and Ermelinda (Alatri) S.; m. Giuseppina Tagliacozzo, July 30, 1935 (div. June 1975); 1 child. Have H.; m. Carol B. Salvadori, Apr. 5, 1975. Dr. Civil Engring., U. Rome, 1930, Dr. Math. Physics, 1933; DSc, Columbia U., 1977; Dr. Fine Letters, New Sch. for Social Rsch., 1990; LHD, Lehman Coll., 1994. Prof. U. Rome (Italy) Sch. Engring., 1932-38, Columbia U., N.Y.C., 1940-90; chmn. Weidlinger Assocs., N.Y.C., 1957-90, hon. chmn., 1991—; founder, chmn. Salvadori Ednl. Ctr. on Built Environment, 1975-91, hon. chmn., 1993—. Author of 21 books; contbr. articles to profl. jours. Recipient over 20 awards from univs., engring. and archtl. socs. and ednl. assns., 1970-92. Fellow ASME, Am. Concrete Inst.; mem. ASCE (hon.), AIA (hon.). Democrat. Achievements include research in applied mathematics and engineering structures; 27 new routes and 3 virgin peaks climbed in the Eastern Alps. Home: 2 Beekman Pl New York NY 10022-8058 Office: Weidlinger Assocs 333 Seventh Ave New York NY 10001

SALVAGGIO, JOHN EDMOND, physician, educator; b. New Orleans, May 19, 1933; s. Louis and Zenobia Ann (Engman-Riley) S.; m. Anne Poillon, Apr. 19, 1958; children: John, Garry, Wayne, Peggy. B.S., Loyola U., New Orleans, 1954; M.D., La. State U., 1957. Diplomate: Am. Bd. Internal Medicine (bd. govs. 1973-81), Am. Bd. Allergy and Immunology (pres. 1975-78). Intern Charity Hosp., New Orleans, 1957-58; resident Charity Hosp., 1958-60; fellow, instr. Mass. Gen. Hosp. and Harvard U., 1961-63; prof. medicine La. State U., 1964-74; Henderson prof. medicine Tulane U., 1974—, chmn. dept. medicine, 1982-87; vice chancellor for rsch. Tulane Med. Ctr., 1988—; vis. prof. U. Colo., 1972-73; mem. pulmonary diseases adv. com. and immunologic scis. study sect. NIH. Contbr. over 400 articles to profl. jours. Served with USAR, 1959-65. Mem. AAAS, ACP, Am. Fedn. Clin. Rsch., Am. Bd. Allergy and Immunology (pres. 1975-78), Am. Acad. Allergy and Immunology (pres. 1985-86), Am. Bd. Internal Med. (bd. govs. 1975-80), Am. Assn. Immunologists, Am. Soc. Clin. Investigation, Am. Thoracic Soc. (governing council 1977-79), Assn. Am. Physicians, Soc. Exptl. Biology and Medicine, Collegium Internat. Allergy, Royal Soc. Medicine. Home: 5726 St Charles Ave New Orleans LA 70115-5052 Office: 1430 Tulane Ave New Orleans LA 70112-2699

SALVAGGIO, TONY JOE, banker; b. Hearne, Tex., Sept. 18, 1931; s. Joe Tony and Bonnie (Piccolo) S.; m. Kathy Skinner; children—Annette, Rosemarie. BBA, Tex. A&M U., 1956; grad., Sch. Banking of South, 1963-65. With Fed. Res. Bank Dallas, 1956—; sr. v.p., cashier, 1970—. Served with USN, 1949-53. Female Lodges: K.C; Rotary. Home: 7751 La Manga Dr Dallas TX 75248-3130 Office: Federal Reserve Bank Dallas 2200 N Pearl St Dallas TX 75201

SALVANESCHI, LUIGI, real estate and development executive, business educator; b. Casale, Italy, 1929; arrived in U.S., 1959; s. Ernesto and Carolina (Bassignana) S.; m. Lenore M. Rickels, Aug. 20, 1958; 1 child, Margherita Lina. Classical Maturity, Valsalice, Torino, Italy, 1950; PhD, Vatican U., Rome, 1958; cert. in real estate, UCLA, 1965. Restaurant mgr. McDonalds Co., Chgo., 1959-61; restaurant mgr. and supr. McDonalds Co., Los Angeles, 1961-63, real estate mgr., 1964-68; v.p. real estate McDonalds Co., Oakbrook, Ill., 1969-83; sr. v.p. real estate and constrn. Kentucky Fried Chicken, Louisville, 1983—; pres., COO, dir. Blockbuster Entertainment, Ft. Lauderdale, Fla., 1989-91; disting. adj. prof. Barry Univ., 1991—; adj. prof. Sch. Bus. U. Louisville, 1987. Served as 2d lt. in Italian Infantry, 1945-46. Recipient Outstanding Italo-Am. award Italian Am. Fedn., 1991; named Colonel of the Commonwealth of Ky., 1984. Mem. Nat. Assn. Real Estate Execs. (co-founder, bd. dirs.). Roman Catholic. Avocations: reading classics in Latin and Greek, mountain hiking. Office: Barry Univ Sch of Bus 11300 NE 2nd Ave Miami FL 33161-6628

SALVATY, BENJAMIN BENEDICT, lawyer; b. Chgo., Dec. 22, 1940; s. Benjamin Benedict and Marion Therese (Ryan) S.; m. Patircia Louise Recor, Aug. 29, 1964; children: Paul Benedict, Kathleen Anne. BBA, U. Notre Dame, 1962; JD, U. So. Calif., 1965. Bar: Calif. 1966, U.S. Dist. Ct. (no., cen., ea. and so. dists.) Calif., U.S.C. Appeals (9th cir.), U.S. Tax Ct., U.S. Supreme Ct. Sr. trial atty. Calif. Dept. Transp., 1966-79; gen. atty. The Atchison, Topeka and Santa Fe Railway Co., 1980-89; sr. ptnr. Hill, Farrer & Burrill, Los Angeles, 1990—. Mem. ABA (litigation sect. urban, state and local govt. law com. on condemnation, zoning and planning com.), Am. Judicature Soc., Internat. Right Way Assn., Irish Am. Bar Assn. (bd. dirs. 1985—, treas. 1991, sec. 1992, v.p. 1992-93, pres. 1993-94), Italian Am. Lawyers Assn., State Trial Attys. Assn. (pres. 1975-79), Calif. State Bar (chmn. condemnation com. 1987-88, vice chmn. 1986-87), Pasadena Bar Assn., L.A. County Bar Assn. (condemnation and land valuation com.). Office: Hill Farrer & Burrill Union Bank Sq 35th Fl 445 S Figueroa St Los Angeles CA 90071-1602

SALVENDY, GAVRIEL, industrial engineer; b. Budapest, Hungary, Sept. 30, 1938; came to U.S., 1968; s. Paul and Katarina (Brown) S.; m. Catherine Vivien Dees, Apr. 1, 1966; children: Laura Dorit, Kevin David. MSc in Engring. Prodn, U. Birmingham, Eng., 1966, PhD, 1968; Doctorate (hon.), Academia Sinica, 1995. Asst. prof. indsl. engring. SUNY, Buffalo, 1968-71; mem. faculty Purdue U., 1971—; prof. indsl. engring., chmn. human factors program, 1977, Fulbright distinguished prof., 1979-80, 81-82, NEC prof. indsl. engring., 1984—; chmn. Internat. Commn. on Human Aspects in Computing, Switzerland, 1986-91. Co-author: Prediction and Development of Industrial Work Performance, 1973, Human Aspects of Computer Aided Design, 1987; sr. editor: Machine-Pacing and Occupational Stress, 1981, Social, Ergonomic and Stress Aspects of Work with Computers, 1987, Designing and Using Human-Computer Interfaces and Knowledge Based Systems, 1989; editor: Handbook of Industrial Engineering, 1982, 2d edit., 1992, Human Computer Interaction, 1984, Handbook of Human Factors, 1987, Cognitive Engineering in the Design of Human Computer Interaction and Expert Systems, 1987; founding editor: Internat. Jour. on Human-Computer Interaction, Internat. Jour. Human Factors in Mfg.; co-editor: Work with Computers: Organizational Management, Stress and Health Aspects, 1989, Human-Computer Interaction: Software and Hardware Interfaces, 1993, Human-Computer Interaction: Applications and Case Studies, 1993, Design of Work and Development of Personnel in Advanced Manufacturing,

1994, Organization and Management of Advanced Manufacturing, 1994; contbr. articles to profl. jours., chpts. to books. Pres. Lafayette Jewish Sunday Sch., 1980-81. Recipient Mikhail Vasilievich Lomonosov medal USSR Acad. Sci., 1991. Fellow NAE, APA, Inst. Indsl. Engrs. (sr., Phil Carroll award 1973), Human Factors Soc. (past officer), Ergonomics Soc. (hon., life mem.). Office: Purdue U Sch Indsl Engring West Lafayette IN 47907

SALVESON, MELVIN ERWIN, business executive, educator; b. Brea, Calif., Jan. 16, 1919; s. John T. and Elizabeth (Green) S.; m. Joan Y. Stipek, Aug. 22, 1944; children: Eric C., Kent Erwin. B.S., U. Calif. at Berkeley, 1941; M.S., Mass. Inst. Tech., 1947; Ph.D., U. Chgo., 1952. Cons. McKinsey & Co., N.Y.C., 1948-49; asst. prof., dir. mgmt. sci. research U. Calif. at Los Angeles, 1949-54; mgr. advanced data systems Gen. Electric Co., Louisville and N.Y.C., 1954-57; pres. Mgmt. Scis. Corp., Los Angeles, 1957-67; group v.p. Control Data/CEIR, Inc., 1967-68; pres. Electronic Currency Corp., 1968—; chmn. OneCard Internat., Inc., 1983-92, Univ. Trans. System Inc., 1992—; founder and pres. Southern Calif. Econ. Alliance, 1992—; bd. dirs. Diversified Earth Scis., Inc., Eco Rx Inc., Eexcel Enterprise Inc., Veritas et Justus Inc., Algeran, Inc., Electronic Currency Corp.; founder Master Card System, Los Angeles, 1966; chmn. Corporate Strategies Internat.; prof. bus. Pepperdine U. 1972-85; adj. prof. U. So. Calif.; adviser data processing City of Los Angeles, 1962-64; futures forecasting IBM, 1957-61; adviser strategic systems planning USAF, 1961-67; info. systems Calif. Dept. Human Resources, 1972-73, City Los Angeles Automated Urban Data Base, 1962-67; tech. transfer NASA, 1965-70, others; mem. bd. trustees, Long Beach City Coll. Contbr. articles to profl. jours. Served to lt. comdr. USNR, 1941-46. Named to Long Beach City Coll. Hall of Fame; recipient Dist. Alumnus 1992 award Calif. Coll. System, 1992. Fellow AAAS; mem. Inst. Mgmt. Sci. (founder, past pres.). Republican. Club: Founders (Los Angeles Philharmonic Orch.), Calif. Yacht. Home: 130 Marguerita Ave Apt 8 Santa Monica CA 90402-1652

SALYER, STEPHEN LEE, broadcast executive; b. Lexington, Ky., July 20, 1950; s. Ralph Conley Salyer and Margaret (Greenlee) Miles; m. Martha Ingels Ruddy, Apr. 21, 1985; children: Samuel Wilmot, Duncan Davis, Clara Josephine. BA, Davidson Coll., 1972; MPA, Harvard U., 1975. Pres. Citizens' Com. on Population and the Am. Future, Washington, 1972-73; cons. to John D. Rockefeller 3d Rockefeller Family Assocs., N.Y.C., 1973-75; assoc. pub. issues program Population Coun., N.Y.C., 1977-79; asst. to the pres. Ednl. Broadcasting Corp., Sta. WNET TV, N.Y.C., 1975-76, v.p. corp. affairs, 1979-80, v.p. program devel. and mktg., 1981-82, sr. v.p. edn. divsn., 1982-86, sr. v.p. mktg. and comm., 1986-88; pres., CEO Pub. Radio International, Mpls., 1988—, also bd. dirs.; bd. dirs. Minn. Meeting; mem. nat. adv. com. Save the Children, 1991—, Nat. Peace Found., 1991—. Coauthor: (with James J. Bausch) Toward Safe, Convenient and Effective Contraceptives, 1978. Mem. Nat. Commn. on Population Growth and the Am. Future, Washington, 1970-72. Mem. Harvard Club (N.Y.C.), Mpls. Club. Avocations: tennis, reading. Home: 1801 Irving Ave S Minneapolis MN 55403-2822 Office: Pub Radio Internat 100 N 6th St Ste 900 A Minneapolis MN 55403-1505

SALZBERG, BETTY JOAN, computer science educator; b. Denver, Jan. 19, 1944; d. Theodore Herbert and Hilda (Herzel) S.; m. Harold Mead Stark, June 21, 1964 (div. 1977); 1 child, Pearl Stark; m. Lawrence Edward Morris, Sept. 2, 1978. BA in Math., UCLA, 1964; MA in Math., U. Mich., 1966, PhD in Math., 1971. Asst. prof. math. Northeastern U., Boston, 1971-77, assoc. prof. math., 1977-82, assoc. prof. Coll. Computer Sci., 1982-90, prof. Coll. Computer Sci., 1990—. Author: An Introduction to Database Design, 1986, File Structures: An Analytic Approach, 1988; contbr. articles to tech. publs. NSF rsch. grantee, 1988—. Mem. Assn. Computing Machinery, Spl. Interest Group Mgmt. of Data Assn. Computing Machinery, IEEE Computer Soc. Avocations: white-water solo canoeing. Office: Northeastern U Coll Computer Sci Boston MA 02115

SALZBERG, BRIAN MATTHEW, neuroscience and physiology educator; b. N.Y.C., Sept. 4, 1942; s. Saul and Betty Bernice (Jacobs) S. BS, Yale U., 1963; AM, Harvard U., 1965, PhD, 1971. Woodrow Wilson fellow in physics Harvard U., Cambridge, Mass., 1963-64, rsch. asst. in high energy physics, 1964-71; rsch. assoc. physiology Yale Med. Sch., New Haven, 1971-75; asst. prof. physiology U. Pa. Sch. Dental Medicine, Phila., 1975-80; assoc. prof. physiology U. Pa., Phila., 1980-82; prof. physiology U. Pa. Sch. Medicine, Phila., 1982-92, prof. neurosci. and physiology, 1992—; Arturo Rosenblueth vis. prof. CINVESTAV, Mexico City, 1987. Contbr. over 100 sci. articles on neurophysiology and biophysics to profl. jours. Trustee Marine Biol. Lab., Woods Hole, Mass., 1980-84, 87—. Guest fellow Royal Soc., Cambridge U., 1991, fellow Japan Soc. for Promotion of Sci., Tokyo, 1989, STEPS fellow Marine Biol. Lab., 1977, 78; recipient Marine Biol. Lab. award, 1981. Fellow Am. Phys. Soc., AAAS; mem. Biophys. Soc. (exec. bd. 1987-90), Soc. Gen. Physiology (coun. 1986-88), Phi Beta Kappa, Sigma Xi. Achievements include co-discovery of voltage-sensitive merocyanine dyes; application of optical methods to cell physiology and neuroscience. Avocation: distance running (2:49:30 in B.A.A. Marathon, 1978). Home: 4632 Spruce St Philadelphia PA 19139-4540 Office: U Pa 234 Stemmler Hall Philadelphia PA 19104-6074

SALZBERG, EMMETT RUSSELL, new product developer; b. N.Y.C., Aug. 15, 1924; s. Herman and Freda (Russell) S.; m. Ilene Roslyn Greenhut, Oct. 29, 1960; children: Shelby Russell, Laurie Russell. Grad., Bronx High Sch. of Sci., 1941; student, Columbia U., CCNY. Pres. Dixey Tapes Corp., Stratford, Conn., 1969-85; sr. product mgr. Tuck Tape, New Rochelle, N.Y., 1986-88; pres. Pickups, Inc., Trumbull, Conn., 1988-94, Dixey Tapes Corp., Stratford, 1993—; cons. Tape div. Shuford Mills, Hickory, N.C., 1990-92. Patentee telephone answering equipment. Mem. Trumbull Yr.-Round. Edn. Feasibility Study Com. Served with U.S. Army, 1943-45, PTO. Mem. Mensa, Inventors Assn. Conn. (co-founder, past mem. exec. bd.). Democrat. Jewish. Avocations: target shooting, photography. Home: 37 Partridge Ln Trumbull CT 06611-4919 Office: Dixey Tapes Corp 959 Main St Stratford CT 06497-7400

SALZER, JOHN MICHAEL, technical and management consultant; b. Vienna, Austria, Sept. 12, 1917; came to U.S. 1940; s. Siegfried and Rose (Deutsch) S.; m. Eva R. Arvay, Mar. 26, 1944; children: Arleen, Ronald, Myra, Gary. BSEE, Case Inst. Tech., 1947, MSEE, 1948; ScDEE, MIT, 1951. Instr. in mechanics and electronics Case Inst. Tech., Cleve., 1947-48; rsch. assoc. Electronic Computer Lab., MIT, Cambridge, Mass., 1948-51; mem. tech. staff Hughes Aircraft Co., El Segundo, Calif., group mgr., 1951-54; asst. dir rsch. lab. Maganvox Co., L.A., 1954-59, dir. systems, 1959; dir. Intellectronics Labs. TRW Inc., 1959-62, spl. asst. to exec. v.p. corp. planning, 1962-63; v.p. tech. and planning Librascope div. Singer Co. Inc., 1963-69; pres. Salzer Tech. Enterprises Inc., tech. and mgmt. cons., Santa Monica, Calif., 1968—. Author: Evolutionary Design of Complex Systems, 1961, Sampled-Data Theory, 1961. Fellow IEEE, Inst. Advancement Engring; mem. Internat. Soc. Hybrid Microelectronics, Semicondr. Equipment and Materials Inst., Sigma Xi, Tau Beta Pi, Eta Kappa Nu. Office: Salzer Tech Enterprises Inc 909 Berkeley St Santa Monica CA 90403-2307

SALZMAN, ARTHUR GEORGE, architect; b. Chgo., June 20, 1929; s. Russell Harvey Salzman and Mildred Olive (Olsen) Erickson; m. Joan Marie Larson, Aug. 16, 1952; children: Lisa Jo Salzman Braucher, David Ralph. BS in Archtl. Engring., U. Ill., 1952; MArch, Ill. Inst. Tech., 1960. Registered architect, Ill. Architect Skidmore, Owings & Merrill, Chgo., 1960, Mies van der Rohe, Arch., Chgo., 1960-69; assoc. The Office of Mies Van Der Rohe, Chgo., 1969-81; v.p. FCL Assocs., Chgo., 1981-86; ex. v.p. Lohan Assocs., Chgo., 1986-91; pvt. practice architecture Evanston, Ill., 1992—; mem. bldgs. restructuring com. City of Chgo., 1994—. Mem. Chgo. Com. on High Rise Bldgs.; bd. dirs. Savoy Aires, Evanston, 1985-88, 90-93, pres. 1992-93; v.p. Chgo. area Unitarian-Universalist Coun., Chgo., 1974-76. Cpl. U.S. Army, 1952-54. Mem. AIA (bd. dirs. Chgo. chpt. 1992—, sec. 1994—), Constrn. Specifications Inst., Bldg. Ofcls. and Code Adminstrs. Internat. (profl.), Coun. on Tall Bldgs. and Urban Habitat, Wind Engring. Rsch. Coun., Precast-Prestressed Concrete Inst., Cliff Dwellers Club. Avocations: community theater, choral singing, sailing. Home: 1018 Greenwood St Evanston IL 60201-4212 Office: 1569 Sherman Ave Ste 200 Evanston IL 60201-4486

SALZMAN, DAVID ELLIOT, entertainment industry executive; b. Bklyn., Dec. 1, 1943; s. Benjamin and Rose Harriet (Touby) S.; m. Sonia Camelia Gonsalves, Oct. 19, 1968; children: Daniel Mark, Andrea Jessica, Adam Gabriel. B.A., Bklyn. Coll., 1965; M.A., Wayne State U., 1967. Dir. TV ops. Wayne State U., 1966-67; producer Lou Gordon Program, 1967-70; program mgr. Sta. WKBD-TV, Detroit, 1970-71; program mgr. Sta. KDKA-TV, Pitts., 1971-72, gen. mgr., 1973-75; program mgr. Sta. KYW-TV, Phila., 1972-73; chmn. bd. Group W Prodns., N.Y.C and Los Angeles, 1975—; founder, pres. United Software Assocs., 1980-81; creator News Info. Weekly Service, 1981; exec. v.p. Teleptictures Corp., 1980-84, vice chmn., 1984; pres. Lorimar Telepictures Corp. (merger Telepictures and Lorimar, Inc.), 1985-90, Lorimar TV, 1986-90; creator Newscope: Nat. TV News Cooperative, 1983; pres., chief exec. officer David Salzman Entertainment, Burbank, Calif., 1990—; co-CEO Quincy Jones-David Salzman Entertainment (QDE), 1993—; exec. prodr. Jenny Jones Show, 1991—; officer Q West, 1994; co-owner QD7 Interactive, 1994; bd. dirs. Premiere Radio, 1994; guest lectr. at schs.; bd. govs. Films of Coll. and Univ. Students. Contbr. articles to Variety and numerous communications trade pubs. Bd. dirs. Pitts. Civic Light Opera, Am. Blood Bank, Pitts., Hebrew Inst., Jewish Community Ctr., Harrison, N.Y., Temple Etz Chaim, USC Sch. Cinema-TV, Emory U. Ctr. for Leadership, Emory Bus. Sch., Bklyn. Coll. Found. Recipient award Detroit chpt. Am. Women in Radio and TV, 1969, award Golden Quill, 1971, award Golden Gavel, 1971, local Emmy award, 1972, award AP, 1974, Gold medal Broadcast Promotion Assn., 1983, Lifetime Achievement award Bklyn. Coll., 1990, Disting. Alumnus award, Golden Plate award Am. Acad. Achievement, 1995; BPME Gold medal San Francisco Film Festival, 1984, N.Y., 1985, Chgo., 1986, Tree of Life award Jewish Nat. Fund, 1988. Mem. Acad. TV Arts and Scis., Nat. Assn. TV Program Execs., Radio-TV News Dirs. Assn., Am. Mgmt. Assn., Am. Film Inst., Brooklyn Coll. Found. Office: QDE Entertainment Ste 503 3800 Barham Blvd Los Angeles CA 90068 "Courage is the first of human qualities because it is the quality which guarantees all the others."

SALZMAN, ERIC, artistic director; b. N.Y.C., Sept. 8, 1933; s. Samuel and Frances (Klenett) S.; m. Lorna Jackson, Dec. 24, 1956; Eva, Stephanie. BA in Music with honors, Columbia U., 1954; MFA, Princeton U., 1956. Music critic N.Y. Times, N.Y.C., 1958-62; dir. music Sta. WBAI-FM, N.Y.C., 1962-63, 68-72; music critic N.Y. Herald Tribune, N.Y.C., 1963-67; asst. prof. Queens Coll. CUNY, Queens, 1967-68; artistic dir. Quog Music Theater, N.Y.C., 1970-80; co-founder, artistic dir. Am. Music Theater Festival, Phila., 1981-93; founder, co-artistic dir. MusicTheater/N.Y., 1994—; mem. guest faculty NYU, Yale U., Banff Ctr. for Arts, Can., Conservatoire Nationale, Lyon, France; organizer ann. conf. Small Scale Opera and Music Theatre, Brussels, 1992, Antwerp, Belgium, 1993, Colmar, 1994. Principal works include: (compositions) String Quartet, 1955, Inventions, 1957, In Praise on the Owl and the Cuckoo, 1963, Foxes and Hedgehogs, 1964, Queens College, 1966, Larynx Music, 1966, Helix, 1971, Fantasy on Lazarus, 1974, Accord, 1975, Variations on Sacred Harp Tunes, 1982, (radio opera) Voices, 1971, (mime-dance prodn.) The Peloponnesian War, 1967, (multimedia participatory work) Feedback 1968, The Nuder Paper Sermon, 1969, (multimedia environ. work) Can Men Survive, 1968, (media poem) Ecolog, 1982, (musical theater prodn.) Saying Something, 1972, Biograffiti, 1972, Lazarus, 1973, (media and live performance piece) Toward a New American Opera, 1985, (adaptations) Strike Up the Band, 1984, Love Life, 1990, The Silent Twins, 1992, (with Michael Stahl) The Conjuror, 1974, (musical theater prodn.) Stauf, 1976, Noah, 1978, The Passion of Simple Simon, 1979, Boxes, 1982 (Seagram Prodn. award), (opera buffa) Civilization and its Discontents, 1980 (Prix Italia award Assn European Broadcasters); prodr., dir. The Unknown Kurt Weill, Silverlake, Civilization and its Discontents, The Tango Project (Record of Yr. award Stereo Rev.), Two to Tango, The Palm Court, The Waltz Project, Moore's Irish Melodies, A Portrait Album, Notebooks of Anna Magdalena Bach, An Old-Fashioned Christmas, Revelation in the Courthouse Park, Casino Paradise; recs. include Civilization and its Discontents, Wiretap, The Nude Paper Sermon, Noah, Accord; author: 20th Century Music: An Introduction, 1988; editor Musical Quar., 1984-91; contbg. editor, critic Stereo Rev., N.Y.C., 1970—; contbr. N.Y. Times, New York Herald-Tribune, N.Y. Mag., others. Fulbright scholar St. Cecilia Acad., 1956-58, Darmstadt Ferienkurse, 1957; recipient Armstrong, Prix Italia radio awards. Mem. Linnaen Soc. (coun. mem.), South Fork Nat. History Soc. (coun. mem.). Avocations: natural history, ornithology. Home: 29 Middagh St Brooklyn NY 11201-1339 Office: MusicTheater/NY 345 E 56th St New York NY 10022

SALZMAN, MARILYN B. WOLFSON, service company executive; b. Chgo., Dec. 25, 1943; d. Joseph and Sera (Krol) Wolfson; 1 son, Lawrence Todd. Student, U. Ill., Barat Coll., Lake Forest, Ill., 1961-64. Adminstrv. project asst. Sci. Research Assocs., Chgo., 1964-70; reporter Suburban Trib of Chgo. Tribune, 1979-80; pres. MWS Assocs., Los Angeles and Fullerton, Calif., 1980—; exec. adminstrv. dir. Crystal Tips of No. Ill., Inc., 1980-83; dir. adminstrn. Ice Dispensers, Inc., 1981-83, Sani-Serv of Ill., Inc., 1981-83; adminstrv. and organizational cons. 1140 Corp., 1980-83; adminstrv. dir. Iceman's Ico Co., Inc., 1980-83; founder, moderator DWC Workshops, 1984; dir. data processing Florence Crittenton Svs., Orange County, 1984-86, dir. MIS, 1986-88, dir. support svcs., 1988-92, bd. dirs. ways and means com., 1991—, dir. adminstrn. & contract compliance, 1992-94, dir. devel. & cmty. svcs., 1994—; pres. MWS Prodns., L.A. and Fullerton, Calif., 1990—; exec. producer (TV series) The State of the Child, 1990-91; panelist computers in residential treatment Child Welfare League Am. Biennial Conf. Workshop, 1986; presenter outcomes and svc. evaluation North Am. Out-of-Home Care Conf., 1991, families & children in residential treatment Calif. State U. Child Devel. Conf., Fullerton, 1994, advancing your message Child Welfare League of Am. Nat. Conf., 1995. Active Friends of Fullerton Library, Boy Scouts Am.; panelist Child Welfare League Am., Biennial Conf. Workshop; chmn. govtl., pub. affairs coms. Orange County Assn. of Children's Svcs.; mem. steering com. Orange County UN Assn. Yr. of Family, 1993—; mem. com. Internat. Yr. of the Family Exhibit & Celebration, Bowers Mus., 1994; mem. planning com. Orange County Summit for Children, 1994—; exec. com. Anne Frank Orange County Organizing Com., 1994—; mem. adv. com. Child Devel. & Family Life Dept., Fullerton Coll., 1994; mem. bd. mgrs. N. Orange County Family YMCA, 1995—, mem. child care adv. com., 1995—; facilitator Orange County Together, 1994—. Mem. Calif. Assn. Svcs. for Children (rsch. and evaluation com. 1993—), Soroptimist Internat. of Fullerton, Mgmt. Forum, Women's Am. ORT, Fullerton C. of C. (indsl. com. 1994—). Contbr. articles to newspapers and indsl. jours.

SALZMAN, RICHARD WILLIAM, artist representative; b. Los Angeles, Nov. 22, 1958; s. Paul and Anne (Meyersburg) S.; student public schs., Los Angeles. Stockboy, Marathon Clothing, Los Angeles, 1976-77, salesman, 1977, sales and mgmt. trainee, 1977-78; br. mgr., San Francisco, 1978-80, San Diego, 1980-82; artist rep., 1982—. Tchr. freelance bus. practices San Diego City Coll. Contbr. illustrations Communication Arts mag., 1992, Graphic Arts of the World. Recipient 2 Gold medals N.Y. Soc. Illustrators. Mem. adv. bd. Fashion Careers of Calif. Mem. Union of Concerned Scientists, Green Peace, Environ. Def. Fund, Coalition for Non-Nuclear World, Communicating Arts Group San Diego (2 Gold awards 1989), Internat. Assn. Bus. Communicators, Soc. Photographers and Artists Reps., Am. Inst. Graphic Arts (founder, v.p. San Diego chpt., mem. nat. task force), Graphic Artist Guild. Democrat. Home: 716 Sanchez St San Francisco CA 94114-2929 Office: Salzman Internat 716 Sanchez St San Francisco CA 94114

SALZMAN, ROBERT JAY, accountant; b. Bklyn., Dec. 7, 1941; s. Irving and Sydelle (Feingold) S.; m. Constance A. Freeman, Sept. 16, 1990. BA, Allegheny Coll., Meadville, Pa., 1962; MBA, U. Pa., 1965; JD, N.Y. Law Sch., 1972. Bar: N.Y. 1973; CPA, N.Y. Acct. N.Y.C., 1965—; pvt. practice Robert J. Salzman, CPA, P.C., N.Y.C., 1970—. Home: 10 East End Ave New York NY 10021 also: 82 Sycamore Dr East Hampton NY 11937 also: 2801 NE 183d St North Miami Beach FL 33160 Office: 845 3d Ave New York NY 10022

SALZSTEIN, RICHARD ALAN, biomedical engineer, researcher; b. Elkins Park, Pa., Sept. 16, 1959; s. Eli and Lorraine (Reese) S.; m. Sharon Lazar; children: Hillary, Lauren. BS in Engring., U. Pa. 1981, MS in Engring., 1982, PhD in Bioengring., 1989. Rsch. fellow U. Pa., Phila., 1981-85; rsch. scientist Hercules, Inc., Wilmington, Del., 1986—. Mem. Soc. for Biomaterials, Orthopaedic Rsch. Soc., Tau Beta Pi. Recipient Kappa Delta award Bioelectrical Repair & Growth Soc., 1985; NSF fellow, 1981-85. Avocations: racquetball, skiing. Office: Hercules Inc Rsch Ctr 500 Hercules Rd Wilmington DE 19808-1513

SAM, DAVID, federal judge; b. Hobart, Ind., Aug. 12, 1933; s. Andrew and Flora (Toma) S.; m. Betty Jean Brennan, Feb. 1, 1957; children: Betty Jean, David Dwight, Daniel Scott, Tamara Lynn, Pamela Rae, Daryl Paul, Angie, Sheyla. BS, Brigham Young U., 1957; JD, Utah U., 1960. Bar: Utah 1960, U.S. Dist. Ct. Utah 1966. Sole practice and ptnr. Duchesne, Utah, 1963-76; dist. judge State of Utah, 1976-85; judge U.S. Dist. Ct. Utah, Salt Lake City, 1985—; atty. City of Duchesne, 1963-72; Duchesne County atty., 1966-72; commr. Duchesne, 1972-74; mem. adv. com. Codes of Conduct of Jud. Conf. U.S., 1987-91, Jud. Coun. of 10th Cir., 1991-93; mem. U.S. Del. to Romania, Aug. 1991. Chmn. Jud. Nomination Com. for Cir. Ct. Judge, Provo, Utah, 1983; bd. dirs. Water Resources, Salt Lake City, 1973-76. Served to capt. JAGC, USAF, 1961-63. Mem. Utah State Bar Assn., Am. Judicature Soc., Supreme Ct. Hist. Soc., Am. Inns of Ct. VII (counselor 1986-89), A. Sherman Christensen Am. Inn of Ct. I (counselor 1989—), Utah Jud. Conf. (chmn. 1982—), Utah Dist. Judges Assn. (pres. 1982-83. Mem. LDS Ch. Avocations: beekeeping, reading, sports, cooking chinese food. Office: US Dist Ct 148 US Courthouse 350 S Main St Salt Lake City UT 84101

SAM, JOSEPH, retired university dean; b. Gary, Ind., Aug. 15, 1923; s. Andrew and Flora (Toma) S.; m. Frances Adickes, Sept. 11, 1945; children—Sherrie, Joseph A., Suzanne F. Student, Drake U., 1942-43; B.S., U. S.C., 1948; Ph.D., Kans. U., 1951. Sr. research chemist McNeil Labs., Phila., 1951-54; research group leader Bristol Labs., Syracuse, N.Y., 1955-57; sr. scientist E.I. duPont de Nemours & Co., Inc., 1957-59; faculty U. Miss. 1959-86, prof. pharm. chemistry, 1961-68, chmn. dept., 1963-68, dir. univ. research, 1968-81, assoc. vice chancellor research, 1981-86; dean U. Miss. (Grad. Sch.), 1968-86; Fulbright lectr. Cairo U., 1965-66. Mem. Am. Pharm. Assn. (found. research achievement award in pharm. and medicinal chemistry 1968), Sigma Xi, Rho Chi, Phi Lambda Upsilon, Phi Kappa Phi. Home: PO Box 351 University MS 38677-0351

SAM, PIERRE DESFORGES, ambassador; b. St. Louis North, Haiti, May 23, 1925; s. Felix D. and Exantucia (Poux) S.; m. Conceptia Geffrar; children: Jean-Renaud, Pierre Richard, Marlene, Donald. BS in Agrl. Engring., U. Haiti, 1945; BSA, U. Mayaguez, P.R., 1946; certification, U. New Mex., 1951; student, IICA, Costa Rica, 1957. Bar: Haiti, 1953. Project mgr. U.S. Ops. Mission, Gonave, St. Raphael, Haiti, 1945-53; nat. supr. U.S. Ops. Mission Extension, Port-Au-Prince, Haiti, 1953-55; project. mgr. SCIPA Haiti, 1955-62; regional officer U.N., Rome, 1962-63; extension officer Gov. of Haiti, Africa, S. Am., Africa, 1963-80; Minister of Planning Gov. of Haiti, Port-Au-Prince, 1981-82, Minister of Agriculture, 1982; Hatian Ambassador Washington, 1986-88; sr. cons., pvt. cons., mgr. U.S. AID/Soc. d'Etudes et de Mise en Valeur, Haiti. Minister of State, Haiti, 1981-82. Recipient rank of Rising Star from Pres. of Taiwan, 1981, Chevalier of the Order of Nat. Merit Haiti; Hon. Citizen of Los Angeles, 1987, Oakland, Calif., 1987. Mem. U.S. Nat. Assn. of Agrl. Engrs., U.S. Acad. of Scis., FAO/UN Internat. Group on Agrl. Extension, Smithsonian. Roman Catholic. Clubs: Nat. Press, Washington Internat. Lodge: Rotary. Avocations: soccer, tennis, music. Office: Embassy of Haiti 2311 Massachusetts Ave NW Washington DC 20008-2802

SAMAAN, NAGUIB ABDELMALIK, endocrinologist; b. Girga, Egypt, Apr. 2, 1925; s. Abdelmalik and Amasil Hanna S.; m. Jean Moffatt, Nov. 18, 1961; children—Sarah Ann, Mary Elizabeth, Jane Susan, Catherine Thia, Michael James. M.B., Ch.B., Alexandria (Egypt) U., 1951; D.M. in Internal Medicine, 1953; Ph.D. in Medicine, U. London, 1964. Rotating intern Alexandria U. Hosp., 1951-52, resident, 1952-54; sr. med. resident, instr., 1954-55; sr. research fellow Chest Inst., Brompton Hosp., London, 1955-56, Neurology Inst., Queen Sq., London, 1956; clin. fellow Postgrad. Med. Sch., London, 1957; clin. asst. prof. dept. endocrinology and therapeutics, asst. physician Royal Infirmary, Edinburgh, Scotland, 1957; sr. med. resident North Cambridge (Eng.) Hosps., 1958-60; staff physician, asst. prof., sr. research fellow Royal Postgrad. Med. Sch., London, 1960-64; research asso., asst. physician and endocrinologist Case Western Res. U., Cleve., 1964-66; staff physician, asst. prof. dept. internal medicine U. Iowa Hosps., Iowa City, 1966-69; med. staff physician and endocrinologist VA Hosp., Iowa City, 1966-69; chief sect. endocrinology U. Tex. M.D. Anderson Hosp. and Tumor Inst., Houston, 1969—; asso. internist, assoc. prof. medicine U. Tex. M.D. Anderson Hosp. and Tumor Inst., 1969-72, internist, prof. medicine, 1972—; Samaan prof. U. Tex. Md. Anderson Cancer Ctr.; prof. medicine and physiology U. Tex. Grad. Sch. Biomed. Scis., Houston, 1969-72, prof., 1972—; prof. internal medicine U. Tex. M.D. Anderson Hosp. and Tumor Inst. and U. Tex. Med. Sch., Houston, 1973—; dep. chmn. dept. of medicine, 1983—; cons., attending physician dept. internal medicine Hermann Hosp., Houston, 1970—. Co-editor: Endocrine Tumors, 1990; contbr. numerous articles to med. jours. Brit. Med. Research Council grantee, 1962-64; NIH grantee, 1969—; Am. Cancer Soc. grantee, 1971—. Fellow Royal Coll. Physicians (Scotland) Royal Coll. Physicians (Eng.), A.C.P.; mem. Brit. Med. Assn., AMA, Am. Endocrine Soc., Am. Fedn. Clin. Research, Am. Physiol. Soc., Fedn. Am. Socs. Exptl. Biology, Central Soc. Clin. Research, Soc. Gynecologic Investigation, N.Y. Acad. Sci., Harris County Med. Soc., Houston Soc. Internal Medicine, Am. Thyroid Assn., Am. Diabetes Assn., Internat. Platform Assn. Club: Nottingham Forest (Houston). Home: 14315 Heatherfield Dr Houston TX 77079-7407

SAMALIN, EDWIN, lawyer, educator; b. N.Y.C., Sept. 19, 1935; s. Harry Louis and Sydell (Fisher) S.; children: David Seth, Andrew Evan, Jonathan Daniel. B.S., U. R.I., 1957; J.D., N.Y. Law Sch., 1962. Bar: N.Y. 1963, U.S. Supreme Ct. 1976. Tax atty. Electric Bond & Share Co., N.Y.C., 1963; ptnr. Samalin & Sklaver, Yorktown Heights, N.Y., 1969-78; pvt. practice law, Yorktown Heights, 1963-69, 78-84; mng. ptnr. Yorktown Office Park Assocs., Yorktown Heights, 1971—; pres. Samalin & Bock, P.C., Yorktown Heights, 1984—; adj. faculty Mercy Coll., Dobbs Ferry, N.Y., 1974-92; commodity coms. Murlas Commodities, Yorktown Heights, 1982-85; ptnr. Patterson (N.Y.) Realty Assocs., 1983—; pres. Sammark Realty Corp., Westchester, N.Y., 1984—, Old Smoke House Realty Corp., 1987—, Atty.'s Asset Mgmt. Corp., Registered Investment Advisors, 1992—; Dem. candidate for County Legislature, 1973. Capt. U.S. Army, 1957-59. Mem. N.Y. State Bar Assn., Westchester County Bar Assn. (chair atty. client dispute com.), Yorktown Bar Assn. (pres. 1982, Man of Yr. 1983), Am. Arbitration Assn. (arbitrator 1974—). Phi Delta Phi. Home: 951A Heritage Hills Dr Somers NY 10589-1913 Office: Samalin & Bock PC 2000 Maple Hill St Yorktown Heights NY 10598-4122

SAMANOWITZ, RONALD ARTHUR, lawyer; b. N.Y.C., June 1, 1944; s. Sam and Thelma (Levin) S.; m. Ann Frieda Weisman, Dec. 18, 1971; 1 child, Samuel. ABA, CUNY, 1965; JD, Bklyn. Law Sch., 1967. Bar: N.Y. 1968, U.S. Dist. Ct. (ea. and so. dists.) N.Y. 1974, U.S. Supreme Ct. 1991. Ptnr. Krakower, Samanowitz & Goldman, N.Y.C., 1968-86, Resnicoff, Samanowitz, Endzweig & Brawer, Great Neck, N.Y., 1986-90, Samanowitz & Endzweig, Great Neck, N.Y., 1990—. Pres. Greater Fresh Meadows Civic Assn., Flushing, N.Y., 1984-85, award for Civic Svc. 1985, Flower Hill Civic Assn., 1992. Mem. Brandeis Lawyers Assn. (sec. 1985—), Queens Bar Assn. (family law com.), Nassau Bar Assn. (plaintiff roundtable 1988—), N.Y. State Trial Lawyers Assn. (gov. L.I. divsn.), Great Neck Lawyers Assn. (pres.). Avocation: marathon running. Office: Samanowitz & Endzweig 98 Cuttermill Rd Great Neck NY 11021-3006

SAMARTINI, JAMES ROGERS, appliance company executive; b. Cleve., Apr. 13, 1935; s. Leonard Henry and Grace Rogers (Tully) S.; m. Irene Ann Kurnava, Sept. 16, 1961 (dec. June 1994); children: David L., James F., Patrick R. AB, Dartmouth Coll., 1957; MBA, Harvard U., 1961. Fin. supr. Ford Motor Co., Dearborn, Mich., 1966-72; v.p. fin. and adminstrn. Thonet Industries Inc., York, Pa., 1972-74; asst. controller Mead Corp., Dayton, 1974-78, assoc. treas., 1974-78, 1978-79, v.p. fin. resources, 1982-86, v.p. chief fin. officer, 1986-91; exec. v.p., chief adminstrv. officer Whirlpool Corp., Benton Harbor, Mich., 1992—; bd. dirs. Peoples State Bank, St. Joseph, Mich. Chmn. bd. trustees Whirlpool Found., 1993—; trustee Dayton Opera Assn., 1977-86, pres., 1985-86; mem. adv. bd. Salvation Army; bd. dirs. Epilepsy Assn. Western Ohio, 1986, S.W. Mich. Symphony Orch., 1991-93. Mem. Fin. Execs. Inst. (dir. 1983-86). Home: 1315 Lake Blvd Saint Joseph MI 49085-1547 Office: Whirlpool Corp 2000 M-63 Benton Harbor MI 49022

SAMEH, AHMED HAMDY, computer science educator; b. Alexandria, Egypt, Nov. 18, 1939; came to U.S., 1963; s. Mohammed and Khadija (Gemei) S.; m. Marilyn Ruth Martin, Dec. 14, 1968; children: Maysa, Leah, Amy. B.Sc., U. Alexandria, 1961; M.S., Ga. Inst. Tech., Atlanta, 1964; Ph.D., U. Ill.-Urbana, 1968. Instr. U. Alexandria, 1961-63; research asst. U. Ill.-Urbana, 1966-68, asst. prof. computer sci., 1968-74, assoc. prof., 1974-80, prof., 1980—. Editor: High Speed Computer Algorithm Organization, 1977; mem. editorial bd. IEEE Trans. on Computers, SIAM Jour. on Sci. and Statis. Computing, and Parallel Computing; contbr. articles to profl. jours. Grantee NSF, Dept. Energy, Air Force Office of Sci. Research. Mem. Assn. Computing Machinery, Soc. Indsl. and Applied Math., IEEE, AAAS. Home: 6 Sunset Ln Saint Paul MN 55127-6454 Office: Univ of Ill 1304 W Springfield Ave Urbana IL 61801-2910

SAMEK, MICHAEL JOHANN, corporation executive; b. Vienna, Austria, Feb. 26, 1920; came to U.S., 1939; s. Berthold and Leontine (Bruell) S.; m. Edith Raymond, Apr. 1948 (div. 1961); m. Stacy Graham, Dec. 20, 1964 (div. 1974). B.S., Vienna, 1938; postgrad., Columbia U., 1949-51. Pres. Computech Inc., N.Y.C., 1956-60; v.p. Data Systems ITT, Paramus, N.J., 1961-64; mgr. dir. internat. Auerbach Corp., Europe and U.S., 1964-69; v.p. Celanese Corp., N.Y.C., 1969-83; pres. Primary Care Software Inc., Riverhead, N.Y., 1987—; chmn. Am. Mgmt. Assn. Info. Systems and Tech. Council, 1960-83; chmn. adv. com. on data processing City of N.Y., 1963—. Served to lt. col. USAF, 1941-45, ETO. Mem. AAAS, AIAA, Assn. Computing Machinery, Soc. Mgmt. Info. Systems, N.Y. Acad. Scis.

SAMEROFF, ARNOLD JOSHUA, developmental psychologist, educator; b. N.Y.C., Apr. 20, 1937; s. Stanley and Zeena (Shapiro) S.; m. Susan C. McDonough, Jan. 2, 1982; children: Shira, Rebecca, Crista, Andrew. BS, U. Mich., 1961; PhD, Yale U., 1965; MA (hon.), Brown U., 1987. Asst. prof. psychology, pediatrics and psychiatry U. Rochester, 1967-70, assoc. prof., 1970-73, prof., 1973-78, dir. developmental psychology tng. program, 1975-78; prof. psychology U. Ill., Chgo., 1978-86, assoc. dir. Inst. for Study Developmental Disabilities, 1978-86; assoc. dir., dir. rsch. Ill. Inst. for Developmental Disabilities, 1978-86; prof. psychiatry and human behavior Brown U., Providence, 1986-92; dir. Developmental Psychopathology Rsch. Ctr., Bradley Hosp., East Providence, 1986-92; prof. psychology, rsch. scientist Ctr. for Human Growth and Devel., U. Mich., Ann Arbor, 1992—; vis. prof. psychology Birkbeck Coll., U. London, 1974-75; vis. scientist Ctr. for Interdisciplinary Rsch., U. Bielefeld, Fed. Republic Germany, 1977-78; W.T. Grant Found. lectr. Soc. for Behavioral Pediatrics, 1984; dir. Summer Inst. on Human Devel. and Psychopathology, Ctr. for Advanced Study in Behavioral Scis., Stanford, Calif., 1989; mem. small grants adv. com. NIH, 1977-81, behavioral scis. assessment panel, 1987-88; mem. organizational planning com. Internat. Conf. for Infant Studies, 1980-84. Editor: (with R. N. Emde) Relationship Disturbances in Early Childhood: A Developmental Approach, 1989; (with F. Kessel and M. Bornstein) Contemporary Constructions of the Child: Essays in Honor of William Kessen, 1991; also monographs; mem. editorial bds. Devel. and Psychopathology, 1988—; Jour. Devel. and Behavioral Pediatrics, 1989-93, Jour. Family Psychology, 1990-91, others. Mem. social and Behavioral scis. rsch. adv. com. March of Dimes Birth Defects Found., 1977-94, rsch. adv. com. Little City Found., 1986-88; bd. dirs. Nat. Ctr. for Clin. Infant Programs, 1986—; mem. program on successful adolescent devel. among youth in high-risk settings John D. and Catherine T. MacArthur Found., 1986—; network on early childhood transitions, 1989-92. GE fellow Yale U., 1961; NIMH predoctoral rsch. fellow Yale U., 1962, NIMH postdoctoral rsch. fellow, 1965-67, Ctr. for Advanced Study in Behavioral Scis. fellow Stanford U., 1984-85. Fellow AAAS, Am. Acad. Mental Retardation, Am. Psychol. Soc., Developmental Psychology and Mental Retardation divs. Am. Psychol. Assn. (mem. program com. developmental psychology div. 1978-90, chair 1979, mem. coun. 1980-83, mem. at large exec. com. 1985-88, pres. devel. psychology divsn. 1995—); mem. AAUP, Soc. for Rsch. in Child Devel. (com. on summer insts. and study groups 1985-88), World Assn. Infant Mental Health, Internat. Soc. for Infant Studies, Soc. for Rsch. on Adolescence.

SAMERS, BERNARD NORMAN, fund raising organization executive; b. N.Y.C., Jan. 25, 1934; s. Abraham and Edith (Slomack) S.; m. Edith Maralyn Rosenblum, Sept. 7, 1958; children: Audrey Meryl, Michael Eric, William David. BS, Queens Coll., 1956; BSIE, Columbia U., 1956; MBA, Harvard U., 1958; Profl. Indsl. Engr., Columbia U., 1968. Registered profl. engr., Calif; Cer: CFRE. Cons. S.B. Littauer & Assocs., N.Y.C., 1956; asst. dir. spl. studies Hudson Pulp & Paper Corp., N.Y.C., 1957; sr. mgmt. scientist Dunlap & Assocs., Inc., Darien, Conn., 1958-66; v.p. Cooper & Co., Mgmt. Cons., Stamford, Conn., 1966-82; v.p. adminstrn. and regional ops. Am. Technion Soc., N.Y.C., 1982-86; exec. v.p. Am. Com. for the Weizmann Inst. of Sci., N.Y.C., 1986—; adj. asst. prof. mgmt. engring. U. Bridgeport, 1972-88; lectr. MBA program U. Conn., 1980-82. Pres. Jewish Edn. in media, 1979, United Jewish Fedn. of Stamford, 1978-79; dir. Coun. of Jewish Fedn., 1979-80; committeeman Dem. City Com., Stamford, 1980-82. Mem. Nat. Assn. Fund Raising Execs., Assn. Jewish Community Orgn. Pers., Ops. Rsch. Soc. of Am. Democrat. jewish. Avocation: abstract painting. Home: 180 Big Oak Rd Stamford CT 06903-4608 Office: Am Com Weizmann Inst Sci 51 Madison Ave New York NY 10010-1603

SAMET, ANDREW, government official; b. Boston, June 29, 1957; s. Theodore S. and Elaine S. (Sloane) S.; m. Kennari S. Sargent, May 10, 1986; 1 child, Daniel Jeremy. BA, Yale U., 1978; MA, Carleton Coll., Ottawa, Ont., Can., 1981; JD, Georgetown U., 1983. Bar: D.C. Assoc. Chapman, Duff and Paul, Washington, 1983-85, Mudge Rose Guthrie Alexander & Ferdon, Washington, 1985-87; legis. counsel Senator Daniel P. Moynihan, Washington, 1987-89, legis. dir., 1989-93; assoc. dep. under sec. for internat. affairs Dept. Labor, Washington, 1993—. Editor: Human Rights Law and Reagan Adminstration, 1984, The U.S.-Israel Free Trade Agreement, 1989; contbr. articles to profl. jours. Democrat. Jewish. Office: Dept of Labor Inernat Labor Affairs 200 Constitution Ave NW Washington DC 20210

SAMET, ANDREW BENJAMIN, lawyer; b. N.Y.C., Dec. 23, 1941; s. Leon and Clara (Belfar) S.; m. Susan McAnalley, Sept. 24, 1965; 1 child, Vanessa. BA, Cornell U., 1962; JD, NYU, 1965. Bar: N.Y. 1966, Mich. 1971. Assoc. atty. Hughes Hubbard & Reed, N.Y.C., 1968-71; with Bendix Corp., Southfield, Mich., 1971-83, assoc. gen. counsel, 1981-83; gen. counsel Allied Corp., Morristown, N.J., 1983—, sec., 1985-86; assoc. gen. counsel AlliedSignal Inc., 1985-86, staff v.p., assoc. gen. counsel, 1986-88, v.p., sec., assoc. gen counsel, 1988-94. Capt. U.S. Army, 1966-68. Decorated Army Commendation medal. Mem. ABA, Mich. State Bar. Office: Allied-Signal Inc PO Box 4000 101 Columbia Rd Morristown NJ 07960-4638

SAMET, JACK L, lawyer; b. N.Y.C., Aug. 6, 1940; s. William and Tillie (Katz) S.; m. Helen Ray, Feb. 12, 1967; 1 son, Peter Lawrence. BA, Columbia U., 1961; JD, Harvard U., 1964. Bar: N.Y. 1964, Calif. 1973. Assoc. Whitman & Ransom, N.Y.C., 1966-69, Hall, Casey, Dickler & Howley, N.Y.C., 1969-73; ptnr. Ball, Hunt, Hart, Brown & Baerwitz, L.A., 1973-81, Buchalter, Nemer, Fields & Younger, L.A., 1981-94, Baker & Hostetler, L.A., 1994—; arbitrator Nat. Assn. Securities Dealers, L.A., 1976—; speaker, panelist Calif. Continuing Edn. of Bar, 1988. Mem. ABA, Sports Club/L.A. Avocations: exercise, reading. Home: 2741 Aqua Verde Cir Los Angeles CA 90077-1502 Office: Baker & Hostetler 600 Wilshire Blvd 12th Fl Los Angeles CA 90017

SAMET, KENNETH ALAN, hospital administrator; b. Bklyn., Mar. 17, 1958; married. BA, Old Dominion U., 1990; MA, U. Mich., 1982. Adminstrv. intern Mt. Vernon Hosp., Fairfax, Va., 1981; adminstrv. resident Washington Hosp. Ctr., 1982-83, pres., 1991—; asst. to pres. Washington Health Care Corp., 1983-85, dir. system devel., 1985-86; v.p. system devel. Medlantic Health Care Group, Washington, 1986-88, exec. v.p. systems, bus. devel., 1988-91; pres. Medlantic Enterprises, Washington, 1988-91. Mem. D.C. Hosp. Assn., Md. Hosp. Assn., Va. Hosp. Assn. (bd. dirs.). Home: 9041 Holly Leaf Ln Bethesda MD 20817 Office: Washington Hosp Ctr 110 Irving St NW Washington DC 20010

SAMFORD, THOMAS DRAKE, III, lawyer; b. Opelika, Ala., Mar. 4, 1934; s. Thomas Drake and Aileen (Maxwell) S., Jr.; m. Jacqueline Screws, June 7, 1955; children: Thomas Drake IV, Jacquelyn, Robert Maxwell, Richard Drake. A.B. magna cum laude, Princeton U., 1955; J.D., U. Ala.,

1961. Bar: Ala. 1961. Owner firm Samford & Samford, 1961-88; judge Mcpl. Ct., Opelika, 1961-88; mem. Ala. Permanent Jud. Commn., 1979-83; gen. counsel Auburn U., 1965-94; lectr. Ala. Law Inst., 1969, Am. Judicature Soc., 1969—. Editor-in-chief: Ala. Law Rev, 1960-61. Dir., bd. trustees Opelika Comty. Chest, 1965-68, pres., 1966-67; bd. dirs. U. Ala. Law Sch. Found., Jr. Achievement Chattahoochee-Lee; elder Presbyn. ch., 1974-94, Meth. ch., 1994—. Recipient John G. Buchanan prize politics, 1955; Farrah, Order Jurisprudence U. Ala., 1956; named one of four Outstanding Young Men in Ala. Jr. C. of C., 1967. Mem. Opelika C. of C. (dir. 1967, pres. 1968), ABA, Lee County Bar Assn. (pres. 1965), Ala. State Bar, U. Ala. Nat. Alumni Assn. (pres. 1966-67), Phi Beta Kappa, Alpha Tau Omega, Phi Delta Phi, Omicron Delta Kappa. Lodge: Kiwanis (bd. dirs. 1966-67, pres. 1969-70). Home: 805 Ridgewood Ct Opelika AL 36801-3525 Office: Auburn Univ 101 Samford Hall Auburn AL 36849-5114

SAMFORD, YETTA GLENN, JR., lawyer; b. Opelika, Ala., June 8, 1923; s. Yetta Glenn and Mary Elizabeth (Denson) S.; m. Mary Austill, Sept. 6, 1949; children: Mary Austill Lott, Katherine Park Alford, Yetta Glenn III (dec.). BS, Ala. Poly. Inst., 1947; LLB, U. Ala., 1949, LLD (hon.), 1995. Bar: Ala. 1949, U.S. Dist. Ct. (mid. dist.) Ala. 1950, U.S. Ct. Appeals (5th cir.) 1961, U.S. Ct. Appeals (11th cir.) 1981. Since practiced in Opelika; ptnr. Samford, Denson, Horsley, Pettey & Martin (and predecessors), 1949—; mem. Ala. Senate from Lee and Russell counties, 1958-62; bd. dirs. Torchmark Corp., Farmers Nat. Bank Opelika; mem. State of Ala. Bd. of Corrections, 1969-75; mem. adv. bd. State Docks, 1987—. Life trustee U. Mobile, 1963-92; trustee emeritus U. Ala., 1972-93. Mem. Ala. Law Inst. Council (exec. com., v.p.), Ala. Acad. of Honor, Phi Delta Phi, Omicron Delta Kappa, Alpha Tau Omega. Republican. Baptist. Lodge: Masons. Home: 615 Terracewood Dr Opelika AL 36801-3850 Office: Samford Denson Horsley Pettey & Martin PO Box 2345 Opelika AL 36803-2345

SAMII, ABDOL HOSSEIN, physician, educator; b. Rasht, Iran, June 20, 1930; came to U.S., 1947; s. Mehdi Ebtehaj and Zahra (Mojdehi-Akbar) S.; m. Shahla Khosrowshahi; children: Ali, Golnaz. Student, Stanford U., 1947-49; BA, UCLA, 1950, MA, 1952; MD, Cornell U., 1956. Intern N.Y. Hosp., N.Y.C., 1956, asst. in medicine, 1956-58; asst. in physiology Cornell U. Med. Sch., N.Y.C., 1958-59; resident and sr. resident N.Y. Hosp., Peter Bent Brigham Hosp. and Mass. Gen. Hosp., Boston, 1959-61; adj. prof. medicine Cornell U. Med. Sch., 1973-79, prof. clin. medicine, 1979—; rsch. fellow Harvard U., Boston, 1959-60; prof. medicine Nat. Univ. Iran, Tehran, 1963-68; med. dir. Pars Hosp., Tehran, 1968-73; dir. div. medicine N.Y. Hosp.-Cornell Med. Coll., White Plains, 1979—; chancellor Reza Shah Kabir Grad. Univ., Tehran, 1973-78; cons. med. rsch. WHO, Geneva, 1973-79; v.p. Imperial Acad. Sci., Tehran, 1974-78. Gen. editor: International Textbook of Medicine, 1981; author, editor: Medical Clinics of North America, 1983, Textbook of Diagnostic Medicine, 1987. Dep. minister, Ministry of Health, Tehran, 1963-65; minister, Ministry Sci. and Higher Edn., Tehran, 1973-75. Fellow Rockefeller Found., Helen Hay Whitney Found. Fellow Royal Soc. of Medicine; mem. N.Y. Acad. Medicine, Harvey Soc. Internat. Soc. Nephrology, Am. Fed. Clin. Rsch. Avocations: music, antiques. Office: NY Hosp CMC WD 21 Bloomingdale Rd White Plains NY 10605-1596 also: 14 E 63rd St New York NY 10021

SAMIOS, NICHOLAS PETER, physicist; b. N.Y.C., Mar. 15, 1932; s. Peter and Niki (Vatick) S.; m. Mary Linakis, Jan. 12, 1958; children: Peter, Gregory, Alexandra. AB, Columbia U., 1953, PhD, 1957. Instr. physics Columbia U., N.Y.C., 1956-59; asst. physicist Brookhaven Nat. Lab., Upton, N.Y., 1959-62, assoc. physicist, 1962-64, physicist, 1964-68, sr. physicist, 1968—, group leader, 1965-75, chmn. dept. physics, 1975-81, dep. dir. for high energy and nuclear physics, 1981, dir., 1982—; adj. prof. Stevens Inst. Tech., 1969-75, Columbia U., 1970—. Contbr. articles in field to profl. jours. Bd. dirs. Stony Brook Found., 1989, Adelphi U., 1989, L.I. Assn., 1990. Recipient E.O. Lawrence Meml. award, 1980, award in physics and math. scis. N.Y. Acad. Scis., 1980; named AUI Disting. Scientist, 1992, W.K.H. Panofsky prize, 1993. Fellow Am. Phys. Soc. (chmn. divsn. of particles and fields 1975-76, chmn. PEP exptl. program com. 1976-78); mem. Internat. Ctr. Future Acceleration, Akademia Athenon (corr. mem.). Achievements include being an expert in field of high energy particle and nuclear physics. Office: Brookhaven Nat Lab Office of Dir Upton NY 11973

SAMMAN, GEORGE, obstetrician, gynecologist; b. Syria, Dec. 12, 1946; came to U.S., 1971; naturalized, 1982; s. Nicolaki and Antoinette (Charaoui) S.; M.D., Damascus U., 1971; m. Husn Massouh, July 4, 1971; children—Fadi, Luna Miriam. Intern, Washington Hosp. Center, 1971-72, resident in ob-gyn., 1972-75, mem. hosp. staff, 1975—, vice chmn. dept. gynecology, 1980, teaching faculty, 1985-88; practice medicine specializing in ob-gyn, Washington, 1975—; Fairfax, Va., 1980—; mem. staff Providence Hosp., 1975—, Columbia Hosp. for Women. Recipient Best Teaching award Washington Hosp. Ctr., 1985, 88. Diplomate Am. Bd. Ob-Gyn. Fellow Am. Coll. Obstetricians and Gynecologists, Am. Fertility Assn.; mem. Med. Soc. D.C. (maternal health com. 1978-80). Melkite Catholic. Home: 10400 Bit & Spur Ln Potomac MD 20854 Office: 2021 K St NWNW Washington DC 20006-2104

SAMMARCO, PAUL WILLIAM, ecologist; b. Hackensack, N.J., Oct. 18, 1948; s. Giacomo and Esther (Galanti) S.; m. Jean Sogioka, May 29, 1971; children: Mimi Cecile, Dustin Paul, Jack Isao. BA, Syracuse U., 1970, postgrad., 1970-71; cert. Marine Biology Lab., Woods Hole, Mass., 1971, Fairleigh Dickinson U. W.I. Lab., U.S. V.I., 1972; PhD, SUNY-Stony Brook, 1977. Teaching asst. Syracuse (N.Y.) U., 1970-71, Discovery Bay Marine Lab., SUNY-Stony Brook Overseas Acad. Program, Jamaica, 1974, SUNY-Stony Brook, 1971-77; asst. prof. Clarkson U., Potsdam, N.Y., 1977-79; vis. asst. prof. tropical ecology, in St. Croix, V.I., SUNY-Potsdam, 1979; sr. rsch. scientist Australian Inst. Marine Sci., Townsville, Queensland, 1979-89, coord. Shelf Seas Rsch. Program 1985-86; dir. environ. rsch. of Resource Assessment Commn. Prime Minister's commn. on natural resources, Canberra, Australia, 1989-91; exec. dir. La. Univs. Marine Consortium, Chauvin, 1991—; dir. inter-univ. seminar program Assn. Colls. St. Lawrence Valley, Potsdam, 1977-79. Composer ballads; former mem. Australian Chamber Choir, Wesley Choir, Canberra; contbr. numerous articles to profl. jours.; editorial advisor Marine Ecology Progress Series, 1985-93; co-editor Proceedings Inaugural Great Barrier Conf., 1983, Proceedings 6th Internat. Coral Reef Symposium, 1988. NSF grantee, 1973-75, Internat. Sci. Exch. award, 1988-89. Mem. Australian Marine Scis. Assn. (keynote speaker 1981, counselor 1984-89, chmn., organizer nat. conf. 1987, chmn. Australia Acad. Sci. Bodem Conf. 1990), Internat. Soc. Reef Studies, Australian Coral Reef Soc., Am. Soc. Limnology and Oceanography, Assn. Island Marine Labs. Carribbean, Smithsonian Assocs., Western Soc. Nat., Australasian Performing Rights Assn., Sigma Xi. Democrat. Methodist. Home: 205 Midland Dr Houma LA 70360-6231 Office: La Univs Marine Consortium 8124 Highway 56 Chauvin LA 70344

SAMMOND, JOHN STOWELL, lawyer; b. Milw., Dec. 27, 1928; s. C. Frederic and Marie (Freitag) S.; m. Cynthia Miller, Feb. 13, 1951 (dec. Dec. 1992); children: Frederic, Christopher, Nicholas, Timothy. BA, Yale U., 1950; SJD, Harvard U., 1955. Bar: Wis. 1955, Fla. 1969, D.C. 1972, Fla. Supreme Ct. as Cir. Ct. mediator, 1990. Assoc. predecessor firm to Quarles & Brady, Milw., 1955-60; ptnr. Quarles & Brady (and predecessor firms), Milw., 1961—, Quarles & Brady, West Palm Beach, Fla., 1969—; bd. dirs. Medalist Industries Inc., Milw., Associated Commerce Bank, Milw., Tropical Plant Rentals Inc., Riverwoods, Ill., Kelley Co. Inc., Milw., others. Bd. dirs., officer Univ. Sch., Milw., Lakeside Children's Ctr., Milw., Palm Beach Habilitation Ctr., Lake Worth, Fla.; sr. warden Christ Episcopal Ch., Whitefish Bay, Wis. Maj. USMCR, 1948-63. Mem. ABA, Wis. Bar Assn., Milw. Bar Assn., Fla. Bar Assn., Palm Beach County Bar Assn., D.C. Bar Assn., Bath and Tennis Club (Palm Beach), Everglades Club (Palm Beach), Milw. Country Club, Milw. Club, Governor's Club (Palm Beach). Republican. Office: Quarles & Brady PO Box 3188 West Palm Beach FL 33402-3188 also: Quarles & Brady 411 E Wisconsin Ave Milwaukee WI 53202-4409

SAMMONS, ELAINE D., corporate executive. Chmn. Sammons Enterprises, Inc., Dallas. Office: Sammons Enterprises Inc 5949 Sherry Ln Ste 1900 Dallas TX 75225*

SAMMONS, JEFFREY LEONARD, foreign language educator; b. Cleve., Nov. 9, 1936; s. Harold Leonard and Therese (Herrmann) S.; m. Kathryn

Josephine Stella, July 1958 (div. 1962); children: Rebecca Kathryn; m. Christa Ann Smith, Oct. 20, 1967; children: Charles Leonard, Harold Hawthorne, Benjamin Gardner. B.A., Yale U., 1958, Ph.D., 1962. Instr., asst. prof. Brown U., Providence, 1961-64; asst. prof. German, Yale U., 1964-67, assoc. prof., 1967-69, prof., 1969—; Leavenworth prof. German, 1979—; mem. editorial bd. Arbitrium, Munich, 1980-87, Suhrkamp/Insel, Boston, 1980—, Mich. Germanic Studies, 1985—. Author: Heinrich Heine: The Elusive Poet, 1969; Six Essays on the Young German Novel, 1972; Literary Sociology and Practical Criticism, 1977; Heinrich Heine: A Modern Biography, 1979, Wilhelm Raabe: The Fiction of the Alternative Community, 1987, The Shifting Fortunes of Wilhelm Raabe, 1992. Guggenheim fellow, 1972-73; Am. Council Learned Socs. fellow, 1977-78, travel grantee, 1983; Duke August Library, Wolfenbuttel Ger. adoptive stipend, 1983. Mem. MLA, Am. Assn. Tchrs. German, Lessing Soc., Goethe Soc. N.Am., Conn. Acad. Arts and Scis., Heinrich-Heine Gesellschaft. Home: 211 Highland St New Haven CT 06511 Office: Dept German PO Box 208210 New Haven CT 06520-8210

SAMO, AMANDO, bishop; b. Moch Island, Federated States of Micronesia, Aug. 16, 1948; s. Benito and Esiper Samo. BA in Psychology, Chaminade U., 1973; diploma in religious edn., EAPI, Manila, Philippines, 1982. Ordained priest Roman Cath. Ch. Parish priest Cath. Ch., Truk, Federated States of Micronesia, 1977-87; bishop Diocese of the Carolines and Marshalls, Truk, 1987—; founder, bd. dirs. Marriage Encounter-Carolines-Marshalls, Truk, 1982-88; dir. ch. leadership tng. programs, Truk, 1986—. Home: PO Box 250, Truk 96942, Federated States Micronesia

SAMOJLIK, EUGENIUSZ, administrator, medical educator; b. Kuchmy-Bialystok, Poland, Aug. 20, 1933; s. Michael and Anastazia S.; m. Anna Morozewicz, Apr. 10, 1965; children: Dorothy, Michael. BS in Biomedicine, U. Warsaw, 1958, PhD in Reproductive Endocrinology, 1964. Rsch. asst. Maternity Inst. Dept. Pharmacology, Warsaw, 1958-62, sr. asst., 1962-66, asst. prof., chief reproductive pharmacology & toxicology Inst. Pharmacy Dept. Pharmacology, Warsaw, 1966-70; assoc. prof., chief hormone rsch. lab. Med. Acad. Dept. Clin. Endocrinology, Warsaw, 1970-73; staff researcher II Syntex, Inc. Rsch. Divsn., Palo Alto, Calif., 1974-75; asst. prof. physiology, dir. radioimmunoassay lab. Milton S. Hershey (Pa.) Med. Ctr., Divsn. Endocrinology, 1975-80; staff endocrinologist VA Med. Ctr. Dept. Medicine, Sect. Endocrinology, East Orange, N.J., 1980-82; dir. endocrine lab. Newark Beth Israel Med. Ctr., Dept. Medicine, 1982—; assoc. prof. medicine U. Medicine & Dentistry-N.J. Med. Sch., Newark, 1982—; vis. researcher UCLA Sch. Medicine, Torrance, Calif., 1973; vis. scientist Nat. Inst. Child Health Human Devel., Reproductive Br., Bethesda, Md., 1973-74; lectr. in field. Mem. internat. adv. bd. Jour. Assisted Reproductive Tech. and Andrology; contbr. articles to profl. jours. Grantee WHO, 1973-74, Ciba-Geigy, 1982-83, Nat. Cancer Inst., 1983-86, 85-88; tng. program fellow Worcester Found. Experimental Biology, Shrewsbury, Mass., 1967-69. Mem. Am. Soc. Andrology, Am. Assn. Clin. Chemistry, Nat. Acad. Clin. Biochemistry, Acad. Medicine N.J., Endocrine Soc. Home: 73 Sykes Ave Livingston NJ 07039 Office: Newark Beth Israel Med Ctr Newark NJ 07112

SAMOLE, MYRON MICHAEL, lawyer, management consultant; b. Chgo., Nov. 29, 1943; s. Harry Lionel and Bess Miriam (Siegel) S.; m. Sandra Rita Port, Feb. 2, 1967; children—Stacey Ann, Karen Lynn, Rena Mara, David Aaron. Student U. Ill., 1962-65; J.D., DePaul U., 1967; postgrad. John Marshall Lawyers Inst., 1967-69. Bar: Ill. 1967, U.S. Dist. Ct. (no. dist.) Ill. 1968, U.S. Dist. Ct. (so. dist.) Fla. 1989, U.S. Ct. Appeals (7th cir.) 1968, Fla. 1981. Pvt. practice, Chgo., 1967-79, Miami, Fla., 1981—; chmn. bd. Fidelity Electronics and subs., Miami, 1969-83; pres. Fidelity Hearing Instruments, Miami, 1984-86, Samole Enterprises, Inc., Miami, 1986—, Fla. Citrus Tower, Inc., Clermont, 1986—; bd. dirs. Enterprise Bank Fla., Miami, 1985-89, The Sports Collection, Inc., Miami, 1987-94; Bd. dirs. South Dade Greater Miami Jewish Fedn., Young Israel of Kendall, Cen. Agy. for Jewish Edn. Jewish Vocat. Service scholar U. Ill., Champaign, 1962-65. Mem. ABA, Chgo. Bar Assn., Ill. State Bar Assn., Fla. Bar Assn., Kendall Bar Assn., Dade County Bar Assn., Ill. Trial Lawyers Assn., Miami C. of C., Phi Alpha Delta. Democrat. Lodges: Masons, Shriners. Office: 9700 S Dixie Hwy Ste 1030 Miami FL 33156-2865

SAMORA, JOSEPH E., JR., lawyer. BA, U. N.Mex., 1978, JD with high honors, 1982. Bar: N.Mex., U.S. Dist. Ct. (fed. dist.) N.Mex., U.S. Ct. Appeals (10th cir.). Jud. clk. to justice N.Mex. Supreme Ct., Sant Fe, 1982-84, gen. counsel, adminstrv. asst. to chief justice, 1986; assoc. atty. Butt, Thornton & Baehr, P.C., Albuquerque, 1984-85; chmn. N.Mex. Pub. Svc. Commn., Santa Fe, 1987—. Contbr. articles to profl. jours. Mem. Multiple Sclerosis Soc., Santa Fe; vol. Big. Bros./Big Sisters, Santa Fe. Scholar U. N.Mex., 1981-82. Mem. ABA (gov. 15th cir. law student div. 1981-82, mem standing com. on rules governing civil and criminal appeals, chmn. pub. utility law com. young lawyers div. 1987-88, Gold Key award 1981-82, one of Twenty Young Lawyers in U.S. Who Make a Difference), State Bar of N.Mex. (pres. young lawyers div. 1985-86), Nat. Assn. Regulatory Commrs. (water com.), U. N.Mex. Alumni Assn. (chmn. class '78 10-yr. reunion celebration 1988), Phi Gamma Delta (grad. advisor, purple legionnaire U. N.Mex. chpt. 1982-84, 89—). Office: NMex Pub Svc Commn PO Box 2205 Santa Fe NM 87504-2205

SAMOUR, CARLOS MIGUEL, chemist. BA in Chemistry, Am. U. Beirut, 1942, MA, 1944; MS in Organic Chemistry, MIT, 1947; PhD, Boston U., 1950. Postdoctoral rsch. fellow Boston U., 1950-52; rsch. chemist The Kendall Co., 1952-57, dir. Theodore Clark Lab. 1957-73, dir. Lexington Rsch. Lab., 1973-81; pres. Samour Assocs., 1981-84; chmn., scientific dir. MacroChem Corp., Lexington, Mass., 1982—; section chmn. Internat. Union Pure and Applied Chemistry, U. Mass., Amherst, 1982; session chmn. Biomaterials, Sardinia, Italy, 1988, internat. conf. MIT, 1982, tech. advisor; pres., chmn. Augusta Epilepsy Rsch. Found., Washington, 1989—; advisor univs. and med. ctrs. Contbr. numerous articles to profl. jours. Mem. Am. Chem. Soc. (cert. merit 1981, adminstr. Kendell award 1964-83), Am. Assn. Pharm. Scis., Controlled Release Soc. Achievements include over 50 U.S. patents and over 200 foreign patents; research in the fields of polymer chemistry, bio-materials, pharmaceuticals and dential materials. Office: Macrochem Corp 110 Hartwell Ave Lexington MA 02173-3134

SAMP, EDWARD JOSEPH, JR., lawyer; b. Madison, Wis., July 5, 1918; s. Edward Joseph and Margaret Helen (Sullivan) S.; m. Mary Lewis Abbott, Oct. 12, 1946; children: Edward, John, Frederick, Richard, Margaret. BA, MA, U. Wis., 1940; LLB, Harvard U., 1946. Bar: Mass. 1948, U.S. Dist. Ct. Mass. 1949. Assoc. Haussermann, Davison & Shattuck, Boston, 1947-49; pvt. practice Boston, 1950-94. Pres. Boston Jaycees, 1950-51; chmn. fund drive Cambridge chpt. ARC, 1952; chmn. fund drive Cambridge TB and Health Assn., 1956; mem. Cambridge Election Commn., 1960-95, chmn., 1980-95. Served to lt. comdr. USNR, 1942-47. Mem. Cambridge, Arlington, Belmont Bar Assns. (pres. 1978), Economy Club (Cambridge), Wardroom Club (Boston), Harvard Club (Boston). Republican. Roman Catholic. Home: 33 Agassiz St Cambridge MA 02140-2801 Office: 6 Beacon St Ste 1115 Boston MA 02108-3802

SAMPAS, DOROTHY M., government official; b. Washington, Aug. 24, 1933; d. Lawrence and Anna Cornelia (Henkel) Myers; m. James George Sampas, Dec. 8, 1962; children: George, Lawrence James. AB, U. Mich. 1955; postgrad. U. Paris, 1955-56; PhD, Georgetown U., 1970; cert. Nat. War Coll., Washington, 1987, Naval Post Grad. Sch., 1993. With Bur. Pub. Affairs Dept. State, Washington, 1958-60, analyst Bur. of Adminstrn., 1973-75, div. chief, dep. chief Office of Position and Pay Mgmt., 1979-83, div. chief Office of Mgmt., 1983-84, dir. Office of Mgmt., 1984-86; vice consul Am. Consulate Gen., Hamburg, Fed. Republic Germany, 1960-62; cons. Trans Century Corp., Washington, 1972; gen. svcs. officer Am. Embassy, Brussels, 1975-79; embassy minister-counselor Am. Embassy, Beijing, 1987-90; minister-counselor U.S. Mission to UN, N.Y.C., 1991-94; am. ambassador to Islamic Republic of Mauritania, 1994—. Presbyterian. Home: 4715 Trent Ct Chevy Chase MD 20815-5516 Office: Am Embassy Nouakchott Dept State Washington DC 20521-2430 also: Am Embassy, Boite Postale 22, Nouakchott Mauritania

SAMPER, JOSEPH PHILLIP, retired photographic products company executive; b. Salt Lake City, Aug. 13, 1934; s. Juan M. and Harriet (Howell) S.; married; children: Joaquin P., Christopher F. With Eastman Kodak Co.,

Rochester, N.Y., 1961—; asst. to gen. mgr. mktg. div. Eastman Kodak Co. (U.S. and Can. photog. div.), 1976-77; asst. v.p., asst. gen. mgr. mktg. div. Eastman Kodak Co. (U.S. and Can. photographic div.), 1977-79; v.p., gen. mgr. mktg. div. Eastman Kodak Co., 1979—, exec. v.p., gen. mgr. photographic div., 1983-86, vice chmn., exec. officer, 1986-90; chief exec. officer, pres. Kinder-Care Learning Ctrs., Inc., 1990—; pres. Sun Microsystems Computer Co., 1994—; bd. dirs. Armstrong World Industries, Inc., Lancaster, Pa., Interpub. Group, N.Y.C., Lifetouch, Inc., Mpls., Sylvan LEarning Systems, Inc., Columbia, Md. Mem. adv. bd. U. Calif. Bus. Sch. With USNR, 1952-56. Recipient Alfred Knight award Am. Grad. Sch. Internat. Mgmt., 1961, Barton Kyle Young award, 1961; Sloan fellow, MIT, 1972-73. Roman Catholic.

SAMPLE, BETTE JEANE, elementary educator; b. Long Beach, Calif., Oct. 20, 1943; d. Dennis Lynn and Norma Dorothy (Ladner) Hart; m. Ronald Charles Sample, Oct. 7, 1967; children: Jennifer Lynne Sample Amend, Leah Anne. BS, Augustana Coll., Sioux Falls, S.D., 1966; MA in Edn., U. Wyo., 1994. Tchr. Whittier Elem. Sch., Colorado Springs, Colo., 1966-67, North Park Elem. Sch., Columbia Heights, Minn., 1967-68; tchr. Gertrude Burns Elem. Sch., Newcastle, Wyo., 1976-88, 2d grade tchr., 1989-90, 1st grade tchr., 1990-95; instr. Ea. Wyo. Coll., Torrington, 1987-92, 95; tchr. English Newcastle Mid. Sch., 1988-89. Grantee Ency. Brittanica, 1991. Mem. NEA, Wyo. Edn. Assn. (Tchr. of Yr. 1991), Newcastle Edn. Assn. Democrat. Lutheran. Home: PO Box 537 Newcastle WY 82701-0537 Office: Gertrude Burns Elem Sch 116 Casper Ave Newcastle WY 82701-2701

SAMPLE, FREDERICK PALMER, former college president; b. Columbia, Pa., May 22, 1930; s. William Walter and Erna Rebecca (Roye) S.; m. Mary Jane Drager, Aug. 19, 1951; children: Jeffrey Lynn, Roger Lee. AB, Lebanon Valley Coll., 1952; MEd, Western Md. Coll., 1956; DEd, Pa. State U., 1968; D in Pedagogy, Albright Coll., 1968. Tchr. Annville (Pa.) High Sch., 1952-53; tchr. Red Lion Area (Pa.) High Sch., 1953-57, prin., 1957-59, supervising prin., 1959-64; supt. Manheim Twp. Sch. Dist., Neffsville, Pa., 1964-68; pres. Lebanon Valley Coll., Annville, Pa., 1968-83; supt. Bellefonte (Pa.) Area Sch. Dist., 1987-92; ednl. cons.; administr. Bucknell U., 1985-87. Mem. Phi Delta Kappa. Republican. Home: PO Box 92 Eagles Mere PA 17731-0092 Despite failures, difficulties, and disappointments I have tried to find the honorable, responsible, productive, true, and humane solutions to problems and make decisions for progress.

SAMPLE, JOSEPH SCANLON, foundation executive; b. Chgo., Mar. 15, 1923; s. John Glen and Helen (Scanlon) S.; m. Patricia M. Law, Dec. 22, 1942 (div.); children: Michael Scanlon, David Forrest, Patrick Glen; m. Miriam Tyler Willing, Nov. 19, 1965. B.A., Yale U., 1947. Trainee, media analyst, media dir. Dancer-Fitzgerald-Sample, Inc., advt. agy., Chgo., 1947-50; v.p., media dir. Dancer-Fitzgerald-Sample, Inc., advt. agy., 1952-53; pres. Mont. Television Network KTVQ, Billings, KXLF-AM-TV, Butte, Mont., KRTV, Great Falls, Mont., KPAX-TV, Missoula, Mont., 1955-84. Pres. Greater Mont. Found., 1986—; chmn. Wheeler Ctr. Mont State U., 1988—. Served with AUS, 1943-46. With U.S. Army, 1950-52. Mem. Rotary, Yellowstone Country Club, Port Royal Club, Hole in The Wall Golf Club, Hilands Golf Club, Naples Yacht Club. Home: 606 Highland Park Dr Billings MT 59102-1909 Office: 14 N 24th St Billings MT 59101-2422

SAMPLE, NATHANIEL WELSHIRE, architect; b. Phila., Apr. 3, 1918; s. Nathaniel Welshire Jr. and Evelyn Aldrich (Hope) S.; m. Virginia Bogert, May 19, 1945; children: Peter, Gregory, Deborah, Phoebe, Joan. BA, Dartmouth Coll., 1940; BArch, Ill. Inst. Tech., 1946. Registered architect, Wis. Archtl. designer Shaw Naess & Murphey, Chgo., 1946-47; designer Weiler, Strang & Assocs., Madison, Wis., 1947-51; project mgr. Weiler, Strang & Assocs., Madison, 1951-58, ptnr., 1958-62; ptnr. Sample & Mullins, Madison, 1962-67, Sample & Potter, Inc., Madison, 1967-84; v.p. Design for Tomorrow, Madison, 1956; pres. Dane County U.N. Assn., Madison, 1965-67; archtl. cons. Mass., N.Y., Ill., 1987—. Prin. works include Sch. Design, a Columbus elem. sch., 1953 (honor award), residence of Shorewood Hills, Wis., 1955 (honor award), Chilren's Treatment Ctr., Madison, 1959, Chgo. Pub. Libr. (1st pl. award nat. competition 1970), design for restoration of 120 Yr. old mansion in Madison for Wis. hdqrs. of Urban League (Preservation award Dane County), 1991. Mem. Dane County Regional Plan Commn., 1981-86, Urban Design Commn., Madison, 1990—; bd. dirs. Madison Downtown Sr. Ctr., 1988—. Lt. (j.g.) USNR, 1942-46, PTO. Fellow AIA; mem. Wis. Soc. Architects (chmn. jury housing for homeless competition 1990, Golden award 1992). Democrat. Mem. Soc. of Friends. Avocations: sports, grandchildren, citizenship. Address: 1105 Rutledge St Madison WI 53703-3825

SAMPLE, STEVEN BROWNING, university president; b. St. Louis, Nov. 29, 1940; s. Howard and Dorothy (Cunningham) S.; m. Kathryn Brunkow, Jan. 28, 1961; children: Michelle Sample Smith, Melissa Ann. BS, U. Ill., 1962, MS, 1963, PhD, 1965; LLD (hon.), U. Sheffield, Eng., 1991; EdD (hon.), Purdue U., 1994; DHL (hon.), Hebrew Union Coll., 1994; DL (hon.), U. Nebr., 1995. Sr. scientist Melpar Inc., Falls Church, Va., 1965-66; assoc. prof. elec. engring. Purdue U., Lafayette, Ind., 1966-73; dep. dir. Ill. Bd. Higher Edn., Springfield, 1971-74; prof. elec. and computer engring. SUNY, Buffalo, 1982-91, pres., 1982-91; pres. U. So. Calif., L.A., 1991—, prof. elec. engring., 1991—; bd. dirs. Ind., First Interstate Bancorp, L.A., Presley Cos, Newport Beach, Calif., Bancorp., Beverly Hills, Calif., Western Atlas Inc., Beverly Hills, Calif.; vice chmn., bd. dirs. Western N.Y. Tech. Devel. Ctr., Buffalo, 1982-91; chmn. bd. dirs. Calspan-UB Rsch. Ctr., Inc., Buffalo, 1983-91; mem. Calif. Coun. Sci. and Tech., Irvine, Calif.; cons. in field. Contbr. articles to profl. jours.; patentee in field. Timpanist St. Louis Philharm. Orch., 1955-58; chmn. Western N.Y. Regional Econ. Devel. Coun., 1984-91; trustee U. at Buffalo Found., 1982-91, Studio Arena Theatre, Buffalo, 1983-91, Western N.Y. Pub. Broadcasting Assn., 1985-91; bd. dirs. Buffalo Philharm. Orch., 1982-91, Regenstrief Med. Found., Indpls., 1982-91, Rsch. Found. SUNY, 1987-91; mem. Gov.'s Conf. on Sci. and Engring. Edn., Rsch. and Devel., 1989-91; chair Calif. Bus.-Higher Edn. Forum; bd. dirs. L.A. chpt. World Affairs Coun., Hughes Galaxy Inst. Edn., L.A., Rebuild L.A. Com., Regenstrief Inst., Indpls., L.A. Metro. Project, Coalition of 100 Club of L.A.; trustee L.A. Ednl. Alliance for Restructuring Now. Recipient Disting. Alumnus award Dept. Elec. Engring. U. Ill., 1980, citation award Buffalo Coun. on World Affairs, 1988, Engr. of Yr. award N.Y. State Soc. Profl. Engrs., 1985, Alumni Honor award Coll. Engring., U. Ill., 1985, Outstanding Elec. Engr. award Purdue U., 1993, Humanitarian award Nat. Conf. Christians and Jews, L.A., 1994, Hollzer Meml. award Jewish Fedn. Coun. Greater L.A., 1994; Sloan Found. fellow, 1962-63, NSF grad. fellow, 1963-65, Am Coun. Edn. fellow Purdue U., 1970-71, NSF. Mem. AAU (chmn. com. on postdoctoral edn. 1994—), IEEE (Outstanding Paper award 1976), Nat. Assn. State Univs. and Land-Grant Colls. (ednl. telecommunications com., 1982-83, chmn. coun. of pres. 1985-86, edn. and tech. com. 1986-87, exec. com. 1987-89), Coun. on Fgn. Rels., Sigma Xi. Episcopalian. Home: 1550 Oak Grove Ave San Marino CA 91108 Office: U So Calif Office of the Pres University Park ADM 110 Los Angeles CA 90089-0012

SAMPLES, RONALD EUGENE, coal company executive; b. Boonville, Ind., Apr. 23, 1926; s. Harold Forest and Hazel Pearl (Grandstaff) S.; student U. Notre Dame, 1944-46; B.S.E.M. N. Mex. Sch. Mines, 1949; m. Virginia Agnes Derr, Feb. 13, 1950; children—Ronald Eugene, II, Rebecca Lee, Thomas Harold, Susan Ann. With Peabody Coal Co., St. Louis, 1949-66, regional chief engr., 1960-66; with Consol. Coal Co., Pitts., 1966-73, 75—, v.p. engring./exploration, 1973, pres., chief operating officer, 1975-77, chmn., chief exec. officer, 1977—; pres. coal and minerals ops. Conoco Inc., 1980—; sr. v.p ops. Amax Coal Co., Indpls., 1973-75, exec. v.p. engring. ops., exploration, purchasing, 1975. Bd. dirs. United Way, Pitts., 1977—. Regional Indsl. Devel. Corp. Southwestern Pa., 1978-79, Allegheny Trails council Boy Scouts Am., 1978-79; mem. sponsoring com. Penn's S.W. Assn., 1978-79; mem. citizen's sponsoring com. Allegheny Conf. on Community Devel., 1978-79; mem. nat. sect. coal industry. corp. campaign Boys Clubs Am., 1978-80. Served with USN, 1944-46. Registered profl. engr., Ind., Pa., Ky., Mont., N.Mex., Utah; registered profl. land surveyor, Ky. Mem. Pa. Soc. Profl. Engrs., AIME, Nat. Coal Assn. (chmn. bd.). Democrat. Clubs: King Coal, St. Clair Country, Duquesne, Renaissance, Rolling Rock, Laurel Valley Golf, Elks. Office: Arch Mineral Corp 1 Cityplace Dr # 3 Saint Louis MO 63141-7014

SAMPRAS, PETE, tennis player; b. Washington, Aug. 12, 1971; s. Sam and Georgia Sampras. mem. U.S. Davis Cup team. Winner tournaments including Phila., 1990, Manchester, 1990, U.S. Open, 1990, 1993, Grand Slam Cup, 1990, L.A., 1991, Indpls., 1991, Lyon, 1991, IBM/ATP Tour World Championship-Frankfurt, 1991, 94, U.S. Pro Indoor, 1992, Lipton Internat., 1993, Wimbledon, 1993, 94, 95, Australian Open, 1994, Italian Open, 1994; ranked # 1 during 1993, 94 season, finalist Australian Open, 1995. 1st male to win the U.S Open, Wimbledon, and the Australian Open in succession, mem. U.S. Davis Cup team, 1991. Office: Assn Tennis Profls 611 Ryan Pla Dr 6th Fl Arlington TX 76011-9990*

SAMPSON, DAPHNE RAE, library director; b. Milw., Aug. 11, 1943; d. Gerald Joseph and Helene Virginia Babbitt; m. Charles Sargent Sampson, Oct. 23, 1971. BA, U. Wis., 1965, MLS, 1966. Reference librr. Def. Intelligence Agy., Washington, 1966-68; sr. reference librr. U.S. Dept. of State, Washington, 1968-78, Exec. Office of the Pres., Washington, 1978-80; chief readers' svcs. Fed. Trade Commn., Washington, 1980-81; chief readers' svcs. U.S. Dept. of Justice, Washington, 1981-84, asst. dir. libr. staff, 1984-86, dep. dir. libr. staff, 1986, acting dir. libr. staff, 1986-87, dir. libr. staff, 1987—, sr. exec. svc., 1995—. Active Berkshire Civic Assn., Alexandria, Va., 1976—. Mem. Am. Assn. Law Librs., Law Librs. Soc. of Washington, Fed. Libr. and Info. Ctr. Com. (bd. mem. 1992). Home: 5838 Wyomissing Ct Alexandria VA 22303 Office: US Dept of Justice Libr Rm 5317 10th & Pennsylvania Ave NW Washington DC 20530

SAMPSON, EARLDINE ROBISON, education educator; b. Russell, Iowa, June 18, 1923; d. Lawrence Earl and Mildred Mona (Judy) Robison; m. Wesley Claude Sampson, Nov. 25, 1953; children: Ann Elizabeth, Lisa Ellen. Diploma, Iowa State Tchrs. Coll., 1943, BA, 1950; MS in Edn., Drake U., 1954; postgrad., No. Ill. U., Iowa State U., 1965-66, 74. Cert. tchr., guidance counselor, Iowa. Tchr. elem. sch. various pub. sch. sys., 1943-48; cons. speech and hearing Iowa Dept. Pub. Instrn., Des Moines, 1950-52; speech therapist Des Moines Pub. Schs., 1952-54, 55; lectr. spl. edn. No. Ill. U., DeKalb, 1964-65; tchr. of homebound Cedar Falls (Iowa) Pub. Schs., 1967-68; asst. prof. edn. U. No. Iowa, Cedar Falls, 1968; asst. prof., counselor Wartburg Coll., Waverly, Iowa, 1968-70; instr. elem. edn., then head of advising elem. edn. Iowa State U., Ames, 1972-82; field supr. elem. edn. U. Toledo, 1988, 89; ind. cons. Sylvania, Ohio, 1989—; cons. Des Moines Speech and Hearing Ctr., 1958-59, bd. dirs., 1962, 63; cons. Sartori Hosp., Cedar Falls, 1967-69; bd. dirs. Story County Mental Health Ctr., Ames, 1972-74. NDEA fellow, 1965. Mem. AAUW, Univ. Women's Club, Zeta Phi Eta. Methodist. Avocations: public speaking on preservation of prose and poetry, reading, music, photography. Home: 4047 Newcastle Dr Sylvania OH 43560-3450

SAMPSON, FRANKLIN DELANO, minister; b. Houston, Jan. 31, 1947; s. Harry Burney and Annie Belle (Lenzia) S.; m. Fannie Marie Iles, Mar. 12, 1972; children: De Anza Michelle, Franklin Delano, Jr., Frederick Dwayne. BA, U. Houston, 1970; D of Ministries (hon.), Mt. Hope Bible Coll., 1978. Ordained to ministry Nat. Bapt. Conv., 1969. Pastor Friendship Missionary Bapt. Ch., Houston, 1972—; moderator Unity Missionary Bapt. Gen. Assn., Houston, 1985—; chmn. Minister's Conf. of Missionary Bapt. Gen. Conv., Dallas, 1987—, Commn. on Orthodoxy of Nat. Bapt. Conv. of Am., Inc., Shreveport, La., 1987—; chief exec. officer Visions of Faith Ministries, Inc., Houston, 1985—. Mem. Bapt. Mins. Assn. of Houston and Vicinity (v.p. 1990—), Unity Missionary Bapt. Gen. Assn. (Houston, moderator 1985-93), Masons. Democrat. Home: 12947 Wincrest Ct Cypress TX 77429-2001 Office: Friendship Missionary Bapt Ch 4812 Bennington St Houston TX 77016-7003

SAMPSON, JOHN EUGENE, food company executive; b. Lincoln, Nebr., Feb. 25, 1941; s. Delbert John and Mary Etta (Dodrill) S.; m. Mary Margaret Treanor, Aug. 14, 1965; children—J. Mark, Sharon. A.B. with distinction, Nebr. Wesleyan U., 1963; M.B.A., Ind. U., 1964. Mgmt. asst., exec. trainee Office Sec. Def., Washington, 1963-64; mem. staff Com. Econ. Devel., Washington, 1964-69; coordinator environ. planning Gen. Mills Inc., Mpls., 1969-72, mgr. devel. planning, 1972-74; dir. corp. planning Central Soya Co. Inc., Ft. Wayne, Ind., 1974-76, v.p corp. planning, 1976-80, v.p corp. planning and devel., 1980-82, v.p. corp. devel., corp. sec., 1982-84; v.p corp. planning and devel. Internat. Multifoods, Inc., 1984—; pres. Sampson Assocs., Inc., 1994—. Mem. bd. govs. Nebr. Wesleyan U., 1974-80; chmn. bd. trustees St. Joseph United Meth. Ch., Ft. Wayne, 1984; bd. dirs., treas. North Ind. United Meth. Found., 1981-84; lay mem. North Ind. Ann. Conf. United Meth. Ch., 1980-84; bd. dirs. Anthony Wayne coun. Boy Scouts Am., 1984; lay mem. Minn. Ann. Conf. United Meth. Church, 1985-91; chmn. conf. bd. devel. Minn. United Meth. Conf., 1986-91; chmn. bd. trustees Hennepin Ave. United Meth. Ch., Mpls., 1990-92, lay leader and chair adminstrv. coun., 1993, 94. Mem. Ind. U. Sch. Bus. Alumni Assn. (pres. 1984-85), Interlachen Country Club. Home: 6612 Gleason Ter Minneapolis MN 55439-1131 Office: Internat Multifoods Inc Multifoods Tower Box 2942 33 S 6th St Minneapolis MN 55402-3601

SAMPSON, JOHN J., lawyer, educator; b. St. Paul, Sept. 30, 1935; s. J.E. and Margaret A. Sampson; m. Joyce C. Hoff, Aug. 6, 1940; children—Margaret J., Eleanor H. LL.B. magna cum laude, U. Minn., 1966. Bar: Calif. 1967, Tex. 1980. Assoc. Morrison-Foerster, San Francisco, 1966-69; asst. gen. csl. U.S. Commn. on Obscenity and Pornography, 1969-70; asst. prof. U. Tex. Sch. Law, Austin, 1970-73, prof., 1973-82, Ben Gardner Sewell prof. law 1982-86; William Benjamin Wynne prof., 1986—. Bd. dirs. Legal Aid Soc. Central Tex.; lectr., legis. draftsman; reporter Nat. Conf. Commrs. Uniform St. Laws, 1990—. Pres., Minn. Law Rev., 1965-66; contbr. numerous articles to legal publs. Mem. State Bar Tex. (editor family law sect. report 1976—.) Office: U Tex Sch Law 727 E 26th St Austin TX 78705-3224

SAMPSON, ROBERT NEIL, association executive; b. Spokane, Wash., Nov. 29, 1938; s. Robert Jay and Juanita Cleone (Hickman) S.; m. Jeanne Louise Stokes, June 7, 1960; children—Robert W., Eric S., Christopher B., Heidi L. B.S. in Agr, U. Idaho, 1960; M.Public Adminstrn., Harvard U., 1974. Soil conservationist Soil Conservation Service, Burley, Idaho, 1960-61; work unit conservationist Soil Conservation Service, Orofino, Idaho, 1962-65; agronomist Soil Conservation Service, Idaho Falls, Idaho, 1967-68; info. specialist Soil Conservation Service, Boise, 1968-70, area conservationist, 1970-72; land use specialist Soil Conservation Service, Washington, 1974-77; dir. environ. services div. Soil Conservation Service, 1977; land use program mgr. Idaho Planning and Community Affairs Agy., Boise, 1972-73; exec. v.p. Nat. Assn. Conservation Dists., Washington, 1978-84, Am. Forestry Assn., Washington, 1984—; instr. soils and land use Boise State U., 1972; dir. Am. Land Forum, Washington, 1978-88. Author: Farmland or Wasteland: A Time To Choose, 1981, For Love of the Land, 1985; contbr. articles to profl. and popular publs. Pres. Orofino Golf Assn., 1966, Clearwater County Search and Rescue Unit, 1966-67; chmn. Nat. Common. on Wildfire Disasters, 1992-94. Recipient President's citation Soil Conservation Soc. Am., 1978; named Boise Fed. Civil Servant of Year Boise Fed. Bus. Assn., 1972. Fellow Soil and Water Conservation Soc. (Hugh Hammond Bennett award 1992); mem. Soc. Am. Foresters, Am. Soc. Assn. Execs. Presbyterian. Home: 5209 York Rd Alexandria VA 22310-1126 Office: Am Forestry Assn 1516 P St NW Washington DC 20005-1932

SAMPSON, RONALD GARY, lawyer; b. Haverhill, Mass., Apr. 8, 1942; s. Courtney Howard and Irene Velma (Sweetser) S. AB, Yale U., 1963; MA, Cambridge U., Eng., 1965; JD, Harvard U., 1968. Bar: Mass. 1969. Asst. prof., asst. dean sch. law U. Conn., 1968-69; assoc. Goodwin, Procter and Hoar, Boston, 1969-75; gen. counsel The Boston Co., 1975—, Boston Safe Deposit and Trust Co., 1975—; bd. dirs. Boston Safe Deposit and Trust Co. N.Y., Boston Hambro Corp., Boston Instl. Svcs. Inc. Trustee Longy Sch. Music, Cambridge, Mass., 1973—, pres. 1986—; dir. Opera Co. Boston, 1978-83. Mem. ABA, Harvard Music Assn. (bd. dirs. 1982—, v.p. 1988—), Handel and Haydn Soc. (gov. 1986—), Cambridge Soc. Early Music (bd. dirs. 1976—). Clubs: Algonquin, Longwood Cricket, Badminton and Tennis.

SAMPSON, SAMUEL FRANKLIN, sociology educator; b. Malden, Mass., Sept. 22, 1934; s. Samuel Daniel and Margaret Louise (Grimes) S.; m. Patricia Katherine Driscoll, Apr. 8, 1972. B.A., U. Okla., 1960, M.A., 1961; Ph.D., Cornell U., 1968. Asst. prof. dept. sociology SUNY, Binghamton, 1965-66; research assoc. dept. sociology Cornell U., Ithaca, N.Y., 1966-67;

lectr., chmn. bd. tutors and advs. Harvard U., Cambridge, Mass., 1967-72; assoc. prof. dept. urban studies and planning MIT, Cambridge, 1971-72; prof. sociology U. Vt., Burlington, 1972—, chmn. dept. sociology, 1972-76, 90—; research and policy cons. Public & Community Agys. and Orgns., 1969—. Gen. editor: Bobbs-Merrill Studies in Sociology, 1970-77; contbr. articles to profl. jours. Served with USAF, 1954-58. Mem. AAUP, AAAS, Internat. Sociol. Assn., Am. Sociol. Assn., Am. Acad. Arts and Scis., Ea. Sociol. Soc., Soc. Study Social Problems, New Eng. Sociol. Assn., Soc. Sci. Study Religion, Internat. Soc. Sociology of Knowledge. Home: 215 S Cove Rd Burlington VT 05401-5445 Office: Dept Sociology Univ Vt 31 S Prospect St Burlington VT 05405-1704

SAMPSON, WILLIAM ROTH, lawyer; b. Teaneck, N.J., Dec. 11, 1946; s. James and Amelia (Roth) S.; 1 child, Lara; m. Drucilla Jean Mort, Apr. 23, 1988. BA with honors in History, U. Kans., 1968, JD, 1971. Bar: Kans. 1971, U.S. Dist. Ct. Kans. 1971, U.S. Ct. Appeals (10th cir.) 1982, U.S. Ct. Claims 1985, U.S. Ct. Appeals (8th cir.) 1992. Assoc. Turner & Balloun, Gt. Bend, Kans., 1971; ptnr. Foulston & Siefkin, Wichita, Kans., 1975-86; shareholder Shook, Hardy & Bacon, Overland Park, Kans., 1987—; presenter legal edn. seminars; speaker to legal orgns., ins. co. seminars and confs.; adj. prof. advanced litigation U. Kans., 1994; mem. faculty trial tactics inst. Emory U. Sch. Law, 1994; lectr. area law schs. Mem. Kans. Law Rev., 1969-71, editor, 1970-71; contbr. articles to legal jours. Chmn. stewardship com. Univ. Friends Ch., Wichita, 1984-86; bd. dirs. Friends U. Retirement Corp., Wichita, 1985-87; chmn. capital fund drives Trinity Luth. Ch., Lawrence, Kans., 1990, 93; mem. ch. coun., 1990-92; bd. dirs. The Lied Carter of Lawrence, Kans. Lt. USN, 1971-75. Fellow Kans. Bar Assn. (chmn. Kans. coll. advocacy 1986, long-range planning, continuing legal edn. com. 1987-88); mem. ABA, Douglas County Bar Assn., Johnson County Bar Assn. (bench-bar com. 1989-93, Boss of Yr. award 1990), Wichita Bar Assn. (bd. dirs. 1985-86), Am. Bd. Trial Advs. (pres. Kans. chpt. 1990-91, nat. bd. mem. 1990-91), Internat. Assn. Def. Coun. (faculty mem. trial acad. 1994), Def. Rsch. Inst. (Kans. chmn. 1990-93, Exceptional Performance Citation 1990, Outstanding State Rep. 1991, 92, 94), Kans. Assn. Def. Counsel (pres. 1989-90, legis. coun. 1991, 93, William H. Kahrs Disting. Achievement award 1994), Kans. U. Law Soc. (bd. govs. 1993—), Am. Inn Ct. (Judge Hugh Means chpt., Master of Bench), Alvamar Country Club, Order of Coif, Delta Sigma Rho, Phi Alpha Theta, Omicron Delta Kappa. Republican. Lutheran. Avocations: jogging, golf, snow skiing, travel, reading. Office: Shook Hardy & Bacon 9401 Indian Creek Pky Overland Park KS 66210-2005

SAMPUGNARO, TRUDY M., principal. Prin. St. Andrew Apostle Sch., Silver Spring, Md. Recipient DOE Elem. Sch. Recognition award, 1989-90. Office: St Andrew Apostle Sch 11602 Kemp Mill Rd Silver Spring MD 20902-1718

SAMRA, HISHAM, pharmaceutical executive. With Ares Serono, Inc., 1988-92; pres. Serono Labs. Inc., Norwell, Mass., 1992—. Office: Serono Labs Inc 100 Longwater Cir Norwell MA 02061-1616

SAMS, JAMES FARID, real estate development company executive; b. Bay City, Mich., Apr. 21, 1932; s. James and Adele (Abuismail) S.; m. Betty Suham Hamady, Aug. 17, 1957; children: James Karl, Alicia Diane, Victoria Saab. BA, Northwestern U., 1954; JD, U. Mich., 1957; LLM, Harvard U., 1959. Com. counsel ABA spl. com. World Peace/Law, Washington, 1960-63; ptnr. Reeves, Harrison, Sams & Revercomb, Washington, 1964-69, Brown & Sams, Washington, 1969-71, Kirkwood, Kaplan, Russin, Veechi & Sams, Beirut, 1971-74; owner, prin. Am. Devel. Services Corp., Washington, 1978—; former chmn. bd. DASI, Inc., Washington, 1974-90; dir. Bristol Compressors, Inc., 1983-86, Nat. Bank Wash., 1986-91; rep. U.S. State Dept. Ams. Abroad, Washington, 1965; del. UN Com. on Internat. Trade Law, N.Y.C., 1970. Contbr. articles to profl. jours. Co-founder, dir. Am. Near East Refugee Aid, Washington, 1968-92; mem. adv. bd. Ctr. for Study of Global South, Am. U., Washington, 1983—; mem. visitors com. U. Mich. Law Sch.; mem. exec. com. Am. Task Force for Lebanon, Washington. Served to lt. U.S. Army, 1957-58. Mem. ABA, Bar Assn. of Washington, Am. Soc. Internat. Law, Nat. Assn. Arab Ams. (pres. 1981, chmn. 1983). Avocations: skiing, sports. Home: 8907 Fernwood Rd Bethesda MD 20817-3015 Office: Am Devel Svcs Corp 5454 Wisconsin Ave Ste 1260 Bethesda MD 20815-6901

SAMS, JOHN ROLAND, retired mission executive, missionary; b. Whatcheer, Iowa, Nov. 1, 1922; s. Bert Willian and Vesta Leora (Wilkins) S.; m. Frances Elizabeth McCluney, July 3, 1924; children: Phyllis Jean, Georgia Ann, Bert Franklin. BS, Iowa State U., 1949; MA, Drake U., 1952; student, Hartford Sem., 1952-54; MA, Chapman Coll., 1972; HHD (hon.), Philippine Christian U., Manila. Tchr. Paullina (Iowa) Pub. Schs., 1949-51; missionary Christian Ch. (Disciples of Christ), Thailand, 1954-67, Philippines, 1968-71; v.p. Am. Leprosy Missions, N.Y.C., 1972-76; exec. v.p. Am. Leprosy Missions, Bloomfield, N.J., 1976-84; pres. Am. Leprosy Missions, Elmwood Park, N.J., 1984-89. Served with USAAF, 1942-46. Mem. United Ch. of Christ. Avocations: travel, reading.

SAMS, ROBERT ALAN, lawyer; b. Mansfield, Ohio, Oct. 17, 1945; s. Ross A. and G. Louise (McFarland) S.; m. Susan M. Danielson, Aug. 26, 1967; children: David R. Tracey M., Daniel R. BA, Denison U., 1967; JD, Vanderbilt U., 1970. Bar: Wis. 1970, U.S. Dist. Ct. (ea. dist.) Wis. 1970, Fla. 1981; bd. cert. estate planning and probate atty. Fla. Assoc. Foley & Lardner, Milw., 1970-77, ptnr., 1977-81; ptnr. Foley & Lardner, Tampa, Fla., 1981—; instr. cert fin. planning courses Am. Coll., 1982-83, Coll. for Fin. Planning, 1984-85; adj. prof. of Law Stetson U. Author: Florida Personal Representative's Guide, 1993; mng. editor: Vanderbilt Law Rev., 1969-70; contbr. articles to profl. jours. Dir. Tampa Bay Estate Planning Coun., 1983-86, Suncoast Chpt. Leukemia Soc. Am., Tampa, 1984-86, Hillsborough County Chpt. Am. Heart Assn., Tampa, 1985-87, Ind. Day Sch., Tampa, 1982-85; svc. asst., adult edn. tchr. Village Presbyn. Ch., 1984—; mem. adv. bd. Child Abuse Coun., Inc., 1984—; mem. planned giving com. Salvation Army, 1987—, Arthritis Found., 1993—; mem. estate planning and endowment com. U. So. Fla. Med. Ctr., 1987—; mem. profl. adv. coun. U. So. Fla., 1993—; mem. adv. bd. Community Found. Greater Tampa, 1990—. Recipient Denison-Vanderbilt Law Scholarship Vanderbilt U., 1967-70, Eddie Morgan Law Scholarship Vanderbilt U., 1969-70. Fellow Am. Coll. Trust and Estate Counsel; mem. ABA (real property, probate and trust sects.), Wis. Bar Assn., Fla. Bar Assn. (probate law com., trust law com.), Hillsborough County Bar Assn. (chmn. cir. probate rules, edn. and liason com. 1986-88), Tampa Bay Chpt. Internat. Assn. for Fin. Planning, Inc. (dir. 1983-86), Order of Coif, Kiwanis, Greater Tampa C. of C., Leadership Tampa. Republican. Avocations: running, archery. Home: 18512 Avocet Dr Lutz FL 33549 Office: Foley & Lardner PO Box 3391 100 N Tampa St Tampa FL 33601-3391

SAMSEL, MAEBELL SCROGGINS (MIDGE SAMSEL), paralegal; b. Yazoo City, Miss., Aug. 15, 1940; d. Robert and Lela Estelle (Hammonds) Scroggins; m. John Sanders Swain, Dec. 30, 1960 (div. Oct. 1968); 1 child, Stacy Melissa Swain Ramsey; m. Howard Swinehart Samsel, Oct. 8, 1981. BA, Miss. Coll., 1963. Sec. Standard Life Ins. Co., Jackson, Miss., 1963-64; legal sec. Gray & Montague Law Firm, Hattiesburg, Miss., 1964-65; personnel sec. Adj. Gen.'s Office, State of Miss., Jackson, 1965-70; paralegal State of Miss., Atty. Gen.'s Office, Jackson, 1970-79, 84-86; sales agt. Prudential Ins. Co. Am., Jackson, 1979-84. Chmn. acquisitions Miss. Mus. Art, Jackson, 1983, acquisitions vol., 1982, 89, chmn. Vols. at the Palette, 1990—, pres. aux., 1991-92, trustee, 1991-92; vol. Miss. Mus. Palette Restaurant, 1988—; chair Miss. Mus. Art Cafe Vols. 1994-95; mem. Jackson Symphony League, 1988—, Miss. Opera Guild, Jackson, 1991—, Friends of the Ballet, 1989—. Named Vol. of the Week, Miss. Mus. Art Palette Restaurant, 1989, Vol. of Yr., Miss. Mus. of Art, 1991-92. Mem. Jackson Assn. Legal Secs. (pres. 1975-76, 77-78, v.p. 1974-75, del. to nat. convs. 1975, 77, Outstanding Legal Sec. of Yr. 1975-76), Miss. Assn. Legal Secs., Nat. Assn. Legal Secs. (chmn. nat. spring bd. meeting 1980), Miss. Coll. Alumni Assn., Petrolwum Aux. (v.p. 1986-87, pres. 1988-89, treas. 1989-90, pres. 1994-95), Revelers Dance Club, Serendipity Bridge Club (treas. 1989-93, v.p. 1991-92, pres. 1992-93), Met. Supper Club. Republican. Baptist. Avocations: fishing, piano, travel. Home: 1206 Bay Vis Brandon MS 39042-8650

SAMSON, ALLEN LAWRENCE, bank executive; b. Milw., Nov. 16, 1939; s. Harry E. and Rose (Landau) S.; m. Vicki Faye Boxer, July 3, 1977; children: Daniel, Rachel; children from previous marriage: Nancy, David. BS, U. Wis., 1962, LLB, 1965. Bar: Wis. 1965. Asst. dist. atty. Milw. County Dist. Attys. Office, 1965-67, dep. dist. atty., 1968-70; assoc. Samson & Nash, Milw., 1967-68; ptnr. Samson, Friebert, Sutton and Finerty, Milw., 1970-73; v.p., sec. Am. Med. Svcs., Inc., Milw., 1973-83, exec. v.p., chief exec. officer, 1983-86, chmn., chief exec. officer, 1986-90; cons. nursing homes Samson Med. Mgmt. Co., Milw., 1990-93; pres. Liberty Bank, Milw., 1993—; pub. mem. nursing home study Wis. Legis. Bur., 1988-89; mem. bd. visitors U. Wis. Law Sch., 1992—; mem. health policy adv. coun. Med. Coll. Wis., 1992—. Trustee Milw. Ballet, 1982-89, Milw. Art Mus., 1985-95, pres. bd. trustees, 1992-95; bd. dirs. War Meml. Corp., 1991—, Jewish Fedn., 1985—, Milw. Jewish Home, Jewish Comty. Ctr., 1993-94; gen. chmn. Wis. Israel Bond Campaign, 1993. Recipient Kaplan prize for econ. devel. Govt. of Israel, 1986. Avocations: tennis, skiing, golf. Office: Liberty Bank 815 N Water St Milwaukee WI 53202 : Liberty Bank 815 N Water St Milwaukee WI 53202

SAMSON, ALVIN, former distributing company executive, consultant; b. N.Y.C., May 2, 1917; s. Morris and Jennie (Buitekant) S.; m. Ann Carol Furmansky, Aug. 15, 1942; children: Leslie Joan, Marla Adriane. Br. mgr. U.S. Hardware and Paper Co., 1947-51; mdse. mgr. U.S. Servateria, 1951-57; dir. purchasing U.S. Consumer Products, Los Angeles, 1959-64; v.p. ops. U.S. Consumer Products, 1964-66, pres., 1966-72; pres. U.S. Consumer Products, San Diego, Bakersfield, Las Vegas, Phoenix, 1966-72, Zelman Co., Los Angeles, San Francisco and Las Vegas, 1968-72, Triple A Corp., Los Angeles, 1966-72, U.S. Consumer Products-Wesco Mdse., Los Angeles, 1972-74; v.p. APL Corp., N.Y.C., 1967-74; pres. USCP-WESCO, 1974-85; cons. A. Samson Cons., Beverly Hills, 1985-92; retired, 1992. Active USCG Aux., 1981—, divsn. capt., 1992—. With USAAF, 1942-45. Named Man of Year Housewares Club So. Calif., 1965. Mem. Housewares Club So. Calif. (pres. 1957, bd. govs. 1955-56), Nat. Assn. Service Merchandisers (dir. 1982-85).

SAMSON, CHARLES HAROLD, JR. (CAR), retired engineering educator, consultant; b. Portsmouth, Ohio, July 12, 1924; s. Charles Harold and Gertrude (Morris) S.; m. Ruth Aileen Baumbach, Sept. 12, 1947; children: Peggy Aileen, Charles Harold III. B.S., U. Notre Dame, 1947, M.S., 1948; Ph.D., U. Mo., 1953. Registered profl. engr., Tex., Ind. Asst. field rep. Loebl, Schlossman and Bennett (architects and engrs.), Chgo., 1948-49; structures engr. Convair Aircraft, Fort Worth, 1951-52; sr. structures engr. Convair Aircraft, 1952-53, project aerodynamics engr., 1956-58, project structures engr., 1958-60; asst. prof. civil engring. U. Notre Dame, 1953-56; office engr. Wilbur H. Gartner & Assocs., South Bend, Ind., 1954; grad. lectr. civil engring. So. Meth. U., Dallas, 1952-53, 56-60; prof. structural engring. and mechanics, depts. aerospace and civil engring. Tex. A&M U., College Station, 1960-64, prof. civil engring., 1964-94, head dept., 1964-79, assoc. head dept., 1989-92, construction area engring. leader, dir. ctr. construction edn., 1992-93; rsch. engr. Tex. Transp. Inst., Tex. A&M U., 1960-62, head structural research dept., 1962-65, acting pres., 1980-81, v.p. planning, 1981-82; pres. S.W. Athletic Conf., 1979-81; v.p. Nat. Collegiate Athletic Assn., 1981-83, mem. council, 1983-85; cons. systems engring. and quality mgmt. Contbr. articles to profl. jours. Served to ensign USNR, 1943-46. Fellow ASCE, Nat. Inst. Engring. Mgmt. and Systems (pres. 1989-90); mem. Am. Soc. Engring. Mgmt., Nat. Soc. Profl. Engrs. (past v.p., chmn. profl. engrs. in edn., pres. 1987-88), Tex. Soc. Profl. Engrs. (past nat. dir., pres. 1973-74), Nat. Assn. Parliamentarians, Am. Pub. Works Assn., Internat. Soc. Systems Sci., Order of the Engr. (chmn., bd. govs., 1989-91), Am. Soc. Quality Control, Project Mgmt. Inst., Design and Constrn. Quality Inst., Nat. Coun. on Systems Engring., Nat. Inst. Engring. Ethics, Sigma Xi, Sigma Gamma Tau, Tau Beta Pi, Phi Kappa Phi, Chi Epsilon. Home: 2704 Camelot Dr Bryan TX 77802-2003

SAMSON, FREDERICK EUGENE, JR., neuroscientist, educator; b. Medford, Mass., Aug. 16, 1918; s. Frederick Eugene and Annie Bell (Pratt) S.; m. Camila Albert; children Cecile Samson Folkerts, Julie Samson Thompson, Renée. DO, Mass. Coll. Osteopathy, 1940; PhD, U. Chgo., 1952. Asst. prof. U. Kans., Lawrence, 1952-57, prof. physiology, 1962-73, chmn., prof. dept. physiology and cell biology, 1968-73; prof. physiology U. Kans. Med. Ctr., Kansas City, 1973-89, prof. emeritus, 1989—; dir. Ralph L. Smith Rsch. Ctr. U. Kans., Kansas City, 1973-89; staff scientist neurosci. rsch. program MIT, Cambridge, Mass., 1968-82, cons., 1982-91; vis. prof. neurobiology U. Catolica de Chile, Santiago, 1972; mem. Inst. de Investigaciones Citologicas, Valenica, Spain, 1981-89; hon. lectr. Mid-Am. State Univs. Assn., 1987. Editor: (with George Adelman) The Neurosciences: Paths of Discovery, II, 1992, (with Merrill Tarr) Oxygen Free Radicals in Tissue Damage, 1993; contbr. articles to profl. publs. Scientist, U.S.A., Spain Friendship Treaty, Madrid and Valencia, 1981. Staff sgt. U.S. Army, 1941-45, PTO. Recipient Rsch. Recognition award U. Kans. Med. Ctr., Kansas City, 1984; Van Lière fellow U. Chgo., 1948; Rawson fellow U. Chgo., 1949-51; USPHS fellow MIT, 1965. Fellow AAAS; mem. Am. Soc. Neurochemistry (chmn. program com. 1980), Am. Soc. Cell Biology (local host com. 1984), Am. Physiol. Soc. (emeritus 1990), Soc. Neurosci. (program com. 1972-73), The Oxygen Soc., N.Y. Acad. Sci., U. Chgo. Kansas City Club (chmn. alumni fund bd. 1975-82, pres. 1979-81), Sigma Xi (regional lectr. 1974-75, pres. Kansas City chpt. 1978, pres. neurosci. chpt. 1978). Avocation: hand balancing. Home: 171 Lakeshore Dr S Lake Quivira KS 66106-9516 Office: U Kans Med Ctr Ralph L Smith Rsch Ctr Bldg 37 Kansas City KS 66160

SAMSON, LINDA FORREST, nursing educator and administrator; b. Miami, Dec. 7, 1949; d. Alvin S. and Grace (Kanner) Forrest; m. Mark I. Samson, Jan. 29, 1972; children: Amy, Josh. BSN, Emory U., 1972, MN, 1973; PhD, U. Ga., 1989. RN, Fla., Ga., N.J., Pa. Nursing instr. Ga. State U., Atlanta, 1974-78; neonatal intensive care nurse Northside Hosp., Atlanta, 1976-78; perinatal clin. specialist Our Lady of Lourdes Med. Ctr., Camden, N.J., 1978-82, per diem staff nurse, ICU nursery, labor and delivery, 1982-88; asst. prof. nursing Kennesaw Coll. Marietta, Ga., 1988-89; asst. prof. Clayton State Coll., Morrow, Ga., 1989-92, head baccalaureate nursing dept., 1991-94, acting dean Sch. Health Scis., 1991-94; dean Sch. Health Scis., 1994—; adj. faculty Gloucester County Coll., 1981-83; adj. clin. preceptor U. Pa. Sch. Nursing, 1981-83, lectr. in perinatal nursing, 1983-88; nursing dir. So. N.J. Perinatal Coop., 1982-84; researcher and lectr. in field. Mem. editorial rev. bds.; contbr. chpts. to textbooks, articles to profl. jours. Bd. dirs., chmn. profl. adv. com. South Jersey chpt. March of Dimes, 1980-85. Named Nurse of Yr. N.J. State Nurses Assn., 1985; recipient Network Edn. grant N.J. State Dept. Health, 1982-84, numerous grants for rsch., 1983-89, Outstanding Svc. award March of Dimes, 1983, Disting. Leadership award March of Dimes, 1984. Mem. ANA (cert. nursing adminstrn. advanced, RNC high risk perinatal nursing), AACN (program com. 1987-88, rsch. com. 1988-89, project devel. task force 1989, strategic planning com. 1989, bd. dirs. 1987-90, bd. dirs. certification corp. 1987-90, chair neonatal and pediatric appeal panels 1992), Nat. Perinatal Assn. (program planning com. 1983-85, resolutions com. 1984-88, state devel. com. spl. interest group task force 1985-88, bd. dirs. 1985-89, chmn. resolutions com. 1988, fin. com. 1989, pub. health policy com.), Ga. Nurses Assn., Ga. Perinatal Assn. (bd. dirs., ex-officio 1989—), Phila. Perinatal Soc., Perinatal Assn. N.J. (pres. 1982-86), Sigma Theta Tau. Home: 2915 Four Oaks Dr Atlanta GA 30360-1744 Office: Clayton State Coll Sch Health Scis PO Box 285 Morrow GA 30260-0285

SAMSON, PERRY J., environmental scientist, educator; b. Binghamton, N.Y., May 18, 1950; s. Perry C. and Ann I. S.; children Karis, Carla. BS, SUNY, Albany, 1972, MS, 1974; PhD, U. Wis., 1979. Rsch. sci. N.Y. State Dept. Environ. Conservation, Albany, 1973-79; asst. prof. U. Mich., Ann Arbor, 1979-85, assoc. prof., 1985-89, prof., 1989—, Arthur Thurnald prof., 1995—; vis. sci. Nat. Ctr. Atmospheric Rsch., Boulder, Colo., 1985-86, U. Corp. Atmospheric Rsch., Boulder, 1994—; head Weather Underground; dir. Lab. Atmospheric Sci. & Environ. Rsch. Author chpts. to books; contbr. articles to profl. jours. Mem. NAS (com. haze in nat. parks and wilderness areas), Am. Meteorol. Soc. (mem. com. atmospheric chemistry), Am. Geophysical Union and Waste Mgmt. Assn. (mem. TT-3 meteorol. com., mem. TE-5 visibility com.). Office: U Mich 1539 Space Rsch Bldg Ann Arbor MI 48109-2143

SAMSON, PETER, lawyer; b. Princeton, N.J., Oct. 26, 1951; s. Hugh and Edith (Willett) S.; m. Lynne W. Coughlin, July 3, 1993; children: David, Brian, Catherine, Molly. BA, U. Pa., 1973; JD, New Eng. Sch. Law, 1976. Bar: Pa. 1976, U.S. Dist. Ct. Pa. 1980, U.S. Ct. Appeals (3d cir.) 1981, U.S. Supreme Ct. 1983. Staff atty. Defender Assn. of Phila., 1976-80; assoc. White & Williams, Phila., 1980-86, ptnr., 1986—; lectr. Temple U. Sch. Law. Mem. ABA, Phila. Bar Assn., Pa. Def. Inst., Assn. of Def. Counsel. Democrat. Avocations: skiing, sailing, wind surfing. Home: 215 Lenoir Ave Wayne PA 19087-3908 Office: White & Williams 1650 Market St Philadelphia PA 19103-7301

SAMSON, RICHARD MAX, investments and real estate executive; b. Milw., June 13, 1946; s. Harry E. and Rose (Landau) S.; m. Nancy K. Pinter; children: Gina Shoshana, Alayna Tamar; (stepson) Christopher P. BA, U. Wis., 1968. Dir., owner The Puppet Co., Jerusalem, 1972-73; pres. Century Hall, Inc., Milw., 1974-75; dir. purchasing Am. Med. Svcs., Inc., Milw., 1973-74, v.p., 1974-82, exec. v.p., 1982-86, pres., 1986-90; pres. Samson Investments, Milw., 1990—; bd. dirs. Liberty Bank, Milw.; sec. Super Sitters, Mequon, Wis., 1987—. Pres. bd. Theatre X, Milw., 1982, Holton Youth Ctr., Milw., 1994; v.p. bd. ArtReach, Milw., 1987; bd. dirs. P'nai Or Religious Fellowship, 1988-93, Children's Outing Assn., 1991—, Milw. Jewish Coun., 1992-94; mem. funding bd. Wis. Community Fund, 1989-93. Recipient Humanitarian Peace award Ecumenical Refugee Coun., 1989. Mem. Ams. for Peace Now (bd. dirs. 1990—). Avocations: chess, comic collecting, puppetry. Office: Samson Investments 100A Pleasant Milwaukee WI 53212

SAMSOT, ROBERT LOUIS, newspaper editor, consultant; b. New Orleans, July 20, 1943; s. Robert Desposito and Mary Helen (Dohan) S.; m. A. Michael Newton, June 9, 1965; children: Kathleen Anderson Samsot English, Robert Dohan. BA in Journalism, U. N.C., Chapel Hill, 1965; cert. in Bus. Adminstrn., Rockhurst Coll., 1982. Reporter Rocky Mountain News, Denver, 1965-67, The Comml. Appeal, Memphis, 1967-72; reporter, editor Newsday, L.I., N.Y., 1972-80; Gannett profl.-in-residence reporter U. Kans., Lawrence, 1980-81; met. editor The Kansas City (Mo.) Times, 1981-84; city editor The Plain Dealer, Cleve., 1984-87; lifestyle editor, dep. editor N.J., dep. editor nat. The Phila. Inquirer, 1987—; cons. W.K. Kellogg Nat. Fellowship, Battle Creek, Mich., 1984-93; freelance writer, 1965—. Youth soccer coach Swarthmore N.J., 1976-80, dir., 1979-80, Shaker Heights, Ohio, 1984-87, Swarthmore (Pa.) Recreation Assn., 1987-88; coach Johnson County (Kans.) Soccer League, 1983-84; bd. dirs. Suffolk County Heart Assn., L.I., 1974-75. Mem. Nat. Assn. Hispanic Journalists. Democrat. Roman Catholic. Avocations: travel, fishing, outdoor sports. Home: 610 Strath Haven Ave Swarthmore PA 19081 Office: The Phila Inquirer 400 N Broad Philadelphia PA 19101

SAMTER, MAX, physician, educator; b. Berlin, Germany, Mar. 3, 1908; came to U.S., 1937; s. Paul and Claire (Rawicz) S.; m. Virginia Svarz Ackerman, Oct. 17, 1947; 1 dau., Virginia Claire. Student, U. Freiburg, Germany, 1926, U. Innsbruck, Austria, 1928; M.D., U. Berlin, 1933. Diplomate: Am. Bd. Internal Medicine (past chmn. bd. allergy), Am. Bd. Allergy and Immunology. Intern, Medizinische Universitätsklinik der Charité, Berlin, 1931-32, resident internal medicine, 1932-33; practice medicine Berlin-Karow, Germany, 1933-38; resident internal medicine & hematology Johns Hopkins Hosp., 1938-39; resident anatomy U. Pa. Sch. Medicine, 1939-43; research asso. dept. biochemistry U. Ill., Chgo., 1946-47, from instr. to full prof. dept. medicine, 1948-69, prof. medicine Coll. Medicine (formerly Abraham Lincoln Sch. Medicine), 1969—, assoc. dean for clin. affairs, 1974-75; vis. scholar, immunology Weizmann Inst. of Sci.; chief staff U. Ill. Hosp., 1974-75; dir. inst. allergy & clin. immunology Grant Hosp., Chgo., 1975-83, sr. cons., 1983-93; rsch. sci. otolaryngology, head & neck surg. U. Ill. Coll. Med., Chgo., 1994—; cons. in allergy U.S. VA, 1962—. Editor: American Lectures in Allergy, 1950, (with Oren C. Durham) Regional Allergy, 1954, (with Harry L. Alexander) Immunological Diseases, 1965, 71, 78, 88, Excerpts from Classics in Allergy, 1969, rev. edit. (with Sheldon G. Cohen), 1992; (with Charles W. Parker) Hypersensitivity to Drugs, 1972; also articles in field. Served to capt. M.C. AUS, 1943-46, ETO. Recipient Disting. Faculty award U. Ill. Coll. Med. 1987. Fellow ACP; mem. AMA, Am. Acad. Allergy (past pres.), Internat. Assn. Allergology and Clin. Immunology (past pres., Disting. Svc. award 1991), German Soc. Allergology and Clin. Immunology (hon.), Phila. Coll. Physicians (hon.), Interasma (hon.), Sigma Xi, Alpha Omega Alpha. Home: 645 Sheridan Rd Evanston IL 60202-2533*

SAMUEL, ATHANASIUS YESHUE, archbishop; b. Hilwah, Syria, Dec. 25, 1907; s. Sowmey Malkey and Khatoun Malkey (Hido) S. Student, St. Mark's Sem., 1923-27, 29-31, Cairo Theol. Coll., 1927-29; DD (hon.), Gen. Theol. Sem., N.Y.C., 1989. Ordained priest Syrian Orthodox Ch. of Antioch, 1932; sec. to Syrian orthodox patriarch of Antioch, 1931-32; father superior St. Mark's Monastery, Jerusalem, 1933-43; patriarchal vicar of Jerusalem, 1943-46; archbishop, 1946-52; patriarchal del. to U.S.A. and Can., 1949-57; archbishop to U.S.A. and Can., 1957—. Author: Treasure of Qumran, 1966, Liturgy of St. James, 1967, Rites of Baptism, Holy Matrimony and Burial, 1974, Book of Church Festivals, 1984, Anaphoras, The Book of the Divine Liturgies, 1991, The Shorter Daily Prayer Book for the Faithful, 1993, Prayer Book for Various Occasions for the Use of the Clergy, 1993. Decorated by Emperor Haile Selassie I gold cross and papal medallion Pope Paul VI, cross Knights of St. John of Jerusalem, Grand Cross of St. Ignatius Theophoros; proclaimed Dean of Bishops of the Holy See of Antioch, 1989. Mem. World Council Chs., Nat. Council Chs. of Christ in U.S.A. Home and Office: 49 Kipp Ave Lodi NJ 07644-2945

SAMUEL, GERHARD, orchestra conductor, composer; b. Bonn, Germany, Apr. 20, 1924; came to U.S., 1939, naturalized, 1943; s. Arthur and Hilde (Behr) S. Student violin with Samuel Belov, chamber music with Jacques Gordon (scholarship); B.Mus. cum laude, Eastman Sch. Music, 1945; choral conducting with Hermann Genhart, conducting with Paul White and Howard Hanson, 1945; student of Serge Koussevitsky, Tanglewood, Mass., 1945-47; student, also Boris Goldowsky; student of Paul Hindemith (scholarship), Yale U., Mus.M. (Haupt prize), 1947; Ph.D. (hon.), Calif. Coll. Arts and Crafts. Fulbright grantee for study in Europe, 1949; exec. com. San Francisco Composers Forum, 1959-62; mem. composers workshop San Francisco Conservatory Music, 1960; prof. music Calif. Inst. Arts, to 1976; condr. Contemporary Ensemble Concert Series, U. Cin. Coll.-Conservatory of Music, 1976—; lectr. in field; guest condr. Oakland Calif./ Ballet Co. Condr.: Ballet Ballads, Music Box Theatre, Broadway, 1947-48; rsch. in France and Italy; condr. concerts Am. contemporary music, Paris, 1948-49, Accademia Chigiana (1st prize), Siena, Italy, 1949; assoc. condr. Mpls. Symphony Orch., 1949-59; condr., Ballets Concertants, Mpls., 1950-59, Collegium Musicum, Mpls., 1952-59, Mpls. Civic Opera Co., 1954-59; mus. dir. Grand Marais (Minn.) Music Festival, 1957-59, Minn. Centennial Music Festival, 1958, Oakland (Calif.) Symphony Orch., 1959-71; mus. dir., condr. San Francisco Ballet, 1961-70; founder, condr. Cabrillo Music Festival, 1962-68, West Coast New Music Ensemble, 1968-70, condr., mus. dir. Oakland Chamber Orch., 1963-69; assoc. condr. Los Angeles Philharmonic, 1970-74; mus. dir., condr., Ojai (Calif.) Festival, 1970-71, Pacific N.W. Ballet Co., 1982-83; artistic dir. L.A. Philharmonic Docents; guest condr. Am. Symphony, Lincoln Center, N.Y.C., 1964, Denver Symphony, 1965, San Francisco Spring Opera, 1965, 66, Am. Symphony Orch., 1965, Winnipeg (Can.) Symphony, 1967, Rochester Philharmonic Orch., 1973, Ives-Schoenberg Festival, Washington, 1974, Fresno Philharmonic, San Francisco Symphony, Vancouver Opera Orch., ann. European, Far Eastern and S.Am. concert tours; condr. Grand Teton Music Festival, 1992; also concerts on TV, with Opera Co. of Phila., youth orchs.; composer numerous works including Twelve on Death and No, In Memoriam D.Q., What of My Music, Into Flight From ..., Looking at Orpheus Looking, On A Dream, Requiem for Survivors, Fortieth Day, Beyond McBean, Au Revoir to Lady R., The Relativity of Icarus, Three Hymns to Apollo, Dirge for John Cage, Left Over Mirrors, Music for Four; commd. major orchs., prominent artists; condr. German premiere Hans Rott's Symphony in E with Sudwestfunk Orch., 1993 ; dir. orch. activities Coll. Conservatory of Music, Cin., from 1976; music dir., condr. Cin. Chamber Orch., 1983-91, Cin. Philharm. Orch., 1976—; invited participant Lincoln Ctr.'s Mozart Bicentennial Celebration, premiere of Outcries and Consolations, L.A., 1990; conducts and recs. (world premieres) Charles Ives (Larry Austin) Universe Symphony, Schubert's opera Der Graf von Gleichen, 1993—; recs. for CRI, Everest, Laurel, Orion, Hyperion, Desto, Delos, Centaur, ACOMA and Vienna Modern Masters

labels. Mem. adv. panel State Dept. Cultural Exchange; mem. music council Young Musicians Found. Recipient Nat. Endowment for Arts Composition award, 1974-75, Composer's Showcase N.Y. award, 1976, 77, 78, Post-Corbett award, 1987, Meet the Composer award, 1990, George Rieveschl prize U. Cin., 1992, Alice M. Ditson award Columbia U., 1994; Rockefeller Found. grantee. Mem. ASCAP (ann. award 1970—), Cin. Composers Guild, Nat. Assn. Composers. Achievements include a CD ecording of String Quartets, Transformations and locturne on and Impossible Dream, 1996. Home: 412 Liberty Hill #2-C Cincinnati OH 45210-1498 Office: Coll Conservatory Music Cincinnati OH 45221-0003

SAMUEL, HOWARD DAVID, union official; b. N.Y.C., Nov. 16, 1924; s. Ralph E. and Florence (Weingarten) S.; m. Ruth H. Zamkin, Apr. 15, 1948; children: Robert H., Donald F., William H. BA, Dartmouth Coll., 1948. Various positions Amalgamated Clothing and Textile Workers (formerly Amalgamated Clothing Workers Am.), N.Y.C., 1949-60; asst. pres. Amalgamated Clothing and Textile Workers (formerly Amalgamated Clothing Workers Am.), 1960-64, v.p., 1966-77; dep. under sec. Bur. Internat. Labor Affairs Dept. Labor, Washington, 1977-79; pres. indsl. union dept. AFL-CIO, Washington, 1979-92; v.p. New Sch. for Social Rsch., N.Y.C., 1964-65, Econ. Strategy Inst., 1992—; vice-chmn. N.Y. Urban Coalition, 1968-74; mem. governing bd. Common Cause, 1971-77; sec. Nat. Com. Full Employment, 1975-77, sec.-treas. 1977-89; mem. Pres.'s Commn. on Indsl. Competitiveness, 1983-85; sr. fellow Coun. on Competitiveness, 1993—, vice chmn. 1986-92; mem. U.S. Dept. Labor Task Force on Econ. Adjustment nd Worker Dislocation, 1985-87; mem. vis. com. advanced tech., Nat. Inst. Standards and Tech., 1995—. Author: (with Stephen K. Bailey) Congress at Work, 1952; Government in America, 1957; Editor: Toward a Better America, 1968. Mem. Nat. Manpower Adv. Com., 1969-74; mem. Commn. Population Growth and the Am. Future, 1970-72; mem. Def. Mfg. Bd., 1988-89, Def. Sci. Bd., 1989-92; chmn. White Plains Dem. Com., 1960-64; vice-chmn. Westchester County com., 1957-70, alt. del. nat. conv., 1964; mem. Nat. Dem. Charter Revision Com., 1972-73; exec. dir. Nat. Labor Com. McGovern-Shriver, 1972; del. Dem. Conv. on Party Orgn. and Policy, Kansas City, 1974, Nat. Dem. Conv., 1976; trustee Carnegie Corp., 1971-77, Joint Coun. Econ. Edn., 1971-77; bd. dirs. ACLU, 1966-68; trustee Brookings Instn.; overseer RAND Inst. for Civil Justice, 1987-93. With AUS, 1943-46. Mem. Coun. on Fgn. Rels., Phi Beta Kappa. Office: Coun on Competitiveness 900 17th St NW Washington DC 20006-2500

SAMUEL, ROBERT THOMPSON, optometrist; b. Kansas City, Mo., June 27, 1944; s. Manlius Thompson and Helen Evelyn (Syverson) S. B.A. William Jewel Coll., 1966; postgrad. U. Mo.-Kansas City, 1967, M.S. U. Mo., 1968; D. Optometry, U. Tenn.-Memphis, 1971. Cert. optometrist, Mo. Buyer Recco, Inc., Kansas City, Mo., 1963-67; histology lab. instr. William Jewell Coll., Liberty, Mo., 1965-66; pvt. practice optometry Gladstone, Mo., 1972—; panel Dr. Ford Motor Co., Claycomo, Mo., 1985—, Union Pacific R.R., Kansas City, 1985—, TWA Airlines, 1990, Union Carbide, 1990. Publicity coord. Rep. Party, Kansas City, Mo., 1975-76; chmn. Save Your Vision Week, Kansas City, 1977; mem. Theatre League of Kansas City, 1976—, Kansas City Mus., 1986—, Friends of Art, 1985, Friends of Mo. Town 1855, 1980—. Recipient Outstanding Young Men of Am. award Jaycees, 1978, Good Citizens award DAR, 1962. Mem. Am. Optometric Assn., Mo. Optometric Assn., Optometric Soc. Greater Kansas City, Heart of Am. Contact Lens Congress, Am. Acad. Sports Vision, Vol. Optometric Svcs. for Humanity, Smithsonian Assocs, Kappa Alpha Order (treas. 1966). Republican. Lutheran. Lodge: Lions (exec. bd. dirs. Lions Eye Clinic 1974-84, bd. dirs. Lions Eye Clinic 1982—, Outstanding Svc. award 1973, 74, editor Lions Optometric Ctr. Quar., 1974-84). Avocations: photography, music, piano, swimming, travel. Home: 6325 N Monroe Ave Kansas City MO 64119-1923 Office: 2700 NE Kendallwood Pky Ste 109 Kansas City MO 64119-2071

SAMUELS, ABRAM, stage equipment manufacturing company executive; b. Allentown, Pa., Sept. 15, 1920; s. Irving and Ann (Friedman) S.; m. Harriet Ann Goodman, Sept. 1, 1945; children: Margaret A. Samuels Berger, Katherine E., Sally R. Samuels Slifkin, John A., Dorothy M. Samuels Lampl, Caroline J. Samuels Bagli. B.S., Lehigh U., 1942; auditor philosophy, Princeton U., 1962-65. Pres. Automatic Devices Co., Allentown, 1946-75, chmn. exec. com., 1987-92; chmn. bd. Automatic Devices Co., 1975-87, 93—; chmn. bd. Mchts. Bank, 1981-85, chmn. exec. com., 1985-91; past guest lectr. Cedar Crest Coll., 1969-71, 84, Muhlenberg Coll., 1977-82, 92. Author: Where the Colleges Rank, 1973. Pres. Samuels Family Found., 1959—; past pres. Pa. Soc. for Crippled Children and Adults, 1957-58; past pres., hon. bd. dirs. Lehigh County Crippled Children's Soc., 1949-51; past pres. Lehigh County Humane Soc., 1960-64, Cedar Crest Coll. Assocs., 1968-70; bd. dirs. Allentown Hosp., 1977-88, chmn. bd., 1987; vice chmn. Allentown Hosp.-Lehigh Valley Hosp. Ctr., 1988; pres. Lehigh County Hist. Soc., 1976-78; past bd. dirs. Nat. Soc. for Crippled Children and Adults, Pa. Mental Health Assn., Merchants Bank, 1965-91, Lehigh County Indsl. Devel. Corp., Pa. Stage Co., 1983-84, Health East, Inc., 1985-91, Nightingale Awards of Pa., 1989-91; trustee St. Augustine's Coll., 1970-77, 92-95, Allentown YWCA, 1977-83; bd. dirs. Fund to Benefit Children and Youth of Lehigh Valley Inc. With AUS, 1942-46. Recipient Benjamin Rush award Lehigh County Med. Soc., 1954, Allentown Human Relations award, 1979; named Outstanding Young Man of Year Jr. C. of C., 1954. Mem. ASCAP, Hon. First Defenders, C. of C. (past v.p. 1960), Pa. German Soc., Am. Soc. Psychical Rsch. (trustee 1985-91, treas. 1990), Princeton Club (N.Y.C.), Rotary (pres. Allentown club 1955-56, dist. gov. 1964-65). Republican. Office: 2121 S 12th St Allentown PA 18103-4751

SAMUELS, CYNTHIA KALISH, communications executive; b. Pitts., May 21, 1946; d. Emerson and Jeanne (Kalish) S.; m. Richard Norman Atkins, Sept. 12, 1971; children: Joshua Whitney Samuels Atkins, Daniel Jonathan Samuels Atkins. BA, Smith Coll., 1968. Press aide McCarthy for Pres. Campaign, Washington, 1968; assoc. producer Newsroom program Sta. KQED, San Francisco, 1972-73; with CBS News, 1973-80, researcher, Washington, 1969-71, documentary researcher, N.Y.C., 1973-74, asst. fgn. editor, 1974-76, asst. N.Y. bur. chief, 1976-80; writer, field producer Today program NBC News, N.Y.C., 1980-84; polit. producer Today program, 1984-89; planning producer, 1988-89; sr. producer Main Street program NBC News, N.Y.C., 1987; founding exec. producer Channel One Program, 1989-92; exec. v.p. Whittle Communications, N.Y.C., 1989-94; now interactive TV and multi-media cons., 1994—. Author: It's A Free Country!: A Young Person's Guide to Politics and Elections, 1988; contbr. book revs. to N.Y. Times Book Rev., Washington Post Book World. Recipient Emmy award No. Calif. Acad. TV Arts and Scis., 1974, Columbia DuPont citation, 1975, Media Access award Calif. Office of Handicapped, 1991, Silver award Nat. Mental Health Assn., 2 Bronze awards Nat. Assn. Edn. in Film and TV, 1993.

SAMUELS, DONALD L., lawyer; b. Washington, May 8, 1961; s. Jack Donald Samuels and Francis Diane (Katcher) Yeoman; m. Linda Marie Tveidt, Aug. 17, 1986. AB, Brown U., 1983; JD, Columbia U., 1986. Bar: Calif. 1986, U.S. Dist. Ct. (cen. dist.) Calif. 1986, U.S Dist. Ct. (no., ea. and so. dists.) Calif. 1988, U.S. Ct. Appeals (9th cir.) 1989. Law clk. U.S. Dist. Ct. (cen. dist.) Calif., L.A., 1986-87; assoc. Sidley & Austin, L.A., 1987-94, ptnr., 1994-95; ptnr. Samuels & Samuels, L.A., 1995—. Mem. ABA, Los Angeles County Bar Assn., Phi Beta Kappa. Home: 2011 S Canfield Ave Los Angeles CA 90034-1110 Office: Samuels & Samuels 2029 Century Pk E Ste 2718 Los Angeles CA 90067

SAMUELS, ERNEST, author, educator; b. Chgo., May 19, 1903; s. Albert and Mary (Kaplan) S.; m. Jayne Porter Newcomer, Aug. 24, 1938; children: Susanna, Jonathan, Elizabeth. Ph.B., U. Chgo., 1923, J.D., 1926, A.M., 1931, Ph.D., 1942. Bar: Ill. Franklyn Bliss Snyder prof. English, Northwestern U., 1942-71; chmn. English dept., 1964-66; Leo S. Bing vis. prof. U. So. Calif., 1966-67; Fulbright lectr. Inter-University Chair in Am. Studies, Belgium, 1958-59. Author: Business English Projects, 1936, The Young Henry Adams, 1948, Henry Adams: The Middle Years, 1958, Henry Adams: The Major Phase, 1964, Bernard Berenson: The Making of a Connoisseur, 1979 (Carl Sandburg award 1981), Bernard Berenson: The Making of a Legend, 1987, Henry Adams, 1989; editor: Adams, History of the United States, 1967, The Education of Henry Adams, 1973, Writings of Henry Adams, 1983, Henry Adams: Selected Letters, 1992; mem. editorial bd.: Am. Lit., 1964-71; mem. adv. bd. publ., Adams Papers; assoc. editor:

Letters of Henry Adams, vols. I-III, 1983, vols. IV-VI, 1988. Mem. Ill. Commn. of Scholars, 1966-71, Council of Scholars, Library of Congress, 1980-81. Recipient Bancroft award and Parkman award for Henry Adams, 1959, Pulitzer prize in biography, 1965, Friends of Lit. award for Henry Adams, 1965; Guggenheim fellow, 1955-56, 71-72. Mem. Nat. Council Tchrs. English (dir. 1956-57), Mass. Hist. Soc. (corr.), Coll. English Assn. (pres. Chgo. area 1957), Am. Studies Assn. (pres. Wis.-No. Ill. chpt. 1960-61), MLA, Tau Delta Phi. Address: 3116 Park Pl Evanston IL 60201

SAMUELS, LESLIE B., federal agency administrator, lawyer; b. St. Louis, Nov. 10, 1942; s. Joseph E. and Dorothy J. (Bernstein) S.; m. Judith B. Thorn, June 19, 1966 (div. Aug. 1976); children: Colin T., Polly B.; m. Augusta H. Gross, Nov. 8, 1980. BS in Econs., U. Pa., 1963; LLB magna cum laude, Harvard U., 1966; postgrad., London Sch. Econs., 1966-67. Bar: N.Y., U.S. Dist. Ct. (so. dist.) N.Y., U.S. Tax Ct.; CPA. Tax analyst Gulf Oil Co., London, 1967-68; assoc. Cleary, Gottlieb, Steen & Hamilton, N.Y.C., 1968-75, ptnr., 1975-93; asst. sec. for tax policy U.S. Dept. Treasury, Washington, 1993—. Editor Law Rev.; contbr. articles to profl. jours. Dir. Lower Manhattan Cultural Coun., N.Y.C., 1981-93; active Carter-Mondale Transition Planning Group, Washington, 1976-77. Fulbright fellow London Sch. Econs., 1966-67. Mem. N.Y. State Bar Assn., Assn. of Bar of City of N.Y., Harvard Club (N.Y.C.). Democrat. Home: 1165 5th Ave New York NY 10029-6931

SAMUELS, MARWYN STEWART, geography educator; b. Utica, N.Y., Jan. 31, 1942; s. Hyman and Florence (Copeland) S.; m. Carmencita; 1 child, Haim-Dovio Rizal. BA, Denver U., 1964, MA, 1967; PhD, U. Washington, 1971. Lectr. Hebrew U., Jerusalem, Israel, 1971-72; asst. prof. U. B.C., Vancouver, Can., 1972-76, assoc. prof., 1977-85; prof. Syracuse (N.Y.) U., 1985—; dir. fgn. and comparative studies Maxwell Sch. Pub. Affairs, 1988—. Author: Contest for South China Sea, 1982. Exec. dir. Sun Yat Sen Garden Soc., Vancouver, 1980-85. Mem. Assn. for Asian Studies, Assn. Am. Geographers. Office: Syracuse U Dept Geog Syracuse NY 13244-0003

SAMUELS, NATHANIEL, business executive, government administrator; b. Chgo., Oct. 20, 1908; s. Maurice and Sarah (Altman) S.; m. Mary Elizabeth Hyman, May 10, 1952; children—Geoffrey, Neil. B.S., Harvard U., 1930; read law privately in Chgo. law office, 1931-35. Bar: Ill. 1935. Practice law Chgo., 1935-42; dep. under sec. state for econ. affairs U.S. State Dept., 1969-72; U.S. alt. gov. IMF, IBRD, Inter-Am. Devel. Bank, Asian Devel. Bank, 1969-72, Overseas Pvt. Investment Corp.; spl. advisor, dir. div. Indsl. Resources Mut. Security Agy., Paris, 1952-53; with Kuhn, Loeb & Co., 1955-69, mng. ptnr., 1966-69; adv. dir. Lehman Bros. Kuhn Loeb, Inc., 1977-85; mng. dir. Shearson Lehman Hutton, 1985-88; bd. dirs. Global Bancorporation; gen. council Assicurazioni Generali, Trieste-Venice, Transocean Holding Corp., N.Y., Scor U.S. Corp., Scor Reinsurance Co., N.Y., Hayward & Co. Ltd., London,SAFRA AGF Reins. Corp. of U.S., 1995, Unione Italiana Reinsurance Co. of Am., Inc., 1994, Jefferson Ins. Co. of N.Y., chmn. 1978—, chmn. emeritus, numerous other nat. and internat. cos.; chmn. exec. bd. Ctr. for Strategic and Internat. Studies, Washington, 1993; past mem. vis. com. to Russian Research Ctr. Harvard U., John F. Kennedy Sch. Govt. and Ctr. for Internat. Affairs Harvard U. Past chmn. editorial bd. The Washington Quar.; contbr. articles to profl. jours. Mem. Council on Fgn. Relations, N.Y., Atlantic Council of U.S., Washington, British-N. Am. Com., Washington, London, Internat. Inst. for Strategic Studies, London, Com. on Changing Internat. Realities, Washington; mem. adv. bd. Internat. Mgmt. and Devel. Inst.; mem. Bretton Woods Com., Washington, U.S. Mission for Econ. Affairs U.S. Embassy, London, 1945-46; bd. dirs. The Americas Soc. (hon.); mem. U.S. Mission for Econ. Affairs U.S. Embassy, London, 1945-46. Served to 1st lt. AUS, 1942-46; ETO, SHAEF. Mem. U.S. C. of C. (past mem. exec. com., chmn. comml. policy com.). Clubs: Harvard, Century Assn., University (N.Y.C.); Met. (Washington). Home: 775 Park Ave New York NY 10021-4253 Office: Lehman Bros Inc World Fin Ctr New York NY 10285

SAMUELS, REUBEN, engineering consultant; b. Suffern, N.Y., Jan. 11, 1926; s. M.S. and Ida Samuels; m. Diane Joyce Limenfeld, Sept. 16, 1948; children: Julie Ellen, Adam Henry. Student, MIT, 1943-44; BSCE, Dartmouth Coll., 1946; MSCE, Harvard U., 1948, postgrad., 1951-54. Registered profl. engr., N.Y., N.J., Conn., Va., Pa., D.C., Md., Mass.; lic. arbitrator. Found. engr. Mueser, Rutledge, Wentworth & Johnson, 1948-50; v.p., chief engr. Thomas Crimmins Contracting Co., 1950-82, vice chmn., 1982-86, chmn., 1986-90; pres. Crimmins, Samuels & Assocs., 1980-90, Crimmins Constructors, Inc., 1987-90; v.p Tishman Constrn. Corp., 1990-91; prin. engring. cons. Parsons Brinckerhoff, N.Y.C., 1991—; arbitrator Am. Arbitration Assn.; mem. Soil Mechanics and Found. Group Bldg. Code Com., N.Y.; past overseer Thayer Sch. Engring.-Dartmouth Coll.; mem. geotech. bd. NAS, 1991-94; mem. geologic site investigation subcom., mem. parent U.S. Nat. Com. on Tunnelling Tech./NAS. Co-author: Construction Rock Work Guide, 1960's. Past. pres. Paramus Bd. Edn., Bergen County Fedn. Sch. Bds. Ensign CEC, USNR, 1943-47. Recipient Outstanding Achievement in Constrn. award, 1988. Fellow ASCE (nat. com. on deep founds.); mem. ASTM, Am. Constrn. Inst., Boston Soc. Civil Engrs., Dartmouth Engring. Soc. (past pres.), Harvard Engring. Soc. (past pres.), Nat. Acad. Engring. The Moles (past pres.), Sigma Xi. Avocations: gardening, reading. Office: Parsons Brinckerhoff Inc 195 Harwood Pl Paramus NJ 07652 Office: Parsons Brinckerhoff 1 Penn Plz New York NY 10119

SAMUELS, SHELDON WILFRED, philosophy educator, writer; b. St. Johnsville, N.Y., Dec. 7, 1929; s. Max and Ethel (Feynman) S.; m. Morjean Rogoff, July 6, 1952; children: Charles A., Susan L. AB, U. Chgo., 1951, postgrad., 1951-56; postgrad., State U. N.Y., 1964-66, USPHS Tng. Program, 1960-66. Mem. adminstrv. staff U. Chgo., 1952-60; dir. pub. info. Air Pollution Control Bd., N.Y. State Health Dept., 1960-66; pub. health advisor USPHS, Washington, 1967-69; chief field service br. Air Programs Office EPA, Washington, 1970-71; dir. health, safety and environment Indsl. Union Dept. AFL-CIO, Washington, 1971-94; adj. prof. State U. N.Y., 1964-66, U. Cin., 1971-73, Mt. Sinai Sch. Medicine, 1973—; Johns Hopkins U., Balt., 1994—; mem. coun. grad. med. edn. HHS, 1987-88; cons. Carter's Safety and Health Fund, 1994—; mem. com. on genetic screening policy Congl. Office of Tech. Assessment, 1988-91; mem. hazardous materials com. Sierra Club, 1985—; exec. v.p Ramazzini Inst., 1992-93, v.p. policy studies, 1995—. Contbg. editor Am. Jour. Indsl. Medicine; contbr. articles, studies on environ. health, philosophy and pub. policy to lay and profl. jours. Past mem. tech. adv. bd. Dept. Commerce, com. on standards ILO; past mem. nat. cancer adv. bd., chmn. subcom. environ. carcinogenesis, mem. com. on risk assessment, mem. com. on cancer control Nat. Cancer Inst.; past mem. task force on research priorities Nat. Inst. Environ. Health Scis.; past mem. com. on regulating chems., com. on food policy and com. on saccharine Nat. Acad. Scis.; founding officer Workers Inst. for Safety and Health, Occupational Health Legal Rights Found.; exec.,v.p. Workplace Health Fund, 1983—; exec. dir. Albert Schweitzer Edn. Found., 1959-60; bd. visitors Chesapeake Biol. Lab., U. Md., 1985-89, Ctr. Environ. Policy, U. Md., 1989-92; mem. Vol. Speakers Program Dept. State and Dept. Labor. Recipient ann. Dubos award René Dubos Ctr., 1989, William Steiger award Am. Conf. Govtl. Indsl. Hygienists, 1987. Fellow N.Y. Acad. Scis., Collegium Ramazzini; mem. Am. Coll. Toxicology (past councilor), Environ. and Occupational Helath Sci. Inst. (adv. bd.), Am. Assn. Bioethics. Home: PO Box 50 Solomons MD 20688-0050 Office: Ramazzini Inst PO Box 1570 Solomons MD 20688

SAMUELS, WILLIAM MASON, physiology association executive; b. Dover, Ohio, Jan. 17, 1929; s. William Mason and Anne Frieda (Fankhauser) S.; m. Joanne Gorenflo, Oct. 2, 1971; children: Robert Lee, Ann Frances. A.B.,U. Ky., 1951; postgrad., Georgetown U., 1952. Mng. editor for Ind., Courier-Jour. & Times, Louisville, 1955-65; dir. office of v.p. U. Ky. Med. Center, Lexington, 1965-70; exec. dir. Am. Soc. Allied Health Professions, Washington, 1970-78, Am. Assn. Blood Banks, Washington, 1978-80, Nat. Soc. Med. Research Washington, 1980-84, Am. Physiol. Soc., Bethesda, Md., 1984-92; retired, 1992—. Contbr. articles to profl. jours. Mem. secretariat Nat. Commn. Health Certifying Agys.; v.p. Coalition Health Funding; cons. to fed. agys.; vol. Habitat for Humanity, Boca Raton. With USAF, 1951-53, USAFR, 1954-76, lt. col. ret. Named Ky. Man of Yr. Sigma Phi Epsilon, 1968. Mem. Am. Soc. Assn. Execs., Am. Optometric Assn. (mem. coun. on edn., coun. on optometric clin. care), Health Staff

Soc., Washington Soc. Assn. Execs., Pinehurst (N.C.) Country Club, Lions. Presbyterian. Home: 3190 Leewood Terr L-101 Boca Raton FL 33431-6508 Home (summer): 11700 Happy Choice Ln North Potomac MD 20878-2453

SAMUELSEN, ROY, bass-baritone; b. Moss, Norway, June 12, 1933; came to U.S., 1950, naturalized, 1954; s. Ragnar Andreas and Margaret Olivia (Evensen) S.; m. Mary Lou Thorne, May 25, 1955; children—Eric Roy, Robert Ragnar, Rolf Harold. B.S. in Music Edn, Brigham Young U., 1961; Mus.M. in Performance, Ind. U., 1963; diploma, Acad. of West, Santa Barbara, Calif., 1960; student voice, Joseph Heuler, Lotte Lehmann, Victor Fuchs, Frank St. Leger, Paul Matthen Charles Kullman. Sheet metal worker Utah, 1951-61. Performed with, Norwegian Opera Co., guest soloist, Norwegian Singing Soc. Am. convs., also with, Am. orchs., prof. music, Ind. U. Opera Theatre, Bloomington, 1963—, rec. artist., (regional winner Met. Opera Auditions, 1960, San Francisco Opera Auditions 1961). Served with Mil. Police U.S. Army, 1953-55. Recipient Lotte Lehmann award Acad. of West, 1960. Mem. AAUP, Nat. Assn. Tchrs. of Singing, Am. Guild Mus. Artists. Democrat. Mormon. Home: 3615 S Oakridge Dr Bloomington IN 47401-8974 Office: Ind U Bloomington IN 47401 *My success in life is a direct reflection upon the standards set by my parents during my early life and by trying to live according to the teachings of my adopted church. These influences, along with my wife's total devotion, have encouraged me and continue to encourage me in my private and professional life.*

SAMUELSON, CECIL O., health care facility executive; b. 1942. BS, U. Utah, MS, MD. V.p. health scis. U. Utah, Salt Lake City, 1970-90; with Intermountain Health Care, Inc., Salt Lake City, 1990—; dean IHC Hosps. Inc., Salt Lake City, 1990—. Office: IHC Hospitals Inc 36 S State St Ste 2100 Salt Lake City UT 84111-1404

SAMUELSON, DERRICK WILLIAM, lawyer; b. Mpls., July 24, 1929; s. Oscar W. and Ruth (Hill) S.; m. Diana L. Webster, Aug. 10, 1957; children: David W., Deirdre W. B.S., U.S. Mil. Acad., 1951; LL.B., Harvard U., 1957. Bar: N.Y. 1958. Assoc. firm Lowenstein, Pitcher, Hotchkiss, Amann & Parr, N.Y.C., 1957-60; staff atty. internat. div. Warner-Lambert Pharm. Co., Morris Plains, N.J., 1960-63; corporate atty. Olin Mathieson Chem. Corp., N.Y.C., 1964-65; v.p., gen. counsel ITT World Communications Inc., N.Y.C., 1965-70, ITT Asia Pacific, Inc., N.Y.C., 1970-81; sr. counsel ITT Corp., N.Y.C., 1981-87, asst. gen. counsel, asst. sec., 1987-92; of counsel Mulvaney, Kahan & Barry, San Diego, 1991—. Pres. Am-Indonesian C. of C., 1976-79, Smoke Rise Club, 1976-77, 88-89; chmn. Am. ASEAN Trade Coun., Inc., 1978-92. With U.S. Army, 1951-54. Mem. ABA, Am. Arbitration Assn.'s Panel of Neutrals. Home: 2940 Via Asoleado Alpine CA 91901-3182

SAMUELSON, ELLEN BANMAN, state legislator; b. Mathiston, Miss., Dec. 11, 1930; d. Alvin Kornelius and Florence Ellen (True) Banman; m. Armin Otto Samuelson, June 22, 1952; children: Alida Jayne, Ronald Ramin, Eric Carl, Mark Alan. BS, Kans. State U., 1952, MS, 1974. Tchr. elem. sch. Newton (Kans.) Pub. Schs., 1952-53, tchr. home econs., 1957-58; tchr. home econs. Hesston (Kans.) Unified Sch. Dist. 460, 1965-79; prof. home econs. Bethel/Hesston Coll., North Newton, Hesston, kans., 1979-82, Bethel Coll., North Newton, 1982-87; cons., 1987-88; legislator ho. of reps. State of Kans., Topeka, 1989—. Precinct committeewoman Rep. Ctrl. Com., Harvey County, Kans., 1956-68, 88—; mem., sec. Harvey County Extension Coun., 1960-64; mem. Family Life Adv. Coun. for Community Mental Health, Kans., 1967-71, Ct. Appointed Spl. Advocate Adv. Bd., Harvey County, 1991—; mem. Hertzler Rsch. Found. Bd., 1993—. Mem. Am. Home Econs. Assn. (speaker ann. meeting student sect. 1989), Am. Vocat. Home Econs. Assn., Kans. Home Econs. Assn. (past sec., past pres. bd. dirs.), Kans. Vocat. Home Econs. Assn. (past pres. bd. dirs. 1971-80), Kans. State U. Alumni Assn., Kans. State U. Coll. Human Ecology Alumni (bd. dirs. 1991-94), Harvey County Rural Life, Soroptomists, Delta Kappa Gamma (pres. 1984-86), Kappa Omicron Phi. Methodist. Office: House Reps State House Topeka KS 66612

SAMUELSON, MARVIN LEE, veterinarian; b. Oketo, Kans., July 25, 1931; s. Eben R. and Mabel M. (Brown) S.; m. Judith Ann Mooney, Aug. 13, 1973 (div. 1995); children: John, Jennifer; children by previous marriage: Valorie, Vonna, Melanie. BS, Kans. State U., 1956, DVM, 1956. Staff veterinarian Carthage (Mo.) Vet. Svcs., 1956, San Pedro (Calif.) Animal Hosp., 1958-61; ptnr., mgr. Clarmar Animal Hosp., Torrance, Calif., 1961-63; owner, dir. South Shore Pet Clinic, San Pedro, Calif., 1963-73; assoc. prof. Coll. Veterinary Medicine Kans. State U., Manhattan, 1973-87; dir. Veterinary Teaching Hosp. Tex. A&M U., College Station, 1987-91, asst. to dean for pub. programs Coll. Vet. Medicine, 1991-92; dir. Animal Dermatology and Allergy Clinic, Topeka, 1992—. Contbr. book chpts. to vet. textbooks, articles to profl. jours. Mem. Jaycees, San Pedro, 1958-61; pres. Lions Club, 1963-64; v.p San Pedro C. of C., 1972; precinct committeeman Wildcat Twp., Manhattan, 1985-87. 1st lt. U.S. Army, 1956-58. Recipient Disting. Teaching award Kansas State U., 1978. Mem. Am. Acad. Vet. Dermatology (sec.-treas. 1986-91), Am. Vet. Allergy (bd. dirs. 1983-91), Am. Vet. Medicine Assn. (edn. com. vet. fgn. grads. 1994—), Am. Assn. Vet. Clinicians (pres. 1990-91), Tex. Vet. Med. Assn., Kans. Vet Med. Assn. (Kans. Vet. of Yr. 1992), Kans. Bd. Vet. Examiners (pres.), Calif. Vet. Med. Assn., So. Calif. Vet. Med. Assn. (pres. 1972), Soc. for Internat. Vet. Symposium (pres.-elect 1991), Alpha Zeta. Democrat. Methodist. Avocation: farming. Office: Animal Dermatol & Allergy Clinic 2147 SW Westport Dr Topeka KS 66614

SAMUELSON, PAUL ANTHONY, economics educator; b. Gary, Ind., May 15, 1915; s. Frank and Ella (Lipton) S.; m. Marion E. Crawford, July 2, 1938 (dec.); children: Jane Kendall, Margaret Wray, William Frank, Robert James, John Crawford, Paul Reid.; m. Risha Eckaus, 1981; stepdaughter, Susan Miller. BA, U. Chgo., 1935; MA, Harvard U., 1936, PhD (David A. Wells prize 1941), 1941; LLD (hon.), U. Chgo., Oberlin Coll., 1961, Boston Coll., 1964, Ind. U., 1966, U. Mich., 1967, Claremont Grad. Sch., 1967, Seton Hall U., 1971, U. N.H., 1971, Keio U. 1971, Widener Coll., 1982, Cath. U. at Riva Aguero U., Lima, Peru, 1980, Harvard, 1972, Gustavus Adolphus Coll., 1974, U. So. Calif., 1975, U. Pa., 1976, U. Rochester, 1976, Emmanuel Coll., 1977, Stonehill Coll., 1978, Indiana U. of Pa., 1993; DLitt (hon.), Ripon Coll., 1962, No. Mich. U., 1973, Valparaiso U., 1987, Columbia U, 1988; LHD (hon.), Williams Coll., 1971; DSc (hon.), U. Mass., 1972, U. R.I., 1972, Tufts U., 1988, East Anglia U., Norwich, Eng., 1966; D (hon.), U. Catholique de Louvain, Belgium, 1976, City U., London, 1980, New U. Lisbon, 1985, Univ. Nat. de Educacion a Distancia, Madrid, 1989, Univ. Politecnica de Valencia, Spain, 1991. Prof. econs. MIT, 1940-65, inst. prof., 1966, prof. emeritus, 1986; mem. staff Radiation Lab., 1944-45; prof. internat. econ. relations Fletcher Sch. Law and Diplomacy, 1945; cons. Nat. Resources Planning Bd., 1941-43, WPB, 1945, U.S. Treasury, 1945-52, 61-74, Bur. Budget, 1952, RAND Corp., 1948-75, Fed. Res. Bd., 1965—; council Econ. Advisers, 1960-68; econ. adviser to Pres. Kennedy; sr. adviser Brookings Panel on Econ. Activity; mem. spl. common on social scis. NSF, 1967-68; cons. Congl. Budget Office, Federal Reserve Bd., 1965—; Gordon Y Billard Fellow MIT, Boston, 1986—; vis. prof of polit. econ. Ctr. Japan-U.S. Bus. and Econ. Studies, NYU, 1987—; Stamp Meml. lectr., London, 1961, Wicksell lectr., Stockholm, 1962, Franklin lectr., Detroit, 1962; Carnegie Found. reflective year, 1965-66; John von Neumann lectr. U. Wis., 1971; Gerhard Colm Meml. lectr. New Sch. for Social Research, N.Y.C., 1971; Sulzbacher Meml. lectr. Columbia Law Sch., N.Y.C., 1974; J. Willard Gibbs lectr. Am. Math. Soc., San Francisco, 1974; John Diebold lectr. Harvard, 1976; Alice E. Blurneuf lectr. Boston Coll., 1981, Horowitz lectr. Jerusalem and Tel Aviv, 1984, Marschak Meml. lectr. UCLA, 1984, Tennenbaum lectr. Ga. Inst. Tech., 1985, Julis Steinberg Meml. lectr. Wharton Sch., 1986, Godkin lectr. Harvard, 1986, Woodward lectr. U. British Columbia, 1987, lectr. Harvard 350 Symposium, Harvard U., 1986, Olin lectr. U. Va., 1989, Commemorative lectr. Stonehill Coll., 1990, Lionel Robbins Meml. lectr. Claremont Coll., 1991; mem. nat. advisory com. Inst. for Rsch. on Poverty. Author: Foundations of Economic Analysis, 1947, enlarged edit., 1983, Economics, 1948-91, Readings in Economics 1955-73, (with R. Dorfman and R.M. Solow) Linear Programming and Economic Analysis, 1958, Collected Scientific Papers, 5 vols., 1966, 72, 78, 86; co-author numerous other books.; contbr. numerous articles to profl. jours.; columnist Newsweek, 1966-81; assoc. editor: Jour. Pub. Econs., Jour. Internat. Econs., Jour. Fin. Econs., Jour. Nonlinear Analysis; adv. bd. Challenge Mag.; editorial bd. Proceedings Nat. Acad. Scis. Chmn. Pres.'s Task Force Maintaining Am.

Prosperity, 1964; mem. Nat. Task Force on Econ. Edn., 1960-61; econ. adviser to Pres. John F. Kennedy, 1959-63; mem. adv. bd. Nat. Commn. Money and Credit, 1958-60. Hon. fellow London Sch. Econs. and Polit. Sci. Guggenheim fellow, 1948-49; Ford Found. Research fellow, 1958-59; recipient David A. Wells prize Harvard U., 1941, John Bates Clark medal Am. Econ. Assn., 1947, Alfred Nobel Meml. prize , 1970, medal of Honor U. Evansville, Ill., 1970, Albert Einstein Commemorative award, 1971, Alumni medal U. Chgo., 1983, Britannica award, 1989, Gold Scanno prize, Naples, Italy, 1990; Paul A. Samuelson Professorship established in his name, MIT, 1991. Fellow Brit. Ac. (corr.), Am. Philos. Soc., Econometric Soc. (v.p. 1950, pres. 1951), Am. Econ. Assn. (hon.; pres. 1961); mem. AAAS, Com. Econ. Devel. (commn. on nat. goals, research adv. bd. 1959-60), Internat. Econ. Assn. (pres. 1966-68, hon. pres.), Nat. Acad. Scis., Leibniz-Akademie der Wissenschaften und der Literatur (corr. mem. 1987—) Nat. Assn. of Investment Clubs (Disting. Svc. award in Investment Edn. 1974), Club of Econ. and Mgmt. (medal, hon. Valencia, Spain 1990), Phi Beta Kappa, Omicron Delta Epsilon (trustee). Home: 94 Somerset St Belmont MA 02178-2010 Office: MIT Dept Econs E52 # 383C Cambridge MA 02139

SAMUELSON, ROBERT JACOB, journalist; b. N.Y.C., Dec. 23, 1945; s. Abraham and Joan (Kahn) S.; m. Judith Herr, July 10, 1983; children: Ruth, Michael, John. AB in Govt., Harvard U., 1967. Reporter Washington Post, 1969-73; free-lance writer Washington, 1973-76; reporter; columnist National Jour. mag., Washington, 1976-84; columnist Newsweek, Washington, 1984—; columnist Washington Post, 1977—.

SAN AGUSTIN, JOE TAITANO, Guam senator, financial institution executive, management researcher; b. Agana, Guam, Oct. 15, 1930; s. Candido S. and Maria P. (Taitano) San A.; m. Carmen Santos Shimizu, June 18, 1955; children: Mary, Ann, Joe, John. BA, George Washington U., 1954, MA, 1965. Chief budget and mgmt. Office of Govt. Guam, Agana, 1966-68; dir. dept. adminstrn. Govt. Guam, Agana, 1968-74; senator Guam Legislature, Agana, 1976—, minority leader 16th Guam Legislature, 1981-82, vice-speaker 17th and 18th Guam Legislature, 1983-86, chmn. com. on ways and means 17th and 18th Guam Legislatures, 1983-86, chmn. com. on health, edn. and welfare 19th Guam Legislature, 1987, chmn. com. on edn., 1991, econ. com.; speaker 20th, 21st, 22nd Guam Legislature, 1989—, chmn. econ. com. Guam Legis., 1995—, bd. dirs. Bank of Guam, Agana. Democrat. Roman Catholic. Office: 155 Hessler Pl Agana GU 96910-5004

SAN ANTONIO MENDOZA, OSCAR ANIBAL, state legislator; b. Isabela, P.R., Jan. 17, 1945; s. Giordano A. and Maria Teresa (Mendoza) San A.; m. Ana I. Rivero, Jan. 21, 1966; children: Oscar A., Silvia M., Ana Maria. BS, U. Catolica P.R., Ponce, 1966. Med. rep. Merck, Sharp & Dohme, Carolina, 1967-70, Schering Plough P.R. Inc., Carolina, 1970-84; mem. Ho. of Reps., San Juan, 1985—. Treas. Partido Popular Democratico, Isabela, 1982-84, campaign dir. mgr., 1986-94. Mem. Lions, Phi Sigma Alpha. Roman Catholic. Avocations: reading, diving, swimming. Home: Ave Estacion # 61 Isabela PR 00662-2808 Office: Camara de Reps Capitolio San Juan PR 00662

SANBORN, ANNA LUCILLE, pension and insurance consultant; b. Bklyn., Mar. 29, 1924; d. Peter Francis and Matilda M. (Stumpp) Galligen; B.A., Bklyn. Coll., 1945; 1 son, Dean Sanborn. Head dept. benefit and estate planning Union Central Life Ins. Co., N.Y.C., 1949-51; adminstr. employee benefits Seaboard Oil Co., N.Y.C., 1952-56; with Frank J. Walters Assocs., Inc., N.Y.C., 1957—, pres., 1970—. Bd. dirs. Archdiocesan Service Corp. Mem. Am. Acad. Actuaries, Republican. Roman Catholic. Home: 58-11 Seabury St Elmhurst NY 11373 Office: Frank J Walters Assocs 58-13 Seabury St Flushing NY 11373-4825

SANBORN, DAVID, alto saxophonist; b. St. Louis, MO, 1945. Student, Northwestern Univ., Univ. of Iowa. Ind. jazz saxophonist, 1975—. Rec. artist: (with James Taylor) How Sweet It Is, (with David Bowie) Young Americans, (with Gil Evans) Priestess, (with Bob James) Double Vision, (solo albums) Taking Off, 1975, Sanborn, 1976, Promise Me the Moon, 1977, Heart to Heart, 1978, Hideaway, 1980, Voyeur, 1981, Grammy awd., 1981), As We Speak, 1982, Backstreet, 1983, Straight to the Heart, 1984, Close Up, 1988 (Grammy awd., 1989), Upfront, 1992, Hearsay, 1994, Pearls, 1995; music for film: Lethal Weapon 2, 1989; host and co-producer of "The Jazz Show," NBC-Radio; TV appearances: host of Night Music, 1988-89, regular guest on Late Night with David Letterman, 1982-94.

SANBORN, GEORGE FREEMAN, JR., genealogist; b. Laconia, N.H., Jan. 18, 1944; s. George Freeman and Charlotte (Dearborn) S.; m. Melinde Laura Lutz, Mar. 30, 1984; children: Ruth Alice, Lowell Freeman. AB, Boston U., 1967; AM, U. Ill., 1968; MEd, U. N.H., 1981. French tchr. Souris (P.E.I., Can.) Regional H.S., 1968-69; French and occupational studies tchr. Massey-Vanier H.S., Cowansville, Que., Can., 1969-70; French and English tchr. Kings Coll. Sch., Windsor, N.S., Can., 1970-71; translator, revisor Province of N.B., Fredericton, 1971-73; sr. govt. revisor Province of Ont., Toronto, 1973-75; French and Spanish tchr. Tilton (N.H.) Sch., 1978-80; living unit coord. Laconia (N.H.) State Sch., 1982-83; ref. libr. New Eng. Hist. Geneal. Soc., Boston, 1983-85, acquisitions libr. and tech. svcs. dir., 1985—. Editor The N.H. Geneal. Record, 1990-93; compiler Vital Records of Hampton, N.H., 1992; contbr. articles to profl. jours. Fellow Am. Soc. Genealogists; mem. Soc. of the Cin. in the State of N.H., Soc. of Mayflower Descendants in the State of N.H., New Eng. Hist. Geneal. Soc., P.E.I. Geneal. Soc., N.H. Soc. Genealogists (pres. 1988—), Geneal. Soc. Vt. (chair publs. com. 1992—). Democrat. Presbyterian. Avocations: gardening, bantam raising, Scottish Gaelic language, P.E.I. history, antique glass and china. Home: 24 Thornton St Derry NH 03038-1628 Office: New Eng Hist Geneal Soc Libr 99-101 Newbury St Boston MA 02116

SANBRAILO, JOHN A., mission director; b. San Francisco, July 26, 1943; s. John and Ann (Schonfeld) S.; m. Cecilia Del Pozo, Jan. 12, 1974. B in Econs., U. Calif., Berkeley, 1965; M in Econs., San Francisco State U., 1969; MPA, Harvard U., 1976. Vol. U.S. Peace Corps., Sucre State, Venezuela, 1965-68; credit union and coop. extension agt. U.S. Peace Corps., Washington; internat. devel. intern US AID, Washington, 1969-70; chief project devel. Nicaragua, project devel. officer Ecuador US AID, 1970-75; dir. policy planning and budgeting, chief fin. officer Latin Am. and Caribbean Bur. US AID, Washington, 1976-79; dir. US AID Mission, Quito, Ecuador, 1979-82, 93—, Lima, Peru, 1983-86, Tequcigalpa, Honduras, 1987-91, San Salvador, El Salvador, 1991-93; career minister US Sr. Fgn. Svc. Decorated Honduran Cong., 1991, Govt. Peru, 1986, Govt. Ecuador, 1982. Office: USAID Quito Ecuador Unit 5330 APO AA 34039

SANCETTA, CONSTANCE ANTONINA, oceanographer; b. Richmond, Va., Apr. 17, 1949; d. Anthony Louis and Joyce Louise (Kellogg) S. BA, Brown U., 1971, MSc, 1973; PhD, Oreg. State U., 1976. Rsch. assoc. Stanford (Calif.) U., 1977-78; assoc. rsch. scientist Columbia U., N.Y.C., 1979-84, rsch. scientist, 1985-87, sr. rsch. scientist, 1988-94; assoc. program mgr. divsn. ocean sci. NSF, Washington, 1992—; mem. adv. com. divsn. ocean sci. NSF, 1981-86, 89-92. Editl. bd. Marine Micropaleontology, Oceanography, 1983—; contbr. articles to profl. jours. Fellow AAAS, Geol. Soc. Am.; mem. Am. Quaternary Soc. (councilor 1988-90), Am. Geophys. Union (sec. ocean sci. sect. 1988-90), Oceanography Soc. (councilor 1989-93), Paleontol. Rsch. Instn. (trustee 1991-92). Home: 1637 Irvin St Vienna VA 22182 Office: NSF Rm 725 4201 Wilson Blvd Arlington VA 22230

SANCHEZ, DAVID ALAN, science administrator; b. San Francisco, Jan. 13, 1933; m. Joan Patricia Thomas, Dec. 28, 1957; children: Bruce, Christina. BS, U. N.Mex., 1955; MS, U. Mich., 1960, PhD, 1964. Instr. U. Chgo., 1963-65; from asst. to assoc. to full prof. UCLA, 1966-77, assoc. dean grad. sch., 1972-73; prof. U. N.Mex., Albuquerque, 1977-86, chmn. dept. math., 1983-86; v.p., provost Lehigh U., Bethlehem, 1986-90; asst. dir. math. and phys. scis. NSF, Washington, 1990-92; dep. assoc. dir. rsch. and edn. Los Alamos (N.Mex.) Nat. Lab., 1992-93; vice chancellor acad. affairs Tex. A&M System, College Station, 1993—. Author books; contbr. articles to profl. jours. Served as 1st lt. USMC, 1956-59. Mem. Am. Math. Soc. Council, Math. Assn. Am. Avocations: fishing, bridge. Office: Tamus State Hdqs Bldg College Station TX 77843-1138

SANCHEZ, GILBERT, university president, microbiologist, researcher; b. Belen, N.Mex., May 7, 1938; s. Macedonio C. and Josephine H. Sanchez; m. Lorena T. Tabet, Aug. 26, 1961; children—Elizabeth, Phillip, Katherine. B.S. in Biology, N.Mex. State U., 1961; Ph.D. in Microbiology, U. Kans., 1967. Research asst. U. Kans., Lawrence, 1963-67; research assoc., postdoctoral fellow Rice U., Houston, 1967-68; prof. N.Mex. Inst. Tech., Socorro, 1968-79; dean grad. studies Eastern N.Mex. U., Portales, 1979-83; v.p. acad. affairs U. So. Colo., Pueblo, 1983-85; pres. N.Mex. Highlands U., Las Vegas, 1985—; cons. NIH, NSF, Solvex Corp., Albuquerque, 1979-83; bd. dirs. Fed. Res. Bank, Denver. Contbr. numerous articles to profl. jours. Patentee in field. Pres. Socorro Sch. Bd., 1974-79, Presbyn. Hosp. Bd., Socorro, 1977-79. Research grantee Dept. Army, 1976-79, N.Mex. Dept. Energy, 1979-83, NSF, 1979. Mem. Am. Soc. Microbiology, Am. Soc. Indsl. Microbiology, AAAS, Am. Assn. Univs. and Colls. (bd. dirs. 1988-90), Hispanic Assn. Univs. and Colls. (pres. 1986-89). Roman Catholic. Lodge: Rotary. Avocations: auto mechanics; welding; woodworking; golf. Office: NMex Highlands U Las Vegas NM 87701

SANCHEZ, LEONEDES MONARRIZE WORTHINGTON (DUKE DE LEONEDES), fashion designer; b. Flagstaff, Ariz., Mar. 15, 1951; s. Rafael Leonedes and Margaret (Monarrize) S. BS, No. Ariz. U., 1974; studied, Fashion Inst. Tech., N.Y.C., 1974-75; AA, Fashion Inst. D&M, L.A., 1975; lic., La Ecole de la Chambre Syndical de la Couture Parisian, Paris, 1976-78. Lic. in designing. Contract designer/asst. to head designer House of Bonnet, Paris, 1976—; dress designer-in-residence Flagstaff, 1978—; mem. faculty No. Ariz. U., Flagstaff, 1978-80; designer Ambiance, Inc., L.A., 1985—; designer Interiors by Leonedes subs. Studio of Leonedes Couturier, Ariz. 1977, Calif., 1978, London, Paris, 1978, Rome, 1987, Milan, Spain, 1989; designer Liturgical Vesture subs. Studio of Leonedes Couturier; CEO Leonedes Internat.; owner, COO, designer Leonedes Internat., Ltd., London, Milan, Paris, Spain, Ambian Ariz, Calif., Appolonian Costuming, Ariz., London, Milan, Paris, El Castillo de Leonedes, Sevilla, Spain, Villa Apollonian de Leonedes, Mykonos, Greece; cns. House of Bonnet, Paris, 1976—, Bob Mackie, Studio City, Calif., 1974-75. Bd. dirs. Roman Cath. Social Svcs., 1985-86, Northland Crisis Nursery, 1985—; bd. dirs., chmn. Pine Country Transit, 1986-88; pres. Chicanos for Edn.; active master's swim program ARC, Ariz., 1979—; eucharistic min., mem. art and environ. com., designer liturgical vesture St. Piux X Cath. Ch.; vol. art tchr., instr. St. Mary's Regional Sch., Flagstaff, 1987-90, vol. art dir.; mem. Flagstaff Parks and Recreation Commn., 1994—; citizen's adv. com. master plan. Decorated Duke de Leonedes (Spain), 1994; recipient Camellian Design award 1988, Atlanta. Mem. AAU, Am. Film Inst., Am. Assn. Hist. Preservation, Costume Soc., Am. Nat. Physique Com., Internat. Consortium Fashion Designers, Nat. Cath. Ednl. Assn., La Legion de Honour de la Mode Parisienne, Social Register Assn., Phi Alpha Theta (historian 1972-73, pres. 1973-74), Pi Kappa Delta (pres. 1972-73, historian 1973-74). Republican. Avocations: body building, swimming. Address: El Castilla de Leonedes, Seville Spain also: Villia de Apollonian de Leonedes, Mykonos Greece

SANCHEZ, MARY ANNE, secondary school educator; b. Galesburg, Ill., Aug. 4, 1939; d. Stephen Mingare and M. Margaret Kennedy; m. J. Manuel Sanchez, Dec. 26, 1980. BS in Edn., Western Ill. U., 1961; MA, Ill. State U., 1970. Tchr. Montgomery County Bd. Edn., Chevy Chase, Md., Hillsborough County Bd. Edn., Tampa, Fla.; tchr. Stanford, Ill., Titusville, Fla. Mem. Nat. Coun. for Social Studies, Fla. Coun. for Social Studies, Adult Edn. Assn. Home: 2715 W Ivy St Tampa FL 33607-1922

SANCHEZ, RAFAEL CAMILO, physician; b. Tampa, Fla., July 18, 1919; s. Francisco and Catalina (Mateo) S.; children: Stephen Francis, John Thomas, David Lear. B.S., Loyola U., New Orleans, 1940; M.D., La. State U., 1950. Diplomate: Am. Bd. Family Practice; bd. dirs. 1976-79, assoc. exec. dir. 1979-84). Intern U.S. Marine Hosp., New Orleans, 1950-51; gen. practice medicine New Orleans, 1951-52; med. educator, dir. continuing med. edn. La. State U., 1963-77, prof. family medicine, 1979-84; prof. family medicine East Carolina U. Sch. Medicine, Greenville, 1984-90, prof. emeritus, 1990—; dir. family practice residency program Charity Hosp. of Bogalusa, La., 1977-79; dir. Continuing Med. Edn.; med. dir. Nat. Med. Info. Network. Served with AUS, 1944-46. Recipient Recognition award Soc. of Tchrs. of Medicine, 1987, Willard M. Duff award Accreditation Coun. for Continuing Med. Edn. Fellow AMA, Am. Acad. Family Physicians (Thomas W. Johnson award 1978, Presdl. award 1983, Pres.'s award 1989); mem. Network for Continuing Med. Edn. (med. dir.), Nat. Med. Info. Network of the World Med. Comms. Orgns. (med. dir.). Am. Omega Alpha. Democrat. Roman Catholic. Office: PO Box 20035 Greenville NC 27858-0035

SANCHEZ, ROBERT FORTUNE, archbishop; b. Socorro, N.Mex., Mar. 20, 1934; s. Julius C. and Priscilla (Fortune) S. Student, Immaculate Heart Sem., Santa Fe, 1954, N.Am. Coll., Gregorian U., Rome, 1960. Ordained priest Roman Cath. Ch., 1959; prof. St. Piux X High Sch., Albuquerque, 1960-68; dir. extension lay vols. Archdiocese Santa Fe, 1965-68, chmn. priest personnel bd., 1968-72, vicar gen., 1974, archbishop, 1974-93; rep. instl. ministry pastoral care N.Mex. Council Chs., 1968; pres. Archdiocesan Priests Senate, 1973-74; rep. region X Nat. Fedn. Priests Councils, 1972-73; bd. dirs. Mexican Am. Cultural Center; mem. regional com. Nat. Conf. Cath. Bishops, N.Am. Coll., Rome; pres. N.Mex. Conf. Chs.; gen. sec. U.S. Cath. Conf./Nat. Conf. Cath. Bishops, 1991. Mem. U.S. Cath. Conf. (chmn. ad hoc com. Spanish speaking). Office: Archdiocese Santa Fe The Cath Ctr 4000 Saint Josephs Pl NW Albuquerque NM 87120-1714*

SANCHEZ, ROBERT FRANCIS, journalist; b. Bradenton, Fla., Jan. 1, 1938; s. Robert and Frances Alice (Thompson) S. B.S. in English Edn., Fla. State U., 1959, M.S., 1962, postgrad., 1971-74. Mem. faculty Fla. State U., Tallahassee, 1962-67; mem. faculty Fla. A&M U., Tallahassee, 1968-71; writer, editor Tallahassee Democrat, 1965-74; editorial writer Miami Herald, 1974—. Co-recipient Pulitzer Prize, 1983. Mem. Phi Delta Kappa, Sigma Delta Chi. Republican. Methodist. Home: 7000 Miller Rd Miami FL 33155-5615 Office: Miami Herald 1 Herald Plz Miami FL 33132-1693

SANCHEZ, VICTORIA WAGNER, science educator; b. Milw., Apr. 11, 1934; d. Arthur William and Lorraine Marguerite (Kocovsky) Wagner; m. Rozier Edmond Sanchez, June 23, 1956; children: Mary Elizabeth, Carol Anne, Robert Edmond, Catherine Marie, Linda Therese. BS cum laude, Mt. Mary Coll., 1955; MS, Marquette U., 1957; postgrad., U. N.Mex., 1979-86, U. Del., 1990. Cert. secondary tchr., N.Mex. Chemist Nat. Bur. Standards, Washington, 1958-60; tchr., chmn. sci. dept. Albuquerque Pub. Schs., 1979-94; chmn. pub. info. area conv. Nat. Sci. Tchrs. Assn., 1984, mem. sci. rev. com. Albuquerque Pub. Schs., 1985-86, 92-93, dedication of N.W. Regional Sci. Fair, 1994, Gov.'s Summit on Edn., 1991, 92, Gov.'s Steering Com. Systemic Change in Math. and Sci. Edn. Bd. dirs. Encino House, Albuquerque, 1976-92, treas., 1977-79; leader Albuquerque troop Girl Scouts U.S., 1966-77. Named Outstanding Sci. Tchr., NW Regional Sci. Fair, Albuquerque, 1983, 88, 90; recipient St. George's award N.Mex. Cath. Scouting Com., 1978, Focus on Excellence award ASCD, 1985, 89, Presdl. awards for excellence in sci. and math. Mem. AAUW (officer Albuquerque br. 1976-77, N.Mex. divsn. 1977-78), NSTA, N.Mex. Sci. Tchrs. Assn. (treas. 1988-90), Albuquerque Sci. Tchrs. Assn. (treas. 1984-85, v.p., pres.-elect 1986-87, pres. 1987-88, Svc. to Sci. award 1994), N.Mex. Acad. Sci., Am. Coun. on Edn. (math. and sci. edn. nat. com. 1990—), DuPont Honors Workshop for Tchrs., Albuquerque Rose Soc. (sec. 1962-63). Democrat. Roman Catholic. Avocations: reading, fishing, hiking, needlecraft, camping. Home: 7612 Palo Duro Ave NE Albuquerque NM 87110-2315

SAND, LEONARD B., federal judge; b. N.Y.C., May 24, 1928. B.S., NYU, 1947; LL.B., Harvard, 1951. Bar: N.Y. 1953, U.S. Supreme Ct. 1956, D.C. 1969. Clk. to dist. ct. judge N.Y., 1952-53; asst. U.S. atty. So. Dist. N.Y., 1953-54; asst. to U.S. Solicitor Gen., 1956-59; mem. firm Robinson, Silverman, Pearce, Aronsohn Sand and Berman, N.Y.C., 1960-78; judge U.S. Dist. Ct. So. Dist. N.Y., 1978—; adj. prof. law NYU. Note editor: Harvard Law Rev, 1950-51. Del. N.Y. State Constl. Conv., 1967; v.p. treas. Legal Aid Soc. Trial Lawyers; mem. ABA, Assn. Bar City N.Y. (v.p.), N.Y. State Bar Assn., Fed. Bar Coun. Office: US Dist Ct US Courthouse 500 Pearl St New York NY 10007-1501

SAND, PHYLLIS SUE NEWNAM (PHYLLIS SUE NEWNAM), retired special education educator; b. Epworth, N.D., Feb. 12, 1931; d. Zelnoe Jackson and Susie Ella (Lindley) Newnam; m. Shirley Sylvester Sand, Aug. 24, 1952; children: Thomas Richard, James Waldow, Catherine Roberta, Constance Renae. AA, Minot State Tchrs. Coll., 1952; BS in Edn., U. N.D., 1970, MEd, 1971. Cert. profl. educator, N.D., tchr., Minn. Tchr. various rural schs. in Ward and Cavalier Counties, Ward County and Cavalier County, N.D., 1950-53; cons., tchr. Griggs, Steele, & Trail Spl. Edn. Unit, N.D., 1976-78; diagnostician, tchr. learning disabled Larimore (N.D.) Elem., 1978-92. Mem. NEA (life), N.D. Edn. Assn. (life), Coun. for Exceptional Children, N.D. Ret. Tchrs. Assn., Greater Grand Forks Ret. Tchrs. Assn., Delta Kappa Gamma (pres. 1990-92, v.p. 1988-90, program chmn.). United Methodist. Avocations: sewing, reading, quilting, travel, family history. Home: 418 Conklin Ave Grand Forks ND 58203-1669

SAND, THOMAS CHARLES, lawyer; b. Portland, Oreg., June 4, 1952; s. Harold Eugene and Marian Anette (Thomas) S.; m. Rhonda Diane Laycoe, June 15, 1974; children: Kendall, Taylor, Justin. Student, Centro des Artes y Lenguas, Cuernavaca, Mex., 1972; BA in Engl., U. Oreg., 1974; JD, Lewis and Clark Coll., 1977. Bar: Oreg. 1977, U.S. Dist. Ct. Oreg. 1977, U.S. Ct. Appeals (9th cir.) 1984. Assoc. Miller, Nash, Wiener, Hager & Carlsen, Portland, 1977-84, ptnr., 1984—; mem. Oreg. State Bar Com. on Professionalism, 1989, chmn., 1990; dir. young lawyers divsn. Multnomah County Bar Assn., 1980; spl. asst. atty. gen. Wasco County 1983 Gen. Election; speaker in field. Contbr. articles to legal jours. and procs. Mem. U.S. Dist. Ct. of Oreg. Hist. Soc., 1990—; bd. dirs. Portland Area Coun. of Camp Fire, Inc., 1978-90, pres., 1984-86, 1st v.p., 1982, 83, strategic planning com., overall camping com.; bd. dirs. Oreg. Indoor Invitational Track Meet, Inc., 1982-84. Recipient Boss of the Yr. award Portland Legal Secs. Assn., 1989. Mem. ABA (securities litigation com., subcom. on broker-dealer litigation), Oreg. Bar Assn., Multnomah Bar Assn. (bd. dirs. task force on structure and orgn. 1989, chmn. com. on professionalism 1988, nominating com. 1986, participating atty. in N.E. legal clin. Vol Lawyers project, award of merit for svc. to profession 1988), Securities Industry Assn. (compliance and legal divsn.), Northwestern Sch. of Law, Lewis and Clark Coll. Alumni Assn. (bd. dirs. 1992), Valley Comm. Presbyterian Ch., Multnomah Athletic Club, Univ. Club, Portland Golf Club. Avocations: golf, guitar, camping, river rafting, children's sports. Office: Miller Nash Wiener Hager & Carlsen 111 SW 5th Ave Ste 3500 Portland OR 97204

SANDAGE, ALLAN REX, astronomer; b. Iowa City, June 18, 1926; s. Charles Harold and Dorothy (Briggs) S.; m. Mary Lois Connelley, June 8, 1959; children: David Allan, John Howard. AB, U. Ill., 1948, DSc (hon.), 1967; PhD, Calif. Inst. Tech., 1953; DSc (hon.), Yale U., 1966, U. Chgo., 1967, Miami U., Oxford, Ohio, 1974, Graceland Coll., Iowa, 1985; LLD (hon.), U. So. Calif., 1971; D Honoris Causa, U. Chile, 1992. Astronomer Mt. Wilson Obs., Palomar Obs., Carnegie Instn., Washington, 1952—; Peyton postdoctoral fellow Princeton U., 1952; asst. astronomer Hale Obs., Pasadena, Calif., 1952-56; astronomer Obs. Carnegie Instn., Pasadena, Calif., 1956—; sr. rsch. astronomer Space Telescope Sci. Inst. NASA, Balt., 1986—; Homewood Prof. of Physics Johns Hopkins U., Balt., 1987-89; vis. lectr. Harvard U., 1957; mem. astron. expdn. to South Africa, 1958; cons. NSF, 1961-64; Sigma Xi nat. lectr., 1966; vis. prof. Mt. Stromlo Obs., Australian Nat. U., 1968-69; vis. rsch. astronomer U. Basel, 1985-92, vis. prof., 1994; vis. rsch. astronomer U. Calif., San Diego, 1985-86; vis. astronomer U. Hawaii, 1986; Lindsey lectr. NASA Goddard Space Flight Ctr., 1989; Jansky lectr. Nat. Radio Astron. Obs., 1991; Grubb-Parsons lectr. U. Durham, Eng., 1992. Assoc. editor Ann. Rev. Astronomy and Astrophysics, 1990—. With USNR, 1944-45. Recipient Pope Pius XI gold medal Pontifical Acad. Sci., 1966, Rittenhouse medal, 1968, Presdl. Nat. Medal of Sci. 1971, Adon medal Obs. Nice, 1988, Crafoord prize Swedish Royal Acad. Scis., 1991, Tomalla Gravity prize Swiss Phys. Soc., 1993; Fulbright-Hays scholar, 1972. Mem. Lincei Nat. Acad. (Rome), Am. Astron. Soc. (Helen Warner prize 1960, Russell prize 1973), Royal Astron. Soc. (Eddington medal 1963, Gold medal 1967), Astron. Soc. Pacific (Gold medal 1975), Royal Astron. Soc. Can., Franklin Inst. (Elliott Cresson medal 1973), Phi Beta Kappa, Sigma Xi. Home: 8319 Josard Rd San Gabriel CA 91775-1003 Office: 813 Santa Barbara St Pasadena CA 91101-1232

SANDAGE, CHARLES HAROLD, advertising educator; b. Hatfield, Mo., Aug. 21, 1902; s. Moses and Almatie (Bissell) S.; m. Dorothy Briggs, Aug. 5, 1924 (dec. 1970); 1 child, Allan R.; m. Elizabeth Smith Danner, 1971. Student, Graceland Coll., Lamoni, Iowa, 1921-23; A.B., State U. Iowa, 1926, M.A., 1927, Ph.D., 1931; postgrad., U. Ill., 1928. Tchr. Dunlap Twp. High Sch., 1923-25; asst. prof. econs. Simpson Coll., Indianola, Iowa, 1927-28; asst. prof. bus. U. Kans., Lawrence, 1928-29; asst., then assoc. prof. bus. Miami U., Oxford, Ohio, 1929-35; prof., head dept. mktg. Miami U., 1937-46; asst. chief, then chief div. transp. and communications Bur. Census, U.S. Dept. Commerce, Washington, 1935-37; lectr. advt. U. Pa., Phila., 1936-37; prof. advt. U. Ill.-Urbana, 1946-68, prof. emeritus, 1968—; cons. FCC, 1957-58; lectr. mktg. Evening Coll., U. Cin., 1930-35, 37-39; vis. prof. bus. research Harvard U., 1943-44; v.p., dir. research Inst. Transit Advt., 1944-45; pres. Farm Research Inst., 1946—; mem. Nat. Adv. Bd. Author: Advertising Theory and Practice, 1936, 12th edit. (with V. Fryburger and K. Rotzoll), 1989, Radio Advertising for Retailers, 1945, Changing Perspectives in Marketing, 1951, (monograph) Qualitative Analysis of Radio Listening in Two Illinois Counties, 1948, Building Audiences, 1951, (with V. Fryburger) The Role of Advertising, 1960, The Promise of Advertising, 1961, (with A. Barban) Readings in Advertising and Promotion Strategy, 1968, (with K. Rotzell and J. Haefner) Advertising in Contemporary Society, 1976; contbg. author Marketing by Manufacturers, 1946, rev. edit., 1951, Roads to be Taken, 1993; also articles. Recipient Advt. Gold Medal award, 1964; named to Advt. Hall of Fame, 1985. Mem. Am. Mktg. Assn. (bd. dirs. 1944-47, 54-56, v.p. 1956-57), Am. Acad. Advt., Am. Assn. Pub. Opinion Research, Phi Beta Kappa, Lambda Delta Sigma, Delta Sigma Pi, Kappa Tau Alpha, Alpha Delta Sigma. Office: Farm Rsch Inst 717 Philo Rd Ste 29 Urbana IL 61801-6044

SANDALLS, WILLIAM THOMAS, JR., financial services company executive; b. Newport, R.I., Jan. 7, 1944; s. William Thomas Sr. and Marion Harriett (Hellman) S.; m. Katharine Anne Flood, June 22, 1968; children: William Thomas III, Benjamin Flood (dec. 1987), Katharine Anne. BA cum laude in Indsl. Adminstrn., Yale U., 1966; MBA, Harvard Grad. Sch. Bus. Adminstrn., 1972; MS in Taxation, Bentley Coll., 1979. CPA, Mass. With Arthur Andersen & Co., Boston, 1972-74; with BayBanks, Inc., Boston, 1974-91; COO MAsterCard Internat. Inc., 1991—; dir.-at-large Bank Adminstrn. Inst. Overseer Boston's Mus. Sci. Lt. USN, 1966-70, Vietnam. Clubs: Union, Harvard, Yale (N.Y.C.); Boston Econ. Office: MasterCard Internat Inc 888 Seventh Ave New York NY 10106

SANDALOW, TERRANCE, law educator; b. Chgo., Sept. 8, 1934; s. Nathan and Evelyn (Hoffing) S.; m. Ina Davis, Sept. 4, 1955; children: David Blake, Marc Alan, Judith Ann. AB, U. Chgo., 1954, JD, 1957. Bar: Ill. 1958, Mich. 1978. Law clk. to judge Sterry R. Waterman U.S. Ct. Appeals (2d cir.), 1957-58; law clk. to justice Potter Stewart U.S. Supreme Ct., Washington, 1958-59; assoc. Ross, McGowan & O'Keefe, Chgo., 1959-61; assoc. prof. law U. Minn., Mpls., 1961-64, prof., 1964-66; prof. law U. Mich., Ann Arbor, 1966—, dean Law Sch., 1978-87, Edson R. Sunderland prof. law, 1987—. Author: (with F.I. Michelman) Government in Urban Areas, 1970, (with E. Stein) Courts and Free Markets, 1982; contbr. to legal jours., periodicals. Mem. Mpls. Commn. Human Relations, 1965-66. Fellow Ctr. Advanced Study in Behavioral Scis., 1972-73. Fellow Am. Acad. Arts Scis.; mem. Order of Coif, Phi Beta Kappa (hon.). Office: U Mich Law Sch 409 Hutchins Hall Ann Arbor MI 48109-1215

SANDBANK, HENRY, photographer, film director; b. Burg, Germany, Mar. 20, 1932; came to U.S., 1939, naturalized, 1950; s. Sylvan and Bella (Spatz) S.; m. Judith Lebow, July 4, 1952; children: Kenneth, Laura, Lisa, David. Ed. pub. schs. Partner Beach & Sandbank, Syracuse, N.Y., 1960-63; sr. ptnr. Sandbank & Ptnrs., N.Y.C., 1963-88; pres., film dir. Sandbank Films Co., Inc., N.Y.C., 1972—; dir. Vantage Films, 1979—; sr. ptnr. Sandbank Kamen & Ptnrs., 1992-94; lectr. Syracuse U., 1972, Mus. Modern Art, 1994, for Eastman Kodak, Tokyo, 1994; cons. Fashion Inst. Tech., 1974-80. Recipient Gold Medal awards Art Dirs. and Copywriters Show, Gold medal Film Festival of the Americas, several Clio and Andy awards, Cannes Festival award, Gold medal for film documentary Houston Internat.

Film Festival 1980). Served to sgt. AUS, 1952-54, Korea. Mem. Am. Soc. Mag. Photographers (chmn. exec. com. 1978-79, Outstanding Achievement award 1981), Soc. Photographers in Communications (trustee 1974-81, 2d v.p. 1975-76, 1st v.p. 1977, chmn. exec. com. 1979). Home: 24 Nutmeg Dr Greenwich CT 06831-3211 Office: 140 Old Saw Mill River Rd Hawthorne NY 10532-1515

SANDBERG, HAROLD RAYMOND, civil engineer; b. Galesburg, Ill., Dec. 28, 1919; s. Oscar I. and Esther O. (Gustafson) S.; m. Alice Louis Bendt, May 24, 1942; children: Diane Louise, Eric Bruce. BS in CE, U. Ill., 1942, MS inCE, 1947. Registered profl. engr. 13 states. Field engr. Dravo Corp., Pitts., 1942-44; instr. Coll. Engring., U. Ill., Urbana, 1946-47; design engr. Alfred Benesch & Co., Chgo., 1947-56; project mgr. Alfred Benesch & Co., 1956-64, v.p., 1964-71, pres., 1971-83, chmn. bd., 1983—; chmn. Indsl. Adv. Bd. Coll. Engring., U. Ill., Chgo., 1988—. Author/editor: Design of Concrete Bridges, 1988; contbr. articles to profl. jours. Chmn. Plan Commn., Mundelein, Ill. Recipient Loyal award, Ill. Alumni Assn., 1983; named Chgo. Civil Engr. of the Yr., ASCE, 1983. Fellow Cons. Engrs. Coun. of Ill. (pres. 1980-81), ACI (bd. dirs. 1988—), ASCE; mem. Structural Engrs. Assn. Ill. (John Parmer award 1983, pres. 1978-80), Ill. C. of C. (bd. dirs. 1981-87). Lutheran. Home: 155 N Harbor Dr Apt 4702 Chicago IL 60601-7325 Office: Alfred Benesch & Co 205 N Michigan Ave Ste 1700 Chicago IL 60601-5891*

SANDBERG, IRWIN WALTER, electrical and computer engineering educator; b. N.Y.C., Jan. 15, 1934; s. Ben and Estelle (Hornick) S.; m. Barbara A. Zimmerman, June 15, 1958; 1 dau. Heidi L. Student, CCNY, 1951-53; B.E.E., Poly. Inst. Bklyn., 1955, M.E.E., 1956, D.E.E., 1958. Tech. aid Bell Telephone Labs., Inc., Murray Hill, N.J., summer 1954, mem. tech. staff, 1958-67, head systems theory research dept., 1967-72, mem. math. and statis. research ctr., 1972-86; prof. elec. and computer engring. U. Tex., Austin, 1986—; now holder Cockrell Family Regents Chair in Engring. U. Tex.; engr. Wheeler Labs., Great Neck, N.Y., summer 1955; vis. prof. U. Calif.-Berkeley, 1965; U.S. del. Union Radio Scientifique Internationale, Munich, Ger., 1966; U.S. nat. inst. rep. Advanced Study Inst. on Network and Signal Theory, NATO, Bournemouth, Eng., 1972; lectr. study inst. NATO (Knokke), Belgium, 1966, NATO, Copenhagen, 1970; disting. invited speaker Asilomar Conf., 1973-74; main lectr. European Conf. on Circuit Theory and Design, The Hague, 1981; advisor Inst. Electronics, Info. and Communication Engrs., Tokyo. Patentee (in field). Recipient Best Paper award Asilomar Conf., 1970, Achievement award IEEE Circuits and Systems Soc., 1986, Classic Paper citation ISI press, 1984, Outstanding Alumnus award Poly. U., 1993. Fellow IEEE (adminstrv. com. group circuit theory 1969-70, vice chmn. group circuit theory 1971-72, Centennial medal), AAAS; mem. NAE, Soc. for Indsl. and Applied Math., Eta Kappa Nu, Sigma Xi, Tau Beta Pi. Home: 8505 Hickory Creek Dr Austin TX 78735-1527 Office: Univ Tex Dept Elec Comp Engr Austin TX 78712

SANDBERG, ROBERT ALEXIS, former research organization administrator; b. Spokane, Sept. 20, 1914; s. Robert A. and Faye P. (Davis) S.; m. Ruth Margaret Cheatham, Apr. 1, 1934 (dec. July 1985); children—Robert Howard, William, Douglas; m. Evelyn M. Lake, May 16, 1987. A.B., Wash. State U., 1936, A.M., 1937; postgrad., Northwestern U., 1937-38, U. Ill., 1939-41. Instr. speech U. Ill., 1939-42; exec. asst. to pres. Wash. State U., 1945-52; v.p. pub. affairs and advt. Kaiser Aluminum and Chem. Corp., Oakland, Calif., 1965-72; sr. v.p. Kaiser Industries, Inc., Oakland, 1972-74; sr. adv. Electric Power Research Inst., Palo Alto, Calif., 1974-80; ret., 1980; cons. in comm. and pub. rels., 1980—. Author: Everyday Business Speech, 1942, Handbook of Public Speaking, 1940, Effective Speaking in Business, 1960. Dir. fund raising Eastern area A.R.C., 1941-45; Trustee Inst. Ednl. Devel.; bd. dirs. Advt. Council. Mem. Pub. Rels. Soc. Am. (accredited, accreditation bd. 1968—), Newcomen Soc., Sigma Delta Chi. Home: 735 Arroyo Ct Lafayette CA 94549-5311

SANDBORN, VIRGIL ALVIN, civil engineer, educator; b. Conway Springs, Kans., Apr. 30, 1928; s. Kenneth Arthur and Mamie Una (Durham) S.; m. Virginia Ruth Cerny, June 12, 1955; children: Peter Alan, Patricia Marie. B in Aero. Engring., U. Kans., 1950; M in Aero. Engring., U. Mich., 1953. Aero. research scientist NACA-NASA, Cleve., 1951-62; cons. scientist AVCO R&AD, Wilmington, Mass., 1962-63; prof. Colo. State U., Ft. Collins, 1963—; vis. scientist NASA-Ames Research Ctr., Moffett Field, Calif., 1972-73, Navy Underwater Ctr., Newport, R.I., 1984-85. Author: Resistance Temperature Transducers, 1972, Classnotes for Experimental Methods in Fluid Mechanics, 1981. Mem. AIAA, Sigma Xi. Home: 917 Cheyenne Dr Fort Collins CO 80525-1559 Office: Colo State U Fort Collins CO 80523

SANDBULTE, AREND JOHN, utility executive; b. Sioux Center, Iowa, Dec. 9, 1933; s. Ben and Rena (Rensink) S.; m. Verna VanDeBerg, June 30, 1953; children: Ruth Marie, Gregory Bern, Kristin Ann, Rachel Lynn. B.S. in Elec. Engring., Iowa State U., 1959, M.B.A., U. Minn., 1966. Registered profl. engr., Minn., N.D., Wis. Rate engr. No. States Power Co., Mpls., 1959-64; with Minn. Power, Duluth, 1964—, asst. v.p. budgets and corp. planning, 1972-74, v.p. corp. planning, 1974-76, v.p. fin., chief fin. officer, 1976-78, sr. v.p. fin. and adminstrn., chief fin. officer, 1978-80, exec. v.p., chief fin. officer, 1980-83, exec. v.p., chief operating officer, chief fin. officer, dir., 1983-84, 1983-89, pres., chief oper. officer, 1984-88, pres., chief exec. officer, 1988-89, chmn., pres., chief exec. officer, 1989—, also bd. dirs.; bd. dirs. Norwest Bank Duluth Community Bd., Royal D. Alworth Jr. Inst. Internat. Studies, Assn. Edison Illuminating Cos., Iowa State U. Elec. Engring. Adv. Bd., Lake Superior Cen. Bd., Minn. Bus. Ptnrship., St. Mary Parish Land Co., Utech Venture Capital Corp., Kitchi Gammi Club. Bd. dirs. N.E. Minn. Devel. Assn., 1987-88, St. Luke's Found., 1985—; trustee Coll. St. Scholastica, Duluth, 1979—, vice chmn. bd., 1983, chmn. bd., 1984-87; dir. St. Luke's Hosp., Duluth, 1977-88, chmn. bd., 1982-84; trustee Duluth YMCA, 1977—; bd. dirs. Ordean Found., 1983—; Minn. Safety Coun., 1986-88, bd. dirs. United Way, 1984—, campaign chmn., 1986, chmn. bd. 1989—. Served with U.S. Army, 1954-55. Recipient Nikola Tesla award Midwest Area Power Utilities, 1975; named Boss of Year, Duluth Jaycees, 1974. Mem. IEEE, Engrs. Club No. Minn., Minn. C. of C. (bd. dirs. industry sect. 1984—), Duluth Area C. of C. (pres. 1982), North Cen. Electric Assn. (pres. 1987-88, exec. com. 1988—), Edison Elect. Inst. (chief exec. officer steering com. on global climate change 1990—, policy com. on environment 1990—, chief exec. officer steering com. on the Staggers Rail Act 1990—), Minn. Bus. Partnership (exec. com., co-chair steering com.). Republican. Presbyterian. Clubs: Mpls.; Kitchi Gammi (Duluth); Northland Country. Home: 2930 London Rd Duluth MN 55804-2004 Office: Minn Power 30 W Superior St Duluth MN 55802-2093

SANDBURG, HELGA, author; b. Maywood, Ill., Nov. 24, 1918; d. Carl and Lilian (Steichen) S.; m. George Crile Jr., Nov. 9, 1963; children by previous marriage: John Carl Steichen, Paula Steichen Polega. Student, Mich. State Coll., 1939-40, U. Chgo., 1940. Dairy goat breeder, also personal sec. to father, 1944-51; sec. manuscripts div., asst. for keeper of collections Library of Congress, 1952-56; adminstrv. asst. for papers of Woodrow Wilson, 1958-59; writer, lectr., 1957—. Author: (novels) The Wheel of Earth, 1958, Measure My Love, 1959, The Owl's Roost, 1962, The Wizard's Child, 1967; (non-fiction) Sweet Music, A Book of Family Reminiscence and Song, 1963; (with George Crile, Jr.) Above and Below, 1969; (poetry) The Unicorns, 1965; To A New Husband, 1970, The Age of the Flower, 1994; (young adult novels) Blueberry, 1963; Gingerbread, 1964; (juveniles) Joel and the Wild Goose, 1963; Bo and the Old Donkey, 1965, Anna and the Baby Buzzard, 1970; Children and Lovers: 15 Stories by Helga Sandburg, 1976; (biography) A Great and Glorious Romance: The Story of Carl Sandburg and Lilian Steichen, 1977; "...Where Love Begins", 1989; (with Diane Leslie) Joel and The Wild Goose, Contempory Musical Fantasy, 1991, also numerous short stories; rep. in collections.; contbr.short stories, poems, articles to popular mags. including Seventeen. Recipient Va. Quar. Rev. prize for best short story, 1959, Borestone Mountain poetry award, 1962, Poetry award Chgo. Tribune, 1970; 2d prize 7th Ann. Kans. Poetry Contest, Florence Roberts Head Ohioana Book award, 1990; grantee Finnish Am. Soc. and Svenska Inst., 1961. Mem. Authors Guild, Poetry Soc., Am. Milk Goat Record Assn., Am.-Scandinavian Found., Nat. Nubian Club, Coun. Save the Dunes, Am. Luxembourg Soc., Acad. Am. Poets. Address: 2060 Kent Rd Cleveland OH 44106-3339

SANDE, THEODORE ANTON, architect, educator, foundation executive; b. New London, Conn., Nov. 21, 1933; s. Lars Anton and Viola (Edgcomb) S.; m. Solveig Inga-Maj Imselius, Aug. 6, 1960; children: Susanne Ingrid, Lars Michael. BSc in Architecture, R.I. Sch. Design, 1956; MArch, Yale U., 1961; PhD, U. Pa., 1972; grad. Cultural Instns. Mgmt. Program, Mus. Collaborative, 1983; postgrad., Attingham (Eng.) Summer Sch., 1980. Vis. prof. history of architecture Rensselaer Poly. Inst., fall 1973-74, U. Pa., 1976-77; adj. prof. Am. studies and history Case-Western Res. U., 1981—; vis. lectr. in historic preservation Cleve. State U., summer 1994; lectr. art Williams Coll., 1972-75; attended teleconfs. non-profit orgn. mgmt. Drucker Found., 1992. Designer, Arkitekt, Hakon Ahlberg, SAR, Arkitekt, Stockholm, 1960, designer, Washburn, Luther & Rowley, Architects, Attleboro, Mass., 1961-62, Barker & Turoff, Architects, Providence, 1962-63, jr. partner, Turoff Assocs., Architects, 1964-67, partner, Turoff & Sande Architects, Providence, 1968-70, prin., Ted Sande, Architect, Cranston, R.I. 1970, Cleve., 1993—; author: Industrial Archaeology: A New Look at the American Heritage, 2d edit, 1978; contbg. author: Guidebook to Philadelphia Architecture, 1974; editor: New England Textile Mill Survey, 1971; co-editor: Historic Preservation of Engineering Works, 1981; contbr. articles to profl. jours.; two-man show drawings, Providence Art Club, 1970. Dir. profl. svcs. office hist. properties Nat. Trust Hist. Preservation, Washington, 1975-77, dir. planning and devel., 1977-78, acting v.p. office hist. properties, 1978-79, v.p., 1979-80; mem. Old Georgetown Bd. Nat. Commn. Fine Arts, 1979-81; exec. dir. Western Res. Hist. Soc., Cleve., 1981-93, exec. dir. emeritus, 1993—; cons. architecture Mus. and Hist. Soc. Mgmt., Historic Preservation and Archtl. Hist., 1993—; co-chmn. Conf. Indsl. Archeology, Smithsonian Instn., 1971; active Shaker Heights Landmark Commn., 1982-84, Cleve. Landmarks Commn., 1985—, Leadership Cleve. Class 86/87, Ohio Gov.'s Commn. on the Bicentennials the NW Ordinance and U.S. Const., 1986-89, Cleve. Bicentennial Commn., 1992-94; trustee Univ. Circle Inc., 1981-93, Cleve. Restoration Soc., 1985—, Lake View Cemetery Found., 1985—, Nat. Rock and Roll Mus. and Hall Fame, mem. exec. bldg. com., 1993—, instnl. rep. Cleve. Arts Consortium, 1987-93; pres. Cleve. Restoration Soc., 1994—. Mem. AIA (architect mem., com. hist. resources 1972-74), SAR, Soc. Indsl. Archeology (co-founder, 1st pres. 1971-72, dir. 1973-76, project supr. handbook, gen. chmn. 15th ann. conf.), Soc. Archtl. Historians (preservation com. 1972-74), Internat. Com. for Conservation of Indsl. Heritage (chmn. bd. dirs. 1978-81), Ohio Mus. Assn. (trustee 1982-87), Am. Assn. Mus., Rowfant Club, Philos. Club Cleve. (past pres.). Episcopalian. Home: 13415 Shaker Blvd Cleveland OH 44120-1548

SANDE, THOMAS PAUL, toy manufacturing company executive; b. Grand Forks, N.D., Dec. 6, 1935; s. Gerald Elliot and Colleta Barbara (Backes) S.; m. Audrey Joan Hoffer, June 29, 1963; children: Theodore, Matthew. BBA, U. N.D., 1957. CPA. Audit mgr. Price Waterhouse and Co., 1957-72; v.p., treas., controller Monroe Auto Equipment Co., 1972-78; corp. controller Dayton-Walther Corp., 1978-84; sr v.p. fin., chief fin. officer Coleco Industries Inc., Avon, Conn., 1984—.

SANDEEN, RODERICK COX, newspaper editor; b. Mpls., Apr. 27, 1943; s. Clair William and Mary Ethel (Cox) S.; B.S. in Journalism, U. Colo., 1969; m. Patricia Anne McDermott, June 10, 1972; children—Peter, Mark. Reporter, The New Haven Post-Register, 1969-70; reporter Post-Register, Idaho Falls, Idaho, 1972-73; reporter, editor Idaho Statesman, Boise, 1973-78, mng. editor, 1978—. Office: The Freedom Forum 1101 Wilson Blvd Arlington VA 22209

SANDEFUR, JAMES TANDY, mathematics educator; b. Madison, Ind., Apr. 25, 1947; s. James Tandy and Evelyn (Gayle) S.; m. Mary Elizabeth Epes, Sept. 6, 1969 (div. 1982); m. Helen Moriarty, Apr. 14, 1984; 1 child, Scott David. BA, Vanderbilt U., 1969; MA, U. Denver, 1971; PhD, Tulane U., 1974. Prof. math. Georgetown U., Washington, 1974—; vis. assoc. prof. U Iowa, Iowa City, 1988-89; math. cons. It's Academic TV show Altman Prodns., Washington, 1985—; prin. investigator, dir. math. modelling workshop NSF, Washington, 1988-91. Author: Discrete Dynamical Systems: Theory and Applications, 1990, Discrete Dynamical Modeling, 1993; adv. bd. to Annenberg/CPB math. and sci. project's Guide to Math and Science Reform; contbr. articles to math. jours. Program dir. in Instrl. Materials Devel. for Div. of Materials, Devel., Rsch. and Informal Sci. Edn.; directorate for Edn. and Human Resources NSF. NSF grantee, prin. investigator Tchr. Leadership Inst., 1993—. Mem. Math. Assn. Am. (chmn. minicourse com.), Nat. Coun. Tchrs. Math. (adv. panel Yearbook Discrete Math.), Am. Contract Bridge League (chpt. bd. dirs. 1983-85). Democrat. Avocations: bridge, tennis, skiing. Office: Georgetown U Dept Math Washington DC 20057

SANDEFUR, THOMAS EDWIN, JR., tobacco company executive; b. Cochran, Ga., Dec. 4, 1939; s. Thomas Edwin and Elsie (Camp) S.; m. Annette Crawford Meginniss, May 8, 1965. B.S. in Bus. Acctg., Ga. So. U., 1963. Sales and mktg. positions R.J. Reynolds Tobacco Co., Winston-Salem, N.C., 1964-76, sr. v.p. advt. and brand mgmt., 1976-79; sr. v.p. R.J. Reynolds Internat., Winston-Salem, N.C., 1979-81; exec. v.p. Europe, Geneva, 1981-82; sr. v.p. internat. mktg. Brown & Williamson Tobacco Corp., Louisville, 1982-84, exec. v.p., 1984-85, pres., COO, 1985-93, chmn., CEO, 1993—; bd. dirs. Bank Louisville. Bd. dirs. Wesleyan Coll., LA. Bantle Inst., Greater Louisville Fund for Arts, Cathedral Heritage Found., Boy Scout coun. Louisville; bd. overseers U. Louisville; bd. adv. coun. Ga. So. Coll., Nat. Assn. Mfrs. Mem. Am. Wholesale Marketers Assn. Office: Brown & Williamson Tobacco Corp 1500 Brown Williamson Tower Louisville KY 40202

SANDELL, WILLIAM, production designer. Art dir.: (films) Fast Charlie...the Moonbeam Rider, 1979; prodn. designer: (films) The Pack, 1977, The Clones, 1977, Piranha, 1978, The Promise, 1979, Serial, 1980, Blood Beach, 1981, (with Joe Aubel) Dead and Buried, 1981, Airplane II: The Sequel, 1982, Young Lust, 1982, The Wild Life, 1984, St. Elmo's Fire, 1985, Robocop, 1987, Big Business, 1988, Total Recall, 1990, Nothing But Trouble, 1991, Newsies, 1992, Hocus Pocus, 1993, The Flintstones, 1994. Office: care Art Directors Guild 11365 Ventura Blvd #315 Studio City CA 91604*

SANDENAW, THOMAS ARTHUR, JR., lawyer; b. Harlowton, Mont., Mar. 17, 1936; s. Thomas A. Sr. S.; m. Colleen A. Andrews, June 3, 1956 (div. May 1981); children: Cheryl Lea, Kevin K., Dana Scott; m. Deborah Rose Hammel, Sept. 26, 1981. BS, Mont. State U., 1958; JD, U. N.Mex., 1967. Bar: N.Mex. 1967, U.S. Dist. Ct. N.Mex. 1968, U.S. Ct. Appeals (10th cir.) 1968. Atty. Wilkinson, Durrett & Conway, Alamogordo, N.Mex., 1968-69, Spence & Sandenaw, Alamogordo, N.Mex., 1969-71, Shipley, Durrett, Conway & Sandenaw, Alamogordo, N.Mex., 1971-77; judge 12th jud. dist. Lincoln and Otero Counties, Alamogordo, N.Mex., 1978-79; atty. Overstreet & Sandenaw, Alamogordo, N.Mex., 1979-82; ptnr. Weinbrenner, Richards, Paulowsky, Sandenaw & Ramirez, Las Cruces, N.Mex., 1982-92; pvt. practice Las Cruces, N.Mex., 1992—. Dri. St. Lukes Health Care, Las Cruces, 1992, Mesilla Valley Hospice, Las Cruces, 1992—, Am. S.W. Theatre Co., Las Cruces, 1992-93. Mem. ABA (law practice mgmt. tort and ins. practice litigation), Am. Bd. Trial Advocates, Am. Bd. Profl. Liability Attys. (diplomat 1993—), Nat. Bd. Trial Advocacy (cert. civil trial practice 1989), State Bar N.Mex. (chmn. pub. rels. com. 1967-68), N.Mex. Defense Lawyers Assn. (sec. 1984-85, v.p. 1985-86, pres. 1987-88, bd. dirs. 1983—, chmn. Amicus Curie com. 1991—), Dona Ana County Bar Assn., Assn. Def. Trial Attorneys, Rotary (past pres. Rio Grande chpt.). Republican. Lutheran. Avocations: skiing, sailing, woodworking. Office: 545 S Melendres St Ste C Las Cruces NM 88005-2805

SANDER, DONALD HENRY, soil scientist, researcher; b. Creston, Nebr., Apr. 21, 1933; s. Paul L. and Mable O. (Wendt) S.; m. Harriet Ora Palmateer, Dec. 27, 1953; children: Ben, Joan. BS, U. Nebr., 1954, MS in Agronomy, 1958, PhD in Agronomy, 1967. Soil scientist researcher USDA Forest Svc., Lincoln, Nebr., 1958-64; asst. prof. agronomy, soil fertility specialist Kans. State U., Manhattan, 1964-67; prof. agronomy, extension soils specialist U. Nebr., Lincoln, 1967—. Contbr. over 40 articles to jours. including Soil Sci. Soc. Am. Jour. 1st lt. U.S. Army, 1954-56, Korea. Recipient USDA Superior Svc. award, 1987, Soil Sci. Applied Rsch. award, 1989, Great Plains Leadership award, Denver, 1990,. Fellow Am. Soc. Agronomy (Agronomic Achievement award 1985), Soil Sci. Soc. Am.; mem.

Gama Sigma Delta, Sigma Xi. Republican. Presbyterian. Avocation: woodworking. Home: 6548 Darlington Ct Lincoln NE 68510 Office: Univ Nebr Dept Agronomy Lincoln NE 68583

SANDER, FRANK ERNEST ARNOLD, law educator; b. Stuttgart, Germany, July 22, 1927; came to U.S. 1940, naturalized 1946; s. Rudolf and Alice (Epstein) S.; m. Emily Bishop Jones, Apr. 26, 1958; children: Alison Bishop, Thomas Harvey, Ernest Ridgway Sander. A.B. in Math. magna cum laude, Harvard U., 1949, LL.B. magna cum laude, 1952. Bar: Mass. 1952, U.S. Supreme Ct 1952. Law clk. to Chief Judge Magruder U.S. Ct. Appeals, 1952-53; law clk. to Justice Frankfurter, U.S. Supreme Ct., 1953-54; atty. tax div. Dept. Justice, 1954-56; with firm Hill & Barlow, Boston, 1956-59; mem. faculty Harvard Law Sch., 1959—, prof. law, 1962—, Bussey prof., 1981—, assoc. dean, 1987—; spl. fields fed. taxation, family law, welfare law, dispute resolution; chmn. Council on Role of Cts.; mem. panels Am. Arbitration Assn., Fed. Mediation and Conciliation Service; chmn. Council on Legal Edn. Opportunity, 1968-70; cons. Dept. Treasury, 1968; treas. Harvard Law Rev., 1951-52. Author: (with Westfall and McIntyre) Readings in Federal Taxation, 2d edit., 1983, (with Foote and Levy) Cases and Materials on Family Law, 3d edit., 1985, (with Gutman) Tax Aspects of Divorce and Separation, 4th edit., 1985, (with Goldberg and Rogers) Dispute Resolution, 2d edit., 1992. Mem. tax mission Internat. Program Taxation to Republic of Colombia, 1959; mem. com. on civil and polit. rights President's Commn. on Status of Women, 1962-63; trustee Buckingham Browne and Nichols Sch., 1969-75; chmn. Mass. Welfare Adv. Bd., 1975-79. With AUS, 1945-46. Recipient Whitney North Seymour medal Am. Arbitration Assn., 1988, spl. award for disting. svc. to dispute resolution Ctr. for Pub. Resources, 1990. Mem. ABA (chmn. standing com. dispute resolution 1986-89, Kutak medal 1993), Boston Bar Assn., Phi Beta Kappa. Home: 74 Buckingham St Cambridge MA 02138-2229 Office: Law Sch Harvard U Cambridge MA 02138

SANDER, RAYMOND JOHN, government executive; b. N.Y.C., July 4, 1944; s. Raymond John and Rose Marie (Nigrelli) S.; m. Sheryl Swed; children: Raymond Paul, Christy. BS, Fordham Coll., 1965; MA, U. Md., 1971. With CIA, Washington, 1966-73; asst. dir. mgmt. program, budget staff Dept. Justice, Washington, 1973-77; dir. office mgmt. planning Dept. Transp., Washington, 1977-81; exec. dir. Urban Mass Transit Adminstrn., Washington, 1981-88; dir. trade and comml. programs Am. Inst. in Taiwan, Arlington, Va., 1988—. Office: Am Inst in Taiwan 1700 N Moore St Arlington VA 22209-1903

SANDER, RUDOLPH CHARLES, investment banker; b. Phila., Aug. 10, 1930; s. Rudolph Carl and Loleita (Kuenstner) S.; m. Julia Agnes Boyce, Sept. 19, 1959; children: Mark, Robert, Jeffrey. Cert. fin. planner. Ptnr. Butcher and Sherrerd, Phila., 1952-74, Butcher and Singer, Inc., Phila., 1974-76; exec. v.p. Janney Montgomery Scott, Inc., Phila., 1977—; chmn. bd. Addison Capital Shares, Bala Cynwyd, Pa.; bd. dirs. Pa. Ins. and Annuity Grp., Phila, Pa. Diversified Ins. and Annuity Corp., Phila. Mem. devel. bd. Del. County Community Hosp., Upper Darby, Pa., 1987—. Mem. Nat. Assn. Security Dealers (bd. govs. 1987—), Phila. Securities Assn., Investment Traders Assn. Phila. Club: Bond of Phila. (pres. 1977-78). Avocations: golf, reading. Home: 505 Oriole Ln Villanova PA 19085-1934 Office: Janney Montgomery Scott Inc 5 Penn Plz Philadelphia PA 19103

SANDERCOX, ROBERT ALLEN, college official, clergyman; b. Akron, Ohio, May 20, 1932; s. Monroe J. and Elverda (Arnold) S.; m. Nancy Lee Wertz, Sept. 13, 1958; children—Alison Grace, Megan Louise, Robert Philip. B.A. Bethany Coll., W. Va., 1954; M.Div., Yale U., 1957; postgrad., U. Buffalo, W.Va. U.; LittD, Bethany Coll., 1989. Ordained to ministry Christian Ch. (Disciples of Christ). Asst. minister Park Ave Christian Ch., N.Y.C., 1954-57; asst. provost Bethany Coll., 1957-60, v.p., dean students, 1960-75, v.p. dir. devel., 1975-79, interim pres., 1979-80, v.p., provost for coll. advancement, 1980-89, sr. v.p., 1989—. Trustee Christian Ch. Disciples of Christ in W.Va., Parkersburg, 1984-88; chmn. Brooke County Landmarks Commn., 1988—. Recipient Alumni Disting. Service award Bethany Coll., 1982. Mem. Coun. for Advancement and Support Edn., Duquesne Club (Pitts.), Internationale (Washington), Order of Symposiarch, Rotary, Kiwanis (pres. 1967), Alpha Sigma Phi (nat. treas. 1982-84, v.p. 1984-86, grad. sr. pres. 1986-88, bd. dirs., trustee Ednl. Found. 1982—, chmn. Ednl. Found. 1994—, Delta Beta Xi svc. award 1960). Democrat. Home: Highland Hearth Bethany WV 26032 Office: Bethany Coll Office of VP Bethany WV 26032

SANDERS, AARON PERRY, radiation biophysics educator; b. Phoenix, Jan. 12, 1924; s. DeWitt and Ruth (Perry) S.; m. Betty Mae Gelein, Aug. 11, 1944 (div.); children: Merle Sanders Inland, Julie Sanders Jacome, James DeWitt; m. Georgia Anne Bullock, Nov. 26, 1972; 1 dau., Kai Marie. B.S., U. Tex., El Paso, 1950; M.S. (AEC fellow), U. Rochester, 1952; Ph.D., U. N.C., 1964. Diplomate: Am. Bd. Health Physics. Baggage clk., ticket agt. Greyhound Bus Lines, Phoenix, 1942; dispatcher, ticket agt. Greyhound Bus Lines, El Paso, Tex., 1946-50; asso. health physicist Brookhaven Nat. Lab., Upton, N.Y., 1951-53; instr. physics, radiol. safety officer N.C. State Coll., 1953; instr. radiology Duke Med. Center, Durham, N.C., 1953-56; dir. radioisotope lab. Duke Med. Center, 1953-65; asso. in radiology Duke Med. Ctr., 1956-57, asst. prof., 1957-64, assoc. prof., 1964-65, assoc. prof., dir. radiobiology, 1965-70, prof., dir. div. radiobiology, 1970-83, prof. emeritus, 1983—; chmn. Biomed. Physics Dept. King Faisal Specialist Hosp., Riyadh, Saudi Arabia, 1984-86; Fulbright sr. lectr. radiol. physics, Argentina, 1958-59; cons. N.C. Bd. Health, 1961-76; mem. N.C. Radiation Protection Commn., 1976-83, chmn., 1978-79. Contbr. articles to profl. jours. Served with USNR, 1942-45. Mem. AAAS, Am. Assn. Physicists in Medicine, AAUP, Soc. Exptl. Biology and Medicine, Health Physics Soc., Soc. Nuclear Medicine, Biophys. Soc., Radiation Research Soc., Undersea Med Soc., Sigma Xi, Sigma Pi Sigma. *Each individual has an obligation to himself and society to pursue an education to his maximum capability. This capability should then be used in his career in an effort to contribute to society as much, or more, than he receives. In work and personal relations you must never deny a man the dignity of his work by ridicule or denigration, and you must never use people.*

SANDERS, ADRIAN LIONEL, education consultant; b. Paragould, Ark., Aug. 3, 1938; s. Herbert Charles and Florence Theresa (Becherer) S.; m. Molly Jean Zecher, Dec. 20, 1961. AA, Bakersfield Coll., 1959; BA, San Francisco State U., 1961; MA, San Jose State U., 1967. 7th grade tchr. Sharp Park Sch., Pacifica, Calif., 1961-62; 5th grade tchr. Mowry Sch., Fremont, Calif., 1962-64; sci. tchr. Blacow Sch., Fremont, Calif., 1964-76; 5th grade tchr. Warm Springs Sch., Fremont, 1977-87, 5th grade gifted and talented tchr., 1987-94; edn. cons., 1994—. Mem. San Jose Hist. Mus. Assn., 1980—, Nat. Geog. Soc., Washington, 1976—, Alzheimer's Family Relief Program, Rockville, Md., 1986; vol. 7 km. Race for Alzheimer's Disease Willow Glen Founders Day, San Jose, 1988-92. Named Outstanding Young Educator, Jr. C. of C., Fremont, Calif., 1965. Mem. Smithsonian Assocs., U.S. Golf Assn. Avocations: photography, travelling, visiting presidents' birthplaces, collecting license plates, collecting matchbooks worldwide. Home and Office: 15791 Rica Vista Way San Jose CA 95127-2735

SANDERS, ALEXANDER MULLINGS, JR., judge; b. Columbia, S.C., Sept. 29, 1938; s. Alexander Mullings Sr. and Henrietta Courtrier (Thomas) S.; m. Zoe Caroline Dutrow; 1 child, Zoe Caroline. BS, U. S.C., 1960, LLB, 1962; LLM, U. Va., 1990. Bar: S.C. 1962, U.S. Dist. Ct. S.C. 1962, U.S. Supreme Ct. 1975, U.S. Ct. Appeals (4th cir.) 1976. Sr. ptnr. Sanders & Quackenbush, Columbia, 1974-83; of counsel Adams & Quackenbush, Columbia, 1983; chief judge S.C. Ct. Appeals, Columbia, 1983-92; pres. Coll. Charleston, S.C., 1992—; adj. faculty U. S.C., Columbia, 1965-92, Harvard U. Law Sch., Cambridge, Mass., 1983-93. Mem. S.C. Ho. Reps., Columbia, 1966-74, S.C. Senate, Columbia, 1976-83. Served with USAR, 1956. Mem. ABA, S.C. Bar Assn. Office: College of Charleston Charleston SC 29424

SANDERS, BARRY, football player; b. Wichita, July 16, 1968; s. William and Shirley Sanders. Student, Okla. State U., 1986-89. With Detroit Lions, 1989—. Recipient Heisman Trophy award, 1988; named Sporting News Coll. Football Player of Yr., 1988, NFL Rookie of Yr., 1990; named to Sporting News Coll. All-Am. team, 1987, 88, All-Pro team, 1989-91, 93, Pro

Bowl, 1989-93. Office: Detroit Lions 1200 Featherstone Rd Pontiac MI 48342-1938*

SANDERS, BERNARD (BERNIE SANDERS), congressman; b. Bklyn., Sept. 8, 1941; s. Eli and Dorothy (Glassberg) S.; m. Jane O'Meara, 1988; children: Levi, Heather, Carina, David. B.A., U. Chgo., 1964. Freelance writer, carpenter, youth counselor, 1964-76; with Govt. Vt., 1965-66; dir. Am. People's Hist. Soc., Burlington, Vt., 1976-81; mayor of Burlington, 1981-89; mem. U.S. House of Reps. from Vt., 102nd-104th Congresses from Vt., 1991—. Chairperson, Vt. Liberty Union Party, 1975-76, candidate for gov., 1972, 76, 86, U.S. Senate, 1971, 74; mem. Com. on Banking and Fin. Svcs., Com. on Govt. Reform and Oversight. Mem. Vt. League Cities and Towns. Jewish. Author filmstrips and articles on social, hist. and polit. subjects. Office: 213 Cannon Washington DC 20515-4501*

SANDERS, BRICE SIDNEY, bishop; b. Nashville, Oct. 15, 1930; s. Walter Richard and Agnes Mortimer (Jones) S.; m. Nancy Elizabeth Robinson, Aug. 22, 1953; children—Richard Evan, Robert Wesley, Lynne Elizabeth. B.A., Vanderbilt U., 1952; M.S.T., Episcopal Div. Sch., Cambridge, Mass., 1955; D.D. (hon.), Va. Theol. Sem., 1980, U. South, Sewanee, Tenn., 1984. Ordained to ministry. Rector St. James Ch., Union City, Tenn., 1955-58, Good Shepherd Ch., Knoxville, 1958-61, Eastern Shore Chapel, Virginia Beach, Va., 1961-70; assoc. dean Va. Theol. Sem., Alexandria, 1970-75; dean St. Andrews Cathedral, Jackson, Miss., 1975-79; bishop Diocese of East Carolina, Kingston, N.C., 1979—. Home: 2112 Sparre Dr Kinston NC 28501-1926 Office: Diocese of E Carolina PO Box 1336 Kinston NC 28503-1336

SANDERS, CHARLES ADDISON, pharmaceutical company executive, physician; b. Dallas, Feb. 10, 1932; s. Harold Barefoot and May Elizabeth (Forrester) S.; m. Elizabeth Ann Chipman, Mar. 6, 1956; children: Elizabeth, Charles Addison, Carlyn, Christopher. MD, U. Tex., 1955. Intern, asst. resident Boston City Hosp., 1955-57, chief resident, 1957-58; clin. and rsch. fellow in medicine Mass. Gen. Hosp., Boston, 1958-60; chief cardiac catheterization lab. Mass. Gen. Hosp., 1962-72, gen. dir., 1972-81, physician, 1973-81, program dir. myocardial infarction rsch. unit, 1967-72; exec. v.p. E.R. Squibb and Sons, 1981-84; exec. v.p. Squibb Corp., 1984-88, vice chmn., 1988-89; chief exec. officer Glaxo Inc., Research Triangle Park, N.C., 1989-94, chmn., 1992—; assoc. prof. medicine Harvard U. Med. Sch., 1969-80, prof., 1980-83; bd. dirs. Merrill Lynch and Co., Inc., Glaxo p.l.c., Morton Internat., Reynolds Metals Co., Mt. Sinai Med. Ctr., N.Y.C.; chmn. Commonwealth Fund N.Y.C.; mem. Inst. Medicine. Mem. editorial bd. New Eng. Jour. Medicine, 1969-72. Chmn. Project Hope. Capt. USAF, 1960-62. Mem. ACP, Am. Fedn. for Clin. Rsch., Am. Heart Assn., Mass. Med. Soc., Am. Physiol. Soc., Am. Clin. and Climatol. Soc., Am. Coll. Cardiology, Am. Soc. for Clin. Investigation, Soc. Hosp. Adminstrs. Methodist. Office: Glaxo Inc PO Box 13408 Durham NC 27709-3408

SANDERS, CHARLES FRANKLIN, corporate executive; b. Louisville, Dec. 22, 1931; s. Charles Franklin and Maragret Rhea (Timmons) S.; m. Marie Audrey Galuppo, Dec. 29, 1956; children: Karen Lynn, Craig Joseph, Keith Franklin. B.Chem. Engring., U. Louisville, 1954, M.Chem. Engring., 1958; Ph.D., U. So. Calif., 1970. Research engr. Exxon Research and Engring. Co., Linden, N.J., 1955-62; asst. prof. engring. Calif. State U., Northridge, 1962-68, assoc. prof., 1968-71, prof., 1971-82, chmn. dept., 1969-72, dean Sch. Engring. and Computer Sci., 1972-81; pres., chief exec. officer, dir. Rusco Industries, Los Angeles, 1981-82; exec. v.p. Energy Systems Assocs., Tustin, Calif, 1982-89; exec. v.p. Energeo, San Francisco, 1989—, also bd. dirs.; v.p. tech. Smith-Bellingham Capital, San Francisco, 1989-91; bd. dirs. Advanced Combustion Tech., Kailua-Kona, Hawaii. Bd. dirs. San Fernando Valley Child Guidance Clinic, 1979-81. Served to 1st lt. U.S. Army, 1956-57. NSF fellow, 1965-67. Mem. AICE, NSPE, Calif. Soc. Profl. Engrs., Am. Soc. for Engring. Edn. Republican. Office: 155 Bovet Rd # 150 San Mateo CA 94402-3180

SANDERS, DAVID P., lawyer; b. Chgo., Sept. 24, 1949. BA with distinction, U. Wis., 1971; JD, Georgetown U., 1974. Bar: Ill. 1974, U.S. Ct. Appeals (7th and 4th cirs.) 1974, U.S. Dist. Ct. (no. dist. trial bar) Ill. 1974. Ptnr. Jenner & Block, Chgo.; adj. prof. trial advocacy Northwestern U. Chgo., 1981-91. Editor Am Criminal Law Rev., 1974. Mem. ABA, Chgo. Coun. Lawyers (chmn. fed. jud. evaluation com. 1989—, mem. def. counsel sect. libel def. resource ctr.). Office: Jenner & Block One IBM Plz Chicago IL 60611

SANDERS, DEION LUWYNN, baseball and football player; b. Ft. Myers, Fla., Aug. 9, 1967. Student, Fla. State U. Baseball player N.Y. Yankees, 1988-90, Atlanta Braves, 1991-94, Cin. Reds, 1994—; football player Atlanta Falcons, 1989-94, San Francisco 49ers, 1994—. Named to Sporting News Coll. All-Am. football team, 1986-88, Sporting News NFL All-Pro Football Team, 1991, 92, 94, Pro Bowl team, 1991-94; recipient Jim Thorpe award. NFL kickoff return leader, 1992, Nat. League Triples Leader, 1992. also: Cin Reds 100 Riverfront Stadium Cincinnati OH 45202*

SANDERS, FRANKLIN D., insurance company executive; b. Newton, Mass., Apr. 24, 1935; s. Franklin and Ethel Shiner (Dulaney) S.; m. Jane Gray Collier, June 18, 1960; children—Cynthia, Franklin D., Nancy, Carolyn. A.B., Amherst Coll., 1957; M.B.A., Harvard U., 1959. With 1st Boston Corp., N.Y.C., 1960-86, mng. dir., 1976-86; pres. Aegis Ins. Services Inc., Jersey City, 1986—; treas., bd. dirs. Assoc. Electric & Gas Ins. Services Ltd., Hamilton, Bermuda. Chmn. Republican Exec. Com., Bernardsville, N.J., 1965-72, Bernardsville Zoning Bd. of Adjustment, 1966—. Episcopalian. Clubs: Down Town, Harvard (N.Y.C.); Somerset Hills Country (Bernardsville), Mid-Ocean (Bermuda). Avocations: sailing, skiing, golf. Home: RR 2 34 Post Kunhardt Rd Bernardsville NJ 07924-1522 Office: Aegis Ins Svcs Inc Harborside Fin Ctr 700 Plaza II Jersey City NJ 07311-3994

SANDERS, FRED JOSEPH, aerospace company executive; b. Tulsa, June 18, 1928; s. Charles Frederick and Mary Ethel (White) S.; m. Marceline Frances Shaw, May 19, 1951; 1 son, Fred William. A.A., Spartan Coll., 1947; M.S.M.E., St. Louis U., 1961. Design engr. McDonnell Aircraft Co., St. Louis, 1947-66; program mgr. Skylab Program, McDonnell Douglas, Huntington Beach, Calif., 1967-74; dir. product devel. McDonnell Douglas, Huntington Beach, 1975-76, v.p., 1977-84; v.p., gen. mgr. McDonnell Douglas Astronautics Co., St. Louis, 1985-88, ret., 1988. Served as capt. U.S. Army, 1954-56. Recipient Public Service award NASA, 1974. Asso. fellow AIAA. Roman Catholic. Home: 4 Broadview Farm Rd Saint Louis MO 63141-8501

SANDERS, FREDERICK, meteorologist; b. Detroit, May 17, 1923; s. Frederick William and Dorothy Gail (Martin) S.; m. Nancy Seabury Brown, Nov. 30, 1946; children: Christopher Martin, John Arnold, Frederick Duncan. B.A., Amherst Coll., 1944; Sc.D., M.I.T., 1954. Forecaster U.S. Weather Bur., N.Y.C., 1947-49; teaching asst. MIT, 1949-51, instr. meteorology, 1951-56, asst. prof., 1956-59, asso. prof., 1959-69, prof., 1969-84, prof. emeritus, 1984—; cons. in field. Author: (with H.C. Willett) Descriptive Meteorology, 1955, (with D.M. Houghton) Weather at Sea, 1988; editor Monthly Weather Rev., 1986—; contbr. numerous articles to profl. jours. Served with USAAF, 1942-46. Recipient award for applied research Nat. Weather Assn., 1978; NSF grantee, 1958—; NOAA grantee, 1956-78; Office Naval Research grantee, 1979-92; USAF grantee, 1954-78. Fellow AAAS, Am. Meteorol. Soc.; mem. Royal Meteorol. Soc. (fgn.). Club: Eastern Yacht (Marblehead, Mass.). Home and Office: 9 Flint St Marblehead MA 01945-3716

SANDERS, FREDRIC M., lawyer; b. N.Y.C., Jan. 10, 1941; s. Louis and Ruth (Appel) Samanowitz; m. Susan Sanders, June 11, 1961; children: Lauren, Lawrence. BA, Queens Coll., 1961; JD, Harvard U., 1964. Bar: N.Y. Assoc. Rubin Baum & Levin, N.Y.C., 1964-67; Hess Segall, N.Y.C., 1967-74; ptnr. Hess Segall Guterman Pelz et al (merged with Loeb and Loeb, 1986), N.Y.C., 1974-86, Loeb and Loeb, N.Y.C., 1986—. Mem. ABA, N.Y. State Bar Assn., Assn. of Bar of City of N.Y. Office: Loeb and Loeb 345 Park Ave New York NY 10154-0001

SANDERS, GERALD HOLLIE, communications educator; b. Mt. Vernon, Tex., Dec. 10, 1924; s. Elmer Hugh and Velma Mae (Hollowell) S.; m. Mary Dean Crew, July 18, 1947; children: Michael Dwaine, Rose Ann, Susan Kathleen, Randall Wayne. BA, Southeastern Okla. U., 1947; MA, Tex. Tech U., 1969; PhD, U. Minn., 1974. Program dir. Sta. WEWO, Laurenburg, N.C., 1947-49; sports dir. Sta. KFYO, Lubbock, Tex., 1949-50; gen. mgr. Sta. KLVT, Levelland, Tex., 1950-51, 53-54; sports dir. Sta. KCUL, Ft. Worth, 1954-55; asst. mgr. Sta. KDAV, Lubbock, 1955-57; mgr. Sta. KCBD, Lubbock, 1957-58; owner Sta. KSEL, Lubbock, 1958-67, Sta. KBUY, Amarillo, Tex., Sta. KERB, Kermit, Tex., Sta. KBEK, Elk City, Okla., Sta. KZZN, Littlefield, Tex.; lectr. communications The Coll. of Wooster, Ohio, 1967-68, asst. prof., 1968-75, assoc. prof., 1975-81, chmn. dept. communication, 1974-81; chmn. dept. communication Miami U., Oxford, Ohio, 1981-92, prof. emeritus comm., 1992—; disting. lectr. Jinan U., Zhong Shan U., Fudan U., Nanjing U., Beijing U., China, 1989; cons. in field, Oxford, 1982—. Author: Introduction to Comtemporary Academic Debate, 1983; also articles. Active Political Campaigns. Served to col. USMC, 1943-46, PTO, 1951-53, Korea. Recipient Disting. Svc. award Delta Sigma Rho-Tau Kappa Alpha, 1991, Am. Forensic Assn., 1991. Mem. Am. Forensic Assn. (pres. 1978-82), Speech Communication Assn., Speech Communication Assn. of Ohio (pres. 1976-77, Disting. Svc. award 1978), Cen. States Speech Assn., Am. Soc. Trial Cons. Presbyterian. Avocations: sports, political campaigns. Home: 200 Country Club Dr Oxford OH 45056-9002 Office: Miami U Dept Communication Oxford OH 45056

SANDERS, HANK, state senator, lawyer; b. Blackshear, Ala., Oct. 28, 1942; s. Sam and Ola Mae (Norman) S.; m. Rose M. Gaines, Jan. 23, 1970; children: Malika A., Kindaka J., Ainka M., Nigist Eyob, Jerusalem Eyob, Maurice Watson, Charles Watson. BS, Talladega Coll., 1967; JD, Harvard U., 1970. Bar: Ala. 1971. Mng. ptnr. Chestnut, Sanders, Sanders & Pettaway, P.C., Selma, Ala., 1972—; mem. Ala. Senate, Montgomery, 1983—, chmn. fin. and taxation com., mem. rules com., 1991-94; newspaper columnist Sketches, Greene County Dem., 1987. Author: (play) The Moment of Truth, 1969, (short stories) Down Home, 1983. Co-founder, pres. Ala. New South Coalition, Montgomery, 1988-90; co-founder, bd. dirs. 21st Century Youth Leadership, Selma, 1986—; co-founder Campaign for New South, Selma, 1984-87; chmn. bd. dirs. Nat. Voting Rights Mus., Selma, 1992. Recipient Nat. Community Svc. award Emergency Land Fund, Atlanta, M.L. King Community Svc. award, Selma, 1994; named Legislator of Yr., Ala. Legis. Black Caucus, NASW, 1990. Mem. Ala. State Bar, Ala. Lawyers Assn. (co-founder, pres. 1974), Nat. Conf. Black Lawyers, Nat. Caucus Black State Legislators. Democrat. Baptist. Avocations: reading, writing, sports. Office: Chestnut Sanders Sanders & Pettaway PC PO Box 1305 1405 Jefferson Davis Selma AL 36702 also: PO Box 1305 Selma AL 36702-1305

SANDERS, HAROLD BAREFOOT, JR., federal judge; b. Dallas, Tex., Feb. 5, 1925; s. Harold Barefoot and May Elizabeth (Forrester) S.; m. Jan Scurlock, June 6, 1952; children—Janet Lea, Martha Kay, Mary Frances, Harold Barefoot III. BA, U. Tex., 1949, LLB, 1950. Bar: Tex. bar 1950. U.S. atty. No. Dist. Tex., 1961-65; asst. dep. atty. gen. U.S., 1965-66; asst. atty. gen., 1966-67; legis. counsel to President U.S., 1967-69; partner firm Clark, West, Keller, Sanders & Butler, Dallas, 1969-79; U.S. dist. judge for No. Dist. Tex., Dallas, 1979—, chief judge, 1989-95. Mem. Tex. Ho. of Reps., 1952-58; Dem. nominee U.S. Senate, 1972. Lt. (j.g.) USNR, World War II. Mem. ABA (chmn. nat. conf. fed. trial judges 1988-89), Fed. Bar Assn. (Disting. Svc. award Dallas 1964), Dallas Bar Assn., State Bar Tex. (jud. conf. U.S. 1989-92, jud. panel on multidistrict litigation 1992—), Blue Key, Phi Delta Phi, Phi Delta Theta. Methodist. Office: US Courthouse 1100 Commerce St 15th Fl Dallas TX 75242

SANDERS, HOWARD, investment company executive; b. Phila., June 30, 1941; s. Louis and Freda (Liss) S.; m. Dale Rosenberg, Dec. 15, 1963; children: Lee Michael, Kimberly Joy. B.S. in Acctg., Temple U., 1962; M.Acctg., Ohio State U., 1963. C.P.A. Acct., Price, Waterhouse & Co., Phila., 1962-65; asst. prof. acctg. Temple U., 1965-72; v.p. Revere Fund, Inc., Phila., 1966-76; pres. Revere Mgmt. Co., Inc., Phila., 1966-72; chmn. bd. Ladies Center of Nebr., Inc., 1976—, Volk Footwear and Findings Co., 1977-78, Mister Plywood Enterprises, Inc., 1970-82; pres. Sanders Fin. Mgmt., Inc., Fort Lauderdale, 1972—; chmn. bd. Am. Carpet Backing Distbg. Inc., 1978-80, Polis-Sanders Real Estate Corp., 1981—. Contbg. author: How to Start a Mutual Fund, 1970. Mem. adv. bd. Phila. Assn. for Retarded Children, 1970-72; chmn. bd. Women's Med. Center of Providence, Inc., 1977—, Women's Med. Center of North Jersey, Inc., 1977-82, Women's Med. Center of Atlanta, Inc., 1977—, Cherry Hill Women's Center, Inc., 1978—, Metairie Women's Center of New Orleans, Inc., 1980-84, Hartford Gynecol. Center, 1980—, Kaiser Aluminum and Chem. Co. fellow, 1962-63. Mem. Am. Inst. C.P.A.s, Pa. Inst. C.P.A.s (award for paper 1961), Phila. Jaycees (dir. 1966), Nat. Assn. Accts., B'rith Shalom Assn., Beta Gamma Sigma, Beta Alpha Psi, Tau Epsilon Phi. Home and Office: 410 Sea Turtle Ter Fort Lauderdale FL 33324-2814 *My life has been guided by careful attention to words which are rapidly disappearing from the "Dictionary of American Life". I have concentrated on integrity, prudence, brevity, clarity, ego control and true friendship. In all dealings I insist upon mutual benefit, taking great effort to assure that the opposite party receives a slightly larger gain. My goal is total value received for all. I attempt to mix my love for life and humor in all my relationships.*

SANDERS, IRWIN TAYLOR, sociology educator; b. Millersburg, Ky., Jan. 17, 1909; s. Robert Stuart and Lucy (Taylor) S.; m. Margaret Rydberg, June 23, 1934; children: Gerda S. (Groff), Robert Stuart. Student, Tenn. Mil. Inst., 1920-25; A.B., Washington and Lee U., 1929; student, Theol. Sem., Princeton, 1932-33; Ph.D., Cornell U., 1938; D.Pedagogy (hon.), R.I. Coll., 1981; Litt.D. (hon.), Washington and Lee U., 1981. Instr. American Coll., Sofia, Bulgaria, 1929-32; dean American Coll., 1934-37; asst. prof. sociology Ala. Coll., 1938-40; successively asst. prof., asso. prof., prof., head dept. sociology, distinguished univ. prof. U. Ky., 1940-56; lectr. sociology Harvard Sch. Pub. Health, 1958-62; chmn. dept. sociology and anthropology Boston U., 1960-63, 69-72, prof. sociology, 1972-77, Univ. lectr., 1973-74, also co-dir. community sociology tng. program; research dir. Assos. Internat. Research, Inc., Cambridge, Mass., 1956-60; asso. dir. Internat. Tng. and Research Program, Ford Found., 1962-66; v.p. Edn. and World Affairs, 1967-69; social science analyst Bur. Agrl. Econ., U.S. Dept. Agr., summer 1943; sr. social scientist Bur. Agrl. Econ., U.S. Dept. Agr. (Office Fgn. Agrl. Relations), 1943; social sci. Bur. Agrl. Econ., U.S. Dept. Agr. (Extension Service), summer 1944; agrl. attaché Am. Embassy, Belgrade, Yugoslavia, 1945-46; research assoc. Harvard, 1952-53; cons. rural welfare division FAO. Author: Balkan Village, 1949, The Community, 1958, 3d rev. edit., 1975, Rainbow in the Rock, People of Rural Greece, 1962, Rural Society, 1977; co-author: Alabama Rural Communities, 1940, Sociological Foundations of Education, 1942, Kentucky: Designs for Her Future, 1944, Farmers of the World, 1945, Making Good Communities Better, 1950, Bridges to Understanding: International Programs at U.S. Colleges and Universities, 1970; Editor: Societies Around the World, 1953, Collectivization of Agriculture in Eastern Europe, 1958, The Professional School and World Affairs, 1968; series editor: Social Movements: Past and Present, 1980-95. Bd. dirs. Am. Farm Sch., Thessaloniki, Greece, Sofia Am. Schs., Inc., Assn. for Study Southeastern Europe, Bucharest, Rumania. Decorated Royal Order of Phoenix Greece). Mem. Am. Sociol. Soc. (disting. cmty. sect. award 1983), Eastern Sociol. Soc., So. Siol. Soc. (pres. 1955-56), Rural Sociol. Soc. (pres. 1956-57, Disting. Rural Sociologist 1993), New Eng. Sociological Assn. (Apple award 1993), Am. Sociol. Advancement Slavic Studies, Bulgarian-Am. Studies Assn. (hon. pres.), Modern Greek Studies Assn. (council), Am. Assn. for S.E. European Studies (pres. 1980), Société European de Culture (Venice), Rumanian Studies Soc. (council), Bulgarian Acad. Scis. (fgn. mem.), Am. Assn. for Promotion Bulgarian Culture (hon. pres.), Cornell Club (N.Y.), Univ. Club (Boston), Phi Beta Kappa, Omicron Delta Kappa, Kappa Phi Kappa, Delta Sigma Rho, Delta Upsilon. Democrat. Presbyterian. Home: 400 School St Wellesley MA 02181-4715 Office: 96 Cummington St Boston MA 02215-2407

SANDERS, JACK FORD, physician; b. St. Louis, Mich., July 16, 1918; s. Ford and Viva (Marvin) S.; m. Gretchen A. Jellema, Feb. 2, 1945; children—Karen Jean, Vicki Leigh, Mary Beth, Donald Curtis, Wendy Lynn. B.S. summa cum laude, Alma Coll., Mich., 1939; M.D., U. Mich., 1945; LL.D., Northwood Inst. Diplomate Am. Bd. Internal Medicine; cert. flight instr. aircraft and instruments, airplane single and multi-engine land

and sea; flight safety counselor FAA; CAP check pilot; sr. aviation med. examiner. Intern Henry Ford Hosp., 1945-46, resident in internal medicine, 1947-50; practice medicine specializing in internal medicine Northwood U., Alma, Mich.; sr. attending physician internal medicine Butterworth Hosp., Blodgett Hosp., Grand Rapids, Mich.; cons. St. Mary's Hosp., Grand Rapids, Ferguson-Droste-Ferguson Hosp.; med. dir. Mich. Masonic Hosp., Alma, 1960—; med. dir. rehab. div., chmn. dept. medicine, chief staff Gratiot Community Hosp.; chmn. dept. medicine Tri-County Hosp., Edmore, Mich.; clin. assoc. prof. medicine Coll. Human Medicine, Mich. State U.; mem. Com. on Aging, Gov's Adv. Coun. on Heart Disease, Cancer and Stroke; del White Ho. Conf. on Aging; bd. dirs. Mich. Masonic Home and Hosp.; chmn. bd. Cen. Mich. Wendy's, Inc.; sec., treas. Gratiot Aviation, Inc. Chmn. bd. govs. Mich.; bd. dirs. Northwood U., Gratist Cmty. Airport Bd. Instr. ACTS, U.S. Air Corps and lt. (j.g.) M.C., USNR, WWII. Fellow ACP, Am. Geriatrics Soc.; mem. AMA, Mich. State Med. Soc., Gratiot Med. Soc., Kent Med.Soc., Gratiot-Isabella-Clare County Med. Soc. (pres. 1965), Am. Diabetes Assn., Am. Heart Assn., Am. Multiple Sclerosis Soc., Mich. Crippled Children and Adults Soc., East Cen. Mich. Health Svc. Assn., Masons (33d degree), Rotary, Phi Sigma Phi. Home: 250 Purdy Dr Alma MI 48801-2174 Office: Mich Masonic Hosp Alma MI 48801-2174

SANDERS, JACK THOMAS, religious studies educator; b. Grand Prairie, Tex., Feb. 28, 1935; s. Eula Thomas and Mildred Madge (Parish) S.; m. M. Patricia Chism, Aug. 9, 1959 (dec. Oct. 1973); 1 son, Collin Thomas; m. Susan Elizabeth Plass, Mar. 3, 1979. B.A., Tex. Wesleyan Coll., 1956; M.Div., Emory U., 1960; Ph.D., Claremont Grad. Sch., 1963; postgrad., Eberhard-Karls U., Tuebingen, Germany, 1963-64. Asst. prof. Emory U., Atlanta, 1964-67, Garrett Theol Sem., Evanston, Ill., 1967-68, McCormick Theol. Sem., Chgo., 1968-69; assoc. prof. U. Oreg., Eugene, 1969-75, prof., 1975—, head dept. religious studies, 1973-80, 85-90. Author: The New Testament Christological Hymns, 1971, Ethics in the New Testament, 1975, 2d edit., 1986, Ben Sira and Demotic Wisdom, 1983, The Jews in Luke-Acts, 1987, Schismatics, Sectarians, Dissidents, Deviants: The First One Hundred Years of Jewish-Christian Relations, 1993; editor: Gospel Origins and Christian Beginnings, 1990, Gnosticism and the Early Christian World, 1990; mem. edit. bd. Jour. Bibl. Lit., 1977-83. Mem. policy bd. Dept. Higher Edn. Nat. Council Chs., N.Y.C., 1971-73. NDEA grad. study fellow, 1960-63; Fulbright Commn. fellow, 1963-64; Am. Council Learned Socs. travel grantee, 1981; NEH fellow, 1983-84. Mem. AAUP (chpt. pres. 1981-82), Studiorum Novi Testamenti Soc., World Union Jewish Studies, Assn. for Jewish Studies, Soc. Bibl. Lit. (regional sec. 1969-76, sabbatical rsch. award 1976-77), Archeol. Inst. Am. (chpt. pres. 1988-89), Soc. for Sci. Study of Religion, Assn. for Sociology Religion. Democrat. Home: 2555 Birch Ln Eugene OR 97403-2191 Office: Dept Religious Studies U Oreg Eugene OR 97403

SANDERS, JACQUELYN SEEVAK, psychologist, educator; b. Boston, Apr. 26, 1931; d. Edward Ezral and Dora (Zoken) Seevak; 1 son, Seth. BA, Radcliffe Coll., 1952; MA, U. Chgo., 1964; PhD, UCLA, 1972. Counselor, asst. prin. Orthogenic Sch., Chgo., 1952-65; research assoc. UCLA, 1965-68; cons. Osawatomie State Hosp. (Kans.), 1965-68; asst. prof. Ctr. for Early Edn., L.A., 1969-72; assoc. dir. Sonia Shankman Orthogenic Sch., U. Chgo., 1972-73, dir., 1973-93, dir. emeritus, 1993—; curriculum cons. day care ctrs. L.A. Dept. Social Welfare, 1970-72; instr. Calif. State Coll., L.A., 1972; lectr. dept. edn. U. Chgo., 1972-80, sr. lectr., 1980-93, clin. assoc. prof. dept. psychiatry, 1990-93, emeritus, 1993—; instr. edn. program Inst. Psychoanalysis, Chgo., 1979-82. Author: Greenhouse for the Mind, 1989; editor: (with Barry L. Childress) Psychoanalytic Approaches to the Very Troubled Child: Therapeutic Practice Innovations in Residential & Educational Settings, 1989, Severly Disturbed Children and the Parental Alliance, 1992, (with Jerome M. Goldsmith) Milieu Therapy: Significant Issues and Innovative Applications, 1993; contbr. articles to profl. jours. UCLA Univ. fellow, 1966-68; Radcliffe Coll. Scholar, 1948-52. Mem. Am. Orthopsychiat. Soc., Am. Psychol. Assn., Am. Assn. Children's Residential Ctrs. (pres.). Clubs: Quadrangle, Radcliffe of Chgo. (sec/treas. 1986-87, pres. 1987-89); Harvard of Chgo. (bd. dirs. 1986—). Home: 5842 S Stony Island Ave Apt 2G Chicago IL 60637-2023

SANDERS, JAMES ALVIN, minister, biblical studies educator; b. Memphis, Nov. 28, 1927; s. Robert E. and Sue (Black) S.; m. Dora Cargille, June 30, 1951; 1 son, Robin David. BA magna cum laude, Vanderbilt U., 1948, BD with honors, 1951; student, U. Paris, 1950-51; PhD, Hebrew Union Coll., 1955; DLitt, Acadia U., 1973; STD, U. Glasgow, 1975; DHL, Coe Coll., 1988, Hebrew Union Coll., 1988. Ordained teacher Presbyn. Ch., 1955; instr. French Vanderbilt U., 1948-49; faculty Colgate Rochester Div. Sch., 1954-65, assoc. prof., 1957-60, Joseph B. Hoyt prof. O.T. interpretation, 1960-65; prof. O.T. Union Theol. Sem., N.Y.C., 1965-70, Auburn prof. Bibl. studies, 1970-77; adj. prof. Columbia, N.Y.C., 1966-77; prof. Bibl. studies Sch. Theology and Grad. Sch., Claremont, Calif., 1977—; ann. prof. Jerusalem Sch. of Am. Schs. Oriental Rsch., 1961-62; fellow Ecumenical Inst., Jerusalem, 1972-73, 85; Ayer lectr., 1971, 79, Shaffer lectr., 1972, Fondren lectr., 1975, Currie lectr., 1976, McFadin lectr., 1979, Colwell lectr., 1979; guest lectr. U. Fribourg, Switzerland, 1981, 90, Hebrew Union Coll., 1982, 88, Oral Roberts U., 1982, Tulsa U., 1982, Ind. U., 1982, Coe Coll., 1983, Garrett Sem., 1984, Pepperdine U., 1985, Western Sem., 1985, Bethany Sem., 1986; lectr. Union Sem. Sesquicentennial, 1987, U. Wis., 1987, U. Chgo., 1987; Gray lectr. Duke U., 1988; guest lectr. Notre Dame U., Georgetown U., Tex. Christian U., 1989, Alexander Robertson lectr. U. Glasgow, 1990-91, Gustavson lectr. United Theol. Sem., 1991; assoc. program lectr. Smithsonian, 1990, Am. Bible Soc. Sesquicentennial, 1991, U. N.Mex., 1992, 94, Am. Interfaith Inst., 1992, Georgetown U., 1992; Lily Rosmen lectr. Skirball Mus., 1992; vis. prof. U. N.Mex., 1992, Southwestern U., 1992, Calif. Luth. U., 1992, 94, Willamette U., 1993, Peter Craigie lectr. U. Calgary, 1993, U. So. Ariz., 1993; Samuel Iwry lectr. John Hopkins U., 1993; lectr. San Diego State U., 1994, Creighton U., 1995, The Mercantile Libr., N.Y.C., 1995; mem. internat. O.T. text critical com. United Bible Socs., 1969—; exec. officer Ancient Bibl. Manuscript Ctr. for Preservation and Rsch., 1977-80, pres., 1980—. Author: Suffering as Divine Discipline in the Old Testament and Post-Biblical Judaism, 1955, The Old Testament in the Cross, 1961, The Psalms Scroll of Qumran Cave 11, 1965, The Dead Sea Psalms Scroll, 1967, Near Eastern Archaeology in the Twentieth Century, 1970, Torah and Canon, 1972, 74, Identité de la Bible, 1975, God Has a Story Too, 1979, Canon and Community, 1984, From Sacred Story to Sacred Text, 1987, Luke and Scripture, 1993; editor: Paul and the Scriptures of Israel, 1993; also numerous articles; mem. editorial bd. Jour. Bibl. Lit., 1970-76, Jour. for Study Judaism, Bibl. Theology Bull., Interpretation, 1973-78, New Rev. Standard Version Bible Com. Trustee Am. Schs. Oriental Research. Fulbright grantee, 1950-51, Lilly Endowment grantee, 1981, NEH grantee, 1980, 91-92; Lefkowitz and Rabinowitz interfaith fellow, 1951-53, Rockefeller fellow, 1953-54, 85, Guggenheim fellow, 1961-62, 72-73, Human Scis. Rsch. fellow, 1989. Mem. Soc. Bibl. Lit. and Exegesis (pres. 1977-78), Phi Beta Kappa, Phi Sigma Iota, Theta Chi Beta. Home: PO Box 593 Claremont CA 91711-0593 Office: Ancient Bible Manuscript Ctr PO Box 670 Claremont CA 91711-0670

SANDERS, JAMES GRADY, biogeochemist; b. Norfolk, Va., June 10, 1951; s. Allen Buford and Maple Seretha (Myers) S.; m. Carmen Lee Nance, Aug. 19, 1972. BS in Zoology, Duke U., 1973; MS in Marine Scis., U., 1975, PhD in Marine Scis., 1978. Postdoctoral investigator Woods Hole (Mass.) Oceanographic Inst., 1978-80; vis. scientist Chesapeake Biol. Lab. U. Md., Solomons, 1980-81; asst. curator Benedict (Md.) Estuarine Rsch. Lab. Acad. Natural Scis., 1981-85, assoc. curator Benedict (Md.) Estuarine Rsch. Lab., 1985-89, curator Benedict (Md.) Estuarine Rsch. Lab. 1989—, dir. Benedict (Md.) Estuarine Rsch. Lab., 1983—; cons. EPA Sweden, Stockholm, 1985-90; mem. Md. Sea Grant Adv. Com., College Park, 1983-90, Environ. Commn., Calvert City, Md., 1981-88; mem. enbiron. biology panel Office R & D EPA, Washington, 1986-95; regional rep. Coastal Resources Adv. Commn., Md., 1983-86. Contbr. over 60 articles to sci. jours. Grantee NOAA, 1981—, EPA, 1983—. Mem. AAAS, Am. Soc. Limnology and Oceanography, Soc. for Environ. Toxicology and Chemistry, Estuarine Rsch. Fedn. (treas 1994—). Achievements include first identification of relationships between algal growth and chemical transformations of arsenic in aquatic systems. Office: Acad Natural Scis Benedict Estuarine Rsch Ctr 10545 Mackall Rd Saint Leonard MD 20685

SANDERS, JAMES JOSEPH, architect; b. Clearwater, Kans., 1936. BS in Architecture, U. Wash., 1963; MS in Architecture, Columbia U., 1964.

Registered arch., Wash., 1968, Mont., 1993; cert. Nat. Coun. Archtl. Registration Bd. Designer Jerome Menell/Charles Eames, N.Y.C., 1963-64; designer/draftsman Foote Okerlund and Zieger, Seattle, 1964-65; assoc. designer, project arch. Naramore Bain Brady and Johanson, Seattle, 1965-68; asst. prof., lectr. dept. architecture U. Wash., Seattle, 1968-76; prin. James J. Sanders Arch. and Urban Designer, Seattle, 1968-76; project dir., designer TRA Architecture Engring. Planning Interiors Ltd., Seattle, 1977—; prin. TRA Architecture Engring. Planning Interiors Ltd., 1991—. Prin. works include Farm Products Rsch. Lab. at U. Wash., Bellevue (Wash.) C.C., Pike St. Hill Climb, Seattle, UNICO, Seattle, Doha (Qatar) Internat. Airport, McCarran Internat. Airport, Las Vegas, Dulles Internat. Airport, Washington, Wash. State Conv. and Trade Ctr., Seattle, Providence Conv. Ctr., New Denver Internat. Airport Concourses, Wash. State Patrol Hdqrs. Bldg., others. Chmn. Pike Pl. Market Hist. Commn., 1981; past bd. dirs. Allied Arts of Seattle; active Leschi Improvement Coun., Seattle, Madrona Cmty Coun., Seattle; profl. soccer referee WSSA, 1974-85. Grad. scholar Columbia U. Fellow AIA (past chmn. Honor awrds com., pre. Seattle chpt. 1993-94, recipient Student Gold medal, Scholar for Design, Home awards); mem. Seattle Architecture Found. (bd. dirs.). Office: TRA Seattle 215 Columbia Seattle WA 98104

SANDERS, JAY WILLIAM, audiology educator; b. Balt., July 26, 1924; s. Jay Will and Mary Magdalene (Fisher) S.; m. Mary Elizabeth St. John, Aug. 27, 1950; children—Mary Jean, John Jay, Elizabeth Ann. A.A., Louisburg Coll., 1948; B.A., U. N.C., 1950; M.A., Columbia U., 1951; Ph.D., U. Mo., 1957; postgrad. (spl. fellow), Northwestern U., 1962-64. Instr. speech U. Mo., Columbia, 1952-57; from asst. prof. to assoc. prof. Trenton (N.J.) State Coll., 1957-62; asst. prof. audiology Vanderbilt U. Sch. Medicine, Nashville, 1964-65, assoc. prof., 1965-71, prof., 1971-87, prof. emeritus, 1987—; chmn. Tenn. State Bd. Examiners for Speech Pathology and Audiology, 1973-79. Contbr. chpts. to textbooks, articles to profl. jours. Served with U.S. Navy, 1942-45. Recipient various awards; Nat. Inst. Neurol. Diseases and Blindness spl. fellow, 1962-64. Fellow Am. Speech and Hearing Assn.; mem. Am. Acad. Audiology, Tenn. Speech-Lang.-Hearing Assn., Phi Beta Kappa. Home: 5518 Vanderbilt Rd Old Hickory TN 37138-1133 Office: Wilkerson Hearing & Speech Ctr 1114 19th Ave S Nashville TN 37212

SANDERS, JIMMY DEVON, university official; b. Montgomery, Ala., Nov. 6, 1945; s. Harold Wright Sanders and Elsie M. (Huett) Harris; m. Linda Ruth Sweatt, Mar. 25, 1966; children: Richard Devon, Robert Pearson. B Gen. Studies, U. Nebr., Omaha, 1968; MPA, U. Okla., 1973, U. So. Calif., 1988; D Pub. Adminstrn., U. So. Calif., 1989. Commd. officer USAF, 1964, advanced through grades to lt. col., 1985, various health svc. adminstrv. positions, 1964-83; dir. base med. svcs. USAF, San Vito dei Normanni, Italy, 1980-83; sr. health policy analyst Dept. Def., Washington, 1983-88; ret., 1988; assoc. prof. mgmt. and healthcare mgmt. Marymount U., Arlington, Va., 1988-91; dir. Atlantic region Troy State U., Norfolk, Va., 1991-94; dir. Fla. region Troy State U., Ft. Walton Beach, 1994—; health care cons. various hosps. and cities, 1987—, Ret. Officers Assn., Arlington, 1988-90. Fellow Am. Coll. Health Care Execs.; mem. Assn. Mgmt. (dir. orgnl. studies, editor Procs. 1994). Republican. Lutheran. Avocations: walking, reading, golf. Home: 381 Santa Rosa Blvd Fort Walton Beach FL 32548 Office: Troy State U PO Box 2829 Fort Walton Beach FL 32549

SANDERS, JOHN LASSITER, retired academic administrator; b. Four Oaks, N.C., June 30, 1927; s. David Hardy and Louie Jane (Lassiter) S.; m. Ann Beal, Aug. 14, 1954; children—Tracy Elizabeth Sanders Justus, Jane Nesbit, William Hardy. A.B., U. N.C., 1950, J.D., 1954. Bar: N.C. 1955. Law clk. to judge U.S. Ct. Appeals, 1954-55; pvt. practice Raleigh, N.C., 1955-56; mem. faculty Inst. Govt., U. N.C., Chapel Hill, 1956-94, dir., 1962-73, 79-92, v.p. planning at univ., 1973-78. Served with USNR, 1945-46. Recipient Thomas Jefferson award U. N.C., 1987. Mem. N.C. Bar Assn. Democrat. Baptist. Home: 1107 Sourwood Dr Chapel Hill NC 27514-4914 Office: U NC Inst Govt Cb 3330 Knapp Bldg Chapel Hill NC 27514

SANDERS, JOHN LYELL, JR., educator, researcher; b. Highland, Wis., Sept. 11, 1924; s. J. Lyell and Grace Ann (Waters) S.; m. Mary Jane Wade, Apr. 23, 1960; children: Alice Elizabeth, William Lyell, Jeanne Frances. BS, Purdue U., 1945; MS, MIT, 1950; PhD, Brown U., 1954; AM, Harvard U., 1960. Section head Nat. Adv. Com. for Aeronautics, Langley Field, Va., 1954-58; lectr. Harvard U., Cambridge, Mass., 1958-60, prof., 1960—; bd. of editors jour. of Math. and Physics, 1963-69; editor's bd. S.I.A.M. Jour. of Applied Math., 1969-79; adv. bd. Acta Mechanica Sinica, Beijing, 1990—. Fellow AAAS, ASME, Am. Acad. Mechanics; mem. Sigma Xi. Democrat. Roman Catholic. Office: Harvard Univ 312 Pierce Hall Cambridge MA 02138

SANDERS, JOHN MONCRIEF, lawyer; b. Houston, Feb. 22, 1936; s. John Austin and Elizabeth (Moncrief) S.; m. Ann Clark, Aug. 13, 1960; children—Julie, Scott. A.B. cum laude, Baylor U., 1957, J.D. cum laude, 1960. Bar: Tex. 1960. Ptnr. Fulbright & Jaworski, Houston, 1973—, Trustee Baylor U., 1981-90. Fellow Houston Bar Found.; mem. ABA, Houston Bar Assn., State Bar Tex., Tex. Assn. Bank Counsel (dir., pres. 1982), Phi Alpha Delta. Office: Fulbright & Jaworski 1301 Mckinney St Ste 5100 Houston TX 77010-3036

SANDERS, JOSEPH STANLEY, lawyer; b. L.A., Aug. 9, 1942; s. Hays and Eva (Cook) S.; m. Melba Binion, Mar. 17, 1984; children: Alexandria, Chelsea; children by previous marriage: Edward Moore, Justin Hays. BA, Whittier Coll., 1963; BA, MA (Rhodes scholar), Magdalen Coll., Oxford U., 1965; LLB, Yale U., 1968. Bar: Calif. 1969. Dir. summer projects Westminster Neighborhood Assn., Los Angeles, 1966-67; Dir. pro tem, instr. polit. sci. Yale U. Transitional Year, 1967-68; staff atty. Western Center on Law and Poverty, Los Angeles, 1968-69; exec. dir. Lawyers Com. for Civil Rights Under Law, Los Angeles, 1969-70; assoc. law firm Wyman, Bautzer, Finell, Rothman & Kuchel, Beverly Hills, Calif., 1969-71; partner Rosenfeld, Lederer, Jacobs & Sanders, Beverly Hills, 1971-72, Sanders & Tisdale, Los Angeles, 1972-78, Sanders & Dickerson, Los Angeles, 1978—. Co-founder Watts Summer Festival, 1966; co-chmn. Whittier Coll. Alumni Fund, 1970-71; mem. Yale Law Alumni Com. on Curriculum Reform, 1970; coordinator Calif. Conf. Black Attys., 1969; chmn. membership drive Dist. 8, Boy Scouts Am., L.A. , 1971; mem. L.A. World Affairs Coun., 1970-74, Com. on Fgn. Affairs, 1971-75; bd. dirs. West L.A. United Way, 1970, Black Arts Coun., Econ. Resources Corp., L.A. Beautiful, L.A. Coun. for Internat. Visitors, Cape of Good Hope Found., NCAA Found., Overland Park, Kans., 1991—, Westminster Neighborhood Assn., 1991—; mem. L.A. Meml. Coliseum Commn.; trustee Whittier Coll., 1973-90, 93—, Mus. Contemporary Art, NCAA Found., 1991—; pres. L.A. Recreation and Parks Commn.; chmn. United Way Task Force on Youth Unemployment, L.A.; mem. adv. bd. Pub. Radio Station, KCRW, 1991—; dir. met. transp. authority L.A. County, 1993—. Recipient Ten Outstanding Young Men of Am. award, 1971. Mem. Langston Bar Assn., Los Angeles County Bar Assn. Club: Mason. Home: 2015 Wellington Rd Los Angeles CA 90016-1824 Office: Sanders & Dickerson 2015 Wellington Rd Los Angeles CA 90016-1801

SANDERS, KEITH PAGE, journalism educator; b. Ashland, Ohio, Sept. 25, 1938; s. Merwin Morse and Phyllis Pearl (Snyder) S.; m. Jane Carmel Adams, June 11, 1966; children: Paige Ann, Kevin Scott. BS in Journalism, Bowling Green State U., 1960; MS in Journalism, Ohio U., 1964; PhD in Mass. Comm., U. Iowa, 1967. Sports editor Ashland (Ohio) Times Gazette, 1960-61, Dover (Ohio) Daily Reporter, 1961-62; instr. journalism Bowling Green (Ohio) State U., 1963-64, U. Iowa, Iowa City, 1965-67; prof. journalism U. Mo., Columbia, 1967—, assoc. dean grad. studies Sch. Journalism, 1986-87, 90-91; exec. dir. Kappa Tau Alpha, Columbia, 1991—; cons. in field. Contbr. articles to profl. jours. including Journalism Quar., Mass Media Rev. Jour. Broadcasting, Electronic Jour. of Comm.; assoc. editor Mass Comm. Rev., 1981-92, editl. bd., 1972—; editl. bd. Journalism Monographs, 1973-80. Named O.O. McIntyre Disting. Prof., U. Mo., 1993; recipient Award for Outstanding Journalist U. Mo. Alumni Assn., 1986. Mem. Internat. Soc. for Sci. Study of Subjectivity (treas. 1990—), Assn. for Edn. in Journalism/Mass. Comm. (Trayes Prof. of the Yr. 1987), Soc. of Profl. Journalists, Kappa Tau Alpha, Omicron Delta Kappa. Avocations: bowling, golf, fishing. Home: 6551 Creasy Spring Rd Columbia MO 65202 Office: Univ of Missouri Dept Journalism Box 838 Columbia MO 65205

SANDERS, KEITH R., university chancellor; b. Benton, Ill., July 31, 1939; m. Carol Dial, 1961; 1 child, Mark Andrew. BS, So. Ill. U., 1961, MS, 1962; PhD in Communication, U. Pitts., 1968. Asst. prof. speech George Washington U., Washington, 1962-66; instr. So. Ill. U., Carbondale, 1967-68, asst. prof., 1969-72, assoc. prof., 1972-77, prof. speech communications, 1977-89, officer govtl. rels. So. Ill. U. System, 1980-83, prof., dean Coll. Communication and Fine Arts, 1983-89; chancellor U. Wis., Stevens Point, 1989—. Author: (with Lynda Kaid and Robert Hirsch) Political Campaign Communication, 1974; co-editor, contbr.: (with Dan Nimmo) The Handbook of Political Communication, 1981; (with Dan Nimmo and Lynda Kaid) Political Communication Yearbook, 1985; (with Dan Nimmo and Lynda Kaid) New Perspectives on Political Advertising, 1986, (with Lynda Kaid and Jacques Gestle) Mediated Politics in Two Cultures, 1991; founder, editor Polit. Communication Rev., 1974-90; cons. editor Human Communication Rsch., 1976-79, Cen. States Speech Jour., 1979-80; contbg. editor: Communication Yearbook III and IV, 1978-80. Pres. Ill. Arts Alliance, Ill. Arts Alliance Found., 1987-88. Am. Coun. on Edn. fellow, 1980-81; honored by Ill. Gen. Assembly, 1983. Mem. So. Ill. U. Alumni Assn. (pres. 1977-78). Home: 2351 Rainbow Dr Plover WI 54467-2464 Office: U Wis Stevens Point WI 54481-3897

SANDERS, LAWRENCE, author; b. Bklyn., 1920. BA, Wabash Coll., 1940. Staff mem. Macy's Dept. Store, N.Y.C., 1940-43; novelist, 1969—. Author: The Anderson Tapes, 1970 (Edgar award best 1st mystery novel Mystery Writers Am. 1970), The Pleasures of Helen, 1971, Love Songs, 1972, The First Deadly Sin, 1973, The Tomorrow File, 1975, The Tangent Objective, 1976, The Marlow Chronicles, 1977, The Second Deadly Sin, 1977, The Tangent Factor, 1978, The Sixth Commandment, 1978, The Tenth Commandment, 1980, The Third Deadly Sin, 1981, The Case of Lucy Bending, 1982, The Seduction of Peter S., 1983, The Passion of Molly T., 1984, The Fourth Deadly Sin, 1985, The Loves of Harry Dancer, 1986, The Eighth Commandment, 1986, Tales of the Wolf, 1986, The Dream Lover, 1987, Caper, 1987, The Timothy Files, 1987, Timothy's Game, 1988, Capital Crimes, 1989, Stolen Blessings, 1989, Sullivan's Sting, 1990, The Seventh Commandment, 1992, McNally's Luck, 1992, McNally's Secret, 1992, McNally's Risk, 1993, Private Pleasures, 1993, The Great Coaster Ride, 1993, McNally's Caper, 1994, McNally's Trail, 1995; (as Mark Upton) Dark Summer, 1979. Served as sgt. USMC, 1943-46. Office: care Putnam Publishing Group 200 Madison Ave New York NY 10016*

SANDERS, LEWIS A., investment research and management executive. Former pres., chief oper. officer Sanford C. Bernstein & Co., Inc., N.Y.C., chmn., CEO, 1993—. Office: Sanford C Bernstein & Co Inc 767 5th Ave Fl 22 New York NY 10153-0185

SANDERS, MARLENE, academic administrator, educator, freelance broadcast journalist; b. Cleve., Jan. 10, 1931; d. Mac and Evelyn (Menitoff) Sanders; m. Jerome Toobin, May 27, 1958 (dec. Jan. 1984); children: Jeff, Mark. Student, Ohio State U., 1948-49. Writer, prodr. Sta. WNEW-TV, N.Y.C., 1955-60, P.M. program Westinghouse Broadcasting Co., N.Y.C., 1961-62; asst. dir. news and public affairs Sta. WNEW, N.Y.C., 1962-64; anchor, news program ABC News, N.Y.C., 1964-68, corr., 1968-72, documentary prodr., writer, anchor, 1972-76, v.p., dir. TV documentaries, 1976-78; corr. CBS News, N.Y.C., 1978-87; host Met. Week in Review, 1988-90; host Thirteen Live Sta. WNET-TV, 1990-91; prof. dept. journalism NYU, 1991-93; adj. prof. journalism, adminstr. Columbia U. Grad. Sch. Journalism, N.Y.C., 1994—. Co-author: Waiting for Prime Time: The Women of Television News, 1988. Recipient award N.Y. State Broadcasters Assn., 1976, award Nat. Press Club, 1976, Emmy awards, 1980, 81, others. Mem. Am. Women in Radio and TV (Woman of Yr. award 1975, Silver Satellite award 1977), Women in Comm. (past pres.), Soc. Profl. Journalists.

SANDERS, PAUL HAMPTON, lawyer, retired educator, arbitrator/mediator; b. Sherman, Tex., Feb. 26, 1909; s. Jewell Richard and Louisa Jane (Gaskill) S.; m. Pauline Cameron, Feb. 23, 1935. A.B., Austin Coll., 1931, LL.D., 1960; J.D., Duke U., 1934. Bar: Tex. 1934, Ga. 1944, N.C. 1946, Tenn. 1951. Practiced with Leo Brewer, San Antonio, 1934; asst. to dir. of nat. bar program Am. Bar Assn., Chgo., 1934-36; asst. prof. law Duke U., 1936-40, assoc. prof. law, 1940-45, prof. law, from 1946; practiced with firm of Wilson and Sanders, Atlanta, 1946-47; vis. prof. law Sch. Jurisprudence, U. Calif. at Berkeley, 1947-48; prof. law Vanderbilt U., 1948-74, prof. emeritus, 1974—; past lectr. Sch. Medicine, adj. prof. mgmt. Grad. Sch. Mgmt.; regional atty. U.S. Dept. of Labor, 1951-53; prin. mediation officer Nat. War Labor Bd., Washington, 1942; regional atty., hdqrs. Nat. War Labor Bd., Atlanta, 1942-44, regional vice chmn., 1944; regional atty. Nat. Wage Stblzn. Bd., Atlanta, 1946; past lectr. Nashville Sch. Social Work; cons. Fed. Civil Rights Commn., 1958-61; dir. Race Relations Law Reporter, 1955-59; apptd. mem. bd. inquiry, labor disputes in atomic energy installations, Oak Ridge, also Ky.; pub. mem., chmn. Industry Com. on Minimum Wages, Puerto Rico, 1950, 56-58, 60-61, 63, 67, 69, 71, 73, 75, 77; apptd. mem. various Presdl. emergency boards to consider labor disputes. Assoc. editor: Law and Contemporary Problems, 1937-46; editor symposia on Unauthorized Practice of Law, The Wage and Hour Law, Governmental Tort Liability, Alcoholic Beverage Control, Combating the Loan Shark, Labor in Wartime and Labor Dispute Settlement, all in Duke Univ., 1938-46; contbr. articles to profl. jours. Indsl. relations specialist, 12th Naval Dist. 1944-46, San Francisco; lt. USNR, 1945-53. Mem. ABA (council mem., sec. labor relations sect. 1949-52), Am. Law Inst. (life), Nat. Acad. Arbitrators (past mem., past bd. govs., regional chmn. Southeastern states 1968-74), Am. Arbitration Assn. (labor panel), Nat. Conf. Jud. Councils, Soc. Profls. in Dispute Resolution, Scholarship Soc., Order of Coif, Pi Gamma Mu, Phi Delta Phi. Democrat. Baptist (vice chmn. Christian Life Commn., So. Bapt. Conv. 1953-59). Club: University (Nashville). Home: Apt 320 115 Woodmont Blvd Nashville TN 37205-2269 My primary interests as a law teacher and arbitrator have centered in systematic study of the processes of dispute settlement and conflict resolution, particularly in the labor relations field. This reflects a conviction that building "community" is the essence of civilization and that there needs to be individual and group commitment to understanding and utilizing the arts of peaceful accomodation. Social conflict is as inevitable as change. All too frequently, however, we show that we have not learned to distinguish, and maintain the proper balance, between the productive and counterproductive aspects of such conflict.

SANDERS, PHAROAH, saxophonist, composer; b. Little Rock, Oct. 13, 1940. Student, Oakland Jr. Coll., Calif. Saxophonist N.Y.C., 1962-66, John Coltrane, 1966-67, Alice Coltrane, 1967-69; leader own group, 1969—. Albums include Jewels of Thought, Journey to the One, Karma, Live, Pharoah, Rejoice, Tauhid, Thembi, Love Will Find a Way, Heart Is a Melody, 1984, Shukuru, Impulse, 1987, Oh Lord, Let Me Do No Wrong, 1989, Moon Child, 1990, Welcome to Love: Pharoah Sanders Plays Beautiful Ballads, 1991, Shukuru, 1992, A Prayer Before Dawn, 1993; composer: songs, including Prince of Peace, The Creator Has a Master Plan; guest artist Sonny Sharaock's Ask the Ages, 1991. Office: care Ted Kurland Assocs 173 Brighton Ave Allston MA 02134-2003*

SANDERS, PHYLLIS ADEN, retired radio and television broadcaster; b. Buenos Aires, June 27, 1919; d. Fred and Anna Almeda (Pettit) Aden; BA, Occidental Coll., 1941; MA, Scarritt Coll., 1943; m. Olcutt Sanders, Apr. 8, 1947; children: Lynn Edwin, Marta Almeda, Jay Olcutt, Fred Aden, R. Elizabeth. Formerly tchr., lectr., workshop leader on changing roles of women, 1973-75; producer, host weekly radio interview show Changing World of Women, Sta. WNYC, N.Y.C., 1972-79; TV reporter, host, commentator on women's issues Sta. WNYC-TV, N.Y.C., 1975-78; regular weekly commentator Prime of Your Life, NBC-TV, N.Y.C., 1979-83; reporter Age Whys, AM Phila., Sta. WPVI-TV, 1981-83; producer, host weekly series Growing Older with Style, WCAU-TV, Phila., 1983-84, feature reporter Noonbreak, 1984, senior reporter NEWS, 1987—; producer, host series on aging WHYY-TV, 1984-85; reporter, interviewer Modern Maturity TV series on aging, nat. PBS-TV, 1986-88; host weekly talk show Over 50 Sta. WCAU-TV, 1989—. Community relations dir. Town of New Castle (N.Y.), 1972-73, originator, coordinator Community Day, New Castle, 1971; coordinator N.Y.C. women's adv. com. on meeting with network mgmt., 1976-77. Recipient award N.Y. chpt. NOW, 1973, N.J. Women, 1976; named to Phila. Mayor's Sr. Citizen Honor Roll, 1984. Mem. AFTRA, Nat. Acad. TV Arts and Scis., Women's Inst. for Freedom of Press, ACLU,

Friends Com. on Nat. Legis., NOW, Older Women's League, Occidental Coll. Alumni (award 1985). Mem. Soc. of Friends. Home: 142 Medford Leas Medford NJ 08055

SANDERS, RICHARD HENRY, lawyer; b. Chgo., Apr. 10, 1944; s. Walter J. and Marian (Snyder) Sikorski; m. Sharon A. Marciniak, July 8, 1967 (div. Oct. 1979); 1 child, Douglas Bennett. BS, Loyola U., Chgo., 1967; JD, Northwestern U., 1969. Bar: Ill. 1969, Ind. 1990, D.C. 1990, U.S. Dist. Ct. (no. dist.) Ill. 1970, U.S. Dist. Ct. (no. and so. dists.) Ind. 1990, U.S. Dist. Ct. Appeals (7th cir.) 1990, U.S. Supreme Ct. 1990. Assoc. Vedder, Price, Kaufman & Kammholz, Chgo., 1969-76, ptnr., 1976—, mem. exec. com., 1991-93; gen. counsel Ancilla Systems Inc., Chgo., 1985-95; adj. prof. Northwestern U. Sch. Law, 1994—. Mem. adv. coun. campaign com. Greater Chgo. divsn. March of Dimes, 1993—. Mem. ABA, Ill. Bar Assn. (chmn. health sect. 1989-90), Chgo. Bar Assn., Ind. Bar Assn., D.C. Bar Assn., Am. Acad. Hosp. Attys., Cath. Health Attys., Ill. Assn. Hosp. Attys., Chgo. Commons Assn. (adv. bd. dirs., sec. 1989-91), Northwestern U. Sch. Law Alumni Assn. (bd. dirs. 1985-90), Univ. Club, Evanston Golf Club (Skokie). Avocations: skiing, driving, photography, golf. Office: Vedder Price Kaufman & Kammholz 222 N La Salle St Chicago IL 60601-1003

SANDERS, RICHARD KINARD, actor; b. Harrisburg, Pa., Aug. 23, 1940; s. Henry Irvine and Thelma S. BFA, Carnegie Inst. Tech., 1962; postgrad. (Fulbright scholar), London Acad. Music and Dramatic Art, 1962-63. pres. Blood Star, Inc. Mem. various acting cos., Front St., Memphis, Champlain Shakespeare Festival, Vt., Center Stage, Balt., N.Y. Shakespeare Festival, N.Y.C., Chelsea Theater Center, N.Y.C., Mark Taper Forum, Los Angeles, Arena Stage, Washington; appeared on: (Broadway) Raisin; (TV series) Les Nessman on WKRP in Cincinnati and The New WKRP in Cincinnati, Paul Sycamore in You Can't Take It With You, Mr. Beanley in Spenser; writer of many episodes of WKRP and other situation comedies; writer NBC movie Max and Sam; numerous TV and film appearances. Vol. Peace Corps, Northeastern Brazil, 1966-69. Recipient Buckeye Newshawk award, 1974-79, Silver Sow award, 1979. Mem. Writers Guild Am., Screen Actors Guild, AFTRA, Actors Equity Assn. Office: care Blood Star Inc 10866 Wilshire Blvd Ste 1100 Los Angeles CA 90024-4335

SANDERS, RICHARD LOUIS, assistant managing editor; b. Rockville Centre, N.Y., July 14, 1949; s. Louis Chadrone and Grace Marie (Clarke) S.; m. Laurie Anne Miroff, July 24, 1970. BFA in Film, NYU, 1976. Sr. editor Us mag., N.Y.C., 1978-83, exec. editor, 1983-85; sr. editor People mag., N.Y.C., 1985-91; gen. editor Entertainment Weekly, N.Y.C., 1991-92, assistant mng. editor, 1993—. Office: Entertainment Weekly 1675 Broadway New York NY 10019

SANDERS, RICKY WAYNE, professional football player; b. New Orleans, La., Aug. 30, 1966. Student, Southwest Texas State U. With Houston Gamblers, USFL, 1984-86, N.J. Generals, USFL, 1986, Washington Redskins, 1986-94, Atlanta Falcons, 1994—. Played in Super Bowl XXII (1987) and XXVI (1991). Office: Atlanta Falcons 2745 Burnett Rd Suwanee GA 30174*

SANDERS, ROBERT MARTIN, commodity trader; b. Amsterdam, The Netherlands, Feb. 8, 1928; came to U.S., 1941, naturalized, 1949; s. Hugo Benjamin and Jean (van der Linden) S.; m. Ingrid Vera Borchardt, Apr. 12, 1959 (dec. Jan. 1993); children: Mark Robert, Steven George. BA, Queens Coll., 1948; MS, Columbia U., 1950; postgrad., New Sch. Social Research, 1953-61. Research asst. The Netherlands Govt., 1948-50; with fgn. acctg. dept. Colgate-Palmolive-Peet, 1950; with A.C. Israel Commodity Co., Inc., N.Y.C., 1952-71, asst. mgr. rubber dept., 1963-67, mgr. rubber dept., 1967-71, asst. v.p., 1967-70, v.p., 1970-71; v.p. ACLI Internat., Inc., 1971-81; pres. A.C. Israel Rubber Co. div., 1971-76, ACLI Rubber Co., 1976-81; v.p. ACLI Commodity Services, Inc., 1975-81; dir. ACLI (Malaysia), Kuala Lumpur, 1975-81; pres. Clinton Internat., Inc., 1982—; mem. N.Y. Cocoa Exchange, 1975-78; U.S. rep. Internat. Natural Rubber Orgn., 1982—. Bd. dirs. Family Resources, 1983—. With AUS, 1950-52. Mem. Internat. Rubber Assn. (pro-tem. com. 1970-71, mgmt. com. 1971-81, dep. chmn. 1974-77), Am.-Indonesian C. of C. (bd. dirs. 1974-80, v.p. 1979-80), Am. Importers Assn. (bd. dirs. 1975-77), Rubber Trade Assn. N.Y. Inc. (bd. dirs. 1970-74, 76-79, 81, v.p. 1972-73, 73-74, pres. 1972, 78-79). Home: 310 Clinton Ave Dobbs Ferry NY 10522-3023 Office: Clinton Internat Inc 547 Saw Mill River Rd Ardsley NY 10502-2143

SANDERS, ROGER COBBAN, radiologist; b. London, June 17, 1936; s. Douglas William and Angela (Cobban) S.; children—Nicolette, Nigel; m. Barri Standish, May 26, 1991. M.A., Oxford U., 1960; B.M., B.CH., F.R.C.R., 1971. Diplomate: Am. Bd. Radiology. Intern United Oxford (Eng.) Hosp., 1964-65; sr. house officer neurology dept., 1965-66, resident in radiology, 1967-70; mem. faculty Johns Hopkins Hosp., Balt., 1971-89; assoc. prof. radiology Johns Hopkins Hosp., 1975-86, prof. radiology, 1986-89; med. dir. Ultrasound Inst. Balt., 1989—; clin. prof. radiology, ob/gyn. U. Md., 1990—. Author: (with A.E. James) Principles and Practice of Ultrasonography in Obstetrics and Gynecology, 3d edit., 1984, Clinical Sonography, A Practical Guide, 1984, 2d edit., 1992, Atlas of Ultrasonic Normal Variants, 1992; editor: Ultrasound Quarterly. Fellow Royal Coll. Radiologists, Am. Coll. Radiologists (sec. 1984-86), Am. Inst. Ultrasound in Medicine; mem. Soc. Radiologists in Ultrasound (pres. 1976), Brit. Ultrasound Soc., Radiol. Soc. N.Am., Am. Coll. Radiology. Mem. Soc. Friends. Home: 34 E Montgomery St Baltimore MD 21230-3847 Office: Ultrasound Inst Balt # 252 10751 Falls Rd Lutherville MD 21093

SANDERS, SHARON RAYE (SHARRI), telecommunications executive, educator; b. Dayton, Ohio, Aug. 25, 1942; d. Robert J. Rapa and Mildred B. Wallace; m. Robert Meredith Sanders, Dec. 28, 1961; children: Robert E., Kenneth B. (dec.). Tchr. cert., U. Tex., 1989, 90. Various positions Rockwell Internat, Bastian-Blessing, others, Mich. and Ill., 1960-79; adminstrv. asst. Tex. Tech. Sch. Medicine, Lubbock, 1980, Thermex Energy Corp., Dallas, 1980-81; exec. asst. Bonser-Philhower Sales, Richardson, Tex., 1982; owner, operator SRS Bus. Svc. Secretarial/Printing, Kaufman, Tex., 1982-89; tchr. Kaufman High Sch., 1989-92; prin. ptnr. MetCom of East Tex., Chandler, Tex., 1993—. Author: What's Cooking?, 1988; contbr. poetry to anthologies; contbg. writer Kaufman Herald, 1988-89, The Secretary mag., 1991. Pres. PTA, Allegan, Mich., 1973, sec., 1974; sec. ladies aux. Forest Grove Property Owners Assn., 1993-94; bd. dirs. Forest Grove Property Owners Assn., 1994—. Recipient Engraved Appreciation award Student Boyd/Graphic Arts, Kaufman High Sch., 1992, 20th Century award for Achievement in Edn., 1994. Mem. NAFE, Nat. League Am. Pen Women (2d place writing contest award 1988), Tex. Printing Instrs. Assn. (sec. 1992), Kaufman C. of C. (bd. dirs. 1983-86), Chandler Lioness Club (co-first v.p., 1995—). Avocations: oil painting, writing, quilting. Office: MetCom of East Tex PO Box 1590 Chandler TX 75758-1590

SANDERS, STEVE, singer; b. Richland, Ga., Sept. 17; s. Herbert and Lorraine Sanders; m. Janet Sanders (div.); 4 children. Mem. Oak Ridge Boys, 1987—; rhythm guitar, now singer. Albums include Heartbeat, 1987, Monongahela, 1988, Unstoppable, 1991, The Long Haul, 1992, Back to Back, 1994; songs written include Live in Love, 1982; appeared in Broadway prodn. The Yearling; appeared in film Hurry Sundown, 1967; TV appearances include Gunsmoke, Noon Wine. Avocations: scuba diving, fishing. Office: The Oak Ridge Boys 329 Rockland Rd Hendersonville TN 37075-3423*

SANDERS, STEVEN GILL, telecommunications executive; b. Chgo., Aug. 23, 1934; s. Raymond E. and Mildred (Gostow) S.; m. Gretchen Griffith, Jan. 15, 1959 (div. 1985); children: Steven Gill, Meghan Griffith; m. Nancy Lee Wolf, Sept. 23, 1989. BS, MIT, 1958; postgrad., Rutgers U., 1960-61; PhD, U.SC., 1965. Instr. mechanics U.S.C., Columbia, 1964-65; asst. prof. So. Ill. U. Edwardsville, 1965-67, assoc. prof., 1969-75, prof. physics, 1975-79, chmn. physics faculty, 1967-71; resident rsch. asst. Agronne (Ill.) Nat. Lab., 1971-72; pres., gen. mgr. No. Ark. Tel. Co., Flippin, 1977—, Nova Systems, Flippin, 1981-92. Contbr. articles on physics to sci. publs. Fellow NSF, 1971. Mem. AAAS, IEEE (sr.), Am. Phys. Soc., U.S. Tel. Assn. (new svcs. and tech. issues subcom. 1991-92, Supercom program com. 1993-94), Ark. Tel. Assn. (pres. 1992, bd. dirs. 1985—), Western Rural Tel. Assn. (bd. dirs. 1993—, chmn. Western Alliance Universal svc. com. 1994—), Ark. C. of C. (bd. dirs. 1989-94), Sigma Xi. Home: 220 N Cardinal Dr Mountain

Home AR 72653-3754 Office: No Ark Tel Co 301 E Main St Flippin AR 72634

SANDERS, STEVEN PAUL, lawyer; b. Mattoon, Ill., Jan. 7, 1950; s. Paul Henry and Frances Ann (Pierce) S.; m. Nancy Kay Hoffman, Aug. 15, 1970; children: Meghan Elizabeth, Benjamin Steven. BA, U. Ill., 1972; JD magna cum laude, Ind. U., 1975. Bar: Ind. 1975, Mo. 1977, Ill. 1977, U.S. Dist. Ct. (so. dist.) Ind. 1975, U.S. Dist. Ct. (ea. dist.) Mo. 1977, U.S. Dist. Ct. (so. dist.) Ill. 1978, U.S. Ct. Appeals (7th and 8th cirs.). Assoc. White, Pierce, Beasley & Gilkison, Muncie, Ind., 1975-76, Coburn, Croft, Shepherd, Herzog & Putzell, St. Louis, 1976-79; assoc. Shepherd, Sandberg & Phoenix, St. Louis, 1979-81, ptnr., 1981-88; ptnr. Armstrong, Teasdale, Schlafly & Davis, St. Louis, 1988—. Mem. ABA, Ill. State Bar Assn., Mo. State Bar Assn., St. Louis Bar Assn., Assn. Def. Counsel of St. Louis (pres. 1983). Office: Armstrong Teasdale Schlafly & Davis 1 Metropolitan Sq Saint Louis MO 63102-2740

SANDERS, TED, state official. Supt., pub. instr. Dept. Edn. Office: Edn Dept 65 S Front St Columbus OH 43266

SANDERS, WALLACE WOLFRED, JR., civil engineer; b. Louisville, June 24, 1933; s. Wallace Wolfred and Mary Jane (Brownfield) S.; m. Julia B. Howard, June 9, 1956; children—Linda, David. B.C.E., U. Louisville, 1955; M.S., U. Ill., Urbana, 1957, Ph.D., 1960; M.Engring., U. Louisville, 1973. Research asst., then research assoc. U. Ill., 1955-60, asst. prof., 1960-64; mem. faculty Iowa State U., Ames, 1964—; prof. civil engring. Iowa State U., 1970—, assoc. dir. engring. research, 1980-91, assoc. dean research, 1988-91, interim asst. vice provost for research and advanced studies, 1991-92; cons. to govt. and industry. Contbr. numerous papers to profl. jours. Bd. dirs. Northcrest Retirement Community, Ames, 1976-82, 1992—, pres., 1987-91. Mem. ASCE (R.C. Reese research prize 1978), Am. Welding Soc. (Adams Meml. membership award 1971), Am. Ry. Engring. Assn., Am. Soc. Engring. Edn. Baptist. Home: 1809 Maxwell Ave Ames IA 50010-5539 Office: Iowa State U 374 Town Engring Bldg Ames IA 50011

SANDERS, WALTER JEREMIAH, III, electronics company executive; b. Chgo., Sept. 12, 1936. BEE, U. Ill., 1958. Design engr. Douglas Aircraft Co., Santa Monica, Calif., 1958-59; applications engr. Motorola, Inc., Phoenix, 1959-60; sales engr. Motorola, Inc., 1960-61; with Fairchild Camera & Instrument Co., 1961-69; dir. mktg. Fairchild Camera & Instrument Co., Mountain View, Calif., 1961-68, group dir. mktg. worldwide, 1968-69; pres. Advanced Micro Devices Inc., Sunnyvale, Calif., until 1987, chmn. bd., chief exec. officer, 1969—. Author: chmn. Semicondr. Industry Assn. (co-founder, dir.), Santa Clara County Mfg. Group (co-founder, dir.). Office: Advanced Micro Devices Inc PO Box 3453 One AMD Pl Sunnyvale CA 94086-3453*

SANDERS, WAYNE R., manufacturing executive; b. Chgo., July 6, 1947; s. Ralph G. and Bernice F. (Swanson) S.; m. Kathleen E. Lessard, Aug. 22, 1970; children: Tracy, Amy, Megan. BCE, Ill. Inst. Tech., 1969; MBA, Marquette U., 1972. Fin. analyst Ford Motor Co., Dearborn, Mich., 1972-75; sr. fin. analyst Kimberly-Clark Corp., Neenah, Wis., 1975, dir. bus. planning internat., 1976-80, dir. bus. planning U.S. consumer bus., 1980-81; v.p. strategic planning Kimberly-Clark of Can., Toronto, Ont., 1981-82, pres., 1982-85; sr. v.p. Kimberly-Clark Corp., Dallas, 1986; pres. infant care sector Kimberly-Clark Corp., Neenah, Wis., from 1987; former pres. personal care div. Kimberly-Clark Corp., pres., chief oper. officer world consumer, nonwovens and svc. and indsl. ops., 1990—; pres., CEO Kimberly-Clark Corp., Dallas, 1990-91, chmn., CEO, 1992—, chmn. bd., CEO, 1992—. Elected mem. Neenah Sch. Bd., 1980-81; nat. trustee Boys and Girls Clubs Am., 1994; trustee Marquette U., Milw. Roman Catholic. *

SANDERS, WILLIAM EUGENE, marketing executive; b. Asheboro, N.C., Nov. 16, 1933; s. Arthur Ira and Picola (Loftin) S.; m. Velma Elizabeth Sumner, June 8, 1957; children: William Eugene Jr., George Herbert Sumner. AB in Polit. Sci., U. N.C., 1956, postgrad. in Law, 1956-57. Marketing rep. Encyclopaedia Britannica, Greensboro, N.C., 1957-60, Am. Pubs., Chgo., 1960-66; pres. S&W Distbrs., Inc., Greensboro, 1966—. Little league coach Civitans, Greensboro, 1967-68. With U.S. Army Res., 1957-63. Named Hon. Amb. Dept. of Labor, Ky., 1976, Ky. Col., 1976, Hon. Mem. La. Lt. Gov. Staff, 1984; recipient Cert. Appreciation Jefferson Davis Parish Libr., Jennings, La., 1986. Mem. State Libr. Assns. Va., W.Va., La., Gen. Alumni Assn. (co-chairman Greensboro chpt. 1979-80), Chi Phi. Democrat. Presbyterian. Avocations: billiards, golf, fishing. Office: S&W Distbrs Inc 1600H E Wendover Ave Greensboro NC 27405-6766

SANDERS, W(ILLIAM) EUGENE, JR., physician, educator; b. Frederick, Md., June 25, 1934; s. W(illiam) Eugene and E. Gertrude (Wilburn) S.; m. Christine Culp, Feb. 22, 1974. A.B., Cornell U., 1956, M.D., 1960. Diplomate: Am. Bd. Internal Medicine. Intern Johns Hopkins Hosp., Balt., 1960-61; resident Johns Hopkins Hosp., 1961-62; instr. medicine Emory U. Sch. Medicine, Atlanta, 1962-64; chief med. resident, instr. U. Fla. Coll. Medicine, Gainesville, 1964-65; asst. prof. medicine and microbiology U. Fla. Coll. Medicine, 1965-69, assoc. prof., 1969-72; prof., chmn. dept. med. microbiology, prof. medicine Creighton U. Sch. Medicine, Omaha, 1972—; cons.-in-research Fla. Dept. Health and Rehab. Services, 1966—. Editor: Am. Jour. Epidemiology, 1974—; contbr. sci. articles to profl. jours. Served as med. officer USPHS, 1962-64. Recipient NIH Research Career Devel. award, 1968-72; John and Mary R. Markle scholar in acad. medicine, 1968-73. Mem. Am. Soc. for Microbiology, Infectious Diseases Soc. Am., Soc. for Epidemiol. Research, Am. Lung Assn., Thoracic Soc., N.Y. Acad. Scis., Phi Beta Kappa, Sigma Xi, Phi Kappa Phi. Achievements include patent on enocin antibiotic and RBE limonene and perrilyl alcohol. Home: T-1004 Woodcliff RR 2 Fremont NE 68025-9619 Office: Creighton U Sch Medicine Omaha NE 68178 Each day provides more challenges and more opportunities than the preceding. No individual can possibly cope with each of these in any given day. Success depends upon establishing priorities and maintaining them. Fight only those battles and pursue with fervor only those opportunities that improve both one's self and one's fellow man.

SANDERS, WILLIAM EVAN, bishop; b. Natchez, Miss., Dec. 25, 1919; s. Walter Richard and Agnes Mortimer (Jones) S.; B.A., Vanderbilt U., 1942; B.D., U. of South, 1945, D.D., 1959; S.T.M., Union Theol. Sem., 1946; m. Kathryn Cowan Schaffer, June 25, 1951; 4 children. Curate St. Paul's Episcopal Ch., Chattanooga, 1945-46; asst. St. Mary's Cathedral, Memphis, 1946-48, dean, 1948-62; bishop coadjutor Tenn., Knoxville, after 1962, now bishop Eastern Tenn., 1985— Address: PO Box 3807 Knoxville TN 37927-3807

SANDERS, WILLIAM GEORGE, public relations executive; b. Sacramento, Jan. 11, 1932; s. Samuel S. and Alice M. (Trow) S.; m. Teresa Helsel, Oct. 20, 1979. Student, Contra Costa Jr. Coll., 1950-51; B.A. in Journalism, U. Oreg., 1957; postgrad. cinema dept., U. So. Calif., 1962. Reporter Roseburg (Oreg.) News-Rev., 1957; group advt. mgr. Montgomery Ward & Co., Oakland, Calif., 1957-61; advt. public relations dir. Jacuzzi Research, Inc., Berkeley, Calif., 1964-65; asst. v.p. cons. communications Airborne Freight Corp., San Mateo, Calif., 1966-67; sr. editor Motor Trend Mag. Hollywood, Calif., 1971-87; exec. v.p., assoc. pub. Four Wheeler Mag., Canoga Park, Calif., 1971-87; pres. William Sanders & Assocs., Sepulveda, Calif., 1987—; sr. editor Off Road Mag., 1988—. Editor: automotive sect. World Year Book, 1970, 71. Served with Signal Corps U.S. Army, 1952-54, Korea. Decorated U.S. Korean Svc. medal W/1 Bronze Svc. star, U.N. Svc. medal, Nat. Def. Svc. medal, Singman Rhee citation Korea. Mem. Calif. Assn. Four Wheel Dr. Clubs, Specialty Equipment Mfrs. Assn., Am. Automotive Writers and Broadcasters Assn., Chi Psi. Winner Baja 1000 Off Rd. Race for prodn. 4 wheel dr. class, 1973, 4th Pl. Baja 1000, 1979.

SANDERS-CHILDEARS, LINDA, banker; b. Council Bluffs, Iowa, Jan. 25, 1950; d. Nolan Glen and Mary Lucile (Dunken) Jackson. Grad., U. Wis., Inst. Banking; student, U. Colo., U. Denver. Various positions First Nat. Bank Bear Valley (name changed to United Bank Bea, Colo., 1969-79; v.p. adminstr. First Nat. Bancorp., 1979-83; pres., CEO, Equitable Bank of Littleton, 1983—; founder The Fin. Consortium; pres., CEO, Young Ams. Bank, Denver, 1987—; also vice-chmn. bd. dirs.; chmn. bd., pres. Young Ams. Edn. Found. Contbr. articles to Time and Newsweek. Bd.

dirs. Cherry Creek Art Festival, Denver 1989—, now chmn.-elect, Grad. Sch. Banking, Colorado Student Loan Program, Denver; vice chmn. Nat. Assembly; past dir. Jr. Achievement, Panorama Products and Svcs., Mile High United Way; mem. adv. bd. Campfire Coun. Colo., nat. past pres. Named hon. life mem. Nat. CampFire, past chmn., numerous other awards Camp Fire Inc. Mem. Am. Bankers Assn. (past chmn. Edn. Found., edn. coun.). Found. Tchg. Econs. (trustee), Colo. Bankers Assn. Republican. Office: Young Ams Bank 311 Steele St Denver CO 80206-4453

SANDERSON, ARTHUR CLARK, engineering educator; b. Providence, Oct. 23, 1946; s. Robert Leroy and Julia Ayer (Oldham) S.; m. Susan Rita Walsh, Aug. 14, 1971; children: Angeline Mirada, Andrew McWain. BS, Brown U., 1968; MS, Carnegie-Mellon U., 1970, PhD, 1972. Rsch. engr. Westinghouse Electric Corp., Pitts., 1968-70; vis. rsch. scientist Delft (The Netherlands) U. Tech., 1972-73; prof. Carnegie-Mellon U., Pitts., 1973-87, co-dir. robotics inst., 1981-87; rsch. dir. Philips Rsch. Labs., Briarcliff Manor, N.Y., 1985-87; prof., dept. chmn. Rensselaer Poly. Inst., Troy, N.Y., 1987—; vis. prof. Univ. Iberoamericana, Mexico City, 1975-77. Contbr. over 180 chpts. to books, articles to profl. jours. Fellow AAAS, IEEE (pres. robotics and automation soc. 1989, 90); mem. AIAA (mem. space automation and robotics tech. com.), Am. Assn. Artificial Intelligence, Soc. Mfg. Engrs. Home: 523 Hancock Rd Williamstown MA 01267-3011 Office: Rensselaer Poly Inst 110 8th St Troy NY 12180-3522

SANDERSON, DAVID R., physician; b. South Bend, Ind., Dec. 26, 1933; s. Robert Burns and Alpha (Rodenberger) S.; divorced, 1978; children: David, Kathryn, Robert, Lisa; m. Evelyn Louise Klunder, Sept. 20, 1980. BA, Northwestern U., 1955, MD, 1958. Cons. in medicine Mayo Clinic, Rochester, Minn., 1965-87, chmn. dept. Thoracic Disease, 1977-87; cons. in medicine Mayo Clinic Scottsdale, Ariz., 1987—, chmn. dept. internal medicine, 1988—, vice chmn. bd. govs., 1987-94; assoc. dir. Mayo Lung Project, Nat. Cancer Inst., Rochester. Contbr. articles to profl. jours. Recipient Noble award, Mayo Found., Rochester, "Significant Sig" award, Sigma Chi Fraternity, Ill., 1989, Chevalier Jackson award, Am. Bronchoesophagologic Assn., Fla., 1990. Fellow ACP, Am. Coll. Chest Physicians (gov. for Minn. 1981-87); mem. Am. Bronchoesophagologic Assn., World Assn. for Bronchology, Internat. Bronchoesophagologic Assn., Internat. Assn. Study of Lung Cancer, AMA. Presbyterian. Home: 10676 E Bella Vista Dr Scottsdale AZ 85258-6086 Office: Mayo Clinic Scottsdale 13400 E Shea Blvd Scottsdale AZ 85259-5499

SANDERSON, DENNIS CARL, theater director, educator; b. Akron, Ohio, Jan. 20, 1935; s. Carl A. Sanderson and Gladys M. (Minter) Sanderson Buchmiller; m. Carol Ann Heitzman, May 13, 1961; children: Dennis Douglas, Diana Dawn. MA, Kent State U., 1963; PhD, Mich. State U., 1973. Dir. theatre Newberry (S.C.) Coll., 1963-73, Francis Marion U., Florence, S.C., 1973—; chmn. div. humanities Newberry Coll., 1971-73; chair, prof. dept. fine arts Francis Marion U., 1985—, C.B. and Marlene Askins prof. art; chmn. Art's Alive Spring Arts festival, Florence, 1985—; cons. in field. Dir. plays including Grease, 1981, Children of a Lesser God, 1983, Hedda Gabler, 1984, The Comedy of Errros, 1985, The Rimers of Eldritch, 1986, Royal Gambit, 1988, South Pacific, 1988, Out Town, 1989, Working, 1990; scenic designer plays Bell, Book, & Candle, 1985, The Foreigner, 1987. Pres. Dem. Com. Precinct 14, Florence, 1980-90. Luth. Ch. Am. fellow, 1966; faculty grantee Newberry Coll., 1970. Mem. Southeastern Theatre Assn., Am. Theatre in Higher Edn., S.C. Theatre Assn. (bd. dirs. 1988), Rotary (bd. dirs. 1987-90), Lions Internat., Sierra Club, Alpha Psi Omega, Phi Delta Theta (treas. 1960-61). Democrat. Lutheran. Avocations: coaching basketball and baseball, wood carving, research. Office: Francis Marion U PO Box 100547 Florence SC 29501

SANDERSON, DOUGLAS JAY, lawyer; b. Boston, Apr. 21, 1953; s. Warren and Edith S. Sanderson; m. Audrey S. Goldstein, June 6, 1982; children: Scott M.G., Phoebe H.G. BA, Trinity Coll., Hartford, Conn., 1974; JD, George Washington U., 1977. Bar: Va. 1977, D.C. 1978, U.S. Dist. Ct. (ea. dist.) Va. 1978, U.S. Ct. Appeals (4th cir.) 1978. Assoc. Bettius, Rosenberger & Carter, P.C., Fairfax, Va., 1977-82; ptnr. Bettius & Sanderson, P.C. and predecessor firms, Fairfax, 1982-86; co-owner Miles & Stockbridge P.C., Fairfax, 1986—; br. head Miles & Stockbridge, Fairfax, 1990-94; trustee Cambridge Ctr. Behavioral Studies, Cambridge, 1981-90. Editor: Consumer Protection Reporting Svc., 1976-77. Bd. dirs. Legal Svcs. No. Va., Inc., 1991—, pres., 1993—. Mem. ABA, Va. Bar Assn., Fairfax Bar Assn., Ctrl. Fairfax C. of C. (bd. dirs. 1988-93). Avocations: sports, reading. Office: Miles & Stockbridge PC 11350 Random Hills Ste 500 Fairfax VA 22030-7429

SANDERSON, EDWARD FRENCH, state official; b. Evanston, Ill., June 25, 1947; s. Edward Gatewood and Barbara (French) S.; m. Carol Clo; children: David, Sarah, Katherine. BA, Wesleyan U., 1969; MA, Brown U., 1974. Exec. dir. Providence Hist. Dist. Commn., 1975-80; dep. dir. R.I. Hist. Preservation Commn., Providence, 1980-84, exec. dir., 1984—; sec. Nat. Conf. of State, Washington, 1989-91; dir., 1985-91; bd. dirs. R.I. Hist. Soc., Providence, 1987-93; commr. Blackstone Valley Nat. Heritage Corridor, Washington, 1988—. Author: Providence, R.I., 1986 (Downing Prize 1987). Office: RI Hist Preservation Commn Old State House 150 Benefit St Providence RI 02903-1209

SANDERSON, ERIC GEORGE (SANDY SANDERSON), broadcast executive; b. Toronto, Ont., Can., Oct. 10, 1948; s. George Douglas and Miriam W. (House) S.; m. Anne Chard, May 23, 1970; children: Timothy, Katherine. Student, U. Toronto, 1965-66, U. Western Ont., 1967-68. Morning announcer, program dir. Radio Sta. CKAR, Huntsville, Ont., 1970-73; prodn. dir. Radio Sta. CJBK, London, Ont., 1973; creative dir. Radio Sta. CKGM, Montreal, Que., Can., 1974-77; asst. program dir. Radio Sta. WABC, N.Y.C., 1977-80; program dir. Radio Sta. WLS, Chgo., 1980-81; dir. programming ABC Radio Network, N.Y.C., 1982; program dir. Radio Sta. CFTR, Toronto, 1983-85, v.p. programming, 1986, sr. v.p., gen. mgr., 1988-90; sr. v.p. programming Rogers Broadcasting Ltd., Toronto, 1987-88, exec. v.p., gen. mgr. stas. CFTR-AM and CHFI-FM, 1990—. Bd. dirs. Found. to Assist Canadian Talent on Record. Mem. Mayfair Lakeshore Tennis Club, Toronto Athletic Club. Avocations: squash, golf, tennis. Office: Rogers Broadcasting Ltd, 44 Victoria St, Toronto, ON Canada M5C 1H3

SANDERSON, FRED HUGO, economist; b. Germany, Apr. 15, 1914; came to U.S., 1937, naturalized, 1944; s. Siegfried and Maria (Schulze) S.; m. Elisabeth Doepfer, Jan. 3, 1938. Lic.Sc.Econ., U. Geneva, Switzerland, 1935; A.M., Harvard U., 1942, Ph.D, 1943. Research asst. Dept. Agr., 1938-42; research asso. com. on research in social scis. Harvard U., 1938-43, teaching fellow, 1942-43; economist OSS, 1943-45; chief Central European econ. sect. div. research for Western Europe Dept. of State, 1946-48, chief Western European econ. br., 1948-52, chief regional econ. staff, 1952-55, asst. chief div., 1955-57, chief div. of research Western Europe, 1957-58; alt. U.S. rep. European Payments Union, 1958-59; dir. finance div. U.S. Mission to OEEC, Paris, 1959-62; chief foodstuffs div. Dept. State, 1963-67; dir. Office Food Policy and Programs, 1967-69, adviser internat. finance, 1970; detailed to Pres.'s Commn. on Internat. Trade and Investment Policy, 1970-71; mem. planning and coordination staff State Dept., 1971-73; fgn. service officer, 1955-73; sr. fellow Brookings Instn., Washington, 1974-83, Resources for Future, Washington, 1983-92, Nat. Ctr. for Food and Agrl. Policy, Washington, 1992—; on leave under Rockefeller Fgn. Svc. award to study econ. effects of European coal and steel cmty., 1956-57; cons. to econ. adviser OMGUS, Berlin, 1948; detailed to Pres.'s Materials Policy Commn., 1951; professorial lectr. Sch. Advanced Internat. Studies Johns Hopkins U., 1973-94. Author: Methods of Crop Forecasting, 1954 (David A. Wells prize), Japan's Food Prospects and Policies, 1978, (with S. Roy) Food Trends and Prospects in India, 1979; contbr. to: Resources for Freedom, Vol. III, 1952, The Struggle for Democracy in Germany (G. Almond, editor), 1949, Strains in International Finance and Trade, 1974, The Great Food Fumble, 1975, U.S. Farm Policy in Perspective, 1983, World Food Prospects to the Year 2000, 1984, Agriculture and International Trade, 1988; co-author/editor: Agricultural Protectionism in the Industrialized World, 1990. Mem. Am. Econ. Assn., Am. Agrl. Econ. Assn. Home: 5017 Westport Rd Chevy Chase MD 20815-3714 Office: Nat Ctr for Food and Agrl Policy Washington DC 20036

SANDERSON, GARY WARNER, food company executive; b. Thermal, Calif., Dec. 17, 1934; s. Syl Z. and Inez (Goodpasture) S.; m. Irene Elizabeth Blocker, Aug. 15, 1953; children: Phillip Paul, Jennifer Ellen Sanderson Bakshi, Peter George, Andrew Forest. BS with honors, U. Calif. at Davis, 1956; PhD, U. Nottingham, 1962. Biochemist, head biochemistry div. Tea Rsch. Inst. of Ceylon, Talawakelle, Sri Lanka, 1963-66; from group leader of tea rsch. sect. to dir. beverage product R&D sect. Thomas J. Lipton, Inc., Englewood Cliffs, N.J., 1966-77; from v.p. rsch. to v.p. techs. Universal Foods Corp., Milw., 1978—; adj. prof. chemistry U. New Rochelle, N.Y., 1985; mem. biology adv. bd. Marquette U., 1987—; bd. adv. Food Rsch. Inst. U. Wisc. Madison, 1990—. Contbr. articles to profl. jours.; patentee in tea processing. Councilman City of Englewood, N.J., 1976-78; pres. City Coun., Englewood, 1977. Woodrow Wilson fellow U. Calif.-Davis, 1957-58; recipient Fulbright scholarship, 1960-62. Mem. Am. Chem. Soc. (chmn. N.Y. sect. 1976-77, treas. midwest regional meeting 1986, 92), Inst. Food Technologists (chmn. biotech. div. 1986-87), Biochem. Soc. (London), Wis. Biotech. Assn. (bd. dirs. 1993—), Wis. Assn. Rsch. Mgmt. (pres. 1992-94, Friends U. Nottingham in Am. (pres. 1994—), Cream City Cycle Club (ride leader 1988—, v.p. 1993—). Democrat. Unitarian. Avocations: bicycling, hiking, camping. Office: Universal Foods Corp 433 E Michigan St Milwaukee WI 53202-5106

SANDERSON, JAMES RICHARD, naval officer, planning and investment company consultant; b. Selma, Calif., Dec. 27, 1925; s. Charles Maxwell and Edith (Wente) S.; m. Betty Lee Bradley, Sept. 19, 1947. Student, U. Calif.-Berkeley, 1943-44, U. Wash., 1944, U. Willamette, 1944-45; grad., USNR Midshipman Sch. at Columbia U., 1945, Nat. War Coll., 1966; student, Gen. Line Sch., Monterey, Calif., 1953, Sr. Officers Ship Material Mgmt. Course, Idaho Falls, Idaho, 1979; B.A. in Internat. Affairs, George Washington U., 1968. Served as enlisted man U.S. Naval Res., 1943-45; commd. ensign USN, 1946, advanced through grades to vice adm., 1980; gunnery officer U.S.S. Mansfield, 1946-47, U.S.S. Bausell, 1947-48; flight trainee Naval Air Sta., Pensacola, Fla., 1949, Corpus Christi, Tex., 1950; served in Attack Squadron 195, Alameda, Calif., 1950-52; flight instr. Naval Air Sta., Pensacola, 1953-55; served in Attack Squadron 16, 1955-57; air ops. officer on staff Comdr. Carrier Div. Four, U.S.S. Forrestal, 1957-60; ops. officer Attack Squadron 43, Naval Air Sta., Oceana, Va., 1960-62; comdg. officer Attack Squadron 76, 1962-63; comdr. Attack Carrier Air Wing Three in U.S.S. Saratoga, 1963-65; spl. support plans officer, Pacific Area Strategic Plans and Policy Div., Office of Chief of Naval Ops., Washington, 1966-67; exec. asst. and sr. aide to dep. chief. naval ops., 1967-69; comdg. officer U.S.S. Ranier, 1969-70; dep. chief of staff for ops. and plans U.S. Sixth Fleet, 1970-71; comdg. officer U.S.S. Saratoga, 1971-73; dep. comdr. Naval Striking and Support Forces, So. Europe, Naples, Italy, 1973-76; vice dir. ops. Joint Chiefs of Staff, Washington, 1976-77; asst. dep. chief naval ops. for plans, policy and ops., 1977-79; comdr. Task Force Sixty, U.S. 6th Fleet, 1979-80, Carrier Group Two, 1979-80, Battle Force Sixth Fleet, 1979-80, Carrier Striking Force So. Region, 1979-80; dep. and chief staff, comdr. in chief Atlantic/U.S. Atlantic Fleet, Norfolk, Va., 1980-83; ret., 1983; exec. cons. Exec. Planning & Investment Co., Inc., Virginia Beach, Va., 1983—; sr. v.p. for corp. ops. Computer Dynamics, Inc., 1984-86; asst. to pres. Eastern Computers, Inc., 1986—; cons., prin. Exec. Planning and Investment Co., Inc., 1986—. Decorated D.S.M., Legion of Merit with 3 gold stars, D.F.C., Meritorious Service medal, Air medal with 4 gold stars, Navy Commendation medal with combat distinguishing device. Mem. Calif. Alumni Assn., George Washington Alumni Assn., Nat. War Coll. Alumni Assn., Naval Acad. Athletic Assn., Assn. Naval Aviation, Tailhook Assn., Smithsonian Assn., Regent Nat. Eagle Scout Assn. (Disting. Eagle Scout award 1994), Nat. Skeet Shooting Assn., Eye Found., Nat. Assn. Investment Clubs, Nat. Wildlife Assn., Order Daedalians, Army Navy Country CLub, Masons (33 degree), Shriners, Knight Templer, Sojourners. Club: Army Navy Country (Arlington, Va.). Lodges: Masons (33 degree), Shriners, Knight Templer, Sojourners. Office: Eastern Computers Inc 596 Lynnhaven Pkwy Virginia Beach VA 23452

SANDERSON, WILLIAM FLETCHER, JR., federal judge; b. Battlecreek, Mich., June 26, 1943; s. William F. Sr. and Jean (Dunning) S.; m. Sandra Kathleen Gregg, June 24, 1967; children: William F. III, Virginia Kathleen. BA, Vanderbilt U., 1965; JD, U. Tex., 1968. Asst. city atty. City of Dallas, 1968-69; asst. U.S. Atty. (no. dist.) Tex. U.S. Dept. Justice, Dallas, 1969-77; assoc. Stubbman, McRae, Sealy, Laughlin & Browder, Midland, Tex., 1977-79; U.S. Magistrate judge U.S. Dist. Ct. (no. dist.) Tex., Dallas, 1979—; mem. U.S. Judicial Conf. Com. on Adminstrn. Office U.S. Cts., Washington, 1992—. Bd. dirs. Greater Dallas Community of Chs. Recipient Cross and Flame award United Meth. Ch., Richardson, Tex., 1988. Mem. ABA, Tex. Bar Assn., Dallas Bar Assn., Fed. Magistrate Judges Assn. (pres. 1991-92). Office: US Dist Ct 1110 Commerce St Rm 14e9 Dallas TX 75242-1001

SANDESON, WILLIAM SEYMOUR, cartoonist; b. Mound City, Ill., Dec. 16, 1913; s. William Stephen and Jessie Mae (Mertz) S.; m. Ione Wear, June 4, 1938 (dec. 1975); 1 son, William Scott; m. Ruth Cress, Dec. 31, 1978. Student, Chgo. Acad. Fine Arts, 1931-32. Free-lance cartoonist for nat. mags., 1932-37; editorial cartoonist New Orleans Item-Tribune, 1937-41; cartoonist, picture editor and art dir. St. Louis Star-Times, 1941-51; editorial cartoonist Ft. Wayne (Ind.) News-Sentinel, 1951-82; ret., 1982. Drew daily cartoon feature for, Star-Times, Sketching Up With the News. Recipient Honor medal Freedoms Found., 1952, 53, 56, George Washington Honor medal, 1954, 55, 57, 58, 59, 60, Disting. Service award, 1961-72, cartoon award, 1982; Ind. Sch. Bell award, 1967, Disting. Service awards, 1971-76, prin. cartoon award, 1977, cartoon award, 1978; co-recipient Pulitzer Prize for gen. local reporting, 1982. Mem. Nat. Cartoonist Soc., Assn. Am. Editorial Cartoonists. Congregationalist. Club: Fort Wayne Press (pres. 1965). Home: 119 W Sherwood Ter Fort Wayne IN 46807-2846 Office: Fort Wayne News Sentinel Fort Wayne IN 46802 *Until I'm listed in WHO WAS WHO, I intend to dip my brush in a mixture of self-improvement, stubbornness, and sincere thoughtfulness of my fellow American.*

SANDIDGE, KENT, III, magistrate judge; b. Nashville, Dec. 28, 1929; s. Kent and Mildred Adele (Regen) S.; m. Paula Conaway, Aug. 21, 1965; children—Kent IV, Beth Regen, Mark Conaway, Scott Overton. B.A., Vanderbilt U., 1952, J.D., 1956. Bar: Tenn. 1956, U.S. Dist. Ct. (mid. dist.) Tenn. 1957, U.S. Ct. Appeals (6th cir.), 1966, U.S. Supreme Ct., 1968. Assoc. Manier, Crouch, White & Herod, Nashville, 1956-64; asst. U.S. atty. Middle Dist. Tenn., Dept. Justice, 1965-69; ptnr. Lackey, Harwood, Sandidge & Alexander, Nashville, 1969-72; magistrate judge U.S. Dist. (mid. dist.) Tenn., Nashville, 1972—. Served to lt. USN, 1952-54. Mem. Nashville Bar Assn., Tenn. Bar. Presbyterian. Office: US District Court 762 US Courthouse 801 Broadway Nashville TN 37203

SANDITEN, EDGAR RICHARD, investment company executive; b. Okmulgee, Okla., Feb. 1, 1920; s. Herman and Anna (Sanditen) S.; m. Isabel Raffkind, Jan. 26, 1945; children: Linda Caryl, Judith Marie, Ellen Jane, Michael Jay. Student, Western Mil. Acad., 1934-37; B.S. in Bus., Okla. U. 1941. With Otasco, Inc., Tulsa, 1941-87, pres., 1974-77, chmn., chief exec. officer, 1977-83, chmn., 1983-87; chmn. employees retirement trust, 1985-87; prin., chmn. Sanditen Investments, Inc., Tulsa, 1987—; bd. dirs. Bank of Okla. Trust Co.; fin. advisor Bank of Okla., 1978-84. Chmn. United Jewish Appeal, Tulsa, 1959; mem. bd. dirs. Jewish Fedn. Tulsa, 1960-62 (Honor award 1960), YMCA, 1966—, Am. Cancer Soc., 1978-80, Tulsa Met. Ministry, 1977-78, Simon Estes Ednl. Found., 1982-88, March of Dimes, 1983—; mem. adv. com. Jr. League, 1977—; Girl Scouts USA, 1987—; chmn. Tulsa Charity Horse Show, 1969-71, 80-84; bd. dirs. Tulsa Opera, 1979-90 (v.p. 1989, Champion Fundraiser 1989, 91, 92), Tulsa Ballet Theater (Dimedici award 1989), Tulsa Econ. Devel. Commn., 1970-84; bd. dirs. Temple Israel Found., 1968-70, chmn., 1979-80; mem. B'Nai Emunah Synagogue; pres. Temple Israel, 1968-70; trustee Children's Med. Center, 1983—; bd. dirs. St. John Med. Ctr., 1973-82 (chmn. 1979-81), St. John Found. 1983-89 (chmn. 1983-85) Tulsa Jewish Retirement and Health Care Ctr., 1986—, Tulsa Ctr. for the Homeless, 1991—, Fenster Mus., 1986—, NCCJ, 1983—, pres. 1985-87; mem. adv. bd. dirs. U. Okla.Coll. Bus. Adminstrn., 1986-91; hon. chmn. founder Ronald McDonald House, 1991. Served with USAAF, 1943-46. Recipient Nat. Humanitarian award Nat. Jewish Hosp., 1987, Brotherhood award NCCJ, 1991, Alfred Aaronson Community Rels. award, 1993; named Boss of Yr., Am. Bus. Women's Assn., 1976. Mem. Tulsa Jr. C. of C. (honor award 1943), Okla. C. of C. (bd. dirs. 1978-87), Tulsa C. of C. (bd. dirs. 1977-83, v.p. 1978-79), Quarter Century Club

Automotive Industry, So. Hills County Club (bd. dirs. 1990—, fin. chmn., exec. com., v.p. 1992, pres. 1995), Summit Club (bd. dirs. 1971-77). Office: Sanditen Investments Ltd 3314 E 51st St Ste 207K Tulsa OK 74135-3527

SANDLER, ABRAHAM, minister. Missionary Jewish Ministry Dist. of Christian and Missionary Alliance. Office: Jewish Ministry Dist 9820 Woodfern Rd Philadelphia PA 19115

SANDLER, BERNICE RESNICK, women's rights specialist; b. N.Y.C., Mar. 3, 1928; d. Abraham Hyman and Ivy (Ernst) Resnick; children: Deborah Jo, Emily Maud. BA cum laude, Bklyn. Coll., 1948; MA, CCNY, 1950; EdD, U. Md., 1969; LLD (hon.), Bloomfield Coll., 1973, Hood Coll., 1974, R.I. Coll., 1980, Colby-Sawyer Coll., 1984; LHD (hon.), Grand Valley State Coll., 1974; Dr. Pub. Service (hon.), North Adams State Coll., 1985; LLD (hon.), Goucher Coll., 1991; LHD (hon.), Plymouth State Coll., 1992, Wittenberg U., 1993. Research asst., nursery sch. tchr., employment counselor, adult edn. instr., sec.; psychologist HEW, 1970; tchr. psychology Mt. Vernon Coll., 1970; head Action Com. for Fed. Contract Compliance, Women's Equity Action League, 1970-71; edn. specialist U.S. Ho. Reps., Washington, 1970; dep. dir. Womens Action program, HEW, Washington, 1971; dir. project on status and edn. of women Assn. Am. Colls., Washington, 1971-91; sr. assoc. Ctr. for Women Policy Studies, 1991-94; sr. scholar in residence Nat. Assn. Women in Edn., Washington, 1994—; cons., 1991—; expert witness, 1990—; writer, 1971—; vis. lectr. U. Md., 1968-69; adv. bd. Women's Equity Action League Ednl. and Legal Def. Fund, 1980—, trustee, 1974-80, Women's Equity Action League, 1971-78; adv. com. Math./Sci. Network, 1979, Wider Opportunities for Women, 1978-85, Women's Legal Def. Fund, 1978-84; adv. bd. N.J. project Inst. for Rsch. on Women Rutgers U., New Brunswick, 1987—; Nat. Coun. for Alternative Work Patterns Inc., 1978-85, Women's Hdqs. State Nat. Bank for Women's Appointments, 1977-78, and others. Mem. adv. bd. Jour. Reprints Documents Affecting Women, 1976-78, Women's Rights Law Reporter, 1970-80; editor: About Women On Campus (newsletter), 1991—; contbr. articles to profl. jours. Mem. bd. overseers Wellesley Coll. Ctr. for Rsch. on Women, 1975-87; bd. dirs. Ctr. for Women's Policy Studies, 1972-75; mem. exec. com. Inst. for Ednl. Leadership, 1982-87, mem. program adv. com., 1987—, chair bd. dirs., 1981, chair adv. com., 1975-81; mem. affirmative action com., task force on family, nat. affairs commn. Am. Jewish Com., 1978, bd. dirs. D.C. chpt.; tech. adv. com. Nat. Jewish Family Ctr., 1980-89; adv. coun. Ednl. Devel. Ctr., 1980-85; adv. bd. Urban Inst., 1981-85, Women Employed Inst., 1981-84, Ex-New Yorkers for N.Y., 1978-79; mem. adv. com. Arthur and Elizabeth Schlesinger Libr. History of Women in Am., 1981-85; nat. adv. com. Shelter Rsch. Inst., Calif., 1980-82; chair adv. panel project on self-evaluation Am. Insts. for Rsch., 1980-82; bd. dirs. Equality Ctr., 1983, Evaluation and Tng. Inst., Calif., 1980, Inst. for Studies in Equality, 1975-77. Recipient Athena award Intercollegiate Assn. Women Students, 1974, Elizabeth Boyer award Women's Equity Action League, 1976, Rockefeller Pub. Svc. award Princeton U., 1976, Women Educators award for activism, 1987, Anna Roe award Harvard U., 1988, Readers Choice honors Washington Woman Mag., 1987, Woman of Distinction award Nat. Assn. Women in Edn., 1991, Georgina Smith award AAUP, 1992, Woman of Achievement Turner Broadcasting System, 1994; named one of 100 Most Powerful Women Washingtonian Mag., 1982, one of the nation's 100 Most Important Women, Ladies Home Jour., 1988. Mem. Assn. for Women in Sci. Found. (bd. dirs. 1977—), Am. Soc. Profl. and Exec. Women (adv. bd. 1980). Avocations: birding, music, swimming, hiking. Office: Nat Assn Women in Edn Ste 850 1350 Connecticut Ave NW Washington DC 20036

SANDLER, GERALD HOWARD, aerospace executive; b. N.Y.C., Sept. 17, 1934; s. Irving and Sally S.; m. Ann Sandler; children: Eric, Steven. BS, CUNY, 1956, MS, 1957. Pres. Grumman Data Systems & Svcs., Bethpage, N.Y. Author: System Engineering, 1963. Home: 46 Bonnie Dr Westbury NY 11590-2804

SANDLER, HERBERT M., savings and loan association executive; b. N.Y.C., Nov. 16, 1931; s. William B. and Hilda (Schattan) S.; m. Marion Osher, Mar. 26, 1961. BSS, CCNY, 1951; JD, Columbia U., 1954. Bar: N.Y. 1956. Asst. counsel Waterfront Commn. N.Y. Harbor, 1956-59; partner firm Sandler & Sandler, N.Y.C., 1960-62; pres., dir., mem. exec. com. Golden West Savs. & Loan Assn. and Golden West Fin. Corp., Oakland, Calif., 1963-75; chmn. bd., co-chief exec. officer, dir., mem. exec. com. World Savs. & Loan Assn. and Golden West Fin. Corp., Oakland, 1975—; charter mem. thrift instns. adv. coun. to Fed. Res. Bd., 1980-81; former mem. legis. and regulation com. Calif. Savs. and Loan League. Pres., trustee Calif. Neighborhood Services Found.; chmn. Urban Housing Inst.; mem. policy adv. bd. Ctr. for Real Estate and Urban Econs. U. Calif., Berkeley. With U.S. Army, 1954-56. Office: Golden W Fin Corp 1901 Harrison St Oakland CA 94612-3574

SANDLER, IRVING HARRY, art critic, art historian; b. N.Y.C., July 22, 1925; s. Harry and Anna (Robin) S.; m. Lucy Freeman, Sept. 4, 1958; 1 child, Catherine Harriet. BA, Temple U., 1948; MA, U. Pa., 1950; PhD, NYU, 1976. Instr. in art history NYU, 1960-71; prof. art history SUNY, Purchase, 1971—; art critic N.Y. Post, N.Y.C., 1960-65. Author: The Triumph of American Painting: A History of Abstract Expressionism, 1970, The New York School: Painters and Sculptors of the Fifties, 1978, Alex Katz, 1979, Al Held, 1984, American Art of the 1960s, 1988; editor (with Amy Newman) Defining Modern Art: Selected Writings of Alfred H. Barr Jr., 1986. John Simon Guggenheim fellow, 1965; Nat. Endowment for Arts fellow, 1977. Mem. Coll. Art Assn., Internat. Assn. Art Critics. Home: 100 Bleecker St New York NY 10012-2202 Office: SUNY Div Visual Arts Purchase NY 10577

SANDLER, JENNY, dancer; b. N.Y.C.. Scholarship student, The Joffrey Ballet Sch. Dancer Joffrey II Dancers, N.Y.C., 1988-90, The Joffrey Ballet, N.Y.C., 1990—. Featured in mag. Mirabella, Aug., 1994. Office: The Joffrey Ballet 25 E 9th St #7A New York NY 10003

SANDLER, LUCY FREEMAN, art history educator; b. N.Y.C., June 7, 1930; d. Otto and Frances (Glass) Freeman; m. Irving Sandler, Sept. 4, 1958; 1 child, Catherine Harriet. B.A., Queens Coll., 1951; M.A., Columbia U., 1957; Ph.D., NYU, 1964. Asst. prof. NYU, 1964-70, assoc. prof., 1970-75, prof. fine arts, 1975-86, Helen Gould Sheppard prof. art history, 1986—, chmn. dept., 1975-89; editorial cons. Viator, UCLA, 1983—. Author: The Peterborough Psalter in Brussels, 1974, The Psalter of Robert De Lisle in the British Library, 1983, Gothic Manuscripts 1285-1385, 1986, 'Omne Bonum': A Fourteenth-Century Encyclopedia of Universal Knowlege, 1995; editor: Essays in Memory of Karl Lehmann, 1964, Art the Ape of Nature: Studies in Honor of H.W. Janson, 1981, Monograph Series, 1970-75, 86-89, Gesta, 1991-94; asst. editor Art Bull., 1964-67, mem. editl. bd., 1994; mem. editl. bd. Jour. Jewish Art, 1978, Speculum, 1994. Trustee Godwin-Ternbach Mus., Queens Coll., 1982-94. NEH fellow, 1967-68, 77; fellow Pierpont Morgan Library; Guggenheim fellow, 1988-89. Fellow Soc. Antiquaries (London); mem. AAUP, Coll. Art Assn. (pres. 1981-84), Medieval Acad. Am., Internat. Ctr. Medieval Art (adv. bd., bd. dirs. 1976-80, 84-87, 89-92, 95—). Home: 100 Bleecker St Apt 30A New York NY 10012-2207 Office: NYU Dept Fine Arts New York NY 10003

SANDLER, MARION OSHER, savings and loan association executive; b. Biddeford, Maine, Oct. 17, 1930; d. Samuel and Leah (Lowe) Osher; m. Herbert M. Sandler, Mar. 26, 1961. BA, Wellesley Coll., 1952; postgrad., Harvard U.-Radcliffe Coll., 1953; MBA, NYU, 1958; LLD (hon.), Golden Gate U., 1987. Asst. buyer Bloomingdale's (dept. store), N.Y.C., 1953-55; security analyst Dominick & Dominick, N.Y.C., 1955-61; sr. fin. analyst Oppenheimer & Co., N.Y.C., 1961-63; sr. v.p., dir. Golden West Fin. Corp. and World Savs. & Loan Assn., Oakland, Calif., 1963-75, vice chmn. bd. dirs., CEO, mem. exec. com., dir., 1975-80, pres., co-chief exec. officer, dir., mem. exec. com., 1980-93, chmn. bd. dirs., CEO, mem. exec. com., 1993—; pres., chmn. bd. dirs., CEO Atlas Assets, Inc., Oakland, 1987—, Atlas Advisers, Inc., Oakland 1987—, Atlas Securities, Inc., Oakland, 1987—; mem. adv. com. Fed. Nat. Mortgage Assn., 1983-84. Mem. Pres.'s Mgmt. Improvement Coun., 1980, Thrift Insts. Adv. Coun. to Fed. Res. Bd., 1989-91, v.p., 1990, pres., 1991; mem. policy adv. bd. Ctr. for Real Estate and Urban Econs. U. Calif., Berkeley, 1981—, mem. exec. com. policy adv. bd., 1985—; mem. ad hoc com. to rev. Schs. Bus. Adminstrn. U. Calif., 1984-85; vice chmn. industry adv. com. Fed. Savs. and Loan Ins. Corp., 1987-88, Ins.

Corp., 1987-88; bd. overseers NYU Schs. Bus., 1987-89; mem. Glass Ceiling Commn., 1992-93. Mem. Phi Beta Kappa, Beta Gamma Sigma. Office: Golden W Fin Corp 1901 Harrison St Oakland CA 94612-3588

SANDLER, MICHAEL DAVID, lawyer; b. Los Angeles, Feb. 27, 1946. AB, Stanford U., 1967; JD, Yale U., 1972. Bar: Calif. 1973, D.C. 1973, Wash. 1985. Assoc. Steptoe & Johnson, Washington, 1972-75, 77-79, ptnr., 1980-85; spl. asst. to legal adviser Dept. of State, Washington, 1975-77; ptnr. Foster, Pepper & Shefelman, Seattle, 1985—; adj. prof. law Georgetown U., Washington, 1979, 81-82, U. Wash., Seattle, 1985-92. Vol. Peace Corps, Ethiopia and Ghana, 1968-70. Mem. ABA (chair-elect sect. of internat. law and practice). Office: Foster Pepper & Shefelman 1111 3rd Ave 34th Fl Seattle WA 98101

SANDLER, PAUL MARK, lawyer; b. Balt., June 7, 1945; s. Edward Barry and Dorothy (Livingston) S.; m. Margaret Batten, Dec. 29, 1974; children: Douglas, David. BA, Hobart Coll., Geneva, N.Y., 1967; JD, Georgetown U., Washington, 1971. Bar: Md. 1972, D.C. 1972, U.S. Dist. Ct. Md. 1972, U.S. Ct. Appeals (4th cir.) 1972. Assoc. Ulman & Cohan, Balt., 1972-77; ptnr. Freishtat & Schwartz, Balt., 1977, Freishtat & Sandler, Balt., 1978—; adj. prof. appellate practice U. Balt., 1974-84; lectr. in field; mem. Speedy Trial Planning Grp., U.S. Dist. Ct. of Md., mem. adv. com. on admission of attys. to fed. practice. Author: Pattern Examinations of Witnesses for the Maryland Lawyer, 1987, Pleading Causes of Action in Maryland, 1991, editor: The Maryland Appellate Practice Handbook, 1978; bd. editors Trial Diplomacy Jour., 1983-84. Bd. dirs. Easter Seal Soc. of Md., St. Joseph Hosp. Found., 1989—, chmn. fund raising campaign, 1990-93; chmn. V.I.P. Panel, Nat. Easter Seal Telethon, 1988—; bd. trustees Balt. County Community Colls., 1977-80; mem. Balt. County Bd. Social Svcs., 1981-83. With USAFR, 1968-72. Mem. ABA (co-chmn. sect. litigation legis. com. 1989—, other coms. in past), Md. Bar Assn. (founder and 1st chmn. litigation sect. 1980-81, mem. litigation sect. coun. 1981—), J. Dudley Digges Inn of Ct. (master of bench). Avocations: reading, writing, horseback riding, fishing, hiking. Office: Freishtat & Sandler 201 E Baltimore St Ste 1500 Baltimore MD 21202-1505

SANDLER, RICHARD JAY, lawyer; b. N.Y.C., Aug. 26, 1947; s. Albert and Ruth (Marcus) S.; m. Ronda Muir, Feb. 27, 1982; children: Elizabeth Muir, Russell Muir. BA summa cum laude, Princeton U., 1969; JD, Harvard U., 1972. Assoc. Davis, Polk & Wardwell, N.Y.C., 1972-79, ptnr., 1979—; ptnr. Davis, Polk & Wardwell, Paris, 1982-85. Mem. ABA. Avocations: collecting art, skiing, tennis, reading, antiques. Office: Davis Polk & Wardwell 450 Lexington Ave New York NY 10017

SANDLER, ROBERT MICHAEL, insurance company executive, actuary; b. N.Y.C., Apr. 20, 1942; s. Albert and Ruth (Marcus) S.; m. Annette L. Marchese, Aug. 18, 1963; children—David, Glenn. B.A. in Math., Hofstra U., 1963. Various actuarial positions Met. Life, N.Y.C., 1963-68; various actuarial positions Am. Internat., N.Y.C., 1968-80; v.p. casualty actuary American Internat. Group, Inc., N.Y.C., 1980-84, sr. v.p., sr. actuary, sr. claims officer, 1984—; dir. various subs. Mem. Casualty Actuarial Soc. (assoc.), Am. Acad. Actuaries, Internat. Actuarial Assn., Am. Internat. Underwriters (chmn. 1994—). Republican. Home: 3 Crestwood Dr Bridgewater NJ 08807-2209 Office: Am Internat Group 70 Pine St New York NY 10270-0001

SANDLER, ROSS, law educator; b. Milw., Jan. 31, 1939; s. Theodore T. and Laurette (Simons) S.; m. Alice R. Mintzer, Sept. 15, 1968; children: Josephine, Jenny, Dorothy. AB, Dartmouth Coll., 1961; LLB, NYU, 1965. Bar: N.Y. 1965, Fla. 1965. Assoc. atty. Cahill Gordon Reindel & Ohl, N.Y.C., 1965-68; asst. U.S. atty. So. Dist. N.Y., 1968-72; assoc. atty. Trubin Sillcocks Edelman & Knapp, N.Y.C., 1972-75; sr. staff atty. Natural Resources Def. Coun., N.Y.C., 1975-81, 83-86; spl. advisor to mayor City of N.Y., 1981-82; exec. dir. Hudson River Found., N.Y.C., 1983-86; commr. N.Y.C. Dept. Transp., 1986-90; ptnr. Jones Day Reavis & Pogue, N.Y.C., 1991-93; law prof. N.Y. Law Sch., 1993—, dir. Ctr. for N.Y.C. law, 1993—; mem. N.Y.C. Procurement Policy Bd., 1994—; vis. lectr. Yale Law Sch., New Haven, 1977; adj. prof. law NYU Law Sch., 1976—; chair, mem. N.Y.C. Taxi and Limousine Commn., 1980-90. Co-author: A New Direction in Transit, 1978; columnist Environ. Mag., 1976-80; contbr. book chpt., op-ed columns, articles to profl. jours.; lectr. environ. law; speaker confs. Trustee Woods Hole (Mass.) Rsch. Ctr., 1983—; mem. exec. com. Hudson River Found., 1986—. Recipient Pub. Interest award NYU Law Alumni, 1987, Louis J. Lefkowitz award Fordham Law Sch. Urban Law Jour., 1989. Mem. City Club of N.Y. (chair 1992-93, trustee). Office: NY Law Sch 57 Worth St New York NY 10013-2926

SANDLER, STANLEY IRVING, chemical engineering educator; b. N.Y.C., June 10, 1940; s. Murray C. and Celia M. (Kamenetsky) S.; m. Judith Katherine Ungar, June 17, 1962; children: Catherine Julietta, Joel Abraham, Michael Howard. BChemE, CCNY, 1962; PhD, U. Minn., 1966. NSF postdoctoral fellow Inst. Molecular Physics, U. Md., College Park, 1966-67; successively asst. prof., assoc. prof., prof. dept. chem. engring. U. Del., Newark, 1967-82, H.B. du Pont Prof., 1982—, chmn. dept., 1982-86, dir. Ctr. for Molecular and Engineering Thermodynamics, 1992—, interim dean Coll. of Engring., 1992; vis. prof. Imperial Coll., London, 1973-74, U. Nat. del Sur, Bahia Blanca, Argentina, 1985, Tech. U., Berlin, 1981, 88-89, U. Queensland, Brisbane, Australia, 1989; cons. maj. oil and chem. cos. Author: Chemical and Engineering Thermodynamics, 1977, 2d rev. edit., 1989; editor: Fluid Properties and Phase Equilibria, 1977, Chemical Engineering Education in a Changing Environment, 1989, Kinetic and Thermodynamic Lumping of Multicomponent Mixtures, 1991, Models for Thermodynamic and Phase Equilibria Calculations, 1993; mem. adv. bd. Jour. Chem. Engring. Data, Chem. Engring. Edn., Indsl. Engring. Chem. Rsch., Indian Chem. Engr., Engring. Sci. and Tech. (Malaysia); also numerous articles. Mem. adv. bd. chem. engring. La. State U., Carnegie-Mellon U. Recipient U.S. sr. Scientist award Alexander von Humboldt Found., 1988, Francis Alison award U. Del., 1993, Ashton Cary award Ga. Tech. U., 1994, Phillips Lecture award Okla. State U., 1993. Mem. AICE (jour. adv. bd., Profl. Progress award 1984), Am. Chem. Soc. (award Del. sect. 1989), Am. Soc. Engring. Edn. (lectr. chem. engring. div. 1988), Cosmos Club (Washington). Jewish. Avocations: jogging, philately. Home: 202 Sypherd Dr Newark DE 19711-3627 Office: U Del Dept Chem Engring Newark DE 19716

SANDLER, SUMNER GERALD, medical educator; b. Lawrence, Mass., Jan. 13, 1935; s. Maurice Lewis and Dorothy Gretchen (Alman) S.; m. Katherine Cushing Rosenberg, May 9, 1969; children: Lisah, David, Jonathan, Joel. AB, Princeton U., 1957; MD, NYU, 1962. Diplomate Am. Bd. Internal Medicine, Am. Bd. Pathology (blood banking). Intern NYU-Bellevue Hosp. Ctr., N.Y.C., 1962-63, assoc. med. resident, 1963-64; clin. assoc. NCI, NIH, 1964-66; hematology fellow NYU-Bellevue Hosp. Ctr., N.Y.C., 1966-68; clin. assoc. NIH, 1964-66; teaching asst. NYU Sch. Medicine, N.Y.C., 1966-67; instr. medicine Georgetown U., Washington, 1968-72, asst. prof. medicine, 1970-72, prof. medicine and pathology, 1991—; sr. lectr. Hebrew U.-Hadassah Med. Ctr., Jerusalem, 1972-78, assoc. prof. medicine, 1977-78; assoc. dir. blood svcs. nat. hdqs. ARC, Washington, 1978-84, assoc. v.p., 1984-90, med. dir., 1989-90, chief med. officer, 1990-91; med. dir. Nat. Reference Lab., ARC, Rockville, Md., 1978—; sr. lectr. Hebrew U. Sch. Medicine, Jerusalem, 1972-77, assoc. prof. medicine Hebrew U. Hadassah Sch. Medicine, Jerusalem, 1977-78; head blood bank, Hadassah U. Hosp., Jerusalem, 1972-78; profl. lectr. dept. medicine, George Washington U. Sch. Medicine, Washington, 1988-91, others. Editor: Immunobiology of the Erythrocyte, 1980, Autologous Transfusion, 1983, Advances in Immunobiology, 1984; mem. editl. bd. Haematologia, 1990—, Transfusion, 1982—. Lt. Comdr. USPHS, 1964-66; capt. med. corps. reserve, Israel Def. Forces, 1976-81; bd. mgrs. Adas Israel Congregation, Washington, 1986-92. Recipient Vicenniel medal Georgetown U., Washington, 1989. Fellow Am. Coll. Physicians, Coll. Am. Pathologists; mem. Internat. Soc. Blood Transfusion (counsellor 1986-91, v.p. 1991-94, Svc. award 1990), Am. Assn. Blood Banks, Leukemia Soc. Am. (med. adv. bd. 1970-72, D.C. chpt. chmn. 1971-72, bd. dirs. 1970-72), Israel Soc. Hematology and Blood Transfusion (exec. com. 1976), Am. Soc. Hematology, Internat. Retrovirology Assn., others. Jewish. Avocation: Torah Bible study. Home: 5808 Ogden Ct Bethesda MD 20816 Office: Georgetown U Med Ctr 3800 Reservoir Rd NW Washington DC 20007

SANDLER, THOMAS R., accountant; b. Mt. Kisco, N.Y., Dec. 16, 1946; s. Louis and Susan (Rosen) S.; m. Alison G. Corneau, Aug. 26, 1972; children—Justin C., Shawn A. B.S. summa cum laude, Ithaca Coll., 1968; M.S., SUNY-Binghamton, 1972. C.P.A., N.Y., Colo. 1982. Asst. acct. KPMG Peat Marwick, White Plains, N.Y., 1972; mgr. KPMG Peat Marwick, Phoenix, 1975; sr. mgr. KPMG Peat Marwick, N.Y.C., 1978; ptnr. KPMG Peat Marwick, Denver, 1981-92; ptnr. in-charge corp. recovery svcs. KPMG Peat Marwick, N.Y.C., 1993-94; mng. ptnr. BDO Seidman, Denver, 1994—. Contbr. articles to profl. jours. Past trustee, past pres. Colo. Children's Chorale; treas., past pres., gov., mem. exec. com., committeeman Colo. Golf Assn.; committeeman U.S. Golf Assn. bd. dirs. Pacific Coast GOlf Assn. Served with USMC, 1968-70. Mem. Colo. Soc. C.P.A.s (chmn. real estate and govt. acctg. com.), Am. Inst. C.P.A.s. Clubs: Columbine Country (Littleton, Colo.); Whippoorwill Country (Armonk N.Y.); Bear Creek Golf. Home: 4 Spyglass Dr Littleton CO 80123-6656 Office: BDO Seidman South Tower 600 17th St Ste 2400 Denver CO 80202

SANDLOW, LESLIE J., physician, educator; b. Chgo., Jan. 7, 1934; s. Harry H. and Rose (Ehrlich) S.; m. Joanne J. Fleischer, June 16, 1957; children; Jay, Bruce, Lisa. BS, U. Ill., 1956; MD, Chgo. Med. Sch., 1960. Intern Michael Reese Hosp. and Med. Ctr., Chgo., 1961, med. resident, rsch. fellow gastrointestinal rsch., 1961-64, physician-in-charge clin. gastroenterology lab., 1963-74, asst. attending physician, 1964-67, assoc. attending physician, 1967-72, vice chmn. divsn. gastroenterology, dir. ambulatory medicine, 1968, dir. ambulatory care, 1969-76, attending physician, 1972—, assoc. med. dir., 1972-73; clin. asst. Chgo. Med. Sch., 1963-68, clin. instr., 1966; asst. prof. dept. medicine Pritzker Sch. Medicine, U. Chgo., 1973-76, assoc. prof., 1976-85, prof., 1985-90; prof. clin. medicine and med. edn. Coll. Medicine, U. Ill., Chgo., 1990-91, prof. medicine and med. edn., 1992—; dep. v.p. profl. affairs Michael Reese Hosp. and Med. Ctr., 1973-78, dir. Office Ednl. Affairs, 1976-81, assoc. v.p. acad. affairs, 1978-82, dir. quality assurance program, 1981-91, v.p. planning, 1982-83, v.p. profl. affairs and planning, 1983-88, dir. divsn. internal medicine, 1986-93, v.p. profl. and acad. affairs, 1988-91, med. dirs. acad. and med. affairs, 1992-94; med. dir. Michael Reese Health Plan, Inc., 1972-74, interim exec. dir., 1976-77; cons. gastroenterologist Ill. Ctrl. Hosp., 1978-80; vis. prof. Pontifica U. Catolica Rio Grande do Sul, Brazil, 1978, U. Fed. Espirito Santo, Brazil, 1978, Nordic Fedn. for Med. Understanding, Akureyri, Iceland, 1978, Seoul Nat. U. Sch. Medicine, 1981, Coll. Physicians and Surgsons, Kharachi, Pakistan, 1994, U. Tex., Ft. Worth, 1977, U. Ariz., Tucson, 1977, Loyola U. Med. Sch., Maywood, Ill., 1979; cons. in field; coord. Health Scis. Librs. in Ill.; mem. Midwest Med. Libr. Network; mem. subcom. on delivery of ambulatory med. care Inst. Medicine Chgo.; mem. cmty. resources task force Interinstnl. Cardiovascular Ctr.; chmn. steering group Ill. Regional Med. Program; past co-chmn. curriculum com. U. Chgo. Reviewer Rsch. in Med. Edn./Assn. Am. Med. Colls., 1985—, Acad. Medicine/Assn. Am. Med. Colls., 1989; contbr. numerous articles to profl. publs. Mem. Skokie (Ill.) Bd. Health, 1973-85, chmn., 1976-85; bd. dirs. Group Health Assn. Am., 1976-78, Portes Ctr., 1980—; bd. dirs. Good Health Program Skokie Valley Hosp., 1978-80; bd. dirs., exec. com. Rsch. and Edn. Found. of Michael Reese Hosp. Med. Staff, 1992—. Recipient numerous grants, including NIH, 1988, Michael Reese Hosp. Found., 1994-95, Chgo. Cmty. Trust, 1994-95. Fellow Am. Coll. Gastroenterology; mem. N.Y. Acad. Scis., Inst. Medicine, Assn. Am. Med. Colls., Am. Coll. Physician Execs. (co-chair resource mgmt. com. of quality assurance forum), Soc. Dirs. Med. Coll. Continuing Med. Edn., Soc. Dir. Rsch. in Med. Edn. Home: 2314 Lincoln Park West Chicago IL 60614 Office: U Ill Coll Medicine-Med Edn M/C 784 105 CMW 1819 W Polk St Chicago IL 60613

SANDMAN, DAN D., lawyer. BA, Ohio State U., 1970, JD, 1973. Bar: Ohio 1973, Pa. 1995. Gen. counsel, sec. Marathon Oil Corp., 1986-92, USX Corp., Pitts., 1992—. Office: USX Corp 600 Grant St Pittsburgh PA 15219-4776

SANDMAN, PETER M., communications risk consultant; b. N.Y.C., Apr. 18, 1945; s. Howard Edwin and Gertrude Leah (Orgel) S.; m. Susan Marie Goertzel, June 18, 1967 (div. 1975); m. Jody Sue Lanard, June 10, 1990; children: Alison, Jennifer; 1 stepchild, James Sachs. BA in Psychology, Princeton U., 1967; MA in Comm., Stanford U., 1968, PhD, 1971. Reporter Toronto (Ont.) Star, Can., 1966; stringer Time, 1966-67; instr. comm. Stanford (Calif.) U., 1968-70; instr. journalism Calif. State Coll., Hayward, 1970; sr. editor The Magazine, 1970; asst. prof. Ohio State U., Columbus, 1971-72; asst. prof. natural resources, journalism U. Mich., Ann Arbor, 1972-75, assoc. prof. natural resources, 1975-77; assoc. prof. comm., coord. Cook Coll. comm. program Rutgers U., New Brunswick, N.J., 1977-83, prof. journalism, 1983-94, prof. dept. human ecology, 1992-94; adj. prof., 1994—; adj. prof. TV, radio Ithaca (N.Y.) Coll., 1976, grad. program in pub. health Rutgers U., 1986—; dept. environ. and comty. medicine Robert Wood Johnson Med. Sch., Rutgers U., 1987—; adv. com. environ./occupational health info. program, 1984-89; founder, dir. environ. comm. rsch. program N.J. Agrl. Exptl. Sta., Rutgers U., 1986-92; vis. scholar urban and environ. policy Tufts U., Medford, Mass., 1990-91; rsch. prof. George Perkins Marsh Inst., Clark U.; comm. coun. Environ. Def. Fund, 1985—; bd. advisors grad. program in tech. and sci. comm. Drexel U., Phila., 1988—; cons. on comm. ACP, 1979-78, The Cousteau Soc., 1977-79, Pres. com. on the accident at Three Mile Island; specialist in comm. coop. ext. svc. U.S. Dept. Agr., 1977-86; cons. risk commn. office policy analysis EPA, 1986-88; exec. com. Sci. Writing Educators Group, 1978-81; cons. ARCO Chem., Boise Casade, Chevron, Ciba-Geigy, Consumers Power, Dow, Du Pont, Johnson and Johnson, Wax, Procter and Gamble, Union Carbide, others. Cons. editor Random House, 1982-89, McGraw-Hill, 1989-94, Holt, Rinehart and Winston, 1978-81; contbg. editor Apt. Life, 1971-75; freelance writer, 1966—; editl. bd. Pub. Rels. Rsch. Ann., 1981-91, Jour. Pub. Rels. Rsch., 1991-94; editl. adv. bd. Environ. and Behavior, 1976-86; contbr. articles to profl. jours. Bd. dirs. N.J. Environ. Lobby, 1984-90, Nuclear Dialogue Project, 1985-90, pres. 1986-90; pub. info. com. N.J. chpt., Am. Cancer Soc., 1981-86, vice chair, 1983-86; comm. coord. N.J. Campaign for a Nuclear Weapons Freeze, 1982-85; socioeconomic subcom., com. on biotechnology agr. div., Nat. Assn. State Univs.and Land Grant Colls., 1988-90; bd. advisors, Environ. Scientists for Global Survival, 1988-91; sci. review panel, radium/randon adv. bd., N.J. Dept. EPA, 1987-88; com. to survey the health effects mustard gas and lewisite, Inst. Medicine, NAS, 1992. Mem. AAUP, ACLU (bd. dirs. N.J. chpt. 1984-87), Assn. for Edn. in Journalism and Mass Comm., Environ. Def. Fund, Investigative Reports and Editors, Nat. Assn. Profl. Environ. Communicators, Sci. Writing Educators Group, Soc. for Risk Analysis, Soc. Environ. Journalists, Soc. Profl. Journalists, Sigma Delta Chi. Home: 54 Gray Cliff Rd Newton Center MA 02159-2017

SANDMEYER, ROBERT LEE, university dean, economist; b. Evansville, Ind., June 12, 1929; s. Orville G. Sandmeyer and Elizabeth Chandler; m. Loretta Mae Jacobs, Aug. 5, 1950; children: Karen, Bridgit, Barbara, Robert C. B.A., Ft. Hays State U., 1956; M.S., Okla. State U., 1958, Ph.D., 1962. Instr. Ft. Hays (Kans.) State U., 1957-58; instr. Iowa State U., 1958-59; asst. prof. econs. Ariz. State U., 1961-62; asst. prof. Okla. State U., 1962-65, assoc. prof., 1965-70, prof., dean Coll. Bus. Adminstrn., 1977-94, dean emeritus Coll. Bus. Adminstrn., 1994—; econ. adv. Ariz. Gov.'s Tax Study Com., 1961-62; adv. Okla. Gov.'s Com. on Mental Health, 1963; bd. dirs. Reading & Bates Corp.; adviser to faculty of econs. and adminstrv. scis. United Arab Emirates U., 1994-95. Contbr. articles to profl. publs. With USN, 1947-51. Mem. So. Econ. Assn., Phi Kappa Phi, Beta Gamma Sigma. Democrat. Roman Catholic. Office: Okla State U Coll Bus Adminstrn Stillwater OK 74078

SANDNER, JOHN FRANCIS, commodity futures broker, lawyer; b. Chgo., Nov. 3, 1941; s. James and Margaret (Elmore) S.; m. Carole Ruth Erhardt, Feb. 14, 1970; children: Kathleen Dyan, Christopher John, Angela Marie, Michael John, Nicholas James, Allysann Elizabeth. BA, So. Ill. U., 1965; JD, U. Notre Dame, 1968. Bar: Ill. 1968, U.S. Dist. Ct. 1969, U.S. Supreme Ct. 1975. Pvt. practice Chgo., 1968—; mem. Chgo. Merc. Exch., 1971-91; sr. policy advisor, 1989-91; chmn. bd. govs. Chgo. Merc. Exch., 1980-82, 86-89, 91—; mem. Internat. Monetary Market, 1973—; pres. John F. Sandner & Assocs. (commodity futures brokers), Chgo., 1973—, RB & H Fin. Svcs., L.P., Chgo., 1978—; law adv. coun. mem. U. Notre Dame, 1988—. Bd. dirs. Fund for Integrative Health and Ednl. Rsch., 1981, Jones Inst. for Reproductive Medicine, Ea. Va. Med. Sch., 1984—; Northern Ill. Coun. Alcoholism and Substance Abuse, 1990; mem. Ill. Vol. Parole Officer Program, 1976-78; commr. Prospect Heights (Ill.) Park Dist., 1977-

78; trustee Found. for Brain Life Research, 1983—; trustee U. Notre Dame, 1993—, Rush-Presbyn. St. Lukes Med. Ctr., 1992—; mem. adv. bd. Mercy Hosp., 1988—, Chgo. Cares, 1993—. Named Man of Yr. by Juvenile Diabetes Found., 1993. Mem. ABA, Am. Arbitration Assn., Ill. Bar Assn., Chgo. Bar Assn. (arbitration com. 1976-77, mental health com. 1976-77), Nat. Futures Assn. (bd. dirs. 1982, chmn. cen. region bus. conduct com. 1982—), Notre Dame Law Assn. (bd. dirs. 1984—), Internat. Press Ctr. (founding bd. dirs.), Econ. Club Chgo. Office: Chicago Mercantile Exchange 30 S Wacker Dr Chicago IL 60606-7402

SANDOR, ELLEN RUTH, artist; b. N.Y.C., Apr. 22, 1942; d. Julius and Matilda (Greene) Simon; m. Richard L. Sandor, June 27, 1963; children: Julie, Penya. BA, Bklyn. Coll., 1963; postgrad., U. Calif., Berkeley, 1968-72; MFA, Sch. of Art Inst. of Chgo., 1975. Dir., founder (Art)n Lab. Northwestern U., Evanston, Ill., 1982—; adj. artist Nat. Ctr. for Supercomputing Applications, Urbana-Champaign, Ill., 1987—; grad. advisor Sch. of Art Inst. Chgo., 1989; adj. assoc. prof., grad. advisor U. Ill. at Chgo., 1988—; speaker, lectr., presenter in field. Patentee for computer-generated autostereography method apparatus Barrier-Strip and Lenticular Autostereogram; co-inventor PHSColograms and Stealth Negative PHSColograms—3D imaging press supporting large-scale full color images with depth; exhbns. include Imaging Antarctica, Linz, Austria, 1986, High Technology and Art, Chunichi Shimim Kaka-ku Mus., Tokyo, 1986, Cinderella Rockefeller Feature, N.Y.C., 1989, Beautiful Stranger Feature, N.Y.C., 1989, Dorothy, Ctr. for Contemporary Art, Chgo., 1989, SIGGRAPH '89 Travelling Art Show, Boston, 1989, Strange Attractors: Signs of Chaos, The New Mus. of Contemporary Art, N.Y.C., 1989, Daydreams to Bitstreams, NAS, Washington, 1989, Photography: Inventions and Innovations, Art Inst. Chgo., 1989-90, A New Generation Part I: Chicago Artists, Carnegie-Mellon Art Gallery, Pitts., 1990, SIGGRAPH '90 Travelling Art Show, Dallas, 1990, Art Futura, Barcelona, Spain, 1991, The Third Emerging Expression Biennial: The Third Dimension and Beyond, Bronx Mus., N.Y.C., 1991, Matter Over Mind = Sculpture, Fermilab, Batavia, Ill., 1991, Retretti Art Centre, Punkaharju, Finland, 1991, Exploratorium, San Francisco, 1991, SIGGRAPH '91 Travelling Art Show, Las Vegas, Nev., 1991, From Media to Metaphor 1991—; Art and the Computer, Idmi-Istituto Dalle Molle di Metodologie Interdisciplinari, Lugano, Switzerland, 1991, La Cité des Arts et des Nouvelles Technologies de Montréal, Que., 1991, Science in Depth travelling PHSCologram exhbn., NASA/AMES Rsch. Ctr., Moffett Field, Calif., 1991—, Computer Mus., Boston, 1991, Mus. Sci. & Industry, Chgo., 1990-91, From Media to Metaphor: Art About Aids, Emerson Gallery, Clinton N.Y., 1992, Ctr. Contemporary Art, Seattle, 1992, Sharadin Art Gallery, Kutztown (Pa.) U., 1992, 3Dmt, Montreal, 1992, CyberArts, Pasadena, Calif., 1992, SIGGRAPH '92 Art Show, Chgo., 1992, Computer Art Pushing the Boundries, State Ill. Gallery, 1992, New Work Feature, N.Y.C., 1992, Images Du Futur '92, Montreal, 1992, Spain Today, Spanish Pavilion Expo '92, Seville, Spain, 1992, Entourage: Exhibitions, Rosenwald-Wolf Gallery, U. of Arts, Elkins Park, Pa., 1992, Electronic Expressions.2, Allegheny Coll., Meadville, Pa, 1992, Musee d'Art Contemporian de Montreal, 1992-93, Grey Art Gallery, N.Y.U., 1993, Tomorrow's Realities, SIGGRAPH '93, Anaheim Calif., 1993, The New Image Montage '93, Rochester, N.Y., 1993, Digital Art/Digital Design, Saatchi and Saatchi, N.Y.C., 1993, Sony Gallery Chgo., 1993, (Art)n: Virtual Photography, 1993, Rhona Hoffman Gallery, Chgo, 1993, Editions Rhona Hoffman Gallery, Chgo., 1993, Gahlberg Gallery-The Coll. of DuPage, Ill., 1994, The Martin Luther King Jr. Performing and Cultural Arts Complex, Columbus, Ohio, 1995, Triennale di Milano, Italy, 1995, Art Chgo., 1995, Oskar Friedl Gallery, Chgo., 1995; exhibited in collections AT&T Bell Labs., Murray Hill, N.J., Eastman Kodak Co., Rochester, N.Y., Electronic Visualization Lab., U. Ill. at Chgo., IBM TJ Watson Rsch. Ctr., Yorktown Heights, NASA/AMES Rsch. Ctr., Moffett Field, Nat. Ctr. for Supercomputing Applications, Urbana-Champaign, Rsch. Inst. of Scripps Clinic, La Jolla, Calif., Monsanto Corp., St. Louis, McDonald's Corp., Northbrook, Ill., Fla. State U., Tallahassee, U. Chgo., Northwestern U., Chgo., Lockheed Aero. Systems Co., So. Calif., Anheuser Busch., St. Louis, Ont. Sci. Ctr. Toronto, Idaho Nat. Engring. Lab., Idaho Falls, and numerous others; subject in numerous publs., articles, revs.; co-author tech. papers. Bd. dirs. Soc. for Outsider, Intuitive and Visionary Art, Chgo., 1991, Randolph Street Gallery, Chgo., New Art Examiner, Chgo., 1985—, The Body Politic, Chgo. NOW, Berkeley, Calif., 1970-72; bd. mem. devel. com. Sch. of Art Inst. of Chgo., 1980-85. Grantee IPP Lithocolor, Chgo., 1985-91, Eastman Kodak Co., Rochester, N.Y., 1989-87, ACM Siggraph, N.Y.C., 1990. Mem. IEEE, Arts Club of Chgo. Democrat. Jewish. Avocation: art collection. Home: 1301 N Astor St Chicago IL 60610-2186 Office: (Art)n Lab IIT BIRL Northwestern U 1801 Maple Ave Evanston IL 60201-3135

SANDOR, GEORGE NASON, mechanical engineer, educator; b. Budapest, Hungary, Feb. 24, 1912; came to U.S., 1938, naturalized, 1949; s. Alexander S. and Maria (Adler) S.; m. Magda Breiner, Dec. 5, 1964; stepchildren: Stephen Gergely, Judith Patricia Gergely (Mrs. J. Peter Vernon). Diploma in Mech. Engring, Poly. U. Budapest, 1934; D. Eng. Sci., Columbia U., 1959; D (hon.), Budapest Technol. U., 1986. Registered profl. engr., Fla., N.J., N.Y., N.C., cert. of qualification Nat. Council Engring. Examiners. Asst. to chief engr. Hungarian Rubber Co., Budapest, 1935-36; mfg. dept. head Hungarian Rubber Co., 1936-38; design engr. Babcock Printing Press Corp., New London, Conn., 1939-44; v.p., chief engr. H.W. Faeber Corp., N.Y.C., 1944-46; chief engr. Time Inc. Graphic Arts Research Labs., Springdale, Conn., 1946-61, Huck Co., Inc., N.Y.C., 1961; assoc. prof. mech. engring. Yale, 1961-66; prof. mech. engring. Rennselaer Poly. Inst., Troy, N.Y., 1966-67; Alcoa Found. prof. mech. design, chmn. machines and structures div. Rennselaer Poly. Inst., 1967-75; rsch. prof. mech. engring. U. Fla., Gainesville, 1976-89, rsch. prof. emeritus 1989—; dir. mech. engring. design and rotordynamics labs. U. Fla., 1979-87; instr. engring. U. Conn. Extension, New London and Norwich, 1940-44; lectr. mech. engring. Columbia U., N.Y.C., 1961-62; dir. Huck Design Corp., Huck Co., Inc., Montvale, N.J., 1964-70; cons. engr., printing equipment and automatic machinery, mech. engring. design, 1961—; cons. NSF Departmental and Instl. Devel. Program, 1970-72; cons. nat. materials adv. bd. Nat. Acad. Scis., 1974; cons. Xerox Corp., Burroughs Corp., Govt. Products div. Pratt & Whitney Aircraft Co., Time Inc., also others, 1961-92; prin. investigator, co-investigator NSF, U.S. Army Research Office and NASA sponsored research at Yale U.; dir. and co-dir. NSF, U.S. Army Research Office and NASA sponsored research at Rensselaer Poly. Inst.; and U. Fla. at Gainesville; chief U.S.A. del. to Internat. Fedn. for Theory Machines and Mechanisms, 1969-75; cons. for materials conservation through design Office Tech. Assessment, Congress U.S., 1977. Author: (with others) Mechanical Design and Systems Handbook, 1964, 2d edit., 1985, Linkage Design Handbook, 1977, Mechanism Design-Analysis and Synthesis, vol. 1, 1984, 2d edit., 1991, Advanced Mechanism Design, Analysis and Synthesis, vol. 2, 1984; mem. editorial bd. Jour. Mechanism, 1966-72, Machine and Mechanism Theory, 1972—, Robotica, 1982—; contbr. articles to profl. jours. Recipient Outstanding Achievement awrd Northctrl. sect. Fla. Engring. Soc., 1983; Fla. Blue Key Leadership award for disting. faculty mem. U. Fla., 1985; elected hon. mem. Internat. Fedn. for Theory Machines and Mechanisms, 1987, Hungarian Acad. Scis., Budapest, 1993. Fellow ASME (life, Machine Design award 1975, mechanisms com. award 1980, hon. mem. 1991); mem. NSPE, Am. Soc. Engring. Edn. (Ralph Coats Roe award 1985), N.Y. Acad. Scis., Am. Acad. Mechanics, Hungarian Acad. Scis. (hon. mem. 1993), Flying Engrs. Internat., Sigma Xi, Tau Beta Pi, Pi Tau Sigma. Achievements include patent for rotary-linear actuator for robotic manipulators, and 5 others. Home: 136 Broadview Acres Highlands NC 28741 *Find out what is expected of you and try to fulfill those expectations to the best of your ability.*

SANDOR, GYORGY, pianist; b. Budapest, Hungary; came to U.S., 1938, naturalized, 1943; s. Ignac and Zsenka (Czipszer) S.; 1 child, Michael. Student, Liszt Ferenc Conservatory, Budapest, 1927-33; studied piano with, Bela Bartok; composition with, Zoltan Kodaly. Mem. piano faculty Julliard Sch., 1982—. Made concert debut, Budapest, 1931; toured, Europe, 1931-38, Am. debut Carnegie Hall, N.Y.C., 1939, touring throughout U.S., Mexico, Can., W.I., North Africa, South Africa, C.Am., S.Am., Europe, Australia, Far East; rec. with N.Y. Philharm. and Phila. orchs., also solo rec. (Grand Prix du Disque for rec. entire piano repertory of Bela Bartok's works 1964); rec. entire solo piano repertory of Prokofiev, 1967, Kodály, 1973; author: On Piano Playing, 1981; world premiers include Bartok's 3d Piano Concerto, Ormandy and Phila. Orch., 1946, Dance Suite, Carnegie Hall, 1945, Concerto for Orch., piano version by Bartok, 1990,

Sony Classical, Vox Candide Turnabout, Trio, Philips Records; recs. include entire Bartók piano repertory, 1995.

SANDOR, THOMAS, biochemist; b. Budapest, Hungary, Nov. 3, 1924; emigrated to Can., 1950; s. Miksa and Iren (Forstner) S.; m. Vera Varkonyi, July 5, 1949; 1 dau., Catherine-Susanne. Dipl. Chem., U. Budapest, 1948; Ph.D., U. Toronto, 1960. Attaché de recherche Inst. A. Fournier, Paris, 1949-50; rsch. fellow Hosp. for Sick Children, U. Toronto, Ont., 1951-56; rsch. biochemist Hotel Dieu Hosp., Montreal, Que., Can., 1956-59; sr. rsch. assoc., endocrinology lab. Hosp. Notre Dame, Montreal, 1959-93; rsch. asst. prof. medicine U. Montreal, 1961-67, rsch. assoc. prof., 1967-70, rsch. prof., 1970-92; hon. prof. McGill U., Montreal, 1969-92; career investigator Med. Research Council of Can., 1962-91; rsch. prof. emeritus Louis C. Simard Rsch. Ctr., Hosp. Notre Dame, U. Montreal, 1992—; vis. prof. zoology U. Sheffield, Eng., 1970-71, 79-80; vis. prof. biochemistry U. Buenos Aires, 1974; lectr. numerous univs., symposia, Can., U.S., U.K., France, Italy, Ger., Spain, India, Hong Kong. Corr. editor: Jour. Steroid Biochemistry, 1970-79; Mem. editorial bd.: Gen. and Comparative Endocrinology, 1974-81; Contbr. chpts. on steroid biochemistry to books, articles to profl. jours. Gouverneur à vie Hôpital Notre-Dame, Montreal. Recipient Nuffield Found. Travelling Fellowship, 1964; recipient Schering Travelling Fellowship, 1966, Science Research Council (U.K.) sr. vis. research fellowship, 1970-71, 79-80. Fellow Royal Soc. Can.; mem. Can. Biochem. Soc., Endocrine Soc. (Travelling Fellowship 1968), Biochem. Soc. (Gt. Britain), Soc. for Endocrinology (Gt. Britain), Am. Soc. Zoologists, European Soc. Comparative Endocrinologists (founder mem.), AAAS, Order Chemists of Que., Canadians for Health Research (bd. dirs. 1976-79, 82-86). Office: Hôpital Notre Dame, CP 1560 Succ C, Montreal, PQ Canada H2L 4K8

SANDORFY, CAMILLE, chemistry educator; b. Budapest, Hungary, Dec. 9, 1920; emigrated to Can., 1951, naturalized, 1957; s. Kamill and Paula (Fenyes) S.; m. Rolande Cayla, Aug. 24, 1971. B.Sc., U. Szeged, Hungary, 1943, Ph.D., 1946; D.Sc., Sorbonne, U. Paris, 1949; PhD (hon.), U. Moncton, N.B., Can., 1986, U. Szeged, Hungary, 1988. Attache de recherches Centre Nationale de la Recherche Scientifique, Paris, France, 1947-51; postdoctoral fellow Nat. Research Council of Can., 1951-53; asst. prof. chemistry U. Montreal, Que., Can., 1954-56; assoc. prof. U. Montreal, 1956-59, prof., 1959—; vis. prof. U. Paris, 1968, 74, univs. in Naples, Italy, 1969, Rio de Janeiro, Brazil, 1970, 82, Lille, France, 1987. Author: Les Spectres Electroniques en Chimie Theorique, 1959, Electronic Spectra and Quantum Chemistry, 1964, (with R. Daudel) Semi-empirical Wave-Mechanical Calculations on Polyatomic Molecules, 1971. Recipient Prix Marie-Victorin Que., 1982, medal Chem. Inst. Can., 1983, Sci. prize of Que., 1964, Herzberg medal, 1980, Killam Meml.scholar, 1978, Compagnon de Lavoisier (Que.), 1992, Heyrovsky gold medal Czech Acad. Sci., 1993. Fellow Royal Soc. Can., Internat. Acad. Quantum Molecular Sci., Hungarian Acad. Sci. Rsch. over 250 publs. in chemistry. Address: 5050 Roslyn, Montreal, PQ Canada H3W 2L2

SANDOVAL, ARTURO, jazz musician; b. Havana, Cuba, Nov. 6, 1949; came to U.S., 1990; s. Arturo and Cira (Arocha) S.; m. Carmen Marianela, Oct. 17, 1975; 1 child, Arturo Jr. Prof. Fla. Internat. U.; lectr. in field; featured artist Dizzy Gillespie UN Orch., Live at Royal Festival Hall album (Grammy 1991). Performed with Cuban Orch. Modern Music; guest artist BBC Symphony, London, Leningrad Symphony; founding mem. Irakere mus. group; albums include Flight to Freedom, I Remember, Clifford (2 Grammy nominations), Dream Come True, Danzon (Dance On), Tumbaito. Recipient Grammy award for Irakere, 1980, also 4 Grammy nominees; named Cuba's Best Instrumentalist, 1982, 83, 84, Golden Feather Artist of Yr., L.A. Times, 1991. Roman Catholic. Home: 101 S. Royal Poinciana Miami FL 33166*

SANDOVAL, RIK (CHARLES SANDOVAL), broadcasting executive; b. Chgo., May 20, 1952; s. Placido Jr. and Ophelia (Lugo) S. BA in Communications, Columbia Coll., 1974. With prodn. dept. Sta. WSNS-TV, Chgo., 1971-72; dir., producer Sta. WCAE-TV, St. John, Ind., 1972-73; producer Sta. WBBM-FM, Chgo., 1973-74; prodn. mgr. Sta. WLS-TV, Chgo., 1972-76, on-air mgr., 1976-77; sr. publicist, producer Sta. KABC-TV, Hollywood, Calif., 1977-79; dir. creative svcs. Sullivan & Assocs, L.A., 1979-81; producer ABC, Hollywood, 1981-82; pres. Sandoval Prodns., Studio City, Calif., 1982-87; sr. v.p. The Agy., Studio City, 1987-88; pres. Tri-Mark Group, Inc., Studio City, 1988-92; dir. world wide ops. publicity MGM Studios, Culver City, Calif., 1992; mgr. interactive video prodn. Entergamement, Inc., L.A., 1993-94; dir. ops. GTE Interactive Media, Carlsbad, Calif., 1994—; Judge The Clio Awards; prodr., writer Miss Hawaiian Tropic Beauty Pageant, 1992; head writer Mad Scientist Toon Club, 1993. Producer, writer: (broadcast promotions) A.K.A. Pablo, 1984 (Silver award), Entertainment Tonight, 1984 (Silver award), Hunter, 1985, People, 1985 (Telly award, 1985, Gold Statuette award); head writer Mad Scientist Toon Club, 1993. Mem. NOSOTROS, L.A., 1987. Recipient 8 Clio nominations, 1977, 79-81, 2 Gold medals Internat. Radio Festival N.Y., 1985, 4 Bronze Telly awards, 1983-88, Silver Telly award, 1988, 2 ITVA awards, 1988, 3 Silver Telly awards, 1991, 4 Silver Telly awards, 1992, 2 Bronze Telly awards, 1992. Mem. Broadcast Promotion Mktg. Execs. (Gold medal, Silver medal 1985, 2 Bronze Telly award statuettes 1989, Silver Telly award statuette 1989. ITVA award), Nat. Assn. Broadcasters (cert. merit 1974), The Publicist Guild, Acad. TV Arts and Scis. Roman Catholic. Avocations: Art Deco antiques, fine wine collector, karate, pre-Columbian artifacts, modern art collector. Home: 7522 High Ave La Jolla CA 92037

SANDQUIST, ELROY CHARLES, JR., lawyer; b. Chgo., Dec. 18, 1922; s. Elroy Carl and Lillian (Peterson) S.; m. Sally Patricia Dunham, Mar. 15, 1945; children: Deirdre, Elroy Charles III, Peter, Ellen. BS, U.S. Naval Acad., 1943; JD, Northwestern U., 1950. Bar: Ill. 1950. Assoc. Peterson, Ross, Schloerb & Seidel, Chgo., 1950-57, ptnr., 1960—; asst. state's atty. County of Cook, Ill., 1957-60; mem. Ho. of Reps. State of Ill., Springfield, 1977-83; legis. coord. County of Cook, 1983-91. Pres. Child Svc., Park Ridge, Ill., 1985-88. Lt. USN, 1943-46. Mem. City Club Chgo. (pres. 1966-68). Republican. Methodist. Home: 353 W Belden Ave Chicago IL 60614-3817 Office: Peterson Ross Schloerb 200 E Randolph Dr # 7300 Chicago IL 60601-6401

SANDQUIST, GARY MARLIN, engineering educator, researcher, consultant, author; b. Salt Lake City, Apr. 19, 1936; s. Donald August Sandquist and Lillian (Evaline) Dunn; m. Kristine Powell, Jan. 17, 1992; children from previous marriage: Titia, Julia, Taunia, Cynthia, Carl; stepchildren: David, Michael, Scott, Diane, Jeff. BSME, U. Utah, 1960, PhD in Mech. Engring., 1964, MBA, 1995; MS in Engring. Sci., U. Calif, Berkeley, 1961; postdoctoral fellow MIT, 1969-70. Registered profl. engr., Utah, N.Y., Minn., Calif.; cert. health physicist, cert. quality auditor. Staff mem. Los Alamos (N.Mex.) Sci. Lab., 1966; rsch. prof. surgery Med. Sch., U. Utah, Salt Lake City, 1974—, prof., dir. nuc. engring., mech. engring. dept., 1975—, acting chmn. dept., 1984-85; expert in nuclear sci. Internat. Atomic Energy Agy., UN, 1980—; chief sci. Rogers and Assocs. Engring. Corp., Salt Lake City, 1980—; vis. sci. MIT, Cambridge, Mass., 1960-70; advisor rocket design Hercules, Inc., Bachus, Utah, 1962; sr. nuc. engr. Idaho Nat. Engring. Lab., Idaho Falls, Idaho, 1963-65; cons. various cos.; cons. nuclear sci. State of Utah, 1980—. Author: Geothermal Energy, 1973; Introduction to System Science, 1984. Comdr. USNR, 1954-56, Korea. Recipient Glen Murphy award in nuclear engring. Am. Soc. Engring. Edn., 1984. Fellow ASME, Am. Nuclear Soc.; mem. Am. Soc. Quality Control, Am. Health Physics Soc., Alpha Nu Sigma of Am. Nuclear Soc., Sigma Xi, Tau Beta Pi, Pi Tau Sigma. Republican. Mormon. Home: 2564 Neffs Circle Salt Lake City UT 84109-4055 Office: U Utah 1206 Merrill Engring Bldg Salt Lake City UT 84112

SANDRICH, JAY H., television director; b. L.A., Feb. 24, 1932; s. Mark R. and Freda (Wirtschafter) S.; m. Nina Kramer, Feb. 11, 1952 (div.); children: Eric, Tony, Wendy; m. Linda Green Silverstein, Oct. 4, 1984. BA, UCLA, 1953. Producer (TV show) Get Smart, 1965; dir. (TV shows) He and She, 1967, Mary Tyler Moore Show, 1970-88, Soap, 1977-79, Cosby Show, 1984-92; dir. (films) Seems Like Old Times, 1980, For Richer, For Poorer (HBO), 1992. Served to 1st lt. Signal Corps U.S. Army, 1952-55. Mem. Dirs. Guild Am. (award 1975, 85, 86), TV Acad. Arts and Scis. (Emmy award 1971, 73, 85, 86).

SANDRIDGE, WILLIAM PENDLETON, JR., lawyer; b. Winston-Salem, N.C., Jan. 27, 1934; s. William Pendleton and Kathryn (Mosby) S.; m. Jane Carolyn Yeager, Dec. 10, 1966; children: Jane, William. AB, U. N.C., 1956; LLB, U. Va., 1961. Bar: N.C. 1961. Ptnr. Womble Carlyle Sandridge & Rice, Winston-Salem, 1962—. Chmn., bd. dirs. Horizons Residential Care Ctr., 1980, Food Bank N.W. N.C., Inc., 1988-89. Mem. ABA. Office: Womble Carlyle Sandridge & Rice PO Box 84 1600 One Triad Pk Winston Salem NC 27102

SANDROK, RICHARD WILLIAM, lawyer; b. Evergreen Park, Ill., July 8, 1943; s. Edward George and Gertrude Jeanette (Van Stright) S.; m. Rebecca Fittz, June 9, 1973; children: Richard William Jr., Alexander Edward, Philip Robert, Erika Joy. BA, Wheaton (Ill.) Coll., 1965; JD, U. Ill., 1968. Bar: Ill. 1968, U.S. Dist. Ct. (no. dist.) Ill. 1971. Assoc. Hinshaw Culbertson Moelmann Hoban & Fuller, Chgo. and Wheaton, 1971-75; ptnr. Hinshaw Culbertson Moelmann Hoban & Fuller, Wheaton, 1976-89, Lisle, Ill., 1989—. Reviewer: Legal Checklists. Capt. U.S. Army, 1969-71. Mem. ABA, Ill. Bar Assn., Chgo. Bar Assn., Am. Arbitration Assn. (arbitrator), DuPage County Bar Assn. (chmn. med./legal com. 1978-79), Assn. Def. Trial Attys., Def. Rsch. Inst. Home: 818 Revere Rd Glen Ellyn IL 60137-5537 Office: Hinshaw & Culbertson 4343 Commerce Ct Ste 415 Lisle IL 60532-3655

SANDS, DON WILLIAM, agricultural products company executive retired; b. Durant, Okla., Aug. 30, 1926; s. William Henry and Mary (Crutchfield) S.; m. Joan Cantrell, Mar. 28, 1947; children: Susan Sands Hendrix, Stan W., Steve J. B.S., Southeastern Okla. State U., 1949. Office mgr. Durant Cotton Oil & Peanut Corp., Okla., 1947-53; asst. mgr. Greenwood Products Co., Graceville, Fla., 1953-57; with Cotton Producers Assn. (changed name to Gold Kist Inc., 1970); exec. v.p., mem. exec. com. Gold Kist Inc., Atlanta, 1978-84, pres., chief oper. officer, mem. exec. com., 1984-88, pres., chief exec. officer, chmn. exec. com., 1989-91; chmn. Golden Poultry Co., Inc. subs. Gold Kist Inc., Atlanta, 1987-92; bd. dirs. Nat. Data Corp., Atlanta, Ga. World Congress Ctr., Atlanta, Bus. Coun. Ga., So. Ctr. for Internat. Studies; chmn. bd. Golden Poultry Co., Inc., Atlanta; mem. Atlanta Dist. Export Coun.; audit com. Nat. Data Corp., Atlanta, 1980. Mem. adv. bd. Inst. Internat. Edn., Atlanta, 1980, Japen-U.S. S.E. Assn., 1975; bd. dirs. Ga. Bd. Industry and Trade, 1979, Bus. Coun. Ga., So. Ctr. for Internat. Studies, Atlanta; chmn. bd. trustee, mem. fin. com. Ga. Coun. on Econ. Edn.; active Pleasant Hill Presbyn. Ch., Duluth, Ga.; chmn. Ga. World Congress Ctr. With USN, 1944-46. Named to Nat. Peanut Coun. Hall of Fame, 1992. Mem. Nat. Coun. Farmer Coops., Ga. C. of C. (bd. dirs.), Japan-Am. Soc. Ga. (chmn. bd. dirs.), S.E. U.S./Japan Assn. (bd. adv. bd., chmn.), Atlanta Athletic Club (gen. chmn. 1990 U.S. Womens Open, pres.), St. Ives Country Club (pres. 1990-95). Democrat. Presbyterian (elder). Office: Gold Kist Inc 244 Perimeter Center Pky NE Atlanta GA 30346-2302

SANDS, DONALD EDGAR, chemistry educator; b. Leominster, Mass., Feb. 25, 1929; s. George and Emily (Parker) S.; m. Elizabeth Stoll, July 28, 1956; children: Carolyn Looff, Stephen Robert. BS in Chemistry, Worcester Poly. Inst., 1951; PhD in Phys. Chemistry, Cornell U., 1955. Sr. chemist Lawrence Livermore (Calif.) Lab., 1956-62; asst. prof. chemistry U. Ky., Lexington, 1962-65, assoc. prof., 1965-68, prof., 1968—, dir. gen. chemistry, 1974-75, assoc. dean arts and sci., 1975-81, acting dean, 1978, 80-81, assoc. v.p., 1981-82, assoc. vice chancellor, 1982-84, vice chancellor acad. affairs, 1984-89; sect. head sci. and engring. edn. dept. NSF, 1989-91; mem. staff dept. chemistry U. Ky., Lexington, 1991—, chmn. dept. chem., 1993—. Author: Introduction to Crystallography, 1969, Vectors and Tensors in Crystallography, 1982. Mem. Am. Chem. Soc. (chmn. Lexington 1972), Am. Crystallographic Assn., AAAS, N.Y. Acad. Scis., Sigma Xi (chmn. Lexington 1975), Omicron Delta Kappa. Democrat. Avocations: reading, hiking, music, art. Home: 335 Cassidy Ave Lexington KY 40502-2559 Office: U Ky Dept Chemistry Lexington KY 40506

SANDS, EDITH SYLVIA ABELOFF (MRS. ABRAHAM M. SANDS), finance educator, author; b. Bklyn.; d. Louis and JEnnie (Goldstein) Abeloff; m. Abraham M. Sands, June 5, 1932; children: Stephanie Lou Sands Ferski, John Eliot. B.A., Adelphi Coll., 1932; M.B.A., Baruch Sch. Bus. Adminstrn., CCNY, 1956; Ph.D., NYU, 1961; cert. fin. planner, Adelphi U., 1985. Asst. prof. L.I. U., Bklyn., 1961-65, assoc. prof., 1965-69, prof., 1969-81, prof. fin. emeritus, 1981—, chmn. dept. finance, 1962-72; prof. fin., cons. Touro Coll. N.Y.C., 1981—, chmn. dept. fin.; participant in person-to-person citizen ambassador program, China, 1987. Author: How to Select Executive Personnel, 1963; contbr. articles to profl. jours.; editor jour. industry studies for investment decisions. Corr. sec. Welfare Council Bklyn. Cancer Com., 1956-58; mem. council Friends of Adelphi Coll. Library, 1955-60; pres. Foster Care Aux., 1959-61; bd. dirs. Nat. Council Jewish Women, 1935-38; mem. community com. Bklyn. Mus., 1950-52; mem. women's aux. Prospect Heights Hosp., 1954-56, Bklyn. Eye and Ear Hosp., 1950-53; mem. asso. bd. Jewish Child Care Assn., 1959-61; chmn. bd. dirs. Friends Bklyn. Center Libraries, L.I. U. Recipient Alumni Achievement award Baruch Alumni Assn., CCNY, 1969; L.I. U. Assn. award of appreciation, 1978. Mem. AAUW, AAUP, Nat. Assn. Personal Fin. Advs., Am. Econ. Assn., Met. Econ. Assn., Fedn. Woman Shareholders (exec. com.), Econ. History Assn., Am. Finance Assn., Acad. Mgmt., AIMR, Soc. Advancement Mgmt., Am. Mgmt. Assn., N.Y. Soc. Security Analysts (Vol. of Yr. award 1990-91), Am. Statis. Assn., Fin. Mgmt. Assn., Met. Econ. Assn., Inst. Cert. Fin. Planners, Internat. Assn. for Fin. Planning registered/lic. fin. planner, registered investment adviser), Acad. Fin. Svcs., Beta Gamma Sigma Alumni N.Y. (pres. 1967-70), City Coll. Alumni Assn., NYU Grad Sch. Bus. Adminstrn. Alumni Assn. (dir. 1968-85, treas. 1975-77), Adelphi Coll. Alumnae Assn. (chpt. pres. 1957-59), Nat., N.Y. assns. bus. economists, Money Marketeers NYU (dir. 1973-75), Women's Econ. Roundtable, Nat. Economists Club, Beta Gamma Sigma (nat. exec. com. 1972-76), Phi Sigma Sigma (chpt. archon 1931-32). Clubs: Women's City, City College, NYU Finance (v.p. 1973-75), Money Marketeers, Business Forum, NYU, Princeton in N.Y. (guest mem.). Home: 874 Carroll St Brooklyn NY 11215-1702

SANDS, FRANK MELVILLE, investment manager; b. Kansas City, Mo., Sept. 5, 1938; s. Melville Reynolds Sands and Louise (Eviston) Olmstead; m. Marjorie Kay Root, July 20, 1963; children: Frank M. Jr., Katharine I., Laura E. BA, Dickinson Coll., 1960; MBA, U. Va., 1963. CFA. Security analyst Loomis Sayles & Co., Boston, 1969-72; sr. v.p., dir. David L. Babson & Co., Inc., Boston, 1972-83, Eppler, Guerin & Turner, Inc., Dallas, 1983-86; chief investment officer Folger Nolan Fleming Douglas, Inc., Washington, 1986-92; pres. Sands Capital Mgmt., Arlington, Va., 1992—. Treas., bd. dirs. Arlington Hosp. Found., 1987-93; treas., mem. bd. trustees Arlington Community Found., 1994—; mem. bd. dirs. The Bank of Northern Va., 1995—. 1st lt. U.S. Army, 1960-61. Mem. Washington Soc. Investment Analysts, Inc. Office: Sands Capital Mgmt Inc 1100 N Glebe Rd Arlington VA 22201-4798

SANDS, I. JAY, corporate executive, business, marketing and real estate consultant, lecturer, realtor, analyst; b. N.Y.C. B.A., NYU; J.D., Columbia U. Bar: N.Y., U.S. Supreme Ct. Mng. partner Korvette Bldg. Assocs., N.Y.C.; mng. dir., founder, chmn. bd. dirs., sec. First Republic Corp. Am.; chief exec. officer, sec. First Republic Corp., N.Y.; gen. partner Velvex Mid-City Parking Center, N.Y.C., Manhattan Parking Assocs.; dir., chmn. First Republic Underwriters, Inc.; pres., dir. Waltham Mgmt. Inc., Mass.; partner Cypress Parking Assocs., Cypress Plaza Shopping, Pompano Beach, Fla.; partner Sheraton Hotel Randolph House Co., Syracuse, N.Y.; partner Beau Rivage Hotel Co., Bal Harbour, Fla., Gulf Assocs., Fla., Sahara Motel Assocs., Miami Beach, Fla.; chmn. Waltham (Mass.) Engring. & Research Co.; gen. partner Allstate Ins. Bldg. Co., N.Y.C., Fairfax Bldg. Assocs., Kansas City, Mo., Engring. Bldg. Assocs., Chgo., Manhattan Parking Co., Williamsbridge Assocs., N.Y.C., First Republic Funding Life Ins. Agy., N.Y.C.; gen. partner Chateau Motel Atlantic Co., Miami Beach; gen. partner Syracuse-Randolph House Hotel, N.Y.C., Marchwood Realty Co., Phila., Video Film Center Assocs., N.Y.C., Hempstead Real Estate Enterprises, N.Y.C., Imperial Sq. Assocs., N.Y.C., DeMille Theatre Co., N.Y.C., Ohio Indsl. Assocs., Cleve., Pelham Park Assocs., Phila., Peoria (Ill.) Parking Assocs.; chmn., dir. Triple P Parking Corp., Peoria, Ill., Square Mgmt. Corp., N.Y.C., Park Circle Apts., Inc., N.Y.C., Holme Circle Apts., Inc., Phila.; pres., dir., sec. F.S. Mgmt. Corp., N.Y.C.; founder, chmn. exec. com., sec., dir. Imperial Sq. Mgmt. Corp., Hempstead, N.Y.; chmn. bd., chmn.

exec. com., sec., dir. Nat. Med. Industries, Inc., Health Insts. Leasing Corp., Am. Med. Computer Corp.; pres. Med. Contract Supply Corp., City Capital Corp., N.J., Claredon Co., N.Y.C.; vis. lectr., instr. entrepreneurship, real estate, commi. mktg. NYU, New Sch. for Social Research, U. Fla.; gen. agt. Northeastern Life Ins. Co., Patriot Life Ins. Co., Citizens Life Ins. Co.; expert witness in corp. and securities litigations. Past trustee Baldwin Sch., N.Y.C.; hon. trustee Pres. Harry S. Truman Libr. Served with AUS. Harlan Fiske Stone fellow Columbia U., 1975; named Man of Yr., Real Estate Weekly. Mem. Nat. Real Estate Club, N.Y. Real Estate Bd., Columbia U. Law Sch. Alumni Assn. (class chmn. 1978). Clubs: Shriners, Masons (32 deg.).

SANDS, MARVIN, wine company executive; b. Cleve., Jan. 28, 1924; s. Mack E. and Sally (Kipnis) S.; m. Marilyn Alpert, May 30, 1947; children: Laurie, Richard, Robert. BSBA, U. N.C., 1946. Chmn., dir. Canandaigua Wine Co., Inc., N.Y., 1945—; pres., dir. Tenner Bros., Inc., Patrick N.C., 1965—, Roberts Trading Corp., Canandaigua, 1959—; v.p., dir. Bisceglia Bros. Wine Co., Madera, Calif., 1975—. Pres. F.F. Thompson Health System, Inc., 1990—; past pres., dir. F.F. Thompson Hosp., Canandaigua, 1970—, Finger Lakes Area Hosp. Corp., Geneva, N.Y., 1980—; trustee YMCA, Canandaigua. Served with USN, 1943-46. Mem. Nat. Wine Assn. (treas., dir.), N.Y. State Finger Lakes Wine Growers Assn. (past pres., bd. dirs. 1979—), Assn. Am. Vintners (bd. dirs.). Office: Canandaigua Wine Co Inc 116 Buffalo St Canandaigua NY 14424-1086

SANDS, MATTHEW LINZEE, physicist, educator; b. Oxford, Mass., Oct. 20, 1919; m. Freya Kidner, 1978; children: Michael, Richard, Michele. B.A., Clark U., 1940; M.A., Rice Inst., 1941; PhD, MIT, 1948. Physicist U.S. Naval Ordnance Lab., 1941-43, Los Alamos Sci. Lab., 1943-46; research asso., then asst. prof. physics Mass. Inst. Tech., 1946-50; sr. research fellow, asso. prof., prof. physics Calif. Inst. Tech., 1950-63; prof., dep. dir. Linear Accelerator Center, Stanford, 1963-69; prof. physics U. Calif-Santa Cruz, 1969-85, prof. emeritus, 1985—, fellow Kresge Coll.; vice chancellor for sci., 1969-72; pres. Sands-Kidner Assocs., Inc., 1986-90; vis. prof. U. Paris-Sud, spring 1976; Mem. Commn. Coll. Physics, 1960-66, chmn., 1964-66; cons. Office Sci. and Tech., ACDA, Inst. Def. Analyses, 1962-67; mem. Pugwash Conf. Sci. and World Affairs, 1960-63; cons. on accelerator physics, 1975—. Author: (with W.C. Elmore) Electronics-Experimental Techniques, 1948, (with R.P. Feynman and R.B. Leighton) The Feynman Lectures on Physics, 3 vols, 1965, (with others) Physical Science Today, 1973; also articles.; Mem. editorial bd.: Il Nuovo Cimento, 1972-85. Fulbright scholar Italy, 1952-53. Fellow Am. Phys. Soc.; mem. Am. Assn. Physics Tchrs. (Disting. Service award 1972), Fedn. Am. Scientists, AAAS. Spl. research electronic instrumentation for nuclear physics, cosmic rays, accelerators, high-energy physics, sci. edn., sci. and public affairs, electron storage rings. Office: 160 Michael Ln Santa Cruz CA 95060-1704

SANDS, RICHARD E., food products executive; b. Canandaigua, N.Y., Mar. 3, 1951; s. Marvin Sands and Marilyn Alpert; m. Sharon Gillick, Apr. 1991. BA in Psychology, U. Vt.; postgrad., U. Calif.; M, PhD, U. N.C. Teaching rsch. asst. psychology dept. U. N.C., Chapel Hill, 1974-79; exec. trainee Canandaigua Wine Co. Inc., 1979-82, exec. v.p., 1982-86, pres., chief oper. officer, 1986—; now CEO Canadaigua Wine Co. Inc., 1993—. Office: Canandaigua Wine Co Inc 116 Buffalo St Canandaigua NY 14424-1086

SANDSON, JOHN I., physician, educator, retired university dean; b. Jeannette, Pa., Sept. 20, 1927; s. Abraham and Dora (Whitman) S.; m. Hannah E. Ney, June 17, 1957; children: Jennifer, Thomas. Student, St. Vincent Coll.; MD, Washington U., St. Louis, 1953. Diplomate Am. Bd. Internal Medicine. Resident in internal medicine Columbia-Presbyn. Med. Ctr., N.Y.C., 1953-56; chief resident Bronx (N.Y.) Mcpl. Hosp. Ctr., 1956-57; from instr. to prof. medicine Albert Einstein Coll. Medicine, Bronx, 1957-74, from asst. to assoc. dean, 1969-74; med. dir. Hosp. Albert Einstein Coll. Medicine, Bronx, 1969-74; prof. medicine Boston U., 1974—, dean Sch. Medicine, 1974-88, dean emeritus, 1988—; mem. Mass. Health Coordinating Com., Boston, 1984-87. Mem. pub. com. New Eng. Jour. Medicine, 1977-89, advisor, 1990—. Trustee Univ. Hosp., Boston, 1974-88, Louis E. Wolfson Found., Boston, 1984—, Whitaker Health Sci. Fund, Cambridge, Mass., 1977-91; pres. Mass. chpt. Arthritis Found., 1990-91, chmn., 1991-93. Served with U.S. Army, 1946-47. Recipient Doris Carr award Health Planning Council, 1981, Maimonides award Anti-Defamation League, 1986, Mayor's award for Disting. Svc. to Boston City Hosp., 1991. Fellow Am. Rheumatism Assn. (founding); mem. AMA, AAAS (study group project on liberal edn. in sci. 1987-90), Am. Soc. for Clin. Investigation, Assn. Am. Physicians, Mass. Med. Soc., Mass. Soc. Med. Rsch. (pres. Waltham 1987-91, chmn.-elect 1991, chmn. 1993—), Alzheimer's Disease and Related Diseases Assn. (bd. dirs. 1989-91), Alpha Omega Alpha, Saint Botolph Club (Boston). Avocation: gardening. Office: Boston U Sch of Medicine Office of the Dean Emeritus 80 E Concord St Boston MA 02118-2394

SANDSTEAD, HAROLD HILTON, medical educator; b. Omaha, May 25, 1932; s. Harold Russel and Lula Florence (Hilton) S.; m. Kathryn Gordon Brownlee, June 6, 1959 (dec. May 13, 1989); m. Victoria Regan Liddle, Feb. 14, 1990 (div. Oct. 1993); children: Eleanor McDonald, James Brownlee, William Harold. BA, Ohio Wesleyan U., 1954; MD, Vanderbilt U., 1958. Diplomate Am. Bd. Internal Medicine, Am. Bd. Nutrition. Intern, asst. resident in internal medicine Barnes Hosp. Washington U., St. Louis, 1958-60; asst. resident in pathology Vanderbilt Hosp., Nashville, 1960-61; asst. surgeon USPHS U.S. NAMRU 3, Cairo, Egypt, 1961-63; asst. resident in internal medicine Thayer VA Hosp. Vanderbilt, Nashville, 1963-64; chief resident in internal medicine Vanderbilt Hosp., Nashville, 1964-65; instr. internal medicine, asst. prof. biochemistry Med. Sch. Vanderbilt U., Nashville, 1965-70, asst. prof. internal medicine, assoc. prof. nutrition, 1970-71; dir. USDA-ARS Human Nutrition Rsch. Ctr., Grand Forks, N.D., 1971-84; adj. prof. biochemistry and internal medicine Sch. Medicine U. N.D., Grand Forks, 1971-84; dir. USDA-ARS Human Nutrition Rsch. Ctr. on Aging, Boston, 1984-85; prof. nutrition Tufts U., Medford, Mass., 1984-85; prof. preventive medicine and community health U. Tex. Med. Br., Galveston, 1985—; chmn. preventive medicine and community health Med. Br. U. Tex., Galveston, 1985-90, prof. internal medicine, human biol. chemistry & genetics, 1986—; cons. NAS, NRC, NIH, WHO, USDA; Joseph Goldberger vis. prof. AMA, 1976, Ellen Swallow Richards Meml. lectr., 1984; W.O. Atwater lectr. USDA, 1984; Sam E. and Mary F. Roberts lectr., 1985, Raymond Ewell Meml. lectr.; 1985; Welcome prof. in basic sci. Fedn. Am. Socs. Exptl. Biology, 1988. Contbr. articles to profl. jours. Recipient Future Leader award Nutrition Found., 1968-70, Hull Gold medal AMA, 1970. Fellow ACP; mem. Am. Inst. Nutrition (Mead Johson award 1972), Cen. Soc. Clin. Rsch., Am. Soc. Clin. Nutrition (various office including pres.), So. Soc. Clin. Investigation, Alpha Omega Alpha. Avocations: gardening, fishing, reading. Office: U Tex Med Br Ewing Bldg K09 Galveston TX 77555-1109

SANDSTROM, DALE VERNON, state supreme court judge; b. Grand Forks, N.D., Mar. 9, 1950; s. Ellis Vernon and Hilde Geneva (Williams) S.; m. Gail Hagerty, Mar. 27, 1993; 1 child, Carrie; 1 stepchild, Jack. BA, N.D. State U., 1972; JD, U. N.D., 1975. Bar: N.D. 1975, U.S. Dist. Ct. N.D. 1975, U.S. Ct. Appeals (8th cir.) 1976. Asst. atty. gen., chief consumer fraud and antitrust div. State of N.D., Bismarck, 1975-81, securities commr., 1981-83, pub. svc. commr., 1983-92, pres. commn., 1987-91, justice Supreme Ct., 1992—; chair N.D. Commn. on Cameras in the Courtroom, 1993—; mem. exec. com. N.D. Jud. Conf., 1995—; mem. Gov.'s com. on Security and Privacy, Bismarck, 1975-76, Gov.'s com. on Refugees, Bismarck, 1976; chmn. Gov.'s com. on Comml. Air Transp., Bismarck, 1983-84. Mem. platform com. N.D. Reps., 1972, 76, exec. com., 1972-73, 85-88, dist. chmn., 1981-82; former chmn. bd. deacons Luth. Ch.; mem. ch. coun., chair legal and constl. rev. com. Evang. Luth Ch. Am., 1993—. Mem. ABA, N.D. Bar Assn., Big Muddy Bar Assn., Nat. Assn. Regulatory Utility Commrs. (electricity com.), N.A. Assn. Securities Adminstrs., Order of De Molay (grand master 1994-95, mem. Internat. Supreme coun., Legion of Honor award), Nat. Eagle Scouts Assn., Shriners, Elks, Eagles, Masons (chmn. grand youth com. 1979-87, Youth Leadership award 1986). Lodges: Shriners, Elks, Eagles, Masons (chmn. grand youth com. 1979-87, Youth Leadership award 1986). Office: State ND Supreme Court Bismarck ND 58505

SANDT, JOHN JOSEPH, psychiatrist, educator; b. N.Y.C., June 29, 1925; s. John Jacob and Victoria Theodora Sandt; m. Mary Cummings Evans,

Sept. 14, 1946; children: Christine, Karen, John K., Kurt, Colin, Carol; m. Mary W. Griswold, July 10, 1992. BA, Vanderbilt U., 1948; MA, Yale U., 1951; MD, Vanderbilt U., 1957. Instr. English Vanderbilt U., Nashville, 1951-52, Syracuse (N.Y.) U. Coll., 1960-61; intern SUNY Upstate Med. Ctr., Syracuse, 1957-58, resident, 1958-61; instr. psychiatry Southwestern Med. Sch., Dallas, 1961-63; chief psychiatry VA Med. Ctr., Dallas, 1961-63; chief outpatient clinic Dept. Mental Health, Springfield, Mass., 1963-66; asst. prof. psychiatry U. Rochester (N.Y.) Med. Sch., 1966-75, clin. assoc. prof. psychiatry, 1975—; chief psychiatry Clifton Springs (N.Y.), 1985-88, VA Med. Ctr., Bath, N.Y., 1988—; cons. psychiatry VA Med. Ctr., Northampton, Mass., 1965-66, Springfield Coll., 1966-84; Brockport (N.Y.) State Coll., 1966-75, Fairport (N.Y.) Bapt. Home, 1966-88; asst. dir. ind. study program U. Rochester Med. Sch., 1971-75. Author: Clinical Supervision of Psychiatric Resident, 1972; contbr. articles on psychiat. consultation and treatment to profl. jours. Vestryman All Saints Episcopal Ch., South Hadley, Mass., 1963-66. With USNR 1944-46, PTO. Nathaniel Currier fellow Yale Grad. Sch., 1948-49. Mem. Am. Psychiat. Assn., Am. Assn. Geriatric Psychiatry, AAAS, Med. Soc. N.Y. State. Office: VA Med Ctr Bath NY 14810

SANDUJA, MOHAN L., chemist, researcher, executive; b. New Delhi, Aug. 17, 1935; naturalized; parents Lorienda Ram and Viran (Bai) S. BS in Chemistry, U. Delhi, India, 1956, MS in Chemistry, 1958; PhD in Chemistry, Queens U., Kingston, Ont., Can., 1972. Postdoctoral fellow Queens U. 1972-74; postdoctoral fellow Study of Kinetics of Reactions Queens Coll. CUNY, N.Y.C., 1977-79; rsch. fellow Hosp. for Special Surgery Cornell U. Med. Coll., N.Y.C., 1974-77; v.p. R & D Polymer Rsch. Corp. of Am., Bklyn., 1979—. Contbr. articles to Can. Jour. Chemistry, others. Achievements include patents (with others) for Titanium Dioxide Dispersions and Processes for their Production, for Decorating Bowling Balls; patents pending (with others) for development of hygroscopic coating for alumnium substrate, for bacteriastatic activated carbon and purification of water therewith, for coating composition for nylon and polyester fabrics used in the manufacture of automobile air bags for flame retardancy, anti-fraying and controlled gas permeability. Home: 14490 41st Ave Apt 508 Flushing NY 11355-1522 Office: Polymer Rsch Corp Am 2186 Mill Ave Brooklyn NY 11234-6308

SANDVICK, FREDERICK, gaming company executive, lawyer, accountant; b. Bay Village, Ohio, Mar. 6, 1956. BS, San Diego State U., 1979; JD, U. San Diego, 1987, diploma in taxation law, 1988. Bar: Calif., U.S. Dist. Ct. (so. dist.) Calif.; CPA. Staff acct., ptnr. J.H. Cohn & Co., San Diego, 1979-90; exec. v.p., CFO Jackpot Enterprises, Inc., Las Vegas, Nev., 1990—; cons., Las Vegas, 1990—. Recipient scholarship U. San Diego, 1986. Mem. AICPA, ABA, Calif. Soc. CPAs. Office: Jackpot Enterprises Inc 1110 Palms Airport Dr Las Vegas NV 89119

SANDWEISS, JACK, physicist, educator; b. Chgo., Aug. 19, 1930; s. Charles Ray and Florence (Hymovitz) S.; m. Letha Ann Boeck, Jan. 16, 1956; children: Daniel Howard, Anne Florence, Benjamin Lewis. Student, UCLA, 1948-50; B.S., U. Calif., Berkeley, 1952, Ph.D., 1957. Research assoc. Radiation Lab., U. Calif., Berkeley, 1957; instr. Yale U., New Haven, 1957-59; asst. prof. Yale U., 1959-62, assoc. prof., 1962-64, prof. physics, 1964—, Donner prof. physics, 1980—, former chmn. dept. physics; cons. Brookhaven Nat. Lab., Fermi Nat. Accelerator Lab.; chmn. high energy physics adv. panel Dept. Energy-NSF, 1982-86. Editor Phys. Rev. Letters, 1988—; contbr. articles to profl. jours. Fellow Am. Phys. Soc. (chmn. div. particles and fields 1980); mem. NAS, AAAS. Home: 248 Ogden St New Haven CT 06511-1221 Office: Yale Univ Sloane Physics Lab New Haven CT 06520*

SANDWEISS, MARTHA A., museum director, author, American studies educator; b. St. Louis, Mar. 29, 1954; d. Jerome Wesley and Marilyn Joy (Glik) S. BA magna cum laude, Radcliffe Coll., 1975; MA in History, Yale U., 1977, MPhil in History, 1981, PhD, 1985. Smithsonian-Nat. Endowment Humanities fellow, Nat. Portrait Gallery, Washington, 1975-76; curator photographs Amon Carter Mus., Ft. Worth, 1979-86, adj. curator photographs, 1987-89; dir. Mead Art Mus. Amherst Coll., 1989—, adj. assoc. prof. of fine arts and Am. studies, 1989-94, assoc. prof. Am. studies, 1994—. Author: Carlotta Corpron: Designer with Light, 1980, Masterworks of American Photography, 1982, Laura Gilpin: An Enduring Grace, 1986, (catalogue) Pictures from an Expedition: Early Views of the American West, 1979; co-author: Eyewitness to War: Prints and Daguerreotypes of th Mexican War, 1989; editor: Historic Texas: A Photographic Portrait, 1986, Contemporary Texas: A Photographic Portrait, 1986, Denizens of the Desert, 1988, Photography in Nineteenth Century America, 1991; co-editor: Oxford History of the American West, 1994. Fellow Ctr. for Am. Art and Material Culture, Yale U., 1977-79, NEH, 1988. Office: Amherst Coll Mead Art Mus Amherst MA 01002

SANDY, STEPHEN, writer, educator; b. Mpls., Aug. 2, 1934; s. Alan Francis and Evelyn Brown (Martin) S.; AB, Yale U., 1955; AM, Harvard U., 1958, PhD, 1963; m. Virginia Scoville, 1969; children: Nathaniel Merrill, Clare Scoville. Instr., Harvard U., 1963-67; vis. prof. U. Toyko, 1967-68; asst. prof. Brown U., Providence, 1968-69; mem. faculty Bennington (Vt.) Coll., 1969—; McGee prof. of writing Davidson (N.C.) Coll., 1994; lectr. U. R.I., 1969; prof. Harvard U. Summer Sch., 1986, 87, 88; poetry workshop dir. Chautauqua Instn., 1975, 77, Johnson (Vt.) State Coll., 1976, 77, Bennington Coll., summers 1978-80, 1989, Bennington Writing Seminars Program, 1994—, Wesleyan Writers Conf., 1981; councillor for English, Harvard Med. Soc. Coun., 1969-74. With U.S. Army, 1955-57. Dexter fellow, 1961; Yaddo fellow, 1963-68, 76, 93; Huber Found. grantee, 1973; Vt. Coun. Arts grantee, 1974; recipient Fulbright postdoctoral award, 1967-68; invited poetry fellow Breadloaf Writers Conf., 1968; nominee for Pulitzer prize, 1971. Fellow Ingram Merrill Found., 1985, MacDowell Colony fellow, 1986, 93, Blue Mt. Ctr. fellow, 1985, 88, creative writing fellow Nat. Endowment for the Arts, 1988, Vt. Coun. on Arts fellow, 1988—; mem. Signet Soc., Elizabethan Club. Author: Stresses in the Peaceable Kingdom, 1967, Roofs, 1971, End of the Picaro, 1977, The Hawthorne Effect, 1980, The Raveling of the Novel: Studies in Romantic Fiction from Walpole to Scott, 1980, Riding to Greylock, 1983, To a Mantis, 1987, Man in the Open Air, 1988, The Epoch, 1990, Thanksgiving Over the Water, 1992; translator Seneca's Oetaeus, 1994. Home: W St Box 524 North Bennington VT 05257 Office: Bennington Coll Bennington VT 05201

SANDY, WILLIAM HASKELL, training and communications systems executive; b. N.Y.C., Apr. 28, 1929; s. Fred and Rose S.; AB, U. Md., 1950, JD, 1953; postgrad. Advanced Mgmt. Program, Harvard Bus. Sch., 1970-71; m. Marjorie Mazor, June 15, 1952; children: Alan, Lewis, Barbara. Admitted to Md. bar, 1953; planner-writer, account exec., account supr. Jam Handy Orgn., Detroit, 1953-64, v.p., 1964-69, sr. v.p., 1969-71; pres. Sandy Corp., Troy, Mich., 1971-88; chmn., 1988—. Author: Forging the Productivity Partnership, 1990. Bd. govs. Northwood Inst., 1976-80; bd. dirs. Cranbrook Sci. Inst., Met. Ctr. High Tech., 1993; pres. Graphic Arts Coun., 1992-93; trustee Detroit Inst. Arts, 1992-93; v.p. nat. exec. coun. Harvard Bus. Sch., 1985-89; mem. Bloomfield Hills Zoning Bd., Walsh Coll. President's Adv. Coun.; city commr. City of Bloomfield Hills, Troy Downtown Devel. Authority. Mem. Am. Mktg. Assn. (pres. Detroit chpt. 1975), Am. Soc. Tng. and Devel., Southeastern Mich. Better Bus. Bur. (bd. dirs.), Adcraft Club, Nat. Assn. Ednl. Broadcasters. Clubs: Harvard Bus. Sch. (pres. Detroit club 1983-85), The Hundred. Home: 596 Rudgate Rd Bloomfield Hills MI 48304-3355 Office: Sandy Corp 1500 W Big Beaver Rd Troy MI 48084-3541

SANELLO, FRANK ANTHONY, journalist, columnist; b. Joliet, Ill., May 17, 1952; s. Frank Anthony and Evelyn Justine (Stiglic) S. BA with honors, U. Chgo., 1974; MA, UCLA, 1976. Mng. editor Eastside Sun, L.A., 1977; tech. writer Litton Data Systems, Van Nuys, Calif., 1977-79; columnist Cashbox mag., Hollywood, Calif., 1979, United Features Syndicate, L.A., 1986—; film crtic Daily News, Van Nuys, 1982-84; reporter UPI, L.A., 1984, People mag., L.A., 1984—. Mng. editor Real Estate Illustrated, Van Nuys, 1980. Democrat. Avocations: gourmet cooking, weight training. Home: 1155 N La Cienega Blvd #107 West Hollywood CA 90069-2457

SANETO, RUSSELL PATRICK, pediatrician, neurobiologist; b. Burbank, Calif., Oct. 10, 1950; s. Arthur and Mitzi (Seddon) S.; m. Kathleen D. Saneto. BS with honors, San Diego State U., 1972, MS, 1975; PhD, U. Tex.

Med. Br., 1981; DO U. Osteo. Medicine and Surgery, 1994. Teaching asst. San Diego State U. 1969-75; substitute tchr. Salt Lake City Sch. Dist., 1975; teaching and research asst. U. Tex. Med. Br., 1976-77, NIH predoctoral fellow, 1977-81, postdoctoral fellow, 1981; Jeanne B. Kempner postdoctoral fellow UCLA, 1981-82, NIH postdoctoral fellow, 1982-87; asst. prof. Oreg. Regional Primate Rsch. Ctr. div. Neurosci., Beaverton, 1987-89; asst. prof. dept. cell biology and anatomy Oreg. Health Scis. U., Portland, 1988-90, U. Osteo. Medicine & Surgery, 1991-94, Cleve. Clinic, 1994—; lectr. rsch. methods Grad. Sch., 1982; vis. scholar in ethics So. Baptist Theol. Sem., Louisville, 1981. Contbr. articles to profl. jours. Recipient Merit award Nat. March of Dimes, 1978; named one of Outstanding Young Men in Am., 1979, 81, one of Men of Significance, 1985. Mem. AAAS, Bread for World, Save the Whales, Sierra Club, Am. Soc. Human Genetics, Winter Confs. Brain Research, Neuroscis. Study Program, N.Y. Acad. Scis., Am. Soc. Neurochem., Soc. Neurosci., Am. Soc. Neurochemistry, Soc. Neurosci., World Runners Club, Sigma Sigma Phi. Democrat. Mem. Evangelical Free Ch.

SANFELICI, ARTHUR H(UGO), editor, writer; b. Haledon, N.J., May 23, 1934; s. Hugo and Anna (Schilder) S.; m. Betty Louise Van Riper, Aug. 10, 1957; children: Brian Arthur, Amy Elizabeth, Gary Hugh, Bruce Richard. Attended, Lehigh U., 1952-55. Assoc. editor Flying Mag., N.Y.C., 1961-64; mng. editor Am. Aviation Mag., Washington, 1964-68; dist. sales mgr. Gates Learjet Co., N.Y.C., 1969-71; exec. editor Airport World Mag., Westport, Conn., 1971-74; spl. project editor Aircraft Owners & Pilots Assn., Washington, 1974-75, mng. editor Pilot mag., 1975-79, editor AOPA Newsletter, AOPAirport Report, Gen. Aviation Nat. Report, 1979-88; pub. cons., 1989-90; sr. editor Flight Safety Found., Washington, 1989-92; editor S-Cubed divsn. Maxwell Labs., Alexandria, Va., 1992—. Editor, compiler: Yesterday's Wings; Editor Aviation History Mag., Leesburg, Va., 1990—. Served with USAF, 1955-60. Mem. Nat. Aeronautic Assn., Washington Ind. Writers, Aero Club of Washington, Shenandoah Astron. Soc. Home: 5 Oak Shade Rd Sterling VA 20164 Office: Maxwell Labs S-Cubed Divsn 4700 King St Ste 400 Alexandria VA 22302-1272

SANFELIPPO, PETER MICHAEL, cardiac, thoracic and vascular surgeon; b. Milw., Nov. 1, 1938; s. Michael L. and Genevieve M. (Gagliano) S.; m. Cecelia Monica Reuss, May 25, 1968. MD, Marquette U., Milw., 1965; MS in Surgery, U. Minn., 1976. Diplomate Am. Bd. Surgery, Am. Bd. Thoracic Surgery, Am. Bd. Gen. Vascular Surgery. Intern Sacred Heart Hosp., Spokane, Wash., 1965-66; gen. surgery fellow Mayo Grad. Sch. Medicine, Rochester, Minn., 1966, 69-73; residency in thoracic surgery USAF Med. Ctr., Lackland AFB, Tex., 1973-75; thoracic surgeon USAF Med. Corps, various locations, 1966-78; pvt. practice cardiac, thoracic and vascular surgery Ohio Heart & Thoracic Surgery Ctr., Columbus, 1978-91; prof. cardiothoacic and vascular surgery U. Tex. Health Ctr., Tyler, Tex., 1991—. Contbr. articles to profl. jours. Lt. col. USAF, 1966-78. Decorated Air Force Commendation medal. Fellow ACS, Am. Coll. Cardiology, Am. Coll. Angiology, Am. Coll. Chest Physicians; mem. AMA. Avocations: scouting, camping, photography, gardening.

SANFILIPPO, ALFRED PAUL, pathologist, educator; b. Racine, Wis., Aug. 30, 1949; s. Paul Joseph and Therese (Rhode) S.; m. Janet Lee Thompson, 1973; children: Lisa, Joseph. Student, Max Planck Inst. Exptl. Med., Gottingen, Germany, 1966-68, U. Pa., 1969-70; BA and MS in Physics, U. Pa., 1970; postgrad., Duke U., 1972-75, PhD in Immunology, 1975, MD, 1976. Diplomate Am. Bd. Pathology; lic. physician N.C., Md. Postdoctoral rschr. divsn. tumor virology dept. surgery, 1976-79; intern in anatomic pathology Duke U. Hosp., 1976-77, resident in anatomic and clin. pathology, 1977-79; asst. prof. pathology and exptl. surgery, lectr. immunology Duke U., Durham, 1979-84, from assoc. prof. to prof. pathology, 1984-93, from assoc. prof. to prof. exptl. surgery, 1985-93, prof. immunology, 1990-93; attending pathologist Duke U. and Durham VA Hosps., 1979-93; staff mem. Duke Surg. Pvt. Diagnostic Clinic, 1979-93; dir. Transplantation Lab. Durham VA Hosp., 1979-93; dir. immunopathology Duke U. Med. Ctr., 1982-93, exec. com. dept. pathology, 1989-91; pathologist-in-chief Johns Hopkins Hosp., Balt., 1993—; Baxley prof., dir. dept. pathology Johns Hopkins U., Balt., 1993—; adj. prof. pathology and immunology Duke U., 1993—, clin. rsch. unit sci. adv. com., 1988-91, at-large rep. basic sci. faculty steering com., 1989-91, dir. interdisciplinary program in transplantation, 1991-93; mem. Duke Comprehensive Cancer Ctr., 1979-93; chmn. comprehensive transplant ctr. planning com. Johns Hopkins Med. Instns., 1993—, mem. physician coun. for Atlantic Alliance, 1994—; med. bd. Johns Hopkins Hosp., 1993—, strategic planning work group, 1993—, quality assessment and improvement coun., 1994—, re-engring. steering com., 1994—; Osler prof., dir. medicine search com. Johns Hopkins U. Sch. Medicine, 1994—, DeVelbiss fund com., 1994—, Clayton fund com., 1993—, Shelley vis. prof. com., 1993—, faculty compensation com., 1993—, bd. dirs. clin. practice assn., 1993—; mem. orgn. student reps. Assn. Am. Med. Colls., 1973-75; sec. Carolina Organ Procurement Agy., 1987-89, exec. com., 1987-93, v.p., 1989-91, pres., 1991-93; com. med. student affairs N.C. Med. Soc., 1972-76, del. Durham County, 1974; cons. Battelle Human Affairs Rsch. Ctrs., Seattle, 1985-93, NSF of Switzerland, 1992-93, also numerous U.S. govt. adv. coms.; speaker and presenter in field. Guest editor: Human Immunology, Vol. 14, 1987; mem. editl. bd. Transplantation, 1985—, Pathobiology, 1989—, Transplantation Now (Japan) 1989—, Pathology, Rsch. and Practice, 1990—, Human Immunology, 1992—, Lab. Investigation, 1993—, Xeno, 1994—; reviewer Am. Jour. Kidney Diseases, Am. Jour. Ophthalmology, Am. Jour. Pathology, Hepatology, Jour. of AMA, Jour. Am. Soc. Nephrology, Jour. Clin. Investigation, Jour. Leukocyte Biology, Kidney Internat., others; contbr. numerous articles to profl. jours. Recipient Kermit G. Osserman award Myasthenia Gravis Found., 1976, Wiley D. Forbus award N.C. Soc. Pathologists, 1979, Reach for Sight Physician Investigator award, 1990; NIH predoctoral fellow Duke U., 1970-76, fellow in exptl. pathology Duke U., 1978-79; numerous rsch. grants. Fellow Coll. Am. Pathologists, Am. Soc. Clin. Pathologists (coun. on edn. and rsch. 1994—); mem. AMA (Physician Recognition award 1979-84), Am. Assn. Immunologists, Am. Soc. Investigative Pathology, U.S.-Can. Acad. Pathology, Southeastern Organ Procurement Found. (sci. projects and publs. com. 1980—, organ preservation com. 1981-83, exec. com. 1992—, sec. 1992-93, treas. 1993-94, v.p. 1994-95, bd. dirs. med. svcs. 1992—, pres. med. svcs. 1994-95), Transplantation Soc., Am. Soc. Histocompatibility and Immunogenetics (chmn. clin. affairs com. 1987-90, chmn. cornea transplant standards subcom. 1985-86), Assn. for Rsch. in Vision and Ophthalmology, Am. Soc. Transplant Physicians (pres.-elect 1984-85, pres. 1985-86, chmn. sci. studies com. 1991-92), Am. Soc. Nephrology, N.C. Kidney Coun. (rep. histocompatibility 1981-92), Md. Soc. Pathologists, Assn. Pathom. grad. med. edn. 1994—), Alpha Omega Alpha. Office: John Hopkins U Sch of Medicine 720 Rutland Ave Baltimore MD 21205

SANFORD, BRUCE WILLIAM, lawyer; b. Massena, N.Y., Aug. 5, 1945; s. Doris (Suhrland) Sanford; m. Marilou Green, May 17, 1980; children: Ashley Anne, Barrett William. BA, Hamilton Coll., 1967; JD, NYU, 1970. Bar: N.Y. 1970, Ohio 1971, D.C. 1981, Md. 1985. Staff reporter Wall St. Jour., 1966-67; assoc. Baker and Hostetler, Washington, 1971-79, ptnr., 1979—. Author: Sanford's Synopsis Law of Libel and Privacy, rev. edit., 1991, Libel and Privacy, 2nd edit., 1991. Trustee Nat. Symphony Orch. Assn.; bd. dirs. Thomas Jefferson 1st Amendment Ctr., U. Va., Charlottesville. Mem. ABA (governing bd., forum com. on communication law, chmn. defamation torts com. 1985-86). Office: Baker & Hostetler 1050 Connecticut Ave NW Washington DC 20036-5303

SANFORD, CHARLES STEADMAN, JR., banker; b. Savannah, Ga., Oct. 8, 1936; s. Charles Steadman and Ann (Lawrence) S.; m. Mary McRitchie, June 19, 1959; children: Ann Whitney, Charles Steadman III. BA, U. Ga., 1958; MBA, U. Pa., 1960. V.p. nat. div., relationship mgr. Bankers Trust Co., N.Y.C., 1961-68, 1st v.p., asst. to head resources mgmt., 1969-71, sr. v.p., 1973, head recources mgmt., from 1972, exec. v.p., 1974, pres., 1983-86, dep. chmn., from 1986, chmn., chief exec. officer, 1987—; mem. mgmt. com., 1979—; chmn. N.Y. Clearing House Com., 1987-88; bd. dirs. J.C. Penney Co., Mobil Corp. Mem. Bus. Roundtable; bd. overseers Wharton Sch., U. Pa. With arty. U.S. Army, 1958-59. Mem. Coun. Fgn. Rels. Office: Bankers Trust NY Corp 130 Liberty St New York NY 10015

SANFORD, DAVID BOYER, writer, editor; b. Denver, Mar. 4, 1943; s. Filmore Bowyer and Alice Irene (Peterson) S. B.A. with honors, U. Denver,

1964; M.S. in Journalism with honors, Columbia U., 1965. With New Republic mag., Washington, 1965-76; mng. editor New Republic mag., 1970-76, Politics Today (formerly Skeptic), Santa Barbara, Calif., 1976-78; contbg. editor Politics Today (formerly Skeptic), 1978-79; editorial writer Los Angeles Herald Examiner, 1978-79; mng. editor Harper's mag., N.Y.C., 1979-80; editor Wall St. Jour. mag., 1980-81; sr. spl. writer Wall Street Jour., 1981—; syndicated columnist, 1970-71; commentator Can. Broadcasting Corp., 1967-76; judge Heywood Broun award Newspaper Guild, 1971; mem. print screening com. Champion-Tuck awards, 1985, 86, Judge Wuxtry award, 1990. Author: Who Put the Con in Consumer?, 1972, Me and Ralph, 1976; editor, co-author: Hot War on the Consumer, 1970. Centennial scholar, 1964; recipient N.Y. Newspaper Guild fellow, 1964-65; recipient Sackett Law prize Columbia, 1965, Eckenberg prize, 1965; Gold award N.Y. Art Dirs. Club, 1977; Wuxtry award for disting. achievement in headline writing, Internat. Soc. for Gen. Semantics, 1989. Mem. Phi Beta Kappa, Omicron Delta Kappa. Democrat. Home: 118 Prospect Park W Brooklyn NY 11215-4270

SANFORD, DAVID HAWLEY, philosophy educator; b. Detroit, Dec. 13, 1937; s. Hawley Seager and Alice Katherine (Brown) S.; m. Anne Irene Zeleney, July 10, 1965; children: Daria Margaret, Katherine Eugenia. Student, Oberlin Coll., 1955-57; B.A., Wayne State U., 1960; Ph.D., Cornell U., 1966. Instr., asst. prof. philosophy Dartmouth Coll., Hanover, N.H., 1963-70; assoc. prof. Duke U., Durham, N.C., 1970-78; prof. Duke U., 1978—, chmn. dept., 1986-89; vis. faculty U. Oreg., U. Mich., Dalhousie U. Author: If P, then Q: Conditionals and the Foundations of Reasoning, 1989, paperback edit., 1992; contbr. articles to profl. jours. Samuel S. Fells fellow, 1962-63, NEH fellow, 1974-75, 82-83, 89-90, Nat. Humanities Ctr. fellow, 1989-90. Mem. Am. Philos. Assn. (exec. com. Eastern div. 1979-81), N.C. Philos. Soc. (pres. 1983-85), Soc. for Philosophy and Psychology, Phi Beta Kappa. Home: 2227 Cranford Rd Durham NC 27706-2507 Office: Duke Univ Dept Philosophy Durham NC 27708

SANFORD, FREDERIC GOODMAN, career officer; b. Williamsport, Pa.; m. Mary Jane Sharpless. BA, Haverford Coll., 1962; MD, U. Pa., 1966. Diplomate Am. Bd. Radiology. Commd. ensign USN, 1962, advanced through grades to rear adm., 1991; intern Robert Packer Hosp., Guthrie Clinic, Sayre, Pa., 1966-67; bn. surgeon 11th Engrs. Bn. 3d Marine Div., Republic of Vietnam, 1967-68; gen. med. officer San Francisco Bay Naval Dispensary, Hunter's Point, 1968-69; resident in radiology Naval Hosp., Bethesda, Md., 1972-73; head radiation therapy div. Naval Hosp., Portsmouth, Va., 1972-73; fellow in radiation therapy Med. Coll. Va., Richmond, 1973-74; head radiation therapy div., program dir. therapeutic radiology tng. program, chmn. radiology dept., dir. ancillary svcs., exec. officer Naval Hosp., San Diego, until 1986; comdg. officer Naval Hosp., Newport, R.I., 1986-88; mem. staff Surgeon Gen.'s Office, Washington, 1988-89, med. insp. gen., 1991-92; comdg. officer Naval Hosp., Long Beach, Calif., 1989-91; med. officer USMC, 1992-93; comdr. Naval Med. Ctr., Oakland, Calif., 1993-94; asst. chief operational medicine and fleed support Bureau of Medicine and Surgery, Washington, 1994—. Decorated Legion of Merit, Meritorious Svc. medal, Vietnamese Cross Gallantry, Combat Action ribbon, other awards. Fellow Am. Coll. Radiology; mem. AMA, Radiol. Soc. N.Am., Am. Radium Soc. Office: Bureau of Medicine & Surgery Navy Dept Washington DC 20372

SANFORD, JAMES KENNETH, public relations executive; b. Clyde, N.C., Jan. 23, 1932; s. James Edward S. and Bernice (Crawford) Peebles; m. Alice Pearl Reavis, Sept. 22, 1957; children: Timothy, Scott, Jeannette. AA, Mars Hill (N.C.) Coll., 1952; AB, U. N.C., 1954, MA, 1958. Pub. rels. officer Asheville (N.C.) United Appeal, 1954; reporter, copy editor Winston-Salem (N.C.) Jour., 1957-59, asst. state editor, 1959-61, news editor, 1961-63, editorial writer, 1963-64; dir. pub. info. and publs. U. N.C., Charlotte, 1964-94; pub. rels. cons. Charlotte, N.C., 1994—; cons. Commn. on Future of Mars Hill Coll., 1990-91, City of Charlotte, 1991. Co-author: Fifty Favored Years, 1972; contbr. numerous articles to mag. and newspapers. Active attractions com. Charlotte Conv. and Visitors Bur., 1994—. Internat. House Bd., 1995, adv. com. Sta. WTVI Pub. TV, Charlotte, 1986-94; chmn. bd. deacons local ch., 1994-95. With U.S. Army, 1954-56. Elected to N.C. Pub. Rels. Hall of Fame, 1995. Fellow Pub. Rels. Soc. Am. (chmn. S.E. dist. 1991); mem. Coll. News Assn. Carolinas (Lewis Gaston award 1982), Charlotte Pub. Rels. Soc. (pres. 1974, Infinity award 1986), Coun. for Advancement and Support Edn. (asst. dist. chmn. 1975-76), Phi Kappa Phi. Baptist. Avocations: writing, hiking, photography. Home and Office: 1216 Braeburn Rd Charlotte NC 28211-4769

SANFORD, JAY PHILIP, physician, government official; b. Madison, Wis., May 27, 1928; s. Joseph Arthur and Arlyn (Carlson) S.; m. Lorraine Burklund, Apr. 7, 1950; children: Jeb, Nancy, Sarah, Philip, Catherine. M.D., U. Mich., 1952; D of Mil. Medicine (hon.), Uniformed Svcs. U. Health Sci., 1991. Intern Peter Bent Brigham Hosp., Boston, 1952-53; research fellow Harvard Med. Sch., Boston, 1953-54; resident Duke U. Hosp., Durham, N.C., 1956-57; practice medicine specializing in internal medicine Dallas, 1957-75; mem. faculty U. Tex. Southwestern Med. Sch. at Dallas, 1957-75; prof. internal medicine, 1965-75; dean F. Edward Hebert Sch. Medicine, Uniformed Services U. Health Scis., Bethesda, Md., 1975-90; pres. Uniformed Services U. Health Scis., 1981-90, dean emeritus, 1990—; clin. prof. internal medicine U. Tex. Southwestern Med. Sch., 1992—; chief microbiology lab. Parkland Meml. Hosp., Dallas, 1957-75, pres. med. staff, 1968-69; mem. adv. coun. Dallas Health and Sci. Mus., 1968-75; chmn. Am. Bd. Internal Medicine, 1978-79; mem. Gov.'s Commn. Phys. Fitness, 1971-75; bd. regents Nat. Libr. Medicine, 1984-90; mem. Accreditation Coun. on Grad. Med. Edn., 1987-92, chmn. transitional yr. residency rev. com., 1989-92, chmn., 1990-91; mem. attending staff Parkland Mem. Hosp.; cons. Dallas Vet. Administrn. Ctr. Contbr. articles to profl. jours. With M.C., U.S. Army, 1954-56; col. Res., 1983—. Decorated Medal of Honor du Service de Sante des Armees, France, 1991; recipient cert. of award Div. Health Moblzn. USPHS, 1963, 64, Prizer award for CD, 1965, Presdl. citation for Health Moblzn. Planning, 1970, Disting. Pub. Svc. medal Dept. Def., 1982, 91. Fellow Am. Acad. Microbiology, ACP (master); mem. Inst. Medicine of NAS, Assn. Am. Physicians, Nat. Inst. Allergy and Infectious Diseases (chmn. tng. grant com. 1971, adv. coun. 1979-90), Am. Fedn. Clin. Research (pres. 1968-69), Am. Soc. Microbiology, Central Soc. Clin. Rsch., Soc. Exptl. Biology and Medicine, Am. Soc. Clin. Investigation, Soc. Med. Consultants to Armed Forces (pres. 1976-77, John R. Seal award 1988, 91), Am. Thoracic Soc., Infectious Disease Soc. Am. (pres. 1978-79, Bristol award 1981, E.H. Kass lectr. 1994), Sigma Xi, Alpha Omega Alpha, Phi Kappa Phi. Home: 4509 Edmondson Ave Dallas TX 75205-2605 Office: 5910 N Central Expy Ste 1955 Dallas TX 75206-5106

SANFORD, KATHERINE KOONTZ, cancer researcher; b. Chgo., July 19, 1915; d. William James and Alta Rachel (Koontz) S.; m. Charles Fleming Richards Mifflin, Dec. 11, 1971. BA, Wellesley Coll., 1937; MA, Brown U., 1939, PhD, 1942; DSc (hon.), Med. Coll. Pa., 1974, Cath. U. Am., 1988. Teaching asst. Brown U., Providence, 1937-39, rsch. asst., 1939-41; instr. biology Western coll., Oxford, Ohio, 1941-42, Allegheny Coll., Meadville, Pa., 1942-43; asst. dir. Johns Hopkins Nursing Sch., Balt., 1943-47; rsch. biologist Nat. Cancer Inst. NIH, Bethesda, Md., 1947-74; head cell physiology and oncogenesis sect. Lab. Biochemistry, Bethesda, 1974-77; chief in vitro carcinogenesis sect. Nat. Cancer Inst. NIH, Bethesda, 1979—. Contbr. 150 articles to profl. jours. Ross Harrison fellow, 1954. Mem. Phi Beta Kappa, Sigma Xi. Home: 101 Stuart Dr Dover DE 19901-5817 Office: Nat Cancer Inst In Vitro Carcinogenesis Bethesda MD 20892

SANFORD, LEROY LEONARD, rancher; b. Sanford Ranch, Wyo., June 24, 1934; s. Claude Leonard and Herminnie May (Brockmeyer) S.; m. Barbara Jo Shackleford, June 15, 1965 (dec. Oct. 1965); stepchildren: Christina Pedley, Marlena McCollum, Diana Sumners; 1 foster child, Catherine Frost. Cert. satellite geodecy, Johns Hopkins U., 1971; cert. astron. geodecy, U.S. Geol. Survey-Branch R & D, 1971. Cert. Geodesic Surveyor. Rancher Sanford Ranch, Douglas, Wyo., 1952-57; topographer, photogrametrist U.S. Geol. Survey-Topog. Divsn.-Hdqs., Denver, 1957-81; rancher Sanford Ranch, Douglas, 1981—; speaker various schs. and coms. Congl. Svc. medal U.S. Congress, 1972. Mem. NRA (endowment), Am. Solar Energy Soc., Antarctican Soc., Wyo. Farm Bur. Republican. Avocation: photography. Home: 400 Windy Ridge Rd Douglas WY 82633-0145

SANFORD, MARSHALL (MARK SANFORD), congressman; b. Ft. Lauderdale, Fla., May 28, 1960; m. Jenny Sanford; 2 children. BA, Furman U., 1983; MBA, U. Va., 1988. With Goldman Sachs, 1988, CRC Realty, 1988-89; prin. Southeastern Ptnrs., 1989—, Norton & Sanford, 1993—; mem. 104th Congress from 2d S.C. dist., 1995—. Republican. Office: Us Ho of Reps Washington DC 20515

SANFORD, RICHARD D., computer company executive; b. 1944. With Arthur Andersen Co., N.Y.C., 1968-77; exec. v.p. Commodore Internat. Ltd., 1977-81; chmn. CEO, former pres. Intelligent Electronics Inc., Exton, Pa., 1982—. With USMC, 1964-68. Office: Intelligent Electronics Inc 411 Eagleview Blvd Exton PA 19341-1139*

SANFORD, SARAH J., nurse, health care executive; b. Seattle, July 20, 1949; d. Jerome G. and Mary L. (Laughlin) S. BS in Nursing, U. Wash., 1972, MA in Nursing, 1977. Cert. in advanced nursing adminstrn. Critical care staff nurse Valley Gen. Hosp., Renton, Wash., 1972-75, Evergreen Gen. Hosp., Kirkland, Wash., 1975-76; instr. nursing Seattle Pacific U., 1977-79; with Overlake Hosp. Med. Ctr., Bellevue, Wash., 1979-88, critical care coord., 1979-80, dir. acute care nursing, 1980-82, assoc. adminstr., 1982-83, sr. v.p. patient care, 1983-88; exec. dir. AACN, Aliso Viejo, Calif., 1988-90, chief exec. officer, 1990—; bd. dirs. Found. for Critical Care, Washington, 1989-91, Partnership for Organ Donation, Boston, 1990—. Co-editor: Standards for Nursing Care of the Critically Ill, 1989; contbr. articles to books and jours. Fellow Am. Acad. Nursing; mem. AACN (pres. 1984-85, bd. dirs. 1981-83), ANA, Soc. for Critical Care Medicine, Am. Orgn. Nurse Execs., Sigma Theta Tau. Office: AACN 101 Columbia Aliso Viejo CA 92656-1491

SANFORD, TERRY, lawyer, educator, former U.S. senator, former governor, former university president; b. Laurinburg, N.C., Aug. 20, 1917; s. Cecil and Elizabeth (Martin) S.; m. Margaret Rose Knight, July 4, 1942; children: Elizabeth Knight, Terry. AB, U. N.C., 1939, JD, 1946; 30 hon. degrees from colls. and univs. Bar: N.C. 1946, D.C. 1979. Asst. dir. Inst. Govt., U. N.C., 1940-41, 46-48; spl. agt. FBI, 1941-42; prvt. practice Fayetteville, 1948-60; ptnr. Sanford, Adams, McCullough & Beard, Raleigh, N.C. and Washington, 1969-85, prof. pub. policy, 1992—; mem. 99th-102d Congresses from N.C., Washington, 1986-93; ptnr. McNair Sanford P.A., Raleigh, 1993—; pub. gov. Am. Stock Exchange, 1977-83; dir. Study of Am. States, Duke U., 1965-68; mem. Carnegie Commn. Edn. TV, 1964-67; pres. Urban Am., Inc., 1968-69; chmn. ITT Internat. Fellowship Com., 1974-86, Am. Coun. Young Polit. Leaders, 1976-86; pres. U.S. Del. Inter-Parliamentary Union, 1988-90. Author: But What About the People?, 1966, Storm Over the States, 1967, A Danger of Democracy, 1981. Sec.-treas. N. C. Port Authority, 1950-53; mem. N.C. Senate, 1953-54; pres. N.C. Young Dem. Clubs, 1949-50; del. Nat. Dem. Conv., 1956, 60, 64, 68, 72, 84, 88, 92; chmn. Nat. Dem. Charter Commn., 1972-74; mem. governing bd. Nat. Com. for Citizens in Edn. Am. Art Alliance; trustee Am. Council Learned Socs., 1970-73, Nat. Humanities Center, 1978-86, Meth. Coll., 1958-94, Howard U., 1968-86; chmn. N.C. Mus. Art, 1993—; bd. dirs. Children's TV Workshop, 1967-71, Council on Founds., 1971-76, N.C. Outward Bound, 1981-88; chmn. bd. trustees U.N.C., 1961-65; chmn. So. Regional Edn. Bd., 1961-63, Sta. ACSN (The Learning Channel), 1980-86, Assn. Am. Univs., 1980-81, Nat. Civic League, 1985-86. Served to lt. AUS, 1942-46. Mem. ABA, Am. Acad. Polit. and Social Sci., Coun. Fgn. Rels., Am. Judicature Soc., Nat. Acad. Pub. Adminstrn., AAAS, Phi Beta Kappa. Methodist. Office: McNair and Sanford Law Firm 234 Fayetteville St Raleigh NC 27601-1867

SANGER, ALEXANDER CAMPBELL, family planning executive; b. N.Y.C., Nov. 25, 1947; s. Grant and Marjery Edwina (Campbell) S.; m. Lisa-Margaret Stevenson, Oct. 31, 1970, (div. July, 1978); m. Jeannette Kittredge Watson, Dec. 21, 1978; children: Ralph, Andrew, Matthew. AB, Princeton U., 1969; MBA, JD, Columbia U., 1974; LLM, NYU, 1985. Bar: N.Y. 1974, Fla. Ptnr., assoc. White and Case, N.Y.C., 1974-88; CEO Sanger Plastics, Union, N.J., 1988-90, Old Line Plastics, Forest Hill, Md., 1990; pres., CEO Planned Parenthood of N.Y.C., 1991—. bd. dirs. Planned Parenthood of N.Y.C., 1984-90, Pierpont Morgan Libr., 1988-90; active alumni coun. Princeton (N.J.) U., 1984-89. Sgt. Air N.G., 1969-70. Mem. Unitarian Ch. Office: Planned Parenthood NYC 26 Bleecker St New York NY 10012-2413

SANGER, GAIL, lawyer; b. N.Y.C., Feb. 4, 1945; d. Maury Daniel and Ethel (Seley) S.; m. Albert M. Fenster, June 16, 1985; children: Robert Jonathan Fenster, Amanda Ruth Fenster. BA cum laude, Bryn Mawr Coll., 1965; LLB cum laude, U. Pa., 1968. Bar: N.Y. 1968. Assoc. Hughes Hubbard & Reed, N.Y.C., 1968-72; assoc. Proskauer Rose Goetz & Mendelsohn, N.Y.C., 1972-76, ptnr., 1976—. Editor: University of Pennsylvania Law Review, 1966-68; contbr. articles to profl. jours. Bd. overseers U. Pa. Law Sch., 1988-91. Mem. ABA, Assn. Bar City N.Y., N.Y. County Lawyers Assn. (chair corp. law com. 1990-93), Order of Coif. Avocation: dressage riding. Office: Proskauer Rose Goetz & Mendelsohn 1585 Broadway New York NY 10036-8200

SANGER, JOHN MORTON, lawyer, urban planner; b. Dallas, July 18, 1943; s. Morton H. and Hortense (Landauer) S.; m. Ellen Ramsey, Aug. 1, 1981; 1 child, Catherine Shea. AB magna cum laude, Harvard U., 1965, JD magna cum laude, 1968, M. in City Planning, 1969. Bar: Calif. 1971, U.S. Dist. Ct. (no. dist.) Calif. 1971, U.S. Ct. Appeals (9th cir.) 1971. Pres., owner John M. Sanger Assocs. cons. firm, San Francisco, 1971-84; counsel Pettit & Martin, San Francisco, 1984-87, ptnr., 1987-94; ptnr. Sanger & Olson, 1995—; lectr. U. Calif., Berkely, 1974-75, 77, San Francisco State U., 1979-80; adj. prof. grad. program U. Miami Law Sch., 1994—. Pres., mem. San Francisco Pub. Utilities Commn., 1978-85; mem. exec. bd. Assn. Bay Area Govts., 1981-83; chair, bd. dirs. Margaret Jenkins Dance Co., San Francisco, 1976-83; bd. dirs. San Francisco Art Inst., 1993—, Children's Place, 1993—. Mem. Bar Assn. San Francisco (chair com. on urban planning and land use), Urban Land Inst. (assoc.), Am. Planning Assn., Lambda Alpha. Democrat. Jewish. Office: Sanger & Olson 12th Fl 1 Embarcadero Ctr San Francisco CA 94111

SANGER, STEPHEN W., consumer products company executive; b. 1945. With General Mills, Inc., Mpls., 1974—; v.p., gen. mgr. Northstar Divsn. General Mills, Inc., 1983, v.p., gen. mgr. new bus. devel, 1986, pres. Yoplait USA, 1986, pres. Big G Divsn., 1988, sr. v.p., 1989, vice chmn. bd., 1992—, pres., 1993—. Treas. Guthrie Theatre Found., Mpls. Office: Gen Mills Inc General Mills Blvd One Minneapolis MN 55426-1347

SANGERMAN, HARRY M., lawyer; b. Chgo., Ill., Jan. 13, 1941. BS, U. Ill., 1962; JD, Northwestern U., 1965. Bar: Ill. 1965. Ptnr. McDermott, Will & Emery, Chgo. Mem. ABA, Chgo. Bar Assn. Office: McDermott Will & Emery 227 W Monroe St Chicago IL 60606

SANGIOVANNI-VINCENTELLI, ALBERTO LUIGI, electrical engineering and computer science educator, consultant; b. Milan, Italy, June 23, 1947; came to U.S., 1975; s. Antonio and Rosetta (Zerbi) S.; m. Annamarie Corsi, June 24, 1972; 1 son, Andrea. Dr.Engring., Politecnico di Milano, 1971. Lectr. elec. engring. Politecnico di Milano, 1971-74, assoc. prof., 1974-76; research assoc. U. Calif., Berkeley, 1975, vis. asst. prof., 1976-77, asst prof. elec. engring. and computer scis., 1977-80, assoc. prof., 1980-83, prof., 1983—, vice chmn. grad. matters dept. elec. engring., 1982-86; vis. scientist IBM T.J. Watson Research Ctr., 1980; cons. in residence Harris Semicondr. div. Harris Corp., 1981; vis. prof. MIT, 1987; cons. to industry; corp. fellow Thinking Machines Co., Harris Co.; bd. dirs Viewlogic, PIE Design, Cadence Design Systems. Assoc. editor: IEEE Trans. on Circuits and Systems, 1979-81, IEEE Trans. on CAD of Integrated Circuits, 1981-86; guest editor spl. issue: Trans. on Circuits and Systems, 1981; contbr. articles to profl. jours. Recipient Disting. Teaching award U. Calif., 1981, Best Paper Design Automation Conf., 1982, 83, Best Presentation Design Automation Conf., 1982, Guillemin-Cauer Circuits and Systems Soc. award, 1981-82, Darlington award 1986; Italian Govt. fellow, 1971-74; Fulbright fellow, 1975; Blanceflor-Stiftelsen-Ludovisi Fodd Bildt grantee, 1976. Fellow IEEE (exec. v.p. Circuits and Systems Soc., Grad. Tchg. award 1995); mem. Assn. Computing Machinery. Home: 200 Tunnel Rd Berkeley CA 94705-2831 Office: Dept Elec Engring U Calif Berkeley CA 94720

SANGMEISTER, GEORGE EDWARD, congressman, lawyer; b. Joliet, Ill., Feb. 16, 1931; s. George Conrad and Rose Engaborg (Johnson) S.; m. Doris Marie Hinspeter, Dec. 1, 1951; children: George Kurt, Kimberley Ann. BA, Elmhurst Coll., 1957; LLB, John Marshall Law Sch., 1960, JD, 1970. Bar: Ill. 1960. Ptnr. McKeown, Fitzgerald, Zollner, Buck, Sangmeister & Hutchison, 1969-89; justice of peace, 1961-63; states atty. Will County, 1964-68; mem. Ill. Ho. of Reps., 1972-76, Ill. Senate, 1977-87, 101st-103rd Congresses from 4th (now 11th) Dist. Ill., 1989-95; ret., 1995. Chmn. Frankfort Twp. unit Am. Cancer Soc., Will County Emergency Housing Devel. Corp.; past trustee Will County Family Svc. Agy.; past bd. dirs. Joliet Jr. Coll. Found., Joliet Will County Ctr. for Econ. Devel., Silver Cross Found., Silver Cross Hosp. With inf. AUS, 1951-53. Mem. ABA, Ill. Bar Assn., Assn. Trial Lawyers Am., Am. Legion, Frankfort (past pres.), Mokena C. of C., Old Timers Baseball Assn., Lions. Home: 20735 S Wolf Rd Mokena IL 60448

SANGREE, WALTER HINCHMAN, social anthropologist, educator; b. N.Y.C., June 15, 1926; s. Carl Micheal and Constance (LaBoiteaux) S.; m. Mary Lucinda Shaw, June 14, 1952 (div. Jan. 1986); children: Margaretta Elizabeth, Mary Cora; m. Ilse Michaels, Dec. 31, 1988. A.B., Haverford Coll., 1950; M.A., Wesleyan U., 1952; Ph.D., U. Chgo., 1959. Asst. prof. anthropology U. Rochester, N.Y., 1957-64; assoc. prof. U. Rochester, 1964-73, prof., 1973—, chmn. dept. anthropology, 1974-77, acting chmn. dept., 1990; vis. scholar dept. anthropology Harvard U., 1979-80; vis. scholar Ctr. for Population Studies, Harvard U., 1986-87. Author: Age, Prayer & Politics in Tiriki, Kenya, 1966; contbr. articles to profl. jours. Co-clk. Rochester Friends Meeting, 1977-79. Fulbright scholar U.K. and Kenya, 1954-56; NSF research fellow Nigeria, 1963-65. Mem. AAAS, Am. Anthrop. Assn., Internat. African Inst., Royal Anthropol. Soc. Gt. Britain and Ireland, Sigma Xi. Democrat. Mem. Soc. of Friends. Home: 254 Highland Pky Rochester NY 14620-2508 Office: U Rochester Dept Anthropology Rochester NY 14627

SANHUEZA, HERNAN, demographer, physician; b. Santiago, Chile, Aug. 17, 1935; came to U.S., 1972; s. Hernan and Elena (Luco) S.; m. Karen Beattie, Apr. 14, 1989 (div.); children: Hernan Jr., Claudia. BA in Biology, Nat. Inst. Luis Campino, Santiago, 1953; MD, U. Chile, 1961; MS in Med. Demography, London Sch. Hygiene & Tropical Medicine, 1971. Mem. staff Felix Bulnes Hosp., Santiago, 1961-72; asst. prof. preventive medicine Sch. Pub. Health, Santiago, 1969-72; med. dir. Internat. Planned Parenthood Fedn., N.Y.C., 1972-78, regional dir., 1978—; exec. coord. Inter-Am. Parliamentary Group Population & Devel., N.Y.C., 1983—. Author: The Population of Latin America, 1984. Office: IPPF WHR Inc 902 Broadway Fl 10 New York NY 10010-6002

SANI, ROBERT LEROY, chemical engineering educator; b. Antioch, Calif., Apr. 20, 1935; m. Martha Jo Marr, May 28, 1966; children: Cynthia Kay, Elizabeth Ann, Jeffrey Paul. B.S., U. Calif.-Berkeley, 1958, M.S., 1960; Ph.D., U. Minn., 1963. Postdoctoral researcher dept. math Rensselaer Poly. Inst., Troy, N.Y., 1963-64; asst. prof. U. Ill., Urbana, 1964-70, assoc. prof. 1970-76; prof. chem. engring. U. Colo., Boulder, 1976—; co-dir. Ctr. for Low-g Fluid Mechanics and Transport Phenomena, U. Colo., Boulder, 1986-89, dir., 1989—; assoc. prof. French Ministry Edn., 1982, 84, 86, 92, 94; cons. Lawrence Livermore Nat. Lab., Calif., 1974—. Contbr numerous chpts. to profl. publs.; mem. editorial bd. Internat. Jour. Numerical Methods in Fluids, 1981—, Revue Européenne des Éléments Finis, 1990—,. Guggenheim fellow, 1970. Mem. AICE, Soc. for Applied and Indsl. Math., World User Assn. in Applied Computational Fluid Dynamics (bd. dirs.). Democrat. Office: U Colo Dept Chem Engring Campus Box 424 Boulder CO 80309

SANJIAN, AVEDIS KRIKOR, Armenian studies educator; b. Marash, Turkey, Feb. 24, 1921; came to U.S., 1949; s. Krikor and Nazli (Kalayan) S.; m. Helen Karaghuzian, Nov. 11, 1950; 1 child, Gregory Shahan. BA in English, Am. U., Beirut, 1949; MA in English, U. Mich., 1950, PhD in Nr. Eastern Studies, 1956; LHD (hon.), U. La Verne/Am. Armenian Internat. Coll., 1986. Postdoctoral research fellow Harvard U., Cambridge, Mass., 1957-61, asst. prof. Armenian studies, 1961-65; assoc. prof. Armenian studies UCLA, 1965-68, prof., 1968—; holder Narekatsi endowed chair for Armenian studies, 1969—; dir. Nr. Eastern Summer Inst UCLA, summer 1968, chmn. dept. Nr. Eastern langs. and cultures, 1970-74. Author: The Sanjak of Alexandretta (Hatay): A Study in Franco-Turco-Syrian Relations, 1956, A Grammar of Classical Armenian, 1963, The Armenian Communities in Syria under Ottoman Dominion, 1965, Colophons of Armenian Manuscripts, 1301-1480: A Source for Middle Eastern History, 1969, A Catalogue of Medieval Armenian Manuscripts in the United States, 1976, (with Andreas Tietze) Eremya Chelebi Kömürjian's Armeno-Turkish Poem "The Jewish Bride," 1981, The Private Letters of the Poet Vahan Tekeyan, 1983, David Anhaght: The "Invincible" Philosopher, 1986, (with Thomas F. Mathews) Armenian Gospel Iconography: The Tradition of the Glajor Gospel, 1991; author numerous articles, book revs. Chmn. bd. trustees Dickranian Armenian Sch., L.A., 1981-88; trustee Am. Armenian Internat. Coll., La Verne, Calif., 1978—; bd. dirs. Armenian Assembly of Am., Washington, 1974-84. Recipient Ouzounian Lit. prize Tekeyan Cultural Assn., Beirut, 1984, St. Sahak-St. Mesrop medal Catholicos Vazgen I of Holy Etchmiadzin, Armenia, 1986, Mesrop Mashtots medal Matenadaran (Library of Manuscripts), Yerevan, Armenia, 1986, Meritorious Achievement award Com. for Cultural Relations with Armenians Abroad, Yerevan, 1986, Cert. Appreciation Chancellor Charles Young UCLA, 1986. Mem. Middle East Studies Assn., Am. Oriental Soc., Middle East Inst., Soc. for Armenian Studies (editor jour. 1985-91, Best. Scholarly Jour. award). Mem. Armenian Apostolic Ch. Home: 545 Muskingum Pl Pacific Palisades CA 90272-4257 Office: Nr Eastern Langs and Cultures UCLA Los Angeles CA 90024

SANKOVICH, JOSEPH BERNARD, cemetery management consultant; b. Johnstown, Pa., Feb. 6, 1944; s. Joseph George and Helen Mary (Kasprzyk) S. Student, St. Francis Sem., 1964-68; BA, St. Francis Coll., 1966; postgrad., St. John Provincial Sem., 1968-69; MA, U. Detroit, 1973. Cert. cemetery exec., cath. cemetery exec., profl. cons. Assoc. pastor St. Mary's Ch., Nanty Glo, Pa., 1970-71, Sacred Heart Ch., Dearborn, Mich., 1971-74; dir. Mt. Kelly Cemetery, Dearborn, 1972-84; admissions counselor U. Detroit, 1974-81; dir. religious edn. St. James Ch., Ferndale, Mich., 1981-84; exec. Diocesan Cemetery Cons., Wyoming, Pa., 1984-86; dir. cemeteries Archdiocese of Seattle, 1986-91; mgmt. cons., owner Joseph B. Sankovich & Assocs., Edmonds, Wash., 1991—; cons. Archdiocese St. Paul and Mpls., 1990—, Diocese San Diego, 1991—, Archdiocese Santa Fe, 1991—, Diocese Tucson, 1991—, Diocese Toledo, 1992—, Diocese Saginaw, 1992—, Archdiocese Edmonton, Alta., Can., 1993—, Diocese Monterrey, 1993—, Diocese Fresno, 1994—; mem. Task Force on Cremation of Bishops Com. on Liturgy Nat. Conf. Cath. Bishops, 1990-92; instr. Am. Cemetery Assn. Univ. Ops./Maintenance, 1994. Author, editor: Directory of Western Catholic Cemeteries, 1992, 94; author mgmt. assessments, sales programs, market analyses, 1986—; contbr. articles to profl. jours. Mem. Am. Cemetery Assn., Nat. Cath. Cemetery Conf., Wash. Interment Assn. (bd. dirs. 1990-91), Cath. Cemeteries of the West (founder 1987, governancy com. 1987-90). Avocations: travel, reading, scuba diving. Home: Joseph B Sankovich & Assocs 24006 92d Ave W Edmonds WA 98020

SANKOVITZ, JAMES LEO, development director, lobbyist; b. St. Paul, July 3, 1934; s. John L. and Mabel A. (Hanrahan) S.; m. Margaret E. Mathews, Aug. 3, 1957; children: Richard, Therese, Patrick, Margaret, Katherine. BS in Journalism, Marquette U., 1956; MA in Speech, U. Denver, 1963. Dir. pub. rels. Coll. of St. Mary of the Wasatch, Salt Lake City, 1956-57; dir. pub. rels. Colo. Sch. of Mines, Golden, 1957-63; assoc. dir. devel. Marquette U., Milw., 1963-66, dir. alumni fund, 1966-67, dir. alumni rels., 1967-69, asst. v.p. univ. rels., 1969-70, v.p. univ. rels., 1970-78, v.p. govtl. rels., 1978-86, v.p. govtl. and community affairs, 1986—. Contbr. articles to profl. jours. Founding dir. Univ. Nat. Bank, Milw., 1971-74; bd. dirs. St. Coletta Sch. Jefferson, Wis., 1970-76, 86-93, chair, 1974-76. Mem. Nat. Assn. for Ind. Colls. and Univs. (bd. dirs. Washington 1986-90), Disting. Svc. award 1986), Assn. Jesuit Colls. and Univs. (fed. affairs cons. Washington 1974-90), Assn. Cath. Colls. and Univs. (fed. affairs cons. Washington 1974-85, Blue Key, Alpha Sigma Nu. Roman Catholic. Avocations: woodworking, reading. Home: 4057 N Prospect Ave Milwaukee WI 53211-2121 Office: Marquette U 1324 W Wisconsin Ave Milwaukee WI 53233-2241

SANKS, CHARLES RANDOLPH, JR., psychotherapist, clergyman; b. Yonkers, N.Y., Feb. 14, 1928; s. Charles Randolph and Myrtle Elizabeth (Bunn) S.; m. Jacquelyn Gibson, Nov. 11, 1949; children—Charlene Cynthia Saunders, Valeri Ann. B.A. cum laude, Stetson U., 1956; B.Div., Southeastern Sem., 1960; M.Th., Union Sem., 1961; postgrad., U. Salamanca, Spain, 1975; D.Ministry, Wesley Theol. Sem., 1977. Ordained to ministry Baptist Ch., 1957. Minister Judson Meml. Bapt. Ch., Fayetteville, N.C., 1957-60; interim minister First Bapt. Ch. of South Miami, Fla., 1961-62, Sunset Heights Bapt. Ch., Hialeah, Fla., 1962; sr. minister Starling Ave. Bapt. Ch., Martinsville, Va., 1963-69; assoc. pastor 1st Bapt. Ch., Washington, 1969-82, minister to Pres. U.S., 1976-80; developer ministry to community foster-care patients, 1975; dir. Pastoral Counseling Ctr. Greater Marlboro, Md., 1982-87; sr. counselor Washington Pastoral Counseling Service, 1982—; dir. clin. mgmt. Washington Pastoral Counseling Service, 1988—; ptnr. Pastoral Psychotherapy Assocs., Washington, 1984—; fellow Am. Assn. Pastoral Counselors, 1984—; trainer Journeyman Program, Fgn. Mission Bd., So. Bapt. Convention, 1968; mem. exec. com. D.C. Bapt. Conv., 1971-77; leader, speaker in liturgics and worship N.C. Bapt. Conv. Conf., 1972, 75; mem. Pastoral Psychotherapy Assocs., Washington, 1981-84; lectr. on worship and liturgics So. Bapt. Theol. Sem., Louisville, 1978; lectr. Stetson U., Deland, Fla., 1978, So. Ecumenical Conf., Atlanta, 1978. Bd. dirs. Uplift House, Washington, 1970-73, Day Care Ctr., Martinsville, Va., 1963-69, Big Brother Orgn. and Sheltered Workshop, Martinsville, Va., 1963-69. Served to cpl. USMC, 1946-49. Fellow Interpreters' House, Lake Junaluska, N.C., 1968-79; guest Oxford U., Eng., 1981. Mem. Am. Digestive Disease Soc. (bd. dirs. 1979-87). Democrat. Baptist. Avocations: travel; horseback riding; music; art. Home: 1090 Larkspur Ter Rockville MD 20850-1002

SANKS, ROBERT LELAND, environmental engineer, emeritus educator; b. Pomona, Calif., Feb. 19, 1916; s. John B. and Nellie G. (Church) S.; m. Mary Louise Clement, May 16, 1946 (dec. Oct. 1994); children: Margaret Nadine, John Clement. Registered profl. engr., Mont. Draftsman City of La Habra Calif., 1940; asst. engr. Alex Morrison cons. engr., Fullerton, Calif., 1941; jr. engr. U.S. Army Engrs., Los Angeles, 1941-42; asst. research engr. dept. civil engring. U. Calif.-Berkeley, 1942-45; structural engr. The Austin Co., Oakland, Calif., 1945-46; instr. dept. civil engring. U. Utah, Salt Lake city, 1946-49; asst. prof. U. Utah, Salt Lake City, 1949-55, assoc. prof., 1955-58; structural engr. The Lang Co., Salt Lake City, 1950; instrument man Patti McDonald Co., Anchorage, 1951; checker Western Steel Co., Salt Lake City, 1952; structural engr. Moran, Proctor, Meuser and Rutledge, N.Y.C., 1953, F.C. Torkelson Co., Salt Lake City, 1955; soils engr. R.L. Sloane & Assocs., Salt Lake City, 1956; prof., chmn. dept. civil engring. Gonzaga U., Spokane, Wash., 1958-61; prof. dept. civil engring.-engring. mechanics Mont. State U., Bozeman, 1966-82, prof. emeritus, 1982—; vis. prof. U. Tex.-Austin, 1974-75; part-time sr. engr. Christian, Spring, Sielbach & Assoc., Billings, Mont., 1974-82; cons. engr., 1945—; lectr. at pumping sta. design workshops, 1988—; assoc. specialist San. Engring. Research Lab., 1963-65, research engr., 1966. Author: Statically Indeterminate Structural Analysis, 1961; co-author: (with Takashi Assano) Land Treatment and Disposal of Municipal and Industrial Wastewaters, 1976, Water Treatment Plant Design for the Practicing Engineer, 1978; editor-in-chief: Pumping Station Design, 1989 (award Excellence profl. & scholarly pub. div. Assn. Am. Pubs. 1989); contbr. articles on civil engring. to profl. publs. Named to Wall of Fame, Fullerton High Sch., 1987; NSF fellow, 1961-63. Fellow ASCE (chmn. local qualifications com. intermountain sect. 1950-56, pres. intermountain sect. 1957-58); mem. Am. Water Works Assn. (life, pres. Mont. sect. 1981-82, George Warren Fuller award), Mont. Water Environ. Fedn., Assn. Environ. Engring. Profs., Rotary, Sigma Xi, Chi Epsilon. Home: 411 W. Dickerson St Bozeman MT 59715-4538 Office: Mont State U Dept Civil Engring Bozeman MT 59717

SAN MARTIN, ROBERT L., federal official. MME, U. Fla., PhD ME. Prof. mech. engring. New Mexico State U.; dep. asst. sec. renewable energy, solar energy, field ops. Office Conservation and Renewable Energy, Washington, 1978—; dep. asst. sec. utility techs. Office Energy Efficiency and Renewable Energy (formerly Office Conservation and Renewable Energy), Washington, 1990—; acting asst. sec. Office Energy Efficiency and Renewable Energy, 1993—; past chair Renewable Energy Working Party Internat. Energy Agy.; past dir. New Mexico Solar Energy Inst., New Mexico Energy Inst. Mem. ASME (former chair solar divsn.), Am. Solar Energy Soc. (past bd. dirs.). Office: US Dept Energy Energy Efficiency & Renewable Energy 1000 Independence Ave SW Washington DC 20585-0001

SAN MIGUEL, SANDRA BONILLA, social worker; b. Santurce, P.R., May 23, 1944; d. Isidoro and Flora (Carrero) Bonilla; m. Manuel San Miguel, July 12, 1969. BA, St. Joseph's Coll., 1966; MS in Social Work, Columbia U., 1970. Case worker Dept. Labor, Migration Div., N.Y.C., 1966-68; clin. social worker N.Y.C. Housing Authority, N.Y.C., 1968-69, Children's Aid Soc., N.Y.C., 1969-71; sr. social worker Traveler's Aid Soc., San Juan, P.R., 1971-74; coord., supr. Dept. Addiction Control Svcs., San Juan, P.R., 1974-77; substance abuse div. dir. Seminole County Mental Health Ctr., Altamonte Springs, Fla., 1978-81; cons. pvt. practice Hispanic Cons. Svcs., Winter Springs, Fla., 1982—; adj. prof. Seminole Community Coll., Lake Mary, Fla., 1986-90; sch. social worker I Seminole County Pub. Schs., Sanford, Fla., 1986-91, lead sch. social worker, 1991—; mem. pres.'s minority adv. coun. U. Ctrl. Fla., 1982—; vice chair, 1982-86, chair, 1986-90; mem. bd. regents EEO adv. com. State Univ. System Fla., 1985-89; bd. dirs. Seminole Community Mental Health Ctr., 1986—, v.p., 1988-90, pres., 1990-91; mem. Fla. Consortium on Tchr. Edn. for Am. Minorities, 1990—; mem. local com. Hispanic Info. and Telecomms. Network, 1990; mem. Seminole County (Fla.) Juvenile Justice Coun., 1993—; mem. statewide student svcs. adv. com. Dept. Edn., Fla., 1993—. Columnist Minority Corner, 1988-92. Mem. NASW, Fla. Assn. Sch. Social Workers (co-founder minority caucus 1988, columnist quar. newsletter Minority Corner 1988-92, bd. dirs. 1989—, sec. 1990-92, v.p. 1992-93, pres. 1993-94), Collegiate Social Workers P.R., Columbia U. Alumni Assn., St. Joseph's Coll. Alumni Assn. Home: 1214 Howell Creek Dr Winter Springs FL 32708-4516 Office: Seminole County Pub Schs 1401 Magnolia Ave Sanford FL 32771-2999

SANNEH, LAMIN, religion educator; married; 2 children. MA in Arabic and Islamic Studies, U. Birmingham, Eng., 1968; postgrad., Near East Sch. Theology, Beirut, 1968-69; PhD in African Islamic History, U. London, 1974. Resident tutor Ctr. for Study of Islam and Christianity, Ibadan, Nigeria, 1969-71; vis. scholar U. Sierra Leone, Freetown, 1974-75; lectr. U. Ghana, Legon, 1975-78, U. Aberdeen, Scotland, 1978-81; asst. prof., then assoc. prof. history of religion Harvard U., Cambridge, Mass., 1981-89; prof., chmn. Coun. on African Studies Yale U., New Haven, 1989—; cons. World Coun. Chs., 1974-79, The Africans TV series, PBS, 1986, Program on Christian-Muslim Rels. in Africa, 1988—; Prof. Lamin Sanneh Found., Banjul, The Gambia; instr. San Francisco Theol. Sem., San Anselmo, Calif., 1987, Iliff Sch. Theology, Denver, 1988; Disting. Staley Christian lectr. Mennonite Brethren Bible Coll., Winnipeg, Can., 1988; lectr. Princeton (N.J.) Theol. Sem., 1988; Gest lectr. Haverford (Pa.) Coll., 1988; Mars lectr. Northwestern U., 1988; Spriggs lectr. Protestant Episcopal Theol. Sem., Alexandria, Va., 1990; Cullum lectr. Augusta Coll., U. Ga., 1990; vis. fellow Clare Hall, Cambridge (Eng.) U., 1995; participant various acad. confs. Author: West African Christianity: The Religious Impact, 1983, Translating the Message: The Missionary Impact on Culture, 1989, The Jakhanke Muslim Clerics: A Religious & Historical Study of Islam in Senegambia (c. 1250-1905), 1990, Encountering the West: Christianity and the Global Cultural Process, 1993; also articles; co-editor Jour. Religion in Africa, 1979-84; mem. adv. bd. Studies in Interreligious Dialogue; editor-at-large The Christian Century; contbg. editor Internat. Bull. Missionary Rsch. Decorated comdr. de l'Ordre Nat. du Lion (Senegal); recipient award Theol. Edn. Fund, 1971-74, award U. London, 1972, Carnegie Truste of Univs. of Scotland, 1980. Mem. Internat. Acad. Union (consultative mem. Africa com.), Ecumenical Assn. African Theologians (exec. com.), Royal African Soc. Home: 47 Morris St Hamden CT 06517-3426 Office: Yale U Div Sch 409 Prospect St New Haven CT 06511-2167

SANNER, ROYCE NORMAN, lawyer; b. Lancaster, Minn., Mar. 9, 1931; s. Oscar N. and Clara (Hermanson) S.; m. Janice L. Sterne, Dec. 27, 1972; children—Michelle Joy, Craig Allen. BS, Moorhead State U., 1953; LLB cum laude, U. Minn., 1961. Bar: Minn. 1961, U.S. Dist. Ct. Minn. 1961, U.S. Supreme Ct. 1981. Tchr. English Karlstad (Minn.) High Sch., 1955-57; counsel IDS Life Ins. Co., Mpls., 1961-68; v.p., gen. counsel IDS Life Ins. Co., 1969-72, exec. v.p., gen. counsel, 1972-77; dir. corp. devel. Investors

Diversified Svcs., Inc., Mpls., 1968-69; v.p. gen. counsel Investors Diversified Svcs., Inc., 1975-78; v.p. Investors Diversified Svcs., Inc. (Benefit Plans Svc. Group), 1978-80, v.p., gen. counsel, 1980-82; v.p. law Northwestern Nat. Life Ins. Co., Mpls., 1982-83; sr. v.p., gen. counsel, sec., 1983—; sr. v.p., gen. counsel, sec. ReliaStar Fin. Corp., Mpls., 1988—; bd. dirs. Riverside Med. Ctr., Friendship Ventures, Inc., Minn. Life & Health Ins. Guaranty Assn., chmn.; bd. dirs. Mass Life & Health Ins. Guaranty Assn., Fairview Hosp. and Healthcare Svcs., vice chmn.; Served with U.S. Army, 1953-55. Mem. ABA, Am. Soc. Corps. Secs., Minn. Bar Assn., Hennepin County Bar Assn., Fed. Bar Assn., Assn. of Life Ins. Counsel, Minn. Corp. Counsel Assn., Mpls. Club, Rotary. Home: 4811 Westminster Rd Minnetonka MN 55345-3723 Office: ReliaStar Financial Corp 20 Washington Ave S Minneapolis MN 55401-1908

SANNUTI, PEDDAPULLAIAH, electrical engineering educator; b. Rajupalem, Andhra-Pradesh, India, Apr. 2, 1941; came to U.S., 1965; m. 1965; children: Aruna, Arun. PhD, U. Ill., Urbana, 1968. Asst. prof. dept. elec. and computer engring. Rutgers U., Piscataway, N.J., 1968-71, assoc. prof., 1971-76, prof., 1976—. Fellow IEEE. Office: Rutgers Univ Dept Elec & Computer Engring Piscataway NJ 08855-0909

SANNWALD, WILLIAM WALTER, librarian; b. Chgo., Sept. 12, 1940; s. William Frederick and Irene Virginia (Stanish) S.; children: Sara Ann, William Howard. B.A., Beloit Coll., 1963; M.A.L.S., Rosary Coll., River Forest, Ill., 1966; M.B.A., Loyola U., Chgo., 1974. Mktg. mgr. Xerox Univ. Microfilms, 1972-75; assoc. dir. Detroit Public Library, 1975-77; dir. Ventura (Calif.) County Library, 1977-79; city libr. San Diego Public Libr., 1979—; vis. instr. mktg. San Diego State U. Author: Checklist of Library Building Design Considerations, 2d edit., 1992; chairperson editorial adv. bd. Pub. Libr. Pres. Met. Libraries Sect., 1989. Recipient Outstanding Prof. award and Outstanding Mktg. Prof. award, 1985; Award of Merit AIA San Diego chpt., 1988. Mem. ALA, Calif. Library Authority for Systems and Services (pres. congress of mems. 1980), Calif. Library Assn. Roman Catholic. Home: 1201990 Calle De Medio El Cajon CA 92019-4905 Office: San Diego Pub Libr 820 E St San Diego CA 92101-6416

SANO, ROY I., bishop. Ordained to ministry United Meth. Ch., later consecrated bishop; appointed Bishop Rocky Mountain Conf., United Meth. Ch., Denver. Office: PO Box 6006 Pasadena CA 91102

SANSONE, TORRY MARK, association executive; b. Chgo., Oct. 12, 1940; s. Vincent Anthony and Dorothy Ann (Scolaro) S. B.A, St. Mary's Sem., Perryville, Md., 1963; postgrad., De Andreis Inst. Theology, Lemont, Ill., 1964-67; STL, Lateran U., Rome, 1968. Dean of men St. John's Sem., Camarillo, Calif., 1968-71; exec. dir. Am. Student Dental Assn., Chgo., 1972-80, Emergency Nurses Assn., Chgo., 1981-89, Soc. Nuclear Medicine, Reston, Va., 1989—. Mem. Am. Soc. Assn. Execs. Home: Soc of Nuclear Medicine 136 Madison Ave Fl 8 Washington DC 10016-6711 Office: Soc Nuclear Medicine 1850 Samuel Morse Dr Reston VA 22090-5316

SANSTEAD, WAYNE GODFREY, state superintendent, former lieutenant governor; b. Hot Springs, Ark., Apr. 16, 1935; s. Godfrey A. and Clara (Buen) S.; m. Mary Jane Bober, June 16, 1957; children: Timothy, Jonathan. B.A. in Speech and Polit. Sci, St. Olaf Coll., 1957; M.A. in Pub. Address, Northwestern U., 1966; Ed.D., U. N.D., 1974. Tchr. Luverne, Minn., 1959-60; dir. forensics Minot (N.D.) High Sch., 1960-71, tchr. social sci., 1960-78; mem. N.D. Ho. of Reps., 1965-70, 83-85, N.D. Senate, 1971-73; lt. gov. N.D. Bismarck, 1973-81; supt. pub. instrn. N.D. Bismarck, 1985—. Served with AUS, 1957-59. Recipient Disting. Alumnus award St. Olaf Coll., 1991; named Outstanding Freshman Senator A.P., 1971, Outstanding Young Educator, N.D. Jr. C. of C., 1967, Outstanding Young Man, Minot Jr. C. of C., 1964; Coe Family Found. scholar, 1963, Eagleton scholar Rutgers U., 1969. Mem. N.D. Edn. Assn., NEA (legis. com. 1969—), Central States Speech Assn., Am. Forensic Assn., Jr. C. of C., Sons of Norway. Democrat. Lutheran (chmn. Western N.D. research and social action com. 1962-68). Clubs: Elk, Toastmaster. Home: 1120 Columbia Dr Bismarck ND 58504-6514 Office: Dept Pub Instrn 600 E Boulevard Ave Bismarck ND 58505-0660

SANSWEET, STEPHEN JAY, journalist, author; b. Phila., June 14, 1945; s. Jack Morris and Fannie (Axelrod) S. BS, Temple U., 1966. Reporter Phila. Inquirer, 1966-69; reporter Wall Street Jour., Phila., 1969-71, Montreal, Que, Can., 1971-73; reporter Wall Street Jour., L.A., 1973-84, dep. bur. chief, 1984-87, bur. chief, 1987—; lectr. bus. journalism U. So. Calif., L.A., 1984-87. Author: The Punishment Cure, 1976, Science Fiction Toys and Models, 1981, Star Wars: From Concept to Screen to Collectible, 1992, Tomart's Guide to Worldwide Star Wars Collectibles, 1994; consulting editor: Star Wars Galaxy, 1993, 2d series, 1994. Recipient award for best fire story Phila. Fire Dept., 1968, Pub. Svc.-Team Mem. award Sigma Delta Chi, 1977; finalist Loeb award, 1990. Mem. Soc. Profl. Journalists. Avocation: collecting toys and movie memorabilia. Office: Wall Street Jour 6500 Wilshire Blvd Ste 1500 Los Angeles CA 90048 also: The Wall Street Journal 200 Liberty St New York NY 10281

SANT, JOHN TALBOT, lawyer; b. Ann Arbor, Mich., Oct. 7, 1932; s. John Francis and Josephine (Williams) S.; m. Almira Steedman Baldwin, Jan. 31, 1959; children: John Talbot Jr., Richard Baldwin, Frank Williams. AB, Princeton U., 1954; LLB, Harvard U., 1957. Bar: Mo. 1957. Assoc. Thompson, Mitchell, Douglas & Neill, St. Louis, 1958-60; atty. McDonnell Aircraft Co., St. Louis, 1960-61, asst. sec., 1961-62, sec., 1962-67; sec. McDonnell Douglas Corp., St. Louis, 1967-76, asst. gen. counsel, 1969-74, corp. v.p. legal, 1974-75, corp. v.p., gen. counsel, 1975-88, bd. dirs. 1978-82, sr. v.p., gen. counsel, 1988-91; ptnr. Bryan Cave, 1991—. Vestry of St. Michael and St. George, St. Louis, 1979-82, 87-90, 93—; bd. dirs. Grace Hill Neighborhood Svcs. St. Louis, 1987—. Mem. ABA (pub. contracts sec., coun. 1987-91), Am. Law Inst., Mo. Bar. Assn., St. Louis Bar Assn. Home: 9 Ridgewood St Saint Louis MO 63124-1849 Office: Bryan Cave 1 Metropolitan Sq Saint Louis MO 63102-2750

SANTACANA, GUIDO E., physiology educator; b. Placetas, Las Villa, Cuba, Dec. 25, 1932; came to U.S., 1963; s. Guido and Concepcion (Sanchez) S.; m. Maria E. Laffitte, May 27, 1978; 1 child, Guido E. BS, Coll. Agrl. and Mech. Arts, Mayaguez, P.R., 1975; PhD, Med. Sci. Campus, San Juan, P.R., 1982. Instr. dept. nat. sci. Sacred Heart U., Santurce, P.R., 1976-84, asst. prof. dept. natural sci., 1981-83; asst. prof. dept. physiology S.J.B. Sch. Med., Hato Rey, P.R., 1981-83; asst. prof. dept. physiology Universidad Central del Caribe Sch. Medicine, Bayamon, P.R., P.R., 1984-86, prof., chmn. dept. physiology, 1986—; dir. grad. program Universidad Central del Caribe Sch. Medicine, Bayamon, P.R. Contbr. articles to sci. jours. Recipient Sci. award Bausch & Lomb, San Juan, P.R., 1971, Rsch. Ctr. for Minority Instns. rsch. grant NIH, Bayamon, P.R., 1986—, Minority Access to Rsch. Careers Program faculty fellowship NIH, San Juan, 1979-82. Mem. AAVSO Assn. (Boston), Am. Physiol. Soc. (Porter physiology devel. grants com.), Am. Assn. Chmn. Depts. Physiology, Soc. Exptl. Biology and Medicine. Roman Catholic. Avocations: amateur radio, fishing, astronomy. Office: Universidad Cen del Caribe Sch Medicine Dept Physiology PO Box 60327 Bayamon PR 00960-6032

SANTA-COLOMA, BERNARDO, secondary school educator, counselor; b. N.Y.C., May 31, 1934; s. Bernardo Santa-Coloma Sr. and Belma Remotti; m. Sofia A. Santa-Coloma, Dec. 22, 1981; childen: Ananda, Anita. BA in Humanistic Psychology, U. Calif., Santa Cruz, 1973; MA in Integral Counseling Psychology, Calif. Inst. Integral Studies, San Francisco, 1976; MEd in Secondary Edn., U. Nev., Las Vegas, 1979; postgrad., U. Houston; EdD in Human Svcs. Counseling Spec., U. Sarasota. Cert. secondary edn. and ESL tchr.; lic. profl. counselor, lic. marriage and family therapist, Tex., nat. cert. counselor. Mem. tchr. corps., vol VISTA, Las Vegas, Nev., 1976-79; family counselor, English tutor Diocese of Matamoros and Valle Hermoso Tamps, Mexico, Cath. Family Svcs. and Vol. Ednl. and Social Svcs., Amarillo, Tex., 1980-82; grad. asst. Pan Am. U., Brownsville, Tex.; at-risk program, low-level reading instr. Brownsville Ind. Sch. Dist., 1984-94; basic skills instr. James Pace High Sch., Brownsville; counselor and psychotherapist Family Effectiveness and Devel. Program, Kids in Crisis Teenage Crisis Hotline; basic adult reading instr. Southmost Coll.; at-risk tchr., guidance counselor, family therapist Brownsville Ind. Sch. Dist. Alternative Ctr. (La Casa Home for Boys), 1994—. Contbr. articles to profl. jours. in U.S. and Mex. in-

cluding Integracion Integral, Journey in Matamoros. Vol. VISTA, 1976-79, VISTA Tchr. Corps, Las Vegas, Peace Corps, Thailand, 1979, Vol. Edn./ Soc. Svc., Tex., Mex., 1980-82. With USN, 1952-56, medic neuropsychology wards, San Diego and Guam. Scholar U. Calif.-Santa Cruz, 1971-73, Calif. Inst. Integral Studies, 1974-76, U. Nev. tchr. corps, 1977-79, Feuerstein's Instrumental Enrichment Program (3-level cert.). Home: PO Box 724 Brownsville TX 78522-0724 also: Brownsville Country Club Amigoland Villa Condos 2009 Madero Dr Brownsville TX 78521-1734

SANTANA, CARLOS, guitarist; b. Autlan de Navarro, Mexico, July 20, 1947. prin. Guts and Grace Records, 1993. Played guitar in Tijuana nightclubs; recorded with Mike Bloomfield and Al Kooper's Super Session; founder, guitarist: rock band Santana, 1966—; appeared at Woodstock Festival, 1969; rec. artist, Columbia Records, 1969—; albums include: Santana, 1968, Abraxas, 1970, Santana III, 1972, Caravanserai, 1972, Welcome, 1973, Greatest Hits, 1974, Barboletta, 1974, Lotus, 1975, Amigos, 1976, Festival, 1977, Moonflower, 1977, Inner Secrets, 1979, Marathon, 1979, Swing of Delight, 1980, Zebop, 1981, Shango, 1982, Havana Moon, 1983, Beyond Appearances, 1985, Freedom, 1987, Viva Santana!, 1988, Doin' It, 1990, Spirits Dancing In the Flesh, 1990, Milagro, 1992, Brothers, 1994, Sacred Fire: Live in South America, 1995; solo albums include Devadip Carlos-Oneness: Silver Dreams, Golden Reality, 1979, Blues for Salvador, 1987; world-wide concert tours with Santana Band; performed and recorded with Buddy Miles, Herbie Hancock, McCoy Tyner, John McLaughlin, Jose Feliciano, Wayne Shorter and Alice Coltrane, Aretha Franklin, Olatunji . Recipient Gold Medal award, 1977, Grammy award, 1989. Office: Santana Mgmt PO Box 881630 San Francisco CA 94188-1630 *Keep an open heart, focus on the positive, be true to your innermost feelings, but most of all make time to visit the Lord within.*

SANTANGELO, MARIO VINCENT, dental association executive, educator; b. Youngstown, Ohio, Oct. 5, 1931; s. Anthony and Maria (Zarlenga) S.; student U. Pitts., 1949-51; D.D.S. Loyola U. (Chgo.), 1955, M.S., 1960. Instr. Loyola U., Chgo., 1957-60, asst. prof., 1960-66, chmn. dpt. radiology, 1962-70, dir. dental aux. utilization program, 1963-70, assoc. prof., 1966-70, chmn. dept. oral diagnosis, 1967-70, asst. dean, 1969-70; practice dentistry, Chgo., 1960-70; cons. Cert. Bd. Am. Dental Assts. Assn., 1967-76, VA Research Hosp., 1969-75, Chgo. Civil Service Commn., 1967-75; counselor Chgo. Dental Assts. Assn., 1966-69; mem. dental student tng. adv. com. Div. Dental Health USPHS, Dept. Health, Edn. and Welfare, 1969-71; cons. dental edn. rev. com. NIH, 1971-72; cons. USPHS, HEW, Region IV, Atlanta, 1973-76, Region V, Chgo., 1973-77; mem. Commn. on Dental Edn. and Practice, Fedn. Dentaire Internationale, 1984-92. Bd. visitors Sch. Dental Medicine, Washington U., St. Louis, 1974-76. Served to capt. USAF, 1955-57. Recipient Dr. Harry Strusser Meml. award NYU Coll. Dentistry, 1985. Fellow Am. Coll. Dentists; mem. AMA (mem. edn. work Group 1982-86), Assembly Specialized Accrediting Bodies (council on postsecondary accreditation 1981-92, award of Merit 1992), Am. Assn. Dental Schs., Odontographic Soc. Chgo., Am. (asst. sec. council dental edn. 1971-81, acting sec. 1981-82, sec. 1982-90, dir., 1990-92, asst. sec. commn. on dental accreditation 1975-81, acting sec. 1981-82, sec. 1982-90, dir., 1990-92, acting sec. commn. on continuing dental edn. 1981-82, sec. 1982-85), Ill., Chgo. dental assns., Am. Acad. Oral Pathology, Am. Acad. Dental Radiology, Canadian Dental Assn. (commission on dental accreditation award of merit 1992), Am. Acad. Oral Medicine, Am. Assn. Dental Examiners (hon. 1993), Omicron Kappa Upsilon (pres. 1967-68), Blue Key, Xi Psi Phi. Contbr. articles to profl. jours. Home: 1440 N Lake Shore Dr Chicago IL 60610-1682

SANTANIELLO, ANGELO GARY, state supreme court justice; b. New London, Conn., May 28, 1924; s. Samuel C. and Katie Santaniello; m. Catherine A. Driscoll, June 1948 (dec.); children—Samuel Gary, Lisa Mary; m. Catherine M. Cooper Sept. 27, 1968; 1 child, Maria Roberta. B.A., Coll. Holy Cross, 1945; JD, Georgetown U., 1950. Bar: Conn. 1950, U.S. Dist. Ct. Conn. Sole practice, New London, 1950-53; sr. ptnr. Santaniello & Satti, 1953-61, Santaniello Satti Wilensky & Schwartz, 1962-65; judge Conn. Cir. Ct., 1966-71, Conn. Ct. Common Pleas, 1971-73; judge Conn. Superior Ct., 1973-85, administrv. judge, 1978-85, chief adminstrv. judge, 1979-85; assoc. justice Conn. Supreme Ct., Hartford, 1985-87, sr. assoc. justice, 1987-95; asst. prosecuting atty. New London Police Ct., 1951-55. Trustee, New London Pub. Library, Mitchell Coll., Lawrence and Meml. Hosp.; bd. dirs. Holy Cross Alumni, Am. Cancer Soc., New London Fed. Savs. and Loan; chmn. New London Republican Party, 1956-65; nat. committeeman Conn. State Young Reps., 1959-61; legal counsel Conn. State Senate Rep. Minority, 1961-65; campaign mgr. to gubernatorial candidate, 1962; mem. athletic council Holy Cross Coll., 1971-77, chmn., 1972-73; bd. of trustees Mitchell Coll., 1976-89, chmn., 1988-91. Served to lt. (j.g.) USNR, 1942-46. Recipient Columbus award Italian-Am. Civic Assn., 1964; In Hoc Signo award Holy Cross Coll. 1976; 1st Humanitarian award Eastern Conn. Conf. March of Dimes, 1983. Mem. New London Bar Assn., Conn. Bar Assn., Am. Justinian Soc., Holy Cross Alumni Assn. (pres. 1981-82). Roman Catholic. Home: 25 Shirley Ln New London CT 06320-2929 Office: 70 Huntington St New London CT 06320-6113 also: 70 Huntington St New London CT 06320-6113

SANTARELLI, EUGENE DAVID, air force officer; b. Canton, Ohio, Aug. 14, 1944; s. Inez Louize Santarelli; m. Barbara Olsen, July 9 (div. 1974); m. Denniseen Kay Bright, Dec. 3, 1976. BBA, U. Notre Dame, 1966; M in Mil. Sci., U.S. Army Command and Staff Coll., Ft. Leavenworth, Kans., 1980; M in Adminstrn. and Mgmt., Troy (Ala.) State U., 1981; Grad. Nat./ Internat. Security Mgmt., U. Harvard, 1993. Commd. 2d lt. USAF, 1966, advanced through grades to maj. gen., 1993; staff officer Hdqrs. Tactical Air Command, Langley AFB, Va., 1980-81, asst. sr. officer matters, 1981-82; asst. dir. ops. 363d Tactical Fighter Wing, Shaw AFB, S.C., 1982-84; student Air War Coll. Maxwell AFB, Ala., 1984-85; dir. USAF Bd. Structure, Office Vice Chief of Staff, Washington, 1985-87; vice comdr., then comdr. 52d Tactical Fighter Wing, Spangdahlem Air Base, Fed. Republic Germany, 1987-89; exec. officer Office Chief of Staff, Washington, 1989-90; comdr. 836th Air Div., Davis-Monthan AFB, Ariz., 1990; comdr. 4404th Comp Wing USCENTAF Forward, Dhahran, Saudi Arabia, 1991; comdr. 355th Wing Davis-Monthan AFB, Ariz., 1992-93; comdr. NATO Combine Air Ops. Ctr. 3, Sembach, Germany, 1993—, 17th Air Forces, Sembach, 1993—; dir. ops. Pacific Air Forces, Hickman AFB, HI, 1995—. Co-chmn. Combined Fed. Campaign, Tucson, 1990-93. Mem. Air Force Assn., VFW, Order of Daedalians, Rotary. Roman Catholic.

SANTE, WILLIAM ARTHUR, II, aerospace and manufacturing company executive; b. N.Y.C., July 16, 1943; s. William Arthur and Grace Elizabeth (Burnat) S.; m. Kathleen Margaret Rourke, July 2, 1966; children: Jennifer, William, Timothy. BS, U. Detroit, 1965; MBA, U. Pitts., 1981. CPA, Mich. Mgr. Deloitte & Touche, Detroit, 1965-78; gen. auditor Rockwell Internat., Pitts., 1978—. Mem. Am Inst. CPA's, Mich. Assn. CPA's, Inst. Internal Auditors. Republican. Roman Catholic. Clubs: Shannopin (Pitts.), Rivers (Pitts.). Office: Rockwell Internat Corp 625 Liberty Ave Pittsburgh PA 15222-3110

SANTEN, ANN HORTENSTINE, broadcasting executive; b. New Orleans, May 23, 1938; d. Jacob L. and Martha Taylor (Grace) Hortenstine; m. Harry H. Santen, Oct. 4, 1958; children: Edward, Sally, Matthew. Student Smith Coll., 1956-58; BFA, U. Cin., 1979. Assoc. producer Sta.-WGUC, Cin., 1974-77, chief music producer, 1977-79, music dir., 1977-89, internat. coordinator, 1981-89, exec. dir., gen. mgr., 1989—; cons. Radio Nederland, The Netherlands, 1978—, Deutsche Welle, Fed. Republic Germany, 1980—; v.p., dir. Am. Music. Ctr.; producer radio series Festival! (Oebie award 1982). Adviser Cin. Composers Guild League, 1979—; head media panel Ohio Arts Coun., Columbus, 1987-88; trustee Cin. Opera, 1980-84; panelist Ohio Arts Coun., 1985-88; mem. radio projects adv. panel NEA, 1987, 88, 93. Named Producer of Yr., Ohio Ednl. Broadcasters, 1983; recipient Deems Taylor Broadcast award ASCAP, 1989. Mem. Coll. Conservatory Music Alumni Assn. (trustee 1981-85), Taft Mus. Com. 1991—). Avocations: skiing, climbing. Office: Sta WGUC-FM 1223 Central Pky Cincinnati OH 45214-2812

SANTER, RICHARD ARTHUR, geography educator; b. Detroit, Sept. 26, 1937; s. Arthur James and Hazel Luella (Houghten) S.; m. Ruth Margaret Boyce, Aug. 29, 1959; children: Carolyn M., Catherine R. BS, Ea. Mich. U., 1959, MS, 1965; PhD, Mich. State U., 1970. Cert. secondary tchr., Mich. Tchr. geography Wyandotte (Mich.) Pub. Schs., 1963-66; prof. geography

Ferris State U., Big Rapids, Mich., 1969—; cons. Graphic Learning Corp., Tallahassee, 1983, Humanities Coun. West Cen. Mich., Big Rapids, 1987—; coord. govs. conf. Upper Great Lakes Commn., Bid Rapids, 1980. Author: Michigan: Heart of Great Lakes, 1977, Geography of Michigan and the Great Lakes Basin, 1993; author (atlas) Green Township Atlas, 1974; contbg. auditor: Michigan Visions of Our Past, 1989. Mem., mapper Green Twp. Plan Commn., Paris, Mich., 1973-74; co-chmn. Mecosta County Bicentennial Commn., Big Rapids, 1974-75; mem. Mecosta County Zoning Commn., Big Rapids, 1978-81; bd. dirs., elder United Ch., Big Rapids, 1970-81; bd. dirs., elder United Ch., Big Rapids, 1970-81; mem. Mich. conf. United Ch. of Christ, Commn. of Ch. and Pastoral Ministries, 1988-91; chmn. 1993 commn. Ferris State U., 1990-93; mem. bd. of trust Hist. Soc. Mich., 1993—. 1st lt. U.S. Army, 1959-62. Recipient Recognition award Population Action Coun., 1983, Certs. of Appreciation, Mich. Sesquicentennial Commn., 1987, The Population Inst., 1987, Nat. Geography Bee, 1989-95. Mem. Assn. Am. Geographers, Nat. Coun. for Geog. Edn. (Mich. coord. 1970-74), Mich. Acad. Sci., Arts and Letters (sect. chmn. 1974-75, 94-95, instn. rep. 1988-89), Phi Delta Kappa (chmn. 1990-91). Presbyterian. Avocation: outdoor nature recreation. Office: Ferris State Univ Dept Social Scis Geography 901 S State St Big Rapids MI 49307-2251

SANTIAGO, BENITO RIVERA, professional baseball player; b. Ponce, P.R., Mar. 9, 1965; m. Bianca Santiago; 1 child, Benny Beth. Baseball player San Diego Padres, 1982-92, Florida Marlins, 1992—. Named Nat. League Rookie of Yr. Baseball Writers' Assn. Am., 1987, Sporting News All-Star Team, 1987, 89, 91, 92; recipient Gold Glove award, 1988-90, Silver Slugger award, 1987-88, 90-91; holder maj. league rookie record for most consecutive games batted safely. Office: Florida Marlins 2269 NE 199th St Miami FL 33180*

SANTIAGO, CARLOS, minister. Supt. Ea. Spanish Ministry Dist. of the Christian and Missionary Alliance. Office: Ste 3000 6220 S Orange Blossom Trl Orlando FL 32809-4630

SANTIAGO, JUAN JOSE, secondary school president; b. San Juan, P.R., July 8, 1931; s. Juan Jose and Mercedes (Asenjo) S. BA and BS, Colegio de Belen, Habana, Cuba, 1957; licensee in philosophy, Cath. U., Quito, Ecuador, 1958; licensee in theology, Woodstock Coll., 1965; D in Missiology, Gregorian U., Rome, 1988. Prof. Interdiocesan Seminary, Aibonito, P.R. 1958-59, Colegio San Ignacio, Rio Piedras, P.R., 1959-61; spiritual dir. Interdiocesan Seminary, Aibonito, 1966-67, Major Seminary, Ponce, P.R., 1967-68; vocation dir. Soc. of Jesus, San Juan, 1969-74; pres. Colegio San Ignacio, Rio Piedras, 1972-78, 88—, prof., 1983-84, prin., 1984-88; Pres. adv. bd. P.R. Symphony Orch., 1986-92. Author: Frutos de Soledad, 1978, Y el rio sigue fluyendo, 1989; contbr. articles to profl. jours. Mem. Am. Soc. for Psychical Rsch., Soc. for Psychical Rsch. (assoc.), Acad. Cath. Hispanic Theologians of the U.S., Cath. Theol. Soc. Am., Internat. Yoga Tchrs. Assn. (Australia). Roman Catholic. Avocations: reading, music, photography, writing. Home and Office: 1940 Sauco St Santa Maria San Juan PR 00927

SANTIAGO, JULIO VICTOR, medical educator, researcher and administrator; b. San German, Puerto Rico, Jan. 13, 1942. BS, Manhattan Coll., 1963; MD, U. Puerto Rico, 1967. Diplomate Am. Bd. of Internal Medicine, 1975. Fellow in metabolism and endocrinology Washington U., St. Louis, 1972-74; chief resident Barnes Hosp., St. Louis, 1974-75; dir. divsn. of endocrinology and metabolism Dept. of Pediatrics, 1984—; program dir. Diabetes Rsch. and Tng. Ctr. Wash. U. Sch. Medicine, 1991—, prof. of medicine, pediatrics, 1983—. Assoc. editor Diabetes, 1977-79, 91—. Mem. Am. Soc. for Clin. Investigation, Soc. for Pedatric Rsch., Am. Diabetes Assn. Home: 4 Forest Pky Manchester MO 63021 Office: Washington U Sch Medicine St Louis Hosp 1 Childrens Place Saint Louis MO 63110

SANTIAGO, NELLIE, state legislator; m. Ben Fernandez. BA, Hunter Coll., 1970; MA, Columbia U., 1972; PhD, U. Mass., 1977. Dir. chronic mental health svcs. Jefferson County Health Dept., Birmingham, Ala., 1978-84; administr. Bklyn. Manor Home for Adults, 1987-92; asst. bur. dir. N.Y. State Health, Albany, 1984-87; mem. N.Y. State Senate, Albany, 1992—; health care adminstrn. cons.; mem. adj. faculty U. Ala., Birmingham, 1978-84; mem. White House Conf. on Families, 1980. Recipient Pub. Health award Kings County Dist. Atty., 1992, also awards from Johns Hopkins U. Sch. Hygiene and Pub. Health, SUNY Ctr. for Women in Govt.. Office: NY State Senate Legis Office Bldg Rm 513 Albany NY 12247

SANTIAGO-NOA, VICTOR MANUEL, psychiatrist; b. San Juan, P.R., Feb. 29, 1944; s. Victor M. and Lydia M. (Noa) S.; m. Olga Carrion, June 15, 1968 (div. Aug. 1975); children: Cecile, Mara; m. Nancy Hernandez, Apr. 3, 1980; children: Vivienne, Joseph. Student, U. P.R., 1968, MD, 1972, postgrad., 1977. Instr. U. P.R., San Juan, 1977-80; asst. med. dir. P.H.P., Ft. Chaffee, Ark., 1980-81; clin. dir. geriatrics dept. Danville (Pa.) State Hosp., 1982-84; clin. dir. children Manchester (N.H.) Mental Health, 1984-87; staff psychiatrist Lakeshore Hosp., Manchester, 1987-88; med. dir. outpatient children York (Pa.) Hosp., 1988-90; pvt. practice Monroeville, Pa., 1990-94; cons. P.R. Dept. Health, 1977-80, VA Hosp., San Juan, 1981-82, Union-Snyder Mental Health, Lewisburg, Pa., 1982-84, Allegheny Valley Mental Health, 1989-94. Author: short story Muneca, 1971, Labor de la noche a medias, 1971, The Wake, 1986, Diez Cuentos Encantados y un desenconto, 1992. Vice pres. bd. Latin Am. Ctr., Manchester, 1986. Recipient Exemplary Psychiatrist award Nat. Alliance for the Mentally Ill, 1993. Mem. Am. Psychiat. Assn. Avocations: writing, poetry, woodworking, computers, reading.

SANTINI, JOHN AMEDEO, educational consultant; b. Detroit, Nov. 4, 1926; s. Amedeo Enrico and Ida Mercurio (LaFata) S.; m. Mary Beverly Bergman, Aug. 11, 1956 (div. 1982); children—Maria Bettina, Lucia Bianca, John Amedeo. B.A., U. Chgo., 1948; J.D., Wayne State U., 1953; M.A., U. Mich., 1960; Ed.D., Harvard, 1965. Bar: Mich. 1954. Prodn. engr. Fisher body div. Gen. Motors Corp., 1949-51; pvt. practice Detroit, 1954-56; tchr. elem. and middle grades St. Clair Shores and Grosse Pointe, Mich., 1956-60; elem. sch. prin. Chagrin Falls, Ohio, 1960-62; dir. curriculum study Brockton, Mass., 1963-64; supt. schs. Farmington, Conn., 1964-66, New Haven, 1966-69; prof. edn., chmn. dept. edn. Conn. Coll., New London, 1969-85, edn. cons., 1985—; lectr. edn. Western Res. U. 1962; vis. prof. edn. adminstrn. U. Bridgeport, 1971, U. Conn., 1974; cons. edn., Sarasota (Fla.) County, 1963—, Walpole, Mass., 1964, West Hartford, Conn., 1973. Mem. Old Lyme Park and Recreation Commn.; bd. mgrs. Old Lyme-P.G. Noyes Library, 1980—; mem. arbitration panel Conn. Dept. Edn., basic skills adv. com., 1980—; tchr. presp. program rev. com, 1979—. Served with USAAF, World War II. Mem. ABA (adv. commn. on youth edn. for citizenship), Mich. Bar Assn., Am. Fedn. Musicians, Am., Conn., New Eng. assns. sch. supts., Nat., Conn., Mich. edn. assns., Nat. Orgn. Legal Problems of Edn., AAUP, Conn. Assn. Colls. and Univs. for Tchr. Edn. (pres. 1973-74), Conn. Profs. Ednl. Adminstrn. (pres. 1973-74), Phi Kappa Phi, Phi Delta Kappa. Presbyn. (deacon). Home: 110 Tremain St N Mount Dora FL 32757-5678

SANTMAN, LEON DUANE, lawyer, former federal government executive; b. Phila., July 29, 1930; s. Elmer William and Anna Mary (Moffitt) S.; m. Juliet Gloria Peacock, June 16, 1952; 1 dau., Lorri Leigh Santman Myers. BS, U. S., COAST Guard Acad., 1952; LLB, U. Houston, 1953; LLM, George Washington U., 1968. Bar: Tex. 1963, Md. 1974. Commd. ensign U.S. Coast Guard, 1952, advanced through grades to comdr., 1967, ret., 1972; assoc. gen. counsel Cost of Living Council, Washington, 1972-74; asst. gen. counsel U.S. Dept. Transp., Washington, 1974-77; dir. Materials Transp. Bur., 1977-85; dir. ship ops. Maritime Adminstrn., 1985-88. Episcopalian.

SANTNER, THOMAS, statistics educator, consultant, researcher; b. St. Louis, Aug. 29, 1947; s. Joseph Frank and Margaret Ann (Dolak) S.; m. Gail DeFord, Aug. 29, 1970; children—Emily, Matthew, Abigail, Dominick. B.S., U. Dayton, 1969; M.S., Purdue U., 1971, Ph.D., 1973. Asst. prof. Cornell U., Ithaca, N.Y., 1973-80, assoc. prof., 1980-86, prof., 1986-89, dir. stats. ctr., 1982-86; prof. Ohio State U., 1990—, chair dept. statistics, 1992—; cons. Hosp. for Spl. Surgery, N.Y.C., 1981—. Editor: Design of Experiments: Ranking and Selection, 1984. Contbr. articles to prof. jours. NSF fellow; recipient numerous grants. Mem. Inst. Math. Stats., Biometric Soc., Am. Statis. Assn. Home: 1042 Putney Dr Columbus OH 43085-2903 Office: Ohio State U Dept Stats Columbus OH 43210

SANTO, RONALD JOSEPH, lawyer; b. Detroit, Jan. 11, 1940; s. Joseph P. and Mary L. (Benzi) Angelosanto; m. Donna L. Macidoni, May 15, 1965; children: Michael, Donielle, Jason. AB, U. Detroit, 1962; JD, U. Mich., 1965. Bar: Mich., U.S. Ct. Appeals (6th cir.). Ptnr. Dykema, Gossett, Spencer, Goodnow & Trigg, Detroit, 1965—; chmn. bd. Bon Secours Hosp., Grosse Pointe, Mich., 19846. Contbr. articles to profl. jours. Office: Dykema Gossett PLLC 400 Renaissance Ctr Detroit MI 48243-1507

SANTOMENNA, ROBERT CHARLES, lawyer; b. Bayonne, N.J., July 24, 1934; s. Dominick R. and Janet (Swane) S.; m. Cornelia Frohman, Apr. 12, 1958; children: David T., Paul R. BA, Middlebury Coll., 1956; LLB, Columbia U., N.Y.C., 1961. Bar: Mass. 1961, Maine 1991. Law clk. to justice Mass. Supreme Jud. Ct., Boston, 1961-62; assoc. Goodwin, Procter & Hoar, Boston, 1962-64; assoc. counsel New. Eng. Mut. Life, Boston, 1964-71; assoc. Hale & Dorr, Boston, 1971-73, ptnr., 1973-91; of counsel and ptnr. Beagle, Pearce, Feller and Ridge, Portland, Maine, 1991-93; ptnr. Drummond & Drummond, Portland, Maine, 1993—; co-chmn. Columbia Law Sch. Legal Aid Soc., N.Y.C., 1960-61. Mem. Zoning Bd. Appeals, Carlisle, Mass., 1987-91, Bldg. Com., Carlisle, 1969-72; mem., chmn. Sch. Com., Carlisle, 1969-72. Named Stone Scholar Columbia Law Sch., 1961. Mem. ABA, Mass. Bar Assn., Me. State Bar Assn., Mass. Conveyancers Assn. Episcopalian. Avocations: sailing, skiing. Office: Drummond & Drummond One Monument Way Portland ME 04101

SANTOMERO, ANTHONY M., business educator; b. N.Y.C., Sept. 29, 1946; s. Camillo and Jean (Oddo) S.; m. Marlena Belviso, Aug. 21, 1971; children—Jill Renee, Marc Anthony. AB, Fordham U., 1968; PhD, Brown U., 1971; EDhe (hon.), Stockholm Sch. Econs., 1992. Successively asst. prof., assoc. prof., prof. fin. Wharton Sch., U. Pa., Phila., 1972-84, R.K. Mellon prof. fin., 1984—, vice dean, dir. grad. div., 1984-87, dep. dean, 1990-94; asst. prof. econs. Baruch Coll., CUNY, 1971-72; vis. prof., European Inst. Advanced Studies in Mgmt., Brussels, 1977-78, Stockholm Sch. Econs., 1989-90, Gothenberg U., 1989-90, U. Rome, 1994; formerly vis. prof. Ecole Superieure des Sciences Economiques and Commerciales, France, 1977-78; bd. dirs. The Zweig Fund, The Zweig Total Return Fund, Temp. Investment Fund Inc., PNC Fund; trustee Trust for Fed. Securities, 1991—, Mcpl. Fund for Temp. Investment, 1991—, Portfolios for Diversified Investment, 1991—; rsch. assoc. NYU Ctr. for Japan-U.S. Bus. and Econ. Studies, 1999—. Author: Current Views on Bank Capital, 1983; assoc. editor Jour. Fin., Jour. Banking and Fin., 1978—, Jour. Money, Credit and Banking, 1980—, Jour. Eocns. and Bus., 1979—, Jour. Econs. and Bus., 1979—, Jour. Bank Rsch., Jour. Fin. Rsch., Jour. Fin. Svc. Rsch., 1992—; contbr. numerous articles to profl. jours. Mem. European Fin. Assn. (exec. com. 1984-87), Am. Fin. Assn., Am. Econs. Assn. Roman Catholic. Home: 310 Keithwood Rd Wynnewood PA 19096-1816 Office: U Pa Wharton Sch Philadelphia PA 19104

SANTOR, KEN, state treasurer. Real estate developer, gen. contractor, treas. state of Nev., 1987—. Served with USMC, Korea. Office: Office of State Treas Capitol Bldg Carson City NV 89710

SANTORO, ANTHONY RICHARD, academic administrator; b. Feb. 2, 1939; m. Carol Lynne; 1 child, Melissa. AB, Coll. of the Holy Cross, 1960; MA, U. Calif., 1962; PhD, Rutgers U., 1978. Instr. history, dir. 2-yr. social sci. div., dept. history and govt. Monmouth Coll., West Long Branch, N.J., 1963-67; v.p. for adminstrn., chair depts history and philosophy, registrar Briarcliff Coll., Briarcliff Manor, N.Y., 1967-77; v.p. Devel. and Coll. Rels. Ladycliff Coll., Highland Falls, N.Y., 1977-88, v.p. devel. and coll. rels., 1977-88; pres. St. Joseph's Coll., North Windham, Maine, until 1987, Christopher Newport U., Newport News, Va., 1987—. Author: Theophanes Chronograhia: A Chronicle of 8th Century Byzantium, 1982; co-author: An Eyewitness to History: The Short History of Nikephoros the Patriarch of Constantinople, 1991. Office: Christopher Newport U Office of Pres Newport News VA 23606

SANTORO, CARMELO JAMES, electronics executive; b. Port Chester, N.Y., July 18, 1941; s. Frederick James and Celeste (Fraioli) S.; m. Elizabeth Higgins, June 23, 1963 (div. July 1980); m. Nancy Jo Kested, Sept. 6, 1980; children: Suzan, Patricia, Stephen, Steven. BS, Manhattan Coll., 1963; PhD, Rensselaer Poly. Inst., 1968. Ops. mgr. Motorola, Inc., Phoenix, 1968-76; v.p. mfg. Am. Micro Systems, Santa Clara, Calif., 1976-80; v.p. integrated cirs. RCA, Somerville, N.J., 1980-82; pres., chmn., chief exec. officer Silican Systems, Tustin, Calif., 1982—; bd. dirs. Ashton-Tate, Torrence, Calif., Dallas Semiconductor. Bd. dirs. Orange County Performing Arts Ctr., Newport Beach, Calif., 1989. Republican. Avocations: golf, sports cars, guitar. Office: AST Research Inc PO Box 19658 Irvine CA 92713

SANTORUM, RICK, U.S. Senator; b. Winchester, Va., May 10, 1958; s. Aldo and Catherine (Dughi) S.; m. Karen Garver, June 2, 1990; children: Elizabeth Anne, Richard John Jr. BA with honors, Pa. State U., State College, 1980; MBA, U. Pitts., 1981; JD, Dickinson Sch. Law, 1986. Bar: Pa. 1986. Adminstrv. asst. State Sen. Doyle Corman, Harrisburg, Pa., 1981-86; exec. dir. local govt. com. Pa. State Senate, Harrisburg, 1981-84, exec. dir. transp. com., 1984-86; assoc. atty. Kirkpatrick and Lockhart, Pitts., 1986-90; mem. 102nd-103rd Congresses from 18th Pa. dist., Washington, D.C., 1991-95; U.S. Senator Penn., 1995—; mem. spl. com. on aging, Ag, Nutrition and Forestry Com., Armed Svcs. Com., Rules and Administrn. Com. Bd. dirs. Mt. Lebanon Extended Day Program, 1987-91; mem. Child Advocacy Project, 1987-91. Mem. Allegheny County Bar Assn., Tyrolean Soc. Western Pa., Italian Sons and Daus. Assn., Rotary. Republican. Roman Catholic. Avocations: golf, cross country skiing, racquet sports. Home: 127 Seminole Dr Pittsburgh PA 15228-1528 Office: US Senate 120 Russell Senate Office Bldg Washington DC 20510-3803*

SANTOS, ADELE NAUDE, architect, educator; b. Cape Town, South Africa, Oct. 14, 1938; came to U.S., 1973; d. David Francois Hugo and Aletta Adèle Naudé. Student, U. Cape Town, South Africa, 1956-58; Diploma, Archtl. Assn., 1961; MArch in Urban Design, Harvard U., 1963; M in City Planning, U. Pa., 1968, MArch, 1968. Pvt. practice architecture with Antonio de Souza Santos, 1966-73; ptnr. Interstudio, Houston, 1973-79; assoc. prof. architecture Rice U., Houston, 1973-78, prof., 1979; prof. architecture and urban design, dept. architecture U. Pa., Phila., 1981-90; founding dean Sch. Architecture U. Calif., San Diego, 1990-94; pvt. practice architecture and urban design Adele Naude Santos, Architect, Phila., 1979-90, Adele Naude Santos and Assocs., San Diego and Phila., 1991—; prof. architecture Coll. Environ. Design U. Calif., Berkeley, 1994—; founding dean Sch. of Architecture, U. Calif., San Diego, 1990—. Project dir., co-filmmaker for 5 part series, 1979-80. Wheelwright Travelling fellow, Harvard U., 1968; NEA grantee, 1976, Tex. Com. for Humanities grantee, 1979; recipient (with Hugo Naudé) Bronze medal for House Naudé Capt. Inst. South African Architects, 1967, award for public TV program So. Ednl. Communications Assn., 1980, 3d place award Inner city Infill Competition, 1986; winner Internat. Design Competition, Hawaii Loa Coll., hon. mention Cin. Hillside Housing Competition and City Visions, Phila., 1986; winner competition for Franklin/La Brea Affordable Housing Project Mus. Contemporary Art and Community Redevel. Agy. City L.A., 1988, Pa. Soc. Architects design award for Franklin/La Brea Multi-Family Housing, 1988; winning entry collaborative competition for amphitheater, restaurant and natural history mus., Arts Pk. La., 1989; winner competition for 24-unit residential devel., City of Camden, N.J., 1989, for New Civic Ctr., City of Perris, Calif., 1991. Office: 2527 South St Philadelphia PA 19146-1037 also: 2947 1st Ave San Diego CA 92103-5906

SANTOS, GEORGE WESLEY, physician, educator; b. Oak Park, Ill., Feb. 3, 1928; s. George and Emma (Gast) S.; m. Joanne Agnes Corrigan, June 7, 1952; children: Susan Elizabeth, George Wesley II, Kelly Anne, Amy Coburn. SB, MIT, 1951, MS in Phys. Biology, 1951; MD, Johns Hopkins U., 1955; Doctoris Medicinae Gradum Honoris Cause, U. Munich, Fed. Republic Germany, 1989. Intern Johns Hopkins Hosp., Balt., 1955-56, asst. resident, 1958-60; scholar Leukemia Soc., N.Y.C., 1961-66; faculty Johns Hopkins Sch. Medicine, Balt., 1962—; assoc. prof. medicine, 1968-73, prof. oncology and medicine, 1973-94; prof. emeritus, 1994—; asst. physician in chief Balt. City Hosp., 1963-77; mem. Cancer Clin. Investigative Rev. Com., 1969-73; mem. extramural sci. adv. bd. Meml. Sloan-Kettering Cancer Ctr., 1977-79; mem. Immunology-Epidemiology Spl. Virus Cancer Program, 1969-73; chmn. bone marrow transplant registry ACS, 1969-73; mem. In-

ternat. Com. Organ Transplant Registry ACS, 1969-73; mem. cell biology-immunology-genetics rsch. evaluation com. VA, 1969-71. Assoc. editor Cancer Rsch., 1978-81; mem. bd. editorial advisors Jour. Immunopharmacology, 1978—; mem. editorial bd. Blood, 1983—. With USNR, 1956-58. Recipient Disting. Achievement in Cancer Rsch. award Bristol Meyers, 1988. Mem. Am. Soc. Hematology, Transplantation Soc. (counselor 1971-73), Am. Assn. Immunologists, Leukemia Soc. Am. (bd. dirs. 1973—), Internat. Soc. Exptl. Hematology (councillor 1973, pres. 1981), Am. Assn. Cancer Rsch., Am. Soc. Clin. Investigation, Nat. Multiple Sclerosis Soc. (chmn. adv. com. on drug devel. 1981-82, mem. adv. com. on drug devel. 1981—). Home: 307B Mariners Point Hilton Head Island SC 29926

SANTOS, LEONARD ERNEST, lawyer; b. Caracas, Venezuela, Aug. 5, 1946; s. Paul Joseph and Frieda (Epstein) S.; m. Jeannie Bernadette Niedermeyer, Oct. 28, 1978; children: Jonathan, Matthew, Andrew. BA cum laude, Tufts U., 1967; JD, NYU, 1971. Bar: Ariz. 1972, D.C. 1972, U.S. Dist. Ct. D.C. 1972, U.S. Ct. Appeals (9th and 5th cirs.) 1972, U.S. Supreme Ct. 1972. Law clk. to cir. judge U.S. Ct. Appeals (9th cir.), San Francisco, 1971-72; assoc. Hogan & Hartson, Washington, 1972-76; sr. atty. internat. affairs U.S. Dept. Treasury, Washington, 1976-83; internat. trade counsel U.S. Senate Fin. Com., Washington, 1983-87; ptnr. Verner, Liipfert, Bernhard, McPherson & Hand, Washington, 1987-89, Perkins Coie, Washington, 1989—. Note and comment editor NYU Law Jour., 1970; contbr. legal publs. Exec. dir. Dole for Pres. campaign, Washington, 1988. Republican. Roman Catholic. Avocations: architecture, economics. Office: Perkins Coie 607 14th St NW Washington DC 20005-2000

SANTSCHI, PETER HANS, marine sciences educator; b. Bern, Switzerland, Jan. 3, 1943; came to U.S., 1976; s. Hans and Gertrud (Joss) S.; m. Chana Hoida, Mar. 28, 1972; children: Rama Aviva, Ariel Tal. BS, Gymnasium, Bern, 1963; MS, U. Bern, 1971, PhD summa cum laude, 1975; Privatdozent, Swiss Fed. Inst. Tech., Zurich, Switzerland, 1984. Lectr. chemistry Humboltianum Gymnasium, Bern, 1968-70; teaching rsch. asst. U. Bern, 1970-75; rsch. scientist Lamont-Doherty Geol. Obs., Columbia U., Palisades, N.Y., 1976-77; rsch. assoc. Lamont-Doherty Geol. Obs. Columbia U., Palisades, N.Y., 1977-81; sr. rsch. scientist Lamont-Doherty Geol. Obs., Columbia U., Palisades, N.Y., 1981-82, Swiss Inst. Pollution Control, Zurich-Duebendorf, Switzerland, 1982-88; prof. oceanography Tex. A&M U., College Station, 1988—; prof. marine scis. Tex. A&M U., Galveston, Tex., 1988—; sect. head chem. oceanography dept. oceanography Tex. A&M U., College Station, 1990—; head isotope geochemistry and radiology sect. Swiss Inst. Water Resources and Water Pollution Control, Zurich, 1983-88; mem. rev. panel on chem. oceanography NSF, 1990-91. Contbr. articles to profl. jours. Cpl. Swiss Army, 1964-65. Mem. AAAS, Am. Chem. Soc., Am. Geophys. Union, Oceanography Soc., Am. Soc. Limnology and Oceanography. Avocation: swimming. Office: Tex A&M U Galveston TX 77553-1675

SANTULLI, THOMAS VINCENT, surgeon; b. N.Y.C., Mar. 16, 1915; s. Frank and Amalia (Avagliano) S.; m. Dorothy Muriel Beverly, Apr. 10, 1941 (dec.); children: Thomas Vincent Jr., Robert B.; m. Patricia Rita, May 28, 1982. BS, Columbia, 1935; M.D., Georgetown U., 1939. Intern N.Y. Polyclinic Hosp., 1939-41, resident, 1941-44; prof. surgery Columbia U., N.Y.C., 1967-81, prof. emeritus, 1981—; chief pediatric surg. service emeritus Babies Hosp., Columbia-Presbyn. Med. Center, N.Y.C., 1955-81; attending surgeon emeritus Presybn. Hosp., Columbia-Presbyn. Med. Center. Mem. Am. Surg. Assn., Am. Pediatric Surg. Assn. (pres. 1980-81), A.C.S., British Assn. Pediatric Surgeons, N.Y. Pediatric Surg. Soc. (pres. 1967-69). Office: Babies Hosp 3959 Broadway New York NY 10032-1537

SANYOUR, MICHAEL LOUIS, JR., financial services company executive; b. Richmond, Va., Aug. 24, 1930; s. Michael Louis, Sr. and Betty (Toobert) S.; m. Therese Marie McCarthy, June 1, 1951; children: Jeffrey, Mark, Jennifer, Florence, Norman, Ned. A.A., Union Coll., 1952; S.B., Rutgers U., 1954, postgrad., 1978-82; M.B.A., Harvard U., 1956; postgrad., Am. Coll., 1987-92. CLU, ChFC. Vice pres. Harbridge House, Inc., Boston, 1956-63; also dir; corp. v.p. mktg. Volkswagen of Am., Inc., Englewood Cliffs, N.J., 1963-70; pres., chief exec. officer Subaru of Am., Pennsauken, N.J., 1970-75, also dir.; exec. v.p., dir. Sci. Mgmt. Corp., 1975-82; pres., chief exec. officer Wofac Co., Bridgewater, N.J., 1975-82; pres., chief exec. officer, dir. Metrologic Instruments Inc., Bellmawr, N.J., 1982-85; pres., chief operating officer, dir. Avant-Garde Computing, Inc., Mt. Laurel, N.J., 1985-86; principal, dir. CMS Cos., Phila., 1986—; bd. dirs. CSS Industries Inc., Gordon Wahls Co. Contbr. to: Chief Executive's Handbook, 1975, Am. Mgmt. Assn.'s Publs., 1990. Trustee, pres. West Jersey Chamber Music Co., 1987-88; councilman Moorestown, N.J., 1988—; bd. dirs. Union League of Phila., Meml. Health Alliance, ARC of Burlington County, 1989-94, Coriell Inst. for Med. Rsch., World Affairs Coun. Phila., 1992—; bd. dirs. Phila. Pres.' Orgn., vice chmn., 1992-93, chmn., 1993-94; chmn. maj. gifts com. HBS Class of '56, 35th Reunion, 1990-92, class sec., 1986—. With USNG, 1948-54. Recipient Alumni award Rutgers U., 1954, awards Am. Cancer Soc., 1978, 79. Mem. World Pres's. Orgn., Am. Mensa Ltd., Automotive Orgn. Team, World Affairs Council Phila., South Jersey C. of C. (v.p., dir.), Beta Gamma Sigma, Delta Sigma Pi. Clubs: Harvard (N.Y.C.); Union League (Phila.), Harvard Bus. Sch. (Phila.) (pres. 1980-81, chmn. 1983-84, dir. 1984—); Moorestown Rotary (pres.1987-88, dir.). Home: 201 E Maple Ave Moorestown NJ 08057-2011 Office: 1926 Arch St Philadelphia PA 19103-1444

SANZO, ANTHONY MICHAEL, health care executive; b. Bayonne, N.J., June 13, 1954; married. BA, Allegheny Coll., 1976; MA, Duke U., 1978. Dir. ambulatory care svcs. Meml. Hosp. Burlington County, Mt. Holly, N.J., 1979; adminstrv. resident Presbyn. U. Hosp., Pitts., 1978-79, asst. dir., 1980-82, v.p., 1982-84, sr. v.p., COO, 1985-86; sr. v.p., COO Allegheny Gen. Hosp., Pitts., 1986-87, pres., CEO, 1988—; adj. educator in field. Contbr. articles to profl. jours. Home: Blackburn Rd Sewickley PA 15143-8386 Office: Allegheny Gen Hosp 320 E North Ave Pittsburgh PA 15212-4756

SANZONE, DONNA S., editor-in-chief; b. Bklyn., Apr. 4, 1949; d. Joseph J. Seitz and Faye (Brooks) Rossman; m. Charles F. Sanzone, Jan. 2, 1972; children: Danielle, Gregory. BA magna cum laude, Boston U., 1970; MA, Northeastern U., 1979. Grad. placement specialist Inst. Internat. Edn., N.Y.C., 1970-72; adminstr. AFS Internat. Scholarships, Brussels, 1972-74; editor Internat. Ency. Higher Edn., Boston, 1974-76; editor G.K. Hall & Co., Phila., Boston, 1977-81, exec. editor, 1981-91, editor-in-chief, 1991—. Contbg. author: Access to Power, 1981. Mem. ALA, Assn. Am. Publs., Assn. Coll. and Rsch. Librs., Libr. and Info. Tech. Assn. Office: G K Hall & Co 18 Pine St Weston MA 02193-1804

SAPAROFF, PETER M., lawyer; b. Boston, Oct. 27, 1942; s. Michael and Delphine (Campbell) S.; m. Lisa Duberg, Feb. 9, 1992; children: Heather, Michael. AB, Harvard U., 1964, JD, 1967. Bar: Mass. 1967, N.Y. 1981, U.S. Supreme Ct. 1982. Ptnr. Gaston & Snow, Boston, 1973-91, Palmer & Dodge, Boston, 1991—. Mem. ABA (various coms.). Congregationalist. Avocation: sports. Office: Palmer & Dodge 1 Beacon St Boston MA 02108-3106

SAPER, CLIFFORD BAIRD, neurobiology and neurology educator; b. Chgo., Feb. 20, 1952; s. Julian and Susan Menkin S.; m. Barbara Susan Farby, Aug. 26, 1973; children: Rebecca Michelle, Leah Danielle, Sean Zachary. BS, U. Ill., 1972, MS, 1972; MD, Washington U., 1977, PhD, 1977. Diplomate Am. Bd. Psychiatry and Neurology. Intern Jewish Hosp., St. Louis, 1977-78; resident New York Hosp., N.Y.C., 1978-81; asst. prof. Washington U., St. Louis, 1981-84, assoc. prof., 1984-85; assoc. prof. U. Chgo., 1985-88, prof., 1988-92, chmn. com. on neurobiology 1987-92; James Jackson Putnam prof. neurology and neurosci. Harvard Med. Sch., 1992—; chmn. deptt. neurology Beth Israel Hosp., Boston, 1992—. Editor-in-chief Jour. of Comparative Neurology, 1994—; contbr. articles to profl. jours. Mem. Am. Neurol. Assn., Am. Acad. Neurology, Am. Physiol. Soc., Soc. for Neurosci. Office: 330 Brookline Ave Boston MA 02215

SAPERS, CARL MARTIN, lawyer; b. Boston, July 16, 1932; s. Abraham E. and Anne (Herwitz) S.; m. Judith H. Thompson, Nov. 29, 1959; children: Jonathan Simonds, Rachel Elizabeth, Benjamin Lovell. AB, Harvard U., 1953, JD, 1958. Bar: Mass. 1958. Assoc. Hill, Barlow, Goodale & Adams, Boston, 1958-65; ptnr. Hill & Barlow, Boston, 1965—; counsel Mass. Crime Commn.; spl. asst. atty. gen. criminal div. Commonwealth of Mass., 1963-65;

adj. prof. Harvard Grad. Sch. Design, 1983—; spl. cons. Mass. Ethics Commn., 1978-79. Moderator Town of Brookline, 1982-91; trustee Nat. Bldg. Mus., 1990—; bd. dirs. Boston Archtl. Ctr., 1993—; active Mass. Bd. Registration in Medicine, 1995—. With U.S. Army, 1953-55. Recipient Allied Professions medal AIA, 1975. Mem. AIA (hon.), Boston Bar Assn. (coun. 1970-73, 91—), Am. Arbitration Assn. (bd. dirs. 1987—, Whitney North Seymour medal 1991), Am. Coll. Constrn. Lawyers (bd. govs. 1989—, pres. 1993), Handel & Haydn Soc. (bd. govs. 1988—). Home: 26 Chesham Rd Brookline MA 02146-5811 Office: Hill & Barlow One International Pl Boston MA 02110

SAPERSTEIN, DAVID ALLAN, novelist, screenwriter, film director; b. N.Y.C., 1937; s. Louis and Celia S.; m. Ellen Mae Bernard; children: Ivan, Ilena. Student, CCNY Film Inst., CCNY. With CBS-TV Ed Murrow Show-Person To Person; owner, writer, producer, dir. Skyline Films, Inc., 1963-83; asst. prof. of film NYU Grad. Sch., Tisch Sch. of the Arts, 1992-93. Lyricist 40 pub. songs; theatrical prodns. include musicals Blue Planet Blue, Clowns; Author: Cocoon, 1985, Fatal Reunion, 1987, Metamorphosis, 1988, Red Devil, 1989, Funerama, 1994; movies include Cocoon (Best Original Story for Screen, 1985, 2 Academy awards); writer, dir. My Sister's Keeper, Personal Choice (Beyond The Stars), Hearts & Diamonds; writer Torch, Sara Deri, Queen of America, Italian Ices, Joshua's Golden Band, Roamers, Vets, Do Not Disturb, Snatched, Jack in the Box, School House, Point of Honor, Roberto!, The John Gill Story: In Defense of Ivan the Terrible, Joshua's Golden Band, Fighting Back; writer, dir. music videos Dr. Bill, Teenage Mutant Ninja Turtles, Fallow Angel, Wowii; dir. over 300 TV commercials; writer, dir. over 200 documentaries, corp. and indsl. films, videos including Dance of the Athletes (Emmy nomination), Explorations in Aqua-Space, Rodeo: A Matter of Style. Recipient Cine Golden Eagle award, N.Y. Film Festival award, San Francisco Film Festival award, Venice Film Festival award, Melbourne Film Festival award, N.Y. Art Dirs. award, Chgo. Film Festival award. Mem. Writer Guild of Am., Dir. Guild of Am. Office: Ebbets Field Prodns Ltd Wykagyl Station PO Box 42 New Rochelle NY 10804-0042

SAPERSTEIN, GUY T., lawyer; b. June 20, 1943. AB, U. Calif., Berkeley, 1966, JD, 1969. Bar: Colo. 1969, Calif. 1970, U.S. Dist. Ct. Colo., U.S. Dist. Ct. (no., ea. and ctrl. dists.) Calif., U.S. Ct. Appeals (9th and 10th cirs.), U.S. Supreme Ct. Ptnr. Saperstein, Mayeda & Goldstein, Oakland, Calif. Contbr. articles to profl. jours. Reginald Heber Smith fellow, 1969-71. Mem. ABA (labor and employment law sect.), State Bar Calif., Calif. Trial Lawyers Assn. Office: Saperstein Mayeda & Goldstein 1300 Clay St 11th Fl Oakland CA 94612

SAPERSTEIN, LEE WALDO, mining engineering educator; b. N.Y.C., July 14, 1943; s. Charles Levy and Freda Phyllis (Dornbush) S.; m. Priscilla Frances Hickson, Sept. 16, 1967; children: Adam Geoffrey, Clare Freda. BS in Mining Engring., Mont. Sch. Mines, 1964; PhD in Engring. Sci., Oxford U., 1967. Registered profl. engr., Ky., Mo., Pa. Laborer, miner, engr. The Anaconda Co., Butte, Mont., and N.Y.C., 1963-64; asst. prof. mining engring. Pa. State U., University Park, 1967-71; assoc. prof. Pa. State U. 1971-78, prof., 1978-87, sect. chmn., 1974-87; prof., chmn. dept. mine engring. U. Ky., Lexington, 1987-93; dean, prof. mining engring. Sch. Mines and Metallurgy U. Mo., Rolla, 1993—; chmn. engring. accreditation commn., 1989-90, bd. dirs. Accreditation Bd. for Engring. and Tech., 1992—, ABET fellow. Contbr. articles to refereed jours. Rhodes scholar Oxford U., 1967. Mem. AIME, NSPE, ASEE, Soc. Mining Engrs., Am. Assn. Rhodes Scholars. Home: 801 Laurel Dr Rolla MO 65401-3841 Office: U Mo 305 V H Mcnutt Hall Rolla MO 65401

SAPERSTEIN, MARC ELI, religious history educator, rabbi; b. N.Y.C., Sept. 5, 1944; s. Harold Irving and Marcia Belle (Rosenblum) S.; m. Roberta Shapiro, June 17, 1970; children: Sara Michal, Adina Ruth. AB, Harvard U., 1966, PhD, 1977; student, Pembroke Coll., U. Cambridge, Eng., 1966-67; MA, Hebrew U., Jerusalem, 1971, Hebrew Union Coll., N.Y.C., 1972. Ordained rabbi, 1972. Lectr. in Hebrew lit. Harvard U., Cambridge, Mass., 1977-79; lectr. in Jewish studies Harvard U. Divinity Sch., 1979-81, asst. prof. Jewish studies, 1981-83, assoc. prof., 1983-86; Gloria M. Goldstein prof. Jewish history and thought Washington U., St. Louis, 1986—, chmn. program Jewish and Near Eastern Studies, 1989—; rabbi Temple Beth David, Canton, Mass., 1973-86; mem. exec. bd. Cen. Conf. Am. Rabbis, 1985-87. Author: Decoding the Rabbis, 1980, Jewish Preaching, 1200-1800, 1989, Moments of Crisis in Jewish-Christian Relations, 1989, also articles; editor: Essential Papers on Messianic Movements and Personalities in Jewish History, 1992. Fellow Charles and Julia Henry Fund, 1966-67, Am. Coun. Learned Socs., 1983-84, Inst. Advanced Studies Hebrew U., Jerusalem, 1989, Am. Acad. for Jewish Rsch., 1994—; Danforth Found. Kent fellow, 1973-77. Mem. Assn. Jewish Studies (bd. dirs. 1983—), Phi Beta Kappa. Home: 7445 Oxford Dr Saint Louis MO 63105 Office: Washington U Dept History Saint Louis MO 63130

SAPERSTON, HOWARD TRUMAN, SR., lawyer; b. Buffalo, Oct. 30, 1899; s. Willard W. and Julia (Wilson) S.; m. Nan Basch, Oct. 5, 1937; children: Howard Truman, Willard B. Student, Cornell U., 1917; LLB, Syracuse U., 1921, LLD (hon.), 1969. Bar: N.Y. 1922. Since practiced in Buffalo; mem. Saperston and Day, P.C. Assoc. editor: Cornell U. Daily Sun, 1918. Mem. Nat. coun., mem. exec. com. Buffalo coun. Boy Scouts Am.; pres., gov. United Jewish Fedn., 1948-51; pres. Community Vol. Svc. Bur., 1946-47; bd. dirs. United Fund, 1950-68, 1973-74, trustee, 1950—; bd. dirs. Buffalo chpt. ARC, 1948—; gen. chmn. Community Chest-ARC campaign United Fund, 1955; v.p. Federated Health Fund Buffalo, 1948-49; mem. adv. bd. Cerebral Palsy Assn. Western N.Y., 1953-68; bd. dirs. Buffalo Tennis Found., 1970-72; mem. exec. bd., co-chmn. Buffalo chpt. NCCJ, 1962-65; v.p. Coun. Jewish Fedns. and Welfare Funds for N.Y., Ont., 1935-50; bd. dirs. Jr. Achievement of Niagara Frontier, 1960—, Arthritis Found., 1978-88; pres. United Jewish Fedn., 1952-55, Community Chest, 1956-57; trustee Union of Am. Hebrew Congregations, 1956; pres. Temple Beth Zion, 1953-55; hon. chmn. Temple Beth Zion Endowment Fund; nat. coun. Joint Def. Appeal, Am. Jewish Joint Distbn. Com.; del. bd. Community Welfare Coun.; dir. Western N.Y. Traffic Coun.; N.Y. State assoc. chmn. U.S. Olympic Com., 1976; regent Canisius Coll., 1955-70, trustee, 1970-77; mem. coun. U. Buffalo, 1957-63; chmn. bd. dirs. Chmns. Club of Erie County Rep. Party, 1965-72, pres., 1978-80; bd. visitors Syracuse U. Coll. Law, 1960—mem. deans adv. com. U. Buffalo Coll. Law, 1955-65; bd. dirs. Bradley Sch. Music, 1960-85; trustee Buffalo Gen. Hosp., pres., 1969-72; trustee, mem. adv. com. Children's Hosp., 1962-69; mem. governing com. Buffalo Found., 1960-77, chmn., 1972-75; chmn. United Negro Coll. Fund, 1951-52, gen. chmn., 1953; bd. dirs. Greater Buffalo Devel. Found., 1960-68, Buffalo Urban League, 1942-65, Meals on Wheels, 1981-87; mem. devel. bd. U. Buffalo, 1957-62; mem. Pres.' Assocs. State U. N.Y. at Buffalo; dir. Jewish Ctr. Buffalo, 1940-43; mem. adv. bd. Camp Lakeland, 1950-75; chmn. Erie County Republican Fin. Com., 1954-73, 78-79. Officer U.S. Army, World War I, Officers Tng. Camp. Named one of 6 outstanding citizens Buffalo Eve. News, 1955; recipient Brotherhood award NCCJ, 1956, President's medal Canisius Coll., 1963, Silver Beaver award Boy Scouts Am., 1964, Nat. award NCCJ, 1966, Disting. Citizen's award Canisius Coll., 1968, Chancellor's award SUNY-Buffalo, 1982, Outstanding Citizen's award Syracuse U. Club of Buffalo, 1982, Outstanding Citizen Am. Jewish Comm. 1987, Lawyer of Yr. award Erie County Bar Assn., 1986, Citizen of Yr. award Am. Jewish Com., 1987, Lifetime Svc. award Jr. Achievement of Western N.Y., 1989, Bronze Leadership award, 1989. Mem. Am., N.Y., Erie County bar assns., Lawyers Club Buffalo, Greater Buffalo Advt. Club (sec.-treas. 1934), 100 Club of Buffalo, Am. Legion, C. of C., Am. Arbitration Assn. (dir. 1960-70), Buffalo Hist. Soc., Buffalo Pub. Libr. (life), Buffalo Fine Arts Acad. (life), Buffalo Soc. Natural Scis., Grovesnor Soc., The Soc. of the Buffalo (Ann. award 1989), Cornell Spike Shoe Soc., Zeta Beta Tau. Jewish (temple pres., trustee). Clubs: Mason (Shriner); Wilmont Country (pres. 1936-38, 43), Buffalo, Westwood Country (pres. 1948), Cornell, Syracuse, Automobile, 100, Marshall, Mid-Day, Capitol Hill, Saturn. Home: 226 Depew Ave Buffalo NY 14214-1622 Office: 1100 MIT Ctr 3 Fountain Plz Buffalo NY 14203-1486

SAPICO, FRANCISCO LEJANO, internist, educator; b. Manila, July 18, 1940; came to U.S., 1967; s. Urbano Loyola and Asuncion Limon (Lejano) S.; m. Margaret Mary Armstrong, Nov. 7, 1969; children: Erica Anne, Derek Armstrong. AA, U. Philippines, 1960, MD, 1965. Diplomate Am. Bd. Internal Medicine, Am. Bd. Infectious Diseases. Rotating intern, resident in internal medicine Philippine Gen. Hosp.-U. Philippines, Manila, 1964-67; resident in internal medicine SUNY Upstate Med. Ctr., Syracuse, 1967-69; fellow in infectious diseases UCLA Ctr. for Health Scis., 1969-71; fellow in infectious diseases Wadsworth VA Hosp., L.A., 1971-72, staff physician dept. medicine, 1972-77; physician specialist dept. medicine Rancho Los Amigos Med. Ctr., Downey, Calif., 1977—; adj. asst. prof. medicine UCLA Sch. Medicine, 1972-77; asst. prof. medicine U. So. Calif. Sch. Medicine, L.A., 1977-82, assoc. prof., 1982-90, prof., 1990—. Contbr. articles to med. jours., chpts. to books. Judge Fullerton (Calif.) Youth Sci. Fair, 1982-86, Orange County Sci. and Engring. Fair, Fullerton, 1984; coach, asst. coach Fullerton Rangers Youth Soccer Club, 1982-89. Fellow ACP, Infectious Diseases Soc. Am.; mem. Am. Soc. Microbiology, Am. Fedn. Clin. Rsch., Am. Soc. Tropical Medicine and Hygiene, Soc. Hosp. Epidemiology Am. Republican. Avocations: soccer, tennis, camping, fishing. Office: Rancho Los Amigos Med Ctr 7601 Imperial Hwy Downey CA 90242-3456

SAPIENZA, JOHN THOMAS, lawyer; b. South Orange, N.J., Feb. 26, 1913; s. James C. and Rosalie (Giaimo) S.; m. Virginia H. Gignoux, Feb. 12, 1972; children by previous marriage: John Thomas, James K. A.B. summa cum laude, Harvard U., 1934, LL.B. magna cum laude, 1937. Bar: N.Y. 1938, D.C. 1943. Law clk. Judge A.N. Hand, N.Y.C., 1937-38, Justice Stanley Reed, Washington, 1938-39; assoc. firm Wright, Gordon, Zachry & Parlin, N.Y.C., 1939-41; assoc. firm Covington & Burling, Washington, 1941-48, ptnr., 1949-87, ret. ptnr., 1987—; dir. Hiram Walker-Gooderham & Worts Ltd., 1971-86, Hiram Walker & Sons, Inc., 1971-86, Hiram Walker Resources Ltd., 1981-86, Wyman Gordon Co., 1973-83; dir. Am. Security Bank, N.A., 1975-83, dir. emeritus, 1983-88. Pres.: Harvard Law Rev, 1936-37. Trustee George Washington U., 1978-88, hon. trustee, 1988—. Served to lt. comdr. USNR, 1943-46. Mem. Am., D.C., Fed. bar assns., Am. Law Inst., Confrerie des Chevaliers du Tastevin, Phi Beta Kappa. Clubs: Burning Tree (Washington), Metropolitan (Washington); Farmington Country (Charlottesville, Va.). Home: 635 Worthington Dr Apt 300 Charlottesville VA 22903-4660 Office: Covington & Burling PO Box 7566 1201 Pennsylvania Ave NW Washington DC 20004-2401

SAPINSKY, JOSEPH CHARLES, magazine executive, photographer; b. N.Y.C., Dec. 13, 1923; s. Simon Moses and Janet (Charles) S.; m. Jane Tomney, Oct. 21, 1970; children—Michael Joseph, Jane Anne, Laura Alexandra. Certificate illustration, Pratt Inst., 1943; certificate advt. design, 1947. Art dir. Today's Living, N.Y. Herald Tribune, N.Y.C., 1960-63; art dir. N.Y. Mag., N.Y.C., 1963-65; asso. art dir., dir. photography Sat. Evening Post, N.Y.C., 1965-67; dir. publs. I.O.S., Geneva, 1967-69; art dir. This Week, N.Y.C., 1969, Jock N.Y. mag., N.Y.C., 1970; dir. publs. I.I.G., London, 1970; art dir. Woman's Day mag., N.Y.C., 1971-83; exec. art dir. Woman's Day Spls., N.Y.C., 1983-92; comml. photographer, 1992—; cons. art dir. Infinity mag., N.Y.C., 1971-73; instr. dept. photography Sch. Visual Arts, N.Y.C., New Sch., N.Y.C. Served with USNR, 1943-46; capt. Res. ret. Recipient numerous art dir. awards. Mem. Am. Soc. Mag. Photographers, Soc. Illustrators, Am. Soc. Mag. Editors, Am. Inst. Graphic Arts, Soc. Publ. Designers, Res. Officers Assn. Home: 76 Bank St New York NY 10014-2124

SAPINSLEY, LILA MANFIELD, state official; b. Chgo., Sept. 9, 1922; d. Jacob and Doris (Silverman) Manfield; Ba, Wellesley Coll., 1944; D. Pub. Service, U. R.I., 1971; D. Pedagogy, R.I. Coll., 1973, LHD, Brown U., 1993; m. John M. Sapinsley, Dec. 23, 1942; children—Jill Sapinsley Mooney, Carol Sapinsley Rubenstein, Joan Sapinsley Lewis, Patricia Sapinsley Levy. Mem. R.I. Senate, 1972-84, minority leader, 1974-84; dir. R.I. Dept. Community Affairs, 1985; chmn. R.I. Housing and Mortgage Fin. Corp., 1985-87; Commr. R.I. Pub. Utilities Commn., 1987-93. Mem. R.I. Gov.'s Commn. on Women; commr. Edn. Commn. of States; pres. bd. trustees Butler Hosp., 1978-84; trustee R.I. State Colls., 1965-70, chmn., 1967-70; trustee U. R.I. R.I. Coll. Found.; bd. dirs. Miriam Hosp., Hamilton House, Trinity Repertory Co., Lincoln Sch., Wellesley Center for Research on Women, 1980, Providence Pub. Libr. Recipient Alumnae Achievement award Wellesley Coll., 1974; Outstanding Legislator of Yr. award Republican Nat. Legislators Assn., 1984. Republican. Jewish. Home: 25 Cooke St Providence RI 02906-2022

SAPOLSKY, HARVEY MORTON, political scientist, educator; b. Haverhill, Mass., Feb. 21, 1939; s. Abraham and Anne Betty (Selig) S.; m. Karen P. Stenbo, Aug. 27, 1966. BA, Boston U., 1961; MPA, Harvard U., 1963, PhD, 1967. Mem. faculty MIT, 1966—, prof. polit. sci., 1977—; dir. communications forum, 1987—; dir. def. and arms control program, 1989—; dep. dir. Univ. Health Policy Consortium, 1978-83. Vis. prof. U. Mich., 1971-72; cons. Artificial Heart Assessment Panel Nat. Heart and Lung Inst., Washington, 1972-73; mem. Ethics and Health Policy Panel Hastings (N.Y.) Ctr., 1979-80; mem. com. on Fed. Rsch. on Effect of Ionizing Radiation NRC, Washington, 1980-81; mem. com. on Risk Perception and Comm. NRC, 1987-88; mem. Sec. of Energy's Task Force on Alternative Futures for Dept. of Energy Labs., 1994-95. Author: The Polaris System Development, 1972, (with D. Altman and Richard Greene) Health Planning and Regulation, 1981, (with A. Drake, S. Finkelstein) The American Blood Supply, 1982, Science and the Navy, 1990; editor: Consuming Fears: The Politics of Product Risks, 1986; co-editor: Federal Health Programs, 1981, (with S. Altman), 1981, (with R. Crane, W.R. Newman and E. Noam) The Telecommunications Revolution, 1992; also articles. Mem. AAAS (sec. sect. social and econ. scis. 1988-91), Am. Polit. Sci. Assn., Nat. Acad. Social Ins., Coun. on Fgn. Rels. Home: 37 Edgemoor Rd Belmont MA 02178-3916 Office: MIT Def Arms Control Studies Pro E38-600 Cambridge MA 02139

SAPORTA, JACK, psychologist, educator; b. N.Y.C., Oct. 21, 1927; s. David and Victoria (Fils) S.; m. Judith Hammond, May 28, 1967 (div. 1979); children: David, Victoria. AB cum laude, Adelphi U., 1951; PhD, U. Chgo., 1962. Diplomate Am. Bd. Profl. Psychology; lic. clin. psychologist. Pvt. practice, 1962—; supt. Tinley Park (Ill.) Mental Health Ctr., 1975-82; dir. chief manpower tng. and devel. Ill. Dept. Mental Health, Chgo., 1978-82; dean, prof. Forest Inst. Profl. Psychology, Des Plaines, Ill., 1982-85; coord. studies Fielding Inst., Santa Barbara, Calif., 1984—; prof. Ill. Sch. Profl. Psychology, Chgo., 1985—; mem. adj. faculty psychology Lake Forest Grad. Sch. Mgmt., 1987—; mem. Ill. State Clin. Psychology Lic. and Disciplinary Com., Springfield, Ill., 1984-93; profl. staff Forest Hosp., Des Plaines, 1977—; med. staff Luth. Gen. Hosp., Park Ridge, Ill., 1986—. Served with U.S. Army, 1946-47, Germany. Named Educator of Yr., Forest Inst., 1982, Outstanding Faculty Mem. Lake Forest Grad. Sch. Mgmt. Fellow Acad. Clinical Psychology, Nat. Tng. Labs. Inst. (mem. faculty); mem. APA (accreditation site vis. team), Am. Acad. Psychotherapists, Ill. Psychol. Assn., Chgo. Psychol. Assn. (exec. bd.). Avocations: tennis, computers, sailing, do-it-yourself home projects. Home: 3201 California Ave Rolling Meadows IL 60008-2226 Office: 2604 E Dempster St Des Plaines IL 60016-5312

SAPOS, MARY ANN, advertising agency executive. Formerly with Al Paul Lefton, Inc.; pres., CEO, Hutchins/Young & Rubicam, Rochester, N.Y. Office: Hutchins/Young & Rubicam 400 Midtown Tower Rochester NY 14604-2069

SAPP, A. EUGENE, JR., electronics executive; b. Winston-Salem, N.C., 1933; married. BEE, Ga. Inst. Tech., 1959. With Tex. Instruments Inc., 1959-62, SCI Systems Inc. Hunstville, Ala., 1962—; v.p. SCI Systems Inc. 1973-80, exec. v.p., 1980—, now pres., chief oper. officer. Office: SCI Systems Inc PO Box 1000 Huntsville AL 35807-4001

SAPP, DONALD GENE, minister; b. Phoenix, Feb. 27, 1927; s. Guerry Byron and Lydia Elmeda (Snyder) S.; m. Anna Maydean Nevitt, July 10, 1952 (dec.); m. Joann Herin Mountz, May 1, 1976; children: Gregory, Paula, Jeffrey, Mark, Melody, Cristine. AB in Edn., Ariz. State U., 1949; MDiv, Boston U., 1952, STM, 1960; D Ministry, Calif. Grad. Sch. Theology, 1975. Ordained to ministry Meth. Ch., 1950. Dir. youth activities Hyde Park (Mass.) Meth. Ch., 1950-52; minister 1st Meth. Ch., Peabody, Mass., 1952-54, Balboa Island (Calif.) Community Meth. Ch., 1954-57, Ch. of the Foothills Meth., Duarte, Calif., 1957-63; sr. minister Aldersgate United Meth. Ch., Tustin, Calif., 1963-70, Paradise Valley (Ariz.) United Meth. Ch., 1970-83; dist. supt. Cen. West Dist. of Desert S.W. Conf. United Meth. Ch., Phoenix, 1983-89. Editor Wide Horizons, 1983-89; contbr. articles to profl. jours. Chaplain City of Hope Med. Ctr., Duarte, 1957-63; trustee Plaza

Community Ctr., L.A., 1967-70; corp. mem. Sch. Theology at Claremont, Calif., 1972-80; pres. Met. Phoenix Commn., 1983-85; del. Western Jurisdictional Conf. United Meth. Ch., 1984, 88; bd. dirs. Coun. Chs., L.A., 1963-67, Orange County (Calif.) Human Rels. Coun., 1967-70, Interfaith Counseling Svc. Found., 1982-89, Wesley Community Ctr., Phoenix, 1983-89; mem. gen. conf. United Meth. Ch., 1988. With USN, 1945-46. Mem. Ariz. Ecumenical Coun., Bishops and Exec. Roundtable, Rotary (pres.), Kappa Delta Pi, Tau Kappa Epsilon. Democrat. Avocation: overseas travel. Home: 5225 E Road Runner Rd Paradise Valley AZ 85253

SAPP, JOHN RAYMOND, lawyer; b. Lawrence, Kans., June 18, 1944; s. Raymond Olen and Amy (Kerr) S.; m. Linda Lee Tebbe, July 3, 1965; children: Jeffrey, Jennifer, John. BA, U. Kans., 1966; JD, Duke U., 1969. Bar: Wis. 1969, U.S. Dist. Ct. (ea. dist.) Wis. 1969, U.S. Ct. Appeals (7th cir.) 1974, U.S. Ct. Appeals (4th cir.) 1984, U.S. Supreme Ct. 1974. Assoc. Michael, Best & Friedrich, Milw., 1969-76, ptnr., 1976-90, mng. ptnr., 1990—; dir. Roadrunner Freight Systems, Milw., 1992—, Aarrow Elec. Signs, Inc., Shawno, Wis., 1990. Bd. dirs. Milw. Symphony, 1981—, mem. exec. com., 1993—; bd. dirs. Boy Scouts Am., Milw., 1986—, pres. 1990; mem. Milw. Arts Bd., 1990, Greater Milw. Com.; assoc. bd. dirs. Zool. Soc., 1992—. Avocations: golf, curling, print collecting. Office: Michael Best & Friedrich 100 E Wisconsin Ave #3300 Milwaukee WI 53202

SAPP, MARY ELLEN, state official, educator; b. Bethesda, Md., Aug. 6, 1945; d. Richard Friend and Anne Carr (Garges) S. BA in Math., Incarnate Word Coll., 1968; MS in Health Care Adminstrn., Trinity U., 1972; M in Theol. Studies, Oblate Sch. Theology, San Antonio, 1984. Tchr. Archdiocese of San Antonio, 1965-71; adminstrv. resident Spohn Hosp., Corpus Christi, 1971, Morningside Manor, San Antonio, 1972; exec. dir. St. Benedict Health Care Ctr., San Antonio, 1972-85, Benedictine Health Resource Ctr., Austin/San Antonio, 1985-89, Tex. Dept. Aging, Austin, 1992—; town meeting specialist Alamo Area Coun. of Govts., San Antonio, 1990-91; pres. Tex. Conf. Cath. Health Facilities, Austin, 1980-81; cmty. advisor San Antonio Light Newspaper, 1989-91; mem. adj. faculty Inst. on Aging Incarnate Word Coll., San Antonio, 1991-93; active Tex. Indigent Health Care Task Force, Austin, 1983-84. Recipient Headliners award for pub. endeavors Women in Comm., 1990; named Regional Citizen, Alamo Area Coun. Govts., 1987. Avocations: music, art, poetry, hiking. Office: Tex Dept Aging 1949 IH 35 South Austin TX 78711

SAPP, NEIL CARLETON, international airline pilot, industrial consultant; b. Miami, Fla., Nov. 22, 1939; s. Alfred Eli and Vera May (Crowson) S.; m. Peggy Joe Brotherton, June 10, 1962; children: Erin Lynn, Kerrie Ellen. BS, U.S. Naval Acad., 1962; postgrad., U. Miami, Coral Gables, Fla. Commd. ensign U.S. Navy, 1962, advanced through grades to lt.; fighter pilot U.S. Navy, Virginia Beach, Va., 1962-67; resigned U.S. Navy, 1967; capt. Nat. Airlines, Miami, Fla., 1967-80, Pan Am. World Airways, Inc., Miami, 1980-91, Delta Air Lines, Inc., N.Y.C., 1991—; mng. ptnr. Sapp & Slaton Fin. Concepts Group, Coral Gables, Fla., 1981-85; chmn., chief exec. officer, pres. U.S. Indsl. Dynamics Corp., Miami, 1988—; pres., COO Iowa Acquisition Group, Inc., 1990-91; v.p. mktg. and corp. devel. The Systema Group, Inc., Miami, 1993—; past chmn. internat. ops., vice-chmn. master exec. coun. Nat. Airline Pilots Assn., Miami; past chmn. spl. corp. ops., profl. standards, flight standard and tng. Pan Am. N.Y.; bd. dirs. World Export/Import Marts, Ltd., Waterloo, Iowa, 1989—; bd. advisors The Cesne Inst., Waterloo, 1988—. Officer affiliate admissions com., U.S. Naval Acad. 1967—; bd. dirs. St. Thomas Sch., Miami, 1976-77; co-pres. Coral Gables Sr. High Sch. PTA, 1983-84; vol. Informed Families of Dade County, Miami, 1984—; vestry St. Thomas Ch., Miami, 1976-79. Mem. Internat. Platform Assn., Delta Airline Pilots Assn. (chmn. profl. stds., flight stds. and tng. 1991-93), Assn. Naval Aviation, Tailhook Assn., U.S. Naval Acad. Alumni Assn., Am. Legion, Naval Inst., Navy League of the U.S., Beach Colony Club, Miami Club, Army-Navy Club Washington, Riviera Country Club, Fisher Island Club. Episcopalian. Avocations: reading, tennis, golf, economics, computers. Home: 7201 SW 47th Ct Miami FL 33143-6109

SAPP, WALTER WILLIAM, lawyer, energy company executive; b. Linton, Ind., Apr. 21, 1930; s. Walter J. and Nona (Stalcup) S.; m. Eva Kaschner, July 10, 1957 (dec.); children: Karen Elisabeth, Christoph Walter; m. Blake Anderson, June 10, 1994. AB magna cum laude, Harvard, 1951; JD summa cum laude, Ind. U., 1957. Bar: Ind. 1957, N.Y. 1959, Colo. 1966, U.S. Supreme Ct. 1972, Tex. 1977. Pvt. practice Paris, 1957-60, 63-66; practice in Paris, France, 1960-63, Colorado Springs, 1966-76; assoc. atty. Cahill, Gordon, Reindel & Ohl, Paris, 1960-63, N.Y.C. 1957-60, 63-65; partner Cahill, Gordon, Reindel & Ohl, 1966; gen. counsel Colo. Interstate Corp., 1966-76, v.p., 1968-76, sec., 1971-76, sr. v.p., dir., exec. com., 1973-75, exec. v.p., 1975-76; v.p. Coastal States Gas Corp., 1973-76; sr. v.p., gen. counsel Tenneco, Inc., Houston, 1976-82, sec., 1984-86; pvt. practice Houston, 1992—; Editor-in-chief Ind. U. Law Jour., 1956-57. Trustee Houston Ballet, 1982-85, Awty Internat. Sch., 1989—, vice-chmn., 1994—; bd. dirs. Harris County Met. Transit Authority, 1982-84, Houston Internat. Protocol Alliance, 1992-94, Houston Symphony, 1989—, v.p., 1991-94; adv. bd. Inst. for Internat. Edn. S.W. region, 1987—, chmn., 1992-94, Internat. and Comparative Law Ctr. Southwestern Legal Found., 1976-92. Lt. USNR, 1951-54. Mem. ABA, N.Y. State Bar Assn., Tex. Bar Assn., Assn. Bar City of N.Y., Houston Bar Assn., Order of the Coif, French-Am. C. of C. (bd. dirs. 1987-92), Alliance Francaise Houston (bd. dirs. 1991-94). Mem. United Ch. of Christ. Office: 1 West Loop South Ste 100 Houston TX 77027

SAPPENFIELD, CHARLES MADISON, architect, educator; b. Columbia, S.C., Mar. 17, 1930; s. Charles Madison and Elizabeth Olive (Moss) S.; m. Mary Frances McGowan Dec. 14, 1963 (div. June 1990); children—Charles Ross, Sarah Kathleen. B.Arch., N.C. State U., 1956; Cert., Denmark's Royal Acad., Copenhagen, 1961. Registered architect, Ind., Tenn., N.C. Asst. prof. N.C. State U., Raleigh, 1956-57, asst. prof., 1961-63; head archtl. firm C.M. Sappenfield, Asheville, N.C. and Muncie, Ind., 1961—; assoc. prof. Clemson U., S.C., 1963-65; prof. architecture Ball State U., Muncie, Ind., 1965-94, prof. emeritus, 1994—, dean, 1965-81, dean emeritus, 1994—. dir. Design Indiana, 1983-88; awards juror Interfaith Forum on Religious Art and Architecture, 1981, Am. Cons. Engrs. Council, 1982; mem. accreditation teams Nat. Archtl. Accrediting Bd., 1967-82. Archtl. works include: Dormitories, U. N.C., Gumpert residence, Dave residence. Pres. Asheville Art Mus., N.C. 1964-65; chmn. Ind. Commn. on Aging, Indpls., 1983-85; pres. Alpha Day Care Ctr. for Elderly, Muncie, 1985; mem. State Planning Adv. Commn., Indpls., 1974-82. Served with U.S. Army. Recipient Gold medal for service Ball State U., 1983; named Sagamore of the Wabash, Gov. of Ind., 1982. Fellow AIA (dir. nat. bd. dirs. 1989-92); mem. Ind. Soc. Architects (pres. 1976), Ind. Archtl. Found. (chmn. 1975), Am. Soc. Landscape Architects (awards juror 1983), Danish Fedn. Architects (hon., Aeresmedallion 1987), Fulbright Alumni Assn., Alpha Rho Chi. Republican. Episcopalian. Lodges: Rotary, Civitan. Avocations: bicycling, racquetball, photography. Home and Office: 2900 W Torquay Rd Muncie IN 47304-5294

SAPSOWITZ, SIDNEY H., entertainment and media company executive; b. N.Y.C., June 29, 1936; s. Max and Annette (Rothstein) Sapsowitz; m. Phyllis Skopp, Nov. 27, 1957; children: Donna Dawn Chazen, Gloria Lynn Aaron, Marsha Helene Gleit. BBA summa cum laude, Paterson (N.J.) State Coll. 1980. Various fin. and oper. systems positions Metro Goldwyn Mayer, Inc., N.Y.C., 1957-68; exec. v.p. Penta Computer Assoc. Inc., N.Y.C., 1968-70, Cons. Actuaries Inc., Clifton, N.J., 1970-73; CFO Am. Film Theatre, N.Y.C., 1973-76; exec. v.p., CFO Cinema Shares Internat Distrb. Corp., N.Y.C., 1976-79; sr. cons. Solomon, Finger & Newman, N.Y.C., 1979-80; exec. v.p., chief fin. officer Metro Goldwyn Mayer, Inc., L.A., 1980-85; various positions leading to exec. v.p. fin. and adminstrn., CFO MGM/UA Entertainment Co., Culver City, Calif., 1985-86; also bd. dirs. MGM/UA Entertainment Co., L.A.; fin. v.p. chief bus. and ops. officer, Office of Pres. dir. United Artists Corp., Beverly Hills, Calif., 1986-87; chmn. bd., CEO MGA/UA Telecommunications Corp., Beverly Hills, 1986-89; sr. exec. v.p., dir., mem. exec. com. MGA/UA Communications Co., 1986-89; chmn., CEO Sid Sapsowitz & Associates, Inc., 1989—. Pres., Wayne Conservative Congregation, N.J., 1970-77. Mem. Am. Mgmt. Assn., Am. Film Inst., Acad. Motion Picture Arts and Scis., Fin. Exec. Inst., TV Acad. Arts and Scis., KP (chancellor comdr.).

SAPUTRA, DANIEL, agricultural engineering educator; b. Padangsidempuan, Indonesia, Aug. 9, 1958; s. Adam and Hanna Saputra; m. Liniyanti D. Oswari, Sept. 19, 1984; children: Danny Matthew, Joshua Michael, Irene Ruth. Sarjana, Bogor (Indonesia) Agrl. U., 1982; MS in Agrl. Engring., U. Ky., 1988, PhD, 1992. Site mgr. P.T. Layaniraya, Tarakan, Indonesia, 1982-83; supervision head P.T. Trans Intra Asia, West Aceh, Indonesia, 1983-84; lectr. Coll. Agr. U. Sriwijaya, Palembang, Indonesia, 1985—, head food process engring., 1993—. Contbr. articles to profl. jours.; patentee in field. Mem. Am. Soc. Agrl. Engrs., Indonesian Soc. Agrl. Engrs. Seventh Day Adventist. Office: U Sriwijaya Coll Agrl, JLN Padang Selasa #524, Palembang 30139, Indonesia

SARACHIK, MYRIAM PAULA, physics educator; b. Antwerp, Belgium, Aug. 8, 1933; came to U.S., 1947; d. Solomon and Sarah (Segal) Morgenstein; m. Philip E. Sarachik, Sept. 6, 1954; 1 child, Karen Beth. AB, Barnard Coll., 1954; MS, Columbia U., 1957, PhD, 1960. Rsch. assoc. IBM Watson Labs., Columbia U., N.Y.C., 1960-61; mem. tech. staff Bell Telephone Labs., Murray Hill, N.J., 1962-64; asst. prof. physics CCNY, 1964-67, assoc. prof., 1967-70, prof., 1970—; advisor NSF, NRC. Contbr. over 70 articles to profl. jours. Fellow Am. Phys. Soc. (various offices and coms.), N.Y. Acad. Scis.; mem. NAS. Office: CCNY Physics Dept Convent Ave and 138 St New York NY 10031

SARANDON, SUSAN ABIGAIL, actress; b. N.Y.C., Oct. 4, 1946; d. Phillip Leslie and Lenora Marie (Criscione) Tomalin; m. Chris Sarandon, Sept. 16, 1967 (div. 1979); children: Eva Maria Livia Amurri, Jack Henry Robbins, Miles Guthrie Robbins. B.A. in Drama and English, Cath. U. Am., 1968. Actress: (plays) include An Evening with Richard Nixon, 1972, A Coupla White Chicks Sittin' Around Talkin', 1980-81, A Stroll in the Air, Albert's Bridge, Private Ear, Public Eye, Extremities, 1982, (films) Joe, 1970, Lady Liberty, 1972, The Rocky Horror Picture Show, 1975, Lovin' Molly, 1974, The Front Page, 1974, The Great Waldo Pepper, 1975, Dragon Fly, 1976, Crash, 1976, The Other Side of Midnight, 1977, The Last of the Cowboys, 1978, Checkered Flag or Crash, 1978, Pretty Baby, 1978, King of the Gypsies, 1978, Something Short of Paradise, 1979, Loving Couples, 1980, Atlantic City, 1980 (Prix Genie Best Fgn. Actress award 1981, Acad. award nominee 1981), Tempest, 1982 (Venice Film Festival Best Actress 1982), The Hunger, 1983, Buddy System, 1984, Compromising Positions, 1985, The Witches of Eastwick, 1987, Bull Durham, 1988, Sweet Hearts Dance, 1988, A Dry White Season, 1989, The January Man, 1989, White Palace, 1990, Thelma and Louise, 1991 (Acad. award nominee 1992), Golden Globe award nominee 1992), The Player, 1992, Light Sleeper, 1992, Bob Roberts, 1992, Lorenzo's Oil, 1992 (Acad. award nominee 1993), The Client, 1994 (Acad. Awd. nom., Best Actress), Little Women, 1994, Safe Passage, 1994; TV appearances The Haunting of Rosalind, 1973, F. Scott Fitzgerald and The Last of the Belles, 1974, Who Am I This Time, 1982, A.D., 1985. Mussolini: The Deline and Fall of Il Duce, 1985, (TV series) A World Apart, 1970-71, Search for Tomorrow, 1972-73. Mem. AFTRA, Screen Actors Guild, Actors Equity, Acad. Motion Picture Arts and Scis., NOW, MADRE, Amnesty Internat., ACLU. Office: Internat Creative Mgmt Martha Luttrell 8942 Wilshire Blvd Beverly Hills CA 90211*

SARANOW, MITCHELL HARRIS, investment banker, financial consultant; b. Chgo., Oct. 14, 1945; B.S.B.A. with high distinction, Northwestern U., 1967; J.D. cum laude, Harvard U. 1971; M.B.A. with distinction (George F. Baker scholar), Harvard U. Bus. Sch., 1971; m. Linda Lee Billig, Sept. 8, 1973; children: Jennifer Wynne, Julie Ann, William L., David M. Bar: Ill. 1971, Mo. 1976, D.C. 1984; Assoc. firm Mayer, Brown & Platt, Chgo., 1971-73; investment banker Becker and Warburg, Paribas Group, Inc., Chgo., 1973-75; v.p. fin. and law Sunmark Cos., St. Louis, 1975-79; v.p. fin., chief fin. officer CFS Continental, Inc., Chgo., 1979-83; pres., The Saranow Co., Chgo., 1983—; chmn. Fluid Mgmt. L.P., Wheeling, Ill. 1987; cons., dir. MidAtlantic Cable TV, Inc., Washington, 1983—. C.P.A., Ill. Mem. Am. Bar Assn., Beta Gamma Sigma, Phi Epsilon Pi. Clubs: Econs., Standard; Harvard Bus. Sch. Century. Office: Saranow Co 1023 Wheeling Rd Wheeling IL 60090-5714

SARAS, JAMES J., agricultural products, grain company executive; b. 1933. BA, Stanford U., 1955. Peach grower Modesto, Calif., 1955—; chmn. Tri-Valley Growers, 1979—, CEO, 1987—, dir. Office: Tri-Valley Growers Inc 1255 Battery St San Francisco CA 94111-1174

SARASON, IRWIN G., psychology educator; b. Newark, Sept. 15, 1929; s. Max and Anna Sarason; m. Barbara June Ryrholm, Sept. 19, 1953; children: Suzanne, Jane, Donald. BA, Rutgers U., Newark, 1951; MS, U. Iowa, 1953; PhD, Ind. U., 1955. Lic. psychologist, Wash. Intern clin. psychology VA Hosp., West Haven, Conn., 1955-56; asst. prof. psychology U. Wash., Seattle, 1956-59, assoc. prof., 1959-65, prof., 1965—. Co-author: Abnormal Psychology, 1972, 8th edit., 1996; editor: Jour. Personality and Social Psychology, 1985-91; author over 250 articles. The Netherlands Inst. for Advanced Study fellow, Wassenaar, 1975, 85. Fellow APA, Japan Soc. for Promotion of Sci., AAAS, Western Psychol. Assn. (pres. 1978-79), Wash. State Psychol. Assn. (pres. 1965). Avocations: travel, music, reading. Home: 13516 42d Ave NE Seattle WA 98125 Office: U Wash Dept Psychology Seattle WA 98195

SARASTE, JUKKA-PEKKA, conductor; b. Heinola, Finland, 1956. With Finnish Radio Symphony Orch., 1978—, prin. condr., 1987—; prin. condr. Scottish Chamber Orch., 1987-91; music dir. The Toronto Symphony Orch., 1987-91. Guest conductor Helsinki Philharm., Beijing Ctrl. Opera Orch., Symphonic Orch. Chengdu, Rotterdam Philharm. Orch., Chamber Orch. Europe, Bavarian Radio Symphony Orch., Junge Deutsche Philharmonie, Detroit Orch., Minn. Orch., Vienna Symphony Orch., Rome's Santa Cecilia Orch., Orch. Deutsche Opera Berlin, Swedish Radio Symphony Orch., Scottish Chamber Orch., Norddeutschen Rundfunks Symphony Orch., L.A. Philharm.; co-founder Avantil Chamber Orch.; conductor over 30 recordings with Finnish Radio Symphony Orch. and Scottish Chamber Orch. Recipient First prize Scandinavian Conducting Competition, 1981. Office: Radio Symphony Orch, Yleisradio Ja 14, SF-00240 Helsinki 24, Finland also: Toronto Symphony Orch, Ste 550, 212 King St W, Toronto, Canada M5H 1K5

SARAT, AUSTIN D., jurisprudence and political science educator; b. Fall River, Mass., Nov. 2, 1947; s. Joseph George and Lillian (Sock) S.; children: Lauren, Emily. BA in Polit. Sci., Providence U., 1969; MA in Polit. Sci., U. Wis., 1970, PhD in Polit. Sci., 1973; JD, Yale U., 1988. Rsch. assoc. Yale Law Sch., 1976-81; sr. staff civil litigation rsch. project U. Wis. Sch. Law, 1979-81; rsch. assoc. U. Wis. Law Sch., 1981-83; William Nelson Cromwell prof. jurisprudence and polit. sci. Amherst (Mass.) Coll., 1974—; cons. Nat. Adv. Commn. on Small Claims Cts., 1976-77, Pub. Mgmt. Svcs., 1977-78, Law Enforcement Assistance Adminstrn., 1977-78, Nat. Ctr. for State Cts., 1977-78, NAS, 1979, Yankelovich, Skelley & White, 1980, Hampshire Coll., 1983, Vt. Law Sch., 1983, Modern Media Inst., 1983-84, Porter, Morris, Arthur and Wright, 1984; dir. NEH summer seminar for coll. tchrs., 1986. Author: (with Malcolm Feeley) The Policy Dilemma: Federal Crime Policy and the Law Enforcement Assistance Administration 1968-78, 1980, (with Stan Wheeler and Ken Mann) Sitting in Judgment: The Sentencing of White Collar Criminals, 1988; editor and co-author: American Court Systems, 1978, 2d edit., 1988; also numerous articles and rev. essays, book revs.; sr. editor Yale Law Jour., 1987-88; co-editor Studies in Law, Politics and Society; assoc. editor Justice Quar., 1986—; mem. editorial bd. Law and Society Rev., 1977-78; editorial adv. bd. Yale Jour. of Law and the Humanities. Woodrow Wilson fellow, 1969-70, Russell Sage fellow Yale Law Sch., 1973-74, Karl Lowenstein fellow in polit. sci. and jurisprudence, 1985-86, vis. fellow Centre for Socio-Legal Studies, Oxford U., 1985-86, vis. sr. rsch. fellow Am. Bar Found., 1987-88; NSF grantee, 1972-73, 81, 85. Mem. Am. Polit. Sci. Assn. (Corwin award com. 1981, 87), Law and Society Assn. (program com. for 1986 ann. meeting, trustee 1987-81, 86-88, exec. com. bd. trustees 1986-88), Am. Judicature Soc. (program com. 1978-80). Office: Amherst Coll Dept Of Polit Sci Amherst MA 01002

SARAZEN, RICHARD ALLEN, media company executive; b. Bklyn., June 27, 1933; s. Nicholas and Anna M. (Isacco) S.; children: Richard, Theresa, Mary, Barbara, David, Russell, Christina, Andrea. B.B.A., Hofstra U., 1955. CPA, N.Y., Pa., Calif. Acct. Arthur Young & Co., N.Y.C., 1955-58; ptnr. Alexander Grant & Co., N.Y.C., 1958-67; v.p. fin. Seeburg Corp., Chgo.,

1967-69; mng. ptnr. Alexander Grant & Co., Pitts., Los Angeles, 1969-74; exec. v.p. News Am. Pub., Inc., N.Y.C., 1974-80; chmn. bd. XCor Internat., Inc., N.Y.C., 1980-82; sr. exec. v.p., bd. dir. The News Corp. Ltd., Sydney, Australia, 1982—. Bd. dirs. N.Y.C. Center Found. Mem. AICPA, N.Y. State Soc. CPAs. Republican. Roman Catholic. Club: Chgo. Athletic. Home: 165 Galway Rd Windham NY 12496 Office: News Am Pub Inc 1211 Ave of the Americas New York NY 10036-8701

SARAZIN, CRAIG LEIGH, astronomer; b. Milw., Aug. 11, 1950; s. Valley V. and Martha V. (Gustafson) S.; m. Jane Curry, June 12, 1971; children: Stephen N., Andrew T. BS in Physics, Calif. Inst. Tech., 1972; MA in Physics, Princeton U., 1973, PhD in Physics, 1975. Millikan fellow Calif. Inst. Tech., Pasadena, 1975; mem. Inst. Advanced Study, Princeton, N.J., 1975-77; asst. prof. U. Va., Charlottesville, 1977-79, assoc. prof. dept. astronomy, 1979-86, prof., 1986—, chair dept., 1992-95; vis. asst. prof. U. Calif., Berkeley, 1979; vis. scientist Nat. Radio Astronomy Obs., Charlottesville, 1977-82; vis. prof. physics Inst. Advanced Study, 1981-82; JILA vis. fellow U. Colo., Boulder, 1985-86; mem. com. on Space Astronomy Astrophysics, Washington, 1984-86, mem. x-ray astronomy working group, 1989-94; mem. AXAF users com., 1993—; mem. ASCA users com., 1995—. Author: X-ray Emission from Clusters of Galaxies; contbr. numerous articles to profl. jours. NSF grantee, 1981-86, NASA grantee, 1979-82, 86—; recipient Haren Fischer Physics prize Calif. Inst. Tech., 1971. Mem. Am. Astron. Soc., Internat. Astron. Union. Home: 2574 Kimbrough Cir Charlottesville VA 22901-9516 Office: Leander J McCormick Obs Dept of Astronomy U of Va PO Box 3818 Charlottesville VA 22903-0818

SARBANES, PAUL SPYROS, senator; b. Salisbury, Md., Feb. 3, 1933; s. Spyros P. and Matina (Tsigounis) S.; m. Christine Dunbar, June 11, 1960; children—John Peter, Michael Anthony, Janet Matina. A.B., Princeton, 1954; B.A. (Rhodes scholar), Oxford (Eng.) U., 1957; LL.B. Harvard, 1960. Bar: Md. bar 1960. Law clk. to judge Morris Soper U.S. Ct. Appeals (4th cir.), 1960-61; asso. Piper & Marbury, Balt., 1961-62; administrv. asst. Walter W. Heller; chmn. Council Econ. Advisers, 1962-63; exec. dir. Charter Revision Commn., Balt., 1963-64; asso. Venable, Baetjer & Howard, Balt., 1965-70; mem. Md. Ho. of Dels., 1967-71, 92d Congress from 4th Dist. Md., 93d-94th congresses from 3d Dist. Md.; U.S. senator from Md., 1977—. Democrat. Greek Orthodox. Office: US Senate 309 Hart Senate Bldg Washington DC 20510 also: Tower I Ste 100 100 S Charles St Baltimore MD 21201

SARBIN, HERSHEL BENJAMIN, management consultant, business publisher, lawyer; b. Massillon, Ohio, Dec. 30, 1924; s. Joseph I. and Sarah Charlotte (Reich) S.; m. Susan Chaffman, July 24, 1973; children by previous marriage: Penelope Sarbin Burke, Richard, Barbara; 1 stepdau., Caroline Cooley. A.B., Western Res. U., 1946; J.D., Harvard U., 1950. Bar: Ill. 1950, N.Y. 1953. Assoc. firm Lewis and MacDonald, N.Y.C., 1953-58; with Ziff-Davis Pub. Co., 1950-81; pub. Popular Photography mag., 1965-66, sr. v.p. co., 1967-74; assoc. pub. Travel Weekly, 1967-68, pub., 1969-74, pres., pub. dir., chief exec. officer photog. div., 1968-69, pres. Pub. Transp. and Travel div., 1970-74; pres. Ziff-Davis Pub. Co., 1974-78; exec. v.p. Ziff Corp., 1978-81, also dir.; chmn., pres. Hershel Sarbin Assocs., Inc., 1981—; vis. assoc. prof. Fla. Internat. U., 1980; mem. exec. com., nat. photography coordinator Pres.'s Council Youth Opportunity, 1968; fed. commr. Nat. Commn. on New Technol. Uses of Copyrighted Works, 1975-78; mem. policy rev. bd. Public Agenda Found.; pres., CEO Cowles Bus. Media, Inc., 1991-95; Sr. Advisor Cowles Media, 1995. Author: (with George Chernoff) Photography and the Law, 1958, rev. edit., 1977. Mem. exec. com. Westchester County (N.Y.) Soc. Bd., 1964-66; mem. ethical practices com. N.Y. Sch. Bd. Assn., 1965-68; pres. Hastings-on-Hudson Bd. Edn., 1966-67. Served with AUS, 1946-47. Mem. Phi Beta Kappa. Clubs: Harvard, Sky (N.Y.C.); Bedford Golf and Tennis (N.Y.). Home: 756 Guard Hill Rd Bedford NY 10506 Office: 6 Riverbend Ctr 911 Hope St Stamford CT 06907

SARCHET, BERNARD REGINALD, retired chemical engineering educator; b. Byesville, Ohio, June 13, 1917; s. Elmer C. and Nellie Myrtle (Huff) S.; m. Lena Virginia Fisher, Dec. 13, 1941; children: Renee Erickson, Dawne, Melanie Koewing. BS in Chem. Engring., Ohio State U., 1939; MS in Chem. Engring., U. Del., 1941. From engr. to dir. comml. devel. Koppers Co., Inc., Pitts., 1941-67; prof. and founding chmn. dept. engring. mgmt. U. Mo., Rolla, 1967-88; mgmt. cons. Sarchet Assocs., Rolla, 1975—. Coauthor: Supervisory Management (Essentials), 2nd edit. 1976, Management for Engineers, 1981; contbr. articles to profl. jours. Mem. Planning Commn. Beaver, Pa., 1955-58; dir. Billy Graham Film Crusades, Rolla, 1969-75; area dir. Here's Life America, Rolla, 1977. Recipient Profl. Achievement award U. Del., 1952, Freedom Found. awards, 1974-75, Fellow Mem. awd., Am. Soc. for Engineering Educ., 1992. Fellow Am. Soc. Engring. Mgmt. (founding pres., bd. dirs. 1979—), Am. Soc. Engring. Edn. (chmn. 1976). Achievements include patent on composition for producing detergent polyglycol condensation products; led in developing engineering management for engineers. Home: PO Box 68 Rolla MO 65401-0068

SARCHI, BERNARD, healthcare administrator; b. Holyoke, Mass., May 28, 1943; s. Edmund and Clare Olive (Collins) S.; m. Ruth Ann Huddleson; 1 child, Pamela. AA, Mohegian Community Coll., Norwich, Conn., 1977; BA, Annhurst Coll., Woodstock, Conn., 1979; MS, DePaul U., Chgo., 1987. Specialist Gen. Dynamics, Groton, Conn., 1965-68; buyer Eldridge Hardware Co., Inc., Taftville, Conn., 1968-74; asst. coach Annhurst Coll., 1977-79; head coach Woodstock Sch., 1979-80; field rep. Blinded Vets Assn., Washington, 1980-82; asst. chief VA Med., Chgo., 1982-83; reg. cons. VA Blind Rehab. Svc., Washington, 1983-84; dir. prosthetic VA Med. Ctr. West Side, Chgo., 1984—; cons. VA, 1983-84; bd. dirs. thrift stores DAV, Chgo., 1987—, state comdr., 1991-93, nat. exec. com., 1992—. Cubmaster Boy Scouts Am., Norwich, 1960-65, dist. commr., 1966-75; mem. Commn. on Vets. Affairs, Chgo., 1986—. Recipient Silver Beaver, Boy Scouts Am., 1972, Bronze Peligen, 1971. Republican. Roman Catholic. Avocations: football, baseball, basketball, soccer, swimming, running. Office: VA Med Ctr 820S S Damen Ave # 121 Chicago IL 60612-3728

SARD, GEORGE, public relations company executive; b. N.Y.C., May 13, 1953. BA, Clark Univ., 1975. Pub. rels. writer Clark Univ., 1975-78; dir. pub. rels. East N.Y. Svgs. Bank, 1978-80; acct. exec. Adams & Rinehart, Inc. (now Ogilvy Adams & Rinehart), 1980-82, v.p., 1982-86; pres., chief operating officer Adams & Rinehart, Inc. (now Ogilvy Adams & Rinehart), N.Y.C., from 1986; now chmn./N.Y. Ogilvy Adams & Rinehart, N.Y.C.; chmn., CEO Sard Verbinnen & Co., N.Y.C., 1992—. Office: Sard Verbinnen & Co 630 3rd Ave New York NY 10017-6705

SARDANIS, ANDREW S., investment company executive. With Zambian Ministeries of Fin., Comm., and Industry, Zambia, Africa, 1965-1970; chmn. ITM Corp, N.Y.C., 1970—. Office: ITM Corp 126 E 56th St New York NY 10022-3613

SARDI, MAURICE CHARLES, contract furniture company executive; b. Jamestown, N.Y., Mar. 25, 1935; s. Charles John and Margaret Mary (Mistretta) S.; m. Jacqueline Ann Lawrence, May 3, 1958; children: Christopher Lawrence, Charles John, Elizabeth Ann, Maureen Rose. BSEE, U. Notre Dame, 1957; MBA, George Washington U., 1966. With Westinghouse Electric Corp., 1971-90, group mktg. mgr. Constrn. Group, 1973-74, div. gen. mgr. Semiconductor Div., 1974-77; gen. mgr. mktg. ops. Westinghouse Elevator Co., Short Hills, N.J., 1977-81; div. gen. mgr. Westinghouse Furniture System, Grand Rapids, Mich., 1981-84; v.p. corp. rels. Westinghouse Electric Corp., Pitts., 1984-88, exec. v.p. Comml. Group and Corp. Resources, 1988-90, chmn., chief exec. officer The Knoll Group, 1990—. Bd. dirs., past chmn. Allegheny County Commn. for Workforce Excellence, Pitts., 1976—; mem. steering com. Leadership Pitts, 1986; mem. Pa. State Job Tng. Coordinating Coun., 1987—; bd. dirs. Pitts. Ballet Theatre, 1989—. Mem. Pitts. Field Club, Laurel Valley Golf Club. Republican. Roman Catholic. Office: The Knoll Group 6 Gateway Ctr Pittsburgh PA 15222-1318

SARDIÑA, ADOLFO F. See ADOLFO

SAREERAM, RAY RUPCHAND, naval officer; b. Orangevale, Calif., Feb. 16, 1938; s. Charles and Lajwanti (Ram) S.; m. Catherine Marie Glancey,

May 6, 1967; children: Catherine M., Thomas C., Stephanie E. BA, Sacramento State Coll., 1960; MBA, U. Mich., 1973. Commd. ensign USN, 1962, advanced through grades to rear adm., 1989; dir. supply program and policy div. (N41) USN, Washington. Roman Catholic. Home: 5817 Colfax Ave Alexandria VA 22311-1013 Office: USN Supply Program & Policy Div (N41) Office Chief Naval Ops Washington DC 20350-2000

SARGEANT, ERNEST JAMES, lawyer; b. Spokane, Wash., Sept. 26, 1918; s. Ernest Edward and Louise (McWhinnie) S.; m. Helene Sophie Kazanjian, Jan. 29, 1944. B.A. cum laude, Harvard U., 1940, LL.B. magna cum laude, 1947. Bar: Mass. 1947. Assoc. Ropes & Gray, Boston, 1947, 52-56, ptnr., 1956-90, of counsel, 1991—; lectr. law Harvard U. Law Sch., Cambridge, Mass., 1961-62, 65-92; adj. prof. Boston Coll. Law Sch., 1990—. Grad. treas. Harvard Law Rev., Cambridge, 1971—. Capt. U.S. Army, 1942-46, 51-52. Mem. Am. Law Inst. (council), ABA, Boston Bar Assn. Clubs: Union (Boston); Country (Brookline, Mass.). Home: 24 Highgate Wellesley Hills MA 02181-1420 Office: Ropes & Gray 1 International Plz Boston MA 02110-2624

SARGENT, ARLENE HONDL, nursing educator; b. Little Falls, Minn., Jan. 11, 1944; d. Anton Clarence and Eleanor (Buerman) Hondl; m. Kenneth William Sargent, June 16, 1972; children: Lisa, Michelle. BS, Coll. St. Catherine, St. Paul; MS, U. Minn., 1972; EdD, No. Ill. U., 1980. Staff nurse U. Wash. Hosp., Seattle, 1969-70; asst. head nurse U. Minn. Hosp., Mpls., 1970-72; instr. nursing Loyola U., Chgo., 1972-75; asst. prof. No. Ill. U., De Kalb, 1975-79; chmn. dept. nursing U. Dubuque, Iowa, 1980-83; prof. Holy Names Coll., Oakland, Calif., 1983-89, chairperson of nursing, 1989—, coord. of BSN teleconf. program, 1994—; cons. Mercy Health Ctr., Dubuque, 1980-83; reviewer textbooks Mosby & W.B. Saunders Pub. Co., vis. prof. Kumomoto U., Japan, 1994. Chmn. bioethics com., Lafayette, Calif., 1985—. Mem. Am. Nurses Assn., Calif. Nurses Assn., Am. Assn. Adult Continuing Edn., Sigma Theta Tau, Kappa Delta Pi, Pi Lambda Theta. Presbyterian. Avocations: running, reading. Home: 15 Sessions Rd Lafayette CA 94549 Office: Holy Names Coll 3500 Mountain Blvd Oakland CA 94619-1699

SARGENT, CHARLES LEE, recreation vehicle and pollution control systems manufacturing company executive; b. Flint, Mich., Mar. 22, 1937; s. Frank T. and Evelyn M. (Martinson) S.; m. Nancy Cook, June 9, 1962; children: Wendy L., Joy A., Candace L. B ME, GM Inst., 1960; MBA, Harvard U., 1962. Reliability engr. AC Spark Plug div. GM, Flint, 1962-63; with Thetford Corp., Ann Arbor, Mich., 1962-95, pres., chmn. bd. dirs., 1974-95; ret., 1995; pres., chmn. bd. dirs Thermassan Corp., 1969-72; bd. dirs. First of Am. Bank Ann Arbor, 1976-94, First of Am. Bank-Mich., 1995—; trustee Lincoln Cons. Schs., 1973-77; GMI Engring. and Mgmt. Inst., Flint, 1989—. Patentee in field. Elder Presbyn. Ch. Recipient Entrepreneurial Achievement award GMI, 1989; named Entrepreneur of the Yr., Harvard Bus. Sch. Club of Detroit, 1981. mem. Barton Hills Country Club (bd. dirs. 1985-87, pres. 1987), Harvard Bus. Sch. Club of Detroit (bd. dirs. 1983-93). Avocations: traveling, golf. Home: 3774 Cracker Way Bonita Springs FL 33923

SARGENT, DAVID JASPER, university official; b. Manchester, N.H., Aug. 5, 1931; s. Merton Jasper and Marguerite (Riley) S.; student U. N.H., 1949-51; J.D. magna cum laude, Suffolk U., Boston, 1954, LL.D. (hon.), 1978; m. Shirley Woodbury Swift, Dec. 21, 1951. Bar: N.H., 1954, Mass., 1954; U.S. Supreme Ct. 1978. Assoc. Kowal and Sargent, Boston, 1954-57; mem. faculty Suffolk U. Law Sch., Boston, 1957-73, prof. law, 1961-73, dean, 1973-89, pres., 1989—; chmn. Chief Justice's Commn. Future of the Cts., 1989; cons. Am. Trial Lawyers Assn., 1957-81; mem. Mass. Jud. Selection Com., 1974-77, Nat. Bd. Trial Advocacy, 1978—. Trustee, Anatolia Coll. Thessaloniki, Greece. Recipient Nat. Service award Am. Trial Lawyers Assn., 1968; Outstanding Alumnus award Suffolk U. Law Sch., 1978; hon. mem. Minn. Bar. Mem. ABA, Am. Law Inst., Mass. Bar Assn. (chmn. com. trial practice 1974-77, chmn. subcom. ct. unification 1976), N.H. Bar Assn. Episcopalian. Club: Masons. Contbr. articles to legal publs. Home: 83 Church St Winchester MA 01890-2545 Office: Suffolk U President's Office 25th Fl 1 Beacon St Boston MA 02108-2770

SARGENT, HENRY BARRY, JR., holding company executive; b. Jackson, Miss., June 19, 1934; s. Henry Barry and Grace Richmond (Ellis) S.; m. Caroline Huey, Aug. 8, 1964 (div. 1978); children: Catherine Sargent Warshawsky, Carolyn, Henry B. III; m. Claire King, Dec. 23, 1978. BA, Ariz. U., 1956; MS, Columbia U., 1957. Various positions Ariz. Pub. Svc. Co., Phoenix, 1957-67, contr., 1967-69, v.p. mktg. then customer svc., 1969-75, v.p. fin., 1975-81, also bd. dirs., exec. v.p., 1981-86; exec. v.p., chief fin. officer Pinnacle West Capital Corp., Phoenix, 1985—, also bd. dirs.; bd. dirs. MeraBank, Phoenix, Magma Copper Co., San Manuel, Ariz. Pres., dir. Phoenix Symphony Assn., 1969-79; chmn. Nat. Alliance Businessmen, Phoenix, 1970-71; chmn. Ariz. Theatre Co., Phoenix and Tucson, 1985—; chmn. Cen. Phoenix Com., 1987—. Mem. Phi Beta Kappa. Republican. Episcopalian. Clubs: Phoenix Country; Univ. (N.Y.C.). Avocations: theater, sports, music, reading. Home: 2201 N Central Ave Phoenix AZ 85004-1424 Office: Pinnacle W Capital Corp 411 N Central Ave Phoenix AZ 85004-2115

SARGENT, JAMES CUNNINGHAM, lawyer; b. New Haven, Feb. 26, 1916; s. Murray and Mary Hale (Cunningham) S.; m. Rebecca Porteous Jackson, Jan. 23, 1943; children: Stephen Denny, James Cunningham, Felicity Hale, Sarah Blanchard. Grad., Taft Sch., 1935; B.A., U. Va., 1938, LL.B., 1940. Bar: N.Y. 1940, D.C. 1961. With Clarke & Baldwin, N.Y.C. 1940-41; trial atty. Consol. Edison Co. of N.Y., 1941-51; asst. atty. gen., elections fraud bur. State of N.Y., 1948; law asst. appellate div. N.Y. Supreme Ct., 1951-54; asso. atty. Spence & Hotchkiss, N.Y.C., 1954-55; regional adminstr. SEC, N.Y.C., 1955-56; mem. SEC, 1956-60; asst. gen. counsel CIT Finance Corp., N.Y.C., 1960-64; mem. Whitman & Ransom (and predecessors), 1964-94; guest lectr. corporate securities U. Va. Law Sch., 1958-60, Practicing Law Inst., 1962—. Served from pvt. to capt. USAAF, 1942-46. Mem. St. Andrews Soc., Bar Assn. City N.Y., N.Y. County Lawyers Assn., ABA, Fed. Bar Assn., Fed. Bar Coun., Va. Bar Assn. (hon.), U. Va. Law Sch. Alumni Assn. (pres.), Order of Coif, Sky Club, Univ. Club (N.Y.C.), Church Club (N.Y.C.), Downtown Assn. (N.Y.C.), Capitol Hill Club (Washington), Army-Navy Club (Washington), Farmington Country Club, Phi Delta Phi. Episcopalian. Home: 310 E 84th St New York NY 10028-4405 Office: Whitman & Ransom 200 Park Ave New York NY 10166-0001

SARGENT, JAMES O'CONNOR, freelance writer; b. N.Y.C., June 15, 1918; s. Joseph Hughes and Maryann Josephine (O'Connor) S.; m. Mildred Elizabeth Clark, apr. 19, 1949. Student, British Intelligence Sch., Calcutta, India, summer 1944, Fordham U., 1949-51. Ghostwriter, freelance writer, 1949—; founder Washington Writers Group, Washington, 1960—. Author: (novellas) You Don't Bury on Christmas, 1960, Interregnum in a Commune, 1968, The Button Man, 1969, Moon in Pisces, 1970, Death in Saigon, 1971, Last Minuet in Washington, 1973, (screenplay) Queen Victoria and Lady Flora, 1993, (play) Loss of Innocence, 1994; pub. over 1500 works. Liaison with Peiping Aviators Assn., 1995. Maj. USAF, 1942-47. Decorated Bronze Star, Chinese medal of freedom. Mem. 14th USAF Assn., 528th Fighter Squadron Assn. (officer). Avocations: walking 5 miles per day, genealogy, World War I & II history, friendships. Home: 1019 Stillbrook Rd Pensacola FL 32514-1629

SARGENT, JOHN TURNER, publisher; b. Lawrence, N.Y., June 26, 1924; s. Charles and Dagmar (Wetmore) S.; m. Neltje Doubleday, May 16, 1953 (div.); children—Ellen, John Turner; m. Elizabeth Nichols Kelly, Dec. 21, 1985. Copywriter, advt. mgr., editor Doubleday & Co., N.Y.C., 1945-54; former gen. mgr. Garden City Books; bus. mgr., dir. Doubleday & Co., Inc., 1955-60, pres., 1961-78, former chmn. bd., chmn. exec. com., also bd. dirs., ret.; dir. Grumman Corp., Centennial Ins. Co.; trustee East Rivers Savs. Bank, Atlantic Mut. Ins. Co. Trustee N.Y. Zool. Soc., N.Y. Pub. Library, Kipsbay Boys Club, Alger Fund, Castle Convertible Fund; bd. dirs. Am. Acad. in Rome. Clubs: Knickerbocker, Century Assn., Maidstone.

SARGENT, JOSEPH DENNY, insurance executive; b. West Hartford, Conn., Sept. 11, 1929; s. Thomas Denny and Elizabeth (Owen) S.; m. Mary A. Tennant, June 25, 1955; children: Robert Tennant, Thomas Denny II, Mary Diane, Suzanne Davis. Grad., St. Paul's Sch., Concord, N.H., 1948;

BA, Yale U., 1952. With Conning & Co., Inc., Hartford, Conn., ptnr., 1957—; mng. ptnr. Conning & Co., Inc., 1986-92; chmn., chief exec. officer Conning & Co., 1986-91, chmn., 1992; chmn. Conning Internat., London, 1986-92; vice chmn. Conning & Co., 1993—, also bd. dirs., 1993—; bd. dirs. Beekley Corp., Bristol, Conn., Trenwick Reins., Stamford, Conn., Exec. Risk Ins. Co., Simsbury, Conn., MMI Co., Chgo., Blanch, Mpls., Mut. Risk, Bermuda, Policy Mgmt. Sys., Columbia, S.C., Corning & Co., Hartford; chmn. Conn. Surety Corp., Hartford, Bradley, Foster & Sargent, Hartford; trustee McLean Fund; chmn., treas. SKI Ltd.; chmn. Beazley Furlonge Holdings, Ltd., London. Past trustee Wadsworth Atheneum; past trustee Children's Svcs. of Conn.; trustee Hartford Hosp. Mem. Yale Club (Hartford), Hartford Club, Hartford Golf Club. Home: 25 Colony Rd West Hartford CT 06117-2215 Office: City Place II 185 Asylum St Hartford CT 06103-3401

SARGENT, LIZ ELAINE (ELIZABETH SARGENT), safety consulting executive; b. Meadville, Pa., Apr. 17, 1942; d. Melvin Ellsworth and Roberta Jean (Beach) Taylor; m. Lawrence Sargent, Sept. 6, 1969; 1 child, Kathy-Dawn. Allegheny Coll., 1964; AA cum laude, Cuyahoga C.C., Cleve., 1987, Assoc. in Transp. cum laude, 1989; BA, Ithaca Coll., 1993. Car distbr. Norfolk and Western R.R., Cleve., 1963-69; account mgr. Ill. Cen. R.R., Cleve., 1970-73; traffic coord. Carlon Pipe, Mantua, Ohio, 1973-75; chief dispatcher X.L. Trucking, Coshocton, Ohio, 1975-77; corp. log auditor Anchor Motor Freight, Beachwood, Ohio, 1977-78; cons. Saf-T, Parma, Ohio, 1978-84; v.p. safety Saf-T, Shaker Heights, Ohio, 1987-91; dir. safety Sherwin Williams, Cleve., 1984-87; pres. Safety Advisors for Transp., Inc., Beachwood, Ohio, 1991—; speaker Coshocton (Ohio) Traffic Club, 1984, Am. Indsl. Hygiene, Cleve., 1985. Author: Hall Chemical-Safety Procedures, 1983-84, Progressive Insurance, 1987, RL Lipton Co. manual, 1995; contbr. articles to profl. jours. Chairperson intergenerational com. Ch. in Aurora, Ohio, 1984-86; bd. dirs. Shaker Heights Teen Recreational Com., 1984-87. Delta Nu Alpha scholar, 1977. Mem. Ohio Trucking Assn. (nat. safety coun.), Cleve. Bd. Realtors, Motor Fleet Safety Suprs. (nat. com.), Fleet Maintenance Coun., Phi Theta Kappa. Republican. Avocations: interior design, painting, writing poetry and short stories, dried floral arrangements, hiking. Office: Saf-T 14716 Rockside Rd Maple Heights OH 44137-4016

SARGENT, MALCOLM LEE, research biochemist, research geneticist, botany educator and researcher; b. Grayling, Mich., Sept. 14, 1937; 3 children. BS, U. Mich., 1960; PhD in Biology, Stanford U., 1966. Asst. prof. botany U. Ill., Urbana, 1968-73, assoc. prof. plant biology, 1973—. Botany fellow NIH, 1966-68; recipient Stanley Greene award Internat. Assn. Bryologists, 1993. Mem. Am. Bryology and Lichenological Soc., Am. Soc. Plant Physiology, Genetics Soc. Am. Achievements include research in biochemical-genetics of circadian rhythms and development in Neurospora and other fungi, reproductive and developmental physiology of bryophytes. Office: U Ill Dept Plant Biology 265 Morill Hall Urbana IL 61801*

SARGENT, MURRAY, III, physicist, educator, software engineer; b. N.Y.C., Aug. 18, 1941; s. Murray Jr. and Lucy (Garfield) S.; m. Helga Reineke, May 21, 1967; children: Nicole, Christine. BS in Physics, Yale U., 1963, MS, 1964, PhD, 1967. Postdoctoral researcher Yale U., New Haven, Conn., 1967; mem. tech. staff Bell Telephone Labs., Holmdel, N.J., 1967-69; prof. optical sci. U. Ariz., Tucson, 1969—; sr. software design engr. Microsoft, Redmond, Wash., 1992—; vis. prof. U. Stuttgart, 1975-76, Max Planck für Festkorperforschung, 1975-76, Max Planck für QuantenOptik, 1982-92, U. Toronto, 1991; pres. Scroll Systems, Inc., Tucson, 1981—. Author: Laser Physics, 1977, Interfacing Microcomputers, 1981, IBM PC from Inside Out, 1984, Elements of Quantum Optics, 1991, Semiconductor Laser Physics, 1993, The PC from the Inside Out, 1994. Recipient U.S. Sr. Scientist award Humboldt Stiftung, 1975. Fellow Optical Soc. Am.; mem. Am. Phys. Soc., Sigma Xi. Republican. Avocations: music, hiking, bicycling. Office: Microsoft One Microsoft Way Redmond WA 98052

SARGENT, NOEL BOYD, electrical engineer; b. Cleve., Dec. 5, 1943; s. William Boyd and Jennie Parkin (Wheeler) S.; m. Joan Marie Hodan, Aug. 21, 1965; children: Andrew, Jeffrey. BS in Engring., Cleve. State U., 1970. Broadcast engr. Stas. WVIZ-TV, WERE am-fm, WKSU, Cleve., 1960-65; electronics technician NASA-Lewis Rsch. Ctr., Cleve., 1965-70, engr. aeroacoustics, 1970-76, rsch. engr., 1976-83, sr. engr. launch vehicles, 1983-87, tech. asst., 1988—. Mem. Soc. Automotive Engrs. (vice chmn. 1992—, sec. 1988-92), IEEE. Avocations: soccer, amateur radio. Office: NASA-Lewis Rsch Ctr 21000 Brookpark Rd Cleveland OH 44135-3127

SARGENT, PAMELA, writer; b. Ithaca, N.Y., Mar. 20, 1948. BA, SUNY, Binghamton, N.Y., 1968, MA, 1970. Am. editor: The Bull. of the Sci. Fiction Writers Am., Johnson City, N.Y., 1983-91; mng. editor Binghamton, 1970-73, asst. editor, 1973-75; editor (anthology) Women of Wonder, 1975, Bio-Futures, 1976, More Women of Wonder, 1976, The New Women of Wonder, 1978, (with Ian Watson) Afterlives, 1986, Women of Wonder, The Classic Years, 1995, Women of Wonder, The Contemporary Years, 1995, Nebula Awards 29, 1995; author: Starshadows, 1977, The Best of Pamela Sargent, 1987, Cloned Lives, 1976, The Sudden Star, 1979, Watchstar, 1980, The Golden Space, 1982, The Alien Upstairs, 1983, Earthseed, 1983, Eye of the Comet, 1984, Homesmind, 1984, Venus of Dreams, 1986, The Shore of Women, 1986, The Best of Pamela Sargent, 1987, Alien Child, 1988, Venus of Shadows, 1988, Ruler of the Sky, 1993, (Nebula Best Novelette award 1992, Locus Best Novelette award 1993). Office: PO Box 486 Johnson City NY 13790-0486 also: care Richard Curtis Assocs Inc 171 E 74th St New York NY 10021

SARGENT, ROBERT GEORGE, engineering educator; b. Port Huron, Mich., June 14, 1937; s. George O. and Marie L. (Roome) S.; m. Dorothy Baum, 1970; 1 dau., Tiffany. BSE, U. Mich., 1959, MS, 1963, PhD, 1966. Elec. engr. Hughes Aircraft Co., Culver City, Calif., 1959-61; faculty mem. Syracuse U., 1966—, asst. prof., 1966-70, assoc. prof., 1970-81, prof. indsl. engring. and ops. research, 1982—, chmn. dept., 1982-85, prof. elec. and computer engring., 1994—; vis. faculty Cornell U., 1981-82; bd. dirs. Winter Simulation Conf., 1974-84, chmn. bd., 1979-81, gen. chmn., 1977; chmn. TIMS Coll. on Simulation and Gaming, 1978-80. Dept. editor: Communications of Assn. Computing Machinery, 1980-85; editorial adv. bd. ACM Transactions on Modeling and Simulations, 1990—; contbr. articles to profl. jours. Recipient Service award Winter Simulation Conf., 1984. Mem. Assn. Computing Machinery (nat. lectr. 1985-89, Svc. award 1985), Ops. Rsch. Soc. Am., Inst. Mgmt. Scis. (Disting. Svc. award for Simulation 1985), Inst. Indsl. Engrs. (Svc. award 1985), Soc. Computer Simulation (bd. dirs. 1984-87), Computer Soc. of IEEE (mem. exec. com. simulation 1985—). Office: Syracuse U Dept Indsl Engring and Ops Rsch 439 Link Hall Syracuse NY 13244

SARGENT, THOMAS ANDREW, political science educator, university program director; b. Indpls., Apr. 24, 1933; s. Thomas Edward and Inez (Secrest) S.; m. Cecily Constance Fox-Williams, 1965 (dec.); children: Sarah Beatrice, Andrew Fox; m. 2d Frances Petty, 1987. BA, DePauw U., 1955, Greencastle, Ind., 1955; MA, Fletcher Sch. Law and Diplomacy, Tufts U., 1959, MA in Law and Diplomacy, 1968, PhD, 1969. With First Nat. City Bank, N.Y.C., 1959-64; asst. accountant, 1963-64; asst. sec. Irving Trust Co., N.Y.C., 1964-66; mem. faculty Ball State U., Muncie, Ind., 1969-89, dir. London Ctr., 1973-74, chmn. polit. sci. dept. 1977-80, prof. polit. sci., 1979-89, prof. emeritus, 1989—, acting asst. to dean Coll. Scis. and Humanities, 1981-82, assoc. dean Coll. Scis. and Humanities, 1982-85, dir. spl. programs Minnetrista Ctr., 1985-87; dir. E.B. Ball Ctr., Muncie, 1987-89, dir. emeritus, 1989—. Contbg. editor: Ripon Forum, 1973-78. Bd. dirs., exec. v.p. Ea. Ind. Community TV, Muncie, 1974-76, pres., 1976-77; mem. nat. bd. govs. Ripon Soc., Washington, 1976-84; mem. Indpls. Com. Fgn. Relations, 1977—; bd. dirs. Hist. Muncie, Inc., 1979-85, pres., 1980; bd. dirs. Muncie Civic Theatre Assn., 1978-81, 90—, v.p., 1992—; exec. dir. Ind. Consortium for Internat. Programs, 1982-88; mem. Ind. Real Estate Commn., 1983-91; trustee DePauw U., 1983—; bd. dirs. Muncie Symphony Orch., 1985—, pres. 1991-93; mem. bd. govs. Minnetrista Cultural Ctr., Muncie, 1989-94, chmn., 1992-94; bd. dirs. Arts Ind., Inc., 1992—; Muncie Children's Mus., 1994—. 1st lt. USAF, 1955-58. Named Sagamore of Wabash, 1988. Mem. Am. Polit. Sci. Assn., Am. Acad. Polit. Sci., Delaware County Hist. Alliance (bd. dirs. 1980-86, 87—, pres. 1987-91), Soc. Profl. Journalists, Del. Country Club, Muncie Club, Columbia Club (Indpls.), Maxinkuckee Yacht Club

(Culver, Ind.), Rotary, Phi Delta Theta. Republican. Methodist. Address: 2207 W Wiltshire Rd Muncie IN 47304

SARGENT, THOMAS JOHN, economics educator; b. Pasadena, Calif., July 19, 1943; s. Charles Robert and Helen Alma (Drucker) S.; m. Judith Leslie Tam, Sept. 3, 1964 (div. Apr. 1982); children: Robert John, Judy Tam, Anne Catherine. B.A., U. Calif.-Berkeley, 1964; Ph.D., Harvard U., 1968. Research assoc. Carnegie-Mellon U., Pitts., 1967; assoc. prof. U. Pa., Phila., 1970-71; assoc. prof., prof. econs. U. Minn., Mpls., 1971—; researcher Nat. Bur. Econ. Research, 1969-73, 79—; advisor Fed. Res. Bank, Mpls., 1971—. Author: Macroeconomic Theory, 1979; co-editor: Rational Expectations and Econometric Practice, 1981. Recipient Univ. medal U. Calif.-Berkeley, 1964; recipient Mary Elizabeth Morgan prize dept. econs. U. Chgo., 1979; fellow Nat. Acad. Scis., 1983, Am. Acad. Arts and Scis., 1983. Fellow Econometric Soc.; mem. Am. Econ. Assn., Phi Beta Kappa. Office: Stanford U Hoover Institute Stanford CA 94305

SARGENT, WALLACE LESLIE WILLIAM, astronomer, educator; b. Elsham, Eng., Feb. 15, 1935; s. Leslie William and Eleanor (Dennis) S.; m. Anneila Isabel Cassells, Aug. 5, 1964; children: Lindsay Eleanor, Alison Clare. B.Sc., Manchester U., 1956, M.Sc., 1957, Ph.D., 1959. Research fellow Calif. Inst. Tech., 1959-62; sr. research fellow Royal Greenwich Obs., 1962-64; asst. prof. physics U. Calif., San Diego, 1964-66; mem. faculty dept. astronomy Calif. Inst. Tech., Pasadena, 1966—; prof. Calif. Inst. Tech., 1971-81, Ira S. Bowen prof. astronomy, 1981—; Thomas Gold lectr. Cornell U., 1994-95. Contbr. articles to profl. jours. Alfred P. Sloan fellow, 1968-70. Fellow Am. Acad. Arts and Scis., Royal Soc. (London); mem Am. Astron. Soc. (Helen B. Warner prize 1969, Dannie Heineman prize 1991), Royal Astron. Soc. (George Darwin lectr. 1987), Astron. Soc. Pacific (Bruce Gold medal 1994), Internat. Astron. Union. Club: Athenaeum (Pasadena). Home: 400 S Berkeley Ave Pasadena CA 91107-5062 Office: Calif Inst Tech Astronomy Dept 105-24 Pasadena CA 91125

SARGENTICH, LEWIS D., legal educator; b. 1944. A.B., Occidental Coll., 1965; B.A., U. Sussex, Eng., 1967; J.D., Harvard U., 1970. Bar: D.C. 1972. Law clk. to assoc. justice Thurgood Marshall, U.S. Supreme Ct., Washington, 1970-71; staff counsel Washington Residential Project, 1971-72; assoc. gen counsel United Mine Workers, Washington, 1973-74; asst. prof. Harvard U., Cambridge, Mass., 1975-79, prof., 1979—. Office: Law Sch Harvard U Cambridge MA 02138

SARICH, VINCENT M., anthropologist, educator; b. Chicago, Ill., Dec. 13, 1934; s. Matt and Manda Saric; m. Jorjan Snyder; children: Kevin, Tamsin. BS, Ill. Inst. Tech., 1955; PhD, U. Calif., Berkeley, 1967. Instr. anthropology Stanford U., Berkeley, Calif., 1965; asst. prof. anthropology U. Calif. Berkeley, Berkeley, Calif., 1967-80; assoc. prof. U. Calif. Berkeley, 1970-81; prof., 1981—. Office: U Calif Dept of Anthropology 232 Kroebel Hall Berkeley CA 94720

SARIDIS, GEORGE NICHOLAS, electrical, computers and system engineering educator, robotics and automation researcher; b. Athens, Greece, Nov. 17, 1931; came to U.S., 1961, naturalized, 1971; s. Nicholas and Anna (Tsofa) S.; m. Panayota Dimaregona, Apr. 10, 1985. Diploma in Mech. and Elec. Engring., Nat. Tech. U., Athens, 1955; MS in Elec. Engring., Purdue U., 1962, PhD, 1965. Instr. Nat. Tech. U., 1955-63, Purdue U., West Lafayette, Ind., 1963-65, asst. prof., 1965-70, assoc. prof., 1970-75, prof., 1975-81; prof. elec., computer and system engring. Rensselaer Poly. Inst., Troy, N.Y., 1981—; dir. Robotics and Automation Lab., 1982—; dir. NASA Ctr. for Intelligent Robotic Systems for Space Exploration, 1988-92; engring. program dir. NSF, Washington, 1973. Author: Self-Organizing Control of Stochastic Systems, 1977, Stochastic Processes Estimation and Control, 1995; co-author: Intelligent Robotic Systems: Theory and Applications, 1992; also numerous articles, reports. Co-author: Intelligent Robotic Sys.; co-editor, contbg. author: Fuzzy Automata, 1977; editor, contbg. author: Advances in Automation and Robotics, Vol. 1, 1985, Vol. 2, 1990. Fellow IEEE (founding pres. robotics and automation council 1981-84, Centennial medal 1984, Disting. Mem. award 1989); mem. ASME, Soc. Mfg. Engrs./Robotics Internat.-Machine Vision Assn. (sr.), Am. Soc. Engring. Edn., N.Y. Acad. Scis. Home: 38 Londonwood Ave Loudonville NY 12211 Office: Rensselaer Poly Inst NASA Ctr Intelligent Robotic School of Engineering Troy NY 12180-3590

SARIS, PATTI B., federal judge; b. 1951. BA magna cum laude, Radcliffe Coll., 1973; JD cum laude, Harvard U., 1976. Law clerk to Hon. Robert Braucher Mass. Supreme Judicial Ct., 1976-77; atty. Foley Hoag & Eliot, Boston, 1977-79; staff counsel U.S. Senate Judiciary Com., 1979-81; atty. Berman Dittmar & Engel, Boston, 1981-82; chief civil divsn. U.S. Atty.'s Office, 1984-86; U.S. magistrate judge U.S. Dist. Ct. Mass., 1986-89; assoc. justice Mass. Superior Ct., 1989-94; dist. judge U.S. Dist. Ct. Mass., 1994—; mem. com. on civil rules Supreme Judicial Ct. Comments editor civil rights Civil Liberties Law Rev. Bd. trustees Beth Israel Hosp.; active Wexner Heritage Found. Nat. Merit scholar, 1969; recipient award Mothers of Murdered Children, 1993. Mem. Nat. Assn. Women Judges, Am. Jewish Com., Women's Bar Assn. (bd. dirs. 1982-86), Mass. Bar Assn., Mass. Assn. Women Judges, Boston Bar Assn., Boston Inns Ct., Phi Beta Kappa. Office: John W McCormack Courthouse 90 Devonshire St Rm 707 Boston MA 02109-4583

SARJEANT, WALTER JAMES, electrical and computer engineering educator; b. Strathroy, Can., Apr. 7, 1944; s. Walter Burns and Margaret (Laurie) S.; m. Ann Richards, June 30, 1972; children: Eric, Cheryl. BSc in Math, Physics, U. Western Ont., Can., 1966, MSc in Physics, 1967, PhD in Physics, 1971. Asst. dir. R&D Gen-Tec Inc., Quebec City, Que., Can., 1971-73; program mgr. Lumonics Rsch. Ltd., Ottawa, Ont., Can., 1973-75; staff scientist Nat. Rsch. Coun., Ottawa, Ont., Can., 1975-78; project leader Los Alamos (N.Mex.) Nat. Lab., 1978-81; James Clerk Maxwell prof. elec. and computer engring. SUNY, Buffalo, 1981—; dir. High Power Electronics Inst. Author: High Power Electronics, 1989. Fellow IEEE; mem. Electromagnetics Acad., Electrostatics Soc., N.Y. Acad. Scis., Rotary, Eta Kappa Nu. Office: SUNY Elec Engring Dept PO Box 601900 312 Bonner Hall Buffalo NY 14260

SARKISIAN, CHERILYN See CHER

SARLE, CHARLES RICHARD, health facility executive; b. Saratoga Springs, N.Y., Sept. 21, 1944; s. John Robert and Marjorie Elizabeth (Swick) S.; m. Marion D. Wallace, June 21, 1968; children: Richard Charles, Robert Edmond. BBA cum laude, Northeastern U., 1968; MBA, Babson Coll., 1973. CPA, Mass., Vt.; cert. mental health adminstr. Staff acct. Price Waterhouse & Co., Boston, 1968-70; George Kanavich, CPA, Wellesley, Mass., 1970-72; controller Human Resource Inst., Boston, 1972-73, adminstr., 1973-77; controller Brattleboro (Vt.) Retreat, 1977-78, dir. adminstrn., 1978-85, v.p., 1985-88, chief exec. officer, 1988—; bd. dirs., treas. Prouty Child Devel. Ctr., Brattleboro, 1983—; speaker in field. Mem. commn. Vt. Health Bldg. Fin. Agy., 1978—; alt. Va. Rep. Caucus, 1983; regent A.C.H.E. Va. Recipient recognition award Brattleboro C. of C., 1985. Fellow AICPA, Mass. Soc. CPAs, Am. Coll. Healthcare Execs.; mem. Am. Hosp. Assn. (del.-at-large 1988—, del.-at-large to regional policy bd.), Nat. Assn. Pvt. Psychiat. Hosps. (bd. dirs. polit. action com. 1983—), Vt. Soc. CPAs (Community Svc. award 1984), Hosp. Fin. Mgmt. Assn. (hosp. cost com. 1985—), Rescue, Inc. (trustee 1982-83). Republican. Avocations: skiing, fishing, tennis, photography. Home: PO Box 104 Brattleboro VT 05302-0104 Office: Brattleboro Retreat 75 Linden St Brattleboro VT 05301-4807

SARN, JAMES, physician, health association administrator; b. Orange, N.J., July 17, 1941; s. Chester Walter and Grace Marie (Lang) S.; m. Leslie Barton Warren, June 28, 1971; children: Fiona Rachel, Audrey Pearmain, Nicola Warren, Philip Hamilton. BS, U.S. Military Acad., 1963; MPH, U. N.C., 1972; MD, Duke U., 1973. Diplomate Bd. Med. Examiners. Dir. health, nutrition, population USAID, Managua, Nicaragua, 1974-78; dir. disease control Ariz. Dept. Health Svcs., Phoenix, 1978-80, health dir., 1980-83; agency dir. health and population U.S. Agency Internat. Devel., Washington, 1983-85; dir. health, nutrition, population U.S. Agency Internat. Devel., Khartoum, Sudan, 1985-87; dir. health and nutrition U.S. Agency

Internat. Devel., Cairo, Egypt, 1987-91; dep. asst. sec. internat. and refugee health Dept. Health and Human Svcs., Washington, 1991-93; dir. health, nutrition and population Save The Children, Westport, Conn., 1993—. Contbr. articles to profl. jours. U.S. delegate Internat. Conf. Nutrition, Rome, Italy, 1992, Pan Am. Health Orgn. Governing Coun., Washington, 1991-93, World Health Assembly, Geneva, 1991-93; mem. bd. Nat. Coun. Internat. Health, Washington, 1984, 85, 91-93. Capt. U.S. Army 1963-68, Vietnam. Recipient Bronze Star U.S. Army, 1965, 68, Medal Honor 1st Class Govt. Vietnam ,1968, Peacemaker medal Govt. Brazil, 1965, Surgeon General's Exemplary Svc. award Pub. Health Svc. Dept. Health and Human Svcs., 1993. Mem. AMA, APHA, Am. Coll. Preventative Medicine, Am. Soc. Tropical Medicine, Nat. Coun. Internat. Health (bd. dirs. 1991—). Home: 426 Judd Rd Easton CT 06612 Office: Save the Children 54 Wilton Rd Westport CT 06880-3108

SARNA, NAHUM MATTATHIAS, biblical studies educator; b. London, Eng., Mar. 27, 1923; came to U.S., 1951, naturalized, 1959; s. Jacob and Milly (Horonzick) S.; m. Helen Horowitz, Mar. 23, 1947; children: David E. Y., Jonathan D. BA, U. London, 1944, MA, 1946; minister's diploma, Jews Coll., London, 1947; PhD, Dropsie Coll., Phila., 1955; D Hebrew Letters (hon.), Gratz Coll., Phila., 1984; LHD (hon.), Hebrew Union Coll.-Jewish Inst. Religion, 1987; D Hebrew Lit., Hebrew Coll., Boston, 1991. Asst. lectr. Hebrew, Univ. Coll., London, 1946-49; lectr. Gratz Coll., Phila., 1951-57; librarian Jewish Theol. Sem.; also asst. prof. Bible Tchrs. Inst., 1957-63, assoc. prof. of Bible, 1963-65; assoc. prof. Bibl. studies Brandeis U., Waltham, Mass., 1965-67; Dora Golding prof. Bibl. studies Brandeis U., 1967-85, prof. emeritus, 1985—, chmn. dept. Near Eastern and Judaic studies, 1969-75, chmn. humanities council, 1980-81; vis. prof. Bible Dropsie Coll., 1967-68; vis. prof. religion Columbia U., 1964-65, 92, Yale U., 1992-94; vis. disting. prof. Fla. Atlantic U., 1995. Author: Understanding Genesis, 1966, Exploring Exodus, 1986, Commentary to Genesis, 1989, Commentary to Exodus, 1991, Songs of the Heart: An Introduction to the Book of Psalms, 1993; co-author: A New Translation of the Book of Psalms, 1973, The Book of Job, A New Translation with Introductions, 1980; editor, translator: Jewish Publ. Soc. Bible, 1966-85; editorial bd. Jour. Bibl. Lit, 1973-75, Soc. Bibl. Lit. Monograph Series, 1975—; deptl. editor Ency. Judaica; gen. editor Jewish Publ. Soc. Bible Commentary series, 1974—; editor Proceedings of the American Academy for Jewish Research; mem. editorial adv. bd. Biblical Archaeology Rev., Moment Mag.; contbr. to Ency. Judaica, 1972, Ency. Brit., 1974, Ency. Religion, 1986, Anchor Bible Dictionary, 1992, Oxford Companion to the Bible, 1993; also articles to scholarly jours. Assoc. trustee Am. Sch. Oriental Research; trustee, mem. exec. com. Boston Hebrew Coll.; acad. adv. coun. Nat. Found. Jewish Culture; trustee Annenberg Rsch. Inst., 1990—. Recipient Jewish Book Ann. award, 1967, Jewish Cultural Achievement award in Bibl. scholarship, 1994; Am. Coun. Learned Socs. fellow, 1971-72, Moses A. Dropsie fellow U. Pa., 1993, Inst. Advanced Studies fellow Hebrew U., 1982-83. Fellow Royal Asiatic Soc., Am. Acad. Jewish Research; mem. Soc. Bibl. Lit. and Exegesis, Am. Oriental Soc., Israel Exploration Soc., Archons of Colophon, Palestine Exploration Soc. Bibl. Colloquium, Assn. for Jewish Studies (hon. sec.-treas. 1972-79, pres. 1983-85). Home: 7886 Chula Vista Crescent Boca Raton FL 33433

SARNAT, BERNARD GEORGE, plastic surgeon, educator, researcher; b. Chgo., Sept. 1, 1912; s. Isadore M. and Fanny (Sidran) S.; m. Rhoda Elaine Gerard, Dec. 25, 1941; children: Gerard, Joan. SB, U. Chgo., 1933, MD, 1937; MS, DDS, U. Ill., 1940. Diplomate Am. Bd. Plastic Surgery. Intern Los Angeles County Gen. Hosp., 1936-37; resident oral and plastic surgery Cook County Hosp., Chgo., 1940-41; asst. to Dr. Marshall Davison (gen. surgery), Chgo., 1942-43, Drs. Vilray P. Blair and Louis T. Byars (plastic and reconstructive surgery), St. Louis, 1943-46; practice medicine specializing in plastic surgery Chgo., 1946-56, Beverly Hills, Calif., 1956-91; asst. histology U. Ill. Coll. Dentistry, 1937-40, prof., head dept. oral and maxillofacial surgery, 1946-56; asst. dept. surgery Washington U. Sch. Medicine, St. Louis, 1944-46; prof., dir. dept. oral and plastic surgery St. Louis U. Coll. Dentistry, 1945-46; clin. assoc. prof. surgery (plastic surgery) U. Ill. Coll. Medicine, 1949-56; adj. prof. oral biology Sch Dentistry UCLA, 1969—, mem. Dental Rsch. Inst., 1974—, adj. prof. plastic surgery Sch. Medicine, 1974—; attending staff Cedars-Sinai Med. Ctr., L.A., 1956-91, emeritus, 1991—, mem. staff, sr. rsch. scientist, chief plastic surgery, 1961-81; cons. in gen., plastic and maxillofacial surgery VA Regional Office, Chgo., until 1956; lectr. in field. Sr. author: (with Dr. Isaac Schour) Oral and Facial Cancer, 2d edit., 1957, (with Dr. Daniel Laskin) Surgery of the Temporomandibular Joint, 1964; editor: (with Daniel Laskin) The Temporomandibular Joint A Biological Basis for Clinical Practice, 4th edit., 1991, (with Andrew D. Dixon) Factors and Mechanisms Affecting Growth of Bone, 1982, Normal and Abnormal Bone Growth: Basic and Clinical Research, 1985, Fundamentals of Bone Growth: Methodology and Applications, 1991; contbr. chpts. to textbooks, articles to surg. and sci. jours., other pubs. Co-winner Joseph A. Capps prize for med. rsch., 1940, Frederick B. Noyes prize, 1940; recipient Kerbs award for rsch. plastic and reconstructive surgery, 1950, 1st prize, sr. award Found. Am. Soc. Plastic and Reconstructive Surgeons, 1957, Nat. Achievement award medicine Phi Epsilon Pi, 1964, 1st prize Am. Rhinologic Soc., 1980, medal Hebrew U., Jerusalem, 1985, medal Tel Aviv U., 1985, Disting. Svc. Alumni award U. Chgo. Pritzker Sch. of Medicine, 1987, hon. award Am. Soc. Maxillofacial Surgeons, 1990, Dallas B. Phemister Profl. Achievement award Dept. Surgery U. Chgo., 1993, Disting. Alumnus award U. Ill. Coll. Dentistry, 1994, Craniofacial Biology Rsch. award Internat. Assn. for Dental Rsch., 1995. Fellow ACS, AAAS, Am. Assn. Plastic Surgeons (hon.); mem. Calif. Med. Soc., L.A. Med. Soc., Am. Soc. Plastic and Reconstructive Surgeons, Plastic Surgery Rsch. Coun. (founding mem. 1955, chmn. 1957), Calif. Soc. Plastic Surgeons, Beverly Hills Acad. Medicine (pres. 1962-63), Internat. Assn. Craniofacial Biology, Am. Assn. Phys. Anthropologists, Internat. Assn. Study Dento-Facial Abnormalities (hon.), Sigma Xi, Omicron Kappa Upsilon, Zeta Beta Tau, Phi Delta Epsilon, Alpha Omega (Internat. Achievement medal 1988). Home: 1875 Kelton Ave Apt 301 Los Angeles CA 90025-4576

SARNELLE, JOSEPH R., electronic publishing specialist, magazine and newspaper editor; b. Bklyn., Aug. 24, 1951; s. Alphonse Louis and Julie Lena (Mingarelli) S.; m. Ruth Patricia Cullen, Aug. 5, 1982; children: Cullen Joseph, D'Arcy Emilie. BA, Cornell U., 1973; postgrad., Sch. Visual Arts, N.Y.C., 1976-77, The New Sch., N.Y.C., 1979-80. Graphic artist Lewahl KC Graphics, N.Y.C., 1974-76; editor United Bus. Publs., N.Y.C., 1976-79; mng. editor Lebhar-Friedman Inc., N.Y.C., 1979-88; assoc. mng. editor HomeOwner Mag., N.Y.C., 1988-90; sr. composition specialist Info. Builders Inc., N.Y.C., 1990—; cons. video Markham-Novelle Pub. Rels., N.Y.C., 1988-89; cons. Best info. Family Media, N.Y.C., 1990-91. Author, dir. (videos) J. Roland Pepe's Guide to New York City, 1980, Underground Roundup, 1981. Recipient McMullen scholar, Cornell U., Regents scholar, State of N.Y., 1969; Best Headline of Year award Lebhar-Friedman Inc., 1982. Mem. Bestinfo Users' Group of N.Y., 1990, Mensa. Office: Info Builders Inc 1250 Broadway New York NY 10001-3701

SARNI, VINCENT ANTHONY, manufacturing company executive; b. Bayonne, N.J., July 11, 1928; s. Alfred M. and Louise M. (Zoratti) S.; m. Dorothy Bellavance, Nov. 4, 1950; children: Louise Marie, Karen Lee, Vincent Anthony. B.S., U. R.I., 1949; postgrad., N.Y. U., 1950-52, Harvard U., 1973; LL.D. (hon.), Juniata Coll., 1979, U. R.I., 1985; DSc (hon.), New England Inst. Tech., 1991. Plant acct. Rheem Mfg. Co., Linden, N.J., 1950-53; dir. mfg. services Crown Can Co., Phila., 1953-57; dir. mktg. services Olin Corp., Stamford, Conn., 1957-68; with PPG Industries, Inc., Pitts., 1968—; v.p. mktg. indsl. chem. dept. PPG Industries Inc., Pitts., 1968-69, v.p., gen. mgr. indsl. chem. dept., 1969-75, v.p., gen. mgr. chem div., 1975-77, group v.p. chems. group, 1977-80; sr. v.p. PPG Industries Inc. (parent co.), Pitts., 1980-83, vice chmn., 1984, chmn., chief exec. officer, 1984—; bd. dirs. PNC Fin. Corp., Hershey Foods Corp., Pitts. Baseball Assocs.; chmn., chief exec. officer Inst. for Tng. of Handicapped in Advanced Tech. Chmn. Allegheny Conf. on Community Devel.; trustee U. R.I. Found., Juniata Coll., Carnegie-Mellon U.; bd. dirs. Pitts. Guild for Blind, 1980, Allegheny Gen. Hosp.; mem. bus. adv. coun. U. R.I., 1975—; chmn. Pitts. Opera Soc.; bd. dirs. River City Brass Band; chmn. Nat. Orgn. on Disability. Mem. Chem. Mfrs. Assns., Soc. Chem. Industry, Bus. Higher Edn. Forum, Bus. Roundtable, The Bus. Coun., Duquesne Club, Rolling Rock Club, Laurel Valley Country Club, Chartiers Country Club, Allegheny Club, Point Judith Country Club. Office: PPG Industries Inc 3503 Wagon Wheel Wichita Falls TX 76310-1423 also: Pitts Pirates 600 Stadium Cir Pittsburgh PA 15212

SARNO, MARIA ERLINDA, lawyer, scientist; b. Manila, Philippines, July 26, 1944. BS in Chemistry magna cum laude, U. Santo Tomas, Philippines, 1967; MS in Chemistry summa cum laude, Calif. State U., Long Beach, 1975; JD cum laude, Western State U., 1993. Bar: Calif. 1994, U.S. Patent Office, 1993. Instr. U. Santo Tomas, Philippines, 1967-68; sr. chemist, analytical rsch. and quality assurance Rachelle Labs., Long Beach, Calif., 1969-74; teaching/rsch. asst. Calif. State U., Long beach, 1971-73; mgr. in charge of radioisotope section Curtis Nuclear Lab., L.A., 1974; assoc. chemist, asst. to dir. quality control Nichols Inst., San Pedro, Calif., 1974-75; mgr. rsch. and devel. Baxter Healthcare, Hyland, Calif., 1975-91; legal coord. sci. affairs Immunotherapy div. Baxter Biotech, Irvine, Calif., 1991-93, mgr. regulatory affairs, 1994-95; sole practice, 1995—. Editorial bd: (tech. editor) Western State U. Law Review; Contbr. articles to profl. jours.; patentee in field. Mem. ABA, OCAABA, Am. Chem. Soc., Am. Intellectual Property Law Assn., Orange County Bar Assn., LACBA, Phi Kappa Phi, Phi Delta Gamma,. Home: 12541 Kenobi Ct Cerritos CA 90701

SARNOFF, ALBERT, communications executive; b. N.Y.C., July 19, 1925; s. Morris and Clara (Oppenheimer) S.; m. Nancy Hanak, July 25, 1968; children: Gary, Ken, Doug. B.A., Yale U., 1947. Buyer R.H. Macy & Co., N.Y.C., 1950-52; v.p. Pease & Elliman, N.Y.C., 1952-58; pres. Club Razor Blade Mfg. Co., N.J., 1958-62; sr. v.p., treas. Warner Communications Inc., N.Y.C., 1962-90; sr. cons. Time Warner Inc., 1990—. Mem. Metropolis Country Club, City Athletic Club, El Cabellero. Office: Warner Comm Inc 75 Rockefeller Plz New York NY 10019

SARNOFF, JILL ROBIN, lawyer; b. Bklyn., Mar. 18, 1954; d. Alvin Martin and Barbara Elaine (Lesser) S. BA, U. Rochester, N.Y., 1976; JD, NYU, 1979. Bar: N.Y. 1980, U.S. Dist. Ct. (so. dist.) N.Y. 1980, Calif. 1984, U.S. Dist. Ct. (cen. dist.) Calif. 1984. Assoc. Hopgood, Calimafde, Kalil, Blaustein & Lieberman, N.Y.C., 1979-81, Lieberman, Rudolph & Nowak, N.Y.C., 1982-83; trademark atty. Carter-Wallace, Inc., N.Y.C., 1982-83, Blakely, Sokoloff, Taylor & Zafman, Beverly Hills, Calif., 1983-86; trademark counsel Apple Computer, Inc., Cupertino, Calif., 1986-89, sr. trademark counsel, 1989—. Mem. ABA, N.Y. State Bar Assn., Calif. Bar Assn. (exec. com. intellectual property sect. 1990—), U.S. Trademark Assn., San Francisco Patent and Trademark Law Assn. Office: Apple Computer Inc 20525 Mariani Ave Cupertino CA 95014

SARNOFF, LILI-CHARLOTTE DREYFUS (LOLO SARNOFF), artist, business executive; b. Frankfurt, Germany (Swiss citizen), Jan. 9, 1916; came to U.S., 1941, naturalized, 1941; d. Willy and Martha (Koch von Hirsch) Dreyfus; m. Stanley Jay Sarnoff, Sept. 11, 1948; children: Daniela Martha Bargezi, Robert L. Grad. Reimann Art Sch. (Germany), 1934, U. Berlin, 1935; student U. Florence (Italy), 1948-54. Rsch. asst. Harvard Sch. Pub. Health, 1955-89; rsch. assoc. cardiac physiology Nat. Heart Inst., Bethesda, Md., 1954-59; pres. Rodana Rsch. Corp., Bethesda, 1959; v.p. Catrix Corp., Bethesda, 1958-61; inventor FloLite light sculptures under name Lolo Sarnoff, 1968; one-woman shows include Agra Gallery, Washington, 1969, Corning Glass Ctr. Mus., Corning, N.Y., 1970, Gallery Two, Woodstock, Vt., 1970, Gallery Marc, Washington, 1971, 72, Franz Bader Gallery, Washington, 1976, Gallery K, Washington, 1978, 81, Alwin Gallery, London, 1981, Galerie von Bartha, Basel, Switzerland, 1982, Gallery K, Washington, 1982, 83, 84, 85, 87, 88, 89, 90, 91, La Galerie L'Hotel de Ville, Geneva, Switzerland, 1982, Pfalzgalerie, Kaiserlautern, Fed. Republic of Germany, 1985, Gallery K, Washington, 1987-91, Galerie Les Hirondelles, Geneva, 1988, Rockville (Md.) Civic Ctr., 1988, Washington Square Sculpture Group, 1989, Internat. Sculpture Congress, Washington, 1990; represented in collections: Fed. Nat. Mortgage Assn., Washington, Brookings Inst., Washington, Corning Glass Ctr. Mus., Nat. Air and Space Museum, Washington, Kennedy Ctr., Washington, Nat. Acad. Sci., Chase Manhattan Bank, N.Y.C., Israel Mus., Jerusalem, Nat. Mus. Women in the Arts, Washington, others. Past trustee Nat. Ballet, Mt. Vernon Coll.; founder, pres. Arts for the Aging, Inc., Bethesda, Md., 1988—; active Washington Opera Soc., Washington Ballet Soc.; bd. overseers Corcoran Gallery Art, 1991. Recipient Gold medal Accademia Italia delle Arti e del Lavoro, 1980. Mem. City Tavern Club (Washington), Cosmos Club. Democrat. Co-inventor electrophrenic respirator; inventor flowmeter. Home: 7507 Hampden Ln Bethesda MD 20814-1331

SARNOFF, THOMAS WARREN, television executive; b. N.Y.C., Feb. 23, 1927; s. David and Lizette (Hermant) S.; m. Janyce Lundon, May 21, 1955; children: Daniel, Timothy, Cynthia. Grad., Phillips Acad., 1939-43; student, Princeton, 1943-45; B.S. in Elec. Engring., Stanford U., 1948, postgrad. Sch. Bus. Adminstrn., 1948-49; D.H.L., Columbia Coll. Engaged in prodn. and sales with ABC, Inc., 1949-51; prodn. Metro-Goldwyn-Mayer, 1951-52; with NBC, 1952-77; v.p. prodn. and bus. affairs NBC (Pacific div.), 1956-60, v.p. adminstrn. West Coast, 1960-62, v.p. charge West Coast, 1962-65, staff exec. v.p. West Coast, 1965-77; pres. NBC Entertainment Corp., 1972-77, Sarnoff Internat. Enterprises, 1977-81, Sarnoff Entertainment Corp., 1981—; exec. v.p. Venturetainment Corp., 1981-87, pres., 1987—. Exec. producer Bonanza: The Next Generation, 1987, Bonanza: The Return, 1993, Back to Bonanza Retrospective, 1993, Bonanza: Under Attack, 1995. Mem. Calif. Commn. for Reform Intermediate and Secondary Edn. Pres., Research Found., St. Joseph Hosp., Burbank, 1965-73, Permanant Charities Com. of Entertainment Industries, 1971-72; nat. trustee Nat. Conf. Christians and Jews. Served with Signal Corps AUS, World War II. Mem. Acad. TV Arts and Scis. (chmn. trustees 1972-74, chmn. past pres.'s coun. 1989-92), Acad. TV Arts and Scis. Found. (pres. 1990—). Office: 2451 Century Hl Los Angeles CA 90067-3510

SARNOFF, WILLIAM, publishing company executive; b. Mt. Vernon, N.Y., May 22, 1929; s. Morris and Clara (Oppenheimer) S.; m. Pam Martin, Dec. 24, 1955; children—Jeffrey, Richard, Nancy. BA, Stanford U., 1950; MBA, Harvard U., 1952. Treas. Club Razor Blade Mfg. Co., Newark, 1955-62; v.p. Warner Communications, Inc., N.Y.C., 1962-75; chmn. Warner Pub. Svcs., and predecessor firms, N.Y.C., 1975—. Trustee Horace Mann Sch., Beth Israel Hosp. Served with USAF, 1952-54. Office: Warner Books Inc 1271 Avenue of the Americas New York NY 10020-1300

SAROKIN, H. LEE, federal judge; b. Perth Amboy, N.J., Nov. 25, 1928; s. Samuel O. and Reebe (Weinblatt) S.; m. Marjorie Lang, Apr. 23, 1971; children: James Todd, Jeffrey Scott, Abby Jane. AB, Dartmouth Coll., 1950; J.D., Harvard U., 1953. Bar: N.J. 1954. Assoc. Lasser, Lasser, Sarokin & Hochman, Newark, 1955-58; partner Lasser, Lasser, Sarokin & Hochman, 1958-79; asst. county counsel Union County, N.J., 1959-65; U.S. dist. judge Dist. of N.J., Newark, 1979-94; U.S. ct. appeals judge Dist. Ct. Appeals of N.J., Newark, 1994—. Fellow Am. Bar Assn.; mem. Am. Law Inst.; Mem. N.J. Bar Assn., Essex County Bar Assn., Fed. Bar Assn. Office: US Dist Ct PO & Courthouse PO Box 419 Newark NJ 07101-0419

SARPKAYA, TURGUT, mechanical engineering educator; b. Aydin, Turkey, May 7, 1928; came to U.S., 1951, naturalized, 1962; s. Hasip and Huriye (Fetil) S.; m. Gunel Ataisik, Aug. 26, 1963. B.S. in Mech. Engring., Tech. U. Istanbul, 1950, M.S., 1951; Ph.D. in Engring. U. Iowa, 1954. Research engr. MIT, Cambridge, 1954-55; asst. prof. U. Nebr., 1957-59, assoc. prof., 1959-62, prof. mech. engring., 1962, distinguished prof., 1962-66; research prof. U. Manchester, Eng., 1966-67, U. Gottingen, Fed. Republic of Germany, 1971-72; prof. mech. engring., distinguished prof. mech. engring. U.S. Naval Postgrad. Sch., Monterey, Calif., 1967-71, 72—, Disting. engring. prof. mech. engring., 1975—; Cons. aerospace industry, 1967—, petroleum industry, 1976—. Author: Mechanics of Wave Forces on Offshore Structures, 1981; mem. editorial bd. Zentralblatt fur Mathematik; editor: Procs. Heat Transfer and Fluid Mechanics Inst., 1970; contbr. chpts. to many books and over 200 papers on fluid dynamics. Served with C.E. AUS, 1955-57. Fellow Royal Instn. Naval Architects, AIAA, ASME (Lewis F. Moody award 1967, exec. bd. fluids engring. fivsn., chmn. review com., Freeman Scholar award 1988, Engring. award 1991, Fluids Engring. award 1990); mem. ACME (Collingwood prize 1957, Offshore Mechanics and Arctic Engring. award 1993), Heat Transfer and Fluid Mechanics Inst. (chmn., Am. Inst. Aeros. and Astronautics, Am. Soc. Engring. Edn. Achievements include patent for fluidic elements. Home: 25330 Vista Del Pinos Carmel CA 93923-8804 Office: Naval Postgrad Sch Mech Engring Code ME-SL Naval Postgraduate Sch Monterey CA 93943

SARPONG, PETER KWASI, bishop; b. Maase-Offinso, Ashanti, Ghana, Feb. 26, 1933; s. Peter Donkor and Anna Yaa Nkansah. Student, St. Theresa's Maj. Sem., 1954-56, St. Peter's Maj. Sem., Cape Coast, Ghana, 1957-59; Licentiate in Sacred Theology, U. St. Thomas Aquinas, Rome, 1962, STD, 1963; Diploma in Anthropology, M of Letters in Social Anthropology, U. Oxford, Eng., 1965; DSc (hon.), U. Sci. and Tech., Kumasi, Ghana, 1979. Ordained priest Roman Cath. Ch., 1959. Chancellor Cath. Diocese of Kumasi, 1960-61; chaplain Okomfo Anokye Hosp., Kumasi; rector St. Peter's Maj. Sem., 1967-70; bishop of Kumasi, 1970—; chancellor Cath. Inst. West Africa, Port Harcourt, Nigeria, 1985—; Ghana rep. Synod of Bishops, Rome, 1971; rep. Bishops for Promotion of Christian Unity, Rome, 1972; consultor Papal Commn. for Justice and Peace, Rome, 1972-76, also West African regional corr.; West African regional liaison Secretariat for Christian Unity, Rome, Secretariat for Non-Believers; mem. com. for African internal affairs Pan African Bishop's Conf.; v.p. Cath. Bishop's Conf. of Ghana, 1982-88, pres., 1988-91; mem. standing com. Symposium of Episcopal Confs. of Africa and Madagascar. Author: The Sacred Stools of the Akan, 1971, Ecumenical Relations in Ghana, 1973, Some Christian Reflections on Poverty, Ghana in Retrospect, 1974, The One Honest Man, Ashanti Girl's Nubility Rites, 1977, Culture and the Kingdome, Guidelines on Priestly Life and Ministry, 1981, Essays on the University Student and Other Topics, 1982, The African Experience, 1987, African Theology: A Simple Description, Justice and Development in Africa: The Challenge of the 1990s, 1988, The Ceremonial Horns of the Ashanti, The Veneration of Ancestral Blackened Stool Among the Asante, 1995; translator ch. texts from English and Latin into Asante lang.; contbr. numerous articles to profl. jours. and mags. Chmn. coun. U. Sci. and Tech., Kumasi, 1972-77; chmn. Com. Planning for Pre-Univ. Edn., 1974-77, Authorship Devel. Fund, 1974-77; chmn. bd. govs. Nat. Cultural Centre, Kumasi, 1974-77; mem. Ghana Red Cross; mem. Coun. of State, 1980-81. Decorated by Govt. of Dahomey (now People's Republic of Benin), 1972; recipient Freedom award City of Tuskegee, Ala., 1973, prize for Disting. Writers, Ghana Book Devel. Coun., Asanteman award Asantehene, 1991. Avocations: chess, draught, football, writing, dancing. Address: Office of Bishop, PO Box 99, Kumasi Ghana

SARPY, LEON, lawyer; b. New Orleans, Nov. 25, 1907; s. Henry Leon and Anita Louise (Staigg) S.; m. Courtney Dickinson, July 7, 1938 (dec. Mar. 1945); children: Courtney Anne, H. Leon; m. Eleanor Legier, July 17, 1948; 1 son, John Robert. A.B., Loyola U., New Orleans, 1928, LL.B., 1931, LL.D. (hon.), 1961; LL.M., Georgetown U., 1932. Bar: La. 1931. Practice law New Orleans, 1932; mem. firm Chaffe, McCall, Phillips, Toler & Sarpy, 1948—; lectr. Loyola U. Law Sch., 1934-87, prof., 1992—; Sarpy Endowed prof., 1992—; dist. rent atty. OPA, 1942-43; reporter La. Criminal Code, 1942, La. Code Civil Procedure, 1960. Contbr. to legal jours. Chmn. CSC New Orleans, 1952-63; chmn. civic luncheon for Pres. deGaulle of France, 1960; pres. Asso. Catholic Charities New Orleans, 1953-54; mem. Audubon Park Commn., 1963-70; bd. pres. New Orleans United Fund, 1959-60; bd. dirs. Greater New Orleans Homestead Assn., 1940-87; chmn. adv. bd. Convent Good Shepherd, 1957-58; trustee St. Mary's Dominican Coll., 1963-67; chmn. Community Chest of New Orleans, 1970-73; adv. bd. Loyola U., 1964-72, Tulane Admiralty Inst., 1966-87. Mem. La. N.G., 1925-28; Mem. USCG Temp. Res., 1944-45. Decorated Legion of Honor France; named Outstanding Alumnus, Jesuit High Sch., New Orleans, 1964; recipient Brotherhood award NCCJ, 1964, Gold medal St. Mary's Dominican Coll., 1970, Pres.' medal Loyola U., 1989, Alexis deTocqueville award United Way, 1989; named Rex of New Orleans Mardi Gras, 1972; cert. appreciation Outstanding Community Svc. ARC, 1992. Mem. ABA (ho. dels. 1965-70), La. Bar Assn. (pres. 1964-65), New Orleans Bar Assn. (pres. 1951-60), Am. Law Inst., La. Law Inst. (v.p. 1961-68, pres. 1968-73, chmn. 1980-86), Inst. Jud. Adminstrn. (N.Y.), Southwest Legal Found. (chmn. research fellows 1970-72), Order of Coif, Blue Key, Delta Theta Phi. Clubs: Boston (New Orleans), Round Table (New Orleans) (pres. 1964-66), Serra (New Orleans) (pres. 1960-61); Order of St. Lazarus. Home: 455 Walnut St New Orleans LA 70118-4933 Office: 2300 Energy Centre 1100 Poydras St New Orleans LA 70163-1100

SARRIS, ANDREW GEORGE, film critic; b. Bklyn., Oct. 31, 1928; s. George Andrew and Themis (Katavolos) S.; m. Molly Clark Haskell, May 31, 1969. A.B., Columbia, 1951. Film critic Village Voice, N.Y.C., 1960-89, N.Y. Observer, 1989—; editor-in-chief Cahiers du Cinema in English; instr. Sch. Visual Arts, 1965-67; asst. prof. N.Y. U., 1967-69; assoc. prof. films Columbia Sch. Arts, N.Y.C., 1969-81, prof., 1981—. Author: The Films of Josef Von Sternberg, 1966, Interviews with Film Directors, 1967, The Film, 1968 The American Cinema, 1968, Confessions of a Cultist, 1970, The Primal Screen, 1973, The John Ford Movie Mystery, 1976, Politics and Cinema, 1978. Served with Signal Corps AUS, 1952-54. Guggenheim fellow, 1969. Mem. Am. Film Inst. (dir.), Soc. Cinema Studies, Nat. Soc. Film Critics, N.Y. Film Critics. *I keep on working toward that last deadline.*

SARRIS, SHIRLEY CORNELIA, publishing company executive; b. N.Y.C., July 25, 1938; d. Reuben Alexander and Sarah Sonia (Kahan) Kopatz; m. George Sarris, June 27, 1959 (dec. 1960). BA, CCNY, 1966; MA, U. Chgo., 1967. Mgr. rights, contracts Promo Coord Basic Books, N.Y.C., 1967-68; mgr. mktg. Swallow Press, Chgo., 1968-70; dir. mktg. John Wiley and Sons, N.Y.C., 1979-74, Arno Press, N.Y.C., 1974, Franklin Watts, N.Y.C., 1974-75, R.R. Bowker, N.Y.C., 1975-78; founder, pres. Sarris Bookmktg. Service, N.Y.C., 1978-92; pres. Thomson Learning divsn. Info. Reference Group Internat. Thomson Pub., N.Y.C., 1992—; leader seminar Folio, 1977—. Woodrow Wilson fellow, 1966; named One of 70 Women Who Made a Difference in the World of Books, Women's Nat. Book Assn., 1987. Mem. ALA, Publs. Mktg. Group, Book Industry Study Group, Am. Booksellers Assn. Democrat. Office: Thomson Learning Divsn Info Reference Group 1 Penn Plz Fl 41 New York NY 10011

SARRY, CHRISTINE, ballerina; b. Long Beach, Calif., May 25, 1946; d. John and Beatrice (Thomas) S.; m. Jim Varriale, Sept. 12, 1984; 1 child, Maximilian Sarry Varriale. With Joffrey Ballet, 1963-64; With Am. Ballet Theatre, 1964-68, prin. dancer, 1971-74; leading dancer Am. Ballet Co., 1969-71; ballerina Eliot Feld Ballet, 1974-81; mem. faculty New Ballet Sch., also freelance guest tchr. Performed ballets for Agnes DeMille, Antony Tudor, Jerome Robbins, Eliot Feld; appeared at White House, 1963, 67; U.S. Dept. State tours include, Russia, 1963, 66, S.Am., 1964, 76, various tours of N.Am., Orient, Europe, various appearances U.S. nat. TV; partnered by Mikhail Baryshnikov.

SARSON, EVELYN PATRICIA See KAYE, EVELYN PATRICIA

SARSON, JOHN CHRISTOPHER, television producer, director, writer; b. London, Jan. 19, 1935; s. Arnold Wilfred and Annie Elizabeth (Wright) S.; m. Evelyn Patricia Kaye, Mar. 25, 1963; children: Catharine May, David Arnold. BA with honors, Trinity Coll., Cambridge, Eng., 1960, MA, 1963. Dir. Granada TV, Manchester, Eng., 1960-63; producer, dir. Sta. WGBH-TV, Boston, 1963-73; pres. Blue Penguin, Inc., Boulder, Colo., 1974—; v.p. TV programming Sta. WYNC-TV, N.Y.C., 1989-90; dir. Pub. Broadcasting Assocs., Newton, Mass.; cons. to numerous pub. TV stations. Creator, producer MAsterpiece Theatre, PBS, 1970-73, Zoom, PBS, 1971-73; producer Live From the Met, PBS, 1977-79, Kid's Writes, Nickelodeon, 1982-83, American Treasure, a Smithsonian Journey, 1986, Spotlight Colorado, 1991, PArenting Works, 1993, Club 303, 1994. Served with Royal Navy, 1956-57. Recipient Emmy award, 1973, 74, Peabody award Ohio State U., 1978, Internat. Emmy award, 1983, Nat. Acad. TV Arts and Scis. Gov.'s award, 1991. Mem. Dirs. Guild Am., Nat. acad. TV Arts and Scis. (gov. Heartland chpt.). Avocations: music; cooking; gardening; travel. Home and Office: 3031 5th St Boulder CO 80304-2501

SARSTEN, GUNNAR EDWARD, mechanical engineer, construction executive; b. N.Y.C., Jan. 5, 1937; s. Peder and Jenny E. (Brynthe) S.; m. Marie E. Smulktis, Aug. 27, 1976; children: Jan, Janine, Thomas. BSME, Stevens Inst. Tech., 1958; postgrad., U. Pa., 1962-65; D Engring. (hon.), Spring Garden Coll., 1988. Registered profl. engr., 17 states. Test engr. Duquesne Light Co., Shippingport, Pa., 1958; with United Engrs. & Constructors, Phila., 1961-90, engring. asst. 1961-64, supervising mech. engr., 1964-67, supervising power engr., 1967-70, project engring. mgr., 1970-75, asst. chief mech. engring., 1975-77, mgr. dept. power engring., 1977-80, v.p. power, 1980-83, pres., chief exec. officer, 1983-90; pres., COO Morrison Knudsen Corp., 1990-94; chmn., CEO MK Internat. Group, San Francisco,

1994—; now mem. bd. dirs. Morrison Knudsen Corp., Boise, Idaho; dep. chmn. Fed. Res. Bank Phila., 1989-90; bd. dirs. Leopard Lake Farms, Inc., Pa., Allegheny Power System, Inc., N.Y.C., Neutron Tech., Boise, Idaho; exec. com. Internat. Energy Devel. Coun.; presenter in field. Contbr. numerous tech. papers to profl. jours. Bd. dirs., vice chmn. Greater Phila. Econ. Devel. Coalition, 1987-90; bd. dirs. Penjerdel Coun., Phila., 1988-90; trustee Spring Garden Coll., 1988-90; mem. Chesapeake Bay Found., Balt., 1987—. Lt. USAF, 1958-61. Recipient Thomas Alva Edison award, 1990; named Engr. of Yr. Engring. Socs. Pa. and N.J., 1988. Mem. ASME (Delaware Valley Engr. of Yr. award 1988), IEEE, Am. Nuclear Soc., Am. Nuclear Energy Coun., U.S. Coun. Energy Awareness, Gibson Island (Md.) Club, Yacht Squadron Club, Tau Beta Pi. Avocations: sailing, gardening. Home: PO Box 459 Belle Haven VA 23306-0459 Office: MK Internat Group 180 Howard St San Francisco CA 94105•

SARTO, GLORIA ELIZABETH, obstetrician/gynecologist, educator; b. Racine, Wis., Oct. 20, 1929; d. Nicolas Peter and Alida Marie (Heusdens) S. RN, St. Luke's Hosp., Racine, 1950; BS, U. Wis., 1955, MD, 1958, PhD, 1971. Diplomate Am. Bd. Obstetrics and Gynecology. Intern Cleve. Met. Gen. Hosp., 1958-59; resident Dept. Ob/Gyn. Univ. Hosp., Madison, Wis., 1959-63; asst. prof. dept. gynecology and obstetrics U. Wis., Madison, 1966-70; assoc. prof. U. Wis., Madison 1970-75; prof. U. Wis., Madison, 1975-76, assoc. chair dept., 1762-76; prof. dept. ob-gyn U. Wis., Milw., 1983-86, chair dept., 1983-85; prof. dept. ob-gyn, from asst. chair to vice-chair dept. Northwestern U., Chgo., 1976-83; prof. dept. ob-gyn U. N.Mex., Albuquerque, 1986—, chair dept., 1986—. Author: (with others) Comparative Mammalian Cytogenetics, 1969, Obstetrics and Gynecology, 3d edit., 1977, 4th edit., 1982, 5th edit., 1986, Gynecology and Obstetrics, Vol.1, 1978, Controversies in Contraception, 1979, Genetic and Environmental Factors in Experimental and Human Cancer, 1980, Clinics in Obstetrics and Gynaecology, Vol. 7, 1980, Critical Care for Surgical Patients, 1982, Genetics in Obstetrics and Gynecology, 1982, Gynecologic Signs and Symptoms, 1983, The Cytogenetics of the Mamallian X Chromosome, 1983, Cytogenetics and Cell Genetics, 1987, also abstracts, revs., trans.; contbr. numerous articles to profl. jours. NIH spl. fellow, 1963, N.Y. Acad. Sci. fellow, 1971. Fellow ACS, Am. Coll. Obstetricians and Gyncologists; mem. AAAS, AAUW, AMA, Albuqueque Obstet. and Gynecol. Soc., Am. Coll. Nurse/Midwives (cons.), Am. Fertility Soc., Am. Genetic Assn., Am. Gynecol. and Obstet. Soc., Am. Med. Women's Assn. (1st v.p. Chgo. br. 1981-83), Am. Soc. Human Genetics, Assn. Profs. Gynecology and Obstetrics, Assn. for Women in Sci., Birth Defect and Clin. Genetic Soc., Cen. Assn. Obstetricians and Gynecologists, Greater Albuqueque Med. Assn., Gynecol. Urology Soc., Hasting Ctr. Inst. Soc. Ethics and Life Scis., N.Y. Acad. Sci., Soc. Gynecologic Investigation, Tissue Culture Assn., Sigma Xi, Alpha Omega Alpha (Cen. Assn. Ob-Gyn award 1973). Office: U NMex Sch Medicine Dept Ob-Gyn 2211 Lomas Blvd NE Univ Of New Mexico NM 87131

SARTOR, ANTHONY JOSEPH, environmental engineer; b. Englewood, N.J., Mar. 28, 1943; s. John and Catherine (Dottino) S. Sr.; m. Maria C. Crisonio, Dec. 26, 1964; children: Lisanne, Colette (twins), John. BS in Engring., Manhattan Coll., 1964; MS in Engring., Mich. U., 1965, PhD, 1968. Devel. engr. Celanese Co., 1968-70; sr. water quality engr. Con Edison, N.Y.C., 1970-72; mgr. environ. affairs N.Y. Power Pool, 1972-74; pres. Sartor Assocs., Warren, N.J., 1974-77; exec. v.p., treas., sec. Paulus, Sokolowski, Sartor, Inc., Warren, 1977—; commr. N.J. Sports and Exposition Authority, 1992. Trustee Richard J. Hughes Found., Inc.; active Environ. Commn., Fanwood, N.J., gov.'s transition team N.J. Dept. Environ. Projection. Recipient Disting. Service award Fanwood-Scotch Plains Jaycees. Mem. Am. Chem. Soc., Am. Inst. Chem. Engrs., Na.t Soc. Environ. Engrs., Jaycees (past bd. dirs., pres.), UNICO (Environ. Sci. award), Italian-Am. Club, Sigma Xi, Phi Lambda Upsilon. Club: Italian-Am. (Fairview, N.J.). Home: 19 Kevin Rd Scotch Plains NJ 07076-2211 Office: PO Box 4039 67A Mountain Boulevard Ext Warren NJ 07059-5626

SARTOR, DANIEL RYAN, JR., lawyer; b. Vicksburg, Miss., June 2, 1932; s. Daniel Ryan and Lucy Leigh (Hubbs) S.; m. Olive Guthrie Moss, Oct. 12, 1957; children—Clara M., Daniel Ryan, Walter M. B.A., Tulane U., 1952, LL.B., 1955. Bar: La. 1955. Instr. Tulane U., New Orleans, 1955-56, asst. prof., 1956-57; ptnr. Snellings, Breard, Sartor, Inabnett & Trascher, Monroe, La., 1957—. Contbr. articles to profl. jours. Fellow Am. Coll. Trust and Estate Counsel, Am. Bar Found., La. Bar Found.; mem. La. State Law Inst. (mem. council 1969—, sec. civil law sect. 1969—), La. State Bar Assn. (chmn. sect. on trust estate, probate and immovable property 1973-74, bd. govs. 1974-75). Democrat. Methodist. Clubs: Lotus (Monroe), Tower. Home: 2405 Pargoud Blvd Monroe LA 71201-2326 Office: Snellings Breard Sartor 1503 N 19th St Monroe LA 71201-4960

SARTORE, JOEL, photojournalist; b. Ponca City, Okla., June 16, 1962; s. John Edward and Sharon Lee (Meese) S.; m. Kathleen Louise Vestecka, June 21, 1985; 1 child, Cole Woodrow. B in Journalism, U. Nebr., 1985. Photo intern The Witchita Eagle, 1984; staff photographer, 1985-88, asst. dir. photography, 1989, dir. photography, 1990; photographer Nat. Geographic Washington, 1991, contract photographer, 1992—. Recipient Award of Excellence Pictures of the Yr. Competition U. Mo., 1992. Mem. Nat. Press Photographer's Assn. (dir. region 7 1990). Methodist. Avocations: fishing, antique restoration. Office: Nat Geog Soc Photo Dept 1145 17th NW Washington DC 20036

SARTORELLI, ALAN CLAYTON, pharmacology educator; b. Chelsea, Mass., Dec. 18, 1931; m. Alice C. Anderson, July 7, 1969. B.S., New Eng. Coll. Pharmacy Northeastern U., 1953; M.S., Middlebury (Vt.) Coll., 1955; Ph.D., U. Wis., 1958; M.A. (hon.), Yale U., 1967. Rsch. chemist Samuel Roberts Noble Found., Ardmore, Okla., 1958-60; sr. rsch. chemist Samuel Roberts Noble Found., 1960-61; mem. faculty dept. pharmacology Yale Sch. Medicine, New Haven, Conn., 1961—, prof., 1967—, head devel. therapeutics program Comprehensive Cancer Center, 1974-90, chmn. dept. pharmacology, 1977-84, dep. dir. Comprehensive Cancer Ctr., 1982-84, dir. Comprehensive Cancer Ctr., 1984-93, Alfred Gilman prof. pharmacology, 1987—; prof. epidemiology, 1991—; Charles B. Smith vis. rsch. prof. Meml. Sloan-Kettering Ctr., 1979; William N. Creasy vis. prof. clin. pharmacology Wayne State U., 1983; Mayo Found. vis. prof. oncology Mayo Clinic, 1983; Walter Hubert lectr. Brit. Assn. Cancer Rsch., 1985; Pfizer lectr. in clin. pharmacology U. Conn. Health Ctr., 1985; William N. Creasy vis. prof. clin. pharmacology Bowman Gray Sch. Medicine, 1987; Wellcome vis. prof. basic sci. U. Pitts. Sch. Medicine, 1990; mem. sci. adv. bd. ImmunoGen, Inc., 1981—, U. Ind. Cancer Ctr., 1992, Cancer Inst. N.J., 1993—, Cell Pathways, Inc., 1993—; chmn. cancer sci. adv. bd. ViraChem, Inc., 1986-93, The Liposome Co., 1986—, OncoRx, Inc., 1993—; chmn. vis. sci. adv. com. Columbia U. Comprehensive Cancer Ctr., 1986—; chmn. pres.'s cancer adv. bd. Fox Chase Cancer Ctr., 1992—; mem. cancer clin. investigation rev. com. Nat. Cancer Inst., 1968-72, mgmt. cons. to dir. divsn. cancer treatment, 1975-77, bd. sci. counselors, divsn. cancer treatment, 1978-81, chmn. com. to establish nat. coop. drug discovery groups, 1982-83, chmn. special review com. Outstanding Investigator grant applications, 1992, chmn. ad hoc contracts tech. rev. group, 1993; mem. instl. rsch. grants com. Am. Cancer Soc., 1971-76, coun. analysis and projection, 1978-79; cons. in biochemistry U. Tex. M.D. Anderson Hosp. and Tumor Clinic, Houston, 1970-76; cons. Sandoz Forschungs-Institut, Vienna, Austria, 1977-80; mem. exptl. therapeutics study sect. NIH, 1973-77, working cadre nat. large bowel cancer project, 1973-76; mem. adv. com. Cancer Rsch. Ctr., Washington U. Sch. Medicine, 1971-75, SLSB Partners, L.P., 1992—; mem. sci. adv. com. U. Iowa Cancer Ctr., 1979-83; mem. external adv. com. Wis. Clin. Cancer Ctr., 1978-79, Duke Comprehensive Cancer Ctr., 1983—; mem. external adv. bd. U. Ariz. Cancer Ctr., 1982-92, U. So. Calif. Cancer Ctr., 1983-93, Clin. Cancer Rsch. Ctr., Brown U., 1980-86; mem. nat. program com. 13th Internat. Cancer Congress, 1979-81; cons. Bristol-Myers Co., 1982-93, mem. selection com. prize in cancer rsch., 1977-85, chmn. 1979-81, chmn. selection com. award for disting. achievement in cancer rsch., 1989-92; bd. advisors Drug and Vaccine Devel. Corp. (Ctr. for Pub. Resources), 1980-81, Specialized Cancer Ctr., Mt. Sinai Med. Ctr., 1981-90, Grace Cancer Drug Ctr., Roswell Park Meml. Inst., 1986-89; mem. med. and sci. adv. com. grants rev. subcom. Leukemia Soc. Am., 1984-88; bd. dirs. Metastasis Rsch. Soc., 1984-90; mem. program planning com. Mary Lasker-Am. Cancer Soc. Conf., 1986; mem. external sci. rev. com. Massey Cancer Ctr., 1989—; bd. visitors Moffit Cancer Ctr. U.S. Fla., 1989—; mem. ad hoc cons. group for cancer ctrs. program Nat. Cancer Adv. Bd., 1989-92; dep. dir. Cancer Prevention Rsch.

Unit for Conn., 1989—, acting dir., 1991-93; mem. nat. bd. Cosmetic Toiletry and Fragnance Assn.'s Look Good...Feel Better Program, 1989-91; mem. organizing com. Conf. on Bioreductive Drug Activation, 1993-94; chmn. bd. special cons. Inst. for Cancer Therapeutics, 1993—. Regional editor Am. Continent Biochem. Pharmacology, 1968—, exec. editor, 1993—; editor-in-chief Cancer Communications, 1989-91, Oncology Rsch., 1993—; editor Handbuch der experimentellen Pharmakologie vols. on antineoplastic and immunosuppressive ages on cancer chemotherapy Am. Chem. Soc. Symposium, 1976; exec. editor Pharmacology and Therapeutics, 1975—; mem. editorial bd. Internat. Ency. Pharmacology and Therapeutics, 1972—, Seminars in Oncology, 1973-83, Chemico-Biol. Interactions, 1975-78, Jour. Medicinal Chemistry, 1977-82, Cancer Drug Delivery, 1982-85, Jour. Enzyme Inhibition, 1984—, Anti-Cancer Drug Design, 1984—, Jour. Liposome Rsch., 1986-92, In Vivo, 1990—, Cancer Biotherapy, 1992, Cancer Rsch., Therapy, and Control, 1993—; mem. adv. bd. Advances in Chemistry Series, ACS Symposium Series, 1977-80; mem. editorial adv. bd. Cancer Rsch., 1970-71, assoc. editor, 1971-78, Current Awareness in Biol. Scis., Current Advances in Pharmacology and Toxicology, 1983—, Cancer Cells, 1989-91; mem. exec. adv. bd. Ency. of Human Biology, 1987-90, Dictionary of Sci. and Tech., 1989-91; editorial cons. Biol. Abstracts, 1984—; contbr. articles to profl. jours. Bd. dirs. Shubert Performing Arts Ctr., 1992—, Shubert Opera Bd., 1991—, chmn., 1993—. Recipient Outstanding Alumni award Northeastern U., 1987, Mike Hogg award M.D. Anderson Cancer Ctr., U. Tex., 1989, Alumni Achievement award Middlebury Coll., 1990. Fellow AAAS, N.Y. Acad. Scis.; mem. Am. Assn. Cancer Rsch. (dir. 1975-78, 84-87, chmn. publs. com. 1981-88, v.p. 1985-86, fin. com. 1985-88, exec. com. 1985-89, chmn. exec. com. 1987, pres. 1986-87, chmn. awards com. 1987, chmn. nominating com. 1993—), Am. Chem. Soc., Am. Soc. Microbiology, Am. Soc. Biochemistry and Molecular Biology, Am. Soc. Cell Biology, Am. Soc. Pharmacology and Exptl. Therapeutics (award in exptl. therapeutics 1986, award com. 1988, chmn. 1992), Assn. Am. Cancer Insts. (v.p. 1986, bd. dirs. 1986-89, liaison rep. to Nat. Cancer Inst. 1986, pres. 87-88, chmn. bd. dirs. 1989), Inst. of Medicine of Nat. Acad. Scis. (com. on govt. industry collaboration in biomed. rsch. and edn. 1989, mem. Forum on Drug Devel. and Regulation 1989—), Conn. Acad. Sci. and Engring., Coun. Biology Editors. Home: 4 Perkins Rd Woodbridge CT 06525-1616 Office: Yale U Dept Pharmacology 333 Cedar St New Haven CT 06510-3206•

SARTORI, GIOVANNI, political scientist; b. Florence, Italy, May 13, 1924; s. Dante and Emilia (Quentin) S.; 1 child, Ilaria. PhD, U. Florence, 1956; Doctor honoris causa, U. Genoa, 1992; Georgetown U., 1994. Prof. polit. sci. U. Florence, 1956-76, dean faculty of polit. scis., 1968-71; prof. polit. sci. Stanford U., 1976-79; Albert Schweitzer prof. in the humanities Columbia U., N.Y.C., 1979—; fellow Ctr. Advanced Study Behavioral Scis., 1971-72; sr. fellow Hoover Instn., 1976-79. Author: Democratic Theory, 1962, Parties and Party Systems: A Framework for Analysis, 1976, La Politica, 1979, The Theory of Democracy Revisited, 1987, Elementi di Teoria Politica, 1990, Seconda Repubblica?, 1992, Democrazia, 1993, Comparative Constitutional Engineering, 1994. Guggenheim fellow, 1979, Russell Sage Found. fellow, 1988-89. Mem. Am. Acad. Arts and Scis, Accademia dei Lincei. Home: 25 Central Park W Apt 270 New York NY 10023-7203 Office: Sch Internat Affairs 420 W 118th St Rm 1234 New York NY 10027

SARTORIUS, PETER S., lawyer; b. Jan. 15, 1947. BA, Williams Coll., 1968; JD, U. Va., 1974. Bar: Pa. 1975. Law clk to Hon. Leonard P. Moore U.S. Ct. Appeals (2nd cir.), 1974-75; ptnr. Morgan, Lewis & Bockius, Phila. Office: Morgan Lewis & Bockius 2000 One Logan Sq Philadelphia PA 19103

SARVER, EUGENE, finance educator; b. N.Y.C., July 15, 1943; s. Edmund and Stella (Bodek) S.; m. Vivian J. Ortega, Jan. 1, 1992. BA, Haverford Coll., 1965; MA, Johns Hopkins U., 1967; postgrad., U. N.C., 1967-69; ArtsD, Idaho State U., 1973. Lectr. in polit. sci. U. N.C., Greensboro, 1969-72; chief economist, corp. fin. advisor Credit Lyonnais-U.S. Group (#2 French Bank), N.Y.C., 1974-79; v.p., mgmt. cons. Chemical Bank, N.Y.C., 1979-84; dir. banking programs N.Y. Inst. Fin., N.Y.C., 1984-85; asst. chmn., assoc. prof. fin. Lubin Grad. Sch. Bus., Pace U., N.Y.C., 1985—; vis. prof. Internat. Fin. and Banking U. Malta, 1993; guest lectr. Ind. U. Sch. Bus.; cons. INFORMASI Indonesian Bus. Data Ctr., Jakarta, Malaysian Indsl. Devel. Authority, MTB Banking Corp., Republic Nat. Bank of N.Y., Swiss Banking Corp., Bank of Valletta Malta, Chemical, Chase, Citibank, Nomura Securities Internat., Global Mgmt. Inc. (U.S., Russia), World Trade Inst. of the Port Authority of N.Y. and N.J.; cross-cultural cons. Moran, Stahl and Boyer Internat. (subs. Prudential Ins. Co.). Author: The Eurocurrency Market Handbook, 1988, 2d edit., 1990; contbr. articles to The Malta Bus. Weekly, Third World ann. edit., Bank of Valletta Rev., Currency Forecasters Digest, Jour. of Commerce, The World and I, Money and Investments, Jour. Fin. Planning Treasury Mgr.; TV commentator on Financial Fitness. Pres., Haverford (Pa.) Young Democrats, 1964-65; candidate City Coun., Greensboro, 1971; elected bd. dirs. Am. Heritage (Mutual) Fund and Am. Heritage Growth Fund; elected gov. The Money Marketeers, 1990-93. Mem. N.Y. Assn. Bus. Economists (chmn. conf. com. 1989), Money Marketeers, Met. Econs. Assn., Assn. Downtown Economists, AAUP (pres. 1980—), Am. Fin. Assn., Fin. Mgmt. Assn., Mensa, Bradford Country Club. Democrat. Avocations: travel, skiing, furniture design. Home: 241 W 97th St Apt 8M New York NY 10025-6209 Office: Pace U Lubin Grad Sch Bus 1 Pace Plz New York NY 10038-1502

SARWAR, BARBARA DUCE, school system administrator; b. Mpls., Aug. 9, 1932; d. Harold Taylor and Barbara (Thayer) Duce; m. Mohammad Sarwar, Dec. 28, 1972; children: Barbara, Sarah, Franklin. BS, U. Colo., 1972; M Spl. Edn., Ea. N.Mex. U., 1975, Edn. Specialist, 1979. Cert. tchr., adminstr., N.Mex. Tchr. 2d grade, English as 2d lang. Lake Arthur (N.Mex.) Mcpl. Schs., 1972-74; tchr. spl. edn. Artesia (N.Mex.) Pub. Schs., 1974-79, ednl. diagnostician, 1979-88, dir. spl. edn., 1988—. Contbr. to profl. publs. Pres. Altrusa Club Artesia, 1981-82, 86-87, The Arc of Artesia, 1990-92. Named Employee of Yr. Arc of N.Mex., 1994. Mem. NEA, Artesia Edn. Assn. (pres. 1978-79), Internat. Reading Assn. (pres. Pecos Valley chpt. 1975-76, sec. N.Mex. unit 1977-78), Nat. Assn. Sch. Psychologists, N.Mex. Sch. Adminstrs. Assn., Phi Kappa Phi, Phi Delta Kappa. Avocations: reading, sewing, golf. Home: PO Box 1493 Artesia NM 88211-1493 Office: Artesia Pub Schs 1106 W Quay Ave Artesia NM 88210-1493

SARWER-FONER, GERALD JACOB, physician, educator; b. Volkovsk, Grodno, Poland, Dec. 6, 1924; arrived in Can., 1932, naturalized, 1935; s. Michael and Ronia (Caplan) Sarwer-F.; m. Ethel Sheinfeld, May 28, 1950; children: Michael, Gladys, Janice, Henry, Brian. B.A., Loyola Coll. U., Montreal, 1945, M.D. magna cum laude, 1951; D.Psychiatry, McGill U., 1955. Diplomate: Am. Bd. Psychiatry and Neurology. Intern. Univ. Hosps. U. Montreal Sch. Medicine, 1950-51; resident Butler Hosp., Providence, 1951-52, Hosps. Western Res. U., Cleve., 1952-53, Queen Mary Vets. Hosp., Montreal, 1953-55; lectr. psychiatry U. Montreal, 1953-55; lectr., assoc. prof. McGill U., 1955-70; prof. psychiatry U. Ottawa, Ont., 1971—, prof., chmn. psychiatry, 1974-86; dir. dept. psychiatry Ottawa Gen. Hosp., 1971-87; dir. Lafayette Clinic, Detroit, 1989-92; prof. psychiatry Wayne State U., Detroit, 1989—; cons. in psychiatry Ottawa Gen. Hosp., Royal Ottawa Hosp., Nat. Def. Med. Ctr., Children's Hosp., Nat. Def. Med. Ctr., Children's Hosp. of Eastern Ont., Ottawa, Windsor (Ont.) Western Hosp. Ctr., Ottawa Sch. Bd.; Z. Lebensohn lectr. Silbey Meml. Hosp. Cosmos Club, Washington, 1991. Editor: Dynamics of Psychiatric Drug Therapy, 1960, Research Conference on the Depressive Group of Illnesses, 1966, Psychiatric Crossroads-the Seventies, Research Aspects, 1972; editor in chief Psychiat. Jour. U. Ottawa, 1976-90, emeritus editor in chief, 1990—; mem. editorial bds. of numerous internat. and nat. profl. jours.; editor numerous audio-video tapes; contbr. numerous articles to profl. jours. Bd. govs. Queen Elizabeth Hosp., Montreal, 1966-71; life gov. Queen Elizabeth Hosp. Found.; cons. Protestant Sch. Bd., Westmount, Que., 1966-71; advisor Com. on Health, City of Westmount, 1969-71. Served to lt. col. Royal Can. Med. Corps, 1949-62. Recipient Sigmund Freud award Am. Acad. Psychoanalytic Physicians, 1982, William V. Silverberg Meml. award Am. Acad. Psychoanalysis, 1990, Poca award Assn. Psychiat.c Out Patient Ctrs. Am., 1990; Simon Bolivar lectr. Am. Psychiat. Assn., New Orleans, 1981; Can. Decoration Knight of Malta. Fellow AAAS, Royal Coll. Physicians and Surgeons Can. (mem. spl. psychiat. com. 1958-64, exec. sec. test psychiat. com. 1987-89), Royal Coll. Psychiatry (Found. fellow), Am. Coll. Neuropsychopharmacology (charter, life), Can. Coll. Neuropsychopharmacology (life, hon. found.), Internat. Coll. Psychosomatic Medicine (sec.-gen. 1979-83), Am. Psychiat. Assn. (life), Am.

Orthopsychiat. Assn. (life), Am. Coll. Psychiatrists (bd. regents 1978-80, emeritus fellow), Am. Psychopathol. Assn., Am. Coll. Psychoanalysts (pres. elect 1983, pres. 1984-85, Henry Laughlin award 1986), Am. Coll. Mental Health Adminstrn., Benjamin Rush Soc. (founding mem., councillor), World Psychiat. Assn. (chair Sci. program VI World Congress 1974, v.p. sect. on edn. 1989—, mem. internat. adv. com. 9th World Congress Rio de Janeiro 1993, mem. nominating com.), Collegium Internat. Neuropsychopharmacology; mem. Am. Acad. Psychiatry and the Law (sr., pres. 1977, Silver Apple award), Soc. Bio. Psychiatry (sr. mem., H. Azina Meml. lectr. 1963, pres. 1983-84), Can. Psychoanalytic Soc. (pres. 1977-81), Can. Assn. Profs. of Psychiatry (pres. 1976-77, 82-86), Am. Assn. for Social Psychiatry (v.p. 1987-89, pres. elect 1990, pres. 1992-94), Mich. Psychoanalytic Soc., Cosmos Club, Royal Can. Mil. Inst. Club. Home and Office: 3220 Bloomfield Shore Dr West Bloomfield MI 48323-3300

SASAHARA, ARTHUR ASAO, cardiologist, educator, researcher; b. Del Rey, Calif., May 11, 1927; s. Harold Hango and Blanche (Takayama) S.; m. Alice Ann Guenther, Apr. 2, 1955; children: Ann Mariko, Claire Michiko, Ellen Reiko, Karen Hideko, Mark Tadao. AB, Oberlin Coll., 1951; MD, Case Western Res. U., 1955; AM (hon.), Harvard U., 1974. Diplomate Am. Bd. Internal Medicine. Intern Boston City Hosp., 1955-56; jr. asst. med. resident Mass. Gen. Hosp., Boston, 1956-57; fellow in cardiology West Roxbury VA Med. Ctr., Mass., 1957-58, Children's Hosp. Med. Ctr., Boston, 1958-59; sr. resident in medicine Yale-New Haven Med. Ctr., 1959-60; asst. chief med. svc., dir. cardiopulmonary lab., dep. chmn. rsch. and edn. com. VA Hosp. West Roxbury, 1960-70, chief cardiopulmonary sect., 1971-74, assoc. chief staff for rsch. and edn., 1970-76; chief med. svc., 1974-82; chief med. svc. West Roxbury-Brockton VA Hosp., 1982-87; prof. medicine Harvard Med. Sch., Boston, 1974-93; prof. emeritus Harvard Med. Sch., 1993—; cons. cardiovascular-pulmonary diseases Boston, 1975-87; cons. pediatric cardiology Children's Hosp. Med. Ctr., Boston, 1976-86; physician Brigham and Women's Hosp., Boston, 1979-82, sr. physician, 1982—; dir. Thrombolytics Rsch. Pharm. Products Divsn. Abbott Labs., Abbott Park, Ill., 1987-95, sr. med. dir., 1995—. Author-editor: Pulmonary Embolic Disease, 1965, Pulmonary Emboli, 1975; contbr. articles to profl. jours.; designer constant infusion med. pump, Harvard Apparatus Co., 1973; editorial bd. Jour. Nuclear Medicine, 1981-83, Am. Jour. Medicine, 1971-72, Circulation, 1973-78, VASA, 1978-85, Jour. Cardiovascular Medicine, 1980-86, Primary Cardiology, 1986-89. With U.S. Army, 1945-47. NIH grantee, 1963-82; VA grantee, 1961-87. Fellow ACP, Am. Coll. Chest Physicians, Am. coll. Cardiology; mem. AAAS, Am. Fedn. Clin. Rsch., Internat. Soc. Thrombosis and Thrombolysis, Alpha Omega Alpha. Democrat. Episcopalian. Home: 1094 Linda Ln Glencoe IL 60022-1147 Office: Abbott Labs R D Ap9 Apt 9 Abbott Park IL 60064

SASAKI, CLARENCE TAKASHI, surgeon, medical educator; b. Honolulu, Jan. 24, 1941; s. Tsutomu and Carla Harumi (Mirikitani) S.; m. Carolyn Elizabeth Lindahl, June 26, 1967; children: Peter Gordon, John Eric. B.A., Pomona Coll., 1962; M.D., Yale U., 1966. Diplomate: Am. Bd. Otolaryngology. Intern San Francisco Hosp., U. Calif., 1966-67; resident in surgery Dartmouth Med. Sch., 1967-68; resident in otolaryngology Yale U. Med. Sch. Hosps., New Haven, 1968-73, faculty mem., 1973—, assoc. prof., 1977-82, prof. surgery, 1982—, chief sect. otolaryngology, 1981—; Charles Ohse prof. surgery Yale U. Med. Sch. Hosps., 1988—. Author: Surgery of the Skull Base, Head and Neck Surgery, Vol. 1 Atlas Otolarynogology, Vocal Fold Physiology, Laryngeal Function in Phonation and Respiration, Neurological Diseases of the Larynx; mem. editorial bd. profl. jours. Served to maj. M.C. U.S. Army, 1968-70. Recipient award Fowler Triological Soc., 1979. Mem. Am. Acad. Otolaryngology (1st prize clin. research), Am. Soc. Head and Neck Surgery (council), Assn. Research Otolaryngology, Am. Laryngol. Rhinol. and Otol. Soc. (coun. sec. ea. sect. 1990), New Eng. Otolaryngology Soc. (pres. 1987, council), Assn. Acad. Depts. Otolaryngolgy (council), Am. Laryngol. Assn., Pan Pacific Surg. Assn. Soc. for Neurosci., Soc. Neurovascular Surgery, Soc. for Head and Neck Surgeons, Am. Neurotolog. Soc., Pan Am. Assn. Oto-rhino-laryngology and Bronchoesophagology, Conn. Med. Soc., N.Y. Acad. Scis., Soc. Univ. Otolaryngologists, Collegium Orlas, Cartesian Soc., Am. Bronchoesophagological Assn., N.Am. Skull Base Soc., Laryngol. Cancer Assn. (Padua), Am. Otol. Soc., Dysphagia Rsch. Soc. (treas., pres.-elect), Phi Beta Kappa, Sigma Xi. Clubs: Lawn; Mory's (New Haven); Yale (N.Y.C.). Office: Yale U Med Sch Dept Surgery PO Box 208041 333 Cedar St New Haven CT 06520-8041

SASAKI, MIKIO, import/export company exeutive. Pres., ceo Mitsubishi Int'l Corp., N.Y.C. Office: Mitsubishi International Corp 520 Madison Ave New York NY 10022

SASAKI, TATSUO, musician; b. Okayama, Japan, Mar. 30, 1944; s. Koichi and Fumiko Sasaki; m. Shigeko Hayashi, Apr. 9, 1972; children: Jun Daniel, Maki Elisabeth. BA in Music, Tokyo U. of Arts, 1965; postgrad., Juilliard Sch. Music, 1965-67. Percussionist Am. Symphony, N.Y.C., 1966-67; solo timpanist Am. Wind Symphony, Pitts., 1966-67; asst. timpanist Israel Philharm. Orch., Tel Aviv, 1967-69; percussionist Japan Philharm. Orch., Tokyo, 1969-72; prin. timpanist Orch. Sinfonica Brazileiro, Rio de Janeiro, 1972-73, San Diego Symphony and San Diego Opera, 1973—; xylophone recitalist in U.S., Europe, Japan; spl. mem. Japan Xylophone Assn., Tokyo, 1971—; dir. Pacific Xylo-Marimba Trio, San Diego, 1974-76; dir. xylophone soloist Internat. Chamber Concert, Dusseldorf, Fed. Republic Germany, 1975—; dir. Sasaki/Rhein Brass Quintet, Dusseldorf, 1988—. Performer (album) Xylophone Artistry, 1983, (compact disk) Xylophone Artistry, Musical Heritage Soc., 1994. Fulbright scholar U.S. govt., 1965-67. Avocations: golfing, skiing, shogi (japanese chess). Home: 5842 Henley Dr San Diego CA 92101-4302 Office: San Diego Symphony 1245 7th Ave San Diego CA 92101-4302

SASAYAMA, TAKAO, electronics company executive; b. Tokyo, June 29, 1937; s. Shigetaro and Kimiko (Tsukada) S.; m. Fumiko Waga; children: Tomoo, Mizuko. BS, Keio U. Tokyo, 1963; PhD, Keio U. 1983. Rsch. scientist Hitachi Ltd., Hitachi, Japan, 1963-75; sr. researcher Hitachi Ltd., 1976-85; gen. mgr. Hitachi Am., Ltd., Tarrytown, N.Y., 1986—; v.p. Hitachi Am., Ltd., 1987—. Inventor automotive electronics and semiconductor devices; author sci. papers. Fellow Am. Soc Automotive Engrs., Japan Soc. Automotive Engrs. (Nakagawa prize 1983), IEEE; mem. Am. Phys. Soc., European Phys. Soc. Avocation: noh-play singing. Office: Hitachi Am Ltd 50 Prospect Ave Tarrytown NY 10591-4625

SASDI, GEORGE P., utilities company executive; b. Budapest, Hungary, Mar. 4, 1934; came to U.S., 1963; s. Miksa and Margaret (Krausz) S.; m. Susan T. Feldman, July 17, 1964; children: Richard, David. Diploma in Elec. Engring., Tech. U. Budapest, 1956; BS in Elec. Engring., U. Toronto, 1959. Registered profl. engr., Mass. Engr. Gatineau Power Co., Hull, Que., Can., 1959-63; with New Eng. Electric System, Westborough, Mass., 1963-93; planning engr. New England Power Service Co., Boston, 1963-69; project mgr. mgmt. info. systems New England Power Service Co., 1969-70; head engring. computer applications dept., New England Power Service Co., Westboro, Mass., 1970-73, project mgr. power plant projects, 1973-75, dir. power plant engring., 1975-77, v.p., chief engr., 1977-81; v.p., chief engr. New England Power Co., Westboro, Mass., 1984-91; also bd. dirs. New Eng. Power Co., Westboro, Mass.; pres. New Eng. Power Co., 1990-91, vice chmn., 1991-93; v.p., chief engr. New England Electric System, Westboro, Mass., 1985-87, sr. v.p., chief engr., 1987-91; dir. New England Wholesale Electric Co., 1988-91; pres. Elec. Power Consultancy, Newton, Mass., 1991—; mem. Electric Power Rsch. Inst. Generation and Storage Div. Com. 1988-90, Energy Mgmt. and Utilization Div. Com., 1985-87; mem. rsch. adv. com. Electric Power Rsch. Inst., 1991-93, chmn. membership and policy subcommittee, 1993-94; Utility Air Regulatory Group Steering-Audit Com., 1985-91; bd. dirs. New Eng. Electric Transmission Corp., New Eng. Hydro-Transmission Corp., New Eng. Hydro-Transmission Corp., New Eng. Hydro-Transmission Electric Co., Inc.; New Eng. Hydro Fin. Co., Inc. Narragansett Energy Resources Co., 1990-91. Mem. Internat. Energy Adv. Coun. Fletcher Sch. Law and Diplomacy Tufts U., 1984—; mem. elec. engring. dept. adv. com. Worcester Polytech. Inst., 1990-94; pres. Hungarian Am. Bus. Coun., 1993—. Mem. IEEE (sr. mem., past chmn. power engring. com. Boston chpt. 1972), Am. Soc. Macro Engring., Edison Electric Inst. (engring., operating and standards exec. adv. com. 1983-90). Avocations: hiking, conservation of natural resources.

SASENICK, JOSEPH ANTHONY, health care company executive; b. Chgo., May 18, 1940; s. Anthony E. and Caroline E. (Smicklas) S.; m. Barbara Ellen Barr, Aug. 18, 1962; children: Richard Allen, Susan Marie, Michael Joseph. BA, DePaul U., 1962; MA, U. Okla., 1966. With Miles Labs., Inc., Elkhart, Ind., 1963-70; product mgr. Alka-Seltzer, 1966-68, dir. mktg. grocery products div., 1968-70; with Gillette Corp., Boston, 1970-79; dir. new products/new ventures, personal care div. Gillette Corp., 1977; v.p. diversified cos. and pres. Jafra Cosmetics Worldwide, 1977-79; mktg. dir. Braun AG, Kronberg, W. Ger., 1970-73; chmn. mng. dir. Braun U.K. Ltd., 1973-77; with Abbott Labs., North Chicago, 1979-84; corp. v.p., pres. consumer products div. Abbott Labs., 1979-84; pres., chief exec. officer Moxie Industries, 1984-87, Personal Monitoring Technologies, Rochester, N.Y., 1987; pres. Bioline Labs., Ft. Lauderdale, Fla., 1988; mng. dir., ptnr. Vista Resource Group, Newport Beach, Calif., 1988-90; pres., CEO, Alcide Corp., Redmond, Wash., 1991-92, CEO, 1992—. Mem. Knollwood Club, El Niguel Club, Landmark Club, Wash. Athletic Club. Home: 1301 Spring St Seattle WA 98104 Office: Alcide Corp 8561 154th Ave NE Redmond WA 98052

SASLOW, GEORGE, psychiatrist, educator; b. N.Y.C., Dec. 5, 1906; s. Abram and Becky (Zinkoff) S.; m. Julia Amy Ipcar, July 28, 1928; children: Michael G., Rondi, Steven, Marguerite. ScB magna cum laude, Washington Sq. Coll. NYU, 1926; postgrad., U. Rochester, 1926-28; PhD in Physiology, NYU, 1931; MD cum laude, Harvard U., 1940. Instr., asst. prof. biology N.Y. U., 1928-37; vis. research asso. physiology Cornell Med. Coll., 1935-36, U. Rochester Sch. Medicine, 1936-37; research asso. physiology Harvard Sch. Pub. Health, 1937-40; neurology-neurosurgery intern Boston City Hosp., 1940-41; resident Worcester State Hosp., 1941-42; chief resident psychiatry Mass. Gen. Hosp., Boston, 1942-43; staff Mass. Gen. Hosp., 1955-57; instr., successively asst., asso. prof., prof. psychiatry Washington U. Sch. Medicine, 1943-55; staff Barnes Hosp., St. Louis, 1943-55; practice of psychiatry, 1943—; clin. prof. psychiatry Harvard, 1955-57; prof. psychiatry U. Oreg. Med. Sch., Portland, 1957-74; head dept. U. Oreg. Med. Sch., 1957-73, prof. emeritus, 1979—; chief mental health and behavioral sci. edn., chief psychiatry service VA Hosp., Sepulveda, Calif., 1974-79; prof. psychiatry in residence UCLA, 1974-79; mem. Psychiat. Security Rev. Bd., 1983—. Fellow Nat. Tng. Labs. Fellow Am. Psychiat. Assn. (life, mem. task force on nomenclature and statistics), Am. Coll. Psychiatrists (charter); mem. AMA, Assn. for Advancement Behavioral Therapy, Delta Soc. (bd. dirs. 1986—). Home: 02403 SW Greenwood Rd Portland OR 97219-8394

SASMOR, JAMES CECIL, publisher representative, educator; b. N.Y.C., July 29, 1920; s. Louis and Cecilia (Mockler) S.; 1 child from previous marriage: Elizabeth Lynn; m. Jeannette L. Fuchs, May 30, 1965. BS, Columbia U., 1942; MBA, Calif. Western U., 1977, PhD, 1979. Cert. Am. Bd. Med. Psychotherapists, sex educator Am. Assn. Sex Educators, Counselors and Therapists, Healthcare Risk Mgr. Am. Inst. Med. Law, diplomate Am. Bd. Sexology. Advt. sales exec. 1946-59; registered rep. Nat. Assn. Security Dealers, 1956-57; founder, owner J.C. Sasmor Assocs. Publishers' Reps., N.Y.C., 1959-89; co-founder, pres., dir. adminstrn. Continuing Edn. Cons., Inc., 1976—; pub. cons., 1959—; clin assoc., U. So. Fla. Coll. of Medicine, 1987-89; adj. faculty Coll. Nursing, 1980-89, dir. Ednl. Counseling Comprehensive Breast Cancer Ctr., U. So. Fla. Med. Ctr., 1984-89, client librn. mental health inst., 1979-89. Team tchr. childbirth edn. Am. Soc. Childbirth Educators; bd. dirs. Tampa chpt. ARC, also chmn. instructional com. on nursing and health, Sedona Ariz. unit Am. Cancer Soc., co-chmn. adult edn. com.; county nursing ednl. cons. ARC. With USN, 1942-58, PTO; lt. USNR ret. Recipient cert. appreciation ARC, 1979, Dept. Health and Rehab. Svcs. award for Fla. Mental Health Inst. Svc., 1980, Cert. of Appreciation Am. Fgn. Svc. Assn., 1988. Internat. Coun. of Sex Edn. and Parenthood Am. U. fellow, 1981—. Mem. NAACOG (bd. dirs. Tampa chpt.), Nat. Assn. Pubs. Reps. (pres. 1965-66), Am. Soc. Psychoprophylaxis in Obstetrics (dir. 1970-71), Am. Soc. Childbirth Educators (co-founder, dir. 1972—), Internat. Coun. Women's Health Issues (chmn. resources com.), Health Edn. Media Assn., Nursing Educators Assn. Tampa, Lions (bd. dirs. Found. Ariz., pres. Sedona club). Author: Economics of Structured Continuing Education in Selected Professional Journals'; contbr. chpts. to Childbirth Education: A Nursing Perspective; contbr. articles to profl. jours. Home: 235 Arrowhead Dr Sedona AZ 86351-8900 Office: PO Box 2282 Sedona AZ 86339-2282

SASS, DONALD JAY, anesthesiologist; b. Balt., July 12, 1934; s. Albert Roy and Ruth Ellen (Smith) S.; m. Elizabeth Anne Bridges, Aug. 15, 1959 (div. Aug. 4, 1976); children: David J., Christin L. Sass Cross, Elizabeth A.; m. Eleanor Elsie Perry, Oct. 6, 1978. BS, Johns Hopkins U., 1955, MS, 1957; MD, Stanford U. Sch. Medicine, 1964. Diplomate Am. Bd. Anesthesiologists, Nat. Bd. Med. Examiners. Fellow in physiology Mayo Grad. Sch. Medicine, Rochester, Minn., 1968-72; head biophysics dept. Naval Med. Rsch. Inst., Bethesda, Md., 1972-76; resident in anesthesia U.S. Naval Hosp., Bethesda, 1976-78; fellow in cardiac anesthesia Mass. Gen. Hosp., Boston, 1978-79; asst. chief anesthesia U.S. Naval Hosp., 1979-81, chief anesthesia 1981-84; chief anesthesia Kaiser Permanente Hosp., Oakland, Calif., 1984-94; staff anesthesiologist, sr. physician Kaiser Permanente Hosp., 1994—; assoc. prof. Uniformed Svcs. Health Scis., Bethesda, 1979-84. Capt. U.S. Navy, 1964-84. Mem. Am. Soc. Anesthesiologists, Calif. Soc. Anesthesiologists, Calif. Med. Assn. Republican. Avocations: collecting antique Jaguars and MGs. Home: 6353 Ascot Dr Oakland CA 94611 Office: Kaiser Permanente Hosp 280 W MacArthur Blvd Oakland CA 94611

SASS, RONALD LEWIS, biology and chemistry educator; b. Davenport, Iowa, May 26, 1932; s. Erwin Leese and Flora Alice (Puck) S.; m. Joyce R. Moorhead, 1951 (div. 1968); children: Dennise, Andria; m. Margaret Lee Macy, Apr. 4, 1969; children: Hartley, Dennis. BA, Augustana Coll., Rock Island, Ill., 1954; PhD, U. So. Calif., L.A., 1957. Chemist U.S. Army, Rock Island (Ill.) Arsenal, 1951-54; asst. prof. Rice U., Houston, 1958-62, assoc. prof., 1962-66, prof., 1966—, chmn. biology, 1981-87; co-dir. Rice Ctr. for Edn., Houston, 1988—; chair Rice Earth Systems Inst., Houston, 1990—; cons. EPA, Washington, 1990—, Coll. Bd., N.Y.C., 1988—. Contbr. articles on chemistry, biology and biochemistry to profl. jours. NSF predoctoral fellow U. So. Calif., 1954-57, fellow AEC, 1957-58, Guggenheim fellow, 1965, sr. rsch. fellow NRC, 1988. Mem. Internat. Geospher-Biosphere Program (com. chair 1990—). Avocations: tennis, fishing. Home: 2406 Wordsworth St Houston TX 77030-1834 Office: Rice U Ecology & Evolutionary Biology Houston TX 77251

SASSAMAN, ANNE PHILLIPS, science administrator; b. La Grange, Ga., Jan. 7, 1944; d. Joe and Bessie (Lewis) Phillips; m. John Robert Ball, Aug. 13, 1966 (div.); children: Kristen Anne, John Robert; m. Jan Frederick Sassaman, Oct. 1, 1983. BS with honors, Auburn U., 1965; PhD, Duke U., 1970. Rsch. assoc. depts. surgery, medicine, biochemistry Duke U., Durham, N.C., 1970-74; rsch. chemist FDA, Bethesda, Md., 1974-76; scientist-adminstr. Nat. Heart, Lung & Blood Inst., Bethesda, 1976-79, chief blood diseases br., 1979-86; dir. div. extramural rsch. and tng. Nat. Inst. Environ. Health Scis., NIH, Research Triangle Park, N.C., 1986—. Contbr. rsch. articles on biochemistry of thrombosis and thrombolysis to sci. jours. Mem. exec. com. coun. on thrombosis Am. Heart Assn., Dallas, 1979-86; bd. dirs. Wyngate Daycare Assn., Bethesda, 1976-78; mem. exec. bd. Am. Field Svc. Chpt., Chapel Hill, N.C., 1989-92; vol. Am. Heart Assn., March of Dimes. Mem. AAAS, Am. Soc. Hematology, Internat. Soc. Thrombosis and Haemostatis, N.C. Soc. Toxicology, Assn. for Women in Sci., Sigma Xi. Democrat. Methodist. Home: 534 Caswell Rd Chapel Hill NC 27514-2704 Office: Nat Inst Environ Health Scis PO Box 12233 Durham NC 27709-2233

SASSEEN, ROBERT FRANCIS, university president; b. Bklyn., June 6, 1932; s. Robert B. and Teresa M. (Regan) S.; divorced; children: Robert V., Christopher J., Patricia M., Timothy P., Katherine A. BA in Polit. Sci, U. Notre Dame, Ill., 1957; MA, U. Chgo., 1959, PhD, 1961. Instr. polit. sci. Marquette U., Milw., 1960-62; asst. prof. honors div. U. Santa Clara, Calif., 1962-65; from lectr. to prof. polit. sci. San Jose (Calif.) State U., 1965-72, chmn. dept., 1971-72, assoc. acad. v.p., dean faculty, 1972-81; pres. U. Dallas, 1981—. Author articles in field. Mem. AUS, 1951-54. Mem. Legatus Club. Roman Catholic. Office: U Dallas Office of Pres 1845 E Northgate Dr Irving TX 75062-4736

SASSER, WILLIAM JACK, government official; b. Arcadia, Okla., Aug. 12, 1934; married; childrren: Sam, Steve, Susan, Sandra. BS in Sociology and Psychology, Okla. Bapt. U., 1956; postgrad., S.W. Bapt. Sem., 1957-60, George Washington U., 1966. Lic. comml. pilot with instrument rating. Air traffic control specialist S.W. region FAA Air Route Traffic Control Ctr., Ft. Worth, 1963-65, pers. officer, 1970-71; tech. intern FAA, Washington, 1965-66; employee devel. officer S.W. region FAA, Houston and Ft. Worth, 1966-70; chief tng. br. pers. div. Gt. Lakes region FAA, Des Plaines, Ill., 1971-73; with exec. devel. program Gt. Lakes and ctrl. regions FAA, Des Plaines, Kansas City, Mo., 1973-75; asst. chief airports div. ctrl. region FAA, Kansas City, 1975-76, mgr., 1977-87; mgr. airports div. S.W. region FAA, Ft. Worth, 1987-89, dep. regional adminstr. S.W. region, 1989—. Home: Rt 1 Box 314 Decatur TX 76234 Office: FAA 2601 Meacham Blvd Fort Worth TX 76193-0002

SASSO, CASSANDRA GAY, lawyer; b. Washington, Feb. 5, 1946; d. Phillip Francis and Lois Aileen (Ayers) S.; m. David John Stephenson, Jr., Feb. 12, 1982; 1 child, Gabriel David. BS magna cum laude, U. Nebr., 1967; MA, U. Calif., Santa Barbara, 1970; JD, Northwestern U., 1974. Bar: Ill. 1974, Colo., 1976. Law clk. Schiff Hardin & Waite, Chgo., 1973; assoc. Sidley & Austin, Chgo., 1974-75; instr. antitrust and securities U. Denver Law Sch., 1978-79, 1985-87; instr. trial practice U. Colo. Law Sch., Boulder, 1983-86; instr. Nat. Inst. Trial Advocacy, 1985—; ptnr., trial lawyer Sherman & Howard, Denver, 1976-91; ptnr. Kutak Rock, Denver, 1991—. Bd. dirs. Colo. Jud. Inst., 1982-88, v.p. 1984; bd. dirs. Colo. Lawyers Com., Denver, 1980-82, Legal Aid Soc. of Met. Denver, 1981-83; mem. Denver Com. Fgn. Rels., 1981—; chmn. bd. dirs. Colo. ACLU, Denver, 1982-83; mem. steering com. Colo. Lawyers for Nuclear Arms Edn., Denver, 1982-83, ABA (securities litigation com. 1988—), Chgo. Council Lawyers (sec. 1974-75), Denver Bar Assn. (bd. trustees 1978-81), Colo. Trial Lawyers Assn. (bd. dirs. 1984-85), Alpha Omicron Pi, Mortar Bd. Democrat. Presbyterian. Home: 108 S Dexter Denver CO 80222 Office: Kutak Rock 717 17th St Ste 2900 Denver CO 80202-3429

SASSO, SANDY, rabbi; b. Phila., Jan. 29, 1947; d. Israel and Freda (Plotrick) Eisenberg; m. Dennis Sasso, June 25, 1970; children: David Aryeh, Debora Shoshana. BA magna cum laude, Temple U., 1969, MA in Religion, 1972. Ordained rabbi, 1974. Rsch. assoc. Jewish Reconstructionist Found., N.Y.C., 1974-76; rabbi Congregation Beth-El Zedeck, Indpls., 1977—; lectr. Jewish Welfare Bd. Lecture Bur., 1972-77. Bd. dirs. Julian Mission, 1978-79; mem. adm. coun. Women's Health Resource Ctr., 1983—. Recipient Woman of Yr. award Brith Sholom Women, 1975. Mem. Reconstructionist Rabbinical Assn. (pres. Wyncote, Pa. chpt.), Nat. Coun. Jewish Women (edn. and pub. affairs coms.), N.Y. Bd. Rabbis, Coalition for Alternatives in Jewish Edn., NCCJ (exec. bd. 1978-79). Office: Reconstructionist Rabbinical Church Rd Greenwood Ave Wyncote PA 19095

SASSOON, JANET, ballerina, educator; b. Sorabaya, Indonesia, Sept. 2, 1936; came to U.S., 1937; d. Edward and Flora (Bar) S.; m. John Roland Upton Jr., Aug. 7, 1983. Began training with Christensen brothers, Ricky Asgruth, and Gisella Caccialarya, San Francisco; Studied with Leo Staats, Lubov Egorova, Olga Preobrajenska, Mathilde Kshessinskaya, Paris, 1951. Dancer Grand Ballet du Marquis de Cuevas, Paris, 1952-55, Chgo., Utah and San Francisco Ballets, 1955; prima ballerina Berlin Ballet, 1956; assoc. dir. Acad. of Ballet, San Francisco, 1974—; condr. master classes in ballet, movement therapy for numerous profl. dancers including Natalia Makarova. Avocations: cooking, gardening, writing. Office: 2121 Market St San Francisco CA 94114-1321

SASSOON, VIDAL, hair stylist; b. London, Jan. 17, 1928; s. Nathan and Betty (Bellin) S.; divorced 1980; children—Catya, Elan, Eden, David. Student, NYU. Founder, former chmn. bd. Vidal Sassoon, Inc. (beauty treatment products, appliances), Europe and Am.; pres. Vidal Sassoon Found.; lectr. in field. Author: autobiography A Year of Beauty and Health, 1976. Served with Palmach Israeli Army. Recipient award French Ministry of Culture, award for services rendered Harvard Bus. Sch.; Intercoiffure award Cartier, London, 1978; Hair Artists Internat. fellow. Clubs: Anabelle (London, Eng.), Ambassadeurs (London, Eng.), Claremont (London, Eng.); Le Club (N.Y.C.). Office: Vidal Sassoon Inc 2029 Century Park E Los Angeles CA 90067-1906

SATA, LINDBERGH SABURO, psychiatrist, physician, educator; b. Portland, Oreg., Jan. 6, 1928; s. Charles Kazuo and Ito (Kojima) S.; m. Yuriko Kodama, Aug. 19, 1956; children: Roberta, Camille, Holly, John. BS, U. Utah, 1951, MD, 1958, MS, 1964. Intern U. Utah Coll. Medicine, Salt Lake Gen. Hosp., 1958-59; resident in psychiatry, 1959-62, chief resident in psychiatry, 1961-62; adminstrv. chief resident neurology U. Utah Coll. Medicine, VA Hosp., Salt Lake City, 1960-61; fellow Inst. for Mental Retardation, Letchworth Village, Thiells, N.Y., 1962; intern Behavioral Sci. Intern Program Nat. Tng. Labs., Bethel, Maine, 1966; instr. U. Utah, 1962-64; asst. prof. The Psychiat. Inst. U. Md., Balt., 1964-67, assoc. prof., 1967-68; assoc. prof. U. Wash., Seattle, 1968-77, asst. dean, 1969-70, prof., 1977-78; prof., chmn. St. Louis U. Sch. Medicine, 1978-94, prof. emeritus, chmn. emeritus, 1994—. Fellow Am. Coll. Psychiatrists, Am. Psychiat. Assn., Pacific Rim Coll. Psychiatrists (founding); mem. Am. Assn. for Social Psychiatry. Office: 1606 Riverview Dr NE Auburn WA 98002

SATCHER, DAVID, public health service officer, federal official; b. Anniston, Ala., Mar. 2, 1941; s. Wilmer and Anna S; m. Nola; children: Gretchen, David, Daraka, Daryl. BS, Morehouse Coll., 1963; MD, PhD, Case Western Reserve Univ., 1970. Pres. Meharry Med. Coll., Nashville; now dir. Centers for Disease Control and Prevention, Atlanta, 1993—. Office: Ctr Disease Control & Prevention 1600 Clifton Rd NE Bdlg 1 Atlanta GA 30333

SATCHLER, GEORGE RAYMOND, physicist; b. London, June 14, 1926; came to U.S., 1959; s. George Cecil and Georgina Lillie (Strange) S.; m. Margaret Patricia Gibson, Mar. 27, 1948; children: Patricia Ann, Jacqueline Helen. BA, Oxford U., 1951, MA, 1951, D Phil., 1955, DSc, 1989. Research fellow Clarendon Lab., Oxford U., 1954-59, 71; research assoc. physics dept. U. Mich., 1956-57; physicist Oak Ridge Nat. Lab., 1959—, assoc. dir. physics div., 1967-74, theoretical physics dir., 1974-76, distinguished research staff mem., 1976—. Author: (with D.M. Brink) Angular Momentum, 1962, Introduction to Nuclear Reactions, 1980, Direct Nuclear Reactions, 1983; contbr. research articles to profl. jours. Served with RAF, 1944-48. Corp. rsch. fellow, 1976—. Fellow Am. Phys. Soc. (mem. exec. com. nuclear physics div. 1974-75, T.W. Bonner prize 1977). Home: 973 W Outer Dr Oak Ridge TN 37830-8608 Office: Oak Ridge Nat Lab PO Box 2008 Oak Ridge TN 37831-6373

SATEREN, TERRY, theater technical production; b. Madison, Wis., Dec. 5, 1943; s. Leland Bernhard and Eldora (Johnson) S. BA, Augsburg Coll., 1968. Tech. prodn. dir. Guthrie Theatre, Mpls., 1974-78, dir. prodn., 1985-87; dir. exhibits Sci. Mus. Minn., St. Paul, 1978-85; tech. prodn. dir. Seattle Repertory Theatre, 1987—; cons. acad. and community theaters and museums, 1974—, U. Minn., 1992; Master class lectr. U. Wash., Seattle, 1989-91; adj. prof. U. Wash., 1991-92. Designer: (operas) Three Penny Opera, 1972, Newest Opera in the World, 1972, Don Giovanni, 1973; commd. sculptor numerous inds., chs. and acad. instns., 1966—. Pres.'s scholar Valparaiso (Ind.) U., 1967. Mem. U.S. Inst. Theatre Tech. Avocations: scuba diving, mountain climbing, travel, museums. Home: 7341 23d Ave NW Seattle WA 98117-5661 Office: Seattle Repertory Theatre 155 Mercer St Seattle WA 98109-4639

SATHE, SHARAD SOMNATH, chemical company executive; b. Bombay, Oct. 10, 1940; came to U.S., 1967; s. Somnath Waman and Kamala S. (Bhave) S. m. Usha Moreshwar Tamhankar, Feb. 6, 1969; children: Vandana, Swapna. BS, U. Bombay, 1960; B in Pharmacy, Banaras Hindu U., 1963; PhD, Ind. U., 1971. Rsch. asst. CIBA Rsch. Ctr., Bombay, 1964-67; postdoctoral fellow Rsch. Triangle Inst., Raleigh, N.C., 1971-73; rsch. chemist Mallinckrodt, Inc., St. Louis, 197-379, tech. supr., 1979-81, group leader, 1981-87, mgr. R & D, 1989-94; assoc. dir. rsch., 1995—. Patentee in field; contbr. articles to profl. jours. Pres. India Student Assn., Bloomington, Ind., 1969-70; mem. bd. of trustees India Assn. of St. Louis, 1980-85; pres. Sangeetha, St. Louis, 1986-87. Fellow Am. Inst. Chemistry, N.Y. Acad. Scis.; mem. Am. Chem. Soc. Avocations: music, tennis, reading. Office: Mallinckrodt Inc 2D And Mallinckrodt St Saint Louis MO 63147

SATHER, EVERETT NORMAN, accountant; b. Story City, Iowa, July 20, 1935; s. George John and Laura Josephine (Bakka) S.; m. Patricia Ann Johnson, Apr. 24, 1955; children: Kimberly L., Kristine J., Kendall D. Student, Am. Inst. Bus., Des Moines, 1953-55. CPA, Iowa, Nebr., Ill. Office mgr. Story Polk Farm Svc., Nevada, Iowa, 1955-57; office mgr., bookkeeper Capital City Electric Co., Des Moines, 1958-59; staff acct. Willard C. Randol, CPA, Des Moines, 1959-60, Ryun, Givens and Co., Des Moines, 1960-63; acct. Everett N. Sather, CPA, Des Moines, 1963-66; acct., ptnr. Denman and Co., Des Moines, 1966—; pres., chmn. Ankeny (Iowa) Nat. Bank, 1972-82; pres. Triple K Ltd., Ankeny, 1983—, Boone (Iowa) Speedways, Inc., 1976—. Active Polk County Bd. Rev., Des Moines, 1970—; chmn. bd. Greater Des Moines Aviation Expo, 1992—; treas. Des Moines Grand Prix, 1988—. Staff sgt. Iowa Air NG, 1957-63. Mem. AICPA, Ill. Soc. CPAs, Iowa Soc. CPAs, Rotary (bd. dirs. 1990-93, pres. 1994-95), Zagszig Shrine, Scottish Rite, MAsons. Lutheran. Avocation: sports. Office: Denman and Co 1601 22nd St Ste 400 West Des Moines IA 50266-1453

SATHER, GLEN CAMERON, professional hockey team executive, coach; b. High River, Alta., Canada, Sept. 2, 1943. Former professional hockey player; pres., gen. mgr. Edmonton Oilers, Nat. Hockey League, Alta., Can., coach, 1977-89, now alt. gov.; coach winning team in Stanley Cup competition, 1987. Recipient Jack Adams Award for NHL Coach of the Yr., 1986. Office: care Edmonton Oilers, Northlands Coliseum, Edmonton, AB Canada T5B 4M9*

SATHRE, LEROY, mathematics educator, consultant; b. Cleve., June 4, 1936; s. Louis and Hazel Irene (Pletcher) S.; m. B. Ann Sathre, May 30, 1968 (div. May 1983); m. Winona Sechrist, Aug. 30, 1984. BA, DePauw U., 1958; MS, U. Fla., 1960; postgrad., U. Calif., Santa Barbara, 1963-65. Reliability engr. N.Am. Aviation, Downey, Calif., 1960-62; statistician Gen. Electric Co., Daytona Beach, Fla., 1965-67; instr. St. Johns River Jr. Coll., Palatka, Fla., 1968-70; prof. Valencia C.C., Orlando, Fla., 1970-94, dept. chmn., 1994—; pres. faculty senate Valencia City Coll., 1974-75; sec., treas. United Community Coll. Faculty of Fla., Tallahassee, 1976-80; textbook reviewer various pubs. Mem. Math. Assn. Am., Fla. Math. Assn. of Two Yr. Colls., Am. Math. Assn. Two Yr. Colls. Democrat. Methodist. Office: Valencia Community Coll 701 N Econlockhatchee Trl Orlando FL 32825-6404

SATHYAMOORTHY, MUTHUKRISHNAN, engineering researcher, educator; b. Sathanur, Tamil Nadu, India, Feb. 21, 1946; s. Kuppusamy and Visalakshi Muthukrishnan; m. Chitra Subbiah, May 26, 1971; children: Mohanakrishnan, Kumaran. B in Civil Engring., U. Madras, India, 1967; M in Engring. Mechanics, Indian Inst. of Tech., Madras, India, 1969, PhD in Aero. Engring., 1973. Lectr. Indian Inst. of Tech., Madras, India, 1969-74; rsch. fellow U. Birmingham, Eng., 1974-76; asst. prof. Clarkson U., Potsdam, N.Y., 1979-82, assoc. prof., 1982-92, assoc. prof., exec. officer, 1992-94, prof., exec. officer, 1994—; vis. rsch. faculty U. Calgary, Can., 1977-79. Contbn. author: Handbook of Civil Engineering Practice, 1988; editor: Material Nonlinearity in Vibrations, 1985. Recipient Appreciation cert. U.S. Army, 1990, Outstanding Advisor award Clarkson U., 1993. Fellow ASME (mem. nat. student sect. com. 1992-94, mem. gen. awards com. 1994—, Nat. Faculty Advisor award 1993); mem. AIAA (sr.), Aero. Soc. India. Avocations: overseas travel, camping, photography, fishing. Home: 177 Regan Rd Potsdam NY 13676 Office: Clarkson U Mech Engring Dept Potsdam NY 13699-5725

SATIN, JOSEPH, language professional, university administrator; b. Phila., Dec. 16, 1920; s. Reuben Philip and Harriet (Price) S.; m. Selma Rosen (dec. 1978); children: Mark, Diane; m. Barbara Jeanne Dodson (dec. 1987); m. Terrye Sagan, 1992. BA, Temple U., 1946; AM, Columbia U., 1948, PhD, 1952. Instr. integrated studies W.Va. U., Morgantown, 1952-54; prof. English and Comparative Lit. Moorhead (Minn.) State U., 1954-63; chmn. dept. English and Journalism Midwestern U., Wichita Falls, Tex., 1963-73; dean Sch. Arts and Humanities Calif. State U., Fresno, 1973-89; mgr. concert series Moorhead State U., 1956-61; mem. nat. bd. cons. NEH, Washington, 1979—; dir. London semester Calif. State U., Fresno, 1982-92, dir. Frank Lloyd Wright Auditorium project. Author: Ideas in Context, 1958, The 1950's: America's "Placid" Decade, 1960, Reading Non-Fiction Prose, 1964, Reading Prose Fiction, 1964, Reading Drama, 1964, Reading Poetry, 1964, Shakespeare and His Sources, 1966, Reading Literature, 1968, The Humanities Handbook (2 Vols.), 1969; editor: Frank Lloyd Wright-Letters to Apprentices, 1982, Letters to Architects, 1984, Letters to Clients, 1986, Treasures of Taliesin, 1985, The Guggenheim Correspondence, 1986, Frank Lloyd Wright: His Living Voice, 1987, Frank Lloyd Wright, The Crowning Decade, 1989; translator: Federico Fellini, Comments on Film, 1987; contbr. to Ency. Internat. Edn., 1978; dir. Univ. Press, Calif. State U., 1982-92. Served with U.S. Army, 1943-46, ETO. Jewish. Avocations: creative writing, music, parcheesi. Home: 65 Maywood Dr San Francisco CA 94127-2007

SATINE, BARRY ROY, lawyer; b. N.Y.C., July 25, 1951; s. Norman S. and Fay (Mekles) S.; m. Janice Bea Halfond, Aug. 4, 1974; children: David, Leah. B.A., CCNY, 1972; J.D., George Washington U., 1975. Bar: N.Y. 1976, D.C. 1977, U.S. Dist. Ct. (so. dist.) N.Y. 1978, U.S. Supreme Ct. 1979, U.S. Dist. Ct. (ea. dist.) N.Y. 1982, U.S. Ct. Appeals (2d cir.) 1989. Trial atty. U.S. Civil Service Commn., Washington, 1975-78; atty. AT&T, N.Y.C., 1978-81, N.Y. Tel. Co., N.Y.C., 1981-82; mem. assoc Surrey & Morse, N.Y.C., 1982-84, ptnr., 1985; ptnr. Jones, Day, Reavis & Pogue, 1986—. Mem. ABA (litigation sect., internat. litigation com.), Assn. of Bar of City of N.Y. (litigation com.). Office: Jones Day Reavis & Pogue 599 Lexington Ave New York NY 10022-6030

SATINOVER, JEFFREY BURKE, psychiatrist, health science facility administrator, lecturer, author; b. Chgo., Sept. 4, 1947; s. Joseph and Sena (Rotman) S.; m. Julie Rachel Leff, June 10, 1982; Sarah Katherine, Anne-Rebecca, Jenny Leigh. BS, MIT, 1971; EdM, Harvard U., 1973; MD, U. Tex., 1982; Diplomate, C.G Jung Institute, Zurich, Switzerland, 1976. Diplomate Am. Bd. Psychiatry and Neurology, added qualifications in geriatric psychology. Fellow dept. psychiatry and child psychiatry Yale U., New Haven, 1982-86; founder, exec. dir. Sterling Inst., Stamford, Conn., 1985-92; med. dir. Temenos Inst., Westport, Conn., 1984—; pvt. practice, Westport, 1992—; mem. pastoral care ministries, pres., bd. dirs. C.G. Jung Found. N.Y., 1988-92; bd. dirs., mem. catchment area coun. S.W. Regional Mental Health Bd., 1988-92; William James lectr. psychology and religion Harvard U., 1975; mem. Lower Fairfield County Regional Action Coun. Against Substance Abuse, 1990-92. Author: Homosexuality and the Politics of Truth, 1994, The Empty Self: Gnostic Foundations of Modern Identity, 1994, Skein of Darkness, Skein of Gold, 1995; contbg. author: Jungian Psychotherapy, 1984, Science and the Fragile Self, 1990, Jungian Analysis, 1993; contbr. articles to profl. jours., pub. policy jours. Founder, exec. bd. com. Save Our Schs., 1994—; trustee Family Inst. of Conn.; bd. lay ministry St. Paul's, Westport, 1994—; bd. govs. Toward Tradition; active nat. physician's resource coun. Focus on the Family. Recipient Seymour Lustman Rsch. award Yale U., 1983, 85. Mem. AMA, Am. Psychiat. Assn. (Burroughs-Wellcome fellow 1983-85), Am. Psychosomatic Soc., Am. Acad. Psychomatics, Internat. Assn. Analytical Psychology (diplomate), Aspetuck Valley Country Club, Alpha Omega Alpha. Republican. Jewish. Avocations: tennis, harpsichord, jazz keyboard. Home: 38 Steep Hill Rd Weston CT 06883-1822 Office: 29 E Main St Westport CT 06880-3749

SATINSKAS, HENRY ANTHONY, airline services company executive; b. Kaunas, Lithuania, Dec. 22, 1936; came to U.S., 1949; s. Henry Francis and Donna (Olechnavicius) S.; m. Lucia Aldona Sestakauskas, Dec. 7, 1963; children: Henry Arnold, Paul Steven (dec.), Laura Monica. Student, Drexel U., 1957-60; BS in Bus. Adminstrn., Temple U., 1963. Mgmt. trainee Pub. Service Coordinated Transp., Maplewood, N.J., 1964; asst. garage supr. Jersey City, 1965-66; charter service mgr. Suburban Transit Corp., New Brunswick, N.J., 1966-68; gen. mgr. Ave B and E Byway Transit Co., N.Y.C., 1968-71; St. John's (Newfoundland, Can.) Transp. Commn., 1971-73; asst. dir. transp. planning Montgomery County Govt., Rockville, Md., 1973-76; gen. mgr. Airway Limousine Service subs. Hudson Gen. Corp., Balt., 1976-78; dir. transp. services Airway Services subs. Hudson Gen. Corp., Jamaica, N.Y., 1978-81; v.p. Hudson Gen. Corp., Great Neck, N.Y., 1981—. Mem. adv. coun. on edn. Province of Newfoundland and Labrador, St. John's, 1972; bd. dirs. Greater Jamaica Devel. Corp., 1987-90. Republi-

can. Roman Catholic. Avocations: reading, gardening, travel, biking. Home: 35 Woodvale Dr Syosset NY 11791-1213 Office: Hudson Gen Corp 111 Great Neck Rd Great Neck NY 11021-5402

SATINSKY, BARNETT, lawyer; b. Phila., June 17, 1947; s. Alex and Florence (Talsky) S.; m. Fredda Andrea Wagner, June 17, 1973; children: Meagen, Sara Beth, Jonathan. AB, Brown U., 1969; JD, Villanova U., 1972. Bar: Pa. 1972, U.S. Dist. Ct. (ea. dist) Pa. 1975, U.S. Dist. Ct. (mid. dist.) Pa. 1975, U.S. Ct. Appeals (3d cir.) 1981. Law clk. Phila. Ct. Common Pleas, 1972-73; dep. atty. gen. Pa. Dept. Justice, Harrisburg, 1973-75; 1st asst. counsel Pa. Pub. Utility Commn., Harrisburg, 1975-77, chief counsel, 1977; assoc. Fox, Rothschild, O'Brien & Frankel, Phila., 1978-81, ptnr., 1981—. Children Svcs. Rev. com., United Way Southeast Pa., 1984-86; bd. dirs. ACLU, Harrisburg, 1973-74, Voyage House, Inc., 1994—. Mem. ABA (pub. utility, labor and employment law sects., employee benefits com. 1984—), Pa. Bar Assn. (labor rels., pub. utility law sects. 1980—, pub. utility law com., governing coun. 1991-93), Phila Bar Assn. (labor law pub. utility law coms. 1980—, chmn. oub. utility law com. 1988-91), Nat. Assn. Coll. and Univ. Attys., Nat. Assn. Regulagory Commrs. (staff subcom. law 1977), Tau Epsilon Rho Law Soc., Soc. for Human Resource Mgmt. Democrat. Jewish. Office: Fox Rothschild O'Brien & Frankel 2000 Market St Philadelphia PA 19103-3291

SATO, EUNICE NODA, former mayor, consultant; b. Livingston, Calif., June 8, 1921; d. Bunsaku and Sawa (Maeda) Noda; m. Thomas Takashi Sato, Dec. 9, 1950; children—Charlotte Patricia, Daniel Ryuichi and Douglas Ryuji (twins). AA, Modesto Jr. Coll., 1941; BA, U. No. Colo., 1944; MA, Columbia U., 1948. Public sch. tchr. Mastodon Twp. Schs., Alpha, Mich., 1944-47; ednl. missionary Reformed Ch. Am., Yokohama, Japan, 1948-51; coun. mem. City of Long Beach, Calif., 1975-86; mayor, 1980-82; sec. corp. bd. Los Angeles County Health Systems Agy., 1978-79. Monthly contbr. articles to 2 neighborhood papers, 1975-86. Bd. dirs. Long Beach chpt. ARC, 1975—, mem. exec. com., 1978-91, 93—, past v.p., pres.; bd. dirs. Goodwill Industries, 1978-82 ; trustee St. Mary's Bauer Med. Ctr., 1977—; pres. Industry Edn. Coun., Long Beach, 1984-86, mem. exec. bd., 1984—; bd. dirs. Industry Edn. Coun. of Calif., treas. So. Calif. Consortium of I.E.C., 1986-87, pres., 1988-89; mem. State Adv. Group on Juvenile Justice and Delinquency Prevention, 1983-91, Calif. Coun. Criminal Justice, 1983—, legis. com. Girl Scout coun. Calif., 1986-92, chair, 1991-92; bd. dirs. Long Beach council Girl Scouts U.S., 1986-92, Region III United Way, 1974-88; mem. Asian Pacific adv. com. Calif. Dept. Rehab., 1985-87, recreation commnr. City of Long Beach, 1985-86, pub. safety policy com. League Calif. Cities, 1981-86, community econ. and housing devel. com. So. Calif. Assn. Govts., 1976-86, Calif. Task Force to Promote Self-Esteem and Personal and Social Responsibility, 1987-90; Long Beach chpt. pres. NCCJ, 1987-88; pres. Internat. Community Coun., 1986-87, Japanese Am. Reps., 1987, 88; presdl. appointee Nat. Adv. Coun. Ednl. Rsch. and Improvement, 1991-94; pres. Aux. to Sch. Theology, Claremont, 1990-91, exec. bd. 1989-91; chair selection com. Leadership Long Beach, 1990-91, sec. exec. bd., 1991-92; chair adv. bd. AIESEC, 1990-92, Long Beach Area Rep. Party, 1990-92; mem. cen. com., L.A.; sec.-gen. coun. on fin. and administrn. United Meth. Ch., 1992—; appointed by Gov. to commn. on teacher credentialing State Calif., 1994. Recipient Outstanding Service award Long Beach Coordinating Council, 1969, Mother of Yr. award Silverado United Meth. Ch., 1973, Hon. Service award Calif. PTA, 1963, Continuing Service award, 1974, hon. life membership award Nat. PTA, 1974, Outstanding Laywoman of Yr. award Long Beach Area Council Chs., 1976, Woman of Yr. award State Women's Council-C. of C., 1979, Women of Yr. award Long Beach Internat. Bus. and Profl. Women's Club; Nat. Merit award DAR, 1982; Citizen of Yr. award Los Altos YMCA, 1982, Citizen of Yr. award Calif. Community Pool for Handicapped, 1982; Outstanding Citizen award Torch Club of Long Beach, 1983, W. Odie Wright award Industry Edn. Coun., 1990, Humanitarian award NCCJ, 1992. Mem. Alpha Iota (hon.). Republican. Methodist. Home: Bixby Village 551-101 Pittsfield Ct Long Beach CA 90803

SATO, GORDON HISASHI, retired biologist, researcher; b. Los Angeles, Dec. 17, 1927; married; 6 children. BA, U. Calif., 1950; PhD in Biology, Calif. Inst. Tech., 1955; DSc (hon.), SUNY, Plattsburgh, 1987. Tchg. asst. in microbiology Calif. Inst. Tech., Pasadena, 1953-55; fellow in virology and jr. asst. virologist U. Calif., Berkeley, 1955-56; fellow, instr. biophysics U. Colo. Med. Sch., 1956-58; from asst. prof. to prof. biochemistry Brandeis U., 1958-69; prof. biology U. Calif., San Diego, 1969-83; dir., chief exec. officer W. Alton Jones Cell Sci. Ctr., Lake Placid, N.Y., 1983—; Hon. prof. biology Tsinghua U., Beijing, Xiamen U., Peoples Rep. China; Disting. Rsch. prof. Clarkson U., Potsdam, N.Y., 1987, dir. lab. molecular biology; mem. panel molecular biology study sect. NIH; mem. Coun. for Tobacco Rsch.; bd. sci. counsellors Nat. Inst. Diabetes, Digestive and Kidney Diseases. Editor in chief: In Vitro Cellular Developmental Biology. Mem. NAS, Am. Acad. Arts and Scis., Am. Assn. Immunologists, Endocrine Soc., Assn. Biol. Chemistry. Achievements include research of animal cell culture, endocrinology, bacteriophage. Office: W Alton Jones Cell Sci Ctr 10 Old Barn Rd Lake Placid NY 12946-1099

SATO, HIROSHI, materials science educator; b. Matsuzaka, Mie, Japan, Aug. 31, 1918; came to U.S., 1954; s. Masayoshi and Fusae (Oohara) S.; m. Kyoko Amemiya, Jan. 10, 1947; children: Norie M., Nobuyuki Albert, Erika Michiko. BS, Hokkaido Imperial U., Sapparo, Japan, 1938, MS, 1941; DSc, Tokyo U., 1951. Rsch. assoc. faculty sci. Hokkaido Imperial U., Sapparo, 1941-42, asst. prof. Inst. Low Temperature Sci., 1942-43; rsch. physicist Inst. Phys. and Chem. Rsch., Tokyo, 1943-45; prof. Tohoku Imperial U., Sendai, Japan, 1945-57; rsch. physicist Westinghouse Rsch. Labs., Pitts., 1954-56; prin. scientist Sci. Lab., Ford Motor Co., Dearborn, Mich., 1956-74; prof. materials engring. Purdue U., West Lafayette, Ind., 1974—, Ross Disting. prof. engring., 1984-89; Ross Disting. prof engring. emeritus Purdue U., West Lafayette, 1989—; affiliate prof. dept. materials sci. U. Washington, Seattle, 1986-89; collaborator Los Alamos (N.Mex.) Nat. Lab., 1989—; vis. prof. U. Grenoble, France, 1967, Tokyo Inst. Tech., 1979, Tech. U. Hannover, Fed. Republic Germany, 1980-81; cons. Oak Ridge (Tenn.) Nat. Lab., 1978, 80. Contbr. over 260 articles to profl. jours., chpts. to books. Recipient U.S. Sr. Scientist award Alexander von Humboldt Found., 1980; fellow John Simon Guggenheim Meml. Found., 1966, Japan Soc. for Promotion Sci., 1979. Fellow Am. Phys. Soc.; mem. Japan Phys. Soc., Am. Ceramic Soc., Metall. Soc.-AIME, Japan Inst. Metals (hon. 1985—, Prize of Merit 1951). Office: Purdue U Sch of Materials Engring 1289 MSEE Bldg Lafayette IN 47907-1289

SATO, MOTOAKI, geologist, researcher; b. Tokyo, Japan, Oct. 11, 1929; came to U.S., 1955, 63; s. Iwazo and Kyoko (Ito) S.; m. Ellen B. Leukunen, Feb. 11, 1961 (div. Sept. 1978); children: Emily Coates, Alice Isomé, Thomas Bartlett. BS in Geology, U. Tokyo, Japan, 1953, MS in Geology, 1955; PhD in Geology, U. Minn., 1959. Research asst. dept. geophysics Univ. Minn., Mpls., 1956-58; rsch. fellow in geophysics dept. geol. scis. Harvard Univ., Cambridge, Mass., 1958-61; assoc. prof. geology Inst. Thermal Springs Research, Misasa, Tottori, Japan, 1961-63; research geologist U.S. Geological Survey, Washington, 1963-65; geologist, project chief U.S. Geological Survey, Washington/Reston, Va., 1965—; prin. investigator Lunar Sample & Sci. Program, NASA, 1971-80. Contbg author books and articles in profl. jours. Fulbright/Smith-Mundt fellow Inst. Internat. Edn., 1955-57, Gilbert fellow U.S. Geol. Survey, Reston, Va., 1982-83. Mem. Am. Geophysical Union, Geochemical Soc., Geological Soc. Washington (2d v.p. 1982-83), Geochemistry Div. Am. Chem. Soc. Home: 11173 Lake Chapel Ln Reston VA 22091-4308 Office: US Geol Survey 959 National Ctr Reston VA 22092
Remember that we did not design the way Nature works; Nature designed us, too. So let's listen ever so carefully, with an open mind, to what Nature is trying to tell us.

SATO, RICHARD MICHIO, consulting engineering company executive; b. Paia, Maui, Hawaii, Dec. 30, 1934; s. Shinichi and Namie (Hanazawa) S.; m. Althea Reiko Ouye; children: Janice Muraoka, Kelvin. BSCE, U. Hawaii, 1956. Registered civil/structural engr., Calif., Hawaii. Civil and structural engr. Dalton Dalton Assocs., L.A., 1960-62; structural engr. William M. Taggart, SE, L.A., 1962-67; project coord. Office of Univ. Planning U. Hawaii, Honolulu, 1967-69; project engr. T.Y. Lin Hawaii, Honolulu, 1969; pres. Sato & Assocs., Inc. (formerly Richard M. Sato & Assoc. & Sato & Kuniyoshi, Inc.), Honolulu, 1969—. 1st lt. U.S. Army, 1957-59. Mem. Am. Concrete Inst., Prestressed Concrete Inst., Structural Engrs. Assn. Hawaii

(pres. 1976), Consulting Engrs. Coun. Hawaii, Hui Kokua Kinipopo (pres. 1993—), U. Hawaii Pres.'s Club, U. Hawaii Alumni Assn., Chi Epsilon. Avocations: golf, sports fan. Office: Sato & Assocs Inc 2046 S King St Honolulu HI 96826

SATO, TADASHI, artist; b. Maui, Hawaii, Feb. 6, 1923. Student, Honolulu Sch. Art, Bklyn. Mus. Art Sch., New Sch. Soc. Rsch. Exhbns. include Guggenheim Mus., N.Y.C., 1954, Honolulu Acad. Arts, 1957, Pacific Heritage Exhibit, L.A., 1963, McRoberts and Tunnard Ltd., London, 1964, White House Festival Arts, Washington, 1965, Berlin Art Festival, 1967, Japanese C. of C., Honolulu, 1993-94, Maui Cmty. and Cultural Assn., 1994; represented in permanent collections Albright-Knox Art Gallery, Buffalo, Guggenheim Mus., Whitney Mus. Am. Art, N.Y.C., Honolulu Acad. Arts, U. Art Gallery, Tucson, (mosaic) Hawaii State Capitol Bldg., State Libr. Aina Haina, Oahu, State Hosp., Kea-lakekua, Hawaii, Wailulu War Meml. Gymnasium, Maui, Krannert Art Mus., Ill., U. Nebr.; executed murals Halekulani Hotel, Honolulu, (mosaic) West Maui Recreation Ctr., (oil) Bay Club, Kapalua, Maui; retrospective Hui No Eau, Makawao, Maui, 1992. Office: PO Box 476 Lahaina HI 96767-0476

SATORIUS, JOHN ARTHUR, lawyer; b. Berwyn, Ill., Aug. 20, 1946; s. Woodrow Wilson and Frances Jane (Embshoff) S.; m. Linda Kay Grove, Dec. 26, 1968; children: Katherine, Joseph. BA summa cum laude, U. Va., 1968; MA, Harvard U., 1972, JD cum laude, 1975, PhD, 1977. Bar: Minn. 1975. Assoc. Fredrikson & Byron PA, Mpls., 1975-81, ptnr., 1981—, also bd. dirs.; bd. dirs. Bellcomb Techs., Mpls. Editor Contract Law in Minnesota, 1993. Bd. dirs. Childrens Theater Co., Mpls. With U.S. Army, 1968-70, Vietnam. Named Vol. of Yr. Met. Econ. Devel., 1986. Mem. Rotary. Avocations: wilderness canoe activities, traveling, reading. Office: Fredrikson & Byron PA 1100 International Ctr 900 2d Ave S Minneapolis MN 55419

SATOVSKY, ABRAHAM, lawyer; b. Detroit, Oct. 15, 1907; s. Samuel and Stella (Benenson) S.; m. Toby Nayer, Sept. 4, 1938 (dec.); children: Sheldon Baer, James Bennett. B.A., U. Mich., 1928, J.D., 1930. Bar: Mich. 1930, U.S. Supreme Ct. 1930. Assoc. William Henry Gallagher, Detroit, 1930-65; Bldg. chmn. lawyers com. United Found. and Torch Dr. Co-chmn. profl. divsn. Allied Jewish Campaign; adv. coun. United Synagogue Am.; del. Jewish Cmty. Coun. Detroit; v.p. Mosies Chetim Orgn. Detroit; bd. dirs. Detroit Svc. Group, past chmn. fgn. mission; active fund raiser Greater Miami United Jewish Appeal; mem. fund dr. com. U. Mich. Law Sch.; trustee Clover Hill Park Cemetery, 1978-81, trustee emeritus, 1982—; bd. dirs. Congregation Sharrey Zedek, Southfield, Mich., past pres., 1959-62. Recipient Sem. award Jewish Theol. Sem. Am., 1952; citation of merit Jewish Welfare Fedn., Detroit; Jerusalem award State of Israel Bond Orgn.; numerous other awards. Mem. ABA, Mich. Bar Assn., Detroit Bar Assn. (mem. pub. adv. com. jud. candidates), Oakland County Bar, Nat. Fedn. Jewish Men's Clubs (founder, past pres., hon. life pres. Gt. Lakes regional award 1977, Ma'Asim Tovim (Good Deeds) award 1989), Am. Arbitration Assn., Jewish Hist. Soc. Mich. (mem. adv. bd.), Am. Jewish Hist. Soc., Am. Judicature Soc., Men's Club Congregation Shaarey Zedek (past pres., hon. life pres.), Standard Club, B'nai B'rith (past pres. Detroit), Hadassah (life), Phi Beta Delta (merged with Pi Lambda Phi). Home: 6187 Forest Grove West Bloomfield MI 48322 also: 20379 W Country Club Dr Apt 2334 Aventura FL 33180 Office: 28455 Northwestern Hwy Southfield MI 48034-1895 *With a desire and willingness to improve my profession, my religious beliefs, and help the community, I have devoted a good portion of my time and efforts for those purposes. I, too, have been enriched by the association, have hopefully directed and encouraged others, and hope to continue to do so.*

SATRE, PHILIP GLEN, business executive, lawyer; b. Palo Alto, Calif., Apr. 30, 1949; s. Selmer Kenneth and Georgia June (Sterling) S.; m. Jennifer Patricia Arnold, June 30, 1973; children: Malena Anne, Allison Neal, Jessica Lilly, Peter Sterling. BA, Stanford U., 1971; JD, U. Calif.-Davis, 1975; postgrad sr. exec. program MIT, 1982. Bar: Nev. 1975, Calif. 1976. Assoc. Vargas & Bartlett, Reno, 1975-79; v.p., gen. counsel, sec. Harrah's, Reno, 1980-83, sr. v.p., 1983-84, pres. Harrah's East, Atlantic City, 1984; pres., CEO Harrah's Hotels and Casinos, Reno, 1984-91; dir, sr. v.p. Gaming Group The Promus Cos., Inc., Memphis, 1988-91, pres., COO, 1991-94, pres., CEO, 1994—; dir., treas. Nat. Judicial Coll., Reno. Mem. ABA, Nev. Bar Assn., Calif. Bar Assn., Order of Coif, Phi Kappa Phi, Stanford Alumni Assn. (pres. Reno chpt. 1976-77), Young Pres. Orgn. Office: The Promus Cos Inc 1023 Cherry Rd Memphis TN 38117-5423

SATRUM, JERRY R., chemicals company executive; b. 1933. BS, Oreg. State U., 1967. With Ga.-Pacific Corp., Atlanta, 1968-84; v.p., treas. fin. and adminstr. Ga. Gulf Corp., 1984-89, pres., COO, 1989—, now CEO, 1992—, also bd. dirs. Office: Georgia Gulf Corp 400 Perimeter Center Ter NE Atlanta GA 30346-1227

SATTERFIELD, CHARLES NELSON, chemical engineer, educator; b. Dexter, Mo., Sept. 5, 1921; s. Charles David and Hermine (Weber) S.; m. Anne Pettingell, July 6, 1946; children—Mark Edward, Joye. B.S. cum laude, Harvard U., 1942; M.S., MIT, 1943, Sc.D., 1946. Registered profl. engr., Mass. Asst. prof. chem. engring. Mass. Inst. Tech., Cambridge, 1946-53; asso. prof. Mass. Inst. Tech., 1953-59, prof., 1959—; Lectr. indsl. chemistry Harvard, 1948-57; cons.on rocket propellants Dept. Def., 1952-60; mem. com. chem. kinetics NRC, 1960-66; chmn. ad hoc panel on abatement nitrogen oxide emissions from stationary sources Nat. Acad. Engring., 1970-72; indsl. cons. to major cos. in petroleum and chem. industries. Co-author: Thermodynamic Charts for Combustion Processes, 1949, Hydrogen Peroxide, 1955 (translated into Russian 1957), Role of Diffusion in Catalysis, 1963; author: Mass Transfer in Heterogeneous Catalysis, 1970 (translated into Russian 1976), Heterogeneous Catalysis in Practice, 1980 (translated into Russian 1984), repub. as Heterogeneous Catalysis in Industrial Practice, 1991, also more than 140 tech. papers; mem. editl. adv. bd. Indsl. and Engring. Chemistry, 1966-68, Advances in Chemistry Series, 1971-73, 82-86, Energy and Fuels, 1990—, Applied Catalysis, 1995—. Fellow Am. Acad. Arts and Scis.; mem. Am. Chem. Soc., Am. Inst. Chem. Engrs. (Wilhelm award 1980), Sigma Xi, Tau Beta Pi. Patentee in field. Home: 38 Tabor Hill Rd Lincoln MA 01773-2906 Office: Dept Chem Engring Mass Inst Tech Cambridge MA 02139

SATTERTHWAITE, CAMERON B., physics educator; b. Salem, Ohio, July 26, 1920; s. William David and Mabel (Cameron) S.; m. Helen Elizabeth Foster, Dec. 23, 1950 (div. July 31, 1979); children: Mark Cameron, Tod Foster, Tracy Lynn, Keith Alan, Craig Evan (dec.). B.A., Coll. Wooster, 1942; postgrad., Ohio State U., 1942-44; Ph.D., U. Pitts., 1951. Chemist Manhattan dist. project Monsanto Chem. Co., Dayton, Ohio, 1944-47; research chemist DuPont, Wilmington, Del., 1950-53; researcher, adv. physicist Westinghouse, Pitts., 1953-61; asso. prof. physics U. Ill., Urbana, 1961-63; prof. U. Ill., 1963-79, prof. emeritus, 1979—; prof. physics Va. Commonwealth U., Richmond, 1979-85; prof. emeritus Va. Commonwealth U., 1985—, chmn. dept. physics, 1979-82; program dir. NSF, 1975-76; field sec. Friends Com. on Nat. Legis., 1988-90. Contbr. articles to profl. jours. Sch. dir., Monroeville, Pa., 1959-61; trustee, mem. fin. com. Southeastern Univs. Research Assn., 1980-85; Democratic nominee for U.S. Congress, 1966; del. to Dem. Nat. Conv., 1968, 72. Fellow Am. Phys. Soc.; mem. AAAS, Fedn. Am. Scientists (chmn. 1968), Sigma Xi. Patentee in field. Home: Unit # 1 803 S Coler Ave Urbana IL 61801-4009

SATTERTHWAITE, FRANKLIN BACHE, JR., management educator, consultant; b. Mt. Holly, N.J., Apr. 30, 1943; s. Franklin Bache and Emily Vaux (Cresson) S.; m. Antonia Mitchell, Oct. 6, 1987 (div. Oct. 1992); m. Martha Werenfels, May 21, 1994; 1 child, Peter Franklin. AB, Princeton U., 1965; M in Urban Studies, Yale U., 1968, MPhil, 1972, PhD, 1975. Sci. faculty Escola Americiana, Rio Janeiro, Brazil, 1965-66; planner Nat. Inst. Mental Health, Chevy Chase, Md., 1968-70; cons. Battelle Meml. Inst., Columbus, Ohio, 1971-72; touring squash pro W.P.S.A., N.Am., 1976-84; sr. cons. Brown Cronson Assocs., N.Y.C., 1981-87; prin. Frank Satterthwaite, N.Y.C., 1982-95, R.I., 1995—; asst. prof. Johnson & Wales U., Providence, 1993—; cons. Cost of Living Coun., Washington, 1972-73. Author: The Three-Wall Nick and Other Angles, 1979. Lt. USPHS, 1968-70. Mem. Am. Mktg. Assn., Acad. Mgmt. Avocations: squash (World Profl. Vets. Squash Champion 1984), tennis, golf, piano, travel. Home: 81 Strathmore Rd

Cranston RI 02905-3722 Office: Johnson and Wales U 8 Abbott Park Pl Providence RI 02903-3703

SATTERTHWAITE, HELEN FOSTER, state legislator; b. Blawnox, Pa., July 8, 1928; d. Samuel J. and Lillian (Schreiber) Foster; B.S. in Chemistry, Duquesne U., 1949; m. Cameron B. Satterthwaite, Dec. 23, 1950 (div. July 1979); children: Mark Cameron, Tod Foster, Tracy Lynn, Keith Alan, Craig Evan (dec.). Biol. technician U.S. Dept. Agr., 1967-68; research asst. Iowa State U. Coll. Agr., 1971; lab. technician U. Ill. Coll. Agr., 1968-70; rsch. chemist E.I. duPont de Nemours & Co., Wilmington, Del., 1951-53; rsch. asst. Gulf R & D, Harmarville, Pa., 1950; natural sci. lab. technician U. Ill. Coll. Vet. Medicine, 1971-74; rep. Gen. Assembly Ill., 1974-92, majority leader, 1991-92, sch. fin. task force, 1990-92; chairperson House com. on higher edn., 1983-91, vice-chairperson elem. and secondary edn., 1983-91; mem. Commn. on Mental Health and Devel. Disabilities, 1975-85, mem. exec. com., 1977-85, vice chairperson, 1979-85; mem. Commn. to Visit and Examine State Instns., 1977-85, Ill. Coun. Mental Health, 1992—, task force on global climate change, 1991—, League Women Voters, treas. 1994-95, Bus. & Profl. Women's Club, treas. 1993-94, sec. 1994-95. Bd. dirs. East Central Ill. Health Systems Agy., 1977-79, Champaign County Med. Health Ctr. 1993—, Girls Inc. 1992—, Champaign County (Ill.) United Way, 1970-74, mem. budget com., 1973-74, mem. joint rev. com. on funding Champaign County Mental Health Programs, 1973; co-chairperson Task Force on Mental Retardation for Champaign County Mental Health Bd., 1973; mem. Ill. Developmental Disability Advocacy Authority, 1977-85, vice chmn., 1979-80; chairperson Ill. House Democratic Study Group, 1979-81; mem. Edn. Commn. of the States, 1985-92; mem. Nat. Conf. State Legis. Commn. on Labor and Edn., 1985-92. Recipient Freshman Legislator of Yr. award Ill. Edn. Assn., 1975; commendation Ill. State's Attys. Assn., 1975; Best Legislator award Ind. Voters Ill., 1976, 78, 80, 82, 84, 86, 88, 90; cert. honor Assn. Students Govts., 1977; Disting. Service cert. Am. Vets. World War II, Korea and Viet Nam, 1977; Environ. Legis. of Yr. award Ill. Environ. Council, 1977, 79, 81, 83; Meritorious Svc. award Champaign County Council on Alcoholism, 1978, Ill. Community Coll. Trustees Assn., 1996; Perfect Voting Record award Ill. Credit Union League, 1979, Ill. Wildlife Fedn., 1979; cert. spl. recognition Ill. Women's Polit. Caucus, 1979, 80, Public Service award Izaak Walton League, 1980, Friend of Edn. award Ill. State Bd. Edn., 1985, Cert. of Appreciation Champaign County Urban League, 1987, Resolution of Honor Ill. Libr. Assn., 1987, 100 percent award Ill. State Coun. Sr. Citizens Orgns., 1989, Dare to be Great award Ill. Women Adminstrs., 1989; named Person of Yr., Champaign County Mental Health Assn., 1981, Pub. Citizen of Yr., Illini Dist. and Ill. chpt. Nat. Assn. Social Workers, 1981, Legislator of Yr., Ill. Assn. Sch. Social Workers, 1989. Mem. Ill. Conf. Women Legislators (co-convenor 1981-83), Nat. Order Women Legislators (dir. Region IV 1982, treas. 1983-84), Delta Kappa Gamma. Quaker. Office: Rm 2031 Stratton Office Bldg Springfield IL 62706

SATTERWHITE, WILLIAM T., lawyer, energy company executive; b. Baytown, Tex., 1933. Grad., Baylor U., 1956, LLB, 1958. Now sr. v.p., gen. counsel, chief legal officer ENSERCH Corp., Dallas. Office: Ensersh Corp 300 S St Paul St Dallas TX 75201-5598*

SATTLER, ROLF, plant morphologist, educator; b. Göppingen, Germany, Mar. 8, 1936; arrived in Can., 1962; s. Otto and Emma (Mayer) S.; m. Liv Hamann, May 1, 1963 (div. 1985). PhD, U. Munich, 1961. Asst. prof. McGill U., Montreal, Que., Can., 1964-69, assoc. prof., 1969-77, prof., 1977—. Author: Organogenesis of Flowers 1973 (Lawson medal 1974), Biophilosophy, 1986; editor: Theoretical Plant Morphology, 1978, Axioms and Principles of Plant Construction, 1981; contbr. articles to profl. jours. NATO fellow, 1962-64. Fellow Royal Soc. Can., Linnean Soc. London; mem. Can. Bot. Assn., Bot. Soc. Am., Can. Soc. for Theoretical Biology, Internat. Soc. for History, Philosophy and Social Studies of Biology, Sci. and Med. Network, Internat. Assn. for New Sci., Ctr. for Process Studies, Sigma Xi. Office: McGill U, 1205 Dr Penfield Ave, Montreal, PQ Canada H3A 1B1

SATUR, NANCY MARLENE, dermatologist; b. Philipsburg, Pa., Apr. 12, 1953; d. Nicholas and Mary (Kutzer) S.; m. John David Lortscher, Oct. 20, 1979; children: David Nicholas, Glenn William, Stephen John. BS magna cum laude, Pa. State U., 1974; MD, Thomas Jefferson U., 1976. Diplomate Am. Bd. Dermatology. Intern Allentown (Pa.) Gen. Hosp., 1976-77; resident in pathology U. Ill. Hosp., Chgo., 1978-79; resident in dermatology Case Western Res. U. Hosp., Cleve., 1979-82; dermatologist Encinitas, Calif. 1985—; sr. instr. dermatology Case Western Res. U. Hosp., 1982-83, sr. clin. instr. dermatology, 1983-84. Fellow Am. Acad. Dermatology; mem. Am. Soc. Dermatologic Surgery, Am. Soc. Laser Medicine and Surgery, N.Am. Soc. Phlebology, San Diego Dermatologic Soc., Pacific Dermatologic Assn. Office: 477 N El Camino Real C-300 Encinitas CA 92024

SATURNELLI, ANNETTE MIELE, school system administrator; b. Newburgh, N.Y., Dec. 1, 1937; d. William Vito and Anna (Marso) M.; m. Carlo F. Saturnelli, Oct. 15, 1960; children: Anne, Karen, Carla. BA, Vassar Coll., 1959; MS, SUNY, New Platz, 1978; EdD, NYU, N.Y.C., 1993. Rsch. chemist Lederle Labs/Am. Cyanamid, Pearl River, N.Y., 1959-64; sci. coord. Marlboro (N.Y.) Cen. Sch. Dist., 1974-84; state sci. supr. N.Y. State Dept. Edn., Albany, 1984-86; dir. sci. edn. Newburgh (N.Y.) City Sch. Dist. 1986—; project dir., proposal reviewer NSF, Washington, 1984—; state coord. N.Y. State Sci. Olympiad, 1985-86; mem. Gov. Cuomo's Task Force on Improving Sci. Edn., Albany, N.Y., 1989—; mem. adv. bd. N.Y. State Systemic Initiative, 1993—, N.Y. State Tech. Edn. Network, 1993—. Author: Focus on Physical Science, 1981, 87; editor: Transforming Testing in New York State—A Collection of Past, Present and Future Assessment Practices, 1994. NSF 3-yr. summer sci. camp grantee, 1995, 96, 97; recipient Presdl. award Excellence in Sci. Tchg., Washington, 1983. Mem. ASCD, Nat. Sci. Tchrs. Assn. (exemplary sci. tchrs. award 1982), N.Y. State Sci. Suprs. (bd. dirs., pres. 1991), Sci. Tchrs. Assn. N.Y. State (outstanding sci. tchrs. award 1983, fellows award 1990, pres. 1993), Phi Delta Kappa. Home: 3 Taft Pl Cornwall On Hudson NY 12520-1713 Office: Newburgh Free Acad 201 Fullerton Ave Newburgh NY 12550-3798

SATYAPRIYA, COMBATORE KESHAVAMURTHY, geotechnical engineering executive; b. Bangalore, Mysore, India, Jan. 27, 1949; came to U.S., 1972; s. C.V. and C.V. (Vedamma) Keshavamurthy; m. Indira Muthanna, Nov. 1, 1976; children: Ajay S., Anand A., Divya S. BCE, Bangalore U., 1969, MCE, 1971; MS, Worcester (Mass.) Poly. Inst., 1972. Registered profl. engr., Ohio, Md., Va., W.Va., Washington, Pa., Ind., Ky., Fla. Staff engr. Mason & Ray Inc., Columbus, Ohio, 1976-77; sr. geotech. engr. Resource Internat. Inc., Columbus 1977-78; staff engr. CTL Engring. Inc., Columbus, 1978-79, dept. head geotech. engring., 1979-80, v.p., 1981-83, exec. v.p., 1983-86; mgr. ops. Washington Testing, Inc., Fairfax, Va., 1981-82; pres. CTL Engring. Inc., Columbus, 1986—; mem. control group Placement & Improvement, Columbus, 1982—. Contbr. articles to profl. jours. Fellow ASCE (pres. Ctrl. Ohio chpt. 1978-79, tech. com. on placement and improvement of soils 1982—); Mem. ASTM (coms. E-06, D-18, D-20), Indian Geotech. Soc., Rotary, Chi Epsilon. Home: 8015 Flint Rd Columbus OH 43235 Office: CTL Engring Inc 2860 Fisher Rd Columbus OH 43204-3538

SATZ, LOUIS K., publishing executive; b. Chgo., Apr. 28, 1927; s. Harry Addison and Faye (Pollen) S.; m. Adele Wallenstein, Mar. 2, 1976 (dec.); children: Jay, Jonathan. B.S. in Mktg., U. Ill., 1949. Circulation dir. Books Devel. Corp., Chgo., 1953, Guns mag., Jr. Arts and Activities, 1961; wholesaler sales mgr., then v.p., dir. sales Bantam Books, Inc., N.Y.C. 1962-80; sr. v.p., dir. diversified markets Bantam Books, Inc., 1980-84; pub. Passport Books, Lincolnwood, Ill., 1985-88; pres. Louis K. Satz Assocs., Pub. Cons., N.Y.C., 1988-91; ptnr. Scott/Satz Group, Pub. Cons., Walnut Creek, Calif., 1991—; guest lectr. Sarah Lawrence Coll. Pub. Sch., Pace U.; faculty Hofstra U., Denver Pub. Inst.; bd. dirs. N.Y.S. Book Country, Brandeis U. Pub. Scholarship Fund, Oscar Dystel Fellowship NYU. Served with AUS, World War II, ETO. Decorated Army Commendation medal. Mem. Am. Assn. Pubs. (chmn. small books mktg. div. 1975). Office: Scott/Satz Group 539 Monarch Ridge Dr Walnut Creek CA 94596-2955

SATZ, MICHAEL ELLIS, insurance executive; b. N.Y.C., Oct. 30, 1948; s. Louis and Rose (Schiff) S.; m. Marietta Maldonado Staples, Mar. 3, 1978; children: William Harrington, Marisa Blanca. BA, Cornell U., 1970; JD,

Harvard U., 1974. Bar: N.Y. Assoc. Willkie Farr and Gallagher, N.Y.C., 1974-82; gen. counsel Ambac Indemnity Corp., N.Y.C., 1982-85, chief operating officer, 1985-87; chmn., chief exec. officer Capital Re Corp., N.Y.C., 1987—; founder Assn. Fin. Guaranty Insurors, N.Y.C., 1986; lectr. pub. adminstrn. NYU; panelist Bond Atty.'s Workshop, Chgo., 1979-83, 85-87. Contbr. articles to profl. jours. Bd. advisors Outward Bound U.S.A. Mem. ABA, N.Y. State Bar Assn., Assn. of Bar of City of N.Y., Cornell Club, Harvard Club. Avocations: travel, riding, scuba diving. Office: Capital Re Corp 787 7th Ave New York NY 10019-6018

SAUCIER, GENE DUANE, state legislator, import/export company executive; b. Dallas, Sept. 25, 1931; s. Albert L. and Myrtle Irene (West) S.; m. Marilyn Emmy Cox, Dec. 27, 1952 (div. Sept. 1980); children: Alan, Steve, Renee; m. Giulia Riga LaCagnina, Nov. 28, 1981. BS in Agronomy Soils, Miss. State U., 1953; MS in Counseling, U. So. Miss., 1970, EdD in Adult Edn., 1978. Builder, developer Saucier Co., Hattiesburg, Miss., 1957-70; dir. admissions U. So. Miss., Hattiesburg, 1970-74, dean spl. acad. svcs., 1974-84, asst. v.p. bus. and fin., 1984-93; rep. Miss. Ho. of Reps., Jackson, 1993—; importer tractors from China. Scoutmaster Boy Scouts Am., 1960-70, chmn. camping and activities Pine Burr Area, 1970. 1st lt. USAF, 1953-56. Mem. Res. Officers Assn., Am. Assn. Collegiate Registrars and Admissions Officers (mem. adv. bd. 1985-86), So. Assn. Collegiate Registrars and Admissions Officers (bd. dirs. 1981, local arrangements chmn. 1981, v.p. admissions and fin. aid 1982-83, pres. 1985-86), Miss. Assn. Collegiate Registrars and Admissions Officdrs, Miss. Forestry Assn. (exec. bd. dirs. 1992-94, bd. dirs. 1992-94), Miss. Nature Conservancy, Forrest/Lamar Forestry Assn. (pres. 1989-92), Sigma Chi, ODK, Phi Delta Kappa, Omicron Delta Kappa. Office: 41 Saucier Rd Hattiesburg MO 39402

SAUCIER LUNDY, KAREN, college dean, educator; b. Hattiesburg, Miss., Oct. 7, 1954; d. William Marshall and Ruth (Landers) S.; m. Joel Christopher Lundy, Dec. 27, 1986; 1 child, Marshall Parker. BS in Nursing, U. So. Miss., 1975; MS in Community Health Nursing, U. Colo. Health Scis. Ctr., 1978; MA in Sociology, U. Colo., Boulder, 1987, PhD in Sociology, 1987. RN. Clin. nurse U. Miss. Med. Ctr., Jackson, 1976-77; clin. specialist HEW, USPHS, Atlanta, 1978-80; clin. instr. U. Miss. Med. Ctr. and Med. Sch., 1980-81; asst. prof. Loretto Heights Coll., Denver, 1983-85; instr. U. Colo., Boulder, 1982-85; prof., dean sch. nursing Delta State U., Cleveland, Miss., 1985-90; assoc. prof., U. So. Miss., Hattiesburg, 1990-92, 1992—; mem. Miss. Bd. Nursing, 1990-94. Author: Community Health, 1987, nursing text, 1991, Family and Community Health Nursing, 1991 (AJN Book of the Year 1991). Vol. Spl. Olympics, Miss., Fla., 1979-80; mem. ARC, 1978-82; cons. Sierra Club, Denver, 1977-78, Headstart, Tampa, Fla., 1978-79; bd. dirs. March of Dimes, Jackson, 1977-81, Am. Cancer Soc., 1985—. Am. Coll. Test Merit scholar 1972-75; USPHS fellow, 1977; named Educator Nurse of Year Miss. Nurses' Assn., 1989. Mem. ANA, Am. Sociol. Assn., So. Sociol. Assn., Nat. League Nursing (accreditation site visitor 1988—), Kappa Delta. Democrat. Avocations: photography, tennis. Home: PO Box 927 89 James Switzer Rd Purvis MS 39475-0927 Office: U So Miss Sta Box 5095 Hattiesburg MS 39406-5095

SAUER, CONRAD FREDERICK, IV, food products executive; b. Richmond, Va., May 28, 1949; s. Conrad F. III and Barbara (Boyd) S.; m. Patricia Totty, Nov. 3, 1973; children: Ashley, Jennifer. BA, Hampden-Sydney Coll., 1972. Mgmt. trainee C.F. Sauer Co., Richmond, 1972-80, asst. v.p., officer, 1980-85, officer, dir., v.p., 1985—. Avocations: hunting, fishing, biking, swimming. Office: CF Sauer Co 2000 W Broad St Richmond VA 23220-2006

SAUER, DAVID ANDREW, writer, computer consultant; b. Urbana, Ill., Feb. 25, 1948; s. Elmer Louis and Frances (Hill) S. BA, Northwestern U., 1970; MS, Simmons Coll., 1975. Reference libr. Boston U., 1976-78, bibliographer, 1978-84, sci. bibliographer, 1984-88, head Stone Sci. Libr., 1988-94. Co-author: Internet for Windows, 1994, WinComm Pro: The Visual Learning Guide, 1995, ProComm Plus V2 for Windows: The Visual Learning Guide, 1995. Mem. S.W. Corridor Project, Boston, 1977-87, Forest Hills Neighborhood Improvement Assn., Boston, 1977-90, Forest Hills/Woodbourne Neighborhood Group, 1991-94. Mem. ALA, Spl. Librs. Assn., Assn. Coll. and Rsch. Librs., Geoscience Info. Soc., N.E. Map Orgn., San Diego Computer Soc., Boston Computer Soc. Democrat. Home and Office: 1034 La Tierra Dr San Marcos CA 92069

SAUER, ELISSA SWISHER, nursing educator; b. Williamsport, Pa., Jan. 9, 1935; d. Oliver S. and Emily Louisa (Gehron) Swisher; m. Raymond James Sauer, Nov. 27, 1964. Diploma, Reading Hosp. Sch. Nursing, 1957; BS, Albright Coll., Reading, 1958; MS in Nursing, U. Pa., Phila., 1964. Nurse Community Health and Med. Assn., Ardmore, Pa., 1966-67; pub. health coord. Albert Einstein Med. Ctr., 1967-68; pvt. duty nurse, 1968-73; clin. faculty Schuylkill County AVTS, 1973-74; prof. nursing Reading (Pa.) Area Comunity Coll., 1975-80; oncology nurse adminstr.-educator Comprehensive Community Cancer Ctr., Allentown, Pa., 1978-85; exec. dir. Holy Family Home Health Care, Orwigsburg, Pa., 1985-89; dir. nursing program, chair health svcs. div. Reading Area Community Coll., 1989—. Author instr.'s manual and procedure manual to accompany Fundamentals of Nursing: Human Health and Function, 1992. Mem. Pa. Nurses Assn. (Dist. 2 Adminstr. award 1992), Pa. League for Nursing, Sigma Theta Tau. Home: 475 Marshall Dr Orwigsburg PA 17961-1617 Office: Reading Area C C PO Box 1706 10 S 2d St Reading PA 19603-1706

SAUER, GEORGIA BOORAS, newspaper writer; b. Kalamata, Greece, May 9, 1946; came to U.S., 1946; d. Peter P. and Angela (Dimopoulos) Booras; m. Mark Sauer, Jan. 4, 1969; children: Peter, Alexander. BS, U. Ill., 1968. Obituary and feature writer Champaign (Ill.)-Urbana Courier, 1966-68; reporter Times-Democrat, Davenport, Iowa, 1968; reporter, travel writer, copy editor Chgo. Tribune, 1969-70, fashion and feature writer, asst. Lifestyle editor, 1971-75; reporter Home Furnishings Daily, Fairchild Publs., N.Y.C., 1970-71; fashion reporter, Sunday women's editor N.Y. Daily News, N.Y.C., 1975-76; fashion editor St. Louis mag., 1981-86; became feature writer St. Louis Post-Dispatch, 1986-91; fashion editor Pitts. Post Gazette, 1993—. Pres. bd. dirs. League Chapel Nursery Sch.; bd. dirs. Martha's Shelter, St. Louis, 1985-91, DG Found. for Visually Impaired Children, St. Louis, 1985-91, St. Louis Pub. Libr., 1987-91, Payback, St. Louis, 1987-91; mem. Jr. League St. Louis and Pitts.; bd. dirs. Three Rivers South, Pitts., Ozanam Cultural Ctr., mem. bd. parents coun. Shadyside acad., mem. devel. com. Greek Orthodox. Office: Pittsburgh Post-Gazette 34 Blvd of the Allies Pittsburgh PA 15222

SAUER, GORDON CHENOWETH, physician, educator; b. Rutland, Ill., Aug. 14, 1921; s. Fred William and Gweneth (Chenoweth) S.; m. Mary Louise Steinhilber, Dec. 28, 1944; children: Elisabeth Ruth, Gordon Chenoweth, Margaret Louise, Amy Kieffer.; m. Marion Green, Oct. 23, 1982. Student, Northwestern U., 1939-42; B.S., U. Ill., 1943, M.D., 1945. Diplomate: Am. Bd. Dermatology and Syphilology. Intern Cook County Hosp., Chgo., 1945-46; resident dermatology and syphilology N.Y. U.-Bellevue Med. Center, 1948-51; dermatologist Thompson-Brumm-Knepper Clinic, St. Joseph, Mo., 1951-54; pvt. practice Kansas City, Mo., 1954—; mem. staff St. Luke's, Research, Kansas City Gen. hosps.; asso. instr. U. Kans., 1951-56, vice chmn. sect. dermatology, 1956-58, asso. clin. prof., 1960-64, clin. prof., 1964-93; clin. prof. emeritus, 1993—; head sect. dermatology U. Kans., 1958-70; clin. asso., acting head dermatology sect. U. Mo., 1955-59, cons. dermatology, 1959-67, clin. prof., 1967—; cons. Munson Army Hosp., Ft. Leavenworth, Kans., 1959-68; Mem. dermatology panel, drug efficacy panel Nat. Acad. Sci.-FDA, 1967-69. Author: Manual of Skin Diseases, 6th edit., 1991, Teen Skin, 1965, John Gould Bird Print Reproductions, 1977, John Gould's Prospectuses and Lists of Subscribers to his work on Natural History: with an 1866 Facsimile, 1980, John Gould The Bird Man, 1982; editor: Kansas City Med. Bull., 1967-69; contbr. articles to profl. jours. Bd. dirs. Kansas City Area coun. Camp Fire Girls Am., 1956-59, Kansas City Lyric Theatre, 1969-74, Kansas City Chamber Choir, 1969-74, Chouteau Soc., 1985—, U. Mo.-Kansas City Friends of Libr. 1988-92; bd. dirs. Mo. br. The Nature Conservancy, 1984-91. Sr. asst. surgeon USPHS, 1946-48. Named Dermatology Found. Practitioner of Yr., 1992. Fellow Am. Acad. Dermatology and Syphilology (dir. 1975-79, v.p. 1980); mem. Mo., Jackson County med. socs., Mo. Dermatol. Soc. (pres. 1974-75), Dermatology Found. (trustee 1978-83), Am. Ornithol. Union, Wilson Ornithol. Soc., Royal Australasian Ornithologists Union, Soc. Bibliography

Natural History, Am. Dermatol. Assn., Alpha Delta Phi, Nu Sigma Nu. Presbyterian. Office: 6400 Prospect Ave Kansas City MO 64132-1181

SAUER, HARRY JOHN, JR., mechanical engineering educator, university administrator; b. St. Joseph, Mo., Jan. 27, 1935; s. Harry John and Marie Margaret (Witt) S.; m. Patricia Ann Zbierski, June 9, 1956; children: Harry John, Elizabeth Ann, Carl Andrew, Robert Mark, Katherine Anne, Deborah Elaine, Victoria Lynn, Valerie Joan, Joseph Gerard. B.S., U. Mo.-Rolla, 1956, M.S., 1958; Ph.D., Kans. State U., 1963. Instr. mech. engring. Kans. State U., Manhattan, 1960-62; sr. engr., cons. Midwest Rsch. Inst., Kansas City, Mo., 1963-70; mem. faculty dept. mech. and aerospace engring. U. Mo., Rolla, 1957—, prof., 1966—, assoc. chmn., 1980-84, dean grad. study, 1984-92; cons. in field; mem. Gov.'s Commn. on Energy Conservation, 1977; mem. Mo. Solar Energy Resource Panel, 1979-83. Co-author: Environmental Control Principles, 1975, 4th edit., 1985, Thermodynamics, 1981, Heat Pump Systems, 1983, Engineering Thermodynamics, 1985, Principles of Heating, Ventilating and Air Conditioning, 1991, 2d edit., 1994; contbr. articles to profl. jours. Pres. St. Patrick's Sch. Bd., 1970-72, St. Patrick's Parish Council, 1975-76. Recipient Ralph R. Teetor award Soc. Automotive Engrs., 1968; Hermann F. Spoehrer Meml. award St. Louis chpt. ASHRAE, 1979; also disting. service award, 1981, E. K. Campbell award of merit, 1983. Mem. ASME, ASHRAE, NSPE, Soc. Automotive Engrs., Am. Soc. Engring. Edn., Mo. Soc. Profl. Engrs., Mo. Acad. Sci., Sigma Xi. Roman Catholic. Home: 10355 College Hills Dr Rolla MO 65401 Office: U Mo Rolla MO 65401

SAUER, JAMES EDWARD, JR., hospital administrator; b. Sanborn, N.D., Feb. 14, 1934; s. James Edward and Rose Marie (Grafton) S.; m. Sharon Ann Groom, Aug. 18, 1962; children—Scott Michael, Jeffrey William, Steven Douglas. BS in Bus. Adminstrn., U. N.D., 1956; M.H.A., U. Minn., 1964. Administrv. asst. Meth. Hosp., Madison, Wis., 1961-62; adminstrv. resident San Jose Hosp. and Health Ctr., Calif., 1963-64; asst. administr. Providence Hosp., Portland, Oreg., 1967-69, assoc. administr., 1969-73; pres., exec. dir. Calif. Hosp. Med. Ctr., Los Angeles, 1973-79; administr. St. Joseph Med. Ctr., Burbank, Calif., 1979—; mem. hosp. adv. com. Blue Cross So. Calif. 1976-79. Trustee, Sisters of Providence in Calif., 1979—; mem. exec. com. retirement bd. Sisters of Providence, 1983—. Contbr. articles to profl. jours. Served to capt. USAF, 1956-62. Fellow Am. Coll. Hosp. Adminstrs.; mem. Am. Hosp. Assn. (chmn. 1982-84), Oreg. Conf. Cath. Hosps. Assn. (pres. 1973-74), Hosp. Council So. Calif. (bd. dirs. 1975-81, exec. com. 1977-81, chmn. 1979-80), Calif. Hosp. Assn. (trustee 1979-84, chmn. 1983, Walker Fellow 1983), Calif. Assn. Cath. Hosps. (trustee 1981-82), Am. Arbitration Assn. (Los Angeles adv. council), Hollywood Acad. Medicine, Central Area Teaching Hosps. (bd. dirs. 1976-79). Lodge: Rotary. Office: Alexander & Alexander 55 S Lake Ave Ste 500 Pasadena CA 91101-2602

SAUER, JANE TAYLOR, nursing administrator, medical-surgical nurse; b. Phila., Sept. 4, 1943; d. Paul R. and Mary Elizabeth (Taylor) Davidson; m. Eugene Sauer, Feb. 14, 1982; children: Kelly, Adrian. ADN, Shoreline Community Coll., Seattle, 1976; BA, Pa. State U., State College, 1966; BSN, Loretto Heights Regis Coll., 1988; postgrad., U. Colo., 1989—. Staff nurse Swedish Med. Ctr., Englewood, Colo., asst. nurse mgr., nurse mgr., dir. med./surg. CCU; v.p. nursing. Friends of Nursing scholar, 1988; recipient Margaret Metzger award, 1989. Mem. Colo. Soc. for Nurse Execs., Sigma Theta Tau.

SAUER, KENNETH, chemistry educator; b. Cleve., June 19, 1931; s. Raymond Harvey and Beatrice Ruth (Hemke) S.; m. Marjorie Wright, June 24, 1958; children: Robert, Terence, Rodney, Peter. A.B., Oberlin Coll., 1953; M.A., Harvard U., 1954, Ph.D., 1958. Asst. prof. Am. U., Beirut, 1957-60; USPHS fellow U. Calif., Berkeley, 1960-63, asst. prof. chemistry, 1963-66, assoc. prof., 1966-72, prof., 1972—, vice chmn. chemistry dept., 1990-92; faculty sr. scientist Chem. Biodynamics Lab., Lawrence Berkeley Lab., Berkeley, 1963—. Author: (with I. Tinoco, J. Wang) Physical Chemistry, 1977, 2d edit., 1985; contbr. numerous articles to sci. jours. Recipient Alexander von Humboldt award, 1985-86, McKnight Found. award, 1983; Guggenheim Meml. Found. fellow, 1976-77; NSF grantee, 1968, 72, 76, 78, 79, 82, 85, 87, 91; USDA grantee, 1983, 85, 87. Mem. Am. Chem. Soc., Biophys. Soc., AAAS (fellow 1976—), Am. Soc. Photobiology (Rsch. award 1993), Am. Soc. Plant Physiology, AAUP, Phi Beta Kappa, Sigma Xi. Office: U Calif Dept Chemistry Berkeley CA 94720

SAUER, KENNETH H., bishop. Bishop Luth. Ch. Am., Columbus, Ohio. Office: Evangelical Lutheran Church 8765 W Higgins Rd Chicago IL 60631-4101

SAUER, NORMAN GARDINER, judge, attorney; b. Independence, Iowa, Aug. 28, 1921; s. Olvin Charles and Dorothy (Geiser) S.; m. Irene Manuth, Sept. 14, 1947; children: Georg, James, Vicki, Douglas. BS, U.S. Mil. Acad., 1945; JD, Gonzaga U., Spokane, Wash., 1975. Atty. pvt. practice, Republic, Wash., 1976-77; prosecuting atty. Ferry County, Republic, Wash., 1977-82; atty. pvt. practice, Republic, Wash., 1983-88; dist. court judge Ferry County, Republic, Wash., 1989—; judge pro tem Ferry County Dist. Court, Republic, Wash., 1982-88; superior court commr. Ferry County Superior Court, Republic, Wash., 1989-92; mcpl. court judge City of Republic, Wash., 1989-92. Chmn. Rep. Ctl. Com., Ferry County, Wash., 1976. Lt. col. USAF, 1964-70. Home: 87 N Klondike Rd Republic WA 99166 Office: PO Box 526 Republic WA 99166

SAUER, RICHARD JOHN, association executive; b. Walker, Minn., Nov. 15, 1939; s. Herman and Katherine Elizabeth (Rieder) S.; m. Elizabeth Louise Hornstein, Aug. 18, 1962; children: Michele, Alison, Maria, Peter. BS in Biology, St. John's U., Collegeville, Minn., 1962; MS in Zoology, U. Mich., Ann Arbor, 1964; PhD in Entomology, N.D. State U., 1967. Asst. prof. biology St. Cloud (Minn.) State U., 1967-68; asst. prof., then assoc. prof. entomology Mich. State U., East Lansing, 1968-76, acting assoc. dir. Mich. Agrl. Expt. Sta., 1975-76; prin. entomologist Coop. State Rsch. Svc., USDA, Washington, 1974-75; prof., head dept. entomology Kans. State U., Manhattan, 1976-80; dir. Agrl. Expt. Sta. U. Minn., St. Paul, 1980-89, v.p. agriculture, forestry and home econs., 1983-89; interim pres. U. Minn., Mpls., 1988-89; pres., CEO Nat. 4-H Coun., Chevy Chase, Md., 1989—. Mem. Entomol. Soc. Am. (pres. N.Cen. br. 1989-90), Am. Soc. Assn. Execs. Roman Catholic. Home: 1523 Ivystone Ct Silver Spring MD 20904-5476 Office: Nat 4-H Coun 7100 Connecticut Ave Chevy Chase MD 20815-4999

SAUER, ROBERT C., religious organization administrator. 3d v.p. Luth. Ch.-Mo. Synod, St. Louis. Office: 1333 S Kirkwood Rd Saint Louis MO 63122-7226

SAUERBREY, ELLEN ELAINE RICHMOND, radio talk show host; b. Balt., Sept. 9, 1937; d. Edgar Arthur and Ethel Frederika (Landraf) Richmond; m. Wilmer John Emil Sauerbrey, June 27, 1959. AB summa cum laude in Biology and English, Western Md. Coll., 1959. Biology instr., chmn. sci. dept. Baltimore County Sch. System, 1959-64; dist. mgr. Baltimore County U.S. Census, 1970; Md. Ho. of Dels., Annapolis, 1978-95, minority leader, 1986-95; radio talk show host Sta. WBAL; Rep. candidate for Gov., 1994. Del. Rep. Nat. Convs., 1968, 76, 84, 88, 92, mem. credentials com., 1984, platform com., chmn. subcom. on economy, 1977; vice chmn. Rep. State Ctrl. Com. of Balt. County, 1966-71; trustee Md. Coun. Econ. Edn., Franklin Sq. Hosp.; nat. chmn. Am. Legis. Exec. Coun., 1990-91; Rep. candidate Gov. Md., 1994. Named Legislator of Yr., Md. Assn. Bldrs. and Contrs., 1982, Am. Legis. Exec. Coun., 1986, Western Md. Coll. Alumni of Yr., 1988, Outstanding Legis. Leader, Am. Legis. Exec. Coun., 1992; recipient Pvt. Property award Greater Balt. Bd. Realtors, 1984. Mem. DAR, Md. Fedn. Rep. Women, Am. Legis. Exch. Coun. Found. (chmn. emeritus, legislator of yr. 1986), Nat. Taxpayers Union, Md. Farm Bur., Women Legislators of Md., Md. Conservation Union, Beta Beta Beta. Presbyterian. Avocations: gardening, travel.

SAUERHAFT, STAN, public relations executive, consultant; b. N.Y.C., Nov. 25, 1926; s. Al and Rae S.; m. Rosalie Cynthia Tolkin, Oct. 28, 1951; children: Richard Craig, Douglas Clark, Robert James. BA, U. Mich., 1948, MA, 1949. Editor, scriptwriter Paramount News, 1950-51; scriptwriter Hearst Metrotone News, N.Y.C., 1951-52; editor Food Bus. Mag., N.Y.C.,

1952-53; acct. supr. Selvage, Lee & Chase, N.Y.C., 1953-55; v.p., mem. creative plans bd. Communications Counselors, Inc. McCann-Erickson, N.Y.C., 1955-59; pres. Chase and Sauerhaft Assocs., N.Y.C., 1959-65; exec. v.p., dir., mem. mgmt. com. Hill & Knowlton, Inc., N.Y.C., 1965-86; vice chmn. bd. , dir. Burson-Marsteller, U.S., 1987-88; vice chmn., dir. Burson-Marsteller Internat., 1988—; instr., lectr. Columbia U. Grad. Sch., 1962-65, NYU Grad. Bus. Sch., 1984-87. Author: The Merger Game, 1971; co-author: Image Wars, 1989; contbr. bus. articles and chpts. to anthologies. Chmn. West Point Civilian Adv. Com., N.Y., 1980—; mem. exec. com. of bd. Inst. for Pub. Rels. Rsch. and Edn., 1984—, LS&A Coll. of U. Mich., 1990—; mem. adv. bd. U. Mich. Staff sgt. AUS, 1945-46. Coll. of Fellows Pub. Rels. Soc. Am. (nat. accreditation bd. 1981-83), Pub. Rels. Soc. N.Y. (pres. 1983-85); mem. Soc. Profl. Journalists, Authors Guild, Pub. Affairs Coun., Am. Platform Tennis Assn. (v.p.), U. Mich. Alumni Club, Union League Club N.Y. (chmn. pub. affairs com. 1980-84), Burning Tree Country Club (Greenwich, Conn.), Wiindmill Club, Seabrook Island Club (S.C.). Republican. Avocations: golf, platform tennis, bridge. Home: 21 Windmill Pl Armonk NY 10504-2830 Office: Burson-Marsteller 230 Park Ave S New York NY 10003-1513

SAUERS, CLAYTON HENRY, financial executive; b. Mont., Apr. 7, 1926; m. Patricia Davis; children: Gale Elizabeth, Peter D. BS, U. Wash., 1948; MBA, Harvard U., 1951. Credit analyst The Northern Trust Co., Chgo., 1951-54; exec. v.p. A.B. Dick Co., Chgo., 1954-79; v.p. fin., chief fin. officer West Point (Ga.) Pepperell Inc., 1979—. With USN, 1944-46, PTO. Mem. Fin. Execs. Inst. (pres. Chgo. chpt. 1974-75). Republican. Mem. Christian Science Ch. Office: West Point-Pepperell Inc PO Box 71 West Point GA 31833-0071

SAUFFERER, WILLIAM CHARLES, health center executive; b. Faribault, Minn.; s. William Carl and Dorothy F. (Martin) S.; m. Mardell Haiby, Apr. 23, 1960; children: Nancy, Kari, Scott. BA in Econ. and History, U. Minn. 1958. Asst. administr. Faribault (Minn.) Regional Ctr., 1960-84, chief exec. officer, 1984-90, regional mgr., 1990—; cons. Bus. Planning Group, Inc., Farmington Hills, Mich., 1980—. Pres. River Bend Nature Ctr., Faribault, 1989-91; dir. Hannah Lips Found., 1988—; bd. dirs. Faribault Community Quality project Minn. Coun. for Quality, 1988—. With USAF, 1950-53, Korea. Recipient Citation of Honor Gov. Minn., 1978, Citation for Exec. Service State of Minn., 1981. Mem. Nat. Assn. Supts. of Pub. Residential Facilities for the Mentally Retarded, Minn. Congress of Advocates for the Retarded, Faribault Area C. of C. (bd. dirs. 1987-90), Faribault Exch. Club (sec. 1986-88, bd. dirs. 1988-90, pres. 1990-91). Democrat. Lutheran. Avocations: camping, fishing, stained glass design, reading. Home: 6400 French Lake Trl Faribault MN 55021-7482 Office: Faribault Regional Ctr 802 Circle Dr Faribault MN 55021-6399

SAUFLEY, WILLIAM EDWARD, banker, lawyer; b. Washington, Mar. 7, 1956; s. Franklin Dewit and Ruth Constance (Wright) S.; m. Leigh Ingalls, Jan. 3, 1981. BA, Dartmouth Coll., 1977; JD, U. Maine, 1980. Bar: Maine 1980, U.S. Dist. Ct. Maine 1980. Of counsel Maine Legislature, Augusta, 1981-84; v.p. counsel Maine Savs. Bank, Portland, 1984-88, gen. counsel, sec., 1988-91; corp. sec. The One Bancorp, Portland, 1984-91, gen. counsel, 1989-91; sr. v.p., gen. counsel Fleet Bank of Maine, Portland, 1992-94; of counsel Monaghan, Leahy, Hochadel & Libby, Portland, 1995—. Trustee 75 State St Home for Elderly, Portland, 1986-92. Mem. ABA (bus. law sect.), Maine Bar Assn. (corp. sect., consumer law sect.). Democrat. Roman Catholic. Avocations: photography, computers. Home: 51 Bramblewood Dr Portland ME 04103-3796 Office: Monaghan Leahy Hochadel & Libby 95 Exchange St Portland ME 04112-7046

SAUL, B. FRANCIS, II, bank executive; b. Washington, Apr. 15, 1932; s. Andrew Maguire and Ruth Clark (Sheehan) S.; m. Elizabeth Patricia English, Apr. 30, 1960; children: Sharon Elizabeth, B. Francis III, Elizabeth Willoughby, Andrew Maguire II, Patricia English. Grad. Georgetown Prep. Sch., 1950; BS, Villanova U., 1954, DCS (hon.), 1989; LLB, U. Va., 1957. Bar: D.C. 1959. Chmn., pres. B.F. Saul Co., Chevy Chase, Md., 1957—; chmn., trustee B.F. Saul Real Estate Investment Trust Co., Chevy Chase, 1964—; With Chevy Chase Bank, F.S.B. 1969—, chmn., chief exec. officer, founder; chmn. Fin. Gen. Bankshares, Inc., 1978-82; chmn., CEO, trustee Saul Ctrs., Inc., 1993—; chmn. bd. dirs. 1st am. Bankshares, Inc., Washington, 1978-85; dir. Colonial Williamsburg Hotel Properties, Inc., 1983—; fin. cons. Archdiocese of Washington, 1990—; mem. bd. advisors CLW Life and Annuity Acquisition Corp., 1994—. Trustee Fed. City Coun., Nat. Geographic Soc., 1985—, Suburban Hosp., 1972-76; dirs. Wadsworth Preservation Trust, 1983—; trustee Brookings Inst., 1987-93, hon. trustee, 1993—; trustee Corcoran Gallery Art, Washington, 1972-90; mem. vis. com. Sch. Architecture U. Va., 1985—; bd. dirs. Garfinckel, Brooks Bros., Miller & Rhoads, 1970-81, Madeira Sch., Greenway, Va., 1978-88, Portsmouth Abbey Sch., R.I., 1979-84, United World Coll. of Am. West, Montezuma, N.Mex., 1982-85, D.C. Fund for Creative Space, 1980-82, D.C. chpt. ARC, 1964-86; chmn. Folger Shakespeare Libr. Com., 1985—; pres. D.C. Soc. for Crippled Children, 1973-75. Mem. Mortgage Bankers Assn. Met. Washington (pres. 1968), Nat. Assn. Real Estate Investment Trusts (pres. 1973-74), Alfalfa Club, Alibi Club, Met. Club, Knights of Malta, Chevy Chase Club, Burning Tree Club, Friendly Sons of St. Patrick (pres. 1992), Wianno Club, The Brook Club, Farmington Country Club, Roman Catholic. Home: 1 Quincy St Chevy Chase MD 20815-4226 Office: BF Saul Co 8401 Connecticut Ave Chevy Chase MD 20815-5897

SAUL, GEORGE BRANDON, II, biology educator; b. Hartford, Conn., Aug. 8, 1928; s. George Brandon and Dorothy (Ayers) S.; m. Sue Grau Williams, Mar. 28, 1953. A.B., U. Pa., 1949, A.M., 1950, Ph.D. 1954. From instr. to assoc. prof. Dartmouth, 1954-67; prof. biology Middlebury (Vt.) Coll., 1967—, chmn. dept., 1968-76, 91-93, v.p. acad. affairs, 1976-79; Research asso. Calif. Inst. Tech., 1964-65; NSF postdoctoral fellow U. Zurich, Switzerland, 1959-60; vis. scientist Boyce Thompson Inst. for Plant Research, Yonkers, N.Y., 1972-73. Author papers in field. Fellow AAAS; mem. Pa. Acad. Sci., Genetics Soc. Am., Am. Genetics Assn., Radiation Research Soc., N.Y. Acad. Scis., Sigma Xi. Club: Lion. Home: Munger St RR 3 Box 2575 Middlebury VT 05753 Office: Middlebury Coll Dept Biology Middlebury VT 05753

SAUL, JOHN WOODRUFF, III, writer; b. Pasadena, Calif., Feb. 25, 1942; s. John Woodruff and Adeline Elizabeth (Lee) S. Student, Antioch Coll., 1959-60, Cerritos Coll., 1960-61, Mont. State U., Missoula, 1961-62, San Francisco State Coll., 1963-65. In various positions primarily in L.A. and San Francisco, 1965-76. Author: Suffer The Children, 1977, Punish the Sinners, 1978, Cry for the Strangers, 1979, Comes the Blind Fury, 1980, When the Wind Blows, 1981, The God Project, 1982, Nathaniel, 1984, Brainchild, 1985, Hellfire, 1986, The Unwanted, 1987, The Unloved, 1988, Creature, 1989, Second Child, 1990, Sleep Walk, 1990, Darkness, 1991, Shadows, 1992, Guardian, 1993, The Homing, 1994, Black Lightning, 1995; also other novels under pseudonyms. Bd. dirs. Seattle Theatre Arts, 1978-80; bd. govs. Tellurian Communities, Inc., Madison, Wis.; v.p. Chester Woodruff Found., N.Y.C. Mem. Authors Guild. Democrat. Swedenborgian. Office: care Jane Rotrosen 318 E 51st St New York NY 10022-7803 For a writer, the education of experience is without doubt the best education.

SAUL, KENNETH LOUIS, retired utility company executive; b. Columbus, Ohio, Aug. 29, 1923; s. Aloysius Louis and Ruth Geneva (Duke) S.; m. Shirley Ann Todd, Feb. 14, 1953; children: Carl, Deborah, Kenneth, Mark, Lori, Richard. BBA, Ohio State U., 1949. Various mgmt. positions Columbus & So. Ohio Elec. Co., 1955-70, asst. controller, 1970-74; v.p., controller Tucson Elec. Power, 1974-84, sr. v.p., chief fin. officer, 1984-88, also bd. dirs.; bd. dirs. Ohio Steel Products, Columbus, Engring. Rsch. Assocs., Tucson. Chmn. bd. Bishop Hartley High Sch., Columbus, 1967-73; treas., bd. dirs. United Way, Tucson, 1975-81, Carondelet Health Care, Tucson, 1982-85, St. Joseph's Hosp., Tucson, 1976-82. Staff sgt. USAAF, 1943-45, PTO. Mem. Nat. Assn. Accts., Skyline Country Club (pres. 1979-80), SMOO Investment Club (pres. 1970-73). Republican. Roman Catholic. Avocations: golf, swimming, baseball, football. Home: 6260 E Placita El Vuelo Tucson AZ 85715-1284

SAUL, NORMAN EUGENE, history educator; b. LaFontaine, Ind., Nov. 26, 1932; s. Ralph Odis and Jessie (Neff) S.; m. Mary Ann Culwell, June 27, 1959; children: Alyssa, Kevin, Julia. B.A., Ind. U.- Bloomington, 1954;

M.A., Columbia U., 1959, Ph.D., 1965; postgrad., Leningrad State U. (USSR), 1960-61. Instr. history Purdue U., 1962-65; asst. prof. Brown U., 1965-68; vis. assoc. prof. Northwestern U., 1969-70; assoc. prof. U. Kans., Lawrence, 1970-75, prof. history, 1975—, chmn. dept. history, 1981-89. Author: Russia and the Mediterranean 1797-1807, 1970, Sailors in Revolt, 1978, Distant Friends: The United States and Russia, 1763-1867, 1991. Fulbright scholar U.S. Edn. Commn., London, 1954-55, U.S. Edn. Commn., Helsinki, 1968-69; Soviet Am. Exch. scholar Internat. Rsch. and Exch. Bd., Moscow, 1973-74, 91-92; fellow Ford Found., 1957-59, Kennan Inst., 1976, 84, 91, 95, Hall Ctr. for Humanities, 1989, 95; recipient Byron Caldwell Smith Book award for Distant Friends Hall Ctr. for Humanities, 1993. Mem. Am. Hist. Assn., Am. Assn. Advancement of Slavic Studies, Kans. State Hist. Soc. Home: 1002 Crestline Dr Lawrence KS 66049-2607 Office: Dept of History U of Kans Lawrence KS 66045

SAUL, PETER, artist; b. San Francisco, Aug. 16, 1934. Student, Stanford U., Calif. Sch. Fine Arts, 1950-52; B.F.A., Washington U., St. Louis, 1956. One-man shows at Allan Frumkin Gallery, Chgo., 1961, 63, 64, N.Y.C., 1962, 63, 64, 66, 70, 84, 87, Frumkin & Struve Gallery, Chgo., 1983, 84, Galerie Breteau, Paris, 1962, 64, 67, La Tartaruga, Rome, 1963, Rolf Nelson Gallery, 1963, Notizie Gallery, 1964, Galerie Darthea Speyer, Paris, 1969, Musée St. Etienne, France, 1971, Frumkin Adams Gallery, N.Y.C., 1989-90, Gelene Thomas R. Monahan, Chgo., 1990, Galene du Ctr., Paris, 1991, Tex Gallery, 1987-90, many others; exhibited in group shows at Salon des Seunes Peintres, Paris, 1959, 60, Dayton Art Inst., 1961, U. Colo., 1962, Chgo. Art Inst., 1962, 63, 64, U. Mich., 1963, Musee Cantonal des BeaxArts, Lausanne, I Salon Internat. de Galeries Pilotes, 1963, Abbey Saint-Pierre, Ghent, 1963, Brandeis U., Recent Am. Drawings, 1964, The Hague, New Realism, 1964; represented in permanent collections at Art Inst. Chgo., Oberlin Coll., Whitney Mus. Am. Art, N.Y.C., Mus. Modern Art, N.Y.C., others. Recipient New Talent award Art in America mag. 1962. William and Noma Copley Found. grantee, 1962; recipient Nat. Endowment Arts grant, 1980. Address: Galerie Thomas R Monahan 1038 N La Salle Chicago IL 60610

SAUL, RALPH SOUTHEY, financial service executive; b. Bklyn., May 21, 1922; s. Walter Emerson and Helen Douglas (Coutts) S.; m. Bette Jane Bertschinger, June 16, 1956; children: Robert Southey, Jane Adams. B.A., U. Chgo., 1947; LL.B., Yale U., 1951. Bar: D.C. 1951, N.Y. 1952. With Am. Embassy, Prague, Czechoslovakia, 1947-48; assoc. firm Lyeth & Voorhees, N.Y.C., 1951-52; asst. counsel to Gov. N.Y. State, 1952-54; staff atty. RCA, 1954-58; with SEC, 1958-65, dir. div. trading and markets, 1963-65; v.p. corporate devel. Investors Diversified Services, Inc., Mpls., 1965-66; pres. Am. Stock Exchange, N.Y.C., 1966-71; co-CE, chmn. mgmt. com. First Boston Corp., 1971-74; chmn., chief exec. officer INA Corp., Phila., 1975-82, CIGNA Corp., Phila., 1982-84; bd. dirs. PH-II, Inc., Saint Gobain Corp., Commonwealth Ventures, Phila. Ventures Liberty Fund, Am. Bldgs. Co. HoraceMann Educator Corp. Trustee Com. for Econ. Devel., Brookings Inst.; chmn. Ednl. Quality Work Force Adv. Bd. With USNR, 1943-46, PTO. Mem. ABA, N.Y. Stock Exch. (regulatory adv. com.), Union League , Merion Golf Club, Links Club. Home: 549 Avonwood Rd Haverford PA 19041-1602 Office: Cigna Corp One Logan Square PO Box 7716 18th and Cherry Sts Philadelphia PA 19192

SAUL, STEPHANIE, journalist; b. St. Louis, Jan. 28, 1954; d. Elmer William and Nancy (Cromer) S.; m. Walt Bogdanich, Jan. 2, 1982; children: Nicholas Walter, Peter Eric. BA, U. Miss., 1975. Reporter New Albany (Miss.) Gazette, 1974, Clarion-Ledger, Jackson, Miss., 1975-80, The Plain Dealer, Cleve., 1980-84; nat. corr. Newsday, Melville, N.Y., 1984—. Recipient Silver Gavel award ABA, 1980, George Polk award for regional reporting, 1981, Nat. Press Club award, 1990, IRE award Investigative Reporters and Editors, 1995, Headliner award Atlantic City Press Club, 1995, Roy Howard award Scripps Howard Found., 1995, Pulitzer prize for investigative reporting, 1995. Office: Newsday 235 Pinelawn Rd Melville NY 11747-4250

SAUL, WILLIAM EDWARD, academic administrator, civil engineering educator; b. N.Y.C., May 15, 1934; s. George James and Fanny Ruth (Murokh) S.; m. J. Muriel Held Eagleburger, May 11, 1976. BSCE, Mich. Tech. U., 1955, MSCE, 1961; PhD in Civil Engring., Northwestern U., 1964. Registerd profl. engr., Wis., Idaho, Mich., profl. structural engr., Idaho. Mech. engr. Shell Oil Co., New Orleans, 1955-59; instr. engring. mechanics Mich. Tech. U., Houghton, 1960-62; asst. prof. civil engring. U. Wis., Madison, 1964-67, assoc. prof., 1967-72, prof., 1972-84; dean Coll. Engring., prof. civil engring. U. Idaho, Moscow, 1984-90; prof. civil engring. Mich. State U., East Lansing, 1990—, chair dept. civil and environ. engring., 1990—; cons. engr., 1961—; bd. dirs. Idaho Rsch. Found., 1984-90; vis. prof. U. Stuttgart, Fed. Republic Germany, 1970-71. Co-editor of Methods of Structural Analysis, 1976. Fulbright fellow 1970-71; von Humboldt scholar, 1970-71. Fellow ASCE (vis. sect. 1983-84); mem. NSPE, Mich. Soc. Profl. Engrs., Internat. Assn. Bridge and Structural Engrs., Am. Concrete Inst., Am. Soc. Engring. Edn., Sigma Xi, Phi Kappa Phi, Tau Beta Pi, Chi Epsilon. Avocations: hiking, reading, travel, gadgets. Home: 1971 Cimarron Dr Okemos MI 48864-3905 Office: Mich State U A349 Engring Bldg East Lansing MI 48824

SAULS, DON, religious organization administrator, clergyman; b. Eureka, N.C.; m. Marie Brown; children: Donna, Dale. B in Sacred Lit., Holmes Sch. of the Bible, Greenville, S.C., 1967; B Sacred Lit., N.C. State U., 1984; postgrad., N.C. Wesleyan Coll. Ordained to ministry Pentecostal Free Will Bapt. Ch., 1966. Pastor Pentecostal Free Will Bapt. Ch., Benson, N.C., 1967-74, gen. dir. Christian Edn. dept., 1971-84, gen. supt., 1984—; tchr. Heritage Bible Coll., Dunn, N.C., 1971—, also trustee; chmn. bd. dirs , sec., mem. bd. adminstrn. Pentecostal Fellowship N.Am., 1988-91; lectr. U.S. and abroad. Columnist Messenger, 1984—; contbr. articles to jours. in field. Mem. Kiwanis (former pres. Dunn club, bd. dirs.). Office: Pentecostal Free Will Bapt Ch PO Box 1568 Dunn NC 28335-1568

SAULSBURY, RUTH EVA, retired special education educator; b. Madison County, Miss., Mar. 26, 1920; d. Samuel Paul and Sarah Libby (Thomas) Johnson; m. Otis Samuel Saulsbury; children: Byron Henry, Nelda Kaye, Onwin Samuuel. BS, Tougaloo Coll., 1944; MEd, DePaul U., 1981. Cert. tchr., Miss., Ill., Del., La. Tchr. Sts. Indsl. Sch., Lexington, Miss., 1944-46, Union Parish Sch., Farmerville, La., 1946-47, Dunbar High Sch, Chgo. Elem. Schs., 1948-50, Delena Day Elem., Chgo., 1963-65, Garfield Elem. Sch., Chicago Heights, Ill., 1965-81, Chipman Jr. High Sch., Harrington, Del., 1981-93. Adult Sun. Sch. tchr. Calvary Assembly of God, Dover, Del., 1985-91; vol. tchr. South Area Lit. Coun., so. suburbs Ill. Mem. ASCD, Coun. Exceptional Children, Smithsonian Assoc. Democrat. Pentecostal. Avocations: reading, flower gardening, fishing. Home: 14302 Tracy Ave Riverdale IL 60627

SAUMIER, ANDRE, finance executive; b. Montreal, Que., Can., Aug. 26, 1933; s. Robert and Georgette (Sansoucy) S.; children—Sonia, Genevieve, Verushka. BA, U. Montreal, 1950; LTh, Angelicum U., Rome, 1955; MA, U. Chgo., 1958; MBA, Harvard U., 1962. Research assoc. Battelle Inst., Columbus, Ohio, 1962-63; dir. research Urban Affairs Council, Ottawa, Ont., Can., 1963-67; asst. dep. minister rural devel., regional devel., urban affairs Can. Govt., Ottawa, Ont., Can., 1967-75; dep. sec. to cabinet, dep. minister of mines, water & energy Que. Govt., Quebec City, 1975-79; sr. v.p. Richardson Greenshields Co., Montreal, 1979-85; pres., chief exec. officer Montreal Stock Exchange, 1985-87; chmn. Saumier Morrisson & Davidson Inc., Investment Bankers, Montreal, 1987-89, Saumier Freres Conseil, Fin. Advisors, Montreal, 1989—; bd. dirs., chmn. Societe Nationale de L'Amiante, Montreal; chmn. Sebentar Holdings Inc., Unilever Can., Inc., Toronto, Alyvanor Inc., Montreal, Virage Prodns., Inc.; vice chmn. Simpa Inc., Montreal, Vista Info. Tech. Inc., Can. Golden Fund Inc., Can. ASEAN Ctr., Singapore; advisor World Resources Inst., Washington, Ministry of Fin. of Indonesia, Jakarta, Ministry of Fin. of Gabon, Libreville, Ministry of Fin. of Kazakhstan, Almaty; bur. de consultation de Montreal, City of Montreal, Que. Contbg. author books on environment. Bd. govs. Nouveau-Monde Theater, Montréal, 1983—, Quebec Press Coun. Found. Decorated officer Nat. Order of Niger, 1972, Order of St.-Lazarus of Jerusalem, 1987; recipient Merit award Montreal C. of C., 1985, 88. Home: 65 St Paul W Apt 403, Montreal, PQ Canada H2Y 3S5 Office: Saumier Freres Conseil, 5 Place Ville-Marie Ste 1234, Montreal, PQ Canada H3B 2G2

SAUNBY, JOHN BRIAN, petrochemical company executive; b. Hull, Eng., Mar. 7, 1933; came to U.S., 1959; s. Clive Henry and Frances Evelyn (Smith) S.; m. Eileen Mary Hillman, Sept. 1, 1956; children: Carole, Linda. B.S. in Chem. Engring., Birmingham U., Eng., 1954, Ph.D., 1957. Postdoctoral fellow NRC, Ottawa, Can., 1957-59; chem. engr. Union Carbide Corp., South Charleston, W.Va., 1959-65, group leader, 1965-73, assoc. dir., 1973-80, dir. licensing, 1978-80, dir. rsch. and devl., 1980-92; cons. R&D NSF EPSCOR program, 1992—; chmn. NSF Exptl. Program for Stimulation of Competitive Rsch., W.Va., 1980-85, 89-92; W.Va. rep. So. Tech. Coun., 1989-92. Patentee in field. Bd. dirs. Kanawha Valley Youth Orch., Charleston, 1972-78, pres., 1972-78; bd. dirs. W.Va. Opera Theater, Charleston, 1978-79; mem. arts and scis. adv. bd. W.Va. U., 1985-92. Fellow Trinidad Leaseholds Ltd., 1954-56; fellow Shell Petroleum Co., 1956-57. Mem. Am. Inst. Chem. Engrs. Club: Les Amis du Vin (Charleston).

SAUNDERS, ALEXANDER HALL, real estate executive; b. Tallahassee, Oct. 5, 1941; s. Irvin Jasper and Perry Frances (Watson) S.; m. Pamela Wightman, July 24, 1970; 1 child, Anne Marguerite. AA, Norman Coll., 1961; BA, Mercer U., 1966. Planning administr. Ga. Dept. Corrections, Atlanta, 1969-70; mgmt. analyst Ga. Dept. Transp., Atlanta, 1970-71, tng. adminstr., 1971-72, asst. to research and devel., 1972-73, adminstr., asst. to dir., 1974-82; pres. ERA Towne Square Realty, Inc. Stone Mountain, Ga., 1982—. Named one of Top Real Estate Execs. in Am., ERA, 1987. Mem. Nat. Assn. Realtors, Ga. Assn. Realtors, DeKalb Bd. Realtors, ERA North Ga. Brokers Coun. (trustee 1983-86, pres. 1988-89, v.p. dir. fin. 1989-), Metro Listing Svc., U.S. C of C, DeKalb C. of C., Better Bus. Bur., Alpha Tau Omega, Delta Theta Phi. Avocations: tennis, racquet ball, golf.

SAUNDERS, ARLENE, opera singer; b. Cleve., Oct. 5, 1935. MusB, Baldwin-Wallace Coll., 1957. Tchr. voice Rutgers U., New Brunswick, N.J., 1987-88; tchr. classical vocal repertoire Abraham Goodman Sch., N.Y.C., 1987-88; advisor, tchr. vocal dept. NYU, 1990—, tchr. master classes, head opera dept., 1993; tchr. master classes Baldwin Wallace Coll., Santa Fe Opera Co., etc.; founder, dir. Opera Mobilè, Inc., N.Y.C., 1991—; adjudicator Met. Opera Regional Auditions, Liederkranz Voice Auditions, etc. Debut Milan Opera, 1961; Met. Opera debut in Die Meistersinger, 1976; specializes in Strauss and Wagner; performer with Phila. Opera, Lyric Opera, Houston Opera, Covent Garden, London, Teatro Colon, Buenos Aires, San Francisco Opera, Vienna Staatsoper, Paris Opera, Australian Opera, Sydney, Berlin Deutsche Opera, Munich Staatsoper, Hamburg State Opera, 1963-86, Rome Opera, Brussels Opera, Maggio Musicale, Florence, Italy, Geneva (Switzerland) Opera, Berlin Festival, Lisbon Opera, Glyndebourne Festival Opera, Eng., English Opera North, Boston Opera, N.Y.C. Opera; performed world premieres of Beatrix Cenci, 1971, Jakobowsky und der Oberst, 1965, Help, Help, The Globolinks, 1968, Ein Stern Geht Auf Aus Jaakob, 1970 (Gold medal Vercelli (Italy) voice competition); appeared in opera films including Arabella (title role), Meistersaenger (Eva), Marriage of Figaro (Countess), Help, Help the Globolinks (Mme. Euterpova), Der Freischuetz (Agathe), Gasparone (Carlotta); recs. for Philips and Victor. N.Y.C. Mayor's award, 1962; Kammersängerin Hamburg, 1967. Mem. Pi Kappa Lambda (Epsilon Phi chpt.). Address: 535 E 86th St New York NY 10028-7533

SAUNDERS, CHARLES ALBERT, lawyer; b. Boulder, Colo., Jan. 18, 1922; s. Charles and Anna (Crouse) S.; m. Betti Friedel, Oct. 18, 1946; children—Melanie, Stephen, Cynthia, Shelley. BA, U. Houston, 1942; LLB, U. Tex., 1945. Bar: Tex. bar 1945. Since practiced in Houston; partner firm Fulbright & Jaworski, 1959—; dir. Brookside Corp. Editor: How to Live—and Die—With Probate, 8 vols, 1968, Texas Estate Administration, 1975. Bd. dirs. Houston Symphony Soc., 1964—; bd. dirs. Am. Lung Assn., San Jacinto, 1965—, pres., 1972-73. Mem. Am. Bar Assn., State Bar Tex., Houston Bar Assn., Am. Coll. Trust and Estate Coun. (regent 1972-80, pres. 1978-79). Republican. Presbyterian. Home: 19 Willowron Dr Houston TX 77024-7618 Office: Fulbright & Jaworski 1301 Mckinney St Houston TX 77010-3029

SAUNDERS, CHARLES BASKERVILLE, JR., retired association executive; b. Boston, Dec. 26, 1928; s. Charles Baskerville and Lucy (Carmichael) S.; m. Margaret MacIntire Shafer, Sept. 9, 1950; children—Charles Baskerville III, George Carlton, Margaret Keyser, Lucy C., John R. Grad., St. Mark's Sch., 1946; A.B., Princeton, 1950. News reporter, polit. columnist Ogdensbury (N.Y.) Jour., 1950-51; edn. reporter Hartford (Conn.) Times, 1951-53; asst. dir. pub. relations Trinity Coll., Hartford, 1953-55; asst. dir. pub. info. Princeton, 1955-57; legis. asst. Sen. H. Alexander Smith, 85th Congress, 1957-58; asst. to asst. sec. for legislation HEW, 1958-59; asst. to sec. Arthur S. Flemming, 1959-61, dep. asst. sec. for legislation, 1969-71; asst. to pres. Brookings Instn., 1961-69; dep. commr. of edn. for external affairs U.S. Office Edn., 1971-77; dep. asst. sec. for edn. HEW, 1973-74; dir. govt. relations Am. Council on Edn., 1975-78, v.p. for govt. relations, 1978-87, sr. v.p., 1987-92. Author: Brookings Institution: A Fifty-Year History, 1966, Upgrading the American Police, 1970. Mem. Montgomery County Bd. Edn., 1966-70; trustee Montgomery Coll., 1969-70, Md. Higher Edn. Commn., 1989— (chmn. 1994—); chmn. bd. dirs. Md. Higher Edn. Loan Corp., 1994—. Republican. Presbyterian. Home: 7622 Winterberry Pl Bethesda MD 20817-4848

SAUNDERS, DEBRA J., columnist; b. Newton, Mass., Dec. 8, 1954. BA in Latin and Greek, U. Mass., Boston, 1980. Asst. dir. Arnold Zenher Assocs., 1982-83; writer/rschr., account exec. Todd Domke Assocs., Sacramento, 1983-84, Russo Watts & Rollins, Sacramento, 1985-86; asst. to Rep. Leader Calif. Legislature, Sacramento, 1987-88; columnist, editl. writer L.A. Daily News, 1988-92; columnist San Francisco Chronicle, 1992—; leader study group on polit. speechmaking Harvard U., Cambridge, Mass., 1984; tchr. editl. and column writing UCLA Ext., 1992. Office: San Francisco Chronicle 901 Mission St San Francisco CA 94103-2905

SAUNDERS, DERO AMES, writer, editor; b. Starkville, Miss., Sept. 27, 1913; s. Madison and Erin (Hearon) S.; m. Beatrice Nair, May 23, 1936; children: David, Richard. A.B., Dartmouth Coll., 1935; A.M., Columbia U., 1938. Lectr., lecture mgr. contbr. to various mgs., 1936-42; with Fgn. Econ. Adminstrn., Washington and Cairo, Egypt, 1943-45; chief Fgn. Econ. Adminstrn. (Middle East div.), 1945; asso. editor Fortune mag. 1945-57; v.p. Med. and Pharm. Info. Bur., 1957-59; lectr. Hunter Coll., 1960-61, 67—; associate editor Forbes mag., 1960-62, sr. editor, 1962-66, exec. editor, 1966-81, contbg. editor, 1982—. Contbg. author: Why Do People Buy?, 1953, The Changing American Market, 1954; Editor: The Portable Gibbon, 1952, The Autobiography of Edward Gibbon, 1961; co-editor: The History of Rome, 1958; chmn. editorial bd.: Dartmouth Alumni mag., 1983-85. Pres. Dartmouth Alumni Council, 1970-71; Prin. U.S. civilian rep. Middle East Supply Center, 1945. Clubs: Players (N.Y.C.); Heights Casino (Bklyn.). Home: 446 W 22d St New York NY 10011 Office: 60 Fifth Ave New York NY 10011-8865

SAUNDERS, DONALD HERBERT, utility company executive; b. Gallipolis, Ohio, Dec. 1, 1935; s. Clyde Edwin and Daisy Mae (Betz) S.; m. Dolores Marie Martin, Jan. 4, 1958; children: Scott, Glenn, Laura, El-len. BBA, U. Toledo, 1957, MBA, 1964. Budget and statis. analyst Toledo Edison Co., 1957-60, supr. customer records and acctg., 1960-63, supr. property acctg., 1963-66, mgr. gen. acctg., 1966-68, asst. contr., dir. acctg. records, 1968-71, contr., dir. acctg., 1971-79, treas., 1979-86, v.p. fin. and adminstrn., 1986-90, v.p. adminstrn. and govtl. affairs, 1990, pres. 1990—. Treas. City of Oregon, Ohio, 1972—; mem. adv. bd. St. Charles Hosp., Oregon, 1981—; trustee Metro Toledo YMCA, 1980—, St. Charles and Mercy Hosp., 1989—, United Way, Toledo, 1991, chmn. 1993; bd. dirs. Corp. for Effective Govt., 1987—, Pub. Broadcasting Found. N.W. Ohio, 1991—, Toledo coun. Boy Scouts Am. 1991—, Toledo chpt. ARC, 1991—; mem. Ohio Electric Utility Inst. Bd., 1991—. Named Outstanding Citizen of Oregon, Oregon C. of C., 1983. Mem. Fin. Execs. Inst. (sec. Toledo chpt. 1986-87, treas. 1987-88, 2nd v.p. 1988-89, 1st v.p. 1989-90, pres. 1990-91), Toledo C. of C. (named one of Outstanding Young Men of Toledo 1970), Air Force Assn., N.G. Assn., N.G. Assn. Club, The Oregonian Club (past. pres.), U. Toledo Alumni Assn., Toledo Automobile (mem. corp. bd. 1984—), Masons, Blue Key. Republican. Avocations: golf, hunting, fishing. Home: 239 Ponderosa Dr Oregon OH 43616-2229 Office: Toledo Edison Co 300 Madison Ave Toledo OH 43652-0002

SAUNDERS, DONALD LESLIE, hotel executive, commercial real estate company executive; b. Brookline, Mass., Jan. 28, 1935; s. Irving Matthew Saunders and Shirley Brown; m. Liv Ullmann; children—Lisa M., Pamela R., Linn B. AB in Econs., Brown U., 1957; grad., Inst. Real Estate Mgmt., 1963; LLB (hon.), Pine Manor Coll., 1989. Real estate broker, R.I., Mass. Chmn., CEO Saunders Real Estate Corp., Boston, 1957—; owner Saunders Real Estate and Hotels, Boston; chmn., treas. The Boston Pk. Plz. Hotel and Towers, 1976—; gen. ptnr. The Boston Plaza Hotel L.P.; co-owner Copley Square Hotel, Boston; bd. dirs. Hotel Lenox of Boston Inc. Bd. dirs. Park Sch. Corp., Brookline, Mass.; founder Farview Inc.; pres. Farview Inc., Brown U. comml. real estate devel. co.; vice chmn. facilities and design com. Brown U., trustee emeritus, 1972—; mem. nat. adv. com. U.S. Com. for UNICEF; trustee Boston Ballet Co.; bd. dirs. Jerusalem Inst. Mgmt. Inc. at Harvard Bus. Sch. Recipient Nat. Jewish Hosp. and Research Ctr. Nat. Asthma Ctr. Humanitarian award, 1979, Back Bay Fedn. Community Devel. Ann. award, 1981, Historic Neighborhoods Found. award, 1986. Mem. Internat. Hotel Assn., Inst. Real Estate Mgmt. (key 2299), Nat. Assn. Realtors, Great Boston Real Estate Bd., Ocean Reef Club (Racquet Club, Harbor Course Club), Brown U. Club, Lotos Club, The Players, Union League Club, Hope Club, Boston Tennis and Racquet Club, Ea. Point Yacht Club, Belmont Country Club, Bay Club, Downtown Club, Union Club Boston. Office: Saunders Real Estate Corp 20 Park Plz Boston MA 02116-4399

SAUNDERS, DORIS EVANS, editor, educator, business executive; b. Chgo., Aug. 8, 1921; d. Alvesta Stewart and Thelma (Rice) Evans; m. Vincent E. Saunders Jr., Oct. 28, 1950 (div. 1963); children: Ann Camille, Vincent E. III. B.A., Roosevelt U., 1951; M.S., M.A., Boston U., 1977; postgrad., Vanderbilt U., 1984. Sr. library asst. Chgo. Pub. Library, 1942-46, prin. reference librarian, 1946-49; librarian Johnson Pub. Co., 1949-66, dir. book div., 1961-66, 73-77; prof., coord. print journalism Jackson (Miss.) State U., 1977—, acting chair dept. mass communication, 1990—, chair, 1991—; Disting. minority lectr. U. Miss., Oxford, 1986; pres. Ancestor Hunting, Inc., Chgo., 1982—; dir. community rels. Chgo. State Coll., 1968-70; acting dir. instnl. devel. and community rels Chgo. State Coll., 1969-70; columnist Chgo. Daily Defender, 1966-70, Chgo. Courier, 1970-73; staff assoc. Office of Chancellor, U. Ill. at Chgo. Circle, 1970-73. Host: radio program The Think Tank, 1971-72; writer, producer: (TV) Our People, 1968-70; producer, host: Faculty Review Forum, Sta. WJSU, 1987—; author: Black Society, 1976; assoc. editor: Negro Digest mag, 1962-66; editor: The Day They Marched, 1963, The Kennedy Years and the Negro, 1964, DuBois: A Pictorial Biography, 1979, Wouldn't Take Nothin' for My Journey (L. Berry), 1981; compiler, editor: The Negro Handbook, 1966, The Ebony Handbook, 1974; pub. Kith and Kin; contbr. to profl. jours., mags. Bd. dirs. Arts Alliance, Jackson-Hinds County, Miss., 1993; mem. com. on ministry and commn. on racism Diocese of Miss. Mem. NAACP, Nat. Assn. Black Journalists, Assn. for Edn. in Journalism and Mass Comms., Black Coll. Comms. Assn. (v.p., pres. elect). Democrat. Episcopalian. Office: Jackson State U Dept Mass Communication PO Box 18067 Jackson MS 39217 also: PO Box 2413 Chicago IL 60690

SAUNDERS, ERIC DON, retail company executive; b. Woodbury, N.J., Sept. 14, 1942; s. Donald Herbert and Eula (Loomis) S.; m. Barbara Jeanne Andrews, Apr. 2, 1966; children: Drew Donald, Taryn Leigh. BA, Rutgers U., 1964. Dir. manpower planning Sears, Roebuck & Co., Chgo., 1976-78; territory ops. mgr. Sears, Roebuck & Co., Atlanta, 1978-80; dir. field planning Sears, Roebuck & Co., Chgo., 1980; group mgr. Sears, Roebuck & Co., Atlanta, 1981-82; v.p. ops. Sears, Roebuck & Co., Chgo., 1982-83; exec. v.p. midwest ter. Sears, Roebuck & Co., Skokie, Ill., 1983—. Mem. Beta Pi. Republican. Clubs: Knollwood (Lake Forest, Ill.); Metropolitan (Chgo.). Home: 575 Turicum Rd Lake Forest IL 60045-3365 Office: Sears Roebuck & Co 3333 Beverly Rd Hoffman Estates IL 60179 also: Sear Roebuck & Co Sears Towers Chicago IL 60684

SAUNDERS, GEORGE LAWTON, JR., lawyer; b. Mulga, Ala., Nov. 8, 1931; s. George Lawton and Ethel Estell (York) S.; children: Kenneth, Ralph, Victoria; m. Terry M. Rose. B.A., U. Ala., 1956; J.D., U. Chgo., 1959. Bar: Ill. 1960. Law clk. to chief judge U.S. Ct. Appeals (5th cir.), Montgomery, Ala., 1959-60; law clk to Justice Hugo L. Black U.S. Supreme Ct., Washington, 1960-62; assoc. Sidley & Austin, Chgo., 1962-67, ptnr., 1967-90; founding ptnr. Saunders & Monroe, Chgo., 1990—. With USAF, 1951-54. Fellow Am. Coll. Trial Lawyers; mem. ABA, Ill. State Bar Assn., Chgo. Bar Assn., Order of Coif, Chgo. Club, Tavern Club, Point-O'Woods Club, Quadrangle Club, Law Club, Legal Club, Phi Beta Kappa. Democrat. Baptist. Home: 179 E Lake Shore Dr Chicago IL 60611-1351 Office: Saunders & Monroe 205 N Michigan Ave Chicago IL 60601-5914

SAUNDERS, JAMES C., neuroscientist, educator; b. Elizabeth, N.J., May 8, 1941; s. Charles Oliver and Elizabeth Veronica (Drake) S.; m. Elaine Priscilla Edwards, Oct. 14, 1967; children: Breton Morris, Drew Charles. BA, Ohio Wesleyan U., 1963; MA, Conn. Coll., 1965, U. Pa., 1979; PhD, Princeton U., 1968. Lectr. dept. psychology Monash U., Victoria, Australia, 1969-72; rsch. assoc. Cen. for Deaf, St. Louis, 1972-73; asst. prof., then prof. dept. otorhinolaryngology U Pa., Phila., 1973-92, acting dir. Inst. Neurol. Scis., 1980-83, prof., 1984—; guest scientist Karolinska Inst., Stockholm, 1984-85; exec. com. CHABA, Nat. Rsch. Coun., Washington, 1986-89; chmn. disorders rev. com. NIDCD, Bethesda, Md., 1987-89; mem. exec. coun. Assn. Rsch. Otolaryngology, Chgo., 1988-91; mem. com. on hearing and bioacoustics Nat. Inst. on Deafness and Other Communications Disorders. Contbr. chpts., rev. papers to books on biology of hearing; contbr. articles on auditory neurobiology to profl. jours; author abstracts of meeting presentations on hearing. Recipient Basic Sci. Rsch. award Am. Acad. Otolaryngology, 1978, 87, Pa. Acad. Otolaryngology, 1982, Basic Sci. Excellence award (Claude Pepper award) NIDCD, 1988, Lindback award for disting. teaching U. Pa., 1992. Mem. AAAS, Acoustical Soc. Am., Soc. Neurosci., N.Y. Acad. Sci., Sigma Xi (legal cons. effects of noise on hearing). Democrat. Office: U Pa 5 Silverstein ORL 3400 Spruce St Philadelphia PA 19104 Home: 417 Bryn Mawr Ave Bala Cynwyd PA 19004-2619

SAUNDERS, KENNETH D., insurance company executive, consultant, arbitrator; b. Chgo., Jan. 4, 1927; s. Maurice and Mildred (Cochrane) S.; m. Jean S. Davies, Dec. 17, 1949; children: Karen Saunders Waugh, William Thomas. A.B., Dartmouth Coll., 1949. With Continental Casualty Co., Chgo., 1949-59; asst. v.p. Continental Casualty Co., 1957-59; exec. asst. Standard Accident Ins. Co., Detroit, 1959-62; with Combined Ins. Co. Am., Chgo., 1962-86; v.p. Combined Ins. Co. Am., 1969-74, sr. v.p., 1974-86; with Rollins, Burdick, Hunter, 1986-87. With USMC, 1945-46. Mem. Health Ins. Assn. Am. (com. leader), Chgo. Group Ins. Assn. (past treas., dir.), Internat. Ins. Soc. (charter mem.), Am. Arbitration Assn. (panel). Clubs: Economic (Chgo.), Tavern (Chgo.), Exmoor Country (Ill.), John's Island (Fla.). Office: 1418 Woodhill Dr Northbrook IL 60062-4661

SAUNDERS, NORMAN THOMAS, military officer; b. Amityville, N.Y., Oct. 19, 1942; s. Norman George and Marjory (Scott) S.; m. Christine Patricia Miller, Feb. 24, 1968; children: Thomas, Carré. BS, USCG Acad., 1964; MS, Naval Postgrad. Sch., Monterey, Calif., 1972; grad., Nat. War Coll., 1985. Commd. officer USCG, 1964, advanced through grades to Radm., 1985; br. chief edn. and tng. div. USCG, Washington, 1972-76; exec. officer USCG COURAGEOUS, Port Canaveral, Fla., 1976-78; spl. projects officer personnel div. USCG, Washington, 1978-79, br. chief personnel div., 1979-82; comdg. officer USCG DEPENDABLE, Panama City, Fla., 1982-84; spl. projects officer research and devel. USCG, Key West, Fla., 1985-86; comdr. USCG Group, Key West, 1986-88; chief intelligence and law enforcement br. 7th CG Dist., Miami, Fla., 1988-90; chief, ops. div. 7th USCG Dist., Miami, 1990-91; comdr. 2nd USCG Dist., St. Louis, 1991-93, mil. personnel command, Washington, 1993-94; chief Office of Law and Der. Ops., 1994—. Mem. Mil. Order World Wars, Naval Order U.S., Coast Guard Combat VA, Ret. Officers Assn., Sigma Xi. Republican. Methodist. Avocations: running, tennis, fishing, reading. Home: 13479 Point Pleasant Dr Chantilly VA 22021-2446

SAUNDERS, PAUL CHRISTOPHER, lawyer; b. N.Y.C., May 21, 1941; s. John Richard and Agnes Grace (Kelly) S.; m. Patricia Newman, Sept. 14, 1968; children—Paul Christopher, Michael Eagan. A.B., Fordham Coll., 1963; J.D., Georgetown U., 1966; Certificat d'Études Politiques, Institut d'Études Politiques, Paris, 1962. Bar: N.Y. 1966, D.C. 1967, U.S. Supreme Ct. 1969, U.S. Ct. Appeals (2d cir.) 1971, U.S. Ct. Appeals (5th cir.) 1980, U.S. Ct. Appeals (11th cir.) 1981, U.S. Ct. Appeals (6th cir.) 1982, U.S. Ct. Appeals (9th cir.) 1985, U.S. Ct. Appeals (4th cir.) 1986, U.S. Ct. Appeals (3rd cir.) 1988. Assoc. Cravath, Swaine & Moore, N.Y.C., 1971-77, ptnr., 1977—. Mem. bd. editors Georgetown Law Jour., 1965-66; editor-in-chief The Advocate, 1969-70. Trustee Fordham U.; mem. bd. regents Georgetown U.; bd. visitors Georgetown U. Law Ctr., vice chmn., 1994-95; trustee, vice chmn. Fordham Prep. Sch., 1986-94; v.p., bd. dirs. Legal Aid Soc., 1983-88; dir., trustee Lawyers Com. to Civil Rights Under Law; mem. Cardinal's Com. of Laity, 1982-90. Capt. JACG U.S. Army, 1967-71. Decorated Knight of Malta, 1982, Meritorious Svc. medal. Fellow Am. Bar Found.; mem. ABA, N.Y. State Bar Assn., Assn. of Bar of City of N.Y., Phi Beta Kappa, Pi Sigma Alpha. Democrat. Roman Catholic. Clubs: Apawamis, Westchester Country (Rye, N.Y.). Home: 1220 Park Ave New York NY 10128-1733 also: 455 Polly Park Rd Rye NY 10580 Office: Cravath Swaine & Moore Worldwide Plz 825 8th Ave New York NY 10019-7416

SAUNDERS, PETER PAUL, investor; b. Budapest, Hungary, July 21, 1928; emigrated to Can., 1941, naturalized, 1946; s. Peter Paul and Elizabeth (Halom) Szende; m. Nancy Louise McDonald, Feb. 11, 1956; children: Christine Elizabeth McBride, Paula Marie. Student, Vancouver Coll., 1941-44; B.Com., U. B.C., 1948. Acct. Canadian Pacific Rly. Co., 1948-50; founder, pres. Laurentide Fin. Corp., Ltd., 1950-66, vice chmn., 1966-67; pres. Coronation Credit Corp. Ltd., Vancouver, B.C., Can., 1968-78, Versatile Corp. (formerly Coronation Credit Corp. and Cornat Industries Ltd.), Vancouver, B.C., Can., 1978-87; prin., pres. Saunders Investment Ltd., Vancouver, 1987—; bd. dirs. Computrol Security Systems Ltd., Wajax Ltd., Greene Valley Concessions, Boreal Ins. Inc., Molnar Capital Corp.; mem. Vancouver adv. bd. Nat. Trust Co. Ltd.; pres., dir. Harlan Fairbanks Co. Ltd. Past pres. Vancouver Symphony Soc., 1968-70, Can. Cancer Soc., B.C. and Yukon Region, 1975-77, Vancouver Art Gallery Assn., 1981-83; chmn. Vancouver Opera Round Table, 1984-92; bd. dirs. Coun. for Bus. and the Arts in Can., B.C. and Yukon Div. Arthritis Soc. Mem. Vancouver Club, Vancouver Lawn Tennis and Badminton Club, Shaughnessy Golf and Country Club, Royal Vancouver Yacht Club, Thunderbird Country Club (Rancho Mirage, Calif.). Avocations: golf, skiing, hunting, boating. Home: 3620 Alexandra St, Vancouver BC Canada V6J 4B9 Office: Saunders Investment Ltd, PO Box 49352 Bentall Ctr, Vancouver, BC Canada V7X 1L4

SAUNDERS, R. REED, financial services company executive; b. Manchester, N.H., Feb. 27, 1948; children: Hunter, Ramsey. BA in English, Dartmouth Coll., 1970, MBA, 1972. Dir. mktg. Tonka Corp., Hopkins, Minn., 1972-78; v.p. advt. HBM, Boston, 1978-81; v.p. mktg. IDS Fin. Corp., Mpls., 1981-86, sr. v.p. mktg., 1986-88, sr. v.p. field resource mgmt., 1988—, also bd. dirs. IDS Fin. Services Inc., Mpls., 1987—, also bd. dirs. Clubs: Wayzata Country; Voyageur Outward Bound. Home: 20625 Bayview Ct Excelsior MN 55331-9272 also: 11 Cleveland Rd Marblehead NH 03455 Office: IDS Fin Svcs Inc IDS Tower 10-T29 Unit 75 Minneapolis MN 55440

SAUNDERS, RAYMOND JENNINGS, artist, educator; b. Pitts., Oct. 28, 1934. Student (Nat. Scholastic scholar), Pa. Acad. Fine Arts, U. Pa., Barnes Found.; B.F.A., Carnegie Inst. Tech., 1960; M.F.A., Calif. Coll. Arts and Crafts. Teaching asst. Calif. Coll. Arts and Crafts, 1960-61; resident Am. Acad. in Rome, 1964-66; art and urban affairs cons. N.Y.C. Bd. Edn. and Human Resources Adminstrn., 1967; mem. faculty Calif. Coll. Arts and Crafts, Oakland, 1988—. Vis. artist, R.I. Sch. Design, 1968, artist-in-residence, vis. artist and critic at various art schs., univs., 1968—; subject of profl. articles.; show Stephen Wirtz Gallery, 1989; one-man shows include San Francisco Mus. Modern Art, 1971, Seattle Art Mus., 1981, Pa. Acad. Fine Arts, 1990, Tampa Mus. Art, 1992, Stephen Wirtz Gallery, San Francisco, 1993, Galerie Resche, Paris, 1993, Oakland Mus., 1994, M.H. de Young Meml. Mus., San Francisco, 1995; represented in permanent collections, Mus. Modern Art, N.Y., Whitney Mus. Am. Art, N.Y., Phila. Mus. Art, Chrysler Mus., Va.; author: Black is a Color, 1968. Served with U.S. Army, 1957-59. Recipient Thomas Eakins prize, Schwabacher-Frey award San Francisco Mus. Art Ann., 1961, award Nat. Inst. Arts and Letters, 1963, Prix de Rome Am. Acad. in Rome, award City of Phila., Atwater Kent award Soc. Four Arts, 1970, Granger Meml. award Pa. Acad. Fine Arts, 1972, Art award KQED, 1975, Guggenheim award, 1976, Nat. Endowment for Arts award, 1977, 84; Cresson European traveling scholar. Address: 49 Geary St Fl 3 San Francisco CA 94108-5705

SAUNDERS, ROGER ALFRED, hotel group executive; b. Brookline, Mass., Feb. 14, 1929; s. Irving Matthew and Shirley (Brown) S.; m. Nina Ann Alexander, Oct. 4, 1953 (dec. 1991); children: Gary L., Jeffrey G., Todd R., Tedd R. A.B., Miami U., 1951; H.H.D. (hon.), Stonehill Coll., 1981, New Eng. Sch. Law, 1982, Johnson and Wales U., 1990; cert. hotel adminstr., Mich. State U., 1985. Treas. Copley Square Hotel, Boston, 1951—; pres., CEO Lenox Hotel, Boston, 1963—; founder Saunders Hotels Group, Boston, 1962—; CEO Boston Park Plaza Hotel Operating Co. Inc., 1976—; gen. ptnr. Boston Park Plaza Hotel Ltd Partnership; chmn. Greater Boston Hotel and Restaurant Health and Pension Funds, 1971-82; trustee Am. Hotel Found., Inc.; bd. dirs. Friends of Copley Sq. Pres. Back Bay Assn., 1974-76, bd. dirs., exec. com.; trustee Women's Edn. and Indsl. Union, 1984-87, bd. dirs., adv. Council Freedom Trail; bd. overseers Children's Hosp., New Eng. Med. Center, Boston, Mus. Fine Arts, 1986-88, 92—; Wang Ctr. for Performing Arts (life trustee); trustee, exec. com. Beth Israel Hosp.; mem. Boston Kyoto Sister City Found., Corp. Mass. Gen. Hosp.; bd. dirs Boston Mcpl. Research Bur., 1982-87, World Affairs Council Boston; bd. advisors Stonehill Coll.; mem. bd. corp. New Eng. Med. Center Hosp., 1981-94; mem. adv. council Ho. of Reps. Tourism and Travel Caucus, 1980-84; mem. corp. Mus. of Sci., 1982-89 Mass. Gen. Hosp., 1985—; chmn. Mass. Film Commn., 1984; appointed Civilian Aide to Sec. of Army for Mass., 1987—; bd. overseers Boston Symphony Orchestra. Served with Air Force N.G., 1951-54. Recipient Hotel and Restaurant Industry Leadership award of New Eng., 1977; Grand Bostonian award Boston's 350th Anniversary Celebration, 1978; resolution of recognition Boston City Council, 1978, 80, 82; Humanitarian award Nat. Jewish Hosp. and Research Ctr., Denver, 1979; cert. of merit U.S. Congl. Travel and Tourism Caucus; Hist. Neighborhood Found. award, 1986; Community Enrichment award Am. Jewish Com., 1990; honoree NCCJ, 1985; named Yankee Travel Exec. of Yr., 1991. Fellow Inst. Cert. Travel Agts.;mem Internat. Assn. of Skal Clubs (exec. com., past pres.), Am. Hotel and Motel Assn. (chmn. 1991), Am. Hotel and Motel Assn. (nat. pres. 1990), New Eng. Innkeepers Assn. (v.p. 1981-85), Mass. Hotel Assn. (pres. 1963-65), Greater Boston Hotel Assn. (bd. dirs., pres. 1966-68), Boston C. of C. (v.p. 1973-78), Confrerie de la Chaine des Rotisseurs (chargé de Mission 1988—), Les Amis de Escoffier (exec. com 1983—), World Affairs Council Boston (bd. dirs.), Algonquin Club, Badminton and Tennis Club (Boston), Longwood Cricket. Founder first non-profit N.Am. Hotel Reservation Center. Office: 64 Arlington St Boston MA 02116-3912

SAUNDERS, RON, lawyer, former state legislator; b. Key West, Fla., Oct. 30, 1954; s. Jack and Edith (Hill) S. BS with high honors, U. Fla., 1976, JD, 1979. Bar: Fla. 1979. Pvt. practice Key West, 1979—; mem. Fla. Ho. of Reps., 1986-94, chmn. appropriations com., 1990-92, chmn. cmty. affairs com., 1992-94. Pres. Key West Jaycees, 1981-82; chmn. bd. trustees Fla. Keys Community Coll., 1983-86. Named Outstanding Chpt. Pres., Fla. Jaycees, 1982, Most Effective Mem., Fla. Ho. of Reps., 1991, 92, Mem. Fla. Bar Assn. (bd. govs. young lawyers sect. 1982-86). Democrat. Episcopalian. Address: PO Box 10923 Tallahassee FL 32302

SAUNDERS, RUBIE AGNES, former magazine editor, author; b. N.Y.C., Jan. 31, 1929; d. Walter St. Clair and Rubie Gwendolyn (Ford) S. B.A., Hunter Coll. CUNY, 1950. Editorial asst. Parents Mag. Enterprises, Inc., N.Y.C., 1950-51; editorial asst. Parents Mag. Enterprises, Inc., 1951-53, asst. editor, 1953-54, mng. editor, 1954-60; editor Young Miss mag., 1960-80, editorial dir., 1967-80; instr. Inst. Children's Lit., 1980—. Author: Calling All Girls Party Book, 1966, Marilyn Morgan, R.N., 1969, Marilyn Morgan's Triumph, 1970, Concise Guide to Baby Sitting, 1972, Concise Guide to Smart Shopping and Consumerism, 1973, Quick and Easy Housekeeping, 1977, The Beauty Book, 1983, Good Grooming for Boys, 1989, Good Grooming for Girls, 1989. Bd. dirs. Feminist Press, New Rochelle Coun. on Arts; mem., v.p. New Rochelle Bd. Edn., 1991—. Named Outstanding Grad., 1960, elected to Hunter Coll. Hall of Fame, 1972; recipient 25 Yr. service award Cub Scout Pack 371, Bklyn., 1985. Mem. Westchester-Putnam Sch. Bds. Assn. (exec. com.). Home: 26 Glenwood Ave New Rochelle NY 10801-3602

SAUNDERS, RUSSELL JOSEPH, utility company executive; b. San Mateo, Calif., Oct. 4, 1937; s. Russell Lyall and Beatrice Virginia (Clyne) S.; m. Joan Virginia Donahue, Jan. 6, 1989; children from previous marriage: Shelli Marie, Laura Lee. Student, Stanford, 1955-56, San Mateo Coll., 1956-57, San Jose State Coll., 1957-61; BS in Acctg. and Fin., Grad. Sch. Bus. Adminstrn., Harvard U., 1970. Acct. Consol. Freighways, Inc., Menlo Park, Calif., 1958-66, dir. budgets, 1966; dir. finance Freightliner Corp., Portland, Oreg., 1966-67, v.p., finance, treas., 1967—, sr. v.p., 1973, also bd. dirs.; v.p. fin. Diamond Reo Trucks, Inc., Lansing, Mich., 1974-75; sr. v.p., controller Envirotech Corp., Menlo Park, 1975-82; v.p. fin. Baker Hughes Process Techs., Houston, 1982-91; v.p. fin., CFO, corp. sec. S.W. Water Co., West Covina, Calif., 1992-94, Phase Metrics, Inc., 1994—; dir. Freightliner Can., Ltd., Calif. Domestic Water Co. Mem. Multnomah County Tax Supervising and Conservation Commn., 1973-74; trustee Oreg. Mus. Sci. and Industry, Portland, 1970—, pres., 1973-74; dir. Found. Oreg. Research and Edn., 1973—. Mem. Planning Execs. Inst. (pres. 1965-66), Stanford Alumni Assn., Harvard Bus. Sch. Alumni Assn., Alpha Eta Sigma. Home: 6431 Lago Grande Dr Bonsall CA 92003 Office: 3978 Sorrento Valley Blvd San Diego CA 92121

SAUNDERS, SALLY LOVE, poet, educator; b. Bryn Mawr, Pa., Jan. 15, 1940; d. Lawrence and Dorothy (Love) S. Student, Sophia U., Tokyo, Japan, 1963, U. Pa., Columbia; B.S. George Williams Coll., 1965. Tchr. Shipley Sch., Bryn Mawr, 1962-65, Agnes Irwin Sch., Wynnewood, Pa., 1964-65, Montgomery County Day Sch., Wynnewood, 1962, Miquon (Pa.) Sch., Waldron Acad., Merion, Pa., 1965-66, Phelps Sch., Malvern, Pa., 1965-70, Frankford Friends Sch. Phila., 1965-66, Haverford (Pa.) Sch., 1965-66, Friends Sem. Sch., N.Y.C., 1966-68, Ballard Sch., N.Y.C., 1966-67, Lower Merion Sch., Ardmore, Pa., nights 1967-71, Univ. Settlement House, Phila., 1961-63, Navajo Indian Reservation, Fort Defiance, Ariz., 1963, Young Men's Jewish Youth Center, Chgo., 1964-65, Margaret Fuller Settlement House, Cambridge, Mass., 1958-61; poetry therapist Pa. Hosp. Inst., 1969-74; also drug rehab. house Pa. Hosp. Inst., Phila.; poet in residence Tyrone Guthrie Ctr., Newbliss, Ireland, Aug. 1988; poetry workshop leader Pendle Hill Quaker Ctr., Wallingford, Pa., Apr. 1988; poetry week leader Ferry Beach, Saco, Maine, summer 1988; pioneer in poetry therapy. Poet, 1946—; poems pub. in periodicals including others; author: Past the Near Meadows, 1961, Pauses, 1978, Fresh Bread, 1982, Random Thoughts, 1992, Patchwork Quilt, 1993; contbr. poems to newspapers. Mem. Acad. Am. Poets, Nat. Fedn. State Poetry Socs., Am. Poetry League, Nat. League Am. Pen Women, Poetry Therapy Assn. (v.p.), Avalon Orgn., Authors Guild, Nat. Writers Club, Pen and Brush Club, N.H., Pa. poetry socs., Cath. Poetry Soc. (asso.), Fla. State Poetry Soc. (asso.). Episcopalian. Home: 2030 Vallejo St Apt 501 San Francisco CA 94123-4854 Office: 609 Rose Hill Rd Broomall PA 19008-2254 *So often during my life I have found great comfort and strength in writing and reading poetry. With my poetry I want to help others to get in touch with their own powers. Poetry, to me, is a rare and beautiful freedom and this is what I want to share with others.*

SAUNDERS, TERRY ROSE, lawyer; b. Phila., July 13, 1942; d. Morton M. and Esther (Hauptman) Rose; m. George Lawton Saunders Jr., Sept. 21, 1975. BA, Barnard Coll., 1964; JD, NYU, 1973. Bar: D.C. 1973, Ill. 1976, U.S. Dist. Ct. (no. dist.) Ill. 1976, U.S. Ct. Appeals (7th cir.) 1976, U.S. Supreme Ct. 1983. Assoc. Williams & Connolly, Washington, 1973-75; assoc. Jenner & Block, Chgo., 1975-80, ptnr., 1981-86; ptnr. Susman, Saunders & Buehler, Chgo., 1987-94; pvt. practice Law Offices of Terry Rose Saunders, Chgo., 1995—. Author: (with others) Securities Fraud: Litigating Under Rule 10b-5, 1989. Mem. ABA (co-chair class actions and derivative suits com. sect. litigation), Ill. State Bar Assn., Chgo. Bar Assn., NYU Alumni Assn. (bd. dirs. 1985—). Office: 30 N LaSalle St Chicago IL 60602

SAUNDERS, THOMAS A., III, investment company executive. Chmn. of the bd. Morgan Stanley & Co. Inc., N.Y.C.

SAUNDERS, TONI LYNNE, construction company executive; b. Columbus, Ohio, Aug. 19, 1949; d. Larry Brook Wells and Mildred Carole (Talbott) Cozart; m. William Kenneth Riley, May 13, 1969 (div. Mar. 1971); m. Albert Eugene Saunders, Sept. 28, 1971; 1 child, Randy Lee Saunders. Grad. high sch., Xenia, Ohio, 1967. Corp. sec. Ind. Horizontal Boring, Inc., Indpls., 1981-82; pres., chmn. bd. Ind. Horizontal Boring, Inc., New Palestine, Ind., 1982—; also bd. dirs. Ind. Horizontal Boring, Inc. Indpls. Mem. adv. com. Nontraditional Role Model Linkages Project/Ind. Region Eight Taskforce, 1988. Mem. NAFE, Nat. Assn. Women in Constrn. (v.p. Indpls. chpt. 1988-89, pres. 1990-91, bd. dirs. as immediate past pres., fundraiser 1984, 85, 86, chmn. women's bus. enterprise com. 1984-86, mem. long range planning com. 1988-89, profl. edn. com. 1988-89, chmn. ways and means com. 1991-92, pres. elect 1989-90, pres. 1990-91, immediate past pres. & bd. dirs. 1991-92, Region 4 nat. car. day com. 1991-92), Nat. Assn. Self-Employed, Nat. Fedn. Ind. Businesses, Associated Builders and Contractors, Nat. Women's Bus. Enterprise Assn. (rep. to Ind. women's bus. devel. ctr. adv. counsel, bd. dirs. 1990-91, 91-92, editor newsletter), Ind. Women's Bus. Enterprise Assn., Inc. (chpt. sec. 1988-90, bd. dirs. 1990-92), Am. Subcontractors Assn. (co-chair minority and women bus. enterprise, bd. dirs. 1992—). Avocations: reading, writing, swimming, oil painting, refinishing old furniture. Office: Ind Horizontal Boring Inc PO Box 197 New Palestine IN 46163-0197

SAUNDERS, WARD BISHOP, JR., retired aluminum company executive; b. Gilroy, Calif., Nov. 26, 1919; s. Ward Bishop and Lamira (Doan) S.; m. Elaine McDermott, Oct. 11, 1942; children: Douglas L., Myra K., Leslie J. B.S., U. Calif.-Berkeley, 1942; J.D., Stanford U., 1948. Bar: Calif. 1948, U.S. Dist. Ct. (no. dist.) Calif. 1948, U.S. Supreme Ct. 1956. Atty. Kaiser Aluminum & Chem. Corp., Oakland, Calif., 1951-65, div. v.p., 1965-71; v.p. Kaiser Aluminum & Chem. Corp., Oakland, 1971-84; dir. Volta River Authority, Accra, Ghana, Aluminium Bahrain, Manama, Bahrain, Hindustan Aluminium Co., Bombay, India; mng. dir. Volta Aluminium Co. Ltd., Tema, Ghana, 1971-84; pres. Kaiser Aluminum Salaried Retirees Assn., 1991-93. Served to lt. USNR, 1942-46. Mem. State Bar Calif., Alameda County Bar Assn., Kaiser Aluminum Salaried Retirees Assn. (bd. dirs. 1988-94), Commonwealth Club. Republican. Unitarian. Home: 6123 Estates Dr Oakland CA 94611-3117

SAUNDERS, WILLIAM HUNDLEY, JR., chemist, educator; b. Pulaski, Va., Jan. 12, 1926; s. William Hundley and Vivian (Watts) S.; m. Nina Velta Plesums, June 25, 1960 (dec. June 1982); children: Anne Michele, Claude William. B.S., Coll. William and Mary, 1948; Ph.D., Northwestern U., 1952. Research assoc. Mass. Inst. Tech., 1952-53; mem. faculty U. Rochester, 1953—, prof. chemistry, 1964-91, faculty sr. assoc., 1991—, chmn. 1966-70. Author: Ionic Aliphatic Reactions, 1965, (with A.F. Cockerill) Mechanisms of Elimination Reactions, 1973, (with L. Melander) Reaction Rates of Isotopic Molecules, 1980; contbr. articles to profl. jours. Guggenheim fellow, 1960-61; Sloan Found. fellow, 1961-64; NSF sr. postdoctoral fellow, 1970-71. Mem. Am. Chem. Soc., Royal Soc. Chemistry, Phi Beta Kappa, Sigma Xi, Phi Lambda Upsilon. Home: 15 Parkwood Ave Rochester NY 14620-3401 Office: U Rochester Chemistry Dept Rochester NY 14627

SAUNDERS, WILLIAM LOCKWOOD, financial consultant; b. Seattle, Dec. 13, 1911; s. William Guy and Elizabeth (Ruggles) S.; m. Marjorie Allen, Nov. 30, 1945 (dec.); 1 dau., Mary Lee; m. Margaret Cella, Feb. 13, 1959. B.A., U. Wash., 1948; M.B.A., Northwestern U., 1950. Resident mgr. Drumheller Ehrlichman & White, Aberdeen, Wash., 1933-36; with H.L. Saunders (investments), 1936-42; sales mgr. H. Irving Lee & Co., San Jose, Calif., 1946; fin. cons., 1946-48; with A.G. Becker & Co., Inc., Chgo., 1949—; v.p. A.G. Becker & Co., Inc., 1951—; dir., 1960—; chmn. Oceanatic Steamship Co., 1958-61; pres. Gisholt Machine Co., Madison, Wis., 1963-66; also dir.; chmn. Long Island Tankers, 1958-60; dir. Oregon Am. Lumber Co., 1951-53, Pacific Far East Line, 1957-61, Gilman Engring. & Mfg., 1963, Enterprises Internat., Inc., 1973—; The George E. Taylor Fgn. Affairs INst., 1986—. Bd. dirs. John A. Johnson Found. Served to lt. comdr. USNR,

1943-46. Mem. Bohemian Club (San Francisco), Lighthouse Point Yacht and Racquet Club (Fla.), Beta Gamma Sigma, Alpha Sigma Phi. Congregationalist. Home: The Highlands Seattle WA 98177 also: 1212 Highway Aia Villa # 16 Hillsboro Bch FL 33062 Office: PO Box 33250 Seattle WA 98133-0250

SAUNTRY, SUSAN SCHAEFER, lawyer; b. Bangor, Maine, May 7, 1943; d. William Joseph and Emily Joan (Guenter) Schaefer; m. John Philip Sauntry, Jr., Aug. 18, 1968; 1 child, Mary Katherine. BS in Foreign Service, Georgetown U., 1965, JD, 1975. Bar: D.C. 1975, U.S. Dist. Ct. D.C. 1975, U.S. Ct. Appeals (D.C. cir.) 1975, (4th cir.) 1977, (6th cir.) 1978, (10th cir.) 1983, U.S. Supreme Ct. 1983. Congl. relations asst. OEO, Washington, 1966-68; program analyst EEO Com., Washington, 1968-70, U.S. Dept. Army, Okinawa, 1970-72; assoc. Morgan, Lewis & Bockius, Washington, 1975-83, ptnr., 1983-94; of counsel Howe, Anderson & Steyer, PC, Washington, 1994—. Co-author: Employee Dismissal Law: Forms and Procedures, 1986; contbr. articles to profl. jours. Mem. ABA, D.C. Bar Assn., D.C. Women's Bar Assn., Am. Assn. Univ. Women, USA, Phi Beta Kappa, Pi Sigma Alpha. Democrat. Office: 1747 Pennsylvania Ave NW Ste 1050 Washington DC 20006

SAUR, KLAUS G., publisher; b. Pullach, Germany, July 27, 1941; s. Karl-Otto and Veronika (Bossmann) S.; m. Lilo Stangel, Oct. 5, 1940; children: Klaus Peter, Annette. Grad. Comml. Coll. Munich; PhD honorus causa Philipps U., Marburg, Simmons Univ. Coll., Boston. Pub. mgr. Vulkan-Verlag, Essen, 1962-63; pub. K.G. Saur Verlag, Munich, 1963-66, pub., pres., 1966—; chmn. export com. German Book Trade, Frankfurt, 1979—. Editor, founder World Guide to Libraries. Hon. fellow U. Graz, Austria; hon. senator Ludwig-Maximilian U., Munich. Recipient Munich Honor medal, 1994. Mem. German Pubs. Assn. (pres.), Deutsche Bibliothek Frankfurt-Leipzig-Berlin (bd. dirs. 1978, chmn. bd.), Frankfurt Book Fair (chmn. bd.), German Museum Munich (bd. dirs. 1976), Rotary. Office: K G Saur Verlag KG, Ortlerstr 8, D-81373 Munich 70, Germany also: K G Saur 121 Chanlon Rd New Providence NJ 07974

SAURBIER, SCOTT ALAN, lawyer; b. Evergreen Park, Ill., Apr. 14, 1947; s. Richard George and Lois M. (Swisher) S.; m. Catherine Francis Wrobel, June 26, 1981. BS, Cen. Mich. U., 1969; JD, Wayne State U., 1972. Bar: Mich. 1972, U.S. Dist. Ct. (ea. and we. dists.) Mich. 1972. Prin. Scott A. Saubier & Assocs., Detroit; lectr., speaker various hosps., orgns., ins. cos. Author: Keys to 1994 Medicial Malpractice Tort Reform. Mem. ABA, Mich. Bar Assn., Detroit Bar Assn., Am. Soc. of Law and Medicine, Assn. Mich. Hosp. Assn., Mich. Soc. Hosp. Risk Lawmakers, Def. Trial Counsel, Mich. Def. Trial Counsel, Am. Soc. Hosp. Attys. Office: Scott A Saurbier & Assocs 150 W Jefferson Ste 1300 Detroit MI 48223

SAUSMAN, KAREN, zoological park administrator; b. Chgo., Nov. 26, 1945; d. William and Annabell (Lofaso) S. BS, Loyola U., 1966; student, Redlands U., 1968. Keeper Lincoln Park Zoo, Chgo., 1964-66; tchr. Palm Springs (Calif.) Unified Sch., 1968-70; ranger Nat. Park Svc., Joshua Tree, Calif., 1968-70; zoo dir. The Living Desert, Palm Desert, Calif., 1970—; natural history study tour leader internat., 1974—; part-time instr. Coll. Desert Natural History Calif. Desert, 1975-78; field reviewer conservation grants Inst. Mus. Svcs., 1987—, MAP cons., 1987—; panelist, 1992—; internat. studbook keeper for Sand Cats, 1988—, for Cuvier's Gazelle, Mhorr Gazelle, 1990—; co-chair Arabian Oryx species survival plan propogation group, 1986—; spkr. in field. Author Survival Captive Bighorn Sheep, 1982, Small Facilities- Opportunities and Obligations, 1983; wildlife illustrator books, mags, 1970—; editor Fox Paws newsletter Living Desert, 1970—, ann. reports, 1976—; natural sci. editor Desert Mag., 1979-82; compiler Conservation and Management Plan for Antelope, 1992; contbr. articles to profl. jours. Past bd. dirs., sec. Desert Protective Coun.; adv. coun. Desert Bighorn Rsch. Inst., 1981-85; bd. dirs. Palm Springs Desert Resorts Convention and Visitors Bur., 1988-94; bd. dirs., treas. Coachella Valley Mountain Trust, 1989-92. Named Woman Making a Difference Soroptomist Internat., 1989, 93. Fellow Am. Assn. Zool. Parks and Aquariums (bd. dirs., accredation field reviewer, desert antelope taxon adv. group, caprid taxon adv. group, felid taxon adv. group, small population mgmt. adv. group, wildlife conservation and mgmt. com., chmn. ethics com. 1987, mem. com., internat. rels. com., ethics task force, pres'. award 1972-77, outstanding svc. award 1983, 88, editor newsletter, Zool. Parks and Aquarium Fundamentals 1982); mem. Internat. Species Inventory System (mgmt. com., policy adv. group 1980-88), Calif. Assn. Mus., Calif. Assn. Zoos and Aquariums, Internat. Union Dirs. Zool. Gardens, Western Interpretive Assn. (so. Calif. chpt.), Am. Assn. Mus. Arboreta and Botanical Gardens So. Calif. (coun. dirs.), Soc. Conservation Biology, Nat. Audubon. Soc., Jersey Wildlife Preservation Trust Internat., Nature Conservancy, East African Wildlife Soc., African Wildlife Found., Kennel Club Palm Springs (past bd. dirs., treas. 1978-80), Scottish Deerhound Club Am. (editor SCottish Deerhounds in N.A., 1983, life mem. U.K. chpt.). Avocations: pure bred dogs, dressage, painting, photography. Office: The Living Desert 47 900 Portola Ave Palm Desert CA 92260

SAUSSELE, CHARLES WILLIAM, marking systems company executive; b. St. Louis, July 25, 1933; s. Charles W. Sr. and Else (Fenn) S.; m. Isobel G. Goodsir, July 22, 1961; children: Jeffrey G., John C. BS in Mech. Engring., U. Mo., Rolla, 1956; M Automotive Engring., Chrysler Inst., Highland Park, Mich., 1958; MBA, Mich. State U., 1978. Rsch. engr. Chrysler Corp., Highland Park, 1956-61; engring. mgr. Holley Carburetor div. Colt Industries, Warren, Mich., 1961-71; sales/mktg. mgr. Borg & Beck div. Borg-Warner, Sterling Heights, Mich., 1971-81; v.p. sales/mktg. Russell Birdsall & Ward Corp., Mentor, Ohio, 1981-86; v.p., gen. mgr. Borries Marking Systems, Ann Arbor, Mich., 1986—; cons. SAB Automotive, Kansas City, Mo., 1981-82. Inventor Diesel Combustion System, Automotive Emission Devel. Capt. U.S. Army, 1956-58. Mem. Soc. Automotive Engrs., Soc. Mfg. Engrs., Pi Tau Sigma. Avocations: travel, sailing, photography, tennis. Home: 37656 N Laurel Park Dr Livonia MI 48152-2662 Office: Borries Marking System 3135 S State St Ste 108 Ann Arbor MI 48108-1653

SAUSSER, ROBERT GARY, retired army officer; b. St. Benedict, Pa., Apr. 6, 1941; s. Robert Jacob and Maxine Larue (Earley) S.; married Nov. 2, 1963; 1 child, Geoffrey Robert. BS, U.S. Mil. Acad., West Point, N.Y., 1963; MS, Ind. U., 1971. Commd. 2d lt. U.S. Army, 1963, advanced through grades to brig. gen., 1989; ops. officer 25th Div. Arty., Schofield Barracks, Hawaii, 1977-78; comdr. 1st Bn., 8th F.A., Schofield Barracks, 1978-80; pers. officer 7th Inf. Div., Ft. Ord, Calif., 1980-83; student U.S. Army War Coll., Carlisle Barracks, Pa., 1983-84; comdr. 25th Div. Arty., Schofield Barracks, 1984-86; exec. asst. to Comdr. in Chief, Combined Forces Command, Seoul, Republic of Korea, 1986-88; chief of staff U.S. Army I Corps, Ft. Lewis, Wash., 1988-89; chief U.S. Mil. Assistance Group Manila, 1989-92; dep. comdr. U.S. Army Pacific, Ft. Shafter, Hawaii, 1992; asst. divsn. comdr. 6th Inf. Divsn. U.S. Army Pacific, Ft. Richardson, Alaska, 1992-93; ret., 1993; bd. dirs. Army, Air Force Exch. Svc., Dallas, 1992-93. Decorated Bronze Star, Legion of Merit, D.S.M., Def. Superior Svc. medal. Mem. Assn. U.S. Army, U.S. Army F.A. Assn., West Point Alumni Assn. Republican. Avocation: golf.

SAUSVILLE, EDWARD ANTHONY, medical oncologist; b. Albany, N.Y., Apr. 3, 1952; s. Edward Adolphus and Pauline (Zamenick) S.; m. Carol Ann Cassidy, Feb. 1, 1975; children: Justin, Brendan, Elizabeth, Rebecca, Paul. BS, Manhattan Coll., 1973; MD, PhD, Albert Einstein Coll. Medicine, 1979. Med. house staff Brigham & Women's Hosp., Boston, 1979-82; med. staff fellow Nat. Cancer Inst., Bethesda, Md., 1982-85; sr. investigator Nat. Cancer Inst., Bethesda, 1985-88, 90—; assoc. prof. medicine Georgetown U. Sch. Medicine, Washington, 1988-90. Author: (book chpt.) "Lung Cancer" in Kelley Textbook Internal Medicine, 1989; contbr. articles to New Eng. Jour. Medicine, Jour. Biol. Chemistry, Cancer Rsch. Mem. Am. Assn. Cancer Rsch., Am. Soc. Clin. Oncology, Am. Soc. Biochem. Molecular Biology, Am. Fedn. Clin. Rsch., Phi Beta Kappa, Alpha Omega Alpha. Achievements include research on mechanisms of bleomycin action in bombesin-related peptic gene expression and response in lung cancer; optimal treatment and staging of cutaneous T-cell lymphoma. Home: 709 Bonifant Rd Silver Spring MD 20905 Office: Nat Cancer Inst Devel Ther Program EPM 843 Bethesda MD 20892

SAUTER, VAN GORDON, communications executive; b. Middletown, Ohio, Sept. 14, 1935; s. Freeman and Cornelia (Banker) S.; children: Mark Allen, Jeremy Banker. B.A., Ohio U., 1957; M.A., U. Mo., 1959. Reporter, New Bedford (Mass.) Standard-Times, 1959-63; staff writer Detroit Free Press, 1963-67, Chgo. Daily News, 1967-68; news and program dir. WBBM-CBS Radio, Chgo., 1968-71; exec. producer CBS News (radio), 1971; dir. news WBBM-TV, CBS, Chgo., 1972-74; Paris bur. chief CBS News, 1974-76; v.p. program practices CBS TV Network, N.Y.C., 1976-77, 86; v.p., gen. mgr. Sta. KNXT-TV, CBS, Los Angeles, 1977-80; pres. CBS Sports, N.Y.C., 1980-82; pres. CBS News, 1982-83, exec. v.p., 1983-86; exec. v.p. CBS, Inc., 1986; contbr. articles Los Angeles Times, ind. TV project cons., 1986—; pres. Fox News div. Fox Inc., L.A., 1992—. Co-author: Nightmare in Detroit, 1968, Fabled Land, Timeless River, Life Along the Mississippi, 1970. Mem. Radio TV News Dirs. Assn., Sigma Delta Chi.

SAUTTER, DIANNE LEE, children's museum director; b. Highland, Ill., July 15, 1949; d. Albert L. and Harriett (Kraft) S. BS in spl. and elem. edn. with honors, U. Ill., 1971. Spl. edn. tchr. Chopin Elem. Sch., Chgo., 1971-72; tchr. Walt Disney Magnet Sch., Chgo., 1972-75; exec. dir. Edn. Resource Ctr., Chgo., 1975-78; dir. devel. Bus. Profl. People for Pub. Interest, Chgo., 1978-83; exec. dir. Express- Ways Children's Mus., Chgo., 1983—. Community advisor Jr. League of Chgo., 1983—; exec. com. mem. Chgo Coalition for Arts in Edn., 1986-88; alumnus leadership Greater Chgo. Class of 1988-89. Avocations: skiing, sailing, reading. Office: Chicago Children's Museum 435 E Illinois St Ste 370 Chicago IL 60611-4364

SAUTTER, RICHARD DANIEL, physician, administrator; b. Ord, Nebr., Dec. 30, 1926; s. Daniel August and Theresa May (Ries) S.; m. Rosemary Elizabeth Graham, Aug. 4, 1952; children—Ann Elizabeth, Daniel Richard, Michael Graham, Mark Allen. B.S., U. Nebr., Lincoln, 1948; M.D., U. Nebr., Omaha, 1953. Diplomate Am. Bd. Surgery, Am. Bd. Thoracic Surgery. Intern Highland Alameda County, Oakland, Calif., 1953-54; resident, instr. in gen. surgery State Univ. of Iowa, Iowa City, 1954-61; thoracic and cardiovascular surgeon Marshfield Clinic, Wis., 1961—, dir. med. edn., 1975—; exec. dir. Marshfield Med. Research Found., Wis., 1977—; asst. dean for clin. affairs U. Wis., Madison, 1984—; resident St. Joseph's Hosp., Marschfield, Wis.; mem. alcohol and other drug abuse research adv. com. Dept. Health and Social Services, State of Wis., 1985—. Contbr. numerous articles to profl. jours., chpts. to books; patentee in field; mem. editorial bd. Wis. Med. Jour., 1977—, assoc. editor, 1986-87, med. editor, 1987—. Bd. dirs. State Med. Jour. Advt. Bur. Served with U.S. Army, 1944-45; PTO. Grantee NIH, 1968-70, 70-71, Nat. Heart-Lung Inst., 1971, 71-72, 73-83, 74-77, others. Fellow ACS (nat. and Wis. chpt.); mem. Am. Assn. Thoracic Surgery, Soc. Thoracic Surgeons, Central Surg. Assn., Wis. Surg. Soc., Wis. Heart Club, Wood County Med. Soc., Am. Heart Assn. (council on thrombosis), Wis. State Med. Soc., Western Surg. Assn., Soc. for Clin. Trials Inc. Lodge: Elks. Avocations: fishing; gardening. Home: 1000 N Oak Marshfield WI 54449-5703*

SAUVAGE, LESTER ROSAIRE, health facility administrator, cardiovascular surgeon; b. Wapato, Wash., Nov. 15, 1926; s. Lester Richard Sauvage and Laura Marie Brouillard; m. Mary Ann Marti, June 9, 1956; children: Lester Jr., John, Paul, Helen, Joe, Laura, William, Mary Ann. Student, Gonzaga U., 1942-43, DSc (hon.), 1982; MD, St. Louis U., 1948; Honoris Causa (hon.), Seattle U., 1976. Diplomate Nat. Bd. Med. Examiners, Am. Bd. Surgery, Am. Bd. Thoracic Surgery. Intern King County Hosp., Seattle, 1948-49, surg. resident, 1949-50, sr. resident, 1955-56; sr. resident Children's Med. Ctr., Boston, 1956-58; rsch. assoc. dept. surgery U. Wash., Seattle, 1950-52; sr. resident in thoracic surgery Boston City Hosp., 1958; pvt. practice Pediatric and Cardiovascular Surgeons, Inc., Seattle, 1959-91; founder, med. dir. Hope Heart Inst. (formerly Reconstructive Cardiovascular Rsch. Ctr.), Seattle, 1959—; clin. prof. surgery sch. medicine U. Wash.; chmn. dept. surgery, dir. surg. rsch. Providence Med. Ctr., Seattle; dir. cardiac surgery Children's Orthopedic Hosp. and Med. Ctr.; presenter in field, 1974—. Author: Prosthetic Replacement of the Aortic Valve, 1972; mem. editorial bd. Annals Vascular Surgery; contbr. over 200 rsch. papers to profl. jours. Capt. M.C., U.S. Army, 1952-54. Recipient Vocat. Svc. award Seattle Rotary Club, 1977, Humanitarian award Human Life Found., 1977, Brotherhood award Nat. Conf. Christians and Jews, 1979, Clemson award Soc. Biomaterials, 1982, Jefferson award Am. Inst. Pub. Svc., Seattle Post-Intelligencer, 1983, Gov.'s Disting. Vol. award, 1983, Spotlight award Am. Soc. Women Accts., 1985, Wash. State Medal of Merit, 1987, Seattle 1st Citizen award, 1992. Mem. AMA, Am. Acad. Pediatrics (surg. sect.), Am. Assn. Thoracic Surgery, Am. Coll. Cardiology, Am. Coll. Chest Physicians, Am. Coll. Surgeons, Am. Heart Assn., Am. Pediatric Surg. Assn., Neurovascular Soc. N.Am. (founding mem.), Wash. State Heart Assn., Wash. State Med. Assn., North Pacific Pediatric Soc., North Pacific Surg. Soc., N.W. Soc. Clin. Rsch., Pacific Assn. Pediatric Surgeons, Pacific Coast Surg. Assn., New Eng. Soc. Vascular Surgery (hon.), Seattle Surg. Soc., King County Med. Soc., Internat. Cardiovascular Soc., Soc. Artificial Internal Organs, Soc. Clin. Vascular Surgery (hon.), Soc. Vascular Surgery, Acad. Surg. Rsch., Alpha Omega Alpha, Alpha Sigma Nu. Roman Catholic. Achievements include research in synthetic blood vessel grafts, vascular surgical techniques, prediction and prevention of thrombotic complications of atherosclerosis, endothelial cell function and vascular autografts.

SAUVAGEAU, PHILIPPE, library director; b. Trois-Rivières, Que., Can., June 11, 1940; s. Lorenzo and Laurette (Forest) S. BA, Seminaire St.-Joseph, Trois-Rivieres, 1961; B of Libr. Scis., U. Montréal, 1962. Assoc. libr. Svc. des Bibliothèque de la Mauricie, Trois-Rivières, 1962-64; administr. Bibliothèque Régionale du Nord de l'Outaouais, 1964-70, Bibliothèque Centrale de prêt de l'Outaouais et du Saguenay-Lac, St. Jean, 1971-75; dir. Bibliothèque Que., Can., 1975-80; gen. dir. Institut Canadien de Que., 1980-89; pres. gen. dir Bibliothèque Nationale du Que., 1989—; cons. various orgns. including Agence de Coopération Culturelle et Technique, Paris, Benin, Senegal, 1986-87, Bibliothèque de l'Assemblee Nationale, Que., 1983. Author: Comment Diffuser La Culture, 1969; contbr. articles to jours. Pres. Secrétariat Permanent des Peuples Francophones, Que., 1979-89; administr. Fest. du Film Que., 1986-87; mem. Conf. Canadienne des Arts, 1970—. Decorated Chevalier de l'Ordre des Arts et des Lettres Min. Culture and Communication of the French Govt., 1988; recipient Prix de Développement Culturel "La Laurentienne", Couns. Culture Que., 1986; named adminstr. of cultural devel. Conseil de la Culture de la Region de Que., 1985. Mem. Le Trident (dir. 1976), Com. Internat. des Bibliothèque Publiques, Assn. L'Avancement Scis. et Tech. de la Docum., Can. Libr. Assn., L'Institut Quebecois de Recherche sur la Culture (adminstr. 1991-93). Club: Garnison. Office: Bibliothèque Nat de Quebec, 125 rue Sherbrooke W, Montreal, PQ Canada H2X 1X4

SAUVEY, DONALD (ROBERT), retired musical instrument company executive; b. Green Bay, Wis., Mar. 15, 1924; s. Irving and Alice (LaBelle) S.; m. Shirley Ann Capelle, Nov. 24, 1949. Student, Am. TV Lab., 1942-43; cert. electronic tech., Milw. Sch. Engring., 1947. Sales mgr. Conn Organ Co., Elkhart, Ind., 1960-65; dir. mktg. Electro Music, Pasadena, Calif., 1965-70; v.p., gen. mgr. Electro Music, 1970-73, Gulbransen Organ Co. subs. CBS, Chgo., 1973-75; pres., chief exec. officer Hammond Organ Chgo., 1975-85; pres., dir. Hammond Internat. Can., Ltd., Agincourt, Ont.; v.p. Organos Hammond de Mex. S.A. de C.V., Mexico City; dir. Hammond Organ U.K. Ltd., Milton Keynes, Eng.; Nihon Hammond, Osaka, Japan, Marmon Co. Mem. businessmen's adv. council Forty-Plus of Chgo., Inc., 1977—. Served with USAAF, 1943-46. Mem. Am. Music Conf. (dir.), Nat. Assn. Music Mchts. Republican. Roman Catholic. Elks. Patentee in field.

SAVA, SAMUEL G., educational association administrator. Exec. dir. Nat. Assn. of Elementary Sch. Principals (NAESP), Alexandria, Va. Office: NAESP 1615 Duke St Alexandria VA 22314

SAVAGE, ANNE, zoologist, researcher; b. Milw., Apr. 21, 1961; d. William and Ann Lesley (Styring) S. BA, U. Wis., 1983, PhD, 1990. Rsch. assoc. U. Wis., Madison, 1990—; affiliate scientist Wis. Regional Primate Rsch. Ctr., Madison, 1990—; dir. rsch. Roger Williams Park Zoo, Providence, 1990—; adj. asst. prof. Brown U., Providence, 1990—. Mem. Am. Assn. Zoology, Parks and Aquariums (rsch. coord. com., S.Am. taxon adv. group Bethesda chpt. 1991—), Internat. Soc. Primatologists, Am. Soc. Primatologists, Sigma Xi. Office: Roger Williams Park Zoo Elmwood Ave Providence RI 02907

SAVAGE, ARTHUR L., professional hockey team executive; b. Amarillo, Tex., July 3, 1951; s. Kyle and Rhoda Lou (McClendon) S.; m. Susan Elizabeth Black, May 26, 1970; children: Jeffrey Alan, Brent Thomas. BA, Tex. Tech U., 1973. CPA, Calif. Acct. Deloitte Haskins & Sells, L.A. and San Francisco, 1973-79; ptnr. Bunje Dowse & Co., 1979-86; pres. Savage & Assocs., 1986—; pres. Cleve. Cavaliers, 1988-89, also bd. dirs.; chief exec. officer San Jose (Calif.) Sharks, NHL, 1990—; bd. dirs. Nationwide Advt., 1983—. Office: 525 West Santa Clara St San Jose CA 95113

SAVAGE, BLAIR DEWILLIS, astronomer, educator; b. Mt. Vernon, N.Y., June 7, 1941; s. Rufus Llewellyn and Christine (Burney) S.; m. Linda Jean Wilber, June 25, 1966; children: Reid Hamilton, Keith Wesley. B.Engring. Physics, Cornell U., 1964; M.S., Princeton U., 1966, Ph.D., 1967. Research assoc. Princeton U., 1967-68; asst. prof. U. Wis., Madison 1968-73, assoc. prof., 1973-78, prof. astronomy, 1978—, chmn. dept., 1982-85; vis. fellow Joint Inst. Lab. Astrophysics, Boulder, Colo., 1974-75; investigator space astronomy projects NASA, 1968—; bd. dirs. Wis., Ind. 1; Yale Nat. Optical Astronomy Obs. Telescope Consortium, 1990—. Contbr. articles to profl. jours. Peyton fellow Princeton U., 1964-66; NASA fellow Princeton U., 1966-67; research grantee NASA, NSF, 1968—. Mem. Am. Astron. Soc. (councilor 1994-97), Internat. Astron. Union, Nat. Rsch. Coun. (space sci. bd. mem. 1985-88, chmn. com. for space astronomy and astrophysics 1985-88, astronomy and astrophysics survey com. 1989-90), Assn. for Univ. Rsch. in Astronomy (bd. dirs. 1989-92), Tau Beta Pi. Home: 4015 Hiawatha Dr Madison WI 53711-3037 Office: Dept Astronomy U Wis 475 N Charter St Madison WI 53706-1582

SAVAGE, CHARLES FRANCIS, lawyer; b. Bklyn., Oct. 2, 1942; s. Charles Lincoln and Frances Regis (Moran) S.; m. Maria Ania Bojcun, July 1, 1967; children: Charles F.I., Michael R. BA, Columbia U., 1963, JD, 1966. Bar: N.Y., 1966, Fla. 1977, Colo. 1981. Assoc. Cadwalader, Wickersham & Taft, N.Y.C., 1966-70; sec., gen. counsel Belco Petroleum Corp., N.Y.C., 1970-75, v.p. planning and devel., 1975-77; also bd. dirs. Belco Petroleum Corp.; v.p., gen. counsel Fla. Gas Co., Winter Park, 1977-78; asst. gen. counsel conservation and solar applications U.S. Dept. of Energy, Washington, 1978-79, dep. gen. counsel legal svcs., 1979-81; v.p.-legal, sec. Ensource, Inc., Denver, 1981-86; ptnr. Holland & Hart, Denver, 1986-93, Heppenstall, Savage, Hillyard & Muller, L.L.C., 1993—. Mem. ABA, N.Y. Bar Assn., Fla. Bar Assn., Colo. Bar Assn., Assn. Bar City N.Y., Denver Bar Assn., N.Y. County Lawyers Assn., Fed. Energy Bar.

SAVAGE, EDWARD WARREN, JR., physician; b. Macon, Ga., July 7, 1933; s. Edward Warren and Mildred Eleanor (Goodwin) S.; m. Carole Porter, June 6, 1959; children: Cheryl, Racheal, Edward Warren. A.B., Talladega Coll., 1955; postgrad., St. Louis U., 1955; M.D., Meharry Med. Coll., 1960. Diplomate: Am. Bd. Obstetrics and Gynecology. Intern St. Joseph's Hosp., Syracuse, N.Y., 1960-61; resident Kings County Hosp.-State U. N.Y., Bklyn., 1963-67; USPHS fellow in gynecol. cancer State U. N.Y. Downstate Med. Center, Bklyn., 1967-69; asst. instr. State U. N.Y. Downstate Med. Center, 1964-66, instr., 1966-69; dir. gynecologic oncology U. Ill. Chgo., 1970-73; asst. prof. U. Ill., 1969-73, assoc. prof., 1973; med. dir. King/Drew Med. Ctr., L.A., 1993—; assoc. prof. Sch. Medicine Charles R. Drew Med. Sch., L.A., 1973-80, prof., 1980—, dean clin. affairs, 1993—; mem. staff St. Francis Hosp. of Lynwood, Centinela Hosp. Med. Ctr., UCLA Hosps. and Clinics; adj. assoc. prof. UCLA Sch. Medicine, 1977, prof., 1986—. Contbr. numerous articles to profl. publs. Exec. bd. Los Angeles Community Cancer Control., 1977. Served as capt. M.C. USAF, 1961-63. Fellow ACS, Am. Coll. Obstetricians and Gynecologists; mem. Soc. Gynecologic Oncologists, Am., Western Assn. Gynec. Oncologists (pres. 1980-81), Nat., Golden State med. assns., AAUP, Am. Soc. Colposcopy and Cervical Pathology (dir. 1973-80), Chgo. Gynecol. Soc., Am. Cancer Soc., Ill., Los Angeles Obstet. and Gynecol. Socs. (pres. 1989-90), Charles R. Drew Med. Soc. Office: 12021 Wilmington Ave Los Angeles CA 90059-3019 *I am the product of two wonderful parents whose support and ideals, inclusive of a strong work ethic, allowed me to be prepared for the several fortuitous opportunities that presented themselves. My hope is that somehow my life will be a positive statement to those who know me.*

SAVAGE, JAMES CATHEY, III, lawyer, military officer, educator; b. Nashville, June 26, 1947; s. James C. Jr. and Mary (Estes) S.; m. Annette Egan, Aug. 5, 1975 (div.); children: Sean Patrick, Catriona Sarah; m. Clara Parra, Nov. 25, 1986; children: James C. IV, Anthony Joseph. BS, Austin Peay St. U., 1968; JD, Memphis State U., 1973; MS in Criminal Justice, Troy State U., 1977; LLM, John Marshall Law Sch., 1978, Georgetown U., 1981; LLD (hon.), North Tenn. Bible Inst., 1981. Bar: Tenn. 1973, U.S. Supreme Ct. 1977, D.C. 1981, Md. 1982; cert. tchr. Commd. 1st lt. U.S. Army, 1973, advanced through grades to lt. col, 1988; enlisted ranger and edn. dir. U.S. Army, Vietnam, 1969-70; ins. adjuster Tenn. Co., Molloy & Leary, Bituminious Casualty, 1971-73; judge adv. U.S. Army, Ga., Germany, 1973-77; vets. and contracts atty. V.A. Gen. Counsel, Washington, 1978-82; fgn. mil. sales atty. USAF Electronic Systems Ctr., Hanscom AFB, Mass., 1983-86; chief counsel U.S. Army Materials Tech. Lab, Watertown, Mass., 1986-92, U.S. Army Rsch. Lab, Watertown, Mass., 1992-95; lt. col. civil air patrol CAP Group I Mass., 1989-93; army reserve asst. counsel Defense Contract Mgmt., Boston, 1992-95; gen. atty. Soldier Sys. Command, Natick, Mass., 1995—; adj. prof. City Colls. Chgo., Troy State U., Phillips Coll., John Marshall Law Sch., Middlesex, C.C., U. of Andes, 1974-92. Weekly show host Assembly (BCAT-TV), Burlington, Mass., 1989-93; contbr. articles to profl. jours. Dep. dir. Internat. Rescue Com./Army Res. Project Resettlement for Refugees, Washington, 1980-82; canvasser Am. Heart Assn., Burlington, 1989-92; lay min. Christian Chs., 1974—; chmn. bd. deacons, mem. pastor/parish, pers., parish counsel and nomination coms. Burlington Congl. Ch., 1986—; mem. Christian Legal Soc., 1980—, Inst. Religion and Democracy, 1980—, United Ch. Bd. World Ministries, 1993—; corp. mem., asst. sec. Christian Mil. Fellowship, 1984—; comdr., exec. officer New England Selective Svc. Sys., 1986-92; officer Christian Fellowship, 1988—; mem. Cultural Coun. Town of Burlington. Decorated Bronze Star and 25 other mil. medals; named Mass. Citizen of Yr. Am. Legion, 1985; recipient Exceptional Profl. award, 1985, Excellence in Govt. and Outstanding Community Svc. awards, Boston, 1987, 92, Fed. Exec. Bd., mil., edn. and community svc. recognition resolution Mass. Ho. of Reps. 1992. Mem. Fed. Bar Assn. (nat. chmn. internat. procurement com. 1985-88, vice-chmn. 1979-90, past pres. Mass. chpt. 1985-86, nat. del., Disting. Svc. award), New Eng. Chpt. Judge Advocates Assn. (pres./v.p. 1983-84, 89-90), Res. Officers Assn. (nat. judge adv. 1993-94, state pres. 1993-94, pres.-elect 1992-93, state v.p. for Army 1990-92, state judge adv. 1985-86, pres. William Tudor and N.E. Civil Affairs chpts. 1984-89, Nat. Disting. Svc. awards), Nat. Civil Affairs Assn. (Nat. Disting. Svc. award), DAV (life, Honor Guard Burlington chpt. 113 1985-93), VFW (life, state judge adv. and sr. vice comdr.-All Am. Post 1982-83), AMVETS (life, post comdr.and state judge adv. 1982-83), 75th Ranger Regiment Assn. (nat. dir. 1987-90), Vietnam Vets. Am. (life, sec. D.C. chpt. 1980), Phi Delta Kappa (treas. Harvard U. chpt. 1990-92), Phi Alpha Delta. Avocations: computers, and guitar and trumpet playing. Home: 39 Purity Springs Rd Burlington MA 01803-2423 Office: Soldier Sys Command Legal Office Kansas St Natick MA 01760

SAVAGE, JAMES CRAMPTON, geophysicist; b. Dallas, Sept. 18, 1926; s. John Francis and Georgia (Williford) S.; m. Jane Farish, Dec. 28, 1992. BS, U. Ariz., 1950; PhD, Calif. Inst. Tech. 1957. Asst. prof. U. B.C., Vancouver, Can., 1958-64; assoc. prof. U. Minn., Mpls., 1964-65, U. Toronto, Ont., Can., 1965-69; geophysicist U.S. Geol. Survey, Menlo Park, Calif., 1969—. With U.S. Army, 1944-46. Fellow Am. Geophys. Union (Whitten medal 1989, pres. tectonophysics sect. 1980-82); mem. AAAS, Seismology Soc. Am. (pres. 1978-79). Democrat. Home: 451 Menlo Oaks Dr Menlo Park CA 94025 Office: US Geol Survey 345 Middlefield Rd Menlo Park CA 94025

SAVAGE, JAMES FRANCIS, editor; b. Boston, July 23, 1939; s. James and Hanora (Enright) S.; m. Sharon Kaye Base, May 29, 1965; 1 son, Sean. A.A., Boston U., 1959, B.S., 1961. Reporter Quincy (Mass.) Patriot Ledger, 1961-63; reporter Miami (Fla.) Herald, 1963-67, investigative reporter, 1967-78, investigations editor, 1978-84, assoc. editor investigations, 1984—; investigative reporter Boston Herald Traveler, 1967. Served with AUS, 1962. Recipient Nat. Headliners award, 1969, Fla. Press Assn. award, 1972, George Polk Meml. award for investigative reporting, 1973, 80, Pub. Service award Nat. A.P. Mng. Editors, 1974, 80, award Fla. Soc. Newspaper

Editors, 1974, 75, Nat. Disting. Service award Sigma Delta Chi, 1979, 87, Pulitzer Prize Staff award for Nat. Reporting, 1987, Outstanding Investigative Reporting award Investigative Reporters and Editors, 1988, Disting. Alumni award Boston U. Coll. Communications, 1990, Pulitzer Prize Staff Pub. Svc. award, 1993; Profl. Journalism fellow Stanford, 1974-75. Home: 1004 Orange Is Fort Lauderdale FL 33315-1651 Office: 1 Herald Plz Miami FL 33132-1609

SAVAGE, JOHN EDMUND, computer science educator, researcher; b. Lynn, Mass., Sept. 19, 1939; s. Edmund J. and Eldora A. (Guay) S.; m. Patricia Joan Landers, Jan. 29, 1966; children: Elizabeth, Kevin, Christopher, Timothy. ScB, MIT, 1962, ScM, 1962, PhD, 1965. Mem. tech. staff Bell Telephone Labs., Holmdel, N.J., 1965-67; prof. computer sci. Brown U., Providence, 1967—; chmn. dept. computer sci., 1985-91; vis. prof. U. Paris, 1980-81, Warwick U., Eng., 1991-92; mem. dept. vis. com. elec. engring. and computer sci. MIT, 1991—; cons. in field. Author: The Complexity of Computing, 1976; (with others) The Mystical Machine, 1986; editor: (with Thomas Knight) Advanced Research in VLSI and Parallel Systems, 1992; chair editl. bd. Computing Rsch. News, 1990—; editl. bd. Jour. Computer and Sys. Scis., 1993—; patentee data scrambler, 1970, means and methods for generating permutation of a square, 1976. Mem. MIT Corp. visiting com. dept. elec. engring. and computer sci. Fulbright-Hays grantee, 1973; NSF fellow, 1961, Guggenheim fellow, 1973. Fellow IEEE; mem. Assn. Computing Machinery, Computing Rsch. Assn. (bd. dirs. 1990—), Sigma Xi, Tau Beta Pi. Avocations: reading, skiing, bicycling. Office: Brown U Dept Computer Sci Dept Computer Sci 115 Waterman St Providence RI 02912-9016

SAVAGE, JOHN P., provincial official; b. Newport, South Wales, Nova Scotia; married; 7 children. Grad., Queen's Coll. Med. Sch., Belfast, No. Ireland, 1956. Mayor Town of Dartmouth, Can., 1985-92; premier, min. intergovtl. affairs, min. aboriginal affairs, pres. exec. coun. Govt. of Nova Scotia, Halifax, 1993—; co-chair Nova Scotia Round Table on Environment and Economy. Active Dartmouth Sch. Bd., 1978, chair bd. dirs., 1984, 85. Office: Office of the Premier, 1700 Granville St 7th Fl PO Box 726, Halifax, NS Canada B3J 2T3

SAVAGE, KAY WEBB, lawyer, health center administrator, accountant; b. Piedmont, Ala., Mar. 30, 1942; d. Robert Benjamin and Ellon Marie (Posey) Webb; m. Perry Lauren Savage, Nov. 18, 1961; children: Perry Lauren Jr., Shannon Hunter. BS in Secondary Edn., Jacksonville State Coll., Ala., 1963, AB, 1964; BS, Birmingham-So. Coll., 1987; JD, U. Ala., 1989. Bar: Ala. 1989; CPA, Ala.; cert. secondary tchr., Ala. Tchr. English, Hokes Bluff High Sch., Gadsden, Ala., 1963-64; tchr. sci. and math. McArthur Sch., Birmingham, Ala., 1964-68; tchr. sci. Mountain Brook Jr. High Sch., Birmingham, 1968-69; acct. Robert Resha, CPA, Birmingham, 1984-86; pvt. practice acctg. Birmingham, 1986—, pvt. practice law, 1989—; administr. Ala. Orthopaedic and Spine Ctr., Birmingham, 1987—; pres. Aleco, Inc., Birmingham, 1990—, Savage Enterprises, Birmingham, 1985—; bd. dirs. Assoc. Agys. Am., Coastal Bend Oil & Gas Co., Piedmont Ednl. Trust. Pres., sec. Snowcrest Condominium Assn., Snowshoe, W.Va., 1984-88; mem. exec. bd. Rep. Congl. Leadership Coun., Washington, 1988—; mem. Senatorial Trust, Washington, 1989, Presdl. Roundtable, Washington, 1989—, Piedmont Schs. Found., Birmingham Olympic Com., 1990—, Birmingham So. Coll. Arts Coun., 1992—; also gala advisor; v.p. United Cerebral Palsy, mem. multiple sclerosis class, 1995; sponsor U.S. Olympic Team; bd. dirs. Piedmont Schs. Found., mem. scholarship com.; del. 1st Moscow Conf. on Law and Econ. Coop.; mem. exec. com. Com. for Fair Cts., 1994—; legis. chmn. Jefferson County Med. Alliance, 1994—, Ala. Med. Alliance, 1995; bd. dirs. Ednl Meml. Found., 1994—. Fulbright fellow, 1964; recipient (5) Am. Jurisprudence awards. Mem. AAUW, Ala. Bar Assn., Ala. Soc. CPAs, Birmingham Bar Assn., Med. Group Mgmt. Assn., Bones Orthopedic Mng. Group, Attys. at Law and CPA U.S.A., Am. Soc. Law and Medicine, Pilot Lawyers Assn., Assn. Agys. Am. (bd. advisors), Coastal Ben Oil and Gas (bd. dirs.), Exec. Women Internat., C. of C. (bd. dirs. 1994—), Ninety Nines, Rotary Club Internat. (dir.), Sigma Delta Kappa (svc. award 1989), Sigma Kappa Delta, Sigma Tau Delta, Pi Gamma Mu. Avocations: flying, scuba diving, snow skiing, whitewater paddling, travel. Home: 3815 River View Cir Birmingham AL 35243-4801 Office: 52 Med Park East Dr Ste 115 Birmingham AL 35243

SAVAGE, M. SUSAN, mayor. Student, U. Aix-Marseilles, Aix-en-Provence, France, 1969, City of London Poly., Eng., 1972; BA in Sociology with honors, Beaver Coll., 1974. Pre-trial rep. Phila. Ct. Common Pleas, 1974-75; criminal justice planner Montgomery County Criminal Justice Unit, 1975-77; exec. dir. Met. Tulsa Citizens Crime Com., 1977-87; vol. coord. Vote Yes For Tulsa, 1987; chief of staff to mayor City of Tulsa, 1988-92, mayor, 1992—. Active Lee Elementary Sch. PTA; bd. dirs., treas. Okla. Crime Prevention Assn.; bd. dirs. Youth Svcs. of Tulsa County, 1984-88, pres., 1986-87; co-chair Safe Streets/Enhanced 911 Steering Com., 1987; mem. C. of C. Task Force/Community Edn. Network, 1983. Office: Office of Mayor City Hall Rm 1115 200 Civic Ctr Tulsa OK 74103-3827

SAVAGE, MICHAEL THOMAS, government office executive; b. Oroville, Calif., Oct. 22, 1934; s. Guy Thomas Savage and Sarah Mery (Bennett) Barber; m. Robin Kendall Ward, Apr. 4, 1966; children: Mark McNeer, Kelly Robin. BA in Polit. Sci., U. Calif., Berkeley, 1956, MA in Polit. Sci., 1959; postgrad., Woodrow Wilson Sch., 1969-70. Field renewal rep. Community Devel. Programs, San Francisco, 1959-64, acting chief, chief of ops. br., 1964-66, dir. field svcs. divsn., 1966-68, deuuty regional dir. renewal assistance, 1968-70; various positions Office of Orgn. and Mgmt., Washington, 1970-74, dir. office of mgmt. systems, acting dir., 1974-76, deputy dir. office mgmt., 1976-79; dir. office housint ops. and field monitoring Office of Community Planning and Devel., Washington, 1979-82, program advisor to asst. sec., enterprise zone coord., 1982-86, deputy dir. office block grant assistance and zone coord., 1986—; urban policy advisor Chmn. Ho. Govt. Ops. Com., Washington, 1990-93. Editorial bd.: Econ. Devel. Quar.; contbr. articles to profl. jours. Officer, supporter Great Falls (Va.) Players, 1983-94; co-chair No. Va. alumni recruiting com. Pa. State U. No. Va., 1992-94. 2d lt. U.S. Infantry, 1959. Recipient Mid Career fellowship Nat. Inst. Pub. Affairs, Washington, 1969; named LEGIS fellow Office Pers. Mgmt., Washington, 1990. Avocations: little theater, softball. Home: 436 River Bend Rd Great Falls VA 22066-4017

SAVAGE, NAOMI, photographer; b. N.J., June 25, 1927; d. Samuel and Elsie (Ray) Siegler; m. David C. Savage, Oct. 11, 1950; children—Michael, Lourie. Student, Bennington Coll., 1945-47; pvt. photography study with Man Ray, 1948-49. Free lance photographer including portraits, Versailles, tennis, dental and opthal. equipment, trees, flowers, abstract designs, masks, hands; photographer variety of techniques including photo-engraving, photograms, photo-collages, combination negative-positive photos, porcelain photos. Cassandra Found. grantee, 1970; Nat. Endowment for Arts photography fellow, 1971; recipient One-Show-Silver award Art Dirs. Club N.Y., 1976. Mem. Friends Photography, Internat. Center Photography. Home and Studio: 41 Drakes Corner Rd Princeton NJ 08540-7520 Gallery: Snyder Fine Art 20 W 57th St New York NY 10019

SAVAGE, NEVE RICHARD, marketing executive; b. Harrow, Eng., Nov. 18, 1944; came to U.S., 1970, naturalized, 1983; s. Richard Marshall and Joan Muriel (Eperon) S.; m. Alan Elizabeth Freeman, Apr. 29, 1972; children: Sarah-Jane, Megan, Truan. B.A., U. Oxford (Eng.), 1966, M.A., 1968. Account supr. Garland-Compton Advt., London, 1966-70; sr. v.p. Compton Advt., N.Y.C., 1970-77; dir. Compton Advt., 1980-83; exec. v.p. Cadwell Davis Savage Advt., N.Y.C., 1977-82; exec. v.p. internat. Wells, Rich, Greene, Inc., N.Y.C., 1983-86; vice chmn. Kornhauser & Calene Inc., 1986-88; exec. group dir. Ogilvy & Mather, 1988-94; v.p. mktg. McCaw Cellular Comm., Kirkland, Wash., 1994—.

SAVAGE, PHILLIP HEZEKIAH, federal agency administrator; b. Balt., Aug. 13, 1932; s. Abraham and Ivory F. (Robinson) Shpritz; m. Phyllis Millard; children: Kim Yvette, Jan Miriam, Kirk Phillip; m. Diane Bradford Geers, June 24, 1972; children: Rebekah Ann, Elisabeth Bradford. BA, Morgan State U., 1970. MA, Antioch Sch. Law, 1988. Dir. NAACP, N.Y.C. and Phila., 1960-72, ARA Svcs. Inc., 1972-74; mgr. equal employment opportunity tng. project Gen. Acctg. Office, Washington, 1975-76; dir. equal employment opportunity office SEC, Washington, 1976-84; dir. pub.

employment divsn. HUD, Washington, 1984-89, exec. asst. to asst. sec., 1989-92, dep. asst. sec. ops. and mgmt., 1992-94; sr. advisor to supt. D.C. Pub. Schs., 1994-95; sr. advisor, dep. asst. sec. HUD, 1995—. Arbitrator Better Bus. Bur., Office Common Ownership Communities and Office Consumer Affairs, Montgomery County, Md.; past chair Partnership Fund for Compensation of Victims of Hate, Violence, Montgomery County; past pres. Inter-racial Family Circle; mem. River Rd. Unitarian Ch. With USAF, 1950-53. Recipient Giraffe award, 1988. Avocations: reading, walking, travelling. Home: 7223 Marbury Ct Bethesda MD 20817 Office: HUD Fair Housing and Equal Opportunity 451 7th St SW Washington DC 20410

SAVAGE, RANDALL ERNEST, journalist; b. Commerce, Ga., Mar. 3, 1939; s. Ernest Kyle and Sara Beatrice (Collins) S.; m. Joyce Carol Martin, Nov. 26, 1964 (div. May 1984); children: Kimberly Dawn, Bradley Kyle; m. Mary Elizabeth Hallmark, Aug. 4, 1984; children: Brock Morgan, Laura Marie, Shaw Hamilton. Student, U. Md.-European Div., RAF Bentwaters, Eng., 1967-69; B.A. in Journalism, U. Ga., 1972. Service sta. worker Collins Service Sta., Commerce, Ga., 1958; billing clk. Benton Rapid Express, Atlanta, 1958-61; truck driver So. Oil Co., High Point, NC, 1964-65; reporter Commerce News, Ga., 1972; sr. spl. projects reporter Macon Telegraph and News, Ga., 1972—. Served with U.S. Army, 1961-64; with USAF, 1966-69. Recipient 3rd place in news AP, Atlanta, 1976, 2nd place in news AP, Atlanta, 1976, 1st place in sports AP, Atlanta, 1984; 2d place in news Green Eyeshades award, 1976; Pulitzer prize, 1985, Outstanding Alumnus award Henry W. Grady Coll. of Journalism and Mass Communication, U. Ga., 1989. Baptist. Avocations: jogging; softball; fishing; free-lance writing. Home: 3269 Lennox Dr Macon GA 31204-1054 Office: Macon Telegraph & News Po Box 4167 120 Broadway Macon GA 31201-3444

SAVAGE, RICHARD T., manufacturing company executive; b. 1939. BS, Ohio State U., 1961. With Gen. Motors, 1961-70; v.p. mfg. Blackstone Corp., Jamestown, N.Y., 1979-81; with Modine Mfg. Co., 1970-79, v.p., 1981-83, group v.p. original equipment, 1983-89, pres., COO, 1989—, CEO, 1990—. With USAFR, 1956-62. Office: Modine Mfg Co 1500 De Koven Ave Racine WI 53403-2552*

SAVAGE, ROBERT HEATH, advertising executive; b. Chillicothe, Ohio, Nov. 24, 1929; s. Russell Heath and Frances (Hunt) S.; m. Lorna Dale, May 2, 1970. B.A., Principia Coll., 1951; M.B.A., Harvard U., 1956. Brand mgr. Procter & Gamble, Cin., 1956-60; sr. v.p., mgmt. supr., dir. Ogilvy & Mather, Inc., N.Y.C., 1960-71; mktg. mgr. personal products div. Lever Bros., N.Y.C., 1971; exec. v.p. Botsford Ketchum, Inc., San Francisco, 1972, pres., 1972-78, chmn., 1978-81; pres. KM&G Internat., Inc., 1978-81, Saatchi and Saatchi Compton, Inc., N.Y.C., 1981-83; mng. dir. Henson Assocs., N.Y.C., 1983-86; ptnr. CMA Assocs., Fairfield, Conn., 1987—; mngt. cons., sports and video mktg. cons., 1987—. With USMCR, 1951-54. Mem. Am. Assn. Advt. Agys., Gipsy Trail Club, Naples Bath and Tennis Club, Fairfield County Hunt Club. Home and Office: 5 Crooked Mile Rd Westport CT 06880

SAVAGE, SALLY P., lawyer; b. Sept. 28, 1951. Student, Duke U., 1969-71; BA in Polit. Sci. and History, Macalester Coll., 1973; JD with honors, U. Idaho, 1977. Asst. atty. gen. edn. div. Office Atty. Gen. State of Wash., Olympia, 1977-78; asst. atty. gen. Wash. State U. div. State of Wash., Pullman, 1978-80, sr. asst. atty. gen., 1980—. Mem. Nat. Coll. and Univ. Attys. (continuing legal edu. and nominations coms.; intellectual property sect., speaker ann. conf. 1979, 81), Phi Beta Kappa. Home: RR 1 Box 79 Pullman WA 99163-9711 Office: Wash State U 436 French Adminstrn Bldg Pullman WA 99164

SAVAGE, SANDRA HOPE SKEEN, mathematics educator, curriculum writer; b. Charleston, W.Va., Apr. 4, 1938; d. Raymond and Freda (Burgess) Skeen; m. Steven William Savage, Aug. 17, 1963; 1 child, Samantha. BS in Secondary Edn. Math and English, Bob Jones U., 1960; MS in Math., Ill. Inst. Tech., 1966; EdD in Math. Edn., Columbia U., 1976. Cert. tchr., Calif., N.Y., Ill., Fla., W.Va., Minn. Math. tchr. S. Charleston Jr. High Sch., 1960-61, Citrus Grove Jr. High Sch., Miami, Fla., 1961-62, Skiles Jr. High Sch., Evanston, Ill., 1962-65, Evanston Twp. High Sch., 1965-67, White Plains (N.Y.) High Sch., 1967-68; chmn. math. dept. The Scarborough Sch., Scarborough-on-Hudson, N.Y., 1968-71; math. tchr. Alexander Ramsey High Sch., Roseville, Minn., 1971-72, Minnehaha Acad., Mnpls., 1971-72; lectr. math. Pace U., Westchester County, N.Y., 1972-73; team leader, math. tchr. Fox Lane Mid. Sch., Bedford, N.Y., 1973-74; prof. math. Orange Coast Coll., Costa Mesa, Calif., 1977—; lectr. math. edn. North Park Coll., Chgo., 1965; judge Odyssey of the Mind Competition, 1995; math. media cons. Annenberg Found., Washington, 1991; cons Business Link, Costa Mesa, 1990—. Speaker Expanding Your Horizons Women's Conf., Irvine, Calif., 1984-87; guild mem. Orange County Performing Arts Ctr., Costa Mesa, 1985-87; asst. troop leader Girl Scouts Am., Laguna Niguel, Calif., 1985-87; active Geneva Presbyn. Ch., Laguna Hills, Calif., 1983—. Recipient Cerit. Nat. Merit Scholarship Corp., 1956, Tchr. of Yr. award Orange County Tchrs., 1994, Nat. Inst. for Staff and Orgn. Devel. awrd U. Tex., 1993, U.S.A. Today Teaching Excellence award, 1993; Dept. Edn. Nat. Workplace Literacy Program grantee, 1995. Fellow NSF (grantee 1983); mem. AAUW, Am. Math. Assn. Two Yr. Colls., Math. Assn. Am., Assn. for Women in Sci., Calif. Math. Coun., Orange County Math. Assn. (sec. 1982-83), Phi Delta Kappa (pres. Trabuco chpt. 1986-87, 95—). Democrat. Avocations: music, computer graphics, poetry. Home: 12 Novilla Laguna Beach CA 92607-8915 Office: Orange Coast Coll PO Box 5005 2701 Fairview Rd Costa Mesa CA 92626-5561

SAVAGE, SCOTT DAVID, broadcast executive; b. Newark, Nov. 10, 1954; s. Philip and Charlotte Jean (Figman) S.; m. Anne Marthine Aldrich, Aug. 24, 1975 (div. Mar. 1992); children: Daniel, Ellen; m. Marilyn Massucci, May 4, 1993. BA, Pa. State U., 1975. Account exec., sales mgr. Stas. WMAJ and WXLR, State College, Pa., 1974-77, Westinghouse Broadcasting Co., Pitts., N.Y.C., Ft. Wayne, Ind., 1977-80; dir. sports mktg. Sta. WTOP, Washington, 1981-84; gen. sales mgr. Sta. WCBM, Balt., 1984-85; sta. mgr., gen. sales mgr. Sta. WNEW, N.Y.C., 1985-88; v.p., gen. mgr. Tex. State Network, Dallas, 1988-90; exec. v.p., chief oper. officer Pinnacle Broadcasting Co., Dallas, 1990-91; v.p., gen. mgr. Stas. KYNG-FM, KSNN-FM, Dallas, 1992—. Recipient Award of Excellence, Am. Women in Radio & TV, 1994. Mem. Assn. Radio Mgrs. (pres. 1995). Office: Radio Stas KYNG-FM and KSNN-FM Dallas TX 75251

SAVAGE, STEPHEN MICHAEL, lawyer; b. Norwich, Conn., Apr. 23, 1946; s. Alfred and Iva (Allen) S.; m. Lois Palestine, July 4, 1968; children: Meredith, William, Sam. BA, U. Pa., 1968; JD, Harvard U., 1973. Bar: Ariz. 1973, U.S. Dist. Ct. Ariz. 1973. With Fennemore Craig, Phoenix, 1973—, chmn. mgmt. com., 1988—. Bd. dirs. Ariz. Diabetes Assn. Phoenix, 1983-87, Ariz. Mus. Sci. and Tech., Phoenix, 1992—; chmn. bd. dirs. All Saints' Episcopal Day Sch., Phoenix, 1988; comdr., pres. Mounted Sheriff's Posse Maricopa County, Phoenix, 1992-93. Mem. ABA, State Bar Ariz. (chmn. sect. corp., banking and bus. law 1983-84), Maricopa County Bar Assn., Assn. Corp. Growth, Phoenix Country Club. Avocations: team roping, golf. Office: Fennemore Craig 2 N Central Ave Ste 2200 Phoenix AZ 85004-2390

SAVAGE, TERRY RICHARD, information systems executive; b. St. Louis, Oct. 21, 1930; s. Terry Barco and Ada Vanetta (Cochran) S.; m. Gretchen Susan Wood, Stpe. 26, 1964; children: Terry Curtis, Christopher William, Richard Theodore. AB, Washington U., St. Louis, 1951, MA, 1952; PhD, U. Pa., 1954. Mgr. system software IBM Rsch., Yorktown Heights, N.Y., 1956-63; dir. data processing Documentation Inc., Bethesda, Md., 1963-64; mgr. info. systems Control Data Corp., Rockville, Md., 1964-67; dir. rsch. Share Rsch. Corp., Santa Barbara, Calif., 1967-68; computer-aided acquisition and logistic support program mgr. TRW, Redondo Beach, Calif., 1968-92; ret., ind. cons. pvt. practice, 1992—; mem. expert witness cons. U.S. Congress, 1981, 84, 88, 89; bd. dirs. Savage Info. Svcs., Inc., Torrance, Calif. Contbr. articles to profl. jours. Bd. dirs. ABC-Clio Press, Santa Barbara, 1970-75, Help the Homeless Help Themselves, Rancho Palos Verdes, Calif., 1988—, ChorusLiners, Rancho Palos Verdes, 1983—, Savage Info. Svcs., Inc., Torrance, Calif., 1992—. Mem. Cosmos Club. Home and Office: 30000 Cachan Pl Palos Verdes Peninsula CA 90275-5412

SAVAGE, THOMAS JOSEPH, college president, governance and planning consultant, educator, priest; b. Medford, Mass., Oct. 28, 1947; s. Frank James and Viola Augustine (Ballou) S. B.A. summa cum laude, Boston Coll., 1971; M. City Planning, U. Calif.-Berkeley, 1973; M. Pub. Policy, Harvard U., 1982, EdD, 1985. Assoc. Cheswick Ctr., Boston, 1973-83, dir., 1984—; assoc. Instl. Strategies Assocs., Cambridge, Mass., 1975-87; asst. acad. v.p. Fairfield (Conn.) Univ., 1986-88; pres. Rockhurst Coll., Kansas City, Mo., 1988—; adj. faculty Lesley Coll., Cambridge, 1982-85; cons. Lilly Endowment, Indpls., 1983-87; chmn. planning com. Jesuits New Eng. Province, Boston, 1985-88. Author: Seven Steps to a More Effective Board, 1994, The Goverance of Catholic Health Care Institutions, Catholic Health Assn., Spring, 1988; also articles. Del. Bridges for Peace, Soviet Union, 1985; Trustee Regis Coll., 1989—, Loyola, Balt., 1989-95, St. Louis U., 1991—, Loyola Marymount, 1994—; bd. dirs. Valentine-Radford Comm., 1992—, Preferred Health Profls., 1992—, Kauffman Found., 1993—, Menninger Clinic, 1993—, Kans. City Bd. Trade, 1994—. Mellon fellow, 1971-73. Mem. Am. Planning Assn., Nat. Planning Assn., AAAS, Assn. Jesuit Colls. and Univs. (bd. dirs. 1989—), World Future Soc., Bostonian Soc., Phi Beta Kappa. Roman Catholic. Club: Harvard. Academic Address: Rockhurst Coll 1100 Rockhurst Rd Kansas City MO 64110-2561

SAVAGE, WALLACE HAMILTON, lawyer; b. Houston, Nov. 21, 1912; s. Homer H. and Mary (Wallace) S.; m. Dorothy Harris, Oct. 12, 1940; children—Virginia Wallace (Mrs. A. Lee McAlester), Dorothy Harris. B.S., U. Va., 1933; J.D., Harvard, 1936. Bar: Tex. 1937, Colo. 1937. Practiced in Dallas; Dallas County chmn., nat. vice chmn. Citizens Com. Hoover Report, 1952-54; mem. dir. Citizen's Com. for Reorgn. Exec. Branch of Govt., 1954-59. Author: A Bait of Perjury, 1970. Mayor pro tem City of Dallas, 1947-49, mayor, 1949-51; chmn. Dallas County Democratic Com., 1952-54, Tex. Dem. Com., 1952-54 . Served as comdr. USNR, 1941-45. Univ. fellow U. Colo., 1936-37. Mem. Am., Dallas bar assns., State Bar Tex., Phi Delta Phi. Clubs: Dallas Country, Idlewild, Terpsichorean. Home: 5703 Swiss Ave Dallas TX 75214-4638

SAVAGE, WILLIAM WOODROW, education educator; b. Onley, Va., Jan. 9, 1914; s. Frank Howard and Florence Elmira (Twyford) S.; m. Margaret Jane Clarke; children—Earl R., William W. A.B., Coll. William and Mary, 1937; M.A., U. Chgo., 1946, Ph.D., 1955; student, U. Va., summer 1951. Research editor, div. rural research Fed. Emergency Relief Adminstrn., Richmond, Va., 1935-36; div. mgr. Montgomery Ward & Co., Newport News, Va., 1937-38; statis. worker WPA, Richmond, 1938-39; counselor Va. Consultation Service, Richmond, 1939-42; acting dir. Va. Consultation Service, 1942-45; asst. state supr. guidance and consultation services Va. Dept. Edn., 1946-47; dean Longwood Coll., Farmville, Va., 1947-52; project coordinator, asso. dir. Midwest Adminstrn. Center, U. Chgo., 1952-56; dean Coll. Edn., U. S.C., 1956-65, prof. edn., 1956-79; curator U. S.C. Mus. Edn., 1973-85. Author: Interpersonal and Group Relations, 1968; Co-author: Readings in American Education, 1963; Editor: Work and Training, monthly Va. Bd. Edn., 1941-47, Administrator's Notebook, monthly Midwest Adminstrn. Center, 1954-56, U. S.C. Edn. Report, 1957-65, 67-85; adv. com.: Sch. Rev., 1954-56; Contbr. articles to jours. Mem. visitation and appraisal com. Nat. Coun. for Accreditation Tchr. Edn., 1964-67; bd. dirs. Friends of Libr., Va. Commonwealth U. Mem. S.C. Assn. Sch. Adminstrs., U. S.C. Soc., Wardlaw Club (pres. 1974-75), Order of White Jacket, Phi Delta Kappa. Methodist. Home: 1100 German School Rd Richmond VA 23225-4275

SAVAGE, XYLA RUTH, government official; b. Norman, Okla., Dec. 17, 1937; d. Joel Frederick and Thelma Gladys (Burgess) Church; B.A., U. Okla., 1969; postgrad. U.S. Dept. Agr., 1971; m. John W. Savage, Jr., Jan. 18, 1955 (dec. Oct. 1982); children—Mark Wayne, John Christian. Interior designer Sears, Roebuck and Co., Petersburg, Va., 1966-67; head tech. illustration dept. ITT, Bladensburg, Md., 1967-69; supr. publs. dept. NASA, Greenbelt, Md., 1969-71; supr. illustration dept. VA, Washington, 1971-72; mgr. forms design and visual communications dept. Bur. Labor Stats., Washington, 1972—; instr. design U.S. Dept. Agr. Grad. Sch., evenings 1972—. Mem. Presidential sub-com. Questionnaire Design, 1987; chmn. publicity Band Parents; officer, parents orgn. Mem. Bus. Forms Mgmt. Assn., Printing Industries Am. Mem. Christian Ch. Author: Forms Design, 1975. Home: 12901 Chalfont Ave Fort Washington MD 20744-2728 Office: 441 G St NW Rm 2862 Washington DC 20212-0003

SAVAGEAU, MICHAEL ANTONIO, microbiology and immunology educator; b. Fargo, N.D., Dec. 3, 1940; s. Antonio Daniel and Jennie Ethelwin (Kaushagen) S.; m. Ann Elisa Birky, July 22, 1967; children—Mark Edward, Patrick Daniel, Elisa Marie. B.S., U. Minn., 1962; M.S., U. Iowa, 1963; Ph.D., Stanford U., 1967, postgrad., 1968-70; postgrad., UCLA, 1967-68. Research fellow UCLA, Los Angeles, 1967-68; lectr. Stanford U., Calif., 1968-69; from asst. to full prof. U. Mich., Ann Arbor, 1970—; sr. research fellow Max Planck Inst., Göttingen, Fed. Republic of Germany, 1976-77; fellow Australian Nat. U., Canberra, 1983-84; prof. microbiology and immunology U. Mich., Ann Arbor, 1978—, chmn. dept., 1982-85, 92—, prof. chem. engring., dir. cellular biotech. labs., 1988-91; dir. NIH trng. program in Cellular Biotechnology, 1991-92; cons. NIH, Bethesda, Md., 1981-82, 94-95, Upjohn Co., Kalamazoo, 1979-81, Synergen, Boulder, Colo., 1985-87; Found. for Microbiology lectr., 1993-95. Author: Biochemical Systems Analysis, 1976; mem. editl. bd. Math. Scis., 1976—, editor, 1995—; mem. editl. bd. Jour. Theoretical Biology, 1989—, Nonlinear World, 1992—, Nonlinear Digest, 1992—; co-editor Math. Ecology, 1986—; contbr. articles to profl. jours. Australian Nat. U. fellow, 1983-84; Guggenheim Found., fellow N.Y.C., 1976-77; Fulbright Found., sr. research fellow, Washington, Fed. Republic of Germany, 1976-77; sr. fellow Mich. Soc. Fellows, 1990-94; grantee NIH, NSF, 1964—. Mem. AAAS, Am. Chem. Soc., Am. Soc. Microbiology, IEEE (sr.), Soc. Indsl. and Applied Math., Biophys. Soc., Soc. Gen. Physiologists, Soc. Math. Biology (bd. dirs. 1987—). Office: U Mich Dept Microbiology and Immunology 5641 Med Scis II Ann Arbor MI 48109-0620

SAVARD, CLAUDE A., food service executive. Pres., coo Provigo Corp., San Rafael, Calif. Office: Provigo Distbn Inc, 800 Dorchester Blvd W, Montreal, PQ Canada H3B 4S7

SAVARD, DENIS JOSEPH, professional hockey player; b. Pointe Gatineau, Que., Can., Feb. 4, 1961. With Chgo. Black Hawks, 1980-90, Montreal Canadiens, 1990-93, Tampa Bay Lightning, 1993—; mem. Stanley Cup championship team 1982; player NHL All-Star games, 1982-84, 86, 88, 91. Recipient Michel Briere trophy, 1979-80. Office: Chgo Blackhawks 1901 W Madison St Chicago IL 60612*

SAVARD, SERGE, professional hockey team executive; b. Montreal, Que., Can., Jan. 22, 1946. Hockey player Montreal Canadiens, 1966-81, mng. dir., 1983—; hockey player Winnipeg Jets, 1981-83; v.p. hockey, mng. dir. Montreal Canadiens. Winner Conn Symthe trophy, 1969, Bill Masterton Meml. trophy, 1979; named to Hockey Hall of Fame, 1986. Office: Montreal Canadiens, 2313 St Catherine St W, Montreal, PQ Canada H3H 1N2*

SAVARESE, RALPH J., lawyer; b. N.Y.C., Sept. 4, 1936. BBA, Iona Coll., 1958; LLB, Fordham U., 1961; postgrad., U. Mich., 1961-63. Bar: N.Y. 1962, D.C. 1963. Ptnr. Howrey & Simon, Washington. Grad. Law Study fellow U. Mich., 1961-63. Office: Howrey & Simon 1299 Pennsylvania Ave NW Washington DC 20006-2402

SAVAS, EMANUEL S., public management educator; b. N.Y.C., June 8, 1931; s. John and Olga (Limbos) S.; m. Helen Andrew, Dec. 25, 1955; children: Jonathan, Stephen. BA, U. Chgo., 1951, BS, 1953; MA, Columbia U., 1956, PhD, 1960. Control systems cons. IBM, Yorktown Heights and White Plains, N.Y., 1959-65; urban systems mgr. N.Y.C., 1966-67; 1st dep. city adminstr. Office of Mayor of N.Y.C., 1967-72. Mayor's Urban Action Task Force, 1969-72; prof. pub. mgmt. Columbia U., N.Y.C., 1972-83; dir. Center for Govt. Studies Columbia U., 1973-83, assoc. dir. Center for Policy Rsch., 1973-81; asst. sec. for policy devel. and rsch. HUD, Washington, 1981-83; prof. mgmt. Baruch Coll./CUNY, 1983-94, prof. public policy, 1994—; dir. public policy program, 1994—; chm. dept. mgmt., 1986-93; dir. Privatization Rsch. Orgn., 1986—; cons. NSF, Nat. Bur. Standards, Am. Paper Inst., Nat. Endowment for Arts, HUD, Dept. Transp., World Bank, AID, U.S. Dept. State, President's Commn. on Privatization, UN, UN

Devel. Program, ILO, UNIDO, USIA, also others; mem. voting bd. Blue Cross and Blue Shield Greater N.Y., 1976-79, bd. dirs., 1979-81; mem. Pres.-Elect's Urban Affairs Task Force, 1980, N.Y. State Senate Adv. Commn. on Privatization, 1990—; dir. U.S.-USSR Joint Project on Mgmt. Cities, 1973-81; advisor on privatization Govt. Poland, 1990-92, Govt. Lesotho, 1992, Govt. Ukraine, 1993. Author: Computer Control of Industrial Processes, 1965, Organization and Efficiency of Solid Waste Collection, 1977, Privatizing the Public Sector, 1982, Moscow's City Government, 1985, Privatization, 1987, 15 fgn. edits., others; editor: Alternatives for Delivering Public Services, 1977, Privatization for New York, 1992; mem. editorial bd. Urban Affairs Quar., Privatization Report, Privatization Watch, State and Local Govt. Rev.; contbr. 110 articles to profil. jours. Mem. N.Y.C. Mayor-elect Giuliani transition team, 1993, N.Y. Gov.-elect Pataki transition team, 1994. With U.S. Army, 1953-54, Korea. Recipient Systems Sci. and Cybernetics award IEEE, 1968, Louis Brownlow award Am. Soc. Public Adminstrn., 1970, Honor award Templeton Found., 1989, Leadership award Nat. Coun. Pub.-Private Partnerships, 1993. Mem. Sigma Xi, Psi Upsilon. Greek Orthodox. Club: City of N.Y. (trustee 1974-77, Richard Childs award 1979). Office: CUNY Baruch Coll Box F-1228 17 Lexington Ave New York NY 10010-5526

SAVCHENKO, ALLA, ballet mistress; arrived in Can., 1981; Diploma of excellence, Moscow Ballet Sch. Mem. Bolshoi Ballet, 1953-74; ballet mistress, choreographer Sovrenennik Theatre, Moscow, 1974-79; regisseur Royal Winnipeg Ballet, 1981-89, ballet mistress, 1989-90, sr. ballet mistress, 1989—. Leading roles include Humpbacked Horse, The Nutcracker, The Stone Flower, Fire of Paris, Cinderella, Swan Lake, The Sleeping Beauty. Office: Royal Winnipeg Ballet, 380 Graham Ave, Winnipeg, MB Canada R3C 4K2*

SAVEKER, DAVID RICHARD, naval and marine architectural engineering executive; b. San Jose, Calif., Jan. 10, 1920; s. William Thomas and Bernice (Lloyd) S.; m. Jessie Mae Walters, June 19, 1941 (dec. Jan. 1995); children: William, Linda, Richard (dec.). AA, San Jose State Coll., 1939; AB, Stanford U., 1941; cert. in naval architecture, U.S. Naval Acad., 1942; SM, MIT, 1946. Registered profl. engr., Calif. Commd. ensign USN, 1941, advanced through grades to capt., 1960, ret., 1968; assoc. prof. Calif. Poly. State U., San Luis Obispo, 1969-80; pres. D.R. Saveker Naval Architecture, Pismo Beach, Calif., 1980—; assoc. Mac Kinnon Searle Consortium, Alexandria, Va., 1991—. Inventor sinusoidal structure and applications. Research grantee NASA/Stanford Lab., 1973. Mem. Marine Tech. Soc., Soc. Naval Architects and Marine Engrs., Tau Beta Pi. Democrat. Methodist. Club: Cosmos (Washington). Avocations: history, music, water colors. Home: 711 Hanford St Pismo Beach CA 93449-2347

SAVELKOUL, DONALD CHARLES, lawyer; b. Mpls., July 29, 1917; s. Theodore Charles and Edith (Lindgren) S.; m. Mary Joan Holland, May 17, 1941; children: Jeffrey Charles, Jean Marie, Edward Joseph. BA magna cum laude, U. Minn., 1939; JD cum laude, William Mitchell Coll. Law, 1951. Bar: Minn. 1951, U.S. Dist. Ct. Minn. 1952, U.S.C. Ct. Appeals (8th cir.) 1960, U.S. Supreme Ct. 1971. Adminstrv. work various U.S. govt. depts., including Commerce, War, Labor, Wage Stblzn. Bd., 1940-51; mcpl. judge Fridley, Minn., 1952-53; pvt. practice law Mpls., St. Paul, Fridley, 1951—; chmn. bd. dirs. Blaine State Bank; pres. Blaine Bldg. Corp.; mem. faculty William Mitchell Coll. Law, 1952-59, corp. mem., 1956—; sec. Fridley Recreation and Svc. Co., 1955—; mem. Minn. Legislature, 1967-69. Mem. Gov.'s Com. Workers Compensation, 1965-67, Gov.'s Adv. Coun. on Employment Security, 1957-60; chmn. Fridley Police Civil Svc. Commn., 1962-63; gen. counsel Minn. AFL-CIO Fedn. Labor, 1952-71. 1st lt. AUS, 1943-46. Decorated Bronze Star; recipient Disting. Alumni award Coll. Liberal Arts U. Minn., 1976. Mem. ABA, Minn. Bar Assn. (chmn. 1957-58, bd. dirs. 1958-62, 68-69, labor law sect.), Hennepin County Bar Assn., Justice William Mitchell Soc., Am. Legion, U. Minn. Pres.'s Club, Phi Beta Kappa. Roman Catholic. Home: 916 Moore Lake Dr W Minneapolis MN 55432-5148

SAVELL, EDWARD LUPO, lawyer; b. Atlanta, Apr. 29, 1921; s. Leon M. and Lillian (Lupo) S.; m. Bettie Patterson Henry, Oct. 11, 1944; 1 dau., Mary Lillian Savell Clarke. B.B.A., Emory U., 1947, LL.B., 1949. Bar: Ga. 1948. Assoc. A.C. Latimer, Atlanta, 1948-53; ptnr. Carter, Latimer & Savell, Atlanta, 1953-56, Woodruff, Latimer & Savell (and successor firms), Atlanta, 1956-87; of counsel Savell & Williams, Atlanta, 1987—; instr. John Marshall Law Sch., 1951-55; dir. Legal Aid Soc., 1955-58; arbitrator Am. Arbitration Assn. and Fulton Superior Ct. Contbr. articles to legal jours. With USAAF, 1942-45, CBI. Fellow Internat. Acad. Trial Lawyers (pres. 1978-79, Dean of Acad. 1976); mem. Atlanta Bar Assn. (sec.-treas. 1953-54), ABA, State Bar Ga., Ga. Def. Lawyers Assn. (founder, v.p.), Internat. Assn. Ins. Counsel, Atlanta Claims Assn., Lawyers Club Atlanta, Chi Phi, Phi Delta Phi. Presbyterian. Clubs: Cherokee Town and Country, Commerce, Univ. Yacht (past commodore). Office: Savell and Williams 2600 Marquis I Tower 245 Peachtree Center Ave NE Atlanta GA 30303-1222

SAVELLI, ANGELO, artist; b. Pizzo Calabria, Italy, Oct. 30, 1911; came to U.S., 1954; s. Giorgio and Maria (Barone) S.; m. Elizabeth Fisher Friedman, Jan. 10, 1953; 1 stepdau., Ellen. Student, Ginnasio Vibo Valentia, C.Z., 1928, Maturità Artistica Liceo Artistico, Rome, 1932; diploma, Acad. diBelle Arti, Rome, 1936. Prof. Liceo Artistico, Rome, 1940, 43, 48, 54; instr. New Sch. Social Research, 1959-65; assoc. prof. fine arts Grad. Sch. Fine Arts, U. Pa., 1960-70; vis. artist Cornell U., 1974, U. Tex.-Arlington, 1977-82. Exhibited one man shows, Galleria Roma, 1941, Galleria Cairola, Genoa, Italy, 1942, Galleria del Naviglio, Milan, Italy, 1947, 54, 61, Centre d'Art Itallienne, Paris, 1952, The Contemporaries, N.Y.C., 1955, Castelli Gallery, N.Y.C., 1958, Galleria del Cavallino, Venice, Italy, 1958, Tweed Mus., U. Minn., Duluth, 1960, Peter Deitsch Gallery, N.Y.C., 1962, Art Alliance, Phila., 1963, D'Arcy Galleries, N.Y.C., 1963, XXXII Internat. Biennale, Venice, 1964, Henri Gallery, Washington, 1969, Peale Gallery, Phila., 1969, Lorenzelli Arte, Milano, 1981, L'Arco Studio Internazionale d'Arte Grafica, Roma, 1981, Editalia, Roma, 1981, Gimpel-Hanover-Andre Emmerich Gallery, Zurich, 1981; group shows Quadriennale di Roma, 1943, 49, 60, Biennale of Venice, 1950, 52, 64, Castelli Gallery, Balt. Mus. Art Gallery, 1957, De Cordova Mus., Lincoln, Mass., 1963, White Chapel Gallery, London, 1963, Bklyn. Mus., 1957, 60, 62, 64, 66, Library of Congress, 1959, 63, 66, U.S.A. Cultural Exchange in 5 Russian Cities, 1963, Whitney Rev., 1965, Whitney Mus. Ann., 1966, Internat. Graphic Show, Yugoslavia, 1964, Janis Gallery, N.Y.C., 1966, Jewish Mus., N.Y.C., 1964, Internat. de Gravure, Tokyo, 1964, Mus. Modern Art, 1966, 67, Galleria Naz D'Arts Moderna, Rome, Museo Civico, Phila. Mus. Art, 1966, Everson Mus., Syracuse, N.Y., 1972, Tweed Mus., Duluth, 1973, Stout U. Art Gallery, Menomonie, 1973, Zoller Gallery Pa. State U., 1975, Hutchinson Gallery, N.Y.C., 1978, Parson-Dreyfuss Gallery, N.Y.C., 1978, Padiglione d'Arte Comtemporanea, Milano, 1984, Studio Bonifacio, Genova, 1986, Castello Murat, Pizzo Calabro, 1986, Pinacoteca Comunale, Arona, 1986, Art Coop. Palladio, Zurich, 1987, Studio Brazzani, 1987, Torino, Studio d'Ars, Milano, 1987; represented in permanent collections Torino, Italy, Mus. Modern Art, N.Y.C., Cin. Mus. Art, Tweed Mus., Chase Manhattan Bank, Nelson Rockefeller Collection, Arnold Maremont Collection, N.Y. Pub. Library, Art Mus., Helsinki, Finland, Victoria and Albert Mus., London, Phila. Mus. Art, Nat. Collection Fine Arts, Smithsonian Instn, Wichita (Kans.) Art Mus., Contemporary Art Mus. Milano, Contemporary Art Mus. Gibellina, Italy. Recipient Fellowship for study in Paris, 1948; recipient Grand Prize per L'Incisione XXXII Venice Biennale, 1964, Am. Acad. of Arts and Letters award, 1983, Silver trofy Città Della Magna Graecia, 1987; Guggenheim fellow, 1979-80; grant Pollock-Krasner, 1987. Studio: 431 Broome St New York NY 10013-2622 Address: Butler Inst of Am Art 524 Wick Ave Youngstown OH 44502

SAVETH, EDWARD NORMAN, history educator; b. N.Y.C., Feb. 16, 1915; s. Isidor and Eva (Vasa) S.; m. Harriet Obstler, June 22, 1975; 1 child by previous marriage, Henry. B.S.S., CCNY, 1935; M.A., Columbia U., 1937, Ph.D., 1946. Prof. history Grad. Faculty New Sch. for Social Research, N.Y.C., 1960-63; Fulbright prof. Kyoto U., Kyoto, Japan, 1964-65; prof. Dartmouth Coll. 1965-66; Disting. vis. prof. Tex. Lutheran Coll. Seguin, 1966-67; Disting. prof. SUNY-Fredonia, 1967-85; adj. prof. SUNY, Buffalo, 1987—; lectr. USIA, Nepal, 1965, Morocco, 1977; Fulbright prof. Hebrew U., Jerusalem, 1981; vis. prof. U. Rochester, 1972; lectr. Beijing Tchrs. Coll., 1989. Author: American historians and European Immigrants,

1947; author, editor: Understanding the American Past, 1954, Henry Adams, 1963, American History and the Social Sciences, 1964; revisions editor: Ency. Americana, 1962; contbr. numerous articles to mags. Mem. Am. Hist. Assn., Orgn. Am. Historians. Home: 11 High Ct Buffalo NY 14226-0001 Office: SUNY Buffalo NY 14260

SAVIA, ALFRED, conductor. Asst. condr. Omaha Symphony, 1976-78; asst. condr. Fla. Symphony Orch., 1978-78, assoc. condr., 1979-86, prin. guest condr., 1986-87; asst. condr. Colo. Philharm., 1979-81; resident condr. New Orleans Symphony, 1986-88, assoc. condr., 1988-89; resident condr. Philharm. Orch. Fla. (now Fla. Philharm. Orch.), 1987-89; music dir. Evansville (Ind.) Philharm., 1989—; assoc. condr. winter season Indpls. Symphony Orch., 1990—, artistic dir., prin. condr. summer season, 1991—. Guest condr. Indpls. Symphony, New Orleans Symphony, Kitchener-Waterloo Symphony, Can., Presdl. Symphony Ankara, Turkey, Aalborg Symphony, Denmark, Korea Philharm., San Antonio Symphony, Alabama Symphony, Hudson Valley Philharm., Fla. Symphony Orch., Colo. Philharm., Denver Chamber Orch., Lubbock Symphony, Nebr. Chamber Orch., Miami Ballet, Orlando Opera Co., others. Recipient High Fidelity Musical Am. Young Artist award, 1985. Office: Evansville Philharm Orch PO Box 84 Evansville IN 47701-0084 also: Stanton Cons & Mgmt 45-05 Newtown Rd Astoria NY 11103

SAVICH, RENÉ, broadway theater executive, producer; b. Chgo., Nov. 14, 1947; d. Nicholas and Elizabeth (Szakurski) S. BS, Northwestern U., 1969. Asst. house mgr. Minskoff Theatre, N.Y.C., 1973; mem. mgmt. staff The Shubert Orgn. Inc., N.Y.C., 1975-77, mgr. dept. maintenance, 1977-80; asst. house mgr. The Shubert Theatre, N.Y.C., 1975-77, Plymouth Theatre, N.Y.C., 1978; house mgr. Barrymore Theatre, N.Y.C., 1978-79; mgr. co. The Elephant Man, N.Y.C., 1980; house mgr. Playhouse Theatre, N.Y.C., 1980-81, Cort Theatre, N.Y.C., 1981-85, Golden Theatre, N.Y.C., 1985-86, Booth Theatre, N.Y.C., 1987—. Producer off-Broadway plays including Wine Untouched, 1979, Lou, 1981, Punchy, 1983. Mem. Assn. of Theatrical Press Agts. and Mgrs., Actors Equity Assn., Treas. and Ticket Sellers Union. Office: The Shubert Orgn Inc 234 W 44th St New York NY 10036-3909

SAVIKAS, VICTOR GEORGE, lawyer; b. Pitts., Mar. 13, 1941; s. Victor E. and Bertha (Takach) S.; m. Barbara Klabisch, Sept. 5, 1964 (div. Mar. 1989); children: Elizabeth, Adam, Andrew; m. Muriel Spencer Shankman, Apr. 21, 1990. BA, DePaul U., 1967, JD, 1968. Bar: Calif. 1989, Ill. 1968, D.C. 1971, U.S. Dist. Ct. (no. dist.) Ill. 1968, U.S. Dist. Ct. (cen. dist.) Calif. 1989. Atty., ptnr. Friedman & Koven, Chgo., 1968-75; ptnr. Karon, Savikas & Horn, Chgo., 1975-88, Keck, Mahin & Cate, Chgo., 1988-89; ptnr.-in-charge Keck, Mahin & Cate, L.A., 1989—; instr. DePaul U. Coll. Law, Chgo., 1976-78. Co-editor Ct. of Appeals for Fed. Cir. newsletter, 1983-87. Mem. Spl. Commn. on Adminstrn. of Justice in Cook County, Chgo., 1984-87. Fellow Am. Coll. Trial Lawyers; mem. ABA, Assn. Bus. Trial Lawyers, L.A. County Bar Assn., Ill. State Bar Assn., Fed. Cir. Bar Assn. Office: Jones Day Reavis & Pogue 555 W 5th St Ste 4600 Los Angeles CA 90013

SAVILLE, DUDLEY ALBERT, chemical engineering educator; b. Lincoln, Nebr., Feb. 25, 1933; s. George A. and Alta (Goddard) S.; m. Joy Wagner, Mar. 7, 1959; children: Alexander, Andrea. B.S., U. Nebr., 1954, M.S., 1959; Ph.D. U. Mich., 1966. Engr. Carbide & Carbon Chem. Co. (Institute), W. Va., 1954-55; research engr. Chevron Research Corp. (Richmond), Calif., 1959-61, Shell Devl. Co., Emeryville, Calif., 1966-68; asst. prof. Princeton U. (N.J.), 1968-71, assoc. prof., 1971-77, prof. dept. chem. engring., 1977. Assoc. editor Jour. Physico-Chem. Hydrodynamics, 1980-87; mem. adv. bd. Jour. Colloid Interface Sci., 1992—; contbr. articles to sci. jours. Served to 1st lt. USAF, 1955-58. Mem. Am. Inst. Chem. Engrs., Am. Chem. Soc., Am. Phys. Soc. Office: Princeton U Dept Chem Engring Princeton NJ 08544

SAVILLE, THORNDIKE, JR., coastal engineer, consultant; b. Balt., Aug. 1, 1925; s. Thorndike and Edith Stedman (Wilson) S.; m. Janet Foster, Aug. 28, 1950; children: Sarah, Jennifer, Gordon. A.B., Harvard U., 1947; M.S., U. Calif.-Berkeley, 1949. Research asst. U. Calif., Berkeley, 1947-49; hydraulic engr. Beach Erosion Bd. and Coastal Engring. Research Center, Ft. Belvoir, Va., 1949-81; chief research div. Beach Erosion Bd. and Coastal Engring. Research Center, 1964-71, tech. dir., 1971-81. Contbr. over 75 articles to engring. and sci. publs. Served with USAAF, 1943-46. Recipient Meritorious Civilian Service award Dept. Army, 1981. Fellow AAAS, Wash. Acad. Scis., ASCE (Huber award 1963, Moffatt-Nichol award 1979, Internat. Coastal Engring. award 1991); mem. Am. Geophys. Union, Internat. Assn. for Hydraulic Research, Nat. Acad. Engring., Permanent Internat. Assn. Navigation Congresses (hon., U.S. commr. emeritus 1987—), Am. Shore and Beach Preservation Assn. (bd. dirs. 1976—, v.p. 1988—), Cosmos Club (Washington). Home and Office: 5601 Albia Rd Bethesda MD 20816-3304

SAVIN, ROBERT SHEVRYN, health care products company executive; b. Bridgeport, Conn., Mar. 17, 1925; s. Harry and Agnes (Jacobs) S.; m. Barbara Low, July 15, 1951; children: Deborah Joyce, Scott Martin. Student U. Bridgeport. Pres. Savin Jewelers, 1948-55, also dir.; salesman IPCO Corp., White Plains, N.Y., 1955-61, v.p., dir., 1962-66, pres., chief exec. officer, 1966-73, chmn., 1973-77, chmn., pres., 1977-84, chmn. chief exec. officer, 1984—. Chmn. United Home for Aged Hebrews; co-pres. Am. Friends of Hebrew U., N.Y.; bd. dirs. Nat. Sports. Served with U.S. Army, 1943-46. Mem. Hosp. Industry Assn., Old Oaks Country Club. Home: 1045 Nautilus Ln Mamaroneck NY 10543-4705 Office: IPCO Corp 411 Theo Fremd Ave Fl 2 Rye NY 10580

SAVIN, SAMUEL MARVIN, geologist; b. Boston, Aug. 31, 1940; s. George and Sarah (Lewiton) S.; m. Norma Goulder, Nov. 4, 1978; children: Robert Goulder, Lisa Rebecca. B.A., Colgate U., 1961; Ph.D., Calif. Inst. Tech., 1967. Asst. prof. geol. scis. Case Western Res. U., Cleve., 1967-73, assoc. prof., 1973-76, prof., 1976—; dept. chmn., 1977-82, assoc. dean Coll. Arts and Scis., 1993—; industry fellow Marathon Oil Co., Denver, 1976; mem. adv. panel earth scis. NSF, 1978-81. Assoc. editor Geochimica et Cosmochimica Acta, 1976-79, Marine Micropaleontology, 1979-87, Palaeogeography/Palaeoclimatology/ Palaeoecology, 1987-95; contbr articles to sci. jours.; producer ednl. TV documentaries. Trustee Cleve. Hearing and Speech Ctr., 1995—. Fellow AAAS, Geol. Soc. Am.; mem. Am. Assn. Petroleum Geology, Am. Geophys. Union, Geochem. Soc. (councillor 1988-91), Clay Minerals Soc. (councillor 1978-80, 92-95), Nat. Assn. Geology Tchrs., No. Ohio Geol. Soc. (pres. 1988-89), Soc. Econ. Paleontologists and Mineralogists. Home: 2236 Demington Dr Cleveland OH 44106-3358 Office: Case Western Res U Dept Geol Scis Cleveland OH 44106

SAVINELL, ROBERT FRANCIS, engineering educator; b. Cleve., May 26, 1950; s. Robert D. and Lotte R. Savinell; m. Coletta A. Savinell, Aug. 23, 1974; children: Teresa, Robert, Mark. BSChemE, Cleve. State U., 1973; MS, U. Pitts., 1974, PhD, 1977. Registered profl. engr., Ohio. Rsch. engr. Diamond Shamrock Corp., Painesville, Ohio, 1977-79; assoc. prof. U. Akron, Ohio, 1979-86; prof. Case Western Reserve U., Cleve., 1986—; dir. Ernest B. Yeager Ctr. for Electrochem. Scis., 1991—. Divsn. editor Jour. Electrochem. Soc., 1988-91; N.Am. editor Jour. Applied Electrochemistry, 1991—; contbr. articles to profl. jours. Named Presd.l Young Investigator, NSF, Washington, 1984-89, Outstanding Engring. Alumnus, Cleve. State U., 1984. Mem. AIChE (program chmn. 1986-92), Electrochem. Soc. (divsn. officer 1992—). Avocations: sailing, skiing. Office: Case Western Reserve U Dept Chem Engring AW Smith Bldg Cleveland OH 44106

SAVINI, TOM, make-up artist, actor, director; b. Pitts.; m. Nancy Hare, 1984. Film work includes Deathdream, 1972, Deranged, 1974, Martin, 1976, Dawn of the Dead, 1978, Effects, 1980, Eyes of a Stranger, 1980, Friday the 13th, 1980, Friday the 13th IV, The Burning, 1981, Maniac, 1981, The Prowler, 1981. Alone in the Dark, Creepshow, 1982, Midnight, 1983, Friday the 13th-The Final Chapter, 1984, Invasion U.S.A., 1985, Day of the Dead, 1985, The Texas Chainsaw Massacre, Part II, 1987, Monkey-Shines: An Experiment in Fear, 1988, Red Scorpion, 1989, Two Evileyes, 1990, Heartstopper, 1992, Trauma, 1993, H.P. Lovecrafts Necronomicon, 1994, Mr. Stitch, Ghostwriter, Killing Zoe; dir. Night of the Living Dead, 1990; actor appearances include Knightriders, 1981, The Ripper, 1986; dir. Night of the Living Dead, 1990, episodes Tales from The Darkside; writer: Grand Illusions, 1983, Grand Illusions Books II, 1988. *

SAVIT, CARL HERTZ, geophysicist; b. N.Y.C., July 19, 1922; m. Sandra Kaplan, July 6, 1946; children: Mark, Deborah Savit Pearlman, Judith Savit Simon. B.S. with honors, Calif. Inst. Tech., 1942, M.S., 1943, postgrad., 1943-44, 46-48. Statis. cons. Long Range Meteorology Project, U.S. Air Force, 1943-44; assoc. prof. math. San Fernando Valley State Coll., Northridge, Calif., 1959-60; chief math. Western Geophys. Co, Litton Industries, Inc., 1948-60, dir. systems research, 1960-65, v.p. research and devel., 1965-70, sr. v.p., 1971-86; cons. in field, 1986—; asst. for earth, sea, air sci. to U.S. Pres.'s Sci. Adv.; chmn. Interagy. Com. for Atmospheric Scis., 1970-71; mem. panel On-Site Inspection Unidentified Seismic Events, 1961; mem. Pres.'s panels on Disposition of Oil Leasing in the Santa Barbara Channel, Offshore Pollution, 1969; mem. U.S. Initiatives in Transp., 1971; mem. U.S. del. to, USSR, 1971; mem. Assembly Math. and Phys. Scis., Nat. Acad. Scis./NRC, 1977-80; mem. com. on seismology NAS/NRC, 1971-75, chmn., 1972-74, mem. U.S. nat. com. on tunneling, 1972-75, chmn. subcom. on tech. data and info., 1972-75, mem. panel on earthquake prediction, NAS/NRC, 1973-75, 87-90; dir. Nat. Ocean Industries, Assn., 1972-81, vice chmn. bd., 1973-75, chmn. bd., 1975-76; mem. nat. adv. com. Tex. Marine Biomed. Inst., 1973-78; mem. U.S. Coastal Zone Mgmt. Adv. Com., 1975-78; mem. energy research adv. bd. U.S. Dept. Energy, 1978-81, chmn. com. on geothermal energy, 1979-81; chmn. vis. com. U. Tex. Inst. for Geophysics, 1984—; mem. OCS policy com. Dept. Interior, 1985-89; mem. computer systems tech. adv. com. U.S. Dep. Com., 1989-90, mem. nat. sea grant rev. panel, 1990-94; adj. prof. geophysics Rice U., 1988-94; vis. prof. Netherlands Nat. U. at Utrecht, 1990. Author: Introduction to Geophysical Prospecting; also articles. Served as 2d lt. USAAF, 1944-46. Recipient Litton Advanced Tech. award, 1980; named Inventor of Yr. Houston Intell Property Law Assn., 1988. Fellow Geol. Soc. Am.; mem. European Assn. Exploration Geophysicists, Marine Tech. Soc. (Compass award for disting. achievement 1979), Soc. Exploration Geophysicists (named Classic Author of Geophysics 1960, editor jour. 1967-69, pres. 1971-72, chmn. 43d ann. meeting 1973, Kauffman gold medal 1979, hon. mem.), Acoustical Soc. Am., Am. Mgmt. Assn. (mem. research and devel. council 1974-76), Internat. Assn. Geophysics. Contractors (pres. 1973-75 Disting. Achievement award), World Geol. Congress 1989 (hon.), Nat. Acad. Engring., Sigma Xi. Club: Cosmos (Washington). Patentee in field. Address: 201 Vanderpool Ln No 49 Houston TX 77024-6125

SAVITSKY, DANIEL, engineer, educator; b. N.Y.C., Sept. 26, 1921; s. Maxim and Anna (Oleksiw) S.; m. Mary Wysocki; children: Jean, James, Anne. BCE, CCNY, 1942; MSc, Stevens Inst. Tech., 1952; PhD, NYU, 1971. Registered profl. engr., N.Y. Structural engr. EDO Corp., College Point, N.Y., 1942-44; aero. rsch. scientist Nat. Adv. Com. for Aero., Langley Field, Va., 1944-47; prof. emeritus Stevens Inst. Tech., Hoboken, N.J., 1947—; cons. U.S. Navy; chmn. high speed vehicle com. Internat. Towing Tank Conf., 1978-88. Author: (with others) Yearbook of Science and Technology, 1987; patentee hydrofoil controls. Mem. Soc. Naval Architects and Marine Engrs. (Adm. Cochrane award 1967), Am. Soc. Naval Engrs., Niantic Bay Yacht Club (Conn.), Sigma Xi. Roman Catholic. Avocations: sailing, skiing, tennis. Home: 597 Delcina Dr Westwood NJ 07675-6111 Office: Davidson Lab 711 Hudson St Hoboken NJ 07030-5953

SAVITZ, DAVID BARRY, lawyer; b. Wilkes-Barre, Pa., June 6, 1943; s. Sam and Isabelle (Weber) S.; 1 child, Curtis; m. Robin Kash, Dec. 13, 1987; 2 children: Rachel Childs and Kristin Childs. BA, Pa. State U., State Coll., 1965; JD, U. Colo., Boulder, 1968. Bar: Colo. 1968, U.S. Dist. Ct. Colo. 1969, U.S. Ct. Appeals (10th cir.) 1973, U. S. Supreme Ct. 1978. Pvt. practice Denver, 1968—; instr./lectr. Denver Police Dept., 1976,77; lectr. Colo. Criminal Def. Bar, Denver, 1979,82; instr. 1988-90, 93, APA, Dallas, 1985; instr./judge Univ. Denver Law School, 1986-90. Contbr. articles to profl. jours. Bd. dirs. Kempe Children's Found., Denver, 1992-93, chmn. speaker's bur., 1992-93; active Survivors' United Network Legal Task Force, Denver, 1992. Recipient David Caul Mem. award Internat. Soc. Study Multiple Personality and Dissociation, 1991. Mem. ABA, Nat. Assn. Criminal Def. Lawyers, Am. Trial Lawyers Assn., Colo Criminal Def. Bar, Colo. Trial Lawyers Assn., Colo. Bar Assn. Avocations: jogging, biking. Home: 22434 Anasazi Way Golden CO 80401 Office: # 600 950 S Cherry St Denver CO 80222

SAVITZ, MARTIN HAROLD, neurosurgeon; b. Boston, Jan. 20, 1942; s. Nathan and Bernice Beatrice (Segal) S.; m. Susan Rayna Gordon, June 23, 1968 (div. Sept. 1977); 1 child, Sean Isaac; m. Harmony Gwynne Keys, Oct. 28, 1979; 1 child, Ariel Austryn. AB, Harvard U., 1963; MD, Hahnemann, 1969. Diplomate Am. Bd. Neurol. Surgery, Am. Bd. Clin. Neurosurgery (head examination com. 1995—), Nat. Bd. Med. Examiners. Intern Boston City Hosp., 1969-70; resident Mount Sinai Hosp., N.Y.C., 1970-74; clin. instr. dept. neurosurgery Mt. Sinai Sch. Medicine, N.Y.C., 1974-82, asst. clin. prof., 1982-86, assoc. clin. prof., 1986-95; attending neurosurgeon Nyack (N.Y.) Hosp., Good Samaritan Hosp., Rockland County, N.Y., 1974—; mem. pres.'s coun. Harvard Coll., 1991—, marshall of commencement, 1993—; mem. alumni bd. trustees Hahnemann U., 1991-94. Contbg. editor Mt. Sinai Jour. Medicine, 1976-90, asst. editor, 1990—; mem. editorial bd. Jour. Orthopaedic Neurol. Medicine and Surgery, 1991—, Internat. Surgery, 1995—; contbr. 2 chpts. to textbooks; contbr. over 70 articles to profl. jours. Fellow ACS, Internat. Coll. Surgeons (chmn.-elect U.S. sect. neurosurgery 1992—, chmn. 1993, exec. com. 1994, chmn.-elect 1995), N.Y. Acad. Medicine, Phila. Coll. Physicians, Am. Acad. Neurol. Ortho. Surgery (bd. dirs. 1994—); Am. Bd. Forensic Examiners; mem. AMA, Am. Assn. Neurol. Surgeons, N.Y. Soc. Neurosurgery, Congress Neurol. Surgeons, N.Y. State Neurosurg. Soc., Am. Assn. for Advancement of Surgery, Internat. Fedn. of Surg. Colls, Am. Assn. Physicians, Internat. Soc. Minimal Intervention in Spinal Surgery, Hastings Ctr., Alpha Omega Alpha. Jewish. Home: Hobbit Holw New City NY 10956 Office: 55 Old Turnpike Rd Ste 101 Nanuet NY 10954-2449

SAVITZ, MAXINE LAZARUS, aerospace company executive; b. Balt., Feb. 13, 1937; d. Samuel and Harriette (Miller) Lazarus; m. Sumner Alan Savitz, Jan. 1, 1961; children: Adam Jonathan, Alison Carrie. BA in Chemistry magna cum laude, Bryn Mawr Coll., 1958; PhD in Organic Chemistry, MIT, 1961. Instr. chemistry Hunter Coll., N.Y.C., 1962-63; sr. electrochemist Mobility Equipment Rsch. and Devel. Ctr., Ft. Belvoir, Va., 1963-68; prof. chemistry Federal City Coll., Washington, 1968-72; program mgr. NSF, Washington, 1972-74; dir. FEA Office Bldgs. Policy Rshc. U.S. Dept. Energy, Washington, 1974-75, dir. div. indsl. conservation, 1975-76, from dir. div. bldgs. and community systems to dep asst sec., 1975-83; pres. Lighting Rsch. Inst., 1983-85; asst. to v.p. engring. Ceramic Components div. The Garrett Corp., 1985-87; gen mgr. Ceramic Components div. AlliedSignal Aerospace Co., Torrance, Calif., 1987—; lectr. in field; bd. dirs. Am. Coun. for Energy Efficient Economy, 1984—, Internat. Inst. Energy Conservation, 1984—, Energy Found., 1991—; cons. State Mich. Dept. Commerce, 1983, N.C. Alternative Energy Corp., 1983, Garrett Corp., 1983, Energy Engring. Bd., Nat. Rsch. Bd., 1986-93, Office Tech. Assessment, U.S. Congress Energy Demand Panel, 1987-91, nat. materials adv. bd. NRC, 1989-94; bd. dirs. U.S. Advanced Ceramic Assn., 1989—, chmn., 1992; mem. adv. com. div. ceramics/materials ORNL, 1989-92, mem. adv. com. div. energy, 1992—; mem. adv. bd. Sec. of Energy, 1992—; mem. Def. Sci. Bd., 1993—; mem. visiting com. adv. tech. Nat. Inst. Stds. & Tech., 1993—. Editor Energy and Bldgs.; contbr. articles to profl. jours. Policy com. mem. NAE, 1991—. NSF postdoctoral fellow, 1961, 62, NIH predoctoral fellow, 1960, 61. Mem. Nat. Acad. Engring. Office: AlliedSignal Ceramic Components Divsn 2525 W 190th St Torrance CA 90504-6002

SAVITZ, SAMUEL J., actuarial consulting firm executive; b. Phila., Dec. 23, 1936; s. Paul and Ann (Gechman) S.; BS in Bus. Adminstrn., Temple U., 1958; postgrad. U. Pa., 1960-62, Temple U., 1965; m. Selma Goldberg, June 15, 1958; children: Jacqueline Beverly, Steven Leslie, Michelle Lynn. Pension analyst Provident Mut. Life Ins. Co., Phila., 1958-61; v.p. The Wirkman Co., Phila., 1961-64; pres. Samuel J. Savitz & Assoc., Inc., Phila., 1964-86; chmn. bd., cons. Exec. Compensation Plans, Inc., Phila., 1980-86; sr. prin. Laventhol & Horwath, Phila., 1986-90; pres., chief exec. officer Savitz Orgn., Inc., 1990—; vis. lectr. U. Pa., Phila., 1960, La. State U., 1972-74; faculty Villanova U., 1971-75; cons. in field. Mem. pension com. Fedn. Jewish Agys., Phila., 1960; bd. dirs. Am. Weizmann Inst. Sci., 1984-85, Phila. All-Star Forum, 1987—; Mann Music Ctr., 1992—. With USAR, 1954-62. Mem. Am. Soc. Pension Actuaries (dir. 1969-75). Jewish. Club: Locust. Contbr. articles in field to profl. jours. Home: 470 Conshohocken State Rd

Bala Cynwyd PA 19004-2639 Office: 1845 Walnut St Philadelphia PA 19103-4728

SAVNER, DAVID A., lawyer; b. Chgo., Mar. 15, 1944. BA, Northwestern U., 1965, JD magna cum laude, 1968. Bar: Ill. 1968. Ptnr. Jenner & Block, Chgo. Editor Northwestern U. Law Review, 1967-68. Mem. ABA, Chgo. Bar Assn., Chgo. Coun. Lawyers, Order of Coif. Office: Jenner & Block 1 IBM Plz Chicago IL 60611

SAVOCA, ANTONIO LITTERIO, technology company executive; b. Cleve., Aug. 10, 1923; s. Peter Louis and Angelina Nancy (Ragonese) S.; m. Charlene Henson, Sept. 27, 1952; 1 child, Gina Savoca Rose. BBA, U. Okla., 1958. Mgr. dept. proposals Wasatch div. Thiokol Corp., Brigham City, Utah, 1963-66, asst. to gen. mgr., 1966-68, dir. fin. and adminstrn., 1968-74, sr. v.p., gen. mgr., 1974-83; pres., chief exec. officer Transpace Carriers, Inc., Greenbelt, Md., 1983-86; mgmt. cons. various cos., 1986-89; pres., chief exec. officer Atlantic Rsch. Corp. subs. Sequa Corp., Alexandria, Va., 1989—, also bd. dirs.; sr. v.p. Sequa Corp., N.Y.C., 1991—; chmn. bd. Kollsman Mfg. Inc. Co., 1991—; bd. dirs. No. Va. Tech. Coun. Chmn. U.S. Savs. Bond Campaign, Alexandria, 1991. Lt. col. USAF, 1942-63; ETO; Korea. Mem. Nat. Assn. Mfrs., Air Force Assn., Assn. U.S. Army, Am. Def. Preparedness Assn., Italy-U.S. Bus. Conf. (bd. dirs.), Navy League, U.S. Space Found., Hon. Utah Cols., The Robert Trent Jones Golf Club, Ogden Golf and Country Club, Tower Club. Republican. Roman Catholic. Office: Atlantic Rsch Corp 1577 Spring Hill Rd Ste 600 Vienna VA 22182

SAVOCCHIO, JOYCE A., mayor; b. Erie, Pa.; d. Daniel and Esther S. BA in History, Mercyhurst Coll., 1965; MEd, U. Pitts., 1969; cert. secondary sch. adminstrn., Edinboro U., 1975; DHL (hon.), Gannon U., 1990. Tchr. social studies Erie Sch. Dist., 1965-85, asst. prin. Strong Vincent High Sch., 1985-89, tchr. coord. high sch. task force, 1971-75; pres. Erie Edn. Assn., 1975-76; mem. coun. City of Erie, 1981-90, pres. coun., 1983, mayor, 1990—; bd. dirs., co-chair legis. com. Pa. League of Cities and Municipalities; mem. subcoms. on transp. and communications U.S. Conf. of Mayors; bd. dirs. State Job Tng. Partnership Bd.; mem., sec. Electoral Coll. for Commonwealth of Pa.; mem. various coms. Erie Sch. Dist. Past pres. Erie Hist. Mus.; past mem. editorial bd. Erie Hist. Soc.; mem. Pa. Gov.'s Flagship Commn., Community Task Force on Drug and Alcohol Abuse; bd. dirs. Pa. League Cities and Mcpls., co-chair legis. com.; mem. subcoms. Transp. and Communications U.S. Conf. Mayors; mem., sec. Electoral Coll. Commonwealth Pa.; bd. dirs. State Job Tng. Partnership Bd. Named Woman of Yr., Dem. Women Erie, 1981, Italian Am. Women's Assn., 1987; recipient Disting. Alumna award Mercyhurst Coll., 1990, Community Svc. award Roosevelt Mid. Sch., 1990, Disting. Citizen award French Creek coun. Boy Scouts Am., 1991. Mem. Delta Kappa Gamma. Roman Catholic. Office: Office of Mayor Mcpl Bldg 626 State St Erie PA 16501-1128

SAVOIE, LEONARD NORMAN, transportation company executive; b. Manchester, N.H., Aug. 8, 1928; s. Joseph Peter and Angelina (Desmarais) S.; m. Elsie Anne Berscht, June 9, 1951; children: Deborah Anne, Judith Lynn, Andrew Peter. B.S., Queen's U., 1952; M.B.A., U. Detroit, 1955. Indsl. engr. Kelsey-Hayes Can. Ltd., Windsor, Ont., Can., 1952-60; mgmt. cons. P.S. Ross & Partners, Toronto, Ont., 1960-64; pres., gen. mgr. Kelsey-Hayes Can. Ltd., 1964-70; pres., chief exec. officer Algoma Central Ry., Sault Ste. Marie, Ont., 1970-93, vice-chmn., 1993—; bd. dirs. Can. Gen. Ins. Co., E-L Fin. Corp. Ltd., Empire Life Ins. Co., Newaygo Forest Products Ltd., Gt. Lakes Power Ltd. Bd. dirs. United Appeal. Mem. Profl. Engrs. Ont., Engring. Inst. Can., Canadian, Sault Ste. Marie chambers commerce. Clubs: Rotary, Toronto, Toronto Ry, Sault Ste. Marie Golf. Office: Algoma Cen Ry, 289 Bay St, Sault Sainte Marie, ON Canada P6A 4Z2

SAVOY, DOUGLAS EUGENE, bishop, religion educator, explorer, writer; b. Bellingham, Wash., May 11, 1927; s. Lewis Bell and Maymie (Janett) S.; m. Elvira Clarke, Dec. 5, 1957 (div.); 1 son, Jamil Sean (dec.); m. Sylvia Ontaneda, July 7, 1971; children: Douglas Eugene, Christopher Sean, Sylvia Jamila. Student, U. Portland, 1947-8; DST, D Canon and Sacred Law, Jamilian U. of the Ordained, 1980; PhD in Theology, DD (hon.), Tech. Inst. Bibl. Studies, Nev., 1990. Ordained to ministry Internat. Community of Christ Ch., 1962, bishop, 1971. Cardinal head bishop Internat. Community of Christ Ch., 1971—; lectr. in ministerial tng. studies, 1972—; pastor Univ. Chapel, Reno, 1979—; founder Jamilian Parochial Sch., 1976; chancellor, founder Sacred Coll. of Jamilian Theology; pres., founder Jamilian U. of the Ordained, 1980; pres. Advs. for Religious Rights and Freedoms; chmn. World Coun. for Human Spiritual Rights, 1984—; head Jamilian Order of Patriarchs, 1990—; engaged in newspaper pub. West Coast, 1949-56; began explorations in jungles east of Andes in Peru to prove his theory that high civilizations of Peru may have had their origin in jungles, 1967; pres., founder Andean Explorers Club, Found.; Reno; pres., Advocates for Religious Rights and Freedoms; chmn., World Coun. for Human Spiritual Rights. Author: Antisuyo, The Search for Lost Cities of the High Amazon, 1970, Vilcabamba, Last City of the Incas, 1970, The Cosolargy Papers, vol. 1, 1970, vol. 2-3, 1972, The Child Christ, 1973, Arabic edit., 1976, Japanese edit., 1981, The Decoded New Testament, 1974, Arabic edit., 1981, The Millenium Edition of the Decoded New Testament, 1983, On The Trail of The Feathered Serpent, 1974, Code Book and Community Manual for Overseers, 1975, Prophecies of Jamil, First Prophecy to the Americas, Vol. 1, 1976, Second Prophecy to the Americas, 1976, The Secret Sayings of Jamil, The Image and the Word, Vol. 1, 1976, Vol. 2, 1977, Project X—The Search For the Secrets of Immortality, 1977, Prophecy to the Races of Man, Vol. 2, 1977, Solar Cultures of The Americas, 1977, Dream Analysis, 1977, Vision Analysis, 1977, Christoanalysis, 1978, The Essaei Document: Secrets of an Eternal Race, 1978, Millennium edit., 1983, The Lost Gospel of Jesus: Hidden Teachings of Christ, 1978, Millennium edit., 1983, Secret Sayings of Jamil, Vol. 3, 1978, Vol. 4, 1979, Prophecy to The Christian Churches, 1978, The Sayings, vol. 4, 1979, Solar Cultures of Oceania, 1979, Prophecy of The End Times, Vol. 4, 1980, The Holy Kabbalah and Secret Symbolism, Vols. 1 and 2, 1980, Solar Cultures of China, 1980, Christotherapy, 1980, Christophysics, 1980, Christodynamics, 1980, Code Book of Prophecy, 1980, The Sayings, vol. 5, 1980, vol. 6, 1981, Solar Cultures of India, 1981, Prophecy on the Golden Age of Light and the Nation of Nations, Vol. 5, 1981, Solar Cultures of Israel, vol. 3, 1981, The Counsels, 1982, Prophecy of the Universal Theocracy, vol. 6, 1982, Prophecy of the New Covenant, vol. 7, 1982, The Book of God's Revelation, 1983, Miracle of the Second Advent, 1984, Clerical Studies in Theology, Book I, Book II, Book III, Book IV, Transformative Theology: The School of Revelation, Transformative Theology: The School of Prophecy, Liturgical Theology: Preparation for Advanced Degrees, 1993; over 300 audio tape rec. lectures, 1974—, numerous others.; documentary film on Gran Vilaya, 1989; wrote, dir. videos Royal Roads to Discovery, Mystery of the Essenes of Old Israel, Secrets From the High Andes of Peru, 1993; contbr. articles on Peruvian cultures to mags., also articles on philosophy and religion; discoverer lost city of Incas at Vilcabamba Cuzco, numerous ancient cities in Amazonia including Gran Pajaten, Gran Vilaya, Monte Peruvia, Twelve Cities of the Condor. Trustee in Trust Episcopal Head Bishop Internat. Community of Christ. Served with AS USNR, 1944-46. Decorated officer Order of the Grand Cross (Republic of Peru), 1989; recipient numerous exploring awards including over 40 Flag awarndean Explorers Club, 1958-85 and Explorer of the Century trophy Andean Explorers Found., 1988, Silver Hummingbird award Ministry Industry and Tourism of Peru, 1987, medal of Merit Andres Reyes, 1989. Mem. Geog. Soc. Lima, Andean Explorers Found, Ocean Sailing Club, World Coun. for Human Spiritual Rights, Advs. for Religious Rights and Freedoms, Authors Guild. Clubs: Explorers (N.Y.C.); Andean Explorers Found. and Ocean Sailing. Home: 2025 La Fond Dr Reno NV 89509-3025 Office: 643 Ralston St Reno NV 89503-4436 *One who makes dreams come true is that person who gets an idea, figures out how to make it work and then throws all of his energy into the project, stopping at nothing.*

SAVRANN, RICHARD ALLEN, lawyer; b. Boston, July 29, 1935; s. Abraham B. and Doris (Curhan) S.; m. Diane Barbara Kleven, Dec. 22, 1957; children: Stephen Keith, Russell Carl. BA, Harvard U., 1956, JD, 1959. Bar: Mass. 1959, U.S. Dist. Ct. Mass. 1963, U.S. Ct. Appeals (1st cir.) 1965. Exec. Klev Bro. Mfg., Derry, N.H., 1959-63; assoc. Law Office of Jerome Rappaport, Boston, 1963-68; asst. atty. gen. Commonwealth of Mass., Boston, 1968-70; ptnr. Newell, Savrann & Miller, Boston, 1970-75; sr. ptnr. Kunian, Savrann & Miller, Boston, 1976-81, Singer, Stoneman, Kunian & Kurland, P.C., Boston, 1981-88, Singer, Kunian • Kurland, P.C., Boston,

1988-90; sr. ptnr, Curhan, Kunian, Goshko, Berwick and Savrann, P.C., Boston, 1990-92; ptnr. Burns and Levinson, Boston, 1993—; dir. Comite Internat. de Scientifiques pour la Sante el l'Environment, Paris, 1993—. Mem. Andover (Mass.) Housing Authority, 1972-0, chmn., 1984-90; pres. Hospice of Greater Lawrence, North Andover, Mass., 1984; bd. dirs. Boston Latin Sch. Found., 1987, clk., 1992—; bd. dirs. Comite Internat. de Sci. pour La Santé et l'Environ., Paris, 1993—. Mem. FBA, Am. Trial Lawyers Assn., Mass. Bar Assn., Boston Bar Assn., Indian Ridge Country Club, Eastpointe Golf and Racquet Club (Palm Beach Gardens, Fla.), Harvard Club (Andover) (pres. 1985—), Harvard Club. Avocations: golf, opera. Home: 11 Sheridan Rd Andover MA 01810-5109 Office: Burns and Levinson 125 Summer St Boston MA 02110-1616

SAVRIN, LOUIS, lawyer; b. Phila., Jan. 20, 1927; s. William Philip and Anna (Sass) S.; m. Barbara J. Schwimmer, Jan. 16, 1954; children: Jonathan Eric, Philip Wade, Daniel Scott. B.S., N.Y. U., 1948; J.D., U. Pa., 1951. Bar: N.Y. 1952. Atty. tax dept. Arthur Young & Co. (C.P.A.'s), N.Y.C., 1951-55; pvt. practice N.Y.C., 1955—; gen. counsel, sec. Pickwick Internat., Inc., N.Y.C., 1965-77. Assoc. editor: U. Pa. Law Rev, 1949-51. Mem. sch. bd. Dist. 21, Bklyn., 1962-68. With AUS, 1945-46. Mem. N.Y. State Bar Assn., N.Y. County Lawyers Assn., Real Estate Tax Rev. Bar Assn.; mem. B'nai B'rith (pres. lodge 1957-59, named to lodge Hall of Fame 1967, Torch of Freedom award Anti-Defamation League 1982). Club: Mason. Home: 907 Lake Plymouth Dr Newton NJ 07860-8921 Office: 60 E 42d St New York NY 10017

SAWABINI, WADI ISSA, retired dentist; b. Jaffa, Palestine, Jan. 14, 1917; s. Issa J. and Julia C. (Malak) S.; m. Harriet Colgate Abbe Lack, Aug. 6, 1949; children—Wadi' Issa, Frederick Lack, Stuart John, Julia Malak. Student, College des Ecoles Chrétiennes, 1924-32; D.D.S., Am. U. Beirut, 1940. Grad. study Forsyth Dental Infirmary, 1940-41; intern Med. Center Hosp. Vt. (formerly DeGoesbriand Meml. Hosp.), Burlington, 1941-42; attending staff; assoc. pvt. practice Dr. Charles I. Taggart, 1942-51; pvt. practice Burlington, 1951-88, ret.; instr. oral pathology U. Vt., 1951-58; dir. U. Vt. (Sch. Dental Hygiene), 1953-72; asst. prof. oral hygiene U. Vt. (Coll. Medicine), 1958-72; chief dental staff Mary Fletcher Hosp., 1958-68, assoc. prof. dept. allied health scis., 1969-72. Mem. adv. bd. Vt. Pub. Health Dept.; mem. Vt. Bd. Health, 1980-86; v.p. bd. dirs. Overlake Day Sch., 1962-63; mem. Ethan Allen Homestead Fundraising Com., 1990—. Paul Harris fellow Burlington Rotary. Fellow Internat. Coll. Dentists (mem. exec. council 1950-54), Am. Coll. Dentists; mem. Vt. Dental Soc. (pres. 1956-57, mem. bd. rev., Disting. Service award 1972), New Eng. Dental Soc., Champlain Valley Dental Soc., C. of C., ADA, Fedn. Dentaire Internat. Republican. Episcopalian (vestryman). Clubs: Mason (Shriner), Rotary (dir. 1955-56, pres. 1961-62), Ethan Allen (Burlington). Home: Bldg O Apt 2 Gardenside Shelburne VT 05482-7316

SAWALLISCH, WOLFGANG, conductor; b. Munich, Germany, Aug. 26, 1923; s. Wilhelm and Maria (Obermeier) S.; ed. Wittelsbacher Gymnasium of Munich, Musikalische Ausbildung, pvt. music studies; m. S. Mechthild, 1952. Condr., Augsburg, 1947-53; musical dir. Aachen, 1953-58, Wiesbaden, 1958-60, Cologne Opera, 1960-63; condr. Hamburg Philharm. Orch., 1960-73, hon. mem., 1973—; prin. condr. Vienna Symphony Orch., 1960-70, hon. mem.; also prof. Staatliche Hochschule für Musik, Cologne, 1960-63; musical dir. Bayerische Staatsoper Munich, 1971-92, dir. Staatsoper Munich, 1982-92, hon. mem., 1992; permanent condr. Teatro alla Scala, Milan; condr. many festivals; rec. artist U.S. and Britain; hon. condr. NHK Symphony Orch., Tokyo, 1967; artistic dir. Suisse Romande Orch., Geneva, 1973-80; music dir. Phila. Orch., 1993-94. Recipient Accademico Onorario Santa Cecilia, 1975; decorated Osterreichisches Ehrenkreuz für Kunst und Wissenschaft, Bundesverdienstkreuz, Bayerischer Verdienstorden, Grosses Bundesverdienstkreuz mit Stern (Fed. Republic Germany), Order of the Rising Sun Japan; recipient Bruckner-Ring, Vienna Symphony Orch., 1980; Bayerisches Maximilians-order für Wissenschaft and Kunst, 1984, Chevalier dans L'ordre National de la Légion d'Honneur de France, 1991. Mem. Richard Strauss Gesellschaft Munich (pres. 1976). Office: Phila Orch Acad of Mus Ste 400 1420 Locust St Philadelphia PA 19102-4223*

SAWCHUK, RONALD JOHN, pharmaceutical scientist, educator; b. Toronto, May 29, 1940; s. John Alexander and Mary (Skorupa) S.; m. Rosslyn Andrea Murison, July 8, 1967; children: David, Heather, Holly. BSc in Pharmacy, U. Toronto, 1963, MSc in Pharmacy, 1966; PhD Pharm. Chemistry (Pharmacokinetics), U. Calif., San Francisco, 1972. Lic. pharmacist, Ont. Asst. prof. Coll. Pharmacy, U. Minn., Mpls., 1971-76, assoc. prof., 1976-83, prof., 1983—, acting chmn. 1983-86, dir. grad. studies, 1983-89, 92-94, dir. Clin. Pharmacokinetics Lab., 1982—; expert cons. FDA, 1982-84; cons. to Epilepsy br. NIH; cons. to pharm. industry. Contbr. articles in pharmacokinetics and bioanalysis to sci. jours. Fellow AAAS, Am. Assn. Pharm. Scientists; mem. Am. Assn. Colls. Pharmacy, N.Y. Acad. Scis., U. S. Pharmacopeial Conv. Co. of Revision, Controlled Release Soc., Rho Chi. Lutheran. Achievements include establishment of methods for individualizing aminoglycoside dosing regimens in patients, drug distribution and elimination studies utilizing microdialysis. Avocations: winter sports, travel, photography. Home: 1762 20th Ave NW Saint Paul MN 55112-5419 Office: Coll Pharmacy U Minn 308 Harvard St SE Minneapolis MN 55455-0353

SAWDEI, MILAN A., lawyer; b. Bakersfield, Calif., Aug. 23, 1946. BA, U. Calif., Long Beach, 1969; JD, W.S.U., 1975. Bar: Calif. 1975, U.S. Dist. Ct. (ctrl. dist.) Calif. 1975. House counsel Sanyo Electric, Inc., 1975-77; assoc. counsel Brown Co. (Gulf & Western), 1978-80; divsn. counsel Petrolane, Inc., 1980-83; sr. counsel Bergen Brunswig Corp., Orange, Calif., 1983-90, v.p., chief legal officer, 1990-92, exec. v.p., chief legal officer, sec., 1992—. Mem. ABA, Am. Corp. Counsel Assn., Am. Soc. Corp. Secs., L.A. County Bar Assn. Office: Bergen Brunswig Corp 4000 Metropolitan Dr Orange CA 92668-3502

SAWDEY, RICHARD MARSHALL, lawyer; b. Buffalo, Jan. 8, 1943; s. Marshall Douglas and Eleanor Katherine (Reichman) S.; m. Judith Hollister Helgeson, Aug. 12, 1967; children—David Marshall, Karin Elizabeth. B.S., Mich. State U., 1965; J.D., U. Mich., 1968. Bar: Ill. 1968. Assoc. McBride, Baker, Wienke & Schlosser, Chgo., 1968-73; atty. R.R. Donnelley & Sons, Chgo., 1974-75, asst. sec., 1975-83, sec., 1983-85; v.ps., sec., 1985-88; Of counsel Hoogendoorn, Talbot, Davids, Godfrey & Milligan, Chgo., 1988—. Mem. ABA, Am. Soc. Corp. Secs., Chgo. Bar Assn. Office: Hoogendoorn Talbot Davids Godfrey & Milligen 122 S Michigan Ave Ste 1220 Chicago IL 60603-6107

SAWHILL, ISABEL VAN DEVANTER, economist; b. Washington, Apr. 2, 1937; d. Winslow B. and Isabel E. Van Devanter; m. John C. Sawhill, Sept. 13, 1958; 1 son, James W. B.A., NYU, 1962, Ph.D., 1968. Policy analyst Office Sec. HEW, 1968-69, Office Mgmt. and Budget, 1969-70; asst. prof. econs. Goucher Coll., Balt., 1969-73; sr. research assoc. Urban Inst., 1973-77, program dir., 1975-77, program dir., sr. fellow, 1980-93; dir. Nat. Commn. Employment Policy, Washington, 1977-79; program assoc. dir. Office Mgmt. and Budget, 1993-95; sr. fellow and Arjay Miller chair in pub. policy Urban Inst., 1995—; vis. prof. Georgetown U. Law Ctr., 1990-91. Author: The Reagan Record, 1984, Challenge to Leadership, 1988. Past mem. Sec. of Labor's commn. on workforce quality and labor mkt. efficiency, Ctr. Strategic and Internat. Studies commn. on strenghtening of Am., NRC bd. on sci., tech., and econ. policy; bd. dirs. Assembly of Am., Manpower Demonstration Res. Corp., Resources of the Future, vice-chair. Mem. Am. Econ. Assn. (mem. exec. com.), Assn. Pub. Polit. Analysis and Mgmt. (pres. 1988), Phi Beta Kappa. Office: 2100 M St NW Washington DC 20037

SAWHILL, JOHN CRITTENDEN, businessman, economist, university president, government official; b. Cleve., June 12, 1936; s. James Mumford and Mary Munroe (Gipe) S.; AB, Princeton U., 1958; PhD, N.Y. U., 1963; m. Isabel Van Devanter, Sept. 13, 1958; 1 child, James W. With Merrill, Lynch, Pierce, Fenner & Smith, Washington, 1958-60; asst. dean, prof. NYU Sch. Bus. Adminstrn., 1960-63, pres. NYU Washington Sq., 1975-79; dir. credit rsch. and planning Comml. Credit Co., Balt., 1964-66, sr. v.p., 1968-73; sr. assoc. McKinsey & Co., Washington, 1966-68; assoc. dir. natural resources Office Mgmt. and Budget, Washington, 1973-74; adminstr. Fed. Energy Adminstrn., Washington, 1973-75; dep. sec. Dept. Energy, Washington, 1979-80; chmn. U.S. Synthetic Fuels Corp., Washington, 1980; bd.

dirs. McKinsey & Co., Inc., Washington, 1980-90, Pacific Gas & Electric Co., NACCO Industries, Vanguard Group. Pres. The Nature Conservancy, Arlington, Va., 1990—; chmn. bd. trustees Whitehead Inst. Biomed. Rsch.; trustee Princeton U.; mem. Coun. on Fgn. Rels.; mem., dir. Trilateral Commn. Mem. AAAS (dir.), Met. Club (Washington), Chevy Chase Club (Md.), River Club (N.Y.C.). Office: The Nature Conservancy 1815 N Lynn St Arlington VA 22209-2003

SAWICKI, THOMAS, health care company executive; b. Seattle, July 29, 1945; s. Robert Alfred and Bernice Camille (Sokolowski) S.; m. Sandra Jeanne Douglas; 1 dau., Christine Dawn. BS in Zoology, U. Ill., 1968; MBA in Health and Hosp. Adminstrn., U. Fla., 1973. Assoc. dir. Morton F. Plant Hosp., Clearwater, Fla., 1973-77; v.p., asst. regional dir. ea. region Am. Med. Internat., Inc., Atlanta, 1977-81, group v.p., regional dir. so. region, 1981-83; group v.p., regional dir. Tex. south region Am. Med. Internat., Inc., Houston, 1985-86; sr. v.p., regional dir. Houston region Am. Med. Internat., Inc., 1986-88; sr. v.p., regional dir. cen. region Am. Med. Internat., Inc., Denver, 1988—; dir. divestiture ops., 1989-90; pres. ARA Living Ctrs., Inc., Houston, 1983-85; pres., chief exec. officer P/SL Healthcare System, Denver, 1991—; chmn. adv. bd. exec. program in health care fin. U. N.C., Chapel Hill, 1982-84; dir. divestiture ops. Am. Med. Inst., Inc., 1989-90; pres., chief exec. officer P/SL Healthcare System, 1991—. Mem. Tex. Comm. on Health Care Reimbursement Alternatives, Austin, 1988; official N.W. Age Group Swim League, Houston, 1987-88; bd. dirs. Nat. Coun. Health Ctrs., Washington, 1983-85, Tex. Assn. Bus., Austin. 1985-88; active United Way, Clearwater and Houston, 1973—. Lt. USN, 1968-71. Fellow Am. Coll. Health Care Execs. Republican. Roman Catholic. Avocations: tennis, golf, family activities. Home: 9355 Riviera Hills Dr Englewood CO 80111-3453 Office: Presb/St Lukes Health System 55 Madison St Ste 700 Denver CO 80206-5423

SAWIN, NANCY CHURCHMAN, educator, artist, historian; b. Wilmington, Del., June 21, 1917; d. Sanford W. and Ellen (Quigley) S. BA, Principia Coll., 1938; MA, U. Del., 1947; D.Ed., U. Pa., 1962; PhD (hon.), Golden Beacom Coll., 1987. With Sanford Sch., Hockessin, Del., 1938-74; dean girls Sanford Sch., 1945-62, head sch., 1962-74; coordinator student services U. Del. Div. Continuing Edn., Newark, 1974-77; edhl. cons. DuPont Co., ICI Ams., 1976-80; chmn. Del. State Sci. Fair com., 1962; mem. com. Jr. Sci. and Humanities Symposium, 1962-76; mem. English, lang. arts adv. com. State Dist., 1965-68; sec., dir. Recreation, Promotion and Service, Inc., 1963-74; mem. All-Am. Hockey Team, 1948-59. Exhibited one-person exhbns.; editor: The Eagle, 1961-62; co-pub., illustrator: Between the Bays, Delaware Sketchbook, Backroading through Cecil County, Brick and Ballast; author, illustrator: Up the Spine and Down the Creek, Locks Traps and Corners, China Sketchbook, A Hockessin Diary, Privy to the Council, The Oulde King's Roade, North from Wilmington by Oulde Roads and Turnpikes, 1992, Once Upon a Time in the Country, 1994. Trustee Golday Beacom Coll., pres., 1974-81, mem. safety coun., 1964-74; pres. Del. Sports Hall of Fame, 1982—; pres. bd. dirs. Del. Soc. for Preservation of Antiquities, 1986-88, chair, 1990—; chair fundraising com. Hockessin County Libr., 1989-94. 2d lt. CAP, 1942-45. Recipient Medal of Merit U. Del., 1989, DAR History medal, 1990; named to Del. Sports Hall of Fame, 1977; charter mem. U.S. Field Hockey Hall of Fame, 1988; named to Hall of Fame of Del. Women, 1991, Wall of Fame U. Del., 1991. Mem. Headmistress Assn. East, Del. Art Mus., Rehoboth Art League, Middle Atlantic States Assn. Colls. and Secondary Schs. (past pres.), Commn. on Secondary Schs., Red Clay Creek Assn., Internat. Fedn. Women's Hockey Assns. (past pres.), U.S. Field Hockey Assn. (past pres., named to Sports Hall of Fame 1987), Del. Field Hockey Assn. (past pres.), Nat. League Am. Pen Women, DAR (History medal), Daus. of Founders and Patriots, Nat. Soc. New Eng. Women, Daus. Colonial Wars, Del. Greenbank Questars (pres. 1993-94), Delta Kappa Gamma (past pres.), Pi Lambda Theta. Republican. Presbyterian (elder). Club: Quota (pres. Wilmington 1971-73, gov. 10th Dist. 1979-80). Address: North Light Studio 147 Sawin Ln Hockessin DE 19707-9713

SAWINSKI, VINCENT JOHN, chemistry educator; b. Chgo., Mar. 28, 1925; s. Stanley and Pearl (Gapinski) S.; m. Florence Whitman, Aug. 24, 1952; children—Christine Frances, Michael Patrick. B.S., Loyola U., 1948, M.A., 1950, Ph.D., 1962. Instr., asst. prof. chemistry, physiology and pharmacology Loyola U., Chgo., 1949-67; supervisory research chemist VA, Hines, Ill., 1961-66; assoc. prof. chemistry, phys. sci. City Colls. Chgo., 1967-71, prof., 1971-91, prof. emeritus, 1991—, chmn. phys. sci. dept. Wright campus, 1971-91. Contbr. articles to profl. jours. Served with U.S. Army, 1945-46. Fellow AAAS, Am. Inst. Chemists; mem. Am. Chem. Soc., Nat. Sci. Tchrs. Assn., Sigma Xi. Home: 1945 N 77th Ct Elmwood Park IL 60635-3623 Office: 4300 N Narragansett Ave Chicago IL 60634-4276

SAWIRIS, MILAD YOUSSEF, statistician, educator; b. Cairo, Jan. 11, 1922; came to U.S., 1966, naturalized, 1972; s. Youssef Sawiris and Faika Botros Samaan. B.Sc., Cairo U., 1942, diploma in edn., 1944, diploma higher edn., 1959; M.A., U. London, 1963, Ph.D., 1965; M.S., Stanford U., 1975. Tchr. math. Egyptian Govt. schs., 1944-48, 57-61, Sudan Govt. schs., 1948-57; mem. faculty Calif. State U., Sacramento, 1966-86, prof. emeritus, 1986—. Author research papers. Mem. Am. Statis. Assn. Mem. Coptic Orthodox Ch. Home: 8308 Caribbean Way Sacramento CA 95826-1657

SAWOROTNOW, PARFENY PAVLOVICH, mathematician, educator; b. Ust Medveditskaya, Russia, Feb. 20, 1924; came to U.S., 1949, naturalized, 1965; s. Pavel Ivanovich and Anna Davidovna (Soloviev) S.; student U. Graz (Austria), 1946-49; M.A. (Peirce scholar), Harvard U., 1951, Ph.D. (Shattuck fellow), 1955. Teaching fellow Harvard U., 1953-54; instr. math. Cath. U. Am., Washington, 1954-57, asst. prof., 1957-62, asso. prof., 1962-67, prof., 1967—. NSF grantee, 1967, 70; with Georgetown U. and George Washington U., 1971, 77. Mem. Am. Math. Soc., Math. Assn. Am., Calcutta Math. Soc., N.Y. Acad. Scis., AAUP, Sigma Xi. Mem. Eastern Orthodox Ch. Contbr. articles to and referred papers for math. rsch. jours. Home: 6 Avon Pl Hyattsville MD 20782-3328 Office: Cath U Am Dept Math 4th and Michigan Ave NE Washington DC 20064

SAWTELL, STEPHEN M., private investor, lawyer; b. St. Paul, Jan. 17, 1931; s. William Amos and Helen Mary (Fiegenbaum) S.; m. Helen Elizabeth Wencel, June 27, 1956; children: Stephen, Katherine H. Student, Northwestern U., 1948-50; BSc in Law, U. Nebr., 1956, JD, 1957; postgrad., Stanford U., 1974. Bar: Nebr. 1957. With No. Natural Gas Co. (now Enron, Inc.), Omaha, 1957-85, Dubuque Packing Co. of Omaha, 1987-88, CENI Corp., JinNeb Beef Ltd., Dalien, China, 1987-89; of counsel McMannama and Assocs., Inc., Omaha, 1988—. Pres. Omaha Symphony Assn., 1969-71, Jr. Achievement Omaha, 1975, Omaha Sister City Assn., 1974-83; chmn. Omaha Com. on Fgn. Rels., 1975-81; mem. bd. advisors Salvation Army, 1981—. With AUS, 1952-55. Named Omaha's Outstanding Young Man of Year Omaha Jr. C. of C., 1963. Mem. Masons, Rotary, Omaha Club, Omaha Country Club. Congregationalist. Home: 702 Ridgewood Ave Omaha NE 68114-5360

SAWYER, CHARLES HENRY, anatomist, educator; b. Ludlow, Vt., Jan. 24, 1915; s. John Guy and Edith Mabel (Morgan) S.; m. Ruth Eleanor Schaeffer, Aug. 23, 1941; 1 dau., Joan Eleanor. B.A., Middlebury Coll., 1937, D.Sc. (h.c.), 1961; student, Cambridge U., Eng. 1937-38; Ph.D., Yale, 1941. Instr. anatomy Stanford, 1941-44; assoc., asst. prof., assoc. prof., prof. anatomy Duke U., 1944-51; prof. anatomy UCLA, Los Angeles, 1951-85; prof. emeritus UCLA, 1985—, chmn. dept., 1955-63, acting chmn., 1968-69, faculty research lectr., 1966-67. Editorial bd.: Endocrinology, 1955-59, Proc. Soc. Exptl. Biology and Medicine, 1959-63, Am. Jour. Physiology, 1972-75; Author papers on neuroendocrinology. Mem. Internat. Brain Research Orgn. (council 1964-68), AAAS, Am. Assn. Anatomists (v.p. 1969-70, Henry Gray award 1985), Am. Physiol. Soc., Am. Zool. Soc., Neurosci. Soc., Endocrine Soc. (council 1968-70, Koch award 1973), Am. Acad. Arts and Scis., Nat. Acad. Scis., Soc. Exptl. Biology and Medicine, Soc. Study Reprodn. (dir. 1969-71, Hartman award 1977), Internat. Neuroendocrine Soc. (council 1972-76), Hungarian Soc. Endocrinology and Metabolism (hon.), Japan Endocrin Soc. (hon.), Phi Beta Kappa, Sigma Xi. Home: 466 Tuallitan Rd Los Angeles CA 90049-1941 Office: U Calif Sch Medicine Los Angeles CA 90024

SAWYER, CHRISTOPHER GLENN, lawyer; b. Winston-Salem, N.C., Sept. 20, 1950; m. Julia Ann Fergerson; children: Frances Elizabeth, Christopher Glen Jr. BA, U. N.C., 1972; MDiv, Yale U., 1975; JD, Duke U., 1978. Bar: Ga. 1978, N.C. 1978. Assoc. Alston & Bird, Atlanta, 1978-85, ptnr., 1985—; lectr. at profl. seminars. Bd. dirs. Lee Harper and Dancers, 1982-88, chmn., 1983-86; mem. exec. com. Atlanta Crime Coordination Com., 1979-80; chmn. Ga. adv. bd. trustees The Trust for Public Land, 1990—, chmn. adv. bd. 1991—, bd. dirs. 1993—; clk. of sessions Trinity Presbyterian Ch., 1992-93. Mem. ABA, Ga. Bar Assn. (consumer rights and remedies com. 1980-81), N.C. Bar Assn., Nat. Conf. Bar Pres., The Nature Conservancy of Ga. (bd. dirs. 1990—), chmn., nat. real estate adv. bd., 1992—), Atlanta Bar Assn. (pres. 1989-90, bd. dirs 1983—, exec. com. 1984-85, 87—), Atlanta Coun. Young Lawyers (bd. dirs. 1979-84), Atlanta Vol. Lawyers Found. (bd. dirs.), Lawyers Club of Atlanta, Atlanta Botan. Gardens, Atlanta Hist. Soc., Atlanta Music Festival Assn., Friends of Atlant Zoo, High Mus. Art, Yale Club of Ga. Presbyterian. Office: Alston & Bird 1 Atlantic Ctr 1201 W Peachtree St NW Atlanta GA 30309-3400

SAWYER, (L.) DIANE, television journalist; b. Glasgow, Ky., Dec. 22, 1945; d. E.P. and Jean W. (Dunagan) S.; m. Mike Nichols, Apr. 29, 1988. BA, Wellesley Coll., 1967. Reporter Sta. WLKY-TV, Louisville, 1967-70; adminstr. press office White House, 1970-74; rschr. Richard Nixon's memoirs, 1974-78; gen. assignment reporter, then Dept. State corr. CBS News, 1978-81; co-anchor Morning News CBS, from 1981, co-anchor Early Morning News, 1982-84; corr., co-editor 60 Minutes CBS-TV, 1984-89; co-anchor Prime Time Live ABC News, 1989—; co-anchor Day One, 1995—; co-anchor Day One ABC News. Recipient Peabody award for Pub. Svc., 1988, Robert F. Kennedy award, 8 Emmy awards, Spl. Dupont award. Mem. Coun. Fgn. Rels. Office: PrimeTime Live 147 Columbus Ave 3rd Fl New York NY 10023-5900

SAWYER, FORREST, newscaster; b. Lakeland, Fla.. BA, U. Fla., 1971, MA, 1976; student, U. Tex., Austin. Reporter, news dir. various radio stas., 1974-80; anchorman Sta. WAGA-TV (CBS affiliate), Atlanta, 1980-85; co-anchor Early Morning News CBS, N.Y.C.; now corr. Nightline ABC, N.Y.C., substitute anchor Nightline, anchor World News Sunday; anchor World News Sunday ABC News Day One, N.Y.C.; corr. covering Persian Gulf war for ABC-TV, 1991. Office: Day One 147 Columbus Ave Fl 8 New York NY 10023-5900

SAWYER, GRANT, lawyer; b. Twin Falls, Idaho, Dec. 14, 1918; s. Harry William and Bula Bell (Cameron) S.; m. Bette Norene Hoge, Aug. 1, 1946; 1 child, Gail. BA, Linfield Coll., 1939; student, U.Nev., Reno, 1940-41; JD, Georgetown U., 1948. Bar: Nev. 1948, D.C. 1948, U.S. Dist. Ct. Nev. 1967, U.S. Ct. Appeals (9th cir.) 1974, U.S. Supreme Ct. 1959. Pvt. practice Elko, Nev., 1948-50; dist. atty. Elko County, Nev., 1950-58; gov. State of Nev., 1959-67; sr. ptnr. Lionel Sawyer & Collins, Las Vegas, 1967—. Author books and articles on gaming. Mem. bd. regents U. Nev., 1957-58; Dem. nat. committeeman for Nev., 1968-88; chmn. Nev. Commn. on nuclear Projects, 1985—; mem. adv. bd. Aid for Aids of Nev., 1987—; trustee Bluecoats, Inc., 1987—; mem. exec. com. U.S. Las Vegas Found., 1988; mem. nat. adv. coun. ACLU, 1988—; bd. dirs. Nat. Jud. Coll., 1991-94. Pvt. to 1st lt. U.S. Army, 1942-46, PTO. Mem. ABA, Nev. Bar Assn., D.C. Bar Assn., Am. Judicature Soc., Phi Delta Phi. Office: Lionel Sawyer & Collins 300 S 4th St Stop 1700 Las Vegas NV 89101-6034

SAWYER, HELEN ALTON, artist; b. Washington; d. Wells Moses and Kathleen Alton (Bailey) S.; m. Jerry Farnsworth, Aug. 8, 1925. Student, Master's Sch., Dobbs Ferry, 1914-18; studied art with Johansen and Hawthorne. Painter, artist in oil and water color, lithographer; exhibited at principal galleries and museums of U.S.; represented permanent collections numerous museums,including Whitney Mus. Am. Art, Pa. Acad., Toledo Mus., Syracuse U. Mus., John Herron Mus., Indpls., Atlanta Mus., Amherst Coll. Mus., Williams Coll. Mus. Art, Chrysler Mus., U. Fla. Mus. Collection, others; IBM collection, Libr. of Congress, C & O. R.R. collections, Norfolk Mus., Samuel P. Harm Mus. of Art, Gainesville, Fla., Holyoke Pub. Mus.; contbr. articles and verse to jours. Recipient numerous awards, honors. Mem. N.A.D., Nat. Arts Club, Provincetown, Yonkers, Sarasota art assns., Audubon Artists, Nat. Assn. Women Artists. Home: 3482 Flamingo Ave Sarasota FL 34242-1004 also: Corbina Galleries 1472 Main St Sarasota FL 34236*

SAWYER, HOWARD JEROME, physician; b. Detroit, Nov. 17, 1929; s. Howard C. and Dorothy M. (Risley) S.; m. Janet Carol Hausen, July 24, 1954; children: Daniel William, Teresa Louise. BA in Philosophy, Wayne State U., 1952, MD, 1962, postdoctoral, 1969-72. Diplomate Am. Bd. Preventive Medicine in Occupational and Environ. Medicine. Intern William Beaumont Hosp., Royal Oak, Mich., 1962-63, resident in surgery, 1963-64; chief physician gen. parts div. Ford Motor Co., Rawsonville, Mich., 1964-66; med. dir. metall. products dept. Gen. Electric Co., Detroit, 1966-73; chem. and metal div. Gen. Electric Co., 1972-73; staff physician Detroit Indsl. Clinic, Inc., 1973-74; pres., med. dir. OccuMed Assocs., Inc., Farmington Hills, Mich., 1974-84; dir. OccuMed div. Med. Service Corp. Am., Southfield, Mich., 1984-86; dir. occupational, environ. and preventive medicine Henry Ford Hosp., 1987-91, cons., 1991—; adj. asst. prof. occupational and environ. health scis. Wayne State U., 1974—; lectr. Sch. Pub. Health, U. Mich., Ann Arbor, 1977—; cons. med. dir. St. Joe Minerals Corp., 1976-87, Chesbrough Pond's Inc., 1979-83; cons. Anaconda, Bendix, Borg Warner Chems., Fed. Mogul, Gen. Electric, Gt. Lakes Chems., other corps. Contbr. articles to profl. jours., chpts. to textbooks. Fellow Am. Coll. Preventive Medicine, Am. Occupational and Environ. Med. Assn., Mich. Occupational and Environ. Med. Assn. (pres. 1986), Am. Acad. Occupational Medicine; mem. AMA, Detroit Occupational Physicians Assn. (pres. 1984), Mich. State Med. Soc., Oakland County Med. Soc., Am. Indsl. Hygiene Assn., Mich. Indsl. Hygiene Soc. Office: Sawyer Med Cons PC 7072 Edinborough Dr West Bloomfield MI 48322-4025

SAWYER, JOHN, professional football team executive; s. Charles S.; m. Ruth Sawyer; children: Anne, Elizabeth, Catherine, Mary. Pres., part owner Cin. Bengals, Nat. Football League; pres. J. Sawyer Co., Ohio, Miss., Mont., Wyo. Office: J Sawyer Co Provident Tower Cincinnati OH 45202 Office: Cin Bengals 200 Riverfront Stadium Cincinnati OH 45202*

SAWYER, MARY CATHERINE, hospital administrator; b. Borger, Tex., Dec. 8, 1931; d. Andrew Rodgers and Mary Elizabeth (Slater) Hill; m. Edmond Eugene Sawyer, Aug. 26, 1963; children: Slater Shane, Anthony Barrett, Maronda Rae. BBA, Tex. Tech U., 1956; cert. in med. records, U. Tex. Med. Br., Galveston, 1957. Registered med. adminstr.; cert. coding specialist. Med. record adminstr. Taylor Hosp., Inc., Lubbock, Tex., 1957-63; pvt. practice cons. Paris, Tex., 1963-79; med. record adminstr., coding specialist St. Joseph's Hosp., Paris, 1979—. Mem. DAR (sec. 1989-91, treas. 1991-93, 1st vice regent 1994—, def. chmn. 1990-94), Gordon Country Club, Phi Gamma Nu. Methodist. Avocation: genealogy. Home: PO Box 128 Deport TX 75435 Office: St Joseph's Hosp PO Box 9070 Paris TX 75461

SAWYER, RAYMOND LEE, JR., motel chain executive; b. New Orleans, Oct. 7, 1935; s. Raymond Lee Sawyer and Eloise Falvy (Searcy) Easley; m. Dolores Jean Young, June 11, 1960; children: Lisa Kay, Linda Fay. BA, Northwestern State U., 1959. Art dir., advt. mgr. Natural Food and Farming Mag., Atlanta, Tex., 1959-66, editor, 1963-66; asst. editor, editor Tourist Court Jour./Southwest Water Works Jour., Temple, Tex., 1966-73; editor Tourist Court Jour./Southwest Water Works Jour., Temple, 1973-75; founding ptnr., sr. v.p. Budget Host Inns, Ft. Worth, 1975-83, pres., chief exec. officer, 1983—. Named Man of Yr. Motel Brokers Assn. Am., 1974; recipient Bob Gresham Meml. award Nat. Innkeeping Assn., 1975. Mem. Am. Automobile Assn., mem. lodging adv. panel 1990—). Methodist. Avocations: photography, writing. Office: Budget Host Inns PO Box 14341 Arlington TX 76094-1341

SAWYER, RAYMOND TERRY, lawyer; b. Cleve., Oct. 1, 1943; s. R. Terry and Fanny Katherine (Young) S.; m. Katherine Margaret Schneider, Aug. 5, 1972; children: Margaret Young, John Terry. BA, Yale U., 1965; LLB, Harvard U., 1968. Bar: Ohio 1969, U.S. Dist. Ct. (no. dist.) Ohio 1970. Assoc. Thompson, Hine and Flory, Cleve., 1968-76, ptnr., 1976-83,

—; exec. dir. Ohio Housing Fin. Agy., Columbus, 1983-84; counsel to Gov. Richard F. Celeste, Columbus, 1984-85, chief of staff, 1985-86. Vol. VISTA, East Palo Alto, Calif., 1968-69; mem. Tech. Leadership Coun., Leadership Cleve., 1986-87, Cleve. Found. Study Commn. on Med. Rsch. Edn., 1991-92; mem. Ohio Bd. Regents, Columbus, 1987—, chmn., 1992-93; trustee Cleve. Ballet, 1987—, Cleve. Orch., 1993—, Western Res. Hist. Soc.; bd. dirs. Premix, Inc., North Kingsville, Ohio; chmn. George W. Codrington Charitable Found. Named Man of Yr. Womanspace, 1982. Mem. ABA, Ohio State Bar Assn. (chair corp. law com. 1993-95), Clevel. Bar Assn., Yale U. Alumni Assn. (pres. Cleve. chpt. 1980-81). Democrat. Presbyterian. Office: Thompson Hine and Flory City Bank Bldg 1100 National Cleveland OH 44114-3070

SAWYER, RICHARD, art director, production designer. Art dir.: (films) In Search of Noah's Ark, 1977, FM, 1978, Melvin and Howard, 1980, The Hand, 1981, The Border, 1982, Twilight Zone-The Movie ("Back There"), 1983, (TV movies) Rich Men, Single Women, 1990; prodn. designer: (films) Where the Buffalo Roam, 1980, Things Are Tough All Over, 1982, Off the Wall, 1983, Bachelor Party, 1984, Lost in America, 1985, Moving Violations, 1985, Three Amigos, 1986, Vibes, 1988, Big Man on Campus, 1989, (with Jeremy Railton) The Two Jakes, 1990, Innocent Blood, 1992, (TV movies) Mother and Daughter: The Loving War, 1980, Coward of the County, 1981, Lottery!, 1983, The Gambler, 1983, Shattered Vows, 1984, C.A.T. Squad, 1986. Office: The Lyons/Sheldon Agency 8344 Melrose Ste 20 Los Angeles CA 90069*

SAWYER, ROBERT MCLARAN, history educator; b. St. Louis, Nov. 12, 1929; s. Lee McLaran and Harrie (Alcock) S.; m. Patricia Ann Covert, Nov. 23, 1955; children—Ann Marie, Lee McLaran, Gail Louise. B.S., S.E. Mo. State Coll., 1952; M.A., U. Ill., 1953; Ph.D., U. Mo., 1966. Tchr. Rolla (Mo.) Public Schs., 1955; asst. prof., then asso. prof. history U. Mo., Rolla, 1956-67; mem. faculty U. Nebr., Lincoln, 1967—; prof. history of edn. U. Nebr., 1969—, chmn. dept. history and philosophy of edn., 1975-81; mem. council U. Nebr. (Coll. Arts and Scis.), 1979—; vis. prof. Ark. State U., Jonesboro, summer 1966; proposal reviewer Nat. Endowment Humanities, 1979. Author: The History of the University of Nebraska, 1929-1969, 1973, The Many Faces of Teaching, 1987, The Art and Politics of College Teaching, 1992, The Black Student's Guide to College Success, 1993, The Handbook of College Teaching, 1994; also articles, revs. Served with AUS, 1953-55. Mem. Orgn. Am. Historians, History Edn. Soc., Am. Ednl. Studies Assn., Soc. Profs. Edn., Phi Alpha Theta, Phi Delta Kappa. Home: 2640 S 35th St Lincoln NE 68506-6623 Office: Univ Nebr 29 Henzlit Hall Lincoln NE 68588

SAWYER, THOMAS C., congressman; b. Akron, Ohio, Aug. 15, 1945; m. Joyce Handler, 1968; 1 child, Amanda. BA, U. Akron, 1968, MA, 1970. Pub. sch. tchr. Ohio; adminstr. state sch. for delinquent boys; legis. agt. Ohio Pub. Utilities Commn.; mem. Ohio House Reps., Columbus, 1977-83; mayor City of Akron, 1984-86; mem. 100th-104th Congresses from 14th Ohio dist., Washington, D.C., 1987—; mem. econ. & ednl. opportunity com., postal pers. Democrat. Office: US Ho of Reps 1414 Longworth Bldg Washington DC 20515-3514*

SAWYER, THOMAS HARRY, health care facility administrator; b. Lake Providon, La., Jan. 14, 1941; s. Narvin Hersey and Billie (Byatt) S.; m. Barbara Gertrude Richey, June 5, 1960; children: Thomas R., Paul B. BS, La. Tech. U., 1964, MBA, 1965. Asst. adminstr. Lincoln Gen. Hosp., Ruston, La., 1965-70; asst. adminstr. Baton Rouge Gen. Hosp., 1970-79, exec. v.p., 1979-81, pres., 1981-84; pres. Gen. Health, Inc., Baton Rouge, 1984—; sec. Sunhealth Enterprises, Charlotte, N.C., 1987—. Pres. La. Arts and Scis. Found., Baton Rouge, 1987. Mem. Am. Coll. of Home Health Care Execs., Healthcare Fin. Mgmt. Assn. (past pres. La. chpt.), La. Hosp. Assn. (pres. 1988-89), Met. Kiwanis (pres. 1984), Bocago Racquet Club (pres. 1982), Baton Rouge C. of C. (v.p. 1988), Rotary, Baton Rouge Roundtable. Republican. Avocations: golf, tennis, hunting, skiing. Home: 12400 Jefferson Hwy Apt 512 Baton Rouge LA 70816-6212 Office: Baton Rouge Gen Med Ctr PO Box 2511 Baton Rouge LA 70821

SAWYER, THOMAS WILLIAM, air force officer; b. Turlock, Calif., Nov. 19, 1933; s. Everett Edward and Marie Georgine (Gunderson) S.; m. Faith Barry Martin, Feb. 16, 1957; children: William Everet, John Martin, Susan Quincy. BS in Mil. Sci., U. Nebr., 1965; MS in Internat. Rels., George Washington U., 1974. Enlisted U.S. Air Force, 1952, commd. and advanced through grades to maj. gen., 1983; comdr. 57th Fighter Squadron, Keflavik, Iceland, 1971-73; chief internat. relations div. Hdqrs. U.S. Air Force, Washington, 1974-77; vice comdr. 20th Air Div., Fort Lee, Va., 1977-78; mil. asst. to Sec. Air Force, 1978-80; comdr. 26th Air Div., Luke AFB, Ariz., 1980-82; dep. ops. NORAD and Space Command, Colorado Springs, Colo., 1982-86; retired USAF, 1986; founder, pres. Aerospace Network Inc., 1986. Bd. dirs Pikes Peak chpt. ARC, Colo./Wyo. chpt. Am. Def. Preparedness Assn. Decorated Disting. Service medal, Def. Disting. Service medal, Legion of Merit with 2 oak leaf clusters, Silver Star (2). Mem. Phoenix C. of C. (bd. dirs. 1980-82), Colorado Springs C. of C. Avocations: nat. security affairs, woodworking, automobile bldg. Home: 10 W Cheyenne Mountain Blvd Colorado Springs CO 80906-4335 Office: Aerospace Network Inc 10 W Cheyenne Mountain Blvd Colorado Springs CO 80906-4335

SAWYER, WILBUR HENDERSON, pharmacologist, educator; b. Brisbane, Australia, Mar. 23, 1921; s. Wilbur Augustus and Margaret Henderson S.; m. Marian Gholson Kittredge, Nov. 14, 1942 (dec. Mar. 1982); children: Wilbur Kittredge, Robert Kittredge, Thomas Kittredge, Richard Kittredge; m. Pomona Jean Mitchell, Aug. 28, 1982. A.B., Harvard U., 1942, M.D., 1945, Ph.D., 1950. Instr. biology Harvard U., Cambridge, Mass., 1950-53; asst. prof. physiology NYU Med. Sch., N.Y.C., 1953-57; asso. prof. pharmacology Columbia U. Coll. Physicians and Surgeons, N.Y.C., 1957-64; prof. Columbia U. Coll. Physicians and Surgeons, 1964-78, Gustavus A. Pfeiffer prof., 1978-90, prof. emeritus, 1991—. Contbr. articles on exptl. endocrinology, physiology and pharmacology to profl. jours. Served to lt. (j.g.) M.C., USN, 1946-48. Recipient Lederle Med. Faculty award NYU, 1955-57; Fulbright-Hays Sr. scholar, 1974; Commonwealth Fund travelling fellow, 1965. Fellow AAAS; mem. Am. Soc. Zoologists, Am. Physiol. Soc., Soc. Gen. Physiologists, Soc. Exptl. Biology and Medicine, Endocrine Soc., Am. Soc. Pharmacology and Exptl. Therapeutics, Harvey Soc., Soc. Endocrinology, Alpha Omega Alpha. Home: 1490 Kings Ln Palo Alto CA 94303-2836

SAWYER, WILLIAM DALE, physician, educator, university dean, foundation administrator; b. Roodhouse, Ill., Dec. 28, 1929; s. Cloyd Howard and Eva Collier (Dale) S.; m. Jane Ann Stewart, Aug. 25, 1951; children—Dale Stewart, Carole Ann. Student, U. Ill., 1947-50; MD cum laude, Washington U., St. Louis, 1954; ScD (hon.), Mahidol U., Bangkok, 1988; DPH (hon.), Chiang Mai U., Thailand, 1993. Intern Washington U.-Barnes Hosp., 1954-55, resident, 1957-58, fellow, 1958-60; asst. prof. microbiology Johns Hopkins U., Balt., 1964-67; prof., chmn. dept. microbiology Rockefeller Found.-Mahidol U., Bangkok, 1967-73, Ind. U. Sch. Medicine, Indpls., 1973-80; prof. depts. medicine, microbiology and immunology Wright State U., Dayton, Ohio, 1981-87, dean Sch. Medicine, 1981-87; pres. China Med. Bd. N.Y., Inc., 1987—; adj. prof. biology Ball State U., Muncie, Ind., 1987-88; hon. prof. microbiology Sun Yat Sen U. Med. Sci., 1987; hon. prof. Peking Union Med. Coll., 1989; hon. advisor Beijing Med. U.; cons. U.S. Army Med. R & D Command, WHO Immunology Ctr., Singapore, 1969-73; mem. bd. sci. advisers Armed Forces Inst. Pathology, 1975-80, chmn., 1979-80; adj. prof. medicine and microbiology and immunology N.Y. Med. Coll., Valhalla, 1990—. Contbr. numerous articles to profl. jours. Mem. Lobund adv. bd. U. Notre Dame. Served to maj. M.C., UAS, 1955-64. Recipient Gold medal of merit Airlangga U., Indonesia, 1992, Pub. Health Recognition award Asia-Pacific Acad. Consortium Pub. Health, 1993. Fellow ACP; mem. AAAS, Am. Soc. Microbiology (br. pres. 1976), Sci. Rsch. Soc. Am., Am. Fedn. Clin. Rsch., Ctrl. Soc. Clin. Rsch., Infectious Diseases Soc. Am., Soc. Exptl. Biology and Medicine, Am. Acad. Microbiology, Am. Assn. Pathologists, Assn. Am. Med. Colls. (coun. deans 1980-87), Phi Beta Kappa, Sigma Xi, Alpha Omega Alpha. Office: China Med Bd of NY Inc 750 3rd Ave New York NY 10017-2703

SAWYERS, ELIZABETH JOAN, librarian, administrator; b. San Diego, Dec. 2, 1936; d. William Henry and Elizabeth Georgiana (Price) S. A.A.,

Glendale Jr. Coll., 1957; B.A. in Bacteriology, UCLA, 1959, M.L.S., 1961. Asst. head acquisition sect. Nat. Library Medicine, Bethesda, Md., 1962-63, head acquisition sect., 1963-66, spl. asst. to chief tech. services div., 1966-69, spl. asst. to assoc. dir. for library ops., 1969-73; asst. dir. libraries for tech. services SUNY-Stony Brook, 1973-75; dir. Health Scis. Library Ohio State U., Columbus, 1975-90, spl. asst. to dir. Univ. librs., 1990—. Mem. Assn. Acad. Health Scis. Library Dirs. (sec./treas. 1981-83, pres. 1983-84), Med. Library Assn., Am. Soc. for Info. Sci., Spl. Libraries Assn., ALA. Office: Ohio State Univ Librs 1858 Neil Ave Columbus OH 43210-1225

SAWYERS, JOHN LAZELLE, surgeon; b. Centerville, Iowa, July 26, 1925; s. Francis Lazelle and Almira (Baker) S.; m. Julia Edwards, May 25, 1957; children: Charles Lazelle, Al Baker, Julia Edwards. A.B., U. Rochester, 1946; M.D., Johns Hopkins U., 1949. Diplomate: Am. Bd. Surgery (dir. 1981-87), Am. Bd. Thoracic Surgery. House officer surgery Johns Hopkins Hosp., Balt., 1949-50; asst. resident, resident in surgery Vanderbilt U. Hosp., Nashville, 1953-58; practice medicine specializing in surgery Nashville, 1958—; surgeon Edwards-Eve Clinic, 1958-60; chief surg. service Nashville Gen. Hosp., 1960-77; surgeon-in-chief St. Thomas Hosp., Nashville, 1977-82; prof. surgery Vanderbilt U., Nashville., chmn. dept. surgery, dir. sect. surg. scis., 1983—. Bd. dirs. Davidson County unit Am. Cancer Soc. Served from lt. (j.g.) to lt. M.C. USNR, 1950-52. Fellow A.C.S. (gov. 1974-80, pres. Tenn. chpt. 1974); mem. Am. Surg. Assn. 1st v.p. 1994), Southeastern Surg. Congress (pres. 1980), So. Surg. Assn. (pres. 1987), Halsted Soc. (pres. 1981). Home: 403 Ellendale Ave Nashville TN 37205-3401 Office: Vanderbilt U Dept Surgery T # 2116 Nashville TN 37232

SAWYIER, CALVIN P., lawyer; b. Chgo., Oct. 7, 1921. AB, Chgo. U., 1942, MA, 1942; LLB, Harvard U., 1947. Bar: N.H. 1948, Ill. 1949. Ptnr. Winston & Strawn, Chgo. Mem. ABA, Ill. State Bar Assn., Chgo. Bar Assn., Chgo. Coun. Lawyers, Phi Beta Kappa. Office: Winston & Strawn 35 W Wacker Dr Chicago IL 60601-1614

SAWYIER, DAVID R., lawyer; b. Chgo., Feb. 2, 1951. BA, Harvard U., 1972, JD, 1977; MA, Oxford U., 1974; diploma law, Cambridge U., 1979. Bar: Ill. 1977, D.C. 1978. Law clerk U.S. Ct. Appeals D.C. cir., 1977-78; ptnr. Sidley & Austin, Chgo. Mem. ABA (bus. law sect.), Chgo. Bar Assn. (futures sect.). Office: Sidley & Austin 1 First Nat Plz Chicago IL 60603

SAX, HELEN SPIGEL, lawyer; b. Phila., June 2, 1915; d. D. Hays and Erna (Sultan) Solis-Cohen; m. Herbert Spigel, Aug. 31, 1939; children—Frank, Robert, James; m. James E. Sax, June 15, 1969. B.A., Swarthmore Coll., 1937; LL.B., U. Pa., 1940. Bar: Ill. 1941, Pa. 1945. With War Labor Bd., Chgo., 1940-41; mem. Wolf Block Schorr & Solis-Cohen, Phila., 1945—. Trustee Rosenbach Mus. and Libr., 1969—, Nat. Mus. Am. Jewish History, 1975—; bd. dirs. Big Bros.-Big Sisters Assn. Phila; mem. women's bd. Thomas Jefferson U. Hosp.; mem. adv. bd. Phila. Found.; mem. Juvenile Justice Alliance-Citizens Crime Commn.; former pres., mem. citizens com. Girl Scouts of Greater Phila. Mem. ABA, Pa. Bar Assn., Phila. Bar Assn., Phila. Lawyers Club, Phi Beta Kappa. Office: Wolf Block Schorr SE Corner 15th Chestnut St Philadelphia PA 19102

SAX, JOSEPH LAWRENCE, lawyer, educator; b. Chgo., Feb. 3, 1936; s. Benjamin Harry and Mary (Silverman) S.; m. Eleanor Charlotte Gettes, June 17, 1958; children—Katherine Elaine, Valerie Beth, Anne-Marie. AB, Harvard U., 1957; JD, U. Chgo., 1959; LLD (hon.), Ill. Inst. Tech., 1992. Bar: D.C. 1960, Mich., 1961, U.S. Supreme Ct. 1969. Atty. Dept. Justice, Washington, 1959-60; pvt. practice law Washington, 1960-62; prof. U. Colo., 1962-65, U. Mich., Ann Arbor, 1966-86; counselor U.S. Sec. Interior, Washington, 1994—; vis. prof. U. Calif. Law Sch., Berkeley, 1965-66, 86, U. Paris I, 1981, 82, Stanford Law Sch., 1985; fellow Ctr. Advanced Study in Behavioral Scis., 1977-78; cons. U.S. Senate Com. on Pub. Works, 1970-71; mem. cons. council Conservation Found., 1969-73; mem. legal adv. com. Pres.'s Council on Environ. Quality, 1970-72; mem. environ. studies bd. Nat. Acad. Sci., 1970-73; mem. Mich. Environ. Rev. Bd., 1973-74. Author: Waters and Water Rights, 1967, Water Law, Planning and Policy, 1968, Defending the Environment, 1971, Mountains Without Handrails, 1980, Legal Control of Water Resources, 1991. Bd. dirs. Environ. Law Inst., Washington, 1970-75; trustee Center for Law and Social Policy, 1970-76; regional gov. Internat. Coun. Environmental Law; gov.'s rep. Gt. Lakes Task Force, 1984-85. With USAF, 1960. Fellow AAAS; mem. University Club (San Francisco)

SAX, MARTIN, crystallographer; b. Wheeling, W.Va.. BS, U. Pitts., 1941, PhD in Phys. Chemistry, 1961. Rsch. chemist Trojan Powder Co., 1941-44, Glyco Products Co., 1951-59; asst. biochemist W. Pa. Hosp., 1946-57; postdoctoral crystallographer U. Pitts., 1961-63, asst. rsch. prof., 1963-66; rsch. chemist and dir. biocrystallography lab. Vets. Affairs Med. Ctr., Pitts. 1966—, assoc. chief staff R&D—, 1972—; adj. assoc. prof. crystallographer U. Pitts., 1966-71, adj. prof., 1971—. Mem. AAAS, Am. Crystallography Assn., Am. Chem. Soc. Achievements include research in three dimensional structures and the functions of biological macromolecules as ascertained by x-ray diffractions from single crystals. Office: U Drive C Vets Adminstn Med Ctr Rsch Svc Pittsburgh PA 15240

SAX, ROBERT EDWARD, food service equipment company executive; b. Phila., Nov. 2, 1938; s. Sam and Jessie (Sirisky) S.; m. Rochelle E. Sax, Jan. 11, 1959; children: Nathan, Beverly. Student, U. Pa., 1960-66; Diploma, Xerox Systems, 1987. Pres. Robert E. Sax Assocs., Inc., Blackwood, N.J., 1965-79; sr. sales mgr. Household Internat., Inc, Veron Hills, Ill., 1979-90; v.p. nat. accounts True Food Svc. Equipment, O'Fallon, Mo., 1990—. Author: It's Yours Just Ask, 1975. Pres. ARCH, Berlin, N.J., 1971. Named Man of Yr. WPEN Radio Sta., Camden, N.J., 1969. Mem. NHRA, Masons. Home: 305 Old Orchard Rd Cherry Hill NJ 08003-1216

SAX, STANLEY PAUL, manufacturing company executive; b. Cin., Sept. 1, 1925; s. Ben Philip and Goldie (Quitman) S.; children: Steven Jay, David Jay; m. Patricia Moran Leach, June 14, 1970; children: Cathy, Carolyn. A.B., U. Wis., 1948. Researcher Market Research Co. Am., Chgo., 1942; instr. U. Wis., 1948; v.p., dir. Am. Buff Co., Detroit, 1948-57; exec. v.p., dir. Am. Buff Co., Chgo., 1957—; pres. Speedway Buff Co.; pres., chmn. bd., dir. J.J. Siefen Co., 1961—; chmn. bd., pres. Sax Abrasive Corp., 1961—, Sax Cal. Corp., 1962—, Klem Chem. Corp., 1963—, Stan Sax Corp., Seco Chems., Inc., 1965—; chmn. bd. Buckingham Products Co., McAleer Mfg. Co., 1968—, Sax Realty Investment Corp., 1967—, Globe Compound Corp. 1971—, Goodison Mfg. Co., 1972—, Ana, Inc., 1974—; partner S & D Leasing Co. Contbr. articles to profl. jours. Trustee Sax Family Found.; nat. trustee Balt. Mus. Art; bd. dirs. Med. Center Crippled Children and Adults. Served to lt. AUS, 1943-46; to lt. col. Res. 1946—. Recipient Wis. scholar award. Mem. Mil. Order World Wars, Metal Finishing Suppliers Assn. (trustee), Detroit C. of C, Detroit Inst. Arts (patron), Friends of Am. Wing (Founders Soc.), Friends of Henry Ford Mus., Pres.'s Soc., Am. Electroplaters Soc., Am. Soc. for Abrasives, Soc. Mil. Engrs., Young President's Orgn., World Presidents Orgn., Chief Execs. Orgn., Amateur Athletic Union, Soc. Die Casting Engrs., Res. Officers Assn., V.F.W., Wis. Alumni Assn., Winterhur Collectors Circle Mt. Vernon 100, Phi Beta Kappa, Alpha Phi Omega, Phi Kappa Phi, Psi Chi, Phi Eta Sigma. Clubs: Elk (Detroit), Rotarian. (Detroit), Economic (Detroit), Renaissance (Detroit); Recess, Army-Navy. Lender furnishings to diplomatic reception rooms, Nat. Portrait Gallery, Smithsonian Inst.; benefactor fine arts com. Dept. State. Home: 1340 Pembroke Dr Bloomfield Hills MI 48304-2653 Office: 101 S Waterman St Detroit MI 48209-3065

SAXBE, WILLIAM BART, lawyer, former government official; b. Mechanicsburg, Ohio, June 24, 1916; s. Bart Rockwell and Faye Henry (Carey) S.; m. Ardath Louise Kleinhans, Sept. 14, 1940; children: William Bart, Juliet Louise Saxbe Blauch, Charles Rockwell. A.B., Ohio State U., 1940; LL.B., 1948; hon. degrees, Central State U., Findlay Coll., Ohio Wesleyan U., Walsh Coll., Capital U., Wilmington Coll., Ohio State U., Bowling Green State U. Bar: Ohio 1948. Practiced in Mechanicsburg, 1948-55; partner Saxbe, Boyd & Prine, 1955-58; mem. Ohio Gen. Assembly, 1947-48, 49-50; majority leader Ho. Reps., 1951-52, speaker, 1953-54; atty. gen. Ohio, 1957-58, 63-68; partner Dargusch, Saxbe & Dargusch, 1960-63; mem. U.S. Senate from Ohio, 1969-74; atty. gen. U.S., 1974; ambassador to India, 1975-77; partner firm Chester, Saxbe, Hoffman & Wilcox, Columbus, Ohio, 1977-81; of counsel firm Jones, Day, Reavis & Pogue, Cleve., 1981-84, Pearson, Ball &

Dowd (merger Pearson, Ball & Dowd and Reed, Smith & McClay), Washington, 1984-93; ind. spl. counsel Central States Teamsters Pension Fund, 1982—; of counsel Chester Willcox & Saxbe, Columbus, Ohio, 1994—. Served with 107th Cav. AUS, 1940-42; Served with 107th Cav. USAAF, 1942-45; col. Res. Mem. Am., Ohio bar assns., Am. Judicature Soc., Chi Phi, Phi Delta Phi. Republican. Episcopalian. Clubs: Mason (33d degree) (Columbus), University (Columbus); Columbus Athletic (Columbus), Columbus (Columbus), Scioto Country (Columbus); Urbana (Ohio) Country; Burning Tree Country (Bethesda, Md.); Country of Fla. (Boynton Beach). Home: 1171 N Ocean Blvd Gulf Stream FL 33483-7273 Office: 4600 N Ocean Blvd Boynton Beach FL 33435-7312

SAXBERG, BORJE OSVALD, management educator; b. Helsinki, Finland, Jan. 25, 1928; came to U.S., 1950, naturalized, 1966; s. Oskar Valdemar and Martha (Granberg) S.; m. A. Margrete Haug; children: Bo Erland Haug, Bror Valdemar Haug. B.A., Swedish Sch. Bus. and Econs., 1950; B.S., Oreg. State U., 1952; M.S., U. Ill., 1953, Ph.D., 1958. Teaching asst., instr. U. Ill., 1953-57; prof. dept. mgmt. and orgn. U. Wash., 1957—; asso. dean U. Wash. (Bus. Sch.), Washington, 1980-81, chmn. dept. mgmt. and orgn., 1972-76, chmn. faculty senate, 1980-81, chmn. dept. mgmt. and orgn., 1989-93; dir. program in entrepreneurship and innovation, 1993—; cons. in field. Author: (with R. Joseph Monsen) The Business World, 1967, (with H.P. Knowles) Personality and Leadership Behavior, 1971, (with R.A. Johnson) Management, Systems and Society, 1976, (with B. Mar) Managing High Technology, 1985. Ford Found. fellow, 1960-61. Mem. Am. Sociol. Assn., Rainier Club, Swedish Club (Seattle). Home: 7336 58th Ave NE Seattle WA 98115-6257 Office: Univ of Wash Grad Sch of Bus Seattle WA 98195

SAXBY, LEWIS WEYBURN, JR., glass fiber manufacturing company executive; b. Oak Park, Ill., Dec. 17, 1924; s. Lewis Weyburn Saxby and Dorothy (Porter) Willey; m. Kathryn Hutchinson, Sept. 7, 1947; children: Steven Lewis, Ann, Jane Porter. BS, U. Calif., Berkeley, 1945; MBA, Stanford U., 1948. Prodn. trainee Owens-Corning Fiberglas Corp., Newark, Ohio, 1948-49; prodn. scheduler Santa Clara, Calif., 1949-51; estimator salesman San Francisco, 1951-52, dept. supr., 1952-56; br. mgr. Sacramento, Calif., 1956-58; br. mgr. Detroit, 1958-60, mgr. supply and contracting East, 1960-61; mgr. supply and contracting Toledo, 1961-66, v.p., mgr. supply and contracting, 1966-70, v.p. mech. products and constrn. services, 1971-74, v.p. mech. ops. div., 1974-78, sr. v.p., 1978—; bd. dirs. OC-Birdair, Inc., Buffalo. Nat. bd. dirs. Jr. Achievement, Inc., Colorado Springs, 1979—, chmn. com., 1980—; bd. dirs., chmn. com. Toledo Conv. and Visitors Bur., 1986-87. Served to ensign USNR, 1942-46, PTO. Recipient Gold Leadership award Jr. Achievemnt, Inc., 1981. Mem. Nat. Insulation Contractors (chmn. com. 1984—, Man of Yr. 1985). Republican. Presbyterian. Club: Inverness (Toledo) (bd. govs. 1976-80). Avocations: golf, tennis, travel, photography, snorkeling. Office: Owens-Corning Fiberglas Corp Fiberglas Towers Toledo OH 43614

SAXE, DEBORAH CRANDALL, lawyer; b. Lima, Ohio, July 23, 1949; d. Robert Gordon and Lois Barker (Taylor) Crandall; m. Robert Saxe, June 3, 1989; children: Elizabeth Sara, Emily Jane. BA, Pa. State U., 1971; MA, UCLA, 1973, JD, 1978. Bar: Calif. 1978, D.C. 1979, U.S. Dist. Ct. D.C 1979, U.S. Dist. Ct. (ea. dist.) Calif. 1981, , U.S. Dist. Ct. (ctrl. dist.) Calif. 1982, U.S. Dist. Ct. (no. and so. dists.) Calif. 1987, U.S. Ct. Appeals (4th and D.C. cirs.) 1979, U.S. Ct. Appeals (6th cir.) 1985, U.S. Ct. Appeals (8th and 9th cirs.) 1987, U.S. Ct. Appeals (2nd cir.) 1990, U.S. Supreme Ct. 1985. Assoc. Seyfarth, Shaw, Fairweather & Garaldson, Washington, 1978-83; assoc. Jones, Day, Reavis & Pogue, Washington, 1983-85; assoc. Jones, Day, Reavis & Pogue, L.A., 1985-87, ptnr., 1988—; judge pro tem, Small Claims Ct., L.A., 1985-88. Co-author: Advising California Employers, 1990; contbg. editor Employment Discrimination Law, 1989. Bd. dirs. Pediatric and Family Med. Ctr., L.A., 1990-91. Mem. ABA (labor law sect. 1978—), Calif. Bar Assn. (labor law sect. 1985—), L.A. County Bar Assn. (labor law sect. 1985—, mem. exec. com. 1988—), Pi Lambda Theta, Phi Beta Kappa. Office: Jones Day Reavis & Pogue 555 W 5th St Ste 4600 Los Angeles CA 90013-1025

SAXE, EDWARD A., lawyer; b. Cambridge, Mass., July 5, 1933; s. Harry and Mildred (Pord) S.; m. Claire Sue Rosenthal, Dec. 23, 1956; children: James, Judith. AB, cum laude, Harvard U., 1954, LLB cum laude, 1957. Bar: Mass. 1957, U.S. Dist Ct. Mass. 1957, U.S. Tax Ct. 1957. Assoc. Sheridan & Randall, Framingham, Mass., 1957-58; exec. v.p. Eli Sandman Co., Worcester, Mass., 1958-59; mng. ptnr., chmn. Peabody & Brown, Boston, 1959-85; pres. Related Cos. Northeast, Inc., Boston, 1985-89; ptnr. Fine & Ambrogne, Boston, 1989-90, Bingham, Dana & Gould, Boston, 1990—. Trustee Beth Israel Hosp., Boston, 1980—, Combined Jewish Philathropies, Boston, 1970—; chmn. Town of Framingham (Mass.) Personnel Bd., 1963-66; adv. mem. Mayor's Office Cultural Affairs, Boston, 1975-78. With USAR, 1956-62. Mem. ABA, Mass. Bar Found. (life), Boston Bar Assn, Wightman Tennis Club (pres. 1975-76). Avocations: tennis, skiing, bicycling. Office: Bingham Dana & Gould 150 Federal St Boston MA 02110-1726

SAXE, LEONARD, social psychologist, educator; b. N.Y.C., June 12, 1947; s. Theodore and Marjorie (Mayers) S.; m. Marion Gardner, Aug. 9, 1970; 1 child, Daniel. BS in Psychology, U. Pitts., 1969, MS in Psychology, 1972, PhD in Social Psychology, 1976. Asst. instr. U. Pitts., 1973-75; asst. then assoc. prof. psychology Boston U., 1976-88, assoc. dir. Ctr. Applied Social Sci., 1982-84, dir., 1984-87; rsch. prof. Heller Sch. Social Welfare Brandeis U., Waltham, Mass., 1988-90, adj. prof. psychology, adj. rsch. prof., 1990—; prof. psychology Grad. Ctr. CUNY, 1991—; head social-personality psychology, 1991—; Fulbright sr. lectr. U. Haifa, Israel, 1981-82; mem. task force Children's Mental Health Rsch. Inst. Medicine-NAS, 1988-89; rev. coms. HHS-Healthcare Fin. Administr. NIMH, Nat. Inst. Drug Abuse, Dept. Edn.; cons., contractor Office Tech. Assessment, U.S. Congress, 1980-88. Author: (with others) Children's Mental Health: Problems and Treatment, 1987, (with M. Fine) Social Experiments: Methods for Design and Evaluation, 1981; editor: (with M.J. Saks) Advances in Applied Social Psychology, Vol. 3, 1986, (with D. Koretz) New Directions for Program Evaluation, 1982, (with D. Bar-Tal) The Social Psychology of Education: Theory and Research, 1978; contbr. chpts. to books, articles to profl. jours.; assoc. and mng. editor Personality and Social Psychology Bull., 1978-81; ad hoc reviewer various jours., book reviewer various pubs. Congl. fellow Office Tech. Assessment, 1979. Fellow APA (bd. dirs. sect. social and clinical responsibility 1985-88, Disting. Contbn. award 1989), AAAS, Soc. Psychol. Study Social Issues (coun. 1982-84, 87-89). Office: CUNY Grad Ctr 33 W 42nd St New York NY 10036-8003

SAXE, THELMA RICHARDS, secondary education educator, consultant; b. Ogdensburg, N.J., Apr. 21, 1941; d. George Francis and Evelyn May (Howell) Richards; m. Kenneth Elwood Meeker, Jr., June 22, 1957 (div 1965); children: Sylvia Lorraine Meeker Hill, Michelle Louise Meeker Aromando, David Sean (dec.); m. Frederick Ely Saxe, Feb. 18, 1983; stepchildren: Jonathan Kent, Holly Harding Schenker. BA, William Paterson Coll., Wayne, N.J., 1972, MEd, 1975, postgrad., 1983-84; Dyslexia cert., Fairleigh Dickinson U., 1994. Cert. paralegal, dyslexia specialist Fairleigh Dickonson U. Tchr. handicapped Sussex (N.J.)-Wantage Regional Sch. Dist., 1972-75; resource rm. tchr. Sussex County Vo-Tech Sch., Sparta, N.J., 1975-77; learning cons. Sussex County Vo-Tech Sch., 1977-83; learning specialist Bennington-Rutland Supervisory Union, Manchester, Vt., 1986-87; learning cons. Stillwater (N.J.) Twp. Sch., 1987-88, Independence Twp. Cen. Sch. Great Meadows, N.J., 1989; learning cons., tutor in pvt. practice specializing dyslexia Sparta, 1986—; asst. prin. Harmony Twp. Sch., Harmony, N.J., 1989-92; coordinator gifted/talented Sussex Vo-Tech, 1980-83; coordinator child study team Stillwater Twp. Sch., 1987-88. Mem. Coun. Exceptional Children, Learning Disabilities Assn., Orton Dyslexia Soc., N.J. Assn. Learning Cos., Kappa Delta Pi. Republican. Presbyterian. Avocations: music, singing, piano, autoharp, skiing, hiking, travel. Home and Office: 17 Park Rd Sparta NJ 07871-2002

SAXENA, ARJUN NATH, physicist; b. Lucknow, India, Apr. 1, 1932; s. Sheo and Mohan (Piyari) Shanker; came to U.S., 1956, naturalized, 1969; BSc, Lucknow U., 1950, MSc, 1952, profl. cert. in German, 1954; Post MS diploma, Inst. Nuclear Physics, Calcutta, India, 1955; PhD, Stanford U., 1963; m. Veera Saxena, Feb. 9, 1956; children: Rashmi, Amol, Varsha, Ashvin. Rsch. asst. Stanford U., 1956-60; mem. tech. staff Fairchild

Semicondr. Co., Palo Alto, Calif., 1960-65; dept. head Sprague Electric Co., North Adams, Mass., 1965-69; mem. tech. staff RCA Labs., Princeton, N.J., 1969-71; pres., chmn. bd. Astro-Optics, Phila., 1972; pres. Internat. Sci. Co., Princeton Junction, N.J., 1973—; disting. vis. scientist Centre de Récherches Nucléaires, Strasbourg, France, 1973, 77; sr. staff scientist, mgr. engring. Data Gen. Corp., Sunnyvale, Calif., 1975-80; mgr. process tech. Signetics Corp., Sunnyvale, 1980-81; Gould AMI Semicond., dir. advanced process devel. Gould AMI Semicondrs., Santa Clara, Calif., 1981-87; dir. Ctr. for Integrated Electronics, prof. dept. elec. and computer system engring. Rensselaer Poly. Inst., Troy, N.Y., 1987—; disting. vis. scientist Inst. Microelectronics, Stuttgart, Germany, 1993-94. Treas. Pack 66, Boy Scouts Am., W. Windsor, N.J., 1970-74. Recipient Disting. vis. scientist award State of N.J., 1975. Mem. Am. Phys. Soc., IEEE, Electrochem. Soc., Stanford Alumni Assn. (life). Contbr. articles on semicondr. tech., optics, nuclear and high-energy physics to sci. jours., 1953—; patentee in field. Home: 2 Birch Hill Rd Ballston Lake NY 12019-9370 Office: Rensselaer Poly Inst Ctr Integrated Electronics Dept Elec/Computer Sci Engring Troy NY 12180-3590

SAXENA, ASHOK, materials engineering educator, consultant; b. Jhansi, India, Aug. 28, 1948; came to U.S., 1970; s. Ram K. and Shanti (Verma) S.; m. Madhu Chhanda Narain; children: Rahul, Anjali. B in Tech., Indian Inst. Tech., 1970; MS, U. Cin., 1972, PhD, 1974. Rsch. metallurgist Nat. Steel Co., Weirton, W.Va., 1974-76; sr. engr. Westinghouse R & D Ctr., Pitts., 1976-80, fellow scientist, 1981-85; sr. devel. mgr. H.A.L., Bangalore, India, 1980; reader, assoc. prof. Banaras (India) Hindu U., 1980-81; prof. Ga. Inst. Tech., Atlanta, 1985—, also dir. Composites Edn. and Rsch. Ctr., 1991-94, dir. Sch. of Materials Scis. and Engring., 1993—; cons. Westinghouse Electric Co., Pitts., 1985—, Babcock & Wilcox, Barberton, Ohio, 1985-88, Detroit Edison Co., 1986-88, Structural Integrity Assocs., San Jose, Calif., 1987—, S.W. Rsch. Inst., San Antonio, 1991—. Developer software package; contbr. articles to profl. jours. Fellow ASTM (officer 1989—, George Irwin medal 1992); mem. metallurgical Soc., Sigma Xi. Avocations: bridge, reading, traveling. Home: 3539 Princeton Corners Ln Marietta GA 30062-5596 Office: Ga Inst Tech Sch Materials Engrin Atlanta GA 30332-0245

SAXENA, BRIJ B., biochemist, endocrinologist, educator. PhD, India; DSc, U. Muenster, W.Ger.; PhD, U. Wis., 1961. Asst. prof. biochemistry and endocrinology N.J. Coll. Medicine., 1966-74; assoc. prof. biochemistry Cornell U. Med. Coll., N.Y.C., 1974—; prof. biochemistry Cornell U. Med. Coll., 1974—, prof. endocrinology, 1981—, dir. div. reproductive endocrinology. Contbr. 200 articles to profl. jours. Recipient Career Scientist award N.Y.C. Health Research Council; Upjohn research award; Campoz da Paz award. Fellow Royal Soc. Medicine (London); mem. Am. Soc. Biol. Chemists, AAAS, Endocrine Soc., Harvey Soc., Am. Physiol. Soc., Am. Chem. Soc. Office: Cornell Univ Med Coll 1300 York Ave New York NY 10021-4896

SAXER, RICHARD KARL, metallurgical engineer, retired air force officer; b. Toledo, Aug. 31, 1928; s. Amand Bernard and Gertrude Minnie (Kuebeler) S.; m. Marilyn Doris Mersereau, July 19, 1952; children—Jane Lynette, Robert Karl, Kris Renee, Ann Luette. Student, Bowling Green State U., 1946-48; BS, U.S. Naval Acad., 1952; MS in Aero. Mechanics Engring., Air Force Inst. Tech., 1957; PhD in Metall. Engring., Ohio State U., 1962; grad. Armed Forces Staff Coll., 1966, Indsl. Coll. Armed Forces, 1971. Commd. 2d lt. U.S. Air Force, 1952, advanced through grades to lt. gen., 1976; electronics officer, mech. officer (4th Tactical Support Sqadron, Tactical Air Command), Sandia Base, N.Mex., 1953-54; electronics and mech. officer, spl. weapons assembly sect. supr. (SAC 6th Aviation Depot Squadron), French Morocco, 1954-55; project engr. mech. equipment br. Air Force Spl. Weapon's Center, Kirtland AFB, N.Mex., 1957-59; project officer Nuclear Safety div., 1959-60; assoc. prof. dept. engring. mechanics Air Force Inst. Tech., 1962-66; asso. prof., dep. dept. head USAF Acad., 1966-70; comdr., dir. Air Force Materials Lab., Wright-Patterson AFB, Ohio, 1971-74; dep. for Reentry System Space and Missile Systems Orgn., 1974-77; dep. for aero equipment Aero. Systems Div., 1977-80, dep. for tactical systems, 1980, vice comdr., 1981-83; aero. systems div. dir. Def. Nuclear Agy., 1983-85, ret., 1985; pres. R.K. Saxer & Assocs., 1985-91; CEO Universal Tech. Corp., Dayton, Ohio, 1991—; research and tech. com. materials and structures NASA, 1973-74; chmn. planning group aerospace materials Interagy. Council Materials, 1973-74; mem. Nat. Mil. Adv. Bd., 1971-74, NATO adv. group for research and devel., 1973-74. Contbr. articles to profl. jours. Decorated Def. Disting. Svc. medal, Legion of Merit, Meritorious Service medal USAF, D.S.M., Joint Svc. Commendation medal, Air Force Commendation medal with 3 oak leaf clusters, Army Commendation medal U.S., Def. Superior Service medal, Cross of Gallantry with palm Vietnam, Def. Meritorious Service medal; recipient Disting. award for systems mgmt. Air Force Assn., 1979; Disting. Alumnus award Ohio State U., 1986. Mem. Air Force Assn.. Am. Def. Preparedness Assn. (pres. Dayton 1977-78), Sigma Xi, Phi Lambda Epsilon, Alpha Sigma Mu, Masons, Shriners. Home: 215 Dalfaber Ln Springboro OH 45066

SAXL, JANE WILHELM, state legislator; b. N.Y.C., Aug. 26, 1939; d. Seymour F. and Doris (Fuld) Wilhelm; m. Joseph Saxl, Nov. 17, 1957; children: Susan S., Ruth L., Mary-Anne, Michael V. BA, Sangamon State U., 1973, MA, 1974. City councilor City of Bangor, Maine, 1987-93; mem. Maine Ho. Reps., Augusta, 1992—. sec./treas. Penobscot Valley Coun. Govts., 1988-91. Active Bangor Sch. Bd., 1984-87, Family Planning Maine, Natural Resources Coun., Penobscot Dem. Com.; bd. dirs. Bangor Beautiful, Bangor Conv. and Visitors Bur.; past chmn. Bangor Recycling. Mem. LWV (pres. Maine chpt. 1987-93), Nat. League State Legislators, Nat. Women's Polit. Caucus, Maine Women's Lobby, Friends of Bangor Pub. Libr., Spruce Run Assocs.. Maine Audubon Soc.. Tuesday Forum, Women's Legis. Lobby, N.Y. Pub. Libr. Democrat. Jewish. Avocations: bird watching, fly fishing. Home: 37 Pond St Bangor ME 04401 Office: Maine Legislature State House Sta # 3 Augusta ME 04330

SAXON, DAVID STEPHEN, physics educator, university official; b. St. Paul, Feb. 8, 1920; s. Ivan and Rebecca (Moss) S.; m. Shirley Goodman, Jan. 6, 1940; children: Margaret Elizabeth, Barbara Susan, Linda Caroline, Catherine Louise, Victoria Jean, Charlotte Mala. BS, MIT, 1941, PhD, 1944; various hon. degrees. Research physicist Radiation Lab., Mass. Inst. Tech., 1943-46, Philips Labs., 1946-47; mem. faculty U. Calif., Los Angeles, 1947-75; prof. physics U. Calif., 1958-75, chmn. dept., 1963-66, dean phys. scis., 1966-68, vice chancellor, 1968-75, provost, 1974-75, pres., 1975-83, pres. emeritus, 1983—; mem. corp. MIT, 1977-90, life mem., 1990—, chmn. corp., 1983-90, hon. chmn., 1990-95; vis. scientist Centre d'Etudes Nucléaires, Saclay, France, 1968-69; vis. prof. faculty scis. U. Paris, Orsay, France, 1961-62; cons. to rsch. orgns., 1948—; mem. tech. adv. coun. Ford Motor Co., 1979-94. Author: Elementary Quantum Mechanics, 1968, (with A.E.S. Green and T. Sawada) The Nuclear Independent Particle Model, 1968, (with Julian Schwinger) Discontinuities in Wave Guides, 1968, (with William B. Fretter) Physics for the Liberal Arts Student, 1971. Mem. Mass. Ctr. Excellence, 1985-91; mem. com. to visit Med. Sch., Sch. Dental Medicine, Harvard U., 1985-90. Decorated Royal Order of No. Star; Guggenheim fellow Niels Bohr Inst. Theoretical Physics, Copenhagen, 1956-57, 61-62; Fulbright grantee, 1961-62. Fellow Am. Phys. Soc., Am. Acad. Arts and Scis., AAAS; mem. Am. Assn. Physics Tchrs., Am. Inst. Physics, Am. Philosophy Soc., Phi Beta Kappa, Sigma Xi, Sigma Pi Sigma. Spl. research theoretical physics, nuclear physics, quantum mechanics, electromagnetic theory, scattering theory. Home: 1008 Hilts Ave Los Angeles CA 90024-3215

SAXON, FRANKLIN N., finance executive; b. Charlotte, N.C., July 26, 1952; s. James H. and Frances (Shiver) S.; m. Abigail F. Stuckey, June 2, 1979 (div. Feb. 1982). BS in Acctg. with honors, U. N.C., Charlotte, 1977. CPA, N.C. Sr. auditor Coopers and Lybrand, Charlotte, 1979-81, audit supr., 1981-82, audit mgr., 1982-83; v.p., corp. controller Culp, Inc., High Point, N.C., 1983-85, v.p., chief fin. officer, 1985—. Treas., bd. dirs. Community Health Assn., Charlotte, 1979-81; loaned exec. United Way, High Point, 1985. Scholarship grantee, U. N.C., 1967-77. Mem. Am. Inst. CPA's, N.C. Soc. CPA's, Fin. Execs. Inst. Republican. Presbyterian. Avocations: running, scuba diving, piano. Home: 3730 Briarwood Ave High Point NC 27265-1256 Office: Culp Inc 101 S Main St High Point NC 27261-2686

SAXON, JANET D., federal government official. Chief adminstrv. law judge U.S. Internat. Trade Commn., Washington. Office: US Internat Trade Commn Chief Adminstrv Law Judge 500 E St NW Washington DC 20436-0003

SAXON, JOHN DAVID, lawyer, policy analyst, educator; b. Anniston, Ala., July 21, 1950; s. J.Z. and Sarah Elizabeth (Steadham) S.; m. Elizabeth Lord, Mar. 10, 1973. BA with honors, U. Ala., 1972, JD, 1977; grad. Exec. Program Stanford U., 1986; MA, U. N.C., 1973. Bar: Ala. 1977, U.S. Dist. Ct. (no. dist.) Ala. 1977, U.S. Supreme Ct. 1983, U.S. Dist. Ct. (mid. dist.) Ala. 1989, U.S. Dist. Ct. (so. dist.) Ala. 1990, U.S.C. Ct. Appeals (11th cir.) 1990, U.S. Ct. Appeals (5th cir.) 1992. Adminstrv. asst. to acting chief exec. officer U. Ala.-University, 1976-77; assoc. Sirote, Permutt, Friend, Friedman, Held & Apolinsky, P.A., Birmingham, Ala., 1977-78; spl. asst. to Vice Pres. U.S., Washington, 1978-79; counsel subcom. on jurisprudence and govt. rels. Com. on Judiciary, U.S. Senate, Washington, 1979-80, counsel Select Com. on Ethics, 1980-83; dir. corp. issues RCA, Washington, 1983-86; Washington rep., Gen. Electric Co., 1986-87; assoc. counsel U.S. Senate Select com. on secret mil. assistance to Iran and the Nicaraguan Opposition, 1987-88; spl. counsel U.S. Senate Armed Svcs. com., 1988; counsel, Johnston, Barton, Proctor, Swedlaw & Naff, Birmingham, 1988-90; atty. Gathings & Davis, Birmingham, 1990-92; ptnr. Cooper, Mitch, Crawford, Kuykendall & Whatley, 1992—; adj. instr. polit. communication U. Md., 1982-83; instr. speech communication U. Ala.-University, 1973; instr. speech communication and mgmt. Brewer Jr. Coll., Tuscaloosa, 1975-77; adj. instr. civil litigation Samford U., Birmingham, 1977-78; adj. prof. Washington Coll. Law The Am. U., 1988; vis. scholar The Hastings Ctr., 1983; mem. Am. Observer Delegation, Kettering Found., U.S.-China Task Force, 1986; bd. dirs. White House Fellows Found., 1981-84 , pres., 1983-84; mem. bd. advisers Center for Publ. Law and Service, U. Ala. Sch. Law, 1976-83; bd. trustees Farrah Law Soc., 1988-94, vice-chmn., 1990-92, chmn., 1992-94; bd. dirs. exec. com. mem. U. Ala. Law Found.; mem. Pres.'s Commn. White House Fellowships, 1983-84, 93—; mem. Washington Local Devel. Corp, 1986-88; chmn. Ala. Clinton for Pres. Campaign, 1992; mem. platform com. Dem. Nat. Conv., 1992; mem. policy adv. com. The Coalition for Excellence in Edn., chmn., 1991-92; The A+ Rsch. Found.; mem. bd. advisors N.E. Ala. Devel. Forum, 1992—, Nat. Governing Bd. Common Cause, 1992—, Leadership Birmingham Class of 1993-94; mem. pres. adv. coun. Birmingham So. Coll., 1993—; mem. adminstrv. bd. First United Meth. Ch., 1994—; co-chmn. Birmingham Boys Choir Found., 1994—; asst. scoutmaster Troop 57 Boy Scouts of Am.; pres. Southside Baseball, 1995—; adv. com. The Blackburn Inst., U. Ala.; bd. dirs. Miles Coll. Ctr. for Cmty. Econ. Devel., 1995—. Served to 2d lt. U.S. Army, 1974, capt. Res. White House Fellow, 1978-79; named Disting. Mil. Grad., U. Ala., 1972. Mem. ABA (spl. com. litigation sect.), Ala. Bar Assn., Birmingham Bar Assn. (chmn. profl. ethics com. 1991-92, mem. grievance com. 1992—), Ala. Trial Lawyers Assn. (bd. govs. 1990—), White House Fellows Assn. (pres. 1983-84), Kiwanis Club (Birmingham), Scabbard and Blade, The Order of Barristers, Bench and Bar (Outstanding Sr. award 1977), Downtown Dem. Club (pres. 1992-93), Omicron Delta Kappa, Omicron Delta Epsilon, Phi Alpha Theta, Pi Sigma Alpha. Methodist. Contbr. articles to newspapers and legal publs., chpts. to books.

SAXON, VIRGINIA M., nursing administrator; b. Etowah County, Ala., Mar. 3, 1939; d. Grey Allen and Dorothy Idalene (Sheffield) Miller; m. Richard Earl Saxon, Jr., June 8, 1957; children: Richard Earl III, Clifford Allen. ADN magna cum laude, Gadsden (Ala.) State Jr. Coll., 1978; BSN with honors and distinction, Jacksonville (Ala.) State U., 1980, MBA, 1985. RN, Ala. Sec.-treas. Clark Memls., Gadsden; clin. supr. Bapt. Meml. Hosp., Gadsden, asst. dir. nursing, v.p. nursing svcs. Mem. ANA, Am. Orgn. Nurse Execs., Am. Coll. Health Care Execs., Am. Heart Assn. (bd. dirs.).

SAXTON, H. JAMES, congressman; b. Scranton, Pa., Jan. 22, 1943; s. Hugh R. and Helen M. (Billings) S.; m. Helen Jean Gadomski, June 9, 1965; children—Jennifer, James Martin. B.A., East Stroudsburg State Coll., 1965; postgrad. in elem. edn., Temple U., 1967-68. Tchr. Bordentown Pub. Schs., Bordentown, N.J., 1965-68; realtor Jim Saxton Realty Co., Bordentown, N.J., 1968-85; assemblyman N.J. State Assembly, Trenton, 1975-81; state senator N.J. State Senate, Trenton, 1981-84; mem. 99th-104th Congresses from 13th (now 3rd) N.J. dist., Washington, D.C., 1984—; mem. nat. security com., resources subcom. on fisheries, wildlife & oceans, mem. joint econ. com.; mem. travel and tourism caucus, maritime caucus, mem. port caucus environ. and energy study conf., Rep. study com., Stripers Ltd. (99th Congress); sec. N.J. Congl. Del., Washington, 1985-89. Active Boy Scouts Am., Burlington Council. Bordentown C. of C. Club: Leadership Found. N.J. Lodge: Elks. Office: US Ho of Reps 339 Cannon House Office Bldg Washington DC 20515-3003*

SAXTON, JAMES, congressman; children: Martin, Jennifer. Tchr., small businessman; mem. U.S. Ho. of Reps., Washington, 1984—; vice-chmn. joint econ. com. U.S. Ho. of Reps., 104th Congress, Washington, chmn. Ho. subcom. Fisheries, Wildlife and Oceans; mem. Ho. Nat. Security Com. U.S. Ho. of Reps., Washington. Republican. Office: House Reps 339 Cannon House Office Bldg Washington DC 20515-3003 also: 7 Hadley Ave Toms River NJ 08753 also: 1 Maine Ave Cherry Hill NJ 08034*

SAXTON, WILLIAM MARVIN, lawyer; b. Joplin, Mo., Feb. 14, 1927; s. Clyde Marvin and Lea Ann (Farnan) S.; m. Helen Grace Klinefelter, June 1, 1974; children: Sherry Lynn, Patricia Ann Painter, William Daniel, Michael Lawrence. A.B., U. Mich., 1949, J.D., 1952. Bar: Mich. Mem. firm Love, Snyder & Lewis, Detroit, 1952-53; mem. firm Butzel, Long, Detroit, 1953—, now dir., chmn., chief exec. officer; lectr. Inst. Continuing Legal Edn.; sec., bd. dirs. Fritz Broadcasting, Inc., 1983—; mem. mediation tribunal hearing panel for 3d Jud. Dist. Mich., 1989—. Trustee Detroit Music Hall Ctr. Soc. for the Performing Arts, 1984—; trustee Hist. Soc. U.S. Dist. Ct. (ea. dist.) Mich., 1992—, pres., 1993-94. Recipient Distinguished award Mich. Road Builders Assn., 1987. Master of Bench Emeritus Am. Inn of Court; fellow Am. Coll. Trial Lawyers, Am. Bar Found., Mich. Bar Found.; mem. ABA, Detroit Bar Assn. (dir. 1974-79), Mich. Bar (mem. atty. discipline panel), Detroit Indsl. Rels. Rsch. Assn. (treas. 1980—, v.p. 1982, pres. 1984-85), Mich. Young Lawyers (pres. 1954-55), Am. Law Inst., Fed. Bar Assn., Indsl. Rels. Rsch. Assn. Am. Arbitration Assn., U.S. 6th Cir. Ct. Appeals (life, mem. jud. conf., mem. bicentennial com.), Detroit Golf Club (dir. 1983-89), Detroit Athletic Club. Office: Butzel Long 150 W Jefferson Ave Ste 900 Detroit MI 48226-4430

SAY, ALLEN, children's writer, illustrator; b. Aug. 28, 1937; s. Masako Moriwaki; m. Deirdre Myles, Apr. 18, 1974; 1 child, Yuriko. Pub. EIZO Pr., Berkeley, 1968. Author, illustrator: Dr. Smith's Safari, 1972, Once Under the Cherry Blossom Tree: An Old Japanese Tale, 1974, The Feast of Lanterns, 1976, The Bicycle Man, 1982, A River Dream, 1988, The Lost Lake, 1989, Tree of Cranes, 1991, Grandfather's Journey, 1993 (Caldecott medal 1994, Boston Globe/Horn Book award 1994), The Stranger in the Mirror, 1995; author: The Innkeeper's Apprentice, 1989, El Chino, 1990; illustrator: A Canticle to the Waterbirds, 1968, Two Ways of Seeing, 1971, Magic and Night River, 1978, The Lucky Yak, 1980, The Secret Cross of Lorraine, 1981, How My Parents Learned to Eat, 1984 (Horn Book honor list 1984, Christopher award 1985), The Boy of the Three Year Nap, 1988 (Boston Globe/Horn Book award 1988, Caldecott honor book 1989). Office: care Houghton Mifflin 222 Berkeley St Boston MA 02116-3748*

SAYATOVIC, WAYNE PETER, manufacturing company executive; b. Cleve., Feb. 8, 1946; s. Peter and Margaret Ann (Nestor) S.; m. Janice Elaine Zajac, July 27, 1968; children: Jason Scott, Jamie Elizabeth. BA in Econs., Syracuse U., 1967, MBA in Fin., 1969. Fin. mgmt. program Gen. Electric Co., Syracuse, N.Y., 1969-72; fin. and cost acctg. mgr. Lubriquip div. Houdaille Industries Inc., Solon, Ohio, 1972-75; contr. Hydraulics div. Houdaille Industries Inc., Buffalo, 1975-77, Strippit div Houdaille Industries Inc., Akron, N.Y., 1977-79; treas. Houdaille Industries Inc., Ft. Lauderdale, Fla., 1979-86; v.p., treas., sec. Houdaille Industries Inc., Northbrook, Ill., 1986-88; v.p., treas., sec. IDEX Corp., Northbrook, 1988-91, v.p. fin., CFO, sec., 1992-94; sr. v.p. fin., CFO, sec., 1994—. Mem. Mfrs.' Alliance for Productivity & Innovation (fin. coun.). Office: IDEX Corp 630 Dundee Rd Northbrook IL 60062-2762

SAYER, JOHN SAMUEL, retired information systems consultant; b. St. Paul, July 27, 1917; s. Arthur Samuel and Genevieve (Ollis) S.; m. Elizabeth Hughes, June 9, 1940; children: Stephen, Susan, Kathryn, Nancy. BSME, U. Minn., 1940. Registered profl. engr., Del.; lic. profl. engr. Info. Industries Assn. Sect. mgr. E.I. Du Pont de Nemours & Co, Wilmington, Del., 1940-60; exec. v.p. Documentation Inc., Washington, 1960-63; v.p. corp. devel. Aurbach Corp., Phila., 1963-65; exec. v.p. Leasco Systems & Rsch., Bethesda, Md., 1966-70, Leasco Info. Products, Silver Spring, Md., 1971-74; pres. Remac Info. Corp., Gaithersburg, Md., 1975-82; cons. John Sayer Assocs., Gaithersburg, 1983-94; numerous presentations in field. Contbr. numerous articles to profl. jours. Recipient Info. Product of Yr. award Info. Industries Assn., 1973. Mem. ASME, Assn. Info. and Image Mgmt., Am. Inst. Info. Sci. Achievements include direction of work leading to critical path method of planning and scheduling, technical word thesarus, microfiche, data base publishing.

SAYER, MICHAEL, physics educator; b. Newport, Gwent, Wales, Nov. 6, 1935; emigrated to Can., 1960, naturalized, 1965; s. Charles Claude and Elizabeth Mary (Southcott) S.; m. Anne Moira Rogers, Aug. 27, 1960; children: Jane, Suzanne, Andrew, Christopher. BSc, U. Birmingham, Eng., 1957; PhD, U. Hull, Eng., 1961. Registered profl. engr. Postdoctoral fellow U. B.C., Vancouver, 1960-62; asst. prof. physics Queen's U., Kingston, Ont., 1962-67, assoc. prof., 1967-73, prof., 1973—, head dept. physics 1977-82; assoc. dean for research Faculty Applied Sci. Queen's U., 1984-87; prof. materials and metallurgical engring. Queens U., Kingston, 1990—; sr. indsl. fellow, dir. research Almax Industries Ltd., 1987-88; vis. fellow Sheffield U., Eng., 1972-73; dir. Cansort Devices Ltd., Kingston, 1977—; vis. asst. prof. Trent U., Peterborough, Ont., 1965-66; mem. Can. Engring. Accreditation Bd., 1987-94. Contbr. articles to profl. jours.; patentee in field. Grantee Natural Sci. and Engring. Research Council Can., 1962—; recipient Silver Medal for Tech. Transfer Can. Award for Excellence, 1986. Fellow Royal Soc. Can., Can. Ceramic Soc. (pres. 1987-88, editor Can. Ceramic Quar. 1986—); mem. Am. Ceramic Soc., Materials Rsch. Soc., Assn. Profl. Engrs. Ont. Roman Catholic. Home: 97 Yonge St, Kingston, ON Canada K7M 1E4 Office: Queen's Univ, Dept Physics, Kingston, ON Canada K7L 3N6

SAYERS, GALE, computer company executive, retired professional football player; b. Wichita, Kans., May 30, 1943; s. Roger Earl and Bernice (Ross) S.; m. Ardythe Elaine Bullard, Dec. 1, 1973; children: Gale Lynne, Scott Aaron, Timothy Gale, Gaylon, Guy, Gary. Student phys. edn., Kans. U., N.Y. Inst. Finance. Running back Chgo. Bears Profl. Football Team, 1965-72; then asst. to athletic dir. Kans. U.; athletic dir. So. Ill. U., to 1981; v.p. mktg. Computer Suppy by Sayers, Northfield, Ill., 1984-86; pres. Crest Computer Supply Co., Skokie, Ill., 1986—; columnist Chgo. Daily News. Author: (with Al Silverman) I Am Third, 1970. Co-chmn. legal def. fund sports com. NAACP; co-ordinator Reach-Out program, Chgo.; hon. chmn. Am. Cancer Soc.; commr. Chgo. Park Dist. Recipient numerous awards for playing, also holder numerous Nat. Football League records; named to Pro Football Hall of Fame, 1977. Mem. Kappa Alpha Psi. Office: Crest Computer Supply Co 7855 Gross Point Rd Ste 1H Skokie IL 60077-2646

SAYERS, KEN W(ILLIAM), writer and public relations executive; b. N.Y.C., July 31, 1942; s. William Verey and Doris Edith (Weale) S.; m. Rose Mary Beirao, Aug. 20, 1965; children: Wendy Elizabeth Sayers Rehnberg, Matthew Verey. BA in Journalism, CCNY, 1965; postgrad., Columbia U., 1970. Dep. chief book br. Office Asst. Sec. of Def. for Pub. Affairs, Washington, 1967-69; mgr. rsch. and analysis DMS, Inc., Greenwich, Conn., 1969-72; mgr. rsch. and publs. Lulejian & Assocs., Inc., Falls Church, Va., 1972-74; mgr. internat. pub. affairs Am. Cyanamid Co., Wayne, N.J., 1974-77; various positions IBM Corp., 1977—; pres. Halyard Ptnrs., Ridgefield, Conn., 1994—. Co-author: Anchors and Atoms, It Was a Very Good Year; author: Industrial Lasers; editor: Missiles and Spacecraft, World Aircraft Forecast; contbr. articles to profl. jours. Exec. officer Queens Nautical Cadets, Astoria, N.Y., 1963-65. Lt. USN, 1965-69. Decorated Joint Svc. Commendation medal. Home: 342 Limestone Rd Ridgefield CT 06877-2635 Office: IBM Corp 20 Old Post Rd Armonk NY 10504-1343

SAYERS, MARTIN PETER, pediatric neurosurgeon; b. Big Stone Gap, Va., Jan. 2, 1922; s. Delbert Bancroft and Loula (Thompson) S.; m. Marjorie W. Garvin, May 8, 1943; children: Daniel Garvin, Stephen Putnam, Julia Hathaway Bolton, Elaine King Buck. B.A., Ohio State U., 1943, M.D. 1945; postgrad., U. Pa., 1948-51. Intern Phila. Gen. Hosp., 1945-46; resident in neurosurgery U. Pa. Hosps., Phila., 1948-51; practice medicine specializing in neurosurgery Columbus, Ohio, 1951—; mem. faculty Ohio State U., Columbus, 1951-87, clin. prof. neurosurgery, 1968-87, emeritus; chief dept. pediatric neurosurgery Ohio State U., 1960-87; cons. Bur. Crippled Children Services Ohio.; Neurosurgeon Project Hope, Ecuador, 1964, Ceylon, 1968, Cracow, Poland, 1979. Served as lt. M.C., USN, 1946-48. Mem. Am. Assn. Neurol. Surgeons (chmn. pediatric sect.), Congress Neurol. Surgeons (pres.), Neurosug. Soc. Am. (pres.), Am. Soc. Pediatric Neurosurgery, Soc. Neurol. Surgeons. Office: 931 Chatham Ln Columbus OH 43221-2417

SAYERS, RICHARD JAMES, newspaper editor; b. Oil City, Pa., Mar. 16, 1947; s. Theodore Roosevelt and Ardella (Hanna) D.; m. Mary Catherine Smith, Nov. 22, 1974; children—Kelly Lyn, Rachel Richelle, Christopher Alan, Shannon Marie. Student, Albany Bus. Coll., Rochester Ins. Tech. Sports writer Rochester Times-Union, N.Y., 1969-74; sports editor Port Huron Times Herald, Mich., 1974-76; exec. sports editor Boston Herald Am., 1976-79; asst. mng. editor Detroit News, 1979-89; sr. editor THE NATIONAL Sports Daily, N.Y.C., 1989-91; editor Conn. Post, Bridgeport, 1991—. Grad. Multicultural Mgmt. Program fellow U. Mo., 1988. Presbyterian. Home: 98 Neponsit St Stamford CT 06902

SAYERS, ROGER, academic administrator. Pres U. Ala., Tuscaloosa. Office: The U Ala Office of the Pres Tuscaloosa AL 35487

SAYES, JAMES OTTIS, religion educator, minister; b. Hudson, La., Nov. 16, 1922; s. Archie Lee and Alma Urania (Reid) S.; m. Delia Nell Melton, Oct. 29, 1944; children: James Melton, Deena Jan Sayes Thomas. BTh, So. Nazarene U., Bethany, Okla., 1944; postgrad., Cen. Bapt. Theol. Sem., Kansas City, Kans., 1944-45; BD, Nazarene Theol. Sem., Kansas City, Mo., 1947; MRE, DRE, So. Bapt. Theol. Sem., Ft. Worth, 1951, 55. Pastor Ch. of the Nazarene, Neosho, Mo., 1947-48, Maryville, Mo., 1948-50; pastor Arlington Heights Ch. of the Nazarene, Ft. Worth, 1951-54; assoc. pastor First Ch. Nazarene, Little Rock, 1954-56; prof. Olivet Nazarene U., Kankakee, Ill., 1956-94, prof. emeritus, 1994—; pastor Ch. of the Nazarene, Orland Park, Ill., 1985-88; pres. Ministerial Assn., Maryville, 1950. Mem. Am. Theol. Soc., Wesleyan Theol. Soc., Religious Educators Assn. Avocations: collecting dated R.R. nails, golf, horseback riding. Home: 480 S Bresee Ave Bourbonnais IL 60914-2265 Office: Olivet Nazarene U Kankakee IL 60901

SAYETTA, THOMAS CHARLES, physics educator; b. Williamsport, Pa., Apr. 12, 1937; s. Morris and Gladys Pauline (Sunderland) S.; m. Patsy Anne Sherrill; 1 child, Susan Leigh. BS in Physics, U. S.C., 1959, PhD in Physics, 1964. Teaching asst. physics dept. U. S.C., Columbia, 1956-59; engr. RCA, Camden, N.J., 1959-60; teaching asst. physics dept. U. S.C., Columbia, 1960-63, rsch. asst. physics dept., 1963-64; prof. physics East Carolina U., Greenville, N.C., 1964—. Asst. editor Internat. Jour.. Math. and Math. Sci., 1979-83. Nat. treas. Chi Beta Phi, 1974-82. With USNR, 1954-62. Mem. Am. Assn. Physics Tchrs., Sigma Xi (pres. East Carolina U. chpt. 1970-71). Avocations: tennis, jogging. Home: 1117 Hillside Dr Greenville NC 27858-4522 Office: Physics Dept East Carolina U Greenville NC 27858

SAYKALLY, RICHARD JAMES, chemistry educator; b. Rhinelander, Wis., Sept. 10, 1947; s. Edwin L. and Helen M. S. BS, U. Wis., Eau Claire, 1970; PhD, U. Wis., Madison, 1977. Postdoctoral Nat. Bur. Standards, Boulder, Colo., 1977-79; asst. prof. U. Calif., Berkeley, 1979-83, assoc. prof., 1983-86, prof., 1986—, vice chmn. dept. chemistry, 1988-91; Bergman Lectureship Yale U., 1987; Merck-Frost lectr. U. B.C., 1988; Bourke Lectureship Royal Soc. Chemistry, 1992, L.J. Bircher Lectureship, Vanderbilt U., 1993; prin. investigator Lawrence Berkeley Lab., 1983-91; prin. investigator Lawrence Berkeley Lab., 1983-91; prin. investigator program Sci. for Sci. NSF; mem. Laser Sci. Topical Group Fellowship Com., 1993—; mem. internat. steering com. 12th Internat. Conf. on Laser Spectroscopy, 1995; lectr. U. Alta. (Can.), 1995. Contbr. over 160 articles to profl. jours.; editl. rev.

bd. Jour. Chem. Physics, 1993-95, Molecular Physics, 1983—, Chem. Physics Letters, 1987—, Spectroscopy Mag., 1986—, Rev. of Sci. Instruments, 1987-90. Dreyfuss Found. fellow, 1979; presdl. investigator NSF, 1984-88; recipient Bomem Michelson prize for spectroscopy, 1989, E.K. Plyler prize for molecular spectroscopy, 1989, Disting. Alumnus award U. Wis., Eau Claire, 1987, E.R. Lippincott medal OSA, SAS, 1992, Disting. Tchg. award U. Calif., Berkeley, 1992; Churchill fellow Cambridge U., 1995. Fellow Am. Phys. Soc., Royal Soc. Chem.; mem. AAAS, AAUP, Optical Soc. Am., Am. Chem. Soc. (Harrison Howe award 1992). Office: University of California Dept of Chemistry 419 Latimer Hall #1460 Berkeley CA 94720-1460

SAYLER, J. W., JR., insurance company executive. With Bus. Mens Assurance Co. of Am., Kansas City, Mo., 1957-1990, pres. and coo, 1990—. Office: Bus Mens Assurance Co of Am PO Box 419458 Kansas City MO 64141-6458

SAYLER, RICHARD H., lawyer; b. Rochester, N.Y., Jan. 24, 1945. AB, Dartmouth Coll., 1966; JD, U. Mich., 1969. Bar: N.Y. 1970, Ohio 1985. Law clk. to Hon. Lumbard U.S. Ct. Appeals (2nd cir.), 1969-70; law clk. to Hon. White U.S. Supreme Ct., 1970-71; spl. asst. to asst. atty. gen. Antitrust Divsn., U.S. Dept. Justice, Washington, 1972-74; ptnr. Jones, Day, Reavis & Pogue, Cleve. Office: Jones Day Reavis & Pogue N Point 901 Lakeside Ave E Cleveland OH 44114-1116

SAYLES, EDWARD THOMAS, theatrical producer; b. Auburn, N.Y., Feb. 19, 1952; s. Thomas Edward and Gilda Marie (Campolieto) S.; m. Sue Ann Kocks (div.); children: Austin, Celeste. BA, SUNY, Cortland, 1974; MA, Bowling Green (Ohio) State U., 1980. Producing dir. Uptown Stage, Cortland, 1975-76, Trotwood (Ohio) Circle Theatre, 1976-80, First St., Dayton, 1978-80, Merry-Go-Round Playhouse, Auburn, N.Y., 1980—; instr. SUNY, Cortland, 1975-76, guest prof., 1985-87; N.Y. State Coun. on the Arts, 1986—. Dir. collaborator original plays including Alice in Wonderland, 1985 (Nat. Showcase award 1988), Pictures at an American Exhibition, 1988; arranger A Modern Survey, 1985. Trustee Cayuga County United Way, Auburn, 1988—, Tomato Festival, 1987-89, Conf. Help for Alcohol and Drug Abuse, 1984-87. Recipient Creative Support award Nat. Endowment for the Arts, 1977-80, Ohio Arts Coun., 1977-80, Dayton (Ohio) Found., 1977-80, N.Y. State Coun. on the Arts, 1980-89. Mem. Owasco Country Club (bd. dirs.), Phi Alpha Theta (v.p. 1973), Alpha Psi Omega (v.p. 1974). Roman Catholic. Office: Merry Go Round Playhouse PO Box 506 Auburn NY 13021-0506

SAYLES, JOHN THOMAS, film director, writer, actor; b. Schenectady, Sept. 28, 1950; s. Donald John and Mary (Rausch) S. BS, Williams Coll., 1972. Author: Pride of the Bimbos, 1975, Union Dues, 1979, Thinking in Pictures: The Making of the Movie "Matewan," 1987, The Anarchists Convention, 1979, Los Gusanos, 1991; short stories I-80 Nebraska, M.490 - M.205, 1975 (O Henry award), Breed, Golden State, 1977 (O Henry award), Hoop; writer, dir. plays: New Hope for the Dead, 1981, Turnbuckle; screenwriter: Piranha, 1978, The Lady in Red, 1979, Battle Beyond the Stars, 1980, Alligator, 1981, The Challenge, 1982, Enormous Changes at the Last Minute, 1985, Wild Thing, 1987, The Clan of the Cave Bear, 1988, Breaking In, 1989; screenwriter, actor: The Howling, 1981; dir., screenwriter, actor: Return of the Secaucus Seven, 1980 (Los Angeles Film Critcs award, 1980), Lianna, 1983, The Brother From Another Planet, 1984, Matewan, 1987, Eight Men Out, 1988, City of Hope, 1991; dir., screenwriter: Baby, It's You, 1983, Passion Fish, 1992; actor: Hard Choices, 1986, Something Wild, 1986, Little Vegas, 1990, Straight Talk, 1992, Malcolm X, 1992, Matinee, 1993, My Life's in Turnaround, 1994; dir. Bruce Springsteen music videos Born in the U.S.A., I'm on Fire, Glory Days; TV work includes A Perfect Match, Unnatural Causes, Shannon's Deal, spl. Mountain View. MacArthur Found. grantee. Office: Paramount Pictures 5555 Melrose Ave Los Angeles CA 90038-3197 Office: Paradigm Ste 2600 10100 Santa Monica Blvd Los Angeles CA 90067*

SAYLES, LEONARD ROBERT, management educator, consultant; b. Rochester, N.Y., Apr. 30, 1926; s. Robert and Rose (Sklof) S.; m. Kathy Ripin; children: Robert, Emily. BA with highest distinction, U. Rochester, 1946; PhD in Econs. and Social Sci, MIT, 1950. Asst. prof. Cornell U., 1950-53, U. Mich., 1953-56; prof. emeritus Grad. Sch. Bus. Adminstrn., Columbia U., 1956-91, prof. bus. adminstrn., 1962—, head div. indsl. relations and orgnl. behavior, 1960-72; adviser to adminstr. NASA, 1966-71; sr. rsch. scientist Ctr. for Creative Leadership, Greensboro, N.C., 1988-94; Disting. vis. lectr. McGill U., 1974; bd. govs. Center for Creative Leadership, 1984-88. Author: (with G. Strauss) The Local Union, 1953, Managerial Behavior, 1964, Human Behavior in Organizations, 1966, (with E. Chapple) Measure of Management, 1961, Behavior of Industrial Work Groups, 1958, Individualism and Big Business, 1963, (with W. Downing) How Managers Motivate, 1971, (with M. Chandler) Managing Large Systems; Organizations for the Future, 1971, 2d edit., 1993, (with G. Strauss) Personnel, 4th edit, 1980, Managing Human Resources, 2d edit, 1981, Leadership, 1979, (with R. Burgelman) Inside Corporate Innovation, 1985, Managing in Real Organizations, 1989, The Working Leader, 1993; mem. editorial bd. Human Orgn., 1957-62. Fellow Am. Anthropol. Assn.; mem. Phi Beta Kappa.

SAYLES, THOMAS DYKE, JR., banker; b. Newton Center, Mass., Jan. 16, 1932; s. Thomas Dyke and Eleanor (Norton) S.; m. Patricia Blake, Dec. 11, 1954; children: Lynn Diane, Richard Norton, Stephen Dyke. A.B., Dartmouth, 1954; M.A., N.Y. U., 1961. With Mfrs. Hanover Trust Co., N.Y.C., 1958-70; v.p. Mfrs. Hanover Trust Co., 1966-70, sr. v.p., 1970; dir. Summit Trust Co., Summit, N.J., 1968—; exec. v.p., chief adminstrn. officer Summit Trust Co., 1970, pres., 1971-80, chmn., 1971-94; chmn., pres., chief exec. officer Summit Bancorp., 1974-87, chmn., chief exec. officer, 1987-94, chmn., 1994—; bd. dirs. Selective Ins. Group, Inc. Trustee Overlook Hosp., 1972-80, Drew U., 1984—, Papermill Playhouse, 1991—, NCCJ, 1991—, N.J. Israel Commn., 1991. With USAF, 1955-58. Mem. Chatham (N.J.) Jr. C. of C. (dir. 1965), N.J. State C. of C. (trustee 1992—). Clubs: Baltusrol (Springfield); Canoe Brook (Summit), Pine Valley. Home: 58 Lincoln Ave Chatham NJ 07928-2062 Office: Summit Bancorp One Main St Chatham NJ 07928

SAYLOR, LARRY JAMES, lawyer; b. Biloxi, Miss., Nov. 7, 1948; s. Rufus Don and Alice Julia (Kidd) S.; m. Mary L. Mullendore, Dec. 27, 1975; children: David James, Stephen Michael. AB in Political Sci., Miami U., Oxford, Ohio, 1970; M in City and Regional Planning, Ohio State U., 1976; JD, U. Mich., 1976. Bar: D.C. 1976, Mich. 1977, U.S. Ct. Appeals (D.C. cir.) 1977, U.S. Ct. Appeals (6th cir.) 1978, U.S. Supreme Ct. 1981, U.S. Ct. Appeals (10th cir.) 1982. Law clk. to presiding judge U.S. Ct. Appeals (D.C. cir.), Washington, 1976-77; ptnr. Miller, Canfield, Paddock and Stone, Detroit, 1977—. Article editor Mich. Law Rev., 1975-76; contbr. articles to profl. jours. 1st lt. USAF, 1970-72. Mem. ABA (antitrust and litigation sects.), Mich. Bar Assn., (chair antitrust sect.), D.C. Bar Assn., World Trade Club, Detroit Econ. Club. Avocations: skiing, woodworking. Home: 455 Lakeland St Grosse Pointe MI 48230-1654 Office: Miller Canfield Paddock & Stone 150 W Jefferson Ave Ste 2500 Detroit MI 48226-4415

SAYLOR, MARK JULIAN, editor; b. Wellsville, N.Y., Mar. 19, 1954; s. Richard Samuel and Naomi (Roth) S.; children: Samuel, Benjamin, Katie. BA cum laude, Harvard Coll., 1976. Staff writer Ark. Democrat, Little Rock, 1976-77; staff writer San Jose (Calif.) Mercury News, 1977-81, asst. met. editor, 1981-82, govt. and politics editor, 1982-85; asst. city editor San Diego County edit. LA Times, L.A., 1985-89, city editor San Diego edit., 1989-91, Calif. editor, 1991-95; entertainment editor Business, 1995—. Avocation: chess master. Office: LA Times Times Mirror Sq Los Angeles CA 90053

SAYLOR, PETER M., architect; b. Phila., July 26, 1941; s. Harry T. and Dorothy (Johnson) S.; m. Caroline Mercalf, Apr. 4, 1970; children: Thomas S., Elizabeth B. B.Arch., U. Pa., 1963, M.Arch., 1965. Registered architect, Pa., N.J., Conn., Ohio, Minn. Architect Mitchell-Giurgola, Phila., 1967-70; ptnr. firm Dagit-Saylor Architects, Phila., 1970—; design critic, juror U. Pa., 1975—; bd. dirs. Found. for Architecture, Phila., 1980-90. V.p. Chestnut Hill Community Assn., Phila., 1979; bd. dirs. All Saint's Hosp., Wyndmoor, Pa., 1981-86. Recipient various bldg. design award. Fellow AIA (bd. dirs. Phila. chpt. 1973-82, chpt. pres. 1981-82); mem. Pa. Soc. Archs., Chestnut Hill Hist. Soc. (bd. dirs. 1988-95, pres. 1989-92), Phila. Soc. Preservation of

Landmarks (bd. dirs. 1989-95, pres. 1993-94), Phila. Mus. Art (friends bd. dirs. 1990-93), Phila. Cricket Club (bd. dirs. 1985-91), Mask and Wig Club (pres. 1980-81, bd. dirs. 1970-84). Republican. Episcopalian. Office: Dagit-Saylor Archs Land Title Bldg Ste 1100 100 S Broad St Philadelphia PA 19110

SAYLOR, STEVEN WARREN, writer prose, fiction; b. Port Lavaca, Tex., Mar. 23, 1956; s. Lyman Harrison and Lucy Lee (Reeves) S. BA History, U. Tex., 1978. Author: Roman Blood, 1991, Arms of Nemesis, 1992, Catilina's Riddle, 1993 (Lambda Literary award 1994); contbr. short stories, essays to numerous mags. Mem. Mystery Writers of Am. (Robert L. Fish Meml. award 1993). Avocations: bicycling, furniture making, travel. Office: St Martins Press 175 Fifth Ave New York NY 10010

SAYRE, DAVID, physicist; b. N.Y.C., Mar. 2, 1924; s. Ralph E. and Sylvia (Rosenbaum) S.; m. Anne Bowns, Dec. 26, 1947. BS, Yale U., 1944; MS, Auburn U., 1948; PhD, Oxford (Eng.) U., 1951. Staff mem. radiation lab. MIT, Cambridge, 1943-46; rsch. assoc. U. Pa., Phila., 1951-55; mathematician IBM Corp., N.Y.C., 1955-59, corp. dir. programming, 1959-62; mem. rsch. staff IBM T.J. Watson Rsch. Ctr., Yorktown Heights, N.Y., 1962-90, ret., 1990; cons. U.S. Office Naval Rsch., London, 1951; mem. U.S.A. Nat. Com. for Crystallography, 1952-55, 81-84, vice chmn., 1984-86; vis. fellow All Souls Coll., Oxford U., 1972-73. Co-author: Waveforms, 1947; editor: Computational Crystallography, 1983; co-editor: Structural Studies on Molecules of Biological Interest, 1983, X-Ray Microscopy II, 1988; contbr. numerous articles to profl. jours. Trustee Village of Head-of-the-Harbor, L.I. N.Y., 1975-95. Mem. Am. Crystallographic Assn. (treas. 1952-55, pres. 1983, Fankuchen award 1989). Episcopalian. Achievements include devel. of atomicity-based direct phasing method for x-ray crystallography, (with others) of first FORTRAN compiler and first virtual computer system; contbns. to x-ray microscopy; observation (with others) of x-ray diffraction pattern from single biol. cell.

SAYRE, EDWARD VALE, chemist; b. Des Moines, Sept. 8, 1919; s. Edward Agnew and Audrey (Vale) S.; m. Virginia Nelle Rogers, Oct. 20, 1943. B.S., Iowa State U., 1941; A.M., Columbia U., 1943, Ph.D., 1949. Mgr. research sect. Manhattan Dist. project Columbia U., 1942-45; research chemist Eastman Kodak Research Labs., Rochester, N.Y., 1949-52; sr. chemist Brookhaven Nat. Lab., Upton, N.Y., 1952-84; research phys. scientist Smithsonian Instn., Washington, 1984—; dir. research Museum Fine Arts, Boston, 1975-80. sr. scientist, 1980-84; sr. scientist Alexander von Humboldt Found., 1980; vis. lectr. Stevens Inst. Tech., 1955-61; adj. prof. fine arts Inst. Fine Arts, N.Y. U., 1960-74; distinguished vis. prof. Am. U. Cairo, 1970; Regents prof. U. Calif., Irvine, 1972; mem. sci. advisory council Winterthur Mus. Contbr. numerous articles on research to profl. jours.; assoc. editor Archaeometry, 1969-93, Art and Archaeology Tech. Abstracts, 1970-87, Jour. Archaeol. Sci., 1971-77. Guggenheim fellow, 1969; recipient U.S. sr. scientist award Alexander von Humboldt Found., 1980-81, George von Hevesy medal, 1984. Fellow Internat., Am. insts. for conservation hist. and artistic works; mem. Am. Chem. Soc. Club: Cosmos. Home: 2106 Wilkinson Pl Alexandria VA 22306-2540

SAYRE, E(NOCH) PHILLIP, political scientist, state official; b. Humboldt, Iowa, Apr. 19, 1926; s. Enoch Franklin and Grace Irene (Rusk) S.; m. Mary-Ellen Silverstone, May 25, 1957; children: Michael Franklin, Elisabeth Carol Sayre Lozinsky. BA, U. Wash. 1950; postgrad., Georgetown U., 1951-54. Campaign mgr. for Henry Jackson and Senator W.G. Magnuson, Skagit County, Wash., 1950; mem. campaign staff Henry Jackson for U.S. Senate, Wash., 1953; adminstrv. asst. to Congressman John Lesinski, U.S. Ho. of Reps., Washington, 1954-56; ins. agt. State Mut. Life Assurance Co., Washington, 1956-62; staff assoc. J.D. Marsh & Assocs., Inc., Washington, 1962-64; dir. fin. planning, supr. ins. Capital Plans, Washington, 1964-68; v.p., registered prin. Diversified Planning Corp., Washington, 1968-70; adminstrv. analyst dept. fiscal svcs. Md. Gen. Assembly, Annapolis, 1970-80, sr. adminstrv. analyst, 1980—; staff dir. Md. Commn. on Intergovtl. Cooperation, 1974-78. Chmn. legis. com. Young Dems. Co., 1954-56; co-founder Md. Com. for Fair Representation, 1960-62; chmn. issues com. We. Suburban Dem. Club Montgomery County, Md., 1962-64; mem. Md. Constl. Conv. Commn., 1965-67; co-chmn. Dem. Com. for Constn., Md., 1968; mem. steering com. Citizens for Proposed Constn. Md., 1968. Recipient resolution Md. Ho. of Dels., 1963, 65, Young Dem. of Yr. award Young Dems. Md., 1965, Outstanding Civic Achievement award Young Dems. Montgomery County, 1965. Mem. Am. Soc. for Pub. Adminstrn., World Future Soc., Bannockburn Civic Assn., Bannockburn Cmty. Club, Washington Ethical Soc. Avocations: reading, futurist interests, walking, outdoors, nature. Home: 6809 Laverock Ct Bethesda MD 20817-4912

SAYRE, FRANCIS BOWES, JR., clergyman; b. Washington, Jan. 17, 1915; s. Francis Bowes and Jessie Woodrow (Wilson) S.; m. Harriet Taft Hart, June 8, 1946; children: Jessie Wilson, Thomas Hart, Harriet Brownson, Francis Nevin. A.B. cum laude, Williams Coll., 1937, D.D. (hon.), 1963; M.Div., Episcopal Theol. Sch., Cambridge, Mass., 1940; L.H.D. (hon.), Wooster Coll., 1956; D.D. (hon.), Va. Theol. Sch., 1957, Wesleyan U., Conn., 1958, Hobart Coll., 1966; S.T.D. (hon.), Queen's U., Belfast, 1966; Litt.D. (hon.), Lehigh U., Ursinus Coll., 1973. Ordained to ministry Episcopal Ch., 1940; asst. minister Christ Ch. Cambridge, 1940-42; indsl. chaplain Diocese of Ohio, Cleve., 1946-51; rector St. Paul's Ch., East Cleveland, Ohio, 1947-51; dean Washington Cathedral, 1951-78; asso. dir. Woodrow Wilson Internat. Center for Scholars, Washington, 1978-79; Chmn. bd. Detroit Indsl. Mission, 1956-68; chmn. U.S. Com. for Refugees, 1958-61. Bd. dirs. Presbyn. Ministers Fund; pres. Martha's Vineyard Hosp., 1981-83. Served as chaplain USNR, 1942-46. Recipient Clergyman of Yr. award Religious Heritage Am., 1976; Disting. Pub. Service medal NASA, 1977. Mem. Sigma Phi.

SAYRE, JEAN WILLIAMS, librarian, educator. BA in Biology, U. Minn., Duluth, 1973; MA in Libr. Sci., U. Minn., 1975. Intern May Clinic Med. Libr., Rochester, Minn., 1974; substitute libr. Mpls. Pub. Libr., 1974-76; med. libr. Golden Valley (Minn.) Health Ctr., 1975-76; info. coord. Am. Med. Systems Inc., Mpls., 1976-77; asst. dir. S.W. Area Health Edn. Ctr. Libr. U. N.D., Fargo, 1978-80; chief libr. VA Med. Ctr., Iowa City, 1981; asst. dir. med. libr., asst. prof. med. libr. sci. Sch. Medicine Mercer U., Macon, Ga., 1981-87; cons., libr. Rowland Med. Libr. U. Miss. Med. Ctr., Jackson, 1988-89; dir. and chief med. libr. Oliver Ocasek Regional Med. Info. Ctr., asst. prof. libr. and info. sci. Coll. Medicine Northeastern Ohio U., Rootstown, 1989—; cons., presenter in field; advisor Mercer U., 1982-86, Ohio U. Libr. Coun. Contbr. articles to profl. jours. Mem. Ptnrs. Edn., 1984-87. Recipient Frank Bradway Rogers Info. Advancement award, 1992. Mem. Med. Libr. Assn. (cert.), Acad. Health Info. Profls. (disting.), Spl. Librs., Midwest Med. Libr. Assn., Northeastern Ohio Maj. Acad. Libr. Dirs. Coun., Ohio Health Scis. Libr. Assn., Tri-County Bioscis. Librs. Home: 164 Milton Dr Tallmadge OH 44278-1669 Office: Northeastern Ohio U Coll Medicine PO Box 95 4209 State Route 44 Rootstown OH 44272-9698

SAYRE, JOHN MARSHALL, lawyer, former government official; b. Boulder, Colo., Nov. 9, 1921; s. Henry Marshall and Lulu M. (Cooper) S.; m. Jean Miller, Aug. 22, 1943; children: Henry M., Charles Franklin, John Marshall Jr., Ann Elizabeth Sayre Taggart (dec.). BA, U. Colo., 1943, JD, 1948. Bar: Colo. 1948, U.S. Dist. Ct. Colo. 1952, U.S. Ct. Appeals (10th cir.) 1964. Law clk. trust dept. Denver Nat. Bank, 1948-49; asst. cashier, trust officer Nat. State Bank of Boulder, 1949-50; ptnr. Ryan, Sayre, Martin, Brotzman, Boulder, 1950-66, Davis, Graham & Stubbs, Denver, 1966-89, of counsel, 1993—; asst. sec. of the Interior for Water and Sci., 1989-93. Bd. dirs. Boulder Sch. Dist. 3, 1951-57; city atty. City of Boulder, 1952-55; gen. counsel Colo. Mcpl. League, 1956-63; prin. counsel No. Colo. Water Conservancy Dist. and mcpl. subdist., 1964-87, spl. counsel, 1987, bd. dirs. dist., 1960-64; former legal counsel Colo. Assn. Commerce and Industry. Lt. (j.g.) USNR, 1943-46. Decorated Purple Heart. Fellow Am. Bar. Found. (life), Colo. Bar Found; mem. ABA, Colo. Bar Assn., Boulder County Bar Assn. (pres. 1959), Denver Bar Assn., Nat. Water Resources Assn. (Colo. dir. 1980-89, 93—, pres. 1984-86), Denver Country Club, Denver Club, Mile High Club, Phi Gamma Delta, Phi Beta Kappa. Republican. Episcopalian. Office: Davis Graham & Stubbs PO Box 185 Denver CO 80201-0185 Home: 355 Ivanhoe St Denver CO 80220

SAYRE, KENNETH MALCOLM, philosophy educator; b. Scottsbluff, Nebr., Aug. 13, 1928; s. Harry Malcolm and Mildred Florence (Potts) S.; m. Lucille Margaret Shea, Aug. 19, 1958 (dec. Apr. 1980); children—Gregory, Christopher, Jeffrey; m. Patricia Ann White, Apr. 4, 1983. A.B., Grinnell Coll., Iowa, 1952; M.A., Harvard U., 1954, Ph.D., 1958. Asst. dean Grad. Sch. Arts and Letters Harvard U., Cambridge, Mass., 1953-56; systems analyst MIT, Cambridge, Mass., 1956-58; from instr. to prof. philosophy U. Notre Dame, Ind., 1958—, dir. Philosophic Inst., 1966—. Author: Recognition, 1965, Consciousness, 1969, Plato's Analytic Method, 1969, Cybernetics and the Philosophy of Mind, 1976, Moonflight, 1977, Starburst, 1977, Plato's Late Ontology, 1983. Served with USN, 1946-48. NSF grantee, 1962-79. Mem. Am. Philos. Assn., Phi Beta Kappa. Home: 910 Weber Sq South Bend IN 46617-1850 Office: Univ Notre Dame Dept Philosophy Notre Dame IN 46556

SAYRE, LARRY D., religious organization executive. Dir. Am. Baptist Church Greater Indpls. Region. Office: American Baptist Churches of USA 1350 N Delaware St Indianapolis IN 46202-2415

SAYRE, ROBERT FREEMAN, English language educator; b. Columbus, Ohio, Nov. 6, 1933; s. Harrison M. and Mary (White) S.; (divorced); children—Gordon, Nathan, Laura; m. Hutha Refle, May 7, 1988. B.A., Wesleyan U., Middletown, Conn., 1955; Ph.D., Yale U., 1962. Instr. English U. Ill., Urbana, 1961-63; Fulbright lectr. Lund (Sweden) U., 1963-65; mem. faculty U. Iowa, 1965—, prof. English, 1972—; dir. inter-profl. seminars NEH, 1978, 79; Fulbright lectr. Montpellier, France, 1984; exch. prof. U. Copenhagen, 1988-89; mem. adv. bd. Leopold Ctr. for Sustainable Agr., 1994—. Author: The Examined Self: Benjamin Franklin, Henry Adams and Henry James, 1964, Adventures, Rhymes and Designs of Vachel Lindsay, 1968; Thoreau and the American Indians, 1977; editor: A Week on the Concord and Merrimac Rivers, Walden, The Maine Woods, Cape Cod (H.D. Thoreau), 1985, Take This Exit: Rediscovering the Iowa Landscape, 1989, New Essays on Walden, 1992, American Lives: An Anthology of Autobiographical Writing, 1994; contbr. articles and revs. to profl. jours. Guggenheim fellow, 1973-74. Mem. Am. Studies Assn., MLA. Office: U Iowa English Dept Iowa City IA 52242

SAYRE, ROBERT MARION, ambassador; b. Hillsboro, Oreg., Aug. 18, 1924; s. William Octavius and Mary (Brozka) S.; m. Elora Amanda Moyhihan, Dec. 29, 1951; children: Marian Amanda, Robert Marion, Daniel Humphrey. B.A. summa cum laude, Willamette U., 1949; J.D. cum laude (Alexander Welborn Weddell Peace prize 1956), George Washington U., 1956; M.A., Stanford U., 1960; LL.D. Willamette U., 1965. Bar: D.C. 1956, U.S. Ct. Appeals 1956, U.S. Supreme Ct. 1962. Joined U.S. For. Service, 1949; econ. adviser on Latin Am., 1950-52, mil. adviser, 1952-57, officer charge inter-Am. security affairs, 1955-57; polit. counselor embassy Lima, Peru, 1958-59; fin. attache embassy Havana, Cuba, 1960; exec. sec. Task Force Latin Am., State Dept., 1961, officer charge Mexican affairs, 1961-63; dep. dir. Office Caribbean and Mexican Affairs, 1963-64; dir. Office Mexican Affairs, 1964; sr. staff mem. White House, 1964-65; dep. asst. sec. Bur. Inter-Am. Affairs, Dept. State, 1965-67; acting asst. sec. Dept. State, 1968—; Am. ambassador to Uruguay, 1968-69, to Panama, 1969-74; sr. insp. Dept. State, 1974-75, insp. gen., 1975-78; ambassador to Brazil, 1978-81; chmn. U.S. Interdepartmental group on Terrorism, dir. Counter-terrorism and Emergency Planning Dept. State, 1981-84, sr. insp., 1985-86; prinr. IRC Group, Inc., 1986-87; sr. assoc. Global Bus. Access, Ltd., Washington, 1995—, 1995—; adv. to U.S. rep.OAS, 1985-87; OAS under sec. for mgmt., 1987-94; sr. councilor Atlantic Coun. U.S.; mem. Washington Inst. Fgn. Affairs. Capt. AUS, WWII; col. Res., ret. Decorated So. Cross (Brazil); Cross of Balboa (Panama); recipient Outstanding Employee award Dept. State, 1952, Superior Honor awards, 1964, 75, Disting. Honor award, 1978, Outstanding Performance award, 1982, 83, 84, 85, Presdl. Meritorious award, 1986, Fgn. Svc. Cup award, 1990. Mem. Blue Key, Phi Delta Theta, Phi Eta Sigma, Tau Kappa Alpha. Episcopalian. Club: Cosmos, Dacor. Home: 3714 Bent Branch Rd Falls Church VA 22041-1028 Office: Global Business Access Ltd Ste 400 1825 I St NW Washington DC 20006

SAYRE, WILLIAM HEYSHAM, banker; b. Montclair, N.J., Apr. 1, 1933; s. William Heysham and Lee (Stuart) S.; m. Eleanor deVore, June 18, 1955; children: Carolyn Beldon, Catherine Brooks, Robert deVore, William H. BBA, Lehigh U., 1958; postgrad., Harvard Bus. Sch., 1976. Asst. treas. Fidelity Bank, Phila., 1962-66, asst. v.p., 1966-70, v.p., 1970-73, sr. v.p., 1973-75; exec. v.p. Fidelity Bank N.A., Phila., 1975—, sr. credit officer, 1982—. Contbg. author: The Banker's Handbook, 1978. bd. dirs., past chmn., chief exec. officer Cathedral Village, Phila.; treas. Cathedral chpt. Episcopal Diocese of Pa. Mem. Am. Bankers Assn. (cert. commil. lender 1976), Robert Morris Assocs. (nat. pres. 1987-88, pres. Phila. chpt. 1979-80, chmn. policy div. 1980-81, bd. dirs., chmn. chpts. council div. 1982-84). Home: 850 Mt Pleasant Rd Bryn Mawr PA 19010-1824 Office: Fidelity Bank Broad & Walnut Sts Philadelphia PA 19109

SAYWELL, WILLIAM GEORGE GABRIEL, foundation administrator; b. Regina, Sask., Can., Dec. 1, 1936; s. John Ferdinand Tupper and Vera Marguerite S.; m. Helen Jane Larmer; children: Shelley Jayne, William James Tupper, Patricia Lynn. BA, U. Toronto, 1960, MA, 1961, PhD, 1968; LLD, U. B.C., 1994. Asst. prof. dept. East Asian studies U. Toronto, Ont., Ont., Can., 1963-69; asst. prof. U. Toronto, Ont., Can., 1969-71, assoc. prof., 1971-82, prof., 1982-83, chmn. dept., 1971-76; prof. dept. history, pres. Simon Fraser U., Burnaby, B.C., Can., 1983-93; pres., chief exec. officer Asia Pacific Found. of Can., Vancouver, B.C., 1993—; sinologist and 1st sec. Can. Embassy, Peking, 1972-73; dir. U. Toronto-York U. Ctr. Modern East Asia, 1974-75; prin. Innis Coll., 1976-79; vice provost U. Toronto, 1979-83; dir. Westcoast Energy, Spar Aerospace. Author articles and revs. on Chinese affairs to profl. jours. Decorated Order B.C. Office: Asia Pacific Found Can, 666-999 Canada Pl, Vancouver, BC Canada V6C 3E1

SAZAMA, THOMAS JOHN, circuit judge; b. Chippewa Falls, Wis., Feb. 24, 1946; s. John James and Mary Janese (Cline) S.; m. Mary Margaret Wanicek, Aug. 30, 1975; children: Stephen E., Caroline A., Andrew J. BA, U Wis., 1968; JD, Marquette U., 1973. Bar: Wis. 1973, U.S. Dist. Ct. (ea. and we. dists.) Wis. 1973. Asst. dist. atty. Chippewa County, Wis., 1973-75 dist. atty., 1976-80; ptnr. Falkenberg & Sazama, Cadott, Wis., 1975-85, Sazama Law Offices, S.C., Chippewa Falls, Wis., 1985-94; magistrate judge U.S. Dist. Ct. (we. dist.) Wis., Madison and Chippewa Falls, 1991-94; circuit judge Chippewa County, Wis., 1995—; bd. dirs. XMI Corp., Chippewa Falls. With U.S. Army, 1970-71, Vietnam. Mem. Elks. Roman Catholic. Avocations: golf, lawn work. Home: 5728 Redwood Dr Chippewa Falls WI 54729 Office: 711 N Bridge St Chippewa Falls WI 54729

SAZDANOFF, CATHERINE ANN, lawyer; b. Norwich, N.Y., Sept. 22, 1956; d. James Albert and Caroline Louise (Jansen) Buzard; m. Michael Louise Sazdanoff, May 31, 1980. BA in English, U. Notre Dame, 1978; JD, Northwestern U., 1981. Bar: Ill. 1981, U.S. Dist. Ct. (no. dist.) Ill. 1981, U.S. Ct. Appeals (7th cir.) 1983. Assoc. Isham, Lincoln & Beale, Chgo., 1981-84; atty. Abbott Labs., North Chicago, Ill., 1984-85, sr. atty., 1985—. Mem. ABA, Chgo. Bar Assn. Republican. Roman Catholic. Office: Abbott Labs 1 Abbott Park Rd Abbott Park IL 60064-2204

SAZEGAR, MORTEZA, artist; b. Tehran, Iran, Nov. 11, 1933; s. Hassan Ali and Zahra (Frootan) S.; m. Patricia Jean Kaurich, July 13, 1959. B.A., U. Tex., El Paso, 1955, B.S., 1956; postgrad., Baylor U. Coll. Medicine, 1956-57, Cornell U., 1958-59. One man exhibitions include, Poindexter Gallery, N.Y.C., 1964, 67, 69, 71, 73, 75, 77, group exhibitions include, Detroit Inst. Arts, 1965, Chgo. Art Inst., 1965, Univ. Art Mus., U. Tex., Austin, 1965, 72, Whitney Mus. Am. Art, 1970, Cleve. Mus. Art, 1972, Corcoran Gallery Art, Washington, 1973, Tyler Sch. Art, Temple U., Phila., 1979; represented in permanent collections, Whitney Mus. Am. Art, N.Y.C., San Francisco Mus. Modern Art, Riverside Mus., N.Y.C., U. Mass. Amherst, Corcoran Gallery Art, Prudential Ins. Corp. Am., Mus. Contemporary Art, Tehran, Iran. Mem. Artists Equity Assn. Democrat. Address: RR 1 Cochranville PA 19330

SAZIMA, HENRY JOHN, oral and maxillofacial surgery educator; b. Cleve., Dec. 25, 1927; s. Henry Charles and Frances (Mahr) S.; m. Carol Ann Watson, Sept. 10, 1955; 1 child, Holly Ann Sazima Davani. BS, Case Western Res. U., 1948, DDS, 1953; grad. sch. medicine, U. Pa., 1956-57;

grad. sch. edn., Chapman Coll., 1967-69. Diplomate Am. Bd. Oral and Maxillofacial Surgery. Chief maxillfacial div. Naval Support Act, Saigon, Republic of Viet Nam, 1969-70; chmn. dental dept. Naval Med. Ctr., Phila., 1971-73, San Diego, 1979-80; spl. asst. dentistry Sec. Def. Health Affairs, Washington, 1973-77; comdg. officer Naval Dental Ctr., Parris Island, S.C., 1977-79; dep. chief dental div. Bur. Medicine and Surgery, Washington, 1980-82; comdg. officer Nat. Naval Dental Ctr., Bethesda, Md., 1982-83; dir. resources div. Chief Naval Ops., Washington, 1983-84; dep. commdr. for readiness and logistics Naval Med. Command, Washington, 1984-87, ret. rear admiral, 1987; now clin. assoc. prof. oral and maxillofacial surgery Georgetown U. Med. Ctr.; exec. dir. Acad. Dentistry Internat., 1988—; cons., lectr., researcher in field. Co-author: Management of War Injuries, 1977; contbr. articles to profl. jours. Recipient Residents award St. Vincent Charity Hosp., 1957. Fellow Am. Coll. Dentists, Assn. Oral and Maxillofacial Surgeons, Internat. Assn. Oral and Maxillofacial Surgeons, Acad. Dentistry Internat.; mem. Brit. Soc. Oral and Maxillofacial Surgeons, European Assn. Maxillofacial Surgery, Assn. Mil. Surgeons of U.S. (chmn. internat. com. 1984-86, Margetis award 1971), Internat. Coll. Dentists (dep. regent 1971-87), Omicron Kappa Upsilon, Delta Tau Delta, Psi Omega. Republican. Roman Catholic. Club: Mil. Order of CARABAO. Avocations: sports, tennis, music, travel. Home: 4924 Sentinel Dr Apt 105 Bethesda MD 20816-3506 Office: Acad Dentistry Internat 5125 Macarthur Blvd NW Ste 50 Washington DC 20016-3300

SBARBARO, ROBERT ARTHUR, banker; b. Bklyn., Jan. 24, 1933; s. John Vincent and Louise Olga (Perigone) S.; m. Kathleen Ann Noonan, Sept. 12, 1959; children—Robert, Paul, Nancy. B.A., Wagner Coll., 1954; grad., Stonier Sch. Banking, Rutgers U., 1977. CFP. Programming mgr. IBM, 1956-59; regional ops. mgr. Univac, 1959-65; asst. v.p., mgr. Computax Corp., N.Y.C., 1965-70; sr. v.p. Irving Trust Co., N.Y.C., 1970-89; pres. SPAR Cons., Montvale, N.J., 1989—. Mem. Montvale (N.J.) Recreation Commn., 1979-80; treas. Pascack Hills High Sch. Parents Assn., 1978-79; trustee Wagner Coll. Served with U.S. Navy, 1954-56. Recipient Alumni Achievement award Wagner Coll., 1987—. Mem. Data Processing Mgmt. Assn., Am. Banking Assn., Data Security Inst., Internat. Assn. for Fin. Planning. Republican. Roman Catholic. Avocation: sports. Home: 14 Sunrise Dr Montvale NJ 07645-1044 Office: SPAR Cons 14 Sunrise Dr Montvale NJ 07645-1044

SBORDON, WILLIAM G., publisher; b. Detroit, June 17, 1928; s. Victor George and Ernestine Marie (Schaible) S.; m. Edna Helen Nitkowski, June 18, 1949; children—Sharon A., William G., Carol M., David J., Edna J., James V. M.E., Wayne U., 1949. Dist. mgr. Plant Operation Mgmt., Detroit, 1965-69; dist. mgr. Design News, Detroit, 1969-76, Detroit mgr., 1972-76; nat. sales mgr. Modern Materials Handling, Boston, 1976-78, assoc. pub., 1978-80, v.p., pub., 1980—; v.p., pub. Cahners Pub. Co., Newton, Mass., 1980-93, v.p., pub. OEM Group, 1993—. Mem. Bus. and Profl. Advt. Assn., Materials Handling Inst., Materials Handling Equipment Dist. Assn., Nat. Wooden Pallet and Container Assn., Inst. Caster Mfrs., Materials Handling Industry Am. (vice chmn.), Materials Handling Edn. Found., Inc. (pres.), Univ. Club. Roman Catholic. Avocations: gardening; woodworking; building. Office: Modern Materials Handling Cahners Publishing Co 275 Washington St Newton MA 02158-1611

SCAGLIONE, ALDO DOMENICO, language educator; b. Turin, Italy, Jan. 10, 1925; came to U.S., 1951, naturalized, 1958; s. Teodoro and Angela (Grasso) S.; m. Jeanne M. Daman, June 28, 1952 (dec. June 1986); m. Marie M. Burns, Aug. 28, 1992. D.Modern Letters, U. Torino, 1948. Lectr. U. Toulouse, France, 1949-51; instr. Italian U. Chgo., 1951-52; mem. faculty U. Calif., Berkeley, 1952-68, prof. Italian and comparative lit., 1963-68, chmn. dept. Italian, 1963-65; W.R. Kenan prof. Romance langs., comparative lit. U. N.C., Chapel Hill, 1968-87; Italian prof. NYU, N.Y.C., 1987—, chmn. Italian dept., 1989-93, Erich Maria Remarque prof. lit., 1991—; vis. prof. Romance langs. Yale, 1965-66; vis. prof. comparative lit. Grad. Center, City U. N.Y., 1971-72; vis. prof. Italian, U. Va., fall, 1986; H.F. Johnson research prof. Inst. for Research in Humanities, Madison, Wis., 1981-82; Asso. Columbia U. Renaissance Seminar. Author: Nature and Love in the Late Middle Ages, 1963, Ars Grammatica, 1970, The Classical Theory of Composition, 1972, The Theory of German Word Order, 1981, Komponierte Prosa von der Antike bis zur Gegenwart, 2 vols., 1981, The Liberal Arts and the Jesuit College System, 1986, Knights at Court: Courtliness, Chivalry, and Courtesy from Ottonian Germany to the Italian Renaissance, 1991; also articles; editor: Orlando Innamorato, Amorum Libri, 2 vols., rev. edit., 1963, Francis Petrarch, Six Centuries Later: A Symposium, 1975, Ariosto 1974 in America, 1976, The Emergence of National Languages: A Symposium, 1984, The Divine Comedy and The Encyclopedia of Arts and Sciences, 1987, The Image of the Baroque, 1995, Series L'Interprete and Speculum Artium, Longo Editore, Ravenna, 1976—, (with Peter Lang) Series Studies in Italian Culture: Literature in History, 1989—; editor: Italian Culture, 1978-80; gen. editor: Romance Notes and N.C. Studies in Romance Langs. and Lits., 1971-75; assoc. editor: Romance Philology, 1963—, N.C. Studies in Comparative Literature, 1968-87, Studies in Philology, 1969-87, Amsterdam Studies in the History of Linguistics, 1973—, Annali d'Italianstica, 1983—, The Comparatist, 1983—, Differentia, 1984—, Italica, 1984—; U.S. corr.: Studi Francesi, 1961—. Chmn. Berkeley campus campaign Woodrow Wilson Nat. Found., 1964-65. Served with Italian Liberation Army, 1944-45. Decorated Knight Order of Merit (Italy); Fulbright fellow, 1951; Guggenheim fellow, 1958; Newberry Library sr. resident fellow Chgo., 1965; fellow Southeastern Inst. for Medieval and Renaissance Studies, 1968; fellow Cini Found. Program in Medieval and Renaissance Culture, 1973; fellow German Acad. Exchange, W.Ger., 1977, 80; fellow Rockefeller Found. Conf. and Study Center, Bellagio, Italy, 1978; dir. NEH Seminar for Coll. Tchrs., Chapel Hill, N.C., 1981. Mem. MLA (exec. coun. 1981-85), Internat. Linguistic Assn., N.Am. Assn. for History of Lang. Scis. (pres. 1989-92), Am. Boccaccio Assn. (pres. 1980-81), Am. Assn. Italian Studies (v.p. 1981-83, hon. pres. 1988-89), Renaissance Soc. Am., Dante Soc. Am. (coun. 1975-78, 81-83, 89-92), Am. Assn. Tchrs. Italian, Medieval Acad. Am., Am. Comparative Lit. Assn., Renaissance Soc. No. Calif. (pres. 1962-63). Home: 3 Reading Ave Frenchtown NJ 08825

SCALA, GALE G., lawyer; b. Jacksonville, Fla., Nov. 11, 1948; d. Peter Paul Jr. and Helen Carol (Burjnowski) Gwiazdowski; m. John Warren Moscow, Sept. 15, 1973 (div. Dec. 1977); m. James Robert Scala, Aug. 28, 1987. AB, Boston U., 1970, JD, 1973. Bar: N.Y. 1974, U.S. Dist. Ct. (so. dist.) N.Y. 1975, U.S. Ct. Appeals (2nd cir.) 1975 . Asst. corp. counsel Law Dept City of N.Y., 1974-77; assoc. Marshell, Bratter, Green, Allison & Tucker, N.Y.C., 1977-82; ptnr. Dechert, Price & Rhoads, N.Y.C., 1982—. Mem. Assn. Bar City N.Y. (bd. dirs. real estate tax rev. 1979—, v.p. 1982—, certiorari and condemnation 1986—), Inst. Property Taxation. Office: Dechert Price & Rhoads 477 Madison Ave New York NY 10022-5802

SCALA, JAMES, health care industry consultant, author; b. Ramsey, N.J., Sept. 16, 1934; s. Luigi and Lorene (Hendrickson) S.; m. Nancy Peters, June 15, 1957; children: James, Gregory, Nancy, Kimberly. B.A., Columbia U., 1960; Ph.D., Cornell U., 1964; postgrad., Harvard U., 1968. Staff scientist Miami Valley Labs., Procter and Gamble Co., 1964-66; head life scis., dir. fundamental research Owens Ill. Corp., 1966-71; dir. nutrition T.J. Lipton Inc., 1971-75; dir. health scis. Gen. Foods Corp., 1975-78; v.p. sci. and tech. Shaklee Corp., San Francisco, 1978-85, sr. v.p. sci. affairs, 1986-87; lectr. Georgetown U. Med. Sch., U. Calif.-Berkeley extension. Author: Making the Vitamin Connection, 1985, The Arthritis Relief Diet, 1987, 89, Eating Right for a Bad Gut, 1990, 92, The High Blood Pressure Relief Diet, 1988, 90, Look 10 Years Younger, Feel 10 Years Better, 1991, 93, Prescription for Longevity, 1992, 94, If You Can't/Won't Stop Smoking, 1993; editor: Nutritional Determinants in Athletic Performance, 1981, New Protective Roles for Selected Nutrients, 1989; columnist Dance mag.; contbr. articles on nutrition and health scis. to profl. publs. With USAF, 1953-56. Disting. scholar U. Miami, Fla., 1977, Fla. Atlantic U., 1977. Mem. AAAS, Am. Inst. Nutrition, Am. Coll. Nutrition, Brit. Nutrition Soc., Sports Medicine Coun., Am. Soc. Cell Biology, Inst. Food Technologists, Astron. Soc. Pacific (bd. dirs., chmn. devel. coun.), Am. Dietetic Assn., Olympic Club (San Francisco), Oakland Yacht Club, Sigma Xi. Republican. I am in awe of the incredible resiliency of living things, but most of all the human spirit.

SCALA, SINCLAIRE MAXIMILIAN, aerospace engineer, retired; b. Charleston, S.C., June 27, 1929; s. George and Goldie (Bocker) S.; m. Enid

Joan Perlin, Mar. 25, 1951; children: Howard Alexander, Richard Perlin, Susanna Linda. BME cum laude, CCNY, 1950; postgrad., Columbia U., 1950, NYU, 1950-51; MME, U. Del., Newark, 1953; MA, Princeton U., 1955, PhD, 1957; MBA, U. Pa., 1978. Advanced devel. engr. Westinghouse Elec. Corp., Lester, Pa., 1951-53; rsch. fellow Princeton (N.J.) U. James Forrestal Rsch. Ctr., 1953-56; rsch. engr. GE, Phila., 1956-58, cons. high altitude gas dynamics, 1958-59, mgr. high altitude aerodynamics, 1959-64, mgr. theoretical fluid physics, 1964-68, mgr. fluid physics projects, 1968-69, mgr. environ. scis. lab., 1969-73, chief scientist, 1973-74, sr. cons. scientist, 1974-80, tech. dir. in adv. R & D program, 1974-80, mgr. adv. weapons concepts, 1980-82, tech. dir. profl. devel. and edn. program, 1974-82, chmn. rsch. & engring. productivity coun., 1979-82; v.p. advanced engring. Fairchild Republic Co., Farmingdale, N.Y., 1982-83, v.p. advanced systems & tech. devel., 1983-84, v.p. strategic def., 1984-85, v.p. research, 1985-86, dir. rsch. and advanced product devel., 1986-87; dir. advanced programs Grumman Aircraft Systems, Bethpage, N.Y., 1987-91; dir. bus. planning Grumman Corp. Ops., Bethpage, 1991-94, ret., 1994; lectr. dept. physics Temple U., Phila, 1960-61; guest lectr. MIT, 1964-66; Colloquium lectr. various univs. to date; gen. chmn. AFOSR/GE Symposium on Dynamics of Manned Lifting Planetary Entry, Phila., 1962; mem. NASA Research & Tech. Adv. Subcom. on Fluid Mechanics, Washington, 1965-70; mem. indsl. and profl. adv. council dept. aerospace engring. Pa. State U., 1969-73; cons. Engring. & Tech. Socs. Council of Delaware Valley, Inc., Phila. 1980-82; active various symposiums. Contbr. articles to profl. jours.; patentee in field. Pres. Wyncote-West Elkins Park Community Council, Montgomery Co., Pa., 1963-65; v.p. Cheltenham Council Civic Assns., 1964-65; bd. dirs. Parents Assn. Syracuse U., 1969-73; panel mem. Continuing Edn. Com. Commonwealth of Pa., 1976-77. Recipient Alumni award in mech. engring. CCNY, 1950; NYU teaching fellow, 1950-51, Guggenheim fellow, 1953-55, Bakhmeteff fellow, 1955-56. Fellow AIAA (assoc.); mem. Air Force Assn., Am. Def. Preparedness Assn., Am. Soc. Engring. Edn., Assn. for Unmanned Vehicle Systems, Nat. Mgmt. Assn., N.Y. Acad. Sci., Tech. Mktg. Soc. Am., U.S. Space Found., Army Aviation Assn. of Am., World Future Soc., Sigma Xi, Tau Beta Pi, Pi Tau Sigma. Home: 2107 Alexis Ct Tarpon Springs FL 34689-2053

SCALAPINO, DOUGLAS JAMES, physics educator; b. San Francisco, Dec. 10, 1933; s. John and Marie Constance (Pederson) S.; m. Diane Holmes Lappe, June 19, 1955; children: Lisa, Leigh, Kenneth, Lynne, Anne. BS, Yale U., 1955; PhD, Stanford U., 1961. Rsch. assoc. Washington U., St. Louis, 1961-62; rsch. assoc. U. Pa., Phila., 1962-64, asst. prof., 1964-66, assoc. prof., 1966-68, prof., 1968-69; vis. prof. U. Calif., Santa Barbara, 1968-69, prof., 1969—; prin. investigator Inst. for Theoretical Physics, Santa Barbara, 1979—; cons. E.I. Du Pont De Nemours & Co. Inc., Wilmington, Del., 1963-88; Faculty Rsch. lectr., U. Calif., Santa Barbara, 1983; IBM Almaden Rsch. Ctr., San Jose, Calif., 1989—; mem. sci. adv. bd. Superconductor Techs.Inc., Santa Barbara, 1987—; fellow Los Alamos Nat. Lab., 1992—. Contbr. articles to profl. jours. Fellow Alfred P. Sloan Found., 1964-66, fellowship, Guggenheim Found., 1976-77.; grantee NSF, U.S. Dept. Energy, pvt. corps., 1965—. Mem. NAS, Am. Acad. Arts and Scis., Phi Beta Kappa, Sigma Xi. Office: U Calif Dept Physics Santa Barbara CA 93106

SCALAPINO, LESLIE, poet; b. Santa Barbara, Calif., July 25, 1947; d. Robert Anthony and Dee (Jessen) S.; m. Wesley St. John, 1968 (div.); m. Tom White, 1987. BA, Reed Coll.; MA, U. Calif., Berkeley. co-publisher O Books. Author: O and Other Poems, 1975, The Woman Who Could Read the Minds of Dogs, 1976, Instead of an Animal, 1978, This Eating and Walking at the Same Time Is Associated All Right, 1979, Considering How Exaggerated Music Is, 1982, That They Were at the Beach, 1985, How Phenomena Appear to Unfold, 1990, The Return of Painting, the Pearl, and Orion: A Trilogy, 1991, Crowd and Not Evening or Light, 1992, Objects in the Terrifying Tense Longing from Taking Place, 1993, Goya's L.A., 1994, Defoe, 1995; editor: O One-An Anthology, 1988, O Two-An Anthology: What Is the Inside, What Is the Outside?, 1991, War: O-Three, 1991, Talking in Tranquility: Interviews with Ted Berrigan, 1991, Subliminal Time-O Four, 1993. Nat. Endowment for Arts fellow, 1976, sr. fellow, 1986. Office: 5729 Clover Dr Oakland CA 94618*

SCALES, JAMES RALPH, history educator, former university president; b. Jay, Okla., May 27, 1919; s. John Grover and Katie (Whitley) S.; m. Elizabeth Ann Randel, Aug. 4, 1944 (dec. Aug. 1992); children: Laura (dec.), Ann Catherine. B.A., Okla. Baptist U., 1939; M.A., U. Okla., 1941, Ph.D., 1949; postgrad., U. Chgo., 1941-42, 47-49, U. London, 1958; LL.D., Alderson Broaddus Coll., 1971, Duke U., 1976; Litt.D., No. Mich. U., 1972; L.H.D., Belmont Abbey Coll., 1981, Winston-Salem State U., 1984, William Jewell Coll., 1989. Reporter Miami (Okla.) News Record, 1934-35, Shawnee (Okla.) News-Star, 1935-36; instr. Okla. Baptist U., Shawnee, 1940-42, asst. prof., 1946-47, assoc. prof., 1947-51, prof. history, govt., 1951-61, v.p., 1950-53, exec. v.p., 1953-61, pres., 1961-65; dean arts and scis. Okla. State U., Stillwater, 1965-67; pres. Wake Forest U., Winston-Salem, N.C., 1967-83, Worrell prof. Anglo Am. studies, 1983—; founder Cimarron Rev., 1967. Mem. Pres.'s Com. Edn. Beyond High Sch., 1957; mem. adv. com. U.S. Army Command and Gen. Staff Coll., Ft. Leavenworth, Kans., 1969-72, chmn., 1971-72; mem. U.S. del. UNESCO, 1978-81. Co-author: Oklahoma Politics: A History, 1983. Okla. del. Dem. Nat. Conv., 1956; bd. dirs. N.C. Civil Liberties Union; trustee Belmont Abbey Coll., 1977-80; mem. Bapt. Joint Com. on Pub. Affairs, 1990—. Signal officer USN, 1942-45. Named to Okla. Hall of Fame, 1983. Mem. Am. Hist. Assn., Am. Polit. Sci. Assn., AAUP, So. Assn. Bapt. Colls. (pres. 1969-70), Am. Guild Organists, N.C. Assn. Ind. Colls. (pres. 1969-71), Winston-Salem C. of C. (dir.), Nat. League for Nursing (hon.), Cherokee West, Phi Beta Kappa, Omicron Delta Kappa, Baptist (deacon). Clubs: Rotary (Winston-Salem); University (N.Y.C.); Twin City (Winston-Salem); Bay Hill Golf and Country (Orlando, Fla.); Cape Fear (Wilmington, N.C.); Miles Grant Country (Port Salerno, Fla.); Reform (London). Home: 5401 Indiana Ave A2 Winston Salem NC 27106-2809

SCALES, RICHARD LEWIS, manufacturer's representative; b. Indpls., Nov. 16, 1928; s. Ortho Lorton and Nina L. (Julian) S.; m. E. Jean Rankin, Dec. 21, 1951; children: Richard, Allan, Anne. BSME, Purdue U., 1952. Rsch. and devel. engr. Bell Labs./Western Electric, Chgo. also Whippany, N.J., 1955-58; sales engr. Bodine Electric Co., Chgo., 1958-61; dist. sales mgr. Wabash (Ind.) Magnetics, 1961-66; founder, chmn. bd. (emeritus) Richard Scales Assocs., Wabash, 1966—, RSA Inc., Wabash, 1985—. Contbr. articles to mag. Elder, Presbyn. Ch. Lt. USNR, 1952-55, Korea. Mem. AAAS, Rotary (past pres. Wabash club, Paul Harris fellow 1987). Republican. Avocations: computers, photography. Home: 550 Sommers Ave Wabash IN 46992-2021 Office: Richard Scales Assocs Inc 84 W Market St Wabash IN 46992-3127

SCALETTA, PHILLIP RALPH, III, lawyer; b. Iowa City, Iowa, Dec. 18, 1949; s. Phillip Jasper and Helen M. (Beedle) S.; m. Karen Lynn Scaletta, May 13, 1973; children: Phillip, Anthony, Alexander. BSIM, Purdue U., 1972, MS, 1972; JD, Ind. U., 1975. Bar: Ind. 1975, U.S. Dist. Ct. Ind. 1975, Ill. 1993. Assoc. Ice Miller Donadio & Ryan, Indpls., 1975-81, ptnr., 1981—. Contbr. articles to profl. jours. Chmn. Ind. Continuing Legal Edn. Found., Indpls., 1989; mem. Environ. Quality Control Water Com., 1988—. Mem. Ind. Bar Assn., Indpls. Bar Assn., Def. Rsch. Inst., Internat. Assn. Def. Counsel, Gyro Club Indpls. (v.p. 1992-93, pres. 1993-94, bd. dirs 1990—). Avocations: golf, skiing, tennis. Home: 7256 Tuliptree Trl Indianapolis IN 46256-2136 Office: Ice Miller Donadio & Ryan 1 American Sq Indianapolis IN 46282-0001

SCALI, JOHN ALFRED, journalist; b. Canton, Ohio, Apr. 27, 1918; s. Paul M. and Lucy (Leone) S.; m. Helen Lauinger Glock, Aug. 30, 1945 (div. 1973); children: Donna Claire Scali Bordley, Paula Lucia Scali Wolf, Carla Scali Byrd; m. Denise St. Germain, Mar. 4, 1973. B.S. in Journalism, Boston U., 1942. Reporter Boston Herald, 1942, Boston bur. U.P., 1942-43; war corr. A.P., 1943-44, diplomatic corr. Washington Bur., 1945-61; diplomatic corr. ABC News, Washington, 1961-71; spl. cons. for fgn. affairs to Pres. U.S., 1971-73; U.S. ambassador to UN, N.Y.C., 1973-75; sr. corr. ABC News, Washington, 1975—. mem. adv. council Ariz. Heart Inst. mem. Internat. Heart Inst., Council Am. Ambassadors. Recipient Man of Year award in journalism Boston U., 1965, High Achievement award, 1986, Spl. award Overseas Press Clubs, 1965, Journalism award U. So. Calif., 1964, spl.

award Washington chpt. Nat. Acad. Arts and Scis., 1964; John Scali award created by Washington chpt. AFTRA, 1964. Mem. A.F.T.R.A.; Council on Fgn. Relations, Sigma Delta Chi. Club: Nat. Press (Washington). Office: ABC News Washington Bur 1717 Desales St NW Washington DC 20036-4407

SCALIA, ANTONIN, U.S. supreme court justice; b. Trenton, N.J., Mar. 11, 1936; s. S. Eugene and Catherine Louise (Panaro) S.; m. Maureen McCarthy, Sept. 10, 1960; children—Ann Forrest, Eugene, John Francis, Catherine Elisabeth, Mary Clare, Paul David, Matthew, Christopher James, Margaret Jane. A.B., Georgetown U., 1957; student, U. Fribourg, Switzerland, 1955-56; LL.B., Harvard, 1960. Bar: Ohio 1962, Va. 1970. Assoc. Jones Day Cockley & Reavis, Cleve., 1961-67; assoc. prof. U. Va. Law Sch., 1967-70; prof. law U. Va., 1970-74; gen. counsel Office Telecommunications Policy, Exec. Office of Pres., 1971-72; chmn. Adminstrv. Conf. U.S., Washington, 1972-74; asst. atty. gen. U.S. Office Legal Counsel, Justice Dept., 1974-77; vis. prof. Georgetown Law Center, 1977, Stanford Law Sch., 1980-81; vis. scholar Am. Enterprise Inst., 1977; prof. law U. Chgo., 1977-82; judge U.S. Ct. Appeals (D.C. cir.), 1982-86; justice U.S. Supreme Ct., Washington, 1986—. Editor: Regulation mag, 1979-82. Sheldon fellow Harvard U., 1960-61. Office: US Supreme Ct Supreme Ct Bldg 1 1st St NE Washington DC 20543-0002

SCALISE, FRANCIS ALLEN, adminstrator, consultant; b. Rochester, N.Y., Dec. 16, 1930; s. Sam and Margaret Rose (Seran) Scalise; children: Allen, Stephen. BS in Elem. Edn., SUNY, Brockport, 1952; MEd in Ednl. Adminstrn., U. Rochester, 1956. Tchr. Virgil I. Grissom Sch. 7, Rochester, 1955-60, acting prin., 1960-61; prin. Gen. Elwell S. Otis Sch. 30, Rochester, 1962-67, Susan B. Anthony Sch. 27, Rochester, 1967-71; prin. Dr. Louis A. Cerulli Sch. 34, Rochester, 1971-90, ret.; supr. student tchr. satellite sch., SUNY, Brockport, 1976-90; workshop presenter Wayne County Schs., Goldsboro, N.C., 1988. Team capt. new bldg. drive YMCA, Rochester, 1983; vol. ptnr. Compeer Psychiat. Program, Rochester, 1988; vol. Monroe County Dem. Com., Rochester, 1986, 89, 90. Recipient Community Svc. awards Neighborhood Hope, 1990, Rochester Police Dept., 1990. Mem. Sch. Adminstrs. Assn. N.Y. State, Adminstrs. and Suprs. Assn. Rochester, Phi Delta Kappa. Roman Catholic. Avocations: racquetball, world travel, photography. Home: 1000 East Ave 508 Rochester NY 14607

SCALISE, GEORGE MARTIN, electronics company executive; b. Warren, Pa., May 1, 1934; m. Dorothea K. McDonald, Apr. 28, 1962; children: Kathleen Marie, George Edward, Craig Thomas. B.S.M.E., Purdue U., 1956. Engr. CBS Electronics, Lowell, Mass., 1958-61; asst. gen. mgr. Motorola, Phoenix, 1961-67; gen. mgr. Motorola, Geneva, 1968; group dir. adminstrn. Fairchild, Mountain View, Calif., 1968-70, v.p., gen. mgr., 1970-74; v.p. adminstrn. and internat. ops. Advanced Micro Devices, Sunnyvale, Calif., 1974-81, sr. v.p., 1981-87; pres., chief exec. officer Maxtor Corp., San Jose, Calif., 1987—; dir. Microelectronics & Computer Tech. Corp.; chmn. bd. Semicondr. Research Corp., Research Triangle Park, N.C.; adviser U.S.-Japan Work Group on High Tech. Industries, 1983, U.S.-Japan Common Market Businessmen Adv. Group; adv. panel Tech. and Am. Econ. Transition, Office of Tech. Assessment. Mem. adv. council Engring. Found., U. Tex.-Austin Served with U.S. Army, 1956-58. Mem. Semicondr. Industry Assn. (chmn. pub. policy com. 1982—). Roman Catholic. Office: Maxtor Corp 211 River Oaks Pky San Jose CA 95134-1913

SCALISH, FRANK ANTHONY, labor union administrator; b. Cleve., Nov. 5, 1940; s. John T. and Tillie M. (Rockman) S.; m. Carla Rita Cinti, 1960; children: John M., Frank A., Tina Marie. Grad. high sch., Cleve. Bus. agt. Local Union #1 Textile Processors Svc. Trades, Health Care Profl. and Tech. Employees Internat., Cleve., 1962—; sec., treas. Local Union #1, Cleve., 1978—; v.p. Internat. Union, Chgo., 1969-84, gen. pres., 1984—. Bd dirs. Cleve. Opera Theater, 1981-84. Recipient Israel Solidarity award Israeli Bonds, 1983. Roman Catholic. Avocations: hunting, fishing, golf, grandchildren. Office: Texile Processors Service Trades Health Care Prof Tech Employees 303 E Wacker Dr Ste 1109 Chicago IL 60601-5212

SCALLEN, STEPHEN BURNS, law educator; b. Mpls., Aug. 24, 1932; s. Raymond A. and Lenore (Kaine) S. m. Chacké Yeterian, Dec. 28, 1963; children: Julie Ann, Nora Lynn. BA, Coll. St. Thomas, 1954; JD, U. Minn., 1959; MBA, U. Chgo., 1989. Bar: Minn. 1959, D.C. 1960. Assoc. Covington & Burling, Washington, 1959-61; prof. law U. Minn., Mpls., 1961—; cons., 1961—; rsch. fellow Harvard Law Sch., 1965-66; vis. prof. Jean Moulin U., Lyon, France, 1981, 82, Jiling U., Peoples Republic of China, 1984. Pres. Minn. Law Rev., 1958-59; contbr. articles to profl. jours. Trustee St. Thomas Acad., Mendota, Minn., 1982-88, Visitation Sch., Mendota, 1984-91. Capt. USAF, 1955-57. Mem. ABA, Minn. State Bar Assn., Hennepin County Bar Assn. Home: 3574 Northome Rd Wayzata MN 55391-3019 Office: U Minn Law Sch 229 19th Ave S Minneapolis MN 55455-0400

SCALLEN, THOMAS KAINE, broadcasting executive; b. Mpls., Aug. 14, 1925; s. Raymond A. and Lenore (Kaine) S.; m. Bille Jo Brice; children by previous marriage: Thomas, Sheila, Patrick, Eileen, Timothy and Maureen (twins). BA, St. Thomas Coll., 1949; JD, U. Denver, 1950. Bar: Minn. Asst. atty. gen. State of Minn., Mpls., 1950-55; sole practice Mpls., 1955-57; pres. Med. Investment Corp., Mpls., 1957—; Internat. Broadcasting Corp. Mpls., 1977—; owner Harlem Globetrotters; pres., exec. producer Ice Capades; chmn. bd. dirs. Century Park Pictures Corp., Los Angeles, Calif.; bd. dirs. Blaine-Thompson Co., Inc., N.Y.C; chmn. Apache Plastics, Inc., Stockton, Calif. Served with AUS. Mem. World Pres. Orgn., Minn. Club, Calhoun Beach Club, L.A. Athletic Club. Clubs: University (St. Paul, Mpls.), Rochester (Minn.) Golf and Country, Edina (Minn.) Country, Athletic (Mpls.). Home: Heron Cove Windham NH 03087 Office: Internat Broadcasting Corp 80 S 8th St IDS Center #4701 Minneapolis MN 55402-2113

SCALLEY, JOHN J., automotive parts company executive; b. 1930. BS, Ga. Inst. Tech., 1951. With Genuine Parts Co., Atlanta, 1951—, various mgmt. positions, 1951-74, v.p. S.E. div., 1974-77, now exec. v.p. Office: Genuine Parts Co 2999 Circle 75 Pky NW Atlanta GA 30339-3050

SCAMMELL, MICHAEL, foreign language educator, translator, writer; b. Lyndhurst, Hampshire, Eng., Jan. 16, 1935; s. Frederick George Talbot and Estelle Constance (Ayling) S.; m. Erika Roettges, Feb. 17, 1962 (div.); m. Rosemary Alise Nossiff, Aug. 11, 1990. BA with 1st Class Honours in Modern Langs., Nottingham (Eng.) U., 1958; PhD in Slavic Langs. and Lits., Columbia U., 1985. Lectr. in English Lang. and Lit. U. Ljubljana, Yugoslavia, 1958-59; instr. Russian Lang. and Lit. CCNY, 1961-63; dir. East European exchange program, N.Y. Inst. Humanities N.Y.U., N.Y.C., 1982-84; prof. dept. Russian Lit. Cornell U., Ithaca, N.Y., 1987—, chair dept., 1987-92, dir. Soviet and East European Studies program, 1989-92; bd. dirs. Internat. Ctr. Devel. Policy; freelance translator N.Y., London, 1962-65, London, 1967-71; lang. supr., programme asst. external svcs. East European divsn., BBC, London, 1965-67; vis. prog. dept. Russian Lit. Cornell U., Ithaca, 1986-87. Author: Blue Guide to Yugoslavia, the Adriatic Coast, 1969, Solzhenitsyn, a Biography, 1984 (L.A. Times Book prize 1984, Silver PEN award 1985); editor: Russia's Other Writers, 1970, La letteratura contemporanea nell'Europa dell'Est, 1977, Unofficial Art from the Soviet Union, 1977; translator: Cities and Years (Konstantin Fedin) 1962, Crime and Punishment (Fyodor Dostoyevsky) 1963, The Gift (Vladimir Nabokov) 1963, The Defence (Vladimir Nabokov) 1964, Childhood, Boyhood & Youth (Leo Tolstoy) 1964, My Testimony (Anatoly Marchenko) 1969, To Build a Castle (Vladimir Bukovsky) 1978; author introduction Ressurection (Leo Tolstoy) 1963; contbg. translator various Slavic poetry anthologies; contbr. articles to profl. jours., reviews to newspapers. Internat. adv. com. Robert F. Kennedy Meml. Human Rights award, Washington, 1985—. Cadet, Brit. Intelligence Corps, 1953-55. Post-grad. fellow Columbia U., 1959-61, sr. vis. fellow, 1981-83, fellow, then assoc. fellow, N.Y.U., 1982-86, fellow Kennan Inst. Advanced Russian Studies, 1985, Post-doctoral fellow Harvard U., 1986; grantee Rockefeller Found., 1979, Ford Found., 1981-82, Leverhulme Trust, 1981-82; recipient Writers' bursary award Arts Coun. Gt. Britain 1981, Humanities Divsn. award Ford Found., 1982-83. Mem. PEN (v.p. 1984—), Internat. Acad. Scholarship and the Arts (bd. dirs. 1986—). Avocations: theatre, tennis, sailing. Office: Cornell U Dept Russian Literature 236 Goldwin Smith Hall Ithaca NY 14853-3201

SCAMMON, RICHARD MONTGOMERY, political scientist; b. Mpls., July 17, 1915; s. Richard Everingham and Julia (Simms) S.; m. Mary Stark Allen., Feb. 20, 1952; 1 dau., Anne Valerie. A.B., U. Minn., 1935; A.M., U. Mich., 1938. Rsch. sec., radio office U. Chgo., 1939-41; with Office Mil. Govt. for Germany, U.S., 1945-48; chief, div. rsch. for Western Europe Dept. of State, 1948-55; dir. Elections Rsch. Center, 1955-61, 65—; elections cons. NBC News, 1965-89; vis. fellow Am. Enterprise Inst.; mem. Israeli-Am. Electoral Conf., 1989; cons. to State Dept., 1979-80; dir. Bur. Census, Dept. Commerce, 1961-65. Co-author: The Real Majority; Editor: America Votes, America at the Polls. Chmn. U.S. delegation observe elections in, USSR, 1958; chmn. Pres.'s Commn. Registration and Voting Participation, 1963; mem. OAS electoral mission to, Dominican Republic, 1966; mem. Pres.'s Commn. to observe elections in Viet Nam, 1967; chmn. U.S. Select Commn. Western Hemisphere Immigration, 1966-68; pres. Nat. Council on Pub. Polls, 1969-70; mem. Pres.'s Commn. on Fed. Statistics, 1970-71, U.S. delegation Gen. Assembly UN, 1973, U.S. delegation observe elections in El Salvador, 1982; mem. Nat. Bipartisan Commn. on Central Am., 1983-84. Served with U.S. Army, 1941-46. Mem. Am. Polit. Sci. Assn., Am. Acad. Polit. and Social Sci., Acad. Polit. Sci. Club: Cosmos (Washington). Home: 5508 Greystone St Chevy Chase MD 20815-5534

SCANDALIOS, JOHN GEORGE, geneticist, educator; b. Nisyros Isle, Greece, Nov. 1, 1934; s. George John and Calliope (Broujos) S.; m. Penelope Anne Lawrence, Jan. 18, 1961; children: Artemis Christina, Melissa Joan, Nikki Eleni. B.A., U. Va., 1957; M.S., Adelphi U., 1960; Ph.D., U. Hawaii, 1965; D.Sc. (hon.), Aristotelian U. Thessaloniki, Greece, 1986. Assoc. in bacterial genetics Cold Spring Harbor Labs., 1960-62; NIH postdoctoral fellow U. Hawaii Med. Sch., 1965; asst. prof. Mich. State U., East Lansing, 1965-70; assoc. prof. Mich. State U., 1970-72; prof., head dept. biology U. S.C., Columbia, 1973-75; prof., head dept. genetics N.C. State U., Raleigh, 1975-85; disting. univ. research prof. N.C. State U., 1985—; mem. Inst. Molecular Biology and Biotechnology, Research. Ctr. Crete, Greece; vis. prof. genetics U. Calif., Davis, 1969; vis. prof. OAS, Argentina, Chile and Brazil, 1972; mem. recombinant DNA adv. com. NIH. Author: Physiological Genetics, 1979; editor: Developmental Genetics, Advances in Genetics, Current Topics in Medical and Biological Research; co-editor: Isozymes, 4 vols., 1975, Monographs in Developmental Biology, 1968-86; molecular biology editor Physiol. Plant, 1988—. Served with USAF, 1957. Alexander von Humboldt travel fellow, 1976; mem. exchange program NAS, U.S.-USSR. Fellow AAAS; mem. Genetics Soc. Am., Am. Soc. Biochemistry and Molecular Biology, Am. Genetic Assn. (pres.), Soc. Devel. Biology (dir.), Am. Inst. Biol. Scis., Am. Soc. Plant Physiologists, N.Y. Acad. Scis., Sigma Xi. Office: NC State U Dept Genetics PO Box 7614 Raleigh NC 27695

SCANDARY, E. JANE, special education educator, consultant; b. Saginaw, Mich., Sept. 12, 1923; d. Leonard William and Reva Charlotte (Smith) Leipprandt; m. Theodore John Scandary; children: John S., Robert G. BA, Mich. State U., East Lansing, 1945, EdS, 1963, PhD, 1968; MEd, Wayne State U., 1951. Cert. secondary and spl. edn. tchr., Mich. Therapist speech and lang. Ann J. Kellogg Sch., Battle Creek, Mich., 1945-47; supr. speech therapy programs Wayne County Schs., Detroit, 1948-52; supr. programs for phys., hearing and visually impaired Ingham Intermediate Schs., Mason, Mich., 1960-78; spl. edn. cons. Mich. Dept. of Edn., Lansing, 1978-87, Livingston Intermediate Schs., Howell, Mich., 1987—; rsch. assoc. Mich. State U., East Lansing, 1965-66, adj. prof., 1969-75, 81-82; mem. adv. com. China-U.S. Sci. Exchange Program Spl. Edn.; guest lectr. seminars spl. edn. Australia, Eng., Iran, Israel, Aruba, Germany, Scotland. Contbr. articles to profl. jours. Vol. Physically Impaired Assn. of Mich. Assistance Ctr., Lansing, 1987-89; chair Mich. Dept. Edn. Futures Com., 1992, editor, chair Task Force Futures in Spl. Edn; 2000 AD and Beyond, 1992. 1st Chance Early Childhood grantee, 1972-78; recipient Resolution of Tribute Mich. State Senate, 1986; Scandary award for outstanding contbrs. early childhood edn. established in her name, 1990. Mem. Nat. Coun. Exceptional Children (field editor 1976-86, pres. div. physically handicapped 1982-83), Internat. Coun. Edn. Visually Handicapped, World Future Soc. Avocations: painting, writing, reading, creative sewing.

SCANDLING, WILLIAM FREDRIC, retired food service company executive; b. Rochester, N.Y., June 17, 1922; s. Fredric D. and Helen T. (Moran) S.; m. Margaret Warner, Apr. 19, 1949 (dec.); 1 child, Michael. A.B., Hobart Coll., 1949, LL.D. (hon.), 1967. Co-founding ptnr. ALS & Co., Geneva, N.Y., 1948, Saga Corp., Geneva, N.Y., 1949; co-founding ptnr. Saga Corp. (ALS and Saga Corp. merged) Menlo Park, Calif., 1962, dir.; 1949-86, sec.-treas., 1949-68, pres., 1968-78, founder, dir., 1978-86; dir. Empire Broadcasting Corp., 1975-82; pres. Auburn Broadcasting Corp., Calif., 1975-82, dir., 1982-86. Trustee Hobart and William Smith Coll., Geneva, 1967—, chmn. 1971-82; trustee Deep Springs Coll., Calif., 1984-92, Nat. Council Salk Inst.; chmn., bd. dirs. Community Found. Santa Clara County, Calif., 1988-91. With USAAF, 1943-45. Mem. Kappa Alpha Soc., Menlo Country Club ((Woodside, Calif.), Seneca Yacht Club (Geneva), Genesee Valley Club (Rochester, N.Y.). Home: 38 Barry Ln Menlo Park CA 94027-4023

SCANDURA, JOSEPH MICHAEL, education researcher, software engineer; b. Bay Shore, N.Y., Apr. 29, 1932; s. Joseph and Lucy Stella S.; m. Alice Baker Scandura; children—Jeanne, Janette, Joseph, Julie. AB, U. Mich., 1953, MA, 1955; PhD, Syracuse U., 1962; postdoctoral, Stanford U., summer 1964, 68-69, U. Calif.-Berkeley, summer 1968, MIT, summer 1972; postgrad., U. Kiel, W.Ger., 1975, Inst. Ednl. Tech., Italy, summer 1978. Tchr. math., sci. White Plains, Bay Shore, 1953-56; instr. math., head wrestling coach Syracuse U., N.Y., 1956-63; asst. prof. edn., math. SUNY-Buffalo, 1963-64; research asst. prof. math. edn. Fla. State U., Tallahassee, 1964-66; dir. instructional systems, structural learning U. Pa., Phila., 1966—; founder, chmn. Intelligent Micro Systems, Narberth, Pa., 1978—; chmn. bd. sci. advisors MERGE Rsch. Inst., 1973; cons. jours., govt. agys., pub. cons., 1967—; cons. U.S. Office Edn., NSF, NAS, Tex. Instruments, Borg-Warner, U.S. Army; organizer, lectr., participant profl. confs., 1963—; dir. NATO Advanced Study Inst. on Structural Process Theories of Complex Human Behavior, 1977; coach undefeated Ea. Intercollegiate Wrestling Championship Team, 1963. Author: Mathematics - Concrete Behavioral Foundations, 1971, (with others) An Algorithmic Approach to Mathematics - Concrete Behavioral Foundations, 1971, Structural Learning I - Theory and Research, 1973, Problem Solving - A Structural Process Approach with Instructional Implications, 1977, (with A.B. Scandura) Structural Learning and Concrete Operations - An Approach to Piagetian Conservation, 1980, Cognitive Approach to Software Development, 1988, Prodoc (comprehensive suite of software devel. and maintenance tools), 1989, Cognitive Approach to Software Engineering and Re-engineering, 1991, Research on Program Modification under program control, 1992, NATO Advanced Study Inst., 1993, Automated Software Conversions and Re-engineering, 1993; contbr. over 170 articles to profl. jours.; editor: Research in Mathematics Education, 1967, Structural Learning II - Issues and Approaches, 1976, (with C.J. Brainerd) Structural Process Models of Complex Human Behavior, 1978; developer, producer numerous computer-based instructional systems and software devel. systems; patentee in field. Recipient Rensselaer award, 1949, Bausch and Lomb award, 1949, Nat. AAU Wrestling Champion and Outstanding Wrestler award, 1955; Fulbright scholar, 1975-76; U.S. Office Edn. fellow, 1978-79. Fellow APA (chmn. E.L. Thorndike award com. 1974-79); mem. AAUP, IEEE, Assn. Computing Machinery, Am. Ednl. Rsch. Assn. (past com. chmn.), Nat. Coun. Tchrs. Math. (past fed. funds com. chmn.), Math. Assn. Am., Psychonomic Soc., Structural Learning Soc. (chmn. 1969-80, 85-88, 95—, editor in chief Jour. Structural Learning 1976-90, Jour. Structural Learning and Intelligent Systems 1990—), Unif. Profs. for Acad. Order, Phi Kappa Phi, Phi Eta Sigma, Phi Delta Kappa. Home: 1249 Greentree Ln Narberth PA 19072-1219 Office: U Pa Instructional Systems Philadelphia PA 19104 *Accomodation to – as well as leadership of – groups, institutions and/or societies is an essential ingredient of success in most walks of life. There are circumstances, however, which require inner direction, whether developing a new scientific paradigm or standing firm against political pressures. Although vindication is rarely complete and often delayed, following one's best instincts yields its own rewards—perhaps the satisfaction of ultimately being proven right but more often simply knowing one did what had to be done.*

SCANLAN, JAMES PATRICK, philosophy and Slavic studies educator; b. Chgo., Feb. 22, 1927; s. Gilbert Francis and Helen (Meyers) S.; m. Marilyn A. Morrison, June 12, 1948.; BA, U. Chgo., 1948, MA, 1950, PhD, 1956.

Research fellow Inst. Philos. Research, San Francisco, 1953-55; instr. Case Inst. Tech., Cleve., 1955-56; from instr. to assoc. prof. Goucher Coll., Balt., 1956-68; prof. dir. Slavic Ctr. U. Kans., Lawrence, 1968-70; prof. Ohio State U., Columbus, 1971-91, dir. Slavic Ctr., 1988-91, prof. emeritus, 1992—; vis. rsch. scholar Moscow State U., 1964-65, 69, Acad. Scis. USSR, Moscow, 1978, 93, fgn. vis. fellow Slavic Rsch. Ctr., Hokkaido U., Sapporo, Japan, 1987-88. Author: Marxism in the USSR, 1985; editor: Historical Letters by Peter Lavrov, 1967, Soviet Studies in Philosophy, 1987-92, Russian Studies in Philosophy, 1992—, Technology, Culture and Development: The Experience of the Soviet Model, 1992, Russian Thought After Communism, 1994; co-editor: Russian Philosophy, 1965, Marxism and Religion in Eastern Europe, 1976. Served with USMC, 1945-46. Woodrow Wilson Internat. Ctr. fellow, 1982; recipient Translation award Nat. Translation Ctr., 1967, Faculty Research award Fulbright-Hays, 1982-83. Mem. Am. Philos. Assn., Am. Assn. Advancement Slavic Studies, Phi Beta Kappa. Home: 1000 Urlin Ave Apt 206 Columbus OH 43212-3324

SCANLAN, JOHN DOUGLAS, foreign service officer, former ambassador; b. Thief River Falls, Minn., Dec. 20, 1927; s. Paul Douglas and Ruby (Bennes) S.; m. Margaret Anne Calvi; children: Kathleen, Michael, Malia, John. B.A., U. Minn., 1952, M.A. in Russian Studies, 1955. Instr. U. Minn., 1955; Soviet research analyst U.S. Dept. State, Washington, 1956-58; third sec. Am. Embassy, Moscow, 1958-60; cultural attache Am. Embassy, Warsaw, 1961-65; second sec. Am. Embassy, Montevideo, 1966-67; prin. officer Am. Consulate, Poznan, Poland, 1967-69; sr. rep. to U.S. Dept. Defense, Washington, 1969-71; desk officer U.S.-Soviet bilateral relations, 1971-73; polit. counselor Am. Embassy, Warsaw, 1973-75; mem. state exec. seminar Washington, 1975-76; spl. asst. to Dir. Gen. of Fgn. Service, 1976-77; dep. dir. for Europe, USIA, 1977-79; dep. chief Mission in Belgrade, Yugoslavia, 1979-81; dep. asst. sec. of state for European affairs, 1981-82; fgn. affairs fellow Fletcher Sch. Law and Diplomacy, Tufts U., 1983-84; chmn. U.S. del. to Conf. on Security and Coop. in Europe, Cultural Forum Preparatory Conf., Budapest, 1984; amb. to Yugoslavia, Am. Embassy, Belgrade, 1985-89; dep. comdt. U.S. Army War Coll., Carlisle Barracks, Pa., 1989-91; v.p. East EUR, ICN Pharmaceuticals Inc.; mem. bd. Am. Drug Co., Project on Ethnic Rels.; mem. Kissinger-Sobchak St. Petersburg Commn., CSIS U.S.- European-Poland Action Commn.; adv. coun. ABA CEELI project. Mem. Planning Commn., Falls Church, Va., 1972-73, City Council, 1975-79. Recipient Presdl. Meritorious Service award for Diplomacy, 1984.

SCANLAN, JOHN JOSEPH, retired bishop; b. Ihiscarra, County Cork, Ireland, May 24, 1906; came to U.S., 1930; s. Peter Scanlan and Katherine Coleman. Student, Hallows Coll., Dublin, Ireland, 1923-30; LLD (hon.), Portland U., 1966; LHD (hon.), U. Hawaii, 1980. Ordained priest Roman Cath. Ch., 1930. Asst. pastor Archiodese of San Francisco, 1930-50, pastor, 1950-54; aux. bishop Diocese of Honolulu, 1954-67, ordinary bishop, 1968-81, adminstr., 1981-82, ret., 1982; dir. archdiocesan coun. cath. men Archdiocese of San Francisco, 1952-54; mem. Cath. Philosophic Assn., San Francisco, 1940-50. Mem. Nat. Coun. Cath. Bishops. Home: Nazareth House 245 Nova Albion Way San Rafael CA 94903

SCANLAN, MICHAEL, priest, academic administrator; b. Far Rockaway, N.Y., Dec. 1, 1931; s. Vincent Michael and Marjorie (O'Keefe) S. BA, Williams Coll., 1953; JD, Harvard U., 1956; MDiv, St. Francis Sem., Loretto, Pa., 1975; LittD (hon.), Coll. Steubenville, 1972; LLD (hon.), Williams Coll., Williamstown, Mass., 1978; PdD (hon.), St. Francis Coll., Loretto, Pa., 1987. Ordained priest Roman Catholic Ch., 1964; Cross Pro Ecclesia et Pontifice, 1990. Acting dean Coll. Steubenville, Ohio, 1964-66, dean, 1966-69; rector pres. St. Francis Major Sem. Loretto, Pa., 1969-74; pres. Franciscan U. Steubenville, 1974—; mem. Pa. Fullbright Com., 1974; pres. FIRE Cath. Alliance for Faith, Intercession, Repentence and Evangelism, 1984—. Author: The Power in Penance, 1972, Inner Healing, 1974, A Portion of My Spirit, 1979, The San Damiano Cross, 1983, Turn to the Lord-A Call to Repentance, 1989, The Truth About Trouble, 1989; mem. editorial bd. New Covenant mag., 1985-92. Mem. Diocese of Steubenville Ecumenical Commn., 1964-69; bd. dirs. Rumor Control Ctr., Steubenville, 1968-69, C. of C., Steubenville, 1976-79; bd. trustees St. Francis Prep. Sch., Spring Grove, Pa., 1969-74; vice-chmn., bd. trustees St. Francis Coll., Loretto, Pa., 1969-74; trustee United Way, Steubenville, 1975-80; chmn. nat. svc. com. Cath. Charismatic Renewal, 1975-78. Staff judge adv. USAF, 1956-57. Mem. Assn. Ind. Colls. and Univs. Ohio (sec. 1980-82), Nat. Cath. Edn. Assn. (vice-chmn. 1968-69), Cath. Edn. Assn. Pa. (chmn. sem. divsn. 1973), Ea. Major Sem.Rectors (sec. 1969), Fellowship of Cath. Scholars, Legatus. Roman Catholic. Avocations: tennis, golf. Office: Franciscan U Franciscan Way Steubenville OH 43952 *If you are going to change something, you've got to live on vision, before you live on reality. You have to be so inspired by the vision, that you keep telling everybody until it gets in them, and they start living it with you.*

SCANLAN, RICHARD THOMAS, classics educator; b. St. Paul, May 30, 1928; s. Robert Lawrence and Catherine (Krackroth) S.; m. Donna Mary Campion, Dec. 29, 1951; children: John, Susan, Catherine, Anne, Margaret. B.S., U. Minn., 1951, M.A., 1952. Tchr. Hastings High Sch., Minn., 1953-55, Edina High Sch., Minn., 1955-67; prof. classics U. Ill., Urbana, 1967—; ednl. cons. 1960-75. co-author: Power in Words, 1983; computer courses, 1975, 77; Myths of Greece and Rome, 1986. Pres. bd. trustees Champaign Libr., 1980-92. With U.S. Army, 1946-48, Italy. Named Excellent Tchr. Am. Classical League, 1966; recipient Silver medal Nat. Coun. for Advancement of Edn., 1985. Mem. Am. Philol. Assn., Am. Classical League, Archaeol. Assn., Classical Assn. (Excellent Tchr.award 1974). Roman Catholic. Home: 2103 Noel Dr Champaign IL 61821-6552 Office: Univ of Ill Dept of Classics Urbana IL 61801

SCANLAN, THOMAS CLEARY, publishing executive, editor; b. Birmingham, Mich., May 18, 1957; s. Thomas Matthew and Emily (Cleary) S.; m. Sally Sachs, June 20, 1981; children: Bridget C., Thomas M., Patrick J. BS, St. Louis U., 1979. Salesman Walter Heller Co., Chgo., 1979-82; pub., editor Surplus Record, Inc., Chgo., 1982—. Office: Surplus Record Inc 20 N Wacker Dr Chicago IL 60606-2806

SCANLAN, THOMAS JOSEPH, college president, educator; b. N.Y.C., Mar. 5, 1945; s. Thomas Joseph and Anna Marie (Schmitt) S. BA in Physics, Cath. U. Am., 1967; MA in Math., NYU, 1972; PhD in Bus. Adminstrn., Columbia U., 1978. Prin. Queen of Peace High Sch., North Arlington, N.J., 1972-75; dir. fin., edn. N.Y. Province, Bros. of Christian Schs., Lincroft, N.J., 1978-81; vice chancellor Bethlehem (Israel) U., 1981-87; pres. Manhattan Coll., Bronx, N.Y., 1987—; trustee Commn. Ind. Colls. & Univs., 1994—, First Xerox Life Ins. Co., 1993—. Trustee Lewis U., Romeoville, Ill., 1987—; bd. trustees Commn. on Ind. Colls. & Univs., 1994—, Assn. Cath. Colls. and Univs., 1994—. Recipient Pro Ecclesia et Pontifice medal, Pope John Paul II, Vatican City, 1986. Mem. Bros. of Christian Schs., Am. Coun. Edn., Assn. Cath. Colls. and Univs. (trustee 1994—), Assn. Cath. Colls. and Univs., Nat. Assn. Ind. Colls. and Univs., Nat. Collegiate Athletic Assn. (mem. pres. commn.), Metro Atlantic Athletic Assn., Equestrian Order of the Holy Sepulchre of Jerusalem, Phi Beta Kappa, Beta Gamma Sigma. Avocations: tennis, reading, movies. Office: Manhattan Coll Manhattan Coll Pky Bronx NY 10471-3913

SCANLON, ANDREW, structural engineering educator. Prof. structural engring. Pa. State U., University Pk. Recipient Le Prix P.L. Pratley award Can. Soc. Civil Engring., 1990. Office: Pa State U 212 Sackett Bldg University Park PA 16802

SCANLON, CHARLES FRANCIS, army officer, retired, defense consultant; b. Nashville, Jan. 31, 1935; s. Francis James Gordon and Dorothy Rose (Compton) S.; m. Barbara Jean Schoen, Oct. 9, 1954; children: Teri, Brett, Ashlyn, Kellie. BA in Polit. Sci., U. Fla., 1960; grad., Command and Gen. Staff Coll., Ft. Leavenworth, Kans., 1970, Naval War Coll., Newport, R.I., 1977; MA in Am. Studies, U. Hawaii, 1974; postgrad., Pa. State U., 1982, Harvard U., 1984, 1992. Commd. 2d lt. U.S. Army, 1960, advanced through grades to maj. gen., 1988; chief collection U.S. Army Europe, Heidelberg, Germany, 1977-78; comdg. officer 66th Mil. Intelligence Brigade, Munich, 1978-80; chief ops. U.S. Army Intelligence and Security Command, Arlington, Va., 1980-82; exec. officer Dept. Army Asst. Chief Staff Intelligence, Washington, 1982-83; dep. commdr. gen. U.S. Army Intelligence and Security Command, Arlington 1983-85; dir. estimates Def.

Intelligence Agy., Washington, 1985-86, dir. attaches, 1986-90; comdg. gen. U.S. Army Intelligence and Security Command, Ft. Belvoir, Va., 1990-93; ret., 1993; pres. Def. and Internat. Consulting Svcs. Consulting Svcs. Scantec, Ltd., Fairfax Station, Va., 1993—. Decorated Def. D.S.M., Army D.S.M., Nat. Intelligence D.S.M., Legion of Merit with 3 oak leaf clusters, Bronze Star with 2 oak leaf clusters. Mem. Assocn. U.S. Army, Nat. Mil. Intelligence Assn. (pres. 1974-76), Sigma Nu. Baptist. Avocations: boating, scuba diving, racquetball, soaring, reading. Home: 8036 Oak Hollow Ln Fairfax Station VA 22039 Office: 9419 Braymore Cir Fairfax Station VA 22039 also: 3048 Savannah Way Melbourne FL 32933

SCANLON, DOROTHY THERESE, history educator; b. Bridgeport, Conn., Oct. 7, 1928; d. George F. and Mazie (Reardon) S.; A.B., U. Pa. 1948, M.A., 1949; M.A., Boston Coll., 1953; Ph.D., Boston U., 1956; postdoctoral scholar Harvard U., 1962-64, 72. Tchr. history and Latin Marycliff Acad., Winchester, Mass., 1950-52; tchr. history Girls Latin Sch., Boston, 1952-57; prof. Boston State Coll., 1957-82, Mass. Coll. Art, 1982—. Recipient Disting. Service award Boston State Coll., 1979, Faculty Award of Excellence, Mass. Coll. Art, 1985, Faculty Disting. Service award, Mass. Coll. Art, 1987. Mem. Pan-Am. Soc., Latin Am. Studies Assn., Am. Hist. Assn., Orgn. Am. Historians, Am. Studies Assn., Am. Assn. History of Medicine, History of Sci. Soc., AAUP, AAUW, Phi Alpha Theta, Delta Kappa Gamma. Author: Instructor's Manual to Accompany Lewis Hanke, Latin America: A Historical Reader, 1974; contbr. Biographical Dictionary of Social Welfare, 1986. Home: 140 Thornton Rd Chestnut Hill MA 02167-3638 Office: Mass Coll Art Dept History 621 Huntington Ave Boston MA 02115-5878

SCANLON, EDWARD C., clinical psychologist; b. Bradford, Pa., Dec. 3, 1931; s. Edward John Scanlan and Martha (Karlous) Charles; m. Constance Morgan, May 19, 1962 (div. Jan. 1976); 1 child, Heather Marie. AB cum laude, SUNY, Buffalo, 1954; EdM, Harvard U., 1958, EdD, 1961; postgrad., Columbia U. Lic. psychologist, Pa. Assoc. prof. Lehigh U., Bethlehem, Pa., 1961-66; acad. dean Montgomery County C.C., Conshahocken, Pa., 1966-69; acting. dir. home sch. Wilkes Coll., Wilkes Barre, Pa., 1968-71; clin. psychologist dept. human svcs. mental health and mental retardation Easton, Pa., 1972—; vis. prof. clin. psychology Clinic Mental Health and Mental Retardation, Pottsville, Pa., 1971-72. Capt. USAF, 1954-57. Thayer scholar Harvard U. Mem. APA, Pa. Psychol. Assn., Harvard Club of Phila., Lehigh Country Club, Masons, Phi Beta Kappa. Democrat. Anglican. Avocations: classic automobiles, psychoanalytic studies.

SCANLON, EDWARD F., surgeon, educator; b. Waynesburg, Pa., Sept. 15, 1918; s. Hugh and Ellen S.; m. Virginia K. Scanlon, June 26, 1948; children: Cathy, Mary, Sally. B.S., Kenyon Coll., 1940, D.Sc. (hon.), 1983; M.D., Columbia U., 1943. Intern St. Luke's Presbyn. Hosp., Chgo., 1944; resident in surgery St. Luke's Presbyn. Hosp., 1946-50, Meml. Sloan Kettering, N.Y.C., 1950-53; fellow Meml Sloan Kettering, 1953; mem. staff Evanston Hosp, Ill., 1953-89; chmn. dept. surgery Evanston Hosp, 1974-86; mem. faculty dept. surgery Northwestern U. Med. Sch., Chgo., 1953—, prof. surgery, 1971—, chief surg. oncology, 1974-86, emeritus prof. 1989—. Mem. editorial adv. bd. Cancer Treatment Reports, 1976-80, Jour. Surg. Oncology, 1982-93, Internat. Jour. Breast and Mammary Pathology, 1982-93, Seminars in Surg. Oncology, 1982-93; contbr. articles to med. jours. Bd. dirs. Evanston Hosp., 1977-86. Served with M.C., U.S. Army, 1944-46. Recipient Am. Cancer Soc. annual divisional award, 1978; Hayes Martin lectr., 1979; James Ewing lectr., 1984. Fellow ACS (bd. govs. 1971-76); mem. Soc. Surg. Oncology (pres. 1974-75), Am. Cancer Soc. (pres. 1980-81), Internat. Union Against Cancer (com. internat. collaborative activities), Am. Surg. Assn., Soc. Head and Neck Surgeons (treas. 1974), Western Surg. Assn., Central Surg. Assn., Chgo. Surg. Soc., Phi Beta Kappa. Home: 1338 Edgewood Ln Northbrook IL 60062-4716

SCANLON, EUGENE FRANCIS, lawyer; b. Pitts., Oct. 15, 1947; s. Eugene F. and Ann Elizabeth (Boyle) S.; married; children: Brian P., Bradley M. BA, U. Pitts., 1969; JD, Duquesne U., 1972. Bar: Pa. 1972, U.S. Dist. Ct. (we. dist.) Pa. 1972, U.S. Ct. Appeals (3d cir.) 1973, U.S. Supreme Ct. 1983. Assoc. Dickie, McCamey & Chilcote, P.C., Pitts., 1972—. Bd. dirs. Pitts. sect. Am. Cancer Soc., 1980-87, Pitts. sect. Cystic Fibrosis Found. 1985—, pres. bd. dirs., 1992—. Mem. ABA, Pa. Bar Assn., Allegheny County Bar Assn., Internat. Assn. Def. Counsel, Pa. Def. Inst. (bd. dirs. 1980-87, pres. 1984-85). Democrat. Roman Catholic. Office: Dickie McCamey & Chilcote 2 Ppg Pl Ste 400 Pittsburgh PA 15222-5491

SCANLON, JANE CRONIN, mathematics educator; b. N.Y.C., July 17, 1922; d. John Timothy and Janet Smiley (Murphy) Cronin; m. Joseph C. Scanlon, Mar. 5, 1953 (div.); children: Justin, Mary, Anne, Edmund. Student, Highland Park Jr. Coll., 1939-41; BS, Wayne State U., 1943; MA, U. Mich., 1945, PhD, 1949. Mathematician Air Force Cambridge Research Center, 1951-54; instr. Wheaton Coll., Norton, Mass., 1954-55; asst. prof. Poly. Inst. Bklyn., 1957-58, asso. prof., 1958-60, prof., 1960-65; prof. math. Rutgers U., New Brunswick, N.J., 1965-91, prof. emerita, 1991—; cons. Singer-Kearfott Div., Naval Research Lab. Office Naval Research Fellow Princeton, 1948-49; Horace H. Rockham Postdoctoral fellow U. Mich., 1950-51, Rutgers Research Council fellow, 1968-69, 72-73; NSF vis. professorship for women Courant Inst., NYU, 1984-85. Author: Fixed Points and Topological Degree in Nonlinear Analysis, 1964, Advanced Calculus, 1967, Differential Equations: Introduction and Qualitative Theory, 1980, 2d edit., 1994, Mathematics of Cell Electrophysiology, 1980, Mathematical Aspects of Hodgkin-Huxley Neural Theory, 1987. Mem. Am. Math. Soc., Soc. for Indsl. and Applied Math., Math. Assn. Am., Internat. Soc. Chronobiology. Home: 110 Valentine St Highland Park NJ 08904-2106 Office: Rutgers U Dept Math New Brunswick NJ 08903

SCANLON, PATRICK MICHAEL, lawyer; b. Welch, W.Va., May 16, 1940; s. John Michael Scanlon and Jean Elizabeth (Hatfield) Irving; m. Joyce Janifer Haythorn, Feb. 27, 1965 (div. 1980); children: Alison Margaret, Janifer Colleen; m. Laura Reeves, Mar. 15, 1980; 1 child, Patrick Reeves. BA in Polit. Sci., U. Fla., 1965; JD, Stetson U., 1968. Bar: U.S. Dist. Ct. (no. dist.) Fla. 1969, U.S. Dist. Ct. (mid. dist.) Fla. 1971, U.S. Ct. Appeals (5th cir.) 1972, U.S. Supreme Ct. 1973, U.S. Ct. Appeals (6th cir.) 1975, Appeals (11th cir.) 1981, U.S. Dist. Ct. D.C. 1983. Assoc. Adair, Goldthwaite, Stanford, Atlanta, 1968-71, ptnr., 1971-76; v.p. treas. Adair, Goldthwaite & Daniel, P.C., Atlanta, 1976-80; exec. v.p. Adair & Goldthwaite, P.C., Washington, 1980-81; exec. v.p. Adair, Scanlon & McHugh, P.C., Washington, 1981-87, pres., 1987-88; gen. counsel Communications Workers of Am., Washington, 1988—; bd. dirs. AFL-CIO Lawyers Coordinating Com., Washington, 1988—; mem. Lawyers Adv. Panel, 1988—. Contbr. articles to profl. jours. With USNR, 1961-63. Mem. ABA (co-chair equal employment opportunity com. of labor and employment law sect. 1992-94). Democrat. Avocations: running, camping. Office: Communications Workers Am 501 3rd St NW Washington DC 20001-2760

SCANLON, PETER REDMOND, accountant; b. N.Y.C., Feb. 18, 1931; s. John Thomas and Loretta Dolores (Ryan) S.; m. Mary Jane E. Condon, Mar. 7, 1953; children: Peter, Barbara, Mark (dec.), Brian, Janet. BBA in Acctg., Iona Coll., 1952, LLD (hon.), 1992. CPA, N.Y. Mem. profl. staff Coopers & Lybrand, N.Y.C., 1956-66, ptnr., 1966-91, vice chmn., 1976-82, chmn., chief exec. officer, 1982-91, ret. chmn., 1991—; hon. ptnr. N.Y.C. Partnership, 1991. Lt. USN, 1952-56. Decorated Knight of Malta, Knight Holy Sepulchre; recipient Arthur A. Loftus award Iona Coll., 1974, Trustee award, 1990, Crain's N.Y. All Star award, 1990, Best in Class award Conf. Bd. Youth Edn., 1991. Mem. AICPA, N.Y. State Soc. CPAs, N.Y. Athletic Club. Roman Catholic. Office: Coopers & Lybrand 1251 Ave Of The Americas New York NY 10020-1104

SCANLON, ROSEMARY, economist; b. Inverness, N.S., Can., Dec. 25, 1939; d. Donald Angus and Mary Agnes (MacDonald) MacLellan; A.B., St. Francis Xavier U., N.S., 1959; M.A. (Ford Found. Scholar) U. New Brunswick, 1960; P.M.D., Harvard Bus. Sch., 1981; m. Michael Scanlon, Apr. 24, 1965 (div. 1979); children: Sean Donald, Jennifer; instr. econs. Coll. of William and Mary, Williamsburg, Va., 1960-63; asst. prof. Old Dominion U., Norfolk, Va., 1963-65; econ. analyst Port Authority of N.Y. and N.J., 1969-93; sr. economist for regional research, 1977-80, mgr. econ. devel. planning, N.Y.C., 1980-83, chief economist 1983—; asst. dir. Planning and Devel.

Dept., 1985; apptd. dep. state contr., N.Y.C., 1993; bd. dirs. Nova Scotia Power, Inc. Bd. dirs. Rsch. Found. SUNY, 1987-93. Recipient Salute to Women in Business award YWCA of N.Y.C., 1980, Outstanding Achievement award, Exec. Dirs. award. Mem. Am. Econ. Assn., Nat. Council for Urban Econ. Devel. (bd. dirs.1982-88). Author: The Arts as an Industry in N.Y.-N.J., 1983, The Arts as an Industry, 1993, The Regional Economy in 1995, The Regional Economy, 1993; (with others) Cities in a Global Soc., 1989; contbr. articles to profl. jours. Home: 10 Clinton St Apt 9T Brooklyn NY 11201-2709 Office: 270 Broadway New York NY 10007

SCANLON, TERRENCE MAURICE, research foundation adminstrator; b. Milw., May 1, 1939; s. Maurice John and Anne (Hayes) S.; m. Judy Ball, June 14, 1969; children: Michael Mansfield, Justin Ball, Brendan Hayes. BS, Villanova U., 1961. Staff asst. The White House, Washington, 1963-67; with SBA, Washington, 1967-69; with Dept. of Commerce, Washington, 1969-83, mem. office Minority Bus. Enterprise, 1969-80, with Internat. Trade Adminstrn., 1980-81, with Minority Bus. Devel. Agy., 1981-83; mem. Consumer Product Safety Commn., Washington, 1983-89, vice chmn., 1983-84, chmn., 1985, 86-89; v.p., treas. The Heritage Found., Washington, 1989-91, v.p. corp. rels., 1991-94; chmn., pres. Capital Rsch. Ctr., Washington, 1994—. Am. Polit. Sci. Assn. Congl. fellow, 1967-68. Mem. Sovereign Mil. Order of Malta, University Club. Home: 4510 Dexter St NW Washington DC 20007-1115 Office: Capital Rsch Ctr Ste 800 727 15th St NW Washington DC 20005

SCANLON, THOMAS MICHAEL, lawyer; b. Indpls., Apr. 20, 1909; s. John H. and Anna C. (Ferriter) S.; m. Grace L. Barnett, July 10, 1937; children: Thomas M., Christopher G. A.B., Butler U., 1932; LL.B., Ind. U., 1935. Bar: Ind. 1935. Asso. Noel, Hickam, Boyd & Armstrong, Indpls., 1935-40; assoc. Barnes, Hickam, Pantzer & Boyd, 1940-43, ptnr., 1943-82; of counsel Barnes & Thornburg, 1982—; mem. Ind. Bd. Law Examiners, 1942-43, 47-52. Co-author: Preparation for Trial. Trustee emeritus Butler U. Served to lt. comdr. USNR, 1943-46. Fellow Am. Bar Found., Ind. Bar Found. (50-yr. award for disting. svc. 1986), Indpls. Bar Found.; mem. ABA (chmn. sect. antitrust law 1973-74), Ind. Bar Assn. (pres. 1955-56), Indpls. Bar Assn., Bar Assn. 7th Fed. Cir. (pres. 1956-57), Am. Law Inst. (life), Am. Coll. Trial Lawyers, Delta Tau Delta, Phi Delta Phi. Clubs: Lawyers of Indianapolis (Indpls.) (pres. 1964-65), Indpls. Literary (Indpls., pres. 1990-91), Woodstock (Indpls.), Players (Indpls., pres. 1956-57). Home: 9570 Copley Dr Indianapolis IN 46260-1430 Office: Merchants Bank Bldg Indianapolis IN 46204

SCANNELL, DALE PAUL, dean, university educator; b. Iowa City, Mar. 3, 1929; s. Paul A. and Florence (Fieseler) S.; children:—Steven, Jeffrey, Susan, Janet. B.A., U. Iowa, 1951, M.A., 1955, Ph.D., 1957. Tchr. Iowa City High Sch., 1950-51, 53-58; acting asst. prof. edn. U. Calif. at Berkeley, 1958-59; asst. prof. U. Kans., 1959-62, asso. prof., 1962-64, prof., 1964-67; assoc. dean U. Kans. (Grad. Sch.), 1963-67; prof. edn. U. Iowa, 1967-69; dean Sch. Edn. U. Kans., 1969-85; dean Coll. Edn. U. Md., College Park, 1985-91; prof. edn. Ind. U., Bloomington, 1991—; vis. prof., Lester prof. tchr. edn. U. S.C., 1993-94. Author: (with others) Tests of Academic Progress, 2d edit., 1971, Tests of Achievement and Proficiency, Form T, 1978, Form G, 1985, Form H, 1986, Form J, 1989, (with Oscar Haugh) Form K, 1993, Form L, 1993, Form M, 1995, Writing, Listening Supplements, 1986, (with A.J. Edwards) Educational Psychology, 1968, (with V.H. Noll and Robert Craig) Introduction to Educational Measurement, 4th edit., 1979, (with H.S. Holl and Rachel Noll) Introductory Readings in Educational Measurement, 1972, (with D.B. Tracy) Testing and Measurement in the Classroom, 1975. Served to lt. USAF, 1951-53. Mem. AAUP, Am. Ednl. Research Assn., Nat. Council Measurements in Edn., Phi Delta Kappa. Congregationalist. Club: Kiwanis. Home: 501 Copley Pl Indianapolis IN 46290 Office: Ind Univ Bloomington IN 47405 Office: IUPUI Indianapolis IN 46202

SCANNELL, WILLIAM EDWARD, aerospace company executive, consultant, psychologist; b. Muscatine, Iowa, Nov. 11, 1934; s. Mark Edward and Catharine Pearson (Fowler) S.; m. Barbara Ann Hoemann, Nov. 23, 1957; children: Cynthia Kay, Mark Edward, David Jerome, Terri Lynn, Stephen Patrick. BA in Gen. Edn., U. Nebr., 1961; BS in Engring., Ariz. State U., 1966; MS in Systems Engring., So. Meth. U., 1969; PhD, U.S. Internat. U., 1991. Commd. 2d lt. USAF, 1956, advanced through grades to lt. col., 1972; B-47 navigator-bombardier 98th Bomb Wing, Lincoln Air Force Base, Nebr., 1956-63; with Air Force Inst. of Tech., 1963-65, 68-69; chief mgmt. engring. team RAF Bentwaters, England, 1965-68; forward air contr. 20th Tactical Air Support Squadron USAF, Danang, Vietnam, 1970-71; program mgr. Hdqrs. USAF, Washington, 1971-74, staff asst. Office of Sec. Def., 1974-75, ret., 1975; account exec. Merrill Lynch, San Diego, 1975-77; program engring. chief Gen. Dynamics, San Diego, 1977-79, engring. chief, 1979-80, program mgr., 1980-83; mgr. integrated logistics support Northrop Corp., Hawthorne, Calif., 1984-88; mgr. B-2 program planning and scheduling Northrop Corp., Pico Rivera, Calif., 1988-91; pres. Scannell and Assocs., Borrego Springs, Calif., 1991—; mem. adj. faculty U.S. Internat. U., San Diego. Decorated DFC with three oak leaf clusters, Air medal with 11 oak leaf clusters. Mem. APA, Calif. Psychol. Assn., Soc. Indsl. and Orgnl. Psychology, Inst. Indsl. Engrs., Coronado Cays Yacht Club, Psi Chi. Republican. Roman Catholic. Home: 717 Anza Park Trail Borrego Springs CA 92004 Office: Scannell and Assocs PO Box 2392 Borrego Springs CA 92004

SCARBOROUGH, CHARLES BISHOP, III, broadcast journalist, writer; b. Pitts., Nov. 4, 1943; s. Charles Bishop and Esther Francis (Campbell) S.; m. Linda Anne Gross, Dec. 14, 1972; children: Charles Bishop IV, Elizabeth Anne; m. Anne Ford Uzielli, Oct. 2, 1982; m. Ellen Carol Ward, Sept. 25, 1994. B.S., U. So. Miss., 1969. Prodn. mgr. Sta.-WLOX-TV, Biloxi, Miss., 1966-68; reporter, anchorman Sta.-WDAM-TV, Hattiesburg, Miss., 1968-69; reporter, anchorman, mng. editor Sta.-WAGA-TV, Atlanta, 1969-72; reporter, anchorman Sta.-WNAC-TV, Boston, 1972-74, NBC News, N.Y.C., 1974—. Author: (novels) Stryker, 1978, The Myrmidon Project, 1981, Aftershock, 1991. Served with USAF, 1961-65. Recipient award for journalism AP (9), 1969-72, Emmy awards (22), 1974-94, award Aviation/Space Writers Assn., 1977, 78, 88, UPI award for journalism N.Y. Press Club award, 1988, 89, Sigma Delta Chi award, Deadline Club award, Terry Anderson Journalism award Working Press Assn. N.J., 1992. Mem. Phi Kappa Phi. Office: NBC News 30 Rockefeller Plz New York NY 10112-0002

SCARBOROUGH, CLAUDE MOOD, JR., lawyer; b. Columbia, S.C., Dec. 7, 1929; s. Claude M. and Gelene (Stallworth) S.; student U. of South, 1947-49; A.B., U.S.C., 1951, LL.B., 1952; m. Sarah Carpenter, June 30, 1955; children—Sarah Catherine, Elizabeth Ann, Claude M. III, Gelene Bivins. Admitted to S.C. bar, 1952, U.S. Dist. Ct., 1956; U.S. Ct. Appeals, 1957; assoc. firm Nelson, Mullins & Grier, Columbia, S.C., 1955-61, ptnr. Nelson, Mullins, Riley & Scarborough, 1961—, mng. ptnr., 1964—; mem. Columbia adv. bd. Nat. Bank S.C., 1979—, chmn., 1982-92, also dir.; dir. NBSC Corp., Forest Lake Travel, Inc. Spl. hearing officer U.S. Dept. Justice, 1962-68. Trustee Legal Aid Soc. Richland Co., 1960-67, pres., 1960-64; mem. Gov.'s Com. to Study Police and Community Relations, 1975-76; mem. indsl. adv. bd. S.C. Dept. Corrections, 1974-76; bd. dirs. S.C. Orch. Assn., Ctrl. Carolina Community Found., United Way of the Midlands, Palmetto Soc. of United Way, past chair, Columbia Mus. of Art, Midlands Bus. Forum, Palmetto Project Adv-Bd., U. S.C. Sch. Law Partnership Bd., Greater Columbia Chamber Econ. Devel. Task Force, Com. of 100, 1980-85, chmn. 1983-84; bd. trustees Episc. Diocese of Upper S.C., 1981—, pres., 1985—; chmn. bd. dirs. S.C. Research Authority, 1983-87, S.C. Coord. Coun. for Econ. Devel., 1984-87. Served to 1st Lt. AUS, 1952-55. Recipient Order of Palmetto Gov. S.C., 1986. Fellow Am. Bar Found.; mem. Greater Columbia C. of C. (pres. 1986-87, dir. 1985-89), S.C. C. of C. (bd. dirs. 1990-93), Internat. Assn. Ins. Counsel, Am. S.C. (treas. 1968-72, exec. com. 1972-74, chmn. exec. com. 1973-74 pres. 1975-76, bd. dirs. 1975—), Richland County bar assns., S.C. Bar Found. (bd. dirs. 1976-81, chmn. bd. 1977-80, founding fellow), U.S. 4th Circuit Jud. Conf. (permanent mem.), S.C. Def. Attys. Assn., Def. Research Inst., Am. Judicature Soc. (Herbert Harley award 1976), The Forum (past pres.),Phi Delta Phi. Episcopalian (lay reader, vestryman, warden). Clubs: Palmetto, Summit, Capital City, Forest Lake Country, Kiwanis. Home: 1514 Tanglewood Rd Columbia SC 29205-1448

Office: Nelson Mullins et al 3rd Fl Keenan Bldg 1330 Lady St Columbia SC 29201-3300

SCARBOROUGH, JOE, congressman; b. Atlanta, Apr. 9, 1963; m. Melanie Scarborough; 2 children. BA, U. Ala., 1985; JD, U. Fla., 1990. Atty., 1990—; mem. 104th Congress from 1st Fla. dist., 1995—. Tchr. Sunday sch. 1st Bapt. Ch. Mem. Young Lawyer's Assn., Fellowship Christian Athletes. Republican. Office: US Ho of Reps Washington DC 20515

SCARBROUGH, ROBERT HENRY, JR., coast guard officer; b. Hawkinsville, Ga., Mar. 12, 1923; s. Robert Henry and Janet Augusta (Burton) S.; m. Walterene Brant, July 1, 1946; children—Robert Henry, James Burton. BS, U.S. Mcht. Marine Acad., 1944; BBA, U. Hawaii, 1969, MBA, 1971; M.S., George Washington U., 1971, Armed Forces Staff Coll. 1963, Nat. War Coll., 1971. Commd. lt. (j.g.) USCG, 1949; advanced through grades to vice adm., 1978; chief Office of Ops. USCG, 1974-75, chief of staff, 1975-77, comdr. 9th Coast Guard Dist., 1977-78; vice comdt. USCG, Washington, 1978-82; ret. USCG, 1982; exec. dir. Navy League U.S., 1982-84; pres. Polaris Potomac Corp., 1985—. With USNR, 1942-49. Decorated Legion of Merit, D.S.M. Mem. Beta Gamma Sigma. Office: 5357 37th St N Arlington VA 22207-1312

SCARBROUGH, CLEVE KNOX, JR., museum director; b. Florence, Ala., July 17, 1939; s. Cleve Knox and Emma Lee (Matheny) S. B.S., U. No. Ala., 1962; M.A., U. Iowa, 1967. Asst. prof. art history U. Tenn., 1967-69; dir. Mint Mus. Art, Charlotte, N.C., 1969-76. Hunter Mus. Art, Chattanooga, 1976—; pres. N.C. Mus. Coun., 1976; bd. mem. adv. com. Tenn. Arts Commn., 1976-77, chmn. visual arts com., 1978—; mem. art selection com. TVA, 1983—, Provident Life Ins. Co., 1983—; cons. Mus. Assessment Program, 1984-94; grant evaluator Inst. Mus. Svcs., 1985-86; mem. art adv. com. First Tenn. Corp., 1991; lectr. Tenn. Gov.'s Conf. on the Arts, 1991. Compiler, editor: North Carolinians Collect, 1970, Pre Columbian Art of the Americas, 1971, Graphics by Four Modern Swiss Sculptors, 1972, British Paintings from the North Carolina Museum, 1973, Montain Landscapes by Swiss Artists, 1976. Mem. Chattanooga Landmark Com.; mem. City Planning Bd.; Bd. dirs. Chattanooga Conv. and Visitors Bur., 1977-79; advisor Chattanooga Cen. City Council, 1981-85, Tenn. State Mus., 1981, mem. Am. Federation of Arts Adv. Bd., 1987—. Served with USN, 1962-64. Mem. Am. Assn. Museums (accreditation vis. com. 1985-94), Southeastern Mus. Conf. (coun. 1976-80, 86-88, chmn. publs. com. 1979, rep. to Am. Assn. Mus.; bd. dirs. 1986-88), Rotary. Office: Hunter Mus Art 10 Bluff View St Chattanooga TN 37403-1197

SCARBROUGH, FRANK EDWARD, government official; b. Knoxville, Tenn., Sept. 27, 1942; s. James L. and Anna Dale (Edwards) S.; m. Deborah Griffin, Feb. 4, 1972; 1 child, Elizabeth Anne. BS, U. Tenn., 1964; AM, Harvard U., 1966, PhD, 1971. Rsch. assoc. U. Bern, Switzerland, 1971-73; instr. U. Pa., Phila., 1973-76; chemist food additive rev. FDA, Washington, 1977-80, chief regulatory affairs staff, 1980-86, dep. dir. Office Nutrition, 1986-89, dir. Office Nutrition, 1989-92, dir. Office Food Labeling, 1992—. Contbe. author: Food Labeling, 1994. Recipient award of merit FDA, 1985, Superior Svc. award USPHS, 1991, Disting. Svc. award HHS, 1993. Mem. Am. Chem. Soc., Am. Soc. Clin. Nutrition, Inst. Food Technologists. Office: FDA Office of Food Labeling 200 C St SW Washington DC 20204

SCARDINA, FRANK JOSEPH, real estate executive; b. Chgo., Feb. 18, 1948; s. Joseph Samuel and Marian Florence (Bogseth) S.; m. Diane Lynne Stern, Sept. 1, 1968; children: Brian Joseph, Kevin Stanley, Adam Charles, Todd Richard. BA in Econs. U. Denver, 1969; JD, U. Calif., Berkeley, 1972. Bar: Calif. 1972. Assoc. Mitchell, Silverberg & Knupp, L.A., 1975-77, Chickering and Gregory, San Francisco, 1972-75; corp. counsel Kaufman and Broad, Inc., L.A., 1978; v.p., gen. counsel, 1979-80; pres. Kaufman and Broad Communities, Inc., 1981-89, Kaufman and Broad of So. Calif., 1985—; vis. lectr. Law Sch. U. So. Calif. 1987—; mem. L.A. Blue Ribbon Com. for Affordable Housing, 1988. Pres. Bon Vivant Homeowners Assn., 1976-77; founding pres. Lindley Oaks Parents-Tchrs. Assn., 1979-80. Home: 28850 Countryside Dr Agoura Hills CA 91301-2747

SCARDINO, ALBERT JAMES, journalist; b. Balt., Sept. 22, 1948; s. Peter Lester and Mary Katherine (Mangelsdorf) S.; m. Marjorie Beth Morris, Apr. 19, 1974; children—Adelaide Katherine Morris, William Brown, Albert Henry Hugh. B.A., Columbia U., 1970; M.J., U. Calif.-Berkeley, 1976. Editor Ga. Gazette, Savannah, 1978-84; corr., editor N.Y. Times, N.Y.C., 1985-89; press sec. Mayor of N.Y.C., 1990-91; ind. journalist, 1991—. Editor, producer documentary film: Guale, 1976 (numerous awards 1976). Recipient Pulitzer Prize, 1984. Mem. Internat. Soc. Weekly Newspaper Editors (bd. dirs. 1983-86, Golden Quill award 1982), Columbia Coll. Alumni Assn. (sec. 1990-93). Home: 19 Empire House, Thurloe Pl, London SW7 2RU, England

SCARDINO, MARJORIE MORRIS, publishing company executive; b. Flagstaff, Ariz., Jan. 25, 1947; d. Robert Weldon and Beth (Lamb) Morris; m. Albert James Scardino, Apr. 19, 1974; children: Adelaide Katherine Morris, William Brown, Albert Henry Hugh. BA, Baylor U., 1973; JD, San Francisco. Ptnr. Brannen Wessels & Searcy, Savannah, Ga., 1976-85; pub. Ga. Gazette Pub. Co., Savannah, 1978-85; pres. The Economist Newspaper Group, Inc., N.Y.C., 1985-93; worldwide mng. dir. Economist Intelligence Unit, N.Y.C., 1992-93; chief exec. The Economist Group, London, 1993—; bd. dirs. The Economist Newspaper, Ltd., ConAgra, W.H. Smith; mem. vis. com. New Sch. for Social Rsch., N.Y.C., 1989—. Bd. dirs. Atlantic Coun., 1989, Pub. Radio Internat., 1993—. Office: The Economist Group, 25 St James's St, London SW1A 1HG, England also: The Economist 8th Fl 111 W 57th St New York NY 10019

SCARDINO, MICHAEL CHRISTOPHER, advertising executive; b. Elmhurst, N.Y., Oct. 12, 1948; s. Michael Vincent and Dorris Fulghum (Tidwell) S.; m. Barbara Anne White, Aug. 21, 1971; children: Emily Katherine, Sarah Elizabeth, Charlotte Anne. BA, Vanderbilt U., 1970. Chief instr. Sch. Modern Photography, N.J., 1971-73; E. Coast editor Petersen's Photographic Mag., N.Y.C., 1973-74; copy contact Dentsu Corp. Am., N.Y.C., 1974-80; v.p., copy supr. Ally & Gargano Inc., N.Y.C., 1980-84; v.p., assoc. creative dir. J. Walter Thompson Inc., N.Y.C., 1984-87; v.p., group head Chiat/Day Inc., N.Y.C., 1987-88; sr. v.p., group head Lord, Einstein, O'Neill & Ptnrs., N.Y.C., 1988-90; exec. v.p., creative dir. Wells, Rich, Greene Inc., N.Y.C., 1990—, Young & Rubicam, N.Y.C., 1993—. 2d Lt. USNG, 1970-76. Recipient Gold Lion Cannes Festival, France, 1989. Office: Lord Dentsu & Ptnrs 810 7th Ave New York NY 10019-5818

SCARF, HERBERT ELI, economics educator; b. Phila., July 25, 1930; s. Louis H. and Lena (Elkman) S.; m. Margaret Klein, June 28, 1953; children: Martha Anne Samuelson, Elizabeth Joan Stone, Susan Margaret Merrell. AB, Temple U., 1951; MA, Princeton U., 1952, PhD, 1954; LHD (hon.), U. Chgo., 1978. With RAND Corp., Santa Monica, Calif., 1954-57; asst. and assoc. prof. stats. Stanford U., Calif., 1957-63, fellow Ctr. for Advanced Study, 1962-63; vis. assoc. prof. Yale U., New Haven, 1959-60, prof. econs., 1963-70, Stanley Resor prof. econs., 1970-78, Sterling prof. econs., 1979—; dir. Cowles Found. Research in Econs., Yale U., 1967-71, 1981-84, div. social sciences, 1971-72, 1973-74. Author: Studies in the Mathematical Theory of Inventory and Production, 1958, Computation of Economic Equilibria, 1973. Editor: Applied General Equilibrium Analysis, 1984. Recipient Lanchester prize Ops. Research Soc. of Am., 1974, Von Neumann medal, 1983; named Disting. fellow Am. Econ. Assn., 1991. Fellow Econometric Soc. (pres. 1983); mem. Am. Acad. Arts and Sciences, Nat. Acad. of Sciences, Am. Philos. Soc. Democrat. Jewish. Clubs: New Haven Lawn (Conn.), Yale (N.Y.C.). Office: Yale U Cowles Found Rsch Econs PO Box 208281 New Haven CT 06520-8281

SCARF, MARGARET (MAGGI SCARF), author; b. Phila., May 13, 1932; d. Benjamin and Helen (Rotbin) Klein; m. Herbert Eli Scarf, June, 1953; children: Martha Samuelson, Elizabeth Stone, Susan Merrell. BA, South Conn. State U., 1989. Writer in residence Jonathan Edwards Coll., Yale U.; contbg. editor New Republic, Washington, DC, 1978—, Self Mag., N.Y.C., 1991—; assoc. fellow Jonathan Edwards Coll. Yale U., New Haven, 1979, 81, 83; sr. fellow Bush Ctr. in Child Devel. and Social Policy, Yale U., 1991—; mem. adv. bd. Am. Psychiat. Press. Author: Meet Benjamin

Franklin, 1968, Antarctica: Exploring the Frozen Continent, 1970, Body, Mind, Behavior, 1976 (Nat. Media award Am. Psychological Assn. 1977), Unfinished Business: Pressure Points in the Lives of Women, 1981, Intimate Partners: Patterns in Love and Marriage, 1987; contrb. numerous articles to jours. including N.Y. Times mag. and book rev., Psychology Today. Recipient Nat. Media award Am. Psychol. Found., 1971, 74, Conn. UN award Outstanding Conn. Women, 1987; Ford Found. fellow, 1973-74, Neiman fellow Harvard U., 1975-76, Ctr. Advanced Study in Behavioral Scis. fellow, 1977-78, 85-86, Alicia Patterson Found. fellow, 1978-79. Mem. Conn. Soc. Psychoanalytic Psychologists, Am. Psychiat. Press (mem. adv. bd. 1992), Lawn Club, Elizabethans. Avocations: reading, hiking, swimming. *

SCARFF, EDWARD L., diversified company executive; b. 1930. BS, Mich. Tech. U., 1954. With Ansul Chem. Co., 1953-56, Stanford Research Inst. 1956-60; dir. investment research Investors Diversified Services, Inc., 1960-63; pres. chief exec. officer N. Am. Securities Co., 1963-65; v.p., then pres. Transam. Corp., 1965-71; pres. Edward L. Scarff and Assocs., San Francisco, 1971—; with Arcata Corp., San Francisco, 1971—, now chmn. bd. dirs., also bd. dirs. Office: Arcata Corp Press St Kingsport TN 37660

SCARFIOTTI, FERDINANDO, production designer. Prodn. designer: (films) The Conformist, 1971, Death in Venice, 1971, Avanti!, 1972, Last Tango in Paris, 1973, Daisy Miller, 1974, American Gigolo, 1980, Flash Gordon, 1980, Honky Tonk Freeway, 1981, Cat People, 1982, Bring on the Night, 1985, The Last Emperor, 1987 (Academy award best art direction 1987), Mamba, 1988, Toys, 1992 (Academy award nomination best art direction 1992). Office: care Art Directors Guild 11365 Ventura Blvd #315 Studio City CA 91604*

SCARINGI, MICHAEL JOSEPH, lawyer, consultant; b. Seattle, May 9, 1944; m. Suzan Jean Allyn, Sept. 9, 1967; children: Anthony, Marco. AA, Highline Coll., Seattle, 1965; BA, Seattle U., 1967, MA, 1970; grad. law clerkship, Wash. State Bar Assn., 1987. Bar: Wash. 1989, U.S. Dist. Ct. (we. dist.) Wash. 1989. Cons. Wash. State Dept. Trans., Seattle, 1970—; atty. pvt. practice, Seattle, 1989—. Home: PO Box 670 Mercer Island WA 98040-0670 Office: 1299 156th Ave NE Ste 120 Bellevue WA 98007-4599

SCARLETT, HAROLD O., retired retail executive, consultant; b. Detroit; s. Howard O. and Irene J. (LaSprance) S.; m. Helen L. Steigerwalt, Apr. 15, 1950. B.S. in Mech. Engring., Purdue U., 1949. Registered profl. engr., Mich. Design engr. Detroit Edison Co., 1949-52; air conditioning engr. S.S. Kresge Co., Detroit, 1952-55, chief mech. supt., 1955-65, asst. mgr. constrn. dept., 1965-69, gen. mgr., 1969-73; v.p. constrn. K mart Corp., Troy, Mich., 1973-87; pres. Huck Fixture Co. subs., Quincy, Ill, 1969-79; chmn. Huck Fixture Co. subs, Quincy, Ill, 1979-87; Mem. corp. Merrill Palmer Inst., Detroit, 1980; corp. mem. Boys & Girls Clubs, 1983, Naples Bd. Appeals, 1990—. Served with U.S. Army, 1942-45, PTO. Mem. Pi Tau Sigma, Tau Beta Pi. Home and Office: 626 Parkview Ln Naples FL 33940-3737

SCARMINACH, CHARLES ANTHONY, lawyer; b. Syracuse, N.Y., Feb. 19, 1944; s. John Louis and Lucy (Egnoto) S.; m. Carol Cramer, Dec. 26, 1986; children: John, Catherine, Karen, Charles, Robert. MA, U. Buffalo, 1965; JD, Syracuse U., 1968. Bar: N.Y. 1968, S.C. 1974. Gen. counsel Sea Pines Co., Hilton Head Island, S.C., 1973-78; sole practice, Hilton Head Island, 1978-83; ptnr. Novit & Scarminach, P.A., Hilton Head Island, 1983-93. Chmn. bd. Sea Pines Montessori Sch., Hilton Head Island, 1979-83; bd. dirs. Hilton Head Preparatory Sch., 1984-93, chmn. bd. trustees 1986-93. Maj. U.S. Army, 1968-73. Mem. ABA, S.C. Bar Assn., N.Y. State Bar Assn. Democrat. Roman Catholic. Club: Sea Pines. Home: 11 Governors Rd Hilton Head Island SC 29928-4153 Office: Novit & Scarminach PA PO Box 14 Hilton Head Island SC 29938-0014

SCARNE, JOHN, game company executive; b. Steubenville, Ohio, Mar. 4, 1903; s. Fiorangelo and Maria (Tamburro) S.; m. Steffi Kearney, 1956; 1 son, John Teeko. Student pub. schs., Guttenberg, N.J. Pres. John Scarne Games, Inc., North Bergen, N.J., 1950—; gaming cons. Hilton Hotels Internat. Magician stage, screen and television; Author: Scarne on Dice, 1945, Scarne on Cards, 1950, Scarne on Card Tricks, 1950, Scarne on Magic Tricks, 1952, Scarne's New Complete Guide to Gambling, 1962, The Odds Against Me, 1967, Scarne's Encyclopedia of Games, 1973, The Mafia Conspiracy, 1976, Scarne's Guide to Casino Gambling; Scarne's Guide to Modern Poker; contbr. to World Book Ency, 1970, Ency. Brit, 1975. Cons. to U.S. Armed Forces, 1941-45. Named Man of Year for Police Chiefs of U.S., 1960. Office: 8900 Blvd East North Bergen NJ 07047-2707

SCARPA, ANTONIO, medicine educator, biomedical scientist; b. Padua, Italy, July 3, 1942; s. Angelo and Elena (DeRossi) S. MD cum laude, U. Padua, 1966, PhD in Pathology, 1970; MA (hon.), U. Pa., 1978. Asst. prof. biochemistry, biophysics U. Pa., Phila., 1971-73, assoc. prof., 1976-80, prof., 1980-86, dir. biomed. instrumentation group, 1983-86; prof. dept. pathology Jefferson U., Phila., 1986—; prof., chmn. dept. physiology Case Western Res. U., Cleve., 1986—, dir. tng. ctr., program project, 1983—; prof. medicine, 1989—; cons. study sect. NIH, Bethesda, 1984—, Am. Heart Assn., Dallas, 1986-91; pres., assoc. chair dept. phsiology, 1993-94. Editor (books): Frontiers of Biological Energetics, Calcium Transport and Cell Function, Transport ATPases, Membrane Pathology, Membrane and Cancer Cells; editor (jours.) Archives Biochemistry and Biophysics, Cell Calcium, Biochemistry Internat.; mem. editorial bd. Circulation Rsch., 1978-81, Biophys. Jour., 1979-82, Jour. Muscle Rsch., 1979—, Magnesium, 1982—, Physiol. Revs., 1982-90, FASEB Jour., 1987-92, Molecular Cellular Biochemistry, 1988—; contbr. numerous articles to profl. jours. Mem. Am. Soc. Physiologists, Am. Soc. Biol. Chemistry, Biophys. Soc. (exec. coun. 1980-83, 85-89, 94-98), U.S. Bioenergetics Group (program chmn. 1974-75, 82, 83, exec. officer 1985—, asst. chmn. dept. physiology, pres. 1993-95). Avocations: farming, sailing, painting. Office: Case Western Reserve Univ Dept Of Physiology Cleveland OH 44106

SCARPINO, PASQUALE VALENTINE, environmental microbiologist; b. Utica, N.Y., Feb. 13, 1932; s. Antonio and Mary Ann (Lia) S.; m. Flora Jean Heid, May 24, 1986; 1 child, Andrea Lia; 1 stepchild, Kimberly Sue Cooper. B.A. magna cum laude, Utica Coll., Syracuse U., 1955; M.S., Rutgers U., 1958, Ph.D. (USPHS fellow), 1961. Asst. prof. biol. scis. Fairleigh Dickinson U., Madison, N.J., 1961-63; mem. faculty U. Cin., 1963—, prof. environ. engring., 1970—, prof. environ. health, 1986—; interim dir. office minority affairs coll. engring., 1987; chmn. water subcom. Cin. Environ. Task Force, 1972-73; chmn. Cin. Citizen-Scientist Com. Drinking Water Quality, 1975-82, 87—; chmn. water com. Cin. Environ. Adv. Council, 1975-76, chmn. nuclear safety com., 1979-82, chmn. environ. adv. council, 1980-82; mem. pub. interest adv. com. Ohio River Valley Water Sanitation Commn., 1981-85, chmn. 1984-85, commr. from Ohio 1985-92, sec., 1987-88, vice chmn., 1988-89, chmn. of commn., 1989-90, chmn. tech. com., 1987-88, chmn. program and fin. com., 1988-89; chmn. tech. adv. com. Cin. Right-to-Know Ordinance, 1983-88; trustee from U.S. to Ohio River Basin Consortium for Research and Edn., 1985—; chmn., organizer of Consortium's 8th Ann. Sci. Symposium, 1992, sec.-treas., 1992—. Contbr. articles to profl. jours. Mem. adv. council Cin. Experience, 1973-80. Recipient Pres. U. Cin. Excellence in Community Service award, 1975, Tristate Air Com. award, 1977, Alumni Achievement award Utica Coll. Alumni Assn., 1983, Man of Yr. award Cin. United Italian Soc., 1988, Disting. Scientist of Yr. award Cin. Tech. Socs., 1992; grantee USPHS, 1965-68, Space Inst., 1967-69, EPA, 1969—, Dept. Def., 1983-85, Nat. Inst. Environ. Health Scis., 1988-91. Fellow Am. Acad. Microbiology (chmn. com. on use of microorganisms in rsch. 1987-90, mem. nomination com.); mem. Am. Soc. Microbiology (chmn. com. edn. 1970-72, chmn. com. role microbiology in edn. of other disciplines 1972-73), Soc. Indsl. Microbiology, Soc. Risk Analysis, Water Environment Fedn., Am. Water Works Assn., Engrs. and Scientists of Cin. (pres.-elect 1992-93, pres. 1993-94), Internat. Assn. on Water Quality, Kiwanis Internat. (pres. Cin. chpt. 1988-90), Sigma Xi (pres. Cin. chpt. 1985-87). Home: 3843 Middleton Ave Cincinnati OH 45221-1126 Office: U Cin 720 Rhodes Hall Cincinnati OH 45221 *I have found that in striving for goals, the scientist must have the courage to report his results, have patience, use knowledge wisely and develop good judgment. But most of all, he/she must develop wisdom—an understanding of how to apply the knowledge that has been extracted from nature for the betterment of Man.*

SCARPITTI, FRANK ROLAND, sociology educator; b. Butler, Pa., Nov. 12, 1936; s. Frank and Geneva (Costanza) S.; m. Ellen Louise Canfield, Sept. 5, 1959; children: Susan, Jeffrey. B.A., Cleve. State U., 1958; M.A., Ohio State U., 1959, Ph.D., 1962. Research asso. Ohio State U. Psychiat. Inst., Columbus, 1961-63; asst. prof. Rutgers U., 1963-67; asso. prof. sociology U. Del., 1967-69, prof., 1969—, chmn. dept., 1969-80, 88-94; cons. state and fed. govts.; Bd. dirs. Joint Commn. on Criminology and Criminal Justice Edn. and Standards, 1977-81. Author: Schizophrenics in the Community, 1967, Combatting Social Problems, 1967, Youth and Drugs, 1970, Group Interactions as Therapy, 1974, Social Problems, 1974, 77, 80, Deviance: Action, Reaction, Interaction, 1975, Women, Crime and Justice, 1980, The Young Drug User, 1980, Poisoning for Profit, 1985, Social Problems, 1989, 92, Social Problems: The Search for Solutions, 1994; contbr. articles to profl. jours. Recipient Hofheimer prize for research Am. Psychiat. Assn., 1967; mem. Danforth Found. asso. program. Mem. Am. Sociol. Assn., Am. Soc. Criminology (v.p. 1978-79, pres.-elect 1979-80, pres. 1980-81), AAUP, Alpha Kappa Delta, Phi Kappa Phi, Omicron Delta Kappa. Home: 104 Radcliffe Dr Newark DE 19711-3147

SCARR, SANDRA WOOD, psychology educator, researcher; b. Washington, Aug. 8, 1936; d. John Ruxton and Jane (Powell) Wood; m. Harry Alan Scarr, Dec. 26, 1961 (div. 1970); children: Phillip, Karen, Rebbecca, Stephanie; m. Charles Callan Walker, Aug. 9, 1982 (div. 1994). AB, Vassar Coll., 1958; AM, Harvard U., 1963, PhD, 1965. Asst. prof. psychology U. Md., College Park, 1964-67; assoc. prof. U. Pa., Phila., 1967-71; prof. U. Minn., Mpls., 1971-77, Yale U., New Haven, 1977-83; Commonwealth prof. U. Va., Charlottesville, 1983—, chmn. dept. psychology, 1984-90; mem. nat. adv. bd. Robert Wood Johnson Found., Princeton, N.J., 1985-91; mem. coordinating council psychology SUNY Bd. Regents, N.Y., 1984-92; prof. Kerstin Hesselgren, Sweden, 1993-94; bd. dirs. KinderCare Learning Ctr., Inc., also chmn. bd. dirs. Author: Race, Social Class and Individual Differences in IQ, 1981, Mother Care/Other Care, 1984 (Nat. Book award APA 1985), Caring for Children, 1989; editor Jour. Devel. Psychology, 1980-86, Current Directions in Psychol. Sci., 1995-97. Fellow Ctr. for Advanced Studies, Stanford U., Calif., 1976-77; grantee NIH, NSF, others, 1967—. Fellow AAAS, APA (chmn. com. on human research 1980-83, council of reps. 1984—, bd. dirs. 1988—, Award for Disting. Contbn. to Research on Pub. Policy 1988), Am. Psychol. Soc. (bd. dirs. 1991—, James McKeen Cattell award 1993); mem. Am. Acad. Arts and Scis., Behavior Genetics Assn. (pres. 1985-86, mem. exec. council 1976-79, 84-87), Soc. for Research in Child Devel. (governing council 1974-76, 87-93, chmn. fin. com. 1987-89, pres. 1989-91), Internat. Soc. for Study of Behavioral Devel. (exec. bd. 1987-94). Democrat. Avocations: dogs, gardening. Home: 1243 Maple View Dr Charlottesville VA 22902 Office: U Va Dept Psychology Charlottesville VA 22903

SCARRITT, THOMAS VARNON, newspaper editor; b. Tuscaloosa, Ala., Jan. 28, 1953; s. Charles Wesley and Valerie (Varnon) S.; m. Kathryn Rush Hubbard, Dec. 28, 1973; children: Sara Kathryn, Thomas Varnon Jr. BA in Journalism, U. N.C., 1974; MBA, Samford U., 1995. Reporter The Birmingham (Ala.) News, 1975-79, Washington corr., 1979-83, news editor, 1983-85, editorial page editor, 1986-89, exec. editor, 1989— mem. Am. Soc. Newspaper Editors, Soc. Profl. Journalists (pres. Ala. profl. chpt. 1988-89), Kiwanis (Birmingham), Phi Beta Kappa. Episcopal. Home: 4240 Clairmont Ave Birmingham AL 35222 Office: The Birmingham News 2200 4th Ave North Birmingham AL 35202

SCARSE, OLIVIA MARIE, cardiologist, consultant; b. Chgo., Nov. 10, 1950; d. Oliver Marcus and Marjorie Ardis (Olsen) S. BS, North Park Coll., 1970; MD, Loyola U., Maywood, Ill., 1973. Diplomate Am. Bd. Internal Medicine, Am. Bd. Cardiovascular Diseases. Surg. intern Resurrection Hosp., Chgo., 1974; resident in internal medicine Northwestern U., Chgo., 1974-77; cardiovascular disease fellow U. Ill., Chgo., 1977-80; dir. cardiac lab. Cook County Hosp., Chgo., 1981; dir. heart sta. MacNeal Hosp., Berwyn, Ill., 1983; dir. electrophysiology Hines VA Hosp., Maywood, Ill., 1984-85; dir. progressive care Columbus Hosp., Chgo., 1985-88, pvt. practice, 1984—; pvt. practice Ill. Masonic Hosp., Chgo., 1989—. Pillsbury fellow Pillsbury Fund, 1980. Fellow Am. Coll. Cardiology; mem. AMA, ACP, Chgo. Med. Assn., Ill. State Med. Assn., Am. Heart Assn., Crescent Countries Found. for Med. Care, Cen. Ill. Med. Review Orgn. Avocations: musician, ballet and tap dancer, actress, model, singer. Home and Office: 2650 N Lakeview # 4109 Chicago IL 60614

SCASSA, EUGENE L., ambassador; b. Monaca, Pa., Feb. 6, 1939; married; 3 children. Student, Geneva Coll., 1957-58, 60-61, Fla. State U., 1963-64. With Fgn. Svc., 1962; comm. and records clk. U.S. Embassy, Panama, 1962-64; comm. officer U.S. Embassy, Quito, Ecuador, 1964-65; adminstrv. asst. U.S. Embassy, Libreville, Gabon, 1965-67; spl. asst. Bur. African Affairs, 1967-69; adminstrv. officer, consular officer U.S. Consulate, Mozambique, 1969-71; adminstrv. officer U.S. Embassy, Madagascar, 1971; adminstrv. and consular officer U.S. Consulate Gen., Monterrey, Mex., 1971-73; adminstrv. officer U.S. Embassy, Lusaka, Zambia, 1973-74, Reykjavik, Iceland, 1974-77; adminstrv. and conf. officer U.S. Mission, Geneva, 1978-80; adminstrv. counselor U.S. Embassy, Jidda, Saudi Arabia, 1980-82; with Nat. War Coll., 1982-83; divsn. chief bur. pers. Dept. of State, 1983-85, dep. exec. dir. bur. inter-Am. affairs, 1985-86, exec. dir., 1986-90, U.S. amb. to Belize, 1990—. With U.S. Army, 1958-60. Office: Belize Us Dept Of State Washington DC 20521

SCATURRO, PHILIP DAVID, investment banker; b. Newark, Dec. 8, 1938; s. Charles and Rose (Montino) S. BA, Williams Coll., 1960; JD, Columbia U., 1963, MBA, 1963. Analyst Ladenburg, Thalmann & Co., N.Y.C., 1964-67; v.p. Sellin, Forbes & Smith, N.Y.C., 1967; v.p. Allen & Co. Inc., N.Y.C., 1967-71, mng. dir., exec. v.p., 1977—; gen. ptnr. R&S Assocs., N.Y.C., 1972-76; pvt. investor, N.Y.C., 1976-77; bd. dirs., chmn. compensation com., mem. audit com. United Asset Mgmt. Co.; bd. dirs. Savoy Pictures Entertainment, Inc., N.Y.C., Asquith Ct. Ltd. London. Bd. dirs., exec. com., chmn. fin. com. N.Y.C. Opera; trustee, exec. com., chmn. audit com. New Sch. for Social Rsch.; mem. com. on alt. investments Williams Coll. Mem. Univ. Club (N.Y.C.). Avocations: Opera, music, theatre, wine, fly fishing. Office: Allen & Co 711 5th Ave New York NY 10022-3109

SCAVULLO, FRANCESCO, photographer; b. Staten Island, N.Y., Jan. 16, 1929; s. Angelo and Margaret (Pavis) S.; m. Carol McCallson, 1952. Student pub. schs., N.Y.C. Asst. photographer Horst at Vogue Studio, N.Y.C., 1946-48; photographer Seventeen mag., N.Y.C., 1948-50, Town and Country mag., 1950, Harper's Bazaar mag., 1960, Cosmopolitan mag., 1965—, Vogue mag., 1970; owner The Scavullo Gallery, 1988. Represented in permanent collection, Met. Mus. Art., Amon Carter Mus., Ft. Worth; author: Scavullo on Beauty, 1976, Scavullo Men, 1977, Scavullo Women, 1982, Scavullo, 1984. Recipient Photograph of Yr. award, 1977, numerous awards advt. art dirs. clubs. Mem. Dirs. Guild Am. Roman Catholic. Studio: 212 E 63rd St New York NY 10021-7604

SCEARCE, P. JENNINGS, JR., engineering executive. BS in Elec. Engring., N.C. State U. With ManTech Internat., Vitro Corp.; with Sequa Corp., Rockville, Md., 1976—, v.p. ops., sr. v.p., gen. mgr. def. systems divsn., ARC profl. svcs. group. Mem. Am. Soc. Naval Engrs., Am. Soc. Quality Control, Armed Forces Comm. and Electronics Assn., Quality and Productivity Mgmt. Assn. (v.p. Chesapeake coun.), Navy League U.S. (life). Office: Atlantic Rsch Corp 1375 Piccard Dr Rockville MD 20850-4311

SCEARSE, PATRICIA DOTSON, nurse educator, college dean; b. Wabash, Ind., Sept. 4, 1931; d. Claude Richard and Lilly Etta (Colvill) D.; m. Vernon Quinton Scearse, June 26, 1955 (dec. Mar. 1990); 1 child, Victoria Lynn Lenderman. BS, Earlham Coll., 1955; MS, U. Colo., 1968; D in Nursing Sci., U. Calif., San Francisco, 1974. RN. Staff nurse Reid Meml. Hosp., Richmond, Ind., 1954-55; head nurse, instr. Hillcrest Bapt. Hosp., Waco, Tex., 1955-56; instr. Sch. Nursing Candler Hosp., Savannah, Ga., 1956-60; adminstrv. asst., edn. cons. Wyo. State Bd. Nursing, Cheyenne, 1964-68; asst. prof. San Diego State U., 1969, Ball State U., Muncie, Ind., 1969-71; assoc. prof., area chairperson U. Mich., Ann Arbor, 1974-80; prof., dean Coll. Nursing Tex. Christian U., Ft. Worth, 1980-95, emeritus dean, prof., 1995—. Pub. policy editor Jour. Profl. Nursing, Phila., 1986-89; editorial cons. Jour. Pub. Health Nursing, New Haven, 1984-89; contbr. articles to profl. jours. Recipient Outstanding Nurse award Sigma Theat Tau, Beta

Alpha, Ft. Worth, 1986; Kennedy Inst. Ethics postdoctoral fellow, Georgetown U., 1978. Mem. ANA, APHA (bd. govs. 1976), Am. Assn. Colls. of Nursing (bd. dirs. 1982-84, 85-87), Nat. League for Nursing, Coun. Baccalaureate and Higher Degree Programs (bd. rev.), Assn. Community Health Nurse Educators (named Great 100 Nurses 1992). Home: 5511 Ledgestone Dr Fort Worth TX 76132-2342

SCELSA, JOSEPH VINCENT, sociologist; b. N.Y.C., Dec. 7, 1945; s. Albert John and Katherine Mary S.; A.A., LIU, 1966, B.A., 1968; M.A., City U. N.Y., 1973, M.S.Ed., 1978; M.A., Columbia U., 1983, Ed.D., 1984; m. Joyce Ann Tisi, Nov. 13, 1981; 1 child, Jonathan. Counselor, tchr. N.Y.C. Bd. Edn., 1970-78, coord. career and occupational edn., 1979; coord. specialized counseling CUNY, 1979-81; pvt. practice counseling, N.Y.C., 1975—; lectr. grad. faculty Herbert H. Lehman Coll., 1980—; dir. Calandra Inst. CUNY, 1984—. Cert. sch. counselor, N.Y. Active Coun. of 1000 Nat. Italian-Am. Found; past vice chair multi cultural adv. bd. N.Y.C. Bd. Edn., 1990-91; N.Y. State Mentoring Program Adv. Bd., 1990—; bd. dirs. Nat. Ethnic Coalition Orgns., 1990—, Coalition Italo-Am. Assn., 1986—; Italian Apostalate, N.Y., 1993. Recipient Disting. Alumni award LIU, 1985, Organizational Leadership award Coalition Italo-Am. Assns., Inc., 1988, Americus award Bronx Community Coll., 1989, Role Model award Club DaVinci, 1990, Inte I-A Student Assn. award, CUNY, 1991, Intergroup Rels. Chancellor's award, 1994, FIERI Leadership award, 1993, Philip Mazzei award, 1993; named Cavaliere of Order of Merit Republic of Italy, 1992; Italian fellow John Jay Coll., 1993. Mem. Am. Counseling Assn., Am. Mental Health Counselors Assn. (cert. of recognition 1979, counselor of yr. 1983-84), Nat. Acad. Cert. Clin. Mental Health Counselors, Nat. Bd. for Cert. Counselors, Am.-Italian Hist. Assn., N.Y. State Mental Health Counselors Assn. (past pres., Outstanding Work award 1980), Ill. Club. Home: 41 Carwall Ave Mount Vernon NY 10552-1211 Office: CUNY Grad Ctr 33 W 42d St New York NY 10036

SCEPANSKI, JORDAN MICHAEL, librarian, administrator; b. Yonkers, N.Y., Nov. 21, 1942; s. Michael James and Margaret (Witko) S.; m. H. Lea Wells, Apr. 18, 1981; children—Kathryn Mary, Jordan Wells, Jennifer Elizabeth. BS, Manhattan Coll., 1964; MLn, Emory U., 1967; postgrad., U. N.C., Charlotte, 1976-77; M.B.A., U. Tenn., Nashville, 1982. Vol. Peace Corps, Turkey, 1964-66; adult services librarian Uniondale Pub. Library, N.Y., 1967-68; various profl. staff positions ALA, Chgo., 1970-73; asst. dir. library, asst. prof. U. N.C., Charlotte, 1974-78; dir. central library Vanderbilt U., Nashville, 1978-84; dir. univ. library and learning resources Calif. State U., Long Beach, 1984—; mgmt. intern Joint Univ. Librs., Nashville, 1977-78; cons./trainer Assn. Rsch. Librs., 1979-80; Fulbright lectr. Hacettepe U., Ankara, Turkey, 1981-82; cons. Coll. Charleston, S.C., No. Ky. U., Highlands Heights, Elon Coll., N.C.; facilitator, trainer U. Notre Dame, South Bend, Ind., U. Nebr., Lincoln, U. Wyo.; founding mem. IBM Informa; bd. dirs. VTLS Inc. Contbr. articles to profl. jours. cons. Calif. State U., L.A. Served with U.S. Army, 1968-70. Recipient K.G. Saur award Coll. and Research Libraries publ., 1988; sr. fellow UCLA, 1983; faculty/librarian coop. research grantee Council on Library Resources, 1983. Mem. ALA (chair internat. rels. round table 1990-91), Western Assn. Schs. and Colls. (accreditation vis. team); Freedom to Read Found., Fulbright Alumni Assn., Jane Austen Soc. (bd. dirs.), Jane Austen Soc., S.W. Am.-Turkish Assn. So. Calif., Beta Phi Mu, Phi Beta Delta. Democrat. Roman Catholic. Home: 6714 E Los Arcos St Long Beach CA 90815-2409 Office: Calif State U-Long Beach U Libr Long Beach CA 90840

SCHAACK, PHILIP ANTHONY, retired beverage company executive; b. Evanston, Ill., June 6, 1921; s. Harry Charles and Lora Mary (Colford) S.; m. Elizabeth Eberhart, Mar. 27, 1943; children: Susan, Laura, Betsy. Student, Northwestern U., 1943; LLD (hon.), Ill. Benedictine Coll., 1977. Vice-pres. Joyce Beverages/Chgo., 1957-60; v.p. Joyce Beverages/Ill., Joliet, 1960-63, exec. v.p., 1963-65, pres., 1965-85; dir. Joyce Beverages/Ill. Retired ir. First Midwest Bank; past chmn., trustee Ill. Benedictine Coll.; vice-chmn. nat. devel. coun. Sisters of Providence. With USN, 1942-45. Mem. Chgo. Golf Club, Innisbrook Golf Club, Minocqua Country Club, Timber Ridge Country Club. Republican. Roman Catholic. Home: 1480 Aberdeen Ct Naperville IL 60564-9797

SCHAAF, MARTHA ECKERT, author, library director, musician; b. Madison, Ind., Sept. 21, 1911; d. Frederick William and Julia (Richert) Eckert; m. Clarence William Schaaf, Dec. 27, 1941 (dec. 1987); 1 child, Susan Elizabeth Lee. AB with distinction, Ind. U., 1933; MLS, Columbia U., 1945; postgrad., Butler U., Ind. U. Lic. tchr. English, French, Spanish tchr., music tchr., libr. dir. Twp. System, Crothersville, Ind., 1936-38; libr. music instr. Angola, Ind., 1938-39, Howe High Sch., Indpls., 1939-42; libr. dir. Reitz High Sch., Evansville, Ind., 1942; county libr. organizer County Brs. Libr., Columbus, Ga., 1943; hosp. libr. dir. Camp Van Dorn, Woodville, Miss., 1943-44; organized libr. Bulova Sch. for Disabled Vets., L.I., N.Y., 1944-45; organized bus. rsch. libr. Eli Lilly & Co., Indpls., 1946-50; rsch. libr. Wallace Collection Inst. Hist. Soc. Libr., 1958-61; dir. Pub. Libr., Pompano Beach, Fla., 1967-72; prin. Ind. Spl. Libr. Assn., 1948. Author: Lew Wallace: Boy Writer, 1961, Duke Ellington: Music Master, 1975; contbg. author: War Paint and Wagon Wheels, 1968, Reading Incentive Series, 1969; contbr. articles to profl. jours. Named Valedictorian, Madison (Ind.) High Sch., 1929; recipient History award Daughters Am. Revolution, 1930, C. of C. award Pompano Beach, Fla., 1970, Lit. Music award NLAPW; Disting. Alumni award Ind. U., Bloomington, 1983, literary, music awards, Nat. League of Am. Pen Women. Mem. Nat. League Am. Pen Women, Mortar Board, U. Ind. Alumni Assn., Columbia U. Alumni Assn., Phi Beta Kappa, Pi Lambda Theta, Chi Omega. Avocations: piano, organ, choral direction, composing. Home: 6065 S Verde Trl Apt G119 Boca Raton FL 33433-4410

SCHAAF, MIV, writer, graphic designer, composer; b. Oct. 3, 1920; m. Alfred Musso, 1959; 1 child, Gia Musso. BA, Mich. State U., 1943; postgrad., Humboldt State U., 1988—. Owner Miv Schaaf Assocs., 1954—; seminar tchr. UCLA, U. Calif. Irvine, Scripps Coll., 1977—; del. White House Conf. Libs., 1979; judge Robert B. Campbell book collection UCLA, 1980; speaker in field. Author: Who Can Not Read About Crocodiles, 1988; columnist L.A. Times, 1972-87; writer North Coast Jour., 1993—; writer 156 poems; composer some 160 songs, including Songs of Age and Songs of Rage. Pres. Archtl. Panel, L.A., 1951-69; founder Pasadena Cultural Heritage Commn., 1973. Recipient Premier award Pasadena Heritage, 1977, Met. Coop. Libr. System and Calif. Libr. Assn. award, 1982, Gold Crown award Pasadena Arts Coun., 1983. Avocation: playing cello. Home: 83 Wilson Ln Fieldbrook CA 95519

SCHAAP, MARCIA, special education educator; b. Grand Rapids, Mich., May 21, 1938; d. Wiliam Jr. and Margaret D. (Dekker) Hertel; m. Richard A. Schaap, June 16, 1962; children: Sandra, Linda, Kathy, Esther. AB in Edn., Calvin Coll., 1962; MS in Spl. Edn., Chgo. State U., 1984. Cert. tchr., Mich. 2d grade tchr. West Side Christian Sch., Grand Rapids, 1960-62; 2d grade tchr. Roseland Christian Sch., Chgo., 1963, with remedial reading dept., 1984-85, with chpt. I remedial computers dept., 1986, learning disabilities resource, author, dir., 1987-92; tutor St. Paul Luth. Sch., Dolton, Ill., 1992—; Salem Luth. Sch., Blue Island, Ill., 1992—; owner, dir. Marcia's Music and Tutoring, South Holland, Ill.; mem. ABLE. Mem. Nat. Learning Disabilities Assn., Ill. Learning Disabilities Assn., Chgo. Learning Disabilities Assn., Orland C.H.I.L.D. Assn., Nat. Music Tchrs. Assn., South Suburban Music Tchrs. Assn., Orton Dyslexia Assn. Advocates Behind Legal Edn., Nat. Piano Tchrs. Orgn., Ill. State Music Tchrs. Assn., Christian Educators Assn. Home and Office: 643 E 162nd Pl South Holland IL 60473-2302

SCHAAP, RICHARD JAY, journalist; b. N.Y.C., Sept. 27, 1934; s. Maurice William and Leah (Lerner) S.; m. Barbara M. Barron, June 20, 1956 (div. 1967); children: Renee Beth, Michelle Anne; m. Madeleine Gottlieb, Aug. 29, 1967 (div. 1980); children: Jeremy Albert, Joanna Rose; m. Patricia Ann McLeod, May 17, 1981; children—Juryan Dean, David Maurice. BS, Cornell U., 1955; MS, Columbia U., 1956. Sr. editor Newsweek, N.Y.C., 1956-63; city editor N.Y. Herald Tribune, 1964-66; correspondent NBC, N.Y.C., 1971-80, ABC, N.Y.C., 1980—; host of The Sports Reporters ESPN, 1990—. Author 28 books including RFK, 1967, Turned On, 1967, (with Jerry Kramer) Instant Replay, 1968, (with Jimmy Breslin) 44, 1980, Steinbrenner!, 1982, The 1984 Olympic Games, 1984, (with Jerry Kramer)

Distant Replay, 1985; (with Billy Crystal) Absolutely Mahvelous, 1986; (with Phil Simms and Phil McConkey) Simms to McConkey, 1987, (with Bo Jackson) Bo Knows Bo, 1990. Served to lt. U.S. Army, 1957-58. Recipient Emmy awards for Sid Caesar profile 1984, sports features 1986, Tom Waddell profile 1988, commentaries 1992, 94, Columbia Sch. Journalism Alumni award, 1994. Office: ABC News 47 W 66th St New York NY 10023-6201

SCHABER, GORDON DUANE, law educator, former judge; b. Ashley, N.D., Nov. 22, 1927; s. Ronald and Esther (Schatz) S. A.B. with distinction, Sacramento State Coll., 1949; J.D. with honors, U. Calif. at San Francisco, 1952; LL.D., McGeorge Sch. Law, 1961, John Marshall Law Sch., 1983, Widener U., Del. Law Sch., 1984; LLD, Southwestern U., 1994. Bar: Calif. 1953. Pvt. practice Sacramento, 1953-65; ptnr. firm Schaber & Cecchettini, Sacramento, 1953-65; prof., asst. dean McGeorge Coll. of Law (now McGeorge Sch. Law of U. Pacific), Sacramento, 1953-56, asst. dean, 1956, acting dean, dean, prof. law, 1957-91, univ. counsellor, disting. prof. law, 1991—; presiding judge Superior Ct. Sacramento County, 1965-70; dir. Air Calif., 1974-81, Westgate Corp., 1979-82, Sacramento Cablevision, 1980-82, Capitol Bank of Commerce, vice chmn., 1987-90; chmn. bd. dirs. River City Cablevision Inc.; mem. Calif. Bd. Control, 1962-64; chmn. Greater Sacramento Plan Com., 1970; cons. on establishment Sch. Law at U. Puget Sound, 1970-71; cons. study on jud. workload Jud. Council Calif., 1971-72; mem. Adv. Com. to Chief Justice Calif. on Superior Ct. Mgmt., 1971; cons. vehicle theft study Calif. Hwy. Patrol, 1972; panelist Sacramento Bee Secret Witness Program, 1971-90; mem. adv. com. to Calif. Office Econ. Opportunity, Calif. Legal Services Expt., 1972; vice chmn. Calif. Ednl. Facilities Authority, 1978—; bd. dirs. Nat. Center Adminstrv. Justice, 1978; mem. President's Adminstrn. Justice Task Force, 1980; mem. Joint Task Force on Student Fin. Aid Com. and Govt. Rels., 1988-90, Com. to Study the Law Sch. Process, 1989-90, Ind. Law Sch. Com., 1989-90. Author: Contracts in a Nutshell, 1975, 3d rev. edit., 1990, Procedural Guide for the Evaluation and Accreditation of Court Facilities, 1977, (with others) The Twentieth Century and the Courthouse, 1977; contbr. articles to profl. jours., book reviewer. Mem. Sacramento-San Joaquin chpt. Muscular Dystrophy Assn. Telethon Gift com. 1980, Sierra Found. for Health (One Hundred Million Dollar Health Trust), 1987—, adv. bd. Performing Arts Fund, Sacramento Bee, 1987—, exec. com. Sacramento Area Commn. on Mather Conversion, 1989-90, law sch. admission coun., Fin. Aid Svcs. Com., 1989-90; past mem., bd. advisors Mental Health Soc. Sacramento, Better Bus. Bur., League of Women Votors; trustee Stanford Homes Found., 1980-87; bd. dirs. Sacramento Regional Foundation, 1982-87, Sutter Hosps. of Sacramento, 1978; mem. bd. advisors Coll. Public Interest Law, Pacific Legal Found., 1974—; vice chmn. Calif. Edn. Facilities Authority, 1978; chmn. Sacramento County Democratic Central Com., 1960-64; mem. Dem. State Central Com., 1960-64, 74-82; trustee Sierra Found. for Health, 1987—; Hon. Lorenzo Patino Scholarship trust, 1984; active numerous other civic coms. Named Sacramento County Young Man of Yr., 1962, Trial Judge of Yr. Calif. Trial Lawyers Assn., 1969, Humanitarian of Yr. Sacramento County Bar Assn., 1990, Sacramentan of Yr. Sacramento C. of C., 1994, Outstanding Alumnus Hastings Coll., 1994; recipient Legal Edn. and Jud. award Am. Trial Lawyers Assn., 1965, Order of Hornet Calif. State U., Sacramento, 1972, award Citizenship and Law Related Edn. Ctr., 1994, Silver Hope award Multiple Sclerosis Soc., 1994. Fellow Am. Bar Found.; mem. ABA (council sect. legal edn. and admissions to bar 1975, chmn. 1981, sec. 1982-92, adv. com. pres.-elect on competence of lawyers continuing edn. 1978, numerous other coms., Robert J. Kutak award 1991), Sacramento Bar Assn. (v.p. 1970), State Bar Calif. (mem. com. legislation 1969-89, spl. com. appellate cts. 1970-72, long range adv. planning com. 1972-89, vice chmn. com. law sch. edn. 1973, chmn. 1974, mem. commn. to study bar examination processes 1976-80, Merit Selection Com., others), Am. Judicature Soc., Order of Coif, Phi Delta Phi. Clubs: Commonwealth, Comstock, Sutter, Sacramento/Capitol, many others. Home: 937 Piedmont Dr Sacramento CA 95822-1701 Office: U Pacific McGeorge Sch Law 3200 5th Avecramento CA 95817-2705

SCHACHMAN, HOWARD KAPNEK, molecular biologist, educator; b. Phila., Dec. 5, 1918; s. Morris H. and Rose (Kapnek) S.; m. Ethel H. Lazarus, Oct. 20, 1945; children—Marc, David. BSChemE, Mass. Inst. Tech., 1939; PhD in Phys. Chemistry, Princeton, 1948; DSc (hon.), Northwestern U., 1974; MD (hon.), U. Naples, 1990. Fellow NIH, 1946-48; instr., asst. prof. U. Calif., Berkeley, 1948-54, assoc. prof. biochemistry, 1954-59, prof. biochemistry and molecular biology, 1959-91; prof. emeritus dept. molecular and cell biology U. Calif. at Berkeley, 1991-94; prof. grad. sch., 1994—; prof. grad. sch. U. Calif. at Berkeley, 1994—, chmn. dept. molecular biology, dir. virus lab., 1969-76; mem. sci. coun. and sci. adv. bd. Stazione Zoologica, Naples, Italy, 1988—; cons. bd. sci. Meml. Sloan-Kettering Cancer Ctr., 1988—; mem. sci. adv. com. Rsch. 1 Am., 1990—; William Lloyd Evans lectr. Ohio State U., 1988, Carl and Gerty Cori lectr. Washington State U. Sch. Medicine, 1993; faculty rsch. lectr. U. Calif., Berkeley, 1994. Author: Ultracentrifugation in Biochemistry, 1959; developer of ultracentrifuge as a tool for studying macromolecules of biol. interest; condr. studies on structure and function of regulatory enzyme: aspartate transcrabamylase. Mem. bd. sci. counselors Cancer Biology and Diagnosis divsn. Nat. Cancer Inst., 1989-92; spl. advisor to dir. NIH, 1994—. Lt. USNR, 1945-47. Recipient John Scott award, 1964, Warren Triennial prize Mass. Gen. Hosp., 1965, Alexander von Humboldt award, 1990, Berkeley citation for disting. achievement and notable svc. U. Calif., 1993; Guggenheim Meml. fellow, 1956. Mem. AAAS, NAS (chmn. biochemistry 1990-93, panelist sci. responsibility and conduct of rsch. 1990-92), Am. Chem. Soc. (award in chem. instrumentation 1962, Calif. sect. award 1958), Am. Soc. Biochemistry and Molecular Biology (pres. 1987-88, chmn. pub. affairs com. 1989—, Merck award 1986, Herbert A. Sober award 1994), Fedn. Am. Socs. for Exptl. Biology (pres. 1988-89, pub. affairs exec. com. 1989—, pub. svc. award 1994), Sigma Xi. Achievements include development of the ultracentrifuge as a tool for studying macromolecules of biological interest; studies on structure and function of a regulatory enzyme: Aspartate transcarbamylase. Office: U Calif Berkeley Dept Molecular and Cell Bio MCB Stanley ASU 229 Stanley Hall # 3206 Berkeley CA 94720-3206

SCHACHT, HENRY BREWER, diesel engine manufacturing company executive; b. Erie, Pa., Oct. 16, 1934; s. Henry Blass and Virginia (Brewer) S.; m. Nancy Godfrey, Aug. 27, 1960; children: James, Laura, Jane, Mary. BS, Yale U., 1956; MBA, Harvard U., 1962; DSc (hon.), DePauw U., 1982; MA (hon.), Yale U., 1988. Sales trainee Am. Brake Shoe Co., N.Y.C., 1956-57; investment mgr. Irwin Mgmt. Co., Columbus, Ind., 1962-64; v.p. fin. Cummins Engine Co., Inc., Columbus, 1964-66; v.p., cen. area mgr. internat. Cummins Engine Co., Inc., London, 1966-67; group v.p. internat. and subsidiaries Cummins Engine Co., Inc., 1967-69; pres. Cummins Engine Co., Inc., Columbus, 1969-77, CEO, 1977-94, chmn., 1977—; bd. dirs. AT&T, CBS, Chase Manhattan Corp., Chase Manhattan Bank N.A., Alcoa. Trustee emeritus The Culver Ednl. Found.; active Bus. Coun., Coun. Fgn. Rels.; mem. The Assocs., Harvard Bus. Sch., The Bus. Enterprise Trust; hon. trustee Brookings Instn., Com. Econ. Devel., Yale Corp.; chmn. trustees Ford Found.; sr. mem. Conf. Bd. With USNR, 1957-60. Mem. Tau Beta Pi. Republican. Office: Cummins Engine Co Inc PO Box 3005 Columbus IN 47202-3005

SCHACHT, HENRY MEVIS, writer, consultant; b. Pasadena, Calif., Feb. 28, 1916; s. Henry and Amelia (Claussen) S.; m. Mary Joan Turnbull, Dec. 30, 1937; children—Henry John, Linda Jean. B.A., U. Calif.-Berkeley, 1936. Info. specialist U. Calif.-Berkeley, 1936-42; dir. agr. NBC, San Francisco, 1942-59, ABC, San Francisco, 1959-60; agrl. columnist San Francisco Chronicle, 1959-93; dir. agrl. info. U. Calif., 1961-65; v.p. corp. relations, corp. sec. Calif. Canners & Growers, San Francisco, 1965-81; freelance writer, 1936—; cons. radio-TV to FAO of UN, Cairo, 1963, Mexico City, 1965, Tokyo, 1966; dir. Calif. Co. for Internat. Trade; dir. Agrl. Issues Ctr., U. Calif. Pres. U.S. Fruit Export Coun., 1972-75; exec. sec. Commn. Calif. Agr. and Higher Edn., 1993-95; adv. bd. Agrl. Issues Ctr. U. Calif., 1990—. Mem. Pub. Relations Soc. Am., Pub. Relations Roundtable San Francisco, Nat. Assn. Farm Broadcasters, Agrl. Relations Council, Nat. Canners Assn. (dir. 1966-81). Home: 60 Hiller Dr Oakland CA 94618

SCHACHT, JOCHEN HEINRICH, biochemistry educator; b. Königsberg, Fed. Republic Germany, July 2, 1939; came to U.S., 1969; s. Heinz and Else (Sprenger) S.; m. Helga Hildegard Seidel, Jan.27, 1967; children: Miriam Helga, Daniel Jochen. BS, U. Bonn, Fed. Republic Germany, 1962; MS in

Chemistry, U. Heidelberg, Fed. Republic Germany, 1965, PhD in Biochemistry, 1968. Asst. research chemist, Mental Health Research Inst. U. Mich., Ann Arbor, 1969-72, from asst. prof. to assoc. prof. biochemistry, Dept. Biol. Chemistry & Otolaryngology, 1973-84, prof., 1984—, chmn. grad. program in physiol. acoustics, 1981—; vis. prof. Karolinska Inst., Stockholm, 1979-80; acting dir. Kresge Hearing Rsch. Inst., U. Mich., 1983-84, assoc. dir., 1989—; mem. hearing rsch. study sect. USPHS, NIH, Nat. Inst. Neurol. and Communicative Disorders and Stroke, 1986-89, Task Force Nat. Strategic Rsch. Plan, Nat. Insts. Deafness and Communication Disorders, USPHS, NIH. Author over 100 articles, book chpts., revs.; co-editor Neurochemistry of Cholinergic Receptors, 1974. Fogarty Sr. Internat. fellow NIH, 1979, Sen. J. Javitz Neurosci. investigator, 1984; recipient Cherchour Etranger research award INSERM, Paris, 1986, Animal Welfare award Erna-Graff Found., Berlin, 1987, Disting. Faculty Achievement award U. Mich., 1989. Mem. Deutsche Gesellschaft für Biologische Chemie, Am. Soc. Neurochemistry, Internat. Soc. Neurochemistry, Soc. for Neurosci., Assn. for Research in Otolaryngology, Am. Soc. Biol. Chemists. Avocations: photography, travel. Office: U Mich Kresge Hearing Rsch Inst Ann Arbor MI 48109-0506

SCHACHT, LINDA JOAN, broadcast journalist; b. Berkeley, Calif., Sept. 11, 1944; d. Henry Mevis and Mary (Turnbull) S.; m. John Burdette Gage, May 1, 1976; children: Peter Turnbull, Katharine Burdette. BA, U. Calif., Berkeley, 1966, MJ, 1978. Reporter Sta. KQED-TV, San Francisco, 1974-76, Sta. KPIX-TV, San Francisco, 1976—; vis. faculty Grad. Sch. Journalism U. Calif., Berkeley, 1990—. Reporter Dem. conv., 1980 (Emmy award 1981), investigative article on second mortgage brokers, 1977 (Emmy award), on children as witnesses, 1984 (Calif. State Bar award 1985, ABA award 1986). Mem. Nat. Acad. TV Arts and Scis.

SCHACHT, RICHARD LAWRENCE, philosopher, educator; b. Racine, Wis., Dec. 19, 1941; s. Robert Hugo and Alice (Munger) S.; m. Judith Rowan; children: Eric Lawrence, Marshall Robert. B.A., Harvard U., 1963; M.A., Princeton U., 1965, Ph.D., 1967; postgrad, Tübingen U., Fed. Republic Germany, 1966-67. Asst. prof. U. Ill., Urbana-Champaign, 1967-71, assoc. prof., 1971-80, prof. philosophy, 1980—, Jubilee prof. of Liberal Arts and Scis., 1990—, chmn. dept., 1980-91, interim dean Coll. Liberal Arts and Scis., 1994; vis. prof. U. Oreg., 1969, U. Pitts., 1973, U. Mich., 1979; vis. scholar Tübingen U., 1975. Author: Alienation, 1970, Hegel and After, 1975, Nietzsche, 1983, Classical Modern Philosophers, 1984, The Future of Alienation, 1994, Making Sense of Nietzsche, 1995; editor: Nietzsche Selections, 1993, Nietzsche, Genealogy, Morality, 1994, Internat. Nietzsche Studies. Mem. Am. Philos. Assn. (chair com. on status and future of the profession), N.Am. Nietzsche Soc. (exec. dir.), Internat. Sociol. Assn. (v.p., research com. on alienation theory), AAUP. Office: U Ill Dept Philosophy 105 Gregory 810 S Wright St Urbana IL 61801

SCHACHT, RONALD STUART, lawyer; b. Stamford, Conn., Nov. 7, 1932; s. Saul Albert and Faye Dorothy (Gittleman) S.; m. Natalie Helene Goldman, June 17, 1956; children—Patti Ellen, Bonnie Anne, Cindy Joy. B.S., U. Conn., 1954; LL.B., NYU, 1957, LL.M., 1966. Bar: N.Y. 1957, D.C. 1980. Tax atty. IRS, N.Y.C., 1957-62; assoc. Proskauer Rose Goetz & Mendelsohn, N.Y.C., 1962-69, ptnr., 1969—, mng. ptnr., 1981-84, mem. exec. com., 1985—; lectr. Practising Law Inst., NYU Inst. Fed. Taxation; adj. asst. prof. Sch. Continuing Edn. NYU, 1970-72. Bd. dirs. Congregation Agudath Shalom, Stamford, 1968-73; mem. com. Fedn. Jewish philanthropoies, N.Y.C., 1972-80. Mem. N.Y. State Bar Assn., Assn. of Bar of City of N.Y., N.Y. County Lawyers Assn. (bd. dirs. 1977-83, chmn. ins. com. 1975-85), Newfield Swim Club (bd. dirs. 1967-70, pres. 1969), Phi Kappa Phi, Gamma Chi Epsilon. Democrat. Jewish. Home: 245 E 54th St New York NY 10022-4707 Office: Proskauer Rose Goetz & Mendelsohn 1585 Broadway New York NY 10036-8200

SCHACHTER, BARRY, economist; b. Providence, R.I., Aug. 17, 1954; s. Hyman and Fannie (Dunder) S.; m. Joanne Fitzsimmons, Sept. 13, 1981; 1 child, Devra Fitzsimmons. BS in Econs., Bentley Coll., 1976, AS in Acctg., 1976; MA in Econs., Cornell U., 1979, PhD, 1982. From instr. to assoc. prof. dept. Econs. Rutgers U., New Brunswick, N.J., 1980-82; from asst. prof., to assoc. prof. Simon Fraser U., Burnaby, B.C., 1982-88; assoc. prof. Tulane U., New Orleans, 1988-92; fin. economist divsn. econ. analysis Commodity Futures Trading Commn., Washington, 1990-94; fin. economist risk analysis divsn. Comptroller of the Currency, Washington, 1994—; vis. asst. prof. U. Utah, Salt Lake City, 1987-88; vis. scholar rsch. dept. Internat Monetary Fund, Washington, 1992-93; ad hoc referee Can. Coun. Killam Fellowship, 1988, Econ. Inquiry, 1983-84, Fin. Review, 1985, 89-90, Jour. Fin. Rsch. 1987-93, Fin. Mgmt., 1989-90, Jour. Bus. and Rsch., 1988, Jour. Fin., 1989, 91, Quarterly Jour. Econs., 1989, Jour. Money, Credit and Banking, 1989, Jour. Econ. Theory, 1990, Jour. Banking & Fin., 1990-93, Jour. Fin. Edn., 1990, Review of Quantatative Fin. and Acctg., 1991-92, Internat. Review Econs. and Fin., 1992, Soc. Scis. and Humanities Rsch. Coun. Can. 1993; speaker in field; presenter various confs. Contbr. articles to profl. jours., chpts. to books, annuals, proceedings; assoc. editor Internat. Rev. of Fin. Analysis, 1990—, Jour. Derivatives, 1993—, Fin. Mgmt., 1993—, Jour. Banking & Finance, 1995—, Jour. Fin. Engring. 1995—. Rsch. grantee Simon Fraser Univ., 1982, 84, 86, Inst. Quantitative Rsch. Fin., 1990; recipient Best Paper award Internat. Options Market, 1984. Mem. Am. Econs. Assn., Am. Fin. Assn., Fin. Mgmt. Assn., Internat. Assn. Fin. Engrs., Western Fin. Assn. Office: Comptroller of the Currency Risk Analysis Divsn 250 E St SW Washington DC 20219

SCHACHTER, HARRY, biochemist, educator; b. Vienna, Austria, Feb. 25, 1933; came to Can., 1951; s. Asher and Miriam (Freund) S.; m. Judith Jakubovic, Dec. 23, 1958; children: Aviva, Asher. BA, U. Toronto, 1955, MD, 1959, PhD, 1964. From assist. prof. to assoc. prof. dept. biochemistry U. Toronto, 1964-72, prof., 1972—, chmn., 1984-89; sr. scientist Rsch. Inst. Hosp. for Sick Children, Toronto, 1976—; head biochemistry rsch. divsn. Rsch. Inst. Hosp. for Sick Children, 1976-89.

SCHACHTER, MAX, retired engineering services company executive; b. N.Y.C., Aug. 22, 1913; s. Morris and Rebecca (Sirota) S.; m. Ida Jensky, June 25, 1934; 1 son, Robert. Student, N.Y. U., 1932, CCNY, 1932-36, Cooper Union, 1942. Registered profl. engr., N.Y., N.J. Machine designer Torrington Mfg. Co., Conn., 1941-43, Machine & Tool Design Co., N.Y.C., 1943-48; chief engr. machine design div. Am. Machine & Foundry, Bklyn., 1949-51; chmn. Atlantic Design Co., Inc., Livingston, N.J., 1951-89, ret., 1989. Trustee, now pres. Ruth Gottscho Kidney Found., 1960—. Mem. ASME. Jewish.

SCHACHTER, MICHAEL BEN, psychiatrist; b. Bklyn., Jan. 15, 1941; s. Saul and Ann (Palestine) S.; m. Margaret Josephine Kavanagh, July 22, 1967 (div. Mar. 1979); children: Brian Joseph, Amy, Stefan James; m. Marlene Helen Brodsky, Aug. 22, 1982 (div. Mar. 1993); children: Adam Elliot, Jason Neil; m. Lisa Lackhai, July 19, 1993. BA, Columbia Coll., 1961, MD, 1965. Diplomate Am. Bd. Psychiatry and Neurology in Psychiatry, Am. Bd. Chelation Therapy. Med., surg. and pediatric intern Hosp. for Joint Diseases and Med. Ctr., N.Y.C., 1965-66; resident psychiatry Downstate Med. Ctr., Kings County Hosp., Bklyn., 1966-69; staff psychiatrist Bklyn. Community Counseling Ctr., 1968-69; staff psychiatrist Rockland County Community Mental Health Ctr., Pomona, N.Y., 1971, dir. emergency and admissions, 1971-72, dir. outpatient clinic, 1972-74; founder, dir. Michael B. Schachter M.D., P.C. formerly Mountainview Med., Suffern, N.Y., 1974—; bd. dirs. Am. Bd. Chelation Therapy, 1983-88. Author: (with David Sheinkin and Richard Hutton) The Food Connection, 1979, Food, Mind and Mood, 1980, 2d edit., 1987, The Natural Way To a Healthy Prostate, 1995; contbr. articles to profl. jours. Maj. USAF, 1969-71. Recipient Appreciation award NHF, 1979, Carlos Lamar Pioneer Meml. award Am. Acad. Med. Preventics, 1979, Merit award Am. Acad. Craniomandibular Disorders, 1981, Physician's Recognition awards AMA. Fellow Am. Coll. for Advancement in Medicine (v.p. 1985-87, pres.-elect 1987-89, pres. 1989-91); mem. Am. Psychiat. Assn., Am. Acad. Environ. Medicine, Am. Coll. Nutrition, Found. for Advancement Innovative Medicine (v.p. 1986-94, pres. 1994—). Avocations: running, basketball, swimming, tennis, golf. Office: 2 Executive Blvd # 202 Suffern NY 10901-4164

SCHACHTER, OSCAR, lawyer, educator, arbitrator; b. N.Y.C., June 19, 1915; s. Max and Fannie (Javits) S.; m. Mollie Miller, Aug. 9, 1936 (dec.

July 1980); children: Judith (Mrs. John Modell), Ellen (Mrs. John P. Leventhal); m. Muriel L. Sackler, June 14, 1982. BSS, Coll. City N.Y., 1936; JD, Columbia, 1939. Bar: N.Y. 1939. Editor-in-chief Columbia Law Rev., 1938-39; pvt. practice N.Y.C., 1939-40; atty. U.S. Dept. of Labor, Washington, 1940; chief nat. defense sect. in law dept. FCC, 1941; sect. of law com. and advisor on internat. communications Bd. of War Communications, 1941-42; prin., divisional asst., adviser on wartime econ. controls and on European liberated areas U.S. Dept. State, 1942-43; asst. gen. counsel UNRRA, 1944-46; drafting officer UNRRA council sessions, 1944-45; legal adv. UNRRA del. to USSR and Poland, 1945; legal counselor UN, 1946-52, dir. gen. legal div., 1952-66; dep. exec. dir., dir. studies UN Inst. for Tng. and Research, 1966-75; lectr. law Yale U. Law Sch., 1955-71; Carnegie lectr. Hague Acad. Internat. Law, 1963-82; Rosenthal lectr. Northwestern U. Law Sch., 1974; prof. Law Sch. and Faculty Internat. Affairs Columbia U., 1975—, Hamilton Fish prof. internat. law and diplomacy Law Sch. and Faculty Internat. Affairs, 1980-85, prof. emeritus Law Sch. and Faculty Internat. Affairs, 1985—; vis. prof Harvard Law Sch., 1982; chmn. legal com. UN Maritime Conf., 1948; legal com. UNESCO, 1948; past dir. Gen. Legal Div. of UN; served as legal adviser various internat. confs. and UN couns. and coms.; sec. legal adv. com. UN Atomic Energy Commn., 1946-47; vice chmn. Internat. Investment Law Conf., 1958; exec. sec. Internat. Arbitration Conf., 1958; mem. panel arbitrators Internat. Ctr. for Settlement of Investment Disputes, 1980-87; judge Ct. Arbitration in Canada-France Maritime Boundary dispute, 1989-92; expert advisor UN com. on transnational sorps., 1990-93. Author: Relation of Law, Politics and Action in the U.N, 1964, Sharing the World's Resources, 1977, International Law in Theory and Practice, 1985, rev. edit., 1991; co-author: Across the Space Frontier, 1952, Toward Wider Acceptance of UN Treaties, 1971, International Law Cases and Materials, 1980, 3rd edit., 1993; contbr. articles and monographs on internat. law, internat. instns., legal philosophy, human rights, internat. peace and security, internat. resources to legal jours.; editor-in-chief Am. Jour. Internat. Law, 1978-84, hon. editor, 1985—; co-editor: Competition in International Business, 1981; editorial bd. Marine Policy. Bd. dirs. Internat. Peace Acad., 1970-82. Recipient Friedman award Columbia Law Sch., 1983, Carl Fulda award U. Tex. Law Sch., 1990, Columbia Law medal for excellence, 1991. Fellow Am. Acad. Arts and Scis., World Acad. Art and Sci.; mem. ABA, Am. Soc. Internat. Law (pres. 1968-70, hon. v.p., exec. coun., hon. pres. 1994—, Manley Hudson medal 1981, Cert. of Merit for creative scholarship 1992), Coun. on Fgn. Rels., Inst. de Droit Internat. (v.p. 1991—), Internat. Law Assn., Internat. Astronautical Acad., Phi Beta Kappa. Home: 11 E 86th St New York NY 10028-0548 Office: Columbia U Law Sch New York NY 10027

SCHACHTER, STANLEY, psychology educator; b. N.Y.C., Apr. 15, 1922; s. Nathan and Anna (Fruchter) S.; m. Sophia Thalia Duckworth, June 2, 1967; 1 child, Elijah. BS, Yale U., 1942, MA, 1944; postgrad., MIT, 1946-48; PhD, U. Mich., 1949. From asst. prof. to prof. U. Minn., Mpls., 1949-61; Niven prof. psychology Columbia U., N.Y.C., 1961—; dir. research Orgn. for Comparative Social Research, Amsterdam, The Netherlands, 1952-54; vis. prof. U. Amsterdam, 1952-53, Stanford (Calif.) U., 1960. Author: (with others) Social Pressure Informal Groups, 1950, (with others) When Prophecy Fails, 1956, Psychology of Affiliation, 1959 (AAAS award 1959), Emotion, Obesity and Crime, 1971, (with others) Obese Humans and Rats, 1980; editor (with others): Extending Psychological Frontiers, 1989. Sgt. USAF, 1944-46. Fulbright fellow, 1952, Guggenheim fellow, 1967, Cattell Found. fellow, 1974; hon. research fellow U. London, 1975. Fellow Am. Psychol. Assn. (Disting. Scientific Contbr. award 1969), AAAS (Socio-Psychol. prize 1959), Am. Acad. Art and Scis., Nat. Acad. Sci., Soc. Exptl. Social Psychology (Disting. Scientist award 1984); mem. Cognitive Neurosci. Inst. (bd. dirs. 1980—), Internat. Soc. Emotion (bd. dirs. 1980—), Commn. Behavioral and Social Scis., Century Club (N.Y.C.). Jewish. Club: Century (N.Y.C.). Home: 175 Riverside Dr New York NY 10024-1616 Office: Columbia Univ Dept of Psychology Broadway & West 116th New York NY 10027

SCHAD, JAMES L., bishop; b. Phila., July 20, 1917. Grad. St. Mary's Sem., Balt. Ordained priest Roman Catholic Ch., 1943; ordained titular bishop of Panatoria and aux. bishop of Camden, 1966—; ret. Home: 1730 Kresson Rd Cherry Hill NJ 08003

SCHAD, MIKE, professional football player; b. Trenton, ON, Canada, Oct. 2, 1963. BS, geography, physiology, Queens Coll., Canada, 1986. With L. A. Rams, 1986-89; guard Philadelphia Eagles, 1989-94, Cleveland Browns, 1994—. Dr. Z's All-Pro team, 1994. Office: Cleveland Browns 80 First Ave Berea OH 44017-0679*

SCHAD, THEODORE MACNEEVE, science research administrator, consultant; b. Balt., Aug. 25, 1918; s. William Henry and Emma Margaret (Scheldt) S.; m. Kathleen White, Nov. 5, 1944 (dec. Aug. 1989); children: Mary Jane, Rebecca Christina; m. Margot Cornwell, Mar. 19, 1995. BSCE, Johns Hopkins U., 1939. Registered profl. engr., D.C. Various positions water resources engring. U.S. Army C.E., U.S. Bur. Reclamation, Md., Colo., Oreg. Wash., 1939-54; prin. budget examiner water resources programs U.S. Bur. Budget, Exec. Office of Pres., 1954-58; sr. specialist engring. and pub. works, dep. dir. Congl. Rsch. Svc., Libr. of Congress, 1958-68; staff dir. U.S. Senate Com. Nat. Water Resources, 1959-61; exec. dir. Nat. Water Commn., 1968-73; exec. sec. Environ. Studies Bd., 1973-77; dep. dir. Commn. Natural Resources, NAS, Washington, 1977-83; exec. dir. Nat. Ground Water Policy Forum, 1984-86; sr. fellow Conservation Found., Washington, 1986—; U.S. commr. Permanent Internat. Assn. Nav. Congresses, Brussels, 1963-70, commr. emeritus, 1987—; cons. U.S. Senate Com. Interior and Insular Affairs, 1963, U.S. Ho. of Reps. Com. Sci. and Tech., 1962-65, U.S. Office Saline Water, 1965-67, A.T. Kearney, Inc., Alexandria, Va., 1979-80, Chesapeake Rsch. Consortium, 1984, Ronco Cons. Corp., 1986—, Gambia River Basin Devel. Commn., Dakar, 1986-87, Apogee Rsch. Corp., 1987—, Office Tech. Assessment, U.S. Congress, 1992—. Contbr. articles to Ency. Brit. and profl. jours. Treas. Nat. Speleol. Found., 1961-65, trustee, 1965—; bd. dirs. Vets. Coop. Housing Assn., Washington, 1958-81, v.p., 1960-72. Recipient Meritorious Svc. award U.S. Dept. Interior, 1950, Icko Iben award Am. Water Resources Assn., 1978, Henry P. Caulfield medal, 1990. Fellow ASCE (treas. Nat. Capital chpt. 1952-55, v.p. 1967, pres. 1968, Julian Hinds prize 1991); mem. AAAS, Nat. Speleol. Soc., Am. Water Works Assn. (hon.), Am. Geophys. Union, Am. Acad. Environ. Engrs., Nat. Acad. Pub. Adminstrn., Permanent Internat. Assn. Nav. Congresses, Internat. Commn. Irrigation and Drainage, Potomac Appalachian Trail Club, Cosmos Club, Colo. Mountain Club (Denver), Seattle Mountaineers Club. Home: 4540-25th Rd N Arlington VA 22207-4102 Office: The Conservation Found 1260-24th St NW Washington DC 20037

SCHADE, CHARLENE JOANNE, adult and early childhood education educator; b. San Bernardino, Calif., June 26, 1935; d. Clarence George Linde and Helen Anita (Sunny) Hardesty; m. William Joseph Jr., Apr. 12, 1958 (div., 1978); children: Sabrina, Eric, Camela, Cynthia; m. Thomas Byron Killens, Sept. 25, 1983. BS, UCLA, 1959. Tchr. dance & pe L.A. Unified Secondary Schs., Calif., 1959-63; dir., instr. (Kindergym) La Jolla YMCA, Calif., 1972-76; instr. older adult San Diego Community Colls., 1977—; artist in residence Wolf Trap/Headstart, 1984-85; workshop leader S.W. Dance, Movement and Acro-Sports Workshop, prime-time adult activities coord., 1988—, Am. Heart Assn., Arthritis Found., Am. Lung Assn.; cons. to Calif. Gov.'s Coun. of Phys. Fitness, 1993; workshop leader AAHPERD Calif. Assn. HPERD, Head Start, San Diego Assn. Young Children, Calif. Assn. Edn. Young Child, Calif. Kindergarten Assn., Assn. Childhood Edn. Internat., IDEA Internat. Assn. Fitness Profls., San Diego C.C., Am. Soc. on Aging, 1977—; feature guest Sta. KFMB and KPBS TV shows, San Diego, 1980-88. Author: Move With Me From A to Z, 1982, Move With Me, One, Two, Three, 1988; co-author: Prime Time Aerobics, 1982, Muevete Conmigo, uno, dos, tres, 1990; co-writer: Guide for Physical Fitness Instructors of Older Adults, Grant Project, 1990, The Empowering Teacher, 1990, Handbook for Instructors of Older Adults, 1994. Dir. We Care Found., San Diego, 1977-79, Meet the Author programs San Diego County Schs., 1988—; founder SOLO, San Diego, 1981-83; adminstr., v.p. ODEM chpt. Toastmasters, San Diego, 1982; chmn. People with Arthritis Can Exercise com. San Diego chpt. Arthritis Found., 1994-95; workshop leader Am. Heart Assn., Arthritis Found., Am. Lung Assn. Grantee Video Showcase of Exercises for Older Adults, 1992-93. Mem. AAPHERD (workshop leader), Calif. Assn. Health, Phys. Edn., Recreation and Dance (workshop leader).

Avocations: hiking, dancing, traveling. Office: Exer Fun/Prime Time Aerobic 3089C Clairemont Dr Ste 130 San Diego CA 92117-6767

SCHADE, MALCOLM ROBERT, lawyer; b. Holyoke, Mass., Oct. 23, 1950; s. G. Malcolm and Dorothy Jean (Alderman) S.; m. Charlanne Reid Murray, June 26, 1971. BA magna cum laude, Windham Coll., 1971; JD, Columbia U., 1974, postgrad., 1975-76. Bar: N.Y. 1975, Mass. 1975, U.S. Dist. Ct. (so., ea., we. & no. dists.) N.Y. 1975, U.S. Ct. Appeals (2d cir.) 1975, U.S. Ct. Appeals (1st cir.) 1976, U.S. Supreme Ct. 1978, U.S. Dist. Ct. Vt. 1980, U.S. Ct. Appeals (6th cir.) 1985, U.S. Dist. Ct. (ea. dist.) Mich. 1988. Assoc. Kronish, Lieb, Shainswit, Weiner & Hellman, N.Y.C., 1977-79, Skadden Arps Slate Meagher & Flom, N.Y.C., 1980-83; ptnr. Alexander & Green, N.Y.C., 1984-86, Mudge Rose Guthrie Alexander & Ferdon, N.Y.C., 1987—. Rapporteur (book) American Hostages in Iran, 1985. Trustee Windham Coll., Putney, Vt., 1970-71, 76-80, sec., 1977-80, chmn. bd., 1978-80. Mem. Assn. Bar of City of N.Y. (com. on internat. arms control & security affairs 1979-85), Mass. Bar Assn., Comml. Bar Assn. (London, overseas mem.), Down Town Assn., Larchmont Shore Club, Horseshoe Harbor Yacht Club. Congregationalist. Avocations: sailing, hunting, skiing. Home: 24 Beech Rd New Rochelle NY 10804-4304 Office: Mudge Rose Guthrie Alexander & Ferdon 180 Maiden Ln New York NY 10038-4925

SCHADT, JAMES P., publishing executive. With Procter & Gamble USA, 1960-73, Pepsi Inc., 1973-78, Consolidated Foods Corp., 1978-81; pres., CEO Cadbury Schweppes Inc., 1981-91; pres., COO Reader's Digest Assoc. Inc., Pleasantville, N.Y., 1991-94, pres., CEO, 1994—. Office: Readers Digest Assoc Inc Reader's Digest Rd Pleasantville NY 10570

SCHADT, JAMES PHILLIP, consumer products executive; b. Saginaw, Mich., Aug. 7, 1938; s. Phillip, Jr., and Jean D. (Cardy) S.; BA, Northwestern U., 1960; m. Barbara L. Soldmann, Aug. 16, 1959; children: Lauren C., Andrew F. With Procter & Gamble, 1960-65, Glendinning Cos., 1965-70, Squibb Corp., 1970-73, PepsiCo, 1973-77, Sara Lee Corp., 1977-80; pres. Cadbury Schweppes plc., Stamford, Conn., 1981-91, also dir.; pres., COO, dir. Reader's Digest Assn., 1991-94, dir, pres., CEO, 1994—; bd. dirs. DeWitt Wallace-Reader's Digest Fund, Lila Wallace-Reader's Digest Fund, DeWitt Wallace Fund Meml. Sloat-Kettering Cancer Ctr.; trustee Am. Enterprise Inst., Norwalk (Conn.) Hosp., Northwestern U. Mem. Am. Assn. Pubs., Bus. Roundtable, Conf. Bd., Mag. Pubs. Assn., Heritage Found, Grocery Manufacturers Assn., Blind Brook Club, Chgo. Club, Fairfield County Hunt Club, Country Club Fairfield, John's Island Club, Lotos Club. Home: 17 Owenoke Park Westport CT 06880-6834 Office: Reader's Digest Assn Reader's Digest Rd Pleasantville NY 10570-7000

SCHAECHTER, MOSELIO, microbiology educator; b. Milan, Italy, Apr. 26, 1928; children: Judy, John. Student Central U., Ecuador, 1947-49; MA, U. Kans., 1952; PhD, U. Pa., 1954. Postdoctoral fellow State Serum Inst., Copenhagen, 1956-58; instr., asst. prof., assoc. prof. U. Fla., Gainesville, 1958-62; from assoc. prof. to disting. prof. dept. microbiology Tufts U., Boston, 1962-95, prof. emeritus 1995—; adj. prof. San Diego State U. Editor: Molecular Biology Bacterial Growth, 1985, Escherichia coli and Salmonella Typhimurium, 1987, 95, Mechanisms of Microbiol. Disease, 1989, 92. Mem. Am. Soc. Microbiology (pres. 1985-86, chmn. internat. activities), Am. Soc. Med. Sch. Microbiology Chmn. (pres. 1984-85, chair internat. activities 1986-94), Soc. Gen. Microbiology, Boston Mycol. Club, Sigma Xi. Avocations: field mycology; hiking. Office: San Diego State U Dept Biology San Diego CA 92182

SCHAEDLER, RUSSELL WILLIAM, microbiologist, physicians, educator; b. Hatfield, Pa., Dec. 17, 1927; s. Robert and Sophia Louise (Enz) S. B.S., Ursinus Coll., 1949; M.D., Jefferson Med. Coll., 1953. Intern Jefferson Med. Coll. Hosp., Thomas Jefferson U., Phila., 1953-54; prof., chmn. dept. microbiology Jefferson Med. Coll. Hosp., Thomas Jefferson U., 1968-91, Plimpton-Pugh prof., 1985—; asst. Rockefeller Inst. for Med. Research, asst. physician Hosp. of Rockefeller Inst., 1954-57; asst. prof. Rockefeller Inst., resident asso. physician, 1957-62, asso. prof., physician to Hosp., 1962-68; asso. mem. Armed Forces Epidemiology Bd., Enteric Commn., 1967-72; mem. bacteriology and mycology study sect. NIH, 1970-74, chmn., 1973-74; mem. and chmn. NIH bacteriology and mycology AHR study sect., 1978-82. Mem. editorial bd. Jour. Bacteriology, 1965-69, Jour. Infection and Immunity, 1970-72; contbr. articles to sci. jours. Bd. dirs. Cardeza Found. Served with U.S. Army, 1946-47. Mem. Am. Assn. Immunologists, Am. Soc. Microbiology, Am. Gastroent. Assn., Infectious Disease Soc. Am., Coll. Physicians Phila., Harvey Soc., AAAS, J. Aitken Meigs Med. Assn. N.Y. Tb and Health Assn. (bd. dirs. 1965-68), Sigma Xi, Alpha Omega Alpha. Clubs: Vesper, Sydenham Coterie. Research in anaerobes and microecology of the gut. Home: 320 Delancey St Philadelphia PA 19106-4209 Office: 1020 Locust St Philadelphia PA 19107-6731

SCHAEFER, ADOLPH OSCAR, JR., advertising agency executive; b. Phila., May 21, 1932; s. Adolph Oscar and Jessie Rae (Brooks) S.; m. Leslie C. Maurer, May 4, 1994; children by previous marriage: Jeffrey S., Andrew C.; adopted children: Deborah H., Scott S., Adrian L. Maurer, Senta G. Maurer. B.S. in Econs., Wharton Sch., U. Pa., 1954. With drug products div. Procter & Gamble, Cin., 1954-56; mfrs. rep. Towle & Son Co., Phila., 1956-61; ptnr. Rockett & Schaefer Advt., Phila., 1961-63; v.p. Eldridge Co., Phila., 1963-64; pres. Schaefer Advt. Inc., Valley Forge, Pa., 1964-87, chmn. bd. dirs., 1987-89; chmn. Direct Strategies, Inc., Devon, Pa., 1989-92. Mem. editorial adv. bd.: Pa. Gazette, U. Pa., 1970-72. Mem. alumni bd. mgrs. Episcopal Acad., 1969-73; pres. Valley Forge Gallery, Pa., 1992—; Corporate Insights, Wayne, Pa. Served with U.S. Army, 1954-56. Mem. Bus. and Profl. Advt. Assn. (Hall of Fame 1993), Pa. Soc. SAR, Union League Club, Phi Gamma Delta. Home: PO Box 752 Valley Forge PA 19482-0752

SCHAEFER, C. BARRY, railroad executive, lawyer, investment banker; b. Elizabeth, N.J., Feb. 23, 1939; s. Carl H. and Evelyn G. (Conk) S.; m. Carol Ann Craft, July 11, 1970; children: Sara Elizabeth, Susan Craft. BS in Engring., Princeton U., 1961; MS in Engring., U. Pa., 1962; LLB, Columbia U., 1965; MBA, NYU, 1970. Bar: N.Y. 1966, Nebr. 1972. With Kelly, Drye, Warren, N.Y.C., 1966-69; asst. gen. counsel Union Pacific Corp., N.Y.C., 1969-72; western gen. counsel Union Pacific R.R. Co., Omaha, 1972-74, v.p., western gen. counsel, 1974-77, v.p. law, 1977-82; sr. v.p. planning and corp. devel. Union Pacific Corp., N.Y.C., 1984-88; exec. v.p. Union Pacific Corp., Bethlehem, Pa., 1988; sr. advisor Dillon Read & Co. Inc., 1989-91; mng. dir. The Bridgeford Group, 1992—; dir. Ultramar Corp. Nat. bd. dirs. Jr. Achievement, Colorado Springs, Colo., 1986—. Mem. ABA, Nebr. Bar Assn., Racquet and Tennis Club (N.Y.C.), Round Hill Club (Greenwich, Conn.), Desert Mountain Club (Scottsdale, Ariz.).

SCHAEFER, CARL GEORGE LEWIS, writer, public relations and advertising executive; b. Cleve.; s. George S. and Margaret (Freyberg) S.; m. Virginia Clark, Sept. 2, 1938; 1 dau., Susan Diane Schaefer Francis. A.B., UCLA, 1931. Freelance mag. writer, 1931; pres. Pacific Intercollegiate Press Assn., 1931-32; reporter Hollywood (Calif.) Citizen-News, 1931-35; with Warner Bros.-Seven Arts, Burbank, Calif., 1935-71; dir. internat. relations Warner Bros.-Seven Arts, 1962-71; owner Carl Schaefer Enterprises, Hollywood, 1971—; bur. chief movie/TV mktg. Movie News, Singapore, Antena, B.A., 1975—; coord. internat. poster competition Hollywood Reporter, 1971-82, dir. spl. projects; exec. com. ShoWest, 1978—. Mem. internat. com. Acad. Motion Picture Arts and Scis., 1940—; chmn. internat. Hollywood Mus., 1964; vice chmn. Hollywood-Wilshire council Girl Scouts U.S., 1957-58; mem. Mayor Los Angeles Council Internat. Visitors, 1964—; mem. interview bd. Los Angeles Police Dept., 1965—; mem. adv. com. West Hollywood Hosp., 1983—; mng. dir. Internat. Festival Adv. Council, 1971—; nat. panel consumer arbitrators Better Bus. Bur. Los Angeles, 1984—; co-founder com. Los Angeles Acad. Motion Picture Arts & Scis. Served with OSS, World War II, ETO; ensign Calif. Naval Militia, 1935-36. Decorated Knight of the Royal Order of Merit for Mexico; Legion of Honor France; Ordine al Merito Italy; l'Ordre de la Courrenne Belgium; recipient service plaque Acad. Motion Picture Arts and Scis., The Hollywood Reporter Spl. Key Art award, 1990. Mem. Am. Soc. French Legion of Honor, Assn. Motion Picture and TV Producers (chmn. internat. co. 1967-68, 69-70), Publicists Guild Am. (charter), Internat. Press Photo-Journalists (hon.), Fgn. Trade Assn. So. Calif. (past pres., chmn. bd.), Brit.-Am. (dir.), Los Angeles Chambers Commerce, Culver City C. of C., Western Publs. Assn., Am. Bus.

Press, Blue Key, Sigma Alpha Epsilon, Alpha Delta Sigma. Republican. Methodist. Clubs: Mason (Los Angeles) (Shriner), Press (Los Angeles), Brit. United Services (Los Angeles). Address: 3320 Bennett Dr Hollywood CA 90068-1704 *When I lose my imagination, I'll be more than happy to cash in the chips whatever—and slink off.*

SCHAEFER, CHARLES HERBERT, physiologist, educator; laboratory administrator; b. Albany, Calif., Mar. 24, 1935; s. Charles Christopher and Thelma Ardell (Richard) S.; m. Maud Elizabeth Dawson, Sept. 14, 1967; children—Katherine Marie, Julia Elizabeth. B.S. in Forestry, U. Calif.-Berkeley, 1958, Ph.D., 1962. Insect physiologist U.S. Forest Service, Beltsville, Md., 1962-64; physiologist, toxicologist Shell Devel. Co., Modesto, Calif., 1964-67; lab. dir. Mosquito Control Research Lab., U. Calif.-Parlier, 1967—; cons. WHO; Geneva 1979—. Contbr. articles to profl. jours. Served to capt. U.S. Army, 1958-65. Mem. Entomol. Soc. Am., Entomol. Soc. Can., Am. Mosquito Control Assn. Home: 7740 E Saginaw Way Fresno CA 93727-9525 Office: U Calif Mosquito Control Research Lab 9240 S Riverbend Ave Parlier CA 93648

SCHAEFER, CHARLES JAMES, III, advertising agency executive, consultant; b. Orange, N.J., Dec. 17, 1926; m. Eleanor Anne Montville, Apr. 8, 1961; 1 child, Charles James IV. A.B., Dartmouth Coll., 1948, M. Comml. Sci. Amos Tuck Sch., 1949. V.p. Dickie-Raymond, 1952-67; sr. v.p. Metromedia, 1968-69; exec. v.p., treas. The DR Group, Boston, 1969-76, pres., 1976-87; exec. v.p., dir. Needham Harper Worldwide Inc., N.Y.C., 1984-87; chmn. bd. Marcoa DR Group, Inc., N.Y.C., 1987-88; cons. Rapp Collins Marcoa, N.Y.C., 1989-92; advt. cons., 1992—. Trustee, mem. exec. com. Direct Mktg. Ednl. Found., 1983-89. With USN, 1945-46. Mem. Direct Mktg. Assn. (chmn. awards com. 1971-76, Hall of Fame com. 1978-81, ethics com. 1981-86), Assn. Direct Mktg. Agys. (pres. 1980-82, gen. chmn. Caples awards 1985, Direct Mktg. Day N.Y. 1988, N.Y. Direct Marketer of Yr. award 1987, Silver Apple award 1989, contbr. to jour.), Dartmouth Club of N.Y. (pres. 1968-70), Lotos Club (bd. dirs. 1985-88, treas. 1987-88), Canoe Brook Country Club (Summit, N.J.). Home and Office: 307 Hobart Ave Short Hills NJ 07078-2207

SCHAEFER, DAN L., congressman; b. Gutenberg, Iowa, Jan. 25, 1936; s. Alvin L. and Evelyn (Everson) S.; m. Mary Margaret Lenney, 1959; children: Danny, Darren, Joel, Jennifer. B.A., Niagara U., 1961, LLD (hon.), 1986; postgrad., Potsdam State U., 1961-64. Pub. relations cons., 1967-83; mem. Colo. Gen. Assembly, 1977-78; mem. Colo. Senate, 1979-83, pres pro tem, 1981-82, majority whip, 1983; mem. 98th-103rd Congresses from 6th dist. Colo., Washington, 1983—; mem. house small bus. com., 1983, govt. ops. com., 1983, energy and commerce com., 1984-86 (subcom. on fossil and synthetic fuels; commerce, transp. and tourism; oversight/investigations), environ. and energy study com., 1987— (subcoms. on Transp. and Hazardous materials, Telecom. and Fin.), Energy and Commerce ranking Rep Oversight and Investigations, 1993—, Rep. study com.; mem. house sci. and high tech. task force, mil. reforms caucus, congl. grace caucus; mem. adv. com., com. of concern for Soviet Jewry; mem. exec. bd. Environ. and Energy Study Conf., 1995; chmn. Subcom. on Energy and Power House Commerce Com.; mem. Subcom. on Telecom. in Fin., House Vet. Affairs Com., Subcom. on Edn., Training, Employment and Housing. Pres. Foothills Recreation Bd., 1973-76; sec. Jefferson County Republican Party, Colo., 1975-76. Served with USMCR, 1955-57. Recipient Colo. Park and Recreation citation, 1976; named Elected Ofcl. of Yr., Lakewood/South Jeffco C. of C., 1986, 88, 90, Leadership award U.S. Congl. Adv. Bd., Am. Security Coun. Found.; Taxpayers Friend award Nat. Taxpayer's Union, 1985-86, 88, 90, 91, 92, Golden Bulldog award Watchdog of Treasury, 1985-86, 86-87, 87-88, 88-89, 89-90, 91-92. Mem. C. of C., Beta Theta Pi. Roman Catholic. Lodge: Rotary. Office: House of Representatives 2353 Rayburn House Office B Washington DC 20515

SCHAEFER, DAVID ARNOLD, lawyer; b. Cleve., May 3, 1948; s. Leonard and Maxine V. (Bassett) S.; m. Riki C. Freeman, Aug. 8, 1971; children—Kevin, Lindsey, Traci. BS, Miami U., Oxford, Ohio, 1970; MA, Northwestern, U., 1971; JD, Case Western Res. U., 1974. Bar: Ohio 1974, U.S. Dist. Ct. (no. dist.) Ohio 1974, U.S. Ct. Appeals (6th cir.) 1978, U.S. Supreme Ct. 1978. Ptnr. Guren, Merritt et al, 1980-84, Benesch, Friedlander et al, Cleve., 1984-94; McCarthy, Lebit, Crystal & Hairman, Cleve., 1994—; Author: Deposition Strategy, 1981, 2d edit., 1984; contbr. articles to profl. publs. Soccer coach Ohio Amateur Youth Soccer League, Cleve., 1980-81, 84. Mem. ABA, Ohio State Bar Assn., Ohio Acad. Trial Lawyers (Disting. Svc. award 1980, seminar speaker 1982), Fed. Bar Assn. (pres. elect 1991-92, pres. 1992-93), Nat. Inst. Trial Advocacy (faculty), 8th Dist. Jud. Conf. (life). Office: McCarthy Lebit 1800 Midland Bldg 101 Prospect Ave W Cleveland OH 44115

SCHAEFER, GEORGE LOUIS, theatrical producer and director, educator; b. Wallingford, Conn., Dec. 16, 1920; s. Louis and Elsie (Otterbein) S.; m. Mildred Trares, Feb. 5, 1954. BA magna cum laude, Lafayette Coll., 1941, LittD, 1963; postgrad., Yale Drama Sch., 1942; LHD, Coker Coll., 1973. Producer, dir. TV series Hallmark Hall of Fame, 1955-68; freelance producer, dir., 1945—; assoc. dean sch. theater, film and TV UCLA, 1986-91; artistic dir. N.Y.C. Ctr. Theatre Co., 1949-52; dir. Dallas State Fair Musicals, 1952-58; pres. Compass Prodns., Inc., 1959-86. Dir. Broadway prodns G.I. Hamlet, 1945, Man and Superman, 1947, The Linden Tree, 1948, The Heiress (revival), 1949, Idiot's Delight (revival), 1950, Southwest Corner, 1955, The Apple Cart, 1956, The Body Beautiful, 1958, Write Me a Murder, 1961, The Great Indoors, 1966, The Last of Mrs. Lincoln, 1972, Mixed Couples, 1980; co-producer Broadway and London prodns. The Teahouse of the August Moon, 1953; dir., co-producer Zenda for Los Angeles Civic Light Opera Co., 1963; producer To Broadway with Love for N.Y. World's Fair, 1964; producer, dir. TV spls. Do Not Go Gentle into That Good Night, 1967, A War of Children, Sandburg's Lincoln, 1974-76, In This House of Brede, 1975, Truman at Potsdam, Amelia Earhart, 1976, Our Town, 1977, First You Cry, Orchard Children, 1978, Blind Ambition, Mayflower, 1979, The Bunker, 1981, Jean Harris Trial, 1982, A Piano for Mrs. Cimino, 1982, Deadly Game, 1983, Answers, 1983, Right of Way, 1983, Children in the Crossfire, 1984, Stone Pillow, 1985, Mrs. Delafield Wants to Marry, 1986, Laura Lansing Slept Here, 1988, Let Me Hear You Whisper, 1990, The Man Upstairs, 1992; dir. films An Enemy of the People, Generation, Doctor's Wives, Pendulum, Macbeth; dir. Los Angeles prodn. Leave It To Jane, 1987. Mem. Nat. Council on the Arts, 1983-88. Recipient Emmy awards, 1959, 60, 61, 68, 73, Dirs. Guild Am. TV awards, 1961, 64, 67, 68, Dinneen award Nat. Cath. Theatre Conf., 1964; named Dir. of Yr., Radio-TV Daily, 1957, 60, 63, 65; Am. Theatre fellow, 1995. Mem. Dirs. Guild Am. (v.p. 1961-79, pres. 1979-81), Phi Beta Kappa.

SCHAEFER, GORDON EMORY, food company executive; b. 1932; married. BS, Marquette U., 1956. With Peat, Marwick, Mitchell & Co., 1955-59; treas. Pabst Brewing Co., Milw., 1965-72, v.p. adminstrn., 1972-75, v.p. ops., 1975-76, exec. v.p. ops., 1976-89, cons., 1980—, dir.; pres., dir. Krier Foods Inc., Belgium, Wis., 1981-85, Corrs Beverages, Chgo., 1985-86; dir. bus. devel. Lakeside Packing Co., Manitowoc, Wis., 1989-92; mng. dir. Robertson Assocs., Mfg. Europe Ltd., Cardiff, Wales, U.K., 1993-94; bd. dirs. Fox Fin. Co., Grand Rapids, Mich., Robertson Assocs., Denver; fin. and ops. cons.; owner, operator Schaefer's Orchards. Home: 154 Granville Rd Cedarburg WI 53012-9509

SCHAEFER, HENRY FREDERICK, III, chemistry educator; b. Grand Rapids, Mich., June 8, 1944; s. Henry Frederick Jr. and Janice Christine (Trost) S.; m. Karen Regine Rasmussen, Sept. 2, 1966; children Charlotte, Pierre, Theodore, Rebecca, Caleb. BS in Chem. Physics, MIT, 1966; PhD in Chem. Physics, Stanford U., 1969. Asst. prof. chemistry U. Calif., Berkeley, 1969-74, assoc. prof., 1974-78, prof., 1978-87; Graham Perdue prof., dir. Ctr. for Computational Quantum Chemistry U. Ga. Athens, 1987—; Wilfred T. Doherty prof., dir. Inst. Theoretical Chemistry, U. Tex., Austin, 1979-80; endowed lectr. Nat. U. Mex., 1979, Johns Hopkins U., 1982, Brown U., 1985, U. Canterbury, Christchurch, New Zealand, 1986, U. Kans., 1986, Vanderbilt U., 1988, U. Va., 1988, U. Alta., 1990, U. Guelph, Waterloo, Ont., 1991, Case Western Res. U., 1992, Kans. State U., 1993; Francis A. Schaefer lectr. Covenant Sem., St. Louis, 1995. Author: The Electronic Structure of Atoms and Molecules: A Survey of Rigorous Quantum Mechanical Results, 1972, Modern Theoretical Chemistry, 1977, Quantum Chemistry, 1983, A New Dimension to Quantum Chemistry, 1994; editor

Jour. Molecular Physics, 1991—. Recipient Pure Chemistry award Am. Chem. Soc., 1979, Leo Hendrik Baekeland award, 1983, Centenary medal Royal Soc. Chemistry, London, 1992; Sloan fellow, 1972, Guggenheim fellow, 1976-77; named one of 100 Outstanding Young Scientists in Am., Sci. Digest, 1984, named 3rd Most Highly cited chemist in world Science Watch, 1992. Fellow Am. Phys. Soc., Am. Sci. Affiliation; mem. Internat. Acad. Quantum Molecular Sci. Presbyterian. Office: U Ga Ctr Computational Quantum Chemistry Athens GA 30602

SCHAEFER, J. SCOTT, religious organization administrator. Dir. Dept. of Administration of the Presbyterian Ch., USA, Louisville. Office: Presbyterian Church 100 Witherspoon St Louisville KY 40202-1396

SCHAEFER, JACOB WERNLI, military systems consultant; b. Paullina, Iowa, June 27, 1919; s. Louis B. and Minnie (Wernli) S.; m. Mary Snow Carter, July 26, 1941; children: Joanna, James, Scott. B.M.E., Ohio State U., 1941, D.Sc. (hon.), 1976. Mem. staff Bell Labs., 1941-84; dir. Kwajalein (Marshall Islands) Field Sta., 1963-65; exec. dir. Holmdel, N.J., 1968-80, Murray Hill, N.J., 1980-81; exec. dir. Mil. Systems Div., Whippany, N.J., 1981-84, ret.; pvt. cons., 1984—. Contbr. articles to profl. jours. Pres. Watchung (N.J.) Sch. Bd., 1954-63; trustee Bancroft Sch., Haddonfield, N.J., 1973—; chmn. Watchung Planning Bd., 1967—; mem. Watchung Area council Boy Scouts Am., 1966-69. Served to capt. Ordnance Corps AUS, 1942-46. Decorated Commendation medal; recipient Disting. Alumnus award Ohio State U., 1966, 2 Outstanding Civilian Svc. medals U.S. Army. Fellow IEEE; mem. Nat. Acad. Engring., ASME, Army Ordnance Assn. Republican. Patentee command guidance for anti-aircraft missiles, optical tracking systems for anti-aircraft fire control. Home: 115 Century Ln Watchung NJ 07060-6007

SCHAEFER, JIMMIE WAYNE, JR., agricultural company executive; b. Anna, Ill., Dec. 26, 1951; s. Jimmie Wayne and Wilma Jean (Kinder) S.; m. Melanie Kugel, Apr. 19, 1981; 1 child Jyoti. BS in Agronomy, So. Ill. U., 1974; MSCI, MERU, Switzerland, 1979. Br. mgr. World Plan Exec. Coun., Nashville, 1975-79; pres. Schaefer & Assoc., Inc., Fairfield, Iowa, 1979-82, J.W. Schaefer Mortgage Co., Fairfield, 1981-1982; chmn. chief exec. officer Soil Techs. Corp., Fairfield, 1982—; chmn. bd. Radiance Dairy Corp., Fairfield, 1980—; bd. dirs. FAE Credit Union, Fairfield, 1982-84; cons. BioField Rsch. Inc., Ottawa, Ont., Can., 1985—; lectr. microalgal applications in agr. to ednl. and rsch. instns. in numerous developing countries; mem. adv. bd. Inst. for Agr. and Environ. Studies, Maharishi Internat. U., Fairfield. Author: (with others) Turf Integrated Pest Management Systems, 1988; patentee in field. Mem. Am. Soc. Agronomy, Am. Soc. Agrl. Cons. Avocation: gentleman farmer. Home: RR 4 Box 134 Fairfield IA 52556-9204 Office: Soil Techs Corp RR 4 Fairfield IA 52556-9804

SCHAEFER, JOHN FREDERICK, lawyer; b. Detroit, Mich., Apr. 10, 1943; s. Gilbert Frederick and Mary Cathryn (Henderson) S.; m. Sharon Kathleen Chalmers, May 22, 1976; children: John Frederick Jr., Kimberly Megan, Kelly Leigh, Charles Frederick. Student, U. Notre Dame, 1961-63; BA, Mich. State U., 1965; JD, Detroit Coll. Law, 1968. Bar: Mich. 1969. Ptnr. Buesser, Buesser, Snyder & Blank, Bloomfield Hills, Mich., 1968-73, Williams, Schaefer, Ruby & Williams, Birmingham, Mich., 1973—; adj. prof. domestic rels. Detroit Coll. Law, 1971—; instr. domestic rels. Mich. Jud. Inst., 1980-81; lectr. in field. Contbr. articles to legal jours. Trustee Detroit Coll. Law, 1985—. Fellow Am. Acad. Matrimonial Lawyers (pres. Mich. chpt. 1986-87), State Bar Mich. (family law com. 1972-73, coun. family law sect. 1974—, treas. sec. 1977-78, chmn. 1978-79, mem. fee arbitrator grievance bd. 1976—, com. on character and fitness 1972-75); mem. Detroit Bar Assn. (friend of ct. and domestic rels. com. 1972—, com. on char., 1975-76, mem. pub. adv. com. 1976—), Oakland County Bar Assn. (family law com. 1973—, chmn. com. 1974-77, mem. character and fitness com. 1973). Roman Catholic. Office: Williams Schaefer Ruby & Williams 380 N Woodward Ave Ste 300 Birmingham MI 48009

SCHAEFER, JOHN PAUL, chemist, corporate executive; b. N.Y.C., Sept. 17, 1934; s. Conrad and Meta (Rekelkamm) S.; m. Helen Marie Schwarz, May 18, 1958; children—Ann Marie, Susan Margaret. B.S., Poly. Inst. Bklyn., 1955; Ph.D. in Chemistry, U. Ill., 1958; fellow, Calif. Inst. Tech., 1958-59. Asst. prof. U. Calif. at Berkeley, 1959-60; mem. faculty U. Ariz., 1960—, prof. chemistry, head dept., 1968-70; dean Coll. Liberal Arts U. Ariz., 1970-71, pres., 1971-82; pres. Rsch. Corp., 1982—, also bd. dirs.; chmn. bd., chief exec. officer Rsch. Corp. Techs. Inc., 1988—; bd. dirs. Olin Corp., Rsch. Corp. Techs. Bd. dirs. Tucson Airport Authority; bd. govs. U.S.-Israel Binat. Sci. Found., 1972-77. Mem. AAAS, Nat. Audubon Soc., Tucson Audubon Soc. (pres. 1961-65), Am. Chem. Soc., Ariz. Acad., Nature Conservancy, Newcomen Soc., Sigma Xi, Phi Lambda Upsilon, Phi Kappa Phi. Office: Rsch Corp 101 N Wilmot Ste 250 Tucson AZ 85711-3332

SCHAEFER, MARILYN LOUISE, artist, writer, educator; b. Cedar Rapids, Iowa, Apr. 22, 1913; d. Henry Richard and Maria Augusta (Dickel) S. AA, Monticello Coll. for Women, 1953; BFA, Cranbrook Acad. Art, 1956, MFA, 1960; MA cum laude, U. Chgo., 1958; MA, St. John's Coll., Santa Fe, 1979. Rsch. asst. editor Encyclopaedia Britannica, Chgo., 1960-63; humanities editor Encyclopedia Americana, N.Y., 1964-68; acquisitions editor Litton Ednl. Pub., N.Y., 1968-70; from instr. to prof. art and advt. design dept. N.Y.C. Tech. Coll. CUNY, 1970—; contbg. editor Encyclopedia Americana, 1979—, Coll. Teaching jour., 1979. Contbr. articles to profl. publs. including Art and Auction mag., Art and Antiques mag., Am. Artist mag., Encyclopedia Americana, 1970—. Luce Found. postgrad. study fellow St. John's Coll., 1976-79; Ingram Merrill Found. grantee, 1983-84. Mem. AAUW, CUNY Acad. Arts and Scis. Home: 306 W 76th St New York NY 10023-8065 Office: NYC Tech Coll CUNY 300 Jay St Brooklyn NY 11201-2902

SCHAEFER, ROBERT WAYNE, banker; b. Balt., Feb. 28, 1934; s. Roland Elmer and Lillian (Reid) S.; m. Elaine Lennon, May 18, 1963; children: Linda, Karen. Student, Balt. City Coll., 1949-51; BS in Acctg., U. Balt., 1955; MBA in Fin., Loyola Coll., 1971. C.P.A., Md. With First Nat. Bank of Md., Balt., 1951-55, 59—; comptroller First Nat. Bank of Md., 1961—, v.p., 1965-69, sr. v.p., 1969-73, exec. v.p., 1973—; instr. accounting N.C. State Coll., 1956-58; instr. accounting, econs., taxes, credit Balt. chpt. Am. Inst. Banking, 1960-66. Mem. Balt. City Sch. Bd., 1973-75, Balt. City Bd. Fin.; bd. dirs., treas. Balt. Area United Fund, 1964-79; past bd. dirs. Balt. coun. Boy Scouts Am. Balt. chpt. ARC, Boys Latin Sch.; trustee, pres. Wesley Home for Aged; bd. dirs. Balt. City Aquarium, Roland Park Country Sch., Md. Gen. Hosp., Western Md. Coll. 1981-92, Lyric Theatre, 1985—, Enoch Pratt Libr., 1986-93, Ind. Coll. Fund Md., 1990—, Coun. on Econ. Edn., YMCA Ctrl. Md., 1992, U. Balt. 1st F. SCHAEFER, 1956-58. Mem. Bank Adminstrn. Inst. (past pres., bd. dirs. Balt. chpt.), Md. CPA Assn., Fin. Execs. Inst., U. Balt. Alumni Assn. (bd. dirs. 1972—), U. Balt. Found., Valley Country Club. Republican. Methodist. Bd. dirs., mem. finance com.). Home: 5903 Meadowood Rd Baltimore MD 21212-2436 Office: 1st Md Bancorp 1st Md Bldg 25 S Charles St Baltimore MD 21201-3330

SCHAEFER, THEODORE PETER, chemistry educator; b. Gnadenthal, Man., Can., July 22, 1933; s. Paul Jacob and Margarethe (Wiebe) S.; m. Nicola Caroline Sewell, Dec. 26, 1960; children: Catherine, Dominic, Benjamin. B.S. with Honors, U. Man., 1954, M.S., 1955; D.Phil. (Shell scholar), Oxford (Eng.) U., 1958; D.Sc. (hon. causa), U. Winnipeg, 1982. Prof. chemistry U. Man., Winnipeg, Can., 1958—. Univ. Disting. prof., 1982—; researcher NRC, Ottawa, Can., 1959, 62, Nat. Phys. Lab., Teddington, U.K., 1960, 65, Argonne Nat. Lab., Chgo., 1967, 68; sr. fellow, mem. grants com. NRC, Ottawa.; mem. council Nat. Scis. and Engring. Research Council, Ottawa., 1980-85. Contbr. articles on nuclear magnetic resonance to sci. jours. Recipient Herzberg award Spectroscopy Soc. Can., 1975. Fellow Chem. Inst. Can. (Noranda award 1973), Royal Soc. Can. Home: 210 Oak St, Winnipeg, MB Canada R3M 3R4 Office: Univ of Manitoba, Dept of Chemistry, Winnipeg, MB Canada R3T 2N2 *Persistence can sometimes emulate perspicacity.*

SCHAEFER, THOMAS J., bank executive. CEO Columbia First Bank, Arlington, Va. Office: Columbia First Bank 1560 Wilson Blvd Arlington VA 22209-2409

SCHAEFER, WILLIAM DAVID, English educator; b. Dighton, Mass., May 11, 1928; s. Louis and Elsie K. (Otterbein) S.; m. Josephine R. Lamprecht, Aug. 8, 1958; 1 dau., Kimberly. B.A., NYU, 1957; M.S., U. Wis., 1958, Ph.D., 1962. Mem. faculty UCLA, 1962-90, prof. English, 1970-90, chmn. dept., 1969-71, exec. vice chancellor, 1978-87. Author: James (BV) Thomson: Beyond the City, 1965, Speedy Extinction of Evil and Misery, 1967, Education Without Compromise: From Chaos to Coherence in Higher Education, 1990; contbr. articles to profl. jours., short stories to literary mags. Served with AUS, 1954-56. Fulbright fellow Eng., 1961-62. Mem. MLA (exec. dir. 1971-78). Home: 164 Stagecoach Rd Bell Canyon CA 91307-1044 Office: UCLA 405 Hilgard Ave Los Angeles CA 90024-1301

SCHAEFER, WILLIAM G., lawyer; b. Kansas City, Mo., June 16, 1941; m. Sharon Saylor, Dec. 21, 1963; children: James, Kristen. B.A., U. Kans., 1963; J.D., Harvard U., 1966. Bar: Ill. 1966, D.C. 1978, Md. 1984. Ptnr. Sidley & Austin, Chgo. and Washington, 1966-74, 78-93; v.p., gen. counsel DeKalb Corp., Ill., 1974-77; spl. counsel Bechtel Corp., Gaithersburg, Md., 1993—. Office: Bechtel Corp 9801 Washington Blvd Gaithersburg MD 20878

SCHAEFFER, BRENDA MAE, psychologist; b. Duluth, Minn.; d. Ralph J. Bernice M. (Johnson) Furtman; children: Heidi, Gordon III. BA in Sociology, Psychology and English cum laude, U. Minn., 1962; MA in Human Devel., St. Mary's Coll., Winona, Minn., 1976. Lic. psychologist, Minn. Mem. faculty Coll. St. Scholastica, Duluth, 1976—; trainer, therapist, communications cons. Transactional Analysis Inst., Mpls., 1984-88; owner, clin. dir. Brenda M. Schaeffer and Assocs., Inc., Healthy Relationships, Inc. Birchwood Ctrs., Inc.; vis. prof. U. Minn., Duluth, 1976—; guest lectr. dep. counseling U. Wis., Superior, 1980-81; nat. and internat. lectr. Author: Is It Love or Is It Addiction, 1987, Loving Me, Loving You, 1991, Signs of Healthy Love, Signs of Addictive Love, Power Plays, Addictive Love, Help Yourself Out; mem. editorial bd. Transactional Analysis Jour.; editor Healthy Relationships newsletter. Planner Lake Superior Task Force, Duluth, 1980-83; bd. dirs., sec. Nat. Coun. Sexual Addictions/Compulsions, 1992—, sec. 1994-95; v.p. H. Milton Erickson Inst. Minn., 1992—. Mem. Internat. Transactional Analysis Assn. (1975), Transactional Anaylsis Inst. Minn. (founder, pres. 1984-86), U.S. Assn. Transactional Analysis, Northeast Minn. Transactional Analysis Seminar (founder and chairperson 1977-83). Office: 9531 W 78th St Ste 350 Eden Prairie MN 55344-8000

SCHAEFFER, EDWIN FRANK, JR., lawyer, finance company executive; b. N.Y.C., Nov. 29, 1930; s. Edwin Frank and Rachel Townsend (Bouchier) S.; m. Joan Cameron Sherwood, Apr. 7, 1956; children: Edwin Frank III, Cameron, Donald. AB, Washington and Lee U., 1952; JD, Harvard U., 1955. Bar: Ky, 1955, U.S. Dist. Ct. (ea. and we. dists.) Ky. 1957, U.S. Ct. Appeals (6th cir.) 1957. Assoc., Bullitt, Dawson & Tarrant, Louisville, 1955-60, ptnr., 1960-63; ptnr. Kincaid, Wilson, Schaeffer, Hembree & Kinser, P.S.C., Lexington, Ky., 1963-79, bd. dirs., chmn. bd. dirs., 1979-93; vice chmn., bd. dirs. Ky. Fin. Co., Inc., 1976-84, chmn., 1984-91; bd. dirs. Ky. Central Life Ins. Co., 1976-93, Central Bank & Trust Co., 1974-93, Bd. dirs. Lexington Philharm., 1970-80, United Way, 1976-80, 84-88, Lexington Sr. Corp., 1982—, Hospice of Bluegrass, 1985-91. Served with JAGC, AUS, 1955-57. Fellow Am. Bar Found.; mem. ABA, Ky. State Bar Assn., Fayette County Bar Assn., Louisville Bar Assn., Greater Lexington C. of C. (bd. dirs. 1986-88). Democrat. Presbyterian. Club: Lexington Country. Address: 200 W Vine St Ste 810 Lexington KY 40507-1620

SCHAEFFER, GARY N., mayor; b. York, Pa., May 8, 1948; s. Calvin William and Jane Rae (Desenberg) R.; m. Katherine Lyn Dowler, June 22, 1968; children: Andrew, Ryan. BS, York Coll. of Pa., 1973. Tchr. Upper Adams Sch. Dist., Biglerville, Pa., 1974-75, Dallastown (Pa.) Area Schs., 1975-79, Laramie County Sch. Dist., Cheyenne, Wyo., 1982-89; owner Auto Hosp., Cheyenne, 1979-82; mayor City of Cheyenne, 1989—. Author: Eat your Heart Out, 1979. Sgt. USAF, 1967-71. Mem. Cheyenne C. of C. (bd. dirs. 1989—), Leads (bd. dirs. 1989—), VFW, Am. Legion, Amvets, U.S. Conf. of Mayors (chmn. subcom. on water 1990). Avocations: flying, skiing, horseback riding, auto repair. Home: 418 Lafayette Blvd Cheyenne WY 82009-2098 Office: City of Cheyenne 2101 Oneil Ave Cheyenne WY 82001-3550

SCHAEFFER, GLENN WILLIAM, casino corporate financial executive; b. Pomona, Calif., Oct. 11, 1953; s. William Donald and Mary Louise (Miller) S.; m. Deborah Lynn Helfer, Sept. 6, 1974 (div. Apr. 1981); m. Renee Sue Riebel, May 25, 1985. AB summa cum laude, U. Calif., Irvine, 1974, MA, 1975; MFA, U. Iowa, 1977. Fin. cons. Dean Witter, Los Angeles, 1977-78; assoc. Hill and Knowlton, Inc., Los Angeles, 1978-81; v.p. Ramada Inns, Inc., Phoenix, 1981-84; exec. v.p., chief fin. officer Circus Circus Enterprises, Inc., Las Vegas, Nev., 1984-91; pres. Circus Circus Enterprises, Inc., 1991-93; also bd. dirs. Circus Circus Enterprises, Inc., Las Vegas; ptnr. Gold Strike Resorts, Jean, Nev., 1993-95; pres. Ceres Circus Enterpises, 1995—. Pres. Hitch fellow U. Calif.-Irvine, 1973-74. Mem. Phi Beta Kappa. Avocations: reading, bicycling. Office: Gold Strike Resorts PO Box 19278 Jean NV 89019-9278

SCHAEFFER, LEONARD DAVID, health care executive; b. Chgo., Ill., July 28, 1945; s. David and Sarah (Levin) S.; m. Pamela Lee Sidford, Aug. 11, 1968; children: David, Jacqueline. BA, Princeton U., 1969. Mgmt. cons. Arthur Andersen & Co., 1969-73; dep. dir. mgmt. Ill. Mental Health/Devel. Disability, Springfield, 1973-75; dir. Ill. Bur. of Budget, Springfield, 1975-76; v.p. Citibank, N.A., N.Y.C., 1976-78; asst. sec. mgmt. and budget HHS, Washington, 1978, adminstr. HCFA, 1978-80; exec. v.p., COO Student Loan Mktg. Assn., Washington, 1980-82; pres., CEO Group Health, Inc., Mpls., 1983-86; chmn., CEO Blue Cross of Calif., Woodland Hills, 1986—, WellPoint Health Networks Inc., 1993—; bd. dirs. Allergan, Inc., Irvine, Calif.; bd. councilors U. So. Calif. Sch. Pub. Adminstrn., 1988—; bd. dirs., exec. com. Blue Cross/Blue Shield Assn., Chgo., 1986—; mem. Congl. Prospective Payment Assessment Commn., 1987-93; mem. Pew Health Professions Com., Phila., 1990—; chmn. bd. trustees Nat. Health Found., L.A., 1992—; chmn. Nat. Inst. Health Care Mgmt., 1993—. Mem. editorial adv. bd. Managed Healthcare, 1989—. Bd. govs. Town Hall of Calif., L.A., 1989—. Kellogg Found. fellow, 1981-89, Internat. fellow King's Fund Coll., London, 1990—; recipient Citation/Outstanding Svc., Am. Acad. Pediatrics, 1981, Corp. Social Responsibility award U. Calif., Berkeley, 1987, Disting. Pub. Svc. award HEW, Washington, 1980, Leadership in Health Affairs award Hosp. Coun. So. Calif., 1992. Mem. Cosmos Club, Princeton Club, Regency Club. Office: Blue Cross of Calif 21555 Oxnard St Woodland Hills CA 91367-4999

SCHAEFFER, REINER HORST, air force officer, retired librarian, foreign language professional; b. Berlin, Lichterfelde, Fed. Republic Germany, Jan. 13, 1938; came to U.S. 1958; s. Immanuel Emil and Wilhelmine (Fahrni) Frei-S.; m. Cathy Anne Cormack, Apr. 6, 1966; 1 child, Brian Reiner. Nat. Cert., Bus. Sch., Thun, Switzerland, 1957; B.G.S. in Bus., U. Nebr., 1970; M.P.A. in Orgnl. Behavior, U. Mo., 1972; P.h.D. in Fgn. Lang. Edn., Ohio State U., 1979. Commd. officer USAF, 1958, advanced through grades to lt. col.; instr. German, French USAF Acad., Colorado Springs, Colo., 1975-77, assoc. prof., 1977-81, chmn. German, 1981, dir. librs., 1982-86, prof., 1986-92, dir. Acad. Librs., 1986—. Mem. People to People, Colorado Springs; bd. dirs. Friends of AF Acad. Librs. Named Disting. Grad. Air Force Inst. Tech, Wright-Patterson AFB, Ohio, 1979; recipient 5 Meritorious Service medals, 5 Air Force Commendation medals. Mem. Am. Assn. Tchrs. of German, Swiss Club (pres. Colorado Springs chpt. 1990—, chmn. Lewis Palmer High Sch. accountability com.), Pi Alpha Alpha, Alpha Sigma Alpha. Republican. Avocations: skiing; golfing; hiking; soccer. Home: 515 Celtic Ct Colorado Springs CO 80921-1807 Office: Fgn Lang Ctr LLC 315 E Willamette Ave Colorado Springs CO 80903

SCHAENGOLD, PHILLIP S., hospital administrator; b. Marseilles, France, Nov. 26, 1948; married;. BA, U. Cin., 1971, MA, 1975; Doctorate, S.P. Chase Coll. Law, 1977. Dir. pharm. svcs. Providence Hosp., Cin., 1972-79, risk mgmt. coord., 1979-80; sr. sect. mgr. McDonnell Douglas Auto Co., St. Louis, 1980-82; asst. exec. dir. Menorah Med. Ctr., Kansas City, 1983-85, assoc. exec. dir., COO, 1985-86, pres., 1986-92; pres., CEO Sinai Hosp., Detroit, 1992—. Contbr. articles to profl. jours. Mem. Mich. Hosp. Assn. Home: 767 Fairfax Birmingham MI 48009 Office: Sinai Hosp 6767 W Outer Dr Detroit MI 48235-2899*

SCHAETER, GEORGE A., JR., banking executive. CEO Fifth Third Bancorp, Cin. Office: Fifth Third Bancorp 38 Fountain Square Plz Cincinnati OH 45263

SCHAFER, ALICE TURNER, mathematics educator; b. Richmond, Va., June 18, 1915; d. John H. and Cleon (Dermott) Turner; m. Richard Donald Schafer, Sept. 8, 1942; children: John Dickerson, Richard Stone. A.B., U. Richmond, 1936, D.Sc., 1963; M.S., U . Chgo., 1940, Ph.D. (fellow), 1942. Tchr. Glen Allen (Va.) High Sch., 1936-39; instr. math. Conn. Coll., New London, 1942-44; asst. prof. Conn. Coll., 1954-57, asso. prof., 1957-61, prof., 1961-62; prof. math. Wellesley Coll., 1962-80, Helen Day Gould prof. math., 1969-80, Helen Day Gould prof. math. emerita, 1980—, affirmative action officer, 1980-82; prof. math. Marymount U., Arlington, Va., 1989—; instr. U. Mich., Ann Arbor, 1945-46; lectr. Douglass Coll., New Brunswick, N.J., 1946-48; asst. prof. Swarthmore (Pa.) Coll., 1948-51, Drexel Inst. Tech., Phila., 1951-53; mathematician Johns Hopkins Applied Physics Lab., Silver Spring, Md., 1945; lectr. Simmons Coll., Boston, 1980-88, Radcliffe Coll. Seminars, Cambridge, Mass., 1980-85. Contbr. articles on women in math. and other articles to math. jours. Recipient Disting. Alumna award Westhampton Coll., U. Richmond, 1977; NSF sci. faculty fellow Inst. for Advanced Study, Princeton, N.J., 1958-59. Fellow AAAS (math. sect. A nominating com. 1979-83, mem.-at-large 1983-86, chair-elect sect. A 1991, chair 1992, retiring chair 1993, Assn. for Women in Math. rep., 1993—), AAUP (chmn. nat. com. W 1980-83, mem. nat. coun. 1984-87), Am. Math. Soc. (chmn. postdoctoral fellowship com. 1973-76, affirmative action procedures com. 1980-82, chair com. on Human Rights of Mathematicians 1988-94), Soc. Indsl. and Applied Math., Am. Statis. Assn., Inst. Math. Stats., Nat. Coun. Tchrs. of Math. (chair com. on women 1976-81), Math Assn. Am. (adv. com. for Women and Math. program 1987-89, dir. fund raising 1989-92, lectr. 1982—, chair devel. com. 1988-92), Internat. Congress Mathematicians (mem. fund raising com. 1986), Assn. for Women in Math. (pres. 1973-75, Alice T. Schafer Prize established 1989, chair fund raising com. 1992—, leader math. del. women mathematicians to China 1990, U.S. chair postsecondary math. edn., U.S./China Joint Conf. on Edn. 1992), Cosmos Club, Phi Beta Kappa, Sigma Xi, Sigma Delta Epsilon. Achievements include first study of singularities of space curves in projective differential geometry; research on undulation point of a space curve. Home: 2725 N Pollard St Arlington VA 22207-5038 Office: Marymount U Dept Math 2807 N Glebe Rd Arlington VA 22207-4299

SCHAFER, CARL WALTER, investment executive; b. Chgo., Jan. 16, 1936; s. MacHenry George and Gertrude (Herrick) S.; 1 child, MacHenry George II. BA with distinction, U. Rochester, 1958. Budget examiner Budget Bur., Exec. Office Pres., Washington, 1961-64, legis. analyst, 1964-66, dep. dir. budget preparation, 1966-68, dir. budget preparation, 1968-69; staff asst. U.S. Ho. of Reps. Appropriations Com., 1969; dir. budget Princeton (N.J.) U., 1969-72, treas., 1972-76, fin. v.p., treas., 1976-87, lectr. indsl. adminstrn., 1975; prin. Rockefeller & Co., Inc., 1987-90; pres. Atlantic Found., Princeton, N.J., 1990—; pres., chief exec. officer Palmer Square Inc., 1979-81; trustee, treas. McCarter Theatre Co. Inc., 1974-76; co-chmn. N.J. Gov.'s Task Force on Improving N.J. Econ. and Regulatory Climate, 1982-83; chmn. investment adv. com. Howard Hughes Med. Inst., 1985-92; trustee Am. Bible Soc., 1987-92; trustee, dir. Wainoco Oil Corp., Neutraceutix Inc., Electronic Clearing House Inc., the Paine Webber and Mitchell Hutchins Groups of Mut. Funds, Evans Systems, Inc., Internat. Agritech Resources, Inc., Ardic Exploration and Devel. Ltd., Hidden Lake Gold Mines Ltd., U. Rochester Harbor Br. Inst. Inc., The Jewish Guild For the Blind, The Investment Fund for Founds., The Johnson Atelier and Sch. Sculpture; mem. adv. coun. Domain Ptnrs., The Banbury Fund; mem. internat. adv. coun. Wm. Sword & Co., Inc.; trustee, chmn. fin. com. Chem. Heritage Found. Mem. Am. Coun. Learned Socs. (investment com.), Asset Mgmt. Advisors (investment com.), Rockefeller Ctr. Club (N.Y.C.), Phi Beta Kappa. Home and Office: PO Box 1164 Princeton NJ 08542-1164

SCHAFER, EDWARD T., governor; b. Bismarck, N.D., Aug. 8, 1946; s. Harold and Marian Schafer; m. Nancy Jones; children: Edward Thomas Jr., Ellie Sue, Eric Jones, Kari Jones. BSBA, U.N.D., 1969; MBA, Denver U., 1970. Quality control inspector Gold Seal, 1971-73, v.p., 1974, chmn. mgmt. com., 1975-78; owner/dir. H&S Distbn., 1976—; pres. Gold Seal, 1978-85, Dakota Classics, 1986—, TRIESCO Properties, 1986—, Fish 'N Dakota, 1990-94; gov. State of N.D., 1992—. Chmn. N.D. Micro Bus. Mktg. Alliance; pres. N.D. Heritage Group; adv. coun. Distributive Edn. Clubs of Am.; lectr. Hugh O'Brien Leadership Found.; counselor Junior Achievement; dir. Bismarck Recreation Coun.; trustee Missouri Valley Family YMCA; plankowner USS Theodore Roosevelt; ann. support com. Medcenter One Found.; mem. Bismarck State Coll. Found. Mem. NRA, Theodore Roosevelt Assn. (Theodore Roosevelt Medora Found., United Sportsman of N.D., U. N.D. Pres. Club, U. Mary Pres. Club, Bismarck-Mandan Rotary. Republican. Office: Office of the Governor 600 E Boulevard Ave Bismarck ND 58505-0660

SCHAFER, JAMES HENRY, newspaper company executive; b. Seattle, Apr. 15, 1945; s. Henry and Fayette K. (Boasen) S.; m. Marcia W. Schafer, May 5, 1975; children—Christine Ann, Joel Henry. B.B.A., U. Wash., 1970. Dir labor relations The Bon, Seattle, 1967-79; dir. adminstrn. I.T.T. Rayonier, Seattle, 1979-83; v.p. indsl. relations Seattle Times, 1983—; dir. Health Care Purchasers, Seattle; mem. adv. council Seattle Pacific U., Seattle, 1984—. Bd. dirs. Wash. State Leukemia Soc., N.W. Kidney Found. Mem. C. of C. (leadership tomorrow 1984—). Clubs: Bellevue Athletic, Lakes, Rainier, City (Seattle). Office: Seattle Times PO Box 70 Seattle WA 98111-0070

SCHAFER, JOHN FRANCIS, plant pathologist; b. Pullman, Wash., Feb. 17, 1921; s. Edwin George and Ella Frances (Miles) S.; m. Joyce A. Marcks, Aug. 16, 1947; children—Patricia, James. B.S. Wash. State U., 1942, Ph.D., U. Wis., 1950. Asst. prof. to prof. plant pathology Purdue U., 1949-68; head dept. plant pathology Kans. State U., 1968-72; chmn. dept. plant pathology Wash. State U., Pullman, 1972-80; integrated pest mgmt. coordinator sci. and edn. USDA, 1980-81, acting nat. research program leader plant pathology Agrl. Research Service, 1981-82; dir. cereal rust lab. USDA, St. Paul, 1982-87, biol. sci. collaborator, 1987—; vis. rsch. prof. Duquesne U., 1965-66; adj. prof. plant pathology U. Minn., 1982-92. Contbr. articles to profl. jours.; chpts. to books. Served with AUS, 1942-46. Phi Sigma scholar, 1942. Fellow AAAS, Ind. Acad. Sci., Am. Phytopathol. Soc. (past pres.); mem. Am. Soc. Agronomy, Crop Sci. Soc. Am. Achievements include identification of increased resistance to wheat leaf rust by genetic recombination; demonstration of probabilities of virulence to genetic resistance combinations, of tolerance as a mechanism of disease control, of use of cultivaral diversity for disease protection; bred (with others) over 30 disease resistant cultivars of cereal crops, including Arthur wheat. Home: 1753 Lindig St Saint Paul MN 55113-5505 Office: Univ Minn Cereal Rust Lab Saint Paul MN 55108

SCHAFER, JOHN STEPHEN, foundation administrator; b. N.Y.C., Sept. 5, 1934; s. Stephen James and Siiri (Halmi) S.; m. Gertrud Rosa Fleischmann, June 14, 1958; children: Sylvia F., John Stephen, Karen D., Kristen H. B.A., Rutgers U., 1956, M.B.A., 1963. Advt. research mgr. Union Carbide Corp., N.Y.C., 1959-65; research mgr. Bus. Week, N.Y.C., 1965-66; v.p. Opinion Research Corp., Princeton, N.J., 1966-80; pres. Am. Econ. Found., Cleve., 1981—, trustee, 1975—; v.p., dir. Ams. for Competitive Enterprise System, Phila., 1970-82. Editor Linde Electric Welding Progress, 1959-62, ORC Pub. Opinion Index, 1968-72, AEF Straight Talk, 1981-82, Bellcore Exch., 1993-94. Polit. pollster Ed Clark for U.S. Pres., 1980; chmn. N.J. Libertarian party, 1983; nat. dir. U.S. Jaycees, 1965-66, v.p. N.J., 1964-65. Served to 1st lt. U.S. Army, 1957-59. Mem. Jr. Chamber Internat. (hon. life), Philosophan Soc., Scabbard and Blade, Delta Phi Alpha. Presbyterian. Home: 24 Fayson Lakes Rd Kinnelon NJ 07405-3137

SCHAFER, MICHAEL FREDERICK, orthopedic surgeon; b. Peoria, Ill., Aug. 17, 1942; s. Harold Martin and Frances May (Ward) S.; m. Eileen M. Briggs, Jan. 8, 1966; children—Steven, Brian, Kathy, David, Daniel. B.A., U. Iowa, 1964, M.D., 1967. Diplomate: Am. Bd. Orthopedic Surgery. Intern Chgo. Wesley Meml. Hosp., 1967-68; resident in orthopedic surgery Cook County Program, Northwestern U., Chgo., 1968-72; practice medicine specializing in orthopedic surgery Chgo., 1974—; asst. prof. orthopedic surgery Northwestern U., 1977—; Reyerson prof. and chmn. dept.

orthopedic surgery; asso. attending orthopedic surgeon Northwestern Meml. Hosp., 1974—; adj. staff Children's Meml. Hosp., Chgo., 1974—; cons. VA Lakeside Hosp., 1974—; adv. bd. Center Sports Medicine, Northwestern U., 1976—; panelist Bur. Health Manpower, HEW, 1976; sec.-treas. Orthopedic Research and Edn. Found. Contbr. articles to med. jours. Served to maj. U.S. Army, 1973-74. Fellow Am. Orthopaedic Assn., Am. Acad. Orthopaedic Surgeons, Assn. Bone and Joint Surgeons; mem. AMA, Am. Orthopedic Soc. Sports Medicine, Ill. Med. Soc., Chgo. Med. Soc., Internat. Soc. Study of Pain, Scoliosis Rsch. Soc. Roman Catholic. Home: 1815 Ridgewood Ln W Glenview IL 60025-2205 Office: 303 E Chicago Ave Chicago IL 60611-3008

SCHAFER, RAYMOND MURRAY, composer, author; b. Sarnia, Ont., Can., July 18, 1933; s. Harold J. and Belle (Rose) S.; m. Jean C. Reed, Sept. 18, 1975. Studies with John Weinzweig, Royal Conservatory of Music, 1950-55; L.R.S.M., Royal Coll. and Royal Acad. Music, London, 1954. Artist in residence Meml. U. Nfld., 1963-65; prof. communications studies Simon Fraser U., Burnaby, B.C., Can., 1965-75; author, composer multimedia composition Ra, multimedia composition Princess of the Stars,, 1985. Author: British Composers in Interview, 1963, The Composer in the Classroom, 1965, Ear Cleaning, 1967, The New Soundscape, 1969, The Book of Noise, 1970, When Words Sing, 1970, The Rhinoceros in the Classroom, 1974, E.T.A. Hoffmann and Music, 1975, Creative Music Education, 1976, The Tuning of the World, 1977, The Chaldean Inscription, 1978, The 16 Scribes, 1982, On Canadian Music, 1984, Dicamus et Labyrinthos, 1985, The Thinking Ear, 1986; novel Smoke, 1976; Composer: various works including Music for the Morning of the World, 1972, From the Tibetan Book of the Dead, 1968, String Quartet, 1970, Miniwanka, 1973, Son of Heldenleben, 1968. Recipient Arts award Can. Council, 1968-69, Fromm Music Found. award, 1969, Serge Koussevitzky Music Found. award, 1969, Can. Music Coun. medal, 1972, Leger prize, 1978, Priz Arthur Honegger, 1980, 1st Glenn Gould Prize, 1987, Banff Ctr. Sch. Fine Arts Nat. award, 1985; Guggenheim fellow, 1976. Mem. Can. League Composers. Can. Music Council, Sinfonia, Phi Mu Alpha.

SCHAFER, ROBERT LOUIS, agricultural engineer, researcher; b. Burlington, Iowa, Aug. 1, 1937; s. Marion Louis and Pansy (Head) S.; m. Carolyn Louise Henn, Aug. 1, 1959; 1 child, Elizabeth Diane. BS, Iowa State U., 1959, MS, 1961, PhD, 1965. Agrl. engr. Agrl. Rsch. Svc., USDA, Ames, Iowa, 1959-64, Auburn, Ala., 1964—. Contbr. articles to profl. jours. Fellow Am. Soc. Agrl. Engrs.; mem. Ruritan Nat. (various offices). Home: PO Box 188 Loachapoka AL 36865-0188 Office: USDA Agrl Rsch Svc PO Box 3439 Auburn AL 36831

SCHAFER, RONALD WILLIAM, electrical engineering educator; b. Tecumseh, Nebr., Feb. 17, 1938; s. William Henry and Esther Sophia (Rinne) S.; m. Dorothy Margaret Hall, June 2, 1960; children: William R., John C. (dec.), Katherine L., Barbara Anne. Student, Doane Coll., Crete, Nebr., 1956-59; BEE, U. Nebr., 1961, MEE, 1962; PhD in Elec. Engring., MIT, 1968. Mem. tech. staff Bell Labs., Murray Hill, N.J., 1968-74; John O. McCarty prof. elec. engring. Ga. Inst. Tech., Atlanta, 1974—; Inst. prof., 1991—; chmn. bd. Atlanta Signal Processors Inc., 1983—. Co-author: Digital Signal Processing, 1974, Digital Processing of Speech Signals, 1979, Speech Analysis, 1979, Discrete-Time Signal Processing, 1989, Computer-Based Exercises for Signal Processing Using Matlab. Recipient Class of 34 Disting. Prof. award Ga. Inst. Tech., 1985. Fellow IEEE (Emanuel R. Piore award 1980, Edn. medal 1992), Acoustical Soc. Am.; mem. IEEE Acoustics Speech and Signal Processing Soc. (soc. award 1982), AAAS, Nat. Acad. Engring. Democrat. Methodist. Lodge: Kiwanis. Office: Ga Inst of Tech Dept of Elec Engring Atlanta GA 30332-0250

SCHAFER, SHARON MARIE, anesthesiologist; b. Detroit, Mar. 23, 1948; d. Charles Anthony and Dorothy Emma (Schweitzer) Pokriefka; m. Timothy John Schafer, Nov. 12, 1977; children: Patrick Christopher, Steven Michael. BS in Biology, Wayne State U., 1971, MD, 1975. Diplomate Am. Bd. Anesthesiology. Intern, resident Sinai Hosp. Detroit, 1975-78; pvt. practice anesthesiology Troy, Mich., 1988—. Mem. AMA, Am. Soc. Anesthesiologists. Roman Catholic. Home and Office: 5741 Folkstone Troy MI 48098-3154

SCHAFER, THOMAS WILSON, advertising agency executive; b. Youngstown, Ohio, Sept. 12, 1939; s. Kenneth Charles and Clara Louise (Wilson) S.; m. Anne Kernwein, Jan. 22, 1972; children: Charles Kenneth, Bret Thomas. B.A., Colgate U., 1962. Salesman Gen. Foods Corp., 1962-65; sr. ptnr. Tatham EURO RSCG Advt., Chgo., 1965-93; chmn. Schafer Rsch., Inc., Savannah, Ga., 1993—. Past dir. Off the Street Club. Mem. Chgo. Advt. Fedn. (past exec. v.p.). Clubs: Bob O'Link Golf, Saddle and Cycle, Off The Street. Home: 5 Modena Rd Savannah GA 31411-2136 Office: Schafer Rsch Inc 5 Modena Rd Savannah GA 31411

SCHAFER, WILLIAM HARRY, electric power industry executive; b. South Portsmouth, Ky., Aug. 22, 1936; s. William Harry and Mary Minnie (Papillon) S. AS, Franklin U., 1980; BA, Capital U., 1987; MS, Greenwich U., 1992. Cert. fraud examiner; cert. protection officer. With Columbus (Ohio) So. Power, 1969—, risk mgmt. coord., 1989—; cons. in field. First aid instr. Franklin County ARC, Columbus, 1965-93; mem. Simon Kenton coun. Boy Scouts Am., Columbus. Named Ky. Col., Gov. Ky., 1974, Ky. Adm., 1994, Hon. Lt. Gov., Ohio Lt. gov., 1977; recipient Columbus Mayor's award for Voluntary Svc., 1982, Outstanding Comty. Svc. award Ohio Senate, 1982, Humanitarian Achievement award Columbus Dispatch newspaper, 1983, Silver Beaver award Boy Scouts Am., 1974, 45 Yr. Vets. award, 1992; James E. West fellow Boy Scouts Am., 1995. Mem. Nat. Assn. Cert. Fraud Examiners, Acad. Security Educators and Trainers, Valley Forge Hist. Soc. (life), Ky. Hist. Soc. (life), U.S. Capitol Hist Soc. (supporting founding mem.), Nat. Safety Coun. (camping com. 1974-86), Nat. Fire Protection Assn. (edn. com. 1989-93), Children's Club-Children's Hosp. (charter), Masons, Shriners. Methodist. Avocations: back-packing, travel, humanities. Home: 60 Broadmeadows Blvd Ste 327 Columbus OH 43214-1152 Office: Columbus So Power 215 N Front St Columbus OH 43215-2291

SCHAFFEL, LEWIS, professional basketball team executive; b. Bklyn.; m. Barbara Schaffel. Student, Kans. State U., Harvard U. Law Sch. Players agt. Nat. Basketball Assn.; exec. v.p., gen. mgr. New Orleans Jazz, 1977-78, Atlanta Hawks, 1979-80; owner, mgr. cons. firm N.Y.C.; became exec. v.p., chief operating officer N.J. Nets, 1983; now mng. ptnr. Miami Heat. Office: Miami Heat The Miami Arena Miami Beach FL 33136-4102*

SCHAFFER, DAVID IRVING, lawyer; b. N.Y.C., Oct. 17, 1935; s. Frank and Edith (Montlack) S.; m. Lois Ann Warshauer, June 16, 1957; children: Susan Edith Wenig, Eric Michael. B.A., U. Pa., 1956; LL.B., Harvard U., 1959. Bar: N.Y. 1960. Assoc. Shearman & Sterling, N.Y.C., 1960-65; sec., counsel Yale Express System, Inc., N.Y.C., 1965-66; sr. v.p., gen. counsel, sec. Avis, Inc., Garden City, N.Y., 1966-83; v.p., gen. counsel U.S Surgical Corp., Norwalk, Conn., 1983-86; of counsel Meltzer, Lippe, Goldstein & Wolf, P.C., Mineola, N.Y., 1986-89, ptnr., 1989—; past pres. Nassau County Legal Aid Soc., 1984-86. Bd. dirs. United Community Fund, Great Neck, N.Y., 1980, L.I. Venture Group, 1988—. With USAR, 1960. Mem. ABA, N.Y. State Bar Assn., Nassau County Bar Assn., Harvard Club. Democrat. Home: 31 Amherst Rd Great Neck NY 11021-2910 Office: Meltzer Lippe Goldstein Wolf Schlissel & Sazer PC 190 Willis Ave Mineola NY 11501-2639

SCHAFFER, EDMUND JOHN, management consultant, retired engineering executive; b. N.Y.C., July 28, 1925; m. Muriel Spiro, Aug. 22, 1948; children: Diane Schaffer Garretson, Elaine Schaffer Lukas. BS in Indsl. Engring., Syracuse U., 1950. Sr. staff indsl. engr. Carborundum Co., Niagara Falls, N.Y, 1952-60; mgr. mfg. Ford Motor Co., Detroit, 1952-60; sr. indsl. engr. ITT, N.Y.C., 1960-69, v.p., dir. worldwide indsl. engring. and mfg., 1969-82, ret., 1982; mgmt. cons. Short Hills, N.J., 1983—. With USN, 1943-47. Mem. Canoe Brook Country Club, Johns Island Country Club, Interlachen Country Club. Home: 63 Slope Dr Short Hills NJ 07078-1953

SCHAFFER, EUGENE CARL, education educator; b. Phila., May 10, 1944. BA, Temple U., 1968, EdD, 1976. Dir. field experience Valparaiso U., Valparaiso, Ind., 1974-76; prof. curriculum and instrn. U. N.C., Charlotte, 1976-91, chair dept. curriculum and instrn., 1994—. Co-author:

Recent Advances in School Effects Research, 1994; contbr. articles to profl. jours. Recipient Fulbright scholarship, Japan rsch. fellowship. Mem. Am. Edn. Rsch. Assn., Phi Delta Kappa. Home: 5838 New Combe Ct Charlotte NC 28277

SCHAFFER, KENNETH B., communications executive, satellite engineer, inventor, consultant; b. N.Y.C., Oct. 19, 1947; s. Louis and Rose (Paul) S.; m. Alla Fyodorovna Kliouka, Aug. 26, 1993; 1 child, Kibo Louis. BA, CCNY, 1969. Pres., founder Sound Images, Inc., N.Y.C., 1969-72; exec. v.p. Douglas Internat., N.Y.C., 1972-75; pres., founder Ken Schaffer Group, Inc., N.Y.C., 1975-82, Orbita Techs. Corp. N.Y.C., 1981-86; v.p., founder Belka Internat. Inc., N.Y.C. and Moscow, 1986-91; pres., founder Belcom, Inc., N.Y.C., Moscow, and Almaty, 1991—, also bd. dirs. Recipient Golden Ace award Cable TV Assn., 1989. Mem. Am. Radio Relay League, Aircraft Owners and Pilots Assn., Internet Soc., Moscow Comml. Club. Achievements include invention of wireless guitar, satellite system to intercept internal Soviet television. Avocations: flying, amateur radio, internetworking. Home: 21 W 58 St Penthouse New York NY 10019 Office: Belcom Inc 515 Madison Ave 24 New York NY 10022

SCHAFFER, MONROE S., grocery company executive; b. N.Y.C., Oct. 24, 1917; s. Samuel and Fannie (Schwartz) S.; children—Barbara, Roberta, Gail. B.S., NYU, 1941. Vice pres. Schaffer Leasing Co., N.Y.C., 1965—; pres. Far Choy Trading Co., N.Y.C., 1975—, S. Schaffer Grocery Corp., N.Y.C., 1978—, Larmon Realty Co., N.Y.C., 1980—, Weyman Assocs., 1983—; v.p. Alyim Grocery Co., Marshall Trading Co. Pres. United Way, New Rochelle, N.Y., 1980-82. Club: Ridgeway Country (past pres.). Home: 8 Rolling Hills Ln Harrison NY 10528-1706 Office: S Schaffer Grocery Corp 27 Weyman Ave New Rochelle NY 10805-1410

SCHAFFER, ROBERT WARREN, state senator; b. Cin., July 24, 1962; s. Robert James and Florence Ann (Bednar) S.; m. Maureen Elizabeth Menke, Feb. 8, 1986; children: Jennifer, Emily, Justin. BA in Polit. Sci., U. Dayton, 1984. Legis. asst. State of Ohio, Columbus, 1985; majority adminstrv. asst. Colo. Senate, Denver, 1985-87; Colo. senator representing Dist. 14 Ft. Collins, 1987—; chmn. state affairs com., 1995—; commr. Colo. Advanced Tech. Inst., 1988—; proprietor No. Front Range Mktg. and Distbn., Inc. Mem. Mental Health Bd. Larimer County, 1986-87, Bus. Affairs, Edn., Nat. Conf. State Legislatures Com. on Econ Devel. Commerce; campaign co-chair Arnold for Lt. Gov., Larimer and Weld Counties, 1986; head coach Ft. Collins Youth Baseball, 1986—; chmn. Senate Fin. Com.; Republican candidate for lt. gov., 1994. Mem. Colo. Press Assn., Colo. Press Club, Jaycees (Mover and Shaker award, 1989), KC. Republican. Roman Catholic. Avocations: backpacking, skiing, baseball, painting, reading. Home: 3284 Silverthorne Dr Fort Collins CO 80526 Office: The State Senate State Capitol Denver CO 80203

SCHAFFER, SETH ANDREW, lawyer; b. Bklyn., Jan. 7, 1942; m. Karen (Kiki) Cohn, Dec. 1, 1968; children: Amanda, Julia, James. BA in Econs. magna cum laude, Harvard U., 1963, LLB cum laude, 1967; postgrad., Cambridge (Eng.) U., 1964. Bar: N.Y. 1970, U.S. Dist. Ct. (so. dist.) N.Y. 1973, U.S. Ct. Appeals (2d cir.) 1973, U.S. Supreme Ct. 1980. Tchr. math. and econs. York (Pa.) Country Day Sch., 1967-68; assoc. dir. Vera Inst. Justice, 1969-72; asst. U.S. atty. U.S. Dist. Ct. (so. dist.) N.Y., 1972-75; chief counsel Moreland Act Commn. on Nursing Homes, N.Y., 1975-76; of counsel Stanley S. Arkin, P.C., Attys. at Law, 1976-77; v.p., gen. counsel, sec. of univ. NYU, N.Y.C., 1977-93, sr. v.p., gen. counsel, sec., 1993—; adj. prof. law NYU; chmn. Criminal Justice Agy., N.Y.C.; trustee Manhattan Bowery Corp. Dir. Not for Profit Coordinating Com. N.Y. Henry fellow Cambridge U., Eng., 1964. Mem. Assn. Bar City N.Y., Phi Beta Kappa. Home: 14 Washington Mews New York NY 10003-6608 Office: NYU 70 Washington Sq S New York NY 10012-1091

SCHAFFER, TERESITA CURRIE, federal official; b. Washington, Sept. 28, 1945; d. Francis and Teresita (Sparre) Currie; m. Howard B. Schaffer, Oct. 25, 1971; children: Michael C., Christopher S. AB, Bryn Mawr Coll., 1966; Cert., Institut d'Etudes Politiques, Paris, 1965; postgrad., Georgetown U., 1973-74. Embassy officer U.S. Embassy, Tel Aviv, 1967-69; econ. officer U.S. Embassy, Islamabad, Pakistan, 1975-77; sci. attache U.S. Embassy, New Delhi, 1977-79; polit. analyst U.S. Dept. State, Washington, 1969-71, economist, 1972-73; div. chief, dir. Office Trade U.S. Dept. State, Washington, 1980-84; dir. Office Egyptian Affairs U.S. Dept. State, Washington, 1987-89, dep. asst. sec. for Near East and South Asia, 1989-92; amb. to Sri Lanka and Maldives U.S. Embassy, Colombo, Sri Lanka, 1992—. Author: Profile of Women in Bangladesh, 1986, Survey of Development Projects and Activities for Women in Bangladesh, 1986; chmn. editorial bd. Fgn. Svc. Jour., 1972-74. Mem. Am. Fgn. Svc. Assn. Office: U S Embassy, Colombo Sri Lanka

SCHAFFNER, BERTRAM HENRY, psychiatrist; b. Erie, Pa., Nov. 12, 1912; s. Milton and Gerta (Herzog) S. Student, Harvard U., 1928-29, 32-33; AB, Swarthmore Coll., 1932; MD, Johns Hopkins U., 1937; diploma, William Alanson White Inst., 1953. Diplomate Am. Bd. Psychiatry, Am. Bd. Neurology. Intern Johns Hopkins Hosp., Balt., 1937-38; resident in neurology Mt. Sinai Hosp., N.Y.C., 1938-39; resident in psychiatry Bellevue Hosp., N.Y.C., 1939-40, N.Y. State Psychiat. Inst., N.Y.C., 1946-47; pvt. practice psychiatry and psychoanalysis N.Y.C., 1947—; lectr. Sch. Nursing Cornell U., N.Y.C., 1950-60; mem. faculty, clin. supr. in psychotherapy William Alanson White Inst. Psychoanalysis, 1960—, clin. dir. HIV svc., clin. supr. psychotherapy, 1993—; cons., editor confs. Josiah Macy Jr. Found., 1949, 50, 51; cons. U.S. Children's Bur., 1946-47, Bur. Mental Health, V.I., 1954-60, World Fedn. Mental Health, 1958-68, others; mem. N.Y. County dist. bd. Com. on Gay and Lesbian Issues; cons. WHO, 1960-67; founder, pres. U.S.-Caribbean Aid to Mental Health, Inc., 1960-69; organizer Biennial Caribbean Confs. for Mental Health, 1959-65; organizer, cons. Caribbean Fedn. for Mental Health, 1959-65; mem. rsch. study Pre-Soviet Russian Family and Culture, Columbia U., 1949-51. Mem. editl. bd. Jour. of Gay and Lesbian Psychotherapy, 1987—; author: Father Land: A Study of Authoritarianism in the German Family, 1948; contbr. numerous articles to profl. publs. Recipient Adolf Meyer award for Disting. Svc. in Behalf of Improved Care and Treatment of the Mentally Ill in the Caribbean, 1961. Fellow AMA (life), Am. Psychiat. Assn. (chmn. 1983-86, mem. com. on AIDS N.Y. County dist. br. 1989—, life), Am. Acad. Psychoanalysis (life), Caribbean Psychiat. Assn.; mem. Group for Advancement of Psychiatry (chair internat. rel. com. 1960-65, chair com. on human sexuality 1987—). Avocations: collecting Asian and Indian art. Home and Office: 220 Central Park S New York NY 10019

SCHAFFNER, CHARLES ETZEL, consulting engineering executive; b. N.Y.C., July 21, 1919; s. Louis C. and Christina (Etzel) S.; m. Olga T. Stroedecke, Feb. 13, 1943; children—Charles Etzel II, Linda Jean. B.C.E., Cooper Union, 1941, C.E., 1952; M.C.E., Bklyn. Poly. Inst., 1944; B.S.S.E., U. Ill., 1945, N.Y. U.; D.Sci (hon.), Iona Coll., 1983. Jr. engr. Moran Proctor, Freeman & Mueser, N.Y.C., 1941; instr. Cooper Union, 1941-44; mem. faculty Bklyn. Poly. Inst., 1946-70, prof. engring., 1957-70, adj. prof., 1970-72, asst. dean, 1954-57, assoc. dean, 1957-58, dean, dir. planning, 1958-62, v.p. adminstrn., 1962-70; v.p. Syska & Hennessy, Inc., 1970-73, sr. v.p., 1973-76, exec. v.p., 1976-85, vice chmn., 1985-86, cons., 1987—, also dir.; chmn. nat. adv. bd. Summer Inst. Young Engring. Tchrs., 1959-63; mem. adv. panel NSF, 1960-70; chmn. exec. bd. N.Y.C. Bldg. Code Project, 1962-66; mem. panel 421.00 adv. to bldg. research div. Inst. Applied Tech., Nat. Bur. Standards, 1966-69; mem. bldg., constrn. adv. council Dept. Bldgs. City N.Y., 1966—; mem. bldg. research adv. bd. NRC, 1972-79, vice chmn., 1973-77; chmn., 1977-78, Mayor's Bldg. and Constrn. Adv. Council, 1971-73; exec. dir. Mayor's Fire Safety Com., 1971-73; mem. N.Y.C. Constrn. Industry Advisory Council, 1973—; v.p., bd. dirs. N.Y. Bldg. Congress, 1967-71, sec., 1971-75, chmn. govtl. affairs com., 1977-78, pres., 1979-83, chmn. council pres., 1983-87, chmn. council bus. and labor, 1987-88. Contbr. articles profl. jours. Commr. edn. dist., Locust Valley, N.Y., 1956-59, pres., 1958-59; commr. edn., pres. Central Dist. 3, Oyster Bay, N.Y., 1959-63; Trustee Cooper Union, 1975-78; trustee Cooper Union Research Found. Served with AUS, 1944-46. Named Outstanding Alumnus Cooper Union, 1966; Good Scout of Yr. Boy Scouts Am., 1979; recipient Disting. Alumnus award Poly. Alumni Assn., Alumnus of Year, 1972. Mem. Operation Democracy, ASCE (Civil Engr. of Year 1969), ASTM, Am. Arbitration Assn. (bd. arbitrators), Am. Soc. Engring. Edn. (v.p., gen. council 1965-67,

v.p. fin. 1974-77, dir. 1965-67, 74-77, 78-81, pres. 1979-80), Nat. Inst. Bldg. Scis. (exec. com. consultative council 1978-82, dir. 1982-88), Engrs. Joint Council (dir. 1976-79), Am. Assn. Engring. Socs. (bd. govs. 1979-81, chmn. ednl. affairs council 1979-80), Am. Concrete Inst., N.Y. State Sch. Bds. Assn., N.Y. State Soc. Profl. Engrs. (dir. Nassau County chpt., Engr. of Year, Kings County chpt. 1968), Cooper Union Alumni Assn. (pres. 1973), Tau Beta Pi, Chi Epsilon, Omega Delta Phi. Clubs: Municipal, Nassau. Home and Office: Linden Farms Rd Locust Valley NY 11560

SCHAFFRAN, CHARLES BRAD, investment company executive; b. N.Y.C., Feb. 1, 1950; s. Leonard and Maxine (Bernstein) S.; m. Laurie Lane, Jan. 10, 1981; children: Scott, Zachary. BA with honors, U. Rochester, 1972; JD with distinction, Northwestern U., 1975. Bar: N.Y. 1976. Assoc. Willkie, Farr & Gallagher, N.Y.C., 1975-77; assoc. Schulte Roth & Zabel, N.Y.C., 1977-83, ptnr., 1983-86; dir. alternative investments, ptnr. Weiss, Peck & Greer, N.Y.C., 1986-94; sr. v.p. Alliance Capital Mgmt. Corp., N.Y.C., 1994—; Editor Northwestern U. Law Review, 1974-75. Mem. Investment Mgmt. Com. (chmn. 1989-91), Securities Industry Assn. Home: 215 E 68th St New York NY 10021-5718 Office: Alliance Capital Mgmt Corp 1345 Ave of Americas New York NY 10105

SCHAICH, WILLIAM L., physics educator; b. Springfield, Oct. 15, 1944; s. Wilbur Allison and Lillian Luella (Halfaker) S.; m. Georgia Jeann Loebrich, Dec. 23, 1966; children: Amy C., Lucy B. BS, Denison U., 1966; MS, Cornell U., 1968, PhD, 1970. Post doctoral fellow Bristol, U.K., 1970-71; research asst. U. Calif., LaJolla, Calif., 1971-73; asst. prof. Ind. U., 1973-76, assoc. prof., 1976-80, prof., 1980—. Contbr. articles to profl. jours. Fellow Am. Physical Soc. Office: Ind U Swain Hall W Bloomington IN 47405

SCHAIE, K(LAUS) WARNER, human development and psychology educator, researcher; b. Stettin, Germany (now Poland), Feb. 1, 1928; came to U.S., 1947, naturalized, 1953; s. Sally and Lottie Louise (Gabriel) S.; m. Coloma J. Harrison, Aug. 9, 1953 (div. 1973); 1 child, Stephan; m. Sherry L. Willis, Nov. 20, 1981. A.A., City Coll. San Francisco, 1951; B.A., U. Calif.-Berkeley, 1952; M.S. U. Wash., 1953, Ph.D., 1956. Lic. psychologist, Calif., Pa. Postdoctoral fellow Washington U., St. Louis, 1956-57; asst. prof. psychology U. Nebr., Lincoln, 1957-1964, assoc. prof., 1964-68; prof., chmn. dept. psychology W.Va. U., Morgantown, 1964-73; prof. psychology, dir. Gerontology Research Inst., U. So. Calif., 1973-81; Evan Pugh prof. human devel. and psychology, dir. Gerontology Ctr., Pa. State U., University Park, 1981—; mem. devel. behavior study sect. NIH, Bethesda, Md., 1970-72, chmn., 1972-74, chmn. human devel. and aging study sect., 1979-84, mem. expert panel in comml. airline pilot retirement, 1981, data and safety bd. shep project, 1984-91. Author: Developmental Psychology; A Life Span Approach, 1981; Adult Development and Aging, 1982, 3d rev. edit., 1991; editor: Handbook of Psychology of Aging, 1977, 3d rev. edit., 1990, Longitudinal Studies of Adult Development, 1983, Cognitive Functioning and Social Structure over the Life Course, 1987, Methodological Issues in Research on aging, 1988, Social Structure and Aging: Psychological Processes, 1989, Age Structuring in Comparative Perspective, 1989, The Course of Later Life, 1989, Self-Directedness: Cause and Effects Throughout the Life Course, 1990, Aging, Health Behaviors and Health Outcomes, 1992, Caregiving Systems: Formal and Informal Helpers, 1993, Societal Impact on Aging: Historical Perspectives, 1993, Adult Intergenerational Relations: Effects of Societal Change, 1995, Intellectual Development in Adulthood: The Seattle Longitudinal Study, 1995; editor Ann. Rev. Gerontology and Geriatrics vol. 7, 1987, vol. 11, 1991; contbr. articles to profl. jours. Fellow APA (coun. reps. 1976-79, 83-86, Disting. Contbn. award 1982, Disting. Scientific Conbns. award, 1992), Gerontol. Soc. (Kleemeier award 1987), Am. Psychol. Soc.; mem. Psychometric Soc., Internat. Soc. Study Behavioral Devel. Unitarian. Avocations: hiking; stamps. Home: 1214 Deerfield Dr State College PA 16803-2206 Office: Pa State U Dept Human Devel & Family Study University Park PA 16802

SCHAIRER, GEORGE SWIFT, aeronautical engineer; b. Pitts., May 19, 1913; s. Otto Sorg and Elizabeth Blanche (Swift) S.; m. Mary Pauline Tarbox, June 20, 1935; children: Mary Elizabeth, George Edward, Sally Helen, John Otto. With Bendix Aviation Corp., South Bend, Ind., 1935-37, Consol. Vultee Aircraft Corp., San Diego, 1937-39; joined Boeing Airplane Co., Seattle, 1939, successively chief aerodynamist, staff engr. aerodynamics and powerplant, 1948-51, chief tech. staff, 1951-56, asst. chief engr., 1956-57, dir. research, 1957-59, v.p. research and devel., 1959-73, v.p. research, 1973-78, cons., 1978-88; mem. tech. adv. group USAAF, 1945-46; mem. com. on aerodynamics NACA; mem. tech. adv. panel on aeros. Dept. Def., 1954-61; sci. adv. bd. USAF, 1955-60; cons. ops. evaluation group USN, 1961; panel sci. and tech. manpower Pres.'s Sci. Adv. Com., 1962-64; sci. adv. com. Def. Intelligence Agy., 1966-70; mem. aeros. and space engring. bd. NRC, 1977-79. Contbr. articles to profl. jours. Trustee A Contemporary Theatre. Recipient Spirit of St. Louis award ASME, 1959, Guggenheim medal, 1967. Fellow AIAA (hon. fellow, Sylvanus Albert Reed award 1950, Wright Bros. lectr. 1964); mem. NAE, NAS, Internat. Acad. Astronautics, Am. Helicopter Soc., Soc. Naval Architects and Marine Engrs., Sigma Xi, Sigma Tau. Address: 4242 Hunts Pt Rd Bellevue WA 98004

SCHAKE, LOWELL MARTIN, animal science educator; b. Marthasville, Mo., June 6, 1938; s. Martin Charles and Flora Olinda (Rocklage) S.; m. Wendy Anne Walkinshaw, Sept. 11, 1959; children: Sheryl Anne, Lowell Scott. BS, U. Mo., 1960, MS, 1962; PhD, Tex. A&M U., 1967. Asst. prof. Tex. A&M U., College Station, 1965-67, assoc. prof., 1969-72, prof., 1972-84; asst. prof., area livestock specialist Tex. A&M U., Lubbock, 1967-69; prof., head animal sci. dept. U. Conn., Storrs, 1984-92; prof., chmn. animal sci. dept. Tex. Tech. U., Lubbock, 1992—; developer applied animal ethology program Tex. A&M U., 1970, New Eng. Biotech. Conf. series, 1990, Southeast Beef Forum, 1993; chmn. Am. Registry of Profl. Animal Scientist Com. on Profl. Stds., 1988; chmn. Nat. Com. Exec. Officers of Animal Vet., Dairy and Poultry Sci. Depts., 1992; cons. Alpart, Kingston, Jamaica, 1975, U.S. Feeds Grain Coun., 1970-73, A.O. Smith Products Inc., 1968—, Humphrey Land & Cattle Co., Dallas, 1980-86; lectr. in field. Author: Growth and Finishing of Beef Cattle, A Class Handbook, 1982; contbr. articles to profl. jours. Recipient Innovative Teaching award Tex. A&M U., 1978. Mem. Am. Soc. Animal Sci., Plains Nutrition Coun. (adv. bd. 1967-80, sec.-treas. 1994-95, founder), Nat. Assn. Colls. and Tchrs. Agr., Am. Registry Profl. Animal Scientists (dir. for Northeast 1987-89), Coun. for Agr. Sci. and Tech. World Conf. on Animal Prodn., Am. Soc. Dairy Sci., Gamma Sigma Delta. Republican. Club: Tiger (College Station) (pres.). Avocations: fishing, gardening, outdoor work. Home: 60 Lakeshore Dr S Ransom Canyon TX 79409 Office: Tex Tech U Dept Animal and Food Sci Lubbock TX 79409

SCHALEBEN, ARVILLE, newspaper editor, writer, educator; b. Brown County, Minn., Jan. 25, 1907; s. Wilhelm and Lina (Helling) S.; m. Ida Androvandi, Sept. 14, 1935; children: Joy Schaleben Lewis, Susan Schaleben Wilson, Mary Schaleben Totero, Will. B.A., U. Minn., 1929. With Milw. Jour., 1929-72, reporter, asst. city editor, then city editor, 1936-46, asst. mng. editor, 1946-59, mng. editor, 1959-62, exec. editor, 1962-66, assoc. editor, 1966-72; v.p. The Jour. Co., 1962-68, dir., 1960-72; editor-in-residence U. Wis., Madison, 1972—; also vis. prof. U. Wis.; vis. prof. Medill Sch. Journalism, Northwestern U., 1972—; Riley prof. journalism Ind. U., Bloomington, 1972; lectr. U. Wis., Milw., 1976-77. Author: Your Future in Journalism; editorial bd. This Week mag.; contbr. anthologies: Folks Say of Will Rogers, The American Dream, Headlining America, News Stories of 1933, News Stories of 1934, Fifty and Feisty. Pres. Androvandi, Ltd., Milw. Dir. Fox Point (Wis.) Sch. Bd., 1942-48; mem. President's Com. for Handicapped, 1950-58; chmn. Nicolet High Sch. bldg. com., 1953. Named Wis. Journalist of Year, Soc. Profl. Journalists, 1958; 80; recipient Honor al Merito award N.Am. Assn. of Venezuela. Mem. Wis. AP Assn. (pres.), AP Mng. Editors Assn. (dir.; chmn. news research com. 1965, mem. media competition com., new methods com., com. future newspapers, co-editor 50-yr. associated press history, regent 1965—), Am. Newspaper Pubs. Assn. (mem. news research center steering com. 1964-72), Am. Soc. Newspaper Editors (co-chmn. edn. com., mem. research com., com. edn. for journalism, com. minorities), Internat. Press Inst., Soc. South Pole, Antarctican Soc., Sigma Delta Chi (chmn. Wis. 1958, mem. prof. goals com.). Congregationalist (past chmn. bldg. com.). Clubs: Milw. Press (pres. 1936-39, mem. Found.), Milw. Press (pres. Found. 1975-85, knight of Golden Quill, 1979), Ozaukee Country (Mequon, Wis.), Makai Golf and Tennis (Princeville,

Hanalei, Hawaii). Home: 8254 N Gray Log Ln Milwaukee WI 53217-2862 Office: 333 W State St Milwaukee WI 53203-1305 also: U Wis-Madison Vilas Communications H Madison WI 53706 *In our good earth's eternity, not one among us is more enduring than the least among us unless he so lives to lengthen mankind's future.*

SCHALL, ALVIN ANTHONY, judge; b. N.Y.C., Apr. 4, 1944; s. Gordon William and Helen (Davis) S.; m. Sharon Frances LeBlanc, Apr. 25, 1970; children: Amanda Lanford, Anthony Davis. BA, Princeton U., 1966; JD, Tulane U., 1969. Bar: N.Y. 1970, U.S. Dist. Ct. (so. and ea. dists.) N.Y. 1973, U.S. Ct. Appeals (2d crct.) 1974, D.C. 1980, U.S. Dist. Ct. D.C. 1991, U.S. Ct. Appeals (D.C. crct.) 1991, U.S. Ct. Fed. Claims 1982, U.S. Ct. Appeals (fed. crct.) 1987, U.S. Supreme Ct. 1989. Assoc. Shearman & Sterling, N.Y.C., 1969-73; asst. U.S. atty. ea. dist. N.Y. Borough of Bklyn., 1973-78, chief appeals div., 1977-78; trial atty. civil div. U.S. Dept. Justice, Washington, 1978-87, sr. trial counsel, 1986-87, asst. to atty. gen., 1988-92; ptnr. Perlman & Ptnrs., Washington, 1987-88; judge U.S. Ct. Appeals (fed. crct.), Washington, 1992—. Home: 103 Grafton St Chevy Chase MD 20815-3425 Office: 717 Madison Pl NW Washington DC 20439

SCHALL, LAWRENCE DELANO, economics educator, consultant; b. Los Angeles, Nov. 5, 1940; s. Lee and Lillian (Seltzow) S.; m. Betty Jane Kay, Aug. 6, 1982; children: Michael Kay, Adam Kent. BA, UCLA, 1962; MA in Econs., U. Chgo., 1967, PhD in Econs., 1969. CPA, Wash. Sec.-treas. Permco Inc., Los Angeles, 1959-61; acting asst. prof. econs. U. Wash., Seattle, 1968-69, asst. prof., 1969-72, assoc. prof., 1972-76, prof., 1976—. Author: (with C. W. Haley) The Theory of Financial Decisions, 1972, 2d edit., 1979, Introduction to Financial Management, 1977, 6th edit., 1991, (with K. Henderson and R. May) Evaluating Business Ventures, 1982; contbr. articles to profl. jours. Recipient Bank of Am. Excellence award, 1983, Burlington No. Found. award, 1986, First Interstate Bank award, 1990, Andrew V. Smith award, U. Wash., 1992. Mem. Am. Econ. Assn., Am. Fin. Assn., Fin. Mgmt. Assn., Fin. Execs. Inst. Office: U Wash Sch Bus Adminstrn 261 Mackenzie Hall Dj # 10 Seattle WA 98195

SCHALLENBERGER, CAROLYN, college dean; b. Jacobs Creek, Pa., Aug. 2, 1935; d. George J. and Margaret (Movic) S. BSN, Mt. Mercy.Coll., Pitts., 1959; MS in Nursing, Cath. U. Am., 1962. RN, Pa.; joined Sisters of Mercy, Roman Catholic Ch., 1953. Head nurse Mercy Hosp., Pitts.; instr. Mercy Sch. Nursing, Pitts., dean, assoc. dir.; mem. bd. appeals NLN, CDP Exec. Com. Mem. ANA, Am. Hosp. Assn., Nat. League for Nursing, Pa. Nurses Assn., Inst. for Hosp. Clin. Nursing Edn., Sigma Theta Tau. Home: 1515 Locust St Pittsburgh PA 15219-5131

SCHALLENKAMP, KAY, college administrator; b. Salem, S.D., Dec. 9, 1949; d. Arnold B. and Jennie M. (Koch) Krier; m. Ken Schallenkamp, Sept. 7, 1970; children: Heather, Jenni. BS, No. State Coll., 1972; MA, U. S.D., 1973; PhD, U. Colo., 1982. Prof. No. State Coll., Aberdeen, S.D., 1973-88, dept. chair, 1982-84, dean, 1984-88; provost Chadron (Nebr.) State Coll., 1988-92, U. Wis., Whitewater, 1992—; cons. North Ctrl. Assn., nursing homes, hosps. and ednl. instns. Contbr. articles to profl. jours. Bush fellow, 1980; named Outstanding Young Career Woman, Bus. and Profl. Women's Club, 1976. Mem. Am. Speech and Hearing Assn. (cert.), Rotary. Avocation: martial arts. Office: U Wis Whitewater 800 W Main Whitewater WI 53190

SCHALLER, GEORGE BEALS, zoologist; b. Berlin, May 26, 1933; s. Georg Ludwig S. and Bettina (Byrd) Iwersen; m. Kay Suzanne Morgan, Aug. 26, 1957; children: Eric, Mark. BS. in Zoology, BA in Anthropology, U. Alaska, 1955; Ph.D. in Zoology, U. Wis., 1962. Research assoc. Johns Hopkins U., Balt., 1963-66; research zoologist N.Y. Zool. Soc., Bronx, 1966—, dir. internat. conservation program, 1979-88; adj. assoc. prof. Rockefeller U., N.Y.C., 1966—; research assoc. Am. Mus. Natural History. Author: The Mountain Gorilla, 1963 (Wildlife Soc. 1965), The Year of the Gorilla, 1964, The Deer and the Tiger, 1967, The Serengeti Lion, 1972 (Nat. Bookaward 1973), Golden Shadows, Flying Hooves, 1973, Mountain Monarchs, 1977, Stones of Silence, 1980, The Giant Pandas of Wolong, 1985, The Last Panda, 1993. Ctr. Advanced Study in Behavioral Scis. fellow, Stanford U., 1962; fellow Guggenheim Found., 1971; decorated Order of Golden Ark (The Netherlands), Explorers medal, 1990; recipient gold medal World Wildlife Fudn., 1980. Mem. Explorers Club (hon. dir. 1991). Office: Wildlife Conservation Soc Bronx Park Bronx NY 10462

SCHALLER, JOANNE FRANCES, nursing consultant; b. Columbus, Ga., July 15, 1943; d. John Frank and Ethel Beatrice (Spring) Lanzendorfer; m. Robert Thomas Schaller, Jan. 22, 1977; 1 child, Amy. BS, Pacific Luth. U., 1969; M in Nursing, U. Wash., 1971. House supr. UCLA Hosp., 1971-72; outpatient supr. Harborview Hosp., Seattle, 1973-75; outpatient clinic and emergency room supr. U. Wash. Hosp., Seattle, 1975-77; co-author, researcher with Robert Schaller MD Seattle, 1977-87; prin. Nursing Expert-Standards of Care, Seattle, 1987—; cons. Wash. State Trial Lawyers, Wash. Assn. Criminal Def. Lawyers, 1989—; founder, CEO Present Perfect, Seattle, 1991—. Contbr., editor articles to profl. jours. Bd. dirs. Pacific Arts Ctr., 1992—; vol. guardian ad litem King County Juvenile Ct., 1978—; vol. Make a Wish Found. U.S. Bank, 1984—, Multiple Sclerosis Assn., 1986—, Am. Heart Assn., 1986—, Internat. Children's Festival, 1987—, Seattle Children's Festival, 1987—, Seattle Dept. Parks and Recreation Open Space Com., 1990—, Pacific N.W. Athletic Congress, 1991—, Wash. Fed. Garden Clubs Jr. Advisor, 1992—, Fred Hutchison Cancer Rsch. Ctr., 1993—; mem. parent coun. Seattle Country Day Sch., 1986—; mem. Photo Coun. Seattle Art Mus., 1986—, Native Am. Coun., 1989—; mem. N.W. coun. Seattle Mus., 1992—, mem. NAOO Coun., 1989—, Plestcheeff Inst. Decorative Arts, 1992—; mem. fundraiser Children's Hosp. Med. Ctr., 1977—, Breast Cancer Fund, 1994—, Susan G. Komen Breast Cancer Found., 1994—. Named 1st Migrant Health Care Nurse, State of Wash., 1969, 1st Am. nurse visiting China, 1974. Mem. AAUW, ANA, Wash. State Nurses Assn., U. Wash. Alumni Assn. Avocations: photography, writing, gardening, hiking, music. Home and Office: 914 Randolph Pl Seattle WA 98122-5267

SCHALLERT, EDWIN GLENN, lawyer; b. L.A., Aug. 7, 1952; s. William Joseph and Rosemarie Diane (Waggner) S. AB, Stanford U., 1974; JD, Harvard U., 1981, MPP, 1981. Bar: N.Y. 1974, U.S. Ct. Appeals (7th cir.) 1986, U.S. Ct. Appeals (2d cir.) 1989, U.S. Dist. Ct. (so. dist.) N.Y. 1975. Legis. aid to U.S. rep. Les Aspin Washington, 1975-78, law clk. to Hon. J. Skelly Wright, 1981-82, law clk. to Hon. Thurgood Marshall, 1982-83; assoc. Debevoise & Plimpton, N.Y.C., 1983-89; ptnr. Debevoise & Plimpton, 1989—. Term mem. Coun. o Fgn. Rels., 1983-88. Mem. Internat. Inst. for Strategic Studies, Phi Beta Kappa. Democrat. Avocation: tennis. Office: Debevoise & Plimpton 875 3rd Ave New York NY 10022-6225

SCHALLY, ANDREW VICTOR, endocrine oncologist, researcher; b. Poland, Nov. 30, 1926; came to U.S., 1957; s. Casimir Peter and Maria (Lacka) S.; m. Ana Maria Comaru, Aug., 1976; children: Karen, Gordon. B.Sc., McGill U., Can., 1955, Ph.D. in Biochemistry, 1957; 16 hon. doctorates. Research asst. biochemistry Nat. Inst. Med. Research, London, 1949-52; dept. psychiatry McGill U., Montreal, Que., 1952-57; research assoc., asst. prof. physiology and biochemistry Coll. Medicine, Baylor U., Houston, 1957-62; assoc. prof. Tulane U. Sch. Medicine, New Orleans, 1962-67, prof., 1967—; chief Endocrine Polypeptide and Cancer Inst. VA Med. Ctr., New Orleans; sr. med. investigator VA, 1973—. Author several books; contbr. articles to profl. jours. Recipient Van Meter prize Am. Thyroid Assn., 1969; Ayerst-Squibb award Endocrine Soc., 1970; William S. Middletown award VA, 1970; Ch. Mickle award U. Toronto, 1974; Gairdner Internat. award, 1974; Borden award Assn. Am. Med. Colls. and Borden Co. Found., 1975; Lasker Basic Research award, 1975; co-recipient Nobel prize for medicine, 1977; USPHS sr. research fellow, 1961-62. Mem. NAS, AAAS, Endocrine Soc., Am. Physiol. Soc., Soc. Biol. Chemists, Soc. Exptl. Biol. Medicine, Internat. Soc. Rsch. Biology Reprodn., Soc. Study Reprodn., Soc. Internat. Brain Rsch. Orgn., Mex. Acad. Medicine, Am. Soc. Animal Sci., Nat. Medicine Brazil, Acad. Medicine Venezuela, Acad. Sci. Hungary, Acad. Sci. Russia. Home: 5025 Kawanee Ave Metairie LA 70006-2547 Office: VA Hosp 1601 Perdido St New Orleans LA 70146

SCHAMA, SIMON, historian, educator, author; b. London, England, Feb. 13, 1945; married; 2 children. BA, Cambridge (Eng.) U., 1966, MA in History, 1969. Prof. Humanities Old Dominion Found. Columbia U.,

Cambridge, Mass., 1980—; sr. assoc. Ctr. European Studies Harvard U., Cambridge, Mass. Author: Patriots and Liberators: Revolution in the Netherlands, 1780-1813, 1977 (Wolfson prize for history 1977, Leo Gershoy Meml. prize Am. Hist. Assn. 1978), Two Rothschilds and the Land of Israel, 1979, The Embarrassment of Riches: An Interpretation of Dutch Culture in the Golden Age, 1987, Citizens: A Chronicle of the French Revolution, 1989 (NCR prize for non-fiction), Dead Certainties, 1991, Landscape and Memory, 1995. Office: Columbia U Dept History New York NY 10027

SCHAMBRA, PHILIP ELLIS, federal agency administrator, radiobiologist; b. Saginaw, Mich., Nov. 8, 1934; s. William Philip and Gwendolyn Maude (Leister) S.; m. Uta Gertrude Bossel, Mar. 30, 1967 (div. Aug. 1981); children: Eric William Philip, Kirsten Uta, Heidi Maren; m. Donita Bartels Feldman, Aug. 15, 1990. BA, Rice U., 1956; PhD, Yale U., 1961. Examiner Office of Mgmt. and Budget Exec. Office of Pres., Washington, 1968-71, staff mem. Coun. on Environ. Quality, 1971-74; assoc. dir. Nat. Inst. Environ. Health Scis., Research Triangle Park, N.C., 1974-81; chief internat. coordination Fogarty Internat. Ctr. NIH, Bethesda, Md., 1981-84; sci. attache U.S. Embassy, New Delhi, 1984-88; dir. Fogarty Internat. Ctr. NIH, Bethesda, Md., 1988—. Contbr. articles on radiobiology to profl. jours. Recipient Superior Svc. award USPHS, 1989; Nat. Cancer Inst. fellow, 1958, Rsch. fellow NASA, 1964. Mem. AAAS. Avocations: sailing, racquetball. Home: 9104 Drumaldry Dr Bethesda MD 20817-3341 Office: NIH Fogarty Internat Ctr 9000 Rockville Pike Bethesda MD 20892-0001

SCHANBERG, SAUL MURRAY, pharmacology educator; b. Clinton, Mass., Mar. 22, 1933; m. Rachel Weinbaum, Dec. 18, 1956; children: Laura E., Linda S. B.A., Clark U., 1954, M.A., 1956; Ph.D., Yale U., 1961, M.D., 1964. Cons. Calif. Dept. Mental Health, 1962-65; intern in pediatrics Albert Einstein Med. Ctr., N.Y.C., 1964-65; rsch. assoc. NIMH, 1965-67; asst. prof. Duke U. Med. Ctr., Durham, N.C., 1967-69, assoc. prof., 1969-73, prof. of pharmacology, 1973—; prof. psychiatry Duke U. Med. Ctr., 1983—; assoc. dean Duke U. Med. Ctr. Sch., 1987-93, chair phamacology, 1987-92. Cons. USPHS, Rockville, Md., 1983-84. NIMH grantee, 1968; NIH grantee, 1967. Fellow Am. Coll. Neuropsychopharmacology. Home: 1604 Pinecrest Rd Durham NC 27705-5832 Office: Duke U PO Box 3813 Durham NC 27702-3813

SCHANBERG, SYDNEY HILLEL, newspaper editor, columnist; b. Clinton, Mass., Jan. 17, 1934; s. Louis and Freda (Feinberg) S.; children—Jessica, Rebecca. B.A., Harvard U., 1955. Joined N.Y. Times, 1959, became reporter, 1960; bur. chief N.Y. Times, Albany, N.Y., 1967-69; chief bur. N.Y. Times, New Delhi, India, 1969-73; S.E. Asia corr. N.Y. Times, Singapore, 1973-75; met. editor N.Y. Times, 1977-80, columnist, 1981-85; assoc. editor, columnist Newsday, 1986—. Served with AUS, 1956-58. Recipient Page One award for fgn. reporting Newspaper Guild N.Y., 1972; George Polk Meml. award for fgn. reporting, 1972; spl. award for coverage fall of Phnom Penh, 1975; Overseas Press Club award for fgn. reporting, 1972; for fgn. photography, 1974; Bob Considine Meml. award, 1975; Pulitzer prize, 1975; Front Page award Newspaper Guild; Sigma Delta Chi award for disting. service in journalism. Office: Newsday Inc 2 Park Ave New York NY 10016-5603

SCHANFARBER, RICHARD CARL, real estate broker; b. Cleve., June 11, 1937; s. Edwin David and Helen (Newman) S.; m. Barbara A. Berger, Dec. 21, 1958 (div. Sept. 1981); children: Edwin Jeffrey, Lori Jo, Tammy Joy. Grad., NYU, 1959. Cert. profl. standards insttr.; cert. energy instr.; cert. tchr. Ohio; lic. FCC broadcasters; lic. gun dealer. Pres. Erieview Realty Inc., Gates Mills, 1961—, Miller Warehouse, Gates Mills, 1968—, ERI Travel Co., Gates Mills, 1974—, ERI Sales Co., Gates Mills, 1979—; ptnr. Landwood Assocs. Ltd., Gates Mills, 1986—; pres. Eastgate Travel Svcs., Gates Mills, Ohio, 1987—. Pres. Shaker Hts. (Ohio) Alumni Assn., 1986—, Cleve. Area Bd. Realtors, 1981, Cleve. Warehouseman Assn., 1977-79; chmn. City of Cleve. Landmarks Commn., 1984—. Mem. NRA (life), Nat. Assn. Realtors, Ohio Assn. Realtors, Ohio Hist. Soc., Cleve. Growth Assn., Cleve. Area Bd. Realtors, Cleve. Zool. Soc., Cleve. Mus. Art, Corpus Christi Aquarium Soc., U.S.S. Lexington Mus. on the Bay, Friends Landmark Commn., Early Settlers Assn., Blossom Musical Soc., Mayfield Twp. Hist. Soc., Ashtabula Hist. Soc., We. Res. Hist. Soc. Republican. Jewish. Avocations: woodworking, gun collecting, coin collecting, antiques, travel. Office: Erieview Realty Inc 6719 Sandalwood Dr Gates Mills OH 44040

SCHANFIELD, MOSES SAMUEL, geneticist, educator; b. Mpls., Sept. 7, 1944; s. Abraham and Fannie (Schwartz) S.; m. Nancy Bergren. BA in Anthropology, U. Minn., 1966; AM in Anthropology, Harvard U., 1969; PhD in Human Genetics, U. Mich., 1971. Postdoctoral fellow in immunology U. Calif. Med. Ctr., San Francisco, 1971-74, rsch. geneticist, 1974-75; head of blood bank Milw. Blood Ctr., 1975-78; adj. dir. ARC, Washington, 1978-83; exec. dir. Genetic Testing Inst., Atlanta, 1983-85; lab. dir. Analytical Genetic Testing Ctr., Atlanta and Denver, 1985—; adj. asst. prof. Med. Coll. Wis., Milw., 1976-78; adj. assoc. prof. George Washington U., Washington, 1979-83, Emory U., Atlanta, 1984-89; adj. assoc. prof. Univ. Kans., 1992—; affiliated faculty Colo. State Univ., Fort Collins, 1992—. Author, editor: Immunobiology of the Erythrocyte, 1980; contbg. author: Immunogenetic Factors and Thalassaemia of Hepatitis, 1975; contbr. articles to profl. publs. Recipient Gold medal Latin Am. Congress Hemotherapy and Immunohematology, 1979, R&D 100 award, 1993. Fellow Am. Acad. Forensic Sci.; mem. Am. Soc. Crime Lab. Dirs., Am. Soc. Human Genetics, Human Biology Coun., Phi Kappa Phi. Achievements include discovery of the biological function of GC protein as vitamin D transport protein, of 2 sources of errors in DNA sizings. Office: Analytical Genetic Testing Ctr # 201 7808 Cherry Crk South Dr Denver CO 80231-3218

SCHANK, ROGER CARL, computer science and psychology educator; b. N.Y.C., Mar. 12, 1946; s. Maxwell and Margaret (Rosenberg) S.; m. Diane Levine, Mar. 22, 1970; children: Hana, Joshua. B.S., Carnegie Inst. Tech., 1966; M.A., U. Tex., 1967, Ph.D., 1969; M.A. (hon.), Yale U., 1976. Asst. prof. linguistics and computer sci. Stanford (Calif.) U., 1968-74; rsch. fellow Inst. Semantics and Cognition, Castagnola, Switzerland, 1973-74; assoc. prof. computer sci. Yale U., New Haven, Conn., 1974-76, prof. computer sci. and psychology, 1976-89, chmn. dept. computer sci., 1980-85; John Evans prof. elec. engring. and computer sci., psychology and edn., dir. Inst. for Learning Scis. Northwestern U., Evanston, Ill., 1989—; pres. chmn. bd. Cognitive Sys., Inc., New Haven, 1981-88; pres., chmn. Computeach, Inc., 1982-88; pres. Learning Scis. Corp., 1995—. Author: Conceptual Information Processing, 1975, Dynamic Memory, 1982, (with others) Scripts, Plans, Goals and Understanding, 1977, Cognitive Computer, 1984, Explanation Patterns, 1986, The Creative Attitude, 1988, Tell Me A Story, 1990, The Connoisseur's Guide to the Mind, 1991, Engines for Education, 1995; editor Cognitive Sci. Jour.; inventor computer programs. Mem. Cognitive Sci. Soc. (founder). Office: Northwestern U Inst Learning Scis 1890 Maple Ave Evanston IL 60201

SCHANNEP, JOHN DWIGHT, brokerage firm executive; b. Newport News, Va., May 23, 1934; s. Dwight Bahney and Harriet Louise (Quinn) S.; m. Helen Ann Harris, June 21, 1958; children: John Barton, Dwight David, Timothy Michael, Marie Louise. BS, U.S. Mil. Acad., 1956. Commd. 1st lt. U.S. Air Force, 1956; resigned, 1960; account exec. Dean Witter Reynolds, Phoenix, 1960-68, v.p., resident mgr., Tucson, 1968-83, sr. v.p., 1983-89, ret.; pres. Tucson Stock/Bond Club, 1971-72; bd. dirs. SNEDCO. Author, pub. Schannep Timing Indicator Quar. Letter, 1980—. Pres. Big Bros. Tucson, 1972-74. Mem. Nat. Assn. Security Dealers (Ariz. committeeman and chmn. 1971-73), Tucson C. of C. (v.p. 1971), Pinetop Lakes Golf and Country Club (treas. 1990-91, pres. 1991-93), West Point Soc. (pres. 1967), Lions (pres. Phoenix chpt. 1966). Republican. Episcopalian. Home: 5191 E Hill Place Dr Tucson AZ 85712-1346 Office: Dean Witter Reynolds 7070 N Oracle Rd Ste 100 Tucson AZ 85740-8000

SCHAPERY, RICHARD ALLAN, engineering educator; b. Duluth, Minn., Mar. 3, 1935; s. Aaron and Nellie (Slovut) S.; m. Mable Etta Burns, June 14, 1957; 1 child, Phillip Randal. BS in Mech. Engring. with high distinction, Wayne State U., 1957; MS, Calif. Inst. Tech., 1958, PhD in Aeros, 1962. Mem. faculty Purdue U., Lafayette, Ind., 1962-69; prof. civil and aerospace engring. Tex. A.&M. U., College Station, 1969-80, Disting. prof., 1980-90, Alumni prof., 1980-85, TEES chair, 1985-89, R.P. Gregory chair, 1989-90; dir. Mechanics and Materials Center, 1972-90; The Cockrell Family Regents

chair in engring., prof. U. Tex., Austin, 1990—; Cons. industry, govt. Contbr. to profl. jours. and books. Gen. Motors Corp. fellow, Woodrow Wilson fellow, Douglas Aircraft fellow; Purdue XL grantee; recipient machinery's award for design; Disting. Achievement award for research Tex. A. and M. U., Disting. Engring. Alumni award Wayne State U., 1992. Mem. AIAA, Am. Ceramic Soc., Sigma Xi, Omicron Delta Kappa, Tau Beta Pi. Home: 7133 Valburn Dr Austin TX 78731-1812 Office: U Tex Dept Aerospace/Mechanics Engring Austin TX 78712

SCHAPIRO, DONALD, lawyer; b. N.Y.C., Aug. 8, 1925; s. John Max and Lydia (Chaitkin) S.; m. Ruth Ellen Goldman, June 29, 1952 (dec. Aug. 1991); m. Linda N. Solomon, Oct. 10, 1993; children: Jane G., Robert A. A.B., Yale U., 1944, LL.B., 1949. Bar: N.Y. 1949. Assoc. Paul, Weiss, Rifkind, Wharton & Garrison, N.Y.C., 1949-51; asst. chief counsel subcom. ways and means com. on adminstrn. revenue laws U.S. Ho. of Reps., Washington, 1951-52; assoc. Barrett, Smith, Schapiro, Simon & Armstrong, N.Y.C., 1952-55; partner Barrett, Smith, Schapiro, Simon & Armstrong, 1955-88; ptnr. Chadbourne & Parke, 1988—; vis. lectr. law Yale U. Law Sch., 1949-78, 94—; instr. law and econs., 1944-49. Mem. Order of Coif, Phi Beta Kappa, Phi Delta Phi. Home: 1035 5th Ave New York NY 10028-0135 Office: Chadbourne & Parke 30 Rockefeller Plz New York NY 10112-0001

SCHAPIRO, JEROME BENTLEY, chemical company executive; b. N.Y.C., Feb. 7, 1930; s. Sol and Claire (Rose) S.; B.Chem. Engring., Syracuse U., 1951; postgrad. Columbia U., 1951-52; m. Edith Irene Kravet, Dec. 27, 1953; children: Lois, Robert, Kenneth. Project engr. propellants br. U.S. Naval Air Rocket Test Sta., Lake Denmark, N.J., 1951-52; with Dixo Co., Inc., Rochelle Park, N.J., 1954—, pres., 1966—; lectr. detergent standards, drycleaning, care labeling, consumers standards, orgns., U.S., 1968—; U.S. del. spokesman on drycleaning Internat. Standards Orgn., Newton, Mass., 1971, Brussels, 1972, U.S. del. spokesman on dimensional stability of textiles, Paris, 1974, Ottawa, 1977, Copenhagen, 1981; chmn. U.S. del. com. on consumer affairs, Geneva, 1974, 75, 76, spokesman U.S. del. on textiles, Paris, 1974, mem. U.S. del. on care labeling of textiles, The Hague, Holland, 1974, U.S. del., chmn. del. council com. on consumer policy, Geneva, 1978, 79, 82, Israel, 1980, Paris, 1981; leader U.S. del. com. on dimensional stability of textiles, Manchester, Eng., 1984; fed. govtl. appointee to Industry Functional Adv. Com. on Standards, 1980-81; legal expert drycleaning techniques and procedures. Mem. Montclair (N.J.) Sch. Study Com., 1964-69; co-founder Jewish Focus, Inc., 1991, pub. Sullivan/Ulster Jewish Star. 2d lt. USAF, 1952-53. Fellow ASTM (chmn. com. D-12 Soaps and Detergents 1974-79, mem. standing com. on internat. standards 1980-84, hon. mem. award com. D-13, textiles) mem. AIChE, Am. Nat. Standards Inst. (vice chmn. bd. dirs., 1983-85, exec. com. 1979-81, 83-85, bd. dir. 1979-85, fin. com. 1982-85, chmn. consumer council 1976, 79, 80, 81, mem. steering com. to advise Dept. Commerce on implementation GATT agreements 1976-77, mem. exec. standards coun., 1977-79), internat. standards coun., chmn. internat. consumer policy adv. com. 1978-86), Am. Assn. Textile Chemists and Colorists (mem. exec. com. on rsch. 1974-77, chmn. com. on dry cleaning 1976-88, vice chmn. internat. test methods com.) Am. Chem. Soc., Standards Engring. Soc. (cert.), Internat. Standards Orgn. (mem. internat. standards steering com. for consumer affairs 1978-81), Nat. Small Bus. Assn. (assoc. trustee 1983-85), Jewish (v.p., treas. temple). Lodge: Masons. Home: PO Box 771 Wurtsboro NY 12790-0771 Office: 158 Central Ave PO Box 7038 Rochelle Park NJ 07662-4003

SCHAPIRO, MARY, federal agency administrator, lawyer; b. N.Y.C., June 19, 1955; d. Robert D. and Susan (Hall) S.; m. Charles A. Cadwell, Dec. 13, 1980. BA, Franklin and Marshall Coll., 1977; JD, George Washington U., 1980. Bar: D.C. 1980. Trial atty., 1980-81; counsel to chmn. Commodity Futures Trading Commn., 1981-84; gen. counsel Futures Industry Assn., 1984-88; commr. SEC, Washington, 1988-94; chmn. Commodity Futures Trading Commn. (CFTC), Washington, 1994—. Office: Commodity Future Trading Commn (CFTC) 2033 K St NW Ste 800 Washington DC 20581

SCHAPIRO, MEYER, retired art history educator; b. Shavly, Lithuania, Russia, Sept. 23, 1904; came to U.S., 1907, naturalized; 1914; s. Nathan M. and Fanny (Adelman) S.; m. Lillian Milgram, 1928; children: Miriam, Ernest. A.B., Columbia U., 1924, Ph.D., 1929. Lectr. dept. fine arts and archaeology Columbia U., 1928-36, asst. prof., 1936-46, assoc. prof., 1946-52, prof. art history, 1952-65; Univ. prof. Columbia, 1965-73; prof. emeritus Columbia U., 1973—; Norton prof. Harvard, 1966-67; Slade prof. Oxford U., 1968; lectr. Inst. Fine Arts, N.Y. U., 1932-36, New Sch. Social Rsch., 1938-52, Warburg Inst. (London U.), 1947, 57, Collège de France, Paris, 1974, Cornell. U., Ind. U.; fellow Ctr. for Advanced Study in Behavioral Scis., Stanford, 1962-63. Author articles and books on medieval, modern art; mem. bd. editors: Semiotica, Dissent, Jour. History of Ideas; works of art exhibited 1919-79, Wallach Art Gallery, Columbia U., 1987. Decorated comdt. de l'Ordre des Arts et des Lettres France; recipient award for disting. scholarship in humanities Am. Council Learned Socs., 1960, ann. creative art award for notable achievement Brandeis U., 1966, award for excellence in art history Art Dealers Assn. Am., 1973, Mitchell award, 1980; Aby M. Warburg prize, Hamburg, 1985; Guggenheim fellow, 1939, 1942; MacArthur Found. fellow, 1987. Fellow Am. Acad. Arts and Scis., Am. Philos. Soc., Medieval Acad. Am., Am. Inst. Arts and Letters, Brit. Acad. Address: RR 1 Box 92 South Londonderry VT 05155-9601

SCHAPIRO, MIRIAM, artist; b. Toronto, Ont., Can., Nov. 15, 1923; d. Theodore and Fannie (Cohen) S. BA, State U. Iowa, 1945, MA, 1946, MFA, 1949; hon. doctorate, Wooster Coll., 1983, Calif. Coll. Arts and Crafts, 1989, Mpls. Coll. Art and Design, 1994, Miami U., 1995. co-orginator Womanhouse, Los Angeles, 1972, Heresies mag., N.Y.C., 1975; co-originator feminist art program Calif. Inst. Arts, Valencia, 1971; founding mem. Feminist Art Inst., N.Y.C.; mem. adv. bd. Women's Caucus for Art; assoc. mem. Heresies Collective; lectr. dept. art history U. Mich., 1987. Works in numerous books and catalogues; numerous one-woman shows including, Galerie Liatowitsch, Basel, Switzerland, 1979, Lerner Heller Gallery, N.Y.C., 1979, Barbara Gladstone Gallery, N.Y.C., 1980, Spencer Mus. Art, Lawrence, Kans., 1981, Everson Mus., Syracuse, N.Y., 1981, Galerie Rudolf Zwirner, Cologne, Fed. Republic Germany, 1981, Staatagalerie, Stuttgart, Fed. Republic Germany, 1983, Dart Gallery, Chgo, 1984, Bernice Steinbaum Gallery/Steinbaum Krauss Gallery, N.Y.C., 1986, 88, 90, 91, 94, Brevard Art Ctr. and Mus., Melbourne, Fla., 1991, Guild Hall Mus., East Hampton, N.Y., 1992, ARC Gallery, Chgo., 1993, others; retrospective exhbn., Wooster (Ohio) Coll. Art Mus., 1980; exhibited in numerous group shows, including, Palais de Beaux Arts, Brussels, 1979, Inst. Contemporary Art, Phila., 1979, Delahunty Gallery, Dallas, 1980, Indpls. Mus., 1980, Va. Mus., Richmond, 1980, Laguna Gloria Mus., Austin, Tex., 1980, R.O.S.C., Dublin, Ireland, 1980, Biennale of Sydney, Australia, 1982, Zurich, Switzerland, 1983, Sidney Janis Gallery, N.Y.C., 1984, Am. Acad. Arts and Letters, N.Y.C., 1985, Mus. Modern Art, N.Y.C., 1988, Whyte Mus. Can. Rockies, Banff, Alta., 1991, Nat. Mus. Women in Arts., Wash., 1993, Jane Voorhees Zimmerli art mus. Rutger's U., New Brunswick, N.J., 1994, Mus. of F.A. Boston, 1994, Santa Barbara Mus. of Art, 1994, Hudson River Mus. of Westchester, Yonkers, N.Y., 1995, Bronx Mus. of the Arts, N.Y., 1995; represented in permanent collections, Hirshhorn Mus., Washington, Bklyn. Mus., Met. Mus. Art, N.Y.C., Mus. Contemporary Art, San Diego, Mpls. Inst. Art, Mulvane Art Center, Topeka, Nat. Gallery Art, Washington, N.Y.U., Peter Ludwig Collection, Aachen, Germany, Stanford U., Palo Alto, Calif., Univ. Art Mus., Berkeley, Calif., Whitney Mus., N.Y.C., Worcester (Mass.) Art Mus., also others; author: (books) Women and the Creative Process, 1974, Rondo: An Artists Book, 1988; sculpture Anna and David, Rosslyn, Va., 1987. Guggenheim fellow, 1987, Nat. Endowment for Arts fellow; grantee Ford Found.; recipient numerous other grants and fellowships. Mem. Coll. Art Assn. (past dir.). Address: Steinbaum Krauss Gallery 132 Greene St New York NY 10012-3242 *Process and ideology in an opulent, multilayered, eccentric and hopeful abstract art: 1. The need for order and stability 2. The need to destroy order and stability in order to find something else. 3. Finding something else. Pattern, itself an architectural species, reflects order and stability. Then a need to create chaos as though life itself were taking place. Finally the bonding layer by layer, the interpenetration of paint, fabric, photograph, tea towel, ribbon, lace, and glue. A collage: a simultaneity; a visual dazzlement, a multi-layering, a final message for the senses. And the ideology which inspires the work itself? That is feminism, the wish to have the art speak as a woman speaks. To be sensitive to the material used as though there were a responsibility to history*

to repair the sense of omission and to have each substance in the collage be a reminder of a woman's dreams.

SCHAPIRO, MORRIS A., investment banker; b. Lithuania, Apr. 9, 1903; came to U.S., 1907, naturalized, 1914; s. Nathan M. and Fanny (Adelman) S.; m. Alma Binion Cahn, Mar. 28, 1929; children: Linda S. Collins, Daniel E. BA, Columbia U., 1923, Engr. Mines, 1925, LLD (hon.), 1987. Engr. geologist Am. Metal Co., 1925-27; bank analyst Hoit, Rose & Troster, 1928-31; ptnr. Monahan, Schapiro & Co., 1931-39; chmn. bd. dirs., CEO M.A. Schapiro & Co., Inc., N.Y.C., 1939—; pres. SD Securities, N.Y.C., 1944—; chmn. adv. com. N.Y. State Joint Legis. Com. to Revise Banking Law, 1957-60. Contbr. articles on banking to profl. jours. Mem. Am. Inst. Mining and Metall. Engrs., N.Y. Soc. Security Analysts, Securities Industry Assn. Home: 910 Fifth Ave New York NY 10021-4155 Office: M A Schapiro & Co Inc 1 Chase Manhattan Plz New York NY 10005-1436 also: S D Securities Inc 1 Chase Manhattan Plz New York NY 10005-1401

SCHAPP, REBECCA MARIA, museum director; b. Stuttgart, Fed. Republic Germany, Dec. 12, 1956; came to U.S., 1957; d. Randall Todd and Elfriede Carolina (Scheppan) Spradlin; m. Thomas James Schapp, May 29, 1979. AA, DeAnza Coll., 1977; BBT, BA in Art, San Jose State U., 1979, MA in Art Adminstrn., 1985. Adminstrv. dir. Union Gallery, San Jose, Calif. 1979-82; mus. coordinator de Saisset Mus. Santa Clara (Calif.) U., 1982-86, asst. dir., 1984, acting dir., 1986-87, asst. dir., 1987-89, dep. dir., 1989-92, dir., 1993—. Mem. San Francisco Mus. Modern Art; bd. dirs. Works of San Jose, v.p. 1983-85. Mem. Non-Profit Gallery Assn. (bd. dirs.). Democrat. Avocations: racquetball, Jazzercise, bicycling, camping. Office: De Saisset Museum Santa Clara Univ 500 El Camino Real Santa Clara CA 95053

SCHAPPELL, LOLA IRENE HILL, school system administrator; b. Rochester, N.Y., Feb. 17, 1940; d. Harrison Albert and Bertha May (McIntyle) Hill; m. Kerry W. Washburn, June 11, 1960 (div. Oct. 1968); children: Yvonne Marie Washburn White, Valerie Lee Washburn Anderson; m. Robert Nathaniel Schappell, Dec. 18, 1976. BS in Elem. Edn., SUNY, Brockport, 1962; MS in Edn., Purdue U., 1969; EdD, U. Mass., 1972. Cert. tchr., N.Y., N.C.; curriculum specialist, adminstr., N.C. Ednl. psychologist Belchertown (Mass.) Sch. for Mentally Retarded, 1970-71; dir. reading Albion (N.Y.) Cen. Schs., 1972-73, Mexico (N.Y.) Cen. Schs., 1973-75; asst. prof. Fed. City Coll., Washington, 1975-76; curriculum specialist/reading Charlotte (N.C.)-Mecklenburg Schs., 1976-78, program specialist, 1978-81, asst. prin., 1981-84, elem. prin., 1984-88; elem. prin. Greensboro (N.C.) Pub. Schs., 1988-91, coord. spl. projects and grants, 1991-93; mem. adv. bd. Gethsemane Enrichment Ctr., Charlotte, 1984-88; bd. dirs. Am. Field Svc., Attica, N.Y., 1964-67, N.Y. Baha'i Dist. Teaching Com., Mexico, 1973-75; exec. dir. GPS Excellence Fund, Greensboro, 1991-93; mem. Nat. Baha'i Edn. Task Force, 1995—; speaker in field. Prin. creator acceleration/enrichment program. Participant Guildford Women for Race Rels., Greensboro, 1991-92, Race Rels. Forum, Greensboro, 1992; resource developer Black Child Devel., Greensboro, 1992. Mem. AAUW, ASCD, Phi Delta Kappa. Mem. Baha'i Faith. Avocations: water skiing, swimming, walking, gardening, reading. Home: 401 Chancery Park Ct Kernersville NC 27284-8338 Office: Guilford Co Pub Schs 701 Eugene St Greensboro NC 27401

SCHAR, DWIGHT C., construction company executive; b. 1942. With Ryan Homes, Washington, 1986-77, NVLand, 1977—; with NVR L P, 1980-86, chmn. bd. CEO, 1986—; bd. dirs. NVCompanies Inc. Office: NVR L P 7601 Lewinsville Rd Mc Lean VA 22102-2806

SCHARF, LINDA MARGARET, nursing administrator; b. Buffalo, Sept. 30, 1945; d. Oscar and Winfred (Rohr) Dabritz; m. Harvey Scharf, Aug. 20, 1970; children: Michael, Rebecca. BSN, SUNY, Buffalo, 1967, MS, 1976, postgrad., 1987—. RN, N.Y. In-svc. coord. Millard Fillmore Hosp., Buffalo, asst. dir. nursing; asst. adminstrv. nurse Millard Fillmore Hosps., Williamsville, N.Y.; v.p. nursing Millard Fillmore Suburban Hosp., Williamsville. Anne W. Sengbusch award, 1940; Am. Legion scholar. Mem. Am. Orgn. Nurse Execs., ANA, Sigma Theta Tau.

SCHARF, WILLIAM, artist; b. Media, Pa., Feb. 22, 1927; s. Lester William and Ebba (Anderson) S.; m. Diana Denny, Mar. 11, 1947 (div. 1951); 1 child, William Denny; m. Sally Kravitch, Mar. 25, 1956; 1 child, Aaron Anderson. Student, Barnes Found., 1946-47; cert. in painting, Pa. Acad. of Fine Arts, 1947. Instr. Mus. Modern Art, N.Y.C., 1964, Sch. Visual Arts, N.Y.C., 1965-73, San Francisco Inst. Fine Arts, 1963, 66, 69, 74, 89. One-man shows include David Herbert Gallery, N.Y.C., 1960, 1962, San Francisco Inst. Fine Arts, 1969, Neuberger Mus., Purchase, N.Y., 1976, High Mus., Atlanta, 1978, Armstrong Gallery, N.Y.C., 1987, U. Mich. Mus. Art, Ann Arbor, 1993; exhibited in group shows at Guggenheim Mus., N.Y.C., 1982, Hirschl-Adler Gallery, N.Y.Y., 1980, Smith-Anderson Gallery, Palo Alto, Calif., Nat. Mus. Am. Art, Washington, 1987, 91, 92, American Acad. and Inst. Arts and Letters, N.Y.C., 1989, 91; represented in permanent collections Boston Inst. Contemporary Art, Bklyn. Mus., Solomon R. Guggenheim Mus., N.Y.C., Newark Mus., Nat. Mus. Am. Art, Smith Coll. Mus., Northampton, Mass., Zimmerli Mus., Rutgers U., New Brunswick, N.J., U. Mich. Mus. Art, Phillips Collection, Washington. Trustee Rothko Found., N.Y.C., 1979-87; instr. Art Student's League, N.Y., 1987-94. With USAF, 1945-46. Emmlen Cresson fellow Pa. Acad. Fine Arts, 1948. Mem. Artist Equity Assn., Soc. of Illustrators.

SCHARF, WILLIAM, film editor. Editor: (films) The Prince of Pennsylvania, 1988; (with Stephen A. Rotter) Dirty Rotten Scoundrels, 1988, An Innocent Man, 1989, Rising Son, 1993, Cops and Robbersons, 1994; (with Dede Allen and Vivien Hillgrove Gilliam) Henry & June, 1990. Office: Broder Kurland Webb Uffner Agency 9242 Beverly Blvd Ste 200 Beverly Hills CA 90210*

SCHARFENBERG, DORIS ANN See DORIS ANN

SCHARFF, JOSEPH LAURENT, lawyer; b. New Orleans, Oct. 2, 1935; s. Joseph Roy and Celia Ray (Rosenhein) S.; m. Mary Susan Greulach, June 29, 1963; children: Catherine Elizabeth, Robert Laurent, Anne Victoria. BS in Journalism, Northwestern U., 1957; JD, Harvard U., 1964. Bar: D.C. 1965, U.S. Supreme Ct. 1970, U.S. Ct. Appeals (D.C. cir.) 1965, U.S. Ct. Appeals (2nd cir.) 1980, U.S. Ct. Appeals (5th cir.) 1973, U.S. Ct. Appeals (10th cir.); U.S. Ct. Claims 1965. From assoc. to ptnr. Pierson, Ball & Dowd, Washington, 1964-89; ptnr. Reed Smith Shaw & McClay, Washington, 1989—; mem. adv. bd. Inst. Communications Law Studies Catholic U. Mem. ABA (fair trial-free press com. 1973-76, com. reps. media 1985, co-chmn. 1989-92), Fed. Comm. Bar Assn., Soc. Profl. Journalists, Radio-TV Dirs Assn. (counsel 1965—), Disting. Svc. award 1987). Home: 12000 Turf Ln Reston VA 22091-2123 Office: Reed Smith Shaw & McClay 1200 18th St NW Washington DC 20036-2506

SCHARFF, MATTHEW DANIEL, immunologist, cell biologist, educator; b. N.Y.C., Aug. 28, 1932; s. Harry and Constance S.; m. Carol Held, Dec. 19, 1954; children—Karen, Thomas, David. A.B., Brown U., 1954, DMS (hon.), 1994; M.D., N.Y.U., 1959. House officer II and IV med. service Boston City Hosp., 1959-61; research asso. NIH, 1961-63; asst. prof. Albert Einstein Coll. Medicine, Yeshiva U., Bronx, N.Y., 1963-67; asso. prof. Albert Einstein Coll. Medicine, Yeshiva U., 1967-71; prof. dept. cell biology, 1971—; chmn. dept., 1972-83, dir. div. biol. scis., 1975-81; asso. dir. Cancer Center, 1975-86, dir., 1986—. Served with USPHS, 1961-63. Recipient Alumni Achievement award NYU Sch. Medicine, 1980, N.Y. Acad. Medicine medal, 1990, Commemorative award Albert Einstein Coll. Medicine, 1993. Mem. Am. Assn. Immunologists, Am. Soc. Clin. Investigation, Nat. Acad. Scis., Am. Acad. Arts and Sci., Phi Beta Kappa, Sigma Xi, Alpha Omega Alpha. Office: Albert Einstein Coll Med Cancer Ctr 1300 Morris Park Ave Bronx NY 10461-1975

SCHARLAU, CHARLES EDWARD, III, natural gas company executive; b. Chgo., Apr. 24, 1927; s. Charles Edward II and Esther (Powell) S.; m. Clydene Yvonne Sloop, Aug. 13, 1960; children: Caryn, Robin, Greg, Charles, Marti. LLB, U. Ark., 1951. Bar: Ark. 1951, U.S. Dist. Ct. (western dist.) Ark. 1951, U.S. Supreme Ct. 1958. Atty. Ark. Western Gas Co., Fayetteville, 1951-61, v.p., 1961-68, pres., 1968-78; pres., chmn. S.W. Energy Co., Fayetteville, 1978—; bd. dirs. C.H. Heist Co., Clearwater, Fla., McIlroy

Bank and Trust Co., Fayetteville. Chmn. U. Ark. Devel. Coun., 1989—. With USMC, 1945-46. Mem. ABA, Ark. Bar Assn., So. Gas Assn., Nat. Assn. Mfrs. (bd. dirs. 1986-89), Am. Gas Assn. (bd. dirs. 1987-90), U. Ark. Alumni Assn. (pres. 1972-73), Ark. C. of C. (pres. 1977-79), Beta Gamma Sigma. Methodist. Avocations: reading, tennis, canoeing, sports. Home: 1506 Sunset Pl Fayetteville AR 72701-1627 Office: Ark Western Gas Co 1001 Sain St Fayetteville AR 72703

SCHARLEMANN, ROBERT PAUL, religious studies educator, clergyman; b. Lake City, Minn., Apr. 4, 1929; s. Ernst Karl and Johanna Meta (Harre) S. Student, Northwestern Coll., Watertown, Wis., 1946-49; B.A., Concordia Coll. and Sem., St. Louis, 1952; B.D., Concordia Coll. and Sem., 1955; Dr. theol., U. Heidelberg (Germany), 1957. Ordained to ministry, Lutheran Ch., 1960. Instr. philosophy Valparaiso U., 1957-59; postdoctoral fellow Yale U., 1959-60; pastor Bethlehem Luth. Ch., Carlyle, Ill., 1960-62, Grace Luth. Ch., Durham, N.C., 1962-63; asst. prof. religion U. So. Calif., 1963-64, assoc. prof., 1964-66; assoc. prof. religion U. Iowa, Iowa City, 1966-68, prof., 1968-81; Commonwealth prof. religious studies U. Va., Charlottesville, 1981—; Fulbright-Hayes prof. U. Heidelberg, 1975-76. Author: Thomas Aquinas and John Gerhard, 1964, Reflection and Doubt in the Thought of Paul Tillich, 1969, The Being of God, 1981, Inscriptions and Reflections, 1989, The Reason of Following, 1991; editor Jour. of Am. Acad. Religion, 1980-85; contbr. articles to profl. jours. Mem. Am. Acad. Religion, Am. Theol. Soc., Société Européenne de Culture, Soc. for Philosophy of Religion. Office: Dept of Religious Studies University of Virginia Charlottesville VA 22903

SCHARP, ANDERS, manufacturing company executive; b. Stockholm, June 8, 1934; married. MEngring, Royal Inst. Tech., Stockholm, 1960. Head refrigeration lab. Elektro Helios, 1960-69; v.p. prodn. AB Electrolux, Stockholm, 1969-74, exec. v.p. prodn. and R&D, 1974-81; pres. AB Electrolux, Cleve., 1981-86; pres., CEO AB Electrolux, 1986-91, chmn., CEO, 1991—; chmn. Saab-Scania AB, Linkoping, Sweden, 1990—, AB SKF, Gothenburg, Sweden, 1992—, Incentive AB, Stockholm, 1992—; vice chmn. Investor AB, 1992—, Atlas Copco AB, 1992—; bd. dirs. Email Ltd., Australia. Mem. Royal Swedish Acad. Engring., Swedish Employers Confedn. (bd. dirs.), Assn. Swedish Engring. Industries (bd. dirs.), Fedn. Swedish Industries (bd. dirs.). Office: Electrolux AB, Lilla Essingen, S-105 45 Stockholm Sweden also: White Consol Industries Inc 11770 Berea Rd Cleveland OH 44111-1601*

SCHARP-RADOVIC, CAROL ANN, choreographer, classical ballet educator, artistic director; b. Ypsilanti, Mich., Aug. 9, 1940; d. John Lewis and Mary Vivien (Alther) Keeney; m. Jack Laurel Scharp, July 28, 1958 (div. July 1970); children: Kathryn E., Mark A.; m. Srecko Radovic, Nov. 15, 1989. Studied with Pereslavic, Danilova; student, Harkness Ballet, N.Y.C., Joffrey Ballet, N.Y.C., Eglevsky Ballet, N.Y.C., Briansky Ballet, Darvesh Ballet, N.Y.C.; studied with Jurgen Schneider, Am. Ballet Theatre, 1983-93; studied with Janina Cunova, Luba Gulyeava, Australian Ballet Co., 1983-93; studied with Ninel Kurgapkina, Ludmila Synelnikova, Genhrich Mayorov, Kirov Ballet, 1987-89; studied with Ludmila Sakharova, Perm Ballet, 1993; studied with Ludmila Synelnikova, Bolshoi Ballet Sch., Moscow, 1989; studied with Inna Zubkhovskaya, Alex. Stiopin, Lydia Goncharova, Valentina Chistova, Mararita Zagurskaya, Valentina Rumyantsema, Kirov Ballet Sch., St. Petersburg, Russia, 1993. Ballet mistress Adrian (Mich.) Coll., 1982-84; founder, dir. Ann Arbor (Mich.) Ballet Theatre, 1980—; former regional field judge Nat. Ballet Achievement Fund; dir. seminars Marygrove Coll., Detroit. Choreographer Cinderella, 1980, Nightingale, 1980, Nutcracker, 1984, Carnival of the Animals, 1981, Carmen, 1983, Midsummer Nights Dream, 1982, Vivaldi's Spring, 1990, Opulence, 1984, La Boutique Fontasque, 1995 and others. Recipient Ruth Matt grant for choreography, 1982. Mem. Mich. Dance Assn. Avocations: gardening, reading, writing. Office: CAS Ballet Theatre Sch 548 Church St Ann Arbor MI 48104-2514

SCHARRER, BERTA VOGEL, anatomy and neuroscience educator; b. Munich, Dec. 1, 1906; d. Karl and Johanna V.; widowed. PhD in Zoology, U. Munich, 1930; MD (hon.), U. Giessen, Germany, 1976, U. Frankfurt, Germany, 1992; DSc (hon.), Northwestern U., 1977, U. N.C., 1978, Smith Coll., 1980, Harvard U., 1982, Yeshiva U., 1983, Mt. Holyoke Coll., 1984, SUNY, 1985, U. Salzburg, Austria, 1988; LLD, U. Calgary, Alta., Can., 1982. Research assoc. Research Inst. for Psychiatry, Munich, 1931-34, Neurol. Inst., Frankfurt-am-Main, 1934-37, U. Chgo. Dept. Anatomy, 1937-38, Rockefeller Inst., N.Y.C., 1938-40; instr., fellow Western Res. U. Dept. Anatomy, Cleve., 1940-46; John Guggenheim fellow U. Colo. Dept. Anatomy, Denver, 1947-48, spl. USPHS research fellow, 1948-50; asst. prof. (research) dept. anatomy U. Colo. Sch. Medicine, Denver, 1950-55; prof. anatomy Albert Einstein Coll. Medicine, 1955-77, acting chmn., 1965-67, 76-77, disting. prof. emeritus anatomy and neurosci., 1978—. Decorated Order of Merit (Free State of Bavaria); recipient Kraepelin gold medal, 1978, F.C. Koch award Endocrine Soc., 1980, Nat. Medal Sci., 1983. Mem. NAS, Am. Acad. Arts and Scis., Deutsche Acad. Naturforscher Leopoldina (Schleiden medal 1983), Am. Assn. Anatomists (pres. 1978-79, Henry Gray award 1982), Am. Soc. Zoologists (hon. mem.), Soc. Neurosci., Endocrine Soc. (F.C. Koch award 1980). Achievements include rsch. in comparative neuroendocrinology, neurosecretion, neuroimmunology, neuropeptides. Home: 1240 Neill Ave Bronx NY 10461-1736 Office: Albert Einstein Coll Med Dept Anatomy 1300 Morris Park Ave Bronx NY 10461-1975

SCHARUDA, VICTORIA, lawyer; b. Vineland, N.J., Aug. 3, 1967; d. Victor Scharuda and Elizabeth (Repin) Bennett. BA in History, Ursinus Coll., 1989; JD, Temple U., 1992. Bar: Ga. 1993. Corp. counsel Wells Fargo Armored Svc. Corp., Atlanta, 1993—. Active 1000 Lawyers for Justice, Atlanta, 1993. Recipient James D. Mandarino award Phila. Trial Lawyers Assn., 1992. Mem. NAFE. Avocations: painting, reading, crotcheting, football, softball. Office: Wells Fargo Armored Svc Corp 6165 Barfield Rd Ste 200 Atlanta GA 30328

SCHARY, EMANUEL, artist; b. Feb. 27, 1924; s. Harold and Aliza S.; m. Judith Schary, Sept. 23, 1951; children: Abby, David, Anne. Student, Carnegie Inst. Tech. Sch. Fine Arts, 1945-46, Art Students League, 1946-49, Pratt Graphics Ctr., 1962-63, Edwin Dickenson, Howard Trafton, Frank Reilly, Ivan Olinsky, Robert Hale, Jurgen Fischer. One-man shows, Guild Gallery, N.Y.C., 1978, 80, 81, group shows, Tel Aviv, Kean Coll., Bklyn. Mus., Kansas City Country Club Plaza, Mo., U. Mich., U. Miami, Fla., Nassau Community Coll., Lenox Square Art Festival, Ga., Guild Gallery, N.Y.; represented in permanent collections, Smithsonian Nat. Fine Art Collection, Met. Mus. Fine Art, N.Y., Vatican Mus., Rome, Bklyn Mus., Jewish Mus., N.Y.C., Spertus Mus., Chgo., Madison Art Mus., Wis., Fleming Mus., Vt., Wyo. Art Mus., Laramie, B'nai B'rith Mus., Washington, Mus. of Israel, Jerusalem, Mus. of Haifa, Israel, Bldg. of Chief Rabbinate, Jerusalem, New Britain Mus. Am. Art, Ind. Mus. Am. Art, Ga. Mus. Art, Hofstra U. Mus., Boston Pub. Library, N.Y. Pub. Library, Newark Pub. Library, U. Ariz. Art Mus., Kansas City Art Inst., Library of Congress, in pvt. collections, commns. include, N.Y. World's Fair Pavillion, Weizmann Inst. Sci., 1964; designed 4 stained glass painted windows for Synagogue, Rock Hill, N.Y., 1992, wood sculpture, 1993, Holocaust Meml., 1994. Address: 66 Nottingham Gate Rock Hill NY 12775

SCHATT, PAUL, newspaper editor; b. N.Y.C., Aug. 31, 1945; divorced; children: Suzannah, Andrew. BA with distinction Polit. Sci., English, Ariz. State U., 1967. Editor Ariz. Republic, 1964-66, reporter, 1965-74, urban affairs editor, 1974-75, asst. city editor, 1975-79, chief asst. city editor, 1979-82, asst. met. editor, 1985-86, met. editor, 1986-88, editor edit. pages, 1993—; asst. editor Ariz. Mag., 1981-82, editor, 1982-85; editor edit. pages Phoenix Gazette, 1988-93, The Ariz. Republic, 1993—; vis. lectr. Pub. Affairs Journalism, Ariz. State U., 1976—; instr. Mass. Comm. Dept., 1974-76; dir. Eugene C. Pulliam Fellowship. Phoenix program, 1990—; writing coach, 1989; del. Pre White House Conf. Librs., 1991. v.p. Crisis Nursery, 1984-87, bd. dirs. 1980-87; exec. bd. Hospice of the Valley, 1980-87; pres. Friends of Phoenix Pub. Libr., 1985-86, bd. dirs. 1986—; bd. trustees 1st Amendment Congress, 1989—; bd. dirs. Camelback Hosps. 1982-89, chmn. bd. dirs. 1986-87, Cactus Pine Coun. Girl Scouts Am., 1988-89, Sun Sounds Inc., 1982-89, Valley Leadership Inc., 1991—; alum. assn., 1985-89, Ariz. Zool. Soc., 1991—, Barrow Neurol. Found., 1991—, Kids Voting, 1991-93, Barry Goldwater Inst., 1991-93, Ariz. Club, 1991—. With Ariz. Nat. Guard, 1966-79. Recipient Montgomery award Outstanding Svc. to Community Friends of Phoenix Pub. Libr., 1989; profl. Journalism fellow Stanford U., 1970-71.

Mem. Am. Soc. Newspaper Editors, Soc. Profl. Journalists (pres. Valley of Sun chpt. 1974-75, 83-84, exec. bd. 1988-92), Sigma Delta Chi (co-chair nat. convention 1974). Office: The Ariz Republic Editorial Dept 120 E Van Buren St Phoenix AZ 85004-2227

SCHATTEN, GERALD PHILLIP, cell biologist, educator; b. N.Y.C., Nov. 1, 1949; s. Frank and Sylvia Schatten; m. Heather Aronson, July 4, 1994. BS, U. Calif., Berkeley, 1971, PhD, 1975. Instr. U. Calif., Berkeley, 1975; postdoctoral fellow Rockefeller Found., 1976-77; successively asst. prof., assoc. prof., prof. Fla. State U., Tallahassee, 1979-86; prof. molecular biology, zoology, and ob-gyn. U. Wis., Madison, 1986—, dir. integrated microscopy resource for biomed. rsch., 1986-92; dir. gamete and embryo biol. tng. program, U. Wis., Madison, 1998—. Recipient Rsch. Career Devel. award NIH, 1981-86. Office: Univ Wis 1117 W Johnson St Madison WI 53706-1705

SCHATZ, IRWIN JACOB, cardiologist; b. St. Boniface, Man., Can., Oct. 16, 1931; came to U.S., 1956, naturalized, 1966; s. Jacob and Reva S.; m. Barbara Jane Binder, Nov. 12, 1967; children: Jacob, Edward, Stephen and Brian (twins). Student, U. Man. (Can.), Winnipeg, 1951, M.D. with honors, 1956. Diplomate: Am. Bd. Internal Medicine. Intern Vancouver (B.C.) Gen. Hosp., 1955-56; resident Hammersmith Hosp., U. London, 1957, Mayo Clinic, Rochester, Minn., 1958-61; head sec. peripheral vascular disease Henry Ford Hosp., Detroit, 1961-68; asso. prof. medicine Wayne State U., 1968-71, chief sect. cardiovascular disease, 1969-71; assoc. prof., asso. dir. sect. cardiology U. Mich., 1972-73, prof. internal medicine, 1973-75; prof. medicine John A. Burns Sch. Medicine, U. Hawaii, 1975—, chmn. dept. medicine, 1975-90. Author: Orthostatic Hypotension, 1986; contbr. numerous articles to med. jours. Rockefeller Found. scholar, 1991. Fellow ACP (master, bd. govs. 1984-89, Laureate award Hawaii chpt. 1992), Am. Coll. Cardiology (bd. govs. 1980-84); mem. Am. Heart Assn. (fellow couns. cardiology and circulation), Am. Fedn. Clin. Rsch., Asian-Pacific Soc. Cardiology (v.p. 1987-91), Accreditation Coun. for Grad. Med. Edn. (chmn. residence rev. com. internal medicine), Assn. Profs. Medicine, Hawaii Heart Assn. (pres.), We. Assn. Physicians, Pacific Interurban Club. Jewish. Home: 4983 Kolohala St Honolulu HI 96816-5126 Office: 1356 Lusitana St Honolulu HI 96813-2427

SCHATZ, LILLIAN LEE, playwright, molecular biologist, educator; b. N.Y.C., Apr. 8, 1944; d. Joseph Louis and Rose (Zakalik) S. BA in Biology, SUNY, Buffalo, 1965, MA in Biology, 1970. Cert. h.s. tchr. biology, chemistry, gen. sci., N.Y., 1968. Rsch. asst. dept. biology SUNY at Buffalo, 1965-68, rsch. asst. dept. pharmacology Sch. Medicine, 1969; rsch. assoc. dept. biology SUNY, Buffalo, 1971-74; cancer rsch. scientist dept. viral oncology Roswell Park Meml. Inst., Buffalo, 1969-70; tchr. biology Kenmore East Sr. H.S., Buffalo, 1970-71; playwright Buffalo, 1976—; presenter workshop Rosa Coplon Jewish Home and Infirmary, Buffalo, N.Y., 1982, N.Y. State Community Theater Assn., 1982. Plays include Solomon's Court, 1979, Neshomah, 1983, Bernie, 1985, The Jonah Men, 1991; contbr. rsch. articles to sci. jours. Charter mem. B'not Israel Group Buffalo chpt. Hadassah, life mem. Recipient N.Y. State Regents Coll. Scholarship, 1961-65; semi-finalist Sergel Drama prize Ct. Theatre, U. Chgo., 1985, Nat. Play Award Competition Nat. Repertory Theatre Found., 1981; Playwriting fellow, N.Y. State Creative Artists Pub. Svc. fellow, 1980-81, Roswell Park Meml. Inst. fellow, 1962, Summer Sci. fellow. Democrat. Jewish. Avocations: art, genealogy. Home and Office: 31 Twyla Pl Buffalo NY 14223-1526

SCHATZ, PAUL FREDERICK, laboratory director; b. Cin., Aug. 24, 1944; s. Frederick Vincent and Nell (Sarles) S.; m. Eleanor Mae Smith, Aug. 19, 1967; children: Alexander, Christopher. BA, Colgate U., 1966; PhD in Chemistry, U. Wis., 1971. Lab. dir. U. Wis., Madison, 1971—. Author various computer programs. Mem. Am. Chem. Soc. Office: Univ Wis Dept Chemistry 1101 University Ave Madison WI 53706

SCHATZ, S. MICHAEL, lawyer; b. Hartford, Conn., May 28, 1921; s. Nathan Arthur and Dora (Goldberg) S.; m. Norma Hirshon, Oct. 28, 1945; children—Andrew M., Debra J., Nathan A., Donald N. A.B., Cornell U., 1941, LL.B., 1942. Bar: Conn. bar, N.Y. bar also U.S. Fed. Cts. and U.S. Treasury Dept. Assoc., jr. ptnr., then sr. ptnr. Schatz & Schatz, Ribicoff & Kotkin, Hartford, 1946—; gen. counsel Conn. Vet. Assn., Tobacco Distbrs. Assn. Conn., Conn. State Dental Assn., Outdoor Advt. Assn. Conn.; Dir. Sage-Allen & Co., Inc., Edward Balf Co., Hartford, Dunham-Bush, Inc., West Hartford, Conn. Bank and Trust Co., West Hartford, Atlantic Carton Corp., Norwich, Ripley Co., Inc., Middletown, Conn., Griese Advt. Co., West Hartford; partner B.L. McTeague & Co., Hartford. Editor-in-chief: Cornell Law Quar. Mem. council Cornell U., exec. com. Law Sch.; bd. dirs. Hartford chpt. ARC, 1960-62, U. Conn. Found., St. Francis Hosp. Assn., Conn. Dental Service, Inc., Friends of Sch. Dental Medicine, U. Conn.; corporate mem. Saint Francis Hosp., Hartford Pub. Library, Mt. Sinai Hosp., Hartford. Served to lt. USNR, 1942-46; mem. adv. bd. Cornell Law Sch.; vice chmn. U. Conn. Found.; mem. Devel. Com. Hartford Jewish Endowment Found. Mem. Am., N.Y. State, Hartford County bar assns., State Bar Assn. Conn. (pres. jr. bar sect. 1951, exec. com., asst. sec.-treas. 1956-57, sec. 1957-59), Cornell Law Assn. (pres.) Order of Coif, Phi Beta Kappa, Phi Kappa Phi. Home: 4 Hampton Pl Avon CT 06001-4554 Office: Schatz & Schatz, Ribicoff & Kotkin 90 State House Sq Hartford CT 06103-3702

SCHATZBERG, ALAN FREDERIC, psychiatrist, researcher; b. N.Y.C., Oct. 17, 1944; s. Emanuel and Cila (Diamand) S.; m. Nancy R. Silverman, Aug. 27, 1972; children: Melissa Ann, Lindsey Diamand. BS, NYU, 1965, MD, 1968; MA (hon.), Harvard U., 1989. Diplomate Nat. Bd. Med. Examiners, Am. Bd. Psychiatry and Neurology. Intern Lenox Hill Hosp., N.Y.C., 1968-69; resident in psychiatry Mass. Mental Health Ctr., Boston, 1969-72; clin. fellow in psychiatry Harvard Med. Sch., Boston, 1969-72, asst. prof. psychiatry, 1977-82, assoc. prof., 1982-88, prof., 1988-91; interim psychiatrist-in-chief McLean Hosp., Belmont, Mass., 1984-86; dir. depression rsch. facility, 1985—, vice chief, 1982-84, 86-88; psychiatrist adv. panel Eli Lilly & Co., Indpls., 1986-93; clin. dir. Mass. Mental Health Ctr., Boston, 1988-91; Kenneth T. Norris, Jr. prof. psychiatry and behavioral scis. Stanford U., 1991—; chmn. dept. psychiatry and behavioral scis. Sch. Medicine, 1991—; cons. AMA Videoclinics, Chgo., 1979-83; mem. AMA/FAA panel on health regulations, Chgo., 1984-86; mem. NIMH Biol. Psychopathology, 1991—, chmn., 1993-94. Co-author: Manual of Clinical Psychopharmacology, 1986, 2d edit., 1991; contbr. more than 170 articles, book chpts. to profl. publs.; co-editor: Depression: Biology, Psychodynamics and Treatment, 1978, Hypothalamic-Pituitary-Adrenal Axis, 1988, Textbook of Psychopharmacology, 1995; mem. editl. bd. McLean Hosp. Jour., 1975-88, Jour. Psychiat. Rsch., 1986—, Integrative Psychiatry, 1990—, Harvard Rev. Psychiatry, 1993—, Archives of Gen. Psychiatry, 1995, Psychoneuroendocrinology, 1995, Annals Psychiatry, 1992—, Anxiety, 1993—; assoc. editor-in-chief Depression, 1992—. Maj. USAF, 1972-74. Rsch. grantee NIMH, 1984-87, 94—, Poitras Charitable Found., 1985-93. Fellow Am. Psychiat. Assn.; mem. Am. Coll. Neuropsychopharmacology (coun. 1994—), Am. Psychopath. Assn.; mem. Am. Coll. Psychiatrists, Mass. Psychiat. Soc. (coun. 1987-90), No. Calif. Psychiat. Soc. Avocations: travel, theater, tennis, swimming, fine arts. Office: Stanford U Sch Medicine 401 Quarry Rd Rm 300 Stanford CA 94305-5548

SCHATZBERG, JERRY NED (JERROLD SCHATZBERG), film director; b. N.Y.C., June 26, 1927; s. Abraham and Lillian (Eiger) S.; children: Don S., Steven M. Student, U. Miami, 1947-48. Photography asst. to Bill Helburn, 1954-56; guest lectr. NYU Sch. Cinema Studies. Freelance still photographer and TV comml. dir., 1959-69; contbr. photographs to various mags. including Life; dir. feature films Puzzle of A Downfall Child, 1970, Panic In Needle Park, 1972, Scarecrow, 1973 (Cannes Film Festival Golden Palm), Sweet Revenge, 1977, The Seduction of Joe Tynan, 1979, Honeysuckle Rose, 1980, Misunderstood, 1984, No Small Affair, 1984, Street Smart, 1987, Reunion, 1991; films have appeared in various film festivals; TV Films include: Clinton and Nadine, 1988 (HBO). Served with USN, 1945-47. Mem. Acad. Motion Picture Arts and Scis., Dirs. Guild Am., Writers Guild Am. *

SCHATZKI, GEORGE, law educator; b. 1933. A.B., Harvard U., 1955, LLB, 1958, LLM, 1965. Teaching fellow Harvard U., Cambridge, Mass., 1963-65; prof. law U. Tex.-Austin, 1965-79; dean U. Wash. Sch. Law,

Seattle, 1979-82, prof., 1979-84; dean U. Conn. Sch. Law, Hartford, 1984-90, prof., 1984—; vis. prof. law U. Pa., Phila., 1973-74, Harvard U., Cambridge, Mass., 1977-78; vis. lectr. law Yale U., New Haven, 1993. Co-author: Labor Relations and Social Problems: Collective Bargaining in Private Employment, 1978, Labor and Employment Law, 1988, 2d edit., 1995. Office: U Conn Law Sch 65 Elizabeth St Hartford CT 06105-2213

SCHAUB, HARRY CARL, lawyer; b. Hazleton, Pa., Feb. 3, 1929; s. Harry J. and Lida M. (Fisher) S.; m. Kathryn Klindt Deans, Aug. 14, 1982; children: Lisa A., Irene Cannon, Christian K. BA, U. Pa., 1950; JD, Yale U., 1955; postgrad., Columbia U., 1962. Bar: Pa. 1955. Assoc. Montgomery, McCracken, Walker & Rhoads, Phila., 1955-62; ptnr. Montgomery, McCracken, Walker & Rhoads, 1963—; consul Republic of Austria to State of Pa., 1978-84, consul gen., 1984—. Contbr. articles to profl. jours. V.p., bd. dirs. Luth. Ch. of Holy Communion, Phila., 1975-88; bd. dirs. YMCA Cen., Phila., 1986-91; chmn. bd. dirs. Consular Corps Coll., Richmond, Va., 1987—; mem. The Athenaeum of Phila., 1976—. Capt. U.S. Army, 1951-53. Decorated Golden Medal of Honor 1st class (Austria), 1992; recipient Johann Strauss award City of Vienna, 1979. Mem. ABA, Pa. Bar Assn., Phila. Bar Assn., Internat. Bar Assn., Am. Soc. Internat. Law, Am. Coun. on Germany, Austrian Soc. Pa. (v.p., bd. dirs. 1981—), John Peter Zenger Law Soc. (founder, bd. dirs., pres. 1994—), Union League of Phila., Rittenhouse Club, Mil. Order Fgn. Wars, Phi Beta Kappa, Pi Gamma Mu. Democrat. Lutheran. Home: 1420 Locust St Unit 7K Philadelphia PA 19102 Office: Montgomery McCracken 3 Pkwy 20th Fl Philadelphia PA 19102

SCHAUB, JAMES HAMILTON, engineering educator; b. Moundsville, W.Va., Jan. 27, 1925; s. Carroll Franklin and Lilian Hoyle (Hutchison) S.; m. Malinda Katherine Bailey, June 15, 1948. Student, George Washington U., 1942-43; B.S. in Civil Engring., Va. Poly. Inst., 1948; S.M. in Civil Engring., Harvard U., 1949; Ph.D., Purdue U., 1960. Registered profl. engr., Va. Soils engr. Ore. Hwy. Dept., 1949-50, 51-52; lab. dir. Palmer and Baker, Inc., Mobile, 1952-55; asst. prof. civil engring. Va. Poly. Inst., 1955-58; instr., research engr. Purdue U., 1958-60; prof. civil engring., chmn. dept. W.Va. U., 1960-67, assoc. dean engring., 1967-69; prof. civil engring., chmn. dept. U. Fla. at Gainesville, 1969-87, Disting. Service prof., 1984-92, NSF faculty fellow, 1975-76, affiliate prof. dept. history, 1977-92, Disting Svc. prof. emeritus, 1992—; acad. visitor dept. history of sci. and tech. Imperial Coll., U. London, 1975-76; Edwin P. Conquest chair humanities Va. Mil. Inst., 1986; vis. prof. Swarthmore Coll., spring 1988; cons. engr. to state, fed. and pvt. agys. and cos., 1960—. Co-author 2 books; author tech. papers. Served with inf. AUS, 1943-46; with C.E. 1950-51, ETO, Korea. Recipient Eminent Career award Coll. Engring, U. Fla., 1987. Mem. ASCE (named Engr. of Year, Fla. sect. 1974, William H. Wisely award 1986), Am. Pub. Works Assn. (pres. chpt. 1983-84, nat. dir.-at-large 1983-89), Order of Engr., Golden Key, Chi Epsilon, Phi Kappa Phi, Kappa Sigma, Sigma Xi, Tau Beta Pi. Episcopalian. Home: 4401 NW 15th Pl Gainesville FL 32605-4509

SCHAUB, MARILYN MCNAMARA, religion educator; b. Chgo., Mar. 24, 1928; d. Bernard Francis and Helen Katherine (Skehan) McNamara; m. R. Thomas Schaub, Oct. 25, 1969; 1 dau., Helen Ann. B.A., Rosary Coll., 1953; Ph.D., U. Fribourg, Switzerland, 1957; diploma, Ecole Biblique, Jerusalem, 1967. Asst. prof. classics and Bibl. studies Rosary Coll., River Forest, Ill., 1957-69; prof. Bibl. studies Duquesne U., Pitts., 1969-70, 73—; participant 8 archeol. excavations, Middle East; adminstrv. dir. expedition to the Southeast Dead Sea Plains, Jordan, 1989—; hon. assoc. Am. Schs. Oriental Rsch., 1966-67, trustee, 1986-89; Danforth assoc., 1972-80. Author: Friends and Friendship for St. Augustine, 1964; translator: (with H. Richter) Agape in the New Testament, 3 vols, 1963-65. Mem. Soc. Bibl. Lit., Catholic Bibl. Assn., Am. Acad. Religion. Democrat. Home: 25 McKelvey Ave Pittsburgh PA 15218-1452 Office: Duquesne U Theology Dept Pittsburgh PA 15282

SCHAUB, SHERWOOD ANHDER, JR., management consultant; b. Rahway, N.J., Jan. 8, 1942; s. Sherwood Anhder Sr. and Doris (Beecher) S.; m. Diane Katherine Wells, July 29, 1967; children: Whitney, Kristen. BBA with honors, Nichols Coll., 1964; postgrad. in bus. adminstrn., Fairleigh Dickinson U., 1965-69. Cert. mgmt. cons. Dir. Gilbert Lane, N.Y.C., 1965-67; exec. v.p. Ward Clancy, N.Y.C., 1967-71; founder, chmn., CEO, sr. mng. ptnr. Goodrich & Sherwood Co., N.Y.C. 1971—; pres., chmn., CEO Reed, Cuff & Assocs., 1980-86; CEO Exec. Change, Inc., 1978; mem. adv. bd. Paine Webber; mem. Schwarzkopf Cup select com., 1992-95; mem. adv. bd. Restaurant Assocs. Author: Breakpoints, 1986; contbr. articles on mgmt. to mags. and profl. jours. Congl. advisor Pres. Ronald Reagan, 1986; head Bus. Task Force N.Y. for Reagan Adminstrn., 1987-89; bd. dirs. Conn. Pub. Broadcasting; trustee Nichols Coll., 1992-95, mem. exec. com., 1984-86, presidl. search com. 1995. Decorated Knight Comanderie de Bordeaux 1993 (France); named Outstanding Alumnus, Nichols Coll., 1994; elected to U.S. 100 Top Recruiters, 1990-95. Mem. Nat. Assn. Corp. and Profl. Recruiters, Young Pres. Orgn. (bd. dirs. 1986-88, vice chmn. met. chpt. sounding bd., hospitality, edn. chmn., chpt. chmn. elect 1989), Pvt. Pilots Assn., World Pres. Orgn., Safari Club Internat. (bd. dirs., 1987-89), U.S. Equestrian Team. Congregationalist. Clubs: Chemists, University, Westfield Tennis, New Canaan Racquet, New Canaan Field, Am. Friends of Game Conservancy, Rolling Rock, Weston Gun Club, Mashomak Field and Game, Econ. of N.Y., Explorers (fellow), Madison Ave Sports Car Driving & Chowder Society, Greenwich Polo, Ducks Unlimited (sponsor, co-chmn. So. Conn. 1994, 95), Advt. Sportsmen of N.Y. (bd. dirs., treas.). Avocations: scuba diving, equestrian riding, big and small game hunting, antiques, sporting clays shooting. Office: Goodrich and Sherwood Co Hdqrs 521 Fifth Ave New York NY 10017

SCHAUBERT, DANIEL HAROLD, electrical engineering educator; b. Galesburg, Ill., Feb. 15, 1947; s. Robert Harold and Carolyn Virginia (Dunkle) S.; m. Joyce Marie Conard, June 15, 1968; 1 child, Karen Louise. BSEE, U. Ill., 1969, MS, 1970, PhD, 1974. Rsch. engr. U.S. Army Harry Diamond Labs., Adelphi, Md., 1977-80; rsch. engr., program mgr. U.S. Bur. Radiol. Health, Rockville, Md., 1980-82; prof. elec. engring. U. Mass., Amherst, 1982—; dept. head elec. and computer engring., 1994—. Patentee in field. 1st lt. U.S. Army, 1974-77. Fellow IEEE, IEEE Antennas and Propagation Soc. (membership chair 1980-82, editor newsletter 1982-84, sec.-treas. 1984-88). Office: U Mass Elec and Computer Engring Amherst MA 01003

SCHAUER, FREDERICK FRANKLIN, legal educator; b. Newark, Jan. 15, 1946; s. John Adolph and Clara (Balayti) S.; m. Margery Clare Stone, Aug. 25, 1968 (div. June, 1982); m. Virginia Jo Wise, May 25, 1985. AB, Dartmouth Coll., 1967, MBA, 1968; JD, Harvard U., 1972. Bar: Mass. 1972, U.S. Supreme Ct. 1976. Assoc. Fine & Ambrogne, Boston, 1972-74; asst. prof. law W.Va. U., Morgantown, 1974-76, assoc. prof., 1976-78; assoc. prof. Coll. William and Mary, Williamsburg, Va., 1978-80, Cutler prof., 1980-83; prof. of law U. Mich., Ann Arbor, 1983-90; Frank Stanton prof. of 1st Amendment Kennedy Sch. of Govt., Harvard U., Cambridge, Mass., 1990—; vis. scholar, mem. faculty law Wolfson Coll. Cambridge (Eng.) U., 1977-78; vis. prof. law sch. U. chgo., 1990; vis. fellow Australian Nat. U., 1993; William Morton Disting. Sr. fellow in humanities Dartmouth Coll., 1991. Author: The Law of Obscenity, 1976, Free Speech: A Philosophical Enquiry, 1982 (ABA cert. merit 1983), Supplements to Gunther Constitutional Law, 1983—, Playing by the Rules: A Philosophical Examination of Rule Based Decision-Making in Law and Life, 1991, The First Amendment: A Reader, 1992, The Philosphy of Law, 1995; contbr. articles to profl. jours. Mem. Atty. Gen.'s Commn. on Pornography, 1985-86. Served with Mass. Army N.G., 1970-71. NEH fellow, summer 1980. Fellow Am. Acad. Arts and Scis.; mem. Am. Philos. Assn., Am. Soc. for Polit. and Legal Philosophy, Assn. Am. Law Schs. (chmn. sect. constl. law 1984-86). Office: Kennedy Sch of Govt Harvard U Cambridge MA 02138

SCHAUER, LOUIS FRANK, lawyer; b. Chgo., Dec. 4, 1928; s. Frank William and Mary (Wittich) S.; m. Nancy Clair Wilson, Oct. 5, 1957; 1 son, Christopher. B.S., Northwestern U. 1949; LL.B., Harvard U., 1952. Bar: Ill. 1952. Assoc. law firm Lord, Bissell & Brook, Chgo., 1955-63, ptnr., 1963-92; sec. Arens Industries, Inc.; village atty. Western Springs, Ill., 1973-80. Author: (monograph) Indemnification and Insurance for Directors and Officers, 1989; contbr. articles to profl. jours. Pres. Village of Western Springs, 1981-85; chmn. West Suburban Mass Transit Dist., Western Chgo.

Suburbs, 1971-73; trustee Chgo. Zool. Soc., Brookfield, 1979—, sec., 1993—; bd. dirs. Chgo. Opera Theater, 1988-90. Mem. ABA, Chgo. Bar Assn., Phi Beta Kappa. Clubs: Legal (Chgo.), Law (Chgo.), Union League (Chgo.), LaGrange Country. Home: 178 Maplewood Rd Riverside IL 60546-1844 Office: Lord Bissell & Brook 115 S La Salle St Ste 3200 Chicago IL 60603-3972

SCHAUER, RALPH FLOYD, microelectronics company executive; b. Waterloo, Iowa, May 31, 1930; s. Herman Carl and Louise Emma (Mixdorf) S.; m. Gwen Elaine Maurer, Mar. 31, 1961; children: Wren, Heidi, Rebecca. BSEE, Iowa State U., 1952, MS, 1957, PhD, 1960. Mgr. design, test and research IBM, Fishkill, N.Y., 1960-80; dir. corp. tech. ctr. Wang Labs. Inc., Lowell, Mass., 1980-82; v.p. computer aided design Ford Microelectronics Inc., Colorado Springs, Colo., 1982—. Patentee in field. Pres. Lakeland Sch. Bd., Shrub Oak, N.Y., 1974; Putnam Valley (N.Y.) Free Library, 1968-78. Served to lt. USN, 1952-55. Mem. IEEE. Democrat. Lutheran. Avocations: collecting Am. antique furniture, metal ware, pewter and art. Office: Ford Microelectronics Inc 10340 State Hwy 83 Colorado Springs CO 80908

SCHAUER, WILBERT EDWARD, JR., lawyer, manufacturing company executive; b. Milw., Oct. 28, 1926; s. Wilbert Edward and Gertrude (Nickel) S.; m. Genevieve Stone, June 23, 1951; children—Jeffrey Edward, Constance Emily, Gregory Wilbert, Martha Ann, Jennifer Caroline. B.B.A., U. Wis., 1949, M.B.A., 1950, J.D., 1950. Bar: Wis. 1950. Accountant Pub. Service Commn. Wis., 1950-52; with Rexnord, Inc., Milw., 1952-87; v.p. finance, treas. Rexnord, Inc., 1968-76, v.p. fin. and law, 1977-78, exec. v.p. fin. and adminstrn., 1978-86, vice chmn., 1986-87. Alderman, Brookfield, Wis., 1958-68; pres. Common Council, 1966-68. Clubs: Milwaukee; Westmoor Country (Brookfield, Wis.); Bluemound Golf and Country. Home: 3215 Gulf Shore Blvd N # PH4 Naples FL 33940-3947

SCHAUF, LAWRENCE E., restaurant corporation executive. BA, Wichita State U., 1968; JD, Washburn U., 1971. Bar: Colo. 1971, U.S. Dist. Ct. Kans. 1974, Kans. 1981. Cons. franchising/legal dept. Pizza Hut, Inc., 1986-87, 1st asst. gen. counsel, sr. v.p. govt. rels., 1977-84; sr. v.p. franchising Popingo Video, Inc., 1986; v.p., gen. counsel Wendy's Internat., Inc., Dublin, Ohio, 1987—; co-chmn. legal legis. com. Internat. Franchising Assn., 1988; bd. dirs. Foodservice & Lodging Inst., Ohio Coun. Retail Mchts. Office: Wendy's Internat Inc 4288 W Dublin Granville Rd Dublin OH 43017-2093

SCHAUF, VICTORIA, pediatrician, educator, researcher, consultant; b. N.Y.C., Feb. 17, 1943; d. Maurice J. and Ruth H. (Baker) Bisson; m. Michael Delaney; 2 children. BS with honors in Microbiology, U. Chgo., 1965, MD with honors, 1969. Intern pediatrics U. Chgo. Hosp., 1969-70; resident pediatrics Sinai Hosp. of Balt., 1970-71; chief resident pediatrics Children's Hosp. Nat. Med. Ctr., Washington, 1971-72; rsch. trainee NIH, Bethesda, Md., 1972; asst. prof. microbiology Rush Med. Coll., Chgo., 1972-74; prof. pediatrics, head pediatric infectious diseases U. Ill., Chgo. 1974-84; med. officer FDA, Rockville, Md., 1984-86; chmn. dept. pediatrics Nassau County Med. Ctr., East Meadow, N.Y., 1986-90; prof. pediatrics SUNY, Stony Brook, 1987—; vis. prof. Rockefeller U., 1990-92; mem. vis. faculty Chiang Mai (Thailand) U., 1978; mem. ad hoc com. study sects. NIH, Bethesda, 1981-82; bd. dirs. Pearl Stetler Rsch. Found., Chgo. 1982-84; cons. FDA, 1987-88, 93—; Can. Bur. Human Prescription Drugs, Ottawa, 1990—, biotech. investors, 1993—; course dir. pediatric infectious diseases rev. course Cornell U. Med. Coll., N.Y.C., 1994. Producer TV programs in field; contbr. articles to profl. jours., chpts. to books. Vol. physician Cook County Hosp., Chgo., 1974-84; mem. adv. com. Nat. Hansen's Disease Ctr., La., 1986, Nassau County Day Care Coun., N.Y., 1988-90; mem. adv. bd. Surg. Aid to Children of World, N.Y., 1986-90. Am. Lung Assn. grantee U. Ill., 1977; recipient contract NIH, U. Ill., 1978-81, grantee, 1979-84. Fellow Infectious Diseases Soc. Am.; mem. Pediatric Infectious Diseases Soc. (exec. bd.), Soc. Pediatric Rsch. Am. Pediatric Soc., AAAS, Am. Soc. Microbiology, Am. Acad. Pediatrics, NOW, Phi Beta Kappa, Alpha Omega Alpha. Avocations: organic gardening, walking.

SCHAUFELE, ROGER DONALD, aircraft company executive; b. Mar. 30, 1928; s. Franklin A. and Josephine (Schmidt) S.; m. Barbara Powell Harkness, Oct. 8, 1949; children—Margaret Jo, Roger Donald Jr. B.S. in Aeros., Rensselaer Poly. Inst., 1949; M.S. in Aeros., Calif. Inst. Tech., 1952. With Douglas Aircraft Co., Santa Monica, Calif., 1949-51; with Douglas Aircraft Co., Long Beach, Calif., 1955—, asst. chief aerodynamics, comml. programs, DC-10 dep. dir. aerodynamics, 1967-71, dir. tech., 1971-76, dir. advanced engring. 1976-79, dir. aircraft design, 1979-81, v.p. engring., 1981-87; v.p., gen. mgr. comml. advanced products Douglas Aircraft, Long Beach, Calif., 1987-89, cons., 1989—; mem. aero. adv. com. NASA, Washington, 1981-87; mem. aero. and space engring. bd. NRC, Washington, 1982-85; mem. U. engring. adv. and devel. council Calif. State U.-Long Beach, 1983—; mem. aero. engring. tech. indsl. adv. bd. Ariz. State U., Tempe, 1983-86; mem. com. on sci. and tech. U.S. Ho. Reps., Congl. Adv. Com. on Aeronautics, Washington, 1984-87; Patentee in field. Fellow AIAA, Inst. for Advancement of Engring.; mem. ASME, Soc. Automotive Engrs. (tech. bd. 1983-85, bd. dirs. 1990—), Aero. Club of So. Calif., Tau Beta Pi, Gamma Alpha Rho. Home: 13112 Wheeler Pl Santa Ana CA 92705-1826 Office: Douglas Aircraft Co 3855 Lakewood Blvd M/C 18A-61 Long Beach CA 90846

SCHAUFUSS, PETER, dancer, producer, choreographer, ballet director; b. Copenhagen, Denmark, Apr. 26, 1950; s. Frank Schaufuss and Mona Vangsaae S. Student, Royal Danish Ballet Sch. Apprentice with Royal Danish Ballet, 1965; soloist Nat. Ballet Can., 1967-68, Royal Danish Ballet, 1969-70; prin. with LFB, 1970-74, N.Y.C. Ballet, 1974-77, Nat. Ballet Can., 1977-83; artistic dir. London Festival Ballet (now English Nat. Ballet), 1984-90; ballet dir. Deutsche Oper Berlin, 1990-93, Royal Danish Ballet, 1994—; guest appearances in Can., Denmark, France, Germany, Italy, Japan, U.K., U.S.A., USSR, Austria, S.Am.; presented BBC TV series Dancer, 1984; numerous other TV appearances; created roles include Rhapsodie Espagnole, The Steadfast Tin Soldier (Balanchine), Phantom of the Opera (Petit), Verdi Variations, Orpheus (MacMillan); ballets produced include La Sylphide (London Festival Ballet, Stuttgart Ballet, Roland Petit's Ballet de Marseille, Deutsche Oper Berlin, Teatro Comunale Firenze, Vienna State Opera, Opernhaus Zürich, Teatro dell'Opera di Roma, Hessisches Staatstheater Wiesbaden, Ballet Du Rhin (Royal Danish Ballet), Napoli (Nat. Ballet Can., Teatro San Carlo, Naples, English Nat. Ballet, formerly London Festival Ballet), Folktale (Deutsche Oper Berlin), Dances from Napoli (London Festival Ballet), Bournonville (Aterballetto), The Nutcracker (London Festival Ballet, Deutsche Oper Berlin), Giselle (Deutsche Oper Berlin), Tchiakovsky Trilogy (Deutsche Oper Berlin). Recipient Solo award 2d Internat. Ballet Competition, Moscow, 1973, Star of the Yr. award Abendzeitung, Munich, 1978, Evening Standard award, 1979, Soc. of West End Theatres Ballet award (now Oliver), 1979, Manchester Evening News Theatre awards-dance, 1986, Berlin Co. award for best ballet prodn. Berlinerzeitung, 1991, Edinburgh Festival Critics prize, 1991 , Critics prize Edinburgh Festival, 1991; named Knight of the Dannebrog, 1988. Office: care Papoutsis Rep Ltd, 18 Sundial Ave, London SE25 4BX, England

SCHAUMBERG, WILLIAM LLOYD, retired banker; b. Lincoln, Nebr., May 4, 1923; s. Edward George and Claire Elizabeth (Barentsen) S.; m. Patricia Louise Ward, Sept. 4, 1948; children: DeeAnn, William Ward, Denise Lynn, Kirstin. B.S., U. Nebr., 1947, LL.B., 1949. Bar: Nebr. 1949, Oreg. 1953. Dep. county atty. Lancaster County, Nebr., 1949-51; v.p. 1st Nat. Bank of Oreg., 1952-69, Columbia Mgmt. Co., Portland, Oreg., 1970-73; exec. v.p., mgr. capital mgmt. div. Rainier Nat. Bank, Seattle, 1973-87; dir. Pacific Coast Depository Trust, San Francisco, 1980-88, Pacific Clearing Corp., L.A., 1985-88, BHC Corp., Phila., 1985-88. Bd. dirs. Willamette Valley Camp Fire Girls, 1955-62, pres., 1960-61; bd. dirs. Ind. Colls. Wash.; bd. dirs. Multnomah County chpt. Nat. Found. March of Dimes, 1963-70, pres. Multnomah County chpt., 1968; bd. visitors Puget Sound U.; mem. Trustees Assn. Wash., pres., 1975, 84; mem. adv. com. Fred Hutchinson Cancer Research Ctr., 1983-87. Served with U.S. Army, 1943-46, 51-52. Recipient Gullick award Nat. Campfire Girls, 1961. Mem. Seattle Estate Planning Council, Assn. Corp. Trustees Wash., Beta Theta Pi. Republican. Episcopalian. Clubs: Broadmoor Golf, D'Anza Country. Home: 8520 SE 80th St Mercer Island WA 98040-5637

SCHAUMBURG, HERBERT HOWARD, neurology educator; b. Houston, Tex., Nov. 6, 1932; m. Joanna Jane Austin; children: Barnabas Paul, Kristin Elizabeth. AB cum laude, Harvard Coll., 1956; MD, Washington U., 1960. Instr. in neurology Albert Einstein Coll. of Medicine, N.Y.C., 1964-67, asst. prof. neurology, 1967-69, assoc. prof. neurology, 1972-76, prof., 1976—, vice chmn., 1977-84, acting chmn., 1984-86, chmn., 1986—; instr. pathology Harvard Med. Sch., Boston, 1969-71. Mem. Am. Acad. Neurology, Am. Assn. Neuropathologists, Am. Neurol. Assn., Soc. Toxicology, Soc. Neurosci. Home: 616 King Ave City Island Bronx NY 10464 Office: Albert Einstein Coll Medicine 1300 Morris Park Ave Bronx NY 10461-1975

SCHAUT, JOSEPH WILLIAM, banker; b. Cleve., May 30, 1928; s. Francis Xavier and Emma Gertrude (Urmann) S.; m. Susan Stiver, Apr. 23, 1955; children: Deborah Anne Schaut Payne, Gregory F., Mary Theresa Schaut Bentley, Michael J. B in Social Sci. in Econs., Georgetown U., 1950, JD, 1953. Bar: D.C. 1953, U.S. Mil. Ct. Appeals 1953, U.S. Dist. Ct. D.C. 1953, U.S. Ct. Appeals (D.C. cir.) 1953, Ohio 1954. Tax analyst Republic Steel Corp., Cleve., 1953-60, asst. to sec., 1960-67, asst. sec., 1967-81; dir. corp. properties Republic Steel Corp., 1976-84; corp. sec. Republic Steel Corp., Cleve., 1981-84; bus. cons., 1984-85; sr. trust officer AmeriTrust Co. Nat. Assn., 1986-92; sr. trust officer Soc. Nat. Bank, Cleve., 1992-93, v.p., 1993—. Served to col. USAR, 1950-78. Recipient award Silver Beaver Greater Cleve. council Boy Scouts Am., 1975. Mem. Am. Soc. Corp. Secs. (dir. 1976-79), Ohio State Bar Assn., Greater Cleve. Growth Assn., Delta Theta Phi, Pi Gamma Mu. Roman Catholic. Office: Soc Nat Bank 127 Public Sq Cleveland OH 44114-1216

SCHAWLOW, ARTHUR LEONARD, physicist, educator; b. Mt. Vernon, N.Y., May 5, 1921; s. Arthur and Helen (Mason) S.; m. Aurelia Keith Townes, May 19, 1951; children: Arthur Keith, Helen Aurelia, Edith Ellen. BA, U. Toronto, Ont., Can., 1941, MA, 1942, PhD, 1949, LLD (hon.), 1970; DSc (hon.), U. Ghent, Belgium, 1968, U. Bradford, Eng., 1970, U. Ala., 1984, Trinity Coll., Dublin, Ireland, 1986; DTech (hon.), U. Lund, Sweden, 1987; DSL (hon.), Victoria U., Toronto, 1993. Postdoctoral fellow, research asso. Columbia, 1949-51; vis. assoc. prof. Columbia U., 1960; research physicist Bell Telephone Labs., 1951-61, cons., 1961-62; prof. physics Stanford U., 1961-91, also J.G. Jackson-C.J. Wood prof. physics, 1978, prof. emeritus, 1991—, exec. head dept. physics, 1966-70, acting chmn. dept., 1973-74. Author: (with C.H. Townes) Microwave Spectroscopy, 1955; Co-inventor (with C.H. Townes), optical maser or laser, 1958. Recipient Ballantine medal Franklin Inst., 1962, Thomas Young medal and prize Inst. Physics and Phys. Soc., London, 1963, Schawlow medal Laser Inst. Am., 1982, Nobel prize in physics, 1981, Nat. Medal of Sci., NSF, 1991, Arata award High Temperature Soc. Japan, 1994; named Calif. Scientist of Yr., 1973, Marconi Internat. fellow, 1977. Fellow Am. Acad. Arts and Scis., Am. Phys. Soc. (coun. 1966-70, chmn. div. electron and atomic physics 1974, pres. 1981), Optical Soc. Am. (hon. mem. 1983, dir.-at-large 1966-68, pres. 1975, Frederick Ives medal 1976); mem. NAS, IEEE (Liebmann prize 1964), AAAS (chmn. physics sect. 1979), Am. Philos. Soc., Royal Irish Acad. (hon.). Office: Stanford U Dept Physics Stanford CA 94305

SCHECHNER, RICHARD, theater director, author, educator; b. Newark, Aug. 23, 1934; s. Sheridan and Selma Shapiro (Schwarz) S.; m. Carol Martin; children: Samuel MacIntosh, Sophia Martin. BA, Cornell U., 1956; postgrad., Johns Hopkins U., 1957; MA, State U. Iowa, 1958; PhD, Tulane U., 1962. Asst. prof. theatre Tulane U., 1962-66, assoc. prof., 1966-67; prof. performance studies NYU, 1967-91, Univ. prof., 1991—; co-founder, co-dir. New Orleans Group, 1965-67; founder, dir. Performance Group, N.Y.C. 1967-80; founder, artistic dir. East Coast Artists, 1991—; bd. dirs. Theatre Communications Group, 1977-78; advisor Internat. Theatre Inst., 1975-77; pres. Bunch of Exptl. Theatres, 1975, 77, Fulbright Theatre Discipline Com., 1988-91. Author: Public Domain, 1968, Environmental Theater, 1973, (with others) Theatres, Spaces, Environments, 1975, Essays on Performance Theory, 1977, 2d. edit. 1988, (with others) Macbeth, 1977, The End of Humanism, 1982, Performative Circumstances, 1983, Between Theater and Anthropology, 1985, (with Samuel MacIntosh-Schechner) The Engleburt Stories: North to the Tropics, 1987, The Future of Ritual, 1993; editor: Dionysus in 69, 1970; co-editor: Free Southern Theater, 1968, Ritual, Play, and Performance, 1976, By Means of Performance, 1990; gen. editor: (series) Worlds of Performance, 1993—; editor: The Drama Rev, 1962-69, 85—; contbg. editor, 1971—; adv. editor Jour. Ritual Studies, 1987—; adv. editor Text and Performance Quar., 1988—; dir. Dionysus in 69, 1968, Macbeth, 1969, Commune, 1970, The Tooth of Crime, 1972, Mother Courage, 1975, The Marilyn Project, 1975, Oedipus, 1977, Cops, 1978, The Balcony, 1979, The Red Snake, 1981, Richard's Lear, 1981, The Cherry Orchard, 1983, Prometheus Project, 1985, Don Juan, 1987, Tomorrow He'll Be Out of the Mountains, 1989, Ma Rainey's Black Bottom, 1992, Faust/Gastronome, 1993, Three Sister, 1995. Served with AUS, 1958-60. Recipient Mondello prize, 1985. Contbns. to Theatre Spl. award New England Theare Conf., 1991, Work in Theatre award Towson State U., 1991; grantee John D. Rockefeller 3d Fund, 1971-72, 76, Asian Cultural Coun., 1988; Guggenheim fellow, 1976, Fulbright fellow, 1976, 83, N.Y. Inst. Humanities fellow, 1987—, NEH sr. rsch. fellow, 1988. Office: NYU 721 Broadway 6th Fl Washington Sq New York NY 10003

SCHECHTER, ALLEN E(DWARD), retired publishing company executive; b. Chgo., Dec. 17, 1935; s. Oscar A. and Sarah (Silberman) S.; m. Esther M. Schiller, June 11, 1961; children: Deborah, Daniel. AB, U. Chgo., 1955; JD, Northwestern U., 1958. Bar: Ill. 1958. With Commerce Clearing House, Inc., Chgo., 1959-73, v.p., 1973-92, sr. mgr., 1977-91, asst. to pres., 1991-92. Home: 6747 S Constance Ave Chicago IL 60649-1015

SCHECHTER, ARTHUR LOUIS, lawyer; b. Rosenberg, Tex., Dec. 6, 1939; s. Morris and Helen (Brilling) S.; m. Joyce Proler, Aug. 26, 1965; children: Leslie Schechter Karpas, Jennifer. BA, U. Tex., 1962, JD, 1964; postgrad. U. Houston, 1964-65. Bar: Tex. 1964, U.S. Dist. Ct. (ea. and so. dists.) Tex. 1966, U.S. Ct. Appeals (5th cir.), U.S. Supreme Ct. 1976, cert. Tex. Bd. Legal Specialization to Personal Injury Trial Law, 1964—. Pres. Arthur L. Schechter & Assocs., 1992—; speaker Marine Law Seminar, 1983; speaker in field. Contbr. to Law Rev., 1984. Bd. dirs. Theatre Under the Stars, Houston, 1972-78, Congregation Beth Israel, Houston, 1972-84, pres., 1982-84; pres. Am. Jewish Com., Houston, 1982-84, chmn. fgn. rels. com., chmn. United Jewish Campaign exec. com., chmn. 1993-94; mem. fin. coun. Nat. Dem. Orgn., 1979; trustee, mem. fin. com. Dem. Nat. Com., 1992—; v.p., exec. com. Nat. Jewish Dem. Coun., 1992—; mem. Leadership Cir., Dem. Senatorial Campaign Com.; mem. Deans Council, U. Tex. Law Sch. Found., Austin, 1981-84, U.S. Holocaust Commn.; pres. Beth Israel Congregation, 1988-90; bd. trustees Schlenker Sch. Coun. Recipient Love award Congregation Beth Israel, 1976, Press. award NAACP, 1992, Love award Child Advocate Houston. Mem. ATLA, Tex. Trial Lawyers Assn. (chmn. admiralty sect., presenter 1985-87), Jewish Fedn. Houston (bd. mem., v.p., pres. 1994—), Houston Trial Lawyers Assn., Houston Bar Assn. Democrat. Jewish. Clubs: Westwood Country (bd. dirs., sec.). Home: 19A Westlane Houston TX 77019

SCHECHTER, DANIEL PHILIP, lawyer; b. N.Y.C., Nov. 29, 1942; s. Isadore and Jenny (Waldman) S.; m. Sara P. Howell (div. 1977); children: Matthew, Ellen; m. Elizabeth L. Cooke, Oct. 1, 1983. BA, Columbia U., 1964, LLB, 1967. Bar: N.Y. 1968. Law clk. to judge U.S. Dist. Ct. (so. dist.) N.Y., N.Y.C., 1967-68; assoc. Fried, Frank, Harris, Shriver & Jacobson, N.Y.C., 1968-75, ptnr., 1975—. Mem. ABA, N.Y. City Bar Assn. Club: India House (N.Y.C.). Office: Fried Frank Harris Shriver & Jacobson 1 New York Plz New York NY 10004

SCHECHTER, GERALDINE POPPA, hematologist; b. N.Y.C., Jan. 16, 1938; d. Josif and Victoria (Nosi) P.; m. Alan Neil Schechter, Feb. 6, 1965; children: Daniele Malka, Andrew M.R. AB, Vassar Coll., Poughkeepsie, N.Y., 1959; MD, Columbia U., 1963. Diplomate Am. Bd. Internal Medicine, Am. Bd. Hematology. Intern, resident Presbyn. Hosp., N.Y.C., 1963-65; resident, fellow, rsch. assoc. VA Med. Ctr., Washington, 1965-70, staff physician, 1970-74, chief hematology, 1974—; asst., assoc. prof. medicine George Washington U., Washington, 1971-81, prof. medicine, 1981—; mem. hematology com. Am. Bd. Internal Medicine, Phila., 1985-91, bd. dirs., 1990—. Mem. editorial bd. Blood, 1985-89. Contbr. articles to hematologic jours. Office: VA Med Ctr Hematology Sect 50 Irving St NW Washington DC 20422-0001

SCHECHTER, PAUL J., pharmacologist; b. Bklyn., Aug. 9, 1939; s. Harry and Frances (Maybloom) S.; m. Barbara F. Roth, Dec. 9, 1967; children: Rebecca, Christopher. BS, Columbia U., 1960; PhD, U. Chgo., 1966, MD, 1968. Rsch. asst. U. Chgo., 1966-68; intern Presbyn.-St. Luke's Hosp., Chgo., 1968-69; rsch. assoc. NIH, Bethesda, Md., 1969-71, clin. investigator, 1971-72; jr. asst. resident Georgetown U. Hosp., Washington, 1972-73; chief exptl. therapist Merrell Internat. Rsch. Ctr., Strasbourg, France, 1973-78, dir. clin. rsch., 1978-84; v.p. internat. clin. pharm. Merrell Dow Rsch. Inst., Strasbourg, 1984-88; v.p. clin. rsch. Merrell Dow Rsch. Inst., Cin., 1988-90; v.p. rsch. and devel. Fujisawa Pharm. Co., Deerfield, Ill., 1990—. Contbr. articles, abstracts to profl. publs.; patentee in field. Lt. comdr. USPHS, 1969-72. Recipient Clin. Pharmacol. award Internat. League Against Epilepsy. Mem. numerous profl. orgns. Avocations: tennis, skiing, music.

SCHECHTER, ROBERT SAMUEL, chemical engineer, educator; b. Houston, Feb. 26, 1929; s. Morris Samuel and Helen Ruth S.; m. Mary Ethel Rosenberg, Feb. 15, 1953; children: Richard Marine, Alan Lawrence, Geoffrey Louis. B.S. in Chem. Engring., Tex. A&M U., 1950; Ph.D. in Chem. Engring, U. Minn., 1956. Registered engr., Tex. Asst. prof. chem. engring. U. Tex. at Austin, 1956-60, assoc. prof. 1960-63, prof., 1963—; adminstrv. dir. Ctr. Statis. Mechs. and Thermodynamics, 1968-72, chmn. dept. chem. engring., 1970-73, chmn. petroleum engring. 1975-78, E.J. Cockrell, Jr. prof. chem. and petroleum engring., 1975-81, Dula and Ernie Cockrell prof. engring., 1981-83, Getty prof. engring., 1984-85, Getty Oil Centennial chair in Petroleum Engring., 1985-89, W.A. (Monty) Moncrief Centennial Endowed chair in Petroleum Engring., 1989—; vis. prof. U. Edinburgh, Scotland, 1965-66; Disting. vis. prof. U. Kans., spring 1968; vis. prof. U. Brussels, 1969; Disting. Lindsay lectr. Tex. A&M U., 1993; cons. in field. Author: Variational Method in Engineering, 1967, (with G.S.G. Beveridge) Optimization—Theory and Practice, 1970, Adventures in Fortran Programming, 1975, (with B.B. Williams and J.L. Gidley) Acidizing Monograph, 1979, (with D.D. Shah) Enhanced Oil Recovery by Surfactants and Polymers, 1979; (with Maurice Bourrel) Microemulsions and Related Systems, 1988, Oil Well Stimulation, 1991; contbr. (with D.D. Shah) numerous articles to profl. jours. Served to 1st lt., Chem. Corps AUS, 1951-53. Decorated Chevalier Order Palmes Academique; recipient Outstanding Teaching award U. Tex., 1969, Outstanding Paper award, 1973, Gen. Dynamics award for Excellence in Engring. Teaching, Gen. Dynamics Corp., 1987, Sr. Rsch. award Engring. Rsch. Coun. of Am. Soc. Engring. Educators, 1991, Franklin Carll award Rsch. by Soc. of Petroleum Engrs., 1994. Mem. AIME, Am. Inst. Chem. Engrs., Am. Chem. Soc., Soc. Petroleum Engrs. (John Franklin Carll award 1994), Nat. Acad. Engrs., Sigma Xi, Tau Beta Pi. Developer methods of measuring surface viscosity and ultra low inter-facial tensions; discoverer instability of thermal diffusion. Home: 4700 Ridge Oak Dr Austin TX 78731-4724

SCHECHTER, SOL, clothes company executive; b. 1916; married. With Shirt Mfrs., N.Y., 1936-40, Overndorfer-Marcus Inc., 1940-41; br. owner Atlas Shirt Co. Inc.; prin. Lenoir Shirt Co., Hampton Industries Inc., 1946—. Office: Hampton Industries Inc PO Box 614 2000 Greenville Hwy Kinston NC 28501-1845

SCHECHTER, STEPHEN L, political scientist; b. Washington, Nov. 28, 1945; s. William J. and Blossom (Rapaport) S.; m. Stephanie A. Thompson, Feb. 16, 1993; 1 child, Sarah J.; 1 stepdaughter: Kelly Anne Thompson. BA, Syracuse U., 1967; PhD, U. Pitts., 1972. Acting dir. Ctr. for Study of Federalism/Temple U., 1973-76; asst. to full prof. polit. sci. Russell Sage Coll., Troy N.Y., 1977—; exec. dir. N.Y. State Commn. on Bicentennial of U.S. Constitution, 1986-90; dir. Coun. for Citizenship Edn. Russell Sage Coll., N.Y., 1990—; coord. We The People, 1992—; pres. N.Y. State Coun. on Social Edn., 1992-93; presenter workshops in field. Co-editor: World of the Founders: New York Communities in the Federal Period, 1990, Contexts of the Bill of Rights, 1990, New York and the Union, New York and the Bicentennial, 1990; editor: Roots of the Republic: American Founding Documents Interpreted, 1990, others; contbr. articles to profl. jours., chpts. to books in field; editor: Social Sci. Record, 1991-. Chmn. Rensselaer County Bicentennial Commn., 1991. Mem. Nat. Coun. Social Studies (state del. 1991), Internat. Assn. Ctrs. for Fed. Studies (co-founder 1976), Am. Polit. Sci. Assn., N.Y. State Acad. Pub. Adminstrn., others. Office: Russell Sage Coll 45 Ferry St Troy NY 12180-4115

SCHECKNER, SY, former greeting card company executive; b. N.Y.C., Aug. 8, 1924; s. Morris and Bella S.; m. Georgene W. Carrigan, Aug. 17, 1974; children: Barry David, Michael Matthew, Jeri Bella,. Student, CCNY, U. Pitts., U. Ill. Sr. v.p., dir. Papercraft Corp., Pitts, 1956-75, Am. Greetings Corp., Cleve., 1975-85; pres. Knomark, Inc., Plus Mark, Inc.; gen. ptnr. Doubletree Investments. Vice chmn. bd. trustees Tusculum Coll., Greeneville, Tenn. Served with U.S. Army, 1942-45. Decorated Purple Heart. Office: 1480 S Military Trl West Palm Beach FL 33415-9142

SCHECTER, M., book publishing executive. With Educatinal Reading Service Inc., Mahwah, N.J., 1961-89; pres. Troll Assoc., Mahwah, N.J., 1968—. Office: Troll Associates 100 Corporate Dr Mahwah NJ 07430

SCHECTMAN, HERBERT A., lawyer, corporate executive; b. N.Y.C., Aug. 8, 1930; s. Leon and Ethel (Brown) S.; m. Evelyn P. DePalma, Apr. 15, 1956 (div. 1974); children: Bart T., Robert; m. Lois Regent Driscoll, Apr. 11, 1974. AB, Syracuse U., 1952; MA, Columbia U., 1958, JD, 1958. Bar: N.Y. 1959. Atty. U.S. Govt., Bklyn., 1958-60, The Lummus Co., N.Y.C., 1960-62; assoc. gen. counsel GE Credit Corp., N.Y.C. and Chgo., 1962-67; div. counsel GE, N.Y.C., 1967-69; ptnr. Belfer, Bogart & Schectman, N.Y.C., 1969-74; sr. v.p. ops. and adminstrn., gen. counsel Chrysler Capital Corp. (formerly E.F. Hutton Credit Corp.), Greenwich, Conn., 1974-87; sr. v.p., group exec. mergers, acquisitions and corp. fin. group, 1988-89, exec. v.p., sector exec. merchant banking svcs., 1989-91; sr. v.p. credit and ops. Chrysler Capital Corp. (formerly E.F. Hutton Credit Corp.), Greenwich, 1991—; also bd. dirs. Chrysler Capital Corp. (formerly E.F. Hutton Credit Corp.), Greenwich, Conn.; arbitrator N.Y.C. Civil Ct. Small Claims, N.Y.C., 1974—. Served with USAF, 1951-54; ETO. Mem. N.Y. State Bar Assn., Am. Judges Assn. Office: Chrysler Capital Corp 225 High Ridge Rd Stamford CT 06905-3000

SCHEEDER, LOUIS, theater producer, director, educator; b. N.Y.C., Dec. 26, 1946; s. Louis W. and Julia H. (Callery) S. B.A. in English Lit, Georgetown U., 1968; postgrad., Sch. of Arts, Columbia U., 1968-69; MA in Performance Studies NYU, 1995. Founder, dir. The Classical Studio NYU, 1991—; dir. NYU Tisch Sch. of the Arts, Shakespeare Ensemble, 1989-90; mem. adv. council Nat. Com. on Arts and Edn., 1977-82; mem. D.C. Commn. on Arts and Humanities, 1976-80; bd. advs. New Playwrights' Theatre of Washington, 1975-82; asst. stage mgr. Arena Stage, Washington, 1969-70; dir., producer Folger Theatre Group, Washington, 1973-81; cons. Ctr. for Renaissance and Baroque Studies U. Md., 1984-91; asst. dir. Royal Shakespeare Co. Stratford-Upon-Avon, Eng., 1988. Dir., producer plays including Creeps (Am. premiere), 1973, The Farm (Am. premiere), 1974, The Collected Works of Billy the Kid (Am. premiere), 1975, Henry V, 1976, The Fool (Am. premiere), 1976, Mummer's End (world premiere), 1977, Teeth 'n' Smiles (Am. premiere), 1977, Two Gentlemen of Verona, 1977, Mackerel (world premiere), 1978, Black Elk Speaks (tour), 1978, Richard III, 1978, Whose Life Is It Anyway? (Am. premiere), 1978, Richard II, 1978, As You Like It, 1979, Custer (Kennedy Center), 1979, Charlie and Algernon (Kennedy Center), 1980, Crossing Niagara (Am. premiere), 1981, Love's Labour's Lost, 1981; also dir. Broadway, Off Broadway, regional prodns. including (Broadway) Charlie and Algernon, 1980, (off-Broadway) Creeps, 1973, Passover, 1986, (off-off-Broadway) The Gettysburg Sound Bite, 1989, Brunch At Trudy And Paul's, 1990, The Christmas Rules, 1991, The Monkey Business, 1992; dir. All's Well That Ends Well, 1990; producer How I Got that Story (off-Broadway), 1982, Diamonds (off-Broadway), 1984, Today, I Am A Fountain Pen (off-Broadway), 1986; dir. Man. Theatre Centre, 1982, 83, 84, Nat. Arts Centre, Ottawa, Ont., Can., 1984, Hedda Gabler, Centre Stage, Toronto, 1985, Reg: Life in the Trees, GeVa Theatre, 1991; asst. dir. Broadway prodn. Carrie, 1988. Recipient Dixon award Georgetown U., 1968; alumni achievement award Georgetown U. Alumni Club Met. Washington, 1981; Mayor's Arts award D.C., 1982. Mem. Soc. Stage Dirs. and Choreographers, Episc. Actors Guild (mem. council). Home: 7 Stuyvesant Oval New York NY 10009-1901

SCHEEL, NELS EARL, financial executive, accountant; b. Spencer, Wis., Sept. 25, 1925; s. Roland Edward and Louise Ernestine (Hake) S.; m. Elaine Marie Carlisle, Aug. 28, 1949; children: Thomas W., John E., Martha L., Mark A., Mary E. BS, Youngstown Coll., 1949; MBA, U. Pa., 1950. CPA, Ohio. Staff acct. Lybrand Ross Bros., Cleve., 1950-54; asst. controller Century Foods, Youngstown, Ohio, 1954-62; treas., controller The Bailey Co., Cleve., 1962-63, Golden Dawn Foods, Sharon, Pa., 1963-82; v.p., chief fin. officer Peter J. Schmitt Co., Sharon, 1982-89; cons. to industry Columbiana, 1989- ; part-time faculty Youngstown (Ohio) State U., 1954— . Pres. Crestview Bd. Edn., Columbiana, Ohio, 1970-81. Staff sgt. AUS, 1943-46, PTO, hon. discharge. Mem. Am. Inst. CPA's, Ohio Soc. CPA's.

SCHEELE, PAUL DRAKE, former hospital supply corporate executive; b. Elgin, Ill., Aug. 6, 1922; s. Arthur R. and Helen M. (Christiansen) S. B.A., Coe Coll., 1944; M.B.A., Harvard, 1947. With Am. Hosp. Supply Corp., 1947— ; pres. Harleco div., Phila., 1966-68; group v.p. Am. Hosp. Supply Corp., 1968-70; exec. v.p., also pres. internat. group Am. Hosp. Supply Corp., Evanston, Ill., 1970-74, v.p., asst. to chmn. bd., 1974-81. Chmn. bd. trustees Coe Coll. Served to 1st lt., inf. AUS, 1943-46. Mem. Harvard Bus. Sch. Club, Harvard Club Fla., Econ. Club (Chgo.), Tau Kappa Epsilon, Pi Delta Epsilon.

SCHEELER, CHARLES, construction company executive; b. Balt., June 20, 1925; s. George F. and Catherine Louise (Seward) S.; m. Mary Katherine Scarborough, Aug. 22, 1953; children—Charles D., George D., Donald C. B.S., U. Md., 1948, LL.B., 1952. Bar: Md. 1952; CPA, Md. With C.J. Langenfelder & Son, Inc., Balt., 1949— ; exec. v.p., treas. C.J. Langenfelder & Son, Inc., 1974-77, pres., chief exec. officer, 1977— ; chmn. bd. Rosedale Fed. Savs. & Loan Assn. Served with USN, 1943-46, PTO. Mem. AICPA, Md. Assn. CPAs. Office: 8427 Pulaski Hwy Baltimore MD 21237-3093

SCHEELER, JAMES ARTHUR, architect; b. Pontiac, Ill., Dec. 20, 1927; s. Aman B. and Jane (Steele) S.; m. Barbara Jean Lloyd, Sept. 2, 1950; children: James Erich, Carl Aman, Orissa Jane Elizabeth. B.S. with highest honors, U. Ill., 1951, M.S., 1952; postgrad., U. Liverpool, 1952-53. Grad. asst. U. Ill., Urbana, 1950-52; draftsman-designer Lundeen & Hilfinger, Bloomington, Ill., 1952-53; designer Skidmore, Owings & Merrill, Chgo., 1955-59; partner Richardson, Severns, Scheeler & Assos., Inc., Champaign, Ill., 1959-65; v.p., treas. Richardson, Severns, Scheeler & Assos., Inc., 1965-71; vice chmn. bd., dir. Prodn. Systems for Architects and Engrs., Inc., 1973-81; vis. critic U. Ill., 1959-60. Mem. Plan Commn. Champaign, 1966—, chmn., 1969-71; mem. Champaign County Regional Planning Commn., 1967-71; bd. dirs. Nat. Center for a Barrier-Free Environment, 1978—, pres., 1981. Served with USN, 1946-47. Recipient various archtl. awards.; Francis J. Plym fellow, 1953-54; Fulbright fellow, 1953. Fellow AIA (treas. Central Ill. chpt. 1967-68, sec. 1968-69, pres. 1970-71, nat. dep. exec. v.p. 1971-76, pres. corp. 1974-78, exec. v.p. 1977-78, program devel. group exec. 1976-85, sr. exec. 1985-88, v.p. design practice group 1989, resident fellow 1990—). Fedn. Colls. Architects Republic Mex. (hon.); mem. Ill. Arts Council (archtl. adv. bd. 1966-71), Montessori Soc. Champaign-Urbana (dir. 1964-66), Gargoyle, Scarab, Phi Kappa Phi, Lambda Chi Alpha, Lambda Alpha. Episcopalian. Address: 11179 Saffold Way Reston VA 22090-3824

SCHEER, JULIAN WEISEL, business executive, author; b. Richmond, Va., Feb. 20, 1926; s. George Fabian and Hilda (Knopf) S.; m. Suzanne Fugler Huggan, Oct. 9, 1965; 1 child, Hilary Susannah; children by previous marriage: Susan, David Scott, George Grey. AB, U. N.C., 1950. Reporter Mid-Va. Publs., Richmond, 1939-43; pres. Scheer Syndicate, Chapel Hill, N.C., 1947-53; columnist, reporter Charlotte (N.C.) News, 1953-62; asst. adminstr. pub. affairs NASA, 1962-71; ptnr. Sullivan, Murray & Scheer, Washington, 1971-76; sr. v.p. corp. affairs LTV Corp., Dallas, 1976-93; ptnr. Murray, Scheer, Tapia and Montgomery, Washington, 1993—; bd. dirs. several corps.; mem. adv. coun. NASA. Free-lance writer, author. Bd. dirs. Sch. Journalism, U. N.C. With U.S. Mcht. Marine, 1943-46; with USNR, 1946-53. Mem. Algonquin Soc., City Tavern Club, Sigma Delta Chi, Pi Lambda Phi. Home: 8303 Old Dumfries Rd Catlett VA 22019-9001

SCHEER, MILTON DAVID, physical chemist; b. N.Y.C., Dec. 22, 1922; s. Abraham and Lena (Brauner) S.; m. Emily Hirsch, June 23, 1945; children—Jessica, Richard Mark, Julia Rachel. B.S., CCNY, 1943; M.S., N.Y. U., 1947, Ph.D., 1951. Chemist Bd. Econ. Warfare, Guatemala, C. Am., 1943-44; research asst. N.Y. U., 1947-50; combustion scientist U.S. Naval Air Rocket Test Sta., Dover, N.J., 1950-52; phys. chemist U.S. Bur. Mines, Pitts., 1952-55; research scientist Gen. Electric Co., Cin., 1955-58; phys. chemist Nat. Bur. Standards, Washington, 1958-68; chief photochemistry sect. Nat. Bur. Standards, 1968-70, chief phys. chemistry div., 1970-77; dir. Center for Thermodynamics and Molecular Sci., Nat. Measurement Lab., 1977-80; research scientist chem. kinetics div. Ctr. for Chem. Physics, Nat. Measurement Lab., 1981-85; ptnr. McNesby & Scheer Research Assocs., 1985-89; rsch. cons. U.S. Dept. Energy, Germantown, Md., 1990-94; vis. prof. U. Md., 1980-81; Fulbright scholar U. Rome, 1982-83. Contbr. numerous articles to profl. jours. Served with USN, 1944-46. Fellow Am. Inst. Chemists, AAAS; mem. Am. Chem. Soc., Am. Phys. Soc. Home: 15100 Interlachen Dr Apt 512 Silver Spring MD 20906-5605

SCHEERER, ERNEST WILLIAM, dentist; b. Wabash, Ind., May 18, 1932; s. Ernest William and Anna Lucille (Bahler) S.; m. Ingrid Elvy Yvonne, Sept. 28, 1973. BS, Purdue U., 1954; DDS, Ind. U., 1961. Intern The Queen's Hosp., Honolulu, 1961-62; assoc. Pvt. Dental Practice, Honolulu, 1963-65; owner Pvt. Solo Dental Practice, Honolulu, 1965-75; ptnr. Dental Adminstrn., Honolulu, 1975-78; pres. Scheerer & West Dental Corp., Honolulu, 1978—; chief Dept. Dentistry Queen's Hosp., Honolulu. Contbr. various clin. articles to profl. jours. Mem. Big Bros., Hawaii, 1968-74. Fellow Acad. Gen. Dentistry, Hawaii Acad. Gen. Dentistry (pres.), Am. Coll. Dentists; mem. Am. Dental Assn., Hawaii Dental Assn. (treas.), Internat. Acad. of Gnathology, Pierre Fauchard Soc., Fedn. Dental Internat., Am. Equilibration Soc., Acad. of Osseointegration, Hawaii Med. Library (sec.). Mem. United Ch. of Christ. Club: Honolulu, Pacific. Lodge: Elks. Avocations: tennis, travel, Hawaiian music. Office: Scheerer & West Inc 735 Bishop St Ste 211 Honolulu HI 96813-4884

SCHEERER, PAUL J., lawyer; b. Sturgeon Bay, Wis., 1945. BA, U. Mich., 1967; JD magna cum laude, U. Minn., 1970. Bar: Minn. 1970. Assoc. prof. William Mitchell Coll. Law, 1972-74; ptnr. Dorsey & Whitney, Mpls. Office: Dorsey & Whitney 220 S 6th St Minneapolis MN 55402-4500

SCHEETZ, GEORGE HENRY, library director; b. Columbus, Ohio, July 27, 1952; s. Donald Jean and Betty Jane (Killeen) S.; m. Kathy Charlotte Durley, Apr. 28, 1979; children: Trevor Killeen, Avery Kathleen. AB, U. Ill., 1974, MS, 1976. Reference libr. Bradley U., Peoria, Ill., 1977-78; bus. libr. Peoria Pub. Libr., 1978-79, br. mgr., 1979-82; asst. dir. Ames (Iowa) Pub. Libr., 1982-85; dir. Sioux City (Iowa) Pub. Libr., 1985-92, Champaign (Ill.) Pub. Libr., 1992—; registered agt. Sioux City Pub. Libr. Found., 1990-92; ex officio bd. dirs. Champaign Pub. Libr. Found., 1993—. Author: Place Names of Story County, 1985, Trevor, 1986, Name's Names, 1988; editor: Riverworld War, 1980; contbr. articles to profl. jours. Rep. Jr. League Community Adv. Coun., Sioux City, 1985-89; bd. dirs. Sioux City Concert Course, 1991-92. Named one of Outstanding Young Men of Am., Jaycees, 1979. Mem. ALA, Ill. Libr. Assn. (mem. pub. policy com. 1994-), Am. Name Soc., Ill. State Libr. Adv. Com. (subcom. pub. libr. svc. 1992—), Sci. Fiction Rsch. Assn., Rotary, Sigma Tau Delta, Omicron Delta Kappa. Roman Catholic. Avocations: books and bibliographies, Sherlock Holmes, onomastics, logology, philately. Home: #163 2112 W White St Champaign IL 61821-2935 Office: Champaign Pub Libr 505 S Randolph St Champaign IL 61820-5193

SCHEETZ, SISTER MARY JOELLEN, English language educator; b. Lafayette, Ind., May 20, 1926; d. Joseph Albert and Ellen Isabelle (Fitzgerald) S. A.B., St. Francis Coll., 1956; M.A., U. Notre Dame, 1964; Ph.D., U. Mich., 1970. Tchr. English, Bishop Luers High Sch., Fort Wayne, Ind., 1965-67; acad. dean St. Francis Coll., Fort Wayne, 1967-68; pres. St. Francis Coll., Ft. Wayne, Ind., 1970-93; pres. emeritus; English lang. prof. St. Francis Coll., Ft. Wayne, Ind., 1993—. Mem. Nat. Coun. Tchrs. English, Delta Epsilon Sigma. Office: St Francis Coll 2701 Spring St Fort Wayne IN 46808

SCHEFFLER, ISRAEL, philosopher, educator; b. N.Y.C., Nov. 25, 1923; s. Leon and Ethel (Grünberg) S.; m. Rosalind Zuckerbrod, June 26, 1949; children: Samuel, Laurie. B.A., Bklyn. Coll., 1945, M.A., 1948; M.H.L. Jewish Theol. Sem., 1949; Ph.D. (Ford fellow 1951), U. Pa., 1952; A.M. (hon.), Harvard U., 1959; D.H.L. (hon.), Jewish Theol. Sem., 1993. Mem. faculty Harvard U., 1952-92, prof. edn., 1961-62, prof. edn. and philosophy, 1962-64, Victor S. Thomas prof. edn. and philosophy, 1964-92, professor emeritus, 1992—, hon. research fellow in cognitive studies, 1965-66, co-dir. Research Ctr. for Philosophy of Edn., 1983—; Fellow Center for Advanced Study in Behavioral Scis., 1972-73. Author: The Language of Education, 1960, The Anatomy of Inquiry, 1963, Conditions of Knowledge, 1965, Science and Subjectivity, 1967, Reason and Teaching, 1973, Four Pragmatists, 1974, Beyond the Letter, 1979, Of Human Potential, 1985, Inquiries, 1986, In Praise of the Cognitive Emotions, 1991, Teachers of My Youth, 1995; co-author: Work, Education and Leadership, 1995; editor: Philosophy and Education, 1958, 66; co-editor: Logic and Art, 1972; contbr. articles to profl. jours. Recipient Alumni award of merit Bklyn. Coll., 1967; Disting. Service medal Tchrs. Coll., Columbia, 1980; Guggenheim fellow, 1958-59, 72-73; NSF grantee, 1962, 65. Mem. Am. Acad. Arts and Scis., Am. Philos. Assn., Aristotelian Soc., Philosophy Edn. Soc., Nat. Acad. Edn. (charter), Philosophy of Sci. Assn. (pres. 1973-75). Office: Harvard U Larsen Hall Cambridge MA 02138

SCHEFFLER, LEWIS FRANCIS, pastor, educator, research scientist; b. Springfield, Ohio, Oct. 13, 1928; s. Lewis Francis and Emily Louise (Kloker) S.; m. Willa Pauline Cole, Aug. 9, 1949 (div. 1978); children: Lewis F. Fischer, Richard Thomas, Gary Arlen, Tonni Kay; m. Mary Lee Smith, Apr. 18, 1978; stepchildren: Kimberly McCollum, Jeffrey McIlroy, Kerry Buell. BA in Liberal Arts, Cin. Bible Seminary, 1950; AA in Bus., Jefferson Coll., 1989; MAT, Webster U., 1989. Quality assurance Tectum Corp., Newark, 1954-57; rsch. group leader Owens-Corning Fiberglas, Granville, Ohio, 1957-64; tech. asst. to v.p. R&D and Engring., 1960-61; rsch. administr. Modiglas Fibers Corp., Bremen, Ohio, 1965-68; dir. R & D Flex-O-Lite Corp., St. Louis; pastor Christian Ch., St. Louis, 1971-75; police commns. Brentwood (Mo.) Police Dept., 1975-87; pastor Christian Ch., Potosi, Mo., 1988-89, Slater (Mo.) Christian Ch., 1989-93, Laddonia Christian Ch., 1994—; asst. prof. English lang. and lit. Mo. Valley Coll., Marshall, 1989-93; adj. prof. theology Mo. Sch. Religion, 1993—; organizing co-chmn. aerospace composite materials com. ASTM. 1961; mem. exec. bd. Northwest Area Christian Ch., 1989-93; mem. Coun. of Areas of Mid-Am. Region Christian Ch., 1990-93; cons. in field. Contbr. articles to profl. jours. Patentee in field. Money raiser United Appeal, chaplaincy Blessing Hosp., Quincy, Ill., 1974; vol. Ill. Divsn. Children and Family Svcs., 1972-75; sec. exec. com. N.W. Area Christian Ch. (Disciples of Christ). Mem. Medieval Acad. Am., Mo. Philol. Assn. Avocations: philosophy and pomology. Home: R1 Box 32A Laddonia MO 63352 *Now and then, God has so touched people in such a way that, recognizing it, we think "So that's what God must be like!" and our ethical and moral sensitivities are heightened.*

SCHEFFLER, ROBERT W., insurance company executive; b. Pekin, Ill., Apr. 14, 1940; s. Walter J. Scheffler and Mary H. (Johns) Atterberry; m. Sandra K. Lowry, June 8, 1963; children: Raelynn, Renee. BA, Bradley U., 1964. Automobile ins. underwriter Pekin Ins., 1964-78, asst. underwriting mgr., 1978-81, underwriting mgr., 1981-87, v.p. underwriting, 1987-90, sr. v.p., 1990-91, exec. v.p., 1991—. Mem. Cen. Ill. Chartered Property-Casalty Underwriters. Office: Pekin Life Ins Co 2505 Court St Pekin IL 61558-0002

SCHEFFMAN, DAVID THEODORE, economist, management educator, consultant; b. Milaca, Minn., Dec. 1, 1943; s. David Theodore and Fern Virginia (Maas) S.; m. Cathy Schutz, May 11, 1989. BA, U. Minn., 1967; PhD, MIT, 1971. Lectr. Boston Coll., 1970-71; from asst. prof. to assoc. prof. Univ. Western Ont., London, Can., 1971-81; sr. economist FTC, Washington, 1979-82, dep. dir., 1983-86, dir. bur. econs., 1985-88; Justin Potter prof., prof. bus. strategy and mktg. Vanderbilt U., Nashville, 1989—; prof., dir. Inst. Applied Econs. Concordia U., Montreal, Que., Can., 1982-83; adj. prof. Georgetown U. Law Ctr., Washington, 1986; cons. Ont. Econ. Coun., Toronto, 1973-81, GM, 1977, Cen. Oil Inquiry, Ottawa, Ont., 1982-84, Cen. Govt., Ottawa, 1979—, Can. Competition Tribunal, 1987-89, Can. Bur. Competition Policy, 1988-91, U.S. Sentencing Commn., 1988-89, PepsiCo, 1989-93, Kraft Gen. Food, 1989-92, PacifiCorp, 1989-93, NERA, 1991-93, Boeing, 1992—, LECG, 1993—, Berwind Industries, Inc., 1993—, Comm. Ctrl., Inc., Applied Innovation, Inc. Author: Speculation and Monopoly in Urban Development: Analytical Foundations, 1977, An Economic Analysis of Provincial Land Use Policies in Ontario, 1980, Social Regulation in Markets for Consumer Goods and Services, 1982, An Economic Analysis of the Impact of Rising Oil Prices on Urban Structure, 1983, Strategy, Structure, and Antitrust in the Carbonated Soft Drink Industry, 1992. Recipient Dissertation Fellowship award NSF, 1967-68; vis. scholar U. Minn., 1978. Mem. Am. Econ. Assn., Strategic Mgmt. Soc., Am. Mgmt. Assn., Am. Mktg. Assn. Office: Owen Grad Sch Mgmt Vanderbilt U Nashville TN 37203

SCHEFTNER, GEROLD, marketing executive; b. Milw., June 1, 1937; s. Arthur Joseph and Alice Agnes (Gregory) S.; m. Chantal Scheftner; children: Mark A., Mary L., Michael D. Student, Milw. Bus. Inst., 1953, Great Lakes Naval Acad. Sch. Dental-Med. Surgery, USAF, 1955-56, USAF Inst., 1959, Marquette U., 1959-60. Territorial rep. Mossey-Otto Co., Milw., 1960-63; with Den-Tal-Ez Mfg. Co., Des Moines, 1963—; dir. fgn. affairs Den-Tal-Ez Mfg. Co., 1969-71; dir. Far Ea. affairs, 1971-72, exec. dir. internat. sales/mktg., 1973, v.p., gen. mgr. internat. ops., 1974—, also corp. dir., 1969—; chmn. bd. Den-Tal-Ez Ltd., Gt. Britain, 1974—; pres., mktg. specialist Pennwalt/Jelenko; pres. S&S Scheftner, Ltd, Biel/Bienne, Mainz, Germany, Switzerland subs.; adviser Kuwait M.O.H., Saudi Arabia; pres. mktg. specialist Productivity Tng. Corp., Calif., Tek-Scan Inc. subs. GE, Boston, Swift Instruments, Boston, Oral Logic Inc., Seattle, LMT LAser, San Clemente, Calif.; researcher dental therapy equipment and apparatus Relaxodont (dental patient anxiety relaxer), Temple U, 21st Century Group, Jacksonville, Fla., OralSafe, Inc., Temecula, Calif.; mfr. disposable dental surgery instruments for WHO, Geneva. Pub. Die Produkt Börse-DENTAL. Bd. dirs. Dist. Export Coun. Iowa, 1976-77; mem. Lake Panorama (Iowa) Devel. Assn., 1972-73; chmn. World Trade Coun. Iowa, 1976-77; adv. bd. bldg. program St. Charles Boys Home, Milw., 1963. With USAF, 1955-59. Recipient Presdl. Mgr. of Yr. award Den-Tal-Ez Co., 1967, Lectr. award Faculdade de Odontologia, U. Ribeirao Preto, Brazil, 1974. Mem. Am. Dental Trade Assn., Am. Dental Mfrs. Assn., Hong Kong Dental Trade Assn. (hon.), Saudi Dental Soc. (advisor sci. dental products, concepts), Internat. Platform Assn., Greater Des Moines C. of C. (dir. 1976-77), Lions. Republican. Office: Silbergasse 6, CH-2502 Biel Switzerland *Live enthusiastically, expand your natural attributes, be truthful and sincere, assume responsibility, avoid prejudice of the innocent, respect authority, live for today, but improve tomorrow-pray consistently and confidently, love and be loved, be proud of your noble heritage of being an American.*

SCHEIBE, KARL EDWARD, psychology educator; b. Belleville, Ill., Mar. 5, 1937; s. John Henry and Esther Julia (Friesen) S.; m. Elizabeth Wentworth Mixter, Sept. 10, 1961; children: David Sawyer, Robert Daniel. B.S., Trinity Coll., 1959; Ph.D., U. Calif.-Berkeley, 1963; M.A. (hon.), Wesleyan U., 1973. Faculty mem. Wesleyan U., Middletown, Conn., 1963—, prof. psychology, 1973—, chmn. dept., 1973-76, 79-81, 86-88; v.p. Stonington Inst., 1984-91; dir. Saybrook Counseling Ctr., 1990—; cons. prof. U. So. Calif., 1974; dir. rev. panels NSF Sci. Profl. Devel. Program, 1975-81; cons. Am. Council Edn., 1975-81. Author: Beliefs and Values, 1970, Mirror, Masks, Lies and Secrets, 1979, Studies in Social Identity, 1983, Self Studies: The Psychology of Self and Identity, 1995. Trustee Trinity Coll., Hartford, Conn., 1977-83; moderator congregation First Ch. of Christ, Middletown, 1981-82. Woodrow Wilson fellow, 1959; NSF fellow, 1961; NIMH research grantee, 1964-68; Fulbright fellow Cath. U. Sao Paulo, Brazil, 1972-73, 84. Mem. Am. Psychol. Assn., New Eng. Psychol. Assn., Eastern Psychol. Assn., Conn. Acad. Arts and Scis., Phi Beta Kappa. Congregationalist. Home: 11 Long Ln Middletown CT 06457-4046 Office: Wesleyan U Dept Psychology Middletown CT 06457

SCHEIBEL, ARNOLD BERNARD, psychiatrist, educator, researcher; b. N.Y.C., Jan. 18, 1923; s. William and Ethel (Greenberg) S.; m. Madge Mila Ragland, Mar. 3, 1950 (dec. Jan. 1977); m. Marian Diamond, Sept.

1982. B.A., Columbia U., 1944, M.D., 1946; M.S., U. Ill., 1952. Intern Mt. Sinai Hosp., N.Y.C., 1946-47; resident psychiatry Barnes and McMillan Hosp., St. Louis, 1947-48, Ill. Neuropsychiat. Inst., Chgo., 1950-52; asst. prof. psychiatry and anatomy U. Tenn. Med. Sch., 1952-53, assoc. prof., 1953-55; assoc. prof. UCLA Med. Center, 1955-67, prof. psychiatry and anatomy, 1967—, mem. Brain Rsch. Inst., 1960—, acting dir. Brain Rsch. Inst., 1987-90, dir., 1990—; cons. VA hosps., Los Angeles, 1956—. Contbr. numerous articles to tech. jours, chpts. to books; editorial bd.: Brain Research, 1967-77, Developmental Psychobiology, 1968—, Internat. Jour. Neurosci., 1969—, Jour. Biol. Psychiatry, 1968—, Jour. Theoretical Biology, 1980—. Mem. Pres.'s Commn. on Aging, Nat. Inst. Aging, 1980—. Served with AUS, 1943-46; from 1t. to capt. M.C. AUS, 1948-50. Guggenheim fellow (with wife), 1953-54, 59. Fellow Am. Acad. Arts and Scis., Norwegian Acad. Scis.; mem. AAAS, Am. Psychiat. Assn. (lifetime fellow), Am. Neurol. Assn., Soc. Neurosci., Psychiat. Research Assn., Am. EEG Assn., Am. Assn. Anatomists, Soc. Biol. Psychiatry, Am. Acad. Neurology, So. Calif. Psychiat. Assn. Home: 16231 Morrison St Encino CA 91436-1331 Office: UCLA Los Angeles CA 90024 *Intense personal tragedy can embitter life and choke off further personal creativity. It may also offer the opportunity to open new doors in the discovery of self. I am more aware than ever of my good fortune in having the opportunity to teach, to continue investigative work in the structure and function of the brain, and to give love and care to those who need it. I am more than ever convinced that loving and being loved is the greatest good that we can know, the state in which we most nearly fulfill our roles as human beings.*

SCHEIBEL, JAMES ALLEN, volunteer service executive; b. St. Paul, Aug. 30, 1947; s. Donald Louis and Beverly Wanda (Call) Urista; m. Mary Pat Lee, July 10, 1987.. AA, Nazareth Hall, 1967; BA, St. John's U., 1969; Hon. Doctorate, Coll. St. Catherine, 1993. City coun. aide to Joanne Showalter St. Paul, 1978-79; vol. 15th anniversary VISTA, 1979-80; v.p. Mondale's Youth Employment Task Force, Washington, 1980-81; assoc. dir. Citizen Heritage Ctr., St. Paul, 1981-82; city coun. mem. City of St. Paul, 1982-89, mayor, 1990-94; dir. domestic vol. svc. programs Corp. Nat. Svc., Washington, 1994—; mem. nat. adv. coun. Ctr. for Global Orgn., 1990—; chmn. U.S. Conf. of Mayors Task Force on Hunger, 1990-94; mem. Lifelong Literacy Project, St. Paul, 1990-94; mem. bd. dirs. Nat. Law Ctr. on Homelessness and Poverty. Mem. Partnership for Democracy, Washington, 1988-91. Recipient Spurgeon award, 1985, Am. Jewish Com. Humanitarian award, 1990, Chip Fricke award Nagasaki Sister City Com., 1993, Bravo award St. Paul C. of C., 1993. Office: Corp for Nat Svc Office of CEO Domestic Volunteer Svc Program 1201 New York Ave NW Washington DC 20525*

SCHEIBEL, KENNETH MAYNARD, journalist; b. Campbell, Nebr., May 17, 1920; s. G. Alfred and Rachel Christine (Koch) S.; m. Helen Schmitt, May 14, 1955 (div. Sept. 1977); children: Victor Warren Schmitt, William Becker Schmitt, Kenneth Jr., Sally. Student, George Washington U., 1938-41; BA, U. Va., 1947, MA, 1949. Mag. salesman Periodical Pubs. Service Bur., Inc., 1935-38; reporter Internat. News Service, Washington, 1940-41, Wall St. Jour., Washington, 1949-51; Washington corr. Gannett Newspapers, 1951-63; syndicated columnist N.Am. Newspaper Alliance, 1963-64; chief Washington bur. Donrey Media Group, 1964-67; founder, bur. chief Washington Bur. News, 1967—; founder nat. syndicated column Washington Farm Beat, 1970-85; Washington corr. Wis. State Jour., 1963-66, LaCrosse (Wis.) Tribune, 1963-66, Billings (Mont.) Gazette, 1964-71, V.I. Network, 1966-67, Moline (Ill.) Daily Dispatch, 1967-68, Drovers' Jour., 1967-68, Newport News (Va.) Daily Press & Times Herald, 1969-71, Packer Pub. Co., 1964-74, Gasoline Retailer, 1966-67, Okla., Farmer Stockman; congl. corr. F-D-C Reports, 1975-77; Washington columnist Farm Jour., 1960-75; covered nat. polit. convs., campaigns; v.p. Fraser Assos. (public relations), Washington, 1976-79; Congl. broadcast interviewer. Contbr. nat. mags., newspaper syndicates. Incorporator War Meml. of Korea, Washington, 1981; bd. dirs., treas. Nat. Ctr. Fin. and Econ. Info., U.S.-Saudi Arabian Joint Econ. Commn., Riyadh, 1985-86. Capt. AUS, 1941-45, 755th Tank Bn., 1942-45, Europe, North Africa, Italy. Decorated Bronze star, U.S. Army Occupation medal, Combat Infantryman badge; co-recipient Croix De Guerre (France), Thoth award for excellence in pub. rels., 1980. Mem. Izaak Walton League Am., White House Corrs. Assn., Overseas Press Club of Am., Am. Radio Relay League, Sigma Chi. Presbyn. Clubs: Nat. Press (Washington) (financial sec., gov. 1969-73, vice chmn. bd. 1971), dir. Nat. Press Bldg. Corp. (Washington) (1973, v.p., pres. club and bldg. corp. 1974). Home: 1325 18th St NW Apt 302 Washington DC 20036-6505 *The greatest sins are timidity and self indulgence, the greatest virtue is to love. Live each day, don't fret about yesterday or tomorrow. Enjoy the senses, learn from others, and never forget that both love and hate are returned.*

SCHEIBER, HARRY N., law educator; b. N.Y.C., 1935. BA, Columbia U., 1955; MA, Cornell U., 1957, PhD, 1961; MA (hon.), Dartmouth Coll., 1965. instr. to assoc. prof. history Dartmouth Coll., 1961-68, prof., 1968-71; prof. Am. history U. Calif., San Diego, 1971-80; prof. law Boalt Hall, U. Calif., Berkeley, 1980—, chmn. jurisprudence and social policy program, 1982-84, 90-93, assoc. dean, 1990-93; The Stefan Riesenfeld Prof., 1991—; vice chair Univ. Academic Senate, 1993-94. chair, 1994-95; Fulbright disting. sr. lectr., Australia, 1983, marine affairs coord. Calif. Sea Grant Coll. Program, 1989—. Chmn. Littleton Griswold Prize Legal History, 1985-88; pres. N.H. Civil Liberties Union, 1969-70; chmn. Project '87 Task Force on Pub. Programs, Washington, 1982-85; dir. Berkeley Seminar on Federalism, 1986—; cons. judiciary study U.S. Adv. Commn. Intergovernmental Rels., 1985-88; dir. NEH Inst. on Constitutionalism, U. Calif., Berkeley, 1986-87, 88-91. Recipient Sea Grant Colls. award, 1981-83, 84-85, 86—; fellow Ctr. Advanced Study in Behavioral Scis., Stanford Calif., 1967, 71; Guggenheim fellow, 1971, 88; Rockefeller Found. humanities fellow, 1979, NEH fellow, 1985-86; NSF grantee, 1979, 80, 88-89; Fellow U. Calif. Humanities Rsch. Inst., 1989. Mem. Am. Hist. Assn., Orgn. Am. Historians, Am. Soc. Intl. Law, Agrl. History Soc. (pres. 1978), Econ. History Assn. (trustee 1978-80), Law and Soc. Assn. (trustee 1979-81), Am. Soc. Legal History (pres 1982-86, 90—), Am. Bar Found. (legal history fellowship com. 1982-86), Nat. Assessment History and Citizenship Edn. (chmn. nat. acad. 1986-87), Marine Affairs and Policy Assn. (bd. dirs. 1991—), Ocean Governance Study Group (steering com. 1991—), Internat. Coun. Environ. Law. Author numerous books including: (with L. Friedman) American Law and the Constitutional Order, 1978, 2d edit. 1988; contbr. articles to law revs.and social sci. jours., 1963—. Office: U Calif Berkeley Law Sch Boalt Hall Berkeley CA 94720-2150

SCHEIBER, STEPHEN CARL, psychiatrist; b. N.Y.C., May 2, 1938; s. Irving Martin and Frieda Olga (Schor) S.; m. Mary Ann McDonnell, Sept. 14, 1965; children: Lisa Susan, Martin Irving, Laura Ann. BA, Columbia Coll., 1960; MD, SUNY, Buffalo, 1964. Diplomate Am. Bd. Psychiatry and Neurology. Intern Mary Fletcher Hosp., Burlington, Vt., 1964-65; resident in psychiatry Strong Meml. Hosp., Rochester, N.Y., 1967-70; asst. prof. U. Ariz., Tucson, 1970-76, assoc. prof., 1976-81, prof., 1981-86; exec. sec. Am. Bd. Psychiatry and Neurology, Inc., Deerfield, Ill., 1986-89; exec. v.p. Am. Bd. Psychiatry and Neurology, Inc., 1989—; prof. clin. psychiatry Northwestern U., Chgo. and Evanston, 1986—; adj. prof. psychiatry Med. Coll. Wis., Milw., 1986—. Co-editor: The Impaired Physician, 1983, Certification, Recertification and Lifetime Learning in Psychiatry, 1994; contbr. articles to profl. jours. Mem. med. adv. com. Casas de los Ninos, Tucson, 1974-86, mental health adv. com. Tucson Health Planning Council, 1974-75; med. student interviewer Office of Med. Edn., 1975; mem. Glenbrook (Ill.) North High Sch. Boosters Club, 1988-91. Served as surgeon USPHS, 1965-67. Grantee Group Therapy Outcome Studies on Inpatient Service, 1980, Dialysis and Schizophrenia Pilot Project NIH, 1978; recipient Outstanding Tchr. award U. Ariz., 1986. Fellow Am. Psychiat. Assn. (chmn. imparied physician com. 1985-88, cons. 1988-92), Am. Coll. Psychiatrists (bd. regents 1992—, treas. 1995—), Am. Assn. Dirs. Psychiat. Residency Tng. (pres. 1981-82), Assn. Acad. Psychiatry (Parliamentary sec. 1979*84, treas. 1984-88, pres.-elect 1988-89, pres. 1989-90), Group for Advancement of Psychiatry (invited mem., chmn. mem. edn. com. 1987-91, bd. dirs., sec. 1993—), Oracle Heights Club (pres. 1983-84). Democrat. Jewish. Office: Am Bd Psychiatry & Neurology 500 Lake Cook Rd Ste 335 Deerfield IL 60015-4939

SCHEICH, JOHN F., lawyer; b. Bklyn., Aug. 6, 1942; s. Frank A. and Dorothy (O'Hara) S. BA, St. John's U., N.Y.C., 1963, JD, 1966. Bar: N.Y. 1967, U.S. Ct. Internat. Trade Admission 1969, U.S. Dist. Ct. (ea. and so. dists.) N.Y. 1971, U.S. Ct. Appeals (2d cir.) 1971, U.S. Supreme Ct. 1975,

Pa. 1980. Spl. agt. FBI U.S. Dept. Justice, Washington, 1966-69; asst. dist. atty. Queens County, Kew Gardens, N.Y., 1969-72; pvt. practice John F. Scheich, P.C., N.Y., 1970-76, 79-91; ptnr. Raia & Scheich, P.C., N.Y., 1976-79; sr. ptnr. Scheich & Goldsmith, P.C., Richmond Hill, N.Y., 1991—; lectr. estate planning Nat. Bus. Inst., 1994; mem. assigned counsel panel for indigent defendants in major felony and murder cases 9th and 11th jud. dists. N.Y. State Supreme Ct., Queens County, 1972-94; lectr. Lawyers iin the Classroom, 1979-91; chmn. arbitration panel Civil Ct. City of N.Y., 1981-90; bd. dirs. Ra-Li Brokerage Corp., v.p., 1975—. Editor: Conashaugh Courier, 1989-92; mem. editorial bd., 1988-92; contbg. columnist, 1981-89. Mem. Com. for Beautification of East Norwich, N.Y., 1983—; pres. local chpt. Holy Name Soc., 1971-73; bd. dirs. Conashaugh Lakes Cmty. Assn., Milford, Pa., 1981-90, organizing mem., interim com., 1977-81, sec., 1981-82, v.p., 1982-84, pres., 1984-86; mem. St. Edward's Syosset (N.Y.) Sch. Bd. 1986-90; mem. parish coun. Our Lady of Perpetual Help, Richmond Hill, N.Y., 1976-82, pres., 1978-80, mem. fin. com., advisor to pastor, 1970-82, chmn. fin. com., 1979-82; bd. dirs. Northslope II Homeowners Assn., Shawnee-on-Delaware, Pa., 1988-90, 92-94; mem. East Norwich Rep. Club, 1982—; bd. dirs., 1984-87, 93—, v.p., 1987-89, pres., 1989-93; nat. trust and estate assoc. Meml. Sloane Kettering Cancer Ctr., 1994—; mem. Nat. Rep. Senatorial Com., 1994—; active Internat. Wine Ctr., 1985—, St. Edward the Confessor Ch., Syosset, 1982—, St. Vincent's Ch., Dingman Hills, Pa. 1977—, St. Cominic's Ch., Oyster Bay, N.Y., 1982—, St. John's Ch., St. Petersburg Beach, Fla., 1982—, Lincoln Ctr. Performing Arts, Inc., 1985—, Nat. Rep. Senatorial Com., 1988—, Bravo Soc., 1994—, Concern for Dying, 1984—, Sea Cliff Chamber Players, 1992—. Recipient J. Edgar Hoover award, 1967, award of appreciation, Civil Trial Inst., St. John's U. Sch. of Law, 1991, Disting. Svc. award, 1992, cert. of appreciation Conashaugh Lakes Community Assn., 1990, Dist. Svc. award Kiwanis Club, 1992, Cert. of Merit for Disting. Svc. award Nassau County Exec. Hon. Thomas Gulotta, 1989, Presdl. Order of Merit award Pres. George Bush, 1991, Order of Merit award Nat. Rep. Senatorial Com., 1994; named one of Best Trial Lawyers in the U.S., Town and Country mag., 1985. Mem. ABA (cert. of appreciation Am. Bar Endowment 1992), Assn. Trial Lawyers Am., Pa. Bar Assn., Pike County Bar Assn., N.Y. State Bar Assn., Queens County Bar Assn., Nassau County Bar Assn. N.Y. State Trial Lawyers Assn., Criminal Cts. Bar Assn., Internat. Platform Assn., John Marshall Lawyers Assn. (bd. dirs., pres. 1992—), Soc. Former Spl. Agts. of FBI, N.Y. State Assn. criminal Def. Lawyers, St. John's Coll. Alumni Assn., Asst. Dist. Attys. Assn. Queens County, St. John's U. Sch. of Law Alumni Assn., Friends of the Arts, Cath. Lawyers Guild, KC, Brookhaven Wine Lovers Assn., Phi Alpha Delta. Avocation: collecting fine wines. Home: 170 Sugar Toms Ln East Norwich NY 11732-1153 Office: Scheich & Goldsmith PC 103-42 Lefferts Blvd Richmond Hill NY 11419-2012 also: 109 Newbridge Rd Hicksville NY 11801 also: 3901 Conashaugh Trl Box 4042, Conashaugh Lakes Milford PA 18337

SCHEIDEL, THOMAS MAYNARD, speech communication educator; b. Columbus, Nebr., July 24, 1931; s. Ralph Maynard and Helen Margaret (Beierle) S.; m. Frances Emily Smith, Sept. 4, 1953; children—Susan Jane, Thomas Parker. B.A., Willamette U., Salem, Oreg., 1953; M.A., U. Wash., 1955, Ph.D., 1958. Instr., asst. prof. U. Wash., 1958-60; asst. prof. speech communication Cornell U., Ithaca, N.Y., 1960-63; assoc. prof. U. Ill., 1963-69; prof. U. Wis., Madison, 1969-76; prof., dept. speech communication U. Wash., Seattle, 1976—, assoc. dean humanities, 1988-92; Mem. Speech Communication Assn., Internat. Communication Assn. Author: Persuasive Speaking, 1967, Speech Communication and Human Interaction, 1972, 2d edit., 1976, (with Laura Crowell) Discussing and Deciding, 1979. Home: 5736 60th Ave NE Seattle WA 98105-2036 Office: 205 Raitt Hall Dept Speech Communication Univ of Wash Seattle WA 98195

SCHEIDT, W. ROBERT, chemistry educator, researcher; b. Richmond Heights, Mo., Nov. 13, 1942; s. Walter Martin and Martha (Videtich) S.; m. Kathryn Sue Barnes, Aug. 9, 1964; children: Karl Andrew, David Martin. BS, U. Mo., 1964; MS, U. Mich., 1965, PhD, 1968; postdoctoral studies, Cornell U., 1970. Asst. prof. U. Notre Dame, Ind., 1970-76, assoc. prof., 1976-80, prof., 1980—; vis. prof. U. Wash., Seattle, 1980, U. Paris (Orsay), France, 1991; mem. review sect. Metallobiochemistry NIH, Bethesda, 1991—. Contbr. articles to profl. jours. Fellow AAAS; mem. Am. Chem. Soc. (assoc. editor Chem. Revs. jour. 1980-85), Am. Crystallographic Assn., Sigma X. Democrat. Office: U Notre Dame Dept Chemisty Notre Dame IN 46556

SCHEIFELE, RICHARD PAUL, cosmetics and chemical manufacturing company executive; b. Phila., Mar. 6, 1934; s. E. Paul and Kathryn Edith (Weidner) S.; m. Wanda Louise Bruch, June 15, 1957; 1 child, Kristina Louisa. BCE, Cornell U., 1957. Area mfg. dir. Colgate Palmolive Ltd. S.A., Guatemala City, Guatemala, 1965-68; tech. dir. Toddy Venezolana S.A., Caracas, Venezuela, 1968-69; mfg. dir. Chesebrough-Pond's Inc., Clinton, Conn., 1969-72, dir. internat. mfg., Geneva, 1972-76, corp. v.p. mfg., Greenwich, 1976-82, group v.p., 1982-85, vice chmn., Westport, Conn., 1985—; also bd. dirs. Mem. AAAS, Indsl. Research Inst., Dirs. Indsl. Research. Club: Bailiwick. Avocations: archeology, art, real estate, biking, tennis. Home: 35 Birchwood Dr Greenwich CT 06831-3311 Office: Chesebrough-Pond's Inc Box 6000 33 Benedict Pl Greenwich CT 06836

SCHEIFLY, JOHN EDWARD, retired lawyer; b. Mexico, Mo., Aug. 25, 1925; s. Luke Clauser and Isabella (Sprankle) S.; m. Patricia Ann Lenhart, Dec. 27, 1947; children: John Edward, Jan Ellen. Sc.B., Brown U., 1945; J.D., Washington and Lee U., 1948. Bar: W.Va. 1948, Calif. 1954. Practice law L.A., 1953—; mem. firm Baker, Scheifly & Porter, Huntington, W.Va., 1949-53, McClean, Salisbury, Petty & McClean, L.A., 1953-57, Willis, Butler, Scheifly, Leydorf & Grant (and predecessors), L.A., 1958-81, Bryan, Cave, McPheeters & McRoberts, L.A., 1981-84; mem. firm Morgan, Lewis & Bockius, L.A., 1984-90, counsel, 1990—; lectr. tax law U. So. Calif., 1960-74. Author lectr. fed. tax matters profl. publs., insts. Dir. Presbyn. Intercommunity Hosp., Whittier, Calif., 1994—. Lt. USNR, 1943-46, 51-53. Mem. ABA (mem. coun. sect. taxation 1974-77), State Bar Calif., Los Angeles County Bar Assn. (chmn. tax sect. 1965-66), Jonathan Club (L.A.), Hacienda Golf Club (LaHabra, Calif.), Monterey Country Club (Palm Desert, Calif.). Home: 9441 Friendly Woods Ln Whittier CA 90605-1658 Office: Morgan Lewis & Bockius 801 S Grand Ave Los Angeles CA 90017-4613

SCHEIG, HENRY FREDERICK, fraternal insurance society executive; b. Warren, Ohio, June 14, 1924; s. Henry F. and Martha J. (Zivitz) S.; m. Mary Beardsley, June 8, 1946; children—Kathryn C., William B. B.A. in Math, U. Iowa, 1947, M.S., 1949; LL.D., Valparaiso (Ind.) U., 1976. Asst. sec. Lincoln Nat. Life Ins. Co., 1949-54; with Aid Assn. for Lutherans, Appleton, Wis., 1954—; actuary Aid Assn. for Lutherans, 1958-68, sr. v.p., then exec. v.p., 1964-72, pres., 1972-85, chmn., chief exec. officer, 1985—; dir. Wis. Power & Light Co. Exec. bd. Bay Lakes Council Boy Scouts Am., 1976-85; bd. dirs. Outagamie County Health Center, 1977-85. Served with USAAF, 1943-46. Fellow Soc. Actuaries, Fraternal Actuarial Assn. (pres. 1961-62); mem. Am. Acad. Actuaries (dir. 1971-74), Internat. Actuarial Assn., Wis. Actuaries Club, Wis. Ins. Club, Life Office Mgmt. Assn. (dir. 1974-77), Nat. Fraternal Congress Am. (exec. com. 1971-76, pres. 1974-75, pres. gen. sessions program commn. 1969-71), Wis. Assn. Mfrs. and Commerce (bd. dirs. 1985—), Nature Conservancy (bd. dirs. Wis. chpt. 1984—), Fox Cities C. of C. and Industry (dir. 1975-77). Lutheran. Club: North Shore Country (Menasha, Wis.). Address: 4321 N Ballard Rd Appleton WI 54919-0001*

SCHEIMER, LOUIS, film and television producer; b. Pitts., Oct. 19, 1928; s. Sam and Lena (Kessler) S.; m. Jay Wucher, Dec. 29, 1953; children—Lane, Erika. BFA, Carnegie Inst. Tech., 1952. With various animation studios, 1955-62; founder, pres. Filmation Studios, Woodland Hills, Calif., 1962-89; pres. Lou Scheimer Prodns., Woodland Hills, Calif., 1989—. Producer: (animated TV programs) Archie, 1968, Fat Albert, 1972 (Wilbur award, Scott Newman Drug Abuse Prevention award 1985), Star Trek, 1973 (Emmy award 1974), Isis, 1975, Tarzan, 1976, Space Academy, 1977, He-Man and Masters of the Universe, 1983, She-Ra Princess of Power, 1985, Ghostbusters, 1986, BraveStarr, 1987, Arch Angels, 1995 (feature film) Pinocchio and the Emperor of the Night, 1987, Happily Ever After, 1989. Recipient Christopher award, 1972, Emmy award, 1979. Mem. Nat. Acad. TV Arts and Scis., Motion Picture Acad. Jewish. Office: Lou Scheimer Prodns 20300 Victory Blvd Woodland Hills CA 91364

SCHEIN, EDGAR HENRY, management educator; b. Zurich, Switzerland, Mar. 5, 1928; came to U.S., 1939, naturalized, 1944; s. Marcel and Hilde (Schoenbeck) S.; m. Mary Louise Lodmell, July 28, 1956; children—Louisa, Elizabeth, Peter. Ph.B., U. Chgo., 1946, B.A., 1947; B.A., Stanford U., 1948, M.A., 1949; Ph.D., Harvard U., 1953. Teaching asst. statistics Stanford U., 1947-49; teaching asst. social psychology Harvard U., 1949-52; research psychologist, neuropsychiatry div. Walter Reed Army Inst. Research, also chief social psychology sect., 1952-56; mem. faculty MIT, 1956—, prof. orgnl. psychology and mgmt., 1964—, chmn. orgn. studies group Sloan Sch. Mgmt., 1972-81, Sloan Fellows prof. mgmt., 1978—; mem. adv. bd., exec. com. Nat. Tng. Labs., 1962-64; cons. to govt. and industry, 1956—. Author books and articles in field. Served to capt. AUS, 1950-56. Recipient Aux. Research award Social Sci. Research Council, 1958. Mem. Am. Psychol. Assn., Am. Sociol. Assn., Phi Beta Kappa, Sigma Xi. Office: MIT Sloan Sch Mgmt Cambridge MA 02139

SCHEIN, HARVEY L., communications executive; b. N.Y.C., Sept. 15, 1927; s. Morris and Matilda (Feld) S.; m. Joy Carol Gitlin, Dec. 11, 1963; children: Mark David, Justin Harris. A.B., NYU, 1949; LL.B., Harvard U., 1952. Bar: N.Y. 1953. Asso. Rosenman, Colin, Kaye, Petschek & Freund, N.Y.C., 1952-58; gen. atty. Columbia Records div. CBS, also asst. sec. CBS, 1958-60, div. v.p. internat., 1961-67; pres. CBS Internat. div., 1968-71, CBS Columbia Group, 1971-72; pres., chief exec. officer Sony Corp. Am., 1972-77, chmn., 1977-78; exec. v.p. Warner Communications Inc., 1978-80; pres. Warner Plays, Inc., 1978-80; pres., chief exec. officer Polygram Corp., 1980-83; exec. v.p.; dir. News America Pub. Inc., 1983-88; pres., chief exec. officer Skyband Inc., 1983-88; v.p., bd. dirs. Internat. Fedn. Phonographic Industries, 1969-73; mem. Marconi Internat. Fellowship Council; mem. adv. council Partners of the Americas; asst. sec. Franklin D. Roosevelt Found., 1952-58. Editor: Harvard Law Rev., 1951-52. Served with USNR, 1945. Mem. Phi Beta Kappa.

SCHEIN, PHILIP SAMUEL, physician, educator, pharmaceutical executive; b. Asbury Park, N.J., May 10, 1939; s. Irving and Henrietta (Setzer) S.; m. Dorothy Rosenfeld, May 28, 1967; children: Deborah, Andrew. A.B., Rutgers U., 1961; M.D., SUNY, Syracuse, 1965. Diplomate Am. Bd. Internal Medicine (chmn. med. oncology com. 1980-83). Intern Beth Israel Hosp., Boston, 1966-68, resident, 1968-69, 70-71; sr. house officer Radcliffe Infirmary, Oxford, Eng., 1969-70; instr. medicine Harvard U., 1970-71; sr. investigator Nat. Cancer Inst., Bethesda, Md., 1971-74, head clin. pharm. sect., 1973-74; dir. div. med. oncology Georgetown U. Hosp., 1974-83; sci. dir. Georgetown U. Cancer Ctr., 1974-83; v.p. clin. R & D worldwide Smith Kline and French Labs., Phila., 1983-86; chmn., CEO U.S. Biosci., 1987—; cons. oncology Walter Reed Gen. Hosp., Washington, 1971-84, Clin. Ctr., NIH, 1971-84; assoc. prof. medicine and pharmacology Georgetown U., 1974-77, prof., 1977—; adj. prof. medicine Brown U., 1983—; adj. prof. medicine and pharmacology U. Penn., 1983—; adj. prof. pharmacology Temple U., 1984—; mem. Nat. Pancreatic Cancer Project, 1974-79; chmn. Gastrointestinal Tumor Study Group, 1974-83, FDA adv.com. on oncology drugs, 1979-81, Mid-Atlantic Oncology Program; mem. Nat. Cancer Adv. Bd., 1994—. Fellow Royal Soc. Medicine, ACP, Royal Coll. Physicians London, Royal Coll. Physicians Glasgow; mem. Am. Soc. Clin. Oncology (bd. dirs. 1979-83, pres. 1983), Am. Assn. Cancer Research, Am. Soc. Clin. Investigation, Am. Soc. Hematology, Assn. Am. Physicians, Am. Soc. Clin. Pharmacology Therapeutics, Sigma Xi, Alpha Omega Alpha. Clubs: Cosmos, Union League. Research on mechanisms of action of cancer chemotherapy drugs, prediction and prevention drug toxicity, treatment malignant and hematologic diseases. Office: US Bioscience 100 Front St Conshohocken PA 19428-2800

SCHEIN, VIRGINIA ELLEN, psychologist; b. Rahway, N.J., June 23, 1943; d. Jacob Charles and Anne S.; m. Rupert F. Chisholm. BA cum laude, Cornell U., 1965; PhD, N.Y.U., 1969. Lic. psychologist, Pa. 1 child, Alexander Nikos. Sr. research assoc. Am. Mgmt. Assn., N.Y.C., 1969-70; mgr. personnel research Life Office Mgmt. Assn., N.Y.C., 1970-72; dir. personnel research Met. Life Ins. Co., N.Y.C., 1972-75; asso. prof. Sch. Mgmt. Case Western Res. U., Cleve., 1975-76; vis. assoc. prof. Sch. Orgn. and Mgmt., Yale U., New Haven, 1976-77; assoc. prof. mgmt. Wharton Sch. U. Pa., Phila., 1977-80; mgmt. cons. Virginia E. Schein, Ph.D., P.C., 1975—; assoc. prof. psychology Bernard M. Baruch Coll., City U. N.Y., 1982-85; prof. mgmt. Gettysburg Coll., Pa., 1986—, chair mgmt. dept., 1993—. Co-author: Power and Organization Development, 1988; Author: Working from the Margins, 1995; mem. editorial rev. bds. Women Mgmt. Rev., Acad. Mgmt. Execs.; contbr. articles to profl. jours. Bd. dirs. Family Planning Ctr., Survivors, Inc., past pres. bd.; bd. dirs. Pvt. Industry Coun. Mem. Am. Psychol. Assn. (council reps. 1978-80, com. on women 1980-83), Metro. Applied Psychology (pres. 1973-74), Acad. Mgmt., (rep. orgn. devel. div. 1979-81, mem. exec. com. women mgmt. divsn.), Internat. Assn. Applied Psychology, Am. Psychol. Soc., Psi Chi. Office: Gettysburg Coll Dept Mgmt Gettysburg PA 17325

SCHEINBAUM, DAVID, photography educator; b. Bklyn., Apr. 14, 1951; s. Louis and Rhoda (Feerman) S.; m. Vicki Golden, May 30, 1973 (div. 1975); m. Janet Ann Goldberg-Russek, Mar. 21, 1982; stepchildren: Jonathan Russek, Andrea Russek; 1 child, Zachary. BA, CUNY, 1973. Instr. photography Pace U., N.Y.C., 1974-75, LaGuardia (N.Y.) Community Coll., 1975-78; assoc. prof. art Coll. Santa Fe, 1979-81, 82—, assoc. prof. of art photography, 1981—; printer, asst. to Beaumont Newhall, Santa Fe, 1980-93; printer to Eliot Porter, Santa Fe, 1980-90; co-dir. Scheinbaum & Russek, Ltd., Santa Fe, 1979—. Author: (photographs) Bisti, 1987, Miami Beach: Photographs of an American Dream, 1990; photography exhbns. include Pace U., 1974, Midtown Y Gallery, N.Y., 1977, Santa Fe Gallery for Photography, 1979, 81, The Armory for the Arts, Santa Fe, 1980, 1981, Sea Breeze Gallery, Block Island, R.I., 1982, Highlands U., Las Vegas, N.Mex., 1982, Gov's. Gallery, Santa Fe, 1982, Santa Fe Festival for the Arts, 1982, Coll. Santa Fe, 1983, Dem. Conv. San Francisco, 1984, Mus. Natural History, Albuquerque, Bisti/Miami Beach Photogroup Coral Gables, Fla., 1990, Ctr, Met. Studies U. Mo., St. Louis, 1988, Earthscope Expo '90 Photo Mus., Osaka, Japan, 1990, Jamestown C.C., N.Y., 1990, Neikrug Photo Gallery Internat., Tokyo, 1987; in permanent collections Norton Gallery Mus., West Palm Beach, Fla, Amon Carter Mus., Ft. Worth, N.Mex. State U., Las Cruces, Ctr. Creative Photography, Tucson, Ariz., Mus. Fine Arts, Santa Fe, Bklyn. Mus., U. Okla., Norman, Bibliothèque Nationale France, Paris, Gernsheim Collection. U. Tex., Austin, Albuquerque Mus., Rockwell Mus., Corning, N.Y., Chase Manhattan Bank, N.Y. Pub. Libr., Fogg Art Mus., Harvard U., Met. Mus. Art, N.Y.C., Frito-Lay Collection, Kans. City, Expo 90 Photo Mus., Osaka, Coll. Art Gallery, SUNY, New Paltz, N.Y., Univ. Art Mus., U. N.Mex. Inducted Wall of Fame Kingsborough C.C., N.Y., 1994. Mem. N.Mex. Coun. on Photography (founder, v.p., bd. dirs.), Santa Fe Ctr. Photography (bd. dirs. 1978-85). Jewish. Home: 369 Montezuma Box 345 Santa Fe NM 87501-1882 Office: Coll Santa Fe Saint Michaels Dr Santa Fe NM 87501

SCHEINBERG, LABE CHARLES, physician, educator; b. Memphis, Dec. 11, 1925; m. Louise Goldman, Jan. 6, 1952: children: Susan, David, Ellen, Amy. A.B., U. N.C., 1945; M.D., U. Tenn., 1948. Intern Wesley Meml. Hosp., Chgo., 1949; resident psychiatry Elgin (Ill.) State Hosp., 1950; resident, asst. neurology Neurol. Inst., N.Y., 1952-56; mem. faculty Albert Einstein Coll. Medicine, 1956-93, prof. neurology, asst. dean, 1968-69, assoc. dean, 1969-70, prof. rehab. medicine and psychiatry, dean, 1970-72; dir. neurology Hosp., 1966-73; dir. dept. neurology and psychiatry St. Barnabas Hosp., Bronx, N.Y., 1974-79; prof. neurology Mt. Sinai Med. ctr., N.Y.C., 1993—. Cons. editor: N.Y. Acad. Scis, 1964, 84, editor-in-chief J. Neurologic Rehab. Rehab. Reports, Multiple Sclerosis Research Reports. Served as capt. M.C. USAF, 1951-52. Fellow Am. Acad. Neurology; mem. Am. Neurol. Assn., Am. Assn. Neuro-pathology, Am. Soc. Exptl. Pathology, Phi Beta Kappa, Alpha Omega Alpha. Home: 9 Oak Ln Scarsdale NY 10583-1621 Office: Mt Sinai Med Ctr 5 E 98th St New York NY 10029-6574

SCHEINBERG, PERITZ, neurologist; b. Miami, Fla., Dec. 21, 1920; s. Mendel and Esther Dobrisch (Asch) S.; m. Chantal D'Adesky, Mar. 12, 1971; children: Philip Asch, Richard David, Marissa. A.B. in Chemistry, Emory U., 1941, M.D., 1944. Diplomate: Am. Bd. Internal Medicine, Am. Bd. Psychiatry and Neurology. Intern Grady Hosp., Atlanta, 1944-45; resident in internal medicine and neurology Grady Hosp. and Duke U. Hosp., 1946-50; research asst. prof. physiology U. Miami Med. Research Unit, Miami, Fla., 1950-53; asso. prof. neurology U. Miami Med. Research Unit, 1955-57, prof. neurology, 1957—; chmn. dept. neurology U. Miami Sch. Medicine, 1961—. Author, editor books in field.; contbr. articles to profl. jours. Served with M.C. USNR, 1945-46, 53-55. Fellow ACP, Am. Acad. Neurology; mem. Am. Neurol. Assn. (pres. 1981), Assn. Univ. Profs. Neurology (pres. 1977-78), Am. Heart Assn., Nat. Multiple Sclerosis Soc. (mem. med. adv. bd.). Democrat. Jewish. Office: U Miami Jackson Meml Med Ctr 1611 NW 12th Ave Miami FL 33136-1005

SCHEINBERG, STEVEN ELIOT, investment banker; b. N.Y.C., Mar. 2, 1952; s. Arnold Lewis and Mildred (Schapira) S.; m. Robin Scheinberg; children: Michael Aaron and Andrew Ross (twins), Rachel Lillian. BA in Econs., U. Conn., 1973, MA in Econs., 1976; cert. in real estate, NYU, 1980. Economist Conn. Gen. Assembly, Hartford, 1975-77; dir. mcpl. bond research Shearson Hayden Stone, N.Y.C., 1977-79; sr. assoc. Matthews and Wright Inc., N.Y.C., 1979-80; v.p. dir. mcpl. bond rsch. Shearson/Am. Express, N.Y.C., 1980-82; v.p., dir. equity rsch. S.D. Cohn and Co. N.Y.C., 1982-83; v.p., chief fin. officer Audre Inc., San Diego, 1983-85, also bd. dirs.; mng. dir., bd. dirs. RGS Capital Mgmt. Inc., N.Y.C., 1985-89; v.p., ltd. ptnr. Robert Sheridan and Ptnrs., Miami, Fla., 1989-92; cons. Miami, 1992—. Adminstrv. chmn. bd. govs. U. Conn., 1971-72. Mass. Audubon Soc. fellow, 1974. Mem. Nat. Assn. Bus. Economists. Office: 801 Brickell Ave Ste 944 Miami FL 33131-4945

SCHEINDLIN, RAYMOND PAUL, Hebrew literature educator, translator; b. Phila., May 13, 1940; s. Irving and Betty (Bernstein) S.; m. Shira Ann Joffe, Mar. 1969 (div. 1981); children—Dov Baer, Dahlia Rachel; m. Janice Clair Meyerson, 1986. B.A., U. Pa., 1961; M.H.L. Jewish Theol. Sem., N.Y.C., 1963; Ph.D., Columbia U., N.Y.C., 1971. Ordained rabbi, 1965. Asst. prof. McGill U., Montreal, Que., Can., 1969-72; asst. prof. Cornell U., Ithaca, N.Y., 1972-74; assoc. prof. Jewish Theol. Sem. of Am., N.Y.C., 1974-85, prof. Hebrew lit., 1985—; provost, 1984-90; rabbi Congregation Baith Israel Anshei Emes, Bklyn., 1979-82; mem. publ. com. Jewish Publ. Soc., Phila., 1985-90; mem. internat. adv. com. Ctr. for Judaic Studies U. Pa., 1995—; mem. bd. acad. advisors Catalan Mus. Jewish Culture, Gerona, Spain, 1993—. Translator: (novella) Of Bygone Days by Mendele Mokher Seforim, 1973, Jewish Liturgy: A Comprehensive History by Ismar Elbogen, 1993; author: Form & Structure in the Poetry of Al-Mu'tamid Ibn 'Abbad, 1974, 201 Arabic Verbs, 1978, Wine, Women, and Death: Medieval Hebrew Poems on the Good Life, 1986, The Gazelle: Medieval Hebrew Poems on God, Israel and the Soul, 1991, (libretto) Miriam and the Angel of Death, 1984; mem. editorial com. Prooftexts, 1988—, Edebiyat, 1992—, Studies in Muslim-Jewish Relations, 1992—. Guggenheim fellow, 1988, Annenberg Inst. fellow, 1993; sr. assoc. fellow Oxford Centre for Postgrad. Hebrew Studies. Mem. Soc. for Judeo-Arabic Studies (exec. com.), World Union for Jewish Studies , Assn. Jewish Studies, Jewish Publ. Soc. (bd. dirs. 1987-93). Home: 420 Riverside Dr New York NY 10025-7773 Office: Jewish Theol Sem Am 3080 Broadway New York NY 10027-4650

SCHEINER, JAMES IRA, engineering company executive; b. Mpls., May 7, 1944; s. Samuel L. and Sally Scheiner; m. Kristin Scofield; children: Alec, Zachary, Meredith. BS in Civil Engring., U.S. Mil. Acad., 1965; MPA, MCE, Princeton U., 1967. Registered profl. engr., Pa. Cons., prin. transp. consulting divsn. Booz-Allen and Hamilton, 1971-79; dep. sec. adminstrn. Pa. Dept. Transp., 1979-83; sec. revenue Commonwealth of Pa., 1983-87; v.p. Huth Engrs., Inc., 1987-88; pres. Stoner Assocs., Inc., 1988-91; pres., COO Benatec Assocs., Inc., 1991—. Contbr. articles to profl. jours. Vice chair area bd. Leadership Harrisburg; group chair 1993 campaign cabinet capital region United Way; mem. Pa. Chamber Bus. and Industry Bd.; mem. Harsco Bd.; trustee Harrisburg Area C.C. Capt. CE, U.S. Army, Vietnam, 1967-71. Decorated Bronze Star, Purple Heart; recipient Disting. Svc. award Nat. Gov.'s Assn., 1986. Office: Benatec Assocs 101 Erford Rd Camp Hill PA 17011

SCHEINFELD, JAMES DAVID, travel agency executive; b. Milw., Nov. 11, 1926; s. Aaron and Sylvia (Rosenberg) S.; children from previous marriage: John Stephen, Nancy Ellen, Robert Alan; m. Elna Magnusson, 1994. BA in Econs. magna cum laude, U. Wis., 1949. With Manpower, Inc., 1948-78, salesman, Chgo., 1949-51, br. mgr., 1951-53, nat. sales mgr., Milw., 1953-56, dir. sales, corp. sec., 1956-59, v.p. sales, 1959-62, exec. v.p. mktg., 1962-65, exec. v.p. (sr.), chief ops. officer, 1965-76, v.p. spl. projects, 1976-78, mem. exec. com., bd. dirs., 1959-76, cons., 1978-84; exec. v.p., chief exec. officer, bd. dirs. Transpersonal, Inc., Any Task Inc., Manpower Argentina, Manpower Europe, Manpower Ltd. (U.K.), Manpower Australia, Manpower Japan, Manpower Germany GmbH, Manpower Norway, Manpower Denmark, Manpower Venezuela, 1966-76; pres. Travway Internat. Inc. - Funway Holidays, Funjet, 1976-81, Aide Svcs., Inc., Tampa, Fla., 1976-81; pres., chief exec. officer Travelpower Inc., 1976-84; sr. v.p. Carlson Travel Network, 1984—; mem. Hickory Travel Systems Inc., 1977-85, bd. dirs., 1978-85, pres., 1980-82, pres. emeritus, 1982—. Contbr. articles to profl. jours. Chmn. Cancer Crusade Milw. County, 1970; bd. dirs. Sinai-Samaritan Med. Ctr., Better Bus. Bur. Milw., 1979-90, Found. for Santa Barbara City Coll., 1989—; trustee Santa Barbara Med. Found. Clinic, 1990—; trustee U. Wis.-Milw. Found., 1981-91, mem. bus. adv. bd. U. Wis.-Milw., 1987—; mem. adv. bd. Sch. Fine Arts, U. Wis.-Milw., 1986—; chmn. bus. adv. bd. Santa Barbara City Coll., 1988-97; mem. Greater Milw. Com., 1984—. With USNR, 1944-46. Mem. Nat. Assn. Temporary Services (pres. 1975-76, bd. dirs. 1969-77). Clubs: University (Milw.); Coral Casino (Santa Barbara, Calif.). Lodge: Rotary. Home: 365 El Cielito Rd Santa Barbara CA 93105-2308 Office: 9076 N Deerbrook Trail Milwaukee WI 53223-2474 *I do not often walk or look back where my footprints are. I prefer to walk that part of the beach I have never walked before. I am a person who thinks more about tomorrow than yesterday . . . more about what can be done than what has been done . . . more about challenges than accomplishments. Looking back is helpful only if I can find a sign to help me in my future.*

SCHEINHOLTZ, LEONARD LOUIS, lawyer; b. Pitts., June 2, 1927; s. Bernard A. and Marie (Getzel) S.; m. Joan R. Libenson, Aug. 16, 1953; children: Stuart, Nancy, Barry. B.A., U. Pa., 1948, M.A., 1949; LL.B., Columbia U., 1953. Bar: Pa. 1954, U.S. Ct. Appeals (3d cir.) 1959, U.S. Ct. Appeals (6th cir.) 1968, U.S. Supreme Ct. 1972, U.S. Ct. Appeals (4th cir.) 1973, U.S. Ct. Appeals (5th cir.) 1981, U.S. Ct. Appeals (11th cir.) 1991, U.S. Ct. Appeals (2d cir.) 1993. Assoc. Reed, Smith, Shaw & McClay, Pitts., 1953-62, spl. pttnr., 1962-64, gen. pttnr. 1964—, head labor dept., 1980-86; dir. Am. Arbitration Assn., N.Y.C., 1980—. Author: Exemption Under the Anti-Trust Laws for Joint Employer Activity, 1982, The Arbitrator as Judge and Jury: Another Look at Statutory Law in Arbitration, 1985. Vice chmn. Pa. AAA Fedn., Harrisburg, 1982-85 ; chmn. W. Pa. AAA Motor Club, 1979-82; trustee Montefiore Hosp., Pitts., 1976-79. Served with USN, 1945-46. Mem. ABA, Pa. Bar Assn., Allegheny County Bar Assn. Republican. Jewish. Home: 746 Pinoak Rd Pittsburgh PA 15243-1153 Office: Reed Smith Shaw & McClay Mellon Sq 435 6th Ave Pittsburgh PA 15219-1886

SCHEININGER, LESTER, lawyer, administrator religious organization; b. Steyer, Austria, Aug. 12, 1947; arrived in Can., 1948; s. Joel and Esther (Kramer) S.; m. Judy Weiss, Aug. 10, 1969; children: Pamela Brett, Stephanie Karyn, Samuel Robert. Student, NYU; BA, U. Toronto, 1968; LLB, Osgoode Hall Law Sch., 1971. Bar: Ont. 1973. Ptnr. Bresver Grossman Scheininger & Davis, Toronto, Ont., Can., 1973—; bd. dirs. Coachman Ins. Co.; pres. Jewish Family and Child Svc. Met. Toronto, 1992-83; past chmn. leadership devel. com. Toronto Jewish Congress; year round del. Coun. Jewish Fedns. Contbr. articles to profl. jours. Bd. Jewish edn. Toronto, Associated Hebrew Schs. Toronto, Ulpanot Orot-Or Chaim Yeshiva. Mem. Can. Bar Assn., Law Soc. Upper Can., York County Law Assn. Can. Jewish Cong. (nat. pres. 1989-92, nat. hon. counsel 1986-89, chmn. Ont. region 1983-86), Toronto Jewish Cong. (past v.p., past chmn. leadership devel. com., past exec. com.), Leadership Devel. award 1979). Office: Bresver Grossman Scheininger & Davis, 390 Bay St Ste 2800, Toronto, ON Canada M5H 2Y2 also: Can Jewish Congress, 1590 Ave Docteur Penfield, Montreal, PQ Canada H3G 1C5

SCHEINKMAN, JOSÉ ALEXANDRE, economics educator; b. Rio de Janeiro, Brazil, Jan. 11, 1948; s. Samuel and Sara (Lerner) S.; m. Michele Zitrin, Dec. 14, 1969; 1 child, Andrei Zitrin. B.A., U. Fed. Rio de Janeiro, 1969; M.S., Instituto de Matematica Pura e Aplicado, Brazil, 1970; M.A., U.

Rochester, 1972, Ph.D., 1973. Asst. prof. econs. U. Chgo., 1973-76, assoc. prof., 1976-81, prof., 1981-86, Alvin H. Baum prof. economics, 1987—; v.p. Goldman, Sachs & Co., 1987-89; chmn. econs. dept., 1995—; vis. prof. Instituto de Matematica Pura e Aplicado Brazil, 1979-80, Fundação Getulio Vargas, Brazil, 1979-80, U. Paris, 1985-94; external Prof. Sante Fe Inst., 1989—; Harry Johnson lectr. Royal Econ. Soc./Assn. Univ. Tchrs. in Econs., 1989; cons. Ministry of Planning, Brazil, 1981. Editor: General Equilibrium Growth and Trade, 1975, Jour. Polit. Economy, Chgo., 1983-94; contbr. articles to profl. jours. NSF grantee, 1974, 76, 79, 83, 85, 90, 93. Fellow AAAS, Econometric Soc. Home: 5719 S Kenwood Ave Chicago IL 60637-1743 Office: Univ Chicago 1126 E 59th St Chicago IL 60637-1580

SCHEINMAN, STANLEY BRUCE, venture capital executive, lawyer; b. N.Y.C., Nov. 13, 1933; s. Samuel and Susan Elstein (dec.); m. Janet L. Donnelly, Dec. 30, 1975 (div.); children: Catherine Amy, Anthony Paul, Sarah, Jean, Norah Jane. AB, Cornell U., 1954; MBA, CCNY, 1957; JD (Harlan Fisk Stone scholar), Columbia U., 1960. Bar: N.Y. 1960. Assoc. firm Cravath, Swaine & Moore, N.Y.C., 1960-62; capital projects officer, legis. programs staff coord. AID, Washington, 1962-64; sr. exec. officer Bur. Pvt. Enterprise AID, 1982-83; v.p. fin. and adminstrn. svcs. industries div., also v.p., counsel internat. div. PepsiCo. Inc., 1965-70; v.p. fin. and adminstrn. pharm. div. Revlon, Inc., 1970-72; sr. v.p. MCI Communications, 1972-76; pres., chief oper. officer FSC Corp., Pitts., 1976-81; pres. New Venture Capital Corp., Washington, 1984-85; prin. Re Venture Assocs., Salisbury, Conn., 1985-86; chmn. chief exec. officer Internat. 800 Telcom Corp., Geneva, 1987-88; pres., chief exec. officer Zurich Depository Corp., Manhasset, N.Y., 1988-89; exec. v.p. AMIF&S Ltd., N.Y.C., 1989-91; pres. IT Svc. Corp., Westport, Conn., 1991-92; v.p. ops. and bus. devel. EQ Corp., Westport, 1992—. Mem. Assn. of Bar of City of N.Y., Fgn. Execs. Inst., Internat. Execs. Assn., Paris-Am. Club, Fgn. Svc. Club, Cornell Club. Home: PO Box 3355 Westport CT 06880 Office: 25 Sylvan Rd S Ste D Westport CT 06880

SCHEKMAN, RANDY W., molecular biology administrator, biochemist; b. St. Paul, Dec. 30, 1948; married, 1973; 1 child. BA, UCLA, 1970; PhD in Biochemistry, Stanford U., 1975. Fellow U. Calif., San Diego, 1974-76; from asst. to assoc. prof. U. Calif., Berkeley, 1976-83, prof., 1983—, head divsn. biochemistry and molecular biology, 1990—. Fellow Cystic Fibrosis Found., 1974, Sabbatical fellow John S. Guggenheim Found., 1982. Mem. Am. Soc. Microbiology, Am. Soc. Biochemists & Molecular Biologists. Achievements include research on molecular mechanism of secretion and membrane assembly in eucaryotic cells. Office: U Calif Dept Biochemistry & Molecular Biology Barker Hall Berkeley CA 94720*

SCHELER, BRAD ERIC, lawyer; b. Bklyn., Oct. 11, 1953; s. Bernard and Rita Regina (Miller) S.; m. Amy Ruth Frolick, Mar. 30, 1980; children: Ali M., Maddie H., Zoey B. BA magna cum laude, Lehigh U., 1974; JD, Hofstra U., 1977. Bar: N.Y. 1978, U.S. Dist. Ct. (so. and ea. dists.) N.Y. 1978. Assoc. Weil, Gotshal & Manges, N.Y.C., 1977-81; sr. ptnr., chmn. bankruptcy and restructuring practice Fried, Frank, Harris, Shriver & Jacobson, N.Y.C., 1981—. Rsch. editor Hofstra U. Law Rev., 1975-77. Treas., bus. mgr. Trustees of Gramercy Park, N.Y.C., 1979-87. Mem. ABA (bus. bankruptcy com. corp. banking and bus. law sect., creditors' rights com. litigation sect.), N.Y. State Bar Assn., Assn. Bar City N.Y. (com. on bankruptcy and corp. reorgn. 1991-94), Sigma Alpha Mu. Jewish. Home: 32 Maple Hill Dr Larchmont NY 10538-1614 Office: Fried Frank Harris 1 New York Plz New York NY 10004

SCHELL, ALLAN CARTER, electrical engineer; b. New Bedford, Mass., Apr. 14, 1934; s. Charles Carter and Elizabeth (Moore) S.; m. Shirley T. Sardineer; children: Alice Rosalind, Cynthia Anne. B.S., MIT, 1956, M.S.E.E., 1956, Sc.D., 1961; student, Tech. U. Delft, Netherlands, 1956-57. Research physicist Air Force Cambridge Research Labs., Bedford, Mass., 1956-76; Guenter Loeser Meml. lectr. Air Force Cambridge Research Labs., 1965; dir. electromagnetics directorate Rome Air Devel. Ctr., Bedford, 1976-87; chief scientist Hdqrs. USAF Systems Command, 1987-92; chief scientist, dep. dir. sci. and tech. Hdqrs. USAF Materiel Command, 1992-94; dir. Electro; vis. assoc. prof. MIT, 1974; chair dept. of elec. engring. adv. coun. U. Pa., 1992-94. Contbr. articles to profl. jours.; patentee in field (9). Served as lt. USAF, 1958-60. Recipient Fulbright award, 1956-57, Meritorious Exec. award U.S. Govt., 1989; NSF fellow, 1955-56, 60-61. Fellow IEEE (bd. dirs. 1981-82, editor IEEE Pres. 1976-79, Proc. of IEEE 1990-92); Mem. Am. Def. Preparedness Assn., Antennas and Propagation Soc. of IEEE (pres. 1978, editor tran. 1969-71, John T. Bolljahn award 1966), Internat. Sci. Radio Union (U.S. nat. com.), Sigma Xi, Tau Beta Pi.

SCHELL, BRAXTON, lawyer; b. Raleigh, N.C., Feb. 24, 1924; s. Marshall H. and Margaret (Newsom) S.; m. Ann Cooper Knight, Mar. 30, 1951 (div. 1982); children: Braxton, Richard Knight, James Gray.; m. Mary Rehill, Apr. 16, 1983. Student, N.C. State Coll., 1942-43; B.S., U. N.C., 1948, J.D. with honors, 1951. Bar: N.C. 1951. Since practiced in Greensboro; assoc. Smith, Moore, Smith, Schell & Hunter, Greensboro, 1951-56; ptnr. Smith, Moore, Smith, Schell & Hunter, 1956-85, Smith, Helms, Mullis, and Moore, 1986-87, Schell, Bray, Aycock, Abel & Livingston, 1987—; gen. counsel, dir. Texfi Industries, Inc. Flagler Sys. and The Breakers Palm Beach, Inc.; bd. dirs. Kenan Transport Co. Assoc. editor: N.C. Law Rev. 1950-51. Chmn. Special Liason Tax Com. Southeastern Region, 1960-61; bd. dirs. N.C. Outward Bound Sch., 1975-88, chmn., 1977-80; trustee Outward Bound, Inc., 1978-81; bd. dirs. William R. Kenan Fund for Pvt. Enterprise, Arts and Engring., Tech. and Sci. Served with USAAF, 1942-45. Fellow Am. Bar Found.; mem. Am., N.C. bar assns., Order of Coif, Phi Beta Kappa. Presbyn. Clubs: Greensboro Country (pres. 1971-72), Greensboro City (dir. 1980—). Home: 422B Fisher Park Cir Greensboro NC 27401-1615 Office: Schell Bray Aycock Abel & Livingston 1500 Renaissance Pla Greensboro NC 27420

SCHELL, JAMES EDWARD, II, computer company executive, consultant; b. West Point, Ga., Jan. 21, 1930; s. Nelson Henderson and Mattie Lou (Winkfield) S.; m. Doris Elizabeth Hunter, Jan. 15, 1954; children: James Lawrence, Kenneth Henderson, George Keith, Pamela Noelle Schell Focht, Regina Lisbeth Schell Giszpenc. BA in Math., Physics and French, Morehouse Coll., 1949, LLD (hon.), 1984; postgrad., Calif. State U., Northridge, 1969-72, U. So. Calif., 1984. Instr. USAF Sch. Electronics, Radar Keesler AFB, Miss., 1949-51; electronics engr. Conscript U.S. Army Signal Corps, Ft. Myer, Va., 1951-53; instr. USAF, 1953-54, U.S. Army Electronics Command, Ft. Monmouth, N.J., 1954-57; tech. writer, requirements officer U.S. Army Signal Publs. Agy., 1954-63; chief project mgr.'s staff office U.S. Army Electronics Command, Ft. Monmouth, N.J., 1963-68; mgr. systems engring. Litton Data Systems, Van Nuys, Calif., 1968-71, dir. command and control systems, 1971-79; dir. Ctr. for Tactical Computer Systems U.S. Army Comms. R & D Command, Ft. Monmouth, N.J., 1979-81; program mgr. marine integrated fire and air support systen Norden Systems, Inc., Norwalk, Conn., 1981-82; dir. Ctr. for Tactical Computer Sys. U.S. Army Comms. Electronics Command, Ft. Monmouth, 1982-85; dep. program mgr. Command and Control Sys. U.S. Army CECOM, Ft. Monmouth, 1985-86, dir. ctr. for software engring., 1986-88; exec. dir. HiBisCUn Corp., Ocean, N.J., 1988—; cons. McDonnell Corp., Huntington Beach, Calif., 1988, RAM, Inc., El Paso, Tex., 1990; pres. SOPHSYS, Inc., Ocean, 1988-92; dir. Conf. on Software Engring., Ft. Monmouth, 1988-89; mem. high tech. adv. coun. Monmouth Coll.; mem. adv. bd. Atlanta U. Sci. Rsch. Inst.; hon. mem. faculty Def. Weapon Systems Mgmt. Ctr., 1966; founder Ada Nat. Conf. Bd. and Conf.; cons. on software engring. and tech. project mgmt. Pres. Asbury Park-Neptune (N.J.) br. NAACP, 1960-61; mem. Tinton Falls (N.J.)ú Schs. Bd. Edn., 1963-68. With U.S. Army, 1951-53. Recipient outstanding performance award U.S. Army, 1966, 67, Sec. of Army award for most outstanding achievement in EEO, 1985, Nittany Lion award Pa. State U., 1986, humanitarian award U.S. Army Materiel Command. Negro Bus. and Profl. Womens Clubs, Inc., 1986, comdr.'s award for outstanding achievement in EEO, U.S. Army Materiel Command, 1986, Meritorious Civilian Svc. award Dept. Army, 1986, 88, Humanitarian award Nat. Greater Houston Assn. Tech. Achiever's Assn., 1992, Founder's award Ann. Nat. Conf. on Software Tech., Inc., 1992. Mem. AAAS, Planetary Soc., Assn. U.S. Army, Armed Forces Comm. and Electronics Assn. (bd. dirs. 1979-88), Morehouse Coll. Alumni Assn. Avocations: oil painting, foreign languages, Japanese gardening, anthropology. Home and Office: 9 Old Weathersfield Rd Ocean NJ 07712-3344

SCHELL, JAMES MUNSON, financial executive; b. Kalamazoo, Mich., Mar. 25, 1944; s. Frank John and Shirley I. S.; m. Susan O'Laughlin, Aug. 6, 1966; children: Karen, Michael, Ryan. B.A., Vanderbilt U., 1966; M.B.A., Washington U., 1968. Dir. term and internat. financing Chrysler Fin. Corp., Troy, Mich., 1976-79, v.p., treas., 1980-81; v.p. domestic treasury Am. Express Co., N.Y.C., 1981-82; v.p. fin. resources Hertz Corp., N.Y.C., 1982-83; v.p., chief fin. officer Clabir Corp., Greenwich, Conn., 1983-84; v.p., treas. Fairchild Industries, 1985-87; ind. fin. cons., 1987—; bd. dirs. Jackson-Jordan Corp., CTI Industries. Republican. Roman Catholic. Home: 40 Stony Brook Rd Darien CT 06820-4326

SCHELL, JOAN BRUNING, information specialist, business science librarian; b. N.Y.C., June 9, 1932; d. Walter Henry and Gertrude Emily (Goossen) Bruning; m. Harold Benton Schell, Aug. 27, 1955 (div. 1978); children: Jeffrey Mark, Sue Lynne. AB, Wittenberg U., 1954; postgrad., Syracuse U., 1963, U. Md., 1965-66; MLS, U. Pitts., 1968. Actuarial, claims asst. Nationwide Ins., Columbus, Ohio, 1954-57; tech. report typist Cornell U., Ithaca, N.Y., 1957; bus. libr. asst. U. Pitts., 1969; bus. reference libr. Dallas Pub. Libr., 1971-73, Pub. Libr. Cin. and Hamilton County, Cin., 1973-79; book selection coord. Pub. Libr. Cin. & Hamilton County, Cin., 1979-83, asst. to main libr., 1983-85; literacy tutor Cin. LEARN, 1985-89; recorder feminist lit. Womyn's Braille Press, Mpls., 1985-89; wellness program asst. Times Pub. Co., St. Petersburg, Fla., 1989—; dir. Wittenberg U., Springfield, Ohio, 1988—; bd. dirs. Crazy Ladies Ctr. Inc., Cin., 1989-93; coord. Fla. west coast Old Lesbians Organizing for Change, 1993-95; sec., trustee Clio Found., Inc., 1995—; docent Fla. Internat. Mus., 1994—. Compiler: (reference source) Greater Cincinnati Business Index, 1975-79; editor: New Reference Materials, 1983, 84. Mem. Tampa Bay YWCA Women's Guild, St. Petersburg, 1991—; vol. NOW Elect Women Campaign, St. Petersburg, 1990-92, Senator Helen G. Davis Reelection, St. Petersburg, 1992. Mem. ALA, Spl. Librs. Assn. (treas., archivist 1974-83), Am. Assn. Individual Investors, Laubach Literary Action, Beta Phi Mu Libr. Sci. Hon. Phi Delta Gamma Grad. Women Hon. Avocations: travel, reading, figure skating fan, yoga, swimming. Home: PO Box 7472 Saint Petersburg FL 33734 Office: Times Pub Co 490 First Ave S Saint Petersburg FL 33701

SCHELL, JONATHAN EDWARD, writer; b. N.Y.C., Aug. 21, 1943; s. Orville H. and Marjorie Bertha S. Staff writer New Yorker Mag., N.Y.C., 1967—. Author: The Village of Ben Suc, 1967, The Military Half, 1968, The Time of Illusion, 1975, The Fate of the Earth, 1982. Office: Newsday Inc 235 Pinelawn Rd Huntington Station NY 11747-4226

SCHELL, MAXIMILIAN, actor, director; b. Vienna, Austria, Dec. 8, 1930; s. Hermann Ferdinand and Margarethe (Noé von Nordberg) S. Student, Humanistisches Gymnasium, Basel, Switzerland, Freies Gymnasium, Zürich, Switzerland, also univs., Zürich, Basel and Munich. Various appearances on stage in Switzerland and Germany, 1952-55; German film debut in Children, Mothers and a General, 1955; Am. film debut in Young Lions, 1958; on Broadway stage in Interlock, 1958; prin. roles in films Judgment at Nuremberg, 1961 (Acad. award Best Actor), Five Finger Exercise, 1961, Reluctant Saint, 1962, Condemned of Altona, 1962, Topkapi, 1963, Return from the Ashes, 1965, The Deadly Affair, 1966, Counterpoint, 1967, The Castle, 1968, Simon Bolivar, 1969, First Love, 1970, Pope Joan, 1971, Paulina 1880, 1972, The Man in the Glass Booth, 1974, The Odessa File, 1974, Assassination in Sarajewo, 1975, Cross of Iron, 1976, A Bridge Too Far, 1976, Julia, 1976, The Black Hole, 1979, Players, 1978, Avalanche Express, 1978, The Chosen, 1980, Les Iles, 1981, Man Under Suspicion, 1983, The Assisi Underground, 1984, The Rosegarden, 1989, The Freshman, 1989, Labyrinth, 1990, A Far Off Place, 1993, Little Odessa, 1995; various appearances in stage roles Hamlet, Prince of Homburg, Mannerhouse, Don Carlos, Durell's Sappho, A Patriot for Me, London, 1965, Broadway, 1969, Old Times Vienna, 1972, Everyman, Salzburg Festival, 1978-82, Poor Murderer, Berlin, 1982, Der Seidene Schuh, Salzburg Festival, 1985; producer, dir. films include The Pedestrian, 1973, End of the Game, 1975, Tales from the Vienna Woods, 1978; producer film Ansichten eines Clowns, 1975; dir., co-author screenplay, actor in film First Love, 1969, Marlene, 1983; stage dir. plays include All For the Best, Vienna, 1966, Hamlet, Munich, 1968, Pygmalion, Dusseldorf, 1970; (opera) La Traviata, 1979, Tales from the Vienna Woods, London, 1977, The Undiscovered Country, Salzburg Festival, 1979, 80, opera Cornet, Deutsche Opera, Berlin, 1985, Glaube Liebe Hoffnung, Moscow, 1989; prin. TV film appearances include Heidi, 1968, The Diary of Anne Frank, 1980, Phantom of the Opera, 1983, miniseries Peter the Great, 1984-85, Young Catherine, 1990, Wiseguy, 1990, Miss Rose White, 1991, Stalin, HBO, 1992 (Emmy nomination, Supporting Actor - Miniseries or Special, Cable Ace award, Best Supporting actor). Corporal Swiss Army, 1948-49. Recipient N.Y. Critics Circle award, 1961, 78, 86, Acad. award, 1961, Golden Globe award, 1962, 74, Silver Shell award, 1970, 75, German Fed. award, 1971, 79, 80, 84, Chgo. Film Critics award, 1973, Golden Cup award, Germany, 1974, Gold Hugo award, 1979, Nat. Soc. Film Critics award, 1986; nominated Critics award (Broadway), 1961, Academy award, 1970, 74, 75, 78. Home: Culmannstr 49, 8006 Zurich Switzerland Office: United Talent Agnecy 822 S Robertson Blvd Ste 200 Los Angeles CA 90035 also: Mgmt Erna Baumbauer, Keplerstr 2, 8000 Munich 90, Federal Republic of Germany*

SCHELL, RICHARD A., federal judge; b. 1950. BA, So. Meth. U., 1972, JD, 1975. Bar: Tex. 1975. Asst. dist. atty. Collin County, Tex., 1976; mem. firm Boyd, Veigel & Gay, 1977-81; judge County Ct. Law Collin County, 1982-86, 219th Jud. Dist. Ct. Tex., 1986-88, U.S. Dist Ct. (ea. dist.) Tex., Beaumont, 1988—; instr. rsch. methods and legal writing So. Meth. U., 1975-76. Mem. State Bar Tex. Office: US Dist Ct PO Box 1470 Beaumont TX 77704-1470

SCHELL, WILLIAM H., oil company executive. Exec. v.p. PEPCO div. Pennzoil Co., Houston. Office: Pennzoil Co PO Box 2967 Houston TX 77252-2967

SCHELLEN, NANDO, opera director; b. The Hague, The Netherlands, Oct. 11, 1934; came to U.S., 1993; m. Deborah Raymond, June 19, 1991; 4 children. Managing dir. Netherlands Opera, 1969-79, assoc. gen. dir., 1979-87; gen. artistic dir. Sweelinck Conservatory of Music, Amsterdam, 1990-93; gen. dir. Indpls. Opera, 1993—; freelance stage dir., 1982—. Home: 4635 N Graceland Ave Indianapolis IN 46208 Office: Indpls Opera 250 E 38th St Indianapolis IN 46205

SCHELLENBERG, GERARD DAVID, geneticist, researcher; b. Reedly, Calif., Sept. 29, 1951; s. Ernest David and Clara (Hagen) S.; m. Mary Teresa Ensek, Aug. 23, 1986; children: Zachary David, Sierra Marie. BS in Biochemistry, U. Calif., Riverside, 1973, PhD in Biochemistry, 1978. Rsch. asst. biochemistry U. Calif., Riverside, 1973-78; sr. rsch. fellow med. genetics U. Wash., Seattle, 1978-79, sr. rsch. fellow neurology 1979-82, sr. rsch. fellow genetics, 1982-83, rsch. asst. prof. neurology, 1983-90, rsch. assoc. prof. neurology, 1990—; mem. adv. bd. Jour. Neural Transmission, 1989—; mem. med./sci. adv. bd. Alzheimer's Assn., Chgo., 1990—; mem. Alzheimer's disease med./sci. adv. bd. Am. Health Assistance Found., 1992—. Achievements include identification of chromosome 14 Alzheimer's disease locus. Home: 7031 19th NE Seattle WA 98117 Office: U of Washington School of Medicine Neurology Div Seattle WA 98195

SCHELLENBERG, KARL ABRAHAM, biochemist; b. Hillsboro, Kans., July 13, 1931; s. Theodore R. and Alma Alice (Groening) S.; m. Elizabeth Joan Booker, Aug. 20, 1955; children: Robert, Elizabeth, Richard, Margaret. BS, Coll. William and Mary, 1953; MD, Johns Hopkins U., 1957; PhD, Harvard U., 1964. Asst. prof. Johns Hopkins U., 1968-73; prof., chmn. dept. biochemistry Eastern Va. Med. Sch., Norfolk, 1973—; mem. adv. bd. NSF Middle Atlantic Mass Spectrometry Lab.; mem. adv. com. dept. chem. scis. Old Dominion U.; mem. adv. com. dept. chemistry Coll. William and Mary. Contbr. articles to profl. jours. John and Mary R. Markle Found. scholar, 1965-70; NIH grantee. Mem. Nat. Bd. Med. Examiners (biochemistry test com. 1989-92), Assn. Am. Med. Schs. (panel on the gen. profl. edn. of the physician 1982-84), Assn. Med. Sch. Depts. Biochemistry (sec. 1987-91), Am. Soc. Biol. Chemists, Am. Chem. Soc., N.Y. Acad. Scis., Va. Acad. Scis., Oxygen Soc., Phi Beta Kappa, Sigma Xi (Tidewater, Va. chpt. sec. 1990-91, pres. 1992-93, pres. 1995-96). Club: Pithotomy. Patentee in field. Home:

1332 Lakeview Dr Virginia Beach VA 23455-4130 Office: Eastern Va Med Sch PO Box 1980 Norfolk VA 23501-1980

SCHELLENBERGER, ROBERT EARL, management educator and department chairman; b. Janesville, Wis., July 25, 1932; s. Ervin William and Adelaide Louise (Keller) S.; m. Linda Eula Todd, Dec. 30, 1961; children: Brian T., Keith W., Heidi L. BSBA, U. Wis., 1958, MBA, 1959; PhD, U. N.C., 1963. Personnel supr. Libby McNeill and Libby, Janesville, Wis., 1957-58; from asst. prof. to assoc. prof. chmn. div. stats. dept. bus U. Md., College Park, 1963-68; chair dept. mgmt. So. Ill. U., Carbondale, Ill., 1968-70; dir. planning Sch. Human Resources Devel. So. Ill. U., Carbondale, 1970-71, prof. mgmt., 1968-71; vis. prof., dir. program evaluation Babcock Grad. Sch. Mgmt., Wake Forest U., Winston-Salem, N.C., 1971-73; prof. dept. mgmt. Temple U., Phila., 1973-81, from chmn. dept. mgmt. to asst. to acad. vice chancellor, 1975-77; prof. decision scis. dept., 1989—; pres. Md. Rsch. and Cons., Hyattsville, 1964-67; v.p. Ea. Acad. Mgmt., 1967; cons. Comml. Credit Corp., Balt., 1966. Author: Managerial Analysis, 1967, Policy Formulation, 1978, 2d edit., 1982; co-editor Jour. of Econs. and Bus., 1976; developer (software package) MANYSYM, 1965, 68, 78, 82, 86. Chmn. Utilities Com., Carbondale, 1970-72. Title IV NDEA fellow U. N.C., 1960-62, Earhart Jr. fellow U. Wis. Mem. Assn. for Bus. Simulation, SE Decision Scis. Inst., Decision Scis. Inst. (bd. dirs. 1974-77), Beta Gamma Sigma. Office: East Carolina U Decision Scis Dept Greenville NC 27858

SCHELLER, SANFORD GREGORY, printing company executive; b. Newark, July 7, 1931; s. John Arthur Scheller and Harriet (Gregory) Tate; m. Marjory Meyer, Dec. 31, 1950; children: Sanford Gregory Jr., Douglas Meyer, Bradford John, Frances Scheller Lavin, Eric Bruce. BBA, Westminster Coll., New Wilmington, Pa., 1953. V.p., gen. mgr. St. Regis Corp., N.Y.C., 1978-84, Champion Internat., Stamford, Conn., 1985; pres., chief exec. officer Treasure Chest Advt., Glendora, Calif., 1986—. Republican. Office: Treasure Chest Advt Co Inc PO Box 5016 Glendora CA 91740-0805

SCHELLING, JOHN PAUL, lawyer, consultant; b. Chgo., Aug. 24, 1924; s. Lawrence C. and Hattie (La Bonte) S.; m. V. Jacqueline Davis, Aug. 27, 1945; children: Lawrence, Donna Schelling Scheer, Gloria Schelling Boughers. Student, St. Mary's Coll., Winona, Minn., 1942-43, U. Ill., 1946-47; J.D., Loyola U., Chgo., 1950; postgrad., U. Chgo., 1954-55. Bar: Ill. 1950, Va. 1986. Assoc. McMahon & Plunkett, Chgo., 1950-51; mem. indsl. relations staff Union Asbestos & Rubber Co., Chgo., 1951-56; fin. mgr. Land-Air, Inc. subs. Dynalectron Corp., Chgo., 1956-60; sec. Dynalectron Corp., McLean, Va., 1960-65; v.p. Dynalectron Corp., McLean, 1962-71, v.p., gen. counsel, 1972-76, sr. v.p. fin. and adminstrn. group, 1977-78, sr. v.p. adminstrn. group, 1979-84, sr. v.p. adminstrn. group, gen. counsel, 1984-86, ret., 1986; chmn. Esop com. DynCorp, 1987—. Bd. dirs., v.p. Potomac Hills Citizens Assn., McLean, 1963-64; organizer, mem. bd. dirs., v.p. Highland Swim Club, McLean, Va., 1964-67; bd. dirs. McLean Orch., 1984-86; trustee Fairfax County Pub. Schs. Edn. Found., 1984-86; bd. dirs. Shorewood Property Owners Assn., 1990—, sec.-treas., 1990-92, pres., 1992—. Served with USNR, 1943-46. Mem. ABA, D.C. Bar Assn., Va. Bar Assn., McLean Bar Assn. (bd. dirs. 1988-89), Delta Theta Phi. Home: RR 1 Box 8122 Mineral VA 23117-9713 Office: Dyncorp 2000 Edmund Halley Dr Reston VA 22091-3400

SCHELLING, THOMAS CROMBIE, economist, educator; b. Oakland, Calif., Apr. 14, 1921; s. John M. and Zelda M. (Ayres) S.; m. Corinne T. Saposs, Sept. 13, 1947 (div. 1991); children: Andrew, Thomas, Daniel, Robert; m. Alice M. Coleman, Nov. 8, 1991. AB, U. Calif., Berkeley, 1943; PhD, Harvard U., 1951. U.S. govt. economist Copenhagen, Paris, Washington, 1948-53; prof. econs. Yale U., 1953-58, Harvard U., Cambridge, Mass., 1958—; prof. econs. and pub. affairs U. Md., College Park, 1990—; sr. staff mem. RAND Corp., 1958-59; chmn. rsch. adv. bd. Com. Econ. Devel., 1978-81, 84-85; mem. sci. adv. bd. USAF, 1960-64, def. sci. bd., 1966-70; mem. mil. econ. adv. panel CIA, 1980-85; trustee Aerospace Corp., 1984-93. Author: National Income Behavior, 1951, International Economics, 1958, The Strategy of Conflict, 1960, Arms and Influence, 1966, Micromotives and Macrobehavior, 1978, Choice and Consequence, 1984; co-author: Strategy and Arms Control, 1961. Recipient Frank E. Seidman Disting. award in polit. economy, 1977. Fellow Am. Acad. Arts and Scis., AAAS, Assn. for Pub. Policy Analysis and Mgmt., Am. Econ. Assn. (pres. 1991, Disting. mem. award). Mem. Nat. Acad. Scis. (rsch. award, 1993), Inst. Medicine. Office: Univ Md Sch Pub Affairs College Park MD 20742

SCHELLMAN, JOHN A., chemistry educator; b. Phila., Oct. 24, 1924; s. John and Mary (Mason) S.; m. Charlotte Green, Feb. 10, 1954; children: Heidi M., Lise C. AB, Temple U., 1948; MS, Princeton U., 1949, PhD, 1951; PhD (hon.), Chalmers U., Sweden, 1983, U. Padua, Italy, 1990. USPHS postdoctoral fellow U. Utah, 1951-52, Carlsberg Lab., Copenhagen, 1953-55; DuPont fellow U. Minn., Mpls., 1955-56; asst. prof. chemistry U. Minn., 1956-63; prof. chemistry Inst. Molecular Biology, U. Oreg., Eugene, 1958-63; prof. chemistry, rsch. assoc. Inst. Molecular Biology, U. Oreg., 1963—; vis. Lab. Chem. Physics, Nat. Inst. Arthritis and Metabolic Diseases, NIH, Bethesda, Md., 1980; vis. prof. Chalmers U., Sweden, 1986, U. Padua, Italy, 1987. Contbr. articles to profl. jours. Served with U.S. Army, 1943-46. Fellow Rask-Oersted Found., 1954, Sloan Found., 1959-63, Guggenheim Found., 1969-70. Fellow Am. Phys. Soc.; mem. NAS, Am. Chem. Soc., Am. Soc. Biochemistry and Molecular Biology, Am. Acad. Arts and Scis., Biophys. Soc., Phi Beta Kappa, Sigma Xi. Democrat. Home: 780 Lorane Hwy Eugene OR 97405-2340 Office: Univ Oreg Inst Molecular Biology Eugene OR 97403

SCHELM, ROGER LEONARD, information systems specialist; b. Kingston, N.Y., July 29, 1936; s. Frederick & Elizabeth M. (Wojciehowski) S.; m. Gloria Mae Dutterer, June 13, 1958; children: Sandra Lee Kern, Theresa Jean Sollitto, Ginger Lisa. B.A. in Polit. Sci., Western Md. Coll., 1958; M.A. in Pub. Adminstrn., Am. U., 1970; postgrad., U. Md., 1960-62. Analytic equipment programmer Nat. Security Agy., Ft. Meade, Md., 1958-60; computer cons. various cons. firms Balt. and Washington, 1960-68; mgr. army plans and programs Informatics Inc., Bethesda, Md., 1968; mgr. def. programs Automation Tech. Inc., Wheaton, Md., 1968-69; dir. advanced planning Genasys Corp., Washington, 1969-71; mgr. info. systems Ins. Co. North Am., Phila., 1971-72, sect. mgr. computing ops., 1972-74; mgr. tech. services INA Corp., Phila., 1974-75; mem. spl. tech. projects INA Corp. merger with Conn. Gen. Ins. Co. to form CIGNA Corp. 1982, Phila., 1975-76, asst. dir. tech. services, 1977, asst. dir. spl. tech. projects 1977-78, asst. dir. adminstrn., 1978-79, asst. dir. resource mgmt., data ctr. design, contingency planning, 1979-80; dir. corp. info. tech. now CIGNA Corp., Phila., 1981-82, dir. planning and control ops. div., 1982-83, v.p. strategic planning, systems div., 1983-84, v.p. applied research/expert systems, systems div., 1984-92; co-founder, pres. Schelm Internat., Inc., Cherry Hill, N.J., 1992—; mem. adj. faculty Camden Coll., N.J., 1978-82; mem. Camden County EDP Adv. Com., 1980-82; mem. faculty Drexel U., Phila., 1983-95. Author: Ednl. Computer Mag., 1982; editorial adv. bd., author Small Systems World Mag., 1982-84; editorial adv. bd. Spang-Robinson Report, 1986-87, Machine Intelligence News, 1987—; AI Expert Mag., 1985-88; cons. editor Expert Systems Jour., 1987-91. Tech. advisor various sch. bds., colls., univs. and non-profit orgns. Served to capt. U.S. Army, 1959. Mem. Am. Assn. Artificial Intelligence, Assn. Computing Machinery (founder Delaware Valley chpt. vice. chmn., program chmn. 1983-84, chmn. 1984-85, founder Del. Valley Spl. Interest Group in Artificial Intelligence, 1985, vice chmn. 1985-87), World Future Soc. Home: 506 Balsam Rd Cherry Hill NJ 08003-3202 Office: Schelm Internat Inc PO Box 172 Cherry Hill NJ 08003-0172

SCHELP, RICHARD HERBERT, mathematics educator; b. Kansas City, Mo., Apr. 21, 1936; s. Herbert and Ida (Stuerke) S.; m. Billie Marie Swopes, Dec. 20, 1958; children: Lisa Marie, Richard John. BS, Cen. Mo. U., 1959; MS, Kans. State U., 1961; postgrad., U. Kans., 1968; PhD, Kans. State U., 1970. Assoc. mathematician Johns Hopkins U., 1961-66; instr. math. Kans. State U., 1966-70; asst. prof. math. U. Memphis, 1970-74, assoc. prof. math., 1974-79, prof. math., 1979—; vis. rschr. Hungarian Acad. Scis., 1985, 90, 94, U. Paris-Sud, 1993; presenter in field. Contbr. over 100 articles to profl. jours.; mem. editorial bd. Jour. of Graph Theory, 1981—, co-mng. editor, 1981-86; referee math. jours., reviewer profl. jours. Rsch. grantee U. Memphis, 1973, 79, facil. devel. grantee, 1985; travel and subsistence grantee Internat. Rsch. and Exch. Bd., 1985, 90; grantee NSF, Nat. Security Agy.,

1986-88, 89-92, 94—. Mem. Am. Math. Soc., Am. Math. Assn. Home: 355 Lenora Dr Memphis TN 38117-2102 Office: Univ Memphis Dept Math Memphis TN 38152

SCHEMNITZ, SANFORD DAVID, wildlife biology educator; b. Cleve., Mar. 10, 1930; s. David Arthur Schemnitz; m. Mary Margaret Newby, July 8, 1958; children: Ellen Kay, Steven, Stuart. Student, U. Wis., 1948-50; BS in Wildlife, U. Mich., 1952; MS in Wildlife, U. Fla., 1953; PhD in Wildlife, Okla. State U., 1958. Cert. wildlife biologist. Conservation aide State of Mich. Dept. Conservation, Ann Arbor, 1951-52; game research biologist State of Minn. Dept. Conservation, St. Paul, 1958-59; asst. prof. wildlife Pa. State U., University Park, 1960-61; prof. wildlife resources U. Maine, Orono, 1962-75; dept. head fish and wildlife sci. N.Mex. State U., Las Cruces, 1975-81, prof. wildlife scis., 1981—. Editor: Wildlife Management Techniques Manual, 1980; contbr. articles to profl. jours. Fulbright Prof. Council for Internat. Exchange Scholars, Kathmandu, Nepal, 1983, Kenya, 1990. Mem. Am. Soc. Mammalogists, The Wildlife Soc. (life, S.W. regional rep. 1979-80), Ecol. Soc. Am., Wilson Ornithol. Soc., N.Mex. Wildlife Fedn. (bd. dirs. 1983—), Sigma Xi. Home: 8105 Dona Ana Rd Las Cruces NM 88005-6307 Office: NMex State U Dept Fish & Wildlife PO Box 4901 Las Cruces NM 88003-4901

SCHENCK, BENJAMIN ROBINSON, insurance consultant; b. N.Y.C., July 21, 1938; s. John T. and Harriet Buffum (Hall) S.; m. Sally V. Sullivan, Aug. 27, 1960; children: Steven T., Elizabeth F., Timothy S. B.A., William Coll., Williamstown, Mass, 1960; LL.B., Harvard U., 1963. Bar: N.Y. 1964, Mass. 1978. Asst. counsel to gov. State of N.Y., Albany, 1963-66; assoc. Bond, Schoeneck & King, Syracuse, N.Y., 1966-68; dep. supt., 1st dep. sup. and supt. State of N.Y. Dept. Ins., N.Y.C., 1968-75; sr. v.p. Shearson Hayden Stone Inc., N.Y.C., 1975-77; sr. v.p. State Mut. Life Assurance Co. Am., 1977-86, exec. v.p., 1986-89; pres. Worcester Mut. Ins. Co., 1979-83, Cen. Mass. Health Care, Inc., Worcester, 1989-93. Home: 85 Stockbridge Rd Lee MA 02138 Office: 63 State Rd Great Barrington MA 01230

SCHENCK, FREDERICK A., business executive; b. Trenton, May 12, 1928; s. Frederick A. and Alwilda M. (McLain) S.; m. Quinta Chapman, Jan. 25, 1974. Student, Howard U., 1948-50; B.S., Rider Coll., 1958, M.A., 1976. With N.J. Dept. Community Affairs, 1967-72; dir. youth and family services div. N.J. Dept. Instns. and Agys., 1972-74; dep. dir. administrn. purchase and property div. N.J. Treasury Dept., 1974-77; secretarial rep. Fed. Region II, Dept. Commerce, 1977-78; dep. under sec. Dept. Commerce, 1978-79; v.p. administrn. Resorts Internat. Hotel Casino, Atlantic City, 1979-88; v.p. personnel Cunard Lines Ltd., N.Y.C., 1988-93; self employed mgmt. cons. Secaucus, N.J., 1993—. Mem. N.J. Gov.'s Commn. on Disabled; bd. dirs. Bur. Nat. Affairs Inc. With USNR, 1946-48. Mem. Am. Soc. Public Adminstrn., N.J. C. of C. Presbyterian. Club: Sundowners, Nat. Guardsmen, Inc. Home: 569 Sanderling Ct Secaucus NJ 07094-2220

SCHENCK, JACK LEE, retired electric utility executive; b. Morgantown, W.Va., Aug. 2, 1938; s. Ernest Jacob and Virginia Belle (Kelley) S.; m. Rita Elizabeth Pietschmann, June 7, 1979; 1 son, Erik. B.S.E.E., B.A. in Social Sci., Mich. State U., 1961; M.B.A., NYU, 1975. Engr. AID, Tunis, Tunisia, 1961, Detroit Edison Co., 1962-63; engr., economist OECD, Paris, 1963-70; v.p. econ. policy analysis Edison Electric Inst., N.Y.C. and Washington, 1970-81; v.p., treas. Gulf States Utilities Co., Beaumont, Tex., 1981-92, sr. v.p., CFO, 1992-94, ret., 1994. Mem. Internat. Assn. Energy Econs., Triangle Club, Eta Kappa Nu. Republican.

SCHENCK, JOHN FREDERIC, physician; b. Decatur, Ind., June 7, 1939; s. John C. Schenck and Mildred Blosser; m. Jane Stark, Oct. 12, 1962 (div. 1982); children: Brooke, Kimberly, David; m. Susan J. Kalia, Oct. 8, 1994. BS in Physics, Rensselaer Poly. Inst., 1961, PhD in Physics, 1965; MD, Albany Med. Coll., 1977. Intern Albany (N.Y.) Med. Ctr. Hosp., 1977-78; staff scientist electronics lab GE, Syracuse, N.Y., 1965-73; staff mem., sr. scientist corp. R & D ctr. GE, Schenectady, N.Y., 1973—; assoc. prof. electrical engring. Syracuse U., 1970-73; mem. med. staff Ellis Hosp., Schenectady, 1981—; cons. scientist electronic lab GE, 1965-72; adj. asst. prof. dept. radiology U. Pa., 1983—. Contbr. articles to profl. jours.; 12 patents in field. Recipient S.S. Greenfield award Am. Assn. Physicists in Medicine, 1993. Mem. IEEE, AAAS, Soc. Magnetic Resonance in Medicine, Am. Physical Soc., Sigma Xi. Home: 17 Carrie Ct Niskayuna NY 12309-2223 Office: 4914 Ravine Ct Ann Arbor MI 48105

SCHENDEL, DAN ELDON, management consultant, business educator; b. Norwalk, Wis., Mar. 29, 1934; s. Leonard A. and Marian T. (Koch) S.; B.S. in Metall.Engring., U. Wis., 1956; M.B.A., Ohio State U., 1959; Ph.D. (Ford Found. fellow), Stanford U., 1963; m. Mary Lou Sigler, Sept. 1, 1956; children: Suzanne, Pamela, Sharon. With ALCOA, 1956, U.S. Civil Service, 1959-60, SRI, 1963-65; prof. mgmt., dir. exec. edn. programs Purdue U., 1965—; vis. prof. U. Mich., 1988-89, U. Chgo., 1990-91; pres. Strategic Mgmt. Assocs., Inc. Served with USAF, 1956-59. Fellow Acad. Mgmt.; mem. Strategic Mgmt. Soc. (founding pres., exec. dir.). The Planning Forum. Club: Lafayette Country. Author: (with others) Strategy Formulation: Analytical Concepts, 1978, Divided Loyalties, 1980, Fundamental Issues in Strategy, 1994; editor: (with others) Strategic Management: A New View of Business Policy and Planning, 1979; founding editor Strategic Mgmt. Jour., 1980—. Home: 1327 N Grant St West Lafayette IN 47906-2463 Office: Krannert Grad Sch Mgmt Purdue U West Lafayette IN 47907

SCHENDEL, STEPHEN ALFRED, plastic surgery educator, oral surgeon; b. Mpls., Oct. 10, 1947; s. Alfred Reck and Jeanne Shirley (Hagquist) S.; m. Susan Elizabeth Brown, Aug. 15, 1969; children: Elliott, Mélisande. BA, St. Olaf Coll., Northfield, Minn., 1969; BS with high distinction, U. Minn., 1971, DDS, 1973; diplome asst. etranger with high honors, U. Nantes, France, 1980; MD, U. Hawaii, 1983. Diplomate Am. Bd. Plastic Surgery, Nat. Bd. Med. Examiners, Nat. Bd. Dental Examiners, Am. Bd. Oral and Maxillofacial Surgery (adv. com., bd. examiner 1991—). Fellow in oral pathology U. Minn. Sch. Dentistry, Mpls., 1972; pvt. practice gen. dentistry, then oral-maxillofac. surgery, Honolulu, 1974-75, 80-83; resident in gen. dentistry Queen's Med. Ctr., Honolulu, 1973-74; intern, then resident in oral and maxillofacial surgery Parkland Meml. Hosp., Dallas, 1975-79; resident in gen. surgery Baylor U. Med. Ctr., Dallas, 1983-84; resident in gen. surgery Stanford (Calif.) U. Med. Ctr., 1984-86, resident in plastic surgery, 1986-89, acting assoc. prof. surgery, 1989-91, assoc. prof., 1991-95, head div. plastic and reconstructive surgery, 1992—, dir. residency tng., 1992—, acting chmn. dept. functional restoration, 1994, chmn., 1994—, prof., 1995—; head, plastic surgery, dir. Cranofacial Ctr. Lucile Salter Packard Children's Hosp., Stanford; asst. to Dr. Paul Tessier, Paris, 1987-88; asst. dept. stomatology and maxillofacial surgery Centre Hospitalier Regional Nantes, 1979-80; referee Annals Plastic Surgery, 1989—, Am. Jour. Orthodontics and Dentofacial Orthopedics, 1990—; presenter in field; mem. staff John Peter Smith Hosp., Ft. Worth, 1979; asst. clin. prof. surgery U. Hawaii John A Burns Sch. Medicine, Honolulu, 1980-84; chief plastic surgery svc., mem. med. bd. Lucile Salter Packard Children's Hosp. at Stanford, 1991—; mem. organizing com. 1st Hawaii-Pacific Cleft Palate Program, 1983; mem. in-svc. exam. com. Plastic Surgery Ednl. Found., 1992-93. Assoc. editor Selected Readings in Oral and Maxillofacial Surgery, 1989—; contbr. articles and abstracts to med. and dental jours., chpts. to books. Recipient Disting. Alumnus award St. Olaf Coll., 1993; Fulbright fellow, Nantes, 1979-80, Chateaubriand fellow Govt. of France, 1987-88. Fellow ACS; mem. European Assn. for Cranio-Maxillofacial Surgery, Am. Assn. Oral and Maxillofacial Surgeons (craniofacial com. 1989-91), Am. Soc. Pediats., Soc. Baylor Surgeons (founding), French Assn. Maxillofacial Surgeons (fgn.), Am. Cleft Palate-Craniofacial Assn., Am. Soc. Plaastic and Reconstructive Surgeons (sci. program com. 1992—), Am. Soc. Maxillofacial Surgeons (basic course syllabus com. 1991-93, membership com. 1991—, sci. program com. 1991—, best paper award com. 1991—, craniofacial and maxillofacial com. 1993—, bd. dirs.-at-large 1993—), Calif. carriers adv. com. 1993—), liaison to Am. Assn. Orthodontists 1994—), Assn. Acad. Chairmen Plastic Surgery, Internat. Soc. for Craniofacial Surgery, Zedplast (bd. dirs., surgery com. 1993—), Calif. Med. Assn. (sci. adv. panel on plastic surgery 1992—), Omicron Kappa Upsilon. Avocation: fly fishing. Office: Stanford U Med Ctr NC-104 Div Plastic-Reconstr Surg Stanford CA 94305

SCHENK, DEBORAH HUFFMAN, law educator; b. 1947. BA, Cornell U., 1969; JD, Columbia U., 1972. Bar: N.Y. 1973. From asst. prof. to prof. law Bklyn. Law Sch., 1974-85; prof. law NYU, N.Y.C., 1985—; vis. prof. Harvard U., spring, 1982, NYU, 1983-85; editor-in-chief Tax Law Rev., Yale U., 1989—. Author: Federal Taxation of S Corporation, 1986, supp. 1993. Mem. ABA (tax sect.). N.Y. State Bar Assn. (vice chmn. com. on profl. ethics). Home: 219 Kane St Brooklyn NY 11231-4437 Office: NYU Sch Law 40 Washington Sq S New York NY 10012-1005

SCHENK, GEORGE, oil industry executive; b. 1934. Grad., Fed. Inst. Tech., Zurich, Switzerland, 1956. With JM Huber Corp., 1957—, v.p., 1972-79, corp. v.p., 1979-84, pres., COO, 1984-90, pres., CEO, 1990—. Office: J M Huber Corp 333 Thornall St Edison NJ 08818

SCHENK, JOSEPH B., museum director; b. Mar. 28, 1953; m. Jacqueline Schenk; children: Brian, Stuart. BA in Mus. Staff Preparation, Huntingdon Coll., 1974; MA in Art Edn., Ball State U., 1979; postgrad., U. Calif., Berkeley, 1986. Exhibits asst. Hunter Mus. of Art, Chattanooga, 1974-75; asst. dir. Alford House/Anderson Fine Arts Ctr., Anderson, Ind., 1976, exec. dir., 1976-79; exec. dir. Okefenokee Heritage Ctr., Waycross, Ga., 1979-83; dir. So. Forest World, Waycross, 1979-83, Chattahooche Valley Art Mus., LaGrange, Ga., 1983-88, Fine Arts Mus. of the South at Mobile, Ala., 1988—; bd. dirs. U.S. Sports Acad. Art Mus., 1993—; v.p. Ala. Muss. Assn., 1994—; adv. panelist Profl. Touring Panel Ga. Coun. for Arts, 1983-84, PRACSO Panel Ga. Coun. for Arts, 1984-86, Architecture & Environ. Arts Ind. Arts Commn., 1978-79, Mus. Ind. Arts Commn., 1977-79; Ind. representative Small Mus. Com. Midwest Mus. Conf., 1978-79. Pub. numerous art catalogs; editor newsletter Ga. Assembly of Community Arts Agys., 1987-88. Art juror at numerous pub. and pvt. art shows; bd. dirs. Ga. Alliance for Arts Edn., 1982-84, Assn. Ind. Mus., 1979, Mobile Arts Coun., 1989-90, Ga. Assembly Community Arts Agys., 1986-88; commr. Madison County Hist. Home, Anderson, 1977-79; mem. dedication com., cons. Krannert Fine Arts Ctr., Anderson Coll., 1979; mem. com. forest festival tourism and conventions Waycross/Ware County C. of C., 1979-83; bd. dirs. Southeastern Ga. Travel and Tourism Assn., 1981-83, sec., 1981-82, pres., 1982-83. Grantee Nat. Endowment for Arts, Ala. State Coun. on Arts, Mobile Arts Coun., Ga. Endowment for Humanities, Ga. Coun. Arts, Ala. Arts Found., Inst. Mus. Svcs., Ga. Gov.'s Intern Program, others; recipient Spark Plug of Yr. award Waycross Jaycees, 1981; Mus. Mgmt. Inst. scholar, 1986. Mem. Am. Assn. Mus., Southeastern Mus. Conf., Ala. Mus. Assn. (v.p. 1994—), Rotary, Mobile United. Home: 5000 N Carmel Dr Mobile AL 36608 Office: Fine Arts Mus of the South 4850 Museum Dr PO Box 8426-36689 Mobile AL 36689

SCHENK, LYNN, congresswoman; b. Bronx, N.Y.; m. C. Hugh Friedman. BA, UCLA; JD, U. San Diego; postgrad, London (Eng.) Sch. Econs. Dep. atty. gen. Calif. Atty. Gen.'s Office; atty. San Diego Gas & Electric Co.; spl. asst. vps Nelson Rockefeller and Walter Mondale, Washington, 1976-77; sec. bus., transp. and housing State of Calif., 1980-83; mem. 103rd Congress from 49th Calif. dist., 1993—; founder San Diego Urban Corp, The Women's Bank, The Lawyer's Club. Vice chair bd. dirs. San Diego Unified Port Dist, commr., Ctr. for Nat. Policy, Washington; bd dirs Edmund G "Pat" Brown Inst. Govt. Affairs, Calif. State U., L.A.; trustee Claremont U. Ctr. and Grad. Sch. Recipient Israel Peace medal; named Outstanding Young Citizen San Diego Jaycees.

SCHENK, QUENTIN FREDERICK, retired social work educator, mayor; b. Fort Madison, Iowa, Aug. 25, 1922; s. Fred Edward John and Ida (Sabrowsky) S.; m. Patricia J. Kelley, Aug. 6, 1946 (div. Apr. 1970); children: Fred W. (dec. 1972), Patricia, Karl, Martha; m. Emmy Lou Willson, May 23, 1970. BA, Willamette U., 1948; M.S., U. Wis., 1950, M.S. in Social Work, 1953, Ph.D., 1953. Asst. social work U. Wis.-Madison, 1953-55, prof., chmn. extension social work, 1961-63; prof., former dean Sch. Social Welfare, Milw., 1963-90, prof. emeritus, 1990—; assoc. prof. U. Mo., 1955-61; project specialist Ford Found., 1968-71; Spl. cons. on urban mission in Africa United Presbyn. Ch., 1971—, World Council Chs., 1971—; adviser to Haile Sellassie I U., Addis Ababa, Ethiopia, 1968-71; Alderman City of Cedarburg (Wis.), 1974-82, mayor, 1982-86. Author: (with Emmy Lou Schenk) Pulling Up Roots, 1978, Welfare Society and the Helping Professions, 1981; author sect. on Ethiopia, Welfare in Africa, 1987; contbr. articles, bulls., reports to profl. lit. Mem. Wis. Historic Preservation Negotiating Bd.; chmn. bd. Guest House, Milw., 1987-89. Pilot USNR, 1942-46. Decorated Air medal with 3 gold stars, DFC; recipient Presdl. citation Pres. Harry Truman, 1948. Mem. AAUP, Nat. Trust for Historic Preservation, Am. Sociol. Assn., Council on Social Work Edn., Aircraft Owners and Pilots Assn., Cessna Pilots Assn., Am. Legion. Home: Box 31 550 Graham Ave #409 Eau Claire WI 54701

SCHENK, WORTHINGTON GEORGE, JR., surgeon, educator; b. Buffalo, Feb. 10, 1922; s. Worthington George and Edna (Klein) S.; m. Jean L.K. Lyon, Mar. 9, 1946; children: Martha, Lura, Worthington George III, Elsa, Gregory, Molly, Andrew. B.A., Williams Coll., 1942; M.D., Harvard U., 1945. Diplomate: Am. Bd. Surgery. With U. Buffalo, 1948-66, assoc. prof. surgery, 1959-66; prof. surgery SUNY, Buffalo, 1966-85; acting chmn. dept. surgery SUNY, 1969-72, chmn., 1972-85; dir. surgery Erie County Med. Ctr., Buffalo, 1966-85; ret., 1985. Editorial bd. Current Surgery; contbr. articles to profl. jours. Mem. AMA, Am. So. surg. assns., Am. Assn. Surgery Trauma, Soc. Univ. Surgeons, Soc. Vascular Surgery (past treas., pres. 1976), Soc. Clin. Surgery (sec. 1966-72), Internat. Cardiovascular Soc., ACS, Soc. for Surgery of Alimentary Tract, Surg. Biology Club, Phi Beta Kappa. Home: 38 Front Ave Hanford Bay Silver Creek NY 14136 *It has been a great pleasure to have been involved in the development of vascular surgery from its inception. Retrospectively, my basic laboratory type research contributions now give me the greatest satisfaction, far more than any number of surgical operations. Next in importance is the satisfaction of having turned out more than 25 research fellows.*

SCHENKEL, SUZANNE CHANCE, natural resource specialist; b. Phila., Mar. 12, 1940; d. Henry Martyn Chance II and Suzanne (Sharpless) Jameson; m. John Lackland Hardinge Schenkel, June 15, 1963; children: John Jr., Andrew Chance. BS in Edn., Tufts U., 1962. Tchr. Roland Pk. Country Sch., Balt., 1962-65; exec. dir. Mass. Citizens' Com. for Dental Health, Springfield, 1981-83; pub. editor Women's Investment Newsletter, Longmeadow, Mass., 1985-89; pub. affairs officer USDA's Soil Conservation Svc., Amherst, Mass., 1990-93; program mgr. land and water program divsn. USDA's Soil Conservation Svc., Washington, 1993—; staff Merchant Marine and Fisheries com. U.S. Ho. of Reps., Washington, 1993. Author Wetlands Protection and Management Act. Chmn. Longmeadow (Mass.) Conservation Commn., 1984-90; supr. Hampden County (Mass.) Conservation Dist., 1985-90; bd. dirs., v.p. League of Women Voters of Mass., Boston, 1974-85; exec. com. Water Supply Citizens' Adv. Com., Water Resources Authority, Mass., 1979-90. Mem. Soil and Water Conservation Soc., Nat. Assn. Conservation Dists. Episcopalian. Avocations: golf, tennis, sailing. Home: 1052 Carriage Hill Pkwy Annapolis MD 21401 Office: USDA Natural Resources Conservation Svc/Ecosystem Asst Divsn/PO Box 2890 Washington DC 20013

SCHENKENBERG, MARY MARTIN, principal; b. Oakland, Calif., Nov. 29, 1944; d. Leo Patrick and Florence Kathryn (Brinkoetter) Martin; m. Philip Rawson Schenkenberg III, Aug. 20, 1966; children: Philip Rawson IV, Amy Lynn, Stephen Patrick. BA in English, Fontbonne Coll., 1966; MA Teaching in English, St. Louis U., 1975, PhD in English, 1991. Cert. tchr., Mo. Asst. prof. Fontbonne Coll., St. Louis, 1978-85; English dept. chair Nerinx Hall High Sch., St. Louis, 1979-89; asst. prof. Webster U., St. Louis, 1986-89; co-prin. Nerinx Hall High Sch., St. Louis, 1989-92, prin., 1992—; adj. prof. St. Louis U., 1985-89; advanced placement reader Ednl. Testing Svc., Princeton, N.J., 1986-90. Author: (with others) The English Classroom in the Computer Age, 1991. Bd. pres. Mary, Queen of Peace Sch., St. Louis, 1977. Mem. ASCD, Nat. Coun. Tchrs. English, Greater St. Louis Tchrs. English (bd. dirs. 1989—). Roman Catholic. Avocations: tennis, theater, travel. Office: Nerinx Hall High Sch 530 E Lockwood Ave Webster Groves MO 63119

SCHENK, ALEXANDER MARIAN, Slavic linguistics educator; b. Cracow, Poland, Dec. 20, 1924; came to U.S., 1946, naturalized, 1952; s. Oskar and Gizela (Szaminski) S.; m. Krystyna Czaja, Oct. 15, 1970; children: Alfred R., Michael J., Catherine I. Student, Stalinabad Pedagogical Inst., 1943-46, U. Paris, 1947-48; M.A., Yale U., 1950, Ph.D., 1953. Asst. in instrn. Yale U., New Haven, 1950-52; instr. Yale U., 1952-56, asst. prof., 1956-63, asso. prof., 1963-67, prof. Slavic linguistics, 1967—; vis. prof. Slavic linguistics U. Calif., Berkeley, 1969-70. Author: Polish Declension, 1964, Beginning Polish, 2 vols., rev. edit., 1973; editor: Fifteen Modern Polish Short Stories, 1970, American Contributions to the 10th Internat. Congress of Slavists Linguistics, 1988; co-editor: For Wiktor Weintraub, 1975, The Slavic Literary Languages, 1980, Studies in Slavic Linguistics and Poetics, 1982. Mem. Internat. Linguistic Assn., Conn. Acad. Arts and Scis., Polish Inst. Arts/Scis., Am. Assn. Tchrs. Slavic and E. European Langs., Am. Assn. Advancement Slavic Studies. Office: Yale U Dept Slavic Langs and Lits PO Box 208236 New Haven CT 06520-8236

SCHENKER, CARL RICHARD, JR., lawyer; b. Portland, Oreg., Feb. 28, 1949; s. Carl Richard and Frances Emily (Cole) S.; m. Susan Sherman Richardson, Mar. 29, 1986. BA, Stanford U., 1971, JD, 1974. Bar: Calif. 1974, D.C. 1977, U.S. Dist. Ct. (so. dist.) Calif. 1977, U.S. Supreme Ct. 1978, U.S. Dist. Ct. D.C. 1980, U.S. Ct. Appeals (5th and 11th cirs.) 1981, U.S. Ct. Appeals (D.C. cir.) 1983, U.S. Ct. Appeals (2d cir.) 1992. Law clk. to hon. Shirley M. Hufstedler U.S. Ct. Appeals (9th cir.), L.A., 1974-75; law clk. to Hon. Lewis F. Powell, Jr. U.S. Supreme Ct., Washington, 1975-76; assoc. O'Melveny & Myers, Washington, 1976-82, ptnr., 1982—. Pres. Stanford Law Review, 1973-74; contbr. articles to profl. jours. Mem. ABA, Fed. Bar Assn., D.C. Bar Assn., Phi Beta Kappa. Office: O'Melveny & Myers 555 13th St NW Washington DC 20004

SCHENKER, ERIC, university dean, economist; b. Vienna, Austria, Feb. 24, 1931; came to U.S., 1939, naturalized, 1945; s. Adolph and Olga (Strauss) S.; m. Virginia Martha Wick, Apr. 14, 1963; children: David, Richard, Robert. B.B.A., CCNY, 1952; M.S., U. Tenn., 1955; Ph.D., U. Fla., 1957. Asst. prof. Mich. State U., 1957-59; mem. faculty U. Wis.-Milw., 1959—, prof. econs., 1965—; dean U. Wis.-Milw. (Sch. Bus. Adminstrn.), 1976—; dir. Urban Research Center, 1974-76; asso. dir. Center Great Lakes Studies, 1967-74, sr. scientist, 1974—; asso. dean Coll. Letters and Scis., 1963-69; bd. dirs. Am. Med. Bldgs., Ampco Metal; cons. in field. Author: The Port of Milwaukee: An Economic Review, 1967; co-author: Port Planning and Development as Related to Problems of U.S. Ports and the U.S. Coastal Environment, 1974, The Great Lakes Transportation System, 1976, Port Development in the United States, 1976, Maritime Labor Organizations on the Great Lakes-St. Lawrence Seaway System, 1978, Great Lakes Transportation System in the 80s, 1986; also monographs and articles. Sr. mem. Milw. Bd. Harbor Commrs., 1960-72, chmn., 1965-68; chmn. panel on future port requirements of U.S., Maritime Transp. Research Bd., Nat. Acad. Scis., 1973-76, chmn. panel on reducing tankbarge pollution, 1980-81; mem. pilotage adv. bd. to U.S. sec. transp., 1972-75; trustee Mt. Sinai Med. Ctr. 1984-88; mem. Econ. Progress Authority of Milw. Met. Sewerage Dist., 1983-88, Marine Bd., NAS, 1982-83, Gov.'s Coun. on Econ. Issues, 1983—. Served with AUS, 1952-54. Mem. Am. Econs. Assn., So. Econs. Assn., Phi Kappa Phi, Alpha Kappa Psi, Beta Gamma Sigma, Beta Alpha Psi. Home: 2254 W Dunwood Rd Milwaukee WI 53209-1818

SCHENKER, LEO, retired utility company executive; b. Vienna, Austria, Jan. 3, 1922; came to U.S., 1952, naturalized, 1959; s. Max and Selda Lea (Podhorcer) S.; m. Alda R. Tinson, Jan. 20, 1949; children: Michael Gregory, Deborah Anne. B.S. with first class honors, U. London, 1942; M.A. in Sci. (Can. Inst. Steel Constrn. fellow), U. Toronto, 1950; Ph.D., U. Mich., 1954. Mng. dir. METAG Ltd., London, 1945-48; asst. rsch. engr. Hydro-Electric Power Commn. of Ont. (Can.), Toronto, 1948-52; rsch. assoc. U. Mich., Ann Arbor, 1952-54; with Bell Telephone Labs., 1954-87, various positions, dir. mil. electronic tech., 1968-71; dir. Loop Maintenance Systems Lab., 1971-80, exec. dir. Central Office Ops. div., 1980-83; exec. dir. network system planning div., 1983-84, exec. dir. tech. info. div., 1984-87; adj. prof. electrical engring. Cooper Union, N.Y.C. Served with RAF, 1942-45. Recipient Duggan medal Can. Inst. Steel Constrn., 1950. Fellow IEEE, Sigma Xi, Phi Kappa Phi. Patentee communications tech. field.

SCHENKER, MARC BENET, medical educator; b. L.A., Aug. 25, 1947; s. Steve and Dosella Schenker; m. Heath Massey, Oct. 8; children: Yael, Phoebe, Hilary. BA, U. Calif., Berkeley, 1969; MD, U. Calif., San Francisco, 1973; MPH, Harvard U., Boston, 1980. Instr. medicine Harvard U., Boston, 1980-82; asst. prof. medicine U. Calif., Davis, 1982-86, assoc. prof., 1986-92, prof., 1992—. Fellow ACP; mem. Am. Thoracic Soc., Am. Pub. Health Assn., Soc. Epidemiologic Rsch., Am. Coll. Epidemiology, Soc. Occupl. Environ. Health, Internat. Commn. Occupl. Health, Phi Beta Kappa, Alpha Omega Alpha. Office: U Calif Divsn Occupational & Environ Medicine ITEH Davis CA 95616

SCHENKER, STEVEN, physician, educator; b. Poland, Oct. 5, 1929; came to U.S., 1943, naturalized, 1946; s. Alfred and Ernestyna S.; m. Sally Ann Wood, May 11, 1956; children: Julie C. Schenker Burn, Steven A., David S., Andrew G., Jennifer E.; m. Jo Ann Neumann, Nov. 24, 1985. B.A., Cornell U., 1951, M.D., 1955. Intern Harvard Service-Boston City Hosp., 1955-56, resident in medicine, 1956-58; asst. prof. medicine U. Cin. Sch. Medicine 1961-63; asst. prof. U. Tex., Southwestern Sch. Medicine, 1963-67, assoc. prof. medicine, 1967-70; prof. medicine, biochemistry, dir. div. gastroenterology Vanderbilt U. Sch. Medicine, Nashville VA Hosp., 1970-82; prof. medicine and pharmacology, dir. div. gastroenterology U. Tex. Sch. Medicine, San Antonio, 1982—; chmn. study sect. Nat. Inst. on Alcohol Abuse and Addiction, 1980-83; chmn. study sects. VA, 1985-88. Editor: Hepatology, 1985-90. Contbr. numerous articles in field to profl. jours. Recipient Markle award, 1963; Career Devel. award NIH, 1968; Jurzykowski Found. for Research in Medicine award, 1979, Alcoholism Research Soc. award 1987. Mem. Am. Assn. for Study Study of Liver Diseases (pres. 1980), Am. Soc. Clin. Investigation, Assn. Am. Physicians, Am. Gastroent. Soc., Am. Soc. Pharm. and Exptl. Therapeutics, Am. Soc. Clin. Nutrition, Internat. Soc. for Study of Liver Diseases, Alpha Omega Alpha. Home: 26025 Mesa Oak Dr San Antonio TX 78255-3533 Office: U Tex Med Sch San Antonio TX 78284

SCHENKKAN, ROBERT FREDERIC, writer, actor; b. Chapel Hill, N.C., Mar. 19, 1953; s. Robert Frederic Sr. and Jean (McKenzie) S.; m. Mary Anne Dorward, Dec. 1, 1984; children: Sarah Victoria, Joshua McHenry. BA in Theatre Arts, U. Tex., 1975; MFA in Acting, Cornell U., 1977. Author: (plays) Final Passages, 1981, Derelict, 1982, Intermission, 1982, Lunchbreak, 1982, The Survivalist, 1982 (Best of the Fringe award Edinburgh Festival 1984), Tachinoki, 1987, Tall Tales, 1988 (Playwrights Forum award 1988, Best One Act Plays 1993), Heaven on Earth, 1989 (Julie Harris Playwright award Beverly Hills Theatre Guild 1989), The Kentucky Cycle, 1991 (Pulitzer Prize for drama 1992, L.A. Drama Critics Circle Best Play award 1992, Perez Ctr. West award 1993, Best Play Tony award nominee 1993, Best Play Drama Desk award nominee 1993), Conversations with the Spanish Lady and Other One Act Plays, 1993; actor (TV) Father Brown Detective, 1979, Murder in Cowetta County, 1980, George Washington, 1983, Kane and Abel, 1984, Nutcracker, 1987, (films) Act of Vengeance, 1974, Sweet Liberty, 1986, The Manhattan Project, 1986, Bedroom Window, 1987. Grantee Vogelstein Found., 1982, Arthur Found., 1988, Fund for New Am. Plays grantee 1990, Calif. Arts Coun. grantee, 1991. Mem. SAG, Writers Guild, Dramatists Guild, Actors Equity, Ensemble Studio Theatre.

SCHENKMAN, JOHN BORIS, pharmacologist, educator; b. N.Y.C., Feb. 10, 1936; s. Abraham and Theresa (Moses) S.; m. Deanna Owen, June 5, 1960; children: Jeffrey Alan, Laura Ruth. BA in Chemistry, Bklyn. Coll., 1960; PhD in Biochemistry, SUNY Upstate Med. Ctr., Syracuse, 1964. Postdoctoral fellow U. Pa. Johnson Found., Phila., 1964-67, Inst. Protein Research Osaka U., Japan, 1967-68, Inst. Toxicology Tübingen U., Fed. Republic Germany, 1968; asst. prof. U. Wis. Sch. Medicine, New Haven, 1968-71, assoc. prof., 1971-78; prof., dept. head. U. Conn. Health Ctr., Farmington, 1978-87; prof. U. Conn., Farmington, 1987—. Contbr. articles to profl. jours. Served as sgt. U.S. Army, 1953-55. Research grantee NIH, to profl. jours. Served as sgt. U.S. Army, 1953-55. Research grantee NIH, NSF; recipient Research Career Devel award NIH, 1971-76. Mem. Am. Soc. Biochemists and Molecular Biologists, AM. Soc. Pharmacology Exptl. Therapeutics, Brit. Biochemistry Soc., Soc. Toxicology, Am. Med. Sch. Pharmacologists (councilor 1987-88). Jewish. Avocations: fishing, botany, wine making. Office: U Conn Sch Medicine Dept Phamacology Farmington CT 06030-1505

SCHENTAG, JEROME JOHN, pharmacy educator; b. St. Clair, Mich., Jan. 25, 1950; s. John and Rose (Petracek) S.; m. Rita R. Sloan, June 26, 1976; 1 child, Annie Sloan. BS in Pharmacy, U. Mich., 1973; D. Pharmacy, Phila. Coll. Pharmacy, 1975. Postdoctoral fellow SUNY, Buffalo, 1975-76, asst. prof. of pharmacy, 1976-81, assoc. prof., 1981-86, prof., 1986—; dir. Clin. Pharmacokinetics Lab., Millard Fillmore Hosp., Buffalo. Editor: Applied Pharmacokinetics, 1981, 2d edit., 1985; contbr. over 175 articles to profl. publs. Am. Coll. Clin. Pharmacy fellow, 1985; recipient Disting. Young Alumni award Phila. Coll. of Pharmacy, 1989. Fellow Am. Assn. Pharm. Scientists; mem. Am. Soc. Microbiology. Office: Millard Fillmore Hosp Clin Pharmacokinetics Buffalo NY 14209

SCHEPARTZ, ALANNA, biochemist, educator; b. N.Y.C., Jan. 9, 1962. BS, SUNY, Albany, 1982; PhD in Chemistry, Columbia U., 1987. NIH fellow Yale U., 1987-88, asst. prof., 1988-92, assoc. prof. dept. chemistry, 1992—. Recipient Presdl. Young Investigator award NSF, 1991; Sci. and Engring. fellow David and Lucille Packard Found., 1991. Mem. Am. Chem. Soc. (Arthur C. Cope Scholar award 1995). Achievements include research in bioorganic chemistry. Office: Yale U Dept Chemistry New Haven CT 06511-8161*

SCHEPERS, JAMES STUART, soil scientist; b. Geneva, Nebr., Feb. 10, 1946; s. Stuart Albert and Adelia Louise (Meyer) S.; m. Marilyn La Vonne Cherry, Dec. 29, 1968; children: Michael, Damion, Aaron, Joshua. BS, U. Nebr., 1968, MS, 1970; PhD, U. Ill., 1973. Asst. prof. U. Ga., Athens, 1973-75; soil scientist USDA Agrl. Rsch. Svc., Lincoln, Nebr., 1975—; mem. environ. task force Pioneer HiBred Int., Des Moines, 1991-93; cons. Int. Atomic Energy Agy., Vienna, Austria, 1993. Fellow Am. Soc. Agronomy (Agronomic Achievement award 1993, Weiner L. Nelson Diagnostic award 1994), Soil Sci. Soc. Am.; mem. Internat. Soil Sci. Soc., Soil and Water Conservation Soc. Avocation: woodworking. Office: USDA-Agrl Rsch Svc Dept of Agronomy 113 Keim Hall Lincoln NE 68583-0915

SCHEPISI, FRED, director, screenwriter; b. Melbourne, Australia, Dec. 26, 1939. Student, Assumption Coll., Marcellin Coll. assessor student films Swinburne Inst. Tech., Melbourne; with govt. sponsored exptl. Film Fund; founder prodn. co. The Film Ho. Dir. films including Libido, 1973, Barbarosa, 1982, Iceman, 1984, Plenty, 1985, Roxanne, 1987, The Russia House, 1990, Mr. Baseball, 1992, Six Degrees of Separation, 1993, I.Q., 1994; screenwriter, dir. The Devil's Playground, 1976 (Best Film award Australian Film Inst.), The Chant of Jimmie Blacksmith, 1978, A Cry in the Dark, 1988 (Best Screenplay award Australian Film Inst.). Address: ICM 8942 Wilshire Blvd Los Angeles CA 90211*

SCHEPPACH, RAYMOND CARL, JR., association executive, economist; b. Hamden, Conn., Mar. 28, 1940; s. Raymond Carl and Margret (Barrie) S.; m. Anna Roberts, July 14, 1962 (div. Nov. 1978); children: Kristine, Raymond Scott; m. Trevia Dean, Apr. 28, 1985. B.A., U. Maine, 1962; M.A., U. Conn., 1965, Ph.D., 1970. Vice pres., sr. cons. Jack Faucett Assocs., Chevy Chase, Md., 1969-75; asst. dir. natural resources and commerce Congl. Budget Office, Washington, 1976-80, dep. dir. office, 1980-82; exec. dir. Nat. Govs. Assn., Washington, 1982—. Author: State Projections of the Gross national Product, 1970 and 1980, Transportation Productivity: Measurement and Policy Applications, 1975, Energy Policy Analysis and Congressional Action, 1982, New Directions in Economic Policy: An Agenda for the 1980's, 1984. Served to capt. U.S. Army, 1962-64. Mem. Am. Econ. Assn. Home: 4078 Rosamora Ct Arlington VA 22207-4707 Office: Nat Govs Assn 444 E Capitol St NW Washington DC 20001-1512

SCHER, HOWARD DENNIS, lawyer; b. Ft. Monmouth, N.J., Apr. 23, 1945; s. George Scher and Rita (Eitches) Zar; children: Seth Micah, Eli David. BA, Brandeis U., 1967; JD, Rutgers U., 1971. Bar: Pa. 1971, U.S. Dist. Ct. (ea. dist.) Pa. 1971, U.S. Ct. Appeals (3rd cir.) 1971, U.S. Supreme Ct. 1975. Asst. city solicitor City of Phila., 1971-73; assoc. Goodis, Greenfield, Henry & Edelstein, Phila., 1973-77; assoc. Montgomery, McCracken, Walker & Rhoads, Phila., 1977-80, ptnr., 1980—. V.p. Jewish Employment Vocat. Svcs., Phila., 1988—; trustee Fedn. of Jewish Agys. of Greater Phila.; dir. Akiba Hebrew Acad., Merion, Pa.; mem. pres.'s coun. Brandeis U. Mem. Phila. Bar Assn., Pa. Bar Assn., ABA, Brandeis U. Alumni Assn. (v.p. 1983-87). Home: 2222 Locust St Philadelphia PA 19103-5511 Office: Montgomery McCracken Walker & Rhoads 3 Parkway Fl 20 Philadelphia PA 19102-1321

SCHER, IRVING, lawyer; b. N.Y.C., July 22, 1933; s. Charles and Tillie (Ballenberg) S.; m. Marilyn Deanna Ball, Sept. 11, 1955 (div. 1984); children: Susan, Lisa; m. Amy Lynn Katz, June 8, 1985; 1 child, Sara Katz-Scher. BA, City Coll. N.Y., 1955; JD, Columbia U., 1962. Bar: N.Y. 1963. Assoc. Weil, Gotshal & Manges, N.Y.C., 1962-69, ptnr., 1969—; adj. prof. NYU Sch. Law, 1972—; co-chmn. ann. anti-trust law inst. Practicing Law Inst., N.Y.C., 1976—; adv. bd. Antitrust and Trade Regulation Reports, 1980—. Editor Columbia Law Rev., 1960-61, revs. editor 1961-62; contbr. articles to profl. jours. Served as lt. USNR, 1955-59. Recipient Harlan Fiske Stone scholarship Columbia Law Sch., 1960-62, Nat. Scholarship award Columbia Law Sch., 1961-62, Gluck scholarship Columbia Law Sch., 1960-61. Mem. ABA (chmn. antitrust law section 1988-89), N.Y. State Bar Assn. (chmn. antitrust law section 1980-81). Jewish. Avocations: skiing, theater. Office: Weil Gotshal & Manges 767 5th Ave New York NY 10153-0001

SCHER, ROBERT SANDER, instrument design company executive; b. Cin., May 24, 1934; s. Stanford Samuel and Eva (Ordan) S.; m. Audrey Erna Gordon, Oct. 21, 1961; children: Sarahh, Alexander, Aaron. SB, MIT, 1956, SM, 1958, Diploma in Mech. Engring., 1960, ScD, 1963. Rsch. and teaching asst. MIT, Cambridge, Mass., 1957-62; control system engr. RCA, Hightstown, N.J., 1963-65; engring. mgr. Sequential Info. System, Elmsford, N.Y., 1965-71; tech. dir. Teledyne Gurley, Troy, N.Y., 1971-78, v.p. engring., 1978-86, pres., 1986-92; pres. Encoder Design Assocs., Clifton Park, N.Y., 1993—. Co-author patent Linear Digital Readout, 1965. Mem. ASME, Optical Soc. Am. Jewish. Avocation: chamber music. Home: 2 Laurel Oak Ln Clifton Park NY 12065-4712

SCHER, STANLEY JULES, lawyer; b. Bklyn., Dec. 19, 1929; s. Leo A. and Frances (Goldman) S.; m. Susan Goldman, June 16, 1957; children—William Goldman, Peter Lawrence, Alison Hope. LL.B., Bklyn. Law Sch., 1952. Bar: N.Y. 1954, U.S. Dist. Ct. (so. and ea. dists.) N.Y. 1960, U.S. Supreme Ct. 1970. Ptnr. Tullman, Fisher & Scher, N.Y.C., 1954-62; founder, sr. ptnr. Garbarini & Scher, P.C., N.Y.C., 1962—; med.-legal lectr. physicians, hosps., health-related facilities, 1970—; mem. faculty N.Y. State Trial Lawyers Assn., 1975—; lectr. Nassau Acad. Law, 1984, N.Y. State Bar Assn., 1983. Pres. Baker Hill Civic Assn., Great Neck, N.Y., past zone leader Great Neck North Dem. Com., mem. Nat. CIC Orgn., Great Neck. Served with U.S. Army, 1952-54. Mem. ABA, Assn. Trial Lawyers Am., Soc. Med. Jurisprudence, N.Y. State Bar Assn., N.Y. County Lawyers Assn., Queens County Bar Assn., Nassau County Bar Assn. Jewish. Club: Temple Israel Couples (Great Neck, N.Y.) (past pres.). Lodge: B'nai B'rith. Home: 59 Essex Rd Great Neck NY 11023-1535 Office: Garbarini & Scher PC 1114 Ave Of The Americas New York NY 10036-7703

SCHER, STEVEN PAUL, literature educator; b. Budapest, Hungary, Mar. 2, 1936; came to U.S., 1957, naturalized, 1963; Diploma in piano, Bela Bartok Conservatory of Music, Budapest, 1955; B.A. cum laude, Yale U., 1960, M.A., 1963, Ph.D., 1966. Instr. German, Columbia U., N.Y.C., 1965-67; asst. prof. German, Yale U., New Haven, 1967-70; assoc. prof. Yale U., 1970-74; prof. German and comparative lit. Dartmouth Coll., Hanover, N.H., 1974—; chmn. dept. Dartmouth Coll., 1974-80, acting chmn. dept., 1982-83, Ted and Helen Geisel 3d Century prof. humanities, 1984-89; vis. prof. U. Paderborn, Fed. Republic Germany, summer 1980, Karl-Franzens-U. Graz, Austria, summer 1984; grant reviewer Guggenheim Found., NEH, Am. Council Learned Socs., others; cons. univ. presses and scholarly jours.; lectr. throughout world. Author: Verbal Music in German Literature, 1968; editor: (with Charles McClelland) Postwar German Culture: An Anthology, 1974, 2d edit., 1980, Interpretations: Zu E.T.A. Hoffmann, 1981, (with Ulrich Weisstein) Literature and the Other Arts. Proc. of IXth Congress of Internat. Comparative Lit. Assn., Innsbruck, vol. 3, 1981, Literatur und Musik. Ein Handbuch zur Theorie und Praxis eines komparatistischen Grenzgebietes, 1984, Music and Text: Critical Inquiries, 1992; contbr. ar-

ticles and essays to scholarly jours. Morse fellow, 1969-70; Humboldt fellow, 1972-73; Yale Coll. scholar, 1957-60, grad. fellow, 1960-62; DAAD grantee U. Munich, 1964-65. Mem. MLA (chmn. bibliography com. of div. lit. 1972-86), Am. Comparative Lit. Assn., Internat. Comparative Lit. Assn., Internat. P.E.N. Club. Home: 102 S Main St Hanover NH 03755-2040 Office: Dartmouth College Dept German Dartmouth Hall Hanover NH 03755

SCHER, VALERIE JEAN, music critic; b. Chgo., Jan. 31, 1952; d. Jacob and Klema (Seider) S.; m. David Clark Elliott, Sept. 6, 1980; children: Sabrina, Travis. B in Performance Piano, Northwestern U., Evanston, Ill., 1974, M in Music History, 1976, PhD in Music History, 1978. Asst. music critic Chgo. Daily News, 1975-78; asst. music and dance critic Chgo. Sun-Times, 1978-82; dance critic, asst. music critic Phila. Inquirer, 1982-83; music and dance critic San Diego Tribune, 1984-91, music, dance and theater critic, 1991-92; music critic San Diego Union-Tribune, 1992—. mem. citizens adv. coun. San Diegoito River Park, 1993—. Mem. Music Critics Assn. Avocations: horseback riding, gardening, cooking. Office: San Diego Union-Tribune 350 Camino De La Reina San Diego CA 92108-3003

SCHERAGA, HAROLD ABRAHAM, physical chemistry educator; b. Bklyn., Oct. 18, 1921; s. Samuel and Etta (Goldberg) S.; m. Miriam Kurnow, June 20, 1943; children: Judith Anne, Deborah Ruth, Daniel Michael. B.S., CCNY, 1941; A.M., Duke U., 1942, Ph.D., 1946, ScD. (hon.) 1961; ScD. (hon.), U. Rochester, 1988, U. San Luis, 1992, Technion, 1993. Teaching, research asst. Duke U., 1941-46; fellow Harvard Med. Sch., 1946-47; instr. chemistry Cornell U., 1947-50, asst. prof., 1950-53, assoc. prof., 1953-58, prof., 1958-65, Todd prof. chemistry, 1965-92, Todd prof. chemistry emeritus, 1992—, chmn. dept., 1960-67; vis. assoc. biochemist Brookhaven Nat. Lab., summers 1950, 51, cons. biology dept., 1950-53; vis. lectr. div. protein chemistry Wool Research Labs., Melbourne, Australia, 1959; vis. prof. Soc. for Promotion Sci., Japan, Aug. 1977; mem. tech. adv. panel Xerox Corp., 1969-71, 74-79; Mem. biochemistry tng. com. NIH, 1963-65; mem. research career award com. NIGMS, 1967-71; comm. molecular biophysics Internat. Union for Pure and Applied Biophysics, 1965-69, mem. commn. macromolecular biophysics, 1969-75, pres., 1972-75, mem. commn. subcellular and macromolecular biophysics, 1975-81; adv. panel molecular biology NSF, 1960-62; Welch Found. lectr., 1962, Harvey lectr., 1968, Gallagher lectr., 1968, Lemieux lectr., 1973, Hill lectr., 1976, Venable lectr., 1981; co-chmn. Gordon Conf. on Proteins, 1963; mem. council Gordon Research Confs., 1969-71. Author: Protein Structure: Theory of Helix-Coil Transitions in Biopolymers; co-editor: Molecular Biology, 1961-86; mem. editl. bd. Physiol. Chemistry and Physics, 1969-75, Mechanochemistry and Motility, 1970-71, Thrombosis Rsch., 1972-76, Biophys. Jour., 1973-75, Macromolecules, 1973-84, Computers and Chemistry, 1974-84, Internat. Jour. Peptide and Protein Rsch., 1978—, Jour. Computational Chemistry, 1980—, Jour. Protein Chemistry, 1982—; corr. PAABS Revista, 1971-73; mem. editl. adv. bd. Biopolymers, 1963—, Biochemistry, 1969-74, 85—, Structural Chemistry, 1989-93, Jour. Computational Polymer Sci., 1991—, Jour. Biomolecular NMR, 1991—, Jour. Biomed. Sci., 1994—, Jour. Am. Chem. Soc., 1995—. mem. Ithaca Bd. Edn., 1958-59; Bd. govs. Weizmann Inst., Israel, 1970—; mem. staff Naval Research Lab. Project, Air Force OSRD Project, World War II. Fulbright, Guggenheim fellow Carlsberg Lab., Copenhagen, 1956-57, Weizmann Inst., Israel, 1963; NIH Spl. fellow Weizmann Inst., 1970; Fogarty scholar NIH, 1984, 86, 88-91; recipient Townsend Harris medal CCNY, 1970, Chemistry Alumni Sci. Achievement award 1977, Kowalski medal Internat. Soc. Thrombosis and Haemostasis, 1983, Linderstrøm-Lang medal Carlsberg Lab., 1983, Internat. Soc. of Quantum Chemistry and Quantum Pharmacology award in Theoretical Biology, 1993, gold medal Soc. Polymer Sci. Japan, 1995, Stein & Moore award Protein Soc., 1995. Fellow AAAS; mem. NAS, Am. Chem. Soc. (chmn. Cornell sect. 1955-56, mem. exec. com. div. biol. chemistry 1966-69, vice chmn. div. biol. chemistry 1970, chmn. div. biol. chemistry 1971, Eli Lilly award 1957, Nichols medal 1974, Kendall award 1978, Pauling award 1985, Mobil award 1990, Repligen award 1990), Am. Soc. Biol. Chemists, Biophys. Soc. (coun. 1967-70), Am. Acad. Arts and Scis., N.Y. Acad. Scis. (hon. life), Hungarian Biophys. Soc. (hon.), Phi Beta Kappa, Sigma Xi, Phi Lambda Upsilon. Home: 212 Homestead Ter Ithaca NY 14850-6220

SCHERER, A. EDWARD, nuclear engineering executive; b. Bklyn., May 23, 1942; s. Samuel M. and Margie Scherer. BS in Mech. Engring., Worcester Poly. Inst., 1963; MS in Nuclear Engring., Pa. State U., 1965; MBA, Rensselaer Poly. Inst., Hartford, Conn., 1978. Registered profl. engr., Mass. Asst. to project mgr. Combustion Engring., Inc., Windsor, Conn., 1968-70, reactor project engr., test evaluation engr., 1970-73, asst. project mgr., 1973-75, mgr. nuclear licensing, 1975-80, dir. nuclear licensing, 1980-90, v.p. nuclear quality ABB Combustion Engring. Nuclear Power, 1990-92, v.p. regulatory affairs ABB Combustion Engring. Nuclear Fuel, 1992-93; v.p. bus. devel. ABB Combustion Engring. Nuclear Ops., 1993—; mem. tech. adv. com., mem. issues mgmt. com., mem. standardization oversight com. NUMARC, Washington. Contbr. articles to profl. jours. Capt. U.S. Army, 1965-67, South Vietnam. Named Outstanding Engring. Alumnus, Pa. State U. Fellow ASME; mem. Am. Nuclear Soc., Sigma Xi, Alpha Epsilon Pi (internat. pres. 1982-84, fiscal control bd. 1986—, v.p. Alpha Epsilon Pi Found. 1985—, named Outstanding Engring. Alumnus Penn. State U. 1995). Office: ABB Combustion Engring 1000 Prospect Hill Rd Windsor CT 06095-1574

SCHERER, FREDERIC MICHAEL, economics educator; b. Ottawa, Ill., Aug. 1, 1932; s. Walter King and Margaret (Lucey) S.; m. Barbara A. Silbermann, Aug. 17, 1957; children: Thomas, Karen S. Main, Christina. AB with honors, U. Mich., 1954; MBA with high distinction, Harvard U., 1958, PhD, 1963. Asst. prof. Princeton (N.J.) U., 1963-66; prof. econs. U. Mich., Ann Arbor, 1966-72; chief economist FTC, Washington, 1974-76; prof. econs. Northwestern U., Evanston, Ill., 1976-82; Joseph Wharton prof. polit. economy Swarthmore (Pa.) Coll., 1982-89; Larsen prof. pub. policy and mgmt. Harvard U., Cambridge, Mass., 1989—; vis. prof. Ctrl. European U., Prague, 1993-94. Author: The Weapons Acquisition Process, 1964 (Lanchester prize 1964), Industrial Market Structure and Economic Performance, 1970, 3d rev. edit., 1990, The Economics of Multi-Plant Operation, 1975, Innovation and Growth, 1984, International High-Technology Competition, 1992, Competition Policies for an Integrated World Economy, 1994, Industry Structure, Strategy and Public Policy, 1995; co-author: Mergers, Sell-Offs and Economic Efficiency, 1987; mem. editl. bd. Jour. Indsl. Econs., 1982-89, Jour. Econ. Lit., 1989—; assoc. editor Ency. Econs., 1983—. Mem. adv. panel NSF, Washington, 1980-83, U.S. Office Tech. Assessment, 1989-93. Sr. research fellow Internat. Inst. Mgmt., 1972-74, Am. Stats. Assn. Census fellow, 1989-90; Baker scholar Harvard U., 1957; grantee NSF, 1970, 79, 82; O'Melveny & Myers Centennial Rsch. grantee, 1989. Mem. European Assn. for Rsch. in Indsl. Econs. (co-founder 1974), Internat. J.A. Schumpeter Assn. (pres. 1988-90), Brit-N.Am. Com., Am. Econ. Assn. (v.p. 1988), Indsl. Orgn. Soc. (pres. 1992), So. Econ. Assn. (v.p. 1990). Democrat. Roman Catholic. Avocations: listening to music, musicology. Home: 48 Pier 7 Charlestown MA 02129 Office: Harvard U John F Kennedy Sch Govt Cambridge MA 02138

SCHERER, GEORGE W., research chemist. With Dupont, Inc., Wilmington, Del. Recipient Ralph K. Iler award in the chemistry of colloidal materials Am. Chem. Soc., 1995. Office: Dupont Inc 1007 Market St Wilmington DE 19898*

SCHERER, HAROLD NICHOLAS, JR., electric utility company executive, engineer; b. Plainfield, N.J., Apr. 5, 1929; s. Harold Nicholas and Nora (McDonough) S.; m. Jane Neely, Sept. 6, 1952 (div.); children—Anne Scherer McConnell, Christopher; stepchildren: James, John, Joseph, Jeffery Ludwig, Jean Ludwig Ransdell. B.E., Yale U., 1951, M.B.A., Syracuse U., 1955. Registered profl. engr., N.J., Mass. Various engring. positions Pub. Service Electric and Gas Co., Newark, 1951-63; various engring. positions Am. Electric Power Service Corp., N.Y.C., 1963-68, assoc. chief. elec. engr., 1968-69, chief elec. engr., 1969-73, v.p. elec. engr., 1973-82; v.p. elec. engring. Am. Electric Power Service Corp., Columbus, Ohio, 1982-90; also dir. Am. Electric Power Service Corp.; until 1990; pres. Commonwealth Electric Co., Wareham, Mass., 1990-93, Cambridge Electric Light Co., Canal Electric Co., Com/Steam Co., 1990-93; bd. dirs. Commonwealth Electric Co., Cambridge Electric Light Co., Com/Steam Co., Commonwealth Svcs. Co., Canal Electric Co.; cons. utility mgmt.

and engring., 1993—; mem. Joint U.S.-USSR working group on power transmission, 1975-81, joint U.S.-Italy working group on power transmission, 1979-88; vice-chmn. Am. Nat. Stds., N.Y.C., 1985-87; v.p. U.S. nat. com. 1985-93, pres. 1993—, chmn. U.S. tech. com. Internat. Conf. on Large High Voltage Electric Systems 1985-91, internat. adminstrv. coun., 1988, internat. exec. com. 1993—; mem. engring. rev. bd. Bonneville Power Adminstrn., 1984-94; chmn. elec. systems and equipment com. Edison Electric Inst., 1989-90, pres. power engring. soc. found., 1992—. Contbr. articles to profl. jours. Pres. N.J. Jr. C. of C., 1960-61; councilman City of Plainfield, 1963-65; mem. Watchung (N.J.) Hills Regional H.S. Bd. Edn., 1970-72; pres. Woods at Josephinum Civic Assn., Worthington, Ohio, 1983-84. Recipient Clayton Frost award U.S. Jaycees, 1961, Young Man of Yr. award Plainfield Jaycees, 1963, Lifetime Achievement award T&D Mag., 1990. Fellow IEEE (v.p. power engring. soc. 1988-89, pres. 1990-91, William Habirshaw award for transmission and distbn. engring. 1986); mem. NAE, Tau Beta Pi, Sigma Sigma. Republican. Home and Office: 467 Bay Ln Centerville MA 02632-3352

SCHERER, KARLA, foundation executive, venture capitalist; b. Detroit, Jan. 13, 1937; d. Robert Pauli and Margaret (Lindsey) S.; m. Peter R. Fink, Sept. 14, 1957 (div. July 1989); children: Christina Lammert, Hadley McKenzie Tolliver, Allison Augusta Scherer; m. Theodore Souris, Sept. 5, 1992. Student, Wellesley Coll., 1954-55; BA, U. Mich., 1957. Chmn. Karla Scherer Found., Detroit, 1989—; advisor on shareholders' rights; speaker on corp. governance to various univs. and profl. assns.; condr. workshops in field; leader only successful proxy contest of maj. U.S. publicly held corp., 1988. Trustee Eton Acad., Birmingham, Mich., 1989—; mem. vis. com. Fordham U. Grad. Sch. Bus. Adminstrn.; former mem. bd. dirs. Cottage Hosp., Univ. Liggett Sch., Music Hall, Detroit League for Handicapped; former mem. adv. bd. Wellesley Coll; former mem. Rep. Dennis M. Hertel's Candidate Selection Com. for Armed Svcs. Acads.; mem. U. Mich. Ctr. for the Edn. of Women Leadership Coun. Named Outstanding Woman Leader of Yr. Oakland U., 1990, one of Metro Detroit's Dynamic Women Women's Econ. Club, 1992, Entrepreneur of Yr. Finalist, 1993. Mem. Women's Forum Mich., Econ. Club Detroit (bd. dirs. 1991—), Women's Econ. Club Detroit, Detroit Club, Detroit Athletic Club, Country Club Detroit, Grosse Pointe Club, Renaissance Club (bd. dirs. 1995—). Office: 100 Renaissance Ctr Ste 1680 Detroit MI 48243-1009

SCHERER, NORBERT FRANZ, chemistry educator; b. Milw., July 9, 1960; s. Franz and Ilse B.; m. Seung-Eun Choi, June 2, 1990; 1 child, Matthew S. BS, U. Chgo., 1982; PhD, Caltech., 1989. NSF postdoctoral fellow U. Chgo., 1989-91, postdoctoral assoc., 1991-92; asst. prof. chemistry U. Pa., Phila., 1992—. Contbr. articles to sci. publs. Recipient Nat. Young Investigator award NSF, 1993-98; David and Lucile Packard fellow, 1993-98, Arnold and Mabel Beckman fellow, 1994-96. Mem. Am. Chem. Soc., Am. Phys. Soc., Optical Soc. Am. Office: U Pa Dept Chemistry M/S 6323 Philadelphia PA 19104

SCHERER, ROBERT DAVISSON, retired business and association executive; b. Ironton, Ohio, Jan. 27, 1929; s. Albert C. and Lois (Davisson) S.; m. Margaret Jane Harsh, June 18, 1951; children: Gary, Mark, Thomas. BS in Agr., Ohio State U., 1950. With sales and mktg. depts. Landmark and affiliates, 1955-75; v.p. food div. Landmark, Inc., Columbus, Ohio, 1975-81, sr. v.p. adminstrn., 1982-83, exec. v.p., chief exec. officer, 1983-85; exec. v.p., chief oper. officer Countrymark, Inc., Delaware, Ohio, 1985-86; pres., chief exec. officer Nat. Coop. Bus. Assn., Washington, 1986-93; pres. AGLANDS, Inc., 1993—. Bd. dirs. CARE, N.Y.C. then Atlanta, 1988—; Overseas Co-op. Devel. Commn., Washington, 1986-93, vols. in Overseas Devel. Assistance, Washington, 1986-93; bd. dirs. exec. com. Internat. Co-op. Alliance, Geneva, 1987-93; agr. rep. alumni adv. coun. Ohio State U., 1983-89; mem. Bennett Round Table of Farm Found., AID Adminstr.'s Adv. Com. on Voluntary Fgn. AID, 1988-93; bd. dirs. Citizens Network, Nat. Agrl. Adv. Com., 1987-93. Recipient Disting. Alumni award Ohio State U. Coll. Agr., 1983, Exec. of Yr. award Profl. Secs. Internat., Cen. Ohio, 1984. Mem. Gamma Sigma Delta. Republican. Home: 610 Garden Pky Circleville OH 43113-1422

SCHERER, RONALD CALLAWAY, voice scientist, educator; b. Akron, Ohio, Sept. 11, 1945; s. Belden Davis and Lois Ramona (Callaway) S.; m. Mary Ellen Angel, Aug. 14, 1971; children: Christopher, Maria. BS, Kent State U., 1968; MA, Ind. U., 1972; PhD, U. Iowa, 1981. Research asst. U. Iowa, Iowa City, 1979-81, asst. research scientist 1981-83, adj. asst. prof., 1983-88, adj. assoc. prof., 1988—; adj. assoc. prof. U. Denver 1984-86; asst. adj. prof. U. Colo., Boulder, 1984-93, adj. assoc. prof., 1993—; research scientist The Denver Ctr. for the Performing Arts, 1983-88, sr. scientist, 1988—; lectr. voice and speech sci. Nat. Theatre Conservatory, Denver, 1990-94; asst. clin. prof. Sch. Medicine U. Colo., Denver, 1988—; adj. assoc. prof. U. Okla., 1992—; affiliate clin. prof. U. No. Colo., 1993—; mem. editorial bd. Jour. of Voice, 1987—, sci. adv. bd., 1993—. Author: (with Dr. I. Titze) Vocal Fold Physiology: Biomechanics, Acoustics and Phonatory Control, 1983; contbr. articles to profl. jours. Nat. Inst. Dental Research fellow, 1972-76. Fellow Internat. Soc. Phonetic Scis. (auditor 1988-91); mem. Nat. Ctr. for Voice and Speech (exec. bd. 1990—), Internat. Arts Medicine Assn., Am. Speech-Lang.-Hearing Assn., Acoustical Soc. Am., Internat. Assn. Logopedics and Phoniatrics, Am. Assn. Phonetic Scis. (nominating com. 1985-887), Pi Mu Epsilon, Sigma Xi. Office: Denver Ctr for Performing Arts 1245 Champa St Denver CO 80204-2104

SCHERER, ROSS PAUL, retired sociology educator; b. Fort Wayne, Ind., Mar. 30, 1922; s. Arnold Frederick and Eleanor Margaret (Vonderau) S.; m. Doris Emelie Hoffmeier, July 6, 1946; children: Rebecca A. Koppel, Thomas Ross, Mary Eleanor Scherer Emunds. Student, Concordia Coll., 1939-41; AB, Concordia Sem., 1943, diploma, 1946; AM, U. Chgo., 1947, PhD, 1963. Ordained to ministry Luth. Ch., 1950. Social worker Luth. Child Welfare Assn., Addison, Ill., 1948-50; instr. sociology Valparaiso (Ind.) U., 1950-54, asst. prof. sociology, 1954-63; dir. rsch. ops. Nat. Coun. Chs., N.Y.C.; dir. ministry studies Nat. Coun. Chs., 1963-66; assoc. prof. sociology Loyola U., Chgo., 1966-85, prof. sociology, 1985-90, prof. emeritus, 1990—, chmn. dept., 1967-69, dir. grad. sociology, 1979-82; reviewer Religious Rsch., Soc. Religion, Jour. Sci. Study Religion. Editor: Lutheran Parish in an Urbanized America, 1958, The Church and Its Manpower Management, 1966, American Denominational Organization, 1980. Pres. Faith Luth. Ch., Arlington Heights, Ill., 1971-73; mem. pub. issues com. Ch. Fedn. Chgo., 1974-75; bd. govs. Ctr. for Sci. Study Religion, Chgo., 1984-95. Fellow Am. Sociol. Assn., Religious Rsch. Assn. (v.p. 1974-75, pres. 1975-77); mem. Am. Sociology Assn., M.W. Sociol. Assn., Ill. Sociol. Assn., Assn. for Sociology Religion, Soc. Sci. Study of Religion. Democrat. Home: 202 S Gibbons Ave Arlington Heights IL 60004-6804 Office: Loyola U Dept Sociology & Anthropology Chicago IL 60626

SCHERF, CHRISTOPHER N., association executive; b. N.Y.C., Aug. 8, 1950; s. Richard Edward and Doris Margaret (Farley) S.; m. Diane Frances Koenig, Nov. 13, 1981; children: Casey Lyn, Donna Streit, Donald Makofske. BA, U. Md., 1972. Sports writer Hagerstown (Md.) Morning Herald, 1973, UPI, N.Y.C., 1973-77, The Courier-Jour., Louisville, 1977-78; mgr. media rels. N.Y. Racing Assn., Jamaica, 1978-82; dir. svc. bur. Thoroughbred Racing Assns. of N.Am., 1982-88, exec. v.p., 1988—; also bd. dirs. Thoroughbred Racing Assns. of N.Am., Elkton, Md.; bd. dirs. TRA Ins. Co., TRA Enterprises, Inc.; trustees adv. comm. Am. Horse Coun., 1988—. Co-author: Pro Basketball '76-'77, 1976, Pro Basketball '77-'78, 1977. Mem. Turf Publicists Am., Nat. Turf Writers Assn., Racing Assn. Execs. Office: Thoroughbred Racing Assn(TRA) 420 Fair Hill Dr Elkton MD 21921-2583

SCHERICH, EDWARD BAPTISTE, retired diversified company executive; b. Inland, Nebr., Dec. 3, 1923; s. Clarence H. and Clara E. (Baptiste) S.; m. Hyacinth Rau, Aug. 11, 1945 (div. 1980); children: Carol, Eileen, John; m. Antoinette Currera, 1981; 1 stepdau., Sylvia McNamara. B.B.A., Tulane U., 1948. Acct. Colo. Milling & Elevator Co., Denver, 1948-50; accountant, office mgr. Southdown, Inc., New Orleans, 1950-55; controller Southdown, Inc., 1955-69; v.p. finance, sec., treas. Southdown Sugars Inc., New Orleans, 1970-73; v.p., sec., treas. Southdown Land Co., New Orleans, 1971-75; sec.-treas. Southdown, Inc., Houston, 1975-78; v.p., sec. Southdown, Inc., 1979-84, treas., 1980-83; ind. fin. cons., 1984—; pres. Valmax Inc., 1988—. Served in USNR, 1943-45. Mem. Beta Gamma Sigma. Home: 633 Brouilly Dr Kenner LA 70065 Office: PO Box 641307 Kenner LA 70064-1307

SCHERICH, ERWIN THOMAS, civil engineer, consultant; b. Inland, Nebr., Dec. 6, 1918; s. Harry Erwin and Ella (Peterson) S.; student Hastings Coll., 1937-39, N.C. State Coll., 1943-44; B.S., U. Nebr., 1946-48; M.S., U. Colo., 1948-51; m. Jessie Mae Funk, Jan. 1, 1947; children—Janna Rae Scherich Thornton, Jerilyn Mae Scherich Dobson, Mark Thomas. Civil and design engr. U.S. Bur. Reclamation, Denver, 1948-84, chief spillways and outlets sect., 1974-75, chief dams br., div. design, 1975-78, chief tech. rev. staff, 1978-79, chief div. tech. rev. Office of Asst. Commr. Engring. and Rsch. Ctr., 1980-84; cons. civil engr., 1984—. Mem. U.S. Com. Internat. Commn. on Large Dams. Served with AUS, 1943-45. Registered profl. engr., Colo. Fellow ASCE; mem. NSPE (nat. dir. 1981-87, v.p. southwestern region 1991-93), Profl. Engrs. Colo. (pres. 1977-78), Jefferson County West C. of C. Republican. Methodist. Home and Office: 3915 Balsam St Wheat Ridge CO 80033-4449

SCHERMER, HARRY ANGUS, insurance company executive; b. Dubois, Pa., Apr. 13, 1942; s. Herman Victor and Dorothy Evelyn (Postlethwait) S.; m. Marsha Ann Rockey, Jan. 3, 1970 (div. 1982); m. Linda Lou Smith, Feb. 5, 1983. B.S., Ohio State U., 1964. Chartered fin. analyst, 1971. Various postions Nationwide Ins. Co., Columbus, Ohio, 1965-79, v.p. equity securities, 1979—; v.p. Nationwide Fin. Svcs. Inc., Nationwide Gen. Ins. Co., Nationwide Life Ins. Co., Nationwide Mut. Fire Ins. Co. Mem. Fin. Analysts Fedn., Inst. Chartered Fin. Analysts. Office: Nationwide Mut Ins Co One Nationwide Plaza Columbus OH 43216

SCHERMER, LLOYD G., publishing and broadcasting company executive; b. St. Louis, 1927; married. Student Amherst U., 1950, Harvard U. Grad. Sch. Bus. Adminstrn., 1952. With Lee Enterprises, Inc., Davenport, Iowa, 1955—, pres., chief exec. officer, from 1974, now pres., also dir.; chmn. Newspaper Advt. Bur.; dir. Davenport Bank & Trust Co., NAPP Systems (USA), Inc. Bd. dirs. U. Mont. Found. Mem. Am. Soc. Newspaper Editors, Am. Newspaper Pubs. Assn. (dir.; dir. Found.). Office: Lee Enterprises Inc 130 E 2nd St Davenport IA 52801-1502

SCHERR, ALLAN LEE, computer scientist, executive; b. Balt., Nov. 18, 1940; s. Morris and Sarah (Kratzmar) S.; m. Marsha Kahn, Sept. 2, 1962 (div. 1974); children: Elise A., Stephanie L.; m. Linda Martin, June 8, 1980; 1 child, Katherine M. B.E.E., MIT, 1962, M.E.E., 1963, Ph.D.E.E., 1965. Mgr. time sharing option design System Devel. div. IBM, Poughkeepsie, N.Y., 1967-70; mgr. multiple virtual storage (MVS) project IBM, 1971-74; mgr. distributed systems programming System Communications div. IBM, Kingston, N.Y., 1977-80; dir. communications programming IBM, 1980-81; dir. communications and applications systems corp. staff IBM, Armonk, N.Y., 1981-83; dir. engring. and programming systems products div. IBM, White Plains, N.Y., 1983-86; dir. integrated applications info. systems div. IBM, Milford, Conn., 1986-88, v.p. devel. and integration application systems div., 1988-89, application solutions dir. architecture and devel., Application Solutions Line Bus., 1990-91; v.p. tech. World Wide Cons. Practices IBM Cons. Group, Milford, Conn., 1991-93; ind. cons. bus. process engring. info. tech., tech. mgmt. Weston, Conn., 1993-94; sr. v.p. software engring. EMC Corp., Hopkinton, Mass., 1994—; seminar leader Werner Erhard & Assocs., N.Y.C., 1982-90. Author: An Analysis of Time-Shared Computer Systems, 1966 (Grace Murray Hopper award Assn. Computing Machinery 1975); patentee in field. Mem. The Hunger Project, San Francisco, 1977—. IBM fellow, 1984. Fellow IEEE; mem. Sigma Xi, Tau Beta Pi, Eta Kappa Nu. Democrat. Home: 12 Doeskin Dr Framington MA 01701

SCHERR, BARRY PAUL, foreign language educator; b. Hartford, Conn., May 20, 1945; s. Joseph and Helen Lillian (Shapiro) S.; m. Sylvia Egelman, Sept. 8, 1974; children: Sonia, David. AB magna cum laude, Harvard U., 1966; AM, U. Chgo., 1967, PhD, 1973. From acting asst. prof. to asst. prof. U. Washington, Seattle, 1970-74; from asst. prof. to prof. Russian Dartmouth Coll., Hanover, N.H., 1974—, chair dept. Russian, 1981-90, chair program Linguistics, Cognitive Sci., 1989—; ad hoc svc. Bd. Examiners State N.H. Teacher Certification; co-dir. seminar Soviet Union for Secondary Sch. Tchrs., 1984; co-organizer Internat. Conf. Russian Verse Theory, 1987, Internat. Conf. Anna Akhmatova and the Poets of Tsarskoe Selo, 1989. Author Russian Poetry: Meter, Rhythm, and Rhyme, 1986, Maxim Gorky, 1988; co-trans. The Seeker of Adventure, Alexander Grin, 1989; edit. bd. Slavic and East European Jour.; co-editor Russian Verse Theory: Proceedings of the 1987 Conference at UCLA, 1987, A Sense of Place: Tsarskoe Selo and Its Poets, 1993, A Serve of Place: Tsarskoe Selo and Its Poets, 1993, O Rus! Studia Litteraria Slavica in Honorem Hugh McLean, 1995; contbr. articles to profl. jours. Scholar Harvard Coll., 1963-66; fellow NDEA, 1966-69; grantee Internat. Rsch. and Exchange Bd., 1969-70, NEH, 1987, 89, U.S. Dept. Edn., 1987-89, Dartmouth Coll. Sr. Faculty, 1989; summer rsch. grantee Grad. Sch., Inst. Comparative and Fgn. Area Studies U. Wash., 1973. Mem. MLA (exec. com. assoc. dept. fgn. langs. 1983-85, del. assembly 1986-88), Am. Assn. Advancement Slavic Studies, Am. Assn. Tchrs. Slavic and East European Langs. (pres. 1987-88, founder, past pres. No. New England chpt., numerous coms.). Office: Dartmouth Coll Russian Dept 44 N Coll St Hanover NH 03755-1801

SCHERR, LAWRENCE, physician, educator; b. N.Y.C., Nov. 6, 1928; s. Harry and Sophia (Schwartz) S.; m. Peggy L. Binenkorb, June 13, 1954; children: Cynthia E., Robert W. AB, Cornell U., 1950, MD, 1957. Diplomate Am. Bd. Internal Medicine (bd. dirs., sec.-treas. 1979-86). Intern Cornell Med. div. Bellevue Hosp. and Meml. Center, 1957-58, asst. resident, 1958-59, research fellow cardiorenal lab., 1959-60, chief resident, 1960-61, co-dir. cardiorenal lab., 1961-62, asst. vis. physician, 1961-63, asso. vis. physician, 1963-65, dir. cardiology and renal unit, 1963-67, asso. dir., 1964-67, vis. physician, 1966-68; physician to out-patients N.Y. Hosp., 1961-63, asst. attending physician, 1963-66, asso. attending physician, 1966-71, attending physician, 1971—; asst. attending physician Meml. Sloan-Kettering Cancer Center, 1962-71, cons., 1971—; chmn. dept. medicine North Shore Univ. Hosp., 1967—; dir. acad. affairs, 1969-93, v.p. med. affairs, 1993—; asst. in medicine Cornell U. Med. Coll., 1958-59; research fellow N.Y. Heart Assn., 1959-60, instr. medicine, 1960-63, asst. prof., 1963-66, assoc. prof., 1966-71, David J. Greene Disting. prof., 1971—, assoc. dean, 1969—; career scientist Health Research Coun., N.Y.C., 1962-66; teaching scholar Am. Heart Assn., 1966-67; pres. N.Y. State Bd. Medicine, 1974-75; bd. dirs. Nat. Bd. Med. Examiners, 1976-80; chmn. Accreditation Coun. for Grad. Med. Edn., 1988, N.Y. State Coun. on Grad. Edn., 1987-92. Contbr. articles to profl. jours. Lt. USNR, 1950-53. Fellow N.Y. Acad. Medicine, Am. Heart Assn. (coun. on clin. cardiology); mem. ACP (master, chmn. and gov. Downstate N.Y. region II 1975-80, regent 1980-86, chmn. bd. regents 1985-86; nat. pres.-elect 1986-89, pres. 1987-88, pres. emeritus), AMA, Am. Fedn. Clin. Rsch., Harvey Soc., N.Y. Heart Assn., Nassau County Med. Soc., Assn. Am. Med. Colls., Am. Clin. and Climatologic Assn. Home: 19 Doral Dr Manhasset NY 11030 Office: No Shore Univ Hosp Manhasset NY 11030

SCHERSTEN, H. DONALD, management consultant, realtor, mortgage broker; b. Titusville, Pa., Nov. 6, 1919; s. H.J. and Clara (Brown) S.; m. Katherine Conley; 1 dau. by previous marriage, Sandra S. Hotard. B.S., Temple U., 1941; postgrad., Tulsa U., 1946-48, Columbia U., 1955. With Creole Petroleum Corp. (affiliate Exxon Corp.), 1948-69, successively dist. field chief accountant Cabimas, Venezuela, coordinator procedures, fin. statements and audits, asst. controller, 1951-62; controller Creole Petroleum Corp. (affiliate Exxon Corp.), Caracas, 1962-69; gen. auditor Exxon Corp., N.Y.C., 1969-74; coordinator math., computers, systems Exxon Corp., 1975-76; pres. H. Donald Schersten & Assocs. (Mgmt. Cons.), 1977—, R.J. Reynolds Nabisco, 1977-78; realtor, 1985—; lic. mortgage broker, 1986—. Pres. council Am. Ch. Caracas, 1960. Served to 1st lt. AUS, 1942-45. Named to Acct. Alumni Hall of Fame, Temple U., 1985. Mem. Am. Petroleum Inst. (chmn. audit com. 1974-76), Inst. Internal Auditors (cert.), U.S. Power Squadrons, USCG Aux. (comdr. 1984). Clubs: Internat, Safari, Toastmasters (past pres. Caracas chpt.), Los Rancheros Deep Sea Fishing. Home: Bird Key 454 Partridge Circle Sarasota FL 34236

SCHERTZ, MORRIS, library director; b. N.Y.C., May 3, 1929; s. Jacob Schertz and Frieda (Kerschner) S.; m. Marcia Ruth Lang, Aug. 4, 1959; children—Hannah, Owen, Bonnie, Jessica, Peter. B.A., NYU, 1952; M.L.S., Pratt Inst., 1956. Librarian Bklyn. Pub. Library, Bklyn., 1956-58; curator Colby Coll., Waterville, Maine, 1958-62; dir. library SUNY-Buffalo, 1962-64; assoc. dir. library U. Mass., Amherst, 1964-69; dir. library U. Denver, 1969—. Contbr. articles to profl. jours. Mem. ALA, Colo. Library Assn.,

Colo. Alliance of Research Libraries (bd. dirs., treas., Denver, 1973—). Office: U Denver University Blvd Denver CO 80208-0001

SCHETKY, LAURENCE MCDONALD, metallurgist, researcher; b. Baguio, The Philippines, July 15, 1922; s. Gerald Laurence and Ethyl Jane (McDonald) S.; m. Diane Heiskell, Dec. 12, 1977 (div. Feb. 1986); m. Karen Searles, July 12, 1986; children: Mark Christian. BSChemE, Rensselaer Poly Inst., Troy, N.Y., 1943, MMetE, 1948, PhD, 1953. Registered profl. engr., Mass. Rsch. fellow MIT, Cambridge, 1953-59; v.p. rsch. Alloyd Electronics, Inc., Cambridge, 1959-63; dir. R & D Internat. Copper Rsch. Assn., Inc., N.Y.C., 1963-83; pres. Memory Metals Inc., Stamford, Conn., 1983-86; chief scientist Memry Corp., Brookfield, Conn., 1987—; dir. Photoetching Engring., Inc., Milford, Mass., 1985—. Editor: Beryllium Technology, 2 vol., 1966, The Metallurgy of Copper, 13 vols., 1966-83; author: (with others) Copper in Iron and Steel, 1982; contbr. over 100 articles to physics and metallurgy jours. With USN, 1944-46, PTO. Fellow Alcoa Corp., 1948-53, Am. Soc. Metals, 1984. Fellow Brit. Inst. Metals, Am. Soc. Metallurgy Internat. (life); mem. AIME (life). Republican. Episcopal. Achievements include 5 patents in Electron Beam Technology, Vapor Phase Deposition, Shape Memory Actuators. Home: 77 Rock House Rd Easton CT 06612-1003 Office: Memry Corp 57 Commerce Dr Brookfield CT 06804-3405

SCHEU, DAVID ROBERT, SR., historic site director; b. Milw., Feb. 8, 1944; s. Oscar Charles Jr. and Dorothy Marie (Schmitz) S.; m. Deborah Singleton Hill, Feb. 3, 1968; children: David R. Jr., Stephanie Ann Scheu Aman. BS in Engring., U.S. Naval Acad., 1967; MBA, U. So. Ill., Edwardsville, 1980. Commd. ensign USN, 1967, advanced through grades to capt., 1988; served on USS Sterett, 1967-69, USS Buchanan, 1970-71; stationed at US Naval Acad., 1971-74; served on USS Berkeley, 1975-77; stationed at Fleet Combat Tng. Ctr. Pacific, 1977-80; served on USS Hepburn, 1980-81, USS New Jersey, 1981-83, USS Edson, 1984-86; stationed at Comcargru Seven, 1986-89, Mil. Sealift Command, 1989-91; dir. Battleship N.C. Meml., Wilmington, N.C., 1991—. Bd. dirs. Travel Coun. N.C., Raleigh, 1991—; N.C. Maritime History Coun., Beaufort, 1991—; Cape Fear Coast Conv. and Visitors Bur., Wilmington, 1992. Mem. U.S. Naval Inst., Navy League U.S., S.W. Tourism Scc., Ret. Officers Assn., Hist. Naval Ships Assn. Roman Catholic. Avocations: sailing, jogging. Office: USS NC Battleship Meml PO Box 480 Wilmington NC 28402-0480

SCHEU, LYNN MCLAUGHLIN, scientific publication editor; b. Lancaster, Ohio, July 9, 1942; d. Franklin Neil and Carol Lois (Bigham) McLaughlin; m. Richard V. Scheu, Oct. 14, 1940; children: David Edward, Michael Edward. BS, Auburn U., 1964; postgrad., Ohio State U., 1964-66. English, French tchr. Reynoldsburg (Ohio) H.S., 1966-70; adj. curator mollusks Mus. History & Sci., Louisville, 1978-85; editor Am. Conchologist, Saddlebrook, N.J., 1987—; adv. edtl. bd. Bailey Matthews Shell Mus. & Ednl. Found., Sanibel, Fla., 1988—; bd. dirs. Conchologists Am., 1987—. Exec. bd. Friends of Libr., Louisville, 1989-95; mem. Mayor's Task Force on Librs., Louisville, 1988-89. Avocations: shell collecting, fossils, landscape gardening. Home and Office: 1222 Holsworth Ln Louisville KY 40222

SCHEUER, KATHERINE DUNN, editor; b. Westwood, N.J., Sept. 27, 1937; d. Walter Torrance and Isabel (Colville) D.; m. John W. Scheuer 2d, Sept. 5, 1964; children: Abigail M., John W. 4th. BA, Smith Coll., 1958. Editorial asst. Doubleday & Co., N.Y.C., 1958-60, editor, 1962-69; freelance editor N.Y.C., 1969-75; sr. manuscript editor Cornell U. Press, Ithaca, N.Y., 1975-89, mng. editor, 1989—. Democrat. Office: Cornell U Press Sage House 512 E State St Ithaca NY 14850

SCHEUER, PAUL JOSEF, chemistry educator; b. Heilbronn, Germany, May 25, 1915; came to U.S., 1938; s. Albert and Emma (Neu) S.; m. Alice Elizabeth Dash, Sept. 5, 1950; children: Elizabeth E., Deborah A., David A., Jonathan L.L. BS with high honors, Northeastern U., Boston, 1943; MA, Harvard U., 1947, PhD, 1950. Asst. prof. chemistry U. Hawaii, Honolulu, 1950-55, assoc. prof. chemistry, 1956-61, prof. chemistry, 1961-85, prof. chemistry emeritus, 1985—; vis. prof. Orsted Inst., U. Copenhagen, 1977, 89; Toyo Suisan vis. prof. U. Tokyo, 1992. Author: Chemistry of Marine Natural Products, 1973; editor: (12 series) Marine Natural Products, 1978-93; contbr. 240 articles to profl. jours. Spl. agt. U.S. Army, 1944-46, ETO. Recipient Rsch. Achievement award Am. Soc. Pharmacognosy, 1994; named P.J. Scheuer award Marine Chemists, 1992; NATO fellow, 1975. Fellow AAAS, Royal Soc. Chemistry; mem. Am. Chem. Soc. (sect. chair 1956, 87, Guenther award 1994), Northeastern U. Alumni Assn. (Disting. Alumni award 1984). Office: U Hawaii Chemistry Dept 2545 The Mall Honolulu HI 96822-2275

SCHEUERER, DIANE THOMPSON, home economics educator; b. Stuart, Fla., Jan. 23, 1943; d. Frances Earl Thompson and Ida Ann (Minschke) Nall; m. Daniel Thomas Scheuerer, June 11, 1966; children: Daniel "Todd", David W. BS, Barry Coll., 1965. cert. vocat. home econ. tchr., Fla. Tchr. Melbourne (Fla.) High Sch., 1965-66, Southwest Jr. High, Melbourne, 1966-67, Cen. Cath. High Sch., Melbourne, 1971-79; tchr. edn. of teenage parents Brevard County Sch. Bd., Melbourne, 1979—; adv. bd. mem. Child Care Aide Adv. Com., South Brevard, Fla., 1990—. Active West of EauGallie Civic Assn., Melbourne, 1986—, Ascension Cath. Women's Guild, Melbourne, 1990—. Recipient Nat. Second Place award Nat. FEdn. Indep. Bus., Washington, 1990, Second Place Entrepreneurship award Fla. Coun. on Econ. Edn., Tapma, 1991, Martha Schenck Priv. Enterprise Edn. award U. Cen. Fla., Orlando, 1992, Nat. Hon. Mention award Joint Coun. on Econ. Edn., New Orleans, 1992, Burps, Bibs, Bonnets Leavey award Freedoms Found., Beverly Hills, 1992. Mem. Am. Home Econ. Assn. (local arrangements com.), Fla. Vocat. Assn., Fla. Home Econs. Assn., Cen. Fla. Home Econs. Assn. (sec. 1992—), Brevard Vocat. Assn. Roman Catholic. Avocations: gardening, sewing, club work. Office: Sch Bd Brevard County 1400 Commodore Blvd Melbourne FL 32935

SCHEUERMAN, ELEANOR JOYCE MILLER, medical association administrator; b. Jersey City, N.J., July 7, 1937; d. Lawrence Houseman and Bridie E.J. (Moran) M.; m. William Henry Scheuerman, Jr., Sept. 5, 1969; 1 child, Sheila Brigid. BS in Nursing, Seton Hall, 1959; MA in Pub. Health, N.Y.U., 1964. RN, N.J., Mass. Pvt. duty nurse Jersey City Med. Ctr., 1959-60; pub. health nurse Pub. Health Nursing Svc. of Jersey City, 1959-63, 66; health educator Acad. St. Aloysius, Jersey City, 1962-64; instr. sch. nursing Seton Hall Univ., South Orange, N.J., 1964-67; dir. Pub. Health Nursing Agcy., Washington, N.J., 1967-93; head nurse Hunterdon Devel. Ctr., Clinton, N.J., 1993-93; bd. dirs. Warren County Office on Aging, 1974-93, Legal Svc. of Warren County, 1976-77; med. and health staff chief Warren County Civil Def. and Disaster Control, 1979; info. and referral svc. area com. Warren County Human Svcs., 1985-91, adv. coun., 1983-91, chair protective svcs. com., 1984-91. Chair suprs.' workshop com. Home Health Assembly of N.J., 1974-75; adv. coun. for practical nursing Warren County Vocat. Tech. Sch., 1986-93. Mem. Nat. League for Nursing (bd. dirs. 1977-78), APHA, Am. Sch. Health Assn. (fellow 1965), Am. Nursing Assn. (pub. health sect., membership chair 1960, v.p. dist. 2 1962), N.J. State Nurses Assn. (membership chair 1965), Sigma Theta Tau.

SCHEUPELEIN, ROBERT JOHN, government official; b. Brookhaven, N.Y., May 9, 1932; s. Ernest and Mary (Leonowitz) S.; m. Kathleen Ehrensberger (div. 1980). BA in Chemistry, U. Miami, 1955, MS in Phys. Chemistry, 1956; PhD in Phys. Chemistry, U. Utah, 1961; postgrad., Harvard U., 1982. Rsch. assoc. dermatology Harvard Med. Sch., Cambridge, Mass., 1962-68, assoc. in biophysics and dermatology, 1968-70, prin. assoc. in biophysics, 1970-77; chief dermal and ocular toxicology br. Bur. Foods, FDA, Washington, 1977-79, dir. div. food animal additives, 1979-82; dep. dir. Office Toxicological Scis., Ctr. for Food Safety and Applied Nutrition, Washington, 1983-88, dir. Office Toxicological Scis., 1988-92, dir. Office Rsch. Skills, 1992-94; prin. Weinberg Cons. Group, Washington, 1994—; course dir. skin biology and physiology Harvard-MIT Program in Health Sci., 1971-76; mem. White House USTP Task Force on Chem. Carcinogens, Washington, 1983-85; mem. task force on risk assessment and risk mgmt. HHS, Washington, 1984-85; mem. risk assessment subcom. Nat. Sci. and Tech. Coun., 1994—. Editor: Biological Basis for Risk Assessment of Dioxins, 1991; contbr. articles to sci. jours., chpts. to books. Capt. USAR, 1961-62. Recipient sci. lit. award Soc. Cosmetic Chemists, 1968, citation Bur. Roods, FDA, 1980, award of merit FDA, 1987; sr. exec. fellow Harvard U. John F. Kennedy Sch. Govt., 1982. Mem. AAAS; mem. Soc. for Risk

Analysis. Avocations: tennis, woodworking, ballroom dancing, writing. Home: 5140 Maris Ave Alexandria VA 22304-1963

SCHEURING, GARRY JOSEPH, banker; b. 1939; married. BS, U. Notre Dame, 1961; MBA, U. Chgo., 1964. With Booz, Allen & Hamilton, Inc., 1961-62; with Continental Bank Corp., 1964-91, sr. v.p., then exec. v.p., then sector exec., then vice chmn., also bd. dirs.; now chmn., pres., chief exec. officer Midlantic Corp., Edison, N.J., 1991—, also bd. dirs. Office: Midlantic Corp Metro Park Plz PO Box 600 Edison NJ 08818-0600

SCHEVILL, JAMES ERWIN, poet, playwright; b. Berkeley, Calif., June 10, 1920; s. Rudolph and Margaret (Erwin) S.; m. Margot Helmuth, Aug. 2, 1966; children (by previous marriage): Deborah, Susanna. BS, Harvard U., 1942; MA (ad eundem), Brown U.; LHD (hon.), R.I. Coll., 1986. Mem. faculty San Francisco State Coll., 1959-68, prof. English, 1968, dir. Poetry Center, 1961-68; prof. Brown U., 1969-85, prof. emeritus, 1985—; reader various univs., insts., and orgns. Author: (poems) Tensions, 1947, The American Fantasies, 1951, The Right to Greet, 1955, Selected Poems 1945-59, 1959, Private Dooms & Public Destinations: Poems 1945-62, 1962, The Stalingrad Elegies, 1964, Release, 1968, Violence & Glory: Poems 1962-68, 1969, The Buddhist Car & Other Characters, 1973, Pursuing Elegy: A Poem About Haiti, 1974, The Mayan Poems, 1978, Fire of Eyes: A Guatemalan Sequence, 1979, The American Fantasies: Collected Poems 1945-81, 1983, The Invisible Volcano, 1985, Ghost Names/Ghost Numbers, 1986, Ambiguous Dancers of Fame: Collected Poems 1945-86 Vol. II, 1987, Winter Channels, 1994; (biographies) Sherwood Anderson: His Life and Work, 1951, The Roaring Market and the Silent Tomb, 1956, Bern Porter: A Personal Biography, 1993; (plays) High Sinners, Low Angels, 1953, The Bloody Tenet, 1957, Voices of Mass. and Capital A, 1958, The Black President and Other Plays, 1965, Lovecraft's Follies, 1971, Breakout: In Search of New Theatrical Environments, 1973, Cathedral of Ice, 1975, reprinted in internat. anthology Plays of the Holocaust, 1988, Oppenheimer's Chair, 1985, Collected Short Plays, 1986, Monologue on S.J. Perelman, 1986, Time of the Hand and Eye, 1986, Mother O Or The Last American Mother, 1990, (with Mary Gail) The Garden on F Street, 1992, The Phantom of Life: A Melville Play, 1993, Five Plays, 1993; (novel) The Arena of Ants, 1977; (rec.) Performance Poems, 1984; (translation) The Cid, 1961; editor: Six Historians (by F. Schevill), 1956; (with others) Wastepaper Theatre Anthology, 1978; plays produced in various theaters in U.S. including Guthrie Theatre, Mpls., Magic Theatre, San Francisco, La Mama, N.Y.C., Trinity Repertory Co., Providence, Goodman Theatre, Chgo., Berkeley Repertory Theatre, R.I. Playwrights Theatre, Volkstheater, Rostock, German Dem. Republic, others. Served to capt. AUS, 1942-46. Ford Found. grantee, 1954, 60-61, R.I. Com. on Humanities grantee, 1975; Fund Advancement Edn., 1953-54, Office for Advanced Drama Research fellow, 1957, Rockefeller fellow, 1964, Guggenheim fellow, 1981, McKnight fellow, 1984; recipient Performance prize Nat. Theatre Competition, 1945, 2d prize Phelan Biography Competition, 1954, 2d prize Phelan Drama Competition, 1958, William Carlos Williams award, 1965, Roadsted Found. award, 1966, Gov.'s award R.I., 1975, Best Story of Yr. award Ariz. Quart., 1977; story selected for O. Henry Awards Prize Stories, 1978; award in lit. Am. Acad. and Inst. Arts and Letters, 1991; work commd. by Nat. Council Chs., 1956-61, Fromm Found., 1959, Trinity Repertory Co., R.I. Hosp., 1986, Providence Coll., 1986, Magdalena Group, 1992. Home: 1309 Oxford St Berkeley CA 94709-1424 Office: Brown U Dept English Providence RI 02912

SCHEVING, LAWRENCE EINAR, scientist, anatomy educator; b. Hensel, N.D., Oct. 20, 1920; s. Einar L. and Mary (Brown) S.; m. Virginia M. Krumdick, Aug. 6, 1949; children: Lawrence, Mary, John, Jennifer, Patricia (dec.). BS in Biology, DePaul U., 1949, MS in Zoology, 1950; PhD, Loyola U., Chgo., 1957. Mem. faculty Lewis Coll., Lockport, Ill.; successively instr., asst. prof., asso. prof. and head dept. biol. sci. Lewis Coll., 1950-57; prof. anatomy Chgo. Med. Sch., 1957-67, La. State U. Med. Sch., New Orleans, 1967-70, U. Ark. Coll. Med., Little Rock, 1970-74; Rebsamen prof. anat. sci. U. Ark. Coll. Med., 1974-91, Rebsamen prof. emeritus, 1991—; vis. prof. U. Bergen, Norway, 1952, The Med. Sch. Hanover, Fed. Republic Germany, 1973; dir. chronobiology course Chautauqua series NSF, 1979; dir. NATO Advanced Study Insts., 1979, Workshop on chronobiotech. and chronobiol. engring., 1985; dir. Fedn. Am. Socs. Exptl. Biology summer research conf., Copper Mountain, Colo., 1988; mem. breast cancer task force Nat. Cancer Inst.; mem. U.S. Army med. research and devel. adv. com., 1982—; cons. to VA. Author: Biological Rhythms in Structure and Function, 1981; editor: Chronobiology, 1974, Chronobiotech. and Chronobiol. Engring. 1986, Research Advance in Chronobiology, 1987 (2 vols.); numerous chpts. to books, over 270 articles in field of chronobiology and other biol. areas to profl. jours.; mem. editorial bd.: Chronobiologia, Chronobiology Internat., Am. Jour. Anatomy. Served to capt. AUS, 1940-45; col. Res. Decorated Bronze Star, D.S.M., others; recipient Research award Chgo. Med. Sch. Bd. Dirs., 1962, Most Helpful Prof. award La. State U., 1968, award for Excellence in Nat. Leadership and Lifes Work, Gov. N.D., 1992; named Prof. Year Student Council Chgo. Med. Sch., 1964; recipient Golden Apple award student body U. Ark. Med. Sch., 1972; Alexander von Humboldt Sr. Scientist prize German govt., 1973, Highest Faculty award U. Ark. Med. Soc., 1987, others. Mem. AAAS, Am. Soc. Anatomists, Am. Assn. Cancer Research, Am. Soc. Zoologists, Am. Soc. Photobiology, Internat. Soc. Chronobiology (hon. mem., sec.-treas. 1971-83, pres.-elect 1983-85, pres. 1985-89), So. Assn. Anatomists (past councillor), Am. Indsl. Hygiene Assn. (traditional workshifts com. 1983-89), Sigma Xi (chpt. pres. 1964-65). Roman Catholic. Home: 21020 George Hunt Cir Apt 906 Waukesha WI 53186

SCHEWE, DONALD BRUCE, archivist, library director; b. Cleve., Oct. 28, 1943; s. Norman Edward and Theodora (Robinson) S.; m. Charlene R. Wenz, June 10, 1965; children: Amanda Marie, Ann Elizabeth. BA, U. Nebr., 1964, MA, 1968; PhD, Ohio State U., 1971. Archivist Franklin D. Roosevelt Library, Hyde Park, N.Y., 1972-77, supervisory archivist, 1977-79, asst. dir., 1979-81; dir. Carter Presdl. Materials Project, Atlanta, 1981-86, Jimmy Carter Library, Atlanta, 1986—. Editor: Franklin D. Roosevelt and Foreign Affairs, 1981. With U.S. Army, 1966-68, Vietnam, ret. lt. col. Mem. Am. Records Mgrs. and Adminstrs., Soc. Ga. Archivists, Orgn. Am. Historians. Episcopalian. Lodge: Rotary. Office: Jimmy Carter Libr 441 Freedom Pky Atlanta GA 30307-1498

SCHEXNAYDER, BRIAN EDWARD, opera singer; b. Port Arthur, Tex., Sept. 18, 1953; s. Leonard and Dorothy (Carrier) S.; m. Sherri Scallan, Oct. 2, 1976. BA in Music, U. Southwestern La., 1976; postgrad., Juilliard Sch. Music, 1976-80. Performances with Met. Opera, N.Y.C., Paris Opera Co., Edmonton (Alta., Can.) Opera Co., New Orleans Opera Co., Santiago (Chile) Opera, Winnipeg (Man., Can.), St. Petersburg (Fla.) Opera, Jackson (Miss.) Opera Co., San Francisco Opera, Frankfurt Opera, Hamburg Staatsoper Opera, Oper der Studt Bonn, Spoleto (Italy) Festival of Two Worlds, Cin. Opera, Fla. Grand Opera. Mem. Am. Guild Musicians. Avocations: computers, billiards, remote control airplanes.

SCHEXNAYDER, CHARLOTTE TILLAR, state legislator; b. Tillar, Ark., Dec. 25, 1923; d. Jewell Stephen and Bertha (Terry) Tillar; m. Melvin John Schexnayder Sr., Aug. 18, 1946; children: T. John Jr., Sarah Holden Stephen. BA, La. State U., 1944, postgrad., 1947-48. Asst. editor La. Agrl. Extension, Baton Rouge, 1944; editor The McGehee (Ark.) Times, 1945-46, 48-53; editor, co-publisher The Dumas (Ark.) Clarion, 1954-85, publisher, 1985—; state rep. Ark. House Reps., Little Rock, 1985—, pres. Ark. Assn. Women, 1955, Nat. Newspaper Assn., Washington, 1991-92, Ark. Press Assn., Little Rock, 1982, Nat. Fedn. Press Women, Blue Springs, Mo., 1977-78, Litte Rock chpt. Soc. Profl. Journalists, 1973; mem. pres.'s coun. Winrock Internat., 1990—. Editor: Images of the Past, 1991. 1st woman mem. Ark. Bd. Pardons and Parole, 1975-80; mem. Ark. Legis. Coun., 1985-92; v.p. Desha County Mus., 1989—; dir. Dumas Indsl. Found., 1986—; exec. com. Ark. Ctrl. Radiation Therapy Inst., 1991-92; mem. adv. bd. Ark. Profl. Women Achievement, 1992; mem. Ark. Rural Devel. Commn., 1991-93; mem. Winrock Internat. Adv. Coun., 1991—. Named Disting. Alumnus Ark. A&M Coll., 1971, Woman of Achievement Nat. Fedn. Press Women, 1970, Outstanding Arkansan C. of C. 1986; recipient Ark. Profl. Women of Distinction award No. Bank, Little Rock, 1990, Emma McKinnery award Nation's Top Cmty. Newspaper Woman, 1980, Journalist award Nat. Conf. of Christians and Jews, 1989, Lifetime Achievement award Nat. Fedn. Press Women, 1992, Outstanding Svc. award Ark. Assn. Elem. Prins.; named to

La. State U. Alumni Hall of Distinction, 1994; named one Top 100 Ark. Women, Ark. Bus., 1995. Mem. Pi Beta Phi (Crest award 1992), Ark. Delta Coun. (chmn. of bd. dirs. 1989—). Democrat. Roman Catholic. Home: 322 Court Dumas AR 71639 Office: Clarion Publishing Co Inc 136 E Waterman Dumas AR 71639

SCHEY, JOHN ANTHONY, metallurgical engineering educator; b. Sopron, Hungary, Dec. 19, 1922; came to U.S., 1962; s. Mihaly and Hedvig Terez (Topfl) S.; m. Margit Maria Sule, Sept. 13, 1926; 1 child, John Francis. Diploma metall. engring., Tech. U., Sopron, 1946; candidate tech. scis., Acad. Scis., Budapest, Hungary, 1953; D of Engring. (hon.), U. Stuttgart, 1987, U. Heavy Industry, Miskolc, Hungary, 1989. Cert. mfg. engr.; registered profl. engr. Chief technologist Iron and Metal Works, Csepel, Hungary, 1947-51; reader Tech. U., Miskolc, Hungary, 1951-56; dept. head Brit. Aluminium Co. Research Labs., 1957-62; metall. advisor Ill. Inst. Tech. Research Inst., Chgo., 1962-68; prof. U. Ill., Chgo., 1968-74; prof. U. Waterloo, Ont., Can., 1974-88, disting. prof. emeritus, 1988; resource person Niagara Inst., Ontario, 1980; course dir. Forging Industry Assn., Cleve., 1978; cons. to various corps. in U.S. and Can. Author: Tribology in Metalworking, 1983, Introduction to Manufacturing Processes, 2d edit., 1987; patentee in field. Recipient W.H.A. Robertson award Inst. Metals, 1966. Fellow Am. Soc. Metals, Soc. Mfg. Engrs. (Gold Medal award 1974); mem. Nat. Acad. Engring., Can. Inst. Mining and Metallurgy (Dofasco award 1984); fgn. mem. Hungarian Acad. Scis. Avocations: music, history, impact of technology on soc.

SCHEY, RALPH EDWARD, manufacturing executive; b. Cleve., 1924; married. B.S., Ohio U., 1948; M.B.A., Harvard U., 1950. Sales trainee Leisy Brewing Co., 1950-51; indsl. engr. Gen. Motors Corp., 1951; exec. v.p. Clevite Corp., 1951-69; pres. Joseph Mellen & Miller Inc., 1959-71; venture capital activities, 1971-74; with Scott & Fetzer Co., Westlake, Ohio, 1974—; pres. Scott & Fetzer Co., 1974-83, chmn. and chief exec. officer, dir., 1976—; pres., 1985-86; dir. Hauserman Co. Served with U.S. Army, 1943-45. Office: Scott Fetzer Co 28800 Clemens Rd Cleveland OH 44145-1134

SCHIAFFINO, S(ILVIO) STEPHEN, retired medical society executive, consultant; b. Bklyn., Nov. 1, 1927; s. Stephen Anthony and Jane (DiDonato) S.; m. Josephine Rose Bovello, Apr. 25, 1954; children—Susan, Stephen. BS, Georgetown U., 1946, MS, 1948, Ph.D. in Biochemistry, 1956. Research biochemist div. nutrition FDA, Washington, 1948-50; asst. br. chief div. FDA, 1954-60; mgr. chemistry dept. Hazelton Labs., Vienna, Va., 1960-61; with NIH, 1961—; scientist adminstr. NIH (Nat. Cancer Inst.), 1961-64, asst. chief research grants rev. br., 1964-69, chief., 1969-72, assoc. dir. for sci. rev., 1972-78, dep. dir. div. research grants, 1978-86; sr. sci. advisor office of extramural research and tng., office of dir. NIH, 1986-87; exec. officer, sci. officer Am. Soc. for Clin. Nutrition, Bethesda, Md., 1987-93; cons., 1993—; cons. in field. Served with AUS, 1950-53. Recipient Superior Service award FDA, 1960, Superior Service award NIH, 1969. Mem. AAAS, Am. Soc. for Clin. Nutrition., Am. Inst. Nutrition.

SCHIAVELLI, MELVYN DAVID, university provost, chemistry educator, researcher; b. Chgo., Aug. 8, 1942; s. Gene James and Frances Elizabeth (Giacomo) S.; m. Virginia Farrell, Sept. 10, 1966; children—Timothy, Karen. BS in Chemistry, DePaul U., 1964; PhD in Chemistry, U. Calif., Berkeley, 1967. Rsch. assoc. Mich. State U., East Lansing, 1967-68; from asst. prof. to assoc. prof. chemistry Coll. William and Mary, Williamsburg, Va., 1968-80; prof. chemistry Coll. William and Mary, Williamsburg, 1980-94, chmn. dept. chemistry, 1978-84, dean Faculty Arts and Scis., 1984-86; provost Coll. William and Mary, 1986-93, acting pres., 1992; prof. chem. and biochem., provost U. Del., Newark, 1994—. Contbr. articles to profl. jours., 1969—. Grantee NSF Petroleum Rsch. Fund, 1969-90. Mem. Am. Chem. Soc., Royal Inst. Chemists, Sigma Xi. Roman Catholic. Office: U Del Office of the Univ Provost 129 Hullihen Hall Newark DE 19716

SCHIAVI, RAUL CONSTANTE, psychiatrist, educator, researcher; b. Buenos Aires, Argentina, Jan. 7, 1930; came to U.S. 1956; s. Constantino and Maria (Acquier) S.; m. Michelle deMiniac, Aug. 8, 1960; children: Isabelle, Nadine, Viviane. MD, U. Buenos Aires, 1953. Diplomate Am. Bd. Psychiatry and Neurology. Fgn. asst. psychiatry U. Paris, 1955-56; resident in psychiatry U. Pa., Phila., 1956-59; instr. psychiatry U. Pa., 1959-61; assoc. College de France, Paris, 1961-63; asst. prof. psychiatry Cornell U., N.Y.C., 1963-66; assoc. prof. psychiatry SUNY, Downstate Med. Ctr., Bklyn., 1966-71, Mt. Sinai Sch. Medicine, N.Y.C., 1971-78; prof. psychiatry Mt. Sinai Sch. Medicine, 1978—; fellow Found. Fund for Rsch. in Psychiatry, 1958-63; cons. NIMH, 1966-70, 77-81; dir. human sexuality program Mt. Sinai Sch. Medicine, 1973—; advisor World Health Orgn., 1989. Contbr. articles to profl. jours., chpts. to books; co-editor Jour. Sex and Marital Therapy; mem. editl. bd. Archives of Sexual Behavior, Hormones and Behavior, Psychosomatic Medicine, Revista Latinoamericana de Sexologia, Quaderni de Sessuologia Clinica, Revista Argentina de Sexualidad Humana, Annual Rev. Sex Rsch. Recipient Rsch. Sci. Devel. award, 1966, Masters and Johnson award Soc. for Sex Therapy and Rsch., 1991; grantee NIH, 1977-80, 87-95, NIMH, 1976-95, others. Fellow Am. Psychopathol. Assn., Psychiat. Rsch. Soc., Am. Psychiat. Assn. (life fellow, cons. 1989, Excellence in Edn. award 1992); mem. AAAS, Am. Psychosomatic Soc. (coun. 1985-88), Internat. Acad. Sex Rsch. (pres. 1995-96), Soc. Sex Therapy and Rsch. (pres. 1984-86), Sex Info and Edn. Coun. of U.S. (bd. dirs. 1979-83), Internat. Soc. Psychoneuroendocrinology, Sigma Xi. Home: 25 E 86th St New York NY 10028-0553 Office: Mt Sinai Sch Medicine 1 Gustave L Levy Pl New York NY 10029-6504

SCHIAVINA, LAURA MARGARET, artist; b. Springfield, Mass., Nov. 27, 1917; d. Joseph A. and Egidia (Bernini) Schiavina; student Traphagen Sch. of Fashion, 1944-46, U. R.I., 1967, Cornell U., 1968, Art Students League, 1973-74. With Eastern States Farmers Exchange, Springfield, 1935-44; with Marsh & McLennan, 1944-75, adminstrv. asst., 1971-75, librarian Wm. M. Mercer, Inc. subs., 1975-80; represented by Z Gallery, N.Y.C. One-woman shows at Little Gallery, Barbizon Hotel, N.Y.C., 1968, Galerie Internat., N.Y.C., 1969, Z Gallery, N.Y.C., 1993, 94; exhibited in group shows at Westfield (Mass.) Coll., 1968, Nat. Acad., N.Y.C., 1969, Bergen Mus. of Art and Sci., Paramus, N.J., 1991, Stuhr Mus. of the Prairie Pioneer, Grand Isle, Nebr., 1990, Nat. Soc. of Painters in Casein and Acrylic, 1992, 94, Washington & Lee U., Lexington, Va., 1993, Darke County Ctr. for Arts, Greenville, Ohio, 1993, NLAPW 1992 Biennial Sumner Mus., Washington, 1992, 1994 Biennial Cork Gallery, N.Y.C.; Lever House, N.Y.C., 1973, 74, 83, 84, 85, 86, 87, Queensboro C.C. Gallery, 1984, 94, Cork Gallery, N.Y.C., 1984, 93, 94, Westbeth Gallery, N.Y.C., 1985, 88, Nat. Arts Club, 1986, 88—, Isis Gallery, 1986, Morin-Miller Galleries, 1988; also various exhbns. with Wall St. Art Assn., Nat. Art League and Jackson Heights Art Club, Audubon Artists, 1969, 86, 88—, Salmagundi Club, 1973—, Nat. Assn. Women Artists travel show centennial exhibits at 5 art ctrs. and mus., 1989, and ann. exhbns., 1989—; represented in pvt. collections. Recipient numerous prizes, awards. Mem. Wall St. Art Assn. (v.p. 1972-76), Audubon Artists, Inc., Nat. Art League, Burr Artists Inc., Nat. Assn. Women Artists, N.Y. Artists Equity, Nat. League Am. Pen Women, Jackson Heights Art Club (pres. 1970-71), Salmagundi Club. Home: 35-25 78th St Jackson Heights NY 11372-4751 Studio: 41 Union Sq W # 406 New York NY 10003-3208

SCHIAVO, A. MARY FACKLER, federal official, lawyer; b. Pioneer, Ohio, Sept. 4, 1955. AB cum laude, Harvard U., 1976; MA, Ohio State U., 1977; JD, NYU, 1980. Bar: Mo. 1980, U.S. Dist. Ct. (we. dist.) Mo. 1980, U.S. Ct. Appeals (8th cir.) 1983, U.S. Ct. Appeals (10th cir.) 1985, U.S. Supreme Ct. 1990, D.C. 1993, Md. 1994. Assoc. Watson, Ess, Marshall & Enggas, Kansas City, Mo., 1980-82; asst. U.S. atty. we. dist. Mo. U.S. Dept. Justice, Kansas City, 1982-85, fed. prosecutor organized crime and racketeering strike force, 1985-86; White House fellow, spl. asst. to U.S. Atty. Gen. U.S. Dept. Justice, Washington, 1987-88; exec. dir. Bush/Quayle '88 Campaign, State of Mo., 1988; atty. McDowell, Rice & Smith, Kansas City, 1989; asst. sec. labor-mgmt. standards U.S. Dept. Labor, Washington, 1989-90; insp. gen. U.S. Dept. Transp., Washington, 1990—; instr. U.S. Atty. Gen.'s Adv. Inst., Washington, 1986, 88, FBI Acad., Quantico, Va., 1988; guest lectr. NYU Sch. Law, 1986, 88, 91; bd. dirs. Dept. Labor Acad., 1989-90, White House Fellows Assn., 1992—, 2d v.p., 1992-93, chair ann. meeting, 1993, 1st v.p., pres.-elect, 1993-94, pres., 1994—; mem. Pres.'s Coun. on Integrity and Efficiency, 1990—, Fed. Investigators assn., Pres. Commn. on White House Fellowships, 1994—. Bd. dirs. Root-Tilden Scholarship program NYU,

1982-89. Recipient Thompson award Ohio State U. Alumni, 1988, Aviation Laurel award Aviation Week and Space Tech. mag., 1992; named one of Top Ten Coll. Women in U.S., 1975, One of Ten Outstanding Young Working Women in Am., 1987, Kansas City Career Woman of Yr., 1988; Ohio State U. fellow, 1976-77; Root-Tilden legal scholar NYU, 1977-79. Mem. ABA (ho. of dels. 1986-89, assembly del. 1986-89, litigation sect. complex crimes com.), Mo. Bar Assn. (bd. govs. 1986-89, chmn. pro bono task force 1984-86, young lawyers coun. 1983-86, Outstanding Svc. award 1986), Exec. Women in Govt., Harvard Club of Washington, Charter 100, Women's Fgn. Policy Group. Avocations: pilot, ventriloquist. Office: US Dept Transp Office of Insp Gen 400 7th St SW Ste 9210 Washington DC 20590

SCHIAVONE, LOUISE L., political correspondent, news analyst; b. N.Y.C., Apr. 10, 1951; d. Rocco Michael and Accursia Theresa (La Rocca) Schiavone; m. Richard Uliano, Oct. 19, 1985; 1 child, Christina Maria. BA in History, Emmanuel Coll., 1972; MS in Journalism, Columbia U., 1978. Press sec., legis. asst., speech writer Office of Congressman Paul Tsongas, Washington, 1975-77; polit. reporter anchor WGST Newsradio, Atlanta, 1978-80; senate corr., polit. reporter Associated Press Radio Network, Washington, 1980—; anchor, guest co-host Newsweek on Air, Newsweek Mag., Washington, 1980—; TV reporter AP TV Direct, 1988-91; guest commentator on polit. affairs Fox TV, C-Span TV, Cable News Network, Washington, 1992—. Mem. Congl. Radio and TV Corrs. Assn. (elected exec. com. 1986-88, 93-95). Roman Catholic. Office: AP Broadcast News Ctr 1825 K St NW Washington DC 20006-1202

SCHIAZZA, GUIDO DOMENIC (GUY SCHIAZZA), educational association administrator; b. Phila., May 17, 1930; s. Guido and Claudina (DiPrinzio) S.; m. Irmgard Heidi Reissmueller, May 15, 1954. BA, Pa. State U., 1952; postgrad., St. Joseph's U., 1954-55, Villanova U., 1954-55, Temple U., 1955-58. Cert. tchr., Pa.; cert. clinician, ednl. specialist, instructional specialist, sch. psychologist, guidance counselor, reading specialist. Speech therapist, lang. arts instr. Commonwealth of Pa., Dept. Edn., 1956-59; founder, clinician, instr., dir., bd. pres. Communicative Arts Ctr., Inc., Drexel Hill, Pa., 1958, Communication Skills Community Resources Ctr., Inc., Drexel Hill, Pa., 1958, 1964—; charter mem. exec. bd., bd. pres. United Pvt. Acad. Schs., Assn. of Pa., Drexel Hill, 1966—; exec. bd. govs., bd. chmn. The Accrediting Commn., Drexel Hill, 1971—; charter mem. Pa. State Univ. Radio and TV Guild, University Park, Pa., 1951—; mem. legis. action com., Pa. State U., Univ. Park, 1988—; cons. communications skills, The Accrediting Commn., 1971—, United Pvt. Acad. Schs. Assn., Pa., 1966—. Founder, chmn., chief exec. officer Am. Ednl. Group, 1991—; chmn. chief exec. officer Internat. Ednl. Group, 1991—; CEO Cmty. Resources Ctr., Drexel Hill, 1991—; project coord. Energy Quest, 1992—; mem. Smithsonian Inst. Nat. Assocs., 1995—; active Nat. Com. to Preserve Social Security and Medicare, Washington, 1986—, Am. Imigration Control Found., Monterey, Va., 1987—, English First, Springfield, Va., 1988—; mem. pres.'s coun. Rep. Nat. Com., 1989—, Nat. Rep. Senatorial Com., 1989—, Rep. Presdl. Task Force, 1989—. 1st Lt. Signal Corps, U.S. Army, 1952-54. Recipient Svc. award United Pvt. Acad. Sch. Assn. Pa., Monroeville, Pa., 1978, Disting. Achievement and Svc. award Bd. Govs. of the Accrediting Commn., Downington, Pa., 1980, Dr. Charles Boehm Edn. of Yr. award, University Park, Pa., 1990, Loyal and Dedicated Svc. award The Accrediting Commn., 1974. Mem. NEA, Libr. of Congress (chartered), Internat. Platform Assn., Pa. Edn. Assn., Jefferson Ednl. Found., World Affairs Coun., Phila. Nat. Congl. Club, Penn. State U. Nittany Lions Club, Penn. State U. Alumni Assn., Penn. State U. Football Lettermen's Club, Smithsonian Inst. Nat. Assocs. Republican. Roman Catholic. Avocations: music, home and garden design, automotive design, reading, golf. Office: The Accrediting Commn 436 Burmont Rd Drexel Hill PA 19026-3630

SCHICK, EDGAR BREHOB, German literature educator; b. Phila., June 28, 1934; s. Claude Ernest and Martha Henrietta (Brehob) S.; m. Margaret Barbara Buehl, Feb. 12, 1938; children: Susanne, Christina. AB magna cum laude, Muhlenberg Coll., 1955; MA, Rutgers U., 1962, PhD, 1965. Asst. prof. German SUNY, Binghamton, 1963-68; asst. to pres. SUNY, Albany, 1968-72, asst. prof., 1968-72; v.p. acad. affairs St. John Fisher Coll., Rochester, N.Y., 1972-78, exec. v.p. 1978-80, assoc. prof., 1972-80; pres. Nasson Coll., Springvale, Maine, 1980-83; provost, v.p. acad. affairs, prof. Eastern Ill. U., Charleston, 1984-87; exec. dir. Bd. Trustees, Md. State Univs. & Colls., Annapolis, 1987-88; vice chancellor for policy and planning U. Md. System, Adelphi, 1988-91; sr. fellow Am. Assn. State Colls. and Univs., 1991-94; cons. Assn. Governing Bds., 1993—; chmn. visitation team Mid. States Assn. Colls. and Schs., Phila., 1975-79; cons. IBM, Yorkville, N.Y., 1968, Nat. Luth. Campus Ministry, 1968-85, USAID, 1992-95. Author: Metaphorical Organicism in the Early Herder, 1971, Shared Visions of Public Higher Education Governance: Structures and Leadership Styles That Work, 1992, The "Local Board" in Multi-Campus Public Universities, 1994; contbr. articles on German lit. and higher edn. to profl. jours. Bd. dirs. United Way, 1981-82, Maine Ind. Colls. Assn., 1981-93, Deaton Hosp., Balt.; pres. Oakleigh Forest Civic Assn. Univ. fellow, Rutgers U., New Brunswick, N.Y., 1962-63; grantee Carnegie Found., Dept. HEW. Mem. Am. Assn. Higher Edn., Am. Assn. Univ. Adminstrs., Am. Assn. Tchrs. German, Assn. for Instl. Rsch., Soc. for Coll. and Univ. Planning, Thomas Mann Soc., Nat. Soc. Fund-Raising Execs. Lutheran. Home: 106 Quinn Rd Severna Park MD 21146-3015

SCHICK, ELLIOT, manufacturing company executive; b. N.Y.C., June 13, 1924; s. Joseph I. and Naomi S. Student Washington and Lee U., 1940-42; B. Adminstrv. Engring., N.Y. U., 1944, M. Adminstrv. Engring., 1949; m. Harriet Schick; children—Debra, Karen. Chief indsl. engr. Emerson Radio & Phonograph Co., 1945-55; plant mgr. Herald Radio & Phono Corp., 1955-60; sr. cons. F.G. Bishop Co., Rockville Center, N.Y., 1960-65; mgmt. cons. Elliot Schick & Co., Bay Harbor Island, Fla., 1965-77; v.p. Matrix Corp., Orangeburg, N.J., 1978-90; pres. Diversified Office Svcs., N.Y.C., 1990—. Registered profl. engr., N.Y. Mem. Am. Inst. Indsl. Engrs. Office: Diversified Office Svcs Message Ctr 11 Penn Plz New York NY 10001-2005

SCHICK, HARRY LEON, investment company executive; b. N.Y.C., Oct. 24, 1927; s. Martin and Sadie (Spitz) S.; m. Eleanor Alter, Oct. 16, 1982; m. Inge Nussbaum, Oct. 12, 1964 (div. Nov. 1971); 1 child, Susan. A.B. magna cum laude, Bklyn. Coll., 1947; M.S., Columbia U., 1948; postgrad., NYU, 1948-52. Securities analyst Sutro Bros., N.Y.C., 1948-52; asst. to pres. Clairdale Enterprises, Inc., N.Y.C., 1953-66; mgr. arbitrage dept. First Manhattan Co., N.Y.C., 1966-69, gen. ptnr., 1969-91, ltd. ptnr., 1992—; lectr. Donaldson Sch. Orgn. and Mgmt., Yale U., New Haven, 1978-88, NYU Grad. Sch. Bus. Adminstrn., N.Y.C., 1977; lectr. in field. Mem. Inst. Chartered Fin. Analysts, Am. Fin. Assn., Am. Econ. Assn., N.Y. Soc. Security Analysts (bd. dirs. 1975-76), Beta Gamma Sigma. Jewish. Home: 215 E 68th St Apt 15Y New York NY 10021-5726 Office: First Manhattan Co 437 Madison Ave New York NY 10022-7001

SCHICK, IRVIN HENRY, educator; b. Wilkes-Barre, Pa., Aug. 10, 1924; s. Irvin and Elizabeth (Valentine) S.; diploma Bliss Elec. Sch., 1947; B.E.E. with distinction, George WashingtonU., 1958; M.S. in Elec. Engring. (NSF fellow), U. Md., 1961; m. Marilyn Freeman, July 17, 1954 (dec. Aug. 1961); m. 2d, Marjorie Bletch Beach, Dec. 23, 1967; 1dau., Carolyn Patricia. Engring. asst. Jeddo-Highland Coal Co. (Pa.), 1942-43; instr. Bliss Elec. Sch., Washington, 1947-50; prof. math. and elec. engring., dept. head Montgomery Coll., Rockville, Md., 1950-65, dir. extension, 1965-67, dean adminstrn., 1967-75, adminstrv. v.p., 1975-78, prof. emeritus, adminstrv. v.p. emeritus, 1978—. Tchr., tutor, cons. indsl. cos. 1949—. Served with USAAF, 1943-46. Mem. AAUP, Montgomery County Edn. Assn., Md. State Tchrs. Assn., IEEE, Am. Assn. Sch. Adminstrs., Internat. Platform Assn., Bliss Elec. Soc. (bd. govs.,past pres.), Tent Troupe Theatrical Organ. (bd. govs.), Theta Tau, Sigma Tau (past pres.), Sigma Pi Sigma, Tau Beta Pi. Home: 105 Fleetwood Ter Silver Spring MD 20910-5512

SCHICK, MICHAEL WILLIAM, public relations executive; b. San Antonio, July 17, 1956; s. Lawrence Martin and Jeanne Frances (McCuen) S.; m. Diana Lynn McGinty, Mar. 14, 1988; 1 child, Tiffany Michele. B in Media Arts with honors, U. S.C., 1979. Dir. prodns., asst. v.p. S.C. Savs. & Loan League, Columbia, 1978-81; dep. press sec., sr. Sen. Strom Thurmond Washington, 1981-85; sr. assoc. Civic Svc. Inc., Washington, 1985—. Co-founder, chmn. First Monday Night, McLean, Va., 1981-94; active Young Reps., Reston, Va., 1990-92, Fourth Presbyn. Ch., Bethesda,

Md., 1988—; chmn. Creative Living Internat., Reston, 1988—. Mem. Am. Assn. Polit. Conss. Republican. Avocations: golf, tennis, soccer, sailing, guitar. Home: 11560 Brass Lantern Ct Reston VA 22094 Office: Civic Svc Inc 1050 Connecticut Ave NW Ste 870 Washington DC 20036

SCHICK, SETH HARVEY, land resource economist; b. Kaysville, Utah, June 8, 1936; s. George and Ruth (Harvey) S.; m. Karren Hodgson, Sept. 2, 1960; children: Jeffery, Scott, Daranee, Alison. BS in Econs., Utah State U., 1962; MS in Econs., N.C. State at Raleigh, Utah State U., 1964; postgrad., U. Ariz., 1967-68. Mktg. rep. Proctor and Gamble, Salt Lake City, 1962; economist Fed. Milk Mktg., Denver, 1964; land resource economist Harza Engring. Co., Chgo., 1965-70; land resource economist Schick Internat., Salt Lake City, 1970-74, pres., land resource economist, 1974—; project economist Tipton Kalmback Co., Denver, 1976, Electro Watt Engring. Co., Zurich, Switzerland, 1984-85; spl. assignmentt resource economist on irrigation systems mgmt. USAID, Sri Lanka, 1987-88; resource economist on irrigation system improvement project Asian Devel. Bank, Leyte Island, Philippines, 1993-94; resource economist pricing culinary water Utah Municipalities, 1994-95, Schick Internat., Inc. Served with USAF, 1954-58. Democrat. Mormon. Office: Schick Internat Inc 3010 First Commerce Ctr 175 W 200 S Salt Lake City UT 84101

SCHICKEL, RICHARD, writer, film critic; b. Milw., Feb. 10, 1933; s. Edward J. and Helen (Hendricks) S.; children: Erika Tracy, Jessica Avery. BS, U. Wis., 1955. Sr. editor Look mag., 1957-60, Show mag., 1960-63; freelance writer, 1963—; film critic Life mag., 1965-72, Time mag., 1973—; cons. Rockefeller Bros. Fund, 1964, Rockefeller Found., 1965; lectr. in history art Yale, 1972, 76; adj. prof. film, U. S. Calif., 1989; pres. Lorac Prodns., 1986—. Author: The World of Carnegie Hall, 1960, The Stars, 1962, Movies: The History of an Art and an Institution, 1964, The Gentle Knight, 1964, The Disney Version, 1968, The World of Goya, 1968, Second Sight: Notes on Some Movies, 1972, His Picture in the Papers, 1974, Harold Lloyd: The Shape of Laughter, 1974, The Men Who Made the Movies, 1975, The World of Tennis, 1975, The Fairbanks Album, 1975, Singled Out, 1981, Cary Grant, A Celebration, 1984, D.W. Griffith: An American Life, 1984, James Cagney, A Celebration, 1985, Intimate Strangers: The Culture of Celebrity, 1985, Striking Poses, 1987, Schickel on Film, 1989, Brando: A Life In Our Times, 1991, Double Indemnity, 1992; co-author: Lena, 1965, The Platinum Years, 1974, Hollywood at Home, 1990, (novel) Another I, Another You, 1978; co-editor: Film 67-68, 1968; producer, dir., writer (TV series) The Men Who Made the Movies, 1973; producer, writer: (TV spls.) Life Goes to the Movies, 1976, SPFX, 1980, Cary Grant, A Celebration, 1989; producer, writer, dir.: (TV spls.) Funny Business, 1978, Into the Morning: Willa Cather's America, 1978, The Horror Show, 1979, James Cagney: That Yankee Doodle Dandy, 1981, From Star Wars to Jedi: The Making of a Saga, 1983, Minnelli on Minnelli: Liza Remembers Vincent, 1987, Gary Cooper: American Life, American Legend, 1989, Myrna Loy: So Nice to Come Home To, 1990, Barbara Stanwyck: Fire and Desire, 1991, Eastwood & Co.; Making Unforgiven, 1992, Hollywood on Hollywood, 1993. Recipient Book prize Brit. Film Inst., 1985; Guggenheim fellow, 1964. Mem. Nat. Soc. Film Critics, N.Y. Film Critics, Dirs. Guild Am., Writers Guild Am.

SCHICKELE, PETER, composer; b. Ames, Iowa, July 17, 1935; s. Rainer Wolfgang and Elizabeth (Wilcox) S.; m. Susan Sindall, Oct. 27, 1962; children: Karla, Matthew. B.A., Swarthmore Coll., 1957; M.S., Juilliard Sch. Music, 1960; PhD (hon.), Swarthmore, 1980. Composer-in-residence Los Angeles High Sch., 1960-61; faculty Swarthmore Coll., 1961-62, Juilliard Sch. Music, 1961-65, Aspen Festival Music, Colo., 1963. Composer: scores for films The Crazy Quilt, 1965, Funny Man, 1967, Silent Running, 1972, several non-theatrical and TV films; arranger for: Joan Baez albums Noel, 1966, Joan, 1967, Baptism, 1968; composer mus. score for film at Tex. pavilion of Hemisfair, San Antonio, 1968; TV appearances include: Profile on the Arts, Camera Three, Bach 'N' Roll, 13 Stars for 13, Dick Cavett Show, Mike Douglas Show, David Frost Show, ABC Comedy News, Tonight Show with Johnny Carson; comedian, recorded: An Evening with P.D.Q. Bach, 1968, P.D.Q. Bach: 1712 Overture and Other Musical Assaults, 1989, Oedipus Tex and Other Choral Calamities, 1990, WTWP-Classical Talkity-Talk Radio, 1991, Music for an Awful Lot of Winds and Percussion, 1992, other comedy albums; mem., The Open Window, chamber-rock trio, 1967-71; composer and lyricist: Oh Calcutta; composer String Quartet No. 1, American Dreams and numerous works for orch., chorus, piano, chamber music, band, organ, voice and instruments, 1953—; creator, host Schickele Mix, Pub. Radio Internat., family concerts with Am. Symphony Orch., 1994—; author: The Definitive Biography of P.D.Q. Bach. Recipient Gershwin Meml. award, 1959, Elizabeth Tow Newman Contemporary Music award, 1964, Grammy awards, 1990-93, Deems Taylor award; Ford Found. grantee. Mem. ASCAP, Am. Music Ctr., Assn. Classical Music, Am. Fedn. Musicians. Avocation: crossword puzzles. Office: ICM Artists care Stewart Warkow 40 W 57th St New York NY 10019

SCHIDLOW, DANIEL, pediatrician, medical association administrator; b. Santiago, Chile, Oct. 23, 1947; m. Sally Rosen; children: David, Michael, Jessica. Grad., U. Chile, 1972. Diplomate Am. Bd. Pediatrics, Am. Bd. Pediatric Pulmonology; lic. in D.C., Pa., N.J. Rotating intern U. Chile Hosp., U. Chile Sch. Medicine, 1971-72, resident in internal medicine, instr. phys. diagnosis, 1972-73; resident, emergency rm. physician in pediatrics E.G. Cortes Hosp. Children, U. Chile, 1973-74; resident in pediatrics Albert Einstein Coll. Medicine Bronx (N.Y.)-Lebanon Hosp. Ctr., 1974-76; fellow pediatric pulmonary medicine St. Christopher's Hosp. Children, Phila., 1976-78; chief sect. pediatric pulmonology dept. pediatrics St. Christopher's Hosp. Children, 1983-94, sr. v.p. clin. affairs, 1994—; from asst. to assoc. prof. pediatrics sch. medicine Temple U., Phila., 1978-90, prof., 1990-94, dep. chmn. dept. pediatrics, 1991-94; prof., sr. vice chmn. dept. pediatrics Med. Coll. Pa./Hahnemann U. Med. Sch., Phila., 1994—; attending physician St. Christopher's Hosp. Children, 1978—; dir. fellowship tng. and edn. program sect. pediatric pulmonology, 1979-91, assoc. dir. pediatric pulmonary and cystic fibrosis ctr., 1981-83, med. dir. dept. respiratory therapy, 1982-88, project dir. Pediatric pulmonary ctr., 1983-86, dir. cystic fibrosis ctr., 1983—, chair capital campaign com. dept. pediatrics, 1987, mem. exec. com. med. staff, 1988—, mem. various coms.; courtesy staff Lancaster (Pa.) Gen. Hosp., 1980-82; cons. divsn. rehab. Pa. Dept. Health, 1983—; mem. promotions com. dept. pediatrics sch. medicine Temple U., 1986—, chmn. com. appointments clin.-educator track 1991—; attending staff no. divsn. Albert Einstein Med. Ctr., 1987—; cons. Nat. Ctr. Youth Disabilities, 1987—; mem. med. adv. coun. Cystic Fibrosis Found., Bethesda, Md., 1987—, trustee, 1990—, med. dir. home care svcs., 1991—, various other positons; consulting staff Temple U. Hosp., 1988—; mem. organizing com. N.Am. Cystic Fibrosis Conf., 1990-93, co-chmn., 1992—; co-chmn. Nat. Concensus Conf. Pulmonary Complications Cystic Fibrosis, McLean, Va., 1992; mem. adv. bd. Phila. Parenting Assocs., 1992—. Reviewer Jour. Pediatrics, Am. Jour. Diseases Children, others. Named Illustrious Guest, City of LaPlata, Argentina, 1992. Fellow Am. Acad. Pediatrics (Pa. chpt., sect. diseases chest), Am. Coll. Chest Physicians (sect. cardiopulmonary diseases children); mem. AAAS, Am. Thoracic Soc. (mem. nominating com. 1993—), Am. Fedn. Clin. Rsch., Chilean Pediatric Soc. (hon.), Pa. Thoracic Soc., Ea. Soc. Pediatric Rsch., Phila. Pediatric Soc. Home: 315 N Bowman Ave Merion Station PA 19066 Office: St Christopher's Hosp Chldn Office Med and Acad Affairs Erie Ave at Front St Philadelphia PA 19134

SCHIEBLER, GEROLD LUDWIG, physician, educator; b. Hamburg, Pa., June 20, 1928; s. Alwin Robert and Charlotte Elizabeth (Schmoele) S.; m. Audrey Jean Lincourt, Jan. 8, 1954; children: Mark, Marcella, Kristen, Bettina, Wanda, Michele. BS, Franklin and Marshall Coll., 1950; MD, Harvard U., 1954. Intern pediatrics and internal medicine Mass. Gen. Hosp., Boston, 1954-55, resident, 1955-56; resident pediatrics U. Minn. Hosp., Mpls., 1956-57, fellow pediatric cardiology, 1957-58, rsch. fellow, 1958-59; rsch. fellow sect. physiology Mayo Clinic and Mayo Found., 1959-60; asst. prof. pediatric cardiology U. Fla., 1960-63, assoc. prof., 1963-66, prof., 1966-92, Disting. Svc. prof., 1992—, chmn. dept. pediatrics, 1968-85, assoc. v.p. for health affairs for external rels., 1985—; dir. div. Children's Med. Svcs., State of Fla., 1973-74. Author: (with L.P. Elliott) The X-ray Diagnosis of Congenital Cardiac Disease in Infants, Children and Adults, 1968, 2d edit., 1979, (with L.J. Krovetz and I.H. Gessner) Pediatric Cardiology, 2d edit., 1979. Mem. AAAS, Inst. Medicine NAS, Am. Acad. Pediatrics (Abraham Jacobi award 1993), AMA (Benjamin Rush award 1993), Am. Coll. Cardiology, Soc. Pediatric Rsch. (emeritus), Fla. Pediatric Soc. (exec. com.), Fla. Heart Assn.

(past pres.), Fla. Med. Assn. (past v.p., bd. govs., pres. 1991-92), Phi Beta Kappa, Alpha Omega Alpha. Home: 2115 NW 15th Ave Gainesville FL 32605-5216

SCHIEFELBUSCH, RICHARD L., research administrator; b. Osawatomie, Kans., July 23, 1918; s. Edward Francis and Emma (Martie) S.; m. Ruth Lenore Magee, Sept. 20, 1942; children—Lary, Carol, Jean. B.S., Kans. State Tchrs. Coll., 1940; M.A. in Speech Pathology and Psychology, U. Kans., 1947; Ph.D. in Speech Pathology, Northwestern U., 1951. Mem. faculty U. Kans., Lawrence, 1946-89, prof. speech pathology and audiology, 1959-69; dir. Speech and Hearing Clinic Schiefelbusch Speech and Hearing Clinic, Lawrence, 1949-56; dir. Bur. Child Research U. Kans., Lawrence, 1955-90, Univ. Disting. prof., 1969-89; Univ. Disting. prof. emeritus, 1989—; chmn. child lang. grad. degree program U. Kans., Lawrence, 1983-89, interim dir. Gerontology Ctr., 1989-91; interim dir. Inst. for Life Span Studies Schiefelbusch Inst. for Life Span Studies, Lawrence, 1989-90; dir. Kans. Center Mental Retardation and Human Devel., Lawrence, 1969-89; co-dir. Kans. Research Inst. Learning Disabilities, Lawrence, 1977-81; sr. scientist VA Hosp., Topeka, 1991-93; cons. in field, dir. research grants. Author book series Language Intervention; also numerous articles in field; mem. editorial bds. profl. jours. Served with USAAF, 1941-46. Recipient Disting. Service award Nat. Assn. for Retarded Citizens, 1983; Disting. Achievement award Pittsburg State U., 1985, Disting. Accomplishment award Am. Assn. Univ. Affiliated Programs, 1987; Fulbright scholar, Australia, 1986. Fellow Am. Assn. Mental Deficiency (Spl. award 1975, Edn. award 1986), Am. Speech and Hearing Assn. (assn. honoree 1976, v.p. edn. and sci. affairs 1980-82); mem. Council Exceptional Children. Home: 3113 Campfire Dr Lawrence KS 66049-2012 Office: U Kans Bur Child Rsch Lawrence KS 66045

SCHIEFFER, BOB, broadcast journalist; b. Austin, Tex.; m. Patricia Penrose; children: Susan, Sharon. B.A. in Journalism, Tex. Christian U. Reporter Ft. Worth Star-Telegram; news anchorman Sta. WBAP-TV, Dallas-Ft. Worth; with CBS News, 1969—, Pentagon corr., 1970-74, White House corr., 1974-79, chief Washington corr., 1982—; anchorman CBS Sunday Night News, 1973-74, Sunday edit. CBS Evening News, 1976—, Monday-through-Friday edits. Morning, 1979-80; co-anchorman CBS Morning News, from 1985; also participant CBS news spls. and spl. reports, including Peace and the Pentagon, 1974, Watergate-The White House Transcripts, 1974, The Mysterious Alert, 1974, 1976, Ground Zero, 1981; Democratic Nat. Conv., 1976, Republican Nat. Conv., Campaign '72; and mem. Emmy award-winning team CBS Evening News with Walter Cronkite, 1971; currently moderator Face the Nation CBS News, chief Washington corr.; co-anchor CBS Weekend News/Sunday News, 1976—. Author: (with Gary Paul Gates) The Acting President, 1989. Recipient various awards Sigma Delta Chi, various awards Tex. Associated Broadcasters, various awards AP Mng. Editors; corecipient Emmy awards. Office: care CBS News Weekend/Sunday News 524 W 57th St New York NY 10019

SCHIEFFER, J. THOMAS, professional baseball team executive. Pres. Texas Rangers. Office: Texas Rangers 1000 Ballpark Way Arlington TX 76011

SCHIELE, PAUL ELLSWORTH, JR., educational business owner, writer; b. Phila., Nov. 20, 1924; s. Paul Ellsworth Sr. and Maud (Barclay) S.; m. Sarah Irene Knauss, Aug. 20, 1946; children: Patricia Schiele Tiemann, Sandra Schiele Kicklighter, Deborah Schiele Hartigan. AT, Temple U., 1949; BA, LaVerne U., 1955; MA, Claremont Associated Colls., 1961; PhD, U.S. Internat. U., San Diego, 1970. Cert. sec tchr., Calif. 1961. Tchr. sci. and math. Lincoln High Sch., Phila., 1956-57, Ontario (Calif.) Sch. Dist., 1957-65; math. and sci. cons. Hacienda La Puente U. Sch. Dist., Calif., 1965-75; asst. prof. Calif. State U., Fullerton, 1975-83; pres., owner Creative Learning Environments and Resources, Glendora, Calif., 1983—, cons. sci. curriculum, 1985—; dir. title III project ESEA, 1974-75, cons. for project, 1975-77; cons. in field. Author: Primary Science, 1972, 2d edit., 1976; editor: A Living World, 1974, 2d edit., 1986; writer 9 sound filmstrips, model units for sci. and math. instrn., 1974-75, cons. for project, 1975-77; cons. in field. Author: Primary Science, 1972, 2d edit., 1976; editor: A Living World, 1974, 2d edit., 1986; writer 9 sound filmstrips, model units for sci. and math. activity books, 10 sci. activities for L.A. Outdoor Edn. Program, 1980; editor 21 sci. and math. activity books; writer, co-dir. (TV) Marine Biology Series, 1970-71; contbr. numerous articles to profl. magazines, 1960-85; writer and designer of 2 sci. ednl. games; designer in field. Apptd. adv. com. Sci. and Humanities Symposium Calif. Mus. Sci. and Industry, 1974; mem. State Sci. Permit Com., Tide Pools of Calif. Coast, 1974-75; active Playhouse 90, Pasadena (Calif.) Playhouse; mem. Friends of Libr., Friends Libr. Found. Mem. Internat. Platform Assn., ABI Rsch. Assn. (bd. govs.), Calif. Elem. Edn. Assn. (hon.), Nat. PTA (hon.), Calif. Inter-Sci. Coun. (pres., chmn. 1971, 72), Elem Sch. Scis. Assn. (past pres., bd. dirs.), Phi Delta Kappa (chartered). Republican. Lutheran. Avocations: travel, etchings, art collecting, fencing. Home: 231 Catherine Park Dr Glendora CA 91741-3018

SCHIER, DONALD STEPHEN, language educator; b. Ft. Madison, Iowa, Sept. 10, 1914; s. Francis and Marcella (Kenny) S. B.A., State U. Iowa, 1936; M.A., Columbia U., 1937, Ph.D., 1941. Mem. faculty State Tchrs. Coll., Bemidji, Minn., 1939-41, 41-42, Ill. Inst. Tech., 1946; mem. faculty Carleton Coll., Northfield, Minn., 1946-80; prof. French Carleton Coll., 1953-80; vis. prof. U. Wis., 1964-65; Brown tutor in French U. of South, Sewanee, Tenn., 1980-81. Author: Louis-Bertrand Castel, 1942; editor: (with Scott Elledge) The Continental Model, 1960, 2d edit., 1970; (Bertrand de Fontenelle), Nouveaux Dialogues des morts, 1965, rev. edit., 1974; translator: Letter on Italian Music (Charles de Brosses), 1978. Mem. selection com. Young Scholar Program, Nat. Found. Arts and Humanities, 1966-67. Served to capt. AUS, 1942-46. Mem. MLA, Am. Assn. Tchrs. French, Am. Soc. Eighteenth-Century Studies. Home: Apt 1106 750 Weaver Dairy Rd Chapel Hill NC 27514-1438

SCHIER, MARY JANE, science writer; b. Houston, Mar. 10, 1939; d. James F. and Jerry Mae (Crisp) McDonald; B.S. in Journalism, Tex. Woman's U., 1961; m. John Christian Schier, Aug. 26, 1961; children—John Christian, II, Mark Edward. Reporter, San Antonio Express and News, 1962-64; med. writer Daily Oklahoman, also Oklahoma City Times, 1965-66; reporter, med. writer Houston Post, 1966-84; sci. writer, univ. editor U. Tex. M.D. Anderson Cancer Ctr., 1984—. Recipient award Tex. Headliners Club, 1969, Tex. Med. Assn., 1972-74, 76, 78, 79, 80, 82 Tex. Hosp. Assn., 1974, 82, Tex. Public Health Assn., 1976, 77, 78, others. Mem. Houston Press Club Ednl. Found. (pres 1992—). Lutheran. Home: 9742 Tappenbeck Dr Houston TX 77055-4102 Office: 1515 Holcombe Blvd Houston TX 77030-4095

SCHIERHOLZ, WILLIAM FRANCIS, JR., real estate developer; b. St. Louis, Oct. 14, 1921; s. William Francis and Florence Cecelia (Wuensch) S.; m. Joan Flavin, Sept. 7, 1947; children—Margaret Ann, John W., William Francis, III. B.S. in Engring. Adminstrn, Washington U., St. Louis, 1943. Vice pres., gen. mgr. Fuel Oil of St. Louis, 1949-55; pres. Chemtech Industries, Inc., St. Louis, 1956-87, chmn. bd., 1991—; with real estate devel. Habitech Devel. Corp., Chesterfield, Mo., 1989-91; bd. dirs. Commerce Bank St. Louis; pres. Affiliated Chem. Group, Ltd., Bermuda; commr. Mo. Hwy. and Transp. Commn., 1982-87. Chmn. Mo. State Com. Reponsible Consumerism, 1977-78; mem. exec. bd. St. Louis area coun. Boy Scouts Am., adv. bd. INROADS, also chmn.; bd. dirs. Jr. Achievement of Miss. Valley; commr. Mo. Highway and Transp. Commn., 1982-87. Served to capt. USAAF, 1943-46. Mem. U.S. C. of C., Mo. C. of C. (dir., exec. com., chmn.) (bd. dirs Yr. 1981). St. Louis Regional Commerce and Growth Assn. (dir., exec. com., chmn.), Am. Assn. Indsl. Mgmt. (pres. 1976, dir.), Chem. Mfg. Assn., NAM, Presidents Assn. Chem. Industry Council Greater St. Louis (pres. 1970), Backstoppers, Affiliated Chem. Group (pres. 1966), Rotary Club St. Louis (pres. 1981-82), Beta Theta Pi (pres. alumni assn. 1967). Clubs: Univ., Mo. Athletic, Rotary (pres. 1981-82). Office: Chemtech Industries Inc 1655 Des Peres Rd Saint Louis MO 63131-1832

SCHIESER, HANS ALOIS, education educator; b. Ulm, Germany, July 15, 1931; came to U.S., 1965; s. Alois and Anna (Stegmann) S.; m. Margret H. Schröer, June 6, 1962; children: Peter, Elisabeth. BA, Kepler Gymnasium, Ulm, 1952; MA in Philosophy, Passau, Fed. Republic Germany, 1959; EdM, Pedagogic Acad., Weingarten, Fed. Republic Germany, 1962; PhD, Loyola U., 1970. Head tchr. Pestalozzischule, Ulm, 1964-65; learning disabilities tchr. Jeanine Schultz Meml. Sch., Skokie, Ill., 1966-67; co-dir. Oak Ther-

apeutic Sch., Evanston, Ill., 1967-70; assoc. prof. to prof. edn. DePaul U., Chgo., 1969-91, prof. emeritus, 1991—; cons. various indsl. and bus. tng. programs, 1978-91; program cons. Delphian Soc., L.A., 1977-90; rschr., tchr. in Germany, 1991—; active in tchr. edn. Midwest Montessori Tchr. Tng. Ctr., Evanston, Ill.; mem. adv. bd. Verein Psychol. Menschenkenntnis Zurich, 1993—. Author chpts. in books; contbr. numerous articles U.S. and German publs.; adv. bd. Ann. Edits. Sociology, Dushkin Pub. Group, 1985-91. Pres. N.Am. Family Svc. Found., Oak Lawn, Ill., 1974-91; pres. emeritus S.O.S. Children's Villages USA, Washington, 1986—; pres. emeritus S.O.S. Children's Village Ill., Inc., Chgo.; pub. policy expert Domestic Issues Heritage Found., 1991—; bd. dirs. Invest-in-Am. Nat. Found., Phila., 1988-90. Rsch. grantee DePaul U., 1985-86, Rsch. sabbatical, 1989. Mem. Am. Ednl. Studies Assn., Nat. Soc. for Study of Edn., Philosophy of Edn. Soc. U.S.A., Soc. Educators and Scholars (bd. dirs. 1984-90), Am. Montessori Soc., Thomas More Gesellschaft/Amici Mori Europe, Phi Delta Kappa (pres. Zeta chpt., Chgo. 1973-75). Home: 136 Dodge Ave Evanston IL 60202 Home: Veilchenweg 9, D-89134 Bermaringen Federal Republic of Germany Office: DePaul U 2323 N Seminary Ave Chicago IL 60614-3211

SCHIESS, BETTY BONE, priest; b. Cin., Apr. 2, 1923; d. Evan Paul and Leah (Mitchell) Bone; m. William A. Schiess, Aug. 28, 1947; children: William A. (dec.), Richard Corwine, Sarah. BA, U. Cin., 1945; MA, Syracuse U., 1947; MDiv, Rochester Ctr. for Theol. Studies, 1972. Ordained priest Episcopal Ch., 1974; priest assoc. Grace Episc. Ch., Syracuse, N.Y., 1975; mem. N.Y. Task Force on Life and Law (apptd. by gov.) 1985—; chaplain Syracuse U., 1976-78, Cornell U., Ithaca, N.Y., 1978-79; rector Grace Episc. Ch., Mexico, N.Y., 1984-89; cons. Women's Issues Network Episc. Ch. in U.S., 1987—; writer, lectr., cons. religion and feminism, 1979—. Author: Take Back the Church, Indeed The Witness, 1982, Creativity and Procreativity: Some Thoughts on Eve and the Opposition and How Episcopalians Make Ethical Decisions, Plumline, 1988, Send in the Clowns, Chrysalis, Journal of the Swidenborg Foundation, 1994. Bd. dirs. People for Pub. TV in N.Y., 1978, Religious Coalition for Abortion Rights; trustee Elizabeth Cady Stanton Found., 1979; mem. policy com. Coun. Adolescent Pregnancy; mem. N.Y. State Task Force Life and the Law, 1983—. Recipient Gov.'s award Women of Merit in Religion, 1984, Ralph E. Kharas award ACLU Cen N.Y., 1986 Goodall disting. alumna award & Hills Sch., 1988, Human Rightes award Human Rights Commn. of Syracuse and Onondaga County, N.Y., 1989; inducted into Nat. Women's Hall of Fame, 1994. Mem. NOW (Syracuse), Internat. Assn. Women Ministers (dir. 1978, pres. 1984-87), Assn. for Vol. Surg. Contraception (exec. com.), Am. Soc. Law and Medicine, Clergy Assn. Diocese of Cen. N.Y. (v.p. 1985—), Na'amat U.S. (hon. life), Mortar Bd., Theta Chi Beta. Democrat. Home and Office: 107 Bradford Ln Syracuse NY 13224-1901 Office: Grace Episcopal Ch Main St Mexico NY 13114

SCHIESSLER, ROBERT WALTER, retired chemical and oil company executive; b. Honesdale, Pa., Oct. 2, 1918; s. Walter A. and Josephine (Herzog) S.; m. Betty Hartman, June 5, 1939; children—Lynn Alice, Dale Ann; m. Florence Cutler, Aug. 16, 1968. B.S., Pa. State U., 1939, Ph.D., 1944; M.S., McGill U., 1941. Research chemist Gen. Electric Co., Schenectady, 1941; from instr. to asso. Prof. chemistry and dir. Am. Petroleum Inst. Research Pa. State U., 1942-55; chemistry and physics cons., 1946-55; tech. dir. Central Research div. Mobil Oil Co., Paulsboro and Princeton, N.J., 1950-60; mgr. central research div., asst. gen. mgr. research dept. Central Research div. Mobil Oil Co., 1960-62, gen. mgr. research dept., 1962-67; v.p. research Mobil Research & Devel. Corp., 1967-68; chmn., pres. Indsl. Reactor Labs., Inc., 1966-67; mgr. long-range planning Mobil Oil Corp., 1968-72, gen. mgr. real estate and land devel., 1972-83; chmn. Mobil Land Devel. Corp., 1972-83; pres. Sandvik, Inc., 1983-84; chmn. bd. trustees Gordon Rsch. Conf., Inc., 1957; mem. bd. Am. Chem. Soc. Peroleum Rsch. Fund, 1955-59, 60-63; Rsch. chemist Can. govt., 1940-41. Co-Author: Chemistry of Petroleum Hydrocarbons, 1954, Discoverer method for prodn. super-explosive used by U.S. and Can., World War II. Recipient award in petroleum chemistry Am. Chem. Soc., 1953; named outstanding young man State Coll. of Pa., outstanding young man Jr. C. of C., 1952; recipient Wisdom award, 1970. Fellow Am. Inst. Chemists, AAAS (v.p. for chemistry, chmn. chemistry sect. 1960); mem. Am. Chem. Soc., AAUP, Sigma Xi, Phi Lambda Upsilon, Phi Eta Sigma. Home: 1500 Palisade Ave Fort Lee NJ 07024-5337

SCHIFF, CRAIG MITCHELL, computer company executive; b. N.Y.C., June 11, 1955; s. Stanley and Bernice Mary (Kostman) S.; m. LuAnn Bellantoni, June 26, 1982; 1 child, Holly Ann. BS in Biology, SUNY, New Paltz, 1977; MBA in Fin., Fordham U., 1987. Programmer NPD Rsch., Floral Park, N.Y., 1977-79; fin. programmer Gulf & Western, N.Y.C., 1979-80; project mgr. GE, N.Y.C., 1980-83; v.p. Hyperion Software (formerly IMRS, Inc.), Stamford, Conn., 1983—. Pres. Majestic Tenants Corp., Forest Hills, 1982—. Democrat. Jewish. Avocations: traveling, videos, reading. Home: 11020 71st Ave Apt 432 Forest Hills NY 11375-4572 Office: Hyperion Software 777 Long Ridge Rd Stamford CT 06902-1247

SCHIFF, DAVID TEVELE, investment banker; b. N.Y.C., Sept. 3, 1936; s. John Mortimer and Edith Brevoort (Baker) S.; m. Martha Elisabeth Lawler, May 11, 1963; children: Andrew Newman, David Baker, Ashley Reynolds. B.Engring., Yale U., 1958. Trainee Chem. Bank N.Y. Trust, N.Y.C., 1959-62; analyst Madison Fund, N.Y.C., 1962; assoc., then partner Kuhn, Loeb & Co., N.Y.C., 1963-77; vice chmn. Kuhn Loeb & Co., 1977; mng. dir. Lehman Bros. Kuhn Loeb Inc., N.Y.C., 1977-83; also dir. Lehman Bros. Kuhn Loeb Inc.; mng. ptnr. Kuhn, Loeb & Co. (formerly KLS Enterprises), 1984—; dir., vice chmn. Am. Crown Life Ins. Co., N.Y.C., 1981-85; bd. dirs. Crown Life Ins. Co., Toronto, 1971-92; mem. lower Manhattan adv. bd. Chem. Bank, 1977-85. Trustee Met. Mus. Art., (Citizens Budget Commn., N.Y.C., Greater N.Y. Coun. Boy Scouts Am.; trustee, chmn. exec. com. The Wildlife Conservation Soc.; trustee Beekman Downtown Hosp., 1966-82, chmn. 1975-79; trustee Brooks Sch., North Andover, Mass., 1972-90, treas. 1987-90; bd. govs. Yale U. Art Galleries, Fed. Hall Meml. Assn.; adv. bd. dirs. Outward Bound, Inc.; mem. Provident Loan Soc. N.Y.; bd. dirs. Am. Hosp. of Paris Found., N.Y.C., 1987. With AUS, 1959. Mem. Econ. Club N.Y.C., Pilgrims U.S., Brook Club, Century Assn., River Club, Maroon Creek Club (Aspen, Colo.), Mill Reef Club (Antigua), Yale Club N.Y.C., Am. Bugatti Club, Vintage Sports Car Club Am. Republican. Episcopalian. Home: 770 Park Ave New York NY 10021-4153 Office: 485 Madison Ave 20th Fl New York NY 10022

SCHIFF, DONALD WILFRED, pediatrician, educator; b. Detroit, Sept. 11, 1925; s. Henry and Kate (Boesky) S.; m. Rosalie Pergament; children: Stephen, Jeffrey, Susan, Douglas. Student, Wayne State U., 1943-44, Oberlin Coll., 1944-45; MD, Wayne State U., 1949. Diplomate Am. Bd. Pediatrics. Intern Detroit Receiving Hosp., 1949-50; resident in pediatrics U. Colo., 1954-55, chief resident in pediatrics, 1955-56; instr. U. Colo. Health Scis. Ctr., Denver, 1956-59, asst. clin. prof., 1959-69, assoc. clin. prof., 1969-78, clin. prof., 1978-87, prof., 1987—; pvt. practice Littleton (Colo.) Clinic, 1956-86, chmn. bd., 1973-79; med. dir. HMO Colo., Denver, 1980-86; med. dir. Child Health Clinic The Children's Hosp., Denver. Contbr. articles to profl. jours. Bd. dirs. Sch. Dist. VI, Colo., 1962; pres. Arapahoe Mental Health Clinic, Denver, 1968-70, bd. dirs., 1964-70; exec. com. State of Colo. Medicaid, Denver, 1981—. With USN, 1944-46, USPHS, 1952-54, Turtle Mountain Indian Reservation, N.D. Recipient 25 Yrs. Teaching award U. Colo. Sch. Medicine, 1981. Mem. Am. Acad. Pediatrics (chmn. Colo. chpt. 1973-79, alternate dist. chmn. 1977-81, chmn. dist. 8 1981-86, nat. pres. 1988-89), Rocky Mountain Pediatric Soc., Colo. Med. Soc. Home: 600 Front Range Rd Littleton CO 80120-4052 Office: The Children's Hosp Child Health Clinic Box BO32 1056 E 19th Ave Denver CO 80218-1007

SCHIFF, EUGENE ROGER, medical educator, hepatologist; b. Cin., Jan. 3, 1937; s. Leon and Augusta (Miller) S.; m. Dana Kendall, Dec. 27, 1965; children: David, Lisa. BA, U. Mich., 1958; MD, Columbia U., 1962. Diplomate Am. Bd. Internal Medicine, Am. Bd Gastroenterology, Nat. Bd. Med. Examiners. Intern and med. resident Cin. Gen. Hosp., 1962-64; med. resident Parkland Meml. Hosp., Dallas, 1966-67; USPHS postdoctoral fellow in gastroenterology Southwestern Med. Sch., U. Tex., Dallas, 1967-69; asst. prof. medicine U. Miami (Fla.) Sch. Medicine, 1969-74, assoc. prof., 1974-78, prof., 1978—, chief div. hepatology, 1971—; dir. Ctr. for Liver Diseases, 1982—; chief hepatology sect. VA Med. Ctr., Miami, 1971—; chmn. adv. com. on gastrointestinal drugs FDA, Rockville, Md., 1983-85, 88-92. Co-

editor: Diseases of the Liver, 5th edit., 1982, 6th edit., 1987, 7th edit. 1993. Lt. comdr. USPHS, 1964-66. Fellow ACP (gov. Fla. chpt. 1984-88), Am. Coll. Gastroenterology (master); mem. AMA, Am. Assn. for Study of Liver Diseases (sec.-treas. 1991—), Internat. Assn. for Study of Liver Diseases, Am. Gastroenterology Assn. (chmn. Biliary Disorders sect.), Argentine Soc. Gastroenterology (hon.). Jewish. Home: 10445 SW 109th St Miami FL 33176-3455 Office: U Miami 1500 NW 12th Ave Ste 1101 Miami FL 33136-1038

SCHIFF, GUNTHER HANS, lawyer; b. Cologne, Germany, Aug. 19, 1927; came to U.S., 1936; s. Hans and Alice (Goldstein) S.; m. Katharine MacMillan, Jan. 27, 1950 (div. 1957); children: Eric Alan, Mary Alice; m. JoAnn R. Schiff; children: Jage, Hans Judson. B.S.F.S., Georgetown U., 1949, J.D., 1952. Bar: D.C. 1952, Calif. 1953. Assoc., ptnr. various firms, Beverly Hills, Calif., 1954—; sec. Los Angeles Copyright Soc., Beverly Hills, 1975-76. Contbr. articles to profl. jours. Pres. Beverly Hills Civil Svc. Commn., 1984-85, 88-89; pres. Free Arts for Abused Children, 1993-94, dir.; chmn. Rent Control Rev. Bd., Beverly Hills, 1980-84; trustee Young Musicians Found. With USNR, 1945-46. Mem. Beverly Hills Bar Assn. (chmn. Resolutions Com. 1977-78), Los Angeles County Bar Assn., ABA, U.S. Copyright Soc., Los Angeles Copyright Soc. Clubs: Lake Arrowhead Country, Calif. Yacht. Avocations: sailing; skiing; golfing. Home: 612 N Foothill Rd Beverly Hills CA 90210-3404 Office: Law Office Gunther H Schiff 9430 W Olympic Blvd Beverly Hills CA 90212-4552

SCHIFF, JEROME ARNOLD, biologist, educator; b. Bklyn., Feb. 20, 1931; s. Charles K. and Molly (Weinberg) S. BA in Biology and Chemistry, Bklyn. Coll. (summer scholar invertebrate zoology Woods Hole Marine Biol. Lab.), 1952; PhD in Botany and Biochemistry, U. Pa., 1956. Predoctoral fellow USPHS, 1954-56; fellow Brookhaven Nat. Labs., summer 1956; rsch. assoc. biology Brandeis U., Waltham, Mass., 1956-57, instr., 1957-58, asst. prof., 1958-61, assoc. prof., 1961-65, prof. biology, 1966—, chmn. dept., 1972-75, Abraham and Etta Goodman prof. biology, 1974—; dir. Inst. Photobiology of Cells and Organelles, 1975-87; summer instr. exptl. marine botany Marine Biol. Lab., Woods Hole, Mass., 1971; sr. investigator explt. marine botany Marine Biol. Lab., 1972-74; dir. programs Exptl. Marine Botany, 1974-79; cons. on devel. biology NSF, 1965-68, cons. on metabolic biology, 1982-86; vis. prof. Tel Aviv U., 1972, Hebrew U., 1972, Weizmann Inst., Israel, 1977; mem. biology grant rev. program U.S.-Israel Binat. Sci. Found., 1974—; mem. corp. Marine Biol. Lab., 1972—. Mem. editorial bd. Developmental Biology, 1971-74, Plant Sci., 1972-78, assoc. editor, 1978-81, chief co-editor, 1981—; asst. editor Plant Physiology, 1964-69, adv. editor, 1969-79; mem. editorial com. Ann. Rev. Plant Physiology, 1974-80; contbr. over 180 articles to profl. jours. Carnegie Instn. fellow in plant biology, 1962-63; Recipient Disting. Alumni award Bklyn. Coll., 1972. Fellow AAAS, Am. Acad. Arts and Scis.; mem. Soc. Devel. Biology (sec. 1964-66, mem. exec. com.), Am. Soc. Biol. Chemists, Am. Soc. Plant Physiologists (mem. exec. com. 1972-88, Disting. Svc. award N.E. sect. 1989), Biophys. Soc., Internat. Phycological Soc., Phycological Soc. Am., Soc. Cell Biology, Soc. Gen. Microbiology, Soc. Protozoologists, Am. Soc. Microbiology, Internat. Soc. Devel. Biologists, Brit. Phycological Soc., Am. Soc. Photobiology, Sigma Xi. Achievements include research in metabolism of protista (algae); in sulfate metabolism by plants and microorganisms; on the pathway of biosynthesis of chlorophylls and carotenoids; on chloroplast and mitochondrial development, replication, function and evolution, particularly in Euglena. Office: Brandeis U Inst for Photobiology of Cells and Organelles Waltham MA 02254

SCHIFF, JOHN JEFFERSON, insurance company executive; b. Cin., Apr. 19, 1916; s. John Jefferson and Marguerite (Cleveland) S.; m. Mary Reid, July 26, 1941; children: John Jefferson, Suzanne, Thomas R. BSc in Commerce, Ohio State U., 1938. Vice chmn. Cin. Ins. Co., 1979—; pres. Cin. Fin. Corp., 1979-91, chief exec. officer, 1987-91; chmn., exec. com. Cin Fin Corp., 1991—; v.p. Deaconess Hosp. of Cin., Griffith Found. for Ins. Chmn. Cin. Art Mus.; trustee Am. Inst. for Property and Liability Underwriters; chmn. investment com. Navy League of the U.S. Served to lt. comdr. Supply Corps, USN, 1942-46. Named Ins. Man of Yr. in Cin., Cin. Ins. Bd., 1977. Mem. Cin. C of C. (v.p. 1972). Republican. Methodist. Clubs: Queen City, Western Hills Country, Cin. Country, Royal Poinciana Golf. Home: 1926 Beech Grove Dr Cincinnati OH 45233-4912 Office: Cin Fin Corp PO Box 145496 Cincinnati OH 45250-5496

SCHIFF, MARGARET SCOTT, newspaper publishing executive. V.p. controller and personnel adminstr. Washington Post. Office: Washington Post Co 1150 15th St NW Washington DC 20071-0002*

SCHIFF, MARTIN, physician, surgeon; b. Phila., July 16, 1922; s. Isidore and Cecelia (Miller) S.; m. Mildred Tepley, Jan. 5, 1946; children: Denise Schiff Simon, Michael, David. BS, Pa. State U., 1943; MD, U. Calif.-Irvine, 1951. Intern L.A. County Gen. Hosp., 1950-51; gen. practice medicine specializing in bariatrics L.A., 1951—; mem. staff Brotman Meml. Hosp.; lectr. L.A. area community colls. Author: Eat & Stay Slim, 1972, Miracle Weight-Loss Guide, 1976, One-Day-At-A-Time Weight Loss Plan, 1980, (5 tapes) Weight Loss Plan for Health, Happiness & A Longer Life Span, 1982, The Thin Connection, 1986. Lt. USN, 1943-45, PTO. Mem. AMA, Calif. Med. Assn., L.A. Med. Assn., Am. Soc. Weight Control Specialists. Home: 1220 Corsica Dr Pacific Palisades CA 90272-4016 Office: 12900 Venice Blvd Los Angeles CA 90066-3543

SCHIFF, STEFAN OTTO, zoologist, educator; b. Braunschweig, Germany, July 22, 1930; came to U.S., 1941, naturalized, 1943; s. Walter and Johanne Ilse (Muller) S.; m. Laura Frances Ward, June 6, 1957; children—Sena, Stefanie. B.S., Roanoke Coll., 1952; Ph.D., U. Tenn., 1964. USPHS trainee, 1961-63; mem. faculty George Washington U., Washington, 1964—, prof. zoology, 1976-95, prof. emeritus, 1995, chmn. dept. biol. scis., 1977-87, dir. grad. genetics program, 1971-95. Author: Twenty-One Afternoons of Biology, 3d edit., 1986, Buttons: Art in Miniature, 1980. Mem. Radiation Rsch. Soc., Sigma Xi. Lutheran. Home: 10710 Howerton Ave Fairfax VA 22030-2917 Office: George Washington U Lisner Hall # 320 Washington DC 20052

SCHIFF, STEVEN HARVEY, congressman, lawyer; b. Chicago, Ill., Mar. 18, 1947; s. Alan Jerome and Helen M. (Ripper) S.; m. Marcia Lewis, Nov. 8, 1968; children: Jaimi, Daniel. BA, U. Ill., Chgo., 1968; JD, U. N.Mex., 1972. Bar: N.Mex. 1972, U.S. Dist. Ct. N.Mex. 1972, U.S. Ct. Appeals (10th cir.) 1980. Asst. dist. atty. Dist. Atty.'s Office, Albuquerque, 1972-77, sole practice, 1977-79; asst. city atty. City of Albuquerque, 1979-81; dist. atty. State of N.Mex., Albuquerque, 1981-89; mem. 101st-104th Congresses from 1st N.Mex. dist., Washington, D.C., 1989—; mem. govt. reform & oversight com. U.S. House of Reps., mem. judiciary com. and standards of ofcl. conduct com., chmn. sci. subcom. on basic rsch.; lectr. U. N.Mex., Albuquerque, 1981—. Chmn. Bernalillo County Rep. Party Conv., Albuquerque, 1984, 87, staff judge adv. N.Mex. Air N.G. JAGC, USAFR. Recipient Law Enforcement Commendation medal SR, 1984. Mem. ABA, Albuquerque Bar Assn., N.Mex. Bar Assn. Republican. Jewish. Club: Civitan. Lodge: B'nai Brith (pres. 1976-78). Home: 804 Summit Ave NE Albuquerque NM 87106-2045 Office: House of Reps 2404 Rayburn Washington DC 20515-3101 also: 625 Silver Ave SW Ste 140 Albuquerque NM 87102*

SCHIFFER, CLAUDIA, model. Model Guess? jeans, 1989—, Revlon cosmetics, Chanel. Runway debut in Chanel fashion show, 1990; appeared on covers of Mademoiselle, Cosmopolitan, Vogue, and over 100 others. Office: Met Model Agy USA 5 Union Sq West New York NY 10003

SCHIFFER, DANIEL L., gas company executive; m. Sheila Schiffer; children: Michael, Eric. AB, Bklyn. Coll., 1964; JD, Cornell U., 1967. Law clk. U.S. Ct. Appeals (2d cir.); pvt. practice N.Y.C.; spl. asst. N.Y. Pub. Svc. Commn., N.Y.C.; now v.p., gen. counsel, sec. MCN Corp., 1989—. Trustee Batsford Gen. Hosp. Mem. ABA, Mich. State Bar Assn., Detroit Bar Assn., Fed. Energy Bar Assn. Avocations: sports, reading, bridge. Office: MCN Corp 500 Griswold St Detroit MI 48226-3700

SCHIFFER, JOHN PAUL, physicist; b. Budapest, Hungary, Nov. 22, 1930; came to U.S., 1947, naturalized, 1953; s. Ernest and Elisabeth (Tornai) S.;

m. Marianne Tsuk, June 28, 1960; children: Celia Anne, Peter Ernest. AB, Oberlin Coll., 1951; MS, Yale U., 1952, PhD, 1954. Research asso. Rice Inst., Houston, 1954-56; asst. physicist Argonne (Ill.) Nat. Lab., 1956-59, asso. physicist, 1960-63, sr. physicist, 1964—, assoc. dir. physics div., 1964-79, 83—, dir. physics div., 1979-82; prof. physics U. Chgo., 1968—; vis. asso. prof. Princeton, 1964; vis. prof. U. Rochester, N.Y., 1967-68; mem. adv. coms. nuclear physics Nat. Acad. Scis.; mem. program adv. or rev. coms. Los Alamos Meson Physics Facility, 1971-73, Ind. U. Cylotron Facility, 1974-77, Lab. for Nuclear Sci., M.I.T., 1975-79, Lawrence Berkeley Lab, Bevalac, 1978-80, Swiss Inst. Nuclear Research, 1981-85, Max Planck Inst. Nuclear Physics, 1982-85; mem. physics adv. panel NSF, 1971-73; mem. Nuclear Sci. Adv. Com. Dept. Energy/NSF, 1981-85, chmn., 1983-85; chmn. program adv. com. CEBAF, 1986-91; mem. subcom. Implementation of 1989 Long Range Plan for Nuclear Sci. Editor: Comments on Nuclear and Particle Physics, 1971-75; assoc. editor Revs. Modern Physics, 1972-77; mem. editorial bd. Phys. Rev. C, 1983-85; editor: Physics Letters, 1978—; mem. editorial com. ann. revs. of nuclear and particle sci., 1987-91; contrb. articles on nuclear structure physics and nuclear reactions to phys. jours. and books. Mem. cold fusion panel Dept. Energy, 1989. Recipient Alexander V. Humboldt Found. sr. U.S. scientist award, 1973-74; Wilbur Cross medal Yale U., 1985; Guggenheim fellow, 1959-60. Fellow AAAS (mem. coun., chair physics sect. 1992-93), Am. Phys. Soc. (chmn. div. nuclear physics 1975-76, Tom W. Bonner prize 1976); mem. NAS. Research on nuclear structure, Mössbauer effect, heavy-ion reactions, pion interactions in nuclei, quark searches, condensation in confined cold plasmas. Office: Physics Division Argonne Nat Lab Argonne IL 60439

SCHIFFMAN, DAVID M., lawyer; b. Chgo., June 8, 1953. AB magna cum laude, Harvard U., 1974, JD cum laude, 1977. Bar: Ill. 1977. Ptnr. Sidley & Austin, Chgo. Mem. ABA (antitrust law sect., bus. law sect. litigation sect.), Chgo. Bar Assn., Chgo. Coun. Lawyers, Phi Beta Kappa. Office: Sidley & Austin 1 First Nat Plz Chicago IL 60603

SCHIFFMAN, GERALD, microbiologist, educator; b. N.Y.C., May 22, 1926; s. Samuel and Mollie (Brookner) S.; m. Lillian Ebert, July 12, 1951; children: Stewart, Howard. B.A. cum laude, NYU, 1948, Ph.D., 1954. Asst. prof. microbiology Coll. Physicians and Surgeons, Columbia U., N.Y.C., 1960-63; asso. prof. dept. research medicine and microbiology U. Pa., Phila., 1963-70; prof. SUNY Health Sci. Ctr., Bklyn., 1970—; cons. Contbr. articles to profl. jours. Served in U.S. Army, 1943-45, ETO. Decorated Bronze Star; recipient Nichols award, 1947; Atomic Energy fellow, 1948-52; NIH grantee, 1974-94. Mem. Am. Assn. Immunologists, Am. Chem. Soc., Am. Soc. Microbiology, AAAS, Harvey Soc., Soc. Complex Carbohydrates, Sigma Xi, Phi Beta Kappa, Mu Chi Sigma, Pi Mu Epsilon. Jewish. Office: 450 Clarkson Ave Brooklyn NY 11203-2012

SCHIFFMAN, HAROLD FOSDICK, Asian language educator; b. Buffalo, Feb. 19, 1938; s. Merl and Mathilda (Keller) S.; m. Marilyn Gail Hornberg, June 10, 1978; 1 son, Timothy Marc Rajendran. B.A., Antioch Coll., 1960; M.A., U. Chgo., 1966, Ph.D., 1969. Lectr. anthropology U. Calif.-Davis, 1966-67; asst. prof. U. Wash., Seattle, 1967-73, assoc. prof., 1973-78, prof., 1978-95, chmn. dept. Asian langs., 1982-87; prof. South Asian studies U. Pa., Phila., 1995—, acad. dir. Penn Lang. Ctr., Luce prof. lang. learning, 1995—; Trustee Am. Inst. Indian Studies, Chgo., 1979-82; lang. dir. Southeast Asian Summer Studies Inst., 1992-93, mem. lang. adv. com., 1993-94. Author: A Grammar of Spoken Tamil, 1979, A Reference Grammar of Spoken Kannada, 1983; co-editor: Dravidian Phonological Systems, 1975; co-author: Language and Society in South Asia, 1981. Pres. bd. dirs. Seattle Pro Musica (choral group), 1976-78; mem. Pacific Northwest Chamber Chorus, Seattle, 1983-87. Sr. fellow Am. Inst. Indian Studies, 1976, 78; grantee U.S. Office Edn., 1971, 74, 78, NEH, 1984-87, Smithsonian Inst., 1984-87, Fulbright Rsch., 1993-94. Mem. Assn. Asian Studies (S. Asia council 1982-85), Am. Inst. Indian Studies (trustee 1979-82), Soc. S. Indian Studies (sec.-treas. 1973-75), Internat. Assn. Tamil Research (v.p. 1987-89). Quaker. Office: U Pa Dept South Asian Studies 820 Williams Hall Philadelphia PA 19104-6305

SCHIFFMAN, JOSEPH HARRIS, literary historian, educator; b. N.Y.C., June 13, 1914; s. Samuel and Norma Minnie (Berger) S.; m. Elizabeth Selsbee, Nov. 29, 1941; children: Jessica, Joshua. B.A, L.I. U., 1937; MA, Columbia U., 1947; PhD, NYU, 1951. Instr. dept. English, L.I. U., 1945-49, asst. prof., 1949-51, assoc. prof., 1951-58, coord. grad. program Am. studies, 1956-58; prof. English Dickinson Coll., Carlisle, Pa., 1958-79, James Hope Caldwell prof. Am. studies, 1968-79, emeritus prof., 1979—, prof. continuing edn., 1979-86, 90-94, chmn. dept. English, 1959-69; sr. Fulbright vis. prof., India, 1964, U. Bordeaux (France), 1965-66, U. Indonesia, 1981-82; vis. prof. Grad. Sch. U. Pa., U., 1960, 67, New Coll., U. South Fla., spring 1981; lectr. U. P.R., 1984, Lifetime Learning, Sarasota, 1984-88, Elderhostel U., Del., 1995; fgn. expert vis. prof. East China Normal U., Shanghai, 1985; founding dir. Am. Studies Rsch. Centre, India, 1964, Am. adv. com., 1990—, Elderhostel U., Del., 1995; lectr. French Ednl. Radio System, 1966, acad. specialist program, Malaysia, Internat. Communication Agy., 1982; PhD theses examiner various univs., India, 1970—; lectr. numerous orgns. including Mark Twain Assn. N.Y., Walt Whitman Birthplace Assn., MLA, Am. Studies Assn., Rotary, Pa. Writers Group, Jewish Community Ctr., Bosler Free Libr., AAUW, YWCA, Bethany Retirement Community, U.S.-China Peoples Friendship Assn., Sr. Action Ctr., Pa. Poets Soc., Harrisburg Manuscript Club, Golden Age Club, Encore Books and Music, Cumberland County Med. Soc. Alliance. With U.S. Army, 1942-45, ETO. Recipient Lindback Found. Disting. Teaching award, 1962, Fulbright-Hays award U.S. State Dept., 1964, 65, 81, Alumni award L.I. U., 1976. Mem. Am. Studies Assn. (pres. Met. N.Y. chpt. 1958-59), MLA (head Am. lit. internat. bibliography com. 1961-64), Nat. Council Tchrs. English. Author: (with Lewis Leary) American Literature: A Critical History from Its Beginning to the Present, Ency. World Lit., 1973, William Faulkner, A Dramatic Evocation, 1981; contbr. articles on Am. writers to lit. jours.; contbr. introductions to Looking Backward (Edward Bellamy), 1959, Brook Farm (Lindsay Swift), 1961, Three Shorter Novels of Herman Melville, 1962; editor: Edward Bellamy, Selected Writings on Religion and Society, 1955, Edward Bellamy, The Duke of Stockbridge, 1962; contbr. numerous book recs. including Idealist, Activist, The Haunted Chamber, The World a Ship, In Search of America, The Roaring Twenties, A Utopian Dream, also revs. to scholarly jours. Home: 551 S Hanover St Carlisle PA 17013-3919 Office: Dickinson Coll Carlisle PA 17013

SCHIFFMAN, ROBERT S., environmental test equipment manufacturing executive; b. Passaic, N.J., Jan. 25, 1944; s. Saul and Lillian (Gold) S.; m. Anita Joyce Sikeman, Aug. 15, 1965; children: Caren L., Glenn H., Robyn L. BSBA in Mgmt., Clark U., 1965; MBA in Mktg., Seton Hall U., 1970. Chmn., pres., CEO, bd. dirs. Tenney Engring. Inc., Union, N.J., 1977—. Mem. Inst. Environ. Sci. (sr.), Aircraft Owners and Pilots Assn. Office: Tenney Engring Inc 1090 Springfield Rd Union NJ 07083-8197

SCHIFFMAN, STEPHAN, management consultant; b. N.Y.C., June 14, 1946; s. Walter and Martha S.; B.S., Ithaca Coll., 1968; MSW, Cornell U., 1969; postgrad U. Md., 1971-72, Detroit U., 1973-73; m. Anne Feinglass, Aug. 25, 1974; children: Daniele Megan, Jennifer Ruth. Prin. Stephan Schiffman Assocs., N.Y.C., 1972—; dir. trng. United Jewish Appeal, N.Y.C., 1975—; practice psychotherapy, N.Y.C., 1976—; speaker on motivation and success, power sales, 1989; dir. D.E.I. Mgmt. Group, N.Y.C., 1979—; prin. Stephan Schiffman Telemarketing, 1992; mem. faculty Adelphi U., Garden City, N.Y., 1976-80; lectr. N.Y. U., 1977-80, New Sch. Social Research, 1978—, Queen's Coll., 1985—, Norwalk Community Coll. 1989;. Author: Cold Calling Techniques that Work, 1991, 3d edit., 1979, cassette edit. 1991, The Consultant's Handbook, 1988, 25 Sales Mistakes, 1990, Power Sales Presentations, 1989, Sales Habits of Highly Successful People, 1991; contbr. articles to profl. jours. Mem. Inst. Mgmt. Cons., Nat. Soc. Fund Raisers (dir.), Am. Mgmt. Assn., TC Acad. Arts and Scis., Soc. Profl. Mgmt. Cons., Am. Soc. Tng. and Devel., N.Y.C. Chamber Commerce and Industry (edn. chair, speaker), Cornell Club. Jewish. Home: 235 E 87th St New York NY 10128-3225 Office: 850 7th Ave Ste 1002 New York NY 10019-5230

SCHIFFMAN, SUSAN STOLTE, medical psychologist, educator; b. Chgo., Aug. 24, 1940; d. Paul R. and Mildred (Glicksman) Stolte; m. Harold Schiffman (div.); 1 child, Amy Lise; m. H. Troy Nagle, July 22, 1989. BA, Syracuse U., 1965; PhD, Duke U., 1970. Lic. psychologist, N.C. Postdoctoral fellow Duke U., Durham, N.C., 1970-72, asst. prof., 1972-77,

assoc. prof., 1978-83, full prof., 1983—; cons., mem. adv. bd. Nutrasweet, Chgo., 1978—, Nestle, Vevey, Switzerland, 1990, Fragrance Rsch. Fund, N.Y.C., 1986—, and others. Author: Introduction to Multidimensional Sealing: Theory, Methods and Applications, 1981, Flavor Set-Point Weight Loss Cookbook, 1990. Nat. Inst. Aging grantee, 1972—. Mem. Assn. Chemoreception Scis., European Chemoreception Rsch. Orgn., Soc. for Neurosci. Office: Duke U Dept Psychology Durham NC 27708-0086

SCHIFFNER, CHARLES ROBERT, architect; b. Reno, Sept. 2, 1948; s. Robert Charles and Evelyn (Keck) S.; m. Iovanna Lloyd Wright, Nov. 1971 (div. Sept. 1981); m. Adrienne Anita McAndrews, Jan. 20, 1983. Student, Sacramento Jr. Coll., 1967-68, Frank Lloyd Wright Sch. Architecture, 1968-77. Registered architect, Ariz., Nev., Wis. Architect Taliesin Associated Architects, Scottsdale, Ariz., 1977-83; pvt. practice architecture Phoenix, 1983—; adj. prof. The Frank Lloyd Wright Sch. of Architecture, 1994, 95. Named one of 25 Most Promising Young Americans Under 35, U.S. mag., 1979; recipient AIA Honor award Western Mountain Region, 1993, Western Home awards Sunset Mag., 1989, 91, AIA Ariz. Merit award, 1993 and numerous others. Home: 5202 E Osborn Rd Phoenix AZ 85018-6137 Office: Camelhead Office Ctr 2600 N 44th St # 208 Phoenix AZ 85008-1521

SCHIFFRIN, ANDRE, publisher; b. Paris, June 12, 1935; came to U.S., 1941; s. Jacques and Simone (Heymann) S.; m. Maria Elena de la Iglesia, June 14, 1961; children—Anya, Natalia. B.A. summa cum laude, Yale U., 1957; M.A. with 1st class honors, Cambridge U., Eng., 1959. With New Am. Library, 1959-63; with Pantheon Books, Inc., N.Y.C., 1962-90, editor, then editor in chief, mng. dir., 1969-90; pub. Schocken Books subs. Pantheon Books Inc., 1987-90; pres. Fund for Ind. Pub. N.Y.C., 1990—; dir., editor in chief The New Press, N.Y.C., 1990—; mem. spl. com. Am. Ctr., Paris, 1994—; vis. fellow Davenport Coll., 1977-79; vis. lectr. Yale U., 1977, 79; bd. dirs. The New Press, N.Y.C. Contbr. articles to profl. jours., N.Y. Times Book Rev., Nation, New Republic. Mem. council Smithsonian Instn., 1969—; bd. dirs. N.Y. Council for Humanities, 1978—, mem. exec. com., 1979-80; bd. dirs. N.Y. Civil Liberties Union; mem. freedom to pub. com. Assn. Am. Pubs., 1976-78; mem. vis. com. history dept. Princeton U., 1978—; mem. freedom to read com. AAUP, 1985—; mem. U.S. cultural del. to Peoples Republic China, 1983, 87. Mellon fellow Clare Coll., 1957, hon. scholar, 1959; hon. fellow Trumbull Coll., Yale U., 1979—; Fulbright travel grantee, 1958-59. Fellow N.Y. Inst. for the Humanities. Home: 250 W 94th St New York NY 10025-6954 Office: The New Press 450 W 41st St New York NY 10036-6807

SCHIFRIN, LALO, composer; b. Buenos Aires, June 21, 1932. Student, Juan Carlos Paz and Olivier Messiaen.; PhD (hon.), RISD, 1989. Tchr. composition UCLA, 1970-71; guest condr. Israel Philharm, L.A. Philharm, L.A. Chamber Orch., Indpls. Symphony, Atlanta Symphony. Argentinian rep., Internat. Jazz Festival, Paris, 1955, formed own jazz group; composer for stage, modern dance, TV; with Dizzy Gillespie's band, 1962; film and TV composer, Hollywood, Calif., 1964—; compositions: (for ballet) Jazz Faust, 1963, (for orch.) Piano Concerto # 1, 1986, Cantos Aztecas, 1989, Concerto for guitar and orch., 1986, Concerto for double bass and orch., 1987, Three tangos for flute, harp and strings, 1987, Dance concertantes for clarinet and orch., 1990, Impressions for trumpet and orch., 1990, La Nouvelle Orleans Woodwind Quitet, 1991, Concerto # 2, 1992, Cantares Argentinos, 1992, Symphony # 1 for orch., 1993 (opera) The Trial of Louis XVI, 1988; theme for TV series Mission: Impossible (2 Grammy awards); film scores include The Cincinnati Kid, 1965, Cool Hand Luke, 1967, The Fox, 1968; film scores include Kelly's Heroes, 1970, W.U.S.A., 1970, Pussycat, Pussycat, I Love You, 1970, Bullit, 1970, Dirty Harry, 1971, THX-1138, 1971, The Beguiled, 1971, Magnum Force, 1973, The Four Musketeers, 1975, The Eagle Has Landed, 1977, Voyage of the Damned, 1976, Rollercoaster, 1977, Telefon, 1977, Boulevard Nights, 1979, The Concorde-Airport '79, 1979, Competition, 1981, Sudden Impact, 1984, The Sting II, 1985, The Fourth Protocol, 1987, The Fourth Protocol, 1987; TV series The Young-Lawyers, Mannix, 'Mission Impossible', Starsky and Hutch; writer orchestration for Grand Finale medley for Carreras, Domingo and Pavarotti, Rome, 1991; commd. Steinway Found piano concerto The Americas, selected by Nat. Symphony Orch., 1992. Recipient 4 Grammy awards, 1967, 1969, 1986, 6 Acad. award nominations Acad. Motion Picture Arts and Scis., 1966, 67, 75, 77, 80, 82, Walk of Fame award Hollywood C. of C.; chevalier de l'Ordre des Arts et des Lettres French gov. Mem. Young Musicians Found. (pres. 1983). Office: CAA 9830 Wilshire Blvd Beverly Hills CA 90212*

SCHIFSKY, CHARLES MARK, magazine editor; b. St. Paul, May 19, 1962; s. William Charles and Kathleen Jeanne (Lau) S.; m. Gina Maria Gelsomino, Oct. 8, 1994. BA in Journalism and Pub. Rels., U. St. Thomas, St. Paul, 1987. With Bill Schifsky Enterprises, St. Paul, 1977-87; pub. rels. rep. Ramsey County Info. Office, St. Paul, 1987; clutch specialist Gary Ormsby Racing, Auburn, Calif., 1988-90; co-crew chief Jack Clark Racing, Indpls., 1990-91; assoc. editor Car Craft mag. Peterson Pub. Co., L.A., 1992-93, editor, 1993—. Mem. Motor Press Guild, Nat. Hot Rod Assn. (mem. top fuel world championship team 1989). Avocations: travel, photography, golf, motorsports. Office: Petersen Pub/Car Craft Mag 6420 Wilshire Blvd Los Angeles CA 90048

SCHIFTER, RICHARD, lawyer, government official; b. Vienna, Austria, July 31, 1923; came to U.S., 1938; s. Paul and Balbina (Blass) S.; m. Lilo Krueger, July 3, 1948; children: Judith, Deborah, Richard P., Barbara, Karen. BS in Social Sci. summa cum laude, CCNY, 1943; LLB, Yale U., 1951; DHL (hon.), Hebrew Union Coll., 1992. Bar: Conn. 1951, D.C. 1952, U.S. Supreme Ct. 1954, Md., 1958. Assoc. Fried, Frank, Harris, Shriver & Jacobson, Washington, 1951-57, ptnr., 1957-84; dep. U.S. rep. with rank of ambassador UN Security Council, N.Y.C., 1984-85; asst. sec. of state for human rights and humanitarian affairs Dept. State, Washington, 1985-92; U.S. rep. UN Human Rights Commn., Geneva, 1983-86, 93; spl. asst. to pres., counselor Nat. Security Coun., Washington, 1993—; head U.S. del. Conf. on Security and Cooperation in Europe Experts Meeting on Human Rights, Ottawa, Ont., Can., 1985, Dem. Insts., Oslo, 1991; bd. dirs. U.S. Inst. Peace, 1986-92; mem. Congl. Commn. on Security and Cooperation in Europe, 1986-92. V.p., pres. Md. Bd. Edn., Balt., 1959-79; chmn. Md. Gov.'s Commn. on Funding Edn. of Handicapped Children, 1975-77, Md. Values Edn. Commn., 1979-83, Montgomery County Dem. Cen. Com., Md., 1966-70; del. Dem. Nat. Conv., 1968; bd. govs., chmn. Nat. Adv. Com., Am. Jewish Com., 1992-93. With U.S. Army, 1943-46, ETO. Recipient Disting. Svc. award Sec. of State, 1992. Mem. Phi Beta Kappa. Democrat. Jewish. Home: 6907 Crail Dr Bethesda MD 20817-4723 Office: Nat Security Coun Washington DC 20506

SCHILD, JOYCE ANNA, otolaryngologist, surgeon; b. Chgo., May 26, 1931; d. William Paul and Helen (Kammer) S.; m. John A. Hegber, Dec. 15, 1973. BS, U. Ill., Chgo., 1954, MD, 1956. Diplomate Am. Bd. Otolaryngology. Intern St. Francis Hosp., Peoria, Ill., 1956-57; residency in otolaryngology U. Ill., Chgo., 1958-61, fellow in bronchoesophagology, 1961-62, clin. instr. to assoc. prof. otolaryngology, 1958-82, interim acting head dept. otolaryngology, 1978-79, prof. otolaryngology head and neck surgery Coll. Medicine, 1982—; mem. staff U. Ill. Hosp., Chgo.; otolaryngologist, surgeon Ill. Eye and Ear Infirmary, Chgo.; from adj. to assoc. attending otolaryngologist Presbyn. St. Luke's Hosp., Chgo. 1964-76; acting head bronchoesophagologist Children's Meml. Hosp., Chgo., 1972-76, cons. staff, 1976—; mem. staff Michael Reese Hosp., Chgo., 1989—; courtesy staff dept. surgery sect. otolaryngology St. Joseph's Hosp., Chgo. 1961-74; numerous presentations and lectrs. in field. Mem. AMA, Am. Acad. Otolaryngol.-Head-Neck Surgery, Ill. State Med. Soc., Chgo. Med. Soc., Am. Laryngol. Assn., Soc. Univ. Otolaryngologists, Am. Laryngol., Rhinol. and Otol. Soc., Am. Soc. Pediatric Otolaryngology, Chgo. Laryngol. and Otol. Soc. (pres. elect 1983-84, pres. 1984-85, coun. mem. 1985-86), Am. Broncho-Esophagological Assn. (v.p. 1977-79, pres. elect 1978-79, pres. 1979-80, thesis com. 1981-82), Am. Coun. Otolaryngology, Soc. Ear, Nose and Throat Advances in Children, Am. Acad. Pediatrics (com. on accident and poison prevention 1982-85), Pan-Am. Assn. Oto-Rhino-Laryngology, Head and Neck Surgery. Office: Ill Eye and Ear Infirmary 1855 W Taylor St Rm 42 Chicago IL 60612-7243

SCHILD, RUDOLPH ERNST, astronomer, educator; b. Chgo., Jan. 10, 1940; s. Kasimir A. and Anneliese (Schuricht) S.; m. Jane H. Struss, July 28, 1982. BS, U. Chgo., 1962, MS, 1963, PhD, 1966. Rsch. fellow Calif. Inst.

Tech., Pasadena, 1966-69; scientific dir., 1.5m Telescope Program Smithsonian Astrophysical Obs., Amado, Ariz., 1969-74; astronomer Harvard-Smithsonian Ctr. for Astrophysics, Cambridge, Mass., 1974—; lectr. Harvard U., 1975-83. Author: (slide set) The Electronic Sky: Digital Images of the Cosmos, 1985, (CD-ROM) Voyage to the Stars: The Rudy Schild Collection; contbr. over 100 articles to scholarly and profl. jours. Mem. Am. Astronomical Soc., Internat. Astronomical Union. Achievements include 2 patents; discovery of gravitational microlensing. Office: Ctr for Astrophysics 60 Garden St Cambridge MA 02138-1596

SCHILDHAUSE, SOL, lawyer; b. N.Y.C., Sept. 5, 1917; s. Jacob and Fannie (Gerber) S.; m. Phyllis Sydell, May 23, 1943 (divorced); children: Susan Schildhause Tash, Peter, Richard. BS, CUNY, 1937; JD, Harvard U., 1940. Bar: N.Y. 1941, D.C. 1972, U.S. Ct. Claims 1975, U.S. Supreme Ct. 1978. Mng. ptnr. Sta. KOMA-AM, Oklahoma City, 1976—; administrv. law judge FCC, Washington, 1963-66, chief cable TV bur., 1966-73; ptnr. D.C. office Farrow, Schildhause & Wilson, 1973—; lectr. Practicing Law Inst., 1985. Mem. ABA (asst. chmn. cable TV com. 1986), FCC Bar Assn. Democrat. Jewish. Club: Harvard (Washington). Office: Farrow Schildhause & Wilson 1400 16th St NW Ste 501 Washington DC 20036

SCHILLER, ALFRED GEORGE, veterinarian, educator; b. Irma, Wis., Dec. 5, 1918; s. Adam and Bertha Schiller; m. Carolyn Capps, Apr. 14, 1944; children: James, Charles. DVM, Mich. State U., 1943; MS, U. Ill., 1956. Bd. cert. vet. surgery. Gen. practice vet. medicine Mpls., 1947-52; from instr. to prof. U. Ill., Urbana, 1952-87, head small animal clinic, 1954-74, asst. head dept. vet. medicine, 1974-76, acting dept. head vet. medicine, 1976-78, acting assoc. dean acad. affairs, 1978-79, acting dir. lab. animal care, 1979-80, asst. dept. head vet. clin. medicine, from 1980, prof. emeritus, 1987—. Contbr. articles to profl. jours. Served to capt. U.S. Army, 1944-47. Recipient Alumni award Mich. State U., 1978. Mem. Am. Vet. Medicine Assn. (various coms.), Ill. State Vet. Medicine Assn. (various coms., Meritorious Svc. award 1972), Am. Coll. Vet. Surgeons (recorder 1968-69, v.p. 1970-71, pres.-elect 1971-72, pres. 1972-73, chmn. 1973-74, exec. sec. 1975-90, Disting. Svc. award 1985).

SCHILLER, ARTHUR A., architect, educator; b. N.Y.C., July 23, 1910; s. Valentine and Rose (Bayer) S.; m. Anne O'Donnell, June 12, 1937; children: Valerie Schiller Schaefer, Virginia Schiller Waicul, Eileen Schiller Toomey. BArch, NYU, 1933; diploma, Beaux Arts Inst. Design, N.Y.C., 1935; MArch, MIT, 1939. Registered architect, N.Y. Architect U.S. Govt., Washington, 1936-38, N.Y.C. Dept. Parks, 1938-47; chief architect Bd. Higher Edn., N.Y.C., 1947-51, dir. architecture and engring., 1951-67; coord. campus planning Queens Coll., N.Y.C., 1967-73; adj. prof. N.Y. Inst. Technology, Old Westbury, 1973-91; cons. Triboro Bridge Authority, N.Y.C., 1946; lectr. CCNY, 1957-67. Mayor Village of Plandome Manor, N.Y., 1965-87, trustee, 1960-65; trustee Sci. Mus. L.I. 1986—. Named Man of Yr. AARP, 1990, Sr. Citizen of Yr. Nassau County, State of N.Y., 1992 . Fellow AIA (pres. Queens chpt. 1957-58); mem. N.Y. State Assn. Architects (dir. 1959-60), Assn. Univ. Architects (emeritus), U.S. Power Squadron (comdr. 1961-62, budget dir. 1988-91), Elks (life). Avocations: boating, gardening, conducting defensive driving courses for older citizens. Home: 15 Luquer Rd Manhasset NY 11030-1015

SCHILLER, DONALD CHARLES, lawyer; b. Chgo., Dec. 8, 1942; s. Sidney S. and Edith (Lastick) S.; m. Eileen Fagin, June 14, 1964; children—Eric, Jonathan. Student, Lake Forest Coll., 1960-63; J.D., DePaul U., 1966. Bar: Ill. 1966, U.S. Dist. Ct. (no. dist.) Ill. 1966, U.S. Supreme Ct. 1972. Ptnr. Schiller, DuCanto & Fleck (formerly Schiller & Schiller and Schiller & DuCanto), Chgo. 1966—; chair domestic rels. adv. com. Cir. Ct. Cook County, 1993—, exec. com., 1986-93; speaker profl. confs. Contbr. chpts. and articles to profl. publs. Mem. steering com. on juvenile ct. watching, LWV, 1980-81. Recipient Maurice Weigle award Chgo. Bar Found., 1978, Disting. Alumni award, DePaul U., 1988, various certs. of appreciation profl. groups; named One of Am.'s Best Divorce Lawyers, Town and Country, 1985, The Nat. Law Jour., 1987, The Best Lawyers in Am., 1987, 89, 91, 93, One of Chgo's. Best Div. Lawyers, Crain's Chgo. Bus., 1981, Today Chgo. Woman, 1985, Inside Chgo. mag., 1988. Fellow Am. Bar Found., Am. Acad. Matrimonial Lawyers (chair continuing legal edn. 1993-94; mem. ABA (chmn. family law sect. 1985-86, mem. Ho. of Dels., 1984, Ill. State del. 1980-84, bd. govs. 1994—, editor in chief Family Law Newsletter 1977-79; mem. editorial bd., assoc. editor Family Adv. Mag., 1979-84, mem., chmn., co-chmn. coms., spkr. confs. meetings), Ill. Bar Assn. (chmn. family law sect. 1976-77, editor Family Law Bull. 1976-77, bd. govs. 1977-83, press. 1981-84, v.p. 1984-86, pres. 1987-88, mem. chmn. various coms., lectr. , incorporator Ill. State Bar Assn. Risk Retention Group, Inc. 1988, press. 1988-89), Chgo. Bar Assn. (chair matrimonial law com. 1977-78); diplomate Am. Coll. Family Law Trial Lawyers. Office: Schiller DuCanto & Fleck 200 N La Salle St Ste 2700 Chicago IL 60601-1089

SCHILLER, ERIC M., lawyer; b. Detroit, Mar. 19, 1946; s. Stanley Schiller and Sara (Barliant) Benson; m. Jill E. Friedman, Aug. 16, 1970; children: Colin, Daniel, Jonathan. BA, Ind. U., 1968; JD, Northwestern U., 1971. Bar: Ill. 1971. Assoc. Sonnenschein Nath & Rosenthal, Chgo., 1971-78, ptnr., 1979—; mem. exec. com. Sonnenschein, Nath & Rosenthal, 1991—; lectr. ALI-ABA. Exec. bd. dirs. Anti-Defamation League of Chgo., 1989-92. Mem. ABA, Chgo. Bar Assn., Chgo. Coun. Lawyers, The Law Club of Chgo., John Henry Wigmore Club of Northwestern U. Law Sch. (exec. com. 1990-93), The Met. Club, Lake Shore Country Club. Home: 7 Rockgate Ln Glencoe IL 60022-1250 Office: Sonnenschein Nath & Rosenthal 8000 Sears Towers Chicago IL 60606

SCHILLER, FRANCIS, neurologist, medical historian; b. Prague, Czechoslovakia, Jan. 23, 1909; came to U.S., 1950; s. Friedrich and Luise (Mannheimer) S. MD, German U. Prague, 1933. Diplomate Am. Bd. Psychiatry and Neurology. With U. Calif. Med. Sch., San Francisco, 1951-79, clin. prof. neurology, 1972, emeritus prof. neurology, 1979; neurologist Kaiser Permanente Med. Group, San Francisco, 1953-78; cons. neurology Pub. Health Svc., San Francisco, 1978-81, VA Compensation & Pension, San Francisco, 1984—; sr. lectr. history and health sci. U. Calif., San Francisco, 1962—. Author: Paul Broca, 1824-80, 1979, A Möbius Strip, 1981; contbr. articles to profl. jours. Fellow Am. Acad. Neurology, San Francisco Neurology Soc.; mem. Internat. Acad. History of Medicine, Bay Area History of Medicine Club (pres. San Francisco cht. 1975-76). Avocations: gardening, piano. Home: 2730 Wawona St San Francisco CA 94116-2866 Office: U Calif Dept History of Health Scis Box 0726 Parnassus Ave 458 San Francisco CA 94122-2721

SCHILLER, HERBERT IRVING, social scientist, author; b. N.Y.C., Nov. 5, 1919; s. Benjamin Franklin and Gertrude (Perner) S.; m. Anita Rosenbaum, Nov. 5, 1946; children: Daniel T., P. Zachary. B in Social Sci., CCNY, 1940; MA, Columbia U., 1941; PhD, NYU, 1960. Teaching fellow CCNY, 1940-41, lectr. econs., 1949-59; economist U.S. Govt., 1941-42, 46-48; mem. faculty Pratt Inst., Bklyn., 1950-63; prof. econs., chmn. dept. social studies Pratt Inst., 1962-63; research asso. Bur. Econ. and Bus. Research, U. Ill. at Urbana, 1963-65, research prof., 1965-70; prof. communication U. Calif., San Diego, 1970-90, prof. emeritus, 1990—; lectr. Bklyn. Acad. Music, 1961-66; vis. fellow Inst. Policy Studies, Wash., 1968; vis. prof. U. Amsterdam, The Netherlands, 1973-74; Thord-Gray vis. lectr. U. Stockholm, 1978; vis. prof. comms. Hunter Coll., CUNY, 1978-79, Am. U., 1991-93, NYU, 1993-95. Author: Mass Communications and American Empire, 1969, rev. edit., 1992, Superstate: Readings in the Military-Industrial Complex, 1970, The Mind Managers, 1973, Communication and Cultural Domination, 1976, Who Knows: Information in the Age of the Fortune 500, 1981, Information and the Crisis Economy, 1984, Culture Inc.: The Corporate Takeover of Public Expression, 1989, (with others) Hope and Folly: The U.S. and UNESCO, 1945-85, 1989; editor Quar. Rev. Econs. and Bus., 1963-70; co-editor: Triumph of the Image: The Media's War in the Persian Gulf, 1992, Beyond National Sovereignty: International Communication in the 1990s, 1993. Served with AUS, 1942-45, MTO. Mem. AAAS, Internat. Assn. Mass Communication Research (v.p.), Internat. Inst. Communications (trustee 1978-84), AAUP (sec. Ill. U.), Phi Beta Kappa. Home: 7109 Monte Vista Ave La Jolla CA 92037-5326 Office: Univ Calif San Diego La Jolla CA 92093

SCHILLER, JAMES JOSEPH, lawyer; b. Cleve., July 1, 1933; s. Jacob Peter and Helen Elizabeth (Tosh) S.; m. Sara Brooke Wilson, Oct. 24, 1964; children: Charles A., Brooke V.G., Kristan W. BS, Case Inst. Tech., 1955; JD, U. Mich., 1961. Bar: Ohio 1962. Assoc. Marshman, Hornbeck & Hollington, Cleve., 1961-68; ptnr. Marshman, Snyder & Seeley, Cleve., 1968-73, Zellmer & Gruber, Cleve., 1973-80, Weston, Hurd, Fallon, Paisley & Howley, Cleve., 1980-88, Porter, Wright, Morris & Arthur, Cleve., 1989—. Campaign mgr. John J. Gilligan for Gov. of Ohio, Cuyahoga County, 1970; campaign dir. U.S. Senator Howard M. Metzenbaum, Cleve., 1973; mem. Ohio Dem. Com., 1970-73; dep. registrar motor vehicles Dept. Hwy. Safety, Cuyahoga County, 1971-74; trustee Greater Cleve. Regional Transit Authority, 1985-87; vestryman Christ Episcopal Ch., Shaker Heights, Ohio, 1974-76, 90-93, clk., 1974-76, sr. warden, 1992-93. Lt (j.g.) USNR, 1955-58. Recipient Cert. Commendation Bd. County Commrs., 1987. Mem. ABA, Ohio State Bar Assn. (ethics com. 1986-88), Cleve. Bar Assn., Rowfant Club (fin. com. 1988, coun. of Fellowes 1990-91, advocate 1992—), Union Club, Cleve. Skating Club. Avocations: sailing, skiing, restoring furniture. Home: 3311 Maynard Rd Cleveland OH 44122-3437 Office: Porter Wright Morris et al 925 Euclid Ave Cleveland OH 44115-1408

SCHILLER, JERRY A., retired manufacturing company executive; b. Moline, Ill., Sept. 2, 1932; s. Walter A. and Mae (Sears) S.; m. Betty Fuller; children: Michele Schiller Smead, Susan Schiller Fortune, Richard, Lisa Schiller Swank, Sandra Schiller Rogers, Sara Schiller Sieflaff. BA in Bus. Adminstrn. and Acctg., Augustana Coll., 1954. CPA, Iowa. Mgr. internal auditing Maytag Co., Newton, Iowa, 1962-75, asst. controller, 1975-84, asst. v.p., controller, 1984-85; v.p., chief fin. officer Maytag Corp., Newton, Iowa, 1985-86, sr. v.p., chief fin. officer, 1986-89, exec. v.p., chief fin. officer, 1989—, also trustee, 1989-93; ret., 1994; bd. dirs. Amerivend, AMAC Ins. Co., treas; mem. various coms. Maytag Mgmt. Club, Newton. Chmn. Newton Community Childrens Day Care Ctr., 1967; pres. Newton YMCA, 1970; auditor Newton Community Ctr. Fund Dr., 1973; various offices Our Savior Luth. Ch., Citizens Com. for Schs.; bd. dirs. Des Moines Ballet, 1986. Recipient Outstanding Religious Leader award Newton Jaycees, 1968, Outstanding Alumni award Augustana Coll.,1990. Mem. Fin. Execs. Inst., Iowa Soc. CPAs, Am. Inst. CPAs. Home: PO Box 515 Newton IA 50208-0515 Office: Maytag Corp 403 W 4th St N Newton IA 50208

SCHILLER, LAWRENCE JULIAN, motion picture producer, director; b. N.Y.C., Dec. 28, 1936; s. Isidore and Jean (Liebowitz) S.; children: Suzanne, Marc, Howard, Anthony, Cameron. B.A., Pepperdine Coll., 1958. Photojournalist Life mag., 1959-69, Paris Match, 1960-69, London Sun Times, 1960-69; Producer, dir.; (films) Hey, I'm Alive, The Winds of Kitty Hawk, Marilyn, Raid on Short Creek, An Act of Love, The Executioner's Song (Emmy award), Peter the Great (Emmy award), By Reason of Insanity, Margret Bourke-White Story, Plot to Kill Hitler, Double Jeopardy; author: Sunshine, Masters of Contemporary Photography, Marilyn; collaborator: (with Albert Goldman) Lenny Bruce, (with Eugene Smith) Minamata, (with Norman Mailer) The Executioner's Song (Pulitzer prize 1980), Oswald's Tale, (with O.J. Simpson) I Want To Tell You. Producer, dir.: (films) Hey, I'm Alive, The Winds of Kitty Hawk, Marilyn, Raid on Short Creek, An Act of Love, The Executioner's Song (Emmy award), Peter the Great (Emmy award), By Reason of Insanity, Margret Bourke-White Story, Plot to Kill Hitler, Double Jeopardy; author: Sunshine, Masters of Contemporary Photography, Marilyn; collaborator: (with Albert Goldman) Lenny Bruce, (with Eugene Smith) Minamata, (with Norman Mailer) The Executioner's Song (Pulitzer prize 1980). Chmn. bd. dirs. Am.-Soviet Film Initiative, 1988; Am. del. Moscow Internat. Forum on Peace, 1987; mem. USSR-USA Bi-Lateral Talks, 1988. Recipient numerous awards in photojournalism Nat. Press Photographers Assn., Acad. award for The Man Who Skied Down Everest, 1975. Mem. Nat. Press Photographers Assn., Calif. Press Photographers Assn., Dirs. Guild of Am., Acad. of Motion Picture Arts and Scis. Democrat. Jewish.

SCHILLER, PIETER JON, venture capital executive; b. Orange, N.J., Jan. 14, 1938; s. John Fasel and Helen Roff (Roberts) S.; m. Elizabeth Ann Williams, Nov. 20, 1965; children:—Cathryn Ann, Suzanne Elizabeth. B.A. in Econs. with honors, Middlebury (Vt.) Coll., 1960; M.B.A., N.Y. U., 1966. Fin. analyst Merck & Co., Inc., N.Y.C., 1960-61; fin. analyst, asst. div. controller, dir. auditing, then asst. controller Allied Chem. Corp., N.Y.C. and Morristown, N.J., 1961-75; treas. Allied Chem. Corp., 1975-79, v.p. planning and devel., 1979-83; Allied Corp. exec. v.p. diagnostic ops. Allied Health & Sci. Products Co., 1983-86; pres. subs. Instrumentation Lab., Lexington, Mass., 1983-86; gen. ptnr. Advanced Tech. Ventures, Boston, 1986—; bd. dirs. Anthra Pharms., Inc., Princeton, N.J., Afferon Corp., Phoenix, HealthShare Tech., Acton, Mass. Chmn. bd. trustees Newark Boys Chorus Sch., 1976-78, pres. bd., 1974-76; trustee Colonial Symphony Soc., 1978-85, v.p., 1980-82, pres. 1982-83, Morris Mus., Morristown, Concord (Mass.) Mus., 1994—; bd. dirs. New Eng. Coun., Boston, 1983-86, Middlebury Coll. Alumni Assnm., 1989—, v.p., 1992-94, pres., 1994—; chmn. allocations com. United Way of Morris County, 1974-79, v.p. bd. dirs., mem. exec. com., 1979-80; trustee Morris Mus. Arts and Scis., 1980-83; co-chmn. devel. com. Lawrence Acad., Groton, Mass., 1988—. Mem. Fin. Execs. Inst. Republican. Episcopalian. Avocations: skiing, photography. Home: 1373 Monument St Concord MA 01742-5309

SCHILLER, ROBERT E., state official. Supt. pub. instrn. Mich. State Dept. Edn., Lansing. Office: Edn Dept PO Box 30008 Lansing MI 48909-7508*

SCHILLER, THOMAS BENNETT, motion picture writer, director; b. Los Angeles, Apr. 12, 1949; s. Robert Achille and Joyce Gloria (Harris) S. Documentary film maker Los Angeles; writer "Saturday Night Live", N.Y.C., 1975-80; writer, dir. MGM, N.Y.C., 1982; writer Paramount Pictures, Hollywood, Calif., 1984; writer, dir. Home Box Office, Los Angeles, 1986; free-lance writer, dir. Los Angeles, 1986—. Producer: (documentary films) Buckminster Fuller on Spaceship Earth, 1968, A Glimpse of De Kooning, 1969, Anais Nin Observed, 1971, The Henry Miller Odyssey, 1974, Henry Miller Asleep and Awake, 1974; writer, dir. (Saturday Night Live segments) Schiller's Reel, 1977-80, (feature film) Nothing Lasts Forever, 1982, (TV film) From Here to Maternity, 1986, Flapjack Floozie, 1988, (TV show) Baby Boom. Recipient 2 Emmy awards for Saturday Night Live, 1976, 77. Mem. ASCAP, Am. Fedn. TV and Radio Actors, Writers Guild of Am. (annual award 1976, 79), Dirs. Guild of Am. Lodge: Masons.

SCHILLER, WILLIAM RICHARD, surgeon; b. Bennett, Colo., Jan. 14, 1937; s. Francis T. and Frances M. (Finks) S.; m. Beverlee Schiller; children from previous marriage: Julie, Lisa. B.S., Drury Coll., Springfield, Mo., 1958; M.D., Northwestern U., 1962. Diplomate: Am. Bd. Surgery; cert. of added qualifications in surg. critical care, 1987. Intern Passavant Meml. Hosp., Chgo., 1962-63; resident Northwestern U. Clin. Trng. Program, Chgo., 1963-68; assoc. prof. surgery Med. Coll Ohio, Toledo, 1970-78; prof. surgery U. N.Mex, Albuquerque, 1978-83; dir. Trauma Ctr. St. Joseph's Hosp., Phoenix, 1983-89; dir. burn and trauma ctr. Maricopa Med. Ctr., Phoenix, 1989—. Contbr. chpts. to books, articles to profl. jours. Served as maj. M.C. U.S. Army, 1968-70, Vietnam. Fellow ACS; mem. Am. Assn. Surgery of Trauma, Central Surg. Assn., Soc. Surgery of Alimentary Tract, Am. Burn Assn., Internat. Soc. of Surgery. Republican. Home: 8226 E Via De La Escuela Scottsdale AZ 85258-3054 Office: Burn and Trauma Ctr Maricopa Med Ctr 2601 E Roosevelt St Phoenix AZ 85008-4973

SCHILLING, ALBERT HENRY, former government agency administrator, corporate environmental consultant; b. Cin., Dec. 6, 1943; s. Albert Henry Schilling and Irene Marie (Curd) Reid; m. Victoria Guy Smith, June 28, 1975; children: Christopher, Charles. BA in History, Harvard U., 1967; MPA, Princeton U., 1971; JD, Rutgers U., 1974. Bar: Mass. 1974. Dir. grad. admission Woodrow Wilson Sch. Princeton (N.J.) U., N.J., 1971-73; counsel Southwest Devel. Coordinator, Boston, 1973-74; mgr. ecology and programming Cen. Transp. Planning Staff, Boston, 1974-75; rsch. scientist Battelle Meml. Inst., Seattle, 1975-85, dir. sci. and govt. study ctr.; dir. statutory rev. project EPA, Washington, 1985-87; dir. office regis. analysis, 1987-89, dir. office of pollution prevention, 1989-90, assoc. asst. administr. for policy, planning and evaluation, 1990-91; v.p. environ. support global project and structured fin. corp. GE Capital, Stamford, Conn., 1991—; adv. bd. Greening of Industry Network, 1991—. Pres. Madrona Community Coun., Seattle, 1979-81; mem. King County Indsl. Bond Adv. Com., Seattle, 1983,

Citizen's Panel on Exec. Reorganization, Seattle, 1979. Mem. Assn. for Pub. Policy Analysis and Mgmt., Bridgewater Hill Assocs. (v.p. 1992—), Harvard Club of Seattle (pres. 1981, 83), Harvard Club of Washington, Harvard Club of Fairfield County. Episcopalian. Avocations: squash, cooking, boatbuilding. Home: 769 Hillside Rd Fairfield CT 06430-2111 Office: GE Capital 1600 Summer St Stamford CT 06905-5125

SCHILLING, ARLO LEONARD, bank executive; b. Huntington, Ind., Oct. 13, 1924; s. Jacob Howard and Nova Elnora (Rusher) S.; m. Gloria Ann Wygant, Oct. 20, 1946; children: Nancy, Emily, Janey. BS in Edn., Huntington Coll., 1948; MS in Edn., Ind. U., 1950; PhD in Econ., Edn. Psychology, Purdue U., 1958. Tchr. Avilla Pub. Schs., Ind., 1948-52; prin. Coesse Pub. Schs., Ind., 1952-55, Montpelier Pub. Schs., Ind., 1955-56; instr. Purdue U., West Lafayette, Ind., 1956-58; asst. supt. Elkhart Pub. Schs., Ind., 1958-60; pres. North Cen. Coll., Naperville, Ill., 1960-75; chmn., dir., vice chair chmn. Harris Bank Naperville, 1975-94; ret.; vice chmn. Paramounts Arts Centre, Aurora, Ill., 1983—; interim pres. Bank Fox Valley, Westmont, 1975-80. Trustee Life North Cen. Coll., Naperville, 1960—. With U.S. Army, 1943-45, ETO. Mem. NEA, Rotary (pres. 1968), Phi Delta Kappa, Kappa Delta Pi. Republican. Methodist. Avocations: gardening, reading, public speaking, fund raising. Home: 38 W 55 Deerpath Rd Batavia IL 60510

SCHILLING, EDWIN CARLYLE, III, lawyer; b. Baton Rouge, Apr. 5, 1943; s. Edwin Carlyle and Ann (LeTarde) S.; m. Lanell Holder, Dec. 18, 1964; children: Joel, Daniel. BA in Physics/Math., Baylor U., 1966; JD, La. State U., 1969. Bar: La. 1969, Colo. 1989, Alaska 1990, U.S. Supreme Ct. 1982, U.S. Ct. Mil. Appeals 1981, U.S. Tax Ct. 1982, U.S. Ct. Appeals (Fed. cir.) 1982. Commd. USAF, 1969-89, advanced through grades to lt. col.; assoc. prof. law USAF Acad., Colo., 1972-76; staff judge advocate Kunsan AB, Korea, 1976-77, Myrtle Beach (S.C.) AFB, 1977-80; dir. USAF Legal Assistance Program, Washington, 1980-83; with Air War Coll., 1983-84; staff judge advocate Elemdorf AFB, Alaska, 1984-87; asst. staff judge advocate Air Force Acctg. and Fin. Ctr., Lowry AFB, Colo., 1987-89; pvt. practice law Aurora, Colo., 1989—. Co-author book: Survival Manual for Women in Divorce, 1990, Survival Manual for Men in Divorce; co-author video tape/manual: How to Successfully Manage Military Divorce, 1990. Sec. Eastridge Civic Assn., Aurora, 1988—; bd. dirs. Consumer Credit Counseling Svc., Anchorage, 1985-87, Myrtle Beach Fed. Credit Union, 1978-81. Mem. ABA (exec. mem. fed. procedures and legislation com.), La. Bar Assn., Colo. Bar Assn., Alaska Bar Assn. Republican. Presbyterian. Avocations: photography, fishing, hiking, camping, amateur radio. Office: 2767 S Parker Rd Ste 230 Aurora CO 80014-2701

SCHILLING, JOHN ALBERT, surgeon; b. Kansas City, Mo., Nov. 5, 1917; s. Carl Fielding and Lottie Lee (Henderson) S.; m. Lucy West, June 8, 1957 (dec.); children: Christine Henderson, Katharine Ann, Jolyon David, John Jay; m. Helen R. Spelbrink, May 28, 1979. A.B. with honors, Dartmouth Coll., 1937; M.D., Harvard U., 1941. Diplomate Am. Bd. Surgery (chmn. 1969). Intern, then resident in surgery Roosevelt Hosp., N.Y.C., 1941-44; mem. faculty U. Rochester (N.Y.) Med. Sch., 1945-53, asst. prof. surgery, 1955-56; prof. surgery, head dept. U. Okla. Med. Sch., 1956-74; prof. surgery U. Wash. Med. Sch., Seattle, 1974—; chmn. dept. U. Wash. Med. Sch., 1975-83, prof. emeritus, 1988—; mem. bd. sci. counselors Nat. Cancer Inst., chmn., 1969; also mem. diagnosis subcom. breast cancer task force; chmn. adv. com. to surgeon gen. on metabolism of trauma Army Med. Research and Devel. Command; mem. surgery study sect., div. research grants NIH; chief surgery USAF Sch. Aviation Medicine, 1953-55; cons. Surgeon Gen. USAF, 1959-75. Author articles, chpts. in books, abstracts, reports.; editorial bd. Am. Jour. Surgery, Annals of Surgery. Served to maj. M.C. USAF, 1953-55. Grantee Army Office Surgeon Gen., 1956-80. Mem. ACS (bd. govs., chmn. com. surg. edn. in med. schs., 1st v.p. 1977-78), Am. S., Western, Pan-Pacific, N. Pacific, Pacific Coast surg. assns., Soc. Univ. Surgeons, Southwestern Surg. Soc., Central Surg. Soc., Southwestern Surg. Congress (hon. mem. 1978), Okla. Surg. Assn. (pres. 1970-71, hon. mem. 1974) Am. Assn. Surgery Trauma, Surg. Biology Club, Am. Physiol. Soc., Soc. Surg. Chmn., Am. Trauma Soc., Seattle Surg. Soc., Soc. Exptl. Pathology, Soc. Surgery Alimentary Tract, Explorers Club, Alpha Omega Alpha. Clubs: Yacht (Seattle), University (Seattle). Home: 9807 Lake Washington Blvd NE Bellevue WA 98004-5431 Office: Dept Surgery (RF-25) Univ Wash Medical Sch Seattle WA 98195

SCHILLING, RICHARD M., lawyer, corporate executive; b. Green Bay, Wis., June 15, 1937; s. Merlin Schilling; m. Eileen M. Schilling, Sept. 6, 1959; children: Sherry Schilling Harlan, Rick. BS, U. Green Bay, 1959; LLB, Harvard, 1962. Atty. with Schiff, Hardin & Waite, Chgo., 1962-69; corp. atty. Sundstrand Corp., Rockford, Ill., 1969—. Mem. Chgo. Bar Assn., Winnebago County Bar Assn., ABA, Machinery and Allied Products Inst. Office: Sundstrand Corp PO Box 7003 4949 Harrison Ave Rockford IL 61125

SCHILLING, WARNER ROLLER, political scientist, educator; b. Glendale, Calif., May 23, 1925; s. Jule Frederick and Pauline Frances de Berri (Warner) S.; m. Jane Pierce Metzger, Jan. 27, 1951 (dec. Nov. 1983); children: Jonathan, Frederick. A.B., Yale U., 1949, M.A., 1951, Ph.D., 1954. Research fellow Center Internat. Studies, Princeton U., 1953-54; asst. prof. internat. relations Mass. Inst. Tech., 1957-58; mem. faculty Columbia U., 1954—, prof. govt., 1967-73, James T. Shotwell prof. internat. relations, 1973—; dir. Inst. War and Peace Studies, 1976-86; cons. occasional lectr. in field. Co-author: Strategy, Politics and Defense Budgets, 1962, European Security and the Atlantic System, 1973, American Arms and a Changing Europe, 1973; Contbr. numerous articles to jours. Served with USAAF, 1944-46. Guggenheim fellow, 1964-65; resident fellow Bellagio Study and Conf. Center, 1975. Mem. Internat. Inst. Strategic Studies, Council Fgn. Relations. Club: Leonia Democratic. Home: 496 Park Ave Leonia NJ 07605-1243 Office: 420 W 118th St New York NY 10027-7213

SCHILLINGER, EDWIN JOSEPH, physics educator; b. Chgo., July 14, 1923; s. Edwin Joseph and Marie (Wolf) S.; m. Carmelita Larocco, Aug. 27, 1949; children—Rosemarie, Mary, Ann, Edwin, Jerome, Elizabeth. B.S., DePaul U., 1944; M.S., U. Notre Dame, 1948, Ph.D., 1950. Mem. faculty DePaul U., Chgo., 1950—, prof. physics, 1963-88, prof. emeritus, 1988—; chmn. dept., 1952-68, 76-79, dean Coll. Liberal Arts and Scis., 1966-70, acting dean, 1980-81; edn. cons. Served with AUS, 1944-46. Decorated Purple Heart; recipient merit award Chgo. Tech. Socs., 1976; AEC fellow, 1948-50. Fellow Am. Phys. Soc.; mem. Am. Assn. Physics Tchrs., AAAS, Ill. Acad. Sci., Chgo. Acad. Tech. (charter mem.), Sigma Xi. Roman Catholic. Home: 7724 W Peterson Ave Chicago IL 60631-2246

SCHILSKY, RICHARD LEWIS, oncologist, researcher; b. N.Y.C., June 6, 1950; s. Murray and Shirley (Cohen) S.; m. Cynthia Schum, Sept. 24, 1977; children: Allison, Meredith. BA cum laude, U. Pa., Phila., 1971; MD with honors, U. Chgo., 1975. Diplomate Nat. Bd. Med. Examiners, Am. Bd. Internal Medicine (subspecialty med. oncology); lic. physician, Mo., Ill. Intern, resident medicine Parkland Meml. Hosp., Southwestern Med. Sch., Dallas, 1975-77; clin. assoc. medicine br. clin. pharmacology br. Div. Cancer Treatment, Nat. Cancer Inst., Bethesda, Md., 1977-80, cancer expert clin. pharmacology br., 1980-81; asst. prof. dept. internal medicine U. Mo.-Columbia Sch. Medicine, 1981-84; asst. prof. dept. medicine U. Chgo. Pritzker Sch. Medicine and Michael Reese Med. Ctrs., 1984-86, assoc. prof. dept. medicine, 1986-89; assoc. dir. joint sect. hematology and med. oncology U. Chgo. and Michael Reese Med. Ctrs., 1986-89; assoc. prof. dept. medicine, assoc. dir. sect. U. Chgo. Pritzker Sch. Medicine, 1989-91, prof. dept. medicine sect. hematology-oncology, 1991—; dir. U. Chgo. Cancer Rsch. Ctr., 1991—; chmn. cancer and leukemia group B U. Chgo. Pritzker Sch. Medicine, Chgo., 1995—; Vivian Saykaly vis. prof. oncology McGill U., 1992; mem. sci. com. 4th Internat. Congress on Anti-Cancer Chemotherapy, 1991—; mem. adv. panel on hematologic and neoplastic disease U.S. Pharmacopeial Conv., 1990—; mem. core grant guidelines subcom. ad hoc com. on planning and issues for cancer ctrs., mem. clin. rsch. subcom., Assn. Am. Cancer Insts., 1992—; mem. cancer ctr. support grant rev. com. Nat. Cancer Inst., NIH, 1992-94; mem. expert panel on advances in cancer treatment, 1992-93. Edit. bd. Investigational New Drugs, 1988—, Jour. Clin. Oncology, 1990-93, Contemporary Oncology, 1991-94, Jour. Cancer Rsch. and Clin. Oncology, 1991—; assoc. editor Clin. Cancer Rsch., 1994—; contbr. articles to profl. jours., chpts. to books. With USPHS, 1977-80.

Recipient Spl. Advancement for Performance award VA, 1983, Fletcher Scholar award Cancer Rsch. Found., 1989; grantee VA, 1981-87, Am. Cancer Soc., 1983-86, 92-95, Ill. Cancer Coun., 1985-86, Michael Reese Inst. Coun., 1985-86, Nat. Cancer Inst., 1987, 88-90, Burroughs-Wellcome Co., 1987-88, NIH/Nat. Cancer Inst., 1988—. Fellow ACP; mem. AAAS, Am. Soc. Clin. Oncology (chmn. pub. rels. com. 1994—), Am. Assn. Cancer Rsch. (chmn. Ill. state legis. com. 1992—), Am. Fedn. Clin. Rsch. (senator Midwest sect. 1983-84, councilor 1983-86, chmn.-elect 1987-88, chmn. 1988-89), Am. Assn. Cancer Edn., Am. Soc. Clin. Pharmacology and Therapeutics, Ctrl. Soc. Clin. Rsch., N.Y. Acad. Scis., Chgo. Soc. Internal Medicine, Sigma Xi, Alpha Epsilon Delta, Alpha Omega Alpha. Office: U Chgo Cancer Rsch Ctr 5841 S Maryland Ave Chicago IL 60637-1470

SCHIMBERG, A(RMAND) BRUCE, retired lawyer; b. Chgo., Aug. 26, 1927; s. Archie and Helen (Isay) S.; m. Barbara Zisook; children: Geoffrey, Kate. Ph.B., U. Chgo., 1949, J.D., 1952. Bar: Ohio 1952, Ill. 1955, U.S. Supreme Ct. 1987. Assoc. Paxton & Seasongood, Cin., 1952-55; ptnr. Schimberg, Greenberger, Kraus & Jacobs, Chgo., 1955-65, Leibman, Williams, Bennett, Baird & Minow, Chgo., 1965-72; ptnr. Sidley & Austin, Chgo., 1972-92, counsel, 1993-94, ret., 1994; lectr. U. Chgo. 1993-94; ret., 1994; gen. counsel Commn. Fin. Assn., 1978-94; mem. editorial bd. Lender Liability News. Mng. and assoc. editor U. Chgo. Law Rev., 1951-52; contbr. articles to legal jours. Bd. dirs. U. Chgo. Law Sch. Alumni Assn., 1969-72; dir. vis. com. U. Chgo. Law Sch., 1980-83. Mem. ABA (chmn. subcom. and charter mem. comml. fin. svcs com.), Am. Coll. Comml. Fin. Lawyers (pres. 1994-95, bd. regents), Ill. Bar Assn. (chair comml. banking, bankruptcy sect. 1972-73), Chgo. Bar Assn. (chair ucc com., 1966, bd. mgrs. 1968-70, chair judiciary com. 1971-72), Law Club Chgo., Mid-Day Club, Lake Shore Country Club. Home: 132 E Delaware Pl # 5002 Chicago IL 60611

SCHIMBERG, HENRY AARON, soft drink company executive; b. Chgo., Mar. 3, 1933; s. Arnold and Judith (Aaron) S.; m. Linda Waxberg, June 21, 1975; children: Aaron David, Alexis Leigh. BA, Beloit Coll., 1954. Exec. v.p. Nehi Royal Crown Corp., Chgo., 1970-76; pres. Royal Crown Bottling Co., Los Angeles, 1976-79; pres. bottling ops. Royal Crown Cola Co., Rolling Meadows, Ill., 1979-82; pres., CEO, bd. dirs. Coca-Cola Bottling Midwest, Mpls., 1982-91, Cen. States Coca-Cola Bottling Co., Springfield, Ill., 1985-91, Coca-Cola Bottling Co. of St. Louis, 1986-91, Cin. Coca-Cola Bottling Co., 1986-91, Mid-States Coca-Cola Bottling Co., Paducah, Ky., 1986-91; pres., COO, bd. dirs. Johnston Coca-Cola Bottling Group, Chattanooga, Tenn., 1986-91, Coca-Cola Enterprises Inc., Atlanta, 1991—, Pacific Coca-Cola Bottling Co., Bellevue, Wash., 1992—, Austin Coca-Cola Bottling Co., Dallas; bd. dirs. Johnston Co. Chattanooga. Cpl U.S. Army, 1954-56. Mem. Minn. Soft Drink Assn. (bd. dirs. 1983—), Wis. Soft Drink Assn., Ill. Soft Drink Assn. (pres. 1974-76), Nat. Soft Drink Assn. (exec. bd. 1986—, chmn. 1994—), Coca-Cola Bottlers Assn. (bd. govs. 1986—). Jewish. Avocations: tennis, skiing. Office: Coca-Cola Enterprises Inc 1 Coca-Cola Plz NW Atlanta GA 30313

SCHIMEK, DIANNA RUTH REBMAN, state legislator; b. Holdrege, Nebr., Mar. 21, 1940; d. Ralph William and Elizabeth Julia (Wilmot) Rebman; m. Herbert Henry Schimek, 1963; children: Samuel Wolfgang, Saul William. AA, Colo. Women's Coll., 1960; student, U. Nebr., Lincoln, 1960-61; BA magna cum laude, U. Nebr., Kearney, 1963. Former tchr. and realtor; mem. Nebr. Legislature, Lincoln, 1989—, chmn. govt., mil. and vets. affairs com., 1993-94, vice chair urban affairs com., 1995—. Chmn. Nebr. Dem. Com., 1980-84; Dem. Nat. Com. woman, 1984-88; past pres., sec. bd. dirs. Downtown Sr. Ctr. Found., mem. exec. com., 1987-88. Mem. NAACP, Nat. Conf. State Legislators Women's Network (bd. dirs.), P.E.O., Soroptomists. Democrat. Unitarian. Home: 2321 Camelot Ct Lincoln NE 68512-1457 Office: State Legislature State Capital Lincoln NE 68516

SCHIMELPFENIG, C(LARENCE) W(ILLIAM), JR., chemistry educator; b. Dallas, Apr. 8, 1930; s. Clarence William and Hulda Anna Louise (Borchardt) S.; m. Dorothy Marie Massey, Apr. 28, 1956; children: Laurel Ann, Gretchen Marie, Michael William. BS, North Tex. State U., 1953, MS, 1954; PhD, U. Ill., 1957. Asst. prof. George Washington U., Washington, 1957-59, U. North Tex., Denton, 1959-62; rsch. chemist E.I. du Pont de Nemours and Co., Wilmington, Del., 1962-72; asst. prof. SUNY, Buffalo, 1973-75, Erskine Coll., Due West, S.C., 1975-76; assoc. prof. Tex. Wesleyan Coll., Ft. Worth, 1976-81, U. North Tex., Denton, 1981-82; prof. chemistry Dallas Bapt. U., 1982-91; adj. prof. chemistry U. Tex., Arlington, 1991—. Patentee chlorination method, moistenable hot melt adhesive; contbr. articles to profl. jours. Dist. commr. Boy Scouts of Am. Wilmington, Del., 1972; mem. Crime Watch Bd., Pantego, Tex., 1987-91; mem. Planning and Zoning Commn., Pantego, 1991—; elder Hanover Presbyn. Ch., Wilmington. Recipient grants Robert A. Welch Found., Houston, 1960-62, '78-81, Silver Beaver award, Boy Scouts of Am., 1973. Mem. Am. Chem. Soc. (program dir. meeting-in-minature, Dallas-Ft. Worth, 1981). Republican. Presbyterian. Avocations: gardening, nature study. Office: U Tex Arlington Dept Chemistry Box 19065 Arlington TX 76019-0065

SCHIMKE, ROBERT TOD, biochemist, educator; b. Spokane, Wash., Oct. 25, 1932; s. Tolbert Daniel and Marion (Evans) S.; m. Faith Fagan, July 5, 1952 (dec. 1958); children: Steven R., Caroline E.; m. Ruth Buddington, Feb. 6, 1959; children: Cynthia E., Allison R.; m. Mary Content, June 16, 1973 (dec. 1975); m. Hope Raymond, June 25, 1977 (div. Apr. 1992); m. Pat Jones, Apr. 11, 1992. A.B., Stanford U., 1954, M.D., 1958. Intern, asst. resident medicine Mass. Gen. Hosp., Boston, 1958-60; commd. officer Lab. Biochemical Pharmacology sect. on pharmacology Nat. Insts. Arthritis and Metabolic Diseases, 1960-63, med. officer internal medicine research, 1963-65, chief sect. biochem. regulation, 1965-66; assoc. prof. pharmacology and biology dept. pharmacology Stanford U., 1966-69, prof., 1969-73, chmn. dept., 1970-73, prof. biology, 1973—, chmn. dept. biol. sci., 1978-82, Am. Cancer Soc. research prof. biology, 1983—, dir. med. scientist tng. program, 1969-75; Mem. molecular biol. study sect. NIH, 1970-74, nat. adv. council on aging, 1978-81; mem. adv. panel on nucleic acid and protein synthesis Am. Cancer Soc., 1971-75, Nat. Acad. Scis., 1976, Am. Acad. Arts and Scis., 1977, Inst. Medicine, Nat. Acad. Scis., 1983. Mem. editorial bd.: Jour. Biol. Chemistry, 1968-72; asso. editor, 1975-81, 83—; editorial bd.: Molecular Pharmacology, 1969-72; exec. editor: Archives Biochem. Biophysics, 1973-75. Named Outstanding Young Scientist of Yr., Md. Acad. Sci., 1964; recipient Chas. Pfizer award Am. Chem. Soc., 1969, Boris Pregel award N.Y. Acad. Scis., 1974, W.C. Rose award in biochemistry Am. Nutrition Found., 1983, Sloan prize Gen. Motors Cancer Rsch. Found., 1985, Lila Gruber Meml. Cancer Rsch. award Am. Acad. Dermatology, 1988. Mem. Am. Soc. Biochemistry Molecular Biology (pres. 1988-89), Phi Beta Kappa, Alpha Omega Alpha. Home: 639 Arastradero Rd Palo Alto CA 94306-3838 Office: Stanford U Dept Biol Scis Stanford CA 94305

SCHIMMEL, PAUL REINHARD, biochemist, biophysicist, educator; b. Hartford, Conn., Aug. 4, 1940; s. Alfred E. and Doris (Hudson) S.; m. Judith F. Ritz, Dec. 30, 1961; children: Kirsten, Katherine. A.B., Ohio Wesleyan U., 1962; postgrad., Tufts U. Sch. Medicine, 1962-63, Mass. Inst. Tech., 1963-65, Cornell U., 1965-66, Stanford U., 1966-67, U. Calif., Santa Barbara, 1975-76; Ph.D., Mass. Inst. Tech., 1966. Asst. prof. biology and chemistry MIT, 1967-71, assoc. prof. 1971-76, prof. biochemistry and biophysics, 1976-92, John D. and Catherine T. MacArthur prof. biochemistry and biophysics, 1992—; mem. NIH Study Sect. Physiol. Chemistry, 1975-79; indsl. cons. on enzymes and recombinant DNA. Author: (with C. Cantor) Biophysical Chemistry, 3 vols., 1980; mem. editorial bd. Archives Biochemistry, Biophysics, 1976-80, Nucleic Acids Rsch., 1976-80, Jour. Biol. Chemistry, 1977-82, Biopolymers, 1977-88, Internat. Jour. Biol. Macromolecules, 1983-89, Trends in Biochem. Scis., 1984—, Biochemistry, 1989—, Accounts of Chem. Rsch., 1989-94, European Jour. Biochemistry, 1991—, Protein Sci., 1991—. Proc. Nat. Acad. of Scis., 1993—. Alfred P. Sloan fellow, 1970-72. Fellow AAAS, Am. Acad. Arts and Scis.; mem. NAS, Am. Chem. Soc. (Pfizer award 1978, chmn. divsn. biol. chemistry 1984-85), Am. Soc. for Biochemistry and Molecular Biology, Protein Soc. Office: MIT Dept Biology Cambridge MA 02139

SCHIMMINGER, ROBIN, state legislator; b. Tonawanda, N.Y., Sept. 17, 1947; s. Linus Joseph and Doris Wilson S.; m. Melinda Downey, Apr. 21, 1978. BA, Canisius Coll., 1969; JD, NYU, 1972. Bar: N.Y. Legislator Erie County Legislature, Buffalo, N.Y., 1974-76, N.Y. State Assembly, Buffalo,

1977—; chmn. N.Y. State Assembly Sml. Bus. Com., Albany, 1985—; Coun. State Govts./Ea. Regional Task Force on Econ. Affairs; mem. Nat. Conf. of State Legislatures. Author: (legislation) N.Y. State Audit and Internal Control Act, 1987, N.Y. State Toxic Torts Law, 1986, N.Y. State Equal Access to Justice Act, 1989, Omnibus Procurement Act, 1992, Excelsior Linked Deposit Act, 1993. Bd. dirs. Buffalo Hearing and Speech Ctr., Better Bus. Bur. of Buffalo, Jr. Achievement of Western N.Y., Cardinal O'Hara High Sch., Tonawanda. Recipient Guardian of Sml. Bus. award, Nat. Fedn. of Ind. Bus., citation for Disting. Svc., Disabled Am. Vets., Pres.'s citation, N.Y. State Osteopathic Med. Soc., Advocacy award Alzheimer's Disease and Related Disorders Assn. of Western N.Y., 1987. Mem. Bar Assn. of Erie County, Buffalo C. of C., N.Y. State Gov.'s Coun. on Phys. Fitness and Sports. Democrat. Roman Catholic. Avocations: tennis, hiking, reading. Office: 3514 Delaware Ave Kenmore NY 14217

SCHIMPF, JOHN JOSEPH, real estate developer; b. Paterson, N.J., May 19, 1949; s. Joseph Stephen and Veronica Barbara (Blad) S.; m. Barbara Ann Reid, June 3, 1972; children: Laryn Michelle, Brian Scott, Alysson Marie. BA magna cum laude in Spanish Lit., Seton Hall U., 1971; MA in Comparative Lit., U. Wis., 1974, MA in Spanish Lit., 1975; MBA in Fin. and Mktg., Columbia U., 1977. Corp. loan officer petroleum div. Chase Manhattan Bank, N.Y.C., 1977-79; mgr. treasury ops. Marsh & McLennan Cos., Inc., N.Y.C., 1980-81; exec. v.p. the Hovnanian Enterprises, Inc., Red Bank, N.J., 1981—; bd. dirs. Hovnanian Enterprises, Inc., Red Bank, N.J., New Fortis Corp., King, N.C. Trustee Brookdale C.C. Found., Lincroft, N.J., Emmanuel Cancer Found., Iselin, N.J.; mem. adv. bd. to chancellor Seton Hall U. Served to 1st lt. U.S. Army, 1971-73. Mem. Nat. Assn. Indsl. and Office Parks, Nat. Assn. Sr. Living Industries. Roman Catholic. Avocations: reading, art, racquetball, traveling. Office: Hovnanian Enterprises Inc 10 Hwy 35 PO Box 500 Red Bank NJ 07701

SCHIMPFF, STEPHEN CALLENDER, internist, oncologist; b. Cleve., Nov. 23, 1941; s. Leo Donald and Lorraine (McClintock) S.; m. Carol Rawstrom, Sept. 2, 1963; 1 child, Elizabeth Callender. BA, Rutgers U., 1963; MD, Yale U., 1967. Diplomate Am. Bd. Internal Medicine, Am. Bd. Med. Examiners. Intern Yale-New Haven Hosp., 1967-68, resident, 1968-69; acting head med. svc. Balt. Cancer Rsch. Program, 1970-71, sr. investigator, 1973-76, head. infection rsch. sect., 1976-81; head infectious diseases and microbiology sect. U. Md., Balt., 1981-83, prof. medicine, 1979, prof. oncology, head divsn. infectious disease, 1979-85, Am. Cancer Soc. prof. oncology, 1985-89, dir. Cancer Ctr., 1982-85; exec. v.p. U. Md. Med. System, 1985—; Co-founder Multinat. Assn. for Supportive Care in Cancer, 1988—. Editor: Comprehensive Textbook Oncology, 1986, 91, Recent Results in Cancer Research—Infectious Complications in Bone Marrow Transplantation, 1993; contbr. articles to profl. jours. Bd. dirs. Md. Hosp. Edn. Inst. 1987—, vice chmn. 1992—, sec. 1991-92; bd. dirs. Md. Cancer Consortium, 1990—; bd. dirs. Md. Easter Seal Soc., 1989-92, vice chmn., 1990-92; leader Girl Scouts U.S., 1982. Fellow ACP, Infectious Diseases Soc. Am.; mem. Am. Soc. Clin. Oncology (sec., treas. 1985-88), Am. Assn. Cancer Rsch., Md. Assn. Nonprofit Orgns. (bd. dirs. 1991—, vice chmn. 1991-94, chmn. 1994—), Alpha Omega Alpha. Home: 10129 Pasture Gate Ln Columbia MD 21044-1735 Office: U Md Med System 22 S Greene St Baltimore MD 21201-1544

SCHINAGL, ERICH FRIEDRICH, health care company executive, physician; b. Vienna, Austria, Sept. 18, 1932; came to U.S., 1969; s. Erich Ernest and Helene (Linke) S.; m. Cynthia Stokes, July 27, 1957; children: Catherine, Robert, Helen. MD, U. Vienna, 1961. Intern dept. internal medicine U. Vienna Med. Sch., 1961-62, resident, 1962-65; med. dir. Pharmacia Internat., Uppsala, Sweden, 1965-67; dir. clin. rsch. Pharmacia AB, Uppsala, 1967-69; med. dir. Pharmacia, Inc., Piscataway, N.J., 1969-84, project dir., 1985-88, dir. spl. projects, 1988-89; v.p. R&D Pharmacia Health Care Group, Piscataway, 1984-87; med. dir. KABI Pharmacia Pharms, Piscataway, 1990-93; dir. therapeutic area Med. Rsch. Ctr. Pharmacia Adria, Dublin, Ohio, 1993—. Fulbright scholar Hamilton Coll., Clinton, N.Y., 1951. Office: Pharmacia Adria 7001 Post Rd Dublin OH 43017-9310

SCHINDEL, DONALD MARVIN, lawyer; b. Chgo., Jan. 5, 1932; s. Harry L. and Ann (Schiff) S.; m. Alice Martha Andrews, Apr. 24, 1960; children—Susan, Judith, Andrea. B.S. in Acctg., U. Ill., 1953; J.D., U. Chgo., 1956. Bar: Ill. 1956. Ptnr. Sonnenschein, Nath & Rosenthal, Chgo., 1956—. Author: Estate Administration and Tax Planning for Survivors, 1987, supplements, 1988—. Pres. Congregation Beth Or, Deerfield, Ill., 1983-85. Fellow Am. Coll. Trust and Estate Counsel; mem. Chgo. Estate Planning Council, ABA, Ill. Bar Assn., Chgo. Bar Assn. (chmn. probate practice com. 1981-82). Clubs: Metropolitan, East Bank (Chgo.). Avocations: tennis, photography, carpentry, running, juggling. Home: 636 Rice St Highland Park IL 60035-5012 Office: Sonnenschein Nath & Rosenthal 8000 Sears Tower 233 S Wacker Dr Chicago IL 60606

SCHINDERLE, ROBERT FRANK, hospital administrator; b. Mayville, Wis., Aug. 3, 1923; m. Elizabeth, June 23, 1949; children—David, Gary, Mary, Brian. B.S., Marquette U., 1949; M.S., Northwestern U., 1959. Asst. office mgr. Western Leather Co., Milw., 1949-51; mgr. bus. office St. Francis Hosp., Peoria, Ill., 1951-55; credit mgr. Mercy Hosp., Chgo., 1955-59, asst. to administr., 1957-58, controller, 1958-59, asst. administr., 1959-65; asst. administr. St. Joseph Hosp., Joliet, Ill., 1965-70, assoc. administr., 1970-71, administr., 1971-76, exec. dir., 1976-86; dir. corp. legis. affairs and devel. Franciscan Sisters Health Care Corp., Mokena, Ill., 1986-89, ret.; chmn. Areawide Hosp. Emergency Services Council. Bd. dirs. Region IX Health Systems Agy., Our Lady of Angels Retirement Home, Joliet, Joliet YMCA, St. Joseph Coll. Nursing, Joliet. Fellow Am. Coll. Hosp. Administrs.; mem. Am. Hosp. Assn., Ill. Hosp. Assn. (chmn. 1975-76), Catholic Hosp. Assn. (dir.), Ill. Cath. Hosp. Assn. (chmn. 1972-73). Roman Catholic. Lodges: Rotary, Elks, KC. Home: 408 W Newkirk Dr Plainfield IL 60544-1838

SCHINDLER, ALBERT ISADORE, physicist, educator; b. Pitts., June 24, 1927; s. Jonas and Esther (Nass) S.; m. Phyllis Irene Liberman, June 17, 1951; children—Janet Mae, Jerald Scott, Ellen Susan. B.S., Carnegie Inst. Tech., 1947, M.S., 1948, D.Sc., 1950. Research asst. Carnegie Inst. Tech., Pitts., 1947-50, research physicist, 1950-51; supervisory rsch. physicist Naval Rsch. Lab., Washington, 1951-75; assoc. dir. research for material sci. and component tech. Naval Research Lab., 1975-85; prof. materials engring. and physics Purdue U., West Lafayette, Ind., 1985-92, cons., 1992—, dir. Ind. Ctr. for Innovative Superconductor Tech., 1988-91, dir. Midwest Superconductivity Consortium, 1990-91; dir. div. materials rsch. NSF, Washington, 1988-90; cons. Recipient E.O. Hulburt award Naval Research Lab., 1956, Nat. Capitol award for applied sci., 1962, Pure Sci. award Naval Research Lab.-Sci. Research Soc. Am., 1965, award Washington Acad. Scis., 1965, USN Disting. Achievement in Sci. award, 1975, Alumni Merit award Carngie Mellon U., 1976, Sr. Exec. Service award Dept. Navy, 1983. Fellow Am. Phys. Soc.; mem. Sigma Xi. (dir.). Home: 6615 Sulky Ln Rockville MD 20852

SCHINDLER, ALEXANDER MOSHE, rabbi, organization executive; b. Munich, Germany, Oct. 4, 1925; s. Eliezer and Sali (Hoyda) S.; m. Rhea Rosenblum, Sept. 29, 1956; children—Elisa Ruth, Debra Lee, Joshua Michael, Judith Rachel, Jonathan David. B in Social Sci., CCNY, 1950; B in Hebrew Letters, Hebrew Union Coll., 1951, M in Hebrew Letters, 1953, DD (hon.), 1977; DHL (hon.), U. S.C., 1987, Lafayette U., 1988; DD (hon.), Hamilton Coll., 1990; LLD (hon.), Coll. of Holy Cross, 1994, Wittenberg U., 1995. Ordained rabbi, 1953. Asst. rabbi Temple Emanuel, Worcester, Mass., 1953-56; assoc., rabbi Temple Emanuel, 1956-59; dir. New Eng. council Union Am. Hebrew Congregations, 1959-63, nat. dir. edn., 1963-67, v.p., 1967-72; pres.-elect, 1972, pres., 1973—; mem. exec. bd. Conf. Pres. Major Am. Jewish Orgns., 1967—, chmn., 1976-78; mem. exec. bd. Hebrew Union Coll./Jewish Inst. Religion, 1967—; v.p. Meml. Found. for Jewish Culture, 1967—, chmn. exec. com., 1994—; v.p. World Jewish Congress; mem. exec. com. World Zionist Orgn., 1973—; mem. exec. com. Joint Distbn. Com., 1987—, sec., 1992-94; bd. govs. Hebrew Union Coll., 1973—; v.p. World Union for Progressive Judaism. Author: From Discrimination to Extermination, 1950; lit. editor: CCAR Jour., 1959-63; founding editor: Dimensions, Reform Judaism's quar. religious thought, 1966—; editor: Reform Judaism's graded text book series, 1963-67. Served with AUS, 1943-46. Decorated Bronze Star, Purple Heart; recipient Solomon Bublick prize Hebrew U. Jerusalem, 1978; Townsend Harris medal CCNY, 1979. Mem.

Am. Assn. Jewish Edn. (exec. bd. 1963-67), Central Conf. Am. Rabbis (exec. bd. 1967—). Home: 6 River Ln Westport CT 06880-1925 Office: Union Am Hebrew Congregations 838 Fifth Ave New York NY 10021-7064 *To live life fully, clinging to its many gifts with all my might—and then, paradoxically, to let go when life compels us to surrender what it gave.*

SCHINDLER, BARBARA FRANCOIS, school administrator; b. Chgo., Oct. 28, 1935; d. Harry and Nellie Irene (Lewis) Francois; m. Charles A. Schindler, Jan. 29, 1955; children: Marian, Susan, Neal. BA, U. Tex., 1960; MA, U. Okla., 1975, PhD, 1984. Cert. tchr., Okla. Tchr. Norman (Okla.) Pub. Schs., 1972-86; exec. dir. Dem. Party Okla. Oklahoma City, 1986-87; tchr. Moore (Okla.) Pub. Schs., 1987-88; curriculum supr. Oklahoma City Pub. Schs., 1988—; mem. sch. bd. Moore-Norman Vocat.-Tech. Sch., Norman, 1979-83; bd. dirs. Law-Related Edn., Oklahoma City; chair Okla. Close-Up, Oklahoma City, 1990-92; community planner U.S.-Japan Ednl. Initiative, 1993. Contbr. chpt. to book For the Man, the Myth and the Era, 1987; author: (supplementary materials) The Oklahoma Story, 1980. Nat. Del. Dem. Party Conv., N.Y.C., 1980, Atlanta, 1988; county party chair Dem. Party, Cleveland County, 1985-87. Recipient Excellence in Teaching award Profl. Educators, 1975; Fulbright fellow, 1992, NEH fellow, 1988; grantee Japan Study Tour Found., 1990. Mem. ASCD, Nat. Coun. for Social Studies (com. mem. 1988—), Nat. Coun. for Econ. Edn. (bd. dirs. 1990—), Okla. Edn. Assn. (bd. dirs. 1978-85), Phi Delta Kappa. Avocations: bridge, hiking. Home: 2000 Morgan Dr Norman OK 73069

SCHINDLER, MARVIN SAMUEL, foreign language educator; b. Boston, Jan. 2, 1932; s. Edward Esau and Esther Marian (Wiseman) S.; m. Roslyn Frances Abt, Aug. 11, 1974; children: Daniel Mark, Lore Elaine, Inge-Marie, Neal Elliott. B.A., U. Mass., 1953; M.A., Ohio State U., 1955, Ph.D., 1965. Instr. German Pa. State U., Pottsville, 1955-59; asst. prof. Ohio State U., 1965-67; assoc. prof. German, asso. dean Grad. Sch. Arts and Scis., U. Va., Charlottesville, 1967-71; prof. German, chmn. dept. fgn. langs. No. Ill. U., DeKalb, 1971-74; prof. German, chmn. dept. Romance and Germanic langs. and lits. Wayne State U., Detroit, 1974-83; dir. Jr. Yr. in Germany Programs Wayne State U., 1975—. Author: The Sonnets of Andreas Gryphius, 1971; asso. editor: German Quar, 1971-78. Fulbright fellow, 1961-62; ehrensenator Albert-Ludwigs Universität, Freiburg;Bundesverdienstkreuz, 1. Klasse, Fed. Republic of Germany. Mem. Am. Assn. Tchrs. German (exec. council), MLA, Assn. Depts. Fgn. Langs. (exec. com., pres. 1981), Midwest Modern Lang. Assn. Home: 10075 Lincoln Dr Huntington Wd MI 48070-1507 Office: 487 Manoogian Hall Wayne State Univ Detroit MI 48202

SCHINDLER, PESACH, rabbi, educator, author; b. Munich, Germany, Apr. 11, 1931; came to U.S., 1940; s. Alexander Moshe and Esther (Zwickler) S.; m. Shulamith Feldman, June 30, 1954; children: Chaya, Gita, Meyer, Nechama, Avi. BA, CCNY Bklyn. Coll., 1953; MS, Yeshiva U., 1964; PhD, NYU, 1972; D Pedagogy (hon.), Jewish Theol. Sem., N.Y.C., 1987. Ordained rabbi, 1956. Dir. edn. Congregation Adath Israel, Toronto, Ont., Can., 1959-65; asst. dir. edn. United Synagogue of Am., N.Y.C., 1965-72; dir. Ctr. for Conservative Judaism United Synagogue of Am., Jerusalem, 1972—; asst. prof. Hebrew U., Jerusalem, 1975—; faculty U. Toronto Sch. Theology Jewish Studies Program in Jerusalem, 1986—, Sem. Jewish Studies, Jerusalem, 1988—; mem. internat. bd. Yad Vashem, Jerusalem, 1980—. Author: Hasidic Responses to the Holocaust in the Light of Hasidic Thought, 1990; contbr. numerous articles to profl. jours. Founding mem. Hebrew U. Orch., Jerusalem, 1988. Mem. Rabbinical Assembly (rabbinic ct. on conversion 1988—, com. on Jewish law 1990—), Educators Assembly, Jerusalem Long Distance Running Club (chmn. 1984-87). Office: United Synagogue Conservative Judaism, PO Box 7456, Jerusalem 94205, Israel *Therfore faith is confrontation with the incredulous and with doubt. The struggle for redemption is therefore confrontation with the non-redemptive. Both represent a form of creation ex-nihilo—a marvelous gift from the Almighty to even the humblest human being, His partner in the constant drama in the response to life.*

SCHINDLER, PETER DAVID, child and adolescent psychiatrist; b. Berlin, Germany, Jan. 12, 1931; came to U.S. 1936; s. George David and Elizabeth (Sonntag) S.; m. Marianne Gertrude Leber; children: Thomas Kevin, Claudia Elizabeth. BA, Lafayette U., 1952; MD, U. Basel, Switzerland, 1960. Diplomate Am. Bd. Psychiatry and Neurology, Am. Bd. Child Psychiatry. Intern Stamford (Conn.) Hosp., 1960-61; resident adult psychiatry Temple U. Med. Sch. and Hosp., Phila., 1962-63; resident child psychiatry St. Christopher's Hosp. for Children, Temple U. Med. Sch., 1963-65; resident psychoanalytic, adult, adolescent and child tng. Phila. Psychoanalytic Inst., 1963-76; pvt. practice West Chester, Pa., 1965—; mem. staff adolescent psychiatry Chester County Mental Health Ctr. (now Family Svc.-Mental Health Ctrs. Chester County), West Chester, Pa., 1965-66; med. dir. Chester County Mental Health Ctr. (now Family Svc.-Mental Health Ctrs. Chester County), Pa., 1966-74; cons. Chester County Mental Health Ctr. (now Family Svc.-Mental Health Ctrs. Chester County), West Chester, Pa., 1974—; dir. child/adolescent psychiatry div. A.I. duPont Inst., Wilmington, Del., 1990—; cons. Child Diagnostic and Devel. Clinic, Dept. Devel. Medicine, Alfred I. duPont Inst., Wilmington, 1965—, dir. dept. psychol. medicine, 1979-83; cons. Vis. Nurse Assn. Del., Sch. Wellness Ctrs. Del., 1994—; chief psychiat. cons. A.I. duPont Sch. Dist., Wilmington, 1966-78; vol. faculty assoc. clin. prof. Thomas Jefferson U., Phila., 1980—; mem. staff Chester County Hosp., 1971—; cons. Presbyn. Children's Sch., Rosemont, Pa., 1965-77, Paoli (Pa.) Meml. Hosp., 1966—; Chester County Sch. Dist., 1968-69, West Chester U., 1972-75, lectr. 1969-70; cons. St. Mary's Providence Sch., Elverson, Pa., 1972-76, Westtown (Pa.) Sch., 1977—; mem. ad hoc ethics com. Med. Ctr. Del., Wilmington, 1984-87, profl. entries com. dept. psychiatry, 1989; cons. child/adolescent psychiatry div. child mental health, State of Del., Wilmington, 1985—; cons. in field The Melmark Home, Berwyn, Pa., 1984—; speaker in field. With U.S. Army, 1953-54. Fellow Am. Acad. Child and Adolescent Psychiatry (mental retardation com. 1987—), Am. Acad. Pediatrics (assoc. 1982—); mem. AMA (Pysician's Recognition award), Am. Psychiat. Assn., Chester County Med. Soc., Del. Psychiat. Assn., Med. Soc. Del. (physicians health com. 1979—), New Castle County Med. Soc., Pa. Med. Soc., Pa. Psychiat. Assn., Phila. Psychoanalytic Soc., Soc. Liaison Psychiatry, Sigma Xi. Avocation: sailing. Home and Office: 814 Denton Hollow Rd West Chester PA 19382-7023 Office: A I duPont Inst PO Box 269 Wilmington DE 19899-0269

SCHINDLER, WILLIAM STANLEY, retired public relations executive; b. Detroit, Jan. 4, 1933; s. William Henry and Katherine (Schilling) S. Student, Wayne State U., 1950-53. Sr. v.p. Campbell-Ewald Co., Warren, Mich., 1968-85; v.p. pub. rels. Detroit Med. Ctr., 1985-92; interim v.p. Wayne State U., Detroit, 1993; cons. to bus., univs., and founds.; v.p. Sandusky Pub. Co., Mich. Editor: Progress Report-New Detroit, Inc, 1969. Past mem. Detroit Hist. Commn., Detroit Fire Commn.; chmn. Detroit CSC; past pres. Detroit Hist. Soc., Hist. Soc. Mich.; mem. Gov's. Sesquicentennial Commn.; bd. dirs. Adult Well-Being Svcs., Sacred Heart Rehab. Ctr., Brush Park Devel. Authority, Harper Hosp. Aux. With U.S. Army. 1954-56. Decorated Commendation Medal with pendant. Mem. Pub. Rels. Soc. Am., Adcraft Club Detroit, Detroit Press Club, Soms Whiskey Rebellion, Recess Club, Univ. Club, Detroit Athletic Club, Prismatic Club, Box 12 Club. Home: 18771 N 94th Ave Peoria AZ 85382-3694

SCHINE, GERARD DAVID, entertainment company executive; b. Gloversville, N.Y., Sept. 11, 1927; s. J. Myer and Hildegarde (Feldman) S.; m. Anna Kristina Hilievi (Rombin), 1957; children: Anna Vidette Angela, Jonathan Mark, Alexander Kevin, Frederick Berndt, Benjamin Axel, William Lance. Grad., Fessenden Sch., West Newton, Mass., 1941, Phillips Acad., Andover, Mass., 1945; A.B., Harvard U., 1949. Pres., gen. mgr. Schine Hotels, 1950-63; exec. v.p. Schine Enterprises, 1952-57, pres., 1957-63; pres. Ski Dek Corp., 1961-67, David Schine & Co., Inc. Mgmt. Internat., Inc., Auto Inns Am., Inc., 1963-72. Ambassador Hotel Co. Los Angeles, 1960-63, 64-67, David Schine & Co. Inc., 1965-82; now pres. Schine Music, Myhil Music, Schine Prodns. Los Angeles; pres. Studio TV Services, Inc., Los Angeles, 1980-87, Visual Scis., Inc., 1980—, High Resolution TV, Inc., 1982-87, High Resolution Scis., Inc., 1987— Exec. producer: The French Connection, 1971; writer, producer, dir.: That's Action!, 1977; Author articles and pamphlets. Founding mem. Young Pres.' Orgn., 1950-77; adviser, spl. asst. atty.-gen. U.S. charge subversive activities, 1952; assisted investigation Communist infiltration into UN; chief cons. Senate Permanent Subcom. on Investigations, Com. on Govt. Operations, Jan. to Nov. 1953; directed

investigation of Internat. Information Adminstrn., also Voice of America Dept. State, 1953; mem. Los Angeles Citizens Com. for 1960 Democratic Conv.; Trustee Hotel Industry Devel. Fund; past dir. Symphony Club of Miami, Community Concert Assn. Miami Beach, Fla.; past chmn. adv. bd. Conv. Bur., Miami Beach; past mem. citizens adv. com. Hotel Employees Med. Plan; past dir. Com. 1000 for Variety Children's Hosp., Greater Miami Philharmonic Soc., Inc.; nat. bd. trustees City of Hope; past chmn. Miami Beach Com. Opera Guild; trustee Hope for Hearing Fund. Served as lt. U.S. Army Transport Service, 1946-47; with AUS, 1953-55. Mem. Chief Execs. Orgn. Am., Nat. Bus. Aircraft Assn., Aircraft Owners and Pilots Assn., A.I.M. (pres.'s council), So. Fla. Hotel and Motel Assn. (founding pres.), Dade County (Fla.) Devel. Com. Clubs: Lotos; Harvard (N.Y.C.). Home: PO Box 2181 Beverly Hills CA 90213-2181

SCHINK, FRANK EDWARD, electrical engineer; b. N.Y.C., May 14, 1922; s. Frank and Elizabeth (Kreps) S.; m. Barbara Jean McCally, Oct. 26, 1946; children: Stephen Frank, Thomas Ross. BEE, Bklyn. Poly. (now Poly. U. N.Y.), 1952, MEE, 1955. Registered profl. engr., N.Y., N.J. Elec. engr. George G. Sharp, Naval Architect, N.Y.C., 1940-43, 45, Anaconda Co., N.Y.C., 1946-59, Anaconda-Jurden Assocs., N.Y.C., 1959-61; sr. engr. M.W. Kellogg Co., N.Y.C., 1961-62; sr. engr. Port Authority of N.Y. & N.J., N.Y.C., 1962-77, cons. engr., 1977-84, chief elec. engr., 1984-89; pvt. practice elec. cons. Cranford, N.J., 1989—; mem. various coms. ELECTRO Confs., 1976—, past bd. dirs.; mem. adv. coun. N.J. Union County Transp., Westfield, 1977-79; mem. Port Authority Maintenance Improvement coun., N.Y.C., 1979-80; mem. com. IEEE Vehicular Tech. Conf., 1993; lectr. seminars Internat. Elec. Exposition and Congress, 1986, 87. Author/editor: Environmental Impact Assessment, 1977; contbr. articles to profl. jours. Pres. Brookside Civic Assn., Cranford, 1960-62; chmn. Cub Scout and Boy Scouts Troops, Cranford, 1960-65; capt. United Fund, Cranford, 1962; tchr. Am. Coun. for Emigres, N.Y.S., 1975. With U.S. Army, 1943-45, ETO. Fellow IEEE (vice chmn. region I 1986-87; chmn. N.Y. sect. 1984-85, vice chmn. 1982-84, treas. 1981-82, editor N.Y. sect. Monitor 1989-90, life mem. com. 1994—; also various coms.); mem. IEEE Power Engring Soc. (ad com. 1978-87, exec. com. 1983-87, chpts. rep. 1976-80, chmn. Winter Power Cponf., N.Y. 1990—), IEEE Industry Applications Soc. (coun. mem. 1977-90), Tau Beta Pi, Eta Kappa Nu. Republican. Methodist. Home and Office: 14 Middlebury Ln Cranford NJ 07016-1622

SCHINK, JAMES HARVEY, lawyer; b. Oak Park, Ill., Oct. 2, 1943; s. Norbert F. and Gwendolyn H. (Hummel) S.; m. Lisa Wilder Haskell, Jan. 1, 1972 (div. 1980); children—David, Caroline, Elizabeth; m. April Townley, Aug. 14, 1982. B.A., Yale U., 1965, J.D., 1968. Bar: Ill. 1968, Colo. 1982. Assoc. Sidley & Austin, Chgo., 1968; law clk. to judge U.S. Ct. Appeals, Chgo., 1968-69; assoc. Kirkland & Ellis, Chgo., 1969-72, ptnr., 1972—. Sustaining fellow Art Inst. Chgo. Mem. ABA, Ill. Bar Assn., Chgo. Bar Assn., Chgo. Club, Univ. Club, Saddle and Cycle Club, Mid-Am. Club (Chgo.), Econ. Club of Chgo., Chgo. Yacht Club, Denver Athletic Club, Yale Club of N.Y.C., Point O' Woods Golf & Tennis Club (Benton Harbor, Mich.), Vail Racquet Club. Republican. Presbyterian. Home: 1530 N State Pkwy Chicago IL 60610 Office: Kirkland & Ellis 200 E Randolph St Ste 6100 Chicago IL 60601

SCHINNERER, ALAN JOHN, entrepreneur; b. Long Beach, Calif., June 8, 1925; s. Walter John and Esther Schinnerer; m. Barbara Elaine Danziger, Aug. 17, 1951 (div. Aug. 1971); children: Gregory, Scott, Brett, Vicky. AA, Long Beach City Coll., 1948; B of Elec. Engring., U. So. Calif., 1952, postgrad. law, 1956-57, postgrad. bus., 1958-59. Purchasing agt. McCulloch Corp., Los Angeles, 1952-56; systems engr. Hughes Aircraft Co., Culver City, Calif., 1956-59; sales engr. Gilfillan Corp., Los Angeles, 1959-61; mktg. specialist N.Am. Rockwell Corp., Downey, Calif., 1961-68; sr. project engr. Hughes Aircraft Co., El Segundo, Calif., 1968-74, dir. satellite tests, 1974-76, assoc. program mgr., 1976-84; pres., owner, founder Calif. Classic Boats, Huntington Beach, 1979—; founding ptnr. Looking Glass Cellars, Murrieta, Calif., 1995—. Author: (catalog) Parts for Antique and Classic Chris-Craft, Dodge, Gar Wood and Hacker Runabouts, 1979-95. Bd. dirs. Antique Powercraft Hist. Soc., 1984-85. Served with USN, 1943-46, PTO. Mem. Antique and Classic Boat Soc. (founding pres. So. Calif. chpt. 1983-86), Garwood Soc., Delta Tau Delta. Republican. Clubs: Chris-Craft Antique Boat, Porsche of Am., Tahoe Yacht (Tahoe City, Calif.). Home: 5581 Ridgebury Dr Huntington Beach CA 92649-4825 Office: Calif Classic Boats 3267 Grant St Long Beach CA 90804

SCHINSKI, VERNON DAVID, navy officer; b. Chgo., Feb. 20, 1941; s. Leo August and Avis Amelia (Aldrich) S.; m. Vivian Elaine Mishler, Aug. 21, 1965; children: Victoria Joy, Valorie Lynn. BS in Biology, Goshen Coll., 1964; MS in Biology, Wayne State U., 1966; PhD in Zoology, U. Md., 1975. Commd. USN, 1966, advanced through grades to capt., 1985; rsch. parasitologist Navy Labs., Oakland, Bethesda, Md., Ethiopia, Egypt, 1966-81; exec. officer Navy Med. Rsch. Inst., Bethesda, 1981-83; commdg. officer Navy Med. Rsch. Labs., Philippines and Indonesia, 1983-85; sr. program analyst med. rsch. health affairs Dept. of Def., Washington, 1985-87; commdg. officer Navy Health Scis. Edn. & Tng. Command, Bethesda, 1987-90; dir. health affairs sec. of Navy, Washington 1990-91; chief staff health affairs Asst. Sec. Def., Washington, 1991-92; assoc. dean Uniformed Svcs. U., Bethesda, 1992—; mem. adv. coun. NIH-Nat. Inst. Gen. Med. Scis., Bethesda, 1985-87, NIH-Nat. Ctr. Rsch. Resources, Bethesda, 1993—; AIDS/HIV policy coms. Dept. Def., VA, NIH, Washington, 1985-87. Contbr. articles to profl. jours. Chmn. bd. trustees Youth for Christ, Montgomery County, Md., 1992—. Decorated Legion of Merit; Navy fellow U. Md., College Park, 1974-75. Mem. Am. Soc. Parasitologists, Am. Soc. Tropical Medicine and Hygiene, Helm Soc. Washington, Assn. Mil. Surgeons U.S., Am. Assn.Med. Adminstrs. Methodist. Avocation: painting - Appalachian Svc. Project. Office: Uniformed Svcs U 4301 Jones Bridge Rd Bethesda MD 20814-4712

SCHIPPER, MERLE, art historian and critic, exhibition curator; b. Toronto, Ont., Can.; came to U.S., 1943; d. Leon J. and Libby (Genesove) Solway; m. Bernard Schipper, May 22, 1943 (div. Jan. 1980); children: Lee, Amy Schipper Howe. BA, U. Toronto, 1943; MA, UCLA, 1970, PhD, 1974. Instr. extension UCLA, 1974-78, 83-84, lectr. summer session, 1977-79, 84; vis. artist grad. sch. Claremont (Calif.) U., 1979; lectr. U. So. Calif., L.A., 1985; corr. L.A. ARTnews, N.Y.C., 1985-87; columnist ARTScene, L.A., 1987—; project dir. Santa Monica (Calif.) Arts Found., 1987-89; art book reviewer L.A. Daily News, 1990-91; organizer Congress Internat. Assn. Art Critics, 1991; mem. pub. art panel Santa Monica Arts Commn., 1993—; mem. artist selection panel Met. Transp. Assn., Chinatown Sta., 1993. Panelist, mem. grants com. Art Orgn. Dept. Cultural Affairs, L.A., 1984-85; mem. selection com. of sculpture installation Calif. Med. Ctr., L.A., 1986; mem. Rev. Com. Hist. Resources Survey Project, L.A., 1978-85, So. Calif. Com. for Contemporary Art Documentation, L.A., 1985-89. Rsch. fellow Indo-U.S. Subcommn., 1988; travel grantee Ptnrs. of Ams., 1989. Mem. Coll. Art Assn., Internat. Assn. Art Critics. Home and Office: 835 Grant St Apt 3 Santa Monica CA 90405-1328

SCHIPPERS, DAVID PHILIP, lawyer; b. Chgo., Nov. 4, 1929; s. David Philip and Angela Marie (Lyons) S.; m. Jacquelin Joyce Liautaud, Apr. 19, 1952; children: David P. III, Kathleen M., Antoinette M., Ann L., Colleen M., Thomas M., Kevin D., Mary A., Patrick F., Peter A. BA, Loyola U., Chgo., 1955, JD, 1959. Bar: Ill. 1959, U.S. Dist. Ct. (no. dist.) Ill. 1959, U.S. Ct. Appeals (7th Cir.) 1962, U.S. Supreme Ct., 1966, U.S. Dist. Ct. (so. dist.) Ill. 1973, U.S. Ct. Appeals (9th Cir.) 1976, U.S. Ct. Claims 1979, U.S. Ct. Appeals (3d, 4th, 6th, 8th cirs.) 1981, U.S. Ct. Appeals (fed. cir.) 1983, Wis. 1985, U.S. Ct. Mil. Appeals 1987. Service rep. Ill. Bell Telephone Co., Chgo., 1950-59; assoc. Pope, Ballard, Uriell, Kennedy, Shepard & Fowle, Chgo., 1959-62; asst. atty. U.S. Dept. Justice, Chgo., 1962-63, spl. asst. atty. gen., 1963-64, chief organized crime and racketeering sect., 1964-67; ptnr. Schippers, Gilbert & Bailey, Chartered, Chgo., 1967—; adj. prof. Willamette U., Salem, Oreg., 1972—, Loyola U. Sch. Law, Chgo., 1972—; lectr. J.A.G. Sch., Maxwell AFB, Ala., 1988, 89. Active Cath. League Religious Freedom, Chgo., 1986—; Ill. Dept. Law Enforcement Merit Bd., Springfield, 1987-93; Ill. Crime Investigating Com., Chgo., 1969. Recipient Alumni medal of Excellence, Loyola U. 1967, citation Loyola U. Alumni Assn. 1970. Mem. ABA, Fed. Bar Assn., Ill. Bar Assn., Chgo. Bar Assn., Am. Arbitration Assn., Am. Trial Lawyers Assn., Ill. Trial Lawyers Assn., Appellate Lawyers Assn., Nat. Assn. Criminal Def. Lawyers, Chgo. Crime Commn.,

Fed. Criminal Investigators Assn., Markey Inn of Ct. Club. Office: Schippers Gilbert & Baily Chartr 20 N Clark St 36th FL Chicago IL 60602

SCHIRBER, ANNAMARIE RIDDERING, speech and language pathologist, educator; b. Somerset County, N.J., Dec. 18, 1941; d. Pieter C. and Marie Louise (Kerk) Riddering; m. Eric R. Schirber, Aug. 25, 1960; children: Stefan Rene, Ashley Brooke. BA in Speech and Hearing Therapy, Rutgers U., 1964; MA in Edn. of Deaf and Hard of Hearing, Smith Coll., 1968; postgrad., Rutgers U., 1987-93. Cert. tchr. of deaf, hard of hearing, spl. edn., speech correctionist, speech-lang pathologist, N.J. Speech therapist Manatee County Bd. Edn., Bradenton, Fla., 1968-69; speech-lang. specialist Lawrence Twp. Pub. Schs., Lawrenceville, N.J., 1969—; adj. instr. comm. dept. Trenton (N.J.) State Coll., 1983-87; vis. lectr. Rutgers U., New Brunswick, 1993. Author: Teaching Auditory Processing Skills to Children, 1994; co-author: (with Erica Winebrenner) Speech Activities for Children, 1994, Language Activities to Teach Children at Home, 1994. Mem. exec. com. Women's Coll. Symposium, Princeton, N.J., 1982-84; mem. nat. alumnae admissions com. Smith Coll., Northampton, Mass., 1984-86. Grantee Lawrence Twpw. Bd. Edn., 1973, 89, 90. Mem. N.J. Speech-Lang. and Hearing Assn., Cen. Jersey Speech-Lang. and Hearing Assn. (exec. com. 1984, v.p. 1985, pres. 1986-87). Home: 10 Sycamore Ln Skillman NJ 08558-2013 Office: Lawrence Twp Pub Schs Princeton Pike Trenton NJ 08648

SCHIRMEISTER, CHARLES F., lawyer; b. Jersey City, June 18, 1929; s. Charles F. and Louise P. (Schneider) S.; m. Barbara Jean Fredericks, Feb. 9, 1952; children—Pamela, Charles Bradford. B.A., U. Mich., 1951; LL.B., Fordham U., 1956. Bar: N.Y. 1956, U.S. Dist. Ct. (so. dist) N.Y., U.S. Ct. Appeals (2d cir.), U.S. Supreme Ct. 1961. Asst. dist. atty. N.Y. County (N.Y.), 1956-61; assoc. Reid & Priest, N.Y.C., 1961-71, ptnr., 1971—. Trustee, deacon, Community Congregational Ch., Short Hills, N.J.; trustee Ocean Grove (N.J.) Camp Meeting Assn. Served to capt. USMC, 1951-53. Mem. ABA, N.Y. County Lawyers Assn., Fed. Bar Coun., Sigma Alpha Epsilon. Republican. Clubs: University (N.Y.C.), Canoe Brook Country Club (Summit, N.J.). Avocations: tennis, oenology. Home: 15 Beechcroft Rd Short Hills NJ 07078-1648 Office: Reid & Priest 40 W 57th St New York NY 10019-4001

SCHIRMER, HENRY WILLIAM, architect; b. St. Joseph, Mo., Dec. 8, 1922; s. Henry William and Asta (Hansen) S.; m. Jane Irene Krueger; children: Andrew Lewis, Monica Sue, Daniel F. Carr. AS, St. Joseph Jr. Coll., 1942; BArch Design, U. Mich., 1949. Staff architect Eugene Meier, Architect, St. Joseph, 1939, Neville, Sharp & Simon, Kansas City, Mo., 1946, 49, Ramey & Himes, Wichita, Kans., 1950-57; ptnr. Schaefer & Schirmer, Wichita, 1957-60, Schaefer, Schirmer & Eflin, Wichita, 1960-72, Schaefer, Schirmer & Assocs. P.A., Wichita, 1972-76; prin. Henry W. Schirmer, Topeka, 1976-92, Green Valley, 1993—. Editor: Profile Ofcl. Directory of AIA, 1978, 80, 83, 85, 87, 89-90, 91-92, pub., 1985-92; contbr. AIA Handbook; works include Burn Ctr. U. Kans. Med. Ctr., Allen County Community Jr. Coll., Iola, Kans., Rainbow Mental Health Ctr., Kansas City, Kans., Capitol Area Plaza Project, Topeka. Pres. East Br. YMCA, 1954—; bd. dirs. Wichita YMCA, 1956-73; bd. dirs. San Ignacio Heights H.O.A., 1995—. With C.E. U.S Army, ETO. Decorated Purple Heart. Fellow AIA (past pres. Kans. chpt., seminar leader, chmn. nat. com. office mgmt.1976, nat. bd. dirs. 1979-81, treas. 1982-86, fin. com. 1988, nat. documents com. 1978, chmn. nat. com. on project mgmt. 1977, Edward C. Kemper medal 1990); mem. Kans. Bd. Tech. Professions (chmn. bd. 1985, 87), Nat. Coun. Archtl. Registration Bds. (profl. conduct com. 1986-89, procedures and documents com. 1990), Tau Sigma Delta. Lutheran. Home: 4191 S Emelita Dr Green Valley AZ 85614-5614

SCHIRMER, HOWARD AUGUST, JR., civil engineer; b. Oakland, Calif., Apr. 21, 1942; s. Howard August and Amy (Freuler) S.; m. Leslie May Mecum, Jan. 29, 1965; children: Christine Nani, Amy Kiana, Patricia Leolani. B.S., U. Calif., Berkeley, 1964, M.S., 1965. Registered profl. engr., Hawaii, Guam. Engr. in tng. materials and research dept. Calif. Div. Hwys., Sacramento, 1960-64; engring. analyst Dames & Moore, San Francisco, 1964-67; asst. staff engr. Dames & Moore, 1967-68, chief engr., 1969-72; asso. Dames & Moore, Honolulu, 1972-75; partner, mng. prin. in charge Dames & Moore, 1975-78; regional mgr. Dames & Moore, Pacific Far East and Australia, 1978-81; chief operating officer Dames & Moore, Los Angeles, 1981-83; mng. dir. Dames & Moore Internat., Los Angeles, 1983-89; mng. dir. CH2M Hill Internat. Ltd., Denver, 1989-90, pres., 1991; chmn. geotech. engring. com. Am. Cons. Engrs. Council, 1976-78, profl. liability com. 1984—; past chmn. adv. com. for engring. tech. Honolulu Community Coll. Important works include AFDM Berthing Wharf, Pearl Harbor, Aloha Stadium, Hawaii, Century Ctr., Honolulu, Manila Internat. Airport, Philippines. Past mem. instale UCLA Grad. Sch. Mgmt.; chmn. engring. sect., mem. budget com. Aloha United Way, 1974; founder Mauna Kea Ski Patrol, 1969. Fellow ASCE (past chmn. engring. mgmt. exec. com. 1986-87, Edmund Friedman Young Engr. award for profl. achievement 1974, pres. Hawaii sect., internat. activities com., internat. dir. 1989—); mem. Fedn. Internationale des Ingenieurs-Conseils (chmn. standing com. on profl. liability 1986-89, U.S. rep. to com., mem. task com. on constrn. ins. and law), Cons. Engrs. Coun. Hawaii (pres. 1972), Engring. Assn. Hawaii (past dir., 2d v.p.), Internat. Soc. Soil Mechanics and Found. Engring., Am. Public Works Assn. (sec. 1977-78, dir. 1979-80), Soc. Am. Mil. Engrs., Am. Soc. Profl. Engrs. (internat. contact dir. 1989—), Outrigger Canoe Club, Jonathan Club (L.A.), Met. Club (Denver), Chi Epsilon (hon. mem. U. Hawaii), Sigma Phi Epsilon. Republican. Episcopalian. Home: 4061 S Birch St Englewood CO 80110-5031 Office: CH2M Hill Internat Ltd 6060 S Willow Dr Englewood CO 80111-5142*

SCHIRMER, ROBERT HAMILTON, advertising executive; b. Detroit, Mich., July 19, 1940; s. Edward Adolph and Frances (Hamilton) S.; m. Alice Louise Mayes, Feb. 12, 1940; children: Allison, Mark, Cathrine. BA, Denison U., 1962. Account exec. MacManes, John & Adams, Detroit, 1965-68; account supr. Grey Advt., Detroit, 1968-72; Dodge advt. mgr. Chrysler Corp., Detroit, 1972-75, dir. merchandising, 1977-79; sr. v.p. McCann-Erickson, Detroit, 1975-77; exec. v.p. Campbell-Ewald, Detroit, 1979—. Trustee Mercy Coll. of Detroit, 1985—. Served to lt. (j.g.) USN, 1962-65. Mem. Detroit Adcraft Club (bd. dirs. 1984—), Mich. Council Am. Assn. Ad. Agys. (bd. dirs. 1984—). Republican. Episcopalian. Clubs: Orchard Lake (Mich.) Country; Recess (Detroit). Avocations: hunting, carpentry. Office: Lintas-Campbell Ewald 30400 Van Dyke Ave Warren MI 48093-2316 also: Lintas USA 1 Dag Hammarskjold Pla New York NY 10017

SCHIRN, JANET SUGERMAN, interior designer; b. Jersey City, N.Y.; d. Oscar H. and Mary (Lustig) S.; 1 child, Martha. BFA, Pratt Inst.; MFA, Columbia U.; postgrad. in Architecture, U. Ill. Tchr. N.Y.C. Bd. Edn.; dir. N.Y.C. Bd. Adult Edn.; pres. Janet Schirn Design Group, Chgo., N.Y.C., 1950—; prin. The J S Collection, N.Y.C., 1978—; adj. prof. So. Ill. U., 1991-92; mem. adv. bd. Du Pont Co., Monsanto, 1981—, So. Ill. U., 1990—. Contbr. articles to interior design mag. Bd. dirs. Washington Architecture Forum, Chgo. Archtl. Assistance Ctr., 1975, pres., 1982; adv. bd. mem. Mundelein Coll. dept. interior architecture, 1978; mem. Met. Planning Coun., Chgo., 1980—, Art Resources Teaching, 1984—; mem. aux. bd. Sch. of Art Inst., Ill. Arts Alliance. Recipient award Chgo. Lighting Inst., 1989, 92, 93, Villeroy and Boch Gold award, 1990, Designer mag. residential award, 1990, Edward Fields 1st prize Rug Design, 1991, 1st prize project awards ASID, 1993. Mem. UNESCO (steering com. tall bldgs. and urban habitat coun.), Am. Soc. Interior Designers (nat. pres. 1986, nat. treas. 1984, regional v.p. 1981, pres. Il chpt. 1977-78, nat. dir. 1979-83, chmn. pub. affairs 1989), Illuminating Engring. Soc., Am. Inst. Architects (nat. urban planning and design com. 1981-85), The Chgo. Network, Internat. Fedn. of Interior Designers (exec. bd. dirs.). Home: 220 E Walton St Chicago IL 60611-1534 Office: Janet Schirn Design Group 401 N Franklin St Chicago IL 60610-4402 also: 521 Fifth Ave New York NY 10175 also: 821 Delaware Ave SW Washington DC 20024-4207

SCHIRRA, WALTER MARTY, JR., business consultant, former astronaut; b. Hackensack, N.J., Mar. 12, 1923; s. Walter Marty and Florence (Leach) S.; m. Josephine Cook Fraser, Feb. 23, 1946; children: Walter Marty III, Suzanne Karen. Student, Newark Coll. Engring., 1940-42; B.S., U.S. Naval Acad., 1945; D. Astronautics (hon.), Lafayette Coll., U. So. Calif., N.J. Inst. Tech. Commd. ensign U.S. Navy, 1945, advanced through grades to capt., 1965; designated naval aviator, 1948; service aboard battle cruiser Alaska,

1945-46; service with 7th Fleet, 1946; assigned Fighter Squadron 71, 1948-51; exchange pilot 154th USAF Fighter Bomber Squadron, 1951; engaged in devel. Sidewinder missile China Lake, Calif., 1952-54; project pilot F7U-3 Cutlass; also instr. pilot F7U-3 Cutlass and FJ3 Fury, 1954-56; ops. officer Fighter Squadron 124, U.S.S. Lexington, 1956-57; assigned Naval Air Safety Officer Sch., 1957, Naval Air Test Ctr., 1958-59; engaged in suitability devel. work F4H, 1958-59; joined Project Mercury, man-in-space, NASA, 1959; pilot spacecraft Sigma 7 in 6 orbital flights, Oct. 1962; in charge operations and tng. Astronaut Office, 1964-69; command pilot Gemini 6 which made rendezvous with target, Gemini 7, Dec. 1965; comdr. 11 day flight Apollo 7, 1968; ret., 1969; pres. Regency Investors, Inc., Denver, 1969-70; chmn., chief exec. officer ECCO Corp., Englewood, Colo., 1970-73; chmn. Sernco, Inc., 1973-74; with Johns-Manville Corp., Denver, 1974-77; v.p. devel. Goodwin Cos., Inc., Littleton, Colo., 1978-79; ind. cons., 1979-80; dir. Kimberly Clark, 1983-91. Decorated D.F.C.(3), Air medal (2), Navy D.S.M.; recipient Distinguished Service medal (2), also; Exceptional Service medal NASA. Fellow Am. Astronautical Soc., Soc. Exptl. Test Pilots. Home and Office: PO Box 73 Rancho Santa Fe CA 92067-0073

SCHISGAL, MURRAY JOSEPH, playwright; b. N.Y.C., Nov. 25, 1926; s. Abraham and Irene (Sperling) S.; m. Reene Schapiro, June 29, 1958; children: Jane, Zachary. Student, Bklyn. Conservatory of Music, 1948, L.I. U., 1950; LLB, Bklyn. Law Sch., 1953; BA, New Sch. Social Research, 1959. Author: The Typists and The Tiger, London, 1960, N.Y.C., 1963, Ducks and Lovers, London, 1961, Knit One, Purl Two, Boston, 1963, Luv (One of the Best Plays of 1964-65), London, 1963, N.Y.C., 1964, Fragments, Windows and other plays, 1965, Best Short Plays, 1981, 83, 85; original TV plays The Love Song of Barney Kempinski, 1966, Natasha Kovolina Pipishinski, 1976; off-Broadway Fragments, 1967, The Basement, 1967; Jimmy Shine, 1968, 69, Broadway The Chinese, N.Y.C., 1970 (pub. in Best Short Plays of the World Theatre 1973), Dr. Fish, 1970, An American Millionaire, 1974, All Over Town, 1974 (pub. Best Plays 1974-75); screenplay The Tiger Makes Out, 1967, The Pushcart Peddlers, prod. off-off-Broadway, 1979; novel Days and Nights of a French Horn Player, 1980, Walter and the Flatulist; prod. off-regional theatre A Need for Brussels Sprouts, 1981, Play Time, Denver Ctr. Theatre, 1991, The Japanese Foreign Trade Minister, Cleve. Playhouse, 1992, 74 Georgia Ave., 1992, Circus Life, 1992; prod. Broadway Twice Around the Park, 1982; Other Plays, 1983, Closet Madness and Other Plays, 1984, Popkins, Paris, 1990, Play Time, 1991, The Songs of War, 1989; prod. Off Broadway The New Yorkers, 1984, Circus Life, 1995; prodr. Extensions, 1994; co-author: screenplay Tootsie (Winner Los Angeles Film Critics, N.Y. Film Critics, Nat. Soc. Film Critics, Writers Guild Am. award for best comedy); author Luv and Other Plays, 1983, The Rabbi and the Toyota Dealer, 1985, Jealousy, There are No Sacher Tortes in Our Society, 1985, Old Wine in a New Bottle, 1987, Road Show, 1987, Man Dangling, 1988, Oatmeal and Kisses, 1990, (with others) Best Short American Plays of 1991, 92-93, Sexaholics and Other Plays, 1995, Extensions, 1994. Recipient Vernon Rice award outstanding achievement off-Broadway Theatre, 1963; Outer Circle award Outstanding Theatre, 1963; named Outstanding Playwright, 1963. Office: care Bridget Aschenberg Internat Creative Mgmt 40 W 57th St New York NY 10019-4001

SCHIZER, ZEVIE BARUCH, lawyer; b. Bklyn., Dec. 19, 1928; s. David and Bertha (Rudavsky) S.; m. Hazel Gerber, Aug. 23, 1962; children: Deborah Gail, Miriam Anne, David Michael. BA magna cum laude, NYU, 1950; JD, Yale U., 1953. Bar: N.Y. 1954, U.S. Dist. Ct. (so. and ea. dist.) N.Y. 1959, U.S. Ct. Appeals (2d cir.) 1959, U.S. Supreme Ct. 1959. Assoc. Guzik & Boukstein, N.Y.C., 1953-54; teaching fellow NYU, 1954-55; assoc. Philips, Nizer, Benjamin & Krim, N.Y.C., 1955-56, Aranow, Brodsky, Einhorn & Dann, N.Y.C., 1956-57; asst. counsel Appellate Divsn. 2nd Dept., Bklyn., 1957-62; assoc. Hays, Porter, Spanier & Curtis, N.Y.C., 1963-68, ptnr., 1968-85; sec. United Aircraft Products, Inc., Dayton, Ohio, 1970-83; ptnr. Schizer & Schizer, N.Y.C., 1985—. Trustee Bklyn. Pub. Libr., 1966—, pres. 1985-88, N.Y. Young Dem. Club, N.Y.C., 1960-61; trustee East Midwood Jewish Ctr., Bklyn., 1991—. Mem. N.Y. County Lawyers Assn. (mem. profl. ethics com., mem. com. on profl. discipline), Phi Beta Kappa. Democrat. Jewish. Home: 1134 E 23rd St Brooklyn NY 11210-4519 Office: Schizer & Schizer 3 New York Plz New York NY 10004-2441

SCHLAFER, DONALD HUGHES, veterinary pathologist; b. Sidney, N.Y., July 15, 1948; s. Donald Hughes and Mildred (Gamewell) S., Jr.; m. Judith Ann Appleton, Aug. 2, 1980; children: Nathan James, Russell Matthew. BS, Cornell U., 1971, MS, 1975; DVM, N.Y. State Coll. Vet. Medicine, Ithaca, 1974; PhD, Coll. Vet. Medicine, Athens, Ga., 1982. Diplomate Am. Coll. Vet. Pathologists, Am. Coll. Theriogenologists (exec. com. 1993—), Am. Coll. Vet. Microbiologists. Gen. practice vet. medicine Guilderland Animal Hosp., Altamont, N.Y., 1975-77; resident dept. vet. pathology U. Ga., Athens, 1977-79; research pathologist USDA Plum Island Animal Disease Ctr., Greenport, N.Y., 1975-82; asst. prof. dept. vet. pathology Cornell U., Ithaca, 1982-88, assoc. prof., 1988—; dir. Bovine Research Ctr., 1982-91; 1982-91; cons. in field, 1983—. Contbr. articles to profl. publs. Mem. AVMA, Soc. for Study of Reprodn., Soc. for Theriogenology (exec. com. 1993-96), U.S. Animal Health Assn. Office: NY State Coll Vet Medicine Cornell U Ithaca NY 14853

SCHLAFLY, HUBERT JOSEPH, JR., communications executive; b. St. Louis, Aug. 14, 1919; s. Hubert J. and Mary Ross (Parker) S.; m. Leona Martin, June 12, 1944. B.S. in Elec. Engring. U. Notre Dame, 1941; postgrad., Syracuse U. extension, 1946-47. Electronics engr. Gen. Electric Co., Schenectady, 1941-44, Syracuse, 1946-47; project engr. Radiation Lab., Mass., Inst. Tech., 1944-45; dir. TV research 20th Century-Fox Film Corp., N.Y.C., 1947-51; a founder Teleprompter Corp., N.Y.C., 1951, v.p., 1951-74, pres., 1971-72, exec. v.p. tech. devel., 1972-74; pres. Transponder Corp. Greenwich, 1977-86; chmn., chief exec. officer Portel Services Corp., 1984-86; chmn., pres. Portel Services Network, Inc., 1987-91, chmn. bd., 1991—; cons. in field; industry coord., chmn. exec. com., cable tech. adv. com. FCC, 1972-75; adviser comm. telecom. Nat. Acad. Engring.; advisor Sloan Commn. Cable Commns.; mem. engring. adv. coun. U. Notre Dame, 1977—, vice chmn., 1983, chmn., 1984; lectr. in field; dir., sec. Milbrook Corp., 1994—. Author: Computer in the Living Room. Bd. govs. Milbrook Club, 1993—. Recipient Engring. Honor award U. Notre Dame, 1976, Nat. Acad. T.V. Arts and Scis. Emmy award, 1992. Fellow Soc. Motion Picture and TV Engrs.; mem. IEEE (Delmer Ports award 1979, life), Nat. Cable TV Assn. (chmn. standards com. 1965-69, chmn. domestic satellite com. 1971-73, chmn. future svcs. com. 1972, assns. com. 1981, Outstanding Tech. Achievements award 1974), Cable TV Pioneers, Electronic Industries Assn. (chmn. broadband cable sect. 1971-73, founding chmn. broadband communications com.), Soc. Cable TV Engrs. (sr.), Fairfield Found. (hon.); named Notre Dame alumni Man of Yr., 1992. Roman Catholic. Clubs: Milbrook Country, Rotary (pres. Greenwich club 1991-92), Knights of Malta, Knight St. Gregory the Great. Patentee in field. Home and Office: 27 Orchard Dr Greenwich CT 06830-6711

SCHLAFLY, PHYLLIS STEWART, author; b. St. Louis, Aug. 15, 1924; d. John Bruce and Odile (Dodge) Stewart; m. Fred Schlafly, Oct. 20, 1949; children: John F., Bruce S., Roger S., Phyllis Liza Forshaw, Andrew L., Anne V. BA, Washington U., St. Louis, 1944, JD, 1978; MA, Harvard U., 1945; LLD, Niagara U., 1976. Bar: Ill. 1979, D.C. 1984, Mo. 1985, U.S. Supreme Ct. 1987. Syndicated columnist Copley News Svc., 1976—; pres. Eagle Forum, 1975—; broadcaster Spectrum, CBS Radio Network, 1973-78; commentator Cable TV News Network, 1980-83, Matters of Opinion sta. WBBM-AM, Chgo., 1973-75. Author, pub.: Phyllis Schlafly Report, 1967—; author: A Choice Not an Echo, 1964, The Gravediggers, 1964, Strike From Space, 1965, Safe Not Sorry, 1967, The Betrayers, 1968, Mindszenty The Man, 1972, Kissinger on the Couch, 1975, Ambush at Vladivostok, 1976, The Power of the Positive Woman, 1977, First Reader, 1994; editor: Child Abuse in the Classroom, 1984, Pornography's Victims, 1987, Equal Pay for Unequal Work, 1984, Who Will Rock the Cradle, 1989, Stronger Families or Bigger Government, 1990, Meddlesome Mandate: Rethinking Family Leave, 1991. Del. Rep. Nat. Conv., 1956, 64, 68, 84, 88, 92, alt., 1960, 80; pres. Ill. Fedn. Rep. Women, 1960-64; 1st v.p. Nat. Fedn. Rep. Women, 1964-67; mem. Ill. Commn. on Status of Women, 1975-85; nat. chmn. Stop ERA, 1972—; mem. Ronald Reagan's Def. Policy Adv. Group, 1980; mem. Commn. on Bicentennial of U.S. Constn., 1985-91; mem. Adminstrv. Conf. U.S., 1983-86. Recipient 10 Honor awards Freedoms Found., Brotherhood award NCCJ, 1975; named Woman of Achievement in

Pub. Affairs St. Louis Globe-Democrat, 1963, one of 10 most admired women in world Good Housekeeping poll, 1977-90. Mem. ABA, DAR (nat. chmn. Am. history 1965-68, nat. chmn. bicentennial com. 1967-70, nat. chmn. nat. def. 1977-80, 83-95), Ill. Bar Assn., Phi Beta Kappa, Pi Sigma Alpha. Office: Eagle Forum 7800 Bonhomme Ave Saint Louis MO 63105

SCHLAGEL, RICHARD H., philosophy educator; b. Springfield, Mass., Nov. 22, 1925. BS in Pre-Med cum laude, Springfield Coll., 1949; MA in Philosophy, Boston U., 1952, PhD, 1955. Instr. philosophy Coll. of Wooster, 1954-55; instr. Clark U., 1955-56; asst. prof. George Washington U., 1956-62, assoc. prof., 1962-68, prof., 1968—, chmn. dept., 1965-69, 70-71, 77-83, named Elton prof. philosophy, 1986; sabbatical, Paris, with travel throughout Europe, 1962-63, 69-70, 76-77, 83-84, 90-91. Author: From Myth to the Modern Mind: A Study of the Origins and Growth of Scientific Thought, Vol. I, Animism to Archimedes, 1985, Contextual Realism: A Meta-physical Framework for Modern Science, 1986; also articles and revs. Borden Parker Browne fellow, 1953-54. Mem. AAUP, Am. Philos. Assn., Philosophy of Sci. Assn., Washington Philosophy Club (v.p. 1964-65, pres. 1965-66). Office: George Washington U Dept Philosophy Washington DC 20052

SCHLAGETER, ROBERT WILLIAM, museum administrator; b. Streator, Ill., May 10, 1925; s. Herman Pete and Ida (Ladtkow) S.; divorced; children—David Michael, Robert William. Diploma, Karl Ruprecht Univ., Heidelberg, Fed. Republic Germany, 1950; BA, U. Ill., 1950, MFA, 1957. Asst. prof. U. Tenn., Knoxville, 1952-58; dir. Mint Mus. Art, Charlotte, N.C., 1958-66; assoc. dir. Downtown Gallery, N.Y.C., 1966, Ackland Art Ctr., U. N.C., Chapel Hill, 1967-76; dir. Cummer Gallery Art, Jacksonville, Fla., 1976-92. dir. emeritus, 1992—; fine arts cons. corp. and pvt. collecting, 1993—. Author: (exhbn. catalogue) Winslow Homer's Florida, George Inness' Florida, Martin Johnson Heade Florida, Robert Henri-George Bellows. Served with U.S. Army, 1943-45, ETO. Home: 5201 Atlantic Blvd Apt 2 Jacksonville FL 32207-2473

SCHLAIFER, CHARLES, advertising executive; b. Omaha, July 1, 1909; s. Abraham Schlaifer; m. Evelyn Chaikin, June 10, 1934 (dec. Oct. 1978); children: Arlene Lois Silk, Roberta Semer; m. Ann Mesavage, July 31, 1980. Privately ed.; Litt.D. (hon.), John F. Kennedy Coll., 1969. Newspaper reporter Omaha, 1926-29; advt. dir. Publix Tri-States Theatres, Nebr., Iowa, 1929-37; mng. dir. United Artists Theatres, San Francisco, 1937-42; nat. advt. cons. United Artists Producers, 1937-42; nat. advt. mgr. 20th Century-Fox Film Corp., N.Y.C., 1942-45; v.p. charge advt. and pub. relations 20th Century-Fox Film Corp., 1945-49; pres. Charles Schlaifer & Co., Inc., N.Y.C., 1949—; vis. prof. New Sch. Social Research; expert witness U.S. Congl. and Senatorial coms. on mental health, 1949—. Author: Advertising Code, Motion Picture Assn., 1948; co-author: Action for Mental Health, 1961, Heart's Work, 1991; contbr. articles to psychiat. jours. Mem. Pres.'s Com. Employment Handicapped, 1960—; founder, co-chmn. Nat. Mental Health Com., 1949-57; mem. nat. mental health adv. council Surgeon Gen. U.S., 1950-54; sec.-treas. Joint Commn. Mental Illness and Health, 1955-61; vice chmn. Found. Child Mental Welfare, 1963; mem. Gov.'s Youth Council State N.Y.; chmn. N.Y. State Mental Hygiene Facilities Improvement Corp., 1963—, White House Conf. Children, 1970; sec.-treas., bd. dirs. Joint Commn. Mental Health Children; chmn. N.Y. State Facilities Devel. Corp., 1963-78; mem. adv. council NIMH, 1976—; bd. dirs. Hillside Hosp., League Sch. For Seriously Disturbed Children, Menninger Found., Nat. Mental Hygiene Com. Recipient Social Conscience award Karen Horney Clinic, 1972; Hon. fellow Postgrad. Center Mental Health. Fellow Am. Psychiat. Assn. (hon.), Brit. Royal Soc. Health (hon.), Am. Orthopsychiat. Assn. (hon.); Mem. Nat. Assn. Mental Health (founder), Acad. for Motion Picture Arts and Scis., Harmonie Club. Home and Office: 150 E 69th St New York NY 10021-5704

SCHLARMAN, STANLEY GERARD, bishop; b. Belleville, Ill., July 27, 1933. Student, St. Henry Prep. Sem., Belleville, Gregorian U., Rome, St. Louis U. Ordained priest Roman Catholic Ch., 1958, consecrated bishop, 1979. Titular bishop of Capri and aux. bishop of Belleville, 1979-83; bishop of Dodge City Kans., 1983—. Office: Diocese of Dodge City PO Box 137 910 Central Ave Dodge City KS 67801-4513

SCHLATTER, GEORGE H., producer, director, writer; b. Birmingham; m. Jolene Brand; two children. Student, Pepperdine U. Producer numerous shows including (TV series) Dinah Shore Shows, 1957-62, 60-62, Judy Garland Show, 1963, Steve Lawrence Show, 1965, Colgate Comedy Hour, 1967, Laugh-In, 1967-73, 76-77, Bill Cosby Series, 1972-73, Cher, 1975, Real People, 1979; (TV spls.) Grammy Awards 1965, 68, 69, 70, Jonathan Winters, 1964, Meredith Willson, 1964, Danny Thomas, 1964, 65, Ernie Ford, 1967, Laugh-In, 1967, Dinah Shore, 1969, Doris Day, 1974, Cher, 1975, Diana Ross, 1975, Goldie Hawn, 1975, Goldie & Liza Together, 1980, Joe Piscopo, 1986, George Schlatter's Comedy Club Spl., 1988, Beverly Hills 75th Anniversary, 1989, Sammy Davis Jr. 60th Anniversary Celebration, 1989, 25th Anniversary of the Jerry Lewis Labor Day Telethon, 1990, Sinatra 75th: The Best is Yet to Come, 1990, Soc. of Singers Salute to Frank Sinatra, 1990, Real People Reunion Spl., 1991, A Party for Richard Pryor, 1991, (charitable events) Thalians Tribute to Marianne and Kenny Rogers, 1981, Sun Valley Ski Tournament, 1985, 86, Am. Cinematheque Tribute to Eddie Murphy, 1986, to Bette Midler, 1987, to Robin Williams, 1988, Tel Aviv Found. Cinematheque Tribute to Goldie Hawn and Stan Kamen, 1987, AIDS Project Los Angeles Benefit, 1987, Big Sisters Benefit, 1988, Beverly Hills 75th Anniversary Honoring Frank Sinatra, 1989, Paul Newman/Joanne Woodward Event for the Scott Newman Found., 1990, Carousel of Hope Ball (Barbara/Marvin Davis Diabetes Found., 1990. Recipient 5 Emmys, 22 Emmy nominations, Golden Globe awards, Image awards, Monitor awards, Dirs. Guild award, Producers Guild award, Writer's Guild award ; named Internat. Radio and TV Man of Yr.; awarded a star on Hollywood Blvd.'s Walk of Fame. Avocations: skiing, horseback riding, sailing, scuba diving. Office: William Morris Agy 151 S El Camino Dr Beverly Hills CA 90212-2704

SCHLATTER, KONRAD, corporate executive; b. Zurich, Switzerland, Nov. 6, 1935; came to U.S., 1981; m. Janet Dodd; children: Benedict, Katherine, Frederick. BBA, Bus. Sch. Commerce Assn. Coll., Zurich, Switzerland, 1955. With affiliates of CPC Internat., France, Switzerland, England, 1956-67; comptroller CPC Europe div. CPC Internat., Brussels, 1967-70; dir. fin. CPC Asia div. CPC Internat., Hong Kong, 1970-71, v.p. fin., 1971-76, sr. v.p. fin., 1976-79; chmn. CPC Japan div. CPC Internat., Tokyo, 1979-81; comptroller CPC Internat. Inc., Englewood Cliffs, N.J., 1981-87, v.p. fin. planning, reporting, control, 1987—, alsp sr. v.p. and CFO. Trustee Elisabeth Morrow Sch., Englewood Cliffs, mem. fin. com. Englewood Hosp. Mem. Fin. Execs. Inst., N.J. Hist. Soc. (bd. dirs.), Japan Soc., N.Y.C. Office: CPC Internat Inc Box 8000 International Plz Englewood Cliffs NJ 07632

SCHLECK, ROTH STEPHEN, banker; b. Wonewoc, Wis., Nov. 24, 1915; s. Mathias Hubert and Elizabeth Ann (Roth) S.; m. Jeanne Johansen, July 7, 1947; children: Stephen E., Roth Stephen II, Mark T., Julie M. B.A. in Acctg., U.S. Wis., 1938; grad., Central State Sch. of Banking, Wis., 1948; postgrad., U.S. Army Command and Gen. Staff Sch., 1962. Various adminstrv. positions in depts. acctg. and personnel First Wis. Nat. Bank of Milw., 1938-67, head mktg. div., 1963-65, v.p., 1958-67; pres. First Wis. Nat. Bank of Eau Claire, 1967-76; pres. First Wis. Nat. Bank of Madison, 1976-79, chmn. bd., 1979-82, chief exec. officer, 1976-82; prin. Exec. Dynamics, 1982—; pres. Madison Capital Corp.; pres. Eau Claire Indsl. Devel. Corp., 1969-76; v.p. Eau Claire Hotel Corp. 1974-76; dir. Am. Mut. Life Ins. Co., Madison, Wis., First Wis. Corp., Milw. Mem. adv. com. Chippewa Valley council Boy Scouts Am., 1969-76; pres. Central Madison Council, 1978-80; mem. lay adv. bd. Sacred Heart Hosp., Madison, 1978-80; civilian aide to sec. of Army, State of Wis., 1976-78; mem. fin., budget and devel. com. St. Marys Hosp., 1978-80; chmn. Central City Mixed Housing Com., Madison, 1976-80; chmn. bus. adv. bd. Gov.'s Council Econ. Devel. State of Wis., 1965-67; mem. adv. bd. No. Wis. Devel. Center, 1965-67; chmn. resource priorities bd., State of Wis., 1965-67; mem. Nat. UN Com., 1975, 78, 80; bd. dirs. Madison United Way, 1976-78, Eau Claire Found., U. Wis., 1970-76, St. Mary's Hosp. Med. Center, 1970-76, Wis. History Found., 1978—, Madison Art Center, 1978-81, Public Expenditure Survey of Wis., 1970-81. Served with inf. U.S. Army, World War II, PTO. Mem. Nat. Council for

Small Bus. Mgmt., Am. Inst. Banking, Am. Security Council (mem. nat. adv. bd.), Bascom Hill Soc., Badger Bankers, Wis. Bankers Assn. (mem. legis. com. 1976-80), Wis. Econ. Devel. Assn., Eau Claire County Taxpayers Assn., Wis. Alumni Assn., Am. Legion, Assn. of U.S. Army, Ret. Officers Assn., VFW, 127th Inf. Assn., Dane County Public Affairs Council (chmn. 1978-80), Smithsonian Nat. Assos. Club: Executive. Home: 19 Mountain Ash Trl Madison WI 53717-1508 Office: First Wis Natl Bank of Madison 1 S Pinckney St Madison WI 53707 *It is my belief that the enhanced professional management and social consciousness of American business leadership provides an exciting and rewarding future for the entire country. I feel that I have been helpful in encouraging this trend.*

SCHLECK, THOMAS TODD, financial executive; b. Dodgeville, Wis., June 2, 1947; s. Clarence Carl and Helen Gertrude (Zwettler) S.; m. Carol A. Amos, Dec. 1, 1973; children: Erin, Heather, Alexandra, Gregory. BBA in Fin., U. Wis., 1970. V.p. Banl of Am. NT & SA, L.A., 1970-82; v.p., treas. Am. Med. Internat., Beverly Hills, Calif., 1982-88; CFO, treas., dir. EPIC Holdings, Inc., Dallas, 1988—; mem. southwestern adv. bd. Arkwright Mut. Ins. Co.; bd. dirs. EPIC Holdings, Inc. Bd. dirs. Dallas Adult Literacy Coun., 1993-94. Mem. Leading Chief Fin. Officers, Los Cabarellos.

SCHLEEDE, GLENN ROY, energy market and policy consultant; b. Lyons, N.Y., June 12, 1933; m. Sandra Christine Klafehn, Dec. 27, 1958; children: Kristen M., Kimberly J., Kendall E. BA, Gustavus Adolphus Coll., 1960; MA, U. Minn., 1968; advanced mgmt. program, Harvard U., 1987. Research asst. Indsl. Relations Ctr., U. Minn., Mpls., 1960-61; mgmt. intern, then contractor personnel specialist AEC, Argonne, Ill. and Germantown, Md., 1961-65; asst. chief div. natural resources U.S. Office Mgmt. and Budget, Exec. Office of Pres., Washington, 1965-72, exec. assoc. dir., 1981; dep. assoc. dir. Office of Policy Analysis, AEC, Germantown, 1972-73; assoc. dir. energy and sci. Domestic Council, The White House, Washington, 1973-77; sr. v.p. Nat. Coal Assn., Washington, 1977-81; pres. New Eng. Energy Inc., Westborough, Mass., 1982-92, also bd. dirs.; v.p. New Eng. Power Service Co., Westborough, 1982-92, also bd. dirs.; v.p. New Eng. Electric System, Westborough, 1986-92; pres., CEO, dir. Energy Market and Policy Analysis, Inc., Reston, Va., 1992—. Author numerous speeches, papers and congl. testimony on various nat. energy policy issues. Recipient Disting. Alumni in Bus. award Gustavus Adolphus Coll. Alumni Assn., St. Peter, Minn., 1987. Republican. Lutheran. Avocations: reading, travel, carpentry. Home: 1414 Hemingway Ct Reston VA 22094-1241 Office: Energy Market and Policy Analysis Inc PO Box 3875 Reston VA 22090-1875

SCHLEGEL, FRED EUGENE, lawyer; b. Indpls., July 24, 1941; s. Fred George and Dorothy (Bruce) S.; m. Jane Wessels, Aug. 14, 1965; children: Julia, Charles, Alexandra. BA, Northwestern U., 1963; JD with distinction, U. Mich., 1966. Bar: Ind. 1966. Assoc. lawyer Baker & Daniels, Indpls., 1966-72, ptnr., 1972—; vice chmn. Meridian St. Preservation Commn., Indpls., 1975-90; bd. dirs. Indpls. Water Co., IWC Resources Corp. Contbr. articles to profl. jours. Chmn. Indpls. Pub. Schs. Edn. Found., 1988-90; pres. Festival Music Soc., 1974-75, 79, 86-87; bd. dirs. Indpls. Symphony Orch., 1991—, Arts Coun. Indpls. Mem. ABA, Ind. Bar Assn., Fed. Energy Bar Assn., Northwestern U. Alumni Club Indpls. (pres. 1992-94). Republican. Presbyterian. Office: Baker and Daniels 300 N Meridian St Ste 2700 Indianapolis IN 46204-1755

SCHLEGEL, JOHN FREDERICK, management consultant, speaker, trainer; b. Ogden, Utah, Dec. 18, 1944; s. Max Joseph and Mary Georgia (Whittaker) S.; m. Priscilla Mary Hecht, Sept. 8, 1967. BS in Pharmacy, U. Pacific, 1967; D of Pharmacy, U. So. Calif., 1972, postdoctoral fellow, 1972-73, MS in Edn., 1980; ScD in Pharmacy (hon.), Mass. Coll. Pharmacy, 1984, L.I. U., 1985. Lic. pharmacist, Calif., Nev.; cert. assoc. exec. Chief pharmacist U. So. Calif. Sch. Pharmacy, Los Angeles, 1967-73, dir. pharmacy admissions, 1973-75; dir. office student affairs Am. Assn. Colls. Pharmacy, Alexandria, Va., 1975-77, asst. exec. dir., 1977-81, exec. dir., 1981-84; chief exec. officer Am. Pharm. Assn., Washington, 1984-89; exec. v.p., chief exec. officer Am. Acad. Facial Plastic and Reconstructive Surgery, Washington, 1989-92; pres. Schlegel & Assocs., Chevy Chase, Md., 1992—; ptnr. Schlegel & Schuster, Chevy Chase, 1992—; cons. U.S. Govt., VA, HHS, various pharm. cos., assns. and schs. pharmacy. Contbr. over 60 articles on pharmacy, health care and assn. mgmt.; presenter in field. Nat. del. White House Conf. on Aging, Washington, 1981. Disting. alumnus U. So. Calif. Sch. Pharmacy, 1985, U. the Pacific Sch. Pharmacy, 1987. Fellow Am. Soc. Assn. Execs.; mem. Am. Soc. Assn. Execs., Am. Pharm. Assn., Am. Assn. Med. Soc. Execs., Group Health Assn. (trustee, officer), Greater Washington Soc. Assn. Execs., Phi Delta Chi (charter, bd. counsellors). Avocations: tennis, classical music, gardening. Office: 7423 Lynnhurst St Chevy Chase MD 20815-3101

SCHLEGEL, JOHN PETER, university president; b. Dubuque, Iowa, July 31, 1943; s. Aaron Joseph and Irma Joan (Hingtgen) S. BA, St. Louis U., 1969, MA, 1970; BDiv, U. London, 1973; DPhil, Oxford U., 1977. Joined Soc. of Jesus, 1963, ordained priest Roman Cath. Ch., 1973. From asst. prof. to assoc. prof. Creighton U., Omaha, 1976-79, asst. acad. v.p., 1978-82; dean Coll. Arts and Scis. Rockhurst Coll., Kansas City, Mo., 1982-84, Marquette U., Milw., 1984-88; exec. and acad. v.p. John Carroll U., Cleve., 1988-91; pres. U. San Francisco, 1991—; cons. Orgn. for Econ. Devel. and Cooperation, Paris, 1975-76. Author: Bilingualism and Canadian Policy in Africa, 1979; editor: Towards a Redefinition of Development, 1976; contbr. articles to profl. jours. Mem. Milwaukee County Arts Coun., 1986-88; mem. Mo. Coun. on Humanities, Kansas City, Mo., 1984; trustee St. Louis U., 1985-91, Loyola U., Chgo., 1988—, St. Ignatius H.S., Cleve., 1990-91, Loyola Coll. in Md., 1992—; bd. dirs. San Francisco ARC, 1991-94. Oxford U. grantee, 1974-76; Govt. of Can. grantee, 1977-78. Mem. Am. Coun. on Edn., Can. Studies in U.S., Olympic Club, Univ. Club, Bohemian Club. Avocations: racquet sports, classical music, cooking, hiking. Office: U San Francisco Office of Pres 2130 Fulton St San Francisco CA 94117-1080

SCHLEI, NORBERT ANTHONY, lawyer; b. Dayton, Ohio, June 14, 1929; s. William Frank and Norma (Lindsley) S.; m. Jane Moore, Aug. 26, 1950 (div. 1963); children: Anne C. Buczynski, William K., Andrew M.; m. Barbara Lindemann, Mar. 7, 1965 (div. 1981); children: Bradford L., Graham L., Norbert L., Norma Blake, Elizabeth Eldridge. BA, Ohio State U., 1950; LLB magna cum laude, Yale U., 1956. Bar: Ohio 1956, Calif. 1958, D.C. 1963, U.S. Supreme Ct. 1963. Law clk. to Justice Harlan U.S. Supreme Ct., 1956-57; assoc. atty. O'Melveny & Myers, L.A., 1957-59; ptnr. Greenberg, Shafton & Schlei, L.A., 1959-62; asst. atty. gen. U.S. Dept. Justice, Washington, 1962-66; ptnr. Munger, Tolles, Hills & Rickershauser, 1968-70, Kane, Shulman & Schlei, Washington, 1968-70; ptnr.-in-charge Hughes Hubbard & Reed, L.A., 1972-89; pres., CEO Kahala Capital Corp., Santa Monica, Calif., 1983—; spl. counsel Clinicorp Inc., L.A., 1991—. Author: (with M.S. McDougal and others) Studies in World Public Order, 1961 (Am. Soc. Internat. Law ann. book award); State Regulation of Corporate Financial Practices, 1962; editor-in-chief Yale Law Jour., 1955-56. Dem. nominee for Calif. Assembly, 1962, for sec. of state Calif., 1966; bd. dirs. Constl. Rights Found., Japan-Am. Found., Inc. Mem. ABA, Fed. Bar Assn., Am. Judicature Soc., Am. Soc. Internat. Law, Calif. Bar, L.A. County Bar Assn., Yale Club So. Calif., Riviera Country Club (Pacific Palisades, Calif.). Avocations: tennis, golf, skiing, sailing. Office: 2800 28th St Ste 321 Santa Monica CA 90405

SCHLEICHER, NORA ELIZABETH, banker, treasurer, accountant; b. Balt., Aug. 10, 1952; d. Irvin William and Eleanor Edna S.; m. Ray Leonard Settle Jr., July 27, 1985. AA cum laude, Anne Arundel Community Coll., 1972; BS summa cum laude, U. Balt., 1975. CPA, Md. Staff auditor Md. Nat. Bank, Balt., 1975-76, sr. staff auditor, 1976-77, supr. auditing dept., 1977-78; full charge acct. Wooden & Benson, CPA's, Balt., 1978-81; asst. to treas. First Fed. Savs. & Loan Assn., Annapolis, Md., 1981, asst. treas., 1982-83, v.p., 1984; v.p., treas. First Fed Savs. & Loan Assn. (now First Annapolis Bank), 1984—. Bd. dirs., treas. Coll. Manor Community Assn. Mem. AICPA, Md. Assn. CPA's, Fin. Mgrs. Soc., Coll. Manor Community Assn. (bd. dirs., treas.). Methodist. Office: First Annapolis Savs Bank 1832 George Ave Annapolis MD 21401-4103

SCHLEIF, ROBERT F., biology educator; b. Wenatchee, Wash., Nov. 22, 1940; s. Ferber R. and Wilma H. (Chittenden) S.; m. Nyuk Y. Ho, Nov. 25,

1970; 1 child, Kevin O. BS, Tufts U., 1963; PhD, U. Calif., Berkeley, 1967. Postdoctoral Harvard U., Cambridge, Mass., 1969-71; asst. prof. Brandeis U., Waltham, Mass., 1971-74, assoc. prof., 1974-81, prof., 1981-89; prof. biology Johns Hopkins U., Balt., 1989—. Author: Practical Methods Molecular Biology, 1981, Genetics and Molecular Biology, 1985; contbr. articles to profl. jours. Recipient Helen Hay Whitney award, 1970. Office: Johns Hopkins U Dept Biology 34th and Charles Sts Baltimore MD 21218

SCHLEIFER, LEONARD S., pharmaceuticals company executive; b. N.Y.C., July 7, 1952; s. Charles Baker and Florence (Schacht) S.; m. Harriet Partel, Dec. 24, 1974; children: Adam Paul, David Benjamin. AB, Cornell U., 1973; MD, U. Va., 1977, PhD, 1980. Diplomate Am. Bd. Neurology, Nat. Bd. Examiners. Office: Regeneron Pharmaceuticals 777 Old Saw Mill River Rd Tarrytown NY 10591-6700

SCHLEIN, CAROL LESLIE, lawyer; b. Oceanside, N.Y., Apr. 8, 1955; d. Richard Spencer and Betty Lee (Goldman) S. BA, U. Rochester, 1977; JD, N.Y. Law Sch., 1980. Bar: N.Y. 1982. Staff atty. Legal Def. & Edn. Fund, N.Y.C., 1980-82; assoc. Glazer & Gottlieb, N.Y.C., 1983-85; mgr. legal systems Future Info. Systems, N.Y.C., 1985-86; cons. Hildebrandt Inc., Somerville, N.J., 1986-87; pres. Law Office Systems, N.Y.C., 1987—. Contbr. articles to profl. jours. Mem. ABA, N.Y. State Bar Assn. (law office econs. and mgmt. com.), N.J. State Bar Assn. (law office adminstrn. mgmt. com.), N.Y. Women's Bar Assn. Democrat. Jewish. Avocations: volleyball, computers. Home: 201 E 21st St New York NY 10010-6401

SCHLEIN, DOV C., banker. Vice chmn. Republic N.Y. Corp. Office: Republic Nat Bank of NY 452 Fifth Ave New York NY 10018-2706

SCHLENDER, WILLIAM ELMER, management sciences educator; b. Sawyer, Mich., Oct. 28, 1920; s. Gustav A. and Marie (Zindler) S.; m. Lela R. Pullen, June 9, 1956 (dec. June 1983); m. Margaret C. Krahn, Mar. 3, 1987. A.B., Valparaiso U., 1941; M.B.A., U. Denver, 1947; Ph.D., Ohio State U., 1955. With U.S. Rubber Co., 1941-43, 46; asst. prof., assoc. prof. bus. adminstrn. Bowling Green State U., 1947-53; asst. prof. bus. orgn., prof. Ohio State U., 1954-65, asst. dean, 1959-62; assoc. dean Ohio State U. (Coll. Commerce and Adminstrn.), 1962-63; prof. mgmt. U. Tex., 1965-68, chmn dept., 1966-68; dean Cleve. State U. Coll. Bus. Adminstrn., 1968-75, prof. mgmt., 1975-76; Internat. Luth. Laymen's League prof. bus. ethics Valparaiso (Ind.) U., 1976-79, Richard E. Meier prof. mgmt., 1983-86, Richard E. Meier prof. emeritus, 1986—; vis. asso. prof. mgmt. Columbia, 1957-58; vis. prof. mgmt. U. Tex., Arlington, 1981-82; cons. in field; Bd. govs. Internat. Ins. Soc.; bd. dirs. Carrier Enterprises, 1989—. Author: (with M.J. Jucius) Elements of Managerial Action, 3d edit, 1973, (with others) Management in Perspective: Selected Readings, 1965; Editor: (with others) Management in a Dynamic Society, 1965; Contbr. (with others) articles to profl. jours. Served with AUS, 1943-45. Decorated Bronze Star. Fellow Acad. Mgmt.; mem. Indsl. Relations Research Assn., Am. Mgmt. Assn., Internat. Council Small Bus., Assn. Ohio Commodores, Tau Kappa Epsilon, Beta Gamma Sigma, Sigma Iota Epsilon, Pi Sigma Epsilon, Alpha Kappa Psi, Phi Kappa Phi. Club: Rotary. Home: PO Box 446 Sawyer MI 49125-0446 Office: Coll Bus Adminstrn Valparaiso U Valparaiso IN 46383 *I resolved long ago that where I worked and what I did would be guided not by prestige considerations, but by the answers to three questions: (1) Will my work allow me to grow by discovering and developing my capabilities? (2) Will it make a significant contribution to my profession and to the community? (3) Will I enjoy doing it? My career, and my personal philosophy, have these underlying guidelines.*

SCHLENSKER, GARY CHRIS, landscaping company executive; b. Indpls., Nov. 12, 1950; s. Christian Frederick and Doris Jean (Shannon) S.; m. Ann Marie Tobin, Oct. 27, 1979; children: Laura Patricia, Christian Frederick II. Student, Purdue U., 1969-71, 73; A Bus. Adminstrn., Clark Coll., 1979; cert. emergency med. technician, Ind. Vocat. Tech. Inst., Lafayette, 1974. Cert. profl. soil erosion and sediment control specialist. Salesman Modern Reference, Indpls., 1971; orthopaedic technician St. Elizabeth Hosp., Lafayette, 1973-75, asst. mgr. ambulance service, 1975; sales asst. Merck, Sharpe & Dohme, Oakbrook, Ill., 1975-77; v.p. Turfco, Inc., Zionsville, Ind., 1977-84; pres. Turfscape, Inc., Zionsville, 1984—; speaker Midwest Turf Conf., 1991. With U.S. Army, 1971-73. Mem. Nat. Fedn. Ind. Bus., Midwest Turf Found., Better Bus. Bur., Ohio Turf Found., Internat. Erosion Control Assn., Zionsville C. of C., Indpls. Landscape Assn., Phi Kappa Psi. Presbyterian. Avocations: woodworking, golf, bowling.

SCHLESINGER, ALBERT REUBEN, diversified products company executive, controller; b. Pitts., Oct. 25, 1941; s. Harry and Anne (Dugan) S.; m. Joan Saul, Aug. 9, 1964; children: Mara D., Todd E. AS in Acctg. and Taxation, Robert Morris Coll., 1964; BS in Acctg. and Econs., Gannon U., 1966. CPA, Ohio, Ind. Mgr. Schlesingers Food Store, Pitts., 1960-66; mgr. acctg. and auditing Price Waterhouse & Co., Cleve., 1966-76; asst. controller Ball Corp., Muncie, Ind., 1976-87, v.p., controller, 1987—; treas., Tech. Licensing Corp.; bd. dirs. CCD Inc. , v.p. Ball Fgn. Sales Corp., Ball-Can. Holdings Inc. Bd. dirs. Boy's and Girl's Club, Muncie, 1986—; co-chmn. hospitality Sta. WIPB-Telesale 49,Muncie, 1986; v.p. Beth El Temple, Muncie, 1987—. Mem. Tax Execs. Inst., Fin. Execs. Inst., Am. Inst. CPA's, Ohio Soc CPA's. Office: Ball Corp 345 S High St Muncie IN 47305-2326

SCHLESINGER, ARTHUR (MEIER), JR., writer, educator; b. Columbus, Ohio, Oct. 15, 1917; s. Arthur M. and Elizabeth (Bancroft) S.; m. Marian Cannon, 1940 (div. 1970); children: Stephen Cannon, Katharine Kinderman, Christina, Andrew Bancroft; m. Alexandra Emmet, July 9, 1971; 1 son, Robert Emmet Kennedy. AB summa cum laude, Harvard U., 1938, mem. Soc. of Fellows, 1939-42; postgrad. (Henry fellow), Cambridge (Eng.) U., 1938-39; hon. degrees, Muhlenberg Coll., 1950, Bethany Coll., 1956, U. N.B., 1966, New Sch. Social Rsch., 1966, Tusculum Coll., 1966, R.I. Coll., 1969, Aquinas Coll., 1971, Western New Eng. Coll., 1974, Ripon Coll., 1976, Iona Coll., 1977, Utah State U., 1978, U. Louisville, 1978, Northeastern U., 1981, Rutgers U., 1982, SUNY-Albany, 1984, U. N.H., 1985, U. Oxford, 1987, Akron U., 1987, Brandeis U., 1988, U. Mass., Boston, 1990, Hofstra U., 1991, Adelphi U., 1992, Dominican Coll., 1992, Mt. Ida Coll., 1993, Middlebury Coll., 1994, Roosevelt U., 1995. With OWI, 1942-43, OSS, 1943-45; assoc. prof. history Harvard U., 1946-54, prof., 1954-62; vis. fellow Inst. Advanced Study, Princeton, N.J., 1966; Schweitzer prof. humanities CUNY, 1966-95; cons. Econ. Cooperation Adminstrn., 1948, Mutual Security Adminstrn., 1951-52; spl. asst. to Pres. of U.S., 1961-64; mem. jury Cannes Film Festival, 1964; mem. Adlai E. Stevenson campaign staff, 1952, 56; chmn. Franklin Delano Roosevelt Four Freedoms Found., 1983—; trustee Robert F. Kennedy Meml., Twentieth Century Fund; adv. Arthur and Elizabeth Schlesinger Library. Author: Orestes A. Brownson, 1939, The Age of Jackson, 1945 (Pulitzer prize for history 1946), The Vital Center, 1949, (with R.H. Rovere) The General and the President, 1951, The Age of Roosevelt Vol. I: The Crisis of the Old Order 1919-1933, 1957 (Francis Parkman prize Soc. Am. Historians 1957, Frederic Bancroft prize Columbia U. 1958), The Age of Roosevelt Vol. II: The Coming of the New Deal, 1958, The Age of Roosevelt Vol. III: The Politics of Upheaval, 1960, Kennedy or Nixon: Does It Make Any Difference?, 1960, The Politics of Hope, 1963, (with John Blum) The National Experience, 1963, A Thousand Days, 1965 (Pulitzer prize for biography 1966, Nat. Book award 1966), The Bitter Heritage, 1967, The Crisis of Confidence, 1969, (with Lloyd Gardner and Hans Morgenthau) The Origins of the Cold War, 1970, The Imperial Presidency, 1973 (Sydney Hillman Found. award 1973), Robert Kennedy and His Times, 1978 (Nat. Book award 1979), The Cycles of American History, 1986, The Disuniting of America, 1991, The Causes of the Civil War, 1991; contbr. articles to mags. and newspapers; film reviewer: Show mag, 1962-64, Vogue, 1967-72, Saturday Rev., 1977-80, Am. Heritage, 1981-82; editor: Harvard Guide to American History, 1954, Guide to Politics, 1954, Paths to American Thought, 1963, The Promise of American Life, 1967, The Best and the Last of Edwin O'Connor, 1970, History of American Presidential Elections 1789-1972, 1971, 1972-1984, 1986, The Coming to Power, 1972, The Dynamics of World Power: A Documentary History of United States Foreign Policy 1945-1973, 1973, History of U.S. Political Parties, 1973, Congress Investigates, 1975, The American Statesman, 1982, The Almanac of American History, 1983, Running for President, 1994; screenwriter: (teleplay) The Journey of Robert F. Kennedy. Served with AUS, 1945. Decorated comdr. Order of Orange-Nassau (The Netherlands); recipient Nat. Inst. and Am. Acad. Arts and Letters gold medal in history

and biography, 1967, Ohio Gov.'s award for history, 1973, Eugene V. Debs award in edn., 1974, Fregene prize for lit. (Italy), 1983; Guggenheim fellow, 1946; Am. Acad. Arts and Letters grantee, 1944. Mem. Am. Hist. Assn., Orgn. Am. Historians, Soc. Am. Historians (pres. 1989-92), Am. Acad. and Inst. Arts and Letters (pres. 1981-84, chancellor 1984-87), Am. Philos. Soc., Mass. Hist. Soc., Colonial Soc. Mass., Russian Acad. Scis., Franklin and Eleanor Roosevelt Inst. (co-chmn. 1983—), ACLU, Coun. Fgn. Rels., Ams. for Dem. Acti (nat. chmn. 1952-54), Century Assn., Phi Beta Kappa. Democrat. Unitarian. Home: 455 E 51st St New York NY 10022 Office: CUNY 33 W 42nd St New York NY 10036-8099

SCHLESINGER, B. FRANK, architect, educator; b. N.Y.C., Sept. 17, 1925; s. Augustus and Ethel (Brower) S.; m. Draga A. Christy; children: Jeff, Nike, Katherine, Daniel, Christy Anna; 1 stepson, Frances L. Haley Jr. Student, Middlebury Coll., 1946-48; BS, U. Ill., 1950; MArch, Harvard U., 1954. Draftsman Hugh Stubbins Assocs., 1953-55, Marcel Breuer, 1955-56; practice architecture Princeton, N.J., 1956-59, Doylestown, Pa., 1959-69, Phila., 1969-71, Washington, 1971—; instr. archtl. design U. Pa., 1957-60; vis. critic Columbia Sch. Architecture, 1962-63, U. Pa., 1965; KEA disting. prof. Sch. Architecture, U. Md., 1971, prof. architecture, 1971—. With USNR, 1943-46. Recipient design awards Pa. Soc. Archs., 1960-65, 69, 84, Bronze medal, 1965, Silver medal, 1973, Design awards Progressive Arch., 1966, 67, 69, 72, 74, awards Interfaith Forum on Religion, Art and Arch., 1987, 92. Fellow AIA (design awards Phila. chpt. 1960, 61, 63-65, 68, 69, No. Va. chpt. 1975, Washington chpt. 1990, 92); mem. Harvard Grad. Sch. Design Alumni Assn. (pres. 1971-73), Associated Harvard Alumni (dir. 1972). Address: 5053 Massachusetts Ave NW Washington DC 20016-4312

SCHLESINGER, DAVID HARVEY, medical educator, researcher; b. N.Y.C., Apr. 28, 1939; s. Philip T. and Fay (Margolis) S.; m. Joan M. Aurelia; children: Sarah Jane, Karen Louise. BA, Columbia U., 1962; MS, Albany Med. Coll., 1965; PhD, Mt. Sinai Med. and Grad. Sch., 1972. Research fellow in medicine Mass. Gen. Hosp., Harvard Med. Sch., Boston, 1972-75, instr., 1975-77; asst. in biochemistry Mass. Gen. Hosp., Harvard Med. Sch., 1975-77; rsch. assoc. prof. U. Ill. Med. Ctr., Chgo., 1977-81; rsch. prof. exptl. medicine NYU Med. Ctr., N.Y.C., 1981-95; co-dir. neuroscis. sect. mental health clin. rsch. ctr., 1981-90; dir. microsequency and sythesis facility Kaplan Cancer Ctr., 1983-91; co-dir. neuroscis. sect. mental health clin. rsch. ctr., dir. microsequencing and synthesis faculty Kaplan Cancer Ctr., N.Y. med. Ctr., 1983-92; cons. Ortho Pharm. Co., 1977-91, Armour Pharm., 1971-81, Emisphere Techs., Inc., 1987-93; cons. in drug delivery systems. Editor: monograph Neurobyphysical Peptide Hormones and Other Biological Active Peptides, 1981; editor and contbg. author: Macromolecular Sequencing and Synthesis: Selected Methods and Application, 1988. Recipient Lectureship award Fundacion Gen. Mediterranean, Madrid, 1975. Mem. N.Y. Acad. Scis., Am. Physiol. Soc., Am. Soc. Biol. Chemists, Am. Chem. Soc. Office: NYU Med Ctr 550 1st Ave New York NY 10016-6497

SCHLESINGER, EDWARD BRUCE, neurological surgeon; b. Pitts., Sept. 6, 1913; s. Samuel B. and Sara Marie (Schlesinger) S.; m. Mary Eddy, Nov. 1941; children—Jane, Mary, Ralph, Prudence. B.A., U. Pa., 1934, M.D. 1938. Diplomate Am. Bd. Neurosurgery. Mem. faculty Columbia Coll. Phys. and Surg., N.Y.C., 1946—; prof. clin. neurol. surgery Columbia Coll. Phys. and Surg., 1964—, Byron Stookey prof., chmn. dept. neurol. surgery, 1973-80, Byron Stookey prof. emeritus, 1980—; dir. neurol. surgery Columbia Presbyn. Hosp., 1973-80, pres. med. bd., 1976-79; cons. in neurosurgery Presbyn. Hosp., 1980-87, cons. emeritus, 1987—. Author rsch. publs. on uses, effects of curare in disease, lesions of central nervous system, localization of brain tumors using radioactive tagged isotopes, genetic problems in neurosurgery and spinal disorders. Trustee Matheson Found., chmn. Elsberg fellowship com.; trustee Sharon (Conn.) Hosp. Recipient emeritus rsch. award Presbyn. Hosp. Fellow N.Y. Acad. Scis., N.Y. Acad. Medicine; mem. AAAS, AMA, Am. Assn. Neurol. Surgeons, Harvey Soc., Neurosug Soc. Am. (pres. 1970-71), Soc. Neurol. Surgeons, Am. Assn. Surgery of Trauma, Am. Rheumatism Soc., Am. Coll. Clin. Pharmacology and Chemotherapy, Ea. Assn. Electroencephalographers, Sigma Xi. Achievements include investigation of clinical pathological markers of genetic disorders and the syndromes created. Home: PO Box 3239 Fort Lee NJ 07024-9239 Office: 710 W 168th St New York NY 10032-2699

SCHLESINGER, HARVEY ERWIN, judge; b. N.Y.C., June 4, 1940. BA, The Citadel, 1962; JD, U. Richmond, 1965. Bar: Va. 1965, Fla. 1965, U.S. Supreme Ct. 1968. Corp. counsel Seaboard Coast Line R.R. Co., Jacksonville, Fla., 1968-70; chief asst. U.S. atty. Middle Dist. Fla. Jacksonville, 1970-75, U.S. magistrate judge, 1975-91, U.S. Dist. judge, 1991—; adj. prof. U. N. Fla., 1984-91; mem. adv. com. on Fed. Rules of Criminal Procedure to U.S. Supreme Ct., 1986-93; chmn. U.S. Dist. Ct. Forms Task Force, Washington, 1983—. Served to capt. JAGC U.S. Army, 1965-68. Bd. dirs. Pine Castle Ctr. for Mentally Retarded, Jacksonville, 1970-87 , pres., 1972-74. chmn. bd. dirs., 1973-74, 76, trustee Pine Castle Found., 1972-76; trustee Congregation Ahavath Chesed, Jacksonville, 1970—, v.p. 1975-80, pres., 1980-82; v.p. S.E. council Union Am. Hebrew Congregations, 1984-88; asst. commissioner for exploring N. Fla. council Boy Scouts Am., 1983-86, exec. com., 1986—; mem. Boy Scouts Am. Nat. Jewish com. on Scouting Irving, Tex., 1986-93, recipient Silver Beaver award Boy Scouts Am., 1986; trustee River Garden Home for Aged, 1982—, sec., 1985; co-chmn. bd. govs. Jacksonville chpt. NCCJ, 1983—, presiding co-chmn. 1984-89, nat. bd. trustees, N.Y.C., 1986-93. Recipient George Washington Medal Honor, Freedoms Found, Valley Forge, Pa, 1987, Silver Medallion Humanitarian award Nat. COnf. Christians and Jews, 1992. Mem. ABA (fed. rules of evidence and criminal procedure com. 1979—, Flascher award 1989), Va. Bar Assn., Fla. Bar Assn., Fed. Judges Assn., Nat. Council U.S. Magistrates (pres. 1987, v.p. 1985, pres. elect 1986, sec. 1983, treas. 1984), Jacksonville Bar Assn., Fed. Bar Assn. Jacksonville chpt. 1974, 75, 81-82), Am. Judicature Soc. Lodge: Rotary (Paul Harris fellow, pres. S. Jacksonville club). Mason (past master, past venerable master, knights commander of Ct. Honour, Scottish rite bodies), Shriner. Office: 311 W Monroe St PO Box 1740 Jacksonville FL 32201

SCHLESINGER, JAMES RODNEY, economist; b. N.Y.C., Feb. 15, 1929; s. Julius and Rhea (Rogen) S.; m. Rachel Mellinger, June 19, 1954; children: Cora K., Charles L., Ann R., William F., Emily, Thomas S., Clara, James Rodney. A.B. summa cum laude, Harvard U., 1950, A.M., 1952, Ph.D., 1956. Asst. prof., then assoc. prof. U. Va., 1955-63; sr. staff mem. RAND Corp., 1963-67; dir. strategic studies, 1967-69; asst. dir. Bur. Budget, 1969, acting dep. dir., 1969-70; asst. dir. Office Mgmt. and Budget, 1970-71; chmn. AEC, 1971-73; dir. CIA, Feb.-July 1973; U.S. sec. def., 1973-75; vis. scholar Johns Hopkins Sch. Advanced Internat. Studies, 1976-77; asst. to Pres., 1977; sec. Dept. Energy, 1977-79; counselor Ctr. for Strategic and Internat. Studies, Georgetown U., 1979—; sr. adv. Lehman Bros., 1979—; cons. in field. Author: The Political Economy of National Security, 1960, America at Century's End, 1989; co-author: Issues in Defense Economics, 1967. Frederick Sheldon prize fellow Harvard U., 1950-51. Mem. Phi Beta Kappa. Republican. Lutheran. Office: Lehman Bros 800 Connecticut Ave NW Washington DC 20006

SCHLESINGER, JOHN RICHARD, film, opera and theater director; b. London, Feb. 16, 1926; s. Bernard Edward and Winifred Henrietta (Regensburg) S. B.A., Balliol Coll., Oxford U., 1950. Dir. BBC TV, 1958-60. Dir. feature films including A Kind of Loving, 1962 (Golden Bear award Berlin Film Festival), Billy Liar, 1963, Darling, 1965 (N.Y. Critics award), Far From the Madding Crowd, 1966, Midnight Cowboy, 1968 (Acad. award, Brit. Acad. award), Sunday Bloody Sunday, 1970 (David di Donatello award, Brit. Acad. award), Day of the Locust, 1974, Marathon Man, 1976, Yanks, 1979 (Nat. Bd. Rev. award, New Standard award), Honky Tonk Freeway, 1980, Separate Tables, 1982, An Englishman Abroad, 1983 (Brit. Acad. award), The Falcon and the Snowman, 1983, The Believers, 1986, Madame Sousatzka, 1988, Pacific Heights, 1991, The Innocent, 1995; TV Films include: An Englishman Abroad, 1983 (BBC), A Question of Attribution, 1992 (PBS), Cold Comfort Farm, 1994 (BBC); plays Days in the Trees, 1966, I and Albert, 1972, Heartbreak House, 1974, Julius Caesar, 1977, True West, 1981, Les Contes d'Hoffmann, 1980-81 (SWET award), Der Rosenkavalier, 1984-85, Un Ballo in Maschera, 1989; assoc. dir. Nat. Theatre, London, 1973—. Served with Royal Engrs., 1944-48. Recipient David di Donatello Spl. Dir. award, 1980, Shakespeare prize, 1981;

decorated comdr. Order Brit. Empire. Address: 6 Cranley Mansion, 160 Gloucester Rd, London SW7 4QF, England

SCHLESINGER, JOSEPH ABRAHAM, political scientist; b. Boston, Jan. 4, 1922; s. Monroe Jacob and Millie (Romansky) S.; m. Mildred Saks, Sept. 9, 1951; children: Elizabeth Hannah, Jacob Monroe. A.B., U. Chgo., 1942; A.M., Harvard U., 1947; Ph.D., Yale U., 1955. Instr. Boston U., 1947-49; teaching fellow Wesleyan U., Middletown, Conn., 1952-53; mem. faculty Mich. State U., East Lansing, 1953—; prof. polit. sci. Mich. State U., 1963—; vis. prof. U. Calif., Berkeley, 1964-65. Author: How They Became Governor, 1957, Ambition and Politics: Political Careers in the United States, 1966, Political Parties and the Winning of Office, 1991, also articles. Del. Ingham County (Mich.) Democratic Conv., 1966-68. Served with AUS, 1943-45. Cowles fellow, 1950-51; Block fellow, 1951-52; grantee Social Sci. Research Council, 1955-57, 68-69; recipient Distinguished Faculty award Mich. State U., 1976, Sr. Fulbright award for Rsch. Western Europe, 1990—. Mem. Am. Polit. Sci. Assn. (coun. 1981-83, 1st ann. award for outstanding pub. paper 1986, Samuel Eldersveld award for lifetime achievement 1993), Midwest Polit. Sci. Assn. (v.p. 1969-70), So. Polit. Sci. Assn., Mich. Conf. Polit. Scientists, Acad. Polit. Sci. Democrat. Jewish. Home: 930 Roxburgh Ave East Lansing MI 48823-3131 Office: Dept Polit Sci Mich State Univ East Lansing MI 48824

SCHLESINGER, ROBERT WALTER, microbiologist, microbiology educator emeritus; b. Hamburg, Germany, Mar. 27, 1913; came to U.S., 1938, naturalized, 1943; s. Emil and Flora (Strelitz) S.; m. Adeline P. Sacks, Jan. 7, 1942; children: Robert, Ann. Student, U. Hamburg Med. Sch., 1931-34; M.D., U. Basel, Switzerland, 1937. Guest investigator Inst. Bacteriology and Hygiene, U. Basel, 1937-38; intern Beekman Hosp., N.Y.C., Stamford (Conn.) Hosp., 1938-40; fellow, asst. pathology and bacteriology Rockefeller Inst., N.Y.C., 1940-46; assoc. research prof. pathology, head virus research lab. U. Pitts. Sch. Medicine, 1946-47; assoc. mem., div. infectious diseases Pub. Health Research Inst., City of N.Y., Inc., 1947-55; prof., chmn. dept. microbiology St. Louis U. Sch. Medicine, 1955-63; prof. dept. microbiology U. Medicine and Dentistry N.J.-Robt. Wood Johnson Med. Sch., Piscataway, 1963-83, emeritus disting. prof., 1984—, chmn., 1963-80, also acting dean.; cons. Sec. War, 1946; mem., chmn. virology study sect. NIH; mem., chmn. microbiology and infectious disease adv. com. Nat. Inst. Allergy and Infectious Disease, NIH; mem. adv. com. Nat. Cancer Inst.; mem. cell biology and virology adv. com. Am. Cancer Soc. Editor: Virology; contbr. articles to sci. jours., chpts. to books. Served as capt. M.C. AUS, 1944-46. Recipient Humboldt award Fed. Republic Germany, 1981; Guggenheim fellow, 1972-73. Mem. Am. Acad. Microbiology (emeritus), Am. Assn. Immunologists, Am. Soc. Microbiology, Am. Soc. Cancer Rsch., AAAS, Am. Soc. Virology, N.Y. Acad. Scis., Sigma Xi, Alpha Omega Alpha. Home: 15-E Andover Cir Princeton NJ 08540-1722 Office: Robert Wood Johnson Med Sch 675 Hoes Ln Piscataway NJ 08854-5635

SCHLESINGER, RUDOLF BERTHOLD, lawyer, educator; b. Munich, Germany, Oct. 11, 1909; s. Morris and Emma (Aufhauser) S.; m. Ruth Hirschland, Sept. 4, 1942; children: Steven, June, Fay. Dr. Jur., U. Munich, 1933; LLB, Columbia U., 1942; Dr. Jur. (hon.), U. Trento, 1994. Bar: N.Y. 1942, U.S. Supreme Ct. 1946. Law sec. to Chief Judge Irving Lehman, N.Y. Ct. Appeals, 1942-43; confidential law sec. Judges N.Y. Ct. Appeals, 1943-44; asso. Milbank, Tweed, Hope & Hadley, N.Y.C., 1944-48; asso. prof. Cornell U., 1948-51, prof., 1951-75, William N. Cromwell prof. internat. and comparative law, 1956-75; prof. Hastings Coll. Law, U. Calif., 1975—, vis. prof., 1974; Cons. N.Y. State Law Rev. Commn., 1949—; mem. adv. com. internat. rules of jud. procedure, 1959-66; vis. prof. Columbia, 1952, Salzburg Seminar, 1954; Charles Inglis Thomson disting. vis. prof. U. Colo., summer 1976. Author: Cases, Text and Materials on Comparative Law, 4th edit., 1980, (with Baade, Damaska and Herzog) 5th edit., 1988, (with Baade, Herzog and Wise) Supplement to 5th edit., 1994; Formation of Contracts: A Study of the Common Core of Legal Systems, 2 vols., 1968, others; editor-in-chief Columbia Law Rev., 1941-42; bd. editors Am. Jour. Comparative Law; author articles on legal topics. Trustee Cornell U., 1961-66. Carnegie Corp. Reflective year fellowship, 1962-63. Mem. Am. Law Inst. (life), Am. Bar Assn., Internat. Acad. Comparative Law, Phi Beta Kappa, Order of Coif. Home: Comstock Apts #810 1333 Jones St San Francisco CA 94109-4112 Office: Univ Calif Hastings Coll of Law 200 Mcallister St San Francisco CA 94102

SCHLESINGER, SANFORD JOEL, lawyer; b. N.Y.C., Feb. 8, 1943; s. Irving and Ruth (Rubin) S.; children: Merideth, Jarrod, Alexandra; m. Suzanne Beth Mangold, 1994; 1 stepchild, Mariel Mangold. BS in Govt. with hons., Columbia U., 1963; JD, Fordham U., 1966. Bar: N.Y. 1966, U.S. Dist. Ct. (so. and ea. dists.) N.Y. 1967, U.S. Ct. Appeals (2d cir.) 1968, U.S. Ct. Internat. Trade 1969, U.S. Tax Ct. 1993, U.S. Supreme Ct. 1978. Assoc. Frankenthaler & Kohn, N.Y.C., 1966-67; asst. atty. gen. trusts and estates bur. charitable found. div. State of N.Y., N.Y.C., 1967-69; ptnr. Rose & Schlesinger, N.Y.C., 1969-81, Goldshmidt, Oshatz, Powsner & Saft, N.Y.C., 1981-85; ptnr., head trusts and estates dept. Shea & Gould, N.Y.C., 1985-93; ptnr., head wills and estates dept. Kaye, Scholer, Fierman, Hays & Handler, N.Y.C., 1993—; adj. faculty Columbia U. Sch. Law, 1989—; adj. prof. N.Y. Law Sch., 1978—; mem. estate planning adv. com. Practising Law Inst., 1990—; bd. editors N.Y. State Bar Jour., 1995—; bd. advisors and constbrs. Jour. of S Corp. Taxation, 1989—; chmn. adv. bd. Inst. Fed. Taxation, NYU, 1993; lectr. in field; condr. workshops in field. Author: (text) Estate Planning for the Elderly Client, 1984, Planning for the Elderly or Incapacitated Client, 1993; contbr. articles to profl. jours. Mem. adv. bd. Inst. Fed. Taxation NYU, 1988—, chmn., 1993-94; mem. legis. adv. com. Scarsdale (N.Y.) Sch. Bd., 1981-83, mem. nominating com., 1979-82; pres. dist. 17 N.Y.C. Community Sch. Bd., 1970-71; mem. fin. and estate planning adv. bd. Commerce Clearing House, 1988—. Fellow Am. Coll. Trust and Estate Counsel; mem. ABA (chmn. social security and other govt. entitlements com. 1990-91, chmn. probate and trust com.-estate planning, drafting charitable giving coms., 1992-94), Internat. Acad. Estate & Trust Law (academician 1992—), Nat. Acad. Elder Law Attys., Bklyn. Bar Assn., Westchester County Bar Assn., Assn. of Bar of City of N.Y., Consular Law Soc., N.Y. State Bar Assn. (treas. trusts and estates sect. 1991-92, sec. trusts and estates sect. 1992-93, chmn. trusts and estates sect., 1994-95, chmn. exec. com. 1st jud. dist. 1987-91). Avocations: baseball, writing. Office: Kaye Scholer Fierman Hays & Handler 425 Park Ave New York NY 10022-3506

SCHLESINGER, STEPHEN LYONS, nurseryman; b. N.Y.C., July 24, 1940; s. Nathan and Gertrude (Lyons) S.; m. Barbara Bernthal, Feb. 17, 1963; children—Adam Lyons, Lauren Elizabeth. B.A., Williams Coll., 1962; student, U. Paris, 1960-61; M.A. in French, Columbia U., 1964. Lectr. in French Hunter Coll., 1963-64; lectr. in French Columbia U., summers 1963-64; adminstrv. asst. John Simon Guggenheim Meml. Found., N.Y.C., 1965-67, asst. sec., 1967-70, assoc. sec., 1970-73, sec., 1973-88, spl. cons., 1988-89; ind. cons., 1989-90; assoc. dir., dir. maj. gifts The Corella and Bertram F. Bonner Found., Princeton, N.J., 1990-91; nurseryman Dubrow's Nurseries, Livingston, N.J., 1994—. Woodrow Wilson fellow, 1962-63. Home: 17 Prospect Ter Montclair NJ 07042-3204

SCHLESS, PHYLLIS ROSS, investment banker; d. Lewis H. and Doris G. Ross; m. Aaron Backer Schless, July 7, 1970; 1 son, Daniel Lewis Ross. Cert., N.Y. Playhouse Sch. of Theatre, 1962, N.Y. Sch. Interior Design, 1964; B.A. in Econs., Wellesley Coll., 1964; M.B.A., Stanford U., 1966. Assoc. in internat. fin. Kuhn Loeb & Co., N.Y.C., 1966-70; fin. cons., 1971-73; sr. analyst fin. Trans World Airlines, N.Y.C., 1974-79; dir. mergers and acquisitions Am. Can Co., Greenwich, Conn., 1979-82; v.p. mergers and acquisitions Bear, Stearns & Co., N.Y.C., 1982-84; sr. v.p. corp. acquisitions Integrated Resources, 1984-85; chmn., chief exec. officer Ross Fin. Svcs. Group Inc., 1985—; supervisory dir. Merrill Lynch HYTS Funds, 1991—; trustee Merrill Lynch HYTS Funds, 1991—; trustee Nat. Child Labor Com., 1981—, chmn., 1992-94; trustee New World Found., 1986-92, chair fin. com. and treas., 1993-94; trustee A.E. Tinker Fund, 1993—; cin. adv. Children's Theatre, N.Y.C., Parks Dept., 1969; bd. dirs. Stanford Bus. Sch. Club, N.Y., Presdl. Internship Fund Adv. Com., 1994—. Pres. Greater Bridgeport Nat. Coun. Jewish Women, 1972-73, bd. dirs., 1974-75; bd. dirs. Girls Clubs Am., 1975-78, mem. exec. com., 1982-89, pres., 1984-86; bd. dirs. Pauline Koner Dance Co., 1979-81, So. Conn. Child Guidance Clinic, 1981-83, New Canaan United Way, 1981-83; treas. Wellesley Class '64, 1984-89; bd. dirs. Calvary

Hosp. Fund, 1992—; trustee A.R. Tinker Fund, 1993—. Mem. Univ. Club. Home: 985 Fifth Ave 5A New York NY 10021-0142 Office: Ross Fin Svcs Group Inc 122 E 42d St Ste 4005 New York NY 10168

SCHLESSINGER, ARTHUR JOSEPH, physical education educator; b. Mineola, N.Y., June 9, 1945; s. Albert J. and Gladys (Russell) S.; m. Frances D. Schulman, July 23, 1967; children: James R., Caren R. BS in Edn., SUNY, Cortland, 1967; MS in Health Edn., Adelphi U., 1975. Cert. phys. edn. tchr., N.Y. Tchr. phys. edn. Monroe (N.Y.) Woodbury Sch. Dist., 1967-68, Harborfields Sch. Dist., Greenlawn, N.Y., 1968-70; tchr. phys. edn. Comsewogue Sch. Dist., Port Jefferson Station, N.Y., 1970—, track coach, 1972—, soccer coach, 1984—. Recipient Jack Ault Meml. award N.Y. State Sportswriters and Coaches Orgn. for Girls Sports, 1991; named Man of Yr., Port Jefferson, 1991, Section XI Track Coach of Yr., 1987, 89, 90, Section XI Soccer Coach of Yr., 1984, 86, 87, 91. Mem. AAHPED, N.Y. Assn. for Health, Phys. Edn. and Dance, N.Y. United Tchrs., Nat. Soccer Coaches Assn. Am., Port Jefferson Station Tchrs. Assn. (sr. bldg. rep. 1975-85, v.p. 1985-91), Suffolk County Track Coaches Assn. (league chair 1990—), Suffolk County Girls Soccer Coaches Assn. (pres. 1990—). Home: 7 Cottonwood Ave Port Jefferson Station NY 11776-3110

SCHLESSINGER, BERNARD S., retired university dean; b. Toronto, Ont., Can., Mar. 19, 1930; came to U.S. 1938, naturalized, 1948; s. Morris and Eleanor Schlessinger; m. June Hirsch, Dec. 21, 1952; children: Rashelle, Jill, Joel. B.S., Roosevelt U., 1950; M.S., Miami U., Oxford, Ohio, 1952; Ph.D., U. Wis., 1955; M.L.S., U. R.I., 1975. Research chemist Am. Can Co., Barrington, Ill, 1955-56; dept. head Chem. Abstracts, Columbus, Ohio, 1958-66; info. researcher Olin Corp., New Haven, 1966-68; asst. dir. Library Sch., So. Conn. State Coll., New Haven, 1968-74; prof. library sci. U. S.C, 1975-77; dean Library Sch. U. R.I., Kingston, 1977-82; prof. Sch. Libr. Sci. Tex. Woman's U., Denton, 1982-92 ret., 1992. Contbr. articles to profl. jours. Served with USAF, 1956-58. Named Outstanding Alumnus U. R.I. Grad. Library Sch., 1978. Mem. ALA, Tex. Library Assn., Sigma Xi, Phi Lambda Upsilon, Beta Phi Mu. Home: 15707 Hamilton St Omaha NE 68118-2339

SCHLESSINGER, JOSEPH, pharmacology educator. BSc in Chemistry/ Physics magna cum laude, The Hebrew U., Jerusalem, 1968, MSC in Chemistry magna cum laude, 1969; PhD, The Weizmann Inst. Sci., Rehovot, Israel, 1974. Postdoctoral assoc. dept. chemistry Stanford Applied Physics, Cornell U., 1974-76; vis. scientist immunology br. Nat. Cancer Inst., NIH, Bethesda, Md., 1977-78; sr. scientist dept. chem. immunology The Weizmann Inst. Sci., Rehovot, 1978-80, assoc. prof. dept. chem. immunology, 1980-84, prof. dept. chem. immunology, Ruth & Leonard Simon prof., 1984-91; dir. div. molecular biology Biotech. Rsch. Ctr. Meloy Labs., Inc., Rockville, Md., 1985-86, dir. Biotech. Rsch. Ctr., 1986-88; rsch. dir. Rorer Biotech., Inc., King of Prussia, Pa., 1988-90; prof., chmn. dept. pharmcology NYU Med. Ctr., N.Y.C., 1990—. Mem. editorial bds. European Molecular Biology Orgn. Jour., Jour. Cell Biology, Cell Regulation, Cancer Rsch., Receptors, Growth Factors, Cell Crowth & Differentiation, Protein Engineering, Oncogenes and Growth Factor Abstracts; contbr. articles to profl. jours. Recipient Sara Leedy Prize, Weizmann Inst. Sci., 1980, Levinson Prize, 1984; Hestrin Prize, Biochem. Soc. Israel, 1983. Mem. European Molecular Biology Orgn. Office: NYU Med Ctr Dept Pharmacology 550 1st Ave New York NY 10016-6481*

SCHLEUSENER, RICHARD AUGUST, college president; b. Oxford, Nebr., May 6, 1926; s. August William and Katherine Charlotte (Albrecht) S.; m. Elaine Emma Wilhelm, June 12, 1949; children: Kathryn Jeanne Schleusener Miller, Richard Dennis, Rand Lee, Debra Sue, Jeffrey Thomas. B.S., U. Nebr., 1949; M.S., Kans. State U., 1956; Ph.D., Colo. State U., 1958; postgrad., MIT, 1951-52; D.Sc. (hon.), U. Nebr., 1984. Research engr. Colo. State U., 1958-64, dir. Inst. Atmospheric Sci.; prof., head dept. meteorology S.D. Sch. Mines and Tech., Rapid City, 1965-74, v.p., dean engring., 1974-75, acting pres., 1975-76, pres., 1976-86; pres. Black Hills Regional Eye Inst. Found., 1987—; Cons. weather modification Interior Dept., 1964—, U.S. Forest Service, 1966—, UNESCO, 1971—, also pvt. firms. Contbr. articles to tech. jours. Served with USAF, 1950-55. Mem. Am. Meteorol. Soc., Am. Geophys. Union, Rotary, Sigma Xi, Beta Sigma Psi. Lutheran. Home: 315 S Berry Pine Rd Rapid City SD 57702-1923

SCHLEY, REEVE, III, artist; b. N.Y.C., Mar. 11, 1936; s. Reeve and Elizabeth (Boies) S.; m. Georgia Terry, Oct. 5, 1968; children: Marie B., Reeve T. B.A., Yale U., 1959; M.F.A., U. Pa., 1962; studied with, Josef Buchty, Munich, 1954-55. Instr. watercolor NAD, N.Y.C., 1981—. Exhibited in group shows including Spook Farm Gallery, Farm Hills, N.J., 1958, Hunterdon County Art Ctr. Ann., 1959, Pa. Acad., 1966, N.J. State Mus., Trenton, 1967, Tenn. Fine Arts Ctr., Nashville, 1973, Okla. Art Ctr., Oklahoma City, 1974, Butler Inst. Am. Art, Youngstown, Ohio, 1974, Drew U., 1975, Silvermine Guild Artists, 1975, NAD, 1977-78, Bklyn. Mus., 1984; one-man shows Vendo Nubes Gallery, Chestnut Hill, Pa., 1967, 71, Phila. Art Alliance, 1969, Spook Farm Gallery, 1970, Saratoga (N.Y.) Gallery, 1972-75, Graham Gallery, N.Y., 1973-94, N.J. State Mus., 1978, Hull Gallery, Washington, 1978, 80, Byck Gallery, Louisville, 1979, Peale House Gallery, Pa. Acad. Fine Arts, 1980, Gallerie Arnoldi-Livie, Munich, 1985, New Orleans Acad. Fine Arts, 1985; represented in permanent collections N.J. State Mus., Trenton, NAD, Newark Mus., Bklyn. Mus., Yale U. Art Gallery, Heublein Collection, Somerset County Coll., Tenneco Chems. Recipient Ranger Fund purchase prize NAD, 1981, 85, cert. of merit, 1978, 95; Best in Show award Hunterdon County Art Ctr., 1974, Laura M. Gross Meml. award Silvermine Guild Artists, 1975, purchase prize Somerset County Coll. Tri-State Exhbn., 1975, 2d prize for watercolor Somerset Art Assn., 1975; Cresson travel scholar Pa. Acad. Fine Arts, 1962; fellow N.J. Coun. Arts, 1979.

SCHLEY, WAYNE A., postal rate commissioner; b. Hamilton, Mont., May 22, 1940. AA, Shasta Coll., 1960; BS, Sacramento State U., 1963; MS, Am. U., 1974; postgrad., U. Alaska, 1970, Harvard U. Cert. high sch. teaching (lifetime) Calif. Dept. Edn. Tchr., admin. Placer High Sch., Auburn, Calif., 1963-70; spl. asst. to Sen. Ted Stevens, Washington, 1971-77; staff dir. minority and majority subcom. civil svc. Post Office and Gen. Svcs., Washington, 1977-86; minroity staff dir. Senate Com. on Rules and Adminstrn., Washington, 1987-92; commr. U.S. Postal Rate Commn., Washington, 1992—. Chmn. Calif. Teenage Reps., 1963-64; regional v.p. Calif. Young Reps., 1964-66, state sgt. at arms, 1966-67; mem. Placer County Rep. Ctrl. Com., 1965-70. Recipient Cert. Achievement JFK Sch. Govt. Harvard U., 1982. Home: 614 Massachusetts Ave Washington DC 20002 Office: U S Postal Rate Comm 1333 H St NW Washington DC 20268-0001

SCHLEY, WILLIAM SHAIN, otorhinolaryngologist; b. Columbus, Ga., Sept. 21, 1940; s. Frances Brooking Schley and Susie (Smith) Mathews. BA, Emory U., 1962, MD, 1966. Intern mixed surg. The Roosevelt Hosp., N.Y.C., 1966-67; resident in surgery, 1967-68; resident in otorhinolaryngology N.Y. Hosp.-Cornell Med. Ctr., N.Y.C., 1970-73; clin. instr. otorhinolaryngology Cornell U. Med. Coll., 1972-75, clin. asst. prof., 1975-81, assoc. prof., 1982—; acting chmn. dept. otorhinolaryngology, 1988-94; chmn. dept. otorhinolaryngology Cornell U. Med. Coll., 1994—; otorhinolaryngologist to outpatients with pvt. patient privileges N.Y. Hosp., 1973-75, asst. attending otorhinolaryngologist with pvt. patient privileges, 1975-81, assoc. attending, 1982—, acting otorhinolaryngologist-in-chief, 1988-94, otorhinolaryngologist-in-chief, 1994—; assoc. asst. surgeon otolaryngology Manhattan Eye, Ear, Nose and Throat Hosp., 1988—; sec. med. bd. N.Y. Hosp., 1994—. Author: (with others) Pulmonary Diseases of the Fetus Newborn and Child, 1978; contbr. numerous articles to profl. publs. Vestry St. James Ch., N.Y.C., 1994—; mem. ad hoc bd. visitors Emory U., 1994-95. Lt. comdr. USNR. Recipient Eagle Scout Boy Scouts Am., 1954. Fellow ACS (Manhattan dist. #2 com. on applicants 1991—); mem. Am. Acad. Otolaryngology-Head and Neck Surgery, Med. Soc. State of N.Y., N.Y. State Soc. Otolaryngology-Head and Neck Surgery (exec. coun. 1974-80, dist. dir. 1980), County Med. Soc., N.Y. Laryngol. Soc. (sec.-treas. 1981-84, v.p. 1984-85, pres. 1985-86), N.Y. Bronchoscopic Soc. (v.p. 1986-94, pres. 1994—), Assn. Emory Alumni Od Boys 1990—, pres.-elect 1993-94, pres. 1994-95), Omicron Delta Kappa. Episcopalian. Avocations: astronomy, ornithology. Home: 320 E 72nd St New York NY 10021-4769 Office: NY Hosp Starr 541 525 E 68th St New York NY 10021

SCHLICHTING, NANCY MARGARET, hospital administrator; b. N.Y.C., Nov. 21, 1954. B, Duke U., 1976; M, Cornell U., 1979. Adminstrv. resident Meml. Hosp. Cancer, N.Y.C., 1978; fellow Blue Cross-Blue Shield Assn., Chgo., 1979-80; asst. dirs. ops. Akron (Ohio) City Hosp., 1980-81, assoc. dir. planning, 1981-83, exec. v.p. 1983-88; exec. v.p. Riverside Meth. Hosps., Columbus, Ohio, 1988-92, pres., COO, 1992-93; pres., CEO, 1993—. Home: 887 Neil Ave Columbus OH 43215 Office: Riverside Meth Hosps 3535 Olentangy River Rd Columbus OH 43214-3925

SCHLICKAU, GEORGE HANS, cattle breeder, professional association executive; b. Haven, Kans., Nov. 2, 1922; s. Albert Rudulph and Florence Elsabe (Wittorff) S.; m. Lois Marie Ritthaler, Apr. 26, 1955; children: Bruce Alan, Susan Marie, James Darwin, Nancy Ann. Grad. high sch. Breeder registered Schlickau Hereford cattle, Haven, 1943—; pres. Reno County (Kans.) Hereford Assn., 1947-56, treas., 1956-58; dir. Reno County Cattleman's Assn., 1970-74, sec., 1970-71, treas., 1974; dir. Kans. Hereford Assn., 1955-71, 84-90, v.p., 1959, pres., 1960, 61; mem. organizing bd. Kans. Bull Test Sta., county committeeman Kans. Livestock Assn., 1960-75, bd. dirs., 1976-80, v.p. purebred coun., 1990-91, pres. purebred coun., 1992-93; bd. dirs. Am. Hereford Assn., 1969-75, v.p., 1973-74, pres., 1974-75; bd. dirs. Am. Nat. Cattleman's Assn., 1974-76; mem. fgn. trade com. Nat. Cattlemen's Assn., 1990-93. Contbr. articles in field to profl. jours.; exhibitor, also winner numerous awards at major cattle shows across country; guest speaker, judge at numerous Hereford cattle events across country. Host ann. judging sch. and contest for Future Farmers Am. and 4-H youth, 1940-84; dir. Kans. Nat. Jr. Livestock Show, 1973—, sec., 1982-83, chmn., 1984-85, bd. govs., 1988—; bd. dirs. Haven State Bank, 1962—; Equus Beds Groundwater Mgmt. Dist. 2, 1975-79, Beef leader Haven 4-H Club, 1947-67; mem. Haven High Sch. Bd., 1962-65, clk., 1964-65; mem. agrl. adv. com. Hutchinson (Kans.) Cmty. Jr. Coll., Kans., 1974-82; adv. Am. Jr. Hereford Assn., 1977-82; pres. Parent-Tchr. League Luth. Sch., 1979-80, 83-84; mem. zoning bd. City of Haven, 1985-88; bd. dirs. ark Valley Electric Coop. Assn., 1984—, v.p. 1986-90, pres. 1990-93, Dist. IV Kans. Electric Coop., 1986—, chmn., 1992; bd. dirs. Kans. Coop. Coun., 1994—; vice chmn. KACRE, 1992, chmn., 1993; adv. coun. mem. Arthur Capper Coop. Ctr., 1994—. Recipient Am. Farmer Degree award Future Farmers Am., 1942, Reno County Outstanding Young Farmer award Hutchinson Jaycees, 1959, Kans. Hereford Herdsman of the Year award High Plains Jour., 1960, Soil Conservation award Kans. Bankers Assn., 1968, Hon. State Farmer Degree award Future Farmers Am., 1972, Kans. Hereford Breeder of Yr., 1976, Portrait Gallery Outstanding Livestock Breeder award Kans. State U. Block and Bridle Club, 1978, Reno County 4-H Family of Yr. award, 1987, Reno County Farm Focus Family award Hutchinson C. of C., 1989, Stockman of Yr. award Kansas Livestock and Meat Industry Coun., 1994; named Kans. Seedstock Producer of Yr. BIF, 1988; Kans Jr. Livestock Show dedicatory, 1991, Master Farmer, Master Farm Homemaker, 1991. Mem. Kans. Wheat Growers Assn., Kans. Farm Bur., Haven Industries, Inc., Kansas City (Kans.) Hereford Club, Kans. State U. Block and Bridle Club (hon. mem.), Haven Booster Club (sec. 1952-53, pres. 1954-56), Future Farmers Am. (mem. adv. com. Haven chpt. 1971—). Lutheran (mem. sch. bd. 1967-70, chmn. 1969-70; chmn. ch. bd. 8 yrs., chmn. congregation 1984-88, elder 1977-79). Home: 11701 E K96 Hwy Haven KS 67543

SCHLICKE, CARL PAUL, retired surgeon; b. Bklyn., Mar. 16, 1910; s. Carl Paul and Eunice Gertrude (Hope) S.; m. Hilda Meek Hinckley, Aug. 30, 1937; children: Paul, Suzanne Parker. AB, UCLA, 1931; MD, Johns Hopkins Med. Sch., 1935; MS, U. Minn., 1940. Diplomate Am. Bd. Surgery. From surgeon to sr. surgeon Rockwood Clinic, Spokane, 1946-53; from chmn. surgical dept. to bd. dirs. Sacred Heart Hosp. Med. Ctr., Spokane, 1953-81; from clin. assoc. prof. dept. surgery to prof. emeritus U. Washington Sch. Medicine, Spokane, 1969—; commr. Joint Commn. on Accreditation of Hosps. 1967-78. Fellow Am. Coll. Surgeons; mem. AMA, Spokane County Med. Soc., Washington State Med. Assn. (pres. 1965-66), Am. Surgical Assn. (2d v.p. 1976), Spokane Surgical Soc. (pres. 1960), North Pacific Surgical Assn. (pres. 1964), Western Surgical Assn. (pres. 1972), Pacific Coast Surgical Assn. (pres. 1976-77), Internat. Soc. Surgery, Soc. Surgery Alimentary Tract, Surgeon's Travel Club, Mayo Clinic Alumni Assn., Barber Surgeons Pacific NW, Alpha Omega Alpha, Sigma Pi. Republican. Presbyn. Avocations: swimming, canoeing, writing. Home: E 826 Overbluff Rd Spokane WA 99203

SCHLICKEISEN, RODGER O., non-profit environmental organization executive; b. Houston, Jan. 24, 1941; s. Oscar and Elvene Alice (Rennemo) Muirhead; m. Susan Jane Culver, May 23, 1970; 1 child, Derek. BA, U. Wash., 1963; MBA, Harvard U., 1965; DBA, George Washington U., 1978. Loan officer Export-Import Bank of U.S., Washington, 1968-70; pres. Gryphon, Inc., Washington, 1970-74; group dir. com. on budget U.S. Senate, Washington, 1974-79; assoc. dir. econs. and govt. U.S. Office of Mgmt. and Budget, Washington, 1979-80; v.p. Craver, Mathews, Smith & Co., Falls Church, Va., 1980-81, CEO, 1981-87; chief of staff Office of U.S. Senator Max Baucus, Washington, 1987-91; pres., CEO Defenders of Wildlife, Washington, 1991—; bd. dirs. Island Resources Found., St. Thomas, V.I., Ctr. for Policy Alternatives, Washington; bd. advisors Environ. Comms. Orgn., L.A., 1992—, Environ. Media Assn., L.A., 1992—. Contbr. articles to profl. publs. Va. state chmn. Common Cause, Washington, 1971-74. Capt. U.S. Army, 1966-68. Mem. Soc. for Conservation Biology. Office: Defenders of Wildlife 1101 14th St NW Washington DC 20005-5601

SCHLICKMAN, J. ANDREW, lawyer; b. Washington, Mar. 28, 1952. AB, Georgetown U., 1974; JD, U. Chgo., 1978. Bar: Ill. 1978, U.S. Supreme Ct. 1987. Ptnr. Sidley & Austin, Chgo. Coord. author: International Environmental Law and Regulation. Mem. ABA, Ill State Bar Assn., Chgo. Bar Assn., Internat. Bar Assn. Office: Sidley & Austin 1 First Nat Plz Chicago IL 60603

SCHLIEBS, CHARLES ALLAN, lawyer; b. Kansas City, Mo., Dec. 3, 1950; s. Edgar Emil and Elsie Elizabeth (Rosher) S.; m. Melanie Emily Schuldis, Nov. 15, 1981. BA, BS in Econ., U. Pa., 1972; JD, Vanderbilt U., 1975. Bar: Mo. 1975, U.S. Supreme Ct. 1979, Pa. 1984. Assoc. Blackwell Sanders Matheny Weary & Lombardi, Kansas City, 1975-79, ptnr., 1980-82, various corp. positons, 1982-88; ptnr. Jones, Day, Reavis & Pogue, Pitts., 1988-89, adminstv. ptnr., 1989—; mem. internat. adv. bd. U. Pitts. Grad. Sch. Pub. and Internat. Affairs, 1990—, Duquesne U., Palumbo Sch. Bus. Adminstrn., Pitts., 1990—. Mem. ABA, Internat. Bar Assn., Pa. Bar Assn., Duquesne Club. Home: 10 Myrtle Hill Rd Sewickley PA 15143 Office: Jones Day Reavis & Pogue 1 Mellon Bank Ctr Pittsburgh PA 15219

SCHLIEVE, HY C. J., principal; b. Mandan, N.D., Apr. 4, 1952; s. Calvin L. and Loretta L. (Johnson) S.; m. Terri Ann Hansen, Dec. 30, 1977; children: Derek, Aaron, Jessica. BA, N.D. State U., 1974, MS, 1984; EdD, Calif. Coast U., 1994. Tchr., coach Halliday (N.D.) Pub. Sch., 1974-75, Drake (N.D.) Pub. Sch., 1975-76, Montpelier (N.D.) Pub. Sch., 1976-81; prin. Unity Pub. Sch., Petersburg, N.D., 1981-83, Page (N.D.) Pub. Sch., 1983-85; supt. Wolford (N.D.) Pub. Sch., 1985-87, Garrison (N.D.) Pub. Schs., 1987-93; prin. Buhl Joint Sch. Dist. 412, Idaho, 1993-95, Oconto Falls Area Sch. Dist., Wis., 1995—; com. mem. NDASA Rsch and Evaluation, Garrison, 1988-93; fiscal agt. Mo. Hills Consortium, McLean County, N.D., 1989-93; cons. asbestos Garrison Pub. Sch. Dist. 1987-93. Sec. Govtl. Affairs Com., Garrison, 1987-93; mem. Tourism Com., Garrison, 1988-92, Econ. Devel. Com., 1988-89. Recipient Nat. Superintendent of the Yr. awd., North Dakota, Am. Assn. of School Administrators, 1992. Mem. Nat. Assn. Secondary Sch. Prins. (prin. assessor tng. 1990), NSBA Fed. Policy Coords. Network. Avocations: golf, hunting, fishing, bowling, outdoor activities. Home: 175 N Farm Rd Oconto Falls WI 54154 Office: Oconto Falls High Sch 408 Cedar Oconto Falls WI 54154

SCHLINDWEIN, JAMES A., food products company executive; b. 1929; married. Selection mgr. Rath Packing Co., 1948-59; group v.p., dir. Consolidated Foods Corp., 1959-67, 68-75; asst. to v.p. selection and mktg. Hershey Foods Corp., 1967-68; exec. v.p. Wilson Foods Corp., 1975-78; pres. Midwest Quality Beef Co., 1978-80; sr. v.p. Sysco Corp., 1980-83, exec. v.p., 1983—. U.S. Army, 1946-48. Office: Sysco Corp 1390 Enclave Pkwy Houston TX 77077

SCHLINGER, WARREN GLEASON, retired chemical engineer; b. Los Angeles, May 29, 1923; s. William McKinley and Esther (Gleason) S.; m.

Katharine S. Stewart, June 29, 1947; children: Michael S., Norman W., Sarah Lynne. BS, Calif. Inst. Tech., 1944, MS, 1946, PhD, 1949. Registered profl. engr., Calif. Instr. Calif. Inst. Tech., Pasadena, 1949-53; chem. engr. Texaco Inc., Montebello, Calif., 1953-61, supr. research, 1961-69, mgr., 1969-81, assoc. dir., 1981-87, ret. 1987; cons. 1987—. Contbr. numerous articles to profl. publs. Patentee in field. Fellow Am. Inst. Chem. Engrs. (Chem. Engring. Practice award 1981, So. Calif. sect. Tech. Achievement award 1976; Electric Power Research Inst. Achievement award 1985); mem. NAE, Am. Chem. Soc., Sigma Xi, Tau Beta Pi. Clubs: Jonathan (Los Angeles); Calif. Country (Whittier). Home: 3835 Shadow Grove Rd Pasadena CA 91107-2241

SCHLITTER, STANLEY ALLEN, lawyer; b. Decorah, Iowa, Jan. 27, 1950; s. Joseph Everett and Lillian Helena (Helgerson) S.; m. Sheila Lynn Edwards, Sept. 24, 1977; children: Stephanie Anne, Joseph Allen, John Edward. BS, Iowa State U., 1972; JD, U. Iowa, 1977. Bar: Ill. 1977, U.S. Dist. Ct. (no. dist.) Ill. 1977, U.S. Ct. Appeals (7th cir.) 1981, U.S. Ct. Appeals (Fed. cir.) 1982, D.C. 1989. Assoc. Kirkland & Ellis, Chgo., 1977-84, ptnr., 1984-88; ptnr. Kirkland & Ellis, Washington, 1988-91, Jenner & Block, Chgo., 1991—. Mem. ABA, IEEE, Am. Intellectual Property Law Assn. Office: Jenner & Block One IBM Plaza Chicago IL 60611-3608

SCHLOEGEL, GEORGE ANTHONY, banker; b. Gulfport, Miss., June 17, 1940; s. Joseph A. and Nancy (Bertucci) S.; m. Peggy Jay Harry, Mar. 14, 1959; children: Matthew, Melissa, Mark, Michael. B.S., La. State U., 1962; grad. various bank mgmt. courses. With Hancock Bank, Gulfport, 1956-59, 62—; pres. Hancock Bank, 1990—; with Whitney Nat. Bank, New Orleans, 1960-62; bd. dirs. BIPEC of Miss. Pres. Gulfport Mcpl. Separate Sch. Dist., 1971-80, St. James Roman Cath. Ch. Parish Coun., Gulfport, 1972-74, Miss. Gulf Coast Jr. Coll. Found.; mem. adv. bd. Gulfport Salvation Army, 1963-76; commr. Boy Scouts Am., 1970-74; chmn. Miss USA Pageant, 1979-81; mem. Miss. Bd. Econ. Devel., 1980-85; pres. Grad. Sch. Banking, South La. State U., 1990-92. With USNG, 1954-62. Recipient Pine Burr Dist. Scouting award, 1974. Mem. Am. Bankers Assn., Am. Inst. Banking, Bank Mktg. Assn., Miss. Bankers Assn. (v.p.), U.S. Jaycees (v.p. 1969-70, Clayton Frost Meml. award 1969), Miss. Jaycees (pres. 1968-69, Outstanding Young Man award 1965), Gulfport Jaycees (pres. 1965, Disting. Service award 1965). Club: Gulfport Yacht (commodore, 1982-83). Office: Hancock Bank 1 Hancock Plz Gulfport MS 39501-1948

SCHLOEMANN, ERNST FRITZ (RUDOLF AUGUST), physicist, engineer; b. Borgholzhausen, Germany, Dec. 13, 1926; came to U.S., 1954, naturalized, 1965; s. Hermann Wilhelm and Auguste Wilhelmine (Koch) S.; m. Gisela Mattiat, June 19, 1955 (dec. 1990); children: Susan C., Sonia G., Barbara I.; m. Sally (Duren) Heatter, Nov. 5, 1994. BS, U. Göttingen, Fed. Republic of Germany, 1951, MS, 1953, PhD, 1954. With rsch. div. Raytheon Co., Lexington, Mass., 1955-94; electronics sys. divsn., 1994—; cons. scientist, 1964—; vis. assoc. prof. Stanford U., 1961-62; vis. prof. U. Hamburg, Fed. Republic Germany, 1966. Assoc. editor: Jour. Applied Physics, 1974-76; contbr. numerous articles to profl. jours. Recipient T.L. Phillips award for Excellence in Tech., 1990. Fellow IEEE, Am. Phys. Soc., Sigma Xi. Democrat. Unitarian. Achievements include patents in field of magnetic materials and their application to microwave technology. Office: Raytheon Co Electronic Systems Divsn 131 Spring St Lexington MA 02173-7803

SCHLOEMER, PAUL GEORGE, diversified manufacturing company executive; b. Cin., July 29, 1928; s. Leo Bernard and Mary Loretta (Butler) S.; m. Virginia Katherine Grona, Aug. 28, 1954; children: Michael, Elizabeth, Stephen, Jane, Daniel, Thomas. BSME, U. Cin., 1951; MBA, Ohio State U. 1955. R & D engr. Wright Patterson AFB, Dayton, Ohio, 1951-52; R & D officer Wright Patterson AFB, Dayton, 1952; resident engr. Parker Hannifin Corp., Dayton, 1957; also Ea. area mgr. Parker Hannifin Corp., Huntsville, Ala., 1957-65; v.p. aerospace group Parker Hannifin Corp., Irvine, Calif., 1965-77; pres. aerospace group Parker Hannifin Corp., Irvine, 1977, corp. v.p., 1978-81, exec. v.p., 1981; pres. Parker Hannifin Corp., Cleve., 1982-84, CEO, 1984-93, ret., 1993; bd. dirs. Soc. Corp., Cleve., Rubbermaid Inc., AMP Inc., Parker Hannifin Corp., N.A.M. Capt. USAF, 1952-53. Mem. Machinery and Allied Products Inst. (mem. exec. com.), Aerospace Industry Assn., Conf. Bd., Inc., The Country Club, Big Canyon Country Club, The Pepper Pike Club. Republican. Roman Catholic. Office: Parker Hannifin Corp 17325 Euclid Ave Cleveland OH 44112-1290

SCHLOERB, PAUL RICHARD, surgeon, educator; b. Buffalo, Oct. 22, 1919; s. Herman George and Vera (Gross) S.; m. Louise M. Grimmer, Feb. 25, 1950; children: Ronald G., Patricia Johnson, Marilyn A. Hock, Dorothy E. Schloerb Hoban, Paul Richard. A.B., Harvard U., 1941; M.D., U. Rochester, 1944. Intern U. Rochester Med. Sch., 1944-45, asst. resident, 1947-48, instr. surgery, 1952; research fellow, resident Peter Bent Brigham Hosp., Boston, 1948-52; mem. faculty U. Kans. Med. Ctr., Kansas City, 1952-79, prof. surgery, 1964-79, 88—, dean for research, 1972-79, dir. nutritional support svc., 1993—; prof. surgery U. Rochester (N.Y.) Med Sch. 1979-88, adj. prof. surgery, 1988-90; surgeon Strong Meml. Hosp., 1979-88, dir. Surg. ICU, 1979-83, dir. surg. nutritional support service. Contbr. over 100 articles to profl. jours. Served to lt. (j.g.), M.C. USNR, 1944-45; to lt. 1953-55. Mem. Am. Surg. Assn., Soc. U. Surgeons, A.C.S., AAAS, Am. Physiol. Soc., Internat. Soc. Surgery, Central Surg. Assn., Am. Assn. for Surgery of Trauma, Am. Assn. Cancer Research, AMA, Sigma Xi. Office: Dept Surgery U Kansas Med Ctr Kansas City KS 66160

SCHLOM, JEFFREY BERT, research scientist; b. N.Y.C., June 22, 1942; s. David and Anna (Klein) S.; children: Amy Melissa, Steven Michael. BS (Pres.'s scholar), Ohio State U., 1964; MS, Adelphi U., 1966; Ph.D., Rutgers U., 1969. Instr. Columbia Coll. Phys. and Surg., 1969-71, asst. prof., 1971-73; chmn. breast cancer virus segment Nat Cancer Inst., NIH, Bethesda, Md., 1973-76; chief lab. tumor immunology and biology Nat Cancer Inst., NIH, 1983—, head exptl. oncology sect., 1976-83; prof. George Washington U., Washington, 1975—; disting. lectr. Can. Cancer Soc., 1985. Mem. numerous editorial bds.; contbr. numerous articles to profl. jours. Recipient Dir.'s award NIH, 1977, 89. Mem. Am. Assn. Cancer Rsch. (Rosenthal award 1985), Am. Soc. Cytology (Basic Rsch. award 1987). Office: Insts of Health Bldg 10 Rm 8B07 Bethesda MD 20892

SCHLOSBERG, RICHARD T., III, newspaper publishing executive. Pub., CEO L.A. Times. Office: LA Times Times Mirror Sq Los Angeles CA 90053*

SCHLOSS, NATHAN, economist; b. Balt., Jan. 14, 1927; s. Howard L. and Louise (Levi) S.; B.S. in Bus., Johns Hopkins U., 1950; m. Rosa Montalvo, Mar. 1, 1958; children—Nina L., Carolyn D. Buyer, Pacific Coast gen. merchandise office Sears Roebuck & Co., Los Angeles, 1955-60, staff asst. econ. research dept., Chgo., 1960-63; sr. market analyst corp. research dept. Montgomery Ward & Co., Chgo., 1963-65; research mgr. real estate dept. Walgreen Co., Chgo., 1970-72; v.p. research and planning Maron Properties Ltd., Montreal, Que., Can., 1972-74; corp. economist, fin. analyst Real Estate Research Corp., Chgo., 1974-88, sr. v.p., 1986-88, treas., chief fin. analyst, 1982-88; economist Office of Ill. Atty. Gen., Chgo., 1988—; cons. economist, since 1965—; mem. com. on price indexes and productivity fgn. labor Bus. Research Adv. Council of Bur. Labor Stats., Dept. Labor, 1979-88, also chairperson (1985-86), com. on employment and unemployment. Recipient Commendable Svc. award Dept. Labor, 1987. Mem. Plan Commn., Village of Wilmette, Ill., 1975-77, mem. tech. adv. com. on employment and tng. data Ill. Employment and Tng. Council, 1979-82; mem. tech. adv. com. Ill. Job Tng. Coordinating Council, 1983-87. Mem. Am. Mktg. Assn., Nat. Assn. Bus. Economists, Econometric, Lambda Alpha. Contbr. articles on fin. and market analysis of real estate to profl. jours. Home: 115 Hollywood Ct Wilmette IL 60091-3122 Office: 100 W Randolph St Chicago IL 60601-3218

SCHLOSS, SAMUEL LEOPOLD, JR., retired food service executive, consultant; b. Montgomery, Ala., Mar. 30, 1926; s. Samuel Leopold and Amelia (Strauss) S.; m. Burke Hart Klein; children: Stephen, Alyce, Adam. BS in Indsl. Engring., Ga. Inst. Tech., 1947; MS in Indsl. Engring., Columbia U., 1948. Sec. Schloss and Kahn Inc., Montgomery, 1948-56, pres., 1956-86, chmn., 1986-94. Pres. Montgomery Acad., 1979-80, bd. dirs. emeritus, 1982; control bd. Montgomery Com. of One Hundred, 1984-86; bd. dirs. YMCA

Metro Bd. Capt. USAFR, 1960. Mem. Montgomery C. of C. (pres. 1983). Republican. Clubs: Standard (Montgomery) (pres. 1964), Capital City (bd. govs. 1977-80), Wynlakes Golf and Country Club. Lodge: Rotary (pres. 1972-73). Office: Union Bank Tower 60 Commerce St Ste 1210 Montgomery AL 36104

SCHLOSSBERG, FRED PAUL, elementary education educator; b. N.Y.C., May 30, 1944; s. Alexander and Mae S.; divorced; 1 child, Elan. BSBA, Boston U., 1966; M of Phys. Edn., NYU, 1983. Tchr. elem. sch. N.Y.C. Bd. Edn., 1966—; coach local basketball team, North Bellmore, N.Y., 1988—, local baseball team, North Bellmore, 1988-92. Vol. Alcoholics Anonymous, West Hempstead, N.Y., 1987-93; tutor Literacy Vols. Am. Democrat. Avocations: physical fitness, collecting sports and non-sports cards, comic books and memorabilia, music, travel. Home: 2392 Bedford Ave # A Bellmore NY 11710-3619

SCHLOSSBERG, STEPHEN I., management consultant; b. Roanoke, Va., May 18, 1921; s. Morris Joseph and Jennie (Weinstein) S.; m. Mary Coleman Bazelon, 1953 (div. 1958); m. Nancy Kamin, June 6, 1963; children: Mark Jay, Karen Jean. BS in Commerce, U. Va., 1956, LLB, 1957. Asst. mgr. Kanns, Inc., Roanoke, Va., 1945-49; mem. labor organ. staff Internat. Ladies Garment Workers Union, N.Y.C., 1949-54; assoc., ptnr. Van Arkel & Kaiser, Washington, 1957-61; spl. asst. to dir. Fed. Mediation and Conciliation Service, Washington, 1961-63; gen. counsel, dir. govt. relations Internat. Union UAW, Detroit, 1963-81; ptnr. Zwerdling, Schlossberg, Leibig & Kahn, Washington, 1981-85; dept. under sec. for labor-mgmt. relations and coop. programs U.S. Dept. Labor, Washington, 1985-87; spl. advisor to dir. gen. and dir. Wash. br. Internat. Labor Office, 1987-94; cons., advisor in field; former mem. Presdl. Adv. Bd. on Ambassadorial Appointments, Presdl. Commn. on Indsl. Competiveness; adj. prof. of law Georgetown U. Law Ctr., 1962-63, 84-85. Author: Organizing and the Law, 1967, 2d edit. (with Frederick Sherman), 1971, 3d edit. (with Judith Scott), 1983. Served to staff sgt. U.S. Army, 1941-45, ETO. Mem. ABA (commn. on nat. inst. justice, former co-chmn. internat. labor law com., sect. on labor law, former mem. consortium on legal services, former mem. spl. com. on election law), Order of Coif, Raven Soc., Omicron Delta Kappa. Home: 2801 New Mexico NW # PH17 Washington DC 20007 Office: 1000 Connecticut Ave NW Washington DC 20036

SCHLOSSER, ANNE GRIFFIN, librarian; b. N.Y.C., Dec. 28, 1939; d. C. Russell and Gertrude (Taylor) Griffin; m. Gary J. Schlosser, Dec. 28, 1965. BA in History, Wheaton Coll., Norton, Mass., 1962; MLS, Simmons Coll., 1964; cert. archives adminstrn. Nat. Archives and Records Service, Am. U., 1970. Head UCLA Theater Arts Library, 1964-69; dir. Louis B. Mayer Libr. Am. Film Inst., L.A., 1969-88, dir. film/TV documentation workshop, 1977-87; head Cinema-TV Libr. and Archives of the Performing Arts, U. So. Calif., L.A., 1988-91; dir. Entertainment Resources Seminar, 1990; dir. rsch. libr. Warner Bros., 1991—. Project dir.: Motion Pictures, Television, Radio: A Union Catalogue of Manuscript and Special Collections in the Western U.S., 1977. Active Hollywood Dog Obedience Club, Calif. Numerous grants for script indexing, manuscript cataloging, library automation. Mem. Soc. Am. Archivists, Soc. Calif. Archivists (pres. 1982-83), Theater Library Assn. (exec. bd. 1983-86), Women in Film, Spl. Librs. Assn.. Democrat. Episcopalian. Avocations: running, swimming, reading, dog obedience training. Office: Warner Bros Rsch Libr 5200 Lankershim Blvd Ste 100 North Hollywood CA 91601-3100

SCHLOSSER, HERBERT S., broadcasting company executive; b. Atlantic City, Apr. 21, 1926; s. Abraham and Anna (Olesker) S.; m. Judith P. Gassner, July 8, 1951; children: Lynn C., Eric M. A.B. summa cum laude, Princeton, 1948; LL.B., Yale, 1951. Bar: N.Y. 1952. Assoc. firm Wickes, Riddell, Bloomer, Jacobi & McGuire, N.Y.C., 1951-54, Phillips, Nizer, Benjamin, Krim & Ballon, N.Y.C., 1954-57; with NBC, 1957-78; v.p., gen. mgr. subsidiary Calif. Nat. Prodns., Inc., 1960-61, dir. talent and program adminstrn., 1961-62, v.p. talent and program adminstrn., 1962-66; v.p. programs West Coast NBC, 1966-72; exec. v.p. NBC-TV Network, 1972-73, pres., 1973-74, mem. bd. dirs., 1973-78; pres. NBC, Inc., 1974-78, chief exec. officer, 1977-78; exec. v.p. RCA, 1978-85; sr. advisor broadcasting and entertainment Wertheim Schroder & Co., Inc., N.Y.C., 1986—; bd. dirs. Am. TV and Communications Corp. Trustee Internat. Radio and TV Found., 1972-74; former mem. govs. Ford's Theatre Soc.; former trustee Nat. Urban League; chmn. bd. Am. Mus. of the Moving Image. With USNR, 1944-46. Recipient Humanitarian award NCCJ, 1974, Gold Brotherhood award, 1978. Mem. Assn. of Bar of City of N.Y., Am., N.Y. State bar assns., Council on Fgn. Relations, Acad. TV Arts and Scis., Advt. Council (past dir.), Yale Law Sch. Assn., Internat. Radio and TV Soc. (trustee 1973-74), Hollywood Radio and TV Soc. (trustee 1970-72), Phi Beta Kappa (mem. alumni assn. So. Calif. 1970-72, mem. Phi Beta Kappa assocs.). Club: Princeton (N.Y.). Office: Am Mus of the Moving Image 36-01 35th Ave Long Island City NY 11106

SCHLOSSMAN, JOHN ISAAC, architect; b. Chgo., Aug. 21, 1931; s. Norman Joseph and Carol (Rosenfeld) S.; m. Shirley Goulding Rhodes, Feb. 8, 1959; children: Marc N., Gail S. Mewhort, Peter C. Student, Grinnell Coll., 1949-50; BA, U. Minn., 1953, BArch, 1955; MArch, MIT, 1956. Registered architect, Ill., Fla. Archtl. designer The Architects Collaborative, Cambridge, Mass., 1956-57; architect Loebl Schlossman & Hackl and predecessors, Chgo., 1959-65, assoc., 1965-70, prin., 1970—; bd. overseers Coll. Arch. Illinois Inst. Tech., Chgo.; founding bd. dirs. Chgo. Archtl. Assistance Ctr., 1974-79. Chmn. Glencoe Plan Commn., Ill., 1977-82; trustee Com. for Green Bay Trail, Glencoe, 1970-77, Chgo. Architecture Found., 1971-75; bd. dirs. Merit Music Program, Chgo., 1983-93, pres., 1988-90. Named dir. for life Young Men's Jewish Council, Chgo., 1971; Rotch travelling scholar, 1957. Fellow AIA (trustee ins. trust 1971-76, chmn. ins. com. 1974-75, v.p. Chgo. chpt. 1975, chmn. architects liability com. 1976, 80-82, hon. found. trustee 1995—); Archtl. Soc. of Art Inst. Chgo., Tavern Club (gov. 1986-88, v.p. 1990), The Arts Club, Alpha Rho Chi.. Office: Loebl Schlossman & Hackl 130 E Randolph St Ste 3400 Chicago IL 60601-6378

SCHLOSSMAN, STUART FRANKLIN, physician, educator, researcher; b. N.Y.C., Apr. 18, 1935; s. Abe and Pearl (Susser) S.; m. Judith Seryl Rubin, May 25, 1958; children: Robert, Peter. BA magna cum laude, NYU, 1955, MD, 1958; MA, Harvard U., 1975. Intern in medicine med. div. III Bellevue Hosp., N.Y.C., 1958-59, asst. resident in medicine med. div. III, 1959-60; Nat. Found. fellow dept. microbiology Coll. Physicians Columbia U., N.Y.C., 1960-62; Ward hematology fellow dept. internal medicine Sch. Washington U., St. Louis, 1962-63; rsch. assoc. lab. biochemistry Nat. Cancer Inst. USPHS, Washington, 1963-65; clin. instr. in medicine Sch. of Medicine George Washington U., 1964-65; assoc. in medicine, dir. blood bank Beth Israel Hosp., Boston, 1965-66; instr. Med. Sch. Harvard U., Boston, 1966-68, asst. physician, 1967-68, chief clin. immunology, 1971-73; physician Beth Israel Hosp., Boston; —from asst. to assoc. prof. medicine Harvard Med. Sch., Boston, 1968-77, prof., 1977—, Baruj Benacerraf prof. medicine, 1990—, chief div. tumor immunology and immunotherapy Dana-Farber Cancer Inst., 1973—; sr. physician Brigham and Women's Hosp., Boston, 1976—. Mem. editorial bd. Jour. of Immunology, 1969-74, Cellular Immunology, 1970—, Human Immunology, 1979-84, Clin. Immunology and Immunopathology, 1979—, Hybridoma, 1980—, Cancer Investigation, 1981, Stem Cells, 1981, Cancer Revs., 1984—, Internat. Jour. of Cell Cloning, 1983-86; mem. adv. bd. Cancer Treatment Reports, 1976-80; assoc. editor Human Lymphocyte Differentation, 1980-82; contbr. numerous articles to profl. jours. Recipient Solomon Berson Achievement award, 1984, Robert Koch prize and medal, 1984. Fellow AAAS; mem. NAS, Am. Soc. Hematology, Am. Soc. Immunologists, Am. Soc. Clin. Investigation, Assn. Am. Physicians, Inst. of Medicine, Alpha Omega Alpha. Office: Dana-Farber Cancer Inst 375 Longwood Ave Boston MA 02215-5328

SCHLOTFELDT, ROZELLA MAY, nursing educator; b. DeWitt, Iowa, June 29, 1914; s. John W. and Clara C. (Doering) S. BS, State U. Iowa, 1935; MS, U. Chgo., 1947, PhD, 1956; DSc (hon.), Georgetown U., 1972, Adelphi U., 1979, Wayne State U., 1983, U. Ill., Chgo., 1985, Kent State U., 1987, U. Cin., 1989; LHD (hon.), Med. U. S.C. 1976. Staff nurse State U. Iowa, VA Hosp., 1935-39; instr., supr. maternity nursing (State U. Iowa),

1939-44; asst. prof. U. Colo. Sch. Nursing, 1947-48; asst., then asso. prof. Wayne State U. Coll. Nursing, 1948-55; prof., asso. dean Wayne State U. Coll. Nursing (Coll. Nursing), 1957-60; dean Frances Payne Bolton Sch. Nursing, Case Western Res. U., 1960-72, prof., 1960-82, prof. emeritus, 1982—; vis. prof. Rutgers U., 1984-89, 90—, U. Pa., 1985-86; spl. cons. Surgeon Gen.'s Adv. Group on Nursing, 1961-63; mem. nursing research study sect. USPHS, 1962-66; mem. Nat. League for Nursing-USPHS Com. on Nursing Edn. Facilities, 1962-64; mem. com. on health goals Cleve. Health Council, 1961-66; mem. Cleve. Health Planning and Devel. Commn., 1969-72; adv. com. div. nursing W.K. Kellog Found., 1959-67; v.p. Ohio Bd. Nursing Edn. and Nurse Registration, 1970-71, pres., 1971-72; mem. Nat. Health Services Research Tng. Com., 1970-71; mem. supply and edn. panel Health Manpower Com., 1966-67; rev. com. Nurse Tng. Act, 1967-68; bd. visitors Duke U. Med. Center, 1968-70; mem. council, exec. com. Inst. Medicine of Nat. Acad. Scis., 1971-75; mem. nat. adv. health services council Health Services and Mental Health Adminstrn., 1971-75; mem. def. adv. com. on women in services Dept. Def., 1972-75; bd. mem., treas. Nursing Home Adv. and Research Council, 1975—; mem. adv. panel Health Services Research Commn. on Human Resources, Nat. Acad. Sci., 1977-85; cons. Walter Reed Army Inst.; adv. council on nursing, U.S. VA, 1965-69, chmn., 1966-69; mem. Yale U.; Council Com. on Med. Affairs, 1981-86; mem. adv. bd. Scholarly Inquiry for Nursing Practice, 1987—. Mem. editorial bd.: Advances in Nursing Sci, Inquiry, 1982-85, Jour. Nursing Edn., 1982-91; contbr. numerous articles to profl. jours. Bd. vis. Syracuse U., 1990—. Served to 1st lt. Army Nurse Corps, 1944-46. Recipient Disting. Svc. award U. Iowa, 1973, Case Western Res. U., 1991. Fellow Am. Acad. Nursing (v.p. 1975-77), Nat. League Nursing; mem. Am. Nurses Assn. (chmn. commn. on nurse edn. 1967-70, mem. com. for studying credentialling 1976-79, adv. com. W.K. Kellogg Nat. Fellowship program 1981-85), Pi Lambda Theta, Sigma Theta Tau (nat. v.p. 1948-50, selection com., disting. lectr. program 1986-87, Founders award for creativity 1985). Home: 1111 Carver Rd Cleveland OH 44112-3635 Office: 2121 Abington Rd Cleveland OH 44106-2333

SCHLOTTER, WALLY, chamber of commerce executive, television director; b. San Diego. AA in Bus., Grossmont Jr. Coll., 1972; BS in Telecommunications and Film, San Diego State U., 1975; student, Nat. Acad. TV Arts and Scis., 1974. With KPBS-TV, San Diego, 1973-75; asst. to exec. producer Police Story NBC Columbia Pictures TV, San Diego, 1975-76; production coord. nat. TV commls. San Diego, writer, production assistant, production coord., location scout, location mgr., assoc. producer/dir.; assoc. dir., dir. Motion Picture and TV Bur., San Diego; v.p. Greater San Diego C. of C. Creator, producer many fundraisers including San Diego EMMY Awards broadcast to benefit Nat. Acad. TV Arts and Scis. scholarship fund, 1978, 79, Kids Day at the Movies for orphaned children, Oscar Nite Variety Club fundraiser for children. Bd. govs. Muscular Dystrophy Assn.; trustee San Diego Festival of Arts; bd. dirs. Young Friends of the Symphony; active Multiple Sclerosis Soc., Socail Advocates for Youth, others. Recipient Nat. Best of West Producer award, 1975, San Diego Emmy citation for assoc. dir., 1976, Green Derby award Simon and Simon campaign, 1982, Appreciation award SAG, 1985, Headliner of Yr. award, 1986, Outstanding Young Alumnus award, 1986, Outstanding Young Citizen award, 1988, numerous others. Mem. Nat. Acad. TV Arts and Scis. (bd. govs., past v.p., co-founder/chmn. scholarship fund), Am. Film Inst., Variety Club (bd. govs., past chmn. spl. events, past. v.p.), Ad Club. Home: 5551 Candlelight Dr La Jolla CA 92037-7713 Office: 402 W Broadway Ste 1000 San Diego CA 92101-3542

SCHLOTTERBECK, WALTER ALBERT, manufacturing company executive, lawyer; b. N.Y.C., Dec. 22, 1926; s. Albert Gottlob and Maria Louise (Fritz) S.; m. Pauline Elizabeth Hoerz, Sept. 2, 1951; children—Susan, Thomas, Paul. A.B., Columbia U., 1949, LL.B., 1952. Bar: N.Y. 1953. Counsel Gen. Electric Co. (various locations), 1952-87; v.p. corp. counsel Gen. Electric Co. (various locations), N.Y.C., 1970-77; sec. Gen. Electric Co. (various locations), 1975-76, gen. counsel, 1976-87, sr. v.p., 1977-87. Served with USNR, 1944-46. Home: 201 Overlake Dr E Medina WA 98004

SCHLUETER, BERNARD JOSEPH, state official; b. Dubuque, Iowa, Oct. 8, 1940; s. Leo Bernard and Helen Susan (Ott) S.; m. Judith Ann Friedman, Aug. 31, 1963; children: Ann, Bart, Gregory, Martin, Luke, Nathan, Tobias, Rachael. BA, Loras Coll., Dubuque, 1963; MA in Hosp. Adminstrn., U. Iowa, 1965. Asst. adminstr. St. Francis Hosp., Peoria, Ill., 1964-69; assoc. adminstr. Holy Family Hosp., Manitowoc, Wis., 1969-72; pres., CEO, Mercy Med. Ctr., Oshkosh, Wis., 1972-86; adminstr., CEO Parma Gen. Hosp., Cleve., 1986-93; dep. dir. Ohio Dept. Health, Columbus, 1993—; mem. adv. bd. Parmadale, Parma, Ohio, 1986-91, Marycrest, Brecksville, Ohio, 1990-92. Active numerous polit. campaigns. Recipient Disting. Alumnus Pub. Svc. award Loras Coll., 1984, commendation State of Ohio. Fellow Am. Coll. Healthcare Execs. Roman Catholic. Home: 5716 Chatterfield Dr Dublin OH 43017 Office: Ohio Dept Health 246 High St Columbus OH 43266

SCHLUETER, DAVID ARNOLD, law educator; b. Sioux City, Iowa, Apr. 29, 1946; s. Arnold E. and Helen A. (Dettmann) S.; m. Linda L. Boston, Apr. 22, 1972; children: Jennifer, Jonathan. BA, Tex. A&M U., 1969; JD, Baylor U., 1971, LLM, U. Va., 1981. Bar: Tex. 1971, D.C. 1973, U.S. Ct. Mil. Appeals 1972, U.S. Supreme Ct. 1976. Legal counsel U.S. Supreme Ct., Washington, 1981-83; assoc. dean St. Mary's U., San Antonio, 1984-89, prof. law, 1986—; reporter Fed. Adv. Com. on Criminal Rules, 1988—; chmn. JAG adv. council, 1974-75. Author: Military Criminal Justice: Practice and Procedure, 1982, 3d edit., 1992; (with others) Military Rules of Evidence Manual, 1981, 3d edit., 1991, Texas Rules of Evidence Manual, 1983, 3d edit., 1991, Texas Evidentiary Foundations, 1992, Military Evidentiary Foundations, 1994; contbr. articles to legal publs. Maj. JAGC, U.S. Army, 1972-81. Fellow Tex. Bar Found. (life), Am. Bar Found. (life); mem. ABA (vice chmn. criminal justice sect. coun. 1991-94, vice chmn. com. on criminal justice and mil. 1983-84, chmn. standing com. on mil. law 1991-92, chmn. editorial adv. bd., Criminal Justice Mag., 1989-91), Tex. Bar Assn. Republican. Lutheran. Office: St Marys U Sch Law 1 Camino Santa Maria St San Antonio TX 78228-5433

SCHLUTER, PETER MUELLER, electronics company executive; b. Greenwich, Conn., May 24, 1933; s. Fredric Edward and Charlotte (Mueller) S.; m. Jaquelin Ambler Lamond, Apr. 18, 1970 (div. June 1990); children: Jane Randolph, Charlotte Mueller, Anne Ambler. BME, Cornell U., 1956; postgrad. Harvard U. Grad. Sch. Bus. Adminstrn., 1982. Sr. engr. Thiokol Chem. Corp., Brigham City, Utah, 1958-59; asso. Porter Internat. Co., Washington, 1960-65, v.p., 1965-66, pres., treas., dir., 1966-70; pres., treas. dir. Zito Co., Derry, N.H., 1970-72; internat. bus. cons., Washington, 1972-74; v.p., dir. Buck Engring. Co. Inc., Farmingdale, N.J., 1975, pres., chief exec. officer, dir., 1975—; hon. mem. City and Guilds of London Inst. Mem. Republican Inaugural Book and Program Com., 1969; mem. community adv. bd. Monmouth council Girl Scouts U.S.; mem. adv. council Monmouth (N.J.) Coll. Sch. Bus. Admin.; bd. dirs. United Way of Monmouth County; trustee Monmouth Med. Ctr.; N.Am. rep., mem. presidium WORLD DIDAC, Bern, Switzerland. Fellow City and Guilds of London Inst. (hon.); mem. World Assn. Mfrs. and Distributors of Ednl. Materials (N.Am. rep.), Metropolitan Club Washington, Rumson Country Club, Pi Tau Sigma. Home: 4 Quaker Ln Little Silver NJ 07739-1806 Office: PO Box 686 Farmingdale NJ 07727-0686

SCHLUTH, MICHAEL VERNON, advertising agency executive; b. Phila., Aug. 8, 1944; s. Frank Charles and Charlotte Laurel (Hanwell) S.; A.S. in Mktg., La Salle Coll., 1968; m. Nancy Jane Weller, Jan. 14, 1967; children—Lori Ann, Donna Jean, Michael Philip. Advt. sales rep. Phila. Newspapers, Inc., 1968-75; pres. Alstin Advt., Inc., Phila., 1975—; owner, pres. Lordon-Michaelson Assocs., 1984—. Bd. dirs. Meadowbrook Sch., Pa. Served with U.S. Army, 1963-65. Office: 1435 Walnut St Philadelphia PA 19102-3201

SCHMALBECK, RICHARD LOUIS, university dean, lawyer; b. Chgo., Dec. 31, 1947; s. George Louis and Betty Jeanne (Stevens) S. AB in Econs. with honors, U. Chgo., 1970, JD, 1975. Bar: Ohio 1975, D.C. 1977. Asst. to dir. and economist Ill. Housing Devel. Authority, Chgo., 1971-73; assoc. Vorys, Sater, Seymour & Pease, Columbus, Ohio, 1975-76; spl. asst. to assoc. dir. for econs. and govt. Office of Mgmt. and Budget, Washington, 1976-77;

assoc. Caplin & Drysdale, Washington, 1977-80; assoc. prof. law Duke U., Durham, N.C., 1980-84, prof. law, 1984-90, 93—, vice chmn. acad. coun., 1984-85; dean U. Ill. Coll. Law, Champaign, 1990-93. Assoc. editor U. Chgo. Law Rev., 1974-75; contbr. articles to profl. jours. Mem. ABA (articles editor jour. 1977-80), Am. Law Inst., Phi Beta Kappa. Office: Duke University Sch of Law Box 90360 Durham NC 27708-0360

SCHMALE, ALLEN LEE, financial services company executive; b. Addieville, Ill., Feb. 12, 1933; s. Arnold August and Leona Karoline (Becker) S.; m. Lorraine Marie Loyet, July 19, 1952; children: Judith Ann, Arnold August II, Michelle Lee, René Cerise, Allen Kent. CLU, ChFC. Salesman Western & So. Life Ins. Co., St. Louis, 1955-56, Monarch Life Ins. Co., St. Louis, 1956-58, Mass. Indemnity & Life Ins., St. Louis, 1958-65; pres. Schmale Fin. Svcs., Inc., Okawville, Ill., 1965-88, chmn., 1988—, also bd. dirs. Trustee Village of Okawville, 1976-80, mem. bus. devel. com.; vice chmn. Washington County (Ill.) Rep. Com.; coord. Edgar for Gov., Ill. 1990, 94; pres. St. Peters Ch., 1975-77; br. officer Walnut St. Securities Inc. Recipient Contbns. to Growth award Belleville (Ill.) Area Coll., 1977. Mem. Am. Soc. CLU and ChFC, East Side Life Underwriters (pres. 1971-72), Million Dollar Roundtable, Ill. Life Underwriters (bd. dirs. 1975-78), Nat. Assn. Life Underwriters (del. 1971), Estate Planning Coun. St. Louis, Okawville Comty. Club (pres. 1974-76). Republican. Avocation: golf. Home: 5304 County Hwy 6 Okawville IL 62271 Office: Schmale Fin Svcs Inc 611 S Front St Okawville IL 62271

SCHMALENBERGER, JERRY LEW, pastor, seminary administrator; b. Greenville, Ohio, Jan. 23, 1934; s. Harry Henry and Lima Marie (Hormel) S.; m. Carol Ann Walthall, June 8, 1956; children: Stephen, Bethany Allison, Sarah Layton. BA, Wittenberg U., 1956, DDiv (hon.), 1984; MDiv, Hamma Sch. Theology, Springfield, Ohio, 1959, D of Ministry, 1976. Ordained to ministry Luth. ch., 1959. Dir. Camp Mowana, Mansfield, Ohio, 1958-59; pastor 3d Luth. Ch., Springfield, 1959-61, 1st Luth. Ch., Bellefontaine, Ohio, 1961-66; sr. pastor 1st Luth. Ch., Tiffin, Ohio, 1966-70, Mansfield, 1970-79; sr. pastor St. John's Luth. Ch., Des Moines, 1979-88; pres., prof. parish ministry Pacific Luth. Theol. Sem., Berkeley, Calif., 1988—; co-dir. Iowa Luth. Hosp. Min. of Health Program, Des Moines, 1986-88; Roland Payne lectr. Gbarnga (Liberia) Sch. Theology, 1987; lectr. Luth. Theol. Sem., Hong Kong, 1994, The United Theol. Coll., Kingston, Jamaica, 1994. Author: Lutheran Christians' Beliefs Book One, 1984, Book Two, 1987, Iowa Parables and Iowa Psalms, 1984, Saints Who Shaped the Church, 1986, Stewards of Creation, 1987, Nights Worth Remembering, 1989, The Vine and the Branches, 1992, Call to Witness, 1993, Plane Thoughts on Parish Ministry, 1994, Invitation to Discipleship, 1995; columnist Rite Ideas, 1987-88. Bd. dirs. Grand View Coll., Des Moines, 1980-88, Wittenberg U., Springfield, Ohio, 1974-87, Luth. Social Services of Iowa, 1980-87, chmn. pre fund drive, 1988; bd. dirs. Planned Parenthood of Mid-Iowa, Des Moines, 1987-88; dir. Evang. Outreach/Luth. Ch. Am., 1983-85; mem. Iowa Luth. Hosp. Charitable Trust, 1986-88; chair Com. for Homeless Fund, Des Moines, 1986. Named Outstanding Alumni Wittenberg U., 1965, Young Man of Yr. Tiffin Jaycees, 1965, Man of Yr. Bellefontaine Jaycees, Disting. Alumni award Trinty Sem., Columbus, 1989. Mem. NAACP, Acad. Preachers, Acad. Evangelists (organizer 1986—), Kiwanis, Rotary. Avocations: historical research and writing, travel, boating. Home & Office: 2770 Marin Ave Berkeley CA 94708-1597 *Personal philosophy: Not perfect, but forgiven, we find real life in living ours for others.*

SCHMALENSEE, RICHARD LEE, economist, government official, educator; b. Belleville, Ill., Feb. 16, 1944; s. Fred and Marjorie Jane (Veigel) S.; SB, MIT, 1965, PhD, 1970; m. Edeth Diane Hawk, Aug. 19, 1967; children: Alexander Clayton, Nicholas Hawk. Asst. prof., assoc. prof. econs. U. Calif., San Diego, 1970-77; assoc. prof. applied econs. Sloan Sch. Mgmt., M.I.T., Cambridge, 1977-79, prof., 1979-86, prof. econs. and mgmt., 1986-89, Gordon Y Billard prof., 1988—; dir. MIT Ctr. for Energy and Environ. Policy Rsch., 1991—; dir. L.I. Lighting, Co.; mem. Pres.'s Coun. Econ. Advisors, 1989-91; NSF grantee, 1975-77, 81-83; research fellow U. Louvain (Belgium), 1973-74, 85. Fellow AAAS, Econometric Soc.; mem. Am. Econ. Assn. (nominating com. 1987, exec. com. 1993—). Author: The Economics of Advertising, 1972; The Control of Natural Monopoly, 1979; co-author: Markets for Power, 1983, Economics, 1988; co-editor: Handbook of Industrial Organization, 1989; mem. editorial bd. Jour. Indsl. Econs., 1981-89, Am. Econ. Rev., 1982-86, Internat. Jour. Indsl. Orgns., 1982-89, Jour. Econs. & Mgmt. Strategy, 1993—, Jour. Econ. Perspectives, 1993—. Home: 20 Malia Ter Chestnut Hill MA 02167-1326 Office: MIT 50 Memorial Dr Rm E52-456 Cambridge MA 02142-1347

SCHMALSTIEG, WILLIAM RIEGEL, Slavic languages educator; b. Sayre, Pa., Oct. 3, 1929; s. John William and Dorothy Augusta (Riegel) S.; m. Emily Lou Botdorf, Mar. 28, 1952; children: Linda, Roxanne. BA, U. Minn., 1950; postgrad., Columbia U., 1952; MA, U. Pa., 1951, PhD, 1956; PhD (hon.), Vilnius U., 1994. Instr. U.Ky., Lexington, 1956-59; asst. prof. Lafayette Coll., Easton, Pa., 1959-63; assoc. prof. U. Minn., Mpls., 1963-64; prof. Pa. State U., University Park, 1964—, head dept. Slavic langs., 1969-91; mem. Internat. Commn. Balto-Slavic Linguistics, 1973—; appointed Edwin Erle Sparks prof. Slavic Lang., 1990. Author: (with L. Dambriunas and A. Klimas) An Introduction to Modern Lithuanian, 1966, 4th edit., 1990, 5th edit., 1993, An Old Prussian Grammar, 1974, Studies in Old Prussian, 1976, Indo-European Linguistics, 1980, An Introduction to Old Church Slavic, 1976, 2d edit., 1983, A Lithuanian Historical Syntax, 1988, (with Warren Held and Janet Gertz) Beginning Hittite, 1988; editor: Gen. Linguistics, 1971-82. Served to 1st lt. U.S. Army, 1952-54. NEH grantee, 1978-79, Fulbright grantee and exch. scholar Acad. Scis., Vilnius, USSR, 1986; recipient Humanities medal Pa. State U., 1983, Friend of Lithuania award Knights of Lithuania, 1990; named Disting. Alumnus Breck Sch., 1990. Mem. Assn. Advancement Baltic Studies (pres. 1982-84), Am. Assn. Tchrs. of Slavic and East European Langs. Episcopalian. Home: 814 Cornwall Rd State College PA 16803-1430 Office: Dept Slavic Langs Pa State U University Park PA 16802

SCHMALZ, CARL NELSON, JR., artist, educator, printmaker; b. Ann Arbor, Mich., Dec. 26, 1926; s. Carl Nelson and Esther Dorothy (Fowler) S.; m. Dolores Irene Tourangeau, Dec. 2, 1950; children—Stephen Theodore (dec.), Mathew Nelson, Julia Irene. A.B., Harvard U., 1948, M.A., 1949, Ph.D., 1958; M.A. (hon.), Amherst Coll., 1969. Teaching fellow in fine arts Harvard U., Cambridge, Mass., 1950-52; asst. prof. Bowdoin Coll., Brunswick, Maine, 1953-62; curator, asst dir. Walker Art Mus., 1953-62; asst. prof. Harvard U., 1960; prof. Amherst Coll., 1962-95, prof. emeritus, 1995—; lectr. in field. Author: Watercolor Lessons from Eliot O'Hara, 1974, Watercolor Your Way, 1978, Finding and Improving Your Painting Style, 1986, paperback, 1992; exhibited in one-man shows including Cambridge (Mass.) Art Assn., 1948, Laing Gallery, Portland, Maine, 1955, Amherst (Mass.) Coll., 1963, U. Mass., 1965, W.C. Rawls Mus., Va., 1972, Concord (Mass.) Art Assn., 1974, Govt. House, Hamilton, Bermuda, 1979, Jones Library, Amherst, Mass., 1979, The Arlington, Kennebunkport, Maine, 1980, Harmon-Meek Gallery, Naples, Fla., 1987, 91, 92, Gallery at 6 Deering St., Portland, Maine, 1987, 91, Fretz Gallery, Portland, 1988-87; exhibited in group shows including Jordan Marsh Co., 1947, 48, 50, 71, 72, 73, Colby Coll., 1958, Carnegie Inst., Pitts., 1963, FAR Gallery, N.Y.C., 1964-68, Am. Watercolor Soc., 1966, 68, 70, Bowdoin Coll. Mus., 1973, Balt. Watercolor Soc., 1976, Boston Atheneum, 1979, Watercolor U.S.A. Honor Soc., 1989, 91, Maine Art Gallery, 1991; represented in permanent collections: Walker Art Mus., Brunswick, Maine, Jones & Laughlin Steel Corp., Diners Club Am., Kalamazoo Art Center, Hampshire Coll., Zanesville Art Inst., Blue Cross/Blue Shield; work published in various pubs. including The Artist's Guide for Using Color, 1992, The Artist's Mag., 1994, Splash 3: Ideas and Inspirations, 1994. Mem. exec. bd. Interfaith Housing Corp., Amherst, 1966-76; pres. bd. trustees Amherst Day Sch., 1966-69; mem. Pelham Arts Lottery Coun., 1984-90; v.p. bd. dirs. Portland Mus. Art, 1957-62. Bacon fellow, 1951; recipient 1st prize watercolor Cambridge Art Assn. Ann., 1947; 1st prize for traditional watercolor Virginia Beach Boardwalk Show, 1965; South Mo. Trust purchase award Watercolor U.S.A., 1970; 1st prize watercolor 30th Ann. Kennebunk River Club Show, 1985. Mem. Coll. Art Assn., Watercolor U.S.A. Honor Soc. Democrat.

SCHMALZRIED, MARVIN EUGENE, financial consultant; b. Dighton, Kans., Nov. 11, 1924; s. Carl D. and Marie M. (Bahm) S.; m. Jean Landino Nov. 27, 1946; children—Darlene, Candace, Cynthia, Derek, Valerie,

Rebecca. B.B.A., Northwestern U., 1949; LL.B., U. Conn., 1955. Bar: Conn. bar 1955; C.P.A., Conn. Acct. Webster, Blanchard & Willard, CPA's (named changed to Price Waterhouse & Co.), Hartford, Conn., 1950-55; contr., asst. treas. J.B. Williams Co., Glastonbury, Conn., 1955-57; treas., sec. Curtis 1000, Inc. (name changed to Am Bus. Products, Inc.), Atlanta, 1957-61; asst. to pres. Am Home Products Corp., N.Y.C., 1961-63, comptroller, 1964-67, v.p., 1967-72, sr. v.p., 1972-84; pres. Venda Vid, Inc., N.Y.C., 1986-90; sr. v.p. View-Master Ideal Group, Inc., N.Y.C., 1987-90; exec. v.p. Strategics Inc., 1993—; bd. dirs. Am. Bus. Products, Inc., Atlanta. Recipient Gold medal Conn. Soc. C.P.A.'s, 1953. Mem. AICPA, ABA, Old Greenwich Friday Evening Reading Soc. (pres.). Club: Darien Country. Home and Office: 26 Cove Ave Norwalk CT 06855

SCHMANDT-BESSERAT, DENISE, archaeologist, educator; b. Ay, France, Aug. 10, 1933; came to U.S., 1965, naturalized, 1970; d. Victor and Jeanne (Crabit) Besserat; m. Jurgen Schmandt, Dec. 27, 1956; children: Alexander, Christopher, Philip. Ed., Ecole du Louvre, 1965. Research fellow in Near Eastern Archaeology Peabody Mus. Harvard U., Cambridge, Mass., 1969-71; fellow Radcliffe Inst., Cambridge, 1969-71; asst. prof. Middle Eastern studies U. Tex., Austin, 1972-81, assoc. prof., 1981-88, prof., 1988—; acting chief curator U. Tex. Art Mus., 1978-79; vis. assoc. prof. U. Calif., Berkeley, 1987-88. Author: Before Writing, 1992; adv. editor Tech. and Culture, 1978-92; mem. adv. bd. Visible Language, 1985—; mem. editorial bd. Written Communication, 1993—; contbr. articles to profl. jours. Recipient Kayden Nat. U. Press Book award, 1993; Wenner-Gren Found. grantee, 1970-71; USIA. Am. Ctr. Oriental Rsch. fellow, 1994-95; NEA grantee, 1974-75, 77-78; NEH grantee, 1992; am. Coun. Learned Socs. grantee, 1984; NEH fellow, 1979-80; U.S. Info. Inst. for Rsch. in Humanities fellow, 1984-85; Deutscher Akademischer Austauschdienst grantee, 1986. Mem. Am. Oriental Soc., Archeol. Inst. Am. (governing bd. 1983-89), Am. Anthropol. Assn., Am. Schs. of Oriental Rsch., Centro Internationale Ricerche Archeologiche Anthropologiche e Storiche (Rome). Office: U of Tex Austin TX 78712

SCHMEER, ARLINE CATHERINE, cancer research development chemotherapy scientist; b. Rochester, N.Y., Nov. 14, 1929; d. Edward Jacob and Madeline Margaret (Haines) S. BA, Coll. St. Mary of the Springs, Columbus, Ohio, 1951; MS in Biology, Notre Dame U., 1961; PhD in Biomedicine, U. Colo., 1969; DSc (hon.), Albertus Magnus Coll., New Haven, Conn., 1974, SUNY, Potsdam, 1990. Chmn. sci. dept. Watterson High Sch./Diocese of Columbus, 1954-59, St. Vincent Ferrer High Sch./Archdiocese of N.Y., N.Y.C., 1959-62; chmn. dept. biology Ohio Dominican Coll., Columbus, 1963-72; chmn. dept. anti-cancer agents of marine origin Am. Cancer Rsch. Ctr., Denver, 1972-82; dir. Mercenene Cancer Rsch. Inst. Hosp. St. Raphael, New Haven, 1982-93; sr. prin. investigator Marine Biol. Lab., Woods Hole, Mass., 1962-72; corp. mem., mem. libr. com., 1964—; rsch. prof. Med. Sch., U. Würzburg, Fed. Republic Gemany, 1969-70; pres., chief exec. officer Med. Rsch. Found., 1972—; participant, contbr. Internat. Cancer Congress, 1966—. Contbr. articles to biol. publs. Grantee Am. Cancer Soc., 1965; NSF fellow, 1957-62, NIH, 1966-69; recipient numerous teaching awards, Ohi Acad. Scis. and others. Fellow Royal Microscopical Soc. Eng. (life); mem. N.Y. Acad. Sci. (life), Am. Soc. Cell Biology, Internat. Cancer Congresses. Roman Catholic. Avocations: photography, fishing. Office: Mercenene Cancer Rsch Inst 790 Prospect St New Haven CT 06511

SCHMELING, GARETH, classics educator; b. Algoma, Wis., May 28, 1940; married. B.A., Northwestern Coll., 1963; M.A. (Knapp fellow), U. Wis., 1964, Ph.D. (Knapp travelling grantee 1965-66, Univ. fellow 1967-68), 1968. Asst. prof. classics U. Va., 1968-70; assoc. prof. U. Fla., 1970-74, prof., 1974—; chmn. classics, 1974—; chmn. humanities, 1974-76; dir. Center for Studies in Humanities, 1978-87, prin. investigator Humanities Perspectives on Professions, 1975-87, acting chmn. dept. philosophy, 1986-88; vis. prof. U. Colo., Boulder, 1992; panelist, research div. Nat. Endowment for Humanities, also mem. nat. bd. consultants. Translator and author introduction: Cornelius Nepos: Lives of Famous Men, 1971; author: Petronius' Satyricon, 1971, Ovid's The Art of Love, 1972, Chariton and the Rise of Ancient Fiction, 1974, Homer's the Odyssey, 1974, A Bibliography of Petronius, 1977, Xenophon of Ephesus, 1980, Historia Apollonii Regis Tyri, 1988; contbr. numerous articles, revs. to profl. jours.; editor: Newsletter Petronian Soc, 1970—; editorial com.: U. Fla. Press Humanities Monographs, 1978—. Named 1 of 5 Tchrs. of Yr. for Arts and Scis. U. Fla., 1973; recipient Rome prize Am. Acad., 1977-78; U. Va. faculty fellow, summer 1969, summer 1970; U. Fla. fellow, summer 1971, summer 1974; Nat. Endowment for Humanities fellow, 1973-74; Am. Council Learned Socs. summer fellow, 1974; Am. Philos. Soc. grantee, 1970, 71, 72, 77-78, 84-85; U. Fla. grantee, 1977-78. Fellow Am. Acad. in Rome; mem. Am. Philol. Assn., Am. Classical League, Vergilian Soc., Classical Assn. of Middle West and South (sec.-treas. 1975-82, pres. 1985-86). Home: 320 NW 30th St Gainesville FL 32607-2524 Office: Dept Classics U Fla Gainesville FL 32611

SCHMELTZER, DAVID, lawyer; b. N.Y.C., Mar. 8, 1930; s. Harry Schmeltzer and Julia Hoffman Liebman; m. Louise Rose Levy, June 10, 1962; 1 child, Daniel Havram. BA, LL.U., 1957; LLB, Bklyn. Law Sch. 1960. Bar: N.Y. 1961. Assoc. Charles Struckler Law Office, N.Y.C., 1960-61; mng. atty. Otterbourg, Steindler, Houston & Rosen, N.Y.C., 1961-62; pub. counsel U.S. Maritime Adminstrn., Washington, 1962-66; atty. Dept. Commerce, Washington, 1966; asst. chief counsel Nat. Hwy. Traffic and Safety Ad, Washington, 1967-73; asst. gen. counsel Consumer Product Safety Commn., Washington, 1973-75, dep. gen. counsel, 1975-77, acting gen. counsel, 1976-77, asst. exec. dir. compliance, 1977—; instr. U. Md. Univ Coll., College Park, 1979-90; mng. dir. Inst. Safety Analysis, Rockville, Md., 1981. Avocation: tennis. Home: 9424 Garden Ct Potomac MD 20854-3964 Office: US Cons Prod Safety Commn Compliance & Enforcement Office 4330 East West Hwy Bethesda MD 20014

SCHMELTZER, EDWARD, lawyer; b. N.Y.C., Aug. 22, 1923; s. Harry A. and Julia (Hoffman) S.; m. Elizabeth Ann Cooper, June 19, 1949; children: Henry Cooper, Elizabeth Sabine. B.A., Hunter Coll., 1950; M.A., Columbia U., 1951; J.D., George Washington U., 1954. Bar: D.C. 1954, U.S. Supreme Ct 1958. Economist PHA, 1951-53; econ. cons. 1953-54; trial atty. Fed. Maritime Bd. Maritime Adminstrn., 1955-60; dir. bur. domestic regulation Fed. Maritime Commn., 1961-66, mng. dir., 1966-69; ptnr. Morgan, Lewis & Bockius, 1969-76, Schmeltzer, Aptaker & Shepard, 1976—; U.S. rep. 12th Diplomatic Conf. on Internat. Maritime Law, Brussels, 1967, 13th Diplomatic Conf., Brussels, 1968. Mem. bd. editors: Jour. Maritime Law and Commerce; contbr. articles to profl. jours. Served with USAAF, 1943-46. Recipient Fed. Maritime Commn./ Distinguished Service award, 1969. Mem. Maritime Adminstrv. Bar Assn. (pres. 1971-73). Club: Cosmos (Washington). Home: 10412 Buckboard Pl Rockville MD 20854-3805 Office: The Watergate 2600 Virginia Ave NW Washington DC 20037-1905

SCHMELZER, HENRY LOUIS PHILLIP, lawyer, financial company executive; b. Concord, Mass., Aug. 10, 1943; s. Frank Elden and Carroll (Blanning) S.; m. Cynthia E. Livingston, Sept. 28, 1978. B.A., U. Maine, 1965; J.D., George Washington U., 1968. Bar: Mass. 1971. Atty. State Mut. Life Assurance Co., Worcester, Mass., 1970-72; various positions New Eng. Securities Corp., Boston, 1972-90, pres., dir., 1991-92; v.p. New Eng. Mut. Life Ins. Co., 1983-87; pres., trustee New Eng. Funds, 1992—; bd. dirs. Back Bay Advisors. Bd. overseers U.S.S. Constitution Mus. Capt. M.I., U.S. Army, 1968-70, Vietnam. Decorated Bronze Star with oak leaf cluster. Mem. Investment Co. Inst. (legis. com.), U. Maine Devel. Coun., Boston Com. on Fgn. Rels., Portland (Maine) Yacht Club. Unitarian. Office: New Eng Funds LP 399 Boylston St Fl 10 Boston MA 02116-3305

SCHMEMANN, SERGE, journalist; b. Paris, Apr. 12, 1945; arrived in U.S., 1951; s. Rev Alexander and Juliana (Ossorguine) S.; m. Mary Schidlovsky, Sept. 13, 1970; children: Anne, Alexander, Nathalie. BA cum laude, Harvard U., 1967; MA, Columbia U., 1971; LittD (hon.), Middlebury Coll., 1995. Desk editor AP, N.Y.C., 1972-75, UN corr., 1975-77, South Africa corr., 1977-79, Moscow corr., 1979-80; Moscow bur. chief N.Y. Times, 1980-87, 91-95, Bonn bur. chief, 1987-90, Jerusalem bur. chief, 1995—. Contbr. articles to profl. publs. With U.S. Army, 1968-70 Vietnam. Recipient Hal Boyle award, Overseas Press Club, 1986, Pulitzer Prize for Coverage of German Reunification, 1991. Mem. Phi Beta Kappa.

Avocations: piano, carpentry. Office: NY Times 229 W 43rd St New York NY 10036-3913

SCHMERGEL, GABRIEL, pharmaceutical company executive; b. Budapest, Hungary, May 14, 1940; came to U.S., 1956, naturalized, 1962; s. Geza and Elizabeth (Kovacs) S. BSME, Rensselaer Poly. Inst., 1962; MBA (Baker scholar), Harvard U., 1967; PhD (hon.), Worcester Poly. Tech. Inst., 1988. With Baxter Travenol Labs., Inc., 1967-81; gen. mgr. Baxter Travenol Labs., Gmbh, München, Fed. Republic Germany, 1969-71, Baxter Belgium, Brussels, 1971-74; area dir. Baxter Travenol Labs., Inc., Deerfield, Ill., 1974-75; v.p. Baxter Travenol Labs., Inc., Europe, Brussels, 1975-79; pres. internat. Baxter Travenol Labs., Inc., Deerfield, Ill., 1979-81; pres., chief exec. officer Genetics Inst., Cambridge, Mass., 1981—. Bd. govs. New Eng. Med. Ctr.; trustee Mass. Biotech. Rsch. Inst. Served to 1st lt. Ordnance Corps U.S. Army, 1962-63. Mem. ASME, Pharm. Mfrs. Assn., Indsl. Biotech. Assn. (past pres. 1986).

SCHMERLING, ERWIN ROBERT, volunteer, retired government official; b. Vienna, Austria, July 28, 1929; came to U.S., 1955, naturalized, 1962; s. Heinrich H. and Lily (Goldsmith) S.; m. Esther M. Schmerling, Apr. 5, 1957; children: Susan D., Elaine M. BA, Cambridge U., 1950, MA, 1954, PhD in Radio Physics, 1958; grad., Advanced Mgmt. Program, Harvard, 1969, Fed. Exec. Inst., 1975. Asst. prof. elec. engring. Pa. State U., University Park, 1955-60, assoc. prof., 1960-62, 63-64; staff scientist NASA-Hdqrs., Washington, 1962-63, program chief ionospheric physics, magnetospheric physics, space plasma physics, 1964-82; asst. dir. space and earth scis. Goddard Space Flight Ctr., NASA, Greenbelt, Md., 1984-86; chief data system scientist Office Space Science and Applications NASA Hdqrs., Washington, 1986-88; SAIS program scientist NASA, Washington, 1988-89; data system scientist solar system exploration div. NASA Hdqrs., Washington, 1989-90, program mgr. astrophysics data systems, 1991-94; with Svc. Corps of Retired Execs. (SCORE); mem. U.S. coms. III and IV Internat. Sci. Radio Union, 1985—, sec. U.S. Com. III, 1966-69, chmn., 1969-72; chmn. subcom. C1 Com. Space Rsch. (COSPAR), 1984-88; mem. Adv. Group Aerospace Research and Devel.; vis. scholar Stanford U., 1983; cons. RCA, Gen. Electric, 1959-62. Contbr. papers to profl. jours. Recipient medal for contributions to internat. geophys. programs Soviet Geoph. Fellow IEEE (mem. wave propagation standards com.); mem. Am. Geophys. Union, AAAS, Sigma Xi. Home: 9917 La Duke Dr Kensington MD 20895-3140

SCHMEROLD, WILFRIED LOTHAR, dermatologist; b. Munich, Germany, Dec. 30, 1919; came to U.S., 1956; s. Wilhelm and Frieda (Hinterwinkler) S.; m. Perlette J. Joers, 1962 (div. Apr. 1974); children: Klaus, John, Will, James, Susan, Paul, Carl, Mike, Tom, Marianne. Abiturient, Altes Realgymnasium, 1938; MD, U. Munich, 1945. Bd. cert. dermatologist, dermatopathologist. Intern U Munich Med. Faculty, 1945-46; asst. UN Hosp., Munich, 1946-50, Max Plank Inst., Munich, 1951-52, U. Erlangen, Germany, 1952-53, U. Munich, 1953-56; intern Fairview Park Hosp., Cleve., 1956-57; asst. U. Ill., Chgo., 1957-60, instr., 1960-75, clin. asst. prof., 1975—; dermatologist pvt. practice, Carol Stream, Ill., 1959—, dermatopathologist, 1978—. Contbr. articles to profl. jours. Charter mem. founders club Ctrl. DuPage Hosp., Winfield, Ill., 1963. Fellow AMA, Am. Acad. Dermatology (life), German Dermatological Soc. (life), Am. Soc. Dermatopathology, Ill. Dermatological Soc., Ill. State Med. Soc., Chgo. Dermatological Soc. Roman Catholic. Avocations: opera, travel, anthropology, archaeology, history. Office: Mona Kea Med Park 507 Thornhill Dr # B Carol Stream IL 60188-2703

SCHMERTMANN, JOHN HENRY, civil engineer, educator, consultant; b. N.Y.C., Dec. 2, 1928; s. Johannes Conrad Schmertmann and Margaret Anna (Carstens) Schmertmann Ottesen; m. Pauline Anne Grange, Aug. 11, 1956; children—Carl, Gary, Neil, Joy. B.S.C.E., MIT, 1950; M.S.C.E., Northwestern U., 1954, Ph.D. in Civil Engring., 1962. Registered profl. engr., Fla. Soils engr. Mueser Rutledge Cons. Engrs., N.Y.C., 1951-54; soils engr. C.E., U.S. Army, Wilmette, Ill., 1954-56; asst. prof. civil engring. U. Fla., Gainesville, 1956-62; assoc. prof. U. Fla., 1962-65, prof., 1965-79, adj. prof., 1979-91, prof. emeritus, 1991—; prin. Schmertmann & Crapps, Inc., Gainesville, 1979—; postdoctoral fellow Norwegian Geotech. Inst., Oslo, 1962-63; vis. scientist div. bldg. research NRC Can., Ottawa Ont., 1971-72. Author numerous profl. papers. Fellow ASCE (br. pres. 1972, Collingwood prize 1956, Norman medal 1971, State of the Art award 1977, Middlebrooks award 1981, Terzaghi lectr. 1989), Fla. Engring. Soc.; mem. Nat. Acad. Engring., ASTM (subcom. chmn. 1974—). Republican. Lutheran. Avocation: sport fishing. Office: Schmertmann & Crapps Inc 4509 NW 23rd Ave Ste 19 Gainesville FL 32606

SCHMERTZ, ERIC JOSEPH, lawyer, educator; b. N.Y.C., Dec. 24, 1925; married; 4 children. A.B., Union Coll., 1948, LL.D. (hon.), 1978; cert., Alliance Francaise, Paris, 1948; J.D., NYU, 1954. Bar: N.Y. 1955. Arbitrator rep. Am. Fedn. State, County and Mcpl. Employees, AFL-CIO, N.Y.C., 1950-52; asst. v.p., dir. labor tribunals Am. Arbitration Assn., N.Y.C., 1952-57, 59-60; indsl. relations dir. Metal Textile Corp. subs. Gen. Cable Corp., Roselle, N.J., 1957-59; exec. dir. N.Y. State Bd. Mediation, 1960-62, corp. dir., 1962-68; labor-mgmt. arbitrator N.Y.C., 1962—; mem. faculty Hofstra U. Sch. Bus., 1962-70; prof. Hofstra U. Sch. Law, 1970—, Edward F. Carlough disting. prof. labor law, 1981—, dean Sch. Law, 1982-89; of counsel Rivkin, Radler, Kremer, 1989—; commr. labor rels. City of N.Y., 1990-91; 1st Beckley lectr. in bus. U. Vt., 1981; bd. dirs. Wilshire Oil Co.; mem. N.Y. State Pub. Employment Rels. Bd., 1991—; cons. and lectr. in field. Co-author: (with R.L. Greenman) Personnel Administration and the Law, 1978; contbr. chpts. to books, articles to profl. jours.; to profl. law confs., seminars and workshops. Mem. numerous civic orgns. Served to lt. USN, 1943-46. Recipient Testimonial award Southeast Republican Club, 1969; Alexander Hamilton award Rep. Law Students Assn.; Eric J. Schmertz Disting. Professorship Pub. Law and Pub. Svc. established Hofstra Law Sch., 1993. Mem. Nat. Acad. Arbitrators, Am. Arbitration Assn. (law com.), Whitney North Seymour Sr. medal 1984), Fed. Mediation and Conciliation Svc., N.Y. Mediation Bd., N.J. Mediation Bd., N.J. Pub. Employment Rels. Bd., Hofstra U. Club, Princeton Club. Office: 275 Madison Ave New York NY 10016

SCHMERTZ, HERBERT, public relations and advertising executive; b. Yonkers, N.Y., Mar. 22, 1930; s. Max and Hetty (Frank) S.; children: Anthony, Lexy, Nicole, Thomas, Conor. AB, Union Coll., 1952, LLD (hon.), 1977; LLB, Columbia U., 1955. Bar: N.Y. State 1959. With Am. Arbitration Assn., N.Y.C., 1955-61; gen. counsel, asst. to dir. Fedn. Mediation and Conciliation Svc., N.Y.C., 1961-66; with Mobil Oil Corp., N.Y.C., 1966—; pres. Mobil Shipping and Transp. Co., 1973-74; v.p. pub. affairs Mobil Oil Corp., 1974-88; pres. The Schmertz Co., Inc., N.Y.C., 1988—Washington, 1990—. Author: Good-bye to the Low Profile, 1986; co-author Takeover, 1980. Appointee Pres.'s Commn. on Broadcasting to Cuba, U.S. Adv. Commn. on Pub. Diplomacy; mem. adv. coun. NYU Sch. Arts; bd. dirs. USO Met. N.Y.C.; trustee Media Inst.; bd. govs. Media and Society Seminars Columbia U. Grad. Sch. Journalism. Served with CIC U.S. Army, 1955-57. Mem. Coun. Fgn. Rels., N.Y. Athletic Club. Democrat. Jewish. Office: Schmertz Co Inc 1185 Ave of the Americas 8th FL New York NY 10036-2601 also: Schmertz Co Washington 555 13th St Ste 1300 E Washington DC 20004-1109

SCHMERTZ, MILDRED FLOYD, editor, writer; b. Pitts., Mar. 29, 1925; d. Robert Watson and Mildred Patricia (Floyd) S. B.Arch., Carnegie Mellon U., 1947; M.F.A., Yale U., 1957. Archtl. designer John Schurko Architect, Pitts., 1947-55; assoc. editor Archtl. Record, N.Y.C., 1957-65; sr. editor Archtl. Record, 1965-80, exec. editor, 1980-85, editor-in-chief, 1985-90; vis. lectr. Yale Sch. Architecture, 1979—. Editor, contbr.: New Life for Old Buildings; other books on architecture and planning. Bd. mgrs. Jr. League, City of N.Y., 1964-65; commr. N.Y. Landmarks Preservation Commn., 1988-91. Fellow AIA; mem. Archtl. League N.Y., Mcpl. Art Soc. N.Y., Century Assn. (N.Y.C.). Home and Office: 310 E 46th St New York NY 10017-3002

SCHMETTERER, ROBERT ALLEN, advertising executive; b. N.Y.C., Nov. 23, 1943; s. Robert Mayer and Rosalie (Fernandez) S.; children: Adam, Tyler; m. Stacy Lynn Chiarello, Sept. 26, 1987. B.S., Fairfield Dickinson U., 1967, M.B.A., 1970. Sales promotion mgr. Brit. Motor Corp., Leonia, N.J., 1963-68; market research dir. Volvo, Rockleigh, N.J., 1968-71; v.p.

market rsch. Scali, McCabe, Sloves Inc., N.Y.C., 1971-73, sr. v.p. dir. account service, 1974-79, exec. v.p., chief oper. officer, mng. dir., 1979-84; pres., chief exec. officer/worldwide HCM, N.Y.C. and Paris, 1984-87; pres., ptnr. Messner, Vetere, Berger, Carey, Schmetterer, N.Y.C., 1987—; bd. dirs. N.Y.C. Partnership, 1987—. Mem. Advt. Club N.Y. (dir. 1983). Home: Snedens Landing Palisades NY 10964 Office: Messner Vetere Berger McNamee Schmetterer 350 Hudson St New York NY 10014-4504

SCHMID, HARALD HEINRICH OTTO, biochemistry educator, academic director; b. Graz, Styria, Austria, Dec. 10, 1935; came to U.S., 1962; s. Engelbert and Annemarie (Kletetschka) S.; m. Patricia Caroline Igou, May 21, 1977. MS, U. Graz, 1957, LLD, 1962, PhD, 1964. Rsch. fellow Hormel inst. U. Minn., Austin, 1962-65, rsch. assoc., 1965-66, asst. prof., 1966-70, assoc. prof., 1970-74, prof., 1974—; cons. NIH, Bethesda, Md., 1977—; acting dir. Hormel inst. U. Minn., 1985-87, exec. dir., 1987—; lectr. Mayo Med. Sch., Rochester, Minn., 1990—. Mng. editor Chemistry and Physics of Lipids, Elsevier Sci. Publs., Amsterdam, The Netherlands, 1984—; contbr. numerous articles to profl. jours. Rsch. grantee NIH, 1967—. Mem. AAAS, Am. Soc. Biochemistry and Molecular Biology, Am. Chem. Soc., The Oxygen Soc. Avocations: yacht racing, downhill skiing, tennis, classical music. Home: RR 3 Box 246 Austin MN 55912 Office: U Minn Hormel Inst 801 16th Ave NE Austin MN 55912

SCHMID, RUDI (RUDOLF SCHMID), internist, educator, university official; b. Switzerland, May 2, 1922; came to U.S., 1948, naturalized, 1954; s. Rudolf and Bertha (Schiesser) S.; m. Sonja D. Wild, Sept. 17, 1949; children: Isabelle S., Peter R. B.S., Gymnasium Zurich, 1941; M.D., U. Zurich, 1947, Ph.D., U. Minn., 1954. Intern U. Calif. Med. Center, San Francisco, 1948-49; resident medicine U. Minn., 1949-52, instr., 1952-54; research fellow biochemistry Columbia U., 1954-55; investigator NIH, Bethesda, Md., 1955-57; assoc. medicine Harvard U., 1957-59, asst. prof., 1959-62; prof. medicine U. Chgo., 1962-66; prof. medicine U. Calif., San Francisco, 1966-91, prof. emeritus, 1991—, dean Sch. Medicine, 1983-89, assoc. dean internat. relations, 1989—; Cons. U.S. Army Surgeon Gen., USPHS, VA. Mem. editorial bd. Jour. Clin. Investigation, 1965-70, Blood, 1962-75, Gastroenterology, 1965-70, Jour. Investigative Dermatology, 1968-72, Annals Internal Medicine, 1975-79, Proceedings Soc. Exptl. Biology and Medicine, 1974-84, Chinese Jour. Clin. Scis., Jour. Lab. Clin. Medicine, 1991—, Hepatology Comm. Internat. (Japan), 1993—; cons. editor Gastroenterology, 1981-86. Served with Swiss Army, 1943-48. Master ACP; fellow AAAS, N.Y. Acad. Scis., Royal Coll. Physicians; mem. NAS, Am. Acad. Arts and Scis., Assn. Am. Physicians (pres. 1986), Am. Soc. Clin. Investigation, Am. Soc. Biol. Chemists, Am. Soc. Hematology, Am. Gastroenterol. Assn., Am. Assn. Study Liver Disease (pres. 1965), Internat. Assn. Study Liver (pres. 1980), Swiss Acad. Med. Scis. (mem. senate), Leopoldina, German-Am. Acad. Coun. Research in metabolism of hemoglobin, heme, prophyrins, bile pigments and liver. Home: 211 Woodland Rd Kentfield CA 94904 Office: U of Calif Med Sch Office of Dean PO Box 0410 San Francisco CA 94143-0410

SCHMID, WILFRIED, mathematician; b. Hamburg, Germany, May 28, 1943; came to U.S., 1960; s. Wolfgang and Kathe (Erfling) S. BA, Princeton U., 1964; MA, U. Calif., Berkeley, 1966, PhD, 1967. Asst. prof. math. U. Calif., Berkeley, 1967-70; prof. math. Columbia U., 1970-78, Harvard U., 1978—; vis. mem. Inst. for Advanced Study, Princeton, 1969-70, 75-76; vis. prof. U. Bonn, 1973-74. Editor Springer Ergebnisse der Mathematik, Jour. Am. Math. Soc.; contbr. articles to profl. jours. Sloan fellow, 1968-70, Guggenheim fellow, 1975-76, 88-89. Home: Silver Hill Rd Lincoln MA 01773 Office: Harvard U Dept Mathematics Cambridge MA 02138

SCHMIDHAUSER, JOHN RICHARD, political science educator; b. N.Y.C., Jan. 3, 1922; s. Richard J. and Gertrude (Grabinger) S.; m. Thelma Lorraine Ficker, June 9, 1952; children: Steven, Paul, Thomas, John C., Martha, Sarah, Susan. B.A. with honors, U. Del., 1949; M.A., U. Va., 1952, Ph.D., 1954. Instr. U. Va., 1952-54; prof. constl. law U. Iowa, 1954-64, prof. polit. sci., 1967-73; prof. polit. sci. U. So. Calif., 1973-92, prof. emeritus, 1993—; mem. 89th Congress 1st dist. Iowa.; research fellow Research Inst. on Jud. Process, Social Sci. Research Council, 1958; sr. fellow law and behavorial scis. U. Chgo., 1959-60; Talbot vis. prof. govt. U. Va., 1982-83. Author: The Role of Supreme Court as Final Arbiter in Federal-State Relations, 1789-1957, 1958, The Supreme Court; Its Politics, Personalities and Procedures, 1960, Constitutional Law in the Political Process, 1963, (with Berg) The Supreme Court and Congress, 1972, (with Berg and Hahn) American Political Institutions and Corruption, 1976, (with Totten) Whaling in Japan-U.S. Relations, 1978, Judges and Justices, 1979, Constitutional Law in American Politics, 1984, Comparative Judicial Politics, 1987; also numerous articles in jours. Chmn. Citizens Action Com. for Fair Representation in Iowa Legislature, 1961; dist. chmn. Operation Support Pres. Kennedy and Johnson, 1961—; chmn. Johnson County Dem. Ctrl. Com., 1961-64; del. Iowa Dem. Convs., 1956, 58, 60, 62; mem. Dem. Nat. Com. Alumni Coun., 1986—; chmn. Santa Barbara, Calif. Dem. Ctrl. Com., 1991-92; mem. exec. com. Los Padres chpt. of the Sierra Club, 1992—; sec. Santa Barbara Dem. League, 1993—. With USNR, 1941-45, PTO. Recipient Raubenheimer award U. So. Calif., 1991, Golden Key award for Comparative Rsch. 1991. Mem. Iowa City Mgr. Assn. (bd. reps. 1956-59, chmn. handbook revision 1958), Internat. Polit. Sci. Assn. (chmn. research com. for comparative jud. studies 1980-88), Am. Polit. Sci. Assn., Midwestern Polit. Sci. Assn., Western Polit. Sci. Assn. (v.p., program chmn. 1980-81, pres.-elect 1981-82), AAUP (sec.-treas. State U. Iowa 1958-59, mem. com. on relationship fed. and state govt. to higher edn., mem. exec. com. U. So. Calif. chpt. 1983-92), Humanities Soc., Raven Soc., Phi Beta Kappa, Phi Kappa Phi. Unitarian (chmn. Iowa City Soc. Men's Club 1960-61). Home: 726 Arbol Verde St Carpinteria CA 93013-2508 *For the young today the opportunity for a good education puts them at the threshold of great opportunities. I encourage them to enjoy that with the same spirit that my generation experienced.*

SCHMIDLY, DAVID J., dean; b. Levelland, Tex., Dec. 20, 1943; m. Janet Elaine Knox, June 2, 1966; children: Katherine Elaine, Brian James. BS in Biology, Tex. Tech U., 1966, MS in Zoology, 1968; PhD in Zoology, U. Ill., 1971. From asst. prof. to prof. dept. wildlife fisheries scis. Tex. A&M U., College Station, 1971-82, prof., 1982—, head dept. wildlife, 1986-92; CEO, campus dean Tex. A&M U., Galveston, 1992—; chief curator Tex. Coop. Wildlife Coll., College Station, 1983-86; v.p. Tex. Inst. Oceanography, 1992—; cons. Nat. Park Svc., Wildlife Assocs., Walton and Assocs., Continental Shelf Assn., LGL; press adv. com. Tex. A&M U., 1983—; charter mem. Tex. A&M U. Faculty Senate, 1983-85; chmn. Scholarship Com., 1978-82; lectr. various workshops and seminars. Author: The Mammals of Trans-Pecos Texas including Big Bend National Park and Guadalupe Mountains National Park, 1977, Texas Mammals East of the Balcones Fault Zone, 1983, The Bats of Texas, 1991, The Mammals of Texas, 1994; contbr. articles to profl. jours. Trustee Tex. Nature Conservancy, 1991—. Recipient Dist. Prof. award Assn. Grad. Wildlife and Fisheries Scis., 1985, Donald W. Tinkle Rsch. Excellence award Southwestern Assn. Naturalists, 1988, Diploma Recognition La Universidad Autonoma de Guadalajara, 1989, La Universidad Autonoma de Tamaulipas, 1990. Fellow Tex. Soc. Sci. (bd. dirs. 1979-81); mem. AAAS, Am. Soc. Mammalogists (life, editor Jour. Mammalogy 1975-78), Am. Inst. Biol. Scis. (bd. dirs. 1993—, coun. affiliate socs. 1989—), Am. Naturalist, Soc. Marine Mammalogy (charter mem.), Soc. Systematic Zoology, The Wildlife Soc. Soc. Conservation Biology, Nat. Geog. Sci. Soc., S.W. Assn. Naturalists (life mem., bd. govs. 1980-86, 91—, pres. 1981, trustee 1986—), Tex. Mammal Soc. (pres. 1985-86), Assn. Systematic Collections (bd. dirs.), Chihuahuan Desert Rsch. Inst. (v.p. bd. scientists 1982—, bd. dirs. 1991), Mexican Soc. Mammalogists, Sigma Xi (v.p. 1986-87, pres. 1987-88), Disting. Scientist award 1991), Beta Beta Beta. Phi Sigma, Phi Kappa Phi. Home: 54 Adler Cir Galveston TX 77551-5828 Office: Tex A&M U at Galveston Office of Dean PO Box 1675 Galveston TX 77553-1675

SCHMIDMAN, JO ANN, artistic director. BFA, Boston U., 1970. Performer Joseph Chaikin's Open Theatre, N.Y.C.; artistic dir., writer, actor, prodr., light and concept designer Omaha Magic Theatre, 1968—; project dir., fiscal agt. for more than 90 found., corp., govt. grants; lectr. internationally; condr. workshops in ensemble acting, directing, collaborative theatre, performance art and storytelling; tchr. playwriting and poetry at various univs.; reporter Theatre Program, NEA, 1980—, mem. artistic advancement com., 1987-89, 92, chmn., 1988-89, mem. theatre overview panel, 1988; mem. Japanese-Am. Fellowship Com., 1987. Contbg. writer: 100,001 Horror Stores of the Plains, 1976, This Sleep Among Women, 1978, Running Gag, 1980 (commd. perfs. 1980 Winter Olympics); dir., performer: (with Sora Kimberlain) Yellow Strapping, 1980, (with Kimberlain) Blue Tube, 1980, (with Kimberlain) White Out, 1980, (with Kimberlain) Reflected Light, 1980, Change Yer Image, 1981, Aliens Under Glass, 1982, Velveeta Meltdown, 1982, Watch Where We Walk, 1983, (with Megan Terry) X-Rayed-Iate: E-Motion in Action, 1984, Astro*Bride, 1984, (with Terry) Sea of Forms, 1986, (with Terry) Walking Through Walls, 1987, (with Terry) Babes Unchained, (with Terry and Kimberlain) Body Leaks, 1990, Belches on Couches, 1993; dir.: (with Terry, Kimberlain, and Calif. State students) Cancel That Last Thought or See the 270 Foot Woman in Spandex, 1989, (with Terry and Kimberlain) Sound Fields, 1991, (with Terry) Remote Control, 1994, (with Terry and Kimberlain) Star Path Moon Stop, 1995; editor (with Terry and Kimberlain) Right Brain Vacation Photos, 1972-92; performer: Terminal, Open Theatre, 1971-73; contbg. writer, performer: Mutation Show and Nightwalk, Open Theatre, 1970-73 (Obie award); prodr., dir., performer numerous plays. Artist-in-the-Schs. in Performing Arts grantee Nebr. Arts Coun. Home: 2309 Hanscom Blvd Omaha NE 68105 Office: Omaha Magic Theatre 325 S 16th St Omaha NE 68102

SCHMID-SCHOENBEIN, GEERT WILFRIED, biomedical engineer, educator; b. Albstadt, Baden-Wurttemberg, Germany, Jan. 1, 1948; came to U.S., 1971; s. Ernst and Ursula Schmid; m. Renate Schmid-Schoenbein, July 3, 1976; children: Philip, Mark, Peter. Vordiplom, Liebig U., Giessen, Germany, 1971; PhD in Bioengring., U. Calif., San Diego, 1976. Staff assoc. dept. physiology Columbia U., N.Y.C., 1976-77, sr. assoc., 1977-79; asst. prof. dept. applied mechs. & engring. scis. U. Calif., San Diego, 1979-84, assoc. prof., 1984-89, prof., 1989—. Editor: Frontiers in Biomechanics, 1986, Physiology and Pathophysiology of Leukocyte Adhesion, 1994. Recipient Melville medal ASME, 1990. Fellow Am. Inst. for Med. & Biol. Engring., Am. Heart Assn.; mem. Biomed. Engring. Soc. (pres. 1991-92), Am. Microcirculatory Soc., European Microcirculatory Soc., Am. Physiol. Soc. Achievements include bioengineering research of cardiovascular disease. Office: U Calif San Diego Dept Bioengineering La Jolla CA 92093-0412

SCHMIDT, ADOLPH WILLIAM, retired ambassador; b. McKeesport, Pa., Sept. 13, 1904; s. Adolph and Louise (Schmidt) S.; m. Helen Sedgley Mellon, June 27, 1936; children:—Helen Schmidt Claire, Thomas M. A.B., Princeton U., 1926, LL.D. (hon.), 1977; M.B.A., Harvard U., 1929; certificates, U. Dijon, U. Berlin and U. Paris, Sorbonne, 1926-27; LL.D. (hon.), U. Pitts, 1954, U. N.B., 1973; L.H.D., Chatham Coll., 1965, Carnegie-Mellon U., 1981. Officer Mellon Nat. Bank and affiliated orgns., Pitts., 1929-42; chmn. bd., dir. Columbia Radiator Co., McKeesport, 1939-42; mem. exec. com., dir. Pitts. Coal Co., 1940-42; v.p., gov. T. Mellon & Sons, Pitts., 1946-69; trustee A.W. Mellon Ednl. and Charitable Trust, pres., 1954-65; trustee Old Dominion Found., 1941-69, Carnegie Inst., 1965—; ambassador to Can. Ottawa, Ont., 1969-74; U.S. del. Conf. on North Atlantic Community, Bruges, Belgium, 1957, Atlantic Congress, London, Eng., 1959, Atlantic Conv. NATO Nations, Paris, France, 1962; adviser to U.S. delegation Econ. Commn. for. Europe, Geneva, Switzerland, 1967; bd. govs. Atlantic Inst., Paris; bd. dirs. Atlantic Council U.S., Washington. Co-founder Pitts. Playhouse, 1934, Pitts. Symphony, 1937; pres. Presbyn.-Univ. Hosp., 1946-47; 1st chmn. Three Rivers Arts Festival, 1960; pres., chmn. Allegheny Conf. on Community Devel., Pitts., 1956-61; vice chmn. Urban Redevel. Authority, 1954-59; 1st chmn. Southwestern Pa. Regional Planning Commn., 1960; mem. bus. and internat. coms. Nat. Planning Assn., 1955-69; mem. Can.-Am. Com., 1974-80; chmn. Pa. State Planning Bd., 1955-68; dir. Population Crisis Com., Washington, 1965-69, Population-Environment Balance, Inc., 1973-89; mem. bd. visitors and govs. St. Johns Coll., Annapolis, Md. and Santa Fe, N.Mex., also chmn., 1956, 62; mem. grad. council Princeton U. Served from capt. to lt. col. U.S. Army, 1942-46; with OSS in Africa and Europe; Allied Control Commn. Berlin. Awarded Bronze Star, Two Battle Stars; Benjamin Rush award Allegheny Co. Med. Soc., 1950; David Glick award World Affairs Council, 1965. Mem. Coun. Fgn. Rels., Mil. Order World Wars, Coun. Am. Ambs. Republican. Presbyterian. Clubs: Links, Anglers (N.Y.C.); Duquesne (Pitts.), Pitts. Golf; Laurel Valley Golf, Rolling Rock (Ligonier, Pa.); Metropolitan (Washington). Home: RR 4 Ligonier PA 15658-9804

SCHMIDT, ALLEN EDWARD, religious foundation administrator; b. Barriere, B.C., Can., Oct. 30, 1932; s. Ernst Waldemar and Agda Elvira (Rosen) S.; m. Catherine Edith Lee, June 19, 1954; children: Rebecca Lee Wade, Leanne Ruth Birdwell, Joseph Allen. BA with honors, Hardin-Simmons U., 1957; MDiv, Golden Gate Bapt. Sem., 1962. Owner, operator trucking co. Barriere, 1949-52; founding pastor Tolenas Bapt. Ch., Fairfield, Calif., 1960-61, Pike Rd. Bapt. Ch. Surrey, B.C., 1961-66, Royal Heights Bapt. Ch., Delta, B.C., 1966-81; Can. ch. coord. N.W. Bapt. Conv., Portland, Oreg., 1981; exec. dir., treas. Can. Conv. of So. Baptists, Cochrane, Alta., Can., 1985—. Pres. PTA, Surrey, 1977-79, Surrey Ministerial, 1975-77, N.W. Bapt. Conv., Portland, 1976-78, exec. bd. dirs., chmn., 1971-75. Home: 128 Riverview Cir, Cochrane, AB Canada T0L 0W4 Office: Can Conv So Baptists, Bag 300, Cochrane, AB Canada T0L 0W0

SCHMIDT, ARTHUR, film editor. Editor: (films) (with Jim Clark) The Last Remake of Beau Geste, 1977, Coal Miner's Daughter, 1980 (Academy award nomination best film editing 1980), The Escape Artist, 1982, Firstborn, 1984, The Buddy System, 1984, (with Harry Keramidas) Back to the Future, 1985, Fandango, 1985, (with Gib Jaffe) Ruthless People, 1986, Who Framed Roger Rabbit?, 1988 (Academy award best film editing 1988), (with Keramidas) Back to the Future II, 1989, (with Keramidas) Back to the Future III, 1990, (with Dov Hoenig) The Last of the Mohicans, 1992, Death Becomes Her, 1992, (with Jim Miller) Addams Family Values, 1993, Forrest Gump, 1994 (Academy award best film editing 1994). Office: care Motion Picture Editors 7715 Sunset Blvd #220 Los Angeles CA 90046*

SCHMIDT, ARTHUR LOUIS, retired state senator, businessman; b. Cold Spring, Ky., May 1, 1927; s. Joseph E. and Elizabeth (Bertsch) S.; m. Marian Seibert, Apr. 28, 1951; children: Karen, Marianne. Mgr. mktg. Cin. Bell, 1946-83; dir. Provident Bank of Ky., 1964-93. Mem. City Council, Cold Spring, Ky., 1962-63; mem. Ky. Ho. of Reps., 1963-83; mem. Ky. Senate, 1983-92.

SCHMIDT, BENNO CHARLES, investment company executive; b. Abilene, Tex., 1913; m. Nancy Montgomery Fleischmann; children: Benno, Ralph, Thomas (dec.), John and William (twins). BA, LLB, U. Tex., 1936; LLD (honoris causa), Columbia U.; LHD (hon.), N.Y. Med. Coll. Mem. law faculty U. Tex., 1936-40; Thayer teaching fellow Harvard U. Sch. Law, Cambridge, 1940-41; with Office Gen. Counsel, War Prodn. Bd., Washington, 1941-42; gen. counsel Office Fgn. Liquidation Commn., Dept. State, Washington, 1945-46; mng. ptnr. J.H. Whitney & Co., N.Y.C., 1946-92, sr. ptnr., 1993—; chmn. exec. com., dir. Freeport-McMoRan Inc.; bd. dirs. Genetics Inst., Gilead Scis., Matrix Pharms., Vertex Pharms.; past dir., officer numerous bus. enterprises with holdings in U.S., Australia and Western Europe including Schlumberger Ltd., CBS, Inc., Memorex Crop., Gen. Signal Corp., Transco Energy Co., San Jacinto Petroleum, Global Marine, Inc., others. Chmn. Pres.'s Cancer Panel, 1971-80; mem. Pres.'s Biomed. Rsch. Panel, 1975-76; chmn. Bedford-Stuyvesant Devel. & Svcs. Corp., 1969-84, Fund for City N.Y., 1968-77, Roosevelt Island Devel. Corp., 1969-76; pres. Am. Australian Assn., 1971-86, Thomas Payne Schmidt Found., 1972-86; chmn. bd. Meml. Sloan-Kettering Cancer Ctr., 1982-90, hon. co-chmn., 1990—; trustee Gen. Motors Cancer Rsch. Found., Whitney Mus. Am. Art, 1965-84, Carnegie Found. for Internat. Peace, 1977-81; mem. chancellor's coun., devel bd. U. Tex.; mem. centennial comm., Rockefeller U. Coun., U. Tex. Served to col. AUS, 1942-45. Decorated Legion of Merit, Bronze Star; Legion d'Honneur, Croix de Guerre with palms, French medal of Merit; named Disting. Alumnus U. Tex., 1969, Outstanding Alumnus Law Sch., 1981; recipient cert. of award Am. Assn. Cancer Research, 1971, Clement Cleveland award for disting. service in crusade to control cancer N.Y.C. div. Am. Cancer Soc., 1972, Nat. award for disting. service, 1974, Papanicolaou award for disting. service to cancer control, 1974, James Ewing Soc. Ann. award for outstanding contbns. in fight against cancer, 1975, Alfred P. Sloan, Jr. Meml. award N.Y.C. div. Am. Cancer Soc.; 1977, Stanley P. Reimann medal The Fox Chase Cancer Center, Phila., 1977, medal City of Rotterdam, 1977; NIH Dir.'s award, 1978, Bristol-Myers award for disting. service in

cancer research, 1979. Mem. Am. Australian Assn.,The Thomas Payne Schmidt Found. (pres.), Alpha Omega Alpha (hon.).

SCHMIDT, BENNO CHARLES, JR., lawyer, educator; b. Washington, Mar. 20, 1942; s. Benno Charles and Martha (Chastain) S.; children by previous marriage—Elizabeth, Benno III; m. Helen Cutting Whitney, 1980; 1 child, Christina. BA, Yale U., 1963, JD, 1966; LLD (hon.), Princeton U., 1986; LittD (hon.), Johns Hopkins U., 1987; LLD (hon.), Harvard U., 1987. Bar: D.C. 1968. Law clk. Chief Justice Earl Warren, U.S. Supreme Ct, Washington, 1966-67; spl. asst., asst. atty. gen. Office Legal Counsel U.S. Dept. Justice, Washington, 1967-69; Harlan Fiske Stone prof. constl. law Columbia U., N.Y.C., 1969-86, dean Law Sch., 1984-86; pres., prof. law Yale U., New Haven, 1986-92; pres., CEO The Edison Project, Knoxville, Tenn., 1992—. Author: Freedom of the Press versus Public Access, 1976; (with A.M. Bickel) The Judiciary and Responsible Government 1910-1921, 1984. Dir. Nat. Humanities Ctr., Chapel Hill, N.C., 1985—. Office: The Edison Project 333 Main St Knoxville TN 37902

SCHMIDT, BERLIE LOUIS, agricultural research administrator; b. Treynor, Iowa, Oct. 2, 1932; s. Hans Frederick and Louisa Amalie (Guttau) S.; m. Joanne Doris Bruning, Sept. 4, 1954 (dec. Apr. 1982); children: Brian, Luanne Schmidt Code, Kevin, Kimberly Schmidt Nelson, Christy; m. Bonnijane G. Mehlhop, June 14, 1986. B.S., Iowa State U., 1954, M.S., 1959, Ph.D., 1962. Soil scientist Soil Conservation Svc. USDA, Council Bluffs, Iowa, 1954-57; grad. rsch. assoc. Iowa State U., Ames, 1957-62; asst. prof. agronomy Ohio State U., Wooster, 1962-65, assoc. prof., 1965-69; prof., assoc. chmn. dept. agronomy Ohio State U. Columbus, 1969-75, prof., chmn. dept. agronomy, 1975-86, prof., coord. Conservation Tillage Systems Program, 1986-87; soil scientist, program mgr. water quality program Coop. State Rsch. Svc., USDA, Washington, 1987—; program dir. Nat. Rsch. Initiative Competitive Rsch. Grants Program, 1994—. Editor: Determinants of Soil Loss Tolerance, 1982; contbr. articles to sci. jours. Elder Worthington United Presbyterian Ch., 1983. With U.S. Army, 1954-56, PTO. Fellow Am. Soc. Agronomy, Ohio Acad. Sci.; mem. Soil and Water Conservation Soc. Am. (Outstanding mem. award All-Ohio chpt. 1977), Soil Sci. Am., Coun. Agrl. Sci. and Tech. Republican. Home: 2103 Kedge Dr Vienna VA 22181-3211 Office: USDA CSRS 329 Aerospace Bldg Washington DC 20250

SCHMIDT, CHARLES J., library administrator. Office: Mid Ga Regional Libr 1180 Washington Ave Macon GA 31201-1790

SCHMIDT, CHARLES T., JR., labor and industrial relations educator. Prof., dir. labor and indsl. rels. rsch., labor arbitrator. Office: University of Rhode Island Labor Research Ctr Adams House Kingston RI 02881

SCHMIDT, CHAUNCEY EVERETT, banker; b. Oxford, Ia., June 7, 1931; s. Walter Frederick and Vilda (Saxton) S.; m. Anne Garrett McWilliams, Mar. 3, 1954; children: Carla, Julia, Chauncey Everett. B.S., U.S. Naval Acad., 1953; M.B.A., Harvard U., 1959. With First Nat. Bank, Chgo., 1959-76; v.p., gen. mgr. br. First Nat. Bank, London, Eng., 1965-68; v.p. for First Nat. Bank, Europe, Middle East, Africa, 1968-69; sr. v.p. First Nat. Bank, Chgo., 1969-72; exec. v.p. First Nat. Bank, 1972, vice chmn. bd., 1973, pres., 1974-76; chmn. bd., chief exec. officer, dir. Bank of Calif. N.A., San Francisco, 1976—; chmn. bd., pres., chief exec. officer, dir. BanCal Tri-State Corp., 1976—; dir. Amfac, Inc., Honolulu; mem. Adv. Council Japan-U.S. Econ. Relations; adv. bd. Pacific Rim Bankers Program. Exec. bd. and pres. San Francisco Bay Area council Boy Scouts Am.; council SRI Internat.; bd. dirs. Bay Area Council; bd. govs. San Francisco Symphony; trustee U.S. Naval War Coll. Fedn., Newport, R.I. Served with USAF, 1953-56. Mem. Assn. Res. City Bankers, Am. Bankers Assn., Internat. Monetary Conf., Calif. Bankers Clearing House Assn. (dir.), Calif. Roundtable (dir.), Japan-Calif. Assn. Clubs: Comml. (Chgo.); Bankers (San Francisco), Bohemian (San Francisco). Home: 234 Albion Ave Woodside CA 94062-3602 Office: One Bush St San Francisco CA 94104-1300

SCHMIDT, CHUCK, professional football team executive; b. Detroit, Jan. 22, 1947; m. Sharon Schmidt; children: Scott, Krista, Matthew. Degree in bus., U. Mich.; grad. degree in fin., Wayne State U. Formerly with Ernst and Whinney; CPA Detroit Lions, from 1976, also contr., then v.p. fin., until 1987, exec. v.p., chief oper. officer, 1989—. Bd. dirs., secs., treas. Detroit Lions Charities; bd. dirs. CATCH, Pontiac (Mich.) Devel. Found. Office: Detroit Lions 1200 Featherstone Rd Pontiac MI 48342-1938*

SCHMIDT, CLAUDE HENRI, retired research administrator; b. Geneva, Switzerland, May 6, 1924; came to U.S.; 1935; s. Roger Auguste Schmidt and Lucette (Henriette) Wuhrman; m. Melicent Esther Hane, June 25, 1953; children—Valerie Lynn, Jeffrey Allan. A.B., Stanford U., 1948, M.A., 1950; Ph.D., Iowa State U., 1956. With Agrl. Rsch. Svc., USDA, 1956-88; rsch. entomologist Orlando, Fla., 1956-62; project leader Fargo, N.D., 1964-67; br. chief Beltsville, Md., 1967-72; area dir. N. Cen. region Fargo, 1972-82, lab. dir., 1982-88, acting dir. Red River Valley Agrl. Rsch. Ctr., 1988; collaborator, 1988—; entomologist IAEA, Vienna, Austria, 1962-64; sec. Nat. Mosquito Fish and Wildlife Commn., Washington, 1968-72. Editor Leafy Spurge News, 1994—; contbr. articles to profl. jours. Served with AUS, Signal Corps 1942-46, to 1st lt. Med. Service Corps, 1950-53. Fellow Washington Acad. Sci., AAAS; mem. Am. Mosquito Control Assn. (pres. 1981-82), Am. Chem. Soc., Entomol. Soc. Am. Republican. Lodge: Elks. Home: 1827 3rd St N Fargo ND 58102-2335

SCHMIDT, CYRIL JAMES, librarian; b. Flint, Mich., June 27, 1939; s. Cyril August and Elizabeth Josephine S.; m. Martha Joe Meadows, May 22, 1965; children: Susan, Emily. BA, Cath. U. Am., 1962; MSLS, Columbia U., 1963; Ph.D., Fla. State U., 1974. Asst. bus. and industry dept. Flint Pub. Library, 1963-65; reference librarian Gen. Motors Inst., Flint, 1965; asso. librarian S.W. Tex. State U., San Marcos, 1965-67; head undergrad. libraries, asst. prof. Ohio State U., 1967-70; dir. libraries SUNY, Albany, 1972-79; also mem. faculty SUNY (Sch. Library and Info. Sci.); univ. librarian Brown U., Providence, 1979-81; exec. v.p. Rsch. Libraries Group, Stanford, Calif., 1981-89; prin. cons. Schmidt & Assocs., Palo Alto, Calif., 1989—; univ. prof., libr. San Jose (Calif.) State U., 1992—. Author papers in field. Libr. Svcs. Act fellow, 1962-63, Higher Edn. Act fellow, 1970-72. Mem. ALA, ACLU, Pi Sigma Alpha, Beta Phi Mu. Home: 244 Forest Ave Palo Alto CA 94301-2510 Office: San Jose State U 1 Washington Sq San Jose CA 95192

SCHMIDT, EDWARD CRAIG, lawyer; b. Pitts., Nov. 26, 1947; s. Harold Robert and Bernice (Williams) S.; m. Elizabeth Lowry Rial, Aug. 18, 1973; children: Harold Robert II, Robert Rial. BA, U. Mich., 1969; JD, U. Pitts., 1972. Bar: Pa. 1972, U.S. Dist. Ct. (we. dist.) Pa. 1972, U.S. Ct. Appeals (3d. cir.) 1972, U.S. Ct. Appeals (D.C. cir.) 1975, U.S. Supreme Ct. 1981, U.S. Ct. Appeals (9th cir.) 1982, U.S. Ct. Appeals (6th cir.) 1987, U.S. Ct. Appeals (11th cir.) 1990, U.S. Ct. Appeals (2d cir.) 1992, U.S. Ct. Appeals (4th cir.) 1994. Assoc. Rose, Schmidt, Hasley & Di Salle, Pitts., 1972-77, ptnr., 1977-90, Jones, Day Reavis & Pogue, Pitts.; mem. adv. com. Superior Ct. Pa., 1978-80. Co-editor; Antitrust Discovery Handbook-Supplement, 1982; asst. editor: Antitrust Discovery Handbook, 1980; contbr. articles to profl. jours. Bd. dirs. Urban League, Pitts., 1974-77. Mem. Supreme Ct. Hist. Soc., Pa. Bar Assn., D.C. Bar Assn., Allegheny County Bar Assn. (pub. rels. com. coun. civil litigation sect. 1977-80), Internat. Acad. Trial Lawyers, Acad. Trial Lawyers Allegheny County (bd. govs. 1985-87), Assn. Def. Trial Attys., U. Pitts. Law Alumni Assn. (bd. govs. 1980). Clubs: Rolling Rock (Ligonier, Pa.), Duquesne (Pitts.), Longue Vue (Pitts.). Republican. Home: 159 Washington St Pittsburgh PA 15218-1351 Office: Jones Day Reavis & Pogue One Mellon Bank Ctr 31st Fl 500 Grant St Pittsburgh PA 15219-2502

SCHMIDT, FRANK BROKER, executive recruiter; b. Shamokin, Pa., Aug. 8, 1939; s. Frank Wilhelm and Doris (Maurer) S.; children by previous marrage: Susan E., Tracie A.; m. Elizabeth Mallen, Mar. 18, 1989; children: Alexandra M., Frank W.M. BS, U. Pa., 1962; MBA, Case Western Res. U., 1969; cert. brewmaster, Siebel Inst. Brewing Tech., Chgo., 1964. With Carling Brewing Co., Cleve., 1964-69, mgr. sales and advt. div., brand mgr., 1969-70; advt. and merchandising mgr. The Pepsi-Cola Co., Purchase, N.Y., 1970-71, dir. mktg. programs, then dir. mgmt. devel., 1971-74; mgr. sales and mktg. The Olga Co., Van Nuys, Calif., 1974-75; pres. F.B. Schmidt, Internat., L.A., 1975—. Author: Draft Beer Manual, 1967, Assn. Nat. Advertisers Computerized Media System, 1970. Mem. Calif. Exec. Recruiters Assn., Wharton Alumni Assn., Personnel Cons. Am. (region chmn. 1981-83, chmn. 92-95), Am. Mktg. Assn. Republican. Avocations: automobile racing, flying, marathon bicycling. Office: 30423 Canwood St Ste 239 Agoura Hills CA 91301-4318

SCHMIDT, FRED (ORVAL FREDERICK SCHMIDT), editor; b. Lone Wolf, Okla., Sept. 17, 1922; s. Otto Frederick and Mabel Marie (Johnson) S.; m. Eleanor Minerva Austin, Jan. 15, 1949; 1 son, Frederick Curtis. Student, U. Okla., 1941-42, Chgo. Sch. Photography, 1947-48. Photographer, color technician James Israel Studio, Mt. Vernon, Ohio, 1949-55; from adminstrv. asst. to mng. editor Profl. Photographers Am., Inc., 1955-74; editorial dir. Photomethods, N.Y.C., 1974-85, Internat. TV, 1983-85, Photo/Design, 1984-85; exec. editor Video Mgr., 1985-88; cons. editor Tape/Disc Bus., 1987-89; tchr. photojournalism Milw. Area Tech. Coll., 1965-66, mem. adv. bd., 1972-74; lectr. No. Ill. U., 1968-73; sec. Profl. Photographers, Ohio, 1954-55. Co-author: Opportunities in Photography, 1978. Bd. advisers Chgo. Internat. Film Festival, 1967-75. Served with USCGR, 1942-46. Recipient Nat. award Profl. Photographers Am., 1964. Mem. Am. Soc. Photographers (hon. assco.), Yugoslavia Fedn. Profl. Photographers (hon.), Profl. Photographers of Israel, Internat. TV Assn. (Svc. award). Home and Office: 138 Joralemon St Brooklyn NY 11201-4714

SCHMIDT, FRED C., architect; m. Kathleen Schmidt; children: Erin K., Kirstin M., Bren F. BArch, U. Okla., 1974; student, Seville (Spain) Coll. Arch., U. Seville, U. Grenoble, France. Arch. Frankfurt Short Bruza Assocs., Oklahoma City; adj. prof., design critic Coll. Architecture U. Okla., 1989, 91, 93, 94; chmn. archtl. adv. com. Alliance for Cultural Affairs, Oklahoma City; chmn. nat. urban design competition Oklahoma City Urban Renewal Authority; bd. dirs. DesignWorks; spkr. in field. Author: Space by Design, 1987, The Oklahoma City Walk, 1987, 88, 89, The Pocket Guide to Architectural Learning, 1992; co-author: The Creative Book Design, 1987, The Classroom Companion, 1987, The Architectural Mentor Program, 1987, In Shape for Learning, 1991; author, designer: U.S. Space Station Kit, 1987; editor: Cadet Manual, 1988, Architecture by Alphabet, 1988. Recipient Spl. award Oklahoma City Pub. Schs., 1987, Spl. Contbg. award Oklahoma Aerospace Found., 1987, Bruce Miller award City of Oklahoma City, 1990. Fellow AIA (mem. acad. of architecture for health 1992-94, mem. environ. edn. com. 1989-91, chair, 1991, mem. state coun. Okla. chpt. 1990-92, Ctrl. Okla. chpt. bd. dirs. 1987-92, v.p. 1988, pres.-elect 1990, pres. 1991, Spl. award for cadet activity instr. 1987, Spl. award for mentor program 1988, Spl. award for edn./space architecture, 1989, Outstanding Member award 1989, Spl. award in shape for learning 1991, Outstanding Svc. award 1991), Okla. Found. for Architecture (mem. exec. bd. 1990-94, pres. 1993-94), Okla. State Bus. and Edn. Coun., Okla. Aerospace Found. Office: Frankfurt Short Bruza Assoc 5701 N Shartell Ste 210 Oklahoma City OK 73118

SCHMIDT, GENE EARL, hospital administrator; b. Goessel, Kans., Aug. 5, 1942; s. Arthur K. and Hedwig (Neufeld) S.; m. Marcia K. Hiebert, June 24, 1966; 1 child, William. BA in Social Scis., Bethel Coll., 1964; MHA, U. Minn., 1970. Adminstr. Brook Lane Psychiat. Ctr., Hagerstown, Md., 1966-68; exec. dir. Community Mental Health Ctr., Indpls., 1970; asst. adminstr. Children's Hosp., Columbus, Ohio, 1970-73; exec. v.p. St. Francis Hosp., Miami Beach, Fla., 1973-86; pres. Hutchinson (Kans.) Hosp. Corp., 1986—. Pres. Am. Cancer Soc., Hutchinson, 1990-92; bd. dirs. Tng. and Evaluation Ctr. for Handicapped, ARC, Hutchinson, 1988—, chmn., 1993; mem. advance gifts chmn. United Way, Hutchinson, 1992. Fellow Am. Coll. Healthcare Execs.; mem. Kans. Hosp. Assn. (bd. dirs. 1989-94), Greater Hutchinson C. of C. (chmn. 1992), Rotary. Republican. Presbyterian. Home: 2503 Briarwood Ln Hutchinson KS 67502-1803 Office: Hutchinson Hosp 1701 E 23rd Ave Hutchinson KS 67502-1191

SCHMIDT, GEORGE, physicist; b. Budapest, Hungary, Aug. 1, 1926; s. Laszlo Schmidt and Katalin Wellisch; m. Katalin Varkonyi, June 26, 1955; children: Franklin R., Ronald W. Diploma in Elec. Engring., Tech. U., Budapest, 1950; PhD in Physics, Hungarian Acad. Scis., Budapest, 1956; M in Engring., Stevens Inst. Tech., 1961. Sr. lectr. Israel Inst. Tech., Haifa, Israel, 1957-58; asst. prof. Stevens Inst. Tech., Hoboken, N.J., 1959-61, assoc. prof., 1961-63, prof. physics, 1963-83, George Meade Bond Chair physics and engring. physics, 1983—; vis. prof. U. Wis., 1965, UCLA, 1972-73; vis. scientist Culham Labs., Culham, Eng., 1965, Ecole Polytechnique, Paris, 1979-80; cons. Sci. Applications Inc., Washington, 1981—, Poly. U. of N.Y., 1984—, Berkeley Assocs., Washington, 1985. Author: Physics of High Temperature Plasmas, 1966, 2nd rev. edit., 1979; contbr. sci. articles to profl. jours. Recipient Research award Stevens Inst. Tech., 1961. Fellow Am. Phys. Soc.; mem. N.Y. Acad. Scis. Office: Stevens Inst of Tech Dept Of Physics Hoboken NJ 07030

SCHMIDT, HAROLD EUGENE, real estate company executive; b. Cedar Rapids, Iowa, Oct. 12, 1925; s. Alfons W. and Lillie (Schlegel) S.; m. Lucy Hermann, Apr. 13, 1957; children: Harold, Sandra. B.S. in Civil Engring, U. Iowa, 1949; M.S. in San. Engring, MIT, 1953. Research and devel. engr. Chgo. Pump Co., 1949-51; engr. A.B. Kononoff, Miami, Fla., 1956-58; with Gen. Devel. Corp., Miami, 1958-82; v.p. utilities, asst. v.p. ops. Gen. Devel. Corp., 1967-72, v.p., 1972-81, v.p. community div., 1973-81, sr. v.p., 1981-82; pres. Gen. Devel. Utilities Inc., 1972-82, Kingsway Properties, Inc. 1982—; dir. Port Charlotte Bank, Fla. Served to capt. USAF, 1951-56. Mem. Am. Water Works Assn., Water Pollution Control Fedn., Sigma Xi, Chi Epsilon. Home and Office: 12313 Kingsway Cir Lake Suzy FL 33821-9539

SCHMIDT, HERMAN J., former oil company executive; b. Davenport, Iowa, Feb. 26, 1917; s. Herman and Lillian (Beard) S.; m. Eileen Carpenter, Dec. 20, 1967; children: Paul David, Sarah Louise. AB, U. Iowa, 1938; JD, Harvard U., 1941. Bar: N.Y. 1943. With Cravath, Swaine & Moore, 1941-44, 47-51; tax counsel Socony Mobil Oil Co. Inc. (now Mobil Corp.), N.Y.C., 1951-55, adminstrv. asst. to gen. counsel, 1955, assoc. gen. counsel, 1955-56, gen. counsel, 1956-59, exec. v.p., 1959-74, vice chmn., 1974-78, dir., 1957-78; pres. Mobil Internat. Oil Co., 1959-63; bd. dirs. H.J. Heinz Co., MAPCO, Inc., Hon Industries, Inc. Former chmn. bd. trustees Am. Enterprise Inst.; hon. life trustee U. Iowa Found. Served to 1st lt. M.I. Corps, AUS, 1944-47. Mem. Harvard Law Rev. Assn., Blind Brook Club (Ryebrook, N.Y.), Phi Beta Kappa, Phi Gamma Delta. Home: 15 Oakley Ln Greenwich CT 06830-3025

SCHMIDT, JAKOB EDWARD, medical and medicolegal lexicographer, physician, author, inventor; b. Riga, Livonia, Latvia, June 16, 1906; came to U.S., 1924, naturalized, 1929; s. Michael E. and Rachel I. (Goldman) S. Grad., Balt. City Coll., 1929; Ph.G., U. Md., 1932, BS in Pharmacy, 1935, MD, 1937, postgrad., 1939. Intern Sinai Hosp., Balt.; gen. practice medicine Balt., 1940-53; resident Charlestown, Ind., 1953—; indsl. physician Ind. Ordnance Works, 1953-54; med. and medicolegal lexicographer, 1950—; pres. Sculptural Med. Jewelers, 1973-76; mem. revision com. U.S. Pharmacopeia XI. Columnist What's the Good Word, Balt. Sun; Sharpen Your Tongue, Am. Mercury; The Medical Lexicographer, Modern Medicine; Medical Semantics, Medical Science; Underworld English, Police; Medical Vocabulary Builder, Trauma; English Word Power and Culture, Charlestown Courier, Understanding Med. Talk; assoc. med. editor, Trauma, 1959-88; editor: Medical Dictionary, 1959—; compiler: 50,000-word vocabulary test, 1956; contbr. numerous articles to med. jours., lay press, including Esquire, Playboy, also to press svcs., including UPI, NANA, others; cons. JAMA on med. terminology, also cons. med. terminology to legal profession and cts., to mfrs. on med. tradenames and trademarks; author: Terminology of Sensual Emotions, 1954, Medical Terms Defined for the Layman, 1959, REVERSICON, A Physician's Medical Word Finder, 1958, Medical Discoveries, Who and When, 1959, Dictionary of Medical Slang and Related Expressions, 1959, Narcotics, Lingo and Lore, 1959, The Libido, Its Scientific, Lay, and Slang Terminology, 1960, Baby Name Finder—The Source and Romance of Names, 1961, Schmidt's Illustrated Attorneys' Dictionary of Medicine and Word Finder, 1962, One Thousand Elegant Phrases, 1965, Medical Lexicographer, A Study of Medical Terminology, 1966, The Cyclopedic Lexicon of Sex Terminology, 1967, Police Medical Dictionary, 1968, Practical Nurses' Medical Dictionary, 1968, A Paramedical Dictionary, 1969, 2d edit., 1973, Structural Units of Medical and Biological Terms, 1969,

English Word Power for Physicians and other Professionals, 1971, English Idioms and Americanisms, 1972, English Speech for Foreign Students, 1973, Textbook of Medical Terminology, 1973, Visual Aids for Paramedical Vocabulary, 1973, Analyzer of Medical-Paramedical Vocabulary, 1973, Index of Medical-Paramedical Vocabulary, 1974, Schmidt Diccionario para Auxiliares de la Medicina, 1976, Literary Foreplay, 1983, Romantic's Lexicon, 1987, Schmidt's Illustrated Attorneys' Dictionary of Medicine and Word Finder, 18th edit., 4 vols., 1981, 28th edit., 5 vols., 1995. Recipient Owl gold medal Balt. City Coll., 1929; Rho Chi gold medal U. Md. Sch. Pharmacy, 1932; gold medal for excellence in all subjects, 1932; cert. of honor U. Md. Sch. Medicine, 1937; award and citation N.Y. met. chpt. Am. Med. Writers' Assn., 1959. Mem. Am. Dialect Soc., Natural History Soc., Am. Name Soc., Am. Med. Writers' Assn., Internat. Soc. Gen. Semantics, AMA, Med. and Chirurgical Faculty of Md., Balt. City Med. Soc., Nat. Assn. Standard Med. Vocabulary, Nat. Soc. Lit. and Arts, Authors' Guild, Authors' League, Am. Mus. Natural History, Counteau Soc., Smithsonian Instn., Planetary Soc., Nat. Writers' Club, Rho Chi, others. Achievements include invention of iodine-pentoxide-shunt method and apparatus for detection of carbon monoxide in oxygen, atmosphere, and medicinal gases; shock-proof electric fuse; magnetic needle finger ring; prosthetic mammary papilla; discovered effect of cesium and related metals on oxidation of organic matter in lakes, ponds and drinking water, the TV eye phenomenon, others. Home: 934 Monroe St Charlestown IN 47111-1557

SCHMIDT, JAMES CRAIG, retired bank executive, bankruptcy examiner; b. Peoria, Ill., Sept. 27, 1927; s. Walter Henry and Clara (Wolfenbarger) S.; m. Jerrie Louise Bond, Dec. 6, 1958; children: Julie, Sandra, Susanne. Student, Ill. Wesleyan U., 1945, 48-50, Ph.B. in Bus. Adminstrn, 1952; postgrad., U. Ill. Coll. Law, 1950-52; J.D., DePaul U., 1953. Spl. agt. Fidelity & Deposit Co., Chgo., 1956-58; with Home Fed. Savs. & Loan Assn., San Diego, 1958-67; asst. sec. bus. and transp. State of Calif., 1967-69; vice-chmn., pres. Gt. Am. Bank, San Diego, 1969-88; pres. Conf. Fed. Savs. and Loans of Calif., 1974-75; mem. Calif. Toll Bridge Authority, 1969-74; mem. Calif. State Transp. Bd., 1972-78; past chmn. San Diego Bal. Commn. Task Force. Pres. San Diego Holiday Bowl Football Game, 1986; dir. Friends of Legal Aid; bd. dirs. Greater San Diego Sports Assn., Californians for Better Transp. Served with USN, 1945-48. Mem. Calif. Bar Assn., Ill. Bar Assn., Calif. League Savs. Instns. (chmn. 1986-87), Calif. C. of C. (bd. dirs. 1987-90), U.S. Savs. Instn. League (exec. com. 1983-86), San Diego Country Club, univ Club, Sigma Chi, Phi Delta Phi. Home and Office: Ste 0-2 8380 Hercules St La Mesa CA 91942-2922

SCHMIDT, JAMES ROBERT, facilities engineer; b. Rome, N.Y., Sept. 22, 1932; s. Floyd Vincent and Sophia Louise (Halupka) S.; m. Suzanne Mae Thrasher, Mar. 27, 1965; children: Mark Adrian, Tara Lee. AAS, Mohawk Valley Community Coll., 1951; BS, Utica Coll., 1962; MBA, Syracuse U., 1967. Registered profl. engr., N.Y.; Mass. Draftsman Rome (N.Y.) Cable Corp., 1951-55; designer, 1956-67, project coord., 1968-69; sr. project engr. Xerox Corp., Webster, N.Y., 1970-81; mgr. plant engring. Savin corp., Binghamton, N.Y., 1982-83; constrn. surveillance Horizons Tech./USAF, Thule, Greenland, 1983-84; sr. facilities engr. Horizons Tech., Billerica, Mass., 1984—. Chmn. Community Action Steering Com., Lee Center, N.Y., 1968; mem. ch. ofcl. bd. Meth. Ch., Shortsville, N.Y., 1979. With U.S. Army, 1951-54. Mem. Am. Inst. Plant Engrs., Am. Mil. Engrs., Cogeneration Inst. (charter), Assn. Energy Engrs., Nat. Soc. Profl. Engrs. Achievements include research on add-on system to control electrical surges in an electrical supply cable; modification of FAA radar towers, buildings and services. Office: Horizons Tech Inc 700 Tech Park Dr Billerica MA 01821

SCHMIDT, JEAN MARIE, microbiology educator; b. Waterloo, Iowa, June 5, 1938; d. John Frederick and Opal Marie (Lowe) S. BA, U. Iowa, 1959, MS, 1961; PhD, U. Calif., Berkeley, 1965. NIH postdoctoral fellow U. Edinburgh, Scotland, 1965-66; asst. prof. Ariz. State U., Tempe, 1966-71, assoc. prof., 1971-79, prof. microbiology, 1979—, assoc. dir. for biology Cancer Rsch. Inst., 1982—, acting chair dept. microbiology, 1988-89. Author: (with others) Bergey's Manual of Systematic Bacteriology, 1989; contbr. articles to jours. NSF grantee, 1981. Fellow AAAS; mem. Am. Soc. Microbiology (divsn. chmn. 1979-80), Phi Beta Kappa, Sigma Xi. Democrat. Methodist. Avocations: backpacking, photography, piano.

SCHMIDT, JOHN R., lawyer; b. Chgo., Nov. 24, 1943; s. Edward F. and Josephine (Riggen) S.; m. Janet Gilroy, Apr. 24, 1982; 1 child, Laura. BA, Harvard U., 1964, JD, 1967. Bar: Ill. 1967, U.S. Dist. Ct. (no. dist.) Ill. 1972, U.S. Supreme Ct. 1972. Assoc. Mayer, Brown & Platt, Chgo., 1967-73, ptnr., 1973-84; ptnr. Skadden, Arps, Slate, Meagher & Flom, Chgo., 1984-93; amb. chief U.S. negotiator Uruguay Round of World Trade Talks, Geneva, 1993—. Contbr. articles to profl. jours. Chmn. Ill. Guardianship and Advocacy Commn., 1979-82, Met. Pier and Exposition Authority, Chgo., 1989—; chief of staff City of Chgo., 1989; co-chmn. Citizens for Ct. Reform, Chgo., 1986-92; trustee Ill. Inst. Tech., 1991-93, Chgo. Symphony Orch., 1978-93. Recipient Judge Learned Hand Human Rels. award Am Jewish Com., 1992. Fellow Am. Bar Found.; mem. ABA, Chgo. Coun. Lawyers (pres. 1974-76). Office: US Trade Rep Office 600 17th St NW Rm 121 Washington DC 20501

SCHMIDT, JOHN RICHARD, agricultural economics educator; b. Madison, Wis., July 3, 1929; s. Oscar John and Alma Theodora (Ula) S.; m. Rosemary Pigorsch, Oct. 7, 1951; children: Janet, Deborah, Allen. B.S., U. Wis., 1951, M.S., 1953; Ph.D., U. Minn., 1960. Asst. prof. agr. econs. U. Wis., Madison, 1956-61; asso. prof. agrl. econs. U. Wis., 1961-65, prof., 1965—, chmn. dept. agrl. econs., 1966-70; dir. North Ctrl. Computer Inst., 1981-92; farm mgmt. cons. Am. Farm Bur. Fedn., Chgo., 1962; cons. Banco de Mexico, 1972-84, IBRD (World Bank), 1973—; Agrl. Devel. Bank Iran, 1974-76; mem. adv. bd. Internat. Devel. Inst., 1983. Contbr. articles to tech. jours., also monographs, bulls. Bd. dirs. U. Wis. Credit Union, 1968-77, pres., 1969-75. Served with AUS, 1953-54. Mem. Am. Agrl. Econs. Assn., Western Farm Econs. Assn., Delta Theta Sigma (nat. sec. 1962-64), Gamma Sigma Delta (pres. Wis. chpt. 1975). Lutheran (mem. ch. council 1967-69, 72-75, pres. 1974-75, mem. Wis.-Upper Mich. Synod Sem. com. 1972-75). Club: Rotary. Home: 106 Frigate Dr Madison WI 53705-4426 Office: U Wis 516 Taylor Hall 427 Lorch St Madison WI 53706-1503

SCHMIDT, JOHN THOMAS, neurobiologist; b. Louisville, Sept. 25, 1949; s. Adolph William and Olivia Ann (Hohl) S.; m. Marilyn Joan Gough, Jan. 6, 1979; children: Sarah, Benjamin. BS in Physics, U. Detroit, 1971; PhD in Biophysics, U. Mich., 1976. Postdoctoral assoc. Nat. Inst. for Med. Rsch., London, 1976-77, Vanderbilt U. Med. Sch., Nashville, 1977-80; asst. prof. biol. scis. SUNY, Albany, 1980-85, assoc. prof. biol. scis., 1985-94, prof. biog. scis., 1994, dir. Neurobiology Rsch. Ctr., 1988—. Editor: Activity-Driven CNS Changes, 1991. Mem. Soc. for Neuroscis. (treas. Hudson Berkshire chpt. 1981-83, pres. 1987-89), N.Y. Acad. Scis. Office: SUNY Neurobiology Rsch Ctr 1400 Washington Ave Albany NY 12222

SCHMIDT, JOHN WESLEY, agronomy educator; b. Moundridge, Kans., Mar. 13, 1917; s. John J. and Kathrina (Sperling) S.; m. Olene Lucile Hall, June 23, 1943; children: Karen, Vicki, Wesley, Loren, Jerold. BA, Tabor Coll., Hillsboro, Kans., 1947; MS, Kans. State U., 1949, DSc, 1940, PhD, U. Nebr., 1952. Asst. agronomist Kans. State U., Manhattan, 1951-54; assoc. agronomist Kans. State U., 1954; assoc. prof. agronomy U. Nebr., Lincoln, 1954-62; prof. U. Nebr., 1962-80, Regents prof., 1980-85, prof. emeritus, 1986—. Recipient Outstanding Rsch. and Creativity award U. Nebr.-Lincoln, 1979, Nat. award for excellence in agrl. sci. Nat. Agrl.-Mktg. Assn., 1984. Fellow Am. Soc. Agronomy (Agronomic Rsch. award 1989), Crop Sci. Soc. Am. (Crop Sci. award 1975, DeKalb Crop Sci. career award 1982); mem. Sigma Xi, Phi Kappa Phi, Gamma Sigma Delta (internat. award for disting. svc. in agr. 1969). Republican. Methodist. Office: U Nebr Dept Agronomy East Campus Lincoln NE 68583

SCHMIDT, JULIUS, sculptor; b. Stamford, Conn., June 2, 1923; s. Louis Frank and Susie (Koment) S.; m. Carolyn Marsha Wolf (div.); children: Ania J., Ianos; m. Mary Katherine Powers, 1981 (div.); 1 child, Araan J. Student, Okla. A&M U., 1950-51; B.F.A., Cranbrook Acad. Art, 1952, M.F.A, 1955; student, Ossip Zadkine, Paris, 1953, Accademia di Belle Arti, Florence, Italy, 1954. Chmn. sculpture dept. Kansas City Art Inst., 1954-59, R.I. Sch. Design, 1959-60, U. Calif.-Berkeley, 1961-62, Cranbrook Acad. Art, 1962-70, U. Iowa, Iowa City, 1970-93; ret., 1993. 34 one-man shows 1953—; exhib-

ited in group shows Allen Meml. Art Mus., Oberlin, Ohio, 1958, Arts Club of Chgo. and Milw. Art Center, 1958, Art Inst. Chgo., Mus. Modern Art, N.Y.C., 1960, Whitney Mus., 1960-63, Gallerie Claude Bernard, Paris, 1960, Guggenheim Mus., 1962, San Francisco Mus. Art, 1962, Phila. Art Alliance, 1963, Battersea Park, London, 1963, Sao Paolo Bienal, Brazil, 1963, White House Festival of Arts, Washington, 1965, Bienale Middleheim, Belgium, 1971; represented in permanent collections Nelson Gallery-Atkins Mus., Kansas City, Mo., Art Inst., Chgo., Mus. Modern Art, N.Y.C., Mus. U. Nebr., Whitney Mus. Am. Art, N.Y.C., Krannert Art Mus., Urbana, Ill., Washington, U., Walker Art Center, Mpls., Albright-Knox Mus., Buffalo, Detroit Inst. Art, U. Calif. Art Mus., Cranbrook Acad. Art, Mich., Princeton Mus. Art, Hirshhorn Mus., Washington, numerous others. Served with USNR, World War II. Guggenheim fellow, 1963-64. Address: 5 Highview Knoll NE Iowa City IA 52240

SCHMIDT, KENNETH MARTIN, investment banker; b. Rockville Centre, N.Y., Feb. 12, 1945; s. Ernest M. and Elsa E. (Ey) S.; m. Terry E. Acquasanta, Apr. 27, 1968; 1 dau. Tracy. BA, Rutgers U., 1967; M.B.A., Western New Eng. Coll., 1970. Comml. officer Trust Co. Bank Ga., N.Y.C., 1971-73; investment officer Mellon Bank N.A., N.Y.C., 1973-75; mng. dir., head pub. fin. Dillon Read & Co., Inc., N.Y.C., 1975—. Served to capt. USAF, 1967-71. Mem. Municipal Bond Club N.Y. Republican.

SCHMIDT, KLAUS DIETER, management consultant, university administrator, marketing and management educator; b. Battersea, Germany, May 8, 1930; came to U.S., 1949, naturalized, 1952; s. Kurt Heinrich and Luise (Kruger) S.; B.A. in Econs., U. Calif., Berkeley, 1951; M.B.A., Stanford U., 1953; Ph.D. in Bus. Adminstrn., Golden Gate U., 1978; m. Lynda Hollister Wheelwright, June 29, 1950; children: Karen, Claudia. Buyer, jr. mdse. mgr. Broadway Hale, 1952-54; sales mgr. Ames Harris Neville Co., 1954-56, ops. mgr., 1956-57; gen. mgr. Boise Cascade Corp., 1957-60; pres., chmn. bd. Kimball-Schmidt Inc., San Rafael, Calif., 1960-73, chmn. subs. Kalwall Pacific, 1962-67, chmn. subs. AFGOA Corp., 1966-69; asst. prof. mgmt. and mktg. San Francisco State U., 1970-75, assoc. prof. mgmt., 1975-80, prof. mgmt. and mktg-83, chmn. dept. mgmt. and mktg., 1979-85, prof. emeritus, 1989—; assoc. dean sch. bus. emeritus, 1985-88; chmn. Schmidt Cons. Group, 1988—; dir. Ctr. for World Bus., 1976-88, dir. U.S.-Japan Inst., 1981-88, editor-in-chief Sch. Bus. Jours., 1980-88; U.S. negotiator on Afghanistan issue, 1980-88; mem. Dept. Commerce Dist. Export Council, 1982-88; research cons. SRI Internat. Republican. Club: University (San Francisco). Author 20-booklet series Doing Business In ..., 1978-80. Office: PO Box 269 Brooklin ME 04616-0269

SCHMIDT, KLAUS FRANZ, advertising executive; b. Dessau, Germany, May 25, 1928; came to U.S., 1951; naturalized, 1957; s. Franz and Elfriede (Klamroth) S.; m. Gisela Garbrecht, June 19, 1954; children: Dagmar Schmidt Etkin, Ena Schmidt. Student, Coll. of Journalism, Aachen, Germany, 1947-48, Sch. of Design and Printing, Bochum, Germany, 1948-50; BA, Wayne State U., 1956. Printer, compositor, 1948-56; type dir. Mogul Williams & Saylor, N.Y.C., 1956-59, Doyle, Dane, Bernbach, N.Y.C., 1959-61; type dir. Young & Rubicam, N.Y.C., 1961-68, v.p., dir. print ops., 1968-75, v.p., dir. creative support, 1975-85, sr. v.p., mgr. prodn. svcs., 1985-91; advt./graphic arts cons., 1991—; co-organizer Vision Congress Internat. Ctr. for Communications Arts & Scis., N.Y.C., 1965, 67, 69, 77; chmn., bd. trustees Internat. Ctr. Typographic Arts, N.Y.C. 1969-70. Am. editor Der Druckspiegel, 1957-64; contbg. editor Print Mag., 1968—, The Dunn Report, 1991—. Recipient Typomundus award, 1964, Internat. Book Exhbn. award, Leipzig, Germany, 1965. Mem. Print Advt. Assn. (chmn. N.Y. chpt. 1969-71, nat. sr. v.p. 1971-75), Am. Assn. Advt. Agys. (chmn. subcom. on phototypography 1969-75), Digital Distbn. of Advt. to Publ. Assn. (vice chmn. 1991-95), N.Y. Type Dirs. Club (pres. 1984-86, awards 1962, 64-66, 68, 69), N.Y. Art Dirs. Club (v.p. 1984-86), Advt. Prodn. Club (pres. 1982-84), Gravure Advt. Coun. (chmn. 1970-72). Home and office: 549 Munroe Ave Tarrytown NY 10591

SCHMIDT, L. LEE, JR., university official; b. Mullinville, Kans., Oct. 2, 1937; s. Lester Lee and Mary (Gilliam) S.; m. Sarah Sue Lookinghill, Aug. 12, 1961; children: Suzanne, Jon. B.S. in Bus. Adminstrn., U. Ark., 1962, Ph.D., 1971; M.B.A., Tex. Tech U., 1963. CPA, Colo. Audit sr. Ernst & Young, Fort Worth, 1963-66; mgr. acctg. The Western Co., Fort Worth, 1966-67; asst. prof. U. Tex.-Arlington, 1967-68; instr. U. Ark., Fayetteville, 1968-71; prof. acctg., chmn. dept. Colo. State U., Ft. Collins, 1971-87, assoc. dean Coll. Bus., 1988-92; assoc. dean Coll. Bus. Adminstrn., U. Tex., El Paso, 1992—; speaker in field. Contbr. articles to profl. jours. Served with USN, 1955-58. Earhart Found. fellow, 1968-69. Mem. AICPA, Am. Acctg. Assn., Fin. Execs. Inst., Beta Gamma Sigma, Beta Alpha Psi. Office: U Tex Coll Bus Adminstrn El Paso TX 79968

SCHMIDT, LANNY D., chemical engineering educator and researcher, physical chemist; b. Waukegan, Ill., May 6, 1938; married, 1962; 2 children. BS, Wheaton Coll., 1960; PhD in Phys. Chemistry, U. Chgo., 1964. Rsch. assoc. in phys. chemistry U. Chgo., 1964-65; assoc. prof. U. Minn., Mpls., 1965-69, prof. chem. engring., 1969—. Recipient Alpha Sigma Chi award AIChE, 1993. Mem. Am. Chem. Soc., Am. Phys. Soc., Am. Vacuum Soc., Nat. Acad. Engring. Achievements include research in surface chemistry and physics, adsorption, catalysis, electron microscopy, auger electron spectrometry, kinetics. Office: Dept Chem Engring & Materials Sci U Minnesota Minneapolis MN 55455-0373*

SCHMIDT, MAARTEN, astronomy educator; b. Groningen, Netherlands, Dec. 28, 1929; came to U.S., 1959; s. Wilhelm and Antje (Haringhuizen) S.; m. Cornelia Johanna Tom, Sept. 16, 1955; children: Elizabeth Tjimkje, Maryke Antje, Anne Wilhelmina. B.Sc., U. Groningen, 1949; Ph.D., Leiden U., Netherlands, 1956; Sc.D., Yale U., 1966. Sci. officer Leiden Obs., The Netherlands, 1953-59; postdoctoral fellow Mt. Wilson Obs., Pasadena, Calif., 1956-58; mem. faculty Calif. Inst. Tech., 1959—, prof. astronomy, 1964—, exec. officer for astronomy, 1972-75, chmn. div. physics, math. and astronomy, 1975-78; mem. staff Hale Obs., 1959-80, dir., 1978-80. Co-winner Calif. Scientist of Yr. award, 1964. Fellow Am. Acad. Arts and Scis. (Rumford award 1968); mem. Am. Astron. Soc. (Helen B. Warner prize 1964, Russell lecture award 1978), NAS (fgn. assoc., recip. James Craig Watson Medal, 1991), Internat. Astron. Union, Royal Astron. Soc. (assoc., Gold medal 1980). Office: Calif Inst Tech 105 24 Robinson Lab 1201 E California Blvd Pasadena CA 91125-0001

SCHMIDT, MARK ALAN, information systems executive; b. Lebanon, Oreg., Mar. 21, 1948; s. Lawrence Edward and Shirley Jean (Cone) S.; m. Maren Stark, Jan. 12, 1974; children: Dana, Hannah. BS magna cum laude, U. Ark. at Little Rock, 1977. Vol. Peace Corps, Washington, 1968-69; contractor, carpenter various locations, 1970-75; systems engr., SE mgr. IBM, Little Rock and St. Louis, 1977-87; dir. tech. devel. Wal-Mart Stores, Inc., Bentonville, Ark., 1987-89, sr. dir. info. svcs., 1989-91, v.p. info. tech. and telecommunications, 1991—. Office: Wal-Mart Stores Inc 702 SW 8th St Bentonville AR 72716-0001

SCHMIDT, MICHAEL JACK, former professional baseball player; b. Dayton, Ohio, Sept. 27, 1949; m. Donna Wightman; children: Jessica Roe, Jonathan Michael. BBA, Ohio U., Athens. With Phila. Phillies, 1972-89. Nat. League Player in All-Star Game, 1974, 76, 77, 79-84, 86, 87; named Most Valuable player, National League, 1980,1981, 1986., Most Valuable Player 1980 World Series; recipient 10 Golden Glove awards; inducted into Baseball Hall of Fame, 1995. Address: care Phila Phillies PO Box 2575 Philadelphia PA 19147-0575*

SCHMIDT, NANCY J., anthropologist, educator; b. Cin., May 17, 1936; d. Leon Herbert and Ida (Genther) S. B.A., Oberlin Coll., 1958; M.A., U. Minn., 1961; Ph.D., Northwestern U., 1965; M.L.S., Ind. U., 1971. Asst. prof. anthropology St. Lawrence U., Canton, N.Y., 1966-68; asst. prof. anthropology Stanislaus State Coll., Turlock, Calif., 1968-70; assoc. prof. anthropology Rockford Coll., Ill., 1971-74; vis. assoc. prof. anthropology and African Studies U. Ill., Urbana, 1974-77; librarian Harvard U. Tozzer Library, Cambridge, Mass., 1977-84; African studies area specialist, adj. prof. anthropology Ind. U., Bloomington, 1984—; with cooperative Curriculum Devel. Ctr., Manitowoc, Wis., summer 1967, African Outreach Workshop U. Ill., spring-summer 1974, Twentieth Century Children's Writers St. James Press, London, 1977, 82, 89, NSF, Chautauqua course

Visual Evidence and Women's Roles, Nov. 1976, Apr. 1977. Author: Children's Fiction about Africa in English N.Y., 1981, Subsaharan African Films and Filmmakers: A Preliminary Bibliography, 1986, Subsaharan African Films and Filmmakers: An Annotated Bibliography, 1988; Supplement to Children's Books on Africa and their Authors, N.Y., 1979; Children's Books on Africa and Their Authors N.Y., 1975, Reports on AIDS in the African Press: An Annotated Bibliography, 1988, Supplement, 1990, Subsaharan African Films and Filmmakers 1987-92: An Annotated Bibliography, 1994; founder, editor: Anthropological Lit. Jour., 1978-84; editor Africana Libraries Newsletter, 1986-91; contbr. articles to profl. jours. Founding mem. Sinnissippi chpt. Nat. Audubon Soc., Rockford, Ill., 1972. Mem. ALA, African Lit. Assn. (exec. coun. 1983-85), African Studies Assn. (bd. dirs. 1994—), Africana Librs. Coun. (chmn. 1992-93, editor newsletter), Internat. Union Anthropol. and Ethnol. Scis. (commn. on documentation 1973—), Soc. for Humanistic Anthropology (book rev. editor 1982-85, editorial bd. 1990-93), Am. Anthrop. Assn. (anthropology curriculum study project Chgo. 1963-65), Assn. for Study African Lit., Soc. Visual Anthropology (bd. dirs. 1986-91). Office: Ind U Main Library E660 Bloomington IN 47405

SCHMIDT, PATRICIA FAIN, nurse educator; b. Chgo., June 17, 1941; d. Lawrence D. and Catherine B. (Schira) Fain; m. Donald W. Schmidt, July 16, 1966; children: Kathryn, Kristine, Michael. BSN, Coll. of St. Teresa, 1963; MSN, Marquette U., 1965; EdD, U.S. Internat. U., 1981. Instr. Coll. of St. Teresa, Winona, Minn.; asst. prof. San Diego State U.; assoc. prof. Palomar Coll., San Marcos, Calif. Mem. Sigma Theta Tau. Home: 12573 Utopia Way San Diego CA 92128-2229

SCHMIDT, PAUL JOSEPH, physician, educator; b. N.Y.C., Oct. 22, 1925; s. Joseph and Anna (Schwanzl) S.; BS Fordham U., 1948; MS, St. Louis U., 1952; MD, NYU, 1953; m. Louise Kern Fredericks, June 18, 1953; children: Damien, Matthew, Thomas, Maria. Intern, St. Elizabeth's Hosp., Boston, 1953-54; staff assoc. Nat. Microbiol. Inst., Bethesda, Md., 1954-55; chief blood bank dept. NIH, Bethesda, Md., 1955-74, asst. chief clin. pathology dept., 1963-65; sr. asst. surgeon, USPHS, 1954, advanced through grades to med. dir., 1964-74; assoc. clin. prof. pathology, then clin. prof. Georgetown U., Washington, 1965-75; dir. S.W. Fla. Blood Bank, Inc., Tampa, 1975-90, pres. 1987-90; head transfusion medicine, Transfusion Medicine Acad. Ctr., 1991—; prof. pathology U. So. Fla., Tampa, 1975—; cons. com. on Blood, AMA, 1964-69; tech. adv. Blood Transfusion Rsch. div. US Army, 1966-74; res. adv. com. Blood Program, ARC, 1967-73; com. Human Rsch., ARC, 1968-74; council on Immunohematology, Am. Soc. Clin. Pathologists, 1968-74; com. Anticoagulant Solutions, NRC-Nat. Acad. Sci., 1968-70; com. Plasmapheresis, NRC-Nat. Acad. Sci., 1969-70; com. Blood Bank Programs, N.Y.C., 1969-70; com. Component Therapy, NRC-Nat. Acad. Sci., 1969; com. standards, Am. Assn. Blood Banks, 1970-85 (chmn. 1981-85); Task Force on Blood Banking, dept. HEW, 1972-73; adv. com. Blood Diseases and Resources, Nat. Heart Lung Blood Inst., 1975-79; cons. to surgeon gen. U.S. Navy, 1976; dir. clin. svcs. ARC Blood Svcs., San Juan, P.R., 1993—; clin. prof. pathology U. P.R., 1993—. Mem. svc. and rehab. com. Fla. div. Am. Cancer Soc., 1976-84; bd. dirs. ARC, Tampa 1978-83 (v.p. 1980); com. Transfusion Transmitted Viruses, Coll. Am. Pathologists 1981-91; com. Transfusion Medicine, Coll. Am. Pathologists, 1981-92; bd. dirs. Am. Blood Commn., 1985-87. Served with U.S. Army, 1944-46. Recipient Jour. Club Rsch. award, NYU, 1952, Silver medal Spanish Red Cross, 1960; Emily Cooley award Am. Assn. Blood Banks, 1974, John Elliott award, 1993. Diplomate Am. Bd. Pathology, Nat. Bd. Med. Examiners. Fellow Coll. Am. Pathologists (emeritus); mem. Am. Assn. Blood Banks (pres. 1987-88), Am. Assn. History Medicine, Internat. Assn. History Medicine, Internat. Soc. Blood Transfusion, Fla. Assn. Blood Banks (pres. 1980-81), Cosmos, Rotary. Roman Catholic. Contbr. articles to profl. jours., editorial bd. Transfusion, 1968—, Annals Clinical Lab. Sci., 1971-74, Blood, 1976-77; editor: Progress in Transfusion and Transplantation; described etiology of renal failure after hemolytic blood transfusion reactions, 1967, Rh null disease, 1967. Office: PO Box 2125 Tampa FL 33601-2125

SCHMIDT, PAUL WICKHAM, lawyer; b. Milw., June 25, 1948; s. Edmund Julian and Barbara (Wickham) S.; m. Cathryn Ann Piehl, June 27, 1970; children: Thomas Wickham, William Piehl, Anna Patchin. BA cum laude, Lawrence U., 1970; JD cum laude, U. Wis., 1973. Bar: Wis. 1973, U.S. Dist. Ct. (we. dist.) Wis. 1973, U.S. Supreme Ct. 1982, D.C. 1988. Atty. advisor Bd. Immigration Appeals, Washington, 1973-76; gen. atty. office of gen. counsel Immigration and Naturalization Service, Washington, 1976-78, acting gen. counsel, 1979-81, 86-87, dep. gen. counsel, 1978-87; assoc. Jones, Day, Reavis & Pogue, Washington, 1987-89, ptnr., 1990-92; mng. ptnr. Fragomen, Del Ray & Bernsen, P.C., Washington, 1993-95; chmn. Bd. of Immigration Appeals, Falls Church, Va., 1995—. Mem. ABA, D.C. Bar Assn., Wis. Bar Assn., Fed. Bar Assn. (immigration sect.). Avocations: soccer coaching, gardening, camping, history. Home: 711 S View Ter Alexandria VA 22314-4923 Office: Fragomen Del Ray & Bernsen PC 1212 New York Ave NW Washington DC 20005

SCHMIDT, PETER, construction company executive; b. 1927. With Philip Holzmann AG, Frankfurt, Fed. Republic Germany, 1963—; pres. Philip Holzman USA, Inc., Wilmington, Del.; also bd. dirs. Office: Philipp Holzmann USA Inc 1 S Executive Pk JA Jones Dr Charlotte NC 28287

SCHMIDT, PETER GUSTAV, shipbuilding industry executive; b. Tumwater, Wash., Dec. 3, 1921; s. Peter G. and Clara Louise (Muench) S.; m. Elva Mary Ingalls, Dec. 3, 1945; children: Mimi Schmidt Fuelling, Jill Schmidt Crowson, Janet Schmidt Mano, Hans. BSME, U. Wash., 1948; MS in Naval Architecture and Marine Engring., U. Mich., 1950. Naval architect Nat. Steel Shipbldg. Corp., San Diego, 1950-52, Carl J. Nordstrom/P. Spaulding, Seattle, 1952-53; pres. Marine Constrn. & Design Co., Seattle, 1953—, Astilleros Marco Chilena Ltd., Santiago, Chile, 1960—, Marco Peruana S.A., Lima, Peru, 1965—, Marco Espãna, Bilbao and Canary Islands, Spain, 1970—, Marco Panama, Panama City, 1976—, Campbell Industries, San Diego, 1979—. Author papers on fishing gear and vessels. Served to lt (j.g.) USN, 1942-45, PTO. Recipient Puget Sound's Maritime Man of Yr. award Puget Sound Press Assn., 1975. Mem. Soc. Naval Architects and Marine Engrs., Wash. State Boatbuilders Assn. (pres. 1956-58), Alpha Delta Phi. Avocations: competitive sailing, classical music. Office: Marine Constrn & Design 2300 W Commodore Way Seattle WA 98199-1226

SCHMIDT, PETER R., anthropology educator. AB in History with honors, Stanford U., 1965; MA, UCLA, 1967; PhD, Northwestern U., 1974. Asst. prof. anthropology Brown U., Providence, 1971-81, assoc. prof., 1981-88; rsch. assoc. U. Dar es Salaam, Tanzania, 1976-80, assoc. prof. history, coord. and founder archaeology unit, 1985-87; assoc. prof. anthropology U. Fla., Gainesville, 1988—, dir. Ctr. for African Studies, 1988—; chmn. Adv. Coun. Profl. Archaeologists, 1975-76; state archaeologist State of Idaho, 1975-76; mem. rev. bd. Nat. Hist. Register, R.I., 1978-84; commr. R.I. Hist. Preservation Commn., 1978-84; pres. Found. African Prehistory and Archaeology, 1981—; acad. specialist to Omar Bongo U., Gabon, 1984; vis. assoc. prof. anthropology U. Calif., Berkeley, 1984; program dir. for African exchs. Brown U., 1984-88; Fulbright vis. expert to Omar Bonto U., Gabon, 1986; presented papers in field. Author: Historical Archaeology: A Structural Approach in an African Culture, 1978; prodr., dir. (film): Beating the Bellows: An Archaeological Experiment in African Iron Technology, 1982; prodr. (film): The Tree of Iron: Advanced African Iron Technology, 1988; contbr. articles to profl. jours. Fulbright fellow, 1981; grantee NSF, 1969-70, 75-77, 78-80, 82, Wenner Gren Found., 1973, Fulbright, 1982, Social Sci. Rsch. Coun., 1983, NEH, 1983, Ford Found., 1984; Fulbright scholar U. Dar es Salaam, 1985-87; recipient Excellence award Soc. Visual Anthropology, 1988, Golden Apple award Nat. Film Festival-San Francisco, 1988, Red Ribbon award Am. Film and Video Festival-Chgo., 1989. Mem. Soc. Africanist Archaeologists (mem. steering com. 1982-84, mem. exec. bd. 1990-92, pres. 1988-90). Office: U Fla Ctr African Studies 427 Grinter Hall Gainesville FL 32611

SCHMIDT, RICHARD EDWARD, manufacturing company executive; b. Beatrice, Nebr., Mar. 12, 1932; s. Edward C. and Edna Ruth (Timken) S.; m. Lois Beth Lowell, Dec. 30, 1953; children: Cheryl, Linda, Douglas. BA in Chemistry, U. Kans., 1954. V.p. Beckman Instruments, Fullerton, Calif., 1956-75; group pres. G.D. Searle & Co., Chgo., 1975-79; div. pres. Warner

Lambert, Morris Plains, N.J., 1979-84; chmn., chief exec. officer Milton Roy Co., St. Petersburg, Fla., 1984—; adv. bd. BIMECO, Largo, Fla., 1985—. Bd. dirs. Bayfront Med. Ctr. Inc., 1987. 1st lt. USAF, 1954-56. Mem. Am. Mgmt. Assn., The Conference Bd. Exec. Coun., Mfrs. Alliance for Productivity and Innovation (pres. coun.), Sci. Apparatus Mfg. Assn., Instrument Soc. Am. Feather Sound Country Club (Clearwater, Fla.), St. Petersburg Yacht Club.

SCHMIDT, RICHARD FREDERICK, business executive; b. N.Y.C., Mar. 11, 1930; s. George and Hermine (Hanatschek) S.; m. Faith Segui, Sept. 12, 1958; children: Julia, Carl. B.A., Princeton U., 1953; M.B.A., U. Pa., 1960. Fin. analyst Gen. Motors Corp., Detroit, 1960-61, Ford Motor Co., 1961-63; asso., mgmt. cons. McKinsey & Co., N.Y.C., 1963-69; dir. fin. planning Reuben H. Donnelly Corp., N.Y.C., 1969, v.p. fin. 1969-72, v.p. fin. and adminstrn., 1972-74; pres. Mgmt. Cons. div. Dun & Bradstreet Corp., N.Y.C., 1974-79, sr. v.p. planning and devel., 1976-81, exec. v.p. fin. and planning, 1982—; also dir. Served with AUS, 1953-54. Mem. Fin. Execs. Inst. Republican. Clubs: Sky, Bronxville Field. Home: 5 Fordal Rd Bronxville NY 10708-2404 Office: The Dun & Bradstreet Corp 299 Park Ave New York NY 10171-0002

SCHMIDT, RICHARD MARTEN, JR., lawyer; b. Winfield, Kans., Aug. 2, 1924; s. Richard M. and Ida (Marten) S.; m. Ann Downing, Jan. 2, 1948; children—Eric, Gregory, Rolf (dec.), Heidi. A.B., U. Denver, 1945, J.D., 1948. Bar: Colo. bar 1948, D.C. bar 1968. Dep. dist. atty. City and County of Denver, 1949-50; mem. firm McComb, Zarlengo, Mott & Schmidt, Denver, 1950-54; ptnr. Schmidt & Van Cise (and predecessor), Denver, 1954-65; 65; gen. counsel USIA, 1965-68; ptnr. Cohn and Marks, Washington, 1969—; counsel spl. agrl. investigating subcom. Counsel Am. Soc. Newspaper Editors, 1968—; mem. Gov.'s Coun. Local Govt., Colo., 1963-64; chmn. Mayor's Jud. Adv. Com., Denver, 1963-64, Gov.'s Supreme Ct. Nominating Com., 1964-65; mem. Gov.'s Oil Shale Adv. Com., 1963-65, Colo. Commn. on Higher Edn., 1965; mem. bd. Nat. Press Found., 1993—. Trustee U. Denver. Mem. ABA (chmn. standing com. on assn. communications 1969-73, chmn. forum com. on communications 1979-81, co-chmn. nat. conf. lawyers and reps. of media 1984—), Colo. Bar Assn. (gov.), Denver Bar Assn. (pres. 1963-64), D.C. Bar Assn., Cosmos Club (Washington). Episcopalian. Home: 115 5th St SE Washington DC 20003-1123 Office: Cohn and Marks 1333 New Hampshire Ave NW Washington DC 20036-1573

SCHMIDT, RICHARD S., federal judge; b. Boulder, Colo., Nov. 23, 1948; children: Kristin Winfree, Madeline Mason. JD, U. Tex., 1973. Bar: Tex. 1973, La. 1978. Ptnr. Smitherman, Lunn, Chastain & Hill, Shreveport, La., 1978-87; bankruptcy judge U.S. Courts, Corpus Christi, Tex., 1987—. Capt., judge adv. USAF, 1973-78. Office: US Bankruptcy Ct 615 Leopard St Ste 110 Corpus Christi TX 78476-2200

SCHMIDT, ROBERT, mechanics and civil engineering educator; b. Ukraine, May 18, 1927; came to U.S., 1949, naturalized, 1956; s. Alfred and Aquilina (Konotop) S.; m. Irene Hubertine Bongartz, June 10, 1978; children: Ingbert Robert. Student, UNRRA-Univ., Munich, 1946-47, Technische Hochschule Karlsruhe, Germany, 1947-49; BS, U. Colo., 1951, MS, 1953; PhD, U. Ill., 1956. Tech. draftsman Kalisch, Poland, 1943-45; rsch. asst. U. Ill., 1953-56; asst. prof. mechanics U. Ill., Urbana, 1956-59; assoc. prof. U. Ariz., Tucson, 1959-63; prof. mechanics and civil engring. U. Detroit, 1963—, chmn. civil engring. dept., 1978-80; rschr. in linear and nonlinear theory of elasticity, theories of arches, plates, and shells, and approximate methods of analysis. Editor: Indsl. Math., 1969—; book reviewer Applied Mechanics Rev., Indsl. Math. jour.; contbr. over 135 articles to profl. jours. With C.E., U.S. Army, 1951-52. Grantee NSF 1960-78. Mem. AAUP, ASCE, ASME (cert. recognition 1972), Am. Acad. Mechanics (a founder), Indsl. Math. Soc. (pres. 1966-67, 81-84, 1st Gold award 1986), Sigma Xi. Avocations: biosophy, walking, bicycling, swimming. Office: U Detroit Mercy Coll Engring and Sci Detroit MI 48219-0900

SCHMIDT, ROBERT CHARLES, JR., finance company executive; b. Oklahoma City, Apr. 2, 1942; s. Robert Charles and Francis Laura (Schiele) S.; m. Susan G. Dietz-Hermange, Nov. 8, 1974; children: Laura Stewart, Elizabeth Berry. B.A., Westminster Coll., Fulton, Mo., 1964; postgrad., U. Okla., 1972, London Grad. Sch. Bus. Studies, 1974-76. Exec. trainee First Nat. Bank in St. Louis, 1967-68, comml. banker, 1968-74, v.p., mgr. client services div., 1974-76; v.p. treasury ops. Am. Express Co., N.Y.C., 1976-81, dep. treas., 1981-86; chmn. bd. Am. Express Export Credit Corp., 1982-86; group v.p., gen. mgr. Nat. Data Corp., Atlanta, 1986-88, exec. v.p., 1988-89; exec. v.p. Capital Guaranty Corp., San Francisco, 1989-91; pres. Tampsco Enterprises, Inc., St. Louis, 1993; ptnr. The Whitelaw Group, St. Louis, 1994—; pres. Benefit Info. Techs., Inc., St. Louis, 1995—; cons. City of N.Y., 1977. Loaned exec. United Fund, St. Louis, 1973. Served with U.S. Army, 1965-67. Decorated Army Commendation medal; recipient cert. of merit USO, 1966, Alumni Achievement award Westminster Coll., 1977. Mem. Treas. Group (chmn. 1982-83), Noonday Club (St. Louis), Crystal Downs Country Club (Frankfort, Mich.), Beta Theta Pi. Republican. Episcopalian. Office: 300 Hunter Ave Saint Louis MO 63124-2081

SCHMIDT, ROBERT L, export company executive; b. 1937. Grad., U. Ill., Champaign. With Ford Motor Co., Chgo., 1957-63, Internat. Minerals & Chem. Corp, Chgo., 1963-82; exec. v.p. Phosphate Chem. Export Assn., Des Plaines, Ill., 1982—. Office: Phosphate Chem Export Assn 9399 W Higgins Rd 900 Des Plaines IL 60018

SCHMIDT, ROBERT MILTON, physician, scientist, educator; b. Milw., May 7, 1944; s. Milton W. and Edith J. (Martinek) S.; children Eric Whitney, Edward Huntington. AB, Northwestern U., 1966; MD, Columbia U., 1970; MPH, Harvard U., 1975; PhD in Law, Medicine and Pub. Policy, Emory U., 1982. Diplomate Am. Bd. Preventive Medicine. Resident in internal medicine Univ. Hosp. U. Calif.-San Diego, 1970-71; resident in preventive medicine Ctrs. Disease Control, Atlanta, 1971-73; commd. med. officer USPHS, 1971; advanced through grades to comdr., 1973; dir. hematology div. Nat. Ctr. for Disease Control, Atlanta, 1971-78, spl. asst. to dir., 1978-79, inactive res., 1979—; clin. asst. prof. pediatrics Tufts U. Med. Sch., 1974-86; clin. asst. prof. medicine Emory U. Med. Sch., 1971-81, clin. asst. prof. community health, 1976-86; clin. assoc. prof. humanities in medicine Morehouse Med. Sch., 1977-79; attending physician dept. medicine Wilcox Meml. Hosp., Lihue, Hawaii, 1979-82, Calif. Pacific Med. Ctr., San Francisco, 1983—; dir. Ctr. Preventive Medicine and Health Research, 1983—; dir. Health Watch, 1983—; sr. scientist Inst. Epidemiology and Behavioral Medicine, Inst. Cancer Research, Calif. Pacific Med. Ctr., San Francisco, 1983-88; prof. hematology and gerontology, dir. Ctr. Preventive Medicine and Health Rsch., chair health professions program San Francisco State U., 1983—; cons. WHO, FDA, Washington, NIH, Bethesda, Md., Govt. of China, Mayo Clinic, Rochester, Minn., Northwestern U., Evanston, Ill., U. R.I., Kingston, Pan Am. Health Orgn., Inst. Pub. Health, Italy, Nat. Inst. Aging Rsch. Ctr., Balt., U. Calif., San Diego, U. Ill., Chgo., Columbia U., N.Y.C., Brown U., Providence, U. Calif., L.A., Harvard U., Boston, U. Chgo., Emory U., Atlanta, Duke U., N.C., U. Tex., Houston, Ariz. State U., U. Hawaii, Honolulu, U. Paris, U. Geneva, U. Munich, Heidelberg U., U. Frankfurt, U. Berlin, Cambridge (Eng.) U., U. Singapore, others; vis. rsch. prof. gerontology Ariz. State U., 1989-90; mem. numerous sci. and profl. adv. bds., panels, coms. Mem. editorial bd. Am. Jour. Clin. Pathology, 1976-82, The Advisor, 1988—, Generations, 1989—, Alternative Therapies in Health and Medicine; book and film reviewer Sci. Books and Films, 1988—; author: 17 books and manuals including Hematology Laboratory Series, 4 vols., 1979-86, CRC Handbook Series in Clinical Laboratory Science, 1976—; assoc. editor: Contemporary Gerontology, 1993—; contbr. over 260 articles to sci. jours. Alumni regent Columbia U. Coll. Physicians and Surgeons, 1980—. Northwestern U. scholar, 1964-66; NSF fellow, 1964-66; Health Professions scholar, 1966-70; USPHS fellow, 1967-70; Microbiology, Urology, Upjohn Achievement, Borden Rsch. and Virginia Kneeland Frantz scholar awards Columbia U., 1970; recipient Am. Soc. Pharmacol. and Exptl. Therapy award in pharmacology, 1970, Commendation medal USPHS, 1973, Leadership Recognition awards San Francisco State U., 1984-89, 91-94, Meritorious Performance and Profl. Promise award, 1989, Meritorious Svc. award, San Francisco State U., 1992, Student Disting. Teaching and Svc. award Pre-Health Professions Student Alliance, 1992. Fellow ACP (commentator ACP Jour. Club/Annals of Internal Medicine 1993—), AAAS (med. scis. sect.), Royal Soc. Medicine (London), Gerontol. Soc. Am., Am.

Geriatrics Soc., Am. Coll. Preventive Medicine (sci. com.), Am. Soc. Clin. Pathology, Internat. Soc. Hematology; mem. AMA, Am. Med. Informatics Am. Pub. Health Assn., Internat. Commn. for Standardization in Hematology, Am. Soc. Hematology, Internat. Soc. Thrombosis and Hemostasis, Acad. Clin. Lab Physicians and Scientists, Am. Assn. Blood Banks, Nat. Assn. Advisors for Health Professions (bd. dirs.), Am. Assn. Med. Informatics (chair prevention and health evaluation informatics WG), Calif. Coun. Gerontology and Geriatrics, Am. Coll. Occupational and Environ. Medicine, Assn. Tchrs. Preventive Medicine (edn. com., rsch. com.), Am. Soc. Microbiology, Am. Soc. Aging (editorial bd. 1—, Dychtwald Pub. Speaking award 1991), N.Y. Acad. Sci., Internat. Health Evaluation Assn. (vice pres. for Ams. 1992—, bd. dirs., pres. 1994—), Golden Key (hon. faculty mem.), Army and Navy Club (Washington), Harvard Club (N.Y.), Sigma Xi, others. Home: 25 Hinckley Walk San Francisco CA 94111-2303 Office: HEALTH WATCH Program 2100 Webster St Ste 508 San Francisco CA 94115-2381

SCHMIDT, RONALD HANS, architect; b. Hoboken, N.J., Sept. 9, 1938. BArch., Syracuse U., 1961. Sr. designer Skidmore, Owings & Merrill, N.Y.C., 1963-68; ptnr., dir. archtl. design Grad. Partnership, Newark, 1968-81; pres., chief exec. officer Ronald Schmidt & Assocs., P.A., Hackensack, N.J., 1981—. Recipient numerous awards. Office: 222 Grand Ave Englewood NJ 07631-4352

SCHMIDT, RUTH ANN, retired college president; b. Mountain Lake, Minn., Sept. 16, 1930; d. Jacob A. and Anna A. (Ewert) S. B.A., Augsburg Coll., Mpls., 1952; M.A., U. Mo., 1955; Ph.D., U. Ill., 1962; LLD, Gordon Coll., 1987. Asst. prof. Spanish Mary Baldwin Coll., Staunton, Va., 1955-58; asst. prof. Spanish SUNY-Albany, 1962-67, assoc. prof., 1967-78, dean of humanities, 1971-76; prof. and provost Wheaton Coll., Norton, Mass., 1978-82; pres. Agnes Scott Coll., Decatur, Ga., 1982-94; chair Women's Coll. Coalition, 1986-88. Author: Ortega Munilla y sus novelas, 1973, Cartas entre dos amigos del teatro, 1969. Trustee Gordon Coll., Wenham, Mass., 1980-86, Lyon Coll., 1993—; bd. dirs. DeKalb C. of C. 1983-85, Atlanta Coll. Art, 1984-94; mem. exec. com. Women's Coll. Coalition, 1983-88; v.p. So. Univ. Conf., 1993. Named Disting. Alumna Augsburg Coll., 1973. Mem. Assn. Am. Colls. (dir. 1979-82, treas. 1982-83), Soc. Values in Higher Edn., Am. Coun. Edn. (commn. on women in higher edn. 1985-88), AAUW, Assn. Pvt. Colls. and Univs. Ga. (pres. 1987-89), Internat. Women's Forum, Young Women's Christian Assn. Acad. Women Achievers. Democrat. Presbyterian.

SCHMIDT, STANLEY ALBERT, editor, writer; b. Cin., Mar. 7, 1944; s. Otto Elliott William and Georgia (Metcalf) S.; m. Joyce Mary Tokarz, June 9, 1979. BS, U. Cin., 1966; MA, Case Western Res. U., 1968, PhD, 1969. Asst. prof. physics Heidelberg Coll., Tiffin, Ohio, 1969-78; free-lance writer Lake Peekskill, N.Y., 1968—; editor Analog Sci. Fiction and Fact Dell Mags., N.Y.C., 1978—; mem. bd. advisors Nat. Space Soc., Washington, 1982—. Author: Newton and the Quasi-Apple, 1975, The Sins of the Fathers, 1976, Lifeboat Earth, 1978, Analog Yearbook II, 1981, Analog's Golden Anniversary Anthology, 1980, Analog: Readers' Choice, 1981, Analog's Children of the future, 1982, Analog's Lighter Side, 1982, Analog: Writers' Choice, 1983, War and Peace: Possible Futures from Analog, 1983, Aliens from Analog, 1983, Writer's Choice, Vol. II, 1984, From Mind to Mind, 1984, Analog's Expanding Universe, 1986, Tweedlloop, 1986, Unknown, 1988, Unknown Worlds, 1989, Analog Essays in Science, 1990. Writing Science Fiction and Fantasy, 1991; contbr. stories to science fiction mags., articles to mags., chpts. to books. Mem. Sci. Fiction and Fantasy Writers Am., Am. Assn. Physics Tchrs., Am. Fedn. Musicians. Avocations: photography, hiking, linguistics, cooking, flying. Office: Analog Sci Fiction 1540 Broadway New York NY 10036-4039

SCHMIDT, STEPHEN C., computer company executive; b. Tacoma, Wash., Nov. 12, 1945; s. Carl Joseph and Patricia Theresa (Nelson) S.; m. Frances Crespo, div. 1972; m. Barbara Sue Levine, Nov. 12, 1973; 1 child, Michelle Catherine. BA, U. Miami, 1967; MS in Computer Sci., U. So. Calif., 1970. Gen. mgr. Burroughs Corp., Calif., 1966-82; v.p. product mgmt. Tandem Computers Inc., Cupertino, Calif., v.p. ops., sr. v.p., gen. mgr.; vice chmn. AEA Semiconductor Task Force, 1986-89. Dir. Villa Montalvo Bd. Trustees, Saratoga, Calif., 1985-90. Office: Tandem Computers Inc 19333 Vallco Pky Cupertino CA 95014-2506

SCHMIDT, STEPHEN CHRISTOPHER, agricultural economist, educator; b. Isztimer, Hungary, Dec. 20, 1920; came to U.S., 1949, naturalized, 1965; s. Francis Michael and Anne Marie (Angeli) S.; m. Susan M. Varszegi, Dec. 20, 1945; children—Stephen Peter, David William. Dr.Sc., U. Budapest, Hungary, 1945; Ph.D., McGill U., Montreal, Que., Can., 1958. Asst. head dept. Hungary Ministry Commerce, Budapest, 1947-48; asst. prof. U. Ky., Lexington, 1955-57, Mont. State U., Bozeman, 1957-59; asst. prof. U. Ill., Urbana-Champaign, 1959-63, assoc. prof., 1963-70, prof. agrl. mktg. and policy, 1970-91, prof. emeritus, 1991—. Fulbright grantee Bulgaria, 1992-93; Ford Found. fellow, 1959; Agrl. Devel. Coun. grantee, 1966, U. Man. Rsch., 1968-69, Ford Found. rsch. grantee, 1973, 74, Whitehall found. grantee, 1979, Internat. Inst. Applied Systems Analyses (Laxenburg, Austria) rsch. scholar, 1976-77, USDA Intergovtl. Personnel Act grantee, 1983-84. Mem. Am. Agrl. Econs. Assn. (award 1979), Internat. Assn. Agri. Economists, Am. Assn. Advancement Slavic Studies, Ea. Econ. Assn., Sigma Xi, Gamma Sigma Delta. Office: 1301 W Gregory Dr Urbana IL 61801-3608

SCHMIDT, STEPHEN ROBERT, lawyer; b. Louisville, Jan. 29, 1948; s. Adolph William and Olivia Ann (Hohl) S.; m. Wanda Jean Owen, Aug. 17, 1974; children: Johannes, Kathryn. AB, St. Louis U., 1969; Fulbright fellow, Universität Hamburg, 1969-70; MA, Ohio State U., 1971, JD, 1974. Assoc. Brown, Todd & Heyburn PLLC, Louisville, 1974-79, mem, 1980—. Co-author: Bad Faith Litigation in Kentucky, 1992, Insurance Coverage Law in Kentucky, 1994; editor Ohio State Law Jour., 1973-74; contbr. articles to profl. jours. Named one of Outstanding Young Men of Am. Jaycees, 1983. Mem. ABA (chair comml. torts com., torts and ins. practice sect. 1995-96, speaker ann. meeting 1993, 94), Ohio State U. Alumni Club (pres. Louisville 1983, 86, 93, treas. 1987-95), Fulbright Assn., Order of Coif, Phi Beta Kappa. Avocations: photography, computers, playing cards, golf. Office: Brown Todd & Heyburn PLLC 3200 Providian Ctr 400 W Market St Louisville KY 40202-3363

SCHMIDT, TERRY LANE, health care executive; b. Chgo., Nov. 28, 1943; s. LeRoy C. and Eunic P. S.; children: Christie Anne, Terry Lane II. B.S., Bowling Green State U., 1965; M.B.A. in Health Care Adminstrn, George Washington U., 1971. Resident in hosp. adminstrn. U. Pitts. Med. Center, VA Hosp., Pitts. 1968-69; adminstrv. asst. Mt. Sinai Med. Center, N.Y.C., 1969-70; asst. dir. Health Facilities Planning Council of Met. Washington, 1970-71; asst. dir. dept. govtl. adminstrn A.M.A., Washington, 1971-74; pres. Terry L. Schmidt Inc. Physician Svcs. Group, San Diego, 1974—; assoc. chief operating officer Emergency Health Assocs. P.C., Phoenix, 1989-91; Charleston Emergency Physicians, S.C., 1990—, Joplin Emergency Physican Assocs., 1991-92, Big Valley Med. Group, 1991-92, Blue Ridge Emergency Physicians, P.C., 1992-93, Berkeley Emergency Physicians, P.C., 1992-93; pres. Med. Cons. Inc., 1983-84; v.p. Crisis Communications Corp. Ltd., 1982-90; pres. Washington Actions on Health, 1975-78; partner Washington counsel Medicine and Health, 1979-81; pres. Ambulance Corp. Am., La Jolla, Calif., 1984-87; chmn., pres. Univ. Inst., 1992—; lectr., part-time faculty dept. health care adminstrn. George Washington U., 1969-84, preceptor, 1971-84; adj. prof. grad. sch. Pub. Health San Diego State U., 1989—, preceptor, 1989—, clin. prof., 1995—; asst. prof. Nat. Naval Sch. Health Care Adminstrn., 1971-73; faculty CSC Legis. Insts., 1972-76, Am. Assn. State Colls. and U. Health'Org. Insts.; mem. adv. com. ambulatory care standards Joint Commn. Accreditation of Hosps., 1971-72; guest lectr. health care adminstrn. Nat. U., San Diego, 1992—; adj. prof. Bus. Adminstrn. U.S. Internat. U., San Diego, 1994—. Author: Congress and Health: An Introduction to the Legislative Process and the Key Participants, 1976, A Directory of Federal Health Resources and Services for the Disadvantaged, 1976, Health Care Reimbursement: A Glossary, 1983, Health Reform: A Glossary, 1994; mem. editl. adv. bd.: Nation's Health, 1971-73; contbr. articles to profl. jours. Bd. dirs. Nat. Eye Found., 1976-78. Mem. Am. Hosp. Assn., Med. Group Mgmt. Assn., Hosp. Fin. Mgmt. Assn., Med. Group Mgrs., Assn. Venture Capital Groups (bd. dirs. 1984-89), Med.

Adminstrs. of Calif., San Diego Venture Group (chair 1984-87), U. Calif. San Diego Venture Group (chair 1984-87), U. Calif. San Diego Faculty Club, University Club (life), Nat. Dem. Club (life), Nat. Rep. Club (life), Capitol Hill Club (life), Alpha Phi Omega (pres. Bowling Green alumni chpt. 1967-70, sec.-treas. alumni assn. 1968-71). Office: 9191 Towne Ctr Dr Ste 360 San Diego CA 92122

SCHMIDT, THOMAS CARSON, international development banker; b. York, Pa., Oct. 15, 1930; s. George Small and Josephine Foot (Reifsnider) S.; m. Lucy Carter Searby, Aug. 21, 1954 (div. May 1980); children: Peter, Lucy, Thomas.; m. Robin G. Berry, Nov. 26, 1983; 1 stepdau., Julia Barclay. A.B., Princeton U., 1952; M.Div., Va. Sem., 1955; Ph.D. in Policy Scis., SUNY, 1971. Ordained priest Episcopal Ch., 1955; rector St. Alban's Ch., Bogota, Colombia, 1955-58; asst. St. James, New London, Conn., 1958-61; rector St. Andrew's, Longmeadow, Mass., 1961-68; on leave serving Diocese Zululand-Swaziland, South Africa, 1965-66; mgmt. cons., 1968-71; asst. commr. edn. State of R.I., 1971-73; mem. R.I. Gov.'s Policy and Program Rev. Staff Providence, 1973-75; commr. edn. State of R.I., 1975-80; v.p. Partners of the Americas, 1980-81; mgmt. cons. nat. and fgn. firms, 1981-83, 94—; pub. adminstrn. specialist Internat. Bank Reconstrn. and Devel. (World Bank), 1983-89, sr. gen. educator, 1989-94. Chmn. manpower task force R.I. Health Sci. Edn. Coun., 1973-75, mem. exec. bd., 1973-75; mem. edn. com. Maine Coun. Chs.; bd. dirs. Cmty. Bldg. Trust; mem. fin. com., adult edn. com., pub. rels. com. Mid-Coast Friends Meeting. Mem. Internat. Soc. Ednl. Planners (treas. 1973), Internat. Assn. Applied Social Scientists, Council Chief State Sch. Officers (bd. dirs. 1976-80), State Higher Edn. Exec. Officers Assn. (legis. com.), Am. Assn. State Colls. and Univs. (legis. com.), SUNY Buffalo Alumni Assn. (dir.). Home: HC 61 Box 63 Bristol ME 04539-8803

SCHMIDT, THOMAS JOSEPH, JR., lawyer; b. New Haven, Jan. 16, 1945; s. Thomas Joseph and Rosemary (O'Shaughnessy) S.; m. Linda Diane Crider, Nov. 16, 1974; children: Elizabeth Anne, Thomas Joseph III, Karen Diana. AB, Xavier U., 1967; JD, U. Cin., 1970. Bar: Ohio 1970, U.S. Ct. Mil. Appeals 1970. Commd. 2d lt. U.S. Army, 1967, advanced through grades to capt., 1969; legal officer U.S. Army Corps Engrs., Ft. Hayes, Ohio, 1967-68, Ft. Knox, Ky., 1969-70; atty. U.S. Army JAGC, Ft. Benning, Ga., 1971-75; asst. counsel Midland Enterprises Inc., Cin., 1975-77, assoc. gen. counsel, 1977-83, gen. counsel, 1983-87, gen. counsel, sec., 1987—. Republican. Roman Catholic. Office: Midland Enterprises Inc 1400 580 Building Cincinnati OH 45202

SCHMIDT, THOMAS MELLON, lawyer; b. Pitts., Feb. 18, 1940; s. Adolph William and Helen Sedgely (Mellon) S.; m. Hannah Knowlton Wright, June 21, 1963 (div. 1983); children: Elizabeth, Helen, Josie; m. Susan Elizabeth Scott, Sept. 5, 1992. AB in History and Humanities, Princeton U., 1962; JD, Harvard U., 1965. Bar: Pa. 1966, U.S. Dist. Ct. (we. dist.) Pa., 1966. Assoc. Kirkpatrick & Lockhart, Pitts., 1965-70; adj. prof. law Duquesne U., Pitts., 1973-74; dir. Fallingwater and Pitts. Park and Playground Fund Western Pa. Conservancy, Pitts., 1975—, v.p., counsel, 1970—; developer residential subdivsn. St. Johns County, Fla., 1975-88; advisor Land Conservation Law Inst., San Francisco, 1990—; trustee Whitney Lab., Marineland, Fla., 1993, Morris Arboretum, Phila., 1990—; bd. dirs., past pres. Frank Lloyd Wright Bldg. Conservancy, Oak Park, Ill., 1989-93. Author: (monograph) Laws which Regulate Land Use in Pennsylvania, 1975. Trustee St. BBarnabbus Health System, Pitts., 1978—, Laurel Found., Pitts., 1993; Carnegie Mus. of Natural History, Pitts., 1994; vice chmn. Pitts. Hist. Rev. Commn., 1987—. Recipient citation AIA, 1982, Take Pride in Pa. award, 1986, Nat. Environ. Achievement award, 1993, Wright Spirit award, 1993. Mem. ABA, Allegheny County Bar Assn., Am. Assn. Mus., Rolling Rock Club, Pitts. Golf Club, Anglers Club N.Y. Republican. Episcopalian. Avocations: horticulture, oil painting, travel. Home: 1060 Highmont Rd Pittsburgh PA 15232-2905 Office: Western Pa Conservancy 316 4th Ave Pittsburgh PA 15222-2002

SCHMIDT, W. ROBERT, school system administrator. Supt. schs. Diocese of Davenport, Iowa. Office: St Vincent Ctr 2706 N Gaines St Davenport IA 52804-1914

SCHMIDT, WALDEMAR ADRIAN, pathologist, educator; b. L.A., Aug. 22, 1941; s. Waldemar Adrian and Mary Charlotte (Parker) S.; m. Karmen LaVer Bingham, Feb. 1, 1963; children: Rebecca, Sarah, Waldemar, Diedrich. BS, Oreg. State U., 1965; PhD, U. Oreg., 1969, MD, 1969. Intern U. Oreg. Hosps. and Clinics, Portland, 1969-70, resident, 1970-73; pathologist LDS Hosp., Salt Lake City, 1973-77; prof. pathology U. Tex. Med. Sch., Houston, 1977-91, Oreg. Health Sci. U. and VA Med. Ctr., Portland, 1991—. Author: Principles and Techniques of Surgical Pathology, 1982; editor Cytopathology Annual, 1991—. Asst. scoutmaster Boy Scouts Am., Houston, 1982-91. Maj. U.S. Army, 1970-76. Mem. Coll. Am. Pathologists (program com.), Sigma Xi, Alpha Omega Alpha. Avocations: photography, silviculture. Office: VA Med Ctr 3710 SW US Veterans Hosp Rd Portland OR 97207

SCHMIDT, WILLIAM C., chemical company executive; b. Niles, Mich., Sept. 27, 1938; s. Felix A. and Anna (Reifschneider) S.; m. Bethany Ann Boyd, Dec. 17, 1966; 1 child, Craig W. B.B.A., U. Mich., 1960, M.B.A. 1961. Cert. Mgmt. Acct. Various acctg. positions Dow Chem. Co., Midland, Mich., 1961-73; controller Dow Chem. Pacific Ltd., Hong Kong, 1973-78; area controller Dow Chem. Co., Midland, Mich., 1978-82, asst. corp. controller, 1982—; v.p., chief fin. officer DowElanco, Indpls., 1989—; bd. dirs. Noble Ctrs. Chmn. bd. dirs. Midland Hosp. Ctr., 1986-89; bd. dirs. Mid-Mich. Health Care Corp., 1983-89, chmn. bd., 1986-88; treas., bd. dirs. Indpls. Symphony Orch., 1992—. Cpl. U.S. Army, 1962-64. Mem. Inst. Mgmt. Accts., Inst. Cert. Mgmt. Accts. (regent 1985-89), Am. Indsl. Health Coun. (treas. 1986-87), Fin. Execs. Inst. Ind. C of C. (bd. dirs. 1992—). Methodist. Home: 4958 St Charles Pl Carmel IN 46033-5936 Office: DowElanco 9330 Zionsville Rd Indianapolis IN 46268-1104

SCHMIDT-MONGE, ROBERTO, federal judge; b. San Juan, P.R.; m. Abbie Quiñones; children: Abbie E., Arlene J. Roberto, Richard, Astrid. BA, U. P.R., 1956, LLB, 1958. Bar: U.S. Ct. Appeals (1st cir.) 1984, P.R. Supreme Ct. 1958, U.S. Supreme Ct. 1984. Judge U.S. Dist. Ct., 1959-61; pvt. practice, 1961-69; judge Superior Ct., 1969-78; chmn. rev. bd. Electoral Rev. Bd., 1978-82; superior judge San Juan, P.R., 1982-84; solicitor gen. Commonwealth of P.R., 1984; pvt. practice, 1985; U.S. Magistrate judge U.S. Dist. Ct., San Juan, P.R., 1985—. Bd. dirs. Colegio Marista; mem. govt. Judicial Evaluation Com., pres. Club House, Inc. With P.R.NG, 1948-51; in Korea, 1951-52; 2nd lt. inf., 1956. Mem. P.R. Bar Assn. (bd. dirs., mem. judicial evaluation com. 1992), Fed. Bar Assn. (bd. dirs.). Home: 151 San Tomas St Reparto El Pilar Rio Piedras PR 00926 Office: US Dist Ct 181 Federal Bldg 150 Carlos Chardon Ave San Juan PR 00918

SCHMIDT-NIELSEN, BODIL MIMI (MRS. ROGER G. CHAGNON), physiologist; b. Copenhagen, Denmark, Nov. 3, 1918; came to U.S., 1946, naturalized, 1952; d. August and Marie (Jorgensen) Krogh; m. Knut Schmidt-Nielsen, Sept. 20, 1939 (div. Feb. 1966); children: Astrid, Bent, Bodil; m. Roger G. Chagnon, Oct. 1968. D.D.S., U. Copenhagen, 1941, D.Odont., 1946, Ph.D., 1955; D.Sc. (hon.), Bates Coll., 1983. Faculty Duke, Durham, N.C., 1952-64; prof. biology Case Western Re. U., Cleve., 1964-71, chmn. dept., 1970-71, adj. prof., 1971-74; trustee Mt. Desert Island Biol. Lab., Maine, research scientist, 1971-86, exec. com. 1978-85, v.p., 1979-81, pres., 1981-83; adj. prof. Brown U., Providence, 1972-78; dept. physiol. U. Fla., Gainesville, 1987—; Mem. tng. grant com. NIGMS, 1967-71. Author: August and Marie Knoph, Lives in Science, 1995; editor: Urea and the Kidney, 1970; assoc. editor: Am. Jour. Physiology: Regulatory, Integrative and Comparative Physiology, 1978-81. Trustee Coll. of Atlantic, Bar Harbor, Maine, 1972-92. Recipient Career award NIH, 1962-64, John Simon Guggenheim Meml. fellow, 1952-53; Bowditch lectr., 1958, Jacobaeus lectr., 1974. Fellow AAAS (dir. coun. 1977-79), N.Y. Acad. Sci., Am. Acad. Arts and Scis.; mem. Am. Physiol. Soc. (coun. 1971-77, pres. 1975-76, Ray G. Daggs award 1989, Orr Reynolds award 1994, August Knogh lectr. 1994), Soc. Exptl. Biology and Medicine (coun. 1969-71). Research, publs. on biochemistry of saliva, water metabolism of desert animals, comparative kidney physiology, comparative physiology of excretory organs. Home: 4426 SW 103d Ct Gainesville FL 32608 Office: U Fla Dept Physiology Gainesville FL 32605

SCHMIDT-NIELSEN, KNUT, physiologist, educator; b. Norway, Sept. 24, 1915; came to U.S., 1946, naturalized, 1952; s. Sigval and Signe Torborg (Sturzen-Becker) Schmidt-N. Mag. Scient., U. Copenhagen, 1941, Dr. Phil., 1946; Dr. Med. (hon.), U. Lund, Sweden, 1985; D in Philosophy (hon.), U. Tondheim, Norway, 1993. Research fellow Carlsberg Labs., Copenhagen, 1941-44, Carlsberg Labs. U. (Copenhagen), 1944-46; research assoc. zoology Swarthmore (Pa.) Coll., 1946-48; docent U. Oslo, Norway, 1947-49; research assoc. physiology Stanford U., 1948-49; asst. prof. Coll. Medicine, U. Cin., 1949-52; prof. physiology Duke U., Durham, N.C., 1952—; James B. Duke prof. physiology Duke U., 1963—; Harvey Soc. lectr., 1962; Regents' lectr. U. Calif. at Davis, 1963; Brody Meml. lectr. U. Mo., 1962; Hans Gadow lectr. Cambridge (Eng.) U., 1971; vis. Aggasiz prof. Harvard, 1972; Wellcome vis. prof. U. S.D., 1988; mem. panel environmental biology NSF, 1957-61; mem. sci. adv. com. New Eng. Regional Primate Center, 1962-66; mem. nat. adv. bd. physiol. research lab. Scripps Instn. Oceanography, U. Calif. at San Diego, 1963-69, chmn., 1968-69; organizing com. 1st Internat. Conf. on Comparative Physiology, 1972-80; pres. Internat. Union Physiol. Scis., 1980-86, mem. U.S. nat. com. 1966-78, vice chmn. U.S. nat. com., 1969-78; mem. subcom. on environmental physiology U.S. nat. com. Internat. Biol. Programme, 1965-67; mem. com. on research utilization uncommon animals, div. biology and agr. Nat. Acad. Scis., 1966-68; mem. animal resources adv. com. NIH, 1968; mem. adv. bd. Bio-Med. Scis., Inc., 1973-74; chief scientist Scripps Instn. Amazon expdn., 1967. Author: Animal Physiology, 3d. edit, 1970, The Physiology of Desert Animals; Physiological Problems of Heat and Water, 1964, How Animals Work, 1972, Animal Physiology; Adaptation and Environment, 1975, 2d edit., 1979, 3d edit., 1983, Scaling: Why is Animal Size So Important?, 1984; sect. editor Am. Jour. Physiology, 1961-64, 70-76; editor Jour. Applied Physiology, 1961-64, 70-76; mem. editorial bd. Jour. Cellular and Comparative Physiology, 1961-66, Physiol. Zoology, 1959-70, Am. Jour. Physiology, 1971-76, Jour. Applied Physiology, 1971-76, Jour. Exptl. Biology, 1975-79, 83-86; cons. editor: Annals of Arid Zone, 1962—; hon. editorial adv. bd. Comparative Biochemistry and Physiology, 1962-63; chief editor News in Physiol Scis., 1985-88, cons. editor, 1988—; contbr. articles to sci. publs. Guggenheim fellow, 1953-54; grantee Office Naval Rsch., 1952-54, 58-61, UNESCO, 1953-54, Office Q.M. Gen., 1953-54, Office Surgeon Gen., 1953-54, NIH, 1955-86, NSF, 1957-61, 59-60, 60-61, 61-63; recipient Rsch. Career award USPHS, 1964-85, Internat. prize for biology Japan Soc. for the Promotion of Sci., 1992. Fellow AAAS, N.Y. Acad. Sci., Am. Acad. Arts and Scis.; mem. NAS, N.C. Acad. Sci. (Poteat award 1957), Am. Physiol. Soc., Am. Soc. Zoologists (chmn. div. comparative physiology 1964), Soc. Exptl. Biology, Royal Danish Acad., Acad. Scis. (France) (fgn. assoc.), Royal Norwegian Soc. Arts. and Sci., Norwegian Acad. Scis. and Letters, Physiol. Soc. London (assoc.), Royal Soc. London (fgn.); hon. mem. Am. Soc. Zoologists, Harvey Soc., Zool. Soc. London, Deutsche Ornitologengesellshaft. Office: Duke Univ Dept Zoology Box 90325 Durham NC 27708-0325

SCHMIEDER, FRANK JOSEPH, banker, business executive; b. Granite City, Ill., June 26, 1941; s. Frank John and Ione Mina (Scheller) S.; m. Anne Loraine Murray, Aug. 26, 1961; children: Kevin Frank, Craig Michael. BS (Nat. Merit scholar, State Assembly scholar), U. Ill., 1963, MA, 1964; postgrad. (U. Ill. grad. research fellow), Mass. Inst. Tech., 1966, Stanford U., 1977. Asst. to v.p. indsl. relations Cummins Engine Co., Columbus, Ind., 1964-66, mgr. corp. devel. systems, 1966-68; dir. corp. planning Samsonite Co., Denver, 1969-71; v.p. finance, 1971-73; v.p., treas. Fairchild Camera & Instrument Corp., Mountain View, Calif., 1973-76; v.p. adminstrn. Peterson, Howell & Heather Inc., Hunt Valley, Md., 1976-79, sr. v.p., chief fin. officer, 1979-81, exec. v.p., chief fin. officer, 1981-87; COO Mason Best Mcht. Bank, Dallas, 1987-89; exec. v.p. Greyhound Lines, Inc., 1989-90, pres., COO, 1990-91, CEO, 1991—; pres., bd. dir. Vail Restaurant & Food Services, 1973—; spl. cons. on econs. and efficiency to Gov. Colo., 1968; bd. dirs. EIL Instruments, 1984—, Aviation Office of Am., Plexus Fin. Services, Aviation Internat. Airline. Author: Application of Game Theory to Collective Bargaining, 1965. Bd. dirs. Retarded Children Unltd., 1969-71; dir. Council Econ. Edn. in Md., 1983—. Mem. Nat. Assn. Accountants (award of merit 1971), Am. Econ. Assn., Inst. Mgmt. Sci. Republican. Roman Catholic. Home: 6 Southern Hills Ct Frisco TX 75034 Office: Greyhound 15110 Dallas Pky Ste 400 Dallas TX 75248

SCHMIEGE, ROBERT, railroad executive; b. Madison, Wis., May 24, 1941; married. AB, U. Notre Dame, 1963, JD, 1966. Atty. Nat. Ry. Labor Conf., Chgo., 1966-68, Chgo. and North We. Railway Co., Chgo., 1968-74; asst. v.p. labor rels. Chgo. and North We. Railway Co. (formerly Chgo. and North We. Transp. Co.), Chgo., 1976-79, v.p. labor rels., 1979-84, sr. v.p. adminstrn., 1984-88, chmn., pres., chief exec. officer, 1988-95; atty. So. Pacific Railway Co., L.A., 1974-75; ptnr. Albert & Schmiege, L.A., 1975-76; bd. dirs. Chgo. & North Western Transp. Co., Chgo. Office: Chgo and North Railway Co 165 N Canal St 8N Chicago IL 60661

SCHMIEL, DAVID GERHARD, clergyman, religious education administrator; b. Cedarburg, Wis., Dec. 10, 1931; s. Gerhard August and Frieda Helena (Labrenz) S.; m. Shirley Ann Friede, July 6, 1957; children: Mark, Peter, Steven, Daniel, Julia. BA, Northwestern Coll., 1953; ThD, Concordia Sem., 1967. Pastor St. Paul's Luth. Ch., Gresham, Nebr., 1958-60, Onalaska, Wis., 1960-62; prof. St. Paul's Coll., Concordia, Mo., 1962-70; prof., dean Concordia Coll., St. Paul, 1970-81; dean instrn. Concordia Sem., St. Louis, 1981-82; pres. Concordia Coll., Ann Arbor, Mich., 1983-91; dir. theol. edn. svc. Luth. Ch.-Mo. Synod, St. Louis, 1991-93; pres. Concordia Theol. Sem., Ft. Wayne, Ind., 1993—. Author: Via Propria and Via Mystica...Gerson, 1969. Found. for Reformation Rsch. Jr. fellow, Southeastern Inst. for Medieval and Renaissance Studies, Jr. fellow, 1965, 66, 68. Office: Concordia Theol Sem 6600 N Clinton St Fort Wayne IN 46825

SCHMIT, LUCIEN ANDRÉ, JR., structural engineer; b. N.Y.C., May 5, 1928; s. Lucien Alexander and Eleanor Jessie (Donley) S.; m. Eleanor Constance Trabish, June 24, 1951; 1 son, Lucien Alexander, III. B.S., MIT, 1949, M.S., 1950. Structures engr. Grumman Aircraft Co., Bethpage, N.Y., 1951-53; research engr., aerodynamics engr., aeroelastic and structures lab. MIT, 1954-58; asst. prof. engring. (Case Inst. Tech.), 1958-60, assoc. prof., 1961-63, prof., 1964-70; prof. engring. and applied sci. UCLA, 1970-91, Rockwell prof. aerospace engring. emeritus, 1991—; mem. sci. adv. bd. USAF, 1977-84. Contbr. numerous articles on analysis and synthesis of structural systems, finite elements methods, design of fiber composite components and multidisciplinary design optimization to profl. jours. Fellow AIAA (Design Lecture award 1977, Structures, Structural Dynamics and Materials award 1979, Multidisciplinary Design Optimization award 1994), ASCE, Am. Acad. Mechanics; mem. NAE. Home: 712 El Medio Ave Pacific Palisades CA 90272-3451 Office: UCLA 5532 Boelter Hall Los Angeles CA 90024

SCHMITT, BERNARD W., bishop. Ordained priest Roman Cath. Ch., 1955, ordained to episcopacy, 1988. Titular bishop Walla Walla, Wash., 1988-89; bishop Diocese of Wheeling-Charleston, W.Va., 1989—. Office: Chancery Office Box 230 1300 Byron St Wheeling WV 26003-3315

SCHMITT, GEORGE FREDERICK, JR., materials engineer; b. Louisville, Nov. 3, 1939; s. George Frederick and Jane Limbird (Hurst) S.; m. Ann Cheatham, July 31, 1965; 2 children. BS, U. Louisville, 1962, MS, 1963; MBA, Ohio State U., 1966. Asst. dir. nonmetallic materials div. USAF Materials Lab., Wright Patterson AFB, Ohio, 1966—, advanced engring devel. mgr., 1986-90; chief plans and programs br. USAF Materials Lab., Wright AFB, Ohio, 1989-90; guest lectr. U. Dayton, 1970, 95, Cath. U., 1973, U. Mich., 1975. Contbr. articles profl. jours. Mem. Kettering (Ohio) Civic Band, 1965—, Affiliate Socs. Council of Dayton, 1972-81. Served to 1st lt. USAF, 1963-66. Named Fed. Profl. Employee of Yr. Dayton, 1972, One of Ten Outstanding Engrs., Engrs. Week, 1975, Air Force Meritorious Civilian Svc. award, 1994. Fellow Soc. for Advancement Materials and Process Engrs. (Best Paper award 1973, nat. sec. 1975-76, nat. membership chmn. 1977-79, nat. v.p. 1979-81, nat. pres. 1981-82, chmn. long-range planning com. 1983-87); mem. AIAA (materials tech. com.), ASTM (rec. sec. 1972-75, chmn. com. on erosion and wear 1976-79, chmn. liaison subcom. 1979-83, award of merit 1981), Am. Chem. Soc. Affiliate Socs. Coun. Dayton (chmn. 1978-79). Republican. Lutheran. Home: 1500 Wardmier Dr Dayton OH 45459-3354 Office: WL Materials Directorate Wright-Patterson AFB MLB Wright-Patterson AFB Dayton OH 45433

SCHMITT, GEORGE JOSEPH, chemist; b. Farmingdale, N.Y., June 21, 1928; s. Joseph Frank and Carolyn (Henych) S.; m. E. Christine Schneider, Feb. 10, 1952; children: Paul, Carol, Mark, David. BS in Chemistry, Bklyn. Poly. Inst., 1950; PhD in Chemistry, SUNY, Syracuse, 1960. Chemist Am. Cyanamid, Bound Brook, N.J., 1953-57; chemist Allied Chem., Morristown, N.J., 1960-61, group leader, 1961-63, assoc. dir. rsch., 1963-69, mgr. rsch., 1969-80, dir. Polymer Lab., 1980-89, dir. Structural Polymers Lab., 1989-94; ret.; adv. bd. N.J. R & D Coun., 1982-85. 1st lt. U.S. Army, 1950-53. Named NSF fellow, 1957-60. Mem. Am. Chem. Soc., Soc. for Advancement Materials and Processing Engring., Sigma Xi. Achievements include research on polymer synthesis, structure/property relationships, bipolar membranes, advanced composites, bioresorbable polymers, electrically conducting polymers composite armor.

SCHMITT, HARRISON HAGAN, former senator, geologist, astronaut, consultant; b. Santa Rita, N.Mex., July 3, 1935; s. Harrison A. and Ethel (Hagan) S. BA, Calif. Inst. Tech., 1957; postgrad. (Fulbright fellow), U. Oslo, 1957-58; PhD (NSF fellow), Harvard U., 1964; hon. degree, Franklin and Marshall Coll., 1977, Colo Sch. Mines, 1971, Rensselaer Poly Inst., 1973. Geologist U.S Geol. Survey, 1964-65; astronaut NASA, 1965; lunar module pilot Apollo 17, 1972, spl. asst. to adminstr., 1974; asst. adminstr. Office Energy Programs, 1974; mem. U.S. Senate, N.Mex., 1977-83; cons., 1983—; mem. Pres.' Fgn. Intelligence Adv. Bd., 1984-85, Army Sci. Bd., 1985-90, Pres.' Ethics Commn., 1989; chmn. tech. adv. bd. Army Rsch. Lab.; adj. prof. U. Wis., 1995—; chair, pres. Annapolis Ctr., 1994—; bd. dirs. Sunwest Fin. Svcs., Orbital Scis. Corp. Trustee The Lovelace Insts. Recipient MSC Superior Achievement award, 1970, Disting. Svc. medal NASA, 1973, Lovelace award NASA, 1989, Gilbert award GSA, 1989. Mem. AAAS, Geol. Soc. Am., Am. Geophys. Union, Am. Assn. Petroleum Geologists. Home: PO Box 14338 Albuquerque NM 87191-4338

SCHMITT, JOHANNA MARIE, plant population biologist, educator; b. Phila., Mar. 12, 1953; d. William Francis and Laura Belle (Wear) S.; m. Darrell Marion West, Aug. 6, 1983. BA, Swarthmore (Pa.) Coll., 1974; PhD, Stanford U., 1981. Postdoctoral rsch. assoc. Duke U., Durham, N.C., 1981-82; asst. prof. Brown U., Providence, 1982-87, assoc. prof. biology, 1987-94, prof., 1994—; mem. adv. panel NSF on population biology, 1989; mem. R.I. Task Force, New Eng. Plant Conservation program, 1991—. Assoc. editor Evolution, 1990-92; contbr. articles to profl. jours. including Evolution, Ecology, Am. Naturalist, Jour. Ecology, Nature. Bd. dirs. Sojourner House, Providence, 1989-92. NSF grad. fellow, 1974, mid. career fellow, 1992-93; rsch. grantee, 1984—; recipient faculty award for women, 1991—. Mem. Soc. for Study of Evolution (coun. mem. 1990-92, exec. v.p. 1994—), Bot. Soc. Am., Ecol. Soc. Am., Am. Soc. Naturalists. Achievements include research on ecological genetics of natural plant populations: density-dependent phenomena, gene flow and population structure, inbreeding depression, the evolution of sex, maternal effects, seed ecology, natural selection, evolution of plasticity, adaptive significance of phytochrome, ecological risks of transgenic plants. Office: Brown Univ Dept Ecology & Evolutionary Sci Providence RI 02912

SCHMITT, KARL MICHAEL, retired political scientist; b. Louisville, Ky., July 22, 1922; s. Edward Peter and Mary Ann (Iula) S.; m. Grace Bernadette Leary, June 18, 1949; children: Karl, Edward, Barbara, William, Michael. B.A., Cath. U. Am., 1947, M.A., 1949; Ph.D., U. Pa., 1954. Teaching asst. U. Pa., 1948-50; instr. history Niagara U., 1950-54, asst. prof., 1954-55; research analyst U.S. Dept. State, 1955-58; asst. prof. dept. govt. U. Tex., 1958-63, assoc. prof., 1963-66, prof., 1966-91, prof. emeritus, 1991—, chmn., 1975-80; vis. prof. U. Calif., Los Angeles, summer 1959, Nat. War Coll., 1970-71; vis. sr. fellow U. Manchester, Eng., 1988-89; cons. Dept. of State, 1962-70. Author: Communism in Mexico; A Study in Political Frustration, 1965, Mexico and the United States, 1821-1973: Conflict and Coexistence, 1974, others. Contbr. articles to profl. jours. Served with U.S. Army, 1943-45. Decorated Purple Heart. Mem. Tex. Cath. Hist. Assn. (pres. 1976-77). Roman Catholic. Home: 2603 Pinewood Ter Austin TX 78757-2136 Office: Dept Govt U Tex Austin TX 78712

SCHMITT, NEIL MARTIN, biomedical engineer, electrical engineering educator; b. Pekin, Ill., Oct. 25, 1940; married; 2 children. BSEE, U. Ark., 1963, MSEE, 1964; PhD in Electrical Engring., So. Meth. U., 1969. Systems engr. IBM Corp., 1966-67; engr. Tex. Instruments, Inc., 1967-70; assoc. prof. U. Ark., Fayetteville, 1970-80, prof. elec. engring., 1980—, dean of engring., 1983—. Grantee NSF, 1971-72. Mem. IEEE, NSPE (v.p. 1989-90), Biomed. Engring. Soc. Achievements include research in health care delivery systems, early detection of heart disease. Office: U Ark Engring Rsch Ctr Fayetteville AR 72701

SCHMITT, RICHARD, philosopher, educator; b. Frankfurt/Main, Ger., May 5, 1927; came to U.S., 1946, naturalized, 1952; s. Julius and Elisabeth Dorothea S. B.A., U. Chgo., 1949, M.A., 1952; Ph.D., Yale U., 1956. Instr. philosophy Yale U., 1956-58; mem. faculty Brown U., 1958—, prof. philosophy, 1968—; vis. prof. Stanford U., 1966-67, U. Calif., Santa Barbara, 1971-72, Miles Coll., summer 1964, U. Mass., Boston, 1974. Author: Martin Heidegger and Engels: A Critical Reconstruction, 1987, Beyond Separateness, 1995; editor: (with T.E. Moody) Alienation and Social Criticism, 1993. Alfred Hodder fellow, 1963-64; Guggenheim fellow, 1965-66. Mem. Am. Philos. Assn. Office: Brown U Dept Philosophy 79 Waterman St Providence RI 02912-9079

SCHMITT, ROBERT CHRISTIAN, architect, interior designer; b. Las Vegas, N.Mex., Aug. 21, 1946; s. Robert Mikelsen and Alice Gertrude (Hastings) S.; m. Marilyn Clewley Merchant, Sept. 6, 1969; children—Sabina Hastings, Cullen Carrier. B.Arch., U. Ariz., 1970; M.Arch., Harvard U., 1972. Registered architect, Mass., S.C., Fla., N.C. Designer S.B.A. & A. Architects, Boston, 1969-70, E. Flansburgh & Assocs., Cambridge, Mass., 1970-73; design mgr. Sea Pines Co., Hilton Head, S.C., 1973-75, Kiawah Island Co., Charleston, 1977-79; project architect DRA Architects, Wellesley, Mass., 1975-77; prin., owner Glick, Schmitt & Assocs., Charleston, S.C., 1979—. Recipient Aurora Design award Southeastern Builders Conf., 1983, 84. Mem. AIA (pres. 1985—), Constrn. Specifications Inst., Am. Soc. Interior Designers. Republican. Club: James Island Yacht. Avocations: sailing; tennis; photography. Home: 678 Deepwood Dr Charleston SC 29412-9104 Office: Glick Schmitt & Assocs 247 Meeting St Ste 100 Charleston SC 29401-1609

SCHMITT, ROLAND WALTER, retired academic administrator; b. Seguin, Tex., July 24, 1923; s. Walter L. and Myrtle F. (Caldwell) S.; m. Claire Freeman Kunz, Sept. 19, 1957; children: Lorenz Allen, Brian Walter, Alice Elizabeth, Henry Caldwell. BA in Math, U. Tex., 1947, BS in Physics, 1947, MA in Physics, 1948; PhD, Rice U., 1951; DSc (hon.), Worcester Poly. Inst., 1985, U. Pa., 1985; DCL (hon.), Union Coll., 1985; DL (hon.), Lehigh U., 1986; DSc (hon.), U. S.C., 1988, Universite De Technologie De Compiegne, 1991; DL (hon.), Clarkson U., St. Rose, 1992, Russell Sage, 1993. With GE, 1951-88; R & D mgr. phys. sci. and engring. GE, Schenectady, 1967-74; mgr. energy sci. and engring R & D GE 1974-78, v.p. corp. R & D, 1978-82, sr. v.p. corp. R & D, 1982-86, sr. v.p. sci. and tech., 1986-88, ret. 1988; pres. Rensselaer Poly. Inst., Troy, N.Y., 1988-93; bd. dirs. Gen. Signal Corp., Reveo, Inc.; mem. Tech. adv. bd. Chrysler Corp., 1990-93; chmn. sci. adv. bd. Motorola; past pres. Indsl. Rsch. Inst., 1988; mem. energy rsch. adv. bd. U.S. dept. Energy, 1977-83; chmn. CORETECH, 1988-93; mem. Com. on Japan NRC, 1988-90, Comml. Devel. Ind. Adv. Group, NASA, 1988-90; exec. com. Coun. on Competitiveness, 1988-93; chmn. NRC Panel on Export Controls, 1989-91; mem. Dept. Commerce Adv. Commn. on Patent Law Reform, 1990-92; mem. adv. bd. Oak Ridge Nat. Lab., 1993. Trustee N.E. Savs. Bank, 1978-84; bd. advisors Union Coll., Schenectady, 1981-84, Argonne Univs. Assn., 1979-82, RPI, 1982-88; bd. govs. Albany Med. Ctr. Hosp., 1979-82, 88-90; bd. dirs. Sunnyview Hosp. and Rehab. Ctr., 1978-86, Coun. on Superconductivity for Am. Competitiveness, 1988-89; mem. exec. com. N.Y. State Ctr. for Hazardous Waste Mgmt., 1988-89; chmn. Office of Tech. Assessment adv. panel on industry and environment; mem. Nat. Commn. Ill. Inst. Tech., 1993-94. With USAAF, 1943-46. Recipient RPI Community Svc. award, 1982, award for disting. contbns. Stony Brook Found., 1985, Rice U. Disting. Alumni award, 1985, IRI Medalist award, 1989, Royal Swedish Acad. of Engring. Sci., 1990; named Fgn. Assn. of Engring. Acad. of Japan. Fellow AAAS, IEEE (Centennial medal 1984, Engring. Leadership award 1989, Founders medal 1992, Hoover medal

1993), Am. Phys. Soc. (Pake award 1993), Am. Acad. Arts and Scis.; mem. NAE (coun., com. tech., mgmt. and capital in smaller cos.), Coun. Sci. Soc. (pres. exec. bd. 1993—), N.Y. Acad. Scis. (pres. coun. 1993—), Nat. Sci. Bd. (chmn. 1982), Dirs. Indsl. Rsch., Rensselaer Alumni Assn. (Disting. alumni award 1993). Office: Ste 459 400 Clifton Corporate Pkwy Clifton Park NY 12065

SCHMITT, WILLIAM HOWARD, cosmetics company executive; b. Sterling, Ill., Oct. 27, 1936; s. Alfred William and Katherine Henrietta (Skow) S.; m. Antionette Marie Payne, Mar. 22, 1960; children: Hilary Ann, Andrea Kay, Joseph Michael. BS in Pharmacy, Drake U., 1958. Rsch. assoc. G.D. Searle, Skokie, Ill., 1963-66; assoc. dir. rsch. Alberto Culver, Melrose Park, Ill., 1966-71; dir. product devel. Chesebrough-Pond's USA, Trumbull, Conn., 1971-74; dir. internat. Chesebrough-Pond's Inc., Trumbull, Conn., 1974-83, group dir. R&D, 1983-85, v.p. R&D, 1985-89, sr. v.p. R&D, 1989—; chmn. sci. adv. commn. Cosmetics, Toiletry and Fragrance Assn., Washington, 1994—. Author: (with others) An Overview of World-Wide Regulatory Programs, 1984; editor: Cosmetics and Toiletries Industry, 1992; patentee in toiletry and cosmetics field. Pres. Suburban Sportsman's Club. Lt. USAF, 1959-62. Mem. Soc. Cosmetic Chemists, Am. Assn. for Dental Rsch. Avocations: boating, hunting, fishing. Office: Chesebrough-Ponds Inc 40 Merritt Blvd Trumbull CT 06611-5413

SCHMITT, WOLFGANG RUDOLPH, consumer products executive; b. Koblenz, Germany, Mar. 12, 1944; s. Josef H. and M.H. (Baldus) S.; m. Toni A. Yoder, June 30, 1974; children: Christopher, Corey, Clayton. BA, Otterbein Coll., 1966; AMP, Harvard U. Bus. Sch., 1986. With Rubbermaid Inc., Wooster, Ohio, 1966—, pres., gen. mgr. housewares products div., 1984-91, exec. v.p., bd. dirs., 1987-91, pres., chief operating officer, 1991—; chmn., CEO, 1993—; bd. dirs. Parker Hannifin Corp., Kimberly-Clark Corp. Pres. bd. dirs. Wooster United Way, 1987; bd. dirs. Otterbein Coll., 1992—. Republican. Avocations: archaeology, tennis, sailing. Office: Rubbermaid Inc 1147 Akron Rd Wooster OH 44691-6000

SCHMITTER, CHARLES HARRY, electronics manufacturing company executive, lawyer; b. Paterson, N.J., Feb. 4, 1928; s. Charles and Jennie (Schoe) S.; m. Margaret Ann Roose, Oct. 24, 1964 (dec. Dec. 1989). A.B. magna cum laude, Rutgers U., 1948; J.D., Columbia, 1953. Bar: N.Y. bar 1956, Mich. bar 1960. Asso. atty. firm Cravath, Swaine & Moore, N.Y.C., 1955-59; asst. sec. Ford Motor Co., 1959-64; corp. sec. Sperry Rand Corp. (now Unisys Corp.), N.Y.C., 1964-87, ret., 1987. Served with AUS, 1953-55. Mem. Am. Bar Assn., Am. Soc. Corp. Secretaries, Phi Alpha Delta, Theta Chi. Club: Rockefeller Center Luncheon (N.Y.C.). Home: 420 E 51st St New York NY 10022-8014

SCHMITZ, CHARLES EDISON, evangelist; b. Mendota, Ill., July 18, 1919; s. Charles Francis Schmitz and Lucetta Margaret (Foulk) Schmitz Kaufmann; m. Eunice Magdalene Ewy, June 1, 1942; children: Charles Elwood, Jon Lee. Student, Wheaton Coll., 1936-37, 38, 39; BA, Wartburg Coll., Waverly, Iowa, 1940; BD, Wartburg Theol. Sem., Dubuque, Iowa, 1942, MDiv, 1977. Ordained to ministry Luth. Ch., 1942. Founding pastor Ascension Luth. Ch., L.A., 1942-48, Am. Evang. Luth. Ch., Phoenix, 1948-65; dir. intermountain missions, founding pastor 14 Evang. Luth. Parishes, Calif., Ariz., N.Mex., 1948-65; evangelist Am. Luth. Ch., Mpls., 1965-73; sr. pastor Peace Luth. Ch., Palm Bay, Fla., 1973-89; pastor-at-large Am. Evang. Luth. Ch., Phoenix, 1989—; charter mem. Navajo Luth. Mission, Rock Point, Ariz., 1960—; pastoral advisor Ariz. Luth. Outdoor Ministry Assn., Prescott, 1958-65, 89—; Kogudus Internat. Retreat master and chaplain, Fla., Berlin and Marbach, Germany, 1990; mem. transition team Fla. Synod Evang. Luth. Ch. Am., 1985-89. Author: Evangelism for the Seventies, 1970; co-author: ABC's of Life, 1968; assoc. editor Good News mag., 1965-71. Founder, chmn. Ariz. Ch. Conf. on Adult and Youth Problems, 1956-65; vice chmn. synod worship & ch. music com. Am. Luth. Ch., Mpls., 1960-66; chmn. Space Coast Luth. Retirement Ctr., Palm Bay, Fla., 1985-89; chaplain Ariz. chpt. Luth. Brotherhood, 1991—. Named Citizen of Yr., Palm Bay C. of C., 1979. Mem. Nat. Assn. Evangelicals, German Am. Nat. Congress (nat. chaplain), Lions (officer Phoenix and Palm Bay clubs 1952—), Ariz. Dist. 21A chaplain 1994—), Kiwanis (bd. dirs. L.A. chpt. 1942-48). Republican. Home: 12444 W Toreador Dr Sun City West AZ 85375-1926 *The truly modern person today who, like the scribes of old, would aspire to fulfillment in leadership would do well to remember Jesus' words: "Therefore every scribe who has been trained for the Kingdom of Heaven is like the master of a household who brings out of his treasure what is new and what is old." (Matt. 13:52).*

SCHMITZ, DENNIS MATHEW, English language educator; b. Dubuque, Iowa, Aug. 11, 1937; s. Anthony Peter and Roselyn S.; m. Loretta D'Agostino, Aug. 20, 1960; children—Anne, Sara, Martha, Paul, Matthew. B.A., Loras Coll., 1959; M.A., U. Chgo., 1961. Instr. English Ill. Inst. Tech., Chgo., 1961-62, U. Wis., Milw., 1962-66; asst. prof. Calif. State U., Sacramento, 1966-69, assoc. prof., 1969-74, prof., 1974—; poet-in-residence, 1966—. Author: We Weep for Our Strangeness, 1969, Double Exposures, 1971, Goodwill, Inc., 1976, String, 1980, Singing, 1985, Eden, 1989, About Night: Selected and New Poems, 1993. Recipient Discovery award Poetry Center, N.Y.C., 1968; winner First Book Competition Follett Pub. Co., 1969; di Castagnola award Poetry Soc. Am., 1986; Shelley Meml. award Poetry Soc. Am., 1987; NEA fellow, 1976-77, 85-86, 92-93, Guggenheim fellow, 1978-79. Mem. PEN, Assoc. Writing Programs. Roman Catholic. Office: Calif State U Dept English 6000 J St Sacramento CA 95819-2605

SCHMITZ, DOLORES JEAN, secondary education educator; b. River Falls, Wis., Dec. 27, 1931; d. Otto and Helen Olive (Webster) Kreuziger; m. Karl Matthias Schmitz Jr., Aug. 18, 1956; children: Victoria Jane, Karl III. BS, U. Wis., River Falls, 1953; MS, Nat. Coll. Edn., 1982; postgrad., U. Minn., Mankato, 1969, U. Melbourne, Australia, 1989, U. Wis., Milw., 1989, Carroll Coll., 1990, Cardinal Stritch, 1990. Cert. tchr., Wis. Tchr. Manitowoc (Wis.) Pub. Schs., 1953-56, West Allis (Wis.) Pub. Schs., 1956-59, Lowell Sch., Milw., 1960-63, Victory Sch., Milw., 1964; tchr. Palmer Sch., Milw., 1966-84, 86-94, unit leader, 1984-86; ret., 1994; co-organizer Headstart Tchg. Staff Assn., Milw., 1968; insvc. organizer Headstart and Early Childhood, Milw., 1969-92; pilot tchr. for Whole Lang., Hi-Scope and Math. Their Way, 1988-93; bd. dirs. Curriculum Devel. Ctr. of Milw. Edn. Ctr., 1993-94. Author: (curriculum) Writing to Read, 1987, Cooperation and Young Children (ERIC award 1982), Kindergarten Curriculum, 1953. Supporter Milw. Art Mus., Milw. Pub. Mus., Milw. County Zoo, Whitefish Bay Pub. Libr., Earthwatch, Riveredge Nature Ctr.; vol. fgn. visitor program Milw. Internat. Inst., 1966-94, holiday folk fair, 1976-94, Earthwatch, 1989; lobbyist Milw. Pub. Sch. Bd. and State of Wis., 1986-93; coord. cmty. vols., 1990-94. Grantee Greater Milw. Ednl. Trust, 1989. Mem. NEA (life), ASCD, Milw. Kindergarten Assn. (rec. sec. 1986-93), Nat. Assn. for Edn. of Young Children, Tchrs. Applying Whole Lang., Wis. Early Childhood Assn., Milw. Tchrs. Ednl. Assn. (co-chmn. com. early childhood 1984-86), Assn. for Childhood Edn. Internat. (charter pres. Manitowoc chpt. 1955-56), Milw. Educating Computer Assn., Alpha Psi Omega. Roman Catholic. Avocations: bicycling, nature. Home: # 9 312 8th Ave N Tierra Verde FL 33715-1801

SCHMITZ, JOHN ALBERT, veterinary pathologist; b. Silverton, Oreg., Oct. 21, 1940; s. John J. and Ann G. (Wavra) S.; m. M. Charlene Busch, Aug. 7, 1971. D.V.M., Colo. State U., 1964; Ph.D., U. Mo., 1971. Asst. prof. vet. sci. dept. U. Nebr., Lincoln, 1971-72, prof., head vet., biomed. sci. dept. 1984—; assoc. prof., asst. dean Coll. Vet. Medicine, Oreg. State U., Corvallis, 1972-78, prof., dir. Vet. Diagnostic Lab., 1978-84. Contbr. articles to profl. jours. Mem. AVMA (rsch. coun.), Am. Assn. Vet. Lab. Diagnosticians (bd. govs.), Nebr. Vet. Med. Assn. (bd. dirs.), Am. Coll. Vet. Pathologists, Internat. Acad. Pathologists. Office: U Nebr Dept Vet & Biomed Sci Fair St At E Campus Loop Lincoln NE 68583-0905

SCHMITZ, ROBERT ALLEN, publishing executive, investor; b. Chgo., Jan. 19, 1941; s. John and Lee (Zeal) S.; m. Jenny Ann Quest, Aug. 23, 1969 (div.); children: Alexander, Nicholas, Lara, Maximilian. BA with distinction, U. Mich., 1963; MBA, MIT, 1965. Asst. to pres. Lima (Peru) Light and Power Co., 1965-67; acquisition analyst W.R. Grace Co., N.Y.C., 1967-69; asst. to chmn. N.W. Industries, N.Y.C., 1969-70; prin. McKinsey & Co., Inc., N.Y.C., 1970-82; v.p. books Dow Jones & Co., N.Y.C., 1982-88; chmn.,

pres., founder Quest Capital Ltd., 1989—; investment cons. Soros Fund Mgmt., 1990-92; mgn. dir., sr. ptnr. Trust Co. of the West, 1993—; mem. adv. bd. Coll. Commerce De Paul U., Chgo., 1985—; bd. dirs. Nilfisk PLC, Copenhagen, Adams Rite Sabre, Inc., Glendale, Calif., Superior Fireplace Co., Fullerton, Calif., Houston Goods Co., Chgo., Archibald Candy Co., Chgo., US Media Group, Inc., Cyrstal City, Mo., Ctrl. Valley Publ., Mercaed, Hobby Products Co., Inc., Penrose, Colo., Ind. Media Group, Chippewa Falls, Wis. Pres. Cultural Arts Ctr. Found., Homewood, Ill. Mem. Assn. Am. Pubs. (chmn. higher edn. div. 1989). Office: Trust Co of the West 200 Park Ave Ste 2200 New York NY 10166-0001

SCHMITZ, ROGER ANTHONY, chemical engineering educator, academic administrator; b. Carlyle, Ill., Oct. 22, 1934; s. Alfred Bernard and Wilma Afra (Aarns) S.; m. Ruth Mary Kuhl, Aug. 31, 1957; children—Jan, Joy, Joni. B.S. in Chem. Engring., U. Ill., 1959; Ph.D. in Chem. Engring., U. Minn., 1962. Prof. chem. engring. U. Ill., Urbana, 1962-79; Keating-Crawford prof. chem. engring. U. Notre Dame, Ind., 1979—; chmn. dept. chem. engring., 1979-81, dean engring., 1981-87; v.p., assoc. provost U. Notre Dame, 1987—; cons. Amoco Chems., Naperville, Ill., 1967-79; vis. prof. Calif. Inst. Tech., Los Angeles, 1968-69, U. So. Calif., Los Angeles, 1968-69. Contbr. articles to profl. jours. Served with U.S. Army, 1953-55. Guggenheim Found. fellow, 1968. Mem. Nat. Acad. Engring., Am. Inst. Chem. Engrs. (A.P. Colburn award 1970, R.H. Wilhelm award 1981), Am. Chem. Soc., Am. Soc. for Engring. Edn. (George Westinghouse award 1977). Roman Catholic. Home: 16865 Londonberry Ln South Bend IN 46635-1444 Office: U Notre Dame 202 Adminstrn Notre Dame IN 46556

SCHMITZ, SHIRLEY GERTRUDE, marketing and sales executive; b. Brackenridge, Pa., Dec. 19, 1927; d. Wienand Gerard and Florence Marie (Grimm) S. BA, Ariz. State U., 1949. Tchr., guidance counselor Mesa High Sch., Ariz., 1949-51; area mgr. Field Enterprises Ednl. Corp., Phoenix, 1951-52, dist. mgr., 1952, regional mgr., 1953-55, br. mgr., Montreal, Que., Can. 1955-61, nat. supr., Chgo., 1961-63, asst. sales mgr., 1963-65, nat. sales mgr., 1965-70; v.p., gen. sales mgr. F.E. Compton Co. div. Ency. Brit., Chgo., 1970-71, exec. v.p., dir. sales, 1971-73; pres. CHB Port-A-Book Store, Inc., 1973-76; gen. mgr. Bobbs-Merrill Co., Inc., publs., 1976-82; v.p. sales U.S. Telephone Communications of Midwest, Inc., Chgo., 1982-83; exec. v.p. sales and market devel. Entertainment Publs., Corp., Birmingham, Mich., 1983-89, sr. v.p. mktg. and sales, Troy, Mich., 1989-92; prin. S.G. Schmitz and Assocs., Chgo., 1992—; bd. dirs. Ariz. Tech. Incubator; bd. advisors Ctr. Advancement of Small Bus., Ariz. State U. Sch. Bus; bd. dirs. Spectral, Inc., Colourtech, Inc. Recipient Twin award Nat. Bd. YWCA, 1987. Recipient Honors award Beta Gamma Sigma, 1995, Disting. Achievement award Ariz. State U., 1995. Mem. USGA (assoc.), Internat. Platform Assn., Am. Mgmt. Assn., Nat. Bus. Incubation Assn., Nat. Geographic Soc., Nat. Space Soc., World Future Soc., Ariz. State U. Alumni Assn. Republican. Roman Catholic. Home: 93 Miller Rd Hawthorn Woods IL 60047-1395

SCHMOKE, KURT L., mayor; b. Balt., Dec. 1, 1949; m. Patricia Schmoke; children: Katherine, Gregory. BA, Yale U., 1971; JD, Harvard U., 1976. Former assoc. Piper & Marbury; former pvt. practice; asst. U.S. atty Balt.; state's atty. Maryland, 1982-87; mayor Baltimore, 1987—; apptd. mem. White House Domestice Policy Staff, 1977-78; former mem. Gov.'s Commn. on Prison Overcrowding; former mem. Md. Criminal Justice Coord. Coun. & Task Force to Reform Insanity Def.; founder Balt. Community Devel. Financing Corp., 1988—. Rhodes Scholar Yale U. Office: Office of the Mayor 100 Holliday St Baltimore MD 21202-3417*

SCHMOLKA, LEO LOUIS, law educator; b. Paris, Apr. 25, 1939; came to U.S., 1944; s. Francis and Irene S.; m. Lucille J. Schoenbaum, July 29, 1965; children—Andrew, Gregory. A.B., Dartmouth Coll., 1960; LL.B., Harvard U., 1963; LL.M., NYU, 1971. Bar: N.Y. 1964. Assoc. Weil, Gotshal and Manges, N.Y.C., 1964-71; ptnr. Weil, Gotshal and Manges, 1971-81, of counsel, 1981—; adj. asst. prof. law NYU Law Sch., 1971-75; adj. assoc. prof. law NYU Law Sch., 1975-76, adj. prof., 1977-80, assoc. prof., 1981-84, prof., 1985—, mem. faculty, dir. IRS/NYU continuing profl. edn. program, 1987—; vis. adj. prof. law U. Miami Sch. Law, Fla., 1977, 80; vis. lectr. continuing legal edn. various univs. and tax insts., 1973—; cons. Am. Law Inst., 1979-86, U. Miami Estate Planning Inst., 1976-80; cons. U.S. Treasury Dept. Office Tax Policy, Washington, 1994—. Contbr. articles to legal jours. Fellow Am. Coll. Trust and Estate Counsel; mem. ABA, N.Y. State Bar Assn. (chmn. com. on income taxation estates and trusts 1973-75, estate and gift tax 1976-77, mem. exec. com. tax sect. 1978), Internat. Acad. Estate and Trust Law (academician). Office: NYU Law Sch 40 Washington Sq S Rm 440 New York NY 10012-1099

SCHMOLL, HARRY F., JR., lawyer, educator; b. Somers Point, N.J., Jan. 20, 1939; s. Harry F. Sr and Margaret E. Schmoll; m. Rita L. Miescier, Aug. 29, 1977. BS, Rider Coll., 1960; JD, Temple U., 1967. Bar: Pa., D.C. 1969, N.J. 1975. With claims dept. Social Security Adminstrn., Phila., 1960-67; staff atty. Pa. State U., State College, 1968-69; regional dir. Pa. Crime Commn., State College, 1969-70; campaign aide U.S. Senator Hugh Scott, Harrisburg, Pa., 1970; pvt. practice law, State College, 1970-74, Manahawkin, N.J., 1975—; instr. criminal justice Pa. State U., University Park, 1969-74, assoc. prof. criminal justice, bus. law Burlington County Coll., Pemberton, N.J., 1974-92, prof., 1992—, pres. elect edn. assn., 1992-93, pres. edn. assn., 1993-94; judge mcpl. ct., Stafford Twp., 1982-85. Gen. counsel German Heritage Coun. of N.J., Inc.; active Barnegat Twp. Rent Control Bd., 1991, Barnegat Twp. Zoning Bd., 1994. Author: New Jersey Criminal Law Workbook, 1976, 2nd edit. 1979. Mem. Stafford Twp. Com., 1979-81, dep. mayor, 1979. Trustee Pheasant Run Homeowners Assn., Barnegat, N.J., 1992-95. Mem. Pa. Bar Assn., N.J. Bar Assn., Ocean County Bar Assn., German-Am. Club of So. Ocean County (past pres.). Office: 6 Citrus Ct Barnegat NJ 08005-3126

SCHMULTS, EDWARD CHARLES, lawyer; b. Paterson, N.J., Feb. 6, 1931; s. Edward M. and Mildred (Moore) S.; m. Diane E. Beers, Apr. 23, 1960; children: Alison C., Edward M., Robert C. B.S., Yale U., 1953; J.D., Harvard U., 1958. Bar: N.Y. 1959, D.C. 1974. Assoc. White & Case, N.Y.C., 1958-65; ptnr. White & Case, 1965-73, 77-81; gen. counsel Treasury Dept., Washington, 1973-74; undersec. Treasury Dept., 1974-75; dep. counsel to Pres. U.S., 1975-76; dep. atty. gen. of U.S. Dept. Justice, Washington, 1981-84; sr. v.p. external rels., gen. counsel GTE Corp., Stamford, Conn., 1984-94; lectr. securities laws. Bd. dirs. GP Fin. Corp., Germany Fund, Future Germany Fund; trustee Edna McConnell Clark Found.; chmn. bd. trustees Refugee Policy Group. With USMC, 1953-55. Mem. A.B.A., N.Y. State, Fed. bar assns., Assn. Bar City N.Y., Adminstrv. Conf. U.S. (council 1977-84). Clubs: Sakonnet Golf (Little Compton, R.I.); Metropolitan (Washington).

SCHMUTTENMAER, CHARLES A., chemistry educator. Prof. chemistry dept. Yale U., New Haven, Conn. Recipient Chemistry grant Camille & Henry Dreyfus Found., 1994. Office: Yale U Dept Chemistry New Haven CT 06520*

SCHMUTZ, ARTHUR WALTER, lawyer; b. Akron, Ohio, Aug. 2, 1921; s. Paul Edward and Barbara (Williams) S.; m. Elizabeth Moore, June 17, 1951; children: David H., Stuart R., Jonathan M., Anne Marie. AB summa cum laude, Johns Hopkins U., 1949; LLB cum laude, Harvard U., 1952. Bar: Calif. 1953. Assoc. Gibson, Dunn & Crutcher, L.A., 1952-59, ptnr., 1960-69, sr. ptnr., 1969-86, adv. ptnr., 1987-90, adv. counsel, 1991—; bd. dirs. H.F. Ahmanson & Co. Home Savs. Am., L.A., Ducommun Inc., L.A. Trustee Orthopaedic Hosp., L.A. With USAAF, 1942-45. Decorated Bronze Star. Fellow Am. Bar Found.; mem. Calif. Club, La Jolla Beach and Tennis Club, Lakeside Golf Club, Phi Beta Kappa. Office: 333 S Grand Ave Los Angeles CA 90071-1504

SCHMUTZ, CHARLES REID, university foundation executive; b. Youngstown, Ohio, Jan. 26, 1942; s. Charles Edward and Alice Mae (Bliss) S.; m. Judith Rhodes Seiple, June 19, 1965; children: Charles Reid Jr., Andrew Edward, Jill Caroline. AB in Econs., Brown U., 1964. Lab. technician The Standard Slag Co., Youngstown, 1964-65; direct salesman The Standard Slag Co., Cleve., 1965-69; mktg. and prodn. scheduler The Standard Slag Co., Youngstown, 1969-73, mktg. and indsl. engr., 1973-85, gen. mgr. v.p. ops., 1985-89; pres. Youngstown State U. Found., 1989—; bd. dirs. StanCorp., Youngstown. Bd. dirs. Youngstown Playhouse, Jr. Achievement Mahoning

Valley. Named to Hall of Fame, Ohio Aggregates Assn., 1990. Mem. Rotary. Methodist. Avocations: golf, tennis.

SCHMUTZ, JOHN F., chemical company executive, corporate lawyer. BS, Cornell U.; JD, Georgetown U. Bar: Del. 1958. Now gen. counsel, sr. v.p. E.I. du Pont de Nemours & Co., Wilmington, Del. Office: E I du Pont de Nemours & Co 1007 N Market St Wilmington DE 19898

SCHMUTZHART, BERTHOLD JOSEF, sculptor, educator, art and education consultant; b. Salzburg, Austria, Aug. 17, 1928; came to U.S., 1958, naturalized, 1963; s. Berthold Josef and Anna (Valaschek) S. Student, Acad. for Applied Art, Vienna, Austria, 1956. Cert. fed. tchr., Austria. Prof. Wekschulheim Felbertal, Salzburg, 1951-58; sculptor Washington, 1959-60; tchr. Longfellow Sch., Bethesda, Md., 1960-63; prof., chmn. dept. sculpture Corcoran Sch. Art, Washington, 1963-94, prof. emeritus, 1994—; lectr. Smithsonian Instn., Washington, 1968—. One-man shows include Fredericksburg Gallery Fine Art, Va., 1967-73, Franz Bader Gallery, Washington, 1978, 81, 83, 86, 88; group shows include Nat. Collection Fine Arts, Washington, 1961-70, High Mus. Art, Atlanta, 1965, Ark. Art Ctr., Little Rock, 1966, Birmingham Mus. Art, Ala., 1967, Hirschhorn Mus. and Sculpture Garden, Washington, 1981, Nat. Gallery Modern Art, New Delhi, 1990; represented in permanent collections Hirschhorn Collection; designer fountain, Gallery of Modern Art, Fredericksburg, 1967; author: The Handmade Furniture Book, 1981; contbr. articles to profl. jours. Fine arts panelist D.C. Commn. for Arts, 1973-79; chmn. bd. Market Five Gallery, Washington, 1978-82; bd. dirs. Franz Bader Gallery, Washington, 1981-86; trustee Arts for the Aging, Inc., Washington, 1990—. Recipient 1st prize Washington Religious Arts Council, 1960, for sculpture, Little Rock, 1966, Louisville, 1968, Silver medal Audubon Soc., Washington, 1971. Mem. Guild for Religious Architects, Artists Equity Assn. (pres. D.C. chpt. 1973-75), AAUP, Am. Austrian Soc. (pres. 1968-70, exec. com.), Soaring Soc. Am. Home: 32 Layline Ln Fredericksburg VA 22406-4061

SCHNABEL, JOHN HENRY, music educator; b. Evansville, Ind., Mar. 15, 1915; s. Arthur John and Myrtle L. (Walters) S.; m. Emily H. Wepfer, June 28, 1938; children: Jack D. (dec.), Julia Belle Schnabel Klinke, Diane Schnabel Williams Clayton (dec.), Kathlee Mae Schnabel Wong. B.S., Evansville Coll., 1939; Mus.M., Northwestern U., 1947; Ed.D., Ind. U., 1954; B. A. in Fine Arts, So. Ill. U.-Edwardsville, 1975. Dir. bands Evansville Coll., 1937-39; supr. music Carlisle-Haddon Twp. schs., Carlisle, Ind., 1939-42; supr. music, dir. bands Jasper (Ind.) High Sch., 1942-49; assoc. prof. music, dir. bands Panhandle A. and M. Coll., Goodwell, Okla., 1949-52; prin. Stratford (Tex.) Ind. Sch., 1952-53; grad. asst. Ind. U., 1953-54; vis. prof. Miami U., Oxford, Ohio, 1954-55; dir. admissions Park Coll., Parkville, Mo., 1955-57; registrar, dir. admissions So. Ill. U., Edwardsville, 1957-67, mem. faculty, 1957-80, prof. edn., 1973-80, prof. emeritus, 1980—, head fine arts div., 1961-62, dir. teaching learning centers, 1972-75, coordinator computer based instrn. lab., 1977-80; cons. computer assisted instrn., 1980-90, mgmt. cons., 1980—; chmn. bd., chief exec. officer George G. Fetter Co., Louisville, 1970—. Author: An Evaluation of Extra-Class Activities, 1966, Ten Years of University Progres, 1967; others; contbr. workshops in oboe and watercolor. Oboist, mem. bd. dirs. Alton (Ill.) Civic Symphony, 1957-61; oboist other orchs., 1929—; adv. council Ednl. Resources Info. Center Ednl. Facilities, U. Wis., Madison, 1965-67; Bd. dirs. Alton Meml. Hosp., 1967—. Served with AUS, 1945. Mem. Assn. Collegiate Registrars (chmn. facilities com. 1965-67), Am. Assn. Collegiate Registrars and Admissions Officers, Am. Assn. Sch. Adminstrs., Council Ednl. Facilities Planning, Am. Assn. Higher Edn., Assn. Ednl. Data Systems, Assn. Devel. Computer Based Instrnl. Systems, Internat. Double Reed Soc. (patron), Phi Delta Kappa, Phi Mu Alpha, Kappa Kappa Psi. Methodist. Club: Rotary. Home and Office: 2305 Fairview Dr Alton IL 62002-5627

SCHNABEL, JULIAN, artist; b. 1951. B.F.A., U. Houston, 1972; postgrad., Whitney Mus. Ind. Study Program, N.Y.C., 1973-74. Exhibited one-man shows, Contemporary Art Mus., Houston, 1976, Galerie Dezember, Dusseldorf, West Germany, 1978, Mary Boone, N.Y.C., 1979, Daniel Weinberg Gallery, San Francisco, 1979, Bruno Bischofberger, Zurich, Switzerland, Young-Hoffman Gallery, Chgo., 1980, Mary Boone-Leo Castelli, N.Y.C., 1981, Stedelijk Mus. Amsterdam, Holland, 1982, Bruno Bischofberger, Zurich, Switzerland, 1982, Los Angeles County Mus. Art, 1982, U. Art Mus., Berkeley, Calif., 1982, The Tate Gallery, London, 1982, Mary Boone, N.Y.C., 1982, Bruno Bischofberger, Zurich, Switzerland, 1983, Leo Castelli, N.Y.C., 1983, Akron Art Mus., 1983, Leslie Waddington Gallery, London, 1983, Daniel Templon Gallery, Paris, 1983, Galerie Mario Diacono, Rome, 1983, Akira Ikeda Gallery, Tokyo, 1983, Donald Young Gallery, Chgo., 1983, Martine Hamilton Gallery, N.Y.C., Pace Gallery N.Y., 1984, Whitney Mus., 1988, San Francisco Mus. Modern Art, 1988, Mus. Fine Arts, Houston, 1988, Mus. Contemporary Art, Chgo., 1990, numerous others; group shows, Hidden Houston, U. St. Thomas, 1971, La. Gallery, Houston, 1972, W.I.S.P. Exhibiton, Whitney Mus. Am. Art, N.Y.C., 1974, Holly Solomon Gallery, N.Y.C., 1977, Rennaissance Soc., U. Chgo., 1979, Daniel Templon, Paris, 1980, L'Amerique Aux Independants, Grand Palais, Paris, 1980, Mary Boone, N.Y.C., 1980, La Biennale di Venezia, Venice, Italy, 1980, Indpls. Mus. Art, 1980, The Royal Acad., London, 1981, Whitney Mus. Am. Art, N.Y.C., 1981, Addison Gallery, Andover, Mass., 1981, Basel Kunstmuseum, Switzerland, 1981, Gayden Gallery, MIT, Cambridge, 1981, Kinsthallen, Goteborg, Sweden, 1981, Frankfurter Kunstverein, Frankfurt, West Germany, 1982, Inst. Contemporary Art, Boston, 1982, Whitney Mus. Am. Art, N.Y.C., 1982, Mus. Contemporary Art, LaJolla, Calif, 1982, Stedelijk Mus., Amsterdam, 1982, Art Inst. Chgo., 1982, la Biennale di Venezia, Venice, Italy, 1982, Fort Worth Art Mus., 1982, Milw. Art Mus., 1982, Stifelsen Karlsvik 10, Stockholm, 1983, Whitney Mus. Am. Art, N.Y.C., 1983, The Hirshhorn Mus., Washington, 1983, Nat. Mus. Art, Osaka, 1983, Bklyn. Mus., 1983, Mary Boone Gallery, N.Y.C., 1983, 64th Whitney Biennial, 1987; author: Nicknames of Maitre D's and Other Excerpts From Life, 1988. Office: Pace Gallery NY 32 E 57th St New York NY 10022-2513

SCHNABEL, ROBERT VICTOR, retired academic administrator; b. Scarsdale, N.Y., Sept. 28, 1922; s. Frederick Victor and Louise Elizabeth (Frick) S.; m. Ellen Edyth Foelber, June 7, 1946; children: Mark F., Philip P. Student, Concordia Sem., St. Louis, 1943-45; AB, Bowdoin Coll., 1944; MS, Fordham U., 1951, PhD, 1955; LLD (hon.), Concordia Coll., 1988. Tchr. St. Paul's Sch., Ft. Wayne, Ind., 1945-49; prin. St. Matthew's Sch., N.Y.C., 1949-52; assoc. supt. edn. Central Dist., Luth. Ch.-Mo. Synod, 1952-56; asst. prof. philosophy Concordia Sr. Coll., Ft. Wayne, 1956-60, assoc. prof., 1960-65, prof., acad. dean, 1966-71; pres. Concordia Coll., Bronxville, N.Y., 1971-76; acad. v.p., dean Wartburg Coll., Waverly, Iowa, 1976-78; pres. Valparaiso (Ind.) U., 1978-88; cons. Luth. Ch.-Am., 1977-88. Contbr. articles to profl. jours. Mem. AAUP, Luth. Acad. Scholarship, Assoc. Colls. Ind., Nat. Assn. Colls. and Univs., Rotary, Phi Delta Kappa. Office: Valparaiso Univ 23 Huegli Hall Valparaiso IN 46383

SCHNABEL, ROCKWELL ANTHONY, ambassador; b. Amsterdam, Holland, Dec. 30, 1936; came to U.S., 1957; s. Hans and Wilhelmina S.; m. Marna Belle Del Mar, 1964; children: Mary Darrin, Christy Ann, Everton Anthony. Student, Trinity Coll., Haarlem, Netherlands, 1951-56. Pres. Unilife Assurance Group S.H. Luxembourg, 1974-78; dir. Bateman Eichler, Hill Richards, Los Angeles, 1967-82, sr. v.p., 1969-82, vice chmn. bd., chmn. exec. com., 1978-82; pres. Bateman Eichler Hill Richard Group, Los Angeles, 1981-83; amb. to Finland U.S. Dept. State; under sec. for travel and tourism U.S. Dept. Commerce, Washington, 1989-91, dep. sec., 1991-92; ptnr. Trident Capital Ptnrs. Inc., L.A., 1992—. Pres. L.A. Pension Bd., Calif., 1982; mem. L.A. Olympic Organizing Com., 1983-84. With Air NG, 1958-64. Decorated comdr. Order of Good Hope, South Africa, Grand Cross of Lion of Finland; recipient Gold medal Dutch Govt., U.S. Dept. Commerce, medal of honor the Netherlands Olympic Com. Mem. L.A. Beach Club, Calif. Club, Regency Club. Office: Trident Capital Inc 355 S Grand Ave Sye 4295 Los Angeles CA 90071

SCHNABLE, GEORGE LUTHER, chemist; b. Reading, Pa., Nov. 26, 1927; s. L. Irvin and Laura C. (Albright) S.; m. Peggy Jane Butera, May 4, 1957; children: Lee Ann, Joseph G. BS, Albright Coll., 1950; MS, U. Pa., 1951, PhD, 1953. Project engr. Lansdale (Pa.) Tube Co., 1953-58; engring. specialist Philco Corp., Lansdale, 1958-61; mgr. materials and processes Philco-Ford Corp., Blue Bell, Pa., 1961-71; head process rsch. RCA Labs.,

Princeton, N.J., 1971-80, head device physics and reliability, 1980-87; head device physics and reliability David Sarnoff Rsch. Ctr., Princeton, 1987-91; ind. tech. cons. Schnable Assocs., Lansdale, 1991—. Author: (with others) Advances in Electronics and Electron Physics, 1971, The Chemistry of the Semiconductor Industry, 1987, Microelectronics Reliability, 1989, Microelectronics Manufacturing Diagnostics Handbook, 1993; editor spl. issue RCA Rev., 1984; divsn. editor Jour. of Electrochem. Soc., 1978-90; contbr. 80 articles to profl. publs. With U.S. Army, 1946-47. Fellow AAAS, Am. Inst. Chemists, Electrochem. Soc. (chm. Phila. sect. 1969-71); mem. IEEE (sr.) (assoc. guest editor Proceedings 1974), Alpha Chi Sigma, Phi Lambda Upsilon, Sigma Xi. Achievements include 39 patents (several with others); contributions to semiconductor device fabrication technology and reliability. Home and Office: Schnable Assocs 619 Knoll Dr Lansdale PA 19446-2925

SCHNACK, GAYLE HEMINGWAY JEPSON (MRS. HAROLD CLIFFORD SCHNACK), corporate executive; b. Mpls., Aug. 14, 1926; d. Jasper Jay and Ursula (Hemingway) Jepson; student U. Hawaii, 1946; m. Harold Clifford Schnack, Mar. 22, 1947; children: Jerrald Jay, Georgina, Roberta, Michael Clifford. Skater, Shipstad & Johnson Ice Follies, 1944-46; v.p. Harcliff Corp., Honolulu, 1964—, Schnack Indsl. Corp., Honolulu, 1969—, Nutmeg Corp., Cedar Corp.; ltd. ptnr. Koa Corp. Mem. Internat. Platform Assn., Beta Sigma Phi (chpt. pres. 1955-56, pres. city council 1956-57). Established Ursula Hemingway Jepson art award, Carlton Coll., Ernest Hemingway creative writing award, U. Hawaii. Office: PO Box 3077 Honolulu HI 96802-3077 also: 1200 Riverside Dr Reno NV 89503

SCHNACK, LARRY GENE, university chancellor; b. Harlan, Iowa, Mar. 19, 1937; s. Alvin and Twyla (Kulbom) S.; m. Carol Jean Hansen, Sept. 1, 1955; children—Lorrie, Kevin, Mark, Rachelle. B.S. in Gen. Sci., Iowa State U., 1958, Ph.D. in Organic Chemistry, 1965. Tchr. Emmons High Sch., Minn., 1958-61; mem. faculty, adminstr. U. Wis.-Eau Claire, 1965—, prof. chemistry, 1981—, chancellor, 1985—; bd. dirs. Firstar Bank, No. States Power Co. Mem. Eau Claire Area Indsl. Devel. Corp., Momentum Chippewa Valley. Recipient DuPont Teaching award Iowa State U., 1965, Distging. Service award Nat. Residence Hall Hon., Eau Claire, Wis., 1984. Mem. Eau Clair Country Club, Rotary (past pres. local club), Eau Claire C. of C. Office: U Wis Office of Chancellor Eau Claire WI 54702-4004

SCHNACKENBERG, GJERTRUD CECELIA, poet; b. Tacoma, Aug. 27, 1953; d. Walter Charles and Doris Ione (Strom) S.; m. Robert Nozick, Oct. 5, 1987. BA summa cum laude, Mount Holyoke Coll., 1975, LittD (hon.), 1985. Author: (poetry) Portraits and Elegies, 1982, The Lamplit Answer, 1985, A Gilded Lapse of Time, 1992. Poetry fellow The Bunting Inst. of Radcliffe Coll., 1979-80, NEA, 1985-86, The Guggenheim Found., 1986-87; recipient Rome prize AAAL, 1983, Lit. Lion award N.Y. Pub. Libr., 1993. Office: care Farrar Straus & Giroux Inc 19 Union Sq West New York NY 10003*

SCHNACKENBERG, ROY LEE, artist; b. Chgo., Jan. 14, 1934; s. Elmer J. and Hazel (Bard) S.; children: Marke, Douglas; m. Shirley Goldman, 1986. B.F.A., Miami U., Oxford, Ohio, 1956. One-man shows include, Joachim Gallery, Chgo., 1962, Main St. Galleries, Chgo., 1963, 64, 66, 68-69, Michael Wyman Gallery, Chgo., 1972, Esther Robles Gallery, Los Angeles, 1973; group exhbns. include print and drawing biennial, Art Inst. Chgo., 1961, Chgo. and Vicinity Show Art Inst. Chgo., 1961, 62, 64, 66-69, 73, 78, Soc. Contemporary Art, Art Inst. Chgo., 1962, 70, New Horizons in Sculpture, Chgo., 1962, 2d ann. art dealers show, N.Y., 1963, Ill. Biennial Show, Champaign, 1965, 67, Twelve Chgo. Artists, Walker Mus., Mpls., 1965, also, , Mulvane Art Center, Topeka, 1965, 50 States of Art Exhibit, Burpee Mus., Rockford, Ill.; Recent Aquisitions Exhbn., Whitney Mus., 1967, also, ann. exhbn. painting and sculpture, 1967, 68-69, 69-70, No. Ill. U. group exhbn., Normal, 1968-69, Western Ill. U. show, Macomb, 1968-69, Ill. Arts Council traveling Sculpture exhbn., 1968-69, Des Moines Art Center exhbn., 1969-70, Am. Realists, Konsthallen, Gotenborg, Sweden, 1970, The Art of Playboy World Tour, Milan, 1971,, Dept. Interior Bicentennial Exhbn., Corcoran Gallery, Washington, 1976,, nat. tour 200 Years of Illustration, N.Y. Hist. Soc.; Zriny-Hayes Gallery, Chgo., 1978, Mitchell Mus., Champaign, Ill., 1980, Continuity and Change, Chgo. Artists, 1983, Snead Gallery, Rockford, Ill., 1985, 89, 91, 93, 94, Chgo. Arts Club; executed mural Crucible, South Chgo. Savs. Bank, 1977; 2d ann. art dealers executed mural, S.E. Savs. & Loan, 1979; represented in permanent collections, Whitney Mus. Am. Art, N.Y.C., Art Inst. Chgo., Mus. Contemporary Art, Chgo., Burpee Art Mus., Rockford, Ill., others. Served with AUS, 1956-58. Recipient Joseph R. Shapiro award New Horizons in Sculpture, Chgo., 1962; Slobe award, 1964; Viehler award, 1965; Logan medal, 1973; Municipal award, 1974; all Art Inst. Chgo.; recipient purchase prize Burpee Mus., 1965, Copley Found. award N.Y.C., 1967. Mem. Arts Club of Chgo., Chgo. Yacht Club.

SCHNADIG, EDGAR LOUIS, entrepreneur, management consultant; b. Chgo., June 11, 1917; s. Edgar Louis Sr. and Nell Jane (Fackson) S.; m. Isabel O. Oliver, Dec. 18, 1938; children: Jo-Ann S. Innerarity, Ruth Jean (dec. 1970). A in Bus. Adminstrn., Cen. YMCA Coll., Chgo., 1938. Agt. Fidelity Mut. Life Ins. Co., 1935-48, James H. Brennan Agy., Chgo., 1938-48; pres. City Property Redevel. Corp., Chgo., 1941-45; organizer, pres. Edgar L. Schnadig & Assoc., Inc., 1945-51; owner, operator Indian Country Lodge, Tucson, 1947-50; mfg. rep., organizer Oliver Splty. Co., Tucson, 1951-54; pres. High Value Premium Co., Inc., Tucson, 1954-57; mgmt. cons., mfg. rep. Tucson and El Paso, Tex., 1958-61; dist. rep. Nat. Foreman's Inst., 1961-62; pres. Bray Rsch. and Y-tronics, Inc., El Paso, 1962-65; owner Internat. Bus. Coll. of El Paso, Inc., 1966-70; owner, operator Guaranty Real Estate And Trust #1, El Paso, 1993—; pres. Bus. Equities, Inc., El Paso, to 1993; gen. ptnr. Edgar L. Schnadig (formerly Guaranty Real Estate and Trust #1), El Paso, 1971—. Pres. El Paso Coun. Arts and Humanities, 1975-76; bd. dirs. Internat. Assn. for Visual Arts, Inc., 1992—; sec. 1993-94; charter mem. Reg. Presdl. Task Force, Washington, 1984-92; precinct chmn. El Paso County Rep. Orgn., 1990-92; mem. Internat. Soc. Appraisers, Chgo., 1984-88; apptd. El Paso rep. Taxpayers Action Network, 1991-93; charter mem. Citizens Against Govt. Waste, 1991—; active Fine Art Mus. El Paso, El Paso Artists Scholarship Fund, El Paso Artists Hall of Fame, Nationwide Artist Price Info. Exchange. Avocations: art collecting, photography. Home: 245 Ridgemont Dr El Paso TX 79912-5328

SCHNAIBERG, ALLAN, sociology educator; b. Montreal, Que., Can., Aug. 20, 1939; came to U.S., 1964; s. Harry and Belle (Katzoff) S.; m. Edith L Harshbarger, Sept. 1, 1981; children by previous marriage: Lynn Renee, Jill Ann. B.S., McGill U., 1960; M.A., U. Mich., 1964, Ph.D., 1968. Analytical chemist Can. Nat. Rys., Montreal, 1960-61; materials and process engr. Canadair, Ltd., Montreal, 1961-63; asso. dir. West Malaysian Family Survey, Kuala Lumpur, 1966-67; prof. sociology Northwestern U., Evanston, Ill., 1969—; chmn. dept. sociology Northwestern U., 1976-79; cons. Wissenschaftszentrun, Berlin. Author: The Environment: From Surplus to Scarcity, 1980; co-author: Environment and Society: The Enduring Conflict, 1994; co-editor: Distributional Conflicts in Environmental Resource Policy, 1986. Population Council fellow, 1967-68; Nat. Inst. Child Health and Human Devel. research grantee, 1970-72. Mem. Am. Sociol. Assn. (Disting. Contbn. award environ. sociology sect. 1984, chmn. environ. and tech. div. 1991-93), Soc. for Study Social Problems (chmn. environ. problems divsn. 1978-80, mem. C. Wright Mills com. 1979). Home: 6615 N Fairfield Ave Chicago IL 60645-4405 Office: 1810 Chicago Ave Evanston IL 60208-0001 *Learn conventional wisdom, but be prepared to challenge it at all times. What most people agree upon is often wrong, though they won't welcome you bringing this to their attention.*

SCHNAITMAN, WILLIAM KENNETH, finance company executive; b. Talbot County, Md., May 12, 1926; s. William and Catherine Almeda (Cheezum) S.; m. Beverly June Marshall, July 13, 1963. Student, Strayer Bus. Sch., Balt., 1943. Clk. Comml. Credit Co., Balt., 1944-70; asst. sec. Comml. Credit Co., 1970-72, treas., 1972-75, dir. cash mgmt., 1976-87, ret., 1987. With AUS, 1944-46, ETO. Home: 12520 Wye Ln Wye Mills MD 21679-2050

SCHNAKENBERG, DONALD G., financial administrator; b. Queens, N.Y., Dec. 6, 1939; s. Herman G. and Rose (Conte) S. BS in Acctg., Bklyn. Coll., 1960; MBA in Mgmt. with honors, Pace U., 1969. Acct. Rosen, Futterman & Berylson CPA's, N.Y.C., 1960-62; sr. acct. Fluhr, Massen &

Light CPA's, N.Y.C., 1963; tax examiner N.Y. State Tax Commn., N.Y.C., 1963-65; acct. N.Y.C. Housing and Redevel. Bd., N.Y.C., 1965-67; sr. acct. N.Y.C. Bd. Edn., N.Y.C., 1967-68, N.Y.C. Housing and Redevel., N.Y.C., 1968; prin. budget examiner Bur. of Budget Office of Mayor, N.Y.C., 1968-76; fin. dir. N.Y.C. Coun., 1976-89; chief fin. officer Lower Eastside Svc. Ctr., N.Y.C., 1989-90; chief fin. officer Promesa Inc., Bronx, 1990-91, cons., 1991-93; CFO Am. Chess Found., N.Y.C., 1993-94; cons., 1994—. Mem. Am. Mgmt. Assn., Govt. Fin. Officers Assn., JFK Dem. Club, Manhattan Chess Club. Democrat. Roman Catholic. Avocations: opera, classical music, chess, reading, football. Home: 12335 82nd Rd Apt 7K Kew Gardens NY 11415

SCHNALL, EDITH LEA (MRS. HERBERT SCHNALL), microbiologist, educator; b. N.Y.C., Apr. 11, 1922; d. Irving and Sadie (Raab) Spitzer; AB, Hunter Coll., 1942; AM, Columbia U., 1947, PhD, 1967; m. Herbert Schnall, Aug. 21, 1949; children: Neil David, Carolyn Beth. Clin. pathologist Roosevelt Hosp., N.Y.C., 1942-44; instr. Adelphi Coll., Garden City, N.Y., 1944-46; asst. med. mycologist Columbia Coll. Physicians and Surgeons, N.Y.C., 1946-47, 49-50; instr. Bklyn. Coll., 1947; mem. faculty Sarah Lawrence Coll., Bronxville, N.Y., 1947-48; lectr. Hunter Coll., N.Y.C., 1947-67; adj. assoc. prof. Lehman Coll., City U. N.Y., 1968; asst. prof. Queensborough Community Coll., City U. N.Y., 1967, assoc. prof. microbiology, 1968-75, prof., 1975—, adminstr. Med. Lab. Tech. Program, 1985—; vis. prof. Coll. Physicians and Surgeons, Columbia U., N.Y.C., 1974; advanced biology examiner U. London, 1970—. Mem. Alley Restoration Com. N.Y.C., 1971—; mem. legis. adv. com. Assembly of the State of N.Y., 1972. Mem. Community Bd. 11, Queens, N.Y., 1974—, 3d vice-chmn., 1987-92, 2nd vice chmn., 1992—; public dir. of bd. dirs. Inst. Continuing Dental Edn. Queens County, Dental Soc. N.Y. State and ADA, 1973—. Rsch. fellow NIH, 1948-49; faculty rsch. fellow, grantee-in-aid Rsch. Found. of SUNY, 1968-70; faculty rsch. grant Rsch. Found. City U. N.Y., 1971-74. Mem. Internat. Soc. Human and Animal Mycology, AAAS, Am. Soc. Microbiology (coun., N.Y.C. br. 1981—, co-chairperson ann. meeting com. 1981-82, chair program com. 1982-83, v.p. 1984-86, pres. 1986-88), Med. Mycology Soc. N.Y. (sec.-treas. 1967-68, v.p. 1968-69, 78-79, archivist 1974—, fin. advisor 1983—, pres. 1969-70, 79-80, 81-82), Bot. Soc. Am., Med. Mycology Soc. Americas, Mycology Soc. Am., N.Y. Acad. Scis., Sigma Xi, Phi Sigma. Clubs: Torrey Botanical (N.Y. State); Queensborough Community Coll. Women's (pres. 1971-73) (N.Y.C.). Editor: Newsletter of Med. Mycology Soc. N.Y., 1969-85; founder, editor Female Perspective newsletter of Queensborough Community Coll. Women's Club, 1971-73. Home: 21406 29th Ave Flushing NY 11360-2622

SCHNALL, FLORA, lawyer; b. Bklyn., Oct. 7, 1935; d. Benjamin and Jean (Heilweil) S. B.A. magna cum laude, Smith Coll., 1956; J.D., Harvard U., 1959. Asst. counsel to Gov. Nelson A. Rockefeller State of N.Y., Albany, 1959-60; assoc. Milbank, Tweed, Hadley & McCloy, N.Y.C., 1960-69; ptnr. Milbank, Tweed, Hadley & McCloy, 1984—; from assoc. to sr. ptnr. Rosenman Colin Freund Lewis & Cohen, N.Y.C., 1969-84. Contbg. author: Real Estate Titles. Bd. dirs. Northside Ctr. Child Devel., Inc., N.Y.C., 1980—, Citizens Housing and Planning Council, N.Y.C., 1982—. Mem. ABA (real property probate sect., coun. 1987—), N.Y. State Bar Assn. (editor real property law sect. of newsletter 1980-86, chmn. 1989, ho. of dels. 1986-89), Assn. of the Bar of N.Y.C. (chmn. real property com. 1990—), Am. Coll. Real Estate Lawyers (bd. govs. 1984-89, pres. 1989-90). Club: India House. Office: Milbank Tweed Hadley & McCloy 1 Chase Manhattan Plz New York NY 10005-1401

SCHNAPF, ABRAHAM, aerospace engineer, consultant; b. N.Y.C., Aug. 1, 1921; s. Meyer and Gussie (Schaeffler) S.; m. Edna Wilensky, Oct. 24, 1943; children: Donald J., Bruce M. BSME, CCNY, 1948; MSME, Drexel Inst. Tech., 1953. Registered profl. engr., N.J. Devel. engr. on lighter-than-air aircraft Goodyear Aircraft Corp., Akron, Ohio, 1948-50; mgr. fire control system def. electronics RCA, Camden, N.Y., 1950-55, mgr. airbourne navigation system, aerospace weapon system, 1955-58; program mgr. TIROS/ TOS weather satellite systems RCA Astro-Electronics, Princeton, N.J., 1958-70, mgr. satellite programs, 1970-79, prin. scientist, 1979-82; cons. Aerospace Systems Engring., Willingboro, N.J., 1982—; lectr., presenter on meteor. satellites, space tech., communication satellites. Sgt. USAF, 1943-46. Recipient award Nat. Press Club Washington, 1975, award Am. Soc. Quality Control-NASA, 1968, Pub. Svc. award NASA, 1969, cert. of appreciation U.S. Dept. Commerce, 1984; inducted into Space Tech. Hall of Fame, 1992; named to 5000 Personalities of the World, named Internat. Man of Yr., 1992-93. Fellow AIAA; mem. Am. Astro. Soc., Am. Meterol. Soc., Space Pioneers, N.Y. Acad. Scis. (mem. think tank week sessions 1980's), N.J. Arbitration Soc. Home and Office: 41 Pond Ln # 160 Willingboro NJ 08046-2756

SCHNARE, ROBERT EDEY, JR., library director; b. Morristown, N.J., Dec. 31, 1944; s. Robert Edey and Olive Margaret (Flatt) S.; m. MaryKay Wise, Aug. 29, 1970; 1 child, Katharine Grace. BA, William Paterson Coll., 1967; MLS, U. Pitts. 1968; MA, U. Conn., 1971. Reference librn. history dept. Conn. State Libr., Hartford, 1968-73; head spl. collections U.S. Mil. Acad. Libr., West Point, N.Y., 1973-86; librn. dir. U.S. Naval War Coll., Newport, R.I., 1986—; chmn. Consortium of R.I. Acad. and Rsch. Librs., Providence, 1991-93; bd. dirs. Coalition of Libr. Advocates, Providence, 1991—; chmn. edn. and tng. com. R.I. Preservation Planning Grant, 1991-92; del. White House Conf. on Libr. and Info. Svcs., 1990—; chmn. preservation working group New England Libr. Network, Newton, Mass., 1992—; mem. com. on mgmt. Anne S.K. Brown Mil. Collection, 1987—; mem. Mid-Atlantic Archivist Conf., 1973—; mem. preservation working group Fed. Libr. Info. Ctr. Com., 1991—. Publ. editor Conservation Adminstrn. News, 1979-87, mem. editl. bd., 1987-94; contbr. articles to profl. jours, chpt. to book; compiler Union List of Mil. Edn. Coordinating Com. Library Resources, 1994. Chmn. gifted adv. coun. Providence Bd. Edn., 1990-92; chmn. stewardship St. Martin's Episcopal Ch., Providence, 1990; vol. Providence schs., 1992—. Named Disting. Grad., William Paterson Coll., 1987; recipient Disting. Svc. award Conservation Adminstrn. News, 1987, 94, Comdr.'s award for civilian svc. U.S. Mil. Acad., 1987. Mem. ALA, Spl. Librs. Assn., Assn. for Study Conn. History, New Eng. Archivists. Office: US Naval War Coll Libr 686 Cushing Rd Newport RI 02841

SCHNECK, DANIEL JULIO, biomedical engineer, educator; b. Mendoza, Argentina, Oct. 28, 1941; came to U.S., 1945; s. Leon and Charlotte (Briefwechsler) S.; m. Judith Ann Kooistra, July 6, 1967; children: Patricia Jean, Cynthia Ann. BS in Mech. Engring., CCNY, 1963; MS, NYU, 1966; PhD, Case-Western Res. U., 1973. Lic. profl. engr., N.Y.; Va. Clk.-typist Lafayette Radio Corp., Queens, N.Y., 1958-60; usher Sta. WCBS-TV, N.Y.C., 1960-61; design engr. United Staple Corp., N.Y.C., 1961-62; biomechanics rsch. tech. rsch. div. NYU, 1962-63, project engr. rsch. div., 1963-66; rsch. assoc. N.Y. Med. Coll., 1966-68, instr. in surg. pathology, 1968-69; rsch. assoc. Case-Western Res. U., Cleve., 1969-73; prof. engring. sci. and mechanics, dir. biomed. engring. Va. Poly. Inst. and State U., Blacksburg, 1973—; cons. Radford (Va.) Community Hosp., 1976—, VA Hosp., Salem, Va., 1976—; vis. scholar Naval Med. Rsch. Inst., Bethesda, Md., 1983-86; summer faculty fellow Aerospace Med. Rsch. Lab., Wright-Patterson AFB, Ohio, 1976. Author: Engineering Principles of Physiologic Function, 1990, Clinical Internship Manual for Biomedical Engineers, 1981, Mechanics of Muscle, 1985, Biofluid Mechanics, 1980; contbr. numerous articles to profl. jours. Mission pilot CAP, Cleve., 1969-73; vol. Cleve. Soc. for Blind, 1969-73, Radford Community Hosp., 1980—, Montgomery County Pub. Sch. System, Christiansburg, Va., 1980—, mem. sch. bd., 1990. Paul Harris fellow Rotary, 1984, USPHS rsch. fellow, 1969; named Outstanding Educator of Yr. Soc. for Engring. Sci., 1976; recipient Hometown Hero award St. WDBJ-TV, 1987. Fellow Biomed. Engring. Soc. (pres. 1990—); mem. ASME, Am. Soc. for Engring. Edn. (chmn. bioengring. div. 1983-84, pres. Blacksburg chpt. 1985-86), Am. Acad. Mechanics, Soc. for Scientific Exploration, Sigma Xi. Avocations: playing violin, sports, flying, music, cooking. Home: PO Box 396 Christiansburg VA 24073-0396 Office: Va Poly Inst and State U Mail Code Esm # 0219 Blacksburg VA 24061

SCHNECK, JEROME M., psychiatrist, medical historian, educator; b. N.Y.C., Jan. 2, 1920; s. Maurice and Rose (Weiss) S.; m. Shirley R. Kaufman, July 24, 1943. AB, Cornell U., 1939; MD, SUNY-Bklyn., 1943. Diplomate Am. Bd. Psychiatry and Neurology. Intern Interfaith Med. Ctr.,

1943; mem. psychiat. staff Menninger Clinic, Topeka, 1944-45, L.I. Coll. Hosp., 1947-48, Kings County Hosp., 1948-70, SUNY Hosp., Bklyn., 1955-70; assoc. vis. psychiatrist Kings County Hosp., 1949-70; mem. psychiat. staff State U. Hosp., Bklyn., 1955-70; pvt. practice N.Y.C., 1947—; attending psychiatrist St. Vincent's Hosp. and Med. Ctr. N.Y., 1970—, hon. sr. psychiatrist, 1990—; psychiat. cons. VA Regional Office, 1947-48, N.Y. State Dept. Social Svcs., 1977-83, N.Y. State Dept. Civil Svcs., 1978-84, N.Y. State Office Ct. Adminstrn., 1978-85, N.Y. State Dept. Edn., 1981-83; dir. Mt. Vernon Mental Hygiene Clinic, 1947-52; assoc. chief psychiatrist Westchester County Dept. Health, 1949-50, cons., 1951-52; clin. instr. L.I. Coll. Medicine, 1947-50; clin. assoc. SUNY Coll. Medicine, Bklyn., 1950-53, asst. prof., 1955-58, assoc. prof., 1958-70; supervising psychiatrist Community Guidance Svcs., 1955-70; cons. coun. on mental health AMA, 1956-58; cons. NBC, 1962, Ctr. Rsch. in Hypnotherapy, 1964-70; vis. lectr. N.Y. Med. Coll.-Met. Hosp., 1965; faculty Am. Inst. Psychotherapy and Psychoanalysis, 1970-85. Author: Hypnosis in Modern Medicine, 1953, 2d edit., 1959, Spanish lang. edit., 1962, 3rd edit., 1963, Studies in Scientific Hypnosis, 1954, A History of Psychiatry, 1960, The Principles and Practice of Hypnoanalysis, 1965 (Best Book award Soc. For Clin. and Exptl. Hypnosis 1965); editor: Hypnotherapy, Hypnosis and Personality, 1951; author over 400 med. and sci. publs., book chpts., articles; mem. bd. editors: Personality: Symposia on Topical Issues, 1960-61, Jour. Integrative and Eclectic Psychotherapy, 1986-89; contbg. editor Psychosomatics, 1961-75; mem. editorial bd. Voices—The Art and Science of Psychotherapy, 1965; features editor The Interne, 1942, co-editor, 1943. Capt. AUS, 1945-47. Recipient Clarence B. Farrar award Clarke Inst. of Psychiatry, U. Toronto, 1976. Fellow AAAS, APA, Am. Med. Authors, Acad. Psychosomatic Medicine, Am. Psychiat. Assn. (life), Soc. for Clin. and Exptl. Hypnosis (life, founder, founding pres. 1949-56, exec. coun. 1949—, assoc. editor jour. 1953—, award of Merit 1955, Gold medal 1958, Bernard B. Raginsky award 1966, Shirley Schneck award 1970, Roy M. Dorcus award 1980, Spl. Presdl. award 1986), Am. Acad. Psychotherapists (co-founder, v.p. 1956-58), Am. Med. Writers Assns., Am. Soc. Psychoanalytic Physicians (founding fellow, bd. dirs. 1958-62), Am. Soc. Clin. Hypnosis (life), Internat. Soc. Clin. and Exptl. Hypnosis (co-founder, bd. dirs. 1958-68, founding fellow), Internat. Acad. Eclectic Psychotherapists (charter fellow); mem. AMA, Soc. Acad. Achievement (charter), Soc. Apothecaries London, Inst. Practicing Psychotherapists, Pan Am. Med. Assn. (v.p. sect. clin. hypnosis 1960-65, N.Am. v.p. 1966), N.Y. Soc. Med. History (exec. com. 1956-62), Am. Bd. Med. Hypnosis (founder, pres. 1958-60, life bd. dirs.), Inst. Rsch. in Hypnosis Inc. (bd. dirs. and bd. editors 1957-70), Am. Assn. History Medicine, History of Sci. Soc., Assn. Advancement Psychotherapy (charter), Can. Med. History Assn., N.Y. Soc. Clin. Psychiatry (chmn. com. on history of psychiatry), Charles F. Menninger Soc., Sigma Xi. Address: 26 W 9th St New York NY 10011-8971

SCHNECK, PAUL BENNETT, computer scientist; b. N.Y.C., Aug. 15, 1945; s. Irving and Doris (Grossman) S.; m. Marjorie Ann Axelrod, Feb. 5, 1967; children: Phyllis Adele, Melanie Jane. BS, Columbia U., 1965, MS, 1966; PhD, NYU Courant Inst. Math. Scis., 1979. Computer scientist Inst. for Space Studies, N.Y.C., 1970-76; program mgr. Goddard Space Flight Ctr., Greenbelt, Md., 1976-79; asst. to dir. Goddard Space Flight Ctr., Greenbelt, 1979-80, chief info. extraction div., 1980-81, asst. dir., 1981-83; head info. sci. div. Office of Naval Rsch., Arlington, Va., 1983-85; dir. Supercomputing Rsch. Ctr., Bowie, Md., 1985-93; chief scientist Inst. Defense Analyses, 1993; fellow Mitre Corp., McLean, Va., 1993-94, dir. info. sys. and fellow, 1994—; vice chmn. bd. Nat. Info. Tech. Ctr., 1993, chmn. bd. dirs. 1994, mem. exec. com. 1994—; mem. adv. bd. dept. computer scis. U. Md., College Park, 1989—; tchr. Columbia U., Johns Hopkins U., U. Md. Author: Supercomputer Architecture, 1987; contbr. articles to Ency. of Computer Sci. and Tech., Ann. Rev. of Computer Sci., Ency. Phys. Sci. and Tech. Yearbook. Fellow IEEE; mem. Assn. for Computing Machinery, Brit. Computer Soc. Achievements include design and implementation of the science supervisory system in use at NASA from 1968-83, on the IBM 360/95 and 370/165, and the Amdahl 470/V6, V7; and of the vector/parallel compiler. Office: Mitre Corp 7525 Colshire Dr Mc Lean VA 22102

SCHNECK, STUART AUSTIN, neurologist, educator; b. N.Y.C., Apr. 1, 1929; s. Maurice and Sara Ruth (Knapp) S.; m. Ida I. Nakashima, Mar. 2, 1956; children—Lisa, Christopher. B.S. magna cum laude, Franklin and Marshall Coll., 1949; M.D., U. Pa., 1953. Diplomate Am. Bd. Psychiatry and Neurology (bd. dirs., sec. 1990-91, v.p. 1991-92, pres. 1992-93). Intern Hosp. U. Pa., Phila., 1953-54; resident in medicine U. Colo. Med. Center, Denver, 1954-55, 57-58, resident in neurology, 1958-61; instr. neurology U. Colo. Sch. Medicine, 1959-61; instr. neuropathology Columbia U., N.Y.C., 1961-63; vis. fellow in neurology Vanderbilt Clinic, Columbia-Presbyn. Med. Center, N.Y.C., 1961-63; asst. prof. neurology and pathology U. Colo., 1963-67, assoc. prof., 1967-70, prof., 1970—, assoc. dean clin. affairs Sch. Medicine, 1984-89; cons. Fitzsimons Army Hosp., VA, Nat. Jewish Hosp.; pres. med. bd. Univ. Hosp., Denver, 1983-89, bd. dirs., 1989-90. Contbr. articles to profl. jours. Served with USAF, 1955-57. USPHS fellow, 1961-63. Mem. AAAS, Denver Med. Soc., Am. Acad. Neurology, Am. Assn. Neuropathologists, Am. Neurol. Assn., Colo. Assn. Clin. Neurologists, Alpha Omega Alpha (bd. dirs. 1979-89, treas., pres. 1990-93). Office: 4200 E 9th Ave Denver CO 80220-3706

SCHNEEMAN, BARBARA OLDS, nutrition educator, dean; b. Seattle, Oct. 3, 1948; d. William Arthur and Rose (Antush) Olds; m. Paul Schneeman, Mar. 23, 1974; 1 child, Eric. BS, U. Calif., Davis, 1970, PhD, 1974. Postdoctoral fellow Children's Hosp., Oakland, Calif., 1974-76; mem. faculty U. Calif., Davis, 1976—, chair dept. nutrition, 1988-93, dean Coll. Agriculture and Environ. Sci., 1993—; vis. scientist Cardio Vascular Rsch. Inst., U. Calif., San Francisco, 1991-92; trustee Internat. Life Sci. Inst. North Am., Washington, 1989—; mem. dietary guidelines adv. com. USDA, HHS, Washington, 1989-90. Assoc. editor Jour. Nutrition, 1991-94, 94-95; contbr. over 100 articles to profl. jours. Fellow arteriosclerosis coun. Am. Heart Assn. Recipient Internat. Fibre award Farma Foods, Denmark, 1989. Mem. Am. Inst. Nutrition (treas. 1988), Am. Physiol. Soc., Inst. Food Tech. (Samuel Prescott award 1985). Office: Univ Calif Coll Agriculture/Envir Sci 228 Mrak Hall Davis CA 95616

SCHNEEMANN, CAROLEE, painter, performing artist, filmmaker, writer; b. Pa., Oct. 12, 1939. B.A., Bard Coll., 1960; M.F.A., U. Ill., 1961. Originated Kinetic Theater, 1962; with Judson Dance Theater, 1962-66; performance works, film showings throughout U.S. and Europe; (erotic film) Fuses, 1964-68 (Spl. Jury Selection Cannes 1968); (most recent film) Kitch's Last Meal, 1973-78; (video tapes) Up To and Including Her Limits, 1974-77, Interior Scroll, 1975, ABC-We Print Anything—In The Cards, 1976-77; Homerunmuse, 1977; performance installations include Palazzo Reale, Milan, Italy, Art Inst. Chgo., 1980; performance tour Fresh Blood—A Dream Morphology, France, Belgium, Holland, 1981; books Part Of A Body House Book, 1972, Cezanne, She Was A Great Painter, 1974, ABC-We Print Anything-In The Cards, 1977, More Than Meat Joy, Complete Performance Works and Selected Writings, 1979; retrospective exhibit: Max Hutchison Gallery, 1982; exhbns. Whitney Mus., 1984, 85; U.S. travelling exhbn. sculpture with video, 1986. Creative Artists Public Service Program fellow, 1978-79; N.Y. State Council on Arts grantee, 1968; Nat. Endowment for Arts grantee, 1974, 77-78, 83. Office: 437 Springtown Rd New Paltz NY 12561-3027

SCHNEEWIND, JEROME BORGES, philosophy educator; b. Mt. Vernon, N.Y., May 17, 1930; s. Jerome John and Charlotte (Borges) S.; m. Elizabeth G.R. Hughes, Feb. 23, 1963; children: Sarah, Rachel, Hannah. B.A., Cornell U., 1951; M.A., Princeton U., 1953, Ph.D., 1957. Instr. philosophy U. Chgo., 1957-60, Princeton U., 1960-61; asst. prof. Yale U., 1961-63; assoc. prof. philosophy U. Pitts., 1964-68, prof., 1968-75, dean Coll. Arts and Scis., 1969-73; v.p.; provost Hunter Coll., CUNY, 1975-81; prof. philosophy Johns Hopkins U., Balt., 1981—, chmn. dept., 1981-91; philosophy adviser Ency. Americana, 1967—; mem. adv. bd. sci. tech. and values program NEH, 1975-78; mem. Coun. for Phil. Studies, 1975-80. Author: Backgrounds of English Victorian Literature, 1970, Sidgwick's Ethics and Victorian Moral Philosophy, 1977; editor: Moral Philosophy From Montaigne to Kant, 1990; editorial bd. Victorian Studies, 1968-75, The Monist, 1969-76, Am. Philosophy Quar., 1975-77, Philos. Studies, 1975-78, Jour. of History Ideas, 1985—, pres. bd. dirs., 1988—; contbr. articles on ethics and history of ethics to pubs. Served with Signal Corps, AUS, 1954-56. Mellon postdoctoral fellow, 1963-64; Guggenheim, 1967-68; Am. Council Learned Socs. grantee, 1973; NEH sr. fellow, 1974, Ctr. for

Advanced Study in the Behavioral Scis., 1992-93. Mem. Am. Philos. Assn. (exec. com. Ea. divsn. 1964-67, chmn. com. on teaching philosophy 1973-78, nominating com. 1986-88, v.p. Ea. divsn. 1994-95, pres. 1995—). Office: Philosophy Dept Johns Hopkins U Baltimore MD 21218

SCHNEIDER, ADELE SANDRA, clinical geneticist; b. Johannesburg, South Africa, Mar. 21, 1949; came to U.S., 1976, naturalized, 1981; d. Michael and Annette (Sive) S.; m. Gordon Mark Cohen, July 2, 1978; children: Jeffrey, Brian, Adrienne. MB, BChir, Witwatersrand U., Johannesburg, South Africa, 1973. Intern in internal medicine Baragwanath Hosp., Johannesburg, 1974, intern in gen. surgery, 1974; sr. house officer in pediatrics Coronation Hosp., Johannesburg, 1975; sr. house officer in radiation therapy Johannesburg Gen. Hosp., 1975-76; resident in pediatrics Wilmington (Del.) Med. Ctr., 1976-78; fellow in clin. genetics and metabolic diseases Children's Hosp. of Phila., 1978-81, staff physician Cystic Fibrosis Clinic, 1987-88; staff pediatrician Children's Rehab. Hosp., Phila., 1981-82, dir. pediatrics, 1982-87, acting med. dir., 1984-85; clin. instr. dept. pediatrics Jefferson Med. Coll., Phila., 1982-84, clin. asst. prof. dept. pediatrics, 1984—; clin. geneticist Hahnemann Univ. Hosp., Phila. 1987-90, asst. clin. prof. dept. pediatrics and neoplastic diseases, 1987-90; clin. geneticist Albert Einstein Med. Ctr., Phila., 1990-92, acting dir. med. genetics, 1992-93, dir. clin. genetics program, 1993—; mem. courtesy faculty Sch. Medicine Temple U., Phila., 1987; clin. geneticist St. Christopher's Hosp. for Children, Phila., 1987; genetics cons. dept. pediatrics Bryn Mawr (Pa.) Hosp.; presenter, lectr. in field. Contbr. articles to profl. jours. Bd. dirs. Phila. Parenting Associates, 1986-93. Fellow Am. Coll. Med. Genetics; mem. Am. Soc. Human Genetics, Am. Chem. Soc. Office: Albert Einstein Med Ctr Dept Pediatrics 5501 Old York Rd Philadelphia PA 19141-3098

SCHNEIDER, ALLAN STANFORD, biochemistry and pharmacology educator, biomedical research scientist; b. N.Y.C., Sept. 26, 1940; s. Harry and Edith (Gonsky) S.; m. Mary-Jane Beekman Tunis, Dec. 14, 1968; children: Henry Seth, Joseph Benjamin. B.Chem. Engring., Rensselaer Poly. Inst., 1961; M.S., Pa. State U., 1963; Ph.D., U. Calif.-Berkeley, 1968. Chem. engr. E.I. du Pont de Nemours & Co. Exptl. Sta., Wilmington, Del., 1963-64; postdoctoral fellow Weizmann Inst. Sci., Rehovot, Israel, 1969-71; staff fellow NIH, Bethesda, Md., 1971-73; assoc. Sloan-Kettering Inst. Cancer Research, N.Y.C., 1974-80, assoc. mem., 1980-85; asst. prof. Cornell U. Grad. Sch. Med. Scis., N.Y.C., 1974-80, assoc. prof. biochemistry, 1981-83, assoc. prof. cell biology and genetic, 1983-85, chmn. biochemistry unit Sloan-Kettering div., 1982-83; assoc. prof. pharmacology and toxicology Albany (N.Y.) Med. Coll., N.Y., 1985-86, prof. pharmacology and toxicology, 1986-94; prof. pharmacology and neurosci. Albany (N.Y.) Med. Coll., 1995—; dir. grad. studies Albany (N.Y.) Med. Coll., N.Y., 1987-91; vis. prof. Weizmann Inst. Sci., Rehovot, Israel, 1987; vis. rsch. scholar U. Bergen, Norway, 1989. Contbr. chpts to books, sci. articles to profl. jours. Rsch. grantee Am. Cancer Soc., 1980-83, Am. Heart Assn., 1977-82, 90-93, NIH, 1982—, NSF, 1977-79, Cystic Fibrosis Found., 1980-82; established investigator Am. Heart Assn., 1977-82. Mem. Am. Soc. Biochemistry and Molecular Biology, Biophys. Soc., Soc. Neurosci., Am. Heart Assn. (coun. on basic sci. 1977-95), Phi Lambda Upsilon, Tau Beta Pi. Achievements include first isolation and characterization of chromaffin cells of the adrenal gland now widely used as a model neuronal cell culture system; determination of the relation between cytosolic calcium signals and neurohormone (adrenaline) secretion, relevant to cellular mechanism of hormone and neurotransmitter release; spectroscopic characterization of protein structure in situ in biomembranes and cells; theoretical and experimental analysis of optical activity spectra of turbid biological suspensions; research on neurochemistry of adrenal chromaffin cells, regulation of hormone and neurotransmitter release and mechanisms of nicotine dependence. Office: Dept Pharmacology & Neurosci Albany Med Coll A 136 Albany NY 12208

SCHNEIDER, ARTHUR PAUL, retired videotape and film editor, author; b. Rochester, N.Y., Jan. 26, 1930; s. Mendell Phillip and Frieda (Bl) S.; m. Helen Deloise Thompson, June 5, 1954; children: Robert Paul, Lori Ann. Student, U. So. Calif., 1953. With NBC, 1951-68, film and videotape editor, 1953-60, developer double system method of editing video tape, 1958; pres. Burbank (Calif.) Film Editing, Inc., 1968-72, Electronic Video Industries Inc., 1977-79; supr. video tape editing Consol. Film Industries Inc., Hollywood, Calif., 1972-76, editorial supr., 1980-83; pvt. practice editing, 1983-88; cons., lectr., author. Film and tape editor all: Bob Hope shows, 1960-67; supr. NBC kinescope and video tape editors (1966-67); video tape editor: Laugh-In series, 1967-68; video tape editor: Comedy Shop Series, 1977-80; post-prodn. cons. to Video Systems and Broadcast Engring. mag.; video tape editor: TV series Sonny & Cher, 1973, Sonny Comedy Revue, 1974, Tony Orlando and Dawn, 1974, Hudson Bros, summer 1974, Dean Martin Series, 1975-76, Mickey Mouse Club Series, Walt Disney Prodns., 1976, Redd Foxx Series, 1977; author: Electronic Post Production and Videotape Editing, 1989, Electronic Post Production Terms and Concepts, 1990; contbr. articles to publs. in field. Recipient Broadcast Preceptor award San Francisco State U., 1975; named hon. Ky. Col. Mem. Acad. Television Arts and Scis. (Emmy nominations and Emmy award for video tape editing 1966, 68, 73, 84, gov. 1977-80, sec. 1980-81), Am. Cinema Editors (life), Soc. Motion Picture and TV Engrs., Delta Kappa Alpha (life). Home: PO Box 156 Fish Camp CA 93623-0156

SCHNEIDER, ARTHUR SANFORD, physician, educator; b. Los Angeles, Mar. 24, 1929; s. Max and Fannie (Ragin) S.; m. Edith Kadison, Aug. 20, 1950; children: Jo Ann Schneider Farris, William Scott, Lynnellen. B.S., UCLA, 1951; M.D., Chgo. Med. Sch., 1955. Diplomate Am. Bd. Internal Medicine, Am. Bd. Pathology. Intern, Wadsworth VA Hosp., Los Angeles, 1955-56; resident Wadsworth VA Hosp., 1956-59, chief clin. pathology sect., 1962-68; mem. faculty UCLA, 1961-75, clin. assoc. prof., 1971-75; chmn. dept. clin. pathology City of Hope Med. Ctr., Duarte, Calif., 1968-75; prof., chmn. dept. clin. pathology Whittier Coll., 1974-75; prof., chmn. dept. pathology Chgo. Med. Sch., 1975—; chief lab. service VA Med. Ctr., North Chicago, Ill., 1975-86, chief lab. hematology, 1986-94. Contbr. numerous chpts. to books and articles to med. jours. Served to capt. M.C., USAF, 1959-61. Fellow ACP, Coll. Am. Pathologists, Am. Soc. Clin. Pathologists; mem. AAUP, AMA, Internat. Acad. Pathology, Am. Assn. for Investigative Pathology, Assn. Pathology Chairmen, Acad. Clin. Lab. Physicians and Scientists, Am. Soc. Hematology, Am. Assn. Blood Banks, Am. Soc. Clin. Rsch., Ill. Med. Soc., Lake County Med. Soc., Sigma Xi, Alpha Omega Alpha, Phi Delta Epsilon. Office: Chgo Med Sch 3333 Green Bay Rd North Chicago IL 60064-3037

SCHNEIDER, BENJAMIN, psychology educator; b. N.Y.C., Aug. 11, 1938; s. Leo and Rose (Cohen) S.; m. H. Brenda Jacobson, Jan. 29, 1961; children: Lee Andrew, Rhody Yve. BA, Alfred U., 1960; MBA, CUNY, 1962; PhD, U. Md., 1967. Lic. psychologist, Md. Asst. prof. adminstrv. scis. and psychology Yale U., New Haven, 1967-71; prof. psychology-mgmt. U. Md., College Park, 1971-79, prof. psychology and mgmt., 1982—; John A. Hannah prof. orgnl. behavior Mich. State U., East Lansing, 1979-82; v.p. Orgnl. and Pers. Rsch., Inc. Author: (with D.T. Hall) Organizational Climates and Careers, 1973, Staffing Organizations, 1976, 2d edit. (with N. Schmitt), 1986; (with F.D. Schoorman) Facilitating Work Effectiveness, 1988, Organizational Climate and Culture, 1990, (with D.E. Bowen) Winning the Service Game, 1995; mem. editl. rev. bd. Acad. Mgmt. Jour., 1971-86, Adminstrv. Sci. Quar., 1976-82, Jour. Applied Psychology, 1988—, Brit. Mgmt. Jour., 1989—, Internat. Jour. Svc. Industry Mgmt., 1989—, Pers. Psychology, 1994—. Fulbright grantee, 1973-74. Fellow APA, Am. Psychol. Soc., Soc. for Indsl. and Orgnl. Psychology (pres. 1984-85), Acad. Mgmt. (pres. orgnl. behavior div. 1982-83). Home: 8122 Thoreau Dr Bethesda MD 20817-3105 Office: U Maryland Dept Psychology College Park MD 20742

SCHNEIDER, BERNARD, industrial machinery executive; b. 1944. Student, U. Munich, 1966-71. With Enka-Glanzstoff, Wuppertal, Germany, 1972-76; dir. Fichtel & Sachs AG, Schweinfurt, Germany, 1976-92; exec. v.p. Mannesmann Capital Corp., N.Y.C., 1992—. Lt. German Army, 1964-66. Office: Mannesmann Capital Corp 450 Park Ave # 24 New York NY 10022-2605

SCHNEIDER, CALVIN, physician; b. N.Y.C., Oct. 23, 1924; s. Harry and Bertha (Green) S.; A.B., U. So. Calif., 1951, M.D., 1955; J.D., LaVerne (Calif.) Coll., 1973; m. Elizabeth Gayle Thomas, Dec. 27, 1967. Intern Los

Angeles County Gen. Hosp., 1955-56, staff physician, 1956-57; practice medicine West Covina, Calif., 1957—; staff Inter-Community Med. Ctr., Covina, Calif. Cons. physician Charter Oak Hosp., Covina, 1960—. With USNR, 1943-47. Mem. AMA, Calif., L.A. County med. assns. Republican. Lutheran. Office: 224 W College St Covina CA 91723-1902

SCHNEIDER, CARL EDWARD, law educator; b. Exeter, N.H., Feb. 23, 1948; s. Carl Jacob and Mabel Dot (Jones) S.; m. Joan L. Wagner, Jan. 6, 1976. BA, Harvard Coll., 1972; JD, U. Mich., 1979. Curriculum specialist Mass. Tchrs. Assn., Boston, 1972-75; law clk. to judge U.S. Ct. Appeals (D.C. cir.), Washington, 1979-80; law clk. Potter Stewart U.S. Supreme Ct., Washington, 1980-81; asst. prof. law U. Mich., Ann Arbor, 1981-84, assoc. prof. law, 1984-86, prof. law, 1986—. Author: (with Margaret F. Brinig) An Invitation to Family Law, 1995; editor: (book) The Law and Politics of Abortion, 1980; contbr. articles to profl. jours. Fellow Am. Council of Learned Socs., Ford Found., 1988. Mem. Order of Coif. Office: U Mich Law Sch 625 S State St Ann Arbor MI 48109-1215

SCHNEIDER, CARL W., lawyer; b. Phila., Apr. 27, 1932; s. Nathan J. and Eleanor M. (Milgram) S.; m. Mary Ellen Baylinson; children—Eric, Mark, Adam, Cara. B.A., Cornell U., 1953; LL.B. magna cum laude, U. Pa., 1956. Bar: Pa. 1957. Law clk. U.S. Ct. Appeals (3d cir.), Phila., 1956-57; sr. law clk. U.S. Supreme Ct., Phila., 1957-58; assoc. Wolf, Block, Schorr and Solis-Cohen, Phila., 1958-65; ptnr. Wolf, Block, Schorr and Solis-Cohen, 1965—; spl. advisor divsn. corp. fin. SEC, Washington, 1964; lectr. securities law U. Pa., 1968-70, vis. assoc. prof., 1978-81, acting dir. Ctr. for Study Fin. Instns., 1978-81, acting dir. Ctr. for Study Fin. Instns.; bd. editors and advisors Rev. Securities and Commodities Regulations. Author: SEC Consequences of Corporate Acquisitions, 1971; also numerous articles; mem. editorial adv. bd. Securities Regulation Law Jour. Pres. Found. of Jewish Families and Children's Svc., Phila.; bd. dirs. Phila. Geriatric Ctr. Mem. ABA, Fed. Bar Assn., Pa. Bar Assn., Phila. Bar Assn. (chmn. sect. corp. banking and bus. law 1972). Home: 235 Linden Dr Elkins Park PA 19027 Office: Wolf Block Schorr Packard Bldg 12th Fl SE Corner 15 Chestnut St Philadelphia PA 19122

SCHNEIDER, CHARLES I., newspaper executive; b. Chgo., Apr. 6, 1923; s. Samuel Hiram and Eva (Smith) S.; m. Barbara Anne Krause, Oct. 27, 1963; children: Susan, Charles I. Jr., Kim, Karen, Traci. BS, Northwestern U., 1944. Indsl. engr., sales mgr., v.p. mktg. Curtis-Electro Lighting Corp., Chgo., 1945-54, pres., 1954-62; pres. Jefferson Electronics, Inc., Santa Barbara, Calif., 1962-64; pres. 3 sub., v.p., asst. to pres. Am. Bldg. Maintenance Industries, Los Angeles, 1964-66; group v.p. Times Mirror Co., Los Angeles, 1966-88; ret. Times Mirror Co.; pvt. investor and cons., 1988—; bd. dirs. Jeppesen Sanderson, Inc., Denver, Graphic Controls Corp., Buffalo, Regional Airports Improvement Corp. Bd. regents Northwestern U., Evanston, Ill.; trustee, past pres. Reiss-Davis Child Study Center, L.A.; bd. govs., past pres. The Music Ctr.; trustee The Menninger Found.; pres. St. John's Hosp. and Health Ctr. Found., Santa Monica, Calif. Served with AUS, 1942-44. Mem. Chief Execs. Orgn. (past pres., bd. dirs.). Clubs: Standard (Chgo.); Beverly Hills Tennis (Calif.); Big. Ten of So. Calif. Avocations: tennis, squash, music, reading. Home: 522 N Beverly Dr Beverly Hills CA 90210-3318 Office: 1801 Ave Of The Stars Ste 709 Los Angeles CA 90067 *An individual's growth and success as a manager are in direct proportion to his or her ability to develop, motivate and lead able, capable people.*

SCHNEIDER, CRAIG WILLIAM, biology educator, research botanist; b. Manchester, N.H., Oct. 23, 1948; married, 1972; 3 children. BA, Gettysburg Coll., 1970; PhD in Botany, Duke U., 1975. From asst. to assoc. prof. Trinity Coll., Hartford, Conn., 1975-87, prof. biology, 1987—. Mem Phycological Soc. Am. (Gerald W. Prescott award 1993), Internat. Phycological Soc., Brit. Phycological Soc., Sigma Xi. Achievements include research in benthic algal studies on the Southeastern United States continental shelf and in Bermuda, benthic algal ecology in Connecticut, life-history cultural studies, red-algal morphological studies. Office: Trinity Coll Dept Biology 300 Summit St Hartford CT 06106-3105*

SCHNEIDER, DAN W., lawyer, consultant; b. Salem, Oreg., Apr. 28, 1947; s. Harold Otto and Frances Louise (Warner) S.; m. Nancy Merle Schmalzbauer, Mar. 29, 1945; children: Mark Warner, Edward Michael. BA cum laude, St. Olaf Coll., 1969; JD, Willamette U., 1974; LLM, Columbia U., 1975. Bar: Oreg. 1974, D.C. 1978, Ill. 1987. Trial atty. U.S. Dept. Justice Antitrust, Washington, 1975-79; dep. assoc. dir. U.S. SEC, Washington, 1979-86; gen. ptnr. Schiff Hardin & Waite, Chgo., 1986—; bd. dirs. NygaarArt, Northfield, Minn. Contbr. articles to profl. jours. Trustee, sec. Ill. Acad. Fine Arts, Chgo., 1990—; mem. adv. bd. Steensland Art Mus., Northfield, 1990—. Recipient 1st prize Nathan Burkan Law Essay Competition ASCAP, N.Y., 1974, Christie award Securities Transfer Assn., 1987. Mem. Metropolitan Club, Chgo. Avocations: art collecting, art writing, music composition. Office: Schiff Hardin & Waite 7400 Sears Towers Chicago IL 60606

SCHNEIDER, DAVID J., psychology educator, academic administrator; b. Indpls., July 24, 1940; s. Joseph C. and Ruby Marie (Disque) S.; m. Doris Elizabeth Lieben, Dec. 21, 1962; children: Kristen Lynn, Caitlin Ann. BA, Wabash Coll., 1962; PhD, Stanford U., 1966. Asst. prof. Amherst (Mass.) Coll., 1966-71; assoc. prof. Brandeis U., Waltham, Mass., 1971-75; assoc. prof. U. Tex. San Antonio, 1975-78, prof., 1978-88; prof. Rice U., Houston, 1989—; vis. assoc. prof. Stanford (Calif.) U., 1970-71; vis. prof. Ind. U., Bloomington, 1987-88; chmn. psychology Rice U., 1990—. Author: Person Perception, 1979, Introduction to Social Psychology, 1988; editor (periodical) Social Cognition, 1980-92. Home: 2107 Southgate Blvd Houston TX 77030-2111 Office: Rice Univ PO Box 1892 Psychology Dept 6100 S Main Houston TX 77251

SCHNEIDER, DAVID MILLER, lawyer; b. Cleve., July 27, 1937; s. Earl Philip and Margaret (Miller) S.; children by previous marriage Philip M., Elizabeth Dale. BA, Yale U., 1959; LL.B., Harvard U., 1962. Assoc. Baker & Hostetler, Cleve., 1962-72, ptnr., 1972-89; sr. v.p., chief legal officer Progressive Casualty Ins. Co., Cleve., 1989—; sec. The Progressive Corp., Cleve., 1989—. Trustee Alcoholism Svcs. of Cleve., 1977—, pres., 1980-82, chmn., 1982-84; v.p. Ctr. for Human Svcs., Cleve., 1980-83; trustee Cleve. chpt. NCCJ, 1986—. Mem. ABA, Ohio Bar Assn., Bar Assn. Cleve., Union Club, Tavern Club, Hunt Club, Town Club (Jamestown, N.Y.), Ojibway Club (Pointe au Baril, Ont., Can.). Republican. Episcopalian. Home: 2767 Belgrave Rd Cleveland OH 44124-4601 Office: The Progressive Corp 6300 Wilson Mills Rd Cleveland OH 44143-2109

SCHNEIDER, DONALD FREDERIC, banker; b. N.Y.C., Nov. 12, 1939; s. Charles and Lillian (Anton) S.; m. Mary Patricia McCafferty, Sept. 7, 1963; children—Laurie, John. B.S., Lehigh U., 1961; M.B.A., N.Y. U., 1968. Mgmt. trainee Marine Midland Bank, N.Y.C., 1961-65, asst. sec., 1965-68, asst. v.p., 1968-69, v.p., 1969-79; v.p. 1st Nat. Bank Chgo., 1979-87; fin. cons. Cigna Individual Fin. Svcs. Co., Chgo., 1987; v.p. Irving Trust Co./Bank of N.Y., 1987-90, Citibank N.A., N.Y.C., 1990—; mem. corp. trust activities com. Am. Bankers Assn., fiduciary and securities ops. exec. com. Mem. Am. Soc. Corporate Secs. (pres. Chgo. region 1987), Securities Transfer Assn. Home: 88 Penwood Rd Basking Ridge NJ 07920-2240 Office: Citibank NA 111 Wall St New York NY 10043-0001

SCHNEIDER, DUANE BERNARD, English literature educator, publisher; b. South Bend, Ind., Nov. 15, 1937; s. William H. and Lillian L. (Pitchford) S.; children: Jeffrey, Eric, Lisa, Emily. BA, Miami U., Oxford, Ohio, 1958; M.A., Kent State U., 1960; Ph.D., U. Colo., 1965. Instr. engring. English U. Colo., 1960-65; asst. prof. English Ohio U., Athens, 1965-70, assoc. prof., 1970-75, prof., 1975—, chmn. Faculty Senate, 1981-83, chmn. dept. English, 1983-86; dir. Ohio U. Press, 1986—; editor, pub. Croissant & Co., 1968—. Author: (with others) Anais Nin: An Introduction, 1979; cons. editor: (with others) Thomas Wolfe Rev., 1977—; contbr. (with others) numerous articles to scholarly jours. Mem. Thomas Wolfe Soc. (trustee, pres. 1979-81). Home: PO Box 282 Athens OH 45701-0282 Office: Ohio University Press Scott Quadrangle Athens OH 45701

SCHNEIDER, EDWARD LEE, botanic garden administrator; b. Portland, Oreg., Sept. 14, 1947; s. Edward John and Elizabeth (Mathews) S.; m. Sandra Lee Alfarone, Aug. 2, 1968; children: Kenneth L., Cassandra L. BA, Cen. Wash. U., 1969, MS, 1971; PhD, U. Calif., Santa Barbara, 1974. From asst. to assoc. prof. botany S.W. Tex. State U., San Marcos, 1974-84, prof., 1984-94, chmn. biology dept., 1984-89, dean sci., 1989-92; dir. Santa Barbara (Calif.) Botanic Garden, 1992—. Contbr. articles to profl. jours. NSF grantee, 1980, 90; recipient Presdl. Rsch. award S.W. Tex. State U., 1985. Fellow Tex. Acad. Sci. (pres. 1992-93); mem. Internat. Water Lily Soc. (bd. dirs., sec. 1989—), Internat. Pollination Congress, Nat. Coun. Deans, Tex. Assn. Deans. Home: 1140 Tunnel Rd Santa Barbara CA 93105-2134 Office: Santa Barbara Botanic Garden 1212 Mission Canyon Rd Santa Barbara CA 93105-2199

SCHNEIDER, EDWARD LEWIS, medicine educator, research administrator; b. N.Y.C., June 22, 1940; s. Samuel and Ann (Soskin) S. BS, Rensselaer Poly. Inst., 1961; MD, Boston U., 1966. Intern and resident N.Y. Hosp.-Cornell U., N.Y.C., 1966-68; staff fellow Nat. Inst. Allergy and Infectious Diseases, Bethesda, Md., 1968-70; research fellow U. Calif., San Francisco, 1970-73; chief, sect. on cell aging Nat. Inst. Aging, Balt., 1973-79, assoc. dir., 1980-84, dep. dir., 1984-87; prof. medicine, dir. Davis Inst. on Aging U. Colo., Denver, 1979-80; dean Leonard Davis Sch. Gerontology U. So. Calif., L.A., 1986—, exec. dir. Ethel Percy Andrus Gerontology Ctr., 1986—, prof. medicine, 1987—, William and Sylvia Kugel prof. gerontology, 1989—; sci. dir. Buck Ctr. for Rsch. in Aging, 1989—; cons. MacArthur Found., Chgo., 1985-93, R.W. Johnson Found., Princeton, N.J., 1982-87, Brookdale Found., N.Y.C., 1985-89. Editor: The Genetics of Aging, 1978, The Aging Reproductive System, 1978, Biological Markers of Aging, 1982, Handbook of the Biology of Aging, 1985, 95, Interrelationship Among Aging Cancer and Differentiation, 1985, Teaching Nursing Home, 1985, Modern Biological Theories of Aging, 1987, The Black American Elderly, 1988, Elder Care and the Work Force, 1990. Med. dir. USPHS, 1968—. Recipient Roche award, 1964. Fellow Gerontology Soc., Am. Soc. Clin. Investigation; mem. Am. Assn. Retired Persons, U.S. Naval Acad. Sailing Squadron (coach 1980-86). Office: U So Calif Andrus Gerontology Ctr Los Angeles CA 90089-0191

SCHNEIDER, GENE W., cable television company executive, movie theater executive; b. Enid, Okla., Sept. 8, 1926; s. Harry W. and Gladys C. (Campbell) S.; m. Phyllis Gertrude Stelter, Jan. 23, 1954 (dec. 1975); children: Mark Lyle, Marta Gene Schneider Randell, Tina Michele, Carla Gene; m. Louise Huguette Rouillier, June 21, 1977; children: Michele Marie Seiver, Kim Marie Crosby, Carter John Price. BS in Engring., U. Tex., 1949. Registered profl. engr. With Continental Oil Co., 1949-51, Kwik Kafe Koffee Service, 1951-52, United Artists Entertainment Co. (and predecessors), 1952—; chmn. United Artists Entertainment Co. (and predecessors), Denver; bd. dirs. Turner Broadcasting, Atlanta, C-SPAN, Washington, Blockbuster Entertainment Corp., Ft. Lauderdale, Think Entertainment, Studio City, Calif.; chmn. United Internat. Holdings Inc., 1989—. Active Hope for the Children, St. Joseph's Hosp. Assn. Bd., others. Served with USN, 1944-46. Mem. Nat. Cable TV Assn. (bd. dirs.), Econ. Club Colo. (founding mem.). Republican. Clubs: Vintage (Indian Wells, Calif.); Cherry Hills Country (Englewood, Colo.), Glenmoor Country. Avocations: golf, tennis, hunting, fishing. Home: 6 Sunrise Dr Englewood CO 80110-4107 Office: United Artists PO Box 5227 Englewood CO 80155-5227

SCHNEIDER, GEORGE T., obstetrician-gynecologist; b. New Orleans; s. George Edmond Schneider and Erna Marie Kraft; 1 child, Lynne Schneider Cantrell. Diploma, U. Heidelberg, Fed. Republic Germany, 1938; BS, Tulane U., 1941, MD, 1944. Intern Touro Infirmary, New Orleans, 1944-45, resident ob-gyn, 1945-47; resident ob-gyn U.S. Naval Hosp., Creat Lakes, Ill., 1947-48; vice chmn. Ochsner Med. Instns., New Orleans, 1960-86, cons., 1986—; prof. ob-gyn Sch. Medicine, La. State U., New Orleans, 1965—. Contbr. numerous articles to profl. jours. Bd. dirs. Assn. Internat. Edn., Houston, 1984—, YMCA New Orleans, 1985—, Am. Cancer Soc. La. Lt. USNR, 1945. Recipient Cert. of Merit Cancer Soc. El Salvador, 1980; named hon. counsul Honduras, 1988. Fellow ACS, Am. Coll. Ob-Gyn; mem. Ob-Gyn Soc. New Orleans (past pres.), Internat. Soc. Reproductive Medicine (past pres.), Hospitaliers Order St. Lazarus. Presbyterian. Office: Ochsner Med Instns 1514 Jefferson Hwy New Orleans LA 70121-2483

SCHNEIDER, GEORGE WILLIAM, horticulturist, educator, researcher; b. East Canton, Ohio, Apr. 4, 1916; s. John W. and Cleta (Harter) S.; m. Bernice M. Youtz; children: William Wayne, George Russell. BS, Ohio State U., 1938, MS, 1939; PhD, Rutgers U., 1950. Grad. instr. Ohio State U., Columbus, 1939; instr. N.Mex. State Coll., Las Cruces, 1939-46; asst. prof. Rutgers U., New Brunswick, N.J., 1946-50; from assoc. prof. to prof. horticulture N.C. State U., Raleigh, 1950-58; head dept. horticulture U. Ky., Lexington, 1958-60, assoc. dir. extension, 1960-69, prof. hort., 1969—; chmn. extension bd. U. Wis., Madison, 1966, ECOP Com. on Devel., Washington, 1968-69. Author: Fruit Growing, 1963; contbr. articles to profl. jours. Chmn. First Meth. Ch., Lexington, 1965. Lt. (j.g) USN, 1943-46, ATO. Fellow AAAS, Am. Soc. Hort. Sci. (pomology chmn.). Home: 249 Greenbriar Rd Lexington KY 40503-2633

SCHNEIDER, HAROLD JOEL, radiologist; b. Cin., Aug. 9, 1923; s. Henry W. and Sarah Miriam (Hauser) S.; m. Mary Zipperstein, Dec. 23, 1945; children—Jill, Elizabeth, Ann, Jane. M.D., U. Cin., 1947. Diplomate Am. Bd. Radiology. Intern Cin. Gen. Hosp., 1947-48, resident in radiology, 1953-56; resident in surgery Holzer Hosp. and Clinic, Gallipolis, Ohio, 1948-49; gen. practice medicine Dayton, Ohio, 1949-50; asst. prof. radiology U. Ala. Med. Sch., Birmingham, 1956-59; assoc. prof. radiology U. Cin. Med. Center, 1959-69, prof. radiology 1969-91, prof. emeritus, 1991—; dir. diagnostic radiology Christian R. Holmes Hosp., 1959-91; former cons. Cin. VA Hosp. Contbr. articles to profl. jours. Served to lt. USNR, 1950-52. Fellow Am. Coll. Radiology; mem. Radiol. Soc. N.Am., Am. Roentgen Ray Soc., Ohio Radiol. Soc., Ohio Med. Soc., Greater Cin. Radiol. Soc., Cin. Acad. Medicine. Home: 7290 Elbrook Ave Cincinnati OH 45237-2946

SCHNEIDER, HOWARD, lawyer; b. N.Y.C., Mar. 21, 1935; s. Abraham and Lena (Pincus) S.; m. Anne Evelyn Gorfinkle; children—Andrea Rose, Jeffrey Winston. AB, Cornell U., 1956, JD with distinction, 1959. Bar: N.Y. 1959, D.C. 1976. Assoc., then ptnr. Stroock & Stroock, N.Y.C., 1959-75; gen. counsel Commodity Futures Trading Commn., Washington, 1975-77, Rosenman & Colin, N.Y.C., 1977—. Contbr. articles to profl. jours. Served to capt. USAR, 1956-66. Mem. Assn. Bar of City of N.Y. (chmn. com. 1982—), Harmonie Club (N.Y.C.). Republican. Jewish. Home: 830 Park Ave New York NY 10021-2757 Office: Rosenman & Colin 575 Madison Ave New York NY 10022-2511

SCHNEIDER, JAN, obstetrics and gynecology educator; b. Prague, Czechoslovakia, Dec. 10, 1933; came to U.S., 1963, naturalized, 1967; s. Evzen and Erika S.; m. Sandra Wilson, May 20, 1961; children—Hana, Donald, Kathryn, Jonathan. M.B., U. London, 1957; M.P.H., U. Mich., 1967. Prof. ob-gyn, chief obstetric service dept. ob-gyn U. Mich. Med. Sch., Ann Arbor, 1963-77; prof., chmn. ob-gyn Med. Coll. Pa. and Hahnemann U., Phila., 1977—. Editor: (with R. J. Bolognese and R. H. Schwarz) Perinatal Medicine, 2d edit, 1981. Fellow Am. Coll. Obstetricians and Gynecologists, Soc. Perinatal Obstetricians, Am. Gynecol. and Obstet. Soc., Phila. Obstet. Soc. Presbyterian. Office: Med Coll Pa 3300 Henry Ave Philadelphia PA 19129-1121

SCHNEIDER, JANET M., arts administrator, curator, painter; b. N.Y.C., June 6, 1950. d. August Arthur and Joan (Battaglia) S.; m. Michael Francis Sperendi, Sept. 21, 1985. BA summa cum laude, Queens Coll., CUNY, 1972; spl. study fine arts Boston U. Tanglewood Inst. 1971. With Queens Mus., Flushing, N.Y., 1973-89, curator, 1973-75, program dir., 1975-77, exec. dir., 1977-89. Collections arranged include: Sons and others, Women Artists See Men (author catalog), 1975, Urban Aesthetics (author catalog), 1976, Masters of the Brush, Chinese Painting and Calligraphy from the Sixteenth to the Nineteenth Century (co-author catalog), 1977, Symcho Moszkowicz: Portrait of the Artist in Postwar Europe (author catalog), 1978, Shipwrecked 1622, The Lost Treasure of Philip IV (author catalog), 1981, Michelangelo: A Sculptor's World (author catalog), 1983, Joseph Cornell: Revisited (author catalog), 1992, Blueprint for Change: The Life and Times of Lewis H. Latimer (co-author catalog), 1995. Chmn. Cultural Instns. Group, N.Y.C.,

1986-87; mem. N.Y.C. Commn. for Cultural Affairs, 1991-93; bd. dirs. N.Y.C. Partnership, 1987-88, Gallery Assn. N.Y. State 1979-81. Mem. Artists Choice Mus. (trustee 1979-82), Am. Assn. Mus., Phi Beta Kappa.

SCHNEIDER, JOANNE, artist; b. Lima, Ohio, Dec. 4, 1919; d. Joseph and Laura (Office) Federman; m. Norman Schneider, May 15, 1941; children—Melanie Schneider Tucker, Lois Schneider Oppenheim. B.F.A. Syracuse U., 1941. One-man shows John Heller Gallery, N.Y.C., 1954, 55, 57, 58, Tirca Karlis Gallery, Provincetown, Mass., 1963, Frank Rehn Gallery, N.Y.C., 1965, 66, 69, 72, 75, Elaine Benson Gallery, Bridgehamton, N.Y., 1972, 74, 79, 85, St. Mary's Coll., St. Mary's City, Md., 1978, Alonzo Gallery, N.Y.C., 1978, Discovery Art Gallery, Clifton, N.J., 1978; group shows include Whitney Mus., N.Y.C., Pa. Acad. Arts, Corcoran Galleries, Washington, Toledo Mus., U. Nebr., Everson Mus., Syracuse, N.Y.; represented in permanent collections Met. Mus. Art, N.Y.C., Colby Coll., Syracuse U., Butler Inst., St. Mary's Coll., U. Notre Dame, Guild Hall, East Hampton, N.Y. Recipient Audubon Artists Stanley Grumbacher Meml. award, 1972. Address: 35 E 75th St New York NY 10021-2761 *A life spent in pursuit of creative expression is a fuller, more satisfying life.*

SCHNEIDER, JOHN ARNOLD, business executive; b. Chgo., Dec. 4, 1926; s. Arnold George and Anna (Wagner) S.; m. Elizabeth C. Simpson, Oct. 20, 1951; children: Richard Ward, William Arnold, Elizabeth Anne. B.S., U. Notre Dame, 1948. Exec. assignments with CBS-TV, in Chgo. and N.Y.C., 1950-58; v.p., gen. mgr. sta. WCAU-TV, Phila., 1958-64; sta. WCBS-TV, N.Y.C., 1964-65; pres. CBS TV Network, 1965-66, CBS/Broadcast Group, 1966-69, 71-77; exec. v.p. CBS, Inc., 1969-71, sr. v.p. from, 1977; pres., chief exec. officer Warner Amex Satellite Entertainment Corp., 1979-84. Trustee, mem. exec. com. U. Notre Dame; trustee Com. for Econ. Devel. Served with USNR, 1943-46. Roman Catholic. Club: Indian Harbor Yacht. Home: North Cove Rd Old Saybrook CT 06475

SCHNEIDER, JOHN DAVID, theatre director, playwright, actor, jazz singer; b. Fond du Lac, Wis., June 7, 1948; s. David Elmer and Bernice Catherine (Pable) S. BA, St. Norbert Coll., 1970. Mem. Theatre X, Milw., 1971—; also artistic dir., 1978—, profl. playwright, 1973—; vocalist, leader John Schneider Orch., Milw., 1988—. Author: (plays) Scenarios For the Living/For the Dead, 1989; author numerous plays. Recipient New Works award Wis. Arts Bd., 1990; NEA fellow, 1988, Milwaukee County fellow, 1991, Program Devel. grantee Theatre Comms. Group-Pew Charitable Trust, 1992. Office: Theatre X PO Box 92206 Milwaukee WI 53202-0206

SCHNEIDER, JOHN HOKE, health science administrator; b. Eau Claire, Wis., Sept. 29, 1931; div.; 2 children. B.S. in Chemistry, U. Wis., Madison, 1953, M.S. in Exptl. Oncology, 1955, Ph.D., 1958. Rsch. asst. McArdle Meml. Lab., U. Wis., 1953-58; asst. prof. biochemistry Am. U. Beirut, 1958-61, Vanderbilt U. Med. Sch., 1961-62; editor in chief Biol. Abstracts, Phila., 1962-63; grants assoc. tng. program NIH, Bethesda, Md., 1963-64; sci. and tech. info. specialist, office program planning and analysis Nat. Cancer Inst., 1964-74, dir. internat. cancer rsch. data bank program, 1974-84, sci. rev. adminstr., grants rev. br., 1984-89, program dir. cancer trng. br., 1989—. Author numerous papers on nucleic acid rsch. and info. sci. Recipient numerous achievement awards. Mem. AAAS, Phi Beta Kappa, Sigma Xi. Office: Nat Cancer Inst EPN Bldg Rm 520 Bethesda MD 20892

SCHNEIDER, KEITH HILARY, news correspondent, journalist; b. White Plains, N.Y., Apr. 19, 1956; s. Martin Herbert and Jo-Anne Rosalyn (Spitzer) S.; m. Florence Marianne Barone, Oct. 20, 1984. BA, Haverford Coll., 1978. Reporter Wilkes-Barre (Pa.) Times Leader, 1978-80, The News and Courier, Charleston, S.C., 1980-81; editor S.C. Featured, Charleston, 1981-83, News West, Sacramento, Calif., 1983-85; corr. Washington Bur., N.Y. Times, 1985-87, nat. corr., 1987—. Recipient Judson Chapman award for pub. svc., 1980 and Feature Writing award, 1981 S.C. Press Assn., Columbia, George Polk Meml. award for environ. reporting, 1984, George Polk Meml. award for nat. reporting, 1989 L.I. Univ., N.Y. Jewish. Avocations: hiking, climbing, running, weight lifting, writing. Home: 12178 Nurnberger Rd Thompsonville MI 49683 Office: New York Times Washington Bur 1627 I St NW 7th Fl Washington DC 20006-4007

SCHNEIDER, MARK, political science educator; b. N.Y.C., Oct. 28, 1946; s. Irving and Ida (Schwartz) S.; m. Susan Roth, June 27, 1986; children: Johanna, Elizabeth. BA, Bklyn. Coll., 1967; PhD, U. N.C., 1974. Asst. prof. polit. sci. U. Mich., Ann Arbor, 1973-74; asst. prof. polit. sci. SUNY, Stony Brook, 1974-78, assoc. prof., 1978-85, prof., 1985—, chmn. dept., 1986—; Fulbright sr. lectr., India, 1980-81. Author: The Competitive City, 1989, Public Entrepreneurs, 1995; contbr. articles to profl. jours. Mem. Am. Polit. Sci. Assn., Midwest Polit. Sci. Assn. Office: SUNY Dept Polit Sci Stony Brook NY 11794

SCHNEIDER, MARK LEWIS, government official; b. Newark, Dec. 31, 1941; s. Benjamin and Ruth (Kobran) S.; m. Susan Gilbert, June 20, 1965; children: Aaron Mitchell, Miriam Beth. A.B. in Journalism with honors, U. Calif., Berkeley, 1963; M.A. in Polit. Sci., San Jose State Coll., 1965. Reporter UPI, San Francisco, 1963-64, San Francisco Call Bull., 1965; vol. Peace Corps, El Salvador, 1966-68; reporter Washington News Call Bull., 1969-70; mem. staff U.S. Senate Judiciary Subcom., 1970-71; legis. asst. to Sen. Edward M. Kennedy, 1971-77, 80-81; mem. U.S. Senate del. North Atlantic Assembly, 1971-73; dep. asst. sec. for human rights Dept. State, Washington, 1977-79; mem. del. UN Gen. Assembly, 1978, UN Human Rights Commn., 1979; coordinator policy planning, sr. adviser Pan Am. Health Orgn., 1981-93; adminstr. for Latin Am. and Caribbean USAID, 1993—; lectr. Kennedy Inst. Politics, Harvard U., 1976. Bd. dirs. Internat. Human Rights Law Group. Fulbright fellow, 1976; Recipient F.W. Richardson award Calif. Press Assn., 1963. Mem. Am. Polit. Sci. Assn., Latin Am. Studies Assn. Democrat. Jewish. Home: 3517 Tilden St NW Washington DC 20008-3122

SCHNEIDER, MARTIN AARON, photojournalist, ecologist, engineer, writer, artist, television director, public intervenor, educator, university instructor, lecturer; b. N.Y.C., Sept. 23, 1926; s. Morris and Florence (Frohlich) S. Stuyvesant Science, 1941-44, CUNY, 1947-52. Editor Nocturne; freelance artist, 1941—, freelance photographer, 1954—; photojournalist Life, Time, Newsweek, Sports Illustrated, N.Y. Times, NBC-TV, Ency. Britannica, Mpls. Tribune, 1960—; Time Annual Year in Review, Grolier Ency., Crowell-Collier Ency., NBC Startime, Variety, Time-Life: Ecology, Saturday Review of Literature; ecologist, USPHS, U.S. Senate, U.S. EPA, N.Y.C.EPA, N.Y. State Dept. Environ. Conservation, N.Y.C. Dept. Air Pollution, 1964—; product safety engineer, designer, builder, crash-safety, pollution and radiation monitoring, multi-alternate fuel, laboratory vehicle, 1967—, instr., lectr. NYU, Cornell U., Ithaca, NY, New Sch. Social Rsch., N.Y.C., SUNY, Albany, Cooper Union Advancement Science and Art, N.Y.C., CUNY, Iowa U., lectr. in field, 1969—; pub. intervenor, N.Y.C. Health Dept., N.Y. State Health Dept., N.Y. State Dept. Environ. Conservation, Gov. Rockefeller's State Study Commission for N.Y.C. (Scott Commission), U.S. District Ct., N.Y. Supreme Ct.; People of N.Y.C., N.Y.C. Council, N.Y. Attorney General, 1970— . TV news guest NBC Today, CBS, ABC, 1970—; radio news guest NBC, CBS, NPR, 1970—; TV and radio commentator NBC, CBS, ABC, PBS, FOX, 1970—; author: Breath of Death, 1972, Consumer Genocide, 1992; The Schneider Tapes, 1996, War Against War, ed. 1996; co-author: America-Photographic Statements, 1972, Eye of Conscience, 1974; dir., prodr., writer, videographer, cinematographer (TV documentaries) Environment Crusade, CBS, 1970, The Poisoned Air, CBS, 1970, Killers of the Environment, NBC, 1971, Censorship of Pollution Solutions by Media and Government, PBS, 1974, No Justice for Victims-Criminals Only, 1992; contbr. N.Y. Times, Ency. Britannica, Macmillan Ency. of Photographic Artists, N.Y. Village Voice Whole Earth Ranger: "Ecology's Batman", New World Or No World (Frank Herbert) 1970—; photography exhibited at Mus. Modern Art, N.Y.C., 1958—, George Eastman House Mus., Rochester, N.Y., 1963, 64—, Libr. Congress, 1970, Smithsonian Instn., 1972—, Art Inst. Chgo., 1973—, Whitney Mus., N.Y.C., 1978—; painting exhibited at Guggenheim Mus., N.Y.C., 1943; film exhibited at Am. Mus. Natural History, N.Y.C., 1969-72. Served with U.S. Army Paratroopers, 1944-46, PTO. Fellowship grantee Creative Artists Pub. Svc., 1977, 78; recipient TV Franny Consumer Advocacy award, 1974, for work that was a basis for the first Clean Air Act of 1970. Jewish. Office: 1501 Broadway Ste 2907 New York NY 10036-5502 *Where millions are*

endangered where my work makes a difference--despite gunfire, vehicle sabotage, censorship--there is no dream for me in moving mere mountains, but only in moving man to move himself.

SCHNEIDER, MATTHEW ROGER, lawyer; b. N.Y.C., Nov. 7, 1948; s. Theodore David Schneider and Rosalind (Schwartz) Werner; m. Marjorie Ann Friedlander, Mar. 6, 1976; children: Adam Benjamin, Emily Beth. BA, Cornell U., 1970; student, Georgetown U., 1971; JD, Cath. U., Washington, 1974. Bar: D.C. 1976, U.S. Dist. Ct. D.C. 1994. Staff asst. U.S. Senate Jud. Com., Washington, 1973-74; counsel U.S. Senate Govt. Ops. Com., Washington, 1974-77; spl. asst. Office of Sec. Def., Washington, 1977-79; dir. legis. affairs SEC, Washington, 1979-81, sr. counsel, divsn. corp. fin. 1981-82; chief of staff U.S. Senator Jeff Bingaman, Washington, 1983-85; prin. Law Office Matthew Schneider, Washington, 1985-87; ptnr. Willkie, Farr & Gallagher, Washington, 1987— . Bd. dirs. Capitol Hill Hosp., Washington, 1981-87, Epilepsy Found. for Nat. Capital Area. Avocations: biking, singing, guitar. Office: Willkie Farr & Gallagher 1155 21st St NW Washington DC 20036-3308

SCHNEIDER, MICHAEL JOSEPH, biologist; b. Saginaw, Mich., Apr. 21, 1938; s. Michael Elias and Jane (Moffitt) S.; m. Janet Marie Potter, Nov. 24, 1967. B.S., U. Mich., 1960; M.S., U. Tenn., 1962; Ph.D. (Hutchinson Meml. fellow 1963-64, John M. Coulter research fellow 1964-65), U. Chgo., 1965. Resident research asso. Nat. Acad. Scis., Beltsville, Md., 1965-67; USPHS fellow U. Wis., Madison, 1967-68; asst. prof. biology Columbia U., 1968-73; mem. faculty U. Mich., Dearborn, 1973—, prof. biology, 1975—, chmn. dept. natural scis., 1975-80, 83-89, assoc. provost for acad. affairs, 1990, interim provost, vice chancellor for acad. affairs, 1991; vis. prof. Plant Research Lab., Mich. State U., East Lansing, 1980-81. Contbr. articles profl. jours. Mem. AAAS, Am. Soc. Plant Physiologists, Am. Soc. Photobiology, Sigma Xi. Home: 48511 Meadow Ct Plymouth MI 48170-3256 Office: U Mich-Dearborn Dept Nat Scis Dearborn MI 48128-1491

SCHNEIDER, NORMAN M., food manufacturing company executive; b. N.Y.C., Feb. 5, 1911; s. David and Edith S.; m. JoAnne Federman, May 15, 1940; children: Melanie Schneider Tucker, Lois Schneider Oppenheim. B.A., U. Scranton, 1932. Partner Norsid Co., N.Y.C., 1932-46; founder, pres. Allison Mfg. Co., N.Y.C., 1946-70; pres. and chmn. leisure products div. Beatrice Co. Inc., Chgo., 1970-81; mgmt. cons. Beatrice Co. Inc., 1981-86; pres. Schneider Assocs., N.Y.C., 1987—; mem. N.Y. Bd. Trade; bd. dirs. Park Electrochem. Corp., Toys R Us, Datascope Corp. Recipient Man of Yr. award Boy Scouts Am. Mem. Explorers Club, Harmonie Club. Office: 46 E 70th St New York NY 10021-4928

SCHNEIDER, PETER RAYMOND, research scientist, juvenile justice consultant; b. Muskogee, Okla., Aug. 8, 1939; s. Leo Frederick and Tillie Oleta (Cannon) S.; m. Anne Larason, Jan. 22, 1964 (div. 1983); children: Christopher, Geoffrey; m. Adrienne Armstrong, Dec. 19, 1986; 1 child, Robbie. BS, Okla. State U., 1966, MS, 1968; PhD, Ind. U., 1974. News editor No. Va. Sun, Arlington, 1961-62; news writer AP, Balt., 1962, Balt. News-Am., 1962-65; asst. prof. U. Oreg., Eugene, 1974-76; pres. Inst. of Policy Analysis, Eugene, 1976-83; v.p. Am. Justice Inst., Sacramento, 1983; dir. Ctr. for Assessment of The Juvenile Justice Ctr., Sacramento, 1983; v.p. Nat. Partnership, Washington, 1985; sr. rsch. scientist Pacific Inst. for Rsch. and Evaluation, Bethesda, Md., 1984-92, dir. justice div., 1986-89; pres. Inst. of Policy Analysis, Vienna, Va., 1992—; lectr. on restitution, juvenile justice and drug abuse. Contbr. numerous articles to profl. jours., chpts. to books. Recipient Julia Lathrop award Am. Criminal Justice Assn., 1985, 8 major grants, 1976—, including U.S. Dept. Justice. Mem. Am. Polit. Sci. Assn., Am. Restitution Assn., Pi Sigma Alpha, Sigma Delta Chi, Phi Kappa Phi, Omicron Delta Kappa, Phi Kappa Theta. Avocations: flying, tennis, selling wine. Home: 9025 Streamview Ln Vienna VA 22182-1726 Office: Inst Policy Analysis 8133 Leesburg Pike Ste 260 Vienna VA 22182

SCHNEIDER, PHYLLIS LEAH, writer, editor; b. Seattle, Apr. 19, 1947; d. Edward Lee Booth and Harriet Phyllis (Ebbinghaus) Russell; m. Clifford Donald Schneider, June 14, 1969; 1 child, Pearl Brooke. B.A., Pacific Luth. U., 1969; M.A., U. Wash., 1972. Fiction, features editor Seventeen Mag., N.Y.C., 1975-80; mng. editor Weight Watchers Mag., N.Y.C., 1980-81; editor YM mag., N.Y.C., 1981-86. Author: Parents Book of Infant Colic, 1990, Kids Who Make a Difference, 1993, Straight Talk on Women's Health: How to Get the Health Care You Deserve, 1993, Hot Health Care Careers, 1993, What Kids Like To Do, 1993. Recipient Centennial Recognition award Pacific Luth. U., 1990. Democrat. Episcopalian.

SCHNEIDER, RAYMOND CLINTON, architect, educator; b. Smyrna, N.Y., Dec. 10, 1920; s. George William and Helen (Carey) S.; m. Margaret Maude Pearce, Sept. 16, 1943 (dec. Aug. 3, 1982); children: Stephen Eric, Martha Anne (dec.), Pearce Clinton.; m. Ruth Brown Martsolf, Jan. 2, 1983 (div. Jan. 1986); m. Gertraude R. McMullen, May 28, 1986 (div. Sept. 1988); life ptnr. M. Maxine La Shell. B.S. in Architecture, Kans. State U., 1949, M.S. in Edn., 1952; Ed.D., Stanford U., 1955. Registered architect, Kans. Architect firms in Salina and Manhattan, Kans., 1947-51; assoc. dir. sch. planning lab., asso. dir. W. Regional Center Ednl. Facilities Lab., also research asso., lectr. edn. Stanford U., Palo Alto, 1955-62; head personnel subsystems sect., systems tech. lab. Sylvania Corp., Mountain View, Calif., 1962-63; dir. research and planning Porter, Gogerty, Meston, San Jose, Calif., 1963-64; assoc. prof. edn. and architecture U. Wash., Seattle, 1964-78; prof. architecture and edn. U. Wash., 1978-82, prof. emeritus, 1983—; asst. to dean, 1964-73, dir. grad. program architecture, 1976-83, exhibiting artist and sculptor, 1946—, cons. in field. Author articles in field, chpts. in books. Served with AUS, 1942-46. Kellogg fellow, 1953-54; Masonite Co. fellow, 1954-55; Borg-Warner Co. fellow, 1954-55. Mem. VFW (life), Am. Assn. Retired Persons, Am. Legion. Address: 4406 SW 29th Ter Topeka KS 66614-3102

SCHNEIDER, RICHARD GRAHAM, lawyer; b. Bryn Mawr, Pa., Aug. 2, 1930; s. Vincent Bernard and Marion Scott (Graham) S.; m. Margaret Peter Fritz, Feb. 15, 1958; children: Margaret W., Richard Graham, John F. BA, Yale U., 1952; JD, U. Pa., 1957. Bar: Pa. 1958. Assoc. Dechert Price & Rhoads, Phila., 1957-66; ptnr. Dechert Price & Rhoads, 1966— . Case editor U. Pa. Law Rev., 1956-57. Trustee Baldwin Sch., Bryn Mawr, 1971-79; trustee Episcopal Acad., Merion, Pa., 1976-83. 1st lt. USAF, 1952-54, PTO. Mem. ABA, Pa. Bar Assn., Phila. Bar Assn., Order of Coif, Merion Cricket Club, Merion Golf Club, Yale Club (pres. 1966-68). Republican. Presbyterian. Office: Dechert Price & Rhoads 4000 Bell Atlantic Tower 1717 Arch St Philadelphia PA 19103-2713

SCHNEIDER, RICHARD T(HEODORE), optics research executive, engineer; b. Munich, July 29, 1927; came to U.S., 1961; s. Wilhelm and Martha E. (Hofmann) S.; m. Lore M. Reinhard, May 16, 1950; children: Ursula M. Schneider Long, Richard W. Diploma in physics, U. Stuttgart, Fed. Republic of Germany, 1958, PhD, 1961. Registered profl. engineer, Calif. Teaching asst. U. Stuttgart, 1958-61; sect. chief Allison div. Gen. Motors Corp., Indpls., 1961-65; assoc. prof. U. Fla., Gainesville, 1965-68, prof., 1968-88, prof. emeritus, 1988-90; pres. Eye Rsch. Lab., Inc., Alachua, Fla., 1984-90; chief scientist RTS Labs., Inc., Alachua, 1984-92; cons. Allison div. Gen. Motors Corp., Indpls., 1965-67; IPA assignment Eglin AFB, Ft. Walton Beach, Fla., 1983; liaison scientist USN Office Naval Rsch., London, 1975. Editor: Uranium Plasmas, 1971; patentee in field; contbr. articles to profl. jours. Recipient Medal for Exceptional Sci. Achievement, NASA, 1975, Outstanding Tech. Achievement award, Fla. Engring. Soc., 1978. Mem. Optical Soc. Am., Am. Phys. Soc., Internat. Soc. for Optical Engring., Sigma Xi, Tau Beta Pi (Eminent Engr. 1970). Avocation: flying airplanes. Home: 17 Alachua Highlands Alachua FL 32615-9561 Office: Eye Rsch Lab 1663 Technology Ave Alachua FL 32615-9400

SCHNEIDER, ROBERT JEROME, lawyer; b. Cin., June 22, 1947; s. Jerome William and Agnes (Moehringer) S.; m. Janice Loraine Eckhoff, Dec. 13, 1968; children: Aaron Haisley, Jared Alan, Margot Laraine. B.S. in Mech. Engring., U. Cin., 1970, J.D., 1973. Bar: Ill. 1973, U.S. Dist. Ct. (no. dist.) Ill. 1973, U.S. Ct. Appeals (7th cir.) 1973, U.S. Ct. Appeals (fed. cir.) 1973-82. Ptnr. Mason, Kolehmainen, Rathburn & Wyss, Chgo., 1973-82; ptnr., chmn. intellectual property dept. McDermott, Will & Emery, Chgo. 1982-94; ptnr. intellectual property and tech. svcs. group Keck Mahin & Cate, Chgo., 1994— . Mem. ABA, ASME, Ill. Bar Assn., Chgo. Bar Assn.,

Licensing Execs. Soc., Intellectual Property Law Assn. Chgo. (sec. 1981-83), Fedn. Internat. des Conseils en Proriete Industrielle, Assn. Internationale Pour la Protection de la Propriété Industrielle, Internat. Trademark Assn., Am. Intellectual Property Law Assn., Inter-Pacific Bar Assn., Tower Club (bd. govs. 1988—, v.p. 1994—). Republican. Roman Catholic. Home: 1609 Asbury Ave Winnetka IL 60093-1303 Office: Keck Mahin & Cate 77 W Wacker Dr Chicago IL 60601-1693

SCHNEIDER, SOL, electronic engineer, consultant, researcher; b. N.Y.C., Feb. 24, 1924; s. David Schneider and Noami (Savin) S.; m. Rhoda Botwinick, Apr. 16, 1950; children: Sandra E., Barry. BA, CUNY Bklyn. Coll., 1946; MS, NYU, 1949. Supervisory physicist U.S. Army Electronics Tech. and Devices Lab., Ft. Monmouth, N.J., 1948-80, chief pulse power and plasma devices, 1956-80; cons. Rockwell Internat., Canoga Park, Calif., 1980-81, U.S. Army Pulse Power Ctr., Ft. Monmouth, 1982—, SRI, Internat., Menlo Park, Calif., 1983-91, Vitronics, Inc., Eatontown, N.J., 1987—; adj. prof. Southwestern U. Dept. Tech., Clear Water, Fla., 1980-86; cons. Los Alamos (N.Mex.) Nat. Lab., 1980-81; mem. USN Pulsed Power Tech. Adv. Group, Washington, 1978-80, SDIO Pulsed Power Tech. Adv. Group, 1983-93; assoc. mem. Adv. Group on Electronic Devices, Dept. Def., Washington, 1970-80. Contbr. articles to profl. jours.; holder 14 patents. With U.S. Army, 1943-46, ETO. Recipient Spl. Act award Sec. Army, 1963, U.S. Army R&D Achievement award Dept. Army, 1963, 78, Army Sci. award, 1978. Fellow IEEE (chmn./editor symposium proc. 1957-80, chmn. emeritus power modulator symposium 1981—, co-chmn. high voltage workshop 1989-90, exec. com. 1991—, High Voltage award 1991, Germeshausen award 1992); mem. Am. Phys. Soc. (exec. com. gaseous electronics conf. 1961-66, sec. 1964, exec. com. electron and atomic physics divsn. 1965-66). Home: 100 Arrowwood Ct Red Bank NJ 07701

SCHNEIDER, STEPHEN HENRY, climatologist, environmental policy analyst, researcher; b. N.Y.C., Feb. 11, 1945; s. Samuel and Doris C. (Swarte) S.; married, 1978; 2 children. BS, Columbia U., 1966, MS, 1967, PhD in Mechanical Engring., 1971; DSc (hon.), N.J. Inst. Tech., 1990, Monmouth Coll., 1991. NAS, NRC postdoctoral research assoc. Goddard Inst. Space Studies NASA, N.Y.C., 1971-72; fellow advanced study program Nat. Ctr. Atmospheric Research, Boulder, Colo., 1972-73, scientist, dep. head climate project, 1973-78, acting leader climate sensitivity group, 1978-80, head visitors program and dep. dir. advanced study program, 1980-87; sr. scientist Nat. Ctr. Atmospheric Research, Boulder, 1980; head interdisciplinary climate systems sect. Nat. Ctr. Atmospheric Research, Boulder, Colo., 1987-92; prof. Nat. Ctr. Atmospheric Rsch., Stanford (Calif.) U., 1992—; affiliate prof. U. Corp. Atmospheric Rsch. Lamont-Doherty Geol. Obs., Columbia, U., 1976-83; mem. Carter-Mondale Sci. Policy Task Force, 1976; sci. adviser, interviewee Nova, Sta. WGBH-TV, Planet Earth, Sta. WQED-TV; mem. internat. sci. coms. climatic change, ecology, energy, food and pub. policy; expert witness congl. coms.; mem. Def. Sci. Bd. Task Force on Atmospheric Obscuration. Author: (with Lynne E. Mesirow) The Genesis Strategy: Climate and Global Survival, 1976, (with Lynne Morton) The Primordial Bond: Exploring Connections between Man and Nature through Humanities and Science, 1981, (with Randi S. Londer) The Coevolution of Climate and Life, 1984, Global Warming: Are We Entering the Greenhouse Century?, 1989, (with W. Bach) Interactions of Food and Climate, 1981, (with R.S. Chen and E. Boulding) Social Science Research and Climate Change: An Interdisciplinary Appraisal, 1983, (with K.C. Land) Forecasting in the Social and Natural Sciences, 1987; editor: Climatic Change, 1976—; contbr. sci. and popular articles on theory of climate, influence of climate on soc., relation of climatic change to world food, population, energy and environ. policy issues, environ. aftereffects of nuclear war, carbon dioxide greenhouse effect, pub. understanding sci. Recipient Louis J. Battan Author's award Am. Meteorol. Soc., 1990; named one of 100 Outstanding Young Scientists in Am. by Sci. Digest, 1984; MacArthur Found. Prize fellow John D. and Catherine T. MacArthur Found., 1992. Fellow AAAS (Westinghouse award 1991), Scientists Inst. for Pub. Info.; mem. U.S. Assn. Club Rome, Am. Meteorological Soc., Am. Geophysical Union, Nat. Fedn. Am. Scientists. Office: Stanford U Nat Ctr Atmospheric Rsch Stanford CA 94305-5020*

SCHNEIDER, STEVEN ARNOLD, educational administrator, consultant; b. Montclair, N.J., Mar. 18, 1950; s. Morton Macy Schneider and Betty Lee (Randolph) Baron; m. Susan Hall Arbuckle, Aug. 16, 1987; 1 child, Ayelet. AB in Biol. Scis., U. Calif., Berkeley, 1972; sci. teaching credential, Calif. State U., San Jose, 1973; PhD in Design and Evaluation of Edn., Stanford U., 1989. Life teaching credential, Calif. Tchr. biology Piedmont Hills High Sch., San Jose, 1973-78; tchr. physics, chmn. sci. dept. Santa Cruz (Calif.) High Sch., 1978-83; instr. sci. edn. U. Calif., Santa Cruz, 1983-85; sci. supr. Stanford (Calif.) U., 1985-88; sci. edn. cons. Woodside (Calif.) Rsch. Consortium, 1988—; program dir. for sci. and math. Far West Lab., San Francisco, 1989—; cons. SRI Internat., Menlo Park, Calif., 1988—, Stanford U., 1989—, NSF, Washington, 1990-91. Contbr. articles to profl. jours. Bd. dirs. YMCA, Woodside, 1989-90; advisor Monterey Bay Aquarium, Monterey, Calif., 1991—. Mem. NSTA, AAAS, Am. Ednl. Rsch. Assn., Phi Delta Kappa. Avocations: swimming, water polo. Home: 4140 Jefferson Ave Woodside CA 94062

SCHNEIDER, THOMAS RICHARD, hospital administrator; b. Cin., July 16, 1944; s. Richard Arthur and Janet (Tingley) S.; m. Judith Ann Johnson, June 10, 1967; children: Gregory Thomas, Marcia Kay, Jill Elise. BS in Bus. Adminstrn., Miami U., Oxford, Ohio, 1966; MHA, U. Minn., 1968. Asst. adminstr. Meml. Hosp. of South Bend, Ind., 1971-77, Ft. Hamilton-Hughes Meml. Hosp., Hamilton, Ohio, 1977-82; assoc. adminstr. Ft. Hamilton-Hughes Meml. Hosp., 5, Ohio, 1982-84, assoc. adminstr., chief oper. officer, 1984-85, v.p. ops. and profl. svcs., 1985-91; adminstr. Shriners Hosp. for Crippled Children, Shreveport, La., 1992—; chmn. health careers Greater Cin. Hosp. Coun., 1983-90; mem. adv. bd. Xavier U. Ctr. for Health Mgmt. Edn., Cin., 1985-91; trustee Cmty. Blood Ctr., Dayton, Ohio, 1985-91. Trustee, 1st v.p. YMCA of Hamilton-Fairfield, 1990; chmn. city charter comms. com. City of Hamilton, 1990; chmn. pub. svc. div. United Way of Hamilton-Fairfield, 1988-90. Mem. Med. Svc. Corps. USN, 1968-71. Recipient Disting. Svc. award YMCA, 1992, Gt. Am. Family award of honor, 1990, Proclamation, Mayor and City Coun. of Hamilton, 1992. Fellow Am. Coll. Healthcare Execs.; mem. Rotary Internat., Masons, Shriner. Republican. Methodist. Avocations: fishing, golf, boating, reading, clowning. Home: 535 Northpark Dr Bossier City LA 71111 Office: Shriners Hosp 3100 Samford Ave Shreveport LA 71103

SCHNEIDER, VALERIE LOIS, speech educator; b. Chgo., Feb. 12, 1941; d. Ralph Joseph and Gertrude Blanche (Gaffron) S. BA, Carroll Coll., 1963; MA, U. Wis., 1966; PhD, U. Fla., 1969; cert. advanced study Appalachian State U., 1981. Tchr. English and history Montello High Sch. (Wis.), 1963-64; dir. forensics and drama Montello High Sch., 1963-64; instr. speech U. Fla., Gainesville, 1966-68, asst. prof. speech, 1969-70; asst. prof. speech Edinboro (Pa.) State Coll., 1970-71; assoc. prof. speech East Tenn. State U., Johnson City, 1971-76, prof. speech, 1976—; instr. newspaper course Johnson City Press Chronicle, 1979, Elizabethton Star, Erwin Record, Mountain City Tomahawk, Jonesboro Herald and Tribune, 1980; mem. investor panel USA Today, 1991-92. Editor East Tenn. State U. evening and off-campus newsletter, 1984-91; assoc. editor: Homiletic, 1974-76; columnist Video Visions, Kingsport Times-News (Tenn.), 1984-86; book reviewer Pulpit Digest, 1986-90; contbr. articles on speech to profl. jours. Chmn. AAUW Mass Media Study Group Com., Johnson City, 1973-74. Recipient Creative Writing award Va. Highlands Arts Festival, 1973; award Kingsport (Tenn.) Times News, 1984, 85, Tri-Cities Met. Advt. Fedn., 1983, 84; Danforth assoc., 1977; finalist Money mag. contest 'Best Personal Fin. Mgrs', 1994. Mem. Speech Communication Assn. (Tenn. rep. to states adv. council 1974-75), So., Tenn. (exec. bd. 1974-77, publs. bd. 1974-78, pres. 1977-78), Religious Speech Communication Assn. (Best article award 1976), Tenn. Basic Skills Council (exec. bd. 1979-80, v.p. 1980-81, pres. 1981-82), AAUW (v.p. chpt. 1974-75, pres. 1975-76, corp. rep. for East Tenn. State U. 1974-76), So. Assn. Continuing Higher Edn., Bus. and Profl. Women's Club (chpt. exec. bd. 1973-74, v.p. 1976-77), Mensa, Delta Sigma Rho-Tau Kappa Alpha, Phi Delta Kappa, Delta Kappa Gamma, Pi Gamma Mu. Presbyterian. Home: 3201 Buckingham Rd Johnson City TN 37604-2715 Office: East Tenn State U PO Box 23098 Johnson City TN 37614-0124

SCHNEIDER, WILLIAM CHARLES, aerospace consultant; b. N.Y.C., Dec. 24, 1923; s. Charles J. and Margaret (Stoeffler) S.; m. Roseann Vasco, Oct. 6, 1964; children: Catherine M., Jeanne M., Robert J., Robert Sherer. BS, MIT, 1949; MS, U. Va., 1952; D in Engring., Cath. U. Am., 1976. Rsch. scientist NACA Langley Rsch. Ctr., Hampton, Va., 1949-55; asst. br. head Air-to-Air Missiles Bur. Aeros., Washington, 1955-60; dir. space vehicles USN Bur. Weapons, Washington, 1960-61; dir. space systems Internat. Tel. & Tel., Nutley, N.J., 1961-63; dep. dir. Gemini program Office Manned Space Flight NASA Hdqrs., Washington, 1963-65; dir., dep. dir. operations, mission dir. Office Manned Space Flight NASA Hdqrs. (Gemini program), 1965-66; dir. Apollo Applications Missions, 1966-67, Apollo Mission dir., 1967-68, dir. Skylab program, 1968-74, dep. assoc. adminstr. for space transp. systems, 1974-78, assoc. adminstr. for space tracking and data systems, 1979-80; v.p. mgmt. and product assurance Systems Group Computer Scis. Corp., Falls Church, Va., 1980-83; v.p. control systems Computer Scis. Corp., Falls Church, 1983-85, v.p. devel., 1985-90; cons., 1990—; mem. life scis. strategic planning bd. NASA, life scis. div. working group, aerospace medicine adv. com. NASA, mem. space sta. adv. com.; mem. adv. space tech. com. NRC; bd. dirs. Spacetech Inc. Mem. bd. visitors Cath. U. Served with USNR, 1942-46. Recipient Exceptional Service medal NASA, 1965, Distinguished Service medal, 1968-73, Outstanding Leadership medal, 1980; Apollo Group Achievement award, 1969; Astronautics Engr. award, 1974; Robert J. Collier trophy, 1974; Am. Astronautical Soc. Space Flight award, 1974. Fellow AIAA, Internat. Acad. Astronautics, Planetary Soc., Am. Astron. Soc. (v.p.); mem. VFW, Armed Forces Comm. and Electronics Assn., Energy Mgmt. and Control Soc., NASA Alumni League (treas.), Brit. Interplanetary Soc. Home and Office: 11801 Clintwood Pl Silver Spring MD 20902-1707

SCHNEIDER, WILLIAM GEORGE, chemist, research consultant; b. Wolseley, Sask., Can., June 1, 1915; s. Michael and Phillipina (Krauschaar) S.; m. Jean Purves, Sept. 2, 1940; children: Judith Schneider Saunders, Joanne Schneider Spurrier. B.Sc., U. Sask., 1937, M.Sc., 1939, D.Sc., 1969; Ph.D., McGill U., 1941, D.Sc., 1970; D.Sc. (hon.), York U., 1966, Meml. U., 1968, McMaster U., 1969, Laval U., 1969, Moncton U., 1969, U. N.B., 1970, U. Montreal, 1970, Acadia U., 1976, U. Regina, 1976, Ottawa U., 1978; LL.D., U. Alta., 1968, Laurentian U., 1968. Head phys. chemistry sect., div. chemistry NRC Can., Ottawa, Ont., 1946-63; dir. div. pure chemistry NRC Can., 1963-65, v.p., 1965-67, pres., 1967-80; research cons., 1980—. Author: (with J.A. Pople, H.J. Bernstein) High Resolution Nuclear Magnetic Resonance, 1959; contbr. articles to profl. jours. Decorated Order of Can., 1977. Fellow Royal Soc. Can. (Henry Marshall Tory medal), Royal Soc. London, Chem. Inst. Can. (medal 1969, Montreal medal 1973); mem. Internat. Union Pure and Applied Chemistry (pres. 1983-85). Office: Unit # 2, 65 Whitemarl Dr, Ottawa, ON Canada K1L 8J9

SCHNEIDER, WILLIAM GEORGE, former life insurance company executive; b. Shenandoah, Iowa, Jan. 18, 1919; s. Fred M. and Abba F. (Ferguson) S.; m. Phyllis Welch, Mar. 28, 1943; children—Stephen F., Richard W. B.A., State U. Iowa, 1940; postgrad., N.Y. U. With Met. Life Ins. Co., 1940-41, 45-46; with Bankers Life Co. (now named Prin. Fin. Group), Des Moines, 1946-84; sr. v.p. Bankers Life Co., 1970-82, exec. v.p., 1982-84, ret., 1984. Served with AUS, 1941-45. Fellow Soc. Actuaries; mem. Am. Acad. Actuaries, Phi Beta Kappa. Republican. Clubs: Des Moines, Des Moines Golf and Country. Home: 3662 Ingersoll Ave Apt 414 Des Moines IA 50312-3422

SCHNEIDER, WILLYS HOPE, lawyer; b. N.Y.C., Sept. 27, 1952; d. Leon and Lillian (Friedman) S.; m. Stephen Andrew Kals, Jan. 21, 1979; children: Peter, Josefine. AB, Princeton U., 1974; JD, Columbia U., 1977. Bar: N.Y. 1978, U.S. Dist. Ct. (ea. and so. dists.) N.Y. 1978, U.S. Tax Ct. 1979. Law clk. to judge U.S. Dist. Ct. (ea. dist.), Bklyn., 1977-78; assoc. Paul, Weiss, Rifkind, Wharton & Garrison, N.Y.C., 1978-83; ptnr. Kaye, Scholer, Fierman, Hays & Handler, N.Y.C., 1983—. Contbr. articles to profl. jours. Mem. ABA, N.Y. State Bar Assn., Assn. of Bar of City of N.Y. Home: 320 West End Ave New York NY 10023-8110 Office: Kaye Scholer Fierman Hays & Handler 425 Park Ave New York NY 10022-3506

SCHNEIDER, WOLF, magazine editor, writer; b. N.Y.C., Mar. 5, 1953; d. Mortimer Stanley and Helene Carol (Werner) S. BA, CCNY, 1975; MA, U. So. Calif., 1976. Disc jockey Sta. KNCN-FM, Corpus Christi, Tex., 1977-78; producer Sta. KMET-FM, L.A., 1980-85; editor Videopreview mag., L.A., 1986; film reporter The Hollywood Reporter, L.A., 1987-88; dir. pub. rels. Showtime Networks, L.A., 1989-90; editor Am. Film Mag., L.A., 1990-92; film columnist L.A. Weekly, 1995—; panel moderator NCTA Conv., 1985, panel moderator Billboard Am. Film Inst. Video Conf., 1987; guest lectr. Assn. of Film Commrs. Cineposium, L.A.1988; awards judge Nat. Cable Forum Ace awards, L.A., 1986, 88; course instr. Am. Film Inst., L.A., 1991, 92. Contbr. articles to profl. jours., popular mags. Mem. publicity com. IFP West, L.A., 1989-90. Mem. PEN/West, 1990—, AFI, 1989—. Avocation: horseback riding. Office: LA Weekly 6715 Sunset Blvd Los Angeles CA 90028

SCHNEIDERMAN, DAVID ABBOTT, publisher, journalist; b. N.Y.C., Apr. 14, 1947; s. Robert D. and Mary (Torres) S.; m. Peggy Rosenthal, Sept. 19, 1981. BA, Johns Hopkins U., 1969, MA, 1970. Asst. to the editor op-ed page N.Y. Times, 1970-74, op. editor, 1974-78; editor in chief Village Voice, N.Y.C., 1979-87, pub., 1985-88, 91—, pres., 1985—; publ. 7 Days, N.Y.C., 1988-90; pres. Stern Pub., 1995—; chmn. L.A. (Calif.) Weekly Inc., 1995—; mem. libr. coun. Johns Hopkins U. Office: Village Voice 36 Cooper Sq New York NY 10003 also: LA Weekly 6715 Sunset Blvd Los Angeles CA 90028

SCHNEIDERMAN, HERBERT BARRY, hospital administrator; b. St. Louis, Dec. 15, 1945; m. Eilene Schneiderman; children: Jeffrey, Greg. BA, U. Mo., 1967; MA, Washington U., St. Louis, 1969. Adminstrv. asst. St. Mary's Hosp., East Saint Louis, Ill., 1969-71, asst. adminstr., 1971-74; from assoc. dir. to asst. dir. St. Louis U. Hosps., 1974-83; exec. dir. Univ. Hosp., St. Louis, 1983—; cons. Inst. Health Mgmt., St. Louis, 1980-81; lectr., preceptor St. Louis grad. health adminstrn. program, St. Louis, 1981—. Fellow ACHE; mem. ARC, Mid-Am. Transplant Assn. Jewish. Home: 491 Whitree Ln Chesterfield MO 63017-2449 Office: St Louis U Hosp 3635 Vista At Grand Blvd Saint Louis MO 63110

SCHNEIDERMAN, IRWIN, lawyer; b. N.Y.C., May 28, 1923; s. Meyer and Bessie (Klein) S.; m. Roberta Haig, Nov. 28, 1966; 1 child, Eric T. BA, Bklyn. Coll., 1943; LLB cum laude, Harvard U., 1948. Bar: N.Y. 1949, D.C. 1952. Assoc. Cahill Gordon & Reindel, N.Y.C., 1948-59, ptnr., 1959-89, sr. counsel, 1990—; bd. dirs. Contel Cellular Inc.; spl. cons. to chmn. SEC, 1981-82, mem. adv. com. on tender offers, 1983. Trustee Bklyn. Coll. Found., 1983—; co-chmn. N.Y.C. Opera, 1993—; chmn. bd. WNYC Found., 1993—; bd. dirs. City Ctr. Music and Drama, Inc., 1990—, N.Y.C. NARAL, 1990—; Lincoln Ctr. for the Performing Arts, Inc., 1994—. Lt. (j.g.) USNR, 1943-46. Mem. Harvard Club. Home: 203 E 72d St New York NY 10021 Office: Cahill Gordon & Reindel 80 Pine St New York NY 10005-1702

SCHNEIDERMAN, RICHARD STEVEN, museum official; b. Lakehurst, N.J., June 27, 1948; s. Rubin and Dorothy (Fleer) S.; m. Kathleen Alyse Matteson, Sept. 1, 1969; children: Matthew, Adam, Justin, Jessica. BA, Hartwick Coll., 1970; MA, U. Cin., 1973; PhD, SUNY-Binghamton, 1976. Lectr. dept. art SUNY-Binghamton, 1974, 76; adj. prof. art history Tompkins-Courtland Community Coll., 1976; curator prints and drawings Ga. Mus. Art, Athens, 1976-86, acting dir., 1980-81, dir., 1981-86; dir. N.C. Mus. Art, Raleigh, 1986-93; lectr. various civic, fraternal and profl. orgns. Author: A Catalogue Raisonne of the Prints of Sir Francis Seymour Haden, 1983, A Catalogue Raisonne of the Prints of Charles Meryon, 1990; contbr. papers to profl. lit. 1976-81. Trustee Athens-Clarke Heritage Found., 1982-85. U. Cin. Dept. Art History grad. scholar, 1972; U. Cin. univ. grad. scholar, 1972-73; SUNY-Binghamton Grad Provost's grantee for travel, 1974-75; Samuel H. Kress research grantee Kress Found., 1975-76. Mem. Print Council Am., Coll. Art Assn. Am., Am. Assn. Mus., Internat. Council on Mus., Assn. Art Mus. Dirs. Office: 4600 Forestville Rd Raleigh NC 27604-9723

SCHNEIER, HARVEY ALLEN, physician, pharmaceutical researcher; b. Rochester, N.Y., Jan. 5, 1942; s. Jacob G. and Rose (Ergort) S.; m. Lynn C. Teitelbaum, Aug. 9, 1964 (div. Dec. 1981); m. Barrie Mandel; children: Matthew, Margo, Jonathan. AB, Columbia U., 1963, MD, 1967. Diplomate Am. Bd. Internal Medicine. Asst. chief gen. med. svc. Walter Reed Army Med. Ctr., Washington, 1971-72; assoc. in medicine Columbia-Presbyn. Med. Ctr., N.Y.C., 1973-75, asst. attending physician, 1975-89, assoc. attending physician, 1989—; assoc. med. dir. Forest Labs., Inc., N.Y.C., 1993—; asst. prof. clin. medicine Columbia P&S, 1975-89, assoc. clin. prof., 1989—; corp. med. cons. United Brands Co., N.Y.C., 1980-92; cons. Am. Bd. Internal Medicine, Phila., 1991—. Served to maj. M.C. U.S. Army, 1969-73. Decorated Meritorious Svc. medal. Mem. ACP, AMA, Alpha Omega Alpha. Avocations: theater, folk art collecting. Home: 25 Harrison St New York NY 10013 Office: Forest Labs Inc 909 3d Ave New York NY 10022

SCHNEITER, GEORGE MALAN, golfer, development company executive; b. Ogden, Utah, Aug. 12, 1931; s. George Henery and Bernice Slade (Malan) S.; B. Banking and Fin., U. Utah, 1955; m. JoAnn Deakin, Jan. 19, 1954; children: George, Gary, Dan, Steve, Elizabeth Ann, Michael. With 5th Army Championship Golf Team U.S. Army, 1955-56; assoc. golf pro Hidden Valley Golf Club, Salt Lake City, 1957; golf pro Lake Hills Golf Club, Billings, Mont., 1957-61, sec., 1957-61, pres., 1964—; pres. Schneiter Enterprises, Sandy, Utah, 1974—; developer Schneiter's golf course, 1973—, and subdiv., 1961—; player PGA tour 1958-78; sr. player PGA tour, 1981—. With U.S. Army, 1955-56. Winner Utah sect. Sr. Championship, Wyo. Open Super Sr. Championship, Salt Lake City Parks Tournament, Vernal Brigham Payson Open, Yuma Open, Ariz.; named U.S. Army Ft. Carson Post Golf Champ, 5th Army Championship Golf Team, 1955-56. Mem. PGA, Am. Mormon, Salt Lake City C. of C., Internat. Golf Course Supertaints Assn. Office: 8969 S 1300 E Sandy City Chamber UT 84094-1965 *Personal philosophy: I think everyone should try to make the world a better place to live than it was when we entered it and we should try to help each other and live in peace.*

SCHNELL, CARLTON BRYCE, lawyer; b. Youngstown, Ohio, Jan. 1, 1932; s. Carlton Wilhelm and Helen Jean (Alexander) S.; m. Dorothy Stewart Apple, Aug. 15, 1953; children—Laura, Margaret, Heidi. B.A., Yale U., 1953, LL.B., 1956. Bar: Ohio 1956. Assoc. Arter & Hadden, Cleve., 1956-65, ptnr., 1966—, mng. ptnr., 1977-82; mng. ptnr. Arter & Hadden, Washington, 1982-84. Exec. comm. mem. Greater Cleve. Growth Assn., Cleve., 1983—; chmn. Build Up Cleve., 1981-89; profl. chmn. United Way, Cleve., 1983; co-chmn. Charter Rev. Commn., Cleve., 1983-84; pres. Citizen's League Rsch. Inst., 1992—. Named Vol. of Yr., Leadership Cleve., 1985. Mem. Tex. Club Cleve. (pres. 1972-73), Cleve. Tax Inst. (chmn. 1978), Ohio C. of C. (trustee 1977-80). Republican. Presbyterian. Clubs: Union, Pepper Pike. Avocations: golf; tennis. Home: 31450 Shaker Blvd Cleveland OH 44124-5153 Office: Arter & Hadden 1100 Huntington Blvd Cleveland OH 44115

SCHNELL, GARY DEAN, zoology educator, administrator; b. Lyons, Kans., July 30, 1942. BS in Biology, Ctrl. Mich. U., 1964; MS in Biology, No. Ill. U., 1966; PhD in Zoology, U. Kans., 1969. Grad. asst. dept. biol. scis. No. Ill. U., 1964-66; grad. teaching asst. depts. zoology and biology U. Kans., 1966-68, NSF grad. fellow, 1968-69; coord. origin and structure of ecosystems integrated rsch. program Internat. Biol. Program, 1969-70; rsch. assoc. dept. zoology U. Tex., Austin, 1969-70; assoc. in ornithology Natural History Mus. U. Kans., 1979—; curator of birds Okla. Mus. Natural History (formerly Stovall Mus. Sci. and History) U. Okla., Norman, 1971—, head curator for zoology Okla. Mus. Natural History, 1972-74, head curator for life scis. Okla. Mus. Natural History, 1974—, interim dir. Okla. Mus. Natural History, 1979-80, 82-83, from asst. to assoc. prof. dept. zoology, 1970-83, prof. dept. zoology, 1983—, dir. Okla. Biol. Survey, 1978—; vis. rsch. assoc. dept. biology and Ctr. for Evolution and Paleobiology U. Rochester, 1977-78; OU assocs. lectr. U. Okla., 1984-85; chair local com. ann. meeting Internat. Numerical Taxonomy Group, 1980; mem. The Coun. Soc. Systematic Zoology, 1980-86; mem. steering com., prin. lectr. NATO Advanced Study Inst. Numerical Taxonomy, 1981-82; lectr. U.S. Army Corps Engrs., Chgo., 1982; sec. Assn. Systematic Collections, 1983-86; invited mem. Pre-SOPS panel S.W. Fisheries Ctr. NOAA, La Jolla, Calif., 1983; mem. postdoctoral and midcareer fellowship adv. panel divsn biotic systems and resources NSF, 1991; vice chair Consortium State Biol. Surveys, 1993—; cons. in field. Author: (with J.A. Grzybowski) Oklahoma Ornithology: An Annotated Bibliography, 1984, (with D.S. Wood) Distributions of Oklahoma Birds, 1984, Oklahoma Mammalogy: An Annotated Bibliography and Checklist, 1989; author: (with others) A Symposium on Ecosystematics, 1972, Academic American Encyclopedia, 21 vols., 1980, Mammalian Population Genetics, 1981, Numerical Taxonomy, 1983, foreward to My Way to Ornithology, 1992, Oklahoma Almanac, 85th edit., 1993-94, 1993; asst. editor Systematic Zoology, 1967-68, mng. editor, 1968-69, editor, 1983-86; editor IBP Inter-Am. News, 1969-70; sci. editor Am. Birds, 1975-90; contbr. numerous articles to profl. jours. Bd. dirs. Cleveland County Bird Club, 1971-73, v.p., 1973-75; mem. animal rsch. coun. Oklahoma City Zoo, 1972-85, mem. exec. com., 1974-77; chair nominating com. Cleveland County Audubon Club, 1975-76; merit badge counselor zool. projects Cub Scouts Am., 1975-76; merit badge counselor Boy Scouts Am., 1981-89, coord. spl. field projects in natural history, 1982, 84, 85, 86, 88; mem. selection com. Okla. conservation achievement awards Okla. Wildlife Fedn., 1978-83, chair, 1982-83, chair nongame com., 1978-82, bd. dirs., 1978-85, mem. exec. com., 1979-83; mem. adv. com. Sutton urban wilderness area Parks and Recreation Dept. City of Norman, 1978—; mem. water quality monitoring adv. com. Okla. State Dept. Health, 1978-85; mem. task force for developing model fish and wildlife plan Okla. Dept. Mines, 1978-80; mem. gov's pollution contol task force State of Olka., 1980-81; mem. controlled indsl. waste coun. Dept. of Health State of Okla., 1981-90; mem. panel of judges to recommend recipient 1st achievement award for new scholars Conf. So. Grad. Schs., 1985; judge Okla. duck stamp competition Okla. Dept. Wildlife Conservation, 1986; expert evaluator, enforcement U.S. Fish and Wildlife Svc., 1988-91; mem. natural resources cabinet State of Okla., 1988-90; mem. enironment subcabinet State of Okla., 1990-92. Recipient NSF award U. Mich. Biol. Sta., 1963, 64, 65; grantee U. Okla., 1970, 73, 74, 75, 76, 77-78, 78, 80-81, 81, 81-82, 82-83, 82, 85-87, 87, 88-89, NSF, 1971-75, 72-74, 78-81, 82-83, 84-86, Okla. U. Rsch. Inst., 1972, U.S. Army Constrn. Engring. Rsch. Lab., 1979, 79-80, 80, 81, 81-82, 88, 88-89, 88-90, 89-90, 90-91, 90-92, 91-92, 91-93, 92, 92-93, 93, 92-94, 93-94, 93-95, 94—, Okla. Conservation C979, NOAA, 1979-81, 84, 90, Okla. Dept. Wildlife Conservation, 1979-80, 85, 85-86, 89-90, 92-93, Okla. Dept. Tourism and Recreation, 1981-82, Kerr Found., 1982-84, NEH, 1983-85, Okla. Found. for Humanities, 1983, U.S. Dept. Interior, 1983-85, 85-86, NUS Corp. 1984-85, U.S. Fish and Wildlife Svc., 1988-89, 89, 89-90, 89-91, 89-94, U.S. Dept. Agriculture, 1988-89, Nature Conservancy, 1988-89, 92-92, 93-94, 93-94, Univ. Rsch. Fund, 1989, U.S. Forest Svc., 1989-92, U.S. Army, 1991, 91-92, U.S. Dept. Def., 1991-92, 93-94, 92—, 93—, U.S. Dept. Army, 1991-93, 92, 92-93, 92-94, Colo. State U., 1992, Okla. Dept. Transp., 1993, 93-94, 94—, Heatherly Mining Co., 1993, Woodward-Clyde Fed. Svcs., 1993-94, Nat. Parks Svc., 1993-95, U.S. Dept. Interior, Fish and Wildlife Svc., 1993-95. Fellow AAAS, Am. Ornithologists' Union (editorial asst. The Auk 1966-67, editor 1991—, chair local and sci. program com. ann. meeting 1991, sci. collections com., chair com. for permanent secretariat 1982-84, co-chair sci. program com. 1983-84, chair 1988-88, com. honoraria for officers 1984, program coord. asst. to sec. 1988-91, The Coun. 1988—, program coord. joint meeting with Cooper Ornithol. Soc. 1989-90); mem. Am. Soc. Mammalogists, Am. Soc. Naturalists, Okla. Acad. Sci., Okla. Ornithol. Soc. (book com. 1982-90, grantee 1982-83), Okla. Wildlife Fedn., Southwestern Assn. Naturalists (bd. govs. 1973-78, 81-83, 86-91, 93—, student awards com. 1978-80, pres.-elect 1981-82, pres. 82-83, chair local com. arrangements ann. meeting 1986, program com. ann. meeting 1986, Robert I. Packard Outstanding Educator award 1994, awards com., 1994—), Assn. Field Ornithologists, Cooper Ornithol. Soc. (membership com. 1972-75, assoc. editor The Condor 1974-83, The Coun. 1974-81, nominating com. for honorary mems. 1975-79, chair local meeting 1991, joint meeting with Wilson Ornithol. Soc. 1988-91), Classification Soc. (editorial bd. classification lit. automated search svc. 1984-86), Soc. Study Evolution, Soc. Systematic Biology, Soc. Marine Mammalogy, Wilson Ornithol. Soc. chair Edwards' prize com. 1977-78), Nature Conservancy, Sigma Xi. Home: 4106 Coventry Ln Norman OK 73072 Office: U of Okla Dept Zoology and Okla Biol Survey 111 E Chesapeake St Norman OK 73019

SCHNELL, GEORGE ADAM, geographer, educator; b. Phila., July 13, 1931; s. Earl Blackwood and Emily (Bernheimer) S.; m. Mary Lou Williams, June 21, 1958; children: David Adam, Douglas Powell, Thomas Earl. BS, West Chester U., 1958; MS, Pa. State U., 1960, PhD, 1965; postdoctoral study, Ohio State U., 1965. Asst. prof. Coll. SUNY, New Paltz, 1962-65, assoc. prof., 1965-68, prof. geography, 1968—, founding chmn. dept., 1968—; vis. assoc. prof. U. Hawaii, summer 1966; cons. community action programming, 1965; manuscript reader, cons. to several pubs., 1967—; founder, founding bd. mem. Inst. for Devel., Planning and Land Use Studies, 1986—; cons. Mid-Hudson Pattern for Progress, 1986, Open Space Inst., 1987, Mid-Hudson Regional Econ. Devel. Coun., 1989, Urban Devel. Corp., 1989-90, 93, Tech. Devel. Ctr., 1991, Catskill Ctr., 1991, Ednl. Testing Svc., 1993; mem. exec. bd. Hudson Valley Study Ctr.; cons. depts. of geography, 1988—. Author: (with others) The Local Community: A Handbook for Teachers, 1971, The World's Population, Problems of Growth, 1972, Pennsylvania Coal: Resources, Technology, Utilization, 1983, West Virginia and Appalachia: Selected Readings, 1977, Hazardous and Toxic Wastes: Technology, Management and Health Effects, 1984, Environmental Radon: Occurrence, Control and Health Hazards, 1990, Natural and Technological Disasters: Causes, Effects and Preventive Measures, 1992, Conservation and Resource Management, 1993; co-author: (with M.S. Monmonier) The Study of Population: Elements, Patterns, Processes, 1983, (with Monmonier) Map Appreciation, 1988; editor: (with G.J. Demko and H.M. Rose) Population Geography: A Reader, 1970; contbr. articles to profl. jours.; presenter papers to more than 60 ann. meetings of scholarly and profl. socs. Appt. mem. local bds. and coms. Town and Village of New Paltz, and New Paltz Ctrl. Sch. Dist., 1965—; elder Reformed Ch. of New Paltz. With AUS, 1952-54. Recipient Excellence award N.Y. State/United Univ. Professions, 1990; Disting. Alumnus award West Chester U., 1994. Mem. Assn. Am. Geographers, Pa. Geog. Soc. (mem. editl. bd. Pa. Geographer, Disting. Geographer award 1994), Pa. Acad. Sci. (assoc. editor jour. 1988—). Home: 29 River Park Dr New Paltz NY 12561-2636 Office: SUNY Coll at New Paltz Dept Geography 75 S Manheim Blvd New Paltz NY 12561

SCHNELL, JOSEPH, dancer; b. Marin County, Calif.. Student, Sch. Am. Ballet, 1983; scholarship student, The Joffrey Ballet Sch., 1984-85. Dancer Joffrey II Dancers, N.Y.C., 1984, The Joffrey Ballet, N.Y.C., 1987—. Office: The Joffrey Ballet 130 W 56th St New York NY 10019-3818*

SCHNELL, ROBERT LEE, JR., lawyer; b. Mpls., Sept. 20, 1948; s. Robert Lee and Dorothy Mae (Buran) S.; m. Jacqueline Irene Husak, Dec. 19, 1969 (div. Aug. 1988); children: Robert Lee III, Elizabeth Anne, Jennifer Irene; m. Julie Ann Bemlott, Sept. 29, 1989; children: Helen Bridget, Michael Henry. BA cum laude, Princeton U., 1970; JD magna cum laude, Harvard U., 1974. Bar: Minn. 1974, U.S. Dist. Ct. Minn. 1974, U.S.C. Ct. Appeals (8th cir.) 1975, U.S. Supreme Ct. 1990. Assoc. Faegre & Benson, Mpls., 1974-81, ptnr., 1982—. Bd. dirs. United Way of Mpls., 1992-93. Office: Faegre & Benson 2200 Norwest Ctr 90 S 7th St Minneapolis MN 55402

SCHNELL, ROGER THOMAS, retired military officer, state official; b. Wabasha, Minn., Dec. 11, 1936; s. Donald William and Eva Louise (Barton) S.; m. Barbara Ann McDonald, Dec. 18, 1959 (div. Mar. 1968); children: Thomas Allen, Scott Douglas; m. Young H. Kim, Sept. 25, 1987 (div. Nov. 1993); children: Eunice, Candice. A in Mil. Sci., Command and Gen. Staff Coll., 1975; A in Bus. Administn., Wayland Bapt. U., 1987. Commnd. 2d lt. Alaska N.G., 1959, advanced through grades to col., 1975; shop supt. Alaska N.G., Anchorage, 1965-71, personnel mgr., 1972-74, chief of staff, 1974-87, dir. logistics, 1987; electrician Alaska R.R., Anchorage, 1955-61, elec. foreman, 1962-64; dir. support personnel mgmt. Joint Staff Alaska N.G., 1988-92, ret.; personnel mgr. State of Alaska, 1992; asst. commr. dept. mil. and vets. affairs State of Alaska, Ft. Richardson, 1992-95, dep. commr. dept. mil. and vets. affairs, 1995—. Mem. Fed. Profl. Labor Relations Execs. (sec. 1974-75), Alaska N.G. Officers Assn. (pres. 1976-78, bd. dirs. 1988—), Am. Legion, Amvets. Republican. Methodist. Lodge: Elks. Avocations: bowling, photography. Home: 6911 Hunt Ave Anchorage AK 99504-1891 Office: Dept Mil and Vets Affairs State of Alaska PO Box 5800 Camp Denali Bldg #4900 Fort Richardson AK 99505-0800 *Personal philosophy: Success is built on honesty, hard work, determination, committment and the ability to make personal sacrifices to strive for high professional goals. Always keep a positive attitude and treat each person as you would like to be treated.*

SCHNELL, RUSSELL CLIFFORD, atmospheric scientist, researcher; b. Castor, Alta., Can., Dec. 12, 1944; s. Henry Emmanuel and Anna (Traudt) S.; m. Suan Neo Tan, May 25, 1974; children: Alicia, Ryan. BSc with distinction, U. Alta. (Can.), Edmonton, 1967; MSc, Meml. U., St. John's, Nfld., Can., 1968; MSc, U. Wyo., 1971, PhD, 1974. Research scientist U. Wyo., Laramie, 1971-74, Nat. Ctr. Atmospheric Research and NOAA, Boulder, Colo., 1974-76; dir. Mt. Kenya Study World Meteorol. Orgn. div. UN, Nairobi, Kenya, 1976-78; research scientist U. Colo., Boulder, 1979-82, dir. Arctic Gas and Aerosol Sampling Program, 1982-92, fellow Coop. Inst. Research in Environ. Scis., 1985-92; dir. Mauna Loa Observatory, Hilo, Hawaii, 1992—; mem. aerobiology com. Nat. Acad. Sci., 1976-79; cons. UN, Geneva, 1977-80, Shell Devel., Modesto, Calif., 1978-79, Holme, Roberts & Owen, 1990-92; mem. adv. bd. Frost Tech., Norwalk, Conn., 1983-85; bd. dirs. TRI-S Inc., Louisville, Colo., Magee Sci.,. Editor Geophys. Research Letters, Arctic Haze Edit., 1983-84; discovered bacteria ice nuclei, 1969; patentee in field; contbr. articles to profl. jours. Bd. dirs. Boulder Valley Christian Ch., 1978-91; chmn. Boulder Council Internat. Visitors, 1983-85. Rotary Internat. fellow, 1968-69. Mem. Am. Geophys. Union, AAAS, Am. Meteorol. Soc. (cert. cons. meteorologist), Internat. Assn. Aerobiology, Soc. Cryobiology, Sigma Xi, Sigma Tau. Avocations: travel, real estate investing, public speaking, flying. Home: 1 Kahoa Rd Hilo HI 96720-2205 Office: Mauna Loa Observatory PO Box 275 Hilo HI 96721-0275

SCHNELLE, KARL BENJAMIN, JR., chemical engineering educator, consultant, researcher; b. Canton, Ohio, Dec. 8, 1930; s. Karl Benjamin and Kathryn Emily (Hollingsworth) S.; m. Mary Margaret Dabney, Sept. 8, 1954; children: Karl Dabney, Kathryn Chappell. BS, Carnegie Mellon U., 1952, MS, 1957, PhD, 1959. Registered profl. engr., Tenn. Chem. engr., shift foreman Organics area Pitts. Plate Glass Co., New Martinsville, W.Va., 1952-54; asst. prof. chem. engring. Vanderbilt U., 1958-61, assoc. prof., 1961-64, assoc. prof. environ. and air resources engring., 1967-70, prof., 1970-80, chmn. div. socio-technol. systems, 1972-75, chmn. environ. and water resources engring., 1975-76, chmn. environ. engring. dept., 1976-80, chmn. chem. engring. dept., 1980-88, prof. chem. and environ. engring., 1980—; Alexander Head disting. svc. prof., 1995-96; v.p. ECCE, Nashville, 1983-88, pres., 1989—; mem. Air Pollution Control Bd., State Tenn., 1978-82, 82-87; Fulbright prof. U. Liege, Belgium, 1977; invited prof. Universite Catholique de Louvain, Belgium, 1982; vis. prof. chem. engring. Danish Tech. Inst., Lyngby, Denmark, 1988-89. Fellow AICE; mem. Air and Waste Mgmt. Assn., Instrument Soc. Am., Am. Soc. Engring. Edn., Am. Soc. Environ. Engrs., Sigma Xi, Phi Kappa Phi, Tau Beta Pi. Office: Vanderbilt U PO Box 1683 Station B Nashville TN 37235

SCHNEPS, JACK, physics educator; b. N.Y.C., Aug. 18, 1929; s. Elias and Rose (Rephen) S.; m. Lucia DeMarchi, Mar. 11, 1960; children: Loredana, Melissa, Leila. B.A., N.Y. U., 1951; M.S., U. Wis., 1953, Ph.D., 1956. Asst. prof. physics Tufts U., 1956-60, assoc. prof., 1960-63, prof., 1963—, chmn. dept. physics, 1980-89; vis. scientist European Orgn. Nuclear Research, Geneva, Switzerland, 1965-66; lectr. Internat. Sch. Elementary Particle Physics, Yugoslavia, 1968; vis. research fellow Univ. Coll., London, Eng., 1973-74; vis. prof. Ecole Polytechnique, Palaiseau, France, 1982-83, The Technion, Haifa, Israel, 1989-90. Contbg. author: Methods in Subnuclear Physics, Vol. IV, 1970; editor Proc. of Neutrino 88, 1989; contbr. articles to profl. jours. NSF postdoctoral fellow U. Padua, Italy, 1958-59. Fellow Am. Phys. Soc.; mem. European Phys. Soc., AAUP, Phi Beta Kappa, Sigma Xi. Home: 3 Foxcroft Rd Winchester MA 01890-2407 Office: Dept Physics Tufts U Medford MA 02155

SCHNERING, PHILIP BLESSED, investment banker; b. Detroit, Dec. 26, 1917; s. Otto Young and Dorothy (Russell) S.; m. Ruth Scott, June 10, 1940; children: Sally, Sandra, Philip S., Judith, Wendy. BA, U. Chgo., 1939. Salesman, retail crew worker, factory trainee Curtiss Candy Co., Chgo., 1938-40, salesman supr., 1940, dist. field mgr., 1941-43, asst. to pres., 1943-48, v.p., div. sales mgr., 1948-53, exec. v.p., 1953-58; dir. comml. devel.

McCormick & Co., Inc., Balt., 1958-64; exec. v.p. Farboil Co., Balt., 1965-66; pres. Bowen Co., Balt., 1966-72; investment banker, 1973—; chmn. bd. Curtiss Breeding Svc., Cary, Ill. Vice pres. Balt. Boy Scouts Am.; past pres., dir. Balt. coun. Camp Fire Girls; chmn. nat. bd., dir. fin. com. Nat. Camp Fire Girls; trustee Nat. Coun. Crime and Delinquency; chmn. Md. Commn. Crime and Delinquency; assoc. trustee Northwestern U. Mem. Am. Mgmt. Assn., Soc. Am. Archaeology, Antique Auto Club, Balt. Yacht Club, Green Spring Valley Hunt Club. Home: Hillside Rd Stevenson MD 21153 Office: PO Box 61 Stevenson MD 21153-0061

SCHNEYER, CHARLOTTE ALPER, physiologist, researcher, educator; b. St. Louis, Nov. 21, 1923; d. Nathan and Anna (Schoenfeld) Alper; m. Leon H. Schneyer, June 11, 1945 (dec. Oct. 1976). A.B. with final honors, Washington U., St. Louis, 1945; M.S., NYU, 1947, Ph.D., 1952. Research asst. Marine Biology Lab, Woods Hole, Mass, 1944; grad. teaching fellow NYU, 1945-52; rsch. assoc. U. Ala., Birmingham, 1952-55, asst. prof. dentistry 1955-59, assoc. prof. dentistry, 1959-64, prof. dentistry, 1964—, asst. prof. physiology, 1962-65, assoc. prof. physiology, 1965-67, prof., 1967—, dir. Lab. Exocrine Physiology, 1977—, sr. scientist Cystic Fibrosis Rsch. Ctr., 1981—; grant reviewer NSF, NIH; mem. spl. grants rev. com. Nat. Inst. Dental Rsch., 1979-82; mem. gen. med. scis. coun. NIH, 1972-76; honored invitee to numerous internat. symposia. Co-editor: Secretory Mechanisms of Salivary Glands, 1967; contbr. chpts. to numerous books; manuscript reviewer Am. Jour. Physiology, Jour. Autonomic Nervous System, Archives Oral Biology, Jour. Oral Pathology, Jour. Dental Rsch., Proc. Soc. Exptl. Biology and Medicine (mem. editorial bd. 1980-86), Clin. Investigation, others. adj. curator art glass Birmingham Mus. Art, 1985—. Nat. Inst. Dental Rsch. rsch. grantee, 1958—; presented room of art glass and art pottery to Birmingham Mus. of Art, honoring Dr. Leon H. Schneyer, 1981—. Mem. Am. Physiol. Soc., Soc. for Exptl. Biology and Medicine, Hungarian Dental Assn. (hon.), Internat. Assn. for Dental Rsch. (first recipient Salivary Rsch. award 1991), Sigma Xi, Omicron Kappa Upsilon (hon.), Alpha Lambda Delta. Avocations: painting; enameling; art glass; composing music; bicycling. Office: U Ala Lab Exocrine Physiology University Sta Birmingham AL 35294

SCHNITZER, IRIS TAYMORE, financial management executive; b. Cambridge, Mass., Aug. 3, 1943; d. Joseph David and Edith (Cooper) Taymore; m. Stephen Mark Schnitzer, Sept. 10, 1966. BA in Econs., Boston U., 1967; postgrad., Mass. Sch. Law, 1992—. Lic. real estate broker, life ins. advisor, life ins. and health ins. broker; registered rep. NASD; CFP; CLU; cer. in fin. counseling, advanced pension planning. Real estate broker Woods Real Estate, Braintree, Mass., 1968; real estate broker, property mgr. Village Gate Realty, Brockton, Mass., 1969; agt. Prudential Ins., Boston, 1970-73; supr. edn. and advanced underwriting, agt. Northwestern Mutual Life, Boston, 1973-78; fin. planning cons. Iris Taymore Schnitzer Assocs., Boston, Mass., 1973-79; trainer fin. planners Gerstenblatt Co., Newton, Mass., 1978-79; founder, pres. The Fin. Forum, Inc., Boston, 1979-91, TFF, Inc. at the Chase Exchange, N.Y.C., 1980-83; pres. I&S Assocs., Boston, 1991-93; v.p. Fleet Investment Svcs., Boston, 1993—; bd. dirs., clk. Mister Tire, Inc., Abington, Mass.; arbitrator Nat. Assn. Securities Dealers, 1992—. Contbr. articles to profl. jours. Chmn. credit com., bd. dirs. Mass. Feminist Fed. Credit Union, Boston, 1975-77; bd. dirs. Ledgewood, Brookline, Mass., 1967-70, LWV, Brockton, Mass., 1968-70, NOW, Boston, 1972-73; bd. govs. Women's City Club, Boston, 1976-80; pres. Mass. divsn. Women's Equity Action League, 1977-79; life mem. Navy League U.S, Boston, 1985—; treas., bd. dirs. Festival of Light and Song, 1989-92; bd. dirs. Achievement Rewards for Coll. Scientists, Boston, 1991-93, 94-95; mem. steering com. Fleet Bank of Mass. United Way, 1994—. Named One of the Best Fin. Planners in the U.S., Money Mag., 1987, to Mutual Funds Panel, Sylvia Porter's Personal Fin. Mag., 1988, 89. Mem. Am. Assn. Individual Investors (pres. Boston chpt. 1987-89, bd. dirs. 1985—), Boston Estate Planning Coun., Boston Club. Avocations: sailing, gardening, interior and fashion design, animals, classical music. Office: Fleet Investment Svcs MABOFO5A 75 State St Boston MA 02109-1807

SCHNITZER, JAN EUGENIUSZ, medical educator, scientist; b. Pitts., June 24, 1957. BSChemE, Princeton U., 1980; MD, U. Pitts., 1985. Assoc. rsch. scientist Sch. Medicine Yale U., New Haven, Conn., 1985-90; asst. prof. San Diego Sch. Medicine U. Calif., La Jolla, 1990-93; sr. asst. prof. Med. Sch. Harvard U., Boston, 1994—. Mem. editl. bd. Am. Jour. Physiology-Heart, 1993—. Recipient Investigator award Am. HEart Assn. and Gerentech, 1993—; grantee NIH, 1989—. Office: Harvard U Med Sch Beth Israel Hosp Path 99 Brookline Ave Rsch N Boston MA 02215

SCHNITZER, ROBERT C., theater administrator; b. N.Y.C., Sept. 8, 1906; s. Louis and Clara (diBilliani) S.; m. Marcella Abels Cisney, June 7, 1953. Grad., Horace Mann Sch. for Boys, 1923; A.B., Columbia U., 1927. State dir. Del., asst. dep. nat. dir. Fed. Theatre Project, 1936-39; exec. dir. Civic Theatre, Kalamazoo, Mich., 1939-40; faculty Vassar Coll., 1941-42, Smith Coll., 1942-43, Columbia U. Sch. Dramatic Arts, 1948-54; cons. Martha Graham Sch. Dance, Rollins Sch. Theatre, Randall Sch. Theatre, Dramatic Workshop of New Sch., Denver Red Rocks Theatre, Utah Centennial, 1945-49; vets. counselor Nat. Theatre Conf., 1945-46; gen. mgr. ANTA Exptl. Theatre, 1946-47, recipient Sidney Howard award, ANTA Album, 1951, Cheryl Crawford Prodns., 1952-53, Gilbert Miller Prodns., 1953-54, Am. Nat. Theatre and Acad. Internat. Cultural Exchange, profl. agt. for Dept. State, 3500 Am. performers to over 100 fgn. countries, 1954-60; gen. mgr. overseas tour Theatre Guild Am. Repertory Co. under auspices of Dept. State, 1960-61; exec. dir. Theatre Profl. Theatre Program U. Mich., prof. theatre arts, Ann Arbor, 1961-73, prof. emeritus and exec. dir. emeritus, 1974—; co-founder, exec. dir. Univ. Resident Theatre Assn., 1969-74, cons., 1974—; del. U.S. Nat. Conf. on UNESCO, 1953-57, 1st Inter-Am. Conf. Exchange Persons, 1958; vis. theatre expert German Fgn. Office Cultural Exchange Program, 1965; cons. to pres. U. Bridgeport for Coll. Fine Arts, 1975-87; disting. vis. prof. U. Miami, Fla., 1980, U. Bridgeport, Conn., 1981; co-founder Westport Arts Ctr., 1984, interim pres., 1985, v.p., 1986, chmn. bd. 1987-89, chmn. emeritus, 1989—; mem. Fulbright selection com. theatre arts, 1955-59, Mich. Council Arts, 1961-73; hon. bd. dirs. Westport/Weston Arts Council, 1969-84. Stage mgr., actor, Theatre Guild, Walter Hampden, Katherine Cornell, other Broadway cos., 1927-36; owner, dir., Robin Hood Summer Theatre, Arden, Del., 1933-40; gen. mgr. U.S. participation, Denmark Hamlet Festival, Elsinore, 1949, 1st Am. Ballet Theatre tour, Europe, 1950, U.S. ofcl. participation, Berlin Festivals, 1951-53, U.S. participation, Congress Cultural Freedom Festival, Paris, 1952, U.S. Salute to France, Paris, 1955; arranged visits to U.S., Greek Nat. Theatre, 1952, Yugoslav Nat. Folk Ballet, 1956, Shanta Rao East Indian Dance Co., 1957; Contbr. articles in field to various publs. Served with ARC, 1943-45, CBI. Recipient Pres.'s Citation U. Mich., 1971, Arts Mgmt. Career Award for services to Am. theatre, 1971; Rockefeller Found. grantee, 1948; grad. fellowship in theatre adminstrn. named in honor U. Mich., 1974; Robert C. Schnitzer collection established at George Mason U. Mem. Coll. Fellows of Am. Theatre (life), Actors Equity Assn., Am. Nat. Theatre and Acad., Assn. Theatrical Press Agts. and Mgrs., Nat. Coun. Arts and Govt., Nat. Theatre Conf., Theatre Libr. Assn., U.S Inst. Theatre Technicians, The Players Club, The Century Club. Home: 9 Riverbank Rd Weston CT 06883-2316

SCHNITZLEIN, HAROLD NORMAN, anatomy educator; b. Hannibal, Mo., Aug. 29, 1927; s. Harold Daniel and Martha Anna (Wilhelm) S.; m. Harriett Elizabeth Scheidker, June 2, 1949; children: Jan Elizabeth, Paul Norman, Daniel Richard, Thomas Harry. AB, Westminster Coll., Fulton, Mo., 1950; MS, St. Louis U., 1952, PhD, 1954. USPHS fellow Dept. Anatomy St. Louis U., 1951-54; instr. anatomy U. Ala., Birmingham, 1954-57, asst. prof., 1957-62, assoc. prof., 1962-70, prof., 1970-73; chmn., prof. anatomy U. S. Fla. Coll. Medicine, Tampa, 1973-78, prof. 1978-85, prof. anatomy and radiology, 1985-93, prof. anatomy, radiology, neurology, 1985-93; clin. prof. radiology U. Diagnostic Inst., Tampa, 1993—. Coauthor: Correlative Comparative Anatomy Vertebrate Tel., 1982, Imaging Anatomy: Head and Spine, 2d edit., 1990. Sgt. USAAF, 1946-47. Office: U Diagnostic Inst Tampa FL 33612

SCHNOBRICH, ROGER WILLIAM, lawyer; b. New Ulm, Minn., Dec. 21, 1929; s. Arthur George and Amanda (Reinhart) S.; m. Angeline Ann Schmitz, Jan. 21, 1961; children: Julie A. Johnson, Jennifer L. Holmers, Kathryn M. Kubinski, Karen L. Holetz. BBA, U. Minn., 1952, JD, 1954. Bar: Minn. 1954. Assoc. Fredrikson and Byron, Mpls., 1956-58; pvt. prac-

tice Mpls., 1958-60; ptnr. Popham Haik, Schnobrich & Kaufman, Mpls., 1960—; bd. dirs. numerous corps., Mpls. With U.S. Army, 1954-56. Mem. ABA, Minn. Bar Assn., Hennepin County Bar Assn., Order of Coif, Law Rev. Roman Catholic. Avocations: family, jogging, reading, golf. Home: 530 Waycliffe N Wayzata MN 55391 Office: Popham Haik Schnobrich & Kaufman 3300 Piper Jaffray Tower 222 S 9th St Minneapolis MN 55402

SCHNOLL, HOWARD MANUEL, investment banking and managed asset consultant; b. Milw., June 6, 1935; s. Nathan P. and Della (Fisher) S.; m. Barbara Ostach, Dec. 3, 1988; children: Jordan, Terry, Jeffrey, Robert, Tammy, Daniel. BBA, U. Wis., 1958. CPA, Wis.; cert. mgmt. cons. Mng. ptnr. Nankin, Schnoll & Co., Milw., 1966-86; mng. ptnr., bd. dirs. BDO Seidman, 1986-90; pres., chief oper. officer Universal Med. Bldgs., L.P., Milw., 1990, also bd. dirs.; pres. Howard Schnoll & Assocs., Milw., 1991; mng. dir. Grande, Schnoll & Assocs., Milw., 1992-93; exec. mng. dir., COO Glaisner, Schiffarth, Grande & Schnoll, Ltd., Milw., 1993—. Bd. dirs. Milw. World Festival, Inc., 1968—, City of Festivals Parade, Milw., 1983—, Aurora Health Care Ventures, Milw. Heart Rsch. Found., Milw. Heart Inst., Arthritis Found.; pres. Milw. Coun. on Alcoholism and Drug Dependance, 1993—, bd. dirs.; treas. Am. Heart Assn., Milw., 1978-82; capt. United Way, Milw., 1985; mem. Greater Milw. Com. Nat. Found. Ileitis and Colitis, Milw. chpt. Served to sgt. U.S. Army, 1956-63. Mem. AICPA, Wis. Inst. CPAs, Acct. Computer Users Tech. Exchange, Brynwood Country Club (bd. dirs., treas.), B'nai Brith (pres. 1960-62). Jewish. Avocations: golf, tennis. Office: Glaisner Schiffarth Grande & Schnoll 250 E Wisconsin Ave Ste 800 Milwaukee WI 53202-4205

SCHNUCK, CRAIG, grocery stores company executive; b. 1948. MBA, Cornell U., 1971. With Schnuck Markets, Inc., Hazelwood, Mo., 1971—, v.p.; 1975-76, exec. v.p. sec., 1976-83, pres., chief exec. officer, 1983—, also bd. dirs. Office: Schnuck Markets Inc PO Box 46928 Saint Louis MO 63146-6928

SCHNUCKER, ROBERT VICTOR, history and religion educator; b. Waterloo, Iowa, Sept. 30, 1932; s. Felix Victor and Josephine (Maasdam) S.; m. Anna Mae Engelkes, Sept. 18, 1955; children: Sarai Ann, Sar Victor, Christjahn Dietrich. AB, NE Mo. State U., 1953; BD, U. Dubuque, 1956; MA, U. Iowa, 1960, PhD, 1969. Ordained to ministry Presbyn. Ch., 1956/. Pastor United Presbyn. Ch. USA, Springville, Iowa, 1956-63, Meth.-Presbyn. Ch., Labelle, Mo., 1976—; asst. prof. N.E. Mo. State U., Kirksville, 1963-65, assoc. prof., 1965-65, prof., 1969—; dir. Thomas Jefferson U. Press; supr. Bible exam. Presbyn. Ch. USA, Louisville, 1977-89; bd. dirs. Ctr. for Reformation Rsch., St. Louis, 1984—; pres. Conf. of Hist. Jours., 1993. Author: A Glossary of Terms for Western Civilization, 1975, Helping Humanities Journal Survive, 1985, History Assessment Test, 1990; editor: Calviniana, 1989, Historians of Early Modern Europe, 1976-93, Network News Exch., 1978-88; pres. 1st and 2d Editing History, Conf. for Hist. Jour., 1985—; book rev. editor, mng. editor 16th Century Jour., 1972—; pub. 16th Century Essays and Studies, 1980—; contbr. articles to profl. jours. Fellow Soc. Sci. Study of Religion, 1988; NEH grantee for jour. pubs., 1980. Mem. AAUP, Am. Acad. Religion, Renaissance Soc. Am., Am. History Assn. (chmn. Robinson prize com. 1987), Am. Soc. Ch. History, Soc. History of Edn., Soc. Bibl. Lit., Soc. for Reformation Rsch., Soc. Scholarly Pubs., Soc. for Values in Higher Edn., Conf. for Hist. Jour., Am. Coun. Learned Soc. (exec. bd. conf. adminstr. officers 1993—, sec., 1994, chmn. 1995-96), Conf. Faith and History, 16th Century Studies Cons. (exec. sec. 1972—).

SCHNUR, ROBERT ARNOLD, lawyer; b. White Plains, N.Y., Oct. 25, 1938; s. Conrad Edward and Ruth (Mehr) S.; children: Daniel, Jonathan. BA, Cornell U., 1960; JD, Harvard U., 1963. Bar: Wis. 1965, Ill. 1966. Assoc. Michael, Best & Friedrich, Milw., 1966-73, ptnr., 1973—; chmn. Wis. Tax News, 1983-90; adj. prof. tax law U. Wis. Law Sch., 1988—. Capt. U.S. Army, 1963-65. Mem. ABA, Wis. Bar Assn. (chmn. tax sect. 1986-88), Milw. Bar Assn. Home: 929 N Astor St Milwaukee WI 53202-3454 Office: Michael Best Friedrich 100 E Wisconsin Ave Milwaukee WI 53202-4107

SCHOBEL, GEORGE, insurance company executive. With Blue Cross Blue Shield of R.I., Providence, 1959—, now sr. v.p. Office: Blue Cross Blue Shield of RI 444 Westminster St Providence RI 02903

SCHOBER, CHARLES COLEMAN, III, psychiatrist, psychoanalyst; b. Shreveport, La., Nov. 30, 1924; s. Charles Coleman and Mabel Lee (Welsh) S.; B.S., La. State U., 1946 M.D., 1949; m. Martha Elizabeth Welsh, Dec. 27, 1947 (dec.); children—Irene Lee, Ann Welsh; m. 2d, Argeree Maburl Stiles, Feb. 4, 1972; 1 son, Charles Coleman. Intern, Phila. Gen. Hosp., 1949-51; resident in psychiatry Norristown (Pa.) State Hosp., 1953-57; practice medicine specializing in psychiatry and psychoanalysis, Phila., 1957-71; asso. clin. dir. Inst. Pa. Hosp., Phila., 1957-60, clin. dir., 1960-64, attending psychiatrist, 1960-68, sr. attending psychiatrist, 1968-71; mem. faculty Phila. Psychoanalytic Inst., 1966-71; clin. instr. U. Pa. Sch. Medicine, 1957-62, clin. asso., 1962-68, clin. asst. prof., 1968-71; prof., chmn. dept. psychiatry La. State U. Med. Center, Shreveport, 1971-73, chief psychiatry service, 1971-73; chief psychiatry service VA Hosp., Shreveport, 1971-73; faculty New Orleans Psychoanalytic Inst., 1972-73; mem. faculty St. Louis Psychoanalytic Inst., 1973-78; clin. prof. psychiatry St. Louis U. Med. Sch., 1973-78; clin. prof. psychiatry St. Louis U. Med. Sch., 1973-78; active med. staff psychiatry St. Louis U. Hosp., 1973-78; cons. psychiatry Jefferson Barracks VA Hosp., St. Louis, 1973-78; pvt. practice medicine, specializing in psychiatry and psychoanalysis, Shreveport, 1978-93; clin. prof. psychiatry, mem. med. staff psychiatry La. State U. Med. Center Hosp., Shreveport, 1978—; chief psychiatry service Schumpert Med. Center, 1982-84; med. and clin. dir. psychiatry Willis Knighton Med. Ctr., 1986-89; adult psychiatric treatment program Charter Forest Hosp., Shreveport, 1989—, prof. psychiat. La. State U. Med. Ctr., Shreveport, 1992—; in-patient svc. psychiat., psychoanalysis out patient clinic, 1992—. Served to capt. M.C., USAF, 1951-53. Diplomate Am. Bd. Psychiatry and Neurology (examiner). Fellow Am. Coll. Psychiatrists, Am. Psychiat. Assn.; mem. Am. Psychoanalytic Assn., AMA, La. Psychiat. Soc., La. Med. Soc., New Orleans Psychoanalytic Soc., Phila. Psychoanalytic Soc. Club: Rotary. Contbr. articles to profl. and med. jours. Home: 626 Wilder Pl Shreveport LA 71104-4326 Office: La State U Med Ctr Dept Psychiatry PO Box 33930 Shreveport LA 71130

SCHOCH, CLAUDE MARTIN, computer scientist, publishing company executive; b. Takoma Park, MD., Jan. 19, 1955; s. Jacques J. and Simone A. (Martin) S.; m. Teresa N. Pritchard, Apr. 4, 1992. Student, Am. U., 1976. Programmer Aircraft Owners & Pilots, Bethesda, Md., 1977-80, Aspen Systems, Rockville, Md., 1980-81; systems programmer Disclosure Inc., Bethesda, 1981-84, systems mgr., 1984-85; pres. Digital Libr. Systems Inc., Bethesda, 1985—, Digital Directory Assistance, Bethesda, 1988—; bd. dirs. Phonedisc USA Corp., Marblehead, Mass., co-dir., 1990—, chmn. of bd., 1992—. Author: (software program) Dialog On Disc, 1986, Phonedisc, 1986. Recipient Chrysties award Bus. Optical Pub. Assn., Dublin, Ohio, 1991. Mem. Potomac T-Bird Club (Washington, pres. 1980-81). Home: 7134 River Rd Bethesda MD 20817-4770 Office: Digital Directory Assistance Inc 6931 Arlington Rd Ste 405 Bethesda MD 20814-5231

SCHOCK, FRANKLIN H., clergy member, church administrator. Supt. Evangelical Congregational Church Retirement Village, Myerstown, Pa. Office: Evang Congl Ch PO Box 186 100 W Park Ave Myerstown PA 17067

SCHOCK, ROBERT NORMAN, geophysicist; b. Monticello, N.Y., May 25, 1939; s. Carl Louis and Norma Adaleth (Greenfield) S.; m. Susan Esther Benton, Nov. 28, 1959; children: Pamela Ann, Patricia Elizabeth, Christina Benton. B.S., Colo. Coll., 1961; M.S., Rensselaer Poly. Inst., 1963, Ph.D., 1966; postgrad., Northwestern U., 1963-64. Cert. Calif. state wine judge. Jr. geophys. trainee Continental Oil Co., Sheridan, Wyo., 1960; jr. geologist Texaco In., Billings, Mont., 1961; teaching asst. Rensselaer Poly. Inst., Troy, N.Y., 1961-63, research asst., 1964-66; research assoc. U. Chgo., 1966-68; sr. research scientist Lawrence Livermore Nat. Lab., U. Calif., 1968—, group leader high pressure physics, 1972-74, sect. leader geoscis. and engring., 1974-76, div. leader earth scis., 1976-81, head dept. earth scis., 1981-87, energy program leader, 1987-92, dep. assoc. dir. for energy, 1992—; pres. Pressure Systems Rsch. Inc.; mem. faculty Chabot Coll., 1969-71; dir. Alameda County Flood Control and Water Conservation Dist., 1984-86;

mem. adv. panel on geoscis. U.S. Energy, 1985-87; chair adv. com. U. Calif. Energy Inst., 1992—. Mem. editorial bd.: Rev. Sci. Instruments, 1975-77; assoc. editor: Jour. Geophys. Research, 1978-80; bd. assoc. editors: 11th Lunar and Planetary Sci.Conf., 1980; mem. adv. bd.: Physics and Chemistry of Minerals, 1983—; research and publs. on high pressure physics, solid state physics, physics of earth interior, rock deformation, research on new window design for high pressure vessels, new deformation apparatus for study solids, energy. Fulbright sr. fellow U. Bonn (Germany), 1973; vis. research fellow Australian Nat. U. Canberra, 1980-81. Mem. AAAS, Am. Geophys. Union, Sigma Xi, Commonwealth of Calif. Club. Office: Lawrence Livermore Nat Lab PO Box 808 Livermore CA 94551-0808

SCHOECK, RICHARD JOSEPH, English and humanities scholar; b. N.Y.C., Oct. 10, 1920; s. Gustav J. and Frances M. (Kuntz) S.; m. Reta R. Haberer, 1945 (div. 1976); children: Eric R., Christine C., Jennifer A.; m. Megan S. Lloyd, Feb. 19, 1977. M.A., Princeton U., 1949, Ph.D. 1949. Instr. English Cornell U., 1949-55; asst. prof., then assoc. prof. U. Notre Dame, 1955-61; prof. English U. Toronto, 1961-71; head dept. English St. Michael's Coll., 1965-70; prof. vernacular lit. Pontifical Inst. Mediaeval Studies, Toronto, 1964-71; dir. rsch. activities Folger Shakespeare Libr., also dir. Folger Inst. Renaissance and 18th Century Studies, 1970-74; adj. prof. English Cath. U. Am., 1972; prof. English, medieval and renaissance studies U. Md., 1974-75; prof. English and humanities U. Colo., Boulder, 1975-89, prof. emeritus, 1987—; chmn. dept. integrated studies U. Colo., 1976-79; chmn. comparative lit., 1983-84; prof. Anglistik Universität Trier, 1987-90, head dept., 1988-89; adj. prof. English U. Kans., Lawrence, 1990—; Vincent J. Flynn prof. letters Coll. St. Thomas, 1960; vis. prof. Princeton U., 1964, U. Dallas, 1985; vis. fellow Inst. Advanced Studies in Humanities, Edinburgh, 1984-85; vis. scholar Corpus Christi Coll., Oxford, 1994; cons. NEH; bd. dirs. Natural Law Inst., U. Notre Dame; advisor Italian Acad. for Advanced Studies in Am., 1993—; fellow Assn. Advancement Edn., 1952-53, Yale U., 1959-60, Can. Coun., 1967-68. Author: The Achievement of Thomas More, 1976, Intertextuality and Renaissance Texts, 1984, Erasmus Grandescens, 1988, (poems) A Raging Against Chaos, 1989, Erasmus of Europe, Vol. I, 1991, Vol. II, 1993, The Eye of a Traveller, 1992, The Knight's Book, 1993; author also numerous articles, papers, revs.; editor: Delehaye's Legends of the Saints, 1961, Editing 16th Century Texts, 1966; (Roger Ascham), The Scholemaster, 1966, Shakespeare Quar, 1972-74, Acta Conventus Neo-Latini Bononiensis, 1985; gen. editor: The Confutation of Tyndale, 3 vols, 1973; co-editor: Voices of Literature, 2 vols, 1964, 66, Chaucer Criticism, 2 vols, 1960, 61, Style, Rhetoric and Rhythm: Essays by M.W. Croll, 1966, Acta Conventus Neo-Latini Torontonensis, 1991; former gen. editor: Patterns of Literary Criticism; spl. editor: Canada vol. Rev. Nat. Literatures, 1977, Sir Thomas Browne and the Republic of Letters, 1982, A Special Number of English Language Notes, 1982; gen. editor (series) Renaissance Masters, 1992—; mem. editorial bds. profl. jours. Served with U.S. Army, 1940-46. Guggenheim Found. fellow, 1968-69; grantee Can. Coun., UNESCO, Am. Coun. Learned Socs., U. Toronto, U. Colo., Brit. Coun.; Fulbright fellow, 1983. Fellow Royal Soc. Can., Royal Hist. Soc.; mem. Internat. Assn. Neo-Latin Studies (pres. 1976-79), MLA, Renaissance Soc. Am., PEN (N.Y.), Can. Humanities Assn., Internat. Assn. U. Profs. English, Assn. Can. Studies in U.S. Home: 232 Dakota St Lawrence KS 66046-4710 *More than a thousand years ago Bede summed up what are for me the principles of my professional career: I have always thought it fitting to learn and to teach and to write.*

SCHOEFFEL, JON MICHAEL, lawyer; b. Beaver Dam, Wis., Oct. 11, 1945; s. Gilbert Edwin and Doris Adeline (Hyne) S.; m. Barbara Ann Kreier, Aug. 31, 1968; children: Melissa Ann, Adam Jon. BA, U. Wis., 1968, JD cum laude, 1971. Bar: Wis. 1971, U.S. Dist. Ct. (we. dist.) Wis. 1971, U.S. Dist. Ct. (ea. dist.) Wis. 1974. Assoc. Lathrop & Clark, Madison, Wis., 1971-74; sr. atty. J.I. Case Co., Racine, Wis., 1974-86; assoc. gen. counsel Bear Automotive Svc. Equipment Co., New Berlin, Wis., 1986-87; gen. counsel Western Pub. Co., Inc., Racine, 1987—. Alt. mem. Mt. Pleasant Zoning Bd. Appeals, Racine, 1986—. Mem. Wis. Bar Assn., Racine County Bar Assn., Am. Corp. Counsel Assn., Order of Coif. Avocation: golf. Office: Hon Industries Inc 414 E 3rd St Muscatine IA 52761-4117

SCHOELKOPF, ROBERT CARL, non-profit organization administrator; b. Reading, Pa., Oct. 4, 1946. Diploma, Reading H.S. Founding dir. Marine Mammal Stranding Ctr., Brigantine, N.J., 1977—; dep. warden U.S. Fish and Wildlife Svc., 1978-81; participant U.S. Congl. Hearings on Pollution, U.S. Senatorial Hearings on Pollution, N.J. Senatorial Hearings on Pollution; co-sponsor Dolphin crisis seminar Monmouth Coll., 1987; bd. dirs. Atlantic County Aquarium Project. Contbr. articles to sci. publs. Mem. environ. com. Atlantic County div. N.J. Tourism Coun.; mem. Brigantine Environ. Commn., N.J. Environ. Edn. Commn. With USN, 1965-69, Vietnam. Recipient spl. award N.J. Coun. Dive Clubs, 1982, award Press Club Atlantic City, 1985, Audubon Conservation award, 1987, N.J. Pride award, 1988, rsch. award Save Our Shores, 1988, Atlantic County Citizen award Am. Legion, 1988, award N.J. Tourism Coun., 1989, 90, N.J. Gov.'s Vol. award 1989, award Greater Mainland C. of C., 1990, Region II Environ. Quality award EPA, 1990, Outstanding Achievement award N.J. Assn. Conservation Dists., 1993, Legion of Honor, Chapel of Four Chaplains, 1994. Home: 3625 Brigantine Blvd Brigantine NJ 08203 Office: Marine Mammal Stranding Ctr PO Box 773 Brigantine NJ 08203

SCHOELLER, DALE ALAN, nutrition research educator; b. Milw., June 8, 1948; s. Arthur B. and Anne Clare (Maas) S.; m. Madeline Mary Juresh, Aug. 22, 1970; children: Nicholas Paul, Gregory Scott, Erica Lee. BS with honors, U. Wis., Milw., 1970; PhD, Ind. U., 1974. Postdoctoral fellow Argonne (Ill.) Nat. Lab., 1974-76; from asst. prof. to prof., also rsch. assoc. U. Chgo., 1976-91, assoc. prof., 1991—; chmn. com. on human nutrition and nutritional biology U. Chgo., 1991—. Author: (book chpt.) Obesity, 1992; co-author: (book chpt.) Annual Review of Nutrition, 1991. Achievements include development of stable isotope methods for the study of human energy metabolism including first human use of doubly labeled water for measurement of free-living total energy expenditure. Avocations: coaching youth sports including basketball, baseball and hockey. Mem. Am. Inst. Nutrition (Mead Johnson award 1987), Am. Soc. for Clin. Nutrition, Am. Soc. for Mass Spectrometry, N.Am. Soc. for Study of Obesity. Office: U of Chgo Pritzker Sch of Medicine 5841 S Maryland Ave Chicago IL 60637

SCHOEMEHL, VINCENT CHARLES, JR., mayor; b. St. Louis, Oct. 30, 1946; s. Vincent Charles and Lucille (Miller) S.; m. Lois Brockmeier, Sept. 18, 1971; children—Timothy Martin, Joseph Vincent. B.A. in History, U. Mo., 1972. Alderman 28th Ward, St. Louis, 1975-81; mayor City of St. Louis, 1981—. Democrat. Roman Catholic. Office: Office of the Mayor 200 City Hall 1200 Market St Saint Louis MO 63103

SCHOEN, ALVIN E., JR., environmental engineer; b. Milford, Conn., Jan. 3, 1945; s. Alvin E. and Thelma (Terrace) S.; m. Mary Ann Kosik; 1 child, Matthew S. BA in Math., U. Conn., 1968, BS in Engring., 1971; MSCE, Polytechnic Inst. of N.Y., 1977; PhD in Environ. Engring., U. Okla., 1994. Registered profl. engr., Ohio, Maine, N.Y., Conn., Mass., N.H., Va., Okla., N.J.; diplomate Am. Acad. Environ. Engrs. Field engr. Mobil Oil Corp., Scarsdale, N.Y., 1973-76, engring. supr., 1976-80; project engr. Mobil Oil Corp., Fairfax, Va., 1980-82; group leader, process engr. Mobil Oil Corp., Oklahoma City, 1985-89; environ. engr. rsch. and devel. Mobil Oil Corp., Princeton, N.J., 1989—; project engr. Arabian Am. Oil, Dhahran, Saudi Arabia, 1982-85; commr. Inland Wetlands Commn., Brookfield, Conn., 1978-80, Environ. Commn., Montgomery Twsp, N.J., 1992-93. 1st lt. C.E., U.S. Army, 1968-70, Vietnam. Fellow ASCE; mem. Am. Petroleum Inst. (mktg. terminal effluent task force, liner work group), Nat. Soc. Profl. Engrs. Water Environ. Fedn., Lions Club Internat. Office: Mobil Rsch and Devel Corp PO Box 1026 Princeton NJ 08543

SCHOEN, LINDA ALLEN, public affairs administrator; b. Lynch, Ky., July 9, 1936; d. Wert Harvey and Mary Mabel (Ramsey) Allen; m. Stanly M. Schoen, Apr. 8, 1972 (div. 1980). BA, Northwestern U., 1958. Rsch. technician G.D. Searle & Co., Chgo., 1958-60; rsch. assoc. sect. com. cutaneous health and cosmetics AMA, Chgo., 1960-75; dir. mktg. svcs. Neutrogena Corp., L.A. 1975-83, dir. mktg. svcs., 1983-87, v.p. pub. affairs, 1987-93; pres. Unltd., 1993—. Mem. IABC, Pub. Rels. Soc. Am., Soc. Cosmetic Chemists, The Fashion Group. Episcopalian. Club: Opera Assn. (Northwestern U. Alumni). Editor The Look You Like column Today's

Health mag., 1962-74; The AMA Book of Skin and Hair Care, 1976, The Look You Like Book, 1989; contbr. articles to Harper's Bazaar, Vogue, Redbook, Beauty Handbook. Mem. Soc. Cosmetic Chemists, Internat. Assn. Bus. Communicators. Episcopalian. Avocations: cross country skiing, travel, opera.

SCHOEN, STEVAN JAY, lawyer; b. N.Y.C., May 19, 1944; s. Al and Ann (Spevack) S.; m. Cynthia Lukens; children: Andrew Adams, Anna Kim. BS, U. Pa., 1966; JD, Cornell U., 1969; MPhil in Internat. Law, Cambridge U. (Eng.), 1979. Bar: N.Mex. 1970, N.Y. 1970, U.S. Dist. Ct. N.Mex. 1973, U.S. Supreme Ct. 1976, U.S. Tax Ct. 1973, U.S. Ct. Internat. Trade 1982. Nat. dir. Vista law recruitment U.S. OEO, Washington, 1970-71; atty. Legal Aid Soc. of Albuquerque, 1971-73; chief atty. N.Mex. Dept. Health and Social Services, Albuquerque, 1973-77; atty. Brennan, Schoen & Eisenstadt, 1979-88, Messersmith, McNeill & Schoen, 1989—; probate judge, Sandoval County, 1990—; arbitrator, NYSE. mem. N.Mex. Supreme Ct. Appellate Rules Com., 1982-92; chmn. rules com. Com. on Fgn. Legal Cons., 1993, Jud. Edn. Planning Com.; mem. Children's Code Rules Com., 1976-78. Bd. dirs., offcer, Placitas Vol Fire Brigade, 1973-86; mem. Albequerque Adv. Com. on Fgn. Trade Zone. Recipient Cert. for Outstanding Svc. to Judiciary N.Mex. Supreme Ct., 1982, cert. of Appreciation, N.Mex. Supreme Ct., 1992, Cert. of Appreciation, N.Mex. Sec. of State, 1980, Cert. of Appreciation, U.S. OEO, 1971, Pro Bono Pub. Svc. award 1989, cert. Recognition Legal Aid, 1994. Mem. Am. Judges Assn., Nat. Coll. Probate Judges, State Bar N.Mex. (past chmn. real property, probate and trust sect. 1989, Outstanding Contbn. award 1989, task force on regulation of advt. 1990-91, past chmn. appellate practice sect. 1991, past chmn. internat. law sect. 1991-92, commn. on professionalism 1992—; organizing com. U.S.-Mex. law inst. 1992), N.Mex. Probate Judges Assn. (chmn. 1993-95), Oxford-Cambridge Soc. N.Mex. (sec.), N.Mex. Assn. Counties (adv. bd.). Home: 14 Rainbow Valley Rd Placitas NM 87043-8801 Office: 5700 Harper Dr NE Ste 430 Albuquerque NM 87109-3573

SCHOEN, WILLIAM JACK, financier; b. Los Angeles, Aug. 2, 1935; s. Jack Conrad and Kathryn Mabel (Stegmayer) S.; m. Sharon Ann Barto, Oct. 1, 1966; children: Kathryn Lynn, Karen Anne, Kristine Lea, William Jack. BS in Fin. magna cum laude, U. So. Calif., 1960, MBA, 1963. Mktg. mgr. Anchor Hocking Glass Co., 1964-68; v.p. sales and mktg. Obear-Nester Glass Co., 1968-71; pres. Pierce Glass Co., Port Allegheny, Pa., 1971-73; pres., chief exec. officer, dir. F.&M. Schaefer Brewing Co., N.Y.C., 1973-81; now chmn., pres. Wilshar Mgmt. Co. Inc., Naples, Fla., 1981—; chmn., pres. Health Mgmt. Assocs. Inc., Naples, 1983—; also bd. dirs. Health Mgmt. Assocs. Inc.; bd. dirs. 1st Union Nat. Bank Fla. Contbr. to indsl. pubins. Served with USMC, 1953-56, Korea. Mem. Phi Kappa Phi. Republican. Episcopalian. Clubs: Union League (N.Y.C.), Port Royal, Quail Creek Country.

SCHOENBAUM, DAVID LEON, historian; b. Milw., Mar. 26, 1935; s. Milton Lionel and Leah (Hertz) S.; m. Tamara Holtermann, June 6, 1963; children—Michael, Miriam. B.A., U. Wis.-Madison, 1955, M.A., 1958; D.Phil., St. Antony's Coll., Oxford U., 1965. Reporter Waterloo Courier, Iowa, 1957-58; copy editor Mpls. Tribune, 1958-59; asst. prof. Kent State U., Ohio, 1966-67; from asst. prof. to prof. history U. Iowa, Iowa City, 1967—; guest prof. U. Freiburg, Fed. Republic Germany, 1974-75, U. Bonn, Fed. Republic Germany, 1989; prof. U.S. Naval War Coll., Newport, R.I., 1976-77, Johns Hopkins Univ. Sch. of Advanced Internat. Studies, Bologna Ctr., Bologna, Italy, 1991-93; occasional free-lance journalist. Author: Hitler's Social Revolution, 1966, The Spiegel Affair, 1968, Zabern 1913, 1983, The United States and The State of Israel, 1993. Fulbright grantee, Bonn. Fed. Republic Germany, 1959; sr. scholar, 1973-74, 88-89; Guggenheim grantee, 1975, German Marshall Fund U.S. grantee, 1986—; sr. scholar Truman Presdl. Library, Independence, Mo., 1982-83; fellow Woodrow Wilson Ctr., 1984-85, German Soc. Fgn. Affairs, Bonn, 1988-89. Jewish. Avocation: chamber music (violin and viola). Home: 617 Holt Ave Iowa City IA 52246-2917 Office: U Iowa Dept History Iowa City IA 52242

SCHOENBAUM, SAMUEL, English educator; b. N.Y.C., Mar. 6, 1927; s. Abraham and Sarah (Altschuler) S.; m. Marilyn Turk, June 10, 1946. B.A., Bklyn. Coll., 1947; M.A., Columbia U., 1949, Ph.D. 1953; D. Litt. (hon.), Susquehanna U., 1986, U. Colo., 1987. Mem. faculty Northwestern U., 1953-75, Franklyn Bliss Snyder prof. English Lit., 1971-75; Disting. prof. English U. City N.Y., 1975-76; Disting. prof. Renaissance lit U. Md., 1976-93, dir. Center for Renaissance and Baroque Studies, 1981—; vis. prof. King's Coll., London, 1961, U. Chgo., 1964, 65, Columbia U., 1966, U. Wash., 1968; Hooker Disting. vis. prof. McMaster U., Ont., Can., 1986; mem. adv. com. Internat. Shakespeare Conf., 1972—; mem. adv. coun. Am. Trust for Brit. Libr.; trustee Folger Shakespeare Libr., 1974-84; hon. mem. Folger Libr. Renaissance Forum, 1993—. Author: Internal Evidence and Elizabethan Dramatic Authorship, 1966, Shakespeare's Lives, 1970, new edit., 1991, William Shakespeare: A Documentary Life, 1975 (Distinguished Service award Soc. Midland Authors 1976), William Shakespeare: A Compact Documentary Life, 1977, rev. edit., 1987, Shakespeare: The Globe and the World, 1979, William Shakespeare: Records and Images, 1981, Shakespeare and others, 1985, Shakespeare: His Life, His Language, His Theater, 1990; editor: (with K. Muir) A New Companion to Shakespeare Studies, 1971, Renaissance Drama, 1964-73; mem. editorial bd. Shakespeare Quar. Guggenheim fellow, 1956-57, 69-70; Nat. Endowment Humanities Sr. fellowship, 1973-74; recipient Huntington Library grant, 1959, 67; Newberry Library grant, 1958; recipient Friends of Lit. non-fiction award for Shakespeare's Lives, 1970. Fellow Royal Soc. Lit. (U.K.); mem. Shakespeare Assn. Am. (trustee 1976-79, 81—; pres. 1980-81), Internat. Shakespeare Assn. (v.p. 1988—), Phi Beta Kappa (hon.). Home: 613 Constitution Ave NE Washington DC 20002-6035

SCHOENBERG, HARRY W., urologic surgeon; b. N.Y.C., July 27, 1927; s. Herman Bernard and Esther (Wechsler) S.; children: Mark, Jennifer, Richard; m. Lelia West. BS, Yale U., 1948; MD, U. Pa., 1952. Asst. instr. in urology U. Pa., Phila., 1958-59, instr. in urology, 1959-60, asst. prof. urology, 1963-65, assoc. prof., 1965-69, prof, 1969-72; asst. urologist Grad. Hosp. U. Pa., Phila., 1960-72; cons. surgeon urologist Pa. Hosp., Phila., 1968-72; sr. surgeon of urology Children's Hosp. of Pa., Phila., 1970-72; prof., chmn. urology St. Louis Univ., Mo., 1972-76; prof., chief of urology U. Chgo., Ill., 1976—. Author: Genitourinary Cancer Surgery; author: (with others) The Care of the Geriatric Patient, Progress in Pyelonephritis, The Management of the Patient with Cancer, Urologic Surgery, The Management of the Patient with Cancer, Urolithiasis Research, Urinary System Malformations in Children, Carcinoma of the Colon and Rectum, Outpatient Surgery, Surgery of the Male Reproductive Tract, Benign Prostatic Hypertrophy, Neurologic Clinics, Diagnosis and Treatment of Erectile Disturbances, Treatment of Erectile Disturbances, Diagnosis and Treatment of Erectile Disturbances, Progress and Controversies in Oncological Urology II, Prognostic Cytometry and Cytopathology of Prostate Cancer, Essays in Surgery, Operative Surgery; co-editor: Diagnosis and Treatment of Erectile Disturbances. A Guide for Clinicians. With U.S. Army, 1954-56. John G. Clark prize for Rsch., 1952, I.S. Ravdin prize for Surgery, 1952. Fellow ACS; mem. Am. Urol. Assn., Am. Assn. Genito-Urinary Surgeons, Soc. of Univ. Urologists, Soc. for Pediatric Urologists. Office: U Chgo Div Biol Scis 5841 S Maryland Ave Chicago IL 60637

SCHOENBERG, LAWRENCE JOSEPH, computer services company executive; b. N.Y.C., July 4, 1932; s. Samuel and Selma (Shapiro) S.; m. Barbara Brizdle, Sept. 15, 1990; children: Douglas, Eric, Julie. A.B., U. Pa., 1953, M.B.A., 1956. Sr. systems analyst IBM, N.Y.C., 1956-59; asst. mgr. systems Litton, Orange, N.J., 1959-61; sr. cons. Computer Scis., N.Y.C., 1961-63; exec. v.p Automation Scis., N.Y.C., 1963-65; chmn., chief exec. officer AGS Computers, Mountainside, N.J., 1966-91; chmn. ITAA (formerly ADAPSO), Arlington, Va., 1983; bd. dirs. Penn-Am. Group, Inc., Morisel Inc., Sungard Inc., Softswitch, Inc., Qstar Inc., Image Bus. Systems Inc.; chmn. Gov. Tech. Svcs., Inc. Contbr. articles to profl. jours. Trustee St. Barnabas Hosp., Charles Babbage Inst., Dickinson Coll., N.J. Community Found.; assoc. trustee U. Pa. Served to cpl. U.S. Army, 1953-55. Mem. Software Industry Assn. (dir. 1976—), Orange Lawn Tennis Club, Germantown Cricket Club, Longboat Key Club, Racquet Club of East Hampton. Office: GTSI Inc PO Box 8460 Longboat Key FL 34228-8460

SCHOENBERG, MARK GEORGE, government agency administrator; b. Bklyn., Nov. 22, 1947; s. Abraham Arthur and Ruth Millie (Dunn) S. BA, Columbia U., 1971, postgrad., 1972-73; postgrad., N.C. State U., 1971-72. Research asst. NIMH-sponsored project at N.C. State U., Raleigh, 1971-72; asst. to pres. Key Electric Ltd., Glen Oaks, N.Y., 1973-76; gen. mgr. Key Electric Ltd., Los Angeles, 1976; asst. to pres. Kalsan Electric, Hempstead, N.Y., 1977; asst. mgr. Lincoln Inn, Rockville Ctr., N.Y., 1978; expert, cons. EPA, Washington, 1978; assoc. dir. U.S. Regulatory Council, Washington, 1979-82; exec. dir. Regulatory Info. Service Ctr., Washington, 1982—. Mem. Sr. Exec. Assn., Train Collectors Assn., Lionel Collectors Club Am. Avocations: healthy gourmet cooking, model railroading, early music, wine collecting. Office: Regulatory Info Svc Ctr Exec Office of Pres 750 17th St NW Ste 500 Washington DC 20006-4606

SCHOENBERGER, JAMES EDWIN, federal agency administrator; b. Dayton, Ohio, Sept. 7, 1947; s. Harry Robert and Elizabeth Jane (Hollenkamp) S.; m. Aura Victoria Montana, June 24, 1977; children: David, Eric. BS in Civil Engring., Purdue U., 1969; MBA, Harvard U., 1971. V.p. ops. for midwestern housing developer Herman Devel. Group, Indpls., 1971-74; various positions New Communities Adminstrn. and with sec. HUD, Washington, 1974-77; assoc. dep. asst. sec., 1981-83; dir. land utilization Peabody Coal Co., St. Louis, 1977-81; sr. v.p. ops. The Investment Group, Washington, 1983-86; gen. dep. asst. fed. housing commr. U.S. HUD, Washington, 1987-89, assoc. gen., dep. asst. sec., 1990—. Roman Catholic. Avocation: computers. Office: HUD 451 7th St SW Rm 9106 Washington DC 20410-0001

SCHOENBLUM, JEFFREY A., law educator; b. 1948. AB, John Hopkins U., 1970; JD, Harvard U., 1973. Law clk. to presiding justice U.S. Ct. Appeals (2d cir.), N.Y.C., 1973-74; assoc. Wilkie, Farr & Gallagher, N.Y.C., 1974-77; asst. prof. Vanderbilt U., Nashville, 1977-80, assoc. prof., 1980-83, prof., 1983—; academician Internat. Acad. Estate of Trust Law; adv. com. ALI Restatement of Prop. 3d/. Fellow Am. Coll. Trust & Estate Counsel. Office: Vanderbilt U Sch Law 21st Ave S Nashville TN 37240

SCHOENBRUN, LARRY LYNN, lawyer; b. Tyler, Tex., Mar. 10, 1940; s. Mano and Elsie (Lefkovitz) S.; m. Celia Roosth, June 30, 1963; children: Benjamin C., Michael E., Kathryn L. AB, U. Tex., 1962, LLB, 1965. Ptnr. Gardere & Wynne, L.L.P., and predecessor firms, Dallas, 1965—. Pres., bd. dirs. Community Homes for Adults, Inc., Dallas, 1986-87; bd. dirs. Jewish Fedn. Greater Dallas, 1987—, treas., 1989-91, v.p., 1991—; vice chmn. Found. Jewish Fedn. Greater Dallas, 1988-91, chmn., 1991—; v.p. Jewish Community Ctr., Dallas; bd. dirs. United Way of Dallas, 1992-95. Recipient Jurisprudence award Anti-Defamation League, 1989. Mem. ABA, Tex. State Bar Assn. (securities com. 1970—, vice chmn. 1974-75, chmn. 1975-77, coun. bus. law sect. 1975-83, vice chmn. 1980-81, chmn. 1981-82), Dallas Bar Assn., Tex. Bus. Law Found. (bd. dirs. 1988—, exec. com. 1988—, chmn. 1989-91). Office: Gardere & Wynne LLP 3000 Thanksgiving Tower 1601 Elm St Dallas TX 75201

SCHOENBUCHER, BRUCE, health physicist; b. Dec. 15, 1943; s. Albert King and Alice Elizabeth (Thomson) S.; m. Patty Jo Parry, Feb. 3, 1965 (div. Feb. 1980); children: Teresa Marie, Bonnie Lynn Schoenbucher Mendoza; m. Nancy Lippincott, Jan. 3, 1987; 1 child, Carly Cramer Cutler. BS in Radiation Protection Engring., Tex. A&M U., 1977, MS in Nuclear Engring., 1982. Lic. med. physicist, Tex.; cert. healthcare safety profl. Health physicist nuclear sci. ctr. Tex. A&M U., College Station, 1971-75, health physicist Coll. Vet. Medicine, 1977-79; mgr. radiation safety programs U. Tex. Med. Br., Galveston, 1980-88, asst. dir. environ. health and safety, 1984-88, radiation safety officer, dir. environ. health and safety, 1988—; radiation safety officer Burn Inst Shriners Hosp. for Crippled Children, Galveston, 1991—; presenter in field. Contbr. articles to profl. publs. With USN, 1962-71. Mem. APHA, Health Physics Soc. (med. sect. exec. bd. 1993—, mem. pub. info. com. 1981-84, chmn. 1982-84), South Sect. Chpt. Health Physics Soc. (chmn. ad hoc com. on licensure of med. physicists, chmn. info. com. 1986-88, treas. 1980-85, pres-elect 1985-86, pres. 1986-87), Am. Assn. Physicists in Medicine, Am. Biol. Safety Assn., Am. Soc. Safety Engrs., Laser Inst. Am., Nat. Fire Protection Assn., Tex. Safety Assn., Galveston C. of C., U.S. Coast Guard Auxilliary, Phi Kappa Phi, Sigma Nu Epsilon, Tau Beta Pi. Office: U Tex Med Br 301 Univ Blvd Galveston TX 77555-0633

SCHOENDIENST, ALBERT FRED (RED SCHOENDIENST), professional baseball coach, former baseball player; b. Germantown, Ill., Feb. 2, 1923; m. Mary Eileen O'Reilly; children: Colleen, Cathleen, Eileen, Kevin. Infielder St. Louis Cardinals, 1945-56, 61-63, N.Y. Giants, 1956-57, Milw. Braves, 1957-61; coach St. Louis Cardinals, 1961-64, 1979—, mgr., 1964-77; coach Oakland Athletics, Calif., 1977-78. Mem. Nat. League All-Star team, 10 times, player in 9 games; mem. World Series Championship team, 1946, 57; managed team to World Series Championship, 1967; inducted into Major League Baseball Hall of Fame, 1989. Office: Saint Louis Cardinals 250 Stadium Plz Saint Louis MO 63102-1722*

SCHOENEBERG, JOYCE EILEEN, secondary school biology educator; b. St. Louis, Jan. 13, 1944; d. John F. and Sophie A. (Nachowiak) Zielinski; m. Carl M. Schoeneberg, Dec. 18, 1971; children: C. Jason, Jennifer. BA in Zoology, Washington U., St. Louis, 1965; MEd in Biology, So. Ill. U., 1972. Cert. secondary biology tchr., Mo. Life sci. tchr. Normandy (Mo.) Sch. Dist., 1965-69; biology tchr. Hazelwood (Mo.) Sch. Dist., 1969-73, Parkway Sch. Dist., St. Louis County, Mo., 1983—; sci. chair Parkway Sch. Dist., St. Louis County, Mo., 1992—. Mem. Sci. Tchrs. Mo., Nat. Assn. Biology Tchrs., Phi Mu (pres. 1964-65). Methodist. Avocations: travel, gardening, tennis, photography. Office: Parkway N High Sch 12860 Fee Fee Rd Saint Louis MO 63146-4498

SCHOENER, THOMAS WILLIAM, zoology educator, researcher; b. Lancaster, Pa., Aug. 9, 1943; s. Harold Cloyd and Alta Marjorie (Hewitt) S.; m. Susan L. Keen, 1985. BA, Harvard Coll., 1965, PhD, 1969. Asst. prof. Harvard Coll., Cambridge, Mass., 1972-73, assoc. prof., 1973-75; assoc. prof. U. Wash., Seattle, 1975-76, prof., 1976-80; prof. U. Calif., Davis, 1980—; chairperson sect. evolution and ecology divsn. biol. scis., 1993—. Mem. editorial bd. dirs. Oecologia, 1984-93, Acta Oecologia, 1989—; past mem. editorial bd. Evolution, Am. Naturalist, Sci.; contbr. chpts. to books, articles to profl. jours. Recipient MacArthur prize Ecol. Soc. Am., 1987; grantee NSF, 1975—, Nat. Geog. Soc.; jr. fellow Harvard U., 1969-72; Guggenheim fellow, 1992-93. Mem. NAS, AAAS, Am. Acad. Arts and Scis., Am. Ornithologists Union (elective), Am. Soc. Naturalists, Ecol. Soc. Am., Am. Soc. Ichthyologists and Nerpetologists, Cooper Ornithol. Soc., Wilson Ornithol. Soc., Am. Arachnological Soc., Bahamas Nat. Trust. Avocations: weight lifting; reading. Office: Univ California Dept Zoology Davis CA 95616

SCHOENFELD, ALAN HENRY, mathematics and education educator; b. N.Y.C., July 9, 1947; s. Neil Howard and Natalie (Weinberg) S.; m. Jean Snitzer, June 14, 1970. BS in Math., Queens Coll., 1968; MS in Math., Stanford U., 1969, PhD in Math., 1973. Lectr. U. Calif., Davis, 1973-75; from asst. prof. to assoc. prof. Hamilton Coll., Clinton, N.Y., 1978-81, U. Rochester, N.Y., 1981-84; lectr. U. Calif., Berkeley, 1975-78, assoc. prof. edn., math., 1985-86, prof., 1986—, chmn. div. edn. in math., sci. and tech. 1987—; chmn. Grad. Group in Sci. and Math. Edn., U. Calif., Berkeley, 1985-87; chief organizer IV Internat. Conf. Math. Edn., 1984. Author: Mathematical Problem Solving, 1985, Mathematical Association of AmericaNotes # 1, Problem Solving, 1983; editor: Cognitive Science and Mathematics Education, 1987, A Source Book for College Mathematics Teaching, 1990, Mathematical Thinking and Problem Solving, 1994, Research in Collegiate Mathematics Education, 1994. Mem. State Calif. Math. Framework Com., 1988-90; mem. advisory panel Calif. Assessment Program 1988—. Grantee NSF, 1979, 85, 87, 90-92, Sloan Found., 1984, 87, Spencer Found., 1983, 93; elected Nat. Acad. Edn., 1994. Mem. Nat. Acad. Edn., Math. Assn. Am. (chmn. teaching undergrad. math. com. 1982-89, mem. editorial bd. Jour. Rsch. Math. Edn. 1982-85, chmn. 1984-85), Am. Ednl. Rsch. Assn. (assoc. com. Spec. Int. Group Math. Edn. 1984-86), Am. Math. Soc. (com. on edn. 1992—), Cognitive Sci. Soc., Nat. Coun. Tchrs. Math. (mem. rsch. adv. com. 1990-93, chair 1992-93), Nat. Bd. for Profl. Teaching Standards (mem. math. panel 1990—), Nat. Rsch. Coun. (math. sci. edn. bd. task force on K-12 1986-88, bd. testing/assessment 1993—).

Avocations: food, wine. Home: 830 Colusa Ave Berkeley CA 94707-1839 Office: U Calif Dept Edn Berkeley CA 94720-1670

SCHOENFELD, HANNS-MARTIN WALTER, accounting educator; b. Leipzig, Germany, July 12, 1928; came to U.S., 1962, naturalized, 1968; s. Alwin and Lisbeth (Kirbach) S.; m. Margit Frese, Aug. 10, 1956; 1 child, Gabriele. MBA, U. Hamburg, Fed. Republic Germany, 1952, DBA, 1954; PhD, U. Braunschweig, Fed. Republic Germany, 1966. Pvt. practice acctg. Hamburg, 1948-54; bus. cons. Europe, 1958-62; faculty accountancy U. Ill., Urbana, 1962—; prof. acctg., bus. adminstrn., 1967—, Weldon Powell prof. acctg., 1976, 80-81, H. T. Scovill prof. acctg., 1985-94; prof. emeritus, 1994—, Office of West European Studies, 1994—; lectr., cons. in bus. and acctg., Eng., Belgium, Austria, Denmark, Brazil, Fed. Republic of Germany, Poland, Japan, Switzerland, Hungary, Czechoslovakia, German Dem. Republic, 1962—; vis. prof. ECON U. Vienna, Austria, 1984—, Handelshochschule, Leipzig, Germany, 1996—. Author: numerous books including Management Dictionary 2 vols., 4th edit, 1971, Cost Accounting, 8th edit, 1974-95, Management Development, 1967, Cost. With German Army, 1944-45. Mem. Am. Acctg. Assn. (dir. internat. sect. 1976-77), Acad. Acctg. Historians (v.p. 1976-77, pres. 1978-79), Acad. Internat. Bus., German Profs. Bus. Adminstrn., German Assn. Indsl. Engring., European Acctg. Assn., Council of European Studies, Internat. Assn. for Acctg. Edn. and Rsch., Beta Gamma Sigma, Beta Alpha Psi. Home: 1014 Devonshire Dr Champaign IL 61821-6620 Office: U Ill 302 Commerce Bldg W 1206 S 6th St Champaign IL 61820-6980

SCHOENFELD, JIM, professional hockey coach. Head coach Washington Capitols, 1994—. Office: Washington Capitols USAIR Arena Landover MD 20785*

SCHOENFELD, MICHAEL P., lawyer; b. Bronx, N.Y., Oct. 17, 1935; s. Jack and Anne S.; B.S. in Acctg., N.Y.U., 1955; LL.B., LL.D., Fordham U., 1958; m. Helen Schorr, Apr. 3, 1960; children—Daniel, Steven, Tracy. Admitted to N.Y. bar, 1959, U.S. Supreme Ct., 1963; atty. Am. Home Assurance Co., N.Y.C., 1958-62; ptnr. firm Schoenfeld & Schoenfeld, Melville, 1959—; v.p. Interstate Brokerage Corp., 1965-84, pres., 1984—; ptnr. Melville Realty Co., 1977—; legal adv. various bus. orgns. Vice pres., trustee Temple Beth David, Commack, N.Y., 1972-75; chmn. Community Action Com. of Dix Hills and Commack, 1970-72, Dix Hills Planning Bd., 1972-74; treas. Dix Hills Republican Club, 1976-80; mem. Huntington (N.Y.) Zoning Bd. Appeals, 1980-91, chmn., 1986-89. Recipient United Jerusalem award Israel Bond Drive, 1977; City of Hope Service award; George Bacon award Fordham Law Sch. Mem. N.Y. State Bar Assn., Suffolk County Bar Assn. Home: 14 Clayton Dr Dix Hills NY 11746 Office: 999 Walt Whitman Rd Huntington Station NY 11747

SCHOENFELD, WALTER EDWIN, manufacturing company executive; b. Seattle, Nov. 6, 1930; s. Max and Edna Lucille (Reinhardt) S.; m. Esther Behar, Nov. 27, 1955; children—Lea Anne, Jeffrey, Gary. B.B.A., U. Wash., 1952. Vice pres., dir. Sunshine Mining Co., Kellogg, Idaho, 1964-69, First N.W. Industries, Inc., 1968-79; chmn. bd., pres. Schoenfeld Industries, Inc. (diversified holding co.), 1968-93; vice chmn., acting pres., CEO, Vans, Inc., 1993—; ptnr. Seattle Mariners Baseball Club, 1977-81, Seattle Sounds Soccer Club, 1974-79; v.p., dir. Chief Execs. Orgn., 1987—; bd. dirs. Hazel Bishop Cosmetics; bd. dirs., vice chmn. Vans Shoes, 1991—; Lee CEO Van's Inc., 1993—; chmn. Schoenfeld Neckwear Corp., Seattle, 1983-87, Taylor & Burke Ltd., U.K., 1987-88, Schoenfeld Group, Seattle, 1987-88; trustee Seattle Found., 1987—, N.W. Artificial Kidney Ctr., Seattle, 1967-88. Bd. dirs. Wash. China Rels. Coun., 1980—, Sterling Recreation Orgn., 1985—; chmn. Access Long Distance of Washington; bd. govs. Weizmann Inst. Sci., Rehovot, Israel, 1980—; trustee Barbara Sinatra Children's Ctr., Eisenhower Hosp., Rancho Mirage, Calif., 1990—. With AUS, 1952-55, Korea. Recipient various service awards. Mem. Chief Execs. Orgn., Seattle C. of C., Wash. Athletic Club, Seattle Yacht Club, Mercer Island Country Club, Tamarisk Country Club (Rancho Mirage, Calif.), Mission Hills Country Club (Rancho Mirage), Rolling Hills Country Club (Bellevue, Wash.), Alpha Kappa Psi. Office: 2001 6th Ave Ste 2550 Seattle WA 98121-2522

SCHOENHARD, WILLIAM CHARLES, JR., health care executive; b. Kansas City, Mo., Sept. 26, 1949; s. William Charles S. and Joyce Evans (Thornsberry) Bell; m. Kathleen Ann Klosterman, June 3, 1972; children: Sarah Elizabeth, Thomas William. BS in Pub. Adminstrn., U. Mo., 1971; M of Health Adminstrn., Washington U., St. Louis, 1975. V.p., dir. gen. svcs. Deaconess Hosp., St. Louis, 1975-78; assoc. exec. dir. St. Mary's Health Ctr., St. Louis, 1978-81; exec. dir. Arcadia Valley Hosp., Pilot Knob, Mo., 1981-82, St. Joseph Health Ctr., St. Charles, Mo., 1982-86; exec. v.p. SSM Health Care System, St. Louis, 1986—; bd. dirs. Mark Twain Bank, 1986—. Contbr. articles to profl. jours. Pres. Shaw Neighborhood Improvement Assn., St. Louis, 1979-80; mem. adv. bd. St. Louis Area chpt. Lifeseekers, 1985-94; bd. mgrs. Kirkwood-Webster (Mo.) YMCA, 1990—, Nat. Affairs Round Table Sen. Christopher Bond, St. Louis, 1990—, nat. adv. coun. Healthcare Forum, 1992—, health care adv. bd. Sanford Brown Colls., 1992—, leadership excellence com. Cath. Health Assn. U.S., 1993—; alt. del. Am. Hosp. Assn. Ho. of Dels., 1993-94; mem. steering com. Greater St. Louis Healthcare Alliance, 1994—; bd. dirs. St. Andrews Mgmt. Svcs., Inc., 1994—, Mid-Am. Transplant Assn., 1995—. With USN, 1971-72, Vietnam. Fellow Am. Coll. Health Care Execs. Am. Legion, Navy League of U.S., Univ. Club St. Louis, Phi Eta Sigma, Pi Omicron Sigma, Delta Upsilon, Delta Sigma Pi. Roman Catholic. Avocations: reading, jogging. Home: 420 Fairwood Ln Saint Louis MO 63122-4429 Office: SSM Health Care System 477 N Lindbergh Blvd Saint Louis MO 63141-7832

SCHOENHERR, JOHN (CARL), artist, illustrator; b. N.Y.C., July 5, 1935; s. John Ferdinand and Frances (Braun) S.; m. Judith Gray; children: Jennifer L., Ian G. BFA, Pratt Inst., 1956. Painter/illustrator book: Owl Moon, 1987 (Caldecott medal 1988). Recipient World Sci. Fiction award World Sci. Fiction Conv., London, 1965, silver medal Phila. Acad. Natural Sci., 1984, purchase award Hiram Blauvelt Art Mus., 1994. Mem. Am. Soc. Mammalogists, Soc. Illustrators, Soc. Animal Artists (medal 1979, 85). Home and Office: 135 Upper Creek Rd Stockton NJ 08559-1209

SCHOENLEIN, ROBERT W., research scientist. Staff scientist Lawrence Berkeley Lab, Berkeley, Calif. Recipient Adolf Comb medal Optical Soc. Am., 1994. Office: Lawrence Berkeley Lab 1 Cyclotron Rd Berkeley CA 94720*

SCHOENRICH, EDYTH HULL, academic administrator, physician; b. Cleve., Sept. 9, 1919; d. Edwin John and Maud Mabel (Kelly) Hull; m. Carlos Schoenrich, Aug. 9, 1942; children: Lola, Olaf. AB, Duke U., 1941; MD, U. Chgo., 1947; MPH, John Hopkins U., 1971. Diplomate Am. Bd. Internal Medicine, Am. Bd. Preventive Medicine. Intern John Hopkins Hosp., Balt., 1948-49, asst. resident medicine, 1949-50, postdoctoral fellow medicine, 1950-51, chief resident, pvt. wards, 1951-52; asst. chief, early child dept. chronic and cmty. medicine Balt. City Hosp., Balt., 1963-66; dir. svc. to chronically ill and aging Md. State Dept. Health, Balt., 1966-74; dir. divsn. pub. health adminstrn. Sch. Pub. Health, John Hopkins U., Balt., 1974-77, assoc. dean academic affairs, 1977-86, dir. part time profl. programs and dep. dir. MPH program, 1986—; prof. dept. health policy and mgmt., 1974—, joint appointment medicine, 1978—. Contbd. articles to profl. jours. Bd. trustees Friends Life Care Cmty., 1984—; Kennedy-Krieger Inst., Balt., 1985—, Vis. Nurses Assn., 1990—. Recipient Stebbins medal John Hopkins U., 1989. Fellow Am. Col. Physicians, Am. Coll. Preventive Medicine; mem. Assn. Tchrs. Preventive Medicine, Am. Pub. Health Assn., Med. Chirurg. Soc. Md., Balt. City Med. Soc., Phi Beta Kappa, Alpha Omega Alpha, Delta Omega. Avocations: gardening, music, theater, swimming. Home: 1402 Boyce Ave Baltimore MD 21204-6512 Office: John Hopkins Hosp Sch Pub Health 615 N Wolfe St Baltimore MD 21205

SCHOENROCK, JAMES V., religious organization administrator. Pres. Bapt. Missionary Assoc. of Am. Office: Baptist Missionary Assoc of Am 611 Butler St Springhill LA 71075

SCHOESLER, MARK GERALD, state legislator, farmer; b. Ritzville, Wash., Feb. 16, 1957; s. Gerald E. and Dorothy (Heinemann) S.; m. Ginger J. Van Aelst, Apr. 8, 1978; children: Veronica, Cody. AA, Spokane (Wash.)

C.C., 1977. Mem. Wash. Ho. of Reps., Olympia, 1992—; asst. majority floor leader, mem. rules, agr. and ecology, fin., and corrections coms. Pres. Wash. Friends Farms and Forests, 1991-92; mem. Cmty. Econ. Revitalization Bd. Mem. Wash. Assn. Wheat Growers (dir. 1990-92). Republican. Mem. United. Ch. Christ. Home: Rte 1 Box 151 Ritzville WA 99169

SCHOETTGER, RICHARD A., physiologist, marine biology researcher, science administrator; b. Arlington, Neb., Oct. 24, 1932; m. Loraine L. Nelson; children: David S., Lisa M. BS, Colo. State U., 1954, MS, 1959, PhD in Zoology, 1966. Physiologist Fish Control Lab., 1962-67, asst. dir. lab., 1967-69; dir. Fish-Pesticide Rsch. Lab., 1969-80; dir. Nat. Fisheries Contaminant Rsch. Ctr. U.S. Fish & Wildlife Svc., Columbia, Mo., 1980—; rsch. assoc. Dept. Nat. Resources U. Mo., Columbia, 1971; adv. com. water quality criteria Nat. Acad. Sci., 1971-72; co-project leader U.S.-U.S.S.R. Environmental Exchange Agreement, 1979—. Mem. Am. Fisheries Soc., Soc. Environmental Toxicology and Chemistry, Sigma Xi. Rsch. toxicity, physiology and exological effects of pesticides and other contaminants in aquatic organisms. Office: Nat Fisheries Contaminant Rsch Ctr 4200 New Haven Rd Columbia MO 65201-9634*

SCHOETTGER, THEODORE LEO, city official; b. Burton, Nebr., Sept. 2, 1920; s. Frederick and Louise Cecelia (Gierau) S.; m. Kathlyn Marguerite Hughey, June 3, 1943; children—Gregory Paul, Julie Anne. B.S. in Bus. Adminstrn. with Distinction, U. Nebr., 1948. C.P.A., Calif. Sr. acct. Haskins & Sells, Los Angeles, 1948-55; controller Beckman Instruments, Inc., Fullerton, Calif., 1955-58; corp. chief acct. Beckman Instruments, Inc., 1958-60; treas. Docummun Inc., Los Angeles, 1960-77; fin. dir. City of Orange, Calif., 1977-93. Mem. fin. com., treas., bd. dirs. Childrens Hosp. Served to lt. USNR, 1942-45. Mem. Calif. Soc. CPA's (nat. dir., v.p., past pres. Los Angeles chpt.), Fin. Execs. Inst., Mcpl. Fin. Officers Assn., Beta Gamma Sigma, Alpha Kappa Psi. Methodist. Clubs: Jonathan, Town Hall. Home: 9626 Shellyfield Rd Downey CA 90240-3418

SCHOETTLE, FERDINAND P., legal educator; b. Phila., Aug. 17, 1933; s. Ferdinand P. and Helen Louise (White) S.; m. E. Bok, Feb. 13, 1965 (div. 1976); m. D. Jean Thomson, Nov. 24, 1979 (div. 1982); children—Michael, Derek. B.A. in History, Princeton U., 1955; LL.D., Harvard U., 1960, M.A. in Econs., 1978, Ph.D., 1983. Bar: Pa. 1961, Minn. 1968. Asst., U.S. Senator J.S. Clark, Washington, 1961-62; assoc. Morgan, Lewis & Bockius, Phila., 1963-67; prof. law U. Minn. Law Sch., Mpls., 1967—; vis. prof. Harvard U., 1972-74, Uppsala U., Sweden, 1984; guest scholar Brookings Inst., Washington, 1992-93. Co-author: State and Local Taxes, 1974. Contbr. articles to profl. jours. Served to lt. USN, 1955-57. Mem. ABA (chmn. taxes and revenue com. 1979-82), Am. Law Inst. (editor tax policy. notes). Home: 312 Severn Ave Ste E-106 Annapolis MD 21403 Office: U Minn Sch Law Minneapolis MN 55455

SCHOETTLER, GAIL SINTON, state official; b. Los Angeles, Oct. 21, 1943; d. James and Norma (McLellan) Sinton; children: Lee, Thomas, James; m. Donald L. Stevens, June 23, 1990. BA in Econs., Stanford U., 1965; MA in History, U. Calif., Santa Barbara, 1969, PhD in History, 1975. Businesswoman Denver, 1975-83; exec. dir. Colo. Dept. of Personnel, Denver, 1983-86; treas. State of Colo., Denver, 1987-94, lt. govern., 1995—; bd. dirs. Nat. Jewish Hosp., Nat. Taxpayers' Union, Douglas County Edn. Found.; past bd. dirs. Pub. Employees Retirement Assn., Mi Casa Resource Ctr., Women's Bank, Denver, Equitable Bankshares of Colo., Equitable Bank, Littleton; chair Colo. Commn. Indian Affairs, Aerospace States Assn.; mem. adv. com. on external regulation of nuclear safety U.S. Dept. Energy, 1995—; mem. bd. trustees U. No. Colo., 1981-87. Mem. Douglas County Bd. Edn., Colo., 1979-87, pres., 1983-87; trustee U. No. Colo., Greeley, 1981-87; pres. Denver Children's Mus., 1975-85. Recipient Disting. Alumna award U. Calif. at Santa Barbara, 1987. Mem. Nat. Women's Forum (bd. dirs. 1981-89, pres. 1983-85), Internat. Women's Forum (mem. bd. dirs. 1981-89, pres. 83-85), Women Execs. in State Govt. (bd. dirs. 1981-87, chmn. 1988), Leadership Denver Assn. (bd. dirs. 1987, named Outstanding Alumna 1985), Nat. Assn. State Treas., Stanford Alumni Assn., Denver Rotary. Democrat.

SCHOETZ, DAVID JOHN, JR., colon and rectal surgeon; b. Milw., Oct. 29, 1948; s. David John and Beverly (Rogers) S.; m. Ruthanne Brennan, Mar. 25, 1972; children: Elizabeth Anne, David John III. BA, Coll. of Holy Cross, 1970; MD, Med. Coll. Wis., Milw., 1974. Resident in surgery Boston U. Med. Ctr., 1974-81; resident in colon/rectal surgery Lahey Clinic Med. Ctr., Burlington, Mass., 1981-82, staff colon-rectal surgeon, 1982—, chmn. dept. colon-rectal surgery, 1987—. Fellow ACS, Am. Soc. Colon Rectal Surgeons; mem. Am. Bd. Colon-Rectal Surgery (pres. 1994-95), Residency Rev. Com. Colon-Rectal Surgery (chmn. 1992—). Office: Lahey Clinic Med Ctr 41 Mall Rd Burlington MA 01803-4521

SCHOFFSTALL, PHIL, school superintendent. Supt. Evansville-Vanderburgh Sch. Dist. Office: Vanderburgh SD 1 SE 9th St Evansville IN 47708-1821

SCHOFIELD, CALVIN ONDERDONK, JR., bishop; b. Delhi, N.Y., Jan. 6, 1933; s. Calvin O. and Mabel (Lenton) S.; m. Elaine Marie Fullerton, Aug. 3, 1963; children: Susan Elaine, Robert Lenton. B.A., Hobart Coll., 1959, S.T.D. (Hon.), 1980; M.Div., Berkeley Div. Sch., 1959, D.D. (hon.), 1979; D.D. (hon.), U. of the South, 1981. Ordained priest Episcopal Ch., 1962; curate St. Peter's Episcopal Ch., St. Petersburg, Fla., 1962-64; vicar St. Andrew's Episcopal Ch., Miami, Fla., 1964-70; rector St. Andrew's Episcopal Ch., 1970-78; bishop coadjutor Diocese S.E. Fla., Miami, 1978-79, bishop, 1980—; exec. bd. Presiding Bishops Fund for World Relief; exec. coun. Episcopal Ch., 1991—. Regent U. of the South, Sewanee, Tenn., 1988—. Capt. chaplain corps USNR, 1960-85; ret., 1985. Mem. Naval Res. Assn., Naval Inst. Republican. Office: 525 NE 15th St Miami FL 33132-1485

SCHOFIELD, DONALD STEWART, real estate investment trust executive; b. Stoneham, Mass., Dec. 5, 1928; s. Roland Walter and Ida Louise (Smith) S.; m. Marion Gertrude Caulk, Dec. 10, 1950; children: Diane Schofield Garretson, Linda Schofield MacAyeal, Lora Schofield Ilhardt. BSBA summa cum laude, Boston U., 1956, MBA, 1957. CPA, Mass. Sr. mgr. Price Waterhouse & Co., Boston, 1956-66; v.p., treas. Wolf Rsch. & Devel. Co., Boston, 1966-68; exec. v.p. Gen. Investment & Devel. Co., Boston, 1969-76; pres. Windsor Investment Co., Boston, 1976-78; pres., chief exec. officer First Union Real Estate Investments, Cleve., 1978-85, chmn., pres., CEO, 1985-93; trustee, 1985-93; chmn., CEO, trustee, 1993—; dir. Nat. City Bank, Cleve.; trustee Univ. Circle Inc., Cleve. Served with Signal Corps. U.S. Army, 1951-52, Korea. Mem. Nat. Assn. Real Estate Investment Trusts (govt. rels. com.), Union Club, The Club at Soc. Ctr. Office: First Union Real Estate Investments 55 Public Sq Ste 1900 Cleveland OH 44113-1901

SCHOFIELD, HERBERT SPENCER, III, insurance executive; b. Mineola, N.Y., May 21, 1942; s. Herbert Spencer Jr. and Katherine Joan (Alcott) S.; divorced; children: Scott, Kate; m. Ruth Marie Mayers, July 14, 1985. BA, Lafayette Coll., Easton, Pa., 1965. CLU, ChFC, cert. ins. cons. Spl. agt. Northwestern Mut., Norwalk, Conn., 1974-93; personal ins. agt. various cos. by contract, Norwalk, 1974-93; pres. Schofield & Co., Glenbrook, Conn., 1993—. Mem. Nat. Assn. Life Underwriters, Estate Planning Coun. Southwestern Fairfield County (exec. bd. 1988-93, 1st v.p membership 1990-91, pres. 1991-92), S.W. Conn. Assn. Life Underwriters (treas. 1977-80), Nat. Trust for Hist. Preservation. Roman Catholic. Avocations: photography, walking, 18th and 19th century American antiques. Office: Schofield & Co PO Box 2916 Glenbrook CT 06906

SCHOFIELD, JOHN TREVOR, environmental management company executive; b. Manchester, Eng., Mar. 1, 1938; s. John and Hilda May (Mumford) S.; m. Jennifer Ann Wood, June 4, 1960 (div. Aug. 1980); children: Karen Jane, Alistair John; m. Susan B. West, July 24, 1982; 1 child, Kimberly. BS, U. Manchester, 1959. Dir. European ops. Borg-Warner Chem. Corp., Amsterdam, The Netherlands, 1964-70; mng. dir. Tunnel Holdings PLC, London, 1970-78; chief exec. officer, pres. Stablex Corp., Radnor, Pa., 1978-81; v.p. internat. Tech. Corp., Torrance, Calif., 1981-91; pres., CEO, chmn. Thermatrix Inc., San Jose, Calif., 1992—; mem. adv.

bd. Cupertino Nat. Bank; sec.-treas. Environ. Export Coun. U.S.A. Mem. Bd. Calif. Environ. Bus. Coun. (co-chmn.), Environ. Tech. Adv. Coun. for Calif. Avocation: public speaking, gourmet cooking. Office: Thermatrix Inc 3590 N 1st St San Jose CA 95134-1805

SCHOFIELD, JOHN-DAVID MERCER, bishop; b. Somerville, Mass., Oct. 6, 1938; s. William David and Edith Putnam (Stockman) S. BA, Dartmouth Coll., 1960; MDiv, Gen. Theol. Sem., N.Y.C., 1963, DD (hon.), 1989. Joined Monks of Mt. Tabor, Byzantine Cath. Ch., 1978; ordained priest Episcopal Ch. Asst. priest Ch. of St. Mary the Virgin, San Francisco, 1963-65, Our Most Holy Redeemer Ch., London, 1965-69; rector, retreat master St. Columba's Ch. and Retreat House, Inverness, Calif., 1969-88; bishop Episcopal Diocese of San Joaquin, Fresno, Calif., 1988—; aggregate Holy Transfiguration Monastery, 1984—; bishop protector Order Agape and Reconciliation, Chemainus, B.C., Can., 1990—. Episcopal visitor to Community of Christian Family Ministry, Vista, Calif., 1991—; trustee Nashotah House Sem., Wis., 1991—. Mem. Episcopal Synod of Am. (founder 1989), Episcopalians United (bd. dirs. 1987—). Republican. Office: Diocese of San Joaquin 4159 E Dakota Ave Fresno CA 93726-5297

SCHOFIELD, PAUL MICHAEL, finance company executive; b. Wilmington, Del., Mar. 30, 1937; s. John Edward and Sabina A. (Clarke) S.; m. Carol Ann Hane, July 11, 1964; children—Paul Michael, Andrew Clarke, Dennis Charles. B.A., LaSalle U., Phila., 1960; postgrad., U. Del., 1963. Asst. treas. Sears Roebuck Acceptance Corp., Wilmington, Del., 1971-73, asst. v.p., 1973-74, treas., 1974-83, v.p., treas., 1983-87; pres., treas. Discover Credit Corp., Wilmington, 1987—. Campaign capt. United Way of Del., 1978; campaign capt. Boys Club Del., 1979. Mem. Del. Fin. Assn. (treas.), Phila. Treas. Club. Democrat. Roman Catholic. Club: Irish Culture of Del. (treas. 1980). Avocations: reading; golf; woodworking. Home: 2014 Delaware Ave Wilmington DE 19806-2208 Office: Discover Credit Corp 3711 Kennett Pike Wilmington DE 19807-2102

SCHOFIELD, ROBERT E(DWIN), history educator, academic administrator; b. Milford, Neb., June 1, 1923; s. Charles Edwin and Nora May (Fullerton) S.; m. Mary-Peale Smith, June 20, 1959; 1 son, Charles Stockton Peale. A.B., Princeton, 1944; M.S., U. Minn., 1948; Ph.D., Harvard, 1955. Research asst. Fercleve Corp. and Clinton Labs., Oak Ridge, 1944-46; research assoc. Knolls Atomic Power Lab., Gen. Electric Co., 1948-51; asst. prof., then assoc. prof. history U. Kans., Lawrence, 1955-60; mem. faculty Case Western Res. U., Cleve., 1960-79, prof. history of sci., 1963-72, Lynn Thorndike prof. history of sci., 1972-79; prof. history Iowa State U., Ames, 1979-93, prof. emeritus, 1993—, dir. grad. program history tech. and sci., 1979-92; mem. Inst. Advanced Study, 1967-68, 74-75; Sigma Xi nat. lectr., 1978-80. Author: The Lunar Society of Birmingham, 1963, Scientific Autobiography of Joseph Priestley: Selected Scientific Correspondence, 1966, Mechanism and Materialism: British Natural Philosophy in an Age of Reason, 1970, (with D.G.C. Allan) Stephen Hales: Scientist and Philanthropist, 1980. Served with AUS, 1945-46. Fulbright fellow, 1953-54; Guggenheim fellow, 1959-60, 67-68. Fellow Am. Phys. Soc., Royal Soc. Arts; mem. History of Sci. Soc., Soc. History Tech., Midwest Junto History of Sci., Am. Soc. 18th Century Studies, Acad. Internat. d'Histoire des Scis. (corr.). Home: 44 Sycamore Rd Princeton NJ 08540-5323

SCHOFIELD, SETH EUGENE, air transport company executive; b. Stafford Springs, Conn., Aug. 22, 1939; s. Seth Herbert and Lola Maria (Venturini) S.; children: Lisa, Deanna; m. Diane Hayes, Jan. 4, 1991. P.M.D., Harvard U. Bus. Sch., 1975. With U.S. Air, Inc., 1957—; asst. v.p. ops. adminstrn. U.S. Air, Inc., Pitts., 1974-76; v.p. ops. adminstrn. U.S. Air, Inc., 1976-77, v.p. ops. mgr., 1977-79, sr. v.p. ops., 1979-81, exec. v.p. ops., 1981-89, vice chmn., exec. v.p. ops., 1989-90, vice chmn., pres. and chief ops. officer, 1990-91, from vice chmn., pres. and chief exec. officer to chmn., 1991—. Campaign coordinator Alleghency County (Pa.) United Way; active in fund raising Cystic Fibrosis Found.; Mem. bd. dirs. Pitts.-Allegheny County chpt. ARC, Erie Ins. Group, Pitts. Nat. Bank and Flight Safety Found.; vice chmn. Greater Pitts. C. of C. Recipient Humanitarian award Red Cross and Am. Heritage Award, 1993; named Man of Yr. for Bus. and Industry. Office: USAIR Inc 2345 Crystal Dr Arlington VA 22227

SCHOFIELD, WILLIAM, psychologist, educator; b. Springfield, Mass., Apr. 19, 1921; s. William and Angie Mae (St. John) S.; m. Geraldine Bryan, Jan. 11, 1946; children: Bryan St. John, Gwen Star. B.S., Springfield Coll., 1942; M.A., U. Minn., 1946, Ph.D., 1948. Diplomate: Am. Bd. Profl. Psychology. Instr. U. Minn., Mpls., 1947-48; asst. prof. U. Minn., 1948-51, assoc. prof., 1951-59, prof. psychology, 1959-88, prof. emeritus, 1988—; vis. prof. U. Wash., 1960, U. Colo., 1965; Cons. VA Hosp., Mpls.; examiner, instr. USCG Aux., 1968—; adv. med. council VA, 1970-75; Mem. med. policy adv. com. Dept. Pub. Welfare Minn., 1960-68; mem. mental health services research rev. com. NIMH, 1969-73; bd. dirs. Profl. Exam. Service, 1976-81; mem. editorial bd. Roche Psychiat. Service Inst.; mem. Minn. State Bd. Psychology, 1983-86. Author: Psychotherapy: The Purchase of Friendship, 1964, 2d edit., 1986, Pragmatics of Psychotherapy, 1988; contbr. articles to profl. jours. Served with USAAF, 1943-46. Fellow Am. Psychol. Assn. (com. on health ins. 1968-71, membership com. 1968-71, sec.-treas. clin. div. 1969-72, chmn. task force on health research 1973-75, chmn. sect. health research div. psychologists in pub. service 1977, mem. com. profl. standards 1982-85, chair com. 1984-85); mem. Midwestern Psychol. Assn., Minn. Psychol. Assn. (exec. sec. 1954-59), AAAS, AAUP, Assn. Am. Med. Colls. (chmn. com. on measurement of personality 1970-74), Sigma Xi, Pi Gamma Mu. Home: 1441 E River Pky Minneapolis MN 55414-3625 Home (winter): #202 1500 Beach Rd Tequesta FL 33469-2826 Office: U Minn Hosp 420 Delaware St SE Minneapolis MN 55455-0374

SCHOGGEN, PHIL H(OWARD), psychologist, educator; b. Tulsa, Aug. 28, 1923; s. Walter B. and Emma F. (Alexander) S.; m. Maxine F. Spoor, June 28, 1944; children: Leida, Christopher, Ann, Susan. AB in Psychology, Park Coll., 1946; MS, U. Kans., Lawrence, 1951, P.h.D. in Psychology, 1954. Asst. prof. psychology U. Oreg., 1957-62, asso. prof., 1962-66; prof., chmn. dept. psychology George Peabody Coll., 1966-75; prof. York U., Toronto, Ont., Can., 1975-77; prof. human devel. and family studies N.Y. State Coll. Human Ecology, Cornell U., 1977-90, prof. emeritus, 1990—, chmn. dept., 1977-82. Author: (with R. G. Barker) Qualities of Community Life, 1973; Behavior Settings: A Revision and Extension of Roger G. Barker's Ecological Psychology, 1989. Served with USNR, 1944-46, 50-51. Mem. APA. Home: 121 Vossland Dr Nashville TN 37205-3617

SCHOGT, HENRY GILIUS, foreign language educator; b. Amsterdam, May 24, 1927; s. Johannes Herman and Ida Jacoba (Van Rijn) S.; m. Corrie Frenkel, Apr. 2, 1955; children—Barbara, Philibert Johannes, Elida. B.A. in French, U. Amsterdam, 1947, B.A. in Russian, 1948, M.A. in Russian, 1951, M.A. cum laude in French, 1952; Ph.D. in French, U. Utrecht, 1960. Docent Russian U. Groningen, The Netherlands, 1953-63; sr. lectr. French U. Utrecht, The Netherlands, 1954-63; master asst. gen. linguistics U. Paris, 1963-64; vis. lectr. Russian and French Princeton (N.J.) U., 1964-66; prof. French and linguistics U. Toronto, Ont., Can., 1966-92. Author: books including Les causes de la double issue de e fermé tonique libre en français, 1960, Le système verbal du français contemporain, 1968, Sémantique synchronique, synonymie, homonymie, polysémie, 1976, (with Pierre Léon and Edward Burstynsky) La phonologie, 1977, Linguistics, Literary Analysis and Literary Translation, 1988. Fellow Royal Soc. Can.; mem. Société de linguistique de Paris, Can. Linguistic Assn. Home: 47 Turner Rd, Toronto, ON Canada M6G 3H7 Office: Dept French, Univ Toronto, Toronto, ON Canada M5S 1A1 *My ideas and goals in life are closely connected with the ideals of a socialist system of distribution of wealth and of individual responsibility towards one's fellow human beings and towards society.*

SCHOLDER, FRITZ, artist; b. Breckenridge, Minn., Oct. 6, 1937; s. Fritz William and Ella Mae (Haney) S.; m. Peggy Stephenson, June 28, 1958 (div. Mar. 1966); 1 son, Fritz VI; m. Romona Attenberger, July 30, 1966 (div. Feb. 1994). Student, Wis. State Coll., 1956-57; AA, Sacramento City Coll., 1958; BA, Sacramento State Coll., 1960; MFA, U. Ariz., 1963, DFA (hon.), 1985; DFA (hon.), Ripon Coll., Wis., 1984, Concordia Coll., Minn., 1986, HHD (hon.), Coll. Sante Fe; DFA (hon.), U. Wis., Superior, 1993. Teaching asst. art Univ Ariz., 1962-64; instr. art history, advanced painting Inst. Am. Indian Arts, 1964-69; artist in residence Dartmouth Coll., 1973; guest artist Santa Fe Art Inst., 1987, Okla. Art Inst., 1980-81, 88, Am. U., Washington,

1990. One-man shows: Crocker Art Gallery, Sacramento, 1959, Coll. Santa Fe, 1967, Roswell (N.Mex.) Art Center, 1969, Tally Richards Gallery Contemporary Art, Taos, N.Mex., 1971, 73, 75, 78, 79, St. John's Coll., Santa Fe, 1972, Cordier & Ekstrom, N.Y.C., 1972, 74, 76, 78, 90, Gimpel & Weitzenhoffer, N.Y.C., 1977, Graphics 1 and 2, Boston, 1977, Smith Andersen Gallery, Palo Alto, Calif., 1979, Plains Mus., Moorhead, Minn., 1980, 1981-89, Scottsdale Center for Arts, 1981, Tucson Mus. Art, 1981, Weintraub Gallery, N.Y.C., 1981, ACA Galleries, N.Y.C., 1984, 86, Sena Galleries West, Santa Fe, N.Mex., 1986, 87, Louis Newman Galleries, L.A., 1985, 87, 90-94, Schneider Mus. Art, Ashland, Oreg., 1990, Alexander Gallery, N.Y., 1991, Riva Yares Gallery, Scottsdale, Ariz., 1992, 94; exhibited group shows: Carnegie Art Inst., Butler Inst. Am. Art, Calif. Palace of Legion of Honor, Houston Mus. Fine Arts, Dallas Mus. Fine Arts, San Francisco Mus. Art, Denver Art Mus., Ft. Worth Art Center, Basel Art 5, Linden Mus., Stuttgart, Philbrook Art Center, Oakland Art Mus., Tucson Art Center, N.Mex. Art Mus., Edinburgh Art Festival, Museo de Bellas Artes, Buenos Aires, Biblioteca Nacional, Santiago, Chile, Mus. voor Landen-Volkenkunder, Rotterdam, Amerika Haus, Berlin Festival, Center for Arts of Indian Am., Washington, Yellowstone Art Center, Nat. Mus. Modern Art, Tokyo, Kyoto, Japan, also other fgn. and Am. shows, Smithsonian tour, Bucharest, Berlin, London, Ankara, Madrid, Belgrade, Athens, 1972-73; represented in permanent collections: Mus. Modern Art, N.Y.C., Art Inst. Chgo., Center Culturel Americain, Paris, Art Gallery Toronto, NEA, Houston Mus. Fine Arts, Boston Fine Arts Mus., Milw. Art Mus., Portland (Oreg.) Art Mus., Dallas Mus. Fine Arts, Bur. Indian Affairs, Mus. N.Mex., Smithsonian Insn., Bklyn. Mus., Phoenix Art Mus., San Diego Fine Arts Gallery, Okla. Art Center, Brigham Young U., Heard Mus., Phoenix, Bibliotheque Nat., Paris, San Francisco Mus. Art, Hermitage Mus., Leningrad, others; Included in: American Prints and Printmakers; Subject of: PBS film Fritz Scholder, 1976, PBS film Fritz Scholder, An American Portrait, 1983; author: Fritz Scholder Lithograph, 1975, 1983, Scholder/Indians, Fritz Scholder, Rizzoli, Fritz Scholder, Paintings and Monotypes, Afternoon Nap, 1991, Live Dog/Evil God, 1992, Fritz Scholder, A Survey of Paintings, 1993, Remnants of Memory, 1993, Fritz Scholder's Book of Symbols for Children, 1994, Fritz Scholder, Thirty Years of Sculpture, 1994; guest artist Santa Fe Art Inst., 1987, Taos Inst. Art, 1990, Am. U., Washington, 1990. Recipient Ford Found. purchase award, 1962, 1st prize W.Va. Centennial Exhbn., 1963, purchase prize 13th S.W. Print Drawing Show, 1963, Hallmark purchase award, 1965, 1st prize Scottsdale Indian Nat., 1966, Grand prize Washington Biennial Indian Show, 1967, Grand prize Scottsdale Indian Nat., 1969, jurors award S.W. Fine Arts Biennial, 1970, 71, 72, prize in painting Am. Acad. and Inst. Arts and Letters, 1977, award in painting Am. Acad. Arts and Letters, 1977, internat. prize in lithography Intergrafiks, Berlin, 1980, 90, N.D. Gov.'s award in arts, 1981, N.Mex. Gov.'s award, 1983, Societaire Salon d'Automne, Paris, 1983, Golden Plate award Am. Acad. Achievement, 1985, Third prize Intergrafiks, 1990, Laird Leadership award in the arts U. Wis., Stevens Point; John Hay Whitney fellow, 1962-63. Address: 118 Cattletrack Rd Scottsdale AZ 85251 *I Believe in Art, Love, and Magic.*

SCHOLEFIELD, PETER GORDON, health agency executive; b. Newport, Wales, June 26, 1925; emigrated to Can., 1947, naturalized, 1952; s. Tom and Margaret (Bithell) S.; m. Erna Mary Cooper, Sept. 29, 1951; children—David, John, Paul. B.Sc., U. Wales, 1944, M.Sc., 1946, D.Sc., 1960; Ph.D., McGill U., Montreal, Que., Can., 1949. From research fellow to prof. biochemistry McGill U., 1949-65, dir. cancer research unit, 1965-69; asst. exec. dir. Nat. Cancer Inst. Can., Toronto, 1969-80; exec. dir. Nat. Cancer Inst. Can., 1980-91, spl. adviser to chief exec. officer, 1991-92; dir. grants and awards Alta. Heritage Found. for Med. Rsch., Edmonton, 1992-94; coord. acad. affairs Samuel Lunenfeld Rsch. Inst. Mt. Sinai Hosp., Toronto, 1994—; chair rsch. and policy com., bd. dirs Alzheimer Soc. of Can., 1994—. Home: 161 Allanhurst Dr, Islington, ON Canada M9A 4K5 Office: Mt Sinai Hosp Samuel Linenfeld Rsch Inst, 600 University Ave, Toronto, ON Canada M5G 1X5

SCHOLER, SUE WYANT, state legislator; b. Topeka, Oct. 20, 1936; d. Zint Elwin and Virginia Louise (Achenbach) Wyant; m. Charles Frey Scholer, Jan. 27, 1957; children: Elizabeth Scholer Truelove, Charles W., Virginia M. Scholer McCal. Student, Kans. State U., 1954-56. Draftsman The Farm Clinic, West Lafayette, Ind., 1978-79; assessor Wabash Twp., West Lafayette, 1979-84; commr. Tippecanoe County, Lafayette, Ind., 1984-90; state rep. Dist. 26 Ind. Statehouse, Indpls., 1990—; asst. minority whip, 1992-94, majority whip, 1994—; mem. Tippecanoe County Area Plan Commn., 1984-90. Bd. dirs. Crisis Ctr., Lafayette, 1984-89, Tippecanoe Arts Fedn., 1990—, United Way, Lafayette, 1990-93; mem. Lafayette Conv. and Visitors Bur., 1988-90. Recipient Salute to Women Govt. and Police award, 1986. Mem. Ind. Assn. County Commrs. (treas. 1990), Assn. Ind. Counties (legis. com. 1988-90), Greater Lafayette C. of C. (ex-officio bd. 1984-90), Sagamore Bus. and Profl. Women, LWV, P.E.O., Purdue Women's Club (past treas.), Kappa Kappa Kappa (past pres. Epsilon chpt.), Delta Delta Delta (past pres. alumnae, house corp. treas.). Republican. Presbyterian. Avocations: golf, needlework, reading. Home: 807 Essex St West Lafayette IN 47906-1534 Office: Indiana Statehouse Rm 3A-4 Indianapolis IN 46204

SCHOLES, EDISON EARL, army officer; b. McCaysville, Ga., Aug. 16, 1939; s. Alvin L. and Marie (Plemmons) S.; m. Elva E. Bussey, June 4, 1961; children: Juana Kimberly Scholes Scherer, Tracy Michele Scholes Heller, Michael Lee. BS in Physics cum laude, No. Ga. Coll., 1961; MS in Ops. Rsch., Naval Postgrad. Sch., 1970; postgrad., Army War Coll., 1980, Harvard Def. Policy Seminar, 1991. Commd. 2d lt. U.S. Army, 1961, advanced through grades to maj. gen., 1991; comdr. A Detachment, 10th Spl. Forces Group, 1st Spl. Forces U.S. ArmyEurope, 1963-66; comdr. Co. D, 2d Bn.(Abn.), 8th Cav., 1st Cav. Div. U.S. Army, Republic of Vietnam, 1967-68; comdr. 1st Bn., 23d Inf., 2d Inf. Div. U.S. Army, Republic of Korea, 1976-77; comdr. 2d Tng. Bn., Sch. Brigade, U.S. Army Inf. Sch. U.S. Army, Ft. Benning, Ga., 1978-79, comdr. 1st Inf. Tng. Brigade, U.S. Army Infantry Tng. Ctr., 1983-85; dep. commanding gen. chief of staff 3d U.S. Army/U.S. Army Cen. Command U.S. Army, Ft. McPherson, Ga., 1986-88; asst. div. comdr. 82d Airborne Div. U.S. Army, Ft. Bragg, N.C., 1988-89, chief of staff XVIII Airborne Corps, 1989-90; dep. commanding gen. XVIII south, Op. Just Cause U.S. Army, 1989-90; dep. commanding gen. XVIII Airborne Corps, Operation Desert Shield/Desert Storm U.S. Army, Saudi Arabia, Iraq, 1990-91; dep. commanding gen. XVIII Airborne Corps U.S. Army, Ft. Bragg, 1991-93; dep. comdr. Allied Land Forces, S.E. Europe NATO, 1993—; postgrad. Harvard Def. Policy Seminar, 1991. Decorated Disting. Svc. medal, Silver Star, Legion of Merit with oak leaf cluster, Bronze Star with V device and 4 oak leaf clusters, Purple Heart with oak leaf cluster, 6 Air medals, Army Commendation medal with V device and oak leaf cluster, Armed Forces Expeditionary medal, Vietnam Svc. medal with 6 campaign stars, Southwest Asia Svc. medal with 3 campaign stars, Combat Infantry badge, Expert Infantry badge, Army Gen. Staff badge, Meritorious Svc. medal, Nat. Def. Svc. medal with oak leaf cluster, Kuwait Liberation medal; Cross of Gallantry with Silver and Bronze Stars and Palm (Republic of Vietnam), S.W. Asia Svc. medal with 3 stars; numerous other domestic and foreign awards and skill badges. Mem. 82d Airborne Divsn. Assn., Spl. Forces Assn. (chpt. XXXIV), U.S. Army Ranger Assn., Assn. of U.S. Army, VFW, Officers' Club. Baptist. Avocations: running, reading, camping, fishing.

SCHOLES, MYRON S., law and finance educator; b. 1941. BA, McMaster U., 1962, MBA, 1964; PhD, U. Chgo., 1969. Instr. U. Chgo. Bus. Sch., 1967-68; prof. U. Chgo., 1976-83; asst. prof. MIT Mgmt. Sch., Cambridge, 1968-72, assoc. prof., 1972-73; assoc. prof. U. Chgo., 1973-75, prof., 1975-79, Edward Eagle Brown prof. fin., 1979-82; dir. Ctr. for Rsch. in Security Prices U. Chgo., 1975-81; prof. law Stanford (Calif.) U., 1983—, Frank E. Buck prof. fin.; sr. rsch. fellow Hoover Instn. Stanford U., 1988—; mng. dir. Salomon Bros., 1991-93, prin. long-term capital mgmt., 1994—. Office: Stanford U Grad Sch Bus Stanford CA 94305

SCHOLES, ROBERT EDWARD, English language educator; b. Bklyn., May 19, 1929; s. Ted H. J. and Leila (Imello) S.; m. Joan Grace Carter, Jan. 6, 1951 (dec. 1971); children—Christine (dec.), Peter; m. Jo Ann Schott Putnam, Jan. 30, 1972; stepchildren—Cynthia, Richard, Gregory, Michael. AB, Yale U., 1950; MA, Cornell U., 1956, PhD, 1959. Instr. English U. Va., Charlottesville, 1959-61; asst. prof. U. Va., 1961-63; assoc. prof. U. Iowa, Iowa City, 1964-66; prof. English U. Iowa, 1966-70, Brown U., Providence, 1970-82; univ. prof. Brown

U., 1982-87, Andrew Mellon prof. humanities, 1987—. Author: The Cornell Joyce Collection, 1961, The Fabulators, 1967, Elements of Fiction, 1968, Structuralism in Literature, 1974, Structural Fabulation, 1975, Fabulation and Metafiction, 1979, Semiotics and Interpretation, 1982, Textual Power, 1985; (with others) The Nature of Narrative, 1966, Elements of Essay, 1969, Elements of Drama, 1970, Elements of Writing, 1972, Science Fiction: History, Science, Vision, 1977, Protocols of Reading, 1989, In Search of James Joyce, 1992; editor: Approaches to the Novel, 1969, Learners and Discerners, 1964, The Philosopher Critic, 1970, Some Modern Writers, 1971, others; (with others) Elements of Literature, 1981, The Practice of Writing, 1985, Bridges to Fantasy, 1982, Fields of Writing, 1985, Text Book, 1988, Hemingway's Genders, 1994, others; contbr. articles to profl. jours. Served with USNR, 1951-55. Andrew Mellon fellow, 1983, Guggenheim fellow, 1977-78, U. Wis. fellow, 1963-64. Mem. MLA (Mina P. Shaugnessy award 1986), PEN, Semiotic Soc. Am., James Joyce Found., Nat. Council Tchrs. English (David H. Russell award 1988), Acad. Lit. Studies, Internat. Assn. Univ. Profs. of English. Democrat. Club: Yale (N.Y.). Avocation: sailing. Home: 20 Fairway Dr Barrington RI 02806-3628 Office: Brown U PO Box 1957 Providence RI 02912-1957

SCHOLFIELD, LINDA KATHERINE, nursing administrator; b. Houston, Aug. 20, 1946; d. Harry Francis and Inez Beatrice (McGuff) Knight; m. Paul Arlo Scholfield, Sept. 5, 1970; children: Christin, Suzanne. Diploma, Meml. Bapt. Sch. Nursing, 1967; BBA, Temple U., 1983, MBA, 1985. Nurse mgr., staff nurse Meml. Bapt. Hosp., Houston, 1967-70; asst. nurse mgr., staff nurse U. Mich. Hosp., Ann Arbor, 1970-75; nurse mgr., staff nurse Med. Coll. Pa. Hosp., Phila., 1975-76; asst. dir., bus. mgr. Abington (Pa.) Meml. Hosp., 1985-86, nurse dir., 1986-89, v.p., 1989—; mem. adv. bd. Ea. Montgomery County Vis. Nurse Assn., Abington, 1988—; bd. dirs. Alliance. Mem. Staff-parish rels. com. Huntingdon Valley (Pa.) Meth. Ch., 1992, chairwoman, mem. worship com., 1993. Mem. Am. Orgn. Nurse Execs. (exec. bd. dirs., co-chair legis. com. 1984—), Pa. Nurse Leaders (pres.-elect 1994—). Methodist. Avocations: traveling, art. Office: Abington Meml Hosp 1200 Old York Rd Abington PA 19001

SCHOLL, ALLAN HENRY, retired school system administrator, education consultant; b. Bklyn., May 6, 1935; s. Joseph Arnold and Edith (Epstein) S.; m. Marina Alexandra Mihailovich, July 3, 1960. BA, UCLA, 1957; MA, U. So. Calif., 1959, PhD in History, 1973. Lic. gen. secondary tchr. (life), administrv. svcs. (life), jr. coll. tchr. (life) Calif. Tchr. social studies L.A. Unified Sch. Dist., 1960-82, adviser social studies sr. high schs. div., 1982-84, dir. secondary social studies Office Instrn., 1984-91; instr. history L.A. City Coll., 1966-69, U. So. Calif., L.A., 1968-69, Community Coll., Rio Hondo, Calif., 1972-74, Cerritos (Calif.) Coll., 1973-74; dir. Almar Ednl. Cons., Pasadena, Calif., 1991—; curriculum writer interactive TV and history teaching and resource guides; edn. cons. Am. Odyssey, 1991; cons. h.s. govt. and U.S. history textbooks, 1987. Author: United States History and Art, 1992; co-author: History of the World, 1990, History of the World: The Modern Era, 1991, 20th Century World History: The Modern Era, 1993, People of African Descent in Nazi Occupied Europe, 1995; contbr. articles to profl. jours. Bd. dirs. Pasadena Chamber Orch., 1977-78, Pasadena Symphony Orch., 1984-85, Pasadena Centennial Com., 1985; mem. exec. bd., chmn. edn. com. Martyrs Meml. and Mus. of Holocaust, 1992—; mem. ednl. adv. bd. Gene Autry Western Heritage Mus., 1992—. With U.S. Army, 1958-59. NDEA fellow Russian lang. studies, 1962; Chouinard Art Inst. scholar, 1952. Mem. Am. Hist. Assn., Nat. Coun. Social Studies, Calif. Coun. Social Studies, So. Calif. Social Studies Assn. (bd. dirs. 1982-84), Assoc. Adminstrs. L.A. (legis. coun. 1984-86), Nat. History Hon. Soc., Crohn's and Colitis Found. Am., Phi Alpha Theta. Avocations: reading, hiking, travel, painting, tennis. Personal philosophy: I have always believed that to achieve in life one should work hard and never give up. That is the only way we can ever hope to make a lasting contribution to society.

SCHOLL, DAVID ALLEN, federal judge; b. Bethlehem, Pa., Aug. 20, 1944; s. George Raymond and Beatrice Roberta (Weaver) S.; m. Cynthia Ann Schuler Vetere, June, 1966 (div. 1972); m. Portia Elizabeth White, May 26, 1973; children: Tracy, Xavier; 1 stepchild, Sierra Milan. AB, Franklin & Marshall Coll., 1966; JD, Villanova U., 1969. Bar: Pa. 1969, U.S. Dist. Ct. (ea. dist.) 1970, U.S. Ct. Appeals (3d cir.) 1971, U.S. Tax Ct. 1975, U.S. Supreme Ct. 1975. Staff atty. Community Legal Services, Inc., Phila., 1969-73, 77-80; exec. dir. Delaware County Legal Assistance Assn., Chester, Pa., 1973-76; mng. atty. Lehigh Valley Legal Services, Bethlehem, Allentown, Pa., 1980-86; judge U.S. Bankruptcy Ct., Phila., 1986-94, chief judge, 1994—. Bd. dirs. Phila. Vols. for Indigent Program, 1988-94, Consumer Bankruptcy Assistance Project, 1992—. Recipient Joseph Harris award Ba'Hais of Lehigh Valley, Bethlehem, 1984. Mem. Pa. Bar Assn. (chairperson consumer law commn., 1983-86), Northampton County Bar Assn. Avocations: baseball, rock music. Home: 118 N Highland Ave Bala Cynwyd PA 19004-3027 Office: US Dist Ct 3118 US Courthouse 601 Market St Philadelphia PA 19106-1723

SCHOLLANDER, WENDELL LESLIE, JR., lawyer; b. Ocala, Fla., May 17, 1943; s. Wendell Leslie and Martha Dent (Perry) S.; m. Jayn Mary Cochran, Aug. 22, 1970; 1 son, Wendell Leslie III. BS, U. Pa., 1966, MBA, 1968; student law, Stetson U., 1969-70; JD, Duke U., 1972. Bar: N.C. 1977, Tenn. 1972, Fla. 1987. With Container Corp. Am., Fernandina, Fla., 1968-69; asso. firm Miller, Martin, Chattanooga, 1972-75; asst. counsel R.J. Reynolds Industries, Inc., 1975-78, assoc. counsel, 1978-79, sr. assoc. counsel, 1979-82, sr. counsel, 1982-85; gen. counsel RJR Archer, Inc., Winston-Salem, N.C., 1979-85, sec., dir., 1978-85; ptnr. Finger, Parker & Avram, Winston-Salem, 1985-87, Schollander, Winston-Salem, 1987—; gen. counsel Splty. Tobacco Council, 1985-87. Mem. ABA, N.C. Bar Assn., Forsyth County Bar Assn., Mil. Hist. Soc. U.K., Mensa, SAR, Phi Delta Phi, Kappa Sigma. Presbyterian. Home: 2011 Georgia Ave Winston Salem NC 27104-3105 Office: 2000 W 1st St Ste 509 Winston Salem NC 27104

SCHOLLE, ROGER HAL, dentist; b. Cleve., Oct. 31, 1936; s. Martin Henry Edward and Irene Frances (Lawrence) S. B.A., Northwestern U., 1958, D.D.S., 1962; M.S., U. Chgo., 1968. Diplomate: Am. Bd. Oral Pathology. Resident trainee in oral pathology U. Chgo. Hosp. and Clinics, 1965-67; asst. sec. Council on Dental Therapeutics, 1968-77; pvt. practice dentistry Chgo., 1970—. Editor: Am. Dental Assn. Jour., Chgo., 1978-86, Ill. State Dental Jour., 1987-93, Chgo. Dental Soc. Rev., 1993—. Bd. dirs. Ill. div. Am. Cancer Soc., 1979-83. Served to capt. M.C. USAF, 1962-64. Fellow Am. Coll. Dentists, Internat. Coll. Dentists, Ondontgraphic Soc. Chgo., Pierre Fouchard Soc.; mem. Omicron Kappa Upsilon, Delta Sigma Delta. Address: 166 E Superior St Chicago IL 60611

SCHOLLMAIER, EDGAR H., pharmaceutical products company executive; b. 1933; married. BA, U. Cin., 1956; MBA, Harvard U., 1958. With Alcon Labs., Inc., Ft. Worth, 1956—, dist. mgr., 1959-61, div. mgr., 1961-62, mgr. program planning, 1962-63, dir. mktg., 1963-64, v.p., gen. mgr. mktg., 1964-71, exec. v.p., 1971-72, chief operating officer, from 1972, pres., 1972—, chmn., chief exec. officer, 1977—, also bd. dirs. Office: Alcon Surgical Inc 6201 S Freeway Fort Worth TX 76134-2099

SCHOLNICK, ROBERT J., college dean, English language educator; b. Boston, June 22, 1941; s. I. Allen and Ruth (Kleiman) S.; m. Sylvia Bette Huberman, June 21, 1964; children: Joshua David, Jonathan Ben. BA, U. Pa., 1962; MA, Brandeis U., 1964, PhD, 1969. Asst. prof. English Coll. William and Mary, Williamsburg, Va., 1967-74, assoc. prof., 1974-80, prof., 1980—, dean grad. studies, 1986—; bd. dirs. Univ. Press of Va., Charlottesville, 1988-92; mem. adv. bd. Am. Periodicals. Author: Edmund Clarence Stedman, 1977; editor Am. Lit. and Sci., 1992; contbr. articles to profl. jours. NEH fellow Coll. Tchrs., 1986-87. Mem. Rsch. Soc. for Am. Periodicals (pres.), B'nai B'rith Va. (Hillel svc. award 1986), Phi Beta Kappa. Avocations: distance running, arts. Home: 149 Indian Springs Rd Williamsburg VA 23185-3938 Office: Coll of William and Mary Williamsburg VA 23185

SCHOLSKY, MARTIN JOSEPH, priest; b. Stafford Spring, Conn., Jan. 16, 1930; s. Sigmund Felix and Mary Magdalen (Wysocki) S. BA, St. John's Sem., 1952, MA in History, 1956; MA in Classical Greek, Cath. U. of Am., 1966. Ordained priest Roman Cath. Ch., 1956. Asst. pastor St. Peter's Ch., Hartford, Conn., 1956-61; prin. St. Peter's Sch., Hartford, 1956-58; instr. St. Thomas Sem., Bloomfield, Conn., 1961-67; admissions dir. St. Thomas Sem., Bloomfield, 1965-67; vocations dir. Archdiocese of Hartford, 1967-78;

chaplain Newington (Conn.) Children's Hosp., 1961-78; weekend asst. St. Mary's Ch., Newington, 1961-78; pastor St. Bartholomew Ch., Manchester, Conn., 1978-90; dean Manchester Deanery, 1989-91; spiritual dir. St. Thomas Aquinas High Sch., New Britain, Conn., 1991-92; weekend asst. St. Francis of Assis Ch., South Windsor, Conn., 1991-92; instr. Holy Apostle's Sem. & Coll., Cromwell, Conn., 1988-94; pastor St. Mary's Ch., East Hartford, Conn., 1992—. Contbr. articles to profl. jours. Home: 36 Griswold St Manchester CT 06040-3928 Office: St Marys Ch East East Hartford CT 06108 Conscience is not our own personal feelings about things; rather, it is our innate awareness of the rightness and wrongness of our deeds as God sees them, an awareness, often denied, that still remains the measure by which God will ultimately judge us all.

SCHOLTEN, PAUL, obstetrician-gynecologist, educator; b. San Francisco, Oct. 14, 1921; s. Henry Francis and Gladys (Lamborn) S.; m. Marion Lucy O'Neil, Feb. 7, 1948; children: Catherine Mary (dec.), Anne Marie, Pauline Marie, Joseph, Stephen, John. AB, San Francisco State U., 1943; postgrad., Stanford U., 1946-47; MD, U. Calif., San Francisco, 1951. Diplomate Am. Bd. Ob-Gyn. Intern San Francisco Gen. Hosp., 1951-52; resident in ob-gyn U. Calif., San Francisco, 1952-55; pvt. practice specializing in ob-gyn San Francisco, 1955-80; coll. physician Student Health Svc. San Francisco State U., 1956-80, dir. women's svcs. Student Health Svc., 1980-91; pvt. practice San Francisco, 1991—; part-time ship's surgeon Delta Lines, 1980-84; assoc. clin. prof. Med. Sch., U. Calif., San Francisco, 1955—, assoc. clin. prof. Nursing Sch., 1987—; preceptor Med. Sch., Stanford U., 1989-91; lectr. on health and wine at numerous univs., profl. groups. Contbr. articles to profl. publs., chpts. to books. Cons. U.S. Wine Inst.; sci. advisor Calif. State Adv. Bd. on Alcohol-Related Problems, 1980-86; bd. dirs. A.W.A.R.E., Century Coun. Sgt. U.S. Army, 1944-46. Mem. AMA, Calif. Med. Assn., Pan Am. Med. Assn., San Francisco Med. Soc. (editor 1971—, historian), San Francisco Gynecol. Soc., Am. Coll. Ob-Gyn., Soc. Med. Friends of Wine (bd. dis. 1955—, past pres.), San Francisco Wine and Food Soc. (bd. dirs. 1960—, past pres.), Internat. Wine and Food Soc. (gov. 1989—, Bronze medal 1989), San Francisco State U. Alumni Assn. (bd. dirs. 1962—), German Wine Soc., Sierra Club. Republican. Roman Catholic. Home and Office: 121 Granville Way San Francisco CA 94127-1133

SCHOLTZ, ELIZABETH, botanical garden administrator; b. Pretoria, South Africa, Apr. 29, 1921; came to U.S., 1960, naturalized, 1978; d. Tielman Johannes and Vera Vogel (Roux) Roos-Scholtz. B.Sc., Witwatersrand U., 1941; D.H.L., Pace U., 1974; D.Sc., L.I. U., 1982. Technician South African Inst. Med. Research, Johannesburg, 1942-44; technician dept. medicine Johannesburg and Pretoria gen. hosps., 1944-46; with Groote Schuur Hosp., Capetown; as technician charge student labs. Groote Schuur Hosp., 1948-52, technician charge hematology lab., 1952-60; mem. staff Bklyn. Bot. Garden, 1960—, asso. curator instrn., 1964-71, acting dir., 1972-73, dir., 1973-80, v.p., 1980-87, dir. emeritus, 1987—; trustee Independence Savs. Bank. Recipient Arthur Hoyt Scott Garden and Horticulture award, 1981, Medal of Honor, Garden Club Am., 1990. Mem. Am. Hort. Soc. (Liberty Hyde Bailey medal 1984), Am. Assn. Bot. Gardens and Arboreta (dir. 1976-79, Award of Merit 1992), Royal Hort. Soc. (Veitch Gold medal 1990), Hort. Soc. N.Y. (bd. dirs. 1988—), Bklyn Heights Casino Club, Cosmopolitan Club. Home: 111 Hicks St Brooklyn NY 11201-1658 Office: Bklyn Bot Garden 1000 Washington Ave Brooklyn NY 11225-1008

SCHOLTZ, ROBERT ARNO, electrical engineering educator; b. Lebanon, Ohio, Jan. 26, 1936; s. William Paul and Erna Johanna (Weigel) S.; m. Laura Elizabeth McKeon, June 16, 1962; children: Michael William, Paul Andrew. BSEE, U. Cin., 1958; MSEE, U. So. Calif., 1960; PhD, Stanford U., 1964. Co-op student Sheffield Corp., Dayton, Ohio, 1953-58; MS and PhD fellow Hughes Aircraft Co., Culver City, Calif., 1958-63, sr. staff engr., 1963-78; prof. U. So. Calif., L.A., 1963—; vis. prof. U. Hawaii, 1969, 78; cons. LinCom Corp., L.A., 1975-81, Axiomatix Inc., L.A., 1980-86, JPL, Pasadena, 1985, Tech. Group, 1987-89, TRW, 1989, Pulson Comm., 1992-93, Colley-Godward, Palo Alto, 1994. Co-author: Spread Spectrum Comm., 3 vols., 1984, Spread Spectrum Communications Handbook, 1994, Basic Concepts in Information Theory and Coding, 1994; contbr. numerous articles to profl. jours. (recipient Leonard G. Abraham Prize Paper award 1983, Donald G. Fink Prize award 1984, Signal Processing Soc. Sr. Paper award 1992). Pres., South Bay Community Concert Orgn., Redondo Beach, Calif., 1975-79. Fellow IEEE (bd. govs. info. theory group 1981-86, bd. govs. communication soc. 1981-83, chmn. fin. com. NTC 1977, program chmn. ISIT 1981). Office: U So Calif Comm Scis Inst Dept Elec Engring Los Angeles CA 90089-2565

SCHOLZ, CHRISTOPHER HENRY, geophysicist; b. Pasadena, Calif., Feb. 25, 1943; s. Joseph George and Elizabeth (Ochsner) S.; m. Paula Hanna, May 19, 1962 (div. 1978); children: Erich Frederich, Adrienne Louise; m. Yoshiko Tsujimura, Feb. 8, 1986. B.S., U. Nev., 1964; Ph.D., M.I.T., 1967. Research fellow Calif. Inst. Tech., Pasadena, 1967-68; research assoc. Lamont-Doherty Geol. Obs., Columbia U., N.Y., 1968-70; sr. research assoc. Lamont-Doherty Geol. Obs., Columbia U., 1970—, assoc. prof. geology, 1971-75, prof., 1975—. Author: The Mechanics of Earthquakes and Faulting, 1990; contbr. articles on earthquakes, deformation of the earth, mech. properties of rock to profl. jours. A.P. Sloan fellow, 1975-77; C.I. Green fellow, 1980-81. Fellow Am. Geophys. Union; mem. Seismol. Soc. Am. Office: Lamont-Doherty Geol Obs Palisades NY 10964

SCHOLZ, GARRET ARTHUR, financial executive; b. Bridgeport, Conn., Sept. 22, 1939; s. Edward G. and Ann E. (Dineson) S.; m. Jeanne L. LaBorde; children: Michael, Stephen, Christopher. B.B.A., U. Oreg., 1961, M.B.A., 1965. Security analyst Equitable Life Assurance, N.Y.C., 1966-68; fin. mgr. Olin Corp., New Haven, 1968-73; asst. treas. McKesson Corp., San Francisco, 1973-81, treas., 1982-90, v.p. fin., 1990—; bd. dirs. Golden State Ins. Co., Hamilton, Bermuda; v.p., treas., ArmorAll Products, Inc., P.C.S., Inc.; bd. dirs. Sunbelt Beverage Corp., Medis Health and Pharm. Svcs. Corp. Trustee McKesson Found., San Francisco; bd. dirs. San Francisco Met. YMCA; bd. dirs. Edgewood Children's Ctr.; mem. adv. com. San Francisco Found. 1st lt. U.S. Army, 1961-64. Mem. Fin. Execs. Inst., Fin. Officers of No. Calif., Bankers Club, Olympic Club , Commonwealth Club. Office: McKesson Corp 1 Post St San Francisco CA 94104-5201

SCHOMER, FRED K., financial executive; b. Chgo., June 21, 1939; s. Harold M. and Jeanette (Gerchikov) S.; m. Sharon Ann Schear, Feb. 8, 1964; children: Marcy, Amy. BA, U. Chgo., 1960, JD, 1962, MBA, 1982. With Beatrice Cos., Chgo., 1963-83; v.p. fin. and adminstrn. Acco World Corp., Northbrook, Ill., 1984-88; exec. v.p., chief fin. officer Gerber Products Co., Fremont, Mich., 1988—. With U.S. Army 1962-63. Avocations: music, theater, golf.

SCHOMER, HOWARD, retired clergyman, educator, social policy consultant; b. Chgo., June 9, 1915; s. Frank Michael and Daisy (Aline) S.; m. Elsie Pauline Swenson, Mar. 23, 1942; children: Karine, Mark, Paul, Ellen. B.S. summa cum laude, Harvard U., 1937, postgrad., 1939-40; student, Chgo. Theol. Sem., 1938-39, 40-41, D.D., 1964; LL.D., Olivet Coll., 1966. Ordained to ministry Congl. Ch., 1941. Student pastor Fitzwilliam, N.H., Oak Park, Ill.; asst. dean U. Chgo. Chapel., 1940-41; counsellor Am. history Harvard U., 1939-40; civilian pub. service Am. Friends Service Com., 1941-45; Am. Bd. Mission fellow to chs. of Europe Chambon-sur-Lignon, France, 1946-55; history tchr., work camp dir. Coll. Cevenol; founder internat. conf. center Accueil Fraternel, Permanent Conf. Protestant Chs. in Latin Countries of Europe; asst. to rapporteur UN Commn. on Human Rights, UN Econ. and Social Council, 1947-48; inter-church aid sec. for Europe World

Council Chs., Geneva, 1955-58; pres., prof. ch. history Chgo. Theol. Sem., 1959-66; exec. dir. dept. specialized ministries Div. Overseas Ministries, Nat. Council Chs. N.Y.C., 1967-70; participant integration demonstrations in Ala., Ga., Washington, Chgo., SCLC, 1960-66; world issues sec. United Ch. Bd. World Ministries, 1971-80; Indochina liaison officer World Council of Chs., 1970-71; United Ch. of Christ officer for social responsibility in investments, 1972-81; founder, dir. Corp. Adv. Services, 1980-90; founder, mem. United Ch. Christ Working Group with United Ch. in German Democratic Rep. and Fed. Rep. of Germany, 1977-86; vis. prof. religion and society Andover Newton Theol. Sch., 1981; vis. lectr. Manchester Coll., St. John's U.; Woodrow Wilson vis. fellow Drew U., 1981; pres. Internat. Fellowship of Reconciliation, 1959-63, v.p., 1963-65; participant 1st-3d assemblies World Council Chs., Amsterdam, 1948, Evanston, 1954, New Delhi, 1961; rep. UN non-govt. orgn. UNIAPAC, 1979-85; pastoral assoc. First Congl. Ch. (United Ch. Christ), Montclair, N.J., 1983-89; delegated observer Vatican Council II, 1963; v.p. Am. Friends Coll. Cevenol., 1981-89; bd. dirs. Interfaith Center for Corp. Responsibility, 1973-81; chmn. exec. com. Freedom of Faith - A Christian Com. for Religious Rights, 1978-81; mem. nat. adv. bd. N.Y. State Martin Luther King Jr. Inst. for Nonviolence, 1989-92. Translator: The Prayer of the Church Universal (Marc Boegner), 1954; editor: The Oppression of Protestants in Spain, 1955, the Role of Transnational Business in Mass Economic Development, 1975; editor-at-large Christian Century, 1959-70; contbr.; Business, Religion and Ethics-Inquiry and Encounter, 1982, Aspects of Hope, 1993; articles to religious and interdisciplinary publs.; corr. in U.S. for Evangile et Liberté, 1988—. Past co-chmn. Chgo. Com. for Sane Nuclear Policy; bd. dirs. World Conf. on Religion and Peace, 1974-84, sec. for Kampuchea issues, 1979-81; former trustee Am. Waldensian Aid Soc.; mem. internat. council Internat. Ctr. Integrative Studies, 1984-91, bd. dirs., 1987-91; trustee Internat. Inst. for Effective Communication, 1987-93; bd. dirs. Alternative Lifelong Learning, 1992—; Cambodian Found. for Justice, Peace and Devel., 1993—. Mem. ACLU, Wider Quaker Fellowship, Fellowship Reconciliation, Ctr. for Theology and the Natural Scis., Outlook Club (Berkeley), Harvard Club San Francisco, Phi Beta Kappa. Home: 1012 Contra Costa Dr El Cerrito CA 94530-2710 The human capacity to hope and the power of hope to achieve either good or evil are astonishing. Reasonable hope for the better calls simply for dedicated effort. Mystical hope for the perfect demands consecrated surrender.

SCHOMMER, CAROL MARIE, principal. Prin. Madonna High Sch. Recipient Blue Ribbon, 1990-91. Office: Madonna High Sch 4055 W Belmont Ave Chicago IL 60641

SCHOMMER, TRUDY MARIE, pastoral minister, religion education; b. Wayzata, Minn., May 18, 1937; d. Edward and Gertrude (Mergen) S. BA, Coll. St. Catherine, St. Paul, 1966; MA, Manhattanville Coll., 1971. Joined Order of Franciscan Sisters of Little Falls, Minn., 1955. Dir. religious edn. St. Pius X, White Bear Lake, Minn., 1971-77; campus min., theology tchr. St. Cloud (Minn.) State Univ., 1977-81; pastoral min. St. Galls, St. Elizabeth, Milw., 1981-85; dir. religious edn. St. Alexander's, Morrisonville, N.Y., 1985-90; pastoral min. of religious edn. St. Mary's, Bryantown, Md., 1990-91; diocesan dir. religious edn. Diocese of New Ulm, Minn., 1991—; exec. bd. mem. Nat. Assembly Religious Women, Chgo., 1974-78. Author: Easiest Gospel Stories Ever, 1993; book reviewer Sister's Today, 1988-91. Mem. Network, Washington, 1978—. Mem. Nat. Cath. Edn. Assn., Nat. Parish Coords. and Dirs. Democrat. Roman Catholic. Home and Office: 1725 Oxford St Apt 201 Berkeley CA 94709-1701 Life is an adventure: a time each of us is given to explore and discover the many ways Christ's life and love permeates the whole world. Life is a challenge: together as Christians we face the many challenges and difficulties of life.

SCHONBERG, ALAN ROBERT, management recruiting executive; b. N.Y.C., Oct. 23, 1928; s. Julius and Evelyn (Guzik) S.; m. Carole May Kreisman, Dec. 27, 1975; children: William, Evelyn, David, Jeffrey. Nat. sales mgr. Majestic Specialties, Inc., Cleve., 1953-63; pres. Internat. Personnel, Inc., Cleve. 1963-65, Mgmt. Recruiters Internat., Inc., Cleve., 1965—. V.p., bd. dirs. Jewish Vocat. Service, Cleve., 1983—; bd. dirs. Mt. Sinai Hosp., Cleve. Served to sgt. U.S. Army, Germany. Named one of Cleve.'s 86 Most Interesting People, Cleve. Mag., 1986. Mem. Internat. Franchise Assn., Internat. Confederation Pvt. Employment Agys. Assns., Am. Mgmt. Assn., Assn. Human Resource Cons. (chmn. 1980—), Org. for Rehab. and Training (ORT). Avocation: world travel. Office: Mgmt Recruiters Internat Inc 1127 Euclid Ave Ste 1400 Cleveland OH 44115-1638

SCHÖNBERG, BESSIE, dance educator; b. Hanover, Germany, Dec. 27, 1906; m. Dimitry Varley Jan. 6, 1934. Studied with Martha Hill, Martha Graham. Dancer Martha Graham Dance Co., N.Y.C., 1931; dance instr. Sarah Lawrence Coll., Bronxville, N.Y., 1936-41, head dance dept., 1941-75, 1941, prof. emerita, 1975—; guest tchr. Ohio State U., Wesleyan U., U. N.H., Amherst Coll., George Mason U., The Art of Movement Ctr., London, Contemporary Dance Ctr., London; presenter workshops Dance Theatre Workshop, N.Y.C., Dance Theatre Harlem, N.Y.C.; dance cons. Hunter Coll., N.Y.C., Oberlin (Ohio) Coll., Dennison U., Wesleyan U.; mem. appeals bd. N.Y. State Coun. on Arts; mem. adv. panel NEA Dance Program; chmn., bd. dirs. Dance Theatre Workshop. Appeared in Martha Graham's dances including Primitive Mysteries, Ceremonials, Heretic, Project in Movement for a Divine Comedy. Mentor fellow NEA, 1994; recipient citation Assn. Am. Dance Cos., 1975, Lifetime Achievement in Dance Bessie award, 1987-88, Gov. Arts award N.Y. State, 1989, Ernie award Dance/USA, 1994; The N.Y. Dance and Performance Awards are named in her honor as The BESSIES. Office: Sarah Lawrence Coll Dept Dance 1 Meadway Bronxville NY 10708

SCHONBERG, HAROLD CHARLES, music critic, columnist; b. N.Y.C., Nov. 29, 1915; s. David and Minnie (Kirsch) S.; m. Rosalyn Krokover, Nov. 28, 1942; m. Helene Cornell, May 10, 1975. BA cum laude, Bklyn. Coll., 1937; MA, NYU, 1938; LittD, Temple U., 1964; LHD, Grinnell Coll., 1967. Assoc. editor Am. Music Lover, 1939-41; contbr. editor Mus. Digest, 1946-48; music critic N.Y. Sun, 1946-50; contbg. editor, record columnist Mus. Courier, 1948-52; music and record critic N.Y. Times, 1950-60, sr. music critic, 1960-80, cultural corr., 1980-85; columnist on The Gramophone of London, 1948-60; judge many internat. piano competitions. Author: The Guide to Long-Playing Records, Chamber and Solo Instrumental Music, 1955, The Collector's Chopin and Schumann, 1959, The Great Pianists, 1963, The Great Conductors, 1967, Lives of the Great Composers, 1970, Grandmasters of Chess, 1973, Facing the Music, 1981, The Glorious Ones-Classical Music's Legendary Performers, 1985, Horowitz: His Life and Music, 1992; illustrated own articles with caricatures; contbg. editor Internat. Ency. Music and Musicians. Served as 1st lt. Airborne Signal Corps AUS, 1942-46. Recipient Pulitzer prize for criticism, 1971. Clubs: Manhattan Chess, Century Assn., Army and Navy. Home: 160 Riverside Dr New York NY 10024

SCHONBERG, WILLIAM PETER, mechanical and civil engineering educator; b. N.Y.C., Mar. 25, 1960; s. Christian and Tamara (Kalnev) S.; m. Jane Heminover, Sept. 7, 1986; children: Christina Carol, Richard William. BSCE cum laude, Princeton U., 1981; MS in Engring., Northwestern U., 1983, PhD, 1986. Asst. prof. civil engring. U. Ala., Huntsville, 1986-91, assoc. prof., 1991-94, prof., 1994—; mem. working group NASA Boeing Space Sta., 1987-90. Contbr. articles to profl. publs. Recipient rsch. and creative works award U. Ala.-Huntsville Found., 1992; Walter P. Murphy fellow, 1981-82, summer faculty fellow NASA, 1987, 88, 94, Air Force Office Sci. Rsch., 1992, 93; grantee U. Ala.-Huntsville Rsch. Inst., 1987-92. Mem. AIAA (Young Engr. of Yr. award 1990, Lawrence Sperry award, 1995), ASME (assoc.), ASCE , Am. Acad. Mechanics, Tau Beta Pi. Avocations: astronomy, stamps, mystery novels, rock & roll music, travel. Office: U Ala Huntsville 4701 University Dr Huntsville AL 35899-0100

SCHONBRUN, MICHAEL KEITH, health care executive; b. N.Y.C., Jan. 26, 1948; s. Arnold Laurence and Madeline (Courland) S.; m. Michelle Fredson, June 6, 1971; 1 child, Ethan F. BA, Yale U., 1969; JD, U. Pa., 1973. Bar: Ohio 1973, Colo. 1976. Gen. counsel Gov.'s Commn. Health Care, Columbus, Ohio, 1973-74; research atty. Spectrum Research Inc., Denver, 1974-75; asst. health affairs Gov.'s Office, State of Colo., Denver, 1975-76; asst. care regulation Colo. Dept. Health, Denver, 1976-79; exec. v.p. Nat. Jewish Ctr. for Immunology and Respiratory Medicine, Denver, 1979-82, pres., 1982-91; sr. v.p. healthcare divsn. Rocky Mountain

Health Care Corp., Denver, 1991-93, Mayfield Fund, Palo Alto, Calif., 1993-94; exec. v.p. VITAS Healthcare Corp., Miami, Fla., 1994—; bd. dirs. Norwest Bank Denver, 1987-93; mem. editl. bd. Healthspan, Inc., Washington, 1984-88; com. chmn. Nat. Gov.'s Assn., Washington, 1977-78. Contbr. articles to profl. jours. Chmn. Met. Air Quality Coun., Denver, 1985-89, Gov.'s Search Com. for Exec. Dir. of State Health Dept., Denver, 1986; mem. Denver organizing com. 1998 Winter Olympic Games, 1989. Mem. Nat. Health Lawyers Assn., Young Pres.'s Orgn. Democrat. Jewish. Club: Yale (N.Y.C.); Meadows (Boulder, Colo.). Avocations: tennis, skiing, travel. Office: VITAS Healthcare Corp 100 S Biscayn Blvd Miami FL 33131

SCHÖNEMANN, PETER HANS, psychology educator; b. Pethau, Fed. Republic Germany, July 15, 1929; came to U.S., 1960, naturalized, 1965; s. Max Paul Franz and Hertha Anna (Kahle) S.; m. Roberta Dianne Federbush, Jan. 29, 1962; children: Raoul Dieter, Nicole Deborah. Vordiplom in Psychologie, U. Munich, 1956; Hauptdiplom in Psychologie, U. Goettingen, 1959; Ph.D., U. Ill., 1964. Thurstone postdoctoral fellow U. N.C. 1965-66; asst. prof., then assoc. prof. Ohio State U., 1966-69; postdoctoral fellow Ednl. Testing Service, Princeton, N.J., 1967-68; vis. prof. Technische Hochschule, Aachen, Fed. Republic Germany, 1981; mem. faculty Purdue U., 1969—; prof. psychology, 1971—; vis. prof. Univs. Munich, Bielefeld and Braunschweig, 1984-85, Nat. Taiwan U., 1992. Author papers in field. Mem. Psychonomic Soc., Soc. Multivariate Exptl. Psychology. Office: Perdue U Dept Psychol Scis West Lafayette IN 47907

SCHONFELD, GUSTAV, medical educator, researcher; b. Mukacevo, Ukraine, May 8, 1934; came to U.S., 1946; s. Alexander Schonfeld and Helena Gottesmann; m. Miriam Steinberg, May 28, 1961; children: Luga Lawrence, Julia Elizabeth, Jeremy David. BA, Washington U., St. Louis, 1956, MD, 1960. Diplomate Am. Bd. Internal Medicine. Intern. Bellevue Med. Ctr. NYU, 1960-61, resident in internal medicine, 1961-63; chief resident in internal medicine Jewish Hosp., St. Louis, 1963-64; NIH trainee in endocrinology and metabolism sch. medicine Washington U., St. Louis, 1964-66, instr. medicine, 1965-66, asst. prof. medicine, 1968-70, assoc. prof. preventive medicine and medicine, 1972-77, prof. preventive medicine and prof. internal medicine, 1977-86, William B. Kountz prof. medicine, 1987—, dir. atherosclerosis and lipid rsch. ctr., 1972—, acting head dept. preventive medicine, 1983-86; rsch. assoc. Cochran VA Hosp., St. Louis, 1965-66, clin. investigator, 1968-70, cons. in internal medicine, 1972—; rsch. flight med. officer USAF Sch. Aerospace Medicine, Brooks AFB, Tex., 1966-68; asst. physician Barnes Hosp., 1972-86; assoc. physician Barnes Hosp., Brooks AFB, 1986—; clin. instr. medicine med. sch. Harvard U., Boston, 1970-72; assoc. prof. metabolism and human nutrition, asst. dir. clin. Sch. Ctr. MIT, Boston, 1970-72; mem. rsch. com. Mo. Heart Assn., 1978-80; expert witness Working Group on Atherosclerosis NHLBI, 1979, Nat. Diabetes Adv. Bd., 1979; mem. endocrinologic and metabolic drugs adv. com. Pub. Health Svc., FDA, 1982-86; mem. nutritional study sect. NIH, 1984-88, spl. reviewer metabolism study sect.; mem. adult treatment guidelines panel Nat. Cholesterol Edn. Program, 1986—; mem. Consesus Devel. Conf. on Triglyceride, High Density Lipoprotein, and Coronary Heart Disease, 1992—; cons. Am. Egg Bd., Am. Dairy Bd., Inst. Shortening and Edible Oils, Ciba-Geigy, Sandoz, Fournier, Parke-Davis, Bristol-Meyers Squibb, Monsanto. Editor: Atherosclerosis; past mem. editorial bd. Jour. Clin. Endocrinology and Metabolism, Jour. Clin. Investigation; mem. editorial bd. Jour. Lipid Rsch. Recipient Berg Prize in Microbiology, 1957, 58; grantee merit status NIH. Fellow ACP; mem. Assn. Am. Physicians, Am. Soc. for Clin. Investigation, Am. Physiol. Soc., Am Soc. Biol. Chemists, Am. Inst. Nutrition, Am. Diabetes Assn., Am. Heart Assn. (program com. coun. on atherosclerosis 1977-80, 86-88, nat. com. 1980-84, pathology rsch. com. 1980-83, awards com. 1992, budget com. 1991), Endocrine Soc., Alpha Omega Alpha. Office: Washington U Sch Medicine Box 8046 660 S Euclid Saint Louis MO 63110

SCHONFELD, RUDOLF LEOPOLD, secondary school educator; b. La Paz, Bolivia, Feb. 2, 1942; came to U.S. 1958; s. Walter and Eva (Fuchs) S.; m. Sonia Nussbaum, July 7, 1963; children: Walter, Miriam Schonfeld Giotta. BA, Wilkes Coll., 1963; MA, Seton Hall U., 1972; PhD, Ludwig Maximillian U., Heidelberg, Ger., 1974. Tchr. Parsippany (N.J.) High Sch., 1963-69, tchr. Spanish and German, 1969-82; supr. world langs. Parsippany-Troy Hills Sch. Dist., 1982—; vice-prin. Brooklawn Mid. Sch., Parsippany, N.J. Author: Voces y Vistas, 1989, Pasos y Puentes, 1989, Arcos y Alamedas, 1989. Mem. Masons (master 1990). Avocations: soccer, reading, counseling, values clarification. Office: Parsippany-Troy Hills 5 Lincoln Ave Lake Hiawatha NJ 07034-2409

SCHONFELD, WILLIAM ROST, political science educator, researcher; b. N.Y.C., Aug. 28, 1942; s. William A. and Louise R. (Rost) S.; m. Elena Beortegui, Jan. 23, 1964; children: Natalie Beortegui, Elizabeth Lynn Beortegui. Student, Cornell U., 1960-61; B.A. cum laude with honors, NYU, 1964; M.A., Princeton U., 1968, Ph.D., 1970. Research asst. Princeton U., 1966-69, research assoc., 1969-70, vis. lectr., 1970; asst. prof. polit. sci. U. Calif.-Irvine, 1970-75, assoc. prof., 1975-81, prof., 1981—, dean Sch. Social Scis., 1982—; sr. lectr. Fond. Nat. de Sci. Politique, Paris, 1973-74; researcher Centre de Sociologie des Organisations, Paris, 1976-78. Author: Youth and Authority in France, 1971, Obedience and Revolt, 1976, Ethnographie du PS et du RPR, 1985. Recipient Disting. Teaching award U. Calif.-Irvine, 1984; Fulbright fellow Bordeaux, France, 1964-65; Danforth grad. fellow, 1964-69; Fulbright sr. lectr. Paris, 1973-74; NSF-CNRS Exchange of Scientists fellow Paris, 1976-78; Ford Found. grantee France, Spain, 1978-79; finalist Profl. Yr. Council for Advancement and Support of Edn., 1984. Mem. Am. Polit. Sci. Assn., Association Francaise de Sci. Pol., Phi Beta Kappa. Office: U Calif Sch Social Scis Irvine CA 92717

SCHONHOLTZ, JOAN SONDRA HIRSCH, banker, civic worker; b. N.Y.C., Sept. 8, 1933; d. Joseph G. and Mildred (Klebanoff) Hirsch; m. George J. Schonholtz, Aug. 21, 1951; children: Margot Beth, Steven Robert, Barbara Ellen. Student, Vassar Coll., 1950-52; B.A., Barnard Coll., 1954; postgrad., Am. U., 1963. Chmn. bd. dirs., founding mem. 1st Women's Bank of Md., Rockville, 1976—; chmn. FWB Bancorp., Rockville, 1992—. Pres. Ft. Benning Med. Wives, Ga., 1962-63; sec. Montgomery County Women's Med. Aux., Md., 1968; bd. dirs. Svc. Guild of Washington, 1968-77, sec., 1969-70, pres., 1975-77; bd. dirs. Pilot Sch. for Blind Multiple Handicapped Children, Washington, 1968-77; bd. dirs. Strathmore Hall Arts Ctr., N. Bethesda, Md., 1992—; spl. gifts chmn. Cancer Soc. Montgomery County, 1968, 69; mem. Washington Adv. Coun. on Deaf-Blind Children, 1972-74; chmn. Friends of Wash. Adventist Hosp., Takoma Park, Md., 1993-94. Recipient Outstanding Service award Service Guild of Washington, 1969. Republican. Jewish. Clubs: Vassar, Barnard. Home: 10839 Lockland Rd Potomac MD 20854-1855

SCHONHORN, HAROLD, chemist, researcher; b. N.Y.C., Apr. 2, 1928; s. Benjamin and Dorothy (Gitlin) S.; m. Esther Matesky, Jan. 17, 1954; children: Deborah, Jeremy. BS, Bklyn. Coll., 1950; PhD, N.Y. Polytech. U., 1959. Mem. tech. staff Bell Labs., Murray Hill, N.J., 1961-84; v.p. R & D Schonhorn Polyken Tech. div. Kendall Co., Lexington, Mass., 1984-93; pres. Schonhorn Consultants, 1993—. Contbr. over 100 articles to profl. jours. Pres. B'nai B'rith Lodge, Summit, N.J., 1970. With U.S. Army, 1953-55, Korea. Mem. Am. Chem. Soc. Achievements include 15 patents.

SCHONWETTER, RONALD SCOTT, physician, educator; b. Miami Beach, Fla., Apr. 24, 1958; s. Morris Jack and Joyce (Trager) S.; m. Rita A. Nemitoff, Mar. 2, 1986; children: Sara Wendi, Rachel Elana, Jonathan Harris. BA in Chemistry and Psychology with high honors, Emory U., 1979; MD, U. South Fla., 1984. Diplomate Am. Bd. Internal Medicine, Nat. Bd. Med. Examiners. Intern in primary care internal medicine Baylor Coll. Medicine, Houston, 1984-85, resident in primary care internal medicine, 1985-87; fellow in geriatric medicine Baylor Coll. Medicine and VA Med. Ctr., Houston, 1987-89; asst. prof. internal medicine divsn. geriatric medicine, dept. internal medicine, coll. medicine U. South Fla., Tampa, 1989-94, assoc. prof. medicine, div. geriatric medicine, 1994—; assoc. med. dir. Hospice Hillsborough, Inc., Tampa, 1989-92, med. dir., 1992—; med. dir. palliative care clinic, 1993—; med. dir. Univ. Village Nursing Ctr., Tampa, 1989-94; staff physician Tampa Gen. Hosp. Skilled Nursing Facility, 1989—; cons. internist suncoast gerontology memory disorder clinic Coll. Medicine, U. South Fla., 1989-93; mem. hospice steering com., 1993—; presenter in field. Contbr. articles to profl. jours. Recipient New Investigator award Am. Geriatric Soc. and Merck U.S. Human Health, 1994. Fellow ACP; mem.

Am. Med. Dirs. Assn. (cert. med. dir.), Am. Geriatrics Soc. (mem. ethics com. 1992—), Nat. Hospice Orgn. (mem. coun. hospice profls. 1994—), Gerontol. Soc. Am., Acad. Hospice Physicians (mem. rsch. com. 1993—). Jewish. Office: U South Fla Coll Medicine Dept Internal Medicine Divsn Geriatric Medicine 12901 Bruce B Downs Blvd Tampa FL 33612-4742

SCHOOLEY, CHARLES EARL, electrical engineer, consultant; b. Archie, Mo., Sept. 18, 1905; s. Charles Elias and Virginia Maria (Bone) S.; m. Dorothy S. Alexander, Apr. 29, 1934 (dec. 1965); 1 dau., Dorothy Virginia; m. Dolores Harter, Apr. 1966 (dec. 1993). B.S. in Elec. Engring. U. Mo., 1928. Registered profl. engr., Ga. With Ozark Utilities Co., Bolivar Telephone Co., Mo. Pacific R.R.; transmission engr. Long Lines dept. Am. Tel. & Tel. Co., St. Louis, Kansas City, N.Y.C., 1927-44; co-axial carrier engr., elec. coordination engr. Am. Tel. & Tel. Co., N.Y.C., 1944-48; div. engr. Am. Tel. & Tel. Co., Washington, 1948-49; facility engr., engr. transmission, comml. devel. engr. Am. Tel. & Tel. Co., 1949-51, toll dialing engr., plant extension engr., system planning engr., operating and engring. dep., 1951-53, asst. chief engr., dir. customer products planning, 1956-57; chief engr. So. Bell Tel. & Tel. Co., Atlanta, 1953-55; v.p. operations, dir. Ind. Bell Telephone Co., Indpls., 1957-59; dir. operations, mem. bd. long lines dept. Am. Tel. & Tel. Co., N.Y., 1959-66; dir., v.p. Transpacific Communications Co., Transocean Cable Ship Co., Eastern Tel. & Tel. Co., 1960-66, 9 other Am. Tel. & Tel. subs; v.p., treas., dir. Eds. Inc., Sharon, Conn., 1970-83. Vice pres. Berkshire Hills (Conn.) Music and Dance Assn., 1970-78; v.p.; treas. Wingspread Found., 1977—; trustee Brevard (N.C.) Music Ctr., 1994—. Recipient Disting. Service to Engring. medal U. Mo., 1960. Fellow IEEE; mem. Ga. Engring. Soc., Met. Club (N.Y.C.), Hendersonville (N.C.) Country Club, QEBH U. Mo., Delta Upsilon (bd. dirs. 1962-70), Eta Kappa Nu. Address: PO Box 746 Hendersonville NC 28793-0746 also: PO Box 633 Winter Haven FL 33882-0633 also: 210 Crooked Creek Rd Hendersonville NC 28739

SCHOOLMAN, ARNOLD, neurological surgeon; b. Worcester, Mass., Oct. 31, 1927; s. Samuel and Sarah (Koffman) Schulman; m. Gloria June Feder, Nov. 10, 1963; children: Hugh Sinclair, (Jill) Annette. Student, U. Mass., 1945-46; BA, Emory U., 1950; PhD, Yale U., 1954, MD, 1957. Diplomate Am. Bd Neurol. Surgery, Nat. Bd. Med. Examiners. Intern U. Calif. Hosp., San Francisco, 1957-58; resident in neurol. surgery Columbia-Presbyn. Med. Ctr., Neurol. Inst. N.Y., N.Y.C. 1958-62; instr. neurol. surgery U. Kans. Sch. Medicine, Kansas City, 1962, asst. prof. surgery, 1964; assoc. prof. U. Mo. Sch. Medicine, Kansas City, 1976; chief sect. neurosurgery Research Med. Ctr., Kansas City, 1982; dir. Midwest Neurol. Inst., 1982-83. Patentee in field. Served with USN, 1946-48. Fellow ACS (mem. Mo. chpt.); mem. AMA, Mo. State Med. Assn., Kansas City Med. Soc., Kansas City Neurosurg. Soc. (pres. 1984-85), Kansas City Neurol. Soc., Rocky Mountain Neurosurg. Soc., Am. Assn. Neurol. Surgeons, AAAS, Mo. Neurol. Soc., Internat. Coll. Surgeons, Congress Neurol. Surgeons, Brit. Royal Soc. Medicine, Phi Beta Kappa, Sigma Xi. Avocation: pilot. Home: 8705 Catalina St Shawnee Mission KS 66207-2351 Office: 1000 E 50th St Ste 310 Kansas City MO 64110-2215

SCHOONHOVEN, RAY JAMES, retired lawyer; b. Elgin, Ill., May 24, 1921; s. Ray Covey and Rosina Madeline (Schram) (White) S.; m. Marie Theresa Dunn, Dec. 11, 1943; children: Marie Kathleen, Ray James, Jr., Pamela Suzanne, John Philip, Rose Lynne. B.S.C., U. Notre Dame, 1943; J.D., Northwestern U., 1948. Bar: Ill. 1949, U.S. Supreme Ct. 1954, D.C. 1973, U.S. Ct. Mil. Appeals 1954. Assoc. Seyfarth, Shaw Fairweather & Geraldson, Chgo., 1949-57, ptnr., 1957-92; ret.; chief rulings and opns. br. Wage Stabilization Bd. Region VII, Chgo., 1951-52. Book rev. editor: Ill. Law Rev., 1948. Served to lt.comdr. USNR, 1942-62. Mem. ABA, Chgo. Bar Assn., Ill. State Bar Assn., Chgo. Athletic Assn., Univ. Club Chgo. Republican. Roman Catholic. Home: 6636 N Ponchartrain Blvd Chicago IL 60646-1428 Office: Seyfarth Shaw Fairweather & Geraldson 55 E Monroe St Ste 4200 Chicago IL 60603-5702 I work hard to preserve our free enterprise system and, hopefully, to make such contribution to our society that it is better for my having been a part of it.

SCHOONMAKER, SAMUEL VAIL, III, lawyer; b. Newburgh, N.Y., Sept. 1, 1935; s. Samuel V. Jr. and Catherine (Wilson) S.; m. Carolyn Peters, Sept. 18, 1965; children: Samuel V. IV, Frederick P. BA magna cum laude, Yale U., 1958, JD, 1961. Bar: Conn. 1961, U.S. Dist. Ct. Conn. 1961, U.S. Dist. Ct. (so. and ea. dist.) N.Y. 1964, U.S. Ct. Appeals (2d cir.) 1964, U.S. Supreme Ct. 1965. Assoc. Cummings & Lockwood, Stamford, Conn., 1961-70, ptnr., 1970—, co-mng. ptnr., 1987-90, mng. ptnr., 1990—, chmn. exec. com., 1987—; state trial referee Conn. Superior Ct., 1989; pres. Schoonmaker Family Assn., New Paltz, N.Y., 1975-77. Sr. topical editor Conn. Bar Jour., 1977-81; mem. bd. editors Fairshare and America Jour., 1992; contbr. articles to profl. jours. Chmn. Conn. Child Support Commn., 1984-86; mem. Conn. Family Support Com., 1986-90; mem. Darien (Conn.) Rep. Town Com., 1974-76, town meeting, 1990—; pres. Youth Tennis Found. New Eng., Needham, Mass., 1975-77; pres. New Eng. Lawn Tennis Assn., 1977-79 (Man of Yr. award 1979). Fellow Am. Acad. Matrimonial Lawyers Conn. (bd. mgrs., Disting. Svc. award 1988), Internat. Acad. Matrimonial Lawyers, Am. Bar Found.; mem. ABA (chmn. family law sect. 1982-83), Conn. Bar Assn. (chmn. family law sect. 1971-74), Conn. Bus. and Industry Assn. (bd. dirs. 1993—), S.W. Conn. Bus. and Industry Assn. (bd. dirs 1990—), Pub. Defenders Assn. (chmn.), Wee Burn Country Club (Darien, Conn., asst. sec.), Yale Club (N.Y.C.), Phi Beta Kappa. Avocation: tennis, platform tennis. Home: 231 Old Kings Hwy Darien CT 06820 Office: Cummings & Lockwood 10 Stamford Forum Stamford CT 06901-3215

SCHOONMAKER POWELL, THELMA, film editor; b. 1945; m. Michael Powell, 1984 (dec. 1990). Editor: (films) Finnegan's Wake, 1965, The Virgin President, 1968, Who's That Knocking at My Door, 1968, Woodstock, 1970 (Academy award nomination best film editing 1970), Raging Bull, 1980 (Academy award best film editing 1980), The King of Comedy, 1983, After Hours, 1985, The Color of Money, 1986, The Last Temptation of Christ, 1988, New York Stories ("Life Lessons"), 1989, GoodFellas, 1990 (Academy award nomination best film editing 1990), Cape Fear, 1992, The Age of Innocence, 1993. Office: care Motion Picture Editors 7715 Sunset Blvd #220 Los Angeles CA 90046*

SCHOONOVER, JEAN WAY, public relations consultant; b. Richfield Springs, N.Y.. AB, Cornell U., 1941. With D-A-Y Pub. Rels., Ogilvy & Mather Co., N.Y.C., 1949-91, D-A-Y Pub. Rels. Inc. and predecessor, N.Y.C., 1949—; owner, pres. Dudley-Anderson-Yutzy Pub. Rels. Inc. and predecessor, N.Y.C., 1970—; chmn. Dudley-Anderson-Yutzy Pub. Relations Inc. and predecessor 1984-88; merger with Ogilvy & Mather, 1983; sr. v.p. Ogilvy & Mather U.S.A., 1984-91; vice chmn. Ogilvy Pub. Relations Group, 1986-91; ind. cons., 1992—; pres. YWCA of the City of N.Y., 1994—; mem., historian, Pub. Relations Seminar; mem. U.S. Dept. Agriculture Agribusiness Promotion Council, 1985—. Trustee Cornell U. 1975-80; mem. Def. Adv. Com. on Women in Svcs., 1987-89. Named Advt. Woman of Yr. Am. Advt. Fedn., 1972, one of Outstanding Women in Bus. & Labor, Women's Equity Action League, 1985; recipient Matrix award, 1976, Nat. Headliner award, 1984, N.Y. Women in Comm., 1976, Leadership award Internat. Orgn. Women Bus. Owners, 1980, Entrepreneurial Woman award Women Bus. Owners N.Y., 1981, Women of Distinction award Soroptimists Internat. N.Y., 1995. Mem. Women Execs. in Pub. Rels. N.Y.C. (pres. 1979-80), Pub. Rels. Soc. Am., Pub. Rels. Soc. N.Y. (pres. 1979), Womens Forum, Women's City Club. Home: 25 Stuyvesant St New York NY 10003-7505

SCHOOR, MICHAEL MERCIER, lawyer, lobbyist; b. Chgo., Feb. 24, 1942; s. Richard Carl and Ethel (Mercier) S.; m. JoLen Marty, Oct. 7, 1961; children: Mark, Marty, Gretchen, William. BA, U. N.Mex., 1969; JD, Georgetown U., 1972. Bar: N.Mex. 1972, D.C. 1973, U.S. Supreme Ct. 1975, U.S. Ct. Claims 1974, U.S. Dist. Ct. D.C. 1974, U.S. Ct. Appeals (10th cir.) 1974. Legis. asst. ADA, Washington, 1970-72; assoc. counsel U.S. Ho. of Reps., Washington, 1977; dir. legis. and govt. affairs Nat. Soc. Profl. Engrs., Washington, 1977-82; dir. Tex. Pub. Policy Found.; Internat. Am. Assn. Clin. Nutritionists; dir. dir. Clin. Nutritionists Cert. Bd., Renown Holding Co., Inc.; various engring. firms. Counsel various polit. orgns.; coach youth soccer. Recipient Outstanding Svc. award N.Mex. Chiropractic Assn. 1975, Nat. Soc. Profl. Engrs., 1982. Mem. N.Mex. Bar Assn., D.C. Bar Assn. Republican. Roman Catholic.

SCHOPF, JAMES WILLIAM, paleobiologist; b. Urbana, Ill., Sept. 27, 1941; s. James Morton and Esther Julie (Nissen) S.; m. Julie Morgan, Aug. 7, 1965 (div. 1979); 1 child, James Christopher; m. Jane Shen, Jan. 16, 1980. A.B. with high honors, Oberlin Coll., 1963; A.M., Harvard U., 1965, Ph.D. (Harvard fellow, NSF fellow), 1968. Research chemist NASA, Ames Research Center, Calif., 1967; mem. lunar sample preliminary exam. team Manned Spacecraft Center, Tex., 1968-71; asst. prof. dept. earth and space scis. UCLA, 1968-70, assoc. prof., 1970-73, prof., 1973—, mem. Inst. Evolutionary and Environ. Biology, 1970-76, mem. Inst. Geophysics and Planetary Physics, 1971—, dean honors div. Coll. Letters and Sci., 1983-85, dir. Ctr. for Study Evolution and Origin of Life, 1985—; Sigma Xi Disting. lectr. 1976, Rubey lectr., 1976, Golden Yr. Disting. lectr., 1980, Faculty Research lectr., 1984; Sigma Xi Disting. lectr. U. Cin., 1980; Disting. lectr. Buffalo Mus. Sci., 1982; J.A. Bownocker lectr. Ohio State U., 1982; vis. lectr. Am. Inst. Biol. Scis. Vis. Biologists Program, 1969-72; M.W. Haas vis. disting. prof. geology U. Kans., 1979; extraordinary vis. prof. exobiology U. Nijmegen, Netherlands, 1980-81; C. O'Neal lectr. Ohio Wesleyan U. 1982; Sandia disting. lectr. U. N.Mex., 1985; Sigma Xi disting. lectr. U. Oreg., 1985; Du Pont disting. lectr. U. Ill., 1985; R. Stanier disting. lectr. U. Calif.-Berkeley, 1987; H.P. Mangelsdorf disting. lectr. U. N.C., 1987; mem. Bot. Soc. Am. del., People's Republic China, 1978; Academia Sinica vis. research scientist, People's Republic China, 1981, 82; mem. NASA Terrestrial Bodies Sci. Working Group, 1975-76, space program adv. council NASA Life Scis. Com., 1976-78, NASA Working Group on Origins of Life, 1978-79, NASA Space Sci. Adv. Com., 1973-82, mem. NASA Life Scis. Strategic Planning Study Com., 1985—; Alan T. Waterman Award com. NSF, 1978-81; mem. working group on precambrian biostratigraphy Internat. Geol. Correlation Program, UNESCO, 1975—; mem. Working Group on Cambrian-Precambrian Boundary, 1976—; mem. adv. com. USSR and Eastern Europe, Commn. Internat. Relations NRC, 1981-85, mem. bd. earth sci. Commn. Phys. Scis., Math. and Resources, 1982-85, mem. space sci. bd., 1983-86; mem . com. on guidelines for paleontol. collecting, 1984-86, sub.-com. on evolution and diversity Commn. on Life Scis., 1986; mem. com. space research Internat. Council Sci. Unions. Mem. editorial bd.: Origins of Life, 1973—, Precambrian Research, 1973—, Evolutionary Theory, 1973—, U. Calif. Press, 1973-82, Paleobiology, 1974-83, Geomicrobiology Jour., 1977—, Evolutionary Monographs, 1977—; contbr. articles to profl. jours. Bd. dirs. Brentwood Glen (Calif.) Assn., 1972-75; trustee UCLA Found., 1983-85. Recipient N.Y. Bot. Garden award Bot. Soc. Am., 1966; Group Achievement award NASA, 1969; Outstanding Paper award Jour. Paleontology, 1971; Charles Schuchert award Paleontol. Soc., 1974; Disting. Teaching award UCLA, 1977; Alan T. Waterman award NSF, 1977; G. Hawk award U. Kans., 1979; spl. recognition diploma NASA, 1979; Outstanding Vol. in Phys. Scis. award Am. Assn. Pubs., 1983; Mark Clark Thompson medal Nat. Acad. Scis., 1986; Guggenheim fellow, 1973; U.S. Nat. Acad. Scis. exchange scientist USSR, 1975. Fellow Geol. Soc. Am. (vice-chmn. Cordilleran sect. 1983-84, chmn. 1984-85); mem. Bot. Soc. Am. (com. on sci. liaison with People's Republic China 1978—), Paleontol. Soc. (mem. Schuchert Award com. 1978-82), Internat. Soc. Study of Origin of Life (treas. 1977-83, nat. meeting adv. com. 1980, 83, 86, councilor, 1983—), Geochem. Soc. (nominating com. 1980-82), Soc. Study of Evolution (edn. com. 1980-83), Am. Philos. Soc., Sigma Xi (treas. UCLA chpt. 1972-74, chpt. v.p. 1984-84, pres. 1984-85). Office: U Calif Dept Earth And Scis Los Angeles CA 90024

SCHOPLER, JOHN HENRY, psychologist, educator; b. Fuerth, Fed. Republic Germany, Nov. 5, 1930; came to U.S., 1938, naturalized, 1943; s. Ernest H. and Erna (Oppenheimer) S.; m. Janice E. Hough, Dec. 12, 1969; children: Kari, Lisa, Andrew, David. B.A., U. Rochester, 1952; M.A., U. N.Mex., 1953; Ph.D., U. Colo., 1958. Mem. faculty U. N.C., Chapel Hill, 1957—; asso. prof. psychology U. N.C., 1964-69, prof., 1969—, chmn. dept., 1976-83; NSF sr. postdoctoral fellow London Sch. Econs. and Polit. Sci., 1966-67, Kenan prof., 1983-84. Author: (with Chester Insko) Experimental Social Psychology, 1972; co-founder, asso. editor: (with John Thibaut) Jour. Exptl. Social Psychology, 1964-69; contbr. (with Chester Insko) articles to profl. jours. Fulbright scholar, 1974-75. Fellow Am. Psychol. Assn., Soc. Psychol. Study Social Issues, N.C. Psychol. Assn.; mem. Soc. Explt. Social Psychology. Office: U NC Dept Psychology Chapel Hill NC 27514

SCHOPPMEYER, MARTIN WILLIAM, education educator; b. Weehawken, N.J., Sept. 15, 1929; s. William G. and Madeleine M. (Haas) S.; m. Marilyn M. Myers, Aug. 9, 1958; children: Susan Ann, Martin William. B.S., Fordham U., 1950; Ed.M., U. Fla., 1955, Ed.D., 1962. Tchr. Fla. pub. schs., 1955-59; instr., then asst. prof. U. Fla., 1960-63; assoc. prof., then prof. edn. Fla. Atlantic U., Boca Raton, 1963-68; dir. continuing edn. Fla. Atlantic U., 1965-67; mem. faculty U. Ark., Fayetteville, 1968—; prof. edn. U. Ark., 1971-93; univ. prof. U. Ark., Fayetteville, 1993—; program coord. for ednl. administrn. U. Ark., 1983-90; mem. Nat. Adv. Coun. Edn. Professions Devel., 1973-76; exec. sec. Ark. Sch. Study Coun., 1976—; evaluator instructional tng. program Nat. Tng. Fund, 1978; bd. dirs. Women's Ednl. and Devel. Inst., 1977-80, Nat. Sch. Devel. Coun., sec., 1989-90, v.p. 1990, pres., 1990-92; mem. oversight com. South Conway (Ark.) County Sch. Dist.; mem. state commn. to study effect of Amendment 59 to Ark. Constn. Author books, monographs, articles in field. Mem. president's coun. Subiaco Acad., 1984-90; chmn. Subiaco Sch. Bd., 1990-93, mem., 1993—. With U.S. Army, 1951-53, Korea. Recipient numerous fed. grants. Mem. NEA, Ark. Edn. Assn. (past chpt. pres.), Ark. Assn. Ednl. Adminstrs., KC, Rotary, Kappa Delta Pi, Phi Delta Kappa, Delta Tau Kappa. Roman Catholic. Home: 2950 Sheryl Ave Fayetteville AR 72703-3542 Office: U Ark 244 Grad Edn Bldg Fayetteville AR 72701 The only really sound investment for a family, a community, or a society is that money spent for the education of its youth.

SCHOR, JOSEPH MARTIN, pharmaceutical executive, biochemist; b. Bklyn., Jan. 10, 1929; s. Aaron Jacob and Rhea Iress (Kay) S.; children: Esther Helen, Joshua David, Gideon Alexander; m. Laura Sharon Struminger, June 14, 1992. B.S. magna cum laude, CCNY, 1951; Ph.D. Fla. State U., 1957. Sr. research chemist Armour Pharm. Co., Kankakee, Ill., 1957-59, Lederle Labs., Pearl River, N.Y., 1959-64; dir. biochemistry Endo Labs., Garden City, N.Y., 1964-76; v.p. sci. affairs Forest Labs. N.Y.C., 1977-94, sr. v.p. scientific affairs emeritus, Forest Labs. 1995—. Editor, contbr.: Chemical Control of Fibrinolysis-Thrombolysis, 1970. Contbr. articles to profl. jours. Patentee in field. USPHS fellow, 1955-57. Fellow Am. Inst. Chemists (cert. profl. chemist), Internat. Soc. Hematology; mem. Am. Chem. Soc. (chmn. Nassau County subsect. 1971-72), Internat. Soc. on Thrombosis and Hemostasis, N.Y. Acad. Scis., AAAS, Phi Beta Kappa, Sigma Xi. Home: 28 Meleny Rd Locust Valley NY 11560-1221

SCHOR, LAURA STRUMINGER, historian, academic administrator; b. N.Y.C., June 24, 1945; d. David Charles and Esther Rachel (Pearl) Gross; children: Eric Alain, Neil Remy; m. Joseph Martin Schor, June, 1992. BA, Queens Coll., CUNY, 1967; MA, U. Rochester, 1970, PhD, 1974. Asst. prof. SUNY, Fredonia, 1973-79; assoc. prof., dir. women's studies U. Cin., 1979-85, prof., vice provost, 1985-89; prof., provost, v.p. acad. affairs Hunter Coll., CUNY, N.Y.C., 1989—. Author: Women and the Making of the Working Class, 1979, What Were Little Boys and Girls Made Of?, 1984, The Odyssey of Flora Tristan, 1988, Les Jolies Femmes d'Edouard de Beaumont, 1994. mem. Internat. Soc. for Study European Ideas, Am. Hist. Assn., French Hist. Assn., Phi Beta Kappa. Office: CUNY-Hunter Coll Office of Provost 695 Park Ave New York NY 10021-5024

SCHOR, STANLEY SIDNEY, mathematical sciences educator; b. Phila., Mar. 3, 1922; s. Joseph and Dorothy (Abrams) S.; m. Irene Sternberg, June 19, 1949; children:-Mark, Robin, Randi. A.B., U. Pa., 1943, A.M., 1950, Ph.D., 1952; certificate, U. Cin., 1944. Instr. U. Pa., Phila., 1950-53, asst. prof. stats., 1953-58, assoc. prof., 1958-64, dir. Nat. Periodic Health Exam. Research Group, 1958-64; dir. dept. biostats. AMA, Chgo., 1964-66; prof. biostats. Chgo. Med. Scis., 1964-66; prof., chmn. dept. biometrics Temple U. Med. Sch., 1966-75, adj. prof., 1975-85; vis. prof. Tel Aviv U. 1973-74, Med. Coll. Pa., 1979; exec. dir. Cbards, Merck Sharp & Dohme, West Point, Pa., 1975-91; clin. prof. Hahnemann Med. Sch., 1975-85; cons. in field. Author: Fundamentals of Biostatistics, 1968; mem. editorial staff Jour. Trauma, 1955-91, Jour. AMA, 1964-94, Chest, 1966-91; contbr. articles to profl. jours. Served with AUS, 1943-46. Fellow Am. Public Health Assn., Am. Statis. Assn., Phila. Coll. Physicians; mem. Biometric Soc., AAUP, Royal Soc. Health, Pi Gamma Mu. Home: 3912 S Ocean Blvd # 1105 Highland Beach FL 33487-0147

SCHORE, ROBERT, social worker, educator; b. N.Y.C., July 29, 1934; s. David and Helen S.; married, three children. Student, Mesivta Tifereth Jerusalem, N.Y.C., 1947-48; BA, CCNY, 1955; MS, Columbia U., 1959; cert. advanced study, SUNY, New Paltz, 1985; postgrad., Postgrad. Ctr. for Mental, Health, 1967, Inst. for Rational-Emotive, Therapy, Bank St. Coll., 1984, Rockland Conservatory Music, 1992—. Diplomate Clin. Social Work, NASW; cert. social worker, impartial hearing officer, sch. dist. adminstr., supr. sch. social workers, N.Y. Social worker Dept. Social Svcs./Child Placement Svcs., N.Y.C., 1956-58, Edwin Gould Found., N.Y.C., 1959-63; with NIMH demo. project Shield Inst., Bronx, N.Y., 1963-65; sch. social worker N.Y.C. Bd. Edn. Bur. Child Guidance, Bronx, 1965-80; sch. social worker Com. on Spl. Edn., Bronx, 1980-85; non-pub. sch. program Bur. Child Guidance, Bronx, 1967-69, with Head Start, 1970; sch. social worker High Sch. Clin. Svcs., Bronx, 1986-91; pvt. practice West Nyack, N.Y., 1992—; psychotherapist Ind. Consultation Ctr., Bronx, 1967, Rockland County Mental Health Ctr., Monsey, N.Y., 1968-69; rsch. assoc., editor/ NIMH demo project Nathan Kline Inst., Orangeburg, N.Y., 1968-85; instr. CCNY, 1966; field instr. NYU, N.Y.C., 1970-73; instr. Rockland C.C., Suffern, N.Y., 1993—; fair hearing officer N.Y. State Edn. Dept., 1992—; adminstrv. intern Clarkstown Sch. Dist., West Nyack, 1984-85; workshop leader in field. Editor: Orb Mag., 1950-51; contb. chpts. to books, articles to profl. jours. Supr., cons. Vol. Counseling Svc., New City, N.Y., 1992-94; bd. dirs. Rockland Hebrew Day Sch., 1986; violinist Riverdale Orchestra, Suburban Symphony of Rockland, Ramapo Orchestral Soc., N.Y. With USAR, 1957-63. Fellow N.Y. Soc. Clin. Social Work; mem. Am. Fedn. Tchrs., N.Y. State United Tchrs., United Fen. Tchrs., Acad. Cert. Social Workers. Jewish. Avocations: photography, music, violin, piano. Office: PO Box 276 Monsey NY 10952-0276

SCHORER, JOSEPH U., lawyer; b. Baraboo, Wis., June 15, 1953. BA, Northwestern U., 1975; JD, Harvard U., 1978. Bar: Calif. 1978, U.S. Dist. Ct. (so. dist.) Calif. 1978, Ill. 1981, U.S. Dist. Ct. (no. dist.) Ill. 1981, U.S. Ct. Appeals (7th cir.) 1982, U.S. Ct. Appeals (5th cir.) 1987, U.S. Ct. Appeals (10th cir.) 1988. Ptnr. Mayer, Brown & Platt, Chgo. Office: Mayer Brown & Platt 190 S La Salle St Chicago IL 60603-3410

SCHORER, SUKI, ballet teacher; b. Boston; d. Mark and Ruth (Page) S.; 1 child, Nicole. Studied with, George Balanchine. With San Francisco Ballet, 1956-59; dancer N.Y.C. Ballet, 1959; prin. N.Y.C. Ballet Co., 1968, artistic assoc. lecture demonstration program, 1972—; mem. faculty Sch. Am. Ballet, 1972—; internat. guest tchr. and lectr. specializing in Balanchine tng. and technique; artist dir., tchr. on Balanchine Essays (videos). Created roles in Balanchine's Harlequinade, Don Quixote, Midsummer Night's Dream, Jewels, La Source, Raymonda Variations; repertory included prin. roles in Apollo, Serenade, Concerto Barocco Symphony in C, La Somnambula, Stars and Stripes, Tarantella, Valse Fantaisie, The Nutcracker, Brahams Schoenberg, La Valse, Western Symphony, Ivesiana, Divertimento # 15, Ballet Imperial, others. Office: Sch of Am Ballet 70 Lincoln Ctr Plz New York NY 10024

SCHORGL, THOMAS BARRY, arts administrator; b. St. Louis, Mar. 1, 1950; s. Francis William and Janet Sarah (Peterson) S.; m. Elizabeth Ann Eades, Aug. 6, 1977; children: Matthew, Ann, Joseph. BFA, U. Iowa, 1973, MA in Drawing, 1974; MFA in Printmaking, Miami U., Oxford, Ohio, 1976; apprenticeship, Atelier, Garrigue, France, 1976; postgrad., U. Notre Dame, 1979. Comml. artist R.H. Donnelly, Chgo., 1977; curator Art Ctr. Inc., South Bend, Ind., 1977-78, dir. acquisg. 1978, exec. dir., 1978-81; account exec. James P. Carroll & Assocs., South Bend, 1981-83; exec. dir Ind. Arts. Commn., Indpls., 1983-94; pres., CEO Culture Works, Dayton, Ohio, 1994—; cons. in field. Chmn. Arts Midwest, 1989-91, treas., 1987, 88; panelist Nat. Endowment for Arts, 1985-90, chmn. grants panel Art is Basic to Edn., 1986-89. Mem. Great Lakes Arts Alliance (sec., treas. 1983-85, merger com.), Affiliated State Arts Agys. Upper Midwest (chmn. program com. 1985—), Arts Midwest (chmn. 1989-91), Nat. Assembly of State Arts Agys. (bd. dirs. 1991—). Avocations: visual arts, antiques, endurance sports. Office: Culture Works 126 N Main St Ste 100 Dayton OH 45402

SCHORNACK, JOHN JAMES, accountant; b. Chgo., Nov. 22, 1930; s. John Joseph and Helen Patricia (Patrickus) S.; m. Barbara Anne Lelli, June 5, 1965; children: Mark Boyd, Anne Marguerite Trueman, Erin Keeley, Tracy Bevan. BS, Loyola U., 1951; MBA, Northwestern U., 1956; grad., Advanced Mgmt. Program, Harvard Bus. Sch., 1969. With Ernst & Young (formerly Arthur Young & Co.), 1955-91, partner, 1964-91; firm dir. personnel Ernst & Young (formerly Arthur Young & Co.), N.Y.C., 1966-71; asst. mng. ptnr. N.Y.C. office Ernst & Young (formerly Arthur Young & Co.), 1971-72, mng. ptnr. 1972-74, mng. ptnr. Chgo. office, 1976-85, mng. ptnr. Midwest region, vice chmn., 1985-91; mem. mgmt. com. Arthur Young & Co.; mgmt. com. Arthur Young & Co.; vice chmn., mng. ptnr. Midwest region Ernst & Young, 1989-91; bd. dirs., chmn. Ernst & Young Found., 1981-91; chmn., bd. dirs., CEO Kraft Seal Corp.; bd. dirs. Binks Mfg. Co., Franklin Park, Ill., North Shore Bancorp, Inc. Exec. bd. Chgo. Youth Ctrs., 1979&, pres., 1984-86; bd. govs. Chgo. Symphony, 1979-85, trustee, 1985—; vol. United Way, 1975-92, dir., 1989-92; vis. adv. com. sch. accountancy DePaul U., 1980-83; mem. Loyola U. Citizens Bd., 1977—, chmn., 1993—; mem. adv. com. Northwestern U. Grad Sch. Mgmt., 1967-91; coun. U. Chgo. Grad. Sch. Bus., 1982-91; bd. dirs. Met. Planning Coun., 1992—; trustee Kohl Children's Mus., 1994—, Lyric Opera, 1984-92, Barat Coll., 1983—, vice chmn., 1985-90, chmn. 1990—; trustee St. Francis Hosp., 1986—, vice chmn., 1991—. Mem. AICPA, Am. Acctg. Assn., Ill. Soc. CPA's, Midwest-Japan Assn. (chmn. 1983—), Japan Am. Soc., 410 Club, Economic Club, Tavern Club, Chgo. Club, Glen View Club, Ocean Club. Home: 314 Regent Wood Rd Northfield IL 60093 Office: Ernst & Young Midwest Regional Office 233 S Wacker Dr Chicago IL 60606 also: Kraft Seal 13777 W Laurel Dr Lake Forest IL 60045-4530

SCHORR, ALAN EDWARD, librarian, publisher; b. N.Y.C., Jan. 7, 1945; s. Herbert and Regina (Fingerman) S.; m. Debra Genner, June 11, 1967; 1 son, Zebediah. BA, CUNY, 1966; MA, Syracuse U., 1967; postgrad., U. Iowa, 1967-71; MLS, U. Tex., 1973. Tchr., rsch. asst. dept. history U. Iowa, 1967-70; govt. pubis. and map libr., asst. prof. Elmer E. Rasmuson Libr., U. Alaska, 1973-78; assoc. prof., dir. libr. U. Alaska, Juneau, 1978-84; prof., dean univ. libr. Calif. State U., Fullerton, 1984-86; pres. The Denali Press, Juneau, 1986—; freelance indexer and bibliographer; vis. lectr. Birmingham (Eng.) Poly., 1981; mem. Alaska Edin. Del. to China, 1975. Author: Alaska Place Names, 1974, 4th edit., 1991, Directory of Special Libraries in Alaska, 1975, Government Reference Books, 1974-75, 1976, 1976-77, 1978, Government Documents in the Library Literature 1909-1974, 1976, ALA RSBRC Manual, 1979, Federal Documents Librarianship 1879-1987, 1988, Hispanic Resource Directory, 1988, 3d edit., 1995, Refugee and Immigrant Resource Directory, 1990, 92, 94; editor: The Sourdough, 1974-75, Directory of Services for Refugees and Immigrants, 1987, 3d edit., 1993, Guide to Smithsonian serial publs., 1987; book reviewer, columnist: S.E. Alaska Empire, 1979—, L.A. Times; contbr. articles to profl. jours. Mem. Auke Bay (Alaska) Vol. Fire Dept.; mem. Juneau Borough Cemetery Adv. Com., 1980-81, Juneau Borough Libr. Adv. Com., 1981-82, Am. Book Awards Com., 1980; mem. strategic com. Juneau Sch. Bd., Juneau Bd. Edn., 1991—, chmn. facilities com., 1994—. Mem. ALA (reference and subscription books rev. com. 1975-86, reference and adult services div. publs. com. 1975-77, Nat. Assn. Hispanic Publications, Mudge citation commn. 1977-79, 84-86, Dartmouth Coll. Medal Commn., Governing Council 1977-84, Dewey medal com. 1984-85, Denali Press award), Alaska Library Assn. (exec. bd. 1974-75, nominating com. 1977-79), Pacific N.W. Library Assn. (rep. publs. com. 1973-75), Assn. Coll. and Research Libraries (publ. com. 1976-80), Spl. Libraries Assn. (assoc. editor geography and map div. bull. 1975-76), Soc. for Scholarly Pub., Internat. Assn. Ind. Pubs (bd. dirs. 1990—), Pub. Mktg. Assn., PEN Ctr. USA West, Amnesty Internat., Explorers Club N.Y., No. Pub. Consortium (regional rep. 1993—). Office: PO Box 1535 Juneau AK 99802

SCHORR, ALVIN LOUIS, social worker, educator; b. N.Y.C., Apr. 13, 1921; s. Louis and Tillie (Godiner) S.; m. Ann Girson, Aug. 21, 1948; children—Jessica Lee, Kenneth L., Wendy Lauren. B.S.S., CCNY, 1941; M.S.W., Washington U., St. Louis, 1943; D.H.L., Adelphi U., 1975. With Family Service No. Va., 1956-58; family life specialist Office Commr. Social Security, 1958-62; vis. prof. London (Eng.) Sch. Econs., 1962-63; acting chief long range research Social Security Adminstrn., 1963-64; dir. research and

planning Office Econ. Opportunity, 1965-66; dep. asst. sec. Dept. Health, Edn. and Welfare, 1967-69; prof. social policy, dir. income maintenance project Brandeis U., 1969-70; dean Grad. Sch. Social Work, N.Y.U., 1970-73; gen. dir. Community Service Soc. N.Y., 1973-77; vis. prof. Cath. U. Am., 1977-79; Leonard W. Mayo prof. Case Western Res. U., 1979-92, Leonard W. Mayo prof. emeritus, 1992—; Fulbright sr. rsch. scholar, 1962-63, vis. prof. Hebrew U., Jerusalem, 1986, Fla. Internat. U., 1995; vis. scholar London Sch. Econs., 1991-92. Author: Filial Responsibility in the Modern American Family, 1961, Slums and Social Insecurity, 1963, Social Services and Social Security in France, 1964, Poor Kids, 1966, Explorations in Social Policy, 1968, Children and Decent People, 1974, Jubilee for Our Times, 1977, Thy Father and Thy Mother, 1980, Common Decency: Domestic Policies After Reagan, 1986, Economic Development in Cleveland: A Dissenting View, 1991; The British Personal Social Services: An Outside View, 1992. Recipient Disting. Service in Social Welfare award Washington U. Alumni Assn., 1969; recipient Michael Schwerner award, 1972. Fellow Nat. Acad. Social Ins.; mem. Phi Beta Kappa. Home: 1701 E 12th St Apt 14tw Cleveland OH 44114-3207 Office: Case Western Res U Mandel Sch Appl Social Sci Cleveland OH 44106

SCHORR, DANIEL LOUIS, broadcast journalist, author, lecturer; b. N.Y.C., Aug. 31, 1916; s. Louis and Tillie (Godiner) S.; m. Lisbeth Bamberger, 1967; children: Jonathan, Lisa. B.S.S., CCNY, 1939; hon. doctorate, Kalamazoo Coll., Columbia Coll., Chgo., Wilkes U., Nebr. Wesleyan U., L.I. U., Brandeis U. Asst. editor Jewish Telegraphic Agy., 1934-41; news editor ANETA (Netherlands) News Agy. in N.Y., 1941-48; freelance corr. N.Y. Times, Christian Sci. Monitor, London Daily Mail, 1948-53; Washington corr. CBS News; also spl. assignments CBS News, Latin Am. and Europe, 1953-55; reopened CBS Moscow Bur., 1955; roving assignments U.S. and Europe, 1958-60; chief CBS News Bur., Germany, Central Europe, 1960-66; Washington corr. CBS, 1966-76; Regents prof. U. Calif., Berkeley, 1977; columnist Des Moines Register-Tribune Syndicate, 1977-80; sr. Washington corr. Cable News Network, 1980-85; sr. analyst Nat. Public Radio, 1985—. Author: Don't Get Sick in America!, 1971, Clearing the Air, 1977. Decorated officer Orange Nassau (The Netherlands), Grand Cross of Merit (Germany); recipient citations of excellence for radio-TV reporting Soviet Union Overseas Press Club, 1956, award for best TV interpretation fgn. news, 1963, ACLU and others awards for pub. suppressed House intelligence report, Emmy awards for coverage Watergate scandal, 1972, 73, 74, Peabody award for lifetime of uncompromising reporting of highest integrity, 1992, George Polk award for radio commentary L.I. U., 1994, Disting. Svc. award Am. Soc. Journalism and Mass Comm., 1994; inducted into Hall of Fame, Soc. Profl. Journalists, 1991. Mem. Am. Fedn. Radio-TV Artists, Council on Fgn. Relations N.Y.C. *Journalism, for more than a half century, has been both profession and outlook on life. I have always felt myself the observer and nonparticipant, the quintessential outsider. I have pursued the sense of things behind the appearance of things, the meaning behind the manipulation. I have fought, with dubious success, against the blurring of the media line between reality and fantasy.*

SCHORR, LISBETH BAMBERGER, child and family policy analyst, author, educator; b. Munich, Jan. 20, 1931; d. Fred S. and Lotte (Krafft) Bamberger; m. Daniel L. Schorr, Jan. 8, 1967; children—Jonathan, Lisa. BA with highest honors, U. Calif., Berkeley, 1952; LHD (hon.), Wilkes U., 1991, U. Md., 1994. Med. care cons. U.A.W. and Community Health Assn., Detroit, 1956-58; asst. dir. Dept. Social Security AFL-CIO, Washington, 1958-65; acting chief CAP Health Svcs., OEO, 1965-66; chief program planning Office for Health Affairs, OEO, Washington, 1967; cons. Children's Def. Fund, Washington, 1973-79; scholar-in-residence Inst. of Medicine, 1979-80; chmn. Select Panel on Promotion Child Health, 1979-80; adj. prof. maternal and child health U. N.C., Chapel Hill, 1981-85; lectr. social medicine Harvard U. Med. Sch., 1984—; dir. project on effective svcs. Harvard U., 1988—; nat. council Alan Gutmacher Inst., 1974-79, 82-85; pub. mem. Am. Bd. Pediatrics, 1978-84; vice chmn. Found. for Child Devel., 1978-84, bd. dirs. 1976-84, 86-94; mem. coun. Nat. Ctr. for Children in Poverty, 1987—; mem. children's program adv. com. Edna McConnell Clark Found., 1987—; bd. dirs. Pub. Edn. Fund Network, 1991-93; co-chair Roundtable on Comprehensive Cmty. Initiatives Aspen Inst., 1992—; mem. bd. on children and families NAS, 1993—; mem. Nat. Commn. State & Local Pub. Svc., 1992-94; mem. task force on young children Carnegie Corp., 1991-94; mem. sec.'s adv. com. Head Start quality and expansion, 1993-94; trustee City Yr.; mem. exec. com. Harvard Project on Schooling and Children. Author: Within Our Reach: Breaking the Cycle of Disadvantage, 1988. Recipient Dale Richmond Meml. award Am. Acad. Pediatrics, 1977, 9th Ann. Robert F. Kennedy Book award, 1989, Nelson Cruikshank annual nat. Coun. Sr. Citizens, 1990, Porter prize, 1993. Mem. Inst. Medicine, NAS, Nat. Acad. on Social Ins., Phi Beta Kappa. Home: 3113 Woodley Rd NW Washington DC 20008-3449

SCHORR, MARTIN MARK, psychologist, educator, writer; b. Sept. 16, 1923; m. Dolores Gene Tyson, June 14, 1952; 1 child, Jeanne Ann. Student Balliol Coll., Oxford (Eng.) U., 1945-46; AB cum laude, Adelphi U., 1949; postgrad., U. Tex., 1949-50; MS, Purdue U., 1953; PhD, U. Denver, 1960; postgrad., U. Tex. Diplomate in psychology, Diplomate Am. Bd. Profl. Disability Cons., Diplomate in Forensic Examiner; lic. clin. psychologist. Chief clin. psychol. svcs. San Diego County Mental Hosp., 1963-77; clin. dir. human services San Diego County, 1963-76; pvt. practice, forensic specialist San Diego, 1962—; forensic examiner superior, fed. and mil. cts., San Diego, 1962—; prof. abnormal psychology San Diego State U., 1965-68; chief dept. psychology Center City (Calif.) Hosp., 1976-79; cons. Dept. Corrections State of Calif., Minnewawa, 1970-73, Disability Evaluation Dept. Health, 1972-75, Calif. State Indsl. Accident Commn., 1972-78, Calif. Criminal Justice Adminstrn., 1975-77, Vista Hill Found., Mercy Hosp. Mental Health, Foodmaker Corp., Convent Sacred Heart, El Cajon, FAA Examiner. Author: Death by Prescription, 1988; dir. Alpha Centauri Prodns. Recipient award for aid in developing Whistle Blower Law Calif. Assembly, 1986. Fellow Internat. Assn. Soc. Psychiatry, Am. Coll. Forensic Examiners; mem. AAAS, PEN, APA, Am. Acad. Forensic Scis., Qualified Med. Evaluator, Internat. Platform Assn., World Mental Health Assn., Mystery Writers Am., Nat. Writers' Club, Mensa. Home: University City 2970 Arnoldson Ave San Diego CA 92122-2114 Office: 275 F St Chula Vista CA 91910 *Personal philosophy: Some wag once said that the hardest thing one learns in life is which bridge to cross and which to burn!.*

SCHORR, MARVIN G., technology company executive; b. N.Y.C., Mar. 10, 1925; s. Samuel and Fannie (Smolen) S.; m. Rosalie Yorshis, Dec. 22, 1957; children: Eric Douglas, Susan Ellen. BS, Yale U., 1944, MS, 1947, PhD, 1949. Research asst., instr. Yale U., New Haven, 1946-47; project dir. physics and electronics div. Tracerlab, Inc., 1940-51; exec. v.p. treas. Tech/ Ops., Inc., Boston, 1951-62, pres., chief exec. officer, 1962-88, chmn. 1988—; spl. cons. USAF, 1951-52; dir. Mass. Tech. Devel. Corp., 1973-76, chmn. bd., 1976-83; dir. Ealing Corp., 1965-76, Hysil Mfg. Co., 1965-78, Dynamics Research Corp., 1978-85, Helix Tech. Corp., Costar Corp. Mem. nuclear engring. adv. com. Lowell Inst. Tech., 1958-68; trustee Park Sch., 1974-80; trustee Am. Coll. Greece, 1970-82, chmn. exec. com., 1980-82, hon. trustee, 1982—; trustee New Eng. Deaconess Hosp., 1972—, vice chmn. bd., 1978-81, chmn., 1981-86. Served with U.S. Army, 1944-46. Fellow AAAS; mem. IEEE, Ops. Research Soc. Am., Am. Phys. Soc., Young Pres. Orgn. (chmn. New Eng. chpt. 1967-68), Boston Com. Fgn. Relations, The Forty-Niners, World Bus. Council, Chief Execs. Orgn., Internat. Bus. Ctr.-Chief Exec. Officers Round Table, Explorers Club. Clubs: Cosmos (Washington); Harvard, St. Botolph, Union (Boston); Yale (Boston and N.Y.C.); Longwood Cricket (Brookline, Mass.). Home: Tech/Ops Corp 1 Beacon St Boston MA 02108

SCHORR, S. L., lawyer; b. N.Y.C., Feb. 19, 1930; s. Charles and Clara (Lerech) S.; m. Eleanor Daru, Mar. 23, 1956; children: Lewis, Andrew, Emily, Roberta. Student, L.I. U., 1948-50; LLB, Blyth. Law Sch., 1953. Bar: N.Y. 1955, Ariz. 1962, U.S. Dist. Ct. Ariz. 1962, U.S. Supreme Ct. 1979. Planning commnr. Pima County, Tucson, 1959-62; asst. city mgr. Tucson, 1962-63; ptnr. Lewis and Roca, Tucson, 1988—; co-chair CLE Seminar on Ballot Box Zoning, U. Ariz., 1991, Ariz. State Bar CLE Seminar on Land Use Regulation and Litigation, 1977, 86, 89. Bd. dirs. Pima Coll., 1966-67; mem. Commn. on Improved Govtl. Mgmt., Tucson, 1974-77, Gov.'s Econ. Planning and Devel. Adv. Bd., Phoenix, 1983-85; chmn. Gov.'s Task Force on Seriously Mentally Ill, Phoenix, 1989-91. Mem. ABA, Ariz.

Bar Assn., Pima County Bar Assn.. Democrat. Office: Lewis and Roca 1 S Church Ave Ste 700 Tucson AZ 85701-1620

SCHORRE, LOUIS CHARLES, JR., artist; b. Cuero, Tex., Mar. 9, 1925; s. Louis Charles and Anna (Barthlome) S.; m. Margaret Phipps Storm, July 17, 1948; children—Alice Ann Schorre Stultz, Martha Schorre Jackson, Robin Elisabeth Schorre Glover. B.F.A., U. Tex., 1948. Instr. art Mus. Fine Arts, Houston, 1950-55; prof. Sch. Architecture, Rice U., 1962-72. One-man shows: Tex. Gallery, Meredith Long Gallery, Contemporary Arts Mus.; paintings and drawings in numerous publs. also pvt. and corp. collections throughout U.S.; Author, editor, art dir.: Life Class, 1968 (gold medals in N.Y.C. and abroad); author: Drawings and Notes, 1975, Drawing and Notes II, 1983. Served with USMCR, 1943-46. Studio: 2406 Tangley St Houston TX 77005-2514 *I am influenced by everything that is happening . . . therefore I am touched by the romance of history, the excitement and depression of now and the anticipation of what is to be. I am motivated by love and hate received and given . . . hopefully I am still a child.*

SCHORSCH, ISMAR, clergyman, Jewish history educator; b. Hannover, Germany, Nov. 3, 1935; m. Sally Korn; children: Jonathan, Rebecca, Naomi. BA, Ursinus Coll., 1957; MA, Columbia U., 1961, PhD, 1969; MHL, Jewish Theol. Sem. Am., 1962; LittD (hon.), Wittenberg U., 1989, Ursinus Coll., 1990. Ordained rabbi, 1962. Instr. Jewish Theol. Sem. N.Y.C., 1964-68; asst. prof. Jewish Theol. Sem. Am., N.Y.C., 1970-72, assoc. prof., 1972-76, prof., 1976—, dean Grad. Sch., 1975-79, provost, 1980-84; asst. prof. Jewish history Columbia U., N.Y.C., 1968-70; bd. dirs. Leo Baeck Inst., 1976, mem. exec. com., 1980, pres., 1985-86, 90—, mem. editorial bd. of yearbook, 1987. Author: From Text to Context: The Turn to History in Modern Judaism, 1994; contbr. articles to Judaism, also other profl. publs. Chancellor Jewish Theol. Sem., 1986—. Chaplain U.S. Army, 1962-64. Recipient Clark F. Ansley award Columbia U. Press, 1969; NEH fellow, 1979-80. Fellow Am. Acad. Jewish Rsch. Office: Jewish Theol Sem 3080 Broadway New York NY 10027-4650

SCHORSKE, CARL EMIL, historian, educator; b. N.Y.C., Mar. 15, 1915; s. Theodore A. and Gertrude (Goldschmidt) S.; m. Elizabeth Gilbert Rorke, June 14, 1941; children: Carl Theodore, Anne (Mrs. J. L. Edwards), Stephen James, John Simon, Richard Robert. AB, Columbia U., 1936; MA, Harvard U., 1937, PhD, 1950; DLitt (hon.), Wesleyan U., 1967, Bard Coll., 1982, Clark U., 1983, New Sch. Social Rsch., 1986, Miami U., 1987, SUNY, Stony Brook, 1988, Monmouth Coll., 1994; DPhil (hon.), U. Salzburg, 1986. Prof. history Wesleyan U., Middletown, Conn., 1946-60; prof. history U. Calif.-Berkeley, 1960-69; prof. history Princeton U., 1969-80, emeritus, 1980—. Author: (with Hoyt Price) The Problem of Germany, 1947, German Social Democracy 1905-17, 1955, Fin-de-Siècle Vienna, 1980. Served to lt. (j.g.) USNR, 1943-46; with OSS, 1941-46. Recipient Austrian Cross of Honor for arts and scis., 1979, Pulitzer Prize for gen. nonfiction, 1981, Grand prize for cultural edn. City of Vienna, 1985; named Officer, French Order Arts and Letters, 1987; MacArthur fellow, 1981-86. Fellow Royal Acad. Fine Arts Netherlands (hon.); mem. Am. Acad. Arts and Scis., Austrian Acad. Scis. (corr.), Am. Hist. Assn. (council 1964-68, Disting. Scholar award 1992), Ctr. Advanced Study Behavioral Sci., Inst. Advanced Study., Getty Ctr. Home: 106 Winant Rd Princeton NJ 08540-6738

SCHORZMAN, CLARICE B., principal. Prin. Jemtegaard Mid. Sch. Recipient Blue Ribbon Sch. award 1990-91. Office: Jemtegaard Mid Sch 35300 SE Evergreen Blvd Washougal WA 98671-9753

SCHOSBERG, PAUL ALAN, trade association executive; b. N.Y.C., Apr. 6, 1938; s. Eugene Louis and Thelma (Siegel) S.; B.A., Middlebury Coll., 1959; postgrad. Columbia U. Law Sch., 1959-60; m. Jane Mindlin, Dec. 21, 1958; children: Jill E., Richard E. Gen. assignment reporter, Westchester Rockland Newspapers, 1960-63; mgr. No. Westchester bur. Reporter Dispatch, White Plains (N.Y.), 1963-64; adminstrv. asst. Congressman Richard Ottinger of N.Y., Washington, 1965-71; adminstrv. asst. Congressman Herman Badillo of N.Y., Washington, 1971-74; pres. N.Y. League, Savs. Instns., Scarsdale, 1974-92; pres., CEO Savs. & Community Bankers Am., Washington, 1992—; faculty Nat. Sch. Banking, Fairfield, Conn., 1994—; appointed to bd. dirs. by Gov. Carey N.Y. State Housing Fin. Agy., 1977, Ctr. for Fin. Studies, 1992—; adv. bd. govs. Ctr. for Banking and Mgmt. Adelphi U. Mem. Am. Soc. Assn. Execs. Author: See How They Run-The Making of a Congressman, 1964, The Picture Life of Herman Badillo, 1972. Office: 900 19th St NW Ste 400 Washington DC 20006-2100

SCHOTLAND, DONALD LEWIS, neurologist, educator; b. Orange, N.J., Sept. 21, 1930; s. Joseph Henry and Elsie (Block) S.; m. Estherina Shems, Jan. 11, 1976; children: John, Thomas, Peter. AB, Harvard U., 1952, MD, 1957; spl. student, MIT, 1955-56; MA (hon.), U. Pa., 1973. Diplomate: Am. Bd. Psychiatry and Neurology. Intern U. Ill. Research and Edn. Hosp., 1957-58; asst. resident in neurology Columbia Presbyn. Med. Center, N.Y.C., 1958-61; asst. neurologist Columbia Presbyn. Med. Center, 1961-65, asst. attending neurologist, 1965-66; asst. in neurology Coll. Physicians and Surgeons, Columbia U., N.Y.C., 1960-61; vis. fellow in neurology Coll. Physicians and Surgeons, Columbia U., 1961-64, assoc. in neurology, 1964-66, asst. prof. neurology, 1966-67; assoc. prof. Sch. Medicine U. Pa., Phila., 1967-72, prof. Sch. Medicine, 1972—; speaker profl. confs., U.S., Can., Italy, Japan, China, France, Israel, Finland. Editor: Diseases of the Motor Unit, 1982; contbr. articles, papers to profl. publs. Served to 1st lt. USAR, 1958-65. NIH postdoctoral fellow, 1961-64; recipient Research Career Devel. award, 1966-67, various grants NIH and Muscular Dystrophy Assn. Fellow Coll. of Physicians of Phila.; mem. Am. Acad. Neurology, Am. Neurol. Assn., Phila. Neurol. Soc., Muscular Dystrophy Assn. (sci. adv. com. 1974-86, chmn. fellowship com. 1974-86, chmn. 6th Internat. Conf. 1980). Home: 1310 Wyngate Rd Wynnewood PA 19096-2455 Office: Hosp of Univ Pa 3400 Spruce St Philadelphia PA 19104

SCHOTLAND, ROY ARNOLD, lawyer, educator; b. Newark, N.J., Mar. 18, 1933; s. Joseph J. and Thelma S. S.; m. Sara Deutch, Mar. 29, 1969; children—Rebecca, Joseph. A.B., Columbia Coll., 1954; LL.B., Harvard U., 1960. Bar: N.Y. 1964. Research asst. Paul Freund Harvard U. Law Sch., 1960-61; clk. Justice William J. Brennan, U.S. Supreme Ct., 1961-62; prof. U. Va. Law Sch., 1964-68; prof. law Georgetown U., Washington, 1970—; bd. dirs. Custodial Trust Co., Torray Fund; adviser Leominster, Inc. Fellow Am. Judicare Soc.; mem. Am. Law Inst. Democrat. Jewish. Office: 600 New Jersey Ave NW Washington DC 20001-2075

SCHOTLAND, SARA DEUTCH, lawyer; b. Washington, May 2, 1948; d. Michael Joseph and Rachel (Fischer) Deutch; m. Roy Arnold Schotland; children: Rebecca, Joseph. AB magna cum laude, Harvard U., 1968; JD, Georgetown U., 1971. Law clk. to Hon. Oscar Davis U.S. Ct. Appeals Fed. Cir., Washington, 1971-72; ptnr. Cleary Gottlieb Steen & Hamilton, Washington, 1972—; adj. prof. George Washington U. Law Ctr., 1995—. Office: Cleary Gottlieb Steen & Hamilton 1752 N St NW Washington DC 20036-2806

SCHOTT, JAMES, educational administrator. Supt. of schs. Orange County, Fla. Office: Orange County SD PO Box 271 Orlando FL 32802-0271

SCHOTT, JOHN (ROBERT), international consultant, educator; b. Rochester, N.Y., Jan. 30, 1936; s. John and Ellen (Waite) S.; m. Diane Elizabeth Dempsey, June 19, 1963; children: Elizabeth Anne (dec.), Jennifer, Jared Reed, George Kermit Alexander. BA magna cum laude, Haverford Coll., 1957; postgrad., Oxford U., 1957-59; PhD, Harvard U., 1964. Resident tutor in govt. Eliot House, Harvard Coll., Cambridge, Mass., 1960-64; inst. polit. sci. Wellesley (Mass.) Coll., 1964-66; policy planning specialist AID, Washington, 1966-67; chief Title IX div. AID, Washington, 1967-68; vis. prof. polit. devel. Fletcher Sch. Law & Diplomacy, Tufts U., Medford, Mass., 1968-70; sr. v.p. Thunderbird Grad. Sch. Internat. Mgmt., Phoenix, 1970-71; cons. internat. affairs Francestown, N.H., 1971-74; pres. Schott & Assocs., Inc., Jaffrey Center, N.H., 1974-93; mem. U.S. Del. World Assembly Internat. Secretariat for Voluntary Service, New Delhi, 1967; advisor Office Prime Minister Royal Thai Govt., Bangkok, 1978-80, Minister Cooperatives Govt. of Indonesia, Jakarta, 1983-84; research asst. spl. appointment The Brookings Inst., Washington, 1960-61;. Author: Kenya Tragedy: European Colonization in East Africa, 1964, Frances' Town: History of Francestown, N.H., 1972, A Five-Year Comprehensive Plan for Development of Agricultural Cooperatives in Thailand, 1979, Recana-Komprehensip Pengembangan Kud, Jakarta, Indonesia, 1985, also various govt. reports and articles in profl. jours. and regional publs.; editor: An Experiment in Integrated Rural Development, 1978. Bd. of Selectmen, Francestown, N.H., 1975-78; trustee Spaulding Youth Ctr., Tilton, N.H., 1971-82, 85-89, pres. bd. trustees, 1972-75; trustee Internat. Inst. Rural Reconstrn., N.Y.C., 1979-89, mem. exec. com., 1985-89; bd. trustees N.H. Pub. Radio, 1990—, chmn., 1993—; mem. spl. study commn. Coop. Extension Svc. State of N.H., 1980-81, also mem. scenic and cultural by-ways com. 1993—; forestry rep. County Extension Coun., Hillsboro County, N.H., 1979-82; pres. N.H. Timberland Owner's Assn., 1989-90, bd. dirs., 1988-91; chmn. N.H. chpt. The Nature Conservancy, 1990-93, hon. trustee, 1993—, chmn. N.H. Timber/Tourism Coalition, 1990-94; vice-chmn. Foresters Lic. Bd. State of N.H., 1990-95; bd. trustees Cheshire Med. Ctr., 1992-94, RiverMead Retirement Cmty., Peterborough, N.H., 1993—. Rotary Found. fellow, 1957-58, Coslett Found. fellow, 1958-59, Harvard Arts & Scis. fellow, 1959-60, Fulbright scholar, 1962-63. Mem. Am. Forestry Inst. (cert. tree farmer). Home and Office: Schott & Assocs Inc PO Box 660 Jaffrey NH 03452-0660

SCHOTT, MARGE, professional baseball team executive; b. 1928; d. Edward and Charlotte Unnewehr; m. Charles J. Schott, 1952 (dec. 1968). Owner Schottco, Cin.; ltd. ptnr. Cin. Reds, 1981-84, gen. ptnr., 1984-85, owner, pres., 1985—, chief exec. officer. Office: Cin Reds 100 Riverfront Stadium Cincinnati OH 45202*

SCHOTTA, CHARLES, economist, government official; b. Kansas City, Mo., Feb. 27, 1935; s. Charles and Katherine (Boyer) S.; m. Sarita Gattis, Sept. 9, 1960. B.A., Tex. Christian U., 1957; M.A., Brown U., 1959, postgrad., 1962-65. Assoc. prof. econ. Va. Tech. Inst. and State U., Blacksburg, 1967-71; dir. econometrics staff U.S. Treasury, Washington, 1971-74, dir. office internat. fin. analysis, 1974-77, dir. office internat. energy policy, 1977-79, dep. asst. sec. commodities and natural resources, 1979-83, dep. asst. sec. Arabian Peninsula affairs, 1983-90; dep. asst. sec. Ea. Europe, Soviet and Mid. Ea. policy, 1990-92; dep. asst. sec. Mid. Ea. and energy policy Dept. Treasury, 1992—; pres. Tech. Assocs., Inc., Blacksburg, Va., 1969-71. Author: Property and Casualty Insurance Ratemaking, 1971; contbr. articles to profl. jours. H.B. Earhart Found. fellow, 1963; Richard D. Irwin Found. fellow, 1964. Presbyterian. Clubs: Cosmos (Washington). Home: 104 Prince St Alexandria VA 22314-3312 Office: US Dept of the Treasury 15th Pennsylvania Ave NW Washington DC 20220

SCHOTTELKOTTE, ALBERT JOSEPH, broadcasting executive; b. Cheviot, Ohio, Mar. 19, 1927; s. Albert William and Venetta (Mentrup) S.; m. Elaine Green, Jan 2, 1988; children: Paul J., Carol A., Matthew J., Joseph G., Louis A., Mary J., Ellen E. Noble, William E., Michael H., Linda Brewer, Martha Schottelkotte, Amy Wholeber. Student pub. and parochial schs. With Cin. Enquirer, 1943-61, successively copy boy, city-wide reporter, columnist, 1953-61; news broadcaster Sta. WSAI, Cin., 1953-59; news broadcaster Sta. WCPO-TV, 1959-94, dir. news-spl. events, 1961-83, sta. dir., 1983-88; gen. mgr. news div. Scripps-Howard Broadcasting Co., 1969-81, v.p. for news, 1971-81, sr. v.p., 1981-93; pres., chief exec. officer, trustee Scripps Howard Found., 1986—. Served with AUS, 1950-52. Recipient Nat. CD award for reporting on subject, 1958, Disting. Broadcaster award Alpha Epsilon Ro, 1990; charter inductee Cin. Journalism Hall of Fame Soc. Profl. Journalists, 1990; inducted into Cin. Broadcasting Hall of Fame, 1992. Mem. Bankers Club, Maketewah Country Club (Cin.), Sea Pines Country Club (Hilton Head, S.C.). Roman Catholic. Home: 401 Keeneland Dr Fort Thomas KY 41075-4029 Office: Scripps Howard 312 Walnut St Cincinnati OH 45202

SCHOTTENFELD, DAVID, epidemiologist, educator; b. N.Y.C., Mar. 25, 1931; m. Rosalie C. Schaeffer; children: Jacqueline, Stephen. AB, Hamilton Coll., 1952; MD, Cornell U., 1956; MS in Pub. Health, Harvard U., 1963. Diplomate Am. Bd. Internal Medicine, Am. Bd. Preventive Medicine. Intern in internal medicine Duke U., Durham, N.C., 1956-57; resident in internal medicine Meml. Sloan-Kettering Cancer Ctr., Cornell U. Med. Coll., N.Y.C., 1957-59; Craver fellow med. oncology Meml. Sloan-Kettering Cancer Ctr., 1961-62; clin. instr. dept. pub. health Cornell U., N.Y.C., 1963-67, asst. prof. dept. pub. health, 1965-70, assoc. prof. dept. pub. health, 1970-73, prof. dept. pub. health, 1973-86; John G. Searle prof., chmn. epidemiology sch. pub. health U. Mich., Ann Arbor, 1986—, prof. internal medicine, 1986—; vis. prof. epidemiology U. Minn., Mpls., 1968, 71, 74, 82, 86; W.G. Cosbie lectr. Can. Oncology Soc., 1987. Editor: Cancer Epidemiology and Prevention, 1982; author 7 books; contbr. over 150 articles to profl. jours. Served with USPHS, 1959-61. Recipient Acad. Career award in Preventive Oncology, Nat. Cancer Inst., 1980-85. Fellow AAAS, ACP, Am. Coll. Preventive Medicine, Am. Coll. Epidemiology, Armed Forces Epidemiology Bd.; mem. Phi Beta Kappa. Office: U of Mich Sch Pub Health Dept Epidemiology 109 Observatory St Ann Arbor MI 48109-2029

SCHOTTENHEIMER, MARTIN EDWARD, professional football coach; b. Canonsburg, Pa., Sept. 23, 1943; m. Patricia Schottenheimer; children—Kristen, Brian. B.A., U. Pitts., 1964. Football player Buffalo Bills, NFL, 1965-68, Boston Patriots, 1969-70; real estate developer Miami and Denver, 1971-74; asst. coach World Football League, Portland, 1974, N.Y. Giants, 1975-77, Detroit Lions, 1978-79; asst. coach Cleve. Browns, 1980-84, head coach, 1985-88; head coach Kansas City Chiefs, 1989—. Office: Kansas City Chiefs 1 Arrowhead Dr Kansas City MO 64129-1651*

SCHOTTENSTEIN, SAUL, retail company executive; b. 1924; married. Pres., dir. Schottenstein Stores, Columbus, Ohio, 1972—. Office: Schottenstein Stores Corp 3241 Westerville Rd Columbus OH 43224-3750 also: Schottenstein Stores Corp 1800 Moler Rd Columbus OH 43207-1680

SCHOTTER, ANDREW ROYE, economics educator, consultant; b. N.Y.C., June 6, 1947; s. I. Harvey and Sara (Rothstein) S.; m. Anne Howland, June 7, 1970; children: Geoffrey, Elizabeth. BS, Cornell U., 1969; MA, PhD, NYU, 1974. Asst. prof. Syracuse (N.Y.) U., 1974-75; asst. prof. NYU, 1975-81, assoc. prof., 1981-86; prof., chmn. econs. dept. NYU, N.Y.C., 1989—, chmn. C.V. Starr Ctr. for Applied Econs., 1986-89; vis. asst. prof. Cornell U., Ithaca, 1974-75; vis. prof. U. Venice, 1993; cons. Gulf & Western Corp., N.Y. 1987, Pegalis & Wachsman, Great Neck, N.Y. 1987-88, Nat. Econ. Rsch. Assocs., White Plains, N.Y., 1989—. Author: Economic Theory of Social Institutions, 1981, Free Market Economics: A Critical Appraisal, 1985, 2d edit., 1990, Microeconomics: A Modern Approach, 1993. Grantee Office of Naval Rsch., 1980-83, NSF, 1988-90. Mem. Am. Econ. Assn., Econometric Soc. Office: NYU Dept Econs 269 Mercer St New York NY 10003-6633

SCHOTTERS, BERNARD WILLIAM, communications company executive; b. Indpls., Nov. 25, 1944; s. Bernard William and Virginia (Hubbard) S.; m. Nancy Fraze, Nov. 13, 1953; children: Payson T., Ian McKiney. BSBA, Washington U., 1967; MBA, Northwestern U., 1968. With Am. Nat. Bank and Trust Co., Chgo., 1972-74; v.p. Wells Fargo Bank, Los Angeles, 1974-83; dir. fin. Tele-Communications, Inc., Denver, 1983-85, v.p. fin., 1985—, dir. subs.; pres. ARP Cable (formerly Group W Cable), N.Y.C., 1987. Served to lt. USN, 1968-72. Club: Denver Cable. Office: Tele-Communications Inc 4643 S Ulster St Denver CO 80237-2863

SCHOTTLAND, CHARLES IRWIN, retired legal educator; b. Chgo., Oct. 29, 1906; s. Harry and Millie (Lustberg) S.; m. Edna Lilyan Greenberg, June 7, 1931; children: Richard R., Mary Elizabeth (dec.). AB, UCLA, 1927; postgrad., N.Y. Sch. Social Work, 1928-29, U. So. Calif. Law Sch., 1929-33; DHL, Boston U., 1969; LLD, Western Mich. U., 1970; DH, Centro Escolar U., Manila, Philippines, 1970, Washington U., 1976; LLD, Emerson Coll., 1972, Brandeis U., 1972; DHL, Adelphi U., 1986. Bar: Calif. 1933. Dir. Modern Social Ctr., L.A., 1929-33; administr. Calif. Relief Adminstrn., 1933-36; exec. dir. Fedn. Jewish Welfare Orgns., L.A., 1936-41; asst. to chief children's bur. Dept. Labor, 1941-42; asst. dir. UNRRA for Germany, 1945, pvt. practice law L.A., 1948-50; dir. Calif. Dept. Social Welfare, 1950-54; lectr. UCLA, 1949-54; commr. social security HEW, 1954-59; dean Florence Heller Grad. Sch. for Advanced Studies in Social Welfare Brandeis U., Waltham, Mass., 1959-70, pres., 1970-72, prof., 1972-79; prof. Ariz. State U., Tucson, 1980-82; Pres. Internat. Coun. Social Welfare, 1968-72, chmn. U.S. com., 1961-66; mem. com. social security experts Internat. Labor Office,

1956-59; prin. adv. U.S. del. UN Social Commn., 1955, 57; mem. adv. bd. Dept. Social Welfare, Commonwealth of Mass., 1964; mem.-at-large Nat. Social Welfare Assembly, 1964-71; mem. task force on financing community health svcs. and facilities Nat. Commn. on Community Health, 1964; mem. Citizens Crusade Against Poverty, 1964; cons. pub. health service Nat. Inst. Mental Health, 1964, chmn. rsch. cons. com., 1973-75; chmn. subcom. on retirement income Nat. Council on Aging, 1964; chmn. task force on social svcs. HEW, 1968; mem. pub. health svcs. Nat. Adv. Mental Health Coun., 1968-72; mem. Milbank Commn. on Pub. Health, 1972-76. Author: The Social Security Program in the United States, 1963, The Welfare State, 1967; mem. editorial bd.: Social Policy and Adminstrn, 1978—, Adminstrn. in Social Work, 1978—. Bd. dirs. Big. Bros. Assn. L.A., 1945—, Nat. Big Bros. Assn., 1975-80, Coun. Internat. Programs, 1980-82; bd. dirs., pres. Nat. Sr. Citizens Law Ctr., 1979-86, 89-92, bd. dirs., 1986-88; chmn. Ariz. del. White House Conf. on Aging, 1980-81, Ariz. Gov.'s Adv. Coun. on Aging, 1983-89; bd. dirs. Pima Coun. on Aging, 1983—; bd. dirs. Nat. Coun. on Aging, 1983—, sec., mem. exec. com., 1988—. Lt. col. AUS, 1942-45, ETO. Decorated by govts. of France, Czechoslovakia, Holland, Greece, Poland; recipient Koshland award Calif. Conf., Social Work, 1954. Mem. Am. Public Welfare Assn., Nat. Assn. Social Workers (chmn. div. social policy and action 1962-66, pres.-elect 1966-67, pres. 1967-68), Nat. Conf. Social Welfare (pres. 1953, 59-60), Am. Public Welfare Assn. (dir.), Western Gerontol. Assn. (dir. 1981-83), Am. Soc. on Aging (pres. 1985-88), Calif. State Bar, Am. Legion, Mil. Order World Wars, Mil. Govt. Assn., Zeta Beta Tau, Pi Sigma Alpha, Pi Kappa Delta. Home: 7405 N Mowry Pl Tucson AZ 85741-2573

SCHOTTLAND, EDWARD MORROW, hospital administrator; b. N.Y.C., Aug. 5, 1946; s. Leo Edward and Harriet (Morrow) S.; m. Nancy Resnick, June 25, 1977; 1 child, David. BA, Queens Coll., CUNY, 1968; MPS, Cornell U., 1973. Asst. adminstr. Mercy Hosp., Rockville Centre, N.Y., 1973-75, asst. adminstr. and dir. planning, 1975-79; pres. Kosair Crippled Children's Hosp., Louisville, 1979-81, sr. v.p., chief adminstrv. officer, 1983-89; v.p. NKC, Inc., Louisville, 1981-83; exec. v.p. The Miriam Hosp., Providence, R.I., 1989—; sr. v.p. Lifespan, Providence, R.I., 1995—; mem. Gov.'s Adv. Council on Med. Assistance. Chmn. Jefferson County Child Abuse Authority, Louisville, 1981-83, dir., 1979-86; bd. dirs. Suicide Prevention and Edn. Ctr., Louisville, 1982-86, Interfaith Health Coun., v.p., 1994—; bd. trustee Barrington (R.I.) Pub. Libr. Fellow Am. Coll. Health Execs. (regent 1994—); mem. Nat. Assn. Children's Hosps. and Related Institutions (bd. dirs.). Home: 3 Stratford Rd Barrington RI 02806-3617 Office: The Miriam Hosp 164 Summit Ave Providence RI 02906-2800

SCHOULTZ, LARS, political scientist, educator; b. San Gabriel, Calif., Aug. 23, 1942; s. Ture Wilhelm and Bernice (Bowie) S.; m. Jane Volland, Jan. 18, 1969; children: Nils Gibson, Karina Anne. BA, Stanford U., 1964, MA, 1966; PhD, U.N.C., 1973. Prof. Miami U., Oxford, Ohio, 1973-77, U. Fla., Gainesville, 1977-79; William Rand Kenaw Jr. prof. polit. sci. U. N.C., Chapel Hill, 1979—. Author: Human Rights and U.S. Policy Toward Latin America, 1981, National Security and U.S. Policy Toward Latin America, 1987, The Populist Challenge, 1983. Sgt. U.S. Army, 1966-67. MacArthur fellow in internat. peace and security MacArthur Found., 1990-91, Fulbright fellow, Rockefeller Found. fellow, Ford Found. fellow, Social Sci. Rsch. Coun., Woodrow Wilson fellow, 1994—. Mem. Latin Am. Studies Assn. (pres. 1991-92, v.p. 1990-91). Democrat. Home: 250 Glandon Dr Chapel Hill NC 27514-3816 Office: U NC Inst Latin Am Studies Chapel Hill NC 27599

SCHOUMACHER, BRUCE HERBERT, lawyer; b. Chgo., May 23, 1940; s. Herbert Edward and Mildred Helen (Wagner) S.; m. Alicia Wesley Sanchez, Nov. 4, 1967; children: Liana Cristina, Janina Maria. BS, Northwestern U., 1961; MBA, U. Chgo., 1963, JD, 1966. Bar: Nebr. 1966, U.S. Dist. Ct. Nebr. 1966, Ill. 1971, U.S. Dist. Ct. (no. dist.) Ill. 1971, U.S. Ct. Appeals (7th cir.) 1979, U.S. Supreme Ct. 1982, U.S. Ct. Fed. Claims 1986. Assoc. Luebs, Tracy & Huebner, Grand Island, Nebr., 1966-67; assoc. McDermott, Will & Emery, Chgo., 1971-76, ptnr., 1976-89; ptnr. Querrey & Harrow, Ltd., Chgo., 1989—; instr. bus. adminstrn. Bellevue Coll., Nebr., 1967-70; lectr. U. Md., Overseas Prodram, 1970. Author: Engineers and the Law: An Overview, 1986; contbg. author: Construction Law, 1986; coauthor: Successful Business Plans for Architects, 1992; contbr. articles to profl. jours. Served to capt. USAF, 1967-71, Vietnam. Decorated Bronze Star, 1971. Fellow Am. Coll. Constrn. Lawyers; mem. ABA, AIA (profl. affiliate), Nebr. Bar Assn., Ill. State Bar Assn. (ad hoc com. large law firms 1992—, chmn. membership and bar activities com. 1988-89, coun. ins. law sect. 1986-91, mem. spl. com. on computerized legal rsch. 1986-87), Chgo. Bar Assn. (chmn. fed. civil procedure com. 1982-83), Def. Rsch. Inst., Ill. Assn. Def. Trial Counsel, Chgo. Bldg. Congress (bd. dirs. 1985—, sec. 1987-89. v.p. 1991-91), Western Soc. Engrs. (assoc.), The Legal Club, The Law Club, Pi Kappa Alpha, Phi Delta Phi. Republican. Methodist. Club: Tower (Chgo). Office: Querrey & Harrow Ltd 180 N Stetson Ave Chicago IL 60601-6710

SCHOWALTER, JOHN ERWIN, child and adolescent psychiatry educator; b. Milw., Mar. 15, 1936; s. Raymond Phillip and Martha (Kowalew) S.; m. Ellen Virginia Lefferts, June 11, 1960; children: Jay, Bethany. BS, U. Wis.-Madison, 1957, MD, 1960. Diplomate Am. Bd. Psychiatry and Neurology (com. on cert. in child psychiatry 1983-85, chmn. 1986-87, bd. dirs. 1993—; cert. in adult and child psychiatry also psychoanalysis. Intern in pediatrics Yale-New Haven Hosp., 1960-61; asst. resident in psychiatry Cin. Gen. Hosp., 1961-63; fellow in child psychiatry Yale Child Study Ctr., 1963-65; psychiatrist Mental Hygiene Clinic U.S. Army, Ft. Ord, Calif., 1965-67; asst. prof. Yale U. Child Study Ctr., New Haven, 1967-70, assoc. prof. Sch. Medicine, 1970-75, dir. tng., 1971—, prof. pediatrics and psychiatry, 1975—, chief child psychiatry, 1982-90, Albert J. Solnit prof. child psychiatry and pediatrics, 1989—; mem. publ. com. Yale U. Press, 1992—; mem. sci. adv. bd. Sophia Found. Med. Rsch., Rotterdam, The Netherlands, 1984-89; dir. mental health and substance abuse Yale Preferred Health Plan, 1995—. Co-author: The Family Handbook of Adolescence, 1979; editor: (with others) The Child and Death, 1983, Death and Children: A Guide for Educators, Parents and Caregivers, 1985, Child Psychiatry, 1986, Children and Death: Perspectives from Birth Through Adolescence, 1987; also numerous articles, book revs.; mem. editorial bd. Pediatrics, 1976-81, Children's Health Care, 1977—, Jour. Am. Psychoanalytic Assn., 1978, Pediatrics in Rev., 1978-85; asst. editor Jour. Am. Acad. Child and Adolescent Psychiatry, 1988—; co-editor Yearbook Psychiatry and Applied Mental Health, 1988—. Capt. U.S. Army, 1965-67. Fellow Am. Acad. Child and Adolescent Psychiatry (sec. 1985-87, pres. 1989-91), Am. Coll. Psychiatrists (com. on hon. fellowships 1988-92, com. on long range planning and policy, 1993—), Am. Acad. Pediatrics (affiliate); mem. Am. Pediatric Soc., Am. Psychoanalytic Assn. (cert.), Group for Advancement Psychiatry (com. on child psychiatry 1981, bd. dirs. 1989-91, pres. 1993-95), Assn. for Care of Children's Health (fellow 1984-86), AMA (residency rev. com. for psychiatry 1983-87, 89-94), Soc. Profs. Child Psychiatry (pres. 1984-86), Western New Eng. Inst. Psychoanalysis (pres. candidates' coun. 1972-73, mem. faculty in child psychoanalysis 1980—, supervisor child psychoanalysis 1984—, pres. 1986-88), Conn. and New Haven med. socs., Conn. Child Psychiatrists (pres. 1979-81), Benjamin Rush Soc., others, Sigma Xi. Lutheran. Home: 606 Ellsworth Ave New Haven CT 06511-1636 Office: Yale U Child Study Ctr PO Box 207900 230 S Frontage Rd New Haven CT 06519-1124

SCHOWALTER, WILLIAM RAYMOND, college dean, educator; b. Milw., Dec. 15, 1929; s. Raymond Philip and Martha (Kowalke) S.; m. Jane Ruth Gregg, Aug. 22, 1953; children: Katherine Ruth, Mary Patricia, David Gregg. BS, U. Wis., 1951; postgrad., Inst. Paper Chemistry, 1951-52; MS, U. Ill., 1953, PhD, 1957. Asst. prof. chem. engring. Princeton U., 1957-63, assoc. prof., 1963-66, prof., 1966-86, Class of 1950 prof. engring. and applied sci., 1986-89, acting chmn. dept. chem. engring., 1971, chmn. dept. chem. engring., 1978-87; assoc. dean Sch. Engring. and Applied Sci., 1971-77; dean Coll. Engring. U. Ill., Urbana, 1989—; Sherman Fairchild Disting. scholar Calif. Inst. Tech., 1977-78; vis. fellow U. Salford, Eng., 1974; vis. sr. fellow Sci. Research Council, U. Cambridge, Eng., 1976; cons. to chem. and petroleum cos.; mem. editorial adv. bd. McGraw-Hill Pub. Co., 1964-92; co-chmn. Internat. Seminar for Heat and Mass Transfer, 1970; mem. vis. com. for chem. engring. MIT, 1979-87, Lehigh U., 1980-87, Stanford U., 1990—; mem. evaluation panel Ctr. Chem. Engring., Nat. Bur. Standards, 1982-88, chmn., 1986-88; mem. commn. engring. and tech. systems NRC, 1983-88; engring. research bd., 1984-86, com. on chem. engring.

frontiers; adv. council chem. engring. Cornell U., 1983-91; adv. council Sch. Engring., Rice U., 1986-92; Reilly lectr. in chem. engring. U. Notre Dame, 1985, Van Winkle lectr. in chem. engring. U. Tex., Austin, 1986, David M. Mason lectr. in chem. engring. Stanford U., 1987; bd. dirs. Champaign Nat. Bank., 1991—. Author: Mechanics of Non-Newtonian Fluids, 1978; co-author: Colloidal Dispersions, 1989; mem. editl. com. Ann. Rev. Fluid Mechanics, 1974-80, Internat. Jour. Chem. Engring., 1974-94, Indsl. and Engring. Chemistry Fundamentals, 1975-78, Jour. Non-Newtonian Fluid Mechanics, 1976—, AIChE Jour., 1979-83; contbr. articles to profl. jours. Mem. State of Ill. Gov.'s Sci. Adv. Com., 1989—. Served with AUS, 1953-55. Recipient Lectureship award Chem. Engring. div. Am. Soc. Engring. Edn., 1971, Disting. Service citation Coll. Engring., U. Wis.-Madison, 1983; Guggenheim fellow, 1987-88. Fellow AIChE (William H. Walker award 1982, bd. dirs. 1992-94); mem. NAE (awards com. 1986-88, chmn. 1987, acad. adv. bd. 1991—, chmn. 1992—, coun. 1994—), Am. Acad. Arts and Scis., Am. Chem. Soc., Soc. Rheology (exec. com. 1977-79, v.p. 1981-83, pres. 1983-85, Bingham medal 1988), Sigma Xi, Tau Beta Pi, Phi Lambda Upsilon, Phi Eta Sigma. Home: 1846 Maynard Dr Champaign IL 61821-5268

SCHRADER, HARRY CHRISTIAN, JR., retired naval officer; b. Sheboygan, Wis., Aug. 4, 1932; s. Harry Christian and Edna Flora (Stubbe) S.; m. Carol Joan Gossman, June 23, 1956; 1 child, Mary Clare. BS, U.S. Naval Acad., 1955; MS, U.S. Naval Postgrad. Sch., 1963. Commd. ensign USN, 1955, advanced through grades to vice adm., 1982; comdr. U.S.S. Tawasa, 1963-64, U.S.S. A. Hamilton, 1970-72, U.S.S. Jackson, 1972-73, U.S.S. Gilmore, 1973-75, U.S.S. Long Beach, 1975-78; dir. MLSF Amphibious, Mine Warfare and Advanced Vehicles div. Office Naval Ops., Washington, 1978-80; comdr. Cruiser Destroyer Group One, San Diego, 1980-82, Naval Surface Forces, U.S. Pacific Fleet, San Diego, 1982-85; ret. USN, 1985; mgr. Middle East/NATO programs, autonetics div. Rockwell Internat., Anaheim, Calif., 1985-87; pres. Coronado (Calif.) Tech. Internat., 1987. Mem. Am. Def. Preparedness Assn., San Diego Oceans Found. (mem. adv. bd.), Sigma Xi.

SCHRADER, HELEN MAYE, retired municipal worker; b. Akron, Ohio, June 8, 1920; d. Simon P. and Helen Cecelia (Fennessy) Eberz; widowed; children: Alfred E., Kathleen Therese Schrader Wein. Notary pub. Inspector and clk. Fed. Govt. agys., 1940; stenographer Chem. Warfare div./ USAF, Akron, 1954; clk., stenographer VA; elected clk./treas. of twp. Springfield (Ohio) Twp., 1956-92. Clk., treas. Springfield Twp., 1956-62; sec. Springfield Dem. Club, Akron, 1957—; sec., treas. Springfield Twp. Civic Club, 1980—. Mem. Summit County Assn. of Trustees and Clks. (sec. 1959-78, 83-92, Svc. plaque 1979, 92). Roman Catholic. Avocations: needlework, flower arranging, crossword puzzles. Home: 693 Neal Rd Akron OH 44312-3709

SCHRADER, HENRY CARL, civil engineer, consultant; b. Chgo., Jan. 5, 1918; s. Henry Fred and Helene (Arkenberg) S.; m. Marium Warner, Aug. 22, 1942; children: Henry Carl, Gary Warner. BS in Civil Engring., U. Ill., 1940, MS in Civil Engring., 1959; diploma Indsl. Coll. Armed Forces, Ft. McNair, D.C., 1962. Registered profl. engr., Ill., Va., Md., D.C., Pa., Mass., N.C. Commd. 2nd lt. U.S. Army, 1940; advanced through grades to maj. gen., 1971; dist. engr. Corps of Engrs., Okinawa, Ryukus Island, 1962-64; chief systems analysis Office Chief Staff Dept Army, Washington, 1966-67, dir. mgmt. info. systems, 1967-70; comdr. 18th Engr. Brigade, Vietnam, 1970-71, comdr. Computer Systems Command, Ft. Belvior, Va., 1971-73; ret., 1973; prin. mktg. Dalton Dalton Newport, Washington, 1973-84; v.p. URS Dalton, 1984-86; v.p. URS Cons., 1986—; specialist high speed ground transp. systems, 1978—. Decorated Air Medal with 2 clusters, Disting. Svc. medal with cluster, Legion of Merit with 3 clusters; Engr. Yr. award Dept. Civil Engring. U. Ill., 1971. Fellow Am. Soc. Civil Engrs., Soc. Am. Mil. Engrs. (dir. 1979-86); mem. Nat. Soc. Profl. Engrs., Am. R.R. and Transportation Bldrs. Assn. (bd. dirs. 1982—, pres. planning and design div. 1988-90, pres. pub./pvt. ventures div. 1990-92, railroads adv. coun. 1977—), Am. Railway Engring. Assn., HighSpeed Rail Assn. (bd. dirs. 1982—, vice chmn. 1990-92, chmn. membership com. 1985—), Army and Navy Club, Bethesda Country Club (dir. 1983-86), Farmington Country Club. Republican. Episcopalian.

SCHRADER, KEITH WILLIAM, mathematician; b. Neligh, Nebr., Apr. 22, 1938; s. William Charles and Gail (Hughes) S.; m. Carol Jean Taylor, Dec. 26, 1960; children: Jeffrey, Melinda. BS, U. Nebr., 1959, M.S., 1961, Ph.D., 1966; postgrad., Stanford U., 1961-63. Engr. Sylvania Co., Mountain View, Calif., 1962-63; asst. prof. dept. math U. Mo.-Columbia, 1966-69, assoc. prof., 1969-78, prof., 1978-79, chmn. dept. math. prof., 1979-82, 85-88, prof. dept. math., 1988—. Bd. dirs. Schrader Inst. Early Learning, Columbia, 1970-83; mem. Planning And Zoning Commn., 1980-90. NASA grantee, 1967-68; NSF grantee, 1969-70. Mem. Am. Math. Soc., Sigma Xi, Sigma Phi Epsilon. Office: Dept Math U Mo Columbia MO 65211-0001

SCHRADER, LAWRENCE EDWIN, plant physiologist, educator; b. Atchison, Kans., Oct. 22, 1941; s. Edwin Carl and Jenna Kathryn (Tobiason) S.; m. Elfriede J. Massier, Mar. 14, 1981. BS, Kans. State U., 1963; PhD, U. Ill., 1967; grad., Inst. Ednl. Mgmt., Harvard U., 1991. Asst. prof. dept. agronomy U. Wis., Madison, 1969-72; assoc. prof. U. Wis., 1972-76, prof., 1976-84; prof., head dept. agronomy U. Ill., Urbana, 1985-89; dean Coll. Agr. and Home Econs. Wash. State U., Pullman, 1989-94, prof. dept. horticulture, 1994—; chief competitive rsch. grants office Dept. Agr., Washington, 1980-81; trustee, treas. Agrl. Satellite Corp., 1991-94. Contbr. chpts. to books, articles to profl. jours. Active Consortium for Internat. Devel., 1989-94, chair fin. com., vice chair exec. com., 1990-92, trustee 1989-94; mem. exec. com. Coun. Agrl. Heads of Agy. 1992-94. Capt. U.S. Army, 1967-69. Recipient Soybean Researchers Recognition award 1983, Disting. Service award in Agriculture Kansas State U., 1987; Romnes Faculty fellow U. Wis., 1979. Fellow AAAS (mem. steering group, sect. agr. 1991-95, chair-elect sect. on agriculture, food and renewable resources 1995—), Am. Soc. Agronomy, Crop Sci. Soc. Am.; mem. Am. Soc. Plant Physiologists (sec. 1983-85, pres. elect 1986, pres. 1987-88), Am. Chem. Soc., Sigma Xi, Gamma Sigma Delta, Phi Kappa Phi, Phi Eta Sigma, Blue Key, Alpha Zeta. Methodist. Home: 3504 Crestview Rd Wenatchee WA 98801 Office: Wash State U Tree Fruit Rsch & Extension Ctr 1100 N Western Ave Wenatchee WA 98801

SCHRADER, LEE FREDERICK, agricultural economist; b. Okawville, Ill., Mar. 11, 1933; s. Fred and Alma (Koenemann) S.; m. Martha Ellen Kohl, Dec. 27, 1958; children—Mark, Katherine, Amanda. B.S., U. Ill., 1955; M.S., Mich. State U., 1958; Ph.D., U. Calif., Berkeley, 1961. Buyer Lever Bros. Co., N.Y.C., 1961-64; economist Armour & Co., Chgo., 1965-66; mem. faculty Sch. Agr. Purdue U., West Lafayette, Ind., 1966—; prof. agrl. econs. Sch. Agr. Purdue U., 1971—. Author: (with R.A. Goldberg) Farmers' Cooperatives and Federal Income Taxes, 1975; contbr. articles to profl. jours. Served with U.S. Army, 1955-57. Mem. Am. Agrl. Econs. Assn. Home: 128 Seneca Ln West Lafayette IN 47906-2041 Office: Purdue U Dept Agrl Econs West Lafayette IN 47907

SCHRADER, MARTIN HARRY, retired publisher; b. Queens, N.Y., Nov. 26, 1924; s. Harry F. and Ida (Spiess) S.; m. Cecelia Sofer, July 7, 1957; children: Howard, Daniel, Esther. B.A., Queens Coll., 1946. Vice Pres. Alfred Auerbach & Co., 1950-60; dir. mktg. House Beautiful mag. N.Y.C., 1960-65; pub. spl. publs. div. House Beautiful mag., 1965-69; pub. Town and Country mag., N.Y.C., 1969-77, Harpers Bazaar, 1977-91; retired, 1991—; v.p. Hearst Mags., 1983-91; lectr. merchandising Fairleigh Dickenson U., 1958-61, Parsons Sch. Design, 1976—, Merchandising New Sch. Grad. Ctr., 1984; advt. Cosmetics Plus, N.Y.C.; cons. Columbia Journalism Review, Sports Traveler Mag. Pro-bono pub. Westchester Arts News/Westchester Arts Coun.; editor Counterpoints/Caramoor Ctr. for Music and the Arts, Katonah, N.Y.; author bi-weekly column Gannett Suburban Newspapers, quarterly column Westchester 60 Plus Mag. Former nat. adv. bd. Salk Inst., La Jolla, Calif.; bd. govs. Coty Fashion Critics Awards.; bd. dirs. Mother's Day Found., Ednl. Found. Fashion Industries. Recipient Human Relations award Am. Jewish Com., 1979. Mem. U.S. Lawn Tennis Assn. (umpire's com. 1961-94). Jewish (trustee temple 1965-94).

SCHRADER, PAUL JOSEPH, film writer, director; b. Grand Rapids, Mich., July 22, 1946; s. Charles A. and Joan (Fisher) S.; m. Jeannine Oppewall (div.); m. Mary Beth Hurt, Aug. 6, 1983. B.A., Calvin Coll., 1968; M.A., UCLA., 1970. Film critic Los Angeles Free Press, Coast mag., 1970-71; editor Cinema mag., 1970. Author: Transcendental Style in Film: Ozu, Bresson, Dreyer, 1972, Schrader on Schrader, 1989; screenwriter: The Yakuza, 1975, Taxi Driver, 1976, Obsession, 1976, Rolling Thunder, 1978, Raging Bull, 1980, The Mosquito Coast, 1986, The Last Temptation of Christ, 1988; screenwriter, prodr.: Old Boyfriends, 1978; screenwriter, dir.: Blue Collar, 1977, Hardcore, 1978, American Gigolo, 1979, Mishima: A Life in Four Chapters, 1985, Light of Day, 1987, Light Sleeper, 1992; dir.: Cat People, 1982, Patty Hearst, 1988, The Comfort of Strangers, 1990. Address: 9696 Culver Blvd Ste 203 Culver City CA 90232 also: care Jeff Berg ICM 8942 Wilshire Blvd Beverly Hills CA 90211*

SCHRADER, THOMAS F., utilities executive; b. Indpls., 1950. Grad. Princeton U., 1972, 78. Pres., chief exec. officer Wis. Gas Co., Milw. Office: Wis Gas Co 626 E Wisconsin Ave Milwaukee WI 53202

SCHRADER, WILLIAM CUTLER, banker; b. St. Paul, Apr. 15, 1933; s. Ernst-Joseph and Lydia (Cutler) S.; m. Carolyn Miller, Aug. 4, 1956; children—Elizabeth, William. B.S., Yale U., 1955; M.B.A., Rutgers U., 1966; A.M.P., Harvard U., 1980. Ops. mgr. Procter & Gamble Co., 1958-68; v.p. prodn. William Underwood Co., Watertown, Mass., 1968-74; sr. v.p. Chem. Bank, N.Y.C., 1974-82; exec. v.p. Shawmut Corp., Boston, 1982-; dir., mem. exec. com./Bank Administn. Inst., Rolling Meadows, Ill., 1980-85; bd. dirs. New Eng. Banking Inst. Bd. dirs. Boston council Boy Scouts Am., Boston, 1983—, Brighter Day, Boston, 1973-74; chmn. Exec. Svc. Corps of New Eng. Served to capt. USMC, 1955-58. Mem. Tau Beta Pi, Beta Gamma Sigma. Clubs: Short Hills, Cohasset Golf, Hingham Yacht, Harvard of Boston. Avocations: tennis; skiing; jogging. Office: Shawmut Corp 1 Federal St Boston MA 02110-2003

SCHRADER, WILLIAM JOSEPH, accountant, educator; b. Leroy, Tex., Sept. 21, 1929; s. Rudolph L. and Lela V. (Gaylor) S.; m. Nancy L. Etnier, Mar. 22, 1953 (dec. 1974); children: Diana, Dale (dec. 1974), Frank; m. Mary Kuhns Maserick, Mar. 6, 1976. BBA, Baylor U., 1950; MBA, Ind. U., 1951; PhD, U. Wash., 1959. CPA, Tex. Acct. Texaco, New Orleans, 1949, A.C. Upleger & Co. (C.P.A.'s), Waco, Tex., 1949-50; instr. U. Wash., Seattle, 1952-54; asst. prof. to prof. accounting Pa. State U., University Park, 1954-91; head dept. accounting and mgmt. info. systems Pa. State U., 1976-86; prof. emeritus, 1992—; bd. dirs. various firms including Ceramic Finishing Co., Ultran Labs., Inc., Applied Sci. Labs., Inc., Cenco Assocs. Inc., 1968—; gen. ptnr. investment partnerships; Fulbright prof. U. Dar es Salaam, 1973-75; vis. prof. U. Zimbabwe, 1987; dir. linkage project with U. Zimbabwe, 1982-87; resident advisor mgmt. tng. project U. West Indies, 1989-90; mem. bd. advs. Inst. of Chartered Accts. of The Caribbean, 1988—; trustee Alpha Real Estate and Mortgage Trust. Author: Income Measurement by Products and Periods, 1959, (with Malcom & Willingham) Financial Accounting: An Events Approach, 1981; contbr. articles to profl. publs. including Jour. of Risk and Ins., Acctg. Rev., Abacus, Fin. Exec., Acctg. Horizons, Acctg. Historians Jour. Active Centre County (Pa.) Task Force on Housing, 1969-70; trustee Fair Housing Inc. Liquidating Trust. Mem. AICPA, AAUP, Am. Acctg. Assn., Acad. Acctg. Historians. Baptist. Clubs: Am. Philatelic Soc., Am. Philatelic Research Library. Home: 305 Adams Ave State College PA 16803-3606 Office: 240 Beam Bus Adminstrn Bldg University Park PA 16802

SCHRADER, WILLIAM P., organization executive, farmer; b. Phoenix; m. Bondena; children: Alissa Schrader Urshel, William P. Jr., Larry, Travis. Student, Ariz. State U. Bd. dirs. Salt River Project, Phoenix, 1964-90, v.p. bd., 1990-94, pres., 1994—; pres. Schrader Farms, Inc. Bd. dirs. Greater Phoenix Econ. Coun., Groundwater Users Adv. Coun.; mem. Maricopa C.C.'s Found., East Valley Partnership, Scottsdale (Ariz.) Mcpl. Corp.; former mayor and mem. city coun. City of Scottsdale; 1st chmn. Parada del Sol, Scottsdale Rodeo. Named to Scottsdale Hall of Fame; named Citizen of Yr., City of Scottsdale. Mem. Am. Pub. Power Assn., Am. Mgmt. Assn., Nat. Water Resources Assn., Colorado River Water Users Assn., Scottsdale C. of C., Scottsdale Jr. C. of C. (life, Disting. Svc. award), Scottsdale Charros (life), White Mountain Country Club, Ariz. Club, Mesa Country Club (Ariz.). Methodist. Home: 5611 Calle Camelia Phoenix AZ 85018-4617 Office: Salt River Project PO Box 52025 Phoenix AZ 85072-2025

SCHRADY, DAVID ALAN, operations research educator; b. Akron, Ohio, Nov. 11, 1939; s. Marvin G. and Sheila A. (O'Neill) S.; m. Mary E. Hilt, Sept. 1, 1962; children: Peter, Patrick, Matthew. BS, Case Inst. Tech., 1961, MS, 1963, PhD, 1965. Prof., chmn. Naval Postgrad. Sch., Monterey, Calif., 1974-76, dean acad. planning, 1976-80, provost and acad. dean, 1980-87, prof. ops. research, 1988—; vis. prof. Cranfield Inst. Tech./Royal Mil. Coll. of Sci., Shrivenham, Eng., fall 1987-spring 88. Contbr. articles to profl. jours. Recipient Goodeve medal Ops. Rsch. Soc., U.K., 1992. Mem. Ops. Rsch. Soc. Am. (pres. 1983-84, Kimball medal 1994), Mil. Ops. Rsch. Soc. (pres. 1978-79, Wanner Meml. award 1984), Internat. Fedn. Ops. Rsch. Socs. (hon. treas. 1988—), Inst. Mgmt. Scis. Avocation: guitar, motor sports. Office: Naval Postgrad Sch Dept Ops Rsch Monterey CA 93943-5000

SCHRAG, ADELE FRISBIE, business education educator; b. Cynthiana, Ky., May 7, 1921; d. Shirley Ledyard and Edna Kate (Ford) S.; m. William Albert Schrag, Apr. 6, 1963; 1 stepchild, Marie Carol. B.S., Temple U., 1942; M.A., N.Y. U., 1944, Ph.D., 1961. Tchr. Manor Twp. High Sch., Millersville, Pa., 1942-43, Downingtown (Pa.) Sr. High Sch., 1943-50; instr., asst. prof. Temple U. Sch. Bus. and Pub. Administrn., Phila., 1950-60; prof. bus. edn. and vocat. edn. Coll. Edn., 1960-85, sr. prof., 1985-88, prof. emeritus, 1988—; vis. lectr. N.Y. U.; cons. Phila. Community Coll., 1967-82. Editor: Business Education for the Automated Office, 1964; author: (with Estelle L. Popham and Wanda Blockhus) A Teaching-Learning System for Business Education, 1975, How to Dictate, 1981, Office Procedures Update, 1982, (with Robert Poland) A Teaching System for Business Subjects, 1988; contbr. articles to profl. jours., chpts. to books. Trustee Meth. Hosp., 1981-85, Sun Cities Symphony Assn., 1988-93, Maricopa Habitat for Humanity, 1994—. Recipient Profl. Panhellenic award, 1963; Kensington High Sch. Alumnae award, 1972. Mem. Nat. Soc. Automation in Bus. Edn. (pres. 1969-73, dir. 1974), Nat. Assn. Bus. Tchr. Edn. (pres. 1983-84), Bus. Edn. Certification Council, Phi Gamma Nu (nat. treas. 1952-54, nat. sec. 1954-56), Delta Pi Epsilon (policy commn. for bus. and econ. edn. 1975-78, dir. research found. 1978-83, pres. research found. 1983). Home: 17838 N Conquistador Dr Sun City West AZ 85375-5118

SCHRAG, EDWARD A., JR., lawyer; b. Milw., Mar. 27, 1932; s. Edward A. and Mabel Lena (Baumbach) S.; m. Leslie Jean Israel, June 19, 1954; children: Amelia Marie Schrag Prack, Katherine Allison Schrag Roberts, Edward A. III (dec.). B.S. in Econs, U. Pa., 1954; J.D., Harvard, 1960. Bar: Ohio 1961. Assoc., then firm partner, now of counsel Vorys, Sater, Seymour and Pease, Columbus, 1960—; sec. Ranco Inc., 1972-87; trustee Lake of Woods Water Co., 1972-91; mem. Ohio div. Securities Adv. Com. Mem. Downtown Area Com., 1970-74. Served to 1t. (j.g.) USNR, 1954-57. Mem. ABA, Ohio Bar Assn. (chmn. corp. law com. 1986-88, chmn. securities regulation subcom., spl. com. bus. cts., bd. govs., corp. counsel sect., chmn. 1991-93), Columbus Bar Assn., Columbus Area C. of C., Navy League, Alpha Tau Omega, Beta Gamma Sigma, Phi Sigma Alpha, Pi Gamma Mu. Episcopalian. Clubs: Kiwanis, Capital, Crichton, Ohio State U. Pres.'s, University. Home: 9400 White Oak Ln Westerville OH 43082-9606 Office: Vorys Sater Seymour & Pease PO Box 1008 52 E Gay St Columbus OH 43216-1008

SCHRAG, KARL, artist; b. Karlsruhe, Germany, Dec. 7, 1912; came to U.S., 1938, naturalized, 1944; s. Hugo and Bella (Sulzberger) S.; m. Ilse Szamatolski, June 12, 1945; children: Peter, Katherine. Art student, Ecole Nationale Superieure des Beaux Arts, Paris, 1931-35; studied with Lucien Simon, Roger Bissiere; student, Art Student's League of New York; and also student, Atelier 17, N.Y.C. Tchr. Bklyn Coll., 1953, Cooper Union, 1954-68; dir. Atelier 17, 1950. Paintings and prints exhibited Art Inst. Chgo., Boston Mus. Fine Arts, Met. Mus. Art, Mus. Modern Art, Whitney Mus. Am. Art, Mus. Modern Art, Paris, Tate Gallery, London, Nat. Inst. Arts, Stockholm, others; one-man shows include Brussels, 1938, U.S. Nat. Mus., 1945, Kraushaar Galleries (19 shows), 1947—, Phila. Art Alliance, 1952, U. Ala., 1948, Maine U., 1953, 58, Wagner Coll., S.I., N.Y., 1955, Assn. Am. Artists, 1971, 80, 86, 90, Nat. Collection Fine Arts, 1972, Bethesda (Md.)

Art Gallery, 1977, Jane Haslem Gallery, Washington, 1987, 89, Bergen Mus. Art, Paramus, N.J., 1993, Sordoni Art Gallery, Wilkes-Barre, Penn., 1993, Bucknell U., 1993, retrospective exhbn. Farnsworth Mus., Rockland, Maine, 1992; represented in over 60 pub. collections, including Mus. Modern Art, Whitney Mus. Am. Art, Solomon R. Guggenheim Mus., Met. Mus. Art, Nat. Gallery, Washington, Bibliotheque Nationale, Paris, Library of Congress, N.Y. Pub. Library, Phila. Mus., Cleve. Mus., Bklyn. Mus., others. Recipient award Bklyn. Mus. Print ann., 1947, 50; purchase award Bradley U., 1952; Erickson prize Soc. Am. Graphic Artists, 1962, 64, 67, 77, 80; Lea prize Phila. Print Club, 1964; Am. Colorprint Soc., 1958, 60, 63, 64; awarded retrospective traveling exhbn. by Ford Found., 1959; Ford Found. fellowship Tamarind Lithography Workshop, 1962; grant Nat. Inst. Arts and Letters, 1966; Childe Hassam Purchase Fund award Am. Acad. Arts and Letters, 1969, 73, 77, Andrew Carnegie prize, 1986. Mem. NAD (B. Altman prize for landscape painting, 1981, 94), At Students League N.Y., Artists Equity, Assn. Am. Graphic Artists. Home: 127 E 95th St New York NY 10128-1723

SCHRAG, PETER, editor, writer; b. Karlsruhe, Germany, July 24, 1931; came to U.S., 1941, naturalized, 1953; s. Otto and Judith (Haas) S.; m. Melissa Jane Mowrer, June 9, 1953 (div. 1969); children: Mitzi, Erin Andrew; m. Diane Divoky, May 24, 1969 (div. 1981); children: David Divoky, Benaiah Divoky; m. Patricia Ternahan, Jan. 1, 1988. A.B. cum laude, Amherst Coll., 1953. Reporter El Paso (Tex.) Herald Post, 1953-55; asst. sec., asst. dir. publs. Amherst Coll., 1955-66, instr. Am. Studies, 1960-64; asso. edn. editor Sat. Rev., 1966-68, exec. editor, 1968-69; editor Change mag., 1969-70; editor at large Saturday Rev., 1969-72; contbg. editor Saturday Review/Education, 1972-73; editorial adv. bd. The Columbia Forum, 1972-75; editorial bd. Social Policy, 1971—; contbg. editor More, 1974-78, Inquiry, 1977-80; editorial page editor Sacramento Bee and McClatchy Newspapers, 1978—; vis. lectr. U. Mass. Sch. Edn., 1970-72; fellow in profl. journalism Stanford U., Palo Alto, Calif., 1973-74; lectr. U. Calif. at Berkeley, 1974-78, 90—; Pulitzer Prize juror, 1988-89. Author: Voices in the Classroom, 1965, Village School Downtown, 1967, Out of Place in America, 1971, The Decline of the Wasp, 1972, The End of the American Future, 1973, Test of Loyalty, 1974, (with Diane Divoky) The Myth of the Hyperactive Child, 1975, Mind Control, 1978; contbr. articles. Mem. adv. com. Student Rights Project, N.Y. Civil Liberties Union, 1970-72; mem. Com. Study History, 1958-72; trustee Emma Willard Sch., 1967-69; bd. dirs. Park Sch., Oakland, Calif., 1976-77, Ctr. for Investigative Reporting, 1979-81; bd. visitors Claremont Grad. Sch. Guggenheim fellow, 1971-72; Nat. Endowment for Arts fellow, 1976-77. Office: Sacramento Bee 21st And Q St Sacramento CA 95852

SCHRAG, PHILIP GORDON, law educator; b. Chgo., Apr. 12, 1943; s. Louis Phillip and Lala D. (Fineman) S.; m. Emily Shiling, June 7, 1964 (div. Aug. 1985); children: David, Zachary; m. Lisa Gabrielle Lerman, Dec. 29, 1985; children: Samuel Lerman, Sarah. AB, Harvard U., 1964; LLB, Yale U., 1967. Bar: N.Y. 1967, D.C. 1981. Asst. counsel NAACP Legal Def. & Edn. Fund Inc., N.Y.C., 1967-70; consumer advv. City of N.Y., 1970-71; assoc. prof. law Columbia U., N.Y.C., 1971-73, prof. law, 1973-77; dep. gen. counsel ACDA, Washington, 1977-81; prof. law Georgetown U., Washington, 1981—; cons. Consumer Protection Bd., N.Y., 1975, Carter-Mondale Transition Planning, 1976, Gov.'s Adv. Coun., P.R., 1970. Author: Counsel for the Deceived, 1972, Consumer Protection Law, 1973, Behind the Scenes: The Politics of a Constitutional Convention, 1985, Listening for the Bomb, 1989. Del. Statehood Constnl. Conv., D.C., 1982; chair Consumer's Adv. Coun., N.Y.C., 1968-70. Office: Georgetown U Law Ctr 1507 Isherwood St NE # 1 Washington DC 20002-5564

SCHRAGE, PAUL DANIEL, fast food executive; b. Chgo., Feb. 25, 1935; s. William and Rose Marie (Bruell) S.; m. Janet Carolyn Sievers, June 15, 1957; children: Paul Daniel, Gordon Clark. B.A., Valparaiso U., 1957; M.S. in Advt., U. Ill., 1959. Media buyer Young & Rubicam Advt., Chgo., 1959-61; brand mgr. Quaker Oats Co., Chgo., 1961-65; salesman This Week mag., Chgo., 1965-66; asso. media dir. D'Arcy Advt., Chgo., 1966-67; sr. exec. v.p., chief mktg. officer McDonald's Corp., Oak Brook, Ill., 1967—; bd. dirs. Safety-Kleen Corp. Office: McDonald's Corp 1 McDonald's Pla Oak Brook IL 60521

SCHRAGE, ROSE, educational administrator; b. Montelimar, France, Apr. 15, 1942; came to U.S., 1947; d. Abraham and Celia (Silbiger) Levine; m. Samuel Schrage, Dec. 12, 1935 (dec. 1976); children: Abraham, Leon. BRE, Beth Rivkah Tchrs. Sem., Bklyn., 1968; Paralegal, Manpower Career Devel. Agy., Bklyn., 1973; MS, L.I. U., 1975; Advanced Cert. Ednl. Adminstrn., Bklyn. Coll., 1983. Cert. sch. dist. administr., guidance counselor, tchr., asst. prin. Sec. N.Y.C., 1964-68; police adminstrv. aide N.Y.C. Police Dept., 1974-75; coordinator state reading aid program Sch. Dist. 14, Bklyn., 1977-78, project dir. Title VII, 1978-81, asst. dir. reimbursable fed. and state programs, 1981-85, dist. bus. mgr., 1985-94, asst. prin., 1994—; chmn. N.Y.C. Bd. Edn. IMPACT Com., Bklyn., 1986—. Author (poem): Never Again, 1983; contbg. editor Chai Today; contbr. articles on current affairs and concerns to profl. jours. Del. Republican. Jud. Conf., 1968; founder, pres Concerned Parents, Bklyn., 1977; radio co-host Israeli War Heroes Fund-Radiothon, Bklyn.; family counselor local social agys., Bklyn. Recipient Cert. of Appreciation as vol. regional coord. N.Y. State Mentoring Program N.Y. Gov. Cuomo, 1991. Mem. Am. Assn. Sch. Adminstrs., Assn. Orthodox Jewish Tchrs. (v.p. exec. bd.), N.Y. State Assn. Sch. Bus. Ofcls., N.Y.C. Assn. Sch. Bus. Ofcls., Coun. Suprs. and Adminstrs. Avocations: tennis, needlepoint, piano, reading, communal activities.

SCHRAGER, JAMES E., financial company executive, educator; b. South Bend, Ind., Apr. 5, 1950; s. Howard W. and Eleanor (Kahn) Schrager; m. Teresa Plank, Feb. 21, 1987; children: Max Plank, Michael Elliot. BA Econs., Oakland U., 1971; MBA Acctg., U. Colo., 1975; JD, DePaul U., 1979; PhD, U. Chgo., 1993. CPA, Ill. Acct. Fleetwood Enterprises, Vacaville, Calif., 1973-74; controller Moduline Inds., Colorado Springs, Colo., 1974-75; acct. Haskins & Sells CPAs, Chgo., 1975-77; ptnr. Schrager Stearns & Co., Chgo., 1978-82; gen. mgr. Colson Equipment, Caruthersville, Mo., 1982-84; v.p., CFO Gatz Bros. & Co., San Francisco, 1984-88, exec. v.p., 1989; pres. Japan Capital Mkts., South Bend, 1989—; sr. lectr. U. Chgo., 1982—; adj. instr. Notre Dame U., South Bend, 1992—. Inventor patent for shock-absorbent stretcher chassis, 1984; contbr. articles to profl. jours. Mem. AICPA, Ill. Inst. Cert. Pub. Accts. Avocations: sailboat racing, skiing.

SCHRAGIS, STEVEN M., publisher, lawyer; b. N.Y.C., Oct. 25, 1956; s. Alvin I. and Carole (Kaskel) S.; m. Donna Reservitz. BS in Econs., Tufts U., 1978; JD, Am. U., 1981. Atty. Finley Kemble Wagner, N.Y.C., 1981-84; real estate developer Carol Mgmt./Doral, N.Y.C., 1984-89; pub. Carol Pub. Group, N.Y.C., 1989—. Office: Carol Pub Group 122 E 42nd St Ste 1601 New York NY 10168-1694

SCHRAM, MARTIN JAY, journalist; b. Chgo., Sept. 15, 1942; s. Marlo Joseph and Charleene Janice (Fidler) S.; m. Patricia Stewart Morgan, May 23, 1964; children—Kenneth Marlo, David Morgan. B.A., U. Fla., 1964. Reporter The Miami (Fla.) News, 1964-65; reporter Newsday, Garden City, N.Y., 1965-67; mem. Washington bur. Newsday, 1967-69, White House corr., 1969-73, chief Washington bur., sr. editor report, 1973-79; writer on the presidency Washington Post, 1979-81, nat. affairs writer, 1981-86; assoc. editor, editor Sunday edits. Chgo. Sun-Times, 1986-87; asst. mng. editor, editor Sunday edits. Rocky Mountain News, Denver, 1987-88; polit. columnist United Feature Syndicate, Newspaper Enterprise Assn., 1989-94; Scripps Howard News Svc., Washington, 1994—; commentator Cable News Network, 1984—; nat. editor Washingtonian Mag., 1988-90; fellow Gannett Ctr. for Media Studies, Columbia U., 1985-86; guest scholar Woodrow Wilson Internat. Ctr., 1990-91. Author: Running for President, A Journal of the Carter Campaign, 1976, Running for President: 1976, The Carter Campaign, 1977; (with others) The Pursuit of the Presidency, 1980, The Great American Video Game: Presidential Politics in the Television Age, 1987, Speaking Freely, 1995; co-editor: Mandate for Change, 1993. Recipient James Wright Brown Meml. award Sigma Delta Chi, 1965, Lowell Mellet award Pa. State U., 1988. Office: 1090 Vermont Ave NW Ste 1000 Washington DC 20005

SCHRAM, RONALD BYARD, lawyer; b. Detroit, Sept. 7, 1942; s. Byron Canby and Mary Louise (Byard) S.; m. Carol Lorraine Anderson, July 19, 1969; children: Laura Mary, Alison Leigh. BA, Dartmouth Coll., 1964; MA in Econs., Cambridge U., England, 1966; JD, U. Mich., 1969, LLM, 1970, SJD, 1971. Bar: Mass. 1970. Assoc. Ropes & Gray, Boston, 1970-78, ptnr., 1978—. Trustee Dartmouth Coll., Hanover, N.H., 1981-92, Dartmouth-Hitchcock Med. Ctr., Lebanon, N.H., 1983-93, New Eng. Sports Mus., Cambridge, Mass., 1984—, Derby Acad., Hingham, Mass., 1982-89. Keasbey Found. fellow, Phila., 1964-66; George M. Humphrey fellow in law econ. policy, U. Mich. Law Sch., Ann Arbor, 1969-70. Mem. Boston Bar Assn., Am. Acad. Hosp. Attys., Phi Beta Kappa. Office: Ropes & Gray 1 International Pl Boston MA 02110

SCHRAMEK, TOMAS, ballet dancer; b. Bratislava, Czechoslovakia, Sept. 11, 1944; emigrated to Can., 1968, naturalized, 1973; s. Hans and Valeria (Neudorfer) S. BA in Fine Arts, Acad. Mus. and Theatre Arts, Bratislava, 1968. Mem. Sluk, Slovakia folk dance ensemble, 1959-68, prin. dancer, 1964-68; dancer Nat. Ballet Can., 1969-71, soloist, 1971-73, prin. dancer, 1973-91, prin. character artist, tchr., coach, 1991—. Mem. Actors Equity Assn., Assn. Can. TV and Radio Artists. Home: 117 Welland Ave, Toronto, ON Canada M4T 2J4 Office: Nat Ballet Canada, 157 King St E, Toronto, ON Canada M5C 169

SCHRAMM, BERNARD CHARLES, JR., advertising agency executive; b. Balt., Jan. 23, 1928; s. Bernard C. and Juliet Marie (Barranger) S.; m. Florence Mae Fangman, 1950; children: Stephanie Schramm McDaniel, Carol Schramm Molander, Bernard Charles III, Claudia Schramm Chitwood. Student, Balt. Poly. Inst., 1942-46. Prodn. mgr. Van Sant, Dugdale & Co., Balt., 1946-52; media dir. AWL Advt., Balt., 1952-55; prodn. Henry J. Kaufman Assocs., Washington, 1955-58; exec. v.p. Avalon Hill Co., Balt., 1958-64; v.p. Cargill, Wilson & Acree Advt., Richmond, Va., 1964-68; pres. William Cook Advt. Inc. (now The William Cook Agy. Inc.), Jacksonville, Fla., 1968-89; chmn. bd. William Cook Advt. Inc. (now The William Cook Agy. Inc.), Jacksonville, 1989—; bd. dirs. Otis F. Smith Found., chmn. 1991-93. Mem. exec. com., v.p. United Way N.E. Fla., 1982-87, bd. dirs., 1982-93; bd. dirs. N.E. Fla. chpt. ARC, 1976-89, chmn., 1980-81; bd. dirs. Fla. C.C. Found., 1976-89; chmn. bd. dirs. Otis F. Smith Found., 1991-93. Mem. Am. Assn. Advt. Agys. (chmn. Fla. coun., 1984-85, elected vice-chmn. So. Region Bd. of Govs., 1988—, chmn., 1989, nat. bd. dirs., mem. agy. mgmt. com., elected chmn. So. Region Bd. Govs. 1989), Jacksonville area C. of C., San Jose Club, River Club (Jacksonville), Ponte Vedra Club. Republican. Roman Catholic. Avocations: golf, reading, spectator sports. Home: 1220 Journeys End Ln Jacksonville FL 32223-1753 Office: William Cook Agy Inc 225 Water St Ste 1600 Jacksonville FL 32202-5156

SCHRAMM, DAVID NORMAN, astrophysicist, educator; b. St. Louis, Oct. 25, 1945; s. Marvin M. and Betty Virginia (Math) S.; m. Judith J. Gibson, 1966; children from previous marriage: Cary, Brett. SB in Physics, MIT, 1967; PhD in Physics, Calif. Inst. Tech., 1971. Rsch. fellow in physics Calif. Inst. Tech., Pasadena, 1971-72; asst. prof. astronomy and physics U. Tex., Austin, 1972-74; assoc. prof. astronomy, astrophysics and physics Enrico Fermi Inst. and the Coll., U. Chgo., 1974-77, prof., 1977—, Louis Block prof. phys. scis., 1982—, prof. conceptual founds. of sci., 1983—, acting chmn. dept. astronomy and astrophysics, 1977, chmn., 1978-84; resident cosmologist Fermilab, 1982-84; cons., lectr. Adler Planetarium, Lawrence Livermore Lab., Los Alamos Nat. Lab.; organizer sci. confs.; frequent lectr. in field; chmn. bd. trustees Aspen Ctr. for Physics; bd. on physics and astronomy, exec. com. NRC, 1990—, chair, 1993—, mem. com. aviation weather systems aeronautics and space engring. bd., 1994—; bd. dirs. Astron. Rsch. Consortium, 1990—; pres. Big Bang Aviation, Inc.; bd. overseers Fermi Nat. Accelerator Lab., 1990—. Co-author: The Advanced Stages of Stellar Evolution, 1977, From Quarks to the Cosmos: Tools of Discovery, 1989, The Shadows of Creation: Dark Matter and the Structure of the Universe, 1991; co-editor: Supernovae, 1977, Fundamental Problems of Stellar Evolution, 1980, Essays in Nucleosynthesis, 1981, Gauge Theory and the Early Universe, 1988, Dark Matter in the Universe, 1990; editor profl. jours.; columnist Outside mag.; contbr. over 350 articles to profl. jours. Recipient Gravity Rsch. Found. prize, 1980, Humboldt award Fed. Republic Germany, 1987-88, Einstein medal Evotos U., Budapest, Hungary, 1989, Grad. Teaching award U. Chgo., 1994. Fellow Am. Acad. Arts and Scis., Am. Phys. Soc. (Lilienfeld prize 1993), Meteoritical Soc.; mem. Nat. Acad. Sci., Am. Astron. Soc. (Helen B. Warner prize 1978, exec. com. planetary sci. div. 1977-79, sec., treas. high energy astrophysics div. 1979-81), Am. Assn. Physics Tchrs. (Richtmeyer prize 1984), Astron. Soc. Pacific (Robert J. Trumpler award 1974), Internat. Astron. Union (comms. on cosmology, stellar evolution, high energy astrophysics), Hungarian Acad. Scis. (hon.), Aircraft Owners and Pilots Assn., British-N Am. Com., Alpine Club, Sigma Xi. Achievements include development of the cosmological interface with particle physics and the use of cosmological arguments to constrain fundamental physics; use of big bang to form the principle argument regarding the cosmological density of normal matter. Home: 155 N Harbor Dr Apt 5203 Chicago IL 60601-7326 Office: U Chgo AAC 140 5640 S Ellis Ave Chicago IL 60637-1433 also: 0150 Pitkin Mesa Dr Aspen CO 81611

SCHRAMM, TEXAS E., football league executive; b. Los Angeles, June 20, 1920; m. Marty Schramm; children: Mardee, Christi, Kandy. Grad., U. Tex. Publicity dir., then gen. mgr. Los Angeles Rams, 1947-57; asst. dir. sports CBS, 1957-60; gen. mgr. Dallas Cowboys, 1960-89, pres., resigned 1989; pres. World League of Am. Football, 1989-91. Named NFL Exec. of the Yr., The Sporting News, 1978; recipient Bert Bell award, 1978; named Dallas Father of the Yr., 1987. Office: NFL 410 Park Ave New York NY 10022

SCHRAUT, KENNETH CHARLES, mathematician, educator; b. Hillsboro, Ill., May 19, 1913; s. Charles Frederick and Theresa (Panska) S.; m. Virginia Haury, Feb. 5, 1952; 1 dau., Marilyn Szorc. A.B. with honors, U. Ill., 1936; M.A., U. Cin., 1938, Ph.D., 1940. Vis. instr. U. Notre Dame, summer 1940; instr. dept. math. U. Dayton, (Ohio), 1940-41; asst. prof. U. Dayton, 1941-44, assoc. prof., 1944-48, prof., 1948-72, chmn. dept. math., 1954-72, Disting. Service prof., 1972—; project dir. Research Ctr., 1951-54; vis. lectr. Ohio State U. Grad. Sch., 1946-49; acting prof. U. Cin. Grad. Sch., 1958-60; dir. NSF Math. Inst., Catholic U., Ponce, P.R., summer, 1959; chmn., bd. dirs. Honor Sems. of Met. Dayton, 1987-93. Recipient Lackner award, 1987. Mem. Am. Math. Soc., Math. Assn. Am., Am. Soc. Engring. Edn. (chmn. math. sect. 1967-68, 78-79, mem. exec. com. 1969-73, 76, program comm. 1977-78), Sigma Xi, Pi Mu Epsilon. Home: 448 Mirage Dr Kokomo IN 46901-7037

SCHRAUTH, WILLIAM LAWRENCE, banker, lawyer; b. Bklyn., Apr. 25, 1935; s. William L. and Louise (Rowland) S.; m. Nancy T. Tollner, Dec. 26, 1959; children—Christopher W., Anne, Michael J., Catherine A. B.A., St. Bonaventure U., Olean, N.Y., 1956; J.D., Fordham U., 1960. Bar: N.Y. 1960. Ptnr., Evans, Severn, Bankert & Peet and predecessor firms, Utica, N.Y., 1962-73; v.p. The Savs. Bank of Utica, 1973-74, exec. v.p., 1974-77, pres., 1977—; trustee RSI Retirement Trust. Bd. dirs. Oneida County Indsl. Devel. Corp., Utica. Mem. C. of C. Greater Utica Area. Republican. Office: The Savs Bank of Utica 233 Genesee St Utica NY 13501-2811

SCHREADLEY, RICHARD LEE, writer, retired newspaper editor; b. Harrisburg, Pa., Jan. 3, 1931; s. Harry Leroy and Flora Rebecca (McQuilken) S.; m. Doris Arlene Sheaffer, Dec. 18, 1952; 1 child, Rhys Leroy. B.A., Dickinson Coll., 1952; M.A., Tufts U., 1968, M.A.L.D., 1969, Ph.D., 1972. Reporter The News and Courier, Charleston, S.C., 1975; assoc. editor The Evening Post, Charleston, 1975-76; editorial page editor The Evening Post, 1976-77, editor, 1977-81; exec. editor The Evening Post and The News and Courier, 1981-88; assoc. editor and sr. writer mil. and polit. affairs The News and Courier, 1989. Author: From the Rivers to the Sea, The United States Navy in Vietnam. Chmn. Fgn. Affairs Forum of Charleston, 1987-88, mem. steering com., 1989. Served to comdr. USN, 1949-52, 56-73. Mem. Navy League, Ret. Officer Assn., Washington Light Infantry, Army-Navy Club of Washington, Country Club of Charleston. Home: 812 Clearview Dr Charleston SC 29412-4511

SCHRECK, ROBERT A., JR., lawyer; b. Buffalo, July 22, 1952. BS in Bus. Adminstrn., Georgetown U., 1974; MBA, Northwestern U., 1975, JD, 1978. Bar: Ill. 1978. Ptnr. McDermott, Will & Emery, Chgo., 1978—.

Mem. ABA, Chgo. Bar Asns., Chgo. Soc. Clubs. Office: McDermott Will & Emery 227 W Monroe St Chicago IL 60606-5016

SCHRECKINGER, SY EDWARD, advertising executive, consultant; b. Bklyn., Jan. 10, 1937; s. Robert and Bessie (Gable) S.; m. Linda Fiarman, Mar. 4, 1962; children: Jamie Fran, Jon Gary. B.F.A., Pratt Inst., 1958. Art dir. Sudler and Hennesey, N.Y.C., 1958-61; sr. art dir. Marschalk Co., N.Y.C., 1961-63; group supr. Grey Advt., N.Y.C., 1963-66; v.p., assoc. creative dir. Hicks & Greist, N.Y.C., 1966-69; sr. v.p., assoc. creative dir. Young & Rubicam Inc., N.Y.C., 1969-88; advert. and mktg. cons. Oceanside, N.Y., 1988—. Recipient Lion Venice Internat. Film Festival, 1972, Andy Ad Club, N.Y., 1965, 86, award Internat. Bus. Assn., Best award Hollywood Radio & TV Soc., 1971, Clio Am. TV Comml. Festival, 1967, 72, 82, 85, Effy, 1985. Jewish.

SCHREIBER, BERTRAM MANUEL, mathematics educator; b. Seattle, Nov. 4, 1940; s. Isador and Amy (Hurwitz) S.; m. Rita Ruth Stusser, June 30, 1963; children: Susannah M. Schreiber Bechhofer, Deborah H. Schreiber Shapiro, Abraham D., Elisabeth T. BA, Yeshiva U., 1962; MS, U. Wash., 1966, PhD, 1968. Asst. prof. Wayne State U., Detroit, 1968-71, assoc. prof., 1971-78, prof., 1978—, chair dept. math., 1987-90; vis. prof. Hebrew U., Jerusalem, 1975, Mich. State U., East Lansing, 1982-83, Nat. U. Singapore, 1992, U. New South Wales, Australia, 1992, Indian Statis. Inst., 1993, Tata Inst. Fund Res., Bombay, 1993, Bar Ilan U., 1993, Tel Aviv U., 1993, U. Utrecht, The Netherlands, 1993, U. Wroclaw, Poland, 1993. Contbr. articles to profl. jours. NSF grantee, 1968-87; Sci. and Engring. Rsch. Coun. Gt. Britain fellow U. Edinburgh, Scotland, 1976. Mem. Am. Math. Soc., Math. Assn. Am., Israel Math. Union, Edinburgh Math. Soc. Achievements include research in the fields of harmonic analysis, topological groups, and probability theory. Office: Wayne State U Dept Math Detroit MI 48202

SCHREIBER, GEORGE RICHARD, association executive, writer; b. Ironton, Ohio, July 4, 1922; s. George Joseph and Marie Frances (Heitzman) S.; m. Veva Jeanette Hopkins, May 14, 1945; children—Susan (Mrs. Arlan Shorey), George, Ellen (Mrs. Norman Hodge). A.B., St. Joseph's Coll., Rensselaer, Ind., 1943, L.H.D., 1974; M.A., U. Chgo., 1944. Exec. editor Billboard mag., 1945-60; editor, pub. Vend mag., 1946-66; editorial dir. Billboard Publs., 1966-70; pres., chief exec. officer Nat. Automatic Mdsg. Assn., Chgo., 1970-88, pres. emeritus, 1988—; mem. staff and faculty U. Chgo., 1944-46. Author: Verses from the River Country, 1941, What Makes News, 1943, Automatic Selling, 1954, A Concise History of Vending in the U.S.A, 1965, revised 2d edit., 1990, The Bobby Baker Affair—How to Make Millions in Washington, 1964; contbg. author: Handbook of Modern Marketing, 1986, Vending For Investors-How to Spot Phony Deals, 1994. Chmn. Glenview (Ill.) Plan Commn., 1962-64, mayor, 1964-67; chmn. Region 1, Chgo. Area Transp. Study Group, 1962-63; bd. dirs. Rockefeller Meml. Chapel, U. Chgo., 1944-45; trustee St. Joseph's Coll., 1964—, chmn., 1970-76, chmn. exec. com., 1978—. Recipient Jesse H. Neal award for editorial achievement, 1964; dedication of St. Joseph's Coll. (Ind.) G. Richard Schreiber Dept. Humanities, 1987. Mem. The Authors Guild Inc., Am. Bus. Press (editorial bd.), Assocs. Council, Am. Soc. Assn. Execs., Tavern Club, Internat. Club, Tower Club. Home: 735 Ravine Ave Lake Bluff IL 60044-2625

SCHREIBER, JEFFREY LEE, computer sales executive; b. Detroit, Jan. 18, 1952; s. Oscar and Rhodine Jean (Magids) S.; m. Ruth Ryan, May 27, 1983; children: Kelley Dawn, Joseph Ryan. BA, Wayne State U., 1975; JD, Coll. of William and Mary, 1978. Asst. to pres. Bramson Pub. Co., Bloomfield Hills, Mich., 1978-80; corp. sec. Oppenheimer Industries, Inc., Kansas City, Mo., 1980-82; mem. corp. legal staff Prime Computer, Inc., Oakbrook Terr., Ill., 1983-86; regional sales mgr. Novell, Inc., Arlington Heights, Ill., 1987-89; area sales mgr. AT&T Global Info. Solutions, Chgo., 1989-92, area network mgr., 1993—. Author, editor: Prime Computer's Business Practices Handbook, 1985. Chmn. youth adv. bd. First Citizens Bank of Troy, Mich., 1974; chmn. maj. acquisitions Little Friends Benefit Auction, Naperville, Ill., 1987; bd. dirs. Naperville United Way, 1988-94, v.p., 1993-94; mem. Naperville Bd. Zoning Appeals, 1990—. Mem. ABA, Chgo. Coun. on Fgn. Rels., Bus. Tech. Assocs.(chartered), Naperville C. of C. (steering com. 1986-87), Jaycees (v.p. Naperville chpt. 1986-87, Key Man award 1987), Coun. Telecomms. Execs. (conf. bd.), Kiwanis (bd. dirs. Oak Park, Mich. chpt. 1973-74), Cress Creek Country Club, Phi Beta Kappa. Avocations: lecturing on business and government ethics. Home: 93 Claremont Dr Naperville IL 60540-4150 Office: AT&T Global Info Solutions 7400 N Caldwell Ave Niles IL 60714-3852

SCHREIBER, MARVIN MANDEL, agronomist, educator; b. Springfield, Mass., Oct. 17, 1925; s. William and Florence Schreiber; m. Phyllis E. Altman, Dec. 18, 1949; 1 child, Michelle. BS, U. Mass., 1950; MS, U. Ariz., 1951; PhD, Cornell U., 1954. Asst. prof. dept. agronomy Cornell U., Ithaca, N.Y., 1954-59; assoc. prof. dept. botany and plant pathology Purdue U., West Lafayette, Ind., 1959-73—, prof., 1973—; rsch. agronomist Agrl. Rsch. Svc. USDA, West Lafayette, 1959—. Fellow AAAS, Am. Soc. Agronomy, Weed Sci. Soc. Am.; mem. Internat. Weed Sci. Soc. (pres. 1979-81), Controlled Release Soc., Coun. Agrl. Sci. and Tech., Sigma Xi. Avocations: golf, gardening. Office: Dept Botany & Plant Pathology Purdue U Lilly Hall Life Scis West Lafayette IN 47907

SCHREIBER, MELVYN HIRSH, radiologist; b. Galveston, Tex., May 28, 1931; s. Edward and Sue Schreiber; m. Laurentina; children—William, Diane, Karen, Lori. M.D., U. Tex. Med. Br., Galveston, 1955. Diplomate: Am. Bd. Radiology (trustee 1987—). Intern U. Tex. Med. Br., Galveston, 1955-56; resident U. Tex. Med. Br., 1956-59, asst. prof. radiology, 1961-64, asso. prof., 1964-67, 1967—, chmn. dept. radiology, 1976-91. Author: (with Robert N. Cooley) Radiology of the Heart and Great Vessels, 1978. Served as capt. M.C. U.S. Army, 1959-61. Markle Found. scholar, 1963-68. Fellow Am. Coll. Radiology; mem. Assn. Univ. Radiologists (pres. 1974-75). Office: U Tex Med Br Dept Radiology Galveston TX 77555

SCHREIBER, PAUL SOLOMON, lawyer; b. Krakow, Poland, Mar. 29, 1941; came to U.S., 1949; s. John and Betty (Silber) S.; m. Joan A. Perlmutter, Mar. 20, 1971; children: Douglas Arun, Stacey Lauren. BS, CCNY, 1963; LLB, NYU, 1966, LLM, 1967; postgrad., U. Paris, 1967-68. Bar: N.Y. 1966. Assoc. Marshal, Bratter, Greene, Allison & Tucker, N.Y.C., 1969-76, ptnr., 1976-82; ptnr. Kramer, Levin, Naftalis, Nessen, Kamin & Frankel, N.Y.C., 1982-94, Shearman & Sterling, N.Y.C., 1994—; bd. dirs. Harbor Trust Co., Hoboken, N.J., 1985-92. Editor: Annual Survey Am. Law; co-author articles, papers and revs. Trustee, v.p. Park Ave. Synagogue, N.Y.C., 1985—; bd. dirs. Am. Friends of the Rambam Med. Ctr., N.Y.C., 1989—, N.Y.C. chpt. of Nat. Multiple Sclerosis Soc., 1991—, Sch. for Strings, 1994—; bd. overseers Rabbinical Sch. Jewish Theol. Sem., 1995—. Arthur Garfield Hayes fellow; Ford Found. fellow. Democrat. Jewish. Office: Shearman & Sterling 599 Lexington Ave New York NY 10022

SCHREIBER, SALLY ANN, lawyer; b. El Paso, Tex., July 23, 1951; d. Warren Thomas and Joyce (Honey) S.; children: Amanda Honey, Ryan Thorp Luther. BA, U. N.Mex., 1973; JD, Stanford U., 1976. Bar: Calif. 1976, Tex. 1977. Assoc. Johnson & Swanson, Dallas, 1976-81, ptnr., 1981-89; mem. firm Johnson & Gibbs, P.C., Dallas, 1989-93; of counsel Cox & Smith, Inc., Dallas, 1993-94; shareholder Munsch Hardt Kopf Harr & Dinan, P.C., Dallas, 1994—; spkr. Advanced Mgmt. Rsch. Internat., Dallas, 1984, U. Tex., Austin, 1984, 89, 91, 93, Houston, 1994, Dallas, 1995, State Bar of Tex., Dallas, 1989, Lubbock, Arlignton, San Antonio, 1990, Houston, 1994, South Tex. Coll. Law, Houston, 1990, 94. Editor Stanford U. Law Rev., 1975-76; co-author paper Internat. Bar Assn., 1986. Bd. dirs. The Lyric Opera of Dallas, 1982-86, bd. trustees, 1986-90; mem. law sch. bd. vis. Stanford (Calif.) U., 1981-84; dir. Tex. Bus. Law Found., 1993—, treas., 1994—. Mem. ABA, Tex. Bar Assn. (revision corp. law com. 1981—, vice chair 1993—, ptnrship. law com. 1985—, ltd. liability company com. 1992—, opinion com. 1989—), Calif. Bar Assn., Dallas Bar Assn. Home: 2737 Purdue Ave Dallas TX 75225-7910 Office: Munsch Hardt Kopf Harr & Dinan PC 4000 Fountain Pl 1445 Ross Ave Dallas TX 75202

SCHREIBER, WILLIAM FRANCIS, electrical engineering educator; b. Bklyn., Sept. 18, 1925; s. William B. and Frances (Diamond) S.; m. Marian Connor, Dec. 29, 1979; children—Robert, Peter, Carol. B.S., Columbia U.,

1945, M.S., 1947; Ph.D., Harvard U., 1953. Jr. engr. Sylvania Co., Bayside, N.Y., 1947-49; scientist Technicolor Corp., Los Angeles, 1953-59; assoc. prof. elec. engring. MIT, Cambridge, 1959-68, prof., 1968-90, Bernard Gordon prof., 1980-83; prof. emeritus EE, sr. lectr. MIT; vis. prof. Indian Inst. Tech., Kanpur, 1964-66, U. Que., Can., 1981, 91-92, Swiss Fed. Inst. Tech., 1990. Contbr. articles to profl. jours. Patentee in field. Served with USNR, 1945-46. Recipient honors award Tech. Assn. Graphic Arts, David Sarnoff gold medal Soc. Motion Picture and TV Engrs., 1990. Fellow IEEE, Soc. Motion Picture and TV Engrs.; mem. Soc. Photo-Optical Instrumentation Engrs., Nat. Acad. Engring. Office: 36-545 MIT Cambridge MA 02139

SCHREIER, PETER, tenor; b. Meissen, Germany, July 29, 1935. Ed., Dresden Hochschule für Musik, Germany. With Dresden State Opera, Germany, 1959-63, Berlin Staatsoper, Germany, 1963. Appearances include Vienna State Opera, Salzburg Festival, La Scala, Milan, Sadler's Wells, London, Met. Opera, N.Y.C., Teatro Colon, Buenos Aires; recital debut London, 1978; debut as conductor, 1969; has conducted recordings of several choral works by J.S. Bach and Mozart. Office: Kammersänger, Calberlastr 13, D-01326 Dresden Germany

SCHREINER, ALBERT WILLIAM, physician, educator; b. Cin., Feb. 15, 1926; s. Albert William and Ruth Mary (Neuer) S.; m. Jean Tellstrom, Dec. 12, 1953; 1 child, David William. BS, U. Cin., 1947, MD, 1949. Diplomate: Am. Bd. Internal Medicine. Clin. investigator VA Hosp., Cin., 1957-59, chief med. service, 1959-68, dir. dept. internal medicine, 1968-93; dir. resident program internal medicine Christ Hosp., Cin., 1978-87; mem. faculty U. Cin. Coll. Medicine, 1955—, assoc. prof. medicine, 1962-67, prof. internal medicine, 1967—; attending physician Cin. Gen. Hosp., 1957—; cons. to med. dir. Gen. Electric, 1987—; med. dirs. United Home Care Hospice, 1993—, United Home Care Agy. Contbr. articles to tech. jours. Bd. dirs., chmn. health com. Community Action Commn., 1968-701 trustee Drake Meml. Hosp., 1975-78, Leukemia Found. Southwest Ohio, Cancer Control, Am. Cancer Soc., bd. dirs. Hamilton County unit, 1990; bd. dirs. Gamble Inst. Med. Rsch., Cin., 1991—. Fellow ACP; mem. N.Y. Acad. Scis., Am. Fedn. Clin. Rsch., Ohio Med. Assn., Ohio Soc. Internal Medicine (trustee 1978, sec.-treas. 1981-85, v.p 1982-83, pres. 1984-85), Clin. Soc. Internal Medicine (pres. 1979-80), Assn. Program Dirs. Internal Medicine, Am. Soc. Clin. Rsch. Program Dirs. Internal Medicine, Am. Leukemia Soc. (med. adv. exec. bd.), Am. Cancer Soc. (bd. dirs. Hamilton County unit 1990), Phi Beta Kappa, Sigma Xi. Episcopalian. Home: 8525 Given Rd Cincinnati OH 45243-1159 Office: 2139 Auburn Ave Cincinnati OH 45219-2906

SCHREINER, GEORGE E., nephrologist, educator, writer; b. Buffalo, Apr. 26, 1922; s. George Frederick and Eleanor (Kreig) S.; m. Joanne Baker, Apr. 3, 1948; children: George F., Mary E., Meredith Schreiner Maclay, William P., Sara B. Schreiner Kendall, Lise Schreiner Salmon, Peter K. (dec.). AB magna cum laude, Canisius Coll., 1943, HLD (hon.), 1973; MD cum laude, Georgetown U., 1946, HLD, 1973, ScD (hon.), 1987. Intern Boston City Hosp., 1946-47; fellow in nephrology N.Y. U., 1947-50; resident in medicine Washington VA Hosp., 1950-51; dir. renal clinic Georgetown U. Hosp., 1951-52, 55-61, instr. medicine, 1955-58, asst. prof. medicine, 1958-61, assoc. prof. medicine, dir. renal and electrolyte div., 1961-70, prof. medicine, dir. nephrology div., 1970-87, Disting. prof. medicine, 1987—; mem. staff Arlington Hosp., D.C. Gen. Hosp.; cons. VA Hosp., Walter Reed Army Hosp., Speakers Bur., Merck, Hoechst-Roussel, Baxter, George E. Schreiner Premed. Ctr., Canisius Coll. Editor in chief Am. Soc. Artificial Internal Organs, 1957-86, editor emeritus, 1986—; editor in chief: Procs. of Clin. Dialysis, Transplant Forum and Controveries in Nephrology, 1979-84; contbr. chpts. to books, articles to profl. jours. Bd. dirs. Washington Heart Assn.; bd. trustees Internat. Soc. for Art Orgns., 1986—; bd. sponsors Nat. Kidney Found.; governing bd. Ctr. for Crisis Counseling, Washington; mem. com. academics, coun. devel., bd. trustees Canisius Coll., Buffalo, 1988-94. Recipient Davidson award Med. Soc. D.C., Pres.'s award, 1979, David Hume award Nat. Kidney Found., 1980, Pub. Svc. award NASA, Nettuno d'Argento award U. Bologna, 1988, Achievement award Am. Assn. Kidney Patients, Laureate award Am. Coll. Physicians, Washington; guest of honor Greece Soc. Nephrology-Internat. Congress on Acute Renal Failure. Fellow ACP, Royal Soc. Physicians and Surgeons (Glasgow, Walton lectr.); mem. Soc. Exptl. Biology, Nat. Drug Rsch. Bd., Am. Soc. Physiology, Am. Soc. Pharmacology and Clin. Therapeutics, So. Salt, Water and Kidney Club, Am. Soc. Artificial Internal Organs (past pres.), Internat. Soc. Artificial Organs (life trustee), Nat. Kidney Found. (past pres.), Internat. Soc. Nephrology (pres. 1978-81, past pres., mem. exec. com. 1981-84), Am. Soc. Nephrology (past pres., John Peters award 1989), Assn. Am. Physicians, Am. Soc. Clin. Investigation, Am. Fedn. for Clin. Rsch. (past pres., past treas.), D.C. Med. Soc., Washington Heart Assn. (past pres.), Renal Transplant Physicians, Coun. Transplantation, Am. Soc. Hypertension, Am. Clin. and Climatologic Assn., Wash. Acad. Medicine (admission com. 1987-90, chmn. 1990), Cosmos Club (Washington), Duckwoods Country Club (Kitty Hawk, N.C.), Tralee Golf Club (Kerry, Ireland). Roman Catholic. Home: PO Box 199 Great Falls VA 22066-0199 Office: Georgetown U Hosp 3800 Reservoir Rd NW Washington DC 20007-2196

SCHREINER, JOHN CHRISTIAN, economics consultant, software publisher; b. Los Angeles, Nov. 2, 1933; s. Alexander and Margaret S.; m. Marie Nielsen, June 19, 1967; children: Christian Alexander, Carl Arthur, Elizabeth, Nathan Alexander. B.S.M.E., U. Utah, 1958; M.B.A., Harvard U., 1960; Ph.D., UCLA, 1970. Chartered fin. analyst. Design engr. Eimco Corp., Salt Lake City and N.Y.C., 1957-59; credit exec. James Talcott, Inc., N.Y.C. and Boston, 1960-65; lectr. mgmt. U. Utah, 1965-66; mem. faculty Grad. Sch. Mgmt., U. Minn., Mpls., 1969-84; chmn. dept. fin. and ins. Grad. Sch. Mgmt., U. Minn., 1973-74, 76-81; pres. The Sebastian Group, Inc., 1984—; dir. Deluxe Corp.; cons. to corps. and govt. agys. Co-author: Executive Recruiting: How Companies Obtain Management Talent, 1960; contbr. articles to profl. jours. Mem. Fin. Execs. Inst., Fin. Analysts Fedn., Tau Beta Pi, Phi Kappa Phi. Republican. Mem. Ch. Jesus Christ of Latter-day Saints (missionary, Ger. 1953-56). Club: Harvard Bus. Sch. Minn. Office: The Sebastian Group Inc 5851 Duluth St Minneapolis MN 55422-3946

SCHREMPF, DETLEF, professional basketball player; b. Leverkusen, Germany, Jan. 21, 1963. Student, U. Washington. Forward Dallas Mavericks, 1985-89, Indiana Pacers, 1989-93, Seattle Supersonics, 1993—; player West German Olympic Team, 1984, 92. Recipient Sixth Man award NBA, 1991, 92; mem. NBA All-Star team, 1993. *

SCHREMS, JOHN JOSEPH (JACK SCHREMS), political science educator; b. Saginaw, Mich., July 8, 1936; s. Michael Clement and Catherine (Berghoff) S.; m. Mellie Tirador, Jan. 2, 1960; children: Juanita, Josephine, Maria, John M., George. BA, Aquinas Coll., 1958; MA, Cath. U. Am., 1960, PhD, 1965. Instr. Mt. St. Mary's Coll., Emmitsburg, Md., 1961-65; asst. prof. Villanova (Pa.) U., 1965-82, assoc. prof., 1982-86, prof., 1986—; chmn. polit. sci. dept. Villanova U., 1988-93, dir. gen. arts maj., 1993—. Author: Principles of Politics, 1986; editor: Intelligibility of Political Philosophy, 1989, Future Politics, 1971; contbr. articles to profl. jours. Roman Catholic. Office: Villanova U Polit Sci Dept Villanova PA 19085

SCHRENK, WALTER JOHN, research chemical engineer; b. Toledo, Feb. 12, 1933. BS, U. Mich., 1955. Sr. rsch. scientist Dow Chem. Co., Midland, Mich., 1955—. Fellow ASME, Soc. Plastics Engrs. (Fred. O. Conley award 1987, Jack Barney award 1987), Soc. Optical Engrs., Polymer Processing Soc. (Hall of Fame 1986); mem. NAE. Achievements include fabrication of polymers and polymer processing with emphasis on multilayer coextrusion of polymer films and sheets, orientation and enhanced properties by control of supramolecular structure thru processing. Office: Dow Chemical Co 2030 Dow Ctr Bldg 1702 Midland MI 48674*

SCHRENK, W(ILLI) JUERGEN, chemicals executive; b. Dachau, Fed. Republic of Germany, June 19, 1945; came to U.S., 1972; s. Willi Schrenk and Irmgard (Urbanek) Meinhardt; m. Ruth Halfenberg, Nov. 10, 1971; 1 child, Ralph Michael. PhD, Cologne U., Fed. Republic of Germany, 1972. Rsch. fellow Harvard Med. Sch., Boston, 1972-73; guest scientist Nat. Cancer Inst., Bethesda, Md., 1972-73; asst. rsch. prof. U. Calif., Santa Barbara, 1974-77; sr. scientist Abbott Labs., North Chicago, Ill., 1977-79; sci. dir. Boehringer Mannheim Corp., Tutzing, Germany, 1979-85; sr. dir. R & D Boehringer Mannheim Corp., Indpls., 1986-89; sr. v.p. R & D Gen-Probe, San Diego, 1989-90; v.p. R & D Wampole Labs., Cranbury, N.J.,

1990-93; v.p. tech. mgmt. Corange Internat. Ltd., Bermuda, 1994—. Contbr. articles to profl. jours; patentee in field. Established nature preserves in U.S. and Fed. Republic of Germany, 1975-85. Fellow Fed. Republic of Germany, 1964-70, Deutsche Forschungs-Gemeinschaft, 1972-74. Mem. Nature Conservancy, World Wildlife Fund. Avocations: nature photography, skiing, hiking, traveling. Home: 1 Stream Valley Ct Laytonsville MD 20882-1273 Office: Corange Technology Office 101 Orchard Ridge Dr Gaithersburg MD 20878

SCHREYER, LESLIE JOHN, lawyer; b. N.Y.C., Apr. 11, 1946; s. Oscar and Greta (Loebl) S.; m. Judith Camps, Sept. 25, 1994; 1 child, Gabrielle. BA, Columbia U., 1967; LLB, Yale U., 1970; LLM in Taxation, N.Y.U., 1977. Bar: N.Y. 1971. Assoc. Chadbourne & Parke, N.Y.C., 1970-71, 72-78, ptnr., 1978-81, 83—; adj. assoc. prof. law NYU, 1990—; cons. Am. Law Inst., Fed. Income Tax Project on Internat. Aspects of U.S. Income Taxation, 1983-91. Author: (with others) Foreign Tax Credit, 1980; contbr. numerous articles to profl. jours. Bd. dirs. The Poster Soc., N.Y.C., 1985-93, 910 Park Ave Corp., 1993-94. Mem. ABA, Internat. Bar Assn., Internat. Fiscal Assn., N.Y. State Bar Assn., Assn. of Bar of City of N.Y., Phi Beta Kappa. Republican. Home: 60 East End Ave New York NY 10028 Office: Chadbourne & Parke 30 Rockefeller Plz New York NY 10112-0001

SCHREYER, WILLIAM ALLEN, retired investment firm executive; b. Williamsport, Pa., Jan. 13, 1928; s. William L. and Elizabeth (Engel) S.; m. Joan Legg, Oct. 17, 1953; 1 child, DrueAnne Frazier. BA, Pa. State U., 1948. With Merrill Lynch, Inc. and predecessors, N.Y.C., 1948-93; CEO Merrill Lynch & Co., N.Y.C., 1984-92, chmn., 1985-93; chmn. emeritus, 1993—; bd. dirs. Schering-Plough Corp., Callaway Golf Co., Deere & Co., True North Comm. Inc., Willis Corroon Group. Trustee Ctr. for Strategic and Internat. Studies, Pa. State U., chmn. bd. trustees. With USAF, 1955-56. Mem. Econ. Club. N.Y., River Club, Links Club, Saturn Club (Buffalo), Springdale Golf Club (Nassau), Bedens Brook Club (Princeton), Eldorado Country Club, Georgetown Club, Met. Club (Washington), Old Baldy Club (Wyo.), Knights of Malta. Roman Catholic. Office: Merrill Lynch & Co Inc 800 Scudders Mill Rd Plainsboro NJ 08536-1606

SCHRIBER, THOMAS JUDE, computer and information systems educator, researcher; b. Flint, Mich., Dec. 28, 1935; s. Francis Charles and Alma Marie (Jeannot) S.; m. Cornelia Ann Sneed, June 24, 1967; children: Sarah Elizabeth, John Cornelius, Maria Adams. B.S., U. Notre Dame, 1957; M.S.E., U. Mich., 1958, M.A. in Math., 1959, Ph.D., 1964. Asst. prof. Eastern Mich. U., Ypsilanti, 1963-66; asst. prof. U. Mich., Ann Arbor, 1966-69, assoc. prof., 1969-72, prof. Grad. Sch. Bus. Adminstrn., 1972—; chmn. simulation using GPSS U. Mich., 1969-92, U. Louvain, Belgium, 1987-89; vis. scholar Stanford U., Palo Alto, Calif., 1972-73, Swiss Fed. Tech. U., Zurich, 1987, Nat. U. Singapore, 1995; cons. Ford Motor Co., Dearborn, Mich., 1970-72, Stanford Research Inst., Palo Alto, 1973, Monsanto Chem. Co., St. Louis, 1978, Wolverine Software Corp., Annandale, Va., 1981-94, Occidental Petroleum, 1982, Exxon Prodn. Research, Houston, 1984-85, Gen. Motors Corp., Troy, Mich., 1984-85, Electronic Data Systems, Troy, 1985-86; chmn. bd. Winter Simulation Conf. Series, 1981-83; mem. U.S.-USSR Joint Sci. and Tech. Exchange Agreements, Moscow, 1977. Author: Fundamentals of Flowcharting, 1969, FORTRAN Case Studies for Business Applications, 1970, Simulation Using GPSS, 1974, An Introduction to Simulation Using GPSS/H, 1991; editor: FORTRAN Applications in Business Administration, 3 vol. series, 1970, 71, 74; co-editor: Proceedings of the 1976 Bicentennial Winter Simulation Conference, 1976; assoc. editor: Internat. Jour. of Flexible Mfg. Systems, 1987-95. NSF fellow, 1957-60; Fulbright fellow, 1961; Office Naval Research grantee, 1981-83. Fellow Decision Scis. Inst.; mem. Assn. Computing Machinery (nat. lectr. 1969-70), Inst. Mgmt. Scis., Ops. Research Soc. Am., Soc. for Computer Simulation. Roman Catholic. Home: 2116 Dorset Rd Ann Arbor MI 48104-2604 Office: U Mich Grad Sch Bus Adminstrn Ann Arbor MI 48109

SCHRIEFFER, JOHN ROBERT, physics educator, science administrator; b. Oak Park, Ill., May 31, 1931; s. John Henry and Louise (Anderson) S.; m. Anne Grete Thomsen, Dec. 30, 1960; children: Anne Bolette, Paul Karsten, Anne Regina. BS, MIT, 1953; MS, U. Ill., 1954, PhD, 1957, ScD, 1974; ScD (hon.), Tech. U., Munich, Germany, 1968, U. Geneva, 1968, U. Pa., 1973, U. Cin., 1977, U. Tel Aviv 1987, U. Ala., 1990. NSF postdoctoral fellow U. Birmingham, Eng., also; Niels Bohr Inst., Copenhagen, 1957-58; asst. prof. U. Chgo., 1958-59; asst. prof., then assoc. prof. U. Ill., 1959-62; prof. U. Pa., Phila., 1962-79; Mary Amanda Wood prof. physics U. Pa., 1964-79; Andrew D. White prof. at large Cornell U., 1969-75; prof. U. Calif., Santa Barbara, 1980-91, Chancellor's prof., 1984-91, dir. Inst. for Theoretical Physics, 1984-89; Univ. prof. Fla. State U., Tallahassee, 1992—, chief scientist Nat. High Magnetic Field Lab., 1992—. Author: Theory of Superconductivity, 1964. Guggenheim fellow Copenhagen, 1967; Los Alamos Nat. Lab. fellow; Recipient Comstock prize Nat. Acad. Sci.; Nobel Prize for Physics, 1972; John Ericsson medal Am. Soc. Swedish Engrs., 1976; Alumni Achievement award U. Ill., 1979; recipient Nat. Medal of Sci., 1984; Exxon faculty fellow, 1979-89. Fellow Am. Phys. Soc. (v.p. 1994, pres.-elect 1995, Oliver E. Buckley solid state physics prize 1986); mem. NAS (coun. 1990—), Am. Acad. Arts and Scis., Coun. Nat. Acad. Sci., Royal Danish Acad. Scis. and Letters, Acad. Sci. USSR. Office: Fla State U NHMFL 1800 E Paul Dirac Dr Tallahassee FL 32306-4005

SCHRIER, ARNOLD, historian, educator; b. N.Y.C., May 30, 1925; s. Samuel and Yetta (Levine) S.; m. Sondra Weinshelbaum, June 12, 1949; children—Susan Lynn, Jay Alan, Linda Lee, Paula Kay. Student, Bethany Coll., W.Va., 1943-44, Ohio Wesleyan U., 1944-45; B.S., Northwestern U., 1949, M.A., 1950, Ph.D. (Social Sci. Research Council fellow, Univ. fellow), 1956. Asst. prof. history U. Cin., 1956-61, assoc. prof., 1961-66, prof., 1966—, dir. grad. studies history, 1969-78, Walter C. Langsam prof. modern European history, 1972-95; Walter C. Langsam prof. history emeritus, 1995—; vis. asst. prof. history Northwestern U., Evanston, Ill., 1960; vis. assoc. prof. history Ind. U., Bloomington, 1965-66; vis. lectr. Russian history Duke U., 1966; disting. vis. prof. U.S. Air Force Acad., 1983-84; dir. NDEA Inst. World History for Secondary Sch. Tchrs., U. Cin., 1965; Am. del. Joint U.S.-USSR Textbook Study Commn., 1989. Author: Ireland and the American Emigration, 1958, reissued, 1970, The Development of Civilization, 1961-62, Modern European Civilization, 1963, Living World History, 1964, rev., 1993, Twentieth Century World, 1974, History and Life: the World and Its People, 1977, rev., 1993, A Russian Looks at America, 1979. Pres. Ohio Acad. History, 1973-74, Midwest Slavic Conf., 1980. Served with USNR, 1943-46, 52-54. Recipient Disting. Svc. award Ohio Acad. History, 1992; Am. Council Learned Socs. fgn. area fellow, 1963-64. Mem. World History Assn. (v.p. 1986-88, pres. 1988-90). Home: 10 Diplomat Dr Cincinnati OH 45215-2073 Office: Univ Cincinnati Dept History Mail Location 373 Cincinnati OH 45221

SCHRIER, STANLEY LEONARD, physician, educator; b. N.Y.C., Jan. 2, 1929; s. Harry and Nettie (Schwartz) S.; m. Peggy Helen Pepper, June 6, 1953; children: Rachel, Leslie, David. A.B., U. Colo., 1949; M.D., Johns Hopkins U., 1954. Diplomate Am. Bd. Internal Medicine (chmn. subsplty. bd. hematology). Intern Oster Med. Service, Johns Hopkins Hosp., 1954-55; resident U. Mich., Ann Arbor, 1955-56, U. Chgo. Hosp., 1958-59; sr. asst. surgeon USPHS, 1956-58; instr. medicine Stanford Sch. Medicine, Calif., 1959-60; asst. prof. medicine Stanford Sch. Medicine, 1960-63, assoc. prof., 1963-72, prof. medicine, 1972—, chief divsn. hematology, 1968-94; vis. prof. Oxford U., Eng., 1975-76, Hebrew U., Jerusalem, 1982-83. John and Mary Markle scholar, 1961; recipient Kaiser award Stanford U., 1972, Kaiser award Stanford U., 1974, 75, David Rytand award, 1982, Eleanor Roosevelt Union Internationale Contre le Cancer award, 1975-76. Mem. Am. Soc. Hematology (exec. com.), Am. Physiol. Soc., Soc. Exptl. Biology and Medicine, Am. Soc. Clin. Investigation, Western Assn. Physicians. Democrat. Jewish. Office: Stanford U Sch Medicine 300 Pasteur Dr Palo Alto CA 94304-2203

SCHRIESHEIM, ALAN, research administrator; b. N.Y.C., Mar. 8, 1930; s. Morton and Frances (Greenberg) S.; m. Beatrice D. Brand, June 28, 1953; children: Laura Lynn, Robert Alan. BS in Chemistry, Poly. Inst. Bklyn., 1951; PhD in Phys. Organic Chemistry, Pa. State U., 1954; DSc (hon.), No. Ill. U., 1991; PhD (hon.), Ill. Inst. Tech., Chgo., 1992. Chemist Nat. Bur. Standards, 1954-56; with Exxon Research & Engring. Co., 1956-83, dir.

corp. research, 1975-79; gen. mgr. Exxon Engring., 1979-83; sr. dep. lab. dir., chief operating officer Argonne Nat. Lab., 1983-84, lab. dir., CEO, 1984—; prof. chemistry dept. U. Chgo., 1984—; Karcher lectr. U. Okla., 1977; Hurd lectr. Northwestern U., 1980; Rosensteil lectr. Brandeis U., 1982; Welch Found. lectr., 1987; com. svc. NRC, 1980—; vis. com. chemistry dept. MIT, 1977-82; mem. vis. com. mech. engring. and aerospace dept. Princeton (N.J.) U., 1983-87, mem. vis. com. chemistry dept., 1983-87; mem. Pure and Applied Chemistry Com.; del. to People's Republic of China, 1978; mem. Presdl. Nat. Commn. on Superconductivity, 1989-91, U.S.-USSR Joint Commn. on Basic Sci. Rsch, 1990—; mem. U.S. nat com. Internat. Union Pure and Applied Chemistry, 1982-85; mem. magnetic fusion adv. com. Div. Phys. Scis. U. Chgo. Magnetic Fusion adv. com. to U.S. DOE, 1983-86; mem. Dept. Energy Rsch. Adv. Bd., 1983-85, Congl. Adv. Com. on Sci. and Tech., 1985—; mem. vis. comes Stanford (Calif.) U., U. Utah, Tex. A&M U., Lehigh U.; bd. govs. Argonne Nat. Lab.; mem. adv. com. on space systems and tech. NASA, 1987—; mem. nuclear engring. and engring. physics vis. com. U. Wis., Madison; mem. Coun. Gt. Lakes Govs. Regional Econ. Devel. Commn. 1987—, rev. bd. Compact Ignition Tomamak Princeton U., 1988-91; advisor Sears Investment Mgmt. Co., 1988-89; bd. dirs. Petroleum Rsch. Fund, ARCH Devel. Corp., HEICO, Valley Indsl. Assn., Coun. on Superconductivity for Am. Competitiveness; mem. State of Ill. Commn. on the Future of Pub. Svc., 1990-92; co-chair Indsl. Rsch. Inst. Nat. Labs./Industry Panel, 1984-87; mem. Nat Acad. Engring. Adv. Commn. on Tech. and Soc., 1991-92, Sun Electric Corp. Bd., 1991-92, U.S. House of Reps. subcom. on Sci.-Adv. Group on Renewing U.S. Sci. Policy, 1992—; mem. Chgo. Acad. of Scis. acad. coun., 1994—. Bd. editors Chem. Tech., 1970-85; mem. editl. bd. Rsch. and Devel., 1988-93, Superconductor Industry mag., 1988—; patentee in field. Mem. spl. vis. com. Field Mus. of Natural History, Chgo., 1987-88; bd. dirs. LaRabida Children's Hosp. and Rsch. Ctr., Children's Meml. Hosp., Children's Meml. Inst. for Edn. and Rsch.; trustee The Latin Sch. of Chgo., 1990-92; adv. bd. WBEZ Chicagland Pub. Radio Community, 1990—; mem. Conservation Found. DuPage County, 1983—, Econ. Devel. Adv. Commn. of DuPage County, 1984-88, State of Ill. Gov.'s Commn. on Sci. and Tech., 1986-90, Inst. for Ill. Council Advisors, 1988—, Ill. Coalition Bd. Dirs., 1989—, Inst. for Ill. Adv. Rev. Panel, 1986-88, NASA Sci. Tech. Adv. Com. Manpower Requirements Ad Hoc Rev. Team, 1988-91, State of Ill. Gov. Sci. and Exec. com., 1989—, U. Ill. Engring. Vis. com., Urbana-Champaign, 1986—; trustee Tchrs. Acad. for Math. and Sci. Tchrs. in Chgo., 1990—. Recipient Outstanding Alumni Fellow award Pa. State U., 1984; Disting. fellow Poly. U., 1989. Fellow AAAS (coun. del. chem. sect. 1986-92, bd. dirs. 1992—, sci. engring. and pub. policy com. 1992, standing com. audit 1992), N.Y. Acad. Scis.; mem. NAE (adv. com. tech. and soc. 1991-92, chair study fgn. participation in U.S. R&D 1993—, mem. program adv. com. 1992—), AIChE (AIChE awards com. 1992-97), Am. Chem. Soc. (Petroleum Chemistry award 1969, chmn. petroleum divsn., councilor, com. on chemistry and pub. affairs 1983-91, joint bd. coun. com. on sci. 1983-87, sci. adv. bd. coun. on chem. rsch. 1987-91), Am. Mgmt. Assn. (R&D coun. 1988—), Nat. Conf. Advancement Rsch. (conf. com. 1985—, site selection com. 1994), Am. Petroleum Inst. (com. on refinery equipment), Gas Rsch. Inst. (rsch. coordilear Soc., Rohm and Haas (bd. dirs.), Indsl. Rsch. Inst. (fed. adv. com. to Fed. Sci. and Tech. Com. 1992—, co-chmn. Nat. Labs. Indsl. Panel 1984-87), Carlton Club (bd. govs. 1992—), Cosmos Club, Chgo. Club, Econ. Club. Comml. Club, Sigma Xi, Phi Lambda Upsilon. Home: 1440 N Lake Shore Dr Apt 31ac Chicago IL 60610-1686 Office: Argonne Nat Lab 9700 Cass Ave Argonne IL 60439-4832

SCHRIEVER, BERNARD ADOLPH, management consultant; b. Bremen, Germany, Sept. 14, 1910; came to U.S., 1917, naturalized, 1923; s. Adolph Niholaus and Elizabeth (Milch) S.; m. Dora Brett, Jan. 3, 1938; children: Brett Arnold, Dodie Elizabeth Schriever Moeller, Barbara Alice Schriever Allan. B.S., Tex. A&M U., 1931; M.S.M.E., Stanford U., 1942; D.Sc. (hon.), Creighton U., 1958, Rider Coll., 1958, Adelphia Coll., 1959, Rollins Coll., 1959; D.Aero. Sc. (hon.), U. Mich., 1961; D.Eng. (hon.), Bklyn. Poly. Inst., 1961; LL.D. (hon.), Loyola U., Los Angeles, 1960. Commd. 2d lt. U.S. Army Air Force, 1938; advanced through grades to gen. U.S. Air Force, 1961; comdr. ICBM Program, 1954-59, AFSC, 1959-66; ret., 1966; chmn. bd. Schriever & McKee, Washington, 1971-87; coms. B.A. Schriever, 1987—; bd. dirs. Emerson Electric Co., Matra Aerospace Inc. Decorated D.S.M., D.S.M. with oak leaf cluster, Legion of Merit, Air medal, Purple Heart; named to Aviation Hall of Fame, 1980; recipient Forrestal award, 1987. Hon. fellow AIAA; mem. NAE, Am. Astron. Soc., Air Force Assn. Club: Burning Tree. Home: 4501 Dexter St NW Washington DC 20007-1116 Office: 2300 M St NW Ste 900 Washington DC 20037

SCHRIEVER, FRED MARTIN, energy, environmental and information technology executive; b. N.Y.C.; s. Samuel and Sara S.; m. Cheri G. Spatt; children: Melissa Ann, Elizabeth Ellen. BME, Poly. U. N.Y., 1956, MME, 1958. Registered profl. engr., N.Y., Wash. cert. mgmt. cons. Chief engr. div. Sperry Corp., N.Y.C., 1956-64; ptnr. Booz, Allen and Hamilton, N.Y.C. and Washington, 1964-71; sr. v.p. Reliance Group Holdings, Inc., N.Y.C., 1971—; chmn., pres. RCG Internat. Inc., N.Y.C., 1971—; chmn. Werner Mgmt. Consultants Inc., RCG Info. Tech., Inc., RCG Moody Ltd.; bd. dirs. RCG Hagler Bailly Inc. Fellow Inst. of Dirs., Inst. Mgmt. Consultants U.K.; mem. ASME, Inst. Mgmt. Consultants. Club: Metropolitan. Home: PO Box 32 Westport CT 06881-0032 Office: RCG Internat Inc 111 W 40th St New York NY 10018-2506

SCHRIMPER, VERNON L., manufacturing, marketing executive; b. Cedar Rapids, Iowa, Mar. 25, 1933; s. Clinton and Marie Lorene (Miller) S.; m. Marlene Lorrene Miller, May 9, 1959; children: Michael Charles, Kenneth Andrew, Laura Marie Schrimper Roling. BSME, Iowa State U., 1955; Cert. in Bus. Mgmt., Alexander Hamilton Inst., 1962. Registered profl. engr., Iowa. Design engr. Iowa Mfg. Co., Cedar Rapids, Iowa, 1955-61; chief research and devel. engr. Iowa Mfg. Co., Cedar Rapids, 1961-72, v.p. engring. dept., 1972-78, exec. v.p. ops. dept., 1978-83; exec v.p. Cedarapids, Inc. (formerly Iowa Mfg. Co.), Cedar Rapids, 1983—. Chmn. product safety coun. Constrn. Industry Mfg. Assn., Milw., 1986-92, legis. com., 1994-95; mem. z.r. adv. com. Am. Road & Transp. Builders, Washington, 1985-95, dir., 1994-95; mem. adv. coun. dept. mgmt. Iowa State U., 1986-88, advisor Coll. Engring., 1989-95; mem. Transp. Rsch. Bd., Washington, 1979-92. Trustee Brucemore Hist. Soc., Cedar Rapids, 1984-91; vice chmn. United Way, Cedar Rapids, 1977-78, dir. 1978-81; charter mem. adv. council dept. mech. engring. Iowa State U., 1987—. Recipient Disting. Svc. award Cedar Rapids Jaycees, 1964. Mem. ASME (sect. chmn. 1965-66), Am. Soc. Testing Materials, Soc. Automotive Engrs., Cedar Rapids Engring. Soc. (chmn. 1960-61), Assn. Asphalt Paving Techologists, Iowa Bus. and Industry Assn. (Legis Com.), Nat. Asphalt Pavement Assn., Constrn. Industry Mfg. Assn. (govt. affairs com. 1990-92), Nat. Stone Assn. (assoc. mem., StonePac Trustee, legis. and health and safety com. 1993-95), Cedar Rapids C. of C. (govt. com. 1956—), Phi Kappa Psi (pres. 1954-55). Republican. Methodist. Clubs: Cedar Rapids Country, Iowa State U. Cyclone, I Club (Cedar Rapids). Avocations: golf, camping, fishing, hunting, travel. Home: 1526 Matterhorn Dr NE Cedar Rapids IA 52402-3355 Office: Cedarapids Inc 916 16th St NE Cedar Rapids IA 52402-4602

SCHRIMSHER, JERRY JAMES, diversified financial services company executive; b. Homegrove, Tex., July 23, 1935; s. Archie A. and Lennie S.; m. Sherry L. Moore, July 29, 1966; children: Tasia C., Jerry J. II, Stan A. B of Career Arts in Mgmt./Aviation, Dallas Bapt. U., 1986; M of Liberal Arts, So. Meth. U., 1992. CLU, ChFC; registered investment advisor, SEC. Gen. foreman Tex. Instruments, Inc., Dallas, 1960-70; v.p. I.R.A., Dallas, 1970-74; pres. Am. Retirement, Dallas, 1974—; mem. Dallas Estate Planning, 1982; accident counselor FAA, Dallas, 1973—. Contbr. articles to profl. jours. With USAF, 1956-60. Mem. U.S. Parachute Assn. (life, bd. dirs. 1970-84), Tex. Parachute Assn. (pres. 1968-69), Dallas Parachute Assn. (pres. 1968-83, chief pilot 1979-83, chief instr. 1966-76). Avocations: flying, skydiving, photography. Home and Office: 1315 Cheyenne Dr Richardson TX 75080-3706

SCHRINER, JON LESLIE, sports medicine physician; b. Flint, Mich., Mar. 9, 1937; s. Alva Niel and Helena Ione (McLean) S.; m. Mary Patricia O'Keefe, May 25, 1963 (div. Oct. 1980); children: Jon, Lindsay, Laura, Joan; m. Delores Korb, Mar. 2, 1985 (div. Apr. 1987); m. Vicki Winlehaus, June 12, 1988. AS, Flint Community Coll., 1957; BA, Eastern Mich. U., 1959; DO, Kirksville Coll., 1963. Intern Flint Osteo. Hosp., 1963-64, staff physician Flushing (Mich.) Med. Ctr., 1963-81; physician, pres. Sports Medicine Rehab. Ctr., Flushing, 1981—; assoc. prof. clin. medicine Mich.

State U., East Lansing; staff St. Joseph's Hosp., Genesee Meml. Hosp.; team physician Flushing Community Schs., 1963—, Flint Gens. Hockey Club, 1980-84, Flint Spirits Hockey Club, 1986—. Contbr. articles to profl. jours. Pres. Bd. Edn. Flushing schs., 1968-76; dir. med. services Bobby Crim Road Race Spl. Olympics, Flint, 1978-86, Buick City Road Race, Flint, 1984-86; bd. dirs. United Way Genesee County, Mich., 1979, Am. Heart Assn., 1987-88. Recipient 23 Yr. Service award Flushing Community Schs., 1986, numerous community awards. Fellow Am. Coll. Sports Medicine; mem. Am. Osteo. Assn., Canadian Am. Med. Dental Assn. (bd. trustees 1986—), Profl. Ski Instrs. Assn. Roman Catholic. Club: Bruin of Genesee County (Sports Med. award 1987). Avocations: skiing, tennis, running, sailing. Home: 8022 Fawn Valley Dr Clarkston MI 48348-4540 Office: Sports Medicine Rehab Ctr 6045 W Pierson Rd Flushing MI 48433-2334

SCHRIVER, JOHN T., III, lawyer; b. Evanston, Ill., May 18, 1945. AB, Coll. of Holy Cross, 1967; JD, Georgetown U., 1971. Bar: Ill. 1971, Fla. 1972. Ptnr. McDermott, Will & Emery, Chgo. Mem. ABA, Chgo. Bar Assn., Fla. Bar. Office: McDermott Will & Emery 227 W Monroe St Chicago IL 60606-5016

SCHROCK, HAROLD ARTHUR, manufacturing company executive; b. Goshen, Ind., Apr. 10, 1915; s. Arthur E. and Anna (Shaner) S.; m. Thelma A. Hostetler, Sept. 3, 1938; children—Sara (Mrs. William Barrett), Susan (Mrs. John Graff), Cinda (Mrs. Stephen McKinney), Douglas. B.A, Goshen Coll., 1937. Chmn. bd. dirs. Starcraft Co., Goshen, 1967-71; pres. Goshen Sash & Door Co., Roper-Wright Mfg. Co., Smoker-Craft, Inc., New Paris, Earthway Products, Bristol, Ind., Goshen Iron & Metal Co.; chmn. 1st Nat. Bank of Goshen; v.p. Ind. Capital Corp., Ft. Wayne; pres. Ivy Terrace, Inc., Goshen, Marque, Inc., Goshen. Past pres. Greater Goshen Assn., Jr. Achievement, Goshen Gen. Hosp., Goshen Pub. Library; pres. Goshen Hosp. Found. Mem. Goshen C. of C. (pres. 1952). Republican. Lutheran (v.p. vestry). Clubs: Elcona Country (Goshen), Maplecrest Country (Goshen); John's Island (Vero Beach, Fla.); Rotary (past pres.). Home: 510 Carter Rd Goshen IN 46526-5210 Office: US 33 E Goshen IN 46526 Also: Goshen Sash & Door Co Inc 603-13 E Purl St Goshen IN 46526

SCHROCK, SIMON, retail executive; b. Oakland, Md., Dec. 28, 1936; s. Noah and Cora (Burkholder) S.; m. Eva Lena Yoder, June 7, 1959 (dec. Apr. 1962); m. Pauline Yoder, Sept. 29, 1963; children: Janice Yvonne, Eldon Laverne, Ivan Dale. With Eastern States Farm Supply Co., Oakland, Md., 1957-59, Children's Hosp., Washington, 1959-61, Copp Properties, 1961-75; pres. Choice Books of No. Va., Fairfax, 1975—; chmn. Choice Books Caribbean, 1976—. Author: Get on With Living, 1976, Price of Missing Life, 1981, One-Anothering, 1986, Vow-Keepers Vow-Breakers, A Smoother Journey, 1994. Contbr. articles to ch. jours. Chmn. Faith Christian Sch. Bd., 1977—; bishop Faith Christian Fellowship, Catlett, Va., 1981—. Avocations: traveling; camping; biking. Office: 11923 Lee Hwy Fairfax VA 22030-6708

SCHROCK, VIRGIL EDWIN, mechanical and nuclear engineer; b. San Diego, Jan. 22, 1926; s. Melvin J. and Madge (Ellis) S.; m. Virginia Lee Whorton, July 27, 1946; children: Douglas Richard, Nancy Grace. B.S., U. Wis., Madison, 1946, M.S., 1948; M.E., U. Calif., Berkeley, 1952. Registered profl. engr., Calif. Instr. U. Wis., 1946-48; mem. faculty U. Calif., Berkeley, 1948—; prof. nuclear engring. U. Calif., 1968—, asst. dean, 1968-74; prof. emeritus, 1991-94; prof. Grad. Sch. U. Calif., 1994—; cons. to govt. and industry. Contbr. articles to profl. jours. Served with USNR, 1943-46, 52-53. Grantee C.I.S.E., Milan, Italy, 1962-63, 74-75, also USAF, USN, AEC, NSF, NRC, Dept. Energy, Electric Power Research Inst.; recipient Glenn Murphy award Am. Soc. Engring. Edn., 1983; Japan Soc. Promotion Sci. research fellow, 1984. Fellow ASME (life, chmn. heat transfer divsn. 1976-77, tech. editor Jour. Heat Transfer 1977-83, Heat Transfer Meml. award 1985, heat transfer divsn. 50th anniversary award 1988, Best Paper award 1991), Am. Nuclear Soc. (chmn. thermal hydraulics divsn. 1980-81, Best Paper award 1985, Best Paper award 6th Internat. Conf. Nuclear Reactor Thermal Hydraulics 1993); mem. Am. Soc. for Engring. Edn. Home: 258 Orchard Rd Orinda CA 94563-3532 Office: U Calif Dept Nuclear Engring Berkeley CA 94720-1730

SCHRODER, ANDREA RUTH LUNDEEN, realtor; b. Moline, Ill., Jan. 10, 1944; d. Clifford Frederick and Betty Bernadine (Turpin) Lundeen; m. Stanley D. Schroder, Nov. 27, 1965; children: Stephanie, Katherine. BS, Iowa State U., 1965. Realtor 1st Realty, Des Moines, 1978-92, Iowa Realty, Des Moines, 1992—. Officer Housing Task Force, Des Moines, 1987-92; commr. Planning and Zoning, Urbandale, Iowa, 1988-92. Mem. Nat. Assn. Real Estate Execs., Urbandale C. of C., Des Moines C. of C., Phi Omicron Upsilon. Republican. Lutheran. Home: 4416 96th Ct Urbandale IA 50322-1364 Office: Iowa Realty 3424 E P True Pky Ste A West Des Moines IA 50265

SCHRODER, DIETER KARL, electrical engineering educator; b. Lübeck, Germany, June 18, 1935; came to U.S., 1964; s. Wilhelm and Martha (Werner) S.; m. Beverley Claire Parchment, Aug. 4, 1961; children: Mark, Derek. BSc, McGill U., Montreal, Que., Can., 1962, MSc, 1964; PhD, U. Ill., 1968. Sr. engr. research and devel. sect. Westinghouse Electric Corp., Pitts., 1968-73, fellow engr., 1973-77, adv. engr., 1977-79, mgr., 1979-81; prof. elec. engring. Ariz. State U., Tempe, 1981—; researcher Inst. Solid-State Physics, Freiburg, Fed. Republic Germany, 1978-79. Author: Advanced MOS Devices, 1987, Semiconductor Material and Device Characterization, 1990; patentee in field; contbr. articles to profl. jours. Fellow IEEE (disting. nat. lectr. 1993-94); mem. Electrochem. Soc., Sigma Xi, Eta Kappa Nu. Mem. Baha'i Faith. Home: 1927 E Bendix Dr Tempe AZ 85283-4203 Office: Ariz State U Dept Elec Engring Tempe AZ 85287-5706

SCHRÖDER, HARALD BERTEL, aerospace industry executive; b. Stockholm, Dec. 31, 1924; s. Bertel and Selma Katarina (Kraepelien) S.; m. Kjerstin Sjögren, Mar. 17, 1949; children: Göran, Hans, Henrik. M in Aeronautics Engring., Swedish Royal Inst. Tech., Stockholm, 1948. Developmental engr. SAAB-Scania AB, Linköping, Sweden, 1957-62, program mgr. SAAB Viggen Fighter Program, 1962-68, v.p aircraft sector, 1971-83; sr. v.p. SAAB aircraft div., gen. mgr. SAAB-Aircraft div., 1983-87; exec. v.p. SAAB-Scania AB, Linköping, Sweden, 1987-91; pres. Industry Group JAS AB, 1980-91; adviser to pres. Saab Mil. Aircraft, 1991-95. Mem. Royal Swedish Acad. War Scis., Swedish Assn. Def. Industries (pres. 1987-89, bd. dirs. 1989-92), Swedish Aerospace Industries Assn. (pres. 1991-94), European Aerospace Industries Assn. (v.p. 1992-94). Home: Banergatan 53, 11522S Stockholm Sweden Office: SAAB-Scania AB, S-58188 Linköping Sweden

SCHRODER, JACK SPALDING, JR., lawyer; b. Atlanta, July 10, 1948; s. Jack Spalding Sr. and Van (Spalding) S.; m. Karen Keyworth, Sept. 1, 1973; children: Jack Spalding III, James Edward. BA, Emory U., 1970; JD, U. Ga., 1973. Bar: Ga. 1973, U.S. Dist. Ct. (no. and so. dists.) Ga. 1973, U.S. Ct. Appeals (5th cir.) 1973, U.S. Ct. Appeals (11th cir.) 1982. Assoc. Alston & Bird, Atlanta, 1973-78, ptnr., 1978—. Co-editor, contbr. author: Georgia Hospital Law Manual, 1979, 84, 92. Participant Leadership Ga., Atlanta, 1986, United Way (chmn. legal div.), Atlanta, 1980. Mem. ABA (vice chmn. medicine and law com. 1989-90), Am. Acad. Hosp. Attys. (bd. dirs. 1994—, chmn. med. staff and physician rels. com. 1991-94), Ga. Acad. Hosp. Attys. (pres. 1981-82), State Bar Ga. (bd. govs. 1987-89), Atlanta Coun. Younger Lawyers (pres. 1977-78), Atlanta Bar Assn. (pres. 1982-83), Atlanta Bar Found. (pres. 1991—). Office: Alston & Bird 1 Atlantic Ctr 1201 West Peachtree St Atlanta GA 30309

SCHRODER, JOHN L., JR., retired mining engineer; b. Martinsburg, W.Va.. BS in Mining Engring., W.Va. Sch. Mines, MS, 1941. Registered profl. engr., W.Va., Ky. Jr. engr. H.C. Frick Coke Co. U.S. Steel, Uniontown, Pa., 1941-44; prodn. safety engr. Gay Coal and Coke Gay Mining Cos., 1946-49.; asst. engr. mine planning U.S. Steel, Gary, W.Va., 1949-51, asst. chief engr., 1951-1953; chief engr. U.S. Steel, Lynch, Gary, Ky., 1953-1958; gen. supt. U.S. Steel, Lynch, 1958-70; gen. mgr. coal ops. U.S. Steel, Pitts., 1970-79, v.p. coal ops. resource devel., 1979-81, pres. subsidiary U.S. Steel Mining Co. Inc., 1981-83, ret. 1983; spl. assst. to the pres. Am Mining Congress, 1983-84; dean Coll. Mineral and Energy Resources W.Va. U., 1984-91, ret., 1991; chmn. Mine Insps. Exam. Bd.; mem Govs. Moore's Energy Task Force. Lt. j.g. USN, 1944-46. Recipient

Howard N. Evanson award Soc. Mining, Metallurgy and Exploration, 1991. Mem. AIME (Erskine Ramsay medal 1992), Nat. Mine Rescue Assn., W.Va. Coal Mining Inst., Old Timers Club, King Coal Club. office: 228 Maple Ave Morgantown WV 26505-6666

SCHRODER, RAYMOND A., petroleum company executive; b. N.Y., 1926. Grad., St. John's U., 1950; JD, NYU, 1962. V.p., gen. tax counsel Exxon Corp., N.Y.C. Office: Exxon Corp 1251 Ave Of The Americas New York NY 10020-1104

SCHRODI, TOM, instructional services director; b. Belleville, Ill., Sept. 24, 1942; s. Walter Joseph and Emma Elizabeth (Bleiker) S.; m. Elizabeth Agnes Clark Schrodi, Aug. 19, 1967; children: Lisa, Tammy, Dawn. BS, Ea. Mich. U., Ypsilanti, 1964; MS, Ea. Mich. U., 1965. Calif. Adminstrv. Credential K-12 and Adult, Calif. Standard Svcs. Credential, Supr. 7-12, Calif. C.C. Credential in History, Calif. Standard Teaching Credential in History. Federal and state project writer Orange Unified Sch. Dist., 1975-80, coord. spl. programs, 1976-79, adminstrv. asst. spl. programs, 1979-80, adminstr. of curriculum, 1980-85, dir. instrnl. svcs., 1985—; coord. career edn. Orange County Consortium K-14, 1972-75; instr. Ctrl. County Regional Occupation Program, 1973-75, Whittier Coll., 1974-82; guest lectr. Calif. State U., Long Beach, 1972-80; cons. Calif. State Dept. Edn. Imperial County Dept. Edn. Author: Visual Communications Cluster Curriculum Guide, 1977, Social Studies Review, 1974, Le Mot Educational Services, 1972; co-author: California's Career Education State Plan, 1978, Comprehensive Career Education System, 1977, Monograph, 1973, Needs Assessment, 1972. Named ASCA Adminstr. of Yr. Curriculum and Instrn., 1993. Mem. Business Industry Coun., Orange Unified Curriculum Coun., Articulation Coun., Partnership Network, Dist. Negotiation Team, ASCD, Calif. Indsl. Edn. Assn., Intercultural Edn. Commn., Orange Suburbia Kiwanis Club, Orange High Sch. Faculty Club, Profl. Assn. Orange Educators. Office: Orange Unified Sch Dist 370 N Glassell St Orange CA 92666-1032

SCHROEDER, AARON HAROLD, songwriter; b. Bklyn., Sept. 7, 1926; s. Max and Pearl (Miller) S. m. Abby Steinberg, Oct. 31, 1967; 1 child, Rachel Amy. Student, music and art high schs., N.Y.C. Contact man Warner Bros. Music, Mills Music; profl. mgr. Charley Barnett; owner A. Schroeder Internat., Ltd. and subs. cos., N.Y.C., 1960-77; founder, pres. Musicor Records, N.Y.C., 1960-65. Mus. dir. film The Four Musketeers; producer TV spl. country music, 1979; composer songs for Fund Drives Berkshire United Way, 1986-87, N.Y. State Dept. Agr., Fairview Hosp., 1988, Operation Earth, 1990; composer songs Not as a Stranger, I Got Stung, Mandolins in the Moonlight, Stuck on You, Twixt Twelve and Twenty, Fools Hall of Fame, Because They're Young, French Foreign Legion, Time and the River, I'm Gonna Knock on Your Door, Rubber Ball, It's Now or Never, Big Hunk of Love, Today's Teardrops, Good Luck Charm, Once She Was Mine; film theme Four Musketeers, She Can Put Her Shoes Under My Bed Anytime, If I Could Only Touch Your Life, We're All In the Same Boat; score for motion picture and TV series Lucky Luke including original songs The Lonesomest Cowboy In the West, Lopin' Along, Lotta Legs' Hotel, Put Your Pistol Back in Your Holster, Cowboy's Lament, numerous others; composer for PBS Pilot "Grover's Corner", 1990, PBS spl. Chanukah at Grover's Corner, 1992; sponsored and pub. numerous award-winning songwriters. Mem. ASCAP (elections bd.), NARAS (gov. 1962). Home: Rd 2 Box 118 Great Barrington MA 01230-9808 Office: 200 W 51st St Ste 706 New York NY 10019*

SCHROEDER, ALFRED CHRISTIAN, electronics research engineer; b. West New Brighton, N.Y., Feb. 28, 1915; s. Alfred and Chryssa (Weishaar) S.; m. Janet Ellis, Sept. 26, 1936 (dec.); 1 dau., Carol Ann Schroeder Castle.; m. Dorothy Holloway, Nov. 21, 1981. BS, MIT, 1937, MS, 1937. Mem. tech. staff David Sarnoff Rsch. Ctr. RCA, Princeton, N.J., 1937—. Contbr. articles to profl. jours. Recipient RCA Lab. awards, 1947, 50, 51, 52, 57, 70. Fellow IEEE (Vladimir Zworykin award 1971); mem. AAAS, Optical Soc. Am., Soc. Motion Picture and TV Engrs. (David Sarnoff Gold medal 1965), Soc. Info. Display (Karl Ferdinand Braun prize 1989), Sigma Xi. Quaker. Achievements include 75 patents for color TV products including shadow mask tube. Home: Apt 1-114 Pennswood Village Newtown PA 18940 Office: SRI Internat David Sarnoff Rsch Ctr Princeton NJ 08540

SCHROEDER, BARBET G., director; b. Teheran, Iran, Apr. 26, 1941. Degree in Philosophy, U. Sorbonne, Paris. Jazz tour operator Europe; photojournalist India; film critic Cahiers du Cinema, L'air de Paris, 1958-63; owner, prin. Films du Losange, 1963—. Film dir.: More, 1969, The Valley, 1972, General Idi Amin Dada, 1974, Mistress, 1975, Koko, the Talking Gorilla, 1978, The Cheaters, 1983, The Charles Bukowski Tapes, 1985, Barfly, 1987, Reversal of Fortune, 1990 (Acad. award nominee best dir. 1990, Golden Globe award nominee best dir. film 1990), Single White Female, 1992, Kiss of Death, 1995; film prodr.: Six in Paris, 1968, (with Pierre Cottrell) My Night at Maud's, 1970, (with Georges Beauregard) The Collector, 1971, Chloe in the Afternoon, 1972, (with Cottrell) The Mother and the Whore, 1973, Perceval, 1978, Improper Conduct, 1983, La Carriere de Suzanne, Mediterranee, Tu Imagines Robinson, Out One, Flocons d'Or, The Marquise of O, Le Passe-Montagne, The Rites of Death, Le Navire Night, Le Pont du Nord; asst. to dir. Jean-Luc Goddard for The Soldiers, 1968; exec. prodr.: Claire's Knee, 1971, Celine and Julie Go Boating, 1974; co-prodr.: Chinese Roulette, 1977, The American Friend, 1977; appeared in films The Soldiers, 1968, Six in Paris, 1968, Celine and Julie Go Boating, 1974, Roberte, 1978, Wait Until Spring, Bandini, 1989, The Golden Boat, 1990; screenwriter: (with Paul Gegauff) More, 1969, The Valley, 1972, Mistress, 1975, The Cheaters, 1983. Office: care Myron S Meisel 3264 Ellenda Ave Los Angeles CA 90034-4403 also: CAA 9830 Wilshire Blvd Beverly Hills CA 90212-1804*

SCHROEDER, BILL E., lawyer; b. Long Beach, Calif., Jan. 16, 1942. BA, Stanford U., 1963; LLB, U. Calif., 1966. Bar: Calif. 1967. Ptnr. Baker & Hostetler, L.A. Mem. ABA, State Bar Calif., L.A. County Bar Assn. Office: Baker & Hostetler 600 Wilshire Blvd Los Angeles CA 90017-3212

SCHROEDER, CHARLES EDGAR, banker, investment management executive; b. Chgo., Nov. 17, 1935; s. William Edward and Lelia Lorraine (Anderson) S.; m. Martha Elizabeth Runnette, Dec. 30, 1958; children: Charles Edgar, Timothy Creighton, Elizabeth Linton. BA in Econs., Dartmouth Coll., 1957; MBA, Amos Tuck Sch., 1958. Treas. Miami Corp., Chgo., 1969-78, pres., 1978—; chmn. Blvd. Bancorp., Inc., 1991-94; bd. dirs Blvd. Bank of Chgo., 1981-91; bd. dirs. Nat.-Standard Co., Niles, Mich. Trustee Northwestern Meml. Hosp., 1985-93, Northwestern U., 1989—. Lt. (j.g.) USN, 1958-60. Mem. Fin. Analysts Soc. of Chgo., Chgo. Club, Glen View Club, Michigan Shores Club, Comml. Club. Office: Miami Corp 410 N Michigan Ave Chicago IL 60611-4211

SCHROEDER, CHARLES HENRY, corporate treasurer; b. Akron, Ohio, May 25, 1942; s. Charles Henry Sr. and Marion Belle (Buzenberg) S.; m. Marilyn Sue Patterson, Aug. 28, 1965; children—Rebecca Lynn, William Charles. B.A., Ohio Wesleyan U., 1964; M.B.A., Case Western Res. U., 1968, Stanford U., 1986. Treas. Ford Corp. subs. Ford Motor Co., South Africa, 1972-75; treas. Ford Microelectronics, Inc., 1980-82, Ford Aerospace Corp., 1978-90; v.p., treas. Loral Aerospace Corp. and Space Systems/Loral, Newport Beach, Calif., 1990—. Mem. Stanford U. Alumni Cons. Team for Orange County non-profit orgns., 1993. Recipient Fin. award for outstanding research Cleve. Soc. Security Analysts, 1967. Mem. L.A. Treas.' Club (pres. 1991—), Case-Western Res. U. Orange County Alumni Assn. (pres. 1990). Republican. Episcopalian. Home: 26336 Golada Mission Viejo CA 92692-3285 Office: Loral Aerospace Corp 3501 Jamboree Rd Ste 500 Newport Beach CA 92660-2964

SCHROEDER, CHRISTOPHER H., law educator; b. 1948. BA, Princeton U., 1968; MDiv, Yale U., 1971; JD, U. Calif., Berkeley, 1974. Bar: Calif. 1974. Assoc. prof. Duke U., Durham, N.C., 1979-85, prof., 1985—; vis. prof. UCLA, 1985-86. Office: Duke U Sch Law Durham NC 27706

SCHROEDER, DAVID HAROLD, health care facility executive; b. Chgo., Oct. 22, 1940; s. Harry T. and Clara D. (Dexter) S.; m. Clara Doorn, Dec. 27, 1964; children: Gregory D., Elizabeth M. BBA, Kans. State Coll., 1965; MBA, Wichita State U., 1968; postgrad., U. Ill., 1968-69. CPA, Ill. Supt.

cost acctg. Boeing Co., Wichita, Kans., 1965-68; sr. v.p., treas. Riverside Med. Ctr., Kankakee, Ill., 1971—; treas. Riverside Health System, 1982—, Kankakee Valley Health Inc., 1985—, Health Info. Systems Coop., 1991—; v.p., treas. Oakside Corp., Kankakee, 1982—; bd. dirs. Harmony Home Health Svc., Inc., Naperville, Ill.; mem. faculty various profl. orgns.; adj. prof. econs. div. health adminstrvn. Gov.'s State U., University Park, Ill., 1990—; trustee Riverside Found. Trust, 1989—, RMC Found., 1989—; Sr. Living Ctr., 1989—. Contbg. author: Cost Containment in Hospitals, 1980; contbr. articles to profl. jours. Pres. Riverside Employees Credit Union, 1976-79; founder Kankakee Trinity Acad., 1980, Riverview Hist. Dist., Kankakee, 1982; pres. Kankakee County Mental Health Ctr., 1982-84, United Way Kankakee County, 1984-85; chmn. Ill. Provider Trust, Naperville, 1983-85; mem. adv. bd. Students in Free Enterprise, Olivet Nazarene U., Kankakee, 1989—; pres. adv. coun. div. health adminstrn. Gov.'s State U., University Park, preceptor, 1987—; trustee, treas. Am. Luth. Ch.; wish granter, Make a Wish Found., 1994—. Capt. U.S. Army, 1969-71. Fellow Am. Coll. Healthcare Execs., Healthcare Fin. Mgmt. Assn. (pres. 1975-76, cert. mgr. patient accounts 1981), Fin. Analysts Fedn.; mem. AICPA, Ill. Hosp. Assn. (chmn. coun. health fin. 1982-85), Inst. Chartered Fin. Analysts, Nat. Assn. Accts., Fin. Exec. Inst., Ill. CPA Soc., Healthcare Fin. Mgmt. Assn. (William G. Follimer award 1977, Robert H. Reeves award 1981, Muncie Gold award 1987, Founders medal of honor 1990), Investment Analysts Soc. Chgo., Inc., Classic Car Club Am., Packard Club, Kiwanis (pres.), Masons, Alpha Kappa Psi, Sigma Chi. Avocations: classic automobile restoration, archl. preservation, computers. Home: 901 S Chicago Ave Kankakee IL 60901-5236 Office: Riverside Med Ctr 350 N Wall St Kankakee IL 60901-2901

SCHROEDER, DONALD PERRY, retired food products company executive; b. Danville, Ill., Nov. 2, 1930; s. Donald Joseph and Pauline Hannah (Critchfield) S.; m. Barbara Ann Engle, Jan. 6, 1951; children: Patricia Ann Schroeder Capizzi, Helen Schroeder Marrano, Jeffrey Joseph. Student, Purdue U., 1949, Stanford U., 1982. Mgr. Schroeders I.G.A. Supermarket, Danville, 1950-57; specialist retail meat J.M. Jones Co., Champaign, Ill., 1957-59, mgr. retail zone, 1959-62, dir. meat ops., 1962-67; dir. customer services Olean (N.Y.) Wholesale Grocery Co., 1967-70; nat. dir. meat Ind. Grocers Alliance, Chgo., 1970-74; dir. meat ops. Fleming Cos., Inc., Topeka, 1974-83; v.p. meat., produce ops. Fleming Cos., Inc., Oklahoma City, 1983-88, v.p. meat ops., 1988-89, ret., 1989; chmn. meat council Ind. Grocers Alliance, Chgo., 1962-87. Bd. dirs. Big Bros./Sisters Greater Oklahoma City, 1984-87, North Side YMCA, Oklahoma City, 1988-90. Mem. Nat. Livestock and Meat Bd. (universal meat cut identity com. 1970-73), United Fresh Fruit and Vegetable (bd. dirs. 1984-87). Republican. Roman Catholic. Avocations: yard and garden work, golf, fishing. Home: 5 Charnela Ln Hot Springs Village AR 71909-3030

SCHROEDER, DOUGLAS FREDRICK, architect; b. Omaha, June 12, 1935; s. Walter Elmer and Ellen Ruth (Niles) S.; m. Joanne Vlecides, July 5, 1980. B.Arch., U. Mich., 1959. Registered Architect, Ill., N.C., Mich. Designer, draftsman C.F. Murphy Assocs., Chgo., 1959-63; architect, sr. architect Skidmore, Owings & Merrill, Chgo., 1964-67; architect, ptnr. Schroeder, Yamamoto & Schreiber, Chgo., 1968-69; ptnr. Hinds & Schroeder, Ltd., Chgo., 1972-74; propr. Douglas Schroeder Assocs., Chgo., 1974-83, 93—; ptnr. Siegel & Schroeder, P.C., Chgo., 1983-91; dir. SGA Planning and Constrn. Cons. Co. div. Goforth Group, Chgo., 1991-93; v.p. Yacht Harbor Mgmt. Co., South Haven, Mich., 1983-88; dir. Inland Architect Mag. Contbr. articles to profl. jours. Bd. dirs. Chgo. Archtl. Assistance Ctr., 1982-84; chmn. Mass. Transp. Crisis Com., Chgo., 1973, Ill. Futures Forum, 1976-77; pres. Ill. Planning and Conservation League, Chgo., 1971-74. Named Outstanding Alumnus Lake Superior State U., 1971. Fellow AIA; mem. Am. Arbitration Assn. (arbitrator). Unitarian. Club: Cliff Dwellers (dir. 1971-74). Home: 700 W Irving Park Rd Apt 4A Chicago IL 60613-3133 Office: Douglas Schroeder Assocs Architects & Planners 625 N Michigan Ave Ste 1600 Chicago IL 60611

SCHROEDER, EDMUND R., lawyer; b. N.Y.C., Feb. 6, 1933; s. Robert C. and Rose A. (Garramone) S.; m. Elaine P. Diserio, Jan. 21, 1961; children: Edmund Jr., Christopher, Elizabeth. AB cum laude, Harvard U., 1953, LLB, 1958. Assoc. Archibald R. Graustein, N.Y.C., 1958-61, Root, Barrett, Cohen, Knapp & Smith, N.Y.C., 1961-67; ptnr. Barrett Knapp Smith & Schapiro, N.Y.C., 1967-88, Lord Day & Lord/Barrett Smith, N.Y.C., 1988-94, Cadwalader, Wickersham & Taft, N.Y.C., 1994—; mem. adv. com. Commodity Futures Trading Commn. on Definition and Regulation of Market Instruments, 1975-76. Contbr. articles to profl. jours. Bd. dirs. Orch. St. Luke's, N.Y.C., 1987— (chmn. exec. com. 1993—); bd. trustees The United Way of Scarsdale-Edgemont, 1990-92; mem. Scarsdale Bd. Edn., 1976-79; co-founder, first chmn. Edn. Through Music, Inc., N.Y.C., 1991—; bd. trustees Hoff-Barthelson Music Sch., Scarsdale, 1974—, chmn. bd., 1986-90, hon. chmn., 1990—; bd. trustees The Nat. Guild Cmty. Schs. Arts, Englewood, N.J., 1992—. Mem. ABA (chmn. com. futures regulation 1981-85), Am Arbitration Assn. (arbitrator), Nat. Futures Assn. (arbitrator), Bar Assn. City N.Y. (founder, first chmn. com. futures regulation 1976-81), Scarsdale Golf Club. Office: Cadwalader Wickersham & Taft 100 Maiden Ln New York NY 10038

SCHROEDER, EDWIN MAHER, law educator, law library administrator, university dean; b. New Orleans, June 25, 1937; s. Edwin Charles and Lucille Mary (Maher) S.; m. Marietta Louise DeFazio, Aug. 1, 1936; children—Edwin Charles II, Jonathan David, Margaret Louise. A.A., St. Joseph Sem., St. Benedict, La., 1957; Ph.B., Gregorian U., Rome, 1959; J.D., Tulane U., 1964; M.S., Fla. State U., 1970. Bar: Mass. 1964. Teaching fellow Boston Coll. Law Sch., 1964-65; asst. prof. law U. Conn., 1965-68; asst. prof., asst. law librarian U. Tex., 1968-69; asst. prof. Fla. State U., 1969-71, assoc. prof., 1971-75, prof., 1975—, dir. Law Library, 1969—, assoc. dean Coll. Law, 1979-83, assoc. dean Coll. Law, 1983-93. Mem. ABA, Am. Assn. Law Libraries (v.p. Southeastern chpt. 1983-84, pres. 1984-85), Order of Coif, Beta Phi Mu. Roman Catholic. Home: 806 Middlebrooks Cir Tallahassee FL 32312-2439 Office: Law Libr Fla State U Coll Law Tallahassee FL 32306

SCHROEDER, FRED ERICH HARALD, humanities educator; b. Manitowoc, Wis., June 3, 1932; s. Alfred William and Sissel Marie (Lovell) S.; m. Janet June Knope, Aug. 21, 1954; 1 child, Erich Karl. BS, U. Wis., 1960; MA, U. Minn., 1963, PhD, 1968. Elementary sch. tchr. various locations, Wis., 1952-60; asst. prof. English U. Minn., Duluth, 1968-71, assoc. prof. English, 1971-74, prof. behavioral sci., 1977-82, prof. humanities, 1974—, dir. Ctr. for Am. Studies, 1986-87, dir. Inst. Interdisciplinary Studies, 1987-90, dir. dept. humanities and classics, 1989-90, dir. grad. liberal studies, 1992—. Author: Joining the Human Race: How To Teach Humanities, 1972, Outlaw Aesthetics: Arts and the Public Mind, 1977; editor Interdisciplinary Humanities (formerly Humanities Edn. jour.), 1983—, 5000 Years of Popular Culture, 1980, 20th Century Popular Culture in Museums and Libraries, 1981, Front Yard America: The Evolution and Meanings of a Domestic Vernacular Landscape, 1993; lectr., writer Nat. Humanities Series, 1969-71. Mem. Minn. Humanities Commn., 1985-90. Woodrow Wilson Nat. Found. fellow, 1960-61, dissertation fellow 1963; NEH scholar, 1969-70; Inst. for Human Values in Medicine fellow, 1976. Mem. Am. Culture Assn. (pres. 1984-87), Nat. Assn. Humanities Edn. (pres. 1987-89, exec. sec.-treas. 1989—), Am. Assn. for State and Local History (seminar instr. 1978-82), Popular Culture Assn. Avocations: collecting art, woodworking, gardening. Home: 5756 N Shore Dr Duluth MN 55804-9660 Office: Dept Interdisciplinary Programs U Minn 10 University Dr Duluth MN 55812

SCHROEDER, HAROLD KENNETH, JR., lawyer; b. Buffalo, Aug. 6, 1936; s. Harold Kenneth and Margaret Mary (Mescall) S.; m. Jean Louise Benbenek, Aug. 20, 1958; children: Mary Margaret, Mark, Keith, Kurt, Jennifer. BS, Canisius Coll., 1958; JD, U. Buffalo, 1961; ML, Georgetown U., 1962. Bar: N.Y. 1961, D.C. 1961, Fla. 1979, U.S. Dist. Ct. (we. dist.) N.Y. 1961, U.S. Ct. Appeals (2d cir.) 1981. Trial atty. U.S. Dept. Justice, Washington, 1962-63; spl. asst. U.S. Atty. D.C. Washington, 1962-63; U.S. Atty. Western Dist. N.Y. U.S. Dept. Justice, Buffalo, 1969-72; ptnr. Hodgson, Russ, Andrews, Woods & Goodyear, Buffalo, 1963-69, sr. ptnr., 1972—; chmn. Fed. Merit Selection Panel for U.S. Magistrate Judge, We. Dist. N.Y., 1989, 92, 94, Merit Selection Panel, Fed. Pub. Defender We. Dist. N.Y., 1991; mem. U.S. Civil Justice Reform Act, N.Y. Author: (with others) Law and Tactics in Federal Criminal Cases, 1964. V.p. Orchard

Park, N.Y. Cen. Sch. Dist., 1972-76, Buffalo Sem., 1972-88. E. Barrett Prettyman fellow Georgetown U., 1961. Mem. Erie County Bar Assn. Avocation: tennis. Office: Hodgson Russ Andrews et al 1800 One M&T Pla Buffalo NY 14203

SCHROEDER, HENRY J., health science organization administrator. Dir. Inst. for the Study of Devel. Disablities, Ind. U., Bloomington, Ind. Office: Ind U Inst Study Devel Disabilities 2853 E 10th St Bloomington IN 47408-2601

SCHROEDER, HENRY WILLIAM, publisher; b. Cleve., Wis., Sept. 7, 1928; s. Henry and Esther Julia (Kammann) S. ; m. Dorothy Hildebrand, Aug. 18, 1956 (div.); children: Susan Schroeder Smith, Katherine Jean Duhamel; m. Elizabeth Churbuck, Aug. 15, 1977 (dec.); children: Joy, Bill, Stephen; m. Mary Vae Legler, Feb. 15, 1992; 1 child, Derek Legler. B.S., U. Wis., 1957, M.S., 1959. Info. dir. Wis. Farm Bur., Madison, 1960-63; asst. dir. pub. relations Credit Union Internat., Madison, 1963-65; editor, co-pub. Verona Press (Wis.), Oreg. Observer (Wis.), 1966—, also v.p. Southwest Suburban Publs., Inc., 1966-80; co-pub. Fitchburg Star, 1974—, also pres. Southwest Suburban Publs. and Schroeder Publs., Inc.; pub. Blade-Atlas, Blanchardville, Wis., 1977-83; pres., pub. Leader Publ. Corp., Evansville, Wis., 1981-88; pub. Community Herald Newspapers Corp., 1988—, Monona Herald and McFarland Life newspapers, Clinton (Wis.) Topper, 1994—. Mem. Gov.'s UN Commn., 1974. Served with USNR, 1949-53. Mem. Wis. Newspaper Assn. (pres. 1983-84), Wis. Newspaper Assn. (bd. dir. 1973-86), WNA Found. (pres. 1990-91), Madison Press Club, Madison Advt. Fedn., Nat. Newspaper Assn. (govt. affairs conf., chmn. services com., state chmn., Better Newspaper Contest), Suburban Newspapers Am., Verona C. of C. (pres. 1970, 91), Madison Club, East Madison Optimists (bd. dirs. 1993—), Masons (master 1970, bd. dirs. jour 1990-93, pres. jour. 1993—), Shriners. Republican. Office: Verona Press 120 W Verona Ave Verona WI 53593-1383

SCHROEDER, HERMAN ELBERT, scientific consultant; b. Bklyn., July 6, 1915; s. Henry W. and Caroline (Schmidt) S.; m. Elizabeth Barnes, June 13, 1938; children: Nancy Schroeder Tarczy, Edward L., Peter H., Martha L. Schroeder Lewis. A.B. summa cum laude, Harvard, 1936, A.M., 1937, Ph.D., 1939. With E.I. du Pont de Nemours & Co., Wilmington, Del., 1938-80; asst. dir. R&D E.I. du Pont de Nemours & Co., 1957-63, dir. R&D, 1963-80; pres. Schroeder Sci. Svcs., Inc., 1980—; sci. cons. Met. Mus. Art, N.Y.C., Smithsonian Instn., Winterthur Mus. Mem. Chester County Sch. Bd., Unionville, Pa., 1950-56; pres. Assn. Harvard Chemists, 1955-56; mem. vis. com. Harvard Chemistry Dept., 1960-72; mem. sci. adv. com. Winterthur Mus.; trustee, chmn. research com. U. Del. Research Found., 1976-84, former v.p. Recipient award Internat. Inst. Synthetic Rubber Producers, 1979, Lavoisier medal DuPont, 1992. Mem. AAAS, Am. Chem. Soc. (Charles Goodyear medal 1984), N.Y. Acad. Scis., Phi Beta Kappa, Alpha Chi Sigma. Home and Office: 74 Stonegates 4031 Kennett Pike Greenville DE 19807 *A life in industrial research has been for me both challenging and rewarding. Forces which impel me are largely the compulsion to look for the new, to change for the better, be it by finding better ways to do things or by inventing products to make the world function better. Gratifyingly, these often make the world aesthetically more pleasant and sometimes cleaner. I am concerned by the growing hostility of society to science and to developments that ensure a more comfortable life and safer food and energy than would otherwise be possible.*

SCHROEDER, JACK WALTER, insurance executive, lawyer; b. Davenport, Iowa, Aug. 21, 1925; s. Walter F. and Flora O. Schroeder; m. Virginia Marie Posateri, Apr. 30, 1947; children: Sandra Jo Schroeder Cangelosi, Walter F. BS, St. Ambrose Coll., Davenport, Iowa, 1949; JD, Drake U., 1952. Bar: Iowa 1952, U.S. Ct. Appeals (fed. cir.) 1952. Mem. Iowa Ho. of Reps., Davenport, Iowa, 1950-54; mem. Iowa Senate, Des Moines, 1955-67, maj. leader, 1959-61; pres. Gen. United Life Ins. Co., Des Moines, 1967-78, U.S. Life Co., 1974-78; cons. life industry, 1978-86; chmn., pres. Birdfinder Corp., Cable TV Co., Sarasota, Fla., 1986-88; pres., chief exec. officer Am. Life and Casualty Ins. Co., Des Moines, Vulcan Life, Birmingham, Ala., 1988—; bd. dirs. Hawkeye Bancorp., Des Moines. Mem. legis. com. Rep. for Gov. of Iowa, 1960; chmn. Iowa Heart Assn., Des Moines, 1968-70. With USN, 1942-47, PTO. Recipient Good Govt. award U.S. Jr. Chamber, 1959. Mem. ABA, Iowa State Bar, Wakonda Club, Longboat Key Club, Rotary, Elks, Masons, Shriners. Republican. Lutheran. Avocations: boating, yachting, piloting, golf. Home: 300 Walnut St # 131 Des Moines IA 50309-2239 Office: Am Life and Casualty Ins Co 405 6th Ave Des Moines IA 50309-2412

SCHROEDER, JOHN H., university administrator, history educator; b. Twin Falls, Idaho, Sept. 13, 1943; s. Herman John and Azalia (Kimes) S.; m. Sandra Barrow; children: John K., Andrew Barrow. BA, Lewis and Clark Coll., Portland, Oreg., 1965; MA, U. Va., 1967, PhD, 1971. Instr. history U. Wis., Milw., 1970-71, asst. prof., 1971-76, assoc. prof., 1976-86, prof., 1986—, Am. Coun. on Edn. fellow, 1982-83, assoc. dean, 1976-82, asst. to vice chancellor, 1982-85, acting vice chancellor, 1985-87, vice chancellor, 1987-90, interim chancellor, 1990-91, chancellor, 1991—; Louis M. Sears Meml. lectr. Purdue U., 1978; bd. dirs. Columbia Health Sys., Inc. Author: Mr. Polk's War: American Opposition and Dissent, 1973, The Commercial and Diplomatic Role of the American Navy 1829-1861, 1985. Bd. dirs. Greater Milw. Com., Milw. Boys and Girls Club, Milw. Pub. Policy Forum, Greater Milw. Edn. Trust; mem. Gov.'s Spl. Commn. on Dental Care. Recipient Edward and Rosa Uhrig award U. Wis.-Milw., 1974, Disting. Teaching award AMOCO/U. Wis.-Milw., 1975. Mem. Orgn. Am. Historians, Soc. for History of Early Republic, Soc. for History of Am. Fgn. Rels., Milw. Rotary. Office: U Wis 2310 E Hartford Ave Milwaukee WI 53211-3165

SCHROEDER, MARY MURPHY, federal judge; b. Boulder, Colo., Dec. 4, 1940; d. Richard and Theresa (Kam) Murphy; m. Milton R. Schroeder, Oct. 15, 1965; children: Caroline Theresa, Katherine Emily. B.A., Swarthmore Coll., 1962; J.D., U. Chgo., 1965. Bar: Ill. 1966, D.C. 1966, Ariz. 1970. Trial atty. Dept. Justice, Washington, 1965-69; law clk. Hon. Jesse Udall, Ariz. Supreme Ct., 1970; mem. firm Lewis and Roca, Phoenix, 1971-75; judge Ariz. Ct. Appeals, Phoenix, 1975-79; U.S. Ct. Appeals (9th cir.), Phoenix, 1979—; vis. instr. Ariz. State U. Coll. Law, 1976, 77, 78. Contbr. articles to profl. jours. Mem. Am. Bar Assn., Ariz. Bar Assn., Fed. Bar Assn., Am. Law Inst., Am. Judicature Soc. Democrat. Club: Soroptimists. Office: US Ct Appeals 9th Cir 6421 Courthouse & Fed Bldg 230 N 1st Ave Phoenix AZ 85025-0230*

SCHROEDER, PATRICIA SCOTT (MRS. JAMES WHITE SCHROEDER), congresswoman; b. Portland, Oreg., July 30, 1940; d. Lee Combs and Bernice (Lemoin) Scott; m. James White Schroeder, Aug. 18, 1962; children: Scott William, Jamie Christine. B.A. magna cum laude, U. Minn., 1961; J.D., Harvard U., 1964. Bar: Colo. 1964. Field atty. NLRB, Denver, 1964-66; practiced in Denver, 1966-72; hearing officer Colo. Dept. Personnel, 1971-72; mem. faculty U. Colo., 1969-72, Community Coll., Denver, 1969-70, Regis Coll., Denver, 1970-72; mem. 93d-104th Congresses from 1st Colo. dist., 1973—; co-chmn. Congl. Caucus for Women's Issues, 1976—; mem. Ho. of Reps., ranking minority mem. judiciary subcom. on the Constitution, mem. Nat. Security Com. Congregationalist. Office: US Ho of Reps 2307 Rayburn House Office Bldg Washington DC 20515*

SCHROEDER, PAUL J., JR., lawyer; b. Mo., 1947. BA magna cum laude, U. Notre Dame, 1969; JD, Washington U., 1972. Bar: Mo. 1972. Ptnr. Bryan Cave, St. Louis. Mem. ABA.

SCHROEDER, ROBERT J., veterinarian, association executive; b. Fort Collins, Colo., Nov. 19, 1921; s. John Henry and Mildred Margaret (McElravy) S.; m. Janice Lorraine Dringman, Aug. 24, 1947; children: Jeri Lee, Craig Reed, Curtis John. DVM, Colo. State U., 1947; postgrad., Army Med. Svc. Meat and Dairy Hygiene Sch., 1951, L.A. County Civil Svc. Commn., 1960. Diplomate Am. Coll. Vet. Preventative Medicine; cert. vet. Calif. 1949. Vet. Food and Mouth Disease Control U.S. Dept. Agrl., Mex., 1947-48; vet. Food and Mouth Disease Control L.A. County Livestock Dept., 1947-50, 52-53, sr. vet., 1953-57, dir., 1957-65; county vet. L.A. Dept. Vets., 1965-72; clin. prof. pathology U. So. Calif., L.A., 1968-79, clin. prof. community medicine and pub. health, 1971-78, prof. emeritus, 1979—; dep. dir. L.A. County Dept. Health Svcs., 1972-78; mem. policy staff L.A.

County Dept. Health Svcs., 1972-78, mem. exec. staff, 1972-78, chmn. programs and priorities task force, 1972-78; cons. N.Am. Rockwell Corp. Life Scis. Opers. of Autonetics, 1968-69, Santa Cruz Island Co., 1953-92; nat. civilian cons. Surgeon Gen. USAF, 1969-71. Ecology and pub. health editor Animal Cavalcade, 1970-72; guest editor: AVMA Jour., 1985-87. Active Citizens Com. for Vet. Med. Sch., 1965-70; chmn. steering com. So. Calif. Sch. Vet. Medicine, 1964-68. 1st lt. U.S. Army, 1943-46, 50-52. Recipient Disting. Svc. award Colo. State U. So. Calif. Alumni Assn., 1967, Disting. Vet. Leadership award So. Calif. Vet. Med. Assn., 1969, Honor Alumnus Achievement award Colo. State U., 1969. Mem. AVMA (Pub. Svc. award 1991, pres. 1967-68, pres.-elect. 1967-68, mem. exec. bd. 1961-66, mem. coun. edn. 1969-74, chmn. com. accreditation on tng. for animal technicians 1972—, mem. AVMA-Am. Assn. Vet. Med. Colls. Liaison com., 1969—), U.S. Animal Health Assn. (mem. exec. com. 1957, chmn. pub. health com. 1958-65, mem. mastitis com. 1965—), Med. Rsch. Assn. Calif. (bd. dirs. 1967—), Calif. Regional Med. Programs Adv. Coun. (mem. area V. adv. coun. 1970-73, chmn. 1973, mem. program evaluation com. 1973—), L.A. Area C. of C. (mem. farm/food/fiber com. 1957—). Home: 9738 Tecum Rd Downey CA 90240

SCHROEDER, STEPHEN ROBERT, psychology researcher; b. Leipsic, Ohio, Oct. 28, 1936. BA, Josephinum Coll., 1958; MA, U. Toledo, 1964; PhD, U. Pitts., 1967. Lic. psychologist, Ohio, N.C. Postdoctoral rsch. assoc. Learning Rsch. and Devel. Ctr., U. Pitts., 1967-68; clin. asst. prof. dept. psychology U. N.C., Chapel Hill, 1968-73, clin. assoc. prof. depts. psychology and psychiatry, 1973-77, rsch. assoc. prof. dept. psychology, 1977-87, rsch. sci. Biol. Scis. Rsch. Ctr., 1973-87, assoc. prof. dept. psychiatry, 1977-86, prof. dept. psychiatry, 1986-87; dir. psychology Murdoch Ctr., Butner, N.C., 1973-75, dir. rsch. and devel., 1975-77; prof. dept. psychology and psychiatry Ohio State U., Columbus, 1987-90, dir. The Nisonger Ctr., 1987-90; prof. dept. human devel. and family life U. Kans., Lawrence, 1990—, prof. dept. pharmacology and toxicology, 1990—, dir. Bur. Child Rsch., 1990—, dir. Schiefelbusch Inst. for Life Span Studies, 1990—; mem. program com. Gatlinburg Conf. on Mental Retardation and Devel. Disabilities, 1977-92, program chmn., 1992—; mem. N.C. divsn. Mental Health and Mental Retardation Rsch. Grants Rev. Bd., 1977-86; mem. statewide lead screening com. N.C. Dept. Meternal and Child Health, 1979-86; founding chmn. Annie Sullivan Enterprises, Inc., 1982-89, active, 1989-92, chmn., 1992—; mem. rsch. grant rev. bd. Ont. Mental Health Found., 1984—; mem. internat. rsch. exch. subcom. for Rsch. in Ednl. Rehab. in U.S. and German Dem. Republic, 1984-90; gen. ad hoc mem. grant rev. bd. NIMH, 1984; mem. mental retardation study com. NICHD, 1989-90; rsch. cons. Am. Occupational Therapy Found.; cons. pediats. ward N.C. Meml. Hosp., 1977-86; cons. civil rights divsn. U.S. Dept. Justice, 1987—; cons. No. Va. Tng. Ctr., 1983-85, 91, Murdoch Ctr., Western Carolina Ctr., Caswell Ctr., 1977-89; bd. dirs. Corp. of Guardianship; active Ohio Devel. Disabilities Planning Coun., 1987-90, Kans. Planning Coun. on Devel. Disabilities Svcs., 1990—, Kans. Prevention Task Force, 1991—, Gov. Task Force on Respite Care, 1991—. Author, editor chpts. to books; editor Am. Jour. Mental Retardation, 1991—; co-editor Jour. Applied Rsch. in Mental Retardation, 1980-86, Rsch. in Devel. Disabilities, 1987—; mem. editl. bd. Jour. Applied Behaviour Analysis, 1973-74, Mental Retardation, 1977-93, Analysis and Intervention in Devel. Disabilities, 1981-82; guest reviewer Jour. Applied Behaviour Analysis, Pediat. Psychology, Am. Jour. Psychiatry, Jour. Autism and Childhood Scizophrenia, Child Devel., Sci., Perceptual and Motor Skills, Pediatrics, Neurotoxicology; contbr. articles, papers to profl. jours. Mem. adv. bd. Ohio United Cerebral Palsy, 1988-90; active Ohio Prevention Coalition, 1987-90. Recipient Karl Heinz Renker medallion for interdisciplinary sci. collaboration German Dem. Republic, 1989. Fellow APA (pres. divsn. 33 mental retardation 1986-87, Nicholas Hobbs award); mem. AAAS, Am. Assn. Mental Retardation, Am. Acad. Mental Retardation, Assn. Advancement Behaviour Therapy (mem. task force on self-injurious behaviour 1981-82), Assn. Behaviour Analysis, N.Y. Acad. Scis., Sertoma Club. Office: U Kansas Schiefelbusch Inst Life Span Studies 1052 Dole Human Devel Ctr Lawrence KS 66045*

SCHROEDER, STEVEN ALFRED, medical educator, researcher, foundation executive; b. N.Y.C., July 26, 1939; s. Arthur Edward and Norma (Scheinberg) S.; m. Sally B. Ross, Oct. 21, 1967; children: David Arthur, Alan Ross. BA, Stanford U., 1960; MD, Harvard U., 1964; LHD (hon.), Rush U., 1994. Am. Bd. Internal Medicine. Intern and resident in internal medicine Harvard Med. Service, Boston City Hosp., 1964-66, 68-70; asst. prof., then assoc. prof. George Washington Med. Ctr., Washington, 1971-76; vis. prof. St. Thomas' Hosp. Med. Sch., London, 1982-83; prof. medicine, chief div. gen. internal medicine, mem. Inst. Health Policy Studies U. Calif., San Francisco, 1976-90; pres. Robert Wood Johnson Found., Princeton, N.J., 1990—; bd. dirs. Chem. Bank, N.J.; cons. various govtl. and philanthropic health orgns. Sr. editor Current Medical Diagnosis and Treatment, 1987-93; mem. editorial bd. New Eng. Mag.; contbr. numerous articles to profl. jours. Mem. U.S. Prospective Payment Assessment Commn., 1983-88. With USPHS, 1966-68. Master ACP; mem. Physicians for Social Responsibility, Am. Pub. Health Assn., Am. Physicians, Inst. Medicine, Soc. Gen. Internal Medicine (past pres.), Phi Beta Kappa, Alpha Omega Alpha. Home: 49 W Shore Dr Pennington NJ 08534 Office: Robert Wood Johnson Found PO Box 2316 Princeton NJ 08543-2316

SCHROEDER, WILLIAM JOHN, electronics executive; b. Havre de Grace, Md., June 9, 1944; s. William Martin and Dorothy Jeanne (McLaughlin) S.; m. Marilee Jane Alne, May 28, 1966; children: Kristen, Kari Britt, Kimberley. BSEE, Marquette U., 1966, MSEE, 1968; MBA, Harvard U., 1972. Devel. engr. Honeywell Inc., Mpls., 1968-70; mgmt. cons. McKinsey & Co., Los Angeles, 1972-76; mgr. product planning Memorex Corp., Santa Clara, Calif., 1976-78; pres. Priam Corp., San Jose, Calif., 1978-85, chmn., 1985-86; pres. Conner Peripherals, Inc., San Jose, 1986-89, vice chmn., 1989-94; CEO Arcada Software Inc., a Conner Co., 1993-94; pres., CEO Diamond Multimedia Systems, Inc., San Jose, Calif., 1994—; bd. dirs. Xircom Corp., Thousand Oaks, Calif. Office: Diamond Multimedia Systems Inc 2880 Junction Ave San Jose CA 95134-1922

SCHROEDER, W(ILLIAM) WIDICK, religion educator; b. Newton, Kans., Nov. 12, 1928; s. William Fredric and Irene (Widick) S.; m. Gayle Eadie, Sept. 1, 1956; children: Scott David, Carla Gayle. BA, Bethel Coll., 1949; MA, Mich. State U., East Lansing, 1952; BDiv, Chgo. Theol. Sem., 1955; PhD, U. Chgo., 1960; DD (hon.), Chgo. Theol. Seminary, 1995. Ordained to ministry Congl. Christian Ch., 1955. Instr. Mich. State U., East Lansing, 1953-54, U. Chgo., 1958-60; from asst. prof. to prof. religion and society Chgo. Theol. Sem., 1960-94, prof. emeritus, 1994—; vis. fellow Mansfield Coll., Oxford, Eng., 1966; vis. scholar Ctr. for Process Studies, Claremont, Calif.; vis. lectr. in ethics and soc. Divinity Sch. U. Chgo., 1967-71, 76; editor Rev. of Religious Rsch., 1964-69. Author: (with Victor Obenhaus) Religion in American Culture: Unity and Diversity in a Midwestern County, 1964; Cognitive Structures and Religious Research, 1970; (with Victor Obenhaus, Larry A. Jones and Thomas P. Sweetser), Suburban Religion: Churches and Synagogues in the American Experience, 1974; (with Keith A. Davis) Where Do I Stand? Living Theological Options for Contemporary Christians, 1973, rev. edit. 1975, 3d edit., 1978; Flawed Process and Sectarian Substance: Analytic and Critical Perspectives on the United Church of Christ General Synod Pronouncement, Christian Faith: Economic Life and Justice, 1990, Toward Belief: Essays in the Human Sciences, Social Ethics, and Philosophical Theology, 1995; co-edited: (with Philip Hefner) Belonging and Alienation: Religious Foundations for the Human Future , 1976; (with Gibson Winter) Belief and Ethics: Essays in Ethics, the Human Sciences and Ministry in Honor of W. Alvin Pitcher, 1978; (with John B. Cobb, Jr.) Process Philosophy and Social Thought, 1981; (with Perry LeFevre) Spiritual Nurture, Congregational Development, 1984, Pastoral Care and Liberation Praxis: Essays in Personal and Social Transformation, 1986, Creative Ministries in Contemporary Christianity, 1991; (with Franklin I. Gamwell) Economic Life: Process Interpretations and Critical Responses, 1988. Mem. Am. Acad. Religion, Am. Sociol. Assn., Soc. for the Sci. Study of Religion, Religious Rsch. Assn., Ctr. for Process Studies, Soc. Christian Ethics. Home: 2738 Virginia Pl Homewood IL 60430-1135 Office: Chgo Theol Sem 5757 S University Ave Chicago IL 60637-1507 *The aims of existence are aesthetic satisfaction and intensity of feeling. In facilitating these aims, the Divine Reality is the locus of potentiality, the mediator of experience, the evoker of feeling and the ultimate recipient of all that has become.*

SCHROEPFER, GEORGE JOHN, JR., biochemistry educator; b. St. Paul, June 15, 1932; s. George John and Catherine Rita (Callaghan) S.; children: Lisa Marie Schoepfer Schwartz, Cynthia Marie Schoepfer Winzenried, Stephanie Marie, Jeanine Marie Schroepfer Smith, Dana Marie Schroepfer Rethwisch. BS, U. Minn., 1955, MD, 1957, Phd, 1961. Intern U. Minn. Hosps., 1957-58; rsch. fellow depts. biochemistry and internal medicine U. Minn., 1958-61, asst. prof. biochemistry, 1963-64; rsch. fellow chemistry dept. Harvard U., Cambridge, Mass., 1962-63; asst. prof. biochemistry U. Ill., 1964-67, assoc. prof., 1967-70; dir. Sch. Basic Med. Scis. U. Ill., Urbana, 1968-1970; prof. U. Ill., 1970-72; prof. biochemistry and chemistry Rice U., Houston, 1972-83, Ralph and Dorothy Looney prof. biochemistry, prof. chemistry, 1983—, dir. lab. basic med. sci., 1987—, chmn. biochemistry dept., 1972-84, sci. dir. Inst. Biosci. and Bioengring., 1987—; vis. scientist Med. Rsch. Coun. Unit Hammersmith Hosp., London, 1961-62; mem. sub-com. on biochem. nomenclature NAS, 1965-68; mem. biochemistry, tng. com. Nat. Inst. Gen. Med. Scis. NIH, 1970-73, ad-hoc com. tng. in biochemistry, 1974; cons. Am. Cyanamid Co., 1984-90, undergrad. biol. scis. edn. panel Howard Hughes Med. Inst., 1988; vis. prof. Sci. and Tech. Agy. Japan, 1993. Assoc. editor Lipids, 1969-76; mem. editorial bd. Jour. Biol. Chemistry, 1974-79, Jour. Lipid Rsch., 1983-88. Fellow AAAS, Arteriosclerosis Coun. of Am. Heart Assn.; mem. Am. Chem. Soc., Am. Soc. Biochemistry and Molecular Biology, Am. Soc. Mass Spectrom, Sigma Xi, Alpha Omega Alpha. Office: Rice U Dept Biochemistry PO Box 1892 Houston TX 77251-1892

SCHROER, BERNARD JON, industrial engineering educator; b. Seymour, Ind., Oct. 11, 1941; s. Alvin J. and Selma A. (Mellencamp) S.; m. Kathleen Dittman, July 5, 1963; children: Shannon, Bradley. BSE, Western Mich. U., 1964; MSE, U. Ala., 1967; PhD, Okla. State U., 1972. Registered profl. engr., Ala. Mech. designer Sandia Labs., Albuquerque, 1962-63; engr. Teledyne Co., Huntsville, Ala., 1964-67, Boeing Co., Huntsville, 1967-70, Computer Sci. Corp., Huntsville, 1970-72; dir. Johnson Ctr. U. Ala., 1972-91, prof., 1991-94, chmn. dept. indsl. and systems engring., 1994—, assoc. v.p. rsch., 1994—; mem. adv. coun. Energy Dept., Montgomery, Ala., 1980-86; bd. dirs So. Solar Energy Ctr., Atlanta, 1980-83; mem. gov.'s cabinet State of Ala., Montgomery, 1982. Author: Modern Apparel Manufacturing Systems and Simulation, 1991; contbr. articles to profl. jours. Named Outstanding Engr., Robotics Internat., 1986, Outstanding Engr., Ala. Soc. Profl. Engrs., 1987; recipient summer traineeship NSF, 1971. Fellow Inst. Indsl. Engr. (pres. 1972, 86, Outstanding Engr. 1973, 77); mem. NSPE, Soc. Computer Simulation, Tech. Transfer Soc., Huntsville Rotary. Lutheran. Home: 716 Owens Dr Huntsville AL 35801 Office: Coll Engring U Ala in Huntsville Huntsville AL 35899

SCHROER, EDMUND ARMIN, utility company executive; b. Hammond, Ind., Feb. 14, 1928; s. Edmund Henry and Florence Evelyn (Schmidt) S.; m. Lisa V. Strope; children: James, Fredrik, Amy, Lisa, Timothy, Suzanne. BA, Valparaiso U., 1949; JD, Northwestern U., 1952. Bar: Ind. 1952. Pvt. practice law Hammond, 1952—; assoc. Crumpacker & Friedrich, 1952; ptnr. Crumpacker & Schroer, 1954-56; assoc., then ptnr. Lawyer, Friedrich, Petrie & Tweedle, 1957-62; ptnr. Lawyer, Schroer & Eichhorn, 1963-66; sr. ptnr. Schroer, Eichhorn & Morrow, Hammond, 1967-77; pres., chief exec. officer No. Ind. Pub. Svc. Co., Inc., Hammond, 1977-93; chmn. No. Ind. Pub. Svc. Co., Hammond, 1978-93, chmn., chief exec. officer, 1989-93, also bd. dirs.; chmn., pres., chief exec. officer NIPSCO Industries, Inc., 1987-93; cons. NIPSCO Industries Inc., Hammond, 1993—; asst. dist. atty., No. Ind., 1954-56; trustee Ill. Ins. Exch., 1993—. Trustee Sch. Bd., Munster, Ind., 1969-71, pres., 1971; fin. chmn. Rep. Party, Hammond, 1958-62; del. Ind. Rep. Conv., 1958, 60, 64, 66, 68. Mem. Fed. Bar Assn., Am. Gas Assn. (com. 1986), Rotary (pres. Hammond club 1968). Lutheran. Home and Office: No Ind Pub Svc Co 5265 Hohman Ave Hammond IN 46320-1721

SCHROER, MARY, state legislator; b. St. Marys, Ohio, Feb. 11, 1947; m. J. Michael Schroer; children: Jennifer, Amy, Rebecca. Student, Washtenaw C.C., Ea. Mich. U. Legis. asst. to State Sen. Lana Pollack Inst. Study of Mental Retardation and Related Disabilities, 1983-92; state rep. 52d dist. State of Mich., 1992—; co-vice chair pub. health com., pub. retirement com.; mem. human svcs. com., children com., ins. com., corrections com. Mem. Washtenaw County (Mich.) Dem. Party, Washtenaw County Area Auto Plant Coaltion, Ann Arbor, Pittsfield Twp. Econ. Deve. Corp. Bd.; past pres. Carpenter Sch. PTO, Ann Arbor; former bd. dirs. Ann Arbor (Mich.) Cmty. Ctr. Roman Catholic. Office: 922 Olds Plz Bldg Lansing MI 48913

SCHROETER, LOUIS C., retired pharmaceutical company executive; b. St. Louis, Dec. 13, 1929; s. Clarence Edward and Eleanor (Schindler) S.; m. Julann Griffin, June 7, 1952; children: John Louis, Lois Celeste, Julie Ann, Robert Louis. BS, St. Louis Coll. Pharmacy, 1952, MS, 1956, DSci. (hon.), 1982; PhD, U. Wis., 1959. Lic. pharmacist, Mo. Rsch. assoc. Upjohn Co., Kalamazoo, 1959-63, head rsch., 1963-66, asst. rsch. mgr., 1966-69, rsch. mgr., 1969-70; exec. dir. Merck, Sharpe & Dohme, West Point, Pa., 1970-73; v.p. pharm. mfg. Upjohn Co., Kalamazoo, 1973-77, v.p. gen. mgr., 1977-85, v.p. worldwide mfg., Eng., 1985-88, corp. sr. v.p., 1988-92; corp. sr. v.p. and asst. to chief exec. officer, 1990-92; chmn. U.S. Pharmacopeia Adv. Panel, 1975; bd. dirs. Nat. Pharm. Coun., Washington, 1979-85, Mich. Pharm. Coun., Lansing, 1981-83; bd. advisers Rsch. Inst. Pharm. Edn., Oxford, Miss., 1985-87. Author: Sulfur Dioxide, 1966, Ingredient X, 1969, Organizational Elan, 1970, Self-Discipline, 1978, Short Stories, 1992. Trustee St. Louis Coll. Pharmacy, 1986-89; chmn. Kalamazoo Symphony Soc., 1980-83, trustee, 1982-87; bd. dirs. Am. Found. Pharm. Edn., N.Y.C., 1985-89. With U.S. Army, 1953-55. Recipient Disting. Svc. to Pharmacy award Alumni St. Louis Coll. Pharmacy, 1968, Citation for Profl. and Literary Accomplishments, U. Wis., 1980. Fellow Acad. Pharm. Scis. (v.p. 1968-69); mem. Am. Pharm. Assn. (mem. exec. com. 1968-72). Republican. Roman Catholic. Avocations: classical music, military history, Roman history, French and German literature.

SCHROETER, RICHARD B., federal official; b. Calif., Sept. 25, 1938; s. David H. and Martha (Berg) S.; m. Eva Wahlang, 1965; children: Jeffry D., Stefanie A. BA, UCLA, 1962, MA, 1966. Fgn. agrl. affairs officer U.S. Mission to European Community, 1970-75; dir., internat. economist market economies divsn. Dept. of Agr., 1975-79, dep. dir. mktg., hort. and tropical products divsn. fgn. agrl. svc., 1979-87, dep. asst. administr., 1987-91, asst. administr., 1991—, acting administr., 1993-94; dep. administr. Intern. Trade Policy, 1994—. Avocations: golfing, fishing. Office: Dept of Agriculture Foreign Agricultural Service 14th & Independence Ave Sw Washington DC 20250

SCHROPP, JAMES HOWARD, lawyer; b. Lebanon, Pa., June 20, 1943; s. Howard J. and Maud E. (Parker) S.; m. Jo Ann Simpson, Sept. 4, 1965; children: James A., John C., Jeffrey M., Jeremy M. BA, U. Richmond, 1965; JD, Georgetown U., 1973. Bar: D.C. 1973, U.S. Supreme Ct. 1980. Asst. gen. counsel SEC, Washington, 1973-79; ptnr. Fried, Frank, Harris, Shriver & Jacobson, Washington, 1979—; adj. prof. Georgetown U., Washington, 1982-86. Mem. ABA (discovery com. litigation sect. 1984-86, tender offer litigation subcom. corp. banking and bus. law sect. 1985-86, task force on broker-dealer compliance supervisory procedures 1987-89). Office: Fried Frank Harris Shriver & Jacobson 1001 Pennsylvania Ave NW Washington DC 20004-2505

SCHROTE, JOHN ELLIS, retired government executive; b. Findlay, Ohio, May 6, 1931; s. Millard L. and Alberta (Ellis) S.; m. Rachel Daly, Mar. 2, 1957; children: James D., Gretchen Schrote Kent. BS in Agriculture, Ohio State U., 1958; MBA, Xavier U., 1964. Buyer-expediter McGraw Constrn. Co., Middletown, Ohio, 1958-59; buyer Armco Corp., Middletown, 1959-66; adminstrv. asst. Congressman D.E. Lukens, Washington, 1967-71; prin. asst. dir. OEO, Washington, 1971-72; spl. asst. sec. USDA, Washington, 1972-76, nat. rep. congl. com., 1976-79, acting asst. sec., 1981-82; adminstrv. asst. Congressman F.J. Sensenbrenner, Jr., Washington, 1979-81, 1984-89; dep. dir. presdl. pers. office The White House, 1982-83; exec. v.p. Bishop Bryant & Assocs., Washington, 1983-84; asst. to sec. and dir. congl. affairs Dept. Interior, Washington, 1989, dep. asst. sec. policy mgmt. and budget, 1989-91, asst. sec. policy mgmt. and budget, 1992-93; retired, 1993. Mem. 1994 Nat. Policy Forum/The Environ. Policy Coun., Currituck County Ext. Svc. Adv. Leadership Coun., Currituck County Rep. Exec. Com., 3d Dist. Rep. Exec. Com., N.C. State Rep. Exec. Com. Episcopalian. Home: PO Box 609 Corolla NC 27927

SCHROTH, PETER W(ILLIAM), lawyer, management and law educator; b. Camden, N.J., July 24, 1946; s. Walter and Patricia Anne (Page) S.; children: Laura Salome Erickson-Schroth, Julia James. AB, Shimer Coll., 1966; JD, U. Chgo., 1969; M in Comparative Law, U.Chgo., 1971; SJD, U. Mich., 1979; postgrad., U. Freiburg, Fed. Republic Germany, Faculté Internationale pour l'Enseignement de Droit Comparé; MBA, Rensselaer Poly. Inst., 1988. Bar: Ill. 1969, N.Y. 1979, Conn. 1985, Mass. 1990. Asst. prof. So. Meth. U., 1973-77; fellow in law and humanities Harvard U., 1976-77, vis. scholar, 1980-81; assoc. prof. N.Y. Law Sch., 1977-81; prof. law Hamline U., St. Paul, 1981-83; dep. gen. counsel Equator Bank Ltd., 1984-87; v.p., dep. gen. counsel Equator Holdings Ltd., 1987-94, v.p., gen. counsel, 1994—; adj. prof. law U. Conn., 1985-86, Western New Eng. Coll., 1988—; adj. prof. of mgmt. Hartford Grad. Ctr., 1988—. Author: Foreign Investment in the United States, 2d edit., 1977, (with Stiefel) Products Liability: European Proposals and American Experience, 1981, Doing Business in Sub-Saharan Africa, 1991; bd. editors Am. Jour. Comparative Law, 1981-84, 91—, Conn. Bar Jour., N.Y. Internat. Law Rev.; contbr. articles to profl. jours. Mem. ABA (editor in chief ABA Environ. Law Symposium 1980-82), Am. Soc. Comparative Law (bd. dirs. 1978-84, 91—), Am. Fgn. Law Assn., Internat. Bar Assn., Internat. Law Assn. (com. multinat. banking), Acad. Internat. Bus., Conn. Civil Liberties Union (bd. dirs. 1985-92), Environ. Law Inst. (assoc.), Columbia U. Peace Seminar (assoc.), Hartford Club (bd. govs. 1995—). Office: Equator House 45 Glastonbury Blvd Glastonbury CT 06033-4411

SCHROTH, THOMAS NOLAN, editor; b. Trenton, N.J., Dec. 21, 1920; s. Frank David and Loretta (Nolan) S.; m. Colette Streit, May 1, 1948 (div. 1958); 1 child, Valerie; m. Patricia Wiggins, Sept. 27, 1958; children: Jennifer, Amy, Anne. Student, Tuck Sch. Bus. Adminstrn., 1942; AB, Dartmouth Coll., 1943. Reporter Time, Washington, 1946-47, UPI, Boston, 1947-48; reporter, news editor Bklyn. Eagle, 1948-51, mng. editor, 1951-55; editorial adviser Magnum Photos, Inc., N.Y.C., 1955; exec. editor, pub. Congl. Quar. Inc. and Editorial Research Reports, Washington, 1955-68; founder, editor Nat. Jour. Ctr. Polit. Rsch., Washington, 1969-70; communications adviser Pub. Broadcasting Environment Ctr., Washington, 1970-71; asst. dir. pub. affairs for communications EPA, Washington, 1970-71, cons., 1972; exec. editor The Ellsworth (Maine) American, 1972-77; co-pub.-editor (with Patricia Schroth) Maine Life Mag., Sedgwick, 1977-81; editorial cons. U. Maine, Bangor, 1976-90; mng. editor South-North News Svc., Hanover, N.H., 1987-91; co-pub. New Leaf Pubs., Sedgwick, Maine, 1990—; editor Improving the U. of Maine trustees' pamphlet; mem. Am. Press Inst. Seminar for Mng. Editors, 1953; bd. dirs. Downeast Transp., Inc., Ellsworth, pres., 1994—. Editor: Congress and the Nation 1946-64—A Review of Government and Politics in the Postwar Years. Elected selectman Town of Sedgwick, 1987, 89, 90; bd. dirs. Blue Hill (Maine) Meml. Hosp., 1978-93, Bangor Symphony Orch., 1981-87; bd. dirs., v.p. Island Nursing Home, Deer Isle, Maine, 1985—; mem. Maine State Dem. Com., Augusta, 1985-92. 1st lt. Army Airways Comm. Sys., USAAF, WWII. Mem. Sigma Delta Chi. Avocations: gardening, walking, music. Home and Office: 50 Benjamin River Rd Sedgwick ME 04676-9729

SCHRUM, ED P., manufacturing company executive; b. 1927. Grad., N.C. State U., 1951. With Carolina Mills, Inc., Maiden, N.C., 1951—, pres., 1976-86, pres., chief exec. officer, treas., 1986—; also bd. dirs. Office: Carolina Mills Inc 618 N Carolina Ave Maiden NC 28650-1100*

SCHRUM, JAKE BENNETT, university administrator; b. Greenville, Tex., Feb. 9, 1946; s. Jake M. and Julia (Bennett) S.; m. Alice Woodman, Dec. 28, 1968; children: Julia Elizabeth, Emily Katharine. B.A., Southwestern U., 1968; M.Div., Yale U., 1973; postgrad. Harvard U., 1983. Ordained to ministry Methodist Ch., 1969. Devel. officer Yale U., New Haven, 1973-77; dir. devel. Muhlenberg Coll., Allentown, Pa., 1977-78; v.p. Tex. Wesleyan Coll., Fort Worth, 1978-82; v.p. univ. rels. Southwestern U., Georgetown, Tex., 1982-85; v.p. Emory U., Atlanta, 1985-91; pres. Tex. Wesleyan U., 1991-95; chmn. CASE; bd. dirs. Bd. Ind. Colls. & Univs. Tex., Bd. Tex. Ind. Coll. Found.; trustee United Way; adv. bd. Fort Worth Habitat for Humanity. Mem. Coun. Advancement and Support Edn., Rotary. Avocations: squash, golf, racquetball, tennis. Office: Texas Wesleyan University 1201 Wesleyan Fort Worth TX 76105

SCHRUPP, WALTER CLAIR, air force officer; b. Canby, Minn., Apr. 29, 1931; s. Walter Henry and Esther Bertina (Berg) S.; m. Faye Hackney, Nov. 23, 1956; children—Walter Clair Jr., Elizabeth Ann, Laurie Marie. B.S., U.S. Mil. Acad., 1954; M.S. in Mech. Engring., U. Nebr., 1963; M.S. in Bus. Adminstrn., George Washington U., 1966; student, Nat. War Coll., 1970-71. Cert. pilot, navigator. Commd. 1st lt. U.S. Air Force, 1956, advanced through grades to maj. gen., 1981, ret., 1985; co-pilot, aircraft comdr. U.S. Air Force, Lincoln AFB, Nebr., 1956-61; served with Space Systems div. Air Force Systems Command, Los Angeles, 1961-65; flight comdr. 366th factical fighter wing Da Nang Air Base, Republic of Vietnam, 1966-67; legis. liaison directorate Office of Sec. of Air Force, Washington, 1967-70; vice comdr. 97th bombardment wing Blytheville AFB, Ark., 1971-72; vice comdr. 7th bombardment wing Carswell AFB, Tex., 1972-74; vice comdr. 17th air div. (provisional) U-Tapao Royal Thai Naval Airfield, Thailand, 1973; chief strategic div., dep. dir. for operational forces, dep. dir. ops. and readiness Washington, 1974-76; chief Air Force sect. Joint U.S. Mil., 1977-79; comdr. 40th air div. Wurtsmith AFB, Mich., 1979-80; vice comdr. 8th Air Force strategic air command Barksdale AFB, La., 1980-83; dep. chief of staff, insp. gen. U.S. Pacific Command, Camp Smith, Hawaii, 1983-85; vice chancellor Nat. U., San Diego, 1985—. Decorated Legion of Merit with one oak leaf cluster, D.F.C., Bronze Star, Def. Meritorious Service medal, Meritorious Service medal, Air medal with seven oak leaf clusters, A.F. Commendation medal with one oak leaf cluster, Purple Heart, Presdl. Unit Citation emblem, Combat Readiness medal, Humanitarian Service medal. Mem. Order of Daedalians, Red River Rats. Club: Pink Fish and Game (Tawas City, Mich.). Avocations: golf, hunting, fishing, jogging, cooking. Office: Waco Regional Airport Rt 10 Box 173-T Waco TX 76708 Home: 11938 Prospect Hill Dr Gold River CA 95670-7519

SCHRUTT, NORMAN, broadcast company executive; b. Buffalo; m. Lynda Schrutt; 2 children. Attended, U. Buffalo. Acct. exec. Sta. WKBW-AM Radio, Buffalo, 1963-70, sales mgr., 1970-77, v.p., gen. mgr., 1977-80; v.p., gen. mgr. Sta. KZLA-AM/FM Radio, L.A., 1980-81; pres., gen. mgr. WKHX-AM/FM, Atlanta, 1981-87; pres. Capital Cities/ABC Radio Networks- Group II, N.Y.C., 1987—; responsible daily ops. of ten stas. including WLS-AM/FM, Chgo., WAML-AM/WRQX-FM, Washington, WBAP-AM/KSCS-FM, Dallas, Fort Worth, WKHX-AM/FM, Atlanta, KQRS-AM/FM, Mpls.; bd. dirs. Better Bus. Bur., Atlanta. Recipient Gabriel award, 1980, Clio award, 1981 for writing and producing pub. svc. Mem. Assn. Country Music Stas., Ga. Assn. Broadcasters, Cobb C. of C. (bd. dirs.), Georgian Club. Office: Capital Cities/ABC Broadcast Group 77 W 66th St New York NY 10023

SCHTEINGART, DAVID EDUARDO, internist; b. Buenos Aires, Oct. 17, 1930; came to U.S., 1957; s. Mario and Flora (Garfunkel) S.; m. Monica Naomi Starkman, July 3, 1960; children: Miriam, Judith, M. Daniel. MD, U. Buenos Aires, 1955. Diplomate Am. Bd. Internal Medicine. Fellow Mt. Sinai Hosp., N.Y.C., 1957-58, Maimonides Hosp., Bklyn., 1958-59; fellow U. Mich., Ann Arbor, 1959-62, instr., 1962-63, asst. prof., 1963-68, assoc. prof., 1968-72, prof., 1972—. Contbr. articles to profl. jours., books. Pres. Beth Israel Congregation, Ann Arbor, 1974-79, Hebrew Day Sch., Ann Arbor, 1984-86, Jewish Fedn. Washtenaw County, Ann Arbor. Recipient rsch. grants NIH, Bethesda, Md., 1985—. Fellow Am. Coll. Physicians; mem. Endocrine Soc., N.Y. Acad. Scis., Am. Soc. Clin. Nutrition, Cen. Soc. Clin. Rsch., Am. Fedn. Clin. Rsch. Jewish. Avocations: tennis, running, community activities. Office: U Mich Med Sch Rm 5570 MSRB II Box 0678 1150 W Medical Center Dr Ann Arbor MI 48109-0678

SCHUBART, MARK ALLEN, arts and education executive; b. N.Y.C., May 24, 1918; s. Henry Allen and Pauline (Wartenberg) S. Student pvt. schs., U.S. and France; studied, piano with Celia Wolberg, theory with Marion Nugent, flute with Ruth Freeman, composition with Roger Sessions. Assoc. editor Eton Pub. Corp., 1937-40; asst. music editor newspaper PM, 1940-44; music editor N.Y. Times, 1944-46; dir. pub. activities Juilliard Sch. Music, 1946-49, dean, v.p., 1949-62; exec. dir. The Lincoln Center Fund, Lincoln Center Performing Arts, Inc., N.Y.C., 1963-66; dir. edn. Lincoln Center Performing Arts, Inc., 1966-75; dir. Lincoln Center Inst., 1975-90, pres., 1990—, chmn. council on ednl. programs; bd. dirs. The MacDowell Colony. Composer two song cycles, opera, concert overture, songs.; Author: Performing Arts Institutions and Young People; Contbr. articles profl. jour. Home: 30 Park Ave New York NY 10016 Office: 70 Lincoln Center Plz New York NY 10023-6548

SCHUBEL, JERRY ROBERT, marine science educator, scientist, university dean and official; b. Bad Axe, Mich., Jan. 26, 1936; s. Theodore Howard and Laura Alberta (Gobel) S.; m. Margaret Ann Hostetler, June 14, 1958; children: Susan Elizabeth, Kathryn Ann. BS, Alma Coll., 1957; MA in Teaching, Harvard U., 1959; PhD, Johns Hopkins U., 1968. Rsch. assoc. Chesapeake Bay Inst., Johns Hopkins U., Balt., 1968-69, rsch. scientist, 1969-74, adj. rsch. prof., assoc. dir., 1973-74; dir. Marine Sci. Rsch. Ctr. SUNY, Stony Brook, 1974-83; dean, leading prof. SUNY, Stony Brook, 1983-94; acting dir. Waste Mgmt. Inst., SUNY, Stony Brook, 1985-87; provost SUNY, Stony Brook, 1986-89; dir. COAST Inst., SUNY, Stony Brook, 1989; Disting. Svc. prof. SUNY, Stony Brook, 1994-95, prof. emeritus, 1995—; pres., CEO The New Eng. Aquarium, Boston, 1994—; hon. prof. East China Normal U., Shanghai, 1985—; asst. exec. com. Commn. on Food, Environment and Renewable Resources, 1993, chair steering com., 1994; mem. governing bd. Regional Marine Rsch. Program, Greater N.Y. Bight, 1993-94. Author: The Living Chesapeake, 1981, The Life and Death of the Chesapeake Bay, 1986; (with H.A. Neal) Solid Waste Management and the Environment, 1987, Garbage and Trash: Can We Convert Mountains Into Molehills?, 1992; editor: (with B. C. Marcy Jr.) Power Plant Entrainment, 1978; (with others) The Great South Bay, 1991; sr. editor Coastal Ocean Pollution Assement News, 1981-86; co-editor in chief Estuaries, 1986-88; editorial bd. CRC Revs. in Aquatic Scis.; contbr. articles to profl. jours. Mem. Environ. Sci. Com. Outer Continental Shelf Adv. Bd., Minerals Mgmt. Svc., 1984-86, chmn., 1986; bd. dirs. N.E. Area Remote Sensing System, 1983-85, L.I. Incubator Corp.; v.p. L.I. Forum for Tech., 1989-92. Recipient L.I. Sound Am. Environment Edn. award, 1987, Stony Brook U. medal, 1989, Matthew Fontaine Maury award, 1990, Ben Gurion U. medal, 1993; Alfred P. Sloan fellow, 1959. Mem. NAS (marine bd. 1989-94, exec. com. 1990, vice chair 1991—, chair 1992-94, com. on Coastal Ocean 1989-93), Nat. Assn. State Univ. and Land Grant Colls. (bd. dirs. marine divsn., chmn. 1990-94), L.I. Environ. Coun., L.I. Marine Resources Adv. Coun. (chair 1990-94), L.I. Rsch. Inst. (bd. dirs. 1992-94), L.I. Environ.-Econ. Roundtable (co-chair 1991-92), Suffolk County Recycling Commn. (chmn. 1987-88), Esuarine Rsch. Fedn. (v.p. 1982-83, pres. 1985-87), N.Y. Sea Grant Inst. (chmn. governing bd. 1988-90, gov.'s task force on coastal resources 1990-91), The Nature Conservancy (trustee L.I. chpt. 1991-94), Franklin Electronic Pubs. (bd. dirs. 1991—), Taproot (bd. dirs. 1988-93, vice chair 1990-93), Sigma Xi, Phi Sigma Pi. Avocation: photography. Home: 10 Thacher St Apt 115 Boston MA 02113 Office: SUNY at Stony Brook Marine Sci Rsch Ctr Stony Brook NY 11794

SCHUBER, WILLIAM PATRICK, lawyer; b. Teaneck, N.J., Apr. 15, 1947; s. William A. and Mary E. (Cleary) S. B.A., Fordham U., 1969, J.D., 1972. Bar: N.J. 1972, U.S. Supreme Ct. 1976. Assoc. Contant, Contant, Schuber, Scherby & Atkins, Hackensack, N.J., 1972-79, ptnr., 1979—; adj. prof. Montclair State Coll., 1983—. Mem. Bergen County Housing Devel. Authority; councilman Borough of Bogota, 1972-79, mayor, 1979-83; mem. N.J. Gen. Assembly, 1981—. Served to capt. USAR, 1969-83. Mem. N.J. Bar Assn., Bergen County Bar Assn., Assn. Trial Lawyers Am., Republican. Roman Catholic. Club: Hackensack Rotary. Home: 1042 Wildwood Rd Oradell NJ 07649-1332 Office: Office the County Exec Admin Bldg Court Plz S 21 Main St Rm 300E Hackensack NJ 07601-7021

SCHUBERT, BARBARA SCHUELE, performing company executive; b. Cleve., Feb. 21, 1939; d. William Edward and Mildred Marianne (Matousek) Schuele; m. John Dwan Schubert, June 15, 1963; children: William Edward, Christopher John, David Matthew. BS in Social Scis., John Carroll U, 1962, MA in English, 1967; MEd, 1980. Cert. secondary tchr., elem. remedial reading tchr., Ohio. Tchr. Sch. on Magnolia, Cleve., 1980-82, Ruffing Montessori, Cleve., 1982-83; tchr. English U. Sch., Chagrin Falls, Ohio, 1983-86; gen. mgr. Ohio Ballet, Akron, 1987-90, assoc. dir., 1990—; bd. trustees Ohio Ballet, 1974-87. Bd. dirs. John Carroll U., 1990—; active Beaumont Sch., Internat. Ballet Coun. Roman Catholic. Club: Cleve. Skating. Office: Ohio Ballet 354 W Market St Akron OH 44303-2027

SCHUBERT, GLENDON, political scientist, educator; b. Oneida, N.Y., June 7, 1918; s. Glendon Austin and Agnes (Rogers) S.; m. Elizabeth Josephine Neal (dec. 1949); children: Frank, James; m. Elizabeth Harris; children: Susan, Kathleen, Robin. A.B., Syracuse U., 1940, Ph.D., 1948. Mem. faculties Syracuse U., 1946-48, UCLA, 1948-49, Howard U., 1949-50, Rutgers U., 1950-51; formerly univ. prof.; Mem. faculties Franklin and Marshall Coll., 1951-52, Mich. State U., 1952-67, U. Minn., 1955; formerly William Rand Kenan, Jr. prof. polit. sci. U. N.C. at Chapel Hill, 1967-68; formerly Univ. prof. York U., 1968-70; now univ. prof. polit. sci. U. Hawaii, 1970—; formerly Rsch. Prof. Polit. Sci. So. Ill. U. at Carbondale, 1986-91; Fulbright lectr. U. Oslo, Norway, 1959-60; fellow Center for Advanced Study in Behavioral Scis., 1960-61; sr. scholar in residence Center for Cultural and Tech. Interchange Between East and West, U. Hawaii, 1963-64, 65; Fulbright-Hays research scholar, Netherlands, 1977; NSF faculty fellow U. Groningen, Netherlands, 1977-78; NATO sr. fellow, U.K.; fellow Netherlands Inst. Advanced Study Humanities and Social Sci., Wassenaar, Netherlands, 1978-79. Author over 25 books; assoc. editor for biosocial behavior The Behavioral and Brain Sci.; adv. editor Jour. Social and Evolutionary Systems, Politics and the Life Scis.; contbr. articles to profl. jours. in biobehavioral and polit. sci., and pub. policy. Served with Signal Intelligence U.S. Army, 1942-46. Decorated Bronze Star; recipient Regents' medal and award for excellence in research U. Hawaii, 1975. Mem. Am. Polit. Sci. Assn. (past mem. exec. coun.), Pacific Life Scis. (past pres.), Internat. Soc. Human Ethology, Phi Beta Kappa. Office: Univ Hawaii Dept Polit Sci 2424 Maile Way Honolulu HI 96822-2223

SCHUBERT, GUENTHER ERICH, pathologist; b. Mosul, Iraq, Aug. 17, 1930; s. Erich Waldemar and Martha Camilla (Zschitzschmann) S.; m. Gisela Schultz, June 13, 1959; children: Frank, Marion, Dirk. MD, University, Heidelberg, Germany, 1957; pvt. docent in pathology, University, Tuebingen, Germany, 1966. Asst. med. dir. University Tuebingen, Fed. Republic of Germany, 1966-76; head Inst. Pathology, Wuppertal, Fed. Republic of Germany, 1976—; chair of pathology U. Witten-Herdecke, Fed. Republic of Germany, 1985—. Co-author: Coloratlas of Cytodiagnosis of the Prostate, 1975, Endoscopy of the Urinary Bladder, 1989; author: Textbook of Pathology, 1981, 87. Mem. Wissenschaftlicher Beirat, Bundesarztekammer, Bonn, Germany, 1976-85; pres. Medizinisch Naturwissenschaftliche Gesellschaft, Wuppertal, 1984-85, Onkologischer Arbeitsgemeinschaft, Wuppertal, 1985-93, OSP Bergisch-Land, 1992—, Bergische Arbeitsgemeinschaft fur Gastroenterologie, Wuppertal, 1987-88, 1990-91, 94-95. Mem. Deutsche Gesellschaft fur Pathologie, Deutsche Gesellschaft fur Nephrologie, Deutsche Gesellschaft fur Urologie, Internat. Acad. of Pathology, Lions. Avocations: music, diving, photography. Home: Am Anschlag 71, D-42ii3 Wuppertal 1, Germany Office: Inst of Pathology, Heusner Strasse 40, 42 283 Wuppertal 2, Germany

SCHUBERT, JOHN EDWARD, former banker; b. Rochester, N.Y., Jan. 22, 1912; s. Charles A. and Matilda M. (von Rohr) S.; m. Margaret Cecelia la Plante, Nov. 11, 1939 (dec. Jan. 1977); children: Susan R. (Mrs. Dennis E. Coyne), Patricia S. (Mrs. Daniel L. Starks); m. Florence Margaret Moran, Nov. 14, 1977 (dec. Dec. 1978); m. Rita H. Strowe, Mar. 27, 1993. Student, Syracuse U., 1929-30; grad., Rochester Bus. Inst., 1932; hon. degree accounting, 1955; grad., Rutgers U. Grad. Sch. Banking, 1950. With Security Trust Co., Rochester, 1930-44; with Community Savs. Bank, Rochester, 1944-77; pres., chief exec. officer Community Savs. Bank, 1965-73, chmn. chief exec. officer, 1973-75, chmn., 1976-77; dir. Seneca Towers, Inc. Rochester Mgmt. Inc.; realtor Real Estate Bd. Rochester; assoc. Red Barn Properties, Inc. Bd. dirs. Met. Rochester Found., Inc., Sr. Citizens Homes, Inc.; bd. dirs. Automobile Club Rochester, pres., 1977; trustee emeritus Rochester Inst. Tech. Mem. Oak Hill Country Club (v.p. 1964-67, bd. govs. 1962-68, 78-81), Beta Gamma Sigma (hon. U. Rochester chpt.). Home: 18 Winding Brook Dr Fairport NY 14450-2541 Office: 6 Schoen Pl Pittsford NY 14534

SCHUBERT, RICHARD FRANCIS, foundation administrator; b. Trenton, N.J., Nov. 2, 1936; s. Yaro and Frances Mary (Hustak) S.; m. Sarah Jane Lockington, Aug. 24, 1957; children: Robyn, David. BA cum laude, Eastern Nazarene Coll., 1958; LLB, Yale U., 1961. Bar: Pa. 1962, U.S. Supreme Ct 1972. Arbitration atty. Bethlehem Steel Corp., Pa., 1961-66; asst. mgr. labor relations Bethlehem Steel Corp., 1966-70; exec. asst. to undersec. labor Washington, 1970; gen. counsel labor, 1971-73, dep. sec. labor, 1973-75; asst. to v.p. indsl. relations Bethlehem Steel Corp., 1973, asst. v.p. public affairs, 1975-77, v.p. public affairs, 1977-79, pres., 1979-80, vice chmn., 1980-82; pres. ARC, 1982-89; pres., CEO Points of Light Found., 1990—; bd. dirs. Weirton Steel, Mgmt. Tng. Corp. Bd. dirs. Nat. Alliance of Bus., Inst. Ethics, Cmty. Hope, Inc.; chmn. Nat. Youth Found., Biorelease Inc., Nazarene Compassionate Ministries; vice chmn. Peter F. Drucker Found. Mem. Pa. Bar Assn., Northampton County Bar Assn., Coun. on Fgn. Rels., Am. Iron and Steel Inst. (past chmn. com. on internat. trade), Ctr. Excellence Govt., Ea. Nazarene Alumni Assn. (pres. 1969-73), Phi Alpha Delta. Mem. Ch. of Nazarene. Home: 7811 Old Dominion Dr Mc Lean VA 22102-2425 Office: 1737 H St Washington DC 20006

SCHUBERT, RONALD HAYWARD, SR., retired aerospace engineer; b. Bklyn., Aug. 25, 1932; s. John and Joan Sarah (Hayward) S.; m. Dorothy May Smith, Mar. 5, 1953 (div. 1961); children: Marcus H., Malcolm F., Ronald J. (dec.), Ann E.; m. Linda Jane van der Ploeg, Mar. 6, 1961 (div. 1988). BA cum laude, Ohio State U., 1956. Assoc. engr. Hughes Aircraft Co., Fullerton, Calif., 1957-61; physicist Nat. Cash Register Co., Dayton, Ohio, 1962-63; sr. research engr. Lockheed Missiles and Space Co., Sunnyvale, Calif., 1963-90. Served as staff sgt. USMC, 1951-54. Recipient Hon. mention Woodrow Wilson Fellowship Com. Mem. Phi Beta Kappa. Democrat. Roman Catholic. Achievements include pioneering work in reconnaissance satellite orbit concealment; devel. of digital computer simulations for all aspects of the aerospace mission and its environment; guidance system and autopilot specialist. Home: 201 W California # 1023 Sunnyvale CA 94086

SCHUBERT, WILLIAM HENRY, curriculum studies educator; b. Garrett, Ind., July 6, 1944; s. Walter William and Mary Madeline (Grube) S.; children by previous marriage: Ellen Elaine, Karen Margaret; m. Ann Lynn Lopez, Dec. 3, 1977; children: Heidi Ann, Henry William. BS, Manchester Coll., 1966; MS, Ind. U., 1967; PhD, U. Ill., 1975. Tchr., Fairmount, Ill. Sierra and Herrick Schs., Downers Grove, Ill., 1967-75; clin. instr. U. Wis., Madison, 1969-73; teaching asst., univ. fellow U. Ill., Urbana, 1973-75; asst. prof. U. Ill., Chgo., 1975-80, assoc. prof., 1981-85, prof., 1985—, coord. secondary edn., 1979-82; coord. instrl. leadership, 1979-85, dir. grad. studies Coll. Edn., 1983-85, coord. grad. curriculum studies, 1985—, coord. edn. studies, 1990-94, chair area curriculum and instruction, 1990-94; vis. assoc. prof. U. Victoria (B.C., Can.), 1981; disting. vis. prof. U. S.C., 1986. Mem. Profs. of Curriculum (factotum 1984-85), Soc. for Study of Curriculum History (founding mem., sec.-treas. 1981-82, pres. 1982-83), Am. Ednl. Rsch. Assn. (chmn. creation and utilization of curriculum knowledge 1980-82, program chmn. curriculum studies div. 1982-83, sec. Div. B 1989-91), Am. Assn. Colls. for Tchr. Edn., John Dewey Soc. (bd. dirs. 1986-95, chair awards com., 1988-90, co-chair lectures commn., 1989-91, pres. elect, 1990-91, pres. 1992-93), Assn. for Supervision and Curriculum Devel. (steering com. of curriculum com. 1980-83, pubs. com. 1987-90, internat. polling panel 1990—), Am. Ednl. Studies Assn., World Coun. for Curriculum and Instrn., Soc. for Profs. of Edn., Nat. Soc. for Study of Edn., Inst. Dem. in Edn., Masons, Scottish Rite, Phi Delta Kappa, Phi Kappa Phi (pres. U. Ill.-Chgo. chpt. 1981-82). Author: (with Ann Lopez) Curriculum Books: The First Eighty Years, 1980; author: Curriculum: Perspective, Paradigm, and Possibility, 1986; editor: (with Ann Lopez) Conceptions of Curriculum Knowledge: Focus on Students and Teachers, 1982, (with Edmund C. Short and George Willis) Toward Excellence in Curriculum Inquiry, 1985, (with George Willis) Reflections from The Heart of Ednl. Inquiry: Understanding Curriculum and Teaching Through the Arts, 1991, (with William Ayers) Teacher Lore: Learning From Our Own Experience, 1992, (with George Willis, R. Bullough, C. Kridel, J. Holton) The American Curriculum: A Documentary History, 1993; assoc. editor: Ednl. Theory; former mem. editorial bd. Ednl. Studies; cons. editor Phenomenology Pedagogy; adv. bd. Teaching Edn.; mem. editorial bd. Ednl. Theory; cons. editor Jour. Curriculum and Supervision; editorial bd. Curriculum and Teaching; reviewing editor Gang Jour.; editor: book series Student Lore, SUNY Press, 1990—; cons. editor Jour. Curriculum Discourse and Dialogue; contbr. over 150 articles to profl. publs. Recipient Scholar-Tchr. award in Coll. Edn., 1988. Home: 727 S Ashland Ave Chicago IL 60607-3165 Office: U Ill Coll Edn M/C 147 1040 W Harrison St Chicago IL 60607-7129

SCHUBERT, WILLIAM KUENNETH, hospital medical center executive; b. Cin., July 12, 1926; s. Wilfred Schubert and Amanda Kuenneth; m. Mary Jane Pamperin, June 5, 1948; children: Carol, Joanne, Barbara, Nancy. BS, U. Cin., 1949, MD, 1952. Diplomate Am. Bd. Pediatrics. Pvt. practice specializing in pediatrics Cin., 1956-63; dir. clin. research ctr. Children's Hosp. Med. Ctr., Cin., 1963-76; dir. div. gastroenterology Children's Hosp., Cin., 1968-79; prof. pediatrics U. Cin., 1969—, assoc. sr. v.p. for children's hosp. affairs Coll. Medicine, 1993—; chief of staff Children's Hosp. Med. Ctr., Cin., 1972-88; chmn. dept. pediatrics U. Cin., 1979-93; dir. Children's Hosp. Rsch. Found., Cin., 1979-93; pres., CEO Children's Hosp. Med. Ctr., Cin., 1983—; v.p. Ohio Solid Organ Transplant Consortium, Columbus 1986-87, pres., 1987-88, alt. trustee, 1988—; regional bd. dirs. Ameritrust Corp., 1988-91; trustee med. rsch. James N. Gamble Inst., Cin., 1989—. Contbr. over 100 articles to profl. jours. Trustee Greater Cin. Hosp. Coun., 1986—, Assn. of Ohio Children's Hosp., Columbus, 1986—, The Springer Sch., Cin., 1994—; chmn. Greater Cin. Hosp. Coun., 1989; co-chmn. Citizen's Com. for Med. Ctr., Cin., 1980-81; chmn. Hosp. Divsn. 1988 Fine Arts Fund, Cin., 1987; hon. trustee Babies' Milk Fund, Children's and Prenatal Clinics, Cin., 1994—. Fellow Am. Acad. Pediatrics; mem. Am. Pediatric Soc. (councillor 1986-93), Soc. Pediatric Research, Assn. Med. Sch. Pediatric Dept. Chmn., Am. Acad. Medicine, AMA, Midwestern Soc. for Pediatric Research, Am. Soc. for Study of Liver Diseases, Central Soc. Clin. Research, Am. Gastroenterological Assn., N.Am. Soc. Pediatric Gastroenterology, Nat. Reye's Syndrome Found. (med. dir. 1976-87), Internat. Assn. Study Liver Diseases. Club: Queen City (Cin.). Office: Children's Hosp Med Ctr 3333 Burnet Ave Cincinnati OH 45229-3039

SCHUCHART, JOHN ALBERT, JR., utility executive; b. Omaha, Nov. 13, 1929; s. John A. and Mildred Vera (Kessler) S.; m. Ruth Joyce Schock, Dec. 2, 1950; children: Deborah J. Kelley, Susan K. Felton. BS in Bus. U. Nebr., 1950; grad., Stanford U. Exec. Program, 1968. With No. Natural Gas Co., Omaha, 1950-71, asst. sec., 1958-60, mgr. acctg., 1960-66, adminstrv. mgr., 1966-71; v.p., treas. Intermountain Gas Co., Boise, Idaho, 1972-75, chief fin. officer, 1973-75; fin. v.p. and treas., chief fin. officer Mont.-Dakota Utilities Co. (now MDU Resources Group, Inc.), Bismarck, N.D., 1976-77, pres., chief oper. officer, 1978-80, pres., 1980-92, CEO, 1980-94, chmn. bd., 1983—, also dir. Contbr. articles to profl. jours. Trustee Bismarck YMCA, N.D. chpt. Nature Conservancy; mem. bd. regents U. Mary, Bismarck; vice chair bus. adv. bd. Coll. Bus., Mont. State U., Billings. With AUS, 1951-53. Recipient Am. Gas Assn. Order of Acctg. Merit merit award, 1978, Scroll and Merit award Adminstrv. Mgmt. Soc., 1972, U. Nebr. at Omaha citation of Alumnus Achievement, 1987, Coll. of Bus. Disting. Achievement award, 1989, CEO of Yr. award Fin. World Mag., 1993, Comm. and Leadership award Dist. 20 Toastmasters Internat., 1994. Mem. Apple Creek Country Club, Mpls. Athletic Club, Elks, Delta Sigma Pi. Republican. Methodist. Home: 1014 Cottage Dr Bismarck ND 58501-2458 Office: MDU Resources Group Inc 400 N 4th St Bismarck ND 58501-4022

SCHUCHERT, JOSEPH, light manufacturing executive. Ceo Kelso & Co. Inc., N.Y.C., 1980—. Office: Kelso Asi Partners 350 Park Ave Fl 21 New York NY 10022-6022

SCHUCK, CARL JOSEPH, lawyer; b. Phila., Nov. 21, 1915; s. Joseph and Christina (Schadl) S.; m. Mary Elizabeth Box, June 7, 1941; children: Mary Ann (dec.), John, James, Catherine, Christopher. BS, St. Mary's Coll., 1937; postgrad., U. So. Calif., 1937-38; JD, Georgetown U., 1941. Bar: D.C. 1941, Calif. 1943, U.S. Supreme Ct. 1952. Atty. Dept. Justice, Washington, 1940-42, Alien Property Custodian, San Francisco, 1942-44; mem. firm Overton, Lyman & Prince, L.A., 1947-79, profl. corp. mem. firm, 1979-85; lectr. Practising Law Inst., 1973; Del. 9th Cir. Jud. Conf., 1963-80, chmn. lawyer-

---

dels. com., 1972, mem. exec. com., 1976-80, chmn. exec. com., 1977-78, mem. sr. adv. bd., 1989-95; mem. disciplinary bd. State Bar Calif., 1970-71. Fellow Am. Coll. Trial Lawyers (chmn. com. on complex litigation 1979-81, regent 1981-85), L.A. County Bar Assn. (trustee 1974-76), Phi Alpha Delta. Club: Chancery (pres. 1984-85). Home and Office: 4723 Cordoba Way Oceanside CA 92056-5109

SCHUCK, JOYCE HABER, author; b. N.Y.C., Dec. 9, 1937; d. Frank F. and Florence (Smith) H.; m. Stephen Martin Schuck, June 15, 1958; children: William David, Thomas Allen, Ann Elizabeth. BA in Human Svcs. and Counseling, Loretto Hts. Coll., Denver, 1982. Counselor, tchr. Vision Quest, Colorado Springs, 1979-82; cons., program designer for govt. agys. Colorado Springs, 1982-85; author, 1987—; asst. to cons. Volusia County Dept. Corrections, Daytona Beach, Fla., 1982; cons. student svcs. program Pikes Peak C.C., Colorado Springs, 1982; cons., designer Juvenile Probation of El Paso County, Colorado Springs, 1982, 4th Jud. Dist./Dist. Atty.'s Office, Colorado Springs, 1984. Author: Political Wives, Veiled Lives, 1991. Cofounder Community Transitions, Colorado Springs, 1984; coord. El. Paso County Shape Up Program, 1982; v.p. Community Coun. of Pikes Peak Region, Colorado Springs, 1983, Women's Found. of Colo., Denver, 1987. Recipient Mayor's award for civic leadership City of Colorado Springs, 1983. Mem. Jr. League of Colorado Springs (sustaining), Salon de Femme (founding). Avocations: tennis, skiing, hiking.

SCHUCK, MARJORIE MASSEY, publisher, editor, authors' consultant; b. Winchester, Va., Oct. 9, 1921; d. Carl Frederick and Margaret Harriet (Parmele) Massey; student U. Minn., 1941-43, New Sch., N.Y.C., 1948, N.Y. U., 1952, 54-55; m. Ernest George Metcalfe, Dec. 2, 1943 (div. Oct. 1949); m. 2d, Franz Schuck, Nov. 11, 1953 (dec. Jan. 1958). Mem. editorial bd. St. Petersburg Poetry Assn., 1967-68; co-editor, pub. poetry Venture Mag., St. Petersburg, Fla., 1968-69, editor, pub., 1969-79; co-editor, pub. Poetry Venture Quar. Essays, Vol. I, 1968-69, Vol. 2, 1970-71; pub., editor poetry anthologies, 1972—; founder, owner, pres. Valkyrie Press, Inc. (name changed to Valkyrie Pub. House 1980), 1972—; cons. designs and formats, trade publs. and ann. reports, lit. books and pamphlets, 1973—; founder Valkyrie Press Roundtable Workshop and Forum for Writers, 1975-79; established Valkyrie Press Reference Libr., 1976-80; pub., editor The Valkyrie Internat. Newsletter, 1986—; exec. dir. Inter-Cultural Forum Villanor Ctr., Tampa, Fla., 1987-94; dir. edn. The Villanor Mus. Fine and Decorative Arts, Tampa, 1994, St. Petersburg, 1994—; pres. Found. for Human Potentials, Inc., Tampa, 1988-94; representative distbr. Marg Art Publs. of India (Bombay), 1992—; mem. pres. coun. U. South Fla., 1993—; lectr. in field. Judge poetry and speech contests Gulf Beach Women's Club, 1970, Fine Arts Festival dist. 14. Am. Fedn. Women's Clubs, 1970, South and West, Inc., 1972, The Sunstone Rev., 1973, Internat. Toastmistress Clubs, 1974, 78, Beaux Arts Poetry Festival, 1983, 89, 92, 93, 94; judge poetry contest Fla. State conf. Nat. League Am. Pen Women, 1989; judge Fla. Gov.'s Screenwriters Competition, 1984—. Corr.-rec. sec. Women's Aux. Hosp. for Spl. Surgery, N.Y.C., 1947-59; active St. Petersburg Mus. Fine Arts (charter), St. Petersburg Sister City Com., St. Petersburg Arts Ctr. Assn.; mem. Orange Belt express com. 1988 Centennial Celebration for St. Petersburg; mem. Com. of 100 of Pinellas County, Inc., exec. bd., 1975-77, membership chmn., 1975-77; pub. rels. chmn. Soc. for prevention Cruelty to Animals, 1968-71, bd. dirs., 1968-71, 75-77; founder, mem. Pinellas County Arts Coun., 1976-79, chmn., 1977-78; mem. grant rev. panel for lit. Fine Arts Coun. of Fla., 1979; mem. pres.'s coun. U. South Fla., 1994—. Named One of 76 Fla. Patriots, Fla. Bicentennial Commn., 1976; a recipient 1st ann. People of Dedication award Salvation Army, Tampa, 1984; named to Poetica Hall of Fame, Tampa Bay Poetry Coun., 1994. Mem. Am. Assn. Museums, Acad. Am. Poets, Fla. Suncoast Writers' Confs. (founder, co-dir., lectr. 1973-83, adv. bd. 1984—), Com. Small Mag. Editors and Pubs., Coordinating Council Lit. Mags., Friends of Libr. of St. Petersburg, Suncoast Mgmt. Inst. (exec. bd.; chmn. Women in Mgmt. 1977-78), Pi Beta Phi. Republican. Episcopalian. Author: Speeches and Writings for Cause of Freedom, 1973. Contbr. poetry to profl. jours. Home and Office: 8245 26th Ave N Saint Petersburg FL 33710-2857

SCHUCK, PETER HORNER, lawyer, educator; b. N.Y.C., Apr. 26, 1940; s. Samuel H. and Lucille (Horner) S.; m. Marcy Cantor, June 26, 1966; children: Christopher, Julie. BA with honors, Cornell U., 1962; JD cum laude, Harvard U., 1965, MA, 1969; LLM, NYU, 1966; MA (hon.), Yale U., 1982. Bar: N.Y. State 1966, D.C. 1972. Practiced law N.Y.C., 1965-68; teaching fellow in govt. Harvard U., 1969-71; cons. (Center for Study of Responsive Law), Washington, 1971-72; dir. Washington office Consumers Union, 1972-77; dep. asst. sec. for planning and evaluation HEW, Washington, 1977-79; vis. scholar Am. Enterprise Inst. for Public Policy Research, Washington, 1979; assoc. prof. law Yale U., 1979-81, prof., 1981-86, Simeon E. Baldwin prof. law, 1986—, dep. dean, 1993-94; vis. prof. Georgetown U. Law Ctr., 1986-87, NYU Law Sch., fall 1994; lectr. profl., acad., bus, univ., govt. and citizen groups. Author: The Judiciary Committees, 1975, Suing Government, 1983, Citizenship without Consent, 1985, Agent Orange on Trial, 1986, enlarged edit., 1987; editor: Tort Law and the Public Interest, 1991, Foundations of Administrative Law, 1994; contbr. articles and revs. to profl. and popular publs. Guggenheim fellow, 1984-85; recipient Silver Gavel award ABA, 1987. Jewish.

SCHUCK, THOMAS ROBERT, lawyer; b. Findlay, Ohio, Feb. 7, 1950; s. Robert Damon and Katherine Margaretta (Beynon) S.; m. Pamela Lee Bakan, Sept. 2, 1979. BA, DePauw U., 1972; MA, U. Kent, U.K., 1974; JD, Harvard U., 1976. Bar: Ohio 1976, U.S. Dist. Ct. (no. dist.) Ohio 1977, U.S. Dist. Ct. (so. dist.) Ohio 1979, Ariz. 1990, U.S. Ct. Appeals (6th cir.) 1978, U.S. Ct. Appeals (9th cir.) 1991. Law clk. U.S. Dist. Ct., Cleve., 1976-79; assoc. Taft, Stettinius & Hollister, Cin., 1979-87, ptnr., 1987—; participant Ohio Bench Bar Conf., Columbus, 1990, 91; barrister Am. Inn of Ct., 1986-87. Contbg. author: Aids and the Law, 2d edit. 1992; contbr. articles to profl. jours. Trustee Mental Health Svcs. East, Inc., Cin., 1985-91; mem. Clermont County Mental Health Bd., Batavia, Ohio; 1992—; mem. May Festival Assocs., Cin., 1984-86; spl. gifts com. Cin. Art Acad., 1987; mem. WGUC Radio Community Bd., 1984-86. Republican Internat. Found. grad. fellow, 1972. Mem. FBA (Cin. chpt. pres. 1994-95), Ohio Bar Assn., Cin. Bar Assn., U.S. Rowing Assn. (judge-arbitre), Harvard Club of Cin. (pres. 1995—), Camargo Hunt, Masons, Delta Chi, Phi Beta Kappa, Phi Eta Sigma, Sigma Delta Chi. Republican. Methodist. Avocations: reading, photography. Home: 189 State Rt 133 Felicity OH 45120-9706 Office: Taft Stettinius & Hollister 1800 Star Bank Ctr 425 Walnut St Cincinnati OH 45202-3957

SCHUCK, VICTORIA, political science educator; b. Oklahoma City, Mar. 16, 1909; d. Anthony B. and Anna (Priebe) S. A.B. with great distinction, Stanford U., 1930, M.A., 1931, Ph.D., 1937; L.H.D. (hon.), Mt. Vernon Coll., 1980. Univ. fellow Stanford U., 1931-33, teaching asst., 1934-35, acting instr., 1935-36, instr., 1936-37; asst. prof. Fla. State Coll. Women, 1937-40; mem. faculty Mt. Holyoke Coll., 1940-77, prof. polit. sci., 1950-77; pres. Mt. Vernon Coll., Washington, 1977-80, ret.; vis. lectr. Smith Coll., 1948-49; vis. prof. Stanford U., summer 1952, vis. scholar polit. sci., 1982—; guest scholar Brookings Instn., 1967-68, summers 68, 70, Woodrow Wilson Ctr. Internat. Scholars, 1980; Prin. program analyst, planning for local bds. OPA, 1942-44; rep. Am. Polit. Sci. Assn. UN World Conf. of UN Decade for Women, Nairobi, Kenya, 1985; sponsor Women's Fgn. Policy Council, N.Y., 1986; cons. Office Temporary Controls, 1945-47; mem. internat. secretariat UN Conf. San Francisco, 1945; mem. Mass. Commn. Interstate Coop., 1957-60, U. Mass. Bldg. Authority, 1960-68; Mass. adv. com. U.S. Commn. Civil Rights, 1962-78; cons. GAO, 1980-82; non-govtl. rep. UN Commn. on Status of Women, Vienna, Austria, 1988. Regional editor: Ency. Brit., 1958-61; co-editor and contbr.: Women Organizing: An Anthology, 1979, New England Politics, 1981; contbr. articles to profl. jours. Mem. Pres.'s Commn. Registration and Voting Participation, 1963; mem. Berkshire Community Coll. Planning Com., 1964-68, Greenfield Community Coll. Planning Com., 1965-68, Mass. Bd. Higher Edn., 1976-77; mem. Town of South Hadley Planning Bd., 1959-67, chmn., 1961-67; trustee U. Mass., 1958-63. Grantee Haynes Found., 1951-52; Grantee Asia Soc., 1971-72. Mem. ASPA, AAUW (pres. Mass. 1946-50, nat. chmn. legis. prog. com., bd. dirs. 1965-69), AAUP (pres. Mt. Holyoke 1962-64), Am. Polit. Sci. Assn. (sec. 1959-60, v.p. 1970-71), New Eng. Polit. Sci. Assn. (pres. 1950-51), Northeastern Polit. Sci. Assn. (pres. 1972-73), Internat. Polit. Sci. Assn., Acad. Coun. on UN System, Supreme Ct. Hist. Soc., Fed. City Coun., Internat. Studies Assn., Mortar Bd. (hon.), Cosmopolitan Club, Cosmos

---

Club, Phi Beta Kappa, Chi Omega. Home: 4000 Cathedral Ave NW Washington DC 20016-5249

SCHUDEL, HANSJOERG, international business consultant; b. Wald, Switzerland, Sept. 27, 1937; s. Rene and Alice S. Ed., Coll. Bus. Adminstrn., Zurich, Switzerland. With Byk-Gulden, Konstanz, Germany and Sao Paulo, Brazil, 1962-69, Hicksville, N.Y., 1964-69; pres., chief exec. officer, dir. Stinnes Corp., N.Y.C., 1971-83; exec. officer Stinnes A.G., Muelheim, Fed. Republic of Germany, 1978-83; rep. for the Americas First Arab Pacific Corp. Ltd., Chappaqua, N.Y., 1984—. Mem. German-Am. C. of C. (bd. dirs. 1976-83), Internat. World Travelers Club, Swiss Soc., Confrerie de la Chaine des Rotisseurs, Order des Coteaux de Champagne, Foothills Assn. (bd. dirs.). Office: First Arab Pacific Corp Ltd 1275 4th St Ste 307 Santa Rosa CA 95404-4049

SCHUDER, RAYMOND FRANCIS, lawyer; b. Wickford, R.I., Dec. 27, 1926; s. Rollie Milton and Selma (Ball) S.; AB, Emory U., 1949, JD, 1951; m. Betty Jo Williams, Mar. 14, 1948; children: Gregg Williams, Glen Arva. Bar: Ga. 1951. With Trust Co., Ga., Atlanta, 1951-54; assoc. firm Wheeler, Robinson & Thurmond, Gainesville, Ga., 1954-59; pvt. practice law, Gainesville, 1959-70, 76—; ptnr. Schuder & Brown, Gainesville, 1971-76; Mcpl. ct. judge, Gainesville, 1956-60, 73-75, Magistrate ct. judge, 1985—; bd. dirs. Lanier Securities, Inc. Supr. Upper Chattahoochee Soil and Water Conservation Dist., 1971-74; chief exec. officer, bd. dirs. Charles Thompson Estes Found., Inc., Gainesville. Cpl. USMCR, 1944-50; 1st lt. USAR, ret. Mem. State Bar Ga. (gov. 1966-70), Gainesville-Northeastern (pres. 1969-70) Bar Assn., Am. Legion, V.F.W., Elks. Methodist. Home: 2224 Riverside Dr Gainesville GA 30501-1232 Office: 500 Spring St E Gainesville GA 30501-3792

SCHUELE, ALBAN WILHELM, chemical company executive; b. Stuehlingen, Baden-Wuerttemberg, Germany, Apr. 28, 1944; came to U.S., 1963; s. Wilhelm and Emma (Utz) S.; m. Grayce Winifred LaGrotta, Jan. 25, 1969; children: Jason Alban, Kathleen Marie. B.S. in Econs., Ariz. State U., 1969; B. Internat. Mgmt., Am. Grad. Sch. Internat. Mgmt. Thunderbird, Glendale, Ariz., 1970. V.p. Chase Manhattan Bank, N.Y.C., 1970-80; treas. Am. Hoechst Corp. (now Hoechst Celanese Corp.), Somerville, N.J., 1980—, v.p., treas., 1985-88; treas. Hoechst-Roussel Pharms., Inc., 1985—, Hoechst-Roussel Agri-Vet Co., 1985—; v.p. quality and communications Hoechst Celanese Corp., 1988—, corp. v.p. and pres. splty. products group, 1989—; treas. P.B. Diagnostics, Inc., 1985—; pres. Hoechst Can., Inc., 1991—, Celanese Can. Inc., 1991—. Roman Catholic. Office: Celanese Can Inc, 800 Boul René-Lévesque O 23e, Montreal, PQ Canada H3B 1X9

SCHUELE, DONALD EDWARD, physics educator; b. Cleve., June 16, 1934; s. Edward and Mildred (Matousek) S.; m. Clare Ann Kirchner, Sept. 5, 1956; children: Donna, Karen, Melanie, Judy, Rachel, Ruth. BS, John Carroll U., Cleve., 1956, MS, 1957; PhD, Case Inst. Tech., 1962. Instr. physics and math. John Carroll U., 1956-59; part-time instr. physics Case Inst. Tech., 1959-62, instr., asst. prof., assoc. prof., 1962-70; mem. tech. staff Bell Telephone Labs., 1970-72; assoc. prof. physics Case Western Res. U., 1972-74, prof., 1974—; dean undergrad. coll., 1973-76, chmn. dept. physics, 1976-78; vice dean Case Inst. Tech., 1978-83, v.p. for undergrad. and grad. studies, 1983-84, dean, 1984-86, prof. physics, 1986-88, dean math. and natural sci., 1988-89, Albert A. Michaelson prof. physics, 1989—, acting chmn. elec. engrng. and applied physics, 1992-93; cons. in field. Co-editor: Critical Revs. in Solid State Scis, 1969-84; contbr. articles to profl. jours.; patentee in field. Mem. adv. bd. St. Charles Borromeo Sch., 1970-72; pres. Seed Found., 1986-89; trustee St. Mary's Sem., 1980-93; mem. Olympic Sports Equipment and Tech. Com., 1982-93; trustee Newman Found., 1983—, Northeastern Ohio Sci. Fair, 1983—; mem. Diocesan Pastoral Coun., 1992-94; active Rep. Presdl. task force. NSF Faculty fellow, 1961-63; recipient Disting. Physics Alumnus award John Carroll U., 1983. Mem. Am. Phys. Soc. (vice chair Ohio sect. 1995—), Am. Assn. Physics Tchrs., North Coast Thermal Analysis Soc., Newman Apostolate, Case Alumni Coun. (life, treas. 1992—), Sigma Xi, Alpha Sigma Nu, Tau Beta Pi. Republican. Roman Catholic. Achievements include patents fluid pressure device, impact wrench torque calibrator. Home: 4892 Countryside Rd Cleveland OH 44124-2513 Office: Case Western Res U 10900 Euclid Ave Cleveland OH 44106-4901

SCHUELKE, JOHN PAUL, religious organization administrator; b. Benton Harbor, Mich., Nov. 5, 1934; s. Alwin E. and Martha M. (Schoeneberg) S.; m. Noreta H. Petersen, Sept. 9, 1956; children: Alvin, Mary, Sheryl, Brian. BS in Acctg., U. Wyo., 1957; LLB (hon.), Concordia U. 1983. CPA. From acct. to sr. acct. Colo. Interstate Gas Co., Colorado Springs, 1957-63; staff acct. Arthur Anderson & Co., Denver, 1963-64; mgr. fin. control Colo. Interstate Corp., Colorado Springs, 1964-67, dir. fin. control, 1967-71; adminstrv. v.p. mfg. divsn. Marsh Instrument Co. subs. Colo. Mfg. Corp., Skokie, Ill., 1971-72; exec. dir. bd. dirs., COO Luth. Ch.-Mo. Synod, St Louis, 1972—; Lectr. in field. scoutmaster Boy Scouts Am., Colorado Springs; governing bd. Com. Luth. Cooperation; former mem. governing bd. Luth. Coun.-USA; mem. St. Matthew Luth. Ch., St. Louis. Recipient God and Country award Eagle Scouts. Mem. Alpha Kappa Psi, Gamma Delta (former pres.). Avocations: traveling, fishing, reading.

SCHUELLER, THOMAS GEORGE, lawyer; b. Budapest, Hungary, Oct. 4, 1936; came to U.S., 1938; s. Herbert H. and Edith (Geiringer) S.; m. Sandra Burke, Sept. 3, 1960 (div. Apr. 1982); children: Katherine, Matthew, John. AB cum laude, Amherst Coll., 1958; LLB, Harvard U., 1962. Bar: N.Y. 1963. Salesman Gen. Mills. Inc., Utica, N.Y., 1958-59; assoc. Hughes Hubbard & Reed, N.Y.C., 1962-69, ptnr., 1969—. Bd. dirs., sec. Ballet Hispanico, N.Y.C., 1987—. Mem. ABA, Assn. of Bar of City of N.Y., Phi Beta Kappa. Home: 169 E 78th St New York NY 10021-0462 Office: Hughes Hubbard & Reed 1 Battery Pk Plz New York NY 10004

SCHUELLER, WOLFGANG AUGUSTUS, architectural educator, writer; b. Aachen, Germany, Sept. 10, 1934; came to U.S., 1964; s. Sepp and Mathilde (Kalfff) S.; m. Ria Herpers, Apr. 22, 1960; 1 child, Uschi. Diploma in Engring. in Civil Engring., FH Aachen, Germany, 1960; BS in Archtl. Engring. with honors, N.D. State U., 1966; MSCE in Structural Engring., Lehigh U., 1968; BArch, Syracuse U., 1971. Registered profl. engr., N.Y., Pa. Supr. constrn., structural engr. Hochtief A.G., Munich and Essen, Fed. Republic of Germany, 1960-63; structural designer Green Blanksteen Russel Assocs., Winnipeg, Man., Can., 1963-64; structural engr. Pioneer Svc. and Engring. Co., Chgo., 1966-67, Richardson, Gordon Assocs., Pitts., 1968-69; prof. architecture Syracuse (N.Y.) U., 1971-82, Va. Poly. Inst., Blacksburg, 1982-94, U. Fla., Gainesville, 1994—. Author: Highrise Building Structures, 1977, Horizontal-Span Building Structures, 1983, The Vertical Building Structures, 1990, The Design of Building Structures, 1995. Mem. ASCE, Nat. Soc. Archtl.Engrs., Soc. for History of Tech., Coun. on Tall Bldgs. and Urban Habitat, Sigma Xi, Phi Kappa Phi, Tau Beta Pi. Achievements include rsch. and pubs. on relationship between bldg. sci., structures in particular, and architecture. Avocations: classical music (opera), jazz, history of art, jogging. Office: U Fla Coll Architecture Gainesville FL 32611-2004

SCHUENKE, DONALD JOHN, insurance company executive; b. Milw., Jan. 12, 1929; s. Ray H. and Josephine P. (Maciolek) S.; m. Joyce A. Wetzel, July 19, 1952; children: Ann, Mary. PhB, Marquette U., 1950, LLB, 1958. Bar: Wis. 1958. Spl. agt. Nat. Life of Vt., 1958-59; real estate rep. Standard Oil Co. of Ind., Milw., 1959-63; atty. Northwestern Mut. Life Ins. Co., Milw., 1963-65, asst. counsel, 1965-67, asst. gen. counsel, 1967-74, v.p., gen. counsel, sec., 1974-76, v.p. investments, 1976-80, pres., 1980—, chief operating officer, 1981-83, pres., chief exec. officer, 1983-89, chmn., chief exec. officer, 1989—; bd. dirs. Mortgage Guaranty Ins. Corp., No. Telecom Ltd., Regis Group. Bd. dirs. Milw. Symphony Orch., Com. Econ. Devel., Marquette U., United Way of Greater Milw., Med. Research Fund, Milw. Redevel. Fund, Badger Meter, Milw. Regional Med. Ctr., Milw. Art Mus., Milw. Boys and Girls Club, Grand Ave Com., Greater Milw. Com., Wis. Taxpayers Alliance, Med. Coll. Wis.; mem. adv. council Am. Heart Assn.; mem. Competitive Wis. Milw. Redevel. Corp. Mem. Wis. Bar Assn., Am. Coun. Life Ins. (bd. dirs.), Met. Milw. Assn. Commerce (bd. dirs.). Club: University (local bd. dirs.). Home: 13600 Park Cir N Elm Grove WI 53122-2557 Office: Northwestern Mut Life Ins Co 720 E Wisconsin Ave Milwaukee WI 53202-4703

SCHUEPPERT, GEORGE LOUIS, financial executive; b. Merrill, Wis., July 1, 1938; s. George Henry and Eleanor Natalie (Pautz) S.; m. Kathleen Kay Carpenter, May 6, 1967; children—Steven Andrew, Stephanie Roanne, Stenning Karl. B.B.A. U. Wis., Madison, 1961; M.B.A. U. Chgo., 1969. Treas., controller Steiger-Rathke Devel. Co., Phoenix, 1964-65; various positions Continental Ill. Nat. Chgo., 1965-76, 1981-86; mng. dir. Continental Ill. Ltd., London, 1977-81; sr. v.p. Continental Ill. Nat. Bank, Chgo., 1982-86; ptnr. Coopers & Lybrand, Chgo., 1986-87; exec. v.p. fin. CBI Industries Inc, Oak Brook, Ill., 1987—; also bd. dirs. CBI Industries Inc, Oak Brook, 1987—; bd. dirs. Wells Mfg. Co. Bd. dirs., chmn. fin. com. Gt. Books Found.; bd. advisors CPA's for Pub. Interest; vice chmn., bd. dirs. De Paul U. Gov. Asst. Project. Lt. (j.g.) USN, 1961-64. Recipient Herfurth award U. Wis., 1960. Mem. Econ. Club Chgo. (bd. dirs., chmn. membership com.). Republican. Avocations: history; civic affairs; architecture; travel; golf. Home: 97 Otis Rd Barrington IL 60010-5129 Office: CBI Industries Inc 800 Jorie Blvd Oak Brook IL 60521-2268

SCHUERMAN, JOHN RICHARD, social work educator; b. Scotts Bluff, Nebr., Feb. 27, 1938; s. Lawrence and Mildred Jeanette (France) S.; m. Charlotte Kavaloski, Sept. 12, 1964; children: Gabrielle Ann, Matthew Lawrence. B.S., U. Chgo., 1960, M.A., 1963, Ph.D., 1970. Social worker Ill. Dept. Mental Health, Chgo., 1963-65; mem. faculty Sch. Social Service Adminstrn., U. Chgo., 1968—, prof. social work, 1978—, asso. dean, 1970-79; mem. Ill. Mental Health Planning Bd., 1971-73; cons. in field. Author: Research and Evaluation in the Human Services, 1983, Multivariate Analysis in the Human Services, 1983, Putting Families First: An Experiment in Family Preservation, 1994. Editor jour. Social Service Rev.; research on child welfare, use of artificial intelligence in social welfare. Home: 1229 E 50th St Chicago IL 60615-2908 Office: 969 E 60th St Chicago IL 60637-2640

SCHUERMAN, NORBERT JOEL, school superintendent; b. DeWitt, Nebr., Dec. 26, 1934; s. Edwin J. and Martha (Finkbener) S.; m. Charlotte Ann Detling, Aug. 6, 1960; children: Robert, Brenda, Todd. B of Music Edn., U. Nebr., 1957, MEd, 1959, EdS in Ednl. Mgmt. and Supervision, 1964, EdD, 1967. Cert. profl. tchr. (life), Nebr. Tchr. Clatonia-Bennet (Nebr.) Pub. Sch., 1954-58; instr., prin. Mullen (Nebr.) Pub. Sch., 1958-61; prin. Ainsworth (Nebr.) Pub. Sch., 1961-63; sr. high sch. vice prin. Lincoln (Nebr.) Pub. Sch., 1963-66, 67-69; sr. high sch. prin. Arapahoe County Sch. Dist. 6, Littleton, Colo., 1969-74; from asst. supt. to assoc. supt. to supt. Omaha Pub. Schs., 1974—; trustee, mem. exec. com. Nebr. Coun. Econ. Edn., 1985—; bd. dirs. Nat. Study Sch. Evaluation, 1986-90, Charles Drew Health Ctr., 1985—, Fontenelle Forest, 1990-92, 95—; bd. trustees Western Heritage Mus., 1994—; mem. exec. com. Coun. Gt. City Schs., 1988—; mem. chancellor's adv. coun. U. Nebr., 1987—; mem. Nat. Urban Edn. Task Froce, 1990—; mem. Nat. Adv. Bd. for Active Citizenship Today, 1992—; mem. bd. advisors Close Up Found., 1992—. Mem. adv. coun. Mid-Am. coun. Boy Scouts Am., 1984—; coun. regents Big Bros./Big Sisters of Midlands, Omaha, 1986—; bd. dirs. United Way of Midlands, 1985—, Fontenelle Forest, 1990-92,95—, chmn. edn. div. campaign, 1985; mem. adv. bd. Omaha Children's Mus., 1988—, bd. trustees Western Heritage Mus., 1994-96. Named Nebr. Supt. of Yr., 1991; recipient Disting. Svc. award Nebr. Coun. Sch. Adminstrs., 1988, awards of honor Nat. Sch. Pub. Rels. Assn., 1991; named to Exec. Educator mag.'s Top 100 Sch. Execs., 1993. Mem. Am. Assn. Sch. Adminstrs. (urban schs. com. 1992—), Nebr. Coun. Sch. Adminstrs., Omaha Sch. Adminstrs. Assn., North Ctrl. Assn. (bd. dirs. 1983-89, chmn. 1987-88), Large City Schs. Supts. (mem. 1992-93), NCCJ (bd. dirs. 1990—), Nebr. Schoolmasters Club, Urban League of Nebr., Nat. Congress Parents and Tchrs. (hon. life), Nebr. Congress Parents and Tchrs., Phi Delta Kappa. Home: 4007 N 94th St Omaha NE 68134-3927 Office: Omaha Sch Dist 3215 Cuming St Omaha NE 68131-2024

SCHUESSLER, ANNEMARIE, pianist, educator; b. Wheaton, Ill., Apr. 20, 1951; d. Joseph John and Maureen Eileen (Harrington) S. MusB, Manhattanville Coll., 1973; MusM, Northwestern U., 1980, MusD, 1987; artists diploma with honors, Hochschule für Musik, Wurzburg, Germany, 1982. Music dir. Am. Mil. Community of Kitzingen, Germany, 1976-78; tchr. Music Arts Sch., Highland Park, Ill., 1978-82, Jack Benny Fine Arts Ctr., Waukegan, Ill., 1982-88; lectr. DePaul U. Sch. Music, Chgo., 1984-88; asst. prof. La. State U. Sch. Music, Baton Rouge, 1988-89, Ithaca (N.Y.) Coll. Sch. Music, 1989-92; asst. prof., piano Ball State U. Sch. Music, Muncie, Ind., 1992—; adj. prof. Suzuki program Wheaton (Ill.) Coll., 1982-88, Triton Coll., River Grove, Ill., 1980-82; adjudicator nat. competitions; vis. asst. prof. Eastman Sch. Music, Rochester, N.Y., 1990-91; adj. instr. Northwestern U., Evanston, Ill., 1980-81; lectr. Kaug Reung, South Korea, 1990; lectr., performer European Piano Tchrs. Assn., Eng., 1991; performer Maly Hall, St. Petersburg, Russia, 1993—. Contbr. articles to profl. jours. Eckstein scholar Northwestern U., 1978—. Mem. ISSTIP, EPTA, Nat. Conf. on Piano Pedagogy, Coll. Music Soc. (Sec. N.E. chpt. 1992-94), Ind. Music Tchrs. Assn. (bd. dirs.), Music Tchrs. Nat. Assn., Pi Kappa Lambda. Avocations: swimming, travel, cooking. Office: Ball State U Sch Music Muncie IN 47305

SCHUESSLER, KARL FREDERICK, sociologist, educator; b. Quincy, Ill., Feb. 15, 1915; s. Hugo and Elsa (Westerbeck) S.; m. Lucille Smith, June 27, 1946; children—Thomas Brian. B.A., Evansville (Ind.) Coll., 1936; M.A., U. Chgo., 1939; Ph.D., Ind. U., 1947. Sociologist Ill. State Prison, 1938; tchr. Highland Park (Ill). High Sch., 1939-40; instr. Vanderbilt U., 1946-47; mem. faculty Ind. U., 1947—, prof. sociology, 1960-76, Distinguished prof. sociology, 1976—, chmn. dept., 1961-69; rsch. cons. Thammasat U., Bangkok, Thailand, 1963; vis. prof. UCLA, 1957, U. Calif.-Berkeley, 1965-66, U. Wash., 1967; guest scholar Ctr. for Survey Rsch., Mannheim (Germany) U., 1979-80, vis. prof., 1980-81; fellow Inst. Sociology, U. Hamburg, Germany, summer 1983; mem. adv. panel sociology NSF, 1962-63; mem. behavioral sect. NIH, 1964-68; mem. social sci. rsch. study sect. NIMH, 1968-69, social sci. tng. study sect., 1969-73; mem. NRC, 1970-75. Author: (with J.H. Mueller) Statistical Reasoning in Sociology, 1961; Social Research Methods; Analyzing Social Data, 1971; (with H. Costner) Statistical Reasoning in Sociology, 3d edit, 1977; (with Dagmar Krebs) Soziale Empfindungen: Ein Interkultureller Skalenvergleich bei Deutschen und Amerikanern, 1987; also numerous articles.; editor: (with Cohen and Lindesmith) The Sutherland Papers, 1956, (with E.H. Sutherland) On Analyzing Crime, 1972, (with Demerath and Larsen) Public Policy and Sociology, 1975, Am. Sociol. Rev., 1969-71, Sociol. Methodology, 1977-79, Musical Taste and Social Background, 1980, Measuring Social Life Feelings, 1982. Served to lt. USNR, 1942-46. Fellow AAAS; mem. Am. Sociol. Assn., Am. Statis. Assn. Home: 1820 E Hunter Ave Bloomington IN 47401-5284

SCHUESSLER, MORGAN MCQUEEN, textile company executive; b. Roanoke, Ala., Aug. 7, 1935; s. John Morgan and Lilia (Murphy) S.; m. Nan Enloe Schuessler, June 1, 1957; children: John, Nan, Sam, Morgan Jr. B in Indsl. Engring., Ga. Inst. Tech.; cert. meteorology, UCLA; MBA, Harvard U. With West Point (Ga.) Pepperell, 1964-71; v.p. ops. Gable Industries, Atlanta, 1971-73; v.p. fin. and adminstrn. Arvida, Miami, Fla., 1973-75; exec. v.p. Coronet Industries, Dalton, Ga., 1975-76; pres. chief exec. officer Desoto Falls, Dalton, 1977-82; pres. Candlewick div. Dixie Yarns, Inc., Dalton, 1982-83; sr. v.p. fin. Dixie Yarns, Inc, Chattanooga, 1983—, also bd. dirs.; bd. dirs. First Union Bank Dalton, Ga., Comml. Banksharers of Roanoke, Ala., Masland Carpets, Inc. Avocations: hunting, fishing. Office: Dixie Yarns Inc PO Box 751 Chattanooga TN 37401-0751

SCHUESSLER FIORENZA, ELISABETH, theology educator; b. Tschanad, Romania, Apr. 17, 1938; parents German citizens; d. Peter and Magdalena Schuessler; m. Francis Fiorenza, Dec. 17, 1967; 1 child, Chris. MDiv, U. Wuerzburg, Federal Republic of Germany, 1962; Dr of Theology, U. Muenster, Federal Republic of Germany, 1970; Lic. Theol. U. Wuerzburg, 1963. Asst. prof. theology U. Notre Dame, South Bend, Ind., 1970-75, assoc. prof., 1975-80, prof., 1980-84; instr. U. Muenster, 1966-67; Talbot prof. New Testament Episcopal Div. Sch., Cambridge, Mass., 1984-88; Krister Stendahl prof. div. in scripture and interpretation Harvard U., Cambridge, Mass., 1988—; Harry Emerson Fosdick vis. prof. Union Theol. Sem., N.Y.C., 1974-75; guest prof. U. Tuebingen, Federal Republic of Germany, 1987, Cath. Theol. faculty Luzern, Switzerland, 1990. Author: Der Vergessene Partner, 1964, Priester für Gott, 1972, The Apocalypse, 1976, Invitation to the Book of Revelation, 1981, In Memory of Her, 1983, Bread not Stone, 1984, Judgement or Justice, 1985, Revelation: Vision of a

Just World, 1991, But She Said - Feminist Practices of Biblical Interpretation, 1992, Discipleship of Equals: A Critical Feminist Ekklesialogy of Liberation, 1993, Jesus: Miriam's Child and Sophia's Prophet, Critical Issues in Feminist Christology, 1994; editor: Searching the Scriptures, 2 vols, 1993, 94; founding co-editor Jour. Feminist Studies in Religion; also editor other works. Mem. Am. Acad. Religion, Soc. Bibl. Lit. (past pres.). Office: Harvard Div Sch 45 Francis Ave Cambridge MA 02138-1994

SCHUETTE, MICHAEL, lawyer; b. Manitowoc, Wis., Apr. 19, 1937; s. Elmer A. and Mary Irene (Hart) S.; m. Mary Dare Whiteside, Oct. 28, 1961; 1 child, Sharon Mary. B.S., Northwestern U., 1959, J.D., 1962. Bar: Ill. 1962, U.S. Dist. Ct. (no dist.) Ill. 1962. With Lord, Bissell & Brook, Chgo., 1961—, ptnr, 1971—; dir. Corralitos Astron. Research Assn., Horizons for Blind. Mem. ABA (past chmn. coal com. natural resources sect.), Chgo. Bar Assn. Club: Law (Chgo.). Office: Lord Bissell & Brook 115 S La Salle St Chicago IL 60603-3801

SCHUETZENDUEBEL, WOLFRAM GERHARD, engineering executive; b. Germany, Feb. 17, 1932; came to U.S., 1958; s. Gerhard Egon and Kaethe (Warmbier) S.; m. Ingeborg Jutta Lesch, Dec.15, 1960. BME, Tech. U. Berlin, 1956, MME, MS in Power Engring., 1958; DSc in Nuclear Engring., U. Beverly Hills, L.A., 1979. Registered profl. engr., Calif. Asst. mgr. boiler engring. dept. Riley Stoker Corp., Worcester, Mass., 1958-61; sect. mgr. systems devel. Combustion Engring., Inc., Windsor, Conn., 1961-68; various tech. mgmt. positions Gen. Atomic Co. (subs. Gulf Oil Corp.), San Diego, 1968-79; dir. utilities Solvent Refined Coal Internat., Inc. (subs. Gulf Oil Corp.), Denver, 1979-81, Gulf Oil Corp., Houston, 1981-82; pres. Endyne Internat., Inc., Houston, 1982-84; v.p. engring. and technology, sr. v.p. ops. Blount Energy Resource Corp., Montgomery, Ala., 1984-91; v.p. Birwelco-Montenay Inc., Miami, Fla., 1991—; fgn. corr. Resch Verlag, Munich, 1975—; bd.dirs. W&E Umwelttechnik A.G., A Previous Blount Co., Zurich, Switzerland, 1986-89. Patentee in field; author, co-author, translator tech. and sci. works. Fellow ASME (past chmn. nuclear heat exchanger com.); mem. Nat. Assn. Corrosion Engrs. (cert. corrosion specialist), Assn. German Profl. Engrs., Assn. Energy Engrs. (sr. mem.), Cogeneration Inst., Integrated Waste Svcs. Assn., Solid Waste Assn. N.Am. Home: 801 Timberlane RD Pike Road AL 36064 Office: Birwelco-Montenay Inc 3225 Aviation Ave Miami FL 33133

SCHUG, KENNETH ROBERT, chemistry educator; b. Easton, Pa., Aug. 27, 1924; s. Howard Lester and Marion Henry (Hulbert) S.; m. Miyoko Ishiyama, June 13, 1948; children: Carey Tyler, Carson Blake, Reed Porter. Student, Johns Hopkins U., 1942-43; B.A., Stanford U., 1945; Ph.D., U. So. Calif., 1955. Instr. Seton Hall Coll., South Orange, N.J., 1948-50; research assoc. U. Wis.-Madison, 1954-56; instr. Ill. Inst. Tech., Chgo., 1956-59, asst. prof., 1959-65, assoc. prof., 1965-75, prof. chemistry, 1975—, chmn. dept. chemistry, 1976-82, 85-87, 89-90; project dir. Chgo. Area Health and Med. Careers Program, 1979—; project co-dir. Sci. and Math. Initiative for Learning Enhancement, 1985—; project dir. Howard Hughes Med. Inst. Undergrad. Biol. Scis. Program, 1992—; cons. Argonne (Ill.) Nat. Lab., 1960-62. Co-author: Eigo Kagoku Ronbun no Kakikata, 1979; contbr. articles to profl. jours. Trustee Michael Reese Health Plan, Chgo., 1976-91, Michael Reese Found., 1991—; bd. dirs. Hyde Park Consumers Coop. Soc., 1982-94. Fulbright scholar, 1964-65; grantee in field. Mem. Am. Chem. Soc. (dir., officer Chgo. sect. 1978-84). Home: 1466 E Park Pl Chicago IL 60637-1836 Office: Ill Inst Tech Div Chemistry IIT Ctr Chicago IL 60616

SCHUH, FRANK JOSEPH, drilling engineering company executive, consultant; b. Columbus, Ohio, Feb. 3, 1935; s. Sebastian and Elizabeth (Zorn) S.; m. Alice Virgene Kasler, June 16, 1956; children: Dwain Joseph, Michael James, Barbara Ann. BS in Petroleum Engring., Ohio State U., 1956, MS in Petroleum Engring., 1956. Registered profl. engr., Ohio. Drilling and rsch. engr. Atlantic Refining Co., Tex., La., 1956-62; mem. drilling engring. staff, dir. engring. Atlantic Richfield Co., Dallas, 1962-82; mgr. drilling rsch., sr. advisor Atlantic Richfield Co., Plano, Tex., 1982-86; v.p. Enertech Engring. & Tech., Dallas, 1986-87; pres. Drilling Tech., Inc., Plano, 1987—; v.p. Supreme Resources Corp., Dallas, 1988-92; founder, 1st pres. Drilling Engring. Assn., Dallas, 1983-85. Author: Drilling Equations, 1975; patentee horizontal drilling, high frequency measurement system; 26 other patents. Precinct, region chmn. Rep. Party, Dallas, 1964-74; vol. bldg. com. Mary Immaculate Ch., Dallas, 1965-66; mem. tech. engring. and devel. com. Ocean Drilling Program, Bryan, Tex., 1980—. Recipient outstanding achievement in field of engring. award Nat. Engrs. Coun., 1980, Robert Earl McConnell award Am. Inst. Mining Engrs., 1994, Ohio State Univ. Coll. of Engring. Benjamin G. Lamme Meritorious Achievement medel, 1995. Mem. NAE, Soc. Petroleum Engrs. (nat. bd. dirs. 1983-86, Drilling Engring. award 1986, Disting. Mem. award 1989), Am. Petroleum Inst. (chmn. com. 6, 1985-88, svc. citation 1986), Am. Assn. Drilling Engrs., Soc. Ind. Profl. Earth Scientists, Petroleum Engrs. Club (pres. 1974-75), Ohio State U. Alumni Club (pres. 1968-69), Dallas-Ft. Worth Oilman's Club (handicapper 1973-86). Avocations: golf, sailing. Office: Drilling Tech Inc 5808 Wavertree Ln Ste 1000 Plano TX 75093-4513

SCHUH, G(EORGE) EDWARD, university dean, agricultural economist; b. Indpls., Sept. 13, 1930; s. George Edward and Viola (Lentz) S.; m. Maria Ignez, May 23, 1965; children: Audrey, Susan, Tanya. BS in Agrl. Edn, Purdue U., 1952, DAgr (hon.), 1992; MS in Agrl. Econs., Mich. State U., 1954; MA in Econs, U. Chgo., 1958, PhD, 1961; prof. (hon.), Fed. U. Vicosa, Brazil, 1965; hon. doctorate Purdue U., 1992. From instr. to prof. agrl. econs. Purdue U., 1959-79; dir. Center for Public Policy and Public Affairs, 1977-78; dep. undersec. for internat. affairs and commodity programs Dept. Agr., Washington, 1978-79; prof. agrl. and applied econs., head dept. U. Minn., 1979-84; dir. agr. and rural devel. World Bank, Washington, 1984-87; dean Humphrey Inst. for Pub. Affairs, U. Minn., 1987—; program advisor Ford Found., 1966-72; sr. staff economist Pres.'s Coun. Econ. Advisors, 1974-75. Author, editor profl. books; contbr. numerous articles to profl. publs. Served with U.S. Army, 1954-56. Fellow AAAS, Am. Acad. Arts and Scis., Am. Agrl. Econs. Assn. (Thesis award 1962, Pub. Rsch. award 1971, Article award 1975, Published Rsch. award 1979, Publ. of Lasting Value award 1988, bd. dirs. 1977-80, pres.-elect 1980-81, pres. 1981-82); mem. Internat. Assn. Agrl. Econs., Am. Econ. Assn., Brazilian Soc. Agrl. Economists. Office: Humphrey Ctr U Minn 301 19th Ave S Minneapolis MN 55455-0429

SCHUHMANN, REINHARDT, JR., metallurgical engineering educator, consultant; b. Corpus Christi, Tex., Dec. 16, 1914; s. Reinhardt and Alice (Shuford) S.; m. Betsy Jane Hancock, Aug. 29, 1937; children—Martha Schuh, Alice Bishop. Student, Calif. Inst. Tech., 1929-31; B.S. in Metall. Engring., Mo. Sch. Mines, 1933; M.S. in Metall. Engring., Mont. Sch. Mines, 1935; Sc.D. in Metallurgy, MIT, 1938, DEng (hon.), Purdue U., 1993. Instr. to assoc. prof. MIT, Cambridge, 1938-54; prof. metall. engring. Purdue U., West Lafayette, Ind., 1954-64, head Sch. Metall. Engring., 1959-64, Ross prof. engring., 1964-81, Ross prof. engring. emeritus, 1981—; Battelle vis. prof. Ohio State U., Columbus, 1966-67; Kroll vis. prof. Colo. Sch. Mines, Golden, 1977; metall. engring. cons., 1946—. Author: Metallurgical Engineering, 1952; contbr. articles to profl. jours.; co-inventor Q-S oxygen process, oxygen sprinkle smelting. Fellow Metall. Soc. of AIME (charter; James Douglas Gold medal 1970, Mineral Industry Edn. award 1975, Extractive metallurgy lectr. 1965, Extractive metallurgy Sci. awards 1995), Am. Soc. for Metals, AAAS; mem. Nat. Acad. Engring., Am. Chem. Soc. Democrat. Episcopalian. Club: Parlor (pres. 1963-64)(Lafayette). Lodge: Rotary. Avocations: classical music; hiking. Home: 1206 Hayes St West Lafayette IN 47906-2318 Office: Purdue U Sch Materials Engring West Lafayette IN 47907

SCHUKER, JILL ANITA, federal official, consultant; b. N.Y.C., Feb. 5, 1946; d. Litman H. and Mildred Frances (Lehrer) S. BA, Skidmore Coll., 1966; MA, Tufts U., 1970. Legis. asst. to senator from Mass. Gen. Ct., Boston, 1969-70; legis. asst. Congressman Michael J. Harrington, Washington, 1970-72; exec. dir. New Eng. Congl. Caucus, Washington, 1973-77; spl. asst., dep. spokeswoman Dept. State, Washington, 1977-79; counselor press and pub. affairs U.S. Mission to UN, N.Y.C., 1979-81; press sec. Gov. Hugh L. Carey, N.Y.C. and Albany, N.Y., 1981-82; sr. counseller, sr. v.p. Hill & Knowlton Pub. Affairs Worldwide, Washington, 1984-93; asst. to sec., dir. pub. affairs Dept. Commerce, Washington, 1993—. Dep. press sec. Shriver for V.P., 1972; comm. dir. Calif. Dukakis for Pres., 1988; internat.

election observer Nat. Dem. Inst. Internat. Affairs, Bulgaria, 1991; surrogate spkr. fgn. policy Clinton for Pres., 1992. Grantee European Cmty., 1976; fellow Ford Found., 1967-68. Mem. Am. Coun. Young Polit. Leaders (bd. dirs. 1990—, grantee to Soviet Union 1979), Coun. Fgn. Rels. Avocations: tennis, piano, reading, theatre. Office: Dept Commerce Public Affairs 14th St & Constitution Ave NW Washington DC 20230

SCHUKER, STEPHEN ALAN, historian; b. N.Y.C., Feb. 16, 1939; s. Louis A. and Millicent (Milchman) S. AB summa cum laude, Cornell U., 1959; AM, Harvard U., 1962, PhD, 1969; divorced; children: Lauren, Daniel. Asst. head hist. rsch. naval history div. Office Chief Naval Ops., 1959-61; instr. history Harvard U., Cambridge, Mass., 1968-69, asst. prof., 1969-74, lectr., 1974-75; vis. assoc. prof. European studies Sch. Advanced Internat. Studies, Johns Hopkins U., Washington, 1977, adj. prof., 1978-83; assoc. prof. history Brandeis U., Waltham, Mass., 1977-82, prof., 1982-91; Commonwealth prof. history U. Va., Charlottesville, 1991-92, William W. Corcoran prof., 1992—; syndic U. Press New Eng., 1979-81; cons. Nat. Commn. Documents and Records Federal Ofcls., 1976, Rockefeller Found., 1981. Lt. USNR, 1959-61. Nat. Endowment Humanities fellow, 1972-73; Am. Council Learned Socs. fellow, 1976-77, 85; sr. fellow USIA-Fulbright Commn., 1984, fellow internat. security John D. and Catherine T. MacArthur Found., 1987-89. Mem. Am. Hist. Assn., Soc. Historians Am. Fgn. Relations. Author: The End of French Predominance in Europe (George Louis Beer prize, Gilbert Chinard prize), 1976, American "Reparations" to Germany, 1919-1933: Implications for the Third World Debt Crisis, 1988; contbr. articles to profl. jours. Office: U Va Corcoran Dept History University Station Charlottesville VA 22906

SCHUKNECHT, HAROLD FREDERICK, physician, educator; b. Chancellor, S.D., Feb. 10, 1917; s. J.G. and Dena (Weeldreyer) S.; m. Anne Bodle, June 30, 1941; children—Judith, James. Student, U. S.D., 1934-36; B.S., S.D. Sch. Med. Scis., 1938; M.D., Rush Med. Coll., 1940; M.S. (hon.), Harvard, 1961; D.Sc. (hon.), U. S.D., 1972. Diplomate: Am. Bd. Otolaryngology. Intern Mercy Hosp., Des Moines, 1940-41; resident U. Chgo. Clinics, 1946-49; asst. prof. otolaryngology U. Chgo., 1949-53; assoc. surgeon Henry Ford Hosp., Detroit, 1953-61; Walter A. Le Compte prof. otology, prof. laryngology Harvard Med. Sch., Boston, 1961-87, prof. emeritus otology, 1987—; chief otolaryngology Mass. Eye and Ear Infirmary, 1961-84, emeritus chief otolaryngology, 1984—. Author nearly 300 jour. articles, more than 70 revs., chpts., editorials, 7 books on anatomy, surgery, pathology of the ear. Recipient Achievement award Deafness Rsch. Found., N.Y.C., Beltone award, Shambaugh prize Collegium ORL, Disting. Alumnus award Rush Med. Coll.; named to S.D. Hall of Fame. Fellow Acoustical Soc. Am., Royal Coll. Surgeons (Glasgow) (hon.), Royal Coll. Surgeons (Edinburgh) (hon.); mem. AMA, Am. Acad. Ophthalmology and Otolaryngology(Disting. award contbns. clin. otology), Am. Triological Soc., Am. Otol. Soc. (award merit), Mass. Suffolk County med. socs., New Eng. Otolaryn. Soc., Soc. Univ. Otolaryngologists, Collegium ORL Amicitiae Sacrum, Deutsche Akademie der Naturforscher Leopoldina, Am. Neurotology Soc., Assn. for Research in Otolaryngology(Award of Merit), Phila. Laryngol. Soc., Sigma Xi; hon. mem. S.D. Acad. Ophthalmology and Otolaryngology, Royal Soc. Medicine (London) (hon.), also otolaryn. socs. in South Africa, Panama, Australia, Nicaragua, Colombia, Japan, Egypt, Austria, Germany. Spl. research pathology ear and physiology hearing. Home: 263 Highland St Weston MA 02193-1111 Office: 243 Charles St Boston MA 02114-3004

SCHULBERG, BUDD, author; b. N.Y.C., Mar. 27, 1914; s. Benjamin P. and Adeline (Jaffe) S.; m. Virginia Ray, July 23, 1936 (div. 1942); 1 dau., Victoria; m. Victoria Anderson, Feb. 17, 1943 (div. 1964); children: Stephen, David; m. Geraldine Brooks, July 12, 1964 (dec. 1977); m. Betsy Anne Langman, June 9, 1979; children: Benn Stuart, Jessica A. Student, Deerfield Acad., 1931-32; AB cum laude, Dartmouth Coll., 1936, LLD, 1960; LittD, Long Island U., 1983; DHL, Hofstra U., 1987. Boxing editor Sports Illustrated; pres., prodr. Schulberg Prodns.; founder, dir. Watts Writers Workshop, L.A., 1965—; founder, chmn. Frederick Douglass Creative Arts Ctr., N.Y.C., 1971—. Screenwriter, Hollywood, 1936-39; writer "The Schulberg Report", Newsday Syndicate; author: What Makes Sammy Run?, 1941, The Harder They Fall, 1947, The Disenchanted, 1950, Some Faces in the Crowd, 1953, Waterfront, 1955 (Christopher award 1955), Sanctuary V, 1969, The Four Seasons of Success, 1972, Loser and Still Champion: Muhammad Ali, 1972, Swan Watch, 1975, Everything that Moves, 1980, Moving Pictures: Memories of a Hollywood Prince, 1981, Love, Action, Laughter and Other Sad Tales, 1990, Sparring with Hemingway: And Other Stories of the Fight Game, 1995; editor: From the Ashes: Voices of Watts, 1967; screenwriter: (films) (with Samuel Ornitz) Little Orphan Annie, 1938, (with F. Scott Fitzgerald) Winter Carnival, 1939, Weekend for Three, 1941, (with Martin Berkeley) City without Men, 1943, Government Girl, 1943, On the Waterfront, 1954 (Academy award best original story and screenplay 1954, N.Y. Critics award 1954, Fgn. Corrs. award 1954, Screen Writers Guild award 1954, Venice Festival award 1954), A Face in the Crowd, 1957 (German Film Critics award 1957), Wind across the Everglades, 1958, (teleplays) The Pharmacist's Mate, 1951; playwright: The Disenchanted: A Play in Three Acts, 1958, What Make's Sammy Run?, 1959, (musical) Senor Discretion Himself, 1985; contbr. to Sports Illustrated, Life, N.Y. Times Book Rev., Esquire, Newsday Syndicate, Los Angeles Times Book Rev., N.Y. Times Sunday Mag., Playboy. Bd. dirs. Westminster Neighborhood Assn., L.A., 1965-68, Inner City Cultural Ctr., L.A., 1965-68; mem. nat. adv. commn. on black participation John F. Kennedy Ctr. for Performing Arts; trustee Humanitas Prize. Lt. (j.g.) USNR, 1943-46, assigned to OSS. Awarded Army Commendation Ribbon for gathering photog. evidence of war crimes for Nuremberg Trial, 1945-46; recipient Susie Humanitarian award B'nai B'rith, Image award NAACP, Journalism award Dartmouth Coll., Merit award Lotos Club, L.A. Community Svc. award, 1966, B'hai Human Rights award, 1968, spl. award for Watts Writers Workshop, New Eng. Theater Conf., 1969, Amistad award, award for work with black writers Howard U., Prix Literaire, Deauville Festival 1989, World Boxing Assn. Living Legend award, 1990, Westhampton Writers Lifetime Achievement award, 1989, Southampton Cultural Ctr. 1st Annual Literature award, 1992, Heritage award Deerfield Acad., 1986. Mem. Dramatists Guild, ASCAP, Authors Guild N.Y.C. (mem. council), ACLU, Writers Guild East (mem. coun.), P.E.N., Sphinx (Dartmouth), Phi Beta Kappa. Office: Ronald S Konecky Theatrical Atty 488 Madison Ave Fl 9 New York NY 10022-5702 also: Russell & Volkening Attn: Miriam Altschuler 50 W 29th St New York NY 10001-4205 also: The Artists Agy care Mickey Freiberg 10000 Santa Monica Blvd Ste 300 Los Angeles CA 90067

SCHULBERG, JAY WILLIAM, advertising agency executive; b. N.Y.C., July 17, 1939; s. Perry and Esther (Eagle) S.; m. Kathryn Carmel Nicholson, Sept. 18, 1968. BS (Founder's Day award 1961), NYU, 1961. With Seagram's Inc., 1962, Grumman Aircraft Co., 1963-66; With Foote, Cone & Belding Inc., 1967-68; with Ogilvy & Mather, Inc., N.Y.C., 1968-87; exec. v.p., head creative dept. Ogilvy & Mather, Inc., 1985-87, also mem. U.S. coun. dirs., 1988—; vice chmn., chief creative officer, bd. dirs. Bozell Worldwide, N.Y.C., 1987—; also bd. dirs. Bozell, N.Y.C., operating bd.; bd. dirs. Ogilvy & Mather Worldwide. Creator advt. campaings for Am. Express, TWA, Maxwell House Coffrr, Country Time, Gen. Foods, Duracell, Hardees, Brit. Tourism, Hershyes, Huggies, Merrill Lynch, N.Y. Times, Excedrin, Milk, Tyco, USAF, Mass. Mut., Venity Fair, Vassrette, others. Developed Big Apple campaign, N.Y.C. with AUS, 1962. Recipient Art Dirs. Club awards, One Show awards, Andy awards, Addy awards, Cannes, Hollywood Festival awards, 6 David Ogilvy awards; named Creative Dir. of Yr. Adweek Mag., 1986. Mem. The One Club, Internat. Rescue Com. (bd. dirs.)

SCHULER, JOHN HAMILTON, holding company executive; b. Birmingham, Ala., Oct. 15, 1926; s. Robert Eustace and Doris (Moughon) S.; m. Elizabeth Locke, Dec. 14, 1954; children—George Augustus Mattison IV, Elizabeth Schuler Ogburn, John Hamilton Jr., Robert Eustace II. B.S. in Indsl. Mgmt., Auburn U., 1952. Vice pres. ops. Anderson Electric Corp., Leeds, Ala., 1957-59, exec. v.p. 1959-66, pres., 1966-69, chmn., chief exec. officer, 1969-72; pres. Schuler Investment Co., Birmingham, Ala., 1972-80; exec. v.p. Steego Corp., West Palm Beach, Fla., 1980—; dir. So. Research Inst., Birmingham, Palm Beach Ventures, Fla., WSEF Corp., Palm Beach. Pres., chmn. Associated Industries of Ala., Birmingham, 1962-64, Birmingham Symphony, 1967-69; pres. Ala. Opera Assn., Birmingham, 1970; mem. exec. com. Republican Party of Ala., Birmingham, 1964-68, Soc. Four

Arts, Palm Beach Preservation Found. Exec. Com.; mem. nat. fin. com. Nat. Rep. Party, 1968-72. Recipient Erskine Ramsay award Citizenship Group, Birmingham, 1969. Mem. Newcomen Soc. Am., AmSouth Bank, NA (dir. 1973-81), Sq. D Corp. (dir. 1972-78), First Nat. Bank (dir. 1970-81). Episcopalian. Clubs: Mountain Brook, Birmingham Country (Birmingham); Everglades Bath and Tennis (Palm Beach); Duquesne (Pitts.). Avocations: tennis; golf. Home: 624 N Lake Way Palm Beach FL 33480-3425 Office: Steego Corp 319 Clematis St Ste 900 West Palm Beach FL 33401

SCHULER, ROBERT HUGO, chemist, educator; b. Buffalo, Jan. 4, 1926; s. Robert H. and Mary J. (Mayer) S.; m. Florence J. Forrest, June 18, 1952; children: Mary A., Margaret A., Carol A., Robert E., Thomas C. BS, Canisius Coll., Buffalo, 1946; PhD, U. Notre Dame, 1949. Asst. prof. chemistry Canisius Coll., 1949-53; asso. chemist, then chemist Brookhaven Nat. Lab., 1953-56; staff fellow, dir. radiation research lab. Mellon Inst., 1956-76, mem. adv. bd., 1962-76; prof. chemistry U. radiation research lab. Carnegie-Mellon U., 1967-76; prof. chemistry, dir. radiation lab. U. Notre Dame, Ind., 1976—; John A. Zahm prof. radiation chemistry U. Notre Dame, 1986—; Raman prof. U. Madras, India, 1985-86; vis. prof. Hebrew U., Israel, 1980. Author articles in field. Recipient Curie medal Poland, 1992. Fellow AAAS; mem. Am. Chem. Soc., Am. Phys. Soc., Chem. Soc., Radiation Research Soc. (pres. 1975-76), Sigma Xi. Club: Cosmos. Office: U Notre Dame Radiation Lab Notre Dame IN 46556

SCHULER, ROBERT LEO, appraiser, consultant; b. Cin., June 15, 1943; s. Del D. and Virginia D. (Heyl) S.; m. Shelagh J. Moritz, Aug. 11, 1962; children: Robert C., Sherry L. V.p. Comprehensive Appraisal Service, Inc., Cin., 1977—; bd. dirs. Hamilton County Regional Planning Commn., Cin., 1987-88; mem. exec. com., past pres. OKI Regional Coun. Govts., Cin., 1981-92. Councilman City of Deer Park, Ohio, 1979-86; trustee Sycamore Twp., 1988-92; Ohio state rep. 36th dist. Mem. Am. Assn. Cert. Appraiser (sr.), Cin. Bd. Realtors, Ohio Assn. Realtors, Jaycees (v.p.). Republican. Roman Catholic. Home: 3648 Jeffrey Ct Cincinnati OH 45236-1544 Office: PO Box 36442 Cincinnati OH 45236-0442

SCHULER, THEODORE ANTHONY, civil engineer, city official; b. Louisville, July 1, 1934; s. Henry R. and Virginia (Meisner) S.; m. Jane A. Bandy, July 29, 1979; children: Marc, Elizabeth, Eric, Ellen. BCE, U. Louisville, 1957, M.Engring., 1973. Registered profl. engr., Tenn., Ky.; registered land surveyor. Design, constrn. engr. Brighton Engring. Co., Frankfort, Ky., 1960-65; design engr. Hensley-Schmidt Inc., Chattanooga, 1965-68, assoc. engr., 1969-73, sr. assoc. mem., 1973-75, prin., asst. v.p., head Knoxville office, 1975-81; chief planning engr. engring. dept. City of Knoxville, 1981—. Served to lt. (j.g.) USNR, 1957-60. Fellow ASCE. Home: 5907 Adelia Dr Knoxville TN 37920-5801 Office: Dept Engring City County-Bldg Rm 483 Knoxville TN 37901

SCHULER, V. EDMUND, light manufacturing executive. With GKN plc, Redditch, England, 1974-1989; chmn. GKN Univ. Transmissions, Auburn Hills, Mich. Office: GKN Universal Transmissions 3300 University Dr Auburn Hills MI 48326

SCHULFER, ROCHE EDWARD, theater executive director; b. Chgo., Sept. 26, 1951; s. Thomas Florian and Tess (Ronk) S.; m. Arlene Lencioni, June 2, 1973 (div. 1979); m. Linda Kimbrough, Aug. 2, 1986. BA in Econs., U. Notre Dame. Box office asst. Goodman Theatre, Chgo., 1973-74, asst. to mng. dir., 1974-77, gen. mgr., 1977-80, mng. dir., producer, producing dir., exec. dir., 1980—. Mem. exec. com. League of Resident Theatres, Chgo., 1981, 83; pres. League of Chgo. Theatres, 1983-85, pres. Chgo. Theatre Found., 1985-87; bd. dirs. Chgo. Theatre Group, Lifeline Theatre, Theatre Comm. Group, Lawyers for Creative Arts. Mem. Am. Arts Alliance (chair), Ill. Art Alliance (pres.), Ill. Arts Coun. Office: Goodman Theatre 200 S Columbus Dr Chicago IL 60603-6402

SCHULHOF, MICHAEL PETER, entertainment, electronics company executive; b. N.Y.C., Nov. 30, 1942; s. Rudolph B. and Hannelore (Buck) S.; m. Paola Nissim, Apr. 17, 1969; children: David Kenneth, Jonathan Nissim. BA, Grinnell Coll., 1964, DSc (hon.), 1990; MS, Cornell U., 1967; PhD (NSF fellow), Brandeis U., 1970. Lic. commd. pilot. Am. research fellow Brookhaven Nat. Lab., Uptown, N.Y., 1969-71; asst. to v.p. mfg. CBS Records, Inc., N.Y.C., 1971-73, mem. exec. com., bd. dirs., 1987—; gen. mgr. bus. products div. Sony Corp., N.Y.C., 1973-77, v.p., 1977-78, sr. v.p., 1978-86; pres. Sony Industries, N.Y.C., 1978-86; chmn. Digital Audio Disc Corp., Terre Haute, Ind., 1986—; pres. Sony Software Corp., 1991—; pres., CEO Sony Corp. Am., 1993; chmn. bd. dirs. Quadriga Art Inc., 1980—; bd. dirs. Sony Corp., Japan, Sony Corp. Am., Sony Pictures Entertainment, Materials Rsch. Corp.; chmn. Sony Music Entertainment. Contbr. articles to profl. jours. Patentee audio disc apparatus, 1986. Trustee Brandeis U., 1990—, Mus. TV and Radio, N.Y.C., Lincoln Ctr. for Performing Arts, Inc., N.Y.C., The Brookings Instn., Washington; bd. dirs. Ctr. on Addiction and Substance Abuse at Columbia U., N.Y.C.; mem. investment and svcs. policy adv. com. to U.S. Trade Rep.; active Coun. Fgn. Rels. NSF fellw Brandeis U. Mem. Am. Phys. Soc. (dir. 1978), Computer and Bus. Equipment Mfrs. Assn. (dir.), Am. Radio Relay League, Aircraft Owners and Pilots Assn., Guggenheim Mus., Whitney Mus., Harmony Club, Gipsy Trail Club, East Hampton Tennis Club, Profile Club, Fenway Golf Club, Atlantic Golf Club. Office: Sony Corp Am 9 W 57th St New York NY 10019-2600

SCHULHOFER, STEPHEN JOSEPH, law educator, consultant; b. N.Y.C., Aug. 20, 1942; s. Joseph and Myrelle S.; m. Laurie Wohl, May 28, 1975; children: Samuel, Jonah. AB, Princeton U., 1964; LLB, Harvard U., 1967. Bar: D.C. 1968, U.S. Dist. Ct. (ea. dist.) Pa. 1973, U.S. Supreme Ct. 1973. Law clk. U.S. Supreme Ct., Washington, 1967-69; assoc. Coudert Freres, Paris, 1969-72; prof. law U. Pa., Phila., 1972-86; prof. U. Chgo., 1986—, speedy trial reporter U.S. Dist. Ct., Wilmington, Del., 1975-80; cons. U.S. EPA, Washington, 1977-78, U.S. Sentencing Commn., Washington, 1987-94. Author: Prosecutorial Discretion and Federal Sentencing Reform, 1979. Editor: Criminal Law and its Processes, 1983, 89, 95; contbr. articles to profl. jours. Trustee, Community Legal Services, Inc., Phila., 1981-86. Walter Meyer grantee Am. Bar Found., 1984. Mem. ACLU (Ill. bd. dirs. 1993—), Law and Soc. Assn. Office: U Chgo Law Sch 1111 E 60th St Chicago IL 60637-2702

SCHULIAN, JOHN (NIELSEN SCHULIAN), screenwriter, author; b. L.A., Jan. 31, 1945; s. John and Estella Katherine (Nielsen) S.; m. Paula Lynn Ellis, Aug. 20, 1977 (div. Oct. 1984). BA, U. Utah, 1967; MS, Northwestern U., 1968. Copy editor Salt Lake City Tribune, 1968; reporter Balt. Evening Sun, 1970-75; sportswriter Washington Post, 1975-77; sports columnist Chgo. Daily News, 1977-78, Chgo. Sun-Times, 1978-84, Phila. Daily News, 1984-86; staff writer Miami Vice, Universal City, Calif., 1986-87, story editor, 1987; story editor The Slap Maxwell Story, North Hollywood, Calif., 1987-88; exec. story editor TV series Wiseguy, Hollywood, 1988-89; co-producer TV series Midnight Caller, Burbank, Calif., 1990; supervising producer Midnight Caller, 1990-91; co-exec. producer TV series Reasonable Doubts, Burbank, Calif., 1991-92; creative cons. TV series The Untouchables, L.A., 1992-93; co-exec. producer TV series Hercules, Universal City, Calif., 1994—. Author: Writers' Fighters and Other Sweet Scientists, 1983; contbg. editor Panorama mag., 1980-81; syndicated columnist UP Syndicate; commentator Nat. Pub. Radio, 1985-86; cons. The Reader's Catalog, 1989; contbr. articles to Playboy, Gentlemen's Quar., Sports Illustrated, The National, L.a. Times; included in The Best Am. Sports Writing, 1994. Mem. Pacific Coast League Hist. Soc. With U.S. Army, 1968-70. Recipient Nat. Headliners Club award, 1980, Column Writing award AP Sports Editors, 1979, 82, Best Sports Stories award, 1983, 84, Nat Fleischer Excellence in Boxing Journalism award Boxing Writers Assn. Am., 1985. Mem. Writers Guild Am., Phi Beta Kappa. Office: Peter Benedek United Talent Agy 9560 Wilshire Blvd Beverly Hills CA 90212-2427

SCHULLER, DAVID EDWARD, cancer center administrator, otolaryngology; b. Cleve., Oct. 20, 1944; married; two children. BA, Rutgers U., 1966; MD cum laude, Ohio State U., 1970. Diplomate Am. Bd. Otolaryngology 1975. Intern dept. surgery U. Hosps. Cleve., 1970-71; resident dept. otolaryngology Ohio State U., Columbus, 1971-72; resident dept. surgery U. Hosps. Cleve., 1972-73; fellow head and neck surgery Pack Med. Found. with John Conley, N.Y.C., 1973; resident dept. otolaryngology Ohio State U. Hosps., Columbus, 1973-75; fellow head and neck oncology and facial plastic and reconstructive surgery U. Iowa, Iowa City, 1975-76; from clin. instr. to prof. and chmn. dept. otolaryngology The Ohio State U., Columbus, 1971—; dir. Compehensive Cancer Ctr. & Arthur G. James Cancer Hosp. and Rsch. Inst., Columbus, 1988—; prof. Sch. Allied Med. Professions The Ohio State U., 1990—; mem., chmn. various coms. Ohio State U. Hosps. and Coll. Medicine, 1976—; dir. CCC head and neck oncology program Ohio State U., 1977—, hosps. physician flr. coord. 10th flr., 1977-82, dir. laser-microsurgery teaching and rsch. lab., 1987-88; mem. various coms. Grant Hosp., 1980-84; mem. Accreditation Coun. for the Grad. Med. Edn. Residency Review Com. for Otolaryngology, 1985—, chmn., 1988—; vis. prof., lectr. numerous instns. Author: (books) (with others) Otolaryngology-Head and Neck Surgery-4 Vols., 1986, Textbook of Otolaryngology-7th Edit., 1988, Otolaryngology-Head and Neck Surgery-Update I, 1988, Musculocutaneous Flaps in Head and Neck Reconstructive Surgery, 1989, Otolaryngology-Head and Neck Surgery Update II, 1990, Otorinolaringologia-Cirugia de Cabeza y Culleo, 1991, Otolaryngology-Head and Neck Surgery-4 Vols., 1992; contbr. chpts. to books and articles to profl. jours.; mem. editorial bd. New Horizons in Otolaryngology/Head and Neck Surgery, 1982-87, The Laryngoscope, 1986—, Am. Jour. Otolaryngology, 1988—, Facial Plastic Surgery Internat. Quar. Monographs, 1992—; mem. rev. bd. Jour. Head and Neck Surgery, 1985—; mem. editorial rev. bd. Otolaryngology-Head and Neck Surgery, 1990—; reviewer New Eng. Jour Medicine, 1992—. Trustee Ohio Cancer Found., 1988—; dir. Am. Bd. Otolaryngology, 1988—. Recipient Cert. of Appreciation, Scioto Meml. Hosp., 1982, Edmund Prince Fowler award Triological Soc., 1984; Henry Rutgers scholar Rutgers U., 1965-66; grantee Nat. Cancer Inst., 1980-88, 90—, Bremer Found., 1982-83, 87-88, Photomedica Inc., 1986-89, Upjohn Co., 1986-90, others. Mem. AMA (mem. rev. panel Archives of Otolaryngology-Head and Neck Surgery 1984—), Am. Cancer Soc. (mem. instl. grant rev. com. 1980—, chmn. rehab. com. Franklin County unit 1981-82, mem. profl. edn. com. 1981—, chmn. 1982-85, v.p. 1982-83, pres. 1986, 87, trustee Ohio divsn. 1988—), Am. Assn. Cosmetic Surgeons, Am. Acad. Facial Plastic and Reconstructive Surgery (mem. rsch. com. 1977-82, chmn. residency rels. com. 1982-85, mem. program com. 1982-85, v.p. mid. sect. 1983-87, chmn. by-laws com. 1988—, treas. 1988—, Honor award 1989), Am. Coll. Surgeons, Am. Cleft Palate Assn., Am. Cancer Insts., Am. Soc. Head and Neck Injury, Am. Acad. Otolaryngology Head and Neck Surgery (mem. editorial bd. self-instructional package program 1982—, del. bd. govs. 1982-87, Honor award 1983), Am. Soc. Laser Medicine and Surgery, Am. Laryngological, Rhinological, Otological Soc., Inc., Am. Laryngological Assn., Am. Soc. Clin. Oncology (mem. program com. 1989—), Am. Assn. Cancer Researchers, Am. Soc. Head and Neck Surgery (mem. coun. 1983-86, chmn. scholastic and fellowship award com. 1984-86, mem. profl. rels. and pub. edn. com. 1989—), Southwest Oncology Group (chmn. head and neck com. 1983—), Ohio State Med. Assn. (pres. sect. otolaryngology 1987—), Ohio Soc. Otolaryngology (pres. 1985, 86, 87), Acad. Medicine of Columbus and Franklin County, Columbus E.E.N.T. Soc., Franklin County Acad. Medicine (mem. profl. rels. com. 1982—), Head and Neck Intergroup (vice-chmn. 1984-86, chmn. 1986-89), Asio State U. Med. Alumni Soc. (class rep. 1980—, v.p. 1987-88, pres. 1989-90), Med. Forum, Med. Review Club, Order of Hippocrates (charter), Alpha Omega Alpha. Office: 456 W 10th Ave Columbus OH 43210-1240 also: Ohio State Univ Comp Cancer Ctr Arthur G James Cancer Hosp 410 W 10th Ave Columbus OH 43210-1236

SCHULLER, DIANE ETHEL, allergist, immunologist, educator; b. Bklyn., Nov. 27, 1943; d. Charles William and Dorothy Schuller. AB cum laude with honors in Biology, Bryn Mawr Coll., 1965. Diplomate Am. Bd. Allergy and Immunology, Am. Bd. Pediatrics, Nat. Bd. Med. Examiniers. M.D., SUNY Downstate Med. Sch., Bklyn., 1970. Intern, then resident in pediatrics Roosevelt Hosp., N.Y.C., 1970-72; resident in allergy Cooke Inst. Allergy, 1972-74; assoc. in pediatrics Geisinger Med. Center, Danville, Pa., 1974-95, dir. dept. pediatric allergy, immunology and pulmonary diseases 1974-95; asst. clin. prof. pediatrics Hershey Med. Coll., Pa. State U., 1974-79, assoc. clin. prof., 1979-88; clin. prof. Jefferson Med. Coll., Phila., 1989-95; mem. Columbia-Montour Home Health Services Adv. Group of Profl. Personnel, 1975—; dir. pediatric allergy, immunology, pulmonology Pa. State U., Milton S. Hershey Med. Ctr., 1995—, prof. pediatrics, 1995—. Bd. dirs. Central Pa. Lung and Health Assn.; bd. dirs., exec. com. Am. Lung Assn. of Pa., sec., 1992—; chmn. Susquehanna Valley Lung Assn., 1983—; mem. scholarship com. Bryn Mawr Club, N.Y., 1970-75. Recipient Physicians Recognition award AMA, 1973-76, 74-76, 75-78, 79-82, 83-86, 1987-90, 91-94. Fellow Am. Acad. Pediatrics, Am. Coll. Allergy Asthma and Immunology (2d v.p., bd. regents 1989-91, pres. com. 1990-93, treas. joint coun. of allergy and immunology 1991-93, v.p. 1992, editorial bd. annals of allergy, v.p.1992-93, pres.-elect 1994, pres. 1994—), Am. Assn. Clin. Immunology and Allergy (regional dir., exec. com.), Joint Coun. Allergy and Immunology (bd. dirs. 1986—), Am. Acad. Allergy and Immunology; mem. Pa., N.Y. State allergy socs., N.Y. State, N.Y. County med. socs. Office: Milton S Hershey Med Ctr Pa State U Hershey PA 17033 also: 11 Brandywine Hershey PA 17033

SCHULLER, GUNTHER ALEXANDER, composer; b. N.Y.C., Nov. 22, 1925; s. Arthur E. and Elsie (Bernartz) S.; m. Marjorie Black, June 8, 1948; children: Edwin Gunther, George Alexander. Student, St. Thomas Choir Sch., N.Y.C.; MusD (hon.), Manhattan Sch. Music, 1987, Northeastern U., 1967, U. Ill., 1968, Colby Coll., 1969, Williams Coll., 1975, Cleve. Inst. Music, 1977, New Eng. Conservatory Music, 1978, Rutgers U., 1980, Manhattan Sch. Music, 1987, Oberlin Coll., 1989. tchr. Manhattan Sch. Music, 1950-63; head composition dept. Tanglewood, 1963-84; pres. New Eng. Conservatory of Music, 1967-77; artistic dir. Berkshire Music Center, Tanglewood, 1969-84, Festival at Sandpoint, 1985—; founder, pres. Margun Music Inc., 1975, GM Recs., 1980. French horn player, Ballet Theatre, then prin. horn player, Cin. Symphony Orch., 1943-45, prin. French horn, Met. Opera Orch., 1945-59, Concerto #1 for Horn, 1945; composer: Quartet for Four Double Basses, 1947, Fantasy for Unaccompanied Cello, 1951, Recitative and Rondo for Violin and Piano, 1953, Music for Violin, Piano and Percussion, 1957, Contours, 1958, Woodwind Quintet, 1958, Seven Studies on Themes of Paul Klee, 1959, Spectra, 1960, Six Renaissance Lyrics, 1962, String Quartet No. 2, 1965, Symphony, 1965, opera The Visitation 1966, opera Fisherman and His Wife, 1970, Capriccio Stravagante, 1972, The Power Within Us, 1972, Tre Invenzioni, 1972, Three Nocturnes, 1973, Four Soundscapes, 1974, Concerto No. 2 for Orch., 1975, Triplum II, 1975, Horn Concerto No. 2, 1976, Violin Concerto, 1976, Diptych for organ, 1976, Sonata Serenata, 1978, Contrabassoon Concerto, 1978, Deaï for 3 orchs., 1978, Trumpet Concerto, 1979, Octet, 1979, Eine Kleine Posaunenmusik, 1980, In Praise of Winds (Symphony for Large Wind Orch.), 1981, Symphony for Organ, 1982, Concerto Quaternio, 1983, Concerto for Bassoon and Orch., 1984, Farbenspiel (Concerto No. 3 for Orch.), 1985, On Light Wings (piano quartet), 1984; author: Horn Technique, 1962, Early Jazz: Its Roots and Development, 1968, Musings: The Musical Worlds of Gunther Schuller, 1985, The Swing Era, 1989; premiere of Symphony for Brass and Percussion, Cin., 1950, Salzburg Festival, 1957, Dramatic Overture, N.Y. Philharm., 1956, String Quartet, Number 1 Contemporary Arts Festival, U. Ill., 1957, String Quartet Number 3, 1986, Concertino for Jazz Quartet and Orch, Balt. Symphony Orch., 1959, Seven Studies on Themes of Paul Klee, Ford Found., commn., Minn. Symphony, 1959, Spectra, N.Y. Philharm. 1960, Music for Brass Quintet, Coolidge Found., Library of Congress, 1961, Concerto No. 1 for Orch, Chgo. Symphony Orch., 1966, Triplum, N.Y. Philharm. commd. Lincoln Center, 1967, Aphorisms for Flute and String Trio commd, Carlton Coll. Centennial, 1967, Eine Kleine Posaunenmusik, 1980, In Praise of Winds, 1983, Concerto Quaternio, N.Y. Philharm., 1983, Duologue for Violin and Piano, Library of Congress, 1984, Farbenspiel, Berlin Philharm., 1985, Concerto for Viola and Orch., 1985, String Quartet No. 3, 1986, Chimeric Images, 1988, Concerto for String Quartet and Orchestra, 1988, Concerto for Flute and Orchestra, 1988, On Winged Flight: A Divertimento for Band, 1989, Chamber Concerto, 1989, Concerto for Piano Three Hands, 1989, Phantasmata for Violin and Marinba, 1989, 5 Impromptus Eng. Horn and String Quartet, 1989, Impromptus and Cadenzas, 1990, Hommage à Rayechla for 8 cellos/or multiples thereof, 1990, A Trio Setting for clarinet, violin, piano, 1990, Violin Concert No. 2, 1991, Sonata Fantasia for piano, 1992, Ritmica Melodia Armonia for piccolo and orchestra, 1992, Of Reminiscences and Reflections for orchestra, 1993 (Pulitzer Prize for music 1994), Brass Quintet No. 2, 1993, The Past is in the Present for orchestra, 1994, Sextet for left hand piano and woodwind quintet, 1994, Concerto for organ and orchestra, 1994, Mondrian's Vision, 1994. Guggenheim fellow, 1962, 63, MacArthur fellow, 1991; recipient Creative Arts award Brandeis U., 1960, Deems Taylor award ASCAP, 1970, Alice M. Ditson Conducting award, 1970, Rodgers and Hammerstein award, 1971, Friedheim award, 1988, William Schuman award Columbia U., 1989, Down Beat Lifetime Achievement award, 1993, Pulitzer prize in music, 1994, BMI Lifetime Achievement award, 1994; named Composer of Yr., Mus. Am., 1995. Mem. Nat. Inst. Arts and Letters, Am. Acad. Arts and Scis. Address: care Margun Music Inc 167 Dudley Rd Newton Center MA 02159 also: care Festival at Sandpoint Box 695 Sandpoint ID 83864*

SCHULLER, ROBERT HAROLD, clergyman, author; b. Alton, Iowa, Sept. 16, 1926; s. Anthony and Jennie (Beltman) S.; m. Arvella DeHaan, June 15, 1950; children: Sheila, Robert, Jeanne, Carol, Gretchen. B.A. Hope Coll., 1947; B.D., Western Theol. Sem., 1950; D.D., Hope Coll., 1973; LL.D., Azusa Pacific Coll., 1970, Pepperdine U., 1976; Litt.D., Barrington Coll., 1977. Ordained to ministry Reformed Ch. in am., 1950; pastor Ivanhoe Ref. Ch., Chgo., 1950-55; founder, sr. pastor Garden Grove (Calif.) Community Ch., 1955—; founder, pres. Hour of Power TV Ministry, Garden Grove, 1970—; founder, dir. Robert H. Schuller Inst. for Successful Ch. Leadership, Garden Grove, 1970—; chmn. nat. religious sponsor program Religion in Am. Life, N.Y.C., 1975—; bd. dirs Freedom Found. Author: God's Way to the Good Life, 1963, Your Future Is Your Friend, 1964, Move Ahead with Possibility Thinking, 1967, Self Love, the Dynamic Force of Success, 1969, Power Ideas for a Happy Family, 1972, The Greatest Possibility Thinker That Ever Lived, 1973, Turn Your Scars into Stars, 1973, You Can Become the Person You Want To Be, 1973, Your Church Has Real Possibilities, 1974, Love or Loneliness— You Decide, 1974, Positive Prayers for Power-Filled Living, 1976, Keep on Believing, 1976, Reach Out for New Life, 1977, Peace of Mind Through Possibility Thinking, 1977, Turning Your Stress Into Strength, 1978, Daily Power Thoughts, 1978, The Peak to Peek Principle, 1981, Living Positively One Day at a Time, 1981, Self Esteem: The New Reformation, 1982, Tough Times Never Last, But, Tough People Do!, 1983, Tough Minded Faith for Tender hearted People, 1984, The Be-Happy Attitudes, 1985, Be Happy You Are Loved, 1986, Success is Never Ending, Failure is Never Final, 1988, Believe in the God Who Believes in You, 1989; co-author: The Courage of Carol, 1978. Bd. dirs. Religion in Am. Life; pres. bd. dirs. Christian Counseling Service; founder Robert H. Schuller Corr. Center for Possibility Thinkers, 1976. Recipient Disting. Alumnus award Hope Coll., 1970, Prin. award Freedoms Found., 1974; named Headliner of Year in Religion, Orange County, 1977, Clergyman of Year, Religious Heritage Am., 1977. Mem. Religious Guild Architects (hon.), AIA (bd. dirs. 1986—). Club: Rotary. Office: Religion in Am Life 12141 Lewis St Garden Grove CA 92640-4618

SCHULMAN, CLIFFORD A., lawyer; b. Dec. 6, 1947; s. George and Henrietta Schulman; m. Michele Weissman, June 28, 1969; 1 child, David Michael. B.S. in Journalism and Communications cum laude, U. Fla., 1969, J.D., 1972. Bar: Fla. 1972, U.S. Supreme Ct. 1981, U.S. Ct. Appeals (5th cir.) 1975. Law clk. to Eugene P. Spellman, Miami, Fla., 1970-71; research aide to Judge Norman Hendry, Miami, 1972-73; asst. county atty. Met. Dade County, Miami, 1973-79; ptnr. Greenberg, Traurig, Askew, Hoffman, Lipoff, Rosen & Quentel, Miami, 1979—. Editor-in-chief continuing legal edn. manual Environ. Regulation and Litigation in Fla., 1981 edit. Mem. Gov.'s Task Force on Biscayne Bay Rules, 1978; del. 57th biennial conv. Am. Hebrew Congregations, 1983. Served to capt. USAR, 1969-73. Mem. Fla. Bar (co-editor environ. law sect. newsletter 1977-80; exec. council environ. and land use law sect. 1979-83, sec.-treas. 1981-83, chmn. 1984-85). Home: 21311 NE 23rd Ave North Miami Beach FL 33180 Office: Greenberg Traurig Hoffman Lipoff Rosen & Quentel PA 1221 Brickell Ave Miami FL 33131

SCHULMAN, GRACE, poet, English language educator; b. N.Y.C.; d. Bernard and Marcella (Freiberger) Waldman. m. Jerome L. Schulman, Sept. 6, 1959. Student, Bard Coll., Johns Hopkins U.; BS, Am. U., 1955; MA, NYU, 1960, PhD, 1971. Prof. Baruch Coll., N.Y.C., 1971—; poetry editor The Nation, N.Y.C., 1971—; adviser Poetry Ctr., N.Y.C.; mem. Brandeis Commn., Translation Ctr. Author: (poetry) Burn Down the Icons, 1976, Hemispheres, 1984, For That Day Only, 1994, (critical study) Marianne Moore: The Poetry of Engagement; translator (postry) At the Stone of Losses, Carmi/Present Tense Award. Fellow Yaddo, 1973, 75, 77, 79, 81, 93, MacDowell Colony, 1973, 75, 77, Rockefeller Inst., 1986. Mem. PEN (past v.p.), Poetry Soc. Am., Nat. Book Critics Cir., Authors Guild. Home: 1 University Pl # 14F New York NY 10003

SCHULMAN, HAROLD, obstetrician, gynecologist, perinatologist; b. Newark, Oct. 26, 1930; m. Rosemarie Vincenti; childrne: Stanley H., Sandra C., Gina M. B.S., U. Fla., 1951; M.D. Emory U., 1955. Am. Bd. Ob-Gyn Am. Bd. Maternal and Fetal Medicine. Intern Jackson Meml. Hosp., Miami, Fla., 1955-56; resident Jackson Meml. Hosp., 1958-61; instr. dept. ob-gyn. U. Miami (Fla.) Sch. Medicine, 1961; instr., asst. prof. dept. ob-gyn. Temple U. Sch. Medicine, Phila., 1961-65; asst. prof. dept. ob-gyn. Albert Einstein Coll. Medicine, Bronx, 1965-67; assoc. prof. Albert Einstein Coll. Medicine, 1968-71, prof., 1971—, acting dept. chmn., 1972-73, chmn., 1973-80; assoc. dir. ob-gyn Bronx Mcpl. Hosp. Ctr., 1967-70, dep. dir., 1970-72; chmn. dept. ob-gyn. Winthrop U. Hosp., Mineola, N.Y., 1984-93; prof. ob-gyn SUNY, Stony Brook; 1984-93. Contbr. articles to profl. pubs. Served to capt. U.S. Army, 1956-58. Am. Cancer Soc. fellow, 1959-60; USPHS trainee, 1965-66. Fellow Am. Coll. Obstetricians and Gynecologists (vice chmn. Dist. II 1972-75); mem. Bronx County Obstet. Soc. (pres. 1974), Soc. for Gynecologic Investigation, AAAS, Assn. Profs. of Ob-Gyn., Obstet. Soc. (sec. 1978-80, pres. 1982-83), N.Y. Obstetrical Soc., Soc. Perinatal Physicians, Am. Gynecologic and Obstetric Soc., Am. Gynecol. Obstetrics, N.Y. Obstetics Soc. (pres. 1982), Phi Beta Kappa, Alpha Omega Alpha; hon. mem. Miami Ob-Gyn. Soc., South Atlantic Obstetricians and Gynecologists Soc., Buffalo Gynecologic and Obstetric Soc. (E.G. Winkler meml. lectr.), Croatian Ultrasound Soc. (hon.). Democrat. Jewish. Office: 4605 N A1A Vero Beach FL 32963-1345

SCHULMAN, JOSEPH DANIEL, physician, medical geneticist, reproductive biologist, educator; b. Bklyn., Dec. 20, 1941; s. Max and Miriam (Grossman) S.; m. Dixie A. King; children: Erica N., Julie K. B.A., Bklyn. Coll., 1961; M.D., Harvard U., 1966. Diplomate Am. Bd. Pediatrics, Am. Bd. Ob-Gyn, Am. Bd. Med. Genetics. Intern, resident in pediatrics Mass. Gen. Hosp., Boston, 1966-68; clin. associate. Nat. Inst. Arthritis and Metabolic Diseases, 1968-70; resident in obstetrics and gynecology and fellow in pediatrics N.Y. Hosp.-Cornell Med. Center, 1970-73; Gilbert and Nat. Found. fellow Cambridge (Eng.) U., 1973-74; head sect. human biochem. genetics Nat. Inst. Child Health and Human Devel., NIH, Bethesda, Md., 1974-83; dir. med. genetics program NIH, Bethesda, Md., 1979-1983; prof. ob/gyn, pediatrics, and genetics George Washington U., 1983-84; dir., CEO Genetics & IVF Inst., Fairfax, Va., 1984—; chmn. Genetics & IVF, Inc., Bethesda, Md., 1988—; prof. human genetics, pediatrics, obstetrics and gynecology Med. Coll. Va., 1984—; with dept. ob-gyn Fairfax Hosp., 1984—; advisor to numerous govt. and private agys. Author 3 books; contbr. numerous articles to med. jours.; editorial bd. Molecular Human Reproduction, 1995—. Served with USPHS, 1968-70, 74-83. Fellow Am. Coll. Obstetricians and Gynecologists; mem. Soc. Pediatric Research, Soc. Gynecologic Investigation, Am. Soc. Clin. Investigation, Am. Soc. Human Genetics, Am. Fertility Soc., Phi Beta Kappa, Sigma Xi. Clubs: Harvard, Cosmos. Office: 3020 Javier Rd Fairfax VA 22031-4627

SCHULMAN, MARK ALLEN, market research company executive; b. Phila., Nov. 15, 1945; s. Morris and Ida (Dunn) S. AB, Washington Coll., Chestertown, Md., 1967; MA, U. Wis., 1968; PhD, Rutgers U., 1979. Dir. div. experimental studies U. Md. Ea. Shore, Princess Anne, Md., 1972-75; sr. project dir. Eagleton Inst. Poll Rutgers U., New Brunswick, N.J., 1975-77; sr. v.p. Louis Harris and Assocs., Inc., N.Y.C., 1977-81; pres. Schulman, Ronca & Bucuvalas, Inc., N.Y.C., 1981—. Bd. visitors and govs. Washington Coll., 1990—. Mem. Am. Assn. Pub. Opinion Rsch. (pres. N.Y. chpt. 1994-95). Office: Schulman Ronca & Bucuvalas Inc 145 E 32d St New York NY 10016

SCHULMAN, MICHAEL ROBERT, lawyer; b. Washington, Sept. 10, 1946; s. James H. and Doris (Greenfield) S.; m. Joan M. Camperlino, Feb. 18, 1978; children: Douglas James, Jacie Lauren. BA, Carnegie-Mellon U., 1968; MA in Teaching, Duquesne U., 1971, JD cum laude, 1977. Bar: Pa. 1977, Tex. 1980. Math. tchr. Allderdice High Sch., Pitts., 1968-76; legal asst. Wheeling-Pittsburgh Steel Corp., Pitts., 1976-77; law clk. to judge U.S. Dist. Ct. (we. dist.) Pa., Pitts., 1977-79; assoc. Vinson & Elkins, Houston, 1980-83; assoc. Johnson & Swanson, Dallas, 1983-84, ptnr., 1984—. Mem. Nat. Assn. Bond Lawyers (panelist 1985), Tex. Bar Assn. Avocations: tennis, karate, skiing, running. Office: Johnson & Gibbs PC 900 Jackson St Dallas TX 75202-4404

SCHULMAN, PAUL MARTIN, advertising executive; b. N.Y.C., Feb. 27, 1940; s. Irving and Tessie (Westman) S.; m. Myra Zivia Rosenbaum, Aug. 25, 1963; children: Irv Jeffrey, Mark Todd. BS, NYU, 1961. Media researcher William Esty Co., N.Y.C., 1962-63, network account exec., 1963-69; network account exec. Doyle, Dane & Bernbach, N.Y.C., 1970-71; v.p., dir. programming Gardner Advt., N.Y.C., 1971-89; pres. Paul Schulman Co., N.Y.C., 1978—; sr. v.p. Advanswers Media/Programming; v.p. Wells, Rich Greene/BDDP; network TV cons. Jay Bernstein Prodns., Los Angeles, 1971—; Universal TV Studios, Los Angeles, 1974—, also others. Contbr. articles to profl. publs., 1977—. Head coach Youth Basketball Assn., Montclair, N.J., 1975-78; head coach indoor soccer Clifton Boys Club, N.J., 1980-84; mgr. Montclair Little League Baseball, N.J., 1980-81; head coach outdoor soccer Montclair Town League and Traveling Team, 1981-82; mem. adv. bd. Count Basie Theatre Red Bank, N.J., 1991—. Served to sgt. U.S. Army, 1961-62. Republican. Jewish. Avocations: tennis, spectator sports, collecting jazz compact discs. Home: 50 Grandview Pl Montclair NJ 07043-2422 Office: Paul Schulman Co 1740 Broadway New York NY 10019-4315

SCHULMAN, SIDNEY, neurologist, educator; b. Chgo., Mar. 1, 1923; s. Samuel E. and Ethel (Miller) S.; m. Mary Jean Diamond, June 17, 1945; children—Samuel E., Patricia, Daniel. B.S., U. Chgo., 1944, M.D., 1946. Asst. prof. neurology U. Chgo., 1952-57, asso. prof., 1957-65, prof., 1965-75, Ellen C. Manning prof., div. biol. scis., 1975—. Served with M.C. AUS, 1947-49. Mem. Am. Neurol. Assn., U. Chgo. Med. Alumni Assn. (pres. 1968-69), Chgo. Neurol. Soc. (pres. 1964-65). Home: 5000 S East End Ave Chicago IL 60615-3140 Office: U Chgo Culver Hall 1025 E 57th St Chicago IL 60637-1508

SCHULMAN, TOM, screenwriter. BA, Vanderbilt Univ. Writer: (films) Dead Poets Society, 1989 (Academy award best original screenplay 1989), What About Bob?, 1991; co-writer: (films) Honey, I Shrunk the Kids, 1989, Second Sight, 1989, Medicine Man, 1992; exec. prodr.: (films) Indecent Proposal, 1993. Office: care CAA 9830 Wilshire Blvd Beverly Hills CA 90212-1825*

SCHULMEYER, GERHARD, manufacturing executive; b. 1938. MS in Mgmt., MIT. With Motorola, Inc., 1979-89; exec. v.p. ABB Asea, Brown, Boveri, Ltd., 1989—; pres., CEO Asea, Brown, Boveri, Inc., 1990—. Office: Motorola Inc 1303 E Algonquin Rd Schaumburg IL 60196 Office: ABB ASEA Brown Boveri PO Box 9308 Stamford CT 06904-9308

SCHULSTAD, EUGENE P., computer company executive; b. Detroit Lanes, Minn., Dec. 26, 1944; s. Eugene P. and Bernice I. (Berg) S.; m. Linda M. Long, June 14, 1968; children: Tara, Tammy, Wendy. BS in Math., Moorhead State U., Minn., 1965; MS in Math., Kans. State U., 1967; MBA, Ind. U., 1975. Mathematician GM, Indpls., 1967-69; branch mgr. Dialog Computing, Indpls., 1969-71; regional mgr. Metri Data Computing, Indpls., 1971-75; v.p., gen. mgr. Cybershare, Ltd., Winnipeg, Manitobal, 1975-77; branch mgr. Metri Data Computing, Louisville, 1977-78; pres. Schulstad, Myers & Assoc., Louisville, 1978-83, Master Software Corp., Indpls., 1983—; treas. Assn. Healthcare Philanthropy, Falls Church, Va., 1988-91, Ind. Chpt., Natl. Fund Raising Execs., Indpls., 1988-91; pres. Ind. Chpt., Nat. Soc. Fund Raising Execs., Indpls., 1992. Mem. Lawrence Roundtable, Rep. Fin. Commn., Indpls., 1991-92. Recipient Pres. award Nat. Soc. Fund Raising Execs., Ind., 1991. Mem. Kiwanis, Columbia Club, Old Oakland Golf Club. Avocations: golf, running, reading, travel.

SCHULT, ROBERT W., food products executive; b. 1949. BA, U. N.C., Durham, 1971. With Nestle Food Co., Glendale, Calif., 1971-91, pres., CEO, 1991—. Office: Nestle Food Co 800 N Brand Blvd Glendale CA 91203-1200

SCHULTE, DAVID MICHAEL, investment banker; b. N.Y.C., Nov. 12, 1946; s. Irving and Ruth (Stein) S.; m. Nancy Fisher, June 30, 1968; children: Michael B., Katherine F. BA, Williams Coll., 1968; postgrad., Exeter Coll., Oxford (Eng.) U., 1968-69; JD, Yale U., 1972. Bar: D.C. 1973. Law clk. to Mr. Justice Stewart, U.S. Supreme Ct., 1972-73; spl. asst. to pres. N.W. Industries, Inc., Chgo., 1973-75; v.p. corp. devel. N.W. Industries, Inc., 1975-79, exec. v.p., 1979-80; sr. v.p. Salomon Bros., Chgo., 1980-84; mng. ptnr. Chilmark Ptnrs., Chgo., 1984—. Editor-in-chief: Yale Law Jour, 1971-72. John E. Moody scholar Exeter Coll., Oxford U., 1968-69. Mem. Washington Bar Assn., Chgo. Club, Racquet Club, Bryn Mawr Country Club. Office: Chilmark Ptnrs 2 N Riverside Plz Ste 1500 Chicago IL 60606-2603

SCHULTE, FRANCIS B., archbishop; b. Philadelphia, PA, Dec. 23, 1926. Grad., St. Charles Borromeo Sem. Ordained priest Roman Catholic Ch., 1952. Apptd. titular bishop of Afufenia and aux. bishop of Phila., 1981-85; bishop Wheeling-Charleston, W.Va., 1985-89; archbishop New Orleans, 1989—. Office: 7887 Walmsley Ave New Orleans LA 70125-3431*

SCHULTE, FREDERICK JAMES, newpaper editor; b. Mpls., June 6, 1952; s. Philip William and Katherine Louise (Regan) S. BA, U. Va., 1974. Contbg. editor, feature writer Washington Times, 1974-75; news reporter Internat. Med. News Group, Washington, 1976-78; med. writer, gen. assignment reporter Sun-Sentinel, Ft. Lauderdale, Fla., 1978-83, investigative team leader, 1983-88, asst. regional editor, 1988-90, investigations editor, 1990—. Author: Fleeced! Telemarketing Rip-Offs and How to Avoid Them., 1995. Recipient Excellence in Med. Journalism award Fla. Med. Assn., 1983, 1st Pl. Investigative Reporting award Fla. Press Club, 1983, 1st Pl. Sustained Coverage award Inland Daily Press Assn., 1983, Non-deadline Reporting prize Sigma Delta Chi, 1983, Green Eyeshade award Sigma Delta Chi, 1983, 1st Pl. Pub. Svc. award Fla. Press Club, 1986, 87, 89, 90, Media Merit award Trial Lawyers Am., 1986, 1st Pl. award Big Bros./Big Sisters Am., 1987, 1st Pl. Pub. Svc. award Fla. Soc. Newspaper Editors, 1987, Children's Express Jounalism award, 1987, 1st Pl. Investigative Reporting award Unity Awards in Media, 1987, Pulitzer Prize finalist, 1987, Worth Bingham Meml. Fund prize, 1989, Cert. of Merit, So. Journalism awards, 1990, Freedom of Info. award AP Mng. Editors Assn., 1990, Lowell Thomas award, 1992, John Hancock award, 1992, Silver Gavel award ABA, 1992, Depth Reporting award Fla. Soc. Newspaper Editors, 1993, Pub. Affairs/Social Issues Reporting award Unity Awards in Media, 1993, George Polk award L.I. U., 1993, Gerald Loeb award U. Calif., 1994. Mem. Investigative Reporters and Editors (S.E. regional coord., Disting. Investigative Reporting award 1985). Office: Sun-Sentinel 200 E Las Olas Blvd Fort Lauderdale FL 33301-2293

SCHULTE, HENRY FRANK, journalism educator; b. Lincoln, Nebr., Sept. 24, 1924; s. Henry F. and Neva Irene (Arnold) S.; m. Irene Nef, May 12, 1951; children: Nancy, Susanne; m. Ann M. Raleigh, Dec. 4, 1994. A.B., McGill U., 1951; M.S., Columbia, 1952; Ph.D., U. Ill., 1966. Editor-corr. U.P.I., London, 1954-56; mgr. U.P.I., Spain, 1956-62; assoc. prof. journalism Pa. State U., 1965-69; chmn. newspaper dept. Syracuse (N.Y.) U., 1969-72, prof. journalism, 1980-94; dean Newhouse Sch. Pub. Communications, 1972-80; cons. Nat. Endowment for Arts; dir. WCNY-TV/FM; external examiner U. W.I., 1975-78; cons. external degree program U. State of N.Y. Author: The Spanish Press, 1470-1966: Print, Power and Politics, 1968; Editor, pub.: Mingote's World, 1957. Chmn. Jesse H. Neal awards judging Assn. Bus. Pubs. Served with AUS, 1945-46. Mem. Internat. Press Inst., Inter-Am. Press Assn., Soc. Profl. Journalists, Women in Communications, Assn. for Edn. in Journalism, N.Y. State Soc. Newspaper Editors (exec. sec. 1969-73), Assn. Edn. in Journalism/Am. Newspaper Publishers Assn. (regional liaison officer 1976-81), Overseas Press Club. Club: Hillsboro (Hillsboro Beach, Fla.). Home: 13 Mccoy Rd Jaffrey NH 03452-1662

SCHULTE, JEFFREY LEWIS, lawyer; b. N.Y.C., July 24, 1949; s. Irving and Ruth (Stein) S.; m. Elizabeth Ewan Kaiser, Aug. 13, 1977; children: Andrew Riggs, Ian Garretson, Elizabeth Alexandra. BA, Williams Coll.,

1971; postgrad., Harvard U., 1971-72; JD, Yale U., 1976. Bar: Pa. 1978, Ga. 1993. Law clk. to hon. John J. Gibbons U.S. Ct. Appeals (3d cir.), Newark, 1976-77; assoc. Schnader, Harrison, Segal & Lewis, Phila., 1977-84, ptnr., 1985-92; founding ptnr. Schnader, Harrison, Segal & Lewis, Atlanta, 1992—. Contbr. articles to profl. jours. Bd. dirs. North Ardmore (Pa.) Civic Assn., pres., 1990; bd. dirs. Main Line YMCA, chmn., 1989-91; active Ardmore (Pa.) Alliance Project. Mem. ABA, Pa. Bar Assn., Phila. Bar Assn., State Bar of Ga., Atlanta Bar Assn., Yale Club (bd. dirs Phila. chpt. 1988-92), Williams Club Phila., Phila. Racquet Club, Merion Cricket Club, Weekapaug (R.I.) Yacht Club, Weekapaug Tennis Club, Yale Club Atlanta, Williams Club Atlanta, Phi Beta Kappa. Office: Schnader Harrison Segal & Lewis 285 Peachtree Center Ave NE Atlanta GA 30303-1229

SCHULTE, JOSEPHINE HELEN, historian, educator; b. Foley, Ala., May 9, 1929; d. Mathias and Theresia (Honner) S. AA, Sacred Heart Jr. Coll., Cullman, Ala., 1949; BS in History, Spring Hill Coll., 1957; MA in History, U. So. Miss., 1961; MA in German, Trinity U., San Antonio, 1976; PhD in History, Loyola U., Chgo., 1969. Steamship agt. Gulf Steamship Agy., Mobile, Ala., 1949-58; translator banks in Mobile, 1949-62; German tchr. Brookley Field AFB, Mobile, 1951-62; adminstrv. asst., rsch. assoc. So. Inst. Mgmt., Louisville, 1959-60; spl. lectr. Spring Hill Coll., Mobile, 1960-63; teaching fellow Loyola U., Chgo., 1966-67; asst. prof. Latin Am. history U. of Americas, Mexico City, 1967-70; from assoc. prof. to prof. St. Mary's U., San Antonio, 1970—, coord. Latin Am. studies program, 1972-90, grad. advisor in history, 1973-94; invited to read a paper Internat. Coloquy, U. Lima, Peru, 1991, U. Yucatan, Mex., 1992, U. Maritima, Valparaiso, Chile, 1993; book reviewer. Author: (with Raymond Schmandt) Civil War Chaplains—A Document From a Jesuit Community, 1962, The Spring Hill College Diary, 1861-65, Gabino Barreda y su mision diplomatica en Alemania, 1878-79 Historia Mexicana, 1974; translator: El Positivismo en Mexico, 1974. Grantee OAS, 1966-67, Newberry Library, 1978, Spanish Govt. and OAS, 1981-82; Fulbright grantee, 1983. Mem. Southwestern Conf. L.Am. Studies, German Geneal. Soc., Cath. Hist. Assn., Gottscheer Rsch. Assn. (bd. dirs.). Roman Catholic. Avocations: photography, genealogy, crocheting, collecting postcards and slides, travel. Home: 1415 Babcock Rd San Antonio TX 78201-6640

SCHULTE, MARGARET FLORENCE, personnel firm executive; b. Lima, Ohio, May 30, 1945; d. Stephan Anthony and Mary Laura (Nartker) S. BBA, Thomas More Coll., Erlanger, Ky., 1967; MBA, Xavier U., 1971. Asst. adminstr. Our Lady of the Way Hosp., Martin, Ky., 1967-73; dir. project rev. Health Systems Agy. Northwestern Pa., Erie, 1975-77; certificate of need dir. W.Va. Dept. Health, Charleston, 1977-78; underwriter Hereth, Orr & Jones Inc., Atlanta, 1978-80; dir. devel. Health Group, Inc., Atlanta, 1980-83; pres. Margaret Schulte & Assocs., Atlanta, 1983-87; exec. v.p. The Regis Group, Ltd., Atlanta, 1987-88. Mem., vol. Ga. Trust for Hist. Preservation, Atlanta, 1983-86; friend High Mus. Art., Atlanta, 1981—. Mem. Am. Coll. Healthcare Execs., Ga. Womens' Health Adminstrn. Network. Republican. Roman Catholic. Office: Healthcare Fin Mgt Assn 2 Westbrook Corp Ctr #700 Westchester IL 60154

SCHULTE, RICHARD FRANK, marketing company executive; b. Covington, Ky., Dec. 13, 1935; s. Cyril J. and Rose M. (Hugenburg) S.; m. Suzanne Rice, Apr. 23, 1960; children: Jeffrey, Molly Ann, Richard Frank, Suzanne. B.S., Xavier U., Cin., 1956. Mktg. exec. Procter & Gamble, Cin., 1959-72; v.p. advt. Deltona Corp., Miami, Fla., 1972-74, sr. v.p. mktg., 1975-79; exec. v.p. Deltona Crop., Miami, Fla., 1979-82; pres., chief exec. officer Deltona Mktg. Corp., Miami, 1982-83; dir. Deltona Corp., 1978-83; pres., chief exec. officer Fla. First Properties Corp., 1983—. Bd. dirs. Cin. chpt. ARC, 1968-72; bd. dirs. St. Joseph Orphanage, Cin., 1968-72; chmn. campaign United Fund, 1966-70; chmn. campaign fund Miami council Boy Scouts Am., 1975. Republican. Roman Catholic. Club: Riviera Country (Miami) (fin. com. 1982-84).

SCHULTE, STEPHEN CHARLES, lawyer; b. Evanston, Ill., June 26, 1952; s. George John and Mary Ruth (Lamping) S.; m. Kathleen Ann O'Donnell, Sept. 4, 1982; children: Kate, Maureen. BA magna cum laude, St. Louis U., 1973, JD, 1976. Bar: Ill. 1976, U.S. Dist. Ct. (no. dist.) Ill. 1976, U.S. Ct. Appeals (7th cir.) 1991. Atty. Perz & McGuire, Chgo., 1976-83; ptnr. Winston & Strawn, Chgo., 1983—. Founder, bd. dirs. Greater Orgn. for Less Fortunate (GOLF), Chgo., 1982—; fundraiser for Maryville Acad.; mem. Glenview Park Dist. Commn., 1989—, v.p., 1991-92, pres., 1992-93. Mem. ABA, Ill. State Bar Assn., Chgo. Bar Assn., Ill. Trial Lawyers Assn., Ill. Assn. Def. Trial Counsel, Chgo. Vol. Legal Svcs., Nat. Legal Aid Defender Assn., Phi Beta Kappa. Avocations: basketball, baseball, golf, music, travel. Home: 1222 Pine St Glenview IL 60025-2918 Office: Winston & Strawn 35 W Wacker Dr Chicago IL 60601-1614

SCHULTE, STEPHEN JOHN, lawyer, educator; b. N.Y.C., July 7, 1938; s. John and Marjorie (Fried) S.; m. Patricia Walker, June 6, 1962 (div.); children: Susan Jean, Jeffrey David, Elizabeth Ann; m. Margaret Van Doren Cook, Mar. 12, 1975. BA, Brown U., 1960; JD, Columbia U., 1963. Bar: N.Y. 1964. Assoc. Lowenstein, Pitcher, Hochkiss & Parr, N.Y.C., 1963-66, Fried, Frank, Harris, Shriver & Jacobson, N.Y.C., 1966-69; founding ptnr. Schulte, Roth & Zabel, N.Y.C., 1969—, also chmn. corp. dept.; adj. prof. law Benjamin N. Cardozo Law Sch., 1992—, Fordham U., 1992—; lectr. in securities law field; panelist various forums. Trustee Choate Rosemary Hall Sch., Wallingford, Conn., 1982—, chmn. investment and fin. com., 1984-85, chmn. devel. com., 1985-86, chmn. nominating com., 1986-89, chmn. bd. trustees, 1990—. Mem. ABA, N.Y. State Bar Assn. (com. on securities regulation), Assn. Bar City N.Y., Norfolk Country Club (Conn.). Office: Schulte Roth & Zabel 900 3rd Ave New York NY 10022-4728

SCHULTES, RICHARD EVANS, ethnobotanist, museum executive, educator, conservationist; b. Boston, Jan. 12, 1915; s. Otto Richard and Maude Beatrice (Bagley) S.; m. Dorothy Crawford McNeil, Mar. 26, 1959; children: Richard Evans II, Neil Parker and Alexandra Ames (twins). AB cum laude, Harvard U., 1937, AM, 1938, PhD, 1941; MH (hon.), Universidad Nacional de Colombia, Bogotá, 1953; DSci (hon.), Mass. Coll. Pharmacy, 1987. Plant explorer, NRC rsch. fellow Harvard Bot. Mus., Cambridge, Mass., 1941-42; research asso. Harvard Bot. Mus., 1942-53; curator Orchid Herbarium of Oakes Ames, 1953-58, curator econ. botany, 1958-85, exec. dir., 1967-70, dir., 1970-85; Guggenheim Found. fellow, collaborator U.S. Dept. Agr., Amazon of Colombia, 1942-43; plant explorer in South Am. Bur. Plant Industry, 1944-54; prof. biology Harvard U., 1970-72, Paul C. Mangelsdorf prof. natural scis., 1973-81, Edward C. Jeffrey prof. biology, 1981-85, emeritus prof., 1985—; adj. prof. pharmacognosy U. Ill., Chgo., 1975—; Hubert Humphrey vis. prof. Macalaster Coll., 1979; field agt. Rubber Devel. Corp. of U.S. Govt., in S.Am., 1943-44; collaborator Instituto Argronômico Norte, Belém, Brazil, 1948-50; hon. prof. Universidad Nacional de Colombia, 1953—, prof. econ. botany, 1963; bot. cons. Smith, Kline & French Co., Phila., 1957-67; mem. NIH Adv. Panel, 1964; mem. selection com. for Latin Am. Guggenheim Found., 1964-85; mem. sci. adv. bd. Palm Oil Rsch. Inst., Malaysia, 1980-89; mem. sci. adv. bd. Shaman Pharmaceuticals, 1988—; chmn. Ethnobotany Specialist Group, Internat. Union Nature, Switzerland; chmn. on-site visit U. Hawaii Natural Products Grant NIH, 1966, Deutche Gesellschaft für Arzneiphanzenforchung, Berlin, 1967, III Internat. Pharm. Congress, São Paulo, I Amazonian Biol. Symposium, Belém, Brazil, Symposium Ethnpharmacologic Search for Psychoactive drugs, San Francisco; others; Laura L. Barnes Annual lectr. Morris Arboretum, Phila., 1969; Koch lectr. Rho Chi Soc., Pitts., 33d Internat. Congress Pharm. Sci., Stockholm, 1971, Chgo., 1974; vis. prof. econ. botany, plants in relation to man's progress Jardin Botánico, Medellín, Colombia, 1973; Cecil and Ida H. Green vis. lectr. U. B.C., Vancouver, Can., 1974; co-organizer Internat. Symposium Erythdroxylon, Equador, 1979, co-dir. phase VII Alpha Helix Rsch. plant medicines Witoto, Bora Indianas, Peru, 1977, 2d Philip Morris Symposium, Richmond, Va., 1975, I Solanacese Conf., U. Birmingham, Eng., 1977, Soc. of Americanists, Manchester, Eng., 1982, Salah Workshop for Conservation of Worldlands, Sultanate of Oman, 1983, Symposium of Environ. Protection, 1992, Etnobotanica-92, Córdoba, Spain, 1992, Spruce Meml. Symposium, Castle Howard, Yorkshire, Eng., 1993, INDERENA Bogotá, 1988, others; organizer Internat. Symposium Erythroxylon, Equador, 1979; vis. scholar Rockefeller Study Cent. Centre, Bellagio, Italy, 1980, 88; cons. Rubber Rsch. Inst., Malaysia, 1988—. Author: (with P. A. Vestal) Economic Botany of the Kiowa Indians, 1941, Native Orchids of Trinidad and Tobago, 1960, (with A. F. Hill) Plants and Human Affairs,

1960, rev. edit., 1968, (with A. S. Pease) Generic Names of Orchids—their Origin and Meaning, 1963, (with A. Hofmann) The Botany and Chemistry of Hallucinogens, 1973, rev. edit., 1980, Hallucinogenic Plants, 1976, Plants of the Gods, 1979, Plant Hallucinogens, 1976, (with W.A. Davis) The Glass Flowers at Harvard, 1982, Where the Gods Reign, 1987, El Reino de los Dioses, 1988, (with R.F. Raffauf) The Healing Forest, 1990, Vine of the Soul: Medicine Men of the Colombian Amazon—Their Plants and Rituals, 1992; contbg. author: Ency. Biol. Scis, 1961, Ency. Brit, 1966, 83, Ency. Biochemistry, 1967, McGraw-Hill Yearbook Sci., Tech, 1937-85, New Royal Horticulture Dictionary (ethnobotany chpt., 1992); author numerous Harvard Bot. Mus. Leaflets.; Asst. editor: Chronica Botanica, 1947-52; editor: Bot. Mus. Leaflets, 1957-85, Econ. Botany, 1962-79; mem. editorial bd. Lloydia, 1965-76, Altered States of Consciousness, 1973—, Jour. Psychedelic Drugs, 1974—; co-editor: series Psychoactive Plants of the World, Yale U. Press, 1987—; mem. adv. bd.: Horticulture, 1976-78, Jour. Ethnopharmacology, 1978—, Soc. Pharmacology, 1976—, Elaeis, 1988—, Flora of Ecuador, 1976—, Jour. Latin Am. Folklore, Ethnobotany (India) (also founding mem.), 1989—, Environ. Awareness (India) 1988—, Bol. Mus. Goeldi (Brazil), 1987—, Environ. Conservation (Geneva), 1987—; contbr. numerous articles to profl. jours. Mem. governing bd. Amazonas 2000, Bogotá; assoc. in ethnobotany Museo del Oro, Bogotá, 1974—; chmn. NRC panels, 1974, 75; mem. NRC Workshops on Natural Products, Sri Lanka, 1975, participant numerous sems., congresses, meetings; mem. adv. bd. Fitzhugh Ludlow Libr., Native Land Found., 1980, Morgan Meml. Archives Chadron State Coll., 1987—, Albert Hofmann Found.; v.p. Margaret Mee Amazon Trust, Royal Bot. Gardens. Decorated Orden de Victoria Regia, Cruz de Boyacá (Colombia); recipient award, 1981, gold medal for conservation presented by Duke of Edinburgh, 1984, Tyler prize for environ. achievement, 1984, Mass. gov.'s recognition award Nat. Sci. Week, 1985, cert. of merit Bot. Soc. Am., 1991, Jannaki-Ammal medal, 1992, Linnean medal 1992, medal Harvard U., 1992, Martín de la Cruz medal, 1992; grantee Rockefeller Found., 1982. Fellow Am. Acad. Arts and Scis., Am. Coll. Neuropsychopharmacology (sci. speaker San Juan, P.R. 1984), Third World Acad. Scis., Acad. Scis. India, Internat. Soc. Naturalists; mem. NAS, Linnean Soc. (London), Academia Colombiana de Ciéncias Exactas, Fisico-Químicas y Naturales, Instituto Ecuatoriano de Ciéncias Naturales, Sociedad Cientifica Antonio Alzate (Mexico), Argentine Acad. Scis., Am. Orchid Soc. (life hon.), Pan Am. Soc. New Eng. (gov.), Soc. Mexicana de Micologie (hon.), Asociación de Amigos de Jardines Botánicos (life), Soc. Econ. Botany (organizer annual meeting 1961, Disting. Botanist of Yr. award 1979), New Eng. Bot. Club (pres. 1954-60), Internat. Assn. Plant Taxonomy, Am. Acad. Achievement, Am. Soc. Pharmacognosy, Phytochem. Soc. N.Am., Sociedad Colombiana de Orquideologia, Soc. Ethnobot. India, Amazon Tropical Biology, Internat. Soc. Ethnobiology, Sociedad Cubana de Botánica, Sigma Xi (pres. Harvard chpt. 1971-72, medal 1985), Phi Beta Kappa (Harvard chpt.), Beta Nu chpt. Phi Sigma (first hon.). Unitarian (vestryman Kings Chapel, Boston 1974-76, 82-85). Home: 78 Larchmont Rd Melrose MA 02176-2906 Office: Bot Museum Harvard U Cambridge MA 02138

SCHULTZ, ALBERT BARRY, engineering educator; b. Phila., Oct. 10, 1933; s. George D. and Belle (Seidman) S.; m. Susan Resnikov, Aug. 25, 1955; children—Carl, Adam, Robin. B.S., U. Rochester, 1955; M.Engring., Yale U., 1959, Ph.D., 1962. Asst. prof. U. Del., Newark, 1962-65; asst. prof. U. Ill., Chgo., 1965-66, assoc. prof., 1966-71, prof., 1971-83; Vennema prof. U. Mich., Ann Arbor, 1983—. Contbr. numerous articles to profl. jours. Served to lt. USN, 1955-58. Rsch. Career award NIH, 1975-80; Javits Neurosci. Investigator award NIH, 1985-92. Mem. NAE, Internat. Soc. for Study of Lumbar Spine (pres. 1981-82), ASME (chmn. bioengring. div. 1981-82, H.R. Lissner award 1990), Am. Soc. of Biomechanics (pres. 1982-83), U.S. Nat. Com. on Biomechanics (pres. 1982-83), Phi Beta Kappa. Office: U Mich 3112 GG Brown Lab Ann Arbor MI 48109-2125

SCHULTZ, ANDREW SCHULTZ, JR., industrial engineering educator; b. Harrisburg, Pa., Aug. 14, 1913; s. Andrew S. and Ada (DeHaven) S.; m. Mary S. Mory, Sept. 2, 1939; children: Susan Tapscott, Andrew M. Student, Phillips (Andover) Acad., 1928-32; B.S., Cornell U., 1936, Ph.D., 1941. Installer N.J. Bell Telephone Co., 1936-37; instr. Sibley Sch. Mech. Engring., Coll. Engring. Cornell U., 1937-41, asst. prof., 1941-46, assoc. prof., 1946-50, prof., head dept. indsl. and engring. adminstrn., 1950-62; dean Coll. Engring. Cornell U., 1963-72, acting dean, 1978, Spencer T. Olin prof. engring., 1973-80, emeritus, 1980—; v.p. Logistics Mgmt. Inst., Wash., 1962-63; chmn. bd. trustees Logistics Mgmt. Inst., 1972-84, trustee, 1985-89. Bd. dirs. Engring. Council Profl. Devel., 1968-73. Served as lt. col. AUS, 1941-46; indsl. service ammunition div. Office Chief Ordnance. Fellow Am. Inst. Indsl. Engrs. (dir. research 1955-62); mem. Am. Soc. Engring. Edn., Triangle, Tau Beta Pi, Pi Tau Sigma, Phi Gamma Delta. Home: 1000 Vicars Landing Way Apt PH I Ponte Vedra Beach FL 32082-3127

SCHULTZ, ARTHUR JOSEPH, JR., retired trade association executive; b. Detroit, June 20, 1918; s. Arthur Joseph and Olive U. (Beauchesne) S.; m. Barbara Farnan, Aug. 20, 1942; children: Arthur, Robert, William, Barbara, John, Karen. Student, Naval War Coll., 1956-57, Brookings Inst., 1962, Naval Line Sch., 1947-48, U. Detroit, 1937-39. Joined U.S. Navy, 1940, commd. ensign, 1940, advanced through grades to capt., 1950; comdg. officer Com. Strike/I. NATO, Verona, Italy, 1959-61, Naval Air Sta., Grosse Ile, Mich., 1961-63, ret., 1963; pres. Chrysler Corp. subs., Highland Park, Mich., 1971-75; dep. adminstr. VA, Washington, 1975-77; pres. Steel Shipping Container Inst., Union, N.J., 1977-89; ret., 1989. Vice pres. Detroit Aviation Commn., 1968-77; bd. dirs. United Way Union County, Elizabeth, N.J., 1981-85, sec./treas., 1983-85; chmn. Hazardous Materials Adv. Com., Washington, 1984-85. Decorated Navy Cross; recipient Meritorious Service award VA, 1977. Mem. Am. Soc. Assn. Execs., Soc. Automotive Engrs., Mil. Order World Wars. Republican. Roman Catholic. Club: Englewood (N.J.) Golf and Country Home: 55 Cayman Isles Blvd Englewood FL 34223-1832

SCHULTZ, ARTHUR WARREN, communications company executive; b. N.Y.C., Jan. 13, 1922; s. Milton Warren and Genevieve (Dann) S.; grad. U. Chgo.; D.Letters (hon.), Rosary Coll.; m. Elizabeth Carroll Mahan, 1949 (div. 1987); children—Arthur Warren, John Carroll (dec.), Julia Hollingsworth; m. Susan Keefe, 1988. With Foote, Cone & Belding Communications, Chgo., 1948-82, v.p., 1957-63, sr. v.p., dir., 1963-69, exec. v.p., 1969, chmn. bd., CEO, 1970-81, chmn. exec. com., CEO, 1981-82; dir. Chgo. Sun-Times Co., Field Adams Co.; vice chmn. Chgo. Sun-Times Newspaper Co., 1989-94. Pres. Cook County Sch. Nursing, 1963-64, Welfare Council Met. Chgo., 1965-67; mem. bus. adv. council Urban League Chgo.. 1971-82; chmn. Nat. Com. to Save Am.'s Cultural Collections, 1990-94; mem. Pres.'s Com. on Arts and Humanities, 1984-93; bd. dirs. Chgo. Crime Commn., 1965-71, Community Fund Chgo., 1966-67, Better Bus. Bur., 1970-78, Lyric Opera Chgo., 1967-77, Chgo. Council Fgn. Relations 1977-86, Chgo. Public TV, 1978-82, Chgo. Central Area Com., 1978-82; trustee YWCA, 1962-74, Calif. Coll. Arts and Crafts, 1985-87; trustee Art Inst. Chgo., 1975—, chmn. bd., 1981-84; trustee U. Chgo., 1977—, Santa Barbara Mus. Art, 1988—; pres., 1989-92. Editor Caring for Your Collections. Served to 1st lt. USAAF, 1943-45. Recipient Alumni Service award U. Chgo., 1986. Mem. Am. Assn. Advt. Agys. (dir. 1968-71, 74-76, chmn. Chgo. council 1964-65, chmn. Central region 1970-71), Delta Kappa Epsilon. Episcopalian. Clubs: Commercial, Old Elm, Valley (Montecito, Calif.), Birnam Wood. Home and Office: 2072 China Flat Rd Santa Barbara CA 93108-2211

SCHULTZ, BARBARA MARIE, insurance company executive; b. Chgo., Sept. 9, 1943; d. Edwin and Bernice (Barstis) Legner; m. Ronald J. Schultz Sr., May 1, 1965; 1 child, Ronald J. Grad. high sch., Chgo. Account rep. Met. Ins. Co., Aurora, Ill., 1981—; qualifier Met. Life Leaders Conf., 1990. Fellow Nat. Assn. Life Underwriters (edn. chmn. 1988-91, nat. quality award Robert L. Rose award 1990, Life Underwriters Tng. Coun. (chmn. 1986-88, citation 1987), South Cook County Assn. Life Underwriters (edn. chmn. 1988-91). Roman Catholic. Avocations: boating, aerobics, fishing. Office: Met Ins Co 15255 94th Ave Orland Park IL 60462-3800

SCHULTZ, BRYAN CHRISTOPHER, dermatologist, educator; b. Evergreen Park, Ill., June 29, 1949; s. Warren H. and Norinne A. (McNamara) S.; m. Cathleen T. Fitzgerald, May 14, 1977; children: Carrie T., Megan C., Erin L. B.S., Loyola U., Chgo., 1971; M.D., Loyola Stritch Sch. Medicine, 1974. Diplomate Am. Bd. Dermatology. Intern St. Joseph's Hosp., Chgo., 1975; resident Northwestern U., Chgo., 1976-79; assoc. clin. prof. Loyola U., Maywood, Ill., 1979—; practice medicine specializing in dermatology, Oak

Park, Ill., 1979—; cons. dermatologist West Suburban Hosp., Oak Park Hosp., Gottlieb Hosp., Westlake Hosp., 1979—. Author: Office Practice of Skin Surgery, 1985. Patentee surgical instrument. Contbr. articles to sci. publs. Supr., founder pub. awareness program for skin cancer Loyola U. Stritch Sch. Medicine, 1983—; operator Ultraviolet-Ozone meter, Ill., 1983—. Mem. Am. Acad. Dermatology, Am. Soc. Dermatologic Surgery, Internat. Soc. Dermatologic Surgery, Soc. Investigative Dermatology, Chgo. Dermatologic Soc., AMA (del. intern and resident sect. 1975), Ill. Dermatologic Soc. (exec. com. 1981, chmn. membership com. 1983-84), Soc. Cosmetic Chemists, Royal Soc. Medicine, Alpha Sigma Nu. Office: Affiliates in Diseases and Surgery of Skin S C 1159 Westgate Oak Park IL 60301

SCHULTZ, CARL HERBERT, real estate management and development company executive; b. Chgo., Jan. 9, 1925; s. Herbert V. and Olga (Swanson) S.; m. Helen Ann Stevesson, June 6, 1948; children: Mark Carl, Julia Ann. B.S. in Gen. Engring., Iowa State U., 1948. With Schultz Bros. Co., 1948—; mdse. mgr. and store planner Schultz Bros. Co., Chgo., 1962-70; v.p. Schultz Bros. Co., Lake Zurich, Ill., 1968-72; pres. Schultz Bros. Co., 1972—, Ill. Schultz Bros. Co., Ind. Schultz Bros. Co., Iowa Schultz Bros. Co., Wis. Schultz Bros. Co. Mem. Lake Bluff (Ill.) Zoning Bd. Appeals, 1976-85, chmn., 1978-85. Served with U.S. Army, 1944-46. Mem. Lake Zurich Indsl. Coun. (sec. 1976), Assn. Gen. Mdse. Chains (dir. 1975-86, exec. com. 1983-86, chmn. nat. conv. 1982), Ill. Retail Mchts. Assn. (dir. 1984-89), Wis. Retail Fedn. (dir. 1981-89). Presbyterian. Club: Bath and Tennis (Lake Bluff). Home: 701 E Center Ave Lake Bluff IL 60044-2607 Office: 785 Oakwood Rd Ste 102S Lake Zurich IL 60047-1549

SCHULTZ, CLARENCE CARVEN, JR., sociology educator; b. Temple, Tex., Oct. 31, 1924; s. Clarence Carven Sr. and Bea Alice (Newton) S.; m. Margie Frances Beran, Oct. 29, 1943; children: Timothy Wayne, Theresa Bea. BS, SW Tex. State U., 1948, MA, 1949; PhD, U. Tex., 1970; AA (hon.), Lee Coll., 1989. Adminstrv. asst. Interstate Theatres, Temple, 1941-42; advt. sales rep. Temple Daily Telegram, 1942-43; asst. mgr. McClellan Stores, Tex., 1946-47; history and sociology instr. S.W. Tex. State U., San Marcos, 1949-52, from asst. prof. to prof., 1965-90, prof. emeritus, 1991; chmn. dept. sociology and anthropology SW Tex. State U., San Marcos, 1971-76, dean Sch. Liberal Arts, 1977-78; teaching fellow U. Tex., Austin, 1952-53; mem. faculty Lee Coll., Baytown, Tex., 1953-65, chmn. div. social scis., 1961-65; curriculum cons. to various pub. schs.; presenter workshops in field. Author: Practical Probation: Handbook, 1972; editor: Family Perspectives, 1975; contbr. articles to profl. jours., chpt. to book. Ens. USNR, 1943-46. Recipient S.W. Tex. Pedogog Teaching Excellence award, 1973, 74, Disting. Tchr. award S.W. Tex. State U. Alumni Assn., 1976, S.W. Tex. Presdl. award for excellence in teaching, 1985, Award of Honor, S.W. Tex. State U. Alumni Assn., 1991; named Piper Prof., Minnie Stevens Piper Found., 1976, Outstanding Former Instr., Lee Coll. Former Students' Assn., 1988; appointed Adm. in Tex. Navy by State Gov., 1969. Mem. Am. Sociol. Assn., Tex. Faculty Assn., NEA, Tex. State Tchrs. Assn., Alpha Chi, Alpha Kappa Delta. Methodist. Home: 604 Franklin Dr San Marcos TX 78666-2426 Office: SW Tex State U Dept Sociology Anthrop San Marcos TX 78666

SCHULTZ, DALE WALTER, state legislator; b. Madison, Wis., June 12, 1953; s. Walter Albert and Lillian (Fortman) S.; m. Rachel Weiss, June 20, 1981; children: Katherine Ann, Amanda. BBA, U. Wis., 1975. Farm mgr. Hillpoint, Wis., 1975—; adminstrv. and legis. asst. Wis. State Senate, Madison, 1976-79; planning analyst State of Wis., Madison, 1979-82, rep., 1982-91; senator Wis. State Senate, Madison, 1991—; mem. joint com. fin. com. ins., Mississippi River pky. commn., Minn.-Wis. boundary commn. Wis. State Senate. Mem. citizens adv. bd. Sauk County (Wis.) Health Care Ctr.; mem. Sauk County Farm Bur. Recipient Disting. Svc. award FFA, 1994; named Legislator of Yr., Wis. Tech. Coll. Assn., 1994-95, Guardian of Small Bus., Nat. Fedn. Ind. Bus., 1994, Legislator of Yr., Vietnam Vets. Assn., 1994. Republican. Club: Rod & Gun (Hillpoint, Wis.). Lodges: Lions, Masons. Home: 515 N Central Ave Richland Center WI 53581 Office: PO Box 7882 Madison WI 53707-7882

SCHULTZ, DEAN M., finance company executive; b. 1947. AB, Colgate U., 1969; JD, Georgetown U., 1972. Ptnr. Robinson, Williams & Angeloff Law Firm, Rochester, N.Y., 1973-80; with First Fed. Savings & Loan Assn., Rochester, 1980-84; sr. v.p., gen. counsel FHLB, N.Y.C., 1984-86, exec. v.p., 1986-91; pres., CEO Fed. Home Loan Bank, San Francisco, 1991—. Office: Fed Home Loan Bank 600 California St San Francisco CA 94108

SCHULTZ, DENNIS BERNARD, lawyer; b. Detroit, Oct. 15, 1946; s. Bernard George and Madeline Laverne (Riffenberg) S.; m. Andi Lynn Leslie, Apr. 18, 1967; 1 child, Karanne Anne. BS, Wayne State U., 1970; JD, Detroit Coll. Law, 1977. Bar: Mich. 1977, US Dist. Ct. (ea. dist.) Mich., U.S. Ct. Appeals (6th cir.), U.S. Dist. Ct. (we. dist.) Pa. V.p. Barkay Bldg. Co., Ferndale, Mich., to 1976; law clk. Hon. George N. Bashara, Mich. Ct. Appeals, Detroit, 1977; shareholder Butzel Long, Detroit, 1978—. Editor-in-chief Detroit Coll. Law Rev. Detroit Coll. Law Alumni Assn. scholar, 1976, Mich. Consolidated Gas Co. scholar, 1977. Mem. Detroit Bar Assn., Mich. Bar Assn. Republican. Roman Catholic. Avocations: boating, biking, golf. Office: Butzel Long 150 W Jefferson Ave Ste 900 Detroit MI 48226-4415

SCHULTZ, DON EDWARD, academic administrator; b. Wewoka, Okla., Jan. 20, 1934; s. Carl Edward and Donna Loretta (Welch) S.; m. Margaret Ann Putman, Aug. 28, 1956 (div. Mar. 1978); children: Steven D., Bradley E., Jeffrey P. BBA, U. Okla., 1957; MA, Mich. State U., 1975, PhD, 1977. Sales mgr. Associated Pubs., Dallas, 1957-59; advt. dir. Tyler (Tex.) Courier-Times, 1959-64; sr. v.p. Tracy-Locke Advt., Dallas, 1965-74; asst. prof. Mich. State U., 1975-77; dir. grad. program in direct mktg. Northwestern U., 1978—; pres. Agora, Inc., Evanston, 1982—. Author: Essentials of Creative Strategy, 1988; co-author: Strategic Advertising. Campaigns, 1989, Essentials of Sales Promotion, 1984, Sales Promotion Management, 1984; editor: Journal of Direct Marketing, 1986—. Mem. Promotion Mktg. Assn. Am. (bd. dirs. 1986), Internat. Advt. Assn. (dir. chmn. internat. 1984), Am. Mktg. Assn., Assn. Edn. in Journalism (chmn. accrediting com.), Dir. Mktg. Assn. Episcopalian. Home: 412 Lee St Apt 1 Evanston IL 60202-1804 Office: Northwestern U 1813 Hinman Ave Evanston IL 60201-5035

SCHULTZ, DOUGLAS GEORGE, art museum director; b. Oakland, Calif., Oct. 3, 1947; s. Leon H. and Teresa (deMonte) S. A.B., U. Calif., Berkeley, 1969, M.A. in History of Art, 1972; grad., Inst. Arts Adminstrn., Harvard U., 1971. Summer intern Nat. Gallery of Art, Washington, 1970; curatorial intern Albright-Knox Art Gallery, Buffalo, 1972; asst. curator Albright-Knox Art Gallery, 1973-75, asso. curator, 1975-76, curator, 1977-79, chief curator, 1980-83, dir., 1983—; adj. prof. art history SUNY, Buffalo, 1975-79; mem. adv. bd. Arts Council of Buffalo and Erie County 1975—. Office: Albright-Knox Art Gallery 1285 Elmwood Ave Buffalo NY 14222-1096

SCHULTZ, EILEEN HEDY, graphic designer; b. Yonkers, N.Y.; d. Harry Arthur and Hedy Evelyn (Morchel) S. B.F.A., Sch. Visual Arts, 1955. Staff artist C.A. Parshall Studios, N.Y.C., 1955-57; editorial art dir. Paradise of the Pacific, Honolulu, 1957-58; graphic designer Adler Advt. Agy., N.Y.C., 1958-59; art dir. Good Housekeeping Mag., N.Y.C., 1959-82; creative dir. advt. and sales promotion Good Housekeeping Mag., 1982-86; creative dir. Hearst Promo, 1986-87; pres. Design Internat., N.Y.C., 1987—. Art dir. editor The Depository Trust Co., 1987—. Art dir., editor, designer, 50th Art Directors Club Annual, 1973; columnist: Art Direction, 1969—. Dir. Sch. Visual Arts, N.Y.C., 1978—; trustee Sch. Art League, 1978—; advisor Fashion Inst. Tech., 1979—; mem. adv. commn. N.Y.C. Community Colls., 1979—. Named Yonkers Ambassador of Good Will to Netherlands, 1955; recipient Outstanding Achievement Sch. Visual Arts Alumni Soc., 1976, Sch. Art League Youth award, 1976. Mem. Art Dirs. Club (pres. 1975-77), Soc. Illustrators (pres. 1991-93), Joint Ethics Com. (chmn. 1978-80), Am. Inst. Graphic Arts, Soc. Publ. Designers, Type Dirs. Club.

SCHULTZ, FRANKLIN M., lawyer; b. Cin., June 16, 1917; s. Max and Goldie (Wise) S.; m. Jean Carol Barnett, Apr. 5, 1946 (dec. 1981); children: William Bb, John M., Katherine, Caroline; m. Virginia B. Henderson, Sept. 4, 1983. B.A., Yale U., 1939, LL.B., 1942. Bar: Ohio 1947, D.C. 1954, Mass. 1985, U.S. Supreme Ct. 1954. Atty. Fed. Power Commn., 1946-47; asso. prof. Ind. U. Sch. Law, Bloomington, 1947-53; with firm Purcell & Nelson, Washington, 1953-80; ptnr. Purcell & Nelson 1957-80, Reavis & McGrath,

Washington, 1980-85; lawyer-in-residence Washington & Lee U. Sch. Law, 1985; vis. prof. U. Iowa Sch. Law, 1986-90; lectr. George Washington U. Law Sch., 1958-59; vis. prof. U. Va. Law Sch., 1975, Washington & Lee U. Sch. Law, 1991-94; mem. ednl. appeal bd. U.S. Dept. Edn., 1974-82. Contbr. articles to profl. jours. Served to capt. AUS, 1942-46. Decorated Bronze stars. Mem. ABA (mem. council adminstrv. law sect. 1966-69, chmn. 1970-71, del. ho. of dels. 1972-74), D.C. Bar (gen. counsel 1977-79, mem. legal ethics com. 1976-81), Am. Law Inst., Am. Bar Found., Adminstrv. Conf. U.S. (council 1980-82). Home: 1953 Martha's Rd Alexandria VA 22307

SCHULTZ, FREDERICK HENRY, investor, former government official; b. Jacksonville, Fla., Jan. 16, 1929; s. Clifford G. and Mae (Wangler) S.; m. Nancy Reilly, Aug., 1951; children: Catherine G., Frederick H., Clifford G. John R. B.A., Princeton U., 1951; postgrad., U. Fla. Sch. Law, 1954-56. With Barnett Nat. Bank, Jacksonville, 1956-57; owner, operator investment firm, from 1957; mem. Fla. Ho. of Reps., 1963-70, speaker of the house, 1968-70; chmn. bd. Barnett Investment Svcs., Inc.; dir. Barnett Banks Inc., to 1979; vice chmn. bd. govs. Fed. Res. System, Washington, 1979-82; bd. dirs. Barnett Banks, Inc., Transco Energy, Inc., Am. Heritage Life Ins. Co., S.E. Atlantic Inc., Riverside Group, Inc., Wickes Lumber Co. Served to lt. U.S. Army, 1952-54, Korea. Decorated Bronze Star. Roman Catholic. Office: PO Box 1200 Jacksonville FL 32201-1200

SCHULTZ, G. ROBERT, lawyer; b. Detroit, Apr. 25, 1934; s. George R. and J. Leone (Spencer) S.; m. Elizabeth Anne Burnett, Aug. 17, 1957; children: Suzanne McAree, Sarah Ovitt, Bruce, Robert, Katherine Brenner, Stephen. BA, U. Mich., 1958; JD, Stetson Coll. Law, 1967. Bar: Fla. 1967, U.S. Dist. Ct. (no., so. and mid. dists.), Fla. 1970, U.S. Supreme Ct. 1970; cert. family mediator. Pvt. practice St. Petersburg, Fla., 1967—. With U.S. Army, 1954-56. Fellow Am. Acad. Matrimonial Lawyers; mem. ABA (family law sect.), Fla. Bar Assn. (bd. cert. marital and family law). Office: 1216 66th St N Saint Petersburg FL 33710-6226

SCHULTZ, HARRY, health science organization administrator. Dir. St. Boniface Gen. Hosp. Rsch. Ctr., Winnipeg, MB, Canada. Office: U Manitoba St Boniface Gen Hosp, 351 Tache Ave, Winnepeg, MB Canada R2H 2A6

SCHULTZ, HEIDI FLYNN, publisher; b. Lawrence, Mass., May 28, 1949; d. Joseph Carter and Helen (Southern) Flynn; m. Jay Magnuson, Nov. 28, 1970 (div. 1973); m. Don E. Schultz, Jan. 2, 1980; stepchildren: Steve, Brad, Jeff. BJ, U. So. Calif., 1971; MS in Mgmt., Northwestern U., 1978. Copywriter CNA Ins., Chgo., 1971-74; mgr. rsch. and promotion McGraw-Hill, Chgo., 1974-76; mgr. circulation Crain Communications, Chgo., 1976-85; dir. circulation Chgo. Mag., 1985-88, dir. ops., 1988-90, pub., 1990—; mem. adv. bd. Apparel Industry Bd., Chgo., 1990. Mem. Chgo. Conf. and Tourism Bur., 1990; bd. dirs. River North Assn., Chgo., 1991. Honoree Chgo. House and Social Svc. Agy., 1992. Mem. City and Regional Mag. Assn. (bd. dirs. 1990). Avocation: travel. Office: Chgo Mag 414 N Orleans St Chicago IL 60610-4418

SCHULTZ, JEROLD MARVIN, materials scientist, educator; b. San Francisco, June 21, 1935; s. Ernst and Florence (Rubin) S.; m. Peggy June Ostrom, July 30, 1960; children: Carrie, Timothy, Peter, Anna. BS, U. Calif., Berkeley, 1957, MS, 1958; PhD, Carnegie-Mellon U., 1965. Intermediate engr. Westinghouse Rsch. Labs., Pitts., 1959-61; mem. faculty U. Del., Newark, 1964—. Author: Polymer Materials Science, 1974, Diffraction for Materials Scientists, 1982; editor: Properties of Solid Polymeric Materials, 1977, Solid State Behavior of Linear Polyesters and Polyamides, 1990; contbr. over 150 articles to profl. jours. Flutist Newark Symphony Orch., 1966—. Recipient Sr. Am. Scientist award Alexander von Humboldt Stiftung, Germany, 1977, 82, Kliment Ohridzki medal Peoples Republic of Bulgaria, 1986. Mem. Am. Phys. Soc., Polymer Processing Soc. Democrat. Episcopalian. Achievements include 8 patents on polymer processing and materials. Office: U Del Materials Sci Program Newark DE 19716

SCHULTZ, JEROME SAMSON, biochemical engineer, educator; b. Bklyn., June 25, 1933; s. Henry Herman and Sally (Warburg) S.; m. Jane Paula Schwartz, Sept. 1, 1955; children: Daniel Stuart, Judith Susan, Kathryn Ann. BS in Chem. Engring., Columbia U., 1954, MS, 1956; PhD in Biochemistry, U. Wis., 1958. Group leader biochem. rsch. Lederle Labs., N.Y., 1958-64; asst. prof. dept. chem. engring. U. Mich., Ann Arbor, 1964-67, assoc. prof., 1967-70, prof., 1970-77, chmn., 1977-85; sect. head, emerging engring. techs. NSF, Washington, 1985-86, dep. dir. cross-disciplinary rsch., 1986-87; dir. Ctr. for Biotech. and Bioengring. U. Pitts., 1987—; prof. chem. engring., 1987—; prof. medicine, 1990—, dir. bioengring. program, 1991—. Editor Biotechnology Progress, 1988—; contbr. articles to profl. jours.; patentee in field. NIH rsch. career devel. awardee, 1970-75. Fellow Am. Inst. for Med. and Biol. Engring. (pres. 1995); mem. AAAS, Am. Chem. Soc. (past chem. biochem. tech. divsn.), AIChE (past chmn. food and bioengring. divsn.), Bioengring. award 1984), Am. Soc. Artificial Internal Organs, Nat. Acad. Engring., Sigma Xi, Phi Lambda Upsilon, Tau Beta Pi. Home: 111 Bentley Dr Pittsburgh PA 15238-2501 Office: U Pittsburgh ctr for biotechnology and bioengineering 300 Technology Dr Pittsburgh PA 15219

SCHULTZ, KATHLEEN ANNE, executive director; b. Lincoln, Nebr., Feb. 9, 1952; d. Robert William and Lois Blanche (Barta) S.; 1 child, Kayla. Exec. sec. course, Lincoln Sch. Commerce, 1971. Legal sec. Wellensiek & Davis, Nebraska City, 1971-73; adminstrv. asst. State Racing Commn., Lincoln, 1973-83; legal sec. Zimmerman & Haszard, Lincoln, 1983-88; membership sec., acting exec. dir. Am. Hist. Soc. Germans, Lincoln, 1988-93, exec. dir., 1993—; adv. bd. mem. Lincoln Area Mus. Assn., 1993—. Mem. adv. bd. Lakeview/Yankee Hill PTO, Lincoln, 1993—, Roper PTO, Lincoln, 1994—. Mem. DAR. Avocations: reading, piano, gardening, antique collector. Office: Am Hist Soc Germans 631 D St Lincoln NE 68502

SCHULTZ, KURT LEE, lawyer; b. Chgo., Feb. 13, 1946; s. William Ernst Schultz and Patricia Marie (Chelminski) Facchine; m. Jane Marmet Lerro, Sept. 9, 1972; children: Jane, Melissa, Katherine, Laura. BA, U. Pa., 1967; JD, Ohio State U., 1972. Bar: Ill. 1972. Law clk. to Judge Richard B. Austin U.S. Dist. Ct. (no. dist.) Ill., Chgo., 1972-73; assoc. Winston & Strawn, Chgo., 1973-78, ptnr., 1978—. Trustee Ravinia Festival, Highland Park, Ill., 1990—; bd. dirs. Youth Guidance, Chgo., 1984—. 1st lt. U.S. Army, 1967-69. Mem. Order of Coif. Office: Winston & Strawn 35 W Wacker Dr Chicago IL 60601-1614

SCHULTZ, LOUIS EDWIN, management consultant; b. Foster, Nebr., Aug. 8, 1931; s. Louis Albert and Lula Pusey (Cox) S.; m. Mary Kathleen Peck, Mar. 3, 1962; children: Kurt Michael, Kristen Leigh. BSEE, U. Nebr., 1959; MBA, Pepperdine U., 1974. Mktg. mgr. Bell & Howell, Pasadena, Calif., 1962-70; dir. mktg. Cogar Corp., Utica, N.Y., 1970-71; product mgr. Pertec Corp., L.A., 1971-73; gen. mgr. Control Data Corp., Mpls., 1973-84; founder, CEO Process Mgmt. Inst. Inc., Mpls., Minn., 1984—; adv. bd. Inst. for Productivity Through Quality, U. Tenn., Knoxville, 1982-84. Author: Managing in the Worldwide Competitive Society, 1984, Quality Management Philosophies, 1985, Profiles in Quality, 1994; co-author: Quality Handbook for Small Business, 1994, Deming, The Way We Knew Him, 1995. Mem. Gov.'s Commn. on Productivity, St. Paul, 1986; chmn. Wirth Park Tree Restoration Com., Mpls., 1983; mem. Productivity Planning Com., St. Paul, 1985—. Staff sgt. USMC, 1952-54; advisor to Deming Forum, 1985—; judge Minn. Quality award, 1992. Recipient Profl. Partnership award U. Minn., 1987. Mem. Am. Soc. Performance Improvement (bd. dirs. 1984-89, outstanding svc. award), Minn. Coun. for Quality (bd. dirs. 1987—), Human Sys. Mgmt. (edtl. bd.), Asia-Pacific Orgn. Quality Control, Toastmasters Internat. Republican. Methodist. Office: Process Mgmt Inst 7801 E Bush Lake Rd Ste 360 Minneapolis MN 55439-3115

SCHULTZ, LOUIS MICHAEL, advertising agency executive; b. Detroit, Aug. 24, 1944; s. Henry Richard and Genevieve (Jankowski) S.; m. Susan Kay Hammel, Sept. 10, 1966; children—Christian David, Kimberly Ann. B.A., Mich. State U., 1967; M.B.A., Wayne State U., 1970. Staff Campbell-Ewald, Warren, Mich., 1967-74; v.p. group dir. Campbell-Ewald, 1975-77, sr. v.p., assoc. dir., 1977-82, group sr. v.p., 1982-83, exec. v.p.,

1984-87; exec. v.p. Lintas: USA, 1987—; chmn. Lintas: WW Media Coun., 1991; mem. devel. council IPG, N.Y.C., 1984—; pres., COO Lintas Mktg. Comms., 1994—; bd. dirs. Lintas USA, Lintas N.Y., Lintas Campbell-Ewald, Lintas Worldwide, Initiative Media Internat. Advisor, Detroit Renaissance Com., 1981-84. With USAR, 1967-73. Mem. Nat. Acad. TV Arts and Scis., Am. Women in Radio and TV, Am. Mktg. Assn., Detroit Advt. Assn., Ad. Club N.Y. (bd. dirs.), Great Oaks Country Club, Adcraft Club, Marco Polo Club, Old Club, Hidden Valley Club, Longboat Key Club. Republican. Roman Catholic. Avocations: golf; tennis; travel. Home: 472 Streamview Ct Rochester MI 48309 Office: Lintas Mktg Comms 30400 Van Dyke Warren MI 48093

SCHULTZ, LOUIS WILLIAM, judge; b. Deep River, Iowa, Mar. 24, 1927; s. M. Louis and Esther Louise (Behrens) S.; m. D. Jean Stephen, Nov. 6, 1949; children: Marcia, Mark, Paul. Student, Central Coll., Pella, Iowa, 1944-45, 46-47; LL.B., Drake U., Des Moines, 1949. Bar: Iowa. Claims supr. Iowa Farm Mut. Ins. Co., Des Moines, 1949-55; partner firm Harned, Schultz & McMeen, Marengo, Iowa, 1955-71; judge Iowa Dist. Ct. (6th dist.), 1971-80; justice Iowa Supreme Ct., 1980-93; county atty. Iowa Couty, 1960-68; ret., 1993. Served with USNR, 1945-46. Mem. Am. Bar Assn., Iowa Bar Assn. (bd. govs.), Iowa Judges Assn. (pres.). Republican. Lutheran. Office: U Iowa Coll Law # 1488 Iowa City IA 52242

SCHULTZ, MICHAEL, stage and film director, film producer; b. Milw., Nov. 10, 1938; s. Leo Schultz and Katherine (Frances) Leslie; m. Gloria Jean Jones. Ed., U. Wis., Marquette U. Dir. stage plays Waiting for Godot, 1966, Song of the Lusitanian Bogey, Negro Ensemble Co., N.Y.C., 1968, and London, 1968, Kongi's Harvest, God Is a (Guess What), Does A Tiger Wear a Necktie, 1969; Broadway debut The Reckoning, 1969, Eugene O'Neill Meml. Theatre, 1969; Operation Sidewinder, Dream on Monkey Mountain, 1970, What the Wineskiners Buy, 1974, Mulebone, Lincoln Ctr., 1991; dir. films including To Be Young, Gifted and Black, 1971, Together for Days, 1973, Cooley High, 1975, Car Wash, 1976, Greased Lightning, 1977, Which Way Is Up?, 1977, Sgt. Pepper's Lonely Hearts Club Band, 1978, Scavenger Hunt, 1979, Carbon Copy, 1981, Bustin Loose, 1983, The Last Dragon, 1985, Krush Groove, 1985, Disorderlies, 1987, Livin' Large, 1991, Ceremonies in Dark Old Men; dir. TV films Benny's Place, 1982, For Us The Living, 1983, The Jerk, Too, 1984, Timestalkers, 1986, Rock n' Roll Mom, 1988, Jury Duty, 1989, Hammer and Slammer, 1990, Dayo, 1992, Picket Fences, 1993-94, Young Indiana Jones, 1994. Office: PO Box 1940 Santa Monica CA 90406-1940*

SCHULTZ, PETER G., chemistry educator. PhD, Calif. Inst. Tech., 1983. Mem. faculty chemistry dept. U. Calif., Berkeley, 1985—, now assoc. prof. NIH Postdoctoral fellow, MIT; recipient Nobel Laureate Signature award for Grad. Edn. in Chemistry, Pure Chemistry award, Harrison Howe award, Am. Chem. Soc., 1993, Arthur C. Cope award, Am. Chem. Soc., 1990, Alan T. Waterman award NSF, 1988, Denkewalter lectr. award Loyola U., 1990, Ernest Orlando Lawrence Meml. award U.S. Dept. Energy, 1991. Office: U Calif Dept Chemistry Dept Chemistry Berkeley CA 94720*

SCHULTZ, PHILIP, poet, novelist, educator; b. Rochester, N.Y., Jan. 6, 1945; s. Samuel B. and Lillian (Bernstein) S. Student, U. Louisville, 1963-65, San Francisco State U., 1965-67; BA in English Lit, U. Iowa, 1968, MFA in Poetry, 1971. Various clerical positions Dept. Social Services, San Francisco, 1969-70; writer-in-residence Kalamazoo Coll., 1971-72; lectr. in poetry Newton (Mass.) Coll. of Sacred Heart, 1973-74; lectr. in writing U. Mass., Boston, 1973-75; tchr. poetry elem. schs. in Mich., 1971-72, Mass., 1974-75, N.Y., 1977-80; dir. founder Writers Studio (pvt. sch.), 1984—; lectr. in creative writing NYU, N.Y.C., 1978-88; dir. grad. creative writing program NYU, 1984-88; mem. faculty Columbia U., 1981-82. Author: (poems) Like Wings (Am. Acad.-Inst. of Arts and Letters award 1979), 1978 (Nat. Book Award nomination 1979), Deep Within the Ravine (Lamont poetry selection Acad. Am. Poets 1984), 1984; (chapbook) My Guardian Angel Stein, 1986; contbr.: numerous poems to lit. jours. and mags. including The Kenyon Review; short stories to lit. jours. (Recipient Kansas City Star Poetry award 1971, Discovery-Nation Poetry award 1976). N.Y. State Council for the Arts fellow, 1976, 80; Nat. Endowment Arts fellow, 1980-81; Fulbright grantee, 1983; N.Y. Found. for Arts fellow, 1985. Mem. Poetry Soc. Am. (governing bd. 1984-88), PEN, Writers Guild Am. East, Authors Guild Inc. Democrat. Jewish. *I place clarity and precision above all else in my work, and if these are the modes of expression, honesty of feeling provides the substance as well as the goal. I believe the art of good writing takes place in the art of revision, which, if taxing, often enough gives me the time to get to the heart of the matter. I choose to write about only those things which I feel most passionate about: the particular circumstances of my life.*

SCHULTZ, RICHARD CARLTON, plastic surgeon; b. Grosse Pointe, Mich., Nov. 19, 1927; s. Herbert H. and Carmen (Huebner) S.; m. Pauline Zimmermann, Oct. 8, 1955; children: Richard, Lisa, Alexandra, Jennifer. McGregor scholar, U. Mich., 1944-49; M.D., Wayne State U., 1953. Diplomate Am. Bd. Plastic Surgery. Intern Harper Hosp., Detroit, 1953-54; resident in gen. surgery Harper Hosp., 1954-55, U.S. Army Hosp., Fort Carson, Colo., 1955-57; resident in plastic surgery St. Luke's Hosp., Chgo., 1957-58, U. Ill. Hosp., Chgo., 1958-59, VA Hosp., Hines, Ill., 1959-60; practice medicine specializing in plastic surgery Park Ridge, Ill., 1961—; clin. asst. prof. surgery U. Ill. Coll. Medicine, 1966-70, assoc. prof. surgery, 1970-76, prof., 1976—, head div. plastic surgery, 1970-87; pres. med. staff Lutheran Gen. Hosp., Park Ridge, 1977-79; vis. prof. U. Pitts., 1972, U. Miss., 1973, U. Pisa, Italy, 1974, Jikei U. Coll. Medicine, Tokyo, 1976, Ind. U., 1977, U. Helsinki, 1977, U. N.Mex., 1978, U. Milan, 1981, So. Ill. Sch. Medicine, 1982, Tulane U. Med. Sch., 1983, Shanghai 2d Med. Coll., 1984, U. Guadalajara (Mex.), 1986, Gazi U., Turkey, 1988; participant, guest surgeon Physicians for Peace, Turkey and Greece, 1988, Israel and Occupied Ters., 1990, Egypt, 1991, Lithuania, Estonia, 1993 (team leader); leader citizen amb. people to people Internat. Del. Plastic Surgeons to Albania & Russia, 1994. Author: Facial Injuries, 1970, 3d edit., 1988, Maxillo-Facial Injuries from Vehicle Accidents, 1975, Outpatient Surgery, 1979. Mem. sect. bd., Lake Zurich, Ill., 1966-72, pres., 1968-72. Chgo. Found. for Plastic Surgery, 1966—. Served to capt. M.C., AUS, 1955-57. Recipient research award Ednl. Found. Am. Soc. Plastic and Reconstructive Surgery, 1964-65, Med. Tribune Auto Safety award, 1967, Robert H. Ivy award, 1969, Disting. Sci. Achievement award Wayne U. Coll. Medicine Alumni, 1975; Sanveneru-Rosselli award, 1981; Fulbright scholar U. Uppsala, Sweden, 1960-61. Fellow ACS (pres. local commn. on trauma 1985-87); mem. Am. Assn. Plastic Surgeons (trustee 1990-91), Am. Soc. Plastic and Reconstructive Surgeons, Midwestern Assn. Plastic Surgeons (pres. 1978-79), Chgo. Soc. Plastic Surgeons (pres. 1970-72), Midwestern Assn. Plastic Surgeons (pres. 1978-79), Am. Soc. Maxillofacial Surgeons (pres. 1988-89, award of honor 1986), Am. Assn. Automotive Medicine (pres. 1970-71, A. Merkin award 1982), Am. Cleft Palate Assn., Am. Soc. Aesthetic Plastic Surgery, Tord Skoog Soc. Plastic Surgeons (pres. 1971-75), Can. Soc. Plastic Surgery, Chilean Soc. Plastic Surgery (corr.), Japanese Soc. Plastic Surgery (corr.), Cuban Soc. Maxillofacial Surgery (corr.). Home: 21150 N Middleton Dr Kildeer IL 60047 Office: 1875 Dempster St Park Ridge IL 60068-1163

SCHULTZ, RICHARD DALE, national athletic organizations executive; b. Grinnell, Iowa, Sept. 5, 1929; s. August Henry and Marjorie Ruth (Turner) S.; m. Jacquilyn Lu Duistermars, June 26, 1949; children: Robert Dale, William Joel, Kim Marie. BS, Cen. Coll., Pella, Iowa, 1950; EdD Honoris Causa, Cen. Coll., 1987; LLD (hon.), Wartburg Coll., 1988, Alma Coll., 1989, Luther Coll., 1991; PhD, U.S. Sports Acad., 1993. Head basketball coach, athletic dir. Humboldt (Iowa) High Sch., 1950-60; freshman basketball coach U. Iowa, Iowa City, 1960-62; head baseball coach, assoc. basketball coach U. Iowa, 1962-70, head basketball coach, 1970-74, asst. v.p., 1974-76; dir. athletics and phys. edn. Cornell U., Ithaca, N.Y., 1976-81; dir. athletics U. Va., Charlottesville, 1981-87; exec. dir. NCAA, Mission, Kans., 1987-94; pres. Global Sports Enterprises, 1994—; mem. honors ct. Nat. Football Found. and Hall of Fame, Nat. Basketball Hall of Fame, 1992; mem. bd. NCAA Found., 1989; organizer Iowa Steel Mill, Inc. Author: A Course of Study for the Coaching of Baseball, 1964, The Theory and Techniques of Coaching Basketball, 1970; contbr. articles to mags. Bd. dirs. Fellowship of Christian Athletes, 1986, chmn. 1990; chmn. Multiple Sclerosis, 1974-75; mem. Knight Found. Commn. on Intercollegiate Athletics, 1990—; mem. adv. com. on svc. acad. athletic programs Def.

Dept. Recipient Disting. Alumni award Ctrl. Coll., Pella, 1970, Lifetime Svc. award U. Iowa, 1994; mem. Basketball Hall of Fame Honor Ct., 1992; inducted into Iowa Baseball Hall of Fame, 1993. Mem. Nat. Assn. Coll. Basketball Coaches, Ea. Coll. Athletic Assn. (mem. exec. com. 1980-81), Am. Basketball Coaches Assn. (Award of Honor 1994), Am. Football Coaches Assn. (lifetime membership award 1995). Home: 12505 Nieman Rd Overland Park KS 66213-2138 Office: Ste 200 1901 W 47th Pl Westwood KS 66205

SCHULTZ, RICHARD OTTO, ophthalmologist, educator; b. Racine, Wis., Mar. 19, 1930; s. Henry Arthur and Josephine (Wagoner) S.; m. Diane Haldane, Sept. 29, 1990; children: Henry Reid, Richard Paul, Karen Jo. B.A., U. Wis., 1950, M.S., 1954; M.D., Albany Med. Coll., 1956; M.Sc., U. Iowa, 1960. Diplomate: Am. Bd. Ophthalmology. Intern, Univ. Hosps., Iowa City, 1956-57; resident in opthalmology Univ. Hosps., 1957-60; chief ophthalmology sect. div. Indian health USPHS, Phoenix, 1960-63; practice medicine specializing in ophthalmology Phoenix, 1963; NIH spl. fellow in ophthalmic microbiology U. Calif., San Francisco, 1963-64; clin. assoc. U. Calif., 1963-64, research assoc., 1963-64; assoc. prof., chmn. dept. ophthalmology Marquette U. Sch. Medicine (now Med. Coll. Wis.), Milw., 1964-68; prof., chmn. Marquette U. Sch. Medicine (now Med. Coll. Wis.), 1968—; dir. Eye Inst.; dir. ophthalmology Milw. Regional Med. Ctr.; mem. nat. adv. eye coun. NIH, 1984-88; cons. VA regional ctr. Milw. Children's, Columbia, Luth. and St. Mary's hosps., Milw. Contbr. articles to profl. jours. Served with USPHS, 1960-63. Fellow Am. Acad. Ophthalmology, ACS, Am. Ophthal. Soc.; mem. Assn. Univ. Profs. Ophthalmology (trustee, pres. 1978), AMA, Am., Milw. ophthalmol. socs., Assn. Research Vision and Ophthalmology, N.Y. Acad. Scis., Research to Prevent Blindness, Oxford Ophthalmol. Congress (Eng.), State Med. Soc. Wis., Wis. Soc. Prevention Blindness, Med. Soc. Milw. County, Milw. Acad. Medicine. Home: 12500 W Grove Ter Elm Grove WI 53122-1973 Office: 8700 W Wisconsin Ave Milwaukee WI 53226-3512

SCHULTZ, ROBERT VERNON, entrepreneur; b. Sterling, Ill., July 2, 1936; s. Wilbur Henry and Eleanor Grace (Love) S.; m. Shelly I. Shaw, Feb. 12, 1970; children: Robert G., Trina R., Cherie A. BBA, Lincoln Mgmt. Sch. of Chgo., 1971; BA in Acctg., Rockford Sch. of Bus., 1975; BS in Christian Edn., Moody Bible Inst., 1983. Asst. to v.p. DeKalb Ogle Tel. Co., Rochelle, Ill., 1969-74; mktg. mgr. Chambers Owen Inc., Rockford, Ill., 1960-69; owner, pres. Schultz Mgmt. and Mktg., St. Charles, Ill., 1970—; pres., owner Investment Internat. Inc., North Aurora, 1988—; Diamond Publs. Inc., North Aurora, 1987—; owner Schultz Internat. Inc., Princeton, Ill.; bus. cons. Network Bus. Opportunity Entrepreneurs Chgo. 1970—; owner Schultz Internat. Inc., Princeton. Editor-in-chief, owner, pres., chmn. bd. Ill. Car Mart, 1988. With U.S. Army, 1957-59. Recipient Quick Silver award Ambs. Internat., 1990. Mem. Internat. Platform Assn., Internat. Speakers Platform Assn., Jaycees (pres. 1968). Republican. Avocation: pilot. Home: PO Box 185 Princeton IL 61356-0185 Office: Schultz Internat Inc PO Box 185 Princeton IL 61356-0185

SCHULTZ, RUTH ANNE, home economics educator, parenting educator, consultant; b. Oneida, N.Y., Jan. 27, 1953; d. Herman Lyon and Anna Marie (Jarvis) S. BS, Cornell U., 1975; MS, Syracuse U., 1982; postgrad., Plattsburgh State U., 1986, 89, L.I. U., 1990—. Cert. tchr., N.Y.; cert. home economist. Tchr. home econs. Phelps-Clifton Springs (N.Y.) Cen. Schs., 1975-77, adult educator, 1976-77, 93; home econs. tchr. Fabius (N.Y.)-Pompey Cen. Schs., 1977-82; home econs. tchr. Chittenango (N.Y.) Cen. Schs., 1982—; adviser Future Homemakers Am. club, 1986—; parenting educator Cornell Coop. Extension, Madison County, Morrisville, N.Y., 1985—; cons. N.Y. Dept. Edn., 1988—. Primary author curriculum materials. Community rep. Madison County Head Start Policy Coun., Morrisville, 1985-88; chmn. program com. Cornell Coop. Extension, Madison County, 1990-92, Long Range Planning Com.; bd. dirs. Community Action Program of Madison County. Recipient N.Y. State Edn. Dept. Region 7 Disting. Occupational Educator ward, 1990. Mem. ASCD, N.Y. State Future Homemakers of Am. (bd. trustees, vice chair), Home Econs. Edn. Assn. (v.p. 1988-90, pres. elect 1990-91, pres. 1991-93, past pres. 1993-94), N.Y. State Home Econs. Tchrs. Assn. (pres. 1986-88, state conv. chmn. 1989-90, legislation co-chmn. 1989-90), N.Y. State Home Econs. Assn. (elem., secondary, adult chmn. 1989-93, New Achiever award, 1988, Tchr. of Yr. 1989), Am. Home Econs. Assn. (nat. leadership com. 1989-91), Cen. N.Y. Home Econs. Tchrs. Assn. (Tchr. of Yr. 1985), N.Y. State Occupational Edn. Assn. (affiliate v.p. 1986-88, state conv. chmn. 1988-89, 93, regional rep. 1994—, Disting. Svc. award 1990), Nat. Assn. Vocat. Home Econs. Tchrs. (spl. award of merit 1991), Am. Vocat. Assn. (region I Vocat. Tchr. of the Year 1994). Democrat. Roman Catholic. Home: RR 3 Cazenovia NY 13035-9803 Office: Chittenango Mid Sch RR 2 1732 Fyler Rd Chittenango NY 13037-9802

SCHULTZ, SAMUEL JACOB, clergyman, educator; b. Mountain Lake, Minn., June 9, 1914; s. David D. and Anna (Eitzen) S.; m. Eyla June Tolliver, June 17, 1943; children: Linda Sue, David Carl. AA, Bethel Coll., 1938; BA, John Fletcher Coll., 1940; BD, Faith Theol. Sem., 1944; MST, Harvard U., 1945, ThD, 1949. Ordained to ministry Christian and Missionary Alliance Ch., 1944; pastor First Meth. Ch., Pine River, Minn., 1940-41, Waldo Congl. Ch., Brockton, Mass., 1944-45, Evang. Bapt. Ch., Belmont, Mass., 1945-47; prof. Gordon Coll., Boston, 1946-47, Bethel Coll. and Sem., St. Paul, 1947-49, St. Paul Bible Inst., 1948-49; prof. Wheaton (Ill.) Coll., 1949-80, prof. emeritus, 1980—, Samuel Robinson prof. Bible and theology, 1955-80, chmn. Bible and philosophy dept., 1957-63, chmn. div. Bibl. edn. and philosophy, 1963-67, chmn. div. Bibl. studies, 1972-79; prof. Old Testament and Bible Exposition Trinity Coll. Grad. Sch. (name now Tampa Bay Theol. Sem.), Dunedin (now Holiday), Fla., 1987-93; prof. Old Testament St. Petersburgh (Fla.) Theol. Sem., adj. prof. St. Petersburgh Jr. Coll., 1995—; interim supply pastor Bible Ch. Winnetka, Ill., 1951, 60; resident supply pastor South Shore Bapt. Ch., Hingham, Mass., 1958-59. Author: The Old Testament Speaks, 1960, 3d edit., 1980, 4th edit., 1990, Law and History, 1964, The Prophets Speak, 1968, Deuteronomy-Gospel of Love, 1971, The Gospel of Moses, 1974, 79, Interpreting the Word of God, 1976, Leviticus-God Dwelling among his People, 1983, The Message of the Old Testament, 1986. Mem. bd. edn. Bethel Coll. and Sem., 1960-65; historian Conservative Congregation Christian Conf., 1980-86; bd. dirs. Inst. in Basic Youth Conflicts, 1965-80, Congl. Christian Hist. Soc., 1984—, Brookwoods Christian Camps and Confs., Inc., Alton, N.H., 1978—; trustee Gordon-Conwell Sem., South Hamilton, Mass., 1980—, Lexington (Mass.) Christian Acad., 1987—. NYU study grantee Israel, 1966, Wheaton Coll. Alumni research grantee, 1958. Mem. Soc. Bibl. Lit., Evang. Theol. Soc. (editor Jour. 1962-75), Near East Archaeol. Soc. (sec., bd. dir.), Wheaton Coll. Scholastic Honors Soc., Phi Sigma Tau. Book the Living and Active Word of God dedicated in his honor, 1983. Home: 143 East St Lexington MA 02173-1913 Love the Lord your God with all your heart and with all your soul and with all your strength and your neighbor as yourself.

SCHULTZ, STANLEY GEORGE, physiologist, educator; b. Bayonne, N.J., Oct. 26, 1931; s. Aaron and Sylvia (Kaplan) S.; m. Harriet Taran, Dec. 25, 1960; children: Jeffrey, Kenneth. A.B. summa cum laude, Columbia U., 1952; M.D., N.Y. U., 1956. Intern Bellevue Hosp., N.Y.C., 1956-57; resident Bellevue Hosp., 1957-59; research assoc. in biophysics Harvard U., 1959-62, instr. biophysics, 1964-67; assoc. prof. physiology U. Pitts., 1967-70, prof. physiology, 1970-79; prof., chmn. dept. physiology U. Tex. Med. Sch., Houston, 1979—, prof. dept. internal medicine, 1979—; cons. USPHS, NIH, 1970—; mem. physiology test com. Nat. Bd. Med. Examiners, 1974-79, chmn., 1976-79. Editor Am. Jour. Physiology, Jour. Applied Physiology, 1971-75, Physiol. Revs., 1975-81, Handbook of Physiology: The Gastrointestinal Tract, 1989-91—; mem. editl. bd. Jour. Gen. Physiology, 1969-88, Ann. Revs. Physiology, 1974-81, Current Topics in Membranes and Transport, 1975-81, Jour. Membrane Biology, 1977—, Biochim. Biophys. Acta, 1987-89; assoc. editor Ann. Revs. Physiology, 1977-81; assoc. editor News in Physiol. Scis. 1989-94, editor, 1994—; contbr. articles to profl. jours. Served to capt. M.C. USAF, 1962-64. Recipient Research Career award NIH, 1969-74; overseas fellow Churchill Coll., Cambridge U., 1975-76. Mem. AAAS, Am. Heart Assn. (established investigator 1964-69), Am. Physiol. Soc. (councillor 1989-91, pres.-elect 1991-92, pres. 1992-93, past pres. 1993-94), Fed. Am. Soc. Exptl. Biology (exec. bd. 1992—), Biophys. Soc., Soc. Gen. Physiologists, Internat. Cell Rsch. Orgn., Internat. Union Physiol. Scis. (chmn. internat. com. gastrointestinal physiology 1977-80, chmn. U.S. nat. com. 1992—), Assn. Am. Physicians, Am. Assn. Ob-Gyn.

(hon. fellow), Assn. Chmn. Depts. Physiology (pres. 1985-86), Sigma Xi, Phi Beta Kappa. Home: 4955 Heatherglen Dr Houston TX 77096-4213

SCHULTZ, T. PAUL, economics educator; b. Ames, Iowa, May 24, 1940; s. Theodore W. and Esther (Werth) S.; m. Judith Hoenack, Sept. 16, 1967; children: Lara, Joel, Rebecca. BA, Swarthmore Coll., 1961; PhD, MIT, 1966; MA (hon.), Yale U., 1974. Cons. Joint Econ. Com., Washington, 1964; researcher econs. dept. Rand Corp., Santa Monica, Calif., 1966-72; dir. population research, 1968-72; prof. econs. U. Minn., Mpls., 1972-75; prof. econs. Yale U., New Haven, 1974—, dir. Econ. Growth Ctr., 1983—; cons. World Bank, Rockefeller Found.; mem. com. on population NAS, Washington, 1987-89, 90-93. Author: Structural Change in a Developing Country, 1971, Economics of Population, 1981; editor: (books) The State of Development Economics, 1988, Investing in Women's Human Capital, 1995, (periodical) Research in Population Economics, 1985, 88, 91; assoc. editor Jour. Population Econs., 1991—, Econ. of Edn. Rev., 1993—. Fellow AAAS (population resources environ. com. 1985-89, nomination com. 1987-90); mem. Am. Econ. Assn., Econometrics Soc., Population Assn. Am. (bd. dirs. 1979-81), Internat. Union for Sci. Study Population, Soc. for Study Social Biology (bd. dirs. 1986-89), European Soc. for Population Econs. (bd. dirs. 1992—, pres. elect 1996), Econ. Rsch. Forum for Arab Countries. Office: Yale U Econ Growth Ctr PO Box 208269 27 Hillhouse Ave New Haven CT 06520-8269

SCHULTZ, THEODORE EDWARD, retail executive; b. Middletown, Conn., Sept. 15, 1945; s. John and Florence Irene (Rogoz) S.; m. Florence Norfleet Taylor, Sept. 2, 1972; children: Lisa, G. Taylor, Thomas. BS, Quinnipiac Coll., 1972; MBA, U. Chgo., 1974. CPA, Ill. Sr. auditor Arthur Young & Co., Chgo., 1974-77; v.p., gen. auditor Exch. Nat. Bank, Chgo., 1977-82, comptr., 1982-86, sr. v.p., treas, chief acctg. officer, 1986-90; chief fin. officer Gander Mountain Inc., Wilmot, Wis., 1990-93; CFO Midco Internat. Inc., 1993—. Served with U.S. Army, 1964-68, Vietnam. Mem. AICPA, Fin. Execs. Inst., Inst. Internal Auditors, Nat. Assn. Accts., Ill. Soc. CPAs (chmn. banking com. 1989-91, mem. coordination and planning com. 1990—), Delta Mu Delta (chpt. pres. 1971-72). Methodist. Avocations: fishing, golf, hunting. Home: 1160 Banbury Circle Naperville IL 60540

SCHULTZ, THEODORE WILLIAM, retired educator, economist; b. Arlington, S.D., Apr. 30, 1902; s. Henry Edward and Anna Elizabeth (Weiss) S.; m. Esther Florence Werth; children: Elaine, Margaret, T. Paul. Grad., Sch. Agr., Brookings, S.D., 1924; B.S., S.D. State Coll., 1927, D.Sc. (hon.), 1959; M.S., U. Wis., 1928, Ph.D., 1930; LL.D. (hon.), Grinnell Coll., 1949, Mich. State U., in 1962, U. III., 1968, U. Wis., 1968, Cath. U. Chile, 1979, U. Dijon, France, 1981; LL.D., N.C. State U., 1984. Mem. faculty Iowa State Coll., Ames, 1930-43; prof., head dept. econs. and sociology Iowa State Coll., 1934-43; prof. econs. U. Chgo., 1943-72, chmn. dept. econs., 1946-61, Charles L. Hutchinson Disting. Service prof., 1952-72, prof. emeritus, 1972—; econ. adviser, occasional cons. Com. Econ. Devel., U.S. Dept. Agr., Dept. State, Fed. Res. Bd., various congl. coms., U.S. Dept. Commerce, FAO, U.S. Dept. Def., Germany, 1948, Fgn. Econ. Adminstrn., U.K. and Germany, 1945, IBRD, Resources for the Future, Twentieth Century Fund, Nat. Farm Inst., others; dir. Nat. Bur. Econ. Research, 1949-67; research dir. Studies of Tech. Assistance in Latin Am.; bd. mem. Nat. Planning Assn.; chmn. Am. Famine Mission to India, 1946; studies of agrl. developments, central europe and Russia, 1929, Scandinavian countries and Scotland, 1936, Brazil, Uruguay and Argentina, 1941, Western Europe, 1955. Author: Redirecting Farm Policy, 1943, Food for the World, 1945, Agriculture in an Unstable Economy, 1945, Production and Welfare in Agriculture, 1950, The Economic Organization of Agriculture, 1953, Economic Test in Latin America, 1956, Transforming Traditional Agriculture, 1964, The Economic Value of Education, 1963, Economic Crises in World Agriculture, 1965, Economic Growth and Agriculture, 1968, Investment in Human Capital: The Role of Education And of Research, 1971, Human Resources, 1972, Economics of the Family: Marriage, Children, and Human Capital, 1974, Distortions of Agricultural Incentives, 1978, Investing in People: The Economics of Population Quality, 1981, Restoring Economic Equilibrium: Human Capital in the Modernizing Economy, 1990, The Economics of Being Poor, 1993, Origins of Increasing Returns, 1993; co-author: Measures for Economic Development of Under-Developed Countries, 1951; editor: Jour. Farm Econs., 1939-42; contbr. articles to profl. jours. Research fellow Center Advanced Study in Behavioral Sci., 1956-57; recipient Nobel prize in Econs., 1979. Fellow Am. Acad. Arts and Scis., Am. Farm Econs. Assn., Nat. Acad. Scis.; mem. Am. Agrl. Econ. Assn., Am. Econ. Assn. (pres. 1960, Walker medal 1972), Am. Philos. Soc., Royal Econ. Soc., Nat. Acad. Edn., others. Home: 5620 S Kimbark Ave Chicago IL 60637-1606 Office: U Chgo Dept Econs 1126 E 59th St Chicago IL 60637-1580

SCHULTZE, CHARLES LOUIS, economist, educator; b. Alexandria, Va., Dec. 12, 1924; s. Richard Lee and Nora Woolls (Baggett) S.; m. Rita Irene Hertzog, Sept. 6, 1947; children: Karen M., Kevin C., Helen L., Kathleen, Carol, Mary. A.B., Georgetown U., 1948, M.A., 1950; Ph.D., U. Md., 1960. Mem. staff Pres.'s Council Econ. Advisers, 1952, 54-58; chmn. Pres.'s Council Econ. Advisors, 1977-81; assoc. prof. econs. Ind. U., 1959-61; prof. econs. U. Md., 1961-87; asst. dir. U.S. Bur. of Budget, 1962-64, dir., 1965-67; sr. fellow Brookings Instn., Washington, 1968-76, 81—. Author: (with others) Setting National Priorities, 6 vols., 1970, 71, 72, 73, 83, 90, The Public Use of Private Interest, 1977, Other Times, Other Places, 1986, (with others) Barriers to European Growth, 1987, (with others) An American Trade Strategy, 1990, Memos to the President, 1992. Served with AUS, 1943-46. Decorated Purple Heart, Bronze Star. Mem. Am. Econ. Assn. (pres. 1984). Office: Brookings Instn 1775 Massachusetts Ave NW Washington DC 20036-2188

SCHULTZ, CHARLES MONROE, cartoonist; b. Mpls., Nov. 26, 1922; s. Carl and Dena (Halverson) S.; m. Joyce Halverson, Apr. 18, 1949 (div. 1972); children: Meredith, Charles Monroe, Craig, Amy, Jill; m. Jean Clyde, 1973. LHD (hon.), Anderson Coll., 1963; DHL (hon.), St. Mary's Coll. of CA, 1969. Cartoonist St. Paul Pioneer Press, Sat. Eve. Post, 1948-49. Created syndicated comic strip Peanuts, 1950—; author of many collections of Peanuts strips and cartoons; screenwriter of several teleplays and feature films based on the Peanuts strip. With U.S. Army, 1943-45. Recipient Outstanding Cartoonist award Nat. Cartoonist Soc., 1955, 1964; Yale Humor award, 1956; School Bell award, Nat. Edn. Assn., 1962; Peabody award and Emmy award for CBS cartoon special "A Charlie Brown Christmas", 1966; Charles M. Schulz award for contribution to the field of cartooning, United Feature Syndicate, 1980. Office: Number One Snoopy Place Santa Rosa CA 95401 also: United Feature Syndicate 200 Park Ave New York NY 10166-0001*

SCHULZ, JUERGEN, art history educator; b. Kiel, Germany, Aug. 18, 1927; came to U.S., 1938; s. Johannes Martin Anson Schulz and Ilse (Lebenbaum) Hiller; m. Justine Hume, Sept. 1951 (div. 1968); children: Christoph (dec.), Ursula, Catherine; m. Anne Markham, May 19, 1969; 1 child, Jeremy. BA, U. Calif., Berkeley, 1950; PhD in Art, U. London, 1958. Reporter San Francisco Chronicle, 1950-51; copy editor UPI, London, 1952-53; from instr. to prof. history of art U. Calif., 1958-68; prof. Brown, Providence, 1968-90, Andrea V. Rosenthal prof. history art and architecture, 1990—; mem. Inst. for Advanced Study, Princeton, N.J., 1971-72. Author: Venetian Painted Ceilings of the Renaissance, 1968, Printed Plans and...Views of Venice, 1971, La cartografia tra scienza e arte, 1990; also articles. Staff sgt. U.S. Army, 1945-48. Decorated grande ufficiale Ordine della Stella della Solidarieta della Repubblica Italiana; Guggenheim fellow, 1966-67. Mem. Ateneo Veneto. Office: Brown U Dept History Art and Architecture PO Box 1855 Providence RI 02912-1855

SCHULZ, KEITH DONALD, corporate lawyer; b. Burlington, Iowa, Dec. 20, 1938; s. Henry Carl and Laura Iral (Bowlin) S.; m. Emily Brook Roane, Apr. 19, 1985; children: Keith Jr., Sarah, Christine, Stefan. BA, U. Iowa, 1960, JD, 1963. Bar: Iowa 1963, Ill. 1986, Wis. 1990. Dep. Sec. of State, State of Iowa, Des Moines, 1965-66; atty. AT&T, Chgo., 1966-67; sec., gen. counsel Borg-Warner Acceptance Corp., Chgo., 1967-74; asst. gen. counsel Borg-Warner Corp., Chgo., 1974-84, v.p., gen. counsel, 1984-88; of counsel Bell, Boyd & Lloyd, Chgo., 1988—. Contbr. articles to Harvard Bus. Rev., Jour. for Corp. Growth. Chmn. bd. Vol. Legal Services Found., Chgo., 1984-91; bd. dirs. Chgo. Metro Ethics Coalition, Community Renewal Soc.,

---

Assn. for Corp. Growth. Mem. Iowa Bar Assn., Chgo. Bar Assn. (chmn. corp. law depts. com. 1983-84), Wis. Bar Assn., Assn. Gen. Counsel, Am. Soc. Corp. Secs., Law Club of Chgo. Clubs: University, Economic (Chgo.). Avocations: tennis, bicycling, skiing. Office: Bell Boyd & Lloyd 70 W Madison St Chicago IL 60602-4284

SCHULZ, MARY ELIZABETH, lawyer; b. New Ulm, Minn., Oct. 6, 1950; d. Paul F. and Elizabeth B. (Wichtel) S. BA cum laude, Mankato State U., 1972; JD, So. Meth. U., 1976. Bar: Tex., 1976, Ky., 1992, Ohio, 1993. Atty. Kagay, Turner, Eyres & Robertson, Dallas, 1976-78; asst. regional counsel U.S. EPA, Dallas, 1978-86; atty. Gardere & Wynne, Dallas, 1986-89, Valvoline, Inc., Lexington, Ky., 1989-90; counsel Olin Corp., E. Alton, Ill., 1990-92; sr. environ. counsel B.F. Goodrich Co., Akron, Ohio, 1992—; mem. adv. bd. Bus. Forum for Environ. Health & Safety, Washington, 1994. Mem. ABA, Fed. Bar Assn. Office: B F Goodrich Co 3925 Embassy Pkwy Akron OH 44333

SCHULZ, MICHAEL ANTHONY, JR., construction company executive, real estate developer; b. New Orleans, Dec. 17, 1934; s. Michael Anthony and Hilda (Monnin) S.; m. Ann Miller Hawkins; 1 child, Terri Lynn Guidry. BS, La. State U., 1959. Registered profl. engr., La., Miss. Plant mgr. Tidewood Corp., Baton Rouge, 1957-58; engr. La. Concrete Products, Baton Rouge, 1959-61; dept. head Wilson P. Abraham, Baton Rouge, 1961-64; mgr. Odis F. Haymon, Baton Rouge, 1964-67; sec., treas. The Bedford Corp., Baton Rouge, 1967-85; pres. Mike Schulz Constrn., Inc., Baton Rouge, 1985-92; coord. facility mgmt. La. Health Care Authority, Baton Rouge, 1992—. Maj. gen. USAR, 1957-93. Fellow Am. Soc. Civil Engrs.; mem. La. Engring. Soc., Soc. Am. Mil. Engrs., Res. Officers Assn., Sr. Army Res. Comdrs. Assn., Am. Arbitration Assn. (panel of arbitrators). Democrat. Episcopalian. Avocations: fishing, gardening. Home: 441 Highland Oaks Dr Baton Rouge LA 70810-5344

SCHULZ, RALPH RICHARD, publishing consultant; b. N.Y.C., June 5, 1928; s. Harry and Margaret (Faecher) S.; m. Joyce S. Woolf, Sept. 9, 1951; children: Laura Krevey, Barbara Tejerina, Susan. BS in Chemistry, CCNY, 1950. Asst. editor McLean-Hunter Pub. Co., Toronto, Can., 1950; assoc. editor McGraw-Hill Pub. Co., N.Y.C., 1951-60, mng. editor, 1960-68, editor-in-chief, 1968-73; dir. McGraw-Hill World News, N.Y.C. 1973-76; v.p. editorial dept. McGraw-Hill Pubs. Co., N.Y.C., 1976-84; sr. v.p. editorial dept. McGraw-Hill, Inc., N.Y.C., 1985-92; pub. cons., 1992—; adj. prof. Grad. Sch. Bus. Adminstrn., Fordham U., 1990—. Author to numerous mag. on bus. and sci. Trustee Correspondents Fund, N.Y.C., 1979—; bd. dirs. Bus. Press Ednl. Found. N.Y.C., 1986—, McGraw-Hill Found., N.Y.C., 1987-92, Copyright Clearence Ctr., N.Y.C., 1983-92. Petty officer USN, 1946-48. Recipient Honor award for disting. svc. in journalism Ohio U., 1972, Jesse H. Neal Editorial Achievement award Am. Bus. Press, 1972. Mem. Am. Soc. Mag. editors (exec. com. 1984-88), Overseas Press Club Am. (bd. dirs. 1969-73), Nat. Press Club, Players Club (bd. dirs. 1974-78), Silurians, Sigma Delta Chi.

SCHULZ, RICHARD BURKART, electrical engineer, consultant; b. Phila., May 21, 1920; s. Herman G. Schulz and Laura (Burkart) Luckenbill; m. Jeannette Charlotte Vollmer, Nov. 22, 1958; 1 child, Steven Edward. BSEE, U. Pa., 1942, MSEE, 1951. Rsch. assoc. U. Pa., Phila., 1942-46; owner Electro-Search, Phila., 1947-55; program devel. coord. Armour Rsch. Found., Chgo., 1955-61; chief electro-interference United Control Corp., Redmond, Wash., 1961-62; chief electro-compatibility Boeing Co., Seattle, 1962-70; staff engr. S.W. Rsch. Inst., San Antonio, 1970-74; sci. advisor IIT Rsch. Inst., Annapolis, Md., 1974-83; mgr. EMC and TEMPEST Xerox Corp., Lewisville, Tex., 1983-87; EMC cons. Carrollton, Tex., 1987—. Contbr. numerous tech. papers to profl. publs. Named Life Master Am. Contract Bridge League. Fellow IEEE (life; Centennial medal 1984, Standards plaque 1991); mem. IEEE Soc. on Electromagnetic Compatibility (life; treas. 1966-67, pres. 1968, bd. dirs. 1961-89, chmn. internat. conf. 1968, tech. program chmn. internat. conf. 1993, L.G. Cumming plaque 1980, Richard R. Stoddart award 1988), Toastmasters Club. Republican. Lutheran. Home and Office: 2030 Cologne Dr Carrollton TX 75007-2334

SCHULZ, ROBERT ADOLPH, management educator, management consultant; b. Long Branch, N.J., Aug. 20, 1943; s. Robert Adolph and Anna Elizabeth (Fuga) S. BA in Math., St. Vincent Coll., Latrobe, Pa., 1965; BS in Mech. Engring., U. Notre Dame, 1966; MBA, U. Pitts., 1967; PhD in Bus. Adminstrn., Ohio State U., 1971. Rsch. asst. Tech. and Bus. Svcs., Ohio State U., Columbus, 1967-68; teaching asst. dept. mktg. Ohio State U., 1968-70; sr. assoc. Mgmt. Horizons, Inc., Columbus, 1970-71; dir. edn. Mgmt. Horizons Data Systems, Columbus, 1971-72, dir. edn., 1972-73; assoc. prof., Faculty of Mgmt. U. Calgary, Alta., Can., 1973-88, acad. dir. petroleum land mgmt., 1983—, prof. mgmt., 1988—, univ. coord. teaching devel. office, 1991—, pres. Myosymmetries Internat. Inc., 1994—; pres. Scenario Mgmt. Cons. Ltd., Calgary, 1987—. Chmn. Align to 21st Century Task Force, Calgary Econ. Devel. Authority, 1989-92; chmn. coordinating com. Calgary Cath. Diocese Synod, 1990—; bd. govs. 1994—, co-chmn. Synod implementation com., 1994—; bd. dirs. Calgary Sponsor and Refugee Soc., 1981-83. Recipient awards for teaching and coaching academic teams, Edn. award City of Calgary, 1995. Mem. Soc. for Teaching and Learning in Higher Edn., Can. Assn. Petroleum Landmen (hon.). Avocations: golf, basketball, jogging. Home: 24-1815 Varsity Estates Dr NW, Calgary, AB Canada T3B 3Y7 Office: U Calgary, Faculty of Mgmt, Calgary, AB Canada T2N 1N4

SCHULZ, ROCKWELL IRWIN, health administration educator; b. Milw., June 30, 1929; s. Irwin W.P. and Ruth Mary (Rockwell) S.; m. Susan Clare Marriott Learmonth; children from previous marriage: Rockwell A., Michael T., Kerry G., David T. BS, Lawrence U., Appleton, Wis., 1951; MHA, U. Minn., 1955; PhD (spl. rsch. fellow HEW 1969-72), U. Wis., 1972. Asst. adminstr. Charles T. Miller Hosp., St. Paul, 1955-56; adminstr. Pember Nuzum Clinic, Janesville, Wis., 1956-61, Meml. Hosp., Manitowoc, Wis., 1961-63; cons. Booz, Allen & Hamilton, Chgo., 1963-66; asst. dean Tulane U. Med. Sch., 1966-67; asso. dean U. Tex. Southwestern Med. Sch., Dallas, 1967-69; mem. faculty U. Wis. Med. Sch., Madison, 1969—, prof. preventive medicine, dir. Internat. Ctr. for Health Services Studies, 1979—; cons. in field. Author: Management of Hospitals, 1976, 2d edit., 1983, Teams and Top Management in British National Health Services, 1984, Management of Hospitals and Health Services: Strategic Issues and Performance, 1990; also articles. Served with USCG, 1951-53. WHO fellow, 1981, Fulbright sr. rsch. fellow, 1985-86; recipient Hubert H. Humphrey award for best articles Jour. Health and Human Resources Adminstr., 1981, Vernon E. Weekworth award for best rsch. paper U. Minn. Hosp. & Health Svcs. Adminstrn., 1992, best paper award health sect. Acad. of Mgmt. 1992. Mem. Am. Acad. Mgmt., Am. Hosp. Assn., Am. Pub. Health Assn., Assn. for Health Svcs. Rsch. Home: 1 Langdon St Madison WI 53703 Address: U Wis Med Scis Ctr 1300 University Ave Madison WI 53706

SCHULZ, RUDOLPH WALTER, university dean; b. Chgo., Aug. 10, 1930; s. Walter Adolph and Minna Louise (Burmeister) S.; m. Charlotte Helen Adams, Sept. 8, 1956; children: Stephanie Sue, Kyle Scott. B.S., Northwestern U., 1954, Ph.D., 1958; M.A., Stanford, 1955. Lectr., research asso. Northwestern U., 1956-58, instr., 1958-59; asst. prof. psychology Carnegie-Mellon U., 1959-60; asst. prof. U. Iowa, 1960-64, asso. prof., 1964-66, prof., 1966—, prof., chmn. dept., 1970-73, dean for advanced studies, 1976-91; cons. in field, mem. NSF fellowship selection panel, 1962-68; NSF vis. scientist, 1962-76; bd. dirs. Midwest Univs. Consortium for Internat. Activities, Inc., 1977-91. Cons. editor: Jour. Exptl. Psychology, 1962-74, Jour. Verbal Learning and Verbal Behavior, 1964-74, Contemporary Psychology, 1970-81; editor: Psychonomic Science, 1971-72, Memory and Cognition, 1972-76; Contbr. articles to profl. jours. Served with USNR, 1950-52. Decorated Air medal.; Old Gold research fellow U. Iowa, 1963; NSF research grantee, 1964-76. Fellow Am. Psychol. Assn., AAAS (mem. council 1974-75) Am. Psychol. Soc. (charter); mem. Psychonomic Soc., Midwestern Psychol. Assn. (sec.-treas. 1973-76, pres. 1978), Sigma Xi. Home: 8 Fairview Knoll NE Iowa City IA 52240-9147

SCHULZ, WILLIAM FREDERICK, human rights association executive; b. Pitts., Nov. 14, 1949; s. William F. and Jean Smith; m. Beth Graham, 1993. AB, Oberlin Coll., 1971; MA, Meadville/Lombard Theol. Sch., 1973, DMin, 1975, DDiv, 1987; MA, U. Chgo., 1974. Minister First Parish

Unitarian Universalist, Bedford, Mass., 1975-78; dir. social responsibility Unitarian Universalist Assn., Boston, 1978-79, exec. v.p., 1979-85, pres., 1985-93; exec. dir. Amnesty Internat. USA, 1994—. Author: Finding Time and Other Delicacies, 1992; editor, contbr. Transforming Words: Six Essays on Preaching, 1984. Bd. dirs. People for the Am. Way, The Communitarian Network. Recipient Albert Francis Christie prize, 1973, 75. Mem. ACLU, Unitarian Universalist Mins. Assn., Internat. Assn. Religious Freedom. Democrat. Home: 10 Castle Harbor Rd Huntington NY 11743

SCHULZE, ARTHUR ROBERT, JR., food company executive; b. LaCrosse, Wis., Jan. 31, 1931; s. Arthur Robert and Elizabeth Margaret (Showers) S.; m. Joan M. Hanifan, June 25, 1955; children: Brett, Mark, David, Anne. BA, Carleton Coll., Northfield, Minn., 1952; MBA with distinction, Harvard U., 1958. With IBM Corp., until 1959; from sales trainee to product mgr. Procter & Gamble Co., Cin., 1959-62, product mgr., 1961-62; product mgr. angel cake mixes Gen. Mills, Inc., Mpls., 1962-63, product mgr. cake mixes, 1963-65, mktg. mgr. baking mixes, 1965-66, mktg. mgr. cereals, 1966-69, asst. gen. mgr. Big G div., 1969-70, v.p., gen. mgr. Golden Valley div., 1970-73, group v.p. consumer foods, 1973-80, exec. v.p., 1981-85, also pres. grocery products food group; exec. v.p., Grocery Products Food Group, 1985-89, vice chmn. bd., 1989—; bd. dirs. Tennant Co., Inc. Gen. Mills, Inter-regional Fin. Corp. Trustee Carleton Coll., Northfield, Minn., 1977—; bd. govs. Meth. Hosp., St. Louis Park, Minn., 1980—. Served with AUS, 1953-56. Recipient Merit award Mpls. United Way. Mem. Cereal Inst. (mem. exec. com., bd. dirs.), Civic League Mpls. Republican. Clubs: Mpls.; Harvard Bus. Sch.; Interlachen Country (Edina, Minn.). Avocation: tennis. Office: Gen Mills Inc 1 General Mills Blvd Minneapolis MN 55426-1347

SCHULZE, ERWIN EMIL, manufacturing company executive, lawyer; b. Davenport, Iowa, May 4, 1925; s. Erwin F. and Hazel (Sorensen) S.; m. Jean E. Steele, June 21, 1952; children: Suzanne Schulze Walker, Donna Schulze Ballard, Stephen Johnson. B.A., De Pauw U., 1947; LL.B., Yale, 1950. Bar: Ill. 1950. Pvt. practice Chgo.; ptnr. Rooks, Pitts, Fullagar & Poust (and predecessor firms), 1950-67, counsel, 1967-80; pres., dir. Standard Alliance Industries, Inc., 1967-79; pres., chief operating officer, dir. Ceco Industries, 1980-85; pres., chief exec. officer The Ceco Corp., 1985-86; pres., chief exec. officer, chmn., dir. Ceco Industries, Inc., 1986-90; mem. adv. coun. zoning, Chgo., 1955-57; chief counsel Standard Forgings Corp., Chgo., 1963-65, exec. v.p., 1965-67; treas., dir. Transue & Williams Steel Forging Corp., Alliance, Ohio, 1965-66; bd. govs. com. on specialist assignment and evaluation and space planning Midwest Stock Exchange, 1979—; dir. AAR Corp., Interlake, Inc., chmn. bd. govs., 1993—. Bd. visitors De Pauw U., 1979-81, trustee, 1981—; co-chmn. Joint Com. Codify Ill. Family Law, 1958-61; mem. Mayor Chgo. Adv. Coun. Juvenile Delinquency, 1958-62; v.p., dir. Midwestern Air Pollution Prevention Assn., 1958-72, chmn. legal com., 1960-63; v.p., dir. Chgo. Tennis Assn., 1964-71; sec., dir. Chgo. Tennis Patrons, 1960-74; chmn. men's ranking com. U.S. Lawn and Tennis Assn., 1961-71. Served as lt. (j.g.) USNR, 1943-46, PTO. Mem. ABA, Ill. Mfrs. Assn. (bd. dirs. 1983—, vice chmn. 1986—, chmn. 1987-89), Nat. Assn. Mfs. (bd. dirs. 1990—), Chgo. Econs. Club, Chgo. Dist. Golf Assn. (bd. dirs. 1990—), Indian Wells Country Club, Legal Club, Shoreacres Club, Phi Beta Kappa. Presbyterian (deacon, elder trustee).

SCHULZE, FRANZ, JR., art critic, educator; b. Uniontown, Pa., Jan. 30, 1927; s. Franz and Anna E. (Krimmel) S.; m. Marianne Gaw, June 24, 1961 (div. 1975); children: F. C. Matthew, Lukas; m. Stephanie Mora, 1992. Student, Northwestern U., 1943; Ph.B., U. Chgo., 1945; B.F.A., Sch. Art Inst. Chgo., 1949, M.F.A., 1950; postgrad., Acad. Fine Arts, Munich, Germany, 1956-57. Instr. art Purdue U., 1950-52; chmn. dept. art Lake Forest (Ill.) Coll., 1952-58, artist-in-residence, 1958-61, prof. art, 1961—, Hollender prof. art, 1974-91; art critic Chgo. Daily News, 1962-78, Chgo. Sun-Times, 1978-85; Chgo. corr. in art Christian Sci. Monitor, 1958-62, Art in Am., 1965—, Art Internat., 1966-67; art and architecture critic The Chicagoan, 1973-74; mem. vis. com. dept. art U. Chgo., 1974—. Author: Art, Architecture and Civilization, 1969, Fantastic Images: Chicago Art Since 1945, 1972, 100 Years of Chicago Architecture, 1976, Stealing Is My Game, 1976, Mies van der Rohe: A Critical Biography, 1985, The University Club of Chicago: A Heritage, 1987, Mariotti, 1988; editor: Mies van der Rohe: Critical Essays, 1989, Mies van der Rohe Archive, 1993; co-editor Chicago's Famous Buildings, 1993, Philip Johnson: Life and Work, 1994; contbg. editor Art News, 1973—, Inland Architect, 1975-94. Trustee Ragdale Found., Lake Forest, 1981—. Recipient Harbison award for tchg. Danforth Found. of St. Louis, 1971; Adenauer fellow, 1956-57; Ford Found. fellow, 1964-65; Graham Found. for Advanced Studies in the Fine Arts fellow, 1971, 81, 93; NEH fellow, 1982, 88; Skidmore Owings & Merrill Found. fellow, 1983; recipient Disting. Svc. award Chgo. Phi Beta Kappa Soc., 1972; Hon. Mention Hitchcock Book award Soc. Archtl. Historians, 1987. Mem. AAUP, Coll. Art Assn. (bd. dirs. 1983-86), Archives Am. Art (adv. com.), Soc. Archtl. Historians. Office: Lake Forest Coll Dept Art Lake Forest IL 60045

SCHULZE, HORST H., hotel company executive. Pres., COO The Ritz Carlton Hotel Co., Atlanta. Office: The Ritz-Carlton Hotel Co 3414 Peachtree Rd NE Ste 300 Atlanta GA 30326-1164*

SCHULZE, RICHARD HANS, engineering executive, environmental engineer; b. Buffalo, May 28, 1933; s. Hans Joachim and Lucy (Kawczynska) S.; m. Jacqueline Van Luppen, Nov. 2, 1957 (div. Aug., 1979); children: Richard H Jr., Linda Schulze Keefer, John; m. Ineke Grooters, Aug. 29, 1987. BSME, Princeton U., 1954; MBA, Northwestern U., 1958. Registered profl. engr., Tex. Rsch. analyst U.S. Steel Corp., Pitts., 1958-60; chief engr. G&H Rsch. and Devel., McKeesport, Pa., 1960-62; cons. Mgmt. and Mktg. Inst., N.Y.C., 1962-63, IITRI mgmt. consulting div., N.Y.C., 1963-64; mkt devel. mgr. Mobil Chem. Co. plastics div., N.Y.C., Jacksonville, Ill., 1964-71; pres. Ecology Audits, Inc. (Core Labs.), Dallas, 1971-74, Trinity Cons., Inc., Dallas, 1974—. Contbr. articles to Jour. of Air and Waste Mgt. Assn., Atmospheric Environment, others; presented papers at sci. symposiums, seminars, confs. Mem. Dallas Symphony Assn., Mus. of Art; bd. dirs. Dallas Opera, 1993—; Lt. (j.g.) USNR, 1954-56. Mem. ASME, TAPPI, Am. Acad. Environ. Engrs. (diplomate), Am. Chem. Soc., Am. Meteorologocal Soc., Air and Waste Mgmt. Assn. (bd. dirs. 1986-89. '90-93, v.p. 1988-89, 1 st v.p. 1990-91, pres. 1991-92, past pres. 1992-93), Am. Inst. Mining, Metallurgical and Petroleum Engrs., Nat. Soc. for Clean Air (UK), Soc Petroleum Engrs., Soc. for Risk Analysis, Semi-Conductor Safety Assn., Verein Deutscher Ingenieure, Assn. Francaise des Ingénieurs et Techniciens de L'environment., Dallas Bar Assn. (environ. law sect., exec. com.),Tech. Assn. Pulp and Paper Industry (air quality com.), Inst. Profl. Environmental Practive (trustee 1993, qualified environmental profl.). Presbyterian. Home: 7619 Marquette Dallas TX 75225 Office: Trinity Cons Inc Ste 1200 12801 N Central Expy Dallas TX 75243

SCHULZE, RICHARD M., consumer products executive; b. 1941. With No. States Sales Co., 1962—; now chmn., CEO, dir. Besy Buy Co., Inc., Eden Prairie, Minn. Office: Best Buy Co 7075 Flying Cloud Dr Eden Prairie MN 55344*

SCHULZE, ROBERT OSCAR, university dean; b. Springfield, Ill., Aug. 6, 1922; s. Walter O. and Lydia I. (Schorr) S.; m. Suzanne Sims, Oct. 23, 1948; children—Peter Compton, Elizabeth Sauter. A.B., U. Mich., 1947, Ph.D., 1956; M.A., Columbia U., 1952. Asst. personnel mgr. Sandia Lab., Albuquerque, 1947-50; teaching fellow sociology U. Mich., 1951-55; instr. sociology Brown U., 1955-57, asst. prof., 1957-61, asso. prof., 1961-66, prof., 1966-70, asst. dean coll., 1959-64, dean, 1964-68; exec. dir. Thomas J. Watson Found., 1968-72; prof. sociology, dean Coll. Arts and Scis., U. No. Colo., Greeley, 1972-87, dean, 1972-87; Faculty research fellow Social Sci. Research Council, 1963-64. Contbr. articles to profl. publs. Chmn. family and children's div., mem. bd. R.I. Council Community Services, 1961-63; bd. dirs. Colo. Humanities Program, 1975-79. Served to warrant officer AUS 1943-46. Decorated Bronze Star. Mem. Vachel Lindsay Assn. (co-founder), ACLU (chmn. Weld County br. 1987-90, bd. dirs. Colo. chpt. 1988-90). Democrat. Home: 1814 Reservoir Rd Greeley CO 80631-6834

SCHULZE, THEODORA ECONOMOU, music director, educator; b. Hammond, Ind., Sept. 19, 1930; d. Xenophon and Emilie (Mueller) Economou; oboist protegee of Alfred Barthel and Kenneth Gekeler, 1943-53;

m. Richard Schulze, Apr. 16, 1950; 1 son, Otto. soloist oboe Am. Conservatory symphony orch., Chgo., 1948-51, music dir., soloist The Telemann Soc., N.Y.C. and Ft. Lauderdale, Fla., 1955—; appearances at Carnegie Hall, Town Hall, N.Y. and other world centers, 1955—; dir. and soloist over 45 recs. on Vox, Nonesuch, Everest, Amphion, other U.S. and overseas labels, 1959—; taught at Carnegie Hall, 1954-63; pedagogical work published by Associated Music Pub., N.Y.C., 1970, author: complete guide to Music Note Reading, 1959, Elements of Musical Style, 1962; editor: 180 Studies for Development of Uniform Velocity & Muscular Control, 1962. Sec. Philharm. Standard Corp., Acton, Mass., 1969-74; producer nat. syndicated radio show "The Age of Telemann", 1961—; with Miami Beach symphony orch., 1974, featured soloist Fla. Pops Orch., 1976-78; appeared with Robert Goulet, Leonard Pennario, other major soloists, 1977—; treas. Amphion Recording Soc. Inc., 1982—, Wynwood Merc. Corp., 1982—; chmn. Gift of Music Program NARAS, Atlanta, 1989-93; pres., CEO Am. Coservatory of Music, 1991—. Office: 16 North Wabash Ave ste 1850 Chicago IL 60602

SCHULZETENBERG, JOHN MARTIN, finance company executive, accountant; b. Greenwald, Minn., Apr. 5, 1946; s. Al and Del Schulzetenberg; m. Jane Planer, June 10, 1968; children: J. Peter, Jay P. BA, St. Cloud (Minn.) U., 1968. CPA, Colo., Minn. With professional staff Touche Ross and Co., Mpls., 1967-77, audit ptnr., 1977-84; mng. ptnr. Touche Ross and Co., Bloomington, Minn., 1985-86, Denver, 1986—; dir. recruiting and tng. Touche Ross and Co., Mpls., 1976-84, Denver, 1986—; mem. mgmt. adv. council Touche Ross and Co., 1979-82; asst. prof. acctg. St. Cloud U. Sch. of Bus., 1973. Bd. dirs., treas. Denver Civic Ventures, 1988; v.p., treas., bd. dirs., Denver Children's Mus., 1988; bd. advisors U. Denver Sch. Accountancy, 1988; found. bd. dirs. and dir. fin. St. Cloud U., 1988. Mem. AICPA (mem. personal fin. statements com. 1987—), Colo. Soc. CPAs (bd. dirs., com. chmn. 1987—), Nat. Assn. Accts. (bd. dirs.). Republican. Office: Touche Ross & Co 1560 Broadway Ste 1800 Denver CO 80202-5151

SCHULZ-WIDMAR, RUSSELL EUGENE, musician, educator, composer; b. Harvard, Ill., July 29, 1944; s. Friederich Wilhelm and Helen (DeVries) Schulz; m. Suzanne Widmar, Aug. 26, 1967; children: John Frederick, Karl Andrew. MusB, Valparaiso U., 1966; SMM, Union Theol. Sem., N.Y.C., 1968; DMA, U. Tex., 1974; postgrad., Royal Sch. Ch. Music, London, summer 1976. Dir. music Univ. United Meth. Ch., Austin, 1971-93, Good Shepherd Episcopal Ch., Austin, 1993—; lectr. Austin (Tex.) Presbyn. Theol. Sem., 1975-91; prof. Episcopal Theol. Sem. S.W., Austin, 1974—; dean Evergreen Music Conf., 1981-87; mem. Standing Commn. on Ch. Music, Episcopal Ch., 1978-85. Editor: (hymnal) Songs of Thanks and Praise, 1980; co-editor: New Hymnal for Colleges and Schools, 1992; chmn. The Hymnal 1982, 1985. Recipient Disting. Alumnus award Valparaiso U., 1988. Mem. Hymn Soc. U.S. and Can. (pres. 1988-90). Office: PO Box 2247 Austin TX 78768

SCHUMACHER, ELIZABETH SWISHER, garden ornaments shop owner; b. Webster City, Iowa, Apr. 1, 1940; d. Andrew Dale and Harriet Elizabeth (Hudson) Swisher; m. H. Ralph Schumacher Jr., July 13, 1963; children: Heidi Ruth, Kaethe Beth. BS, U. Colo., 1961; student, Barnes Found. Sch Horticulture, 1976. Owner Garden Accents, West Conshohocken, Pa., 1979—; lectr. on garden ornaments, hillside gardening, water in the garden, 1979—; exhibitor designer show house Vassar Coll., Phila. area sites, 1984—. Contbr. articles to Fine Gardening, Green Scene, Gardens and Landscapes. Recipient Outstanding Landscaping award Pa. Nurserymen's Assn., 1972, Residential Beautification award Upper Merion Twp., 1974, 76, 86, Exhibit of Distinction award Phila. Flower Show, 1989. Mem. Pa. Hort. Soc. (hotline vol. 1987—), Rhododendron Soc. Am. Office: Garden Accents 4 Union Hill Rd West Conshohocken PA 19428

SCHUMACHER, FREDERICK CARL, former insurance company executive; b. St. Louis, Sept. 5, 1911; s. John Charles Robert and Edna Eugenia (Hanausky) S.; m. Althea Fuqua Hickey, Nov. 4, 1936; children: Nancy S. (Mrs. John D. Dennis), Frederick Carl Jr. A.B., Washington U., St. Louis, 1932; LL.D., Westminster Coll., 1973. With Merc. Ins. Agy., St. Louis, 1933-72; dir. Merc. Ins. Agy., 1966-72, chmn. bd., 1970-72; with Hickey-Mitchell Co., 1937-76, former chmn. bd., dir., pres.; dir. Nat. Home Life Assurance Co., 1945-73, sr. v.p., 1966-69; chmn. bd., dir. Nat. Bonding & Accident Ins. Co., 1967-81, former pres.; former dir. Nat. Liberty Corp., Commerce Bank of St. Louis, Nationwide Corp., Pacific Life Ins. Co., Nat. Services, Inc., Nat. Casualty Co., Mich. Life Ins. Co., Gulf Atlantic Life Ins. Co.; former sr. fellow, chmn. bd. govs Winston Churchill Meml. Library, Fulton, Mo., 1982-92. Alderman, Clayton, Mo., 1953-54; mem. Charter Commn., Clayton, 1955; mem. Citizens Com. for State Reorgn., 1973, 22d Circuit Jud. Commn., 1975-81; founding mem., treas. Mo. Republicans Unlimited, 1959-62; life trustee, former chmn. bd. Westminster Coll.; former bd. dirs. and pres. Child Guidance and Evaluation Clinic, Provident Counseling, Health and Welfare Council; founding mem., former bd. dirs. St. Louis Council on Alcoholism; past trustee Edgewood Children's Center; past bd. dirs. St. Louis County Day Sch., St. Louis Community Sch. Council, Girls' Home, English Speaking Union; former sec., bd. dirs. St. Lukes Hosp.; former pres., dir. Hickey-Schumacher Found. Served to lt. comdr. USNR, 1942-45, ETO, PTO. Mem. Sigma Chi. Presbyterian (former pres. bd. deacons, pres. bd. trustees, clk. of session Ladue Chapel). Clubs: University, St. Louis Country (St. Louis); Belvedere (past pres.), Belvedere Golf (past pres.) (Charlevoix, Mich.). Home & Office: 625 S Skinker Blvd Saint Louis MO 63105-2340

SCHUMACHER, GEBHARD FRIEDERICH BERNHARD, obstetrician-gynecologist; b. Osnabrueck, Fed. Republic Germany, June 13, 1924; came to U.S., 1962; s. Kaspar and Magarete (Pommer) S.; m. Anne Rose Zanker, Oct. 24, 1958; children: Michael A., Marc M. M.D., U. Goettingen and Tuebingen, 1951; Sc.D. equivalent in obstetrics and gynecology, U. Tuebingen, 1962. Intern U. Tuebingen Med. Sch., 1951-52; tng. biochemistry Max Planck Inst. Biochemistry, Tuebingen, 1952-53; tng. biochemistry and immunology Max Planck Inst. Virus Research, 1953-54; resident in ob-gyn U. Tuebingen, 1954-59, tng. internal medicine, 1959, asst. scientist in ob-gyn and biochem. research, 1959-62, dozent in ob-gyn, 1964-65; Research assoc. in immunology Inst. Tb Research, U. Ill. Coll. Medicine, 1962-63; research assoc., asst. prof. ob-gyn U. Chgo., 1963-64; assoc. prof. ob-gyn asst. prof. biochemistry Albany Med. Coll. of Union U., 1965-67; research physician, div. labs. and research N.Y. State Dept. Health, Albany, 1965-67; assoc. prof. ob-gyn U. Chgo.-Chgo. Lying-In Hosp., 1967-73; chief sect. reproductive biology, 1971-91, prof. Immunology, 1974-91; prof. Biol. Sci. Collegiate Divsn. U. Chgo., 1982—; prof. emeritus U. Chgo., 1991—; cons. WHO, NIH, other nat. and internat. orgns.; mem. tech. and sci. adv. bds. Family Health Internat., Cistron Tech. Inc. Author: (with Beller) The Biology of the Fluids of the Female Genital Tract, 1979, (with Dhindsa) Immunological Aspects of Infertility and Fertility Regulation, 1980, (with Kaiser) Human Reproduction, Fertility, Sterility, Contraception, 1981, Spanish edit., 1986; contbr. articles to profl. jours. Fellow Am. Coll. Obstetricians and Gynecologists; mem. Soc. Gynecologic Investigation, Am. Fertility Soc., Soc. Study of Reprodn., Am. Acad. Reproductive Medicine, Am. Soc. Cytology, Am. Assn. Pathologists, Am. Soc. Andrology, Chgo. Assn. Reproductive Endocrinologists (pres. 1985-86), N.Y. Acad. Scis., Deutsche Gesellschaft für Gynakologie und Geburtshilfe, Gesellschaft für Biologische Chemie, Gesellschaft für Immunologie, Deutsche Gesellschaft für Bluttransfusion, Gesellschaft Deutscher Naturforscher und Aerzte. Home and Office: 557 Hamilton Wood Rd Homewood IL 60430-4403

SCHUMACHER, HANS HEINRICH, steel company executive; b. Bad Polzin, Prussia, Germany, Nov. 20, 1933; came to U.S., 1960; s. Karl Heinrich and Helene Erna Martha (Droese) S.; m. Anke Margarethe Johannssen, July 10, 1962 (div. Apr. 1964). BSME, Engring. Acad., Wismar, German Democratic Republic, 1954. Engr. shop and prodn. Mathias Thesen Werft, Wismar, Fed. Republic Germany, 1954-55; project engr. Hauni Maschinenfabrik, Hamburg, Fed. Republic Germany, 1955-56; marine engr. Schlieker Werft, Hamburg, 1956-60; liaison engr. Schlieker Werft, N.Y.C., 1960-62; asst. supr. Hudson Engring. Co., Hoboken, N.J., 1960; marine engr. J.J. Henry Co., Inc., N.Y.C., 1962-63; resident engr. Voest-Alpine Internat. Corp., N.Y.C., 1963-65, pres., dir. 1965—; chmn. Voest-Alpine Can. Corp., Vancouver, B.C., 1987; dir. Va. Crews Coal Co., Welch, W.Va., Third Colony COrp., N.Y.C.; chmn. Vaico, Inc., N.Y.C. Mem. U.S-Austrian C. of C. (dir. N.Y.C.). Clubs: Sixty East (N.Y.C.), Southampton (N.Y.) Beach and Tennis. Avocations: tennis, jogging, anti-

ques. Office: Voest Alpine Internat Corp 60 E 42nd St New York NY 10165-0001

SCHUMACHER, H(ARRY) RALPH, internist, researcher, medical educator; b. Montreal, Feb. 14, 1933; s. H. Ralph and Dorothy (Shreiner) S.; m. Elizabeth Jean Swisher, July 13, 1963; children: Heidi Ruth, Kaethe Beth. B.S., Ursinus Coll., 1955; M.D., U. Pa., 1959. Intern Denver Gen. Hosp., 1959-60; resident in medicine Wadsworth VA Hosp., L.A., 1960-62, fellow in rheumatology, 1962-63; fellow in rheumatology Robert B. Brigham Hosp. and Harvard U. Med. Sch., Boston, 1965-67; chief arthritis-immunology ctr. VA Med. Ctr., Phila., 1967—; faculty mem. U. Pa. Sch. Medicine, Phila., 1967—; prof. medicine, 1979—, acting arthritis div. chief, 1978-80, 91—; vis. scholar NIH, 1994—. Author: Gout and Pseudogout, 1978, Essentials of a Differential Diagnosis of Rheumatoid Arthritis, 1981, Rheumatoid Arthritis, 1988, Case Studies in Rheumatology for the House Officer, 1989, Atlas of Synovial Fluid and Crystal Identification, 1991, A Practical Guide to Synovial Fluid Analysis, 1991; editor: Primer on Rheumatic Diseases, 1981—, Jour. Clin. Rheumatology, 1994—; mem. editorial bd. Jour. Rheumatology, 1973—, Arthritis and Rheumatism, 1981-88, Revue du Rhumatisme, 1992—, Brit. Jour. Clin. Practice, 1992—, New European Rheumatology, 1993—, Japanese Jour. Rheumatology, 1993—; contbr. articles to profl. jours.; lectr., author gardening. Pres. Eastern Pa. chpt. Arthritis Found., 1980-82; chmn., founder Phila. Garden Tours, 1987—; bd. dirs. Hemochromatosis Research Found., 1984—, Am. Bd. Med. Advancement China, 1993—. Served with M.C. USAF, 1963-65. Recipient Van-Breeman award The Netherland Rheumatism Soc., 1988, Philip Hench award Assn. Military Surgeons, 1986; Deposition VA grantee, 1967—, NIH grantee, 1981. Fellow ACP; mem. Am. Coll. Rheumatology (pres. Southeastern region 1981-82), Phila. Rheumatism Soc. (pres. 1980), Phila. Electron Microscopy Soc. (chmn. 1975-76), Rheumatism Soc. Mex., Rheumatism Soc. Australia, Rheumatism Soc. Colombia, Rheumatism Soc. Chile, Rheumatism Soc. Republic of China, Rheumatism Soc. Argentina, Med. Soc. Argentina, Assn. Mil. Surgeons (Philip Hench award 1986), Fedn. Clin. Rsch., AAAS. Office: Hosp U Pa 3400 Spruce St Philadelphia PA 19104 *I try to teach meticulous observation and questioning of dogma both in daily care of patients and in laboratory investigation of the poorly understood rheumatic diseases.*

SCHUMACHER, HENRY JEROLD, former career officer, business executive; b. Torrance, Calif., June 17, 1934; s. Henry John and Rene (Wilcox) S.; m. Barbara Howell, Aug. 24, 1958; children: Sheri Lynn, Henry Jerold II. Student, Stanford U., 1953; B.S., U.S. Mil. Acad., 1957; M.S. Northeastern U., Boston, 1965; M.B.A., Auburn U., 1977. Commd. lt. U.S. Army, 1958, advanced through grades to maj. gen., 1982; army attaché Moscow, 1969-71; chief communications ops. Vietnam, 1971-72; exec. officer Office Chief of Staff, 1972-75; comdr. U.S. Army Communications Command, Panama, 1977-79; dir. network integration, Office Asst. Chief of Staff Automation and Communications, Dept. Army, 1979-81; comdr. The White House Communications Agy., Washington, 1981-82; chief U.S. Army Signal Corps, 1981-83; ret., 1983; sr. v.p. Visa Internat., 1983-86; chief oper. officer Fuel Tech., Inc., Stamford, Conn., 1986-87; pres. IMM Systems, Phila., 1987-89; exec. v.p. Cylink Corp., Sunnyvale, Calif., 1990—. Decorated Def. D.S.M., D.S.M., Legion of Merit. Home: 156 Normandy Ct San Carlos CA 94070-1519 Office: Cylink Corp 910 Hermosa Ct Sunnyvale CA 94086-4111

SCHUMACHER, JOEL, film writer, director; b. N.Y.C., Aug. 29, 1939; s. Francis and Marian (Kantor) S. BA, Parsons U., 1965. Costume designer: (stage) The Time of the Cuckoo, 1974, (films) Play It As It Lays, 1972, The Last of Sheila, 1972, Blume In Love, 1973, Sleeper, 1973, The Prisoner of Second Avenue, 1975, Interiors, 1978; screenwriter: Car Wash, 1976, Sparkle, 1976, The Wiz, 1978; screenwriter, dir.: (films) D.C. Cab, 1983, St. Elmo's Fire, 1985, (TV movies) The Virginia Hill Story, 1974, Amateur Night at the Dixie Bar and Grill, 1979; dir.: The Incredible Shrinking Woman, 1981, The Lost Boys, 1987, Cousins, 1989, Flatliners, 1990, Dying Young, 1991, Falling Down, 1993, The Client, 1994, Batman Forever, 1995; exec. prodr.: Foxfire, 1985, Slow Burn, 1986; writer, exec. prodr.: (TV pilot) Now We're Cookin', 1983; prodn. designer: Killer Bees, 1974. Office: CAA 9830 Wilshire Blvd Beverly Hills CA 90212*

SCHUMACHER, JOHN CHRISTIAN, semiconductor materials and air pollution control equipment manufacturing company executive; b. Spring Valley, Ill., Feb. 8, 1935; s. Joseph Charles and Theresa Isobel (Flynn) S.; children: Jennifer Lea, Jesse Colin, Jacqueline Chanel. B.S., Stanford U., 1956; M.S., M.I.T., 1958; Ph.D., Stanford U., 1973. Research engr. Calif. Inst. Tech., 1958-60; research and teaching asst. M.I.T., 1960-62; dept. mgr. Lockheed Missile & Space Co., Sunnyvale, Calif., 1962-64, program mgr., Lockheed Research, Palo Alto, Calif., 1964-69; research asso., thesis dir. Stanford U., 1969-73; v.p. J. C. Schumacher Co., Oceanside, Calif., 1973-74, pres., 1974-76, pres., chief exec. officer, 1976-86, Diamond Cubic Corp., 1986-87; founder, pres., chief exec. officer, Custom Engineered Materials, Inc., 1987-92; founder J.C. Schumacher Assocs., Carlsbad, Calif., 1992—. Chmn. Oceanside New Bus. and Industry Commn., 1976-78. Mem. Oceanside C. of C. (dir. 1974-78), Electrochem. Soc., Newcomen Soc., IEEE, AAAS, Phys. Soc. Am., Am. Inst. Chem. Engrs. Republican. Club: La Jolla Country. Patentee improved semicondr. device processing materials and equipment; low cost silicon; energy efficient photovoltaic solar cell mfg., air pollution control equipment. Office: 6922 Carnation Dr Carlsbad CA 92009

SCHUMACHER, JON LEE, lawyer; b. Rochester, N.Y., Feb. 28, 1937; s. Howard Alexander and Ruth (Simmons) S.; m. Katherine Truesdell, Apr. 22, 1967; children: Sara Truesdell, Howard Alexander II. AB, Princeton U., 1959; JD, U. Va., 1964. Bar: N.Y. 1964. With Nixon, Hargrave, Devans & Doyle, Rochester, 1964—; mem. mgmt. com., 1986-90, mng. ptnr., 1988-90. Co-author Charitable Giving and Solicitation. Bd. dirs. officer Rochester Area Found., Inc., 1987-94; pres. Estate Planning Coun. Rochester, 1986-87. Lt. (j.g.) USNR, 1959-61. Fellow Am. Coll. Trusts and Estate Counsel; mem. ABA, N.Y. State Bar Assn. (exec. com. trusts and estates law sect. 1985-88, 94—), chmn. estate planning com. 1992-94, sec. 1995), Monroe County Bar Assn. (fedn. pres. 1995-96). Republican. Presbyterian. Clubs: Country of Rochester, Genesee Valley. Avocations: jogging, music. Home: 550 Allens Creek Rd Rochester NY 14618-3406 Office: Nixon Hargrave Devans & Doyle Clinton Sq PO Box 1051 Rochester NY 14603-1051

SCHUMACHER, JOSEPH CHARLES, chemical engineer; b. Peru, Ill., Sept. 15, 1911; s. Joseph F. and Josephine (Mattes) S.; m. Theresa Flynn, Jan. 28, 1933; children—John Christian, Kathleen Schumacher Hoffman, Stephen Joseph, Paul; m. Mary Margaret Maher, Jan. 5, 1985. Student, U. Ill., 1928-30; A.B., U. So. Calif., 1946. Research chemist, prodn. supr. Carus Chem. Co., LaSalle, Ill., 1931-40; research and devel. chem. engr. Fine Chems., Inc., Los Angeles, 1940-41; co-founder Western Electro-chem. Co., Los Angeles, 1941, v.p., dir. research, 1941-54, dir.; research Am. Potash & Chem. Corp., 1954-56, v.p. research, 1956-67; v.p. AFN Inc., 1956-67, Kerr-McGee Chem. Corp., 1967-69; founder J.C. Schumacher Co., Oceanside, Calif., 1971, pres., 1971-74, chmn. bd., 1974-86. Regional editor Electrochem. Soc. Jour., 1953-59; co-author, editor Perchlorates; mem. editorial adv. bd. Research Mgmt., 1963-69; contbr. articles to profl. jours.; patentee in chem. products, processes and apparatus. Trustee Whittier Coll., 1968-77. Recipient Honors award U. So. Calif. Chemistry Alumni Soc., 1962. Mem. Electrochem. Soc. (Vittorio de Nora Diamond Shamrock Engring. and Tech. gold medal 1982), Am. Chem. Soc., Planetary Soc., Sigma Xi, Phi Kappa Theta. Roman Catholic. Clubs: Los Angeles Country, Jonathan. Home and Office: 2220 Ave of Stars West Tower # 704 Los Angeles CA 90067

SCHUMACHER, LARRY P., health facility administrator; b. Waseca, Minn., Apr. 26, 1959; s. James H. and Judith A. (Voight) S.; m. Casey A. Hager, June 26, 1982; children: Matthew, Nicholas, Nathan, Mark. Diploma, Burge Sch. Nursing, 1980; BSN, S.W. Mo. State U., 1983; MS in Nursing, Ind. U., 1985. RN, Iowa; cert. nursing adminstr. advanced, 1989. Dir. critical care and med. nursing Rsch. Med. Ctr., Kansas City, Mo.; v.p. nursing and anesthesia St. Joseph Mercy Hosp., Mason City, Iowa; v.p. patient care svcs. Mercy Hosp., Mason City, Iowa; v.p. patient svcs., chief nursing officer North Iowa Mercy Health Ctr., Mason City; sr. v.p. clin. integration, chief nursing officer North Iowa Mercy Health Sys. Mem. ACHE, ANA, Nat. League Nursing, Am. Orgn. Nurse Execs. Home: 115 10th St NW Mason City IA 50401-2016

SCHUMACHER, ROBERT ALAN, forest products company executive; b. Marshall, Tex., Jan. 13, 1923; m. Dorothy Wemyss, July 23, 1945. B.A., U. Va., 1944. V.p. Groveton (N.H.) Paper Co., 1944-56; pres. Vanity Fair Paper Co., 1956-63; v.p. N.E. div. Ga.-Pacific Corp., Atlanta, 1963-74, sr. v.p. N.E. div., 1974-82, exec. v.p. pulp and paper, 1982-85, pres., chief operating officer, 1985—; also dir. Ga.-Pacific Corp.; dir. KeyCorp.; dir. at large U. Maine Pulp and Paper Found. Bd. dirs. New Canaan (Conn.) chpt. ARC; chmn. Heart Fund, Stamford, Darien and New Canaan, Conn., 1967; chmn. Cancer Fund, New Canaan, 1964; bd. dirs.-at-large U. Maine Pulp and Paper Found. Office: Ga-Pacific Corp 133 Peachtree St NE Atlanta GA 30303-1808

SCHUMACHER, ROBERT DENISON, banker; b. Evanston, Ill., Dec. 16, 1933; s. Frank Ade and Dorothy Ormonde (Hilton) S.; m. Mary Ann Montgomery, Aug. 25, 1956; children—Stephen Michael, Jeffrey Hilton. B.A., Williams Coll., 1956; postgrad., Grad. Bus. Sch. N.Y. U., 1957-59; P.M.D., Harvard Bus. Sch., 1966. With Irving Trust Co., N.Y.C., 1956-89, sr. v.p., 1977-89, mgr. adminstrv. services, 1987-89, ret., 1989. Treas. Calvary, Holy Communion and St. George's Episcopal Ch., 1976-79, warden, 1980-86, 89-93; trustee The Church Club, 1993—, treas., 1994—. Mem. The Church Club. Republican. Home: 431 E 20th St New York NY 10010-7502

SCHUMACHER, ROBERT JOSEPH, petroleum company executive; b. Independence, Kans., Mar. 7, 1929; s. Arthur V. and Margaret F. (Templeman) S.; m. Edith Katherine Kelly, Sept. 30, 1950; children: Mary Beth Schumacher Millett, Kathy, Kyle, William. BS in Commerce, Tex. Christian U., 1950; M Profl. Acctg., U. Tex., 1951. CPA, Tex. Staff acct. Sproles & Woodard, CPA's, Ft. Worth, 1950-52; sec., treas. Sojourner Drilling Corp., Abilene, Tex., 1952-68; ind. oil and gas operator, Ft. Worth, 1967-73; pres., chief exec. officer Texland Petroleum, Inc., Ft. Worth, 1973—; chmn., chief exec. officer Pride Refining, Inc., Abilene, 1989-93; pres., CEO Texland Petroleum Inc., Ft. Worth, Tex., 1973—; bd. dirs. Aztec Mfg. Co., Ft. Worth. Staff sgt. U.S. Army, 1946-48. Republican. Roman Catholic.

SCHUMACHER, WILLIAM JACOB, retired army officer; b. Scranton, Pa., Apr. 15, 1938; s. Jacob and Kathryn Isabel (Williams) S.; m. Sandra Dee Caryl, July 23, 1960; children: Caryl Lee, Leslie Karen. BSEE, Lafayette Coll., 1960; MS in Aerospace Engring., Pa. State U., 1970. Commd. 2d lt. U.S. Army, 1960, advanced through grades to brig. gen., 1989; asst. prof. dept. engring. U.S. Mil. Acad., West Point, N.Y., 1970-73; student Def. Systems Mgmt. Coll., Ft. Belvoir, Va., 1975; asst. project mgr. Office of Project Mgr., Rock Island (Ill.) Arsenal, 1976-78; asst. mgr. conventional ammunition and guided missiles div. Cannon Arty. Weapons System, Picatinny (N.J.) Arsenal, 1978-81; comdg. officer Iowa Army Ammunition Plant, Burlington, 1981-83; student U.S. Army War Coll., Carlisle, Pa., 1983-84; project mgr. for Hellfire U.S. Army Missile Command, Huntsville, Ala., 1984-87; program exec. officer Close Combat Missiles, Huntsville, 1987-88, Fire Support, Huntsville, 1988-90; dep. ammunition, asst. sec. army rsch., devel., acquisition Hdqrs. Army Materiel Command, Washington, 1990-92; dep. comdg. officer Strategic Def. Command, Huntsville, 1992; retired, tech. cons. Garber Internat. Assoc., Inc., Arlington, Va., 1992; gen. mgr. strategic systems Martin Marietta, Arlington, Va., 1992—. Mem. Assn. U.S. Army, Am. Def. Preparedness Assn., Phi Kappa Phi. Avocations: swimming, gardening, book collecting.

SCHUMAKER, CLARENCE JOSEPH, JR., sociologist, educator; b. Fogelsville, Pa., Aug. 25, 1936; s. Clarence Joseph and Frances Irene (Greenwalt) S.; m. M. Jane D. Boucher, June 10, 1961; children: Cheryl Yvonne, Clarence III, Darryl Emile. BA Sociology, La. Coll., Pineville, 1960; MS Sociology, Trinity U., San Antonio, 1962; MS Med. and Hosp. Adminstrn., U. Pitts., 1969; PhD Sociology, Catholic U. Am., 1980. Aerospace med. specialist England AFB USAF Hosp., La., 1955-60; chief patient personnel br. Lackland AFB USAF Hosp., Tex., 1960-61; chief ops. support divsn. Lackland AFB USAF Epidemiological Lab., Tex., 1961-64; dispensary adminstr. Sondrestrom AB Greenland, 1964-65; med. rsch. adminstr. Aeromed. Rsch. Lab. Wright Patterson AFB USAF, Ohio, 1965-66; chief adminstrv. svcs. USAF, 1966-67; adminstrv. resident Wright Patterson AFB USAF Med. Ctr., Ohio, 1968-69; chief support svcs. divsn. Wright Patterson AFB, 1969-72; assoc. adminstr. Clark AB USAF Hosp. Clark, Philippines, 1972-74; health svcs. adminstrv. officer Office Surgeon Gen. USAF, Washington, 1974-75; staff mem. Office Asst. Sec. Defense (Manpower Reserve Affairs and Logistics) U.S. Dept. Defense, Washington, 1975-76, dir. health studies task force Office Planning and Policy Analysis Office Asst. Sec. Defense (Health Affairs), 1976-80; assoc. prof. Extended Degree Programs Ctrl. Mich. U., 1980—; military cons. Health Svc. Studies and Analyses to Sugeon Gen. USAF, 1979; adj. asst. prof. Dept. Family Practice, Sch. Medicine, Uniformed Svcs. Univ. Health Scis., Bethesda, Md., 1981—; Park Coll. Extension program. Ft. Meyer, Va., 1978—, So. Ill. U., 1981—, Bowie (Md.) State Coll., L.A. C.C., 1973-74, U. Md., 1964, Wright State U., 1966-72, Miami Valley Hosp. Sch. Nursing, 1970; rschr. in field, mem. various rsch. teams; spkr. in field. Author, co author numerous articles, audio cassettes in field. Recipient Legion of Merit, 1980, Joint Svc. Commendation medal with oak leaf cluster, 1973, 76, AF commendation medal with oak leaf cluster, 1967, 72, meritorious svc. medal, 1974. Mem. APHA, Am. Coll. Healthcare Execs., Am. Sociol. Assn., Am. Acad. Polit. and Social Scis., Assn. Univ. Programs Health Adminstrn., Alpha Kappa Delta, Pi Gamma Mu. Avocations: golf, motorcycling, reading, collecting B westerns. Home: 5407 Pizarro Ct Clinton MD 20735-2325 Office: Ctrl Mich Univ Wash DC Region 8110 Gatehouse Rd Ste 500 W Falls Church VA 22042-1210

SCHUMAKER, DALE H., paper manufacturing company executive; b. 1933. BS, U. Wis., 1955. Engr. Am. Can Co., Neenah, Wis., 1955-65; with Appleton (Wis.) Papers, Inc., 1965—, v.p. mfg., 1965-79, 1979-84, sr. v.p. mfg., 1984-85, exec. v.p., 1985-86, pres., chief operating officer, 1986—, also bd. dirs. Office: Appleton Papers Inc 825 E Wisconsin Ave Appleton WI 54911-3873

SCHUMAKER, LARRY LEE, mathematics educator; b. Aberdeen, S.D., Nov. 5, 1939; s. Lee B. and Irene Elizabeth (Kelly) S.; m. Gerda Ingeborg Boguszewski, June 10, 1963; 1 child, Annabel Louise. BS in Math., S.D. Sch. of Mines, 1961; MS in Math., Stanford U., 1962, PhD in Math., 1966. Staff mathematician Hughes Aircraft Co., Culver City, Calif., 1961-63; research asst. Stanford U., 1964-65, instr. computer sci. dept., 1966; research mem. Math. Research Ctr., U. Wis., Madison, 1966-68; asst. prof. to assoc. prof. U. Tex., 1968-74, prof. of math., 1974-79; prof. math. Tex. A&M U., 1981-88; dir. Ctr. for Approximation Theory Texas A&M U., 1981-88; prof. of math. Vanderbilt U., Nashville, 1988—; visiting prof. and researcher in field. Author: Approximation Functions, 1967, Approximation Theory I, 1973, Approximation Theory II, 1976, Spline Functions: Basic Theory, 1980, Approximation Theory IV, 1983, Approximation Theory V, 1986, Topics in Multivariate Approximation, 1987, Mathematical Methods in Computer-aided Geometric Design, 1989, Approximation Theory VI, 1989, Approximation Theory VI, Part II, 1989, Approximation Theory VII, 1992, Curves and Surfaces, 1991, Mathematical Methods in Computer-aided Geometric Design II, 1992, Numerical Methods of Approximation Theory, Vol. 9, 1992, Recent Advances in Wavelets, 1993, Curves and Surfaces in Geometric Design, 1994, Wavelets, Images, and Surface Fitting, 1994. Recipient Humboldt Prize Humboldt Found., 1989, Centennial Outstanding Grad. award S.D. Sch. Mines and Tech., 1985, Student Coun. Tchg. Excellence award Tex. A&M U., 1981; named Humboldt fellow, 1978-79. Mem. Soc. for Indsl. & Applied Math., Am. Math. Soc., The Math. Assn. Am.. Office: Vanderbilt U Dept Of Math Nashville TN 37240

SCHUMAN, ALLAN L., chemical company executive; b. 1937. BS, NYU, 1955. With Ecolab Inc., St. Paul, 1957—, v.p. mktg. and nat. acctg., 1972-78, v.p. mktg. devel., 1978-79, now exec. v.p., pres. Ecolab Svcs. Group. Office: Ecolab Inc Ecolab Ctr Saint Paul MN 55102

SCHUMAN, GERALD EUGENE, soil scientist; b. Sheridan, Wyo., July 5, 1944; s. George and Mollie (Michael) S.; m. Mabel F. Kaisler, Mar. 27, 1965; children: William G., Kara L. BS in Soil Sci., U. Wyo., 1966; MS in Soil Sci., U. Nev., 1969; PhD in Agronomy, U. Nebr., 1974. Cert. profl. soil scientist. Soil scientist USDA Agrl. Rsch. Svc., Reno, 1966-69, Lincoln, Nebr., 1969-75; soil scientist USDA Agrl. Rsch. Svc., Cheyenne, Wyo., 1975-77, soil scientist, rsch. leader, 1977—; reclamation cons. HKM Assocs.,

Billings, Mont., 1986-88. Co-editor: Reclaiming Mine Soils, 1987, symposium proc. Soil and Overburden in Reclamation, 1983; contbr. articles to profl. jours., book chpts. Mem., pres. elder, trustee Our Savior Luth. Ch., Cheyenne, 1975—. Recipient Profl. of Yr. award Orgn. Profl. Employees of USDA, 1988. Fellow Am. Soc. Agronomy (cert.), Soil and Water Conservation Soc. (bd. dirs. 1986-89, commendation 1980), Soil Sci. Soc. Am.; mem. Am. Soc. Surface Mining and Reclamation (nat. exec. com. 1991-93, Reclamation rsch. award 1991, pres. 1992-93), Soc. for Range Mgmt. (Man of the Range award Wyo. sect. 1993, Outstanding Achievement award 1994), Internat. Soil Sci. Soc. Avocations: fishing, hunting, traveling. Office: High Plains Grasslands Rsch Sta 8408 Hildreth Rd Cheyenne WY 82009-8809

SCHUMAN, HOWARD, sociologist, educator; b. Cin., Mar. 16, 1928; s. Robert A. and Esther (Bohn) S.; m. Josephine Miles, Sept. 1, 1951; children—Marc, Elisabeth. David. Student, U. Chgo., 1947-48; A.B., Antioch Coll., 1953; M.S. in Psychology, Trinity U., 1956; Ph.D. in Sociology, Harvard, 1961. Research asso. Harvard, 1961-64; asst. prof. U. Mich., Ann Arbor, 1964-67; asso. prof. U. Mich., 1967-71, prof. sociology, 1971—, chmn. dept., 1970-73, dir. Detroit Area Study, 1965-71, program dir. Survey Research Ctr., 1974—, dir. Survey Research Ctr., 1982-90. Author: (with others) Economic Development and Individual Change, Racial Attitudes in Fifteen American Cities, Conversations at Random, Black Racial Attitudes, Questions and Answers in Attitude Surveys, Racial Attitudes in America. Served with AUS, 1954-56. Fellow Am. Acad. Arts and Scis.; mem. Am. Sociol. Soc., Am. Assn. for Pub. Opinion Rsch. (pres. 1985-86). Home: HC 31 Box 477 Phippsburg ME 04562

SCHUMAN, NANCY KATHLEEN, secondary education educator; b. Cleve., May 26, 1946; d. Ralph Henry and Eola Kathleen (Land) S. BA, Wellesley Coll., 1968; MA F.I.S., Cleve. State U., 1988. Cert. tchr., Ohio. Clk. Warner & Swasey Co., Solon, Ohio, 1968-70; bookkeeper J.H. Hinz Co., Cleve., 1970-73; tchr. music Bedford (Ohio) City Schs., 1973—; dir. handbell choirs St. Andrew Episcopal Ch., Mentor, Ohio, 1980—; singer Cleve. Orch. Chorus, 1973-89. Mem. Am. Guild English Handbell Ringers, Mensa, Christian Coalition, Phi Beta (chpt. treas. 1990-95, nat. treas. 1992-95, spl. recognition award 1994). Republican. Episcopalian. Avocations: reading, horseback riding, travel. Home: 5481-D Millwood Ln Willoughby OH 44094 Office: Aurora Upper Intermediate Sch 24200 Aurora Rd Bedford Heights OH 44146

SCHUMANN, WILLIAM HENRY, III, financial executive; b. Iowa City, Aug. 28, 1950; s. William Henry Jr. and Eunice Vere (Doak) S.; m. Denise Suzane Hargrove, Sept. 29, 1979; children: Stefanie Lynn, John William, Kimberly Ann, Robert William. BS, UCLA, 1972; MS, U. So. Calif., 1973. Program mgmt. analyst Hughes Helicopters, Culver City, Calif., 1973-75; mgr. fin. planning Sunkist Growers, Sherman Oaks, Calif., 1975-81; dir. North Am. Ops. Agrl. Chem. Group, FMC Corp., Chgo., 1981—; bd. dirs. Gt. Lakes Advisors. Republican. Office: FMC Corp Agrl Chem Group 1735 Market St Philadelphia PA 19103

SCHUMER, CHARLES ELLIS, congressman; b. Brooklyn, N.Y., Nov. 23, 1950; s. Abraham and Selma (Rosen) S.; m. Iris Weinshall, 1980; 1 child, Jessica Emily. BA magna cum laude, Harvard U., 1971, J.D. with honors, 1974. Bar: N.Y. 1975. Mem. staff U.S. Senator Claiborne Pell, 1973; assoc. Paul, Weiss, Rifking, Wharton and Garrison, 1974; mem. N.Y. State Assembly, 1975-80, chmn. subcom. on city mgmt. and governance, 1977, chmn. com. on oversight and investigation, 1979; mem. 97th-98th Congresses from 16th N.Y. Dist., 99th-104th Congresses from 10th (now 9th) N.Y. dist., Washington, D.C., 1985—; mem. Banking & Fin. Svcs. Com., ranking minority mem. jud. subcom. on crime. Mem. B'nai Brith, Phi Beta Kappa. Democrat. Jewish. Office: US House of Reps Rayburn House Office Bldg Rm 2211 Washington DC 20515*

SCHUMER, WILLIAM, surgeon, educator; b. Chgo., June 29, 1926; s. Solomon and Gussie (Gross) S.; children—Scott, Fern. M.B., Chgo. Med. Sch., 1949, M.D., 1950; M.S., U. Ill., 1966. Diplomate: Am. Bd. Surgery. Intern Mt. Sinai Hosp. Med. Center, Chgo., 1949-50; resident Mt. Sinai Hosp. Med. Center, 1950-54; asst. prof. surgery Chgo. Med. Sch., 1959-65, asst. prof. cardiovascular research, 1964-65; attending surgeon, then asst. chief surgery Mt. Sinai Hosp., Chgo., 1962-65; attending surgeon Hines (Ill.) VA Hosp., 1960-63, VA West Side Hosp., Chgo., 1963-64; dir. surg. service U. Calif. at Davis, Sacramento County Med. Center, 1965-67; chief surg. service VA West Side Hosp., 1967-75; assoc. prof. surgery faculty Abraham Lincoln Sch. Medicine, U. Ill., Chgo., 1967-69; prof. surgery Abraham Lincoln Sch. Medicine, U. Ill., 1969-75; prof. biol. chemistry Grad. Coll., U. Ill. Med. Center, Chgo., 1974-75; mem. staff U. Ill. Hosp., 1967-75; surgery, chmn. dept. U. HEalth Scis./Chgo. Med. Sch., North Chicago, Ill., 1975-90, disting. prof., 1990—; chief surg. service North Chicago VA Med. Center, 1975-79, attending surgeon, 1979-80, chief gen. surg. sect., 1980-82, attending surg. sect., 1983—; chmn. dept. surgery Mt. Sinai Med. Center, Chgo., 1990—; prof. biochemistry U. Health Scis. Chgo. Med. Sch., 1977—; also prof. critical care medicine, disting. prof., 1990—; Mem. numerous coms. VA. Co-editor: Corticosteroids in the Treatment of Shock: Principles and Practice, 1974, Advances in Shock Research, Vol. 2, 1979, Vol. 4, 1980, Vol. 6, 1981, Molecular and Cellular Aspects of Shock and Trauma, Vol. 3, 1983-88; assoc. editor: Circulatory Shock, 1976-79, editor, 1979-88, cons. editor, 1988—; contbr. numerous articles to profl. jours, chpts. to books. Recipient Disting. Alumnus award, 1974, Honors Achievement award Angiology Research Found., 1965, Morris L. Parker award for meritorious research Chgo. Med. Sch., 1976; also numerous awards for sci. exhibits and films. Mem. AAAS, AAUP, ACS, AMA, Am. Assn. Surgery of Trauma, Am. Physiol. Soc., Am. Surg. Assn., Assn. Am. Med. Colls., Assn. VA Surgeons (pres. 1976), Ctrl. Soc. Clin. Rsch., Ctrl. Surg. Soc., Midwest Surg. Soc., Ill. Surg. Soc., Chgo. Shock Soc. (pres. 1978-79), Collegium Internat. Chirurgiae Digestivae, Digestive Disease Found., Inst. Medicine Chgo., N.Y. Acad. Scis., Reticuloendothelial Soc., Soc. Internat. de Chirurgie, Soc. Surgery Alimentary Tract, Soc. Critical Care Medicine, Internat. Fedn. Surg. Colls., Soc. Univ. Surgeons, Surg. Infection Soc., Warren H. Cole Soc., Alumni Assn. U. Ill., Alumni Assn. Chgo. Med. Sch. (pres. Chgo. chpt.), Minn. Surg. Soc. (hon.), Sigma Xi, Alpha Omega Alpha. Office: Mt Sinai Hosp Med Ctr U Health Scis Chgo Med Sch California Ave at 15th St Chicago IL 60608

SCHUMM, STANLEY ALFRED, geologist, educator; b. Kearny, N.J., Feb. 22, 1927; s. Alfred Henry and Mary Elizabeth (Murdock) S.; m. Ethel Patricia Radli, Sept. 3, 1950; children: Brian Murdock, Mary Theresa, Christine Ann. BA, Upsala Coll., 1950; PhD, Columbia U., 1955. Research geologist U.S. Geol. Survey, Denver, 1955-67; prof. geology Colo. State U., Ft. Collins, 1967-86, Univ. disting. prof., 1986—, acting asso. dean, 1973-74; vis. prof. U. Calif., Berkeley, 1959-60, U. Witwatersrand, South Africa, 1975; fellow U. Sydney, Australia, 1964-65, U. New South Wales, 1988; vice chmn. U.S. Nat. Com. Quaternary Research, 1967-70, 1975-82; dist. vis. scientist U. Tex., 1970; vis. lectr. numerous univs. in U.S., vis. scientist N.Z., Europe, Can., Venezuela, Brazil; vis. scientist Polish Acad. Sci., 1969; cons. to govt. agys., engring. firms; prin. geomorphologist, dir. Water Engring. Tech., Davis, Calif., and Ft. Collins, Colo., 1980-91; sr. assoc. Resource Cons. and Engrs., Ft. Collins; prin. investigator research projects NSF, 1969-92, Colo. Agrl. Expt. Sta., 1970-75, Army Research Office, 1970-80, 1982-93, Office Water Research and Tech., 1974-83, Nat. Park Service, 1975-77, Fed. Hwy. Adminstrn., 1978-80, Soil Conservation Service, 1980-85, NASA, 1984-88, Smithsonian Inst., 1986-87, Can. Internat. Devel. Agy., 1991-92. Author: The Fluvial System, 1977, To Interpret the Earth, 1991; co-author: Incised Channels, 1984, Geomorphology, 1985, Experimental Fluvial Geomorphology, 1987; editor: United States Contribution to Quaternary Research, 1969, Rover Morphology, 1972, Slope Morphology, 1973, Drainage Basin Morphology, 1977, Physical Geography of W.M. Davis, 1980, The Variability of Large Alluvial Rivers, 1994; contbr. chpts. to textbooks, articles to profl. jours. Served with USNR, 1944-45. Recipient Disting. Alumnus award Upsala Coll., 1980, L.W. Durrell award Colo. State U., 1980, Linton award Brit. Geomorphology Research Group, 1981, Warren Prize Nat. Acad. Sci., 1986; Harkness fellow U. Canterbury, N.Z., 1983; fellow Japanese Soc. for Advancement of Sci., 1983, Dept. Agr., Republic of South Africa, 1984, Australian Nat. U., 1988; named honor scientist, Colo. State U. chpt. Sigma Xi, 1986. Fellow AAAS, Geol. Soc. Am. (asso. editor 1973-75, vice chmn. geomorphology div. 1978-79, chmn.

1979-80, Kirk Bryan award 1979); mem. Am. Geophys. Union (Horton award 1958, assoc. editor 1973-75), ASCE, Internat. Geog. Union, Assn. Am. Geographers, Internat. Assn. Quaternary Research, Am. Quaternary Assn. (councillor), Sigma Xi (pres. Colo. State U. chpt. 1987-88, honor scientist 1987). Home: 1308 Rollingwood Ln Fort Collins CO 80525-1946 Office: Colo State U Dept Earth Resources Fort Collins CO 80525 also: Ayres Assocs 3665 JF Kennedy Pky Fort Collins CO 80527

SCHUNK, DALE HANSEN, psychology educator; b. Chgo., Aug. 14, 1946; s. Elmer Charles and Mildred Augusta (Hansen) S.; m. Caryl S. Cook; 1 child, Laura. BS, U. Ill.-Urbana, 1968; MEd, Boston U., 1974; PhD, Stanford U., 1979. With NATO, Naples, Italy, 1970-74; teaching asst. Stanford U., 1975, rsch. asst., 1975-79; prof. ednl. psychology U. Houston, 1979-86, U. N.C., 1986—; ednl. cons. Spring Branch Sch. Dist., Houston, 1981—. Contbr. articles to profl. jours. Capt. USAF, 1968-74. Spencer Found. rsch. grantee, 1980, 84, 89; NSF rsch. grantee, 1980, 85. Mem. AAAS, Am. Psychol. Assn. (Early Contbns. to Ednl. Psychology award 1982), N.Y. Acad. Sci., Am. Ednl. Rsch. Assn., Soc. Rsch. in Child Devel. Home: 104 Pitchpine Ln Chapel Hill NC 27514-1640 Office: U NC Sch Edn Peabody Hall CB 3500 Chapel Hill NC 27599

SCHUPAK, LESLIE ALLEN, public relations company executive; b. Spokane, Wash., Apr. 5, 1945; s. Leo and Henrietta (Neumann) S.; m. Dianne Barbara Goldin, June 23, 1968; 1 child, Adam J. BS, Boston U., 1967, MS, 1971. Asst. to pres., account exec. Sperber Assocs., Inc., Boston, 1968-69; account supr. Wilcox & Williams, N.Y.C., 1969-70; v.p., mgr. Daniel J. Edelman, Inc., N.Y.C., 1970-72; mng. ptnr. Kanan, Corbin, Schupak & Aronow, Inc., N.Y.C., 1972—. Pres. Whippoorwill Lake Property Owners Assn., Chappaqua, N.Y., 1984-88. With U.S. Army, 1968-73. Mem. Nat. Investor Rels. Inst., Donald Ross Soc., Metropolis Country Club (White Plains, N.Y.), Met. Golf Assn. Avocations: golf; tennis; fly fishing. Home: 2 Whippoorwill Close Chappaqua NY 10514-2330 Office: KCS&A Pub Rels 820 2nd Ave New York NY 10017-4504

SCHUPP, RONALD IRVING, clergyman, civil rights leader; b. Syracuse, N.Y., Dec. 10, 1951; s. George August and Shirley Louise (Mitchell) S. Ordained ministry, Old Country Ch., 1972; ordained Bapt. ministry, 1976; cert., Moody Bible Inst., 1986; advanced cert., Evang. Tng. Assn., 1992. Missionary, asst. pastor The Old Country Ch. Inc., Chgo., 1972-76; missionary Solid Rock Bapt. Ch., Chgo., 1976-89, Marble Rock Missionary Bapt. Ch., Chgo., 1990—; asst. dir. Uptown Community Orgn., Chgo., 1974-76; dir. Chgo. Action Ctr., 1978-80; bd. dirs. West Englewood United Orgn./Clara's House Shelter, 1991-95 (Recipient Appreciation award, 1992), assoc. chaplain, 1991-95; mem. steering com. 1st Congl. Dist. Ministerial Assn., Chgo., 1993-95, chair housing com., 1993-95. Contbr. articles and poems to numerous periodicals. Mem. Nat. Coalition for the Homeless, 1991—, Nat. Union of the Homeless, 1992—, Chgo. Coalition for the Homeless, 1988—, vol. organizer, 1988-94, mem. empowerment adv. com., 1991-94; mem. Homeless on the Move for Equality, 1990-92, bd. dirs., 1991-92; mem. Chgo. Peace Coun., 1984-87, Voice of Homeless, San Jose, Calif., 1993—, Kansas City Union of Homeless, 1993—; active Pledge of Resistance, Chgo. 1985—; rep. Chgo. Welfare Rights Orgn., 1986-88; activist Chgo. Clergy and Laity Concerned, 1981-87; founding mem. People's Campaign for Jobs, Housing and Food, Chgo., 1992—, chaplain, 1992—; founding mem., missionary People's Ministry Without Walls, Chgo., 1993—; rep. Lakota Nat. Organizing Com., 1993—, League of Indigenous Sovereign Nations of Western Hemisphere, 1993—; representative Alaska Elders Conference, Alaska, 1994—; pres., co-founder Citizens Taking Action, Chgo., 1995—, chair, steering com., 1995—, mem. action com., 1995—; mem., nat. organizer and outreach coord. Nat. People's Campaign, 1995—. Recipient letter of commendation Chgo. Fire Dept., 1983, proclamations Mayor Richard M. Daley, Chgo., 1991, 92, 93, 94, Mayor Joan Barr, Evanston, Ill., 1993, Mayor Lorraine H. Morton, Evanston, 1994, letters of support for anti-apartheid and related work Operation Push 1985-1993, Yogesh K. Gandhi 1987, 1994, Nat. Black United Front, 1989, Cesar Chavez, 1990, NAACP, 1991, Indian Treaty Rights Com., Chgo., 1993, Am. Indian Ctr., Chgo., 1993, Am. Indian Movement, Chgo., 1994, various U.S. senators and congresspersons 1990-93, Coretta Scott King, 1992, Nelson Mandela, Archbishop Desmond Tutu, Janusz Ziolkowski, 1993, The Dalai Lama, 1994; commendation resolution Chgo. City Coun., 1993, South African elections vigil support resolution Chgo. City Coun., 1994; tribute in congl. record Congressman Bobby L. Rush, 1993, Sen. Carol Moseley Braun, 1994; initiated Wa-kin-ya-wicha-ho Thunder Voice by trad. Lakota Elders, 1993; initiated Kiyuyakki Aurora by Inuit Elder Etok, 1994. Mem. Operation Push, Inc., 1985— (citation 1990), NAACP, ACLU, Chgo. Free South Africa (steering com. 1994-94), World Jewish Congress (diplomat), Transafrica. Democrat. Avocations: bicycle riding, poetry. Home and Office: 6412 N Hoyne Ave Apt 3A Chicago IL 60645-5638 *Look inward and see your soul, look outward and serve humanity.*

SCHUR, JEFFREY, advertising executive; b. Capetown, Cape of Good Hope, Union of South Africa, May 3, 1946; Canadian citizen; came to U.S., 1992; s. Lionel Harry and Dorothy (Siman) S.; m. Lucille Stella Breakey, Nov. 30, 1965; children: David Leon, Cynthia-Jean. Diploma in Mktg., Cape Coll. for Advanced Tech., Capetown, 1970. Account exec. J. Walter Thompson, Capetown and Johannesburg, Republic of South Africa, 1969-71; account dir. Ogilvy & Mather, Johannesburg, 1971-76; internat. vp. Latin Am. base Ogilvy & Mather, N.Y.C., 1976-78; account dir. Ogilvy & Mather, Toronto, Ont., Can., 1978-80; sr. gen. mgr., pres. Saatchi & Saatchi, Toronto, 1980-84; pres., chief exec. officer Needham Harper Can., Toronto, 1985-86, Doner Schur Peppler & Assocs., Toronto, 1986-89, Doner Schur Peppler, Toronto, 1989-92; exec. v.p. Earle Palmer Brown, N.Y.C., 1992-94; ptnr. Doig, Elliott, Schur Inc., N.Y.C., 1994—. Dir. Outward Bound, Toronto, 1980-83, Can. Liver Found., Toronto, 1984-86, Toronto Family Svc. Assn., 1985, York Mills Valley Assn., Toronto, 1990-92, Children's Aid, Toronto, 1991-92, S.A. Defence Forces 1st Parachute Bn., 1964-73. Mem. Chartered Inst. Mktg. (lectr. 1971-73, examiner 1973-74, edn. chmn. 1974-75, rsch. award 1970), Devil's Glen Club, Royal Marsh Harbour Yacht Club. Avocations: skiing, scuba, literature, gardening. Office: Doig Elliott Schur Inc 58A W 15th St New York NY 10011

SCHUR, LEON MILTON, educator, economist; b. Milw., Jan. 11, 1923; s. Ben and Bertha (Stein) S.; m. Edith Laiken, Sept. 4, 1949; children—Julie Miriam, Claudia Laiken, Amy Ruth. Student, U. Wis., 1941-43, Dartmouth, 1943-44; B.A., U. Wis., 1946, Ph.D., 1955. From instr. to prof. econs. La. State U., 1954-64; prof. econs., dir. Ctr. Econ. Edn. U. Wis., Milw., 1964—, acting chancellor, 1979-80, chmn. dept. econs., 1987—; vis. prof. Tulane U., 1961, U. Wis., 1962; dir. Univ. Nat. Bank., Wis. Coun. Econ. Edn., 1964—. Contbr. articles to profl. jours. Bernard F. Sliger chair econ. edn. Fla. State U., 1989—; dir. Discovery World Mus. Sci., Econs. and Tech., 1978—. From seaman to lt. (j.g.) USNR, 1943-46. Mem. Am. Econ. Assn., Am. Finance Assn., Am. Assn. U. Profs., Wis. Econ. Assn. (pres. 1975-77), Phi Eta Sigma, Beta Gamma Sigma. Jewish. Home: 173 W Suburban Dr Milwaukee WI 53217-2336

SCHUR, SUSAN DORFMAN, state legislator; b. Newark, Feb. 27, 1940; d. Norman and Jeanette (Handelman) Dorfman; children: Diana Elisabeth, Erica Marlene. BA, Goucher Coll., 1961. Adminstr. fed. housing, fgn. aid, anti-poverty programs, 1961-67; mem. Mass. Housing Appeals Com., 1977-86; mem., v.p. Bd. of Alderman, Newton, Mass., 1974-81; mem. Mass. Ho. of Reps., 1981-94. Mem. Newton Dem. City Com., 1970—.

SCHURE, ALEXANDER, retired university chancellor; b. Can., Aug. 4, 1921; s. Harry Joshua and Bessie (Ginsberg) S.; m. Dorothy Rubin, Dec. 8, 1943 (dec. June 1981); children: Barbara, Matthew, Louis, Jonathan; m. Gail Doris Strollo, Sept. 12, 1984. A.S.T. in Elec. Engring, Pratt Inst., 1943; B.S., CCNY, 1947; M.A., N.Y. U., 1948, Ph.D. 1950, Ed.D., 1953; D.Engring. Sci., Nova U., 1975; DSc, N.Y. Inst. Tech., 1976; LL.D., Boca Raton Coll., 1976, L.I. U., 1983; L.H.D., Columbia Coll., Calif., 1983; D of Pedagogy, N.Y. Chiropractic Coll., 1985. Asst. dir. Melville Radio Insts., N.Y.C., 1945-48; pres. Crescent Sch. Radio and Televison, Bklyn., 1948-55, Crescent Electronics Corp., Bklyn., 1951-55, N.Y. Tech. Inst., Bklyn., 1953-55; pres., chancellor N.Y. Inst. Tech., 1955-91, chancellor emeritus, 1991—; founder Computer Graphics Lab N.Y Inst. Tech., 1985—; chancellor, CEO, Nova U., 1970-85; mem. Fla. State Bd. Ind. Colls. and Univs., 1991—; pres. Vidbits, Inc.; dir. Seversky Electronatom Corp., Executone Inc; cons. N.Y.

State Dept. Edn., U.S. Office Edn., UNESCO; mem. Regents Regional Coordinating Council for Post-Secondary Edn. in N.Y.C., 1973—; Nassau County Consortia on Higher Edn., L.I., 1971—; Alfred P. Sloan Found. adv. com. for expanding minority opportunities in engring., 1974; rep. to Nat. Assn. State Adv. Council, 1975—; chmn. N.Y. Title IV Adv. Council, 1975-77; mem. steering com. L.I. Regional Adv. Council, 1974—; chair Regents Adv. Council on Learning Techs., 1986-88; mem., trustee exec. com. Commn. Ind. Colls. and Univs.; mem. adv. council learning technologies N.Y. State Dept. Edn., 1982—; mem. Accreditation Task Force for Council on Postsecondary Accreditation/SHEEBO Project on Assessing Long Distance Learning Via Telecommunications (Project ALLTEL), 1982—; mem. N.Y. State Motion Picture and TV adv. bd., chairperson tech. com.; dir. numerous research projects; expert witness Ho. Reps. com. of Commn. on Sci. and Astronautics; mem. Fla. State Bd. Ind. Colls. and Univs. Author and-or editor textbooks, film producer; designer automatic teaching machine; built one of first computer-controlled anthropomorphic speech devices, 1959; patentee in field. Pres. bd. dirs., trustee L.I. Ednl. TV Coun., Garden City; bd. dirs. Coun. Higher Ednl. Instns., N.Y.C., 1973-83. Served with Signal Corps AUS, 1942-45. 1st inductee Fine Arts Mus. of Long Island's Computer Hall of Fame, 1986. Mem. IEEE (L.I. sect. Gruenwald award 1988), N.Y. Acad. Sci., Am. Inst. Engring. Edn., N.E.A., Electronic Industries Assn. (chmn. task force curriculum devel.), Phi Delta Kappa, Delta Mu Delta, Eta Kappa Nu. Office: NY Inst Tech Office Chancellor Emeritus Old Westbury NY 11568 *The world is an ever changing, ever challenging reality, filled with opportunities for individual fulfillment and success. A positive philosophy toward life does much to make the realization of individual potential an actuality.*

SCHURE, MATTHEW, college president; b. N.Y.C., May 26, 1948; s. Alexander and Dorothy (Rubin) S.; m. Judith Z. Birchman, Aug. 12, 1973; children: Jared, Deborah. BA magna cum laude with high honors in Psychology, Queens Coll., 1969; MA, Columbia U., 1970, MPH, 1976, PhD, 1976. Lic. psychologist, N.Y. Mem. faculty N.Y. Inst. Tech., Old Westbury, 1969—, research assoc., instr., asst. prof., assoc. prof. behavioral scis., 1969-70, counselor, 1970-72, assoc. dir. Human Resources Devel. Ctr., 1973-77, assoc. dean acad. assessment, 1977-78, dir. Human Resources Devel. Ctr., 1978-81, pres., 1982—; dep. provost, chmn. dept. community medicine N.Y. Coll. Osteo. Medicine, 1981-91. Author: Hannah's Trial: Our Triumph Over Infertility, 1981; contbr. articles and papers in field to profl. pubs. Trustee Commn. on Ind. Colls. and Univs.; 1983-86; St. Barnabas Hosp., L.I. Regional Adv. Coun. on Higher Edn.; chmn. bd. trustees N.Y. State Higher Edn. Svcs. Corp., 1993—; mem. N.Y. State Coun. on Problem Gambling, 1995; chmn. program com. Pvt. Industry Coun., Town of Oyster Bay. Mem. APA, Nassau County Psychol. Assn., Am. Assn. Colls. of Osteo. Medicine (trustee), Phi Beta Kappa. Office: NY Inst Tech PO Box 8000 Old Westbury NY 11568-8000

SCHURMAN, DAVID JAY, orthopaedic surgeon, educator; b. Chgo., Apr. 25, 1940; s. Shepherd P. and Dorothy (Laskey) S.; m. Martha Ellen Rocker, Mar. 8, 1967; children: Hilary Sue, Theodore Shepherd. BA, Yale U., 1961; MD, Columbia U., 1965. Intern Baylor U., Houston, 1965-67; resident in gen. surgery Mt. Sinai Hosp., N.Y.C., 1966-67; resident in orthop. surgery UCLA, 1969-72; asst. rsch. surgeon UCLA Med. Sch., 1972-73; asst. prof. orthopedic surgery Stanford Med. Sch., 1973-79, assoc. prof., 1979-87, prof., 1987—. Capt. USAF, 1967-69. Fellow NIH, 1972-73; grantee NIH, 1976—. Mem. Am. Orthopaedic Assn. (bd. dirs. 1994-95), Clin. Orthopaedics and Related Rsch. (bd. dirs. 1994-95). Office: Stanford U Sch of Medicine R146 Divsn Orthop Surgery 300 Pasteur Dr Stanford CA 94305

SCHURMAN, DONALD PETER, hospital administrator; b. Humboldt, Sask., Can., Mar. 7, 1947; married. BA, U. Sask., 1969; MA, U. Alta., 1978. Sr. v.p. ops. Extendicare Ltd. Toronto, Ont., Can., 1978-81, exec. v.p., 1984-85; exec. dir. Dept. Social Svc., Regina, Sask., Can., 1981; administr. Plains Health Ctr., Regina, Sask., Can., 1981-84; v.p. ops. U. Alta. Hosps., Edmonton, Alta., Can., 1985-87, pres., 1987—; adj. educator in field. Contbr. articles to profl. jours. Home: 14815-45 Ave, Edmonton, AB Canada T6H 5R4 Office: University of Alberta Hospitals, 8440 112th St, Edmonton, AB Canada T6G 2B7

SCHURMAN, JOSEPH RATHBORNE, lawyer; b. N.Y.C., Jan. 5, 1924; s. Jacob Gould and Mary (Cushman) S.; m. Evelyn F. Donoghue, Oct. 21, 1950; children: Elizabeth, Mary, Joseph Jr., Holbrook. Student, Cornell U., 1941-43, U. Minn., 1944; JD, Harvard U., 1949. Bar: N.Y. 1949, Md. 1961. Sole practice Rochester, N.Y., 1949-56; atty. Dept. Army, 1956-58, NSF, 1958-69; gen. counsel NEH, Washington, 1969-82; sec. Nat. Council on Humanities, 1969-82; sole practice N.Y.C. and Md., 1982-94; v.p. Unicorn Rafting Expeditions Inc., Brunswick, Maine, 1984—; cons. Commn. on Govt. Procurement, 1970-72. Mem. N.Y. State Bar Assn., Md. Bar Assn. Roman Catholic. Home and Office: 17 Hesketh St Bethesda MD 20815-4224

SCHURMEIER, L. JON, health care executive; b. Elgin, Ill., Feb. 17, 1937; s. LeRoy H. and June (Zorn) S.; BA, DePauw U., Greencastle, Ind., 1959; MBA, U. Pitts., 1960, MHA, 1970; m. Donna Kay Cunningham, Apr. 1, 1961; children: Kristin, Darla, Steffany. From merchandiser to mgr. Carson Pirie Scott & Co., Chgo., 1963-68; administr. extern Presbyn.-St. Luke's Hosp., Chgo., 1968-69; administr. resident, then asst. administr. Cin. Gen. Hosp., 1969-72; assoc. administr. S.W. Gen. Hosp., Middleburg Heights, Ohio, 1972-81, administr., 1981-83, system pres., 1983—. Adj. clin. prof. U. Pitts.; officer Hudson Younglife, 1981-85; bd. dirs. Westside Imaging Ctr., Hospac, Hudson Girls-Womens Softball League, 1980-89; village councilman, 1984; bd. dirs. Quality Info. Mgmt. Corp. With U.S. Army, 1961-63. Recipient recognition award Seven Hills Neighborhood Houses, Cin., 1972. Fellow Am. Coll. Healthcare Execs. (bd. regents Ohio chpt. 1989-92); mem. Hosp. Fin. Mgmt. Assn., Am. Pub. Health Assn., Ohio Hosp. Assn. (chmn. N.E. Ohio dist., bd. dirs., Ohio dir. health opportunity for change com., OHA past chair), Health Care Administrs. N.E. Ohio, DePauw U. Alumni Assn., U. Pitts. Alumni Assn. Health Administrn. (pres. 1976), Middleburg C. of C., Weymouth Country Club, Union Club Cleve., Tennis Club. Contbr. articles to profl. jours. Home: 20088 Idlewood Dr Strongsville OH 44136 Office: SW Gen Health Ctr 18697 Bagley Rd Cleveland OH 44130-3497

SCHURR, CAROLYN, lawyer; b. Bklyn., Apr. 14, 1964; d. Frederick Stanley and Naomi (Marcus) S. BA, Johns Hopkins U., 1984; JD, U. Chgo., 1987. Bar: N.Y. 1988, D.C. 1988, Conn. 1987, U.S. Dist. Ct. (so. dist., ea. dist.) N.Y. 1988. Assoc. Cravath Swaine and Moore, N.Y.C., 1987-88, Corbin Silverman & Sansevrino, N.Y.C., 1988—; freelance writer ABA Jour., Chgo., 1989—. Mem. ABA, N.Y. Womens Bar Assn., N.Y.C. Bar Assn., Vol. Lawyers for Arts, Lawyers Com. for Human Rights. Home: 360 E 72nd St Apt 2905C New York NY 10021-4767 Office: The Times Mirror Co Times Mirror Sq Los Angeles CA 90053

SCHURR, JOHN MICHAEL, chemistry educator; b. Pittsfield, Mass., Nov. 10, 1937; s. Franklin John and Pauline Virginia (Dean) S.; m. Karen Theresa Martin, Aug. 30, 1958; children: Kerstin Theresa, Rebecca Lynn. BS, Yale U., 1959; PhD, U. Calif., Berkeley, 1964. Rsch assoc. U. Oreg., Eugene, 1964-66; asst. prof. U. Wash., Seattle, 1966-72, assoc. prof., 1972-78, prof., 1978—; vis. scientist EAWAG, Dubendorf, Switzerland, 1974; vis. scholar Kyoto U., Japan, 1987. Assoc. editor: Ann. Rev. Phys. Chemistry, 1976-85; editorial bd. Biophys. Jour., 1983-88; contbr. over 120 papers to sci. jours. Rsch. grantee, NSF, 1970—, NIH, 1980—. Achievements include development of optical methods and theories to study macromolecular Brownian motions, measurement of twisting and bending rigidities of DNA in solution; discovery of novel structural transitions of linear, supercoiled DNAs, of.

SCHURZ, FRANKLIN DUNN, JR., media executive; b. South Bend, Ind., May 22, 1931; s. Franklin Dunn and Martha (Montgomery) S.; m. Robin Rowan Tullis, Nov. 22, 1975 (div. 1985). A.B., Harvard U., 1952, M.B.A., 1956, A.M.P., 1984. Exec. asst. South Bend Tribune, 1956-60, dir., 1961-76, sec., 1970-75, asst. pub., 1971-72, editor, pub., 1972-82, exec. v.p., 1975-76, pres., 1976-82; asst. pub. Morning Herald and Daily Mail, Hagerstown, Md., 1960-62; pub. Morning Herald and Daily Mail, 1962-70, editor, 1966-70; chmn. audit com. AP, 1979-84; pres. Schurz Communications, Inc., 1982—; treas., 1983-89. Chmn. Ind. Arts Commn., 1979-81; bd. regents St. Marys Coll., Notre Dame, Ind., 1977-83; chmn. adv. coun. Coll. Arts and Letters Notre Dame U., 1980-82; bd. dirs. Ind. Endowment Ednl. Excellence Inc., Indpls., 1987-90; mem. pres.'s coun. Ind. U., Bloomington, 1988—. 2d lt. U.S. Army, 1952-54. Recipient Presdl. Award of Merit Nat. Newspaper Assn., 1965, Frank Rogers award Rotary, South Bend, 1980. Mem. Am. Press Inst. (bd. dirs. 1985-94), AP Assn. (exec. com. 1979-84), Chesapeake AP Assn. (past pres.), Md.-Del.-D.C. Press Assn. (past pres.), The Press-Enterprise (bd. dirs. 1992—), Hoosier State Press Assn. (past pres.), Newspaper Advt. Bur. (past bd. dirs.), South Bend Mishawaka Area C. of C. (pres. 1980-82), Am. Soc. Newspaper Editors, Inst. Newspaper Fin. Execs. (past pres.), South Bend Country Club, Nat. Press Club, Sigma Delta Chi. Presbyterian. Home: 1329 E Erskine Manor Hl South Bend IN 46614-2186 Office: Schurz Communications Inc 225 W Colfax Ave South Bend IN 46626-1000

SCHURZ, SCOTT CLARK, journalist, publisher; b. South Bend, Ind., Feb. 23, 1936; s. Franklin Dunn and Martha (Montgomery) S.; m. Kathryn Joan Foley, Aug. 5, 1967; children: Scott Clark, Alexandra Carol, John Danforth. B.A., Denison U., 1957. Asst. instr. U.M.d., 1957-58; administrv. asst. South Bend Tribune, 1960-66; circulation cons. Imperial Valley Press, El Centro, Calif., 1966; asst. to pub. Bloomington (Ind.) Herald-Times/Bedford Times-Mail, 1966-70, pub., 1970—; personnel mgr. Bloomington Herald-Times, 1969-72, promotion mgr., 1969-81, dir. promotions, 1981-86, editor-in-chief, 1977—; editorial chmn. Bedford Times-Mail, 1972-81, editor-in-chief, 1981—; pub., editor-in-chief Sunday Herald Times; pres. Herald-Times, Inc., dir., v.p; dir. Schurz Communications, Inc. Pres., Bloomington Boys' Club, 19701, Jr. Achievement Monroe County, 1971-73; bd. dirs. United Way Monroe County, 1979-81. Served with U.S. Army, 1958-60. Mem. Internat. Newspaper Mktg. Assn. (pres. 1986), Inland Daily Press Assn. (pres. 1989), Newspaper Assn. Am. (bd. dirs. 1992-95), Hoosier State Press Assn. (pres. 1989), Newspaper Advt. Bur. (bd. dirs. 1987-92). Republican. Presbyterian. Office: Herald Times Inc 1900 S Walnut St Bloomington IN 47403

SCHUSSLER, THEODORE, lawyer, physician, educator, consultant; b. N.Y.C., July 27, 1934; s. Jack and Fanne (Blank) S.; m. Barbara Ann Gordon, June 18, 1961; children: Deborah, Jonathan, Rebecca. B.A. in Polit. Sci., Bklyn. Coll., 1955; LL.B., Bklyn. Law Sch., 1958; J.D., Bklyn. Law Sch., 1967; M.D., U. Lausanne (Switzerland), 1974. Bar: N.Y. 1959, U.S. Dist. Ct. (so. and ea. dists.) N.Y. 1975, U.S. Tax Ct. 1961, U.S. Ct. Appeals (2d cir.) 1962, U.S. Supreme Ct. 1975. Clerkship and practice, N.Y.C., 1956, 58-59; legal editor tax div. Prentice-Hall, Inc., Englewood Cliffs, N.J., 1956; vol. criminal law div. Legal Aid Soc., N.Y.C., 1959; atty. legal dept. N.Y.C. Dept. Welfare, 1959-60; sole practice, N.Y.C., 1960—; sr. staff asst. IBM-Indsl. Medicine Program, 1969-70, 74-76; intern in medicine St. Vincent's Med. Center of Richmond, S.I., N.Y., 1976-77; resident emergency medicine, 1977-79, resident in gerontology, chief house physician Carmel Richmond Nursing Home, S.I.; 1978-80; surg. rotation emergency dept. Met. Hosp. Ctr., 1979; house physician dept. medicine Richmond Meml. Hosp. and Health Ctr., 1979-80; gen. practice medicine, 1980—; attending physician, former chief dept. family practice, former chmn. med. care evaluation, med. records and by-laws coms., former physician, advisor emergency dept., former mem. blood transfusion, credential's, emergency dept. coms., former mem. exec. com., mem. med. staff Community Hosp. of Bklyn., 1980-94; attending physician Meth. Hosp., Bklyn., 1984-92; supervising emergency dept. physician, dept. ambulatory care Meth. Hosp., Bklyn., 1980-83; attending physician Kings Hwy. Hosp., 1981-88, coord. emergency dept., 1981; clin. instr. dept. preventive medicine and community health, Downstate Med. Ctr. SUNY, Bklyn., 1981-88, clin. asst. prof., 1988—; SUNY Health Service Ctr. med. dir. divsn. devel. disabilities Mishkon-Jewish Bd. Family & Children's Svc., Bklyn., 1982—; primary care physician Jewish Home and Hosp. for Aged, N.Y.C., 1993-94; co-founder Med. Legal Group; cons. in gerontology Palm Beach Home for Adults, Bklyn., 1980-92; cons. indsl. medicine IBM, 1990-92; tchr., instr., lectr., prof., 1954—; med.-legal cons. to professions of medicine and law; co-founder Med. Legal Group. Dem. County Committeeman, 44th Assembly Dist., Bklyn., del. to judicial conv.; mem. exec. bd. United Ind. Dems. Bklyn. Capt. (med. corp.) USAR. Recipient Pub. and Community Svc. award United Ind. Dems. 44th assembly dist., Bklyn. Fellow Am. Coll. Legal Medicine; mem. Am. Coll. Emergency Physicians (past bd. dir. N.Y. chpt., past chmn. medico-legal com. N.Y. chpt.), Assn. Arbitrators of Civil Ct. of N.Y. (small claims divsn., arbitrator), United Univ. Professions, Bklyn. Law Sch. Alumni Assn. (bd. dirs.), Delta Sigma Rho. Author: Torts; Jurisdiction and Practice in Federal Courts; Constitutional Law; Conflict of Laws; contbr. articles to profl. jours. Home and Office: 760 E 10th St Apt 6H Brooklyn NY 11230-2355

SCHUSTER, ELAINE, civil rights professional, state official; b. Detroit, Sept. 26, 1947; d. William Alfred and Aimee Isabelle (Cote) LeBlanc; m. James William Schuster, Sept. 6, 1969; 1 child, Cambrian James. BA, Wayne State U., 1972, postgrad., 1974-75, paralegal cert., 1991. Asst. payments Mich. Dept. Social Svcs., Detroit, 1972-73; rights rep. Mich. Dept. Civil Rights, Detroit, 1973-80, 82-87, 90, asst. dir. div., 1987-90, supr., 1993-95; court adminstr. Chippewa-Ottawa Conservation Ct., Bay Mills, Mich., 1980-82; quality assurance coord. State Mental Health Facility, Southgate, Mich., 1991-93; acting interim dir. Mich. Indian Commn., Detroit, 1995—. Author: Critique, An Indian Tours Michilimackinac, 1981; contbr. articles and poems to mags. and profl. jours. Bd. dirs. Tri-County Native Ams., Warren, Mich., 1982-89, sec. Native Am. Sesquicentennial subcom., Mich., 1987; mem. Linking Lifetimes, mentor program for Native Am. youth, 1992-93; sec., newsletter editor various civic orgns.; also other polit. and civic activities. Native Am. fellow Mich. State U., 1989. Mem. ACLU (bd. dirs. Union-Oakland county 1987-88). Democrat. Avocations: exploring local historical and natural places of interest, research, middle Eastern dance, fitness. Office: Mich Dept Civil Rights 1200 6th St Detroit MI 48226-2424

SCHUSTER, GARY BENJAMIN, chemistry educator, university dean; b. N.Y.C., Aug. 6, 1946; s. Adolph and Phyllis (Bloch) S.; m. Anita Radice, June 16, 1968; children: Eric, Andrew. BS, Clarkson Coll. Tech., 1968; PhD, U. Rochester, 1971. Fellow Columbia U., 1971-73, 1973-75; asst. prof. chemistry U. Ill., Urbana, 1975-79, assoc. prof., 1979-81, prof., 1981-94, head dept. chemistry, 1990-94; prof. chemistry, dean Coll. Scis., Ga. Inst. Tech., Atlanta, 1994—; cons. Photon Cores, Champaign, Ill., 1980—. With U.S. Army, 1971-73. Grantee NIH, NSF. Mem. Am. Chem. Soc., Am. Assn. Photochemistry and Photobiology, Inter-Am. Photochem. Soc.

SCHUSTER, GARY FRANCIS, corporate relations specialist, former news correspondent; b. Detroit, Jan. 26, 1942; s. Dwayne Alger and Mary Elizabeth (Cullen) S.; m. Barbara Anne Leopold, Aug. 30, 1968; children—Rory Anne, Reid Patrick. B.S. in Journalism/Psychology, Wayne State U., 1966. Gen. assignment reporter Royal Oak (Mich.) Tribune, 1966-68; gen. assignment reporter Detroit News, 1968-70, state capital corr., 1970-74; bur. chief Detroit News, Lansing, 1974-75; chief asst. city editor Detroit News, Detroit, 1975-76; city editor Detroit News, 1976-77, news editor, 1977-78, Washington Bur. chief, 1978-85, White House corr., 1978-85; White House corr. CBS News, 1985-86; pvt. practice media cons., 1986-87; v.p. corp. relations Union Pacific Corp., 1987—. Mem. White House Corrs. Assn. (pres. 1985-86), Saucon Valley Country Club (Bethlehem, Pa.). Roman Catholic.

SCHUSTER, INGEBORG IDA, chemistry educator; b. Frankfurt, W. Ger., Oct. 30, 1937; came to U.S. 1947; d. Ludwig Karl and Mariluise (Kautetzky) S. BA, U. Pa., 1960; MS, Carnegie Inst. Tech., Pitts., 1963; PhD, Carnegie Inst. Tech., 1965. Postdoctoral fellow Bryn Mawr (Pa.) Coll., 1965-67; asst. prof. chemistry Pa. State U., Abington, 1967-73; assoc. prof. chemistry Pa. State U., 1973-83, prof. chemistry, 1983—. Contbr. articles to profl. jours. Huff fellow, 1966; E. Gerry fellow, 1982. Mem. Am. Chem. Soc. Republican. Roman Catholic. Avocations: skiing, violin, cartooning. Office: Pa State Univ 1600 Woodland Rd Abington PA 19001-3918

SCHUSTER, KAREN SUTTON, administrator; b. New Brunswick, N.J., Aug. 26, 1952; d. Alfred Michael and Carmen (Collado) Sutton; m. Derek Vance Schuster, May 31, 1976; children: Sloane, Brooke, Devon, Megan, Christopher. BA, Hofstra U., 1974; postgrad., NYU, 1978-83. Asst. to dir. Mus. Am. Folk Art, N.Y.C., 1975-76, acting dir., 1976-77, bd. dirs. exec. com. officer, 1980-88, gallery dir., 1989-92, dir. ops., 1992-94, dep. dir. planning and adminstrn., 1994-95; v.p. Sotheby's, N.Y.C., 1995—. Bd. dirs.

Family Dynamics, N.Y.C., 1976-80. Mem. Cosmopolitan Club (younger members chmn.), Maidstone Club, Coral Beach Club. Democrat. Episcopalian. Home: 79 E 79th St Apt 9 New York NY 10021 Office: Sotheby's 1334 York Ave New York NY 10021

SCHUSTER, PHILIP FREDERICK, II, lawyer; b. Denver, Aug. 26, 1945; s. Philip Frederick and Ruth Elizabeth (Robar) S.; m. Barbara Lynn Nordquist, June 7, 1975; children: Philip Christian, Matthew Dale. BA, U. Wash., 1967; JD, Willamette U., 1972. Bar: Oreg. 1972, U.S. Dist. Ct. Oreg. 1974, U.S. Ct. Appeals (9th cir.) 1986, U.S. Supreme Ct. 1986. Dep. dist. atty. Multnomah County, Portland, Oreg., 1972; title examiner Pioneer Nat. Title Co., Portland, 1973-74; assoc. Buss, Leichner et al, Portland, 1975-76; from assoc. to ptnr. Kitson & Bond, Portland, 1976-77; pvt. practice Portland, 1977—; arbitrator Multnomah County Arbitration Program, 1985—. Contbr. articles to profl. jours. Organizer Legal Aid Svcs. for Community Clinics, Salem, Oreg. and Seattle, 1969-73; Dem. committeeman, Seattle, 1965-70. Mem. ABA, Multnomah Bar Assn. (Vol. Lawyers Project), NAACP (exec. bd. Portland,Oreg. chpt. 1979—), ACLU, Internat. Platform Assn., Alpha Phi Alpha. Avocations: river drifting, camping, swimming, jogging, karate, writing. Office: 1500 NE Irving St Ste 540 Portland OR 97232-4209

SCHUSTER, ROBERT PARKS, lawyer; b. St. Louis, Oct. 25, 1945; s. William Thomas Schuster and Carolyn Cornforth (Daugherty) Hathaway; 1 child, Susan Michele. AB, Yale U., 1967; JD with honors, U. of Wyo., 1970; LLM, Harvard U., 1971. Bar: Wyo. 1971, U.S. Ct. Appeals (10th cir.) 1979, U.S. Supreme Ct. 1984, Utah 1990. Dep. county atty. County of Natrona, Casper, Wyo., 1971-73; pvt. practice law, Casper, 1973-76; assoc. Spence & Moriarity, Casper, 1976-78; ptnr. Spence, Moriarity & Schuster, Jackson, Wyo., 1978—. Trustee U. Wyo., 1985-89; polit. columnist Casper Star Tribune, 1987—. Ford Found. Urban Law fellow, 1970-71; pres. United Way of Natrona County, 1974; bd. dirs. Dancers Workshop, 1981-83; chair Wyo. selection com. Rhodes Scholarship, 1989—; mem. bd. visitors Coll. Arts and Scis., U. Wyo., 1991—; mem. planning com. Wyo. Dem. Party; mem. platform com. Dem. Nat. Conv. 1992—; mem. Nat. Com., 1992—; mem. Wyo. Public Policy Forum, 1992—; bd. dirs. Community Visual Art Assn. Mem. ABA, Assn. Trial Lawyers Am., Wyo. Trial Lawyers Assn. Home: PO Box 548 Jackson WY 83001-0548 Office: Spence Moriarity & Schuster 15 S Jackson St Jackson WY 83001

SCHUSTER, SEYMOUR, mathematician, educator; b. Bronx, N.Y., July 31, 1926; s. Oscar and Goldie (Smilowitz) S.; m. Marilyn Weinberg, May 2, 1954; children: Paul Samuel, Eve Elizabeth. B.A., Pa. State U., 1947; A.M., Columbia U., 1948; Ph.D., Pa. State U., 1953; postgrad. (fellow), U. Toronto, 1952-53. Instr. Pa. State U., 1950-52; instr. Poly. Inst. N.Y., 1953-54, asst. prof., 1954-56, assoc. prof., 1956-58; vis. assoc. prof. Carleton Coll., Northfield, Minn., 1958-59, assoc. prof., 1959-63, prof. math., 1968—, chmn. dept., 1973-76. William H. Laird prof. math. and liberal arts, 1992-94, William H. Laird prof. emeritus, 1994—; vis. assoc. prof. U. N.C., Chapel Hill, 1961; research assoc. math. dept. U. Minn., Mpls., 1962-63, assoc. prof., 1963-65; assoc. prof. Minn. Math Center, 1965-68; dir. coll. geometry project, 1964-74; dir. Acad. Year Inst. for Coll. Tchrs., 1966-67, NSF Faculty fellow, 1970-71; vis. scholar U. Calif., Santa Barbara, 1970-71, U. Ariz., 1990; guest scholar Western Mich. U., 1976, 81; vis. prof. Western Wash. U., 1983, U. Oreg., 1986. Author: (with K. O. May) Undergraduate Research in Mathematics, 1961, Elementary Vector Geometry, 1962, (with P.C. Rosenbloom) Prelude to Analysis, 1966; also research articles on geometry, graph theory, and analysis.; cons. editor Xerox Pub. Co., 1962-71; assoc. editor, editorial bd.: Am. Math. Monthly, 1969-86; assoc. editor: Indian Jour. Math. Edn., 1976-86; co-producer 12 films on geometry. Served with USNR, 1944-46. Recipient Honor award Am. Film Festival, 1967, Golden Eagle award Cine Film Festival, 1967, 68; named found. fellow Inst. for Combinatorics and Applications. Mem. Math. Assn. Am., Am. Math. Soc., Sigma Xi, Pi Mu Epsilon. Home: 316 Sumner St E Northfield MN 55057-2843

SCHUSTER, TODD MERVYN, biophysics educator, biotechnology company executive; b. Mpls., June 27, 1933; s. David Theodore and Ann (Kaluser) S.; m. Nancy Joanne Barnes, Jan. 25, 1958; 1 child, Lela Alexa. B.A., Wayne State U., 1958, M.S., 1960; Ph.D., Washington U., 1963. Research assoc. Max Planck Inst. Phys. Chemistry, Goettingen, W.Ger., 1963-66; asst. prof. SUNY-Buffalo, 1966-70; assoc. prof. U. Conn., Storrs, 1970-75, prof. biochemistry, biophysics, 1975—; dept. head, 1977-81, dir. Biotech. Ctr., 1986-90; pres., founder Xenogen Inc., 1986-90; vis. prof. Ind. U., Bloomington, 1975, U. Peking, People's Republic of China, 1987; McCollum-Pratt vis. prof. Johns Hopkins U., Balt., 1979-80; mem. NIH grant rev. panels, biophysics and biophys. chemistry panel, 1971-75, biomed. scis. postdoctoral fellowship panel, 1976, Sickle Cell Disease Adv. Panel, 1977; mem. biol. instrumentation rev panel NSF, 1984-90, biol. facilities, 1987-90, sci. and tech. ctrs., 1988-90; mem. BBS adv. coun. NSF, 1989-92; chmn. adv. com. Nat. Cell Culture Ctr., 1990—; program dir. Nat. Analytical Untracentri Fugation Facility, 1987-94. Contbr. research articles on rapid reaction kinetics, biopolymers, hemeprotein structure and function, virus structure and assembly to profl. jours. USPHS fellow, 1959-63, 63-66. Mem. AAAS, Am. Chem. Soc., Conn. Acad. Sci. and Engring., Biophys. Soc., Protein Soc., Am. Soc. Biol. Chemists, Am. Soc. Virology. Home: 556 Wormwood Hill Rd Mansfield CT 06250-1040 Office: U Conn Dept Molecular and Cell Biology PO Box 125 Storrs Mansfield CT 06268-0125 also: Xenogen Inc 321 Fisher Bldg Detroit CT 06269-3125

SCHUTTA, HENRY SZCZESNY, neurologist, educator; b. Gdansk, Poland, Sept. 15, 1928; came to U.S., 1962, naturalized, 1967; s. Jakub and Janina (Zerbst) S.; m. Henryka Kosmal, Apr. 29, 1950; children—Katharine, Mark, Caroline. M.B., B.S., U. Sydney, Australia, 1955, M.D., 1968. Jr. resident, then sr. resident St. Vincent's Hosp., Sydney, 1956-58; acad. registrar, house physician Nat. Hosp. Nervous Diseases, London, 1958-62; neurologist Pa. Hosp., Phila., 1962-73; asso. prof. neurology U. Pa. Med. Sch., 1963-73; prof. neurology, chmn. dept. SUNY Downstate Med. Center, Bklyn., 1973-80; prof. neurology U. Wis. Med. Sch., 1980—. Research on bilirubin encephalopathy, cerebral edema, degeneration and regeneration of muscle. Home: 3510 Blackhawk Dr Madison WI 53705-1406 Office: U Hosp 600 Highland Ave Madison WI 53792-0001

SCHUTTE, ALDEN FREDERICK, advertising agency executive; b. Buffalo, Mar. 24, 1940; s. Henry E. and Doris B. S.; AAS, SUNY, Buffalo, 1959, BS, 1963; postgrad. Harvard Bus. Sch.; m. Susan J. Morrica, Nov. 30, 1968; 1 dau., Jennifer Leigh. Account exec. Whyte Advt., Buffalo, 1964-66; v.p. account service Rich Advt. Co., Buffalo, 1966-71; sr. v.p., creative dir. Post-Keyes-Gardner, Chgo., 1971-74; pres., chief exec. officer Healy-Schutte & Co. of Buffalo, 1974—; bd. dirs. Shea's Buffalo Theater, Buffalo State Coll. Found., Internat. Inst. Gen. campaign chmn. Leukemia Soc. Western N.Y. Mem. Nat. Advertisers, Am. Assn. Advt. Agys. (chmn. N.Y. state council), Internat. Food Mfrs. Assn., Buffalo Area C. of C., Nat. Restaurant Assn. Republican. Office: 1207 Delaware Ave Buffalo NY 14209

SCHUTTE, ANNE JACOBSON, historian, educator; b. Palo Alto, Calif., Apr. 24, 1940; d. David Samuel and Muriel Rose (Ashworth) J.; m. William Metcalf Schutte, Dec. 21, 1967 (div. Jan. 1990). BA in History magna cum laude, Brown U., 1962; AM in History, Stanford U., 1963, PhD in History and Humanities, 1969. Instr. Lawrence U., 1966-69, asst. prof., 1971-77, assoc. prof., 1977-85; prof., 1985-91; prof. U. Va., Charlottesville, 1992—; bd. dirs. Ctr. for Reformation Rsch., 1980-83; mem. exec. com. Newberry Libr. program Assoc. Colls. Midwest, 1981-83, 86-88, 90-91; mem. steering com. Com. Women's Concerns, 1984-85. Author: Pier Paolo Vergerio: The Making of an Italian Reformer, 1977, Printed Italian Vernacular Religious Books, 1465-1550: A Finding List, 1983, Pier Paolo Vergerio e la Riforma a Venezia, 1489-1549, 1988 (trans. Virginia Cappelletti, Anna Maria Fabbrini); editor: Autobiografia di una santa mancata, 1990; translator: Heavenly Supper: The Story of Maria Janis (Fulvio Tomizza), 1991, Varieties of Italian Anticlericalism (Silvana Seidel Menchi), 1993; also articles and numerous revs. We. Regional Alumnae scholar Brown U., 1957-59, 60-62, Stanford U., 1963-65, Stanford U./Italian Govt., 1965-66, Newberry Libr., 1978, S.E. Inst. Medieval and Renaissance Studies, 1979, NEH, 1979-80, 88-89, Gladys Krieble Delmas, 1985; scholar Inst. Reformation Rsch., 1965; Grantee Fulbright Found., 1965-66, Pro Helvetia Found., 1966, Am. Philos. Soc., 1971, NEH 1979-80, 88-89, 95. Mem. Am.

Hist. Soc., Am. Soc. Ch. History (coun.), Coordinating Com. for Women in hist. Profession, Renaissance Soc. Am., 16th Century Studies Conf. (editorial bd. jour. 1972—, v.p. 1973-74, 79-80, pres. 1980-81), Soc. Italian Hist. Socs., Soc. Reformation Rsch. (nominating com. 1981-83, exec. coun. 1987-90, program sec. 1992-95. Office: U Va Dept History Charlottesville VA 22903

SCHUTTER, DAVID JOHN, banker; b. Erie, Pa., Apr. 21, 1945; s. Donald John and Ruth Margaret (Hilbert) S. m. Ellen Carol Hoffman, June 18, 1967; children: David, Erica. BS with honors and distinction, Pa. State U., 1967; postgrad., Mich. State U., 1967-68, Ohio State U., 1973-75; cert., Stonier Grad. Sch. Banking, 1981. Asst. v.p. Huntington Nat. Bank, Columbus, Ohio, 1973-80; v.p. Ameritrust Co., Cleve., 1980-81, v.p., mgr. asset based lending dept., 1981-86, sr. v.p. secured lending div., 1986-89, dep. sr. loan adminstr., 1989-90, sr. cred. pol. off., 1990-92; sr. v.p., regional credit exec. Soc. Nat. Bank, Cleve., 1992-94; exec. v.p., chief credit officer, 1994—; pres. AT Comml. Corp., 1996— panelist Robert Morris Assocs., Cleve., 1981, 93, mem., 1986—, Cleve. Bar Assn., 1986. Served to capt. U.S. Army, 1968-72. Mem. Nat. Comml. Fin. Assn. (bd. dirs. 1986—), Beta Gamma Sigma, Omicron Delta Epsilon. Office: Soc Nat Bank 127 Public Sq Cleveland OH 44114-1216

SCHUTZ, DONALD FRANK, geochemist, corporate executive; b. Orange, Tex., Sept. 22, 1934; s. Theodore J. and Mildred Irene (Chandler) S.; m. Beatriz Valera, May 18, 1958; children: Delfino, Celita. BS in Geology cum laude, Yale U., 1956, PhD in Geology, 1964; MA in Geology, Rice U., 1958. Research staff geologist Yale U., New Haven, 1963-64; mgr. nuclear geochemistry dept. Teledyne Isotopes, Westwood, N.J., 1968-70, v.p. 1970-75, pres., 1975-93; engring. group exec. Teledyne, Inc., Westwood, 1989-92; chief scientist Teledyne Environ. Systems, 1992—; gen. mgr. Teledyne Brown Engring. Environ. Svcs., 1993—; mem. low level waste adv. com. N.J. Dept. Environ. Protection, Trenton, 1988-90; chmn. com. on radioactive materials N.J. BIA, Trenton, 1980-88. Pres. Children's Aid and Adoption Soc. N.J. Inc., Bogota, 1976—, Am. Amateur Judo Found., River Vale, N.J., 1979-89; bd. dirs. Yale U. Alumni Fund, 1988-93. Recipient Antarctic Service medal U.S. Congress, 1964. Mem. Geochem. Soc., Am. Nuclear Soc. (chmn. no. N.J. sect. 1988-89, mem. environ. scis. divsn., bd. dirs., mem. pub. policy com. 1991—, chair-elect 1994), Am. Pub. Health Assn., Geol. Soc. Am., Soc. Petroleum Engrs., Am. Assn. Radon Sci. and Tech. (pres. 1986-89, trans. 1990—), Am. Assn. Petroleum Geologists, Yale Alumni Assn. (bd. dirs. Bergen County and vincinity chpt. 1989—), Sierra Club, Planetar Soc., Sigma Xi. Office: Teledyne Brown Engring Environ Svcs 50 Van Buren Ave Westwood NJ 07675-3242

SCHUTZ, HERBERT DIETRICH, publishing executive; b. Munich, Germany, July 16, 1922; came to U.S. 1924; naturalized, 1930; s. Anton Friedrich and Maria Hedwig (Gross) S.; m. Suzanne Cameron, Mar. 22, 1971; children: Leslie, Suzanne; children by previous marriage: Prescott (dec.), Peter, Jeffrey, Elizabeth. BS, Harvard Coll., 1944. Ptnr. N.Y. Graphic Soc . Ltd., Greenwich, Conn., 1946-66, pres., editor in chief, 1966-81, chmn. bd., 1982-84; v.p. Time Inc., N.Y.C., 1966-81; chmn., pres. Schutz and Co., Fine Arts, Greenwich, 1982—. Served to 1st lt. USMC, 1945-46. Mem. Harvard Club (N.Y.C.), Belle Haven Club, Field Club. Home and Office: The Barn Dewart Rd Greenwich CT 06830-3417 Home (summer): 22 Denison Ave Stonington CT 06378

SCHUTZ, JOHN ADOLPH, historian, educator, former university dean; b. L.A., Apr. 10, 1919; s. Adolph J. and Augusta K. (Gluecker) S. AA, Bakersfield Coll., 1940; BA, UCLA, 1942, MA, 1943, PhD, 1945. Asst. prof. history Calif. Inst. Tech., Pasadena, 1945-53; assoc. prof. history Whittier (Calif.) Coll., 1953-56, prof., 1956-65; prof. Am. history U. So. Calif., L.A., 1965-91; chmn. dept. history U. So. Calif., 1974-76, dean social scis. and communication, 1976-82. Author: William Shirley: King's Governor of Massachusetts, 1961, Peter Oliver's Origin and Progress of the American Rebellion, 1967, The Promise of America, 1970, The American Republic, 1978, Dawning of America, 1981, Spur of Fame: Dialogues of John Adams and Benjamin Rush, 1980, A Noble Pursuit: A Sesquicentennial History of the New England Historic Genealogical Society, 1995; joint editor: Golden State Series; contbg. author: Spain's Colonial Outpost, 1985, Generations and Change: Genealogical Perspectives in Social History, 1986, Making of America: Society and Culture of the United States, 1990, rev. edit., 1992. Trustee Citizens Rsch. Found., 1985—. NEH grantee, 1971; Sr. Faculty grantee, 1971-74. Mem. Am. Hist. Assn. (pres. Pacific Coast br. 1972-73), Am. Studies Assn. (pres. 1974-75), Mass. Hist. Soc. (corr.), New Eng. Hist. Geneal. Soc. (trustee 1988—, editor, author intro. book Boston Merchant Census of 1789, 1989, recording sec. 1995—), Colonial Soc. Mass. (corr.). Home and Office: 1100 White Knoll Dr Los Angeles CA 90012-1353 *The excitement of collegiate activities makes each year an adventure in learning and a renewal of one's youth.*

SCHUUR, DIANE JOAN, vocalist; b. Tacoma, Dec. 10, 1953; d. David Schuur. Ed. high sch., Vancouver, Wash. Albums include Pilot of My Destiny, 1983, Deedles, Schuur Thing, 1986, Timeless (Grammy award for female jazz vocal 1986), Diane Schuur and the Count Basie Orchestra (Grammy award for female jazz vocal 1987), Talkin' 'Bout You, 1988, Pure Schuur, 1991 (reached #1 on Billboard contemporary jazz chart, nominated for Grammy award 1991), In Tribute, 1992, Love Songs, 1993 (Grammy nomination, Best Traditional Vocal), (with B.B. King) Heart to Heart, 1994 (entered at #1 on Billboard contemporary jazz chart); performed at the White House, Monterey Jazz Festival, Hollywood Bowl; toured Japan, Far East, South Am. and Europe. *There is no plateau that can't be reached, no obstacle that can't be overcome if you believe in yourself and your higher power*.

SCHUUR, ROBERT GEORGE, lawyer; b. Kalamazoo, Dec. 5, 1931; s. George Garrett and Louise Margaret (DeVries) S.; m. Susan Elizabeth White, Sept. 28, 1968; children—Arah Louise Adele, Jeremiah Donald Garrett. A.B., U. Mich., 1953, LL.B., 1955. Bar: Mich. 1955, N.Y. 1956. Assoc. Reid & Priest, N.Y.C., 1955-65, ptnr., 1966—. Served with USN, 1956-58. Mem. ABA, N.Y. State Bar Assn., Assn. of Bar of City of N.Y., Phi Beta Kappa. Club: University (N.Y.C.). Home: 163 E 82d St New York NY 10028 Office: Reid & Priest 40 W 57th St New York NY 10019-4097

SCHUYLER, DANIEL MERRICK, lawyer, educator; b. Oconomowoc, Wis., July 26, 1912; s. Daniel J. and Fannie Sybil (Moorhouse) S.; m. Claribel Seaman, June 15, 1935; children: Daniel M., Sheila Gordon. AB summa cum laude, Dartmouth Coll., 1934; JD, Northwestern U., 1937. Bar: Ill. 1937, U.S. Supreme Ct. 1942, Wis. 1943. Tchr. constl. history Chgo. Latin Sch., 1935-37; assoc. Schuyler & Hennessy (attys.), 1937-42, ptnr., 1946-48; ptnr. Schuyler, Richert & Stough, 1948-58, Schuyler, Stough & Morris, Chgo., 1958-76, Schuyler, Ballard & Cowen, 1976-83, Schuyler, Roche & Zwirner, P.C., 1983—; treas., sec. and controller B-W Supercargoes, Inc. div. Borg-Warner Corp., Milw., 1942-46; lectr. trusts, real property, future interests Northwestern U. Sch. Law, 1946-50, assoc. prof. law, 1950-52, prof., 1952-80, prof. emeritus, 1980—. Author: (with Homer F. Carey) Illinois Law of Future Interests, 1941; supplements, 1947, 54; (with William M. McGovern, Jr.) Illinois Trust and Will Manual, 1970; supplements, 1972, 74, 76, 77, 79, 80, 81, 82, 83, 84; contbr. to profl. jours. Republican nominee for judge Cook County Circuit Ct., 1958; bd. dirs., life mem. United Cerebral Palsy Greater Chgo.; bd. dirs. Lawrence Hall Youth Svcs. Fellow Am. Bar Found.; mem. ABA (past mem. ho. of dels., past chmn. sect. real property, probate and trust law), Chgo. Estate Planning Coun. (past pres., Dist. Svc. award 1977), Am. Coll. Trust and Estate Counsel (past pres.), Chgo. Bar Assn. (past chmn. com. on trust law and post-admission edn., past bd. mgrs.), Ill. Bar Assn. (past chmn. real estate and legal edn. sects., past bd. govs.), Wis. Bar Assn., Legal Club, Law Club, Univ. Club, Order of Coif, Phi Beta Kappa, Phi Kappa Psi. Home: 909 W Foster Ave Apt 403 Chicago IL 60640-2515 Office: Schuyler Roche & Zwirner PC Ste 3800 130 E Randolph St Chicago IL 60601-6342

SCHUYLER, ROBERT LEN, investment company executive; b. Burwell, Nebr., Mar. 4, 1936; s. Norman S. and Ilva M. (Hoppes) S.; m. Mary Carol Huston, June 13, 1958; children: Kylie Anne, Nina Leigh, Melynn Kae, Gwyer Lenn. BS, U. Nebr., 1958; MBA, Harvard U., 1960. Asst. to treas. Potlatch Forests, Inc., Lewiston, Idaho, 1962-64; dir. corp. planning Potlatch Forests, Inc., San Francisco, 1964-66; mgr. fin. analysis Weyerhaeuser Co., Tacoma, 1966-68; mgr. investment evaluation dept. Weyerhaeuser Co., 1968-

70, v.p. fin. and planning, 1970-72, sr. v.p. fin. and planning, 1972-85, exec. v.p., chief fin. officer, 1985-91; mng. ptnr. Nisqually Ptnrs., Tacoma, 1991—; chief exec. officer Grande Alberta Paper, Ltd., 1992—; past mem. nat. adv. bd. Chem. Bank, U. Wash. MBA program, coun. fin. exec. Conf. Bd., Pvt. Sector Coun., exec. coun. Am. Paper Inst.; bd. dirs. Multicare Health System, Paragon Trade Brands Inc., One Sport, Inc.; bd. dirs. Tacoma-Pierce County YMCA. Bd. dirs. Tacoma-Pierce County YMCA. Mem. Anglers Club. Home: 12101 Gravelly Lake Dr SW Tacoma WA 98499-1415 Office: Nisqually Ptnrs 621 Pacific Ave Ste 214 Tacoma WA 98402

SCHWAAB, RICHARD LEWIS, lawyer, educator; b. Oconomowoc, Wis., Nov. 15, 1945. s. Thomas L. and Phyllis N. (Lord) S.; m. Lynn Louise Howie; children: Amy, William, Andrew, Matthew. BSChemE, U. Wis., 1967; JD with honors, George Washington U., 1971, LLM in Internat. Law with highest honors, 1979. Bar: Va. 1971, U.S. Dist. Ct. (ea. dist.) Va. 1979, U.S. Supreme Ct. 1980, U.S. Ct. Appeals (fed. cir.) 1982. Ptnr., Stepno, Schwaab & Linn, Arlington, 1972-74, Bacon & Thomas, Arlington, 1974-78, Schwartz, Jeffery, Schwaab, Mack, Blumenthal & Evans, P.C., Alexandria, 1978—; ptnr. in charge, chair dept. intellectual property Foley & Lardner, Washington, 1988—; lectr. law George Washington U., 1978-88, George Mason U., 1989—. Max Planck Inst. Fgn. and Internat. Patent, Copyright and Competition Law fellow, 1971-72. Mem. ABA, Am. Intellectual Property Law Assn., Va. State Bar (gov. 1974-78), Am. Soc. Internat. Law, Internat. Patent and Trademark Assn., Internat. Fedn. Indsl. Property Attys., Christian Legal Soc., Phi Kappa Phi, Tau Beta Pi. Co-author Patent Practice, 6 vols., 1976-93; International Patent Law: EPC & PCT, 3 vols., 1978; Intellectual Property Protection for Biotechnology Worldwide, 1987; contbr. articles to profl. jours. Home: 6326 Karmich St Fairfax VA 22039-1621 Office: Foley & Lardner 3000 K St NW Ste 500 Washington DC 20007-5109

SCHWAB, ARTHUR JAMES, lawyer; b. Pitts., Dec. 7, 1946; s. Earl Walter and Helen Alice (Gascoine) S.; m. Karen Jenny, Sept. 2, 1967; children: John Arthur, Ellen Katherine, David Earl. Student, Muskingum Coll., 1964-65; AB, Grove City Coll., 1968; JD, U. Va., 1972. Bar: Pa. 1972, N.J. 1985, U.S. Dist. Ct. (we. dist.) Pa. 1972, U.S. Dist. Ct. (ea dist.) Pa. 1978, U.S. Dist. Ct. (no. dist) Ohio 1979, U.S. Dist. Ct. S.C. 1980, U.S. Dist. Ct. N.Mex. 1981, U.S. Dist. Ct. Mass. 1984, U.S. Dist. Ct. N.J. 1984, U.S. Ct. Appeals (3d cir.) 1972, U.S. Ct. Appeals (11th cir.) 1982, U.S. Ct. Appeals (4th cir.) 1982, U.S. Ct. Appeals (8th cir.) 1991, U.S. Ct. Appeals (9th cir.) 1995, U.S. Supreme Ct. 1975. Ptnr. Reed, Smith, Shaw and McClay, Pitts., 1973-90; ptnr., chairperson litigation Buchanan Ingersoll, Pitts., 1990—. Mem. editorial bd. Va. Law Rev., Sch. Law U. Va., Charlottesville, 1972. Bd. dirs. Grove City (Pa.) Coll. Mem. Acad. Trial Lawyers Allegheny County (bd. dirs.), Allegheny County Bar Assn. (immediate past pres. civil litigation sect.), Duquesne Club, Rivers Club. Republican. Presbyterian. Home: 212 New England Pl Sewickley PA 15143-1030 Office: Buchanan Ingersoll 5800 USX Tower 600 Grant St Pittsburgh PA 15219

SCHWAB, EILEEN CAULFIELD, lawyer, educator; b. N.Y.C., Feb. 11, 1944; d. James Francis and Mary Alice (Fay) Caulfield; m. Terrance W. Schwab, Jan. 4, 1969; children: Matthew Caulfield, Catherine Grimley, Claire Gillespie. BA, Hunter Coll., 1965; JD, Columbia U., 1971. BA magna cum laude. Bar: N.Y. 1972, U.S. Dist. Ct. (so. and ea. dists.) N.Y. 1975, U.S. Ct. Appeals (2d cir.) 1975, U.S. Tax Ct. 1980, U.S. Ct. Appeals (10th cir.) 1993. Assoc. Poletti Friedin, N.Y.C., 1971-72, Hughes Hubbard & Reed, N.Y.C., 1972-75, Davis Polk & Wardwell, N.Y.C., 1975-81; dep. bur. chief Charities Bu., Atty. Gen. of N.Y., 1981-82; counsel Brown & Wood, N.Y.C., 1983—, ptnr., 1984; adj. prof. N.Y. Law Sch.; mediator atty. disciplinary com. first dept., N.Y. Co-chmn. gift planning adv. com. Archdiocese of N.Y.C. Fellow Am. Coll. Trust and Estate Counsel; mem. N.Y. State Bar Assn. (exec. com. trust and estate sect.), Assn. Bar City N.Y., Phi Beta Kappa. Democrat. Roman Catholic.

SCHWAB, FRANK, JR., management consultant; b. Brookline, Mass., Dec. 19, 1932; s. Frank Sr. and Phyllis (Robinson) F. BA, Rutgers U., 1952; MBA, Harvard Bus. Sch., 1956. Cert. mgmt. cons. Internal auditor Champion Paper, Inc., Hamilton, Ohio, 1956-57; mgmt. engr. Champion Paper, Inc., Pasadena, Tex., 1957-58; cons., assoc. Booz Allen & Hamilton, N.Y.C., 1958-65; dir. trans. planning Planning Rsch. Corp., L.A., 1965; pres., CEO F.R. Schwab & Assocs., N.Y.C., 1965-82; pres., co-CEO Fenvessy & Schwab, N.Y.C., 1982-87; pres., CEO Anderson & Schwab, N.Y.C., 1987—; bd. dirs. Sugarland Oil Corp., N.Y.C., mfrs. and svcs. divsn. nat. mining assns., Washington, Infosafe Corp., N.Y.C. With Nat. Mining Hall of Fame & Mus., Leadville, Colo., 1992—; mem. nominating com. 1st lt. U.S. Army, 1952-54, Korea. Decorated Nat. Def. Svc. medal, Korean Svc. medal with bronze star, Commendation ribbon with medal pendant, UN Svc. medal. Mem. Inst. Mgmt. Cons. (pres. N.Y. chpt. 1975-77), Am. Arbitration Assn. (panel arbitrator), Mil. Order Fgn. Wars (vet. companion), Maidstone Club, Union Club, River Club, King Coal Club. Republican. Avocation: tennis. Office: Anderson & Schwab Inc 444 Madison Ave New York NY 10022-6903

SCHWAB, GEORGE DAVID, social science educator, author; b. Nov. 25, 1931; s. Arkady and Klara (Jacobson) S.; BA, City Coll. N.Y., 1954; MA, Columbia, 1955, PhD, 1968; m. Eleonora Storch, Feb. 27, 1965; children: Clarence Boris, Claude Arkady, Solan Bernhard. Lectr., Columbia Coll. N.Y.C., 1959; lectr. CUNY, 1960-68, asst. prof. history, 1968-72, assoc. prof. history, 1973-79, prof., 1980—. Mem. Columbia U. Seminar on Legal and Polit. Thought; dir. Conf. History and Politics, CUNY. Trustee, pres., mem. exec. com. Nat. Com. Am. Fgn. Policy. Mem. Am. Hist. Assn., Am. Polit. Sci. Assn., Authors Guild, Conf. for Study Polit. Thought, Internat. Conf. for History 2d World War, Internat. Platform Assn. Author: Dayez: Beyond Abstract Art, 1967; Enemy oder Foe, 1968; Switzerland's Tactical Nuclear Weapons Policy, 1969; The Challenge of the Exception: An Introduction to the Political Ideas of Carl Schmitt, 1970, 2d edit., 89; Appeasement and Detente, 1975, 81; Carl Schmitt: Political Opportunist?, 1975; translator: The Concept of the Political with Comments by Leo Strauss (Carl Schmitt), 1976; Legality and Illegality as Instruments of Revolutionaries in their Quest for Power: Remarks Occasioned by the Outlook of Herbert Marcuse, 1978; The German State in Historical Perspective, 1978; Ideology: Reality or Rhetoric?, 1978; Ideology and Foreign Policy, 1978, 81, The Decision: Is the American Sovereign at Bay?, 1978; State and Nation: Toward a Further Clarification, 1980; American Foreign Politics at the Crossroads, 1980; Carl Schmitt: Through a Glass Darkly, 1980; From Quantity and Heterogeneity to Quality and Homogeneity: Toward a New Foreign Policy, 1980; Toward an Open-Society Bloc, 1980; Eurocommunism: The Ideological and Political Theoretical Foundations, 1981; American Foreign Policy at the Crossroads, 1982; A Decade of the National Committee on American Foreign Policy, 1984; trans. Political Theology: Four Chapters on the Concept of Sovereignty (Carl Schmitt), 1985, 88; The Destruction of a Family, 1987; Elie Wiesel: Between Jerusalem and New York, 1990; The Broken Vow, the Good Obtained, 1991; Thoughts of a Collector, 1991; Carl Schmitt Hysteria in the United States, 1992; Contextualizing Carl Schmitt's Concept of Grossraum, 1994; editor Am. Fgn. Policy Interests; series Global Perspectives in History and Politics. Home: 140 Riverside Dr New York NY 10024-2605 Office: CUNY New York NY 10036

SCHWAB, GLENN ORVILLE, retired agricultural engineering educator, consultant; b. Gridley, Kans., Dec. 30, 1919; s. Edward and Lizzie (Sauder) S.; married; children: Richard, Lawrence,Mary Kay. BS, Kans. State U., 1942; MS, Iowa State U., 1947, PhD, 1951; postdoctoral, Utah State U., 1966. Registered profl. engr., Ohio. Instr. to prof. agrl. engring. Iowa State U., Ames, 1947-56; prof. agrl. engring. Ohio State U., Columbus, 1956-85, prof. emeritus, 1985—; cons. Powell, Ohio, 1985—; bd. dirs. Internat. Water Mgmt. Program, Columbus. Co-author: Soil and Water Conservation Engineering, 4th edit., 1993, Agricultural and Forest Hydrology, 1986, Soil and Water Management Systems, 4th edit. 1996; contbr. articles to profl. jours. Served to capt. U.S. Army, 1942-46. Fellow Am. Soc. Agrl. Engrs. (bd. dirs. soil and water div. 1976-78, Hancock Brick and Tile Drainage Engr. 1968, John Deere medal 1987), Am. Soc. Engrs. Edn., Am. Soc. Testing Materials, Soil and Water Conservation Soc. Am., Am. Geophysical Union, Internat. Commn. Irrigation and Drainage. Avocations: rock polishing, wood working, photography, traveling. Home: 2637 Summit View Rd Powell OH 43065-8879 Office: Ohio State U 590 Woody Hayes Dr Columbus OH 43210-1057

SCHWAB, HERMANN CASPAR, banker; b. N.Y.C., Jan. 8, 1920; s. Hermann Caspar and Ruth (Bliss) S.; m. C. Meteer Shanks, July 5, 1955; children: Henry R., Lesley Schwab Forman, Margery Schwab Weekes, Stuart Taylor, George Bliss, Katharine Leonard Schwab Kimmick. Grad., St. Marks Sch., 1937, Yale U., 1941. With Hanover Bank, 1941-44, 46-55, asst. sec., 1949-53, asst. v.p., 1953-55; ptnr. Dick & Merle Smith, 1956; v.p. Empire Trust Co., 1957-66; sr. v.p., 1965-66; with Bank N.Y., 1966-67; sr. v.p. Schroder Trust Co., N.Y.C., 1967-73, dir., 1970-73; pres., dir. Cheapside Dollar Fund Ltd., N.Y.C., 1970-88; sr. v.p. Schroder Capital Mgmt. Inc., N.Y.C., 1973-84, cons., 1984-88; chmn., dir. Schroder Capitol Funds Inc., 1988—. Mayor Oyster Bay Cove, N.Y., 1973-85, trustee, 1965—; trustee St. Lukes-Roosevelt Hosp. Ctr. 2d lt. inf., AUS, 1943-46. Mem. Piping Rock Club (Locust Valley, N.Y.). Home: 34 Northern Blvd Oyster Bay NY 11771

SCHWAB, JOHN HARRIS, microbiology and immunology educator; b. St. Cloud, Minn., Nov. 20, 1927; s. John David and Katherine (Harris) S.; m. Ruth Ann Graves, Sept. 1, 1951; children: Stewart, Thomas, Anna, Kellogg. BS, U. Minn., 1949, MS, 1950, PhD, 1953. Asst. prof. U. N.C., Chapel Hill, 1953-67, prof., 1967—; Cary C. Boshamer prof., 1982—; scientist Lister Inst. Preventive Medicine, London, 1960, MRC Rheumatism Rsch, Unit, Taplow, England, 1968, Radiobiol. Inst., Rijswijk, The Netherlands, 1975, Pasteur Inst., Paris, 1985. Contbr. articles to profl. jours. and chpts. to books. Recipient Faculty Scholar award Josiah Macy Jr. Found., 1975; NIH Spl. fellow, 1960, 68; Fogarty Internat. fellow NIH, Paris, 1985. Mem. Am. Soc. Microbiology (editor Infection and Immunity jour. 1980-85), Am. Assn. Immunologists, AAAS.

SCHWAB, JOHN JOSEPH, psychiatrist, educator; b. Cumberland, Md., Feb. 10, 1923; s. Joseph L. and Eleanor (Cadden) S.; m. Ruby Baxter, Aug. 4, 1945; 1 dau., Mary Eleanor. B.S., U. Ky., 1946; M.D., U. Louisville 1946; M.S. in Physiology (Med. fellow), U. Ill., 1949; postgrad., Duke U. 1951-52, U. Fla., 1959-61. Diplomate: Nat. Bd. Med. Examiners. Intern Phila. Gen. Hosp., 1947-48; resident medicine Louisville Gen. Hosp., 1949-50; adn. officer med. coll. U. Yokohama, 1952-54; internist, psychosomaticist Holzer Clinic, Gallipolis, Ohio, 1954-59; resident psychiatry U. Fla. Hosp., 1959-61; NIMH Career tchr. U. Fla., Gainesville, 1962-64, mem. faculty, 1961-73, prof. psychiatry and medicine, 1967-73, dir. cons. liaison program, 1964-67, rsch. tng. dir., 1965-71; prin. investigator Fla. Health Study, 1969-74; prof., chmn. dept. psychiatry and behavioral scis. Sch. Medicine U. Louisville, 1973-91, prof. psychiatry, 1991-93, prof. emeritus, 1993—, assoc. dir. clin. psychopharm. rsch., 1991—; chmn. epidemiologic studies rev. com. Ctr. for Epidemiologic Studies NIMH, 1973-75, cons. psychiatry br., 1975—; cons. Old Order Amish Study of Depression, 1978—; vol. vis. lectr. Howard U., 1992; ann. vis. lectr. U. Wurzburg, Germany; vis. prof. El-Azar U., Cairo, 1991; prin. investigator LSVL Family Health Study, 1982—. Author: Handbook of Psychiatric Consultation, 1968; also articles; co-author: Sociocultural Roots of Mental Illness: An Epidemiologic Survey, 1978, Social Order and Mental Health, 1979; first author: Family Mental Health, 1993; assoc. editor Psychosomatics, 1985-86; co-editor: Man for Humanity: On Concordance V. Discord in Human Behavior, 1972, Social Psychiatry, vol. 1, 1974, The Psychiatric Examination, 1974. Capt. USAMC, 1949-54. Fellow Am. Coll. Psychiatrists (regent 1977-79), Collegium Internat. Neuro-Psychopharmacologicum, mem. Internat. Assn. Social Psychiatry, AAAS, Am. Psychiat. Assn. (chmn. council research and devel. 1974-75); mem. AMA, Acad. Psychosomatic Medicine (exec. com. 1970-71), Group for Advancement Psychiatry (bd. dirs. 1985-87), So. Med. Assn., Jefferson County Med. Soc., Ky. Psychiat. Assn., Am. Assn. Social Psychiatry (pres. 1971-73), Alpha Omega Alpha (Outstanding Performance award for Affirmative Action U. Louisville 1986), World Assn. Soc. Psychology (internat. adv. com., Rome, 1991), Psychiatrists for Better Psychiat. (pres. 1992—), U. of the World (co-chair health, edn. com. 1992—). Research on applicability of psychiatric concepts to general medicine, sociocultural aspects of mental illness; establishing guidelines for identification and management of medical patients whose illnesses are complicated by emotional stress; epidemiology of mental illness; depression and the family; clinical psychopharmacology, historical and epidemiologic perspectives on the family. Home: 6217 Innes Trace Rd Louisville KY 40222-6008

SCHWAB, KENNETH LYNN, college president; b. Wolcott, Ind., Feb. 5, 1947; m. Patrician N. Schwab; children: Kempten, Carlton, Christopher. BS, Purdue U., 1969; MEd, U. N.C., 1972; EdD, Ind. U., 1978. Spl. edn. tchr. Defiance (Ohio) City Schs., 1969-70; asst. dean students Guilford Coll., Greensboro, N.C., 1970-74, dean of students, 1974-86, asst. to pres. for instnl. planning, 1980-86; sr. v.p. for instnl. planning, 1986-88; exec. v.p. for adminstrn. U. S.C., Columbia, 1988-91; pres., CEO Centenary Coll. La., Shreveport, 1991—. Fellow Am. Coun. on Edn. Office: Centenary College of La PO Box 41188 Shreveport LA 71134-1188

SCHWAB, MICHAEL R., air transportation company executive; b. 1949. Exec. v.p. United Airlines Inc., 1973-91; exec. v.p. ops. USAir Inc., 1991—, USAir Group Inc., 1991—. Office: USAir Group Inc 2345 Crystal Dr Arlington VA 22227

SCHWAB, PAUL JOSIAH, psychiatrist educator; b. Waxahachie, Tex., Jan. 14, 1932; s. Paul Josiah and Anna Marie (Baeuerle) S.; m. Martha Anne Beed, June 8, 1953; children: Paul Josiah III, John Conrad, Mark Whitney. BA, N. Cen Coll., 1953; MD, Baylor U., 1957. Diplomate Am. Bd. Psychiatry and Neurology. Intern Phila. Gen. Hosp., 1957-58; clin. assoc. Nat. Cancer Inst., Bethesda, Md., 1958-60; resident in internal medicine U. Chgo., 1960-62, resident psychiatry, 1962-65, chief resident and instr. psychiatry, 1965; pvt. practice Naperville, Ill., 1965—; lectr. psychiatry U. Chgo., 1968-74, assoc. prof., 1974-79, assoc. prof. clin. psychiatry, 1979—, dir. residency tng. 1976-79, dir. in-patient unit and day treatment program, 1975-79. Contbr. articles to profl. jours. Bd. trustees North Ctrl. Coll., 1981—, chair acad. and student affairs com. 1981-92, chair liaison com., 1983—, vice chair admissions, fin. aid and student devel., 1992-95. Fellow Am. Psychiat. Assn. (Nancy C.A. Roeske award 1991); mem. AMA, Am. Soc. Clin. Psychopharmacology, Acad. Clin. Psychiatrists, Alpha Omega Alpha. Republican. Methodist. Avocations: chess, classical music. Home and Office: 1200 Tall Oaks Ct Naperville IL 60540

SCHWAB, STEWART JON, law educator; b. 1954. BA, Swarthmore U., 1975, MA, 1978; PhD, Mich. U., 1983. Bar: D.C. 1982. Law clk. to Hon. J. Dickson Phillips U.S. Ct. Appeals (4th cir.), 1981-82; law clk. to Hon. Sandra O'Connor U.S. Superior Ct, 1982-83; from asst. prof. to prof. law Cornell U., Ithaca, N.Y., 1983—; vis. fellow Centre Socio-Legal Studies Oxford U., 1990. Mem. Am. Econ. Assn., Am. Judicature Assn., Order of Coif. Office: Cornell Law Sch Myron Taylor Hall Ithaca NY 14853

SCHWAB, SUSAN CAROL, electronics company executive. BA in Polit. Economy, Williams Coll., 1976, MA in Applied Econs., Stanford U., 1977; PhD in Pub. Adminstrn., George Washington U., 1993. U.S. trade negotiator Office of Pres.'s Spl. Trade Rep., Washington, 1977-79; trade policy officer U.S. Embassy, Tokyo, 1980-81; chief economist, legis. asst. for internat. trade for Senator John C. Danforth, 1981-86, legis. dir., until 1989; asst. sec. commerce, dir. gen. U.S. and Fgn. Comml. Svc. Dept. Commerce, 1989-93; with corp. strategy office Motorola, Inc., Schaumburg, Ill., 1993—. Office: Motorola Inc Corporate Strategy Office 1303 E Algonquin Rd Schaumburg IL 60196

SCHWAB, TERRANCE WALTER, lawyer; b. Pitts., May 19, 1940; m. Eileen Caulfield, Jan. 4, 1969; children: Matthew Caulfield, Catherine Grimley, Claire Gillespie. BA magna cum laude, Harvard U., 1962; LLB cum laude, Columbia U., 1966. Assoc. Milbank, Tweed, Hadley & McCloy, N.Y.C., 1966-70; assoc. Kelley, Drye & Warren, N.Y.C., 1970-74, ptnr., 1975—; lectr. various profl. orgns. Assoc. editor: Law Practice of Alexander Hamilton, 1964-1980; contbr. articles to profl. jours. Active Am. Coun. on Germany, N.Y.C., 1987—; trustee, chmn. St. Luke's Chamber Ensemble, N.Y.C., 1980-82; trustee, sec. Caramoor Ctr. for Music and Arts, Katonah, N.Y., 1971—; trustee Sch. of Convent of Sacred Heart, N.Y.C., 1989-92; chmn., 1990-93. Mem. ABA, N.Y. State Bar Assn., Assn. of Bar of City of N.Y., German Am. C. of C., Harvard Club, Quaker Hill Country Club, Hammersly Lake Club, Deutscher Verein, Swiss Soc. N.Y. Office: Kelley Drye & Warren 101 Park Ave New York NY 10178-0062

SCHWABE, ARTHUR DAVID, physician, educator; b. Varel, Germany, Feb. 1, 1924; came to U.S., 1938, naturalized, 1943; s. Curt and Frieda (Roseno) S. M.D., U. Chgo., 1956. Intern UCLA Med. Center, 1956-57, asst. resident, then assoc. resident medicine, 1957-59, chief resident medicine, 1960-61, USPHS fellow gastroenterology, 1959-60; now mem. staff; chief gastroenterology Harbor Gen. Hosp., Torrance, Calif., 1962-67; cons. Wadsworth VA Center, Los Angeles; mem. faculty UCLA Med. Sch., 1961—, asst. prof. medicine, 1962-64, assoc. prof., 1967-71, prof., 1971-89, chief div. gastroenterology, 1967-88, vice chmn. dept. medicine, 1971-74, emeritus prof., 1989—. Contbr. articles to profl. jours. Served with AUS, 1943-46. Recipient UCLA Golden Apple award sr. class UCLA, 1967, 70, Outstanding Tchr. award UCLA Med. House Staff, 1968, 78, Disting. Teaching award UCLA, 1971, S.M. Mellinkoff Faculty award, 1983; Edward F. Kraft scholar, 1951; Ambrose and Gladys Bowyer fellow medicine, 1958-59. Fellow ACP; mem. Am. Gastroenterol. Assn., N.Y. Acad. Sci., So. Calif. Soc. Gastroenterology (pres. 1969), Western Assn. Physicians, Western Soc. Clin. Investigation, Western Gut Club (chmn. 1969-70), Alpha Omega Alpha. Office: 10833 Le Conte Ave Los Angeles CA 90024-1602

SCHWABE, CALVIN WALTER, veterinarian, medical historian, medical educator; b. Newark, Mar. 15, 1927; s. Calvin Walter and Marie Catherine (Hassfeld) S.; m. Gwendolyn Joyce Thompson, June 7, 1951; children: Catherine Marie, Christopher Lawrence. BS, Va. Poly. Inst., 1948; MS, U. Hawaii, 1950; DVM, Auburn U., 1954; MPH, Harvard U., 1955, ScD, 1956. Diplomate Am. Coll. Vet. Preventive Medicine. From assoc. prof. to prof. parasitology and epidemiology, chmn. dept. tropical health, and asst. dir. Sch. Pub. Health, Am. U. Beirut, 1956-66; mem. Secretariat of WHO, Geneva, 1964-66; prof. epidemiology Sch. Vet. Medicine, also Sch. Medicine, U. Calif., Davis, 1966-91, chmn. dept. epidemiology and preventive medicine, 1966-70; assoc. dean Sch. Vet. Medicine, U. Calif., Davis, 1970-71, adj. prof. Agrl. History Ctr., 1984-91, prof. emeritus, 1991—; cons. Futurevet Assocs., Davis and Pedreguer, Spain, 1991—; cons. WHO, UN Environ. Program, FAO, NIH, Pan Am. Health Orgn., UNICEF, Nat. Rsch. Coun.; univ. lectr. U. Sask.; Fulbright vis. prof. Univ. Coll. East Africa, Cambridge (Eng.) U., U. Khartoum; Srinivasan Meml. lectr. U. Madras; Spink lectr. comparative medicine U. Minn.; Franklin lectr. scis. and humanities Auburn U.; Entwhistle lectr. Cambridge U.; Schofield lectr. U. Guelph; mem. Am. Rsch. Ctr. Egypt. Author: Veterinary Medicine and Human Health, 1969, 84, What Should a Veterinarian Do?, 1972, Epidemiology in Veterinary Practice, 1977, Cattle, Priests and Progress in Medicine, 1978, Unmentionable Cuisine, 1980; also articles. Recipient Karl F. Meyer Gold Headed Cane award Am. Vet. Epidemiology Assn., 1985, Disting. Alumnus award Auburn U., 1992. Fellow Am. Pub. Health Assn. (governing coun. 1974-76); mem. AVMA, Am. Soc. Tropical Medicine and Hygiene, History of Sci. Soc., Sudan Studies Assn. Democrat. Mem. Soc. of Friends. Avocations: collecting musical instruments, cooking, raising bamboos. Home (winter): 849 A St Davis CA 95616-1916 Home (summer): Apartado 90, Pedreguer Alicante 03750, Spain

SCHWABE, PETER ALEXANDER, JR., judge; b. Portland, Oreg., July 23, 1935; s. Peter Alexander and Evelyn (Zingleman) S.; A.B., Stanford, 1958; J.D., Willamette U., 1960; m. Bonnie Jean LeBaron, June 21, 1958; children: Mark, Karen, Diane, Patricia, Kurt. Admitted to Oreg. bar, 1960; pvt. practice, Portland, 1960-76; fed. adminstrv. law judge, 1976—. mem. ABA, Oreg. State Bar Assn., Beta Theta Pi, Phi Delta Phi. Home: 4366 Dorking Ct Sacramento CA 95864-6150 Office: 2031 Howe Ave Sacramento CA 95825-0176

SCHWALM, FRITZ EKKEHARDT, biology educator; b. Arolsen, Hesse, Germany, Feb. 17, 1936; came to U.S., 1968; s. Fritz Heinrich and Elisabeth Agnes (Wirth) S.; m. Renate Gertrud Streichhahn, Feb. 10, 1962; children—Anneliese, Fritz-Uwe, Karen. Ph.D., Philipps U., Marburg, Fed. Republic Germany, 1964; Staatsexamen, Philipps U., 1965. Educator boarding sch., Kiel, Fed. Republic Germany, 1956-57; lectr. Folk Universitetet, Stockholm, Sweden, 1959-60; research assoc. U. Witwatersrand, Johannesburg, South Africa, 1966-67, U. Notre Dame, South Bend, Ind., 1968-70; asst. prof., then assoc. prof. Ill. State U., Normal, Ill., 1970-82; assoc. prof. biology, then prof., chair dept. Tex. Woman's U., Denton, 1982—, dir. Animal Care Facility, 1990—, chmn. pro tem grad. coun., 1991-92; coordinator, chmn. S.W. Conf. for Devel. Biology, Denton, 1985, 90. Author: (monograph) Insect Morphogenesis, 1988; mem. editl. bd. Palmer Jour. Rsch., 1994—; contbr. articles to profl. jours. Vice pres. PTA, Normal, 1975. Fellow Anglo-Am. Corp. South Africa, 1966, 67; NATO advanced research fellow, Freiburg, Fed. Republic Germany 1977. Mem. AAAS, Am. Soc. Zoologists, Deutsche Zoologische Gesellschaft, Soc. for Devel. Biology, Phi Kappa Phi (chpt. pres. 1993—). Club: Univ. Denton (pres. 1983-85). Lodge: Kiwanis (v.p. 1987-88, pres. 1988-89). Home: 1116 Linden Dr Denton TX 76201-2721 Office: Tex Woman's U Biology Sci Rsch Lab Denton TX 76204

SCHWAM, MARVIN ALBERT, graphic design company executive; b. Newark, Apr. 18, 1942; s. Meyer and Fannie (Lerman) S.; m. Jeanette Fein, June 13, 1964; children: Frederic, Matthew. BFA, Cooper Union, 1964. Staff artist Doremus & Co., 1964-66; mgr. Flowerental Corp., N.Y.C., 1966-68; pres. M. Schwam Floralart, N.Y.C., 1968-75; exec. v.p.; bd. chmn. Florenco Foliage Systems Corp., N.Y.C., 1975-88; pres. Am. Christmas Decorating Service Inc., N.Y.C.; chmn. bd. Am. Christmas Decorations, Ltd., 1989—; pres. Marc Shaw Graphics, Inc., N.Y.C., Florenco Graphics Systems, Inc.; exec. v.p. Display Arts Worldwide, 1975-88; pres. Creative Animations, Inc., 1988-90; creative dir., v.p. Rennoc Animations, Inc., 1988-90; pres. Almar Communications, Ltd., 1990—, Sayso Communications, Ltd., 1990—, Gay Entertainment TV, Inc., 1992—. Industry chmn. March of Dimes, 1975-78, pres. bd. dirs. Happi Found. for Autistic People, N.Y.C.; trustee Nat. Found. Jewish Genetic Diseases; patron Young Adult Inst. and Workshop, Inc.; co-chmn. restaurant, hotel and entertainment industry luncheon Boy Scouts Am., 1988—; chmn. benefit com. Plan Internat. USA, 1991-92. Recipient award of merit for service to Gen. Motors Corp., 1978, award for Highlight of Christmas, Citibank/Citicorp Center, 1978, Disting. Service award Coler Hosp., 1982-86, Sr. Citizens of Roosevelt Island. Mem. Mcpl. Art Soc. N.Y., Am. Mus. Natural History, Alumni Assn. Cooper Union (2d Century Soc. fellow), Internat. Platform Assn. Designer largest artificial Christmas tree in U.S., Radio City Music Hall, N.Y.C., 1979; decorator Pulitzer Fountain, N.Y.C., 1979-80 Christmas season; chief designer Town Sq., New Orleans, Christmas, 1981, Albany (N.Y.) Tricentennial, 1986; interior landscape designer La. State Pavillion World's Fair, New Orleans, 1984; co-chmn. Nat. Restaurant, Hotel and Entertainment Industry Luncheon, N.Y.C., 1988—. Home: 7 E 17th St New York NY 10003-1913 Office: Am Christmas Decorations Inc 280 E 134th St Bronx NY 10454-4407

SCHWAN, ALFRED, food products executive. Pres., CEO Schwan Sales Enterprises, Inc., Marshall, Minn., 1965—. Office: Schwan Sales Enterprises 115 W College Dr Marshall MN 56258*

SCHWAN, HERMAN PAUL, electrical engineering and physical science educator, research scientist; b. Aachen, Germany, Aug. 7, 1915; came to U.S., 1947, naturalized, 1952; s. Wilhelm and Meta (Pattberg) S.; m. Anne Marie DelBorello, June 15, 1949; children: Barbara, Margaret, Steven, Carol, Cathryn. Student, U. Goettingen, 1934-37; Ph.D., U. Frankfurt, 1940; Doctor habil. in physics and biophysics, 1946; D.Sc. (hon.), U. Pa., 1986. Research scientist, prof. Kaiser Wilhelm Inst. Biophysics, 1937-47, asst. dir., 1945-47; research sci. USN, 1947-50; prof. elec. engring., prof. elec. engring. in phys. medicine, assoc. prof. phys. medicine U. Pa., Phila., 1950-83, Alfred F. Moore prof. emeritus, 1983—; dir. electromed. div. U. Pa., 1952-73, chmn. biomed. engring., 1961-73, program dir. biomed. engr. tng. program, 1960-77; vis. prof. U. Calif.-Berkeley, 1956, U. Frankfurt Fed. Republic Germany, 1962, U. Würzburg, Fed. Republic Germany, 1980-87; lectr. Johns Hopkins U., 1962, U. Drexel U., Phila., 1983-90; W.W. Clyde vis. prof. U. Utah, Salt Lake City, 1980; 10th Lauristan Taylor lectr. Nat. Council Radiation Protection and Measurements, 1986; Fgn. sci. mem. Max Planck Inst. Biophysics, Germany, 1962—; cons. NIH, 1962-90; chmn. nat. and internat. meetings biomed. engring. and biophysics, 1959, 61, 65; mem. nat. advcouncil environ. health HEW, 1969-71; mem. Nat. Acad. Scis.-NRC coms., 1968-87, Nat. Acad. Engring., 1975—. Co-author: Advances in Medical and Biological Physics, 1957, Therapeutic Heat, 1958, Physical Techniques in Medicine and Biology, 1963; editor: Biol. Engring, 1969; co-editor: Interactions Between Electromagnetic Fields and Cells, 1985; mem. editorial bd. Environ. Biophysics, IEEE Transactions Med. Biol. Engring., Jour. Phys.

Med. Biol., Nonionizing Radiation, Bioelectromagnetics; contbr. articles to profl. jours. Recipient Citizenship award Phila., 1952, 1st prize AIEE, 1953, Achievement award Phila. Inst. Radio Engring., 1963, Rajewsky prize for biophysics, 1974, U.S. sr. scientist award Alexander von Humboldt Found., 1980-81, Biomed. Engring. Edn. award Am. Soc. Engring. Edn., 1983, d'Arsonval award Bioelectromagnetics Soc., 1985. Fellow IEEE (Morlock award 1967, Edison medal 1983, Centennial award 1984, Phila. Sect. award 1991, chmn. and vice chmn. nat. profl. group biomed. engring. 1955, 62-68), AAAS, Am. Inst. Med. and Biol. Engring.; mem. Am. Standards Assn. (chmn. 1961-65), Biophys. Soc. (publicity com., council, constn. com.), German Biophys. Soc. (hon.), Soc. for Cryobiology, Internat. Fedn. Med., and Biol. Engring., Bioelectromagnetics Soc., Biomed. Engring. Soc. (founder, dir. 1968-71), Sigma Xi, Eta Kappa Nu. Achievements include discovery of counterion relaxation; dielectric spectroscopy of cells and tissues; nonlinearity law of electrode polarization; rsch. on nonionizing radiation biophysics; fundamentals electromagnetic bioengineering; first standard for safe exposure to electrical fields; biomed. engring. orgn. and edn. Home: 99 Kynlyn Rd Wayne PA 19087-2849 also: 162 59th St Avalon NJ 08202-1207 Office: U Pa Dept Bioengring D2 Hayden Hall Philadelphia PA 19104

SCHWAN, JUDITH ALECIA, photographic researcher; b. Middleport, N.Y., Apr. 16, 1925; d. James William and Mary Alecia (Wythers) S. BSChemE, U. Cin., 1948; MS, Cornell U., 1950. Research scientist Eastman Kodak Co., Rochester, N.Y., 1950-65, lab. head, 1965-68, asst. div. dir. emulsion research div., 1968-71, div. dir. emulsion research div., 1971-75, asst. dir. research labs., 1975-86, dir. photographic research labs., photographic products group, 1986-87, ret., 1987; bd. trustees Eastman Savs. & Loan Assn., Rochester, 1977-87. Patentee in field. Trustee St. John Fisher Coll., Rochester, 1975—; active Meml. Art Gallery, Rochester, Rochester Philharm. Orch., Rochester Mus. and Sci. Ctr., George Eastman House, Rochester; mem. task force Women in Ch. of Rochester Cath. Diocese; mem. econ. pastoral steering com. Rochester Cath. Diocese; mem. parish coun. St. Stephen's Ch., Middleport, N.Y.; mem. Diocesan Pastoral Coun., Buffalo. Recipient Disting. Alumnus award U. Cin. Coll. of Engring., 1976. Fellow Soc. Motion Picture and TV Engrs. (Herbert T. Kalmus Meml award for Outstanding Contbn. in Color Films, 1979); mem. Am. Chem. Soc., Nat. Acad. Engring. Soc. Photographic Scientists and Engrs. Clubs: Shelridge Country (Medina, N.Y.). Home: 45 Park Ave Middleport NY 14105-1354

SCHWANAUER, FRANCIS, philosopher, educator; b. Zsámbék, Hungary, Jan. 20, 1933; came to U.S., 1959; s. Georg and Maria (Keller) S.; m. Johanna Maria Koelln, Sept. 29, 1957; children: Stephan Michael, Miriam Frances. Maturum, Ulrich von Hutten Gymnasium, Korntal, Germany, 1954; Ph.D. U. Stuttgart, Germany, 1959. Asst. prof. Lebanon Valley Coll., Annville, Pa., 1960-62, U. Maine, Orono, 1962-65; asst. prof. U. So. Maine, Portland Gorham, 1965-67, assoc. prof., 1967-72, prof., 1972—. Author: Truth is a Neighborhood with Nothing in Between, 1977, Those Fallacies by Slight of Reason, 1978, No Many is not a One (For the Case is Comparison), 1981, The Flesh of Thought is Pleasure or Pain, 1982, To Make Sure is to Cohere, 1982, Philosophical Fact and Paradox, 1987, Fables from the Fox, 1991. Mem. New England Philos. Assn., Internat. Platform Assn. Democrat. Roman Catholic. Avocation: fishing. Home: 4 Woodmont St Portland ME 04102-2709

SCHWANDA, TOM, religious studies educator; b. E. Stroudsburg, Pa., Oct. 23, 1950; s. Theodore Frank and Madlyn Betty (Backensto) S.; m. Grace Elaine Dunning, July 30, 1977; children: Rebecca Joy, Stephen Andrew. Student, Worcester Polytechnic Inst., 1968-69; BA in Econ., Moravian Coll., 1969-72; student, Gordon-Conwell Sem., 1972-74; MDiv, New Brunswick Sem., 1975; DMin, Fuller Theol. Sem., 1992. Ordained to ministry Reformed Ch. in Am., 1975. Pastor Wanaque (N.J.) Reformed Ch., 1975-87; pastor congl. care Immanuel Reformed Ch., Grand Rapids, Mich., 1987-92; interim sr. pastor Remembrance Reformed Ch., Grand Rapids, 1992-93; rsch. fellow H. Henry Meeter Ctr. for Calvin Studies Calvin Coll., Grand Rapids, 1993—; instr. spirituality and worship Bethlehem Ctr. for Spirituality, Grand Rapids, 1993—; dir. Reformed Spirituality Network, Grand Rapids, 1992—; organizer, convener Gathering Reformed Spirituality, 1993, 94, 95; chair spirituality com. Synod of Great Lakes, 1989—, mem. Christian discipleship com., 1988-94; mem. ch. life, evangelism, missions com. South Grand Rapids Classics, chair, 1992; mem. commn. on worship Reformed Ch. in Am., 1978-94; mem. care of students com. Passaic Classis, 1975, 87, chair, 1978, 83-86, pres., 1979. Contbr. articles to religious jours.; author poetry; manuscript reader, evaluator religious pub. co. Established, managed Wanaque Cmty. Food Pantry, 1977-87; vol. Domestic Crisis Ctr., Grand Rapids, 1988—; bd. dirs. Nat. Inst. Rehabilitation Engring., Hewitt, N.J., 1984—, pres. bd. dirs., 1986—. Recipient Barnabas award Iglesia Cristiana Ebenezer, 1987. Mem. Czechoslovak Soc. Arts and Sci., Czechoslovak Hist. Conf., Soc. for Study of Christian Spirituality. Avocations: running, landscaping, genealogy/family history. Home and Office: 6125 Capitan SE Grand Rapids MI 49546

SCHWANK, JOHANNES WALTER, chemical engineering educator; b. Zams, Tyrol, Austria, July 6, 1950; came to U.S., 1978; s. Friedrich Karl and Johanna (Ruepp) S.; m. Lynne Violet Duguay; children: Alexander Johann, Leonard Friedrich, Hanna Violet. Diploma in chemistry, U. Innsbruck, Austria, 1975, PhD, 1978. Mem. faculty U. Mich., Ann Arbor, 1978—, assoc. prof. chem. engring., 1984-90, acting dir. Ctr. for Catalysis and Surface Sci., 1985-90, prof., interim chmn. dept. chem. engring., 1990-91, assoc. dir. Electron Microbeam Analysis Lab., 1990-91; chmn. dept. chem. engring., 1991—; vis. prof. U. Innsbruck, 1987-88, Tech. U. Vienna, 1988; cons. in field. Patentee bimetallic cluster catalysts, hydrodesulfurization catalysts and microelectronic gas sensors; contbr. over 70 articles to sci. jours. Fulbright-Hays scholar, 1978. Mem. AAAS, Am. Chem. Soc., Am. Inst. Chem. Engrs., Mich. Catalysis Soc. (sec.-treas. 1982-83, v.p. 1983-84, pres. 1984-85), Am. Soc. Engring. Edn. Home: 2335 Placid Way Ann Arbor MI 48105-1205 Office: U Mich Dept Chem Engring 2300 Hayward St Ann Arbor MI 48109-2136

SCHWANN, WILLIAM JOSEPH, publisher, musician, discographer; b. Salem, Ill., May 13, 1913; s. Henry W. and Effie A. (Garthwait) Schwan; m. Aire-Maija Kutvonen, June 1, 1959. Student, Louisville Conservatory Music, 1930-31; A.B., U. Louisville, 1935, D.Mus. (hon.), 1969; D.Mus. (hon.), New Eng. Conservatory Music, 1982; postgrad., Boston U. Sch. Music, 1935-36, Harvard U., 1937-38. Organist, music dir. various chs. Louisville, 1930-35; organ concerts, broadcasts, 1930-40; tchr. organ, piano, organist, music dir. Boston area, 1935-50; music revs. Boston Herald, Boston Transcript, others, 1937-39; owner Record Shop, Cambridge, Mass., 1939-53; mem. staff Radiation Lab., MIT, 1942-45; compiler, pub. 1st Long Playing Record Catalog now known as monthly Schwann-1 Record and Tape Guide, 1949, Artist Listing LP Catalog, semi-ann. Schwann-2 Record and Tape Guide, Schwann Children's Rec. Catalog, Basic Rec. Library, Basic Jazz Record Library, 1953-83, Schwann Record Catalog (now known as quarterly Schwann and Schwann Spectrum Catalogs, ann. Schwann Artist Listing Catalog), 1984—; pres., treas. W. Schwann, Inc., 1957-77; pres., pub., chief exec. officer ABC Schwann Publications, Inc., 1976-83. Editor: White House Record Library Catalog (listing 2,000 RIAA LP record collection presented to White House), Vol. I, 1973, Vol. II, 1981. Trustee Marlboro Sch. Music, Boston Ballet Co.; bd. dirs. Greater Boston Youth Symphony Orch., Longy Sch. Music, Cambridge Soc. Early Music. Recipient Disting. alumnus award U. Louisville, 1980, 1st Alumni Fellows award, 1990, Citation for Disting. Svcs., Music Libr. Assn., 1983, George Peabody medal for outstanding contbns. to music in Am. Peabody Inst., Johng Hopkins U., 1984; Hon. Gold Record award for 35 yrs. of svc. to music industry and pub. Recording Industry Assn. Am., 1984; Disting. Pub. Svc. to Profession Silver medal Boston U., 1985, Disting. Alumni award, 1994; Arion award Cambridge Soc. Early Music, 1991. Mem. Nat. Audubon Soc. (life), Nat. Parks and Conservation Assn. (life), New Eng. Wild Flower Preservation Soc.(life), Save-the-Redwoods League (life), Soc. for Protection N.H. Forests (life), Am. Forestry Assn. (life), Trustees of Reservations (life), Wilderness Soc. (life), Izaak Walton League (life), Nature Conservancy (life), Appalachian Mountain Club (life), Sierra Club (life), Sigma Alpha Iota (hon.). Clubs: St. Botolph, Harvard of Boston, Harvard Mus. Assn. Home and Office: 26 Old Winter St Lincoln MA 01773-3406

SCHWANTNER, JOSEPH, composer, educator; b. Chgo., Mar. 22, 1943; m. Janet Elaine Rossate; 2 children. B.Mus., Chgo. Conservatory Coll.; M.Mus., Northwestern U., 1966, D.Mus., 1968. Teaching fellow Northwestern U., 1966-68; mem. faculty Chgo. Conservatory Coll., 1967-68; asst. prof. Pacific Lutheran U., 1968-69, Ball State U., 1969-70; successively asst. prof., assoc. prof., prof. Eastman Sch. Music, U. Rochester, 1970—; composer-in-residence St. Louis Symphony Orch., 1982-84. Compositions include Aftertones of Infinity (Pulitzer prize for music 1979), Diaphonia Intervallum, Chronicon, Autumn Canticle, Consortium, In Aeternum, Modis Caelestis, Canticle for the Evening Bells, Elixir, Wild Angels of the Open Hills, And the Mountains Rising Nowhere, Sparrows. Recipient Faricy award, 1965, BMI Student award, 1965, 66, 67, Bearns prize Columbia U., 1967; Nat. Inst. Arts and Letters Charles Ives scholar, 1970; N.Y. State Council on Arts Creative Arts Public Service grantee, 1973; NEA grantee; Guggenheim fellow, 1978-79. Office: Eastman Sch Music 26 Gibbs St Rochester NY 14604-2599*

SCHWANZ, H(ERMAN) LEE, publishing company executive; b. Lorimor, Iowa, Apr. 29, 1923; s. Arthur I. and Elva Rae (Caffery) S.; m. Kathleen J. Boland, Sept. 1, 1947; children: Michael L., Leslie Anne Schwanz Satran, Stephen E., Susan E. Schwanz Pigorsch. B.S. in Agrl. Journalism, Iowa State U., 1947. Farm editor Cedar Rapids (Iowa) Gazette, 1947-50; asso. editor Country Gentleman mag. Curtis Pub. Co., Phila., 1950-55; editor, pub. Agrl. Pubs., Milw., 1955-70; pres., pub. Market Communications, Milw., 1970-81, Elmbrook Publishing Co., Brookfield, Wis., 1981-90, H. Lee Schwanz & Assocs., Brookfield, 1990—. Editor Farmer's Digest, 1970-88, Buying for the Farm. 1981-87. Served with 90th inf. div. AUS, 1943-46. Decorated Silver Star. Mem. Westmoor Country Club, Soc. Profl. Journalists. Republican. Methodist. Home and Office: 2645 Maple Hill Ln Brookfield WI 53045-4356

SCHWARCZ, HENRY PHILIP, geologist, educator; b. Chgo., July 22, 1933; s. Arthur and Zita Elizabeth (Strauss) S.; m. Molly Ann Robinson, Dec. 20, 1964; 1 child, Joshua Arthur. A.B., U. Chgo., 1952; M.Sc. in Geochemistry, Calif. Inst. Tech., 1955, Ph.D. in Geology, 1960. Rsch. assoc. E. Fermi Inst., U. Chgo., 1960-62; prof. geology McMaster U., Hamilton, Ont., Can., 1962—, chmn., assoc. mem. dept. anthropology, 1988-91; mem. assoc. com. on meteorites NRC of Can., 1978-86; vis. fellow Clare Hall Coll. Cambridge U., 1991-92, Australian Nat. U., 1995; vis. prof. Hebrew U., Jerusalem, 1992; assoc. mem. dept. anthropology U. Toronto, 1993—; mem. panel refs. Rivista di Antropologia (Roma). Assoc. editor Geochimica et Cosmochimica Acta, 1984—, Jour. Human Evolution, 1994—, Geoarchaeology, 1994—; mem. editorial bd. Jour. Archaeol. Sci., 1986—; contbr. articles to profl. jours., chpts. to books. Fulbright fellow, Pisa, Italy, 1968-69, Killam fellow Can. Coun., 1993—. Fellow Royal Soc. Can., Geol. Soc. Am. (Archeol. Geol. Div. award 1991); mem. Geochem. Soc., Lithoprobe NSERC 1991—), Am. Quaternary Assn., Acad. III Sci. (mem. coun.), Geol. Soc. Am. (chmn. archeol. geol. divsn.). Avocations: playing violin, drawing. Office: McMaster Univ, Dept Geology, Hamilton, ON Canada L8S 4M1

SCHWARCZ, STEVEN LANCE, lawyer, law educator; b. N.Y.C., Nov. 10, 1949; s. Charles and Elinor Schwarcz; m. Susan Beth Kolodny, Aug. 24, 1975; children: Daniel Benjamin, Rebekah Mara. BS summa cum laude, in Aero. Engring., New York U., 1971; JD, Columbia U., 1974. Bar: N.Y. 1975, U.S. Dist. Ct. (so. dist.) N.Y. 1975. Assoc. Shearman & Sterling, N.Y.C., 1974-82, ptnr., 1983-89; ptnr. chmn. structured fin. practice group Kaye, Scholer, Fierman, Hays & Handler, 1989—; adj. prof. law Yeshiva U., Benjamin N. Cardozo Sch. Law, N.Y.C., 1983—; vis. lectr. Yale Law Sch., 1992—; lectr. in law Columbia Law Sch., 1992—. Contbr. articles to profl. jours. Chmn. Friends of the Eldridge St. Synagogue, N.Y.C., 1979—, Legis. Drafting Rsch. Fund. Recipient First Prize award Pub. Speaking Contest, NYU, 1971; George Granger Brown scholar, 1971; NSF grantee in Math., 1969. Fellow Am. Coll. Commercial Fin. Lawyers; mem. Am. Law Inst., Assn. of Bar of City of N.Y. (environ. law com. 1975-78, nuclear tech. com. 1979-81, sci. and law com. 1985—, chmn. 1987—). Tau Beta Pi. Jewish. Office: Kaye Scholer Fierman Hays & Handler 425 Park Ave New York NY 10022-3506

SCHWARCZ, VERA, East Asian studies educator, history educator; b. May 8, 1947; came to U.S. in 1961; BA in French Lit. and Oriental Religions, Vassar Coll., 1969; MA in East Asian Studies, Yale U., 1971; PhD in Chinese History, Stanford U., 1977. Instr. history Stanford U., 1973; lectr. Chinese history Wesleyan U., Middletown, Conn., 1975-77, asst. prof. Chinese history, 1975-83, chair East Asian studies, 1982-84, 85-88, prof. history, 1988—, Mansfield Freeman prof. East Asian studies, 1988—; dir. Mansfield Freeman Ctr. East Asian Studies, 1987-88; bd. dirs. Sino-Judaic Inst.; vis. scholar Beijing U., China, 1983, 86, 89, exchange scholar, 1979-80; vis. scholar Centre de documentation sur la Chine Contemporaine, Paris, 1985, Mishkenot Sha'ananim, Jerusalem, 1991, Chinese Acad. Social Sci. Internat. Inst. Chinese Culture, Beijing, 1989; guest lectr. DAO Assn., Cluj, Romania, 1993; other study trips to Taiwan, Hong Kong, Beijing, Tibet. Author: China: Inside the People's Republic, 1972, Long Road Home: A China Journal, 1984, The Chinese Enlightenment: The Legacy of the May Fourth Movement in Modern China, 1986, Zhongguo de qimeng yundong (China's Enlightenment), 1989, Time for Telling Truth is Running Out: Conversations with Zhang Shenfu, 1992; editorial bd. China Rev. Internat., Bulletin Concerned Asian Scholars, 1979—, History and Theory, 1981-84; contbr. articles to profl. jours.; contbr. poems, fiction to mags.; speaker in field. Guggenheim fellow 1989-90, Founders fellow AAUQ, 1988-89, Faculty fellow Ctr. Humanities Wesleyan U., 1981, Rsch. fellow Social Sci. Rsch. Coun., 1982-83, Advanced Trainee fellow NAS, 1979-80, NDFL fellow 1973-74, Kent fellow Danforth Found., 1971-73, AAUW grantee, 1974-75, Am. Coun. Learned Societies grantee, 1978, Am. Philosophical Soc. grantee, 1981, 85. Mem. AAUP, Assn. Asian Studies (Levenson prize com. 1991-92, chair, 1992-93, coun. confs. 1989—, com. women 1977-78), New Eng. Assn. Asian Studies (pres. 1988-89), Am. Hist. Assn., New Eng. China Faculty Seminar (Harvard), Modern China Faculty Seminar (Columbia), Soc. Values Higher Edn., China Inst. (N.Y.). Office: Wesleyan U Wesleyan Sta Middletown CT 06459

SCHWARDT, SUSAN KELLY, civic organization executive; b. Corning, N.Y., Dec. 26, 1936; d. Merle John and Marcia Phillips (Smith) Kelly; m. David Noel Schwardt, June 6, 1956; children: Ellen Schwardt Popp, Judith Schwardt Bray, Jeffrey David, Kevin John. BA in Psychology, U. Rochester, 1960. Officer LWV, Rochester, N.Y., 1971-84; dir. election law and govt. LWV of N.Y. State, Albany, 1985-87, v.p., 1987-89, pres., 1989-91. Mem. curriculum adv. com. Webster (N.Y.) Cen. Sch. Dist.; 1970s; pres. of congregation First Unitarian Ch., Rochester, 1973-75; mem. Town of Webster/State of N.Y. Waterfront Revitalization Com., 1985-86. Avocations: violin, skiing.

SCHWARTING, ARTHUR ERNEST, university dean; b. Waubay, S.D., June 8, 1917; s. John Ernest and Johanna Martha (Boelte) S.; m. Roberta L. Mitchell, June 14, 1941; children: Jon Michael, Stephen Arthur (dec.), Gerald Allen. B.S., S.D. State U., 1940; Ph.D., Ohio State U., 1943. Instr. U. Nebr., 1943-45, asst. prof., 1945-49; assoc. prof. U. Conn., Storrs, 1949-53; prof. pharmacognosy U. Conn., 1953-81, prof. emeritus, 1981—; dean U. Conn. (Sch. Pharmacy), 1970-80; vis. prof. U. Munich, 1968-69. Author: (with others) Introduction to Chromatography, 1968, 2d edit., 1985; editor: Jour. Natural Products, 1960-76. Mem. Mansfield Bd. Edn., Conn., 1965-70; bd. dirs. Am. Found. Pharm. Edn., 1974-80. Recipient Research Achievement award Am. Pharm. Assn. Found., 1964; U. Conn. Alumni Assn. award for faculty excellence, 1965, Centennial Achievement award Ohio State U., 1970, Disting. Alumnus award S.D. State U., 1986. Fellow AAAS; mem. Am. Assn. Colls. Pharmacy (pres. 1971-72, pres. council deans 1977-78), Am. Pharm. Assn., Am. Soc. Pharmacognosy (hon. mem. 1981), Sigma Xi, Phi Lambda Upsilon, Phi Kappa Phi, Rho Chi. Lutheran. Research and publs. on chemistry and biochemistry of natural drug products. Home: 330 Capstan Dr Placida FL 33946-2222

SCHWARTZ, AARON ROBERT, lawyer, former state legislator; b. Galveston, Tex., July 17, 1926; s. Joseph and Clara (Bulbe) S.; m. Marilyn Cohn, July 14, 1951; children: Richard Austin, Robert Allen, John Reed, Thomas Lee. Pre-law student, Tex. A&M U., 1948; J.D., U. Tex., 1951. Bar: Tex. 1951. Mem. Tex. Ho. of Reps., 1955-59; Mem. Tex. Senate, 1960-

81, past chmn. rules, jurisprudence and natural resources coms.; chmn. Tex. Coastal & Marine Council, U.S. Coastal States Orgn.; bd. dirs. Ins. Corp. of Am., Houston. Contbr. articles to profl. jours. Mem. U. Tex. Med. Br. Devel. Found.; mem. exec. com. Galveston Bay Found; appointed to Tex. Oil Spill Oversight Commn., 1993. Served with USN, 1944-46; to 2d lt. USAFR, 1948-53. Recipient conservation and legis. awards, Outstanding Citizen award Galveston Jr. C. of C., 1981, Man of Yr., People of Vision award Galveston chpt. Soc. for Prevention of Blindness, 1986, Disting. Service award Nat. Hurricane Conf., Tex. Coastal Mgmt. Adv. Com., 1987. Mem. Tex. State Bar Assn., Galveston County Bar Assn. Democrat. Jewish. Home: PO Box 3398 Galveston TX 77552

SCHWARTZ, ALAN E., lawyer; b. Detroit, Dec. 21, 1925; s. Maurice H. and Sophia (Welkowitz) S.; m. Marianne Shapero, Aug. 24, 1950; children: Marc Alan, Kurt Nathan, Ruth Anne. Student, Western Mich. Coll., 1944-45; BA with distinction, U. Mich., 1947; LLB magna cum laude, Harvard U., 1950; LLD (hon.), Wayne State U., 1983, U. Detroit, 1985. Bar: N.Y. 1951, Mich. 1952. Assoc. Kelley, Drye & Warren, N.Y.C., 1950-52; mem. Honigman, Miller, Schwartz & Cohn, Detroit, 1952—; now sr. mem. Honigman, Miller, Schwartz & Cohn; spl. asst. counsel N.Y. State Crime Commn., 1951; dir. Unisys Corp., Detroit Edison Co., Core Industries Inc., Handleman Co., Howell Industries, Inc., Pulte Corp., Comerica Inc. Editor: Harvard Law Rev., 1950. Vice pres., mem. exec. com. Detroit Symphony Orch.; v.p., bd. dirs. United Found.; bd. dirs. Detroit Renaissance, Detroit Econ. Growth Corp., New Detroit, Met. Affairs Corp., Harper-Grace Hosp., Interlochen Arts Acad., Skillman Found.; adv. mem. Arts Commn., City of Detroit. Served as ensign Supply Corps, USNR, 1945-46. Recipient Mich. Heritage Hall of Fame award, 1984, George W. Romney award for lifetime achievement in volunteerism, 1994. Mem. Mich. Bar Assns. Clubs: Franklin Hills Country; Detroit, Economic (dir.). Home: 4120 Echo Rd Bloomfield Hills MI 48302-1941 Office: Honigman Miller Schwartz & Cohn 2290 1st National Bldg Detroit MI 48226

SCHWARTZ, ALAN GIFFORD, sport company executive; b. N.Y.C., Nov. 7, 1931; s. Kevie Waldemar and Vera (Isaacs) S.; m. Roslyn Shulman, Sept. 6, 1958; children: Steven, Andrew, Sally, Elizabeth. BS, Yale U., 1952; MBA, Harvard U., 1954. Ptnr. Gifford Investment Co., Chgo., 1954—; CEO Tennis Corp. of Am., Chgo., 1969—, chmn. bd., 1974—; chmn. exec. com. First Colonia Bankshares, Chgo., 1984—; dir. Mich. Ave. Nat. Bank, Chgo., Comtrex Systems, Inc., Mt. Laurel, N.J.; trustee Roosevelt U., 1994—; mem. bd. dirs. Inst. European & Asian Studies, 1993—, U.S. Tennis Assn., 1994—. Contbr. articles to profl. jours.; editorial cons. Club Industry mag., 1985—. Bd. dirs. Grad. Sch. of Bus., Duke U., Durham, N.C., 1977—, McCormick Boys and Girls Club, 1989—. Elected to Club Industry Hall of Fame, 1987. Mem. Standard Club of Chgo. Jewish. Avocations: travel, tennis. Office: Tennis Corp of Am 2020 W Fullerton Chicago IL 60647

SCHWARTZ, ALAN LEIGH, pediatrician, educator; b. N.Y.C., Apr. 25, 1948; s. Robert and Joyce (Goldner) S.; m. Judith Child, June 22, 1974; 1 child, Timothy Child. BA, Case Western Res. U., 1974, PHD in Pharmacology, 1974, MD, 1976. Diplomate Am. Bd. Pediatrics. Intern Children's Hosp., Boston, 1976-77, resident, 1976-78, fellow Dana Farber Cancer Inst., 1978-80; instr. Harvard Med. Sch., Boston, 1980-81, asst. prof., 1981-83, assoc. prof., 1983-86; prof. pediatrics, molecular biology and pharmacology Washington U. Sch. Medicine, St. Louis, 1986—; vis. scientist MIT, Boston, 1979-82; mem. sci. adv. bd. Nat. Inst. Child Health and Human Devel., NIH, Bethesda, Md., 1988—; investigator Am. Heart Assn. Alumni Endowed Prof. Pediatrics, Wash. U. Sch. Medicine, 1987—. Office: Washington U Sch Medicine Dept Pediatrics Box 8116 1 Children's Pl Saint Louis MO 63110-1093

SCHWARTZ, ALAN VICTOR, advertising agency executive; b. Detroit, July 12, 1948; s. Seymour and Adeline (Goldstein) S.; m. Linda Toba Dershowitz, Aug. 20, 1981; children: Stacy Ilana, Andrew Robert. B.S. with honors, Lehigh U., 1970; M.B.A. with highest honors, Cornell U., 1972. C.P.A., N.Y. Mgr. Price Waterhouse, Huntington, N.Y., 1972-79; v.p. dir. fin. control Doyle Dane Bernbach, N.Y.C., 1979-81; v.p. chief fin. officer Bernard Hodes Advt., N.Y.C., 1981-84; sr. v.p., chief operating and fin. officer, 1984-87, exec. v.p., chief operating and fin. officer, 1987—; bd. mgrs. Evans Tower, treas. 1991-92, pres. 1991-92; Vice campaign chmn. United Way, L.I., 1988. Mem. Nat. Assn. Accts. (various directorships and treas.), N.Y. State Soc. C.P.A.s, Lehigh Alumni Assn. (pres. L.I. chpt. 1977-79, treas. 1975-77). Office: Bernard Hodes Advt 555 Madison Ave New York NY 10022-3301

SCHWARTZ, ALFRED, university dean; b. Chgo., Jan. 8, 1922; s. Isadore and Lena (Ziff) S.; m. Delle Weiss, Aug. 26, 1945; children: Reid Mitchell, Karen Ruth. B.Ed., Chgo. Tchrs. Coll., 1944; M.A. in Polit. Sci., U. Chgo., 1946, Ph.D. in Ednl. Adminstrn., 1949. Tchr. Chgo. pub. schs., 1944-45; contact officer VA, 1946; instr. U. Chgo. Lab. Sch., 1946-50; assoc. prof. edn. Drake U., 1950-56, U. Del.; also exec. sec. Del-Sch. Study Council, 1956-58; dean (Univ. Coll.); prof. Coll. Edn., Drake U., 1958-85, dean, 1964-79, 80-84, dean emeritus, 1985; acting v.p. acad. adminstrn. Coll. Edn., Coll. Edn., 1979-80; cons., 1985—; adviser Iowa Dept. Pub. Instrn.; mem. coordinating bd. Nat. Council Accreditation for Tchr. Edn.; chmn. tchr. edn. and adv. com. Iowa Dept. Pub. Instrn. Author: (with Harlan L. Hagman) Administration in Profile for School Executives, 1954, (with Stuart Tiedeman) Evaluating Student Progress, 1957, (with Willard Fox) Managerial Guide for School Principals, 1965. Mem. Gov.'s Commn. State-Local Relations. Mem. World Council on Curriculum and Instrn., Iowa Assn. Colls. for Tchr. Edn. (pres., exec. sec.), Am. Profs. for Peace in Middle East, Am. Ednl. Research Assn., Iowa Ednl. Assn., NEA, Phi Delta Kappa, Kappa Delta Pi. Home: 3450 3rd Ave Apt 511 San Diego CA 92103-4939

SCHWARTZ, ALLEN G., federal judge; b. Bklyn., Aug. 23, 1934; s. Herbert and Florence (Safier) S.; m. Joan Ruth Teitel, Jan. 17, 1965; children: David Aaron, Rachel Ann, Deborah Eve. BBA, CCNY, 1955; LLB, U. Pa., 1958. Bar: N.Y. 1958. Asst. dist. atty. Office of Dist. Atty., N.Y. County, 1959-62; assoc. firm Paskus Gordon & Hyman, N.Y.C., 1962-65; ptnr. firm Koch Lankenau Schwartz & Kovner, N.Y.C., 1965-69, Dornbush Mensch Mandelstam & Schwartz, N.Y.C., 1969-75; mem. Schwartz & Schreiber, P.C., N.Y.C., 1975-77; corp. counsel City of N.Y., 1978-81; mem. Schwartz Klink & Schreiber, P.C., 1982-87; ptnr. Proskauer Rose Goetz & Mendelsohn, N.Y.C., 1987-94; judge U.S. Dist. Ct. (so. dist.) N.Y., N.Y.C., 1994—; mem. ex officio N.Y.C. Bd. Ethics, 1978-81; pro bono sports commr. City of N.Y., 1982-83. Research editor: U. Pa. Law Rev, 1957-58. Office: US Courthouse 500 Pearl St New York NY 10007

SCHWARTZ, ALLYSON Y., state senator; b. N.Y.C., Oct. 3, 1948; d. Everett and Renee Perl Young; m. David Schwartz, 1970; children: Daniel, Jordan. Ba, Simmons Coll., 1970; MSS, Bryn Mawr Coll., 1972. Founder, exec. dir. Elizabeth Blackwell Health Ctr. for Women, 1975-88; acting commr., 1st dep. commr. Dept. Human Svcs., 1988-90; mem. Pa. State Senate 4th dist., 1990—; minority chmn. Edn. Com., 1994—; mem. Aging and Youth Com., Pub. Health and Welfare Com., Comty. and Econ. Devel. Com. Policy. Mem. Pa. Citizen's Crime Commn. Task Force on Juvenile Justice, 1988-89, Mayor's Task Force on Juvenile Justice, 1988-89, Mayor's Pub.-Pvt. Task Force on Homelessness; bd. dirs., founding mem. Women's Way, 1976-88; chair health com. Nat. Coun. State Legislators, 1994, Ea. Regional Women's Network, 1994. Named Social Worker of Yr. Nat. Assn. Social Workers, 1990. Mem. Child Welfare League. Office: Senate State Capital Harrisburg PA 17101

SCHWARTZ, AMY ELIZABETH, editorial writer, columnist; b. N.Y.C., July 26, 1962; d. Stuart Grad and Doris (Greenburg) S. BA, Harvard U. 1984. Rschr. Harper's mag., N.Y.C., 1984; reporter, rschr. The New Republic, Washington, 1985; rschr. writer The Washington Post, 1985-87, editorial writer, trainee, 1987-89, editorial writer, 1989—. Vol. tchr. Jewish Study Ctr., Washington, 1993-94. Recipient Bernie Harrison Meml. award for commentary Washington-Balt. Newspaper Guild, 1992; Humboldt Found. Chancellors scholar, Bonn, Germany, 1990-91. Mem. Newspaper Guild. Jewish. Office: Washington Post Editorial Page 1150 15th St NW Washington DC 20071-0002

SCHWARTZ, AMY MARGARET, children's book author, illustrator; b. San Diego, Apr. 2, 1954; d. Isador Henry and Eva (Herzberg) S.; m. Leonard Seth Marcus, May 20, 1990; 1 child, Jacob Henry. Student, Antioch Coll., 1972-73; BFA, Calif. Coll. Arts and Crafts, 1975. Author, illustrator: Bea and Mr. Jones, 1982, Begin at the Beginning, 1983, Her Majesty, Aunt Essie, 1984, Mrs. Moskowitz and the Sabbath Candelsticks, 1984, Yossel Zissel and the Wisdom of Chelm, 1986, Oma and Bobo, 1987, Annabelle Swift, Kindergartner, 1988, (with Leonard S. Marcus) Mother Goose's Little Misfortunes, 1991, Camper of the Week, 1991, A Teeny-Tiny Baby, 1994, (with Henry Schwartz) Mak a Face, 1994; illustrator numerous others, including The Purple Coat, 1986, How I Captured a Dinosaur, 1989. Recipient numerous award Parents Choice, 1982, 88; feature book award Parents Choice, 1982, rev. book, 1983; One of Best Books award Sch. Libr. Jour., 1982, 87, 88, starred rev. book, 1984, 93, 94; One of 100 Best Children's Books award N.Y. Pub. Libr., 1983, 88, 90, 94; Children's Choice award Internat. Reading Assn.-CBS, 1984, Nat. Jewish Book award, 1984, award Assn. Jewish Librs., 1984, Christopher award, 1989, Notable Book award ALA, 1987, 88, award Libr. of Congress, 1988, Parents mag., 1988, N.Y. Times Book Review Best Illus. Childrens Book, 1994, N.Y. Times Book Review Notable Childrens Book, 1994. Office: care Jane Feder 305 E 24th St New York NY 10010

SCHWARTZ, ANNA JACOBSON, economic historian; b. N.Y.C., Nov. 11, 1915; married; four children. BA, Barnard Coll., 1934; MA, Columbia U., 1935, PhD, 1964; LittD (hon.), U. Fla., 1987; ArtsD (hon.), Stonehill Coll., 1989; LLD (hon.), Iona Coll. 1992. Researcher USDA, 1936, Columbia U. Social Sci. Research Council, 1936-41; mem. sr. research staff Nat. Bur. Econ. Research Inc., N.Y.C., 1941—; instr. Bklyn. Coll., 1952, Baruch Coll., 1959-60; adj. prof. econs. grad. CCNY, 1967-69, grad. sch. CUNY, 1986—, NYU Grad. Sch. Arts and Sci., 1969-70; hon. vis. prof. City U. Bus. Sch., London, 1984—. Mem. editorial bd. Am. Econ. Rev., 1972-78, Jour. Money, Credit and Banking, 1974-75, 84—, Jour. Monetary Econs., 1975—, Jour. Fin. Svcs. Rsch., 1993—; contbr. numerous articles to profl. jours. Disting. fellow Am. Econ. Assn., 1993. Mem. Western Econ. Assn. (pres. 1987-88). Office: Nat Bur Econ Research 269 Mercer St Fl 8 New York NY 10003-6633

SCHWARTZ, ANTHONY, veterinary surgeon, educator; b. Bklyn., July 30, 1940; s. Murray and Miriam Sarah (Wittes) S.; m. Claudia Rosenberg, July 21, 1963; children: Thomas Frederick, Eric Leigh. Student, Mich. State U., 1957-58; DVM, Cornell U., 1963; PhD, Ohio State U., 1972. Diplomate Am. Coll. Vet. Surgeons (bd. of regents 1989-92). Gen. practice vet. medicine Huntington, N.Y., 1963-66; resident in surgery Animal Med. Ctr., N.Y.C., 1968-69; resident in surgery Ohio State U., Columbus, 1969-70, asst. prof., head sect. small animal surgery, 1973; asst. prof. then assoc. prof. comparative medicine Yale U. Sch. Medicine, New Haven, 1973-79; assoc. prof. then prof., chmn. dept. surgery, assoc. dean Tufts U. Sch. Vet. Medicine, Boston, 1979-89; assoc. dean clin. edn. Tufts U. Sch. Vet. Medicine, 1989-93, prof., chmn. dept. surgery, assoc. dean academic affairs, 1993—; cons. U.S. Surg. Corp., Norwalk, Conn., 1975—. Author: (with others) Small Animal Surgery, 1989; mem. editorial bd.: Vet. Surgery, 1987-90, Jour. Investigative Surgery, 1987—; assoc. editor: Text Book of Small Animal Surgery, 1985; contbr. articles to profl. jours. Capt. U.S. Army Vet Corps, 1966-68. Recipient 1st prize N.Y. State Vet. Med. Soc., 1963; Robert Wood Johnson Health Policy fellow, Washington, 1988-89; NIH grantee, 1975-84. Mem. AVMA (legis. planning com. 1989-92, coun. on govt. affairs 1992—), AAAS, Am. Assn. Immunologists, Am. Assn. Vet. Clinicians, Assn. Am. Vet. Med. Colls. (Washington, exec. dir., treas. 1992-93), Nat. Academies of Practice, Mass. Vet. Med. Assn. (animal welfare com. 1990—, chmn. 1990-91), Sigma Xi, Phi Kappa Phi. Democrat. Jewish. Office: Tufts U Sch Vet Medicine 200 Westboro Rd North Grafton MA 01536-1828

SCHWARTZ, ARNOLD (ARNIE SHAYNE), pharmacologist, biophysicist, biochemist, educator, actor, director, producer; b. Bronx, N.Y., Mar. 1, 1929; s. Saul and Ray S.; m. Ina Price, Dec. 23, 1956; children: Tracy, Stacy. BSc in Pharmacy cum laude, LIU, 1951, DSc (hon.), 1988; MSc, Ohio State U., Columbus, 1957; PhD, SUNY, Bklyn., 1960. Mem. faculty Baylor Coll. Medicine, 1962-77, prof. pharmacology, 1968-72, head div. myocardial biology, chmn. dept. cell biophysics, 1972-77, Disting. Univ. prof., 1989; Edward Wendland prof. materia medica and therapeutics U. Cin. Med. Ctr., 1977-89, chmn. dept. pharmacology and cell biophysics, 1977-94; dir. Inst. Molecular Pharmacology and Biophysics, 1994—; mem. rev. panels Nat. Heart, Lung and Blood Inst. and Am. Heart Assn., 1970-89; pres. Am. sect. Internat. Soc. for Heart Research, 1976-77; pres. drug cons. co. CVR, Inc. Mem. editorial bds. profl. jours.; editor: Methods in Pharmacology Series; contbr. over 400 articles on cardiovascular pharmacology and biochemistry, mechanisms of digitalis and calcium antagonist action, role of calcium in cardiac function, molecular biology of ion channels and receptors to profl. jours. Actor, dir. profl. theatre, TV, cinema, med. and health TV. Served with USAF, 1952-56. Recipient Rsch. Career Devel. award, 1965-72, Samuel Kaplan, M.D. Visionary award S.W. Ohio affiliate Am. Heart Assn., 1992, Rsch. Merit award, 1992, Otto Krayer award in pharmacology Am. Soc. Pharmacology and Exptl. Therapy, 1993, Ariens award in molecular pharmacology Dutch. Pharmacol. Soc., 1993; Josiah Macy scholar Oxford U., 1979-80; NIH fellow, 1960-62; NIH grantee, 1989. Fellow Am. Coll. Cardiology; mem. N.Y. Acad. Sci. Office: Univ Cin Med Ctr 231 Bethesda Ave Cincinnati OH 45267-0001 *The need to discover is of paramount importance.*

SCHWARTZ, ARTHUR LEONARD, pulp company executive, lawyer; b. Bronx, N.Y., Sept. 25, 1941; s. Edward and Ruth (Pruzansky) S.; m. Louis Eleanor Hiltzik, June 16, 1963; children: Peter H., Ellen B. BA, CCNY, 1963; LLB, NYU, 1966, LLM in Taxation, 1967. Bar: N.Y. 1966, U.S. Ct. Appeals (D.C. cir.) 1967, U.S Supreme Ct. 1968. Law clk. Hertz Corp., N.Y.C., 1965-67; staff Income Tax Bur. N.Y.C., 1967; law clk. U.S. Ct. Claims, Washington, 1967-69; assoc. prof. George Washington U. Sch. Law, Washington, 1967-69; staff atty. U.S. Treasury Dept., Tax Legis. Counsel Office, Washington, 1969-71; atty. Roberts & Holland, N.Y.C., 1971-76; tax counsel, v.p. Parsons & Whittemore Inc., N.Y.C., 1976-86, pres., chief exec. officer, 1986—; pres. Ala. River Pulp Co., Monroeville, 1986—; pres. Ala. Pine Pulp Co., 1989—; exec. v.p. St. Anne-Nackawic Pulp and Paper Co. Ltd., N.B., Can.; bd. dirs. Parsons & Whittemore France, Paris. Contbr. articles on tax subjects to profl. jours. Mem. ABA, N.Y. State Bar Assn. Office: Alabama Pine Pulp Co Inc US 84 County Rd 39 Perdue Hill AL 36470

SCHWARTZ, ARTHUR ROBERT, food writer, critic, consultant; b. N.Y.C., Mar. 24, 1947; s. Lawrence and Sydell Bedona (Sonkin) S.; m. Elaine Billie Rothseid, Aug. 16, 1969 (div. 1982). BS in Bus. and Journalism, U. Md., 1968; MA, CUNY, Bklyn., 1970. Editor Bklyn. Graphic, 1968-69; food and wine writer Newsday, L.I., N.Y., 1969-79; exec. food editor N.Y. Daily News, 1979-89, restaurant critic, 1979—; lectr. New Sch. for Social Rsch., N.Y.C., 1987—; TV reporter Sta. WNYW-TV Fox-5, N.Y.C., 1989; talk show host Sta. WOR Radio, 1992—; syndicated food critic. Author: Cooking in a Small Kitchen, 1979, Emergency Meals, 1990, Soup Suppers, 1994; contbr. author: Better Times; also numerous mag. articles. Home and Office: 320 E 42d St New York NY 10017

SCHWARTZ, AUBREY EARL, artist; b. N.Y.C., Jan. 13, 1928; s. Louis and Clara S. Student, Art Students League, Bklyn. Mus. Art Sch., 1969-94; Prof. emeritus Harpur Coll., SUNY, Binghamton, 1994—; prof. art Harpur Coll., SUNY, Binghamton, 1969—. One-man shows Grippi Gallery, N.Y.C., 1958, Art U.S.A., N.Y. Coliseum, N.Y.C., 1959, Contemporary Graphic Art, U.S. State Dept., 1959, group shows include Whitney Mus. Am. Art. N.Y.C., 1957; represented in permanent collections Nat. Gallery Art, Washington, Bklyn. Mus. Art, Phila. Mus. Art, Library Congress, Washington, Art Inst. Chgo. Recipient 1st prize for graphic art Boston Arts Festival 1960; Guggenheim fellow, 1958-60; Tamarind fellow, 1960; N.Y. State CAPS fellow, 1973-74. Home: 104 Main St Afton NY 13730

SCHWARTZ, BERNARD, lawyer, educator; b. N.Y.C., Aug. 25, 1923; s. Isadore and Ethel (Levenson) S.; m. Aileen Haas, Aug. 18, 1950; 1 child, Brian Michael. BSS, CCNY, 1944; LLB, NYU, 1944; LLM, Harvard U., 1945; PhD, Cambridge (Eng.) U., 1947, LLD, 1956; Doctorat d'Universite, U. Paris, 1963. Bar: N.Y. 1945. Mem. law faculty NYU, 1947-92, Edwin D.

Webb prof. law, 1963-92; Chapman Disting. prof. law U. of Tulsa, 1992—; cons. Hoover Commn., 1955; chief counsel, staff dir. spl. subcom. legislative oversight U.S Ho. Reps., 1957-58; Tagore Law lectr., Calcutta, India, 1984; corr. mem. Nat. Acad. Law and Social Scis., Argentina, 1986—. Author: French Adminstrative Law and the Common Law World, 1954, The Supreme Court, 1957, The Professor and the Commissions, 1959, Introduction to American Administrative Law, 1962, The Reins of Power, 1963, Commentary on the Constitution of the U.S., 5 vols, 1963-68, The Roots of Freedom, 1967, Legal Control of Government, 1972, Constitutional Law: A Textbook, 1972, 2d edit., 1979, The Law in America, 1974, Administrative Law, 1976, 3d edit., 1991, The Great Rights of Mankind, 1977, expanded edit., 1992, Administrative Law: A Casebook, 1977, 4th edit., 1994, Super Chief: Earl Warren and His Supreme Court, 1983, Inside the Warren Court, 1983, The Unpublished Opinions of the Warren Court, 1985, Some Makers of American Law, 1985, Swann's Way: The School Busing Case and the Supreme Court, 1986, Behind Bakke: The Supreme Court and Affirmative Action, 1988, The Unpublished Opinions of the Burger Court, 1988, The Ascent of Pragmatism: The Burger Court in Action, 1990, The New Right and the Constitution, 1990, Constitutional Issues: Freedom of the Press 1992, Main Currents in American Legal Thought, 1993, A History of the Supreme Court, 1993. Ann. Survey Am. Law dedicated in his name, 1988. Mem. ABA. Office: U Tulsa Coll Of Law Tulsa OK 74104

SCHWARTZ, BERNARD, physician; b. Toronto, Can., Nov. 12, 1927; s. Samuel and Gertrude (Levinsky) S.; children: Lawrence Frederick, Karen Lynne, Jennifer Carla, Ariane Samara. M.D. U. Toronto, 1951; M.S., State U. Iowa, 1953, Ph.D., 1959. Intern U. Hosps., State U. Iowa, 1951-52, resident ophthalmology, 1951-54; research fellow U. Iowa, 1954-58; asst. prof. to assoc. prof. Downstate Med. Center for State U. N.Y., 1958-68; prof. ophthalmology Tufts U., 1968-93, chmn. dept., 1968-90, prof. emeritus ophthalmology, 1993—. Author: Syphilis and the Eye; Editor in chief of: Survey of Ophthalmology, 1968—; Contbr. articles to profl. jours. Dir. Mass. Soc. Prevention of Blindness. Fellow Am. Acad. Ophthalmology, ACS; mem. Assn. Rsch. in Ophthalmology, New Eng. Ophthalmol. Soc. N.Y. Acad. Medicine, N.Y. Acad. Scis., Soc. Française D'Ophthalmologie, Sigma Xi. Home: 180 Beacon St Boston MA 02116-1455 Office: 20 Park Plz Ste 535 Boston MA 02116-4300

SCHWARTZ, BERNARD See CURTIS, TONY

SCHWARTZ, BERNARD L., electronics company executive; b. 1925. BBA, CCNY, 1948. Ptnr. Schnee, Hover & Schwartz, 1948-62; sr. v.p. APL Corp., Fla., 1962-68; with Leasco Corp., 1969-72; chmn. bd., chief exec. officer Leasco Corp., Miami Beach, 1969-72; with Loral Corp., N.Y.C., 1972—, former pres., 1973-81, chmn., chief exec. officer, 1972—, also dir.; chmn., chief executive officer, K&F Industries, Inc. With U.S. Army, 1943-45. Office: Loral Corp 600 3rd Ave Fl 36 New York NY 10016-1901*

SCHWARTZ, C. EDWARD, hospital administrator; b. Indpls., Oct. 16, 1940; s. Edward and Emily (Workins) S.; children: Ryan, Jeff, Robin. BA in Philosophy, Ky.-Wesleyan Coll., 1962; MDiv., Meth. Theol. Sch., 1965; M in Hosp. Adminstrn., Washington U., 1968. Asst. adminstr. U. Okla. Hosp., Oklahoma City, 1968-72; hosp. adminstr. Muhlenberg Community Hosp., Greenville, Ky., 1972-76; assoc. dir. for hosp. svcs. U. Mich. Hosps., Ann Arbor, 1976-77, chief fin. officer, 1977-79, chief operating officer, 1979-83; hosp. dir. U. Minn. Hosps., Mpls., 1983-87; exec. dir., v.p. health affairs U. Pa., Phila., 1987-90; chief exec. officer U. Nebr. Med. Ctr., Omaha, 1990—; asst. v.p., health scis. U. Minn., Mpls., 1983-87; bd. dirs. MaGee Rehab. Hosp.; vice chmn. Minn. Assn. Pub. Teaching Hosps., Mpls., 1983-87; mem. adv. coun. Leonard Davis Inst., 1988-91. Chmn. bd. dirs. Hopkins-Muhlenberg Community Action Agy., Greenville, 1972-74. Mem. Am. Hosp. Assn., Am. Coll. Hosp. Adminstrs., Minn. Hosp. Assn., Washington U. Alumni Assn. (pres. 1983-85), Assn. Am. Med. Colls. (del. 1983—), Coun. Teaching Hosps. Republican. Methodist. Lodge: Lions. Avocations: skiing, golfing, tennis, running. Home: 725 N 92nd Ct Apt 301 Omaha NE 68114-2669 Office: U of Nebraska Hospital 600 S 42nd St Omaha NE 68198-0001

SCHWARTZ, CARL EDWARD, artist, printmaker; b. Detroit, Sept. 20, 1935; s. Carl and Verna (Steiner) S.; m. Kay Joyce Hofmann, June 18, 1955 (div.); children: Dawn Ellen, Cari Leigh; m. Frieda Nelson, Oct. 17, 1982 (div.). BFA, Art Inst. Chgo. Sch.-U. Chgo., 1957. tchr. art , Chgo., N. Shore Art League, Suburban Fine Arts Center, Deerpath Art League. One-man shows include, South Bend (Ind.) Art Center, Feingarten Gallery, Chgo., 1960, Bernard Horwich Center, Chgo., Covenant Club, Chgo., Barat Coll., Chgo. Pub. Library, Alverno Coll., 1968 Art Center, Rosenberg Gallery, Peoria (Ill.) Art Guild, 1977, Ill. State Mus., 1977 Ill. Inst. Tech., 1978, Miller Gallery, Chgo., 1979, Union League Club, Chgo., 1982, Art Inst. Rental and Sale Gallery, Chgo., 1982, Horwich Gallery, Chgo., 1983, Lake Forest (Ill.) Coll., 1983, Campanile-Capponi Contemporary Gallery, Chgo., 1987, Nagata Gallery, Ft. Myers, Fla., 1988, Jan Cicero Gallery, Chgo., 1990; numerous group shows include 9th Ann. Michigana Exhbt, Detroit (Cloetingh and Deman award 1959), Hyde Park Art Center, Chgo., 1960 (5th Ann. Jury Exhbn. prize), Spectrum Exhbn. '63, Chgo. (1st prize), New Horizons Exhbt, Chgo., 1960 (Joseph Shapiro award), Nat. Design Center, Chgo., 1965 (New Horizons in Painting 1st prize), 3d Ann. Chgo. Arts Competition, 1962 (1st prize), Union League Club, Chgo., 1967 (2d prize), N. Shore Art League Ann. Drawing and Print Show, Chgo., 1965 (1st prize), Artists Guild Chgo., 1965 (prize), McCormack Pl., Chgo., 1965 (1st prize), Detroit Art Inst., 1965 (Commonwealth prize), Park Forest (Ill.) Art Exhbn. 1969 (Best of Show), 14th Ann. Virginia Beach (Va.) Show, 1969 (Best of Show), Suburban Fine Arts Center, Highland Park, Ill., 1970 (prize), 15th Ann. Virginia Beach Show, 1970 (prize), 32d Ann. Artists Guild, Chgo., 1970 (2d prize), N. Shore Art League Print and Drawing Show, 1970 (prize), 16th Ann. Virginia Beach Show, 1971 (2d prize), Ill. State Fair, 1972 (prize), Artists Guild Chgo., 1972 (1st prize), 17th Ann. Virginia Beach Exhbt, 1972 (1st prize), Artists Guild 50th Fine Art Exhbn., Chgo., 1973 (prize), Dickinson State U., 1973 (prize), N. Shore Art League Print Exhbn, 1973 (prize), Lakehurst Exhbt, 1974 (prize), Union League Art Exhbt, 1974 (1st prize) Artists Guild Fine Arts Exhbn., 1974 (best of Show), Bluegrass Painting Exhbn, Louisville, 1975 (award), Union League Art Exhbn, 1976 (prize); represented in permanent collections, Brit. Mus., London, Smithsonian Inst., Washington, Art Inst. Chgo., Jan Cicero Gallery, Chgo., Foster Harmon Gallery, Sarasota, Fla. Home: 13872 Pine Villa Ln Fort Myers FL 33912-1620 *I am a painter of light. I'm intrigued and fascinated with form. To me, there are two worlds-the one we all live in, and the one that I create. Painting is the discipline by which I constantly rediscover both of these worlds.*

SCHWARTZ, CAROL LEVITT, former government official; b. Greenville, Miss., Jan. 20, 1944; d. Stanley and Hilda (Simmons) Levitt; m. David H. Schwartz (dec.); children: Stephanie, Hilary, Douglas. BS in Spl. and Elem. Edn., U. Tex., 1965. Mem. transiton team Office of Pres. Elect, 1980-81; con. office presdl. personnel The White House, Washington, 1981; cons. U.S. Dept. Edn., Washington, 1982; pres. sec. U.S. Ho. Reps., Washington, 1982-83; mem. at large Coun. of D.C., Washington, 1985-89; candidate for mayor, Washington, 1986, 94; vice chmn. Nat. Edn. Commn. on Time and Leaarning, 1992-94, Nat. Adv. Coun. on Disadvantaged Children, 1974-79; lectr. in field; radio commentator, 1990-91. Mem. D.C. Bd. Edn., 1974-82, v.p., 1977-80; bd. dirs. Met. Police Boys and Girls Club, 1st v.p., 1989-93, pres., 1994—, chmn. membership com., 1984-93; mem. adv. com. Am. Coun. Young Polit. Leaders, 1982-90; mem. Nat. Coun. Friends Kennedy Ctr., 1984-91; bd. dirs. Whitman-Walker Clinic, 1988—, St. John's Child Devel. Ctr., 1989-91; trustee Kennedy Ctr. Cmty. and Friends Bd., 1991—; chmn. edn. task force, 1993—; trustee Jewish Coun. on Aging, 1991-93; v.p. adv. bd. Am. Automobile Assn., 1988—. Mem. Cosmos Club. Republican. Jewish.

SCHWARTZ, CHARLES, JR., federal judge; b. New Orleans, Aug. 20, 1922; s. Charles and Sophie (Hess) S.; m. Patricia May, Aug. 31, 1950; children—Priscilla May, John Putney. BA, Tulane U., 1943, JD, 1947. Bar: La. 1947. Ptnr. Guste, Barnett & Little, 1947-70; practiced in New Orleans, until 1970; ptnr. firm Little, Schwartz & Dussom, 1970-76; dist. counsel Gulf Coast dist. U.S. Maritime Adminstrn., 1953-62; judge U.S. Dist. Ct. (ea. dist.) La., New Orleans, 1976—; mem. Fgn. Itelligence Surveillance Ct., 1992—; prof. Tulane U. Law Sch.; lectr. continuing law insts.; mem. Jud.

Conf. Com. U.S. on implementation of jury system, 1981-85; mem. permanent adv. bd. Tulane Admiralty Law Inst., 1984—. Bd. editors Tulane Law Rev. Pres. New Orleans unit Am. Cancer Soc., 1956-57; v.p., chmn. budget com. United Fund Greater New Orleans Area, 1959-61, trustee, 1953-65; bd. dirs. Cancer Assn. Greater New Orleans, 1958—, pres., 1958-59, 72-73; bd. dirs. United Cancer Council, 1963-85, pres., 1971-73; mem. com. on grants to agencies Community Chest, 1965-87; men's adv. com. League Women Voters, 1966-68; chmn. com. admissions of program devel. and coordination com. United Way Greater New Orleans, 1974-77; mem. comml. panel Am. Arbitration Assn., 1974-76; bd. dirs. Willow Wood Home, 1979-85, 1989-92; bd. mgrs. Touro Infirmary, 1992—; trustee Metairie Park Country Day Sch., 1977-83; mem. La. Republican Central Com., 1961-76; mem. Orleans Parish Rep. Exec. Com., 1960-75, chmn., 1964-75; mem. Jefferson Parish Rep. Exec. Com., 1975-76; del. Rep. Nat. Conv., 1960, 64, 68; mem. nat. budget and consultation com. United Community Funds and Coun. of Am., 1961; bd. dirs. Community Svcs. Coun., 1971-73. Served to 2d lt. AUS, 1943-46; maj. U.S. Army Res.; ret. Mem. La. Bar Assn. New Orleans Bar Assn. (legis. com. 1970-75), Fed. Bar Assn. Fgn. Rels. Assn. New Orleans (bd. dirs. 1957-61), 5th Cir. Dist. Judges Assn. (pres. 1984-85), Lakewood Country Club (bd. dirs. 1967-68, pres. 1975-77). Office: US Dist Ct C-317 US Courthouse 500 Camp St New Orleans LA 70130-3313

SCHWARTZ, CHARLES D., broadcast executive; b. Phila., Sept. 6, 1948; s. Howard I. and Jane (Cohen) S.; m. Susan Greenspan, June 28, 1970; children: Daniel, Michael, Amy. BFA, U. Cin., 1970. Media planner, buyer Grey Advt., Inc., N.Y.C., 1970-71; account exec. CBS Radio Spot Sales, CBS, Inc., N.Y.C., 1971-74; retail sales mgr. Sta. WCBS-AM, CBS, Inc., N.Y.C., 1974-75; sales mgr. CBS Radio Spot Sales, CBS, Inc., N.Y.C., 1975-76; gen. sales mgr. Sta. WBBM-AM, CBS, Inc., Chgo., 1976-79; v.p., gen. mgr. Sta. WCAU-AM, CBS, Inc., Phila., 1979-80; pres., chief operating officer Newsystems Group, Inc., Phila., 1980-87; chief executive officer, chmn. Panache Broadcasting, Phila., 1987—. Bd. govs. Likoff Cardiovasc. Inst., Hahneman U., Phila., 1988—; mem. exec. com., 1988—. Avocations: writing, travel. Office: Sta WWDB-FM 166 E Levering Mill Rd Bala Cynwyd PA 19004-2664

SCHWARTZ, CHARLES FREDERICK, economist, consultant; b. Balt., May 2, 1916; s. Charles Herzog and Cora (Miller) S.; m. Marika Rupis, June 7, 1941; children: Mary Louise Schwartz Solomon, Charles Anthony. BA, U. Va., 1936, MA, 1937, PhD, 1939; postgrad., Va. Poly. Inst., 1937-38, Georgetown U., 1941-42. Instr. rural econs. U. Va., 1939-41; economist nat. income div. Office Bus. Econs., U.S. Dept. Commerce, 1941-51, asst. chief, 1951-56, asst. dir. Office Bus. Econs., 1956-59; chief N.Am. div. Western Hemisphere Dept., IMF, 1959-62, asst. dir. Western Hemisphere Dept., 1962-66, dep. dir. rsch. dept., 1966-79, dir. adjustment studies, 1979-83; chmn. investment com. Staff Retirement Plan, IMF, 1979-85, spl. cons., office mng. dir., 1983-86; cons., 1987—; cons. Exec. Office of Pres., mem. adv. coms. on balance of payments stats., 1963-65, 75-76. Author publs. on nat. income, the world economy. Recipient gold medal for exceptional svc. Dept. Commerce, 1951. Mem. Internat. Assn. Rsch. in Income and Wealth, Conf. on Rsch. in Income and Wealth (chmn., exec. com. 1961-62), Am. Econ. Assn., Am. Statis. Assn., Phi Beta Kappa, Theta Delta Chi. Home: 7504 Honeywell Ln Bethesda MD 20814-1028

SCHWARTZ, CHARLES MORRIS, lawyer; b. N.Y.C., Jan. 5, 1948; s. Murray Schwartz and Shirley Phillis (Bomart) Schwartz Dinitz; m. Roberta Sue Dick, June 23, 1968; children: Karen, Jamie. BA, U. Wis., 1969; PhD, NYU, 1973; JD, Harvard U., 1975. Bar: D.C. 1975, Tex. 1977. Assoc. Shaw, Pittman, Potts & Trowbridge, Washington, 1975-77; ptnr. Hughes & Luce, Dallas, 1977—. Mem. ABA, Dallas Bar Assn., North Tex. Center. Avocation: tennis. Home: 4514 Willow Ln Dallas TX 75244-7539 Office: Hughes & Luce 1717 Main St Dallas TX 75201-4605

SCHWARTZ, CHARLES PHINEAS, JR., replacement auto parts company executive, lawyer; b. Chgo., Apr. 23, 1927; s. Charles Phineas and Lavinia Duffy (Schulman) S.; m. Joan Straus, Aug. 12, 1954 (div. 1971); children: Alex, Ned, Debra, Emily; m. Susan Lamm Hirsch, Dec. 18, 1976. A.B., U. Chgo., 1945; LL.B., Harvard U., 1950. Bar: Ill. 1950, N.Y. 1951, U.S. Supreme Ct. 1955. Assoc. Szold & Brandwen, N.Y.C., 1950-52; rsch. assoc., teaching fellow Harvard U. Law Sch., Cambridge, Mass., 1952-56; pvt. practice Chgo., 1956-61; ptnr. Straus, Blosser & McDowell, Chgo., 1961-67; fin. and bus. cons. Chgo., 1967-75, 93—; pres., chief exec. officer Champion Parts Inc., Oak Brook, Ill., 1975-86, chmn. bd., chief exec. officer 1986-92; chmn. emeritus Champion Parts Inc., Oak Brook, 1992—; dir. Supercrete Ltd., Winnipeg, Man., Can., 1964-80, Athey Products Corp., Raleigh, N.C., 1967-86. Trustee, officer Hull House Assn., Chgo., 1958-70; dir., officer Chgo. Fedn. Settlements, 1972-79; dir., officer, pres. Friends of the Parks, Chgo., 1982—; dir., officer, pres. Hyde Park Coop. Soc., 1962-68; pres. U. Cho. Lab. Schs. Parents Assn., 1970-72, 75-77; trustee KAM Isaiah Isrel Congregation, 1975-85. Served with USNR, 1945-46. Recipient Boulton Meml. award for disting. bus. statesmanship and dedicated service rendered to the entire auto parts rebuilding industry Automotive Parts Rebuilders Assn., 1987. Mem. ABA, Motor Equipment and Mfrs. Assn. (dir. 1977-81), Automotive Pres. coun., Heavy Duty Bus. Forum, Automotive Sales Coun., Soc. Autumotive Engrs., Automotive Parts Rebuilders Assn. (dir., officer, chmn. 1988—), Chgo. Coun. Lawyers, Heavy Vehile Maintenance Group officer 1994—). Jewish. Clubs: Quadrangle (Chgo.); Harvard (N.Y.C.). Office: 230 E Ohio St Ste 120 Chicago IL 60611

SCHWARTZ, CHARLES WALTER, lawyer; b. Brenham, Tex., Dec. 27, 1953; s. Walter C. and Annie (Kuehn) S. BS, U. Tex., Austin, 1975, MA, 1980, JD, 1977; LLM, Harvard U., 1980. Bar: Tex. 1977; bd. cert. civil appellate law Tex. Bd. Legal Specialization. Law clk. to judge U.S. Ct. Appeals (5th cir.), Austin, Tex., 1977-79; assoc. Vinson & Elkins L.L.P., Houston, 1980-86, ptnr., 1986—. Contbr. articles to law revs. Mem. ABA, Tex. Bar Assn., Tex. Bar Found., Houston Bar Found., Houston Bar Assn. Am. Law Inst., Tex. Law Rev., Bar Assn. of 5th Cir. Home: 2825 Albans Rd Houston TX 77005-2309 Office: Vinson & Elkins LLP 2300 First City Tower 1001 Fannin Houston TX 77002-6760

SCHWARTZ, CHERIE ANNE KARO, storyteller; b. Miami, Fla., Feb. 24, 1951; d. William Howard and Dorothy (Olesh) Karo; m. Lawrence Schwartz, Aug. 12, 1979. BA in Lit., The Colo. Coll., 1973; MA in Devel. Theater, U. Colo., 1977. Tchr. English, drame, mime, creative writing, speech coach South High Sch., Pueblo, Colo., 1973-76; tchr. drama St. Mary's Acad., Denver, 1979-81; tchr. English and drama Rocky Mountain Hebrew Acad., Denver, 1981-83; full-time profl. storyteller throughout N.Am., 1982—; storyteller, docent, tchr. tng., mus. outreach Denver Mus. Natural History, 1982—; trainer, cons., performer, lectr, keynote speaker various orgns., synagogues, instns., agys., confs. throughout the country, 1982—; co-founder, chairperson Omanim b'Yachad: Artists Together, Nat. Conf. Celebrating Storytelling, Drama, Music and Dance in Jewish Edn., Denver, 1993. Storyteller: (audio cassette tapes) Cherie Karo Schwartz Tells Stories of Hanukkah from Kar-Ben Books, 1986, Cherie Karo Schwartz Tells Stories of Passover From Kar-Ben Books, 1986, Miriam's Tambourine, 1988, Worldwide Jewish Stories of Wishes and Wisdom, 1988; storyteller, actor: (video tape) The Wonderful World of Recycle, 1989; author: (book) My Lucky Dreidel: Hanukkah Stories, Songs, Crafts, Recipes and Fun for Kids, 1994. Title III grantee State of Colo. Edn., Pueblo, 1975-76. Mem. Coalition for Advancement of Jewish Edn. (coord. Jewish Storytelling Conf. 1989—), coord. Nat. Jewish Storytelling Network), Nat. Assn. for Preservation and Perpetuation of Storytelling, Nat. Storytelling Assn., Rocky Mountain Storytelling Guild. Democrat. Jewish. Home: 996 S Florence St Denver CO 80231

SCHWARTZ, CRAIG, osteopath, surgeon. Recipient Robert C. Erwin award Am. Coll. Osteo. Surgeons, 1993. Office: 600 S Dearborn St Philadelphia PA 19128*

SCHWARTZ, DALE MARVIN, lawyer; b. Columbus, Ga., Aug. 20, 1942; s. Sanford and Florence (Casper) S.; m. Susan Ellis, Sept. 12, 1965; children: Lori, Leslye, Laine. Student, Vanderbilt U., 1959-60, George Wash. U., 1964; AB, U. Ga., 1965, JD, 1968. Bar: Ga. 1968, U.S. Ct. Appeals 1975, U.S. Supreme Ct. 1977. Ptnr. Troutman Sanders, Atlanta, 1968—; S.E. counsel to State of Israel, 1976—; mem. Ga. adv. bd. U.S. Civil Rights

Commn., 1986—, chmn., 1991-95; lead counsel Marian Cuban Class Action Litigation, 1981-88; guest Nightline, 60 Minutes, 20/20, CNN, others; adj. prof. Emory U. Shc. of Law, 1988—. Editor: Ga. Law Rev., 1966-68; editl. bd. Immigration Policy and Law, 1988—. Gen. counsel Dem. Party Ga., Atlanta, 1978-80; S.E. chmn. statue of Liberty Ellis Island Fund, N.Y.C., 1985-86; mem. nat. bd. dirs., S.E. vice chmn. Anti-Defamation League, N.Y.C. and Atlanta, 1983—, chmn., 1993—; pres. Jewish Family Svcs., Atlanta, 1984-88; v.p., dir. Hebrew Immigrant Aid Soc., N.Y.C., 1984—; bd. dirs. Ctr. for Human Right and Const. Law, L.A., 1987—, Atlanta Jewish Fedn., 1979-92, Am. Jewish Congress, N.Y.C., 1986-88; pres. Coll. Young Dems. Recipient Young Leadership award Atlanta Jewish Fedn., 1981, Civic Leader award Ga. State U. chpt. Mortar Bd., 1982, Law and Social Action award Am. Jewish Congress, 1984, Civil Liberties award ACLU, Atlanta, 1987. Mem. ABA (coordinating com. on immigration law 1987-94, co-chmn. immigration law com. sect. litigation 1990-92), State Bar Ga., Am. Immigration Lawyers Assn. (bd. dirs. 1980—, nat. pres. 1986-87, Jack Wasserman award for litigation excellence 1988). Avocations: amateur radio, photography, stamp collecting. Home: 650 River Chase Pt NW Atlanta GA 30328-3554 Office: Troutman Sanders 5200 Nat Ins Bank Plz 600 Peachtree St NE Atlanta GA 30308-2216

SCHWARTZ, DANIEL BENNETT, artist; b. N.Y.C., Feb. 16, 1929; s. Bennett Henry and Lillian (Blumenthal) S.; m. Judith Nancy Kass, June 12, 1955 (div. 1980); 1 child, Claudia Bennet. Grad., High Sch. of Music and Art, N.Y.C., 1946; student, Art Students League, 1946, Y. Kuniyoshi; BFA, R.I. Sch. Design, 1949. Instr. pvt. painting class, 1965-81, 90-95, Parsons Sch. Design, 1983. One man shows include Davis Galleries, N.Y.C., 1955, 56, 58, 60, Hirschl & Adler Galleries, N.Y.C., 1963, Maxwell Galleries, San Francisco, 1964, Babcock Galleries, N.Y.C., 1967, F.A.R. Galleries, N.Y.C., 1970, Armstrong Galleries, N.Y.C., 1985, 87, Hammer Galleries, N.Y.C., 1994; exhibited in group shows at Albany Inst. History and Art, Am. Fedn. Arts, Butler Inst. Am. Art, Libr. of Congress, Nat. Acad. Design, Pa. Acad. Fine Art, Whitney Mus. Art, Collection Nat. Portrait Gallery, others; subject of various articles. Louis C. Tiffany Found. grantee, 1956, 60; recipient Purchase prize Am. Acad. Arts and Letters, 1964, 84, 11 Gold medals Soc. Illustrators, N.Y.C., 1960-85, Obrig prize for painting Nat. Acad. Design, 1990, winner 1st Benjamin Altman Figure prize, 1992. Mem. Century Assn. Avocation: jazz piano. Home and Office: 48 E 13th St New York NY 10003-4631

SCHWARTZ, DANIEL C., lawyer; b. Pa., 1943. AB, Stanford U., 1965; JD, George Washington U., 1969. Bar: D.C. 1969. Asst. to dir. Bur. Competition, FTC, Washington, 1973-75, asst. dir. evaluation, 1975-77, dep. dir., 1977-79; gen. counsel Nat. Security Agy., Washington, 1979-81; ptnr. Bryan Cave, Washington. Mem. ABA. Office: Bryan Cave 700 13th St NW Washington DC 20005

SCHWARTZ, DANIEL K., chemistry educator; b. White Plains, N.Y., June 15, 1963; s. Larry and Joan Vida (Oliner) S.; m. Tracey Ray Rangel, July 30, 1994. AB in Chemistry/Physics summa cum laude, Harvard U., 1984, AM in Physics, 1987, PhD in Physics, 1991. Summer rsch. assoc. Woods Hole Oceanographic Inst., 1982; grad. rsch. asst. Harvard U., 1984-91, teaching fellow dept. physics, 1987, resident in chemistry, physics tutor Currier House, 1987-90; postdoctoral assoc. dept. chem. and nuclear engring. U. Calif., Santa Barbara, 1991-92; postdoctoral assoc. dept. chemistry and biochemistry UCLA, 1992-94; asst. prof. dept. chemistry Tulane U., New Orleans, 1994—; presenter in field. Contbr. articles to profl. jours. Exxon Edn. Found. rsch. grantee, Chemistry grantee Camille and Henry Dreyfus Found., 1994; Stone and Webster fellow Harvard U., 1985-86; John Harvard scholar Harvard U., 1981-84. Mem. Am. Chem. Soc., Am. Phys. Soc., Materials Rsch. Soc., Phi Beta Kappa. Office: Tulane U Dept Chemistry New Orleans LA 70118*

SCHWARTZ, DAVID, retail executive; b. 1945. With Skaggs Drug Stores, 1965-77; v.p. rocky mtns. divsn. Albertsons Inc., 1977-86; v.p. drug and mdse. The Kroger Co., 1986-87; pres., COO Perry Drug Stores, Inc., 1987-91; pres., CEO Smitty's Super Value, Inc., 1991-93, Phar-Mor Inc, Youngstown, Ohio, 1993—. Office: Phar-Mor Inc 20 Federal Plz W Youngstown OH 44503

SCHWARTZ, DONALD, chemistry educator; b. Scarsdale, N.Y., Dec. 27, 1927; s. Harry A. and Ethel S.; m. Lois Schwartz, Sept. 8, 1948; children: Leanne, Mark W., Scott B., Bradley F. B.S., U. Mo., 1949; M.S., Mont. State U., 1951; Ph.D., Pa. State U., 1955. Program dir. NSF, 1966-68; asso. dean Grad. Sch., Memphis State U., 1968-70; dean advanced studies Fla. Atlantic U., Boca Raton, 1970-71; v.p., acting dean State U. N.Y., Buffalo, 1971-74; chancellor Ind. U.-Purdue U., Ft. Wayne, Ind., 1974-78; chancellor, prof. U. Colo., Colorado Springs, 1978-83, prof., 1983-93, prof. emeritus, 1993—; cons. in field. Author papers structure of coal and organo-titanium compounds, also on higher edn. Bd. dirs. Colorado Springs Osteo. Found., 1985—. Served with USCG, 1945. Research fellow AEC, 1953-55; N.Y. State fellow, 1947-48. Mem. Am. Chem. Soc., AAAS, Sigma Xi, Phi Lambda Upsilon, Phi Delta Kappa. Clubs: Rotary, Country of Colo, Shriners. Home: 21 Sanford Rd Colorado Springs CO 80906-4219 Office: U of Colo Cragmor Rd Colorado Springs CO 80907 Each can become all that he or she is capable of being through education, hard work and compassion for other human beings. This I believe.

SCHWARTZ, DONALD FRANKLIN, communication educator; b. Jamestown, N.D., Feb. 20, 1935; s. Frank William and Mabel Esther (Williams) S.; m. Lois Carolyn Bonnema, June 26, 1965; children: Daria, Karin, Marc. B.S., N.D. State U., 1957, M.S., 1961; Ph.D., Mich. State U., 1968. Asst. dir. pub. rels. N.D. State U., Fargo, 1959-66, chmn. social scis., 1969-71, chmn. communication, 1967-79; instr. communication Mich. State U., East Lansing, 1966-67; vis. scientist U.S. Dept. Agr., Washington, 1979-80; prof. communication Cornell U., Ithaca, N.Y., 1980—, chmn. dept., 1980-85; vis. scholar U. N.Mex., 1994. Contbr. articles to profl. jours. Recipient Outstanding Svc. award Future Farmers Am., 1976; recipient Svc. award USDA, 1980. Mem. AAUP, Internat. Comm. Assn. (sec., pub. rels. interest group 1992-93), Am. Acad. Mgmt., Am. Soc. Pers. Adminstrn. (chpt. pres. 1976-77), Pub. Rels. Soc. Am. (nat. faculty advisor student assn. 1989-90, vic chair educators sect. 1992, Pres.'s Citation for Leadership 1990, mem. nat. ednl. affairs com. 1993). Roman Catholic. Office: Cornell U Dept Communication 311 Kennedy Hall Ithaca NY 14853-4203

SCHWARTZ, DONALD LEE, lawyer; b. Milw., Dec. 8, 1948; s. Bernard L. and Ruth M. (Marshall) S.; m. Susan J. Dunst, June 5, 1971; children: Stephanie Jane, Cheryl Ruth. BA, Macalester Coll., 1971; JD, U. Chgo., 1974. Bar: Ill. 1974. Assoc. Sidley & Austin, Chgo., 1974-80, ptnr., 1980-88; ptnr. Latham & Watkins, Chgo., 1988—. Chmn. Ill. Conservative Union, 1979-81, bd. dirs. 1977-85. Served with U.S. Army, 1971-77. Mem. ABA (uniform comml. code com., comml. fin. svcs. commn.), Ill. Bar Assn. (sec. comm. banking and bankuprtcy sect. 1982-83), Chgo. Bar Assn. (chmn. comml. law com. 1980-81, fin. insts. com. 1982-83), Ivanhoe Country Club, Monroe Club, Met. Club. Republican. Episcopalian. Avocation: golf. Home: 191 Park Ave Glencoe IL 60022-1351 Office: Latham & Watkins Ste 6800 Sears Tower Chicago IL 60606

SCHWARTZ, DORIS RUHBEL, nursing educator, consultant; b. Bklyn., May 30, 1915; d. Henry and Florence Marie (Shuttleworth) S. BS, NYU, 1953, MS, 1958. RN, N.Y. Staff nurse Meth. Hosp., Bklyn., 1942-43; pub. health nurse Vis. Nurse Assn., Bklyn., 1947-51; pub. health nurse Cornell U. Med. Coll., Cornell-N.Y. Hosp. Sch. Nursing, N.Y.C., 1951-61, tchr. pub. health nursing, geriatric nursing, 1961-80; sr. fellow U. Pa. Sch. Nursing, Phila., 1981-90. Author: Give Us to Go Blithely, 1990 (Book of Yr. award Am. Jour. Nursing 1991); sr. author: The Elderly Chronically Ill Patient: Nursing and Psychosocial Needs, 1963; co-author: Geriatrics and Geriatric Nursing, 1983 (Book of Yr. award Am. Jour. Nursing 1984); contbr. articles to profl. jours. Mem. adv. com. nursing WHO, Geneva, 1971-79; adv. com. Robert Wood Johnson Found., Teaching Nursing Home Project, Princeton, N.J.; U. Pa. Wharton Sch. Study of Continuing Care Retirement Communities, 1981-83. Served to capt. N.C., U.S. Army, 1943-47, PTO. Rockefeller fellow U. Toronto, 1950-51, Mary Roberts fellow Am. Jour. Nursing, 1955, Fogarty fellow NIH, 1975-76; recipient Diamond Jubilee Nursing award N.Y. County RNs Assn., 1979. Fellow Inst. Medicine of NAS, APHA (Disting. Career award nursing sect. 1979), Am. Acad. Nursing (charter,

coun. 1973-74); mem. ANA (Pearl McIver award 1979), Soroptimist (v.p. N.Y.C. club 1974-75), Sigma Theta Tau (Founders award 1979, Mentor award Alpha Upsilon chpt. 1992). Democrat. Mem. Soc. of Friends. Avocations: travel; writing; people.

SCHWARTZ, EDWARD ARTHUR, lawyer, foundation executive; b. Boston, Sept. 27, 1937; s. Abe and Sophie (Gottheim) S.; children: Eric Allen, Jeffrey Michael. AB, Oberlin Coll., 1959; LLB, Boston Coll., 1962; postgrad., Am. U., 1958-59, Northeastern U., 1970; postgrad. exec. program, Stanford U., 1979. Bar: Conn. 1962, Mass. 1965. Legal intern Office Atty. Gen. Commonwealth of Mass., 1961; assoc. Schatz & Schatz, Hartford, Conn., 1962-65, Cohn, Reimer & Pollack, Boston, 1965-67; v.p., gen. coun. sec. Digital Equipment Corp., Maynard, Mass., 1967-88; pres. New Eng. Legal Found., Boston, 1990—, also bd. dirs.; vis. prof. law Boston Coll., 1986, adj. prof., 1987-89; also bd. dirs. The Computer Mus. Editor Boston Coll. Indsl. and Comml. Law Rev, 1960-62, Ann. Survey Mass. Law, 1960-62. Mem. ABA, Mass. Bar Assn., Boston Bar Assn. Home: 62 Todd Pond Rd Lincoln MA 01773-3808

SCHWARTZ, EDWARD J., federal judge. Judge Mcpl. Ct. and Superior Ct., San Diego; judge U.S. Dist. Ct. for So. Dist. Calif., former chief judge, now sr. judge. Office: US Dist Ct 940 Front St San Diego CA 92189-0010

SCHWARTZ, ELEANOR BRANTLEY, academic administrator; b. Kite, Ga., Jan. 1, 1937; d. Jesse Melvin and Hazel (Hill) Brantley; children: John, Cynthia. Student Mercer U., Ga., 1954-55; student U. Va., 1955, Ga. Southern Coll., 1956-57, BBA, Ga. State U., 1962, MBA, 1963, DBA, 1969. Adminstrv. asst. Fin. Agy., 1954, Fed. Govt., Va., Pa., Ga., 1956-59; asst. dean admissions Ga. State U., Atlanta, 1961-66, asst. prof., 1966-70; assoc. prof. Cleve. State U., 1970-75, prof. and assoc. dean, 1975-80; dean, Harzfeld prof. U. Mo., Kansas City, 1980-87, vice chancellor acad. affairs, 1987-91, interim chancellor, 1991-92, chancellor, 1992—; disting. vis. prof. Berry Coll., Rome, Ga., N.Y. State U. Coll., Fredonia, Mons U., Belgium; cons. pvt. industry, U.S., Europe, Can.; bd. dirs. ANUHCO, Rsch. Med. Ctr., Country Club Bank, Toy and Miniature Mus., Menorah Med. Ctr. Found., NCCJ, Econ. Devel. Corp. of Kansas City, Vendo Co. Adv. Com., Midwest Grain Products, Silicon Prairie Tech. Assn. Author: Sex Barriers in Business, 1971, Contemporary Readings in Marketing, 1974; (with Muczyk and Smith) Principles of Supervision, 1984. Chmn., Mayor's Task Force in Govt. Efficiency, Kansas City, Mo., 1984; mem. community planning and research council United Way Kansas City, 1983-85; bd. dirs. Jr. Achievement, 1982-86; Mo. Planning Coun. Devel. Disabilities, 1995—. Recipient Disting. Faculty award Cleve. State U., 1974, Cleve., 60 Women of Achievement Girls Scouts Council Mid Continent, 1983; named Career Woman of Yr. Kansas City, Mo., 1989; recipient disting. svc. award Kansas State U., 1992. Mem. Am. Mktg. Assn., Acad. Internat. Bus., Am. Mgmt. Assn., Am. Case Research Assn., Internat. Soc. Study Behavioral Devel., Greater Kansas City C. of C. (ex. officio, bd. dirs.), Silicon Prairie Tech. Assn. (ex officio, bd. dirs.), Phi Kappa Phi, Golden Key, Alpha Iota Delta.

SCHWARTZ, ELI, economics educator, writer; b. N.Y.C., Apr. 2, 1921; s. Israel and Tillie (Shapiro) S.; m. Renee S. Kartiganer, Aug. 29, 1948; children: Pamela F., Alan G. B.S., Denver U., 1943; M.A., U. Conn., 1948; Ph.D., Brown U., 1952. Instr. U. R.I., Kingston, 1947-48; asst. instr. Brown U., Providence, 1948-51; chief regional economist Office Price Stblzn., Boston, 1951-53; lectr. Mich. State U., East Lansing, 1953-54; asst. prof. econs. Lehigh U., Bethlehem, Pa., 1954-58, assoc. prof., 1958-62, prof., 1962-91, Charles Macfarlane prof. econs., 1978-91, chmn. dept. econs., 1978-84, ret., 1991; cons. econs. and fin., expert witness Schwartz-Aronson Assocs., Bethlehem, 1965—. Author: Corporate Finance, 1962, Trouble in Eden, 1980; editor: Managing Municipal Finance, 1980, 83, 87, Restructuring the Thrift Industry, 1989, Theory and Application of the Interest Rate, 1993. With U.S. Army, 1943-46, ETO. Recipient sr. teaching Lehigh U., 1972; Earhart Found. grantee, 1978. Mem. Am. Econs. Assn., Am. Fin. Assn., Nat. Assn. Forensic Econs. (founding mem.). Jewish. Home: 2655 Nottingham Rd Bethlehem PA 18017 Office: Lehigh U Dept Econs Rauch Ctr 37 Bethlehem PA 18015 If I have achieved any success it is because I am interested in the subject matter of my field. I am fortunate to enjoy reading, teaching, consulting and writing.

SCHWARTZ, ELIAS, pediatrician; b. N.Y.C., Aug. 30, 1935; s. Rubin and Dusha (Premysler) S.; m. Esta Rosenberg, June 12, 1960; children: Samuel Robert. AB, Columbia Coll., 1956; MD, Columbia U., 1960; MA (hon.), U. Pa., 1972. From asst. prof. to assoc. prof. pediatrics Jefferson Med. Coll. Phila., 1967-72; prof. pediatrics Sch. Medicine U. Pa., Phila., 1972—; prof. pediatrics in human genetics Sch. Medicine, 1979—, chmn. dept. pediatrics Sch. Medicine, 1990—; physician-in-chief Children's Hosp. Phila., 1990—; med. adv. bd. Cooley's Anemia Found., N.Y.C., 1976—; policy bd. sickle cell program NIH, Bethesda, Md., 1987—, reviewer's res. 1991—; sci. adv. bd. Enzon, Inc., South Plainfield, N.J., 1992—. Editor Hemoglobinopathies in Children, 1980; contbr. over 200 articles to med. and sci. jours. Active Phila. Healthcare Congress, 1991—. Capt. USAF, 1963-65. Grantee NIH, 1968—. Mem. Am. Soc. Pediatric Hematology/Oncology (pres. 1989-91), Am. Soc. Clin. Investigation, Assn. Am. Physicians, Am. Pediatric Soc., Soc. for Pediatric Rsch. Achievements include rsch. in transfusion treatment of strokes in sickle cell disease, comprehensive program for removal of excess iron in chronically transfused patients, delineation of abnormalities of globin synthesis in several inherited hemoglobin disorders, discovery of genetic defects in several types of thalassemia, cloning and analysis of several human megakaryocyte genes. Office: Children's Hosp Phila 34th St Civic Center Blvd Philadelphia PA 19104

SCHWARTZ, ELLIOTT SHELLING, composer, author, music educator; b. Bklyn, Jan. 19, 1936; s. Nathan and Rose (Shelling) S.; m. Dorothy Rose Feldman, June 26, 1960; children: Nina, Jonathan. A.B., Columbia U., 1957, M.A., 1958, Ed. D., 1962. Instr. music U. Mass., Amherst, 1960-64; asst. prof. music Bowdoin Coll., Brunswick, Maine, 1964-70, assoc. prof., 1970-75, prof. music, 1975—; vis. prof. music Ohio State U., Columbus, 1988-92; vis. composer Trinity Coll. Music, London, 1967, U. Calif. Coll. Creative Studies, Santa Barbara, 1970, 73, 74; composer, pianist, commentator British Broadcast Corp, London, 1972, 74, 78, 83; vis. research musician Center Music Expt., La Jolla, Calif., 1978-79; disting. vis. prof. Ohio State U., 1985-86; music cons. Holt, Rinehart & Winston, Random House, Schirmer Books, N.Y.C., 1977—; vis. fellow Robinson Coll., Cambridge U., U.K., 1993-94. Composer: Island, 1970 (Internat. Gaudeamus prize 1970), Chamber Concertos I-IV, 1977-81, Extended Piano, 1980, Dream Music with Variations, 1983; Four Ohio Portraits, 1986, Memorial in Two Parts, 1989, Elan, 1990, Rows Garden, 1993, Equinox, 1994; author: Electronic Music: A Listener's Guide, 1973, Music: Ways of Listening, 1982, (with Daniel Godfrey) Music Since 1945: Issues, Materials and Literature, 1993; editor: (with Barney Childs) Contemporary Composers on Contemporary Music, 1967; contbr. articles to mus. jours. Nat. Endowment for Arts composition grantee, 1974, 76, 82; Rockefeller Found. residence fellow Bellagio, Italy, 1980, 88; MacDowell Colony resident fellow, 1965, 66; Yaddo residence fellow, 1977; recipient Maine State award Maine Commn. Arts and Humanities, 1970, McKim Commn., 1986. Mem. Am. Music Center (v.p. 1981-87), Coll. Music Soc. (nat. coun. 1982-88, pres. 1988-90), Am. Soc. Univ. Composers (nat. coun. 1968-72, nat. chmn. 1983-88), Am. Composers Alliance (governing bd. 1994—). Home: PO Box 451 10 Highview Rd South Freeport ME 04078 Office: Bowdoin Coll Dept Music Brunswick ME 04011

SCHWARTZ, EUGENE M., art collector, patron; b. Butte, Mont., Mar. 18, 1927. Student, New Sch. Social Rsch., NYU, Columbia U., U. Wash. Mem. acquisitions com. Whitney Mus. Am. Art, N.Y.C., 1967-79, 91—; mem. 20th Century com. Met. Mus. Art, N.Y.C., 1989—; mem. photog. acquaitions com. Mus. Modern Art, N.Y.C., 1993—; collector contemporary Am. art since World War II, chiefly of the sixties; portion of the collection shown as a group at Jewish Mus., Everson Mus. Art, Albany Inst.; individual pieces exhibited at Met. Mus. Art, Mus. Modern Art, Whitney Mus. Am. Art, L.A. County Mus., Tate Gallery, London. Office: 1160 Park Ave New York NY 10028

SCHWARTZ, FELICE N., social activist, educator; b. N.Y.C., Jan. 16, 1925; d. Albert and Rose (Kaplan) Nierenberg; m. Irving L. Schwartz, Jan. 12, 1946; children: Cornelia Ann, Tony, James Oliver. BA, Smith Coll., 1945; LHD (hon.), Pace U., 1980, Smith Coll., 1981, Marietta Coll., 1989,

Chatham Coll., 1990, CUNY Grad. Ctr., 1993, Mt. Holyoke Coll., 1994. Founder, exec. dir. Nat. Scholarship Svc. and Fund for Negro Students, N.Y.C., 1945-51; v.p. prodn. Etched Products Corp., N.Y.C., 1951-54; founder, pres. Catalyst, N.Y.C., 1962-93. Author: Breaking With Tradition: Women and Work, The New Facts of Life, 1992, How To Go To Work When Your Husband Is Against It, Your Children Aren't Old Enough, There's Nothing You Can Do Anyhow, 1968; author numerous articles. Mem. adv. bd. Nat. Women's Polit. Caucus, Nat. Network of Hispanic Women; bd. visitors CUNY Grad. Ctr.; mem. adv. bd. Found. for Student Comm. Woodrow Wilson fellow, 1994—; recipient Mademoiselle medal for singular achievement in edn., 1949, Disting. Alumnae medal Smith Coll., 1976, Susan B. Anthony award NOW, 1981, Boehm Soaring Eagle award Nat. Women's Econ. Alliance, 1987, Sara Lee Corp. Front Runner award, 1987; named Human Resource Profl. of Yr. Internat. Assn. Pers. Women, 1983. Fellow Nat. Acad. Human Resources; mem. Women's Forum, Inc., Global Bus. Network (Woodrow Wilson vis. fellow). Office: 230 Park Ave S New York NY 10003

SCHWARTZ, GARY T., law educator; b. 1940. BA, Oberlin (Ohio) Coll., 1962; JD, Harvard U., 1966. Legal asst. Undersecretary Transp., Washington, 1968-69; prof. UCLA, 1969—. Office: U Calif Sch Law 405 Hilgard Ave Los Angeles CA 90024-1301

SCHWARTZ, GEORGE R., physician; b. Caribou, Maine; m. Kathleen Schwartz; children: Ruth, Rebekah, Rachel, Moses, Abigail, John Gabriel. BS in Chemistry with honors, Hobart Coll., 1963; MD magna cum laude, SUNY, Bklyn., 1967. Diplomate Am. Bd. Family Practice, Am. Bd. Emergency Medicine; cert. CPR instr. Intern King County Hosp., Seattle, 1967-68; instr. dept. medicine U. Wash., Seattle, 1967-68; resident in psychiatry Hillside Hosp., Glen Oaks, N.Y., 1968-69; resident in surgery Ind. U. Med. Ctr., Indpls., 1971-72; instr. emergency medicine Med. Coll. Pa., Phila., 1972-76, dir. emergency svcs., asst. dir. emergency medicine program, 1972-74; dir. emergency medicine West Jersey Hosp., 1974-76; pvt. practice, 1977; assoc. prof., dir. divsn. emergency medicine U. N.Mex., Albuquerque, 1978-83; staff mem. emergency medicine Heights Gen. Hosp., Albuquerque, 1983-85; with Los Alamos (N.Mex.) Med. Ctr., 1985-90; vis. assoc. prof. Med. Coll. Pa., 1991. Author: Geriatric Emergencies, 1984; Co-author: (with Tandberg) Emergency Medicine Continuing Edn. Rev., 1981, 2d edit. 1984, (with Bosker) Geriatric Emergency Medicine, 1990; editor: Principles and Practice Emergency Medicine, 1978, 3d edit., 1992; co-editor Trauma Rounds, 1973-75; editorial bd. Annals Emergency Medicine, 1972-81, Resident and Staff Physician, 1978—, Emergency Med. Abstracts, 1978-85, Med. Exam. Publ. Co., 1981-87; contbr. articles to profl. jours., chpts. to textbooks. Med. dir. The Bridge Counselling Ctrs., Los Alamos, N.Mex., 1988-91; dir. planning com. disaster exercise Phila. Internat. Airport, 1974, Camden County Poison Ctr., 1974-76. Recipient Gallup award, 1973, Giraffe award, 1990. Mem. AAAS, AMA, Am. Coll. Emergency Physicians (pres. N.Mex. chpt. 1980-81), N.Mex. Med. Soc., Univ. Assn. Emergency Physicians (chmn. socio-econ. com. 1976-77), Internat. Emergency Care Assn., Am. Trauma Soc. (founding mem.), Am. Acad. Clin. Toxicology, Am. Acad. Emergency Medicine (founding mem., sec. 1994), Internat. Assn. for Study of MSG and Food Additives (pres. 1988). Achievements include patent for use of a pharmaceutical agent in male impotence; research on computer applications in medicine, new medical diagnostic instruments. Address: 257 Hyde Park Estates Santa Fe NM 87501

SCHWARTZ, GORDON FRANCIS, surgeon, educator; b. Plainfield, N.J., Apr. 29, 1935; s. Samuel H. and Mary (Adelman) S.; m. Rochelle DeG. Krantz, Sept. 5, 1959; children—Amory Blair, Susan Leslie. A.B., Princeton U., 1956; M.D., Harvard U., 1960; MBA, U. Pa., 1990. Intern N.Y. Hosp.-Cornell Med. Ctr., N.Y.C., 1960-61; resident in surgery Columbia-Presbyterian Med. Ctr., N.Y.C., 1963-68; instr. surgery Columbia U., N.Y.C., 1966-68; assoc. in surgery U. Pa., Phila., 1968-70; dir. clin. services Breast Diagnostic Ctr. Jefferson Med. Coll., 1973-78, asst. prof. surgery, 1970-71, assoc. prof., 1971-78, prof., 1978—; practice medicine specializing in surgery and diseases of breast, Phila., 1968—; founder, chmn. acad. com. Breast Health Inst., 1990—. Author: (with R.H. Guthrie Jr.) Reconstructive and Aesthetic Mammoplasty, 1980; editor Cancer Therapy Abstracts, 1976-80; co-editor Breast Disease, an Internat. Jour., 1987—; mem. editl. bd. Breast Jour., 1994—. Mem. Pa. Gov.'s Task Force on Cancer, 1976-82; mem. breast cancer task force Phila. chpt. Am. Cancer Soc.; mem. clin. investigation rev. com. Nat. Cancer Inst., 1992—. Served to capt. AUS, 1961-63. NIH Cancer Control fellow, 1968-69. Mem. ACS, AMA, AAUP, Assn. for Acad. Surgery, Allen O. Whipple Surg. Assn., Soc. Surg. Oncology, Internat. Cardiovasc. Soc., Soc. for Surgery Alimentary Tract, Am. Soc. Clin. Oncology, Soc. for Study Breast Diseases (pres. 1981-83), Soc. Internat. Senologie (treas. 1982-90, v.p. 1990-92, sci. com. 1992—), Pa. Med. Soc., Am. Soc. Transplant Surgeons, N.Y. Acad. Scis., Am. Soc. Artificial Internal Organs, Am. Radium Soc., Philadelphia County Med. Soc., Italian Soc. Senology (hon.), Greek Surg. Soc. (hon.), Union League, Locust Club, Princeton Club (pres. Phila. 1989-91), Princeton Club (N.Y.C.), Princeton Terrace Club, Nassau Club, Phi Beta Kappa, Sigma Xi, Alpha Omega Alpha, Nu Sigma Nu. Republican. Jewish. Home: 1805 Delancey Pl Philadelphia PA 19103-6606 Office: 1015 Chestnut St Fl 510 Philadelphia PA 19107-4305

SCHWARTZ, HARRY, journalist; b. N.Y.C., Sept. 10, 1919; s. Sam and Rose (Schnell) S.; m. Ruth E. Blumner, June 8, 1941; children: William Daniel (dec.), John Leonard, Robert Steven. BA, Columbia U., 1940, MA, 1941, PhD, 1943. Economist War Prodn. Bd., 1942-43; economist OSS, 1944-46; asst. prof. econs. Syracuse U., 1946-48, assoc. prof., 1948-51, prof., 1951-53; mem. editorial bd. N.Y. Times, N.Y.C., 1951-79; disting. prof. SUNY, New Paltz, 1967-79; vis. prof. med. econs. Coll. Physicians and Surgeons, Columbia U., 1974, 78-79, writer in residence dept. surgery, 1979-87; columnist Pharm. Exec. mag., 1981—; Scrip mag., 1984—, Am. Med. News, 1989-91; Backman lectr. med. ethics Hebrew Union Coll., 1981; mem. Nat. Bd. Med. Examiners, 1979-83; Mem. exec. com. N.Y. Blood Center, 1973-87. Author: Russia's Soviet Economy, 1949, China, 1966, Prague's 200 Days, 1968, The Case for American Medicine, 1972, Breakthrough: The Discovery of Modern Medicines at Janssen, 1990; columnist Pvt. Practice mag., 1979-91, editor, 1980-84; mem. editl. bd. Psychiat. Times, 1985-94; contbr. numerous articles to profl. jours., newspapers, including Wall St. Jour., N.Y. Times, USA Today. With U.S. Army, 1943-45. Jewish. Home: PO Box 1169 Scarsdale NY 10583-9169

SCHWARTZ, HARRY KANE, lawyer; b. Phila., Apr. 20, 1934; s. M. Murray and Minne G. (Schoenfeld) S.; m. Marinda Kelley, June 20, 1961; children: Anthony Clark, Amanda Lyle. B.A. summa cum laude, Harvard Coll., 1955; Fulbright fellow, Worcester Coll., Oxford U., 1955-56; LL.B. magna cum laude, U. Pa., 1959. Bar: Pa. 1960, D.C. 1961, U.S. Supreme Ct. 1965. Law clk. U.S. Ct. of Appeals, Washington, 1960-61; asst. U.S. atty., 1961-62; atty. SEC, 1962-63; legis. asst. U.S. Sen. Joseph S. Clark, 1963-66; counsel U.S. Senate Subcom. on Employment, Manpower and Poverty, 1966-68; ptnr. Dechert Price & Rhoads, 1969-76; asst. sec. for legislation and intergovtl. relations HUD, Washington, 1977-78; staff adv. domestic policy staff White House, 1978-79; ptnr. Lane & Edson (P.C.), 1979-88, Dewey, Ballantine, Bushby, Palmer & Wood, Washington, 1988-92; dir. Ct. Preservation Policy Studies, Nat. Trust for Hist. Preservation, 1992-93; spl. projects advisor Office of Cultural Resources, Nat. Park Svc., 1994—; dir. Phila. Urban Coalition, 1974-76; nat. task force dir. Carter-Mondale Campaign, 1976. Served with Army N.G., 1961-65. Fellow Salzburg Seminar in Am. Studies, 1964. Mem. Am., Pa., Phila. bar assns., Order of Coif, Phi Beta Kappa. Democrat. Jewish. Club: Cosmos. Office: 1785 Massachusetts Ave NW Washington DC 20036

SCHWARTZ, HENRY GERARD, surgeon, educator; b. N.Y.C., Mar. 11, 1909; s. Nathan Theodore and Marie (Zagat) S.; m. Edith Courtenay Robinson, Sept. 13, 1934; children: Henry G., Michael R., Richard H. A.B., Princeton, 1928; M.D., Johns Hopkins, 1932. Diplomate: Am. Bd. Neurol. Surgery (chmn. 1968-70). Denison fellow with Prof. O. Foerster, Breslau, Germany, 1931; surg. house officer Johns Hopkins Hosp., 1932-33; NRC fellow Harvard Med. Sch., 1933-35, instr. anatomy, 1935-36; fellow neurol. surgery Washington U. Med. Sch., St. Louis, 1936-37; instr., asst. prof., assoc. prof. neurol. surgery Washington U. Med. Sch., 1937-46, prof., 1946-88, August Busch prof. emeritus, 1988—; acting surgeon-in-chief Barnes and Allied hosps., 1965-67; chief neurosurgeon Barnes, St. Louis Children's

hosps., 1946-74; cons. neurosurgeon St. Louis City, Jewish, Los Alamos (N.M.) hosps.; cons. to surgeon gen. USPHS. to surgeon gen. U.S. Army.; Mem. subcom. neurosurgery NRC; del. World Fedn. Neurosurgery. Mem. editorial bd. Jour. Neurosurgery, chmn. 1967-69, editor, 1975-84. Served with AUS, 1942-45. Decorated Legion of Merit; recipient ofcl. citation and commendation Brit. Army, Harvey Cushing medal, 1979. Fellow ACS (adv. council on neurosurgery 1950, 60, v.p. 1972-73); mem. Soc. Neurol. Surgeons (pres. 1968-69), Am. Acad. Neurol. Surgery (pres. 1951-52), Harvey Cushing Soc. (pres. 1967-68), Am. Neurol. Assn. (hon.), Assn. Research Nervous and Mental Disease, Central Neuropsychiat. Assn. Am., Assn. Anatomists, So. Neurosurg. Soc. (pres. 1953-54), Soc. Med. Cons. to Armed Forces, Am. Surg. Assn. (v.p. 1975-76), Soc. de Neuro-Chirurgie de Langue Francaise, Excelsior Surg. Soc., Johns Hopkins Soc. Scholars, Soc. Internat. de Chirugie (Alpha Omega Alpha leader Am. medicine 1978), World Fedn. Neurosurg. Socs. (hon. pres.), Sigma Xi, Alpha Omega Alpha. Home: 2 Briar Oak Saint Louis MO 63132-4204 Office: Barnes Hosp Pl Saint Louis MO 63110

SCHWARTZ, HENRY GERARD, JR., consulting engineering company executive; b. St. Louis, Aug. 3, 1938; s. Henry Gerard and Edith Childs (Robinson) S.; m. Sally Arlene Dunbar, July 2, 1960; children: Thomas D., Jeffrey R. BS, Washington U., St. Louis, 1961, MS, 1962; PhD, Calif. Inst. Tech., 1966. Registered profl. engr. Mo. project mgr., head environ. div. Sverdrup & Parcel and Assocs., Inc., St. Louis, 1966-72, asst. v.p., 1972-74, v.p. chief engr., 1974-75; v.p. environ. div. Sverdrup Corp., St. Louis, 1975-80, sr. v.p., corp. prin., 1978—, also bd. dirs.; pres. Sverdrup Environ., Inc., St. Louis, 1989-93, 1993—. Contbr. articles to profl. jours. Bd. dirs. United Way, St. Louis, 1985; trustee Sverdrup Charitable Trust, 1987—; chmn. troop com. Boy Scouts Am. St. Louis; deacon, elder Ladue Chapel, St. Louis. Mem. ASCE, NSPE, Water Environ. Fedn. (Arthur Sidney Bedell award 1975, pres. 1986-87, founding chmn. 1990), Civil Engrs. Rsch. Foun. (bd. dirs.), Am. Acad. Environ. Engrs. (diplomate, pres. 1989), Mo. Athletic Club, Media Club, Algonquin Golf Club, St. Louis CLub. Presbyterian. Avocations: skiing, tennis, golf. Home: 10 Deerfield Rd Saint Louis MO 63124-1412 Office: Sverdrup Civil Inc 13723 Riverport Dr Maryland Heights MO 63043

SCHWARTZ, HERBERT FREDERICK, lawyer; b. Bklyn., Aug. 23, 1935; s. Henry and Blanche Theodora (goldberg) S.; m. Gail Lubets, Jan. 23, 1960; children: Wendy Helene, Karen Anne, Peter Andrew; m. Nan Budde Chequer, Mar. 13, 1987; stepchildren: Elizabeth, Anne, Laura. BSEE, MIT, 1957; MA in Applied Econs., U. Pa., 1964, LLB, 1964. Assoc. Fish & Neave, N.Y.C., 1964-70; jr. ptnr. Fish & Neave, 1970-71, ptnr., 1972—, mng. ptnr., 1985-91; lectr. law U. Pa., Phila., 1980-89, adj. prof., 1990—. Medm. adv. bd. PTC Jour., Washington, 1983; Author: Patent Law and Practice Federal Judicial Center, 1988; contbr. articles to profl. jours. Vice-chmn. Jr. Yacht Racing Assn. of L.I. Sound, 1985-88. Fist lt UAS, Signal Corps, 1957-59. Mem. U.S. Trademark Assn., Assn. of Bar of City of N.Y., Am. Intellectual Property Lawyers Assn., N.Y. Intellectual Property Lawyers Assn., Am. Law Inst., Order of Coif, N.Y. Yacht Club, Riverside Yacht Club (bd. govs.). Avocation: racing sailboats. Home: 24 Cherry Tree Ln Riverside CT 06878-2629 Office: Fish & Neave 1251 Avenue Of The Americas New York NY 10020-1104

SCHWARTZ, HERBERT MARSHALL, business executive; b. Miami, Fla., Nov. 15, 1947; s. Harry Spencer and Sandra Rose (Ratthaus) S.; M. Leslie Donna Nadel, Sept. 2, 1974 (div. June 1986); children: Bryan Harris, Sheryl Beth. BA in Bus. and Acctg., U. Ga., 1969. Staff acct. Touche Ross and Co., Atlanta, 1969-70; chief exec. officer P. Gregory's and Jeans Junction, Atlanta, 1970-74, U.S. Postamatic, Inc., Marietta, Ga., 1974—; sr. cons. HMS Bus. Cons., Atlanta, 1981-86; cons., bd. dirs. So. Vending Corp., Dunwoody, Ga., 1988—, Cen. Vending, Inc., Orlando, Fla., 1988—. Invented Honor Vending Machine, 1985, Pastry Machine, 1986. Charter founder Ronald Reagan Rep. Ctr., Washington, 1989; mem. Rep. Senatorial Inner Circle, Washington, 1989; bd. dirs. Etz Chaim Temple, Marietta, 1981-82, fin. dir., 1981-84; mem. site com. selction and Hospice House Atlanta Jewish Community Ctr. Named Runner-Up Businessman of Yr. Atlanta Bus. League, 1973; recipient Gold Medal Award for Outstanding Svc. Spl. Olympics Internat., 1986-89, Appreciation cert. Spl. Olympics Project, 1989, Outstanding Businessman and Distributor award Shipman Mfg., 1986. Mem. U.S. Postage Stamp Assn. (pres. 1977-78), High Mus. Young Profls., B'nai Brith Century Club. Home: 1400 N Riverside Cir NE Atlanta GA 30328-1847

SCHWARTZ, ILSA ROSLOW, neuroscientist; b. Bklyn., Aug. 20, 1941; d. David and Lottie (Warshall) Roslow; m. Alan Gordon Schwartz, July 19, 1964; children: Leah Ellen, Seth Roslow. AB magna cum laude, Vassar Coll., 1962; MS, Yale U., 1964, PhD, 1968. Postdoctoral fellow Albert Einstein Coll. Medicine, Bronx, N.Y., 1968-69; rsch. assoc. ctr. for neural scis. Ind. U., Bloomington, 1970-73, asst. prof. anatomy and physiology, 1973-75; asst. prof. med. scis. Ind. U. Sch. Medicine, Bloomington, 1976-77; vis. rsch. anatomist UCLA Sch. Medicine, 1976-77, asst. prof. in- residence head and neck surgery, 1977-81, assoc. prof., 1981-87; assoc. prof. Yale U. Sch. Medicine, New Haven, 1987-89, prof. surgery (otolaryngology) and neurobiology, 1989—; mem. communicative disorders com. Nat. Inst. Neurol. Communicative Disorders and Stroke, Bethesda, 1981-83, chair, 1983-85; sci. adv. coun. House Ear Inst., L.A., 1989, chair, 1991-94. Recipient Jacob Javits Neurosci. Investigator award Nat. Inst. Neurol. Communicative Disorders and Stroke, 1988-95; grantee NIH, 1973—; fellow Vassar Coll., 1962-63, NIH, 1962-68, 68-69. Mem. Assn. for Rsch. in Otolaryngology (coun. mem. 1986-89, pres. elect 1989-90, pres. 1990-91, past pres. 1991-92), Nat. Inst. on Deafness and Other Communication Disorders (adv. coun. 1989-93), Soc. for Neurosci. (chair Bloomington, Ind. chpt. 1975-76), Am. Assn. Anatomists, Women in Neurosci., AAAS, Friends of NIDCD, Inc. (bd. dirs.). Jewish. Office: Yale U Sch Medicine 333 Cedar St New Haven CT 06510-3289

SCHWARTZ, IRVING DONN, architect; b. Chgo., June 11, 1927; s. Simon S. and Rose P. (Pilot) S.; children—Charles, Linda. B.S., U. Ill., 1949, B.S. in Architecture, 1965, M.S. in Architecture, 1972. Registered architect, Ill. Ind., Fla., D.C., Ohio, Ga., Ala., Calif., N.H., Va., Md., Pa. Chief standard cost and indsl. engring. Lanzit Corrugated Box Co., Chgo., 1950-53; pres. Kaufman, Inc., Champaign, Ill., 1953-60; v.p. Hart Mirror Plate Co., Grand Rapids, Mich., 1953-60; asso. Richardson, Severns, Scheeler & Assos., Inc., Champaign, 1960-71; pres. IDS, Inc., Champaign, 1971-83, ADI, Dallas, 1983-86, IDS/B, Inc., Dallas, 1986—; prof. architecture Grad. Sch. Architecture, U. Ill., 1976-83; assoc. prof. design U. North Tex.; cons. in field. Mem. Champaign County Devel. Council; mem. Model Community Coordinating Council, Champaign; co-chmn. bldg. com. Mercy Hosp.; bd. frat. affairs U. Ill.; bd. dirs. United Fund. Served to 1st lt. U.S. Army, 1945-47. Recipient archtl. design research award, graphic design citation Progressive Architecture mag., 1974. Fellow Am. Soc. Interior Designers (treas. 1976, nat. pres. 1978, Louis Tregre award 1992, Nat. design award 1983); mem. AIA (Design award 1983), Nat. Council Archtl. Registration Bds., Nat. Council Interior Design Qualifications (bd. dirs., pres. 1980), Tex. Assn. Interior Design (pres. 1993). Club: Standard (Chgo.). Home: 4443 Westway Ave Dallas TX 75205-3630 Office: IDS/B Inc 2777 N Stemmons Fwy Ste 1650 Dallas TX 75207-2229

SCHWARTZ, IRVING LEON, physician, scientist, educator; b. Cedarhurst, N.Y., Dec. 25, 1918; s. Abraham and Rose (Doniger) S.; m. Felice T. Nlerenberg, Jan. 12, 1946; children: Cornelia Ann, Albert Anthony, James Oliver. AB, Columbia U., 1939; MD, NYU, 1943. Diplomate Am. Bd. Internal Medicine. Intern, then asst. resident Bellevue Hosp., N.Y.C., 1943-44, 46-47; NIH fellow physiology NYU Coll. Medicine, N.Y.C., 1947-50; Am. Physiol. Soc. Porter fellow, also Gibbs meml. fellow in clin. sci. Rockefeller Inst., 1950-51, Am. Heart Assn. fellow, 1951-52, asst. prof., then assoc., 1952-58; asst. physician, then assoc. physician Rockefeller Inst. Hosp., 1950-58; sr. scientist Brookhaven Nat. Lab., Upton, N.Y., 1958-61, research collaborator, 1961—; attending physician Brookhaven Nat. Lab. Hosp., 1958—; Joseph Eichberg prof. physiology, dir. dept. U. Cin. Coll. Medicine, 1961-65; dean grad. faculties Mt. Sinai Med. and Grad. Schs., CUNY, 1965-80, prof. physiology and biophysics, chmn. dept., 1968-79, exec. officer biomed. scis. doctoral program, 1969-72, Dr. Harold and Golden Lamport disting. prof., 1979—; dir. Ctr. Peptide and Membrane Research Mt. Sinai Med. Ctr., 1979-87; dean emeritus Mt. Sinai Grad. Sch. Biol. Scis., 1980—. Contbr. articles to sci. publs. Pres. Life Scis. Found.,

1962—. Served from 1st lt. to capt., M.C. AUS, 1944-46. Recipient Solomon A. Berson Med. Alumni Achievement award NYU Sch. Medicine, 1973. Fellow A.C.P.; mem. Am. Physiol. Soc., Soc. Exptl. Biology and Medicine, Am. Soc. Clin. Investigation, Am. Fedn. Clin. Research, Biophys. Soc., Endocrine Soc., Harvey Soc., Soc. for Neurosci., Am. Heart Assn., John Jay Assos. Columbia Coll., AAAS, N.Y. Acad. Sci., Sigma Xi, Alpha Omega Alpha. Home: 1120 5th Ave New York NY 10128-0144 also: 9 Thorn Hedge Rd Bellport NY 11713 Office: Mt Sinai Med Ctr Box 932 100th St and Fifth Ave New York NY 10029 also: Med Research Center Brookhaven Nat Lab Upton NY 11973

SCHWARTZ, IRVING LLOYD, retired history educator; m. Rosanne S. Schwartz; children: Barth D., Regina Mara. BA, U. Dayton, 1942; Diplomate, U. Florence, Italy, 1946, Coll. Armed Forces; MA in History, Miami U., 1948. Instr. U.S. Office Edn., Wright-Patterson AFB, Ohio, 1940-43; historian USAF, 1946-47; edn. and tng. specialist, chief spl. rehab. unit VA, Ohio, 1947-50; chief of protocol aeronautical systems USAF, Wright Patterson AFB, 1950-78; prof. history Sinclair Community Coll., Dayton, Ohio, 1978-93, prof. emeritus, 1993—; mem. faculty history dept. U. Dayton, 1953-56. Contbr. articles to profl. jours. Chmn. Gov.'s Help a Disabled Vet. Com., 1945; mem. Mayor's Sister City Com., 1969—; head Dayton com. Bicentennial French Revolution Observances; head Dayton Columbus Quincentary Celebration, 1992; sec. City Plan Bd., Dayton, 1970—; chmn. bd. trustees Dayton and Montgomery County Pub. Libr. System, 1971—; trustee Nat. Aviation Hall of Fame; bd. dirs. Dayton Coun. World Affairs, 1982—. Decorated Chevalier L'Ordre des Palmes Academiques, French Govt., 1990; recipient 2 USAF Exceptional Civilian Svc. award, 1988-89. Mem. Am. Hist. Assn. Home: 2033 Burroughs Dr Dayton OH 45406-4415 Office: Sinclair Community College Dept History 444 W 3rd St Dayton OH 45402-1421

SCHWARTZ, JACK THEODORE, retired publisher; b. N.Y.C., Aug. 24, 1914; s. Nathan and Vera Ida (Rosovsky) S.; m. Pearl Tarnower, May 20, 1941; children: Harriet (Mrs. Tod Johnson), Deborah (Mrs. Gary Raizes). Student, Columbia Coll., 1932-34. Founder, pres. Syndicate Mags., Inc., N.Y.C., 1939-83; founder, pres. Beacon Advt. Assos., Inc., 1950-76; founding partner Beacon Mktg. Consultants, 1959-81; pub. Better Nutrition, Today's Living, Art Material Trade News. Trustee, mem. exec. com. Lesley Coll., Cambridge, Mass.; bd. dirs. Orgn. for Health Initiatives, White Plains, N.Y. Served to 1st lt. AUS, 1943-45. Home: 39 Kenilworth Rd Rye NY 10580-1910 Office: 6 E 43d St New York NY 10017 I feel that the luckiest decision I ever made was the one to balance my business and family lives. I program my family time as carefully as my business time and make sure that my family is never cheated. This, for me, has made for contentment and happiness at home, allowing me to approach my business hours with full concentration and energy.

SCHWARTZ, JEROME MERRILL, lawyer; b. Pittsfield, Mass., Oct. 3, 1952; s. Harry and Pauline (Bricker) S.; m. Gail Eileen Schulman, May 29, 1977; children: Karen Beth, Steven Robert. BSEE magna cum laude, U. Mich., 1974, JD magna cum laude, 1977. Bar: Mich. 1977, U.S. Ct. Appeals (6th cir.) 1979, U.S. Supreme Ct. 1990. Assoc. Dickinson, Wright, Moon, Van Dusen & Freeman, Detroit, 1977-83, ptnr., 1984—. Bd. dirs., chmn.-elect Am. Heart Assn. Mich.; mem. regional adv. bd. Anti-Defamation League. Mem. Detroit Bar Assn., Assn. for Corp. Growth Inc., Comml. Fin. Assn. Edn. Found. (adv. bd.), Nat. Assn. Securities Dealers (panel of arbitrators). Office: 500 Woodward Ave Ste 4000 Detroit MI 48226-3425

SCHWARTZ, JOHN JAMES, association executive, consultant; b. New Rochelle, N.Y., Aug. 28, 1919; s. Edwin Benner and Marjorie Helen (James) S.; m. Katharine S. Sprackling, Jan. 6, 1942; children: Christopher Louis. Grad. high sch., New Rochelle; student, Mercersburg Acad., 1938. Campaign dir. John Price Jones Inc., N.Y.C., 1946-50; dir. pub. relations and fund raising Travelers Aid Soc. N.Y., N.Y.C., 1950-55; dir. devel. Community Service Soc., N.Y.C., 1955-57, Near East Found., N.Y.C., 1957-60; v.p. G.A. Brakeley & Co. Inc., N.Y.C., 1960-61; dir. devel. Fgn. Policy Assn., N.Y.C., 1962-64; founding pres. Greater N.Y. Nat. Soc. of Fund Raising Execs., 1964; asst. v.p. for crusade Am. Cancer Soc., N.Y.C., 1964-66; exec. dir. Am. Fund Raising Counsel, N.Y.C., 1966-68, exec. v.p., 1968-72, pres., 1972-87; founding bd. mem. Ind. Sector, Washington, 1980-85, mem. com. to measurably increase giving; mem., former pres. Com. on Nat. Ctr. for Charitable Stats.; spl. cons. to Com. on Pvt. Philanthropy and Pub. Needs., 1973; chair pvt. adv. group Nat. Assn. Attys. Gen. Model Law Project. Author: Modern American Philanthropy; A Personal Account, 1994. Mem. adv. bd. mgmt. fund-raising NYU Cert. Program; mem. adv. coun. Grad. Sch. Mgmt. & Urban Professions, New Sch. Social Rsch.; active formation of 5 borough coalition Daring Goals for Caring Soc., N.Y.C., 1987; cons. Nat. U. Ctr. on Philanthropy, 1988-91, Community Counselling Svc. Co., Inc., 1988-91; pres. Nat. Philanthropy Day, 1988-90, mem. hon. com., 1991; bd. dirs.-at-large USA World Fund Raising Coun., 1993. Capt. U.S. Army Air Corps, PTO, 1941-46. Recipient Disting. Profl. Service to Philanthropy award Am. Assn. Fund-Raising Counsel, N.Y., 1976, Outstanding Agy. Profl. award United Way Am., Alexandria, 1982. Mem. Nat. Charities Info. Bur. (bd. dirs. 1978-94), Nat. Soc. Fund-Raising Execs. (bd. dirs. 1964-90, past pres.), Fairfield County Assn. for Fund-Raising Dirs. (bd. dirs. 1990—), Am. Assn. Ret. Persons (bd. dirs. Andrus Found. 1983-90), 501C-3 Socs., Princeton Club (N.Y.C.). Democrat. Unitarian. Avocations: writing, ship models, sports cars.

SCHWARTZ, JOHN NORMAN, health care executive; b. Watertown, Minn., Dec. 13, 1945; s. Norman O. and Marion G. (Tesch) S. BA, Augsburg Coll., Mpls., 1967; MHA, U. Minn., 1969. Adminstrv. resident Luth. Hosp. and Med. Ctr., Wheat Ridge, Colo., 1968-69; asst. adminstr. St. Luke's Hosp., Milw., 1969-73, med. adminstr., 1973-75, v.p., 1975-84; sr. v.p. and chief oper. officer Good Samaritan Med. Ctr., Milw., 1984-85, pres. and chief exec. officer, 1985-88; exec. v.p. Aurora Health Care Inc., Milw., 1988-89; gen. mgr. SmithKline Beecham Clin. Labs., Schaumburg, Ill., 1989-90; chief exec. Trinity Hosp. of Advocate Health Care, Chgo., 1991—; bd. dirs. Samaritan Health Plan, Milw., 1984-89. Bd. dirs. Gt. Lakes Hemophilia Found., Milw., 1975-89, Gov.'s appointee to Coun. on Hemophilia and Related Blood Disorders, Madison, 1978, Sullivan Chamber Ensemble, Milw., 1975-84, S. Chgo. YMCA, 1993—. Recipient First Place award Color Photography, Milw. Jour. Co., 1983. Fellow Am. Coll. Health-care Execs. (regent 1993—). Lutheran. Avocations: jogging, photography, music, choral singing. Office: Trinity Hosp 2320 E 93rd St Chicago IL 60617-3909

SCHWARTZ, JOSEPH, English language educator; b. Milw., Apr. 9, 1925; s. Alfred George and Mary (Brandt) S.; m. Joan Jackson, Aug. 28, 1954; 1 son, Adam. B.A., Marquette U., 1946, M.A., 1947; Ph.D., U. Wis., 1952. Teaching asst. Marquette U., Milw., 1946-47; instr. Marquette U., 1947-48, 50-54, asst. prof., 1954-59, assoc. prof., 1959-64, prof., 1964-90, chmn. dept. English, 1963-75, prof. emeritus, 1990—; teaching fellow U. Wis., 1948-50; Chmn. region X Woodrow Wilson Nat. Fellowship Found., 1967-73; pres. bd. edn. Archdiocese of Milw., 1977-79. Author: A Reader for Writers, 3d edit., 1971, Perspectives on Language, 1963, Province of Rhetoric, 1965, Poetry: Meaning and Form, 1969, Hart Crane: A Critical Bibliography, 1970, Hart Crane: A Descriptive Bibliography, 1972, Exposition, 2d edit., 1971, Hart Crane: A Reference Guide, 1983; editor: Renascence mag., 1978-95. Recipient Distinguished Alumni award Marquette U. Sch. Speech, 1967, Outstanding Tchr. award Marquette U., 1974; Ford Found. grantee, 1956; Am. Council Learned Socs. grantee, 1972, 89; HEW grantee, 1966, 67. Mem. Nat. Coun. Tchrs. English (nat. dir. 1965-68), Modern Lang. Assn., Midwest Modern Lang Assn. (exec. com. 1973-76), Fellowship of Cath. Scholars (bd. dirs. 1987-90), Conf. on Christianity and Lit. (bd. dirs. 1987-90), Phi Beta Kappa, Alpha Sigma Nu (bd. dirs.). Republican. Roman Catholic. Home: # 112 8516 W Mequon Rd # 112 Thiensville WI 53097-3100 Office: Marquette U Renascence Brooks Hall Milwaukee WI 53233

SCHWARTZ, JOSEPH, retired container company executive; b. N.Y.C., Apr. 22, 1911; s. Nathan and Ida (Estrich) S.; m. Hazel Shapiro, Dec. 23, 1932; children—Arlene Schwartz Bornstein, Linda Schwartz Rosenbaum. Grad. high sch. Pitt. Mut. Paper Co., Lynn, Mass., 1928-38; treas. Allied Container Corp., Hyde Park, Mass., 1938-56; pres., treas. Allied Container Corp., Dedham, Hyde Park, 1956-84; chmn. bd. Cargal, Ltd., Lod

Israel; ret. v.p. Union Camp Corp., Wayne, N.J. Fellow Brandeis U. Home: #307 3960 Oaks Clubhouse Dr Pompano Beach FL 33069

SCHWARTZ, JULES JACOB, management educator; b. Phila., Apr. 9, 1932; s. Harry J. and Marion E. (Friedmann) S.; m. Sandra Leigh Burgoon, Dec. 18, 1971. B.M.E., U. Del., 1953, M.B.A., 1963; D.B.A. (fellow), Harvard U., 1973, D.H.L. (hon.), 1982. Engr. Westinghouse Electric Co., Phila., 1953; program mgr. Thiokol Chem. Corp., 1957-69; asso. prof., asst. dean Wharton Sch., U. Pa., 1973-77; dean, prof. mgmt. and engring. Sch. Mgmt. Boston U., 1977-80, chmn. univ. faculty, 1991—; bd. dirs. Legal Seafoods Corp., Infinetics Inc., Analogic Corp., Hart, Whitley & Co.; gov. Boston Stock Exchange; cons. Xerox, Internat. Tel. & Tel., Getty Oil, Phila. Nat. Bank, AT&T, New Eng. Telephone Co., A.D. Little, Philip Morris, Bristol Myers, Prime Computer; receiver U.S. Dist. Ct. (Delaware), 1969—. Author: Corporate Policy. Served to lt. col. U.S. Army, 1953-57. Recipient Gen. J. Ernest Smith prize.; Chrysler fellow; Metcalf prize Boston U. Mem. ASME, Am. Inst. Aeros. and Astronautics, Nat. Soc. Profl. Engrs., Tau Beta Pi, Beta Gamma Sigma, Phi Kappa Phi. Clubs: Harvard (N.Y.C. and Boston); Army-Navy (Washington). Patentee in field. Home: 96 Radcliffe Rd Belmont MA 02178-3340 Office: Sch Mgmt Boston U Boston MA 02215

SCHWARTZ, KESSEL, modern language educator; b. Kansas City, Mo., Mar. 19, 1920; s. Henry and Dora (Tanenbaum) S.; m. Barbara Lewin, Apr. 3, 1947; children: Joseph David, Deborah, Edward, Michael. B.A., U. Mo., 1940, M.A., 1941; Ph.D., Columbia U., 1953. Asst. instr. U. Mo., 1940-42; dir. cultural ctrs. in Nicaragua, Ecuador, cultural observer in Costa Rica State Dept., 1946-48; instr. Hofstra, Hamilton, Colby colls., 1948-53; asst. prof. U. Vt., 1953-57; assoc. prof., then prof. modern langs., chmn. dept. U. Ark., 1957-62; prof. modern langs. U. Miami, Fla., 1962-90; chmn. dept. U. Miami, 1962-64, 74-83, dir. grad. studies, 1964-65, 83-90, now emeritus prof.; vis. prof. U. N.C., Chapel Hill, 1966-67. Author: The Ecuadorian Novel, 1953, An Introduction to Modern Spanish Literature, 1967, The Meaning of Existence in Contemporary Hispanic Literature, 1969, Vicente Aleixandre, 1970, Juan Goytisolo, 1970, A New History of Spanish American Fiction, 1972 (named Outstanding Acad. Book of Year, Am. Assn. Coll. and Research Librarians), Studies on Twentieth Century Spanish and Spanish American Literature, 1983; co-author: A New History of Spanish Literature, 1961, rev. edit., 1991, A New Anthology of Spanish Literature, 1968; assoc. editor Hispania, 1965-84; editorial adv. bd.: Anales de Literatura Española Contemporánea Folio; Fiestas (Goytisolo), notes and introduction, 1964; contbr. numerous articles to profl. jours., chpts. to books, ency. Nat. patronato Letras de Oro Spanish Literary Prizes. Served with AUS, 1942-46. July 14, 1989 declared Kessel Schwartz Day in Coral Gables, Miami and Dade County by mayors' proclamation. Mem. MLA (group sec. 1964, group chmn. 1965, chmn. nominating com. for modern Spanish lit. 1966-68), Am. Assn. Tchrs. Spanish and Portuguese (chmn. Peninsular lit. sect. 1972), Internat. Assn. Hispanists, Phi Beta Kappa (pres. So. Fla. chpt. 1977), Phi Sigma Iota, Sigma Delta Pi (nat. Order of Don Quijote award 1984, Order of Discoverers award 1989), Pi Delta Phi, Delta Phi Alpha, Omicron Delta Kappa. Home: 6400 Maynada St Miami FL 33146-3318 *If men loved one another sufficiently, we might not need our legal systems. Given our imperfect nature as human beings, we must believe in some higher goals to give meaning to our lives but be ever vigilant that in the pursuit of success we do not infringe upon the happiness of others or confuse the means with the end.*

SCHWARTZ, LEON, foreign language educator; b. Boston, Aug. 22, 1922; s. Charles and Celia (Emer) S.; m. Jeanne Gurtat, Mar. 31, 1949; children—Eric Alan, Claire Marie. Student, Providence Coll., 1939-41; B.A., U. Calif. at Los Angeles, 1948; certificat de phonetique, U. Paris, 1949; M.A., U. So. Cal., 1950, Ph.D., 1962. Tchr. English, Spanish and Latin Redlands (Calif.) Jr. High Sch., 1951-54; high sch. tchr. Spanish and French, 1954-59; prof. French Calif. State U., Los Angeles, 1959-87, emeritus, 1987—, chmn. dept. fgn. langs. and lit., 1970-73. Author: Diderot and the Jews, 1981. Served as 2d lt. USAAF, 1942-45. Decorated Air medal with 5 oak leaf clusters; recipient Outstanding Prof. award Calif. State U. at Los Angeles, 1976. Mem. Am. Assn. Tchrs. French, Modern and Classical Lang. Assn. So. Calif., Western Soc. 18th Century Studies, Am. Soc. 18th Century Studies, Société Diderot, Phi Beta Kappa, Phi Kappa Phi, Pi Delta Phi, Sigma Delta Pi, Alpha Mu Gamma. Office: Dept Fgn Langs and Literatures Calif State U Los Angeles CA 90032

SCHWARTZ, LILLIAN FELDMAN, artist, filmaker, art analyst, author, nurse; b. Cin., July 13, 1927; d. Jacob and Katie (Green) Feldman; m. Jack James Schwartz, Dec. 22, 1946; children: Jeffrey Hugh, Laurens Robert. RN, U. Cin., 1947; Dr. honoris causa, Kean Coll., 1988. Nurse Cin. Gen. Hosp., 1947; head supr. premature nursery St. Louis Maternity Hosp., 1947-48; cons. AT&T Bell Labs., Murray Hill, N.J., 1968—; pres. Computer Creations Corp., Watchung, N.J., 1989—; cons. Bell Communications Research, Morristown, N.J., 1984-92; artist-in-residence Sta. WNET, N.Y.C., 1972-74; cons. T.J. Watson Rsch. Lab. IBM Corp., Yorktown, N.Y., 1975, 82-84; vis. mem. computer sci. dept. U. Md., College Park, 1974-80; adj. prof. fine arts Kean Coll., Union, N.J., 1980-82, Rutgers U., New Brunswick, N.J., 1982-83; adj. prof. dept. psychology NYU, N.Y.C., 1985-86, assoc. prof. computer sci.; guest lectr. Princeton U., Columbia U., Yale U., Rockefeller U.; mem. grad. faculty Sch. Visual Arts, N.Y.C. 1990—. Co-author: The Computer Artist's Handbook; contbd. articles to profl. jours including Scientific Am., 1995; contbr. chpts. to books, also Trans. Am. Philos. Soc., vol. 75, Part 6, 1985; one-woman shows of sculpture and paintings include Columbia U., 1967, 68, Rabin and Krueger Gallery, Newark, 1968; films shown at Met. Mus., N.Y.C., Franklin Inst., Phila., 1972, U. Toronto, 1972, am. Embassy, London, 1972, L.A. County Mus., Corcoran Gallery, Washington, 1972, Whitney Mus., N.Y.C., 1973, Grand Palais, Paris, Musee Nat. d'Art Moderne, Paris, IBM, and others. Recipient numerous art and film awards, Emmy award Mus. Modern Art, 1984, Computer Graphics World Smithsonian awards for virtual reality, art analysis, inventing computer medium for art and animation, 1993; named Outstanding Alumnus, U. Cin., 1987; grantee Nat. Endowment for Arts, 1977, 81, Corp. Pub. Broadcasting, 1979, Nat. Endowment Composers and Librettists, 1981. Fellow World Acad. of Art and Sci.; mem. NATAS, Am. Film Inst., Info. Film Prodrs. Am., Soc. Motion Picture and TV Engrs., Internat. Sculptors Assn., Centro Studi Pierfrancescani (Sansepolcro, Italy, founding mem.). Pioneer in use of computers as art media; commd. to create computer poster and TV comml. for opening New Mus. Modern Art, 1984; discovered identities of the Mona Lisa, hidden and surface, 1987, and identified steps DaVinci made in transforming Isabella, Duchess of Aragon, into the Mona Lisa using his own features as the model, 1993; discovered perspective used by DaVinci in The Last Supper, 1988; identified time of day and tree of thorns in Piero della Francesca's Resurrection; discovered Elizabeth I is model for Martin Droeshout engraving of Shakespeare, 1991; performed first transmission of computer drawing between U.S. and Germany, 1990; used morphing algorithms to determine Leonardo's creative decision-making steps in transforming the Duchess of Aragon into the Mona Lisa using his own features to segue; discovered metnod Leonardo used to create his Grotesques, 1994. *I have always been provoked by and concerned with the mechanical and technological world around me. I enjoy experimenting with traditional media and combining them with technology today. For example, I used computers as an art medium when computers were solely programmed for scientific purposes. By using the computer to understand the creative process I have made clear the intent of the great masters and applied their decision-making steps to my own work. The excitement in creating is to discover and to make a new world. My present success was achieved in part by being able to make new rules and not be hindered by old or obvious solutions.*

SCHWARTZ, LLOYD, music critic, poet; b. N.Y.C., Nov. 29, 1941; s. Sam and Ida (Singer) S. BA, Queens Coll., N.Y.C., 1962; MA, Harvard U., 1963, PhD, 1976. Classical music editor Boston Phoenix, 1977—; dir. creative writing U. Mass., Boston, 1982-84, 86-88, 1990—; classical music critic Fresh Air Nat. Pub. Radio, Phila., 1987—; prof. English U. Mass. Boston, 1986—. Author: (poems) These People, 1981, (play) These People: Voices for the Stage, 1990, Goodnight, Gracie, 1992; editor: Ploughshares, 1979, Elizabeth Bishop and Her Art, 1983; actor The Spider's Web, 1975-82; dir. These People: Voices for the Stage, 1990, (operas) L'Heure Espagnol (Ravel), 1972, Mavra (Stravinsky), 1973. Recipient Pulitzer prize for criticism, 1994; NEA creative writing fellow in poetry, 1990. Mem. PEN (exec. com. New Eng. chpt. 1983—) PEN Am., Poetry Soc. Am., MLA, New Eng. Poetry

Club. Avocations: collecting old recordings, books. Home: 27 Pennsylvania Ave Somerville MA 02145-2217 Office: Boston Phoenix 126 Brookline Ave Boston MA 02215-3920

SCHWARTZ, LLOYD MARVIN, newspaper and magazine correspondent, broadcaster; b. Bklyn., Mar. 6, 1923; s. Philip and Celia W. Schwartz; m. Doris Grossman, May 19, 1946; children: Ellen, Philip, Laura. BA, NYU, 1944. NYU corr. N.Y. Times, 1942-44; news editor, writer Trade Union Courier, 1943-44; reporter Lima (Ohio) News, 1945; reporter, The White House corr. Fairchild Publs., Washington, 1945-65; Washington bur. chief Fairchild Publs., 1965-88; Congl. corr. Fairchild News Service, 1977-88; panelist, news broadcaster Voice of Am., AFL-CIO, Fairchild Broadcast News and WJR-Detroit; Congl. corr. Van Dahl Publs., Albany, Oreg., 1980-90, mem. Senate and Ho. of Reps. Periodical Press Galleries, 1946-93; Congl. corr. Linn's Stamp News, Sidney, Ohio, 1990-92. Mem. Hollin Hall Sr. Ctr. Camera Club. Democrat. Jewish.

SCHWARTZ, LOUIS BROWN, legal educator; b. Phila., Feb. 22, 1913; s. Samuel and Rose (Brown) S.; m. Berta Wilson, Mar. 29, 1937 (div. 1954); children: Johanna, Victoria; m. Miriam Robbins Humboldt, Sept. 16, 1964. B.S. in Econs, U. Pa., 1932, J.D., 1935. Bar: Pa. 1935, U.S. Supreme Ct. 1942. Atty. SEC, Washington, 1935-39; chief gen. crimes and spl. projects sect. Dept. Justice, 1939-43, chief judgment and enforcement sect. antitrust div., 1945-46; also mem. inter-departmental coms. on war crimes and status-of-forces treaties; prof. law U. Pa. Law Sch., 1946-83, Benjamin Franklin prof., 1964-83; prof. law Hastings Coll. Law, U. Calif., 1983—; vis. prof. Harvard U., Columbia U., U. Calif. at Berkeley, Cambridge (Eng.) U.; Ford vis. Am. prof. Inst. Advanced Legal Studies, U. London (Eng.), 1974; vis. disting. prof. Ariz. State U., 1980; mem. Atty. Gen.'s Nat. Com. Study Antitrust Laws, 1953-55, Pa. Gov.'s Comm. on Penal and Correctional Affairs, 1956-60; adv. commn. Revision Pa. Penal Code, 1963-68; nat. adv. council Nat. Defender Project, 1964-69; dir. Nat. Commn. on Reform of Fed. Criminal Laws, 1968-71; co-reporter Model Penal Code Am. Law Inst., 1962; cons. FTC, Dept. Justice, other agencies. Author: Free Enterprise and Economic Organization, 1959, 6th edit. (with John J. Flynn, Harry First) titled Antitrust and Government Regulation, 1983-85 (2 vols.), Le Système Pénal des Etats-Unis, 1964, Law Enforcement Handbook for Police, 1970, 2d edit., 1979, Proposed Federal Criminal Code, (with Comments and Working Papers), 1971; contbr. numerous articles to profl. jours. Served as lt. (j.g.) USNR, 1944-45. Mem. Ams. Democratic Action (nat. bd.), Am. Law Inst. (adv. com. pre-arraignment code), Order of Coif. Home: 2955 Pierce St San Francisco CA 94123-3824 Office: U Calif Hastings Coll Law 200 Mcallister St San Francisco CA 94102-4978

SCHWARTZ, LOUIS WINN, ophthalmologist; b. Pa., Apr. 19, 1942; s. Edward and Sylvia Beatrice (Winn) S.; m. Linda Weinberg, June 14, 1964; children: Joanne Karen, Geoffrey Paul. AB, Bowdoin Coll., 1963; MD, Jefferson Med. Coll., 1967. Diplomate Am. Bd. Ophthalmology. Intern Phila. Gen. Hosp., 1967-68; resident in ophthalmology Wills Eye Hosp., Phila., 1970-73; ophthalmologist Ophthalmic Assocs., Lansdale, Pa., 1973—; attending surgeon Wills Eye Hosp. Glaucoma Svc., Phila., 1984—; clin. assoc. prof. ophthalmology Jefferson Med. Coll., Phila., 1984—; chief ophthalmology North Penn Hosp., 1995—. Co-author: Laser Therapy of Anterior Segment, 1988, 7 other books; assoc. editor Contact Lens Assn. Ophthalmology Jour., 1988; contbr. numerous articles to profl. jours. Recipient Honor award Am. Acad. Ophthalmology, 1988. Mem. AMA, Am. Glaucoma Soc., Pa. Acad. Ophthalmology, InterCounty Ophthalmol. Soc. (pres. 1985-86), Ophthalmic Club Phila. (pres. 1985-86). Office: Ophthalmic Assocs 1000 N Broad St Lansdale PA 19446-1138

SCHWARTZ, LYLE H., materials scientist, government official; b. Chgo., Aug. 2, 1936; s. Joseph K. Schwartz and Helen (Shefsky) Bernards; divorced; children—Ara, Justin; m. Celesta Sue Jurkovich, Sept. l, 1973. B.S. in Sci. Engring., Northwestern U., 1959, Ph.D. in Materials Sci., 1964. Prof. materials sci. Northwestern U., Evanston, Ill., 1964-84, dir. Materials Research Ctr., 1979-84; dir. materials sci. and engr. lab. Nat. Inst. Standards and Tech., Dept. Commerce, Gaithersburg, Md., 1984—; cons. Argonne Nat. Labs., Ill., 1965-79; vis. scientist Bell Telephone Labs., Murray Hill, N.J., 1971-73. Author: (with J.B. Cohen) Diffraction From Materials, 1977, 2d edit., 1987; numerous articles and papers. NSF fellow, 1962-63; recipient Presdl. Rank Award of Meritorious Exec. for outstanding govt. svc., 1990. Fellow Am. Soc. for Metals; mem. AAAS, AIME, Nat. Acad. Engring., Am. Phys. Soc., Am. Crystallography Assn., Materials Rsch. Soc., Sigma Xi. Office: Nat Inst Standards and Tech Materials Sci & Engring Lab Gaithersburg MD 20899

SCHWARTZ, MARILYN, columnist. Columnist Dallas Morning News. Office: The Dallas Morning News Communications News PO Box 655237 Dallas TX 75265

SCHWARTZ, MARSHALL ZANE, pediatric surgeon; b. Mpls., Sept. 1, 1945; s. Sidney Shay and Peggy Belle (Lieberman) S.; m. Michele Carroll Walker, Oct. 16, 1971; children: Lisa, Jeffrey. BS, U. Minn., 1968, MD, 1970. Diplomate Am. Bd. Surgery, Am. Bd. Pediatric Surgery. Intern N.Y. Hosp., N.Y.C., 1970-71; resident in gen. surgery U. Minn., Mpls., 1971-73, 75-76, rsch. fellow, 1974-75; jr. resident in pediatric surgery Children's Hosp. Med. Ctr., Harvard Med. Sch., 1973-74, sr. resident in pediatric surgery, 1976-77, chief resident in pediatric surgery, 1977-78; instr. Med. Sch. Harvard U., Boston, 1978-79; asst. in surgery Childrens Hosp. Med. Ctr., Boston, 1978-79; asst. prof. Med. Br. U. Tex., Galveston, 1979-81, assoc. prof. Med. Br., 1981-83, chief pediatric surgery Med. Br., 1980-83; assoc. prof. U. Calif., Davis, 1983-86, prof., 1986-92, chief pediatric surgery, 1983-92, chmn. helicopter svcs., programmatic subcom., 1984-86, vice chmn. faculty Sch. Medicine, 1990-91, chmn. faculty Sch. Medicine, 1991-92; prof. surgery and pediatrics George Washington Sch. Medicine, 1992—; surgeon-in-chief, chmn. dept. pediatric surgery Children's Nat. Med. Ctr., Washington, 1992—. Editorial bd. Journal of Pediatric Surgery, 1988—. Pres. bd. dirs. Sacramento Children's Hosp. Found., 1990-92; vice chmn. Bd. of Childrens Faculty Assocs., Childrens Nat. Med. Ctr. Recipient Basil O'Connor Rsch. award March of Dimes Found., 1981, Young Investigator award NIH, 1982, Found. for Children Rsch. award, 1982, James W. McLaughlin award U. Tex., 1983. Fellow ACS; mem. Am. Surg. Assn., Soc. Univ. Surgeon, Am. Pediatric Surg. Assn., Soc. Surgery of the Alimentary Tract, Pacific Assn. of Pediatric Surgeons (pres., pres.-elect). Jewish. Avocations: skiing, fishing, wood working. Office: Children's Nat Med Ctr Dept Pediatric Surgery 111 Michigan Ave NW Washington DC 20010-2970

SCHWARTZ, MARVIN, lawyer; b. Phila., Nov. 3, 1922; s. Abe and Freda (Newman) S.; m. Joyce Ellen Sidner, Sept. 7, 1947; children: John Burkhart, Daniel Bruce, Pamela Louise Pier. LL.B., U. Pa., 1949. Bar: Pa. 1950, N.Y. 1951, D.C. 1955. Law sec. to judge U.S. Ct. Appeals, 3d Circuit, Phila., 1949-50; law sec. to Justice Burton U.S. Supreme Ct., Washington, 1950-51; assoc. Sullivan & Cromwell, N.Y.C., 1951-60; ptnr. Sullivan & Cromwell, 1960-92; mediator U.S. Dist. in So. Dist. N.Y.; arbitrator Am. Arbitration Assn., N.Y. Stock Exch., Nat. Assn. Securities Dealers. Spl. master appellate divsn. 1st dept. Supreme Ct. N.Y.; chmn. Zoning Bd. of Adjustment, Alpine, N.J., 1966-74; mem. Planning Bd., Alpine, 1966-67; bd. overseers U. Pa. Law Sch. Served with Signal Corps U.S. Army, 1943-46. Mem. ABA, N.Y. Bar Assn., Pa. Bar Assn., D.C. Bar Assn., Am. Coll. Trial Lawyers (sec. 1986-88, bd. regents 1981-86, chmn. Downstate N.Y. com. 1976-78), Am. Law Inst. (adviser complex litigation project), Univ. Club (N.Y.C.), Litchfield (Conn.) Country Club. Democrat. Jewish. Office: Sullivan & Cromwell 125 Broad St New York NY 10004-2400

SCHWARTZ, MELVIN, physics educator, laboratory administrator; b. N.Y.C., Nov. 2, 1932; s. Harry and Hannah (Shulman) S.; m. Marilyn Fenster, Nov. 25, 1953; children: David N., Diane R., Betty Lynn. A.B., Columbia U., 1953, Ph.D., 1958, DSc honoris causa, 1991. Assoc. physicist Brookhaven Nat. Labs. 1956-58; mem. faculty Columbia U., N.Y.C., 1958-66; prof. physics Columbia U., 1963-66, Stanford U., Calif., 1966-83; cons. prof. Stanford U., 1983-91; chmn. Digital Pathways, Inc., Mountain View, Calif., 1970-91; assoc. dir. high energy and nuclear physics Brookhaven Nat. Lab., Upton, N.Y., 1991-94; prof. physics Columbia U., N.Y.C., 1991-94, I.I. Rabi prof. physics, 1994—. Co-discoverer muon neutrino, 1962. Bd. govs. Weizmann Inst. Sci. Recipient Nobel prize in physics, 1988, John Jay award Columbia Coll., 1989; Guggenheim fellow, 1968. Fellow Am. Phys.

Soc. (Hughes award 1964); mem. NAS. Home: 61 S Howells Point Rd Bellport NY 11713-2621 Office: Columbia U Dept Physics New York NY 10027

SCHWARTZ, MICHAEL, university president, sociology educator; b. Chgo., July 29, 1937; s. Norman and Lillian (Ruthenberg) S.; m. Ettabelle Slutsky, Aug. 23, 1959; children: Monica, Kenneth, Rachel. BS in Psychology, U. Ill., 1958, MA in Indsl. Relations, 1959, PhD in Sociology, 1962; LLD (hon.), Youngstown State U., 1990. Asst. prof. sociology and psychology Wayne State U., Detroit, 1962-64; asst. prof. sociology Ind. U., Bloomington, 1964, assoc. prof. sociology, 1966-70; prof., chmn. dept. sociology Fla. Atlantic U., Boca Raton, 1970-72, dean Coll. Social Sci., 1972-76; v.p. grad. studies and research Kent (Ohio) State U., 1976-78, interim pres., 1977, acting v.p. acad. affairs, 1977-78, v.p. acad. and student affairs, 1978-80, provost, v.p. acad. and student affairs, 1980-82, pres., 1982-91; pres. emeritus and trustee's prof. Kent State U., 1991—; acting dir. Inst. for Social Rsch., Ind. U., 1966-67; tng. cons. Operation Head Start in Ind., 1964-70; cons. Office of Manpower, Automation and Tng., U.S. Dept. Labor, 1964-65. Cons. editor, Sociometry, 1966-70, assoc. editor, 1970; reader Am. Sociol. Rev. papers; author: (with Elton F. Jackson) Study Guide to the Study of Sociology, 1968; contbr. articles to profl. jours., chpts. to books. Chmn. Mid-Am. Conf. Coun. Pres.; rep. Nat. Coll. Athletic Assn. Pres.'s Commn.; corps evaluators North Ctrl. Assn. Colls. and Schs.; mem. bd. visitors Air U., USAF; mem. Akron (Ohio) Regional Devel. Bd., N.E. Ednl. TV of Ohio, Inc., N.E. Ohio Univs. Coll. Medicine; trustee Akron Symphony Orch. Assn.; mem. State of Ohio Post-Secondary Rev. Entity, 1995. Recipient Disting. Tchr. award Fla. Atlantic U., 1970-71, Meritorious Svc. award Am. Assn. State Colls. and Univs., 1990; Michael Schwartz Ctr., Kent State U., named in his honor, 1991. Mem. Ohio Tchr. Edn. and Cert. Adv. Commn., Akron Press Club, Cleve. Press Club, Pine Lake Trout Club. Office: Kent State U 405 White Hall Kent OH 44242

SCHWARTZ, MICHAEL AVERILL, university dean, pharmaceutical scientist; b. N.Y.C., Aug. 4, 1930; m. Marilyn Ettlinger, Nov. 24, 1954; children: Lori, Sharon. B.S. in Pharmacy, Bklyn. Coll. Pharmacy, 1952; M.S. in Pharmacy, Columbia U., 1956; Ph.D. in Pharmacy; Am. Found. Pharm. Edn. Fellow, U. Wis., 1959. Lic. pharmacist, N.Y., Ill., Fla. Sr. research scientist Bristol Labs., Syracuse, N.Y., 1959-63; asst. prof. pharmaceutics SUNY, Buffalo, 1963-65; asso. prof. SUNY, 1965-70, prof., 1970-78; asst. dean SUNY (Sch. Pharmacy), 1966-70, dean, 1970-76; dean Coll. Pharmacy, prof. pharmaceutics U. Fla., 1978—; mem. U.S. Herbal Pharmacology Del. to People's Republic of China, 1974; cons. to Pharm. industry. Contbr. numerous articles to profl. publs. Served with Med. Service Corps U.S. Army, 1952-54. Fellow AAAS, Acad. Pharm. Scis.; mem. Am. Pharm. Assn. (trustee 1982-84), Am. Chem. Soc., Am. Soc. Hosp. Pharmacists, Am. Assn. Colls. Pharmacy, Fla. Pharm. Assn., Fla. Soc. Hosp. Pharmacists, Sigma Xi, Rho Chi. Office: U Fla PO Box 4J Gainesville FL 32602-0004

SCHWARTZ, MICHAEL JOEL, hospital executive; b. Youngstown, Ohio, Aug. 16, 1941; s. Victor and Ruth Regina (Krause) S.; m. Phyllis JoAnn Colangelo, Sept. 4, 1965; children: Suzanne, David. BS, Va. Mil. Inst., Lexington, 1963; MHA, Duke U., 1971, JD, 1982. Adminstrv. asst. Duke U. Med. Ctr., Durham, N.C., 1971-73; asst. hosp. adminstr. Duke U. Med. Ctr., 1973-78, assoc. hosp. adminstr., 1978-83; pres., chief exec. officer Rome (N.Y.) Hosp. and Murphy Meml. Hosp., 1983-86, Alexian Bros. Hosp., Elizabeth, N.J., 1986—. Editorial bd. Healthcare Exec., 1987—. Div. chmn. United Way of Union County, Elizabeth, 1987—. Capt. USAR, 1967-68. Fellow Am. Coll. Healthcare Execs., Rotary.

SCHWARTZ, MICHAEL ROBINSON, health administrator; b. St. Louis, Mar. 18, 1940; s. Henry G. and Edith C. (Robinson) S.; children: Christine, Richard; m. Kathleen Nowicki, Dec., 9, 1988. AB, Dartmouth Coll., 1962; MHA, U. Minn., 1964. Asst. in adminstrn. Shands Teaching Hosp., Gainesville, Fla., 1966-67; asst. dir. Shands Teaching Hosp., Gainesville, 1967-68, assoc. dir., 1968-73; assoc. adminstr. St. Joseph Mercy Hosp., Pontiac, Mich., 1973-76; pres. St. Joseph Mercy Hosp., 1976-85; exec. v.p. Mercy Health Svcs., Farmington Hills, Mich., 1985—; chief oper. officer Mercy Health Svcs., Farmington Hills, 1988—; exec. v.p. Ea. Mich. region Sisters of Mercy Health Corp., 1991-92; non-resident lectr. U. Mich., 1982—; cons. prof. Oakland U., 1980-88; asst. prof. hosp. adminstrn. U. Fla., 1967-73; pres. Eastern Mich. Regional Bd. Sisters of Mercy Health Corp., 1976-79; bd. dirs. Lourdes Nursing Home, 1973-83, v.p., 1974, pres., 1975; bd. dirs. Oakland Livingston Human Svc. Agy., 1977-81; bd. dirs. Mercy Sch. Nursing, 1976-84, v.p., 1981-84; bd. dirs. United Way-Pontiac/North Oakland, 1976-85, v.p., 1982-84; bd. dirs. Oakland Health Edn. Program, 1977-85, treas., 1978-79; bd. dirs. Blue Cross/Blue Shield of Mich. 1982-86, cons. 1978-86, chair hosp. contingent to participating hosp. agreement adv. com., 1989—; bd. dirs. Greater Detroit Area Health Coun., 1983-88, 93—; chmn. bd. dirs., pres. Accord Ins. Co. Ltd., 1983-88; chmn. bd. dirs. Mercy Alternative, 1986-92, 93—; chmn. bd. dirs. Venzke Svc. Co., 1983-88, pres., 1983-84; chmn., bd. dirs., pres. Venzke Ins. Co. Ltd., 1988—; bd. dirs. Mercy Info. Systems, 1986-92, Pontiac Devel. Found., 1984-86; mem. audit and fin. com. Am. Healthcare Systems, 1988-92; mem. S.E. Mich. Hosp. Coun., chmn. pub. rels. com., 1983-85, bd. dirs. Hosp. Fund 1986—; trustee Sisters of Mercy Health Corp., 1991-93, sec. bd. trustees, 1993. With U.S. Army, 1964-66. Fellow Am. Coll. Healthcare Execs. (mem. exec. com. on higher edn. 1990-93, Mich Regent's award 1992); mem. Mich. Hosp. Assn. (at-large rep. corp. bd. 1990—, exec. com. 1992—), Am. Healthcare Systems Risk Retention Group (bd. dirs. 1990-91), Pontiac Urban League (pers. com. 1979), Comprehensive Health Planning Coun. (com. mem. 1976-81). Office: Mercy Health Svcs 34605 W 12 Mile Rd Farmington MI 48331-3263

SCHWARTZ, MILTON LEWIS, federal judge; b. Oakland, Calif., Jan. 20, 1920; s. Colman and Selma (Lavenson) S.; m. Barbara Ann Moore, May 15, 1942; children: Dirk L., Tracy Ann, Damon M., Brooke. A.B., U. Calif. at Berkeley, 1941, J.D., 1948. Bar: Calif. bar 1949. Research asst. 3d Dist. Ct. Appeal, Sacramento, 1948; dep. dist. atty., 1949-51; practice in Sacramento, 1951-79; partner McDonough, Holland, Schwartz & Allen, 1953-79; U.S. dist. judge Eastern Dist. Calif., U.S. Dist. Ct., Calif., 1979—; prof. law McGeorge Coll. Law, Sacramento, 1952-55; mem. Com. Bar Examiners Calif., 1971-75. Pres. Bd. Edn. Sacramento City Sch. Dist., 1961; v.p. Calif. Bd. Edn., 1967-68; trustee Sutterville Heights Sch. Dist. Served to maj. 40th Inf. Divsn. AUS, 1942-46, PTO. Named Sacramento County Judge of yr., 1990; Milton L. Schwartz Am. Inn of Court named in his honor, Davis, Calif. Fellow Am. Coll. Trial Lawyers; mem. State Bar Calif., Am. Bar Assn., Am. Bd. Trial Advocates, Anthony M. Kennedy Am. Inn of Ct. (pres. 1988-90, pres. emeritus 1990—). Office: US Dist Ct 1060 US Courthouse 650 Capitol Mall Sacramento CA 95814-4708

SCHWARTZ, MISCHA, electrical engineering educator; b. N.Y.C., Sept. 21, 1926; s. Isaiah and Bessie (Weinstein) S.; m. Lillian Mitchnick, June 23, 1957 (div.); 1 son, David; m. Charlotte F. Berney, July 12, 1970. B.E.E., Cooper Union, 1947; M.E.E., Poly. Inst. Bklyn., 1949; Ph.D. in Applied Physics (Sperry Gyroscope grad. scholar), Harvard U., 1951. Project engr. Sperry Gyroscope Co., 1947-52; mem. faculty Poly. Inst. Bklyn., 1952-74, prof. elec. engring., 1959-74, head dept., 1961-65; prof. elec. engring. and computer sci. Columbia U., N.Y.C., 1974-88, Charles Batchelor prof. elec. engring., 1988—; dir. Ctr. for Telecommunications Research, 1985-88; part-time tchr. CCNY, 1952, Adelphi Coll., 1951-52; cons. radiation physicist Montefiore Hosp., N.Y.C., 1954-56; cons. to industry, 1956—; full time cons. NYNEX, July-Dec. 1986; vis. prof. systems sci. dept. UCLA, 1964; dept. elec. engring. and computer sci. Columbia U., 1973-74; vis. sci. IBM Rsch., 1980, 94; chmn. Commn. C, U.S. Nat. Com. Internat. Union Radio Sci., 1977-80; vis. prof. dept. electronic and elec. engring. Univ. Coll., London, 1995; vis. mem. tech. staff AT&T Bell Labs., 1994. Author: Information Transmission, Modulation and Noise, 4th edit, 1990, (with L. Shaw) Signal Processing, 1975, Computer Communication Network Design and Analysis, 1977, Telecommunications Networks, 1987; editor; contbr.: Communication Systems and Techniques, 1966. Served with AUS, 1944-46. NSF sci. faculty fellow, 1965-66; recipient Disting. vis. award Australian-Am. Ednl. Found., 1975, Vis. Scientist award Nippon Tel.& Tel., 1981, Teaching award Columbia U., 1984, Gano Dunn award Cooper Union, 1986; finalist Mayor's Awards for Excellence in Sci. & Tech. City of N.Y., 1992. Fellow AAAS, IEEE (chmn. adminstrv. com. profl. group info. theory 1964-65, bd. dirs. 1978-79, bd. govs. Comm. Soc. 1973-79, v.p. 1982-83, pres. 1984-85, Edn.

medal 1983, IEEE Centennial Hall of Fame 1984, Region 1 award for leadership in mgmt. Ctr. for Telecom. Rsch. 1990, Edwin Armstrong award for contbns. to telecomm. 1994); mem. NAE, AAUP (chpt. pres. 1970-72), Assn. for Computing Machinery, Sigma Xi, Tau Beta Pi, Eta Kappa Nu. Home: 66 Maple Dr Great Neck NY 11021-1928 Office: Columbia U Shapiro CEPSR Rm 806 New York NY 10027

SCHWARTZ, MURRAY LOUIS, lawyer, educator, academic administrator; b. Phila., Oct. 27, 1920; s. Harry and Isabelle (Friedman) S.; m. Audrey James, Feb. 12, 1950; children—Deborah, Jonathan, Daniel. B.S., Pa. State U., 1942; LL.B., U. Pa., 1949; LL.D. (hon.), Lewis and Clark Coll., 1977. Bar: Pa. bar 1950, also U.S. Supreme Ct., D.C. Ct. Appeals 1950. Chemist Standard Oil Ind., Whiting, 1942-44; law clk. Fred M. Vinson, Chief Justice U.S., 1949-51; assoc. firm Shea, Greenman, Gardner & McConnaughey, Washington, 1951-53; spl. asst. to U.S. atty. gen. Office Solicitor Gen., 1953-54; 1st dept. city solicitor City Phila., 1954-56; assoc. firm Dilworth, Paxson, Kalish & Green, Phila., 1956-58; prof. law Law Sch., UCLA, 1958-91, dean, 1969-75; David G. Price and Dallas P. Price prof. of law UCLA, 1988-89, exec. vice chancellor, 1988-91; vice chancellor academic affairs U. Calif, Santa Barbara, 1991-92; interim sr. v.p. acad. affairs U. Calif., 1992-93; chmn. exec. com., bd. dirs. Social Sci. Rsch. Coun., 1981-85; bd. dirs. Mattel, Inc. Author: (with K.L. Karst and A.J. Schwartz) The Evolution of Law in the Barrios of Caracas, 1973, Law and the American Future, 1976, Lawyers and the Legal Profession, 2d edit. 1985; contbr. articles to profl. jours. Served to lt. (j.g.) USNR, 1944-46. Home: 1339 Marinette Rd Pacific Palisades CA 90272-2626

SCHWARTZ, MURRAY MERLE, federal judge; b. 1931. BS, Wharton Sch. U. Pa., 1952; LLB, U. Pa., 1955; LLM, U. Va., 1982. Part-time referee in bankruptcy Dist. of Del., 1969-74; judge U.S. Dist. Ct. Del., 1974—; chief judge, 1985-89. Author: The Exercise of Supervisory Power by the Third Circuit Court of Appeals, 1982. Mem. ABA, Del. State Bar Assn., Am. Judicature Soc. Office: US Dist Ct 844 N King St Wilmington DE 19801-3519

SCHWARTZ, NEENA BETTY, endocrinologist, educator; b. Balt., Dec. 10, 1926; d. Paul Howard and Pauline (Shulman) S. A.B., Goucher Coll., 1948, D.Sc. (hon.), 1982; M.S., Northwestern U., 1950, Ph.D. 1953. From instr. to prof. U. Ill. Coll. Medicine, Chgo., 1953-72; asst. dean for faculty U. Ill. Coll. Medicine, 1968-70; prof. physiology Northwestern U. Med. Sch., Chgo., 1973-74; Deering prof. Northwestern U., Evanston, Ill., 1974—; chmn. dept. biol. scis. Northwestern U., 1974-78. Contbr. chpts. to books, articles to profl. jours. NIH research grantee, 1955—. Fellow AAAS; mem. Am. Acad. Arts Scis., Endocrine Soc. (v.p. 1970-71, mem. coun. 1979-83, pres. 1982-83, Williams award 1985), Soc. for Study of Reprodn. (dir. 1975-77, exec. v.p. 1976-77, pres. 1977-78, Carl Hartman award 1992), Am. Physio. Soc., Soc. for Neurosci., Phi Beta Kappa. Home: 1511 Lincoln St Evanston IL 60201-2338

SCHWARTZ, NORMAN L., lawyer; b. N.Y.C., Nov. 2, 1935; s. Louis and Rose (Tendlar) S.; m. Sandra Jean Coffae, Nov. 20, 1960; children: Debra, Cathy. BBA cum laude, Ohio State U., 1957, JD summa cum laude, 1960; LLM in Taxation, Georgetown U., 1968. Bar: Ohio 1960, D.C. 1968, Fla. 1991, U.S. Ct. Claims 1986, U.S. Tax Ct. 1961, U.S. Supreme Ct. 1967. Pvt. practice Columbus, Ohio, 1960-61, Dayton, Ohio, 1962-64; atty. IRS, Washington, 1964-68; ptnr. Cohen and Uretz, Washington, 1969-85, Morgan, Lewis & Bockius, Washington, 1985-88; atty. Arthur Andersen LLP, Sarasota, Fla., 1988—. Served with USAF, 1961-62; capt. Ohio Air NG 1960-64. Mem. ABA (chmn. com. on S corps. 1973-74 tax sect.). Democrat. Jewish. Avocations: reading, jogging. Home: 4761 Pine Harrier Dr Sarasota FL 34231-3360 Office: Arthur Andersen LLP 2803 Fruitville Rd Sarasota FL 34237-5323

SCHWARTZ, PERRY LESTER, information systems engineer, consultant; b. Bklyn., July 29, 1939; s. Max David and Sylvia (Weinberger) S.; m. Arlene Metz, Jan. 24, 1960; 3 children. BEE, CUNY, 1957-62; MS in Indsl. Engring. and Computer Sci., NYU, 1967. Registered profl. engr., N.J.; registered profl. planner, N.J.; cert. mediator and arbitrator, expert witness communicator. Microwave engr. Airbourne Inst. Lab., Deer Park, N.Y., 1962-63, ITT Fed. Labs., Nutley, N.J., 1963-64; program mgr. Western Electric Co., N.Y.C., 1964-69; dept. head RCA, Princeton, N.J., 1970-71; dir. engring. Warner Communications Inc., N.Y.C., 1972-74; cons. engr. Intertech Assocs., Marlboro, N.J., 1974—; adj. faculty CCNY, 1962-71, Ocean County Coll., Toms River, N.J., 1983-91, Rutgers U., New Brunswick, N.J., 1984-87; lectr. N.J. Dept. Energyu, 1994. Mem. Am. Cons. Engrs. Coun., Nat. Assn. Radio and Telecom. Engrs. (sr. mem., charter mem., cert. master engr. in wire and RF, Cert. of Distinction 1994-95), IEEE (sr.), Intelligent Bldgs. Inst. Found. (steering com. trustee 1982-89), Nat. Soc. Profl. Engrs., Cons. Engrs. Coun. N.J., Am. Arbitration Assn., Zeta Beta Tau (chpt. founder 1958), K.P. Office: Intertech Assoc Pla 79 Marlboro NJ 07746

SCHWARTZ, PETER EDWARD, physician, gynecologic oncology educator; b. N.Y.C., Mar. 28, 1941; s. Bernard and Marcia (Firkser) S.; m. Arlene Harriet Eigen, Aug. 18, 1966; children: Bruce, Andrew, Kenneth. BS, Union Coll., Schenectady, N.Y., 1962; MD, Yeshiva U., N.Y.C., 1966; MA (hon.), Yale U., 1985. Diplomate Am. Bd. Ob-Gyn., Am. Bd. Gynecol. Oncology. Surg. intern U. Ky. Med. Ctr., Lexington, 1966-67; resident in ob-gyn. Yale-New Haven Hosp., 1967-71; fellow in gynecol. oncology U. Tex. M.D. Anderson Hosp., Houston, 1971-73; asst. prof. Yale U. Sch. Medicine, New Haven, 1975-80, assoc. prof., 1980-85, prof., 1985—, now vice chmn. dept. ob-gyn., 1992—. Maj. USAF, 1971-73. John Slade Ely Prof. of obstetrics and gynecology at Yale U. (hon. chair). Office: Yale U Sch Medicine Dept Ob-Gyn 333 Cedar St New Haven CT 06520

SCHWARTZ, R. MALCOLM, management consultant; b. St. Louis, Nov. 15, 1934; s. Joseph Guthrie and Mildred Anne (Miller) S.; m. Carole Ann; children: Douglas William, Stephanie Ann. B.S.E., Princeton U., 1956. Cert.mgmt. cons. Indsl. engr., mfg. supr. Procter & Gamble Mfg. Co., 1956-64; ops. cons. Booz Allen & Hamilton, Inc., N.Y.C., 1964-68; with fin. dept. Insilco Corp., 1968-73; with gen. mgmt. dept. Westinghouse Broadcasting Co., 1973-75; with Booz Allen & Hamilton, N.Y.C., 1976-86, v.p., 1977-83, chief fin. officer, 1981-86, sr. v.p., 1983-86; ptnr. Coopers & Lybrand, N.Y.C., 1986—. Fin. editor: Impact, 1977-94; contbr. articles to profl. publs. Chmn., campaign mgr. local Democratic Party in Conn. and N.J., 1969-79; trustee Human Relations Council Greater New Haven, 1970-72; mem. bd. fin., City of Cheshire (Conn.), 1969-71; trustee, officer Congregation Mishkan Israel, Hamden, Conn., 1969-73. Served with USNR, 1956-59. Mem. Fin. Execs. Inst., Planning Forum. Clubs: Beacon Hill (Summit); Princeton (N.Y.C.). Home: 14 Edgewood Dr Summit NJ 07901 Office: Coopers & Lybrand 1301 Avenue Of The Americas New York NY 10019-6053

SCHWARTZ, RENEE GERSTLER, lawyer; b. Bklyn., June 18, 1933; d. Samuel and Lillian (Neulander) Gerstler; m. Alfred L. Schwartz, July 30, 1955; children—Carolyn Susan, Deborah Jane. A.B., Bklyn, Coll., 1953; LL.B., Columbia U. 1955. Bar: N.Y. 1956, U.S. Dist. Ct. (so. and ea. dists.) N.Y. 1956, U.S. Ct. Appeals (2d cir.) 1956, U.S. Dist. Ct. D.C. 1983, U.S. Supreme Ct. 1986. Ptnr., Botein, Hays & Sklar, N.Y.C., 1955-89, Kronish, Lieb, Weiner & Hellman, N.Y.C., 1990—. Bd. dirs. New Land Found., N.Y.C., 1965—. Mem. Bar Assn. City N.Y. Home: 115 Central Park W New York NY 10023-4153 Office: Kronish Lieb Weiner & Hellman 1114 Avenue Of The Americas New York NY 10036-7701

SCHWARTZ, RICHARD BRENTON, English language educator, university dean, writer; b. Cin., Oct. 5, 1941; s. Jack Jay and Marie Mildred (Schnelle) S.; m. Judith Mary Alexis Lang, Sept. 7, 1963; 1 son, Jonathan Francis. AB, U. Notre Dame, 1963; AM, U. Ill., 1964, PhD, 1967. Instr. English U.S. Mil. Acad., 1967-69; asst. prof. U. Wis.-Madison 1969-72, assoc. prof., 1972-78, prof., 1978-81; assoc. dean U. Wis.-Madison (Grad. Sch.), 1977, 79-81; prof. English, dean Grad. Sch., Georgetown U., Washington, 1981—; interim exec. v.p. for main campus academic affairs, 1991-92; mem. exec. bd. Ctr. Strategic and Internat. Studies, 1981-87. Author: Samuel Johnson and the New Science, 1971, Samuel Johnson and the Problem of Evil, 1975, Boswell's Johnson: A Preface to the Life, 1978, Daily Life in Johnson's London, 1983, Japanese edit., 1990, (novel) Frozen Stare, 1989; editor: The Plays of Arthur Murphy, 4 vols., 1979, Theory and Tradi-

tion in Eighteenth-Century Studies, 1990; contbr. articles to profl. jours. Served to capt. U.S. Army, 1967-69. Nat. Endowment Humanities grantee, 1970, 87; Inst. for Research in Humanities fellow, 1976; Am. Council Learned Socs. fellow, 1978-79; H.I. Romnes fellow, 1978-81. Mem. Mystery Writers Am., Johnson Soc. So. Calif., Am. Soc. Eighteenth-Century Studies, Coun. Grad. Schs., N.E. Assn. Grad. Schs. (exec. com. 1986-88), Assn. Grad. Schs. in Cath. Univs. (exec. com. 1984-87), Assn. Literary Scholars and Critics, N.Am. Conf. Brit. Studies, Alpha Sigma Nu. Roman Catholic. Home: 4132 41st St N Arlington VA 22207-4802 Office: Georgetown U Grad Sch Washington DC 20057

SCHWARTZ, RICHARD DERECKTOR, sociologist, educator; b. Newark, Apr. 26, 1925; s. Selig and Tillie (Derecktor) S.; m. Emilie Zane Rosenbaum, June 30, 1946; children: David, Margaret Jane, Deborah. B.A., Yale U., 1947, Ph.D. in Sociology, 1952; LL.D. (hon.), Am. Internat. Coll., 1977. Research fellow Inst. Human Relations, Yale, 1951-54, instr., asst. prof. sociology and law, 1953-61; faculty Northwestern U., Evanston, 1961-71; prof. sociology Northwestern U., 1964-71, prof. sociology and law, 1966-71; dir. Council Intersocietal Studies, 1965-70, co-dir. law and social sci. program, 1967-70; dean, provost Faculty of Law and Jurisprudence, State U. N.Y. at Buffalo, 1971-76; Ernest I. White rsch. prof. law Syracuse U., 1977—; rsch. cons. Nat. Coun. Juvenile Ct. Judges, 1961-68; lecture tour for U.S. Embassy, India, 1968; adviser U.S. Dept. Justice, 1977-80; cons. U.S. Dept. Transp., 1968-69, Nat. Conf. Commrs. on Uniform State Laws, 1968-70, ABA, 1979-83; mem. com. law enforcement and adminstrn. of justice NAS, 1975-85; fellowship referee Russell Sage Found., 1970-77, NEH, 1972-77, NSF, 1978-81; mem. bd. edn., Orange, Conn., 1954-61; mem. exec. com. Am. Friends Svc. Com., Middle Atlantic Region, 1987-92; chmn. Am. Coalition for Middle East Dialogue, 1990-93. Author: (with others) Society and the Legal Order, 1970, Criminal Law, 1974, Nonreactive Measures in the Social Sciences, 1980, Handbook of Regulation and Administrative Law, 1994; founding editor: Law and Soc. Rev., 1966-69. Served with USNR, 1943-45. Ctr. for Advanced Study in Behavioral Scis. fellow, 1989-90. Fellow AAAS; mem. ABA (nonprofl. legal edn. com. 1986-89), Am. Sociol. Assn., Law and Soc. Assn. (pres. 1972-75). Jewish. Home: 15 Clarmar Rd Fayetteville NY 13066-1603 Office: Syracuse U Coll Law Syracuse NY 13244-1030 *I believe that we could create a better way of life if we structured society to encourage-rather than to penalize-altruism. Although I have not yet contributed much toward achieving such a society, the effort to do so has been satisfying.*

SCHWARTZ, RICHARD FREDERICK, electrical engineering educator; b. Albany, N.Y., May 31, 1922; s. Frederick William and Mary Hoyle (Holland) S.; m. Ruth Louise Feldman, Oct. 25, 1945 (div. Oct. 1977); children: Kathryn Gail, Frederick Earl, Karl Edward, Eric Christian, Frieda Dianne; m. Margaret Owen Camp Boes, May 29, 1982. BEE, Rensselaer Poly. Inst., 1943, MEE, 1948; PhD, U. Pa., 1959. Registered profl. engr., Pa., Mich. Teaching asst., then instr. Rensselaer Poly. Inst., Troy, N.Y., 1946-48; engr. Radio Corp. of Am., Camden, N.J., 1948-51; rsch. staff mem. U. Pa., Phila., 1951-59, mem. faculty, 1959-73; prof. elec. engring., head dept. Mich. Technol. U., Houghton, 1973-79, prof. elec. engring., 1979-85; prof. elec. engring. SUNY, Binghamton, 1985—; vis. asst. prof. U. Mich., Ann Arbor, 1960; cons. Pa. Bar Assn. Endowment, Armstrong Cork Co., Am. electronics Labs., Inc., IBM, RCA, City of Phila., GE. Contbr. articles to profl. jours. Active Delaware County Symphony, Pa., 1867-72, Keeweenaw Symphony Orch., Houghton, 1973-85. With U.S. Army, 1942-46. Mem. IEEE, AAAS, NSPE, Am. Soc. Engring. Edn., Audio Engring. Soc., Acoustical Soc. Am., Catgut Acoustical Soc., Order of Engr., Sigma Xi, Eta Kappa Nu, Tau Beta Tau. Unitarian-Universalist. Avocations: music, fishing, shopwork, the outdoors. Office: SUNY Sch Engring and Applied Sci Binghamton NY 13902

SCHWARTZ, RICHARD JOHN, electrical engineering educator, researcher; b. Waukesha, Wis., Aug. 12, 1935; s. Sylvester John and LaVerne Mary (Lepien) S.; m. Mary Jo Collins, June 29, 1957; children: Richard, Stephan, Susan, Elizabeth, Barbara, Peter, Christopher, Margarett. BSEE, U. Wis., 1957; SM, MIT, 1959, ScD, 1962. Mem. tech. staff Sarnoff Rsch. Labs. RCA, Princeton, N.J., 1957-58; instr. MIT, Cambridge, 1961-62; v.p. Energy Conversions, Inc., Cambridge, 1962-64; assoc. prof. Purdue U., West Lafayette, Ind., 1964-71, prof., 1972—, head dept., 1985—, dir. Optoelectronic Ctr., 1986-89; bd. dir. Nat. Elec. Engring. Dept. Heads Assn.; solar cells cons., 1965—. Contbr. chpts. to books, articles to profl. jours. Served to 2nd lt. U.S. Army, 1957-58. Recipient Disting. Svc. medal U. Wis., 1989, Centennial medal, 1991. Fellow IEEE. Achievements include development of high intensity solar cells, of surface charge transfer device, and of numerical models for solar cells. Office: Purdue U 1285 Elec Engring Elec Engring Rsch Lab West Lafayette IN 47907

SCHWARTZ, ROBERT, automotive manufacturing company executive, marketing executive; b. Atlantic City, N.J., Mar. 9, 1939; s. Robert A. and Irene (Davis) S.; m. Judith H. Amole, Apr. 30, 1961. B.S., Drexel U., 1961; M.B.A., Wash. State U., 1962. With Ford Motor Co., 1964-70; dist. mgr. Simplicity Mfg., Port Washington, Wis., 1970-71; zone mgr. Am. Motors Corp., Boston, 1971-72, N.Y.C., 1972-74; dir. sales ops. Am. Motors Corp., Detroit, 1975; regional mgr. Am. Motors Corp., 1975-76; gen. mgr. Am. Motors Corp. (U.S. sales), 1976-80; mng. dir. Am. Motors Corp. (N.Am. sales and distbn.), 1981-83; pres. Am. Motors Sales Corp., Detroit, 1978-81, v.p. N.Am. sales, 1981-83; v.p. sales and mktg. Rolls-Royce Motors Inc., Lyndhurst, N.J., 1983-85, pres., chief exec. officer, 1986-89; pres. Motors Mgmt., Neptune, N.J., 1989-93; pres., CEO Automotive Ventures, Inc., Wayne, N.J., 1993—. Mem. Metropolitan Club (N.Y.C.).

SCHWARTZ, ROBERT GEORGE, retired insurance company executive; b. Czechoslovakia, Mar. 27, 1928; came to U.S., 1929, naturalized, 1935; s. George and Frances (Antoni) S.; m. Caroline Bachurski, Oct. 12, 1952; children: Joanne, Tracy, Robert G. BA, Pa. State U., 1949; MBA, NYU, 1956. With Met. Life Ins. Co., N.Y.C., 1949-93, v.p. securities, 1962-70, v.p., 1970-75, sr. v.p., 1975-78, exec. v.p., 1979-80, vice chmn. bd., 1980-83, chmn. investment com., 1980-93, chmn. bd., 1983-93, chmn. bd., pres., chief exec. officer, 1989-93; bd. dirs. Met. Life Ins. Co., Potlatch Corp., San Francisco, Lowe's Cos., Inc., North Wilkesboro, N.C., COMSAT Corp., Bethesda, Md., Mobil Corp., Fairfax, Va., Reader's Digest Assn., Inc., Consol. Edison Co. of N.Y., CS First Boston, Inc., Lone Star Industries, Inc., Stamford, Conn. Trustee Com. for Econ. Devel.; bd. visitors Smeal Coll., Pa. State U., mem. nat. devel. coun. With AUS, 1950-52. Mem. Bus. Coun., Springdale Country Club, Sky Club, Blind Brook Country Club, Alpha Chi Rho. Office: MetLife Bldg 200 Park Ave Ste 5700 New York NY 10166

SCHWARTZ, ROBERT M., lawyer; b. Phila., Aug. 6, 1940; s. Nathan and Miriam (Albus) S.; m. Karen Faf, Feb. 11, 1966; children: Eric, Lauren. BS, Pa. State U., 1962; JD, Villanova U., 1965. Bar: Pa. 1965, U.S. Ct. Appeals (3rd cir.) 1965. Law clk. to presiding justice Common Pleas Ct. Montgomery County, Norristown, Pa., 1965; v.p., assoc. counsel Continental Title Ins. Co., Phila., 1969-73; ptnr. in charge real estate group and bus. dept. White and Williams, Phila., 1973—. Speaker numerous lectures and seminars in field. Mem. regional civil rights com. Anti-Defamation League. Capt. JAGC, U.S. Army, 1966-68. Mem. Phila. Bar Assn. (chmn. real property sect. 1983-89, 91, chmn. real property sect. 1986), Am. Coll. Real Estate Lawyers (best lawyers in Am. award 1989—), Am. Land Title Assn. (leader's counsel group 1993—, Order of Coif. Republican. Jewish. Avocations: bridge, tennis. Office: White and Williams One Liberty Pl Ste 1800 1650 Market St Philadelphia PA 19103

SCHWARTZ, ROBERT S., lawyer; b. Bklyn., Jan. 7, 1949. BA cum laude, Cornell U., 1971; JD cum laude, U. Pa., 1974. Bar: Pa. 1974, D.C. 1979. Law clerk to sr. judge U.S. Dist. Ct. dist. Del., 1974-75; trial atty. intellectual property sect. antitrust divsn. U.S. Dept. Justice, 1975-79; ptnr. McDermott, Will & Emery, Washington. Mem. ABA, D.C. Bar. Office: McDermott Will & Emery 1850 K St NW Washington DC 20006-2213

SCHWARTZ, ROBERT TERRY, professional association executive; b. Irvington, N.J., Sept. 29, 1950; s. Edward Herman and Harriet Selma (Rosenstein) S.; m. Carol Fawn Mullenix, July 27, 1975; children: Zachary Jacob, Allison Lizabeth. BFA, Kansas City Art Inst., 1973; M of Indsl. Design, R.I. Sch. Design, 1975. Red Cross project dir. R.I. Sch. Design, Providence,

1975-76; head indsl. design/architecture ARC Nat. Hdqrs., Washington, 1976-88; dir. sci. and tech. Health Industry Mfrs. Assn., Washington, 1988-90; exec. dir., COO Worldesign Found., Great Falls, Va., 1990—. Indsl. Designers Soc. Am., Great Falls, 1990—. Contbr. chpts. to books, articles to profl. jours.; presenter in field; holder 5 patents, 1 trademark. Recipient Project of Merit award Indsl. Design Mag., 1985, Cert. of Achievement, ARC, 1988, Louis B. Tiffany award ARC, 1987, numerous others; Nat. Endowment for the Arts grantee, 1984, 92, 94; EPA grantee, 1992. Mem. Am. Soc. Assn. Execs., Greater Washington Soc. Assn. Execs., Am. Design Coun. (ofcl. rep.). Avocations: Edison antiquities collecting, sailing. Office: Indsl Designers Soc Am 1142 Walker Rd Great Falls VA 22066-1836

SCHWARTZ, ROBERT WILLIAM, management consultant; b. N.Y.C., Oct. 13, 1942; s. Edward and Bertha R. S.; m. Gail Beth Greenbaum, Mar. 18, 1967; children: Jill, Evan. BS, Cornell U., 1967; postgrad., SUNY, Albany, 1970. Assoc. IBM, 1967-68; cons. Peat, Marwick, Mitchell & Co., Albany, 1970-71; v.p. Security Gen. Svcs., Inc., Rochester, N.Y., 1971-73; v.p. fin. and adminstrn. Gardenway Mfg. Co., Troy, N.Y., 1973-77; exec. v.p. United Telecommunications Corp., Latham, N.Y., 1977-79; pres. United Telecommunications Corp., Latham 1980-82; also bd. dir. United Telecommunications Corp.; pres., chmn. Winsource, Inc., Albany, 1985—; Schwartz, Gordon, Haslin & Assoc., Inc., 1985—; bd. dirs. Caddim Corp., Union Nat. Bank, Albany, ESARCO Internat., Inc., Springfield, Mo., LBO Capital Corp., Detroit; adj. prof. Rochester Inst. Tech., 1971-73. Bd. dirs. United Cerebral Palsy of Capital Dist., 1973—; trustee Newman Found., Rensselaer Poly. Inst., 1974-78, Gov. Clinton coun. Boy Scouts Am., SUNY Found. Mem. Am. Mgmt. Assn., Esarco Internat., Assoc. Video Hut, N.Am. Tel. Assn., Assn. for Systems Mgmt., Ft. Orange Club, Econ. Club, Corenell Club (N.Y.C.). Republican. Home: 2 Myton Ln Albany NY 12204-1310 Office: 120 Defreest Dr Troy NY 12180-8360

SCHWARTZ, ROSELIND SHIRLEY GRANT, podiatrist; b. N.Y.C., Apr. 23, 1922; d. Joseph and Amy (Jacobs) Grant; m. Herman Schwartz, Dec. 19, 1943 (dec. Sept., 1980); children: Arthur Zachary, Raymond Dana. BA, NYU, 1943; D Podiatry cum laude, L.I. U., 1947, DPM, 1970; postgrad., L.A. Trade Tech. Coll., 1973-75. Notary pub., Calif. Pvt. practice Podiatry N.Y.C., 1947-73; cons. L.A., 1973-76, travel cons., 1974—; owner, mgr. Ros Travel, 1994—. Bd. dirs. Welfare League for Retarded Children, 1955-73, chmn. Annual Souvenir Jour., 1955-65, Annual Luncheon, 25th anniversary, 1968, pres., 1969-70; pres. Sisterhood of Community Ctr. of Israel, N.Y., 1966-67; Cub den mother Boy Scouts Am., N.Y., 1960-63; class mother Pub. Schs., N.Y., 1960-66, pres. Parents' Assn. Jr. High Sch., N.Y., 1966-69; bd. dirs., pres. Barrington-Terryhill Condominium Assn., 1981—; vol. UCLA, 1981—; mem. Adv. Coms., Nurse Anesthesists, Infant & Child Care, 1981—. Recipient testimonial Community Ctr. Israel, Bronx, N.Y., 1971, award for devoted leadership Welfare League, 1963, 65. Mem. Assn. Wives of Physicians, Podiatry Soc. N.Y. State, Bus. and Profl. Women. Avocations: collecting stamps and coins, travel. Home: 269 W 11th St # 3C New York NY 10014-2493

SCHWARTZ, ROY RICHARD, holding company executive; b. N.Y.C., Mar. 27, 1943; s. Julius and Mildred (Friedman) S.; m. Sharon Massler, June 3, 1965; children: Lisa Beth, Meridith Sara, Greg Mathew. AB, Washington Coll., Chestertown, Md., 1964; JD, Columbia U., 1967. Asst. counsel N.Y.C., 1967-68; assoc. Blumberg, Singer, N.Y.C., 1968-72, Kelly, Drye, N.Y.C., 1969-72; U.S. counsel U.S. Counsel Ltd., N.J., 1972-74; sr. U.S. counsel Imasco Ltd., N.J., 1974-78; pres. Imasco Holdings, N.J., 1978-82; v.p. Imasco Resources, Montreal, 1983; v.p. corp. devel. Imasco Ltd., Montreal, 1984-89, sr. v.p., 1989—; bd. dirs. Ulster Petroleums Ltd. Mem. Montreal Bd. of Trade, Univ. Club. Office: Imasco Ltd, 600 de Maisonneuve Blvd W, Montreal, PQ Canada H3A 3K7

SCHWARTZ, SAMUEL, business consultant, retired chemical company executive; b. Moose Jaw, Sask., Can., Nov. 12, 1927; came to U.S., 1951, naturalized, 1965; s. Benjamin and Rose (Becker) S.; m. Margaret Patterson, Feb. 20, 1956; children: Michael R., Thomas R., David C., Janet C. BA, U. Sask., 1948, B in Commerce, 1950; MBA, Harvard U. 1953. Research assoc. Harvard Bus. Sch., Boston, 1953-57; with Conoco Inc., 1957-83; sr. v.p. coordinating and planning Conoco Inc. Stamford, Conn., 1974-75; sr. v.p. corp. planning Conoco Inc., 1975-78, sr. v.p. adminstrv., 1978-80, group sr. v.p. adminstrv., 1980-83; sr. v.p. adminstrv. E.I. duPont de Nemours & Co., Wilmington, Del., 1983-87, sr. v.p., corp. plans dept., 1987-88; dir. Conoco Inc. Consol. Coal Co., 1981-88. Trustee Inst. for the Future, Menlo Park, Calif., 1975-92, Henry du Pont Winterthur Mus., Winterthur, Del., 1981—, trustee, 1984—, chmn., 1994—.

SCHWARTZ, SEYMOUR IRA, surgeon, educator; b. N.Y.C., Jan. 22, 1928; s. Samuel and Martha (Paul) S.; m. Ruth Elaine Wainer, June 18, 1949; children: Richard, Kenneth, David. BA, U. Wis., 1947; MD, NYU, 1950; PhD (hon.), U. Lund, Sweden, 1989; FRCS (hon.), U. Intern Strong Meml. Hosp., Rochester, N.Y., 1950-51, resident, 1951-52, 54-57; asst. prof. surgery U. Rochester, N.Y., 1959-63, assoc. prof., 1963-67, prof., 1967—, chmn. dept., 1987—, dir. surg. rsch., 1962-82; nat. cons. USAF, 1968-77; mem. surgery study sect. A, NIH, 1974-78. Co-author: Mapping of America, 1980, Surgical Reflections, 1991, Mapping of the French and Indian War, 1994; co-editor: Maingot's Abdominal Operations, 2 edits.; editor-in-chief: Year Book of Surgery, 6 edits., 1969—. Bd. mgrs. Strong Meml. Hosp., Rochester. Lt. (j.g.) USN, 1952-54. Recipient Sesquicentennial medal U.S.C., 1974, Acrel medal Swedish Surg. Assn., 1974, Yandell medal U. Louisville (Ky.), 1978, Roswell Park medal, 1989, Albert Kaiser medal, 1992; John and Mary R. Markle scholar in acad. medicine, 1960. Fellow ACS (regent 1988, chmn. bd. regents 1994—; programs and ethics com. 1989—, Disting. Svc. award 1986), Royal Coll. Surgeons Edinburgh (hon.), Ctrl. Surg. Soc. (pres. 1981-82), So. Surg. Soc., Univ. Surgeons, Soc. Clin. Surgery (pres. 1985), Am. Surg. Assn. (pres. 1993-94), Am. Antiquarian Soc., Grolier Club (N.Y.C.), Cosmos Club (Washington), Genesee Valley Club, Phi Beta Kappa, Alpha Omega Alpha. Avocation: collecting antique maps. Office: U Rochester Med Ctr 601 Elmwood Ave Rochester NY 14642-8410

SCHWARTZ, SHIRLEY E., chemist; b. Detroit, Aug. 26, 1935; d. Emil Victor and Jessie Grace (Galbraith) Eckwall; m. Ronald Elmer Schwartz, Aug. 25, 1957; children: Steven Dennis, Bradley Allen, George Byron. BS, U. Mich., 1957, Detroit Inst. Tech., 1978; MS, Wayne State U., 1962, PhD, 1970. Asst. prof. Detroit Inst. Tech., 1973-78, head divsn. math. sci., 1976-78; mem. rsch. staff BASF Wyandotte (Mich.) Corp., 1978-81, head sect. functional fluids, 1981; sr. staff rsch. scientist GM, Warren, Mich., 1981—. Contbr. articles to profl. jours.; patentee in field. Recipient Gold award Engring. Soc. Detroit, 1989. Fellow Soc. Tribologists and Lubrication Engrs. (treas Detroit sect. 1981, vice chmn. 1982, chmn 1982-83, chmn wear tech. com. 1987-88, bd. dirs. 1985-91, assoc. editor 1989-90, contbg. editor 1989—; Wilbur Deutsch award 1987, P.M. Ku award 1994); mem. Am. Chem. Soc., Soc. Invitro Biology, Soc. Automotive Engrs. (Excellence in Oral Presentation award 1986, 91, 94, Arch T. Colwell Merit award 1991, Lloyd L. Withrow Disting. Spkr. award 1995), Mensa, Classic Guitar Soc. Mich., U.S. Power Squadrons, Detroit Navigators, Sigma Xi. Lutheran. Office: GM NAO Rsch & Devel Ctr 30500 Mound Rd Warren MI 48092-2031 *I've spent a number of very pleasant hours trying to make water behave like oil and alcohol behave like gasoline-a quest no much different from that of the ancient alchemists, who also spent their time trying to convert one substance to another.*

SCHWARTZ, STEPHEN ALLAN, toy company executive; b. Bronx, N.Y., Apr. 18, 1949; s. Edward and Shirley (Silver) S.; m. Hana Solomon, July 4, 1971; children: Joshua, Daniel, Kathryn. BA, NYU, 1971. Mgr. mktg. Ideal Toy Co., Queens, N.Y., 1972-76, Child Guidance, Bronx, 1976-78; dir. mktg. Hasbro, Inc., Pawtucket, R.I., 1978-80, v.p. mktg., 1980-82, sr. v.p. mktg., 1982-87, exec. v.p. mktg., product devel., 1987-89, pres. Playskool div., 1989—. Office: Hasbro Inc 1027 Newport Ave Pawtucket RI 02861-2539

SCHWARTZ, STEPHEN BLAIR, retired information industry executive; b. Chgo., Oct. 19, 1934; s. Herbert S. and Gertrude (Weinstein) S.; m. Nancy Jean Astrof, Dec. 18, 1955; children: Debra Lee Schwartz Zaret, Susan Beth Schwartz Derene. BS in Indsl. Engring., Northwestern U., 1957. With IBM Corp., 1957-92; various mgmt. positions, dir. product programs Harrison, N.Y., to 1977, v.p. Systems Communications div., 1977-81; v.p. Armonk, N.Y., 1982-90; v.p. Am. Far East Corp. subs. IBM Corp. Tokyo, 1982-84; pres., CEO Satellite Bus. Systems, McLean, Va., 1984; v.p., asst. group exec. Telecommunications, 1985-86, v.p., pres. Systems Products Div., 1986-88, v.p., gen. mgr. Application Bus. Systems, 1988-90; sr. v.p. market driven quality Stamford, Conn., 1990-92; bd. dirs. Niagara Mohawk Power Corp., Integrated Surg. Systems, Inc., Western Digital Corp. Mem. PGA Nat. Club (Palm Beach Gardens, Fla.). Republican. Jewish.

SCHWARTZ, STEPHEN LAWRENCE, composer, lyricist; b. N.Y.C., Mar. 6, 1948; s. Stanley Leonard and Sheila Lorna (Siegel) S.; m. Carole Ann Piasecki, June 6, 1969; children—Scott Lawrence, Jessica Lauren. Student, Juilliard Sch. Music, 1960-64; B.F.A., Carnegie Inst. Tech., 1968. Composer/lyricist title song for: Butterflies Are Free, 1969; composer: music and new lyrics for Godspell, 1971; author: (with Leonard Bernstein) English texts for Leonard Bernstein's Mass, 1971; music and lyrics for Pippin, 1972, The Magic Show, 1974, The Baker's Wife, 1976, Children of Eden, 1991; lyrics for Rags, 1986; end credits Life with Mikey, 1993, Pocahontas, 1995, juvenile The Perfect Peach, 1977, The Trip, 1983; four songs, adaptation and direction Working, 1978; music for 3 songs, Personals, 1985; 1 song A My Name is Still Alice, 1993. Recipient Drama Desk awards, 1971, 78, Grammy awards, 1971. Mem. ASCAP, Nat. Acad. Rec. Arts and Scis. Address: care Paramuse Assocs 1414 Avenue of the Americas New York NY 10019

SCHWARTZ, STUART CARL, electrical engineering educator; b. N.Y.C., July 12, 1939; s. Charles M. and Rose (Greenberg) S.; m. Miriam Jane Loewengart, June 11, 1961; children—Julie, Alan. B.S. in Aero. Engring, Mass. Inst. Tech., 1961, M.S. in Aero. Engring, 1961; Ph.D., U. Mich., 1966. Rsch. engr. Jet Propulsion Lab., Pasadena, Calif., 1961-62; asst. prof. dept. elec. engring. Princeton (N.J.) U., 1966-70, chmn., 1985—, assoc. prof., 1970-76, prof., 1976—; assoc. dean Princeton (N.J.) U. (Sch. Engring. and Applied Sci.), 1977-80; vis. asso. prof. (John Simon Guggenheim Meml. fellow) dept. elec. engring. The Technion, Haifa, Israel, 1972-73. Mem. IEEE, Inst. Math. Statistics, Soc. Indsl. and Applied Math. (editor Jour. Applied Math., 1970-76), Sigma Xi, Sigma Gamma Tau, Phi Kappa Phi, Eta Kappa Nu. Office: Princeton U Dept Elec Engring Princeton NJ 08544

SCHWARTZ, THEODORE B., physician, educator; b. Phila., Feb. 14, 1918; s. William F. and Fanny (Farkas) S.; m. Genevieve Etta Bangs, Jan. 9, 1948; children: Richard, Steven, Michael, David, Jonathan, Thomas. B.S., Franklin and Marshall Coll., 1939; M.D., Johns Hopkins U., 1943. Diplomate Am. Bd. Internal Medicine (bd. govs., 1970-78, sec.-treas., 1976-78). Intern Osler Clinic, Johns Hopkins Hosp., 1943-44; asst. resident medicine Salt Lake City Gen. Hosp., 1946-47, resident medicine, 1947-48; fellow medicine Duke U. Med. Sch., 1948-50, asso. medicine, asst. prof. medicine, 1950-55; dir. sect. endocrinology and metabolism Rush-Presbyn.-St. Luke's Med. Center, Chgo., 1955-82; attending physician Rush-Presbyn.-St. Luke's Med. Center, 1960—; chmn. dept. medicine Rush-Presbyn.-St. Luke's Med. Center, 1970-82; cons. endocrinology Hines (Ill.) VA Hosp., 1956-71, Great Lakes Naval Hosp., 1960-74; prof. medicine U. Ill. Coll. Medicine, 1960-71; prof., chmn. dept. medicine Rush Med. Coll., 1971-82; prof. medicine U. Wash., Seattle, 1982—; chief med. services VA Med. Ctr., Boise, 1982-86; Mem. Am. Bd. Med. Specialities, 1972-79. Editor: Yearbook of Endocrinology, 1964-86, endocrinology article Ency. Brit., 1985—; contbr. articles to profl. jours. Bd. dirs. Boise Art Mus., 1984-92. Served with M.C. AUS, 1944-46. Decorated Bronze Star. Fellow ACP (mem. publs. com. 1973-78, chmn. subcom. on aging 1982-85, mem. health and pub. policy com.), Am. Coll. Endocrinology (hon.); mem. Assn. Program Dirs. Internat. Medicine (councilor 1978-80), Am. Fedn. Clin. Rsch., Am. Diabetes Assn., Diabetes Assn. Greater Chgo. (bd. dirs.), Am. Soc. Clin. Investigation, Am. Clin. and Climatol. Assn., Am. thyroid Assn., Endocrine Soc., Ctrl. Clin. Rsch. Club, Ctrl. Soc. Clin. Rsch., Chgo. Soc. Internat Medicine (pres. 1966-67), Phi Beta Kappa, Alpha Omega Alpha. Address: 4820 Roberts Rd Boise ID 83705-2853

SCHWARTZ, VICTOR ELLIOT, lawyer; b. N.Y.C., July 3, 1940. A.B. summa cum laude, Boston U., 1962; J.D. magna cum laude, Columbia U., 1965. Bar: N.Y. 1965, Ohio 1974. Law clk. to judge So. Dist. N.Y., 1965-67; from asst. to assoc. prof. law U. Cin., 1967-72, prof., 1972-79, acting dean, 1973-74; vis. prof. U. Va. Law Sch., 1970-71; adj. prof. law U. Cin., 1985—; ptnr. firm Crowell & Moring, Washington; chmn. Fed. Interagy. task Force on Products Liability, 1976; bd. dirs. Am. Tort Reform Assn.; chmn. Civil Justice Task Force, Am. Legis. Exch. Coun.; adj. prof. law Georgetown U., 1987—; chmn. Dept. of Commerce Task Force on Product Liability and Accident Compensation, 1977-80. Author: Comparative Negligence, 1974, 3d edit., 1994; (with Prosser and Wade) Cases and Materials on Torts, 1976, 9th edit., 1994, How to Prepare for the Multi-State Bar Examination, 1977, Products Liability: Cases and Trends, 1987, Products Liability: Asset Trends, 1988, (with Lee and Kelly) Multistate Legislation, 1985; editor: Columbia Law Rev., 1965; prin. draftsman: Model Uniform Product Liability Act. Recipient Sec. of Commerce award for disting. svc.; named One of 100 Most Influential Attys. in U.S., Nat. Law 3, 1994. Mem. Am. Bar Assn. (chmn. products liability com. 1979, uniform laws com. 1981, torts and ins. practice sect.), Am. Law Inst. (adv. com. Restatement Third of Torts), Phi Beta Kappa. Office: Crowell & Moring 1001 Pennsylvania Ave NW Washington DC 20004-2505 *The greatest joys in life are found in one's relationships, be it business, romance or friendship, with other people.*

SCHWARTZ, WILLIAM, lawyer, educator; b. Providence, May 6, 1933; s. Morris Victor and Martha (Glassman) S.; m. Bernice Konigsberg, Jan. 13, 1957; children: Alan Gershon, Robin Libby. A.A., Boston U., 1952, J.D. magna cum laude, 1955, M.A., 1960; postgrad., Harvard Law Sch., 1956. Bar: D.C. 1956, Mass. 1962, N.Y. 1989. Prof. law Boston U., 1955-91, Fletcher prof. law, 1968-70, Roscoe Pound prof. law, 1970-73, dean Sch. of Law, 1980-88, dir. Ctr. for Estate Planning, 1988-91; univ. prof. Yeshiva U., N.Y.C., 1991—; v.p. for acad. affairs, chief acad. officer, 1993—; counsel Cadwalader, Wickersham and Taft, N.Y.C., Washington, L.A., Palm Beach, 1988—; mem. faculty Frances Glessner Lee Inst., Harvard Med. Sch., Nat. Coll. Probate Judges, 1970, 77, 78, 79, 88; gen. dir. Assn. Trial Lawyers Am., 1968-73; reporter New Eng. Trial Judges Conf., 1965-67; participant Nat. Met. Cts. Conf., 1968; dir. Mass. Probate Study, 1976—; chmn. spl. com. on police procedures City of Boston, 1989, 91; vice chmn. bd. UST Corp., chmn., 1993-94; bd. dirs. Viacom Inc., Viacom Internat. Inc., UST Corp., WCI Steel, Inc.; mem. legal adv. com. N.Y. Stock Exch. Author: Future Interests and Estate Planning, 1965, 77, 81, 86, Comparative Negligence, 1970, A Products Liability Primer, 1970, Civil Trial Practice Manual, 1972, New Vistas in Litigation, 1973, Massachusetts Pleading and Practice, 7 vols., 1974-80, Estate Planning and Living Trusts, 1990, The Convention Method: The Unused Amending Superhighway, 1995, others; note editor: Boston U. Law Rev., 1954-55; property editor: Annual Survey of Mass. Law, 1960—; contbr. articles to legal jours. Bd. dirs. Kerry Found.; trustee Hebrew Coll., 1975—, Salve Regina Univ.; rep. Office Public Info. UN, 1968-73; chmn. legal adv. panel Nat. Commn. Med. Malpractice, 1972-73; examiner of titles Commonwealth of Mass., 1964—; spl. counsel Mass. Bay Transp. Authority, 1979; trustee Yeshiva U. Recipient Homer Albers award Boston U., 1955, John Ordronaux prize, 1955; Disting. Service award Religious Zionists Am., 1977; William W. Treat award; William O. Douglas award. Fellow Am. Coll. Probate Counsel; mem. ABA, Am. Law Inst., Mass. Bar Assn. (chmn. task force tort liability), Nat. Coll. Probate Judges (hon. mem.), Phi Beta Kappa. Office: 500 W 185th St New York NY 10033-4818 *I have been guided by the maxim: "Ideals are like stars. You cannot touch them with your hands, but like the seafaring man, if you choose them as your guide and follow them, you will reach your destiny."*

SCHWARTZ, WILLIAM A(LLEN), broadcasting and cable executive; b. Detroit, Nov. 29, 1938; m. Marlene J. Cohen; children: Jonathan, Cynthia, Michael. BA in Mktg. and Broadcasting, Wayne State U., 1961; postgrad. Bernard Baruch Grad. Sch. Bus.Mgr. research projects NBC, 1963-66; asst. dir. research Columbia Pictures, 1966; v.p., gen. mgr. Sta. WUAB-TV, Cleve., 1968-73; v.p. ops. Telerep, Inc., N.Y.C., 1973-74; v.p., gen. mgr. Sta. KTVU-TV, Oakland, Calif., 1974-79; pres. Cox Broadcasting div., Atlanta, 1979-81; pres. Cox Communications, Inc., Atlanta, 1981-87, chief exec. officer, 1983-87; pres., chief operating officer Cox Enterprises, Inc., Atlanta, 1985-87; chmn., chief exec. officer Capital Cable, 1988—; pres., chief exec.

officer Cannell Communications, L.P., 1989-95, First Media Television, L.P., 1995—. Office: 400 Perimeter Center Ter NE Atlanta GA 30346-1227

SCHWARTZ, WILLIAM B., JR., ambassador; b. Atlanta, Nov. 14, 1921; s. William B. and Ruth (Kuhn) S.; m. Sonia Weinberg, Dec. 3, 1942; children—William B., Arthur Jay, Robert C. B.S., U. N.C., 1942. Various positions, then v.p. Nat. Service Industries, Atlanta, 1945-68; pres. Weine Investment Corp., Atlanta, 1969-77; amb. to Bahamas, 1977-81; bd. dirs. Weine Investment Corp., Balco Energy, Phenix Supply, Artex Internat. Mem. pres.'s council Brandeis U., 1966—, chancellor's club U. N.C., Bd. Councillors Carter Ctr., Emory U.; trustee, past chmn. Atlanta chapt. Am. Jewish Com.; chmn. Chatham Valley Found.; bd. dirs. Met. Atlanta Rapid Transit Authority, 1969-76, vice chmn., 1971-73; bd. dirs. Big Bros. Atlanta, Atlanta Jewish Welfare Fedn.; former mem. Pres.'s Council Oglethorp U.; former mem. bd. dirs. Jewish Home for the Aged; chmn. bd. visitors Emory U., 1966-74. Served with USN, 1942-45. Recipient Man of Yr. award Am. Jewish Com., 1972. Mem. Coun. Am. Ambs. Clubs: Standard (Atlanta), Commerce (Atlanta); East Hill (Atlanta), Lyford Cay (Nassau); Longboat Key (Fla.); City (Sarasota). Lodges: B'nai Brith, Masons, Shriners. Home: 35 Valley Rd NW Atlanta GA 30305-1115 also: 1211 Gulf Of Mexico Dr Longboat Key FL 34228-4602

SCHWARTZBAUER, ROBERT ALAN, lawyer; b. St. Paul, July 5, 1944; s. Bernard S. and Helen B. (Ringus) S.; m. Karen S. Carlson, Sept. 10, 1965; children: Christopher, Jessica, Peter. BA, U. Minn., 1966, JD, 1969. Bar: Minn. 1969. Atty. Dorsey & Whitney, Mpls., 1969-75, ptnr., 1975—. Mem. ABA, Minn. State Bar Assn., Phi Beta Kappa. Avocations: hunting, photography. Office: Dorsey & Whitney 220 S 6th St Minneapolis MN 55402-4500

SCHWARTZBERG, ALLAN ZELIG, psychiatrist, educator; b. Cleve., Dec. 5, 1930; s. Joseph and Jeanette (Epstein) S.; m. Katherine Weiss, June 19, 1955; children: Shana, Robert. BS cum laude, Case Western Res. U., 1951; MD, Ohio State U., 1955. Diplomate Am. Bd. Psychiatry and Neurology. Intern, resident in psychiatry Johns Hopkins Hosp., Balt., 1955-59; pvt. practice, Gaithersburg, Md.; asst. prof. psychiatry Georgetown U. Sch. Medicine, Washington, 1964-66, asst. clin. prof., 1966-79, assoc. clin. prof., 1979-89, clin. prof., 1989—; vis. prof. faculty seminar in community psychiatry Harvard U. Med. Sch., Boston, 1965-67; cons. Walt Whitman High Sch., Bethesda, Md., 1980—, Passage Crisis Ctr., Montgomery County Health Dept., 1974-82, psychiat. tng. br. NIMH, 1971-74. Editor-in-chief Internat. Annals Adolescent Psychiatry, 1988—; co-editor Adolescent Psychiatry, Vols. 8-19; contbr. articles to med. jours. Recipient Vicennial medal Georgetown U., 1984. Fellow Am. Psychiat. Assn., Am. Soc. for Adolescent Psychiatry, Am. Soc. Psychoanalytic Physicians (pres. 1986-87); mem. AMA, Am. Group Psychotherapy Assn., Am. Coll. Psychiatrists, B'nai B'rith, Phi Beta Kappa. Republican. Jewish. Home: 6616 Kenhill Rd Bethesda MD 20817-6014 Office: Suburban Psychiat Assocs 8943 Shady Grove Ct Gaithersburg MD 20877-1308

SCHWARTZBERG, HOWARD, judge; b. Paterson, N.J., Mar. 27, 1930; s. Harry Schwartzberg and Rose Cohen; m. Lita I. Goodstein, June 27, 1954; children—Diane, Robert, Paul. B.A., NYU, 1950, LL.B., 1953, LL.M. in Taxation, 1961. Bar: N.Y. 1954, U.S. Ct. Appeals (2d cir.) 1956, U.S. Dist. Ct. (so. and ea. dists.) N.Y. 1955; Served as clk. for judge U.S. Dist. Ct. (so. dist.) N.Y.; now judge U.S. Bankruptcy Ct., White Plains, N.Y. Contbg. editor: Norton's Bankruptcy Law and Practice, 1980. Editor NYU Law Rev., 1952-53. Served with USNR, 1951-59. Office: US Dist Ct US Courthouse 101 E Post Rd White Plains NY 10601-5018

SCHWARTZBERG, MARTIN M., chemical company executive; b. N.Y.C., Dec. 10, 1935; s. Morris H. and Anne C. (Steskanin) S.; m. Florence M. Bloom, Sept. 22, 1957; children: Steven E., Michael C., Scott A. B ChemE, NYU, 1956; MBA, Wayne State U., 1965. Asst. to div. mgr. Pennwalt Corp., Phila., 1969-72, mgr. mktg. service, 1972-74, asst. to chief exec. officer, 1974-76, mng. dir. chems. Europe, 1976-78, mng. dir. splt. chems., 1978-80, pres. agrichems. div., 1980-85, pres. inorganic chems. div., 1985, v.p. chems., 1985-87, sr. v.p. chems., 1987-89; group pres. Elf Atochem N.Am., Inc. (formerly Pennwalt Corp.), Phila., 1990-94, ret., 1995. Served with U.S. Army, 1959. Mem. Nat. Agrl. Chems. Assn. (bd. dirs. Washington), Sigma Iota Epsilon. Avocations: volleyball, golf.

SCHWARTZEL, CHARLES BOONE, lawyer; b. Louisville, Jan. 4, 1950; s. Charles Joseph and Rosemary Jane (Redens) S.; m. Rose Marie Carlisi, June 20, 1980; children: Sally Ann, Charles Gerard. BA, Vanderbilt U., 1972; JD, U. Tex., 1975. Bar: Tex. 1975. Atty. Vinson & Elkins L.L.P., Houston, 1975—, ptnr., 1983—. Contbr. articles to profl. jours. Councilman City of West University Place, Tex., 1985-89; vol. Trees For Houston, 1985—. Fellow Am. Coll. Trust and Estate Counsel; mem. ABA (chmn. real property, probate and trust law sect. com. on creditors' rights in estates and trusts 1989-93), Tex. Bar Assn., Houston Bar Assn. Roman Catholic. Office: Vinson & Elkins LLP 1001 Fannin Ste 1935 Houston TX 77002-6760

SCHWARTZHOFF, JAMES PAUL, foundation executive; b. Waukon, Iowa, June 24, 1937; s. Harold J. and Mary (Regan) Schwartzhoff; m. Mary Lou Hess, Apr. 23, 1960; children: Tammara, Eric, Stephanie, Mark, Laurie, Michelle, Steven. B. U. Iowa, 1962. Asst. chief auditor Wis. Dept. Tax, Madison, 1962-67; mgr. treas. dept. Mead Johnson and Co., Evansville, Ind., 1967-69; v.p. treas. Kettering Found., Dayton, Ohio, 1969—; chmn., treas. bd. Pastoral Counseling Ctr., Dayton, 1975-81; treas. Ohio River Rd. Runners, Dayton, 1986-87. Treas. Nat. Issues Forums Inst., Coun. Pub. Policy Edn., Ctr. for Community and Ednl. Devel.; mem. Donor's Forum Ohio Fin. Com., 1990-92; mem. investment com. U. Dayton; adv. com. JMB Endowment and Found. Realty Funds, 1991-94. Cpl. U.S. Army, 1957-59. Mem. AICPA, Found. Fin. Officers Group, Southern Ohio Pension Fund Group. Avocations: bicycling, backpacking, photography, woodworking. Office: Kettering Found 200 Commons Rd Dayton OH 45459-2788

SCHWARTZMAN, DAVID, economist, educator; b. Montreal, Que., Can., Apr. 22, 1924; came to U.S., 1954, naturalized, 1964; s. Joseph and Jeannette (Zurick) S.; m. Gertrude Schneiderman, June 17, 1951; children—Michael, Jason, Paul. B.A., McGill U., 1945; postgrad., U. Minn., 1945-46; Ph.D., U. Calif. at Berkeley, 1953. Lectr. McGill U., 1948-51; economist Dominion Bur. Statistics, 1951-53, United 5to $1.00 Stores, Can., 1953-54; instr. Columbia, 1954-58; asst. prof. N.Y.S., 1958-60; assoc. prof. New Sch. for Social Research, N.Y.C., 1960-64; prof. New Sch. for Social Rsch., 1964—, chmn. dept. econs., 1966-76, 83-84; mem. staff Nat. Bur. Econ. Research, 1963-69; prof. environ. medicine and community health state U. N.Y. Downstate Med. Center, part-time, 1969-70; Cons. Royal Commn. on Farm Machinery, Ottawa, Can., 1968-70, U.S. Bur. Census, 1973, anti-trust div. U.S. Dept. Justice, 1973, U.S. Council on Wage and Price Stability, Exec. Office of Pres., 1975-76; adj. mem. Com. on Trade Regulation, N.Y. County Lawyers' Assn., 1976-85; Bd. advisors Inst. Health Economics and Social Studies, 1976-80. Author: Oligopoly in the Farm Machine Industry, 1970, Decline of Service in Retail Trade, 1971, The Expected Return from Pharmaceutical Research, 1975, Innovation in the Pharmaceutical Industry, 1976, Games of Chicken: Four Decades of Nuclear Policy, 1988, Economic Policy: An Agenda for the Nineties, 1989, The Japanese Television Cartel: A Study Based on Matsushita v. Zenith, 1993; contbr. articles to profl. jours. Mem. Am. Econ. Assn. Home: 285 Central Park W New York NY 10024-3006 Office: New Sch for Social Rsch Dept Econs 65 5th Ave New York NY 10003-3003

SCHWARY, RONALD LOUIS, motion picture producer; b. The Dalles, Oreg., May 23, 1944; s. Mitchell Louis and Lorraine (Ablan) S.; children: Brian L., Neil L. BS, U. So. Calif., 1967. Pres. Schwary Enterprises, L.A., 1985—. Prodr. (motion pictures) Ordinary People, 1980 (Golden Globe award 1981, Acad. award 1981), Absence of Malice, 1981, Tootsie, 1982, A Soldier's Story, 1984, Batteries Not Included, 1987, Havana, 1990, Scent of a Woman, 1992, Cops and Robbersons, 1994; (TV series) Tour of Duty, 1987. Mem. Dirs. Guild Am. Roman Catholic.

SCHWARZ, CARL W., lawyer; b. Milw., Jan. 28, 1936. BCE, Cornell U., 1958; JD with honors, George Washington U., 1962, LLM, 1966. Bar: Wis. 1962. D.C. 1969. Trial atty. Antitrust divsn., U.S. Dept. Justice, 1962-64,

Fgn. Commerce Sect., 1964-69; ptnr. McDermott, Will & Emery, Washington. Mem. ABA, Internat. Bar Assn., D.C. Bar, State Bar Wis. Office: McDermott Will & Emery 1850 K St NW Washington DC 20006-2296

SCHWARZ, EGON, humanities and German language educator, author, literary critic; b. Vienna, Austria, Aug. 8, 1922; came to U.S., 1949, naturalized, 1956; s. Oscar and Erna S.; m. Dorothea K. Klockenbusch, June 8, 1950; children—Rudolf Joachim, Caroline Elisabeth, Gabriela Barbara. Ph.D., U. Wash., 1954. Mem. faculty Harvard U., 1954-61; mem. faculty dept. Germanic langs. and lit. Washington U., St. Louis, 1961—, prof. German, 1963—, Rosa May Disting. Univ. prof. in the Humanities, 1975-93, prof. emeritus, 1993—; vis. prof. U. Hamburg, Fed. Republic Germany, 1962-63, U. Calif., Berkeley, 1963-65, Middlebury Coll., 1969, U. Calif.-Irvine, 1977, U. Tübingen, 1986; William Evans prof. U. Otago, Dunedin, N.Z., 1984; Disting. scholar Ohio State U., Columbus, 1987, U. Graz, Austria, 1989, 93, U. Siegen, 1993-94. Author: Hofmannsthal und Calderon, 1962, Joseph von Eichendorff, 1972, Das verschluckte Schluchzen-Poesie und Politik bei Rainer Maria Rilke, 1972, Keine Zeit für Eichendorff: Chronik unfreiwilliger Wanderjahre; an autobiography, 1979, revised and expanded, 1992, Dichtung, Kritik, Geschichte: Essays zur Literatur 1900-1930, 1983, Literatur aus vier Kulturen: Essays und Besprechungen, 1987, also numerous other books. Recipient Joseph von Eichendorff medal, 1986, Austrian Medal of Honor for Arts and Scis., 1991; Guggenheim fellow, 1957-58; Am. Council Learned Socs. grantee, 1962-63; Fulbright fellow, 1962-63; NEH sr. fellow, 1970-71; fellow Center for Interdisciplinary Studies Bielefeld, Ger., 1980-81. Mem. MLA (hon.), Am. Assn. Tchrs. German, German Acad. Lang. and Lit. Home: 1036 Oakland Ave Saint Louis MO 63122-6565 Office: Washington U German Dept Saint Louis MO 63130 *When I was young, heroic phantasies were closer to my heart than ethical ones, desires of self-fulfillment stronger than the hopes for an equitable world. Today my horizon is broader in that I wish for a society where personal satisfactions are not achieved at the expense of others, where the earth which one generation inherits is not left more depleted to the next, a society which does not coerce other societies.*

SCHWARZ, GERARD, conductor, musician; b. Weehawken, N.J., Aug. 19, 1947; s. John and Gerta (Weiss) S.; m. Jody Greitzer, June 23, 1984; children: Alysandra, Daniel, Gabriella, Julian. BS, Juilliard Sch., 1972, MA, 1972; DFA (hon.), Fairleigh Dickinson U., Seattle U.; DMus (hon.), U. Puget Sound. Trumpet player Am. Symphony Orch., 1965-72, Am. Brass Quintet, 1965-73, N.Y. Philharm., 1973-77; trumpet player, guest condr. Aspen Music Festival, 1966-75, bd. dirs., 1973-75; music dir. Erick Hawkins Dance Co., 1967-72, SoHo Ensemble, 1969-75, Eliot Feld Ballet Co., N.Y.C., 1972-78; prin. condr. Waterloo Festival, 1975-93, Music Sch. Princeton (N.J.) U.; music dir. N.Y. Chamber Symphony, 1977—, L.A. Chamber Orch., 1978-86, White Mountains (N.H.) Music Festival, 1978-80, Music Today at Merkin Concert Hall, N.Y.C., 1988-89; music advisor Mostly Mozart Festival, Lincoln Ctr., N.Y.C., 1982-84, music dir., 1984—; music advisor Seattle Symphony, 1983-84, prin. condr., 1984-85, music dir., 1985—; artistic advisor Tokyu Bunkamura's Orchard Hall, Japan, 1994—; mem. faculty Juilliard Sch., N.Y.C., 1975-83, Mannes Coll. Music, 1973-79, Montclair (N.J.) State Coll., 1975-80; guest condr. various orchs. including Phila. Orch., L.A. Philharmonic, St. Louis, Buffalo, Detroit, San Francisco, Atlanta, Houston, Pitts., Minn., Jerusalem Symphony, Israel Chamber Orch., Moscow Philharmonic, Moscow Radio Orch., Orch. Nat. de France, Paris, London Symphony Orch., Frankfurt Radio, Stockholm Radio, Helsinki Philharm., Ensemble InterContemporain, Monte Carlo Philharm., Nat. Orch. Spain, English Chamber Orch., London Symphony, Scottish Chamber Orch., City of Birmingham (Eng.) Symphony, Nouvel Orchestre Philharmonique, Sydney (Australia) Symphony, Melbourne (Australia) Symphony, Orchestre National de Lyon, France, Orchestre Philharm. de Montpellier, France, Washington Opera, Da Capo Chamber Players, 20th Century Chamber Orch., Chamber Music Soc. Lincoln Ctr., San Francisco Opera, Seattle Opera, Tokyu Bunkamura, Japan, Residentie Orch. of The Hague, The Netherlands, St. Louis Symphony, London Mozart Players, Kirov Orch., St. Petersburg, Russia, Tokyo Philharm., Royal Liverpool (Eng.) Philharm., Vancouver (Can.) Symphony Orch., City of London Symphonia, Evian Festival in France, 1994; also numerous appearances on TV; rec. artist Columbia, Nonesuch, Vox, MMO, Desto, Angel, Delos records; record: Seattle Symphony 1994-95 Season, 1995. Bd. dirs. Naumburg Found., 1975—. Recipient award for concert artists Ford Found., 1973, Grammy award nominee, Mumms Ovation award, Record of Yr. awards, Ditson Condrs. award Columbia U., 1989; named Condr. of Yr., Musical Am. Internat. Directory of Performing Artists, 1994. Office: NY Chamber Symphony 1395 Lexington Ave New York NY 10128-1647

SCHWARZ, GLENN VERNON, editor; b. Chgo., Nov. 24, 1947; s. Vernon Edward and LaVerne Louise (Schuster) S.; m. Cynthia Frances Meisenhoelder, June 17, 1984; 1 child, Chloe. BA, San Francisco State U., 1970. Sports writer San Francisco Examiner, 1970-87, sports editor, 1988—. Fundraiser San Francisco Zoological Soc., 1987—. Mem. AP Sports Editors, Baseball Writers Assn. Am. (bd. dirs. 1986-87). Avocation: nature travel. Office: San Francisco Examiner 110 5th St San Francisco CA 94103

SCHWARZ, H. MARSHALL, trust company executive; b. 1936; married. BA, Harvard U., 1958, MBA, 1961. With U.S. Trust Co., N.Y.C., 1967—, chmn, chief exec. officer, 1990—; bd. dirs. Bowne & Co., Inc., Atlantic Mut. Co. Bd. dirs. United Way, N.Y.C.; chmn. ARC in Greater N.Y.C.; trustee Columbia U. Tchrs. Coll., Milton Acad. Camille and Henry Dreyfus Found., Boys Club N.Y. Office: US Trust Co NY 114 W 47th St New York NY 10036-1532

SCHWARZ, J(AMES) CONRAD, psychology educator; b. Hartford, Conn., Sept. 19, 1936; s. William Merlin and Violet May (List) S.; m. Lois J. Stonebraker, 1956 (div. 1981); m. Carolina A.B. Herfkens, Oct. 12, 1984. BS, Pa. State U., 1958; MA, Ohio State U., 1961, PhD, 1963. Lic. clin. psychologist, Conn.; cert. psychologist, N.Y. Rsch. asst. Pa. State U., 1957-58; psychol. trainee Chillicothe (Ohio) VA N.P. Hosp., 1958-60; psychol. intern Columbus (Ohio) VA Out-Patient Clinic, 1960-61; instr. psychology Bowling Green (Ohio) State U., 1962-64, asst. prof., 1964-65; asst. prof., mem. teaching faculty grad. tng. Syracuse U, 1965-70, assoc. prof., 1970-72; assoc. prof., mem. teaching faculty grad. tng. program U. Conn., Storrs, 1972-75, prof., mem. teaching faculty grad. tng. program, 1975—; pvt. practice clin. psychology Mansfield Center, Conn., 1973—; asst. field assessment officer Peace Corps Tng. Programs, 1967-68; clin. psychology cons. VA Out-Patient Clinic, Syracuse, 1968-72, Onodaga Co. Mental Health Clinic, Syracuse, 1969-72; with Windham Pub. Schs.-Project Self-Search, 1974-76; cons. Ea. Conn. Mental Health Group, 1974-83, Bermuda Govt., Child Devel. Project, 1979-82, Optimum Resource, Inc., Software for Learning Disabled Children. Author: Deck-a-Dot Manual: An Educational Card Game Program to Develop Arithmetic Readiness, 1970; If This Is Love, Why Do I Feel So Insecure?, 1989, 90, Teacher's Manual for Optimum Resource Reading Program, 1991; cons. editor Devel. Psychology, 1981-84; co-developer The Optimum Resource Reading Program, 1991; contbr. articles to profl. jours. USPHS fellow, 1958-59, 61-62; grantee Nat. Lab. Early Childhood Edn. Ctr. Syracuse U., 1968-71, NIMH, 1978-83, 84-85, Nat. Inst. Alcohol Abuse and Addiction, 1986-89, U. Conn. Rsch. Found., 1985-87. Mem. APA (div. clin., family psychology), Soc. Rsch. in Child Devel., Sigma Xi, Phi Beta Kappa, Psi Chi, Phi Eta Sigma, Phi Kappa Phi. Avocations: tennis, landscape gardening. Office: U Conn Dept Psychology 406 Babbidge Rd Storrs Mansfield CT 06269-1020

SCHWARZ, JOHN HENRY, theoretical physicist, educator; b. North Adams, Mass., Nov. 22, 1941; s. George and Madeleine (Haberfeld) S.; m. Patricia Margaret Moyle, July 11, 1986. AB, Harvard U., 1962; PhD, U. Calif., Berkeley, 1966. Instr. physics Princeton (N.J.) U., 1966-69, asst. prof., 1969-72; research assoc. Calif. Inst. Tech., Pasadena, 1972-85, prof. theoretical physics, 1985—, Harold Brown prof. theoretical physics, 1989—. Co-author: Superstring Theory, 1987. Trustee Aspen (Colo.) Ctr. for Physics, 1982—. Recipient Dirac medal Internat. Ctr. for Theoretical Physics, 1989; Guggenheim fellow, 1978-79, MacArthur Gound. fellow, 1987. Fellow Am. Phys. Soc., Phi Beta Kappa (vis. scholar 1990—). Office: Calif Inst Tech # 452-58 Pasadena CA 91125

SCHWARZ, JOHN J.H., state senator, surgeon; b. Chgo., Nov. 15, 1937; s. Frank William and Helen Veronica (Brennan) S.; m. Anne Louise Ennis, Jan.

16, 1971 (dec. Feb. 1990); 1 child, Brennan Louise; m. Patricia A. Woodworth, June 8, 1991. BA, U. Mich., 1959; MD, Wayne State U., 1964. Physician, surgeon Battle Creek, Mich., 1974—; mayor City of Battle Creek, 1985-87; senator State of Mich., 1987—, pres. pro tempore, 1994—. Trustee Olivet Coll., 1991—, Wayland Acad., 1992—. Lt. comdr. USN, 1965-67. Mem. AMA, Am. Coll. Surgeons, Am. Soc. for Head & Neck Surgery. Republican. Roman Catholic. Office: State Senate State Capital Lansing MI 48909

SCHWARZ, JOSEPH EDMUND, artist; b. Hartford, Conn., May 13, 1929; s. Jules and Dora (Sklarinsky) S.; m. Jean Bunker Chalmers, Jan. 29, 1951; children: David Bunker, Dina Ruth, Jonathan Chalmers, Adam Jules; m. Sarah Rollings, Oct. 21, 1971. B.F.A. Ohio Wesleyan U., 1950; M.F.A. U. Ill., 1952; Ph.D., Ohio State U., 1957. instr. Ohio State U. 1952-57; assoc. prof. U. Ga., 1957-68; prof., dir. grad. studies Va. Commonwealth U., 1968-73; prof. U. Maine- Machias, 1973-74, Auburn U. Montgomery, Ala., 1977—, head dept. fine arts, 1977—. Exhibited group shows, Butler Art Inst. Ann., 1949-55, Southeastern Ann., Atlanta, 1957, 59-61, 66-67, Chrysler Show, Provincetown, Mass., 1958, Hunter Gallery Ann., Chattanooga, 1960-62, 67, Whitney Ann., N.Y.C., 1958, Montgomery Mus.; represented pub. art collections, Butler Art Inst., Atlanta High Mus., Ball State U., Temple Beth Israel, Hartford, LaGrange Coll. U. Ga. Sch. Law. Home: 165 Vivian Ln Wetumpka AL 36092-4480 Office: Dept Fine Arts Auburn U Montgomery AL 36177 *As a humanist and as a painter, my life's goal is to be actually what I hope I am, that is to realize myself, to develop fully whatever it is that makes my life unique. I want my paintings to be records of my ideas and values, and if it should be that my being and my work have specialty, then I would hope that others would find there compassion and passion, a witnessing of human joy and pain and, finally, affirmation of the beauty of man and of human life.*

SCHWARZ, JOSEPHINE LINDEMAN, retired ballet company director, choreographer; b. Dayton, Ohio, Apr. 8, 1908; d. Joseph and Hannah (Lindeman) S. D.F.A. (hon.), U. Dayton, 1974; H.H.D. (hon.), Wright State U., 1983. Founder, dir. Schwarz Sch. Dance, Dayton, 1927-84, Exptl. Group for Young Dancers (now Dayton Ballet), 1937-79; mem. Weidman Theatre Dance Co., 1934-37; guest tchr., lectr., choreographer Hunter Coll., N.Y.C., YM-YWHA, N.Y.C., also regional dance companies in, Cleve., Phila., Indpls., Houston; pres. N.E. Regional Ballet Assn., 1961; chmn. dance adv. panel Ohio Arts Council, 1967-70; founder, program dir. Nat. Craft Choreography Confs., 1968-70; dance advisory panels Nat. Endowment for Arts, 1975-78; also Ohio Arts Council, 1975-78. Profl. dancer Adolph Bolm's Ballet Intime, Ravinia Opera Ballet, Chgo., 1925-27; European study and performances, 1929-30; author articles. Recipient award Ohio Arts Council, 1977, Spl. Achievement award YWCA, 1982, Brotherhood award Dayton chpt. NCCJ, 1984, Pegasus award Ohioana Library Assn., 1987, Northeast award Regional Dance Am., 1990; inducted into Ohio Women's Hall of Fame, 1991. Mem. Nat. Assn. Regional Ballet (bd. dirs. 1970-75), Am. Dance Guild (award 1985), Friends Dayton Ballet, Dayton Art Inst. Jewish. Home: 350 Ponca Pl # 122 Boulder CO 80303 *There are no short cuts.*

SCHWARZ, MELVIN A., lawyer; b. Cin., Feb. 20, 1950; s. John H. and Ann (Gruenebaum) S.; m. Roberta M. Edge, July 14, 1979; children: Emily, Julia. BA, Johns Hopkins U., 1972; JD, U. Chgo., 1975. Bar: Pa., N.Y., U.S. Dist. Ct. (ea. & mid. dists.) Pa., U.S. Dist. Ct. (ea., so & no. dists.) N.Y., U.S. Ct. Appeals (1st, 2d & 3d cirs.), U.S. Supreme Ct. Assoc. Dechert Price & Rhoads, Phila., 1975-83; ptnr. Dechert Price & Rhoads, N.Y.C., 1983—. Mem. Phila. Bar Assn., assoc. mem. Bar of City of N.Y., Order of Coif, Phi Beta Kappa. Office: Dechert Price & Rhoads 477 Madison Ave New York NY 10022-5802

SCHWARZ, MICHAEL, lawyer; b. Brookline, Mass., Oct. 19, 1952; s. Jules Lewis and Estelle (Kosberg) S. BA magna cum laude, U. No. Colo., 1975; postgrad. U. N.Mex., 1977, JD, 1980; Rsch. reader in Negligence Law, Oxford U., 1978; diploma in Legal Studies, Cambridge U., 1981. Bar: N.Mex. 1980, U.S. Dist. Ct. N.Mex. 1980, U.S. Ct. Appeals (10th, D.C., and Fed. cirs.) 1982, U.S. Ct. Internat. Trade, 1982, U.S. Tax Ct. 1982, U.S. Supreme Ct. 1983, N.Y. 1987. VISTA vol., Albuquerque, 1975-77; rsch. fellow N.Mex. Legal Support Project, Albuquerque, 1978-79; supr. law Cambridge (Eng.) 1980-81; law clk. to chief justice Supreme Ct. N.Mex., Santa Fe, 1981-82; pvt. practice law, Santa Fe, 1982—; spl. prosecutor City of Santa Fe, 1985; spl. asst. atty. gen., 1986-88; mem. editorial bd. Social Security Reporting Svc. Author: New Mexico Appellate Manual, 1990, 2nd. edit., 1994; contbr. articles to profl. jours. Vice dir. Colo. Pub. Interest Rsch. Group, 1974; scoutmaster Great S.W. Area coun. Boy Scouts Am., 1977-79; mem. N.Mex. Acupuncture Licensing Bd., 1983. Recipient Cert. of Appreciation Cambridge U., 1981, Nathan Burkan Meml. award, 1980, N.Mex. Supreme Ct. Cert. Recognition, 1992, 93. Mem. ABA (litigation com. on profl. responsibility, litigation com. on pretrial practice and discovery), Assn. Trial Lawyers Am., State Bar N.Y., N.Mex. State Bar (bd. dirs. employment law sect. 1990—, chair employment law sect. 1991-92), N.Y. Bar Assn., First Jud. Dist. Bar Assn. (treas. 1987-88, sec. 1988-89, v.p. 1989-1990, pres. 1990-91, local rules com. mem. 1989-92), N.Mex. Supreme Ct. (standing com. on profl. conduct 1990—, hearing officer, reviewing officer disciplinary com. 1993—), Am. Inns. of Ct. N.Mex. (barrister), Nat. Employment Lawyers Assn. (Nat. chpt., N.Mex. chpt.), Sierra Club, Amnesty Internat., Nat. Audubon Soc. Home and Office: PO Box 1656 Santa Fe NM 87504-1656

SCHWARZ, RALPH JACQUES, engineering educator; b. Hamburg, Germany, June 13, 1922; naturalized, 1944; s. Simon J. and Anna (Schoendorff) S.; m. Irene Lassally, Sept. 9, 1951; children: Ronald Paul, Sylvia Anne. B.S., Columbia U., 1943, M.S., 1944, Ph.D., 1949; postgrad., Poly. Inst. Bklyn., 1944-45, N.Y. U., 1946-47. Registered profl. engineer. N.Y. Mem. faculty Columbia U. 1943-92 prof. elec. engring., 1958-92, chmn. dept., 1958-65, 71-72, assoc. dean acad. affairs Faculty Engring. and Applied Sci., 1972-75, acting dean, 1975-76, 80-81, vice dean, Thayer Lindsley prof., 1976-92, Thayer Lindsley prof. emeritus, 1992—; cons. systems analysis, communications and noise theory, 1945—; vis. assoc. prof. UCLA, 1956; adviser Inst. Internat. Edn., 1952-65; vis. scientist IBM Research Center, 1969-70. Author: (with M.G. Salvadori) Differential Equations in Engineering Problems, 1954, (with B. Friedland) Linear Systems, 1965. Bd. dirs. Armstrong Meml. Research Found.; trustee Associated Univs., Inc., 1980-92. Fellow IEEE (chmn. circuit theory group 1963-65, Centennial medal 1984); mem. Communications Soc. (bd. govs.), Am. Soc. Engring. Edn., AAAS, Sigma Xi, Tau Beta Pi, Pi Mu Epsilon, Eta Kappa Nu. Home: 33 Wood Ln New Rochelle NY 10804-3709 Office: Columbia U 116th St And Broadway New York NY 10027

SCHWARZ, RICHARD HOWARD, obstetrician/gynecologist, educator; b. Easton, Pa., Jan. 10, 1931; s. Howard Eugene and Blanche Elizabeth (Smith) S.; m. Patricia Marie Lewis, Mar. 11, 1978; children by previous marriage: Martha L., Nancy Schwarz Tedesco, Paul H., Mary Katherine Schwarz Murray. MD, Jefferson Med. Coll., 1955; MA (hon.), U. Pa., Phila., 1971. Diplomate Am. Bd. Ob-Gyn. (examiner 1977—). Intern, then resident Phila. Gen. Hosp., 1955-59; prof. U. Pa., Phila., 1963-78; prof., chmn. Downstate Med. Ctr., Bklyn., 1978-90, dean, v.p. acad. affairs, 1983-89, provost, v.p. clin. affairs, 1988—, interim pres., 1993-94. Author: Septic Abortion, 1968. Editor: Handbook of Obstetric Emergencies, 1984, mem. editorial bd. jour. Ob-Gyn., Milw., 1983-87; contbr. articles to profl. jours. Bd. dirs. March of Dimes, N.Y.C., 1985—. Capt. USAF, 1959-63. Mem. Am. Coll. Obstetricians and Gynecologists (chmn. dist. 2 1984-87, v.p. 1989-90, pres. elect 1990-91, pres. 1991-92). Republican. Presbyterian. Office: Greater NY Hosp Assn Health Sci Ctr 55 W 57th St New York NY 10019

SCHWARZ, RICHARD WILLIAM, historian, educator; b. Wataga, Ill., Sept. 11, 1925; s. George William and Mildred (Imschweiler) S.; m. Joyce Frances Anderson, June 11, 1950; children: Constance Kay, Richard Paul, Dwight Luther. BA, Andrews U., 1949; MS, U. Ill., 1953; MA, U. Mich. 1959, PhD, 1964. Tchr.-librarian Broadview Acad., La Grange, Ill., 1949-53, Adelphian Acad., Holly, Mich., 1953-55; instr. history Andrews U., 1955-58, asst. librarian, 1955-56, acting librarian, 1956-58, asst. prof., 1958-63, assoc. prof., 1963-68, prof., 1968-89, acting chmn. dept. history and polit. sci., 1964-66, prof. emeritus, 1989—, chmn., 1966-77, v.p. acad. adminstrn., 1977-87; reference libr. Berrien Springs Community Libr., 1990-93; vis. instr. Mich. State U., 1967; book reviewer Library Jour., 1957-77. Author: John

Harvey Kellogg, M.D., 1970, Lightbearers to the Remnant, 1979; bd. editors: Studies in Adventist History, 1971-83. Del. Berrien County Republican Conv., 1966, 68, 74. Served with USNR, 1944-46. Mem. Assn. 7th-Day Adventists Historians (pres. 1987), Phi Beta Kappa, Phi Alpha Theta, Phi Kappa Phi. Home: 113 Oakwood Pl Hendersonville NC 28792-9521

SCHWARZ, ROBERT DEVLIN, art dealer; b. Atlantic City, N.J., July 11, 1942; s. Frank Samuel and Marie (Devlin) S.; m. Pamela Pillion; children: Robert, Jr., Elizabeth, Jonathan. BS, Dickinson Coll., 1964. Curator Stephen Girard Collection, Phila., 1970-80; pres., curator The Schwarz Gallery, Phila., 1981—; pres., owner. Author: Catalogue of the Stephen Girard Collection, 1980, A Gallery Collects Peale, 1987. Mem. bd. dirs. Conservation Ctr., 1995. Mem. Art Dealers Assn. Am., Art and Antiques Deales League Am. Republican. Presbyterian. Office: The Schwarz Gallery 1806 Chestnut St Philadelphia PA 19103

SCHWARZ, WOLFGANG, psychologist; b. Stuttgart, Ger., Oct. 30, 1926; s. Mole and Edith (Gutstein) S.; brought to U.S., 1934, naturalized, 1940; A.B., N.Y. U., 1948, A.M., 1949, Ph.D., 1956; m. Cynthia Mae Johnson, Sept. 12, 1949 (div.); children—Amy Maria, Casey Andrew, Darcy Lynn, Priscilla Anne, Lydia Beth, Emily Jane; m. Susan Decker, 1976; children—Jaime Bartholomew, Noah. Intern, Bellevue Med. Center, N.Y., 1949-51; chief psychology Rip Van Winkle Med. Found., Hudson, N.Y., 1951-53; dir. psychology Hillcrest Med. Center, Tulsa, 1953-56, Hollywood Presbyn. Hosp., Los Angeles, 1956-58; cons. psychology Cedars Lebanon Hosp., Los Angeles, 1956-58; spl. cons. to D.C. Govt., 1959-61, NIH, Bethesda, Md., 1962-64; dir. psychol. research Mass. Dept. Mental Health, Boston and Malden, 1965-68; individual practice clin. psychology, Tulsa, 1953-56, Beverly Hills, Calif., 1956-59, Washington, 1959-63, Concord and Malden, Mass., 1963-73, Mt. Kisco, N.Y., 1973—; lectr. U. Tulsa, 1953-54, Hillcrest Med. Center, Tulsa, 1953-56, Los Angeles State Coll., 1956-57; asst. prof. Howard U., 1961; asso. prof. George Washington U., 1961-62; vis. research asst. Harvard Psychiatry, Lab., 1966-68; prof. Malden Hosp., 1968-71; cons. No. Westchester Hosp., 1974—, United Hosp., 1975—, Four Winds Hosp., 1975-80; cons. psychology Peace Corps, Mass., 1969—. Mem. exec. com. Mayor's Model City Program, Malden, 1967-68. Served with USNR, 1945-46. Recipient Founder's Day award N.Y. U., 1956, Individual award USPHS/NIH, 1960-64. Diplomate Am. Bd. Profl. Psychology. Mem. Am., N.Y., Mass. psychol. assns., Washington Soc. History of Medicine (exec. com. 1963-64), N.Y. Acad. Scis., Psi Chi, Beta Lambda Sigma. Author: A Survey of the Mental Health Facilities in the District of Columbia, 1961; also articles. Home: 81 Paulding Dr Chappaqua NY 10514-2818 Office: 121 Smith Ave Mount Kisco NY 10549-2815

SCHWARZENEGGER, ARNOLD ALOIS, actor, author; b. Graz, Austria, July 30, 1947; came to U.S., 1968, naturalized, 1983; s. Karl and Aurelia (Jedrny) S.; m. Maria Owings Shriver, Apr. 26, 1986; children: Katherine Eunice, Christina Aurelia, Patrick. BA in Bus. and Internat. Econs., U. Wis., Superior. Owner prodn. co. and real estate. Actor: (films) Stay Hungry, 1976 (Golden Globe award 1976), Pumping Iron, 1977, The Villain, 1979, Conan, The Barbarian, 1982, Conan, The Destroyer, 1983, The Terminator, 1984, Commando, 1985, Red Sonja, 1985, Raw Deal, 1986, Predator, 1987, Running Man, 1987, Red Heat, 1988, Twins, 1988, Total Recall, 1990, Kindergarten Cop, 1990, Terminator 2: Judgement Day, 1991, The Last Action Hero, 1993, True Lies, 1994, Junior, 1994; (TV movies) The Jayne Mansfield Story, 1980; dir. TV movie Christmas in Connecticut, 1992; host A Very Special Christmas Story; dir. The Switch, Tales from the Crypt, HBO, 1990; author: Arnold: The Education of a Bodybuilder, 1977, Arnold's Bodyshaping for Women, 1979, Arnold's Bodybuilding for Men, 1981, Arnold's Encyclopedia of Modern Bodybuilding, 1985; prodr. bodybuilding video tape. Nat. weight tng. coach Spl. Olympics; vol. prison rehab. programs; chmn. Pres.'s Coun. on Phys. Fitness and Sports, 1990. Bodybldg. champion, 1965-80; named Jr. Mr. Europe, 1965, Best Built Man of Europe, 1966, Mr. Europe, 1966; Internat. Powerlifting Championship, 1966, German Powerlifting Championship, 1968; IFFB (Internat. Fedn. Body Builders) Mr. Internat., 1968, IFFB Mr. Universe (amateur), 1969; NABBA (Nat. Assn. Body Builders) Mr. Universe (amateur), 1967, NABBA Mr. Universe (profl.), 1968, 69, 70; Mr. World, 1970; IFFB Mr. Olympia, 1970, 71, 72, 73, 74, 75, 80; recipient Golden Globe award for Best Newcomer in Films, 1976, Timmie Award The Touchdown Club, 1990; named Video Star Yr. VSDA, 1990; voted Internat. Star of 1984, ShoWest. Office: care ICM 8942 Wilshire Blvd Beverly Hills CA 90211*

SCHWARZER, WILLIAM W, federal judge; b. Berlin, Apr. 30, 1925; came to U.S., 1938, naturalized, 1944; s. John F. and Edith M. (Daniel) S.; m. Anne Halberslaben, Feb. 2, 1951; children: Jane Elizabeth, Andrew William. A.B. cum laude, U. So. Calif., 1948; LL.B. cum laude, Harvard U. 1951. Bar: Calif. 1953, U.S. Supreme Ct. 1967. Teaching fellow Harvard U. Law Sch., 1951-52; asso. firm McCutchen, Doyle, Brown & Enersen, San Francisco, 1952-60; ptnr. McCutchen, Doyle, Brown & Enersen, 1960-76; judge U.S. Dist. Ct (no. dist.) Calif., San Francisco, 1976—; dir. Fed. Jud. Ctr., Washington, 1990-95; sr. counsel Pres.'s Commn. on CIA Activities Within the U.S., 1975; chmn. U.S. Jud. Conf. Com. Fed.-State Jurisdiction, 1987-90; mem. faculty Nat. Inst. Trial Advocacy, Fed. Jud. Ctr., All-ABA, U.S.-Can. Legal Exch., Anglo-U.S. Jud. Exch., 1987, Salzburg Seminar on Am. Studies; adj. prof. Georgetown Law Ctr.; vis. prof. Hastings Coll. Law U. Calif. Author: Managing Antitrust and Other Complex Litigation, 1982, Civil Discovery and Manadatory Disclosure, 1994, Federal Civil Procedure Before Trial, 1994; contbr. articles to legal publs., aviation jours. Trustee World Affairs Coun. No. Calif., 1961-88; chmn. bd. trustees Marin Country Day Sch., 1963-66; chmn. Marin County Aviation Commn., 1969-76; mem. vis. com. Harvard Law Sch., 1981-86. Served with Intelligence, U.S. Army, 1943-46. Fellow Am. Coll. Trial Lawyers (S. Gates award 1992), Am. Bar Found.; mem. ABA (Meador Rosenberg award 1995), Am. Law Inst., San Francisco Bar Assn., State Bar Calif., Coun. Fgn. Rels. Office: 450 Golden Gate Ave San Francisco CA 94102

SCHWARZKOPF, H. NORMAN, retired army officer, engineer; b. Trenton, N.J., Aug. 22, 1934; s. H. Norman and Ruth (Bowman) S.; m. Brenda Holsinger, July 6, 1968; children: Cynthia, Jessica, Christian. BS in engring., U.S. Mil. Acad., West Point, N.Y., 1956; MME, U. So. Calif., Los Angeles, 1964; student, U.S. Army War Coll., Carlisle Barracks, Pa., 1972-73. Commd. 2nd lt. U.S. Army, 1956, advanced through grades to gen., 1988; platoon leader, exec. officer 2nd Airborne Battle Group, 1957-59; platoon leader 6th Inf., Fed. Rep. Germany, 1959; aide-de-camp Berlin Command, Fed. Rep. Germany, 1960-61; lecturer Dept. Mechanics, U.S. Army Military Acad., West Point, NY, Ga., 1965; advisor U.S. Army, Vietnam, 1965-66; commander 1st Battalion, 6th Inf., 198th Inf. brigade, 23rd Inf. Div., Vietnam, 1969-70; chief, Prof. Devel. Section, Inf. branch Office Personnel Operations, Washington, D.C., 1970-72; military asst. Office Asst. Sec. Army, Washington, D.C., 1973-74; dep. comdr. 172d inf. brigade Ft. Richardson, Alaska, 1974-76; comdr. 1st brigade 9th Inf. div., Ft. Lewis, Wash., 1976-78; dep. dir. plans U.S. Pacific Command, Camp Smith, Hawaii, 1978-80; asst. div. comdr. 8th inf. div. (mechanized) U.S. Army Europe, Fed. Republic Germany, 1980-82; dir. mil. personnel mgmt. Office Dep. Chief Staff for Personnel, Washington, 1982-83; comdg. gen. 24th inf. div. (mechanized) Ft. Stewart, Ga., 1983-85; dep. comdr. U.S. forces in Grenada operation, 1983; asst. dep. chief staff ops. Hdqrs. Dept. Army, Washington, 1985-86; comdg. gen. I corps Ft. Lewis, Wash., 1987-88; dep. chief staff for ops. and plans Hdqrs. Dept. Army, Washington, 1987-88; comdr. in chief U.S. Cen. Command, MacDill AFB, Fla., 1988-91, U.S. Forces in Ops. Desert Shield, Desert Storm, Saudi Arabia, 1990-91; U.S. Army Retired, 1992, lecturer, 1993—. Author: (with Peter Petre) It Doesn't Take a Hero, 1992. U.S.A, Vietnam, 1965-66, 1969-70. Decorated Def. D.S.M., D.S.M. with two oak leaf clusters, D.S.M. for USN, D.S.M. for USAF, D.S.M. for USCG, Silver Star with two oak leaf clusters, Def. Superior Svc. medal, Legion of Merit, D.F.C., Bronze Star with three oak leaf clusters, Purple Heart with oak leaf cluster, Combat Infantryman badge, Master Parachutist badge, Gen. Staff Identification badge, Joint Staff Identification badge, Dept. Def. Identification badge, Presdl. Medal of Freedom; Nat. Order of Legion of Honor, hon. pfc. French Fgn. Legion (France); Order of Leopold (Belgium); knight Hon. Order of the Bath (U.K.); Decoration 1st degree (Bahrain); Sash of Honour (Qatar); Medal of Independence (United Arab Emirates); officer Order of King Abd Al Aziz 1st class (Saudi Arabia), Order of Kuwait with Sash of Most Excellent Order (Kuwait). Avocations: hunting, fishing, skeet, trap and sporting clays. Office: care Internat Creative Mgmt Inc 40 W 57th St New York NY 10019-4001

SCHWARZLOSE, RICHARD ALLEN, journalism educator; b. Chgo., Mar. 18, 1937; s. Paul Fowler and Muriel Beth (Kingsley) S.; m. Sally Jean Frye, July 27, 1963; children: Daniel Frye, Rebecca Frye. BS in Journalism, U. Ill., 1959, MA in Polit. Sci., 1960, PhD in Communications, 1965. Reporter, telegraph editor News-Gazette, Champaign, Ill., 1955-62; asst. prof. journalism Purdue U., West Lafayette, Ind., 1965-68; from asst. prof. to prof. journalism Northwestern U., Evanston, Ill., 1968—, assoc. dean Sch. Journalism, 1989-93. Author: Newspapers: A Reference Guide, 1987, Nation's Newsbrokers, 2 vols., 1989-90; author monograph; contbr. numerous articles to profl. jours. Peterson rsch. grantee Am. Antiquarian Soc., Worcester, Mass., 1984. Mem. Assn. for Edn. in Journalism and Mass Communications, Soc. Profl. Journalists. Unitarian. Avocations: biking, conducting seminars with adult groups. Home: 2712 Payne St Evanston IL 60201-2028 Office: Northwestern U Medill Sch Journalism Evanston IL 60208

SCHWARZROCK, SHIRLEY PRATT, author, lecturer, educator; b. Mpls., Feb. 27, 1914; d. Theodore Ray and Myrtle Pearl (Westphal) Pratt; m. Loren H. Schwarzrock, Oct. 19, 1945 (dec. 1966); children: Kay Linda, Ted Kenneth, Lorraine V. BS, U. Minn., 1935, MA, 1942, PhD, 1974. Sec. to chmn. speech dept., U. Minn., Mpls., 1935, instr. in speech, 1946, team tchr. in creative arts workshops for tchrs., 1955-56, guest lectr. Dental Sch. 1967-72, asst. prof. (part-time) of practice adminstrn. Sch. Dentistry, 1972-80; tchr. speech, drama and English, Preston (Minn.) High Sch., 1935-37; tchr. speech, drama and English, Owatonna (Minn.) H.S., 1937-39, also dir. dramatics, 1937-39; tchr. creative dramatics and English, tchr.-counselor Webster Groves (Mo.) Jr. H.S., 1939-40; dir. dramatics and tchr.-counselor Webster Groves Sr. H.S., 1940-43; exec. sec. bus. and profl. dept. YWCA, Mpls., 1943-45; tchr. speech and drama Covent of the Visitation, St. Paul, 1958; editor pro-tem Am. Acad. Dental Practice Adminstrn., 1966-68; guest tchr. Coll. St. Catherine, St. Paul, 1969; vol. mgr. Gift Shop, Eitel Hosp., Mpls., 1981-83, Edina Cmty. Resource Pool, 1992—; cmty. citizen mem. planning, evaluating, reporting com. Edina Pub. Sch. System, 1993—; tutor for reading, writing, and speaking, 1993—; cons. for dental med. programs Normandale Cmty. Coll., Bloomington, Minn., 1968; cons. on pub. rels. to dentists, 1954—; guest lectr. to various dental groups, 1966—; lectr. Internat. Congress on Arts and Communication, 1980, Am. Inst. Banking, 1981; condr. tutorials in speaking and profl. office mgmt., 1985—; owner Shirley Schwarzrock's Exec. Support Svc., 1989—; cons. to mktg. communications mgr. Ergodyne Corp., St. Paul, 1991-92; freelance editor med. support bus., 1992. Author books (series): Coping with Personal Identity, Coping with Human Relationships, Coping with Facts and Fantasies, Coping with Teenage Problems, 1984; individual book titles include: Do I Know the "Me" Others See?, My Life-What Shall I Do With It?, Living with Loneliness, Learning to Make Better Decisions, Grades, What's So Important About Them, Anyway?, Facts and Fantasies About Alcohol, Facts and Fantasies About Drugs, Facts and Fantasies About Smoking, Food as a Crutch, Facts and Fantasies About the Roles of Men and Women, You Always Communicate Something, Appreciating People-Their Likenesses and Differences, Fitting In, To Like and Be Liked, Can You Talk With Someone Else? Coping with Emotional Pain, Some Common Crutches, Parents Can Be a Problem, Coping with Cliques, Crises Youth Face Today, Effective Dental Assisting, (with L.H. Schwarzrock) 1954, 59, 67, (with J.R. Jensen) 1973, 78, 82, (with J.R. Jensen, Kay Schwarzrock, Lorraine Schwarzrock) 1990, Workbook for Effective Dental Assisting, 1960, 68, 73, (with Lorraine Schwarzrock), 1978, 82, 90, Manual for Effective Dental Assisting, 1968, 73, 78, 82, 90; (with Donovan F. Ward), Effective Medical Assisting, 1969, 76; Workbook for Effective Medical Assisting, 1969, 76, Manual for Effective Medical Assisting, 1969, 76; (with C.G. Wrenn) The Coping with Series of Books for High School Students, 1970, 73; The Coping With Manual, 1973, Contemporary Concerns, of Youth, 1980. Pres. University Elem. Sch. PTA, 1955-56. Fellow Internat. Biog. Assn.; mem. Minn. Acad. Dental Practice Adminstrn. (hon.), Minn. Historical Soc., 1992—, Minn. Genealogical Soc., 1992—, Zeta Phi Eta (pres. 1948-49), Eta Sigma Upsilon. Home: 7448 W Shore Dr Edina MN 55435-4022

SCHWARZSCHILD, MARTIN, astronomer, educator; b. Potsdam, Germany, May 31, 1912; came to U.S., 1937, naturalized, 1942; s. Karl and Else (Rosenbach) S.; m. Barbara Cherry, Aug. 24, 1945. Ph.D., U. Goettingen, 1935; D.Sc. (hon.), Swarthmore Coll., 1960, Columbia U., 1973; DSc, Princeton U., 1992. Research fellow Inst. Astrophysics, Oslo (Norway) U., 1936-37, Harvard U. Obs., 1937-40; lectr., later asst. prof. Rutherford Obs., Columbia U., 1940-47; prof. Princeton U., 1947-50, Higgins prof. astronomy, 1950-79. Author: Structure and Evolution of the Stars. Served to 1st lt. AUS, 1942-45. Recipient Dannie Heineman prize Akademie der Wissenschaften zu Goettingen, Germany, 1967, Albert A. Michelson award Case Western Res. U., 1967, Newcomb Cleveland Prize AAAS, 1987, Rittenhouse Silver medal, 1966, Prix Janssen Société astronomique de France, 1970, Medal from l'Assn. Pour le Developpement Internat. de l'Observatoire de Nice, 1986, Gerlach-Adolph von Muenchausen Medaille Goettingen U., 1987, Dirk Brouwer award Am. Astron. Soc., 1991, Balzan prize, 1994. Fellow Am. Acad. Arts and Scis.; mem. Internat. Astron. Union (v.p. 1964-70), Akademie der Naturforscher Leopoldina, Royal Astron. Soc. (asso., Gold medal 1969, Eddington medal 1963), Royal Astron. Soc. Can. (hon.), Am. Astron. Soc. (pres. 1970-72), Nat. Acad. Scis. (Henry Draper medal 1961), Soc. Royale des Sciences de Liege (corr.), Royal Netherlands Acad. Sci. and Letters (fgn.), Royal Danish Acad. Sci. and Letters (fgn.), Norwegian Acad. Sci. and Letters, Astron. Soc. Pacific (Bruce medal 1965), Am. Philos. Soc., Sigma Xi.

SCHWARZSCHILD, PATRICIA MICHAELSON, lawyer; b. Washington, Jan. 15, 1950; d. Louis LeRoy and Katherine Ann (Elmore) Michaelson; m. William Harry Schwarzschild, June 9, 1973 (div.); children—W.H., Michael Todd. B.S., Va. Tech. U., 1972; J.D., Vanderbilt U., 1975. Bar: Va. 1975, U.S. Dist. Ct. (ea. dist.) Va. 1975, U.S. Ct. Appeals (4th cir.) 1981. Staff atty. Va. State Corp. Commn., Richmond, 1975-77; assoc. McGuire, Woods & Battle, Richmond, 1977-81; ptnr. Hunton & Williams, Richmond, 1981—. mem. exec. com., bd. dirs. Va. Capital Representation Resouce Ctr. Bd. dirs. YMCA, Richmond, 1977-83, Richmond Children's Mus., 1980-83, Va. Fedn. Planned Parenthood, Richmond, 1983-86. Fellow Va. Law Found. (exec. coun.); mem. ABA (council on issues affecting legal profession), Va. Bar Assn. (chmn. membership com. 1982-84, bd. govs. litigation section), Va. Bar (fellow young lawyers sect.), Am. Judicature Soc. Club: Westwood Racquet. Office: Hunton & Williams E Tower Riverfront Plz 951 E Byrd St Richmond VA 23219-4074

SCHWARZSCHILD, WILLIAM HARRY, JR., banker; b. Richmond, Va., Sept. 19, 1903; s. William Harry and Rosalie (Held) S.; m. Kathryn Emsheimer, Sept. 6, 1945; children: Kathrin, William Harry. A.B., U. Va., 1923; M.B.A., Harvard, 1925. With J. & W. Seligman & Co., 1926-30; v.p. Central Nat. Bank, 1931-41, exec. v.p., 1945-49, pres., 1949-71, chmn. bd., 1967-73, 76-78, chmn. bd. Central Nat. Corp., 1973-76, chmn. bd. dir., mem. exec. com. Central Nat. Bank, Central-Fidelity Banks, Inc., 1921-78. Chmn. Va. Bd. Vocational Rehab., 1964-73; chmn. gen. fund drive Henrico, Richmond, Chesterfield, ARC, 1952; Trustee Richmond Meml. Hosp. Served to lt. comdr. USNR, 1942-45. Decorated Bronze Star. Mem. Richmond C. of C. (pres. 1955-57), Am. Inst. Banking, Phi Beta Kappa. Clubs: Commonwealth, Fishing Bay Yacht, Westwood Racquet. Home: 210 Overlook Rd Richmond VA 23229-8511 Office: 219 E Broad St Richmond VA 23219-1735

SCHWASS, GARY L., utilities executive; b. Ludington, Mich., Sept. 30, 1945; s. Philip V. and Greta (Beebe) S.; m. Peggy Ann McElroy, Nov. 29, 1968; children: John P., Jeree A. BS, Western Mich. U., 1968; MBA, Eastern Mich. U., 1971. Tchr. maths. Annapolis High Sch., Dearborn Heights, Mich., 1968-71; corp. systems analyst Consumers Power Co., Jackson, Mich., 1971-73; prin. planning analyst Consumers Power Co., Jackson, 1974-78, dir. fin. planning, 1979-80, dir. fin. planning and projects, 1981-83, exec. dir. fin. planning and projects, 1984-85; treas. Duquesne Light Co., Pitts., 1985-88, v.p., 1987—, v.p. finance group, CFO, 1989-94, sr. v.p., CEO, 1995—, v.p. and treas. DQE, Pitts., 1989-94; pres., bd. dirs. Montauk, 1990—, Western Pa. Devel. Credit Corp., Pitts., 1985—; chmn., bd. dirs. Custom Coals Internat., 1991-92; bd. dirs. Duquesne Enterprises, Pitts.; mem. steering com. Edison Electric Inst. Fin., 1991-94; exec. v.p., CEO and treas., 1995—. V.p., treas. bd. dirs. Cath. Social Services, Jackson, 1984-85; bd. dirs. Mercy Health Svcs., Altoona, 1992—, Holy Family Inst., Pitts., 1988-92; v.p., treas. bd. dirs. Holy Family Found., Pitts., 1992—.

Methodist. Avocations: skiing, reading, woodworking. Office: Duquesne Light Co One Oxford Centre 301 Grant St Pittsburgh PA 15279-0001

SCHWATKA, MARK ANDREW, advertising agency executive; b. Oakland, Calif., Mar. 17, 1950; s. Arthur Edward and Beverly Ruth (La Flamme) S.; m. Diana Tompkins; children: Vasiliki, Phoebe, Sophia, Irina. B.A., Loyola U., Los Angeles, 1972. Copywriter Bates Worldwide, N.Y.C., 1973-77, creative supr., 1978-80, creative dir., 1981—. Home: 31 Cherry Ave Larchmont NY 10538-3709

SCHWEBEL, ANDREW I., psychology educator; b. N.Y.C., Feb. 5, 1943; s. Milton and Bernice Lois (Davison) S.; m. Carol Rose Lubinsky, May 25, 1969; children—David, Sara. B.A., Antioch Coll., 1965; M.S., Yale U., 1967; Ph.D., 1969. Lic. psychologist, Ohio; cert. family therapist. Asst. prof. psychology Ohio State U., Columbus, 1969-73; assoc. prof. Ohio State U., 1973-79, prof., 1979—; pvt. practice clin. psychology Columbus, 1977—; psychol. cons. SE Ohio Comprehensive Planning Agy., Cambridge, Ohio, 1970-73; adj. prof. Union for Experimenting Colls. and Univs., Yellow Springs, Ohio, 1971—; cons. Social Ecology Equity Change Quest, Baton Rouge, 1973-75; host Let's Talk It Over, WBNS-AM Radio, Columbus, 1980-81; v.p for human relations New Communities Corp., Columbus; columnist Suburban News Press. Author: Student Teacher's Handbook, 1979, 2d rev. edit., 1992, Personal Adjustment and Growth: A Life-Span Approach, 1983, 2d rev. edit., 1990, A Guide to a Happier Family: Overcoming the Anger, Frustration and Boredom that Destroy Family Life, 1989; co-editor: Mental Health of Ethnic Minorities, 1991; co-author: Understanding and Helping Families: A Cognitive-Behavioral Approach, 1994; assoc. editor Family Relations, 1993—, Jour. of Personal and Interpersonal Loss, 1995—. Bd. dirs. Urban Alternatives, 1976-87, Columbus Fathers, 1977-89, New Communities, 1981—; edn. com. The Wellington Sch.; mem. profl. adv. bd. Peers Unlimited, 1993—; chmn. Gov.'s Com. on Child Support. Recipient award City of Columbus Dept. Devel., 1979, Ohio Dept. Mental Health, 1980-82. Fellow APA; mem. Cmty. Devel. Soc., Internat. Personal Rels. Network, Nat. Coun. for Therapy and Rehab. Through Horticulutre, Nat. Acad. Cert. Family Therapists (adv. bd. 1995—), N.Y. Acad. Scis., Sigma Xi. Office: Ohio State U Dept Psychology 1885 Neil Ave Mall Columbus OH 43210-1222

SCHWEBEL, MILTON, psychologist, educator; b. Troy, N.Y., May 11, 1914; s. Frank and Sarah (Oxenhandler) S.; m. Bernice Lois Davison, Sept. 3, 1939; children—Andrew I., Robert S. A.B., Union Coll., 1934; M.A., SUNY, Albany, 1936; Ph.D., Columbia U., 1949; certificate in psychotherapy, Postgrad. Center for Mental Health, 1958. Diplomate: Am. Bd. Examiners Profl. Psychology; licensed psychologist, N.Y., N.J. Asst. prof. psychology Mohawk Champlain Coll., 1946-49; asst. to prof. edn., dept. chmn., assoc. dean NYU, 1949-67; dean, prof. Grad. Sch. Edn., Rutgers U., New Brunswick, N.J., 1967-77; prof. Grad. Sch. Applied and Profl. Psychology, 1977-85, prof. emeritus 1985—; vis. prof. U. So. Calif., U. Hawaii; lectr. psychologist Postgrad Ctr. for Mental health; cons. NIMH, U.S., state, city depts. edn., ednl. ministries Europe, Asia, UNESCO, univs. and pub. schs.; pvt. cons. psychologist and psychotherapist, 1953—. Author: A Guide to a Happier Family, 1989, Personal Adjustment and Growth, 1990, Student Teachers Handbook, 2d edit., 1992, Interests of Pharmacists, Health Counseling, Who Can Be Educated?; editor: Mental Health Implications of Life in the Nuclear Age, 1986, Facilitating Cognitive Development, 1986, Promoting Cognitive Growth Over the Life Span, 1990, Behavioral Science and Human Survival, The Impact of Ideology on the I.Q. Controversy; editor Peace & Conflict: Journal of Peace Psychology, 1993—; co-editor Bull. Peace Psychology, 1991-94; mem. editorial bd. Am. Jour. Orthopsychiatry, Readings in Mental Health, Jour. Contemporary Psychotherapy, Jour. Counseling Psychology, Jour. Social Issues, others. Mem. sci. adv. bd. Internat. Ctr. for Enhancement of Learning Potential, 1988—; trustee Edin. Law Ctr., 1973-81, Nat. Com. Employment Youth, Nat. Child Labor Com., 1967-75, Union Exptl. Colls. and Univs., 1976-78; pres. Nat. Orgn. for Migrant Children, 1980-85; pres. Inst. of Arts and Humanities, 1984-95. Served with AUS, 1943-46, ETO. Postdoctoral fellow Postgrad. Center for Mental Health, 1954-56; Met. Applied Research Council fellow, 1970-71. Fellow APA, Am. Psychol. Soc., Am. Orthopsychiatry Assn.; Soc. Psychol. Study Social Issues, Jean Piaget Soc. (trustee), Am. Ednl. Rsch. Assn., N.Y. Acad. Scis., Psychologists for Social Responsibility (pres.), Inst. Arts and Humanities Edn. (pres.), Sigma Xi. Home: 1050 George St Apt 17L New Brunswick NJ 08901-1025 Office: Rutgers U Grad Sch Applied and Profl Psychology Piscataway NJ 08854

SCHWEBEL, STEPHEN MYRON, judge, arbitrator; b. N.Y.C., Mar. 10, 1929; s. Victor and Pauline (Pfeffer) S.; m. Louise Ingrid Nancy Killander, Aug. 2, 1972; children: Jennifer, Anna. BA in Govt. magna cum laude with highest honors in govt., Harvard U., 1950; postgrad., Cambridge (Eng.) U., 1950-51; LLB, Yale U., 1954; LLD, Bhopal (India) U., 1983. Bar: N.Y. 1955, U.S. Supreme Ct. 1965, D.C. 1976. Dir. UN hdqrs. office World Fedn. UN Assns., 1950-53; lectr. Am. fgn. policy various univs. U.S. State Dept., India, 1952; research, drafting asst. to Trygve Lie for writing of In the Cause of Peace, 1953; assoc. White & Case, N.Y.C., 1954-59; asst. prof. law Harvard U., Cambridge, Mass., 1959-61; asst. legal advisor U.S. Dept. State, Washington, 1961-66, dep. legal advisor, 1973-81; exec. dir. Am. Soc. Internat. Law, Washington, 1967-72; Burling prof. internat. law Sch. of Advanced Internat. Studies, Johns Hopkins U., Washington, 1967-81; judge Internat. Ct. Justice, The Hague, The Netherlands, 1981—; v.p. Internat. Ct. Justice, The Hague, 1994—; spl. rep. Micronesian claims U.S. Dept. State, 1966-71; legal adviser U.S. del. 16th-20th and 4th Spl. Gen. Assemblies UN; U.S. assoc. rep. Internat. Ct. Justice, 1962, U.S. dep. agt., 1979-80, U.S. counsel, 1980; U.S. rep., chmn. U.S. del. to 1st session UN Spl. Com on Principles Internat. Law concerning friendly relations and cooperation among states, Mexico City, 1964; U.S. rep. on adv. com. UN Program Assistance in Teaching, Study, Dissemination and Wider Appreciation Internat. Law, 1966-74; U.S. counsel Franco-Am. Air Arbitration, 1978; legal adv. U.S. del. to 32d and 33d WHO Assemblies, Geneva, 1979-80; vis. prof. internat. law Australian Nat. U., Canberra, 1969; U.S. rep., chmn. del. 3d session UN Spl. Com. on Question Defining Aggression, Geneva, 1970; counselor internat. law U.S. Dept. State, 1973; U.S. rep., chmn. del. 2d and 4th sessions UNCTAD Working Group on Charter Econ. Rights and Duties of States, Geneva, 1973, Mexico City, 1974; U.S. alt. rep. UN Econ. and Social Council, Geneva, 1974; legal adviser U.S. del. Conf. Internat. Econ. Coop., Paris, 1975; mem. U.S. Tripartite Adv. Com. on Internat. Labor Standards, 1980, Internat. Law Commn., UN, Geneva, 1977-81; spl. rapporteur internat. watercourses Internat. Law Commn., UN, 1977-81, chmn. drafting com., 1978; mem. bd. arbitration Brit. Petroleum v. Iran and Nat. Iranian Oil Co., Paris, 1982-85; pres. arbitration tribunal Marine Dr. Ltd. v. Ghana Investments Ctr. and Govt. of Ghana, 1988-90; chmn. or partyapptd. arbitrator internat. comml. arbitration tribunals, 1988—; mem. exec. com. Commn. Study Orgn. Peace, 1948-61; adv. joint com. law internat. transactions Am. Law Inst. and Am. Bar Assn., 1959-61; nat. chmn. Collegiate Council for UN, 1948-50; pres. Internat. Student Movement for UN, 1950-51; undergrad. orator Harvard U. Commencement, 1950; mem. adv. bd. Ctr. Oceans Law and Policy U. Va., 1975-81; vice chmn. Sec. State's Adv. Com. Pvt. Internat. Law, 1978-79, chmn., 1979-81; mem. internat. adv. bd. Cambridge U. Ctr. for Rsch. in internat. Law, 1983—, mem. bd. electors Whewell Professorship in Internat. Law U. Cambridge, 1983—; mem. overseers' com. to visit Harvard U. Law Sch., 1991—; cons. Ford. Found., 1990; chmn. supervisory bd. Telders Internat. Law Moot Court Competition, The Hague, Netherlands, 1993—, vis. lect. Cambridge U., 1957, Inst. Universitaire de Hautes Etudes Internationales, Geneva, 1980; Carnegie lectr. Hague Acad. Internat. Law, 1972; Brown lectr. Cath. U., 1983; Lauterpacht lectr., Cambridge U., 1983; jurisprudential lectr. U. Wash., 1985; Otto Walter Internat. Fellow, N.Y. Law Sch., 1987; Sherrill lectr. Yale U., 1988; Centennial Morris vis. prof. Chgo.-Kent Coll. of Law, 1988; Page Disting. vis. jurist U. Kans., 1988; Allison lectr. Suffolk Law Sch., 1989; Regents' lectr. U. Calif. Berkeley, 1990; Wing-Tat Lee lectr. Loyola U., 1990; Ford Found. lectr. U. N.Mex., U. Wash., U. Ind., Vanderbilt U., U. Minn., 1991, U. Ca.A., U. Houston, U. Miami, Emory U., Notre Dame U., 1992, U. Iowa, U. Pitts., 1993; Ben C. Green lectr. Case Western Res. U., 1992; Blaine Sloan lectr. Pace U., 1993; Hauser lectr. NYU Law Sch., 1994; Goff lectr., Hong Kong Polytechnic Law Faculty, 1994; pres. Adminstrv. Tribunal Internat. Monetary Fund, 1994—. Author: The Secretary-General of the United Nations, 1952, International Arbitration: Three Salient Problems, 1987, Justice in International Law, 1994; editor: The Effectiveness of International Decisions, 1971; mem. editorial bd. Am. Jour. Internat. Law,

1967-81; chmn. editorial adv. com. Internat. Legal Materials, 1967-73. Frank Knox fellow Harvard U., 1950-51; recipient Gherini prize Yale Law Sch., 1954, Pres. medal Johns Hopkins U., 1992, Harold Weill medal NYU, 1992. Mem. ABA, Am. Soc. Internat. Law (exec. v.p. 1967-73, hon. v.p. 1982—), Internat. Law Assn., Inst. Droit Internat., Coun. Fgn. Rels., Harvard Club (N.Y.C.), Athenaeum (London), Haagsche Club (The Hague), Cosmos Club (Wash.), Phi Beta Kappa. Avocations: music, cycling.

SCHWEBER, SILVAN SAMUEL, physics and history educator; b. Strasbourg, France, Apr. 10, 1928; came to U.S., 1942, naturalized, 1951; s. David and Dora (Edelman) S.; m. Myrna Tapper, June 21, 1951 (div. Feb. 1965); m. Miriam Fields, June 14, 1965; children: Libby Ann, Abigail, Simone Aviva, Howard. B.S., CCNY, 1947; M.S., U. Pa., 1949; Ph.D., Princeton U., 1952. Instr. Princeton U., 1951-52; mem. Inst. Advanced Study, Princeton, N.J., 1955; faculty Brandeis U., Waltham, Mass., 1955—; prof. physics Brandeis U., 1961—, Koret prof. history of ideas, 1982—, dir. Dibner Inst. in History of Sci. and Tech., 1987-89, chmn. physics dept., 1958-61, 64-65, 74-76, chmn. Sch. Sci., 1963-64, 79-80, chmn. history of ideas, 1982-88; vis. prof. MIT, 1961-62, 69-70, Hebrew U., Jerusalem, 1971-72, 80-82, Harvard U., spring semester 1986, 87, 91, fall 1991; vis. fellow Harvard U., 1976-78, 83-84, assoc. history of sci., 1986—. Author: Quantum Field Theory, 2d edit., 1961, QED and the Men Who Made It, 1994. Proctor fellow Princeton U., 1952, NSF postdoctoral fellow Cornell U., 1952-54, sr. postdoctoral fellow Carnegie Inst. Tech., 1955. Fellow AAAS, Am. Acad. Arts and Scis.; mem. Am. Phys. Soc., History of Sci. Soc., Phi Beta Kappa, Sigma Xi. Home: 22 Turning Mill Rd Lexington MA 02173-1318 Office: Brandeis U Dept Physics Waltham MA 02254

SCHWED, PETER, author, retired editor and publisher; b. N.Y.C., Jan. 18, 1911; s. Frederick and Bertie (Stiefel) S.; m. Antonia Sanxay Holding, Mar. 6, 1947; children: Katharine Holding (Mrs. Eric F. Wood), Peter Gregory, Laura Sanxay (Mrs. Michael Sirico), Roger Eaton. Grad., Lawrenceville (N.J.) Sch., 1928; student, Princeton, 1929-32. Asst. v.p. Provident Loan Soc. N.Y., 1932-42; with Simon & Schuster, Inc., N.Y.C., 1946-84; v.p., exec. editor Simon & Schuster, Inc., 1957-62, exec. v.p., 1962-66, pub. trade books, 1966-72, chmn. editorial bd., 1972-82, editorial chmn. emeritus, 1982-84, dir., 1966-72. Author: Sinister Tennis, 1975, God Bless Pawnbrokers, 1975, The Serve and the Overhead Smash, 1976, Hanging In There, 1977, (with Nancy Lopez) The Education of a Woman Golfer, 1979, Test Your Tennis IQ, 1981, Turning the Pages, 1984, Overtime: A 20th Century Sports Odyssey, 1987, How to Talk Tennis, 1988, Quality Tennis After 50...Or 60...Or 70...Or..., 1990, The Common Cold Crusade: A Novel Not to be Sneezed At, 1994; compiler: The Cook Charts, 1949; editor: (with H.W. Wind) Great Stories From the World of Sports, 1958, (with Allison Danzig) The Fireside Book of Tennis, 1972; contbr. articles to jours. Trustee Lawrenceville Sch., 1968-72. Capt. F.A. AUS, World War II. Decorated Bronze Star, Purple Heart. Mem. Authors Guild, P.E.N., Century Assn. Democrat. Home: 151 W 86th St New York NY 10024-3401 *I suppose my guiding principle has been to face up to problems and difficult situations as immediately as I can, even if taking more time to think about them might have resulted in better ideas and actions. But an honest, un-Machiavellian handling of matters, without putting them off while brooding about them, has always struck me as effective when I do it, and appealing when others do. I try to carry this principle through with everyone, from my wife and children, through my office associates, to community affairs. It gives me a reputation ranging from bluntness to rudeness with those whose favorite I may not be, but I would hope one of respect and admiration with those about whom I care.*

SCHWEGLER, ROBERT ANDREW, English language educator; b. Buffalo, N.Y., Oct. 7, 1946; s. Emil A. and Nelo M. S.; m. Nancy Ann Newman, Apr. 6, 1968; children: Brian, Christopher. BA, Hope Coll., 1968; MA, U. Chgo., 1970, PhD, 1978. Instr. U. Cin., 1972-75; asst. prof. Syracuse (N.Y.) U., 1975-78; asst. prof. U. R.I., Kingston, 1978-83, assoc. prof., 1983-91, prof., 1991—; exec. bd. Coun. of Writing Program Adminstrs.; trustee Richard Beal Hist. Collection of Materials in Rhetoric and Composition Studies, Dimond Libr., U. N.H.; presenter confs. in field. Author: Patterns in Action, 1985, 3d edit., 1993, The Little, Brown Handbook: Instructor's Annotated Edit., 1989, Patterns of Exposition 14, 1995, HarperCollins Handbook, 1995, others; contbr. articles to profl. jours. Mem. New Eng. Assn. of Tchrs. of English (bd. dirs. 1984), Nat. Coun. Tchrs. of English, Modern Lang. Assn., Coun. of Writing Program Adminstrs., Conf. on Coll. Composition and Comm. Presbyterian. Avocations: fishing, tennis, gardening. Home: 36 Dunes Rd Narragansett RI 02880 Office: English/Coll Writing Prog Independence Hall Univ Ri Kingston RI 02881

SCHWEGMANN, JOHN F., consumer products company executive. Ceo, gen. manager, partner Schwegmann Giant Super Markets, New Orleans, La., 1967—. Office: Schwegmann Giant Super Markets 5300 Gentilly Rd New Orleans LA 70126

SCHWEGMANN, MELINDA, state official; b. Austin, Tex., Oct. 25, 1946; m. John F. Schwegmann; 3 children. Student, La. State U.; grad. in Edn., U. New Orleans, 1968. Former pub. sch. tchr.; past pres. La. Soc. for Prevention of Cruelty to Animals; lt. gov. La., 1991—. Mem. bd. Schwegmann Giant Super Markets; chmn. bd. Goodwill Industries; bd. dirs. Met. Area Com. New Orleans; sec. bd. dir.s Jr. Achievement; former mem. Jefferson Beautification Com. Office: Office of Lt Gov PO Box 44243 Baton Rouge LA 70804*

SCHWEICKART, JIM, advertising executive, broadcast consultant; b. Toledo, June 25, 1950; s. Norman Marvin and Anne Belle (Cress) S.; m. Deborah J., Aug. 14, 1971; children: Jennifer, Kimberly, Stephen. BA in Polit. Sci, Taylor U., Upland, Ind., 1972. News anchor, announcer Sta. WCMR, Elkhart, Ind., 1967-71; news anchor, disc jockey Sta. WWHC, Hartford City, Ind., 1971-72; gen. mgr. Sta. WTUC, Taylor U., 1971; news dir. Sta. WCMR, Elkhart, 1972-74; news anchor Sta. WOWO, Fort Wayne, Ind., 1974-78, Sta. KDKA, Pitts., 1978-79; gen. mgr. Sta. WBCL-FM, Fort Wayne, 1979-85; owner advt. agy., broadcast cons. Fort Wayne, 1984—. Bd. dirs. Christians for Polit. Alternatives; elder bd. Blackhawk Bapt. Ch. Republican. Baptist.

SCHWEICKART, RUSSELL LOUIS, communications executive, astronaut; b. Neptune, N.J., Oct. 25, 1935; s. George L. Schweickart; children: Vicki Louise, Russell and Randolph (twins), Elin Ashley, Diana Croom; m. Nancy Kudriavetz Ramsey; step-children: Matthew Forbes Ramsey, David Scot Ramsey. B.S. in Aero. Engring, Mass. Inst. Tech., 1956, M.S. in Aeros. and Astronautics, 1963. Former research scientist Mass. Inst. Tech. Exptl. Astronomy Lab.; astronaut Johnson Manned Spacecraft Center, Houston, lunar module pilot (Apollo 9, 1969); dir. user affairs Office of Applications, NASA; sci. adv. to Gov. Edmund G. Brown, Jr. State of Calif., 1977-79; chmn. Calif. Energy Commn., 1979-83, commr., 1979-85; pres., founder Assn. Space Explorers, 1985—; pres. NRS Communications, San Francisco, 1991-94; exec. v.p. CTA Comml. Systems, Rockville, Md., 1994—; cons. and lectr. in field. Trustee Calif. Acad. Sci. Served as pilot USAF, 1956-60, 61; Capt. Mass. Air N.G. Recipient Distinguished Service medal NASA, 1970, Exceptional Service medal NASA, 1974, De La Vaulx medal FAI, 1970, Spl. Trustees award Nat. Acad. TV Arts and Scis., 1969. Fellow Am. Astronautical Soc.; mem. Soc. Exptl. Test Pilots, AIAA, Sigma Xi. Club: Explorers. Office: CTA Comml Systems 6116 Executive Blvd # 800 Rockville MD 20852

SCHWEIG, MARGARET BERRIS, meeting and special events consultant; b. Detroit, Mar. 23, 1928; d. Jacob Meyer and Anne Lucille (Schiller) Berris; m. Eugene Schweig Jr., Nov. 24, 1951 (dec.); children: Eugene III, John A., Suzanne. Student, U. Mich., 1945-47. Founder, pres. St. Louis Scene, Inc., 1975-94. Mem. St. Louis Conv. and Visitors Commn., St. Louis Forum. Mem. Meeting Planners Internat., Am. Soc. Assn. Execs., Profl. Conv. Mgmt. Assn., Nat. Assn. Exposition Mgrs., Internat. Spl. Events Soc., Hotel Sales Mgmt. Assn. (bd. dirs. 1977-80), Regional Commerce and Growth Assn., The Network (pres. 1980-81).

SCHWEIKER, MARK S., lieutenant governor; b. Bucks County, Pa., 1953; s. John and Mary S.; m. Katherine Schweiker; children: Brett, Eric, Kara. BS, Bloomsburg U., 1975; MA in Adminstrn., Rider U., 1983. Merrill Lynch, McGraw Hill; Supr. Middletown Twp., 1979; commr. Bucks

County, Pa., 1987-94; lt. gov., pres. of the senate, chmn. of the bd. of pardons State of Pa., 1995—; former chmn. Dela. Valley Regional Fin. Authority. Former bd. dirs. Bucks County United Way. Recipient Alumnus of Yr. Bloomsburg U., 1990, Outstanding Svc. to Conservation award Nature Conservancy Pa. Branch. Office: 200 Main Capitol Harrisburg PA 17120-0002*

SCHWEIKER, RICHARD SCHULTZ, trade association executive, former senator, former cabinet secretary; b. Norristown, Pa., June 1, 1926; s. Malcolm Alderfer and Blanche (Schultz) S.; m. Claire Joan Coleman, Sept. 10, 1955; children: Malcolm C., Lani, Kyle, Richard S. Jr., Lara Kristi. BA, Pa. State U., 1950; D of Pub. Svcs. (hon.), Temple U., 1970; D.Sc. (hon.), Georgetown U., 1981. Bus. exec., 1950-60; mem. 87th-90th congresses from 13th Dist. Pa., mem. house armed services and govt. ops. coms.; U.S. senator from Pa., 1969-80; mem. appropriations com., ranking mem. Labor-HEW subcom., ranking mem. health and human resources com., ranking mem. health subcom.; sec. HHS, 1981-83; pres. Am. Council Life Ins., Washington, 1983-94; bd. dirs. Tenet Healthcare Corp., LabOne Inc., Univax Biologics Inc.; chmn. Partnership for Prevention, 1991—. Alt. del. Nat. Rep. Conv., 1952, 56, del., 1972, 80; designated v.p. candidate with Reagan for Pres. of U.S., 1976. Served with USNR, World War II. Recipient Disting. Alumnus award Pa. State U., 1970, Dr. Charles H. Best award Am. Diabetes Assn., 1974, Outstanding Alumnus of Yr. award Phi Kappa Sigma, 1982, Gold medal Pa. Assn. Broadcasters, 1982, Nat. Outstanding Svc. award Headstart, 1983, Pub. Svc. Gold medal Surgeon Gen. U.S., 1988, Govt. Achievement award Juvenile Diabetes Found., 1990, Disting. Achievement award Nat. Coun. on Aging, 1991, John Newton Russell award Nat. Assn. Life Underwriters, 1992; named Outstanding Young Man of Yr., Jr. C. of C., 1960. Mem. Phi Beta Kappa. Address: 904 Lynton Pl McLean VA 22102-2113

SCHWEIKERT, NORMAN CARL, musician; b. Los Angeles, Oct. 8, 1937; s. Carl Albert and Hilda (Meade) S.; m. Sally Hardin Haizlip, July 22, 1961; 1 son, Eric Carl. Mus.B. performer's certificate in horn, Eastman Sch. Music, 1961. teaching assoc. Northwestern U., 1973-75, assoc. prof. (part-time), 1975—; horn instr. Nat. Music Camp, Interlochen, 1967; curator Leland B. Greenleaf Collection Mus. Instruments, Interlochen, 1970-71. Successively 4th, 2d and 3d horn with, Rochester Philharmonic, Civic and Eastman-Rochester symphonies, 1955-62, 64-66, instr. horn, mem., Interlochen (Mich.) Arts Quintet, Interlochen Arts Acad., 1966-71, 1st horn, Rochester Chamber Orch., 1965-66, Midland (Mich.) Symphony Orch., 1969-71, 1st horn, soloist, Northwestern Mich. Symphony Orch., 1966-71, Chgo. Little Symphony, tours, 1967, 68, asst. 1st horn, soloist, Chgo. Symphony Orch., 1971-75, 2d horn, Chgo. Symphony Orch., 1975—; appearances with, Eastman Chamber Orch., Rochester Bach Festival, Aspen Festival Orch., Moravian Music Festival, Alaska Festival, Peninsula Music Festival, Rochester Brass Quintet, Canterbury Wind Quintet, Westchester Brass Quintet, Eastman Wind Ensemble, Chgo. Symphony Winds, Quadrangle Chamber Players; soloist, New Japan Philharmonic, rec. artist for, Mercury, Columbia, Everest, C.R.I., Capitol. Mark Ednl., London-Decca, DGG, RCA Victor records, Sheffield Lab, Koch; recitals, also lecture demonstrations.; Contbr. articles to profl. jours. Served with AUS, 1962-64. Recipient certificate of merit City Chgo., 1971. Mem. Internat. Horn Soc. (chmn. organizing com., sec.-treas. 1970-72, adv. coun. 1972-76), Am. Mus. Instrument Soc., Phi Mu Alpha Sinfonia (life alumni mem.), Pi Kappa Lambda. Home: 1491 Edgewood Rd Lake Forest IL 60045-1314 Office: care Chgo Symphony Orch 220 S Michigan Ave Chicago IL 60604-2508

SCHWEINHART, RICHARD ALEXANDER, health care company executive; b. Louisville, Sept. 19, 1949; s. John Lawrence and A. Alicia (Kotheimer) S.; m. Margaret Loraine Hobbs, July 17, 1971; children: John Edward, Jennifer Lynn. AB in Acctg., Bellarmine Coll., 1971. CPA, Ky. Staff Coopers & Lybrand, Louisville, 1971-75; asst. contr. Humana Inc., Louisville, 1975-82, dir. acctg., 1982-83, contr., 1983-85, v.p., contr., 1985-88, v.p. fin., 1988-91, sr. v.p. fin., 1991-93; sr. v.p. fin. Galen Health Care, Inc., Louisville, 1993, Columbia/HCA Healthcare Corp., Louisville, 1993-95; sr. v.p. nonhosp. ops. Columbia/HCA Healthcare Corp., Nashville, 1995—. Bd. dirs. Goodwill Industries Ky., 1988-94, treas., 1989-90, vice chmn., 1991-92, chmn., 1992-93; mem. Leadership Louisville, 1987-88. Mem. AICPA, Ky. Soc. CPAs. Democrat. Roman Catholic. Avocations: golf, genealogy. Office: Columbia/HCA Healthcare 1 Park Plaza Nashville TN 37203-0550

SCHWEITZER, CONRAD, timber company executive; b. 1928. BS, U. So. Calif., 1954. With Ga.-Pacific Corp., Atlanta, 1961—, various mgmt. positions, v.p. ops., 1961-82, sr. v.p., 1982-83, group sr. v.p., 1983-85, exec. v.p., 1985—; exec. v.p. Brunswick Pulp & Paper Co. Served with USMC, 1946-48, 50-52. Office: Ga-Pacific Corp 133 Peachtree St NE Atlanta GA 30303-1801

SCHWEITZER, GEORGE KEENE, chemistry educator; b. Poplar Bluff, Mo., Dec. 5, 1924; s. Francis John and Ruth Elizabeth (Keene) S.; m. Verna Lee Pratt, June 4, 1948; children: Ruth Anne, Deborah Keene, Eric George. BA, Central Coll., 1945, ScD in History, 1964; MS, U. Ill., 1946, PhD in Chemistry, 1948; MA, Columbia U., 1959; PhD in Philosophy, NYU, 1964. Asst. Central Coll., 1943-45; fellow U. Ill., 1946-48; asst. prof. chemistry U. Tenn., 1948-52, assoc. prof., 1952-58, prof., 1960-69, Alumni Distinguished prof., 1970—; cons. to Monsanto Co., Proctor & Gamble, Internat. Tech., Am. Cyanamid Co., AEC, U.S. Army, Massengill; lectr. colls. and univs. Adv. bd. Va. Intermont Coll. Author: Radioactive Tracer Techniques, 1950, The Doctorate, 1966, Genealogical Source Handbook, 1979, Civil War Genealogy, 1980, Tennessee Genealogical Research, 1981, Kentucky Genealogical Research, 1981, Revolutionary War Genealogy, 1982, Virginia Genealogical Research, 1982, War of 1812 Genealogy, 1983, North Carolina Genealogical Research, 1983, South Carolina Genealogical Research, 1984, Pennsylvania Genealogical Research, 1985, Georgia Genealogical Research, 1987, New York Genealogical Research, 1988, Massachusetts Genealogical Research, 1989, Maryland Genealogical Research, 1991, German Genealogical Research, 1992, Ohio Genealogical Research, 1994; also 155 articles. Faculty fellow Columbia U., 1958-60. Mem. Am. Chem. Soc., Am. Philos. Assn., History Sci. Soc., Soc. Genealogists, Phi Beta Kappa, Sigma Xi. Home: 407 Ascot Ct Knoxville TN 37923-5807

SCHWEITZER, JON ANTON, broadcasting executive; b. Milw., Oct. 30, 1957; s. James and Lorraine (Beckman0 S.; m. Leslie B. Block, June 12, 1982; children: Thomas, James. BS, U. Wis., LaCrosse, 1979. Account exec. WMKE/WBCS Radio, Milw., 1982-83, WLPX Radio, Hearst Corp., Milw., 1983-84; account exec. WKIT-FM, WTMJ, Inc., Milw., 1984-86, gen. sales mgr., 1986-89; gen. mgr. KQRC-FM, WTMJ Inc., Kansas City, Mo., 1989—. Mem. Kansas City Radio Broadcasters Assn. (sec. 1992—), Kansas City Media Profls. (Radio Mgr. of Yr. 1991), Kansas City Ad Club. Office: KQRC-FM 4350 Shawnee Mission Pky Shawnee Mission KS 66205-2541

SCHWEITZER, MELVIN L., commissioner, lawyer; b. N.Y.C., Oct. 27, 1944. BA, NYU, 1966; JD, Fordham U., 1969. Bar: N.Y. 1969. Atty. Rogers & Wells, N.Y.C.; commr. The Port Authority of N.Y. and N.J., N.Y.C., 1993—; active Gov. Commn. on N.Y. Fin. Svcs. Industry, 1989. Mem. transition panel N.Y.C. Comptroller's Office, 1973, chair budget subcom., 1989; mem. adv. com. N.Y. State Bd. Elections, 1975-85; counsel, law chmn. N.Y. State Dem. Com., 1974-85. Mem. Assn. Bar City N.Y., Phi Sigma Alpha. Office: Rogers & Wells 200 Park Ave New York NY 10166-0153

SCHWEITZER, N. TINA, photojournalist, television producer, director, writer, international consultant public relations, media relations, government relations; b. Hartford, Conn., Apr. 7, 1941; d. Abraham Aaron Morris and Ruth Blanche (Shifreen) S. BS, Emerson Coll., 1954. Freelance writer Boston and Washington, 1965-67; editor, chief prodn. maj. feature publ., mem. press-info. staff Embassy of Republic of Indonesia, Washington, 1967-68; researcher, writer Congl. Quar., Inc., Washington, 1969-70; owner Schweitzer Assocs., Hartford, Conn. and Washington, 1970-78, 79—; dir. cmty. and govtl. rels. Advocacy Svcs. for the Deaf, West Hartford, Conn., 1978-79; del. White House Coun. Small Bus., 1986; mem. faculty Conn. Re-employment Workshop Middlesex Cmty. Tech. Coll.; profl. model. Corr. The Farmington (Conn.) Valley Herald, 1984; first bus. columnist Hartford

Woman newspaper, 1984; contbr. articles to numerous govtl. and comml. publs.; author: Media Kit, 1978, Women's Job Hunting Guide, 1983, You Can Do It! A Practical Guide for Job Hunting and Career-Changing, 1987, Men On the Tor (Violet Hunter), 1990; writer, designer, producer series of TV videotape pub. svc. announcements on employment deaf or hard-of-hearing, 1983-84; contbr. editorials to TV Stas. WFSB, 1977, 84, 86, WVIT, 1983; writer, ind. producer, dir., talk-show host Sta. WVIT-TV, 1987. Mem. State-wide Health Coordinating Coun., a U.S. Govt./Conn. Health Dept. project, 1978-80; adviser Conn. Office Advocacy to Handicapped; mem. legis. task force State of Conn., 1978-80, 1978-79; del. first Conn. Gov.'s Conf. on Libr. and Info. Svcs., 1978; candidate Conn. Ho. of Reps., 1982; aux. police officer Hartford Police Dept., 1976-77; acting chmn. Comm. Com. Unitarian Meeting House, West Hartford; dir. pub. rels. Greater Hartford Com. UNICEF, 1984-86; affiliated Rep. Town Com., Hartford, 1989; apptd. to Nat. Pub. Rels./Advt. Adv. Coun. Am. Mensa Ltd., 1989; press rep. Mensa Internat. 1st Joint Conf. Am. Coun. Edn. and Conf. European Rectors, 1989. Recipient Presdl. Sports award Pres.'s Coun. on Phys. Fitness and Sports, 1992, 93, 94; fellow John F. Kennedy Presdl. Libr. Mus. Found. Mem. Writers Guild Am., Nat. Writers Union, Nat. Press Photographers Assn., Inter-Am. Press Assn., Mensa, Sherlock Holmes Soc. London, Sigma Delta Chi. Office: Schweitzer Assocs Ste 9P 30 Woodland St Hartford CT 06105

SCHWEITZER, PETER, advertising agency executive; b. Chgo., Aug. 31, 1939; children: Mark, Cynthia, Jenifer, Samantha; m. Elaine Elkin, 1986; children: Dana, Taylor. B.A., U. of Mich., 1961; MBA, W. Mich. U., 1967. With Post div. Gen. Foods, 1961-69; v.p. Grey Advt., 1969-76; sr. v.p. J. Walter Thompson, 1976-79; sr. v.p. mktg. Burger King Corp.; sr. v.p., gen. mgr., then exec. v.p., gen. mgr. J. Walter Thompson USA, Inc.-Detroit; v. chmn. of agency ops. J. Walter Thompson Co., Detroit, 1988—. Office: J Walter Thompson Co 600 Renaissance Ctr Detroit MI 48243-1705 also: J Walter Thompson Co 466 Lexington Ave New York NY 10017

SCHWEITZER, WILLIAM H., lawyer; b. Cleve., June 6, 1944. BA, Trinity Coll., 1966; JD, Georgetown U., 1969. Bar: D.C. 1970. Asst. U.S. atty. U.S. Attys. Office, Washington, 1970-73; mng. ptnr. Baker & Hostetler, Washington. Mem. ABA, D.C. Bar. Office: Baker & Hostetler Washington Sq 1050 Connecticut Ave NW Ste 11 Washington DC 20036-5303

SCHWEIZER, KARL WOLFGANG, historian, writer; b. Mannheim, Fed. Republic Germany, June 30, 1946; came to U.S., 1988; s. Ernest Schweizer; m. Elizabeth Wild, 1969; 1 child, Paul. BA in History, Wilfrid Laurier U., Can., 1969; MA, U. Waterloo, Can., 1970; PhD, Cambridge U., 1976. Prof. history Bishop's U., Lenoxville, Que., Can., 1976-88; chmn. dept. Bishop's U., Can., 1978-79, 82-84, 86; prof., chmn. humanities dept. N.J. Inst. Tech., Newark, 1988-93, prof. history dept. social sci. and policy studies, 1993—; visl. lectr. U. Guelph, Can., 1978-80; rsch. scholar Russian Rsch. Ctr., Ill. 1979-80; acad. visitor London Sch. Econs., 1986, 94, vis. scholar, 1986-87; vis. scholar Queen's U., Ont., Can., 1986-87; Cambridge (Eng.) U., 1994; vis. fellow Darwin Coll., Cambridge, 1987, 94, Princeton U., 1994, Yale U., 1994. Author: Francois de Callieres: The Art of Diplomacy, 1983, Lord Bute: Essays in Reinterpretation, 1988, England, Prussia and the Seven Years War, 1989, Frederick the Great, William Pitt and Lord Bute, 1991; (with J. Osborne) Cobbett in His Times, 1990, Lord Chatham, 1993, Francois de Callieres: Diplomat of the Sun King, 1995; editor: The Devonshire Political Diary, 1757-1762, 1982, Diplomatic Thought 1648-1815, 1982, Warfare and Tactics in The 18th Century, 1984; co-editor: (with J. Black) Essays in European History 1648-1815 in Honour of Ragnhild Hatton, 1985, Politics and the Press in Hanoverian Britain, 1989; contbr. numerous articles to profl. jours. and mags. Mem. N.J. Gov.'s Adv. Panel on Higher Edn. Restructuring, 1994. Recipient thesis defence award Can. Coun., 1976, travel awards Peterhouse Coll., 1971-73, Adelle Mellen prize for outstanding contbn. to scholarship Edwin Mellen Press, 1989, Citation award N.J. Writer's Conf., 1993; fellow U. Waterloo, 1969-70, Province of Ont., 1969-70, Can. Coun., 1970-75; named Wilfred Laurier Proficiency scholar, 1966-69; rsch. grantee Bishop's U., 1977, 78, 80, 82, 83, postdoctoral rsch. grantee Can. Coun., 1977-78, 82-83, grantee Inter-Univ. Ctr. for European Studies, 1978, 81, conf. grantee S.S.H.R.C., 1985; travel grantee NEH, 1991, N.J. Com. for Humanities. Fellow Royal Hist. Soc.; mem. Internat. Commn. on History of Internat. Rels., Cambridge Hist. Soc., North American Conf. on Brit. Studies, Can. Assn. Scottish Studies, Can. Assn. 18th Century Studies, Inst. Hist. Rsch. Avocations: travel, writing, reading. Home: 37 Lenape Trl Chatham NJ 07928-1812 Office: Dept Social Scis and Policy Studies NJ Inst Tech Newark NJ 07102

SCHWEIZER, KENNETH STEVEN, physics educator; b. Phila., Jan. 20, 1953; s. Kenneth Paul and Grace Norma (Fischer) S.; m. Janis Eve Pelletier, Oct. 18, 1986; children: Gregory Michael, Daniel Patrick. BS, Drexel U., 1975; MS, U. Ill., 1976, PhD, 1981. Postdoctoral rsch. assoc. AT&T Bell Labs., Murray Hill, N.J., 1981-83; sr. mem. tech. staff Sandia Nat. Labs., Albuquerque, 1983-91, cons., 1991—; prof. materials sci. engring. and chemistry U. Ill., Urbana, 1991—; chmn. polymers divsn., 1994—. Contbr. articles to profl. jours. Recipient Sandia award for Excellence, 1990, R&D 100 award, 1992. Mem. Am. Phys. Soc. (John H. Dillon medal 1991), Am. Chem. Soc., Sigma Xi, Pi Mu Epsilon. Office: U Ill Dept Materials Sci Engring 1304 W Green St Urbana IL 61801-2920

SCHWEIZER, MELVIN, food products executive. Farmer; dir. Prairie Farms Dairy, Inc. Office: Prairie Farms Dairy Inc 1100 Broadway St Carlinville IL 62626-1183*

SCHWEIZER, PAUL DOUGLAS, museum director; b. Bklyn., Nov. 26, 1946; s. Alvin Charles and Marie Gertrude (Scholtz) S.; m. Jane Kulczycki, June 10, 1978. BA, Marietta Coll., Ohio, 1968; MA, U. Del., 1975, PhD, 1979; postgrad. Mus. Mgmt. Inst., U. Calif., Berkeley, 1990. Instr. art history St Lawrence U., Canton, N.Y., 1977-78; asst. prof. St. Lawrence U., Canton, N.Y., 1978-80; curator St. Lawrence U. (Brush Gallery), Canton, N.Y., 1977-78; dir. St. Lawrence U., Canton, N.Y., 1979-80, Munson-Williams-Proctor Inst. Mus. Art, Utica, N.Y., 1980—. Author exhbn. catalog; contbr. articles to profl. jours. Bd. dirs. Remington Art Mus., Ogdensburg, N.Y., 1979-80, Williamstown (Mass.) Regional Art Conservation Lab., 1981-92, pres., 1988-92. Trustee N.Y. State Assn. Art Museums, 1993—. Rsch. grantee Nat. Endowment for Arts, 1978. Mem. Coll. Art Assn., Assn. Art Mus. Dirs., Otsego Sailing Club (Cooperstown, N.Y.), Alpha Sigma Phi, Omicron Delta Kappa. Office: Munson-Williams-Proctor Inst Mus Art 310 Genesee St Utica NY 13502-4764

SCHWEMM, JOHN BUTLER, printing company executive, lawyer; b. Barrington, Ill., May 18, 1934; s. Earl M. and Eunice (Butler) S.; m. Nancy Lea Prickett, Sept. 7, 1956; children: Catherine Ann, Karen Elizabeth. AB, Amherst Coll., 1956; JD, U. Mich., 1959. Bar: Ill. 1959. With Sidley & Austin, Chgo., 1959-65; with legal dept. R.R. Donnelley & Sons Co., Chgo., 1965-69; gen. counsel R.R. Donnelley & Sons Co., 1969-75, v.p., 1971-75, pres., 1981-87, chmn., 1983-89, dir., 1980-92; bd. dirs. William Blair Mut. Funds, Inc., Walgreen Co., USG Corp. Bd. dirs. Northwestern U., Chgo. Mem. Law Club Chgo., Order of Coif, Phi Beta Kappa. Clubs: Chgo., Univ., Mid-Am., Comml., Hinsdale (Ill.) Golf, Old Elm. Home: 2 Turvey Ct Downers Grove IL 60515-4530 Office: RR Donnelley & Sons Co 750 Warrenville Rd Lisle IL 60532-4345

SCHWENDEMAN, PAUL WILLIAM, lawyer; b. Chgo., Apr. 7, 1945; s. Oscar and Edna Dorothy (Ellis) S.; m. Shirley Anne Starke; children: Paul A., John E., Thomas D. BA in Econs., Carleton Coll.; MSJ, Northwestern U.; JD, Duquesne U. Bar: Pa. 1978. Mgr. divsn. ops. Greater Waterbury (Conn.) C. of C., 1971-75; v.p. Greater Pitts. C. of C., 1975-78; assoc. Kirkpatrick & Lockhart, Pitts., 1978-84, ptnr., 1984—. Lt. USNR, 1971. Office: Kirkpatrick & Lockhart 1500 Oliver Building Bldg Pittsburgh PA 15222-2312

SCHWENDIMAN, GARY, business administration educator; b. Colfax, Wash., Aug. 1, 1940; s. John L. and Naomi (Garner) S.; m. Jill Bateman, June 3, 1966; children: Todd, Heidi, Lisa, Wendy, Julie. B.S. with honors, Wash. State U., 1962; M.S., Brigham Young U., 1968, Ph.D., 1971. Prof. Marshall U., W. Va., 1969-72, Gen. Motors Inst., Flint, Mich., 1972-73; prof., assoc. dean Coll. Bus. Adminstrn. U. Nebr., Lincoln, 1973-77, dean, prof. Coll. Bus. Adminstrn., 1977—; bd. dirs. InaCom, Inc., Nebr. Human

Resources Inst., Midwest Conf. on Bus.; bd. dirs. Gallup, Inc.; ind. adv. com. Savings Assn. Ins. Fund House and Senate Com. on Banking, Housing, and Urban Affairs; chmn. Schwendiman Funds; gen. ptnr. World Mkts. Fund L.P., Cash Alternative Fund L.P., Equity Fund L.P., Banc Fund L.P., Internat. Fund L.P., Global High Performance Fund L.P.; trustee N.R., Inc., Employees Pension Trust. Editor: (with S. M. Lee) Japanese Management, 1982, Management by Japanese Systems, 1982. Bd. dirs. St. Elizabeth Community Health Ctr., Lincoln, Nebr., 1976-78, United Way Lincoln, 1978-80, area council Boy Scouts Am., Lincoln, 1976-80, Gupta Charitable Found.; trustee Jr. Achievement. Mem. Am. Assembly of Collegiate Schs. Bus. (investment com.), Lincoln C. of C. and Industry (edn. com.), Nebr. Coun. Econ. Edn. (exec. com.), Newcomen Soc., Round Table, Polemic Club, Beta Gamma Sigma (bd. govs., chair Investment and Fin. Com.). Office: Univ Nebraska Lincoln Dept Mgmt 256 CBA Lincoln NE 68588-0491*

SCHWENDINGER, CHARLES JOSEPH, public administration educator, researcher; b. Dubuque, Iowa, July 2, 1931; s. Leo James and Loretta Lucille (Meyers) S.; m. Marion Jean Blain, June 11, 1957 (div. 1981); 1 child, Julieanne Schwendinger Wattles; m. Chieko Ikeda, Oct. 13, 1982. BA in History, Va. Mil. Inst., 1957; MPA, U. Okla., 1980, D Pub. Adminstrn., 1991. Commd. 2d lt. U.S. Army, 1957, advanced through grades to lt. col., 1971, served in various locations including Vietnam, 1957-78, ret., 1978; asst. prof. pub. adminstrn. Troy (Ala.) State U., 1986-88, asst. prof., 1989, 91—; lectr. in field. Contbr. to profl. publs. Sgt. U.S. Army, 1949-53. Decorated Bronze Star medal with 2 oak leaf clusters, Air medal. Fellow Pi Alpha Alpha (chpt. pres. 1980-86, 89-90), Pi Sigma Alpha; mem. DAV, VFW, NRA, Am. Soc. Pub. Adminstrn. (coun. mem. Okla. chpt. 1989-90), Internat. City Mgmt. Assn., Am. Legion, Ret. Officers Assn. Roman Catholic. Home: PO Box 6378 Tampa FL 33608-0378 Office: Troy State U Fla Region PO Box 6472 Mac Dill A F B FL 33608

SCHWENGER, FRANCES, library director; b. Hamilton, Ont., Can., Oct. 20, 1936. BA in Psychology and English, U. Western Ont., 1970; MLS, U. Toronto, 1972. Head cataloguing health scis. libr. McMaster U., 1972-74; with Hamilton Pub. Libr., 1974-80, head ctrl. libr., 1980-82; asst. dir. Met. Toronto Ref. Libr., 1982-86, CEO, 1986—. Mem. ALA, Can. Libr. Assn., Ont. Libr. Assn., Internat. Assn. Met. City Librs., Internat. Fedn. Libr. Assns. and Instns. (mem. standing com. pub. librs. 1993—). Office: Met Toronto Libr Bd, Reference Libr 789 Yonge St, Toronto, ON Canada M4W 2G8

SCHWENK, KURT, evolutionary biology educator; b. Bronxville, N.Y., Apr. 7, 1955; s. George Ernest and Ann Barbara (Corbelli) S.; m. Sandford von Eicken, Feb.12, 1988; 1 child, Colton von Eicken Schwenk. AB, Oberlin Coll., 1977; PhD, U. Calif., Berkeley, 1984. Instr. U. Ill., Chgo., 1984-87; lectr. Harvard U., Cambridge, Mass., 1987-89; asst. prof. evolutionary biology, curator mammalogy U. Conn., Storrs, 1989—; assoc. zoology Mus. Comparative Zoology, Harvard U., Cambridge, 1990—. Contbr. articles to profl. jours. U. Calif. regents' fellow, Berkeley, 1982-83; recipient NIH nat. rsch. svc. award Harvard U., 1987-89. Mem. Am. Soc. Zoologists, Am. Soc. Ichthyologists and Herpetologists, The Evolutionists' Soc., Soc. for Study of Amphibians and Reptiles, Sigma Xi. Avocations: leftist politics, backpacking, motorcycles. Office: U Conn Dept Ecology & Evolutionary Biology Storrs Mansfield CT 06269-3043

SCHWENKE, ROGER DEAN, lawyer; b. Washington, Oct. 18, 1944; s. Clarence Raymond and Virginia Ruth (Gould) S.; m. Carol Lynne Flenniken, Nov. 29, 1980; 1 son, Matthew Robert; stepchildren: Tracy L. Wolf Dickey, Mary M. Wolf. BA, Ohio State U., 1966; JD with honors, U. Fla., 1969. Bar: Fla. 1970. Instr. Coll. Law U. Fla., Gainesville, 1969-70; assoc. Carlton, Fields, Ward, Emmanuel, Smith & Cutler, P.A., Tampa, Fla., 1970-74, ptnr., 1975—, adminstr.; dept. head Real Estate, Environ. and Land Use Dept., 1978—; adj. prof. Coll. Law, Stetson U., St. Petersburg, Fla., 1979-80. Author chpt. in Environmental Regulation and Litigation in Florida, 1987; contbr. articles to profl. jours. Mem. diocesan coun. Episc. Diocese SW Fla., 1978-86, mem. standing com., 1990-93. Recipient Gertrude Brick Law Rev. prize U. Fla., 1969. Fellow Am. Coll. Real Estate Lawyers (bd. govs. 1985-88), Am. Law Inst.; mem. ABA (standing com. on environ. law, coun. real property sect. 1981—), Fla. Bar Assn., Air & Waste Mgmt. Assn., Order of Coif, Greater Tampa C. of C. (chmn. environ. coun. 1980-81), Tampa Club. Democrat. Tampa Club. Democrat. Office: Carlton Fields PO Box 3239 Tampa FL 33601-3239

SCHWENN, LEE WILLIAM, retired medical center executive; b. Morrisonville, Wis., Dec. 23, 1925; s. LeRoy William and Vivian Mae (Kramer) S.; m. Glenna Edith Mehne, Jan. 16, 1947; 1 son, William Lee. B.S., U. Wis., 1948; M.P.H., U.N.C., 1956. Tchr. pub. schs. Appleton, Wis., 1948-52; teaching cons. Wis. Health Dept., 1952-53; adminstrv. asst. Madison (Wis.) Health Dept., 1953-57; adminstrv. cons. U.S. Children's Bur., Atlanta Regional Office, 1957-58; adminstr. USPHS, Washington, 1958-66; assoc. dir. D.C. Dept. Health, 1966-70, D.C. Dept. Human Resources, 1970-71; exec. v.p. Maimonides Med. Center, Bklyn., 1971-88, pres., 1988-89, spl. cons. Bd. Trustees, 1989—. Recipient Distinguished Pub. Service award D.C. Govt., 1970. Mem. Am. Pub. Health Assn., Am. Acad. Health Adminstrs., Delta Omega. Home: 1007 Westminster Dr Greensboro NC 27410-4551

SCHWERIN, HORACE S., marketing research executive; b. N.Y.C., Jan. 18, 1914; s. Paul and Rose (Lewis) S.; m. Lorraine Roth, June 14, 1941 (div. Dec. 1969); children—Barbara, Bruce; m. Enid May Highton, Apr. 28, 1973. B.S., Lafayette Coll., 1935; M.A., Kings Coll., London (Eng.) U., 1936; M.S., U. Paris, France, 1937. Gen. mgr., research dir., cons. N.Y. advt. agys., 1936-41; pres. Research Analysts, Inc., 1946; chmn. bd. Schwerin Research Corp., N.Y.C., Toronto, London, Hamburg, to 1968; chmn., pres. Horace Schwerin & Assos., Englewood Cliffs, N.J., 1968-72; dir. marketing devel. Campbell Soup Co., Camden, N.J., 1972—, v.p. market planning Canned Food div., 1977-82, mktg. strategy cons., 1982—; CEO, chmn. Schwerin Murphy, Inc., 1991—. Author: (with Henry H. Newell) Persuasion in Marketing, 1981; also articles on market research, nutrition, use of govt. data bases. Served as capt. U.S. Army, 1946. Decorated Legion of Merit with oak leaf cluster; inducted into Market Rsch. Coun. Hall of Fame, 1992. Mem. Am. Mktg. Assn., Market Rsch. Coun., Can. Club (N.Y.C.), Princeton Club (N.Y.C.). Methodist. Home: 5D Toll Gate Of Moorestown Moorestown NJ 08057 Office: 633 E Main St Moorestown NJ 08057-3059

SCHWERIN, KARL HENRY, anthropology educator, researcher; b. Bertha, Minn., Feb. 21, 1936; s. Henry William and Audrey Merle (Jahn) S.; m. Judith Drewanne Altermatt, Sept. 1, 1958 (div. May 1975); children: Karl Frederic, Marguerite DelValle; m. Partha Louise Hake Buell, Jan. 25, 1979; stepchildren: Tamara, Brent, Taryn. BA, U. Calif., Berkeley, 1958; PhD, UCLA, 1965. Instr. Los Angeles State Coll., 1963; asst. prof. anthropology U. N.Mex., Albuquerque, 1963-68, assoc. prof., 1968-72, prof., 1972—, asst. chmn. dept. anthropology, 1983-85, chmn. dept. anthropology, 1987-93; prof. invitado Inst. Venezolano de Investigaciones Cientificas, Caracas, 1979. Author: Oil and Steel Processes of Karinya Culture Change, 1966, Antropologia Social, 1969, Winds Across the Atlantic, 1970; editor: Food Energy in Tropical Ecosystems, 1985; contbr. articles to profl. jours. V.p. Parents without Ptnr., Albuquerque, 1976-77. Grantee Cordell Hull Found., Venezuela, 1961-62, N.Y. Zool. Soc., Honduras, 1981; Fulbright scholar Cañar, Ecuador, 1969-70, Paris, 1986. Fellow Am. Anthropol. Assn.; mem. Am. Ethnol. Soc., Am. Soc. Ethnohistory (pres. 1975), Southwestern Anthropol. Assn. (co-editor Southwestern Jour. Anthropology 1972-75), N.Mex. Cactus and Succulent Soc. (v.p. 1970-71), Maxwell Mus. Assn. (bd. dirs. 1984-85), Internat. Congress of Americanists (35th-40th, 43d, 46th, 48th), Sigma Xi (chpt. pres. 1980-81). Avocations: photography, gardening, hiking, camping, cycling. Office: U NMex Dept Anthropology Albuquerque NM 87131

SCHWERIN, WARREN LYONS, real estate developer; b. N.Y.C., Sept. 1, 1938; s. Clarence M. III and Helena (Lyons) S.; children: Kathryn Amy, James Warren. BA, Trinity Coll., 1960. Founding ptnr. Omega Properties, N.Y., 1961-70; pres. Arlen Shopping Ctrs., N.Y., 1970-73; pres., co-founder Related Properties, Inc., N.Y.C., 1973—. Past pres. Long Island Hearing and Speech Soc., past treas., trustee Buckley Country Day Sch. Mem.

Internat. Council of Shopping Ctrs., Urban Land Inst. Office: Related Properties 625 Madison Ave New York NY 10022-1801

SCHWERING, FELIX KARL, electronics engineer, researcher; b. Cologne, Nordrhein-Westfalen, Federal Republic of Germany, June 4, 1930; came to U.S., 1964; s. Felix Bernhard and Maria (Heinrichs) S. BS, U. Aachen, Federal Republic of Germany, 1951, Diplom-Ingenieur, 1954, PhD, 1957. Asst. prof. U. Aachen, Federal Republic of Germany, 1956-58; electronic scientist U.S. Army R & D Labs., Fort Monmouth, N.J., 1958-61; project leader AEG-Telefunken, Ulm, Federal Republic of Germany, 1961-64; rsch. scientist U.S. Army Communication Electronics Command, Fort Monmouth, N.J., 1964—; vis. adj. assoc. U.S. Army Rsch. Office, Rsch. Triangle, N.C., 1984-85; vis. prof. N.J. Inst. Tech., Newark, 1986—, Rutgers U., New Brunswick, N.J., 1973-87. Author: (with others) Millimeter Wave Antennas, 1988; author and editor (with others) Microwave Antennas, 1989; mem. editorial bd. Microwave and Optical Tech. Letters, 1988—; contbr. over 30 articles to profl. jours.; patentee in field. Fellow IEEE (Best Paper award Antennas and Propagation Soc. 1961, 82), Internat. Sci. Radio Union, Am. Geophys. Union, Armed Forces Comm. Electronics Assn., Sigma Xi. Roman Catholic. Office: US Army Comm Elec Command Amsel Rd St # C Fort Monmouth NJ 07703

SCHWETZ, BERNARD ANTHONY, toxicologist; b. Cadott, Wis., Nov. 27, 1940; married; 4 children. BS in Biology, U. Wis., Stevens Point, 1962; DVM, U. Minn., 1967; MS in Pharmacology, U. Iowa, 1968, PhD in Pharmacology, 1970. Diplomate Am. Bd. Toxicology. USPHS trainee dept. vet. physiology and pharmacology U. Minn., 1964-66; USPHS trainee dept. pharmacology U. Iowa, 1966-70; toxicologist Dow Chem. U.S.A., Midland, Mich., 1970-78, dir. toxicology rsch. lab., 1978-82; chief sys. toxicity br. divsn. toxicology rsch. and testing NIEHS, Research Triangle Park, N.C., 1982-92, acting dir. environ. toxicology program, 1993; dir. Nat. Ctr. for Toxicol. Rsch., Jefferson, Ark., 1993—; assoc. commr. for sci. FDA, Rockville, Md., 1994—; adj. prof. U. Ark. for Med. Scis., 1993—, Mich. State U., East Lansing, 1973-82, N.C. State U., Raleigh, 1985-93. Assoc. editor Fundamental and Applied Toxicology, 1983-86, editor, 1986-92; editl. adv. bd. Environ. Health Perspectives and Critical Revs. in Toxicology, 1984—; contbr. numerous articles to profl. publs. Recipient Arnold J. Lehman award Soc. of Toxicology, 1991, Dir.'s award NIH, 1991, Founders' award Chem. Industry Inst. of Toxicology, 1994. Mem. Am. Vet. Med. Assn., Soc. Toxicology (charter mem. Mich. chpt., councilor 1984-86, pres. N.C. chpt. 1987, pres. reproductive toxicology specialty sect. 1986), Teratology Soc. (treas. 1978-82), Behavioral Teratology Soc., Phi Zeta. Avocations: fishing, photography. Office: Nat Ctr Toxicol Rsch HFT-1 3900 NCTR Rd Jefferson AR 72079-9502

SCHWIER, FREDERICK WARREN, manufacturing company executive; b. Ft. Wayne, Ind., Sept. 28, 1923; s. Frederick G. and Louise (Kohte) S.; m. Priscilla Lamb Guyton, May 11, 1984; children by previous marriage: Frederick D., Francella L. Student, Mich. State U., 1948-51, Advanced Mgmt. Program, Harvard U., 1978. With Aeroquip Corp., Jackson, Mich., 1951-81, v.p., gen. mgr. AMB div., 1972-74, exec. v.p. AMB div., 1974-76; pres. Aeroquip Corp., 1976-81; exec. v.p. Libbey-Owens-Ford Co., Toledo, 1979-80, pres., chief operating officer, 1980-83; pres., chief exec. officer The ARO Corp., Bryan, Ohio, 1983-86; chmn. Great Lakes Communications, Inc., Toledo, 1987—; dir. Kysor Indsl. Corp., Cadillac, Mich., Tecumseh (Mich.) Products Corp. Trustee Wilberforce U. Served with C.E. AUS, 1943-46. Episcopalian. Clubs: Toledo, Belmont Country (Toledo).

SCHWIETZ, ROGER L., bishop. Ordained priest Roman Cath. Ch., 1967, consecrated bishop, 1990. Bishop Diocese of Duluth, Minn., 1989—. Home: 2830 E 4th St Duluth MN 55812-1501 Office: Diocese of Duluth 2830 E 4th St Duluth MN 55812-1501*

SCHWIND, MICHAEL ANGELO, law educator; b. Vienna, Austria, July 2, 1924; came to U.S., 1951; s. Siegfried and Sali (Salner) S. J.D., U. Central, Ecuador, 1949; LL.M. in Internat. Law, NYU, 1953, LL.B., 1957. Bar: Ecuador 1949, N.Y. 1957, U.S. Supreme Ct. 1967. Pvt. practice N.Y.C., 1957-69; Lectr. law NYU Sch. Law, 1959-63, adj. asst. prof., 1963-64, assoc. prof., 1964-67, prof., 1967-94; prof. emeritus NYU Sch. Law, N.Y.C., 1994—; inter-Am. Law Inst., Inst. Comparative Law, NYU Sch. Law, 1967-71. Bd. editors Am. Jour. Comparative Law. Mem. Am. Arbitration Assn., Am. Fgn. Law assn. (bd. dirs.), Am. Soc. Internat. Law. Office: NYU Sch Law 40 Washington sq S Rm 333 New York NY 10012-1005

SCHWINDT, ROBERT F., diagnostic medical products executive. Ceo., pres. Boehringer Mannheim Corp., Indianapolis, Ind. Office: Boehringer Mannheim Corp PO Box 50457 Indianapolis IN 46250

SCHWING, CHARLES E., architect; b. Plaquemine, La., Nov. 21, 1929; s. Calvin Kendrick and Mary Howard (Slack) S.; m. Cynthia Benjamin, June 14, 1952 (div. 1967); children—Calvin Kendick III, Therra Cynthia; m. Geraldine Fleniken Hofmann, Dec. 27, 1969; 1 stepson, Steven Blake. Student, La. State U., 1947-51; B.S., Ga. Inst. Tech. 1953, B.Architecture, 1954; 3e Assessit d'Architecture, Ecole Des Beaux-Arts. Field insp. Bodman, Murrell and Smith, Baton Rouge, 1954-55; assoc. architect Post & Harelson, Baton Rouge, 1955-59; partner Hughes and Schwing, Baton Rouge, 1959-61; owner Charles E. Schwing, Baton Rouge, 1961-69, Charles E. Schwing & Assocs., Baton Rouge, 1969—; v.p. Schwing Inc., Baton Rouge, 1979-89; pres. Schwing Inc., Plaquemine, La., 1989; mem. La. State Bd. Archtl. Examiners, 1983-95 (pres. 1988-89), Nat. Coun. Archtl. Registration Bds. (chmn. Region III 1988-89, bd. dirs. 1990-93), advt. bd. Architects Nat. Employers Trust. Bd. dirs. Baton Rouge Area Found., 1986-92, treas. 1987-89; bd. dirs. Womens Hosp., 1993-94. Fellow AIA (treas., exec. com., dir. planning com., chmn. finance com. 1976-77, treas., exec. com., dir. fin. com. rsch. corp. 1976-77, treas., dir. found. 1976-77, v.p. 1978, pres.-elect 1979, pres. 1980), Royal Architecture Soc. Can. (hon.); mem. La. Architects Assn. (sec.-treas. 1971, v.p. 1972, pres. 1973), Venezuelan Soc. Architects (hon.), Bolivian Inst. Architects (hon.), C. of C., La. State U. Alumni Fedn., Ga. Tech. Alumni Club, Sigma Alpha Epsilon. Episcopalian. Clubs: Baton Rouge Country, City. Home: Stone's Throw 8655 Jefferson Hwy # 12 Baton Rouge LA 70809 Office: 721 Government St Ste 101 Baton Rouge LA 70802-6096

SCHWINGHAMER, ROBERT JOHN, materials scientist; b. Jasper, Ind., Mar. 12, 1928; s. Robert J. and Eustella (Uebelhor) S.; m. Constance Gramelspacher, Sept. 16, 1950; children: Bettye Lee, Denise, Antoinette, Robyn. B.S. in Elec. Engring. Purdue U., 1950; postgrad., U. Ala., Auburn U., U. Mich.; M.S., M.I.T., 1968. Lead product engr. Sylvania Co., 1950-57; supervisory research engr. Army Ballistic Missile Agy., Dept. Army, 1957-60; sec. br. and div. chief NASA, Marshall Space Flight Center, Huntsville, Ala., 1960-73; dir. materials and processes lab. Marshall Space Flight Ctr., NASA, 1973-89; dep. dir. space transp. systems sci./engring. directorate NASA/Marshall Space Flight Ctr., 1989-94; assoc. dir. tech. Marshall Space Flt. Ctr., 1994—. Contbr. articles to profl. jours. Fellow Soc. for Advancement of Material and Process Engring., Soc. Mfg. Engrs., Am. Soc. Materials Internat.; Assoc. fellow AIAA. Patentee in field. Office: NASA Sci and Engring Directorate Marshall Space Flight Ctr Huntsville AL 35812

SCHWINN, DONALD EDWIN, environmental engineer; b. N.Y.C., July 18, 1935; s. Edwin William and Mary Louise (Conforti) S.; m. Mary Lou De Maria, June 25, 1960; children: Daniel, Michael, Brian, Christine. BS in Civil Engring., The Cooper Union, 1957; MS in Sanitary Engring., MIT, 1959. Diplomate Am. Acad. Environ. Engrs. Sanitary engr. Dorr-Oliver Inc., Stamford, Conn., 1957-62; sanitary engr. Metcalf & Eddy, Boston, 1962-66, exec. engr., 1966-70, v.p., 1970-74; prof. Stearns & Wheler, Cazenovia, N.Y., 1974-88, sr. ptnr., 1988—; mem. study com. water quality policy NAS, 1975-76; advisor to environ. engring. program Cornell U., Ithaca, N.Y., 1976, Syracuse (N.Y.) U., 1987—; mem. US/USSR joint tech. commn. external utility systems HUD, Washington, 1979-85. Sr. author: U.S. EPA Process Design Manual for Upgrading Wastewater Treatment Plants, 1974; contbg. author: Design Manual for Municipal Wastewater Treatment Plants, 1991, U.S. EPA Process Design Manual for Nitrogen Control, 1992; contbr. articles to profl. jours. Co-chmn. Cazenovia Youth Soccer Program 1980-85; mem. Cazenovia Conservation Commn., 1984—,

St. James Choir, Cazenovia, 1990—. Recipient Arthur Sidney Bedell award Water Pollution Control Fedn., 1974, 1st award Consulting Engrs. Coun. N.Y., 1977, Chmn.'s award Water Pollution Control Fedn., 1988. Mem. ASCE, NSPE, Am. Water Works Assn., APWA, Water Environ. Fedn., N.Y. Water Pollution Control Assn. (Kenneth Allen award 1985). Roman Catholic. Achievements include invention and devel. of cyclical nitrogen removal process for removal of nitrogen from sewage.

SCHWINN-JORDAN, BARBARA (BARBARA SCHWINN), painter; b. Glen Ridge, N.J.; d. Carl Wilhelm Ludwig and Helen Louise (Jordan) Schwinn; m. Frank Bertram Jordan, Jr.; children: Janine Jordan, Frank Bertram III. Grad. N.Y. Sch. Fine and Applied Art (Parsons), N.Y. and Paris; student Grand Cen. Art Sch., Art Students League, Grand Chaumiere, Academie Julien-Paris, Columbia U., NAD. Illustrator mags. including Vogue, 1930's, Ladies Home Jour., Saturday Evening Post, Colliers, Good Housekeeping, Cosmopolitan, McCall's, American, Town and Country, 1940's-60's. Women's Jour., Eng., Hors Zu, Fed. Republic Germany, Marie Claire, France, other fgn. publs., 1950's-60's. Portrait painter, including Queen Sirikit, Princess Margaret, Princess Grace; freelance painter, 1970—; one-man shows include Soc. of Illustrators, 1940, 50, Barry Stephens Gallery, 1950, Bodley Gallery, N.Y.C., 1971, 80, C.C., West Mifflin, Pa., 1973, Duquesne U., 1973, Mus. Am. Illustration, N.Y.C., 1991, Illustration House, N.Y.C., 1991, Giraffics Gallery, East Hampton, N.Y., 1991-95 (also rep.); exhibited in group shows including NAD, 1955, Royal Acad., London, Guild Hall, N.Y., 1981, Summit N.J. Art Ctr., 1981, Meredith Long Gallery, Houston, 1983, Mus. Soc. Illustrators, N.Y., 1985, The Marcus Gallery, Sante Fe, 1985, 86, The Gerald Peters Gallery, Santa Fe, 1985, 86, Brandywine Mus., Pa., 1986, New Britain (Conn.) Mus. Am. Art, 1986, Armory Show, N.Y.C., 1992-94, The Women's Ctr., Chapel Hill, N.C., 1993-94, Greenville County Mus. Art, S.C., 1995, The Soc. of the Four Arts, Palm Beach, Fla., 1995, The Hyde Collection, Glens Falls, N.Y., 1995, Ga. Mus. Art, 1995, Heckscher Mus., L.I., N.Y., 1995; works represented Holbrook Collection, Ga. Mus. Art, Eureka Coll., Ill., New Britain Mus. Am. Art, Mus. of Soc. of Illustrators, N.Y.C., Brandywine Mus., Pa., Sanford Low Meml. Collection, Del. Art Mus., Wilmington, Mus. Am. Illustration, N.Y.C., Glenbow Mus., Calgary, Alberta, Can.; represented in traveling show Del. Art Mus. 1994-95; various pvt. and gallery collections; work featured in America's Great Women Illustrators 1850-1950, 1985; lectr., instr. illustration Parsons Sch., 1952-54; founder adv. coun. Art Instrn. Sch., 1956-70. Chmn. art com. UNICEF greeting cards, 1950-61 mem. com. Spence Chapin Sch., Philharm. Soc., 1950's-60's. Winner prizes Art Dirs. Club, 1950, Guild Hall, 1969. Assoc. mem. Guggenheim Mus. Mem. Cosmopolitan Club N.Y. Author: Technique of Barbara Schwinn, 1956; World of Fashion Art, 1968. Home and Studio: 579 Fearrington Post Pittsboro NC 27312

SCHWITTERS, ROY FREDERICK, physicist, educator; b. Seattle, Wash., June 20, 1944; s. Walter Frederick and Margaret Lois (Boyer) S.; m. Karen Elizabeth Chrystal, June 18, 1965; children: Marc Frederick, Anne Elizabeth, Adam Thomas. S.B., MIT, 1966, Ph.D., 1971. Research asso. Stanford U. Linear Accelerator Center, 1971-74, asst. prof., then asso. prof., 1974-79; prof. physics Harvard U., 1979—; former dir. Superconducting Super Collider; now prof. physics U. Tex., Austin; scientist Fermi Nat. Accelerator Lab., 1980-88, dir. Superconducting Super Collider, 1989—. Author papers on high energy physics; asso. editor: Ann. Rev. Nuclear and Particle Sci; div. asso. editor: Phys. Rev. Letters. Recipient Alan T. Waterman award NSF, 1980. Fellow AAAS, Am. Phys. Soc., Am. Acad. Arts and Scis. Home: 1718 Cromwell Hill Austin TX 78703 Office: U Tex Dept Physics Austin TX 78712-1081

SCHWYN, CHARLES EDWARD, accountant; b. Muncie, Ind., Oct. 12, 1932; s. John and Lela Mae (Oliver) S.; m. Mary Helen Nickey, May 25, 1952 (dec.); children: Douglas, Craig, Beth; m. Madelyn Steinmetz. BS, Ball State U., 1957. CPA, Calif., D.C. With Haskins, Sells & Orlando, Chgo., Orlando, Fla., 1958-67; mgr. Deloitte, Haskins & Sells, Milan, Italy, 1967-70, San Francisco, 1970-80; with Deloitte, Haskins & Sells (now Deloitte & Touche), Oakland, Calif., ptnr. in charge, 1980-92, ret., 1992. Bd. dirs. Jr. Ctr. Art and Sci., 1982-89, pres., 1987-88; bd. dirs. trustee Oakland Symphony. 1982-96. 89-91; bd. dirs. Oakland Met. YMCA, 1984-89, Oakland Police Activities League, 1981-91, Joe Morgan Youth Found., 1982-91, Summit Med. Ctr., 1989-94; bd. dirs. Marcus A. Foster Ednl. Inst., 1986—, pres., 1991-93; mem. adv. bd. Festival of Lake, 1984-89, U. Oakland Met. Forum, 1992—; co-chmn. Commn. for Positive Change in Oakland Pub. Schs.; mem. campaign cabinet United Way Bay Area, 1989; bd. regents Samuel Merritt Coll., 1994—. With USN, 1952-56. Recipient Cert. Recognition Calif. Legis. Assembly, 1988, Ctr. for Ind. Living award, Oakland Bus. Arts award for outstanding bus. leader Oakland C. of C., 1992; date of job retirement honored in his name by Oakland mayor. Mem. AICPA (coun. 1987-90), Oakland C. of C. (chmn. bd. dirs. 1987-88, exec. com. 1982-89), Calif. Soc. CPAs (bd. dirs. 1979-81, 83-84, 85-87, pres. San Francisco chpt. 1983-84), Nat. Assn. Accts. (pres. Fla. chpt. 1967), Claremont Country Club (treas., bd. dirs. 1989—), Lakeview Club (bd. govs. 1987-92), Oakland 100 Club (pres. 1994), Rotary (bd. dirs. Oakland club 1986-88, 91-92, treas. 1984-86, pres. 1991-92). Office: Deloitte & Touche 2101 Webster St Fl 20 Oakland CA 94612-3027

SCIAME, JOSEPH, university administrator; b. Bklyn., Sept. 9, 1941; s. Joseph and Sophie (Pintacuda) S. EdB, St. John's U., 1971. Fin. aid officer, asst. to dean of admissions St. John's U., Jamaica, N.Y., 1967-71; fin. aid, 1971-82, dean fin. aid, 1982, v.p. fin. aid and student svcs., 1982-94, v.p. for govt. and community rels., 1994—; pres. N.Y. Assoc. Student Fin. Aid Adminstrn., 1980-82, Ea. Assoc. Student Fin. Aid Adminstrn., 1986-87; chmn. Nat. Assoc. Student Fin. Aid Adminstrn., 1987-88; chairperson Gov. Commn. Sch. Achievement, 1993—, active, 1971—. Chmn. bd. ethics Town of North Hempes, N.Y., 1984—; nat. chmn. bd. dirs. Garibaldi-Meucci Mus., N.Y., 1987-93. Decorated Cavaliere del Merito della Republica Italiana, 1993; recipient Disting. Svc. award Nat. Assn. Student Fin. Aid Adminstrs., 1988, Achievement award N.Y. State Fin. Aid Adminstrs., 1982, Congl. Record award Congress, 1979, 91, 93, 94. Mem. Nat. Assn. Student Fin. Aid Adminstrs. (Disting. Svc. award 1988, Leadership award 1994), Assn. of the Equestrian Order of the Holy Sepulchre (Knight with Grand Cross elevated 1991, Knight invested 1980), Order Sons of Italy in Am. (lodge pres. 1974-75, state pres. 1993—), Futures in Edn. Found. (vice chairperson 1991-93, chairperson 1994—). Roman Catholic. Avocations: walking, cooking, gardening, reading, lecturing. Home: 6 Jones St New Hyde Park NY 11040-1616 also: Trout Ln Southampton NY 11969 Office: St John's U Jamaica NY 11439

SCIANCE, CARROLL THOMAS, chemical engineer; b. Okemah, Okla., Feb. 16, 1939; s. Carroll Elmer and Winifred (Black) S.; BS in Chem. Engring., U. Okla., 1960, M in Chem. Engring., 1964, PhD, 1966; m. Anita Ruth Fischer, Jan. 30, 1960; children: Steven, Frederick, Thomas, Erica. With E.I. duPont de Nemours & Co., Inc., 1966-95, planning mgr. nylon intermediates div., petrochem. dept., Wilmington, Del., 1978-80, tech. mgr., 1980-83, dir. engring. research, engring. dept., 1983-87, prin. cons. corp. research and devel. planning div., 1987-89; mgr. petroleum products R&D div., Conoco, Inc., 1989-93; dir. Environ. Tech. Partnerships, ctrl. R & D dept. DuPont, 1993-95; pres. Sci. Consulting Svcs., Inc. Mem. math. scis. and edn. bd. Nat. Rsch. Coun., 1987-89, adv. bd. NIST for Chem. Sci. & Tech., 1988-94. Served as officer USAR, 1961-63. Fellow Am. Inst. Chem. Engrs. (bd. dirs. materials engring. and scis. div. 1986-92, chmn. new tech. com. 1990-92, govt. rels. com. 1993—), mem. Fedn. Materials Socs. (v.p. 1988-92, pres. 1993-94), Am. Chem. Soc., N.Y. Acad. Scis., Sigma Xi. Home: 9 Aston Circle Hockessin DE 19707

SCIARRATTA, PATRICK LOUIS, director, educator, artistic director; b. Bklyn., Dec. 5, 1951; s. Pasquale Joseph and Antoinette (Angeleri) S.; m. Jane Goodrich Searle, Oct. 19, 1991. BA in Theatre, Queens Coll./CUNY, 1974; MA in Theatre Anthropology, NYU, 1983. Movement program dir. for performing arts dept. Adelphi Univ., Garden City, N.Y., 1976-79; theatre dept. faculty L.I. Univ., Brookdale, N.Y., 1979-81; campus events dir. Iona Coll., Seton Campus, Yonkers, N.Y., 1986-87; performing arts dir. Hunter College, N.Y.C., 1987—; founder, artistic dir., pres., bd. dirs. Bond St. Theatre, N.Y.C., 1976—; founder, dir. Palenville N.Y. Interarts Colony, 1983—; resident dir. Israel Festval, Jerusalem, 1985; artistic dir. Baroness Theatre Lab., N.Y.C., 1988—; critic Show Bus. Mag., 1978-82. Playwright:

The Hunger Artist, 1977; lead actor in Emmy-award-winning prodn. Great Performances Spl.: The Orch., PBS-TV, 1990. Mem. Yorkville Civic Coun. (art com.), N.Y.C., 1991—. Recipient MacArthur award John D. and Catherine MacArthur Found., 1990. Avocations: juggling, circus arts, cooking. Office: Hunter Coll 695 Park Ave New York NY 10021-5085

SCIBELLI, ARTHUR PETER, JR., lawyer; b. Worcester, Mass., June 4, 1956; s. Arthur Peter Scibelli and Nancy (Patch) Dobson. BS in Commerce, U. Va., 1978, JD, 1982. Bar: D.C. 1982, Va. 1982. Assoc. Lane & Edson P.C., Washington, 1982-87; v.p., gen. counsel, sec. Sun Carriers Inc. and subs., Media, Pa., 1987—. Mem. ABA, D.C. Bar Assn., Va. Bar Assn., Transp. Lawyers Assn., Am. Soc. Corp. Secs. Democrat. Roman Catholic. Avocations: boating, racquet sports, stamp collecting. Office: Sun Carriers Inc 119 Jeffrey Ave Holliston MA 01746-2027

SCIESZKA, JON, children's author; b. Flint, Mich., Sept. 8, 1954; s. Louis and Shirley S.; m. Jerilyn Hansen; children: Casey, Jake. BA, Albion Coll., 1976; MFA, Columbia U., 1980. Elem. sch. tchr. The Day Sch., N.Y.C., 1980—. Author: (children's books) The True Story of the Three Little Pigs, 1989, The Frog Prince, Continued, 1991, Knights of the Kitchen Table, 1991, The Not-So-Jolly Roger, 1991, The Good, the Bad and the Goofy, 1992, The Stinky Cheeseman and Other Fairly Stupid Tales, 1992 (Caldecott Medal honor book 1993), Your Mother Was a Neanderthal, 1993, The Book That Jack Wrote, 1994. Office: care Viking Penguin 375 Hudson St New York NY 10014-3658

SCIFRES, DONALD R., semiconductor laser, fiber optics and electronics company executive; b. Lafayette, Ind.; m. Carol Scifres. B.S., Purdue U., 1968; M.S., U. Ill., 1970, Ph.D. 1972. Research and teaching asst. U. Ill., Urbana, 1968-72; research fellow, area mgr. Xerox Corp., Palo Alto, Calif., 1972-83; founder, pres., CEO SDL, Inc., San Jose, Calif., 1983—, chmn., 1992—; nat. lectr. IEEE Quantum Electronics Soc., 1979. Bd. editors Jour. Fiber and Integrated Optics, 1978; mem. editorial adv. bd. Photonics Spectra, 1992—; contbr. articles to tech. jours.; patentee in field. Recipient Disting. Engring. Alumni award Purdue U., 1990, Outstanding Elec. Engr. award, 1992; recipient Engring. Alumni award U. Ill., 1991, Alumni Honor award, 1993; U. Ill. fellow, 1968; Gen. Telephone and Electronics fellow, 1970-72. Fellow IEEE (Jack Morton award 1985, IEEE Lasers and Electro-Optics Soc. (pres. 1992, Engring. Achievement award 1995); mem. Optical Soc. Am., Am. Phys. Soc., Lasers and Electro-Optics Mfg. Assn. (bd. dirs. 1992—, sec. 1994), Tau Beta Pi, Eta Kappa Nu, Phi Eta Sigma. Office: SDL Inc 80 Rose Orchard Way San Jose CA 95134-1356

SCIPIO, (LOUIS) ALBERT, II, aerospace science engineering educator, architect, military historian; b. Juarez, Mex., Aug. 22, 1922; s. Louis Albert and Marie Leona (Richardson) S.; m. Katherine Ruth Janes, Aug. 15, 1942; children: Louis Albert, Karen R. S., Tuskegee Inst., 1943; B.Civil Engring., U. Minn., 1948, M.S., 1950, Ph.D., 1958. Archtl. draftsman McKissack & McKissack, Tuskegee, Ala., 1943; instr. Tuskegee Inst., 1946; designer Long & Thorshov, Mpls., 1948-50; lectr. U. Minn., Mpls., 1950-59; research physicist Hughes Aircraft Co., Culver City, Calif., 1954; Fulbright prof. Cairo U., Giza, Egypt, 1955-56; assoc. prof. mechanics Howard U., Washington, 1959-61; Fulbright prof. Cairo U., Giza, Egypt, 1955-56; dir. grad. studies for engring. and architecture, prof. aerospace engring. Howard U., Washington, 1967-70, Univ. prof. space scis., 1970-87, Disting. Univ. prof. emeritus, 1987—; prof. phys. scis. U. P.R., Mayaguez, 1961-63; prof. aerospace engring. U. Pitts., 1963-67; pub. Roman Publs., Silver Springs, Md., 1981—; cons. in field; author Compendium of Aircraft Stress Analysis and Design, 1956. Author: Principles on Continua with Applications, 1966, Structural Design Concepts, 1967, E.M. Collar Insignia, 1907-1926, 1981, Last of the Black Regulars, 1983, With the Red Hand Division, 1985, The 24th Infantry at Fort Benning, 1986, Pre-War Days at Tuskegee, 1987. Bd. visitors Air Force Inst. Tech., 1979-83. Served with AUS, 1943-46. Mem. N.Y. Acad. Scis., Internat. Assn. Bridge and Structural Engrs., Soc. Natural Philosophy, AIAA, AAAS; mem. Am. Phys. Soc.; mem. NSPE, Co. of Mil. Historians, Coun. on Am. Mil. Past, Phi Beta Kappa, Sigma Xi, Alpha Kappa Mu, Pi Mu Epsilon, Sigma Pi Sigma, Sigma Gamma Tau, Pi Tau Sigma. Home: 12511 Montclair Dr Silver Spring MD 20904-2053

SCIPIONE, RICHARD STEPHEN, insurance company executive, lawyer; b. Newton, Mass., Aug. 27, 1937; s. Charles John and Alice (Scotto) S.; m. Lois Mugford, Aug. 29, 1964; children: Jeffrey Charles, Douglas Loring. BA, Harvard U., 1959; LLB, Boston U., 1962. Bar: Mass. 1962. Atty. John Hancock Mut. Life Ins. Co., Boston, 1965-69, asst. counsel, 1969-74, assoc. counsel, 1975-79, sr. assoc. counsel, 1980-82, 2d v.p., counsel, 1982-84, v.p., gen. solicitor, 1984-85, sr. v.p. and gen. solicitor, 1986-87, gen. counsel, 1987—; chmn. bd. dirs. New England Legal Found.; bd. dirs. John Hancock Advisers/Distbrs.; trustee John Hancock Mutual Funds. Served to capt. U.S. Army, 1962-65. Mem. ABA (dir. New Eng. Coun.), Assn. Life Ins. Counsel (gov. 1994—), Chatham Yacht Club. Office: John Hancock Mut Life Ins Co Box 111 John Hancock Pl Boston MA 02117

SCIRICA, ANTHONY JOSEPH, federal judge; b. Norristown, Pa., Dec. 16, 1940; s. A. Benjamin and Anna (Sclafani) S.; m. Susan Morgan, May 6, 1966; children—Benjamin, Sara. B.A., Wesleyan U., 1962; J.D., U. Mich., 1965; postgrad., Central U., Caracas, Venezuela, 1966. Bar: Pa., 1966, U.S. Dist. Ct. (ea. dist.) Pa., 1984, U.S. Ct. Appeals (3d cir.), 1987. Ptnr. McGrory, Scirica, Wentz & Fernandez, Norristown, Pa., 1966-80; asst. dist. atty. Montgomery County, Pa., 1967-69; mem. Pa. Ho. of Reps, Harrisburg, 1971-79; judge Montgomery County Ct. Common Pleas, Pa., 1980-84, U.S. Dist. Ct. (ea. dist.) Pa., Phila., 1984-87, U.S. Ct. Appeals (3d cir.), 1987—; chmn. Pa. Sentencing Commn., 1980-85. Fulbright scholar Central U., Caracas, Venezuela, 1966. Mem. Montgomery Bar Assn., Pa. Bar Assn., ABA. Roman Catholic. Office: US Courthouse Independence Mall W #22614 601 Market St Philadelphia PA 19106-1723*

SCISCO, PETER LEON, magazine editor, writer; b. Poughkeepsie, N.Y., Apr. 3, 1956; s. Clayton Sterling and Dorothy Patricia (Gantnier) S.; m. Beth Ann Murray, Apr. 14, 1984; children: Taylor Sterling, Jack Edward, Gibson Paul. BA in English, U. Ky., 1983; MA in Composition, U. Mass., 1987. Teaching asst. U. Mass., Boston, 1985; copy editor Micro Market World mag., Framingham, Mass., k1985-86, reporter, 1986-87; free-lance journalist Charlotte, N.C., 1987-88; asst. editor Compute mag., Greensboro, N.C., 1988-89, assoc. editor, 1989, editor, 1989-90, editor in chief, 1990-91; editor The Last Word, Creative Writing Dept., U. Mass., 1985. Author: Big Book of PC Sports, 1991, Police Quest Casebook, 1992, Pro Links, 1992; editor Kids and Computers, 1992-94; contbg. editor Family PC, CD-Rom Today; contbr. articles to jours. in field. Mem. Am. Soc. Mag. Editors. Avocations: guitar, hiking, film, video. Home: 229 Lake Dr Winston Salem NC 27107

SCISM, DANIEL REED, lawyer; b. Evansville, Ind., Aug. 27, 1936; s. Daniel William and Ardath Josephine (Gibbs) S.; m. Paula Anne Sedgwick, June 21, 1958; children: Darby Claire, Joshua Reed. BA, DePauw U., 1958; JD, Ind. U., 1965. Bar: Ind. 1965, U.S. Dist. Ct. (so. dist.) Ind. 1965, U.S. Ct. Appeals (7th cir.) 1967, U.S. Supreme Ct. 1976. Reporter Dayton (Ohio) Jour.-Herald, 1958-59; editor Meade Johnson & Co., Evansville, 1962; first assoc., then ptnr. Roberts, Ryder, Rogers & Scism and predecessor firms, Indpls., 1965-86; ptnr. Barnes & Thornburg, Indpls., 1987—; cons. Ind. Personnel Assn., 1984—. Treas. Marion County chpt. Myasthenia Gravis Found., Indpls., 1970; v.p. Marion County Mental Health Assn., Indpls., 1970-71; pres. The Suemma Coleman Adoption Agy., Indpls., 1973-74; bd. dirs. Ind. Humanities Coun., 1995—. Edwards fellow Ind. U., 1964. Mem. ABA, Ind. Bar Assn., Indpls. Bar Assn., Ind. State C. of C. (social legis. com. 1970-80). Methodist. Clubs: Indpls. Athletic; Woodland Country (bd. dirs. 1984-88) (Carmel, Ind.). Home: 11070 Winding Brook Ln Indianapolis IN 46280-1258 Office: Barnes & Thornburg 1313 Mchts Bank Bldg 11 S Meridian St Indianapolis IN 46204-3506

SCITOVSKY, ANNE AICKELIN, economist; b. Ludwigshafen, Germany, Apr. 17, 1915; came to U.S. 1931, naturalized, 1938; d. Hans W. and Gertrude Margarete Aickelin; 1 dau., Catherine Margaret. Student, Smith Coll., 1933-35; B.A., Barnard Coll., 1937; postgrad., London Sch. Econs., 1937-39; M.A. in Econs., Columbia U., 1941. Mem. staff legis. reference svc., Libr. of Congress, 1941-44; mem. staff Social Security Bd., 1944-46; with Palo Alto (Calif.) Med. Rsch. Found., 1963—, chief health econs. div., 1973-91, sr. staff scientist, 1992—; lectr. Inst. Health Policy Studies, U. Calif., San

Francisco, 1975—; mem. Inst. Medicine of NAS, Nat. Acad. Social Ins., Pres.'s Commn. for Study of Ethical Problems in Medicine and Biomed. and Behavioral Rsch., 1979-82, U.S. Nat. Com. on Vital and Health Stats., 1975-78, Health Resources and Svcs. Adminstrn., AIDS adv. com., 1990-94; cons. HHS, Inst. Medicine Coun. on Health Care Tech. Assessment, 1986-90. Mem. Am. Assn. for Health Svc. Rsch., Am. Pub. Health Assn. Home: 161 Erica Way Menlo Park CA 94028-7439 Office: Palo Alto Med Found Rsch Inst 860 Bryant St Palo Alto CA 94301-2799

SCLAFANI, FRANCES ANN, lawyer, federal agency executive; b. N.Y.C., Aug. 25, 1949; d. Joseph John and Clementina Theresa (Polite) S. BA (hon.), St. John's U., 1971, JD, 1974. Bar: N.Y. 1975, U.S. Dist. Ct. (ea. and so. dists.) N.Y., 1975, U.S. Ct. Appeals (2d cir.) 1975, U.S. Supreme Ct. 1978, U.S. Dist. Ct. D.C. 1987, U.S. Ct. Appeals (D.C. cir.) 1987. Spl. congl. asst. U.S. Congress, Washington, 1971; asst. dist. atty. County of Suffolk (N.Y.), Riverhead, 1974-86; assoc. dir. U.S Office Personnel Mgmt., Washington, 1986—; head of Office Fed. Investigations, Washington, 1986—; bd. fgn. svc. Dept. State, Washington, 1986-90; bd. dirs. Fed. Law Enforcement Tng. Ctr., Glynco, Ga., 1986—; dep. chief Felony Trial Bur., 1981-82, Major Offense Bur., 1982-83. Rep. candidate for N.Y. state atty. gen., 1982; commr. President's Commn. on Organized Crime, Washington, 1983-86, mem. com. on narcotics control and interdiction, 1984-86; rep. to Western Hemisphere Conf. on Narcotics Control, Washington, 1985; faculty U.S. Dept. of Justice Ann. Internat. Drug Traffickers Prosecution Conf., 1983. Recipient award for svc.to victims rights Decision for Women in Commerce and Professions, 1984. Mem. ABA (asst. sec. criminal justice sect. 1980-82), Nat. Dist. Attys. Assn. (assoc. dir. 1980-86), D.C Bar Assn., N.Y. Bar Assn. Roman Catholic. Office: Office of Pers Mgmt Investigations Group 1900 E St NW Washington DC 20415-0002

SCLAR, CHARLES BERTRAM, geology educator, researcher; b. Newark, Mar. 16, 1925; s. Norman and Dorothy (Botvinick) S.; m. Ruth E. Choyke, Feb. 10, 1946; children: David A., Philip J. BS, CCNY, 1946; MS, Yale U., 1948, PhD, 1951. Instr. dept. geology Ohio State U., 1949-51; research petrographer Battelle Meml. Inst. (Minerals Processing div.), Columbus, Ohio, 1951-53, prin. research geologist, 1953-57, asst. tech. cons., 1957-59, asst. tech. cons. chem. physics div., 1959-62, research fellow, 1962-65, assoc. chief, dir. high pressure lab., 1965-68; prof., dept. geol. scis. Lehigh U., Bethlehem, Pa., 1968-90; prof. emeritus Lehigh U., Bethlehem, 1990—; chmn. dept. geol. scis. Lehigh U., Bethlehem, Pa., 1976-85; prin. investigator Apollo program NASA, 1968-78. Contbr. articles to profl. jours.; patentee in field. William E. Ford scholar Yale U., 1947-48, James Dwight Dana fellow, 1948-49. Fellow Mineralogical Soc. Am., Geol. Soc. Am., Soc. Econ. Geol. Home: 2075 Pleasant Dr Bethlehem PA 18015-5134 Office: Lehigh U Dept Earth and Environ Scis 31 Williams Dr Bethlehem PA 18015-3190

SCLATER, JOHN GEORGE, geophysics educator; b. Edinburgh, Scotland, June 17, 1940; s. John George and Margaret Bennett (Glen) S.; children: Iain Andrew, Stuart Michael. B.Sc., Edinburgh U., 1962; Ph.D., Cambridge (Eng.) U., 1966. Research geophysicist Scripps Inst. Oceanography, La Jolla, Calif., 1965-72, prof., 1991—; asso. prof. MIT, 1972-77, prof., 1977-83; dir. Joint Program Oceanography Woods Hole Oceanographic Inst., 1981-83; Shell Cos. chair in geophysics U. Tex., Austin, 1983-91; prof. Scripps Instn. Oceanography, U. Calif., San Diego, 1991—; Sweeney lectr. Edinburgh U., 1976. Contbr. articles to profl. jours. Recipient Rosenstiel award oceanography, 1979, numerous award for publs. Fellow Geol. Soc. Am., Royal Soc. London, Am. Geophys. Union (Bucher medal 1985); mem. NAS (mem. ocean studies bd., 1985-92, chair 1988-91). Home: 4878 Casals Pl San Diego CA 92124 Office: Scripps Instn of Oceanography La Jolla CA 92093-0215

SCOFIELD, GORDON LLOYD, mechanical engineer, educator; b. Huron, S.D., Sept. 29, 1925; s. Perry Lee and Zella (Reese) S.; m. Nancy Lou Cooney, Dec. 27, 1947; children: Cathy Lynne, Terrence Lee. B.M.E., Purdue U., 1946; M.M.E., U. Mo., Rolla, 1949; Ph.D. in M.E, U. Okla., 1968. Instr. mech. engring. S.D. State Coll., Brookings, 1946-47; successively grad. asst., instr., asst. prof., asso. prof., prof. U. Mo., Rolla, 1947-69; prof., head mech. engring.-engring. mechs. dept. Mich. Technol. U., Houghton, 1969-81; disting. prof. mech. engring. S.D. Sch. Mines and Tech., Rapid City, 1981-88; asst. v.p. for acad. affairs S.D. Sch. Mines and Tech. 1981-83, v.p., dean engring., 1984-86; pres. S.D. Sch. Mines and Tech. Found., 1982-90; cons. U.S. Naval Ordnance Test Sta., China Lake, Calif. 1956-71; bd. dirs. Accreditation Bd. for Engring. and Tech.; cons. to industry. Served with USNR, 1943-46. NSF sci. faculty fellow, 1966-67; recipient alumni achievement award U. Mo., Rolla, 1975. Mem. Soc. Automotive Engrs. (pres. 1977), ASME, Am. Soc. Engring. Edn., AIAA, Sigma Xi, Tau Beta Pi, Pi Tau Sigma, Phi Kappa Phi. Home: PO Box 1085 Rapid City SD 57709-1085 Satisfaction comes from sharing achievements. By acknowledging and sharing the importance of others in our success it is possible to accomplish more that is worth remembering.

SCOFIELD, JOHN, jazz guitarist; b. Wilton, Conn., Dec. 26, 1951; s. Leavitt and Anne Fay S.; m. Susan Scofield, 1978; children: Jean, Evan. Student, Berklee Sch. Music, 1970-73. Profl. musician, 1974—; with Billy Cobham George Duke Band, 1974-77; with Dave Liebman quintet, 1978-82; with Miles Davis Band, 1983-85, soloist, collaborating musician, group leader, 1986—; with Enja/rec. artist, 1977-82; Grammavision rec. artist, 1984-89, Blue note rec. artist, 1990—; adv. bd. Guitar Player Mag. Albums include Live, 1977, Rough House, 1978, Shinola, 1982, Still Warm, 1985, Blue Matter, 1986, Loud Jazz, 1987, Pick Hits, 1987, Flat Out, 1989, Slo Soco, 1990, Time on My Hands, 1990, Meant to Be, 1991, Grace Under Pressure, 1992, What We Do, 1993, (with Pat Metheney) I Can See Your House From Here, 1994, Hand Jive, 1994. Recipient numerous Down Beat Mag. Internat. Critic/ Reader Polls. Office: Blue Note Records Avenue of the Americas 35th fl New York NY 10104

SCOFIELD, PAUL, actor; b. Jan. 21, 1922; m. Joy Parker; 2 children. Trained London Mask Theatre Drama Sch., Birmingham Repertory Theatre 1941, 43-46; Stratford-on-Avon Shakespeare Meml. Theatre, 1946-48, Arts Theatre, 1946, Phoenix Theatre, 1947. With H.M. Tennent, 1949-56; assoc. dir. Nat. Theatre, 1970-71; has appeared in Adventure Story, Chekhov's Seagull, Anouilh's Ring Round the Moon, Gielgud's prodn. Much Ado About Nothing, Charles Morgan's The River Line, Richard II, The Way of the World, Venice Preserved, Time Remembered, A Question of Fact, Hamlet, Power and the Glory, Family Reunion, A Dead Secret, Expresso Bongo, The Complaisant Lover, A Man for All Seasons, Stratford Festival, Ont., Can., 1961, Coriolanus, Don Armado, New York, 1961-62, A Man for All Seasons, London, 1962-63, King Lear, N.Y.C, Moscow and Ea. Europe, 1964, Timon, 1965, Staircase, 1966, The Government Inspector, 1967, Macbeth, 1968, The Hotel in Amsterdam, 1968, Uncle Vanya, 1970, The Captain of Kopenik, 1971, Rules of the Game, 1971, Savages 1973, The Tempest, 1974, 75, Dimetos, 1976, Volpone, 1977, The Madras House, 1977, The Family, 1978, Amadeus 1979, Othello, 1980, Don Quixote, 1982, A Midsummer Night's Dream, 1982, I'm Not Rappaport, 1986-87, Heartbreak House, 1992; films: The Train, 1963, A Man for All Seasons (Oscar and N.Y. Film Critics award Moscow Film Festival and Brit. Film Acad. awards), King Lear, 1970, Scorpio, 1972, A Potting Shed, 1981, If Winter Comes, 1981, Song at Twilight 1982, Come into the Garden Maud, 1982, 1919, 1985, Anna Karenina, 1984, Mr. Corbett's Ghost, 1986, The Attic, 1987, Why The Whales Came, 1989, Henry V, 1990, Hamlet, 1990, UTZ, 1991, Quiz Show, 1994; appeared TV Martin Chuzzlewit, 1994. Decorated comdr. Brit. Empire. Address: The Gables, Balcombe Sussex RH17 6ND, England

SCOFIELD, RICHARD MELBOURNE, career officer; b. Hartford, Conn., Apr. 6, 1938; s. Melbourne Frank and Evelyn (Moors) S.; m. Cornelia Ellen Love, Dec. 27, 1961; children: Catherine Scofield Easley, Karen Elizabeth, Elizabeth Ann. BBA, U. Mass., 1960; MBA, Okla. U., 1970; MSSM, U. So. Calif., L.A., 1973. Commd. 2d lt. USAF, 1961, advanced through grades to lt. gen.; 1994; student pilot 3500th Flying Tng. Wing, Reese AFB, Tex., 1961-62; pilot C-130 6550th Ops. Group, Patrick AFB, Fla., 1962-64; pilot C-123 315th Air Div., Danang Air Base, Republic of Vietnam, 1964-65; aerial recovery pilot C-130 6594th Test Squadron, Hickam AFB, Hawaii, 1965-69; grad. student Okla. U., Norman, 1969-70; aerial recovery pilot C-130 OL-1 Satellite Control Facility, Edwards AFB, Calif., 1970-73; student Armed Forces Staff Coll., Norfolk, Va., 1973; chief program evaluation div. E-3A System Program Office, Hanscom AFB, Mass., 1973-76; student Def.

Systems Mgmt. Coll., Ft. Belvoir, Va., 1976; asst. dep. chief of staff, systems Hdqrs. Air Force Systems Command, Andrews AFB, Md., 1976-81; program dir. F-117 System Program Office Aero. Systems Div., Wright-Patterson AFB, Ohio, 1981-83, program dir. B-2 System Program Office, 1983-91; program exec. officer for Bombers, Missiles and Trainers Office of Asst. Sec. of Air Force, Acquisition, Pentagon, Washington, 1991-94; comdr. Aero. Systems Ctr., Wright-Patterson AFB, Ohio, 1994—; ad. prof. Golden Gate U., San Francisco, 1970-76. Decorated DSM, Legion of Merit, DFC, Air medal with ten oak leaf clusters, Meritorious Svc. medal Air Force Commendation medal, Nat. Def. medal. Mem. Air Force Assn. (Ira Eaker fellow 1990), Am. Def. Preparedness Assn. Roman Catholic. Avocation: golf. Home: 29 Westover Ave 88 Wright Ave Wright-Patterson AFB OH 45433 Office: comdr ASC/CC Wright-Patterson AFB OH 45433

SCOGGINS, SAMUEL MCWHIRTER, lawyer; b. Shreveport, La., May 8, 1950; s. Thomas Samuel and Virginia Benton (Vaughan) S.; m. Deborah Bailey, Nov. 26, 1986; children: Christine Crosley, Christopher Mc Whirter. BA with honors, Denison U., 1972; JD, U. Va., 1975. Bar: Ohio, U.S. Dist. Ct. (so. dist.) Ohio. Assoc., Frost & Jacobs, Cin., 1975-82; ptnr., 1982—. Vice chmn. Dan Beard chpt. Nat. Eagle Scout Assn., Cin., 1980-86; trustee Beech Acres, Cin., 1989—, pres. 1991-93, Hist. Southwest Ohio, Inc., 1992-95, Hyde Park Cmty. United Meth. Ch., Cin., 1982-85, Stepping Stones Ctr. for Handicapped, Cin., 1982-91. Mem. Cin. Bar Assn., Ohio State Bar Assn., Cin. Country Club, Indian Hill Club, Sigma Alpha Epsilon. Office: Frost & Jacobs 2500 PNC Ctr 201 E 5th Cincinnati OH 45202

SCOGIN, TROY POPE, publishing company executive, accounts executive; b. Manchester, Ala., Oct. 31, 1932; s. James David and Thelma Katie (Helton) S.; m. Katie Elizabeth Bates, May 26, 1956; children: Norma Kay, Joyce Marie. BA, Howard Coll., 1955; MDiv, So. Baptist Theol. Seminary, Louisville, 1959; MA, Samford U., 1972. Ordained to ministry Baptist Ch., 1956. Pastor West Port (Ky.) Baptist Ch., 1956-58, Providence Baptist Ch., Bellevue, Ohio, 1958-61; chaplain/capt. USAF, Lincoln, Nebr., 1961-64; pastor Sycamore (Ala.) Baptist Ch., 1964-65; sales rep. Houghton Mifflin Co., Boston, 1965-74, regional mgr., 1974-85; asst. to exec. v.p. coll. div., 1989-90, v.p., 1984—, nat. accounts exec., 1990-92; pastor Ross Ave. Bapt. Ch. Intercity Mission, Dallas, 1993—; faculty Eastfield Coll., 1992—. Chmn. bd. deacons Ross Ave. Baptist Ch., Dallas, 1991. Mem. Am. Mgmt. Assn., Am. Soc. Tng. Devel., Nat. Coun. Tchrs. English, Tex. Jr. Coll. Tchrs. Assn., Phi Kappa Phi, Omicron Delta Kappa (nat. leadership fraternity pres. 1954), Alpha Phi Omega (nat. svc. fraternity pres. 1952). Democrat. Avocations: bowling, swimming, fishing, tennis, golf. Home: 15742 Havenrock Cir Dallas TX 75248-4219

SCOGLAND, WILLIAM LEE, lawyer; b. Moline, Ill., Apr. 2, 1949; s. Maurice William and Harriet Rebecca (Lee) S.; m. Victoria Lynn Whitham, Oct. 9, 1976; 1 child, Thomas. BA magna cum laude, Augustana Coll., 1971; JD cum laude, Harvard U., 1975. Bar: Ill. 1975, U.S. Dist. Ct. (no. dist.) Ill. 1975. Assoc. Wildman, Harrold, Allen & Dixon, Chgo., 1975-77, Hughes Hubbard & Reed, Milw., 1977-81; from assoc. to ptnr. Jenner & Block, Chgo., 1981—. Author: Fiduciary Duty: What Does It Mean?, 1989; co-author Employee Benefits Law, 1987. Mem. Phi Beta Kappa, Omicron Delta Kappa. Republican. Office: Jenner & Block 1 IBM Plz Chicago IL 60611

SCOLES, CLYDE SHELDON, library director; b. Columbus, Ohio, Apr. 14, 1949; s. Edward L. and Edna M. (Ruddock) S.; m. Diane Francis, July 14, 1976; children: David, Kevin, Karen, Stephen. BS, Ohio State U., 1971; MLS, U. Mich., 1972. Librarian Columbus Pub. Library, 1972-74; library dir. Zanesville (Ohio) Pub. Library, 1974-78; asst. dir. Toledo-Lucas County Pub. Library, 1978-85, dir., 1985—; adj. lectr., libr. bldg. cons. U. Mich.; v.p. bd. dirs. Read for Literacy. Mem. ALA, Ohio Libr. Assn., Ohio Libr. Coun., Toledo C. of C., Com. of 100, Maumee Hist. Soc. Club: Torch (Toledo). Lodge: Rotary.

SCOLES, EUGENE FRANCIS, legal educator, lawyer; b. Shelby, Iowa, June 12, 1921; s. Sam and Nola E. (Leslie) S.; m. R. Helen Glawson, Sept. 6, 1942; children—Kathleen Elizabeth, Janene Helen. A.B., U. Iowa, 1943, J.D., 1945; LL.M., Harvard U., 1949; J.S.D., Columbia U., 1955. Bar: Iowa 1945, Ill. 1946. Assoc. Seyfarth-Shaw & Fairweather, Chgo., 1945-46; asst. prof. law Northeastern U., 1946-48, assoc. prof., 1948-49; assoc. prof. U. Fla., 1949-51, prof., 1951-56; prof. U. Ill., Champaign, 1958-68; Max Rowe prof. law U. Ill., 1982-89, prof. emeritus, 1989—; vis. prof. McGeorge Law Sch. U. Pacific, Sacramento, 1989-92; prof. U. Oreg., 1968-82, dean Sch. Law, 1968-74, disting. prof. emeritus, 1982—; vis. prof. Khartoum U., Sudan, 1964-65. Author: (with H.F. Goodrich) Conflict of Laws, 4th edit., 1964, (with R.J. Weintraub) Cases and Materials on Conflict of Laws, 2d edit., 1972, (with E.C. Halbach, Jr.) Problems and Materials on Decedents' Estates and Trusts, 5th edit., 1993, Problems and Materials on Future Interests, 1977, (with P. Hay) Conflict of Laws, 2d edit., 1992; contbr. articles to profl. jours.; notes and legislation editor Iowa Law Rev., 1945; reporter Uniform Probate Code Project, 1966-70; mem. joint editorial bd. Uniform Probate Code, 1972—. Mem. ABA, Assoc. Pub. Tchrs. Law, Am. Law Inst., Ill. Bar Assn., Assn. Am. Law Schs. (pres. 1978), Order of Coif. Home: 1931 Kimberly Dr Eugene OR 97405-5849 Office: U Oreg Sch of Law 11th And Kincaid Eugene OR 97403

SCOLES, GIACINTO, chemistry educator; b. Torino, Italy, Apr. 2, 1935; came to Can., 1971; to U.S., 1987; s. Mario and Maria (Fiorio) S.; m. Giok-Lan Lim, Oct. 20, 1964; 1 child, Gigi. Degree in chemistry, U. Genoa, Italy, 1959, Libero Docente, 1968. Asst. prof. U. Genoa, 1960-61, 64-68, assoc. prof., 1968-71; research assoc. U. Leiden, The Netherlands, 1961-64; prof. chemistry and physics U. Waterloo, Ont., Can., 1971-86; Donner prof. sci. Princeton (N.J.) U., 1987—. Editor: Atomic and Molecular Beam Methods, 1987; contbr. numerous articles to profl. jours. Killam fellow Sci. Council Can., 1986; Ellis R. Lippincott Awd., 1995, Optical Soc. Am. Fellow The Chem. Inst. Can.; mem. Can. Assn. Physicists, Am. Phys. Soc., Am. Chem. Soc., Optical Soc. Am. (hon.). Office: Princeton U Dept Chemistry Princeton NJ 08544

SCOLLARD, DIANE LOUISE, secondary education educator; b. Seattle, Mar. 12, 1945; d. James Martin and Viola Gladys (Williams) S. BA in Edn., Wash. State U., 1967; 5th yr. cert. in edn., U. Wash., 1970; cert. edn., Oakland U., 1977. Tchr. Battle Ground (Wash.) Sch. Dist., 1967-70, Lapeer (Mich.) Community Schs., 1970-95. Mem. AAUW, NEA, NAFE, Am. Bus. Women's Assn., Mich. Edn. Assn., Lapeer Edn. Assn. (bldg. rep. 1985, 89), Beta Sigma Phi. Democrat. Episcopalian. Avocations: travel, cooking, movies, collecting thimbles, bowling.

SCOLLARD, PATRICK JOHN, hospital executive; b. Chgo., Apr. 20, 1937; s. Patrick J. and Kathleen (Cooney) S.; m. Gloria Ann Carroll, July 1, 1961; children: Kevin, Maureen, Daniel, Thomas, Brian. BS in Econs., Marquette U., 1959; grad. sr. exec. devel. program, MIT, 1976. With Equitable Life Assurance Soc. U.S., N.Y.C., 1962-79, dir. compensation, 1968-69, asst. v.p., 1969-71, v.p., personnel dir., 1971-75, v.p. administrv. services, 1975-79, v.p. corp. administrv. and employee services, 1978-79; sr. v.p. Chem. Bank, N.Y.C., 1979-80, exec. v.p. 1980-87, chief administrv. officer, 1987-92; pres., CEO St Francis Hosp., Roslyn, N.Y., 1992—; bd. dirs. Work in Am. Mem. adv. bd. Marquette U.; mem. bd. Cath. Charities; former chmn. Woodstock Theol. Ctr.; bd. dirs St. Francis Hosp. With USN, 1959-62. Bd. dirs. Cath. Charities; former chmn. Woodstock Theol. Ctr., St. Francis Hosp. With USN, 1959-62. Office: St Francis Hosp 100 Port Washington Blvd Roslyn NY 11576-1348

SCOLNICK, EDWARD MARK, science administrator; b. Boston, Aug. 9, 1940; s. Barbara (Chasen) Scolnick; m. Barbara Bachrach; children: Laura, Jason, Daniel. AB, Harvard U., 1961; MD, Harvard U. Med. Sch., 1965. Intern Mass. Gen. Hosp., 1965-66, asst. resident internal medicine, 1966-67; research assoc. USPHS, 1967-69; sr. staff fellow lab. biochem. genetics NIH, 1969-70; instr. NIH News, 1970; sr. staff fellow viral leukemia and lymphoma br. Nat. Cancer Inst., 1970-71, spl. advisor to spl. virus cancer program, 1973-78, mem. coordinating com. for virus cancer program, 1975-78, chief lab. tumor virus genetics, head. molecular virology sect., 1975-82; exec. dir. basic research virus and cell biology research Merck Sharp & Dohme Rsch. Labs., West Point, Pa., 1982-83, v.p. virus and cell biology research, 1983-84, sr. v.p., 1984, pres., 1985-93; sr. v.p. Merck & Co., Inc., 1991-93, exec. v.p.,

pres. rsch., 1993—; adj. prof. microbiology Sch. Medicine U. Pa., 1983-86. Editor-in-chief Jour. Virology; mem. editorial bd. Virology; contbr. numerous articles to profl. jours.; Served with USPHS, 1965-67. Recipient Arthur S. Fleming award, 1976, PHS Superior Svc. award, 1978, Eli Lilly award, 1980, Indsl. Rsch. Inst. medal, 1990. Mem. NAS, Am. Soc. Biol. Chemists, Am. Soc. Microbiologists. Home: 811 Wickfield Rd Wynnewood PA 19096-1610 Office: Merck Rsch Labs PO Box 2000 Rahway NJ 07065-0900*

SCONIERS, M. L., bishop. Bishop of Western Fla., Ch. of God in Christ, Orlando. Office: Ch of God in Christ PO Box 5472 Orlando FL 32805

SCOPAZ, JOHN MATTHEW, banker; b. N.Y.C., June 24, 1948; s. John J. and Alice L. (Zustovich) S.; m. Linda N. Nelson, Mar. 17, 1973; children: Jennifer, Lauren, Kristen. BSChemE, Manhattan Coll., 1970; MBA, NYU, 1973. Plant engr. Colgate Palmolive, Jersey City, 1970-72; systems analyst Colgate Palmolive, N.Y.C., 1973-74; mng. dir., v.p. Citicorp (BHC Resources), N.Y.C., 1975-81; exec. v.p. Republic Nat. Bank, N.Y.C., 1981—; chmn., bd. dirs. Republic Info. & Communications Svcs., N.Y.C. Coach Pelham (N.Y.) Little League; bd. dirs., pres. N.Y. League Hard of Hearing. Mem. Am. Mgmt. Assn., N.Y. Clearing House (mem. steering com.). Republican. Roman Catholic. Avocations: family, skiing, tennis. Office: Republic Nat Bank 452 5th Ave New York NY 10018-2706

SCOPES, GARY MARTIN, professional association executive; b. St. Petersburg, Fla., July 16, 1947; s. Louis Martin and Eleanor Beebe (Kurkjian) S.; m. Connie Joy Kowalski, Sept. 16, 1967; children: Darryl, Sandra, Adrian. BA in Rhetoric, U. South Fla., 1971. Cert. assn. exec. (nationally). Lobbyist La. Mcpl. Assn., Baton Rouge, 1972-74; exec. dir. Soc. La. CPAs, Metairie, 1974-84, Tex. Soc. CPAs, Dallas, 1984-87, Inst. Mgmt. Accts. (formerly Nat. Assn. Accts.), Montvale, N.J., 1987—; pres. La. Soc. Assn. Execs., 1980-81, CPA Soc. Execs. Assn., 1982-83, Kaypro Computer Users Group, 1979. 1st lt. U.S. Army, 1966-69. Mem. N.J. Soc. Assn. Execs. (pres.). Avocations: tennis, skiing, golf, fishing, guitar. Home: 1 Van Wyck St Montvale NJ 07645-1025 Office: Institute of Mngmt Accountants 10 Paragon Dr Montvale NJ 07645-1718

SCORCA, MARC AZZOLINI, arts administrator; b. Rockville Centre, N.Y., Sept. 20; s. Louis G. and Rosalie (Tascarella) S. B.A. magna cum laude in History and Music, Amherst Coll. Dir. mktg. Opera Co. of Phila., 1979-80; administrv. asst. N.Y.C. Opera, 1980-81, dir. spl. events, 1981-84; gen. mgr. Chgo. Opera Theatre, 1984-90; exec. v.p., chief exec. officer Opera Am., 1990—, also dir./dir. Pa. Opera Theater, Phila., Am. Arts Alliance, Nat. Music Coun.; dir., pres. Chgo. Music Alliance; panelist NEA, Ill. Arts Coun., Chgo. Office of Fine Arts; mem. Nat. Adv. Coun. Arts in Edn. Home: 108 Tennessee Ave NE Washington DC 20002-6447 Office: Opera Am 777 14th St NW Washington DC 20005-3201

SCORDELIS, ALEXANDER COSTICAS, civil engineering educator; b. San Francisco, Sept. 27, 1923; s. Philip Kostas and Vasilica (Zois) S.; m. Georgia Gumas, May 9, 1948; children: Byron, Karen. B.S., U. Calif., Berkeley, 1948; M.S., M.I.T., 1949. Registered profl. engr., Calif. Structural designer Pacific Gas & Electric Co., San Francisco, 1948; engr. Bechtel Corp., San Francisco, summer 1951, 52, 53, 54; instr. civil engring. U. Calif., Berkeley, 1949-50; asst. prof. U. Calif., 1951-56, asso. prof., 1957-61, prof., 1962-89; asst. dean U. Calif. (Coll. Engring.), 1962-65, vice chmn. div. structural engring, structural mechanics, 1970-73, Nishkian prof. emeritus, 1990—; cons. engring. firms, govt. agys. Contbr. articles on analysis and design of complex structural systems, reinforced and prestressed concrete shell and bridge structures to profl. jours. Served to capt., C.E. U.S. Army, 1943-46, ETO. Decorated Bronze star, Purple Heart; recipient Western Electric award Am. Soc. Engring. Edn., 1978; Axion award Hellenic Am. Profl. Soc., 1979; Best paper award Canadian Soc. Civil Engring., 1982, K.B. Woods award NAS Transp. Rsch. Bd., 1983, Citation U. Calif. Berkeley, 1989, Disting. Engring. Alumnus award Berkeley Engring. Alumni Soc., 1993, Leadership award Am. Segmental Bridge Inst., 1993, Freyssinet medal Internat. Fedn. for Prestressed Concrete, 1994. Fellow ASCE (hon. mem. 1989, Moissieff award 1976, 81, 92, Howard award 1989), Am. Concret Inst.; mem. Internat. Assn. Shell and Spatial Structures (hon., Torroja medal 1994), Structural Engrs. Assn. Calif., Nat. Acad. Engring. Home: 724 Gelston Pl El Cerrito CA 94530-3045 Office: 729 Davis Hall # U Calif Berkeley CA 94720

SCORSESE, MARTIN, film director, writer; b. Flushing, N.Y., Nov. 17, 1942; s. Charles and Catherine (Cappa) S.; m. Laraine Marie Brennan, May 15, 1965 (div.), 1 daughter: Catherine Terese Glinora Sophia; m. Julia Cameron, 1975 (div.), 1 daughter: Dominica Elizabeth; m. Isabella Rosellini, Sept. 29, 1979 (div. 1983); m. Barbara DeFina, Feb. 9, 1985. BS in Film Communications, NYU, 1964, MA in Film Communications, 1966. Faculty asst., then instr. film NYU, N.Y.C., 1963-70. films include: (dir.): The Big Shave, 1968 (also writer), Who's That Knocking at My Door?, 1968 (also writer, assoc. prodr., actor), Boxcar Bertha, 1972 (also actor), Mean Streets, 1973 (also co-writer, actor), Alice Doesn't Live Here Anymore, 1975, Taxi Driver, 1976 (also actor, Palme d'Or Cannes Internat. Film Festival), New York, New York, 1977, The Last Waltz, 1978, Raging Bull, 1980, The King of Comedy, 1983 (also actor), After Hours, 1985, The Color of Money, 1986, The Last Temptation of Christ, 1988, New York Stories (Life Lessons), 1989, GoodFellas, 1990 (also co-writer), Cape Fear, 1991, The Age of Innocence 1993 (also co-writer), Casino, 1995; (prodr.): The Grifters, 1990, Mad Dog and Glory, 1993, Clockers, 1995; (exec. prodr.): Naked in New York, 1994; documentaries include: (editor): Woodstock, 1970 (also asst. dir.), Elvis on Tour, 1973; (assoc. prodr.): Medicine Ball Caravan, 1971; (dir.): Street Scenes 1970, 1970, Italianamerican, 1974, American Boy: A Profile of Steven Price, 1979, Man in Milan, 1990; other film appearances include: Cannonball, 1976, Pavlova: A Woman for All Seasons, 1983, 'Round Midnight, 1986, Akira Kurosawa's Dreams, 1990, Guilty by Suspicion, 1991, Quiz Show, 1994. Recipient Edward L. Kingsley Found. award, 1963-64, 1st prize Rosenthal Found. awards Soc. Cinemetologists, 1964, 1st prize Screen Producer's Guild, 1965, 1st prize Brown U. Film Festival, 1965, also others; named Best Dir. Cannes Film Festival, 1986. Office: Barbara Moskowitz Yohalem Gillman Co 477 Madison Ave Fl 9 New York NY 10022-5802 also: care CAA 9830 Wilshire Blvd Beverly Hills CA 90212-1804

SCORSONE, VINCENT ROBERT, aluminum company executive; b. Mc Keesport, Pa., May 21, 1935; s. Peter and Eva (Cralley) S.; m. Janet Louise Overland, Dec. 15, 1956; children: Valerie J., Grant V. BBA, U. Pitts., 1957. Mgr. transp. Aluminum Co. Am., various location, 1960-73; mgr. production Aluminum Co. Am., Davenport, Iowa and Pitts., 1973-76; works mgr. Aluminum Co. Am., Wenatchee, Wash., 1976-79, Davenport, Iowa, 1979-80; dir. ops. Alcoa Aluminio S.Am., Sao Paulo, Brazil, 1980-81; gen. mgr. primary metals Aluminum Co. Am., Pitts., 1981-82, v.p. primary metals, 1982-84, group v.p. primary metals, 1984-85, group v.p. primary products, 1985-86, group v.p. aerospace and indsl. products, 1986—; bd. dirs. Alcoa Found., Pitts. Mem. N. Cen. Washington Devel. Council, Wenatchee, 1977-78; adv. bd. Mon Valley Renaissance Calif., 1985—, U. Pa., 1985—. Served to 1st lt. U.S. Army, 1957-59. Mem. N. Cen. C. of C. Republican. Methodist. Lodge: Rotary. Office: Aluminium Co Am 1501 Alcoa Bldg Pittsburgh PA 15219

SCORZA, SYLVIO JOSEPH, religion educator; b. Zürich, Switzerland, Mar. 21, 1923; came to U.S., 1929; s. Joseph Peter and Helena Christina (Kopp) S.; m. Phyllis Joan VanSetters, June 6, 1952; children: Christine Marie, Philip Joseph, John Forrest. AA, Woodrow Wilson Jr. Coll., 1942; AB, Hope Coll., 1945; BD, Western Theol. Sem., Holland, Mich., 1953; ThD, Princeton Theol. Sem., 1956; PhD, U. Ill., 1972. Ordained to ministry Ref. Ch. in Am., 1955. Stated supply pastor Hickory Bottom Charge, Loysburg, Pa., 1957-58; prof. religion Northwestern Coll., Orange City, Iowa, 1959-90, prof. emeritus, 1990—; vis. prof. Lancaster (Pa.) Theol. Sem., 1956-57, Western Theol. Sem., Holland, Mich., 1958-59; v.p. Ref. Ch. in Am., N.Y.C., 1988-89, pres., 1989-90, moderator, exec. com. 1990-91. Co-editor: Concordance to the Greek and Hebrew Text of Ruth, The Computer Bible, Septuagint series, Vols. XXX, XXX-B, 1988-89; contbr. articles to profl. jours. County del. Iowa Dems., Ft. Dodge, 1984. Recipient Disting. Alumnus award Hope Coll., 1989, Homecoming Honors award Northwestern Coll. N Club, 1990, Handicapped Person of Siouxland award Siouxland Com. for the Handicapped, 1990, Gov.'s award Iowa Commn. of Persons

with Disabilities, 1990, Victory award Nat. Rehab. Hosp., 1991. Mem. Internat. Orgn. for Septuagint and Cognate Studies, Smithsonian Instsn., Nat. Geog. Soc., Iowa State Chess Assn. (v.p. 1984-85, dir. postal tournament 1987—). Avocations: chess, bridge. Home: 520 2D St SW Orange City IA 51041 Office: Northwestern Coll Orange City IA 51041

SCOTT, A. HUGH, lawyer; b. Auckland, New Zealand, Jan. 10, 1947; came to U.S., 1957; s. John E. and Leona (Lacey) S.; m. Susan Campbell, Dec. 3, 1946; 1 child, Matthew Campbell. BA, Williams Coll., 1968; JD, Columbia U., 1974. Bar: Mass. 1974, U.S. Dist. Ct. Mass 1975, U.S. Ct. Appeals (1st cir.) 1975, U.S. Supreme Ct. 1982. Asst. U.S. atty. U.S. Atty.'s Office, Boston, 1978-83; assoc. Choate, Hall & Stewart, Boston, 1975-78, 83-85, ptnr., 1986—. Lt. (j.g.) USNR, 1968-71. Democrat. Home: 10 Cazenove St Boston MA 02116-6205 Office: Exchange Pl 53 State St Boston MA 02109-2804

SCOTT, A. TIMOTHY, lawyer; b. Natchez, Miss., Feb. 16, 1952; s. John William and Patricia (O'Reilly) S.; m. Nancy E. Howard, June 7, 1976; children: Kevin Howard, Brian Howard. BA in Psychology, Stanford U., 1974, JD, 1977. Bar: Calif. 1977, U.S. Tax Ct. 1978. Assoc. then ptnr. Agnew, Miller & Carlson (now Hufstedler & Klaus), L.A., 1977-83; assoc. Greenberg, Glusker, Claman, Fields & Machtinger, L.A., 1983; ptnr. Sachs & Phelps, L.A., 1983-91; mem. Heller, Ehrman White & McAuliffe, L.A., 1991—; speaker in field. Note editor Stanford Law Rev., 1976-77; contbr. article to profl. pubs., chpt. to book. Mem. ABA, L.A. County Bar Assn. (chmn. real estate taxation com. 1988-91, exec. com., taxation sect. 1989-91), Order of Coif. Democrat. Avocations: volleyball, gardening, Calif. wine, contemporary art. Office: Heller Ehrman White & McAuliffe 601 S Figueroa St Fl 40 Los Angeles CA 90017-3874

SCOTT, ALASTAIR IAN, chemistry educator; b. Glasgow, Scotland, Apr. 10, 1928; came to U.S., 1965; s. William and Nell (Newton) S.; m. Elizabeth Wilson Walters, Mar. 4, 1950; children: William Stewart, Ann Walker. B.Sc., Glasgow U., 1949, Ph.D., 1952, D.Sc., 1964; M.A. (hon.), Yale U., 1968; D.Sc. (hon.), U. Coimbra, Portugal, 1990, U. Pierre & Marie Curie, Paris, 1992. Lectr. organic chemistry Glasgow U., 1957-62; prof. U. B.C., Vancouver, 1962-65, Sussex (Eng.) U., 1965-68, Yale U., 1968-77; disting. prof. Tex. A&M U., 1977-80, Davidson prof. sci., 1982—; prof. dept. chemistry U. Edinburgh, Scotland, 1980-82; cons. in field. Author: Interpretations of Ultraviolet Spectra of Natural Products, 1964; contbr. articles to profl. jours. Recipient rsch. achievement award Am. Soc. Pharmacognosy, 1993. Fellow Royal Soc., Royal Soc. Edinburgh; mem. Am. Chem. Soc. (Ernest Guenther award 1976, A.C. Cope scholar 1992), Chem. Soc. (Corday-Morgan medal 1964, Centenary lectr. 1994), Biochem. Soc., Japan Pharm. Soc. (hon.). Office: Tex A&M U Chemistry Dept College Station TX 77843

SCOTT, ALEXANDER ROBINSON, engineering association executive; b. Elizabeth, N.J., June 15, 1941; s. Marvin Chester and Jane (Robinson) S.; m. Angela Jean Kendall, July 17, 1971; children: Alexander Robinson, Jennifer Angela, Ashley Kendall. B.A. in History, Va. Mil. Inst., 1963; M.A. in Personnel and Counseling Psychology, Rutgers U., 1965. Sales mgr. Hilton Hotels, 1967-70; meetings mgr. Am. Inst. Mining Engrs., N.Y.C., 1971-73; exec. dir. Minerals, Metals and Materials Soc., 1973—. Served with U.S. Army, 1965-67. Decorated Bronze star. Mem. Am. Soc. Assn. Execs. Republican. Baptist. Home: 107 Staghorn Dr Sewickley PA 15143-9506 Office: TMS 420 Commonwealth Dr Warrendale PA 15086-7511

SCOTT, ALICE H., librarian; b. Jefferson, Ga.; d. Frank D. and Annie D. (Colbert) Holly; m. Alphonso Scott, Mar. 1, 1959; children—Christopher, Alison. A.B., Spelman Coll., Atlanta, 1957; M.L.S., Atlanta U., 1958; Ph.D., U. Chgo., 1983. Librarian Bklyn. Pub. Library, 1958-59; br. librarian Chgo. Pub. Library, 1959-72, dir. Woodson Regional Library, 1974-77, dir. community relations, 1977-82, dep. commr., 1982-87, asst. commr., 1987—. Doctoral fellow, 1973. Mem. ALA (councilor 1982-85), Ill. Library Assn., Chgo. Spelman Club, DuSable Mus., Chgo. Urban League. Democrat. Baptist. Office: Chgo Pub Library 400 S State St Chicago IL 60605-1203

SCOTT, ALLEN JOHN, educator; b. Liverpool, England, Dec. 23, 1938; came to U.S., 1969; s. William Rule and Nella Mara (Pieri) S.; m. Nga Thuy Nguyen, Jan. 19, 1979. BA, Oxford (Eng.) U., 1961; PhD, Northwestern U., 1965. Research assoc. dept. town planning U. Coll. London, 1967-69; prof. geography UCLA, 1980—; prof. geography and urgan planning U. Toronto, Ont., Can., 1969-80; dir. Lewis Ctr. for Regional Policy Studies UCLA, 1990-94, assoc. dean Sch. Pub. Policy and Social Rsch., 1994—; Professeur associé U. Paris, 1974. Author: Combinatorial Programming, 1971, Urban Land Nexus, 1980, Metropolis, 1988, New Industrial Spaces, 1988, Technopolis, 1993. Fellow Com. on Scholarly Communication with People's Republic China, 1986. Croucher fellow U. Hong Kong, 1984; Guggenheim fellow, 1986-87. Office: UCLA Sch Pub Policy/Social Rsch Los Angeles CA 90095

SCOTT, AMY ANNETTE HOLLOWAY, nursing educator; b. St. Albans, W.Va., Apr. 10, 1916; d. Oliver and Mary (Lee) Holloway; m. William M. Jefferson, June 22, 1932, (div. Oct. 1933); 1 child, William M. Jefferson, m. Vann Hyland Scott, Mar. 15, 1952, (dec. Dec. 1972). BS in Nursing Edn., Cath. U., Washington, 1948; cert. in psychiat. nursing, U. Paris, Paris, 1959. Indsl. nurse Curtiss Wright Air Plane Co., Lambert Field, St. Louis, 1941-44; faculty St. Thomas U., Manila, Philippines Island, 1948-50; pub. health nurse St. Louis Health Dept., 1951-56; capt. USAF Nursing Corps, Paris, 1956-60; resigned as maj. USAF (Nurse Corps), 1960, 1960; faculty St. Louis State Hosp., 1960-67; dept. head St. Vincents Hosp., St. Louis, 1967-68; faculty RN, creator psychiat. program Sch. of Nursing Jewish Hosp., 1968-72; administrv. nurse St. Louis State Hosp., 1972-84; initiated first psychiatric program sch. nursing, Jewish Hosp. Author: (short story) Two Letters, 1962, (novel) Storms, 1987, Life's Journey, 1993. Past bd. dirs. county bd. Mo. U., 1984-88; hon. citizen Colonial Williamsburg, Va.; mem. Rep. Presdl. Task Force; mem. Women in the Arts '94. Recipient Key to Colonial Williamsburg, Va., Medal of Merit, Rep. Presdl. Task Force, 1992; named to Rep. Presdl. Task Force Honor Roll, 1993, Nat. Women's Hall of Fame, 1995. Mem. AAUW, NAFE, Internat. Fedn. Univ. Women, Internat. Soc. Quality Assurance in Health Care, Am. Biog. Inst. (life, governing bd.), Cambridge Centre Eng., Internat. Platform Assn., Women in Arts. Roman Catholic. Avocations: music, boating, horseback riding, dog sled riding, travel.

SCOTT, ANDREW, corporate executive; b. St. Paul, Apr. 5, 1928; s. Ulric and Annamay (Gorry) S.; m. Kathleen Kennedy, May 7, 1960; children: Andrea Kennedy Scott, Lucia Scott Duff. BS, U. Minn., 1950, LLB, 1952. Bar: Minn. 1952. Ptnr. Doherty, Rumble & Butler, Mpls. and St. Paul, 1952-77; chmn. Andrew Scott Ltd., Mpls., 1978-81; founder, vice chmn. Cray Rsch. Inc., Mpls., 1972—, also bd. dirs. Bd. dirs. Minn. Orchestral Assn., Mpls., 1965-78, First Trust Co., Inc., St. Paul, 1981-90; trustee Mpls. Soc. Fine Arts, 1966-78, Twin City Area Pub. TV Corp., St. Paul, 1967-74, St. Paul Acad./Summit Sch., 1972-75. Mem. ABA, Computer Law Assn. Roman Catholic. Avocations: gardening, tai chi, megalithic cave art, skiing, zazen. Home: 1941 Penn Ave S Minneapolis MN 55405-2210 Office: Cray Rsch Inc 655A Lone Oak Dr Eagan MN 55121-1560

SCOTT, ANNE BYRD FIROR, history educator; b. Montezuma, Ga., Apr. 24, 1921; d. John William and Mary Valentine (Moss) Firor; m. Andrew Mackay Scott, June 2, 1947; children: Rebecca, David MacKay, Donald MacKay. AB, U. Ga., 1941; MA, Northwestern U., 1944; PhD, Radcliffe Coll., 1958; LHD (hon.), Lindenwood Coll., 1968, Queens Coll., 1985, Northwestern U., 1989, Radcliffe Coll., 1990, U. of the South, 1990, Cornell Coll., 1991. Congressional rep., editor LWV of U.S., 1944-53; lectr. history Haverford Coll., 1957-58, U. N.C., Chapel Hill, 1959-60; asst. prof. history Duke U., Durham, N.C., 1961-66; assoc. prof. Duke U., 1968-70, prof., 1971-80, W.K. Boyd prof., 1980-91, W.K. Boyd prof. emerita, 1992—, chmn. dept., 1981-85; Gastprofessor Universität, Bonn, Germany, 1992-93; vis. prof. Johns Hopkins U., 1972-73, Stanford U., 1974, Harvard U., 1984, Cornell U., 1993, Williams Coll., 1994; Times-Mirror scholar Huntington Libr., 1995; vice chmn. Nat. Humanities Ctr., 1991—; mem. adv. com. Schlesinger Libr.; Fulbright lectr., 1962, 92-93. Author: The Southern Lady, 1970, (with Andrew MacKay Scott) One Half the People, 1974, Making the Invisible Woman Visible, 1984, Natural Allies, 1991; editor: Jane Addams,

Democracy and Social Ethics, 1964, The American Woman, 1970, Women in American Life, 1970, Women and Men in American Life, 1976, Unheard Voices, 1993; mem. editorial bd. Revs. in Am. History, 1976-81, Am. Quar., 1974-78, Jour. So. History, 1978-84; contbr. articles to profl. jours. Chmn. Gov.'s Commn. on Status of Women, 1963-64; mem. Citizens Adv. Council on Status of Women U.S., 1964-68. AAUW fellow, 1956-57; grantee NEH, 1967-68, 76-77, Nat. Humanities Ctr., 1980-81; grad. medal Radcliffe Coll., 1986; fellow Ctr. Advanced Study in Behavioral Sci., 1986-87; Fulbright scholar, 1984, 92-93. Mem. Am. Antiquarian Soc., Orgn. Am. Historians (exec. bd. 1973-76, pres. 1983), So. Hist. Assn. (exec. bd. 1976-79, pres. 1989), Soc. Am. Historians, Phi Beta Kappa. Democrat. Office: Duke U Dept History Durham NC 27708

SCOTT, ARNOLD DUANE, lawyer, financial company executive; b. Troy, W.Va., Dec. 16, 1942; s. Russell P. and Geraldine (White) S.; m. Ruth Cottignoli, June 6, 1964; 1 child, Arnold. BA, Alderson-Broaddus Coll., 1964; JD, Rutgers U., 1967. Bar: N.J. 1968, D.C. 1968. Assoc. Carpenter, Bennett & Morrissey, Newark, 1968-69; with Mass. Fin. Services Co., Boston, 1969—, sr. exec. v.p., mem. exec. com. 1985—, also bd. dirs. ; gov. Investment Co. Inst., Washington, 1983—; trustee Mass Investors Trust, 1993—. Mem. Somerset Club. Republican. Episcopalian. Office: Mass Fin Services Co 500 Boylston St Boston MA 02116-3740

SCOTT, AUDREY EBBA, federal agency administrator; b. Boston, Nov. 25, 1935; d. Carl Arthur and Vera (Bisbee) Hallberg; m. John Joseph Scott, May 5, 1962; children: Lawrence, Bryan, Kenneth, Edward. BA, Tufts U., 1957; postgrad., So. Conn. U., 1957-58, Harvard U., 1958; MA, George Washington U., 1990. Tchr. North Haven (Conn.) Sch. System, 1957-59; tchr. U.S. Dept. Def.-Overseas Sch. System, LaRochelle, France, 1959-61, Zama, Japan, 1961-63; councilwoman City of Bowie, Md., 1974-76, mayor, 1976-82; dir. community relations Prince George's Hosp. and Med. Ctr., Cheverly, Md., 1980-81; spl. asst. HUD, Washington, 1981-84, assoc. dep. asst. sec., 1984-86, dep. asst. sec., 1986-88, gen. dep. asst. sec., 1988—; past bd. dirs. Council of Govts., Washington. Pres. Bowie Health Ctr., 1971-75, 82—, Md. Mcpl. League, 1979-80; bd. dirs. Multiple Sclerosis Soc., Washington, 1975—; del. Rep. Nat. Conv., Detroit, 1980; candidate for U.S. Congress from 5th dist. Md., 1981; elder, commr. Nat. Presbytery. Recipient Women Helping Women award Soroptimists, 1982; named Outstanding Mcpl. Ofcl. Mcpl. Assn., 1977, Outstanding Mayor VFW, 1979. Mem. AAUW (program chmn. 1985-87), Rep. Women Capitol Hill. Club: Bus. and Profl. Women's (Bowie) (chmn. status of women com. 1983-84, Woman of Yr. 1984). Home: 12109 Long Ridge Ln Bowie MD 20715-2358 Office: HUD Community Planning & Devel 451 7th St SW Washington DC 20410-0001

SCOTT, BILL, advertising agency executive; b. Phila., Sept. 1, 1949; s. Norris A. and Jean (Satterthwaite) S. BA in Writing, West Chester U., 1971; BS in Radio-TV-Film, Temple U., Phila., 1974. Advt. coord. S.M.S., Malvern, Pa., 1978-81; dir. pub. rels. Thomas R. Sundheim Inc., Jenkintown, Pa., 1981-88; v.p. Kingswood Advt., Inc., Ardmore, Pa., 1988—; cons. Yonex USA, Torrance, Calif., 1989—, Nat. Trust for Historic Preservation, Washington, 1987—. Author: Chinese Kung-Fu, 1976; creator/writer Camp Dog Days comic strip, 1992—. Republican. Episcopalian. Avocations: tennis, running, weightlifting, writing. Home: 77 Croton Rd Strafford PA 19087-2663 Office: Kingswood Advt Inc Cricket Ter Ardmore PA 19003

SCOTT, BRIAN DOUGLAS, association executive; b. Portland, Oreg., Apr. 5, 1958; s. William Craven and Louise (Krengel) S.; m. Debra Suzanne Clem, June 21, 1980 (div. 1986); m. Ruth Elizabeth Pritchard, Aug. 30, 1986. BS, Oreg. State U., 1980; M Landscape Arch., N.C. State U., 1982. Downtown planner City of Raleigh (N.C), 1982-84; dir. design svcs. Oreg. Downtown Devel. Assn., Salem, 1984, program coordinator, 1984-85, pres., exec. dir., 1985—. Editor Oregon's Downtowns: The Next Five Years, 1988 (award 1988); contbr. articles to profl. publs. Mem. Nat. Main St. Network, Internat. Downtown Assn. (bd. dirs. 1991—, Spl. Achievement award 1991, Merit award 1991), Am. Planning Assn., Urban Land Inst. (assoc.). Democrat. Office: Oreg Downtown Devel Assn 921 SW Morrison St Ste 508 Portland OR 97205-2723

SCOTT, BRIAN E., insurance company executive; b. Akron, Ohio, Oct. 2, 1936; s. Parker and Theresa Scott; m. Carole Leiser, Aug. 27, 1960; children—David, Kelly. B.S. in Math., Kent State U., 1962. Actuarial student Aetna Life & Casualty, Hartford, Conn., 1962-67, asst. sec., 1969-73, 1973-76, asst. v.p., 1976-82, v.p., 1982-87, v.p., 1987—. With U.S. Army, 1956-57. Fellow Casualty Actuarial Soc., Am. Acad. Actuaries; mem. Ga. Underwriters Assn. (bd. dirs. 1984—). Republican. Roman Catholic. Club: Avon Golf (pres. 1984—). Home: 78 Brookmoor Dr Avon CT 06001-2301 Office: Aetna Life & Casualty Co 151 Farmington Ave Hartford CT 06156-0002

SCOTT, CAMPBELL, artist; b. Milngavie, Scotland, Oct. 5, 1930; s. Robert and Catherine S. Apprentice woodcarver, Glasgow, Scotland, 1946-51; student, Royal Acad. Art, Copenhagen, 1965-66; studies with, S.W. Hayter, Paris, 1966. Exhbns. include 1st Biennial Internat. Graphics, Krakow, Poland, 1966, 1st Brit. Internat. Print Biennale, Eng., 1969, traveling exhbn., Nat. Gallery Can., Ottawa, 1969, 4th Am. Biennial Engraving, Santiago, Chile, Can. Embassy, Washington, 1971, Pratt Inst., N.Y.C., 1971; represented in permanent collections, Brit. Mus., Bibliotheque Nat., Paris, Scottish Nat. Gallery Modern Art, Montreal Mus. Art, Victoria and Albert Mus., London, Art Gallery of Ont., Toronto, Can.; commd. works include: bronze sculpture, Public Library Niagara Falls, Can., wood sculpture, Public Library, St. Catharines, Can.; mural, The Pumphouse Art Centr Niagara on the Lake, Can. Mem. Print and Drawing Council Can. Address: 89 Byron, Niagara on the Lake, ON Canada L0S 1J0

SCOTT, CAMPBELL, actor; b. N.Y.C., July 19, 1962; s. George C. Scott and Colleen Dewhurst. Appearences include (theatre) The Queen and the Rebels, 1982, The Real Thing, 1984, Our Town, 1984, Hay Fever, 1985, A Man For All Seasons, 1986, Dalliance, 1986, Copperhead, 1987, Ah, Wilderness!, 1987-88, Long Day's Journey Into Night, 1987-88, (TV movies) The Kennedys of Massachusetts, 1990, The Perfect Tribute, 1991, (films) Five Corners, 1987, From Hollywood to Deadwood, 1988, Longtime Companion, 1989, Ain't No Way Back, 1990, The Sheltering Sky, 1990, Dying Young, 1991, Dead Again, 1991, Singles, 1992, Mrs. Parker and the Vicious Circle, 1994, The Innocent, 1994. Office: Paradigm Talent Agency 10100 Santa Monica Blvd 25th Fl Los Angeles CA 90067*

SCOTT, CAROL LEE, child care educator; b. Monte Vista, Colo., Jan. 10, 1944; d. Robert A. and Thelma G. (Allen) Jay; m. Bates E. Shaw, June 4, 1966 (dec. Feb. 1976); children: Crystal A., Sharon L.; m. James W. Scott, July 23, 1977. BA in Home Econs., Friends U., 1965; MS, Okla. State U., 1973. Cert. home economist; lic. profl. counselor. Receptionist Cen. Assembly of God Ch., Wichita, Kans., summer 1965; office worker Henry's Inc., Wichita, 1965-66; tchr. home econs. Wichita High Sch. South, 1966, Cir. High Sch., Towanda, Kans., 1966-68, Fairfax (Okla.) High Sch., 1968-74; tchr. vocat. home econs. Derby (Kans.) High Sch., 1974-75; child devel. specialist Bi-State Mental Health Found., Ponca City, Okla., 1975-87; instr. child care Pioneer Tech. Ctr., Ponca City, 1987—, dir., 1987-89, 93—; cons. Phil Fitzgerald Assocs. Archs., Ponca City, 1980, Head Start Okla., 1981-86; trainer, paraprofl. Child Care Careers, 1980—; validator Nat. Assn. Edn. Young Children 1992—. Contbg. author Child Abuse Prevention Mini Curriculum. Mem. Ponca City Schs., 1982-85, title IV-A parent com., 1985-89; area chmn. Heart Fund, 1985; chmn. edn. com. Dist. XVII Child Abuse Prevention Task Force, Okla., 1985—; treas., 1989—; mem. cultural affairs com. Ponca City Adv. Bd., 1986-89; co-chair Week of the Young Child Com. for Kay County, 1991—. Mem. NEA, Am. Vocat. Assn., Am. Assn. Family and Consumer Scis., Okla. Family and Consumer Scis., Okla. Vocat. Assn., Okla. Assn. Vocat. Home Econs. Tchrs., Okla. Edn. Assn., Okla. Assn. for Edn. Young Children, Okla. Early Childhood Assn., So. Early Childhood Assn., Nat. Assn. for Edn. Young Children (validator for early childhood programs seeking accreditation by divsn. Nat. Acad. Early Childhood Programs 1992—), Friends of Day Care, LWV. Republican. Methodist. Home: 414 Virginia Ave Ponca City OK 74601-3436

SCOTT, CATHERINE DOROTHY, librarian, information consultant; b. Washington, June 21, 1927; d. Leroy Stearns Scott and Agnes Frances (Meade) Scott Schellenberg. AB in English, Cath. U. Am., 1950, MS in Library Sci., 1955. Asst. Librarian Export-Import Bank U.S.A., Washington, 1951-55; asst. librarian Nat. Assn. Home Builders, 1955-62, reference librarian, 1956-62; founder, chief tech. librarian, Bellcomm, Inc., subs. AT&T, Washington, 1962-72; chief librarian Nat. Air and Space Mus., Smithsonian Instn., Washington, 1972-82, chief librarian Mus. Reference Ctr., 1982-88, sr. reference librarian, 1989—; bd. visitors Cath. U. Am. Library Sci. Sch. and Libraries, 1984-93; apptd. by Pres., mem. Nat. Commn. Libraries and Info. Sci., 1971-76. Editor International Handbook of Aerospace Awards and Trophies, 1980, 81; guest editor Aeronautics and Space Flight Collections, 1985, in Spl. Collections, 1984. Vice-chmn. D.C. Rep. Com., 1960-68; mem. platform com. Rep. Nat. Com., 1964, sec., 1968; del. Rep. Nat. Conv., San Francisco, 1964, Miami, Fla., 1968. Recipient Sec.'s Disting. Service award Smithsonian Instn., 1976, Alumni Achievement award Cath. U. Am., 1977, Disting. Fed. Svc. Nat. Commn. Libr. and Info. Sci. medal, 1985. Mem. Spl. Librs. Assn. (pres. Washington chpt. 1973-74, cons. 1976-89, chmn. cons. com. 1994—, chmn. aerospace div. 1980-81, aerospace divsn. 30th anniversary com. 1995, Disting. Svc. award 1982, nat. dir. 1986-89, bd. dirs. 1986-89, 91-94, Washington chpt. awards com. 1990-91, assn. pres.-elect 1991-92, pres. 1992-93, immediate past pres. 1993-94, chair assn. awards and honors 1994-95), Am. Soc. Assn. Execs. (internat. roundtable), Am. Soc. Info. Scis. (com. chmn.), Internat. Fedn. Library Assns. (del. 1976, 83, 85, 88, 89), Friends of Cath. U. Libraries (founder, pres. 1984-88, exec. coun. 1984—), Nat. Fedn. Rep. Women, Rep. Women's Fed. Forum, League Rep. Women D.C. (dir. mem. 1995—), Capital Yacht Club (Washington). Roman Catholic. Office: Smithsonian Instn Cen Ref and Loan SI Librs NHB 27 Washington DC 20560

SCOTT, CHARLES DAVID, chemical engineer, consultant; b. Chaffee, Mo., Oct. 24, 1929; s. Charles Perry and Alma Gertrude (Kendall) S.; m. Alice Reba Bardill, Feb. 11, 1956; children—Timothy Charles, Mary Alice, Lisa Ann. BS in Chem. Engring., U. Mo., 1951; M.S. in Chem. Engring., U. Tenn., 1961, Ph.D., 1966. Registered profl. engr., Tenn. Devel. engr. Union Carbide Corp., Oak Ridge, 1953-57; research engr. Oak Ridge Nat. Lab., 1957-73, sect. chief, 1973-76, assoc. div. dir., 1976-83, research fellow, 1983-86, sr. research fellow, 1987-94; dir. bioprocessing rsch. and devel. ctr., 1991-94; engring. R & D cons., Oak Ridge, 1994—; adj. prof. chem. engring. U. Tenn., Knoxville. Served to 1st lt. AUS, 1951-53. Recipient U.S. Dept. Energy E.O. Lawrence award, 1980, U. Tenn. Nathan W. Doughtery award, 1987, U. Mo. Honor award, 1988, David Perlman award Am. Chem. Soc., 1994; Union Carbide Corp. fellow, 1983; Martin Marietta Sr. Corp. fellow, 1987. Mem. AAAS, Am. Chem. Soc. (chmn. separation sci. subdiv.), Am. Assn. Clin. Chemistry (chmn. com. advanced analytical concepts, nat. award 1980), Am. Inst. Chem. Engrs. (bd. dirs.), Nat. Acad. Engring., Sigma Xi, Alpha Chi Sigma. Lutheran. Contbr. articles to profl. jours.; patentee in field.

SCOTT, CHARLES EDWARD, philosophy educator; b. Oklahoma City, Sept. 3, 1935; s. William Lester and Mildred (McFall) S.; children: Stuart, Rebecca, Charles. BA, So. Meth. U., 1957; BD, Yale U., 1961, MA, 1962, PhD, 1965. Instr. philosophy, dean Berkeley Coll. Yale U., New Haven, 1963-66; asst. prof. philosophy Vanderbilt U., Nashville, 1966-69, assoc. prof., 1969-75, prof., 1975-93, chmn. dept. philosophy, 1979-90; dir. Vanderbilt Ctr. for Humanities, 1987-93; Edwin Eric Sparks prof. philosophy Pa. State U., University Park, 1994—. Author: Boundaries in Mind, 1982, The Language of Difference, 1987, The Question of Ethics, 1990; editor: Martin Heidegger: In Europe and America, 1973, On Dreaming, 1977. Fellow NEH, 1969, 77, von Humboldt Found., 1972-73, Danforth Found. and Soc. for Values in Higher Edn., 1972-73, Fulbright Found., 1957-58. Mem. Am. Philos. Assn. (program com. 1983-84), Soc. for Phenomenology and Existential Philosophy (co-exec. dir. 1986-89), Metaphys. Soc. Am. (exec. com. 1984-87), Phi Beta Kappa. Office: Pa State U Dept of Philosophy State College PA 16801

SCOTT, CHARLES LEWIS, photojournalist; b. Grayville, Ill., Aug. 18, 1924; s. Marvin Joseph and Prudence (Blood) S.; m. Jane Turner, Jan. 14, 1945 (dec. 1983); children—Lyntha Ann, Thomas Marvin; m. Martha McDonald, Aug. 23, 1986. B.S. in Journalism, U. Ill., 1948; M.S., Ohio U., 1970. Photographer Champaign-Urbana (Ill.) Courier, 1946-50, chief photographer, 1953-56; photographer Ill. Natural History Survey, 1946-51, Binghamton (N.Y.) Press, 1951-53; asst. picture editor Milw. Jour., 1956-58; picture editor, 1958-66; graphics dir. Chgo. Daily News, 1966-69; instr. Sch. Journalism, Ohio U., Athens, 1969-70; asst. prof. Sch. Journalism, Ohio U., 1971-72, asso. prof., 1974-76, 76-77, prof., 1977—; dir. Sch. Visual Communication, 1978—; picture editor Chgo. Tribune, 1974-76; dir. photography Rocky Mountain News, Denver, 1987-88; mem. 1995. Served with U.S. Navy, 1942-45. Decorated D.F.C., Air medal (3); recipient numerous awards in regional and nat. news photo contests. Mem. Nat. Press Photographers Assn. (charter mem. Newspaper Photographer of Yr. 1952, Editor of Yr. 1966, Joseph Sprague Meml. award 1975, Robin F. Garland Educator award 1979), Soc. Profl. Journalists, Ohio News Photographers Assn. (Lifetime Achievement award 1995). Presbyterian. Club: Athens Reading. Home: 8559 Lavelle Rd Athens OH 45701-9190

SCOTT, CHARLES R., diversified company executive; b. 1928. BJ, U. Tex., 1949. With advt. dept. Dallas Morning News, 1949-52; mutual fund sales rep. Southwest Capital Corp., 1952-55; pres. Parker Ford and Co., 1957-62; pres., CEO Roberts, Scott & Co., 1962-70; with Triton Group Ltd. (formerly known as Intermark Inc.), La Jolla, Calif., 1970-91, chmn., pres., CEO, 1987-91; pres., CEO The Actava Group, Inc., Atlanta, 1991—. Office: Actava Group Inc 4900 Georgia Pacific Ctr Atlanta GA 30303

SCOTT, CHARLOTTE H., business educator; b. Yonkers, N.Y., Mar. 18, 1925; d. Edgar B. and Charlotte Agnes (Palmer) Hanley; m. Nathan Alexander Scott, Jr., Dec. 21, 1946; children: Nathan Alexander Scott, Leslie Kristin Scott Ashamu. A.B., Barnard Coll., 1947; postgrad., Am. U., 1949-53; M.B.A., U. Chgo., 1964; LL.D., Allegheny Coll., 1981. Research asso. Nat. Bur. Econ. Research, N.Y.C., 1947-48; economist R.W. Goldsmith Assos., Washington, 1948-55, U. Chgo., 1955-56, Fed. Res. Bank, Chgo., 1956-71; asst. v.p. Fed. Res. Bank, 1971-76; prof. bus. adminstrn. and commerce, sr. fellow Tayloe Murphy Inst., U. Va., Charlottesville, 1976-86; prof. commerce and edn. U. Va., Charlottesville, 1986—; bd. dirs. NationsBank of Charlottesville, 1991-93; mem. nat. adv. coun. U.S. SBA, 1979-82; mem. consumer adv. coun. bd. govs. FRS, 1979-82, vice chmn., 1980-81, chmn., 1981-82. Mem. editorial bd. Jour. Retail Banking, 1978-85, Jour. Internat. Assn. Personnel Women, 1981-85; contbr. articles to profl. jours. Pres. women's bd. Chgo. Urban League, 1967-69; mem. Va. Commn. on Status of Women, 1982-85, Gov.'s Commn. on Va.'s Future, 1982-85, Gov.'s Commn. on Efficiency in Govt., 1985-87; treas. Va. Women's Cultural History Project, 1982-85; bd. dirs. Boys and Girls Club of Charlotteville/Albemarle, 1991-93. Mem. Internat. Assn. Personnel Women (v.p. mems. at-large 1980-82), Am. Fin. Assn., Va. Assn. Econs., Acad. Mgmt., Soc. Consumer Affairs Profls. in Bus., Barnard Coll./Columbia U. Alumnae Assn. (bd. dirs. 1977-81, trustee 1977-81). Episcopalian. Home: 1419 Hilltop Rd Charlottesville VA 22903-1226 Office: U Va McIntire Sch Commerce Monroe Hall Charlottesville VA 22903

SCOTT, DALE ALLAN, major league umpire; b. Springfield, Oreg., Aug. 14, 1959; s. Jesse Lee and Betty Ann (Potts) S. AS, Lane C.C., 1979. Radio disc jockey Sta. KBDF, Eugene, Oreg., 1976-81; minor league umpire various orgns., 1981-85; umpire Am. League, 1986—; ofcl. h.s. basketball Portland Basketball Ofcls. Assn., 1986—; ofcl. h.s. football Portland Football Ofcls. Assn., 1989—. Democrat. Office: Am League Profl Baseball 350 Park Ave New York NY 10022

SCOTT, DARREL JOSEPH, healthcare executive; b. Indpls., Sept. 12, 1947; s. Hubert Norris and Beverly June (Hiatt) S.; m. Janice L. Meredith, June 21, 1969; children: Andrew, Brennan. BA, Ind. U., 1969, MHA with high honors, 1971; JD, U. Louisville, 1990. Planning assoc. Ind. Hosp. Assn., Indpls., 1970-72; asst. dir. Welborn Bapt. Hosp., Evansville, Ind., 1972-77, AMA, Chgo., 1977-78; pres., chief exec. officer King's Daus. Hosp., Madison, Ind., 1978-90; v.p. legal svcs. Sisters St. Francis Health Svcs., Mishawaka, Ind., 1990-94, sr. v.p. corp. affairs, 1994—; mem. Ind.

Emergency Med. Services Commn., 1974-75. Bd. dirs. Jefferson County United Way, 1979-85; chair coms. Trinity United Methodist Ch., Madison, 1982, Clay United Meth. Ch., 1992-95. Fellow Am. Coll. Healthcare Execs. Republican. Home: 51563 Fox Pointe Ln Granger IN 46530-8473 Office: Srs of St Francis Hlth Servs PO Box 1290 Mishawaka IN 46546-1290

SCOTT, DAVID BYTOVETZKSI, dental research and forensic odontology consultant; b. Providence, May 8, 1919; 4 children. A.B., Brown U., 1939; D.D.S., U. Md., 1943; M.S., U. Rochester, 1944; Sc.D. (hon.), Med. and Dental Coll. N.J., 1979, U. Louis Pasteur, Strasbourg, France, 1981. Commd. officer, advanced through grades to asst. surgeon gen. USPHS, 1944-65, 75-81; mem. staff Nat. Inst. Dental Rsch., NIH, Bethesda, Md., 1944-56, chief lab. histology and pathology, 1956-65, dir., 1976-82; mem. faculty Case Western Res. U., Cleve., 1965-76, Thomas J. Hill disting. prof. phys. biology Sch. Dentistry., 1965-76, dean Sch. Dentistry, 1969-76; ind. cons. dental rsch. and forensic odontology, 1982—. Recipient Arthur S. Flemming award U.S. Jr. C. of C., 1955, Rsch. Achievement award, Mass. Dental Soc., 1978, Fred Birnberg Dental Rsch. medal, Columbia U., 1978, Callahan Meml. award Ohio Dental Assn., 1985; named to Hall of Fame, Sch. of Dentistry, U. Md., 1990; decorated Order of Rising Sun, Govt. of Japan, 1983. Mem. ADA, Am. Acad. Forensic Sci. (Forensic Odontology award 1981), Electron Micros. Soc. Am., Internat. Coll. Dentists, Am. Coll. Dentists, Internat. Assn. Dental Rsch. (award for Rsch. in Mineralization 1968), Royal Soc. Medicine (hon.), Am. Bd. Forensic Odontology (cert.). Home and Office: 9100 Belvoir Woods Pky Apt 209 Fort Belvoir VA 22060-2713

SCOTT, DAVID J., beverage executive. With Davidson & Omara, N.Y.C., 1981-86, RGR Nabisco, Winston-Salem, N.C., 1981-86; sr. v.p., sec. Heublein Inc., Farmington, Conn., 1986—. Office: Heublein Inc 16 Munson Rd Farmington CT 06032-2000

SCOTT, DAVID KNIGHT, physicist, university administrator; b. North Ronaldsay, Scotland, Mar. 2, 1940; married, 1966; 3 children. BSc, Edinburgh U., 1962; DPhil in Nuclear Physics, Oxford U., 1967. Rsch. officer nuclear physics lab. Oxford U., 1970-73; rsch. fellow nuclear physics Balliol Coll., 1967-70, sr. rsch. fellow, 1970-73; physicist Lawrence Berkeley Lab. U. Calif., 1973-75, sr. scientist nuclear sci., 1975-79; prof. physics, astronomy and chemistry Nat. Superconducting Cyclotron Lab. Mich. State U., East Lansing, 1979-93; Hannah disting. prof. physics, astronomy and chemistry Mich. State U., East Lansing, 1979-86, assoc. provost, 1983-86, provost, v.p. acad. affairs, 1986-92; Hannah Disting. prof. leaning, sci. and soc. Nat. Superconducting Cyclotron Lab. Mich. State U., East Lansing, 1992-93; chancellor U. Mass., Amherst, 1993—. Fellow Am. Phys. Soc. Office: U Mass Office of Chancellor 374 Whitmore Adminstrn Bldg Amherst MA 01003

SCOTT, DAVID WARREN, statistics educator; b. Oak Park, Ill., July 16, 1950; s. John V. and Nancy (Mellers) S.; m. Jean Charlotte Madera, June 15, 1974; children: Hilary Kathryn, Elizabeth Alison, Warren Robert. BA, Rice U., 1972, MA, 1976, PhD, 1976. Asst. prof. Baylor Coll. Medicine, Houston, 1976-79; asst. prof. Rice U., Houston, 1979-80, assoc. prof., 1980-85, chmn. statistics, 1992-93; vis. prof. Stanford U., Palo Alto, Calif. 1985-86; vis. prof. Dept. Def., Ft. Meade, Md., 1993-94. Co-editor: jour. Computational Stats. and jour. Stat. Scis.; contbr. articles to profl. publs.; author: Multivariate Density Estimation, 1992. Grantee NASA, 1982-84, Office Naval Rsch., 1985-93, NSF, 1993—. Fellow Inst. Math. Stats., Am. Statis. Assn.; mem. Am. Statis. Soc. (assoc. editor jour. 1983-94), Inst. Math. Statis. (cons.). Avocations: woodworking, hiking, family. Home: 4143 Marlowe St Houston TX 77005-1953 Office: Rice U Dept Stats PO Box 1892 Houston TX 77251

SCOTT, DEBORAH EMONT, curator; b. Passaic, N.J.; d. Harold and Rhoda (Baumgarten) Emont; m. George Andrew Scott, June 4, 1983; children: Meredith Suzanne, Diana Faith. BA, Rutgers U., 1973; MA, Oberlin Coll., 1979. Asst. curator Allen Meml. Art Mus., Oberlin, Ohio, 1977-79; curator collections Memphis Brooks Mus. Art, 1979-83; curator The Nelson-Atkins Mus. Art, Kansas City, 1983—; project dir. Henry Moore Sculpture Garden, 1986—. Author: (catalogue) Alan Shields, 1983, (essay) Jonathan Borofsky, 1988, (essay) Judith Shea, 1989, (interview) John Ahearn, 1990, (essay) Gerhard Richter, 1990, (essay) Kathy Muehlemann, 1991, (essay) Nate Fors, 1991, (essay) Julian Schnabel, 1991, (essay) Louise Bourgeois, 1994, (essay) Joel Shapiro, 1995. Office: Nelson-Atkins Mus Art 4525 Oak St Kansas City MO 64111-1818

SCOTT, DEBORAH L., costume designer. Costume designer: (films) E.T. The Extra-Terrestrial, 1982, (with Dan Moore) Twilight Zone-The Movie ("Kick the Can", "Nightmare at 20,000 Feet"), 1983, Back to the Future, 1985, About Last Night..., 1986, Armed and Dangerous, 1986, Who's That Girl?, 1987, Moving, 1988, Coupe de Ville, 1990, Defending Your Life, 1991, Eve of Destruction, 1991, Sliver, 1993, Jack the Bear, 1993, Legends of the Fall, 1994. Office: The Gersh Agency 232 N Canon Dr Beverly Hills CA 90210*

SCOTT, DONALD ALLISON, lawyer; b. Phila., Oct. 7, 1929; s. Garfield and Grace Louise (Nevin) S.; m. Jeanne Marie Cooper, June 25, 1955; children: Allison Cooper, Andrew Garfield, John Wallace, Lindsay Nevin. A.B., Princeton U., 1951; J.D., Harvard U., 1956. Bar: Pa. 1958. Law clk. Judge Learned Hand, U.S. Ct. Appeals, 2d Circuit, 1956-57; assoc. firm Morgan, Lewis & Bockius, Phila., 1957-64; ptnr. firm Morgan, Lewis & Bockius, 1964—. Served with USNR, 1951-53. Mem. ABA, Pa. Bar Assn., Phila. Bar Assn., Am. Law Inst., Merion Cricket Club, Paupack Hills Golf Club. Republican. Presbyterian. Home: 714 W Mt Airy Ave Philadelphia PA 19119-3326 Office: Morgan Lewis & Bockius 2000 One Logan Sq Philadelphia PA 19103

SCOTT, DONALD MICHAEL, educational association administrator, educator; b. Los Angeles, Sept. 26, 1943; s. Bernard Hendry and Barbara (Lannin) S.; m. Patricia Ilene Pancoast, Oct. 24, 1964 (div. June 1971); children: William Bernard, Kenneth George. BA, San Francisco State U., 1965, MA, 1986. Cert. tchr. Calif. Tchr. Mercy High Sch., San Francisco, 1968-71; park ranger Calif. State Park System, Half Moon Bay, 1968-77; tchr. adult div. Jefferson Union High Sch. Dist., Daly City, Calif., 1973-87; dir. NASA-NPS Project Wider Focus, Daly City, 1983-90; dir. Geo.S. Spl. Projects Wider Focus, San Francisco, 1990—; also bd. dirs. Wider Focus, Daly City; nat. park ranger/naturalist Grant-Kohrs Ranch Nat. Hist. Site, Deer Lodge, Mont., 1987-88; nat. park ranger pub. affairs fire team Yellowstone Nat. Park, 1988; nat. park ranger Golden Gate Recreation Area, 1988-92; research subject NASA, Mountain View, Calif., 1986, 90; guest artist Yosemite (Calif.) Nat. Park, 1986; nat. park ranger Golden Gate Nat. Recreation Area, Nat. Park Svc., San Francisco, 1986, nat. park svc. history cons. to Bay Dist., 1988-94; adj. asst. prof. Skyline Coll., 1989-94, Coll. San Mateo, 1992-94; NASA aero. edn. specialist, lectr. Okla. State U., 1994—; bd. dirs. Contact. Contbr. articles, photographs to profl. jours., mags. Pres. Youth for Kennedy, Lafayette, Calif., 1960; panelist Community Bds. of San Francisco, 1978-87; city chair Yes on A Com., So. San Francisco, San Mateo County, Calif., 1986; charter mem. Air and Space Mus., Smithsonian Instn., 1995—. Mem. Nat. Sci. Tchrs. Assn., Nat. Coun. Tchrs. Math., Calif. Sci. Tchrs. Assn., Planetary Soc. (charter), Yosemite Assn. (life), Wider Focus, Friends of George R. Stewart. Democrat. Avocations: photography, hiking, camping, travel. Office: PO Box 3099 Costa Mesa CA 92628-3099

SCOTT, EDWARD PHILIP, lawyer; b. Somers Point, N.J., Dec. 17, 1937; s. Harry Edward and Gladys Louise (Atkinson) s.; m. Jane Anne Wilby, June 6, 1961; children: Young-Joon, Edward P. Jr., Lauren, Tracey. BA, Rutgers U., 1959; JD, U. Pa., 1963. Bar: N.J. 1963, D.C. 1968. Assoc. Arnold & Porter, Washington, 1967-68; atty./advisor Peace Corps, Washington, 1968-69; dep. gen. counsel, 1970; dep. dir. Peace Corps, Seoul, Korea, 1971-72; dir. PEace Corps, Korea, Peace Corps, Korea, 1972-73 ; staff atty. Mental Health Law Project, Washington, 1973-77; minority gen. counsel U.S. Senate Com Vets. Affairs, Washington, 1981-86, gen. counsel, 1977-80, 87-90; chief counsel, staff dir. U.S. Senate on Com. Vets. Affairs, Washington, 1990-93; legis. asst. Sen. Alan Cranston, D.C. 1981-88. Author: Mental Health Issues in State Law, 1976. Capt. USAF, 1964-67. Mem. ABA, D.C. Bar Assn., Audubon Naturalist Soc., Montgomery County Road

Runners. Democrat. Avocations: running, birding, scuba diving. Home: 3703 Inverness Dr Chevy Chase MD 20815-5660 Office: Dept Vets Affairs Office Congl Affairs 810 Vermont Ave NW Washington DC 20420

SCOTT, EDWARD WILLIAM, JR., computer company executive; b. Panama City, Panama, May 25, 1938; s. Edward William and Janice Gertrude (Grimison) S.; m. Cheryl S. Gilliland, apr. 23, 1988; children: Edward William, Heather Yolanda Deirdre, Reece Donald. BA, Mich. State U., 1959, MA, 1963; BA, Oxford (Eng.) U., 1962. Personnel specialist Panama Canal Co., 1962-64, staff asst. to dir. personnel, 1964-66; personnel officer IRS, Detroit, 1966-68; staff personnel mgmt. specialist U.S. Dept. Justice, Washington, 1968-69; chief personnel systems and evaluation sect. U.S. Dept. Justice, 1970-72; dir. U.S. Dept. Justice (Office Mgmt. Programs), 1972-74; asso. dep. commr. planning and evaluation U.S. Dept. Justice (U.S. Immigration and Naturalization Service), 1974-75, dep. asst. atty. gen. adminstrn., 1972-75; asst. sec. for adminstrn. (Transp. Dept.), 1977-80; pres. Office Power, Inc., Washington, 1980-81; dir. mktg. Computer Consoles, Inc., 1981-84; v.p. mktg. Dest Systems, 1984-85; dir. govt. mktg. Sun Microsystems, Mountain View, Calif., 1985-88; exec. v.p. Pyramid Tech., Mountain View, 1988-95; chmn. Bea Enterprises, Palo Alto, Calif., 1995—; pres. U.S. Dept. Justice Fed. Credit Union, 1970-73. Recipient Presdl. Mgmt. Improvement certificate, 1971; Spl. Commendation award Dept. Justice, 1973; also Spl. Achievement award, 1976; William A. Jump Meml. award, 1974; presdl. sr. exec. service rank of Disting. Exec., 1980; Mich. State U. Scholar, 1957-60. Mem. Phi Eta Sigma, Phi Kappa Phi. Democrat. Office: Bea Enterprises 2465 E Bayshore Rd Palo Alto CA 94303

SCOTT, ELLIOT, production designer. Prodn. designer: (films) The Americanization of Emily, 1964, The Incredible Sarah, 1976 (Academy award nomination best art direction 1976), Warlords of Atlantis, 1978, The Fifth Musketeer, 1979, Arabian Adventure, 1979, The Watcher in the Woods, 1980, Dragonslayer, 1981, Evil Under the Sun, 1982, The Pirates of Penzance, 1983, Labyrinth, 1985, (with Roger Cain) Who Framed Roger Rabbit?, 1988 (Academy award nomination best art direction 1988), Indiana Jones and the Last Crusade, 1989. Office: care Art Directors Guild 11365 Ventura Blvd #315 Studio City CA 91604*

SCOTT, EUGENIE CAROL, science foundation director, anthropologist; b. LaCrosse, Wis., Oct. 24, 1945; d. Allen K. and Virginia Meliss (Derr) S.; m. Robert Abner Black, Oct. 18, 1965 (div. 1970); m. Thomas Charles Sager, Dec. 30, 1971; 1 child, Carrie Ellen Sager. BS, U. Wis., Milw., 1967, MS, 1968; PhD, U. Mo. 1974. Asst. prof. anthropology U. Ky., Lexington, 1974-82; postdoctoral fellow U. Calif., San Francisco, 1983-84; asst. prof. U. Colo., Boulder, 1984-86; exec. dir., pub. newsletter NCSE Reports, Nat. Ctr. Sci. Edn., Berkeley, Calif., 1987—; bd. dirs. Nat. Pub. Edn. and Religious Liberty, Washington; pub. Bookwatch Revs., 1988-92. Author, editor: Biology Textbook: The New Generation, 1990; prodr. videotape series How Scientists Know About ...; featured guest as sci. authority on creationism and/or pseudosci. Recipient Disting. Alumnus award U. Mo. Arts & Scis., 1993. Fellow Com. for Sci. Investigation Claims of Paranormal (Sci. and Edn. award 1991; mem. Am. Assn. Phys. Anthropology (bd. dirs., exec. com. 1988-93, sec.-treas. 1993—). Office: Nat Ctr Sci Edn PO Box 9477 Berkeley CA 94709-0477

SCOTT, FREDERICK ISADORE, JR., editor, business executive; b. Balt., Oct. 27, 1927; s. Frederick Isadore and Rebecca Esther (Waller) S.; m. Viola Fowlkes, Feb. 4, 1949. B.E. in Chem. Engring, Johns Hopkins, 1950; M.S. in Mgmt. Engring, Newark Coll. Engring., 1956. Chem. process engr. in research and devel. RCA, Harrison, N.J., 1951-59; with Kearfott div. Gen. Precision Aerospace, Little Falls, N.J., 1960-62; asst. sales mgr. Isotopes, Inc., Westwood, N.J., 1964-66; mgr. capacitor sect. Wellington Electronics, Inc., Englewood, N.J., 1967-68; owner F.I. Scott & Assos. (med. equipment), Montclair, N.J., 1968-80; tech. product mktg. and editorial svcs. F.I. scott & Assocs., Check, Va., 1980-86; editor instrumentation publ. Am. Lab. and Internat. Lab., Fairfield, Conn., 1968-80, cons. editor, 1980—; pres. Group Tech., Ltd., 1979—; editor Am. Clin. Lab., 1990—. Served with AUS, 1946-47. Mem. Am. Chem. Soc. (sr.), AAAS, N.Y. Acad. Sci., IEEE (editor newsletter No. N.J. sect. 1957-58, chmn. publs. com. 1958-59), N.Y. Micros. Soc. Home and Office: 1 E Chase St Apt 410 Baltimore MD 21202-2557 *Perhaps the most significant aspect of my life is a long-felt realization that each person is ultimately responsible for his or her condition in life. Application of this principle continually requires that the individual assess a failure in such a way as to determine how his or her actions might have avoided it or, if unavoidable, how its recurrence can be obviated. Accepting responsibility in this manner can, I believe, lead the way toward a society based on a federation of autonomous individuals delegating authority to units of government when appropriate but clearly retaining the capability to recall that delegated authority should it be abused.*

SCOTT, FREDRIC WINTHROP, veterinarian; b. Greenfield, Mass., Nov. 22, 1935; s. Clifton William and Mildred E. (Bradford) S.; m. Lois Ellen Williams, May 26, 1957; children: Duane Douglas, John Gardner, Raymond Clifton. BS in Chemistry, U. Mass., 1958; DVM, Cornell U., 1962, PhD in Virology, 1968. Veterinarian Rutland (Vt.) Vet. Clinic, 1962-64; rsch. veterinarian USDA, Plum Island Animal Disease Ctr., Greenport, N.Y., 1964-65; NIH postdoctoral fellow Cornell U., Ithaca, N.Y., 1965-68, asst. prof. vet. microbiology, 1968-73, assoc. prof. vet. microbiology, 1973-79, prof. microbiology, immunology and parasitology, 1979—; dir. Cornell Feline Health Ctr.; mem. bd. comparative virology WHO/FAO; mem. vet. med. adv. com. Ctr. for Vet. Medicine, FDA, Rockville, Md., 1984-86; mem. vet. sci. tech. adv. coun. Agrl. and Tech. Coll., SUNY, Delhi, 1972-75; cons., rschr. in field. Editor-in-chief Feline Practice Jour.; co-author: Infectious Diseases Domestic Animals, 1988, Infectious Diseases, 1986; contbr. articles to profl. publs.; inventor vaccines. Bd. elders Bethel Grove Bible Ch., 1979-91, 93—; faculty advisor Christian Vet. Fellowship; coach youth baseball and hockey; mem. Town of Ithaca Planning Bd.; mem. troop com. Boy Scouts Am., Ellis Hollow. Nat. Acads. Practice disting. scholar in vet. medicine, 1991—; NIH grantee, 1970-83. Fellow Acad. Feline Practice (bd. dirs. 1991—); mem. AVMA (sci. program com. 1973-81, coun. on biologic and therapeutic agts. 1986-92, chmn. 1987-89), Am. Coll. Vet. Microbiologists (diplomate, examinations com. 1975-79), Am. Soc. Virology, N.Y. State Vet. Med. Soc. (com. on small animal practice 1985-90), So. Tier Vet. Med. Assn., Am. Assn. Feline Practitioners (pres. 1976-78, actv. bd. past pres. 1990—, rsch. award 1975), Am. Animal Hosp. Assn. (Carnation award 1990), Conf. Rsch. Workers on Animal Diseases. Republican. Mem. Evangelical Ch. Avocations: golf, archery, gardening, basketball. Office: Cornell U Coll Vet Medicine Feline Health Ctr Ithaca NY 14853

SCOTT, GARY KUPER, academic administrator; b. Jefferson City, Mo., Jan. 3, 1933; s. Ralph Elmer and Lillian Rachel (Kuper) S.; children—Tina Marie, Lisa René, Corey Kuper. A.A., Jefferson City Jr. Coll., 1953; B.Ed., Western Wash. State Coll., 1960, M.Ed., 1962; Ph.D., U. Minn., 1965. Dir. student counseling center Minot (N.D.) State Coll., 1965-67; faculty, head dept. psychology Lincoln U., Jefferson City, 1967-77, chmn. dept. edn. and psychology, 1979-83, dean Sch. Edn. and Grad. Studies, 1983-85, dir. grad. and continuing edn., 1985-88, dean grad. and continuing edn., 1988-95. Pres. Cole County Mental Health Assn., 1969-70; Bd. dirs. YMCA.; mem. Jefferson City Sch. Bd., 1985-87; mem. Cole County Democratic Com., 1968-70. Mem. Am. psychol. assns. Club: Rotary. Home: 1002 Roseridge Cir Jefferson City MO 65101-3640

SCOTT, GEORGE CAMPBELL, actor, director; b. Wise, Va., Oct. 18, 1927; s. George C. and Helena S.; m. Carolyn Hughs (div.). m. Patricia Reed (div.). m. Colleen Dewhurst, 1960 (div.). m. Trish Van Devere, Feb. 2, 1972; 6 children from previous marriages. Student U. Mo., 1950. Actor stock cos. 1950-57; N.Y.C. debut as Richard III, Shakespeare Festival, 1957; stage appearances include As You Like It, 1958, Children of Darkness, 1958, Antony and Cleopatra 1959, Merchant of Venice, 1960, 62, The Wall, 1960, Desire Under the Elms, 1963, Plaza Suite, 1968, Uncle Vanya, 1974, Andersonville Trial, 1959, Comes a Day, 1959, Present Laughter, 1982, Design for Living, 1984, The Boys of Summer, 1986, On Borrowed Time, 1991, Wrong-turn at Lungfish, 1993; co-founder, Theatre of Mich. Co., Inc., 1961; produced: stage appearances include Great Day in the Morning, 1962; dir., played: title role General Seeger, 1962; dir.: title role All God's Chillun Got Wings, 1975; actor, dir.: title role Death of a Salesman, 1975, Sly Fox, 1976; films include The Hanging Tree, 1959, Anatomy of a Murder, 1959, The Hustler, 1961, The List of Adrian Messenger, 1963, Dr. Strangelove (Or How I Learned To Stop Worrying And Love The Bomb), 1964, The Bible, 1966, Flim-Flam Man, 1967, Patton, 1970, The Hospital, 1971, The Last Run, 1971, They Might Be Giants, 1971, The New Centurions, 1972, Rage (also dir.), 1972, The Day of the Dolphin, 1973, Oklahoma Crude, 1973, The Savage is Loose (also prodr. and dir.), 1974, The Hindenburg, 1975, Beauty and the Beast, 1976, Islands in the Stream, 1977, Crossed Swords, 1978, Movie, Movie, 1978, Hardcore, 1979, The Changeling, 1980, The Formula, 1980, Taps, 1981, Firestarter, The Exorcist III, 1990, The Rescuers Down Under (voice) 1990, Malice, 1993; TV plays include Kraft Mystery Theatre, Omnibus, Playhouse 90, Play of Week, Hallmark Hall of Fame, The Price; others; dir.: The Andersonville Trial (Emmy award for prodn.); TV movies: Jane Eyre, 1971, Fear on Trial, 1975, Oliver Twist, 1982, China Rose, 1983, A Christmas Carol, 1984, Mussolini: The Untold Story, 1985, Choices, 1986, The Last Days of Patton, 1986, The Murders in the Rue Morgue, 1986, Pals, 1987, The Ryan White Story, 1989, Descending Angel, 1990, Finding the Way Home, 1991; TV series East Side/ West Side, 1963, Mr. President, 1986, Traps, 1994. Recipient Clarence Derwent award 1958, Vernon Rice award 1958, Theatre World award 1958, Obie award Village Voice 1958, 63, Golden Globe 1970, refused Oscar for Patton 1971, Emmy for The Price, 1971; Genie (Can.) 1980. Served with USMC, 1945-49. Mem. Actors Equity Assn., Screen Actors Guild, AFTRA, Dirs. Guild Am., Soc. Stage Dirs. and Choreographers. Office: The Charles H. Stern Agency 11755 Wilshire Blvd Ste 2320 Los Angeles CA 90025

SCOTT, GEORGE ERNEST, publisher, writer; b. Detroit, Sept. 12, 1924; s. George Ernest and Ruth Janet (Moffett) S.; m. Lois Aurlie Brown, Mar. 28, 1953; m. Elaine Lorraine Phillips, Feb. 14, 1982. Student, U. Detroit, 1946-47, Woodbury Coll., Los Angeles, 1947-48. With advt. prodn. dept. D.P. Brother Advt., Detroit, 1947-49, Ruthrauff & Ryan Advt., Detroit, 1950-51; advt. account exec. Betteridge & Co. Advt., Detroit, 1951-53; founder, 1954; pub., pres. Scott Advt. & Pub. Co., Livonia, Mich.; owner, pub. Ceramic Arts & Crafts mag., 1955—, Ceramic Teaching Projects and Trade News, quar., 1965—. Songwriter: (words and music) I Want A Lovin' Man, Tropic Memories, A Second Chance at Love, I Think I'm Falling in Love With You, Sing, Sing, Sing at Christmas, Boomerang Lovin' You's the Best Thing Tthat I Do and Over 100 More. With USNR, 1942-46. Mem. Nat. Ceramic Mfrs. Assn. (past dir.), Mich. Ceramic Dealers Assn. (past pres.). Home: 574 Herald St Plymouth MI 48170-1537

SCOTT, HAL S., law educator; b. 1943. AB, Princeton U., 1965; MA, Stanford U., 1967; JD, U. Chgo., 1972. Law clk. to judge U.S. Ct. Appeals D.C. Cir., Washington, 1972-73; to assoc. justice White, U.S. Supreme Ct., Washington, 1973-74; acting prof. law U. Calif.-Berkeley, 1974-75; asst. prof. law Harvard U. Sch. Law, Cambridge, Mass., 1975-79, prof. 1980-90, Nomura prof. internat. fin. systems, 1990—; cons. IBM, N.Y.C., 1977. Contbr. articles to legal jours. Dir. Program on Internat. Fin. Systems. Mem. Internat. Acad. of Consumer and Comml. Law (past pres.). Office: Law Sch Harvard U Cambridge MA 02138

SCOTT, HAROLD LEE, JR., distribution executive; b. Joplin, Mo., Mar. 14, 1949; s. Harold Lee and Avis Viola (Parsons) S.; m. Linda Gale Aldridge, June 7, 1969; children: Eric Sean, Wyatt Parson. BBA, Pitts. State U., Kans., 1971. Br. mgr. Yellow Freight System, Springdale, Ark., 1972-78; mgr. Queen City Warehouse, Springfield, Mo., 1978-79; dir. transp. Wal-Mart Stores, Inc., Bentonville, Ark., 1979-83, v.p. distbn., 1983—; bd. dirs. Pvt. Truck Council, Washington, 1985-86. Republican. Methodist. Avocations: reading, quail hunting. Home: 611 Prairie Creek Rd Rogers AR 72756-3019

SCOTT, HELEN S., law educator; b. 1949. BA, Barnard Coll., 1970; JD, Columbia U., 1977. Bar: N.Y 1978, D.C. 1978. Atty., adviser Office of Chmn. FTC, D.C., 1977-78, atty., adviser Office of Commr., 1978-79; assoc. Shearman & Sterling, N.Y., 1980-82; from asst. prof. to prof. law NYU, N.Y.C., 1983—. Office: NYU Sch Law 40 Washington Sq S New York NY 10012-1099

SCOTT, HENRY LAWRENCE, concert pianist, humorist; b. Tivoli on Hudson, N.Y., Jan. 20, 1908; s. Walter and Mary Wigram (Keeney) S.; m. Mary Bell Bard, Aug. 28, 1938; children: Barbara Bell, Henry Lawrence. Student, Syracuse (N.Y.) U., class 1930; LH.D., Bard Coll., Annandale, N.Y., 1964. head Henry Scott Sch. Modern Piano, N.Y.C.; mem. faculty Champlin Sch., 1940-42; pres., chmn. bd. Solo Theater of Am. Corp., 1948; asst. to pres. Bard Coll., Annandale-on-Hudson, 1966; investment adviser Johnson Lane Space and Smith, 1978-89, Interstate Johnson Lane, 1989—. Teaching and radio, screen, stage and TV work, 1931-41; concert work, throughout U.S., 1939—, debut, Town Hall, 1941, Carnegie Hall, 1945-46, 27 transcontinental concert tours, Carnegie Hall, N.Y.C. (2), Town Hall, N.Y.C. (2), Detroit Town Hall, Kansas City Town Hall, West Point Mil. Academy (12), Akron Concert Course, Fine Arts Series, Worcester, U. Minn. (8), U. Tex. (3), U. Notre Dame (2), Miss Porters Sch., Conn. (2), St. Mark's Sch., Southborough, Mass. (5), So. Ill. U. (10), USAF Acad., 1960, Mt. Mary Coll., Milw., Emanuel Missionary Coll., Mich., Pacific Union Coll., Calif., U. So. Calif., Amherst (Mass.) U., Dartmouth Coll., Purdue U., U. N.C., U. Oreg., Med. Coll. Va., Union Coll., Lincoln, Nebr., U. N.Mex., Teaching and radio, screen, stage and TV work, Woman's Inst., Knoxville Friday Morning Musicales, Syracuse, Meml. Auditorium, Lowell, Mass., Eaton Auditorium, Toronto, Met. Opera House, N.Y.C., U. Wash., U. Utah, U. Fla. (3), U. Ga., Artists Series, San Diego, U. N.C. (3), North-Western State Coll. (7), 6th tour, Can., 1966-67, Hawaiian Islands, Saudi Arabia, 1963; guest artist various orchs. and symphonies; indsl. concerts for, General Electric Co., Eastman Kodak, IBM Corp., others 1958-61; pioneer concert humor; now presenting humorous and ednl. lecture recitals in schs., colls., univs. and concert halls; producer, star: Concerto for Fun, 1949; introduced: Fun at the Philharmonic, 1952; guest appearance: TV show Be Our Guest, 1960; Composer: Clavichord Joe; inventor Technic Mittens for piano practice. Trustee Bard Coll., Annandale, N.Y., 1969-70, Charleston Symphony Orch., 1971-75, Charleston Concert Assn., 1971-78, pres., 1979-84; trustee, 2d v.p. Dock St. Theater, Charleston, 1981-83; founder, chmn. Stockholder Adv. Found., 1975-83, Stockholder Adv. Assn., Inc., 1976-79; bd. visitors Kanuga Episcopal Conf. Ctr., Henderson, N.C., 1985-88; trustee, treas. Dockside Assn., Charleston, 1986-87, pres., 1989-91; life mem. Dutchess County (N.Y.) Hist. Soc. Mem. Carolina Yacht Club (Charleston), Old Town Club (Charleston, pres. 1981-82). Republican. Episcopalian. Address: Dockside Charleston SC 29401 *Fulfillment in life comes from serving and giving. My most frequent prayer is "Lord help me to be a better husband, father and friend".*

SCOTT, HENRY WILLIAM, JR., surgeon, educator; b. Graham, N.C., Aug. 22, 1916; s. Henry William and Claire (Turner) S.; m. Mary Louisa Vanamee, Oct. 17, 1942; children: Henry William III, Mary Elizabeth, Virginia Wright, Patricia Vanamee. A.B., U. N.C., 1937; M.D., Harvard U. 1941; D.Sc. (hon.), U. Aberdeen, 1976. Diplomate: Am. Bd. Surgery (mem. bd. 1956-62, vice chmn. 1961-62). Intern Peter Bent Brigham, Children's hosps., Boston, 1941-43; resident surgery Children's Hosp., 1943-45; Harvey Cushing fellow neurosurgery, 1945-46; resident surgeon Johns Hopkins Hosp., 1946-47; from instr. to asso. prof. surgery Johns Hopkins Med. Sch., 1947-51; prof. surgery, head dept. Vanderbilt U. Sch. Medicine, 1952-82, emeritus prof., 1982—; dir. surgi. scis., 1977-82, emeritus dir., 1982—; surgeon in chief Vanderbilt U. Hosp., 1952-82; clin. prof. surgery Meharry Med. Sch., 1970-82, emeritus, 1982—; mem. surg. study sect. USPHS, 1961-65, chmn. 1966-70; cons. USPHS. Editorial bd.: Surgical Techniques Illustrated, Current Problems in Surgery; contbr. articles to sci. jours. Recipient Disting. Alumnus award U. N.C., 1981, Darlington Sci. award, 1985. Fellow A.C.S. (gov. 1965-67, treas. 1967-72, regent 1972-75, pres. 1975-76, pres. Tenn. chpt. 1968-69), Royal Australasian Coll. Surgeons (hon.), Swedish Surg. Soc. (hon.), So. Surg. Assn. (hon.); mem. Am. Gastroent. Soc., Soc. Vascular Surgery, Am. Assn. Thoracic Surgery, Internat. Soc. Surgery (sec. U.S. chpt. 1957-74, v.p. 1979, pres. 1982-83), Internat. Surg. Group (sec. 1982-83), Internat. Assn. Endocrine Surgeons, Am. Assn. Endocrine Surgeons, Am. Geriatrics Assn., Am. Surg. Assn. (treas. 1958-65, pres. 1973-74), So. Surg. Assn. (pres. 1976-77), Nashville Surg. Soc. (pres. 1964), Soc. Univ. Surgeons (pres. 1960-61), Soc. Clin. Surgery (pres. 1970-72), Deutsche Gesellschaft für Chirurgie (corr.), Internat. Soc. Cardiovascular Surgery, Soc. Surgery Alimentary Tract (pres. 1970-71), Pan Pacific Surg. Assn. (pres. 1980-81), Surg. Biology Club, AMA, So. Med. Assn. (Disting. Service award

1984), Halsted Soc. (pres. 1968-70), Am. Trauma Soc., James IV Surg. Assn. (v.p. 1978-79), Johns Hopkins Soc. Scholars, Phi Beta Kappa, Phi Delta Theta, Nu Sigma Nu, Alpha Omega Alpha. Clubs: Belle Meade Country, Nashville, Le Mirador Country (Switzerland). Home: 1050 Tyne Blvd Nashville TN 37220-1027 also: 424 Ocean House Rd Cape Eliz ME 04107-2622 Office: Vanderbilt U Hosp Nashville TN 37232

SCOTT, H(ERBERT) ANDREW, retired chemical engineer; b. Marion, Va., Mar. 29, 1924; s. Charles Wassum and Carolyn Enyde (Snider) S.; widowed; children: Mark Andrew, Paul Ethan; m. Helen R. LaFollette, July 21, 1984. BSChemE, Va. Tech. Inst. and State U., 1944, MSChemE, 1947. Registered profl. engr., Tenn. Chem. engr. Tenn. Eastman Co., Kingsport, 1947-55, asst. to works mgr., 1955-60, supt. glycol dept., 1960-64, supt. polymers div., 1964-67, dir. engring. div., 1970-87; plant mgr. Holston Def. Corp., Kingsport, 1967-70, dir. systems devel., 1971-73, dir. engring. dvsn., 1974-87; vis. prof. U. Alaska, Fairbanks, 1988-89; mem. standards com. Eastman Kodak Co., Rochester, N.Y., 1982-87. Mem. mayor's adv. com. City of Kingsport, 1971-76; chmn. Kingsport Park Commn., 1976-80. Sgt. AUS, 1944-46. Named Engr. of yr., Tenn. Soc. Profl. Engrs., 1984. Fellow AICE (mem. tech. Inst. Chem. Process Safety 1984-87, vocat. guidance com. 1960-64, chmn. local sect. 1956); mem. Am. Soc. Engring. Edn., Am. Soc. Engring. Mgmt., Kiwanis. Republican. Presbyterian. Achievements include patent in process for manufacture of acetic anhydride, implement pioneering quality management for knowledge workers, design for manufacturing chemicals from coal. Home: 4512 Chickasaw Rd Kingsport TN 37664-2110

SCOTT, HOWARD WINFIELD, JR., temporary help services company executive; b. Greenwich, Conn., Feb. 24, 1935; s. Howard Winfield and Janet (Lewis) S.; B.S., Northwestern U., 1957; m. Joan Ann MacDonald, Aug. 12, 1961; children: Howard Winfield III, Thomas MacDonald, Ann Elizabeth. With R.H. Donnelly Corp., Chgo., 1958-59; sales rep. Masonite Corp., Chgo. also Madison, Wis., 1959-61; sales rep. Manpower Inc., Chgo., 1961-63, br. mgr., Kansas City, Mo., 1963-65, area mgr., Mo. and Kans., 1964-65, regional mgr. Salespower div., Phila., 1965-66; asst. advt. mgr. soups Campbell Soup Co., Camden, N.J., 1966-68; pres. PARTIME, Inc. Paoli, Pa., 1968-74; dir. marketing Kelly Services Inc., Southfield, Mich., 1974-78; pres. CDI Temporary Services, Inc., 1978-91; pres. Dunhill Pers. System, Inc., Woodbury, N.Y., 1991-94; v.p. S.O.S. Temporary Svcs., Salt Lake City; pres. S.O.S. Staffing Svcs., Salt Lake City, 1995—. Trustee Internat. House Phila. Served with AUS, 1957-58. Mem. Nat. Assn. Temporary Services (sec. 1970-71, pres. 1971-73, bd. dirs. 1982-91), Kappa Sigma. Republican. Home: 4030 W Saddleback Rd Park City UT 84060 also: 1204 Annapolis Sea Colony E Bethany Beach DE 19930 Office: SOS Staffing Svcs 1415 S Main Salt Lake City UT 84115

SCOTT, HUGH, III, diesel engine distributor; b. St. Louis, Mar. 24, 1949; s. Hugh and Alice (McAfee) S.; m. Ann Russel Cady, Aug. 7, 1971; children: Hugh IV, Sara Cady. BA, Yale U., 1971. With Western Diesel Svcs., Inc., St. Louis, 1972—, pres., 1977-87, chmn., chief exec. officer, 1987—; chmn., chief exec. officer CK Power Products, Inc., St. Louis, 1985—, Coastal Power Products, Inc., Jacksonville, Fla., 1984-90; bd. dirs. Clayton (Mo.) Savs. and Loan Assn., Boatmen's Trust Co., St. Louis; policyholder adv. com. New Eng. Mutual Life Ins. Co., Boston. Alderman City of Clayton, 1979-87, mayor, 1987-91; bd. dirs. St. Luke's Hosp., St. Louis, 1982-88, Cen. Inst. for Deaf, St. Louis, 1984—; bd. dirs., v.p. V.P. Fair Found., Inc., St. Louis, 1991—; trustee Bellefontaine Cemetary Assn., St. Louis; bd. dirs. St. Louis area coun. Boy Scouts Am., 1988—; elector St. Louis City/County Bd. Electors, chmn., 1990. Mem. Young Pres. Orgn., St. Louis Constrn. Equipment Distbrs. (pres. 1978), Associated Equipment Distbrs. (lt. dir. 1978-80), Mark Twain Summer Inst. (bd. dirs., treas. 1986—), St. Louis Country Club, St. Louis Club. Republican. Episcopalian. Office: Western Diesel Svcs Inc 1424 Ashby Rd Saint Louis MO 63132-1211

SCOTT, HUGH PATRICK, physician, naval officer; b. Phila., Feb. 12, 1938; s. Hugh Patrick and Martha (Papiana) S.; m. Diane Marie Lopatzie, July 1, 1961; children: Karen, Brendan, Catherine. BA, LaSalle Coll., 1960; DO, Phila. Coll. Osteo. Medicine, 1964, LLD (hon.), 1991. Diplomate Am. Osteo. Bd. Ophthalmology and Otolaryngology. Intern Detroit Osteo. Hosp., Highland Park, Mich., 1964-65, resident otorhinolatyngology, 1965-68; lt. med. corps USNR, 1967, advanced through grades to rear adm., 1991; naval med. officer U.S. Naval Dispensary N.O.B., Norfolk, Va., 1968-70, Submarine Squadron 10, Groton, Conn.; Submarine Group 2; naval med. officer Naval Submarine Med. Ctr., New London, Conn., 1975-83; dir. undersea medicine and radiation health Naval Med. Command, Washington, 1983-86; comdg. officer Naval Hosp., Groton, 1986-88, Camp Lejeune, N.C., 1988-90; fleet surgeon Comdr. in Chief, U.S. Pacific Fleet, Pearl Harbor, Hawaii, 1990-91; asst. chief for operational medicine and fleet support Bur. Medicine and Surgery, Washington, 1991-92; dir. med. resources, plans and policy Office Chief of Naval Ops., Washington, 1992-94; asst. clin. prof. medicine Mich. State U., Lansing, Mich., 1970-75; pvt. practice, Madison Heights, Mich., 1970-75; cons. Am. Coll. Undersea and Hyperbaric Medicine, Washington, 1985-86. Decorated Legion of Merit, Gold Star (3). Fellow Osteo. Coll. Ophthalmology and Otolaryngology, Am. Acad. Otolaryngology and Head and Neck Surgery; mem. Am. Osteo. Coll. Otolaryngology—Head and Neck Surgery (pres., chmn. bd. govs.). Republican. Roman Catholic. Home: 3707 Merlin Way Annandale VA 22003-1326

SCOTT, IRENE FEAGIN, federal judge; b. Union Springs, Ala., Oct. 6, 1912; d. Arthur H. and Irene (Peach) Feagin; m. Thomas Jefferson Scott, Dec. 27, 1939 (dec.); children: Thomas Jefferson, Irene Scott Carroll. A.B., U. Ala., 1932, LL.B., 1936, LL.D., 1978; LL.M., Catholic U. Am., 1939. Bar: Ala. 1936. Law libr. U. Ala. Law Sch., 1932-34; atty. Office Chief Counsel IRS, 1937-50, mem. excess profits tax coun., 1950-52, spl. asst. to head appeals div., 1952-59, staff asst. to chief counsel, 1959-60; judge U.S. Tax Ct., 1960-82, sr. judge serving on recall, 1982—. Contbr. articles to Women Lawyers Jour. Bd. dirs. Mt. Olivet Found., Arlington. Mem. ABA (taxation sect.), Ala. Bar Assn., Fed. Bar Assn., D.C. Bar Assn. (hon.), Nat. Assn. Women Lawyers, Nat. Assn. Women Judges, Kappa Delta, Kappa Beta Pi. Office: US Tax Ct 400 2nd St NW Washington DC 20217

SCOTT, ISADORE MEYER, former energy company executive; b. Wilcoe, W.Va., Nov. 21, 1912; s. David and Libby (Roston) S.; m. Joan Rosenwald, Feb. 14, 1943; children: Betsy Scott Kleeblatt, Peggy, Jonathan D. A.B., W.Va. U., 1934, M.A., 1938; J.D., Washington and Lee U., 1937; LLD, West Va. U., 1983. Bar: Va. 1937. Practiced law Richmond, Va., 1937-38; v.p. Lee I. Robinson Hosiery Mills, Phila., 1938-42; with Winner Mfg. Co., Inc., Trenton, 1947-61, v.p., 1947-51, pres., 1951-61; chmn. bd. Tri-Instl. Facilities, Inc., Phila., 1962-78; chmn. bd. TOSCO Corp., Los Angeles, 1976-83, vice-chmn. bd., 1983-87; bd. dir. chmn. Univ. City Assos., Inc. Bd. dirs. S.E. Pa. chpt. ARC, Internat. Rescue Com., Univ. City Sci. Ctr., Phila.; mem. advt. com. Urban Affair Partnership; bd. dirs. emeritus, former mem. exec. com., vice-chmn. Phila. Mus. Art; former mem. World Affairs Council Phila.; mem. Phila. Com. Fgn. Rels.; trustee emeritus Washington and Lee U.; assoc. trustee U. Pa.; trustee George C. Marshall Found. With col. U.S. Army, 1942-46, NATOUSA, ETO. Decorated Legion of Merit, Silver Star, Purple Heart, Bronze Star (U.S.); Crown of Italy; medal of merit Czechoslovakia; Mentioned-in-dispatches, Eng.; fellow Mus. Am. Jewish History. Mem. Va. State Bar, Phila. Club, Gulph Mills Golf, Anglers of Phila, Masons, Phi Beta Kappa, Omicron Delta Kappa, Order of Coif. (hon.). Republican. Jewish. Clubs: Phila.; Gulph Mills Golf, Anglers of Phila. Lodge: Masons.

SCOTT, JAMES J., retired mining engineer; b. Wiota, Wis., Apr. 22, 1928; m. Edna M. Kettler, 1947; 5 children. BS, Mo. Sch. of Mines, 1950; MS, U. Wis., 1959, PhD in Mining Engring., 1962. Mine engr. Bethlehem (Pa.) Steel Co., 1950-53, mine foreman, 1953-57; from instr. to asst. prof. mining U. Wis., 1957-63; assoc. prof. U. Mo., Rolla, 1963-65, prof. mining, 1965-80, chmn. depts. mining & petroleum, 1970-76; gen. mgr. Black River Mine, Marble Cliff Quarries Co., 1967; asst. dir. mining rsch. US Bur. Mines, 1970—; adj. prof. mining engring. U. Mo., Rolla, 1980—; pres. Scott Mine Tech. Svc. Inc. Recipient Rock Mechanics award Soc. Mining Engrs. Mem. Am. Inst. Mining, Metall. and Petroleum Engrs. (Daniel C. Jackling award 1990), Can. Inst. Mining and Metallurgy. Achievements include research in field rock mechanics, mine operational problems, experimental stress analysis, photoelasticity, model studies, stress distribution problems, mine and research management; patentee in field. Home: 16720 State Rte O Rolla MO 65401 Office: Scott MTS Inc HCR 33 Box 36 Rolla MO 65401*

SCOTT, JAMES MARTIN, state legislator, healthcare system executive; b. Fairfax County, Va., June 11, 1938; s. Fred Sharp and Mary Ruth (Bishop) S.; m. Nancy Virginia Cromwell, Nov. 27, 1976; children: Catherine Virginia, Mary Alice. BA in English, U. N.C., 1960, MA in English, 1965; MPA, George Mason U., 1982. Tchr. Edison High Sch., Fairfax, Va., 1963-64; exec. dir. Fairfax Community Action Program, 1966-69, Washington Suburban Inst., Fairfax, 1969-72; bd. suprs. Fairfax County, 1972-76; dir. comminuty affairs Inova Health System, Springfield, Va., 1986-90, asst. v.p.; 1990—; mem. Va. Ho. Dels., Richmond, 1992—; pres. Va. Assn. Counties, Richmond, 1978-79; chair No. Va. Transp. Commn., Arlington, 1982. Pres. Fairfax Fair, 1988-90; bd. dirs. Washington Area Housing Partnership, 1990—, Washington Met. Coun. Govts., 1991—. Recipient David and Betty Scull Pub. Svc. award Washington Met. Coun. Govts., 1983; named Fairfax County Citizen of Yr., Washington Post, 1991. Democrat. Methodist. Avocation: tennis. Office: PO Box 359 Merrifield VA 22116-0359

SCOTT, J(AMES) MICHAEL, research biologist; b. San Diego, Sept. 20, 1941; s. James Melvin Scott and Eileen May (Rose) Scott Busby; m. Sharon Louise Middleton, Dec. 18, 1966; children: Kevin Charles, Heather Ann. BS in biology, San Diego State U., 1966, MA in Biology, 1970; PhD in Zoology, Oreg. State U., 1973. Project dir. U.S. Fish and Wildlife Service, Mauna Loa Station, Hawaii Nat. Park, 1974-84, Condor Research Ctr., Ventura, Calif., 1984-86; leader Coop. Fish and Wildlife Research Unit, Moscow, Idaho, 1986—. Author: (monograph) Forest Bird Communities of the Hawaiian Islands, 1986 (Wildlife Publs. award Wildlife Soc. 1986); editor: Estimating Numbers of Terrestrial Birds, 1981, Hawaii's Terrestrial Ecosystems: Protection and Management, 1985; also articles. Vol. Peace Corps, Colombia, 1963-65; mem. Centennial Commn., State of Idaho, 1989—. Recipient R.E. Dimick award, Oreg. chpt. Wildlife Soc., 1973, Spl. Achievement award U.S. Fish and Wildlife Service, 1978, 81, 87. Mem. Ecol. Soc. Am., Am. Ornithologists Union (elective), Pacific Seabird Group (pres. 1973-75), The Nature Conservancy (bd. dirs. Idaho chpt.). Avocations: bird watching, body surfing, skin diving, stamp collecting. Home: 1130 Kamiaken St Moscow ID 83843-3855 Office: U Idaho Coop Fish and Wildlife Rsch Inst Coll of Forestry Moscow ID 83843

SCOTT, JAMES WHITE, newspaper editor; b. Lebanon, Kans., Feb. 22, 1926; s. James Malcolm and Bernice (White) S.; m. Sammy Peete, June 9, 1950; children: James Peete, Thomas Whiteford, Edward English. B.J., U. Kans., 1950. Reporter Kansas City (Mo.) Times, 1950-54; editorial writer Kansas City (Mo.) Star, 1954-93, nat. affairs writer, arts and entertainment assoc. editor, 1968-77, v.p., 1987-93; editor editorial pages Star and Times, 1977-93, sr. editor, 1993—. Served with AUS, 1944-46, ETO. Mem. Delta Upsilon. Episcopalian. Home: 3204 W 83rd Ter Leawood KS 66206-1304 Office: Kansas City Star 1729 Grand Blvd Kansas City MO 64108-1413

SCOTT, JIMMIE DOW, health facility administrator; b. Milo, Okla., Jan. 1, 1930; s. Preston William and Elnora Mae (Hancock) S.; B. Liberal Studies, U. Okla., 1974, M.P.A., 1976, M.H.R., 1982; m. Wanda Mae Tippit, Oct. 5, 1952; children—Jimmie Dow, Dwain Dawson. Seaman recruit U.S. Navy, 1948, advanced through grades to lt. comdr., 1968; asst. administr. patient affairs, security and edn. U.S. Naval Hosp., Pensacola, Fla., 1959-63; asst. administr. Yokosuka (Japan) Naval Hosp., 1963-67; chief patient relations br. Bur. Medicine and Surgery, Washington, 1967-71; ret., 1971; exec. asst. for adminstrn. Univ. Hosp. and Clinics, Oklahoma City, 1980-83; adminstrv. asst. for adminstrn., assoc. administr. Okla. Meml. Hosp. and Clinics, Oklahoma City, 1983-85; assoc. administr. Okla. Teaching Hosps., Oklahoma City, 1985—. Mem. Am. Acad. Med. Adminstrs., Am. Soc. Public Adminstrs., Am. Coll. Hosp. Adminstrs., Acad. Polit. Sci., Am. Acad. Polit. and Social Sci. Republican. Baptist. Home: 2107 Fox Ave Moore OK 73160-4216 Office: Oklahoma Medical Ct PO Box 26307 Oklahoma City OK 73126-0307

SCOTT, JOANNA JEANNE, writer, English language educator; b. Rochester, N.Y., June 22, 1960; d. Walter Lee and Yvonne (de Potter) S.; m. James Burton Longenbach; 1 child, Kathryn Scott Longenbach. BA, Trinity Coll., Hartford, 1982; MA, Brown U., 1985. Asst. prof. English U. Md., College Park, 1987-88; from asst. to assoc. prof. U. Rochester, N.Y., 1988-95, prof., 1995—. Author: (novels) Fading, My Parmacheese Belle, 1987, The Closest Possible Union, 1988, Arrogance, 1990, (collection of stories) Various Antidotes, 1994 (PEN/Faulkner award nomination 1995). Recipient Richard and Hinde Rosenthal award Am. Acad.-Inst. Arts and Letters, 1991; fellow Guggenheim Found., 1988, MacArthur Found., 1992—. Mem. PEN, Writers of Books (bd. dirs. 1993—). Office: U of Rochester Dept of English Rochester NY 14627

SCOTT, JOHN BROOKS, research institute executive; b. Morenci, Ariz., Aug. 8, 1931; s. Brooks and Lucile (Slagle) S.; m. Jo Ann Rohrbach, June 5, 1987; children from previous marriage: Janice, Steven, Sarah. B.S., U. Ariz., 1957, M.A., 1959. Asst. prof. systems engring. U. Ariz., Tucson, 1959-61; mgr. Bell Aerosystems Co., Tucson, 1961-62; sr. v.p. IIT Research Inst., Annapolis, Md., 1962-90; pres. IIT Research Inst., Chgo., 1990—. Author papers on computer software, electromagnetic compatibility. Past pres. bd. dirs. Md. Hall for Creative Arts, Inc.; past chmn. Md. Hall Found.; mem. bd. govs. IIT Rsch. Inst.; trustee Ill. Inst. Tech. Sr. mem. IEEE, Greater Annapolis C. of C. (pres. 1987); mem. University Club Chgo., Phi Kappa Phi, Sigma Pi Sigma, Pi Mu Epsilon. Home: 215 Cinnamon Ln Edgewater MD 21037-1144 Office: 10 W 35th St Chicago IL 60616-3799

SCOTT, JOHN BURT, life insurance executive; b. St. Louis, July 25, 1944; s. Conley J. and Margaret (Dowdy) S.; m. Darlene Kuhnen Lady, Nov. 18, 1967; children: Kristen, Kathryn. BA in English, U. of South, 1966; MBA in Fin., Loyola U., 1971. Fin. analyst Kemper Nat. Property and Casualty Cos., Chgo., 1967-73; fin. officer Kemper Life, Long Grove, Ill., 1973-77, v.p. ops., 1977-86, pres., chief exec. officer, 1986-87, chmn., pres., chief exec. officer, 1987—; bd. dirs. Fed. Kemper Life Long Grove, Fidelity Life Assn. Long Grove, Kemper Investors Life, Long Grove, Kemper Fin. Cos., Chgo. Am. Coun. Life Insurers, Washington, Ill. Life Ins. Coun., Springfield, Nat. Orgn. Life and Health Guaranty Assn. Bd. dirs., exec. com. Omni Youth Svcs., Buffalo Grove, Ill., 1989—; bd. dirs. Lake County United Way, Life & Health Med. Rsch. Fund. Fellow Life Mgmt. Inst. Episcopalian. Avocations: golf, tennis.

SCOTT, JOHN CARLYLE, gynecologist, oncologist; b. Mpls., Sept. 24, 1933; s. Horace Golden and Grace (Melges) S.; m. Beth Krause, 1958 (div. 1977); m. Paola Maria Martini, Feb. 8, 1986; children: Jeff, David, Suzanne, Danielle. AB, Princeton U., 1956; BS, MD, U. Minn., 1961. Diplomate Am. Coll. Ob-gyn., Pan Am. Ob-gyn. Soc. Intern Sch. Medicine Marquette U., Milw., 1961-62, resident Sch. Medicine, 1962-66; resident Harvard Med. Sch., Boston, 1965; Am. Cancer fellow Marquette Med. Sch., Milw., 1966-67, instr. ob-gyn., 1966-67; clin. instr. ob-gyn. U. Wash. Med. Sch., Seattle, 1968-75, clin. assoc. prof., 1975-85, clin. assoc. prof., 1985—; mem. faculty adv. com. dept. ob-gyn. U. Wash., Seattle, 1973-92. Author: First Aid for N.W. Boaters, 1977; author Am. Jour. Ob-gyn., 1970, 75, 77. Bd. dirs. Renton (Wash.) Handicapped Ctr., 1968-70, March of Dimes, 1974-79; bd. dirs. enabling sys. U. Hawaii, Honolulu, 1977-80. Capt. U.S. Army, 1950-52, Korea. Decorated U.S. senate Medal of Freedom, Bronze and Silver Stars. Fellow ACOG (diplomate), Royal Soc. Medicine (gynecology and oncology sects.), Internat. Coll. Surgeons (sec. U.S. chpt. 1994—, v.p. internat. 1995—); mem. Pan Am. Ob-Gyn. Soc. (diplomate), S.W. Oncology Group, N.W. Oncology Group, Puget Sound Oncology Group, Seattle Gynecol. Soc. (pres. 1978), Baker Channing Soc., Sigma Xi. Avocations: photography, constrn., ornithology, sailing, skiing. Home: 726 16th Ave E Seattle WA 98112 Office: 9730 4th Ave NE Ste 202 Seattle WA 98115

SCOTT, JOHN CONSTANTE, marketing company executive; b. Charleston, S.C., Jan. 31, 1941; s. John C. and Annabelle (Holmes) S.; m. Mary Frances Turner. BS in Psychology, St. Joseph's U., Phila., 1975; JD, Temple U., 1979. Commd. USAF, 1968, advanced through grades to lt. col.; served in Vietnam; resigned, 1972; personnel mgr. Campbell Soup Co., Camden, N.J., 1972-79, corp. mgr. employee relations, 1980-84; v.p. ops. Insilco Corp., Meriden, Conn., 1984-89; v.p. human resources Howmet Corp., Greenwich, Conn., 1989-92; pres. Star Media, Inc. (formerly JMS

Enterprises, Inc.), Greenwich, 1992—. Mem. pres.'s coun. St. Joseph's U., 1985-90. Mem. ABA, N.J. Bar Assn., Pa. Bar Assn., Res. Officers Assn. (life), Greater Meriden C. of C. (bd. dirs. 1986-89). Roman Catholic. Avocations: mountain hiking, flying. Office: 15 E Putnam Ave Ste 320 Greenwich CT 06830-5424 Peace: The product of justice; politics: the major subset of religion; law (human) rules that institutionalize political power (often as not related to justice).

SCOTT, JOHN EDWARD, librarian; b. Washington, Ga., Aug. 12, 1920; s. John Edward and Martha Heard (Williams) S.; m. Dorris Louise Webb, Jan 28, 1948; children—Patricia Louise, Clifford Allen, Martha Ellen. A.B., Morehouse Coll., 1948; B.L.S., Atlanta U., 1949; M.L.S., U. Ill., 1955. Librarian Kans. Tech. Inst., Topeka, 1949-55; circulation librarian Va. State Coll., Petersburg, 1955-56; asst. reference librarian U. Kans., 1956-57; dir. library resources W. Va. State Coll., 1957—. Served with USNR, 1942-46. Mem. AAUP, ALA (councilor 1964—, chmn. coll. libraries sect. 1969-70), Southeastern Library Assn. (treas. 1979—), W.Va. Library Assn. (chmn coll. library sect. 1958-60, pres. 1961-62), Tri-State Assn. Coll. and Research Libraries, Middle Atlantic Regional Library Fedn. (exec. bd.), Kappa Delta Pi, Beta Phi Mu, Alpha Phi Alpha. Home: PO Box 303 Institute WV 25112-0303

SCOTT, JOHN EDWARD SMITH, lawyer; b. St. Louis, Aug. 6, 1936; s. Gordon Hatler and Luella Margarite (Smith) S.; m. Beverly Joan Phillips, Dec. 17, 1960; 1 dau., Pamela Anne. AB, Albion Coll., 1958; JD, Wayne State U., 1961. Bar: Mich. 1961, U.S. Dist. Ct. (ea. dist.) Mich. 1962, U.S. Dist. Ct. (we. dist.) Mich. 1970, U.S. Tax. Ct. 1979, U.S. Ct. Appeals (6th cir.) 1964, U.S. Supreme Ct. 1966. Law clk. Supreme Ct. Mich., Lansing, 1961-62; assoc. Dickinson, Wright, Moon, Van Dusen & Freeman, Detroit, 1962-69, ptnr., 1970—; adj. prof. U. Detroit Law Sch., 1967-71. Supreme Ct. appointee State Bar Rep. Assembly, Detroit, 1972-77; mayor City of Pleasant Ridge, Mich., 1973-81; commr. Mich. Appellate Defender Commn., Detroit, 1979—, chmn., 1992—; hearing referee Mich. Civil Rights Commn., Detroit, 1974-80; chmn. Detroit Legal Aid & Defender Commn., 1972-77; chmn. case flow mgmt. com. Mich. Supreme Ct., 1989-90. Fellow Am. Coll. Trial Lawyers, Internat. Soc. Barristers; mem. ABA (chmn. trial evidence com. sect. litigation 1988-91), Am. Bd. Advs., Internat. Assn. Def. Counsel, Am. Bar Found., Mich. Bar Found., Detroit Golf Club. Office: Dickinson Wright Moon Van Dusen & Freeman Ste 4000 500 Woodward Ave Detroit MI 48226

SCOTT, JOHN PAUL, psychologist, educator, author; b. Kansas City, Mo., Dec. 17, 1909; s. John William and Vivian (Armstrong) S.; m. Sarah Fisher, June 18, 1933 (dec. Sept. 1978); children: Jean Scott Franck, Vivian Scott Hixson, John, David; m. Mary-Vesta Marston, June 30, 1979. BA, U. Wyo., 1930; postgrad., Lincoln Coll., U. Oxford, Eng., 1930-32; PhD, U. Chgo., 1935. Asst. in zoology U. Chgo., 1932-35, prof. biopsychology, 1958; mem. faculty Wabash Coll., Crawfordsville, Ind., 1935-45, prof. zoology, 1942-45, chmn. dept., 1935-45; chmn. div. behavior studies Roscoe B. Jackson Meml. Lab., Bar Harbor, Maine, 1945-58, trustee, 1946-49, sr. staff scientist, 1958-65; rsch. prof. psychology Bowling Green (Ohio) U., 1965-80, Ohio Regents prof., 1968-80, prof. emeritus, 1980—; dir. Ctr. for Rsch. on Social Behavior, 1966-80; rsch. prof. psychology Tufts U., Medford, Mass., 1982-83; mem. Maine Bd. Psychol. Examiners, 1956-59. Author: Animal Behavior, 1958, 72, Aggression, 1958, 75 (with John L. Fuller) Genetics and the Social Behavior of the Dog, 1965, Early Experience and the Organization of Behavior, 1968, (with C.J. Pfaffenberger) Guide Dogs for the Blind, 1976, The Evolution of Social Systems, 1989; also sci. articles, chpts in books; editor: (with Sarah F. Scott) Social Control and Social Change, 1971, (with Basil Eleftheriou) The Physiology of Aggression and Defeat, 1971, (with Edward Senay) Separation and Depression, 1972, Critical Periods, 1978. Rhodes scholar, U. Oxford, 1930-32; recipient Jordan prize Ind. Acad. Sci., 1947, Disting. Alumnus award U. Wyo., 1976, Dobzhansky award for eminent rsch. Behavior Genetics Assn., 1987, Outstanding Achievement award U. Wyo., 1990; Ctr. Advanced Study in Behavioral Scis. fellow, 1963-64. Fellow AAAS, Am. Psychol. Assn., Animal Behavior Soc. (Disting. Animal Behaviorist award 1990), N.Y. Zool. Soc.; mem. Maine Psychol. Assn. (pres. 1953-54), Am. Soc. Zoologists, Am. Eugenics Soc. (v.p. 1963), Ecol. Soc. Am. (chmn. sect. animal behavior and sociobiology 1957-58), Internat. Soc. for Devel. Psychobiology (pres. 1972-78), Internat. Soc. for Rsch. on Aggression (pres. 1973-74), Behavior Genetics Assn. (pres. 1975-76), Phi Beta Kappa, Sigma Xi. Office: Bowling Green State U Bowling Green OH 43403

SCOTT, JOHN WALTER, chemical engineer, research management executive; b. Berkeley, Calif., May 27, 1919; s. John Walter and Cora Viola (Wampfler) S.; m. Jane Ellen Newman, June 27, 1942; children—Nancy, Barbara, Charles, James, Richard. B.S. in Chemistry, U. Calif.-Berkeley, 1941, M.S. in Chem. Engring., 1951. Registered profl. chem. engr., Calif. Process and catalyst research and devel. Chevron Research, Richmond, Calif., 1946-67, v.p., 1967-84, cons., 1985—. Contbr. articles to profl. jours.; patentee in field. Trustee U. Calif.-Berkeley Found., 1985-91; adv. coun. Lawrence Hall of Sci., 1990—; mem. coun. Town of Ross, Calif., 1992—. Capt. U.S. Army, 1941-46. Fellow Am. Inst. Chem. Engrs. (awards com. 1979-84, award 1978), AAAS; mem. Nat. Acad. Engring., Am. Chem. Soc., Am. Petroleum Inst. (chmn. research data info. services 1971-73, 77-80, cert. of appreciation 1983). Avocations: history; travel. Home: PO Box 2004 Ross CA 94957-0668

SCOTT, JOHN WILLIAM, food processing executive; b. Okamoto, Hyogo-Ken, Japan, July 12, 1935; s. John William and Alice Cunningham (Harrison) S.; m. Marilyn Merrill Ackland, July 20, 1962; children: John William, Matthew Thompson, Julia Leigh Harrison, Robert Augustine Thornton. AB, Princeton U., 1958. With CPC, Chgo. and Mexico, 1957-63; ops. mgr. Maizena (CPC), Cali, Colombia, 1964-65; mng. dir. PROMASA (CPC), Guatemala City, Guatemala, 1965-69, IMSA (CPC), Montevideo, Uruguay, 1969-70, Productos Knorr (CPC), Caracas, Venezuela, 1971-75; v.p. consumer div. Refinacoes de Milho (CPC), Sao Paulo, Brazil, 1975-79; mng. dir. Refinerias de Maiz (CPC), Buenos Aires, Argentina, 1979-83; asst. to pres. CPC Internat., Englewood Cliffs, N.J., 1983-84, v.p., 1985—. Bd. dirs. Accion Internat., Boston, 1986—; bd. dirs. Dwight Englewood (N.J.) Sch., 1990—, pres. bd. trustees, 1992—; pres. Englewood Community Chest, 1988. With AUS, 1954-56. Mem. Princeton Club (N.Y.C.), Englewood Field Club. Democrat. Episcopalian. Avocation: squash, sailing. Home: 40 Lydecker St Englewood NJ 07631-3005 Office: CPC Internat Inc International Plaza PO Box 8000 Englewood Cliffs NJ 07632-9976

SCOTT, JOYCE ALAINE, university official; b. Long Beach, Calif., May 21, 1943; d. Emmett Emery Scott and Grace (Evans) Wedum. B.A., U. Conn., 1964; M.A., U. Va., 1966; Ph.D., Duke U., 1973. From instr. to assoc. prof. U. Wyo., Laramie, 1971-74, asst. dean 1974-78, asst. v.p. acad. affairs, 1976-81, assoc. v.p. acad. affairs, 1981-84; provost, v.p. SUNY-Potsdam, 1984-86; exec. v.p. Wichita State U., Kans., 1986-90, v.p. on spl. assignment, 1990-91; sr. cons. Am. Assn. State Colls. and Univs., 1991-92, v.p. acad. and internat. programs, 1992—; mem. Commn. on Ednl. Credit and Credentials of Am. Council on Edn., Washington, 1982-87; cons. faculty Am. Open U., Lincoln, Nebr., 1981-82. Contbr. articles to profl. jours. Mem. MLA, AAUW, AAHE, Am. Assn. Tchrs. French, Phi Beta Kappa, Phi Sigma Iota. Republican. Presbyterian. Office: AASCU 1 Dupont Cir NW Ste 700 Washington DC 20036-1110

SCOTT, JUDITH MYERS, elementary education educator; b. Loredo, Mo., Dec. 29, 1940; d. Wilbur Charles and Dora Emma (Frazier) Myers; m. David Ronald Scott, Dec. 18, 1965; children: Russell Myers, Geoffrey Douglas. BA in Edn., Ariz. State U., 1962, MA in edn., 1970. Cert. tchr. Ariz. Tchr. 2d grade Scottsdale (Ariz.) Elem. Dist., 1962-64; tchr. 1st grade Cahuilla Sch., Palm Springs, Calif., 1965, Palm Crest Sch., La Canada, Calif., 1968-69; tchr. Ak Chin Community Sch., Maricopa, Ariz., 1969-70; grad. asst. Ariz. State U., Tempe, 1970-71; pvt. tutor Tempe, 1970-77; tchr. Dayspring Presch., Tempe, 1978-83; tchr. 3d grade Waggoner Elem. Sch., Kyrene, Ariz., 1984-86; reading specialist Tempe Elem. Sch. Dist., 1986-90, tchr., trainer collaborative literacy intervention program, 1990—; exec. dir. Beauty for All Seasons, Tempe, 1982-86. Coord. New Zealand Tchr. Exch., Tempe Sister Cities, 1992—. Mem. NEA, ASCD, IRA, ARA, Ariz. Sch. Admisntrs., Ariz. Edn. Assn., Tempe Edn. Assn., Internat. Reading Assn. Methodist. Avocations: Painting, reading, hiking. Home: 1940 E Calle De

Caballos Tempe AZ 85284-2507 Office: Tempe Elem Sch Dist 3205 N Rural Rd Tempe AZ 85282

SCOTT, KELLY, newspaper editor. Mng. editor sunday calendar The L.A. Times. Office: LA Times Times Mirror Sq Los Angeles CA 90012-3816*

SCOTT, KENNETH ELSNER, mechanical engineering educator; b. Webster, Mass., May 18, 1926; s. Henry Anderson and Amanda (Elsner) S.; m. Elizabeth Ann Oldham, June 21, 1952; children—Kenneth Elsner, Cynthia Lynne, Jeffrey Alan, Donald Leighton. B.S. in Mech. Engring, Worcester Poly. Inst., 1948, M.S., 1954. Registered profl. engr., Mass. Mem. faculty Worcester Poly. Inst., 1948-91, prof. mech. engring., 1966-91, prof. emeritus, 1991—, George I. Alden prof. engring., 1971-75, inst. dir. audio-visual devel., 1971-74, dir. instructional TV, 1974-90, dir. CAD Lab., 1981-93, acting head dept. mech. engring., 1988-89. Mem. bd. health, Holden, Mass., 1963-70. Served with AUS, 1944-46. Recipient Trustees' award for Outstanding Tchr. of Year, 1971, Western Electric Fund award for excellence in instrn. New Eng. sect. Am. Soc. Engring. Edn., 1972, Teaching Excellence and Campus Leadership award Sears-Roebuck Found., 1990-91. Fellow ASME (exec. com. Worcester sect. 1952-57, sec.-treas. 1955-56, chmn. 1956-57, region I chmn. profl. divs. com. 1957-59, chmn. agenda, audit, budget and nominating com. Worcester 1957-58, chmn. symposium lubrication Worcester sect. 1957-58, chmn. Adm. Earle award com. 1958-59, chmn. devel. com. 1960-61); mem. Am. Soc. Engring. Edn. (sec.-treas. New Eng.), Sigma Xi, Pi Tau Sigma, Tau Beta Pi. Home: 9750 Cypress Lake Dr Fort Myers FL 33919-6064

SCOTT, KENNETH EUGENE, lawyer, educator; b. Western Springs, Ill., Nov. 21, 1928; s. Kenneth L. and Bernice (Albright) S.; m. Viviane H. May, Sept. 22, 1956 (dec. Feb. 1982); children: Clifton, Jeffrey, Linda; m. Priscilla Gay, July 30, 1989. BA in Econs., Coll. William and Mary, 1949; MA in Polit. Sci., Princeton U., 1953; LLB, Stanford U., 1956. Bar: N.Y. 1957, Calif. 1957, D.C. 1967. Assoc. Sullivan & Cromwell, N.Y.C., 1956-59, Musick, Peeler & Garrett, L.A., 1959-61; chief dep. savs. and loan commr. State of Calif., L.A., 1961-63; gen. counsel Fed. Home Loan Bank Bd., Washington, 1963-67; Parsons prof. law and bus. Stanford (Calif.) Law Sch., 1968—; mem. Shadow Fin. Regulatory Com., 1986—; bd. dirs. Benham Capital Mgmt. Mut. Fund, Mountain View, Calif., RCM Capital Funds, San Francisco. Author: (with others) Retail Banking in the Electronic Age, 1977; co-editor: The Economics of Corporation Law and Securities Regulation, 1980. Mem. ABA, Calif. Bar Assn., Phi Beta Kappa, Order of Coif, Pi Kappa Alpha, Omicron Delta Kappa. Home: 610 Gerona Rd Stanford CA 94305-8453 Office: Crown Quadrangle Stanford Law Sch Stanford CA 94305-8610

SCOTT, KENNETH R., transportation executive; b. Iowa City. BCE, U. Iowa, 1960; MCE, U. No., Rolla, 1966. Commd. U.S. Army, 1961, advanced through grades, 1970; airport project engr. Norfolk (Va.) Airport Authority, 1970-72, asst. airport mgr., 1972-74, exec. dir., 1972—; adj. prof. Embry-Riddle Aero. U. at Norfolk Naval Air Sta. and Langley AFB. Bd. dirs. Norfolk Cmty. Promotion Corp., Va. Aviation and Space Edn. Forum. Mem. Am. Assn. Airport Execs., Va. Airport Operators Coun. Office: Norfolk Airport Authority Norfolk Intl Airport Norfolk VA 23518-5897

SCOTT, LARRY MARCUS, aerospace engineer, mathematician; b. Bingham Canyon, Utah, June 14, 1945; s. Wright Marcus Scott and Margaret Ruth (Jackson) Sturzenegger; m. Paula Inger Elisabeth Kjellman, Aug. 21, 1972; children: Paul Marcus, Laura Elizabeth. BS, Brigham Young U., 1971; MS, Boston U., 1983. Engr. lifting body re-entry mechs. Douglas Missile and Space Systems, Sant Monica, Calif., 1965-66; missionary and dist. leader Ch. of Jesus Christ of Latterday Saints, Finland, 1966-69; researcher Math. Dept. Brigham Young U. for Air Force, Provo, Utah, 1969-71; researcher Russian Translation Linguistics Brigham Young U. for Nat. Security Agy., Provo, 1971-72; internship in Plasma Physics, Physics Dept. Brigham Young U., Provo, 1972-73; sci. programmer Lockheed Elect. Co., Edwards AFB, Calif., 1973-75; mathematician 6521 Range Squadron, 6250 Test Wing, Edwards AFB, 1976-80 1982-85; exchange sci. Inst. for Flight Dynamics, DFVLR, Federal Republic Germany, 1980-82; mathematician A.F. Logistics Command, Hill AFB, Utah, 1985-87; software engineer Ball Systems Engring. Div., Edwards AFB, 1987-89; nav. engr. Short Range Attack Missile, 1989-91; avionics engr. F-15E, Edwards AFB, Calif., 1992—. Co-author: Invention disclosure on laser nozzle, 1976, Evaluation of F-15E Operational Flight Program, AF Tech. Report TR 92-021, AFFTC-TR-94-08; author: report for DFVLR in Germany, 1982, USAF Disclosure, 1984; Russian translator Sister Base Program, 1994. Quorum Pres. Ch. of Latter Day Saints, Palmdale, Calif. 1973-74, Lancaster, Calif. 1984-85, Quorum Counselor, Lancaster 1988-90, high counselor, 1994—; asst. varsity scout, Bountiful, Utah 1985-86. Recipient Bank of Am. Language Award, Hawthorne, Calif. 1963, Scholarship to Brigham Young U. 1963, Hon. Cert. Defense Language Inst., Monterey, Calif. 1980. Republican. Avocations: computers, classical music, playing baroque music, musical improvisation, mathematics, genealogy.

SCOTT, LAWRENCE VERNON, microbiology educator; b. Anthony, Kans., Jan. 28, 1917; s. Lawrence Garfield and Mable Grace (Madden) S.; m. Elizabeth Buchanan Rowe, Jan. 28, 1945; children: James Robert, Jean Elizabeth, Lawrence Rowe. B.A., Phillips U., 1940; M.S., U. Okla., Norman, 1947; Sc.D., Johns Hopkins U., 1950. Asst. prof. bacteriology, asso. prof., 1950-58; prof. microbiology and immunology St. Medicine, U. Okla. Health Sci. Center, Oklahoma City, 1958-83, prof. emeritus, 1983—; chmn. dept. microbiology and immunology Sch. Medicine, U. Okla. Health Sci. Center, 1961-83; fellow in tropical medicine La. State U., 1967; cons. microbiologist St. Anthony and VA Hosps., 1957—; vis. prof. U. Otago, Dunedin, N.Z.; condr. microbiol. rsch. South Pole Sta., Antarctica, 1974, 75; participant People to People program to China, 1983, med. missions to Jamaica, 1988-93; invited participant reconciliation trip to Vietnam, 1993. Contbr. writings to profl. publs.; author: Medical Microbiology, 1982. Served to lt. USNR, 1942-46. Recipient Disting. Alumnus award Phillips U., 1968, Superior and Profl. Univ. Svc. award U. Okla., 1984. Mem. Am. Soc. Microbiology, Am. Acad. Microbiology, Assn. Med. Sch. Microbiologists (chmn.), N.Y. Acad. Scis., Okla. Acad. Scis., Am. Soc. Tropical Medicine and Hygiene, Sigma Xi. Democrat. Mem. Christian Church (Disciples of Christ). Condr. research. Home: 4125 NW 61st Ter Oklahoma City OK 73112-1346 Office: PO Box 26901 Oklahoma City OK 73126-0901 Through hard work and education, my goal was to repay society. Thus, it has been important to make a contribution. In all activities, honesty and integrity are central.

SCOTT, LEE HANSEN, retired holding company executive; b. Atlanta, Sept. 25, 1926; s. Elbert Lee and Auguste Lillian (Hansen) S.; m. Margaret Lee Smith, July 20, 1951; children: Bradley Hansen, Randall Lee. B.E.E., U. Fla., 1949. With Fla. Power Corp., St. Petersburg, 1949-94; dir. constrn., maintenance and operating Fla. Power Corp., 1968-71, v.p. customer ops., 1971-77, sr. v.p. ops., 1977-83, pres., 1983-88, chmn. bd., 1988-90, also bd. dirs.; also bd. dirs. Fla. Progress Corp.; retired, 1994; bd. dirs. Sun Banks; cons. in field. Pres. St. Petersburg chpt. ARC, 1977, Pinellas Com. of 100, 1980, Community Services Council, 1970, St. Petersburg Progress, 1983, Bus. and Industry Employment Devel. Council, 1983; chmn. bd. United Way. Served with USAF, 1944-46. Named Mr. Sun of St. Petersburg, 1990. Mem. Fla. Engring. Soc., IEEE, Elec. Council Fla. (pres. 1979), St. Petersburg C. of C. (v.p. 1980), Fla. C. of C. (pres. 1987-88), Pinellas Suncoast C. of C. (past chmn., past bd. trustees). Presbyterian. Home: 601 Apalachee Dr NE Saint Petersburg FL 33702-2766

SCOTT, LEONARD LEWY, JR., mathematician, educator; b. Little Rock, Oct. 17, 1942; s. Leonard Lewy and Mary Ella (Simcoe) S.; m. Mary Ellena Broach; children: Mary Lisette, Walter Lewy. BA, Vanderbilt U., 1964; PhD, Yale U., 1968. Instr. U. Chgo., 1968-70; asst. prof. Yale U., New Haven, 1970-71; from assoc. prof. to prof. U. Va., Charlottesville, 1971-87, McConnell/Bernard prof., 1987—; vis. fellow All Souls Coll., Oxford U., 1992. Mem. editorial bd. Jour. Algebra, 1990—; contbr. articles to profl. jours. including Annals Math, Inventiones, Publ. Math IHES. Rsch. grantee NSF, 1972—, Sci. and Engring. Rsch. Coun. (Eng.), 1983, 92. Mem. Am. Math. Soc. (chmn. S.E. speaker sect. 1985-86, nat. nominating com. 1988-89, editorial bd. Univ. Lectr. Series 1987—, chmn. 1993—). Achievements include origination of maximal subgroups program in finite group theory; development of isomorphism problem for group rings; invention of quasi-hereditary algebras; proof of Carlson's conjecture on group cohomology; demonstration of generic cohomology for finite and algebraic groups. Home: 3250 Tearose Ln Charlottesville VA 22903-9361 Office: U Va Dept Math New Cabell Dr Charlottesville VA 22903

SCOTT, LORRAINE ANN, fraternal organization executive; b. Cleve., Dec. 14, 1947; d. Harry F. and Ann Mae (Dolecek) Dufek; m. John William Scott, Jan. 4, 1969; 1 son, Bruce. BBA, Dyke Coll., Cleve., 1967. Acct., Fulton, Reid & Staples, Cleve., 1967-69; acct., data control Nat. City Bank, Cleve., 1969-70; asst. treas. Independence (Ohio) Bd. of Edn. 1978-80; exec. dir. Nat. Frat. of Phi Gamma Nu, Cleve., 1980—. Mem. Am. Soc. Assn. Execs. Republican. Lutheran. Editor Phi Gamma Nu mag., 1980—.

SCOTT, LOUIS EDWARD, advertising agency executive; b. Waterbury, Conn., June 17, 1923; s. Louis Arthur and Ellen (Eckert) S.; m. Phyllis Corrine Denker, Jan. 27, 1942; children: Susan Louise, Gary Lynn. BS, U. Calif., Berkeley, 1944. Sr. account exec. McCarty Co., L.A. 1946-50; with Foote, Cone & Belding, L.A. 1950-87; v.p. Foote, Cone & Belding, 1956, gen. mgr., 1959, became sr. v.p., 1963, dir., 1961—, chmn. exec. com., 1970-82; chmn. ops. com., pres. Foote, Cone & Belding/Honig, 1975-82; bd. dirs. Smart and Final Corp., Casino Internat., True North Comm.. Chmn. publicity com. Los Angeles Community Chest, 1960; patron mem. Los Angeles YMCA; mem. Freedoms Found.; chmn. So. Calif. advisory bd. Advt. Council; mem. exec. advisory bd. Art Center Coll. Design. Served with U.S. Maritime Service, also USNR, World War II. Named Western Advt. Man of Year, 1972. Mem. Am. Assn. Advt. Agys. (dir., past chmn. Western region), L.A. Advt. Club (dir.), L.A. C. of C., L.A. World Affairs Coun., Town Hall Club, Rio Verde Country Club, Seattle Yacht Club, Cruising Club Am. Home: PO Box 65079 Port Ludlow WA 98365-0079 Office: 101 E Erie St Chicago IL 60611-2811

SCOTT, MANUEL, church administrator. Officer Bd. of Evangelism of the Nat. Baptist Conv. USA, Dallas. Office: Natl. Baptist Conv. USA 2600 S Marsalis Ave Dallas TX 75216

SCOTT, MARIANNE FLORENCE, librarian, educator; b. Toronto, Dec. 4, 1928; d. Merle Redvers and Florence Ethel (Hutton) S. BA, McGill U., Montreal, Que., Can., 1949, BLS, 1952; LLD (hon.), York U., 1985, Dalhousie U., 1989; DLitt (hon.), Laurentian U., 1990. Asst. librarian Bank of Montreal, 1952-55; law librarian McGill U., 1955-73, law area librarian, 1973-75, dir. libraries, 1975-84, lectr. legal bibliography faculty of law, 1964-75; nat. librarian Nat. Library of Can., Ottawa, Ont., 1984—. Co-founder, editor: Index to Can. Legal Periodical Lit, 1963—; contbr. articles to profl. jours. Decorated Officer of the Order of Can., 1995. Mem. Internat. Assn. Law Libraries (dir. 1974-77), Am. Assn. Law Libraries, Can. Assn. Law Libraries (pres. 1963-69, exec. bd. 1973-75, honored mem. 1980—), Can. Library Assn. (council and dir. 1980-82, 1st v.p. 1980-81, pres. 1981-82), Corp. Profl. Librarians of Que. (v.p. 1975-76), Can. Assn. Research Libraries (pres. 1978-79, past pres. 1979-80, exec. com. 1980-81, sec.-treas. 1983-84), Ctr. for Research Libraries (dir. 1980-83), Internat. Fedn. Library Assns. (honor com. for 1982 conf. 1979-82), Conf. of Dirs. of Nat. Libraries (chmn. 1988-92). Home: 119 Dorothea Dr, Ottawa, ON Canada K1V 7C6 Office: Nat Libr Can, 395 Wellington St, Ottawa, ON Canada K1A 0N4

SCOTT, MARY DAVIES, federal judge; b. 1944. BA, Trinity U., San Antonio, 1968; JD, U. Ark., Little Rock, 1978. Admitted to bar, 1979. Bankruptcy judge U.S. Dist. Ct. Ark., Little Rock, 1987—. Office: US Dist Ct 600 W Capitol St PO Box 3201 Little Rock AR 72201

SCOTT, MICHAEL, lawyer; b. N.Y.C., Oct. 11, 1930; s. Irvin Leslie and Dorothy (Chandler) S.; m. Cynthia Ann Meredith, July 17, 1954; children: Elizabeth, Gregory, Andrew. BA, Cornell U., 1952; JD, U. Mich., 1958; diploma, Grad. Inst. of Internat. Studies, Geneva, 1959. Bar: Ohio 1959, D.C. 1971, Calif. 1981. Assoc. Squire, Sanders & Dempsey, Cleve., 1959-67, ptnr., 1967-71; ptnr. Squire, Sanders & Dempsey, Washington, 1971—; pres. Ohio State Legal Services Assn., Columbus, 1969-70, Nat. Capital Area Health Care Coalition, Washington, 1985—. Served to lt. (j.g.) USN, 1952-55. Mem. ABA, Ohio Bar Assn., D.C. Bar Assn., Calif. Bar Assn. Clubs: Met. (Washington), Union (Cleve.). Home: 7133 Deepwood Dr Chagrin Falls OH 44022-2646 Office: Squire Sanders & Dempsey PO Box 407 1201 Pennsylvania Ave NW Washington DC 20004-2401

SCOTT, MICHAEL DENNIS, lawyer; b. Mpls., Nov. 6, 1945; s. Frank Walton and Donna Julia (Howard) S.; m. Blanca Josefina Palacios, Dec. 12, 1981; children: Michael Dennis, Cindal Marie, Derek Walton. B.S., MIT, 1967; J.D., UCLA, 1974. Bar: Calif. 1974, U.S. Dist. Ct. (no. so. and cen. dists.) Calif. 1974, U.S. Patent Office 1974, U.S. Ct. Appeals (9th cir.) 1974, U.S. Supreme Ct. 1978, U.S. Ct. Appeals (fed. cir.) 1989. Systems programmer NASA Electronics Research Lab., Cambridge, Mass., 1967-69, Computer Sciences Corp., El Segundo, Calif., 1969-71, Univac, Valencia, Calif., 1971; from assoc. to ptnr. Smaltz & Neelley, Los Angeles, 1974-81; exec. dir. Ctr. for Computer/Law, Los Angeles, 1977-94; sole practice Los Angeles, 1981-86, 88-89; pres. Law and Tech. Press, 1981-94; ptnr. Scott & Roxborough, Los Angeles, 1986-88, Graham & James, 1989-93; v.p., gen. counsel Sanctuary Woods Multimedia, Inc., San Mateo, Calif., 1993-94; pres., CEO Wildwood Interactive, Inc., Manhattan Beach, Calif., 1994—; of counsel Steinhart & Falconer, 1995—; adj. assoc. prof. law Southwestern U., L.A., 1975-80; chmn. World Computer Law Congress, L.A., 1991, 93. Author: (with David S. Yen) Computer Law Bibliography, 1979, The Scott Report, 1981-86, Computer Law, 1984, Scott on Computer Law, 1991, Multimedia: Law and Practice, 1993; editor in chief: Computer/Law Jour., 1978-94, Software Protection, 1982-92, Software Law Jour., 1985-94, Internat. Computer Law Adviser, 1986-92. Mem. Computer Law Assn. (bd. dirs. 1994—), Calif. State Bar Assn. Office: Wildwood Interactive Inc 4 Arbolado Ct Manhattan Beach CA 90266 also: Steinhart & Falconer 333 Masher St 32nd Fl San Francisco CA 94105

SCOTT, MICHAEL LESTER, artist, educator; b. Lawrence, Kans., Sept. 24, 1952; s. Lester F. and Robbie (Guthrie) S.; m. Cheryl Ann Scott, May 24, 1982; children: Erik, Maxfield. BFA, Kans. City Art Inst., 1976; MFA, U. Cin., 1978. instr. Baker Hunt Found., Covington, Ky., 1986-93, Art Acad. of Cin. Work represented in pub. collections Butler Mus. Art, Youngstown, Ohio, New Orleans Mus. Art, Cin. Art Mus., Mus. Acquisitions of Chgo., J.B. Speed Mus., Bronnin-Foreman, Louisville, Owensboro (Ky.) Mus. Art, Hunter Mus. Art, Chattanooga, Phila. Mus. Art, Manhattan Life, N.Y.C. Mem. Sierra Club, Wilderness Soc., Green Peace, Nature Conservancy, Redwood League, Oxbow Found. Avocation: canoeist. Home and Studio: 2477 Country Pl New Richmond OH 45157 Office: Sherry French 41 W 57th St New York NY 10019

SCOTT, MICHAEL TIMOTHY, lawyer; b. Scranton, Pa., Jan. 12, 1951; s. Thomas F. and Elizabeth (Moran) S.; m. Karen Marian Scott, July 8, 1972; children: Jeffrey, Abigail, Zachary. BS, Pa. State U., 1972; JD magna cum laude, U. Pa., 1976. Bar: Pa. 1976, D.C. 1977. Assoc. Pepper, Hamilton & Scheetz, Phila., 1976-77, ptnr., 1981-87; assoc. Arnold & Porter, Washington, 1977-79; atty. Dept. Justice, Washington, 1979-81; ptnr. Reed, Smith, Shaw & McClay, Phila., 1987—. Contbr. articles to profl. jours. Mem. ABA. Office: Reed Smith Shaw & McClay 2500 One Liberty Pl Philadelphia PA 19103

SCOTT, MIMI KOBLENZ, actress, psychotherapist; b. Albany, N.Y., Dec. 15, 1940; d. Edmund Akiba and Tillie (Paul) Koblenz; m. Barry Stuart Scott, Aug. 13, 1961 (dec. Nov. 1991); children: Karen Scott Zantay, Jeffrey B. BA in Speech, English Edn., Russell Sage Coll., 1962; MA in Speech Edn., SUNY, Albany, 1968; M in Social Welfare, SUNY, 1985; PhD in Psychology, Pacific Western U., Encino, Calif., 1985. Cert. tchr., social worker. Tchr. English, speech Albany Pub. Schs., 1961-63; hostess, producer talkshow Sta. WAST-TV 13, Albany, 1973-75; freelance actress N.Y.C., 1975-77; producer, actress Four Seasons Dinner Theater, Albany, 1978-82; instr. of theatre Albany Jr. Coll., 1981-83; pvt. practice psychotherapy Albany, N.Y., 1985-92; exec. producer City of Albany Park Playhouse, 1989-92; actor self-employed N.Y.C., 1985—; guest psychotherapist Sally Jessy Raphael Show, 1992, 93, Jane Whitney Show, 1994, A Current Affair, 1995, News Talk TV, 1995. Scriptwriter, dir., actress TV

movie, 1984. Event organizer AmFar, 1985; co-chmn. March of Dimes Telethon, 1985-86; fundraiser Leukemia Found., 1987, Aids Benefit, N. Miami Beach, Fla., 1988; elected to SUNY Albany U. Found., 1990. Recipient FDR Nat. Achievement award March of Dimes, 1985, Recognition Cert. Capital Dist. Psychiat. Ctr., 1983, 84, 85; named Woman of Yr. YWCA, 1986, Commr. Albany Tricentennial Celebration, 1986; Mimi Scott Day proclaimed by Mayor of Albany, 1989. Mem. AEA, SAG, AFTRA, NASW. Jewish. Avocations: horseback riding, boating, golf, tennis. Home and Office: 211 West 71st # 6C New York NY 10023

SCOTT, NATHAN ALEXANDER, JR., minister, literary critic, religion educator; b. Cleve., Apr. 24, 1925; s. Nathan Alexander and Maggie (Martin) S.; m. Charlotte Hanley, Dec. 21, 1946; children: Nathan Alexander III, Leslie K. AB, U. Mich., 1944; BD, Union Theol. Sem., 1946; PhD, Columbia U., 1949; LittD, Ripon Coll., 1965, St. Mary's Coll., Notre Dame, Ind., 1969, Denison U., 1976, Brown U., 1981, Northwestern U., 1982, Elizabethtown Coll., 1989; LHD, Wittenberg U., 1965; DD, Phila. Div. Sch., 1967; STD, Gen. Theol. Sem., 1968; LHD, U. D.C., 1976; DD, The Protestant Episcopal Theological Seminary in Va., 1985; HumD, U. Mich., 1988; LHD, Wesleyan U., 1989, Bates Coll., 1990; STD, Univ of the South, 1992; DD, Kenyon Coll., 1993; Ordained priest Episcopal Ch., 1960; canon theologian Cathedral St. James, Chgo., 1967-76. dean of chapel, Va. Union U., 1946-47; instr. humanities, Howard U., 1948-51, asst. prof., 1951-53, assoc. prof., 1953-55; asst. prof. theology and literature, U. Chgo., 1955-58, assoc. prof., 1958-64, prof., 1964-72, Shailer Mathews prof. of theology and lit., 1972-76, prof. English, 1967-76; Commonwealth prof. religious studies, U. Va., 1976-81, William R. Kenan prof. religious studies, 1981-90, prof. English, 1976-90, prof. emeritus, 1990—. Author: Rehearsals of Discomposure: Alienation and Reconciliation in Modern Literature, 1952, The Tragic Vision and the Christian Faith, 1957, Modern Literature and the Religious Frontier, 1958, Albert Camus, 1962, Reinhold Niebuhr, 1963, The New Orpheus: Essays toward a Christian Poetic, 1964, The Climate of Faith in Modern Literature, 1965, The Broken Center: Studies in the Theological Horizon of Modern Literature, 1966, Ernest Hemingway, 1966, The Modern Vision of Death, 1967, Adversity and Grace: Studies in Recent American Literature, 1968, Negative Capability: Studies in the New Literature and the Religious Situation, 1969, The Unquiet Vision: Mirrors of Man in Existentialism, 1969, The Wild Prayer of Longing: Poetry and the Sacred, 1971, Nathanael West, 1971, Three American Moralists: Mailer, Bellow, Trilling, 1973, The Poetry of Civic Virtue: Eliot, Malraux, Auden, 1976, Mirrors of Man in Existentialism, 1978, The Poetics of Belief: Studies in Coleridge, Arnold, Pater, Santayana, Stevens and Heidegger, 1985, Visions of Presence in Modern American Poetry, 1993; co-editor Jour. Religion, 1963-77, (with Ronald Sharp) Reading George Steiner, 1994; adv. editor Religion and Lit., Literature and Theology, Callaloo. Fellow Am. Acad. of Arts and Scis.; mem. Soc. Arts, Religion and Contemporary Culture, Soc. for Values in Higher Edn. (Kent fellow), MLA., Am. Acad. Religion (pres. 1986), Century Assn. (N.Y.C.), Quadrangle Club, Arts Club (Chgo.), Greencroft Club (Charlottesville, Va.). Office: U Va Religion Studies Charlottesville VA 22903

SCOTT, NORMAN LAURENCE, engineering consultant; b. Meadow Grove, Nebr., Oct. 17, 1931; s. Laurence Ray Scott and Ruth Louise Braun; m. Joan Culbertson, Jan. 21, 1956; 1 child, Douglas Jay. BS in Civil Engring., U. Nebr., 1954. Registered profl. engr., Ill., Fla., Md., Minn., Va., Tex.; registered structural engr., Ill. Sales engr. R.H. Wright & Son, Ft. Lauderdale, Fla., 1956-58; mgr. Wright of Palm Beach, West Palm Beach, Fla., 1958-59; exec. sec. Prestressed Concrete Inst., Chgo., 1959-63; gen. mgr. Wiss, Janney, Elstner & Assoc., Northbrook, Ill., 1963-66; pres., chmn. The Consulting Engrs. Group Inc., Mt. Prospect, Ill., 1966—. 1st lt. USAF, 1954-56. Mem. ASCE, Am. Concrete Inst. (pres. 1983-84, Henry C. Turner medal 1993 (hon. mem. 1994), Fedn. Internat. de la Precontraint (medal 1994), Ill. Soc. Profl. Engrs. (pres. North Shore chpt. 1962). Republican. Home: 701 Chatham Rd Glenview IL 60025 Office: The Consulting Engrs Group 55 E Euclid Ave Mount Prospect IL 60056-1287

SCOTT, NORMAN ROSS, electrical engineering educator; b. N.Y.C., May 15, 1918; s. George Norman and Lillias B.H. (Ogg) S.; m. Marjorie M. Fear, Apr. 6, 1950; children: Mari, George, Ian, Charles. BS, MS, MIT, 1941; PhD, U. Ill., 1950. Asst. prof. elec. engring. U. Ill., Urbana, 1946-50; asst. prof. to prof. elec. engring. U. Mich., Ann Arbor, 1951-87, assoc dean Coll. Engring., 1965-68; dean Dearborn Campus U. Mich., 1968-71, prof. emeritus of elec. engring. and computer sci., 1987—; cons. Nat. Cash Register Co., Dayton, 1956-65; mem. math. and computer sci. rsch. adv. com. AEC, Washington, 1961-63. Editor-in-chief IEEE Trans. on Computers, N.Y.C., 1961-65; author: Analog and Digital Computer Technology, 1959, Electronic Computer Technology, 1970, Computer Number Systems and Arithmetic, 1985. Maj. U.S. Army, 1941-46. Fellow IEEE. Home: 2260 Gale Rd Ann Arbor MI 48105-9512 Office: U Mich Eecs Dept Ann Arbor MI 48109

SCOTT, NORMAN ROY, academic administrator, agricultural engineering educator; b. Spokane, Wash., Sept. 6, 1936; s. Roy Samuel and Agnes Sarafia (Lilljegren) S.; m. Sharon R. Cogley, June 17, 1961; children: Robin, Nanette, Shirlene. BS in Agrl. Engring., Wash. State U., 1958; PhD, Cornell U., 1962. Mem. faculty agrl. engring dept. Cornell U., Ithaca, N.Y., 1962—, chmn. agrl. engring. dept., 1978-84, dir. office for rsch. agrl. experimentation sta., 1984-89, v.p. rsch. and advanced studies, 1989—; mem. bd. on agriculture NRC, Nat. Acad. Scis., 1993—. Contbr. articles to profl. jours.; patentee in field. Fellow Am. Inst. for Med. and Biol. Engring. (founding 1991), Am. Soc. Agrl. Engrs. (tech. v.p. 1989-92, pres. elect 1992-93, pres. 1993-94, Henry Glese award 1989); mem. AAAS, N.Y. Acad. Scis., Nat. Acad. Engring., Am. Soc. for Engring. Edn., Instrument Soc. Am. (sr.). Democrat. Methodist. Avocations: sailing, golf. Home: 1662 Taughannock Blvd Trumansburg NY 14886-9120 Office: Cornell U Rsch and Advanced Studies 314 Day Hall Ithaca NY 14853

SCOTT, OLOF HENDERSON, JR., priest; b. Phila., May 13, 1942; s. Olof Henderson and Julia Irene (Rutroff) S.; m. Eva Jakowenko, Sept. 13, 1969; children: Lisa Ann, Christopher Olof, Timothy Nicholas. BA in Physics, Franklin and Marshall Coll., 1964; MS in Nuclear Engring., Pa. State U., 1966; postgrad., St. Vladimir's Orthodox Theol. Sem., 1975-76. Ordained deacon Antiochian Orthodox Christian Ch., 1975, priest, 1976, archpriest, 1988. Ops. engr. S3G ops. Knolls Atomic Power Lab., GE Co., Schenectady, N.Y., 1966-68; project engr. S3G ops. Knolls Atomic Power Lab., GE Co., 1968-69; lead nuclear engr. Seabrook Nuclear project Pub. Svc. Co. of N.H., Manchester, 1969-70; project engr. VEPCO projects Nuclear Energy Systems divsn. Nuclear Energy Systems divsn. Westinghouse Elec. Co., Monroeville, Pa., 1970-72; project mgr. VEPCO projects Nuclear Energy Sys. divsn. Westinghouse Elec. Co., 1972-74, regional sales mgr. WRD mktg., 1974-75; pastor St. George Orthodox Ch., Charleston, W.Va., 1976—; dean of clergy Appalachian-Ohio Valley Deanery, 1976—; spiritual advisor NAC-SOYO of Archdiocese, 1977-82, vice-chmn. inter-orthodox and inter-faith rels., 1987—; mem. exec. bd. W.Va. Coun. Chs., 1977—; bd. govs. Nat. Coun. Chs., 1977—, mem. nominating com., 1979-81, exec. com., 1985—, membership com., 1988-91, unity and rels., 1989-92. Contbr. articles to profl. jours. Bd. dirs. Religious Coalition for Cmty. Renewal in Charleston, 1987—; bd. dirs. Kanawha Home for Children, 1986-89, pres., 1989; mem. long-range planning com. W.Va. State Rep. Assn. Com., 1985-87; mem. W.Va. Ecumenical Coalition on Infant Mortality, 1992—. Mem. Acad. Parish Clergy (pres. W.Va. chpt. 1983-85), Am. Nuclear Soc., St. Vladimir's Theol. Found., Charleston Ministerial Assn., Order of St. John of Jerusalem-Knights Hospitellers (chaplain 1985—), Soc. for Preservation and Encouragement Barbershop Quartet Singing in Am. (v.p. 1984-85), Pa. State Club W.Va. (pres. 1984-88), Alden Kindred of Am., Sigma Pi Sigma, Delta Sigma Phi. Avocations: camping, barbershop quartet, motorcycling. Home: 4409 Staunton Ave SE Charleston WV 25304-1743 Office: St George Orthodox Ch PO Box 2044 Charleston WV 25327-2044 *My thoughts on life are but mere recitations of the Holy Scripture and my feeble attempts at making Those words and Thoughts my own.*

SCOTT, OTTO, writer; b. N.Y.C., May 26, 1918; s. Otto Felix and Katherine (McGivney) S.; m. Rose Massing (div. 1952); 1 child, Katherine; m. Nellie Mouradian (div. 1963); children: Mary, Philipa; m. Anna Barney Scott, Apr. 29, 1963; 1 child, Ann Elizabeth. MA in Polit. Sci., Valley Christian U., Fresno, 1985. Mem. staff United Features Syndicate, N.Y.C., 1939-40; v.p. Globaltronix de Venezuela, Caracas, 1954-56, Mohr Assocs., N.Y.C., 1957-59, Becker, Scott & Assocs., N.Y.C., 1960-63; editor

Bill Bros., N.Y.C., 1964-67; asst. to chmn. Ashland (Ky.) Oil, Inc., 1968, 69; edn. writer, reviewer San Diego Union Tribune, 1970; sr. writer Chalcedon Found., Vallecito, Calif., 1982-94; cons. Ashland Oil, Inc., 1972—; editor, pub. Otto Scott's Compass, Seattle, 1990—. Author: History Ashland Oil (The Exception) 1968, Robespierre: Voice of Virtue (History French Revolution), 1974, The Professional: Biography of J.B. Saunders, 1976, The Creative Ordeal: History of Raytheon Corporation, 1976, James I: The Fool as King, 1976, 86, Other End of the Lifeboat (History of South Africa), 1985, Buried Treasure: The Story of Arch Mineral, 1987, The Secret Six: The Fool as Martyr, 1987, The Great Christian Revolution, 1991. With U.S. Merchant Marine, 1941-47. Mem. Author's Guild, Overseas Press Club, Com. for Nat. Policy, Com. for Monetary Rsch. and Edn., The Southern League. Presbyterian. Office: Otto Scotts Compass Uncommon Books 828 South 299th Pl Federal Way WA 98003

SCOTT, R. J., justice. Chief justice Man. Ct. Appeal, Winnipeg, Can. Office: Court of Appeal, 408 York Ave Law Courts Bldg, Winnipeg, MB Canada R3C 0P9*

SCOTT, RALPH MASON, physician, radiaiton oncology educator; b. Leemont, Va., Nov. 23, 1921; s. Benjamin Thomas and Marion Hazel (Mason) S.; m. Alice Latine Francisco, Dec. 21, 1946; children: Susan Taylor, Ralph Mason, John Thomas. BA, U. Va., 1947; MD, Med. Coll. Va., 1950. Diplomate Am. Bd. Radiology (trustee 1965-76, treas. 1969-70, v.p. 1970-72, pres. 1972-74). Intern Robert Packer Hosp., Sayre, Pa., 1953-54, resident, 1954-57, dir. radiation therapy and nuclear medicine sect., 1957-59; asst. prof. radiology U. Chgo. Med. Sch., 1959-60; assoc. prof. radiology, dir. radiation therapy and radioisotopes U. Louisville Med. Sch., 1960-64, prof., dir. radiation therapy, 1964-77, prof. radiation therapy, 1981-82, dir. J. Graham Brown Regional Cancer Ctr., Health Scis. Ctr., 1981-82; dir. dept. radiation medicine Christ Hosp., Cin., 1982-93; ret.; clin. prof. radiology U. Cin. Coll. Medicine, 1982-93; prof., chmn. dept. therapeutic radiology U. Md. Sch. Med., 1977-80; dir. radiation therapy program div. cancer rsch. resources and ctrs., Nat. Cancer Inst. Am. Cancer Soc., 1972-73; bd. dirs. LADD, 1993—, NKAR, 1993—, Day Spring Inc., 1993—, United Health Care, 1994—. Served to lt. (j.g.) USNR, 1943-46. Fellow Christie Hosp. and Holt Radium Inst., Manchester, Eng., 1956-57. Mem. Am. Roentgen-Ray Soc. (exec. coun. 1968—, chmn. exec. coun. 1972-73), AMA, Am. Coll. Radiology (vice chmn. commn. on cancer 1968-69), Am. Radium Soc., Am. Soc. Therapeutic Radiologists, Assn. U. Radiologists, Radiol. Soc. N.Am., Pi Kappa Alpha, Phi Chi. Home: 5516 Tecumseh Cir Louisville KY 40207

SCOTT, RAYMOND PETER WILLIAM, chemistry research educator, writer; b. Erith, Eng., June 20, 1924; came to U.S., 1969; s. Ronald and Annie (Hoadley) S.; m. Barbara Winifred Doreen Strange, Apr. 20, 1946; children: Kerry Raymond, Kevin Francis. B.Sc., U. London, 1946, D.Sc., 1958. Lab. leader Burroughs Welcome, Dartford, Eng., 1946-48; chief chemist APCM, 1948-52; research mgr. Benzole Producers, Watford, Eng., 1952-60; divisional mgr. Unilever, Sharnbrook and Bedfordshire, Eng., 1960-69; dir. phys. chemistry Hoffamn La Roche, Nutley, N.J., 1969-80; dir. applied rsch. Perkin-Elmer, Norwalk, Conn., 1980-86; research prof. dept. chemistry Georgetown U., Washington, 1986—; rsch. prof. dept. chemistry Birkbeck Coll., London. Author: Liquid Chromatography Detectors, 1977, 3d edit., 1987, Contemporary Liquid Chromatography, 1976, Liquid Chromatography Column Theory, 1991, Silica Gel and Bonded Phases, 1993, Liquid Chromatography for the Analyst, 1994, Chromatography Techniques, 1995; editor: Gas Chromatography, 1960, Small Bore Columns in Liquid Chromatography, 1983. Recipient Tswett medal Am. Internat. Symposia on Chromatography, 1978; recipient Tswett award USSR Tech. Inst. Moscow, 1978, Martin medal in chromatography Chromatography Group Gt. Britain, 1982. Fellow Royal Soc. Chemistry (Chartered Analysis and Instrumentation award 1988), Am. Inst. Chemists (cert.), Am. Chem. Soc. (Chromatography award 1977). Office: Chemistry Dept Georgetown U Washington DC 20057 also: Birkbeck Coll, Chemistry Dept, London England

SCOTT, RICHARD G., church official; b. Pocatello, Idaho, Nov. 7, 1928; s. Kenneth Leroy and Mary Whittle S.; m. Jeanen Watkins, July 16, 1953; 7 children. Degree in mech. engring., George Washington U.; postgrad. in nuclear engring. Mem. staff naval and land based power plants, 1953-65; head North Mission LDS Ch., Cordoba, Argentina, 1965-69; regional rep. in Uruguay, Paraguay, N.C., S.C., Va., Washington LDS Ch., 1969-77, mem. 1st Quorum of Seventy, 1977-83, mem. presidency of 1st Quorum of Seventy, 1983-88, apostle, 1988—. Avocations: jazz and classical music, hiking, birding, painting. Office: LDS Ch 50 E North Temple St Salt Lake City UT 84150

SCOTT, RICHARD JAMIESON, chief justice; b. Winnipeg, Man., Can., Mar. 20, 1938. BA, U. Man., 1959, LLB, 1963. Bar: Manitoba, 1963; appointed Queen's counsel, 1977. Judge Ct. of Queen's Bench, Winnipeg, Man., Can., 1985, assoc. justice, 1985-90; chief justice Ct. of Appeal, Winnipeg, Man., Can., 1990—. Office: Manitoba Ct of Appeal, 226 Law Cts Bldg, 408 York Ave, Winnipeg, MB Canada R3C 0P9

SCOTT, RIDLEY, film director; b. South Shields, Northumberland, Eng., Nov. 30, 1939. Ed., Royal Coll. Art, London. Dir. pictures Boy on Bicycle (first film), The Duellists, 1978, Allen, 1978, Blade Runner, 1982, Legend, 1986, Someone to Watch Over Me (also exec. producer), 1987, Black Rain, 1989, Thelma & Louise,(also co-prodr.) 1991, 1492: Conquest of Paradise (also co-prodr.); co-prodr.: The Browning Version, 1994; exec. prodr.: Monkey Trouble, 1994; also directed of over 3,000 TV commls.; set designer Z-Cars, The Informers series (BBC, London). Winner Design scholarship, N.Y. Office: Percy Main Prodns 5555 Melrose Ave # 117 Los Angeles CA 90038-3149 also: CAA 9830 Wilshire Blvd Beverly Hills CA 90212*

SCOTT, ROBERT ALLYN, college administrator; b. Englewood, N.J., Apr. 16, 1939; s. William D. and Anne F. (Waterman) S.; m. Phyllis Virginia Brice, Mar. 23, 1963; children: Ryan Keith, Kira Elizabeth. BA, Bucknell U., 1961; PhD, Cornell U., 1975. Mgmt. trainee Procter & Gamble Co., Phila., 1961-63; asst. dir. admissions Bucknell U., Lewisburg, Pa., 1965-67; asst. dean Coll. Arts and Scis. Cornell U. Ithaca, 1967-69, assoc. dean, 1969-79, anthropology faculty, 1978-79; dir. acad. affairs Ind. Commn. for Higher Edn., Indpls., 1979-84, asst. commr., 1984-85; pres. Ramapo (N.J.) Coll., 1985—; cons. Sta. WSKG Pub. TV and Radio, 1977-79, also to various colls. and univs., pubs., 1966—; mem. curriculum adv. com. Ind. Bd. Edn., 1984-87, Lilly Endowment Think Tank, 1984-86; nat. adv. panel Ind. 21st Century Schooling Project, 1990-92; sr. cons., chair N.J. Higher Edn. Restructuring Team, 1994; bd. dirs. World Trade Coun., Hackensack Med. Ctr., Hillcrest Health Svc. Systems, Am. Edn. Products, Inc., NCO Investors II, L.P., Proteus Assocs., Inc. Author books and monographs; editorial bd. Cornell Rev., 1976-79; book rev. editor Coll. and Univ., 1974-78; cons. editor Change mag., 1979—; cons. editor Jour. Higher Edn., 1985—; exec. editor Saturday Evening Post book div. Curtis Pub. Co., 1982-85; contbr. articles to sociols., ednl. and popular pubs. Trustee Bucknell U., 1976-78, First Unitarian Ch., Ithaca, 1970-73, 78-79, chmn., 1971-73, Unitarian Universalist Ch. of Indpls., 1980-85. With USNR, 1963-65. Spencer Found. rsch. grantee, 1977; recipient Sagamore of the Wabash award, 1986, Prudential Found. Leader of Yr. award, 1987, Disting. Svc. award West Bergen Mental Health Ctr., 1991, NYU Presdl. medal, 1994. Fellow Am. Anthrop. Assn.; mem. Assn. Study Higher Edn., Am. Sociol. Assn., Am. Assn. Higher Edn., Am. Assn. State Colls. & Univs. (Coll. and Univ. Satellite Ednl. Sys. chair, coun. on Liberal Scis., chair 1990-93), O.E.C.D. (higher edn. program Paris), Am. Coun. on Edn. Commn. on Internat. Edn. (chair), Am. forum, Higher Edn. Colloqi=uium (chmn. 1982-84), N.J. Assn. of Coll. and Univs. (chair 1991-92), Bucknell U. Alumni Assn. (bd. dirs. 1971-80, pres. 1976-78, Outstanding Achievement 1991), Indian Trail Club, Phi Kappa Psi, Phi Kappa Phi. Office: Ramapo Coll 505 Ramapo Valley Rd Mahwah NJ 07430

SCOTT, ROBERT CORTEZ, congressman, lawyer; b. Washington, Apr. 30, 1947; s. Charles Waldo and Mae (Hamlin) S. BA, Harvard U., 1969; JD, Boston U., 1973; LLD (hon.), Commonwealth Coll., Hampton, Va., 1988. Pvt. practice Newport News, 1973—; del. Va. Ho. Dels., Richmond, 1978-83, senator, 1983-92; mem. 103rd-104th Congresses from 3rd Va. dist., Washington, D.C., 1993—; mem. econ. & ednl. opportunity com.; judiciary com. Br. pres. NAACP, Newport News 1974-80; pres. bd. Peninsula Legal Aid Ctr., Hampton, 1977-81; mem. state exec. bd. March of Dimes, Va.,

1987—; chmn. 1st dist. Dem. Party Va., 1980-85; bd. dirs. Hampton Roads March of Dimes; adv. com. Peninsula Boy Scouts Am. Recipient Brotherhood Citation award Nat. Conf. Christians & Jews, 1985, Child Adv. award Va. Acad. Pediatrics, 1987, Disting. Svc. award Va. State Fraternal Order Police, 1987, Outstanding Legislator award So. Health Assn., 1989. Mem. Peninsula C. of C., Alpha Phi Alpha, Sigma Pi Phi. Democrat. Office: US House of Reps 501 Cannon Washington DC 20515*

SCOTT, ROBERT HAL, minister; b. Floydada, Tex., Apr. 2, 1930; s. Samuel Price and Fannie (Miller) S.; m. Carolyn Weaver, July 31, 1950; children: Vicki Lynette Reese, Steven Robert Scott. BA, Pasadena Coll., 1950; DD, Point Loma Coll., 1983. Ordained to ministry Ch. of the Nazarene, 1953. Pastor various Chs. of the Nazarene, Calif., 1950-75; dist. supt. Ch. of the Nazarene/So. Calif. Dist., Orange, Calif., 1986-94, dir. 21st Century Rsch. Inst., 1994—; trustee Pasadena (Calif.) Coll., 1966-75, Point Loma Coll., San Diego, Calif., 1975-86, Nazarene Bible Coll., Colorado Springs, 1976-80. Author: All Over the World, Our Family, 1994; contbr. articles to World Mission mag., 1986—.

SCOTT, ROBERT LANE, chemist, educator; b. Santa Rosa, Calif., Mar. 20, 1922; s. Horace Albert and Maurine (Lane) S.; m. Elizabeth Sewall Hunter, May 27, 1944; children: Joanna Ingersoll, Jonathan Armat, David St. Clair, Janet Hamilton. S.B., Harvard U., 1942; M.A., Princeton U., 1944, Ph.D., 1945. Sci. staff Los Alamos Lab., 1945-46; Frank B. Jewett fellow U. Calif., Berkeley, 1946-48; faculty UCLA, 1948—, prof. chemistry, 1960-92, prof. emeritus, 1993—, chmn. dept., 1970-75. Author: (with J.H. Hildebrand) Solubility of Nonelectrolytes, 3d edit, 1950, rev., 1964, Regular Solutions, 1962, Regular and Related Solutions, 1970; contbr. articles to profl. jours. Guggenheim fellow, 1955; NSF sr. fellow, 1961-62; Fulbright lectr., 1968-69. Fellow AAAS, Am. Phys. Soc.; mem. Am. Chem. Soc. (Joel Henry Hildebrand award 1984), Royal Soc. Chemistry (London), Sigma Xi. Home: 11128 Montana Ave Los Angeles CA 90049-3509

SCOTT, ROBERT LEE, speech educator; b. Fairbury, Nebr., Apr. 19, 1928; s. Walter Everett and Ann Maria (Jensen) S.; m. Betty Rose Foust, Sept. 13, 1947; children—Mark Allen, Janet Lee, Paul Matthew. B.A., U. No. Colo., 1950; M.A., U. Nebr., 1951; Ph.D., U. Ill., 1955. Asst. prof. speech U. Houston, 1953-57; asst. prof. U. Minn., 1957-59, assoc. prof., 1959-63, prof., 1963—. Author: Rhetoric of Black Power, 1969, Moments in the Rhetoric of the Cold War, 1970; contbr. articles to profl. jours. Recipient Teaching award Coll. of Liberal Arts, U. Minn., 1981. Mem. Speech Comm. Assn. (editor Quar. Jour. Speech 1971-74, Winans-Wichelns Rsch. award 1970, Charles H. Woolbert Rsch. award, 1981, Douglas-Ehninger Disting. Scholar award 1989, Disting. Scholar of Assn. 1992), Ctrl. States Speech Assn., Internat. Soc. for Study of Rhetoric. Office: U Minn Dept Speech Communication Minneapolis MN 55455-0194

SCOTT, ROBERT MICHAEL, data processing executive; b. Swainsboro, Ga., May 6, 1950; s. William Hilton and Daphne (Fensom) S.; m. Marcia Lynne Norton, Dec. 20, 1972; children: Allison Marie, Bethany Diane, Katherine Anne. BA in Edn., Fla. Atlantic U., 1972. Consumer lending officer 1st Bank and Trust Co., Boca Raton, Fla., 1972-77; various mgmt. positions First Data Resources, Omaha, 1977-83, v.p., 1983-84, exec. v.p., 1984—; treas. First Data Resources, 1986—, also bd. dirs.; bd. dirs. Deposit Guarantee Bank, Omaha, Profl. On-Line Inc., Saginaw, Mich., Indeserv Inc., Omaha. Bd. dirs. Fontenelle Forest Assn., Omaha, 1986; mem. Salvation Army. Democrat. Office: 1st Data Resources Inc 11718 Nicholas St Omaha NE 68154-3263

SCOTT, ROBERT MONTGOMERY, museum executive, lawyer; b. Bryn Mawr, Pa., May 22, 1929; s. Edgar and Helen Hope (Montgomery) S.; m. H. Gay Elliot, June 30, 1951; children: Hope Tyler Scott Rogers, Janny Scott Ritter, Elliot Montgomery. AB, Harvard U., 1951; LLB, U. Pa., 1954. Ptnr. Montgomery McCracken Walker & Rhoads, Phila., 1961-82, of counsel, 1982-88; spl. asst. to U.S. ambassador to Ct. of St. James, London, 1969-73; hon. Brit. consul Phila., 1979-83; pres., chief exec. officer Phila. Mus. Art, 1982—; bd. dirs. First Fidelity Bancorp. Trustee Phila. Mus. Art, 1965—, Royal Oak Found., 1978-86, Inst. Cancer Rsch., Fox Chase Cancer Ctr., 1960-86, Lankenau Hosp., 1959-86, William Penn Found., 1986-91; pres. Mary Louise Curtis Book Fund., 1989—, Curtis Inst of Music, 1994—; bd. dirs. Glyndebourne Assn. Am., Inc. Recipient Superior Honor award Dept. State, 1973. Fellow Am. Bar Found.; mem. Am. Assn. Mus., Phila. Club, Knickerbocker Club, Locust Club, White's Club. Republican. Home: Ardrossan 807 Newtown Rd Villanova PA 19085 Office: Phila Mus Art Benjamin Franklin Pky PO Box 7646 Philadelphia PA 19101-7646

SCOTT, RODGER GENE, personnel executive; b. Antigo, Wis., July 4, 1931; s. Wyman and Faye (Marshall) S.; m. Norma A. Schoenborn, June 6, 1953; children—Bruce Franklin, Lynnette Gay. Grad., Antigo High Sch., Wis., 1949. Store mgr. Krambo Food Store, Merrill, Wis., 1951-65; store mgr. Sentry Foods, Waukesha, Wis., 1965-66, tng. dir., 1966-67, retail supr., 1967-72, sr. v.p. personnel, 1972—. Mem. ch. council Reformation Luth. Ch., pres., 1982-84. Republican. Home: 8838 Midlake Rd Woodruff WI 54568-9610 Office: Godfrey Co 1200 W Sunset Dr Waukesha WI 53186-6597

SCOTT, RONALD FRASER, civil engineering educator, engineering consultant; b. London, Apr. 9, 1929; came to U.S., 1951; s. Frederick Durham and Catherine Isobel (Fraser) S.; m. Pamela June Wilkinson, May 28, 1959; children—Grant Fraser, Craig Alistair, Roderick Jonathan. B.Sc. in Civil Engring., Glasgow U., 1951; S.M. in Civil Engring., MIT, 1953, Sc.D. in Civil Engring., 1955. Registered engr., Calif. Soils engr. U.S. Army Corps Engrs., Boston, 1955-57; divisional soils engr Racey, McCallum & Assocs., Toronto, Ont., Can., 1957-58; prof. civil engring. Calif. Inst. Tech., Pasadena, 1958—; Dotty and Dick Hayman prof. engring., 1987—; pvt. practice cons. engr. Pasadena, 1958—. Author: Principles of Soil Mechanics, 1963, (with Schoustra) Soil Mechanics and Engineering, 1968, (with Bolt, Horn, MacDonald) Geological Hazards, 1975, Foundation Analysis, 1981. Contbr. articles to profl. jours. Patentee in field. Fellow Guggenheim Found., 1972; Churchill Found., 1972; Rankine Lectureship, Brit. Geotech. Soc., 1987. Mem. ASCE (Huber Research prize 1968, Norman medal 1972, Middlebrooks prize 1981, Terzaghi lectureship 1983), Am. Geophys. Union, Nat. Acad. Engring. Avocations: walking; photography. Office: Calif Inst Tech Mail Sta 104-44 1201 E California Blvd Pasadena CA 91125-0001

SCOTT, SALLY ELAINE, telecommunications manager; b. Chanute, Kans., Mar. 6, 1942; d. Frank L. and Helen E. (Speir) Kenslow; m. Peter K. Scott, Dec. 26, 1966 (div. 1973). Diploma in nursing, Hillcrest Med. Ctr. Tulsa, 1966; BA in Counseling, George Washington U., 1984, MA in Edn., 1988. RN, Okla., Washington; nat. cert. mental health counselor. Occupational health nurse, 1970-81; mgr. employee assistance program Bell Atlantic/C&P Telephone Cos., Washington, 1981-92; mgr. health promotion/employee assistance program Bell Atlantic, Arlington, Va., 1992—. Mem. Employee Assistance Program Profls., Assn. Employee Assistance Program Practitioners, Worksite Intervention Health Promotion Profls. Avocations: sailing, hiking, running. Office: Bell Atlantic 1310 Courthouse Rd Arlington VA 22201

SCOTT, STEPHEN CARLOS, college president; b. Greenville, S.C., Sept. 20, 1949; s. Carlos O'Dell and Christina (Nikitas) S.; m. Patsy Jordan, Apr. 13, 1968; children: Stephanie Christina, Lance Stephen. BA, Clemson (S.C.) U., 1971, MEd, 1975, EdD, 1987. Owner, mgr. Scotty's Inc., restaurant, Clemson, 1967-71; tchr. math. Pickens (S.C.) Sr. High Sch., 1972-74; instr. bus. Tri-County Tech. Coll., Pendleton, S.C., 1974-76, head dept., 1976-78; dir. br. campus Tri-County Tech. Coll., Easley, S.C., 1978-80; dean bus. Greenville Tech. Coll., 1980-85, assoc. v.p., 1985-88; pres. Southeastern C.C., Whiteville, N.C., 1988—; cons. P.C.E. Fed. Credit Union, Liberty, S.C., 1975-88, Jacobs Mfg. Co., Clemson, 1979-80, Flat Rock Shelter Ctr. Easley, 1980-85. Contbr. articles to profl. jours. and mags. Pres. So. Shelter Ctr., Greenville, 1986—, Good Shepherd Found., Whiteville, 1990-92; bd. dirs. Good Shepherd, 1988-91; chmn. Columbus County Sch. Bond Dr., 1989, Am. Heart Fund Drive Columbus County, 1992; co-chmn. Columbus County Long Range Planning Com., 1989-91; vice chmn. Pvt. Industry Coun. Region O, 1992—; founding dir. Habitat for Humanity Columbus County, 1992; co-chmn. bd. dirs. Columbus County Rural Health Ctr., 1994. Recipient award for patriotism U.S. Savs. Bonds Program, 1987. Mem. Am. Assn. Community and Jrs. Colls. (Pres.'s Acad.), Rotary (bd. dirs. Whiteville 1990-92, pres. 1992-93). Presbyterian. Avocations: running, chess, numismatics, reading. Office: Southeastern CC RR 1, Hwy 74-76 Box 151 Whiteville NC 28472

SCOTT, STEVEN DONALD, geology educator, researcher; b. Fort Frances, Ont., Can., June 4, 1941; s. Donald West and Shirley Margaret (Casselman) S.; m. Barbara Joan Armstrong, Dec. 20., 1962; children: Susan Joan, Donald Montgomery. BSc, U. Western Ont., 1963, MSc, 1964; PhD, Pa. State U., State College, 1968. Rsch. assoc. Pa. State U., State Coll., 1968-69; asst. prof. geology U. Toronto, Ont., 1969-72, assoc. prof., 1972-79, prof., 1979—, chmn. geol. engring., 1988—; pres. 507999 Ont. Ltd. Toronto, 1982—; lectr. in field. Contbr. numerous articles to profl. jours. Recipient of Bancroft Awd., 1990, Royal Society of Canada. Fellow Royal Soc. Can. (convenor for earth scis. 1989-90, Bancroft award 1990), Soc. Econ. Geologists (mem. coun. 1986-88, Lindgren award 1978), Mineral. Soc. Am., Geol. Assn Can. (tech. program chmn. ann. meeting 1991), Mineral. Assn. Can. (Past Pres.' award 1984), others. Avocations: travel, fishing, swimming; researcher in marine geology and ore deposits. Office: U of Toronto, Dept Geology, Toronto, ON Canada M5S 3B1

SCOTT, SUSAN, lawyer; b. Orange, N.J., July 25, 1943; d. Bailey Bartlett and Regina Margaret (Butler) S.; m. Robert John Gillispie, Aug. 20. 1966 (div. 1979); children: Robert John Jr., Megan Anne. BA in Math, Catholic U. Am., 1965; JD, Rutgers U., 1975. Bar: N.J. 1975, U.S. Dist. Ct. N.J 1975, U.S. Ct. Appeals (3d cir.) 1988, U.S. Supreme Ct. 1993. Applied math. CIA, Washington, 1965-68; assoc. Pitney, Hardin, Kipp & Szuch, Morristown, N.J., 1975-76; assoc. Riker, Danzig, Scherer, Hyland & Perretti, Morristown, 1979-85, ptnr., 1986—; corp. counsel Allied-Signal, Inc., Morristown, 1977-78; mem. Child Placement Rev. Bd. Morristown,1992—; commr. Morris County Bd. Condemnation, Morristown, 1989—. Mem. ABA, N.J. State Bar Assn., Morris County Bar Assn. Democrat. Roman Catholic. Avocations: tennis, photography. Home: 20 Vinton Rd Madison NJ 07940-2506 Office: Riker Danzig Scherer Hyland & Perretti Headquarters Plz 1 Speedwell Ave Morristown NJ 07960-6838

SCOTT, TERRY LEE, communications company executive; b. Rockford, Ill., Oct. 21, 1950; s. Wilson C. and Marie G. (Bunger) S.; divorced; 1 child, Andrea; m. Jenny Scarborough, Aug. 1, 1981; children: Brady, Tiffany. BS in Acctg. magna cum laude, Bradley U., 1972. CPA Ill., Tex.; cert. info. system auditor. Audit prin. Arthur Young and Co., Dallas, 1972-82; v.p. fin. and adminstrn., treas. Paging Network Inc., Dallas, 1982-90; sr. v.p. Paging Network, Inc., Dallas, 1990-92, pres., CEO, bd. dirs., 1993—. Mem. AICPA, Tex. Soc. CPAs, Phi Kappa Phi, Zeta Pi. Methodist. Home: 1704 Riviera Dr Plano TX 75093-2910 Office: Paging Network Inc 4965 Preston Park Blvd Plano TX 75093-5180

SCOTT, THEODORE R., lawyer; b. Mount Vernon, Ill., Dec. 7, 1924; s. Theodore R. and Beulah (Flannigan) S.; m. Virginia Scott, June 1, 1947; children: Anne Laurence, Sarah Buckland, Daniel, Barbara Gomon. AB, U. Ill., 1947, JD, 1949. Bar: Ill. 1950. Law clk. to judge U.S. Ct. Appeals, 1949-51; sole practice Chgo., 1950—; assoc. Spaulding Glass, 1951-53, Loftus, Lucas & Hammand, 1953-58, Ooms, McDougall, Williams & Hersh, 1958-60; ptnr. McDougall, Hersh & Scott, Chgo., 1960-87; of counsel Jones, Day, Reavis & Pogue, 1987—. Served to 2d lt. USAAF, 1943-45. Decorated Air medal. Fellow Am. Coll. Trial Lawyers.; mem. ABA, Ill. Bar Assn., Chgo. Bar Assn., 7th Circuit Bar Assn. (past pres.), Legal Club Chgo., Law Club Chgo., Patent Law Assn. Chgo. (past pres.), Phi Beta Kappa. Clubs: Union League (Chgo.); Exmoor Country (Highland Park, Ill.). Home: 1569 Woodvale Ave Deerfield IL 60015-2350 Office: Jones Day Reavis & Pogue 77 W Wacker Dr Chicago IL 60601-1629

SCOTT, THOMAS CLEVENGER, lawyer; b. Columbus, Ohio, May 16, 1936; s. Willard Baldwin and Elizabeth (Clevenger) S.; m. Nancy Jo Tiberi, Nov. 11, 1961; children: Amy J., Molly M. BA, Ohio State U., 1958, JD, 1961. Bar: Ohio 1961. Ptnr. McLeskey & McLeskey, Columbus, 1961-79, Loveland, Callard, Clapham & Scott, Columbus, 1979-80, Scott, Kuehnle, Grace & Mills (and predecessor firm Scott, Walker & Kuehnle), Columbus, 1980-86; ptnr. Thompson, Hine & Flory, Columbus, 1986—, ptnr. in charge, 1992—; adj. prof. Ohio State U., Columbus; mem. bd. advisors North Ctrl. Bankruptcy Inst. Capital U. Law Ctr., 1987-90, Midwest Regional Bankruptcy Seminar, 1990—; mem. standing local rules adv. com. U.S. Bankruptcy Ct., 1987-95. Contbr. articles to profl. jours., outlines for confs. and seminars. Mem. ABA, Columbus Bar Assn. (chmn. bankruptcy com. 1986-88), Ohio State Bar Assn., Lawyers Club (pres.). Office: Thompson Hine & Flory One Columbus 10 W Broad St Columbus OH 43215-3435

SCOTT, THOMAS JEFFERSON, JR., lawyer, electrical engineer; b. Montgomery, Ala., Dec. 30, 1943; s. Thomas Jefferson Sr. and Irene (Feagin) S.; m. Betsy Sue Mackta, Apr. 25, 1981; children: Elspeth Watts, Marguerita Taylor, Thomas Jefferson III. BEE, Yale U., 1966, BA in Econs., 1967; JD, Vanderbilt U., 1974. Bar: Va. 1974, D.C. 1975, N.Y. 1980, U.S. Dist. Ct. D.C. 1986, U.S. Dist. Ct. (ea. dist.) Va. 1993, U.S. Tax Ct. 1981, U.S. Ct. Fed. Claims, 1982, U.S. Ct. Appeals (fed. cir.) 1982, U.S. Ct. Appeals (4th cir.) 1993, U.S. Supreme Ct. 1984. Trial atty. civil div. U.S. Dept. of Justice, Washington, 1974-78; assoc. Cooper & Dunham, N.Y.C., 1978-80, sr. trial counsel civil div., 1980-85; ptnr. Pennie & Edmonds, Washington, 1985-90, Howrey & Simon, Washington, 1990—. Capt. USNR, 1966-71. Decorated D.F.C. Mem. ABA, Am. Intellectual Property Law Assn. Office: Howrey & Simon 1299 Pennsylvania Ave NW Washington DC 20004-2402

SCOTT, THOMAS WRIGHT, jazz musician, composer; b. Los Angeles, May 19, 1948; s. Nathan George and Margery (Wright) S. Student, U. So. Calif., 1966-67. Vis. prof. music U. Utah, 1971, Westminster Coll., 1975; clinician Capitol U., Columbus, Ohio, 1973-77. Instrumentalist on saxes, woodwinds, lyricon; rec. artist, arranger and performer on numerous albums, including with: Paul McCartney, George Harrison, Ringo Starr, Barbra Streisand, Carole King, Rod Stewart, Aretha Franklin, Joni Mitchell (as leader of L.A. Express), Steely Dan, Blues Bros., Quincy Jones, Ravi Shankar; producer albums by Doc Severensen, Chevy Chase; composer background music for TV shows: Dan August, Cannon, Barnaby Jones, Streets of San Francisco, Baretta, theme music for TV show Starsky and Hutch; composer TV movies Trouble Comes to Town, 1973, The Girls of Huntington House, 1973, Firehouse, 1973, Class of '63, 1973, Twin Detectives, 1976, Aspen, 1977, The Company Comedy, 1978, Our Family Business, 1981, Family Ties Vacation, 1985, Badge of the Assassin, 1985, The Leftovers, 1986, Not Quite Human, 1987, A Father's Homecoming, 1988, Run Till You Fall, 1988; composer for films The Culpepper Cattle Co., 1972, Conquest of The Planet of The Apes, 1972, Uptown Saturday Night, 1974, The Nine Lives of Fritz the Cat, 1974, Sidecar Racers, 1975, Americathon, 1979, Stir Crazy, 1980, Hanky Panky, 1982, Class, 1983, Going Berserk, 1983, Hard to Hold, 1984, Fast Forward, 1985, The Sure Thing, 1985, Just One of the Guys, 1985, Soul Man, 1986; sound man for films (with Mark Berger, Randy Thorn, David MacMillan) The Right Stuff, 1983 (Acad. Sound award 1983), (with Mark Berger, Todd Boelelheide, Chris Newman) Amadeus, 1984 (Acad. Sound award). Mem. Am. Fedn. Musicians, Nat. Acad. Rec. Arts and Scis. (dir. Los Angeles chpt. 1971-72, Grammy award 1974, chpt. Most Valuable Player 1973, 74, 75, 77), Composers and Lyricists Guild Am. (exec. bd. 1972-73, 80-81). *

SCOTT, TOM KECK, biologist, botanist, educator; b. St. Louis, Aug. 4, 1931; s. George Drake and Mary Ann (Keck) S.; children: David Seymour, Stephen Arthur, John Warner, Cynthia Keck; m. Margaret Ray, Apr. 7, 1990. AB, Pomona Coll., Calif., 1954; MA, Stanford U., 1959, Ph.D., 1961. Rsch. prof. Princeton U., 1963-61; asst. prof., then assoc. prof. biology Oberlin Coll., Ohio, 1963-69; mem. faculty U. N.C., Chapel Hill, 1969—; prof. botany U. N.C., 1972-82, prof. biology, 1982—, chmn. biology curriculum, 1970-75, chmn. dept. botany, 1972-82, dir. rsch., 1985-90; sr. scientist div. life/biomed. scis. and applications NASA, 1994—; vis. rsch. prof. U. Nottingham, Eng., 1967-68; Fulbright sr. lectr. Ege U., Izmir, Turkey, 1972-73; chmn. space biology panel NASA, 1984-89, chmn. plant growth working group, 1989—, cons. space sta. freedom, 1984-88. Author: Plant Regulation and World Agriculture, 1979, The Functions of Hormones from the Level of the Cell to the Whole Plant, 1984, Plant Gravitational and Space Research, 1984. Served with AUS, 1954-56. Danforth assoc., 1974; NATO grantee, 1978; Japanese Soc. for Promotion of Sci. fellow, 1985. Fellow AAAS; mem. Am. Inst. Biol. Scis., Am. Soc. Plant Physiologists (trustee 1979-88, chmn. 84-86), Bot. Soc. Am., NAS (com. on space biology and medicine 1986-92), Am. Soc. Gravitational and Space Biology (bd. govs. 1985-88), Internat. Plant Growth Substance Assn. (bd. govs. 1985-88), Sigma Xi. Achievements include research on characteristics of growth development and hormone translocation in higher plants and gravitational plant biology. Home: 800 E Rosemary St Chapel Hill NC 27514-3722 Office: U NC Dept Biology Coker Hall Clb # 3280 Chapel Hill NC 27599

SCOTT, TONY, film director; b. Newcastle, England, June 21, 1944; m. Donna Wilson. Degree in Fine Arts, Sunderland Art School; postgrad., Leeds Coll. Art, 1969; MFA, Royal Coll. Arts, 1972. Film dir., 1972—. Dir. films including One of the Mission (half-hour film, Brit. Film Inst.), Loving Memory (1-hour feature, Albert Finney), The Hunger, 1983, Top Gun, 1986, Beverly Hills Cop II, 1987, Revenge, 1990, Days of Thunder, 1990, The Last Boy Scout, 1991, True Romance, 1993, Crimson Tide, 1995; formerly dir. TV commls. Recipient numerous Clios, Gold and Silver Lions and various other awards. Office: Totem Prodns 8009 Santa Monica Blvd Los Angeles CA 90046-5008 also: CAA 9830 Wilshire Blvd Beverly Hills CA 90212-1804

SCOTT, W. PETER, bishop. Bishop London (Ont.) Synod United Ch. Can. Office: United Church of Canada, 359 Windermere Rd, London, ON Canada N6G 2K3

SCOTT, WALDRON, mission executive; b. Kansas City, Kans., July 14, 1929; s. Waldron and Audrean (Spurgeon) S.; m. Georgia Dyke; children by previous marriage—Melody, Cheryl, Gregory, Douglas, Linda. B.A., Am. U., Beirut, 1953. Dir. The Navigators, Washington, 1954-59, Middle East and Africa, 1960-66, Asia/Australia, 1967-72; internat. field dir. The Navigators, Colorado Springs, Colo., 1973-74; gen. sec. World Evang. Fellowship, Colorado Springs, 1975-80; pres. Am. Leprosy Missions, Elmwood Park, N.J., 1981-84, Holistic Ministries Internat., Paterson, N.J., 1985—; chair Holistic Ministries Internat., 1994—, Greater Paterson YMCA, 1995—; bd. dirs. Passaic County Cultural and Heritage Coun., Paterson Habitat for Humanity, Christian Leadership in Higher Edn.; adv. coun. Passaic County Human Svcs., Paterson YMCA, Scheffelin Rsch. and Tng. Ctr., Ch. World Svc., Div. Overseas Ministries' Nat. Coun. Chs., Vellore Christian Med. Coll., Paterson Community Health Ctr., Jubilee Svc. Author: Karl Barth's Theology of Mission, 1978, The Paterson Paradigm; Bring Forth Justice, 1980; editor: Serving our Generation, 1980. Chmn. Greater Paterson YMCA, Paterson Coun. Social Svcs., Citizens Alliance for a Drug Free Paterson. Mem. Leadership Paterson Alumni Assn., Am. Soc. Missiology, Nat. Assn. Evangelicals, Evangelicals for Social Action. Mem. Christian Reformed Ch.

SCOTT, WALTER, JR., construction company executive; b. 1931. BS, Colo. State U., 1953. With Peter Kiewit Sons, Inc., Omaha, 1953—, mgr. Cleve. dist., 1962-64, v.p., 1964, exec. v.p., 1965-79, chmn. bd. dirs., 1979—; also pres. Joslyn Art Mus., Omaha. Served with USAF, 1954-56. Office: Peter Kiewit Sons Inc 1000 Kiewit Plz Omaha NE 68131-3302 also: Joslyn Art Mus 2200 Dodge St Omaha NE 68102-1208*

SCOTT, WALTER COKE, retired sugar company executive, lawyer; b. Norfolk, Va., July 20, 1919; s. Walter Coke and Rosemary (White) S.; m. Virginia Kemper Millard, May 14, 1949; children: Mary Lyman (Mrs. K. Logan Jackson), Roberta (Mrs. Frederick Warth), Alexander McRae, Buford Coke. B.S., Hampden-Sydney Coll., 1939; J.D., U. Va., 1948. Bar: Va. 1947, Ga. 1954. Atty. U.S. Dept. Justice, Jacksonville, Fla., 1948; commerce atty. S.A.L. Ry., Norfolk, 1948-54; commerce counsel, gen. solicitor Central of Ga. Ry., Savannah, 1954-60; v.p. Cen. of Ga. Ry., (Norfolk Southern), 1960-62, dir., 1960-88; ptnr. law firm Hitch, Miller & Beckmann, Savannah, 1956-60; sr. v.p., sec. Savannah Foods & Industries, Inc. (formerly Savannah Sugar Refining Corp.), 1962-72, exec. v.p., sec., mem. exec. com., 1972-87, also dir.; exec. v.p., sec. mem. exec. com., dir. Everglades Sugar Refinery, Inc., Clewiston, Fla., 1964-87; sec., mem. exec. com., dir. The Jim Dandy Co., Birmingham, Ala., 1968-81; bd. dirs. 1st Union Nat. Bank Savannah, Atlanta, 1975-91. Pres., chmn. exec. com. Historic Savannah Found., 1963-64; bd. dirs. United Community Services, 1965-68, pres., 1967; gen. chmn. United Community Appeal, 1966; mem. Chatham-Savannah Met. Planning Commn., 1963-68; trustee, chmn. finance com. Telfair Acad. Arts and Scis., 1964-67; trustee, vice chmn. Savannah Country Day Sch., 1967-69, chmn., 1970-72; Bd. dirs., chmn. finance com. Savannah Speech and Hearing Center, 1967-70; bd. dirs. Savannah Symphony Soc., Inc. Mem. Va. State Bar, Ga. State Bar, St. Andrews Soc., Savannah Benevolent Assn. (pres. 1990-92), Kappa Sigma, Omicron Delta Kappa, Phi Alpha Delta, Chi Beta Phi, Pi Delta Epsilon. Episcopalian. Clubs: Chatham, Oglethorpe, Savannah Golf; Farmington Country (Charlottesville, Va.). Home: 56 E 54th St Savannah GA 31405-3314 Office: Savannah Foods & Industries Inc 1st Union Nat Bank Bldg Savannah GA 31401 also: PO Box 339 Savannah GA 31402

SCOTT, WALTER DILL, management educator; b. Chgo., Oct. 27, 1931; s. John Marcy and Mary Louise (Gent) S.; student Williams Coll., 1949-51; BS, Northwestern U., 1953; MS, Columbia, 1958; m. Barbara Ann Stein, Sept. 9, 1961; children: Timothy Walter, David Frederick, Gordon Charles. Cons. Booz, Allen & Hamilton, N.Y.C., 1956-58; assoc. Glore, Forgan & Co., N.Y.C., 1958-63, ptnr. Chgo., 1963-65; ptnr. Lehman Bros., Chgo., 1965-72, sr. ptnr., 1972-73, also bd. dirs.; assoc. dir. econs. and govt. Office Mgmt. and Budget, Washington, 1973-75; sr. v.p. internat. and fin. Pillsbury Co., Mpls., 1975-78, exec. v.p., 1978-80, also bd. dirs.; pres., chief exec. officer Investors Diversified Services, Inc., Mpls., 1980-84, group mng. dir. Grand Met. PLC, 1984-86, also bd. dirs.; chmn. Grand Met U.S.A., 1984-86; prof., sr. Austin fellow Kellogg Grad. Sch. Mgmt., Northwestern U., 1987—; bd. dirs. Kairos, Inc., Chgo. Title and Trust, Intermatic, Inc., Ill. Power Co., Illinova Corp, Orval Kent Food Co. Bd. dirs. Basic Industry Rsch. Lab., Chgo., Cities in Schs. Internat. Urban Assocs., MiAm. Leadership Found. Lt. (j.g.) USN, 1953-56. Home: 55 Meadowview Dr Northfield IL 60093-3547 Office: Northwestern U J L Kellogg Grad Sch of Mgmt Leverone Hall Evanston IL 60208

SCOTT, WILLARD HERMAN, radio and television performer; b. Alexandria, Va., Mar. 7, 1934; s. Willard Herman and Thelma Matti (Phillips) S.; m. Mary Ellen Dwyer, Aug. 7, 1959; children: Mary Phillips, Sally W. B.A. in Philosophy and Religion, Am. U., 1955. With NBC, 1950—; formerly staff announcer children's TV shows Voice of NASA radio show; weather reporter, performer Today Show and NBC Radio, N.Y.C., 1980—; free-lance comml. actor, narrator. Active March of Dimes, Easter Seals, ARC, Am. Cancer Soc., Nat. Symphony of Washington, Nat. Park Service, Alzheimer's Found. Served with USN, 1956-58. Episcopalian. Club: De Molay. Office: NBC Today Program 30 Rockefeller Plz # 304 New York NY 10112-0001*

SCOTT, WILLARD PHILIP, lawyer, corporate executive; b. Columbus, Ohio, Jan. 8, 1909; s. Wirt Stanley and Mabel Lynne (Rond) S.; m. Lucille Westrom, June 27, 1936 (dec); children: Robert W., David W., Anne L.; m. Virginia J. Field, Oct. 30, 1987. A.B. with honors, Ohio State U., 1930; LL.B. (dean's scholar), Columbia, 1933. Bar: N.Y. 1934, D.C. 1934, Okla. 1969. Ptnr. Oliver & Donnally, N.Y.C., 1938-65; Dir. Am. Potash & Chem. Corp., 1951—, v.p., 1955-68, vice chmn. bd., 1968—; v.p., gen. counsel Kerr-McGee Corp. (merged with Am. Potash & Chem.), 1973-75, sr. v.p., 1973-75, cons., 1975-85; gen. counsel Nat. Assn. Mut. Savs. Banks and Savs. Banks Assn. N.Y., 1945-60; counsel bondholders coms. r.r. reorgn. C. & N.-W. Ry., Soo Line, Alton, B. & M. R.R., C., M., St. P. & P. Ry., Fla. East Coast, Central N.J., D. & H. R.R.; dir. 1st Nat. Bank & Trust Co. of Oklahoma City, Transocean Drilling Co. Ltd., Bikita Minerals Ltd. Editor: Business Lawyer, 1958-59; Contbr. articles on corporate law to profl. jours. Trustee, Scarsdale, N.Y., 1951-55, police commr., acting mayor, 1953-55, mayor, 1955-57, mem. bd. appeals, 1957-58; Bd. dirs. Oklahoma City Allied Arts Found., Oklahoma City Symphony Soc.; trustee Okla. Sci. and Arts Found.; bd. advisers Mercy Hosp. Fellow Am. Bar Found.; Southwestern Legal Found.; Mem. Internat. Bar Assn. (patron), ABA (commn. on corporate laws 1947—, chmn. sect. corporate banking and bus. law 1960-61, ho. of dels. 1961-62, chmn. com. ednl. programs), N.Y. Bar Assn., D.C. Bar Assn., Okla. Bar Assn., Am. Law Inst., Assn. Bar City N.Y., Phi Beta Kappa, Phi Kappa Sigma, Phi Delta Phi, Phi Alpha Theta, Pi Sigma Alpha. Republican. Presbyn. Clubs: Union League, Madison Square Garden (N.Y.C.); Metropolitan (Washington); Scarsdale Golf; Oklahoma City Golf and

Country (O, Beacon, Whitehall; Univ. (Chgo.); Calif. (L.A.). Home: 1237 Kenilworth Rd Oklahoma City OK 73114-1212 Office: Kerr-McGee Bldg Oklahoma City OK 73102

SCOTT, WILLIAM BEVERLEY, ichthyologist; b. Toronto, Ont., Canada, July 7, 1917; s. William James and Elsie Irene (Lowry) S.; m. Mildred Grace Fairfield, July 11, 1942; children: Paul James, Patricia Louise. B.Sc., U. Toronto, 1942, Ph.D., 1950; D.Sc., U. N.B., 1985, Queens U., 1994. Curator ichthyology dept. Royal Ont. Mus., Toronto, Ont., Can., 1948-77; assoc. dir. Royal Ont. Mus., 1973-75; dir. Huntsman Marine Lab., St. Andrews, N.B., Can., 1976-82; sr. scientist Huntsman Marine Sci. Centre, 1982—; assoc. prof. to prof. dept. zoology U. Toronto, 1962-83, prof. emeritus, 1983—; bd. dirs. Ont. Council Comml. Fisheries, Port Dover, Ont., Can., 1954-76, Can. Nat. Sportsmen's Shows, Toronto, 1974-78; research assoc. Royal Ont. Mus., Toronto, 1977—; hon. curator Royal Ont. Mus., 1994, curator emeritus, 1994. Author: Freshwater Fishes of Eastern Canada, 1954 (rev. 1974), Fishes Atlantic Coast of Canada, 1966, Freshwater Fishes of Canada, 1973, Atlantic Fishes of Canada, 1988; contbr. articles to profl. jours. Bd. dirs. Met. Toronto Zool. Soc., Can., 1970-75; bd. trustees Can. Nat. Sportsmen's Fund, 1977-85, Sunbury Shores Arts and Nature Ctr., St. Andrews (N.B. Can.), 1965-81, Ross Meml. Mus., 1979-94. Served to capt. Can. Army, 1942-45, PTO. Recipient Can. Centennial medal, 1967; recipient Can. Silver Jubilee medal, 1979. Fellow Royal Soc. Can.; mem. Toronto Sportsmens Assn. (life, bd. dirs. 1955-70); pres. Am. Soc. Ichthyologists and Herpetologists (1972), Can. Soc. Zoologists (hon. life mem., assoc. editor 1973-77), Am. Fisheries Soc. (Award of Excellence 1986), Internat. Game Fish Assn., Am. Inst. Fishery Rsch. Biologists, Nova Scotia Inst. Sci. Anglican. Home: PO Box 369, Brandy Cove Rd, Saint Andrews, NB Canada E0G 2X0

SCOTT, WILLIAM CLEMENT, III, entertainment industry executive; b. N.Y.C., Apr. 25, 1934; s. William Clement and Susan L. (Cameron) S.; m. Cindy L. Taylor, Dec. 5, 1981; children by previous marriage: Katherine Louise, David Campbell. A.B., Coll. William and Mary, Williamsburg, Va., 1956. Self-employed, 1956-64; v.p. Booz-Allen & Hamilton, N.Y.C., 1964-69; group v.p. Cordura Corp., Los Angeles, 1969-72; exec. v.p. Western Pacific Industries, N.Y.C., 1972-76; pres., chief operating officer Western Pacific Industries, 1976-87; pvt. investor N.Y.C., 1987-88; chmn., pres., chief exec. officer Panavision Internat. L.P., Lee Internat., Inc., N.Y.C., 1988—. Bd. dirs., pres. Opera Orch. of N.Y. Republican. Episcopalian. Clubs: Racquet and Tennis, Met. Opera (N.Y.C.); Hay Harbor; Fishers Island Country; Coral Beach (Bermuda). Office: Panavision Internat LP 140 E 45th St New York NY 10017

SCOTT, WILLIAM CORYELL, medical executive; b. Sterling, Colo., Nov. 22, 1920; s. James Franklin and Edna Ann (Schillig) S.; m. Jean Marie English, Dec. 23, 1944 (div. 1975); children: Kathryn, James, Margaret; m. Carolyn Florence Hill, June 21, 1975; children: Scott, Amy Jo, Robert. AB, Dartmouth Coll., 1942; MD, U. Colo., 1944, MS in OB/GYN, 1951. Cert. Am. Bd. Ob-Gyn., 1956, 79, Am. Bd. Med. Mgmt., 1991. Intern USN Hosp., Great Lakes, Ill., 1945-46, Denver Gen. Hosp., 1946-47; resident Ob-Gyn St. Joseph's Hosp., Colo. Gen. Hosp., Denver, 1946-51; practice medicine specializing in Ob-Gyn Tucson, 1951-71; assoc. prof. emeritus U. Ariz. Med. Sch., Tucson, 1971-94, 1994; v.p. med. affairs U. Med. Ctr., Tucson, 1984-94. Contbr. articles to med. jours. and chpt. to book. Pres. United Way, Tucson, 1979-80, HSA of Southeastern Ariz., Tucson, 1985-87; chmn. Ariz. Health Facilities Authority, Phoenix, 1974-83. Served to capt. USNR, 1956-58. Recipient Man of Yr. award, Tucson, 1975. Fellow ACS, Am. Coll. Ob-Gyn, Pacific Coast Ob-Gyn Soc., Ctrl. Assn. of Ob-Gyn; mem. AMA (coun. on sci. affairs 1984-93, chmn. 1989-91), Am. Coll. Physician Execs., Am. Coll. Health Care Execs., Ariz. Med. Assn., La Paloma Country Club. Republican. Episcopalian. Avocations: golf, gardening, photography. Home: PO Box 805 Sonoita AZ 85637

SCOTT, WILLIAM FRED, cultural organization administrator; b. Thomasville, Ga., 1953. B cum laude, Sch. Fgn. Svc., Georgetown U., 1974. Formerly assoc. condr., artistic adminstr. Opera Co of Boston; artistic dir. The Atlanta Opera, 1985—; prin. condr. Opera New England; asst. condr. Atlanta Symphony Orch., 1981—, assoc. condr., 1987—; guest condr. various orgns. including Opera Co. of Boston, Wolf Trap Opera Co., N.Y.C. Opera at Lincoln Ctr., Boston Pro Arte Chamber Orch.; conducted opera workshop in Tel Aviv at request of Israeli Govt., 1983. Operatic debut as condr. Opera Company of Boston, 1975. Office: Atlanta Opera 1800 Peachtree St NW Ste 620 Atlanta GA 30309-2502

SCOTT, WILLIAM HERBERT, state agency administrator; b. Estancia, N.Mex., Mar. 19, 1925; s. Chester Ray and Elizabeth Bryan (McNama) S.; m. Maryann Mavis Munro, Dec. 26, 1952 (div. 1980); children: Jean Ann, Megan Lynne; m. Dorothy Caroline Caster, Apr. 16, 1980. BS in Civil Engring., U. N.Mex., 1949, BBA in Acctg., 1949. CPA, Alaska. Field engr., office mgr. Kincaid & King Constrn., Anchorage, 1949-51; office mgr. M-B Contracting Co., Inc., Anchorage, 1951-52; staff acct. R.L. Rettig, CPA, Anchorage, 1952-54; prtnr. Rettig, Scott & Co., CPAs, Anchorage, 1955-60; mng. ptnr. Scott, McMahon & Co., CPAs, Anchorage, 1960-61, Peat, Marwick Mitchell & Co., Anchorage, 1961-83; cons., 1983-91; exec. dir. Alaska Indsl. Devel., Anchorage, 1991-92, Alaska Permanent Fund Corp., Juneau, 1992-94; sec. Alaska Bd. Pub. Accountancy, 1963-65. Mem. Com. on Operation U.S. Senate, Washington, 1976; honorary consul Denmark, Anchorage, 1963-88. Lt. j.g. USNR, 1942-46, PTO. Named Knight of Dannebrog Queen of Denmark, 1973, 83. Mem. Am. Arbitration Assn. (panel 1984—), Alaska Soc. CPAs (pres., founder 1961-62), AICPA (coun. 1961-62), Anchorage C. of C. (pres. 1966), Alaska State C. of C. (pres. 1968), Alaskan Air Command Civilian Affairs, Sigma Chi. Avocations: tennis, alpine skiing.

SCOTT, WILLIAM PAUL, lawyer; b. Staples, Minn., Nov. 8, 1928; A.L.A., U. Minn., 1949; B.S.L., St. Paul Coll. Law, 1952, J.D., 1954; m. Elsie Elaine Anderson, Feb. 7, 1968; 1 son, Jason Lee; children: William P., Mark D., Bryan D., Scott; stepchildren: Thomas J. (dec.), Terri L. Weeding-Berg. Bar: Minn. 1954. Atty. right of way div. Minn. Hwy. Dept., 1945-52, civil engr. traffic and safety div., 1953-55; practice law Arlington, Minn., 1955-61, Gaylord, Minn., 1963-67; sr. partner firm Scott Law Offices and predecessors, Pipestone, Minn., 1967—; probate, juvenile judge Sibley County, Minn., 1956-61; Minn. pub. examiner, 1961-63; county atty. Sibley County, 1963-68, city atty., Pipestone, 1978—. Formerly nat. committeeman Young Rep. League; Sibley County Rep. chmn., 1961. Served with USMCR, 1946-50; from 2d lt. to lt. col. USAF Res., 1950-77; ret. Recipient George Washington Honor medal Freedoms Found., 1970, 72. Mem. Minn. Bar Assn., TROA, Mensa, V.F.W., DAV, Am. Legion, Res. Officers Assn. Home: PO Box 704 Pipestone MN 56164-0704 Office: Park Plz Offices Pipestone MN 56164

SCOTT, WILLIAM PROCTOR, III, lawyer; b. Berkeley, Calif., Dec. 1, 1946; s. William Proctor Jr. and Marcia (Wood) S.; m. Helen Elizabeth Hiller, June 16, 1968; children: William Proctor IV, Jennifer Anne. BS, MIT, 1968; JD cum laude, U. Pa., 1975. Assoc. Ballard, Spahr, Andrews & Ingersoll, Phila., 1975-82, ptnr., 1982—; regional chmn. MIT Ednl. Coun., 1988—. Lt. (j.g.) USNR, 1969-72. Mem. ABA, Pa. Bar Assn., Phila. Bar Assn., MIT Club of Delaware Valley (mem. exec. com. 1991—). Office: Ballard Spahr Andrews & Ingersoll 1735 Market St Philadelphia PA 19103

SCOTT, W(ILLIAM) RICHARD, sociology educator; b. Parsons, Kan., Dec. 18, 1932; s. Charles Hogue and Hildegarde (Hewit) S.; m. Joy Lee Whitney, Aug. 14, 1955; children: Jennifer Ann, Elliot Whitney, Sydney Brooke. AA, Parsons Jr. Coll., 1952; AB, U. Kans., 1954, MA, 1955; PhD, U. Chgo., 1961. Asst. prof. to assoc. prof. sociology Stanford (Calif.) U., 1960-69, prof., 1969—, chair dept. sociology, 1972-75; courtesy prof. Sch. Medicine, Stanford U., 1972—, Sch. Edn., Grad. Sch. Bus., 1977—; fellow Ctr. for Advanced Study in Behavioral Scis., 1989-90; dir. Orgns. Rsch. Tng. Program, Stanford U., 1972-89, Ctr. for Orgns. Rsch., 1988—; mem. adv. panel Sociology Program NSF, Washington, 1982-84; mem. epidemiol. and svc. rsch. rev. panel NIMH, Washington, 1984-88; mem. Commn. on Behavioral and Social Scis. and Edn., NAS, 1990—. Author: (with O.D. Duncan et al) Metropolis and Region, 1960, (with P.M. Blau) Formal Organizations, 1962, Social Processes and Social Structures, 1970, (with S.M. Dornbusch) Evaluation and the Exercise of Authority, 1975, Organizations: Rational, Natural and Open Systems, 1981, rev. edit., 1992, (with J.W.

Meyer) Organizational Environments: Ritual and Rationality, 1983, edit., 1992, (with A.B. Flood) Hospital Structure and Performance, 1987, (with J.W. Meyer), Institutional Environments and Organizations: Structural Complexity and Individualism, 1994, Institutions and Organizations: Theory and Research, 1995; editor Ann. Rev. of Sociology, 1986-91. Fellow Woodrow Wilson, 1954-55; mem. Nat. Commn. Nursing, 1980-83; chair Consortium Orgns. Rsch. Ctrs., 1989-91; elder First Presby. Ch., Palo Alto, Calif., 1977-80, 83-86. Social Sci. Research Council fellow, U. Chgo., 1959; named Edmund P. Learned Disting. Prof., Sch. Bus. Adminstrn., U. Kans, 1970-71; recipient Cardinal Citation for Disting. Service, Labette Community Coll, Parsons, 1981, Disting. Scholar award Mgmt. and Orgn. Theory div. Acad. Mgmt., 1988. Mem. Inst. Medicine, Am. Sociol. Assn. (chmn. sect. on orgns. 1970-71, mem. coun. 1989-92), Acad. Mgmt., Sociol. Rsch. Assn., Macro-Organizational Behavior Soc., Phi Beta Kappa. Democrat. Presbyterian. Home: 940 Lathrop Pl Palo Alto CA 94305-1060 Office: Stanford U Dept Sociology Bldg 120 Stanford CA 94305

SCOTTI, JAMES VERNON, astronomer; b. Bandon, Oreg., Aug. 22, 1960; s. Paul Carl and Elizabeth Louise (Garoutte) S.; m. Karriaunna K.-R. Harlan, May 15, 1983; children: Jennifer Anne, Christopher James. BS, U. Ariz., 1983. Planetarium asst. Flandrau Planetarium, Tucson, 1979-82; student rsch. asst. Lunar and Planetary Lab., Tucson, 1982-83, rsch. asst., 1983-93, sr. rsch. specialist, 1993—. Mem. Am. Astron. Soc. (assoc.), Div. for Planetary Scis., Assn. Lunar and Planetary Observers (asst. comets recorder). Achievements include being a leading observer of faint comets, being heavily involved in observing comet P/Shoemaker-Levy 9 before and during its impact on Jupiter in July 1994. Office: U Ariz Lunar and Planetary Lab Tucson AZ 85721*

SCOTTI, MICHAEL JOHN, JR., military medical officer; b. N.Y.C., Oct. 30, 1938; s. Michael John and Florence (Ellis) S.; m. Susan Faye Suit, Aug. 25, 1961; children: Michael John III, Pamela Anne, Jennifer Beth. BS, Fordham Coll., 1960; MD, Georgetown U., 1965; postgrad., Indsl. Coll., Washington, 1982-83. Diplomate Am. Bd. Internal Medicine, Am. Bd. Family Practice. Commd. 2d lt. U.S. Army, 1963, advanced through grades to maj. gen., 1990; dir. annulatory care Med. Activity, Landstuhl, Fed. Republic Germany, 1990; dir. residency program Dept. Family Practice, Ft. Gordon, Ga., 1976-79; family practice cons. Surgeon Gen., Washington, 1979-80; dir. Grad. Med. Edn. U.S. Army, Washington, 1980-82; comdr. army hosp. Ft. Polk, La., 1983-86; dir. quality assurance Army Med. Dept, Washington, 1986-88; dir. profl. svcs. Army Med. Dept., 1988-90; comdg. gen. European 7th Med. Comd, Heidelberg, Fed. Republic Germany, 1990—; chmn. Def. Med. Standardization, Ft. Detrick, Md., 1988-90; prof. Uniformed Svcs. U., Bethesda, Md., 1990. Health cons. Nat. PTA, Chgo., 1976-79. Named Person of Yr. Phi Delta Kappa, 1976. Fellow Am. Acad. Family Physicians (vice speaker 1988-90, speaker, bd. dirs. 1990-92), ACP; mem. AMA, Acad. Medicine. Office: 2540 N Randolph St Arlington VA 22207-5218

SCOTT MORTON, MICHAEL STEWART, business management educator; b. Mukden, Manchuria, Peoples Republic of China, Aug. 25, 1937; came to U.S., 1958; s. William and Alice (Gleysteen) S.M.; m. Mary Louise Mansell, June 20, 1964; children: Fiona Margaret, Lesley Elizabeth. Student, Glasgow U., Scotland, 1957-58; BS, Carnegie Mellon, 1961; DBA, Harvard U., 1967. Asst. prof. Sloan Sch. MIT, Cambridge, 1966-69, assoc. prof., 1969-75, Jay W. Forrester prof. mgmt., 1975—; bd. dirs. Dequent Computer Sys.; trustee Met. Life-State St. Author: Decision Support System, 1978, Strategic Control, 1986, Management in the 1990s, 1991; contbr. articles to profl. jours. Mem. Assn. for Computing Machinery, Am. Acctg. Assn., Inst. Mgmt. Sci., Handel and Haydn Soc. (gov.), Fidelco Guide Dog Found. (dir.). Clubs: Somerset, Harvard (Boston). Avocations: sailing, walking. Home: 31 Somerset Rd Lexington MA 02173-3519 also: Ledgrianach, Appin, Argyll Scotland Office: MIT Sloan Sch Mgmt 50 Memorial Dr Cambridge MA 02142-1347

SCOTTO, RENATA, soprano; b. Savona, Italy, Feb. 24, 1935; m. Lorenzo Anselmi. Studied under, Ghirardini, Merlino and Mercedes Llopart, Accademia Musicale Savonese, Conservatory Giuseppe Verdi, Milan. Debut in La Traviata, Teatro Nuevo, Milan, 1954; then joined La Scala Opera Co.; appeared with Met. Opera, N.Y.C., 1965, Convent Garden, Hamburg (Fed. Republic of Germany) State Opera, Vienna (Austria) State Opera, Nat. Theatre Munich, San Francisco Opera, Chgo. Civic Opera, 1988; roles include: Ballo in Maschera, La Sonnambula, I Puritani, L'Elisir d'amore, Lucia di Lammermoor, La Boheme, Turandot, Otello (Verdi), Trovatore, Le Prophete, Madama Butterfly, Adriana Lecouvreur, Norma, Tosca, Manon Lescaut, Rosenkavalier (Marschallin), La Voix Humaine, Pirata; dir. Madama Butterfly, N.Y. Met. Opera, 1986; recordings include Christmas at St. Patrick's Cathedral, French Arias with Charles Rosekrans, Live in Paris with Ivan Davis, Great Operatic Scenes with Jose Carreras. Office: care Robert Lombardo Assocs One Harkness Plaza 61 W 62d St Ste 6F New York NY 10023 also: care Il Teatro la Scala, via Filodrammatici 2, Milan Italy*

SCOTT-WILLIAMS, STEPHANIE, territorial legislator; b. Washington, May 15, 1947; d. John P. and Edna Louise Scott; widowed; children: Travis, Jodianne. Student, Roxborough Meml. Hosp. Sch. Nursing, 1966, Coll. of the V.I., 1967. Interviewer, counselor Div. Pers., St. Thomas, V.I.; counselor Work Incentive Program, St. Thomas; supr. V.I. Employment Security Agy., St. Thomas; program coord. Youth Svc. Adminstrn., St. Thomas, 1980-83; exec. dir. St. Thomas-St. John Youth Multi Svc. Ctr., St. Thomas, 1985-88; pub., editor People's Choice, St. Thomas, 1988; dir. Pub. Edn. on V.I. Status, St. Thomas, 1989; coord. Comprehensive Land and Water Use Plan, St. Thomas, 1990; senator V.I. 19th Legislature, St. Thomas, 1991—. Pres. East End Homeowners Assn., St. Thomas, 1983-84; mem., founder, chmn., bd. dirs. project vital Living in Fuller Expectations Prison Ministry, 1991—. Named Citizen of Yr., St. Thomas-St. John Bd. Realtors, 1986; recipient Woman of Achievement award Caribbean Exec. Women's Network, 1987, Peacemaker award Women's Resource Ctr., 1991; luncheon honoree Senator Robert O'Connor Jr., 1988, Mother's Day honoree Senator Bingley Richardson, 1988. Mem. Nat. Black Caucus of State Legislators, St. Thomas-St. John C. of C. (beautification com.), Rotary Internat., Bus. and Profl. Women's Club. Democrat. Lutheran. Avocations: youth, elderly, disabled. Office: Legis of Virgin Islands Capitol Bldg Charlotte Amalie VI 00801

SCOUTEN, REX W., curator. Curator White House, Washington, D.C.; ex officio mem., Comm. for the Preservation of the White House. Office: White House 1600 Pennsylvania Ave NW Washington DC 20500-0001

SCOUTEN, WILLIAM HENRY, chemistry educator, academic administrator; b. Corning, N.Y., Feb. 12, 1942; s. Henry and M. Anna (Kimble) S.; m. Nancy Jane Coombs, July 16, 1965; children: Lisa, Linda, Michael, William Jr., Thomas, David. BA, Houghton Coll., 1964; PhD, U. Pitts., 1969. NIH postdoctoral fellow SUNY, Stony Brook, 1969-71; asst. prof. Bucknell U., Lewisburg, Pa., 1971-77; assoc. prof. Bucknell U., Lewisburg, 1977-83, prof., 1983-84; chmn. chemistry dept. Baylor U., Waco, Tex., 1984-93; dir. biotech. ctr. Utah State U., Logan, 1993—; vis. scientist for minority inst. Fed. Am. Soc. Exptl. Biology, Washington. Author: Affinity Chromatography, 1981; editor: Solid Phace Biochem., 1983; assoc. editor Internat. Jour. of Bio-Chromatography; mem. editl. bd. Bioconjugate Chemistry, Bioseparation, Jour. Molecular Recognition. Fulbright fellow, 1976; Dreyfus Tchr. scholar, Dreyfus Found., 1976; NSF Sci. Devel. NSF, 1978; Lindbach Disting. Tchr. Bucknell U., 1975. Mem. Am. Soc. Biol. Chemists, Am. Chem. Soc., Internat. Soc. for Biorecognition Tech., Internat. Soc. for Molecular Recognition (pres. 1990-93), Assn. for Internat. Practical Tng. (bd. dirs 1991—). Republican. Baptist. Office: Biotechnology Ctr Utah State U Logan UT 84322

SCOVIL, LARRY EMERY, minister; b. Conneaut, Ohio, Dec. 1, 1950; s. Lynn Edgar and Shirley Jean (Cook) S.; m. Kristine Adell Schulz, Dec. 19, 1970; children: Jennifer, Jarin, Lindsay. B. Music Edn., U. Wis., Oshkosh, 1972; MDiv, Bethel Theol. Sem., 1987. Ordained to ministry Conservative Congl. Christian Conv., 1976. Pastor Zoar Congl. Ch., Mott, N.D., 1975-81, Calvary Evang. Congl. Ch., St. Paul, 1981-86, Emmanuel Congl. Ch., Scottsbluff, Nebr., 1986—; bd. dirs. Conservative Congl. Christian Conf., St. Paul, 1988-91, rec. sec., 1991—, Rocky Mountain area rep., 1989—. Writer,

arranger musical: Joy To The World, 1990. Mem. Panhandle Evang. Ministerial Assn. (pres. 1990—). Republican. Office: Emmanuel Congl Ch 317 W 40th St Scottsbluff NE 69361-4634

SCOVIL, ROGER MORRIS, engineering company executive; b. Greenville, S.C., Apr. 23, 1929; s. Roger Peniston and Sophia Rose (Herbert) S.; m. Mary Earle Nock; children: Randolph, Frances, Elizabeth. Student, Davidson Coll., 1946-48; BS in Civil Engring., N.C. State U., 1951. Registered profl. engr., Ga., S.C., P.R. Project mgr. McKoy-Helgerson Co., Greenville, 1953-63; v.p., maintenance div. mgr. Daniel Constrn. Co., Greenville, 1963-66; v.p., Caribbean div. mgr. Daniel Internat. Corp., San Juan, P.R., 1966-74; v.p. Europe and Middle East Daniel Internat. Corp., Brussels and Jeddah, Saudi Arabia, Saudi Arabia, 1974-79; v.p. internat. mkgt. Daniel Constrn. Co., Greenville, 1980; pres. Polysius Corp., Atlanta, 1981-88; sr. v.p., dir. Lockwood Greene Systems Corp., Atlanta, 1988—; sr. v.p., dir. Lockwood Greene Internat., Atlanta, 1991—. Capt. U.S. Army, 1951-53. Mem. Atlanta World Trade Ctr., Internat. Club Atlanta, Tau Beta Pi, Chi Epsilon. Episcopalian. Home: 6025 Riverwood Dr Atlanta GA 30328-3732 Office: Lockwood Greene Engrs 250 Williams St NW Ste 4000 Atlanta GA 30303-1036

SCOVIL, SAMUEL KINGSTON, mining company executive; b. Cleve., June 15, 1923; s. R. Malcolm and Dorothy Lee (Brown) S.; m. Barbara C. Baker, May 22, 1944; children—Emily, Malcolm (dec.), Samuel, Alexander. B.S., Yale U., 1945; grad., Advanced Mgmt. Program, Harvard, 1962. With Republic Steel Corp., 1947-50; with Cleveland Cliffs Inc. 1950—, mgr. sales, 1960-63, v.p. sales, 1963-69, sr. v.p. sales, 1970-72, sr. v.p., 1972-74, pres., 1974-83, chief exec. officer, 1976—, chmn. bd., 1983—, chmn. exec. com. of bd. dirs., 1988—; bd. dirs. Cleve.-Cliffs, Inc., Holnam Inc. Trustee Univ. Sch., Cleve., Cleve. Clinic Found. Office: Cleve-Cliffs Inc 1100 Superior Ave E Cleveland OH 44114-2501

SCOVILLE, JAMES GRIFFIN, economics educator; b. Amarillo, Tex., Mar. 19, 1940; s. Orlin James and Carol Howe (Griffin) S.; m. Judith Ann Nelson, June 11, 1962; 1 child, Nathan James. B.A., Oberlin Coll., 1961; M.A., Harvard U., 1963, Ph.D., 1965. Economist ILO, Geneva, 1965-66; instr. econs. Harvard U., Cambridge, Mass., 1964-65; asst. prof. Harvard U., 1966-69; assoc. prof. econs. and labor and indsl. relations U. Ill.-Urbana, 1969-75, prof., 1975-80; prof. indsl. rels. Indsl. Rels. Ctr., U. Minn., Mpls., 1979—, dir., 1979-82, dir. grad. studies, 1990—; cons. ILO, World Bank, U.S. Dept. Labor, Orgn. for Econ. Cooperation and Devel., AID; labor-mgmt. arbitrator. Author: The Job Content of the US Economy, 1940-70, 1969, Perspectives on Poverty and Income Distribution, 1971, Manpower and Occupational Analysis: Concepts and Measurements, 1972, (with A. Sturmthal) The International Labor Movement in Transition, 1973, Status Influences in 3rd World Labor Markets, 1991. Mem. Am. Econ. Assn., Indsl. Rels. Rsch. Assn., Internat. Indsl. Rels. Assn. Home: 4849 Girard Ave S Minneapolis MN 55409-2214 Office: U Minn Ind Rels Ctr 271 19th Ave S Minneapolis MN 55455-0430

SCOWCROFT, BRENT, retired air force officer, government official; b. Ogden, Utah, Mar. 19, 1925; s. James and Lucile (Ballantyne) S.; m. Marian Horner, Sept. 17, 1951; 1 dau., Karen. B.S., U.S. Mil. Acad., 1947; M.A., Columbia U., 1953, Ph.D., 1967; postgrad., Georgetown U., 1958. Commd. 2d lt. USAF, 1947, advanced through grades to lt. gen., 1974; asst. prof. dept. social sci. U.S. Mil. Acad., 1953-57; asst. air attache Am. Embassy, Belgrade, Yugoslavia, 1959-61; assoc. prof. dept. polit. sci. U.S. Air Force Acad., Colo., 1962-63; prof., head dept. U.S. Air Force Acad., 1963-64; mem. staff long range planning div. Office Dep. Chief Staff Plans and Ops., Washington, 1964-67; assigned Nat. War Coll., 1967-68; staff asst. Western Hemisphere region Office Asst. Sec. Def. Internat. Security Affairs, Washington, 1968-69; dep. asst. dir. plans for nat. security matters office Dep. Chief Staff Plans and Ops., 1969-70; spl. asst. to dir. Joint Staff, Joint Chiefs of Staff, 1970-71; mil. asst. to Pres., 1972-73, dep. asst. to Pres. for nat. security affairs, 1973-75, asst. to Pres. for nat. security affairs, 1975-77; mem. Pres.'s Gen. Adv. Com. on Arms Control, 1977-80; vice chmn. Kissinger Assocs., Inc., 1982-89; asst. to Pres. Nat. Security Coun., Washington, 1989-93; pres. Forum for Internat. Policy, Washington, 1993—; bd. dirs. Nat. Bank of Washington; chmn. Pres.' Commn. on Strategic Forces; mem. Pres.' Commn. on Def. Mgmt., Pres. Spl. Rev. Bd. on the Iran/Contra Affair. Bd. dirs. Atlantic Council U.S.; Bd. visitors U.S. Air Force Air U., 1977-79; mem. adv. bd. Georgetown Center for Strategic and Internat. Studies. Decorated D.S.M. with two oak leaf clusters, Legion of Merit with oak leaf cluster, Air Force Commendation medal, D.S.M. Dept. Def., Nat. Security medal; recipient Medal of Freedom, 1991; named Hon. Knight Brit. Empire, 1993. Mem. Council Fgn. Relations (bd. dirs.), UN Assn. U.S. (vice chmn.), Am. Polit. Sci. Assn., Acad. Polit. Sci. Mem. Ch. Jesus Christ of Latter-day Saints. Office: 1750 K St NW Ste 800 Washington DC 20006-2300

SCOWCROFT, JOHN ARTHUR, portfolio manager; b. Hammond, Ind., Aug. 3, 1954; s. John Major and Barbara Marie (Caine) S.; m. Carolee Clawson, Sept. 1, 1989. BA, U. Utah, 1977; MBA, U. Chgo., 1983, PhD, 1991. Chartered fin. analyst. Analyst Wasatch Advisors, Salt Lake City, 1975-79; pres. John Scowcroft & Co., 1979-84; mgr. MBS rsch. Merrill Lynch, N.Y.C., 1984-87; pres., vice chmn. Franklin Savings, Ottawa, Kans., 1987—; prin. Houlihan Valuation Advisors, 1992; dir. Oliver, Wyman & Co., N.Y.C., 1994—. Author various books, mag. articles in field, 1983—. Home: 102 NE Crescent Lees Summit MO 64063 Office: Oliver Wyman & Co 666 Fifth Ave New York NY 10103

SCOWCROFT, JOHN MAJOR, petroleum refinery process development executive; b. Ogden, Utah, June 19, 1924; s. John William and Charlene (Major) S.; m. Barbara Marie Caine, Mar. 12, 1951; children: Charlene, John Arthur, Barbara Ann, Sally Caine. BS, U. Utah, 1951; MBA, Northwestern U., 1952. Various mgmt. positions Standard Oil Co. (Ind.), Chgo., N.Y.C., 1952-74; gen. mgr. Deseret Mgmt. Corp., Salt Lake City, 1974-84; founder Utah Tech. Fin. Corp., Salt Lake City, 1984; exec. v.p. Utah Innovation Ctr., Salt Lake City, 1984-86; founder Utah Ventures, Salt Lake City, 1985; pres. Process Innovators, Inc., Salt Lake City, 1986—; bd. dirs.; bd. dirs., cons. small bus. devel. various orgns., Salt Lake City, 1984—; bd. dirs. Naverik Country Stores, Afton, Wyo., IMPETUS, Inc., Spl. Ltd. Ptnr. of Utah Ventures; founding bd. dirs. Deneva Steel. Mem. nat. adv. coun. David Eccles Sch. Bus., U. Utah; regional rep. LDS Ch., 1973-79; mem. Utah Gov.'s Health Care Options Commn. Cash Rsch. grantee U.S. Dept. Energy, 1989, Utah Dept. Energy, 1990, Utah Ctrs. of Excellence, 1989, Utah Tech. Fin. Corp., 1989. Mem. Salt Lake Area C. of C. (chmn. 1983), Alta Club, Rotary Club Salt Lake (treas. 1988-89, pres. 1993-94). Avocations: amateur radio, computers, skiing, hiking. Home: 1292 Federal Heights Dr Salt Lake City UT 84103-4326 Office: Utah Ventures 419 Wakara Way # 206 Salt Lake City UT 84108-1257

SCOZZIE, JAMES ANTHONY, chemist; b. Erie, Pa., Nov. 3, 1943. AB, Gannon Coll., 1965; MS, Case Western Res. U., 1968, PhD in Chemistry, 1970. Jr. rsch. chemist ctrl. rsch. dept. Lord Corp., 1965; rsch. chemist Diamond Shamrock Corp., 1970-72, sr. rsch. chemist, 1972-76, rsch. supr. pharmaceutics, 1976-78, group leader agrl. chemistry, 1978-81, assoc. dir. agrl. chemistry rsch., 1981-83; dir. agrl. chemistry rsch. SDS Biotech Corp., 1983-85, dir. corp. rsch., 1985—; pres. Ricerca, Inc., Painesville, Ohio, 1986—. Chmn. bd. trustees State of Ohio Edison Biotechnology Ctr.; bd. governance Edison Biotechnology Inst. Mem. Am. Chem. Soc. Achievements include research in structure and chemistry of peptide antibiotics, synthesis of biologically active compounds, pesticides, process studies of organic compounds, commercial evaluation, nutrition and animal health, herbicides, plant growth regulants, cardiovascular agents and anti-inflammatory agents. Office: Ricerca Inc PO Box 1000 7528 Auburn Rd Painesville OH 44077

SCRABECK, JON GILMEN, dental eductor; b. Rochester, Minn., Dec. 6, 1938; s. Clarence and Nancy Alma (Brown) S.; m. DeAnn Louise Jacks, June 16, 1962; children: Joan Louise, Erik Jon. Student, Contra Costa Coll., San Pablo, Calif., 1964-66, U. Calif. Berkeley, 1966-67; DDS, UCLA, 1971; MA in Edn., U. Colo., 1985. Pvt. practice, Santa Rosa, Calif., 1971-78; instr. U. Colo. Sch. Dentistry, Denver, 1978-79, asst. prof., 1980-86, dir. patient care, 1979-80, acting dir. clin. affairs, 1980-81; acting assoc. dean U. Colo. Sch. Dentistry, Denver, 1983-84; acting dir. chmn. U. Colo. Sch. Dentistry, Denver, 1984-85; dept. chmn. Marquette U. Sch. Dentistry, Milw., 1986-90, assoc. prof., 1986—, assoc. prof. tenure, 1989, curricular head, 1990—; cons. Dental Student mag.,1983-86, Colo. Bd. Dentistry, Denver, 1985-86, Dentist mag., 1986-90, VA, Milw., 1987-90. Editor Jour. Colo. Dental Assn., 1980-86; contbr. articles and abstracts to dental jours. mem. vol. staff Morey Dental Clinic, Denver, 1982-85, Health Fair, Denver, 1983-85; ofcl. judge S.E. Wis. Sci. Fair, Milw., 1988—. Fellow Internat. Coll. Dentists, Acad. Dental Materials, Am. Coll. Dentists, Pierre Fauchard Acad.; mem. ADA (coun. on journalism 1984-86, coun. on dental rsch. 1986-88, manuscript reviewer 1988—), Acad. Operative Dentistry, Wis. Dental Assn. (assoc. editor Jour. 1987—), Omicron Kappa Upsilon, Alpha Gamma Sigma. Roman Catholic. Avocations: foreign and domestic travel, photography, boating, fishing, water skiing. Home: W349s10140 Bittersweet Ct Eagle WI 53119-1851 Office: Marquette U Sch Dentistry 604 N 16th St Milwaukee WI 53233-2117

SCRANTON, WILLIAM MAXWELL, manufacturing company executive, consultant; b. Scranton, Pa., Mar. 1, 1921; s. William Henry and Dorothy (Bessell) S.; m. Andrea Orne Abbott, Sept. 24, 1949 (dec. Oct. 1991); children: John Selden and Nancy Orne (Mrs. Don J. Sporborg) (twins), James Maxwell, Sarah Abbott. BS in Engring, Princeton U., 1942; MBA, Harvard U., 1948. With Pratt & Whitney Aircraft div. United Aircraft Crop., East Hartford, Conn., 1942-46, 48-50, MPB Corp., Keene, N.H., 1950-77; exec. v.p. MPB Corp., 1953-62, pres., 1962-77, dir., 1959-76; pres., dir. Beede Elec. Instrument Co. Inc., 1977-82; cons., 1983—; mem. adv. bd. Kearsarge Ventures, LP, Manchester, N.H.; dir. Summa Four, Inc. Home: PO Box 491 West Falmouth MA 02574-0491

SCRASE, DAVID ANTHONY, German language educator; b. Upton, Dorset, Eng., Nov. 27, 1939; came to U.S., 1969; s. Robert Stanley and Dorothy Adelaide (Ridgewell) S.; m. Mary Ellen Martin, May 5, 1973 (div. Apr. 1985); 1 child, Anna Rachel Martin-Scrase. BA, Bristol U., 1962; PhD, Ind. U., 1972. Lectr. Zurich U., Switzerland, 1964-68; asst. prof. Oxford Poly., Eng., 1968-69; prof. U. Vt., Burlington, 1971—. Author: Wilhelm Lehmann, A Critical Biography, 1984, Understanding Johannes Bobrowski, 1995; contbr. articles, translations. Recipient fellowships Brit. Acad., London, 1973, Humboldt Found., Bonn, Fed. Republic Germany, 1974, 79. Avocations: reading, music, woodwork, sport. Office: U Vt Dept German Waterman Bldg Burlington VT 05405

SCRIBNER, BARBARA COLVIN, museum administrator; b. Bangor, Maine, Dec. 18, 1926; d. Howard Morton and May Josephine (Tierney) Colvin; m. Harold B. Scribner, Mar. 10, 1956 (dec. June, 1982); 1 child, Scott Colvin. Student Pratt Inst., 1945-46. Assoc. editor McCall's Mag., N.Y.C., 1950-59; assoc. editor Am. Home, N.Y.C., 1960-64, contbg. editor, 1964-67; free-lance writer-editor, N.Y.C., 1968-77; dir. pub. info. Stamford Mus. and Nature Ctr., Conn., 1978—; curator Going to Blazes exhbn., 1988-89, Music Mania exhbn., 1988-89, Antique Toy Banks exhbn., 1990-91, Antique Bottles exhbn., 1992-93, Toy Bldg. Sets Exhbn., 1994—; Bendel Estate Exhibit, 1994—; mem. attractions com. State of Conn., 1982—. Mem. product com. New Eng. U.S.A. Found., 1989-90; American Trail, 1990, Tourism Network Conn., 1992—; exec. bd. Council Darien Sch. Parents, Conn., 1974-82, Episcopal Ch. Women, Darien, 1970-78, Darien High Sch. Parents Assn., 1980-82. Republican. Lodge: Order Eastern Star. Home: 40 Maple St Darien CT 06820-5209 Office: Stamford Mus & Nature Ctr 39 Scofieldtown Rd Stamford CT 06903-4023

SCRIBNER, BELDING HIBBARD, medical educator, nephrologist; b. Chgo., Jan. 18, 1921; s. Carleton Spear and Mary Elizabeth (Belding) S.; m. Elizabeth F. Browne, Dec. 28, 1942 (div. Dec. 1965); children—Peter B., Robert R., Thomas B., Elizabeth A., m. Ethel Victoria Hackett, Jan. 28, 1966. A.B., U. Calif.-Berkeley, 1941; M.D., Stanford U., 1945; M.A., U. Minn., 1951; D. (hon.), U. Goteborg, 1981; postgrad., Med. Sch. London, 1985. Asst. to staff Mayo Clinic, Rochester, Minn., 1950-51; instr. medicine U. Wash., Seattle, 1951-55, asst. prof. medicine, 1955-58, assoc. prof. medicine, 1958-64, prof. medicine, 1964—. Patentee med. device. Served with U.S. Navy, 1941-44. Recipient Gaindner Found. award, Toronto, 1969, David Hume award Nat. Kidney Found., 1975, Mayo Soley award Western Soc. Clin. Investigation, 1982, Jean Hamburger award Internat. Soc. Nephrology, 1987, Gov.'s medal State of Wash., 1989; Markle Found. scholar, 1954-59. Mem. Am. Soc. Clin. Investigation, Am. Soc. Artificial Organs (pres. 1963-64), Am. Soc. Nephrology (pres. 1978-79, John P. Peters award 1986), Assn. Am. Physicians, Inst. Medicine. Office: Univ Wash Divsn Nephrology Mail Stop Rm 11 Seattle WA 98122

SCRIBNER, CHARLES, III, publisher, art historian, lecturer; b. Washington, May 24, 1951; s. Charles and Joan (Sunderland) S.; m. Ritchie Harrison Markoe, Aug. 4, 1979; children: Charles IV, Christopher Markoe. AB, Princeton U., 1973, MFA, 1975, PhD, 1977. Editor Charles Scribner's Sons, N.Y.C., 1975—, dir. subs. rights, 1978-82, pub. paperback div., 1982-83, exec. v.p., 1983-84; v.p. Macmillan Pub. Co., N.Y.C., 1984-94; instr. dept. art and archaeology Princeton U., 1976-77; mem. adv. council Princeton U. Library, 1983—; mem. adv. council dept. art and archaeology Princeton U., 1983-91; trustee Princeton U. Press, 1984-90, Homeland Found., 1987—; bd. advisors Wethersfield Inst., 1985—; bd. editors Met. Opera Guild, 1990-92. Author: The Triumph of the Eucharist - Tapestries by Rubens, 1982, Rubens, 1989, Bernini, 1991. Trustee St. Paul's Sch., Concord, N.H., 1994—. Mem. Americas Princeton U. Press. Roman Catholic. Clubs: Racquet and Tennis (N.Y.C.); Ivy (Princeton); Piping Rock (N.Y.). Avocations: music, art, opera. Office: Charles Scribners Sons 866 3d Ave New York NY 10022

SCRIBNER, RODNEY LATHAM, state official; b. Rumford, Maine, May 6, 1935; s. Dwight Latham and Evaline May (House) S.; m. Evelyn Jean Sanborn, Feb. 28, 1963. B.S. in Marine Sci., Maine Maritime Acad., 1956. C.P.A., Maine. With Mobil Oil Co., N.Y.C., 1958-62; acct. Staples & Boyce, Portland, Maine, 1962-68; mem. Maine Ho. of Reps., 1967-68; dep. commr. Maine Dept. Fin. and Adminstrn., 1968-69, state controller, 1971-72, state budget officer, 1972-73; with Maine Leg. Fin. Office, 1973-74; treas. State of Maine, 1975-76, auditor, 1977; dep. dir. Office Revenue Sharing, U.S. Treas. Dept., Washington, 1977-79; commr. Dept. Fin. and Adminstrn., State of Maine, 1979-87; auditor State of Maine, 1987—; instr. U. Maine, 1971. Treas., United Way of Kennebec County; mem. Augusta Housing Authority, Maine, 1979-89; mem. planning com. Colby Coll. Mgmt. Inst., Waterville, Maine, 1973-89; past treas. Augusta Salvation Army; chmn. Maine Mcpl. Bond Bank, Augusta, 1976-77. Served to lt. (j.g.) USNR, 1956-58. Mem. AICPA, Maine Soc. CPAs (gov. 1983-84, 89—), Am. Soc. Pub. Adminstrn. (pres. Maine chpt. 1972-73), Rotary (treas. 1986-89). Democrat. Baptist. Home: 31 Fairview St Gardiner ME 04345-2807 Office: State of Maine Dept Audit Station #66 Augusta ME 04333

SCRIBNER, RONALD KENT, microbiologist; b. Denison, Tex., June 22, 1948; s. Theodore Roosevelt and Annabelle (Ellis) S. BS, Okla. State U., 1972; MS, L.I. U., 1980. Research supr. Okla. U. Health Sci. Ctr., Oklahoma City, 1980-87; cons. microbiologist N.W. Labs., Oklahoma City, 1989—; prof. biology Oklahoma City C.C., 1986—; cons. The Med. Letter, Phila., 1985—. Author: Nalidixic Acid, Quinolones and Novobiocin in Antimicrobial Therapy in Infants and Children, 1988; contbr. articles to profl. jours. Mem. AAAS, Am. Soc. Microbiology, Am. Soc. Clin. Pathology, S.W. Assn. Clin. Microbiology, Mensa, Nat. Assn. Biology Tchrs., Nat. Sci. Tchrs. Assn. Democrat. Avocations: fishing, golf. Home: 1836 NW 14th St Oklahoma City OK 73106-2016 Office: Oklahoma City CC 7777 S May Ave Oklahoma City OK 73159-4419

SCRICCA, DIANE BERNADETTE, principal; b. Flushing, N.Y., Mar. 18, 1951; d. Dominic John (Scricca) and Anne (Quinterno) Freohlich; m. Mark Scheinbart, Jan. 19, 1975 (div. Dec. 1988); 1 child, Mark Anthony. BA in Social Studies, St. John's U., 1973, MS in Curriculum and Teaching, 1977, D of Adminstrn. and Supervision, 1980. Tchr. social studies various high schs., N.Y.C., 1973-78; coord. spl. edn. Jamaica (N.Y.) High Sch., 1979-81, asst. prin., 1981-87; asst. prin. Ft. Hamilton High Sch., Bklyn., 1987-90; prin. Elmont (N.Y.) Meml. High Sch., 1990—; cons. in field; instr. new tchr., N.Y.C. Bd. Edn., 1982-90, instr., new suprs., 1988-90. Mem. ASCD, Nat. Assn. Secondary Sch. Prins., Am. Assn. Sch. Adminstrs. Avocations: tennis, travel, mus., reading. Home: 8 Bowler Rd East Rockaway NY 11518-1635 Office: Elmont Meml High Sch 555 Ridge Ave Floral Park NY 11003-3524

SCRIGGINS, LARRY PALMER, lawyer; b. Englewood, N.J., Nov. 27, 1936; s. Thomas Dalby and M. Patricia (Fowler) S.; m. Victoria Jackola, Feb. 17, 1979; children: Elizabeth J., Thomas P. AB, Middlebury Coll., 1958; JD, U. Chgo., 1961. Bar: Md. 1962. Law clk. to chief judge Md. Ct. Appeals, 1962; assoc. Piper & Marbury, Balt., 1962-69, ptnr., 1969—, vice chmn. 1988-93, co-chair bus. div., 1990—; mem. legal adv. com. N.Y. Stock Exchange, 1992—; bd. dirs. USF & G Corp., 1979—, Center Stage Assocs., 1979-89, Balt. Choral Arts Soc., 1979—, Balt. Conv. Bur., 1982—, YMCA of Greater Balt., 1987—, Fund for Ednl. Excellence, 1990—, chmn. bd. trustees, 1993—; bd. dirs. Nat. Aquarium in Balt., bd. govs. 1987—. Fellow Am. Bar Found.; mem. Md. Bar Assn. (coun. 1976-78, chmn. 1977-78, chmn. com. on corp. laws 1981-84), ABA (sect. on bus. law, council 1972-76, chair 1991-92, vice-chair and editor in chief The Bus. Lawyer 1989-90, chmn. law and acctg. com. 1985-88), Internat. Bar Assn., Am. Judicature Soc., Am. Law Inst., Task Force on Fin. Instruments, Fin. Acctg. Standards Bd., Am. Inst. CPAs Planning Com. (pub. mem. 1989-92). Contbr. articles to profl. jours. Home: 13 E Eager St Baltimore MD 21202-2513 Office: Piper & Marbury 36 S Charles St Baltimore MD 21201-3020

SCRIMENTI, BELINDA JAYNE, lawyer; b. Dayton, Ohio, Jan. 30, 1956. BS in Journalism, Ohio U., 1978; JD, Ohio State U., 1981. Bar: Ohio 1981, U.S. Dist. Ct. (no. dist.) Ohio 1981, U.S. Dist. Ct. (ea. dist.) Mich. 1983, U.S. Ct. Appeals (3d and 6th cirs.) 1984, U.S. Dist. Ct. Md. 1988, D.C. 1989, U.S. Dist. Ct. D.C. 1989. Assoc. Baker & Hostetler, Cleve., 1981-88; assoc. Baker & Hostetler, Washington, 1988-90, ptnr., 1991—. Contbr. articles to profl. jours. Sec. Chagrin Condominiums Homeowners' Assn., Chagrin Falls, Ohio, 1985-87. Mem. ABA (sect. on litigation, patent, trademarks and copyrights, entertainment and sports law), D.C. Bar Assn. (sects. on copyright, trademarks, patent and entertainment and sport law), Internat. Trademark Assn. (firm rep., coms. 1990—), Internat. Anti-Counterfeiting Coaliton (firm rep.), Womens Bar Assn. D.C. Office: Baker & Hostetler 1050 Connecticut Ave NW Ste 1100 Washington DC 20036

SCRIMSHAW, NEVIN STEWART, physician, nutrition and health educator; b. Milw., Jan. 20, 1918; m. Mary Ware Goodrich, 1941; 5 children. B.A. with honors, Ohio Wesleyan U., 1938; M.A. in Biology, Harvard U., 1939, Ph.D. in Physiology, 1941; M.D. with honors, U. Rochester, 1945; M.P.H. with honors, Harvard U., 1959. Diplomate Am. Bd. Med. Examiners. Intern Gorgas Hosp., C.Z., 1945-46; Rockefeller postdoctoral fellow U. Rochester, N.Y., 1946-47, Merck NRC fellow, 1947-49; asst. resident in ob-gyn Strong Meml. Hosp., Genesee Hosp., N.Y., 1948-49; cons. nutrition Pan-Am. San. Bur. WHO, 1948-49, regional advisor on nutrition, 1949-53; dir. Inst. Nutrition C.Am. and Panama, Guatemala, 1949-61, cons. dir., 1961-65, cons. 1965—; dir. Clin. Research Ctr., MIT, 1962-66, 79-85, dir. internat. food and nutrition program, 1976-88, prof. human nutrition, 1961-76, head dept. nutrition and food sci., 1961-79; Inst. prof. Columbia U., N.Y., 1976-88, prof. emeritus, 1988—, vis. lectr. 1961-66; vis. lectr. Harvard U., 1968-85; vis. prof. Tufts U; mem. govt. adv. com. NIH; chmn. internat. com. NRC; dir. devel. studies div. U.N. U., 1985-86, food nutrition program 1975—. mem. adv. com. WHO, Nutrition Found., others. Contbr. articles to profl. jours.; editor: (with others) Amino Acid Fortification of Protein Foods, 1971, Nutrition, National Development and Planning, 1973, The Economics, Marketing and Technology of Fish Protein Concentrate, 1974, Nutrition and Agricultural Development: Significance and Potential for the Tropics, 1976, Single-Cell Protein: Safety for Animal and Human Feeding, 1979, Nutrition Policy Implementation: Issues and Experience, 1983, Diarrhea and Malnutrition: Interactions, Mechanisms and Interventions, 1983, Chronic Energy Deficiency, 1987, Acceptability of Milk and Milk Products in Populations With Lactose Intolerance, 1988, Activity, Energy Expenditure and Energy Requirements of Infants and Children, 1989, othrs. Recipient Osborne and Mendal award, 1960, Internat. award Inst. Food Technologists, 1969, medal of honor Fundacion F. Cuenca Villoro, Spain, 1978, Bristol-Myers prize, 1988, Alan Shawn Feinstein award, 1991, World Food prize, 1991, also others. Trustee Rockefeller Found., 1971-83, Pan-Am. Health and Edn. Found., 1986-92; pres. Internat. Nutrition Found. for Developing Countries, 1982—. Fellow Am. Inst. Nutrition, Royal Soc. Health, AAAS, Am. Soc. Clin. Nutrition, Am. Pub. Health Assn. (v.p. 1978 award of excellence in promoting and protecting health of people 1974); mem. Am. Coll. Nutrition, NAS (ch. applied biol. section, 1973-76, 88-91), Inst. of Medicine, Am. Acad Astrs., Am. Coll. Preventive Medicine, Am. Bd. Nutrition, Mass. Pub. Health Assn., New Eng. Pub. Health Assn., Mass. Med. Soc., Am. Physiol. Soc., Am. Epidemol. Soc., Internat. Union Nutritional Scis. (pres. 1978-81), Internat. Epidemol. Assn., also others. Home: Sandwich Mountain Farm PO Box 330 Campton NH 03223-0330 Office: PO Box 500 Boston MA 02114-0500

SCRIPPS, CHARLES EDWARD, newspaper publisher; b. San Diego, Jan. 27, 1920; s. Robert Paine and Margaret Lou (Culbertson) S.; m. Louann Copeland, June 28, 1941 (div. 1947); m. Lois Anne MacKay, Oct. 14, 1949 (dec. 1990); children Charles Edward Jr., Marilyn Joy, Eston Mackay, Julia Osborne; m. Mary Elizabeth Breslin, Sept. 7, 1993. Student, Coll. William and Mary, 1938-40, Pomona Coll., 1940-41. Reporter Cleve. Press, 1941; successor-trustee Edward W. Scripps Trust, 1945, chmn. bd. trustees, 1948—; v.p. E.W. Scripps Co., 1946—, chmn., 1953—, also bd. dirs., 1953-94; chmn. exec. com., 1994—; bd. dirs. various Scripps-Howard newspapers and affiliated enterprises. Mem. nat. adv. bd. Salvation Army; trustee Freedoms Found. Served to lt. (j.g.) USCGR, 1942-45. Mem. CAP, Theta Delta Chi. Office: Scripps Howard 312 Walnut St 28th Fl Cincinnati OH 45202

SCRIPPS, EDWARD WYLLIS, newspaper publisher; b. San Diego, May 21, 1909; s. James G. and Josephine (Stedem) S.; m. Betty Jeanne Knight McDonnell, Jan. 31, 1950; children: Edward Wyllis III, Barry Howard. Student, Pomona Coll. Chmn. bd. Scripps League Newspapers, 1931—; mem. St. Francis Yacht Club, Lyford Cay (Nassau, Bahamas), Boars Head Sports Club, Farmington Country Club, Everglades Club, Bath and Tennis Club, Colony Club, Mrs. Club. Home: Eagle Hill HCR 1 PO Box 38 Charlottesville VA 22901-0038 also: 947 N Ocean Blvd Palm Beach FL 33480-3325 Office: Dulles Corner Park 2411 Park S Ste 250 Herndon VA 22071

SCRIVEN, L. E(DWARD), chemical engineering educator, scientist; b. Battle Creek, Mich., Nov. 4, 1931; s. L. Edward and Esther Mabel (Davis) S.; m. Dorene Bates Hayes, June 19, 1952; children: Ellen Dorene, Teresa Ann, Mark Hayes. BS, U. Calif., Berkeley, 1952; MChemE, U. Del., 1954, PhD, 1956. Rsch. engr. Shell Devel. Co., Emeryville, Calif., 1956-59; asst. prof. chem. engring. and fluid mechanics U. Minn., Mpls., 1959-62, assoc. prof., 1962-66, prof., 1966-89, Regents' prof., 1989—, assoc. dept. head, 1975-78, program dir. Ctr. Interfacial Engring., 1988—; cons. in fields; advisor to Humboldt Found., Fed. Republic of Germany; vis. com. to chem. engring. MIT, sci. assoc. Jet Propulsion Lab., 1977, 79; tech. expert UN Indsl. Devel. Orgn., Vienna, Austria, 1979-88; exec. com. on chem. engring. frontiers NRC, 1984-87; mem. NRC Bd. on Chem. Sci. and Tech., 1987-92, chmn., 1992; mem. NRC Commn. on Phys. Scis., Math. and Applications, 1994—; sci. adv. com. Packard Found., 1988—. Editor: Phsiochemical Hydrodynamics (V.G. Levich), 1962; assoc. editor Jour. Fluid Mechanics, 1970-75; adv. editor Jour. Coll. Interfluid Sci., Physics of Fluids, Latin Am. Jour. Chem. Engring. and Applied Chemistry, Internat. Jour. Numerical Methods in Fluid Mechanics; contbr. numerous papers to profl. jours.; patentee in field. Recipient Chem. Engring. award Am. Soc. Engring. Edn., 1968, A.M. Rutherford award, 1979, Minn. Achievement award, 1989, Murphree award Am. Chem. Soc., 1990; Guggenheim fellow, 1969-70, Minn. Supercomputer Inst. fellow, 1984—; named Fairchild Disting. scholar Calif. Inst. Tech., 1989. Mem. NAE, Am. Inst. Chem. Engrs. (mem. nat. program. com. 1964-69, Colburn award 1960, Walker award 1977, Tallmadge award 1992), Am. Phys. Soc., Soc. Petroleum Engrs., Gordon Rsch. Confs., Chem. Soc. (Faraday div.), Soc. Indsl. and Applied Math., Soc. Rheology. Research in capillarity, fluid mechanics and coating processes, porous media, cold-stage electron microscopy, microstructured fluids and interfaces, origins of pattern and form, supercomputer-aided analysis. Office: Univ Minn 151 Amundson Hall 421 Washington Ave SE Minneapolis MN 55455-0373

SCRIVER, CHARLES ROBERT, medical scientist, human geneticist; b. Montreal, Que., Jan., Nov. 7, 1930; s. Walter deM. and Jessie (Boyd) S.; m. E.K. Peirce, Sept. 8, 1956; children: Dorothy, Peter, Julie, Paul. B.A. cum laude, McGill U., Montreal, 1951, M.D.C.M. cum laude, 1955; DSc (hon.), U. Man., 1992, U. Glasgow, 1993, U. Montreal, 1993. Intern Royal Victoria Hosp., Montreal, 1955-56; resident Royal Victoria and Montreal Children's hosps., 1956-57, Children's Med. Center, Boston, 1957-58; McLaughlin travelling fellow Univ. Coll., London, 1958-60; chief resident pediatrics Montreal Children's Hosp., 1960-61; asst. prof. pediatrics McGill U., 1961, prof. biology Faculty of Sci., prof. pediatrics Faculty of Medicine; Alva prof. human genetics, 1994—; mem. med. adv. bd. Howard Hughes Med. Inst., 1981-88; dir. Med. Rsch. Coun. Group in Genetics, 1972-94; assoc. dir. Can. Genetic Diseases Network, 1989—. Co-author: Amino Acid Metabolism and Its Disorders, 1973, Garrod's Inborn Factors in Disease, 1989; sr. editor Metabolic and Molecular Bases Inherited Disease, 1986—; contbr. more than 500 rsch. publs. in field. Decorated Order of Can.; recipient Wood Gold medal McGill U., 1955, Mead Johnson award for rsch. in pediatrics Am. Acad. Pediatrics, 1968, Gairdner Internat. award Gairdner Found., 1979, Ross award Can. Pediatric Soc., 1990; Royal Coll. lectr., 1992, Award of Excellence, Genetic Soc. Can., 1992—, Prix d'Excellence, Inst. Rsch. Clin. de Montreal, 1993; Markle scholar, 1962-67; Med. Rsch. Coun. assoc., 1968-95, Disting. Scientist, 1995—. Fellow AAAS, Royal Soc. Can. (McLaughlin medal 1981), Royal Soc. (London) (Can. Rutherford lectr. 1983); mem. Can. Soc. Clin. Investigation (pres. 1974-75, G. Malcolm Brown Meml. award 1979), Soc. Pediatric Rsch. (pres. 1975-76), Am. Soc. Human Genetics (dir. 1971-74, pres. 1986-87, William Allan award 1978), Am. Pediatric Soc. (pres. 1994-95), Am. Soc. Clin. Investigation, Assn. Am. Physicians, Brit. Pediatric Assn. (50th Anniversary lectr. 1978), Soc. Francaise de Pediat, Am. Acad. Pediatrics (awards). Office: McGill Univ-Montreal, Childrens Hosp Rsch Inst, 2300 Tupper St, Montreal, PQ Canada H3H 1P3

SCRIVER, ROBERT MACFIE, sculptor; b. Browning, Mont., Aug. 15, 1914; s. Thaddeus Emery and Ellison Scriver; m. Mary Helen Strachan, Nov. 27, 1966 (div. Nov. 1970); m. Lorraine, Aug. 15, 1972. Student, Dickinson State Tchr's Coll., N.D., 2 years; Bachelor's degree, Vandercook Sch. Music, Chgo., 1935, Master's degree, 1941; postgrad., Northwestern Univ., summer 1937, U. Wash., summer 1938; D.Arts hon., Carroll Coll. mem. C.M. Russell Adv. Bd., Great Falls, Mont., 1983—. Group of works includes No More Buffalo, 1983 (gold medals 1983), An Honest Try (gold medals), Bob Scriver Hall of Bronze Mus. Mont. Wildlife, 1989; author: No More Buffalo, 1983 (pub. awards 1983), An Honest Try (pub. awards), The Blackfeet, Artists of the Northern Plains, 1990 (pub. awards). Justice of the peace Glacer County, Mont.; city magistrate City of Browning. Served to sgt. USAAF, 1940. Recipient Gold and Silver medals Cowboy Artists Am., Phoenix, Gold and Silver medals Nat. Acad. Western Arts, Oklahoma City, Mont. State Gov.'s award, 1990; honoree Bob Scriver Day State Mont., Helena. Mem. Nat. Sculpture Soc., Nat. Acad. Western Art, Soc. Animal Artists, Browning C. of C. (pres.); mem. emeritus Cowboy Artists Am. Republican. Native American. Lodge: Masons. Office: Museum Mont Wildlife Junction Hwys 2 & 89 Browning MT 59417

SCRIVNER, THOMAS WILLIAM, lawyer; b. Madison, Wis., Sept. 10, 1948; s. William H. and Jane (Gehrz) S.; m. Meredith Burke, Aug. 16, 1980; children: Allison, David. AB, Duke U., 1970, MAT, 1972; JD, U. Wis., 1977. Assoc. Michael, Best & Friedrich, Milw., 1978-85, ptnr., 1985—. Mem. ABA, Wis. Bar Assn., Milw. Bar Assn. (labor sect.), Corp. Practice Inst. (pres. 1989-92). Episcopalian. Home: 4626 N Cramer St Milwaukee WI 53211-1203 Office: Michael Best & Friedrich 100 E Wisconsin Ave Milwaukee WI 53202-4108

SCROGGINS, RICHARD MUIR, real estate executive; b. Detroit, Dec. 11, 1932; s. Olin and Florence Marie (Muir) S.; m. Jeanne Addison Joslyn, June 30, 1956; children: Laura Scroggins Wolf, Lisa, Sarah. BBA, U. Mich., 1955. Salesman , real estate rep. Shell Oil Co., Lansing, Mich., 1958-62; real estate negotiator Burroughs Corp., Detroit, 1962-64; supr. dealership facilities Ford Motor Co., Dearborn, Mich., 1964-68; mgr. dealership facilities and real estate Ford of Europe, London, 1969-74; dir. property mgmt. Ford Motor Land Devel. Corp., Dearborn 1974-75; v.p. real estate Am. Express Co., N.Y.C., 1975-89, sr. v.p. real estate and gen. services and environ. protection officer, 1989—. Chmn. Myasthenia Gravis Found., N.Y.C., 1987—; pres. Rockview Dr. Assn., Greenwich, Conn., 1987—; chmn. Heritage Trail of Lower Manhattan, 1989—; bd.dirs. Downtown-Lower Manhattan Assn., 1990—. 1st lt. USMC, 1955-58. Mem. Nat. Assn. Corp. Real Estate Execs. (Master of Corp. Real Estate award 1982, dir.), Urban Land Inst. Republican. Avocations: sailing, art, antiques, music. Home: 15 Rockview Dr Greenwich CT 06830-4612 Office: Am Express Co Am Express Tower World Fin Ctr New York NY 10285

SCRUGGS, CHARLES G., editor; b. McGregor, Tex., Nov. 4, 1923; s. John Fleming and Adeline (Hering) S.; m. Miriam June Wigley, July 5, 1947; children—John Mark, Miriam Jan. B.S., Tex. A&M U., 1947. Assoc. editor Progressive Farmer, Dallas, 1947-61, editor, 1962—, v.p., 1964—, exec. editor, 1972, editorial dir. 1973—, editor-in-chief, 1982-87; editorial chmn. So. Progress Pubs., 1987-89; pres. Torado Land and Cattle Co., pres. Tex. Comml. Agr. Council 1953-54; chmn. bd. Sunlean Foods, Inc., 1989—. Author: The Peaceful Atom and the Deadly Fly, 1975, American Agricultural Capitalism. Founding gen. chmn. Chancellors' Century Coun., Tex. A&M U. System, 1987-90; Mem. Gov.'s Com. for Agr., 1950, Tex. Animal Health Council, 1955-61; chmn. So. Brucellosis Com., 1956; pres. Tex. Rural Safety Com., 1957-59; chmn. Nat. Brucellosis Com., 1958-59, 71-72; del. World Food Congress, 1963; pub. mem. U.S. del. 17th Biennial Conf. Natural Fibers, Tex. Legislature, 1971; mem. coordinating bd. Tex. Coll. and Univ. System, 1965-69; bd. regents Tex. Tech U., 1971-78; founding pres. S.W. Animal Health Research Found. 1961-63, trustee, 1961—. Served to lt. col. U.S. Army; Res., ret. Recipient Christian Svc. Mass Media award, 1955, Abilene Christian U., Southwestern Cattle Raisers award, 1962, Am. Seed Trade Assn. award, 1963, award of honor Am. Agrl. Editors Assn., 1964, Reuben Brigham award Am. Assn. Agrl. Coll. Editors, 1965, Disting. Svc. award Tex. Farm Bur., 1966, Journalistic Achievement award Nat. Plant Food Assn., 1967, Nat. award for agrl. excellence Nat. Agri-Mktg. Assn., 1983, Agrl. Vision award Nat. Forum for Agr., 1994; named Disting. Alumnus Tex. A&M U., 1982. Mem. Am. Agrl. Editors Assn. (pres. 1963), Am. Soc. Mag. Editors, Tex. Assn. Future Farmers Am. (pres. 1940-41), Dallas Agrl. Club (pres. 1951), Nat. Livestock Confedn. Mexico (hon.), The Austin Club, Headliners Club, Alpha Zeta, Sigma Delta Chi.

SCRUGGS, EARL EUGENE, entertainer; b. Cleveland County, N.C., Jan. 6, 1924; s. George Elam and Georgia Lula (Ruppe) S.; m. Anne Louise Certain, Apr. 18, 1948; children: Gary Eugene, Randy Lynn, Steven Earl. HHD in Folk Music (hon.), Gardner-Webb Coll., 1986. Banjo player, 1945—; formed Earl Scruggs Revue, 1969—; major performances include Carnegie Hall, N.Y.C., Wembley Festival, London, Washington Moratorium for Peace, 1969, also rock festivals, coll. concerts; TV appearances include NET-TV Spl. Earl Scruggs: His Family and Friends, 1971, Midnight Spl., NBC-Harper Valley U.S.A. Spl., NBC Country Music Awards Show, Phil Donahue Show, Mike Douglas Show, Austin City Limits, 1977, The Grand Ole Opry's 60th Anniversary Show, 1985, The Nashville Network spl. The American Music Shop, 1990, The Grand Ole Opry's 65th Anniversary Show, 1991, Country Music Assn. Awards Show, 1991, Country Music Assn. Hall of Fame 25th Anniversary TV show, 1992, The Legend of The Beverly Hillbillies, CBS-TV, 1993, Folk Sound USA-Revlon Revue, The Tonight Show, Les Crane Show, Mac Davis Special, The Johnny Cash Show, The Hootenanny Show, Frank McGee's Here and Now, Ernie Ford Show, Jimmy Dean Show, The Anatomy of Pop, Kraft's American Profile, The Roots of Country, CBS-TV, 1994, Red Hot and Country, TNN-TV, 1995, A Night at the Ryman, TNN-TV, 1995; rec. artist: Columbia Records, 1950—; albums include: Nashvilles Rock, Dueling Banjos, Kansas State, I Saw the Light, Earl Scruggs Revue, Rockin' Cross the Country, Family Portrait, Top of the World, Anniversary Special Vol. I and Vol. II, Live! At Austin City Limits, Earl Scruggs: His Family and Friends Soundtrack, Today and Forever, Bold and New, American-Made, World-Played, others; recorded theme song for TV series The Beverly Hillbillies, 1962, also made guest appearances; composer (with others) movie score Where The Lilies Bloom, 1973, also Earl Scruggs Revue rec. music soundtrack for movie; composer instrumental Foggy Mountain Breakdown (used in movie Bonnie and Clyde), Grammy award 1968, Broadcast Music, Inc. award 1969); star: (movie) Banjo Man, 1975; guest appearance (TV movie) Return of the Beverly Hillbillies, 1981; author: (book) Earl Scruggs and the 5-String Banjo, 1968. Apptd. hon. mem. Lt. Gov.'s Staff, State of Tenn., 1987. Named Artist of Yr. Hi-Fi Inst., 1975, Best Country and Bluegrass Banjoist, Frets mag., 1980; recipient

Country Music award best instrumental group Billboard Mag., 1975, Cert. of Merit Internat. Bluegrass Music Assn., 1988, Order of the Long Leaf Pine award Gov. State of N.C., 1988, cert. appreciation Tenn. Gov. Ned McWherter, 1990, Spl. Citation of achievement recognition of nat. popularity over 1 million broadcasts of Foggy Mountain Breakdown, Broadcast Music, Inc., 1993, others; inducted into Gibson Hall of Fame, 1981, Country Music Assn. Hall of Fame, 1985, Internat. Bluegrass Music Assn. Hall of Honor, 1991; Nat. Heritage fellow NEA, 1989; Nat. Medal of Arts presented by Pres. George Bush at White House, 1992. Developer Scruggs style of banjo playing; inventor Scruggs Tuning Pegs.

SCRUGGS, JACK GILBERT, retired chemical executive; b. Cullman County, Ala., Sept. 9, 1930; s. Carlton Vann and Grace Blanche (Thoroman) S.; m. Anna Faye Thomas, Aug. 21, 1954; children: Pamela Ann, Linda Dianne. BS in Pharmacy, U. Mich., 1952, MS in Pharm. Chem., 1953, PhD in Organic Chem., 1956. Research and devel. mgr. Monsanto Fibers Div., Durham, N.C., 1956-66; tech. v.p. Phillips Fibers Corp., 1966-94. Patentee in polymers and fibers. Pres. Jr. Achievement, Greenville, 1985-86; active Boy Scouts Am.; coach, umpire Little League Baseball, Cary, N.C., 1963-65. Mem. Am. Chem. Soc., Phi Beta Kappa, Sigma Xi, Phi Eta Sigma, Rho Chi, Phi Lambda Upsilon. Republican. Mem. Ch. of Christ. Avocations: golf, racquetball, softball. Home: 614 Devenger Rd Greer SC 29650

SCRUGGS, JOHN DUDLEY, landscape architect; b. Flemingsburg, Ky., May 3, 1911. B.A., Berea Coll., 1933; M.L.A., Harvard, 1938. Co-founder, v.p. Scruggs and Hammond, Inc. (Landscape Architects and Planning Cons.), Lexington, Columbus, Ohio and Peoria, Ill., 1946—; vis. critic U. Ky., Harvard; bd. dirs. Hubbard Ednl. Trust. Served with AUS, 1942-46. Fellow Am. Soc. Landscape Architects (chmn. com. on publ rels 1953-63, com. on biographies of fellows 1976—, coun. of fellows 1983); mem. AIA, Lafayette Club, Harvard Club, Lexington Sports Club, Idle Hour Country Club. Home: 1029 Creekside Ln Ash Grove Pike Nicholasville KY 40356 Office: Scruggs & Hammond Inc 239 N Broadway St Lexington KY 40507-1009

SCUDDER, DAVID BENJAMIN, economist, foundation administrator; b. Evanston, Ill., July 30, 1923; s. Guy and Ruth Marilla (Benjamin) S.; m. Marjorie Adell Buckland, Dec. 27, 1946; children: David Foster, Rexford Guy. BS, Bowling Green State U., 1948; AM, U. Chgo., 1950, postgrad., 1950-51. Economist CIA, Washington, 1951-81, econ. cons., 1981-84; editor, co-pub. World Amateur Dancer, McLean, Va., 1982-84; treas. The Scudder Assn., Inc., Arlington, Va., 1990-92, Boise, Idaho, 1992—. Editor quarterly newsletter The Scudder Assn. Inc, 1989—; contbr. articles and reports to jours. Active Springfield Civic Assn., Fairfax County, Va., 1956-61. With USAF, 1943-45, ETO. Avocations: tennis, ballroom dancing, golf, amateur theater. Home: 1031 Strawberry Ln Boise ID 83712

SCUDDER, EDWARD WALLACE, JR., newspaper and broadcasting executive; b. Newark, Dec. 8, 1911; s. Edward Wallace and Katherine (Hollifield) Scudder; m. Louise Bagby Fry, Jan. 19, 1945; children: Katherine Allison Tiballi, Mary Gale Doe, Edward, Robert. AB, Princeton, 1935. Treas. Newark Evening News, 1950-70; pres. Evening News Pub. Co., 1955-72, Newark Broadcasting, operating Sta. WVNJ, Newark, to 1978; chmn. of bd. Orange Mountain Comm., West Orange, N.J., 1971—. Trustee Paper Mill Playhouse, Millburn, N.J., Newark Mus.; treas. Lake Placid (N.Y.) Edn. Found. Lt. (j.g.) to lt. comdr. USNR Air Force, 1942-46. Mem. Rumson Country Club, Short Hills Club, Gulfstream Golf Club, Gulfstream Bath and Tennis Club, Delray Beach Yacht Club. Home: 1171 N Ocean Blvd Delray Beach FL 33483-7273 Office: PO Box 79 Summit NJ 07902

SCUDDER, RICHARD B., newspaper executive; b. Newark, May 13, 1913; s. Edward W. and Katherine (Hollifield) S.; m. Elizabeth A. Shibley, June 24, 944; children: Elizabeth H. (Mrs. Philip Difani), Charles A., Carolyn (Mrs. Peter M. Miller), Jean (Mrs. Joseph Fulmer). AB, Princeton U., 1935; LHD (hon.), Mon Coll. Reporter Newark News, 1935-37, v.p. 1941-51, pub., 1951-72; reporter Boston Herald, 1937-38; chmn. MediaNews Group, Gloucester County Times, Inc., Garden State Newspapers, Inc., Garden State Paper Co., Denver Newspapers, Inc. Trustee Riverview Hosp., N.J. Conservation Found., Monmouth County Conservation Found.; former trustee Rutgers U.; adv. com. Princeton (N.J.) Environ. Inst. Served from pvt. to maj. AUS, 1941-45. Decorated Bronze Star; recipient TAPPI award, 1971; Nat. Recycling award Nat. Assn. Secondary Materials Industries, 1972; Nat. Resource Recovery Man of Year award, 1978; Papermaker of Year award Paper Trade Jour., 1978. Mem. N.J. Audobon Soc. Clubs: Rumson Country, Seabright Beach, Seabright Lawn Tennis, Mill Reef, Adirondack League. Office: Garden State Paper Company 988 Broad St Passaic NJ 07055

SCUDDER, THAYER, anthropologist, educator; b. New Haven, Aug. 4, 1930; s. Townsend III and Virginia (Boody) S.; m. Mary Eliza Drinker, Aug. 26, 1950; children: Mary Eliza, Alice Thayer. Grad., Phillips Exeter Acad., 1948; A.B., Harvard U., 1952, Ph.D., 1960; postgrad., Yale U., 1953-54, London Sch. Econs., 1960-61. Research officer Rhodes-Livingstone Inst., No. Rhodesia, 1956-57; sr. research officer Rhodes-Livingstone Inst., 1962-63; asst. prof. Am. U., Cairo, 1961-62; research fellow Center Middle East Studies, Harvard U., 1963-64; asst. prof. Calif. Inst. Tech., Pasadena, 1964-66; assoc. prof. Calif. Inst. Tech., 1966-69, prof. anthropology, 1969—; dir. Inst. for Devel. Anthropology, Binghamton, N.Y., 1976—; cons. UN Devel. Program, FAO, IBRD, WHO, Ford Found., Navajo Tribal Coun., AID, World Conservation Union, Lesotho Highlands Devel. Authority, South China Electric Power Joint Venture Corp. Author: The Ecology of the Gwembe Tonga, 1962; co-author: Long-Term Field Research in Social Anthropology, 1979, Secondary Education and the Formation of an Elite: The Ompact of Education on Gwembe District, Zambia, 1980, No Place to Go: The Impacts of Forced Relocation on Navajos, 1982, For Prayer and Profit: The Ritual, Economic and Social Importance of Beer in Gwembe District, Zambia, 1950-1982, 1988, The IUCN Review of the So. Okavango Integrated Water Development Porejct, 1993. John Simon Guggenheim Meml. fellow, 1975. Mem. Am. Anthrop. Assn. (1st recipient Solon T. Kimball award for pub. and applied anthropology 1984, Edward J. Lehman award 1991), Soc. Applied Anthropology, Am. Alpine Club. Office: Calif Inst Tech # 228-77 Pasadena CA 91125

SCUDERI, LOUIS ANTHONY, climatology educator; b. Bklyn., Sept. 13, 1954; s. Louis Samuel Scuderi and Edith Grace Ambrosio; m. Joan E. Drake, Aug. 4, 1979; children: Louis, Benjamin. BA in Geography and Econs., UCLA, 1976, MA in Geography, 1978, PhD in Geography, 1984. Rsch. scientist Calif. Rsch. & Tech., Northridge, 1984-85; rsch. geographer, database mgr. Earth Techs. Corp., Long Beach, Calif., 1985; rsch. scientist Itujhes Aircraft Co., Long Beach, 1985-88; rsch. assoc. Isotope Lab. UCLA, 1986-88; asst. prof. Boston U., 1988—. Contbr. articles to Nature, Quaternavy Rsch., Science, Arctic and Alpine Rsch. Mem. Internat. Soc. for Optical Engring., Assn. of Am. Geographers, Nat. Geographic Soc., Sigma Xi. Achievements include research in solar-climate relationships, effects of volcanic eruptions on climate; creation of three-dimensional computer database for flight simulation and real time infrared simulation. Office: Boston U Dept Geography 675 Commonwealth Ave Boston MA 02215

SCULFORT, MAURICE CHARLES, advertising agency executive; b. N.Y.C., Oct. 26, 1925; s. Edward and Marcelle (Bonnier) S.; children—Raymond J., Jack T. Student, N.Y. U., 1946-50. Sales Sears Roebuck & Co., 1944; abt. Donahue & Coe, 1947; with Compton Advt., Inc., N.Y.C., 1947-85; v.p. Compton Advt., Inc., 1959-69, sr. v.p., 1969-85. Contbr. articles to profl. publs. Active Boy Scouts Am., YMCA. Served with USNR, 1943-46, PTO; Served with USNR, ETO; Served with USNR, MTO. Republican. Home: 4476 NE Ocean Blvd 104C Jensen Beach FL 34957

SCULLEN, THOMAS G., superintendent. Supt. Indian Prairie Community Unit Sch. Dist. 204, Naperville, Ill. Recipient State Finalist for Nat. Supt. of Yr. award, 1993. Office: Indian Prairie CUSD204 PO Box 3990 Naperville IL 60567-3990

SCULLEY, DAVID W., food company executive; b. N.Y.C., July 17, 1946; s. John and Margaret Blackburn (Smith) S.; m. Paula Cook; chil-

dren—Heather Kahrl, David. B.A. in Econs. cum laude, Harvard U., 1968. Group product mgr. Lever Bros. Co., N.Y.C., 1971-73; gen. mgr. mktg. H.J. Heinz-U.K., Middlesex, Eng., 1982-85; pres., chief exec. officer Heinz U.S.A., Pitts., 1985-89, sr. v.p., 1989—, also bd. dirs. Trustee Sewickley Valley Hosp., Pa., 1981; trustee and vice chmn. Allegheny Gen. Hosp., Pitts., 1986—; chmn. D.T. Watson Home Charity Golf Tournament, Sewickley, 1986, Young Pres.'s Orgn. Organization. Clubs: Allegheny Country (Sewickley); Duquesne (Pitts.); Laurel Valley Golf (Ligonier, Pa.). Avocations: golf; tennis; jogging; gardening. Office: H J Heinz Co PO Box 57 600 Grant St Pittsburgh PA 15219-2857

SCULLEY, JOHN, computer company executive; b. N.Y.C., Apr. 6, 1939; s. John and Margaret Blackburn (Smith) S.; m. Carol Lee Adams, Mar. 7, 1978; children: Margaret Ann, John Blackburn, Laura Lee. Student, R.I. Sch. Design, 1960; BArch, Brown U., 1961; MBA, U. Pa., 1963. Asst. account exec. Marschalk Co., N.Y.C., 1963-64, account exec., 1964-65, account supr., 1965-67; dir. mktg. Pepsi-Cola Co., Purchase, N.Y., 1967-69, v.p. mktg., 1970-71, sr. v.p. mktg., 1971-74, pres., chief exec. officer, 1977-83; pres. PepsiCo Foods, Purchase, 1974-77; pres., chief exec. officer Apple Computer Inc., Cupertino, Calif., 1983-1993, past chmn., tech. officer; chmn., CEO Spectrum Cellular Corp. divsn. Spectrum Info. Techs., Dallas; bd. dirs. Comsat Corp. Chmn. Wharton Grad. Exec. Bd., 1980; mem. art adv. com. Brown U., 1980; bd. dirs. Keep Am. Beautiful.; mem. bd. overseers Wharton Sch., U. Pa. Mem. U.S.C. of C. Clubs: Indian Harbor, N.Y. Athletic; Coral Beach (Bermuda); Wharton Bus. Sch. of N.Y. (bd. dirs.); Camden (Maine) Yacht. Office: Spectrum Cellular Corp 2611 Cedar Springs Rd Dallas TX 75701*

SCULLIN, FREDERICK JAMES, JR., federal judge; b. Syracuse, N.Y., Nov. 5, 1939; s. Frederick James and Cleora M. (Fellows) S.; m. Veronica Terek Sauro, Aug. 31, 1984; children: Mary Margaret, Kathleen Susan, Kellie Anne, Rebecca Rose; 1 stepchild, Angel Jenette Sauro. B.S. in Econs., Niagara U., 1961; LL.B., Syracuse U., 1964. Bar: N.Y. 1964, Fla. 1976, U.S. Dist. Ct. (no. dist.) N.Y. 1967, U.S. Supreme Ct. 1971. Assoc. Germain & Germain, Syracuse, 1967-68; asst. dist. atty. Onondaga County, Syracuse, 1968-71; asst. atty. gen. N.Y. State Organized Crime Task Force, 1971-78; dir. regional office N.Y. State Organized Crime Task Force, Albany, 1974-78; chief prosecutor, dir. Gov.'s Council on Organized Crime State of Fla., Tallahassee, 1978—; sole practice Syracuse, 1979-82, U.S. atty. for No. Dist. N.Y., 1982-92; judge U.S. Dist. Ct. (no. dist.) N.Y., 1992—. With U.S. Army, 1964-67, Vietnam; col. USAR. Decorated Air medal, Bronze Star; Cross of Gallantry (Vietnam). Mem. Am. Judicature Soc., ABA, N.Y. State Bar Assn., Fla. Bar Assn., Fed. Bar Assn., Fed. Bar Coun. Office: US Dist Ct US Courthouse 100 S Clinton St Syracuse NY 13261-7255

SCULLION, ANNETTE MURPHY, lawyer, educator; b. Chgo., Apr. 6, 1926; d. Edmund Patrick and Anna (Nugent) Murphy; 1 son, Kevin. B.Ed., Chgo. Tchrs. Coll., 1960; J.D., DePaul U., 1964, M.Ed., 1966; M.Ed., Loyola U., Chgo., 1970; Ed.D., No. Ill. U., 1984. Bar: Ill. 1964, U.S. Dist. Ct. (no. dist.) Ill. 1965, U.S. Ct. Appeals (D.C. cir.) 1978. Lectr. Chgo. Community Coll., 1964-68; pvt. practice law, Chgo., 1964—; asst. prof. bus. edn. Chgo. State U., 1966-69, assoc. prof., 1970-73, prof., 1974—. Club founder, adviser Bus. Edn. Students Assn., Chgo. State U., 1976—; sch. law workshop coordinator Ill. Div. Vocat. and Tech. Edn., 1981. Mem. Nat. Bus. Edn. Assn., Women's Bar Assn. Ill., ABA, Am. Tchr. Edn., Beta Gamma Sigma Home: 386 Muskegon Ave Calumet City IL 60409-2347 Office: Chgo State U 95 And King Dr # 203 Chicago IL 60601

SCULLION, TSUGIKO YAMAGAMI, non-profit organization executive; b. China, June 30, 1946; d. Hajime and Akemi (Murazumi) Yamagami; m. William James Scullion, Nov. 26, 1971; 1 child, James. BA, Baldwin-Wallace Coll., 1970; MA, Sch. Internat. Tng., 1971. Area cons. Conn. AFS Internat./Intercultural Programs, N.Y.C., 1972-73, regional mgr. for Asia and Pacific, 1973-78, dir. internat. ops., 1978-81, v.p. Europe, Africa, Middle East, 1981-83, v.p. program svcs., 1083-85, exec. v.p., 1985-87; exec. v.p. U.S. Com. UNICEF, N.Y.C., 1988—. Bd. dirs. Oberlin Shansi Meml. Assn. Avocations: golf, classical music, ballet. Home: 7 Chasmar Rd Old Greenwich CT 06870

SCULLY, JOHN CARROLL, life insurance marketing research company executive; b. Springfield, Mass., Mar. 16, 1932; s. James and Frances (Carroll) S.; m. Barbara A. Fougere, Sept. 7, 1953; children: Kathleen, Margaret, John, James, Patricia, Mary Ellen, Susan. B.A., Holy Cross Coll., 1953; C.L.U., Boston U., 1963; postgrad., Dartmouth Inst., 1977. With John Hancock Mut. Life Ins. Co., 1953-92; gen. agent John Hancock Mut. Life Ins. Co., Indpls., 1966-75; sr. v.p. agency dept. John Hancock Mut. Life Ins. Co., Boston, 1975-80; pres. retail sector John Hancock Mut. Life Ins. Co., 1980-92; pres., chief. exec. officer Life. Ins. Mktg. Rsch. Assoc., Windsor, Conn., 1992—. Bd. dirs. Greater Boston YMCA, 1975-91; chmn. Mass. campaign Holocaust Meml. Mus., 1985—; div. chmn. United Way, 1985—; bd. dirs. Cath. Charities, 1986—; trustee Springfield Coll., 1986, Suffolk U., 1986. With U.S. Army, 1954-56. Mem. Am. Coll. Life Underwriters, Nat. Assn. Life Underwriters (v.p. Ind. 1973-75), Life Ins. Mktg. and Rsch. Assn. (past chmn.), Gen. Agts. and Mgrs. Assn. (past pres. Indpls. Nat. Mgmt. award 1973-75), Life Underwriter Tng. Coun. (past chmn.), Greater Boston C. of C. (bd. dirs. 1985—), Wellesley Club, Executives Club (past pres.), Algonquin Club (bd. dirs.), Framingham Country Club, Hartford Club, KC. Roman Catholic. Home: 2 Shibah Way Bloomfield CT 06002 Office: Limra Internat PO Box 208 Hartford CT 06141

SCULLY, JOHN THOMAS, obstetrician, gynecologist, educator; b. N.Y.C., Mar. 11, 1931; s. John Thomas and Mildred Frances (Dunstrop) S.; children: John, Helen Mary, Thomas, Nora, James, Sara, Megan, Devin. B.S., Georgetown U., 1952; M.D., U. Mex., 1959. Diplomate Am. Bd. Ob-Gyn. Intern, Nassau Hosp., 1959-60, resident, 1960-63; practice medicine specializing in ob-gyn, 1963—; sr. attending dept. ob-gyn St. Peter's Med. Center, Robert Wood Johnson U. Hosp.; clin. prof. ob-gyn Rutgers U. Med. Sch., 1971—. Fellow ACS, Am. Coll. Ob-Gyn; mem. N.J. Med. Soc., Middlesex County Med. Soc., N.J. Ob-Gyn Soc., N.J. Right to Life (charter). Republican. Roman Catholic. Office: 23 Duke St New Brunswick NJ 08901-1738

SCULLY, JOSEPH C., bank executive; b. 1940. Grad., Loyola U., Chgo., 1962, MBA, 1972. With Dept. Urban Renewal City of Chgo., 1962-63; with St. Paul Bancorp., Inc., Chgo., 1963-80, pres., 1980—, now chmn. bd., CEO. Office: St Paul Bancorp Inc 6700 W North Ave Chicago IL 60635-3937

SCULLY, MARLAN ORVIL, physics educator; b. Casper, Wyo., Aug. 3, 1939; s. Orvil O. and Thelma G. (Thoms) S.; m. Judith Bailey, Aug. 16, 1958; children: James, Robert, Steven. AS, Casper Coll., 1959; BS, U. Wyo., 1961; MS, Yale U., 1963, PhD, 1966. Instr. Yale U., New Haven, 1967-69; asst. prof. MIT, Cambridge, 1969-71, assoc. prof., 1971-72; prof. U. Ariz., Tucson, 1972-80; disting. prof. U. N.Mex., Albuquerque, 1980—; dir., co-founder Radtech, 1984; mem. Joint counm. on Quantum Electronics, Internat. Comm. on Optics; mem. program com. VIIth and VIIIth Internat. Conf. on Quantum Electronics (co-chmn. program com.); panel mem. Internat. Conf. on Hot Electrons in Semiconductors, North Tex. State U.; codir. VIIth Course of NATO Internat. Sch. Quantum Electronics; mem. program com. for OSA sponsored topical meeting on Picosecons Phenomena, Hilton Head, S.C., 1978; invited lectr. U.S.-Japan Coop. Seminar on Laser Spectroscopy, Hakone, Japan, 1977 ; mem. NRC panel on electron, atomic and molecular physics; advisor to ARO Nat. Acad. Panel, Los Alamos Physics Div. Author: (with others) Laser Physics, 1974; contbr. articles to profl. jours. Recipient Elliott Cresson medal The Franklin Inst., 1990; John S. Guggenheim fellow, 1970, Alfred P. Sloan fellow, 1972. Fellow AAAS, Optical Soc. Am. (dir. at large 1978-80, publs. com. 1972, Ives medal com. 1976, chmn. Wood prize com. 1978, Adolph E. Lomb medal 1970; mem. Max Planck Soc. Avocations: cattle ranching, inventing. Home: Scully Farm Estancia NM 87016 Office: Univ N Mex Dept Of Physics Albuquerque NM 87131

SCULLY, SEAN PAUL, artist; b. Dublin, Ireland, June 30, 1945; s. John Anthony and Holly Scully; m. Catherine Lee. Ed., Croydon Coll. Art. With fine art dept. Newcastle (Eng.) U., 1967-71; lectr. Harvard U., Cam-

bridge, Mass., 1972-73, Chelsea Sch. Art, Goldsmiths Sch. Art, London, 1973-75, Princeton (N.J. U., 1978-83; lectr. in painting Parsons Sch. Design, N.Y.C., 1983—. One-man exhbns. in London, L.A., N.Y.C., Berlin, Washington, from 1973; exhbns. at Carnegie Inst., Pitts., Boston Mus. Fine Arts, Chgo. Art Inst., 1987, Univ. Art Mus., Berkeley, Calif., 1987, Whitechapel Art Gallery, London, 1989; works in pub. collections in Eng., U.S.A., Australia, Fed. Republic Germany, Ireland. Recipient Stuyvesant Found. prize, 1970, 72, John Moore Liverpool Exhbn. 8 prize, 1974 and Exhbn. 9 prize; Guggenheim fellow, 1983. Office: Diane Villani Editions 271 Mulberry St New York NY 10012 also: care Mayor Rowan Gallery, 31A Bruton Pl, London W1X 7AB, England

SCULLY, STEPHEN J., plastic surgeon; b. Lawrence, Mass., Jan. 29, 1937; s. Joseph A. and Frances M. (Hart) S.; m. Diane Loretta Lizotte, Apr. 22, 1967; children: Stephen, Christopher, Caroline, Jacqueline. AB summa cum laude, Merrimack Coll., 1958; MD cum laude, Georgetown U., 1962. Surg. resident Tufts New Eng. Med. Ctr., Boston, 1962-67; plastic surg. resident NYU, N.Y.C., 1969-72. Trustee Holy Family Hosp., Methuen, Mass., 1993, Merrimack Coll., North Andover, Mass., 1993. Lt. comdr. USNR, 1967-69. Mem. Am. Soc. Plastic Reconstructive Surgeons, Am. Soc. Aesthetic Plastic Surgery. Roman Catholic. Avocations: photography, skiing. Office: Plastic Cosmetic Reconstr Surgery Inc 451 Andover St North Andover MA 01845

SCULLY, TIMOTHY RICHARD, priest, academic administrator; b. Evanston, Ill., Jan. 18, 1954; s. Thomas Francis and Elizabeth Ann (Joyce) S. BA in Econ., U. Notre Dame, 1976, MDiv in Theology, 1979; MA in Polit. Sci., U. Calif., Berkeley, 1985, PhD in Polit. Sci., 1989. Ordained priest Roman Cath. Ch., 1981. Treas. Holy Cross Fathers, Santiago, Chile, 1980-83; asst. rector St. George's Coll., Santiago, 1980-83; asst. pastor Christ Our Redeemor Parish, Santiago, 1980-83; asst. prof. dept. govt. U. Notre Dame, 1989, v.p., assoc. provost, 1994—; sr. fellow Kellogg Inst. for Internat. Studies, Notre Dame, 1989—. Author: Rethinking the Center, 1991; co-author: Building Democratic Institutions, 1992. Recipient award Social Sci. Rsch. Coun., N.Y., 1989; Fulbright fellow Dept. Edn., 1988; FMRD Found. grantee, 1990. Mem. Phi Beta Kappa. Office: Kellogg Institute Notre Dame IN 46556

SCULLY, VINCENT, art historian, retired educator, writer. Prof. dept. art history Yale U., New Haven, Conn., 1961-91, prof. emeritus, 1991—. Author: Frank Lloyd Wright, 1960, Modern Architecture: The Architecture of Democracy, 1961, Louis I Kahn, 1962, The Architectural Heritage of Newport, Rhode Island, 1640-1915, 1967, American Architecture and Urbanism, 1969, Pueblo Architecture of the Southwest, 1971, The Shingle Style Today: Or the Historian's Revenge, 1974, Pueblo: Mountain, Village, Dance, 1975, The Earth, the Temple, and the Gods: Greek Sacred Architecture, 1979, Robert Stern, 1981, Studies and Executed Buildings by Frank Lloyd Wright, 1986, The Villas of Palladio, 1986, New World Visions of Household Gods and Sacred Places: American Art and the Metropolitan Museum, 1650-1914, 1988, The Architecture of the American Summer: The Flowering of the Shingle Style, 1989, The Architecture of Robert Venturi, 1989, The Great Dinosaur Mural at Yale: The Age of Reptiles, 1990, Architecture: The Natural and the Man-Made, 1991, French Royal Gardens: The Design of Andre Le Notre, 1992. Office: Yale Univ Dept Art History PO Box 2009 New Haven CT 06520

SCULLY, VINCENT EDWARD, sports broadcaster; b. Bronx, N.Y., Nov. 29, 1927; s. Vincent Aloysius and Bridget (Freehill) S.; m. Sandra Hunt, Nov. 11, 1973; children: Michael, Kevin, Todd, Erin, Kelly, Catherine Anne. B.A., Fordham U., 1949. Sports announcer Bklyn. Dodgers Profl. Baseball Team, 1950-57, L.A. Dodgers Profl. Baseball Team, 1957—, CBS-TV, 1975-82, NBC-TV, 1982-89. Served with USNR, 1944-45. Recipient TV award Look mag., 1959; named Sportscaster of Year in Calif., 1959, 60, 63, 69, 71, 73-75; Nat. Sportscaster of Year, 1966, 78, 82; named to Fordham U. Hall of Fame, 1976. Mem. AFTRA, Screen Actors Guild, Catholic Actors, TV Acad. Arts and Scis. Roman Catholic. Clubs: Lambs (N.Y.C.); Bel Air Country, Beach. Office: LA Dodgers 1000 Elysian Park Ave Los Angeles CA 90012*

SCURLOCK, ARCH CHILTON, chemical engineer; b. Beaumont, Tex., Jan. 29, 1920; s. Marvin and Mary (Chilton) S.; m. Maurine Spurbeck, Nov. 27, 1945 (div.); children: Arch, Susan, Marvin Curtis; m. Nancy Morrison Yonick, Nov. 16, 1962; children: Mary, Nancy, Margaret Ann. B.S. in Chem. Engring. U. Tex., 1941, A.B. in Physics, 1941; M.S., Mass. Inst. Tech., 1943, Sc.D., 1948; spl. course meteorology, U. Chgo., 1944. Research asso. chem. engring. dept. Mass. Inst. Tech., 1946-48; asst. dir. chemistry Engring. Research Assocs., 1948-49; pres. Atlantic Research Corp., Alexandria, Va., 1949-62; chmn. bd. Atlantic Research Corp., 1962-65; pres., dir. Research Industries Inc., Alexandria, 1968—; chmn. TransTechnology Corp., 1969-92, Halifax Corp. Served to lt. (s.g.) USNR, 1943-46. Mem. AAAS, AIAA, Am. Inst. Chem. Engrs., Am. Chem. Soc., Am. Phys. Soc., Am. Meteorol. Soc., Am. Def. Preparedness Assn., Combustion Inst., Univ. Club (Washington), Belle Haven (Va.) Country Club, Army Navy Country Club (Va.), Mid-Ocean Club (Tuckers Town, Bermuda), Phi Beta Kappa, Sigma Xi, Tau Beta Pi. Home: 1753 Army Navy Dr Arlington VA 22202-1633 Office: 123 N Pitt St Alexandria VA 22314-3133

SCURRY, RICHARDSON GANO, JR., real estate company financial executive; b. Dallas, June 7, 1938; s. Richardson Gano and Josephine (DuVall) S.; m. Pamela Ruth Edith McGinley, Oct. 11, 1975; children: Richardson, Kristina. BA, U. Tex., 1961; MBA, Stanford U., 1963. Mktg. rep. DP div. IBM, Dallas, 1963-68; mgr. fin. planning, DP group IBM, Harrison, N.Y., 1968-72; exec. asst., group exec. IBM, Armonk, N.Y., 1973; mgr. fin. planning office products div. IBM, Franklin Lakes, N.Y., 1974; mgr. fin. analysis, antitrust litigation IBM, N.Y.C., 1975; controller system communication div. IBM, White Plains, 1976-80; dir. plans, controls internal info. systems & communications IBM Corp., Purchase, N.Y., 1981-84; sr. v.p. fin. Chem. Bank, N.Y.C., 1985-89; pres., chief exec. officer Pearce, Mayer & Greer Realty Corp., N.Y.C., 1989—; v.p. fin., ptnr. Wicker Garden's Children, 1984—; bd. dirs. Info. Mart, Dallas, Firecom, Woodside, N.Y.; treas. bd. dirs. 1158 Fifth Ave. Corp., N.Y.C., 1985-90; mem. real estate coms. Lincoln Ctr., N.Y.C., 1990—. Mem. bus. com. Met. Mus. Art, N.Y.C. 1986—; deacon Brick Presbyn. Ch. Mem. Fin. Exec. Inst. (com. info. mgmt. 1979—, dir. N.Y.C. chpt. 1988-90), Salesmanship Club of Dallas, Union League Club of N.Y.C., Phi Delta Theta. Republican. Home: 1158 Fifth Ave New York NY 10029-6917 Office: Pearce Mayer & Greer Realty Corp 1318 Madison Ave New York NY 10128-1303

SCUSERIA, GUSTAVO ENRIQUE, theoretical chemist; b. San Fernando, Buenos Aires, Argentina, July 30, 1956; came to U.S., 1985; s. Eraldo L. and Alicia (Capitanelli) S.; m. Ana Inés Ilvento, Apr. 17, 1982; children: Ignacio, Tomás. BS, MS, U. Buenos Aires, 1979, PhD in Physics, 1983. Grad. asst. U. Buenos Aires, 1979-83, asst. prof., 1983-85; rsch. assoc. U. Calif., Berkeley, 1985-87; rsch. assoc. U. Ga., Athens, 1987-89; asst. prof. Rice U., Houston, 1989-93, assoc. prof., 1993-95, prof., 1995—. Camille and Henry Dreyfus Teacher scholar Camille and Henry Dreyfus Found., 1992. Mem. AAAS, Am. Chem. Soc., Am. Phys. Soc., Materials Rsch. Soc., Electrochemical Soc. Office: Rice U Dept Chemistry PO Box 1892 Houston TX 77251

SCUTT, DER, architect; b. Reading, Pa., Oct. 17, 1934; s. George W. and Hazel (Smith) S.; student Wyomissing Poly. Inst., 1952-54, Pa. State U., 1956-58; BArch. (Winchester Wirt travel fellow), M.Arch., Yale U., 1961; m. Leena Liukkonen, Feb. 18, 1967; children: Hagen, Kirsti Karina. Design ptnr. Swanke Hayden Connell & Partners, 1975-81; pvt. practice architecture, N.Y.C., 1981—; tchr. architecture Barlow Sch., Amenia, N.Y., 1964-66; vis. critic Yale U., 1982, 83; numerous radio and TV appearances on energy conservation, other subjects. Trustee The Chapin Sch., 1984—, Nat. Maritime Hist. Soc., 1991—, Ocean Liner Mus. N.Y., South St. Seaport Mus., 1994—. Recipient medal AIA, 1961; Rotary Internat. fellow, 1955-56. Fellow Illuminating Engrs. Soc. (bd. mgrs. N.Y. sect. 1971-72, 74-75, v.p. 1972-73, pres. 1973-74, Disting. Service award 1976); mem. AIA (sec. N.Y. chpt. 1970-72, fin. com. 1974-78, Brunner scholarship com. 1975-76, chmn., 1976-77, N.Y. chpt. spl. com. on proposed zoning modifications 1980, 82), Archtl. League N.Y. (chmn. scholarships and award com. 1970-72, exec. com. 1970—, v.p. for architecture 1972-73, N.Y. Bldg. Congress (bd. govs.), v.p. 1984—, v.p. 1985-87, treas. 1987-88, vice-chmn. 1988—), U.S. Inst.

Theatre Tech. (dir. 1970-72). Methodist. Contbr. articles to profl. jours.; lectr. Contbg. editor Lighting Design and Application, 1972—. Project designer, prin. works include: library Barlow Sch., Amenia, 1964, Crossroads Office Bldg., Rochester, N.Y., 1969, One Astor Plaza and Minskoff Theatre, N.Y.C., 1973, Western Union office bldg., Upper Saddle River, N.J., 1973, Equitable Life Assurance Data Center, Easton, Pa., 1973, Creative Perfumery Center, Roure Bertrand DuPont, Teaneck, N.J., 1973, retrofit, 1982, Hercules, Inc. Computer Center, Wilmington, Del., 1974, Northwestern Mut. Life Ins. Co., Milw., 1979, Barnes Group Inc. corp. hdqrs., Bristol, Conn., 1979, Grand Hyatt Hotel, N.Y.C., 1980, 520 Madison Ave., N.Y.C., 1983, Continental Center Office Tower, N.Y.C., 1983, Trump Tower, N.Y.C., 1983, St. Luke's/Roosevelt Hosp. Hand Surgery Clinic, N.Y.C., 1984, U.S. hdqrs, Hong Kong Bank, N.Y.C., 1985, 505 Park Ave. Office Bldg., N.Y.C., 1986, 100 UN Plaza Tower, N.Y.C., 1986, The Corinthian, N.Y.C., 1988, 625 Madison Ave. Office Bldg., N.Y.C., 1988 (Tucker Award of Design Excellence, Bldg. Stone Inst. 1990), The Milan, W. 23d St., N.Y.C., 1988, 575 Lexington Ave. Office Bldg., N.Y.C., 1990, Creative Properties, San Diego, 1990, N.Y. Constrn. Industry Hdqs., N.Y., 1990, The Chapin Sch., N.Y., 1990, KG Land/Nissho, White Plains, N.Y., 1990, IFF Household Products Hdqrs. Bldg., Hazlet, N.J., 1991, 57 West 57th St., N.Y., 1991, Sherry French Gallery, N.Y., 1991, Nat. Maritime Hist. Soc. Hdqs., N.Y., 1991, 823 UN Plz., N.Y., 1991, 450 West 33d St., N.Y., 1991, Golden Gate Bridge, San Francisco, 1992, Kaoping Creek Bridge, Taiwan, 1992, Enhance Reinsurance Corp. Hdqs., N.Y., 1992, Taiwan West Corridor High-Speed Rail Project, Taipei, Taiwan, 1993, Prin. Mut. Life Ins. Co., White Plains, 1993, IFF World Hdqrs., N.Y.C., 1994, 555 Fifth Ave. Office Bldg., N.Y.C., 1994, Givaudan-Roure, Inc., Flavors Hdqs., Clifton, N.J., 1994, Victorian Properties, N.Y., 1994, CIGNA Ins. Group, White Plains, 1994. Office: Der Scutt Architect 44 W 28th St New York NY 10001-4212

SCUTT, ED, English language educator; b. Poughkeepsie, N.Y., Sept. 5, 1943; s. Edward Alvin Scutt and Helen (Jones) Lutz; m. Barbara Scutt, Aug. 25, 1986 (div. June 1989). AA, Dutchess C.C., 1963; BA, Houghton Coll., 1965; MA, SUNY, Buffalo, 1972. Cert. tchr., N.Y. Tchr. LaSalle Sr. High Sch., Niagara Falls, N.Y., 1965-66, Royalton-Hartland Jr.-Sr. High Sch., Middleport, N.Y., 1966-71, Hilton (N.Y.) Ctrl. High Sch., 1972—; summer theater dir. Buck's Rock Camp, New Millford, Conn., 1974-79; presenter, cons. various confs., Washington, Niagara Falls, 1989-92; mem. steering com. Genesse Valley Devel. Learning Group, Rochester, N.Y., 1991—; founding mem. sec. whole lang. support group, 1989—; exec. bd. dirs. Hilton Ctrl. Teaching Assn. Mem. Nat. Coun. Tchrs. English. Avocations: community theater, reading, writing. Home: 65-B Hill Court Cir Rochester NY 14621 Office: Hilton Ctrl High Sch 400 East Ave Hilton NY 14468

SCUTT, ROBERT CARL, lawyer; b. Newark, N.Y., Dec. 24, 1950; s. Charles E. and Lois L. (Armstrong) S. BA, Union Coll., 1973; JD, Duke U., 1976. Bar: N.Y. 1977, U.S. Dist. Ct. (we. dist.) N.Y. 1977, U.S. Tax Ct. 1978. Assoc. Harris, Beach & Wilcox, Rochester, N.Y., 1976-83, ptnr., 1984—. Mem. N.Y. State Bar Assn., Monroe County Bar Assn., Nat. Assn. Health Lawyers. Office: Harris Beach & Wilcox Granite Building 130 E Main St Rochester NY 14604

SCZUDLO, RAYMOND STANLEY, lawyer; b. Olean, N.Y., July 5, 1948; s. Raymond Stanley and Ann Marie (Frisina) S.; m. Jane Marie Ehrensberger, May 9, 1970; children: Gregory Martin, Edward James. BChemE, U. Detroit, 1971; JD, Georgetown U., 1974. Bar: D.C., 1975, U.S. Dist. Ct. (fed. dist.) D.C. 1975, U.S. Ct. Appeals (D.C. cir.) 1975, U.S. Ct. Appeals (5th cir.) 1980, U.S. Supreme Ct. 1981. Assoc. Martin, Whitfield, Thaler & Bebchick, Washington, 1974-78, Verner, Liipfert, Bernhard & McPherson, Washington, 1978-80; ptnr. Verner, Liipfert, Bernhard, McPherson & Hand, Washington, 1981-87, Weil, Gotshal & Manges, Washington, 1987—; bd. dirs. Benlink, Inc., Washington, 1984—; adj. prof. banking law George Washington U. Nat. Law Ctr., 1991—. Contbr. articles on banking to profl. jours. Bd. dirs. Children's Nat. Med. Ctr., Washington, 1985—, chmn. fin. com., 1988-92, vice-chmn. bd., 1989-92, chmn.-elect, 1992, chmn. bd., 1993—; trustee Monsignor Smyth Endowment Fund, Washington, 1994—. Mem. ABA, D.C. Bar Assn., Am. Coll. Investment Counsel. Club: University (Washington). Office: Weil Gotshal & Manges 1615 L St NW Ste 700 Washington DC 20036-5610

SEABORG, GLENN THEODORE, chemistry educator; b. Ishpeming, Mich., Apr. 19, 1912; s. H. Theodore and Selma (Erickson) S.; m. Helen Griggs, June 6, 1942; children: Peter, Lynne Seaborg Cobb, David, Stephen, John Eric, Dianne. AB, UCLA, 1934; PhD, U. Calif.-Berkeley, 1937; numerous hon. degrees; LLD, U. Mich., 1958, Rutgers U., 1970; DSc, Northwestern U., 1954, U. Notre Dame, 1961, John Carroll U., Duquesne U., 1968, Ind. State U., 1969, U. Utah, 1970, Rockford Coll., 1975, Kent State U., 1975; LHD, No. Mich. Coll., 1962; DPS, George Washington U., 1962; DPA, U. Puget Sound, 1963; LittD, Lafayette Coll., 1966; DEng, Mich. Technol. U., 1970; ScD, U. Bucharest, 1971, Manhattan Coll., 1976, U. Pa., 1983. Rsch. chemist U. Calif., Berkeley, 1937-39, instr. dept. chemistry, 1939-41, asst. prof., 1941-45, prof., 1945-71, univ. prof., 1971—, leave of absence, 1942-46, 61-71, dir. nuclear chem. research, 1946-58, 72-75, asso. dir. Lawrence Berkeley Lab., 1954-61, 71—; chancellor Univ. (U. Calif.-Berkeley), 1958-61; dir. Lawrence Hall of Sci. U. Calif., Berkeley, 1982-84, chmn. Lawrence Hall of Sci., 1984—; sect. chief metall. lab. U. Chgo., 1942-46; chmn. AEC, 1961-71, gen. adv. com., 1946-50; research nuclear chemistry and physics, transuranium elements; chmn. bd. Kevex Corp., Burlingame, Calif., 1972-87, Advanced Physics Corp., Irvine, Calif., 1988—; mem. Pres.'s Sci. Adv. Com., 1959-61; mem. nat. sci. bd. NSF, 1960-61; mem. Pres.'s Com. on Equal Employment Opportunity, 1961-65, Fed. Radiation Council, 1961-69, Nat. Aeros. and Space Council, 1961-71, Fed. Council Sci. and Tech., 1961-71, Nat. Com. Am.'s Goals and Resources, 1962-64, Pres.'s Com. Manpower, 1964-69, Nat. Council Marine Resources and Engring. Devel., 1966-71; chmn. Chem. Edn. Material Study, 1959-74, Nat. Programming Council for Pub. TV, 1970-72; dir. Ednl. TV and Radio Center, Ann Arbor, Mich., 1958-64, 67-70; pres. 4th UN Internat. Conf. Peaceful Uses Atomic Energy, Geneva, 1971, also chmn. U.S. del., 1964, 71; U.S. rep. 5th-15th gen. confs. IAEA, chmn., 1961-71; chmn. U.S. del. to USSR for signing Memorandum Cooperation Field Utilization Atomic Energy Peaceful Purposes, 1963; mem. U.S. del. for signing Limited Test Ban Treaty, 1963; mem. commn. on humanities Am. Council Learned Socs., 1962-65; mem. sci. adv. bd. Robert A. Welch Found., 1957—; mem. Internat. Orgn. for Chem. Scis. in Devel., UNESCO, 1981-92, pres., 1981-92, pres. emeritus, 1992—; mem. Nat. Commn. on Excellence in Edn., Dept. Edn., 1981-83; co-discoverer elements 94-102 and 106: plutonium, 1940, americium, 1944-45, curium, 1944, berkelium, 1949, californium, 1950, einsteinium, 1952, fermium, 1953, mendelevium, 1955, nobelium, 1957, seaborgium, 1974; co-discoverer nuclear energy isotopes Pu-239, U-233, Np-237, other isotopes including I-131, Fe-59, Te-99m, Co-60; originator actinide concept for placing heaviest elements in periodic system. Author: (with Joseph J. Katz) The Actinide Elements, 1954, The Chemistry of the Actinide Elements, 1957, (with Joseph J. Katz and Lester R. Morse) 2d ed. Vols. I & II, 1986, The Transuranium Elements, 1958, (with E.G. Valens) Elements of the Universe, 1958 (winner Thomas Alva Edison Found. award), Man-Made Transuranium Elements, 1963, (with D.M. Wilkes) Education and the Atom, 1964, (with E.K. Hyde, I. Perlman) Nuclear Properties of the Heavy Elements, 1964, (with others) Oppenheimer, 1969, (with Ben Loeb) Stemming the Tide, 1987, (with W.R. Corliss) Man and Atom, 1971, Nuclear Milestones, 1972, (with Ben Loeb) Kennedy, Khruschev and the Test Ban, 1981, (with Walt Loveland) Elements beyond Uranium, 1990, (with Ben Loeb) The Atomic Energy Commission Under Nixon, 1992, (with Ray C. Colvig) Chancellor at Berkeley, 1994, (with Ronald L. Kathren, Jerry B. Gough, Gary T. Benefiel) The Plutonium Story: The Journals of Professor Glenn T. Seaborg 1939-1946, 1994; editor: Transuranium Elements: Products of Modern Alchemy, 1978, (with W. Loveland) Nuclear Chemistry, 1982, Modern Alchemy: The Seleced Papers of Glenn T. Seaborg, 1994; assoc. editor Jour. Chem. Physics, 1948-50; mem. editorial adv. bd. Jour. Inorganic and Nuclear Chemistry, 1954-82, Indsl. Rsch., Inc, 1967-75; mem. adv. bd. Chem. and Engring. News, 1957-59; mem. editorial bd. Jour. Am. Chem. Soc, 1950-59, Ency. Chem. Tech., 1975—, Revs. in Inorganic Chemistry, 1977—; mem. hon. editorial adv. bd. Internat. Ency. Phys. Chemistry and Chem. Physics, 1957—; Nuclear Sci. and Techniques, Chinese Nuclear Soc., 1989—; mem. panel Golden Picture Ency. for Children, 1957-61; mem. cons. and adv. bd. Funk and Wagnalls Universal Standard Ency. 1957-61; mem. Am. Heritage Dictionary Panel Usage Cons., 1964-80; contbr. articles to profl. jours. Trustee Pacific Sci. Ctr. Found., 1962-77, Sci. Svc., 1965, pres.

1966-68, chmn., 1988—; trustee Am.-Scandinavian Found., 1968—, Ednl. Broadcasting Corp., 1970-72; bd. dirs. Swedish Coun. Am., 1976—, chmn. bd. dirs., 1978-82; bd. dirs World Future Soc., 1969—, Calif. Coun. for Environ. and Econ. Balance, 1974-83; bd. govs. Am. Swedish Hist. Found., 1972—. Decorated officier Legion of Honor (France); recipient John Ericsson Gold medal Am. Soc. Swedish Engrs., 1948; Nobel prize for Chemistry (with E.M. McMillan), 1951, John Scott award and medal City of Phila., 1953, Perkin medal Am. sect. Soc. Chem. Industry, 1957, U.S. AEC Enrico Fermi award, 1959, Joseph Priestley Meml. award Dickinson Coll., 1960, Sci. and Engring. award Fedn. Engring. Socs., Drexel Inst. Tech., Phila., 1962; named Swedish Am. of Year, Vasa Order of Am., 1962; Franklin medal Franklin Inst., 1963; 1st Spirit of St. Louis award, 1964; Leif Erikson Found. award, 1964; Washington award Western Soc. Engrs., 1965; Arches of Sci. award Pacific Sci. Center, 1968; Internat. Platform Assn. award, 1969; Prometheus award Nat. Elec. Mfrs. Assn., 1969; Nuclear Pioneer award Soc. Nuclear Medicine, 1971; Oliver Townsend award Atomic Indsl. Forum, 1971; Disting. Honor award U.S. Dept. State, 1971; Golden Plate award Am. Acad. Achievement, 1972, Daniel Webster medal, 1976, John R. Kuebler award Alpha Chi Sigma, 1978; Founders medal Hebrew U. Jerusalem, 1981; Great Swedish Heritage award, 1984, Ellis Island Medal of Honor, 1986, Seaborg medal UCLA, 1987, Vannevar Bush award NSF, 1988, Nat. Medal of Sci. NSF, 1991, Royal Order of the Polar Star Sweden, 1992, Profl. Fraternity Assn. Career Achievement award, 1993; Minor Planet 4856-Asteroid Seaborg named in his honor, 1995. Fellow Am. Phys. Soc., Am. Inst. Chemists (Pioneer award 1968, Gold medal award 1973), Chem. Soc. London (hon.), Royal Soc. Edinburgh (hon.), Am. Nuclear Soc. (hon. chair Spl. Panel on Protection and Mgmt. of Plutonium 1994—, Henry DeWolf-Smyth award 1982, Seaborg award 1984, hon. chair Spl. Panel on Protection and Mgmt. of Plutonium 1994—), Calif. Acad. Scis., N.Y. Acad. Scis., Washington Acad. Scis., AAAS (pres. 1972, chmn. bd. 1973), Royal Soc. Arts (Eng.); mem. Am. Chem. Soc. (award in pure chemistry 1947, William H. Nichols medal N.Y. sect. 1948, Charles L. Parsons award 1964, Gibbs medal Chgo. sect. 1966, Madison Marshall award No. Ala. sect. 1972, Priestley medal 1979, pres. 1976, George C. Pimentel award in chem. edn., 1994), Am. Philos. Soc., Royal Swedish Acad. Engring. Scis. (adv. council 1980), Am. Nat., Argentine Nat., Bavarian, Polish, Royal Swedish, USSR acads. scis., Royal Acad. Exact, Phys. and Natural Scis. Spain (acad. fgn. corr.), Soc. Nuclear Medicine (hon.), World Assn. World Federalists (v.p. 1980), Fedn. Am. Scis. (bd. sponsors 1980—), Deutsche Akademie der Naturforscher Leopoldina (East Germany), Nat. Acad. Pub. Adminstrn., Internat. Platform Assn. (pres. 1981-86), Am. Hiking Soc. (bd. dirs 1979-84, v.p. 1980, adv. com. 1984—), Phi Beta Kappa, Sigma Xi, Pi Mu Epsilon, Alpha Chi Sigma (John R. Kuebler award 1978), Phi Lambda Upsilon (hon.); fgn. mem. Royal Soc. London, Chem. Soc. Japan, Serbian Acad. Sci. and Arts. Clubs: Bohemian (San Francisco); Chemists (N.Y.C.); Cosmo), University (Washington); Faculty (Berkeley). Office: U Calif Lawrence Berkeley Lab 1 Cyclotron Rd Berkeley CA 94720

SEABROOK, CHARLES, reporter. Sci. and tech. reporter Atlantic Jour. Constn., Atlanta. Office: Atlanta Journal & Constitution 72 Marietta St NW Atlanta GA 30303-2804

SEABROOK, JOHN MARTIN, retired food products executive, chemical engineer; b. Seabrook, N.J., Apr. 16, 1917; s. Charles Franklin and Norma Dale (Ivins) S.; m. Anne Schlaudecker, Apr. 5, 1939 (div. 1951); children—Carol Ormsby (Mrs. Jacques P. Boulanger), Elizabeth Anne; m. Elizabeth Toomey, 1956; children—John Martin, Bruce Cameron. B.S. in Chem. Engring, Princeton, 1939; LL.D. (hon.), Gettysburg Coll., 1974. Registered profl. engr., N.J., Del. Engr. Deerfield Packing Corp., 1939-41; v.p. Seabrook Farms Co., 1941-50, exec. v.p., 1954-59, dir., 1941-59, pres., 1954-59, chief exec. officer, 1955-59; cons. IU Internat. Corp., Wilmington, Del., 1959; v.p. IU Internat. Corp., 1960-65, dir., 1963-87, pres., 1965-73, 74-78, chief exec., 1967-80, chmn. bd., 1969-82, chmn. exec. com., 1982-87; pres. dir. Cumberland Automobile & Truck Co., 1954-59, Cumberland Warehouse Corp., 1954-59, Salem Farms Corp., N.J., 1948—; dir. Frick Co., Waynesboro, Pa., 1959-69, chmn., 1959-68; chmn., dir. S.W. Fabricating & Welding Co., Inc., Houston, 1964-68; chmn. Divcon, Inc., Houston, 1967-69, dir., 1967-71; pres., dir. Internat. Utilities Overseas Capital Corp., Wilmington, 1966-82, chmn., 1970-80; v.p. Gen. Waterworks Corp., Phila., 1959-66, dir., 1963-71, pres., 1966-68, chmn., 1968-71; chmn., dir. GWC Inc., Phila., 1971-73; pres. Brown Bros. Contractors, Inc., Phila., 1960, dir., 1960-67, chmn., 1965-67; pres. Am. Portable Irrigation Co., Eugene, Oreg., 1961, dir., 1961-68, chmn., 1966-68; chmn., dir. Gotaas-Larsen Shipping Corp., 1963, chmn. 1979, pres., chief exec. officer 1982-88; dir. Amvit Corp., Cleve., 1962-69, chmn., 1964-68; bd. dirs. Echo Bay Mines Ltd., South Jersey Gas Co., Folsom, N.J., South Jersey Industries, Inc., Folsom, Bell Atlantic Corp.; dir. emeritus N.J. Bell Telephone Co. Mem. N.J. Migrant Labor Bd., 1945-67, chmn., 1955-67; mem. N.J. Bd. Higher Edn., 1967-70, Pres.' Air Quality Adv. Bd., 1968-70; bd. dirs. Brandywine Conservancy, Inc., 1972—, pres., 1992-93; trustee Eisenhower Exch. Fellowships, 1974-85; trustee Hitchcock Found., 1991—, chmn., 1993—. Mem. Phi Beta Kappa. Clubs: Racquet and Tennis (N.Y.C.); The Philadelphia (Phila.); Buck's (London, Eng.); Wilmington (Del.); Toronto (Ont.). Home and Office: 55 Nimrod Rd Salem NJ 08079

SEADEN, GEORGE, civil engineer; b. Cracow, May 26, 1936; s. Simon and Mary (Guttman) S.; m. Linda Helen Mutch, Mar. 18, 1978; children: Amy Elisabeth, Maia Claire. BE, McGill U., Montreal, Que., Can., 1958; MS, Harvard U., 1968; postgrad., Northwestern U., 1992. Engr. Gatineau Power, Hull, Que., 1958-59, Ent. Fougerolle, Paris, 1960-62; mgr. Warnock Hersey Ltd., Montreal, 1959-60; assoc. Cartier, Coté, Piette, Montreal, 1962-67; sr. advisor Ministry Urban Affairs, Ottawa, Ont., Can., 1969-71; pres. Archer, Seaden & Assoc., Inc., Montreal, 1971-84; dir. gen. Inst. Rsch. in Constrn. Nat. Rsch. Coun., Ottawa, 1985—; vis. prof. U. Ottawa, 1969-73; mem. Can. Constrn. Rsch. Bd., 1985-91, Constrn. Industry Devel., Can., 1988-93, Civil Engring. Rsch. Found., 1993—, Rsch. Bd. Am.Pub. Works Assn., 1994—; pres. Conseil Internat. du Bâtiment, Rotterdam, The Netherlands, 1989-92; mem. jury to select best Can. constrn. projects and engring. design; lectr. numerous univs., rsch. ctrs. Co-editor: Trends in Building Construction Worldwide, 1989; mem. editl. bd. Bldg. Rsch. and Practice, 1990-94, Constrn. Bldg. Rev., 1991—; contbr. numerous articles to profl. publs. Chmn. bd. dirs. St. Andrew's Ch., Westmount, Que., 1975-82. Home: 80 Lyttleton Gardens, Rockcliffe Park, ON Canada K1L 5A6 Office: Inst for Rsch in Construction, Montreal Rd Bldg M-20, Ottawa, ON Canada K1A 0R6

SEADER, JUNIOR DEVERE, chemical engineering educator; b. San Francisco, Aug. 16, 1927; s. George Joseph and Eva (Burbank) S.; m. Sylvia Bowen, Aug. 11, 1961; children: Steven Frederick, Clayton Mitchell, Gregory Randolph, Donald Jeffrey, Suzanne Marie, Robert Clark, Kathleen Michelle, Jennifer Anne. BS, U. Calif., Berkeley, 1949, MS, 1950; PhD, U. Wis., 1952. Instr. chem. engring. U. Wis., Madison, 1951-52; group supr. chem. process design Chevron Rsch. Corp., Richmond, Calif., 1952-57; group supr. engring. rsch. Chevron Rsch. Corp., 1957-59; prin. scientist heat transfer and fluid dynamics rsch. Rocketdyne div. N.Am. Aviation, Canoga Park, Calif., 1959-65, sr. tech. specialist, summer 1967; prof. chem. engring. U. Idaho, 1965-66; prof. chem. engring. U. Utah, Salt Lake City, 1966—, chmn. dept. chem. engring., 1975-78; tech. cons.; trustee CACHE Corp., Austin, Tex.; inst. lectr. Am. Inst. Chem. Engrs., 1983, also dir., 1983-85. Author 5 books; assoc. editor IEC Rsch. jour.; contbr. articles to profl. jours. Served with USNR, 1945-46. Recipient Disting. Teaching award U. Utah, 1975, Donald L. Katz lectureship, 1990. Fellow Am. Inst. Chem. Engrs. (Computing in Chem. Engring. award 1988); mem. ACS, Sigma Xi, Phi Lambda Upsilon. Heat transfer rsch. connected with the devel. of rocket engines associated with the Apollo and Space Shuttle projects, 1960-65; rsch. on tar sands, process synthesis, catalyst effective factors, finding all roots to solution of nonlinear equations. Home: 3786 Viewcrest Dr Salt Lake City UT 84124-3930 Office: U Utah Dept Chem Engring Meb # 3290 Salt Lake City UT 84112-1180

SEADLER, STEPHEN EDWARD, business and computer consultant, social scientist; b. N.Y.C., 1926; s. Silas Frank and Deborah (Gelbin) S.; AB in Physics, Columbia U., 1947, postgrad. in atomic and nuclear physics, 1947; postgrad. with George Gamow in relativity, cosmology and quantum mechanics, George Washington U., 1948-50; m. Ingrid Linnea Adolfsson, Aug. 7, 1954; children: Einar Austin, Anna Carin. Legal rsch. asst., editor AEC, Washington, 1947-51; electronic engr. Cushing & Nevell, Warner, Inc.,

N.Y., 1951-54; seminar leader, leader trainer Am. Found. for Continuing Edn., N.Y.C. 1955-57; exec. dir. Medimetric Inst., 1957-59; mem. long range planning com., chmn. corporate forecasting com., mktg. rsch. mgr. W. A. Sheaffer Pen Co., Ft. Madison, Iowa, 1959-65; founder Internat. Dynamics Corp., Ft. Madison and N.Y.C., 1965, pres., 1965-70; originator DELTA program for prevention and treatment of violence, 1970; founder ID Center, Ft. Madison, now N.Y.C., 1968, pres., 1968—; mgmt. cons. in human resources devel. and conflict reduction, N.Y.C., 1970-73; pres. UNICON-SULT computer-based mgmt. and computer scis., N.Y.C., 1973—; speaker on decision support systems, internat. affairs and ideological arms control; author/speaker (presentation) Holocaust, History and Arms Control; originator social scis. of ideologics and computer based knowledge systems sci. of ideotopology; spl. works collection accessible via On-line Computer Libr. Ctr. Instr. polit. sci. Ia. State Penitentiary, 1959-62. Served with AUS, 1944-46. Named Man of Yr. Internat. Biog. Ctr., 1993-94. Mem. Am. Phys. Soc., Am. Statis. Assn., Acad. Polit. Sci., Am. Sociol. Assn., IEEE, N.Y. Acad. Sci., Am. Mgmt. Assn. (lectr. 1963-68), Internat. Platform Assn. Unitarian. Lodges: Masons (32 deg.), Shriners. Author: Holocaust, History and Arms Control II, 1990; contbr. Ideologics and ideotopology sects. to Administrative Decision Making, 1977, Societal Systems, 1978; Management Handbook for Public Administrators, 1978; also articles profl. jours. Statement on ideological arms control in Part 4 of Senate Fgn. Relations Com. Hearings on Salt II Treaty, 1979, Ideologics extended to treat ethnic, racial, religious conflict, 1992, with first call for Western Ecumenical Reformation at Morristown, N.J., Unitarian Ch., 1993. Office: 521 Fifth Ave Ste 1700 New York NY 10175-0001

SEAGAL, STEVEN, actor; b. Lansing, Mich., Apr. 10, 1951; m. Kelly LeBrock; children: Anna Aliza, Dominick, Arissa. Studied martial arts under masters, Japan. Founded Aikido Ten Shin Dojo, L.A. Martial arts choreographer The Challenge, 1982; actor, prodr., martial arts choreographer Above the Law, 1988, Marked for Death, 1990; actor, martial arts choreographer Hard to Kill, 1990; actor, prodr. Out for Justice, 1991, Under Siege, 1992, Under Siege 2, 1995; actor, dir., co-prodr. On Deadly Ground, 1994; fight scene choreographer various films. First non-Asian to open martial arts acad. in Japan; black belt numerous martial arts. Office: Creative Artists Agy 9830 Wilshire Blvd Beverly Hills CA 90212*

SEAGER, DANIEL ALBERT, university librarian; b. Jacksonville, Fla., Jan. 1, 1920; s. Harry James and Albertina Adeline (Klarer) S.; m. Helen Ruthe Medearis, Mar. 6, 1943; children: Mary Adele, Susan Kathleen, Dana Ruthe. AA, St. John's Coll., Winfield, Kans., 1941; AB, Okla. Bapt. U., 1948; BA in L.S, U. Okla., 1950, MA, 1953; postgrad., Colo. State Coll. (now U. No. Colo.), 1956-59. Head librarian, prof. English Southwest U., Bolivar, Mo., 1949-53; head librarian, asst. prof. library sci., chmn. dept. Ouachita U., Arkadelphia, Ark., 1953-56; head librarian, head library sci. edn., assoc. prof. library sci. U. No. Colo., Greeley, 1956-66; dir. library services U. No. Colo., 1966-71, coordinator library research and devel., 1971—, prof. library sci., 1984—, chief bibliographer/editor library publns., cons., instr. ednl. media program, 1968-71; libr. cons., 1968—; cons. Ency. Brit. ultramicrofiche project, 1967-69; lectr. in field. Contbr. articles to profl. jours. Mem. book adv. coun. Ednl. for Freedom Found.; mem. Com. library standards Colo. pub. schs., 1960-62; mem. exec. bd. Rocky Mountain Bibliog. Ctr. Research, 1959-60, 65-74, sec., 1961-63; sec. Colo. Council Librarians State-Operated Instns., 1966, chmn., 1968-70; mem. exec. bd. Weld County Assn. Mental Health, 1966, mem. bd. dirs., 1969; mem. Colo. Civil Service Examining Bd., 1961—; mem. U. N.C. Friends Libr., 1984—; Rep. com. chmn., Weld County, 1985-86; deacon, elder Christian Ch. With U.S. Army Signal Corps, WWII, 1942-44, ETO, 1944-45. Recipient several citations of merit profl. orgns. Fellow Intercontinental Biog. Assn.; mem. NEA, AAUP, Am. Library Assn. (library recruitment com. 1957—), Colo. assns. higher edn., United Profs. for Acad. Order Nat. Hist. Soc., Colo. Assn. Sch. Librarians (cons.), Spl. Librarians Assn., ALA (region recruitment rep. 1958—), Utah Library Assn., Kans. Library Assn., Wyo. Library Assn., Nebr. Library Assn., N.D. Library Assn., S.D. Library Assn., Nev. Library Assn., Mountain Plains Library Assn. (treas. 1959-63, exec. sec. 1963-76, spl. hons. plaque 1968, archivist 1974-84, constitution com. 1979, 83, chmn. nominating com. 1980, awards com. 1984, by-laws and amendments coms. 89-91, Pres.'s and Assn.'s Spl. award 17 Years Service award, Spl. Presdl. award 1994), Colo. Library Assn. (auditor), Tex. Library Assn., Southwestern Library Assn., Ill. Library Assn., Calif. Library Assn., Cath. Library Assn., Mich. Library Assn., Ohio Library Assn., N.Y. Library Assn., Pa. Library Assn., Midcontinent Med. Library Assn., Library Automation Research and Cons. Assn., U N.C. Friends of the Libr., 1984, Intercollegiate Studies Inst., Am. Security Council, Alumni Assn. U. No. Colo., Black Silent Majority Com. (hon.), Colo. Council Higher Edn., Colo. Edn. Assn. (mem. coms., del. to convs.), U. No. Colo. Edn. Assn. (treas. 1980-84, sec.-treas. 1984-85), U. Colo. Safety Com., Assn. Coll. and Reference Libraries, Colo. Hist. Soc., Assn. Research Libraries, Colo. Audiovisual Assn., Air Force Assn., Internat. Platform Assn., Acad. Polit. Sci. Columbia, Nat. Geog. Soc., Weld County Assn. Mental Health (mem. bd., chmn. library com.), Am. Judicature Soc., Emeritus Faculty Assn. U. No. Colo., Am. Numis. Assn., Am. Sci. Affiliation, Council on Consumer Info., Smithsonian Assocs., Chem. Abstracts Service Panel, Colo. Gerontol. Soc., Western Gerontol. Soc., Am. Assn. Retired Persons (vote.com.), Audubon Nature Program, Forest History Soc., Journalism Edn. Assn., Greeley Numis. Club, Greeley Jr. C. of C., U. No. Colo. Emeritus Faculty Assn., Nat. Travel Club, Civitan (lt. gov. Mountain Plains dist. 1960-62), Knife and Fork Club, Rep. Club (Washington), Rep. Congl. Club (Washington), Eagles Club, Phi Delta Kappa. Mem. Reformed Christian Ch. Am. Home: 1230 24th Ave Greeley CO 80631-3516

SEAGRAM, NORMAN MEREDITH, corporate executive; b. Toronto, Ont., Can., July 10, 1934; s. Norman Oliver and Constance Beatrice (Mills) S.; m. Joyce Elizabeth McMackon, Aug. 21, 1958; children: Susan Elizabeth, Norman Philip, Joseph Frederick, Samantha. Student, Trinity Coll., Port Hope, Ont.; BASc, U. Toronto, 1958; MSc, U. Birmingham, Eng., 1964. Cons. Associated Indsl. Cons. Ltd. and Mgmt. Scis. Ltd., London, Nairobi, Kenya, Moshi, Tanzania, Harari, Zimbabwe, Halifax, N.S., Can., Toronto, Ont., Can., 1960-68; various mktg. and planning positions The Molson Cos., Molson Breweries of Can. Ltd., 1968-78; pres. Seaway/Midwest Ltd., Toronto, 1978-82, Molson Western Breweries Ltd., Calgary, Alta, Can., 1983-85, Molson Ont. Breweries Ltd., Toronto, 1985-86; exec. v.p. The Molson Cos., Toronto, 1986-92; chmn., CEO Can. Liquid Air, Toronto, 1993—; chmn. Molson Breweries Can. Ltd., Club de Hockey Can. Inc., Vancouver (Can.) Baseball Ltd., Santa Fe Beverage Co., 1986-88; bd. dirs. Assoc. Respiratory Svcs. Inc.; mem. internat. coun. INSEAD. Mem. Bus. Coun. on Nat. Issues, Coun. for Can. Unity, Coun. for Bus. and Arts in Can., Can. Found. for Internat. Mgmt., Inst. Corp. Dirs., Olympic Trust Can., Trinity Coll. Sch. Found. Mem. Engrs. Ont., Alpha Delta Phi, Toronto Club, Toronto Badminton and Racquet Club, Montreal Badminton and Squash Club, Hillside Tennis Club, Empire Club, The Mount Royal Club. Conservative. Anglican. Avocations: tennis, squash, golf, skiing, hockey. Office: 20 York Mills Rd Ste 400, Toronto, ON Canada M2P 2C2

SEAGREN, ALICE, state legislator; b. 1947; m. Fred Seagren; 2 children. BS, SE Mo. State U. Mem. Minn. Ho. of Reps., 1993—. Active Bloomington (Minn.) Sch. Bd., 1989-92. Mem. Bloomington C. of C. (bd. dirs. 1990-92), Phi Gamma Nu, Alpha Chi Omega. Republican. Home: 9730 Palmer Cir Bloomington MN 55437 Office: Minn Ho of Reps State Capitol Saint Paul MN 55155

SEAL, LEO WILLIAM, JR., banker; b. Bay St. Louis, Miss., Sept. 6, 1924; s. Leo William and Rebecca (Baxter) S.; m. Jane Kempe Pringle, Nov. 30, 1974; children: Wallace Lee and Leo William (twins). B.S., Miss State U., 1949. With Hancock Bank, Gulfport, Miss., 1946—, asst. cashier, 1951-58, v.p., 1958-63, became pres., chief exec. officer, 1963, now chmn., CEO; also chmn. Hancock Bank Securities Corp.; Gulfport, Miss.; vice chmn., dir. Bank of Wiggins, Miss., 1967—; dir. Miss. Power Co., Miss. Export R.R. Co., Mosspoint. Served with U.S. Army, 1942-46. Named Alumnus of Yr., Miss. State U., 1983. Mem. Am. Bankers Assn. (state v.p. various terms), Ind. Bankers Assn. Am. (state v.p. various terms), Miss. Bankers Assn. (pres. jr. div. 1961-62), Miss Bankers Assn. (pres. sr. div. 1973-74), State C. of C. (pres. 1968-69), Gulfport C. of C. (pres. 1961-62 Most Outstanding Young Man). Methodist. Lodge: Rotary (pres. Gulfport 1959-60). Office: Hancock Bank 1 Hancock Pla PO Box 4019 Gulfport MS 39502-4019

SEAL, ULYSSES S., animal scientist. Sci. Captive Breeding Specialists Group, Apple Valley, Minn. Recipient R. Marlin Perkins award Am. Assn. Zool. Parks and Aquariums, 1991. Office: Captive Breeding Specialists Group 12101 Johnny Cake Ridge Rd Apple Valley MN 55124*

SEALE, JAMES MILLARD, religious organization administrator, clergyman; b. Middlesboro, Ky., Oct. 4, 1930; s. Albert Tyler and Edith Josephine (Buchanan) S.; m. Mary Dudley Harrod; children: William Alan, Ann Lynn Seale Hazelrigg. BA, Transylvania U., 1952; BD, Lexington Theol. Sem., 1955, MDiv, 1963, D Ministry, 1981. Ordained to ministry Christian Ch. (Disciples of Christ), 1951. Student pastor various Christian Chs., Ky., 1949-54; pastor 1st Christian Ch., Pikeville, Ky., 1954-58, Erlanger (Ky.) Christian Ch., 1958-61; sr. minister 1st Christian Ch., Mt. Sterling, Ky., 1961-70, Paris, Ky., 1978-82; stewardship sec. Gen. Office Christian Ch., Indpls., 1970-74; adminstr. Christian Ch. Home of Louisville, 1974-77; dir. devel. Christian Ch. Homes Ky., Louisville, 1978; pres. Disciples of Christ Hist. Soc., Nashville, 1983-95. Author: A Century of Faith and Caring, 1983, Forward From The Past, 1991; editor jour. Disciplania, 1983-92. Pres. Kiwanis Club, Pikeville, 1957, Mt. Sterling, 1963, lt. gov., Ctrl. Ky., 1965. Avocations: writing, photography, golf, fishing. Office: Disciples of Christ Hist Soc 1101 19th Ave S Nashville TN 37212-2196

SEALE, JOHN CLEMENT, director, cinematographer; b. Warwick, Queensland, Australia, Oct. 5, 1942; s. Eric Clement and Marjorie Lyndon (Pool) S.; m. Louise Lee Mutton, Sept. 23, 1967; children: Derin Anthony, Brianna Lee. Grad. high sch., Sydney, Australia. Camera asst. film dept. Australian Broadcasting Com., 1962-68; freelance technician, camera operator various films, series, commls., 1968-76, dir. photography various film cos., 1976; dir. feature film, Till There Was You, 1989-90. Dir. photography: Goodbye Paradise (Golden Tripod 1982), Careful, He Might Hear You (Best Cinematography 1983), Witness, 1984 (Golden Tripod 1984, Oscar nomination 1986, Brit. Acad. award nomination 1986), The Hitcher, 1985, Children of a Lesser God, 1985 (Golden Tripod 1987), The Mosquito Coast, 1986, Stakeout, 1987, Gorillas in the Mist (Brit. Acad. award nomination 1989, Premier Mag. Cinematographer of the Yr. 1989), Rainman, 1988 (Acad. award nomination 1988, Artistic Achievement award 1989), Dead Poets Society, 1989, The Doctor, 1991, Lorenzo's Oil, 1992, The Firm, 1993, The Paper, 1993, Beyond Rangoon, 1994, The American President, 1995. Recipient Film Critics Cir. Australia 1990 Tribute. Mem. Australian Cinematographers Soc. (named Cinematographer of Yr. 1982, 84). Avocations: building boats, sailing.

SEALE, ROBERT L., state treasurer; b. Inglewood, Calif., Oct. 4, 1941; m. Judy Seale (dec.). BSA, Calif. Poly. U. Former comtr. and sr. fin. officer Rockwell Internat.; sr. accountant Ernst & Ernst, L.A.; mng. ptnr. Pangborn & Co., Ltd. CPA's, 1985-88; now state treas. State of Nev.; trustee, Desert Rsch. Inst. Former treas. Nev. Rep. Party. Office: Office of State Treas Capital Complex Carson City NV 89710

SEALE, WILLIAM EDWARD, finance educator; b. Lynchburg, Va., Feb. 10, 1941; s. Frank Earl and Viola Elizabeth (Parks) S.; m. Patricia Jeanette Marquart, 1962 (div. 1990); children: William E. Jr., James Anthony, Patricia Jeanette; m. Marguerite E. Pelissier, 1992. A.B. in Chemistry, U. Ky., 1963, M.S. in Agrl. Econs., 1969, Ph.D. in Agrl. Econs., 1975. Farm mgmt. specialist U. Ky., Lexington, 1969-74; legis. asst. U.S. Senate, Washington, 1975-79; v.p. Commodity Exchange Inc., N.Y.C., 1979-83; commr. Commodity Futures Trade Commn., Washington, 1983-88; prof. fin., chmn. dept. Sch. Bus. and Pub. Mgmt. George Washington U., Washington, 1988—. Contbr. articles to profl. jours. and mags. Mem. So. Agrl. Econs. Assn., Am. Agrl. Econs. Assn., Am. Fin. Assn., Fin. Mgmt. Assn. Democrat. Roman Catholic. Avocations: yachting, amateur radio. Home: 1936 Franklin Ave Mc Lean VA 22101-5307 Office: George Washington U Dept Fin Washington DC 20052

SEALEY, B. RAPHAEL, classicist, educator; b. Middlesbrough, Yorkshire, Eng., Aug. 14, 1927; came to U.S., 1963; s. Bertram Izod and Florence Gladys (Heath) S.; m. Dagmar Schoelermann, Dec. 19, 1972 (div. Oct. 1977); 1 child, Dorte Freyja. MA, Oxford U., Eng., 1951. Lectr. classics U. Coll. of N Wales, Bangor, 1954-58, U. London, 1958-63; prof. SUNY, Buffalo, 1963-67, U. Calif., Berkeley, 1967—. Author: Essays in Greek Politics, 1967, A History of the Greek City States, 1976, The Athenian Republic, 1987, Women and Law in Classical Greece, 1990, Demosthenes and His Time, 1993, The Justice of the Greeks, 1994. Home: 1206 Milvia St Berkeley CA 94709-1933 Office: U Calif Dept History Berkeley CA 94720

SEALL, STEPHEN ALBERT, lawyer; b. South Bend, Ind., Oct. 24, 1940; s. Stephen Henry and Mildred Rita (MacDonald) S.; m. Barbara Ann Halloran, June 25, 1966; children: John Paul, Edward Andrew, Ann Marie. BA, Purdue U., 1963; postgrad., Cornell U. Grad. Sch. Bus. Adminstrn., 1963; LLB, U. Notre Dame, 1966. Bar: Ind. 1966, U.S. Claims Ct. 1973, U.S. Tax Ct. 1968, U.S. Ct. Appeals (6th cir.) 1980, U.S. Ct. Appeals (7th cir.) 1969, U.S. Supreme Ct. 1973. Assoc. Thornburg, McGill, Deahl, Harman, Carey & Murray, South Bend, 1966-71; ptnr. Barnes & Thornburg and predecessor firm Thornburg, McGill, Deahl, Harman, Carey & Murray, 1972—, vice chmn. exec. and mgmt. coms., 1985—; speaker in field. Mem. editorial bd. Notre Dame Law Rev., 1964-66. Mem. Mayor's Com. on Downtown Devel., South Bend, 1975-77, Mayor's Com. on Utilization of Downtown Bldgs., South Bend, 1988—; trustee Project Future, South Bend, 1986—; dir. Meml. Health Found., 1992—, United Way of St. Joseph County, Inc., 1992—. Fellow Am. Coll. Tax Counsel, Ind. Bar Found.; mem. ABA (taxation sect.), Ind. State Bar Assn. (chmn. taxation sect. 1977-78), Summit Club (chmn. 1976-77), Morris Park Country Club. Democrat. Roman Catholic. Avocations: weightlifting, softball, golf. Home: 17705 Waxwing Ln South Bend IN 46635-1328 Office: Barnes & Thornburg 600 1st Source Bank Ctr 100 N Michigan St South Bend IN 46601-1630

SEALS, DAN WAYLAND, country music singer; b. McCarney, Tex., Feb. 8, 1948. With England Dan & John Ford Coley, 1969-80; recording artist A&M, 1972-80, EMI Records, 1985-86, Liberty Records, 1988-92, Warner Bros., 1992—. Albums (with John Ford Coley) Nights are Forever Without You, 1976, Dowdy Ferry Road, 1977, Dr. Heckle & Mr. Jive, 1979; solo albums Won't Be Blue Anymore, 1985, The Best, 1988, Rage On, 1988, On Arrival, 1990, The Songwriter, 1992, Walking the Wire, 1992, Best of Dan Seals, 1994, Fired Up, 1994; gold #1 single (with John Ford Coley) I'd Really Love To See You Tonight, 1976. Recipient Duet of Yr. award (with Marie Osmond) for Meet Me in Montana from Country Music Assn., 1985, Single of Yr. award for Bop from Country Music Assn., 1988. Office: Warner Bros Records 3300 Warner Blvd Burbank CA 91510*

SEALY, ALBERT HENRY, lawyer; b. Columbus, Ohio, Oct. 23, 1917; s. Albert H. and Lillian E. (Stock) S.; m. Flora Kinkel, Aug. 23, 1947; children: Catherine Ann, Thomas P., Joan Deborah. B.A. summa cum laude, Ohio State U., 1938; LL.B. (J.D.), Harvard, 1941; DL (hon.), Wright State U., 1982. Bar: N.Y. 1942, Ohio 1955. With firm Simpson, Thacher & Bartlett, N.Y.C., 1941-43, 46-55, Smith and Schnacke, Dayton and Columbus, Ohio, 1955-89; sec. Mead Corp., 1964-75. Author: Macro Blueprint, 1986; contbr. articles to profl. jours. Mem. Ohio Ho. of Reps., 1966-68; Chmn. Ohioans for Fair Taxation, 1972—, Ohio Inst. on Pub. Finance, 1973—; chmn. bd. trustees Wright State U., 1977—; exec. dir. Inst. Nat. Econ. and Social Dialogue, 1982-87. Served to lt. USNR, 1943-46. Mem. ABA, Bar Assn. City N.Y., Phi Beta Kappa, Sigma Chi. Home: 3105 Burr St Fairfield CT 06430-1853

SEAMAN, ALFRED BARRETT, journalist; b. Rockville Ctr., N.Y., July 4, 1945; s. Alfred Jarvis and Mary Margaret (Schill) S.; m. Laura Powers Maxwell, Apr. 25, 1970; children: Katherine Maxwell, Margaret Elise Elizabeth Barrett. BA, Hamilton Coll. 1967; MBA, Columbia U., 1971. Reporter Life mag., N.Y.C., 1971-72, Fortune mag. N.Y.C., 1972; corr. Time mag., N.Y.C., 1973, Chgo., 1973-76, Bonn, Germany, 1976-78; bur. chief Time mag., Detroit, 1978-81; dep. bur. chief Time mag., Washington, 1981-83, White House corr., 1984-88; dep. chief corrs. Time mag., N.Y.C., 1988-91, sr. editor, 1991-94, spl. projects editor, 1994— Co-author: Going for Broke: The Chrysler Story, 1981. Alumni trustee Hamilton Coll., Clinton, N.Y., 1990-93, 94—; trustee Village of Irvington, N.Y., 1992-94. With USNR, 1969-71. Mem. Ardsley County Club. Episcopalian. Avoca-

tions: squash, tennis, golf. Home: Ardsley Ave W Ardsley On Hudson NY 10503-7284 Office: Time Mag Rockefeller Ctr New York NY 10020

SEAMAN, ALFRED JARVIS, retired advertising agency executive; b. Hempstead, L.I., N.Y., Sept. 17, 1912; s. Alfred J. and Ellen (Delaney) S.; m. Mary M. Schill, Sept. 26, 1937 (dec. June 1975); children: Marilyn Hollingsworth, Susan, Barry, Deborah; m. Honor S. Mellor, July 16, 1977. BS, Columbia U., 1935; LittD, L.I. U., 1987. Account exec. Fuller & Smith & Ross, Inc., N.Y.C., 1937-41; partner Knight & Gilbert. Inc., Boston, 1941-43; with Compton Advt., Inc., N.Y.C., 1946-59; exec. v.p., creative dir., dir. Compton Advt., Inc., 1954-59; vice chmn. bd., chmn. exec. com. SSC & B, Inc., 1959-60, pres., chief exec. officer, 1960-79, chmn., chief exec. officer, 1979-81; dir., mem. exec. com. Interpublic Group of Cos. Inc. Hon. bd. dirs., adv. council, founding chmn. Advt. Ednl. Found.; bd. dirs., hon. dir. com. Advt. Council.; chmn. planning bd., 1962—, mayor Village Upper Brookville, 1966—; chmn. emeritus Samuel Waxman Cancer Research Found. Lt. USNR, 1943-46. Named to Advt. Hall of Fame, 1983. Clubs: U.S. Sr. Golf Assn., Creek (Locust Valley, L.I.) (pres.), Piping Rock (Locust Valley, L.I.), Racquet and Tennis (N.Y.C.), Links (N.Y.C.), Brook (N.Y.C.), Jupiter Island (Fla.), Nat. Golf Links Am. (Southampton, N.Y.), Seminole (Fla.), Hobe Sound Yacht (Fla.). Home: Wolver Hollow Rd Upper Brookville Oyster Bay NY 11771 also: Jupiter Island 126 Gomez Rd Hobe Sound FL 33455-2424 Office: 666 3rd Ave New York NY 10017-4011

SEAMAN, ARLENE ANNA, musician, educator; b. Pontiac, Mich., Jan. 21, 1918; d. Roy Russell and Mabel Louise (Heffron) S. BS, life cert., Ea. Mich. U., 1939; MMus, Wayne State U., 1951; postgrad., Colo. Coll., 1951-52, Acad. Music, Zermatt Switzerland, 1954, 58, U. Mich. guest conductor Shepherds and Angels, Symphonie Concertante, 1951; asst. conductor Detroit Women's Symphony, 1960-68; adjudicator Mich. State Band and Orch. Festivals, Solo and Ensemble Festivals, 1950-70, Detroit Fiddler's Band Auditions, 1948-52, Mich. Fedn. Music Clubs, 1948-55; instr. Ea. Mich. U., 1939-42, Hartland Sch. Music, 1939-42, Pontiac (Mich.) Pub. Schs., 1942-45, Detroit Pub. Schs., 1945-73, pvt. studio, 1973-90. Performer cello South Oakland Symphony, 1958-65, Detroit Women's Symphony, 1951-68, Riviera Theatre Orch., 1959, 60, Masonic Auditorium Opera, Ballet Seasons, 1959-65, Toledo Ohio Symphony, 1963-70, others; performer trumpet Detroit Brass Quartet, 1974-78; piano accompanist various auditions, recitals, solo and ensemble festivals; composer: Let There Be Music, 1949, Fantasy for French Horn and Symphonic Band, 1951. Mem. Quota Internat., Delta Omicron. Home: 14650 N Alamo Canyon Dr Tucson AZ 85737-8812

SEAMAN, BARBARA (ANN ROSNER), author; b. N.Y.C., Sept. 11, 1935; d. Henry Jerome and Sophie Blanche (Kimels) Rosner; m. Gideon Seaman, Jan. 13, 1957 (div.); children: Noah Samuel, Elana Felicia, Shira Jean. B.A. (Ford Found. scholar), Oberlin Coll., 1956, L.H.D. (hon.), 1978; cert. in advanced sci. writing (Sloan-Rockefeller fellow), Columbia U. Sch. Journalism, 1968. Columnist Brides Mag., N.Y.C., 1964-68; columnist, contbg. editor Ladies' Home Jour., N.Y.C., 1965-69; editor child care and edn. Family Circle, N.Y.C., 1970-73; contbg. editor Omni mag., 1978; cons. FYI, ABC-TV, 1979-80; v.p. for devel. David Brooks Prodns., 1990-94; contbg. editor MS Mag., 1993—; cons. U.S. Senate Subcom. on Monopoly: Nelson Pill Hearings, 1970; presented testimony to Senate and Congressional coms., 1970—; lectr. in field; participant TV discussion shows; tchr. Coll. New Rochelle, 1975, Sagaris Inst., 1975, CUNY, 1993; co-founder Nat. Women's Health Network, 1975—; co-founder Communications Cons. for Choice, 1985-86, Nat. Task Force Sexual Malpractice, 1985-86, Families Against Sexually Abusive Therapists and other profls., 1992—; v.p. Women's Med. Center, N.Y.C., 1971-73; mem. ERA Emergency Task Force, 1979; mem. adv. council Feminist Press, Old Westbury, N.Y., 1975; mem. adv. bd. Feminist Center for Human Growth and Devel., 1979, Women's History Library, Berkeley, Calif., 1973-75; mem. steering com. Women's Forum, 1974; mem. adv. bd. NOW, N.Y., 1973, Women's Guide to Books, 1974, Jewish Women for Affirmative Action, Evanston, Ill., 1973—, Jour. Women and Health, 1975, Jewish Feminist Orgn., N.Y.C., 1975; chair com. domestic violence Nat. Coun. Women's Health, 1993—; judge for various journalism awards. Author: The Doctors' Case Against the Pill, 1969, rev. edit., 1980, 25th anniversary edit., 1995, Free and Female, 1972, (with G. Seaman) Women and the Crisis in Sex Hormones, 1977, Lovely Me: The Life of Jacqueline Susann, 1987; contbg. author: foreword to Lunaception, 1975; The Bisexuals, 1974, Career and Motherhood, 1979, The Hormone Industry, 1994; author (play) I Am a Woman, 1972; contbr. various anthologies including Rooms with No View, 1974, Women and Men, 1975, Seizing Our Bodies, 1978, Encyclopaedia of Childbirth, 1992; narrator (film) Taking Our Bodies Back, 1974; contbr. editorials and revs. to newspapers, popular mags.; books and articles translated into Spanish, German, Dutch, Turkish, Japanese, Hebrew, French, Italian. Alumni cons. women's studies program Oberlin Coll., 1975; mem. motivation com. Am. Cancer Soc., 1973; mem. adv. com. Older Women's Health Project, NYU Med. Ctr., 1980; bd. dirs. Safe Transp. of People, N.Y.C., 1975, Women's Health Newsletter, 1983; adv. bd. DES Action, 1977; cons. Nat. Task Force on DES, 1978; contraceptive research br. HEW, 1980; v.p., bd. dirs. ARM (Abortion Rights Moblzn.), 1981—; mem. hon. bd. Carcinogen Info. Program, St. Louis, 1981; trustee Nat. Coun. on Women in Medicine, 1990—; chmn. adv. bd. Coalition for Family Justice, 1991—; co-chair Domestic Violence com. N.Y. Women's Agenda, 1992-93. Recipient citation for books as first to raise issue of sexism in health care as world-wide issue Library of Congress, 1973, citation as author responsible for patient package inserts on prescriptions HEW, 1970, Matrix award, 1978, Pioneer Woman award Resources Div. of Am. Assn. Ret. Persons, 1986, Athena award Nat. Coun. Women's Health, 1992, Health Advocacy award Health Policy Adv. Ctr., APHA, 1994; inviting com. Am. Writers Congress. Mem. Internat. Women's Forum, N.Y. Women's Forum, PEN, Authors League, Nat. Assn. Science Writers. Address: 110 W End Ave Apt 5D New York NY 10023-6348

SEAMAN, DARYL KENNETH, oil company executive; b. Rouleau, Sask., Can., Apr. 28, 1922. BSME, U. Sask., 1948, LLD (hon.), 1982; LLD (hon.), U. Calgary, 1993. Cert. mech. engr. CEO Bow Valley Industries Ltd., Calgary, Alta., Can., 1962-70, 85-91, chmn., chief exec. officer, 1970-82; chmn. Box Valley Industries Ltd., Calgary, Alta., Can., 1982-85; pres. Bow Valley Industries Ltd., Calgary, Alta., Can., 1985-87; chmn. Bow Valley Industries Ltd., 1991-92; bd. dirs. Renaissance Energy Ltd., Calgary, Trimac Ltd., Potash Corp. Sask. Inc., Encal Energy Ltd., Flowtech Energy Corp., Abacan Resource Corp., Basic Industries Corp.; co-owner, bd. dirs. Calgary Flames Hockey Club; chmn., pres. Dox Investments, Inc. Mem. Royal Commn. Econ. Union and Devel. Prospects for Can., 1982-85; active numerous coms. for fundraising U. Sask.; hon. chmn. The Western Heritage Centre Soc.; chmn. nat. adv. com. Banff Sch. Mgmt. Served with RCAF, 1941-45, North Africa, Italy. There is no repetition since it is indicated as an award you received and as a membership. Mem. Assn. Profl. Engrs., Geologists and Geophysicists (hon. life, Frank Spragins award, 1985, McGill Mgmt. Achievement award, 1979), Order of Canada 1993, Western Heritage Centre Soc., Ranchmen's Club, RAF Club, Earl Grey Golf Club, Calgary Petroleum Club, Calgary Golf and Country Club, U. Calgary Chancellor's Club. Progressive Conservative. Mem. United Ch. Can. Avocations: ranching, golf, hunting, skiing. Home and Office: Dox Investments Inc, 500 333 5th Ave SW, Calgary, AB Canada T2P 3B6

SEAMAN, DONALD ROY, investment company executive; b. b., Rouleau, Sask., Can., July 26, 1925; s. Byron Luther and Letha Mae (Patton) S.; m. Eleanor Victoria Lee, Nov. 4, 1950; children: Victoria Anne, Donna Jane, Lauraine Suzanne (dec.), Marilou Kathleen. B.S.M.E., U. Sask., 1947. Indsl. engr. Canadian Industries Ltd., Kingston, Ont., Can., 1947-50; v.p. Bow Valley Industries, Calgary, Alta., Can., 1950-75, dir., 1950-89, sr. v.p., 1986-87; pres. Bow Valley Resource Services, Calgary, 1976-87; bd. dirs. NuGas Ltd., Northstar Energy Corp., Dominion Explorers Inc., Artisan Drilling Ltd., Best Pacific Resources Ltd., Flowtech Energy Corp., Piper Petroleums Ltd., Ryan Energy Techs., Inc. Trustee Alta. Heritage Found. for Med. Research. Mem. Profl. Engrs. Alta. Clubs: Petroleu, Glencoe, Earl Grey Golf (dir. 1966-72). Office: D R S Resource Investments Inc, 333-5 Ave SW # 500, Calgary, AB Canada T2P 3B6

SEAMAN, IRVING, JR., public relations consultant; b. Milw., July 14, 1923; s. Irving and Anne (Douglas) S.; m. June Carry, June 24, 1950; children: Peter Stewart, Marion Carry, Irving Osborne, Anne Douglas. B.A., Yale U., 1944. With Continental Ill. Nat. Bank & Trust

Co., Chgo., 1947-61; v.p. Continental Ill. Nat. Bank & Trust Co., 1959-61; pres., chief exec. officer, dir. Nat. Boulevard Bank, Chgo., 1961-65; chmn. exec. com., chief exec. officer, dir. Nat. Boulevard Bank, 1966-76; vice chmn. bd., dir. Sears Bank and Trust Co., Chgo., 1976-77; pres., chief operating officer, dir. Sears Bank and Trust Co., 1977-82; sr. cons. Burson-Marsteller, Chgo., 1982-94; chmn. bd. Associated Bank Chgo., 1985—. Mem. Northwestern U. Assn.; life mem. bd. dirs. Lake Forest Hosp.; bd. dirs. United Way of Chgo., 1975-89, pres., 1979; bd. dirs. United Way/Crusade of Mercy, 1980-89, 94—, vice chmn., 1980-81; trustee Chgo. Symphony Orch., 1987—. Served to lt. (j.g.) USNR, WWII. Mem. Commonwealth Club, Econ. Club, Chgo. Club, Comml. Club, Racquet Club, Onwentsia Club, Winter Club, Old Elm Club (Highland Park, Ill.), Shoreacres Club (Lake Bluff, Ill.), Augusta Nat. Golf Club (Ga.), Marsh Landing Club (Fla.). Home: 946 Elm Tree Rd Lake Forest IL 60045-1410 Office: 1E Wacker Dr Chicago IL 60606

SEAMAN, ROBERT LEE, lawyer; b. Long Island, N.Y., Mar. 29, 1942; s. Farrand Robert and Leona (Hicks) S.; m. Carolyn Holmes Hopgood, July 23, 1966; children—Elizabeth, Jennifer, Rebecca. B.A., Harvard U., 1963; LL.B., U. Va., 1966. Bar: N.Y. 1966, Va. 1966. Law clk. to U.S. dist. judge, 1966-68; lectr. U. Va. Grad. Sch. Bus. Adminstrn., 1967-68; assoc. firm Brown, Wood, Ivey, Mitchell & Petty, N.Y.C., 1968-74; officer Phelps Dodge Corp., N.Y.C., 1974-80; ptnr. Seaman, Williamson, Gorayeb & Tidd, N.Y.C., 1981-83; ptnr. Hall, McNicol, Hamilton & Clark, N.Y.C., 1983-86, of counsel, 1986-9; chmn. Friends Work Coll., Lloyd Harbor, N.Y., 1987-89; lectr. in field. Trustee Friends Acad., Locust Valley, N.Y., from 1975. Club: Harvard of L.I. (pres. and dir. 1980-85). Office: 515 Madison Ave New York NY 10022-5403 also: 444 New York Ave Huntington NY 11743-3432

SEAMAN, ROBERT LEROY, technology company executive; b. Auburn, N.Y., Mar. 26, 1924; s. LeRoy John and Alice Mary (Smith) S.; m. Jacqueline Bailey, June 27, 1949; children: Peter B., David S., Richard J. B. Mgmt. Engring., Rensselaer Poly. Inst., 1950; M.S., MIT, 1968. With Ford Motor Co., Detroit, 1950-55; div. controller Curtiss-Wright Corp., Princeton, N.J., 1956-58; internal cons. CBS, Inc., N.Y.C., 1958-60; asst. controller Raytheon Co., Lexington, Mass., 1960-68, dir. planning, 1968, v.p. strategic planning, 1969-89; bd. dirs. Lukens Inc., Integrated Environ. Systems, Lexington Savs. Bank. Co-author: a computer-aided, on-line, planning and analysis system, STEPS, 1968. Served as lt. (j.g.) USNR, 1942-45. Decorated DFC, Air medal with 3 oak leaf clusters. Mem. Fin. Execs. Inst., Planning Forum, Rensselaer Soc. Engrs., Sigma Xi, Tau Beta Pi, Epsilon Delta Sigma. Clubs: N.Y., Univ., Econ. (N.Y.). Home: 17 Hancock St Lexington MA 02173-3443

SEAMAN, ROUAL DUANE, data processing company executive; b. East Chicago, Ind., Apr. 25, 1930; s. Elmer Earl and Roxanna Isabelle (Bennett) S.; m. Sadako Itabashi, July 29, 1957; 1 child, Victor Shayne. Student, U. Mo., 1950-51, Jochi Daigaku, Tokyo, 1956, U. Houston, 1966-69. Mgmt. trainee Gen. Electric Corp., Atomic Energy Commn., Richland, Wash., 1951-52; project mgr. Dynalectron Corp., Ft. Worth, 1952-63; project supr. Apollo Test Facility N.Am. Rockwell Project Apollo, NASA, Houston, 1964-69; mktg. mgr. Gen. Space Corp., Houston, 1969-70; pres. AIM Fin. Systems Group, Inc., Houston, 1970—; bd. dirs. Am. Credit Control; ptnr. Automated Info. Mgmt., 1984—; ptnr. CA$SH Enterprises, 1989—. Author software. Pres. Tex. Intercity Football, Inc., Harris/Galveston County, 1971, League City (Tex.) Little League, 1972; mem. S.W. Football Ofcls. Assn., 1976; mem. Better Bus. Bur., Houston, 1982—. With USAF, 1947-50. Recipient Recognition award Greater Houston Partnership, 1990. Mem. Am. Guild of Patient Mgmt., Houston C. of C., Nat. Fedn. Ind. Businesses, Nat. Assn. Pvt. Enterprise, Tex. Hosp. Assn., Tex. Hosp. Info. Systems Soc., Healthcare Fin. Mgrs. Assn., 100 Club of Houston, Smithsonian Instn., Am. Mus. Natural History. Republican. Christian/Bhuddist. Avocations: golf, baseball, football, gardening, travel. Office: AIM Fin Systems Group Inc 7015 Gulf Fwy Ste # 145 Houston TX 77087

SEAMAN, TONY, university athletic coach. Head coach NCAA Divsn. 1A lacrosse Johns Hopkins Blue Jays, Balt., 1990—. Office: Johns Hopkins U Charles And # 34th Sts Baltimore MD 21218*

SEAMAN, WILLIAM BERNARD, physician, radiology educator; b. Chgo., Jan. 5, 1917; s. Benjamin and Dorothy E. S.; m. Veryl Swick, February 26, 1944; children—Cheryl Dorothy, William David. Student, U. Mich., 1934-37; M.D., Harvard U., 1941. Diplomate: Am. Bd. Radiology. Intern Billings Hosp., U. Chgo., 1941-42; asst. radiology Yale U. Sch. Medicine, 1947-48, instr., 1948-49; instr. radiology Washington U. Sch. Medicine, St. Louis, 1949-51, assoc. prof., 1951-55, prof., 1955-56; prof. radiology, chmn. dept. Coll. Phys. and Surg., Columbia U., 1956-82; James Picker prof. emeritus Columbia U., 1982—; dir. radiology service, trustee Presbyn. Hosp., N.Y.C. Served as maj. USAAF, 1942-46; flight surgeon. Recipient W.B. Cannon medal Soc. Gastro-intestinal Radiologists, 1979, Gold medal Am. Coll. Radiology, 1983. Mem. Radiol. Soc. N.A., Am. Roentgen Ray Soc. (pres. 1973-74, gold medal 1988), Am. Coll. Radiology (pres. 1980-81), Assn. U. Radiologists (pres. 1955-56, Gold medal 1979), N.Y. Roentgen Soc. (pres. 1961-62), N.Y. Gastroent. Soc. (pres. 1965-66), Soc. Chmn. Academic Radiology Depts. (pres. 1967-68), Eastern Radiol. Soc. (pres. 1985-86). Presbyterian. Home: Olympic K 9129 SE Riverfront Terr Tequesta FL 33469

SEAMAN, WILLIAM CASPER, retired news photographer; b. Grand Island, Nebr., Jan. 19, 1925; s. William H. and Minnie (Cords) S.; m. Ruth Witwer, Feb. 14, 1945; 1 son, Lawrence William. Grad. high sch. Photographer Leschinsky Studio, Grand Island; news photographer Mpls. Star & Tribune, 1945-82; ret., 1982. Recipient Pulitzer prize, 1959; also awards Nat. Headliners Club; also awards Nat. Press Photographers Assn.; also awards Inland Daily Press Assn.; also awards Kent State U.; also awards Mo. U.; also awards Local Page One; State A.P. contest; Silver Anniversary award Honeywell Photog. Products, 1975. Mem. Nat. Press Photographers Assn., Sigma Delta Chi. Home: 8206 Virginia Cir S Minneapolis MN 55426-2458

SEAMANS, ROBERT CHANNING, JR., astronautical engineering educator; b. Salem, Mass., Oct. 30, 1918; s. Robert Channing and Pauline (Bosson) S.; m. Eugenia Merrill, June 13, 1942; children: Katherine (Mrs. Louis Padulo), Robert Channing III, Joseph, May (Seamans Baldwin), Daniel M. BS, Harvard U., 1939; MS, MIT, 1942, ScD, 1951; grad. exec. program bus. adminstrn., Columbia U., 1959; DSc, Rollins Coll., 1962, NYU, 1967; DEng, Norwich Acad., 1971, Notre Dame U., 1974, Rensselaer Poly. Inst., 1974, U. Wyo., 1975, George Washington U., 1975, Lehigh U., 1976, Thomas Coll., 1980, Curry Coll., 1982. Successively instr. dept. aero. engring., staff engr. instrumentation lab., asst. prof., project leader instrumentation lab., asso. prof. Mass. Inst. Tech., 1941-55; chief engr. Project Meteor, 1950-53, dir. flight control lab., 1953-55; mgr. airborne systems lab., chief systems engr. airborne systems dept. RCA, 1955-58, chief engr. missile electronics and controls div., 1958-60; asso. adminstr. NASA, 1960-65, dep. adminstr., 1965-68, cons., 1968-69; vis. prof. MIT, 1968, Hunsaker prof., 1968-69; sec. air force, 1969-73; pres. Nat. Acad. Engring., 1973-74; adminstr. ERDA, Washington, 1974-77; Henry R. Luce prof. environment and pub. policy MIT, 1977-84, sr. lectr. dept. aeros. and astronautics, 1984—; dean Sch. Engring., 1978-81; mem. sci. adv. bd. USAF, 1957-62, assoc. adviser, 1963-67. Mem. bd. overseers Harvard U., 1968-74; trustee Mus. Sch., Boston, Sea Edn. Assn.; trustee emeritus Nat. Geog. Soc., Carnegie Inst., Washington, Woods Hole Oceanographic Inst. Recipient Naval Ordnance Devel. award, 1945; Godfrey L. Cabot award Aero Club New Eng., 1965; Distinguished Service medal NASA, 1965, 69; Robert H. Goddard Meml. trophy, 1968; Distinguished Pub. Service medal Dept. Def., 1973; Exceptional Civilian Service award Dept. Air Force, 1973; Gen. Thomas D. White U.S. Air Force Space Trophy, 1973; Ralph Coats Roe medal ASME, 1977; Achievement award Nat. Soc. Profl. Engrs.; Thomas D. White Nat. Def. award, 1980; Exceptional Service award Dept. Air Force, 1985. Fellow Am. Acad. Arts and Scis., Am. Astron. Soc., IEEE, AIAA (hon., Lawrence Sperry award 1951); mem. Internat. Acad. Astronautics, Am. Soc. Pub. Adminstrn., Nat. Acad. Engring., AAAS, Air Force Acad. Found., Fgn. Policy Assn., Coun. on Fgn. Rels., Sigma Xi. Clubs: Harvard (Boston); Manchester Yacht (Mass.); Essex County (Mass.); Chevy Chase, Metropolitan (Washington); Cruising of Am. (Boston Sta.). Office: 33-406 MIT Cambridge MA 02139

SEAMANS, WARREN ARTHUR, museum director; b. Loveland, Colo., Aug. 8, 1935; s. James Lamott and Eleanor Caroline (Baechler) S. BS, Colo. State U., 1957. Pers. officer Stone & Webster Engring. Co., Boston, 1963-64; pers. officer MIT, Cambridge, 1964-66, adminstrn. officer dept. humanities, 1966-71, founding dir. mus., 1971—. Capt. USAF, 1958-63. Mem. Am. Mus. Assn. Democrat. Avocations: history, gardening. Home: RR 1 Box 104A Rumney NH 03266-9706 Office: MIT Mus 265 Massachusetts Ave Cambridge MA 02139-4162

SEAMANS, WILLIAM, writer, commentator, former television-radio journalist; b. Providence, July 8, 1925; s. William and Mary Seamans; m. Jane Kingsbury, Sept. 15, 1951; children: Laurie, Jonathan, Adam. AB, Brown U., 1949; MS, Columbia U., 1952. Freelance journalist, 1952-53; journalist CBS News, 1953-63; producer evening news ABC News, 1963-65; European producer ABC News, London, 1965-70; field producer ABC News, N.Y.C., 1970-72; corr., bur. chief ABC News, Tel Aviv, 1972-92; commentator Vt. Pub. Radio, lectr., freelance writer, 1992—. Producer Nightline in Israel Week (including Palestinian-Israeli town meeting) (Emmy award, Dupont award). Served with inf. AUS, 1942-45. CBS Murrow News fellow Columbia U., 1961-62. Mem. Writers Guild Am., Nat. Acad. TV Arts and Scis. (Emmy award 1961, 89), Overseas Press Club Am. (award for best radio reporting invasion of Cyprus 1974, award for best fgn. affairs documentary Yitzhak Rabin biography 1975), Nat. Press Club (Washington), Fgn. Corrs. Assn. in Israel.

SEAMONS, QUINTON FRANK, lawyer; b. Idaho Falls, Idaho, Mar. 5, 1945; s. Eldon Monroe and Lois (Merrill) S.; m. Michele Geyer Seamons. BA cum laude with honors, Brigham Young U., 1968; JD, U. Utah, 1971. Bar: Utah 1971, D.C. 1976, Ill. 1977, U.S. Supreme Ct. 1975, U.S. Ct. Appeals (7th cir.) 1979, U.S. Dist. Ct. (no. dist.) Ill. 1978. Legis. asst. U.S. Senate, Washington, 1969-71; law clk. Utah Atty. Gen., Salt Lake City, 1970-71; staff atty., legal counsel divsn. mkt. regulation SEC, Washington, 1971-76; ptnr. Wilson & McIlvaine, Chgo., 1976—. Assoc. editor U. Utah Law Jour., 1969; contbr. various articles to profl. jours. Trustee Riverwoods Homeowners Assn., Ill., 1992, Cancer Coun., 1980-84; Vol. Legal Svcs, Chgo., 1993 (bd. dirs., 1994), Northfield Park Dist. Coach, 1978-84, Task Force on SEC Safe Harbor. Hinckley scholar, U. Utah, 1969; recipient Outstanding Young Men of Am. award, 1970, Am. Jurisprudence award Bancroft-Whitney Co. and U. Utah, 1971. Mem. ABA (bus. law sect., task force on SEL safe harbor, litigation sect.), Chgo. Bar Assn. (securities law com., corps. com., class actions com.), Assn. Trial Lawyers Am., Blue Key, Phi Kappa Phi, Phi Alpha Delta, Phi Sigma Alpha. Avocations: sports memorabilia, reading and research of Civil War, Renaissance & Medieval history, book collecting, basketball, health club. Office: Wilson & McIlvaine 500 W Madison St Ste # 3700 Chicago IL 60661-2511

SEAPKER, JANET KAY, museum director; b. Pitts., Nov. 2, 1947; d. Charles Henry and Kathryn Elizabeth (Dany) S.; m. Edward F. Turberg, May 24, 1975. BA, U. Pitts., 1969; MA, SUNY, Cooperstown, 1975. Park ranger Nat. Park Svc., summers 1967-69; archtl. historian N.C. Archives and History, Raleigh, 1971-76, hist. preservation adminstr., 1976-77, grant-in-aid adminstr., 1977-78; dir. Cape Fear Mus. (formerly New Hanover County Mus.), Wilmington, N.C., 1978—; bd. dirs. Bellamy Mansion Found., Wilmington, 1986-89, 91—, Lower Cape Fear Hist. Soc., Wilmington, 1985-88; N.C. rep. S.E. Mus. Conf., 1986-90; field reviewer Inst. Mus. Svcs., 1982—. Contbr. articles to profl. jours. Bd. dirs. Downtown Area Revitalization Effort, Wilmington, 1979-81, Hist. Wilmington Found., 1979-84, pres., 1980-81; mem. Community Appearance Commn., Wilmington, 1984-88, 250 Ann. Commn., Wilmington, 1986-90. Grad. program fellow SUNY, Cooperstown, 1969-70; recipient Profl. Svc. award N.C. Mus. Coun., 1982, Woman of Achievement award YWCA, 1994. Mem. Am. Assn. Mus. (accreditation vis. com. 1983—, reviewer mus. assessment program 1982—), Nat. Trust Hist. Preservation, Southeastern Mus. Conf. (N.C. state rep. 1986-90), N.C. Mus. Coun. (sec.-treas. 1978-84, pres. 1984-86), Hist. Preservation Found N.C. (sec. 1976-78). Democrat. Presbyterian. Home: 307 N 15th St Wilmington NC 28401-3813 Office: Cape Fear Mus 814 Market St Wilmington NC 28401

SEAQUIST, ERNEST RAYMOND, astronomy educator; b. Vancouver, B.C., Can., Nov. 19, 1938; s. Egron Emanuel and Sigrid Alice (Back) S.; m. Gloria Stewart Jenkins, June 11, 1966; children: Jonathan William, Carolyn Suzanne. BASc, U. B.C., Vancouver, 1961; MA, U. Toronto, Ont., Can., 1962, PhD, 1966. Lectr. astronomy U. Toronto, 1965-66, asst. prof., 1966-72, assoc. prof., 1972-78, prof., 1978—, assoc. chm. dept., 1974-88, chmn., 1988—; dir. David Dunlap Obs. U. Toronto, Richmond Hill, Ont., 1988—. Contbr. author: Classical Novae, 1989; also over 150 articles. Rsch. grantee Natural Scis. and Engring. Rsch. Coun. Can., 1967—. Mem. Internat. Astron. Union, Am. Astron. Soc., Can. Astron. Soc. (pres. 1986-88). Avocations: painting and sketching, collecting antiques. Office: U Toronto Dept Astronomy, 60 St George St, Toronto, ON Canada M5S 1A7

SEAR, MOREY LEONARD, federal judge, educator; b. New Orleans, Feb. 26, 1929; s. William and Yetty (Streiffer) S.; m. Lee Edrehi, May 26, 1951; children: William Sear II, Jane Lee. J.D., Tulane U., 1950. Bar: La. 1950. Asst. dist. atty. Parish Orleans, 1952-55; individual practice law Stahl & Sear, New Orleans, 1955-71; spl. counsel New Orleans Aviation Bd., 1956-60; magistrate U.S. Dist. Ct. (ea. dist.) La., 1971-76, judge, 1976—, chief judge, 1992— ; judge Temp. Emergency Ct. of Appeals, 1982-87; adj. prof. Tulane U. Coll. Law; former chmn. com. on adminstrn. of bankruptcy sys. Jud. Conf. U.S., former chmn. adv. com. on bankruptcy rules, mem. exec. com., jud. conf. U.S., former mem. jud. conf. com. on adminstrn. Fed. Magistrates Sys.; mem. cir. coun. 5th Cir. of U.S.; founding dir. River Oaks Pvt. Psychiat. Hosp., 1968. Pres. Congregation Temple Sinai, 1977-79; bd. govs. Tulane Med. Ctr., 1977—; former chmn. Tulane Med. Ctr. Hosp. and Clinic, 1980-85. Mem. ABA, La. Bar Assn., New Orleans Bar Assn., Order of Barristers, Order of the Coif (hon.). Office: US Dist Ct C-256 US Courthouse 500 Camp St New Orleans LA 70130-3313

SEARCY, ALAN WINN, chemist, educator; b. Covina, Calif., Oct. 12, 1925; s. Claude Winn and Esther (Scofield) S.; m. Gail Vaught, Oct. 30, 1945; children: Gay, William, Anne. A.B., Pomona Coll., 1946; Ph.D., U. Calif. at Berkeley, 1950. Faculty Purdue U., 1949-54, asst. prof. chemistry, 1950-54; faculty U. Calif., Berkeley, 1954—, prof., 1958-91, prof. materials sci., 1960-91, prof. emeritus, 1991—, assoc. div. head inorganic materials div. Lawrence Radiation Lab., 1961-64, asst. to chancellor, 1963-64, vice-chancellor, 1964-67, chmn. faculty Coll. Engring., 1969-70, Miller rsch. prof., 1970-71, acting chmn. dept. materials sci. and engring., 1973; assoc. dir. Lawrence Berkeley Lab., head materials and molecular research div., 1980-84; Fulbright lectr. phys. chemistry Inst. Physics, Bariloche, Argentina, 1960; cons. Gen. Motors Tech. Center, 1956-64, Union Carbide, 1956-72, Gen. Atomic, 1957-72; Mem. com. high temperature chemistry NRC, 1961-70. Editor: (with D.V. Ragone, U. Colombo) Chemical and Mechanical Behavior of Inorganic Materials, 1970; editl. adv. bd. High Temperature High Pressure, 1969-93, High Temperature Sci., 1969-94, Advanced in High Temperature Chemistry, 1971-75, Materials Chemistry and Physics, 1976-87, Reactivity of Solids, High Temperature and Materials Science, 1994—; contbr. numerous articles to profl. jours. Served with AUS, 1944-46. Recipient citation for distinction in rsch. U. Calif., Berkeley, 1991; Guggenheim fellow, 1967-68. Fellow Am. Ceramic Soc., AAAS; mem. Am. Chem. Soc., Acad. of Ceramics (charter), Materials Rsch. Assn., Phi Beta Kappa, Sigma Xi. Home: 24 Northampton Ave Berkeley CA 94707-1715

SEARCY, JARRELL D. (JAY), sportswriter; b. Stevenson, Ala., Mar. 26, 1934; s. Harley Johnson and Dovie Mae (Ryan) S.; m. Jackie Lou Hildebrand, Nov. 17, 1957; children—Michael Jarrell, Mark William. Student, U. Tenn., 1953-54, East Tenn. State U., 1956-57. Reporter Kingsport Times-News, Tenn., 1956-57; reporter Chattanooga Times, 1958-64, sports editor, 1964-71; editor/reporter N.Y. Times, N.Y.C., 1972-75; exec. sports editor Phila. Inquirer, 1975-86, sr. writer, 1986—. Author: (with Sam Goldaper) Golden State Warrior, 1975. Mem. Nat. Turf Writers' Assn., Baseball Writers Assn. Am., Football Writers Assn. Am., Nat. Sportswriters and Broadcasters Assn., AP Sports Editors Assn. (pres. 1984-85), Quality Life Assn. (pres. 1990). Avocations: tennis; golf; gardening. Office: Phila Inquirer 400 N Broad St Philadelphia PA 19130-4099

SEARCY, JAY, Sportswriter. Office: The Phila Inquirer 400 N Board St Philadelphia PA 19103

SEARING, MARJORY ELLEN, government official, economist; b. N.Y.C., Mar. 29, 1945; d. William Edgar Searing and Jean Frances (Smith) Searing Fusaro; m. Warren Eugene Lane, Mar. 3, 1977; children—Gary Francis, Jennifer Rebecca, Stephanie Anne. B.A. in Econs., SUNY-Binghamton, 1966; M.A. in Econs., Georgetown U., 1969, Ph.D. in Econs., 1972. Economist Bur. Econs. Analysis U.S. Dept. Commerce, Washington, 1967-73, internat. economist Bur. East-West Trade, 1973-74, dir. Office Internat. Sector Policy, 1980-84, dir. Office Industry Assessment, 1984-86, acting dep. asst. sec. sci. and electronics, 1984-85, dir. Office Multilateral Affairs, 1986-90; dep. asst. sec. for Japan U.S. Dept. Commerce, 1991—; sr. internat. economist Office Trade Policy U.S. Dept. Treasury, Washington, 1974-76, dir. Office East-West Econ. Policy, 1976-79. Contbr. numerous articles to profl. publs. N.Y. State Regents scholar, 1962-65; Georgetown U. fellow, 1966-71. Office: US Dept Commerce Rm 2318 14th & Constitution Ave NW Washington DC 20230-0002

SEARLE, ELEANOR MILLARD, history educator; b. Chgo., Oct. 29, 1926; married. BA, Harvard U., 1948; Licentiate Medieval Studies, Pontifical Inst. Medieval History, 1961, D Medieval Studies, 1972. Lectr. history Calif. Inst. Tech., Pasadena, 1962-63, prof. history, 1979-87, Edie and Lou Wasserman prof. history, 1987—; rsch. fellow Rsch. Sch. Social Sci., Australian Nat. U., 1963-65, fellow, 1965-68; assoc. prof. UCLA, 1969-72, prof., 1972-79; vis. fellow Cambridge U., 1976, 81; vis. rsch. fellow Huntington Libr., 1986—; cons. Huntington Libr., 1980-82. Author: Lordship and Community: Battle Abbey and Its Banlieu, 1066-1538, 1974; editor: The Chronicle of Battle Abbey, 1980; co-editor: Accounts of the Cellarers of Battle Abbey, 1967, Predatory Kinship and the Creation of Norman Power, 840-1066, 1988; contbr. articles to profl. jours. Fellow Royal Hist. Soc., Royal Soc. Antiquaries of London; mem. Am. Hist. Soc., Medieval Acad. Am. (pres. 1985-86), Econ. History Soc., Am. Soc. Legal History, Haskins Soc. (bd. dirs. 1982—, pres. 1990—). Office: Calif Inst Tech Dept History Pasadena CA 91125

SEARLE, LEONARD, astronomer, researcher. Dir. Carnegie Inst. Washington Observatories, Pasadena, Calif. Office: Carnegie Observatories 813 Santa Barbara St Pasadena CA 91101-1232

SEARLE, PHILIP FORD, bank executive; b. Kansas City, Mo., July 23, 1924; s. Albert Addison and Edith (Thompson) S.; m. Jean Adair Hanneman, Nov. 22, 1950 (dec. Nov. 1990); 1 child, Charles Randolph; m. Jean Walker, Oct. 4, 1992 (dec. Oct. 1993); m. Elizabeth Gordon, Nov. 4, 1994. AB, Cornell U., 1949; grad. in banking, Rutgers U., 1957, 64. With Geneva (Ohio) Savs. and Trust Co., 1949-60, pres., 1959-60; pres., sr. trust officer Northeastern Ohio Nat. Bank, Ashtabula, 1960-69; pres., chief exec. officer BancOhio Corp., Columbus, 1969-75; chmn., chief exec. officer Flagship Banks, Inc., Miami, Fla., 1975-84; chmn. bd. Sun Banks, Inc., Orlando, Fla., 1984-85, cons., 1986-94; mem. faculty Sch. Banking, Ohio U., 1959-70, Nat. Trust Sch., Northwestern U., Evanston, Ill., 1965; mem. corp. adv. com. Nat. Assn. Securities Dealers, 1981-83; v.p., mem. fed. adv. coun. to bd. govs. FRS, 1983-85; chmn. Nat. Adv. Bd. to Oversight Bd. for Resolution Trust Corp., 1991-92; bd. dirs. ALLTEL Corp., chmn. audit com. Co-author: The Management of a Trust Department, 1967. Past chmn. bd. regents Stonier Grad. Sch. Banking, Rutgers U., 1974-76, past mem. faculty; trustee Fin. Acctg. Found., Norwalk, Conn., 1989-93. Capt. AUS, 1943-46, 51-52. Decorated Bronze Star; named Outstanding Citizen in Ashtabula County, 1967. Mem. Am. Bankers Assn. (bd. dirs. 1972-74, governing coun.), Bank Adminstrn. Inst. (nat. chmn 1987-88, bd. dirs. Chgo., Ill. 1985-89), Fla. Bankers Assn. (bd. dirs. 1979-81, coun. 1981), Ohio Bankers Assn. (pres. 1970-71), Assn. Bank Holding Cos. (bd. dirs. 1979-81, exec. com. 1981), Fla. Assn. Registered Bank Holding Cos. (pres. 1979-81), Fla. C. of C. (bd. dirs. 1978-82), Royal Poinciana Golf Club (Naples, Fla.), Madison (Ohio) Country Club, Phi Kappa Tau.

SEARLE, RODNEY NEWELL, state legislator, farmer, insurance agent; b. Camden, N.J., July 17, 1920; s. William Albert and Ruby Marie (Barrus) S.; m. Janette Elizabeth Christie, May 17, 1941; children: R. Newell Jr., Linda Jennison, Alan John. B.A., Mankato State U., 1960. Prodn. coordinator Johnson & Johnson, New Brunswick, N.J., 1940-47; farmer Waseca, Minn., 1947—; spl. agt. John Hancock Mut. Ins. Co., Waseca, Minn., 1961-84; mem. Minn. Ho. of Reps., St. Paul, 1957—, speaker, 1979—. Author: Minnesota Standoff—The Politics of Deadlock, 1990. Lay reader St. John's Episcopal Ch., 1952—; chmn. Upper Mississippi River Basin Commn., 1981-82; pres. Minn. State U. Bd., 1981-92; chmn. Minn. Higher Edn. Bd., 1991-92; bd. dirs. Minn. Wellsprings, 1984-90; emeritus mem. adv. bd. Hubert H. Humphrey Inst.; emeritus mem. coun. Minn. Hist. Soc.; bd. dirs. Minn. Agrl. Interpretive Ctr., 1983—. Named Minn. State Tree Farmer of Yr., 1978. Mem. Am. Tree Farm System, Nat. Conf. State Legislators, Minn. Forestry Assn. (bd. dirs. 1991—), Masons, Rotary (pres. club 1968). Republican.

SEARLE, RONALD, artist; b. Cambridge, Eng., Mar. 3, 1920; s. William James and Nellie (Hunt) S.; m. Monica Koenig, 1967. Ed., Cambridge Sch. Art. Author: pub. in U.S. The Female Approach, 1954, Merry England, 1957; (with Kaye Webb) Paris Sketchbook, 1958, The St. Trinian's Story, 1959, Refugees, 1960, (with Alex Atkinson) The Big City, 1958, U.S.A. for Beginners, 1959, Russia for Beginners, 1960, Escape from the Amazon, 1964, Which Way Did He Go?, 1962, From Frozen North to Filthy Lucre, 1964, Those Magnificent Men in Their Flying Machines, 1965, (with Heinz Huber) Haven't we Met Before Somewhere?, 1966, Searle's Cats, 1968, The Square Egg, 1969, Hello: Where Did All the People Go?, 1970, (with Kildare Dobbs) The Great Fur Opera, 1970, The Addict, 1971, More Cats, 1975, Zoodiac, 1978, Ronald Searle Album, 1979, The Situation is Hopeless, 1981, The Big Fat Cat Book, 1982, Winespeak, 1983, Ronald Searle in Perspective, 1985, To the Kwai– and Back, 1986, Something in the Cellar, 1988, Ah Yes, I Remember It Well: Paris 1961-75, 1988, Ronald Searle's Non-Sexist Dictionary, 1989, Slightly Foxed- But Still Desirable, 1989, The Curse of St. Trinian's, 1993, Marquis de Sade Meets Goody Two-Shoes, 1994; contbr. to New Yorker; 1st pub. work appeared in Cambridge Daily News, 1935-39; subject of Ronald Searle : a biography by Russell Davies, 1992; one-man shows include Leicester Galleries, London, 1948, 50, 54, 57, Kraushaar Gallery, N.Y.C., 1959, Blanchini Gallery, N.Y.C., 1963, city mus. Bremen, Hannover, Dusseldorf, Stuttgart, Berlin, 1965, 3d Biennale, Tolentino, Italy, 1965, Galerie Pro Arte, Delmenhorst, Germany, Mus. Art, Bremerhaven, Germany, Galerie Münsterberg, Basle, Switzerland, Galerie Pribaut, Amsterdam, Holland, Wolfgang-Gurlitt Mus., Linz, Austria, Galerie La Pochade, Paris, 1966-71, Art Alliance Gallery, Phila., 1967, Galerie Gurlitt, Munich, 1967-76, Grosvenor Gallery, London, 1968, Galerie Obere Zaune, Zurich, 1968, Galerie Hauswedell, Baden-Baden, 1968, Galerie Brumme, Frankfurt, 1969, Konsthallen, Södertälje, Sweden, 1969, Rizzoli Gallery, N.Y.C., 1969-81, Kunsthalle, Konstanz, 1970, Würzburg, 1970, Galerie Welz, Salzburg, 1971, Galerie Rivolta, Lausanne, 1972, Galerie Gaëton, Geneva, 1972, Bibliothèque Nationale, Paris, 1973, Galerie Würthle, Vienna, 1973, Kulterhaus Graz, Austria, 1973, 79, Galerie Rivolta, Lausanne, 1974, 78, Galerie l'Angle Aigu, Brussels, 1974, 77, Galerie Carmen Casse, Paris, 1975-77, Staatliche Museen Preussicher Kulturbesitz, Berlin, 1976, Galerie Bartsch and Chariau, Munich, 1981, Neue Galerie Wien, Vienna, 1985, 1988, Imperial War Mus., London, 1986, British Mus., London, 1986, Fitzwilliam Mus., Cambridge, 1987, Fine Arts Mus., San Francisco, 1987, Heineman Galleries, N.Y., 1994, Wilhelm Busch Mus., Hannover, 1995, others; contbr. to nat. publs., 1946—; theatre artist: Punch, 1949-61; created series of cartoons on fictitious girls sch., 1941, which became a film series called Belles of St. Trinian's, 1954, Blue Murder at St. Trinian's, 1957, The Pure Hell of St. Trinian's, 1960, The Great St. Trinian's Train Robbery, 1965, Wildcats of St. Trinian's, 1980; films designs include John Gilpin (Brit. Film Inst.), 1951, On the Twelfth Day, 1954 (nominated Acad. award), Energetically Yours, 1957, The Kings Breakfast, 1963, Those Magnificient Men in Their Flying Machines, 1965, Monte Carlo or Bust, 1969, Scrooge, 1970, Dick Deadeye, or Duty Done, 1975. Recipient medal Art Dirs. Club Los Angeles, 1959, medal Art Dirs. Mem. Club Phila., Pa., 1959, gold medal 3d Biennale, Tolentino, Italy, 1965, Prix de la Critique Belge, 1968, medaille de la ville d'Avignon, 1971, Prix de l' Humour S.P.H. Festival d' Avignon, 1971, Prix de l' Humour Noir Granville France, 1971, Prix Internationale Charles Huard France, 1972, Best Advt. Illustration award Nat. Cartoonists Soc.,

1988. Club: The Garrick (London). Home: care Tessa Sayle, 11 Jubilee Pl, London SW 3-3TE England Office: care John Locke Studio 15 E 76th St New York NY 10021-1719

SEARLE, STEWART A., transportation equipment holding company executive; b. Winnipeg, Man., Can., 1923; s. Stewart Augustus and Sally Elizabeth (Appleyard) S.; m. Maudie Jessiman, Nov. 9, 1949; children: Stewart A., David J. Student, Trinity Coll., Port Hope, Ont., Queen's U., Kingston, Ont. Chmn. bd. dirs. Fed. Industries, Ltd., Winnipeg. Served to lt. RCAF. Office: Fed Industries Ltd, 1 Lombard Pl, Winnipeg, MB Canada R3B 0X3

SEARLE, WILLIAM LOUIS, investment company executive; b. Evanston, Ill., Mar. 4, 1928; s. John Gideon and Frances (Crow) S.; m. Sally Burnett, Dec. 4, 1953; children: Marion, Elizabeth Searle Reichert, Louise Searle Klarr. B.A., U. Mich., 1951; postgrad., Harvard, 1969. With G. D. Searle & Co., Chgo., 1953-83; v.p. marketing G. D. Searle & Co., 1965-68, v.p., gen. mgr., 1968-70, sr. v.p., gen. mgr., 1970-72, chmn. bd., 1972-77, vice chmn., 1977-78, chmn. pension com., 1977-83; dir. Kinship Corp., Northbrook, Ill., 1983—. Served with Chem. Corps AUS, 1951. Clubs: Chicago (Chgo.). Office: Kinship Corp 400 Skokie Blvd Ste 675 Northbrook IL 60062

SEARLES, DEWITT RICHARD, retired investment firm executive, retired air force officer; b. Birmingham, Ala., Aug. 7, 1920; s. DeWitt Richard and Miriam (Hostetler) S.; m. Barbara Elizabeth Brown, Jan. 28, 1949; children: Ann Hampton, DeWitt Richard III, Elizabeth Alison. Student, Coll. William and Mary, 1939-41; B.A., U. Md., 1949; M.A., George Washington U., 1964; grad., Army Command and Gen. Staff Sch., Ft. Leavenworth, Kans., 1945, USAF Command and Gen. Staff Coll., Maxwell AFB, Ala., 1956, Nat. War Coll., Washington, 1964. Commd. 2d lt. USAAF, 1942; advanced through grades to maj. gen. USAF, 1971; fighter pilot and squadron comdr. New Guinea and Philippines, 1943-45; wing comdr. 81st Tactical Fighter Wing, Eng., 1965-67; insp. gen. Tactical Air Command, Langley AFB, Va., 1967-69; comdr. 327th Air Div., Taiwan, Republic of China, 1969-71; dep. comdr. 7/13 Air Force, Udorn AFB, Thailand, 1971-72; dep. insp. gen. Hdqrs. USAF, Washington, 1972-74, ret.; asst. v.p. Merrill Lynch, Pierce, Fenner & Smith, Washington, 1974-87, ret., 1987. Decorated D.S.M. with 2 oak leaf clusters, Legion of Merit with oak leaf cluster, D.F.C., Air medal with 7 oak leaf clusters. Home: 1605 Dunterry Pl Mc Lean VA 22101-4318

SEARLES, RICHARD BROWNLEE, botany educator, marine biology researcher; b. Riverside, Calif., June 19, 1936; s. Nathan Francis and Margaret Louise (Ashbrook) S.; m. Georgiana Elizabeth Miller, June 11, 1957; children: Timothy Edward, Andrew Nathan, Elizabeth Louise. AB, Pomona Coll., Claremont, Calif., 1958; PhD, U. Calif., Berkeley, 1965. Asst. prof. botany Duke U., Durham, N.C., 1965-69, assoc. prof., 1969-83, prof., 1983—, chmn. dept., 1991—. Co-author: Seaweeeds of the Southeastern U.S., 1991. Served to 2d lt. U.S. Army, 1961-63, capt. Res. ret. Recipient Gerald W. Prescott Award., 1993, Psychologog. Soc. Am. Mem. Internat. Phycol. Soc., Phycol. Soc. Am., Brit. Phycol. Soc., Oceanographic Soc. Am., Phi Beta Kappa, Sigma Xi. Unitarian. Home: 1800 Woodburn Rd Durham NC 27705-5725 Office: Duke Univ Dept Botany Durham NC 27706

SEARLS, EILEEN HAUGHEY, lawyer, librarian, educator; b. Madison, Wis., Apr. 27, 1925; d. Edward M. and Anna Mary (Haughey) S.; BA, U. Wis., 1948, JD, 1950, MS in Libr. Sci., 1951. Bar: Wis. 1950. Cataloger Yale U., 1951-52; instr. law St. Louis U., 1952-53, asst. prof., 1953-56, assoc. prof., 1956-64, prof., 1964—, law librarian, 1952—. Mem. Am. Lib. Assn., Wis. Bar Assn., Bar Assn. Met. St. Louis, Am. Assn. Law Librs., Mid-Am. Assn. Law Librs., Southwestern Assn. Law Librs., Altrusa Club. Office: 3700 Lindell Blvd Saint Louis MO 63108-3478

SEARS, BRADFORD GEORGE, landscape architect; b. Philmont, N.Y., June 21, 1915; s. Russell Lockwood and Alla (Scutt) S.; m. Ruth Ellen Fox, July 5, 1936; children—Bradford Alan, Brian Scutt, Patricia Ruth. B.S., N.Y. State Coll. Forestry, 1939, M.S., 1948. With State U. N.Y., Syracuse, 1941-76; prof. landscape architecture State U. N.Y., 1950-76, dean landscape architecture, 1968-76, dean emeritus, 1976—; pvt. practice landscape architecture, 1968-76, dean emeritus, 1976—; vis. lectr. Sch. Design, N.C. State U., 1978-83; mem. bd. landscape architecture N.Y. State Dept. Edn., 1967-79. Contbr. articles to profl. jours. and manuals. Fellow Am. Soc. Landscape Architects; mem. (past pres. N.Y. Upstate chpt., past chmn. nat. accreditation bd. for profl. programs), Am. Camping Assn. Methodist. Address: 116 Wellwood Dr Fayetteville NY 13066

SEARS, CURTIS THORNTON, JR., educational administrator; b. Wareham, Mass., Aug. 3, 1938; s. Curtis Thornton Sr. and Ruth (Blake) S.; m. Martha Wilda Colvin, July 5, 1960 (div. May 1977); children: Amy Elizabeth, Leslie Edward; m. Ronnie Spilton, Mar. 23, 1980. AB, W.Va. Wesleyan U., 1961; PhD, U. N.C., 1966. NATO postdoctoral fellow Bristol (Eng.) U., 1966-67; asst. prof. chemistry U. S.C., Columbia, 1967-71; from asst. to assoc. prof. Ga. State U., Atlanta, 1977, assoc. chmn. chemistry dept., 1986-91, assoc. v.p. rsch. and info. tech., 1993-94; reviewer NSF, Washington, 1975—, vis. scientist, 1991-92, 94. Author: Inquiries in Chemistry, 1977, Chemistry for the Health Sciences, 1976, 2d edit., 1982, Aspects of Chemistry, 1979. NATO fellow NSF, 1966; Recipient Teaching award Nat. Sci. Tchrs. Assn., 1973, Arts and Scis. Teaching award Ga. State U., 1977. Mem. Am. Chem. Soc., Royal Soc. Chemistry, Exams. Inst. of Am. Chem. Soc. (chair commn. 1986-91). Methodist. Avocations: cooking, gardening. Office: Ga State U Research Office Atlanta GA 30303

SEARS, EDWARD MILNER, JR., newspaper editor; b. Bluefield, W.Va., Dec. 28, 1944; s. Edward Milner and Helene (Stras) S.; m. Jo Ann Langworthy, May 15, 1971; 1 child, Helene Mateer. B.S. in Journalism, U. Fla., 1967. Makeup editor Atlanta Constn., 1970, news editor, 1971-73, feature editor, 1974, city editor, 1975-76, asst. mng. editor, 1977, mng. editor, 1978-80; mng. editor Atlanta Jour., 1980-82, Atlanta Jour. and Atlanta Constn., 1982-85; editor Palm Beach Post, 1985—. Served with U.S. Army, 1968-69. Mem. Fla. Soc. Newspaper Editors, Am. Soc. Newspaper Editors, Sigma Delta Chi. Home: 230 Dyer Rd West Palm Beach FL 33405-1218 Office: Palm Beach Post 2751 S Dixie Hwy West Palm Beach FL 33405-1298

SEARS, GEORGE AMES, lawyer; b. Chehalis, Wash., Oct. 17, 1926; s. Briton Wallis and Merle (Kelso) S.; m. Mary Ann Deggeller, May 5, 1951; children: Kathrin Elizabeth, Geoffrey John. BA, Yale U., 1949; JD, Stanford U., 1952. Bar: Calif. 1952. Assoc. Pillsbury, Madison and Sutro, San Francisco, 1952-58, ptnr., 1959—, chmn. firm, 1984-89. Bd. dirs. Bay Area Coun., San Francisco, 1984-89, Invest-in-Am. No. Calif. Coun., San Francisco, 1988-90, Marin Conservation League, 1992—; trustee Marin Country Day Sch., Corte Madera, Calif., 1961-65; mem. exec. com. bd. visitors Stanford (Calif.) U. Law Sch., 1982-86; mem. bd. visitors Brigham Young U. Law Sch., Provo, Utah, 1986-88; pres. Stanford U. Law Fund, 1985-86; pres. Legal Aid Soc., San Francisco, 1969-70; mem. Coun. Friends of Bancroft Libr., 1993—. With USN, 1945-46. Fellow Am. Coll. Trial Lawyers, Am. Bar Found.; mem. ABA, Calif. Bar Assn. (chmn. adminstrn. of justice com. 1973-74), San Francisco Bar Assn., Pacific-Union Club, Belvedere Tennis Club. Avocations: reading, music, hiking, tennis. Home: 161 Harrison Ave Sausalito CA 94965-2043 Office: Pillsbury Madison & Sutro 225 Bush St San Francisco CA 94104-4207

SEARS, JOANNE LEWIS, retired educator, author; b. Shreveport, La., Aug. 19, 1930; d. Alfred Raleigh Lewis and Alice Lorene (Featherstone) Barr; m. Arthur Whiting Lynn, Sept. 8, 1951 (div. 1979); children: Robin Lorene, Steven Andrew, Katherine Margaret; m. Donald Albert Sears, Aug. 18, 1989 (dec. May 1994). BA cum laude, Pomona Coll., 1952; MA, Calif. State U., Fullerton, 1965; PhD, U. Calif., Irvine, 1974. Instr. English Fullerton Coll., 1964-65; prof. English, Calif. State U., Fullerton, 1965-92, emeritus prof., 1992—; freelance writer. Mem. Am. Soc. 18th Century Studies. Republican. Home: 1647-A Posilipo Ln Santa Barbara CA 93108

SEARS, JOHN PATRICK, lawyer; b. Syracuse, N.Y., July 3, 1940; s. James Louis and Helen Mary (Fitzgerald) S.; m. Carol Jean Osborne, Aug. 25, 1962; children: James Louis, Ellen Margaret, Amy Elizabeth. B.S.,

Notre Dame U., 1960; LL.B., J.D., Georgetown U., 1963. Bar: N.Y. bar 1963. Clk. N.Y. Ct. Appeals, 1963-65; asso. firm Nixon, Mudge, Rose, Guthrie, Alexander & Mitchell, 1965-66; mem. staff Richard M. Nixon, 1966-69; dep. counsel to Pres. Nixon, 1969-70; ptnr. Gadsby & Hannah, Washington, 1970-75, Baskin & Sears, Washington, 1977-84; sole practice Washington, 1984—; mgr. Ronald Regan's Presdl. Campaign, 1975-76, 79-80; polit. analyst NBC Today Show, 1984-89; mem. Wall Street Jour. bd. of polit. experts, 1984—; columnist LA Times, Newsday, 1992—. Fellow Kennedy Inst. Politics, Harvard, 1970. Home: 2801 New Mexico Ave NW Washington DC 20007-3921 Office: 2021 K St NW Washington DC 20006-1003

SEARS, JOHN WINTHROP, lawyer, administrator; b. Boston, Dec. 18, 1930; s. Richard Dudley and Frederica Fulton (Leser) S.; m. Catherine Coolidge, 1965 (div. 1970). AB magna cum laude, Harvard U., 1952, JD, 1959; MLitt, Oxford U., 1957. Bar: Mass. 1959, U.S. Dist. Ct. Mass. 1982. Rep. Brown Bros. Harriman, N.Y.C., 1959-63, Boston, 1963-66; mem. Mass. Ho. Reps. 1965-68; sheriff Suffolk County, Mass., 1968-69; chmn. Boston Fin. Commn., 1969-70, Met. Dist. Commn., 1970-75; councillor-at-large Boston City Coun., 1980-82; trustee Sears Office, Boston, 1975—; apptd. bd. dirs. Fulbright Scholarship, 1991-93. Contbr. articles to profl. jours. Trustee Christ's Ch., Longwood, Brookline Mass., 1965—, Sears Trusts, Boston, 1975—; hon. trustee J.F. Kennedy Libr., 1991—; bd. dirs. Middlesex Club, Ripon Soc., Mus. Am. Textile Heritage, 1987—, Shirley-Eustis Assoc., Environ. League Mass., 1994—. Rep. candidate Mayor of Boston, 1967, Sec. State, Mass., 1978, Gov. of Mass., 1982; vice chmn. Ward 5 Rep. Com., 1965-69, 75-85; chmn. Rep. State Com., 1975-76, mem., 80-85; del. Rep. Nat. Conv., 1968, 76, State Conv., 1966-92; mem. U.S. Electoral Coll., 1984; bd. dirs. United South End Settlements, 1966—, chmn., 1977-78. Lt. comdr. USNR, 1952-54, 61-62. Rhodes scholar, 1955; recipient Outstanding Pub. Servant award Mass. Legis. Assn., 1975. Mem. Mass. Bar Assn., New Eng. Hist. and Geneal. Soc. (bd. dirs., councillor 1977-82), Mass. Hist. Soc., Handel and Haydn Soc. (gov. 1982-87), Signet Soc., Boston Atheneum, Tennis and Racquet Club, Somerset Club, The Country Club (Brookline), St. Botolph Club, Wed. Evening Club of 1777, Spee Club (Cambridge chpt., pres., trustee), Phi Beta Kappa. Republican. Home: 7 Acorn St Boston MA 02108-3501

SEARS, MARVIN, ophthalmologist, educator; b. N.Y.C., Sept. 16, 1928; s. Louis and Blanche Sears; children: Anne, David, Jonathan, Edward, Benjamin. AB, Princeton U., 1949; MD, Columbia U., 1953. Intern Bellevue Hosp., N.Y.C., 1954; resident in ophthalmology Johns Hopkins Hosp., 1954-61; fellow NIH, 1959-60; chmn. sect. ophthalmology Yale-New Haven (Conn.) Hosp., 1961-71; asst. prof. dept. ophthalmology and visual sci. Yale U. Sch. Medicine, 1961-64, assoc. prof., 1964-69, prof., 1969—, chmn., 1971-93; cons. Vets. Meml. Med. Ctr., Meriden, Conn., 1986—, Princess Margaret Hosp., Nassau, 1982—, Waterbury (Conn.) Hosp., 1975—, William W. Backus Hosp., Norwich, Conn., 1974—, Hosp. Albert Schweitzer, Des Chapelles, Haiti, 1968-83, Jenkins (Ky.) Clinic Hosp., 1968, Hosp. St. Raphael, New Haven, New Britain (Conn.) Gen. Hosp.; chief cons. VA Med. Ctr., West Haven, Conn., 1961—; instr. Johns Hopkins Hosp., 1959-61; vis. prof. dept. ophthalmology U. Puerto Rico; mem. numerous adv. coms. Editorial bd.: Am. Jour. Ophthalmology, 1967-82, Investigative Ophthalmology, 1968-78, Jour. Ocular Pharmacology, 1985—; contbr. articles to profl. jours. Recipient McKosh prize/Epistemology, Princeton U., 1949, Schwenther medal Johns Hopkins Hosp., 1958, Alcon Rsch. Inst. award, 1985, Method to Extend Rsch. in Time award Nat. Eye Inst., 1990—; named Gifford lectr. Chgo. Ophthal. Soc., 1985; endowed professorship established in Sears' name Yale U., 1993. Fellow ACS, Pierson Coll. Yale U.; mem. Am. Acad. Ophthalmology, Am. Ophthal. Soc., Assn. for Rsch. in Vision and Ophthalmology (Jonas S. Friedenwald award 1977), Assn. Univ. Profs. Ophthalmology, Conn. State Med. Soc., Internat. Agy. for Prevention Blindness, Internat. Soc. for Eye Rsch., New England Ophthal. Soc. (award 1969), Pan Am. Assn. Ophthalmology, Soc. Eye Surgeons, Wilmer Residents Assn., Appalachian Mountain Club, Audubon Soc., Lions (Melvin Jones fellow). Jewish. Avocation: mountaineering. Office: Yale Eye Ctr PO Box 208061 330 Cedar St New Haven CT 06520-8061

SEARS, MARY HELEN, lawyer; b. Syracuse, N.Y.; d. James Louis and Helen Mary (Fitzgerald) Sears. AB, Cornell U., 1950; JD with honors, George Washington U., 1960. Bar: Va. 1960, D.C. 1961, U.S. Supreme Ct. 1963. Chemist Allied Chem. and Dye Corp., Syracuse, 1950-52, Hercules Powder Co., Wilmington, Del., 1952-55; patent examiner U.S. Patent Office, Washington, 1955-60; pvt. practice Washington, 1960-61; assoc. Irons, Birch, Swindler & McKie, Washington, 1961-69; mem. firm Irons and Sears, Washington, 1969-84; chmn. trade regulation practice dept. Memel, Jacobs, Pierno, Gersh & Ellsworth, Washington, 1984-87; ptnr., chmn. intellectual property and unfair competition practice dept. Ginsburg, Feldman & Bress, Washington, 1987-91; ptnr., chmn. intellectual property and telecomm. practice group Reid & Priest, Washington, 1991-94; founder, chmn. M. H. Sears Law Firm, 1994—; mem. adv. bd. Boardroom Reports, Inc., N.Y.C., 1980-85; mem. Cornell U. Coun., 1981-87, 89-93, mem. adminstrv. bd., 1984-86. Contbr. articles to various publs. Recipient Outstanding Performance award U.S. Dept. Commerce, 1957. Mem. ABA (co-chmn. appellate practice com., litigation sect. 1989-92), Am. Intellectual Property Law Assn., Am. Chem. Soc., Am. Soc. Internat. Law, Licensing Execs. Soc., Internat. Trademark Assn., Va. State Bar Assn., D.C. Bar Assn., Order of Coif, Phi Alpha Delta. Republican. Office: M H Sears Laro Firm Chartered 2300 N St NW Washington DC 20037

SEARS, ROBERT LOUIS, industrial engineer; b. Oakland, Calif., Jan. 28, 1927; s. Louis Francis and Lucille (Hargreaves) S.; m. Phyllis Ann Barnes, Apr. 30, 1955; children: Stephen A., Jeffrey R., Garth E. BS, U.S. Mil. Acad., 1952; MS in Indsl. Engring., Ariz. State U., 1968. Registered profl. engr., Ariz. Commd. 2d lt. U.S. Army, 1952, advanced through grades to col., 1972, ret. 1973; supt. emergency med. services State of Ariz., 1973-75; gen. mgr. Behavior Modification Clinic, Inc., Phoenix, 1975-78; pres., dir. Indsl. Systems Assocs., Phoenix, 1978-80; assoc. dir. Ariz. Solar Energy Commn., Phoenix, 1980-87; program dir. Cogeneration Research Ctr. for Energy Systems Research Coll. Engring. and Applied Scis. Ariz. State U., Tempe, 1987-89, assoc. dir. program develd., 1990—; pres. Robert Sears and Assocs., 1985—. Decorated Legion of Merit (2). Mem. Nat. Soc. Profl. Engrs., Am. Inst. Indsl. Engrs. (s.r.), Assn. Energy Engrs. (cert., pres. Ariz. chpt. 1986-87, bd. dirs., 1987—), Am. Solar Energy Soc., Am. Cogeneration Assn. (dir. 1990—), Am. Cogeneration Assn., Ariz. Cogeneration Assn. (pres. 1988-90). Republican. Episcopalian. Club: Triathlon Fedn./USA, U.S. Masters Swimming. Contbr. articles to profl. jours.

SEARS, ROBERT STEPHEN, finance educator; b. Odessa, Tex., May 27, 1950; s. William Bethel and Leola Vernon (Little) S.; Reva Dana Flournoy, Aug. 17, 1973; children: Matthew Stephen, Elizabeth Rea. AAS, Odessa Jr. Coll., 1970; BA summa cum laude, Tex. Tech. U., 1973, MS, 1976; PhD, U. N.C., 1980. Supr. Bethel Enterprises, Odessa, Tex., 1973-74; teaching asst. Tex. Tech. U., Lubbock, 1974-76, Lubbock Bankers Assn. prof., dir. Inst. Banking and Fin. Studies, 1988—; teaching asst. U. N.C., Chapel Hill, 1976-79; asst. prof. U. Ill., Champaign, 1979-85, assoc. prof., 1985-88; rsch. prof. Bur. Econ. and Bus., Champaign, 1984; cons. Cameron Brown Mortgage Co., Raleigh, N.C., 1978-80, Howard Savings Bank, Livingston, N.J., 1980; asset mgr., trustee, pvt. investors, 1984—. Author: Investment Management, 1993, (chpt.) Modern Real Estate, 1980, 84; assoc. editor Rev. of Bus. Studies, 1989—, Jour. of Fin. Rsch., 1990—; contbr. articles to profl. jours. Chairman fin. com. Temple Bapt. Ch., Champaign, Ill., 1982, bd. deacons 1982-88, chmn. deacons, lay leader, 1983; Sunday sch. tchr. Carrboro (N.C.) Bapt. Ch., 1977-79; bd. deacons Ind. Ave Bapt. Ch., Lubbock, 1989—; Sunday sch. tchr., 1991—. Rsch. grantee Cameron Brown Mortgage Co., Raleigh, N.C., 1978-80, U. Ill, Champaign, 1980-84, 86-87, Investors in Bus. Edn., Champaign, 1980-81, 84. Mem. Southwestern Fin. Assn. (pres. 1989-90, v.p. and program chmn. 1988-89, sec., treas. 1986-88, dir. 1984-86, program com. 1985-86, 89—), Fin. Mgmt. Assn. (program com. 1986, 89—), So. Fin. Assn. (program com. 1986), Western Fin. Assn. (program com. 1986), Am. Fin. Assn., Ea. Fin. Assn., Alto Lakes Country Club, Lake Ridge Country Club. Republican. So. Baptist. Avocations: golf, walking, participating in sports with my children. Office: Tex Tech U COBA PO Box 4320 Lubbock TX 79409-4320

SEARS, ROLLIN GEORGE, wheat geneticist, small grains researcher; b. Salem, Oreg., Dec. 15, 1950; s. George Lestor and Margret (Mead) S.; m. Donna Jean DeNoma, Sept. 12, 1971; children: Stephanie L., Mark C., Scott N. BS, Montana State U., 1972, MS, 1974; PhD, Oreg. State U., Corvallis, 1979. Asst. prof. N.D. State U., Fargo, 1979-80; asst. prof. Kansas State U., Manhattan, 1980-84, assoc. prof., 1984-89, prof., 1989—. Vestry Episc. Ch., Manhattan, Kans., 1982-85, sr. warden, 1985-87; pres. Manhattan Marlins, 1986-90. Mem. Am. Soc. Agronomy (bd. rep. 1992—), Crop Sci. Soc. Am., Tissue Culture Soc. Am., Internat. Soc. Plant Milec. Biology, Sigma Xi, Alpha Zeta. Avocations: reading, fishing, golf. Office: Kansas State U Agronomy Dept TH Hall Manhattan KS 66506-5501

SEARS, WILLIAM REES, engineering educator; b. Mpls., Mar. 1, 1913; s. William Everett and Gertrude (Rees) S.; m. Mabel Jeannette Rhodes, Mar. 20, 1936; children—David William, Susan Carol. BS in Aero. Engring. U. Minn., 1934; Ph.D, aeronautics, Calif. Inst. Tech. 1938; DSc (hon.), U. Ariz., 1987. Asst. prof. Calif. Inst. Tech., 1939-41; chief aerodynamics Northrop Aircraft, Inc., 1941-46; dir. Grad. Sch. Aero. Engring., Cornell U., Ithaca, N.Y., 1946-63; dir. Center Applied Math., 1964-63; J.L. Given prof. engring., 1962-74; prof. aerospace and mech. engring. U. Ariz., Tucson, 1974-88, prof. emeritus, 1988—; F. W. Lanchester lectr. Royal Aero. Soc., 1973, Gardner lectr. MIT, 1987, Guggenheim lectr. Internat. Congress Aero. Scis., 1988; cons. aerodynamics. Author: The Airplane and its Components, 1941; Editor: Jet Propulsion and High-Speed Aerodynamics, vol. VI, 1954, Jour. Aerospace Scis, 1956-63, Ann. Revs. of Fluid Mechanics, Vol. I. Recipient Vincent Bendix award Am. Soc. Engring. Edn., 1965, Prandtl Ring Deutsche Gesellschaft für Luft-und Raumfahrt, 1974, Von Karman medal AGARD (NATO), 1977, ASME medal, 1989. Fellow AIAA (hon., G. Edward Pendray award 1975, S.A. Reed Aeros. award 1981, Von Karman lectr. 1968); mem. Nat. Acad. Engring. Mex. (fgn.), Am. Phys. Soc. (Fluid Dynamics prize 1992), Nat. Acad. Scis. (award in aero. engring. 1995), Sigma Xi. Home: # 8202 7500 N Calle Sin Envidia Tucson AZ 85718-7305 Office: U Ariz Aerospace & Mech Engring Dept Tucson AZ 85721

SEASE, GENE ELWOOD, public relations company executive; b. Portage, Pa., June 28, 1931; s. Grover Chauncey and Clara Mae (Over) S.; m. Joanne D. Cherry, July 20, 1952; children: David Gene, Daniel Elwood, Cheryl Joanne. A.B., Juniata Coll., 1952; B.D., Pitts. Theol. Sem., 1956, Th.M., 1959; Ph.D., U. Pitts., 1965, M.Ed., 1958; LL.D., U. Evansville, 1972, Butler U., 1972; Litt.D., Ind. State U., 1974; DD, U. Indpls., 1989. Ordained to ministry United Methodist Ch., 1956; pastor Grace United Meth. Ch., Wilkinsburg, Pitts., 1952-63; conf. dir., supt. Western Pa. Conf. United Meth. Ch., Pitts., 1963-68; lectr. grad. faculty U. Pitts., 1965-68; mem. staff U. Indpls., 1968—, asst. to pres., 1968-69, pres., 1970-88, chancellor, 1988-89, pres. emeritus, 1989—; chmn. Sease, Gerig & Assocs., Indpls., 1989—; bd. dirs. Indpls. Life Ins. Co., Nat. City Bank of Ind. Author: Christian Word Book, 1968; also numerous articles. Pres. Greater Indpls. Progress Com., 1972-75; pres. Marion County Sheriff's Merit Bd.; mem. Ind. Scholarship Commn.; cons. Am. Cablevision Indpls.; bd. dirs. Indpls. Conv. Bur., Ind. Law Enforcement Tng. Acad., 500 Festival, Crossroads coun. Boy Scouts Am., Community Hosp. Indpls., St. Francis Hosp. Mem. Internat. Platform Assn., English Speaking Union, Japan-Am. Soc. Ind., Ind. C. of C. (bd. dirs.), Indpls. C. of C. (bd. dirs.), Ind. Schoolmen's Club, Econ. Club of Indpls. (bd. dirs.), Phi Delta Kappa, Alpha Phi Omega, Alpha Psi Omega. Clubs: Mason (Indpls.) (33 deg., Shriner), Kiwanian. (Indpls.), Columbia (Indpls.).

SEASE, JOHN W(ILLIAM), chemistry educator; b. New Brunswick, N.J., Nov. 10, 1920; s. Virgil Bernard and Rosalyn (Summer) S.; m. Mary Lieurance, June 5, 1943; children—Margaret, Catherine, Ann, John Lieurance. A.B., Princeton U., 1941; Ph.D., Calif. Inst. Tech., 1946. Research asst. Nat. Def. Research Com., Calif. Inst. Tech., Pasadena, 1942-45; instr. chemistry Wesleyan U., Middletown, Conn., 1946-48, asst. prof. chemistry, 1948-52, assoc. prof. chemistry, 1952-58, prof. chemistry, 1958-82, E.B. Nye prof. chemistry, 1982-88, prof. emeritus, 1988—. Mem. Portland Sch. Bd., Conn., 1959-65. Mem. AAAS, Am. Chem. Soc. (councilor, sec. chmn. Conn. Valley sect.), Phi Beta Kappa, Sigma Xi. Office: Wesleyan U Dept Chemistry Middletown CT 06459

SEASHORE, MARGRETTA REED, physician; b. Red Bank, N.J., June 20, 1939; d. Robert Clark Reed and Lillie Ann (Heaviland) R.; m. John Seashore, Dec. 26, 1964; children: Robert H., Carl J., Carolyn L. BA, Swarthmore Coll., 1961; MD, Yale U., 1965. Diplomate Am. Bd. Pediatrics, Am. Bd. Med. Genetics, Nat. Bd. Med. Examiners. Intern in pediatrics Yale U. Sch. Medicine, New Haven, Conn., 1965-66, asst. resident in pediatrics, 1966-68; postdoctoral fellow in genetics and metabolism, depts. of pediatrics and medicine Yale U. Sch. Medicine, 1968-70; clin. asst. prof. pediatrics U. Fla. Coll. Medicine, Gainesville, 1970-71; attending physician Hope Haven Children's Hosp., Jacksonville, Fla., 1970-73; asst. prof. pediatrics Duval Med. Ctr., Jacksonville, Fla., 1970-71; attending physician Duvall Med. Ctr. U. Hosp. Jacksonville, 1970-73; asst. prof. pediatrics U. Fla. Coll. Medicine, 1971-73; attending physician Shands Teaching Hosp., Gainesville, Fla., 1971-73; asst. clin. prof. human genetics and pediatrics Yale U. Sch. Medicine, 1974-78; attending physician Yale-New Haven Hosp., 1974—; cons. physician Bridgeport (Conn.) Hosp., 1974—; attending physician Danbury (Conn.) Hosp., 1977—; dir. Genetic Consultation Svc. Yale-New Haven Hosp., 1977-86; from asst. prof. to assoc. prof. human genetics and pediatrics Yale U. Sch. Medicine, 1978-90; cons. physician Lawrence and Meml. Hosp., New London, Conn., 1979—, Norwalk (Conn.) Hosp., 1981—; dir. Genetic Consultation Svc. Yale-New Haven Hosp., 1989—; prof. genetics and pediatrics Yale U. Sch. Medicine, 1990—. Contbr. chpts. to books. Fellow Am. Acad. Pediatrics (chair com. on genetics, 1990-94, mem. screening com. Conn. chpt. 1977—, mem. genetics com. 1989—), Am. Coll. Med. Genetics (founder, mem. screening sub-com. 1993—); mem. AMA, AAAS, Am. Soc. Human Genetics (mem. genetic svcs. com. 1986-91), Soc. Inherited Metabolic Disorders (mem. bd. dirs. 1989—, sec. 1991—), Soc. for the Study of Inborn Errors of Metabolism, New England Genetics Group (co-dir. 1992—, chmn. outreach com. 1979-89, chmn. screening com. 1989-93, mem. steering com. 1979—). Avocations: music, gardening, sewing, computers. Office: Yale U Sch Med Dept Genetics 333 Cedar St New Haven CT 06510-3206

SEASTRAND, ANDREA H., congresswoman; b. Chgo., Aug. 5, 1941; m. Earl Seastrand (dec.); children: Kurt, Heidi. BA in Edn., DePaul U., 1963. Prof. religion U. Santa Barbara; mem. Calif. Assembly, 1990-94, U.S. Ho. of Reps., 1995—; asst. Rep. leader; mem. Rep. caucus; mem. edn. com.; agr. com., consumer protection com., new tech. com., govtl. efficiency com., and ways and means com.; mem. rural caucus and select com. on marine resources. Mem. Calif. Fedn. Rep. Women (past pres.). Office: US Ho of Reps 113 Cannon HOB Washington DC 20515-0522

SEATON, EDWARD LEE, newspaper editor and publisher; b. Manhattan, Kans., Feb. 5, 1943; s. Richard Melvin and Mary (Holton) S.; m. Karen Mathisen, Sept. 4, 1965; children: Edward Merrill, John David. AB cum laude, Harvard U., 1965; postgrad., U. Cen., Quito, Ecuador, 1965-66, U. Mo., 1966-67. Staff writer Courier-Jour., Louisville, 1968-69; editor-in-chief, pub. Manhattan Mercury, 1968—; bd. dirs., officer 12 other newspaper and broadcasting affiliates; mem. adv. com. Knight Internat. Press Fellowship Program; mem. Pulitzer Prize bd. Contbr. articles to profl. jours. Chmn. Alfred M. Landon lecture patrons Kans. State U.; chmn. Latin Am. Scholarship Program Am. Univs., Cambridge, Mass., 1986-87. Decorated comendador Order of Christopher Columbus (Dominican Republic); Fulbright scholar, 1965; recipient Cabot prize Columbia U., 1993. Mem. Am. Soc. Newspaper Editors (treas., pres. found.), Inter-Am. Press Assn. (pres. 1989-90), Ctr. for Fgn. Journalists (bd. dirs.), Internat. Press Inst., Kans. C. of C. and Industry (pres. 1987), Fly Club (Harvard U.). Avocations: tennis, cooking. Office: Manhattan Mercury Osage At N 5th # 5th St Manhattan KS 66502

SEATON, RICHARD MELVIN, newspaper and broadcasting executive; b. Washington, Jan. 25, 1913; s. Fay Noble and Dorothea Elizabeth (Schmidt) S.; m. Mary Holton, June 1, 1936 (dec. 1989); children: Richard H., Frederick D., Elizabeth, Edward L.; m. Eva Lee Sanborn, May 18, 1991. B.S. in Journalism, Kans. State U., 1934. Officer and dir. various cos. comprising Seaton News Media Group, 1937—. Trustee William Allen White Found., Kans. State U. Found.; mem. initial Kans. State Water Resources Bd., 1954-61, initial Kans. Cultural Arts Commn., 1965-67; founder Coffeyville Hist. Mus. Mem. Kans. Press Assn. (pres. 1949), Kans. AP (chmn. 1953), Am. Soc. Newspaper Editors, Internat. Press Inst., Coffeyville C. of C. (pres. 1950-51), Kans. State Hist. Soc. (dir. 1979—), Sigma Delta Chi, Phi Kappa Phi, Beta Theta Pi. Republican. Unitarian. Established R.M. Seaton profl. journalism chair Kans. State U., 1978, Dalton Defenders Meml. Mus., Coffeyville, Kans., 1953, Brown Mansion Mus., Coffeyville, 1973. Office: 218 W 8th St Coffeyville KS 67337-0877

SEATON, ROBERT FINLAYSON, retired planned giving consultant; b. Hancock, Mich., Nov. 28, 1930; s. Donald W. and Mary Lucille (Finlayson) S.; m. Helen Jean Robarts, Apr. 18, 1954; children: Scott, Sandy. B.S., Mich. Technol. U., 1952; M.B.A., Stanford, 1956; postgrad., Ind. U., 1966, U. So. Calif., 1973. Asst. sec. Palo Alto (Calif.) Mut. Savs. and Loan Assn., 1956-60; asst. v.p. Am. Savs. and Loan Assn., Las Vegas, 1963-67; v.p., sec. Fed. Home Loan Bank, Cin., 1967-72; pres., chief exec. officer 2d Fed. Savs. and Loan Assn., Cleve., 1973; pres., chief exec. officer Cardinal Fed. Savs. Bank, Cleve., 1973-87, chmn., 1987-88; sr. v.p. Planned Giving Systems, Inc., Cleve., 1989—, pres., 1990-94. Trustee The Orange Schs. Edn. Found., Univ. Circle, Inc.; v.p. Luth. Housing Corp.; treas. Cleve. Com. on Higher Edn.; adv. bd. Ursuline Coll.; trustee, mem. exec. com. Cleve.-Land-Ohio. Lt. USNR, 1952-54. Republican. Methodist. Home: 16 Pepper Creek Dr Cleveland OH 44124-5248

SEATON, VAUGHN ALLEN, veterinary pathology educator; b. Abilene, Kans., Oct. 11, 1928; m. Clara I. Bertelrud; children: Gregory S., Jeffrey T. BS, Kans. State U., 1954, DVM, 1954; MS, Iowa State U., 1957. Pvt. practice Janesville, Wis., 1954; instr. pathology Vet. Diagnostic Lab. Iowa State U., Ames, 1954-57, from asst. to assoc. prof. pathology Vet. Disgnostic Lab., 1957-64, prof., head Vet. Diagnostic Lab., 1964—; lab. coord. regional emergency animal disease eradication orgn. Animal and Plant Health Inspection Svc. USDA, 1974—; mem. rsch. com. Iowa Beef Industry Coun., 1972-85; mem. adv. bd. Iowa State Water Resources Rsch. Inst., 1973-80; cons. several orgns. Co-author: (monographs) Feasibility Study of College of Veterinary Medicine, 1972, Veterinary Diagnostic Laboratory Facilities-State of New York, 1970; bd. dirs. Iowa State U. Press, 1985-88, mem. manuscript com., 1982-85; contbr. articles to profl. jours. Trustee Ames Pub. Libr., 1979-85; mem. Iowa State Bd. Health, 1971-77, v.p., 1976-77. Mem. AVMA, Am. Assn. Vet. Lab. Diagnosticians (bd. govs. 1973-88, pres. 1968, E.P. Pope award 1980), Am. Coll. Vet. Toxicologists, U.S. Animal Health Assn., iowa Vet. Med. Assn. (pres. 1971), North Cen. Assn. Vet. Lab. Diagnosticians, Western Vet. Conf. (exec. bd. 1986-90, v.p. 1994, pres.-elect 1995, pres. 1996), World Assn. Vet. Lab. Diagnosticians (pres. 1980-86), Masons (bd. dirs. 1985-88), Ames C. of C. (bd. dirs. 1970-73), Phi Kappa Phi, Phi Zeta (pres. 1964), Alpha Zeta, Gamma Sigma Delta. Office: Iowa State U Coll Vet Medicine Vet Diagnostic Lab Ames IA 50011

SEAU, JUNIOR (JR. TIANA SEAU), professional football player; b. Samoa, Jan. 19, 1969. Student, U. So. Calif. Linebacker San Diego Chargers, 1990—; player Super Bowl XXVIV, 1994. Named to Sporting News Coll. All-Am. Team, 1989, to Pro Bowl Team, 1991, 92, 93,to Sporting News NFL All Pro Team, 1992, 93. Office: San Diego Chargers PO Box 609609 San Diego CA 92160-9609*

SEAVER, JAMES EVERETT, historian, educator; b. Los Angeles, Oct. 4, 1918; s. Everett Herbert and Gertrude Lillian (Sharp) S.; m. Virginia Stevens, Dec. 20, 1940; children—Richard Everett, William Merrill, Robert Edward. A.B., Stanford U., 1940; Ph.D., Cornell U., 1946. Asst. instr. history Cornell U., 1940-42, 44-46; instr. Mich. State U., 1946-47; mem. faculty U. Kans., Lawrence, 1947—; prof. history U. Kans., 1960—; prof. emeritus, 1989—; pres. faculty U. Kans., 1972-74, 82-83. Author: The Persecution of the Jews in the Roman Empire, 313-438 A.D, 1952, also numerous articles. Fulbright-Hays grantee Italy, 1953-54; Fulbright-Hays grantee Israel, 1963-64; Carnegie grantee Costa Rica, 1966-67. Mem. Am. Hist. Assn., Am. Philol. Assn., Archaeol. Inst. Am., Am. Numismatic Soc., AAUP, Am. Acad. Rome, U.S. Archives of Recorded Sound. Democrat. Episcopalian. Clubs: Alvamar Tennis, Alvamar Country. Home: 600 Louisiana St Lawrence KS 66044-2336 Office: U Kans Dept History Lawrence KS 66045

SEAVER, RICHARD CARLTON, oil field equipment company executive, lawyer; b. Los Angeles, June 10, 1922; s. Byron D. and Mary Louise (Schmidt) Seaver; children: Richard Carlton, Christopher T., Patrick T., Victoria, Martha. B.A., Pomona Coll., 1946; J.D., U. Calif.-Berkeley, 1949. Bar: Calif. 1950. Assoc. Thelen, Marrin, Johnson & Bridges, Los Angeles, 1950-57; sec., counsel Hydril Co., Los Angeles, 1957-64, pres., 1964-86, chmn., 1986—; dir. DeAnza Land & Leisure Corp. Vice chmn., bd. dirs Seaver Inst.; trustee Los Angeles County Mus. Natural History, Episcopal Diocesan Investment Trust, Doheny Eye Inst., Pomona Coll., Calif. Inst. Arts; bd. dirs. Hosp. of Good Samaritan; bd. dirs., pres. L.A. Music Ctr. Opera Assn.; bd. overseers Hoover Inst., Palo Alto. Served to capt. inf. AUS, 1942-46, PTO. Decorated Bronze Star with oak leaf cluster. Mem. ABA, Calif. Bar Assn., Los Angeles Bar Assn. Republican. Clubs: St. Francis Yacht, Los Angeles Country, Los Angeles Yacht, California (Los Angeles); Newport Harbor Yacht (Balboa). Office: Hydril Co 714 W Olympic Blvd Los Angeles CA 90015-1425

SEAVER, ROBERT LESLIE, law educator; b. Brockton, Mass., June 13, 1937; s. Russell Bradford and Lois (Marchant) S.; m. Marjorie V. Rote, Aug. 21, 1960 (div. 1974); children: Kimberly, Eric, Kristen; m. Elizabeth A. Horwitz, May 22, 1984. AB cum laude, Tufts U., Medford, Mass., 1958; JD, U. Chgo., 1964. Bar: Ohio 1964, U.S. Ct. Appeals (6th cir.) 1964, U.S. Dist. Ct. (so. dist.) Ohio 1965. Assoc. Taft, Stettinius and Hollister, Cin., 1964-66; v.p., sec., gen. counsel IDI Mgmt. Inc., Cin., 1966-74; pvt. practice Cin., 1974-75; prof. law No. Ky. U. Salmon P. Chase Coll. Law, Highland Heights, 1975—; of counsel Cors & Bassett, Cin., 1993—; cons. in field, 1975—. Advisor/editor: Ohio Corporation Law, 1988; contbr. chpts. to books. Advisor subcom. on pvt. corps of Ky. Commn. on Constl. Rev., 1987. With USMC, 1958-61. Recipient Justice Robert O. Lukowsky award of Excellence Chase Law Sch. Student Bar Assn., 1986. Mem. ABA, Ohio Bar Assn., Cin. Bar Assn., No. Ky. Bar Assn., U. Chgo. Law Sch. Alumni Assn. (regional v.p. 1976—). Republican. Unitarian. Avocations: duplicate bridge, history. Home: 826 Woodscene Ct Cincinnati OH 45230-4334 Office: Northern Kentucky U Salmon Chase Coll Law Highland Heights KY 41099

SEAVER, TOM (GEORGE THOMAS SEAVER), former professional baseball player; b. Fresno, Calif., Nov. 17, 1944; s. Charles H. and Betty Lee (Cline) S.; m. Nancy Lynn McIntyre, June 9, 1966; children: Sarah, Anne Elizabeth. Student, Fresno City Coll., 1964, U. So. Calif., 1965-68. Pitcher Jacksonville (Fla.) Suns, 1966; pitcher N.Y. Mets, 1967-77, 83-84, 87, mem. World Series Championship team, 1969; pitcher Cin. Reds, 1977-82, Chgo. White Sox, 1984-86, Boston Red Sox, 1986; announcer N.Y. Yankees WPIX-TV, N.Y.C. Author: (with Lee Lowenfish) The Art of Pitching, 1984, (with Alice Seigel) Tom Seaver's Baseball Card Book, 1985, (with Herb Resnicow) novel Beanball, 1989. Served with USMCR, 1963. Recipient Cy Young award Nat. League, 1969, 73, 75; named Rookie of Yr. Baseball Writers Assn. Am., 1967, Nat. League Pitcher of Yr. Sporting News, 1969, 73, 75, Sportsman of Yr. Sports Illustrated, 1969; named to Nat. League All-Star team, 1969-73, 75-78, to Baseball Hall of Fame Baseball Writers Assn. Am., 1992. Credited with more than 300 career victories; pitched over 3,000 career strikeouts. Office: care Matt Mendola 185 E 85th Ste 18G New York NY 10028*

SEAWELL, DONALD RAY, lawyer, publisher, arts center executive, producer; b. Jonesboro, N.C., Aug. 1, 1912; s. A.A.F. and Bertha (Smith) S.; m. Eugenia Rawls, Apr. 5, 1941; children: Brook Ashley, Donald Brockman. A.B., U. N.C., 1933, J.D., 1936, D.Litt., 1980; L.H.D., U. No. Colo., 1978. Bar: N.C. 1936, N.Y. 1947. With SEC, 1939-41, 45-47, Dept. Justice, Emal Div., 1941-45; pvt. practice Cin., 1966-81; chmn. bd., dir. Gravure West, L.A., 1966-81; dir. Swan Prodns., London; of counsel firm Bernstein, Seawell, Kove & Maltin, N.Y.C., 1979—; chmn. bd., chief exec. officer Denver Ctr. for Performing Arts, 1972—; ptnr. Bonfils-Seawell Enterprises, N.Y.C.; bd. vis. UNC Sch. of the Arts. Chmn. bd. ANTA, 1965—; mem. theatre panel Nat. Coun. Arts, 1970-74; bd. govs. Royal Shakespeare Theatre, Eng.; trustee Am. Acad. Dramatic Arts, 1967—,

Hofstra U., 1968-69, Cen. City Opera Assn., Denver Symphony; bd. dirs., chmn. exec. com. Air Force Acad. Found., Nat. Ints. Outdoor Drama, Walter Hampden Meml. Library, Hammond Mus.; pres. Helen G. Bonfils Found., Denver Opera Found.; dir. Found. for Denver Ctr. for Performing Arts Complex, Population Crisis Com.; bd. dirs Family Health Internat., Found. for Internat. Family Health; bd. visitors N.C. Sch. Arts, 1992—. With U.S. Army, WW II. Recipient Am. Acad. Achievement award, 1980, Tony award for producing On Your Toes, 1983, Voice Research and Awareness award Voice Found., 1983. Mem. Bucks Club (London), Dutch Treat Club (N.Y.C.), Denver Country Club, Denver Club, Cherry Hills Country Club, Mile High Club (Denver), Garden of Gods Club (Colorado Springs, Colo.). Office: Denver Ctr for Performing Arts 1050 13th St Denver CO 80204-2157

SEAWELL, THOMAS ROBERT, artist, retired educator; b. Balt., Mar. 17, 1936; s. Robert James and Cynthia Edith (Bass) S.; m. Barbara Louise Frey, Nov. 30, 1985; children: James Bradford, Lee Thomas, Gustin Charles, Jay Turner Frey. B.F.A., Washington U., 1958; M.F.A., Tex. Christian U., 1960. Mem. faculty dept. art SUNY-Oswego, 1963-91, prof., 1973-91; vis. artist Ox Bow Print Symposium, 1985, Ann. Matrix Artist, U. Dallas, 1989, Midwestern State U., 1993; juror 50th Cooperstown Nat., 1985, Nat. Print Exhbn., Minot State U., N.D., 1985., Rochester Print Club Annual, Meml. Art Gallery U. Rochester, 1988. One-man exhbns. include retrospective U. Md., Baltimore County, 1983, Schoharie County Arts Ctr., 1991, Tyler Art Gallery, SUNY, Oswego, 1991, Univ. Gallery, ETSU, Commerce, Tex., 1995; group exhbns. include Contemporary Am. Prints in Leningrad, USSR, 1983-84, The Collagraph, U. Mont., 1987, SUNY, Oswego, 1988, U. Dallas, 1989, DeCordova Mus., 1991; traveling exhbn. So. Arts Fedn. Traveling Exhbn. "A Sense of Place," 1986—; represented in permanent collections Bklyn. Mus., DeCordova Mus. Art, Rochester Meml. Art Gallery, Pushkin Mus., USSR, Brit. Mus., Munson-Williams-Proctor Inst., Library of Congress, Portland Art Mus.; commd. print editions: Geldermann Securities Ltd., 1985-92. Mem. Boston Printmakers, Phila. Water Color Club, Soc. Am. Graphic Artists. Home (summer): PO Box 14 Sterling NY 13156

SEAWELL, WILLIAM THOMAS, former airline executive; b. Pine Bluff, Ark., Jan. 27, 1918; s. George Marion and Harriet (Aldridge) S.; m. Judith Alexander, June 12, 1941; children: Alexander Brooke, Anne Seawell Robinson. B.S., U.S. Mil. Acad., 1941; J.D., Harvard U., 1949. Commd. 2d lt. U.S. Army, 1941; advanced through grades to brig. gen. USAF, 1959; comdr. 401st Bombardment Group, ETO, World War II, 11th Bomb Wing SAC, 1953-54; dep. comdr. 7th Air Div., 1954-55; mil. asst. to sec. USAF, 1958-59, to dep. sec def., 1959-61; comdt. cadets U.S. Air Force Acad., 1961-63; ret., 1963; v.p. operations and engring. Air Transport Assn. Am. Washington, 1963-65; sr. v.p. ops Am. Airlines, N.Y.C., 1965-68; pres. Rolls Royce Aero Engines Inc. U.S. subsidiary Rolls Royce, Ltd., 1968-71; pres. chief operating officer Pan Am. World Airways Inc., N.Y.C., 1971-72; chmn. bd. Pan Am. World Airways Inc., 1972-81. Decorated Silver Star, D.F.C. with three oak leaf clusters, Air medal with three oak leaf clusters; Croix de Guerre with palm France). Clubs: Wings (N.Y.C.), Pine Bluff Country. Home: 21 Westridge Dr Pine Bluff AR 71603-7149

SEAWRIGHT, JAMES L., JR., sculptor, educator; b. Jackson, Miss., May 22, 1936; s. James L. and Josephine (Power) S.; m. Mabelle M. Garrard, June 22, 1960; 1 child, James Andrew. Student, U. of South, 1953-54, Delta State Coll., 1954-55; B.A. in English, U. Miss., 1957; postgrad., Art Students League of N.Y., 1961-62. Tech. supr. Columbia-Princeton Electronic Music Center, N.Y.C., 1963-69; tchr. Sch. Visual Arts, 1967-69; dir. visual arts program Princeton U., 1972—, prof. coun. of humanities and visual arts, 1992—. Asst. to choreographer, Henry St. Playhouse, N.Y.C., 1962-63, spl. effects, tech. cons., Mimi Garrard Dance Co., N.Y.C., 1964—; sculptor represented in permanent collections, Mus. Modern Art, N.Y.C., Whitney Mus., N.Y.C., N.J. State Mus., Trenton, Guggenheim Mus., N.Y.C., Wadsworth Atheneum, Hartford, Conn., others; pub. commns. for SEA-TAC Internat. Airport, Seattle, Logan Internat. Airport, Boston; also pvt. collections. Served with USN, 1957-61. Recipient Theodoron award Guggenheim Mus., 1969; Graham Found. Advanced Study in Arts fellow, 1970. Mem. Am. Abstract Artists, Phi Delta Theta. Democrat. Episcopalian. Office: 185 Nassau St Princeton NJ 08544-2003

SEAY, FRANK HOWELL, federal judge; b. Shawnee, Okla., Sept. 5, 1938; s. Frank and Wilma Lynn Seay; m. Janet Gayle Seay, June 2, 1962; children: Trudy Alice, Laura Lynn. Student, So. Meth. U., 1956-57; B.A., U. Okla., 1960, LL.B., 1963. Bar: Okla. 1963. Atty. Seminole County, 1963-66; asst. dist. atty., 1967-68, assoc dist. judge, 1968-74; judge Okla. Dist. Ct. 22, 1974-79; judge ea. dist. U.S. Dist. Ct., Okla., 1979—, now chief judge. Mem. ABA, Okla. Bar Assn., Seminole County Bar Assn. Democrat. Clubs: Masons, Elks, Lions. Office: US Dist Ct PO Box 828 Muskogee OK 74402-0828

SEBASTIAN, MICHAEL JAMES, manufacturing company executive; b. Chgo., July 8, 1930; s. Michael and Larraine (DeAmicis) S.; m. Sally Ervin, Nov. 29, 1953; children: Michael, Mark, Lisa. B.S in M.E., Santa Clara U., 1952; A.M.P., Harvard U., 1972. Div. mgr. FMC Corp, Indpls., 1953-77; pres. Rotek, Aurora, Ohio, 1977-78; v.p. Gardner-Denver, Dallas, 1978-79; group pres. Cooper Industries, Dallas, 1979-81; v.p. Cooper Industries, Houston, 1981-82, exec. v.p., 1982—; bd. dirs. Quanex Corp., Gardner Denver Machinery, Inc. Past dir. Weatherford Internat.; mem. adv. bd. U. Houston Ctr. Pub. Policy. Republican. Roman Catholic. Clubs: Petroleum, Lakeside Country (Houston). Avocations: golf; gardening; tennis. Home: 11511 Shadow Way Houston TX 77024-5216 Office: Cooper Industries Inc PO Box 4446 1001 Fannin St Fl 40 Houston TX 77002-6706

SEBASTIAN, PETER, international affairs consultant, former ambassador; b. June 19, 1926; m. Harvel Huddleston, Dec. 11, 1951; 1 child, Christopher. B.A., U. Chgo., 1950; postgrad., U. d'Aix-Marseille, Nice, France, 1949, New Sch. for Social Research, N.Y.C., 1950, Nat. War Coll., 1969-70. Dir., owner cons. co., N.Y.C., 1950-57; U.S. Fgn. Service officer Dept. State, Washington, 1957-76, dep. exec. sec., 1976-77, sr. seminar, 1977-78; U.S. consul gen. Casablanca, Morocco, 1978-80; minister, counselor Am. embassy, Rabat, Morocco, 1980-82; dir. for North Africa Dept. State, Washington, 1982-84; ambassador to Tunisia Tunis, 1984-87; ambassador-in-residence ctr. for Strategic Internat. Studies, Georgetown U., Washington, 1987-88; cons in fgn. affairs to the public and pvt. sector, lectr., 1988—. Contbr. poems to Osmose, 1949; author studies for U.S. Dept. State and other U.S agys. Served to sgt. AUS, 1944-46. Decorated Ouissam Alaouite (Morocco), numerous U.S. mil. decorations; recipient Presdl. Meritorious Service award, 1985. Mem. Am. Fgn. Svc. Assn., Nat. Geog. Soc., Mid. East Inst. Episcopalian. Avocations: painting; drawing; photography.

SEBASTIAN, RICHARD LEE, physicist, executive; b. Hutchinson, Kans., June 22, 1942; s. Leroy Clarence and Marion Alta (Brown) S.; m. Judy Ann French, Dec. 29, 1964; children: Todd Winslow, Alison Louise. A.B. in Math, Princeton U., 1964; Ph.D. in Physics, U. Md., 1970. Staff scientist ENSCO, Inc., Springfield, Va., 1969-72; chief scientist ENSCO, Inc., 1972-73, v.p. research, 1973-83; pres. Wackenhut Research Corp., Springfield, 1980-81; pres., chmn. Digital Signal Corp., Springfield, 1983-91; corp. v.p., gen. mgr. Digital Signal div. Coleman Rsch. Corp., Springfield, 1991—. Mem. Am. Phys. Soc., IEEE, Soc. Exploration Geophysicists. Home: 6128 River Dr Mason Neck VA 22079-4124 Office: Coleman Rsch Corp Digital Signal Div 6551 Loisdale Ct Springfield VA 22150-1808

SEBELIUS, KATHLEEN GILLIGAN, state legislator; b. Cin., May 15, 1948; d. John J. and Mary K. (Dixon) Gilligan; m. Keith Gary Sebelius, 1974; children: Edward Keith, John McCall. BA, Trinity Coll., 1970, MA, U. Kans., 1977. Dir. planning Ctr. for Cmty. Justice, Washington, 1971-74; spl. asst. Kans. Dept. Corrections, Topeka, 1975-78; mem. Kans. Ho. of Reps., 1987—. Founder Women's Polit. Caucus; mem. cmty. adv. com. Youth Ctr. Topeka, Kans. Children's Coalition; precinct committeewoman, 1980-86; mayor-elect, Potwin, 1985-87. Mem. Common Cause (state bd., nat. gov. bd. 1975—), Phi Sigma Alpha. Democrat. Roman Catholic. Home: 224 SW Greenwood Ave Topeka KS 66606-1228

SEBEOK, THOMAS ALBERT, linguistics educator; b. Budapest, Hungary, Nov. 9, 1920; came to U.S., 1937, naturalized, 1944; s. Dezso and Veronica (Perlman) S.; m. Eleanor Lawton, Sept. 1947; 1 child, Veronica C.; m. Jean

Umiker, Oct. 1972; children: Jessica A., Erica L. B.A., U. Chgo., 1941; M.A., Princeton, 1943, Ph.D., 1945; Ph.D. (hon.), U. Budapest, Hungary, 1990; D. (hon.), U. Nacional de Rosario, Argentina, 1991; D.Sc. (hon.), U. So. Ill., 1991. Mem. faculty Ind. U., Bloomington, 1943—, Disting. prof. linguistics, 1967-78, Disting. prof. linguistics and semiotics, 1978-91, Disting. prof. emeritus, 1991—, prof. anthropology, prof. Uralic and Altaic studies, fellow Folklore Inst., mem. Russian and East European Inst., chmn. Research Center for Lang. and Semiotic Studies, 1956-91, chmn. emeritus Grad. Program in Semiotic Studies, 1991—; mem.-at-large NAS-NRC, also mem. various coms.; lectr. various acads. and univs., U.S. and abroad; vis. prof. U. Mich., 1945, 58, U. P.R., 1949, U. N.Mex., 1953, U. Ariz., 1958-59, U. Vienna, 1963, U. Besançon, 1965, U. Hamburg, 1966, U. Bucharest, 1967, 69, U. Ill., 1968, U. Colo., 1969, Stanford U., 1971, U. South Fla., 1972, Linguistic Soc. Am. prof., 1975, Internat. Christian U., Tokyo, 1985, U. Quebec, 1985, El Colegio de Mexico, 1987, U. of Republic, Montevideo, Uraguey, 1987, others; Disting. vis. prof. Internat. Summer Inst. for Semiotic and Structural Studies, 1980-88; cons. Ford Found., Guggenheim Found., Wenner-Gren Found. for Anthrop. Research, U.S. Office Edn., NSF, fellowship div. Nat. Acad. Scis., Can. Council; panel mem. for linguistics Nat. Endowment for Humanities, 1966-67; mem. U.S. del. to permanent council Internat. Union Anthrop. and Ethnol. Scis., 1970-73; U.S. del. Comité International Permanent des Linguistes, 1972—; mem. internat. sci. council Royaumont Center for Sci. of Man, 1973—; exch. prof. NAS-USSR Acad. Scis.; 1973; Regents fellow Smithsonian Instn., 1983-84; adj. fellow Woodrow Wilson Internat Ctr. for Scholars, 1983-84, mem. program on history, culture and soc., 1986-87. Author: Perspectives in Zoosemiotics, 1972, Structure & Texture: Selected Essays in Cheremis Verbal Art, 1974, The Play of Musement, 1981, others; editor-in-chief: Semiotica, 1968—, Current Trends in Linguistics, 1963—, Approaches to Semiotics, 1968-74; editor: Studies in Semiotics, 1974—, others; gen. editor: Advances in Semiotics, 1974—, others; contbr. numerous articles to profl. and scholarly jours. Mem. vis. com. Harvard U., 1973, Simon Fraser U., 1975, Georgetown U., 1977, Vanderbill U., 1977-78. Recipient Pres.' medal of excellence Ind. U., 1991; John Simon Guggenheim Meml. Found. fellow, 1958-59, 81-82, Center for Advanced Study in Behavioral Scis. fellow, 1960-61, 66-67, 71; Fulbright grantee Germany, 1966, 71, Italy, 1969, 71, 87, Argentina, 1987, Uruguay, 1987; NSF sr. postdoctoral fellow, 1966-67; grantee Am. Coun. Learned Socs., Ford Found., Wenner-Gren Found. Anthrop. Rsch., USIA, other fed. agys. Fellow Am. Anthrop. Assn. (disting. service award 1984), Am. Folklore Soc., Soc. Cultural Anthropology, AAAS, Explorers Club, also fgn. linguistic socs.; mem. Internat. Assn. Semiotic Studies (editor-in-chief 1968—, exec. com. 1969—), Linguistic Soc. Am. (sec.-treas. 1969-73, v.p. 1974, pres. 1975, asso. dir. Linguistic Inst. 1958, 75, dir. 1964), Central States Anthrop. Soc. (pres. 1956), Am. Assn. Machine Translation and Computational Linguistics (exec. bd. 1964-66), Animal Behavior Soc. (exec. bd. 1968—), Semiotic Soc. Am. (sec.-treas. 1975, exec. dir. 1976-85, pres. 1984), Sigma Xi, others. Clubs: Cosmos (Washington); University (Chgo.); Princeton (N.Y.C.) ; Internat. House (Tokyo). Home: 1104 W Covenanter Dr Bloomington IN 47401-0010 Office: Indiana U PO Box 10 Bloomington IN 47402-0010

SEBO, STEPHEN ANDREW, electrical engineer, educator, researcher, consultant; b. Budapest, Hungary, June 10, 1934; s. Emery Sebo and Elizabeth Thieben; m. Eva Agnes Vambery, May 25, 1968. MSEE, Budapest Poly-tech. U., 1957; PhD, Hungarian Acad. Sci., 1966. Engr. Budapest Elec. Co., 1957-61; asst. prof. Budapest Poly. U., 1961-66, assoc prof., 1966-68; assoc. prof. Ohio State U., Columbus, 1968-74, prof., 1974—; Am. Electric Power prof. in power sys. engring., 1982—. Recipient Power Educator award Edison Elec. Inst., 1981, Tech. Person of Yr. award Columbus Tech. Coun., 1994. Fellow IEEE (Prize Paper award 1981). Office: Ohio State U Elec Engring 2015 Neil Ave Columbus OH 43210-1272

SEBOK, GYORGY, pianist, educator; b. Szeged, Hungary, Nov. 2, 1922; came to U.S., 1962; s. Vilmos and Klara (Krausz) S.; m. Eva Mandel, Jan. 29, 1957. Ed.; Franz Liszt Acad. Music, Budapest, Hungary. Prof. piano Bela Bartok Conservatory, Budapest, 1949-56; prof. piano Ind. U., Bloomington, 1962—, disting. prof., 1985—; guest prof. Hochschule der Künste, Berlin; hon. life mem. Toho Gakuen Sch. Music, Tokyo; founder, dir. Festival de Zukunft, Ernen, Switzerland. First pub. appearance, 1936, concerts throughout Europe, N.Am., Japan, Africa, 1957—; rec. artist for Erato, Mercury, Philips records. Recipient Internat. Prize, Berlin, Germany, 1951, Liszt Prize, Budapest, 1952, Grand Prix du Disque, Paris, France, 1958; named hon. citizen City of Ernen; 2d Order of Merit Republic of Hungary. Home: Woodcrest 2610 E Second St Bloomington IN 47401

SEBOLD, DUANE DAVID, food manufacturing executive; b. Dorchester, Wis., Mar. 25, 1945; s. Louis J. and Geraldine M. (Herman) S.; m. Kathrin Saunders, June 6, 1970 (dec. Sept. 1973); m. Marcia K. Church, Mar. 19, 1989. BS, U. Wis., Stevens Point, 1967; degree advanced mgmt., Wharton Bus. Sch., 1989. Salesman Ciba-Geigy Corp., San Diego, 1970-73, sales mgr., 1973-76; dir. sales and mktg. Tombstone Pizza Corp., Medford, Wis., 1976-77, v.p. mktg., 1977-80, exec. v.p., gen. mgr., 1980-86, pres., chief exec. officer, 1986-89; chief exec. officer Sebold Enterprises, Medford, 1990—; pres. Nat. Frozen Pizza Inst., McLean, Va., 1985-87; chmn. Tombstone Pizza Found., Medford, 1983—; chmn. policy adv. council Marshfield Med. Research Found., Marshfield; chmn. Tombstone Pizza Exec. Com., Medford, 1986-89. Contbr. articles to mags. mem. Rep. Senatorial Inner Circle, Washington, 1987-88; bd. dirs. Arthritis Found., Milw., 1985-86; guest spkr. U. Wis.-Madison Exec. Program, 1984-90. With USN, 1967-70. Recipient Disting. Alumni award U. Wis., 1994. Mem. Am. Mktg. Assn., Am. Mgmt. Assn., Nat. Mgmt. Assn. (Marketer of Yr. 1979, Gold Knight award of Mgmt. 1988), Safari Club Internat., Ducks Unltd., Found. for N.Am. Wild Sheep, Toastmasters. Roman Catholic. Avocations: hunting, fishing, golf. Home and Office: 5369W N Chelsea Ave Medford WI 54451

SECCHIA, PETER F., ambassador; married; 4 children. BSBA, Mich. State U. Chmn. bd. dirs. The Universal Cos., Inc.; amb. to Italy, Rome, 1989—. Host chmn. Rep. Nat. Com. Midwest Leadership Conf., Grand Rapids, 1985; vice chmn. for midwest Rep. Nat. Com.; mem. exec. com.

Gerald R. Ford Found. Mem. Order Sons Italy (founding pres. West Mich. chpt.). Office: Comml Sect Am Embassy Rome APO AE 09794-9500

SECHREST, WILLIAM B., lawyer; b. Kansas City, Mo., June 29, 1942; s. Harold R. and Mildred J. (Fisher) S.; m. Carol Lynn (dec. Dec. 1978); children: Brett, Trent, Clay; m. Caryn K. Halpern; children: Keller, Edyn. AB, Stanford U., 1964; JD, So. Meth. U., Dallas, 1967. Bar: Tex. 1967, Mo. 1968. Assoc. Shughart, Thomson & Kilroy, Kansas City, 1967-69; ptnr. Akin Vial Hamilton Koch & Tubb, Dallas, 1969-73, Winstead Sechrest & Minick, Dallas, 1973—; past pres. Real Estate Sect. of Dallas Bar. Author: Creation of Joe Bankhead, 1994. Mem. Real Estate Coun., Dallas; pres. Comty. Devel. Assistance Corp. Office: Winstead Sechrest & Minick 5400 Renaissance Tower 1201 Elm St Dallas TX 75270-2016

SECHRIST, CHALMERS FRANKLIN, JR., electrical engineering educator; b. Glen Rock, Pa., Aug. 23, 1930; s. Chalmers F. and Lottie V. (Smith) S.; m. Lillian Beatrice Myers, June 29, 1957; children: Jonathan A., Jennifer N. BEE, Johns Hopkins U., 1952; MS, Pa. State U., 1954, PhDEE, 1959. Sr. engr. Bendix Corp., summers 1952, 53, 54; instr. elec. engring. Pa. State U., 1954-55; staff engr. HRB-Singer, Inc., State College, Pa., 1959-65; asst. prof. elec. engring. U. Ill., Urbana, 1965-67, assoc. prof., 1967-71, prof., 1971—, assoc. head instructional programs dept. elec. and computer engring., 1984-86, asst. dean engring., 1986—; program dir. divsn. undergrad. edn. NSF, Washington, 1992—; acting sci. sect. Sci. Com. on Solar-Terrestrial Physics, 1981; chmn. publs. com. Middle Atmosphere Program, 1980-86, editor handbook, 1981-86. Editor: Proc. Aeronomy Confs, 1965, 69, 72; contbr. articles to profl. jours. NSF grantee. Mem. Edn. Soc. of IEEE (v.p. 1989-90, pres. 1991-92, mem. IEEE edn. activities bd. 1990, 92, 93, mem. tech. activities bd. 1991-92), Am. Geophys. Union, Am. Meteorol. Soc., Am. Soc. for Engring. Edn. Home: 4609 4th Rd N Arlington VA 22203-2347

SECKEL, BROOKE RUTLEDGE, plastic surgeon; b. Columbus, Ohio, Oct. 2, 1943; s. Raymond Clyde and Virginia Caine (Rutledge) S.; m. Deborah Anne Johnson, May 8, 1982; children: Laura, Thomas. BS summa cum laude, Ohio U., 1965; MD, Med. Coll. of Va., 1969. Diplomate Am. Bd. Psychiatry and Neurology, Am. Bd. Emergency Medicine, Am. Bd. Plastic Surgery, Nat. Bd. Med. Examiners; lic. physician, Va., Calif., Mass. Internship in surgery Univ. Hosp., San Diego, 1969-70; jr. asst. resident in neurology, jr. resident Boston City Hosp., Harvard Neurol. Unit, 1971-72, 72-73, chief resident in neurology, 1973-74; instr. in neurology Harvard Med. Sch., Cambridge, Mass., 1974-77; jr. resident in surgery, sr. resident New Eng. Med. Ctr., Boston, 1978-79, 79-80; sr. resident plastic/reconstructive surgery, chief resident Brigham and Women's Hosp. and The Children's Hosp., Boston, 1980-81, 81-82; instr. in surgery Harvard Med. Sch., Cambridge, 1982-85, clin. instr. in surgery, 1986-89, asst. prof. surgery, 1990-93; chmn. dept. plastic and reconstructive surgery Lahey Clinic Med. Ctr., Burlington, Mass., 1986—; courtesy staff The Children's Hosp., Boston, 1982—, New Eng. Deaconess Hosp., Boston, 1986—; assoc. surgeon Brigham and Women's Hosp., Boston, 1982—; dir. Microsurgical Ctr. Lahey Clinic Med. Ctr., 1986—, Plastic Surgery Rsch. Lab., Lahey Clinic Med. Ctr., 1986—, Plastic Surgery Residency Tng. Program, Lahey Clinic Med. Ctr., 1989—. Assoc. editor Jour. of Plastic and Reconstructive Surgery, 1988-94; expert reviewer Jour. of Muscle and Nerve, 1989—; assoc. editor Jour. of Reconstructive Microsurgery, 1990—; author: Plastic Surgery Research Directory, 1990, Facial Danger Zones: Avoiding Nerve Injury in Facial Plastic Surgery, 1993; author of numerous non-print materials including videotapes; contbr. numerous articles to profl. jours. and chpts. to books. Grantee Am. Assn. Plastic Surgeons, 1983, Plastic Surgery Ednl. Found., 1984, Eleanor Naylor Dana Charitable Trust, 1986-90, Donaldson Charitable Trust, 1990, Charles E. Culpeper Found., 1991, 92, The Robert Leet and Clara Guthrie Patterson Trust, 1993, 94. Fellow Am. Coll. Emergency Physicians, Am. Coll. Surgeons; mem. New Eng. Surg. Soc., Soc. Microsurgical Specialists, Assn. Acad. Chmn. Plastic Surgery, Am. Soc. for Aesthetic Plastic Surgery, Am. Assn. Plastic Surgeons, Northeastern Soc. Plastic Surgeons, The Sunderland Soc., Boston Surg. Soc., Plastic Surgery Rsch. Coun., Am. Soc. Plastic and Reconstructive Surgeons, New Eng. Soc. Plastic and Reconstructive Surgeons, Mass. Soc. Plastic Surgery, Mass. Med. Soc., Am. Coll. Emergency Physicians. Home: 21 River St Concord MA 01742-2223 Office: Lahey Clin Med Ctr Plastic Surgery 41 Mall Rd Burlington MA 01805-0001

SECOR, DONALD TERRY, JR., geologist, educator; b. Oil City, Pa., Nov. 22, 1934; s. Donald Terry and Mary Elizabeth (LaRue) S.; m. Dorothy Eisenhart, June 15, 1959; children: Beth Ann, Jane Marie, Carol Lynn. B.S., Cornell U., 1957, M.S., 1959; Ph.D., Stanford U., 1963. Asst. prof. geology U. S.C., Columbia, 1962-66, assoc. prof., 1966-79, prof., 1979—, chmn. dept., 1966-68, 77-81. Am. Assn. Petroleum Geologists Disting. Lectr., 1978-79; recipient U.S.C. Ednl. Found. award, 1991; NSF grantee, 1966-70, 76—, U.S. Geol. Survey grantee, 1979-82. Fellow Geol. Soc. Am.; mem. Am. Geophys. Union, AAAS. Home: RR 1 Box 251 Newberry SC 29108-9738 Office: U SC Dept Geol Scis Columbia SC 29208

SECORD, JAMES ANDREW, researcher, educator; b. Madison, Wis., Mar. 18, 1953; s. John B. and Jane (Kresge) S.; m. P. Anne Sant, Sept. 6, 1980. BA, Pomona Coll., 1975; PhD, Princeton U., 1981. Research fellow Churchill Coll., Cambridge, Eng., 1982-85; lectr. history of sci. Imperial Coll., London, 1985—. Author: Controversy in Victorian Geology, 1986. Contbr. articles to profl. jours. Fulbright-Hays grantee, Eng., 1978-79; Thomas J. Watson Found. fellow, 1975-76. Mem. Brit. Soc. History Sci., History of Sci. Soc. (Zeitlin-ver Brugge prize 1984). Office: Ctr History Sci Medicine Tech, Imperial College, London SW7 2AZ, England

SECORD, LLOYD DOUGLAS, healthcare administrator; b. Lachine, Que., Can., Nov. 22, 1946; s. George William and Gladys Mable (Wilson) S.; m. Louise Margaret Morrison, Dec. 21, 1966; children: Steven Lloyd, Gordon Arthur, Mary Elizabeth. BS in Chemistry, U. New Brunswick, 1968; M of Adminstrn., U. Toronto, Ont., Can., 1970. Cert. accreditation surveyor Can. Coun. on Health Facilities, 1990-92. Adminstry. resident Toronto East Gen. and Orthopaedic Hosp., 1969-70; adminstry. asst. Moncton Hosp., summer 1968, asst. adminstry., 1970-75; exec. dir. Kiwanis Nursing Home Inc., 1975—; facility adminstr. Region 2 Hosp. Corp., Sussex, N.B., Can., 1975—; sec. Sussex Health Ctr. Svcs. Inc., Bryant Dr. Holdings Inc., 1975—, CEO, adminstr. hosp., 1975—; chmn. adv. com. Min. Health; mem. Fundy Linen Svcs. Inc., 1976-92; mem. regional hosp. planning com. Health Region II, 1974-76; commr. of oaths, 1975—. Bd. dirs. Atlantic Bapt. Sr. Citizen's Home Inc., 1973-79, original bldg. com., 1971-74, rec. sec., 1971-74, chmn. bldg. com.; founding chmn. Comty. Based Svcs. Coord. Com. for Sussex, 1981; founding pres. Sussex Sr. Housing Inc., 1981, 82; established Sussex Health Ctr. Svcs. Inc., 1991, Bryant Dr. Holdings Inc., 1992-93; bd. trustees, bd. deacons Sussex United Bapt. Ch.; dir. Sussex br. Order of St. John, 1976-78, 90-92; trombonist Sussex Comty. Adult Band, 1989—. Lord Beaverbrook scholar, Leonard Found. scholar. Fellow Am. Coll. Health Care Execs. (affiliate, regent for Atlantic provinces 1992—; membership oral examiner 1984, 85, 86, 88, 93, mem. ethics com. 1985-88), Can. Coll. Health Svc. Execs. (various provincial coms.), Soc. Mgmt. Accts. (cert., mem. provincial coun. 1977-88, provincial sec.-treas. 1982, provincial chmn. 1987, nat. edn. svcs. com. 1985, 86, nat. bd. 1986, 87, nat. strategic planning com. 1986); mem. New Brunswick Hosp. Assn. (numerous provincial coms.), New Brunswick Assn. Nursing Homes (numerous provincial coms.), Northeastern Can./Am. Health Coun. (Can. co-chmn. 1991-94, co-chair internat. mini conf. on rural health care New London, N.H. 1988, chair bi-ann. conf. Montreal 1991), Provincial Ambulance Operators Assn. (exec. com. 1990—), Sussex and Dist. C. of C. (pres. 1985), Kiwanis Club Sussex Inc. (pres. 1985—). Avocations: band, golf, gardening, painting, education. Office: Sussex Health Ctr, PO Box 5006/Leonard Dr, Sussex, NB Canada E0E 1P0

SECREST, RONALD DEAN, lawyer; b. Kansas City, Mo., Nov. 13, 1951; s. William Francis and Corrine Elizabeth (Clarke) S.; m. Stephanie de Jong, Oct. 8, 1983. BS, Stanford U., 1974; JD, U. Va., 1977. Bar: Tex. 1979, U.S. Dist. Ct. (so. dist.) Tex. 1979, U.S. Ct. Appeals (5th cir.) 1980, U.S. Ct. Appeals (11th cir.) 1981, U.S. Dist. Ct. (no. dist.) Tex. 1986, U.S. Dist. Ct. (we. dist.) Tex. 1989, U.S. Ct. Appeals (10th cir.) 1989, U.S. Supreme Ct. 1990. Law clk. to presiding justice U.S. Ct. Appeals (5th cir.), Houston, 1977-78; ptnr. Fulbright & Jaworski, Houston, 1978-92, Beck, Redden & Secrest, Houston, 1992—. Fellow Tex. Bar Found., Houston Bar Found.;

mem. ABA,. Internat. Assn. Def. Counsel, Tex. Bar Assn., Houston Bar Assn. Home: 11682 Arrowwood Cir Houston TX 77063-1402 Office: Beck Redden & Secrest 1331 Lamar St Ste 1570 Houston TX 77010-3028

SECREST, VICKIE LYNN, nursing administrator; b. Wheeling, W.Va., Aug. 6, 1954; d. Clyde Allen and Loretta Marlene (Hopkins) S. B.S.N., U. Ky., 1976; M.S., Ohio State U., 1979. R.N. Staff/charge nurse Mercy Hosp., Portsmouth, Ohio, 1976-78; head nurse, 1978; nurse coordinator Lexington VA Med. Ctr., Ky., 1979-81, chief nurse trainee, 1981-83; asst. chief nursing service Shreveport VA Med. Ctr., La., 1983-84; assoc. chief nursing service Little Rock VA Med. Ctr., Ark., 1984-87; chief nursing services Wilmington (Del.) VA Med. Ctr., 1987—, Oklahoma City, 1988—. Mem. parish council Roman Cath. Ch., Shreveport, 1983-84; active Lupus Found., Big Bros.-Big Sisters Program. Wharton Nurse Exec. fellow, 1989. Mem. Am. Soc. Nursing Service Adminstrs., Ohio State U. Alumni Assn., Nat. League Nursing, Sigma Theta Tau. Avocations: creative writing; reading; needlepoint; walking; swimming.

SECRIST, RICHARD A., industrial company executive; b. N.Y.C., Oct. 1, 1945; m. Patricia Aljoe; children: Richard Jr., Ryan, Robin, Rudd. BS, U. Fla., 1966, MA, 1967. Sr. mgr. Price Waterhouse, N.Y.C., 1967-77; pres. Gold Fields Am. Corp., N.Y.C., 1977-86; chmn., pres., chief exec. officer Blue Tee Corp., N.Y.C., 1986—, also dir. Mem. Baltusrol Golf Club (Springfield, N.J.), Univ. Club (N.Y.C.). Republican. Episcopalian. Office: Blue Tee Corp 250 Park Ave S New York NY 10003-1402*

SECUNDA, ARTHUR (HOLLAND SECUNDA), artist; b. Jersey City, Nov. 12, 1927; s. Leo Konstantinovich and Catherine (Volkovitzky) S.; m. Gladys Bullis, Mar. 5, 1956 (div. Feb. 1974); 1 child, David Abraham. Student, NYU, 1946, Art Students League N.Y., 1947-48; pvt. study with Ossip Zadkine, Paris, 1949. Art critic Beverly Hills (Calif.) Times, 1959-61; assoc. editor Artforum Mag., 1962-64; art tchr. U. Calif., L.A., Pasadena Art Mus., Long Beach (Calif.) State Coll., Otis Art Inst., L.A.; Curator edn. Santa Barbara Art Mus., 1957-58; guest curator Long Beach Art Mus., 1970; organizer traveling exhibits. Artist: Center Mag., Center Study Democratic Instns., 1969-75; exhibited numerous one-man shows, U.S. and abroad; represented in numerous pub. collections, museums and univs; travelling exhbns. Osaka, Hiroshima, Tokyo, Gifu and Fukui, Japan, 1988. Tamarind fellow, 1969, 73. Mem. Artists Equity. Address: 1223 Wilshire Blvd # 601 Santa Monica CA 90403-5400 Office: Kathy Bianco Fine Arts Internat PO Box 8491 New York NY 10150 *I strive to attain passion and intensity in my work. I am affected strongly by my environment and am attracted to the warm, vibrant colors of the California and Provencal sun.*

SECUNDA, DON ELLIOTT, lawyer, realtor; b. N.Y.C., Aug. 1, 1947; s. Richard N. and Jeannette Lee (Berg) S.; m. Joanne Feil, Nov. 24, 1976; 1 child, Kevin Feil. BA, Queens Coll., 1968; JD, N.Y. Law Sch., 1972. Bar: N.Y. 1973. Ptnr. Whitman & Ransom, N.Y.C., 1987-93, Riukin, Radler & Kremer, N.Y.C., 1994—. Mem. N.Y. County Lawyer's Assn. (chair legis. com. real property sect. 1991—, com. housing preservation and devel. 1976-86). Avocations: tennis, bicycling, hiking, reading. Office: Riukin Radler & Kremer 275 Madison Ave New York NY 10016-1101

SECUNDA, EUGENE, marketing communications executive, educator; b. Bklyn., June 15, 1934; s. Sholom and Betty (Almer) S.; m. Shirley Carol Frummer, Sept. 23, 1961; children—Ruthanne, Andrew. Comml. degree, N.Y. Inst. Photography, 1955; B.S., NYU Sch. Bus., 1956; M.S., Boston U., 1962; PhD, NYU, 1988. News editor Sta.-WBMS, Boston, 1956-57; reporter New London (Conn.) Daily Day, 1958-59; publicist various Broadway shows, 1959-62; sr. publicist 20th Century Fox Film Corp., N.Y.C., 1962-65; with J. Walter Thompson Co., N.Y.C., 1965-73; dir. corp. and public affairs J. Walter Thompson Co., 1974-78, sr. v.p., dir. entertainment group, 1974-80; dir. entertainment div. J. Walter Thompson Co., N.Y.C., 1978-80; sr. v.p., dir. communications services N.W. Ayer Internat., N.Y.C., 1980-82; pres. Barnum/Secunda Assocs., N.Y.C., 1982-85, Secunda Mktg. Communications, N.Y.C., 1985—; adj. prof. advt. NYU, N.Y.C., 1972-85; prof. mktg. and advt. NYU Grad. Sch. Bus., N.Y.C., 1985-88, Baruch Coll., CUNY, 1988-93; prof. mktg. Adelphi U., Garden City, N.Y., 1993—; guest lectr. FBI Acad., Columbia U., UCLA; pres. Secunda Mktg. Communication, N.Y.C., 1985—. Contbr. articles to profl. jours. Mem. Greenwich Village Trust. Served with USAR, 1957-63. Mem. Internat. Communication Assn., Internat. Advt. Assn., TV Acad. Arts and Scis., Mcpl. Arts Soc., First Firday Club, Am. Mktg. Assn. Address: 30 Fifth Ave New York NY 10011-8859

SEDAKA, NEIL, singer, songwriter; b. Mar. 13, 1939; s. Mac and Eleanor (Appel) S.; m. Leba Margaret Strassberg, Sept. 11, 1962; children: Dara Felice, Marc Charles. Grad., Juilliard Sch. Music. Composer numerous popular songs including Breaking Up Is Hard to Do, Stupid Cupid, Calendar Girl, Oh! Carol, Stairway to Heaven, Happy Birthday Sweet Sixteen, Laughter in the Rain, Bad Blood, Love Will Keep Us Together, Solitaire, The Hungry Years, Lonely Night (Angel Face); solo performer worldwide, 1959—; appeared in NBC-TV Special, 1976; recorded numerous albums including In the Pocket, Sedaka's Back, The Hungry Years, Steppin' Out, A Song, All You Need Is the Music, Come See About Me, Greatest Hits, 1988, Oh! Carol and Other Hits, 1990, Timeless, 1992 (Platinum LP). Recipient numerous gold records and industry awards; named to Songwriters' Hall of Fame, 1980; received star on Hollywood Walk of Fame. Mem. AGVA, Am. Fedn. Musicians, AFTRA. Office: c/o Neil Sedaka Music 888 7th Ave Ste 1600 New York NY 10106-0001

SEDARES, JAMES L., conductor; b. Chgo., Jan. 15, 1956. BMusEd, Webster U., 1977; MMusEd, Washington U.- St. Louis, 1979. Assoc. condr. San Antonio Symphony, 1979-89; music dir. Phoenix Symphony Orch., 1989—, also prin. condr. Office: Phoenix Symphony Orch Symphony Hall 3707 N 7th St Ste 107 Phoenix AZ 85014-5094*

SEDDON, JOHANNA MARGARET, ophthalmologist, epidemiologist; b. Pitts.; m. Ralph Hingson, 1974. BS, U. Pitts., 1970, MD, 1974; MS in Epidemiology, Harvard U., 1976. Diplomate Am. Bd. Ophthalmology. Intern Framingham (Mass.) Union Hosp., 1974-75; resident Tufts New Eng. Med. Ctr., Boston, 1976-80; fellow ophthalmic pathology Mass. Eye and Ear Infirmary, Boston, 1980-81, clin. fellow vitreoretinal Retina Svc., 1981-82; instr. clin. ophthalmology Harvard Med. Sch., Boston, 1982-84, asst. prof., asst. surgeon ophthalmolgy, 1984, assoc. prof., 1989—; assoc. surgeon, dir. ultrasound svc. Mass. Eye and Ear Infirmary, Boston, 1989—, orgn. epidemiology rsch. unit, 1984-85, dir. epidemiology unit, 1985—, surgeon in ophthalmology, 1992—; assoc. prof. faculty dept. epidemiology Harvard Sch. Pub. Health, Boston, 1992—; mem. com. vision Commn Behavioral and Social Scis. and Edn., NRC, Washington, 1984; mem. div. rsch. grants NIH, 1987-89, 94—. Author books and articles in field; mem. editl. staff ophthalmic jours. Recipient awards NIH Nat. Svc. Rsch., 1975, 80-81; grantee and prin. investigator Nat. Eye Inst., 1984-95, Nat. Cancer Inst. 1986; med. sch. scholar, 1970-74, Henry H. Clark Med. Edn. Found., 1973. Mem. AMA, APHA, Am. Acad. Ophthalmology (Honor award 1990), Am. Med. Women's Assn., Assn. Rsch. in Vision and Ophthalmology (elected, chair epidemiology sect. 1990, trustee clin. vision epidemiology sect. 1992—, v.p. 1996—), Soc. Epidemiologic Rsch., New Eng. Ophthal. Soc., Am. Coll. Epidemiology, Retina Soc., Macula Soc. Home: 4 Louisburg Sq Boston MA 02108-1203

SEDEI, DONALD JAMES, art director; b. Johnstown, Pa., Nov. 8, 1949; s. Robert Emmett and Mildred Twila (Hornick) S.; m. Joanne Schein, Dec. 1, 1985; children: Richard Scott, Jennifer Elizabeth and David Michael. AA, Art Inst., 1970; BFA, LaRoche Coll., 1972. Designer Fisher Sci. Co., Pitts., 1972-73, art dir., 1973-76; art dir. Gateway Studios, Pitts., 1976-77, HBM Creamer, Pitts., 1977-81; sr. art dir. The Bloom Agy., Dallas, 1981-86, v.p., sr. art dir., 1986—; v.p., creative dir. N.W. Ayer, Dallas, 1988-91; sr. v.p., group creative dir. BBDO Atlanta, 1991-94; creative dir. Temerlin McClain, Dallas, 1994—. V.p. Thumbs-up Enterprises, Pitts., 1980-86; art dir. United Way, Dallas, 1987. Mem. Dallas Soc. Visual Communications. Republican. Avocations: golf, racketball, basketball, weight lifting, remodeling home. Home: 5701 Ridgehaven Dr Plano TX 75093

SEDELMAIER, JOHN JOSEF, film director, cinematographer; b. Orrville, Ohio, May 31, 1933; s. Josef Heinrich and Anne Isabel (Baughman) S.; m. Barbara Jean Frank, June 6, 1965; children: John Josef, Nancy Rachel, Adam Frederich. BFA, Art Inst. Chgo. at U. Chgo., 1955. Dir. art Young and Rubicam, Chgo., 1955-61; dir. art, assoc. creative dir. Clinton E. Frank, Chgo., 1961-64; dir. art, producer J. Walter Thompson, Chgo., 1964-67; pres. Sedelmaier Film Prodns., Chgo., 1967—. Retrospective exhibits Mus. Broadcast Communications, Chgo., 1988, Mus. Broadcasting, L.A., 1991, Mus. TV and Radio, N.Y.C., 1992. Recipient Golden Ducat award Mannheim Film Festival, 1968, Golden Gate award for short film "MROFNOC" San Francisco Film Festival, 1969, numerous Clio awards, 1968-92, numerous Gold, Silver and Bronze Lion awards Cannes Film Festival, 1972-90, Gold Hugo award Chgo. Film Festival, 1976, 91, 2d Ann. IDC Creative award, Chgo., 1980, Internat. Broadcasting award for world's best TV comml., 1980, 86, Clio award for dir. of yr., 1981, London Internat. Advt. awards, 1986-88, numerous awards Internat. Festival of N.Y., 1984-93, Ann. Achievement award Assn. Ind. Comml. Producers, 1988, British Design and Art Direction silver pencils, 1989; named Advt. Person of Yr., Chgo. Advt. Club, 1984, Jewish Communicator of Yr., 1985; named one of 50 Pioneers & Visionaries Who Made TV America's Medium, Advt. Age Mag., 1995; profiled in Communication Arts mag., Mar. 1976, Print mag., Jan. 1982, Fortune mag., June 1983, Newsweek mag., Nov. 1986, numerous others; featured on 60 Minutes, 48 Hours; subject of cover story Esquire mag., Aug. 1983. Office: Sedelmaier Film Prodns Inc 858 W Armitage Ave # 267 Chicago IL 60614-4101

SEDER, ARTHUR RAYMOND, JR., lawyer; b. Oak Park, Ill., Apr. 20, 1920; s. Arthur Raymond and Mary Aline (Grantham) S.; m. Marion Frances Heltzel, Feb. 28, 1942; children: James A., Susan J., Elizabeth A. Student, U. Minn., 1938-39; BSL, Northwestern U., 1946, LLB, 1947. Bar: Ill. 1948, Mich. 1961. Law clk. to Justice Vinson U.S. Supreme Ct., 1948-50; mem. Sidley & Austin., Chgo., 1950-72; pvt. practice Washington 1985—; pres. Am. Natural Resources Co., Detroit, 1973-76; chmn., chief exec. officer, dir. Am. Natural Resources Co., 1976-85; bd. dirs. EnviroSource, Inc. Life trustee Northwestern U., Evanston, Ill. Mem. ABA, Ill. Bar Assn., Mich. Bar Assn. Home: 11221 Crest Hill Rd Marshall VA 22115-9103

SEDERBAUM, ARTHUR DAVID, lawyer; b. N.Y.C., Sept. 14, 1944; s. William and Harriet (Warschauer) S.; m. Francine Haba, Dec. 30, 1967 (div. Aug. 1982); children: Rebecca, David; m. Phyllis Padow, Jan. 18, 1986; 1 child, Elizabeth. AB cum laude, Columbia U., 1965, JD, 1968; LLM, NYU, 1972. Bar: N.Y. 1968, Fla. 1980, U.S. Dist. Ct. (so. and ea. dists.) N.Y. 1972. Assoc. Zissu, Halper & Martin, N.Y.C., 1968-70, Berlack, Israels & Liberman, N.Y.C., 1970-72, Rubin Baum Levin Constant & Friedman, N.Y.C., 1972-76; ptnr. Certilman, Haft, Balin, Buckley, Kremer & Hyman, N.Y.C., 1976-88, Olshan, Grundman, Frome, Rosenzweig & Orens, N.Y.C., 1988-92, Patterson, Belknap, Webb & Tyler, 1992—. Mem. adv. bd. NYU Inst. Fed. Taxation. Author: Setting Up and Executing Trusts, 1988. Recipient J.K. Lasser Tax prize NYU Inst. Fed. Taxation, 1968. Fellow Am. Coll. Trusts and Estates Coun.; mem. ABA, N.Y. State Bar Assn. (vice-chmn. com. on estate planning trusts and estates law sect.), Assn. Bar City N.Y. (com. surrogates cts.), Practising Law Inst. (chmn. income taxation of estates and trusts program). Home: 5 Pheasant Dr Armonk NY 10504-1321 Office: Patterson Belknap Webb & Tyler 1133 Ave of the Americas New York NY 10036

SEDERBAUM, WILLIAM, marketing executive; b. N.Y.C., Dec. 22, 1914; s. Harry and Sarah (Steingart) S.; m. Harriet Warschauer, Aug. 29, 1940; children: Arthur David, Caroline Joan. BS., NYU, 1936, MA, 1943, Ph.D. Assoc. Sigmund Pines Co., Pub. Accts., 1933-35; instr. N.Y.C. pub. schs., 1935-39; restaurant propr., 1939-41; v.p. Schenley Distillers Co., N.Y.C., 1941-61; pres. Distbrs. New Eng., 1956-61, Melrose Distillers Co., 1959-60, Park & Tilford Distillers Co., 1959-61; exec. v.p. Meade & Co., 1961-62; v.p., mktg. dir. J. T. S. Brown Distillers Co., 1962-65; mktg. cons., 1965-67; exec. v.p., gen. mgr. Fulton Distbg. Co., 1967-77; asst. gen. mgr., dir. spl. projects Am. Distbrs Fla., 1977—; instr. acctg. Fla. Jr. Coll., 1984-89. Mem. Eleanor Roosevelt Cancer Com.; mem. U.S. Olympic Games Com.; exec. com. Fedn. Jewish Charities, March of Dimes; bd. dirs. Jacksonville Urban League, 1975-87; mem. Com. of 100; bus. cons. Jr. Achievement Project, Jacksonville; chmn. bd. trustees, pres. men's club Reform Cong. of Merrick, L.I. Recipient Arch award NYU; named Chevalier, Confrerie de la Chaine des Rotisseurs, Bailliage de Jacksonville, Fla. Mem. Jacksonville Wholesale Liquor Assn. (pres. 1970-76), Jacksonville Symphony Assn., Jacksonville Civic Music Assn., Jacksonville C. of C. (econ. edn. com., airline svc. com., hon. adm. of flag ship Am. Airlines), Kappa Phi Kappa. Clubs: River, Carriage (N.Y.C.); NYU, Playboy, Key. Home: 4305 Plaza Gate Ln Apt 201 Jacksonville FL 32217-4439 Office: Am Distbrs Fla 6867 Stuart Ln S Jacksonville FL 32254-3438 *Live life the way it should be the way it is.*

SEDERHOLM, SARAH KATHLEEN (KATHY SEDERHOLM), primary education educator; b. Herrin, Ill., Apr. 17, 1945; d. Clifford Clark and Sarah Kathleen (Cockrum) Hatcher; m. Karl Alexander Sederholm, Aug. 12, 1966; 1 child, Scott Alexander. BS in Edn., No. Ariz. U., 1967; MEd, U. Ariz., 1972. Primary classroom tchr. Tucson Unified Sch. Dist., 1967-69, Marana (Ariz.) Unified Sch. Dist., 1978—. Mem. Ariz. Edn. Assn. (student rels. com. 1992—), Marana Edn. Assn. (assn. rep. 1985-89, 91—), Marana Edn. Assn. (assn. rep. 1985-89, 91-93, treas.), Delta Kappa Gamma (pres. chpt. 1992—). Home: 4302 N Stanley Pl Tucson AZ 85705-1734 Office: Marana Unified Sch Dist 11279 W Grier Rd Marana AZ 85653-9776

SEDGWICK, ALEXANDER, historian, educator; b. Boston, June 8, 1930; s. William Ellery and Sarah (Cabot) S.; m. Charlene Mary Maute, June 24, 1961; children—Catherine Maria, Alexander Cameron. BA, Harvard U., 1952, PhD in History, 1963. Asst. prof. history Dartmouth Coll., 1962-63; assoc. prof. U. Va., Charlottesville, 1963-66; prof. U. Va., 1974—, chmn. history dept., 1979-85, dean Coll. Arts and Scis., 1985-90; dean grad. studies U. Va., Charlottesville, 1990-95; mem. adv. com. in history Sr. Fulbright Awards Council for Internat. Exchange of Scholars. Author: The Ralliement in French Politics 1890-98, 1965, The Third French Republic, 1870-1914, 1968, Jansenism in Seventeenth Century France, Voices in the Wilderness, 1977; co-author: (with others): Church, State and Society Under the Bourbon Kings of France, 1982, For Want of a Horse, 1985, That Gentle Strength, 1980, Les Discour sur les Révolutions, 1991, History Today, 1991, Chroniques de Port-Royal, 1993, 95. Served with U.S. Army, 1952-54. Fulbright fellow, 1960-62; recipient Am. Coun. Learned Socs. grant-in-aid, 1967-78, Am. Philos. Soc. grant-in-aid, 1971. Mem. AAUP (nat. council 1976-79), Soc. French Hist. Studies (sec. 1979-83, pres. 1983-84), Am. Hist. Assn., Century Assn. Home: 1409 Rugby Rd Charlottesville VA 22903-1240 Office: U Va Dept History Randall Hall Charlottesville VA 22903

SEDGWICK-HIRSCH, CAROL ELIZABETH, financial executive; b. Cin., Apr. 16, 1922; d. Howard Malcolm Sedgwick and Lucile Alleen (Willard) Sedgwick-Schenk; m. Donald Sebastian Freeman, Nov. 25, 1944 (div. July 1968); children: Elizabeth P. Freeman Closson, Lucy S. Freeman; m. William Christian Hirsch, June 16, 1983. BS, U. Cin., 1944, postgrad., 1972; postgrad., Art Acad. of Cin., 1953-56; MEd, Xavier U., 1966; MS in Criminal Justice, Xavier U., Cin., 1990. Dir., head tchr. Mason Heart Acad. PreSch., Cin., 1952-53; caseworker dependent children Hamilton County Welfare Dept., Cin., 1959-62; instr. ednl. psychology and child devel. Wright State U., Fairborn, Ohio, 1970-71, 71-72; pres., chief exec. officer Joseph England Hutton Enterprises, Cin., 1979—. Mem. Cin. Women's Club, Coll. Club of Cin. Avocations: golf, swimming, needlework, creative writing. Home: 9092 Lake St Alanson MI 49706 also: 605 E Epworth Ave Cincinnati OH 45232-1705 Office: Joseph England Hutton Enterprises 605 E Epworth Ave Cincinnati OH 45232-1705

SEDLIN, ELIAS DAVID, physician, orthopedic researcher, educator; b. N.Y.C., Jan. 21, 1932; s. Arnold Boris and Sonia Lipschitz Sedlin; m. Barbara Sue Zidell, July 9, 1960; children: Faith Avril, Adrian. BS in Biology, U. Ala., 1951; MD, Tulane U., 1955; D.Med. Sci., U. Gothenburg, Sweden, 1966. Diplomate: Am. Bd. Orthopedic Surgery. Intern Mobile (Ala.) Gen. Hosp., 1955-56; resident Charity Hosp., New Orleans, 1956-57; chief resident Bronx (N.Y.). Mcpl. Hosp., 1959-60; sr. resident Henry Ford Hosp., Detroit, 1960-61, rsch. assoc., emergency room lectr., 1961-63, NIH

fellow, 1963-64; jr. attending physician Detroit Receiving Hosp., 1962-63; spl. NIH fellow dept. orthopedic surgery Sahlgrenska Sjukhuset, Gothenburg, 1964-66; asst. prof. dept. orthopaedic surgery Albert Einstein Coll. Medicine, 1966-69, assoc. prof., 1969-75, prof., 1975—, dir. orthopaedic surgery, 1969-79; prof. orthopaedic surgery Mt. Sinai Sch. Medicine, 1980—, dir. orthopaedic edn. Contbr. to multiple symposia, profl. meetings, also articles to profl. jours. Served to capt. AUS, 1957-59. Fulbright scholar, 1962; NSF postdoctoral fellow, 1964; recipient P.D. McGehee award Mobile Gen. Hosp., 1956; Ludvic Hektoen gold medal AMA, 1963; Nicholas Andry award Assn. Bone and Joint Surgeons, 1964. Fellow ACS, AAAS, Am. Acad. Orthopaedic Surgeons; mem. Orthopaedic Rsch. Soc., Phi Beta Kappa. Office: 5 E 98th St New York NY 10029-6501

SEDRA, ADEL SHAFEEK, electrical engineering educator, university administrator; b. Assuout, Egypt, Nov. 2, 1943; arrived in Can., 1966; s. Chafik and Hélène (Monsour) S.; m. Doris M. Barker, May 5, 1973; children: Paul Douglas, Mark Andrew. BSEE, Cairo U., 1964; MASc in Elec. Engring., U. Toronto, Ont., Can., 1968, PhDEE, 1969. Registered profl. engr., Ont. Instr. Cairo U., 1964-66; asst. prof. elec. engring. U. Toronto, 1969-72, assoc. prof., 1972-78, prof., 1978—, chmn. dept., 1986-93, v.p., provost, 1993—; pres. Elec. Engring. Consociates Ltd., Toronto, 1979-81; bd. dirs. Info. Tech. Rsch. Ctr., Toronto, 1988—. Co-author: Filter Theory and Design, 1978, Microelectronic Circuits, 1982, 3d edit., 1991 (also Spanish, Korean, Greek and Hebrew transls.); contbr. over 120 articles to sci. jours. Recipient Cirs. and Sys. Soc. Edn. award, 1994; Operating grantee Nat. Scis. and Engring. Rsch. Coun. Can., 1970—; fellow Ryerson Poly. Inst., Toronto, 1988. Fellow IEEE (Darlington best paper award 1987); mem. Am. Soc. Engring. Edn. (Terman award 1988), Info. Tech. Assn. Can. (Achievement award 1993), Assn. Profl. Engrs. Ont. Home: 18 High Park Blvd, Toronto, ON Canada M6R 1M4 Office: U Toronto Simcoe Hall, 27 Kings College Cir, Toronto, ON Canada M5S 1A1

SEDWICK, (BENJAMIN) FRANK, language educator; b. Balt., Apr. 7, 1924; s. Benjamin Frank and Louise (Lambert) S.; m. Alice Elvira Magdeburger, June 4, 1949; children: Eric, Lyn, Coralie, Daniel. A.B., Duke, 1945; M.A., Stanford, 1947; Ph.D., U. So. Cal., 1953. Instr. Spanish U. Md., College Park, 1947-49; asst. prof. Spanish and Italian U.S. Naval Acad., 1951-53; asst. prof. Spanish U. Wis.-Milw., 1953-58; prof. Spanish and Italian Ohio Wesleyan U., Delaware, 1958-63; prof. Spanish, head dept. fgn. langs. Rollins Coll., Winter Park, Fla., 1963-80; dir. overseas programs Rollins Coll., 1963-80; freelance writer, 1980—. Author: The Tragedy of Manuel Azaña and the Fate of the Spanish Republic, 1963, A History of the Useless-Precaution Plot in Spanish and French Literature, 1964, El otro and Raquel encadenada, 1960, La forja de los sueños, 1960, La gloria de don Ramiro, 1966, Selecciones de Madariaga, 1969, Conversation in Spanish (co-author French, Italian, English and German edits.), 5th edit., 1988, Conversaciones con madrileños, 1973, Spanish for Careers, 1980 (co-author French and German edits.), The Practical Book of Cobs, 1987, 3d edit., 1995, The Gold Coinage of Gran Colombia, 1991; contbr. articles to profl. jours. Served to lt. USNR, 1942-46, PTO. Home: 2033 Cove Trl Winter Park FL 32789-1158

SEDWICK, JOHN WEETER, judge; b. Kittanning, Pa., Mar. 13, 1946; s. Jack D. and Marion (Hilton) S.; m. Deborah Brown, Aug. 22, 1966; children: Jack D. II, Whitney Marie. BA summa cum laude, Dartmouth Coll., 1968; JD cum laude, Harvard U., 1972. Bar: Alaska 1972, U.S. Dist. Ct. Alaska 1972, U.S. Ct. Appeals (9th cir.) 1973. Lawyer Burr, Pease and Kurtz, Anchorage, 1972-81, 1982-92; dir. div. lands State of Alaska, Anchorage, 1981-82; judge U.S. Dist. Ct. Alaska, Anchorage, 1992—. Mem. membership com. Commonwealth North, Anchorage, 1985; bd. dirs. South Addition Alaska R.R. Com., Anchorage, 1984. Served to sgt. USNG, 1969-72. Mem. ABA, Alaska Bar Assn. (chmn. environ. law sect. 1984, law examiners com. 1986-89, civil rules com. 1990-92, fee arbitration com. 1991-92), Anchorage Bar Assn. Episcopalian. Home: 1112 South St Anchorage AK 99501-4230

SEE, CAROLYN, English educator, book critic; b. Pasadena, Calif., Jan. 13, 1934; d. George Newton Laws and Kate Louise (Sullivan) Daly; m. Richard Edward See, Feb. 18, 1955 (div. June 1959); 1 child, Lisa Lenine; m. Tom Sturak, June 11, 1959; 1 child, Clara Elizabeth Marya. BA, Calif. State U., L.A., 1958; PhD, UCLA, 1963. Prof. English, Loyola Marymount Coll., L.A., 1970-85, UCLA, L.A., 1985—; book critic L.A. Times, 1981-93, Washington Post, 1993—. Author: (novels) Rhine Maidens, 1980, Golden Days, 1986, Making History, 1991, Dreaming: Hard Luck and Good Times In America, 1995, also 3 others. Bd. dirs. Calif. Arts Coun., L.A., 1987-91, Day Break, for homeless, Santa Monica, Calif., 1989—, Friends of English, UCLA, 1990—; buddy for life AIDS Project Los Angeles, AIDS relief, L.A., 1990—. Recipient award Sidney Hillman Found., 1972, Robert Kirsch award L.A. Times, 1994; grantee Nat. Endowment for Arts, 1980, Guggenheim fellow, 1990-91. Mem. Writers Guild Am., Libr. Found. Calif., PEN Ctr. USA West (pres. 1990-91), Nat. Book Critics Cir. (bd. dirs. 1986-90). Democrat. Avocations: gardening, sailing, dancing, brush clearing. Home: PO Box 107 Topanga CA 90290 Office: UCLA Dept English 405 Hilgard Ave Los Angeles CA 90024-1301

SEE, EDMUND M., lawyer; b. Marietta, Ohio, Oct. 9, 1943; s. Edgar Thorpe and Katherine M. (Merriam) S.; m. Ellen Engler, June 5, 1976; children: Kevin, Gregory, Tyler. BA, Wesleyan U., Middletown, Conn., 1965; JD, Harvard U., 1971. Bar: Conn. 1971. Assoc. Day, Berry & Howard, Hartford, Conn., 1971-77; ptnr. Day, Berry & Howard, Hartford, 1978—. Vol. Peace Corps, Gabon, 1965-67, Vista, 1968-69; trustee St. Joseph Coll., 1991—. Mem. Nat. Assn. Bond Lawyers, Conn. Govtl. Fin. Officers Assn. Office: Day Berry & Howard Cityplace 25th Fl Hartford CT 06103-3499

SEE, KAREN MASON, federal judge; b. Springfield, Mo., Jan. 31, 1952; d. Robert Wayne and Mildred Lucille (Stockstill) Mason; m. Andrew B. See, Nov. 24, 1979. BS in Edn. cum laude, SW Mo. State U., 1973; JD, U. Mo., 1978. Bar: Mo. 1978. Tchr. Springfield (Mo.) Dist., 1973-75; law clk. Judge William E. Turnage, Mo. Ct. of Appeals, Kansas City, 1978-79; assoc. atty. Slagle & Bernard, Kansas City, 1979-84, ptnr., 1984-86; judge U.S. Bankruptcy Ct., Kansas City, 1986—; adj. prof. U. Mo. Law Sch., Kansas City. Active Mo. Bicentennial Commn., Jefferson City, 1987—, Kansas City Bicentennial Commn., 1987—; mem. adv. bd. Greater Mo. Focus on Leadership; bd. dirs. Mo. Found. for Women's Resources, Inc.; bd. dirs. Mid-Continent Coun. Girl Scouts U.S.A. Named an Outstanding Young Alumnus S.W. Mo. State U., 1988. Mem. ABA, Mo. Bar Assn. (vice chmn. comml. law com., bd. editors Mo. Bar Jour.), Kansas City Met. Bar Assn., Kansas City Lawyers Assn., Nat. Conf. of Bankruptcy Judges, Am. Judicature Soc., Order of Coif. Avocations: sailing, reading. Office: US Bankruptcy Ct 811 Grand Ave Rm 905 Kansas City MO 64106-1909

SEE, ROBERT FLEMING, JR., lawyer; b. Kansas City, Mo., Apr. 23, 1942; s. Robert Fleming and Betty (Conard) S.; m. Leslie, Apr. 26, 1985. BA with honors, U. Tex., 1964, JD with honors, 1966. Bar: Tex. 1966. Assoc. Locke, Purnell, Rain, Harrell and predecessor, Dallas, 1966, ptnr., 1972, pres., 1989—; speaker in field. Contbg. author: Loan Documentation Guide, 1990. Bd. commrs. Dallas Housing Authority; bd. dirs., chair affordable housing com. Dallas Citizens Coun. Mem. ABA, Tex. Bar Assn., Dallas Bar Assn., Greater Dallas C. of C., North Dallas C. of C., Salesmanship Club Dallas. Office: Locke Purnell Rain Harrell 2200 Ross Ave Ste 2200 Dallas TX 75201-6766

SEEBA, HINRICH CLAASSEN, foreign language educator; b. Hannover, Germany, Feb. 5, 1940; came to U.S., 1967; s. Hinrich and Irmgard (Witte) S. Student, Göttingen, Zürich, Tübingen univs., 1960-67; staatsexamen, U. Tübingen, Fed. Republic of Germany, 1966, PhD, 1967. Asst. prof. German U. Calif., Berkeley, 1968-72, assoc. prof., 1972-76, prof., 1976—, chmn. dept. German, 1977-81, 89-91; vis. prof. Free U. Berlin, 1992, Stanford (Calif.) U., 1994. Author: Kritik des ästhetischen Menschen, 1970, Die Liebe zur Sache, 1973; author, editor: Kleist: Dramen I, 1987, II, 1991; co-editor Politzefs, 1975, Brinkmanfs, 1981; contbr. scholarly papers on German lit. to jours.; editorial bd. Lessing Yearbook, 1979—, Eighteenth Century Studies, 1982-85, The German Quar., 1988-92, 94—, South Cen. Rev., 1988—; adv. bd. German Studies Rev., 1990—, Zeitschrift für Germanistik, 1991—, U. Calif. Press Modern Philology Series, 1992—. Studienstiftung fellow, 1963-68,

Guggenheim Found. fellow, 1970-71. Mem. MLA, Am. Assn. Tchrs. German, German Studies Assn., Philol. Assn. of Pacific, Lessing Soc. (pres. 1985-87), Heine Soc., Grillparzer Gesellschaft, Herder Gesellschaft. Lutheran. Office: U Calif Dept German Berkeley CA 94720

SEEBACH, LYDIA MARIE, physician; b. Red Wing, Minn., Nov. 9, 1920; d. John Henry and Marie (Gleusen) S.; m. Keith Edward Wentz, Oct. 16, 1959; children: Brooke Marie, Scott. BS, U. Minn., 1942, MB, 1943, MD, 1944, MS in Medicine, 1951. Diplomate Am. Bd. Internal Medicine. Intern Kings County Hosp., Bklyn., 1944; fellow Mayo Found., Rochester, Minn., 1945-51; pvt. practice Oakland, Calif., 1952-60, San Francisco, 1960—; asst. clin. prof. U. Calif., San Francisco 1981—; mem., vice chmn. Arthritis Clinic, Presbyn. Hosp., San Francisco, 1961-88, pharmacy com., 1963-78; chief St. Mary's Hosp. Arthritis Clinic, San Francisco, 1968-72; exec. bd. Pacific Med. Ctr., San Francisco, 1974-76. Contbr. articles to med. jours. Fellow ACP; mem. AMA, Am. Med. Womens Assn. (pres. Calif. chpt. 1968-70), Am. Rheumatism Assn., Am. Soc. Internal Medicine, Pan Am. Med. Womens Assn. (treas.), Calif. Acad. Medicine, Calif. Soc. Internal Medicine, Calif. Med. Assn., San Francisco Med. Soc., San Francisco Med. Assn., San Francisco Soc. Internal Medicine, No. Calif. Rheumatism Assn., Internat. Med. Women's Assn., Mayo Alumni (bd. dirs. 1983-89), Iota Sigma Pi. Republican. Lutheran. Avocations: music, cooking, gardening, needlepoint. Office: 490 Post St # 939 San Francisco CA 94102-1410

SEEBART, GEORGE E., insurance executive; b. Niles, Calif., 1928. Grad., Whitman Coll., 1952. V.p. field ops. Farmers Ins. Group Cos.; pres. Mid Century Ins. Co. Office: PO Box 2478 Terminal Annex Los Angeles CA 90051

SEEDLOCK, ROBERT FRANCIS, engineering and construction company executive; b. Newark, Feb. 6, 1913; s. Frank Andrew and Mary Elizabeth (Prosner) S.; m. Hortense Orcutt Norton, Sept. 1, 1937; children: Robert Francis, Elizabeth Munsell Seedlock Morrissette, Walter Norton, Mary Marion. Student Case Inst. Tech., 1931-33; BS, U.S. Mil. Acad., 1937; MS in Civil Engring., MIT, 1940; grad. Armed Forces Staff Coll., 1948, Nat. War Coll., 1958. Registered profl. engr., D.C., Pa. Commd. 2d lt. U.S. Army, 1937, advanced through grades to maj. gen., 1963; asst. to dist. engr., Pitts., 1937-39, Tulsa Aircraft Assembly Plant, 1941; regtl. exec. en. comdr. Engr. Unit Tng. Ctr., Camp Claiborne, La., 1942; asst. theatre engr., CBI, also comdr. Burma Road Engrs., also chief engr. Shanghai Base Command, 1943-45; mem. Gen. Marshall's Mediation Mission, Peking, 1946-47; mem. gen. staff U.S. Army, Mem. Am. del. Far Eastern Commn., 1948-49; aide to chief staff U.S. Army, 1949-54; mem. U.S. del. NATO Ministerial Conf., 1952-53; dep. div. engr. Mediterranean div., 1954-57; mil. asst. to asst. sec. def. for pub. affairs, 1958-62; div. engr. Missouri River, Omaha, 1962-63; sr. mem. UN Mil. Armistice Commn., Korea, 1963-64; dir. mil. personnel Office dep. chief of staff for personnel Dept. Army, 1964-66; dir. mil. constrn. Office Chief of Engrs., 1966; comdg. gen. U.S. Army Engr. Center and Ft. Belvoir, Va., and comdt. U.S. Army Engr. Sch., Ft. Belvoir, 1966-68, ret., 1968; pres. Yuba Industries, Inc., 1968-69, v.p. Standard Prudential Corp. (merged with Yuba Industries), 1969-70; v.p., dir. Petro-Chem. Devel. Co., Inc., N.Y.C., 1968-70, Petchem Constrn. Co., N.Y.C., 1968-70, Petrochem. Isoflow Furnaces, Ltd. (Can.), 1968-70; dir. constrn. and devel. Port Authority of Allegheny County, Pitts., 1970-73; cons. Parsons, Brinckerhoff, Quade & Douglas, N.Y.C., 1973-75; mgr. So. region, 1975-77; dep. project dir. Parsons, Brinckerhoff-Tudor-Bechtel, Atlanta, 1973-77; program dir. Ralph M. Parsons Co., Pasadena, Calif., Phila. and Washington, 1977-83; cons. engr. 1983—; dir. T.Y. Lin Intl., 1985-89; chief liaison, cons. Chinese Acad. Sci. for Beijing Inst. Mgmt., 1985-89; U.S. rep. to Permanent Tech. Com. Number 1 of Permanent Intl. Assn. of Navigation Congresses, 1984-93; pres. First Am. chapt. Burma Star Assn., 1984—; chmn. Sino-Am. Ventures, Inc., 1987—; cons. The Knowledge Co., 1989—, Dove & Assocs., 1990; mem. radio engring. adv. com. Voice of Am., 1990-93. Contbr. to mil. and engring. jours. Bd. dirs. Army and Air Force Exchange and Motion Picture Svc., 1964; mem. Miss. River Commn., 1962-63, Bd. Engrs. Rivers and Harbor, 1962-63, Def. Adv. Commn. Edn., 1964; chmn. Mo. Basin Inter-Agy. Com., 1962-63; fed. rep., chmn. Big Blue River Compact Commn., 1962-63; mem. U.S. Com. on Large Dams, 1962-82; exec. bd. Nat. Capital Area council Boy Scouts Am., 1967-68, Atlanta Area council, 1975-77. Decorated DSM, Legion of Merit with oak leaf cluster; chevalier Legion of Honor (France); 1st class, grade A medal Army, navy, air force, also spl. breast order Yun Hui (China); named Engr. of Yr., Met. Atlanta Engring. Soc., 1976; Ga. Engr. of Yr. in Govt., Ga. Soc. Profl. Engrs., 1976; recipient Silver Beaver award Boy Scouts Am., 1977, Case Alumni Assn. Gold medal, 1985. Fellow Soc. Am. Mil. Engrs. (nat. dir., Cathedral Latin Alumni Assn. Man of the Yr. award 1992); mem. ASCE (hon., aerospace div. program com. 1980-82, sec. exec. com. 1982-83, chmn. 1984-85, editor Jour. Aerospace Engring., 1986-93), Assn. U.S. Army, West Point Soc. N.Y. (life), West Point Soc. Atlanta (pres. 1976), Burma Star Assn. (pres. 1st Am. chpt., 1982—), Sigma Xi, Tau Beta Pi. Roman Catholic. Clubs: Army-Navy Country (sec., chmn. bd. govs. 1952-54, 61-62) (Arlington, Va.); MIT (pres. Shanghai 1946); Met. (N.Y.C.); Oglethorpe (Savannah, Ga.), Ansley Golf (Atlanta).

SEEFELDT, CAROL, education educator; b. St. Louis, May 3, 1935; d. George and Mary (Reznicek) Wohanka; m. Eugene Seefeldt; children: Paul, Andrea. BA, U. Wis., Milw., 1956; MA, U. South Fla., 1968; PhD, Fla. State U., 1971. Reg. tng. officer Fla. Project Head Start, Tallahassee, 1968-71; prof. U. Md., College Park, 1971—. Author: Social Studies for the Preschool and Primary Child, 1992, Continuing Issues in Early Childhood Education, 1990. Bd. dirs. Md. Com. for Children, Balt., 1988-90. Named Disting. Scholar/Tchr., U. Md., 1983—. Mem. Nat. Assn. for Edn. of Young Children (vice chmn. ednl. commn. 1986—), Assn. for Childhood Edn. Internat., Am. Ednl. Research Assn., Phi Delta Kappa. Home: 881 Mt Airy Rd Davidsonville MD 21035-2225 Office: U Md Inst for Child Study College Park MD 20742

SEE FONG CHAN, retired linguist, composer; b. China, Nov. 15, 1922; came to U.S., 1940.; m. Poi Gin Wong, July 24, 1958; 1 child. Owner mfg. co. restaurant equipment, 1949-58, co-owner Chinese restaurant, 1953-72; participant Internat. Conf. of Sino-Tibetan Langs. and Linguistics, 1993, 94, 95. Composer: I Thank You, 1954, Space of Age, 1958. With USN, 1943-45. Achievements include patents of an automatic calculating and printing system with a storage component, controlled fertilizer feeder, ground fertilizer device, liquid-solid dispenser, fertilizer dispenser, automatic electric socket and plug, others. Home: 47-09 Newton Rd Astoria NY 11103*

SEEGAL, HERBERT LEONARD, department store executive; b. Brookline, Mass., Aug. 13, 1915; s. Morris and Rose (Beerman) S.; m. Dorothy Goldstein, June 27, 1941 (div. June 1954); children: Jane Laura, Norma Ann; m. Juanita C. Steele, Feb. 4, 1987. AB, U. Mich., 1937. With R.H. White's, Boston, 1937-41; with Thalhimer's, Richmond, Va., 1941-53, v.p. charge gen. merchandising, 1949-53; sr. v.p. merchandising, dir. Macy's N.Y., N.Y.C., 1953-62; pres. Bamberger's N.J., Newark, 1962-71; dir. R.H. Macy & Co., Inc., 1965—, vice chmn. bd. dirs., 1971-72, pres., 1972-80; cons. Edgars Johannesburg S.A. Mem. N.J. Econ. Stblzn. Bd.; mem. econ. stblzn. com.; regional office Fed. Emergency Mgmt. Agy. Mem. Princeton Club (N.Y.C.), Century Country Club (Purchase, N.Y.). Home: 128 Central Park S New York NY 10019-1565 also: 2451 Windsor Way Ct West Palm Beach FL 33414-7035

SEEGAL, JOHN FRANKLIN, lawyer; b. Newton, Mass., May 21, 1946; s. Samuel Melbourne and Martha (Lewenberg) S.; m. Barbara Ellen Wayne, Apr. 2, 1982. B.A., Harvard U., M.B.A., 1973, J.D., 1973. Admitted to practice Orrick, Herrington & Sutcliffe, San Francisco, 1973-78, ptnr., 1979—. Mem. ABA, Calif. Bar Assn. Republican. Jewish. Office: Orrick Herrington & Sutcliffe 400 Sansome St San Francisco CA 94111

SEEGER, GUENTER OTTO, chef; b. Loffenau, Baden, Germany, Mar. 23, 1949; s. Otto Emil and Margarete (Temme) S.; m. Marion Boehmlander (div. Aug. 1991); children: Diana, Denise. Student, Cook and Hotel Sch., Lucerne, Switzerland. Apprentice Hotel Funk, Dobel, Germany, 1963-66; cook various locations, Switzerland, 1966-77; owner, operator restaurant Pforz Heim, Germany, 1977-84; exec. chef maifar Regent Hotel, Washington, 1984-85; exec. chef dining rm. Ritz-Carlton Hotel, Atlanta, 1985—; pres., cons., produce developer Smi, Inc., Atlanta, 1993. Editor calendars, 1982, 83 (award 1982). Named Best Chef of Atlanta, Atlanta Mag., 1993. Mem.

Chefs Collaborative 2000 (bd. overseers 1994). Avocations: Kung fu. Office: The Ritz-Carlton Buckhead 3434 Peachtree Rd NE Atlanta GA 30326

SEEGER, LEINAALA ROBINSON, law librarian, educator; b. Wailuku, Hawaii, July 2, 1944; d. John Adam and Anna Hiilani (Leong) Robinson; 1 child, Maile Lea. BA, U. Wash., 1966; JD, U. Puget Sound, 1977; M in Law Librarianship, U. Wash., 1979. Bar: Wash. 1977. Reference librarian U. Puget Sound Sch. Law., Tacoma, 1977-79, assoc. law librarian, 1981-86; asst. librarian McGeorge Sch. Law, U. of Pacific, Sacramento, 1979-81; assoc. librarian pub. svc. Harvard Law Sch., Cambridge, Mass., 1986-89; dir. law library, assoc. prof. law U. Idaho Coll. Law, Moscow, 1989—; bd. dirs. Inlan, Spokane, Wash., 1989—. Mem. Palouse Asian-Ams. Assn., Moscow, 1989—. Mem. Wash. STate Bar Assn., Am. Assn. Law Librs. (chmn. minority com. 1990-91, v.p., pres.-elect Western Pacific chpt. 1985-86, 90-91, pres. 1991-92, vice chmn. edn. com. 1991-92, chmn. 1992-93), Idaho Coun. Acad. Librs. Avocations: scuba, snorkeling, wine education, flying, aerobics. Office: U Idaho Coll Laws Moscow ID 83844-2324

SEEGER, MICHAEL, musician, singer, folklorist; b. N.Y.C., Aug. 15, 1933; s. Charles Louis and Ruth Porter (Crawford) S.; m. Marjorie L. Ostrow, Dec. 20, 1960 (div. 1968); children: Kim, Arley, Jeremy; m. Alice L. Gerrard, Aug. 16, 1970 (div.). guest lectr. English dept. U. Calif., Fresno, 1974; mem. jazz/folk/ethnic music sect. Nat. Endowment for Arts, 1973-77; dir. Am. Old Time Music Festival, 1975-78, Rockbridge Mountain Music Conv., Buena Vista, Va., 1986—. Performs Appalachian vocal and instrumental music in a variety of styles at concerts, folk festivals, on radio and TV in U.S. and abroad; also numerous record albums and documentary recordings from traditional folk musicians and dancers; founding mem. New Lost City Ramblers, 1958—, Strange Creek Singers, 1968-76, Bent Mountain Band, 1981. Trustee John Edwards Meml. Found., UCLA, 1962—; bd. dirs. Newport (R.I.) Folk Festival, 1963-71, Nat. Folk Festival, Washington, 1972-78, Smithsonian Am. Folklife Co., 1970-76. Recipient 1st prize banjo category Galax Va. Old Time Fiddlers Conf., 1975; Ralph J. Gleason Meml. award Rex Found., 1994; Grammy nominee for best traditional folk album, 1986, 91, 94; Nat. Endowment Arts grantee, 1975, 82, 84, 87; vis. scholar Smithsonian Instn., 1983; Guggenheim fellow, 1984. Home: PO Box 1592 Lexington VA 24450-1592

SEEGER, PETE, folk singer, songwriter; b. N.Y.C., May 3, 1919; s. Charles Louis and Constance de Clyver (Edson) S.; m. Toshi-Aline Ohta, July 20, 1943; children: Daniel Adams, Mika Salter, Tinya. Student, Harvard U., 1936-38. Teamed with Woody Guthrie, toured south and southwest; an organizer, Almanac Singers, 1940, toured U.S. with group, 1941-42; collaborated on writing labor and anti-Fascist songs; sang on overseas broadcasts, OWI; became nat. dir., People's Songs, Inc., 1946; performed: motion picture film To Hear My Banjo Play, 1946; toured with Progressive Party candidate Henry Wallace; helped organize the Weavers, 1948; appeared nat. radio and TV shows until blacklisted from networks, night clubs and theaters; rec. for, Decca, 1949-52, Folkways, 1953-80, Columbia, 1961-73 toured schs., summer camps, colls., univs. U.S.A. and 35 other countries; assisted orgn., Newport (R.I.) Folk Festivals; songwriter: Where Have All the Flowers Gone, 1961, If I Had a Hammer, (in collaboration with Lee Hays) Kisses Sweeter than Wine, (in collaboration with Weavers) Turn, Turn, Turn, 1959; recent albums include Sing Along, 1980, (with John Hammond) Waist Deep in the Big Muddy and other Love Songs, 1994; TV series Rainbow Quest, 1965; producer ednl. short subjects, Folklore Research Films; performed global singing tour including 24 countries, 1963-64; appeared: Smothers Bros. Show, as network blacklist was lifted, 1967; appeared in: film Tell Me That You Love Me, Junie Moon, 1970; author: American Favorite Ballads, 1961, The Bells of Rhymney, 1964, How To Play The Five-String Banjo, Henscratches and Flyspecks, 1973, The Incompleat Folksinger, 1973, (with Charles Seeger) The Foolish Frog, 1973, Abiyoyo, 1983, (with Robert Reiser) Carry It On, 1986, (with Robert Reiser) Everybody Says Freedom, 1990, Where Have All the Flowers Gone, 1993. Served with U.S. Army, 1942-45. Recipient: Nat. Medal of the Arts, 1994, Kennedy Center Honor, 1994. Pioneered the appreciation of Southern folk music through over 45 years of concerts, recordings and writings, interested many others in the idea of making their own music, revived old music of many types and used music as a means of speaking out against war, racism, poverty, pollution, etc. Office: care Harold Leventhal 250 W 57th St New York NY 10107-0001*

SEEGER, RONALD L., lawyer; b. Prairie Farm, Wis., June 10, 1930; s. John M. and Mildred G. (Moen) S.; m. Theresa A. Seeger, Sept. 3, 1955; children—Mark, Scott, John, Lynn, Eric. B.A., U. Wis., 1951; J.D., U. Minn., 1956. Bar: Minn. 1956, US Dist. Ct. 1957, U.S. Supreme Ct. 1983. Ptnr. Michaels, Seeger, Rosenblad & Arnold (now Dunlap & Seeger PA), Rochester, Minn., 1956—. Counsel, City of Rochester Charter Commn., 1962-74, chmn., 1971-72; pres. Legal Assistance of Olmsted County, 1973-76; bd. dirs., v.p Legal Assistance of Minn., 1972-74; chmn. Gamehaven area Boy Scout Found., 1974-76, now trustee. Served with U.S. Army, 1951-53; Korea. Fellow Am. Bar Found.; mem. ABA (ho. of dels. 1974-80, bd. govs. 1991-95), Minn. State Bar Assn. (bd. govs. 1974-85, pres. 1983-84), Minn. Bar Found. (dir.), Minn. Legal Cert. Bd. (chmn. 1985-90). Home: 524 9th Ave SW Rochester MN 55902-2910 Office: PO Box 549 505 Marquette Bank Bldg Rochester MN 55903

SEEGER, SONDRA JOAN, artist; b. L.A., May 27, 1942; d. Reinhold Josheph and Bertha Catherine (Monese) S.; m. Richard John Pahl, Aug. 18, 1961 (div. 1974); children: Catherine Marie, Douglas Richard, Angela Gay, Susan Joan; m. David Ernest Matteson, Apr. 25, 1990. Student, Marylhurst Coll., 1960. Pvt. practice musician various locations, 1973-81; security guard MGM Hotel, Las Vegas, 1981-82; real estate salesperson Century 21, Kent, Wash., 1983-85; mgr. Viera Land & Cattle, Inc., La Grande, Oreg., 1984-92; freelance artist, Casper, Wyo., 1991—; ptnr. Old West Saddle Shop, Casper, 1989-93, Casper, Wyo., 1993—; com. mem. Oreg. State Forest Practices Com., N.E. Region, 1990-91. Named Union Co. Tree Farmer of Yr., Am. Tree Farm System, 1987. Mem. NRA, Allied Artists, Cider Painters of Am., Australian Soc. of Minature Art, Small Woodlands Assn., Knickerbocker Artists (assoc.), United Pastelists of Am., The Art League of Alexandria, Va., Minature Art Soc. Fla., Oil Painters Am., Wyo. Artists Assn., Cody Country Art Guild, Am. Soc. Classical Realism, Gen. Artist Mem., Internat. Platform Assn., Oreg. Forest Resources Inst. Republican. Avocations: dog obedience tng., hunting, wildlife habitat enhancement. Home and Office: Old West Saddle Shop PO Box 4300 Casper WY 82604

SEEGERS, WALTER HENRY, hematology educator emeritus; b. Fayette County, Iowa, Jan. 4, 1910; s. William and Mary (Wente) S.; m. Lillian Entz, Dec. 31, 1935; 1 child, Dorothy Margaret. B.A., U. Iowa, 1931, M.S., 1932, Ph.D., 1934; D.Sc., Wartburg Coll., 1953; M.D. (hon.), Justus Liebig U., Fed. Republic Germany, 1974; D.Sc. (hon.), Med. Coll. Ohio, 1978. Research fellow U. Iowa, 1931-34, research assoc., 1934-35, 1937-42; research assoc. Antioch Coll., 1936-37; researcher Parke, Davis & Co., Detroit, 1942-45; assoc. prof. physiology Wayne State U. Coll. Medicine, 1945-46, prof., head dept. physiology, 1946-48, prof. physiology and pharmacology, 1948-74, William D. Traitel prof. hematology, 1965-80, emeritus, 1980—, chmn. symposium on blood, 1950-68, dir. Thrombosis Specialized Ctr. of Research, 1972-77; prof. physiology U. Detroit, 1946-51; vis. prof. Baylor U., 1950, 52, U. Uruguay, summer, 1957; vis. scientist, lectr. Rio de Janeiro, 1963; hon. mem. faculty medicine U. Chile; adjunct prof. vis. chair prof. Nat. Taiwan U., 1975; mem. health research facilities sci. rev. com. NIH, USPHS, 1966-70; chmn. subcom. blood coagulation NRC, 1950-53, chmn. panel on blood coagulation, 1953-57; mem. Internat. Com. on Hemostasis and Thrombosis, 1954—; Detroit Mayor's Com. Rehab. Narcotic Addicts, 1961-73; mem. sci. adv. bd. ARC, 1969-72. Author: Prothrombin, 1962; (with E.A. Sharp) Hemostatic Agents, 1948; (with J.M. Dorsey) Living Consciously: The Science of Self, 1959; (with Shirley A. Johnson) Physiology of Hemostasis and Thrombosis, 1967; Prothrombin in Enzymology, Thrombosis and Hemophilia, 1967; Blood Clotting Enzymology, 1967; John M. Dorsey Memorabilia, 1982; (with D.A. Walz) Prothrombin and other Vitamin K Proteins, 1986; contbg. author: The Enzymes. Mem. editorial bd.: Am. Jour. Applied Physiology, 1956-63, Am. Jour. Physiology, 1956-63, Circulation Research, 1954-64, Preparative Biochemistry, 1970-80, Thrombosis Research, 1972. Contbr. articles to profl. jours. Bd. regents Wartburg Coll., 1966-80; mem. bd. Ctr. Health Edn. 1961-80, pres., 1969. Co-recipient Ward Burdick award Am. Soc. Clin.

Pathologists, 1940, James F. Mitchell Found. Internat. award for heart and vascular research, 1969; recipient Commonwealth Fund Spl. award, 1957, Mayo Clinic Vis. Faculty cert., 1964, Disting. Service award Lutheran Brotherhood Ins. Soc., 1967, Acad. Achievement award Probus Club, 1963, Research award Wayne chpt. Sigma Xi, 1957, Disting. Service cert. Wartburg Alumni Assn., 1959, Faculty Service award Wayne State U. Alumni, 1971, Wisdom award honor Wisdom Soc., 1970, Mich. Minuteman Gov.'s award, 1973, H.P. Smith award Am. Soc. Clin. Pathologists, 1978; Disting. Grad. Faculty award Wayne State U., 1980, Med. Sch. Disting. Service award, 1980; commendation Stritch Sch. Medicine, Loyola U., 1980. Fellow N.Y. Acad. Scis.; mem. AAAS, Am. Inst. Chemists, Am. Soc. Hematology, Am. Heart Assn., Am. Chem. Soc., Am. Soc. Biol. Chemists, Soc. Exptl. Biology and Medicine, Am. Physiol. Soc., Detroit Physiol. Soc. (hon., pres. 1948, 80), Can. Physiol. Soc., Mich. Acad. Sci., Harvey Soc. (hon.), Chilean Soc. Transfusion and Hematology (hon.), Am. Coll. Clin. Pharmacology and Chemotherapy, Engring. Soc. Detroit, N.Y. Acad. Scis. (hon. life), Med. Soc. Turkey (hon.), Hematology Soc. Turkey (hon.), Mexican Soc. Hematology (hon.), Japanese Soc. Thrombosis and Hemostasis (hon.), Phi Beta Kappa (hon.), Sigma Xi, Alpha Omega Alpha (hon.), Phi Lambda Upsilon, Alpha Chi Sigma, Phi Beta Pi (hon.). Lutheran. Clubs: Torch, Economics (Detroit). Home: 2857 Ptarmigan Dr Apt 5 Walnut Creek CA 94595-3138

SEEGMAN, IRVIN P., manufacturing company executive; b. 1921; married. Grad., Calif. Inst. Tech., 1942. With Rubber Tech., Mare Island, Calif., 1942-48, Alameda, Calif., 1949-50; with Products Rsch. & Chem. Corp., Glendale, Calif., 1950-89; sr. v.p., dir. Products Research & Chem. Corp., Glendale, Calif., 1960-89; cons. Courtaulds Aerospace, Inc. (formerly Products Rsch. & Chem. Corp.), Glendale, Calif., 1989—. Office: Courtaulds Aerospace Inc PO Box 1800 Glendale CA 91209-1800

SEEHRA, MOHINDAR SINGH, physics educator; b. Panjab, Pakistan, Feb. 14, 1940; came to U.S., 1963; s. Bakhshish Singh and Rattan (Kaur) S.; m. Harbhajan Kaur, May 12, 1963; children: Jasmeet, Parveen. BS, Panjab U., 1959; MS, Aligarh (India) U., 1962; PhD, U. Rochester, 1969. Instr. chemistry Arya Coll., Nawanshahr, India, 1959-60; lectr. physics Jain Coll., Ambala City, India, 1962-63; asst. prof. physics W.Va. U., Morgantown, 1969-73, assoc. prof., 1973-77, prof., 1977-91, Eberly disting. prof. physics, 1992—. Contbr. over 130 articles to profl. jours. Rsch. fellow A.P. Sloan Found., 1973-75, ORAU Summer fellow, 1976, 77, 84, 85; recipient Outstanding Rsch. award Coll. Arts and Scis., U. W.Va., 1985. Fellow Am. Phys. Soc., Materials Rsch. Soc., Carbon Soc., ASM Internat. Office: WVa State U Dept Physics PO Box 6315 Morgantown WV 26506-6315

SEELBACH, WILLIAM ROBERT, management consultant; b. Lakewood, Ohio, Apr. 26, 1948; s. William Fowler and Carolyn (Paisley) S.; m. Nancy Chockley, June 28, 1969; children: Scott, Ryan. BS, Yale U., 1970; MBA, Stanford U., 1972. Assoc. Intasa, Menlo Park, Calif., 1972-74; sr. assoc. Griffenhagen-Kroeger, San Francisco, Calif., 1974-75; assoc. to ptnr. McKinsey & Co., Cleve., 1975-86; pres. Parkwood Corp., 1986-88; chmn. Inverness Ptnrs., Cleve., 1988—; bd. dirs. Lumitex, Inc., Cleve., 1988—. Trustee Work in N.E. Ohio Coun., Cleve., 1984—, Enterprise Devel. Inc., Cleve., 1985—, Playhouse Sq. Found., Cleve., 1986—, Univ. Sch., Cleve. Office: Inverness Ptnrs 25700 Science Pk Dr Beachwood OH 44122 Also: Inverness Castings Group Inc 65059 M 43 Hwy Bangor MI 49013

SEELENFREUND, ALAN, distribution company executive; b. N.Y.C., Oct. 22, 1936; s. Max and Gertrude (Roth) S.; m. Ellyn Bolt; 1 child, Eric. BME, Cornell U., 1959, M. in Indsl. Engring., 1960; PhD in Mgmt. Sci., Stanford U., 1967. Asst. prof. bus. adminstrn. Grad. Sch. Bus. Stanford U., Palo Alto, Calif., 1966-71; mgmt. cons. Strong, Wishart and Assocs., San Francisco, 1971-75; various mgmt. positions McKesson Corp., San Francisco, 1975-84, v.p., chief fin. officer, 1984-86, exec. v.p., chief fin. officer, 1986-89, chmn., chief exec. officer, 1989—; also bd. dirs.; bd. dirs. Armor All Products Corp., Pacific Gas and Electric Co. Bd. dir. Golden Gate Nat. Park Assn. Mem. World Affairs Coun. No. Calif., Bus. Roundtable, Bay Area Coun., Calif. Bus. Roundtable, Bankers Club, St. Francis Yacht Club, Villa Taverna Club, Pacific Union Club. Avocations: sailing, skiing. Office: McKesson Corp 1 Post St San Francisco CA 94104-5201

SEELEY, FRED COOLEY, retail executive; b. Ann Arbor, Mich., Mar. 23, 1942; s. Ralph Kinnie and Charlotte Ruth (Striffler) S.; m. Marlyn Kay Deyo, Nov. 22, 1969; children: Matthew, Marnie. BS, Mich. State U., 1965, MBA, 1972. With Mich. Nat. Bank, Lansing, 1962-65; asst. cashier Bank of Commonwealth, Detroit, 1966-72; mgr. Multivest, Southfield, Mich., 1972-73; sr. v.p. real estate Perry Drug Stores Inc., Pontiac, Mich., 1973—. Dir. Oakland County Econ. Devel. Corp., Pontiac, 1980—, Oakland County Local Devel., Pontiac, 1980—, Pontiac Econ. Devel. Co., 1980—. With USNG, 1966-72. Mem. Nat. Assn. Corp. Real Estate, Internat. Council Shopping Ctrs., Oakland County C. of C. (chmn. bd. dirs. 1982). Avocation: fishing. Office: Perry Drug Stores Inc 5400 Perry Dr PO Box 1957 Pontiac MI 48056

SEELEY, HARRY WILBUR, JR., microbiology educator; b. Bridgeport, Conn., Mar. 5, 1917; s. Harry W. and Genevieve (Quinlan) S.; m. Margaret Johnson, Dec. 21, 1940; children: Gail (Mrs. Frederick Cogswell), Beth (dec.), Carol (Mrs. Daniel Seeley-Teboe). B.S., U. Conn., 1941, M.S., 1942; Ph.D., Cornell U., 1947. Mem. faculty Cornell U., 1947—, prof. bacteriology, 1955—, chmn. sect. microbiology, 1964-68, prof.-in-charge microbiology, 1974-77, acting chmn. dept. microbiology, 1977-78, ret., 1979. Author: Microbes in Action, 1962, 4th edit., 1991, Microbes and Man, 1974. Guggenheim fellow, 1958. Mem. Soc. Microbiology, Am. Soc. Microbiology, Am. Acad. Microbiology, Soc. Applied Bacteriology, Internat. Oceanographic Found., AAAS, Am. Inst. Biol. Scientists, AAUP, Sigma Xi, Phi Kappa Phi. Home: Park Ln Jacksonville NY 14854-0001 Office: Cornell U Wing Hall Ithaca NY 14853

SEELEY, J., photography educator; b. Oct. 23, 1946. BS, SUNY, Buffalo, 1969; MFA in Photography, R.I. Sch. Design, 1971. Tchr. grad. liberal studies program Wesleyan U., 1973—; tchr. summer session SUNY, Albany, 1974; prof. art, photography Wesleyan U., Middletown, Conn., 1972—, chmn. dept. art, dir. studio program, 1986-89; juror Conn. student photographers exhibition U. Bridgeport, 1984, Milford (Conn.) Arts Coun., 1986; featured artist, lectr., workshop leader Focus 91 Conf., Lansing, Mich.; major collaborator with Anne Hyland Conn. Commn. Arts, We. Conn. State U., 1993. Author: High Contrast, 1980, 2d edit., 1992; contbr. articles to profl. jours., photographs to profl. mags. and photography books; one-person shows include Neikrug Gallery, N.Y.C., 1981, Coll. Art and Design, Detroit, 1982, Benjamin Gallery, Bakersfield, Calif., 1982, Ea. Wash. U., Cheney, 1983, Corvallis (Oreg.) Arts Ctr., 1983, Creative Arts Workshop, New Haven, Conn., 1983, Ithaca (N.Y.) Coll., 1984, Artworks, New Haven, 1984, Silver Bullet, Providence, 1984, Zilkha Gallery, Wesleyan U., 1985, Creative Photography Gallery, U. Dayton, Ohio, 1985, DiGiacomo Gallery, Harrington Park, N.J., 1986, U. Gallery, Utah State U., 1987, New Image Gallery, James Madison U., 1987, Faculty Club, Wesleyan U., 1989, U. Conn., Storrs, 1991, Webster U., St. Louis, 1992, Westover Sch., Middlebury, Conn., 1993; exhibited in group shows at Sch. Art, Bowling Green, Ohio, 1981, SUNY Geneseo, 1987, Catskill Ctr. Photography, Woodstock, N.Y., 1981, R.I. Sch. Design, 1982, Sawyer Coll, New London, N.H., 1983, Utah State U., Logan, 1983, Cheney Cowles Mus., Spokane, Wash., 1983, Ctrl. Wash. U., 1983, 86, B.C. Space, Laguana Beach, Calif., 1983, Swen Person Gallery, No. Ill. U., DeKalb, 1984, Catskill Ctr. Photography, Woodstock, 1985, Fla. Inst. Tech., Jensen Beach, 1986, Conn. Pub. TV Juried exhibition, Hartford, 1987, Meriam Perlman Gallery, Chgo., 1987, Sharon (Conn.) Gallery Art, 1989, Graham Horstman Gallery, Dallas, 1990, Zilkha Gallery, Wesleyan U., 1991, John Slade Ely House, New Haven, 1992, Johnson Gallery, U. N.Mex., 1992, Conn. Commn. Arts., Exec. Offices, Hartford, 1993, U. Gallery, U. Ariz., Tucson, 1993, Martin Schweig Gallery, St. Louis, 1993; represented in permanent collections Mus. Modern Art, Internat. Mus. Photography, Eastman House, U. Iowa Art Mus., Time-Life Inc., Aetna, IBM, Carson, Inc., Am. Med. Assn., R.I. Sch. Design, Davison Art Ctr., Wesleyan U., Colo. State U., numerous others. Vol. United Way, 1986—; cons. Ctr. Creative Youth, 1983—, Horizons, New Eng. Craft Program, 1983—; mem. faculty consulting examiners Charter Oak Coll., 1977—; vis. artist Savanna (Ga.) Coll. Art and Design, 1994; mem. Bd. Acad. Awards State of Conn. Recipient Best of Show award N.Am.

Invitational Fla. Inst. Tech., 1986; grantee Conn. Commn. Arts, 1992. Home: 59 South Rd Portland CT 06480 Office: Wesleyan U Art Dept Middletown CT 06459

SEELEY, ROD RALPH, physiology educator; b. Rupert, Idaho, Dec. 29, 1945; s. Earl W. Seeley and Alice E. (Hall) Walker; m. Jeanette Brady, Aug. 27, 1965; children: Teri, Alicia, Christopher, Kara. BS, Idaho State U., 1968; MS, Utah State U., 1971, PhD, 1973. Asst. prof. dept. biol. scis. Idaho State U., Pocatello, 1973-78, assoc. prof., 1978-83, prof., 1983—; chmn. dept., 1986—. Author: Human Anatomy and Physiology, 1989, 3d edit., 1995, Essentials of Anatomy and Physiology, 1991, 2d edit., 1995, Understanding Anatomy and Physiology, 1994; contbr. articles on reproductive physiology to profl. jours. Mem. bd. Sch. Dist. 25, Pocatello, 1982-88, chmn. bd., 1985-87. Recipient Disting. Tchr. award Idaho State U., 1986. Mem. AAAS, Idaho Acad. Sci., Human Anatomy and Physiology Soc., Soc. Study Reproduction, Sigma Xi. Avocations: running, fishing, backpacking, hunting. Office: Idaho State U Dept Biol Scis PO Box 8007 Pocatello ID 83209-8007

SEELIG, GERARD LEO, management consultant; b. Schluchtern, Germany, June 15, 1926; came to U.S., 1934, naturalized, 1943; s. Herman and Bella (Bach) S.; m. Lorraine Peters, June 28, 1953; children: Tina Lynn, Robert Mark and Carol Ann (twins). BEE, Ohio State U., 1948; MS in Indsl. Mgmt, N.Y. U., 1954. Registered profl. engr., Ohio. Electronics engr. Martin Corp., Balt., 1948-50; sr. engr. Fairchild Aircraft Co., Farmingdale, N.Y., 1950-54; program mgr. RCA, Moorestown, N.J., 1954-59, Van Nuys, Calif., 1959-61; div. mgr. Missile & Space Co. div. Lockheed Aircraft Corp., Van Nuys, 1961-63; v.p., gen. mgr. Lockheed Aircraft Corp. (Lockheed Electronics div.), Los Angeles, 1963-68; exec. v.p. Lockheed Electronics Co., Inc., Plainfield, N.J., 1968-69; pres. Lockheed Electronics Co., Inc., 1969-71; group exec., exec. asst. to office of pres. ITT, N.Y.C., 1971-72; corp. v.p. ITT, 1972-79, sr. v.p., 1979-81, exec. v.p., 1981-83; pres. indsl. and tech. sector Allied Corp.; exec. v.p. Allied Corp., Morristown, N.J., 1983-87; disting. exec. lectr. Rutgers Grad. Sch. Mgmt.; exec.-in-residence, vis. prof. Columbia U. Grad. Sch. Bus.; bd. dirs. 5 corps.; cons. various investment firms. Served with AUS, 1944-46. Recipient Disting. Alumnus award Ohio State U., 1987. Fellow AIAA (assoc.); mem. IEEE (sr.).

SEELIG, STEVEN ALFRED, government financial executive; b. N.Y.C., Dec. 24, 1944; s. Henry Walter and Hilde (Oster) S.; m. Gloria Phylis Shidler, June 8, 1969; children: Katherine, Karen, Joanne. BA with hons., Clark U., 1966, PhD, 1971; MA, Washington U., 1968. Instr. Merrimack Coll., North Andover, Mass., 1970-71; economist Fed. Res. Bank of N.Y., N.Y.C., 1971-75; from asst. to assoc. prof. Fordham U., Bronx, N.Y., 1975-78; with Fed. Deposit Ins. Corp., Washington, 1978—, CFO, 1982—, dir. divsn. of liquidation, 1989-92, dir. divsn. of fin., 1992—; mem. adj. faculty Fairleigh Dickinson U., Teaneck, N.J., 1972-77, George Washington U., Washington, 1979-89; cons., lectr. in field. Author: Bank Holding Companies & The Public Interest, 1977; contbr. articles to profl. jours. Pres. Jr. High Sch. PTA, Potomac, Md., 1987-89; mem. adv. com. Appraisal Standards Bd., 1989-91. Mem. Am. Econ. Assn., Am. Fin. Assn., Nat. Soc. Real Estate Fin. (cert.), Omicron Delta Epsilon. Avocation: fishing. Office: Fed Deposti Ins Corp 550 17th St NW Washington DC 20429

SEELMAN, KATHERINE DOLORES, institute administrator; b. Boston, May 26, 1938; d. Frederick George and Loretta (Tetu) S. BA, Hunter Coll., 1964; MA, NYU, 1970, PhD, 1982. Tchr. N.Y.C. Schs., 1966-73; instr., rschr. N.Y. Inst. Tech., NSF, N.Y.C., 1973-75; project mgr. Nat. Coun. Chs., N.Y.C., 1976-82; cons. Am. Assn. Retired Persons, Washington, 1982-83; rsch. scholar Gallaudet U., Washington, 1984-86; dir. pub. edn. Mass. Comm. for Deaf and Hard of Hearing, Boston, 1986-89; rsch. specialist Nat. Coun. on Disability, Washington, 1989-93; dir. program devel. Adminstrn. on Devel. Disability, Washington, 1993-94; dir. Nat. Inst. on Disability and Rehab. Rsch., Washington, 1994—. Switzer scholar Nat. Rehab. Assn., 1991, Disting. Switzer fellow Dept. Edn. Nat. Inst. Disability and Rehab. Rsch., 1985-86; recipient Scholarships NYU, 1973, Am. Law Inst./ABA, 1977, Fellowships NSF, 1974, Resources for the Future, 1976; named to Hall of Fame Alumni Assn. Hunter Coll., 1995. Mem. RESNA, AAAS, Assn. for Advancement of Sci., Soc. for Disability Studies, Nat. Assn. for the Deaf, Self-Help for Hard of Hearing. Home: PO Box 1056 404 Grove Ave Washington Grove MD 20880 Office: Nat Inst Disability and Rehab Rsch 600 Maryland Ave SW Washington DC 20202-2572

SEELY, JAMES MICHAEL, consultant, retired naval officer, small business owner; b. Los Angeles, Oct. 15, 1932; s. Louis K. and Mary Edith (Gleason) S.; m. Gail Margaret Deverman, July 13, 1957; children: Ted Andrew, Nina Marie. BS, UCLA, 1955; MS, George Washington U., 1976. Commd. ensign USN, 1955, advanced through grades to rear adm.; student pilot, 1955-56, attack pilot, 1957-75; comdg. officer Attack Squadron 165, Naval Air Sta. Whidbey Island, Wash., 1972-73; comdr. Carrier Air Wing 9, Naval Air Sta. Lemoore, Calif., 1974-75; comdg. officer U.S. Naval Air Sta., Whidbey Island, 1977-79; dep. dir. DCNO (Air Warfare, OP-50), Pentagon, Washington, 1979-82; dir. Joint Analysis Directorate, Office Joint Chiefs Staff, Washington, 1982-84; comdr. Medium Attack Tactical Electronic Warfare Wing, Pacific Fleet, Naval Air Sta. Whidbey Island, 1984-86; dir. DCNO (Air Warfare, OP-50), Pentagon, 1986-88; dep. comptr. of Navy, Pentagon, 1988-89; ret. Pentagon, 1989; with RRP Def. Cons. Assocs., Arlington, Va., 1989—; Vietnam combat duty with Attack Squadrons 93, 152, 165 flying from aircraft carriers USS Enterprise, Hancock, Bon Homme Richard, Shangri-La and Constellation; 447 combat missions. Decorated Defense Superior Service, Legion of Merit (2), D.F.C. (4), Bronze Star, Air Medal (43). Mem. Naval Inst., Tailhook Assn., Assn. Naval Aviation, Marine Corps Aviation Assn., Red River Valley Fighter Pilots Assn., Navy League, Am. Legion, Am. Def. Preparedness Assn., Assn. Old Crows. Republican. Roman Catholic. Avocations: sports, automobiles. Home: 5730 Shropshire Ct Alexandria VA 22315-4027 Office: RRP Def Cons Assocs 2171 Crystal Dr Arlington VA 22202-3705

SEELY, ROBERT DANIEL, physician, medical educator; b. Woodmere, N.Y., Nov. 4, 1923; s. Harry and Ethel (Weil) S.; m. Marcia Ann Wells, June 19, 1953; children: Ellen Wells, Anne Wells. B.S., NYU, 1943; M.D., Columbia U., 1946. Intern Mt. Sinai Hosp., N.Y.C., 1946-47, asst. resident in medicine, 1950-51, resident in pathology, 1951-52, chief resident in medicine, 1952-53; Sara Welt fellow in cardiovascular research Presbyn. Hosp., N.Y.C., 1953-54; instr. dept. physiology, cardiovascular research Western Res. U., Cleve., 1947-48; chief rheumatic heart disease clinic Mt. Sinai Hosp., N.Y.C., 1961-70, attending physician medicine and cardiology, 1978—, chief of service dept. medicine, 1979—, clin. prof. medicine, cardiology Sch. Medicine, 1970—; practice medicine specializing in cardiovascular disease N.Y.C., 1953—. Contbr. articles to profl. jours. Served to capt. M.C. AUS, 1948-50. Recipient Solomon Berson Meml. award Mt. Sinai Hosp., 1977. Fellow Am. Coll. Cardiology, ACP; mem. N.Y. Heart Assn., AMA, N.Y. County Med. Soc., Soc. Cert. Internists N.Y., Phi Beta Kappa, Alpha Omega Alpha, Beta Lambda Sigma. Office: 994 Fifth Ave New York NY 10028-0100

SEELY, ROBERT FLEMING, lawyer; b. Englewood, N.J., June 21, 1944; s. Harry Gedney and Katharine Elizabeth (Fleming) S.; m. Rebeccah S., June 19, 1976; 1 child, Edward Smith. BA, Princeton U., 1966; JD, Cornell U., 1975. Bar: N.Y. 1976, D.C. 1988, Ill. 1990. Atty. U.S. Customs Svc. Hdqtrs., Washington, 1975-79, U.S. Dept. Commerce, Washington, 1980-87; assoc. Miller & Blume, Washington, 1987-88; ptnr. Katten, Muchin & Zavis, Chgo., 1989—. 1st lt. U.S. Army, 1968-71, Korea. Mem. ABA, Chgo. Bar Assn., Fed. Bar Assn., Internat. Trade Assn. of Greater Chgo. (bd. dirs. 1990—). Office: Katten Muchin & Zavis 525 W Monroe St Ste 1600 Chicago IL 60661-3693

SEEMAN, MELVIN, sociologist, educator; b. Balt., Feb. 5, 1918; s. Morris and Sophie (Kostman) S.; m. Alice Ruth Zerbola, June 30, 1944; children—Teresa E., Paul D. B.A., Johns Hopkins U., 1944; Ph.D., Ohio State U., 1947. Asst. prof. sociology Ohio State U., 1947-52, assoc. prof., 1953-59; prof. UCLA, 1959-88, prof. emeritus, 1988—. Mem. Am. Sociol. Assn. Home: 21532 Paseo Serra Malibu CA 90265-5112 Office: Dept Sociology UCLA 405 Hilgard Ave Los Angeles CA 90024-1301

SEEMAN, PHILIP, pharmacology educator, neurochemistry researcher; b. Winnipeg, Man., Can., Feb. 8, 1934; s. Jacob and Fanny (Wigdor) S.; m. Mary V. Szwarc; children: Marc, Bob, Neil. BS, McGill U., Montreal, Can., 1955, MS, 1956, MD, 1960; PhD, Rockefeller U., 1966. Prof. pharmacology U. Toronto, Can., 1967—, chmn. dept. pharmacology, 1977-87. Author over 300 publs. on dopamine receptors, their discovery, and their changes in brain diseases. Recipient Upjohn award Can. Pharmacology Soc., 1980, John Dewan award Ont. Mental Health Found., 1981, Heinz Lehmann award Can. Coll. Neuropsychopharmacology, 1985, Lieber award Nat. Alliance for Rsch. in Schizophrenia and Depression, 1990, Dean award Am. Coll. Psychiatrists, 1990, Tanenbaum Schizophrenia Rsch. award Can. Psychiat. Rsch. Fedn., 1991, Prix Galien Can., 1994. Fellow Royal Soc. Can.; mem. Am. Soc. Pharmacology, Soc. Neurosci., Am. Coll. Neuropsychopharmacology. Home: 32 Parkwood Ave, Toronto, ON Canada M4V 2X1 Office: U of Toronto Med Scis Bldg, Dept of Pharmacology, Toronto, ON Canada M5S 1A8

SEEMANN, ERNEST ALBRIGHT, lawyer; b. Leipzig, Germany, Oct. 18, 1929; came to U.S., 1959, naturalized, 1964; s. Erich Winrich Albrecht and Käte Renate (Wipper) S.; m. Eola Semple Hamlett, Aug. 6, 1965 (dec.); children: Eric Alexander, Ernest Arthur. Grad. in Classical Langs., Sch. St. Thomas, Leipzig, 1945; J.D., U. Miami, 1981, LL.M. in Internat. Law, 1982. Editor, corp. exec. Verlagsanstalt Hermann Klemm (book pubs.), Freiburg, Germany, 1955-59; dir. U. Ala. Press, 1962-66, U. Miami (Fla.) Press, 1967-74; pres. E.A. Seemann Pub., Inc., Miami, 1974-82; ptnr. Spencer, Bernstein, Seemann & Klein, Miami, 1982-88; prin. Ernest A. Seeman, Esq., Miami, Fla., 1989-92, Cocoa, Fla., 1993-94; prin. Ernst A. Seeman, Esq., Cape Coral, Fla., 1994—. Mem. ABA, Fla. Bar Assn., Deutscher Anwaltverein, Internat. Bar Assn., Schlarafia Amerika (Miami chpt.). Episcopalian. Home: 3706 21st Ave Cape Coral FL 33904 Office: 4729 Del Prado Blvd Cape Coral FL 33904

SEESSEL, ADAM H., writer, journalist; b. Hopewell, N.J., May 18, 1964; s. Thomas Vining and Diane (Weiner) S.; m. Sadie Bridger, May 4, 1991. BA in Religion summa cum laude, Dartmouth Coll., 1985. Staff writer The News and Observer, Raleigh, N.C., 1985-89, The Independent, Raleigh, Durham, N.C., 1989-91; writer Rochester, N.Y., 1991-94, Hopewell, 1995—. Recipient George Polk award L.I. U., 1991. Mem. The Authors Guild, Phi Beta Kappa. Democrat. Avocations: baseball, soccer, rugby, poetry. Home: 422 Hudson St Apt #1 Hoboken NJ 07030

SEESSEL, THOMAS VINING, nonprofit organization executive; b. Chattanooga, Nov. 16, 1937; s. Ben Adolph and Dorothy Anne (Parham) S.; m. Diane Farnham Wiener, Jan. 26, 1963; children: Adam Humphreys, Jessica Parham, Ben Vining. BA, Dartmouth Coll., 1959; MPA, Princeton U., 1964. Asst. to dir. Community Progress, Inc., New Haven, 1964-67; exec. dir. N.J. Housing Fin. Agy., Trenton, 1967-70; sr. program officer The Ford Found., N.Y.C., 1970-74; dep. commr. N.J. Dept. Environ. Protection, Trenton, 1974-75; exec. v.p. Manpower Demonstration Res. Corp., N.Y.C., 1975-78; owner, mgmt. cons. T.V. Seessel Assocs., Hopewell, N.J., 1979-85; exec. dir. Nat. Coun. on Alcoholism, N.Y.C., 1985-88, pres., 1988; pres. Seedco, N.Y.C., 1988—, treas., 1986-88; vis. lectr. Cornell U., Ithaca, N.Y., 1966-68, Princeton (N.J.) U., 1968-69; adj. prof. New Sch. Social Rsch., N.Y.C., 1978-79; mem. tech. adv. com. Adolescent Sch.-based Health Care Svcs. program Robert Wood Johnson Found., Princeton, 1986-91, and nat. adv. com. "Fighting Back" program to combat substance abuse, 1989—. Author numerous articles, speeches and reports on alcoholism, and other health topics and community devel. Mem. bd. edn. Hopewell Valley Regional Sch. Dist., Pennington, N.J., 1971-74; trustee Thomas Edison Coll. N.J., 1979-92, chmn. bd. dirs., 1987-89; bd. dirs. Bus. Employment Found., Paterson, N.J., 1979-87, Freedom Inst., N.Y.C., 1988-91, Nat. Neighborhood Coalition, 1995—; bd. dirs. Ctr. for Sci. in Pub. Interest, 1990-93, treas., 1991-93. Assoc. fellow Branford Coll., Yale U., 1965-70. Mem. Princeton Grad. Alumni (chmn. nominating and awards com. 1978-80), Phi Beta Kappa. Democrat. Club: N.Y. Princeton. Office: Seedco 915 Broadway New York NY 10010-6803

SEEVERS, CHARLES JUNIOR, foundation executive, psychologist; b. Seward, Nebr., May 13, 1925; s. Ferdinand Carl and Hilda Anna (Schultz) S.; m. Florine Marie Viets, June 5, 1949 (dec. 1991); children: Steven, Roger, Sandra, Jane; m. Ruth Ann Krohn Rehschuh, Aug. 28, 1993. AA, St. John's Coll., 1945; BA, Concordia Sem., St. Louis, 1949; MS magna cum laude, St. Francis Coll., Ft. Wayne, Ind., 1965, postgrad., 1966; PhD, U. Notre Dame, 1970. Ordained to ministry Lutheran Ch., 1949; asst. pastor Immanuel Luth. Ch., Balt., 1949-50; pastor St. Paul's Luth. Ch., Kingsville, Md., 1950-57; Bethlehem Luth. Ch., Richmond, Va., 1957-63; sr. pastor Zion Luth. Ch., Ft. Wayne, 1963-66; exec. dir. Assn. for Disabled of Elkhart County, Ind., 1966-82; exec. dir. Aux Chandelles Found., 1982-93, exec. dir. emeritus, 1993; adj. prof. psychology and spl. edn. Ind. U., South Bend, 1972-76; speaker Pres.'s Com. on Mental Retardation 3d Internat. Congress on Prevention of Mental Retardation, Buenos Aries, Argentina, 1986; apptd. del. health psychologist Ind. People to People Internat. Study Mission to Russia, People's Republic China, 1987; 1 cons. Kans. Developmental Disabilities Div., 1972-79, Accreditation Council for Facilities for the Mentally Retarded, Chgo., 1972-80; cons. on assessment of developmentally disabled in various states, 1974—, cons. Leicester, Eng., 1974-75; mem. Ind. Gov.'s Planning and Adv. Bd. for Mental Retardation and Other Developmental Disabilities, 1973-78, chmn., 1976-78; mem. Gov.'s Preventive Health and Handicap Services Coordination Study Commn., 1987-90, Devel. Disabilities Planning Council on Child Health, 1987-90, No. Ind. Health Systems Agy. Central Sub-Area Adv. Council, 1976-78, vice chmn., 1977-78; cons. psychonutrition, 1981-93, emeritus 1993—; regional psychologist Youth for Understanding, 1985-87. Contbr. articles to profl. publs. Home: United Way Execs., Elkhart, 1971-73; bd. dirs. Mill Neck Manor Sch. for the Deaf, L.I., N.Y., 1950-57, Assn. for Retarded Citizens Ind., 1983-89, No. Ind. Health Found., 1981-87; charter mem. Area Vocat. Edn. Adv. Bd., 1973-76; mem. state adv. bd. Prevention: To Be Born Well Curriculum Project, 1977-80; mem. residential services and facilities com. Nat. Assn. Retarded Citizens, 1973-78; mem. No. Ind. Developmental Disabilities Adv. Council, 1977-81, chmn., 1980-81; mem. Dept. Mental Health Multi-Disciplinary Screening Team, 1983-84; mem. bd. teenage parents adv. bd. Elkhart Community Schs., 1984-87; chmn. state policy Ind. Healthy Mothers/Healthy Babies Coalition, 1986-87; hon. chmn. Michiana Fetal Alcohol Syndrome Week, 1986. Recipient United Way Exec. of Yr. award, 1979; Eli Lilly fellow in religion and mental health Ind. U. Med. Center, Indpls., 1964-65; Recipient Liberty Bell award Elkhart Bar Assn., 1974, Outstanding Kindness award Elkhart County Assn. for Retarded, 1974, Concerned for Mankind in Our Nation award Jaycees, 1975, State of Ind. Citizen Participation award Gov.'s Voluntary Action Program, Sagamore of Wabash award Gov. of State of Ind., 1990; elected to Wall of Fame Assn. for Disbaled Elkhart County, Ind., 1985. Mem. Nat. Conf. Execs. of Assns. for Retarded Children (chmn. 1974-75), Am. Psychol. Assn., Soc. Behavioral Medicine, Am. Pub. Health Assn., Nat. Fedn. Parents for Drug Free Youth, Luth. Acad. for Scholarship, Internat. Psychol. Assn., United Cerebral Palsy Am., Luth. Human Relations Assn. Am., Ctr. for Sci. in Pub. Interest, Am. Orthopsychiat. Assn., Elkhart C. of C. (bd. dirs. 1974-76), Am. Council on Drug Edn., Assn. Birth Defect Children, Healthy Mothers/Healthy Babies Coalition, Internat. Council Psychologists. Lodge: Rotary (chmn. community service for affairs conf. dist. 654, 1985-87, pres.-elect 1987-88, gen. chmn. dist. assembly conf. 1986-87, Gov's. award 1987, Chmn. of Yr. 1987). Home: 2103 Norwood Dr Mountain Home AR 72653 *I believe I am a uniquely individual child of God, born to fulfill a purpose for which God continues to give me life each new day. We are joined together in a common effort to fulfill the purpose for which each of us is given life.*

SEEWALD, ELSBETH M., law firm executive, fraternal organization administrator; b. Hamburg, Fed. Republic of Germany, Aug. 24, 1927; came to U.S., 1953; d. Heinrich and Klara (Wohltorf) Bierkarre; m. Bosko Vasich, July 3, 1954 (dec. Dec. 1974); m. George Seewald, Feb. 4, 1978; 1 stepchild, Gerbert. Student, Comml. Coll., Fed. Republic of Germany. With Moehle Mfg. Co., Racine, Wis., 1957-60, Brach & Wheeler, Attys., Racine, 1960-63; mgr. real estate div. Heide, Hartley, Thom, Wilk & Guttormsen, Attys., Kenosha, Wis., 1963-90; nat. pres. German Am. Nat. Congress, Chgo., 1981—. Editor Der Deutsch-Amerikaner, 1981-90. Mem. U.S. German-Am. Youth Exch. Coun., 1990—. Named Honored Am. Ams. By Choice, 1986; recipient Ellis Island Medal of Honor, U.S. Congress, 1986, Officer's Cross of Merit First Class Fed. Republic Germany, 1988, Honorary Citizen-

ship of Dallas, Annette Strauss, Mayor of City of Dallas, 1989. Home: 9804 8th Ave Kenosha WI 53143-7213 Office: German-Am Nat Congress 4740 N Western Ave Fl 2 Chicago IL 60625-2097

SEFCIK, JOHN DELBERT, financial services executive; b. Temple, Tex., Jan. 21, 1921; s. John J. and Annie (Chaloupka) S.; m. Norma Marie Kuzel, May 22, 1942 (div. Sept. 1985); children: John D. Jr., Camille Freitas; m. Christine Gajdica Goodlett, Dec. 13, 1987. Student, Temple Jr. Coll., 1938-39; acctg. grad., Four C. Bus. Coll., 1948-50; A in Mgmt., Brewster Coll., 1956-59; student, So. Meth. U., 1958-70; grad., Civil Def. Staff Coll., Assn. Logistics Ex Sch., Command & Gen. Staff Coll., Indsl. Coll. Armed Forces, Arty. and Civil Affairs Mil. Govt. Sch. Cert. Army logistician. Placement mgr., tax auditor Tex. Employment Commn., 1945-51; with Phoenix Life Ins. Co., 1951-53; mktg. and dist. mgr. Armour Pharm. Co., Inc., 1953-86; regional mgr. ins. and investments, real estate broker Primerica Fin. Svcs., 1987-94. Bd. dirs., gen. chmn. 1st Dallas Mil. Ball, 1965, past pres., 1992-93, mem. to date. With U.S. Army, 1940-45; col. USAR, 1948-78. Decorated Legion of Merit, Bronze Star, Meritorious Svc. medal, Army Achievement medal, Res. Armed Forces medal with 2 H.G. Devices, 2 Battle Stars-ETO, others. Mem. 102d Inf. Divsn. Assn. (life, pres., v.p., bd. dirs., reunion gen. chmn. 1983-89), Res. Officers Assn. (life, nat. chmn. civil preparedness com. 1989-94, numerous other nat. coms., Brigade of Vols., Wall of Gold Waco chpt. pres. 1951-53, Dallas chpt. pres. 1963-65, Army Tex. dept. v.p. 1963-67, 90th divsn. arty. chpt. pres. 1965-66, pres. 1967-68, Tex. dept. nat. councilman 1968-69, Tex. ROA Conv. Gen. chmn. 1981), Mil. Order World Wars (life), Am. Legion (life), Ret. Officers Assn. (life), 2d NF Indian Head Divsn. Assn.

SEFF, LESLIE S., securities trader; b. N.Y.C., Oct. 3, 1950; s. Fredric and Dorothy (Jacobson) S.; children: Dylan, Cortney, Blake, Matthew. BBA in Fin. cum laude with high honors, Hofstra U., Hempstead, N.Y., 1971; MBA, Baruch Coll., N.Y.C., 1980. Co-mgr. Muller & Co., N.Y.C., 1984-88; dir. over-the-counter trading Gruntal & Co., N.Y.C., 1988-92; dir. over-the-counter trading dept. Wagner Stott & Co., N.Y.C., 1992—; Contbr. to Wall Street Jour. and Dow Jones News Svc. Tickertape. Contbr. to Wall Street Jour. and Dow Jones News Svc. Tickertape. Trustee Saddle River (N.J.) Recreation Commn., 1988; active Rep. Eagles, Washington, 1986-87. allied mem. N.Y. Stock Exch. Avocations: tennis, bicycling, playing the harmonica. Office: Wagner Stott & Co 14 Wall St New York NY 10005-2601

SEFFRIN, JOHN REESE, medical society executive; b. Hagerstown, Ind., May 19, 1944; s. Theodore H. and Mary Ellen (Reese) S.; m. Carole Sue Washburn, Apr. 16, 1966; 1 child, Mary. BS in Edn., Ball State U., 1966; MS, U. Ill., 1967; PhD in Health Edn., Purdue U., 1970; DSc (hon.), Ball State U., 1994. Asst. prof. health edn. Purdue U., West Lafayette, Ind., 1970-76; asso. prof. Purdue U., 1976-79; prof. applied health sci., chmn. dept. Ind. U., Bloomington, 1979-92; exec. v.p., chief staff officer Am. Cancer Soc., Atlanta, 1992—; cons. Nat. Dept. Public Instrn., 1979-81, ADA, 1972—; guest lectr. various public health orgns. and schs., 1970—. Contbr. numerous articles on health edn. to profl. publs.; chmn. editorial bd.: Jour. Sch. Health, 1982-85, Smoking and Health Reporter, 1983-88; mem. editorial bd.: Health Edn., 1981-85; cons. editor: Jour. ADA, 1980—. Pres. State Welfare Bd., Dept. Public Welfare, Ind., 1979-80, 83-85; treas. Midwest Nuclear Bd., 1973-76; bd. dirs. Wabash Center for the Mentally Retarded, 1970-73; chmn. community edn. com. Am. Lung Assn., 1981-83, v.p. 1986-88, nat. bd. dirs., 1980—; bd. dirs. Partnership for Prevention...of Premature Death, Disease and Disability, 1991—, Acordia Small Bus. Benefits, Inc., 1992—. Recipient Cert. of Recognition, ADA, 1975, Cert. Appreciation Surgeon Gen. of Pub. Health Svc., 1992; named Sqaavare of Wabash, State of Ind., 1980, 88; Outstanding Alumnus award Ball State U., 1982. Fellow Am. Sch. Health Assn. (mem. governing coun. 1978-81, pres. 1987-88, Howe award 1991), mem. AMA, Nat. Assn. State Bds. of Edn. (comm. on the sch. community role in improving adolescent health 1989—), Assn. for Advancement Health Edn. (bd. dirs. 1989-92), Ind. Assn. Health Educators (pres. 1975-76), Ind. Family Health Coun. (dir. 1979-81, v.p. 1980-81, pres. 1981), Ind. Thoracic Soc. (mem. governing coun. 1977—), Am. Cancer Soc. (dir. Ind. Div. 1977—, chmn. nat. bd. dirs. 1989-91, dir.-at-large to nat. bd. dirs., chmn. nat. pub. edn. com., nat. v.p. 1986-87), Ind. Assn. for Health, Phys. Edn. and Recreation (pres. 1976, Cert. of Appreciation 1977, Honor award 1982), Nat. Interagy. Coun. on Smoking and Health (bd. dirs. 1979—), Phi Delta Kappa, Eta Sigma Gamma. Roman Catholic. Office: Am Cancer Soc 1599 Clifton Rd NE Atlanta GA 30329*

SEGAL, BERNARD GERARD, lawyer; b. N.Y.C., June 11, 1907; s. Samuel I. and Rose (Cantor) S.; m. Geraldine Rosenbaum, Oct. 22, 1933; children: Loretta Joan Segal Cohen, Richard Murry. A.B., U. Pa., 1928, LL.B., 1931, LL.D., 1969; LL.D., Franklin and Marshall Coll., 1953, Temple U., 1954, Dropsie U., 1966, Jewish Theol. Sem. Am., 1977, Vt. Law Sch., 1978, Villanova U., 1980, Georgetown U., 1983; J.S.D., Suffolk U., 1969; D.H.L., Hebrew Union Coll., 1970. Bar: Pa. 1932, D.C. 1976. Mem. faculty U. Pa., 1928-35, 45-47; Am. reporter on contracts Internat. Congress of Law, The Hague, The Netherlands, 1932; asst. dep. atty. gen. Commonwealth of Pa., 1932-33, dep. atty. gen., 1933-34; co-founder Schnader Harrison Segal & Lewis, Phila., 1935—; instr. grad. bus., govt. Am. Inst. Banking, 1936-39; chmn. Schnader Harrison Segal & Lewis, Phila., 1968-86, sr. ptnr., 1986-88, of counsel, 1988—; mem. Bd. Law Examiners, Phila., 1940-46; chmn. Commn. Jud. and Congl. Salaries, U.S. Govt., 1953-55; mem. Atty. Gen.'s Nat. Com. to Study Antitrust Laws, 1953-55; mem. exec. com. Atty. Gen.'s Nat. Conf. on Ct. Congestion, 1958-61; mem. standing com. on rules of practice and procedure Jud. Conf. U.S., 1959-76; co-chmn. Lawyers Com. on Civil Rights Under Law, 1963-65 (Founder award, 25th Anniversary, 1988); chmn. Pa. Jud. Nominating Commn., 1964-66; mem. Nat. Citizens Com. on Community Rels., 1964-74; mem. adv. com. U.S. mission to UN, 1967-68; mem. adv. panel internat. law U.S. Dept. State, 1967-79; mem. Adminstrv. Conf. U.S., 1968-74; chmn. nat. adv. com. on legal svcs. U.S. OEO, 1968-76, chmn. exec. com., 1971-74; chmn. bd. Coun. Legal Edn. Opportunities, 1968-71; mem. Jud. Coun. Pa., 1968-71; coun. World Peace Through Law Ctr., chmn. 1st demonstration trial, Belgrade, Yugoslavia, 1971, coun., 1973—; participant world confs., Athens, Greece, Washington, Geneva, Bangkok, Abidjan, Ivory Coast, Manila and Cairo, chmn. com. on internat. communications, world chmn. World Law Day, Madrid, 1979, Berlin, 1985; mem. U.S. Commn. on Exec., Legis. and Jud. Salaries, 1972-73, 76-77; mem. Appellate Ct. Nominating Commn., 1973-79; mem. U.S. Commn. Revision Fed. Ct. Appellate System, 1974-75; chmn. World Conf. on Peace and Violence, Jerusalem, 1979. Editor-in-chief: Pennsylvania Banking and Building and Loan Law, 3 vols., 1941; editor: The Belgrade Spaceship Trial, 1972; mem. internat. hon. bd. Ency. Judaica; contbr. articles to law revs., other publs. Life trustee, mem. exec. bd. U. Pa., 1959-77, life trustee emeritus, 1977—; mem. bd. overseers U. Pa. Law Sch., 1959—; mem. Commn. on Anti-Poverty Program for Phila., 1967-71, Bus. Leadership Organized for Cath. Schs., 1979—, Commonwealth Commn. on Bicentennial of U.S. Constn., 1986-87; chmn. bd. Coun. Advancement Legal Edn., 1972-77; coun. trustees Hebrew U. Jerusalem; bd. dirs. So. Africa Legal Svcs. and Legal Edn. Project, 1979—, NAACP Legal Def. and Ednl. Fund, Found. Fed. Bar Assn.; bd. govs. emeritus, past v.p., past treas. Dropsie Coll.; trustee emeritus, former exec. com. Albert Einstein Med. Ctr.; trustee Phila. Martin Luther King, Jr. Ctr. Nonviolent Social Change (Drum Major award for legal justice, 1984), 1984—, Found. for the Commemoration of the U.S. Constn., 1986-88, Found. for U.S. Constn., 1988—; bd. dirs. Chapel of Four Chaplains; mem. planning commn. Miracle at Phila., 1986-87. Recipient Arthur von Briesen medal Nat. Legal Aid and Defender Assn., 1970, Nat. Human Rels. award NCCJ, 1972, Herbert Lewis Harley award, Am. Judicature Soc., 1974, World Lawyer award World Peace through Law Ctr., 1975, Judge William H. Hastie award NAACP Legal Def. Fund, 1986, Legion Honor Gold Medallion award Chapel of Four Chaplains, 1988, Nat. Civil Rights award U.S. Atty. Gen. and Lawyers Com. for Civil Rights Under Law, 1969, Ford Found. award to our Counselor on Pub. Interest, 1979, Nat. Award of Merit Fed. Adminstrv. Law Judges Conf., 1984, Pa. Bar Assn. award for Dedicated and Disting. Service, Field of Jurisprudence and Admitice, 1962, 10th Anniversary award Pub. Interest Law Ctr. Phila., 1984; co-recipient Nat. Neighbors Disting. Leadership in Civil Rights award, 1988, ACLU Civil Liberties award, 1991, U. Pa. Law Alumni award of Merit, 1991. Fellow Am. Coll. Trial Lawyers (pres. 1964-65), ABA (pres. 1969-70, Gold medal 1976), Inst. Jud. Adminstrn. (bd. dirs. 1968—), Am. Bar Found. (pres. 1978-79; mem. Jewish Fed. Greater Phila. (mem. emeritus exec. com.), Pa. Bar Assn., Phila. Bar Assn. (chancellor 1952, 53), Pa. Urban Affairs Partnership, Fed. Bar Assn. (nat. coun.), Assn. of Bar of City of N.Y., D.C.

Bar Assn., Am. Arbitration Assn. (former dir.), Am. Law Inst. (1st v.p. 1976-86, 2nd v.p. 1970-75, treas. 1955-69, counselor emeritus 1987—), Am. Judicature Soc. (chmn. 1958-61, bd. dirs. 1956—), Coun. Legal Edn. for Profl. Responsibility (dir.), Fed. Jud. Conf. 3d Cir. (life), World Assn. Lawyers (pres. Am. 1976-86), Nat. Conf. Bar Pres., Taxpayers Forum Pa. (past pres.), Allied Jewish Appeal (past pres., hon. pres.), Legal Aid Soc. Phila. (bd. dirs.), Jewish League Israel (nat. bd.), Jewish Pub. Soc. Am. (life trustee, mem. exec. com.), Jewish Family Svc. (hon. dir.), Order of Coif, Tau Epsilon Rho, Delta Sigma Rho. Republican. Clubs: Locust, Union League, Faculty, Metropolitan (Washington). Home: Philadelphian Apt 19-C-44 2401 Pennsylvania Ave Philadelphia PA 19130 Office: Schnader Harrison Segal & Lewis 1600 Market St Ste 3600 Philadelphia PA 19103-7236

SEGAL, BERNARD LOUIS, physician, educator; b. Montreal, Que., Can., Feb. 13, 1929; came to U.S., 1961, naturalized, 1966; s. Irving and Fay (Schecter) S.; m. Idajane Fischman, Feb. 17, 1963; 1 dau., Jody Segal. B.Sc. cum laude, McGill U., 1950, postgrad., 1950-51, M.D., C.M. high standing, 1955. Diplomate: Am. Bd. Internal Medicine. Intern Jewish Gen Hosp., Montreal, 1955-56; resident Balt. City Hosp., 1956-57, Beth Israel Hosp., Boston, 1957-58, Georgetown Med. Center, Washington, 1958-59, St. George's Hosp., London, Eng., 1959-61; practice medicine specializing in internal medicine and cardiology Phila., 1961—; prof.: sr. attending physician medicine Hahnemann Med. Coll., Phila., 1964—; dir. Phila. Heart Inst., 1987; clin. prof. medicine U. Pa. Med. Ctr., 1987. Author: Auscultation of the Heart, 1965; Editor: Theory and Practice of Auscultation, 1964, Engineering in the Practice of Medicine, 1966, Your Heart, 1972, Arteriosclerosis and Coronary Heart Disease, 1972; Editorial bd.: Am. Jour. Cardiology, 1970—, Clin. Echocardiography, 1978; Contbr. numerous articles on cardiology to med. jours. Fellow ACP, Am. Coll. Cardiology (chmn. scholar-trainee com., trustee 1969-71), Am. Coll. Chest Physicians; mem. N.Y. Acad. Scis., Alpha Omega Alpha. Home: 1156 Red Rose Ln Villanova PA 19085-2121 Office: 38th and Market St Philadelphia PA 19107

SEGAL, CHARLES PAUL, classics educator, author; b. Boston, Mar. 19, 1936; s. Robert and Gladys (Barsky) S.; m. Esther Rogers, Dec. 20, 1961 (div. June, 1979); children: Joshua H., Thaddeus G.; m. Nancy Ann Jones, Jan. 9, 1988; 1 child, Cora M. A.B., Harvard U., 1957, Ph.D., 1961; A.M. (hon.), Brown U., 1969. Teaching fellow, classics tutor Harvard U., Cambridge, Mass., 1959-61, instr., 1963-64; asst. to assoc. prof. classics U. Pa., Phila., 1964-67; assoc. prof. to prof. Brown U., Providence, 1968-78; prof. classics and comparative lit., 1978-86; chmn. classics dept., 1978-81; Benedict prof. classics, prof. comparative lit., 1980-86; prof. classics, comparative lit. Princeton U., 1987-90; prof. Greek and Latin, Harvard U., Cambridge, Mass., 1990—. chmn. classics grad. studies U. Pa., 1967; jr. fellow Ctr. for Hellenic Studies, 1967-68; vis. prof. Intercollegiate Ctr. for Classical Studies, Rome, 1970-72; vis. prof. Brandeis U., 1974; vis. dir. Ecole des Hautes Etudes, Paris, 1975-76; Fulbright exchange lectr. U. Melbourne, Australia, 1978; vis. prof. Greek Columbia U., N.Y.C., 1979; participant 1st and 2d Soviet/Am. Semiotics Colloquia, Am. Council Learned Socs./USSR Acad. Sci., 1980, 83; cons. in field; mem. jury Classical Sch. Am. Acad. Rome, 1972-74, resident in classics, spring 1986; mem. exec. council Ctr. Semiotics, Brown U., 1979-85; chmn. curriculum revision com. Brown U., 1982-84. Author: Landscape in Ovid's Metamorphoses, 1969, The Theme of Mutilation in the Iliad, 1971, Tragedy and Civilization: An Interpretation of Sophocles, 1981, Poetry and Myth in Ancient Pastoral: Essays on Theocritus and Virgil, 1981, Dionysiac Poetics and Euripides' Bacchae, 1982, Pindar's Mythmaking, 1986; Language and Desire in Seneca's Phaedra, 1986; Interpreting Greek Tragedy, 1986, La Musique du Sphinx, 1987, Orpheus: The Myth of the Poet, 1989, Lucretius on Death and Anxiety, 1990, Ovidio e la poesia del mito, 1991, Oedipus Tyrannus: Tragic Heroism and the Limits of poesia del mito, 1991, Oedipus Tyrannus: Tragic Heroism and the Limits of knowledge, 1993, Euripides and the Poetics of Sorrow, 1993, Singers, Heroes and God in the Odyssey, 1994; editor: The Heroic Paradox, 1982, The Rhetoric of Imitation, 1986, Roads to Paradise: Reading the Lives of the Early Saints, 1987; editorial bd. Am. Jour. Semiotics, 1985, Scholars Press, 1982-90, Helios, 1984—, MD, 1985—, Lexis, 1987—; Harvard Studies in Classical Philology, 1994—; contbr. articles to profl. jours. Am. Council Learned Socs. fellow, 1975; NEH grantee, 1977, fellow 1985-86; Guggenheim fellow, 1981-82; sr. fellow Ctr. Hellenic Studies, 1987-92; fellow Ctr. for Advanced Study in Behavioral Scis., 1989-90, fellow Nat. Humanities Center, 1993-94; recipient Prix de Rome Am. Acad. in Rome, 1961-63. Fellow Am. Acad. Arts and Scis.; mem. Am. Philol. Assn. (bd. dirs. 1982-86, pres. 1994), Societa Italiana per lo Studio dell' Antichita Classica (hon.), Virgilian Soc., Classical Assn. New Eng., Internat. Ovid Soc. Office: Harvard U Dept Classics 319 Boylston Hall Cambridge MA 02138

SEGAL, D. ROBERT, publishing and broadcast company executive; b. Oshkosh, Wis., Oct. 30, 1920; s. Morris Henry and Ida (Belond) S.; m. Kathryn McKenzie; children: Jonathan McKenzie, Janet Elizabeth Crane. Currently pres., chief exec. officer, dir. Freedom Newspapers, Inc., Irvine, Calif.; pres. Freedom Communications, Inc., Orange County Cable News, Kinston (N.C.) Free-Press, New Bern (N.C.) Sun Jour., Burlington (N.C.) Times-News, Jacksonville (N.C.) Daily News, WLNE-TV, New Bedford, Mass. and Providence, KFDM-TV, Beaumont, Tex., WTVC-TV, Chattanooga, WRGB-TV, Schenectady, Freedom Newspapers of Fla., Inc., Crawfordsville Jour.-Rev. (Ind.), Greenville (Miss.) Delta Dem. Pub. Co., Dothan (Ala.) Progress.; mng. ptnr. Clovis News-Jour. (N.Mex.), Rio Grande Valley Newspaper Group (Tex.), Gastonia Gazette (N.C.), Lima News (Ohio), Odessa Am. (Tex.), Pampa Daily News (Tex.), Orange County Cablenews Network. Trustee Children's Hosp of Orange County, Calif., Boy Scout Council of Orange County. Served with USAAF, 1942-45. Office: Freedom Newspapers Inc 17666 Fitch Irvine CA 92714-6022

SEGAL, DONALD E., lawyer; b. Houston, Nov. 13, 1947. BA with honors, Brandeis U., 1969; JD, Boston Coll. 1972. Bar: Mass. 1972, D.C. 1973, U.S. Supreme Ct. 1976, U.S. Dist. Ct. (D.C. dist.) 1976. Assoc. chief counsel FDA, Washington, 1979-91; ptnr. Baker & Hostetler, Washington, 1991-93; of counsel Akin, Gump, Strauss, Hauer & Feld, Washington, 1993-95; ptnr. Akin, Gump, Strauss, Hauer & Feld, Washington, 1995—. Mem. ABA, Fed. Bar Assn., Food and Drug Inst. Office: Akin Gump Ste 1100 1333 New Hampshire Ave NW Washington DC 20036-1500

SEGAL, ERICH, author, educator; b. Bklyn., June 16, 1937; s. Samuel Michael and Cynthia (Shapiro) S.; m. Karen James, June 19, 1975; 2 dau., 1 son (dec.). A.B., Harvard U., 1958, A.M., 1959, Ph.D., 1965. Teaching fellow humanities Harvard U., 1959-63; vis. lectr. Yale U., 1964-65, asst. prof., 1965-68, assoc. prof. classics and comparative lit., 1968-73; vis. prof. classical philology U. Munich, Germany, 1973; vis. prof. classics Princeton U., 1974-75, Tel Aviv U., spring 1976; vis. prof. comparative lit. Dartmouth Coll., fall 1976-80; vis. fellow Wolfson Coll., Oxford U., 1978, 79, 80; adj. prof. classics Yale U., 1981-88; hon. research fellow University Coll., London, 1983—; supernumerary fellow Wolfson Coll., Oxford U., 1986—; mem. exec. com. Nat. Adv. Council, Peace Corps, 1970; jury mem. Cannes Film Festival, 1971, Nat. Book Award (Arts and Letters), 1971; lectr. Am. Comparative Lit. Assn., 1971, Am. Philos. Assn., 1971, 72, German Classical Assn., 1974, Boston Psychoanalytic Inst., 1974, Ist. Nazionale del Dramma Antico, Sicily, 1975, Brit. Classical Assn., 1977; William Kelley Prentice Meml. lectr. Princeton U., 1981, Inaugural Andrea Rosenthal Meml. lectr. Brown U., 1992. Author, narrator: TV spl. The Ancient Games, 1972, rebroadcasted 1976; TV commentator track and field events Olympics, 1972, 76, 80; occasional commentator: Wide World of Sports, ABC, Sports World, NBC; host: Mourning Becomes Electra (Masterpiece Theatre), Pub. Broadcasting System, 1978; radio commentator: (in French) Olympics, RTL Radio, Paris, 1972, 76; author: TV spl. Olympathon '80; novels Love Story, 1970, Fairy Tale, 1973, Oliver's Story, 1977, Man, Woman and Child, 1980, The Class, 1985 (Prix Deauville, France 1986, Premio Bancarella Selezione, Italy), Doctors, 1988, Acts of Faith, 1992; book and lyrics Sing Muse, 1961-62; play Odyssey, 1974; lyrics with various composers including Charles Aznavour, Michel Legrand; screenplays (with others) The Beatles' Yellow Submarine, 1968, The Games, 1970, Love Story, 1970 (Golden Globe award Hollywood Fgn. Press Assn., Acad. award nomination best screenplay, Writers Guild nomination, Best Screenplay, 1970), R.P.M, 1970, Jennifer on my Mind, 1971, Oliver's Story, 1978, A Change of Seasons, 1981, Man, Woman and Child, 1983; author: over 70 articles, revs. in profl. jours. including Am. Jour. Philology, Classical Rev.; also N.Y. Times Book Rev., New Republic, Times Literary Supplement (London)), The Independent (London); Washington Post Book Rev., Yale Rev., acad. books; Roman Laughter: The Comedy of Plautus, 1968, rev.

edit., 1987; editor: Euripides: A Collection of Critical Essays, 1968, Oxford Readings in Greek Tragedy, 1983, Plato's Dialogues, 1986; co-editor: Caesar Augustus: Seven Essays, 1984; editor, translator: Plautus: Three Comedies, 1969, reprinted 1985. Co-recipient (with Mother Theresa and Sir Peter Ustinov) Premio San Valentin di Terni award, 1989; Guggenheim fellow, 1968; recipient Presidential Commendation for service to Peace Corps, 1971, Humboldt Stiftung award West Germany, 1973. Mem. ASCAP, Acad. Lit. Studies, Am. Philol. Assn., Am. Comparative Lit. Assn., Writers Guild of Am.-West, Authors League, Soc. Roman Studies (U.K.), PEN, Harvard Club (N.Y.C.), Yale Club (N.Y.C.), Athenaeum (London). Office: Wolfson College, Oxford England OX2 6UD

SEGAL, GEORGE, actor; b. N.Y.C., Feb. 13, 1934; m. Linda Segal. BA, Columbia U., 1955. Actor: (films) The Last Married Couple in America, The Knack, 1961, The Young Doctors, 1961, The Longest Day, 1962, Act One, 1963, The New Interns, 1964, Invitation to a Gunfighter, 1964, Who's Afraid of Virginia Woolf?, 1965, King Rat, 1965, Ship of Fools, 1965, The Lost Command, 1966, The Quiller Memorandum, 1966, The St. Valentines Day Massacre, 1967, Bye Bye Braverman, 1968, No Way To Treat A Lady, 1968, The Southern Star, 1969, The Bridge at Remagen, 1969, The Girl Who Couldn't Say No, 1969, Loving, 1970, The Owl and the Pussycat, 1970, Where's Poppa?, 1970, Born To Win, 1971, The Hot Rock, 1972, A Touch of Class, 1973, Blume in Love, 1973, The Terminal Man, 1974, California Split, 1974, Russian Roulette, 1975, Blackbird, 1975, Duchess and Dirt Water Fox, 1976, Fun With Dick and Jane, 1977, Rollercoaster, 1977, Who Is Killing The Great Chefs of Europe?, 1978, Lost and Found, 1979, Carbon Copy, 1981, Stick, 1985, All's Fair, Look Who's Talking, 1989, For the Boys, 1991, Me, Myself, and I, 1992, Look Who's Talking Now, 1993, (TV movies) including Death of a Salesman, The Desperate Hours, Of Mice and Men, 1981, The Cold Room, 1984, The Zany Adventures of Robin Hood, 1984, Not My Kid, 1985, Many Happy Returns, 1986, Killing 'em Softly, 1986, Of Mice and Men, Trackdown: Finding the Goodbar Killer, 1983, Four Minute Mile, (play) Henceforward, 1987, others; TV series: Murphy's Law, 1988. Recipient Jewish Cultural Achievement award, 1990. Office: Care Ken Starr Star & Co 350 Park Ave New York NY 10022*

SEGAL, GEORGE, sculptor; b. N.Y.C., Nov. 26, 1924; s. Jacob and Sophie (Gerstenfeld) S.; m. Helen Steinberg, Apr. 7, 1946; children—Jeffrey, Rena. BS in Art Edn., N.Y. U., 1950; MFA, Rutgers U., 1963, PhD in Fine Art (hon.), 1970; PhD in Fine Art (hon.), SUNY, Purchase, 1992. One man shows include Hansa Gallery, N.Y.C., 1956-59, Rutgers U., 1958, 63, Green Gallery, N.Y.C., 1960-62, 64, Sonnabend Gallery, Paris, 1963, Schmela Gallery Dusseldorf, 1963, Janis Gallery, N.Y.C., 1965, 67, 68, 70, 71, 73-74, 77, 78, 80, 82, 84, 88, 89, 91, 93, Mus. Contemporary Art, Chgo., 1968, Galerie Speyer, Paris, 1969, 71, Princeton U., 1969, Western Gallery Western Wash. State Coll., 1970, Onnasch Galerie, Cologne, 1971, also European mus. tour, 1971-73, U. Wis., Milw., 1973, Onnasch Galerie, Switzerland, 1974, Andre Emmerich, Zurich, 1975, Dartmouth Coll., 1975, Inst. Contemporary Art, 1976, Nina Freudenheim Gallery, Buffalo, 1976, Art Assn. Newport, R.I., 1976, Suzette Schochet Gallery, 1976, Santa Barbara Mus. Art, 1976, Whitney Mus. Am Art, N.Y.C., 1979, Jacksonville Art Mus., 1982, U. Miami, 1983, Jewish Mus., N.Y.C., Makler Gallery, Phila., 1983, 84, Galleria Il Ponte, Rome, 1984, Evelyn Aimis Fine Art, Toronto, 1984, Galerie Esperanza, Toronto, 1985, 87, Galerie Brusberg, Berlin, 1986, Richard Gray Gallery, Chgo., 1987, Riva Yares Gallery, Scottsdale, Ariz., 1988, Casino Knokke, Belgium, 1989, Galerie Tokoro, Tokyo, 1990, Marguiles/Taplin Gallery, Bay Harbor, Fla., 1990, Art Gallery U. Rochester, N.Y., 1991; retrospective group shows include Sao Paulo Bienal, Janis Gallery, Jewish Mus., N.Y.C., Carnegie Internat., Whitney Mus., others; represented in permanent collections including Mus. Modern Art, Whitney Mus., Mint Mus., Charlotte, N.C., Albright-Knox Mus., Mus. Modern Art, Stockholm, Sweden, Met. Mus. Art, N.Y.C., Guggenheim Mus., N.Y.C., Bklyn. Mus., Art Inst. Chgo., Cleve. Mus. Art, Detroit Mus. Art, Modern Art Mus., Ft. Worth, Newark Mus., Weisman Mus. Contemporary Art, L.A., Pa. Acad. Fine Arts, Phila., Carnegie Mus. Art, Pitts., Portland (Oreg.) Mus. Art, San Francisco Mus. Modern Art, Hirschorn Mus. & Sculpture Garden, Washington, Libr. Congress, Washington, Nat. Gallery Art, Washington, Nat. Portrait Gallery, Washington, Musee d'Art Contemporain, Montreal, Nat. Gallery Art, Ottawa, Can., Art Gallery Ontario, Can., Vancouver Art Gallery, Can., Tamayo Mus., Mexico, Museo de Arte Contemporaneo, Caracas, Venezuela, Musees Royaux des Beaux-Arts, Brussels, Art Mus. of Atenaeum, Helsinki, Finland, Centre Nat. d'Art Contemporain, Paris, Neue Galerie der Stadt Aachen, Germany, Kolnisches Stadtsmuseum, Cologne, Germany, Stadtische Kunsthalle Mannheim, Germany, Staatsgalerie Moderner Kunst, Munich, Germany, Museum Boymans-van Beuningen, The Netherlands, Mus. Modern Art, Teheran, Iran, Israel Mus. Jerusalem, Kunsthaus Zurich, Switzerland, Fukuoka Mcpl. Mus. Art, Japan, Hiroshima (Japan) City Mus. Contemporary Art, Mus. Modern Art, Seibu Takanawa, Karuizawa, Japan, Nat. Mus. Art, Osaka, Japan, Tokyo Ctrl. Mus., Shiga Mus. Art, Japan, and numerous others. Recipient 1st prize Art Inst. Chgo., 1966, award Walter H. Gutman Found., 1962. Office: care Sidney Janis Gallery 110 W 57th St New York NY 10019-3319

SEGAL, GORDON I., retail executive; b. Chgo., Dec. 27, 1938; s. Zalman and Ida (Glick) S.; m. Carole Browe, June 18, 1961; children: Christopher, Katherine, Robert. BS in Bus., Northwestern U., 1960. Founder, pres. Crate & Barrel, Chgo., 1962—; bd. dirs. Continental Bank, Chgo., L. Karp & Sons, Elk Grove Village, Ill., Bio-Logic Systems, Wheeling, Ill. Trustee Northwestern U., Evanston, Ill., 1990, Golden Apple Found., Chgo., 1988, Sta. WTTW-TV, Chgo., 1990, Chgo. Hist. Soc., 1991, Children's Meml. Hosp., Chgo., 1990. Named Man of Yr. City of Hope, 1984; recipient Alumni Merit award Northwestern U., 1988, Brotherhood award Nat. Coun. Christians & Jews, 1990, Steuart Henderson Britt award Am. Mktg. Assn., 1991. Mem. Chgo. Pres. Orgn., Chief Execs. Orgn., World Bus. Coun., The Comml. Club, Econ. Club of Chgo. Office: Crate & Barrel 725 Landwehr Rd Northbrook IL 60062-2393

SEGAL, IRVING EZRA, mathematics educator; b. N.Y.C., Sept. 13, 1918; s. Aaron and Fannie Segal; m. Osa Skotting, 1955 (div. 1977); children: William, Andrew, Karen; m. Martha Fox, 1985; 1 child, Miriam Elizabeth. A.B., Princeton U., 1937; Ph.D., Yale U., 1940. Instr. Harvard U., 1941; research asst. Princeton U., 1941-42, assoc., 1942-43; asst. to O. Veblen, Inst. for Advanced Study, 1945-46; asst. prof. to prof. U. Chgo., 1948-60; prof. MIT, Cambridge, 1960—; vis. assoc. prof. Columbia U., 1953-54; vis. fellow Insts. Math. and Theoretical Physics, Copenhagen, 1958-59; vis. prof. Sorbonne, Paris, France, 1965, U. Lund, Sweden, 1971, Coll. de France, 1977. Author: Mathematical Problems of Relativistic Physics, 1963, (with R.A. Kunze) Integrals and Operators, 1968, Mathematical Cosmology and Extragalactic Astronomy, 1976, (with J.C. Baez and Z. Zhou) Introduction to Algebraic and Constructive Quantum Field Theory, 1992; editor: (with W.T. Martin) Analysis in Function Space, 1964, (with Roe Goodman) Mathematical Theory of Elementary Particles, 1988; contbr. articles to profl. jours. Served with AUS, 1943-45. Recipient Humboldt award, Germany, 1982-83; Guggenheim fellow, 1947, 51-52, 67-68. Mem. Am. Math. Soc., Am. Phys. Soc., Am. Acad Arts and Sci., Royal Danish Acad. Scis., Am. Astron. Soc., Nat. Acad. Sci. Home: 25 Moon Hill Rd Lexington MA 02173-6139 Office: MIT Rm 2-244 Cambridge MA 02139

SEGAL, IRVING RANDALL, lawyer; b. Allentown, Pa., Oct. 15, 1914; s. Samuel I. and Rose (Kantor) S.; m. Eleanor F. Smolens, Dec. 26, 1943; children: Betsy A. Segal Carter, Kathy J., Robert J. BA, U. Pa., 1935; LLB, 1938. Bar: Pa. 1938. Instr. polit. sci. U. Pa., 1938-42; law clk. Ct. Common Pleas No. 4, Phila. County, Pa., 1938-39; assoc. Schnader, Harrison, Segal & Lewis, Phila., 1939-49, ptnr., 1949-92, sr. counsel, 1993—; Permanent mem. Jud. Conf. 3d Circuit U.S. Ct. Appeals; regional rationing atty. OPA, 1942. V.p. Nat. Kidney Disease Found., 1954-59, hon. life del., 1959-64; pres. Nephrosis Found., Phila., 1953-56; bd. mgrs. Woman's Hosp. Phila., 1957-64, v.p., 1962-63; bd. Jewish Edn., Phila., 1948-72; trustee YMHA, YWHA, 1954-58. Served to capt. Judge Adv. Gen. Dept. AUS, 1942-46. Decorated Mil. Commendation medal. Fellow Am. Coll. Trial Lawyers (regent 1976-79, sec. 1979-80); mem. ABA (corrections com. 1971-78, fed. jud. improvements com. 1980-87, jud. selection tenure and compensation com. 1988-93), Pa. Bar Assn., Phila. Bar Assn., Am. Law Inst., Am. Bar Found., Phila. Bar Found., Am. Judicature Soc., World Peace Through Law, Am. Acad. Polit. and Social Sci., Order of Coif, Phi Beta Kappa, Pi Gamma Mu (pres. 1934-35), Delta Sigma Rho. Jewish (dir., v.p. temple). Clubs: Phila. Lawyers, Art

Alliance, Locust, Army and Navy of Washington. Home: 210 W Rittenhouse Sq Apt 2306 Philadelphia PA 19103-4605

SEGAL, JACK, mathematics educator; b. Phila., May 9, 1934; s. Morris and Rose (Novin) S.; m. Arlene Stern, Dec. 18, 1955; children: Gregory, Sharon. B.S., U. Miami, 1955, M.S., 1957; Ph.D., U. Ga., 1960. Instr. math. U. Wash., Seattle, 1960-61; asst. prof. U. Wash., 1961-65, assoc. prof., 1965-70, prof., 1970—, chmn. dept., 1975-78. Author: Lecture Notes in Mathematics, 1978, Shape Theory, 1982. NSF postdoctoral fellow Inst. Advanced Study, Princeton, N.J., 1961-63; Fulbright fellow U. Zagreb, Croatia, 1969-70, U. Coll. London hon. rsch. fellow, 1988; Nat. Acad. Sci. exch. prof. U. Zagreb, Croatia, 1979-80. Mem. Am. Math. Soc. Home: 8711 25th Pl NE Seattle WA 98115-3416 Office: U Washington Dept Mathematics Seattle WA 98195

SEGAL, JOAN SMYTH, library association executive, consultant, organization adminstrator; b. Bklyn., Sept. 14, 1930; d. John Patrick and Anna Catherine (Green) Smyth; m. William Segal, June 25, 1955; children: Harold M., Nora A. BA, Douglass Coll., Rutgers U., 1951; MS in LS, Columbia U., 1955; PhD, U. Colo., 1978. Cert. assn. exec., 1988. Librarian, Math Inst., NYU, 1955-58, Western Interstate Commn. for Higher Edn., Boulder, Colo., 1970-76; library cons., Boulder, 1976-78; resource sharing program mgr. Bibliog. Ctr. for Research, Denver, 1978-80, exec. dir., 1980-84; reton. dir. Assn. of Coll. and Research Libraries, ALA, Chgo., 1984-90; assoc. exec. dir. programs ALA, 1990-93; owner Vintage Ventures, 1993—; trainer library automation, group devel., resource sharing; cons. in field. Contbr. articles to profl. publs. Named Colo. Librarian of Yr., Colo. Library Assn., 1984; named to Douglass Soc. Mem. ALA, Spl. Libraries Assn. (chmn. edn. div. 1981-82), pres. Rocky Mountain chpt. 1981-82, 1994—, bd. dirs. 1983-86), OCLC Network Dirs. (chmn. 1983), Mountain Plains Library Assn., Am. Soc. Assn. Execs. Colo. Soc. Assn. Execs.

SEGAL, JOEL MICHAEL, advertising executive; b. N.Y.C., Sept. 2, 1933; s. Michel M. and Ethel (Meshaloff) S.; m. Alix Hegeler, Aug. 9, 1968; children: Mark J., Gregg F. B.A., Cornell U., 1954; M.B.A., Columbia U., 1960. Media supr. Benton & Bowles, 1960-63; dir. network TV presentations NBC, 1963-65; successively network negotiator, network supr. and v.p., sr. v.p. then exec. v.p. network cable and syndicated broadcasting and dir. Ted Bates & Co., Inc., N.Y.C., 1965-87; exec. v.p. nat. broadcasting McCann-Erickson, N.Y.C., 1988—; bd. dirs. Rigel Inc. Served with AUS, 1956-58. Office: McCann-Erickson USA 750 3rd Ave New York NY 10017-2701

SEGAL, JONATHAN BRUCE, editor; b. N.Y.C., May 12, 1946; s. Clement and Florence Lillian (Miller) S.; m. Haidi Kuhn, June 30, 1974. B.A., Washington Coll., 1966. Writer, editor N.Y. Times, N.Y.C., 1966-73; editor Quadrangle/N.Y. Times Book Co., N.Y.C., 1974-76; sr. editor Simon & Schuster, N.Y.C., 1976-81; exec. editor, editor-in-chief, editorial dir., v.p. Times Books, N.Y.C., 1981-89; editor-at-large Random House, N.Y.C., 1985-89; v.p., sr. editor Alfred A. Knopf, N.Y.C., 1989—. Contbr. articles to popular jours. Democrat. Jewish. Home: 115 E 9th St Apt 12E New York NY 10003-5428 Office: Alfred A Knopf 201 E 50th St New York NY 10022

SEGAL, LORE, writer; b. Vienna, Austria, Mar. 8, 1928; came to U.S., 1951, naturalized, 1956; d. Ignatz and Franzi (Stern) Groszmann; m. David I. Segal, Nov. 3, 1960 (dec.); children: Beatrice Ann, Jacob Paul. B.A. in English, Bedford Coll., U. London, Eng., 1948. Prof. writing div. Sch. Arts, Columbia U., also Princeton U., Sarah Lawrence Coll., Bennington Coll.; prof. English U. Ill., Chgo., 1978-92, Ohio State U., 1992—. Author: Other People's Houses, 1964; Lucinella, 1976, Her First American, 1985; (children's book) Tell Me A Mitzi, 1970, All the Way Home, 1973, Tell Me a Trudy, 1977; The Story of Mrs. Brubeck and How She Looked for Trouble and Where She Found Him, 1981, The Story of Mrs. Lovewright and Purrless Her Cat, 1985; translator: (with W.D. Snodgrass) Gallows Songs, 1968, The Juniper Tree and Other Tales from Grimm, 1973, The Book of Adam to Moses, 1987, The Story of King Saul and King David, 1991; contbr. short stories, articles to N.Y. Times Book Rev., Partisan Rev., New Republic, The New Yorker, others. Guggenheim fellow, 1965-66; Council Arts and Humanities grantee, 1968-69; Artists Public Service grantee, 1970-71; CAPS grantee, 1975; Nat. Endowment Arts grantee, spring 1982, 1987; NEH grantee, 1983; Acad. Arts and Letters award, 1986. Address: 280 Riverside Dr New York NY 10025

SEGAL, MARTIN ELI, retired actuarial and consulting company executive; b. Vitebsk, Russia, Aug. 15, 1916; came to U.S., 1921, naturalized, 1928; s. Isidor and Anna (Title) S.; hon. degrees: L.H.D., Pratt Inst., 1976, Mus.D., Mannes Coll. Music, 1976, L.H.D., Grad. Center CUNY, 1979; LHD (hon.) L.I. U., 1986, NYU, 1988; m. Edith Levy, June 17, 1937; children: Susan Segal Rai, Paul. Various positions in industry, 1935-39; founder The Segal Co., consultants and actuaries, N.Y.C., 1939, pres., chief exec. officer, 1939-67, chmn. bd., 1967-91, chmn. emeritus, 1991—; pres. Wertheim Asset Mgmt. Svcs., Inc., N.Y.C., 1972-75, chmn., bd., 1975-82; ptnr. Wertheim & Co., investment bankers, N.Y.C., 1967-82. Bd. dirs. Helena Rubinstein Found., 1972—; founding chmn. The N.Y. Internat. Festival of the Arts, Inc., 1985—; chmn. bd. Lincoln Ctr. Performing Arts, Inc., 1981-86, chmn. emeritus, 1986—; bd. dirs. Pub. Radio Internat., 1981-94, co-chmn. Conf. on Intellectual Property The Arts and tech., 1994, dir. emeritus, 1994—, Nat. Bldg. Mus., 1983-91; bd. advisers Libr. of Am., 1984—; trustee Am.-Scandinavian Found., 1986-91, adv. trustee, 1991—; bd. visitors Grad. Sch. and Univ. Ctr., CUNY, 1983—; bd. trustees, chmn. exhibitions com. Mus. Modern Art, 1978-81; trustee Inst. for Advanced Study, Princeton, N.J., 1972-91, trustee emeritus, 1991—; pres. Cultural Assistance Ctr., Inc., 1977-82, chmn., 1982-84; founding pres. Film Soc. of Lincoln Ctr., 1968-78, pres. emeritus, 1978—; mem. adv. bd. The Alliance for New Am. Musicals, 1991—; mem. adv. coun. Theatre Devel. Fund, 1992—; bd. dirs. N.Y. Conv. and Visitors Bur., Inc., 1981—; mem. Nat. Bd. of Young Audiences, Inc., 1979—; founding mem. publs. com. The Pub. Interest, 1965—; mem. vis. com., Harvard U. Sch. Pub. Health, 1979-92, dean's coun. Sch. Pub. Health, 1990—; chmn. mayor's Com. on Cultural Policy, 1974; founding chmn. Commn. for Cultural Affairs City of N.Y., 1975, 92, 93, 94, 95; chmn. pub. svc. awards com. Fund for City of N.Y., 1978, 79, bd. dirs. 1978-87; co-chmn. Conf. on Intellectual Property, the Arts and Technology. Decorated Royal Swedish Order of Polar Star, 1984; officer of Arts and Letters, Ministry of Culture of French Govt., 1985; recipient cert. of merit Mcpl. Art Soc., 1974, spl. award Internat. Film Importers and Distbrs. Am., 1973, N.Y.C. Mayor's award of honor for arts and culture, 1982, Ann. award of distinction Mus. City of N.Y. 1982, Concert Artists Guild award, 1983, Disting. Am. of Fgn. Birth award Internat. Inst., N.Y.C., 1985, John H. Finley medal Alumni Assn. CCNY, 1985, Town Hall Friend of the Arts award, 1987, Dirs. Emeriti award Lincoln Ctr. for Performing Arts, Inc., 1987, N.Y. State Gov.'s Arts award (Hon. Mario M. Cuomo), 1989, Pres.'s award Grad. Sch. and Univ. Ctr. of City of N.Y. 1990, City of N.Y. Edn. Fund award LWV, 1984, Songwriter's Hall of Fame Patron of the Arts award, 1988, Nat. Fedn. Music Clubs Presdl. Citation award, 1989, Creative Arts Rehab. Ctr. Pub. Spirit award, 1989, Honor medal The Nat. Arts Club, 1992. Mem. Century assn., City Athletic Club, Players Club. Democrat. Jewish. Office: 1 Park Ave New York NY 10016-5801

SEGAL, MORTON, public relations executive; b. N.Y.C., Mar. 3, 1931. BA, Kenyon Coll., England, 1953; MFA in Dramatic Lit., Columbia U., 1956. Mgr. publicity Paramount Pictures, 1961-63; dir. worldwide publicity and pub. rels. 20th Century Fox, 1963-65; v.p. advt. and publicity MGM, 1965-72; with Allen, Ingersoll, Segal and Henry, 1973-75; prin. ICPR, 1975-79, pres., 1979-86; vice chmn., prin. Dennis Davidson Assocs., 1986—; with L.A. Internat. Film Exposition, 1982-84. Mem. Acad. Motion Picture Arts and Scis. Office: Dennis Davidson Assocs Inc 5670 Wilshire Blvd Ste 700 Los Angeles CA 90036-5607*

SEGAL, ROBERT MANDAL, lawyer; b. Worcester, Mass., Mar. 21, 1915; s. Abe Charles and Bella (Perry) S.; m. Sharlee Mysel, June 17, 1941; children: Terry P., Ellen Huvelle. AB, Amherst Coll., 1936; postgrad., U. Chgo., 1936-38; JD, Harvard U., 1942. Bar: Mass. 1942, U.S. Dist. Ct. Mass. 1946, U.S. Supreme Ct. 1952. Economist U.S. Steel Corp., 1939; sr. ptnr. Segal & Flamm, Boston, 1955-72; New Eng. counsel AFTRA, 1948-86; sr. ptnr. Segal, Roitman & Coleman, Boston, 1972—; lectr. labor law Harvard U. Bus. Sch., 1962-82, Boston Coll. Law Sch., 1979-81, Northeastern U. Labor Inst., U.S. State Dept., 1971, 73; trustee Mass. Continuing Legal Edn., 1970-83; counsel Mass. State Labor Coun., AFL-CIO, 1948-85. Co-author: History of Labor and Employment Section of the ABA, 1946-86, 1986; contbr. articles to profl. jours. Chmn. Harvard U. Law Sch. Rec. Alumni Com., 1973-93; pres. Jewish Cmty. Coun. of Boston, 1975; mem. file Commn. Mass., 1990—; mem. adv. coun. Mass. Perpaid Legal Svcs., 1984—. With U.S. Army, 1943-45. Recipient Cushing-Gavin Labor award, 1986; Brookings Instn. fellow, 1938-39. Mem. ABA (ho. of dels. 1957-58, mem. consortium 1975-80, chmn. labor and employment sect. 1957, co-chmn. membership and fin. com. labor sect. 1978—, forum com. 1984-86), AFTRA (New Eng. counsel 1947-85), Am. Guild of Musical Artists (N.E. counsel 1970—), Screen Actors Guild (New Eng. counsel 1955-88), Mass. Bar Assn., Boston Bar Assn. (mem. coun. 1960-84, co-chmn. labor law sect. 1957-85), Mass. Adv. Bd. of Film Bur., Mass. Prepaid Legal Svcs. Inst. (adv. bd. 1980—), Indsl. Rels. Assn., Mass. Ams. for Dem. Action (chmn. 1960), Harvard U. Law Sch. Alumni Assn. (mem. coun. 1970-73), Phi Beta Kappa, Delta Sigma Rho. Jewish. Home: 50 Longwood Ave # 1112 Brookline MA 02146 also: 6750 Gulf Mexico Dr Longbeach Key FL 34228 Office: Segal Roitman & Coleman 11 Beacon St Boston MA 02108-3002

SEGAL, ROBERT MARTIN, lawyer; b. Atlantic City, N.J., Apr. 7, 1935; s. Nathan Albert and Edna (Dutkin) S.; m. Rhoda Sue Luber, June 8, 1958; children—Deborah Ann, William Nathan, Elizabeth Ann. Student, Cornell U., 1953-54; B.S. in Econs., U. Pa., 1957; LL.B. cum laude, Harvard Law Sch., 1960. Bar: Pa. 1961. Assoc. Wolf, Block, Schorr & Solis-Cohen, Phila., 1960-69, ptnr., 1969—, chmn., exec. com., 1978-79, 82-83, 86-87, 89—; hon. pres. Jewish Employment and Vocat. Svc. Contbr. articles to profl. jours. and mags. Constable of elections Lower Merion Twp., Pa., 1970-72; mem. Rep. Jewish Coalition, 1984-85; bd. dirs. Jewish Family and Children's Agy., Am. Jewish Com., Rosenbach Mus. and Libr., Greater Phila. Urban Affairs Coalition, Phila. Rehab. Plan, Inc. Mem. ABA, Pa. Bar Assn., Phila. Bar Assn., Internat. Coun. Shopping Ctrs., Urban Land Inst. (assoc.), Am. Coll. Real Estate Lawyers, Phila. Bar Found. (trustee 1981-87), Am. Law Inst., Harvard Law Sch. Assn. PHila., Assn. Governing Bds. Univs. and Colls., Atlantic City Country Club, Govs.' Club, Chaine des Rotisseurs, Sunday Breakfast Club, La Coquille Club, Locust Club (bd. dirs. 1983-94), Harvard Club, Beta Gamma Sigma. Avocations: golf, swimming. Home: 1130 Red Rose Ln Villanova PA 19085-2121 Office: Wolf Block Schorr & Solis-Cohen 12th Fl Packard Bldg SE Corner 15 Chestnut St Philadelphia PA 19122

SEGAL, SANFORD LEONARD, mathematics educator; b. Troy, N.Y., Oct. 11, 1937; s. Joseph and Bessie (Katz) S.; m. Rima Maxwell, Sept. 3, 1959; children: Adam, Joshua, Zoë. BA, Washington U., 1958; PhD, U. Colo., 1963. Instr. U. Rochester, N.Y., 1963-64, asst. prof., 1964-70; rsch. fellow U. Vienna, Austria, 1965-66; assoc. prof. U. Rochester, N.Y., 1970-77, assoc. chmn., maths., 1969-79; vis. lectr. U. Nottingham, Eng., 1972-73; prof. U. Rochester, N.Y., 1977—, chmn. maths., 1979-87. Author: (book) Nine Introductions in Complex Variables, 1981; contbr. numerous articles to profl. jours. Fulbright fellow, Mainz, Germany, 1958-59, Fulbright Rsch. fellow, Vienna, Austria, 1965-66; fellow Inst. Math. Para e Applicada, Brazil, 1982, Alexander Von Humboldt Found., Fed. Rep. Germany, 1988. Mem. Am. Maths. Soc., Math. Assn. Am. (various coms. and chmn.) , History Scis. Soc. Democrat. Avocations: gardening, chess, reading. Home: 511 Rockingham St Rochester NY 14620-2519 Office: U Rochester Wilson Blvd Rochester NY 14627

SEGAL, SHELDON JEROME, biologist, educator, foundation administrator; b. N.Y.C., Mar. 15, 1926; s. Morris M. and Florence (Bogan) S.; m. Harriet Ellen Feinberg, May 22, 1961; children: Amy Robin, Jennifer Ann, Laura Jane. BA, Dartmouth Coll., 1947; postgrad., U. Geneva, 1947-48; MS, U. Iowa, 1951, PhD, 1952; MD (hon.), U. Tampere, Finland, 1984, U. Uppsala, Sweden, 1985. Rsch. scientist William S. Merrill Co., Cin., 1952-53; rsch. assoc., asst. prof. U. Iowa, 1953-56; asst. med. dir. Population Coun., N.Y.C., 1956-63, med. dir., 1963-78, v.p., 1969-76, sr. v.p., 1976-78; affiliate Rockefeller U., N.Y.C., 1956-76, adj. prof., 1977-87; dir. population scis. Rockefeller Found., 1978-91; disting. scientist Population Coun., N.Y.C., 1991—; lectr. Columbia U., 1959-61; vis. prof. All-India Inst. Med. Scis., New Delhi, 1962-63, Amir Chand lectr., 1975; mem. Marine Biol. Lab, Woods Hole, Mass.; cons. World Bank, WHO, NIH, Ford Found., Indian Govt., UN Office Sci. and Tech., UN Fund Population Activities; mem. com. on contraceptive tech. NAS, 1977-80, com. on health effects of marijuana Inst. Medicine, 1981-82, NAS com. on demographic impact of contraceptive tech., 1988-89, nat. rsch. con., overview com. for Indo-U.S. sci. initiative, 1985—; adv. com. on human reproduction FDA; cons. to dir. Nat. Inst. Child Health and Human Devel., 1978-80; plenary lectr. 3d World Congress Endocrinology, 1968, Upjohn lectr. Am. Fertility Soc., 1971, plenary lectr. World Fertility Congress, 1975, Sigma Xi lectr. U. Idaho, 1976, plenary lectr. World Congress on Ob-Gyn., 1976, lectr. Chinese Acad. Scis., 1977, Carl Gemzell lectr. U. Uppsala, 1982, Pierre Soupart lectr. Axel Munthe Found., 1988, Alpha Omega Alpha lectr. U. Pa. Coll. Medicine, 1989, plenary lectr. World Congress on Human Reproduction, 1990; hon. prof. Peking Union Med. Coll., Beijing, 1987, Chinese Acad. Scis., 1988; trustee Marine Biol. Lab., 1985—, chmn. bd. trustees, 1991—. Co-editor 8 books; contbr. numerous articles to profl. jours. Trustee Rye Country Day Sch., 1979—, pres. bd. trustees, 1981-85; trustee Ctr. for Reproductive Law and Policy, 1992—. Lt. (j.g.) USNR, 1943-45. Decorated Order Comdr. of Lion (Finland); recipient Honor award Innsbruck U., Austria, hon. citation Pres. of India, 1978, Clarence J. Gamble award World Acad. Arts and Scis., 1980, Joseph C. Wilson award Rochester Assn. for UN, 1981, UN Population award, 1984, Axel Munthe award in medicine Axel Munthe Found., Italy, 1985, Sci. award Planned Parenthood Fedn. Am., 1990, Dmitirus N. Chorafas award in medicine Swiss Acad. Scis., 1995. Fellow AAAS; mem. Royal Coll. Obstetricians and Gynecologists (hon.), Am. Fertility Soc. (hon. v.p. 1975-76, trustee found. 1975-77), Endocrine Soc., Am. Assn Anatomists, Internat. Soc. for Study Reprodn. (pres. 1968-72), Internat. Inst. Embryology, Am. Soc. Zoologists, Coun. Fgn. Rels., Mexican Acad. Medicine (hon.), Inst. Medicine, Dartmouth Club N.Y., Woods Hole Yacht Club. Home: 9 Topland Rd Hartsdale NY 10530-3001 Office: Population Coun One Dag Hammarskjold Plz New York NY 10017

SEGAL, STEPHEN MARTIN, advertising executive; b. N.Y.C., Mar. 22, 1938; s. Abraham and Elsie (Dinberg) S. AB, Cornell U., 1959; postgrad., Columbia U. Grad. Sch. Bus., 1959-60. Media research supr. Grey Advt., N.Y.C., 1962-65; v.p. bus. and media research Marschalk Co., N.Y.C., 1965-70; v.p. mktg. intelligence services McCann-Erickson, Inc., N.Y.C., 1970-74; mgr. mktg. services Lever Bros., N.Y.C., 1976-78; v.p. Tinker Campbell & Ewald, N.Y.C., 1978-80; v.p., dir. media planning Lowe-Marschalk, Inc., N.Y.C., 1980-84, sr. v.p., media dir., 1984, exec. v.p., media dir., 1985—, also bd. dirs., 1984—. Jewish. Office: Lowe-Marschalk Inc 1345 Avenue Of The Americas New York NY 10105-0010

SEGALAS, HERCULES ANTHONY, investment banker; b. N.Y.C., Mar. 21, 1935; s. Anthony Spiros and Katherine A. (Michas) S.; m. Margaret Wharton, Sept. 18, 1956; children—Donnell Anthony, Stephen Wharton, Katherine Lacy. BS, Yale U., 1956. Various engring. and mfg. positions Procter & Gamble Co., Cin., 1956-65; pres. for Latin Am., mgr. Internat. Flavors and Fragrances, N.Y.C., 1965-68; exec. v.p., mem. bd. dirs. William D. Witter Inc., N.Y.C., 1968-76; sr. v.p. Drexel Burnham Lambert Inc., N.Y.C., 1976-87, mng. dir., 1987-88, also bd. dirs., 1976-88; mng. dir. head consumer products investment banking group PaineWebber Inc. Investment Banking Group, N.Y.C., 1988—, also bd. dirs. Bd. dirs. Nantucket Land Coun., Mass., 1982-85; mem. corp. Nantucket Cottage Hosp., 1984-85. Mem. Morriston Field Club, Nantucket Yacht Club (bd. govs. 1987-93, mem. exec. com. 1988-93). Republican. Avocations: tennis, sailing, languages, woodworking. Home: 17 Hilltop Cir Morristown NJ 07960-6312 Office: Paine Webber Inc 1285 Avenue Of The Americas New York NY 10019-6028

SEGALL, HAROLD ABRAHAM, lawyer; b. N.Y.C., May 22, 1918; s. Morris and Mildred (Borkan) S.; m. Edith S. Besser, Jan. 27, 1952; children—Mark E., Grant D., Bruce K. BA with distinction, Cornell U., 1938; LLB cum laude, Yale U., 1941. Bar: N.Y. 1941. Practiced in N.Y.C., 1946—; assoc. mem. firm Gilbert, Segall and Young, 1946-49, ptnr., 1949-93, sr. counsel, 1994—; vis. lectr. Yale U. Law Sch., 1974-75, Yale U. Sch. Orgn. and Mgmt., 1983-85. Author: (with R.B. Kelley) Estate Planning for the

Corporate Executive, 1971, Representing the Seller of a Closely-Held Business, 1973, reprint, 1976; (with J.A. Arouh) How to Prepare Legal Opinions-Boldness and Caution, 1979, reprint, 1990; (with M.S. Sirkin) Providing for Withdrawal from a Joint Venture, 1982, Seventeen Suggestions for Improving Communications with Clients and Colleagues, 1994, reprint, 1995, How to Keep Improving a Highly Successful Law Firm, 1994; contbr. articles to profl. jours. Mem. council State U. N.Y. at Purchase, 1974-79; Counsel United Republican Finance Com., N.Y. State, 1955-61, Rep. City Com., N.Y.C., 1961, Nat. Rep. Citizens Com., 1962, Keating for Senator Com., 1964, Eisenhower 75th Birthday Com., 1965, Friends of the Gov. Wilson Team, 1974, Gov.'s Club, N.Y., 1965-75; trustee, v.p., treas. Philip D. Reed Found. Inc., 1989—; bd. dirs. Oneita Knitting Mills, 1973-83. Served to maj. AUS, World War II, ETO and PTO. Recipient Edgar M. Cullen prize, 1939. Mem. ABA, Bar City N.Y. (com. on trademark and unfair competition 1967-69, chmn. subcom. legislation 1968-69), Jewish Community Center, Order of Coif, Phi Beta Kappa, Phi Kappa Phi, Phi Sigma Delta. Clubs: University (N.Y.C.); Elmwood Country (gov. 1966-70, 73-75). Home: 60 Woodlands Rd Harrison NY 10528-1419 Office: 430 Park Ave New York NY 10022-3505

SEGALMAN, RALPH, sociology educator; b. N.Y.C., July 15, 1916; s. Samuel and Celia S.; m. Anita Cohen, Aug. 25, 1940; children: Robert, Ruth, Daniel. AB in Zoology, Sociology, U. Mich., 1937, MSW, 1944; PhD in Social Psychology, NYU, 1966. Lic. clin. social worker, Calif.; lic. marriage, family, child counselor, Calif. Social worker, exec. dir. various Jewish fedns., community couns., social svc. programs, Sioux City, Iowa, Waterbury, Conn., El Paso, Tex., 1940-65; from asst. to assoc. prof. Grad. Sch. Social Work U. Tex., El Paso, 1965-69, assoc. prof., asst. dean Grad. Sch. Social Work, 1967-69; vis. prof. social work U. Wis., Madison, 1969-70; prof. sociology Calif. State U., Northridge, 1970-86, emeritus prof. sociology 1986—; cons. on social policy, family, public welfare and other issues; keynote spkr. with Alfred Himelson at sessions on the future of the family, Profs. World Peace Acad., Seoul, Korea, 1994. Author: Dynamics of Social Behavior and Development, 1978, The Swiss Way of Welfare, Lessons for the Western World, 1986, (with Asoke Basu) Poverty in America: The Welfare Dilemma, 1981 (Scholarly Work award Calif. State U. 1982), (with David Marsland) Cradle to Grave: Comparative Perspectives on the State of Welfare, 1989; founding consulting editor Jour. of Sociology and Social Welfare; affiliated assoc. editor Jour. Am. Behavioral Sci. Recipient State Israel award, 1963. Fellow AAAS, Found. Jewish Culture, Council Jewish Fedns. and Welfare Funds; mem. Am. Sociol. Assn. Avocations: railroad books, photo collections. Home and Office: 18723 Sunburst St Northridge CA 91324-3828 Home (summer): PO Box 5004 Frazier Park CA 93222-5004

SEGAR, GEOFFREY, retired lawyer; b. Indpls., Jan. 13, 1926; s. Louis H. and Beatrice (Felsenthel) S.; m. Janet Blatt, Jan. 7, 1949; children: Judith Segar Shepherd, Robert, Ann Leh. BS in Bus., Ind. U., 1948, JD, 1952. Bar: Ind. 1952, U.S. Dist. Ct. (so. dist.) Ind. 1952, U.S. Ct. Appeals (7th cir.) 1978, U.S. Supreme Ct. 1983, U.S. Ct. Appeals (8th cir.) 1986. Ptnr. Ice Miller Donadio & Ryan, Indpls., 1952-77, 79-91, ret., 1991; gen. counsel Samaritan Health Svc., Phoenix, 1978; mem. deans adv. com. Ind. U. Med. Sch., 1986—, adv. bd. Ctr. for Law, 1987—; mem. Commn. on Health Policy, Indpls., 1989. Bd. dirs. Hooverwood Nursing Home, Indpls., 1969-88, 92—, Ctrl. Ind. Coun. Aging, 1977, St. Vincents Hosp. and Health Care Ctr., 1991—; pres. Regency Apts. for Elderly, Indpls., 1989-90. With USN, 1944-46. Fellow Am. Coll. Trial Lawyers; mem. Nat. Health Lawyers, Am. Acad. Hosp. Attys. Office: Ice Miller Donadio & Ryan PO Box 82001 Indianapolis IN 46282

SEGARS, JOSEPH M., ambassador; b. Hartsville, S.C., Jan. 6, 1938; married; 1 child, Cheyney. BS, U. Pa., 1961. Vice consul Vienna, 1971-73; with OPS ctr. Dept. of State, 1973-74; desk officer Liberia, Sierra Leone, 1974-76; consulate officer Joberg, 1976-78; acting consul gen. Jamaica, 1978-80; with African studies dept. U. Ind., 1980-81; desk officer for Zimbabwe, Lesotho and Swaziland Dept. of State, 1981-83; consul gen. U.S. Embassy, Lagos, Nigeria, 1983-86; dep. chief mission U.S. Embassy, Dar Es Salaam, Tanzania, 1986-89; career counselor sr. officer divsn. office pers. Dept. of State, 1989-91; U.S. amb. to Cape Verde, 1992—; mem. senior fgn. svc. inst. Dept. of State, 1992. Office: Rua Abilio Macedo 81 CP 201, Praia Cape Verde

SEGER, MARTHA ROMAYNE, financial economist; b. Adrian, Mich., 1932. BBA, U. Mich., 1954, MBA, 1955, PhD, 1971. Began career in econs. dept. GM; later with Fed. Res. Bank Chgo., 3 yrs.; chief economist Detroit Bank & Trust Co., 1967-74; v.p. in charge of econs. and investment Bank of Commonwealth, Detroit, 1971-74; assoc. prof. bus. econs. U. Mich., Ann Arbor, 1976-79; assoc. prof. econs. & fins. Oakland U., Rochester, Mich., 1980; commr. fin. instns. State of Mich., Lansing, 1981-82; prof. fin. Cen. Mich. U., Mt. Pleasant, 1983-84; mem. bd. govs. Fed. Res. System, 1984-91; fin. economist, John M. Olin Disting. fellow Karl Eller Ctr. U. Ariz., Tucson, 1991—. Office: U of Arizona McClelland Hall School of Business Tucson AZ 85721

SEGER, THOMAS M., lawyer; b. Cleve., Oct. 11, 1946. BA, Miami U., 1968; JD, Harvard U., 1972. Bar: Ohio 1972. Law clk. to Hon. Ed McEntree U.S. Ct. Appeals (1st cir.) Ohio, 1972-73; ptnr. Baker & Hostetler, Cleve. Office: Baker & Hostetler 3200 Nat City Ctr 1900 E 9th St Cleveland OH 44114-3303

SEGERSTEN, ROBERT HAGY, lawyer, investment banker; b. Boston, June 24, 1941; s. Wendell C. and Claire H. S.; m. Marie E. Makinen, Feb. 13, 1965; children: Amanda Beth, Vanessa Bryce. A.B., Bates Coll., 1963; J.D., Boston U., 1970. Bar: Mass. 1970. Assoc. Nessen & Csaplar, Boston, 1970-75; v.p. March Co., Boston, 1975-77; pres. March-Eton Corp., Concord, Mass., 1977-82; ptnr. Nessen, Goodwin & Segersten, Concord, 1977-82, Kane & Segersten, Dedham, Mass., 1983-85; pres. Woodbine Optical Corp., Sharon, Mass., 1990—; adj. prof. Sch. Am. Studies, Boston U.; adj. prof. real estate law Bentley Coll. Officer, bd. dirs. Friends of The Jimmy Fund, Boston. Served to lt. USN, 1963-67. Mem. ACLU, Mass. Bar Assn. Democrat. Episcopalian. Home: 64 Folsom Ave Hyannis MA 02601-4823 Office: Route 1 6 Pine Hill Park Sharon MA 02067

SEGESVÁRY, VICTOR GYŐZŐ, retired diplomat; b. Miskolc, Hungary, Feb. 20, 1929; came to U.S., 1984; s. Viktor and Margit (Kovács) S.; m. Andrea Bárczay, Jan. 20, 1955 (div. Nov. 1957); 1 child, Gábor; m. Monika Schwarz, Dec. 28, 1968. PhD in Polit. Sci., Grad. Inst. Internat. Studies, Switzerland, 1968; DD, U. Geneva, 1973. Asst., libr. Reformed Theol. Acad., Budapest, Hungary, 1953-56; sec. gen. African Inst., Geneva, 1961-63; asst. editor, market rsch. officer Bus. Internat. S.A., Geneva, 1963-66; market rsch. officer SESAF S.A., Geneva, 1967-68; chief rsch. dept. Henry Dunant Inst. Internat. Red Cross, Geneva, 1968-71; cons. Internat. Trade Ctr., UNCTAD/GATT, Geneva, 1969-71; tech. advisor market rsch.-market study Internat. Trade Ctr., Algiers, Algeria, 1971-72; sr. trade promotion project mgr. UNCTAD/GATT, Algiers, 1973-74; chief advisor in internat. econ. rels., project mgr. UNCTAD/GATT, Kabul, Afghanistan, 1975-79, Bamako, Mali, 1979-83; sr. advisor, cons. UN Devel. Programme, African countries, 1984-93; sr. advisor, cons. dept. for tech. cooperation for devel. UN, N.Y.C., 1985-88. Author: Le réalisme khouchtchévien-Politique soviétique au Proche-Orient, 1968, La Réforme et l'Islam, 1500-1550, 1973, A Ráday Konyvtár 18. századi története, 1992, Inter-Civilizational Relations and the Destiny of the West: Dialogue or Confrontation?, 1995. Sec.-gen. Internat. Fedn. Students in Polit. Sci., Geneva, 1958-59. Home: 330 E 39th St Apt 21/E New York NY 10016

SEGGER, MARTIN JOSEPH, museum director, art history educator; b. Felixtowe, Eng., Nov. 22, 1946; s. Gerald Joseph and Lillian Joan (Barker-Emery) S.; m. Angele Cordonier, Oct. 4, 1968; children: Cara Michelle, Marie-Claire, Margaret Ellen. B.A., U. Victoria, 1969, Diploma in Edn. 1970; M. in Philosophy, U. London, 1973. Prof. art history U. Victoria, B.C., 1970-74; museologist Royal B.C. Mus., Victoria, 1974-77; dir. Maltwood Art Mus., prof. art history U. Victoria, B.C., 1977—; cons. Nat. Mus. Corp., Ottawa, 1977, UNESCO, O.E.A., Cairo, 1983. Author: exhbn. catalogue House Beautiful, 1975, Arts of the Forgotten Pioneers, 1971, Victoria: An Architectural History, 1979, (commendation Am. Assn. State and Local History 1980), This Old House, 1975, This Old Town, 1979, British Columbia Parliament Buildings, 1979, The Heritage of Canada, 1981,

Samuel Maclure: In Search of Appropriate Form, 1986 (Hallmark award 1987), (a guide) St. Andrew's Cathedral, 1990, The Development of Gordon Head Campus, 1988, An Introduction to Museum Studies, 1989, An Introduction to Heritage Conservation, 1990, Botswana Live, 1994; editl. bd. mem. Managing Leisure: an International Journal, U.K., 1994—. Bd. govs. Heritage Can. Found., 1979-83; chmn. City of Victoria Heritage Adv. Com., 1975-79; bd. dirs. Heritage Trust, 1977-86, B.C. Touring Coun., Sta. CFUV Radio, B.C. Govt. House Found., 1987-93; mem. B.C. Heritage Adv. Bd., 1973-83; councillor City of Victoria, 1987-93; vice-chair Provincial Capital Commn., 1991—; pres. Assn. Vancouver Island Municipalities, 1993-94. Decorated knight Equestrian Order of Holy Sepulchre of Jerusalem; recipient award Heritage Can. Communications, 1976, Heritage Conservation award Lt. Gov. B.C., 1989, Harley J. McKee award Assn. Preservation Technology, 1994. Fellow Royal Soc. Arts; mem. Can. Mus. Assn. (counsellor 1975-77), Internat. Coun. Mus. (exec.), Internat. Coun. Monuments and Sites (bd. dirs. 1980-92), Soc. Study Architecture Can. (bd. dirs. 1979-81), Authors Club (London), Can. Mus. Dirs. Orgn., Canarvon Club. Roman Catholic. Avocations: travel, motor mechanics, walking. Home: 1035 Sutlej St, Victoria, BC Canada V8V 3P2 Office: U Victoria, PO Box 3025, Victoria, BC Canada V8W 2P2

SEGIL, LARRAINE DIANE, former materials company executive; b. Johannesburg, South Africa, July 15, 1948; came to U.S., 1974; d. Jack and Norma Estelle (Cohen) Wolfowitz; m. Clive Melwyn Segil, Mar. 9, 1969; 1 child, James Harris. BA, U. Witwatersrand, South Africa, 1967, BA with honours, 1969; JD, Southwestern U., L.A., 1979; MBA, Pepperdine U., 1985. Bar: Calif. 1979, U.S. Supreme Ct. 1982. Cons. in internat. transactions, L.A., 1976-79; atty. Long & Levit, L.A., 1979-81; chmn., pres. Marina Credit Corp., L.A., 1981-85; pres., chief exec. officer Electronic Space Products Internat., L.A., 1985-87; mng. ptnr. The Lared Group, L.A., 1987—. Bd. govs. Cedars Sinai Med. Ctr., L.A., 1984—; bd. dirs. So. Calif. Tech. Execs. Network, 1984-86. Mem. ABA (chmn. internat. law com. young lawyers div. 1980-84), Internat. Assn. Young Lawyers (exec. coun. 1979-81, coun. internat. law and practice 1983-84), World Tech. Execs. Network (chmn.), Regency Club (house com. 1986). Avocations: piano, horseriding. Office: The Lared Group 1901 Ave of The Stars Ste 280 Los Angeles CA 90067

SEGNER, EDMUND PETER, III, natural gas company executive; b. Dallas, Oct. 23, 1953; s. Edmund Peter Jr. and Martha Fairfax (Smith) S.; m. Kathryn Louise Daily, July 10, 1976; 1 son, Peter Michael. BSCE, Rice U., 1976; MA in Econs., U. Houston, 1980. CPA, Tex. Acct. Touche Ross & Co., Houston, 1976-78; asst. v.p. planning United Gas Pipe Line Co., Houston, 1978-86; asst. v.p. rsch. Drexel Burnham Lambert, N.Y.C., 1986-88; v.p. pub. and investor rels. Enron Corp., Houston, 1988-90; sr. v.p. pub. and gov. rels. investor Enron Corp, Houston, 1990-92, exec. v.p., chief staff, 1992—; lectr. civil engring. Rice U., Houston, 1983-85. Bd. dirs. Zool. Soc. Houston, 1992—, Greater Houston Partnership for Ednl. Excellence, 1991-93, Rice U. Fund Coun., 1992—, Sam Houston Area Coun. Boy Scouts Am., Tex. Nature Conservancy, 1993—; chmn. Community Ptnrs., 1993—. Mem. AICPA, Houston Soc. Fin. Analysts, Petroleum Investor Rels. Assn., Houston City Club, Briar Club, Braeburn County Club, Coronado Club. Republican. Lutheran. Home: 4130 Tennyson St Houston TX 77005-2750 Office: Enron Corp 1400 Smith St Houston TX 77002-7369

SEGRÈ, NINA, lawyer; b. New Haven, Apr. 4, 1940; d. Victor M. and Naomi (Berlin) Gordon; m. Gino Segrè, Dec. 31, 1962 (div. 1983); children: Katia, Julie, Michele; m. Frank F. Furstenberg, Jr., Feb. 2, 1985; stepchildren: Sarah Furstenberg, Ben Furstenberg. BA, Radcliffe Coll., 1961; MAT, Harvard U., 1963; JD, U. Pa., 1974. Bar: Pa. 1974, U.S. Dist. Ct. (ea. dist.) Pa. 1974. Law clk. U.S. Ct. Appeals (3d cir.), Phila., 1974-75; assoc. Dechert Price & Rhoads, Phila., 1976-83, ptnr., 1983-93; ptnr. Segrè & Senser, P.C., Phila., 1993—; adj. prof. Temple U., Sch. Law, 1991; course preparer, panelist Phila. (Pa.) Bar Edn. Ctr., 1994—. Trustee Radcliffe Coll., Cambridge, Mass., 1991—, chair fund com., chair program com.; mem. fin. com. Lynn Yeakel for U.S. Senate, Phila., 1992, Lynn Yeakel for Gov. Pa., 1994. Mem. Phila. Bar Assn. (mem. real property sec., mem. exec. bd.), The Harvard-Radcliffe Club (v.p., mem. exec. bd.), College Works (founder, bd. dirs.). Home: 2316 Delancey Pl Philadelphia PA 19103-6407 Office: Segrè & Senser PC 2 Penn Center Plz Ste 414 Philadelphia PA 19102-1704

SEIBER, WILLIAM JOSEPH, financial and insurance consultant; b. Huntington, W.Va., Dec. 24, 1943; s. Charles Joseph Jr. and Esther (Huddleston) S.; m. Ruby Mae Smith, Mar. 3, 1973 (div. June 1985); children: William Joseph, Scott Joseph; m. Nancy Jeanne Toothman Manfredi, Aug. 3, 1990; stepchildren: Maria C. Manfredi, Anthony C. Manfredi. BBS in Chemistry, Marshall U., 1966, MBA in Fin., 1972, BBA in Acctg., 1973. CLU, CHFC. Analytical chemist Houdaille Industries, Inc., Huntington, W.Va., 1966-67; real estate office mgr. Fla. Tradewinds, Inc., Columbus and Savannah, Ga., 1969-70; asst. prodn. mgr. Chemetron Corp., Huntington, 1970-71; grad. teaching asst. Marshall U., Huntington, 1972-73, instr. acctg., 1977-80; acctg. systems analyst Ashland Oil, Inc., Ashland, Ky., 1973; asst. prof. bus. W.Va. State Coll., Institute, 1980-81, W.Va. U. Grad. Studies, 1981-85; fin. and ins. cons. The Paul Revere Ins. Group, Worcester, Mass., 1973—; mem. Nat. Multistate Ins. Licensing Com., Ednl. Testing Svc. Princeton, N.J., 1983-90; mem. W.Va. Ins. Commrs. Agts. Licensing Adv. Com., Charleston, 1991—, also past chmn.; R&D in field. Fund raiser Salvation Army, Charleston, 1987—; mem. fin. and planned giving com. Cath. Charities, Charleston, 1984—; mem. W.Va. U. Found. Planned Giving Com., 1991—; coach Little League and Sr. League Baseball. 1st lt. U.S. Army, 1967-69. Acad. scholarship and Benedum grantee Marshall U., 1961-66, 70-72; Million Dollar Round Table, 1985-89, 92, 93. Mem. Am. Soc. CLU and ChFC (sec.-treas., pres. Charleston chpt. 1989-91, Pres.'s award 1991), Nat. Assn. Life Underwriters (Charleston chpt.), Nat. Assn. Health Underwriters, Charleston Estate Planning Coun., Cross Lanes Recreation Assn. (bd. dirs. 1986-90). Republican. Roman Catholic. Avocations: tennis, boating, fishing, travel. Home: 17 Hidden Cove Cross Lanes WV 25313 Office: 910 Quarrier St Ste 307 Charleston WV 25301

SEIBERLING, JOHN FREDERICK, former congressman, law educator, lawyer; b. Akron, Ohio, Sept. 8, 1918; s. J. Frederick and Henrietta (Buckler) S.; m. Elizabeth Pope Behr, June 4, 1949; children—John B., David P., Stephen M. AB, Harvard U., 1941; LLB, Columbia U., 1949. Bar: N.Y. 1950, Ohio 1955. Assoc. mem. firm Donovan, Leisure, Newton, Lumbard & Irvine, N.Y.C., 1949-53; atty. Goodyear Tire & Rubber Co., Akron, 1954-71; mem. 92d-99th Congresses from 14th Ohio Dist.; mem. com. on judiciary, com. on interior and insular affairs, chmn. subcom. on public lands; vis. prof. law U. Akron, 1987, 90, dir. Ctr. for Peace Studies, 1991—; ptnr. Goldman, Seiberling, Davis & Tsarnas, Akron, 1988-89. Served to maj. AUS, 1942-46. Mem. ABA. Mem. United Ch. of Christ. Home: 2370 Martin Rd Akron OH 44333-2014

SEIBERT, MARY LEE, college official; b. Evansville, Ind., Jan. 30, 1942; d. Ernest Hensley and Lillian (Schmadel) S.; BS, Ind. U., 1963, MS, 1973, EdD, 1979. Cert. med. technologist, med. asst. supr. Wishard Meml. Hosp., Indpls., 1964-67; chmn. life scis. div. Ind. Vocat. Tech. Coll., Indpls., 1967-73; assoc. prof., program dir. Ind. U. Sch. Medicine, Indpls., 1973-79; assoc. project coordinator Am. Assn. State Colls. and Univs., Washington, 1979-81; dean coll. allied health professions Temple U., Phila., 1981-90; assoc. provost, dean grad. studies Ithaca (N.Y.) Coll., 1990—; vis. prof. U. Tex. Med. Br., Galveston, 1985. Assoc. editor Jour. Med. Tech., 1985-86. Fellow Am. Soc. Allied Health Profs. (hon., chmn. forum on allied health data, rsch. com. 1983-89, bd. dirs. 1990-92, Outstanding mem. award 1986); mem. Am. Soc. Med. Technologists (profl. affairs com. 1986-89), Am. Assn. Med. Assts. (hon.), Nat. Coun. on Health Professions Edn., Nat. Acad. Scis. (bd. health care svcs. inst. of medicine 1993—), Phi Delta Kappa, Pi Lambda Theta. Republican. Avocations: reading, walking, sailing. Home: 16 Bean Hill Ln Ithaca NY 14850-9750

SEIBERT, RUSSELL JACOB, botanist, research associate; b. Shiloh Valley, Ill., Aug. 14, 1914; s. Erwin W. and Helen A. (Renner) S.; m. Isabelle L. Pring, Dec. 26, 1942; children: Michael, Donna, Lisa. A.B., Washington U., St. Louis, 1937, M.S., 1938, Ph.D., 1947. With U.S. Dept. Agr., 1940-50; botanist-geneticist U.S. Dept. Agr.-, Haiti, 1941-42, Peru, 1943-46, Costa Rica, 1947-49; dir. Los Angeles State and County Arboretum, Arcadia, Calif., 1950-55, Longwood Gardens, Kennett Square, Pa., 1955-79; adj.

curator tropical horticulture Marie Selby Bot. Garden, Sarasota, Fla., 1979—; adj. prof. bot. garden mgmt. U. Del., 1967-79; head dept. arboreta and bot. gardens, Los Angeles County, 1952-55; Am. del. Internat. Soc. Hort. Sci., 1960-70; chmn. Am. Hort. Council-U.S.A. (hort. exhbn.), 1960; (floriade), Rotterdam, Holland; v.p. XVII Internat. Hort. Congress, 1966; chmn. Am. Hort. Film Festival, 1964-69. Recipient Frank N. Meyer Meml. medal Am. Genetic Soc., 1966, Arthur Hoyt Scott Garden and Horticulture medal Swarthmore Coll., 1975, Disting. Svc. awrd Hort. Soc. N.Y., 1969, award of merit Am. Assn. Bot. Gardens and Arboreta, 1982. Mem. AAAS, Am. Hort. Soc. (pres. 1964-65, Liberty Hyde Bailey medal 1975), Am. Inst. Biol. Scis., Rotary, Sigma Xi, Phi Sigma, Gamma Sigma Delta. Home: 1613 Caribbean Dr Sarasota FL 34231-5305 Office: Marie Selby Bot Garden Sarasota FL 34230

SEIBOLD, JAMES RICHARD, physician, researcher; b. Washington, Apr. 5, 1950; s. Herman Rudolph and Clara Bond (Taylor) S.; m. Margaret Frances Bennett, Jan. 20, 1968; children: Jon Drew, Zachary Bennett. BS, La. State U., 1972; MD, SUNY, Stony Brook, 1975. Diplomate Am. Bd. Internal Medicine, Am. Bd. Rheumatology. Intern in medicine L.I. Jewish Hosp., New Hyde Park, N.Y., 1975-76, resident in medicine, 1976-78; fellow in rheumatology U. Pitts., 1978-80; asst. prof. medicine Robert Wood Johnson Med. Sch. U. Medicine and Dentistry of N.J., New Brunswick, 1980-86, assoc. prof. medicine Robert Wood Johnson Med. Sch., 1986-92, chief rheumatology Robert Wood Johnson Med. Sch., 1986-91, dir. clin. rsch. ctr. Robert Wood Johnson Med. Sch., 1989—; mem. adv. bd. Ctr. for Advanced Biotech. and Medicine, Piscataway, N.J., 1989—; W. H. Conzen chair clin. pharmacology Schering-Plough Found., Inc., 1989. Author: (chpt.) Rheumatology, 1988, 91; contbr. over 200 articles to profl. jours. Fellow ACP, Am. Coll. Rheumatology (regional coun. 1985). Mem. Soc. of Friends. Home: 16 Durham Rd Skillman NJ 08558 Office: U Medicine & Dentistry NJ Robert Wood Johnson Med Sch 1 Robert Wood Johnson Pl # 19cn New Brunswick NJ 08903-0019

SEIBOLD, RONALD LEE, sociologist, writer; b. Kansas City, Mo., May 8, 1945; s. Dean Phillip and Helen H. (Haney) S.; m. Christine Herbst, June 23, 1971 (div. July 1975). BS, Emporia State U., 1967; MA, Colo. State U., 1969. Dir. chpt. services Alpha Kappa Lambda, Ft. Collins, Colo., 1969-71; v.p. Siever & Assocs., Ft. Collins, 1971-72; pvt. practice sociology research Colo., 1972-75; coodinator Pines Internat., Lawrence, Kans., 1975—, sec., treas., 1976-87, pres., 1987—; pres. Live Foods Co., Lawrence, 1978—. Author: AKL Manual, 1969, Pines...The Wheat Grass People, 1982, Condominium Farming, 1986; editor: Cereal Grass: What's in it for You, 1990, Ceral Grass: Nature's Greatest Health Gift, 1993; contbr. articles to profl. mags. Founder, pres. Midwestern Interfraternity Coun., Emporia, Kans., 1966; pres. Interfraternity Coun., Emporia, 1965; v.p. Collegiate Young Reps., Emporia, 1965; mem. Kans. Organic Producers 1978—, Organic Crop Improvement Assn., 1990—; pres. Wilderness Cmty. Edn. Found., 1989—. George Meredith scholar Emporia State U., 1963. Mem. Nat. Nutritional Foods Assn., Organic Crop Improvement Assn., Lawrence C. of C., U.S. C. of C., Kappa Mu Epsilon, Xi Phi. Presbyterian. Home: 1992 E 1400 Rd Lawrence KS 66044-9803 Office: Pines Internat Inc Box 1107 Lawrence KS 66044-9803

SEID, RUTH (JO SINCLAIR), author; b. Bklyn., July 1, 1913; d. Nathan and Ida S. Grad. John Hay High Sch., Cleve. Various clerical jobs, publicity work, 1943-46; asst. dir. publicity dept. Greater Cleve. chpt. A.R.C., 1945-46. Author: Wasteland, 1946 (exerpts, revs. and notes included in Gay/Lesbian Almanac 1983), reissued, 1987, Sing at My Wake, 1951, (play) The Long Moment, 1951, The Changelings, 1955, reissued, 1985, Anna Teller, 1960, reissued 1992, The Seasons: Death and Transfiguration; A Memoir, 1993; (short stories anthologies) Theme and Variation in the Short Story, 1938, Of the People, 1942, America in Literature, 1944, This Way to Unity, 1945, Social Insight Through Short Stories, 1946, Cross Section, 1947, This Land, These People, 1950; contbr. short stories to anthologies A Treasury of American Jewish Stories, 1958, The American Judaism Reader, 1967, Tales of Our People, 1969, (anthology) Scrittori Ebrei Americani, 2 vols., 1989, America and I. Short Stories by American Jewish Women Writers, 1990, Anthology of Western Reserve Literature, 1992; contbr. to mags. including Readers Digest. Recipient Harper's Prize novel award 1946, 2d prize nat. TV competition Fund for Republic 1956, Ann. Fiction award Jewish Book Council Am. 1956, ann. award Ohioana Library 1956, 61, Brotherhood Week certificate of recognition NCCJ 1956, Lit. award Cleve. Arts prize 1961, Wolpaw Play Writing grant Jewish Community Centers, Cleve. 1969. Mem. Authors Guild Am., P.E.N. Jo Sinclair collection in Mugar Meml. Library, Boston U. Home: 1021 Wellington Rd Jenkintown PA 19046-3827

SEIDE, PAUL, civil engineering educator; b. N.Y.C., July 22, 1926; s. Julius David and Sylvia (Eiler) S.; m. Joan Cecilia Matalka, Jan. 7, 1951; children: Richard Laurence, Wendy Jane Seide Kielsmeier. B.C.E., CCNY, 1946; M. Aero. Engring. U. Va., 1952; Ph.D., Stanford U., 1954. Aero. research scientist Nat. Adv. Commn. for Aeros., Langley AFB, Va., 1946-52; research asst. Stanford Calif. U., 1952-53; research engr. Northrop Aircraft Co., Hawthorne, Calif., 1953-55; head methods and theory sect. TRW Inc., Los Angeles, 1955-60; head methods and research sect. Aerospace Corp., El Segundo, Calif., 1960-65; prof. civil engring. U. So. Calif., L.A., 1965-91, prof. emeritus, 1991—, assoc. chmn. dept. civil engring., 1971-73, 81-83; Albert Alberman vis. prof. Technion-Israel Inst. Tech., Haifa, 1975; vis. prof. U. Sydney, Australia, 1986, U. Canterbury, N.Z., 1986; cons. Northrop Inc., 1972-77, Aerospace Corp., 1966-68, Rockwell Inc., El Segundo, 1982-85. Author: Small Elastic Deformations of Thin Shells, 1975; contbr. numerous articles to profl. jours. NSF fellow, 1964-65. Fellow ASME, Am. Acad. Mechanics; mem. ASCE (life), Tau Beta Pi, Sigma Xi. Democrat. Jewish. Home: 300 Via Alcance Palos Verdes Peninsula CA 90274-1105 Office: U So Calif University Park Civil Engring Dept Los Angeles CA 90089-2531

SEIDEL, FREDERICK LEWIS, poet; b. St. Louis, Feb. 19, 1936; s. Jerome Jay and Thelma (Cartun) S.; children: Felicity, Samuel. AB, Harvard U., 1957. occasional lectr.; Rutgers U., New Brunswick, 1964—; Paris editor, Paris Review, 1961, advisory editor, 1962. Author: (poetry) Final Solutions, 1963, Sunrise, 1979 (Lamont Poetry prize Acad. Am. Poets 1980, Am. Poetry Rev. prize 1980, Nat. Book Critics Circle award for poetry 1981), Men and Woman: New and Selected Poems, 1984, Poems 1959-1979, 1989, These Days, 1989, My Tokyo, 1993. Guggenheim Fellow, 1993. *

SEIDEL, GEORGE ELIAS, JR., animal scientist, educator; b. Reading, Pa., July 13, 1943; s. George E. Sr. and Grace Esther (Heinly) S.; m. Sarah Beth Moore, May 28, 1970; 1 child, Andrew. BS, Pa. State U., 1965; MS, Cornell U., 1968, PhD, 1970; postgrad., Harvard U. Med. Sch., Boston, 1970-71. Asst. prof. physiology Colo. State U., Ft. Collins, 1971-75, assoc. prof., 1975-83, prof., 1983—; vis. scientist Yale U., 1978-79, MIT, 1986-87; mem. bd. on agr. NRC. Co-editor: New Technologies in Animal Breeding, 1981; contbr. articles to profl. jours. Recipient Alexander Von Humboldt award, N.Y.C., 1983, Animal Breeding Research award Nat. Assn. Animal Breeders, Columbia, Mo., 1983, Clark award Colo. State U., 1982, Upjohn Physiology award, 1986; Gov's. award for Sci. and Tech., Colo., 1986. Mem. AAAS, NAS, Am. Dairy Sci. Assn., Am. Soc. Animal Sci. (Young Animal Scientist award 1983), Soc. for Study of Reprodn., Internat. Embryo Transfer Soc. (pres. 1979). Home: 3101 Arrowhead Rd Laporte CO 80535-9374 Office: Animal Reprodn Lab Colo State U Fort Collins CO 80523

SEIDEL, MILTON JOSEPH, government administrator; b. Milw., July 3, 1931; s. Lawrence John and Anna (Norville) S.; m. Katherine Vukelic, Aug. 18, 1956; 1 child, Joseph Lawrence. BS cum laude, St. Louis U., 1956; MS, Washington U., St. Louis, 1963, postgrad., 1963-64. Spl. project engr. Alton (Ill.) Box Bd. Co., 1960-68; dir. mfg. engring. Colt Industries, St. Louis, 1968-71, Kuhlman Corp., Lexington, Ky., 1971-72; mgr. engring. edn. program U.S. Postal Service, Washington, 1972-74; chief Bur. Engraving and Printing, Office of Engring., Washington, 1974; asst. dir. research and engring., 1979-88, asst. dir. tech. 1988—; assoc. prof. Grad. Sch. Engring., George Washington U., Washington 1973—; author, chmn. proceedings Internat. Conf. Machine Inspection Printed Security Documents, 1986, Internat. Conf. on Security Documents in 21st Century, 1987. Author: Economic Analysis for Capital Investment, 1972, Volume Forecasting, 1973, Network Analysis, 1973, Manpower Scheduling, 1974, Electronics Scanning, 1981, Electronic Quality Examination, 1981, Progress of Manufacturing

Operation, 1985, Technology Innovation and Development Program, 1987. Served with U.S. Army, 1948-52. Mem. ASME, Ops. Research Soc. Am., Tech. Assn. Graphic Arts, Am. Soc. Pub. Adminstrn., Sigma Xi, Alpha Eta Rho. Home: 14412 Ansted Rd Silver Spring MD 20905-4410 Office: Bur Engraving and Printing 14th C St SW Washington DC 20228

SEIDELMAN, ARTHUR ALLAN, director; b. N.Y.C.; s. Theodore and Jeanne (Greenberg) S. BA, Whittier (Calif.) Coll., 1958; MA, UCLA, 1960. Adminstr. Forum Theater, Lincoln Ctr., N.Y.C., 1970-72; prodr. LSV Prodns., N.Y.C., 1972-76; v.p. Golden Eagle Prodns., N.Y.C., 1977-79; pres. Entertainment Profls., Inc., L.A., 1980-92, Entpro, Inc., L.A., 1992—. Dir.: (feature films) Rescue Me, The Caller, Children of Rage, Echoes, Ivye, (TV episodes) Hill Street Blues (Emmy, Humanitas awards for "Doris in Wonderland"), Murder She Wrote, Magnum, P.I., Knots Landing, Trapper John, M.D., Fame, A Year in the Life, L.A. Law, Capital News, WIOU, F.B.I. The Untold Stories, Sweet Justice, Amazing Grace, others, (TV movies) Which Mother is Mine? (Emmy award, Christopher award, Golden Halo award), I Love Liberty (Writer's Guild award), A Matter of Time (Emmy award, Chgo. Film Festival Silver plaque, N.Y. Internat. Film Festival Silver plaque), She Drinks a Little (Emmy award, Golden Halo award), Strange Voices, A Place at the Table, Look Away, An Enemy Among Us (Nancy Susan Reynolds award), Poker Alice, Sin of Innocence, Kate's Secret, A Friendship in Vienna (Grand prize N.Y. Internat. Film Festival), The People Across the Lake, Addicted to His Love, The Glory Years, False Witness, The Kid Who Loved Christmas, Body Language, Dying to Remember, Trapped in Space, The Secrets of Lake Success, Amazing Grace (pilot), Wing and a Prayer; directed Broadway and Off-Broadway plays Hamp. Ceremony of Innocence, Awake and Sing, Billy, Inherit the Wind, Justice Box, Vieux Carré, The Most Happy Fella for the N.Y.C. Opera, Gypsy Princess for Opera Pacific, others; host TV series Actors on Acting (Emmy award). Bd. dirs. ACSU So. Calif., L.A., 1986-94, Choreographers Resourcenter, 1993—. Mem. AFTRA, Dirs. Guild, Writers Guild. Democrat. Office: Entpro, Inc 1015 Gayley Ave # 1149 Los Angeles CA 90024-3424

SEIDELMAN, SUSAN, film director; b. Pa., Dec. 11, 1952. Student, Drexel U., NYU. Dir. films Smithereens, 1982, Desperately Seeking Susan, 1985, Cookie, 1989, She-Devil, 1990; dir., co-exec. producer Making Mr. Right, 1987; dir. debut with short film and You Act Like One, Too (Student film award Acad. Motion Picture Arts and Scis.). Office: care Michael Shedler 225 W 34th St Ste 1012 New York NY 10122-0049 also: William Morris Agy 151 El Camino Los Angeles CA 90048*

SEIDEMAN, RUTH EVELYN YOUNG, nurse educator; b. Okeene, Okla., July 7, 1934; d. Ewald Julius and Alma Alexandra (Smith) Kramer; m. Jack Lee Young, Nov. 27, 1954 (div. Mar. 1986); children: Stanley Daryl, Steven Glenn, Roger Neil; m. Walter Elmer Seidman, May 21, 1988. BS, Tex. Woman's U., 1958; MA, U. Okla., 1970, MS, 1975, PhD, 1987. RN, Okla. Staff nurse, supr. U. Hosp., Oklahoma City, Okla., 1955-57; sch. nurse Dallas Pub. Schs., 1958-60; staff nurse St. Francis Hosp., Tulsa, 1963-65, Cen. State Hosp., Norman, Okla., 1966-68; supr. Cen. State Hosp., Norman, 1970-71; instr. Oklahoma City U., 1971-72, Sch. Nursing St. Anthony Hosp., Oklahoma City, 1972-75; asst. prof. Coll. Nursing U. Okla., 1975-82, assoc. prof., 1982—. Author: Community Nursing Workbook:Family as Client, 1983; contbr. articles to profl. jours. Mem. Am. Nurses Assn. (del. 1985—), Midwest Nursing Research Soc., Sigma Theta Tau, Sigma Xi. Avocation: research in parenting and child development. Home: 3104 Canyon Rd Oklahoma City OK 73120-2442 Office: Coll Nursing PO Box 26901 Oklahoma City OK 73126-0901

SEIDEN, HENRY (HANK SEIDEN), advertising executive; b. Bklyn., Sept. 6, 1928; s. Jack S. and Shirley (Berkowitz) S.; m. Helena Ruth Zaldin, Sept. 10, 1949; children: Laurie Ann, Matthew Ian. B.A., Bklyn. Coll.; 1949; M.B.A., CCNY, 1954. Trainee Ben Sackheim Advt. Agy., 1949-51; nat. promotion mgr. N.Y. Post Corp., 1951-53; promotion mgr. Crowell-Collier Pub. Co., Inc., 1953-54; copy group head Batten, Barton, Durstine & Osborn, Inc., 1954-60; v.p., creative dir. Keyes, Madden & Jones, 1960-61; sr. v.p., assoc. creative dir. Marschalk, Inc., 1961-65, chmn. plans bd., 1964-65; creative dir., dir., prin. Hicks & Greist, Inc., N.Y.C., 1965—, sr. v.p., 1965-74, exec. v.p., 1974-83, chief operating officer, 1983—, pres., 1986—; chief exec. officer Ketchum/Hicks & Greist Inc., 1987-89; chmn., chief exec. officer Ketchum Advt., 1989-91; exec. v.p. Ketchum Communications Inc.; bd. dirs. Ketchum Communications Inc., Ketchum Internat. Inc., 1992—; vice chmn. Jordan, McGrath, Case & Taylor, Inc., 1992—; chmn., CEO The Seiden Group, Inc.; guest lectr. Bernard M. Baruch Sch. Bus. and Pub. Adminstrn., CCNY, 1962—, Baruch Coll., 1969—, New Sch. Social Scis., 1968, 72, 73, Sch. Visual Arts, 1979, 80—, Lehman Coll., CCNY, 1980—, Ohio U., 1981, Newhouse Grad. Sch., Syracuse U., 1981, NYU, 1983; cons. pub. rels. and communication to mayor of New Rochelle, N.Y., 1959—, also; mktg. dept. Ohio State U.; Cons. to pres. N.Y.C. City Coun., 1972-73, to postmaster Gen. U.S., 1972-74; communications adviser to Police Commr. N.Y.C., 1973—; hon. dep. commr. N.Y. Police Dept., 1991—; spl. cons. to police commr., 1992—. Author: Advertising Pure and Simple, 1976, Advertising Pure and Simple: The New Edition, 1990; contbg. editor: Madison Ave. mag, 1966—, Advt. Age, Mag. Age; guest columnist: N.Y. Times, 1972. Vice commr. Little League of New Rochelle; bd. dirs. Police Res. Assn. N.Y.C., 1973—, pres. exec. com.; bd. dirs. Cancer Rsch. and Treatment Fund, pres., 1992—, Transmedia Network, Inc.; bd. dirs., exec. v.p. N.Y.'s Finest Found., 1975—; bd. dirs., sr. v.p. Drug Enforcement Agy. Found., 1995—. Recipient award Four Freedoms Found., 1959, award Printers Ink, 1960, promotion award Editor and Publisher, 1955, Am. TV Commls. Festival award, 1963-69, Effie award Am. Mktg. Assn., 1969, 70, award Art Dirs. Club N.Y., 1963-70, award Am. Inst. Graphic Arts, 1963, Starch award, 1969, spl. award graphic art lodge B'nai B'rith Greater N.Y., 1971, 87, award of highest honor The F.B.I. Nat. Acad. 1994. Mem. A.I.M. (asso.), Nat. Acad. TV Arts and Scis., Advt. Club N.Y. (exec. judge Andy awards, award 1963-65), Advt. Writers Assn. N.Y. (Gold Key award for best newspaper and mag. advts. 1962-64), Copy Club (co-chmn. awards com., Gold Key award for best TV comml. 1969), Alpha Phi Omega. Home: 1056 Fifth Ave New York NY 10028-0112 Office: The Seiden Group 445 Park Ave New York NY 10022-2606 *Be yourself but don't take yourself too seriously.*

SEIDENBERG, IVAN G., telecommunications company executive; b. N.Y.C., Dec. 10, 1946; s. Howard and Kitty (Zaretsky) S.; m. Phyllis A. Maisel, Dec. 13, 1969; children: Douglas, Lisa. BS in Math., CUNY, 1972; MBA in Mktg. Mgmt., Pace U., 1980. Various engring. positions N.Y. Tel., 1966-74; dist. mgr. transmission design AT&T, Basking Ridge, N.J., 1974-76; dist. mgr. tech. planning AT&T, Basking Ridge, 1976-78; div. mgr. fed. regulatory AT&T, N.Y.C., 1978-81, asst. v.p. mktg., 1981-83; v.p. fed. relations Nynex Corp., Washington, 1983-86, former v.p. external affairs, former pres. and vice chmn., chmn., 1995—. Served as sgt. U.S. Army, 1966-68, Vietnam. Mem. U.S. Telephone Assn. (bd. dirs. 1985—), Rockland Bus. Council (trustee 1987). Office: Nynex Corp 335 Madison Ave New York NY 10017-4605

SEIDENFELD, GLENN KENNETH, lawyer; b. Waukegan, Ill., Feb. 24, 1914; s. Samuel Milton and Rebecca R. (Rosenblum) S.; m. Mary Louise Liebenstein, Oct. 15, 1917; children: Glenn Jr., John, Leah. BA, Lake Forest Coll., 1935, LittD (hon.), 1984; JD, U. Mich., 1938. Asst. atty. gen. for Lake County, State of Ill., 1938-42; Waukegan, 1957-61; ptnr. Dixon & Seidenfeld, Waukegan, Ill., 1959-63; cir. judge 19th Jud. Cir., State of Ill., 1963-67; appellate judge 2d Appellate Dist., State of Ill., 1967-85; chief judge 19th Jud. Cir., Waukegan, 1964-67; presiding justice 2d Appellate Dist., Elgin, Ill., 1975-84; ptnr. Jenner & Block, Chgo., 1985—. Mem. Waukegan High Sch. Bd. Edn., 1958-62; pres. Ill. Cir. and Appellate Judges Assn., Chgo., 1969. Served to capt. U.S. Army, 1941-46, PTO. Mem. ABA, Ill. Bar Assn., Lake County Bar Assn. Republican. Jewish. Home: 860 N Dewitt Pl Chicago IL 60611-1759 Office: Jenner & Block 1 E Ibm Plz Chicago IL 60611-3608

SEIDENSTICKER, EDWARD GEORGE, Japanese language and literature educator; b. Castle Rock, Colo., Feb. 11, 1921; s. Edward George and Mary Elizabeth (Dillon) S. B.A., U. Colo., 1942; M.A., Columbia U., 1947; postgrad., Harvard U., 1947-48; LittD (hon.), U. Md., 1991. With U.S. Fgn. Service, Dept. State, Japan, 1947-50; mem. faculty Stanford U., 1962-66,

prof., 1964-66; prof. dept. Far Eastern langs. and lit. U. Mich., Ann Arbor, 1966-77; prof. Japanese Columbia U., 1977-85, prof. emeritus, 1986—. Author: Kafu the Scribbler, 1965, Japan, 1961, Low City, High City, 1983, Tokyo Rising, 1990, Very Few People Come This Way, 1994; transl.: (by Murasaki Shikibu) The Tale of Genji, 1976. Served with USMCR, 1942-46. Decorated Order of Rising Sun Japan; recipient Nat. Book award, 1970; citation Japanese Ministry Edn., 1971; Kikuchi Kan prize, 1977; Goto Miyoko prize, 1982; Japan Found. prize, 1984; Tokyo Cultural award, 1985; Yamagata Banto prize, 1992. *"Make yourself a routine and stick to it," said my childhood piano teacher when I went off to college. I have never had, as some people seem to have, great plans for my future; but if a person has a serious routine and sticks resolutely with it, something is bound to get accomplished.*

SEIDERS, JOSEPH ROBERT, service company corporate executive, lawyer; b. Reading, Pa., Oct. 21, 1948; s. Harry Robert and Evelyn Kathryn (Knauer) S.; m. Sharon Ann Hunter, Aug. 21, 1976. BA, LaSalle Coll., Phila., 1970, MBA, 1982; JD, Temple U., Phila., 1974. Bar: Pa. 1974, U.S. Dist. Ct. (ea. dist.) Pa. 1974. Sole practice, Horsham, Pa., 1974-78; of counsel CDI Corp., Phila., 1978—, v.p., sec., 1980-87, sr. v.p., sec., 1987—. Pres., bd. dirs. Lafayette Place Homeowners Assn., 1986—. Mem. ABA, Pa. Bar Assn., Phila. Bar Assn., Nat. Tech. Services Assn. (pres., chmn. legal and legis. com. 1984-87). Republican. Home: 11 Bunker Hill Dr Washington Crossing PA 18977-1415 Office: CDI Corp 1717 Arch St Fl 35 Philadelphia PA 19103-2713

SEIDL, FREDRICK WILLIAM, dean, social work educator; b. Buffalo, Sept. 29, 1940; s. Wolfgang and Anna Clara (Schneider) S.; m. Ann Jane Hazlewood, Apr. 19, 1963; children: Andrew, Barbara. AB, Ohio U., 1962; MSW, SUNY, Buffalo, 1964; PhD, U. Wis., 1970. Asst. prof. U. Minn., Morris, 1964-68; assoc. prof. Wilfred Laurier U., Waterloo, Ont., Can., 1970-72; assoc. prof. U. Wis., Madison, 1972-78, prof., 1978-84, dir. Sch. Social Work, 1980-82; dean, prof. Sch. Social Work SUNY, Buffalo, 1985—; resident Toynbee Hall, London, England, 1991. Author: The Wisconsin Experiment, 1984; contbr. articles on social issues, edn. to jours., 1964—; author, performer: (musical) Hull House: A Folk Music Celebration, 1988, Songs of New Horizons, 1989, Letter From America, 1992, 3 albums of Folk Revival music, 1990-92. Bd. dirs. Child and Family Svcs., Buffalo, 1989—, Gateway Youth and Family Svcs., Williamsville, N.Y., 1989—, United Way, Buffalo, 1989—, Urban League, Buffalo, 1989—; bd. visitors Ohio U., Athens; chair edn. div. Buffalo Philharm. Ann. Appeal; mem. editorial com. Social Work Encyclopedia. Recipient Alumnus of Yr. award SUNY, Buffalo, 1985. Mem. Nat. Assn. Social Workers, Nat. Assn. Deans and Dirs. Social Work Schs., Coun. Social Work Edn. Democrat. Avocations: folk music, canoeing. Home: 69 Symphony Cir Buffalo NY 14201-1203 Office: SUNY Buffalo Sch Social Work 285 Alumni Ave Buffalo NY 14260

SEIDL, JANE PATRICIA, lawyer; b. Stamford, Conn., June 9, 1958; d. Francis Xavier and Frances (Nizolek) S. BA magna cum laude, Boston Coll., 1980; JD, U. Conn., 1985. Bar: Conn. 1985, U.S. Dist. Ct. Conn. 1985. Fin. editor Fin. Acctg. Standards Bd., Stamford, 1980-82; assoc. Schatz & Schatz, Ribicoff & Kotkin, Hartford, Conn., 1985-92; counsel Northeast Utilities, Hartford, Conn., 1992—. Mem. ABA, Conn. Bar Assn., Hartford County Bar Assn., Hartford Assn. Women Attys. (pres. dir 1992—). Avocations: photography, water sports, literature. Office: Northeast Utlities PO Box 270 Hartford CT 06141-0270

SEIDLER, DORIS, artist; b. London, Nov. 26, 1912; m. Bernard Seidler, Sept. 5, 1935; 1 son, David. Group exhbns. include Bklyn. Mus. Bi-Ann., Vancouver Internat., Honolulu Acad. Arts, Pa. Acad. Fine Arts, Phila., Soc. Am. Graphic Artists, Assoc. Am. Artists Gallery, Jewish Mus., N.Y.C., Bklyn. Mus., Albright-Knox, 1994; represented in permanent collections Libr. of Congress, Smithsonian Instn., Washington, Phila. Mus. Art, Bklyn. Mus., Seattle Mus. Art, Whitney Mus., Nat. Gallery Art, Nassau County (N.Y.) Mus. Fine Arts, Brit. Mus., London, Victorial and Albert Mus. London, Pallant House Coll., Eng., Portland Mus. Art, Oreg. Mem. Soc. Am. Graphic Artists (rec. sec. 1964-71, past v.p.). Address: 14 Stoner Ave Great Neck NY 11021-2101

SEIDLER, LYNN L., foundation executive; b. New Brunswick, N.J., Aug. 13, 1936; d. William and Selma (Plapinger) Lopatin; m. Lee J. Seidler, March 26, 1959; 1 child, Laurie K. BA, Lake Erie Coll., Painesville, Ohio, 1958; MA, N.Y.U., 1970. Sec. to dean Lake Erie Coll., 1954-58; exec. sec. Am. Found. Tropical Medicine, N.Y.C., 1958-59; jr. fin. analyst Hemphill Noyes & Co., N.Y.C., 1959-61; coord. pub. rels. Am. Inst. of CPAs, N.Y.C., 1961-63; exec. dir. Shubert Found., N.Y.C., 1975—. Co-author: Social Accounting, 1978. Avocations: scuba diving, swimming, skiing. Office: Shubert Foundation 234 W 44th St New York NY 10041-0001

SEIDLER, NORMAN HOWARD, lawyer; b. N.Y.C., July 5, 1919; s. Charles M. Seidler and Malvina Lassell; m. Muriel P. Tolchin, Nov. 24, 1949; children—Terry Lisa, JoLinda. LL.B., NYU, 1948. Bar: N.Y. Trial atty. U.S. Dept. Justice, Cleve., 1948-55, chief Great Lakes Office antitrust div., 1955-66; chief N.Y. Office antitrust div. U.S. Dept. Justice, N.Y.C., 1966-74; ptnr. Lord, Day & Lord, N.Y.C., 1974—. Served to 1st lt. U.S. Army, 1941-46, ETO. Mem. ABA (antitrust sect., litigation sect.). Home: 1 Copper Beech Pl Merrick NY 11566-3226 Office: Lord Day & Lord 25 Broadway New York NY 10004-1010 Office: Coudert Bros 1114 Avenue Of The Americas New York NY 10036-7701

SEIDMAN, DAVID N(ATHANIEL), materials science and engineering educator; b. N.Y.C., July 5, 1938; s. Charles and Jeanette (Cohen) S.; m. Shoshanah Cohen-Sabban, Oct. 21, 1973; children: Elie, Ariel, Eytan. BS, NYU, 1960, MS, 1962; PhD, U. Ill., 1965. Postdoc. assoc. Cornell U., Ithaca, N.Y., 1964-66, asst. prof. materials sci. and engring., 1966-70, assoc. prof. materials sci. and engring., 1970-76, prof. materials sci. and engring., 1976-85; prof. materials sci. and engring. Northwestern U., Evanston, Ill., 1985—; Lady Davis vis. prof. Hebrew U., Jerusalem, 1978, 80-81, prof. materials sci., 1983-85; sci. cons. Argonne (Ill.) Nat. Labs. 1985-94; vis. prof. Technion, Haifa, 1969, Tel-Aviv U., Ramat-Aviv, 1972; vis. scientist C.E. de Grenoble, 1981, C.N.E.T.-Meylan, 1981, C.E. de Scalay, 1989, U. Goettingen, 1989, 92. Contbr. numerous articles on atomic-scale imperfections in metals and semicondrs., radiation effects, field-ion, atom-probe and electron microscopy, 1964—. Recipient Max Planck Rsch. prize Max-Planck-Gesellschaft and the A. von Humboldt-Stiftung, 1993; Guggenheim fellow, 1972-73, 80-81, Humboldt fellow, 1989, 92; named chair for phys. metallurgy Gordon Conf., 1982. Fellow Am. Phys. Soc.; mem. AIME (Hardy Gold medal 1967), Materials Research Soc., AAAS. Democrat. Jewish. Avocations: reading history and novels, travel. Home: 9056 Tamaroa Ter Skokie IL 60076-1928 Office: Northwestern U MLSF Bldg Evanston IL 60208-3108

SEIDMAN, ELLEN SHAPIRO, lawyer, government official; b. N.Y.C., Mar. 12, 1948; d. Benjamin Harry Shapiro and Edna (Eysen) Stern; m. Walter Becker Slocombe, June 14, 1981; 1 child, Benjamin William. AB, Radcliffe Coll., 1969; JD, Georgetown U., 1974; MBA, George Washington U., 1988. Bar: D.C., 1975. Law clk. U.S. Ct. of Claims, Washington, 1974-75; assoc. Caplin & Drysdale, Washington, 1975-78; atty., advisor U.S. Dept. of Transportation, Washington, 1978-79, dep. asst. gen. counsel, 1979-81; assoc. gen. counsel Chrysler Corp Loan Guaranty Bd., Washington, 1981-84; atty., advisor U.S. Dept. of Treasury, Washington, 1981-86, spl. asst. to the Under Sec. Fin., 1986-87; dir. strategic planning Fed. Nat. Mortgage Assn., Washington, 1987-88, v.p., asst. to chmn., 1988-91, v.p. regulation rsch. and econs., 1991-93; spl. asst. to the pres. for econ. policy The White House, Washington, 1993—. Mem. Women in Housing and Fin. Office: Nat Econ Coun The White House Washington DC 20500

SEIDMAN, HERTA LANDE, international trade and information company executive; married. BA in Econs. and Lit., McGill U. and U. Miami, 1959; MA, Cornell U., 1960. Mgr. shipping and internat. trade bus. devel. firm, 1962-76; dep. comttr. N.Y. State Dept. of Commerce, 1976-79; asst. sec. for trade U.S. Dept. of Commerce Carter Adminstrn., 1979; mng. dir. Philipp Bros. (thereafter Phibro & Phibro-Salomon and Solomon Brothers), 1981-85; co-founder, chmn. Tradenet Corp., N.Y.C., 1985—; dir Atlantic Coun. of U.S.; chmn. Soros Bus. and Mgmt. Found.; vice chair N.Y. Gov.'s Coun. Internat. Bus. Bd. dirs. Jr. Achievement Internat., Albania Am. Enterprise

Fund. Woodrow Wilson fellow, 1960. Mem. Coun. Fgn. Rels. Office: Tradenet Corp 520 Madison Ave New York NY 10022

SEIDMAN, L(EWIS) WILLIAM, television commentator; b. Grand Rapids, Mich., Apr. 29, 1921; s. Frank E. and Esther (Lubetsky) S.; m. Sarah Berry, Mar. 3, 1944; children: Thomas, Tracy, Sarah, Carrie, Meg, Robin. A.B., Dartmouth Coll., 1943; LL.B., Harvard U., 1948; M.B.A., U. Mich., 1949. Bar: Mich. 1949, D.C. 1977. Spl. asst. fin. affairs to gov. of Mich., 1963-66; nat. mng. partner Seidman & Seidman C.P.A.s, N.Y.C., 1969-74; asst. for econ. affairs to Pres. Gerald R. Ford, 1974-77; dir. Phelps Dodge Corp., N.Y.C., 1977-82; vice chmn. Phelps Dodge Corp., 1980-82; dean Coll. Bus. Adminstrn. Ariz. State U., Tempe, 1982-85; chmn. FDIC, Washington, 1985-91; chief commentator Sta. CNBC-TV, 1991; pub. Bank Dir. Mag., 1992; chmn. bd. dirs. Commac Inc., Phoenix; chmn. Detroit Fed. Res. Bank Chgo., 1970, RTC, 1988-91; pres. Leelanau, Inc.; co-chair White House Conf. on Productivity, 1983-84. Served to lt. USNR, 1942-46. Decorated Bronze Star. Mem. D.C. Bar Assn. Clubs: Chevy Chase (Md.); Univ. (N.Y.C.); Crystal Downs (Mich.). Home: 1694 31st St NW Washington DC 20007-2924 Office: 2620 P St NW Washington DC 20007

SEIDMAN, RICKI, federal official. Asst. to the Pres. for scheduling and advance The White House, Washington, 1993—. Office: The White House Office Scheduling and Advance 1600 Pennsylvania Ave NW Washington DC 20500

SEIDMAN, SAMUEL NATHAN, investment banker, economist; b. N.Y.C., Mar. 31, 1934; s. Hyman and Pauline (Seidman) S.; m. Herta Lande, Sept. 4, 1964. B.A., Bklyn. Coll., 1955; Ph.D., NYU, 1964. Instr. Douglass Coll., Rutgers U., New Brunswick, N.J., 1960-62; v.p. Lehman Bros. Internat., N.Y.C., 1962-70; pres. S.N. Seidman & Co. Inc., N.Y.C., 1970—; dir. Amrep Corp., N.Y.C., Harken Oil Corp., Dallas; dir., chmn. Victoria Station Corp., San Francisco, 1985-87; pres., dir. Prodn. Sys. Acquisition Corp. Trustee Mental Health Assn. N.Y., N.Y.C. 1980—. Served to pfc. U.S. Army, 1954-56. Univ. fellow Inst. Labor Relations, NYU, N.Y.C., 1957-58; Fulbright scholar U. Philippines, 1959-60. Mem. Am. Econ. Assn. Club: University (N.Y.C.). Avocations: music; history of Asia. Office: 520 Madison Ave 38th flr New York NY 10022-0010

SEIDNER, FREDERIC JAY, public relations executive; b. Chgo., Mar. 4, 1931; s. Leo and Jewel (Sachs) S.; m. Andrea Pickman; children: Allen P., Cary D., Loren A. B.J., U. Mo., 1953. Editorial writer pub. relations dept. Ill. Bell Telephone Co., 1956-57; with Pub. Relations Bd., Inc., Chgo., 1957—; exec. v.p. Pub. Relations Bd., Inc., 1969—, mng. partner, 1979-85; exec. v.p. Porter Novelli, 1985-88; pres. Seidner Communications Unlimited, 1989—. Home: Chgo. Area Coun. Boy Scouts Am., 1958-66, North Shore Coun., 1967-77; mem. adv. bd. Evanston Theatre Co., 1976-80; mem. exec. com. Jewish Nat. Fund, Ill. region, 1989—; bd. dirs. Mt. Sinai Hosp. Med. Ctr., Chgo., 1961-77, Orch. of Ill. Assn., chmn. mktg. com., 1986-88. Mem. Pub. Rels. Soc. Am. (past chmn. pub. affairs sect.), Soc. Profl. Journalists, Sch. of Journalism Alumni U. Mo. (pres. 1982-90), U. Mo. Alumni Assn. (bd. dirs. 1982-90). Home and Office: 2500 N Lakeview Ave Apt 3502 Chicago IL 60614-1829

SEIFER, JUDITH HUFFMAN, sex therapist, educator; b. Springfield, Ill., Jan. 18, 1945; d. Clark Lewis and Catherine Mary (Fisher) Huffman; married; children: Christopher, Patrick, Andrea. RN, St. John's Hosp./Quincy Coll., 1965; MHS, Inst. Advanced Study Human Sexuality, 1981, PhD, 1986. RN, Ohio; Diplomate Am. Bd. Sexology. Charge nurse Grandview Hosp., Dayton, Ohio, 1967-70; v.p. Sego, Inc., Dayton, 1970-84, pres., 1984—; marital and sex therapist Grandview Ob-Gyn., Inc., Dayton, 1975-87; asst. clin. prof. psychiatry and ob-gyn Wright State U. Sch. Medicine, Dayton, 1985-93; editn. cons., screenwriter The Learning Corp., Ft. Lauderdale, Fla., 1990—; adj. prof. psychology U. Dayton, 1985-90; profl. speaker The Upjohn Co., Kalamazoo, 1986—, CIBA-GEIGY Co., 1987-90; chmn. tech. adv. com. Mercari Comm., Inc., Englewood, Colo., 1988-89; cons. dept. psychology VA Hosp., Dayton, 1990-93. Author, screenwriter film script: Mercari Communications, 1988; guest editor: The D.O., 1985, contbr. articles to profl. jours. Pres. Dayton Osteopathic Aux., 1974-75, Aux. Ohio Osteopathic Assn., Columbus, 1981-82, Sister City Assn., Oakwood, Ohio, 1985-86; bd. dirs. Grace House Sexual Abuse Resource Ctr., Dayton, 1987-89, Planned Parenthood Miami Valley, Ohio, 1985-86, Social Health Assn., Dayton, 1976-87. Grantee Dayton Found.; 1980-82; fellow Masters and Johnson Inst., 1984. Fellow Internat. Coun. Sex Educators, Am. Acad. Clin. Sexologists; mem. Am. Assn. Sex Educators, Counselors and Therapists (cert., rec. sec. 1986-91, pres. 1994—), Am. Coll. Sexologists. Roman Catholic. Avocation: public speaking. Office: Sego Corp 2 Deerfield Rd PO Box 426 Lewisburg WV 24901-0426

SEIFERT, BLAIR WAYNE, clinical pharmacist; b. Regina, Sask., Can., June 5, 1955; s. John Martin and Lottie P. S. (Murray) S. BS in Pharmacy, U. Sask., Saskatoon, 1977; PharmD, U. Tex., 1981. Hosp. pharmacy resident Regina Gen. Hosp., 1977-78; clin. pharmacy resident Bexar County Hosp., San Antonio, 1978-81; asst. dir. pharmacy Thomason Gen. Hosp., El Paso, 1981-83; perinatal clin. pharmacist Victoria (B.C.) Gen. Hosp., 1983-84; pediat. clin. pharmacist Health Scis. Centre, Winnipeg, Man., Can., 1984—; asst. prof. pharmacy U. Man., Winnipeg, 1984—, asst. prof. pediat., 1994—; reviewer Am. Jour. Hosp. Pharmacy, 1988—, Clin. Pharmacy, 1988—, Can. Jour. Hosp. Pharmacy, 1989—; mem. panel examiners Pharmacy Examining Bd. Can., 1992-94; reviewer ind. learning material panel Can. Coun. on Continuing Edn. in Pharmacy, 1994—; lectr. family asthma program Man. Lung Assn., 1985—; spkr. KNOW Drug Program, Man. Pharm. Assn., 1989—; presenter in field. Vol. Man. Riding for the Disabled, Winnipeg, 1987-89, Teddy Bears' Picnic, Children's Hosp. Rsch. Found., 1987, 88, 89, 90, 92, 93, 94, Children's Miracle Network Telethon, Children's Hosp. Rsch. Found., 1987, 88, 89, 90, 91, 92, 93, 94, Can. Nat. Inst. for the Blind, 1990—. Fellow Can. Soc. Hosp. Pharmacists (jr. chmn. Man. chpt. 1987-88, sr. chmn. com. 1988-89, v.p. 1989-90, pres. 1990-91, past pres. 1991-92, mem. corr. edn. com 1988-89, host com. 1990 ann. gen. meeting 1989-90, stds. com. 1990-91, clin. pharmacology adv. com. 1991-93, chmn. intravenous admixture revision task force 1993-95), Man. Pharm. Assn. (edn. com. 1988-89, 91—, planning com. 1989-92). Avocations: reading, horseback riding, figure skating. Office: Health Scis Centre, Dept Pharm Svcs, 820 Sherbrook St, Winnipeg, MN Canada R3A 1R9

SEIFERT, GEORGE, professional football coach; b. San Francisco, Jan. 22, 1940; m. Linda Seifert; children: Eve, Jason. Grad., U. Utah, 1963. Asst. football coach U. Utah, 1964; head coach Westminster Coll., 1965; asst. coach U. Iowa, 1966, U. Oreg., 1966-71; secondary coach Stanford U., 1972-74; head coach Cornell U., 1975-76; from secondary coach to defensive coord. San Francisco 49ers, 1980-89, head coach, 1989—. With AUS, 1963. Office: San Francisco 49ers 4949 Centennial Blvd Santa Clara CA 95054-1229*

SEIFERT, KEITH ANTHONY, mycologist. Rsch. sci. Agri-Food Agr. & Can., Ottawa, Ont., Can. Recipient Alexopoulos prize Mycological Soc. Am., 1993. Office: Agri-Food Agr & Can, Ctr for Land & Biol Resources Rsch, Ottawa, ON Canada K1A 0C6*

SEIFERT, THOMAS LLOYD, lawyer; b. Boston, June 6, 1940; s. Ralph Frederick and Hazel Bell (Harrington) S.; m. Ann Cecelia Berg, June 19, 1965. BS cum laude, Ind. U., 1962, JD cum laude, 1965. Bar: Ill. 1965, Ind. 1965, N.Y. 1979. Assoc. law firm Keck, Mahin & Cate, Chgo., 1965-67; atty. Essex Group, Inc., Ft. Wayne, Ind., 1967-70, Amoco Corp., Chgo., 1970-73; assoc. gen. counsel, asst. sec. Canteen Corp., Chgo., 1973-75; sec., gen. counsel The Marmon Group, Inc. (and predecessor cos.), Chgo., 1975-78; v.p., gen. counsel, sec. Hanson Industries, Inc., N.Y.C., 1978-83; v.p. law, chief fin. officer Petrie Stores Corp., N.Y.C., 1982-83; mem. Finley, Kumble, Wagner, Heine, Underberg, Manley, Myerson & Casey, N.Y.C., 1983-87, Paul, Weiss, Rifkind, Wharton & Garrison, N.Y.C., 1987-91; gen. counsel, chief legal officer Sterling Grace Capital Mgmt., L.P. and affiliated cos., N.Y.C., 1991—. Note editor Ind. Law Jour., 1964-65. Named to Ind. Track and Cross Country Hall of Fame, 1993. Mem. ABA, N.Y. State Bar Assn., Order of Coif, The Creek, Beta Sigma Gamma. Home: Museum Tower 15 W 53d St Apt 31 E New York NY 10019 Office: Sterling Grace Capital Mgmt 515 Madison Ave Ste 2000 New York NY 10022-5403

SEIFERT, WILLIAM WALTHER, electrical engineering educator; b. Troy, N.Y., Feb. 22, 1920; s. Harry Herman and Alice (Turner) S.; m. Sylvia Campbell, Oct. 7, 1943 (dec. Sept. 1949); children: Linda Lee, Charles William; m. Doris Patterson, May 10, 1950 (dec. June 1979); children: Robert Patterson, Camilla Walther (dec. Aug. 1959), Janet. B.E.E., Rensselaer Poly. Inst., 1941; M.S., MIT, 1947; D.Sc., Mass. Inst. Tech., 1951. Instr. Rensselaer Poly. Inst., 1941-44; mem. staff and faculty MIT, 1944-85, prof. elec. engring., 1965-85, prof. emeritus, 1985—, asst. dean engring., 1962-68, dir. project transport, 1964-70, asso. dir. Commodity Transp. and Econ. Devel. Lab., 1970-72, prof. engring. and elec. engring., 1968-74, prof. civil engring., 1974-78, sr. lectr. civil engring., 1978-85; dir. Sahel-Sudano project, 1973-75; dir. rsch. Analysts Rsch. Div., Belmont, Mass., 1991—; pres. Devel. Analysis Assocs., Inc., Cambridge, Mass., 1975-86; pres. Inst. Guilfoyle, 1986—. Author: (with C.W. Steeg, Jr.) Control Systems Engineering, 1960, (with B.A. Schriever) Air Transportation 1975 and Beyond, 1968, (with M.A. Bakr and M.A. Kettani) Energy and Development: A Case Study, 1973; editorial adv. bd., chmn. sci. and tech. com.: World Book Ency., 1963-69. Mem. IEEE (sr.). Home: 7 Longfellow Rd Wellesley MA 02181-5220 Office: 26 Brighton St Belmont MA 02178-4043

SEIFF, ALVIN, planetary scientist, atmosphere physics and aerodynamics consultant; b. Kansas City, Mo., Feb. 26, 1922; s. Harry Louis and Sara Dorothy (Silverstone) S.; m. Robbye Walker, Mar. 27, 1948 (div. Oct. 1959); children: David Wilson, Deborah Ellen Seiff Hedgecock; m. Julia Gwynne Hill, June 23, 1968; children: Michael Harry, Geoffrey Bernard. BS ChemE, U. Mo., 1942; postgrad., U. Tenn., 1946-48, Stanford U., 1959-60. Chem. engr. TVA, Florence, Ala., 1942-43; tech. supr. uranium isotope separ. Tenn. Eastman Corp., Oak Ridge, 1944-45; instr. physics U. Tenn., Knoxville, 1945-48; aero. rsch. scientist NACA Ames Aero. Lab., Moffett Field, Calif., 1948-57; chief supersonic free flight rsch. br. NACA, Moffett Field, 1952-63; chief vehicle environment br. NASA Ames Rsch. Ctr., Moffett Field, 1963-72; sr. staff scientist dir.'s office, 1972-77, sr. staff scientist space sci. div., 1977-86; sr. rsch. assoc. San Jose (Calif.) State U. Found., 1987—; mem. entry sci. team Viking Mars Mission Langley Rsch. Ctr., NASA, Hampton, Va., 1972-77, mem. sci. steering group Pioneer Venus Project Ames Rsch. Ctr., Moffett Field, 1972-82, Galileo Project, sci. group Jet Propulsion Lab., Pasadena, 1979—, mem. sci. team Soviet-French Vega Venus Balloon Mission, 1984-87, chmn. sci. adv. team atmosphere structure and meteorology Mars Pathfinder Mission, 1993—; mem. basic Rsch. Coun., NASA, Washington, 1973-76; Von Karman lectr., 1990. Author and editor: Ballistic Range Technology, 1972; (with others) Venus, 1983; contbr. articles to profl. jours. Recipient Exceptional Scientific Achievement medals NASA, 1978, 81, H. Julian Allen award Ames Rsch. Ctr., 1982. Fellow AIAA (assoc.); mem. Am. Astron. Soc. (div. planetary sci.), Am. Geophys. Union. Avocations: music, piano, gardening, home design and construction. Office: Ames Rsch Ctr Mail Stop 245-2 Moffett Field CA 94035

SEIGEL, DANIEL A., retail executive. With Thrifty Corp., pres., COO, 1990, pres., CEO, also bd. dirs.; also exec. v.p. Pacific Enterprises. Office: Thrifty Corp 3424 Wilshire Blvd Los Angeles CA 90010-2241*

SEIGEL, JERROLD EDWARD, historian, writer; b. St. Louis, June 9, 1936; s. William and Katherine (Ginsberg) S.; m. Jayn Rosenfeld, Aug. 28, 1966; children: Micol, Jessica. A.B., Harvard U., 1958; Ph.D., Princeton U., 1963. Instr. Princeton (N.J.) U., 1962-65, asst. prof., 1965-68, assoc. prof., 1968-78, prof. history, 1978-88; prof. history NYU, N.Y.C., 1988—; Kenan prof., 1994—; vis. prof. history Maitre d'Etudes, Ecoles des hautes études, Paris, 1988-94; finalist Nat. Book Critics Cir., 1987. Author: Rhetoric and Philosophy, 1968, Marx's Fate, 1978, Bohemian Paris, 1986, Private Worlds of Marcel Duchamp, 1995. Fulbright fellow Inst. Internat. Edn., 1961-62; NEH fellow, 1979-80, 87-88. Mem. Phi Beta Kappa. Home: 48 Horatio St New York NY 10014-1614 Office: NYU 19 University Pl New York NY 10003-4501

SEIGEL, STUART EVAN, lawyer; b. N.Y.C., Mar. 25, 1933; s. Philip Herman and Betty Sarah (Leventhal) S.; m. Joyce Roberta Meyers (div.); children: Charles Meyers, Lee Bennett, Suzanne Marcie; m. Sherry Diane Jackson,Sept. 24, 1989. BS, N.Y. U., 1953, LLB, 1957; LLM in Taxation, Georgetown U., 1960. Bar: N.Y. 1958, D.C. 1958. Atty. Office Chief Counsel, IRS, Washington, 1957-65, Office Tax Legis. Counsel, Dept. Treasury, Washington, 1965-69; assoc. tax legis. counsel Office Tax Legis. Counsel, Dept. Treasury, 1968-69; ptnr. firm Cohen and Uretz, Washington, 1969-77; chief counsel IRS, Washington, 1977-79; ptnr. firm Williams and Connolly, Washington, 1979-89, Arnold and Porter, N.Y.C., 1989—; lectr. George Washington U. Sch. Law, 1970-73; adj. prof. law Antioch Sch. Law, 1973-76, Georgetown U. Sch. Law, 1981. Mem. ABA, Am. Law Inst., Am. Judicature Soc., Am. Coll. Tax Counsel, N.Y. State Bar Assn., Assn. of Bar of City of N.Y. Club: Metropolitan (Washington). Office: Arnold and Porter 399 Park Ave New York NY 10022-4614

SEIGLE, HARRY JAY, building supply company executive; b. Elgin, Ill., Nov. 25, 1946; s. Harold T. and Lora (Heimann) S.; m. Susan Gilbert, July 22, 1973; children: Benjamin, Max, Joseph. BA, Washington U., St. Louis, 1968; JD cum laude, Northwestern U., Chgo., 1971. Bar: Ill. 1971. Assoc. Chapman and Cutler, Chgo., 1970-73; pres. Seigle's Home and Bldg. Ctrs., Inc., Elgin, 1973-95, chmn., 1995—; bd. dirs. Lumber Ins. Co., Framingham, Mass.; chmn. Ill. Devel. Fin. Authority. Campaign chmn. United Way Elgin, 1985, pres., 1986; trustee, chmn. Elgin C.C., 1980-93; hon. bd. dirs Elgin Cmty. Crisis Ctr., 1989—; mem. nat. com. Washington U., St. Louis. Recipient Disting. Citizen award Boy Scouts Am., St. Charles, Ill., 1990, Willis A. Reed Humanitarian award United Way Elgin, 1992, Cosmopolitan Disting. Svc. award, 1995; named Retailer of Yr., Bldg. Supply Home Cts., 1989. Mem. Home Builders Assn. Greater Chgo. (v.p. 1991), Ill. C. of C. (chmn. 1990-92), Standard Club (Chgo.). Jewish. Avocations: running, skiing. Office: Seigle's Home & Bldg Ctrs 1331 Davis Rd Elgin IL 60123-1364

SEIGLER, DAVID STANLEY, botanist, chemist, educator; b. Wichita Falls, Tex., Sept. 11, 1940; s. Kenneth R. and Floy M. (Wilkinson) S.; m. Janice Kay Cline, Jan. 20, 1961; children: Dava, Rebecca. BS in Chemistry, Southwestern (Okla.) State Coll., 1961; PhD in Organic Chemistry, U. Okla., 1967. Postdoctoral assoc. USDA No. Regional Lab., Peoria, Ill., 1967-68; postdoctoral fellow dept. botany U. Tex., Austin, 1968-70; asst. prof. botany U. Ill., Urbana, 1970-76, assoc. prof., 1976-79, prof. botany, 1979—, head dept. plant biology, 1988-93; curator U. Ill. Herbarium, 1993—. Editor: Crop Resources, 1977, Phytochemistry and Angiosperm Phylogeny, 1981; contbr. numerous articles to profl. jours. Mem. Phytochem. Soc. N.Am. (pres. 1988-89), Bot. Soc. Am., Am. Chem. Soc., Am. Soc. Plant Taxonomists, Internat. Soc. Chem. Ecology (pres. 1990-91). Mem. Assembly of God Ch. Avocation: genealogy. Home: 510 W Vermont Ave Urbana IL 61801-4931 Office: U Ill Dept Plant Biology 265 Morrill Hall 505 S Goodwin Ave Urbana IL 61801-3707

SEIGLER, RUTH QUEEN, college nursing administrator, consultant, nurse; b. Conway, S.C., July 31, 1942; d. Charles Isaac and Berneta Mae (Weaks) Queen; m. Rallie Marshall Seigler, Sept. 1, 1963; children: Rallie Marshall Jr., Scot Monroe. ADN, Lander Coll., 1962; BSN, U.S.C., 1964, MSN, 1980. Pub. health nurse Richland County Health Dept., Columbia, S.C., 1964-66; dir. nurses Columbia Area Mental Health Ctr., 1966-69; program nurse specialist Midlands Health Dist., 1969-72; discharge planner Richland Meml. Hosp., 1972-73, clin. dir., 1973-75; exec. dir. S.C. State Bd. Nursing, 1976-83; v.p. nursing rsch. Self Meml. Hosp., Greenwood, S.C., 1983-86; exec. dir. S.C. Commn. on Aging, Columbia, 1986-95; asst. dean Coll. Nursing U. S.C., Columbia, 1995—; bd. dirs. Queen Gas Co., Barnwell, S.C.; nurse cons. Creative Nursing Mgmt., Mpls., 1984—. Advisor: The Role of County Mental Health Nurse, 1971. Recipient Disting. Alumni award Lander Coll., 1978, career Woman recognition award Columbia YWCA, 1980, William S. Hall award S.C. Assn. Residential Care Homes, 1988, U.S.C. Coll. Nursing Disting. Alumni award, 1993; named one of Ten Women of Achievement, S.C. March of Dimes, 1987. Mem. Am. Nurses Assn., S.C. Nurses Assn. (sec. 1965-68, bd. dirs. 1986-88, Excellence award 1984, Recognition award 1984), S.C. Hosp. Assn., S.C. Gerontol. Soc., Am. Pub. Health Assn., Columbia Luncheon Club, S.C. Fedn. Older Ams., Evening Mission Action Group, Bd. Nursing Home Examiners, Pilot Club, Inc. (pres. 1988-89), Rotary Internat., Sigma Theta Tau. Presbyterian. Avocations: gardening, traveling. Home: 2220 Bermuda Hills Rd Columbia

SC 29223-6710 Office: U SC Coll Nursing Office Student Svcs Columbia SC 29208

SEIKEL, OLIVER EDWARD, lawyer; b. Akron, Ohio, July 6, 1937; s. Herman William and Josephine Marie (Weaver) S.; m. Meredith Miller. B.S., Mass. Inst. Tech., 1959; J.D., U. Mich., 1962; postgrad. (fellow), U. Hamburg, 1962-63. Bar: Ohio 1963. Assoc. Falsgraf, Reidy, Shoup & Ault, Cleve., 1963-68, ptnr., 1969-71; legal mgr. internat. ops. Midland-Ross Corp., Cleve., 1971-73; sole practice Cleve., 1974-78; ptnr. Seikel & Stinson, Cleve., 1978-86; prin. Burke, Haber & Berick Co., Cleve., 1986-90, McDonald, Hopkins, Burke & Haber Co., L.P.A., Cleve., 1990—; sec. Bearings, Inc. and subs., Cleve., 1974-90, gen. counsel, 1974-89. Trustee Our Lady of the Wayside Home, Avon, Ohio, 1969-88, Gilmour Acad., Gates Mills, Ohio, 1970—; trustee, mem. exec. com. Cath. Charities Corp., Cleve., 1975-88. Fellow Am. Bar Found.; mem. ABA, Ohio Bar Assn., Greater Cleve. Bar Assn., Rotary, Delta Theta Phi. Roman Catholic. Clubs: Cleve. Athletic (Cleve.), Cleve. Yachting (Cleve.), Cleve. City (Cleve.), Cleve. Playhouse (Cleve.). Home: 2 Bratenahl Pl Cleveland OH 44108-1183 Office: McDonald Hopkins Burke Haber Co LPA 2100 Bank One Center 600 Superior Ave E Cleveland OH 44114-2653

SEIL, FREDRICK JOHN, neuroscientist, neurologist; b. Nove Sove, Yugoslavia, Nov. 9, 1933; s. Joseph and Theresa (Krieger) S.; m. Daryle Faith Wolfers, July 2, 1955; children: Jonathan Fredrick, Joel Philip Timothy. BA, Oberlin Coll., 1956; MD, Stanford U., 1960. Intern Kaiser Found. Hosp., San Francisco, 1960-61; resident in neurology Stanford (Calif.) U., 1961-64, fellow in neurology, 1964-66; staff neurologist VA Med. Ctr., Palo Alto, Calif., 1969-76; clin. investigator VA Med. Ctr., Portland, Oreg., 1976-79, staff neurologist, 1979-81, dir. VA office regeneration research programs, 1981—; asst. prof. neurology Stanford U., 1969-75, assoc. prof. neurology Oreg. Health Sci. U., Portland, 1976-78, prof. neurology, 1978—, prof. cell biology and anatomy, 1990—. Editor: Nerve, Organ and Tissue Regeneration: Research Perspectives, 1983, Neural Regeneration, 1987, 94, Current Issues in Neural Regeneration and Transplantation, 1989, Advances in Neural Regeneration Research, 1990, Neural Injury and Regeneration: 1993, Multiple Sclerosis: Current Status of Research and Treatment, 1994; contbr. articles to profl. jours. Served to capt. U.S. Army, 1966-68. Grantee VA, 1970—, NIH, 1986—. Mem. Internat. Brain Rsch. Orgn., Internat. Soc. Develop. Neurosci., Am. Neurol. Assn., Am. Assn. Neuropathologists, Soc. Neurosci., Soc. Exptl. Neuropathology. Democrat. Home: 10306 SW Radcliffe Rd Portland OR 97219-7956 Office: VA Med Ctr Office Regeneration Rs Portland OR 97201

SEILER, STEVEN LAWRENCE, health facility administrator; b. Chgo., Dec. 30, 1941; married. B, U. Ariz., 1963; M, U. Iowa, 1965. Adminstrv. resident Rush-Presbyn.-St. Luke's Med. Ctr., Chgo., 1965, adminstrv. asst., 1965-68; asst. adminstr. Lake Forest (Ill.) Hosp., 1968-71, adminstr., 1971-73, pres., 1973-86; exec. v.p Voluntary Hosps. Am., Park Ridge, Ill., 1987-89, sr. v.p., 1986-92; CEO Good Samaritan Regional Med. Ctr., Phoenix, 1992—; adj. prof. Contbr. articles to profl. jours. Mem. AHA (svc. com.), Ill. Hosp. Assn. (chair 1980-81). Home: 3930 E Rancho Dr Paradise Valley AZ 85253 Office: Good Samaritan Regional Med Ctr 1111 E McDowell Rd Phoenix AZ 85062

SEILHAMER, RAY A., academic administrator. Head Evang. Sch. Theology, Myerstown, Pa. Office: Evang Sch Theol 121 S College St Myerstown PA 17067-1299

SEILHAMER, RAY A., bishop. Bishop United Brethren in Christ. Office: United Brethren in Christ 302 Lake St Huntington IN 46750

SEILS, WILLIAM GEORGE, lawyer; b. Chgo., Aug. 9, 1935; s. Harry H. and Hazel C. (Sullivan) S.; m. Evelyn E. Oliver, Sept. 8, 1956; children: Elizabeth Ann, Ellen Carol, Eileen Alison. A.B., J.D., U. Mich., 1959. Bar: Ill. bar 1959. Since practiced in Chgo.; ptnr. Arvey, Hodes & Costello & Burman, 1968-87; gen. counsel, sec., sr. v.p. Richardson Electronics, Ltd., LaFox, Ill., 1986—. Contbr. articles to profl. jours.; asst. editor: Mich. Law Rev, 1958-59. Mem. Ill. Bar Assn., Order of Coif. Office: Richardson Electronics Ltd 40w267 Keslinger Rd Lafox IL 60147

SEINFELD, JERRY, comedian; b. Bklyn., Apr. 29, 1955; s. Kal and Betty S. Grad. with degree in theatre communications, Queens (N.Y.) Coll., 1976. Former salesman. Stand-up comedian, 1976—; joke-writer (TV series) Benson, ABC, 1980; actor, co-writer, prod. (TV series) Seinfeld, NBC-TV, 1989— (Emmy award Outstanding Comedy Series, 1993, Emmy nomination, Lead Actor - Comedy Series, 1994); writer Jerry Seinfeld-Stand-Up Confidential, 1987; author: Sein Language, 1993. Recipient Am. Comedy award funniest male comedy stand-up, 1988, funniest actor in a TV series, 1992. Jewish. Avocations: Zen, yoga. Office: care Lori Jonas Pub Rels 417 S Beverly Dr Ste 201 Beverly Hills CA 90212-4401*

SEINFELD, JOHN HERSH, chemical engineering educator; b. Elmira, N.Y., Aug. 3, 1942; s. Ben B. and Minna (Johnson) S. BS, U. Rochester, 1964; PhD, Princeton U., 1967. Asst. prof. chem. engring. Calif. Inst. Tech., Pasadena, 1967-70, assoc. prof., 1970-74, prof., 1974—, Louis E. Nohl prof., 1980—, exec. officer for chem. engring., 1973-90, chmn. engring. and applied sci. div., 1990—; Allan P. Colburn meml. lectr. U. Del., 1976; Camille and Henry Dreyfus Found. lectr. MIT, 1979; mem. coun. Gordon Rsch. Confs., 1980-83; Donald L. Katz lectr. U. Mich., 1981; Reilly lectr. U. Notre Dame, 1983; Dean's Disting. lectr. U. Rochester, 1985; Katz lectr. CUNY, 1985; McCabe lectr. N.C. State U., 1986; Lewis lectr. MIT, 1986; Union Carbide lectr. SUNY, Buffalo; Van Winkle lectr. U. Tex., 1988; Bicentennial lectr. La. State U., 1988; Ida Beam lectr. U. Iowa, 1989, David Mason lectr. Stanford U., 1989; Julian Smith lectr. Cornell U., 1990; Merck lectr. Rutgers U., 1991; Henske Disting. lectr. Yale U., 1991; mem. sci. adv. bd. EPA; lectr. Am. Inst. Chem. Engrs., 1980; Centennial lectr. U. Pa., 1993; Miles Disting. lectr. U. Pitts., 1994. Author: Numerical Solution of Ordinary Differential Equations, 1971, Mathematical Methods in Chemical Engineering, Vol. III, Process Modeling, Estimation and Identification, 1974, Air Pollution: Physical and Chemical Fundamentals, 1975, Lectures in Atmospheric Chemistry, 1980, Atmospheric Chemistry and Physics of Air Pollution, 1986, Fundamentals of Air Pollution Engineering, 1988, Distributed Parameter Systems - Theory and Applications, 1989; assoc. editor Environ. Sci., Tech., 1981—; mem. editorial bd. Computers, Chem. Engring, 1974—, Jour. Colloid and Interface Sci, 1978—, Advances in Chem. Engring, 1980—, Revs. in Chem. Engring, 1980—, Aerosol Sci. and Tech., 1981—, Large Scale Systems, 1982—; assoc. editor: Atmospheric Environment, 1976—. Recipient Donald P. Eckman award Am. Automatic Control Coun., 1970, Pub. Svc. medal NASA, 1980, Disting. Alumnus award U. Rochester, 1989; Camille and Henry Dreyfus Found. Tchr. Scholar grantee, 1972. Fellow Japan Soc. Promotion Sci.; mem. AICE (bd. dirs. 1988-91, mem. editl. bd. jour. 1985—, Allan P. Colburn award 1976, William H. Walker award 1986), NAE, Am. Soc. Engring. Edn. (Curtis W. McGraw Rsch. award 1976, George Westinghouse award 1987), Am. Aerosol Rsch. (bd. dirs. 1983—, v.p. 1988-90, pres. 1990-92), Am. Acad. Arts and Scis., Air Waste Mgmt. Assn., Am. Chem. Soc. (Svc. through Chemistry award 1988, Creative Advances in Environ. Sci. and Tech. award 1993), Sigma Xi, Tau Beta Pi. Home: 363 Patrician Way Pasadena CA 91105-1027 Office: Calif Inst Tech Div Engring and Applied Sci Pasadena CA 91125

SEIP, TOM DECKER, securities executive; b. St. Louis, Feb. 15, 1950; s. Norman Walter and Margaret Ann (Decker) S.; m. Linda Shinabarger, Sept. 1976 (div. 1987); children: Parker, Jared; m. Alexa Clay Giddings, Mar. 24, 1990. BA in Psychology, Pa. State U., 1972; postgrad., U. Mich., 1972-74. Regional human resources mgr. Merrill, Lynch, Pierce Fenner and Smith, Inc., N.Y.C., San Francisco, 1975-77; v.p., ptnr. Korn/Ferry Internat., Palo Alto, Calif., 1977-83; v.p. human resources Charles Schwag & Co., Inc., San Francisco, 1983-85; sr. v.p. nat. sales programs Charles Schwab & Co., Inc., San Francisco, 1985-86, sr. v.p. regulatory bus., 1986-88, sr. v.p. ea. div., 1988-91; pres., COO Charles Schwab Investment Mgmt., Inc., San Francisco, 1991—; exec. v.p. The Charles Schwab Corp., San Francisco, 1992—; dir. Ridgefield Devel. Corp., Erie, Pa. Avocation: sailing. Office: Charles Schwab & Co Inc 101 Montgomery St San Francisco CA 94104

SEIPLE, ROBERT ALLEN, Christian relief organization executive; b. Harmony, N.J., Dec. 6, 1942; s. Chris and Gertrude (Crozier) S.; m. Margaret Ann Goebel, May 14, 1965; children: Chris, Amy, Jesse. AB, Brown U., 1965; LHD (hon.), Alderson-Broaddus, 1986, Sioux Falls Coll., 1986, Azusa Pacific U., 1993. Sales rep. Boise Cascade, Mich., 1969-71; dir. athletics Brown U., Providence, 1972-79, v.p. devel., 1979-83; pres. Eastern Coll. and Eastern Bapt. Theol. Sem., St. Davids, Pa., 1983-87, World Vision, Inc., Monrovia, Calif., 1987—; bd. dirs. Stop Cancer, One to One Found.; bd. advisors World Impact, Young Life-Urban Phila., Opportunity Internat. Contbr. articles to mags. Capt. USMC, 1966-69. Decorated D.F.C., 28 Air medals, Vietnam Campaign medal with battle stars; recipient Navy Commendation award. Republican. Baptist. Avocations: deer hunting, trout fishing. Office: World Vision Inc 919 W Huntington Dr Monrovia CA 91016-3111

SEIPPEL, THOMAS J., insurance executive. Pres. Am. Internat. Group Data Ctr. Inc., N.Y.C., also bd. dirs.; v.p. Am. Internat. Group Inc., N.Y.C.; sr. v.p. Commerce and Industry Ins. Co., N.Y.C. Office: Am Internat Group Inc 70 Pine St New York NY 10270-0001

SEIREG, ALI A(BDEL HAY), mechanical engineer; b. Arab Republic of Egypt, Oct. 26, 1927; came to U.S., 1951, naturalized, 1960; s. Abdel Hay and Aisha Seireg; m. Shirley Marachowsky, Dec. 24, 1954; children: Mirette Elizabeth LaFollette, Pamela Aisha. B.Sc. M.E., U. Cairo, 1948; Ph.D., U. Wis., 1954. Lectr. Cairo U., 1954-56; staff adv. engr. Falk Corp., Milw., 1956-59; assoc. prof. theoretical and applied mechanics Marquette U., 1959-64, prof., 1964-65; prof. (Kaiser chair) mech. engring. U. Wis., Madison, 1965—; Ebaugh Prof. U. Fla., Gainesville, 1986—; cons. industry, ednl. and govt. agys.; chmn. U.S. council Internat. Fedn. Theory of Machines, 1974—; co-chmn. 5th World Congress of Theory of Machines, 1979, 1st USSR-USA Conf. on Composite Materials, 1989. Author: Mechanical Systems Analysis, 1969, Biomedical Analysis of Musculoskeletal Structure for Medicine and Sports, 1989; editor Computers in Mechanical Engineering; editor in chief SOMA, Engineering for the Human Body, 1986-90; contbr. numerous articles to profl. jours. Recipient Kuwait prize for sci., 1987. Fellow ASME (Richards Meml. award 1973, Machine Design award 1978, Design Automation award 1990, chmn. div. design engring. 1977-78, chmn. computer tech. 1978-81, mem. policy bd. communications 1978-80, mem. policy bd. gen. engring. 1979-80, chmn. Century II Internat. Computer Tech. Conf. 1980, founding chmn. computer engring. div. 1980-81, v.p. systems and design 1981-85, sr. v.p., chmn. council on engring. 1985-90, pres. Gen. Research Inst. 1984—), Am. Soc. Engring. Edn. (George Westinghouse award 1970), Soc. Exptl. Stress Analysis, Am. Inst. Med. and Biol. Engring. (founding fellow), Am. Gear Mfg. Assn. (E. P. Connell award 1974), Automation Research Council; mem. Chinese Mech. Engring. Soc. (hon.), USSR Acad. Sci. (fgn.), Russian Acad. Sci. (fgn.). Home: 2670 SW 14th Dr Gainesville FL 32608-2049 Office: 1513 University Ave Madison WI 53706-1572 *I have always tried my best to look beyond what I hear, to think beyond what I see, to give more than I receive, and to do good as its own reward.*

SEITA, YUKIFUSA, electronics executive; b. 1944. Grad., Keio U., Tokyo, 1968. With Isuzu Motors, Tokyo, 1968-74, Pioneer Electronic Corp., Tokyo, 1974-79, Pioneer Europe, Brussels, 1979-84, Pioneer Electronic Corp., Tokyo, 1984-90; exec. v.p., COO Pioneer N.Am. Inc., Long Beach, Calif., 1990—. Mem. Laserdisc Fan Club, Inc. (pres. 1994—). Office: Pioneer North America Inc 2265 E 220th St Long Beach CA 90810

SEITEL, FRASER PAUL, public relations executive; b. Jersey City, June 6, 1946; s. Robert and Helen (Barmad) S.; m. Rosemary Kierstein, Dec. 20, 1969; children: Raina, David. BJ, U. Mo., 1964; MA, U. N.D., 1970; MBA, NYU, 1977. Pub. rels. officer Chase Manhattan Bank, N.Y.C., 1970-73, v.p., 1974-85, sr. v.p. dir. pub. affairs, 1985-92; mng. ptnr. Emerald Ptnrs., Ft. Lee, N.J., 1992—; sr. counselor Burson Marsteller, N.Y.C., 1992—; sr. counselor investor rels. and mktg. communications Greater N.Y. Savs. Bank, 1994—; pub. rels. cons. Hill and Knowlton, N.Y.C., 1973; instr. Profl. Devel. Inst., N.Y.C., Ragan Communications, Chgo., Estes Park Inst., Colo. Author: The Practice of Public Relations, 6th edit., 1995; pub. The Public Relations Strategist, 1995—; columnist U.S. Banker, 1989-94, Profil Mag., 1993—; columns editor PRSA Tactics mag., 1994—. Col. USAR, 1969-76. Mem. Pub. Rels. Soc. Am., Bank Mktg. Assn. Avocations: baseball, football, basketball, tai chi, rugby. Home: 12 King Pl Closter NJ 07624-2936 Office: 177 Main St Ste 215 Fort Lee NJ 07024-6936

SEITZ, CHARLES LEWIS, computer scientist and engineer; b. Phila., Jan. 1, 1943; s. Philip Franz Durham and Elaine Marie (Good) S.; m. Jean Marie Austin, July 5, 1963 (div. 1981); children: Elizabeth, Russell. BSEE, MIT, 1965, MS, 1967, PhD, 1971. Asst. prof. computer sci. U. Utah, Salt Lake City, 1970-72; cons. Burroughs Corp., LaJolla, Calif., 1971-78; prof. computer sci. Calif. Inst. Tech., Pasadena, Calif., 1977-94; pres. Myricom, Inc., Arcadia, Calif., 1994—; cons. Strategic Def. Initiative Orgn., Washington, 1985-87; panelist U.S. Congress Office Tech. Assessment, Washington, 1986-87; mem. Computer Sci. and Telecomms. Bd., NRC, 1992—. Contbr. articles to profl. jours; patentee in field. Recipient Goodwin medal MIT, 1968, Leonard G. Abraham award IEEE, 1971, Cert. Appreciation, City Oceanside, Calif., 1984. Mem. NAE, Assn. Computing Machinery, Sigma Xi. Avocations: aerobic flying, hiking. Office: Myricom Inc 325 N Santa Anita Ave Arcadia CA 91006

SEITZ, COLLINS JACQUES, federal judge; b. Wilmington, Del., June 20, 1914; s. George Hilary and Margaret Jane (Collins) S.; m. Virginia Anne Day; children: Virginia Anne, Collins Jacques, Mark, Stephen. A.B., U. Del., 1937, LL.D., 1962; LL.B., U. Va., 1940; LL.D., Widener Coll., 1975, Villanova U. Sch. Law, 1983, Cath. U., 1985, Dickinson Sch. of Law, 1988. Bar: Del. 1940. Vice chancellor Del., 1946; chancellor, 1951-66; judge U.S. Ct. Appeals, 3d Circuit, 1966—, chief judge, 1971-84. Recipient James J. Hoey award, 1954, award NCCJ, 1957, Pro Ecclesia et Pontifice (papal award), 1965, award in law Thomas Jefferson Meml. Found., 1990. Mem. Am., Del. bar assns. Democrat. Roman Catholic. Club: Wilmington. Office: US Ct Appeals 844 N King St Ste 32 Wilmington DE 19801-3519*

SEITZ, FREDERICK, university president emeritus; b. San Francisco, July 4, 1911; s. Frederick and Emily Charlotte (Hofman) S.; m. Elizabeth K. Marshall, May 18, 1935. AB, Leland Stanford Jr. U., 1932; PhD, Princeton U., 1934; Doctorate Hon. Causa, U. Ghent, 1957; DSc (hon.), U. Reading, 1960, Rensselaer Poly. Inst., 1961, Marquette U., 1963, Carnegie Inst. Tech., 1963, Case Inst. Tech., 1964, Princeton U., 1964, Northwestern U., 1965, Poly. Inst. Bklyn., 1967, U. Mich., 1967, U. Utah, 1968, Brown U., 1968, Duquesne U., 1968, St. Louis U., 1969, Nebr. Wesleyan U., 1970, U. Ill., 1972, Rockefeller U., 1981; LLD (hon.), Lehigh U., 1966, U. Notre Dame, 1962, Mich. State U., 1965, Ill. Inst. Tech., 1968, N.Y. U., 1969; LHD (hon.), Davis and Elkins Coll., 1970, Rockefeller U., 1981, U. Pa., 1985, U. Miami, 1989. Instr. physics U. Rochester, 1935-36, asst. prof., 1936-37; physicist research labs. Gen. Electric Co., 1937-39; asst. prof. Randal Morgan Lab. Physics, U. Pa., 1939-41, assoc. prof., 1941-42; prof. physics, head dept. Carnegie Inst. Tech., Pitts., 1942-49; prof. physics U. Ill., 1949-57, head dept., 1957-64, dir. control systems lab., 1951-52, dean Grad. Coll., v.p. research, 1964-65; exec. pres. Nat. Acad. Scis., 1962-69; pres. Rockefeller U., N.Y.C., 1968-78; U. Miami (Fla.), 1989; trustee Ogden Corp., 1977—; dir. tng. program Clinton Labs., Oak Ridge, 1946-47; chmn. Naval Rsch. Adv. Com., 1960-62; vice chmn. Def. Sci. Bd., 1961-63, chmn., 1964-68; sci. adviser NATO, 1959-60; mem. nat. adv. com. Marine Biomed. Inst. U. Tex., Galveston, 1975-77; mem. adv. group White House Conf. Anticipated Advances in Sci. and Tech., 1975-76; mem. adv. bd. Desert Rsch. Inst., 1975-79, Ctr. Strategic and Internat. Studies, 1975-81; mem. Nat. Cancer Adv. Bd., 1976-82; dir. Akzona Inc. Author: Modern Theory of Solids, 1940, The Physics of Metals, 1943, Solid State Physics, 1955, The Science Matrix, 1992, On the Frontier: My Life in Science, 1994. Trustee Rockefeller Found., 1964-77, Princeton U., 1968-72, Lehigh U., 1970-81, Rsch. Corp., 1966-82, Inst. Internat. Edn., 1971-78, Woodrow Wilson Nat. Fellowship Found., 1972-82, Univ. Corp. Atmospheric Rsch., Am. Mus. Natural History, 1975—; trustee John Simon Guggenheim Meml. Found., 1973-83, chmn. bd., 1976-83; mem. Belgian Am. Edn. Found.; bd. dirs. Richard Lounsbery Found., 1980—. Decorated Order of the Brilliant Star (Republic of China); recipient Franklin medal Franklin Inst. Phila., 1965, Hoover medal Stanford U., 1968, Nat. Medal Sci., 1973, James Madison award Princeton U., 1978, Edward R. Loveland Meml. award ACP, 1983, Vannevar Bush award Nat. Sci. Bd., 1983, J. Herbert Holloman award Acta Metallurgica, 1993, Von Hippel award Materials Rsch. Soc., 1993. Fellow Am. Phys. Soc. (pres. 1961); mem. NAS, Am. Acad. Arts and Scis., AIME, Am. Philos. Soc., Am. Inst. Physics (chmn. governing bd. 1954-59), Inst. for Def. Analysis, Finnish Acad. Sci. and Letters (fgn. mem.), Phi Beta Kappa Assos. Address: Rockefeller U 1230 York Ave New York NY 10021-6341

SEITZ, HAROLD A., supermarket executive; b. 1938. Ba, Notre Dame U., 1960. With Jewel Cos., 1960-75; sr. v.p. Loblaw Cos. Ltd., Toronto, Can., 1975-85, Nat. Tea Co., New Orleans, 1985-88; pres. Nat. Tea Co., Hazelwood, Mo., 1989—. Office: Nat Tea Co 6050 N Lindbergh Blvd Hazelwood MO 63042-2804

SEITZ, KARL RAYMOND, editor; b. Corpus Christi, Tex., Sept. 26, 1943; s. Kerlin McCullough and Martha Elizabeth (Tillman) S.; m. Patricia Jean Floyd, June 13, 1970; 1 child, Lee Kerlin. BA, Birmingham So. Coll., 1970. Copy editor Birmingham (Ala.) Post-Herald, 1967-70, asst. news editor, 1970-73, chief editorial writer, 1973-78, editor editorial page, 1978—; dir. Birmingham Post-Birmingham Typographical Union Pension Plan, 1983-90, chmn., 1986-90; dir. Goodfellow Fund, Inc., Birmingham, 1983—, v.p., 1986—. Active Exec. in Resident Birmingham So. Coll., 1987, Leadership Birmingham, 1986; mem. Leadership Birmingham Alumni Assn., 1986—. With USN, 1961-64. Mem. Am. Acad. Polit. and Social Sci., Nat. Conf. Editorial Writers, Acad. Polit. Sci. Home: 1308 Roseland Dr Birmingham AL 35209-3930 Office: Birmingham Post Herald PO Box 2553 Birmingham AL 35202-2553

SEITZ, MELVIN CHRISTIAN, JR., distributing company executive; b. Indpls., Aug. 9, 1939; s. Melvin Christian and Francis Sue (Lee) S.; m. Bette Louise Pierson, May 5, 1941; children: David, Mark, Keith, Cindy. Student Butler U., 1957-60. Salesman, Service Supply Co., Inc., Indpls., 1963-71, sec.-treas., 1971-74, v.p., 1974-81, exec. vp., 1981-83, pres., 1983-94, COO, 1995. Active Met. Devel. Commn. Indpls., 1994—. Served with U.S. Army. Mem. Nat. Fastener Distributor Assn. (bd. dirs.), Cole Roster (bd. dirs.), Sigma Nu. Republican. Mem. Disciples of Christ. Lodges: Masons, Shriners, Scottish Rite. Home: 4716 Northeastern Ave Indianapolis IN 46239-1665 Office: Svc Supply Co Inc Ind 603 E Washington St Indianapolis IN 46204-2693

SEITZ, NICHOLAS JOSEPH, magazine editor; b. Topeka, Kans., Jan. 30, 1939; s. Frank Joseph and Lydia Natalie (Clerico) S.; m. Velma Jean Pfannenstiel, Sept. 12, 1959; children: Bradley Joseph, Gregory Joseph. BA, U. Okla., 1966. Sports editor Manhattan (Kans.) Mercury, 1960-62, Norman (Okla.) Transcript, 1962-64, Okla. Jour., Oklahoma City, 1964-67; mem. staff Golf Digest mag., Norwalk, Conn., 1967—; editor Golf Digest mag., 1973-82; editorial dir. Golf Digest and Tennis, 1982-90; editorial dir. Sports/Leisure div. N.Y. Times Co. Mag. Group, 1991-92, sr. v.p., editor in chief, 1992—; syndicated golf instrn. and commentary CBS Radio Network; commentary ESPN TV Network. Author: Superstars of Golf, 1978, (with Dave Hill) Teed Off, 1977, (with Tom Watson) Getting Up and Down, 1983, Getting Back to Basics, 1991, Tom Watson's Strategic Golf, 1993; contbr. articles to profl. jours; anthologized in: Best Sports Stories. Named Okla. Sports Writer of Year Nat. Sportswriters and Sportscasters Assn., 1965; winner contests Nat. Basketball Writers Assn.; winner contests Golf Writers Assn.; recipient Lincoln A. Werden award for outstanding contbn. to golf journalism, 1993. Home: 36 Hunt St Norwalk CT 06853-1015 Office: 5520 Park Ave Trumbull CT 06611-3400

SEITZ, PATRICIA ANN, lawyer; b. Washington, Sept. 2, 1946; d. Richard J. and Bettie Jean (Merrill) S.; m. Alan Graham Greer, Aug. 14, 1981. BA in History cum laude, Kans. State U., 1968; JD, Georgetown U., 1973. Bar: Fla. 1973, D.C. 1975, U.S. Dist. Ct. (no., mid., so. dists., trial bar) Fla., U.S. Ct. Appeals (5th and eleventh cir.), U.S. Supreme Ct. Reporter Dallas Times Herald, Washington, 1970-73; law clk. U.S. Dist. Ct., Washington, 1973-74; assoc. Steel, Hector & Davis, Miami, Fla., 1974-79, ptnr., 1980—; adj. faculty U. Miami Law Sch., Coral Gables, Fla., 1984-88; faculty Nat. Inst. Trial Advocacy, Boulder, Colo., 1982, 83, Chapel Hill, N.C., 1984, 87, Fla. region, 1989; lectr. in field. Contbr. numerous articles to law jours. Mem. Dade Munroe Mental Health Bd., Miami, 1982-84, United Way of Greater Miami comty. devel. com., 1984-87; chmn. family abuse task force United Way of Greater Miami, 1986; chmn. devel. com. Miami City Ballet, 1986-87, bd. dirs., 1986-90. Fellow Am. Bar Found., Internat. Soc. Barristers; mem. ABA (chmn. various coms. 1979-82), Fla. Bar (bd. govs. young lawyer div. 1981-82, bd. govs. 1986-92, pres. 1993-94), Fla. Assn. Women Lawyers, Fla. Acad. Trial Lawyers, Dade County Bar Assn. (pub. interest law bank). Democrat. Roman Catholic. Avocations: travel, art. Home: 224 Ridgewood Rd Miami FL 33133-6614 Office: Steel Hector & Davis Ste 4000 200 S Biscayne Blvd Miami FL 33131-2313

SEITZ, TIM, church administrator. Pres. Luth. Youth Orgn. Evang. Luth. Ch. Am. Office: Evang Luthern Ch in Am 8765 W Higgins Rd Chicago IL 60631-4101

SEITZ, WALTER STANLEY, cardiovascular research consultant; b. L.A., May 10, 1937; s. Walter and Frances Janette (Schleef) S. BS in Physics and Math., U. Calif., Berkeley, 1959; PhD in Biophysics, U. Vienna, 1981, MD, 1982. Health physicist U. Calif. Radiation Lab., 1959-61; rsch. assoc. NIH at Pacific Union Coll., 1961-63; physicist Lockheed Rsch. Labs., Palo Alto, Calif., 1961-63; staff scientist Xerox Corp., Pasadena, Calif., 1963-66; sr. scientist Applied Physics Cons., Palo Alto, 1966-75; instr. clin. sci. U. Ill Coll. Medicine, Urbana, 1983-84; cons. cardiology Cardiovascular Rsch. Inst. U. Calif. Sch. Medicine, San Francisco, 1987—; sr. scientist Inst. Med. Analysis and Rsch., Berkeley, 1987—. Contbr. articles to profl. jours. Postdoctoral Rsch. fellow, U. Calif. San Francisco, 1984. Fellow Am. Coll. Angiography; mem. AAAS, Royal Soc. Medicine London, N.Y. Acad. Scis., Physicians for Social Responsibility. Avocations: reading, music, hiking. Office: IMAR Cons Inc 38 Panoramic Way Berkeley CA 94704

SEITZ, WESLEY DONALD, agricultural economics educator; b. Wapakoneta, Ohio, Sept. 29, 1940; s. Donald Otto and Irene Katherine (Greubmeyer) S.; m. Janice Ann Parker, June 21, 1964; children: Kimberly, Matthew. BS, Ohio State U., 1962, MS, 1964; PhD, U. Calif., Berkeley, 1968. Asst. specialist, instr. U. Calif., Berkeley, 1967-68; asst. prof. bus. adminstrn. and agrl. econs. U. Ill., Urbana, 1968-72, assoc. prof. agrl. econs., 1972-74, assoc. prof. Inst. Environ. Studies, 1974-79, asst. head agrl. econs., 1979-81, head agrl. econs., 1981-87, prof. agrl. econs., 1987-92, assoc. head agrl. econs., 1992—; com. chmn. Nat. Acad. Sci., Washington, 1979-80, commn. mem., 1980, 85-86; cons. Dept. Interior, Ft. Collins, Colo., 1976; mem. Agrl. Task Force III. EPA, Springfield, 1978-80. Co-editor: Natural Resource Jour., vol. 15, no. 4, 1975; chmn.: Surface Mining: Soil, Coal and Society, 1981; contbr. chpts. to books. Bd. dirs. Univ. YMCA, Urbana, 1974-77; mem. adminstrv. com. Wesley Methodist Ch., 1981—. Served with USAFR, 1962-67. Recipient Disting. Service award Univ. YMCA, Urbana, 1980. Mem. Am. Agrl. Econs. Assn. (chmn. spl. pubis. com.), Soil Conservation Soc. Am. (dir. Ill. chpt. 1980-82), North Central Research Strategy Com. (chmn. 1973-74), Am. Econs. Assn., Assn. Environ. and Resource Economists, Sigma Xi, Gamma Sigma Delta, Phi Kappa Phi (pres. Ill. chpt. 1989-90, chair Resource policy consortium). Home: 4014 Pinecrest Dr Champaign IL 61821-9216 Office: Dept Agrl Economics U Ill 1301 W Gregory Dr Urbana IL 61801-3608

SEIZINGER, BERND ROBERT, molecular geneticist, physician, researcher; b. Munich, Germany, Dec. 27, 1956; came to U.S., 1984; s. August and Mathilde (Haselbeck) S. MD, Ludwig-Maximilians U. Med. Sch., Munich, Germany, 1983; PhD summa cum laude, Max-Planck Inst., Munich, Germany, 1984. Postdoctoral rsch. assoc. Harvard Med. Sch., Boston, 1984-86, instr. neurology, 1986-88, asst. prof., 1988-90, assoc. prof. neuroscience, 1990—; dir. molecular neuro-oncology lab. Mass. Gen. Hosp., Boston, 1989-92, assoc. geneticist, 1990—; v.p. oncology drug discovery Bristol-Myers Squibb Pharm. Rsch. Inst., Princeton, N.J., 1992—; dir. dept. molecular genetics and cell biology, 1992—; co-chmn. Internat. Consortium on Neurofibromatosis, N.Y.C., 1988—; chmn. Comm. on Gene Loss in Human Cancers Intern Human Gene Mapping Conf., Oxford, 1991, Rsch. Adv. Bd. Nat. Neurofibromatosis Found., N.Y.C., 1991—, co-chmn. 1993—; vis. rsch. scientist, assoc. mem. faculty Princeton (N.J.) U., 1993—. Recipient Otto Hahn Medal Max Planck Soc., Munich, Germany, 1983, Jr. Investigators award Nat. Neurofibromatosis Found., N.Y.C., 1985, Wilson S. Stone Meml. award Cancer Rsch., 1987, Rsch. Faculty Scholar award Am. Cancer Soc., Atlanta, 1989. Mem. Nat. Neurofibromatosis Found. (Von Recklinghausen award, 1992), Am. Soc. Human Genetics, Am. Assn. Cancer Rsch. Achievements include discovery of fundamental genetic mechanisms of tumor formation in the human nervous system, chromosomal location of the tumor suppressor genes causing neurofibromatosis type I and II, and von Hippel-Lindau disease; co-discovery of gene for neurofibromatosis type II. Office: Bristol-Myers Squibb Pharm Rsch Inst PO Box 4000 Princeton NJ 08543-4000

SEKANINA, ZDENEK, astronomer; b. Mlada Boleslav, Czechoslovakia, June 12, 1936; came to U.S., 1969; s. Frantisek Sekanina and Hedvika (Kolarikova) Sekaninova; m. Jana Soukupova, Apr. 1, 1966; 1 child, Jason. Diploma, Charles U., Prague, Czechoslovakia, 1959, PhD in Astronomy, 1963. Astronomer Stefanik Obs., Prague, 1959-66, Ctr. for Numerical Math., Charles U., Prague, 1967-68; vis. scientist Inst. d'Astrophysique, Univ. de Liege, Cointe-Ougree, Belgium, 1968-69; physicist Smithsonian Astrophys. Obs., Cambridge, Mass., 1969-80; mem. tech. staff Jet Propulsion Lab., Pasadena, Calif., 1980-81, rsch. scientist, 1981-84, sr. rsch. scientist, 1984—; assoc. Harvard Coll. Obs., Cambridge, 1969-80; mem. NASA Comet Sci. Working Group, 1977-80; cons. Jet Propulsion Lab., 1977-80; prin. U.S. co-investigator Particulate Impact Analyzer Experiment, Dust Impact Detector Sys. Experiment, European Space Agy.'s Giotto Mission to Comet Halley, 1980-89, STARDUST Discovery Mission, 1994—; mem. NASA-European Spacy Agy. Comet Halley Environ. Working Group, 1980-89; discipline specialist Near Nucleus Studies Network, Internat. Halley Watch, 1982-90; mem. imaging sci. subsys. team Comet Rendezvous Asteroid Flyby Mission, 1986-92; mem. sci. definition team ESA/NASA Comet Nucleus Sample Return Mission, 1988—. Editor Comet Halley Archive, 1982-91; mem. editorial bd. Kosmicke Rozhledy, 1963-69. Recipient Exceptional Sci. Achievement medal NASA, 1985; minor planet named Sekanina, 1976. Mem. Internat. Astron. Union (mem. commns. 15, 10, 22, mem. organizing commn. 22 1976-82, organizing commn. 15 1979-85, mem. working group on comets 1988—, assoc. dir. Ctrl. Bur. for Astron. Telegrams 1970-80), COSPAR (working group 3, panel C, exec. mem. 1980-82). Roman Catholic. Office: Jet Propulsion Lab 4800 Oak Grove Dr Pasadena CA 91109-8001

SEKELY, GEORGE FRANK, computer and communications executive; b. Budapest, Hungary, Mar. 22, 1931; came to Can., 1956; s. Alfred and Vilma (Polak) Szekely; m. Veronique M. Dezseny, Apr. 23, 1955; children—Robert F., Sandra M. Diploma civil engring., Tech. U. of Budapest, 1953. Registered profl. engr., Ont., Can. Design engr. Dept. Constrn., Budapest, 1953-56; chief engr. A.M. Lount and Assocs., Toronto, Ont., Can., 1957-59; various mgmt. positions IBM Can., Toronto, 1959-64; mgr. systems engring. tech. programs IBM World Trade, N.Y.C., 1964-69; br. mgr. IBM Can., Montreal, Que., 1969-71; gen. mgr. C&S, Montreal, 1971-72; v.p. computers and communications Can. Pacific Limited, Toronto, 1972-92; pres. CSX Tech., Jacksonville, Fla., 1992—; sr. v.p. CSX Transp., Jacksonville, 1992—; program chmn., sec. Can. Info. Processing Soc., Montreal, 1973-75. Contbr. articles to profl. jours. Home and sch. exec. PTA, Montreal, 1969-71; cub scout exec. Boy Scouts Can., Montreal, 1971-72. Mem. Assn. Profl. Engrs. of Ont., Assn. Am. Railroads (exec. com., chmn. gen. com. data systems divsn. 1976-81), Senneville Yacht Club (commodore 1978-80), Epping Forest Yacht Club, River Club. Avocations: sailing, reading, music. Office: CSX Tech 500 Water St Jacksonville FL 32202

SEKERKA, ROBERT FLOYD, physics educator, scientist; b. Wilkinsburg, Pa., Nov. 27, 1937; s. John Jacob and Vivian Mae (Smith) S.; m. Dianne Thompson, Apr. 30, 1960 (div. Apr. 1981); children: Lee Ann, Robert Thompson; m. 2d Carolyn Lee Confer, May 24, 1981. B.S. in Physics, U. Pitts., 1960; A.M., Harvard U., 1961, Ph.D., 1965. Engr. Westinghouse Research Labs., Pitts., 1965-68, mgr. materials growth and properties dept., 1968-69; lectr. Carnegie-Mellon U., Pitts., 1967-69, assoc. prof., 1969-72, prof. metallurgy and materials sci., 1972-82, dept. head, 1976-82, prof. physics and math., dean Mellon Coll. Sci., 1982-91; Univ. Prof. Carnegie Mellon U., Pitts., 1991—; mem. space studies bd. NRC, 1989-91. Assoc. editor Jour. Crystal Growth, 1971-94; Metallurgical Trans., 1970-76; editorial bd. Applied Microgravity Tech., 1987-90. Past bd. dirs. Forbes Health System, Pitts.; past vice chmn. bd. dirs. NMR Inst.; past mem. rsch. com. Allegheny Singer Rsch. Inst., Pitts.; past bd. dirs. Pitts. Regional Ctr. for Sci. Tchrs. Recipient A.G. Worthing award U. Pitts. 1959; Woodrow Wilson fellow, 1960; NSF fellow, 1962-65; recipient Philip M. McKenna Meml. award, 1980. Fellow Am. Soc. Metals; mem. The Minerals Metals Materials Soc., Am. Assn. Crystal Growth (exec. com.), Internat. Assn. Crystal Growth (co-v.p., Frank prize 1992), Edgewood Country Club, Club One, Phi Beta Kappa, Sigma Xi, Omicron Delta Kappa, Am. Physical Soc. Home: 307 S Dithridge St Apt 407 Pittsburgh PA 15213-3514 Office: Carnegie Mellon U Dept Physics 6319 Wean Hall Pittsburgh PA 15213-3890

SEKHON, KATHLEEN, state legislator; b. 1948; m. David Sekhon; 3 children. BS, U. Minn. Mem. Minn. Ho. of Reps., St. Paul, 1992—, mem. environ. and natural resources com., labor and mgmt. rels. com.; tchr. Home: 6619 189th Ln NW Anoka MN 55303-9519

SEKI, HOKEN S., lawyer; b. Phoenix, Sept. 4, 1935; s. Hozen and Satomi (Shiomasu) S.; m. Frances C. Takamoto, Sept. 12, 1964; 1 child, Chandra. BA, Columbia U., 1957; LLB, Harvard U., 1964. Bar: N.Y., Ill., Calif., U.S. Supreme Ct., U.S. Ct. Appeals, U.S. Dist. Ct. Ptnr. Baker & McKenzie, Chgo., 1973-80, Seki, Jarvis & Lynch, Chgo., 1980-87, Bell, Boyd & Lloyd, Chgo., 1987-92, Foley & Lardner, Chgo., 1992—. V.p. bd. govs. Internat. House U. Chgo.; bd. overseers Ill. Inst. Tech. Chgo.-Kent Coll. Law, pres. bd. dirs. Libr. Internat. Rels.; chmn. bd. trustees Am. Buddhist Acad., N.Y.C.; bd. dirs. Japanese Am. Nat. Mus., L.A.; sec. Chgo.-Osaka Sister Cities Com., Chgo. Mem. Japan Am. Soc. Chgo. (bd. dirs.), Execs. Club Chgo., Chgo. Coun. Fgn. Rels. (mem. Chgo. com.), World Trade Ctr. Chgo. Assn. (bd. dirs.), Harvard Club (N.Y.C.), Univ. Club (Chgo.), Union League Club (Chgo.). Republican. Office: Foley & Lardner 330 N Wabash Ave Chicago IL 60611-3608

SEKITANI, TORU, otolaryngologist, educator; b. Kochi, Japan, May 5, 1932; s. Fusaharu and Miyoko (Tokushige) S.; m. Miyoko Uejo, Dec. 26, 1960; children: Miwako, Yoshiko, Tetsuko. MD, Yamaguchi Med. Sch., 1957. Intern Yamaguchi Med. Sch. Hosp., Ube, Japan, 1957-58, instr., 1962, assoc. prof., 1971, prof., chmn. dept. otolaryngology, 1976-93; emeritus prof. Yamaguchi U. Sch. of Medicine, 1993—; dir. Nat Shimonoseki Hosp, Japan, 1993—; rsch. assoc. Univ. Iowa, Iowa City, 1969-71; head ENT clinic Yamaguchi Cen. Hosp., Hofu, Japan, 1972-74. Author: (with others) Vertigo: Basic and Clinic, 1976, Vestibular Mechanism in Health and Disease, 1978; editor: Vestibular Ganglia and Vestibular Neuronitis, 1988. Mem. Barany Soc., Prosper Meniere Soc., Otorhinolaryngological Soc. Japan, Japan Soc. Equilibrium and Rsch. (exec. com. 1975—). Office: Shimonoseki Nat Hosp, Shimonoseki 751, Japan

SEKLER, EDUARD FRANZ, architect, educator; b. Vienna, Austria, Sept. 30, 1920; came to U.S., 1955; s. Eduard Jakob and Elisabeth (Demmel) S.; m. Mary Patricia May, July 21, 1962. Dipl. Ing., Tech. U., Vienna, 1945; student, Sch. Planning and Regional Research, London, 1947; PhD., London U., 1948; A.M. (hon.), Harvard U., 1960; D Tech. Scis. (hon.), Fed. Inst. Tech., Zurich, Switzerland, 1988. Ptnr. archtl. firm Prehsler and Sekler, Vienna, 1945-95; teaching asst.; lectr. faculty architecture Tech. U., Vienna, 1945-54; vis. prof. architecture Harvard U., Cambridge, Mass., 1955-56, assoc. prof., 1956-60, prof., 1960-91, prof. emeritus, 1991—; Osgood Hooker prof. visual art, 1970-91, prof. emeritus, 1991—; coord. studies Carpenter Ctr. Visual Arts, 1962-65; dir., 1966-76, chmn. dept. visual and environ. studies, 1968-70; expert mem. internat. com. hist. monuments UNESCO, 1951-54; UNESCO advisor to planning and archaeology depts. Govt. of Nepal, 1972-94; cons. Hist. Monuments Office, Vienna, 1975, 89, 91-94; head UNESCO team for masterplan for Conservation Cultural Heritage of Kathmandu Valley, 1975; UNESCO con. masterplan for Sukothai Hist. Park, Thailand, 1978, 84. Author: Point-houses in European Housing, 1952, Wren and His Place in European Architecture, 1956, Proportion, a Measure of Order, 1965, Historic Urban Spaces I-IV, 1962-71, Proposal for the

Urbanistic Conservation of Patan Durbar Square, 1980, Jos. Hoffmann, The Architectural Work, 1982, Die Architektur und die Zeit, 1988; co-author: Kathmandu Valley, The Preservation of Physical Environment and Cultural Heritage, 2 vols., 1975, Le Corbusier at Work: The Genesis of the Carpenter Center for the Visual Arts; archtl. works include restoration ch., Leopoldsberg, nr. Vienna, urban redevel., Alt Erdberg, 1956, Austrian Cultural Inst., N.Y.C., 1962, several housing schemes, Vienna, 1948-68, Telephone Exchange, Vienna, 1970. Mem. Cambridge Arts Council, 1975-84; bd. dirs. Archtl. Heritage, Inc., 1969-75; chmn. Kathmandu Valley Preservation Trust. Decorated Cross of Honor for Scis. and Art (Austria); recipient prize for humanities City of Vienna, 1983, Inst. honors AIA, 1989, Jean Tschumi prize Internat. Union Architects, 1990, Prechtl medal Vienna Tech. U.; Guggenheim fellow, 1961-63. Fellow Am. Acad. Arts and Scis., U.S. Nat. Com. for Internat. Council of Monuments and Sites, Academia Scientiarum et Artium Europa; mem. Internat. Council Monuments and Sites, Soc. Archtl. Historians (dir. 1963-66, 70-73), Archtl. Assn. London, Austrian Chamber Architects, Royal Town Planning Inst. (hon. corr. mem. London), Signet Soc. Office: Grad Sch Design Gund Hall 48 Quincy St Cambridge MA 02138-3804

SEKULA, EDWARD JOSEPH, JR., financial executive; b. Brandonville, Pa., Sept. 2, 1937; s. Edward Joseph and Dorothy May (Fritz) S.; m. Carol Lee Helton, July 13, 1963; 1 child, David. BSBA, Pa. State U., 1961. Dep. fin. officer Aberdeen Proving Ground, Md., 1961-63; with Peat, Marwick, Mitchell & Co., N.Y.C., 1963-77; corp. cont. N.Y.C. Health & Hosp. Corp., 1977-78; dir. fin. Mt. Sinai Med. Ctr., N.Y.C., 1979-82; CFO Vis. Nurse Svc. N.Y., N.Y.C., 1982-86, Wallkill Valley Gen. Hosp., 1986-94; pres. EJ Sekula Ent. Inc.; sec.-treas. Planning Assistance Inc., N.Y.C., 1978—. Mem. parish coun. of deacons Abiding Peace Luth. Ch., 1972-89; cubmaster, com. chmn., Webelos leader Cub Scouts Am., 1974-78; scoutmaster Troop 186, Boy Scouts Am., 1978-85, asst. dist. commr.; vol. fireman Netcong Fire Co. 1, 1974—; co-treas. Lenape Valley Regional High Sch. Band Parents Assn., 1981-83; chmn. environ. commn. Borough of Netcong, 1988—, Lake Musconetcong Regional Planning Bd., 1989—. With U.S. Army, 1961-63; capt. Res. (ret.). Recipient Dist. Award of Merit, Boy Scouts Am. Mem. AICPA, Hosp. Fin. Mgmt. Assn., Home Care Assn., N.Y. Soc. CPAs, Musconetcong Club, Beta Alpha Psi, Phi Kappa Tau. Republican. Lutheran. Fishing, Trout Unltd., Rotary (Paul Harris fellow). Home: 39 Amendola Dr Netcong NJ 07857-1401

SEKULER, ROBERT WILLIAM, psychology educator, scientist; b. Elizabeth, N.J., May 7, 1939; s. Sidney and Mary (Siegel) S.; m. Susan Pamela Nemser, June 25, 1961; children: Stacia, Allison, Erica. A.B., Brandeis U., 1960; Sc.M., Brown U., 1963, Ph.D., 1964; postgrad. (NIH postdoctoral fellow), M.I.T., 1964-65. Prof. psychology Northwestern U., Evanston, Ill., 1973-89, chmn. dept., 1975-79, prof. ophthalmology Med. Sch., 1978-89, prof. neurobiology and physiology, 1982-89, assoc. dean Coll. Arts and Scis., 1985-89, John Evans prof. neurosci., 1986-89; v.p. Optronix, Inc., 1980-82; provost, dean of faculty Brandeis U., Waltham, Mass., 1989-91, Louis and Frances Salvage prof. psychology, 1989—; mem. Ctr. for Study Complex Systems, 1990—; rsch. prof. biomed. engring. Boston U., 1992—; adj. cognitive and neural systems Boston U., 1994—; cons. NSF, NIH, AAAS, USAF, U. Calif, Am. Psychol. Assn.; chmn. NRC-Nat. Acad. Sci. Vision Com.; chmn. NRC Working Group on Visual Function and Aging; chmn. NRC Working Group on Aging Workers and Visual Impairment. Author: (with D. Kline and K. Dismukes) Aging and Human Visual Function, 1981, (with R. Blake) Perception, 1985, 2d edit., 1990, 3rd edit., 1994; editor: Perception & Psychophysics, 1971-86, Jour. Exptl. Psychology, 1973-74, Vision Research Jour., 1974-79, 80-92, Optics Letters, 1977-79, Am. Jour. Psychology, 1979-81, Sensory Processes, 1979-81, Ophthalmic and Physiological Optics, 1986—, Intelligent Systems, 1986-92, Psychology and Aging, 1987-92; contbr. other sci. jours. Grantee Nat. Inst. Neurol. Diseases and Stroke, USAF, NSF, Nat. Eye Inst., Nat. Inst. Aging, USN, James McDonnell Found. Fellow AAAS, Optical Soc. Am., Am. Psychol. Soc.; mem. Assn. Rsch. in Vision and Ophthalmology, Neurosci. Soc., Internat. Neural Network Soc., Psychonomic Soc., Knowles Inst. for Hearing Rsch. (bd. dirs. 1988-90), Sigma Xi. Home: 64 Strawberry Hill Rd Concord MA 01742-5502 Office: Brandeis U Ctr for Complex Systems Waltham MA 02254

SEKULOVICH, MALDEN See MALDEN, KARL

SEKULOW, JAY ALAN, lawyer; b. 1956. BA, JD, Mercer U. Bar: Ga. 1980. Chief counsel Am. Ctr. for Law and Justice, Virginia Beach; adj. prof. law Regent U. Author: From Intimidation to Victory, 1990, Knowing Your Rights, 1993, Students Rights and the Public School. Office: Am Ctr for Law & Justice PO Box 64429 Virginia Beach VA 23467

SELANDER, LARRY, lawyer; b. Chgo., May 28, 1946. BS, U. Notre Dame, 1967; JD, U. Ill., 1972. Bar: Ill. 1972. Ptnr. Keck, Mahin & Cate, Chgo. Mem. ABA, Ill. State Bar Assn., Chgo. Bar Assn. Office: Keck Mahin & Cate 77 W Wacker Dr Ste 4900 Chicago IL 60601-1693

SELBIN, JOEL, chemistry educator; b. Washington, Aug. 20, 1931; s. Abram Jacob and Rose (Aronson) S.; m. Marion F. Kilsheimer, Aug. 28, 1955; children: Eric Allyn, Jeffrey Lynn, Deborah Lyn, Jonathan David. BS, George Washington U., 1953; PhD, U. Ill., 1957. Asst. prof. chemistry La. State U., Baton Rouge, 1957-61, assoc. prof., 1961-67, prof., 1967-91, also dir. Summer Inst. for High Sch. Tchrs., 1984—; spl. vis. prof. U. Colo., Denver, 1991—; speaker Union of Concerned Scientists, 1980—. Author: Theoretical Inorganic Chemistry, 2d edit., 1969; patentee in field; contbr. articles to profl. jours. Grantee Am. Chem. Soc., NSF, Rsch. Corp. Fellow AAAS; mem. Am. Chem. Soc. (Charles E. Coates award 1973), Phi Beta Kappa, Sigma Xi. Office: U Colo Dept of Chemistry Denver CO 80304

SELBY, CECILY CANNAN, dean, educator, scientist; b. London, Feb. 4, 1927; d. Keith and Catherine Anne Cannan; m. Henry M. Selby, Aug. 11, 1951 (div. 1979); children: Norman, William, Russell; m. James Stacy Coles, Feb. 21, 1981. A.B. cum laude, Radcliffe Coll., 1946; Ph.D. in Phys. Biology, MIT, 1950. Teaching asst. in biology MIT, 1948-49; adminstrv. head virus study sect. Sloan-Kettering Inst., N.Y.C., 1949-50; asst. mem. inst. Sloan-Kettering Inst., 1950-55; research assoc. Sloan-Kettering div. Cornell U. Med. Coll., N.Y.C., 1953-55; instr. microscopic anatomy Cornell U. Med. Coll., 1955-57; tchr. sci. Lenox Sch., N.Y.C., 1957-58; headmistress Lenox Sch., 1959-72; nat. exec. dir. Girl Scouts U.S.A., N.Y.C., 1972-75; adv. com. Simmons Coll. Grad. Mgmt. Program, 1977-78; mem. Com. Corp. Support of Pvt. Univs., 1977-83; spl. asst. acad. planning N.C. Sch. Sci. and Math., 1979-80, dean acad. affairs, 1980-81, chmn. bd. advisors, 1981-84; cons. U.S. Dept. Commerce, 1976-77; dir. Avon Products Inc., RCA, NBC, Loehmanns Inc., Nat. Edn. Corp. pres. Am. Energy Ind., 1976; co-chmn. commn. precoll. math. and sci. Nat. Sci. Bd., 1982-83; adj. prof. NYU, 1984-86, prof. sci. edn., 1986—; mem. policy steering com. Gov. Cuomo's Conf. on Sci. and Engring., 1989-90. Contbr. articles to profl. jours., chpt. to book. Founder, chmn. N.Y. Ind. Schs. Opportunity Project, 1968-72; mem. invitational workshops Aspen Inst., 1973, 75, 77, 79; trustee MIT, Bklyn. Law Sch., Radcliffe Coll., Woods Hole Oceanographic Instn., Women's Forum N.Y., Skin Disease Found., N.Y. Hall of Sci., 1982—, vice chmn., 1989—; trustee Girls Inc., 1992—; Nat. Coun. Women in Medicine, 1990—; mem. Yale U. Peabody Mus. Adv. Coun., 1981-89. Recipient Woman Scientist of Yr. award N.Y. chpt. Am. Women in Sci., 1992. Mem. Headmistresses of East (hon., pres. 1970-72), Sigma Xi, Phi Delta Kappa. Clubs: Cosmopolitan (N.Y.C.). Home and Office: 45 Sutton Pl S New York NY 10022-2444 also: 100 Ransom Rd Falmouth MA 02540

SELBY, CLARK LINWOOD, JR., sales executive; b. Miami, Okla., Sept. 20, 1936; s. Clark Linwood and Edith Opal (Clark) S.; m. Patricia Ann Hayes, Dec. 22, 1952; children: Michael Lynn, Robert Clark. Sales engr. Carl Evans Co., Kansas City, Mo., 1962-70; asst. dir. traffic and parking U. Iowa, Iowa City, 1970-72; parking cons. De Leuw and Cather & Co., Chgo., 1972-77; pres. Enterprising Am. Corp., Hutchinson, Kans., 1978-82; dir. mfg. Duncan Industries, Harrison, Ark., 1982-85, dir. internat. sales, 1985-86, v.p. internat. sales, 1987-88, pres. 1988-90, v.p. sales and mktg., 1991-94; pres. Annell Corp., Wichita, Kans., 1991—, bd. dirs.; instr. free trade mktg. Kiev (USSR) Inst., 1991; chmn., sec. Florentine Corp., Flippin, Ark., 1994—; pres., CEO Worldwide Parking, Harrison, 1994—; dir. Eyewear Shoppe, Inc., Hutchinson; chmn. Florentine Corp., Flippin, Ark., 1994.

Inventor in field. Served with USNG, 1955-60. Recipient Presdl. E award for excellences in exporting, 1988. Methodist. Home: 1801 Par Ln Harrison AR 72601-6708 Office: Worldwide Parking Security Plz Ste 203C Harrison AR 72601

SELBY, HUBERT, JR., writer; b. N.Y.C., July 23, 1928; s. Hubert and Adalin (Layne) S.; m. Inez Taylor, Apr. 23, 1955 (div. 1960); children: Claudia, Kyle; Suzanne Schwartzman, Dec. 26, 1969; children: Rachel, William. Student public schs. Bklyn. Author: Last Exit to Brooklyn, 1964, The Room, 1971, The Demon, 1976, Requiem for a Dream, 1978, Song of the Silent Snow, 1986; screenwriter: Day and Night, 1986, Remember the Sabath Day, 1974, Love Your Buddy Week, 1978, Solder of Fortune, 1990. Served with U.S. Mcht. Marine, 1944-46. Mem. Writers Guild Am. (West chpt.), Authors Guild.

SELBY, JEROME M., mayor; b. Wheatland, Wyo., Sept. 4, 1948; s. John Franklin and Claudia Meredith (Hudson) S.; m. Gloria Jean Nelson, June 14, 1969; children: Tyan, Cameronn, Kalen. BS in Math., Coll. Idaho, 1969, MA in Ednl. Adminstrn., 1974; MPA, Boise State U., 1978. Assoc. engr. Boeing Co., Seattle, 1969-71; dir. evaluation WICHE Mountain States Regional Med. Program, Boise, 1971-74; dir. rsch., evaluation Mountain States Health Corp., Boise, 1974-76, with health policy analysis and accountability, 1976-78; dir. health Kodiak (Alaska) Area Native Assn., 1978-83; mgr. Kodiak Island Borough, 1984-85, mayor, 1985—; proprietor Kodiak Tax Svc., 1978—, Registered Guide, Kodiak, 1987—; cons. Nat. Cancer Inst., Washington, 1973-78, others. Contbr. articles to profl. jours. Treas. ARC, Kodiak, 1978-93, bd. dirs., 1977-78, chmn., 1989-90, mem. western ops. hdqrs. adv. bd., 1986-92, mem. group IV and V nat. adv. com., 1986-89, nat. bd. govs., 1989—, chmn. chpt. rels. com., 1994-95; pres. S.W. Alaska Mcpl. Conf., Anchorage, 1988-89, v.p., 1986-87, bd. dirs., 1986—; pres. Alaska Mcpl. League Investment Pool, Inc., 1992—; v.p. Alaska Mcpl. League, 1988-90, pres., 1990-91, bd. dirs., 1988—; mem. Alaska Resource Devel. Coun., 1987—, exec. com., 1989—; mem. policy com. of outer continental shelf adv. bd. U.S. Dept. Interior, 1990—; co-chair Alaska Task Force, 1995; mem. Com. on Oil Pollution Act, 1995; mem. Nat. Assn. Counties, Cmty. and Econ. Devel. Steering Com., 1990—, Alaska govtl. roles task force, 1991-92; chmn. Kodiak Island Exxon Valdez Restoration Com., 1991—; dir. Kodiak Health Care Found., 1992—; co-chmn. Arctic Power, 1993—; mem. bd. dirs. Western Interstate Region Nat. Assn. of Counties, 1993—. Paul Harris fellow, 1987, 88, 91, 92; recipient Outstanding Contbn. award Alaska Mcpl. League, 1994. Mem. Alaska Conf. Mayors, Nat. Soc. Tax Profls., Acad. Polit. Sci., Alaska Mcpl. Mgrs. Assn., Kodiak C. of C. (dir. 1983—) Rotary (mem. bd. dirs. 1989—, treas. 1989-93, v.p 1993-94, pres. elect 1994-95). Office: Kodiak Island Borough 710 Mill Bay Rd Kodiak AK 99615-6398

SELBY, ROGER LOWELL, museum director; b. Phila., July 4, 1933; s. Willard Lowell and Margaret Anne (Gray) S.; 1 child, Christine. A.B., U. Md., 1960; postgrad., Claremont Grad. Sch., 1960-61, Ind. U., 1963-65; doctoral studies in fine arts, U. N.Mex., 1983—. Curator nat. Gallery Art, Washington, 1961-62, Corcoran Gallery Art, Washington, 1965-68; head adm. Wadsworth Atheneum, Hartford, 1968-74; dir. Winnipeg (Man., Can.) Art Gallery, 1974-83, Boca Raton Mus. Art., Fla., 1984—; instr. Corcoran Sch. Art, 1965-68, Hartford Art Sch., 1969-71; Asst., gen. fellow Claremont Grad. Sch., 1960-61; asst. Ind. U., 1963-65; hon. prof. U. Winnipeg, 1979-82. Served with U.S. Army, 1953-55. Recipient Queen's Silver Jubilee medal, 1978. Mem. Assn. Art Mus. Dirs., Canadian Art Mus. Dirs. Orgn. (pres. 1979-81), Can. Mus. Assn. (chmn. fin./exec. com. 1980-81). Home: 365 NW 35th St Boca Raton FL 33431 *Elements of Success: A stubborn dedication towards a goal, nourished by life's varied experiences, coupled with exhaustive thought; a fortunate set of circumstances; the realization that nothing is accomplished alone; and the resolved question—why are we here in the first place.*

SELBY, ROY CLIFTON, JR., neurosurgeon; b. Little Rock, Sept. 28, 1930; s. Roy Clifton Sr. and Annie Mae (Bular) S.; m. Marilyn Triffler, May 12, 1960; children: Brian M.T., Bretta L.T. BSc, MSc, La. State U., 1952; MD, U. Ark., Little Rock, 1956. diplomate Am. Bd. Neurol. Surgery. Intern Montreal Gen. Hosp., 1956-57; resident VA Hosp., Little Rock, Ark., 1957-58, U. Ill. Depart. Neurology and Neurosurgery, Chgo., 1958-61; sr. fellow Neurosurgery Lahey Clinic, Boston, 1961-62; dir. dept. neurosurgery Ministry Health Gen. Hosp., Kuala Lumpur, Malaysia, 1963-70; chmn. dept. neurosurgery Cook County Hosp., Chgo., 1970-74; practice medicine specializing in neurosurgery Texarkana, Tex., 1974-86; assoc. clin. prof. neurosurgery U. Ill., Chgo., 1970-74; prof. Cook County Postgrad. Sch. Med., 1970-74; vis. assoc. prof. Rush Presbyn. Med. Ctr., 1970-74; lectr. dept. psychology E. Tex. U., Texarkana, 1986—. Author short stories; contbr. chpts. to books. Fellow Royal Soc. Medicine; mem. Am. Assn. Neurol. Surgeons, N.Y. Acad. Scis., Soc. Neurol. Lange Francaise, N.Y. Acad. Medicine, French Soc. History of Medicine, Acad. Medicine (Paris), Internat. Soc. Surgery, Am. Osler Soc., Ark. Hist. Soc., Neurosci., Cen. Neuropsychiat. Soc., Inst. Charles DeGaulle, Ala. Hist. Soc., La. Hist. Soc., Sigma Xi, Alpha Omega Alpha. Avocations: reading, writing, gardening. Home: No 7 Sweetbrush Ave Texarkana TX 75503-2004 *The more I learn, the less I feel separated from all creatures; believing in all forms of life highly specialized, though greatly diverse, require respect and reverence.*

SELCER, DAVID MARK, lawyer; b. Cleve., Feb. 12, 1943; s. Lester and Sylvia (Esral) S.; m. Belinda Weine, Aug. 8, 1968 (div. 1986); children: Daniel, Anne, Emily; m. Susan Merwin, Mar. 22, 1993. BA, Northwestern U., 1965; JD, Ohio State U., 1968. Bar: Ohio 1968, Ill. 1969, U.S. Dist. Ct. (so. dist.) Ohio 1971, U.S. Dist. Ct. (no. dist.) Ohio 1973. Ptnr. Porter, Wright, Morris & Arthur, Columbus, Ohio, 1973-78, Krupman, Fromson & Selcer, Columbus, 1979-81, Baker & Hostetler, Columbus, 1981—; adj. prof. Capitol U. Law Sch., Columbus, 1973-74; bd. dirs. Consolidated Stores Corp., 1990-91. Trustee Temple Israel, Columbus, 1987-94; v.p. Jewish Family Svc., 1987-94. Recipient Disting. Service award Columbus Symphony Orch., 1986-87. Mem. ABA (equal employment opportunity subcom. of labor com 1978—), Nat. Labor Relations Bd (asst. bd. mem. 1967-68), Ohio Bar Assn., Columbus Bar Assn. Office: Baker & Hostetler 65 E State St Columbus OH 43215-4213

SELDEN, RICHARD THOMAS, economist, educator; b. Pontiac, Mich., Mar. 31, 1922; s. Arthur Willis and Florence L. (Seeley) S.; m. Martha Mathiasen, Mar. 21, 1953 (div. June 1989); children: Phoebe Serena, Thomas Mathiasen; m. Louise H. Randolph, July 30, 1989; 1 stepdaughter, Laura Peyton Mosca. BA, U. Chgo., 1948, PhD, 1957; MA, Columbia U., 1949. Instr. U. Mass., Amherst, 1949-50; mem. faculty Vanderbilt U., Nashville, 1952-59; asso. prof. Vanderbilt U., 1955-59; research asso. Nat. Bur. Econ. Research, N.Y.C., 1958-59; asso. prof. banking Columbia, 1959-63; economist 1st Nat. City Bank, N.Y.C., 1962-63; prof. econs. Cornell U., 1963-69; Carter Glass prof. econs. U. Va., 1969-94, chmn. dept., 1972-79; Mem. adv. council banking and financial research com. Am. Bankers Assn., 1964-67; U. Va. rep. on univs. Nat. Bur. Com. for Econ. Research, 1969-79. Author: The Postwar Rise in the Velocity of Money, 1962, Trends and Cycles in the Commercial Paper Market, 1963, (with George R. Morrison) Time Deposit Growth and the Employment of Bank Funds, 1965; Contbr. articles to profl. jours. Guggenheim fellow, 1965; Fulbright Advanced Research scholar Brussels, Belgium, 1964-65; Ford Found. faculty fellow Cornell U., 1968-69; Indo-Am. fellow Bombay, India, 1981. Mem. Am. Econ. Assn. Home: PO Box 3 Ivy VA 22945-0003

SELDEN, ROBERT WENTWORTH, physicist, science advisor; b. Phoenix, Aug. 11, 1936; s. Edward English and Mary Priscilla (Calder) S.; m. Mary Tania Hudd, June 1958 (div. 1976); 1 child, Ian Scott; m. Marjorie Anne Harmon, Feb. 20, 1977; children: Brock, Thane, Shawna, Kirsten. BA in Physics cum laude, Pomona Coll., 1958; MS in Physics, U. Wis., 1960, PhD in Physics, 1964. Rsch. assoc. Lawrence Livermore (Calif.) Nat. Lab., 1965-67, staff mem., 1967-73, group leader, 1973-78, asst. assoc. dir., 1978-80; dir. dep. assoc. dir. strategic def. rsch., 1983-84, assoc. dir. theoretical and computational physics, 1984-86, dir. Ctr. for Nat. Securities Studies, 1986-88; chief scientist USAF, Washington, 1991-94; assoc. dir. for lab. devel. Los Alamos Nat. Lab., 1991-94; panel chmn. USAF Sci. Adv. Bd., Washington, 1984-88, 91—; cons. Los Alamos, 1994—; chmn. study group on reactor materials and nuclear explosives U.S. Dept. Energy, 1976-78; mem. ballistic

missile def. techs. adv. panel U.S. Congress Office Tech. Assessment, 1984-85, The Pres.'s Defensive Tech. Study Team, Washington, 1983. Editor Rsch. Jour. Lawrence Livermore Nat. Lab., 1976-77; contbr. sci. and tech. papers to profl. jours. Pres. Livermore Cultural Arts Coun., 1969-72; chmn. Livermore Sister City Orgn., 1973, Planning Commn. City of Livermore, 1971-76; bd. dirs. Orch. of Santa Fe. 1986-88. Capt. U.S. Army, 1964-67. Grad. fellow Edward John Noble Found., 1958-62; recipient Theodore von Karman award for outstanding contbn. to def. sci., 1989. Mem. AAAS, Am. Phys. Soc., N.Y. Acad. Sci., Air Force Assn. Avocations: tennis, hiking, music. Office: 624 La Bajada Los Alamos NM 87544-3805

SELDEN, WILLIAM KIRKPATRICK, educational consultant; b. Oil City, Pa., Nov. 11, 1911; s. Edwin van D. and Cornelia Fuller (Earp) S.; m. Virginia Barr, June 25, 1938; children: Edwin van Deusen, II, Joseph Barr. A.B., Princeton U., 1934; LL.D., Carthage Coll., 1954; Litt.D., Jacksonville U., 1964; L.H.D., Scholl Coll. Podiatric Medicine, 1984. Asst. to faculty dean, coll. dean Princeton U., 1934-37; clk. Eastman Kodak Co., Rochester, N.Y., 1937-38; asst. dir. admissions, admissions officer, asst. coll. dean Brown U., Providence, 1938-43; asst. to pres. Brown U., 1943-45; asst. dean students, dir. admissions Northwestern U., Evanston, Ill., 1945-52; univ. recorder Northwestern U., 1952-53; pres. Ill. Coll., 1953-55; exec. dir. Nat. Commn. on Accrediting, 1955-65; v.p. The Am. Assembly, 1965-66; Ednl. specialist in India U.S. Dept. State, 1965; adv. com. on nursing edn. facilities USPHS, 1964-65; cons. N.J. Dept. Edn., 1966-67; chmn. Spl. Com. on Status of Podiatry Edn., 1960-61; dir. Va. Gov.'s Com. on Nursing, 1967-69; cons., dir. projects numerous profl. assns. and orgns.; exec. com. Coll. Entrance Exam. Bd., 1953; mem. Gov.'s Commn. Higher Edn. Ill., 1954-55; grad. council Princeton U., 1954-56, exec. com., 1989-91; mem. ednl. adv. council NAM, 1954-58; adv. com. Presbyn. Bd. Christian Edn., 1959-63; exec. com. Episcopal Ch. Soc. for Ch. Work, 1962-66, pres., 1964-66; vice chmn. St. John's Orphanage Assn., 1960-65; chmn. adv. com. CIT Fin. Found., 1960-65; past pres. vol. bur. Providence Civilian Def. Council; mem. bd. Vets. Info. Center, Bur. Handicapped; chmn. citizens adv. com. long-range planning Princeton Regional Schs., 1970-71; bd. acad. advisors U.S. Marine Corps Schs., Quantico, 1969-70; dir. health scis. research project New Eng. Bd. Higher Edn., 1974-75; chmn. podiatry edn. feasibility study So. Regional Edn. Bd., 1976-77; trustee Profl. Exam. Service, 1974-76; chmn. adv. com. health programs Ednl. Testing Service, 1976-82; chmn. spl. higher edn. com. ADA, 1978-79; exec. dir. Nat. Bd. Podiatry Examiners, 1978-80; mem. com. for study credentialing in nursing Am. Nurses Assn., 1976-79; mem. council on optometric edn. Am. Optometric Assn., 1977-84; mem. com. on edn. for allied health professions AMA, 1969-70, dir. study accreditation selected health edn. programs, 1971-72. Author: Accreditation—A Struggle Over Standards in Higher Edn, 1960, Woodrow Wilson School, Princeton University, 1984, Princeton Summer Camp, 1987, Vignettes of Princeton University, 1987, Legacy of John Cleve Green, 1988, It's First 100 Years Nassau Club of Princeton, 1989, From These Roots: The Creation of Princeton Day School, 1991, The Heritage of Isabella McCosh: A History of the Health Service at Princeton University, 1991, History of Princeton Theol. Seminary, 1992, Drumthwalket, The Governors Mansion, 1993; contbr. articles to profl. jours. Mem. bd. Evanston YMCA; mem. borough council, Princeton, 1976-78; judge Miss Am. Pageant, 1951; co-chmn. Princeton Joint Mcpl. Consolidation Study Commn., 1978-79; mem. adv. panel ROTC affairs, Dept. Def., 1950-53; bd. dirs. Princeton Prospect Found., 1973-77, chmn., 1979-83, 90-91; sec., treas. Corner House Found., 1981-83; pres. Constitution Hill Property Owners Assn., 1981-86. Recipient Recognition awards Nat. Assn. Schs. Art, 1967, Princeton class of 1934, 71, Am. Podiatry Assn., 1961, 76, United Way of Princeton, 1993; travel and study grantee Ford Found., 1960. Mem. Council Social Work Agys., Fund Advancement Edn. (cons. 1953), Am. Council Edn. (sec. com. on civil def. and higher edn. 1952), Assn. Naval ROTC Colls. (sec.-treas. 1948-53). Home: Loe 105 Pennswood Village Newtown PA 18940-2401

SELDES, MARIAN, actress; b. N.Y.C.; d. Gilbert and Alice (Hall) S.; m. Julian Claman, Nov. 3, 1953 (div.); 1 child, Katharine; m. Garson Kanin, June 19, 1990. Grad., Neighborhood Playhouse, N.Y.C., 1947; D.H.L., Emerson Coll., 1979. Mem. faculty drama and dance div. Juilliard Sch. Lincoln Center, N.Y.C., 1969-91. Appeared with Cambridge (Mass.) Summer Theatre, 1945, Boston Summer Theatre, 1946, St. Michael's Playhouse, Winooski, Vt., 1947-48, Bermudiana Theatre, Hamilton, Bermuda, 1951, Elitch Gardens Theatre, Denver, 1953; Broadway appearances include Medea, 1947, Crime and Punishment, 1948, That Lady, 1949, Tower Beyond Tragedy, 1950, The High Ground, 1951, Come of Age, 1952, Ondine, 1954, The Chalk Garden, 1955, The Wall, 1960, A Gift of Time, 1962, The Milk Train Doesn't Stop Here Any More, 1964, Tiny Alice, 1965, A Delicate Balance, 1967 (Tony award for best supporting actress), Before You Go, 1968, Father's Day, 1971 (Drama Desk award), Mendicants of Evening (Martha Graham Co.), 1973, Equus, 1974-77, The Merchant, 1977, Deathtrap, 1978; off-Broadway appearances include Diffrent, 1961, The Ginger Man, 1963 (Obie award), All Women Are One, 1964, Juana LaLoca, 1965, Three Sisters, 1969, Am. Shakespeare Festival, Stratford, Conn., Mercy Street at Am. Place Theater, N.Y.C., 1969, Isadora Duncan, 1976 (Obie award), Painting Churches, 1983, 84 (Outer Critics Circle award 1984), Other People, Berkshire Theatre Festival, 1969, The Celebration, Hedgerow Theater, Pa., 1971, Richard III, N.Y. Shakespeare Festival, 1983, Remember Me, Lakewood Theatre, Skowhegan, Maine, Gertrude Stein and a Companion, White Barn Theatre, Westport, Conn., 1985, Lucile Lortel Theatre, N.Y.C., 1986, Richard II, N.Y. Shakespeare Festival, 1987, The Milk Train Doesn't Stop Here Anymore, WPA Theatre, N.Y.C., 1987, Happy Ending, Bristol (Pa.) Riverside Theatre, 1988, Annie 2 John F. Kennedy Ctr., Washington, 1989-90, Goodspeed Opera House, Chester, Conn., 1990, A Bright Room Called Day, N.Y. Shakespeare Festival, 1991, Three Tall Women, River Arts, Woodstock, N.Y., 1992, Another Time, Am. Jewish Theatre, 1993, Breaking the Code, Berkshire Theatre Festival, 1993, Three Tall Women, Vineyard Theatre, N.Y.C., 1994, Promenade Theatre, 1994-95; engaged in nat. tour Medea, 1947; U.S. entry Berlin Festival, 1951; motion picture appearances include The Greatest Story Ever Told, Gertrude Stein and a Companion, 1988, In a Pig's Eye, 1988, The Gun in Betty Lou's Handbag, 1992, Tom Sawyer, 1995; (ABC series) Good and Evil, 1991, Murphy Brown, 1992, Truman, 1995; also appeared on CBS Radio Mystery Theater, 1976-81, as well as numerous dramatic shows; author: The Bright Lights, 1978, Time Together, 1981. Bd. dirs. Neighborhood Playhouse, The Acting Co., nat. repertory theatre. Mem. Players Club, Century Assn.

SELDMAN, NEIL NORMAN, cultural organization administrator; b. Bklyn., Aug. 2, 1945; s. Fred Herman and Sylvia (Flaster) S.; m. Laura Jane Klugherz, Feb. 22, 1968; children: Oliver, Chloe. BS in Indsl. and Labor Rels., Cornell U., 1966; MS in Internat. Communism, George Washington U., 1968, PhD in Internat. Rels., 1974. Asst. to pres. B.H. Krueger Co., Bklyn., 1969-72; assoc. prof., lectr. George Washington U., Washington, 1974-76, asst. dir. exptl. program, 1976-77; founder Inst. for Local Self-Reliance (ILSR), Washington, 1974—, pres., 1980—; cons. World Bank/UN Environ. Program, Washington, 1980-81, City Coun., Phila., 1994-90. Author: Common Sense Radicalism, 1976, Waste to Wealth: A Guide for Community Enterprise, 1985; co-author: Integrated Resource Recovery-Recycling from Municipal Refuse: A State-of-the-Art Review & Annotated Bibliography, 1985, Proven Profits from Pollution Prevention, 1986, Garbage in Europe: Economics, Technologies, Trends, 1987; contbr. article to Sci. & Tech. Encyc., 1995. Fabrangen Cheder Jewish Community Orgn.; elected chair Neighborhood Planning Coun., Washington, 1976-82; co-founder D.C. Interracial Coalition for Environ. Equity, Washington, 1989. With NG, 1968-74. Grantee Moriah Fund, 1990, PEW Charitable Trusts, 1991, NSF, 1979-80, H. Heinz Endowment. Jewish. Avocations: fast pitch softball, nineteenth-century literature, French and Russian revolutions. Office: Inst Local Self-Reliance 2425 18th St NW Washington DC 20009

SELECMAN, CHARLES EDWARD, business executive; b. Dallas, Sept. 17, 1928; s. Frank A. and Eloise (Olive) S.; m. Nan Harton Nash, May 11, 1951 (div. 1975); children: Mary Lucinda, Nan Elizabeth, Amy Eloise; m. Judith Wallace Pollard, Feb. 6, 1976 (div. 1984); m. Barbara Ann Calvert, Apr. 18, 1985. B.A., So. Meth. U., 1951. Bus. mgmt. clk. Buick Motor div. Gen. Motor Corp., Dallas, 1951-52; pers. dept. Chance Vought Aircraft, Inc., Dallas, 1952-56; div. pers. mgr. U.S. Industries, Inc., Longview, Tex., 1956-64; div. v.p. mktg. U.S. Industries, Inc., 1964-66; div. exec. v.p. Axelson div. U.S. Industries, Inc., 1966-67, div. pres., 1967; corp. v.p. U.S. Industries, Inc., N.Y.C., 1967-68, corp. exec. v.p., 1968-70, pres., 1970-73; vice chmn., chief exec. officer U.S. Industries, Inc., 1973, also dir.; owner

Charles E. Selecman & Assos., 1974-75; pres., chief exec. officer E.T. Barwick Industries, Inc., 1975-78; ptnr. Marshalsea Texas Partners, Dallas, 1978-86; pres. Marshalsea Industries, Inc., Ft. Worth 1980-83; chmn., pres., chief exec. officer Input/Output Inc., Houston, 1984-93, chmn., 1993—; dir. Triton Oil & Gas Corp., 1975-93. Mem. Soc. Exploration Geophysicists, Sigma Alpha Epsilon. Office: Input/Output Inc 12300 Parc Crest Dr Stafford TX 77477

SELES, MONICA, tennis player; b. Novi Sad, Yugoslavia, Dec. 2, 1973; came to U.S., 1986; d. Karol and Esther Seles. Winner Italian Open, 1990, German Open, 1990, French Open, 1990, 91, 92, Va. Slims, 1990, 91, 92, U.S. Open, 1991, 92, Australian Open, 1991, 92, 93; named Yugoslavia's sportwoman of yr., 1985, World #1 ranked player, 1991, 92. Office: care Internat Mgmt Group 1 Erieview Plz Cleveland OH 44114-1715*

SELF, CHARLES EDWIN, financial consultant, retail company executive; b. Roanoke, Va., June 6, 1934; s. Loy Evry and Louzelle (Childers) S.; m. Phyllis Ann Stevens, Sept. 2, 1961; children: Tim, Randy, Betsy. BA, Randolph Macon Coll., 1956. Budget specialist Gen. Electric Co., Schenectady, N.Y., 1960-64; merchandise contr. Montgomery Ward & Co., N.Y.C., 1964-67; contr. The Hecht Co., Washington, 1967-70; v.p., fin. contr. Zayre Corp., Framingham, Mass., 1970-79; v.p. fin. Wal-Mart Stores, Inc., Bentonville, Ark., 1979-87; pvt. practice fin. cons. Bellingham, Wash., 1987—; mem. fin. steering com. Nat. Mass Retail Inst., N.Y.C., 1980-86; chmn. Nat. Capital Group of Contrs., Washington, 1969; chmn., bd. dirs. Consumers' Choice Inc., Bellingham, Wash., 1990-94; bd. dirs. Bank of Bellingham, No. Automotive Corp., Phoenix. Commr. Conservation Commn., Mass., 1976-79; bd. dirs. Am. Field Svc., Ark., 1984; bd. dirs. Whatcom Mus. History and Art, Bellingham, 1990—, pres., 1994—; trustee Western Found., Western Wash. U., 1991—, St. Luke's Found., 1994—. Lt. USNR, 1956-60. Mem. B'Ham (Wash.) Yacht Club. Republican. Episcopalian. Avocations: boating, fishing, stained glass, woodwork. Home and Office: 324 Bayside Rd Bellingham WA 98225-7802

SELF, JAMES REED, librarian; b. Greeneville, Tenn., May 14, 1944; s. Rex Clive and Ethel (Reed) S.; m. Charlotte Clifford, Mar. 18, 1967; children—Jennifer Reed, Abigail Clifford. B.S., U. Tenn., 1967, M.A. in History, 1970; M.A. in Librarianship, U. Denver, 1971. Reference librarian Ind. U., Bloomington, 1971-78, head undergrad. library, 1978-81; dir. Clemons Library U. Va., Charlottesville, 1982—. Contbr. articles to profl. jours. Mem. ALA, Va. Library Assn. Office: University of Virginia Clemons Library Charlottesville VA 22904

SELF, LARRY DOUGLAS, architectural firm executive; b. Cleburne, Tex., Aug. 14, 1943. BArch, Tex. Tech U., 1968. Registered arch., Mo., Tex.; cert. Nat. Coun. Archtl. Registration Bds. Project designer Hellmuth, Obata & Kassabaum, Inc., St. Louis, 1968—; overseas dir. Hellmuth, Obata & Kassabaum, Inc., Riyadh, Saudi Arabia; dir. design, mng. prin. Hellmuth, Obata & Kassabaum, Inc., Dallas, 1980-91; exec. dir. Europe, bd. dirs. Hellmuth, Obata & Kassabaum, Inc., London, 1992-95, dir. corp. ops., 1995—. Prin. works include Am South/Harbert Plz., Birmingham, Ala., Zale Corp. World Hdqrs., Dallas, Arco Exploration & Prodn., Rsch. Ctr., Plano, Tex., Collin County C.C., Plano, Cmty. Fedn. Ctr., St. Louis, Plano Civic Ctr., Xerox Rsch. Ctr., Palo Alto, Calif., Tuscon Mall, Aetna Life & Casualty Group Benefits Divsn. Hdqrs., Middletown, Conn., Albuquerque Plz. Hyatt Hotel, Riverchase Galleria Wyndham Hote, Birmingham, King Saud Univ., Riyadh, Saudi Arabia, others. Fellow AIA. Office: Hellmuth Obata & Kassabaum 211 N Broadway Saint Louis MO 63102 Home: 7057 Kingsbury Blvd Saint Louis MO 63130

SELF, MADISON ALLEN, chemical company executive; b. Ozawkie, Kans., June 30, 1921; s. Benjamin B. and Margaret E. (Allen) S.; m. Lila M. Reetz, Sept. 1, 1943; 1 son, Murray A. B.S. in Chem. Engring, U. Kans., 1943. Engr. York Corp., 1943-44; salesman and researcher Sharples Chems., Inc., 1944-47; with Bee Chem. Co., Lansing, Ill., 1947-84; chmn. bd., chief exec. officer Bee Chem. Co., until 1984; pres. Allen Fin., Inc., 1984—; chmn. bd. dirs. Tioga Internat., Inc., 1989—. Life trustee Ill. Inst. Tech. Mem. Chief Exec. Orgn., World Pres.'s Orgn., Hinsdale Golf Club. Office: Allen Fin Inc 1440 Huntington Dr Calumet City IL 60409-5464

SELF, PHYLLIS C., health sciences librarian; b. Moline, Ill., Dec. 5, 1946; d. Charles Arthur and Henrietta Mary (Youngvorst) K.; m. David Alfred Self, June 22, 1968; 1 child, Linnea Christine. A.S., Black Hawk Coll., 1966; B.S., U. Ill., 1969, M.L.S., 1974, PhD, 1990. Jr. librarian R.I. Pub. Library, Rock Island, Ill., 1969-70; unit librarian Rockridge Sch. Unit, Edgington, Ill., 1970-71; biology tchr. Northwestern High Sch., Sciota, Ill., 1971-73; asst. phys. sci. librarian U. Ill., Urbana, 1974-75, asst. health scis. librarian, 1975-77, health scis. librarian, 1977-87, asst. dir. pub. services, 1980-84; health scis. librarian U. N.C., Chapel Hill, 1987-89; health scis. libr. dir. Cin., 1989-91; health scis. libr. U. Commonwealth U. Richmond, 1991—; cons. in Sudan WHO, Alexandria, Egypt, 1982. Editor: Physical Disabilities, 1984 (Presdl. commn. award 1985); contbr. articles to profl. jours. Mem. Med. Library Assn. (com. chmn. 1979—, pres. 1980 Midwest chpt.). Internat. Fedn. Librarians. Methodist. Avocations: travel; cooking; golf. Home: 320 Farnham Dr Richmond VA 23236-4025 Office: Va Commonwealth U - Med Coll Va Campus Tompkins McCaw Libr 509 N 12th St Richmond VA 23298-0582

SELFE, EDWARD MILTON, lawyer; b. St. Paul, Sept. 26, 1921; s. Edward Milton and Eleanor (Moen) S.; m. Rena Hill McMurry, July 10, 1950 (div. Oct. 1979); children: Murry, Edward, James; m. Jane Comer Bowron, Dec. 31, 1979. BA, Presbyn. Coll., Clinton, S.C., 1943; LLB, U. Va., 1950. Bar: N.Y., Va., Ala. Asst. prof. law Law Sch., U. Va., Charlottesville, 1950-51; assoc. Shearman & Sterling, N.Y.C., 1951-52; assoc. Bradley Arant Rose White, Birmingham, Ala., 1952-57, ptnr., 1957—; vice chmn. Secor Bank, Birmingham, 1988-91, gen. counsel, 1991-93. Chmn. Birmingham-Jefferson County Transit Authority, 1972-82. Served to capt., inf. U.S. Army, 1943-47, ETO. Decorated Silver Star, Bronze Star (V), Purple Heart. Fellow Am. Coll. Tax Counsel; mem. ABA, Ala. Bar Assn., Birmingham Bar Assn. Democrat. Avocation: tennis (ranked 25th nationally in men's singles-age 70). Home: 2600 Arlington Ave Unit 84 Birmingham AL 35205 Office: Bradley Arant Rose & White 1400 Park Place Tower Birmingham AL 35203-2709

SELFRIDGE, GEORGE DEVER, dentist, retired naval officer; b. Pitman, N.J., Sept. 24, 1924; s. William John and Edith (Gorman) S.; m. Ruth Motisher, 1948; children: Pamela Ruth, Kimberly Dawn, Cheryl Beth. Student, Gettysburg Coll., 1942-43, Muhlenberg Coll., 1943-45; DDS, U. Buffalo, 1947; MA, George Washington U., 1974. Commd. lt. (j.g.) USN, 1948, advanced through grades to rear adm., 1973; intern Naval Dental Sch., Bethesda, Md., 1948-49, Naval Hosp., St. Albans, N.Y., 1949-50; various dental positions USN, 1951-64; sr. dental officer U.S.S. Cadmus, 1964-65, U.S.S. Vulcan, 1965-66, Svc. Force, 1966-64, Submarine Force, Atlantic Fleet, 1967-69; asst. dir. grad. edn. Navy Grad. Dental Sch., Bethesda, 1969-72, comdg. officer, 1973-76; dep. exec. officer Norfolk (Va.) Navy Dental Clinic, 1972-73; ret. USN, 1976; dean Dental Sch., Washington U., St. Louis, 1976-80; dir. dental services Barnes Hosp., St. Louis, 1976-87, Children's Hosp., St. Louis, 1976-87; exec. dir. Am. Bd. Orthodontics, 1986—; mem. adv. bd. VA Hosp., St. Louis, 1977-79; mem. exec. coun. Cen. Region Testing Svc., 1976-86; mem. adv. com. St. Louis Jr. Coll. Dist., 1976-86. Contbr. articles to med. jours. Decorated Legion of Merit; recipient commendation medals. Mem. ADA, Am. Coll. Dentists, Internat. Coll. Dentists (dep. registrar, sec. U.S. sect.), Assn. Mil. Surgeons U.S., Omicron Kappa Upsilon. Republican. Home: 14545 Foxham Ct Chesterfield MO 63017-5620 Office: Am Bd Orthodontics 401 N Lindbergh Blvd Ste 308 Saint Louis MO 63141-7839

SELIG, ALLAN H. (BUD SELIG) professional baseball team executive; b. Milw., July 30, 1934; s. Ben and Marie Selig; m. Suzanne Lappin Steinman, Jan. 18, 1977; children: Sari, Wendy. Grad., U. Wis., Madison, 1956; LHD (hon.), Lakeland Coll., 1989. With Selig Ford (became Selig Chevrolet 1982), West Allis, Wis., 1959-90, pres., owner, 1966-90; with Selig Exec. Leasing Co., West Allis, 1959—, pres., owner, 1977—; part owner Milw. Braves (became Atlanta Braves 1965), 1963-65; co-founder Teams, Inc., 1964; co-owner, pres., chief exec. officer Milw. Brewers Baseball Club, Inc., 1970—; interim commr. Maj. League Baseball, 1991—; bd. dirs. Green Bay

Packers Profl. Football Team. Co-founder Child Abuse Prevention Fund, 1988. With U.S. Army, 1956-58. Recipient Major League Exec. of Yr. award UPI, 1978, Internat. B'nai B'rith Sportsman of Yr. award 1981, Sportsman of Yr. award U.S. Olympic Com., 1988, August A. Busch, Jr. award for long and meritorious svc. to baseball, 1989, Ellis Island Congl. medal of honor, 1993, Anti-Defamation League's "A World of Difference Award" 1994. Office: Milw Brewers Milw County Stadium PO Box 3099 Milwaukee WI 53214

SELIG, KARL-LUDWIG, language and literature educator; b. Wiesbaden, Germany, Aug. 14, 1926; naturalized, 1948; s. Lucian and Erna (Reiss) S. B.A., Ohio State U., 1946, M.A., 1947; postgrad., U. Rome, Italy, 1949-50; Ph.D., U. Tex., 1955. Asst. prof. Romance langs. and lit. Johns Hopkins U., Balt., 1954-58; assoc. prof. U. N.C., Chapel Hill, 1958-61, U. Minn., Mpls., 1961-63; vis. prof. U. Tex., Austin, 1963-64, prof. Romance langs. and lit., 1964-65; Hinchliff prof. Spanish lit. Cornell U., Ithaca, N.Y., 1965-69; dir. grad. studies in Romance lit. Cornell U., Ithaca, 1966-69; prof. Spanish lit. Columbia U., N.Y.C., 1969—; Brown Found. fellow, vis. prof. Spanish and comparative lit. U. of the South, Sewanee, Tenn., 1990; vis. prof. U. Munich, 1963-64, U. Berlin, 1967, U. Greifswald, Germany, 1992-95; cons. prof. Ohio State U., Columbus, 1967-69; vis. lectr. U. Zulia, Maracaibo, Venezuela, 1968; dir. summer seminar NEH, 1975, cons., 1975-77; vis. scholar Ga. U. Sys., 1977; vis. rsch. scholar Fondation Hardt, Vandoeuvres, Switzerland, 1959, Herzog August Bibliothek Wolfenbüttel, Fed. Republic Germany, 1979—; mem. com. grants-in-aid Am. Coun. Learned Soc., 1969-73; chmn. Comparative Lit. Program and Colloquia, Columbia Coll., 1976-88. Author: The Library of Vincencio Juan de Lastanosa, Patron of Gracián, Geneva, 1960, Studies on Alciato in Spain, 1990, Studies on Cervantes, 1992; also numerous articles, revs.; editor: (Thomas Blundeville) of Councils and Counselors, 1963, (with A. G. Hatcher) Studia Philologica et Litteraria in Honorem L. Spitzer, 1958, (with J. E. Keller) Essays in Honor of N. B. Adams, 1966, (with R. Brinkmann) Theatrum Europaeum. Festschrift E. M. Szarota, 1982, (with S. Neumeister) Theatrum Mundi Hispanicum, 1986, (with R. Somerville) Florilegium Columbianum: Essays in Honor of Paul Oskar Kristeller, 1987, (with E. Sears) The Verbal and the Visual: Essays in Honor of William Sebastian Hecksher, 1990, Polyanthea Essays on Art and Literature in Honor of William Sebastian Hecksher, 1993; assoc. editor Modern Lang. Notes, 1955-58; mng. editor Romance Notes, 1959-61; editor U. N.C. Studies in Comparative Lit, 1959-61, Bull. Comediantes, 1959-64, assoc. editor 1964-68, 79—; co-editor Yearbook of Comparative Lit., Vol. IX, 1960; editorial bd. Colección Támesis, London, 1962-79, Romanic Rev., 1969-89, Teaching Lang. Through Lit, 1978-88; assoc. editor Hispania, 1969-74, Ky. Romance Quar, 1973-85; gen. editor Revista Hispánica Moderna, 1971-86; mem. nat. adv. bd. MLA Internat. Bibliography, 1978-88; editorial bd. Yale Italian Studies, 1976-80. Recipient Mark Van Doren award Columbia, 1974, spl. citation Columbia Coll. Alumni Assn., 1991; fellow Fulbright Found., Rome, 1949-50, Newberry Library, 1958, Folger Shakespeare Library, 1959, 63, Belgian Am. Ednl. Found., 1961, 62; sr. fellow Mediaeval and Renaissance Inst. Duke U., 1978; Fulbright research scholar Utrecht, The Netherlands, 1958-59. Mem. MLA (sec., then chmn. Romance sect. 1965-66, chmn. comparative lit. 1973, James Russell Lowell prize com. 1989-90, chmn. 1990), Am. Friends of Herzog August Bibliothek (bd. dirs.), Internat. Assn. Hispanists, Am. Comparative Lit. Assn., Coll. Art Assn., Acad. Lit. Studies, Phi Beta Kappa (hon.). Home: 30 E 37th St New York NY 10016-3012

SELIGER, CHARLES, artist; b. N.Y.C., June 3, 1926; s. George Zekowski and Hortense S.; m. Ruth Lewin, June 20, 1948 (dec. May 1975); children: Robert, Mark; m. Lenore Klebanow, 1975. Ed. by pvt. art instrn., also, WPA Sch., 1940. Robert H. and Clarice Smith Disting. vis. prof. George Washington U., Washington, 1990; lectr. Katonah Art Mus., 1990; panelist Terra Mus. Am. Art, Chgo., 1990, Whitney Mus. Am. Art, N.Y.C., 1990, Michael Rosenfeld Gallery, N.Y.C., 1994. One man shows include Peggy Guggenheim Gallery, N.Y.C., 1945-46, Carlebach Gallery, 1948, DeYoung Meml. Mus., San Francisco, 1949, Whitney Mus. ann., 1949-57, Willard Gallery, N.Y.C., 1951, 53, 55, 57, 61, 62, 66, 68, Seligman Gallery, Seattle, 1955, 58, 65, Nassau Community Coll., N.Y.C., 1965, Wooster Community Art Center, Conn., 1969, Andrew Crispo Gallery, 1973, 75, 76, 78, 80, 81, 83, Mus. Modern Art, Hayden Calhoun Gallery, Dallas, Makler Gallery, Phila., 1979, Miami-Dade Community Coll., 1981, Jacksonville (Fla.) Art Mus., 1981, Gallery Schlesinger-Boisanté, 1985, 86, Guggenheim Mus., 1986, Galerie Lopes, Zurich, Switzerland, 1986, 89, Michael Rosenfeld Gallery, N.Y.C., 1991, 92, 94, others; exhibited in Norlyst Gallery, N.Y.C., 1942, 67 Gallery, N.Y.C., 1943, David Porter Gallery, Washington, 1945, Four Arts Club, Palm Beach, Fla., 1946, Va. Mus. Fine Arts, 1946, U. Iowa, 1946, Salon des Realites Nouvelle, Paris, France, 1948, Bklyn. Mus., 1949, Cornell U., 1951, Art Inst. Chgo., 1961, 64, Syracuse Mus. Fine Arts, 1953, Nebr. Art Assn., 1953, Am. Acad. Arts & Letters, 1965, 67, 68, Smithsonian Inst., 1968, Taft Mus., Cin., 1981, Okla. Art Ctr., 1981, Saidenberg Gallery, N.Y.C., 1983, 89, Wight Art Gallery, UCLS, traveling to Nat. Gallery Modern Art, New Delhi, 1987, 88, Frances Wolfson Art Gallery, Miami, Fla., 1987, Guggenheim Mus., traveling to Venice, Italy, 1987, 88, Sid Deutsch Gallery, N.Y.C., 1989, 90, Weatherspoon Gallery, Greensboro, N.C., 1989; many others.; exhbn. Abstract Expressionism: Other Dimensions traveling to Lowe Art Mus., Coral Gables, Fla, Terra Art Mus., Chgo. (also panelist), Jane Voorhees Zimmerli Art Mus., Rutgers, New Brunswick, 1990, 92; works in permanent collections Addison Gallery, Andover, Mass., Munson Williams Proctor Mus., Utica, N.Y., Guggenheim Mus., Miss. Mus. Art, Whitney Mus., High Mus., Atlanta, Terra Mus. Am. Art, Evanston, Ill., Mus. Modern Art, Chgo. Art Inst., Newark Mus. Art, Iowa State U., Municipal Art Mus., The Hague, Holland, Tel Aviv Mus., Balt. Mus. Art, Hirshhorn Mus. and Sculpture Garden, Met. Mus. Art, N.Y.C., Phillips Collection, Washington, Carnegie Inst., Pitts., Rutgers U., Jane Voorhees Zimmerli Art Mus., New Brunswick, N.J., Worcester (Mass.) Art Mus., Nat. Mus. Am. Art Smithsonian Inst., Washington, others, also numerous pvt. collections; artist, 1960—. Office: Michael Rosenfeld Gallery 24 W 57th St New York NY 10019-3918

SELIGER, MARK ALAN, photographer; b. Amarillo, Tex., May 23, 1959; s. Maurice and Carol Lee (Singer) S. BS, East Tex. State U., 1981. Contbg. photographer Rolling Stone Mag., N.Y.C., 1989-93, chief photographer 1993—. Recipient Excellence in Journalism award Page One, 1988, Excellence awards Comm. Arts, 1988, 89, 90, 91, 92, 93, Creativity certs. Distinction Art Direction Mag., 1989, 93, Merit award Art Dirs. Club, 1991, Distinctive Merit award 1991, 92, Excellence certs. Am. Photography, 1991, 92, Distinctive Merit awards Soc. Pub. Designers, 1992, Distinguished Alumni award East Tex. State U., 1993; Mark Seliger Photography Scholarship named in his honor East Tex. State U., 1994. Mem. Am. Soc. Mag. Photographers. Office: Rolling Stone Mag 1290 Avenue Of The Americas New York NY 10104-0295

SELIGMAN, DANIEL, editor; b. N.Y.C., Sept. 25, 1924; s. Irving and Clare (O'Brien) S.; m. Mary Gale Sherburn, May 23, 1953; children: Nora, William Paul. Student, Rutgers U., 1941-42; A.B., NYU, 1946. Editorial asst. New Leader, 1946; asst. editor Am. Mercury, 1946-50; assoc. editor Fortune, 1950-59, editorial bd., 1959-66, asst. mng. editor, 1966-69, exec. editor, 1970-77, asso. mng. editor, 1977-87, contbg. editor, 1988—; sr. staff editor all Time, Inc. (publs.), 1969-70. Author: A Question of Intelligence: The IQ Debate in America, 1992. Home: 190 E 72nd St New York NY 10021-4370 Office: care Fortune Time And Life Bldg New York NY 10020

SELIGMAN, GEORGE BENHAM, mathematics educator; b. Attica, N.Y., Apr. 30, 1927; s. George Frederick and Florence Rose (Benham) S.; m. Irene Alice Schwieder, July 31, 1959; children: Barbara, Karen. AB, U. Rochester, 1950; MA, Yale U., 1951, PhD, 1954. Instr. math. Princeton (N.J.) U., 1954-56; instr. math. Yale U., New Haven, 1956-57, asst. prof., 1957-60, assoc. prof., 1960-65, prof., 1965-82, James E. English prof., 1982—. Author: Modular Lie Algebras, 1967, Rational Methods, 1976, Constructions of Lie Algebras and Their Modules, 1988; mem. editorial bd. Am. Scientist, 1980-90. With USNR, 1945-46. Mem. AAUP, Am. Math. Soc. (com. mem.), Math. Assn. Am. Democrat. Avocation: gardening. Home: 143 Woodlawn St Hamden CT 06517-1341 Office: Yale U Dept Math 2155 Yale Ave New Haven CT 06515-2254

SELIGMAN, JOEL, law educator; b. N.Y.C., Jan. 11, 1950; s. Selig Jacob and Muriel (Bienstock) S.; m. Friederike Felber, July 30, 1981; children:

Andrea, Peter. AB magna cum laude, UCLA, 1971; JD, Harvard U., 1974. Bar: Calif. 1975. Atty., writer Corp. Accountability Rsch. Group, Washington, 1974-77; prof. law Northeastern U. Law Sch., 1977-83, George Washington U., 1983-86, U. Mich., Ann Arbor, 1987-95; dean law U. Ariz., Tucson, 1995—; prof. law U. Mich., Ann Arbor, 1986-87; cons. Fed. Trade Commn., 1979-82, Dept. Transp., 1983, Office Tech. Assessment, 1988-89. Author (with others) Constitutionalizing the Corporation: The Case for the Federal Chartering of Giant Corporations, 1976, The High Citadel: The Influence of Harvard Law School, 1978, The Transformation of Wall Street: A History of the Securities and Exchange Commission and Modern Corporate Finance, 1982, The SEC and the Future of Finance, 1985, (multivolume) Securities Regulation; contbr. articles to profl. jours. Mem. State Bar Calif., Am. Law Inst. (adv. com., advisor corp. governance project). Office: U Ariz Law Sch Speedway & Mountain Tucson AZ 85721

SELIGMAN, MARTIN E. P., psychologist; b. Albany, N.Y., Aug. 12, 1942; s. Adrian and Irene Seligman; A.B., Princeton U., 1964; Ph.D. in Psychology, U. Pa., 1967; PhD (hon.) Uppsala U., Sweden, 1989; m. Mandy M. Seligman; children—Amanda, David, Lara, Nicole, Darryl. Asst. prof. Cornell U., 1967-70; assoc. prof. psychology U. Pa., 1972-76, prof., 1976—; dir. clin. program, 1980-94; vis. fellow Maudsley Hosp. Inst. Psychiatry, U. London, 1975. Recipient MERIT award, 1991, JAmes McKeen Cattell Fellow award Am. Psychol. Soc., 1995; NIMH grantee, 1969—; NSF fellow, 1963-64, Woodrow Wilson fellow, 1964-65, Guggenheim fellow, 1974-75; Center Advanced Study in Behavioral Scis. fellow, 1978-79; lic. psychologist, Pa. Fellow AAAS, Am. Psychol. Assn. (pres. divsn. clin. psychology 1993-95, William James Fellow award 1992); mem. Eastern Psychol. Assn., Psychonomic Soc., Assn. Advancement Behavior Therapy, Am. Psychopathol. Assn., Am. Psychosomatic Soc., Phi Beta Kappa, Sigma Xi. Author: Helplessness, 1975, Learned Optimism, 1991, What You Can Change & What You Can't, 1993, The Optimistic Child, 1995; contbr. numerous articles to profl. jours. Office: 3815 Walnut St Philadelphia PA 19104-3604

SELIGMAN, RICHARD MICHAEL, lawyer; b. N.Y.C., Feb. 3, 1945; s. Alexander and Sophie (Goldblatt) S.; m. Dana Leslie Corman, Mar. 13, 1969 (div. June 1975); m. Jody Lynn Wittenberg, May 24, 1985. BS, U. Wis., 1966, MBA, 1968; JD, DePaul U., 1973. Bar: Ill. 1973, U.S. Dist. Ct. (no. dist.) Ill. 1973, U.S. Dist. Ct. (so. dist.) Ill. 1975. Asst. counsel Marsh & McLennan Cos., Chgo., 1973-75; sole practice Chgo., 1975; chief counsel Ill. Dept. Ins., Springfield, 1975-76; ptnr. Schiff, Hardin & Waite, Chgo., 1976-85, Katten Muchin & Zavis, Chgo., 1985—. Mem. ABA, Ill. Bar Assn., Chgo. Bar Assn. Democrat. Jewish. Avocations: scuba diving, flying, motorcycling. Home: 786 Hill St Highland Park IL 60035-1165 Office: Katten Muchin & Zavis 525 W Monroe St Ste 1600 Chicago IL 60661-3693

SELIGMAN, THOMAS KNOWLES, museum administrator; b. Santa Barbara, Calif., Jan. 1, 1944; s. Joseph L. and Peggy (Van Horne) S.; children: Christopher, Timothy, Dylan. BA, Stanford U., 1965; BFA with honors, San Francisco Acad. Art, 1967; MFA, Sch. Visual Art, N.Y.C. 1968. Tchr., mus. dir. Peace Corps, Liberia, 1968-70; curator dept. Africa, Oceania and Ams. Fine Arts Museums, San Francisco, 1971-88; dep. dir. edn. and exhbns. Fine Arts Museums, 1972-88, dep. dir. ops. and planning, 1988-91; dir. Stanford (Calif.) U. Mus. Art, 1991—; mem. cultural property adv. com. USIA, 1988-92, Nat. Endowment for Art Indemnity Panel, 1992-95. Author mus. catalogues, articles in field. Trustee Internat. Coun. Mus./Am. Assn. Mus., 1990-94, Am. Fedn. Arts; mem. adv. coun. Acad. Art Coll. Grad. Program. Fellow Nat. Endowment Arts, 1974-75, 87. Mem. Assn. Art Mus. Dirs., Am. Assn. Mus., Leaky Found. Address: Stanford U Mus Art Stanford CA 94305-5060

SELIGSON, CARL H., investment banker; b. N.Y.C., Feb. 25, 1935; s. Harold P. and Lilian (Yohalem) S.; m. Joan Escott, May 19, 1957 (div. Nov. 1969); children: Susan S. Pattenaude, Barbara C.; m. Bonnie Laskin, Mar. 6, 1983. AB, Brown U., 1956; postgrad., NYU Grd. Sch. Bus. Adminstrn., 1961-63. Textile salesman Cohn, Hall, Marx Co., Montreal, Can., 1958-61; security analyst Burnham & Co., N.Y.C., 1961-67, Kuhn, Loeb & Co, N.Y.C., 1967-71; mng. dir. Merrill Lynch Capital Markets, N.Y.C., 1971-87, Kidder, Peabody & Co., N.Y.C., 1987-90; sr. exec. cons. regulated industries Deloitte & Touche, N.Y.C., 1990-92; mng. dir. Prudential Securities, N.Y.C., 1992—. Contbr. articles to profl. jours. including Pub. Utilities Fortnightly, Telephony, Fin. Exec., The Southern Banker, Coal Monthly and Energy News. Bd. dirs. Nuclear Energy Inst., Washington, 1988—. With U.S. Army, 1956-58. Fellow Fin. Analysts Fedn.; mem. Brown U. Club. Democrat. Jewish. Avocations: water sports, travel, theatre. Home: 40 E 94th St New York NY 10128-0709 Office: Prudential Securities 1 New York Plz New York NY 10292-2018

SELIGSON, MITCHELL A., Latin American studies educator; b. Hempstead, N.Y., Nov. 12, 1945; s. Morris and Ethel (Finkel) S.; m. Susan Berk, June 18, 1967; 1 child, Amber Lara. BA, Bklyn. Coll., 1967; MA, U. Fla., 1968; PhD, U. Pitts., 1974. Vol. U.S. Peace Corps, Costa Rica, 1968-70; asst. prof./assoc. prof. U. Ariz., Tucson, 1974-85; prof. U. Pitts., 1986-93, Daniel H. Wallace prof. polit. sci., 1994—, dir. Latin Am. studies, 1986-92, rsch. prof., 1992—; cons. U.S. AID, Guatemala, Honduras, Costa Rica, Ecuador, Jamaica, Panama, El Salvador, 1980—. Author, editor: Peasants of Costa Rica and the Development of Agrarian Capitalism, 1980, The Gap Between Rich and Poor, 1984, Authoritarians and Democrats, 1987, Elections and Democracy in Central America, 1989, reprinted 1995, Development and Underdevelopment, 1993. Fulbright fellow, Costa Rica, 1986, Rockefeller Found. fellow, 1985-86; grantee Social Sci. Rsch. Coun., Ford Found., NSF, Mellon Found., Heinz Endowment. Mem. Am. Polit. Sci. Assn., Latin Am. Studies Assn. (chmn. fin. com. 1991). Office: U Pitts Dept Polit Sci Pittsburgh PA 15260

SELIGMAN, THEODORE H., architect, interior designer, art consultant; b. Kansas City, Mo., Nov. 10, 1930; s. Harry and Rose (Haith) S.; m. Jacqueline Rose, Dec. 27, 1964 (div. 1976). BArch, Washington U., St. Louis, 1953. Registered architect, Mo., Kans. Intern Marshall & Brown, Kansas City, Mo., 1949-54; designer, head design Kivett & Myers, Kansas City, Mo., 1954-62; prin. Design Assocs., 1955—, Atelier Seligman, Kansas City, Mo., 1962-64; pres. Seligson, Eggen, Inc., Kansas City, 1964-73, Seligson Assocs., Inc., Architects Planners, Kansas City, 1973—; vis. lectr. adult edn. U. Mo.-Kansas City, 1958-61, vis. prof., 1989-94; prof. design and profl. architecture course U. Mo./Kansas City, 1994; tchr., critic Kansas City Art Inst., Mo., 1961-64, 71-72, adj. prof., 1986, 89, 91, 92; adj. prof. Kansas State U., 1991-92; vis. prof. Washington U., 1975, 77, 78, 81, 86, 91, U. Kans., Lawrence, 1978, 79, 80, 91, 92; art cons. Design Assocs., Kansas City, Mo., 1975—. Projects pub. in archtl. jours. V.p. Friends of Art Nelson-Atkins Mus. Art, Kansas City, bd. dirs. 1964-67, chmn. selections com., 1981, vis. curator, 1972, 87; chmn. Capitol Fine Arts Commn. Mo., 1983-90, Kansas City Worlds Fair goals and themes subcom., 1985-90; bd. dirs. Westport Tomorrow, Kansas City, 1980-87, Hist. Kansas City Found., 1984-90; pres. Native Sons of Kansas City, 1989, bd. dirs. 1978-94, Westport Cmty. Coun., 1973-75. Recipient Urban Design award Kansas City Mcpl. Art Commn., 1968, 74, 78; Nat. Archtl. award Am. Inst. Steel Constrn., 1970; Nat. award ASID/DuPont Color, 1989. Fellow AIA, Kansas City chpt. AIA (pres. 1983, bd. dirs. 1979-84, Design Excellence award 1966, 68, 70, 74, Cen. States Regional award 1974, 78, Honor award for outstanding service to chpt. and profession 1982-83); mem. Mo. Council Architects, Am. Soc. Interior Designers, Nat. Coun. Archtl. Registration Bds. (task analysis adv. com. 1988-90), Soc. Archtl. Historians (pres. 1973-75). Jewish. Office: Seligson Assocs Inc 106 W 14th St Kansas City MO 64105-1914

SELIN, IVAN, federal official; b. N.Y.C., Mar. 11, 1937; s. Saul and Freda (Kuhlman) Selin; m. Nina Naftal, June 8, 1957; children: Douglas, Jessica. B.E., Yale U., 1957, M.E., 1958, Ph.D., 1960; Dr. es Sciences, U. Paris, 1962. Rsch. engr. Rand Corp., Santa Monica, Calif., 1960-65; systems analyst Dept. Def., Washington, 1965-67, dep. asst. sec. def., 1967-69, acting asst. sec. for systems analysis, 1969-70; founder, chmn. bd. Am. Mgmt. Systems, Inc., Arlington, Va., 1970-89; undersec. state Dept. State, Washington, 1989-91; chmn. NRC, Washington, 1991-95; lectr. UCLA, 1961-63; chmn. mil. econ. adv. panel to CIA, 1978-89. Author: Detection Theory, 1964; contbr. articles to profl. jours. Pres. Corp. Against Drug Abuse, 1988—; bd. dirs. gov. UN Assn. U.S., 1979-89; mem. exec. com. Greater Washington Research Ctr., Fed. City Council. Decorated Disting. Civilian

Svc. medal, 1970; recipient Disting. Svc. medal Sec. of State, 1991; Fulbright scholar, 1959-61; Ford Found. grantee, 1952-54. Mem. Council Fgn. Relations, Fed. City Council Washington (trustee), IEEE (editor Trans. on Ifo. Theory 1960-65), Sigma Xi, Tau Beta Pi. Clubs: Yale, Cosmos. Home: 2905 32d St NW Washington DC 20008-3526 Office: Nuclear Regulatory Commn Washington DC 20555

SELINE, REX, reporter. Bus. reporter The Miami Herald, Fla. Office: The Miami Herald Pub Co One Herald Plz Miami FL 33132-1693

SELKE, CHARLES RICHARD, lawyer, mediator, real estate professional; b. Houston, Dec. 10, 1947; s. Oscar Otto Jr. and Edith Hicks (Hardey) S.; children: Erin Hardey, Lindsay Broussard. BA, U. Tex., 1970, JD, 1972. Bar: Tex., 1972. Pvt. practive Houston, 1974-80; ptnr. Beich & Selke, Houston, 1980-81; sr. v.p., ptnr. The Murphree Co., Houston, 1982-86; sr. v.p. Lowe Enterprises, Inc., Houston, 1987-88, Trione & Gordon, Inc., Houston, 1986-90; exec. v.p. Interstate Realty Corp., Houston, 1990-92; trust mktg. officer No. Trust Bank of Tex., Houston, 1992-93; pres. C. Richard Selke, P.C., Houston, 1994—. Bd. dirs., The McClelland Found., Austin, Tex., 1980—; vestryman, Palmer Meml. Episcopal Ch., Houston, 1986-88. Mem. State Bar Tex., Houston Bar Assn., Tex. Assn. Realtors, Breakfast Club Houston (pres. 1989), Briar Club (bd. dirs.). Avocations: skiing, water sports, marathon running. Home: 3400 Edloe # 301 Houston TX 77027 Office: C Richard Selke PC 3200 Southwest Fwy Ste 3300 Houston TX 77027

SELKIRK, JAMES KIRKWOOD, biochemist; b. N.Y.C., Dec. 3, 1938; s. James Kirkwood and Doris (Schuler) S.; m. Carole Ann Bozzone, Sept. 16, 1961; children: James Kirkwood, David Kirkwood. BS, Coll. Environ. Sci. and Forestry, Syracuse (N.Y.) U., 1964; PhD, Syracue U. Upstate Med. Ctr., Syracuse, 1969. Postdoctoral fellow McArdle Lab. Cancer Rsch., U. Wis., Madison, 1969-72; staff fellow Nat. Cancer Inst., NIH, Bethesda, Md., 1972-74, sr. staff fellow, 1974-75; sr. staff scientist unit leader chem. carcinogenesis biology divsn. Oak Ridge (Tenn.) Nat. Lab., 1975-85; chief carcinogenesis and toxicology evaluation br. nat. toxicology program Nat. Inst. Environ. Health Scis., 1985—, assoc. dir. divsn. toxicology rsch. and testing, 1989-92, chmn. carcinogen mechanism group Lab. Molecular Carcinogenesis, 1992—; adj. prof. Oak Ridge Biomed. Grad. Sch., U. Tenn., 1975-85; mem. breast cancer task force NIH, 1979-82; mem. com. on pyrenes and analogs NAS, 1981-83; chmn. Interagy. Testing Commn., 1986-90. Author rsch. articles, chpts. in books; mem. editorial bd. Carcinogenesis Jour., 1984-87, 91—; Cancer Rsch., 1981-86, Environ. Perspectives, 1993—. With AUS, 1959-61. Recipient U.S. Interagy. Testing Com. Exemplary Svc. award, 1992. Mem. Am. Cancer Soc. (carcinogenesis study sect. 1992—). Home: 113 Basswood Ct Chapel Hill NC 27514-1610 Office: Nat Inst Environ Health Scis PO Box 12333 Durham NC 27708

SELKOE, DENNIS JESSE, neurologist, researcher, educator; b. N.Y.C., Sept. 25, 1943; s. Herbert E. and Mary P. (Lille) S.; m. Polly Ann Strasser, June 24, 1967; children: Gregory, Kimberly. BA, Columbia U., 1965; MD, U. Va., 1969. Diplomate Am. Bd. Psychiatry and Neurology, Nat. Bd. Med. Examiners. Intern in medicine Hosp. U. Pa., Phila., 1969-70; rsch. assoc. NIH, Bethesda, Md., 1970-72; resident in neurology Peter Bent Brigham/Children's Hosp., Boston, 1972-74, chief resident in neurology, 1974-75; rsch. assoc. Harvard U. Med. Sch., Boston, 1975-78, asst. prof. neurology, 1978-82, assoc. prof., 1982-85, assoc. prof. neurology and neurosci., 1985-90, faculty mem. div. on aging, 1980—, prof. neurology and neurosci., 1990—; co-dir. Ctr. Neurologic Diseases Brigham and Women's Hosp., Boston, 1985—; mem. sci. adv. bd. Alzheimer's Disease Assn., Chgo., 1983-89; mem. Gov.'s Commn. on Alzheimer's Disease, Mass., 1985-87. Author over 200 articles, book chpts. on biochemistry and molecular biology of Alzheimer's Disease. Asst. surgeon USPHS, 1970-72. Recipient Wood-Kalb Found. prize Alzheimers Disease Assn., 1984, Med. Rsch. award Met. Life Found., 1986, LEAD award Nat. Inst. on Aging, 1988, NIH Merit award, 1991—; grantee Bristol-Myers Squibb Neurosci., 1990. Fellow Am. Acad. Neurology (Potamkin prize 1989); mem. Am. Neurol. Assn., Soc. for Neurosci., Am. Assn. Neuropathologists, World Fedn. Neurologists, AAAS. Office: Harvard Med Sch Brigham & Womens Hosp 221 Longwood Ave Boston MA 02115-5817

SELKOWITZ, ARTHUR, advertising agency executive; b. N.Y.C., May 26, 1943; s. Harry and Anne (Lichten) S.; m. Betsey Wattenberg, Apr. 15, 1967; children: Adam, Jed. AB, Syracuse (N.Y.) U., 1965. Account exec. Dancer Fitzgerald Sample, 1969-71; with Benton & Bowles, Inc., N.Y.C., 1971-82; v.p., account supr. Benton & Bowles, Inc., 1972-75, sr. v.p., mgmt. supr., 1975-81, sr. v.p., account dir., 1981-82; founder, pres. Penchina, Selkowitz Inc., N.Y.C., 1982-90; exec. v.p. internat. D'Arcy, Masius, Benton & Bowles, N.Y.C., 1990-94, pres. Asia and Pacific, 1995—, also bd. dirs.; bd. dirs. Medicus Group Internat. Dancer Fitzgerald Sample, N.Y.C., 1966-71. Office: 1675 Broadway New York NY 10019-5820

SELL, EDWARD SCOTT, JR., lawyer; b. Athens, Ga., Mar. 13, 1917; s. Edward Scott and Nettie Ruth (Whatley) S.; m. Mary Deupree Eckford, Sept. 14, 1940; 1 son, Edward Scott. A.B., U. Ga., 1937, J.D. cum laude, 1939. Bar: Ga. bar 1938. Ptnr. firm Lewis & Sell, 1940-55, Lane & Sell, 1955-56, Sell & Comer, Macon, Ga., 1956-69, Sell, Comer & Popper, Macon, 1969-80, Sell & Melton, 1980—; city atty., Macon, 1947-53; atty. Macon-Bibb County Planning & Zoning Commn., 1953-65; county atty. Bibb County, Ga., 1965—; lectr. law Mercer U., 1958-60. Trustee Wesleyan Coll., Macon, 1973—. Served with U.S. Army, 1942-46. Decorated Bronze Star, Army Commendation medal. Fellow Am. Bar Found.; mem. State Bar Ga. (bd. govs. 1947-50), Macon Bar Assn. (past pres.), Macon Cir. Bar Assn. (past pres.), Phi Beta Kappa, Phi Kappa Phi, Phi Delta Phi, City Club of Macon, Lions, Shriners, Masons, River North. Clubs: City Club of Macon, Lions, 191, Shriners, Masons, River North. Home: 1644 Hawthorne Rd Macon GA 31211-1213 Office: PO Box 229 Macon GA 31297-2899

SELL, WILLIAM EDWARD, legal educator; b. Hanover, Pa., Jan. 1, 1923; s. Henry A. and Blanche M. (Newman) S.; m. Cordelia I. Fulton, Aug. 20, 1949; 1 son, Jeffrey Edward. AB, Washington and Jefferson Coll., 1944, LHD, 1972, JD, Yale U., 1947; LLD, Dickinson Sch. Law, 1968. Bar: D.C. 1951, Pa. 1952. Instr. law U. Pitts., 1947-49, asst. prof. law, 1949-51, assoc. prof. law, 1953-54, prof. law, 1954-77, assoc. dean, 1957-63, dean, 1966-77, disting. svc. prof. law, 1977-94; emeritus dean, disting. svc. prof. law, 1994—; sr. counsel firm Meyer, Unkovic & Scott, Pitts., 1977-94; vis. prof. U. Mich. Law Sch., 1957; past pres. Pa. Bar Inst.; chmn. bd. St. Clair Health Corp. Author: Fundamentals of Accounting Lawyers, 1960, Pennsylvania Business Corporations, 3 vols., 1969, revised, 1981, Sell on Agency, 1975, also articles; editor: Pennsylvania Keystone Lawyers Desk Library. Past pres., bd. dirs. St. Clair Meml. Hosp.; chmn. St. Clair's Health Corp. With USAAF, WWII. Fellow Am. Bar Found. (life); mem. ABA, Pa. Bar Assn., Allegheny County Bar Assn., Assn. Am. Law Schs., Am. Law Inst. (life), Univ. Club, Phi Beta Kappa, Order of Coif, Pi Delta Epsilon, Phi Gamma Delta, Phi Delta Phi, Omicron Delta Kappa. Presbyterian (elder, deacon). Home: 106 Seneca Dr Pittsburgh PA 15228-1029 Office: U Pitts Sch Law 531 Law Bldg Pittsburgh PA 15260 also: St Clair Health Corp 1000 Bower Hill Rd Pittsburgh PA 15243-1873

SELLA, GEORGE JOHN, JR., chemical company executive; b. West New York, N.J., Sept. 29, 1928; s. George John and Angelina (Dominoni) S.; m. Janet May Auf-der-Heide, May 14, 1955; children: George Caldwell, Jane Ann, Lorie Jean, Michael Joseph, Carlie. B.S., Princeton U., 1950; M.B.A., Harvard U., 1952. With Am. Cyanamid Co., Wayne, N.J., 1954—; corp. v.p. Am. Cyanamid Co., 1977, sr. v.p., 1977-78, vice chmn., 1978-79, pres., 1979-90, chief exec. officer, 1983—, chmn. bd., 1984—; bd. dirs. Union Camp Corp., Equitable Life Assurance Soc. U.S. Bd. dirs. Multiple Sclerosis Soc. With USAF, 1952-54. Mem. NAM (bd. dirs.), Pharm. Mfrs. Assn. (bd. dirs.).

SELLAND, HOWARD M., manufacturing executive; b. 1943. BA, Spring Arbor Coll., 1979; MBA, U. Mich., 1983. Pres. Aeroquip Corp., Maumee, Ohio, 1963-81, 89—, also bd. dirs.; pres. Sterling Engineered Pdts. Inc., 1984-89; exec. v.p. Trinova Corp., 1981-84, 89—. Office: Aeroquip Corp 3000 Strayer Rd Maumee OH 43537-9713 also: Trinova Corp 3000 Strayer Rd Maumee OH 43537-9700 Office: 19700 Hall Rd Clinton Township MI 48038-1478•

SELLARS, VICTOR CAROL GENE, lawyer; b. Dallas, Nov. 30, 1929; s. Rod and Vera (Arnold) S.; m. Barbara Brown, Aug. 28, 1954; 1 son, Glenn S. BBA, U. Tex., Austin, 1958; JD, Baylor U., 1961. Bar: Tex. 1961, U.S. Dist. Ct. (no. dist.) Tex. 1964. Ptnr., Sellars, Terry and Fuller, Dallas County, Tex., 1961-65; atty. advisor Fed. Nat. Mortgage Assn., Dallas, 1965-69, asst. regional counsel, 1969-73, regional counsel Southwestern region, 1973-79, ret., 1979; of counsel L.M. Brazil PC, Emory, Tex. Served to 1st lt. USAF, 1950-55; Korea. Mem. Tex. Bar Assn.

SELLECK, TOM, actor; b. Detroit, Jan. 29, 1945; s. Robert D. and Martha S.; m. Jacquelyn Ray, 1970 (div. 1982); 1 stepson, Kevin; m. Jillie Joan Mack, Aug. 7, 1987; 1 child, Hannah Margaret. Student, U. So. Calif. TV appearances include The Rockford Files, Gypsy Warriors; TV series Magnum P.I. 1980-88; films include Myra Breckinridge, 1970, Seven Minutes, 1971, Daughters of Satan, 1972, Midway, 1976, Coma, 1982, High Road to China, 1983, Lassiter, 1984, Runaway, 1985, Three Men and a Baby, 1987, Her Alibi, 1989, An Innocent Man, 1989, Quigley Down Under, 1990, Three Men and a Little Lady, 1990, Folks!, 1992, Christopher Columbus: The Discovery, 1992, Mr. Baseball, 1992; TV films include Returning Home, 1975, Most Wanted, 1976, The Sacketts, 1979, The Concrete Cowboys, 1979, Divorce Wars, 1982, Louis L'Amour's "The Shadow Riders", 1982; exec. prodr. (series) B.L. Stryker, 1989-90, (TV movie) Revealing Evidence, 1990. Office: ICM 8942 Wilshire Blvd Beverly Hills CA 90211•

SELLER, ROBERT HERMAN, cardiologist, family physician; b. Phila., Mar. 21, 1931; s. David and Elsie (Straussman) S.; m. Maxine Schwartz, June 3, 1956; children: Michael, Douglas, Stuart. A.B., U. Pa., 1952, M.D. 1956. Intern. Grad. Hosp. of U. Pa., Phila., 1956-57; research asst. dept. pharmacology U. Pa., 1953-55; resident in cardiology, research fellow Am. Heart Assn., Phila. Gen. Hosp., 1957-58; resident in internal medicine Albert Einstein Med. Ctr., Phila., 1958-59; chief resident Albert Einstein Med. Ctr. 1959-60; instr. medicine Hahnemann Med. Coll. and Hosp., Phila., 1960-64; asst. prof. Hahnemann Med. Coll. and Hosp., 1964-69, assoc. prof., 1969-72, dir. Service F, 1962-67, asst. coordinator mil. edn. for nat. def., 1961-64, dir. div. family medicine, 1967-72, acting chmn. dept. family medicine and community health, 1972-74, prof. medicine, family medicine and community health, 1973-74; practice medicine, specializing in cardiology Buffalo, 1974—; prof., chmn. dept. family medicine, prof. medicine SUNY-Buffalo, Deaconess Hosp., 1974-82, chmn. dept. family practice and dir. family practice residency program, 1974-82; prof. medicine and family medicine SUNY-Buffalo, 1974—. Author: Differential Diagnosis of Common Complaints, 1986, 2nd edit., 1993; contbr. articles to profl. jours. NIH grantee, 1972-75; Deaconess Hosp. family practice resident tng. grantee, 1975—; health professions spl. projects grantee, 1975—. Fellow ACP, Am. Coll. Cardiology, Am. Acad. Family Physicians, Phila. Coll. Physicians; mem. AMA, N.Y. Med. Soc., Erie County Med. Soc., Am. Fedn. Clin. Research, Am. Heart Assn., Soc. of Tchrs. of Family Medicine, N.Y. Acad. Sci., N.Y. Acad. Family Physicians. Home: 125 Crestwood Ln Buffalo NY 14221-1462 Office: 1542 Maple Rd Buffalo NY 14221-3625

SELLERS, BARBARA JACKSON, federal judge; b. Richmond, Va., Oct. 3, 1940; m. Richard F. Sellers; children: Elizabeth M., Anne W., Catherine A. Attended, Baldwin-Wallace Coll., 1958-60; BA cum laude, Ohio State U., 1962; JD magna cum laude, Capital U. Law Sch., Columbus, Ohio, 1979. Bar: Ohio 1979, U.S. Dist. Ct. (so. dist.) Ohio 1981, U.S. Ct. Appeals (6th cir.), 1986. Jud. law clk. Hon. Robert J. Sidman, U.S. Bankruptcy Judge, Columbus, Ohio, 1979-81; assoc. Lasky & Semons, Columbus, 1981-82; jud. law clk. to Hon. Thomas M. Herbert, U.S. Bankrupcty Ct., Columbus, 1982-84; assoc. Baker & Hostetler, Columbus, 1984-86; U.S. bankruptcy judge So. Dist. Ohio, Columbus, 1986—; lectr. on bankruptcy univs., insts., assns. Recipient Am. Jurisprudence prize contracts and criminal law, 1975-76, evidence and property, 1976-77, Corpus Juris Secundum awards, 1975-76, 76-77. Mem. ABA (corp., litigation sect. 1986—, banking and bus. law sect. 1981—, jud. adminstrv. sect. 1983-84), Columbus Bar Assn., Comml. Law League of Am., Am. Bankruptcy Inst., Nat. Conf. Bankruptcy Judges, Order of Curia, Phi Beta Kappa. Office: US Bankruptcy Ct 124 US Courthouse 85 Marconi Blvd Columbus OH 43215-2823

SELLERS, BARNEY, professional society administrator; b. Bklyn., June 12, 1941; s. Milton Theodore and Alice Margaret (Wilensky) S.; m. Rosalie Bono; children: David, Lori; m. Karla Young, Nov. 1, 1958. BA, CCNY, 1963; MS, Syracuse U., 1972; MLA, Johns Hopkins U., 1991. Rsch. analyst U.S. Commn. on Civil Rights, 1964-66; asst. to dir. Office Civil Rights HEW, 1966-68; dir. project enforcement A. Philip Randolph Inst., 1968-69; Washington rep. Am. Friends Svc. Com., 1969-70; dir. spl. projects Nat. Urban Coalition, 1970-71; staff dir. med. assistance adv. coun. HEW, 1972-74; dir. govt. rels. Nat. Health Coun., 1974-78; dep. dir. Am. Health Planning Assn., 1978-79; dir. office beneficiary svcs. HEW, 1979-82; exec. dir. Am. Soc. Parenteral & Enteral Nutrition, 1982—; cons. McGraw-Hill Health and Medicine Newsletters, Resource Mgmt. Corp., Roy Littlejohn Assocs., Washington Rsch. Project. Vol. Dukakis for Pres., 1988. Mem. Am. Soc. Assn. Execs. (cert., tech. com. Greater Washington 1994—), Second Tuesday Breakfast Club (founder, pres.). Avocations: racquetball, hiking. Home: 9512 Nightsong Ln Columbia MD 21046 Office: Am Soc Parenteral/ Enteral Nutrition 8630 Fenton St Ste 412 Silver Spring MD 20910-3803

SELLERS, FRED WILSON, banker; b. Alexander City, Ala., Apr. 29, 1942; s. Fred Wilson and Helen (Hagan) Sellers); m. Nancy Wilbanks, July 11, 1964; children: Fredrick Hagan, Robert Wilbanks. BS, U. Ala., 1964; MBA, L.I. U., 1966; postgrad., U. Wis., Madison, 1974. CPA, N.C. Ala.; cert. fraud examiner. Staff acct. Ernst & Young, Winston-Salem, N.C. 1966-69; comptr. Citibanc Group, Inc., Andalusia, Ala., 1972-73; various positions, then sr. v.p., dir. internal audit AmSouth Bankcorporation, Birmingham, Ala., 1973—; bd. dirs. Better Bus. Bur., Mobile, Ala., 1984-86. Mem. budget com. United Way, Birmingham, 1982-83. Mem. AICPA, N.C. Assn. CPAs, Ala. Assn. CPAs, Ala. United States Air Force Acad. Parents Club (pres. 1993-94, 94-95), Vestavia Country Club, The Club, Univ. Club (Tuscaloosa). Avocation: travel. Home: 2112 Viking Cir Birmingham AL 35216 Office: AmSouth Bankcorporation PO Box 11007 Birmingham AL 35288

SELLERS, JAMES EARL, theological educator; b. Lucedale, Miss., Nov. 1, 1926; s. Lucius Earl and Grace (McVicar) S. BEE, Ga. Inst. Tech., 1947; MS, Fla. State U., 1954; PhD (Kent fellow), Vanderbilt U., 1958. Asst. prof. Christian ethics and theology Div. Sch. Vanderbilt U., Nashville, 1958-61; assoc. prof. Vanderbilt U., 1961-64, prof., 1964-71, dean Div. Sch., 1964-67; David Rice prof. ethics Rice U., Houston, 1971-93, prof. emeritus, 1993—. Author: The Outsider and the Word of God, 1961, The South and Christian Ethics, 1962, Theological Ethics, 1966, Public Ethics, 1970, Warming Fires, 1975, The Polis in America as Imago Dei, 1984, Tensions in the Ethics of Interdependence, 1986, Medical Ethics and the Civil Rights Movement, 1989, Love and Justice Reconsidered, 1990, Essays in American Ethics, 1991; co-author: The Health-Care Community as a Reservoir of Potential Subjects, 1984; editor-at-large The Christian Century, 1971-86; contbr. articles to Ethical Issues in Am. Life, Lifeboat Ethics. Lt. USNR, 1944-54. Recipient Danforth Rsch. award, France, 1966. Mem. Soc. for Values in Higher Edn., Group for Research in Med-Ethics, AAUP. Home: 2601 S Braeswood Blvd Apt 1501 Houston TX 77025-2816 Office: Rice U Dept Religious Studies 6100 S Main Houston TX 77251 *After more than thirty years of teaching ethics to university students and churchmen, I have concluded that neither "morality" nor "religion" is as basic as the American tradition of justice. If we would rescue the oppressed here or elsewhere, indeed, if we would redeem mankind, we should begin by affirming life with dignity, liberty, and the right of all to the pursuit of happiness, the disadvantaged as well as the advantaged.*

SELLERS, JOEL SCOTT, sports medicine physician; b. Tulsa, Oct. 8, 1957; s. Jimmy Lloyd and Nita (Long) S.; m. Lori Kaye Irwin, Apr. 29, 1988. BA, U. Okla., 1980; DO, Okla. State U., 1985. Intern Phoenix Gen. Hosp., 1985-86; fellow in sports medicine Ctr. Sports Medicine and Orthopedics, Phoenix, 1986-87; staff physician, 1987—; team physician, USA Wrestling Fedn., Stillwater, Okla., 1986—, Ironwood High Sch., Glendale, Ariz., 1986—; consulting physician, Phoenix Suns basketball team, 1986—; area community colls., Phoenix; lectr. intern tng. program, Phoenix Gen. Hosp., 1986; speaker in field; U.S. physician, U.S. vs. USSR Wrestling Dual

Meet, Phoenix, 1988. Contbr. articles on wrestling to various publs. Mem. Am. Osteo. Acad. Sports Medicine, Am. Osteo. Assn. Ariz. Osteo. Assn., Okla. Alumni Assn., Sigma Chi. Democrat. Roman Catholic. Avocations: skiing, weightlifting, cycling, racquetball, golf. Home: 2254 W Mandalay Ln Phoenix AZ 85023-5027

SELLERS, PETER HOADLEY, mathematician; b. Phila., Sept. 12, 1930; s. Lester Hoadley and Therese (Tyler) S.; m. Lucy Bell Newlin, June 21, 1958; children—Mortimer, Therese, Mary, Lucy Bell. B.A., U. Pa., 1953, M.A., 1958, Ph.D., 1965. Math. tchr. Kangaru Sch., Embu, Kenya, 1961-63; programmer U. Pa., Phila., 1958-61; mem. faculty Rockefeller U., N.Y.C., 1966—; Johnson Found. postdoctoral fellow, 1963-65. mem. editorial bd. Genomics, 1986—; author: Combinatorial Complexes, 1979; contbr. articles to profl. jours. Trustee Coll. of the Atlantic, Bar Harbor, Maine, 1985—. Served to lt (j.g.) USNR, 1953-55. Mem. Am. Math. Soc., Math. Assn. Am., Soc. Indsl. and Applied Math. Democrat. Episcopalian. Avocation: boat building. Home: 413 W Stafford St Philadelphia PA 19144-4407 Office: Rockefeller Univ 1230 York Ave New York NY 10021-6341

SELLERS, WALLACE OSBORNE, financial services company executive; b. Jacksonville, Fla., Oct. 14, 1929; s. Elijah Thomas and Naomi (Wallace) S.; m. Elizabeth Naudain Ives, Dec. 15, 1956; children—Wallace, Jr., Susan G., Catherine W. B.A., U. N.Mex., 1951; M.A., NYU, 1956; A.M.P., Harvard, 1975. Chartered fin. analyst. With Merrill Lynch, Pierce, Fenner & Smith Inc., 1951-72; dir. mcpl. and corp. bond div., 1972-75; pres. Merrill Lynch Trading Services, S.A., Geneva, Switzerland, 1973-75, dir. securities research div., 1975-77; v.p. corp. and pub. affairs Merrill Lynch & Co. Inc., 1977-79, dir. planning div. 1979-82, dir. diversification and joint ventures div., 1982-84, sr. v.p., dir. strategic devel., 1984-86; pres., chief exec. officer Enhance Fin. Services, Enhance Reins. Co., 1986—, also bd. dirs.; pres. Merrill Lynch Communications Investments, Inc., v.p. Merrill Lynch Tech. Group, Inc.; bd. dirs. Biotech Capital, Fin. News Network, Santa Monica, Calif., TI Industries, Inc., Vienna, Va., Intex Holdings, Hamilton, Bermuda. Trustee N.Y. Infirmary, Beekman Downtown Hosp., Hudson Inst., Indianapolis, Ind.; bd. dirs. Friends of Women's World Banking, N.Y.; mem. adv. bd. Inst. for Studies in Tech. Mgmt. and Policy, N.Y. Poly. Inst., Bklyn.; Mem. N.Y. Soc. Security Analysts, Fin. Analysts Fedn., Am. Soc. Macro-Engring. (treas., bd. dirs.). Episcopalian. Clubs: Bond, Mcpl. Bond (N.Y.C.); Ridgewood Country (N.J.). Office: Enhance Fin Svcs Group Inc 335 Madison Ave Fl 25 New York NY 10017

SELLERY, J'NAN MORSE, English and American literature educator; b. Oakland, Calif., Jan. 3, 1928; d. Raymond Stephen and Minna Esther (Bourus) Morse; m. Austin R. Sellery, Aug. 30, 1947; children: Stephen Brooke, Edward Austin, Margaret Joan, John Merritt. BA, U. Calif., Riverside, 1965; MA, U. Calif., 1967, PhD, 1970. Asst. prof. Harvey Mudd Coll., Claremont, Calif., 1970-74, assoc. prof. Claremont grad. sch., 1974-80, prof. English Claremont grad. sch., 1980—, Louisa & Robert Miller chair prof. humanities, 1989—; coord. women's studies Claremont Coll., 1988-91; cons. UMI Press, 1989, Conn. Rev., 1988. Books co-editor: Faust Part I, 1969, The Scapegoat, 1972, Bibliography of Elizabeth Bowen, 1981; editor (jours.) Women's Voices, 1986, Gender, 1990; sr. editor Psychol. Perspectives, 1969—; contbr. articles and poetry to mags. and profl. jours. NDEA fellow U. Calif., 1967-70; rsch. grantee Harvey Mudd Coll., 1971-90, NEH summer grantee Yale U., 1979, Mellon grantee in curriculum Claremont Colls., 1989; vis. humanities scholar U. Calgary, Can., 1992. Mem. AAUW (nat. bd. mem. 1982-83, mem. fellowship panel 1989-93), MLA, Nat. Women's Studies Assn. (coord. coun. 1989-92, cons. jour. and book awards 1991—). Office: Harvey Mudd Coll Kingston Hall Kingston Hall Claremont CA 91711

SELLIN, ERIC, linguist, poet, educator; b. Phila., Nov. 7, 1933; s. Thorsten and Amy (Anderson) S.; m. Birgitta Sjöberg, Jan. 25, 1958; children: Frederick, Christopher. BA, U. Pa., 1955, MA, 1958, PhD, 1965. Asst. instr. French U. Pa., Phila., 1955-56, 1957-58, 1959-60; lectr. Am. lit. U. Bordeaux, France, 1956-57; instr. French Clark U., Worcester, Mass., 1958-59; lectr. creative writing U. Pa., 1960-62; instr. French Temple U., Phila., 1962-65; asst. prof. Temple U., 1965-67, assoc. prof., 1967-70, prof., 1970-91, chmn. dept. French and Italian, 1970-73, founder, dir. Center for Study of Francophone Lit. of North Africa, 1981—; prof. French Tulane U., New Orleans, 1991—; chmn. dept. French and Italian, 1995—; USIS lectr., Africa and Near East, 1981-83, 85, 88-91, manuscript reader, cons. to various profl. jours., univ. presses, and founds.; sr. Fulbright-Hays lectr., Algiers, Algeria, 1968-69, Dakar, Senegal, 1978-79. Author: The Dramatic Concepts of Antonin Artaud, 1968, The Inner Game of Soccer, 1976, Soccer Basics, 1977, Reflections on the Aesthetics of Futurism, Dadaism and Surrealism—a Prosody Beyond Words, 1993, (poetry) Night Voyage, 1964, Trees at First Light, 1973, Tanker Poems, 1973, Borne kilométrique, 1973, Marginalia, 1979, Crépuscule prolongé à El Biar, 1982, Nightfall over Lubumbashi, 1982, Night Foundering, 1985, Dead of Noon, 1992; editor: Africana Jour., 1983-87, CELFAN Edit. Monographs, 1987—, CELFAN Rev., 1981—; contbr. over 150 articles to profl. jours. and anthologies. Recipient faculty prize in Romance langs. U. Pa., 1955; Am. Philos. Soc. fellow, 1970, 82, NEH sr. fellow, 1973-74; Temple U. rsch. grantee, 1970, 82; sr. Fulbright-Hays Rsch. scholar Francophone Lit., Rabat, Morocco, 1989. Mem. Am. Assn. Tchrs. French, African Lit. Assn., Phi Beta Kappa. Office: Tulane U Dept French New Orleans LA 70118

SELLIN, IVAN ARMAND, physicist, educator, researcher; b. Everett, Wash., Aug. 16, 1939; s. Petrus and Amelia Fanny (Josephson) S.; m. Helen Kathleen Gill, June 16, 1962; children: Peter Bennington, Frank Erick. Student, Harvard U., 1956-59; MS, U. Chgo., 1960, PhD, 1964. Instr., rsch. assoc. U. Chgo., 1960-65; asst. prof. NYU, 1965-67; rsch. physicist Oak Ridge (Tenn.) Nat. Lab., 1967-70; assoc. prof. U. Tenn., Knoxville, 1970-74, prof., 1974-83, dist. prof., 1983—; adj. rsch. physicist Oak Ridge (Tenn.) Nat. Lab., 1970—; consultant prin. NSF, Washington, 1988-89; mem. Nat. Acad. Scis.-NRC Com. Atomic and Molecular Sci., 1973-76, chmn. 1980-83, mem. panel on accelerator-related atomic and molecular sci., 1978-80, survey on atomic and molecular sci., mem. panel on atomic, molecular and optical physics, NAI-NRC Nat. Physics Survey, 1983-86; vis. Centro Atomico Orgn. of Am. States, Bariloche, Argentina, 1972, 81-82, Humboldt Awardee, Inst. fur Kernphysik der Univ., Frankfurt, 1977, Nobelinstitut/Atomsysik, Stockholm, Sweden, 1977-78, 83; speaker and presenter in field. Editor, co-author (with others): Advances in Atomic and Molecular Physics, 1994, McGraw-Hill Annual Yearbook of Science and Technology, 1978, McGraw-Hill Encyclopedia of Science and Technology, 5th edit., 1982, 7th edit., 1992, Beam Foil Spectroscopy: Vol. 1, Atomic Structure and Lifetimes, Vol. 2, Collisional and Radiative Processes, 1976, Structure and Collisions of Ions and Atoms, 1978, Forward Electron Ejection in Ion Collisions, 1984, Physics Through the 1990's: Atomic, Molecular, and Optical Physics, 1986; contbr. more than 200 articles to profl. jours. Concert mgr. Oak Ridge Civic Music Assn., 1973. Grantee Office of Naval Rsch., 1972-82, NASA, 1972-73, 73-78, NSF, 1973-97; Dept. Energy, 1979-83, Oak Ridge Nat. Lab., 1980-82, NSF Divsn. Internat. Programs, 1986-92; recipient Sr. U.S. Scientist award, Alexander von Humboldt Found., 1977, 86, 88; Fulbright scholar, 1977; rsch. scholar Japan Ministry of Edn., Sci. and Culture, 1994, invited vis. Harvard-Smithsonian Ctr. for Astrophysics, 1995; guest prof. U. Stockholm, 1995. Mem. Fellow Am. Phys. Soc. (vice chmn. 1981, chmn. com. on Constitution and Bylaws, 1982-83, mem. com. on meetings 1991-93, coun. advisor, 1989-93, councillor 1979-83, chmn. publs. com. divsn. of electron and atomic physics 1974-76, mem. program com. 1976-78, mem. nominating com. 1979-83, mem. fellowship com. 1979-83, mem. exec. com., 1979-83; mem. exec. com. Southeastern sect. 1979-93, vice chmn. 1990-91, program chmn. 1990-91, chmn. 1991-92, Jesse Beams medal 1983); mem. Academia European, Cosmos Club. Achievements include research in highly ionized heavy ions, modes of formation and destruction in collisions with target atoms and molecules, and the excitation they induce in dilute gas and dense solid media; use of synchrotron radiation to form and study cold, multiply ionized ions using heavy ion accelerators, synchrotron storage rings, electron spectrometers, x-ray, soft x-ray, and extreme ultra-violet spectrometers, heavy particle spectrometers, and two-dimensional position-sensitive detectors. Office: Oak Ridge Nat Lab MS 6377 PO Box 2008 Oak Ridge TN 37830

SELLIN, THEODORE, foreign service officer, consultant; b. Phila., June 17, 1928; s. Thorsten and Amy (Anderson) S.; m. Taru Jarvi, July 10, 1965;

1 child, Derek. Student, U. Uppsala, Sweden, 1946-48; BA, U. Pa., 1951, MA, 1952. Joined Fgn. Svc., Dept. State, 1952; vice consul Copenhagen, 1952-56; rsch. analyst Dept. State, Washington, 1956-58; program officer Office Internat. Confs., 1965-67; acad. tng. staff U. Ind., 1958-59; 2d sec. Am. Embassy, Helsinki, Finland, 1959-64, 1st sec., polit. officer, 1971-73; 1st sec., labor-polit. officer Am. Embassy, Oslo, 1967-71; polar affairs officer Dept. State, 1975; consul gen. Goteborg, Sweden, 1978-80; fgn. rels. cons. Dept. State, Washington, 1980—. Office: Dept State IS/FPC/CDR Washington DC 20520

SELLMYER, DAVID JULIAN, physicist, educator; b. Joliet, Ill., Sept. 28, 1938; s. Marcus Leo and Della Louise (Plumhoff) S.; m. Catherine Joyce Zakas, July 16, 1962; children: Rebecca Ann, Julia Maryn, Mark Anthony. BS, U. Ill., 1960; PhD, Mich. State U., 1965. Asst. prof. MIT, Cambridge, 1965-72, assoc. prof., 1972; assoc. prof. U. Nebr., Lincoln, 1972-75, prof., 1975—, chmn. dept. physics, 1978-84, George Holmes disting. prof., 1987, dir. Ctr. Materials Rsch., 1988—; cons. Dale Electronics, Norfolk, Nebr., 1980—. Contbr. articles, book revs. to refereed jours. Recipient tech. award NASA, 1972; disting. vis. prof. S.D. Sch. Mines and Tech., Rapid City, 1981. Fellow Am. Phys. Soc. Office: U Nebr Ctr Materials Rsch Lincoln NE 68588-0113

SELLO, ALLEN RALPH, oil company executive; b. Winnipeg, Man., Can., June 22, 1939; m. Mary Lou Sello, June 3, 1972; children: Clint, Monique, Daren. B of Commerce (hon.), U. Man., 1963; MBA, U. Toronto, Ont., Can., 1964. Mgr. mktg. analysis Ford Motor Co. of Can., Oakville, Ont., Can., 1972-75, mgr. product plans, 1975-78, asst. treas., 1978-79; dir. acctg. Gulf Can. Ltd., Toronto, 1979-81, dir. fin. planning, 1981-82, contr., 1982-85; v.p., contr. Gulf Can. Corp., Calgary, Alta., Can., 1985-86; v.p. fin. Gulf Can. Resources, Ltd., Calgary, 1986-88, v.p. fin., chief fin. officer, 1988-95. Mem. Fin. Execs. Inst.; trustee Glencoe Golf and Country Club, Calgary Petroleum Club. Avocations: squash, skiing, tennis, golf.

SELLS, BOAKE ANTHONY, private investor; b. Ft. Dodge, Iowa, June 24, 1937; s. Lyle M. and Louise (Gadd) S.; m. Marian S. Stephenson, June 20, 1959; children: Damian, Brian, Jean Ann. BSC, U. Iowa, 1959; MBA, Harvard U., 1969. Bus. office mgr. Northwestern Bell Tel., Des Moines, 1959-63; salesman Hydraulic Cos., Ft. Dodge, 1964-67; pres. Cole Nat. Corp., Cleve., 1969-83; vice chmn. Dayton Hudson Corp., Mpls., 1983-84, pres., 1984-87, chmn., pres., chief exec. officer Revco D.S., Inc., Twinsburg, Ohio, 1987-92; bd. dirs. Promus Cos., Huffy Corp. Trustee Cleve. Ctr. for Contemporary Art, Cleve. Play House.

SELLS, BRUCE HOWARD, biomedical sciences educator; b. Ottawa, Ont., Can., Aug. 15, 1930; s. Charles Henry and Nell (Worth) S.; m. Bernice May Romain, Sept. 19, 1953; children: Jennifer, Monica, David, Lisa. B.S., Carleton U., 1952; M.A., Queen's U., 1954; Ph.D., McGill U., 1957. Demonstrator McGill U., Montreal, Ont., Can., 1954-57; research assoc. Columbia U., N.Y.C., 1961-62; asst. prof. St. Jude Children's Hosp.-U. Tenn., Memphis, 1962-64; assoc. prof. St. Jude Children's Hosp., Memphis, 1964-72, staff, 1964-72; prof., dir. molecular biology Meml. U. Nfld., St. John's, Can., 1972-83, assoc. dean, 1979-83; prof. molecular biology U. Guelph, Ont., Can., 1983—, dean biol. sci., 1983-95; mem. adv. com. Ont. Health Rsch. Coun., 1992. Contbr. numerous articles to various publs. Adv. Com. Ont. Health Rsch. Coun., 1992—. Research fellow Damon Runyon Meml. Fund, Brussels, 1957-59; research fellow Damon Runyon Meml. Fund, Copenhagen, 1959-60; Killam sr. research fellow U. Paris, 1978-79; grantee NIH, 1963-72, NSF, 1965-69, Med. Research Council Can., 1972, Damon Runyon Meml. Fund for Cancer Research, 1962-76, Nat. Found.-March of Dimes, 1974-78, Muscular Dystrophy Assn. Can., 1974, Nat. Cancer Inst. Can., 1979, Vis. Prof. award Institut Pasteur, Paris, 1989; Exchange fellow Natural Scis. and Engring. Rsch. Coun. of Can., 1994. Fellow Royal Soc. Can. (rapporteur microbiology and biochemistry div. 1985-87, convenor 1987-89); mem. Acad. Sci. of Royal Soc. Can. (life scis. div. fellowship rev. com. 1990-92), Am. Soc. Microbiologists, Can. Assn. Univ. Tchrs., Am. Soc. Biol. Chemists, Am. Soc. Cell Biology, Can. Biochemistry Soc. (Ayerst award selection com. 1990), Med. Rsch. Coun. (Centennial fellowships com., chmn. com. on biotech. devel. grants 1983-85, standing com. for Can. Genetic Disease Network 1991-92, chmn. 1992—), Nat. Rsch. Coun. Can. (biological phenomena subcom. 1983-86, chmn. steering group, sci. criteria for environ. quality com. 1986, E.W.R. Steacie Prize com. 1986-88). Home: Rural Rte 6, Guelph, ON Canada N1H 6J3 Office: U Guelph, 577 Gordon St, Guelph, ON Canada N1G 2W1

SELLS, HAROLD E., retail company executive; b. Ozark, Ark., 1928; married. Various operational, mktg. positions Kinney Shoe Corp., 1945-65, pres. real estate div., 1965-74; with Woolworth Corp (formerly F.W. Woolworth Co.), N.Y.C., 1974—; v.p. real estate F.W. Woolworth Co., N.Y.C., 1974-80, sr. v.p. corp. devel., 1980-81, sr. v.p. internat. ops., property devel., 1982, pres., chief operating officer, 1983-87, chmn., chief exec. officer, 1987—, also bd. dirs.; bd. dirs. Bank of N.Y., Centennial Ins. Co., Atlantic Reins. Co., dir. Kinney Shoe Corp., Richman Bros. Co., F.W. Woolworth Co. Ltd., Canada; trustee Atlantic Mut. Ins. Co. Office: Woolworth Corp Woolworth Bldg 233 Broadway New York NY 10279-0001

SELMAN, ROLAND WOOTEN, III, lawyer; b. Kansas City, Mo., Aug. 16, 1941; s. Roland Wooten Jr. and Dixie R. (Chambliss) S.; 1 child, Kellee Harris. Student, U. Kans., 1959-61, Stetson U., 1961-62; BA, U. Mo., Kansas City, 1963; JD, U. Calif., Hastings, 1971. Bar: Calif. 1972, U.S. Ct. Appeals (9th cir.) 1975, U.S. Supreme Ct. 1975, D.C. 1979, U.S. Ct. Appeals (D.C. cir.) 1980, U.S. Ct. Appeals (Fed. cir.) 1983. Assoc. Pillsbury, Madison & Sutro, San Francisco, 1971-79, gen. ptnr., 1979—; judge pro tem Mcpl. Ct., San Francisco, 1984—. Bd. dirs. Marin Svcs. for Women; planning commr. City of Sausalito, Calif., 1991-93; chmn. Sausalito Planning Commn., 1992-93. Lt. USN, 1963-68. Decorated D.F.C., Air medal. Mem. ABA, Nat. Transp. Safety Bd. Bar Assn., San Francisco Bar Assn., Lawyer-Pilots Bar Assn., Aircraft Owners and Pilots Assn., Order of Coif. Mem. Christian Ch. Avocations: flying, video, scuba diving. Home: 28 Greenwood Bay Dr Belvedere Tiburon CA 94920-2252 Office: Pillsbury Madison & Sutro 235 Montgomery St San Francisco CA 94104-2902

SELTSER, RAYMOND, epidemiologist, educator; b. Boston, Dec. 17, 1923; s. Israel and Hannah (Littman) S.; m. Charlotte Frances Gale, Nov. 16, 1946; children: Barry Jay, Andrew David. MD, Boston U., 1947; MPH, Johns Hopkins U., 1957. Diplomate Am. Bd. Preventive Medicine (trustee, sec.-treas. 1974-77). Am. Bd. Med. Specialties (mem. exec. com. 1976-77). Asst. chief med. info. and intelligence br. U.S. Dept. Army, 1953-56; epidemiologist div. internal health USPHS, 1956-57; from asst. prof. to prof. epidemiology Johns Hopkins U. Sch. Hygiene and Pub. Health, 1957-81, assoc. dean, 1967-77, dep. dir. Oncology Ctr., 1977-81; dean U. Pitts. Grad. Sch. Pub. Health, 1981-87, prof. epidemiology, 1981-88, emeritus dean, prof. epidemiology, 1988—; assoc. dir. USPHS Ctrs. for Disease Control, Rockville, Md., 1988-90; assoc. dir. Ctr. for Gen. Health Svcs. Extramural Rsch. Agy. for Health Care Policy and Rsch., Rockville, 1990—; cons. NIMH, 1958-70, also various govtl. health agys., 1958-79; expert cons. Pres.'s Commn. on Three Mile Island, 1979-80; mem. Three Mile Island Adv. Panel Health, Nat. Cancer Inst. Cancer Control Grant Rev. Com., Pa. Dept. Health Preventive Health Service Block Grant Adv. Task Force, Gov.'s VietNam Herbicide Info. Commn. Pa.; chmn. Toxic/Health Effects Adv. Com., 1985-87. Trustee, mem. exec. com., chmn. profl. adv. com. Harmarville Rehab. Ctr., Pitts., 1982-87; bd. dirs. Health Edn. Ctr., Media Info. Service. Served to capt. AUS, 1951-53, Korea. Decorated Bronze Star; recipient Centennial Alumni citation Boston U. Sch. Medicine, 1973; elected to Johns Hopkins Soc. of Scholars, 1986. Fellow AAAS, Am. Pub. Health Assn. (mem. governing council 1975-77, chmn. EPI sect. council 1979-80), Pa. Pub. Health Assn. (bd. dirs. 1985-88, pres.-elect 1986-88), Am. Coll. Peventive Medicine, Am. Heart Assn.; mem. Am. Epidemiol. Assn., Internat. Epidemiol. Assn., Am. Soc. Preventive Oncology, Am. Cancer Soc. (bd. dirs. Pa. div. 1985-87, mem. exec. com. 1986-87), Assn. Schs. Pub. Health (sec. 1969-71, exec. com., chmn. edn. com. 1983-87), Soc. Med. Cons. Armed Forces, Soc. Epidemiologic Research, Nat. Council Radiation Protection and Measurements (consociate), Johns Hopkins Alumni Coun., Delta Omega, Sigma Xi. Office: Agy Health Care Policy Rsch Ctr Gen Health Svcs Extramural Rsch 2101 Jefferson St Rockville MD 20852

SELTZER, ADA MAY, librarian, medical library director; b. Kempton, Pa., June 7, 1942; d. Clayton Franklin and Dorothea Anna (Oldt) S.; m. John W. Bowen, Dec. 24, 1965 (div. May, 1977). BS, Kutztown U., 1964; MS in Libr. Sci., Fla. State U., 1965; MA, U. S. Fla., 1971. Asst. univ. libr. U. S. Fla., Tampa, 1965-68, assoc. univ. libr., 1968-71, univ. libr. med. ctr., 1971-74; head pub. svc. U. S. Fla. Med. Ctr., 1974-79; vis. instr. U. South Fla. Sch. Libr. Studies, Tampa, 1979-86; asst. dir. U. S Fla. Med. Ctr., Tampa, 1979-86; dir. U. Miss. Med. Ctr., Jackson, 1986—; asst. prof. U. Miss. Health Related Professions, Jackson, 1987—; coninuing edn. instr. Med. Libr. Assn., Chgo., 1979-91; project dir. grants, Fla. Libr. Assn, Orlando, 1981-82, Miss. Health Scis. Info. Network, Jackson, 1989-91, 94—. Author: (book) Instructor's Handbook for Searching Medline, 1986; (manual) Oncology: Concepts and Resources, 1988, revised edit. 1991; editor: Fla. Union List of Serials, 1972; contbr. numerous articles to profl. jours. Mem. Friends of Nat. Libr. of Medicine, Washington, 1986—. Mem. ALA, Acad. of Health Sci. Info. Profls. (disting.), Med. Libr. Assn. (chair chpt. coun. 1992-95, bd. dirs 1992-95, continuing edn. com. 1989-91, so. chpt. MLA coun. rep. 1988-91, chmn. so. chpt. 1982-83), S.E. Libr. Assn., Fla. Libr. Assn. (pres. 1981-82), Fla. Health Scis. Libr. Assn. (pres. 1985-86), Miss. Libr. Assn. Office: Rowland Med Libr U Miss Med Ctr 2500 N State St Jackson MS 39216-4505

SELTZER, BRADLEY MARSHALL, lawyer; b. Massapequa, N.Y., Sept. 26, 1953; s. David John and Faye (Hyman) S.; m. Lisa Gayle Stein, June 23, 1979; children: Samantha, Beth, Lauren Rachel. BA, SUNY, Albany, 1974; JD, George Washington U., 1978. Bar: D.C. 1978, U.S. Tax Ct. 1985. Assoc. Sutherland, Asbill & Brennan, Washington, 1978-86, ptnr., 1986—. Mem. ABA (tax sect. coms. on regulated investment cos. and com. on regulated pub. utilities, steering com. tax sect. D.C. 1983-85, 87—), J. Edgar Murdock Am. Inn f the Ct. Democrat. Jewish. Avocations: basketball, racketball. Home: 6002 Studdard Ct # 302 Alexandria VA 22310-5601 Office: Sutherland Asbill & Brennan 1275 Pennsylvania Ave NW Washington DC 20004-2404

SELTZER, LEO, filmmaker, educator, lecturer; b. Montreal, Que., Can., Mar. 13, 1910; came to U.S., 1916; s. Boris and Atalia (Gerowitz) S.; m. Elaine Basil, Apr. 15, 1941 (div. 1950); children: Janzie, John; m. Dicky Ransohoff, 1951 (div. 1963). BA, U. Mass., 1979. Faculty CCNY, 1949-54, New Sch. Social Research, 1949-51; pres. Leo Seltzer Assocs., Inc., N.Y.C., 1950-90; faculty Columbia U., 1954-60, Phila. Coll. Art, 1955-56, NYU, N.Y.C., 1966-67; dir. audio-visual therapy program pediatrics ward Univ. Hosp., N.Y.C., 1970-76; instr. film prodn. workshop Sch. Visual Arts, N.Y.C., 1969-84; asst. prof. performing and creative arts CUNY, 1977-78; prof. film Bklyn. Coll., 1978-83, prof. emeritus film, 1983—; adj. prof. film Coll. S.I., N.Y.C., 1976-78; lectr. in U.S. and abroad, including Mus. Modern Art, N.Y.C., Marymount Coll., Ghent U., others. Producer, dir. over 60 documentary, social, informational, theatrical and TV films in 35 countries, including First Steps, UN Divsn. Social Affairs, 1947 (Acad. award for best documentary 1948), Fate of a Child, 1949, For The Living, 1952, (with Walter Cronkite) Conquest of Aging, 1958, All the Years, 1959, Jacqueline Kennedy's Asian Journey, 1962, Progress through Freedom (pres. Kennedy's visit to Mex.), 1962, (with Edward R. Murrow) The American Commitment, 1963, Report on Acupuncture, 1977, (with John Huston) Let There Be Light; producer, dir.: Nat. Film Bd. Can., 1941; chief cons. visual aids City of N.Y., 1941-42; producer: N.Y.C. Mcpl. Film and TV Unit Sta. WNYC, 1949-50; film biographer to White House for Pres. Kennedy; exec. producer Quadrant Comms., Inc., 1973-75 (7 citations Cannes and Edinburgh Film Festivals 1948-63); films are in Nat. Archives, Libr. of Congress, in collection and distributed by Mus. Modern Art; photographs are in Houston Mus. Fine Arts collection, Nat. Gallery Can., Visual Studies Workshop, Rochester, N.Y.; reconstructed 6 Am. social documentary films of 1930's for Mus. Modern Art Film Collection, 1976-77; subject of TV program by Bill Moyers, A Walk Through the Twentieth Century; contbr. film footage to Nat. Geographic, Blackside Prodns.; producer TV series The Great Depression. Served as 1st lt. Signal Corps. U.S. Army, 1943-46, ETO. Recipient Acad. award for best documentary, 1948, Silver medals Venice Film Festival, 1949, 63, Freedom's Found. award, 1953, Golden Reel award Scholastic Mag., 1955, Robert Flaherty award CCNY, 1956, Silver medal Atlanta Internat. Film Festival, 1977; honored in Leo Seltzer tribute Mus. Modern Art, 1990. Mem. Dirs. Guild Am. (charter). Research on Early Am. social documentary films. Home and Office: 368 E 69th St New York NY 10021-5706

SELTZER, PHYLLIS ESTELLE, painter, printmaker; b. Detroit, May 17, 1928; d. Max and Lillian (Weiss) Finkelstein; m. Gerard Seltzer, May 31, 1953; children: Kim, Hiram. BFA, U. Iowa, 1949, MFA, 1952; postgrad., U. Mich., 1953-55, Case Western Res. U., 1966-70. Faculty U. Iowa, 1950-52, U. Mich., Ann Arbor, 1954-55, Case Western Res. U., Cleve., 1966-70; program coord. arts and humanities Cleve. State U., 1969-71, Lake Erie Coll., Painesville, Ohio, 1970-72; art interior designer Dalton, VanDijk, Johnson, Cleve., 1973-74; pvt. practice as designer Cleve., 1975-87; lectr. Scuola di Grafica, Venice, Italy, 1994. Designer poster Cleve. Bicentennial, 1975; executed elevator murals Stouffer Inn on Sq. Cleve, wall murals Bistrot des Atistes, Cleve., 1987, Highland Grill, Chgo., 1990, Indian's Administration Bldg. Gateway Commn., Cleve., 1994; 3 commd. paintings for Soc. Nat. Bank, Cleve.; one-person shows include Vixseboxse Gallery, 1983, Old Detroit Gallery, 1985, Women's City Club, 1987, Bonfoey's, Cleve., 1989, 91, Jane Haslem Gallery, Washington, 1990, Galerie Bubaco, Venice, Italy, 1993, Bonfoey Gallery, Cleve., 1994; group shows include Mitchell Mus., Mt. Vernon, Ill., 1979, Associated Am. Artists, N.Y.C., 1986, Nat. Print Exhbn., Trenton, N.J., 1988, Butler Inst. Am. Art, Youngstown, Ohio, 1989, S.W. Tex. State U., San Marcos, 1989, Cleve. Mus. Art, 1990, Art Expo, N.Y.C., 1990, Artlink Contemporary Art Space, Ft. Wayne, Ind., 1990, Jan Cicero Gallery, Chgo., 1991, Bolton Gallery, Cleve. Playhouse, 1992, Wasmer Gallery, Ursuline Coll., Cleve., 1992, N.D. Print and Drawing Annual, U. N.D., 1992, 93, Mansfield Art Center, Ohio, 1992, Americana '92, Hong Kong, 1992, N.Y. Print Fair, 1992, The Hammond Galleries, Lancaster, Ohio, Urban-Suburban, Bonfoey Co., Cleve., Great No. Corp. Ctr., Cleve., Dutchess County Art Assn., Poughkeepsie, N.Y., 1992, Michael Ingbar Gallery of Architecture, N.Y.C., 1992, Jane Haslem, Washington, 1993, Hunterton Art Ctr., Clinton, N.J., 1993, Cleve. Mus. Art, 1993, Ctrl. Pa. Festival of Arts, 1993, Northeastern Ohio Art Dealers Assn. Fine Arts Expo., 1993, Fla. Printmakers Soc., 1993, Cleve. Ctr. Contemporary Arts, 1993, Alexandria Mus. Art, 1993, Cleve. Mus. Art, 1993, Ctrl. Pa. Festival of Arts, 1993, Jan Cicero Gallery, Chgo., 1993, Trenton (N.J.) State Coll., 1993, Bonfoey Co., Cleve., 1993, Hunterdon Art Ctr., Clinton, N.J., 1993, Nat. Printmaking Exhibition, 1993, Jan Cicero Gallery, Chgo., 1994. Sec. Edgewater Homeowners Assn., Cleve., 1976-78. Tiffany fellow, 1952; recipient Cleve. Health Dept. award, 1975, Print Exhbn. award Hudson River Mus., 1987, Printmaking award Nat. Congress Art and Design, 1988, Juror's Merit award Chattahoochee Valley Art Mus., 1991, Purchase award Cleve. Mus. Art, 1993. Mem. Am. Soc. Aesthetics, New Orgn. Visual Arts Cleve. (v.p. 1974), Cleve. Soc. Contemporary Art, Print Club of Cleve. Mus. Art. (pres. 1983-84). Studio: 7431 Detroit Ave Cleveland OH 44102 *I am guided mainly by a need to make a visual contribution to society by adding innovative ways of seeing, as well as by utilizing the new techniques and technologies that are available to the visual artist. In my particular area this means the utilization of new printing processes-e.g. the mylar print, the 2080 Xerox print and the 6500 color Xerox and the laser Canon copier (with heat transfer printing). These new media also lend themselves to the continuance of painting in traditional methods, nevertheless expanding the horizon of surface and color on a single plane.*

SELTZER, RICHARD C., lawyer; b. N.Y.C., Sept. 3, 1943; s. Edward and Beatrice (Fishman) S.; m. Carol Reische, Aug. 31, 1969; children: Wendy, Mark. BA, Harvard U., 1965; JD, Columbia U., 1968. Bar: N.Y. 1969, U.S. Dist. Ct. (so. and ea. dists.) N.Y. 1969, U.S. Ct. Appeals (5th cir.) 1978, U.S. Ct. Appeals (2nd cir.) 1987. Ptnr. Kaye Scholer Fierman Hays and Handler, N.Y.C., 1969—. Mem. ABA, Assn. of Bar of City of N.Y. Office: Kaye Scholer Fierman Hays and Handler 425 Park Ave New York NY 10022-3506

SELTZER, RONALD, retail company executive; b. Boston, Nov. 16, 1931; s. Harold and Molly (Scheinberg) S.; m. Leila Podell, Feb. 24, 1957; children: Marjory, Michael, Barbara, Janet. B.B.A., Boston U., 1953. Asst. employment mgr. Gilchrist Co., Boston, 1956-59; personnel mgr. Bamberger's, Plainfield, N.J., 1959-61; employment and employee relations mgr. Bamberger's, Newark, 1961-66, v.p., store mgr., 1966-67, dir. sales promotion, 1967-70, sr. v.p., dir. stores, 1970-71; exec. v.p. Bamberger's, 1971-81, dir., 1969—; chmn. bd. R.H. Macy, N.Y.C., 1971-81; exec. v.p. ops. Macy N.Y., 1979-80; pres., chief exec. officer Lionel Leisure Inc., 1981-82; Louis Dryfus Retail Inc., 1981-90, bus. cons., 1990—; DWS. Retail Mgmt. Toronto; dir. Bradford Nat. Corp.; cons., pres. R & L Seltzer Assocs. Trustee Urban Coalition, N.J. Safety Council Inc., Garden State Ballet. Served with USNR, 1950-53; Served with AUS, 1953-55. Mem. Greater Newark C. of C. (dir. 1970—, mem. tax task force 1970—). Home: 278 Garfield Ave Oakhurst NJ 07755-1734

SELTZER, RONALD ANTHONY, radiologist, educator; b. Washington, Mar. 7, 1935; s. Lawrence H. and Sarah (Levin)S.; m. Adele Wishnow, June 25, 1961; children: Jeffrey David, Lauren Jill. AB with distinction, U. Mich., 1956; MD with high distinction, Wayne State U., 1960. Diplomate Am. Bd. Radiology. Resident in radiology Mass. Gen. Hosp., Boston, 1961-62, 64-66; asst. prof. radiology Stanford (Calif.) U. Med. Sch., 1966-67, assoc. clin. prof., 1967-73, assoc. clin. prof., 1974-89; pvt. practice San Mateo, Redwood City., Calif., 1967; mem. med. staff Mills Meml. Hosp., San Mateo, Calif., 1967-69; mem. med. staff Sequoia Hosp., Redwood City, 1969—, pres., 1986-88; cons. on radiation exposure divsn. radiol. health USPHS, 1964-67; cons. on nuclear medicine Palo Alto VA Hosp., 1967-75; cons. on computerized reporting in radiology GE, 1975-78; cons. advanced imaging divsn. Xerox Corp., 1978-82; cons. on electronic imaging Stanford Rsch. Internat., 1980-84; bd. dirs. Hosp. Consortium San Mateo County, 1986-88. Contbr. articles on biol. behavior and radiation dosimaty of radioactive materials, diagnostic radiology and uses of computers in medicine to med. jours. Sr. asst. surgeon USPHS, 1962-64. Fellow Inst. Cardiology Gt. Britain; mem. AMA, Calif. Med. Assn., Radiol. Soc. N.Am., Am. Roentgen Ray Soc., Western Angiography Soc. (pres. 1976-78), San Mateo County Ind. Practice Assn. (bd. dirs. Bay Pacific Health Plan 1979-84), Alpha Omega Alpha. Home: 140 Degas Rd Portola Vally CA 94028-7709 Office: Sequoia Hosp Redwood City CA 94062

SELTZER, VICKI LYNN, obstetrician-gynecologist; b. N.Y.C., June 2, 1949; d. Herbert Melvin and Marian Elaine (Willinger) S.; m. Richard Stephen Brach, Sept. 2, 1973; children: Jessica Lillian, Eric Robert. BS, Rensselaer Poly. Inst., 1969; MD, NYU, 1973. Diplomate Am. Bd. Ob-Gyn. Intern Bellevue Hosp., N.Y.C., 1973-74, resident in ob-gyn, 1974-77; fellow gynecol. cancer Am. Cancer Soc., N.Y.C., 1977-78, Meml. Sloan Kettering Cancer Ctr., N.Y.C., 1978-79; assoc. dir. gynecol. cancer Albert Einstein Coll. Medicine, N.Y.C., 1979-83; assoc. prof. ob-gyn., SUNY, Stony Brook, N.Y.C., 1983-89; prof. ob-gyn. Albert Einstein Coll. Medicine, 1989—; chmn. ob-gyn. L.I. Jewish Med. Ctr., 1993—; dir. ob-gyn., Queens Hosp. Ctr., Jamaica, N.Y., 1983—, pres. med. bd., 1986-89. Author: Every Woman's Guide to Breast Cancer, 1987; editor-in-chief: Primary Care Update for the Ob-Gyn, 1993—; editor: Women's Primary Health Care, 1995; mem. editorial bd. Women's Life mag., 1980-82, Jour. of the Jacobs Inst. Women's Health, 1990—; contbr. over 75 articles to profl. jours.; host Weekly Ob-Gyn. TV Program, Lifetime Med. TV. Chmn. health com. Nat. Coun. Women, N.Y.C., 1979—; mem. Mayor Beame's Task Force on Rape, N.Y.C., 1974-76; bd. govs. Regional Coun. Women in Medicine, 1985—; chmn. Coun. on Resident Edn. in Ob-Gyn., 1987—; Galloway Fund fellow 1975; recipient citation Am. Med. Women's Assn., 1973, Nat. Safety Coun., 1978, Achiever award Am. Med. Women's Assn., 1985, Achiever award L.I. Ctr. Bus. and Profl. Women, 1987. Fellow N.Y. Obstet. Soc., Am. Coll. Ob-Gyn (v.p. 1993—, gynecol. practice com. 1981, examener Am. Bd. Obstetrics and Gynecology 1988—); mem. Women's Med. Assn. (v.p. N.Y. 1974-79, editorial bd. jour. 1985—, resident review com. for obstetrics and gynecology 1993—), Am. Med. Women's Assn. (com. chmn. 1975-77, 78-79, editorial bd. jour. 1986—), N.Y. Cancer Soc., NYU Sch. Med. Alumni Assn. (bd. govs. 1979—, v.p. 1987—, pres. 1992—), Alpha Omega Alpha. Office: LI Jewish Med Ctr New Hyde Park NY 11040

SELTZER, WILLIAM, statistician, social researcher; former international organization director; b. N.Y.C., Sept. 22, 1934; s. William B. Seltzer and Edith S. (Goldman) Alt.; m. Jane E. Berger, Nov. 20, 1970; children: Benjamin, Ezra. BA, U. Chgo., 1956. Rsch. asst. Health Info. Found., N.Y.C., 1957-60; statistician U.S. Bur. Census, Suitland, Md., 1960-64; advisor Pakistan Inst. Devel., Econs. and Cen. Statis. Office, Karachi, 1964-68; staff assoc. Population Coun., N.Y.C., 1968-74; br. chief UN Statis. Office, N.Y.C., 1974-86, dir., 1986-93; sr. advisor to under-sec.-gen. Dept. Econ. and Social Info. and Policy Analysis, N.Y.C., 1993-94; vis. schlar Fordham U., N.Y.C., 1995—; mem. com. on population and demography, chair panel on data collection NAS, Washington, 1977-82. Author: Poems, 1960, Populatin and Statistics, 1994; co-author: Population Growth Estimation, 1973; also various UN documents, jour. articles, reports. Fellow Am. Statis. Assn. (chair social stats. sect. 1983-84, chair com. on internat. rels. 1986-87), Royal Statis. Soc. (hon.); mem. Population Assn. Am., Internat. Statis. Inst., Internat. Assn. Official Statisticians. Mem. Soc. of Friends. Office: Fordham U Dept Sociology and Anthropology Dealy Hall Rm 522 441 E Fordham Rd Bronx NY 10458

SELVADURAI, ANTONY PATRICK SINNAPPA, civil engineering educator, applied mathematician, consultant; b. Matara, Sri-Lanka, Sept. 23, 1942; arrived in Can., 1975; s. Kanapathiyar Sinnappa and W. Mary Adeline (Fernando) S.; m. Sally Joyce; children: Emily, Paul, Mark, Elizabeth. Diploma in Engnrg., Brighton Poly., U.K., 1964; Diploma, Imperial Coll./London U., 1965; MS, Stanford U., 1967; PhD in Theoretical Mechanics, U. Nottingham, Eng., 1971; DSc, U. Nottingham, Eng., 1986. Registered profl engr., Can. Staff rsch. engr. Woodward Clyde Assocs., Oakland, Calif., 1966-67; rsch. assoc. dept. theoretical mechanics U. Nottingham, 1969-70; lectr. dept. civil engring. U. Aston, Birmingham, Eng., 1971-75; asst. prof. civil engring. Carleton U., Ottawa, Ont., Can., 1975-76, assoc. prof., 1976-81, prof., 1982-93, chmn. dept., 1982-90, Davidson Dunton Rsch. lectr., 1987; prof., chmn. dept. civil engring./applied mechanics McGill U., Montreal, 1993—; vis. rsch. scientist Bechtel Group, Inc., San Francisco, 1981-82; vis. prof. U. Nottingham, 1986, Inst. de Mécanique de Grenoble, France, 1990; cons. Atomic Energy of Can. Ltd., Pinawa, Man., 1983—, Ministry of Transp. Ont., Toronto, 1984—, Fleet Tech., Ottawa, 1988—, Atomic Energy Control Bd., 1987—. Author: Elastic Analysis of Soil Foundation Interaction, 1979; editor: Mechanics of Structured Media, 1981, Mechanics of Material Interfaces, 1986, Developments of Mechanics, 1987. King George VI Meml. fellow English Speaking Union of Commonwealth, 1965, rsch. fellow SRC, U.K., 1969, Erskine fellow U. Canterbury, New Zealand, 1992. Fellow Am. Acad. Mechanics, Can. Soc. Civil Engring. (Leipholz medal 1991), Assoc. Prof. Engrs. of Ont. (Engring. medal for rsch. 1993), Engring. Inst. Can., Inst. Math. and Its Applications, Internat. Assn. for Computer Methods and Advances in Geomechanics (award for significant paper in the category theory computational analytical 1994). Roman Catholic. Office: McGill U, Dept Civil Engring, Montreal, PQ Canada H3A 2K6

SELVER, PAUL DARRYL, lawyer; b. N.Y.C., May 28, 1947; s. Rene T. Selver and Marilyn (Steiner) Pomerance; m. Ellen J. Roller, Jan. 22, 1984; children: Adam, Max, Katelyn. BA magna cum laude, Harvard U., 1969, JD, 1972. Bar: N.Y. 1973. Assoc. Hale Russell & Gray, N.Y.C., 1972-74; ptnr. Brown and Wood (formerly Tufo and Zuccotti), N.Y.C., 1974-94, Battle Fowler, N.Y.C., 1994—; lectr. of law Columbia U. Law Sch., 1994—; assoc. adj. prof. Sch. Architecture, Planning and Preservation Columbia U., N.Y.C., 1986-88. Author: (N.Y. practice guide book) Real Estate: Land Use Regulations, 1986; edit. bd. Metroplis Mag. 1983-86. Mem. Manhattan Community Bd. #6, N.Y.C., 1974-76, Westside Transit Com., N.Y.C., 1987; bd. dirs. Manhattan Bower Corp., N.Y.C., 1982—, Packer Collegiate Inst., N.Y.C., 1992—. Mem. ABA, Assn. of Bar of City of N.Y., Am. Planning Assn. Office: Battle Fowler 75 E 55th St New York NY 10022

SELVY, BARBARA, dance instructor; b. Little Rock, Jan. 20, 1938; d. James Oliver and Irene Balmat Banks; m. Franklin Delano Selvy, Apr. 15, 1959; children: Lisa Selvy Yeargin, Valerie Selvy Miros, Lauren, Franklin Michael. Student, U. Ctrl. Ark., 1955-57. Founder, dir. Carolina Ballet Theater, Greenville, S.C. 1973—; Advisory bd. dirs. Met. Arts Council and S.C. Governors Sch. Appeared in numerous TV commls., on Goodson-Toddman game show Play Your Hunch, 1958-59; toured Far East with TV show Hit Parade, 1958; named Miss Ark., 1956, Mrs. S.C. 1981; dir. and staged Mrs. Va., Mrs. N.C., Mrs. S.C. pageants; choreographed Little

Theater prodns., Furman U. Opera. Mem. So. Assn. Dance Masters (ballet adviser, regional dir.), Dance Educators Am., Dance Masters of Am., Profl. Dance Tchrs. Home: 206 Honey Horn Dr Simpsonville SC 29681-5814 Office: Carolina Ballet Theatre 872 Woodruff Rd Greenville SC 29607-3538

SELWOOD, PIERCE TAYLOR, lawyer; b. Evanston, Ill., July 31, 1939; s. Pierce Wilson and Alice (Taylor) S.; m. Alexis Fuerbringer, June 8, 1964; children: Allison, Jonathan. AB, Princeton U., 1961; JD, Harvard U., 1964. Bar: Calif. 1965, U.S. Dist. Ct. (cen. dist.) Calif. 1965, U.S. Dist. Ct. (no. dist.) Calif. 1966, U.S. Dist. Ct. (ea. dist.) Calif. 1989, U.S. Ct. Appeals (9th cir.) 1970. Assoc. Sheppard, Mullin, Richter & Hampton, L.A., 1964-70, ptnr., 1971—, chmn. litigation dept., 1986-91; lectr. Calif. Continuing Edn. Bar, Berkley, 1970-84, Practicing Law Inst., N.Y.C., 1980s, ABA Nat. Inst., Chgo., 1986. Mem. ABA (chmn. various subcoms. 1984-89), Calif. Bar Assn., L.A. County Bar Assn., Assn. Bus. Trial Lawyers (bd. gov.s 1977-79), Jonathan Club (L.A.), Princeton Club So. Calif. (pres. 1970-72). Republican. Episcopalian. Avocations: tennis, hiking, camping, travel. Office: Sheppard Mullin Richter & Hampton 333 S Hope St Fl 48 Los Angeles CA 90071

SELWYN, DONALD, engineering administrator, researcher, inventor, educator; b. N.Y.C., Jan. 31, 1936; s. Gerald Selwyn and Ethel (Waxman) Selwyn) Moss; m. Delia Nemec, Mar. 11, 1956 (div. Mar. 1983); children—Laurie, Gerald, Marcia; m. Myra Rowman Markoff, Mar. 17, 1986. B.A., Thomas A. Edison Coll. N.J., 1977. Service engr. Bendix Aviation, Teterboro, N.J., 1956-59; service mgr. Bogue Electric Mfg. Co., Paterson, N.J., 1959; proposal engr. advanced design group Curtiss-Wright Corp., East Paterson, N.J., 1960-64; indl. bioengr., rehab. engring. cons. N.Y.C., 1964-67; pres. bd. trustees, exec. tech. and tng. dir. Nat. Inst. for Rehab. Engring., Hewitt, N.J., 1967—; cons. N.Y. State Office Vocat. Rehab., 1964—, Pres.'s Com. on Employment of Handicapped, 1966—, bus. and industry and for Am. with Disabilities Act compliance, also numerous state rehab. agys., health depts., vol. groups, agys. for handicapped in fgn. countries; cons., trainer computer applications. Contbr. articles on amateur radio, rehab. of severely and totally disabled to profl., gen. mags. Trustee Nat. Inst. for Rehab. Engring., Rehab. Research Center Trust. Decorated Knight of Malta; recipient Humanitarian award U.S. Ho. of Reps., 1972, Bicentennial Pub. Service award, 1975. Mem. Am. Acad. Consultants, I.E.E.E. (sr.), Soc. Tech. Writers and Pubs. (sr.), Nat. Rehab. Assn., N.Y. Acad. Scis., Mensa. Achievements include being the developer or co-developer field-expander glasses for hemianopsia, tunnel and monocular vision, electronic speech clarifiers, electronically guided wheelchairs, off-road vehicles and cars for quadriplegics, others; patentee indsl., mil. and handi-capped rehab. inventions; expert, cons. on handicapped employment, handi-capped product safety including design, manufacture, labelling and user instrnl. material, 1990—. Office: Nat Inst Rehab Engring PO Box T Hewitt NJ 07421-1020 *As I travel the road of life, it becomes more and more evident to me that people matter most, and technology is useful and good only so long as it serves man, and man is not made to serve technology. From technician I have evolved to humanist, using technology only as a tool.*

SELYA, BRUCE MARSHALL, federal judge; b. Providence, May 27, 1934; s. Herman C. and Betty (Brier) S.; m. Ellen Hazel Barnes, Feb. 27, 1965; children: Dawn Meredith Selya Sherman, Lori Ann. B.A. magna cum laude, Harvard U., 1955, J.D. magna cum laude, 1958. Bar: D.C. 1958, R.I. 1960. Law clk. U.S. Dist. Ct. R.I., Providence, 1958-60; assoc. Gunning & LaFazia, Providence, 1960-62; ptnr. Gunning, LaFazia, Gnys & Selya, Providence, 1963-74, Selya & Iannuccillo, Providence, 1974-82; judge U.S. Dist. Ct. R.I., Providence, 1982-86, U.S. Ct. Appeals (1st cir.), Providence, 1986—; judge Lincoln Probate Ct., R.I., 1965-72; mem. R.I. Jud. Council, 1964-72, sec., 1965-70, chmn., 1971-72; mem. Gov.'s Commn. on Crime and Adminstrn. Justice, 1967-69; del. Nat. Conf. on Revisions to Fed. Appellate Practice, 1968-82; mem. various spl. govtl. commns. and adv. groups. Chmn. bd. trustees, Bryant Coll., Smithfield, R. I., 1986-92; bd. trustees, R. I. Hosp. Recipient Louis Dembitz Brandeis medal for disting. legal svc. Brandeis U., 1988, Neil Houston award Justice Assistance of Am., 1992. Mem. ABA, Fed. Bar Assn., Fed. Judges Assn., R.I. Bar Assn. (chmn. various coms.), R.I. Bar Found., U.S. Jud. Conf. (com. on jud. br.), Am. Arbitration Assn., Am. Judicature Soc. (dir.). Jewish. Home: 137 Grotto Ave Providence RI 02906-5720 Office: US Ct Appeals 311 Fed Bldg & US Courthouse Providence RI 02903 also: 1704 McCormack Boston MA 02109

SELZ, PETER HOWARD, art historian, educator; b. Munich, Germany, Mar. 27, 1919; came to U.S., 1936, naturalized, 1942; s. Eugene and Edith S.; m. Thalia Cheronis, June 10, 1948 (div. 1965); children: Tanya Nicole Eugenia, Diana Gabrielle Hamlin; m. Carole Schemmerling, Dec. 18, 1983. Student, Columbia U., U. Paris; MA, U. Chgo., 1949, PhD, 1954; DFA, Calif. Coll. Arts and Crafts, 1967. Instr. U. Chgo., 1951-56; asst. prof. art history, head art edn. dept. Inst. Design, Ill. Inst. Tech., Chgo., 1949-55; chmn. art dept., dir. art gallery Pomona Coll., 1955-58; curator dept. painting and sculpture exhbns. Mus. Modern Art, 1958-65; dir. univ. art mus. U. Calif., Berkeley, 1965-73, prof. history of art, 1965—; Zaks prof. Hebrew U., Jerusalem, 1976; vis. prof. CUNY, 1987; mem. pres.'s council on art and architecture Yale U., 1971-76. Author: German Expressionist Painting, 1957, New Images of Man, 1959, Art Nouveau, 1960, Mark Rothko, 1961, Fifteen Polish Painters, 1961, The Art of Jean Dubuffet, 1962, Emil Nolde, 1963, Max Beckmann, 1964, Alberto Giacometti, 1965, Directions in Kinetic Sculpture, 1966, Funk, 1967, Harold Paris, 1972, Ferdinand Holder, 1972, Sam Francis, 1975, The American Presidency in Political Cartoons, 1976, Art in Our Times, 1981, Art in a Turbulent Era, 1985, Chillida, 1986, Twelve Artists from the GDR, 1989, Max Beckmann: The Self Portraits, 1992, William Congdon, 1992; editor: Art in Am., 1967—, Art Quar., 1969-75, Arts, 1981-92; contbr. articles to art publs. Trustee Am. Crafts Coun., 1985-89, Creators Equity Found., 1980—; Marin Mus. Assn., 1993—; pres. Berkeley Art Project, 1988-93; mem. adv. coun. archives Am. Art, 1971—; project dir. Christo's Running Fence, 1973-76; commr. Alameda County Art Commn., 1990-95; mem. acquisitions com. Fine Arts Mus. San Francisco, 1993—. With OSS AUS, 1941-46. Decorated Order of Merit Fed. Republic Germany; Fulbright grantee Paris, 1949-50; fellow Belgian-Am. Ednl. Found.; sr. fellow Nat. Endowment for Humanities, 1972. Mem. Coll. Art Assn. Am. (dir. 1959-64, 67-71), AAUP, Internat. Art Critics Assn. Office: U Calif Dept Art History Berkeley CA 94720

SEMAK, MICHAEL WILLIAM, photographer, educator; b. Welland, Ont., Can., Jan. 9, 1934; s. John and Lena (Roketsky) S.; m. Annette Antoniuk, Jan. 30, 1960; children: James, Arlene. Student archtl. tech., Ryerson Poly. Inst., 1956-58. Freelance photographer Toronto-Pickering, 1961—; mem. faculty York U., Toronto, 1971—, assoc. prof. photography, 1977—. Exhibitor one-man shows, Image Gallery, N.Y.C., 1972, Il Diaframma Canon Gallery, Milan, Italy, 1976, Enjay Gallery, Boston, 1977, Ukraina Soc., Kiev, U.S.S.R., 1980, 81, group shows, Ont. Art Gallery, 1967, Expo '67 Internat. Exhbn., Montreal, 1967, Neikrug Gallery, N.Y.C., 1971; represented in permanent collections, Nat. Film Bd. Can., Ottawa, Nat. Gallery Can., Ottawa, Mus. Modern Art, N.Y.C., UN, Geneva. Recipient Photo Excellence Gold medal Nat. Film Bd., 1969; recipient Excellence award Pravda newspaper, Moscow, 1970, 71, Excellence diploma Fedn. Intenationale de l'art Photographique, Switzerland, 1972. Home: 1796 Spruce Hill Rd, Pickering, ON Canada L1V 1S4 Office: Dept Photography York U, 4700 Keeles St, Toronto, ON Canada M3J 1P3 *I see many contradictions around us, social realities which I believe rob us of our self-esteem and individuality. Must we continually accept and succumb to the never-ending hot baths for the mind society offers us? I wish my photography and words to disturb the complacent and the sleeper. I offer you cold showers for the mind.*

SEMANIK, ANTHONY JAMES, university program administrator; b. Cleve., Mar. 2, 1942; s. Anthony Joseph and Angela Theresa (Peters) S.; m. Elaine Maria Christian, Apr. 20, 1968. BS in Edn., Kent State U., 1965, MEd, 1969. TV coord. Kent (Ohio) State U., 1967-71; TV producer/dir. High/Scope Ednl. Research Found., Ypsilanti, Mich., 1971-72; dir. learning resource ctr. Mercy Coll. of Detroit, 1972-78; indl. media designer/cons. Detroit, 1972—; pub. affairs specialist Detroit bn. recruiting command U.S. Army, 1980-84; pub. affairs specialist tank-automotive command U.S. Army, Warren, Mich., 1984-85; dir. learning resource ctr. U. Detroit Mercy, 1985—; chair Detroit Ednl. Cable Consortium, 1992—. Producer, designer, dir., editor instructional-educational multimedia and video programs-series for univ. and cable TV, 1985—; editor: (video programs) Elders in the New

Japan, 1987, China and its Elders, 1989. Chmn. Detroit Ednl. Cable Consortium, 1992—. With U.S. Army, 1965-67. Mem. Pub. Rels. Soc. Am., Assn. for Ednl. Communications and Tech., Mich. Assn. Media in Edn., Phi Delta Kappa. Avocations: photography, videography, music, reading. Home: 7176 Green Farm Rd West Bloomfield MI 48322-2824 Office: U Detroit Mercy PO Box 19900 Detroit MI 48219-0900

SEMANS, MARY DUKE BIDDLE TRENT, foundation administrator; b. N.Y., Feb. 21, 1920; d. Anthony Joseph Drexel and Mary (Duke) B.; m. Josiah Trent; m. James H. Semans. Attended, Hewitt Sch., N.Y.; AB in History, Duke U.; LLD (hon.), N.C. Cen. U., 1963; HHD (hon.), Elon Coll., 1965; degree (hon.), Davidson Coll., N.C. Wesleyan Coll., 1982, U.N.C. at Chapel Hill, Duke U., 1983; LLD (hon.), Furman U., 1993. trustee emeritus Duke U., 1961-81; chmn. The Duke Endowment, 1960—; various positions N.C. Sch. Arts, 1981—; former trustee Davidson Coll., N.C. Mus. Art, 1961-83, Shaw U., Converse U., Lincoln Hosp.; vice chmn. The Mary Duke Biddle Found., 1960—; chmn. Angier B. Duke Meml., Exec. Mansion Fine Arts Com., 1965—, Friends of Duke U. Library; pres. Durham Homes, Inc., 1968; mem. bd. dirs. Goodwill Industries of the Rsch. Triangle Area, 1964—, First Union Corp., 1980-82, N.C. State Library, 1958-61, Durham Pub. Library; numerous other positions. Mem. Durham City Coun., 1951-55; mayor pro-tem City of Durham, 1953-55; commencement speaker Duke U., 1983. Recipient Merit award Duke U. Health and Hosp. Adminstrn. Alumni Assn., 1989, Giannini medal for meritorious svc. to N.C. Sch. of the Arts, 1990, Alan Keith-Lucas Friend of Children award N.C. Childcare Assn., 1991, Elna Spaulding award Women-in-Action, 1993, Outstanding Philanthropist award Triangle Chpt. Nat. Soc. Fund Raising Execs., 1993, Sam Ragan award St. Andrews Coll., 1993. Mem. LWV, Bus. and Profl. Women's Club, Altrusa Club, Half Century Club, Rotary Club. Democrat. Methodist. Home: 1415 Bivins St Durham NC 27707 Office: The Mary Duke Biddle Found 1044 W Forest Hills Blvd Durham NC 27707 office: The Duke Endowment 100 North Tryon St Ste 3500 Charlotte NC 28202

SEMANS, TRUMAN THOMAS, investment company executive; b. Oct. 27, 1926; s. William Ritchie and Ann (Thomas) S.; A.B., Princeton U., 1949; postgrad. U. Va. Law Sch., 1950; m. Nellie Merrick, Dec. 14, 1961; children: Truman Thomas, Jr., William Merrick. Chmn. bd., pres. Robert Garrett & Sons, Balt., 1951-74; ptnr. Alex Brown & Sons, Balt., 1974—, mem. exec. com., 1979—, mng. dir., vice chmn. bd., 1987—; exec. com. Duke U. Investment Mgmt. Corp. Trustee Md. Mus. and Hist. Soc., Balt., 1982—, v.p. bd., 1982—; trustee Chesapeake Bay Found., Annapolis, Md., Lawrenceville, (N.J.) Sch., Eaton Found., Mercy Hosp. Balt., Duke U., 1993—; mem. fin. com. Roman Cath. Archdiocese Md. Served with USN, 1944-46; PTO. Mem. The Brook Club, Green Spring Valley Hunt Club, Hamilton St. Club, Va. Hot Springs Golf and Tennis Club, Ivy Club, Seminole Golf Club (West Palm Beach, Fla.), Jupiter Island Club (Hobe Sound, Fla.), Knights of St. Gregory, Knights of Malta. Democrat. Office: Alex Brown & Sons 19-21 South St Baltimore MD 21202

SEMAS, PHILIP WAYNE, editor; b. Gilroy, Calif., Feb. 23, 1946; s. Louis Alexander and Marian (Crapper) S.; m. Robin Lucille Tuttle, Sept. 7, 1967; children—Katherine Lucille, Anna Marian. Student, U. Oreg., 1963-67. Editor Coll. Press Service, Washington, 1967-68; free-lance writer Berkeley, Calif., 1968-69; asst. editor Chronicle of Higher Edn., Balt. and Washington, 1969-76, sr. editor, 1976-78, mng. editor, 1978-88; editor Chronicle of Philanthropy, Washington, 1988—. Recipient Higher Edn. Writers award, AAUP, 1974. Mem. Am. Soc. Mag. Editors. Home: 3403 Notre Dame St Hyattsville MD 20783-1910 Office: Chronicle of Philanthropy 1255 23d St NW Washington DC 20037

SEMAYA, FRANCINE L., lawyer; b. N.Y.C., Mar. 26, 1951; d. Julie and Ann (Tannenbaum) Levitt; m. Richard Semaya, Aug. 3, 1975; children: Stefanie Rachel, David Steven, Scott Brian. BA magna cum laude, Bklyn. Coll., 1973, MS magna cum laude, 1975; JD, N.Y. Law Sch., 1982. Bar: N.Y. 1983, U.S. Dist. Ct. (ea. and so. dists.) N.Y. 1983. Sr. legal analyst, atty. Am. Internat. Group, Inc., N.Y.C., 1977-83; assoc. counsel, asst. v.p. Beneficial Ins. Group, Inc. (formerly Benico, Inc.), Peapack, N.J., 1983-87; v.p., counsel Am. Centennial Ins. Co., Peapack, 1985-87; legal/reins. cons. Peapack, 1987; counsel reins. Integrity Ins. Co. in Liquidation, Paramus, N.J., 1988-91; ptnr. Werner & Kennedy, N.Y.C., 1991—. Editor: Law and Practice of Insurance Insolvency Revisited, 1989. Mem. ABA (chmn. pub. regulation of ins. law com. 1990-91, chair ABA/TIPS pub. rels. com. 1993—, and others, co-editor State Regulation of Insurance 1991), N.Y. State Bar Assn., N.Y. County Lawyers Assn., S.I. Women's Bar Assn. (legis. com. 1983-84), Phi Beta Kappa. Avocations: reading, travel. Office: Werner & Kennedy 1633 Broadway New York NY 10019-6708

SEMBLER, MEL, company executive, former ambassador; b. 1930; m. Betty Schlesinger; children: Steve, Brent, Greg. BS, Northwestern U., 1952. Developer shopping ctrs.; amb. to Australia, Canberra, 1989-93; chmn. bd. The Sembler Co., St. Petersburg, Fla., 1962—; committeeman Rep. Nat. Com., Fla.; fin. chmn. Rep. Party, Fla.; bd. trustees George Bush Presdl. Libr. Found., Eckerd Coll., Internat. Coun. Shopping Ctrs., STRAIGHT Found.; bd. dirs. Pratt Industries, First Union Nat. Bank Fla., Pro Hispanic Polit. Action Com., Bush/Quayle Alumni Assn., Nat. Jewish Coalition, Holocaust Meml. Mus. Madiera Beach; resident mem. Fla. Coun. of 100. Mem. Internat. Coun. Shopping Ctrs. (pres. 1986-87). Office: 5858 Central Ave Saint Petersburg FL 33707-1728

SEMEGEN, PATRICK WILLIAM, lawyer; b. Akron, Ohio, Dec. 23, 1946; s. Stephen T. and Jane F. (Schmiedel) S.; m. Joann Kucharski, Jan. 10, 1975; children: Michael, Peter. BS in Econs., U. Pa., 1968; J.D., U. Mich., 1971. Bar: Ohio 1971, Calif. 1974. Chief crim. div. Summit County Prosecutor, Akron, Ohio, 1972-74; sole practice, Akron and San Diego, 1974-77; litigation counsel Beneficial Corp., Peapack, N.J., 1977-81; v.p. gen. counsel, sec. Western Auto Supply Co., Kansas City, Mo., 1981—, also dir. Contbr. articles to profl. jours. Served to capt. USAR, 1968-71. Mem. ABA, Internat. Franchise Assn., Am. Fin. Services Assn., Am. Corp. Counsel Assn. Office: Western Auto Supply Co 2107 Grand Blvd Kansas City MO 64108-1806

SEMEL, TERRY, motion picture company executive; b. N.Y.C., Feb. 24, 1943; s. Ben and Mildred (Wenig) S.; m. Jane Bovingdon, Aug. 24, 1977; children: Eric Scott, Courtenay Jane, Lily Bovingdon Semel. BS in Acctg., L.I.U., 1964; postgrad. in market research, CCNY, 1966-67. Domestic sales mgr. CBS Cinema Center Films, Studio City, Calif., 1970-72; v.p., gen. mgr. Walt Disney's Buena Vista, Burbank, Calif., 1972-75; pres. W.B. Distbn. Corp., Burbank, 1975-78; exec. v.p., chief operating officer Warner Bros., Inc., Burbank, 1979-80, pres., chief operating officer, from 1980; bd. dirs. Revlon. Pioneer of the Year, 1990, Found. of Motion PicturesPioneers. Office: Warner Bros Inc 4000 Warner Blvd Burbank CA 91522*

SEMELSBERGER, KENNETH J., household products company executive; b. 1936. BBA, Ohio State U., 1970; MBA, Cleve. State U., 1972. Product mgr. Holan Corp., 1954-66; mgr. sales and contracts Barts Corp., 1966-73; with Scott Fetzer Corp., Cleve., 1973—, v.p. mfg., 1974-75, div. pres., 1975-78, group v.p., 1978-83, sr. v.p. fin. adminstrn., 1983-86, pres., chief operating officer, 1986—. Served with AUS, 1959-62. Office: Scott Fetzer Co 28800 Clemens Rd Cleveland OH 44145-1134

SEMERAD, ROGER DALE, management consultant; b. Troy, N.Y., Sept. 9, 1940; s. Ralph Donald and Marjorie (Burdekin) S.; m. Cathryn Lucille Crangle, Nov. 27, 1965; 1 child, Samantha. B.A., Union Coll., 1962. Staff asst. to the Pres. White House, Washington, 1974-76; chmn., chief exec. officer Semerad Assocs. Inc., Washington, 1977-81; chmn. bd. 70001 Ltd., Washington, 1976-85; exec. v.p., trustee Brookings Instn., Washington, 1981-85; asst. sec. labor Dept. Labor, Washington, 1985-87; sr. v.p. policy dept. Am. Express Co., 1988-89; sr. v.p. RJR Nabisco, Inc., 1989-94; pres. RJR Nabisco Found., 1989-94. Co-author: Reinventing Education, 1990. Exec. sec. adv. policy councils Republican Nat. Com., Washington, 1977-80, exec. dir. platform com., 1980; bd. dirs. Bryce Harlow Found., Washington, 1982—, Hudson Inst., Indpls., 1993—; treas. New Am. Schs. Devel. Corp., Va., 1991—; mem. Sec.'s Commn. on Achieving Necessary Skills, Washington, 1990-92; mem. Nat. Coun. on Standards and Testing, Washington, 1991-92. Club: Metropolitan (Washington). Avocation: farming.

SEMERJIAN, HRATCH GREGORY, research and development executive; b. Istanbul, Turkey, Oct. 22, 1943; came to U.S., 1966; s. Krikor and Diruhi (Semerciyan) S.; m. Sona Kohar Kurkciyan, July 12, 1969 (dec. 1983); children: Tamar, Ara; m. Ayda Karabal, Feb. 8, 1986 (div. 1994). BSME, Robert Coll., Istanbul, 1966; MSc in Engring., Brown U., 1968, PhD in Engring., 1972. Rsch. asst. div. engring. Brown U., Providence, 1966-70; lectr. chemistry U. Toronto, Ont., Can., 1971-73; rsch. engr. Pratt & Whitney Aircraft United Technologies Corp., East Hartford, Conn., 1973-77; group leader Ctr. for Chem. Tech. Nat. Bur. Standards (now Nat. Inst. Standards and Tech.), Gaithersburg, Md., 1977-87, divsn. chief Chem. Sci. and Tech. Lab., 1987-92, dir. Chem. Sci. and Tech. Lab., 1992—; organizer tech. sessions, confs. and symposiums for various profl. orgns., 1978—. Contbr. rsch. articles to profl. publs.; editor numerous conf. procs. Mem. parish coun. St. George Armenian Apostolic Ch., Hartford, Conn., 1975-77; chmn. parish coun., dir. choir St. Mary Armenian Apostolic Ch., Washington, 1977—; coach youth soccer Montgomery Soccer, Inc., Rockville, Md., 1978-81; mem. Ani Armenian Choral Group, Washington, 1988—. Hagopian scholar Robert Coll., 1961-64, A.M.&F. corp. fellow, 1965, C.B. Keen fellow Brown U., 1969; recipient Silver medal Dept. Commerce, Washington, 1984; named Fed. Engr. of Yr., NSPE, Washington, 1991. Mem. AAAS, AIAA, ASME, AIChE, Am. Chem. Soc., Combustion Inst. Avocations: soccer, singing, boating. Office: Nat Inst Standards and Tech Bldg 222 Rm A317 Gaithersburg MD 20899

SEMION, A. KAY, editor; b. New Castle, Ind., July 27, 1944; d. Lowell Ernest and T. Byrneta (Byrne) Hooker; m. William Alexander Semion, June 21, 1969; children: Justin Alexander, Sonja Katherine. BA, Purdue U., 1966; AA, Delta Coll., 1974; MA, Wayne State U., 1981. Reporter The Flint (Mich.) Jour., 1966-70, The Daily Eagle, Wayne, Mich., 1970-71, The Bay City (Mich.) Times, 1971-72; copy editor The Ann Arbor (Mich.) News, 1979-83, editl. page editor, 1983—. Newsletter chmn. Lamaze Wayne County, Canton, Mich., 1977-80; leader La Leche League, Canton, 1978-81. Recipient Orthy awards Ch. 19 PBS, Bay City, 1973, 74. Mem. Soc. Profl. Journalists, Nat. Conf. Editl. Writers (chair mem. 1993-95, co-chair mem. svcs. com. 1995—). Home: 41629 Larimore Canton MI 48187 Office: The Ann Arbor News PO Box 1147 Ann Arbor MI 48106

SEMLER, DEAN, cinematographer. Productions include: (film) Let the Balloon Go, 1976, Hoodwink, 1980, The Road Warrior, 1980, Kitty and the Bagman, 1981, Razorback, 1984, The Coca-Cola Kid, 1986, Mad Max Beyond Thunderdome, 1985, TV Film: Passion Flower, 1985, Going Sane 1985, Bulls Eye, 1986, The Lighthorsemen, 1986, Cocktail, 1988, Young Guns, 1988, Farewell to the King, 1987, Dead Calm, 1987, K-9, 1988, Impulse, 1990, Young Guns II, 1990, Dances with Wolves, 1990 (Academy award 1991), City Slickers, 1991, Power of One, 1991, Super Mario Bros, 1992, Last Action Hero, 1992, The Three Musketeers, 1993, The Cowboy Way, 1993, Waterworld, 1994. Mem. Australian Cinematographers Soc.. Office: 4324 Promenade Way Ste 317 Marina Del Rey CA 90292 Office: Smith/Gosnell/Nicholson & Assoc PO Box 1166 1515 Palisades Dr Pacific Palisades CA 90272

SEMLER, JERRY D., insurance company executive; b. Indpls., Mar. 5, 1937; m. Rosemary Semler; children: Mary, Jack, Kristin, Kimberly, Michael, Jeffrey, Sally. BS, Purdue U., 1958; postgrad. bus. exec. program, Stanford U., 1984. CLU; registered health underwriter. With Am. United Life Ins. Co., Indpls., 1959—, pres., 1980-84, pres., chief oper. officer, 1984-89, pres., chief exec. officer, 1989—, chmn. bd., pres., chief exec. officer, 1991—, also bd. dirs.; bd. dirs. MDRT Found. Bd. dirs. United Way Cen. Ind., Indpls. Conv. and Visitors Bur., Jr. Achievement Cen. Ind., Ind. Sports Corp., Ind. C. of C.; bd. dirs., mem. exec. com. Indpls. Downtown Inc.; chmn. bd. Ctr. for Leadership Devel. Inc., Noble Found.; chmn. bd. Ind. Repertory Theatre, Am. Coll. of Sports Medicine Found., Jenn Found., Ruth Lilly Ctr. for Health Edn.; mem. dean's adv. council Purdue U. Krannert Sch. Mgmt.; hon. dir. "500" Festival Assocs., Purdue Univ. Pres.'s Coun.; bd. advisors Ind. U. Sch. Medicine; trustee Eiteljorg Mus.; bd. trustees Indpls. Parks Found.; bd. assocs. Rose Hulman Inst. Tech. With U.S. Army. Mem. Health Ins. Assn. Am., Am. Coll. Life Underwriters, Nat. Assn. Life Underwriters, Million Dollar Round Table (life), Ind. C. of C. (bd. dirs.), Life Office Mgmt. Assn. (bd. dirs.), Assn. Ind. Life Ins. Cos. (pres., mem. exec. com.), Life Ins. Mktg. and Rsch. Assn. (bd. dirs., chmn. bd.), Alpha Tau Omega. Roman Catholic. Office: Am United Life Ins Co 1 American Sq PO Box 368 Indianapolis IN 46206

SEMLYEN, ADAM, electrical engineering educator; b. Gherla, Romania, Jan. 10, 1923; came to Can., 1969; naturalized, 1974; s. Aurel and Anna (Gyorgy) S.; m. Mary Semlyen; 1 dau., Georgeta. Dipl. Ing., Poly. Inst. Timisoara, Romania, 1949; Ph.D., Poly. Inst. Iasi, Romania. Engr. Regional Power Authority, Timisoara, Romania, 1949-51; mem. faculty Poly. Inst. Timisoara, 1949-69, prof., 1968-69; prof. dept. elec. engring. U. Toronto, Ont., Can., 1969-88, prof. emeritus, 1988—. Fellow IEEE; mem. Conf. Internationale des Grands Reseaux Electriques. Home: 65 High Park Ave # 2203, Toronto, ON Canada M6P 2R7 Office: U Toronto Dept Elec & Computer Engring, 10 King's College Rd, Toronto, ON Canada M5S 1A4

SEMMEL, BERNARD, historian, educator; b. N.Y.C., July 23, 1928; s. Samuel and Tillie (Beer) S.; m. Maxine Loraine Guse, Mar. 19, 1955; 1 child, Stuart Mill. B.A., CCNY, 1947; M.A., Columbia U., 1951, Ph.D., 1955; postgrad., London Sch. Econs., 1959-60. With Nat. Citizens Commn. for Pub. Schs. and Coun. for Fin. Aid to Edn., N.Y.C., 1951-55; asst. prof. history Park Coll., Parkville, Mo., 1956-60; mem. faculty SUNY, Stony Brook, 1960-90; prof. history SUNY, 1964-90, chmn. dept., 1966-69; Disting. prof. Grad. Sch. CUNY, 1990—; vis. prof. Columbia U., 1966-67. Author: Imperialism and Social Reform, 1960, Jamaican Blood and Victorian Conscience, 1963, The Rise of Free Trade Imperialism, 1970, The Methodist Revolution, 1973, John Stuart Mill and the Pursuit of Virtue, 1984, Liberalism and Naval Strategy, 1986, The Liberal Ideal and The Demons of Empire, 1993, George Eliot and the Politics of National Inheritance, 1994; editor: Occasional Papers of T.R. Malthus, 1963; editor, translator: Halévy's The Birth of Methodism in England, 1971; editor Jour. Brit. Studies, 1969-74, Marxism and the Science of War, 1981. Rockefeller Found. grantee, 1959-60; Am. Council Learned Socs. fellow, 1964-65; Guggenheim fellow, 1967-68, 74-75; Nat. Humanities Ctr. fellow, 1986-87. Fellow Royal Hist. Soc.; mem. Am. Hist. Assn. (profl. divsn. 1984-86), Conf. Brit. Studies, Phi Beta Kappa. Club: Cosmos. Home: P O Box 1162 Stony Brook NY 11790-1520 Office: CUNY Grad Sch 33 W 42nd St New York NY 10036-8003

SEMOFF, DEIRDRE PAULA, special education administrator, academic director; b. Albuquerque, Oct. 5, 1944; d. Milton C. F. and Padrice (McLaughlin) S. BA in Psychology, San Diego State U., 1971, MA, 1982; doctoral student, Claremont Grad. Sch. Cert. tchr., Calif., learning handicapped tchr., Calif. Specialist San Diego City Schs., 1977-79; coord. for program for learning disabilities San Diego State U., 1980-89; cons. writer Emerson & Stern Software Co., San Diego, 1986-87; faculty spl. edn. San Diego State U., 1987-89; counselor, coord. U. Calif., Berkeley, 1989—; staff advisor for learning disabled diversity in learning. Joint PhD program scholar San Diego State U., 1986, Mus. Dept. scholar U. Ariz., 1964. Mem. Assn. on Higher Edn. and Disability, Calif. Assn. Post-Secondary Educators of Disabled, Coun. for Exceptional Children, Assn. for Hearing Disabilities, Coun. for Learning Disabilities, Computer Using Educators, Pi Lambda Theta. Avocations: swimming, horseback riding, theater, poetry, animal and environmental issues. Office: U Calif Berkeley 230 Golden Bear Ctr Berkeley CA 94720

SEMON, WARREN LLOYD, retired computer sciences educator; b. Boise, Ida., Jan. 17, 1921; s. August and Viola Lorreta (Eastman) S.; m. Ruth Valerie Swift, Dec. 1, 1945; children—Warren Lloyd, Nolan David, Jonathan Richard, Sue Anne. Student, Hobart Coll., 1940-43; S.B., U. Chgo., 1944; M.A., Harvard, 1949, Ph.D., 1954. Lectr. applied math. Harvard U., Cambridge, Mass., 1956-61, asst. dir. computation lab., 1954-61; head applied math. dept. Sperry Rand Research Ctr., Sudbury, Mass., 1961-64; mgr. computation and analysis lab. Burroughs Research Ctr., Paoli, Pa., 1964-67; prof. computer sci. Syracuse (N.Y.) U., 1967-84, prof. emeritus, 1984—, dir. system and information sci., 1968-76, dean Sch. Computer and Info. Sci., 1976-84; cons. USAF, 1957, NSA, 1957, Lockheed Electronics Corp., 1967, Monsanto Co., 1972. Contbr. profl. jours. Served to 1st lt. USAAF, 1943-46, MTO. Fellow IEEE; mem. Assn. Computing Machinery, Math. Assn.

Am., IEEE Computer Soc. (chmn. publs. com. 1972-74, bd. govs. 1973-74, editor-in-chief 1975-76), Sigma Xi. Address: F54807 PO Box 44209 Cincinnati OH 45244-0209

SEMONIAN, ROBERT ALEXANDER, energy and lighting consultant; b. Boston, May 17, 1939; s. Leon Astor and Veron (Agojian) S. BBA, U. Miami, Fla., 1964. Editor The Miami Sunlight, 1962-64; adminstr. cost acctg. Raytheon Co., Bedford, Mass., 1964-68; acct. corp. staff L.F.E. Corp., Boston, 1968-70; cons. Watertown, Mass., 1970-73; mktg. rep. Cenebal Corp., Dedham, Mass., 1973-75; energy/lighting cons. No. Am. Philips Corp., Boston, 1975—; treas. Improper Bostonian Newspaper, Brookline, Mass., 1991—; dir. Communications Engring. Inc., Cambridge, Mass., 1972—, Systems and Analytical Scis., Bedford, 1981—; advisor to newspaper The Impartial Observer, 1985; mem. rsch. bd. advisors The Am. Biog. Inst. Inc., Raleigh, 1992—. Exec. dir. Mass. Conservative Caucus, Marlborough, Mass., 1984—, membership chmn., 1984, program chmn., 1983; chmn. Watertown Rep. Town Com., Mass., 1980-88, advisor, 1972-80, 88—, vice chmn., 1968-72; trustee Cambridge Emergency Relief Trust, 1972—; treas. Reps. for Middlesex County, Weston, Mass., 1972—; treas. Armenian-Am. Rep. Club Mass., Watertown, 1972—, Conservation Commn., Watertown, 1966-69, Reagan Dinner, Waltham, Mass., 1975, Boxborough, Mass., 1977; Mass. state co-chmn. Bush/Quayle, 1988; nat. vice chmn. Armenian Ams. for Bush-Quayle '88 Com., Washington; nat. co-chmn. Armenian-Ams. for Bush/Quayle '92 Com., Washington; mem. exec. com. Am. Bicentennial Presdl. Inaugural Com. for Mass., Washington, 1988-89; Mass. chmn. Nat. Conservative Alliance, Waterloo, Iowa, 1985—, Am. Freedom Coalition Mass., Peabody, 1987—; bd. govs. conv. Am. Freedom Coalition, Washington, 1988, 89; treas. Greater Boston Young Rep. Club, 1968, 9 v.p. 1969-70; mem. exec. com. Mass. Reagan for Pres. Com., 1975-76, state nationalities chmn., 1979-80, state vice chmn., 1979-80, exec. com., 1979-80; del. Rep. Nat. Conv., Detroit, 1980, Dallas, 1984, New Orleans, 1988, Houston, 1992; mem. Watertown Town Mtg., 1965-75; state committeeman Mass. Rep. State Com., Boston, 1972-80, dep. chmn., 1972-80, heritage chmn., 1972-80, exec. com., 1972-80; del. Mass. Rep. Conv., 1972, 74, 78, 82, 86, 90, chief page, 1974; Mass. state nationalities co-chmn. Reagan/Bush Com., Mass., 1980; Watertown chmn. Reagan/Bush Com., 1980, 84, State Legislators Conf., Scottsdale, Ariz., 1985, Washington, 1986, 87, 88; state chmn. Robertson for Pres., 1988; co-chmn. East Coast Conservative PAC, Marlborough, 1986—; mem. Appalachian Nat. Scenic Trail Commn., Harpers Ferry, W.Va., 1986-88; dir. Watertown Better Govt. Assn., 1966—, World Info. Network/N.E. Team, Mt. Vernon, N.H., 1986—; exec. com. Zoryan Inst. Support Com., Cambridge, Mass., 1989—; human resources chmn. Armenia Earthquake Fund, N.E. Relief Ctr., Boston, 1988—; exec. com. Armenia Earthquake Relief Coalition Greater Boston, 1988—; bd. advisors Doctors to The World, Denver, 1989—; mem. exec. com. Watertown/JRASHEN Armenia Friendship Assn., Watertown, 1990—, Watertown chmn. Pierce for Gov. primary election, 1990, Weld for Gov./Cellucci for lt. gov., 1990; co-chmn. Mass. State Buchanan for Pres. com., 1992. Subject 120th Anniversary Bachrach Photographers Exhibit of Successful People, Boston, 1990. Watertown chmn. Pierce for Gov., 1990, Weld for Gov./Cellucci for Lt. Gov., 1990; state co-chmn. Buchanan for Pres. Com., Mass., 1992. Rsch. adv. bd. Am. Biog. Inst., Inc., Raleigh, N.C., 1992—; chmn. adv. com. Silvio O. Conte Ctr., Boston, 1993—. Recipient Svc. award N.Am. Philips Corp., 1978, Merit award for svc. to Armenian victims of earthquake, 1988; Medal of Honor Am. Biographical Inst., Raleigh, N.C., 1993; hon. Lt. Col. Aide-de-Camp in Ala. State Militia, 1986. Advisor The Improper Bostonian, 1991—. Mem. Am. Policy Adv. Council (treas., exec. com. 1983—), Fed. Emergency Mgmt. Agy. (Nat. Def./Exec. Res. 1982—), Nat. Assn. Armenian Studies & Rsch., Watertown/Jrashen Armenia Friendship Town Assn. (exec. com. 1990—), U. Miami Alumni Assn. of New nian Students Assn. (nat. v.p. 1971-72, pres. Boston br. 1970-71, 77-78), Delta Sigma Pi. Mem. Armenian Apostolic Ch. Lodge: Masons. Avocation: politics. Home: 11 Howe St Watertown MA 02172-4210

SEMONIN, RICHARD GERARD, state official; b. Akron, Ohio, June 25, 1930; s. Charles Julius and Catherine Cecelia (Schooley) S.; m. Lennie Stuker, Feb. 3, 1951; children: Cecelia C., Richard G. Jr., James R., Patricia R. BS, U. Wash., 1955. With Ill. State Water Survey, Champaign, 1955-91, chief, 1986-91, chief emeritus, 1991—; adj. prof. U. Ill., 1975-91; chmn. Ill. Low-Level Radioactive Waste Task Group, 1994—. Contbr. chpts. to books and articles to profl. jours.; co-editor: Atmospheric Deposition, 1983. Staff sgt. USAF, 1948-52. Grantee NSF, 1957-76, U.S. Dept. Energy, 1965-90. Fellow AAAS, Am. Meteorol. Soc. (councilor 1983-86); mem. Nat. Weather Assn. (councilor 1978-81), Weather Modification Assn., Ill. Acad. Scis., Sigma Xi. Roman Catholic. Avocations: Civil war, golf, fishing, geneology. Home: 1902 Crescent Dr Champaign IL 61821-5826 Office: Ill State Water Survey 2204 Griffith Dr Champaign IL 61820-7495

SEMPLE, CECIL SNOWDON, retired manufacturing company executive; b. Assam, India, Aug. 12, 1917; came to U.S., 1927, naturalized, 1948; s. Fordyce B. and Anne (Munro) S. B.A., Colgate U., 1939. Buyer R.H. Macy & Co., 1939-42, 46-48; buyer, div. supt. Montgomery Ward, 1948-50; v.p. Nachman Corp., Chgo., 1950-55; sales mgr. radio receiver dept. Gen. Elec. Co., Bridgeport, Conn., 1955-60; mktg. cons. merchandising Gen. Elec. Co., N.Y.C., 1966-67, gen. mgr. audio products dept., 1967-68, dep. div. gen. mgr. housewares div., 1968-69, gen. mgr. housewares div., 1969, v.p., 1969-71, v.p. corp. customer relations, 1971-85; v.p. Rich's Inc., Atlanta, 1960-62, sr. v.p., dir., 1962-66; trustee Peoples Bank., Bridgeport, 1975-89, trustee emeritus. Bd. dirs. Nat. Jr. Achievement Inc., 1974-86, Bridgeport Area Found., 1970-91, dir. emeritus, 1991—; bd. dirs. Bridgeport Hosp., 1970-93, chmn., 1983-89, dir. emeritus, 1993—; bd. trustees Colgate U., 1970-84, vice chmn. 1978-84; trustee emeritus, past pres., bd. dirs. Alumni Corp.; chmn. So. Conn. Health Svc. Inc., 1990-93. Served to maj. USAAF, 1942-46. Mem. St. Andrews Soc. State N.Y. (chmn. bd. mgrs. 1968-70), Delta Kappa Epsilon. Clubs: Brooklawn Country (Fairfield, Conn.), Fairfield Country. Home: 25 Cartright St Bridgeport CT 06604

SEMPLE, LLOYD ASHBY, lawyer; b. St. Louis, June 7, 1939; s. Robert B. and Isabelle A. S.; m. Cynthia T. Semple, Aug. 26, 1961; children: Whitney, Sarah, Lloyd Jr., Terrell. BA, Yale U., 1961; JD, U. Mich, 1964. Bar: Mich. 1964. Assoc. Dykema Gossett, Detroit, 1964-70, ptnr., 1971—; gen. counsel Bundy Corp., Daedalus Enterprises, Inc., Ralph Wilson Enterprises, Copper & Bass Sales. Councilman, mayor pro tem City of Grosse Pointe Farms, Mich., 1975-83; chmn. bd., trustee Harper Hosp.; bd. trustees Detroit Med. Ctr. Corp.; bd. dirs. Detroit Zool. Soc.; dir., trustee Mich. Cancer Found. Mem. ABA, Mich. Bar Assn. Detroit Bar Assn., Country Club (Detroit), Yondotega Club (detroit), Detroit Athelitic Club, Yale Club (N.Y.C.), Bohemian Club (San Francisco. Episcopalian. Home: 57 Cambridge Rd Grosse Pointe MI 48236-3004 Office: Dykema Gossett 400 Renaissance Ctr Detroit MI 48243-1705

SEMROD, T. JOSEPH, banker; b. Oklahoma City, Dec. 13, 1936; s. L.J. and Theda Jo (Hummel) S.; m. Janice Lee Wood, June 1, 1968 (div. 1988); children: Ronald, Catherine, Christopher, Elizabeth; m. Jaye Patricia Hewitt, May 27, 1989; 1 child, Kelsey. B.A. in Polit. Sci., U. Okla., 1958, LL.B. 1963. Bar: Okla. 1963. With Liberty Nat. Bank, Oklahoma City, 1963-81; v.p. Liberty Nat. Bank, 1967-69, sr. v.p. 1969-71, exec. v.p. 1971-73, pres., 1973-81; pres. Liberty Nat. Corp., Oklahoma City, 1976-81; chmn. bd., pres., chief exec. officer United Jersey Banks (name now UJB Fin. Corp.), Princeton, N.J., 1981—; chmn. bd. dirs. United Jersey Bank, Hackensack, N.J., 1981—; chmn. Internat. Fin. Conf., 1994—. Bd. dirs. Fed. Res. Bank of N.Y., 1983-86; trustee, mem. exec. com. Nat. Urban League; mem. bd. advisors Outward Bound, Inc., 1984—; Ind. Coll. Fund N.J., 1986-90; commr. Citizens Commnn. on Aids, 1988-90; mem. regents Stonier Grad. Sch. Banking, Rutgers U., 1983; mem. N.J. Transp. Trust Fund Authority, 1985-87; chmn. The Partnership for N.J., 1989-90, trustee; mem. N.J. Com.-U.S. Savings Bonds com.; chmn. banking industry U.S. Savs. Bonds campaign, 1992-93. 1st lt. U.S. Army, 1958-60. Mem. Am. Bankers Assn. N.J. Bankers Assn., N.J. Bar Assn., Okla. Bar Assn., The Bankers Roundtable (bd. dirs. 1995—), Regional Plan Assn. (bd. dirs. 1989-91), Young Pres. Orgn., Am. Running and Fitness Assn. (bd. dirs. 1983-86), N.J. State C. of C. (bd. dirs., vice-chmn.), The Drumthwacket Found. (chmn. 1990-94), Bedens Brook Club (Skillman, N.J.), River Club (N.Y.C.), Metedeconk (Jackson, N.J.), Coral Beach Club (Bermuda). Democrat. Roman Catholic. Office: UJB Fin Corp PO Box 2066 301 Carnegie Ctr Princeton NJ 08543-2066

SEN, AMARTYA KUMAR, economist, educator; b. Santiniketan, India, Nov. 3, 1933; s. Ashutosh and Amita S. B.A., Calcutta U., 1953; B.A., Cambridge U., 1955, Ph.D., 1958; D.Litt. (hon.), U. Sask., 1979, Visva-Bharati U., 1983, U. Essex, 1984, Georgetown U., 1989, Jodavpur U., 1990, Kalyani U., 1990, Athens U. of Econs. and Bus., 1991, Williams Coll., 1991, London Guildhall U., 1991, New Sch. Social Rsch., 1992, Calcutta U., 1992, Oberlin Coll., 1993, Syracuse U., 1994, Wesleyan U., 1995; D.Sc. (hon.), U. Bath, 1984, U. Edinburgh, 1995, Docteur Honoris Causa U. Caen, 1987, Louvain, 1989, U. Valencia, 1994, U. Zurich, 1994, U. Antwerp, 1995, Dottore ad honorem, U. Bologna, 1988; LL.D. (hon.) U. Tulane, 1990, Queen's U., 1993. Prof. econs. Jadavpur U., Calcutta, 1956-58; fellow Trinity Coll., Cambridge U., 1957-63; prof. econs. Delhi U., 1963-71, London Sch. Econs., 1971-77; prof. econs. Oxford U., 1977-80, Drummond prof. polit. economy, 1980-88; prof. econs. and philosophy Harvard U., 1987—; Lamont U. prof. Harvard U., 1988—, vis. prof., 1986-89; vis. prof. U. Calif., Berkeley, 1964-65; Andrew D. White prof.-at-large Cornell U., Ithaca, N.Y., 1978-84; chmn. expert group role advanced skill and tech. UN, 1967; hon. fellow Trinity Coll., Cambridge, Inst. Social Studies, The Hague, Inst. Devel. Studies, U. Sussex, London Sch. Econs., U. London. Fellow Brit. Acad., Econometric Soc. (past pres.); mem. AAAS (fgn. hon. mem), Am. Econ. Assn. (past pres.), Indian Econ. Assn. (past pres.), Royal Econ. Soc. (v.p.), Indian Econometric Conf., Devel. Studies Assn. (past pres.), Internat. Econ. Assn. (pres. 1986-89, hon. pres.), Agnelli Internat. prize 1990, Alan Shawn Feinstein World Hunger award 1990. Author: Choice of Techniques, 1960; Collective Choice and Social Welfare, 1970, Growth Economics, 1970, On Economic Inequality, 1973, Employment, Technology and Development, 1975, Poverty and Famines: An Essay on Entitlement and Deprivation, 1981, Utilitarianism and Beyond, 1982, Choice, Welfare and Measurement, 1982, Resources, Values and Development, 1984, Commodities and Capabilities, 1985, On Ethics and Economics, 1987, The Standard of Living, 1987, Hunger and Public Action, 1989, Inequality Reexamined, 1992, Quality of Life, 1993, India: Economic Development and Social Opportunity, 1995; contbr. articles to profl. jours. Office: Harvard U Dept Econs Cambridge MA 02138

SEN, ASHISH KUMAR, urban planner, educator; b. Delhi, India, June 8, 1942; came to U.S., 1967, naturalized, 1985; s. Ashoka Kumar and Arati Sen; m. Colleen Taylor. BS with honors, Calcutta U., 1962; MA, U. Toronto, Ont. Can., 1964, PhD, 1971. Research assoc., lectr. dept. geography Transp. Center, Northwestern U., 1967-69; mem. faculty Center Urban Studies, U. Ill., Chgo., 1969—; prof. Center Urban Studies, U. Ill., 1978—, dir. Sch. Urban Planning, 1991; dean Center Urban Studies, U. Ill. (Sch. Urban Scis.), 1977-78, acting dir., 1992; pres. Ashish Sen. and Assocs., Chgo., 1977—. Author: Regression Analysis: Theory, Methods, and Applications, 1990; also articles. Mem. Chgo. Bd. Edn., 1990—, chmn. budget com., 1992—; bd. trustees Asian Inst., 1993—. Fellow Royal Statis. Soc.; mem. Am. Statis. Assn., Inst. Math. Stats., Am. Soc. Planning Ofcls., Regional Sci. Assn., Transp. Rsch. Forum, Transp. Rsch. Bd., Cliffdwellers. Hindu. Home: 2557 W Farwell Ave Chicago IL 60645-4617

SEN, PARESH CHANDRA, electrical engineering educator; b. Patiya, Chittagong, Bangladesh, June 30, 1938; arrived in Can., 1963; s. Judhistir and Jaya Sen; m. Maya Dey, July 21, 1968; children: Sujit, Priya, Debashis. BSc with honors, Calcutta (India) U., 1958, MSc Tech., 1961; MASc., U. Toronto, Ont. Can., 1965; PhD, U. Toronto, 1967. Registered profl. engr., Ont. Elec. engr. TISCO, Dhanbad, India, 1961-62, DVC Maithon, India, 1962-63; teaching asst. U. Toronto, 1963-65, 65-67; rsch. asst. No. Electric Co., Ottawa, Ont., 1965; profl. assoc. Queen's U., Kingston, Ont., 1967-68; asst. prof. elec. engring. Queen's U., Kingston, 1968-73, assoc. prof., 1973-79, prof., 1979—; cons. Urban Transp. Devel. Corp., Alcan Ltd., Kingston, 1975-80; sr. indsl. fellow Inverpower Control Ltd., Toronto, 1985-86. Author: Thyristor DC Drives, 1981, Principles of Electric Machines and Power Electronics, 1989. Fellow IEEE (prize paper award indsl. drive com. 1986); mem. Assn. Profl. Engrs. Ont. Hindu. Avocations: oil painting, reading novels. Office: Queens Univ, Dept Elec Engring, Kingston, ON Canada K7L 3N6

SENDAK, MAURICE BERNARD, writer, illustrator; b. Bklyn., June 10, 1928; s. Philip and Sadie (Schindler) S. Student, Art Students League, N.Y.C., 1949-51; LHD, Boston U., 1977; hon. degree, U. So. Miss., 1981, Keene State Coll., 1986. Window display artist Timely Svc., N.Y.C., 1946; display artist FAO Schwartz, N.Y.C., 1948-51; co-founder, artistic dir. The Night Kitchen, 1990—. One-man shows include Gallery Sch. Visual Arts, N.Y.C., 1964, Rosenbach Found., Phila., 1970, 75, Trinity Coll., 1972, Galerie Daniel Keel, Zurich, 1974, Ashmolean Mus., Oxford, 1975, Am. Cultural Center, Paris, 1978, Pierpont Morgan Library, N.Y.C., 1981; author, illustrator: Kenny's Window, 1956 (Spring Book Fesitval honor book 1956), Very Far Away, 1957, The Acrobat, 1959, The Sign on Rosie's Door, 1960, The Nutshell Library (contains Chicken Soup with Rice, One Was Johnny, Alligators All Around, Pierre: A Cautionary Tale), 1962, Where The Wild Things Are, 1963 (N.Y. Times Best Illustrated Book award 1963, Caldecott medal 1964, Lewis Carroll Shelf award 1964, Internat. Bd. on Books for Young People award 1966, Art Books for Children award 1973, 74, 75, Best Young Picture Books Paperback award Redbook Mag. 1984, Children's Choice award 1985), Hector Protector and As I Went Over the Water: Two Nursery Rhymes, 1965, Higglety, Pigglety, Pop!; or, There Must Be More to Life, 1967 (Am. Book award nomination 1980), In the Night Kitchen, 1970 (N.Y. Times Best Illustrated Book award 1970, Caldecott medal nomination 1971, Art Books for Children award 1973, 74, 75, Redbook Mag. award 1985), Ten Little Rabbits: A Counting Book with Mino the Magician, 1970, Pictures by Maurice Sendak, 1971, Maurice Sendak's Really Rosie, 1975, Some Swell Pup; or, Are You Sure You Want A Dog, 1976, Seven Little Monsters, 1977, Outside Over There, 1981 (N.Y. Times Best Illustrated Book award 1981, Boston Globe/Horn Book award 1981, Caldecott medal nomination 1982, Am. Book award 1982), We Are All in the Dumps with Jack and Guy, 1993, Tsippi, 1994, Moishe, 1994, Max, 1994; illustrator: Atomics for the Millions, 1947, Good Shabbos, Everybody!, 1951, The Wonderful Farm, 1951, A Hole is to Dig, 1952 (N.Y. Times Best Illustrated Book award 1952), Maggie Rose: Her Birthday Christmas, 1952, The Giant Story, 1953, Hurry Home Candy, 1953, Shadrach, 1953, A Very Special House, 1953 (Caldecott medal nomination 1954), I'll Be You and You Be Me, 1954 (N.Y. Times Best Illustrated Book award 1954), Happy Hanukkah, Everybody, 1954, The Tin Fiddle, 1954, Magic Pictures, 1954, Mrs. Piggle-Wiggle's Farm, 1954, The Wheel on the School, 1954, Charlotte and the White Horse, 1955, The Little Cow and the Turtle, 1955, Singing Family of the Cumberlands, 1955, What Can You Do With a Shoe?, 1955, Happy Rain, 1956, The House of Sixty Fathers, 1956, I Want to Paint My Bathroom Blue, 1956 (N.Y. Times Best Illustrated Book award 1956), Birthday Party, 1957 (N.Y. Times Best Illustrated Book award 1957), Circus Girl, 1957, You Can't Get There From Here, 1957, Little Bear, 1957, Along Came a Dog, 1958, No Fighting, No Biting!, 1958, Somebody Else's Nut Tree, 1958, What Do You Say, Dear?, 1958 (N.Y. Times Best Illustrated Book award 1958, Caldecott medal nomination 1959), The Moon Jumpers, 1959 (Caldecott medal nomination 1960), Father Bear Comes Home, 1959 (N.Y. Times Best Illustrated Book award 1959), Seven Tales, 1959, Dwarf Long-Nose, 1960, Little Bear's Friend, 1960, Open House for Butterflies, 1960 (N.Y. Times Best Illustrated Book award 1960), Let's Be Enemies, 1961, The Tale of Gockel, Hinkel and Gackeliah, 1961, What Do You Do, Dear?, 1961, Little Bear's Visit, 1961 (Caldecott medal nomination 1962), Schoolmaster Whackwell's Wonderful Sons, 1962, Mr. Rabbit and the Lovely Present, 1962 (Caldecott medal nomination 1963), The Singing Hill, 1962 (N.Y. Times Best Illustrated Book award 1962), Nikolenka's Childhood, 1963, She Loves Me, She Loves Me Not, 1963, The Bat-Poet, 1964 (N.Y. Times Best Illustrated Book award 1964), How Litte Lori Visited Times Square, 1964, Pleasant Fieldmouse, 1964, Lullabies and Night Songs, 1965, The Animal Family, 1965 (N.Y. Times Best Illustrated Book award 1965), Zlateh the Goat, 1966 (N.Y. Times Best Illustrated Book award 1966), The Golden Key, 1967, Poems from William Blake's Songs of Innocence, 1967, The Big Green Book, 1968, Griffin and the Minor Canon, 1968, A Kiss for Little Bear, 1968 (N.Y. Times Best Illustrated Book award 1968), The Light Princess, 1969 (N.Y. Times Best Illustrated Book award 1969), The Bee-Man of Orn, 1971, Sarah's Room, 1971, The Juniper Tree and Other Tales from Grimm, 1973 (N.Y. Times Best Illustrated Book award 1973), Fortunia: A Tale by Mme. D'Aulnoy, 1974, Fly by Night, 1976 (N.Y. Times Best Illustrated Book award 1976), King Grisly-Beard: A Tale from the Brothers Grimm, 1978, The Nutcracker, 1984 (N.Y. Times Best Illustrated Book award 1984), In Grandpa's House, 1985, The Chil-

dren's Books of Randall Jarrell, 1988, Dear Mili, 1988, I Saw Esau, 1992, The Ubiquitous Pig, 1992; author: Fantasy Sketches, 1970, Collection of Books, Posters, and Original Drawings, 1984, The Love for Three Oranges: The Glyndebourne Version, 1984, Posters, 1986, Caldecott & Co.: Notes on Books and Pictures, 1988, Maurice Sendak Book and Poster Package: Wild Things, 1991; editor: Maxfield Parrish Poster Book, 1974, The Disney Poster Book, 1977; contbr.: The Publishing Archive of Lothar Meggendorfer, 1975, Babar's Anniversary Album, 1981, Masterworks of Children's Literature, Vol. 7, 1984, Victorian Color Picture Books, 1985, Winsor McCay: His Life and Art, 1987, Mickey Mouse Movie Stories, 1988; dir.: lyricist: Really Rosie, 1975; lyricist, set designer: Really Rosie, 1978; lyricist, set designer, costume designer: Where the Wild Things Are, 1980, Higglety, Pigglety, Pop!, 1984; set designer, costume designer: The Magic Flute, 1980, The Cunning Little Vixen, 1981, Love for Three Oranges, 1982, The Goose of Cairo, 1984, Idomeneo, 1988, L'Enfant et les Sortileges, 1989, L'Heure Espagnol, 1989, It's Alive!, 1994, So, Sue Me, 1994; photographer: The Cunning Little Vixen, 1985; designer: (film) The Nutcracker, 1986. Recipient Chandler Book Talk Reward of Merit, 1967, Hans Christian Andersen Internat. medal, 1970, Laura Ingalls Wilder award Assn. Libr. Svc. to Children, 1983. Office: Harper & Row 10 E 53rd St New York NY 10022*

SENDAX, VICTOR IRVEN, dentist, educator, dental implant researcher; b. N.Y.C., Sept. 14, 1930; s. Maurice and Molly R. S.; m. Deborah deLand Cobb, Dec. 17, 1969 (div. June 1976); 1 child, Jennifer Reiland; m. Marcia Ayer Pearson, Dec. 13, 1986; children: Anneliese Chase, Cordelia Ayer. Grad., Tanglewood Music Ctr., 1953; BA, NYU, 1951, DDS, 1955; postgrad., Harvard U. Sch. Dental Medicine, 1969-72. Diplomate Am. Bd. Oral Implantology/Implant Dentistry. Commr. N.Y. State Dental Service Corp., 1969-73; pres. BioDental Research Found., Inc., N.Y.C., 1975—, Victor I. Sendax, D.D.S. P.C., N.Y.C., 1972—; Sendax Dental Implant Magnetics Inc., N.Y.C., 1985—; assoc. attending implantologist St. Lukes-Roosevelt Hosp. Dental Implant Ctr., N.Y.C., 1979—; attending implantologist Beth Israel Hosp., N.Y.C., 1991—, Beth Israel North, N.Y.C., 1991—; pres. Mini Dental Implant Mgmt. Ctrs., Inc.; adj. assoc. prof. implant prosthodontics Columbia U. Sch. Dental and Oral Surgery, N.Y.C., 1974-92; vis. lectr. HA-coated implant systems dept. implant dentistry NYU Coll. Dentistry; faculty 1st dist. Dental Soc. Sch. for Continuing Dental Edn.; mem. dental implant rsch. programs adv. com. Nat. Inst. Dental Rsch., HHS; cons. Julliard Sch. Voice and Drama, N.Y.C., 1972—, Vocal Dynamics Lab. Dept. Otolaryngology, Lenox Hill Hosp., N.Y.C., 1970—; founder Sendax Seminars; 1st dir. implant prosthodontics resident program Columbia U. Sch. Dental and Oral Surgery and Columbia Presbyn. Hosp. Editor: Dental Clinics of North America: HA-Coated Dental Implants, 1992; Mem. editorial bd. Oral Implantology, 1979—; patentee in oral implant magnetics, mini-implants and implant abutments. Bd. dirs. City Ctr. Music and Drama, Inc. div. Lincoln Ctr. Performing Arts, N.Y.C., 1966-75; mem. adv. bd. Amagansett (N.Y.) Hist. Assn., 1969—; trustee Leukemia Soc. Am., N.Y.C., 1967; bd. dirs. Schola Cantorum, 1980-90, Soc. Asian Music, 1965-76. Served to capt. Dental Corps USAF, 1955-57. Recipient Spl. Recognition, Am. Fund Dental Health, 1981, Cert. of Honor, Brit. Dental Implant Assn., 1988. Fellow Am. Coll. Dentists, Internat. Coll. Dentists, Am. Acad. Implant Dentistry (nat. pres. 1981), Royal Soc. Medicine Gt. Britain; mem. ADA (ho. of dels. 1969), Am. Assn. Dental Schs. (chmn. interdisciplinary group on dental implant edn.), Acad. of Osseointegration, Am. Prosthodontic Soc., Am. Equilibration Soc., Am. Analgesia Soc., Fedn. Dentaire Internat., Am. Assn. Dental Rsch. (implant group), Internat. Assn. Dental Rsch., N.Y. Acad. Scis., Japan Soc., Century Assn., Players Club (N.Y.C.), Sigma Epsilon Delta. Home: 70 E 77th St Apt 6A New York NY 10021-1811 Office: Victor I Sendax DDS PC Parkview Dental Implant Condo 30 Central Park S Ste 14B New York NY 10019 I stand in awe of mankinds' eternal need to innovate and push back the frontiers of knowledge, while tempering the harsher realities of existence with a perspective born of our cultural heritage.

SENDER, STANTON P., lawyer; b. Seattle, Nov. 11, 1932; s. James and Lucile J. S.; m. Michelle R. Vale, Mar. 29, 1973; children: Jason, Todd. AB, Harvard U., 1953, JD, 1956. Bar: U.S. Supreme Ct. 1962, D.C. 1969. Asst. atty. gen. Wash. State, Seattle and Olympia, 1956-61; trial atty. gen. counsel's office I.C.C., Washington, 1961-63; transp. counsel U.S. Senate Commerce Commn., Washington, 1963-69; asst. gen. counsel, dir. legal affairs Sears, Roebuck, and Co., Washington, 1969-89; dir. govt. rels. practice group Morgan, Lewis, and Bockius, Washington, 1989—; adj. prof. Georgetown U., 1970-78. Bd. dirs. (by presdl. appointment) U.S. Railway Assn., 1978-81; treas. Nat. Industrial Transp. League, 1976-88. Recipient Outstanding Coun. award Fed. Bar Assn., 1979, Achievement award Traffic Management mag., 1986, Silver Plaque award Nat. Retail Merchants Assn., 1989 ; named Man of Yr. Nat. Industrial Transp. League, 1986. Mem. ABA (vice-chair transp. com. 1989—), Propeller Club of Washington (bd. govs. 1990-95). Office: Morgan Lewis & Bockius 1800 M St NW Washington DC 20036-5869

SENDERLING, JON TOWNSEND, journalist, public affairs specialist; b. Phila.; s. John Chester and Elizabeth (Nogle) S.; m. Elizabeth Marie Broadbent, Mar. 27, 1965; children: Jon, Tracy. Student, Ursinus Coll., 1960, Temple U., 1961-64; student (fellow), Stanford U., 1970. Reporter Bucks County Courier Times, Levittown, Pa., 1966-68, Wilmington (Del.) News-Jour., 1968-70; reporter, mag. writer, columnist, spl. projects editor Trenton (N.J.) Times, 1970-76; gen. assignments editor, state editor, nat.-fgn. editor Dallas Times Herald, 1976-80, editorial page dir., 1981-86; dep. fgn. editor Newsday, Melville, L.I., N.Y., 1987-89; pub. affairs mgr. EDS Corp., Dallas, 1989—. Author: play The Trashman, 1970. Recipient disting. service award for editorial writing Sigma Delta Chi, 1982, also 16 awards state press assns. Office: 5400 Legacy Dr Plano TX 75024-9999

SENDROVIC, ISRAEL, bank executive; b. Liberece, Czechoslovakia, June 19, 1947; s. Jacob Solomon and Frieda (Hirsch) S.; m. Esther Leah Karsh, June 15, 1969; children—Barry Dov, Karen Sue, Rochelle Beth, Deena. B.S. in Math., Bklyn. Coll., 1968; Rabbinical degree, Torah Vodaath Sem., Bklyn., 1969; M.S. in Ops. Research, NYU, 1970. Mem. research staff Riverside Research Inst., N.Y.C., 1968-70; exec. v.p. Fed. Res. Bank N.Y., N.Y.C., 1970—. Avocations: Talmudic studies, Judaica. Office: Fed Res Bank NY 33 Liberty St New York NY 10005-1011

SENECAL, EUGENE GERALD, retail executive; b. Holyoke, Mass., Aug. 19, 1943; s. Raymond Jean and Lottie Barbara (Nowalk) S.; m. Carol Ann Basile, May 3, 1969 (div. 1976); 1 child, Lisa Marie; m. Marie Theresa Doyle, Aug. 15, 1981. Programmer Aetna Ins. Co., Hartford, Conn., 1964; programmer, analyst Conn. Gen. Bloomfield, 1964-66; system-program mgr. Advo System, Hartford, 1966-70; cons. Keane Assocs., East Hartford, Conn., 1970-73; dir. mgmt. info. systems Ames Dept. Stores, Rocky Hill, Conn., 1973-78, asst. v.p., 1978-81, v.p. MIS, 1981-85; pres. Nat. Store Systems, Dallas, 1988-90. USAF, 1961-63. Mem. Assn. Systems Mgmt., Data Processing Mgmt. Assn., Internat. Mass. Retailing Assn. (mgmt. info. systems steering com. 1986-88), Am. Inst. Cert. Computer Profls. Republican. Roman Catholic. Avocations: golf, model ship building. Home: 4632 De Gray Ln Plano TX 75093-7124 Office: Nat Store Systems 3418 Midcourt Rd Ste 119 Carrollton TX 75006-5066

SENECHAL, ALICE R., judge, lawyer; b. Rugby, N.D., June 25, 1955; d. Marvin William and Dora Emma (Erdman) S. BS, N.D. State U., 1977; JD, U. Minn., 1984. Bar: Minn. 1984, U.S. Dist. Ct. Minn. 1984, N.D. 1986, U.S. Ct. Appeals (8th cir.) 1987. Law clk. U.S. Dist Judge Bruce M. Van Sickle, Bismarck, N.D., 1984-86; assoc. Robert Vogel Law Office, Grand Forks, N.D., 1986—; U.S. magistrate judge, 1990—. Office: Robert Vogel Law Office 106 N 3rd St Ste M102 Grand Forks ND 58203-3798

SENEFF, SMILEY HOWARD, business owner; b. Odon, Ind., June 28, 1925; s. Smiley and Ada Fern (Howard) S.; m. Barbara Jean Daum, July 17, 1950 (div. 1966); children: Nancy Kay Secrest, Cheryl Evans; m. Mary Ann Beeler, Mar. 12, 1966; children: Jill Midtbo, Judy Hiland, Jacalyn Harness, Jennifer Sillery, Donald. Student, Duke U., 1945; BS, Ind. U., 1950. Mem. acctg. staff Armour and Co., Indpls., 1950-52, Chevrolet Comml. Body Co., Indpls., 1952-54; owner, mgr. Seneff Hardware and Appliance, Plainfield, Ind., 1955-66, Catalina Motel, Indpls., 1966-73, Smiley's Pancake and Steak, Indpls., 1972—, Smiley's Car Wash, Indpls., 1972—. Mem. County Zoning Bd., 1959-63; Rep. precinct committeeman, del. to state Rep. conv., 1959-63. Mem. Elks, Rotary (pres.), Masons, Scottish Rite, Shriners. Avocations:

golf, swimming, walking. Home: 6002 Mt. Auburn Dr Indianapolis IN 46224 Office: Seneff Inns Inc 1307 S High School Rd Indianapolis IN 46241

SENELICK, LAURENCE PHILIP, theatre educator, director, writer; b. Chgo., Oct. 12, 1942; s. Theodore Senelick and Evelyn Marder Zwick. BA, Northwestern U., Evanston, Ill., 1964; AM, Harvard U., 1965, PhD, 1972. Asst. prof. English Emerson Coll., Boston, 1968-72; from asst. to prof. drama, Fletcher prof. drama and oratory Tufts U., Medford, Mass., 1972—; hon. curator Russian drama & theatre Harvard Theatre Collection, Cambridge, Mass., 1991—. Author: A Cavalcade of Clowns, 1978, Tchaikovsky's Sleeping Beauty, 1978, Gordon Craig's Moscow Hamlet: A Reconstruction, 1982, Serf Actor: The Life and Art of Mikhail Shchepkin, 1984, Anton Chekhov, 1985, The Prestige of Evil: The Murderer as Romantic Hero, 1987; (with P. Haskell) The Cheese Book, 1985; editor: Gneder in Performance, Wanderinf Stars; Plays: The Merchant of Venice, Dead Souls, You Never Can Tell, Tartuffe, The Magic Flute, Le Nozze de Figaro; numerous other; contr. articles to profl. jours. Fellow Guggenheim Found., 1979-80, 87-88, Wissenschaftskolleg zu Berlin, 1984-85; recipient George Freediey award Theatre Libr. Assn., 1988. Mem. Am. Soc. Theatre Rsch. (exec. bd. dirs. 1992—), Internat. Fedn. Theatre Rsch. (univ. commn. 1992—). Avocations: collecting theatricalia, cooking. Office: Tufts U Dept of Drama Leir Hall Medford MA 02155

SENER, JOSEPH WARD, JR., securities company executive; b. Balt., June 30, 1926; s. Joseph Ward and Clara (Hodshon) S.; m. Ann Clark TenEyck, May 3, 1952 (dec. Oct. 1967); children: J. TenEyck, Beverley T., Joseph Ward III; m. Jean Eisenbrandt-Johnston, Feb. 6, 1971. A.B., Haverford (Pa.) Coll., 1950; diploma, Inst. Investment Banking, U. Pa., 1954. With John C. Legg & Co., Balt., 1950-70; gen. partner John C Legg & Co., 1961-70; exec. v.p., dir. Legg, Mason & Co., Inc., Balt., 1970-72; vice chmn. bd. dirs., chief adminstrv. officer Legg Mason Wood Walker, Inc., Balt., 1976-80; bd. dirs. Legg Mason, Inc.; chmn. bd. dirs. Chesapeake Bank and Trust, Chestertown, Md., Chesapeake Bancorp. Trustee Boys' Latin Sch., Balt., pres. bd. trustees, 1980-82; chmn. bd. govs. Chesapeake Bay Maritime Mus. Served with USAAF, 1944-46. Mem. Nat. Assn. Securities Dealers (past dist. chmn.), Balt. Security Analysts Soc. (past pres.), Md. Club (Balt.). Republican. Episcopalian. Office: PO Box 511 Chestertown MD 21620-0511

SENESE, DONALD JOSEPH, former government official; b. Chgo., Apr. 6, 1942; s. Leo Carl and Joan (Schaffer) S.; m. Linda Faye Wall, Dec. 29, 1973; 1 dau., Denise Nicole. B.S in History, Loyola U., 1964, M.A., 1966; PhD, U. S.C., 1970; postgrad., Sophia U., Tokyo, 1970, Nat. Chengchi U., Taipei, Taiwan, 1971; cert. in adminstrv. procedures, U.S. Dept. Agr. Grad. Sch., 1976. Assoc. prof. history Radford U., U., 1969-72; legis. asst. to senator from Va. Senator from Va., 1973; legis. dir. to Rep. from Tex., 1973-76; sr. research assoc. House Republican Study Com., U.S. Ho. of Reps., Washington, 1976-81; asst. sec. for ednl. research and improvement U.S. Dept. Edn., Washington, 1981-85; pres. Senese Edn. Enterprises, Inc., 1985—; dep. asst. sec. to asst. sec. Office Territorial and Internat. Affairs, Dept. Interior, Washington, 1989-93; writer, cons. SEE, Inc., Alexandria, Va.; mem. child care liability task force study, Dept. Labor, 1989. Author: Indexing the Inflationary Impact of Taxes, 1978, Modernizing the Chinese Dragon, 1980, Asianomics: Challenge and Change in Northeast Asia, 1981; editor: Ideas Confront Reality, 1981, Sweet and Sour Capitalism, 1985, Democracy in Mainland China, 1986; co-author: Can The Two Chinas Become One?, 1989; editor: George Mason and The Legacy of Constitutional Liberty, 1989. Vice chmn. Alexandria (Va.) Rep. Com., 1976-78, staff Rep. Nat. Com., 1987-89; mem. Alexandria Hist. Records Commn., 1979-84; mem. Fairfax County History Commn., 1985—, chmn., 1990-91; Fairfax County Bicentennial of U.S. Constn. Com., 1986-91; dir. Nat. Ctr. for Presdl. Rsch., 1987—; dir. opposition rsch. Rep. Nat. Com., 1995—. Recipient William P. Lyons Master Essay award, 1967; Freedoms Found. award, 1981, 85, 90; named Outstanding Man of Yr. Jaycees, 1976, 78, Sec. Labor Exceptional Achievement award, 1990. Mem. Univ. Profs. for Acad. Order, Order Sons of Italy, Pi Gamma Mu, Phi Alpha Theta, Delta Sigma Rho-Tau Kappa Alpha. Roman Catholic. Office: PO Box 6886 Alexandria VA 22306-0886 *It has been important to have a philosophy of government which emphasizes honesty, integrity, a Ciceronian concept of duty, cost-effective public service, and a committment to the American heritage and traditions. These views have been reinforced by the support of family, friends, and a spiritual faith.*

SENFF, MARK D., lawyer; b. Wooster, Ohio, Aug. 13, 1945. BS, Ohio State U., 1968, JD summa cum laude, 1971. Bar: Ohio 1971. Ptnr. Baker & Hostetler, Columbus, Ohio. Editor-in-chief Ohio State Law Jour., 1970-71. Office: Baker & Hostetler Capital Sq 65 E State St Ste 2100 Columbus OH 43215-4260

SENG, ANN FRANCES, civic organization executive; b. Chgo., Jan. 5, 1936; d. William John and Helen Christine (Steger) S. BA, Alverno Coll., Milw., 1957; MA, Loyola U., Chgo., 1970. Tchr. Alvernia High Sch., Chgo., 1958-65; exec. dir. Community House Cath. Charities, Chgo., 1965-67; adminstr. Sch. Sisters St. Francis, Chgo., 1967-69; dir. uptown advocacy program Chgo. Cath. Interracial Coun., 1970-71; community devel. dir. Uptown Ctr. Hull House, Chgo., 1971-81; dir. rsch. and pub. policy Hull House Assn., Chgo., 1981-88; pres., chief exec. officer Chgo. Coun. Urban Affairs, 1988—; bd. dirs. Jane Addams Conf., Chgo., 1987—, Chgo. Capital Fund, 1988—, Women Employed Inst., Chgo., 1988-91. Mem. Pvt. Industry Coun., Chgo., 1988—; vice-chair Chgo. Com. Urban Opportunity, 1988-92. Mem. LWV, NOW, Ill. Women's Agenda (chair 1983-84). Office: Chgo Coun Urban Affairs 6 N Michigan Ave Ste 1308 Chicago IL 60602-4808

SENGSTACKE, JOHN HERMAN HENRY, publishing company executive; b. Savannah, Ga., Nov. 25, 1912; s. Herman Alexander and Rosa Mae (Davis) S.; 1 son, Robert Abbott. B.S., Hampton (Va.) Inst., 1933; postgrad., Ohio State U., 1933. With Robert S. Abbott Pub. Co. (publishers Chgo. Defender), 1934—, v.p., gen. mgr., 1934-40, pres., gen. mgr., 1940—; chmn. bd. Mich. Chronicle, Detroit; pres. Tri-State Defender, Defender Publs., Amalgamated Pubs., Inc.; pub. Daily Defender; pres. Sengstacke Enterprises, Inc., Sengstacke Publs., Pitts. Courier Newspaper Chain; dir. Ill. Fed. Savs. & Loan Assn., Golden State Mut. Life Ins. Co. Mem. exec. bd. Nat. Alliance Businessmen; bd. govs. USO; mem. Ill. Sesquicentennial Commn., Pres.'s Com. on Equal Opportunity in Armed Services; mem. pub. affairs adv. com. Air Force Acad.; trustee Bethune-Cookman Coll., Daytona Beach, Fla., Hampton Inst.; bd. dirs. Washington Park YMCA, Joint Negro Appeal; chmn. bd. Provident Hosp. Recipient Two Friends award Nat. Urban League, 1950; Hampton Alumni award, 1954; 1st Mass. Media award Am. Jewish Com. Mem. Negro Newspaper Pubs. Assn. (founder), Nat. Newspaper Pubs. Assn. (founder, pres.), Am. Newspaper Pubs. Assn., Am. Soc. Newspaper Editors (dir.). Congregationalist. Clubs: Royal Order of Snakes, Masons, Elks, Econs, Chgo. Press. Office: Sengstacke Enterprises Inc 2400 S Michigan Ave Chicago IL 60616-2329 also: Robert S Abbott Pub Co 2400 S Michigan Chicago IL 60616

SENGUPTA, DIPAK LAL, electrical engineering and physics educator, researcher; b. Bengal, India, Mar. 1, 1931; came to U.S., 1959; s. Jayanta Kumar and Pankajini Sengupta; m. Sujata Basu, Aug. 31, 1962; children: Sumit, Mita. BSc in Physics with honors, Calcutta U., India, 1950, MSc in Radio Physics, 1952; PhD, U. Toronto, Ont., Can., 1958. Assoc. rsch. physicist dept. elec. engring. U. Mich., Ann Arbor, 1959-63, rsch. physicist, 1965-75, rsch. scientist, prof. dept. elec. engring., 1975-86; asst. prof. dept. elec. engring. U. Toronto, 1963-64; asst. dir. Cen. Electronics Engring. Rsch. Inst., Pilani, India, 1964-65; prof., chmn. dept. elec. engring. at India, 1992-93; cons. Ford Motor Co., Dearborn, Mich., 1976-77, Battelle Pacific N.W. Labs., Richland, Wash., 1978. Author: Radar Cross Section Analysis and Control, 1991; contr. articles to profl. jours. Fellow IEEE (sect. chmn. award 1969, recognition awards 1978-79); mem. Internat. Radio Scientists Union (sec. commn. B 1976-78), Sigma Xi, Eta Kappa Nu. Office: U Detroit Mercy Dept Elec Engring 4001 W Mcnichols Rd Detroit MI 48219

SENGUPTA, MRITUNJOY, mining engineer, educator; b. Cuttack, Orissa, India, Oct. 24, 1941; came to U.S., 1968; s. Chandi P. and Bani S.; m. Nupur Bagchi, Jan. 15, 1981; children: Shyam S. ME, Columbia U., 1971, MS, 1972; PhD, Colo. Sch. of Mines, 1983. Mining engr. Continental Oil Co., Denver, 1977-78, United Nuclear Corp., Albuquerque, 1978-80, Morrison-

Knudson Co., Boise, Idaho, 1975-77, 80-82; assoc. prof. U. Alaska, Fairbanks, 1983-88, prof., 1989—; cons. UN Devel. Program, 1987. Author: Mine Environmental Engineering, vols. I and II, 1989, Environmental Impacts of Mining, 1992; contr. articles to profl. publs. Recipient Gold medal Mining Metall. Inst. of India, 1976, Nat. Merit scholarship Govt. of India, 1959-63. Mem. NSPE, So. Mining Engrs. Achievements include development of new concepts for mine design in oilshale in Colo. Home: 421 Cindy Dr Fairbanks AK 99701-3220 Office: U Alaska Fairbanks AK 99775

SENHAUSER, DONALD A(LBERT), pathologist, educator; b. Dover, Ohio, Jan. 30, 1927; s. Albert Carl and Maude Anne (Snyder) S.; m. Helen Brown, July 22, 1961; children: William, Norman. Student, U. Chgo., 1944-45; BS, Columbia U., 1948, MD, 1951; grad. with honors, U.S. Naval Sch. Aviation Medicine, 1953. Diplomate Am. Bd. Pathology. Intern Roosevelt Hosp., N.Y.C., 1951-52; resident Columbia-Presbyn. Hosp., N.Y.C., 1955-56, Cleve. Clinic, 1956-60; instr. in pathology Columbia U., 1955-56; fellow in immuno-pathology Middlesex Hosp. Med. Sch., London, 1960-61; mem. dept. pathology Cleve. Clinic Found., 1961-63; assoc. prof. pathology U. Mo., 1963-65; prof., asst. dean Sch. Medicine U. Mo., 1969-70, dir. teaching labs., 1968-70, prof., vice-chmn. dept. pathology, 1965-75; prof., chmn. dept. pathology Coll. Medicine Ohio State U., 1975-92, chair emeritus, 1992, prof. Sch. Allied Med. Professions, 1975—; dir. labs. Ohio State U. Hosps., 1975-92; pres. Univ. Reference Lab., Inc., 1984-86, CEO, 1986-92; bd. dirs. Columbus area chpt. ARC, 1978-82; cons. in field; WHO-AMA Vietnam med. edn. project mem. U. Saigon Med. Sch., 1967-52; vis. scientist HEW, 1972-73; acting dir. Ctrl. Ohio Regional Blood Ctr., 1976-79. Mem. editorial bd. Am. Jour. Clin. Pathology, 1965-76. With USN, 1945-46; lt. M.C. USNR, Korea, China; now capt. USNR ret. Served with USN, 1945-46; served as lt. M.C USNR, Korea, China; now capt. USNR, Ret. Recipient Lower award Bunts Ednl. Found., 1960-61. Mem. AAAS, Coll. Am. Pathologists (bd. govs. 1980-86, v.p. 1989-90, pres.-elect 1990-91, pres. 1991-93, immediate past pres. 1993—, Pathologist of Yr. 1994), Am. Soc. Clin. Pathologists, Assn. Pathology Chmn., Am. Assn. Pathology, Internat. Acad. Pathology, Assn. Am. Med. Colls., Am. Assn. Blood Banks, Ohio Soc. Pathologists (gov. 1979, pres. 1987-89), Ohio Hist. Soc., Columbus Art League, Masons, Sigma Xi. Lutheran. Home: 1256 Clubview Blvd N Columbus OH 43235-1226 Office: 333 W 10th Ave Columbus OH 43210-1239

SENHAUSER, JOHN CRATER, architect; b. New Philadelphia, Ohio, Apr. 7, 1947; s. Edwin Crater and Margaret Jean (Huffman) S.; m. Teri A. Schleyer, June 25, 1988. BS in Architecture, U. Cin., 1971. Registered architect, Ohio, Ky. Designer Jones, Peacock, Garn & Ptnrs., Cin., 1971-72; project architect Smith Stevens Architects, Cin., 1972-76; project mgr. Herrlinger Enterprises, Cin., 1976-79; prin., owner John C Senhauser, Architect, Cin., 1979—; adj. assoc. prof. Sch. Architecture and Interior Design, U. Cin., 1992—. Exhibited in group shows at Toni Birckhead Gallery, 1990, Contemporary Arts Ctr., Cin., 1993, Canton (Ohio) Art Inst., 1993; prin. works include residences. Mem. historic conservation bd. City of Cin., 1986—; mem. dean's adv. coun. Coll. Design Architecture Art and Planning U. Cin., 1990. Recipient Merit award Builder mag., 1985, 88, Grand award, 1990, Grand Best in Region award Profl. Builder, 1990. Mem. AIA (honor award Cin. chpt. 1983, 85, 90, 91, 92, 93, v.p. elect 1990, pres. 1991), Architects Soc. Ohio (bd. dirs., honor award 1985, 90, 91, 93), Home Builders Assn. Greater Cin. Office: 1118 Saint Gregory St Cincinnati OH 45202-1769

SENIOR, ENRIQUE FRANCISCO, investment banker; b. Havana, Cuba, Aug. 3, 1943; came to U.S., 1960; s. Frank and Dolores (Hernandez) Senior; m. Robin Suffern Gimbel, Sept. 7, 1977; children: Tailer, Heather, Fern, Seanna. BA in Architecture, Yale U., 1964, BS in Elec. Engring., 1967; MBA, Harvard U., 1969. Corp. fin. exec. White, Weld & Co., N.Y.C., 1969-73; v.p. Allen & Co., N.Y.C., 1973-80, exec. v.p., mng. dir., 1980—; bd. dirs. Allen & Co., Inc., Air & Water Techs. Corp., Somerville, N.J., Dick Clark Prodns., Inc., Burbank, Calif. Mem. The Brook Club, Piping Rock Club, Farmington Country Club, Phi Beta Kappa, Tau Beta Pi. Avocations: flying, fishing, hunting, skiing, woodworking. Office: Allen & Co Inc 711 Fifth Ave New York NY 10022-3109

SENIOR, THOMAS BRYAN A., electrical engineering educator, researcher, consultant; b. Menston, Yorkshire, Eng., June 26, 1928; came to U.S., 1957; s. Thomas Harold and Emily Dorothy (Matthews) S.; m. Heather Margaret Golby, May 4, 1957; children—Margaret, David, Hazel, Peter. B.Sc., Manchester U., 1949, M.Sc., 1950; Ph.D., Cambridge U., 1954. Sr. sci. officer Royal Radar Establishment, Malvern, Eng., 1952-57; rsch. scientist U. Mich., Ann Arbor, 1957-69, prof. elec. engring., 1969-84, prof. elec. and computer sci., 1984—; Arthur F. Thurnau prof., 1990—, dir. radiation lab., 1975-87, assoc. chmn. elect. engring. & computer sci. dept., 1984-90, acting chmn., 1987-88, assoc. chmn. acad. affairs, 1991—; cons. in field. Author: (with Bowman and Uslenghi) Electromagnetic and Acoustical Scattering by Simple Shapes, 1969; Mathematical Methods in Electrical Engineering, 1986; (with Volakis) Approximate Boundary Conditions in Electromagnetics, 1995; contbr. articles to profl. jours. Fellow IEEE; mem. Internat. Sci. Radio Union (chmn. U.S. nat. com. 1982-84, vice chmn. Com. B. 1985-87, chmn. 1988-90, v.p. 1993—, Van der Pol Gold medal 1993). Home: 1919 Ivywood Dr Ann Arbor MI 48103-4527 Office: U Mich Dept Elec Engring Comp S Ann Arbor MI 48109

SENKAYI, ABU LWANGA, environmental soil scientist; b. Mpigi, Uganda, Oct. 16, 1943; came to U.S., 1973; s. Alamanzane Buza and Manjeri (Nalwoga) Abalyawo; m. Sunajeh Nansamba, Dec. 27, 1969; children: Ali K., Sala N. BS, Makerere U., Kampala, Uganda, 1971, MS, 1973; PhD, U. Calif., Davis, 1977. Rsch. scientist Tex. A&M U., College Station, 1977-87; sr. soil chemist Ebasco Environ. Svcs., Dallas, 1987-90; soil chemist PRC Environ. Mgmt., Inc., Dallas, 1990—; tech. cons. U.S. EPA Region 6. Author 7 book chpts.; contbr. articles to Soil Sci. Soc. Am. Jour., Soil Sci. Jour., Clays and Clay Minerals Jour. Recipient PRC-EMI Exceptional Performance award, 1991. Mem. Soil Sci. Soc. Am., Clay Mineral Soc., Mineral. Soc. Gt. Britain, Sigma Xi. Achievements include investigation of mineralogical weathering processes in soils and problems associated with reclamation of surface-mined lands. Home: 1122 De Havilland Ave Duncanville TX 75137-4742 Office: PRC Environ Mgmt Inc 350 N St Paul St Ste 2600 Dallas TX 75201-4218

SENKIER, ROBERT JOSEPH, foundation administrator, educator; b. Poughkeepsie, N.Y., May 31, 1916; s. Michael J. and Mary Gilberta (Perrin) S.; m. Mary Theresa Kelly, Mar. 21, 1941; children—Pamela Jeanne Senkier Scott, Deborah Ann. A.B., Columbia U. 1939, M.A., 1940, Ed.D. 1961. Mem. bus. faculty Columbia U., 1948-61; asst. dean Columbia U. (Sch. Bus.), 1958-61; prof. mgmt. Seton Hall U., South Orange, N.J., 1962-74; dean Seton Hall U. (Sch. Bus. Adminstrn.), 1962-74; prof. mgmt., dean Grad. Sch. Bus., Fordham U., N.Y.C., 1975-79; exec. dir. Mathers Found., 1982-84; found. cons., 1985—. Author: Revising a Business Curriculum—The Columbia Experience, 1961; contbr. articles to profl. jours. Mem. alumni bd. dirs. Columbia Coll.; mem. John Jay Assocs.; Holy See del. to U.N., 1980-83; trustee Marymount Coll. N.Y.A., 1983-85, Molloy Coll., 1986-89. Served to lt. comdr. USNR, 1944-45. Mem. Acad. Internat. Bus., Columbia Alumni Assn., Phi Delta Kappa, Alpha Kappa Psi, Alpha Sigma Phi, Beta Gamma Sigma. Republican. Roman Catholic. Club: Princeton (N.Y.C.). Home: 6 Amherst Ct Glen Rock NJ 07452-1302 Office: Mathers Found 105 S Bedford Rd Mount Kisco NY 10549-3441

SENNEMA, DAVID CARL, museum consultant; b. Grand Rapids, Mich., July 6, 1934; s. Carl Edward and Alice Bertha (Bieri) S.; m. Martha Amanda Dixon, Feb. 22, 1958; children—Daniel Ross, Julia Kathryn, Alice Dixon. B.A., Albion Coll., 1956. Mgr., Columbia Music Festival Assn., 1964-67; exec. dir. S.C. Arts Commn., Columbia, 1967-70; assoc. dir. Federal-State Partnership and Spl. Projects programs Nat. Endowment for the Arts, Washington, 1971-73; prof. arts adminstrn., dir. community arts mgmt. program Sangamon State U. Springfield, Ill., 1973-76; dir. S.C. Mus. Commn. Columbia, 1976-85; cons. in field. Mem. adv. panel Nat. Endowment for the Arts Music, 1968-70. Chmn. Springfield Arts Commn., 1975-76. Served with U.S. Army, 1957-58. Lodge: Rotary (chmn. cultural affairs com. 1978-80).

SENNETT, HENRY HERBERT, JR., theatre arts educator; b. Atlanta, Feb. 28, 1945; s. Henry Herbert and Betty Ruth (Wilson) S.; m. Beverly Ann

Rodgers, Dec. 9, 1967; children: Cristie Aline, Herbert Alan. BS in Edn., Ark. State U., Jonesboro, 1968; MA, Memphis State U., 1971; MDiv, So. Bapt. Sem., Louisville, 1978; DMin, Midwestern Bapt. Sem., Kansas City, Mo., 1988; MFA, Fla. Atlantic U., 1989. Cert. tchr. Tchr. speech and English Covington (Tenn.) High Sch., 1971-72; freelance designer Lighting by Herb, Memphis, 1972-73; tchr. speech and English Augusta (Ark.) High Sch., 1973-76; instr. drama Jefferson Community Coll., Louisville, 1977-78; pastor Dublin (Ohio) Bapt. Ch., 1979-83, Trinity Bapt. Ch., Searcy, Ark., 1983-85; asst. prof. theatre arts, dept chair Palm Beach Atlantic Coll., West Palm Beach, Fla., 1985—; stress mgmt. cons. Palm Beach County Bd. Edn., West Palm Beach, 1988—; freelance cons. theatrical lighting and design, West Palm Beach, 1986—; cons. drama edn. Fla. Dept. Edn., 1991-94; vis. prof. Midwestern Bapt. Sem., Kansas City, Mo., 1988. Author: Theatre in the Church, 1992, Religion and Dramatics: Essays on the Relationship Between Christianity and the Theatrical Arts, 1994; author: (play) Stars, 1989. 1st lt. U.S. Army, 1968-70, Vietnam; chaplain USAR, 1984—. Mem. Nat. Assn. Schs. Theatre, Fla. Theatre Edn., Fla. Theatre Conf., South Western Theatre Conf., Assn. Theatre Higher Edn., Blue Key Nat. Honor Soc., Theatre Comm. Group, Pi Kappa Phi (pres. 1965-66). Republican. Baptist. Avocations: pastor, author. Office: Palm Beach Atlantic Coll PO Box 24708 West Palm Beach FL 33416-4708

SENNETT, RICHARD, sociologist, writer; b. Chgo., Jan. 1, 1943; s. Maurice and Dorothy S. B.A. in History summa cum laude, U. Chgo., 1964; Ph.D., Harvard U., 1969. Asst. prof. Yale U., 1967-68; dir. Urban Family Study, Cambridge, Mass., 1969-71; mem. faculty NYU, 1971—, Univ. prof. of the humanities, 1984—; founder, dir. N.Y. Inst. Humanities, 1976-79, 81-84; chmn. adv. com. on urban studies UNESCO, 1988—; Sigmund Freud Meml. lectr. U. London, 1977; disting. vis. prof. Coll. de France, Paris, 1980; Henry Luce lectr. Yale U., 1986; vis. prof. humanities Harvard U., 1984; Goethe lectr. U. Frankfurt, Germany, 1991-92; scholar-in-residence Am. Acad., Rome, 1992; rep. Internat. Social Sci. Coun. to UN, 1992—. Author: Families Against the City, 1970, The Uses of Disorder, 1970, The Hidden Injuries of Class, 1972, The Fall of Public Man, 1977, Authority, 1980, The Frog Who Dared To Croak, 1982, An Evening of Brahms, 1984, Palais Royal, 1986, The Conscience of the Eye, 1990, Flesh and Stone, 1994. Fellow Guggenheim Found., 1973, Inst. Advanced Study, 1973-74, 79-80, Nat. Endowment for the Humanities, 1976, Woodrow Wilson Ctr.-Smithsonian Instn., Washington, 1993. Fellow Am. Sociol. Assn.; mem. Internat. Sociol. Assn., Nat. Council Family Relations, PEN (dir. 1977—, v.p. 1979-82). Clubs: Century Assn. (N.Y.C.); Signet Soc. (Harvard). Office: 269 Mercer St Rm 812 New York NY 10003-6633

SENNSTROM, JOHN HAROLD, manufacturing company executive; b. Schenectady, N.Y., Mar. 15, 1941. B.S. in Indsl. Mgmt., Purdue U., 1965; M.B.A., U. Wash., 1982. Prodn. supr. Haller Inc., Northville, Mich., 1965-69; plant mgr. IPM Corp., Columbus, Ohio, 1969-76; mfg. mgr. Fentron Industries, Seattle, 1976-79; pres. Hytek Finishes Co., Kent, Wash., 1979-84, Fentron Bldg. Products Co., Seattle, 1984-87, Demcon Cons. Co., Redmond, Wash., 1987—. Home and Office: 2310 187th Ave NE Redmond WA 98052-6011

SENSEMAN, RONALD SYLVESTER, architect; b. Collingswood, N.J., Oct. 19, 1912; s. Raphael and Louise (Tanner) S.; m. Lois Hatt, Aug. 18, 1935 (dec. Aug. 1979); children: Marilyn Louise (Mrs. John Whitson Rogers), Peggy June (Mrs. James Orvil Hutchinson); m. Claire M. Stoehr, Sept. 8, 1980; children: Deborah Stoehr (Mrs. Tim Darrin), Darice (Mrs. Kevin Lang), Darla (Mrs. Jeffrey Schultz), D'Lynn Stoehr (Mrs. Shean Phelps). Student, Columbia Union Coll., 1931-34, Cath. U. Am., 1934-36. Pvt. practice architecture Met. Washington area, 1935-89; ret.; cons. architect Silver Spring, 1989—; dir. Park Motels Inc., Manor Care, Inc.; pres. Reef Properties Inc., St. Croix, V.I.; lectr. Columbia Union Coll., Seventh Day Adventist Theol. Sem. Archtl. works include: Nat. Indsl. Coll., Army War Coll., Ft. McNair, Washington, Naval War Coll., Newport, R.I., Atlantic Union Coll., South Lancaster, Mass., Columbia Union Coll., Takoma Park, Md., Shady Grove Adventist Hosp., Gaithersburg, Md., others. Republican candidate Md. State Legislature, 1958; Mem. univ. councillors Loma Linda U.; trustee Atlantic Union Coll. Fellow AIA (pres. Md. div. met. Washington chpt. 1947-49, pres. Potomac Valley chpt.); mem. Guild Religious Architecture, Washington Bd. Trade, Washington Building Congress, Prince George's County C. of C., Cath. U. Alumni Assn. (Archtl. Achievement award 1967). Lodge: Rotary. Home: 10718 Gatewood Ave Silver Spring MD 20903-1013

SENSENBRENNER, FRANK JAMES, JR., congressman; lawyer; b. Chicago, Ill., June 14, 1943; s. Frank James and Margaret Anita (Luedke) S.; m. Cheryl Lynn Warren, Mar. 26, 1977; children: Frank James III, Robert Alan. A.B. in Polit. Sci, Stanford U., 1965; J.D., U. Wis., 1968. Bar: Wis. 1968, U.S. Supreme Ct. 1972. Mem. firm McKay and Martin, Cedarburg, Wis., 1970-75; mem. Wis. Assembly, 1969-75; mem. Wis. State Senate, 1975-79, asst. minority leader, 1977-79; mem. 96th-104th Congresses from 9th Wis. dist., Washington, D.C., 1979—; mem. House Jud. Com., House Sci. Com., chmn. subcom. on space and aeronautics. Mem. Am. Philatelic Soc. Republican. Episcopalian. Club: Capitol Hill. Office: US Ho of Reps 2332 Rayburn House Bldg Washington DC 20515-4909

SENSENICH, ILA JEANNE, lawyer, magistrate judge; b. Pitts., Mar. 6, 1939; d. Louis E. and Evelyn Margaret (Harbourt) S. BA, Westminster Coll., 1961; JD, Dickinson Sch. Law, 1964, JD (hon.), 1994. Bar: Pa. 1964. Assoc. Stewart, Belden, Sensenich and Herrington, Greensburg, Pa., 1964-70; asst. pub. defender Westmoreland (Pa.) County, 1970-71; U.S. magistrate judge for We. Dist. Pa., Pitts., 1971—; adj. prof. law Duquesne U., 1982-87. Trustee emeritus Dickinson Sch. Law. Mem. ABA, Fed. Magistrate Judges Assn. (sec. 1979-81, sec. 1988-89, treas. 1989-90, 2d v.p. 1990-91, pres.-elect 1992-93, pres. 1993-94), Pa. Bar Assn., Allegheny County Bar Assn. (fed. ct. sect.), Nat. Assn. Women Judges, Westmoreland County Bar Assn., Allegheny Bar Assn. (civil litigation sect., com. women in law), Am. Judicature Soc., 3d Cir. Jud. Coun. Democrat. Presbyterian. Avocations: skiing, sailing, bicycling, classical music, cooking. Author: Compendium of the Law of Prisoner's Rights, 1979; contbr. articles to profl. jours. Office: 518B Us PO And Courthouse Pittsburgh PA 15219

SENSIPER, SAMUEL, consulting electrical engineer; b. Elmira, N.Y., Apr. 26, 1919; s. Louis and Molly (Pedolsky) S.; m. Elaine Marie Zwick, Sept. 10, 1950; children—Martin, Sylvia, David. B.S.E.E., M.I.T., 1939, Sc.D., 1951; E.E., Stanford U., 1941. Asst. project engr. to sr. project engr., cons. Sperry Gyroscope, Garden City, Great Neck, N.Y., 1941-51; sect. head and sr. staff cons. Hughes Aircraft, Culver City, Malibu, Calif., 1951-60; lab. div. mgr. Space Gen. Corp. Glendale, Azusa, Los Angeles, 1960-67; lab. mgr. TRW Redondo Beach, Calif., 1967-70; cons. elec. engr., Los Angeles, 1970-73; dir. engring. Transco Products, Venice, Calif., 1973-75; cons. elec. engr. in pvt. practice, Los Angeles, 1975—; faculty U. So. Calif., Los Angeles, 1955-56, 79-80. Contbr. articles to profl. jours. Recipient Cert. of Commendation U.S. Navy, 1946; indsl. electronics fellow M.I.T., 1947-48. Fellow IEEE, AAAS; mem. Calif. Soc. Profl. Engrs., Fedn. Am. Scientists, M.I.T. Alumni Assn., Stanford Alumni Assn., Electromagnetics Acad., Sigma Xi, Eta Kappa Nu. Patentee in field. Home: 6011 S Holt Ave Los Angeles CA 90056-1415 Office: PO Box 3102 Culver City CA 90231-3102

SENTELLE, DAVID BRYAN, federal judge; b. Canton, N.C., Feb. 12, 1943; s. Horace Richard, Jr., and Maude (Ray) S.; m. Jane LaRue Oldham, June 19, 1965; children: Sharon Rene, Reagan Elaine, Rebecca Grace. AB, U. N.C., 1965, JD with honors, 1968. Bar: N.C. 1968, U.S. Dist. Ct. (we. dist.) N.C. 1969, U.S. Ct. Appeals (4th cir.) 1970. Assoc. Uzzell & Dumont, Asheville, N.C., 1968-70; asst. U.S. atty. City of Charlotte, N.C., 1970-74, dist. judge, 1974-77; ptnr. Tucker, Hicks, Sentelle, Moon & Hodge, P.A., Charlotte, 1977-85; judge U.S. Dist. Ct. (we. dist.) N.C., Charlotte, 1985-87, U.S. Ct. Appeals D.C., 1987—; adj. prof. Fla. State U. Coll. Law. Contbr. articles to profl. jours. Chmn. Mecklenburg County Rep. Com., 1978-80; chmn. N.C. State Rep. Conv., 1979-80. Chairman feldow, 1967. Mem. ABA, Fed. Bar Assn. (chpt. pres. 1975), Mecklenburg County Bar Assn. Baptist. Lodges: Masons, Scottish Rite, Shriners. Office: US Court of Appeals 333 Constitution Ave Rm 5818 Washington DC 20001-2802

SENTENNE, JUSTINE, corporate ombudsman; b. Montreal, Que., Can.; d. Paul Emile and Irene Genevieve (Laliberte) S. MBA, U. Que., Montreal,

1993, postgrad. McGill U., Ecole Nat. d'Adminstrn. Publique, 1989-91. Fin. analyst, assoc. mgr. portfolio Bush Assocs., Montreal, 1970-82; city councillor, mem. exec. com. City of Montreal and Montreal Urban Com., 1978-82; adminstrv. asst. Montreal Conv. Ctr., 1983; dir. sponsorship Cen. Com. for Montreal Papal Visit, 1984; dir. pub. rels. Coopers & Lybrand, Montreal, 1985-87; exec. dir. Que. Heart Found., 1987-89; corp. ombudsman Hydro-Que., Montreal, 1991—; tchr. DSA program Concordia U.; v.p., bd. dirs. Armand Frappier Found., Can., Chateau Dufresne Mus. Decorative Arts, Montreal, 1985-90; chmn. bd. Wilfrid Pelletier Found., Montreal, 1986-91; bd. dirs. St. Paul's Oratory, 1979-92, Caisse Populaire Desjardins Notre Dame de Grace, Montreal, 1980—; mem. jury John Labatt Ltd., London, Ont., 1982-86. Notre Dame de Grace v.p. riding assoc. Liberal Party of Can., chairperson Women's Commn.; mem. bd. govs. Youth and Music Can., Montreal, 1981-86; chmn. bd. The Women's Ctr., Montreal, 1986-88, Vol. Bur. Montreal, 1986-87; bd. dirs. Palais des Congres de Montreal, 1981-89, Port of Montreal, 1983-84, Can. Ctr. for Ecumenism, Montreal, 1968-85, Villa Notre-Dame de Grace, Montreal, 1979-87, v.p Montreal Diet Dispensary, 1989—, Pathways to Faith, 1990—; bd. mgmt. Saidye Bronfman Ctr. for Arts, 1994—. Named Career Woman of Yr., Sullivan Bus. Coll., 1979; recipient Silver medal Ville de Paris, 1981, Women's Kansas City Assn. for Internat. Rels. and Trade medal, 1982. Fellow Fin. Analysts Fedn. N.Y., Inst. Fin. Analysts, Montreal Soc. Investment Analysts; mem. Cercle Fin. et Placement, Corporation Professionelle des adminstrs. agrées, Assn. Profl. Adminstrs., The Ombudsman Assn. Roman Catholic.

SENTER, ALAN ZACHARY, communications company executive; b. N.Y.C., Nov. 8, 1941; s. Hyman B. and Reva (Cooperwasser) S.; m. Karen G. Yellin, Dec. 26, 1965; children: Marc G., Elise J. BS, U. R.I., 1963; MBA, U. Chgo., 1965. Dir. internat. fin. Xerox Corp., Stamford, Conn., 1975-77; v.p. fin. Latin Am. Xerox Corp., Greenwich, Conn., 1977-79; v.p. fin. bus. products Xerox Corp., Rochester, N.Y., 1979-80; asst. contr. Xerox Corp., Stamford, 1981-85, v.p., treas., 1985-90, v.p. fin., 1990-92; exec. v.p., CFO Internat. Speciality Products/GAF Corp., Wayne, N.J., 1992-94 Nynex Corp., N.Y.C., 1994—; bd. dirs. XL Ins., Bermuda. Capt. USAR, 1966-68, Vietnam. Jewish. Avocations: skiing, tennis. Office: Nynex Corp 335 Madison Ave New York NY 10017

SENTER, JACK, art director, production designer. Art dir.: (TV movies) Kung Fu, 1972, The Execution, 1985, Desperate, 1987, Nutcracker: Money, Madness, and Murder, 1987, (films) No Deposit, No Return, 1976, Obsession, 1976, Freaky Friday, 1976, Oh, God!, 1977, Greased Lightning, 1977, Return from Witch Mountain, 1978, Go Tell the Spartans, 1978, Love and Bullets, 1979, The Man Who Loved Women, 1983, Micki & Maude, 1984, Far and Away, 1992; prodn. designer: (films) Modern Problems, 1981, The New Adventures of Pippi Longstocking, 1988. Office: care Tom Miller The Miller Agency 23236 Lyons Ave Ste 219 Santa Clarita CA 91321*

SENTER, LYONEL THOMAS, JR., federal judge; b. Fulton, Miss., July 30, 1933; s. L. T. and Eva Lee (Jetton) S.; married. B.S., U. So. Miss., 1956; LL.B., U. Miss., 1959. Bar: Miss. 1959. County atty., 1960-64, U.S. commr., 1966-68; judge Miss. Circuit Ct., Circuit 1, 1968-80, U.S. Dist. Ct. (no. dist.) Miss., 1980—. Mem. Miss. State Bar. Democrat. Office: US Dist Ct PO Box 925 Aberdeen MS 39730-0925

SENTER, MERILYN P(ATRICIA), state legislator, retired freelance reporter; b. Haverhill, Mass., Mar. 17, 1935; d. Paul Barton and Mary Etta (Herrin) Staples; m. Donald Neil Senter, Apr. 23, 1960; children: Karen Anne Hussey, Brian Neil. Grad., McIntosh Bus. Coll., 1955. Sec. F.S. Hamlin Ins. Agy., Haverhill, Mass., 1955-60; free lance reporter Plaistow-Hampstead News, Rockingham county newspapers, Exeter and Stratham, N.H., 1970-89; state legislator N.H. Gen. Ct., Rockingham Dist. 9, 1989-90. Sec. Hwy. Safety Com., Plaistow, N.H., 1976—; state rep. N.H. Gen. Ct., Rockingham Dist. 16, 1990—, Rep. com. leader, state rep. Dist. 9, 1991-92, floor leader; sec., bd. dirs. Region 10 Commn. Support Svcs. Inc., Atkinson, N.H., 1982-88; chmn. Plaistow Area Transit Adv. Com., 1990-93; active Devel. Disabilities Coun., 1993—. Named Woman of Yr., N.H. Bus. and Profl. Women, 1983, Nat. Grange Citizen of Yr., 1992. Republican. Avocations: nature, grandchildren, handicapped issues. Home and Office: 11 Maple Ave Plaistow NH 03865-2221

SENTER, WILLIAM JOSEPH, publishing company executive; b. N.Y.C., Dec. 4, 1921; s. Joseph and Sarah (Greenglass) S.; m. Irene Phoebe Marcus, Aug. 3, 1952; children: Adam Douglas, Caren Amy. B.B.A., CCNY, 1947. Chmn. bd., mng. editor Deadline Data, Inc., N.Y.C., 1962-66; pres. Unipub, Inc. (merged with Xerox Corp. 1971), N.Y.C., 1966-72; v.p. planning and devel. Xerox Info. Resources Group (includes AutEx Systems, R.R. Bowker Co., Ginn & Co., Univ. Microfilms Internat., Unipub Inc., Xerox Edn. Publs., Xerox Learning Systems, Xerox Computer Services), Greenwich, Conn., 1973-74; v.p. info. pub. Xerox Info. Resources Group, Greenwich, 1974-75; pres. Xerox Info. Resources Group, 1976-80, chmn., 1980-86; v.p. Xerox Corp., Stamford, Conn., 1978-86; pres. R.R. Bowker Co., N.Y.C., 1974-75. Served with U.S. Army, 1942-46. Mem. Assn. Am. Publs. (dir. 1978-81), Info. Industry Assn. (dir. 1980-83). Office: PO Box 364 Cos Cob CT 06807-0364

SENTER, WILLIAM OSCAR, retired air force officer; b. Stamford, Tex., June 15, 1910; s. William Oscar and Mary Ellen (Futrell) S.; m. Ruth Jane Tinsley, Apr. 10, 1937 (dec. Apr. 1967); children: Suellen, Ruth Jane; m. Carolyn C. Fallon, Jan. 2, 1973. Student, Hardin-Simmons U., 1929; BS, U.S. Mil. Acad., 1933; postgrad., Mass. Inst. Tech., 1938, Air War Coll., 1948-49; Aero. Engr., U. Okla., 1957. Commd. 2d lt. Coast Arty. Corps U.S. Army, 1933, attached to air corps and apptd. student officer, 1933; advanced through grades to lt. gen. USAF, 1963; comdr. Oklahoma City Air Material Area, 1954-57; dir. Procurement and Prodn. Hdqrs., Air Materiel Command Wright-Patterson AFB, 1957-59; asst. dep. chief staff materiel Hdqrs. USAF, 1959-63; dir. petroleum logistics policy Dept. Def., 1963-66, ret., 1966; exec. v.p. Natural Gas Supply Assn., 1966-74. Decorated D.S.M., Legion of Merit with oak leaf cluster. Mem. Air Force Assn., Assn. Grads. U.S. Mil. Acad., Air Force Hist. Found., Order Daedalians, Monarch Country Club. Roman Catholic. Home: 1100 SW Shoreline Dr Apt 200 Palm City FL 34990

SENTURIA, YVONNE DREYFUS, pediatrician, epidemiologist; b. Houston, Jan. 16, 1951. BA in Biology and Sociology, Rice U., 1973; MD, U. Tex., San Antonio, 1977; MSc in Epidemiology, London Sch. Hygiene and Tropical Medicine, 1985. Diplomate Am. Bd. Pedias. Pediat. resident Shands Tchg. Hosp., Gainesville, Fla., 1977-79, Tex. Children's Hosp., Houston, 1979-80; instr., asst. prof. Coll. Medicine, Baylor U., Houston, 1980-82; sr. clin. med. officer Hammersmith and Fulham Health Authority, London, 1982-83; cons. pediatrician Kingston (Eng.) Hosp., 1983, Northwick Park Hosp., London, 1983; rsch. pediatrician Charing Cross Hosp. Med. Sch., London, 1984-85; clin. lectr. Inst. Child Health, London, 1985-88; attending pediatrician and epidemiologist Children's Meml. Hosp., Chgo., 1989—. Fellow Am. Acad. Pediats.; mem. Ambulatory Pediat. Assn., Midwest Soc. Pediat. Rsch. Office: Children's Meml Hosp 2300 Childrens Plz Box 103 Chicago IL 60614

SENZEL, MARTIN LEE, lawyer; b. Rochester, N.Y., June 21, 1944; s. Albert Benjamin and Besse (Lipson) S.; m. Dagni Maren Belgum, Feb. 17, 1980; 1 child, Whitney. Ba, Yale U., 1966, LLB, 1969. Bar: N.Y. 1971, U.S. Dist. Ct. (so. dist.) N.Y., U.S. Ct. Appeals (2nd cir) 1973. Assoc. Cravath, Swaine & Moore, N.Y.C., 1969-77; ptnr. Cravath, Swaine & Moore, 1977—. Mem. ABA, N.Y. State Bar Assn., Assn. Bar City N.Y. Home: 101 Central Park W New York NY 10023-4296 Office: Cravath Swaine & Moore Worldwide Plaza 825 8th Ave New York NY 10019-7416

SEOANE, EMILIO, accountant; b. Havana, Cuba, Oct. 13, 1944; came to U.S., 1960; s. Emilio M. and Carmen Seoane; m. Angeles Gonzalez, Sept. 13, 1988; children: Heidi, Ledu. Acct., Havana U., 1959. Acct. Seoane Book-keeping Svc., Miami, Fla., 1964-66, L.A., 1967-79; acct. Empresa Svcs. Hispanos, Anaheim, Calif., 1980-88, Latinos Enterprise, Inc., Santa Ana, Calif., 1988—. Mem. Nat. Soc. Pub. Accts., Nat. Notary Assn., Am. Soc. Notaries, Nat. Assn. Tax Cons., Nat. Soc. Tax Profls. Republican. Roman Catholic. Avocation: philatelist. Office: Latinos Enterprise Inc 1017 S Fairview St Santa Ana CA 92704-2708

SEPAHPUR, HAYEDEH C(HRISTINE), investment executive; b. Lincoln, Nebr., Dec. 8, 1958; d. Bahman and Marylin Lou (Duffy) S.; m. Bahman Robert Kosrovani, May 2, 1992. BS, Lehigh U., 1983. V.p. Drexel Burnham Lambert Inc., N.Y.C., 1982-90, Donaldson, Lufkin & Jenrette, New York City, 1990-92, Lehman Bros., Inc., N.Y.C., 1992—. Sponsor Jr. Statesmen of Am. Found., Washington, 1976—; charter mem. Nat. Mus. Women in the Arts, Washington, 1985—; bd. dirs. Coll. Express Project, Bronx, N.Y., 1987—; mem. Inst. Asian Studies, St. Thomas Episc. Ch. Mem. Nat. Trust Hist. Preservation, The Asia Soc., Women's Campaign Fund, N.Y. Soc. Libr., Mcpl. Art Soc., French Inst., English Speaking Union, WISH List, Parents League, N.Y. Women's Found., Fin. Women's Assn. (N.Y. chpt.), Persian Heritage Found., Mensa, Gamma Phi Beta. Club: Downtown Athletic (N.Y.C.). Home: 220 E 67th St Apt 12-D New York NY 10021-6263 Office: Lehman Bros Inc 3 World Fin Ctr 200 Vesey St 6th fl New York NY 10285-0600

SEPPALA, KATHERINE SEAMAN (MRS. LESLIE W. SEPPALA), retail executive, clubwoman; b. Detroit, Aug. 22, 1919; d. Willard D. and Elizabeth (Miller) Seaman; B.A., Wayne State U., 1941; m. Leslie W. Seppala, Aug. 15, 1941; children: Sandra Kay, William Leslie. Mgr. women's bldg. and student activities adviser Wayne State U., 1941-43; pres. Harper Sports Shops, Inc., 1947-85, chmn. bd., treas., sec., v.p. 1985—; ptnr. Seppala Bldg. Co., 1971—. Mich. service chmn. women grads. Wayne State U., 1962—, 1st v.p., fund bd., Girl and Cub Scouts; mem. Citizen's adv. com. on sch. needs Detroit Bd. Edn., 1957—, mem. high sch. study com., 1966—; chmn., mem. loan fund bd. Denby High Sch. Parents Scholarship; bd. dirs., v.p Wayne State U. Fund; precinct del. Rep. Party, 14th dist., 1956—, del. convs.; mem. com. Myasthenia Gravis Support Assn. Recipient Ann. Women's Service award Wayne State U., 1963. Recipient Disting. Alumni award Wayne State U., 1971. Mem. Intercollegiate Assn. Women Students (regional rep. 1941-45), Women Wayne State U. Alumni (past pres.), Wayne State U. Alumni Assn. (dir., past v.p.), AAUW (dir. past officer), Council Women as Public Policy Makers (editor High lights) Denby Community Ednl. Orgn. (sec.), Met. Detroit Program Planning Inst. (pres.), Internat. Platform Assn., Detroit Met. Book and Author Soc. (treas.), Mortar Bd. (past pres.), Karyatides (past pres.), Anthony Wayne Soc., Alpha Chi Alpha, Alpha Kappa Delta, Delta Gamma Chi, Kappa Delta (chmn. chpt. alumnae adv. bd.). Baptist. Clubs: Zonta (v.p.); Les Cheneaux. Home: 22771 Worthington Ct Saint Clair Shores MI 48081-2603 Office: Harper Sport Shop Inc 23208 Greater Mack Saint Clair Shores MI 48080-1914

SEPTIMUS, BERNARD MARK, religion educator. Jacob E. Safra prof. of Jewish history and sephardic civilization Harvard U., Cambridge, Mass. Office: Harvard U Dept Jewish History & Sephardic Civilization Cambridge MA 02138

SEPULVEDA, EDUARDO SOLIDEO, chemical engineer; b. Loay, Philippines, Jan. 5, 1945; came to U.S., 1981; m. Consuelo S. Araneta, May 18, 1977; children: Edward, Josephus, Blaise. BSChE, De La Salle U., 1966; M of Chem. Engring., U. Philippines, 1972. Lic. profl. engr., Calif. Instr. U. Philippines, Quezon City, 1968-70; sr. instr. De La Salle U., Manila, Philippines, 1970-71, asst. prof., 1971-73; process engr. Philippines Petroleum Corp., Makati, 1973-74, sr. process engr., 1974-75, mgr. tech. svc., 1975-81; sr. engr. C F Braun & Co., Alhambra, Calif., 1981; prin. engr. Brown & Root Braun, Alhambra, Calif., 1987—; reviewer chem. bd. De La Salle U., 1970-79. Mem. St. John Corregidor Lodge, Manila, 1979. Mem. AICE, Project Mgmt. Inst., Phi Kappa Phi. Achievements include designed and engineered a fluid catalyst transport system to hydrocracker reactor. Home: 3700 Oaklawn Ln Pico Rivera CA 90660-5941 Office: LG Engring Co Ltd, C.P.O. Box 6762, Seoul Korea

SEQUEIRA, LUIS, plant pathology educator; b. San Jose, Costa Rica, Sept. 1, 1927; s. Raul and Dora (Jenkins) S.; m. Elizabeth Steinvorth, May 27, 1954; children: Anabel, Marta, Robert, Patricia. AB, Harvard U., 1949, AM, 1950, PhD, 1952. Plant pathologist United Fruit Co., Coto, Costa Rica, 1953-60; research assoc. N.C. State U., Raleigh, 1960-61; prof. plant pathology U. Wis., Madison, 1961-82, J.C. Walker prof. of plant pathology and bacteriology, 1982—; cons. Agracetus, Madison, 1982-93; mgr. competitive grants program USDA, Washington, 1984-85, chief scientist, 1987-88. Contbr. numerous articles to profl. jours. Recipient E. C. Stakman award U. Minn., 1992. Fellow Am. Phytopathological Soc. (editor-in-chief jour. 1979-81, St. Paul sect. v.p. 1984, pres. elect 1985, pres. 1986, Award of Distinction 1994), Am. Acad. Microbiology; mem. Nat. Acad. Scis., Linnean Soc. London. Democrat. Roman Catholic. Home: 10 Appomattox Ct Madison WI 53705-4202 Office: U Wis Dept Plant Pathology 1630 Linden Dr Madison WI 53706-1598

SEQUIN, CARLO H., computer science educator; b. Winterthur, Switzerland, Oct. 30, 1941; came to U.S., 1970; s. Carl R. and Margarit (Schappi) S.; m. Margareta Frey, Oct. 5, 1968; children: Eveline, Andre. B.S., U. Basel, Switzerland, 1965, Ph.D., 1969. Mem. tech. staff Bell Labs., Murray Hill, N.J., 1970-76; vis. Mackay lectr. U. Calif.-Berkeley, 1976-77, prof. elec. engring. computer scis., 1977—, assoc. chmn. computer sci., 1980-83. Contbr. 150 articles to profl. jours.; author first book on charge-coupled devices; patentee integrated circuits. Fellow IEEE; mem. Assn. Computing Machinery, Swiss Acad. Engring. Scis. Office: U Calif Dept EECS Computer Scis Divsn Berkeley CA 94720-1776

SERAFIN, BARRY D., television news correspondent; b. Coquille, Oreg., June 22, 1941; s. Peter B. and Ina V. Serafin; m. Lynn Van Camp, Aug. 24, 1963; children—Lisa Marie, Sandra Lynn. B.A., Wash. State U., 1964. Producer, dir. Sta. KOAP-TV, Portland, Oreg., 1964-65; reporter Sta. KOIN-TV, Portland, 1965-68, Sta. KMOX-TV, St. Louis, 1968-69; corr. CBS News, Washington, 1969-79; nat. corr. ABC News, Washington, 1979—. (Recipient Emmy award 1974). Office: ABC News Washington Bureau 1717 Desales St NW Washington DC 20036-4407

SERAFIN, DONALD, plastic surgeon; b. N.Y.C., Jan. 18, 1938; s. Stephen Michael and Julia (Sopko) S.; A.B., Duke U., 1960, M.D., 1964; m. Patricia Serafin; children—Allison Elizabeth, Christina Julia, Donald Stephen, Lara Leigh. Surg. intern Grady Meml. Hosp., Atlanta, 1964-65; resident in surgery Emory U. Hosp., Atlanta, 1965-69; asst. resident in plastic and reconstructive surgery Duke U. Med. Center, Durham, N.C., 1971-73, chief resident, 1973-74; Christine Kleinert fellow in hand surgery U. Louisville Hosp., 1972-73; practice medicine specializing in plastic surgery, Durham; mem. staff Durham County Gen. Hosp.; asst. prof. plastic, reconstructive and maxillofacial surgery Duke U., 1974-77, assoc. prof., 1977-81, prof., 1981—; chief div. plastic, reconstructive and maxillofacial surgery; chmn. Plastic Surgery Rsch. Council, 1983. Assoc. editor Jour. Reconstructive Microsurgery. Contbr. articles to profl. jours. Served to maj. M.C., USAF, 1969-71, col. M.C., USAR. Diplomate Am. Bd. Surgery, Am. Bd. Plastic Surgery. Recipient Air Force commedation medal, 1971, U.S. Army commendation medal, 1990. Fellow ACS; mem. Internat. Soc. Reconstructive Microsurgery, Am. Soc. Plastic and Reconstructive Surgeons, Am. Assn. Plastic Surgeons, Am. Soc. Plastic and Reconstructive Surgeons, Am. Assn. Plastic Surgeons, AMA, Plastic Surgery Research Council, N.C. Soc. Plastic, Maxillofacial and Reconstructive Surgeons, Southeastern Soc. Plastic and Reconstructive Surgeons, Southeastern Med. Dental Soc., Sigma Xi. Office: Duke U Med Ctr PO Box 3708 Durham NC 27710

SERAFIN, JAMES ADAM, organization executive, management consultant; b. Redruth, Cornwall, Eng., July 26, 1945; came to U.S., 1945; s. Adam Mieczyslaw and Donna Josephine (Szarnagiel) S.; m. Barbara Ann Waligora, May 2, 1975 (div. Oct. 1983); children: Mara Sonya, Adam James. BA, U. Buffalo, 1969; MA, Syracuse U., 1972. Regional planner Comprehensive Health Planning Coun. Western N.Y., Buffalo, 1971-74; fin. planning cons. Niagara County Mental Health Dept., Lockport, N.Y., 1974-76; dir. planning and allocations United Way Niagara, Niagara Falls, N.Y., 1976-80; exec. dir. Amarillo (Tex.) Community Coun., 1980-83; v.p. ops. Opinions Unltd., Amarillo, 1983-84; dir. mktg. and planning High Plains Bapt. Hosp., Amarillo, 1984-87; dir. planning and bus. devel. St. Joseph Hosp., Denver, 1988-89; exec. dir. Cath. Worker Niagara Falls, 1991-94, Food Bank of We N.Y., 1994—; cons. Human Svcs. Planning Assocs., Lockport. 1974-76; pres. Svcs. & Mgmt. Planning Assocs., Tex., Colo., N.Y. 1974—; vis. guest lectr. Amarillo Coll., West Tex. State U., U. Denver, SUNY, Buffalo, 1974—; grad. instr. U. Denver, 1989; state, regional and nat. conf. and workshop presenter. Contbr. articles to profl. jours. Pres. bd.

dirs. Neighborhood Info. Ctr., Buffalo, 1971-73; mem. steering com. Erie County Execs. Task Force, Buffalo, 1974-76; chmn. Panhandle Drug Abuse Consortium, Amarillo, 1981-85; bd. dirs. Buffalo-Rzeszow Sistr Cities, Inc., 1990—. Mem. Acad. Health Svcs. Mktg. (pres. Colo. chpt. 1989-90), Am. Hosp. Assn. (nat. com. 1988-89), Rotary (program chmn. Amarillo 1983-84). Avocations: snow skiing, golf, hiking, reading nonfiction. Home: 3111 Stanley Rd Grand Island NY 14072 Office: Food Bank of We NY 91-95 Holt St Buffalo NY 14206

SERAFIN, JOHN ALFRED, art educator; b. Washington, Nov. 3, 1942; s. John Bernard and Elizabeth (Pichette) S.; m. Josephine Azzarello, Apr. 12, 1969 (div. 1990); children: John Calvin, Michael Joseph, Mary Elizabeth. Student, Syracuse U., 1967-69, MS, 1974; BFA, U. Utah, 1971. Cert. tchr., N.Y. Graphic artist Sears, Roebuck and Co., Syracuse, 1967-68; dir. advt. Around the Town mag., Syracuse, 1969; tchr. art Blodgett Jr. High Sch., Syracuse, 1971-76, Roberts Elem. Sch., Syracuse, 1986-87, Fowler High Sch., Syracuse, 1976—; yearbook adviser Blodgett Jr. High Sch., 1971-75, coach track, 1971-74, coach cross-country, 1972-74; jr. class adviser Fowler High Sch., 1977-78. Artist mag. cover design U. Utah Pharmacy Mag., 1970, Fine Art Index Internat., 1995 edit., Chgo.; group exhbns. include Syracuse Stage, 1989-92, N.Y. State Fair, 1977, 89, 90, Everson Mus., Syracuse, 1985, Cooperstown (N.Y.) Nat. Show, 1991, Westmoreland Nat. Art Show, Latrobe, Pa., 1995; represented by Montserrat Art Gallery, N.Y.C., Limner Gallery, N.Y.C., Agora Gallery, N.Y.C. Recipient award of Excellence, Manhattan Arts Mag., N.Y.C. Mem. N.Y. State United Tchrs., Syracuse Tchrs. Assn. (rep. 1972-75), Associated Artists Galleries, Nat. Art Educators Assn., Syracuse U. Orange Pack and Alumni Assn., Crimson Club U. Utah Alumni Assn., N.Y. State Art Tchrs. Assn., Cooperstown Art Assn., Elks, Moose Lodge. Democrat. Avocations: Syracuse University sports, brewing, blues music, working out, travel. Home: 1205 Teall Ave Syracuse NY 13206-3467 Office: Fowler H S 227 Magnolia St Syracuse NY 13204-2707

SERAFIN, ROBERT JOSEPH, science center administrator, electrical engineer; b. Chgo., Apr. 22, 1936; s. Joseph Albert and Antoinette (Gazda) S.; m. Betsy Furgerson, Mar. 4, 1961; children: Katherine, Jenifer, Robert Joseph Jr., Elizabeth. BSEE, U. Notre Dame, 1958; MSEE, Northwestern U., 1961; PhDEE, Ill. Inst. Tech., 1972. Engr. Hazeltine Rsch. Corp. Ill. Inst. Tech. Rsch. Inst., 1960-62; assoc. engr., rsch. engr., sr. rsch. engr. Nat. Ctr. for Atmospheric Rsch., Booulder, Colo., 1962-73, mgr. field observing facility, 1973-80, dir. atmospheric tech. div., 1981-89, dir., 1989—; chair modernization com. Nat. Weather Svc. Author: Revised Radar Handbook, 1989; also numerous articles; editl. founder Jour. Atmospheric and Oceanic Tech.; editl. bd. Acta Meteorologica Sinica; patentee in field. Chmn. Citizens Adv. Com., Boulder; speaker various civic groups in U.S. and internationally. Fellow Am. Meteorol. Soc. (mem. exec. com.); Mem. IEEE (sr.), NAE, NAS (human rights commn.), Boulder C. of C., Sigma Xi. Avocations: cycling, golf, fishing, skiing. Office: Nat Ctr Atmospheric Rsch PO Box 3000 1850 Table Mesa Dr Boulder CO 80303-5602

SERAMUR, JOHN C., bank executive; b. 1943. With First Fin. Corp., Stevens Point, Wis., 1966—, now pres., CEO, COO. Office: First Fin Corp 1305 Main St Stevens Point WI 54481-2830

SERAPHINE, DANNY PETER, drummer; b. Chgo., Aug. 28, 1948; s. John and Valentine and Mary (Colangelo) S.; m. Rosemarie Stevenson, June 3, 1967; children: Christine, Danielle. Grad. high sch. Owner night club B. Ginnings, Schaumburg, Ill., from 1974; owner clothing store Peabody's, Chgo., from 1974. Mem. musical group, Chicago, 1967—; co-composer: Lowdown, 1972, Devil's Sweet, 1974, Aire, 1974; albums include Chicago I through Chicago XVIII; (with group Chicago) Chicago 19, 1988, Chicago Transit Authority, 1989, Liberation, 1990. Address: care Warner Bros 75 Rockefeller Plz New York NY 10019-6907*

SERBAROLI, FRANCIS J., lawyer, educator, writer; b. N.Y.C., Feb. 8, 1952. AB, Fordham U., 1973, JD, 1977. Bar: N.Y. 1978, U.S. Dist. Ct. (ea. and so. dists.) N.Y. 1978, U.S. Ct. Appeals (2d and D.C. cirs.) 1979, U.S. Supreme Ct. 1983. Asst. atty. gen. N.Y. State Dept. Law, 1977-80, 82; ptnr. Ober, Kaler, Grimes & Shriver, N.Y.C., 1992—; adj. prof. N.Y. Med. Coll., Valhalla, Pace U., White Plains, N.Y.; health law columnist The N.Y. Law Jour. Bd. trustees Loyola Sch., N.Y.C. Fellow N.Y. Acad. Medicine; mem. Nat. Health Lawyers' Assn., N.Y. State Bar Assn., Assn. of Bar of City of N.Y. Office: Ober Kaler Grimes & Shriver 1345 Ave of the Americas New York NY 10105

SERBEIN, OSCAR NICHOLAS, business educator, consultant; b. Collins, Iowa, Mar. 31, 1919; s. Oscar Nicholas and Clara Matilda (Shearer) S.; m. Alice Marie Bigger, Sept. 16, 1952; children: Mary Llewellyn Serbein Parker, John Gregory. BA with highest distinction, U. Iowa, 1940, MS, 1941; PhD, Columbia U., 1951. Grad. asst. math. U. Iowa, Iowa City, 1940-41; clk. Met. Life Ins. Co., N.Y.C., 1941-42; lectr. U. Calif., Berkeley, summer 1948, 50; lectr., asst. prof., assoc. prof. Columbia U., N.Y.C., 1947-59; prof. ins. Stanford (Calif.) U., 1959-89, dir. doctoral program Grad. Sch. Bus., 1960-64, prof. emeritus ins., 1989—; cons. Ins. Info. Inst., N.Y.C., 1971-78, N.Am. Re-Assurance Life Service Co., Palo Alto, 1973, SRI Internat., Menlo Park, Calif., 1980-81, other bus.; cons., expert witness various law firms. Author: Paying for Medical Care in the U.S., 1953, Educational Activities of Business, 1961; co-author: Property and Liability Insurance, 4 ed., 1969, Risk Management: Text and Cases, 2 ed., 1983; also articles. Bd. dirs. Sr. Citizens Coord. Coun., Palo Alto, 1986-89, dir. emeritus 1990—. Maj. USAF, WWII. Decorated Bronze Star, 1944. Mem. Am. Risk and Ins. Assn., Western Risk and Ins. Assn., Phi Beta Kappa, Sigma Xi, Beta Gamma Sigma. Democrat. Methodist. Club: Stanford Faculty. Avocation: gardening. Home: 731 San Rafael Pl Stanford CA 94305-1007 Office: Stanford U Grad Sch Business Stanford CA 94305

SEREBRIER, JOSÉ, musician, conductor, composer; b. Montevideo, Uruguay, Dec. 3, 1938; came to U.S., 1956; s. David and Frida (Wasser) S.; m. Carole Farley, Mar. 29, 1969; 1 child, Lara Adriana Francesca. Diploma, Nat. Conservatory, Montevideo, 1956, Curtis Inst. Music, 1958; BA, U. Minn., 1960; studied with Aaron Copland, Antal Dorati, Pierre Monteux. Ind. composer, condr., 1955—; apprentice condr. Minn. Orch., 1958-60; assoc. condr. Am. Symphony Orch., N.Y.C., 1962-66; music dir. Am. Shakespeare Festival, 1966; composer-in-residence Cleve. Orch., 1968-71; artistic dir. Internat. Festival of Ams., Miami, 1984—, Festival Miami, 1985—; guest condr. numerous orchs. including London Symphony, London Philharm., Paris Radio, Cleve. Symphony Orch., Phila. Symphony Orch., Pitts. Symphony Orch.; founder, artistic dir. Festival Miami (internat. arts festival), 1984. Composer: (for orch.) Variations on a Theme from Childhood, (for chamber) Symphony for Percussion, Concerto for Violin and Orch. (recorded by Royal Phila. Orch. on ASV), also works for chorus, voice, keyboard; recs. for RCA, CRI, ASV, KEM, Disc, Trax Clasique, EMI, Tioch, Chandos, Varese-Sarabande Decca, IMG, Pickwick, with various orchs.; condr. for many recs. including Sibelius Symphony No. 1, Holst's The Planets, Carmen, Poulenc's opera La Voix Humaine, Shostakovich Film Suites vol. 1 (Deutsche Schallplatten award 1988), Carole Farley Sings French Songs (Deutsche Schallplaten award 1988), (home video) Kultur, Prokoviev's Alex Nevsky, Beethoven's Eroica and Tchaikovsky Symphony No.1 with Sydney and Melbourne Symphony Orch., Mendelssohn Symphonies, Beethoven Symphonies, Blochs Violin Concerto and Serebriers Poema Elegiaco CD, 1992, Laserdisc of Operas The Telephone By Menotti and La Voix Humaine By Poulenc with Scottish Chamber Orch., 1992, Royal Philharm. Orch., 1992. Recipient Ford Found. Condr.'s award, Alice M. Ditson award, 1976, commn. award Nat. Endowment Arts, 1978, Deutsche Schall Platten Critics award, Music Retailers Assn. award for Best Symphony Rec., 1991; Guggenheim fellow, 1958-60; Rockefeller Found. grantee, 1968-70. Mem. Am. Symphony Orch. League, Am. Music Ctr., Am. Fedn. Musicians. Home and Office: 20 Queensgate Gardens, London SW7 5LZ, England *A composer has the duty to communicate with his audience. The academic-intellectual composer of the 50's has become obsolete. Writing just for one's colleagues has fortunately been proven a dead-end.*

SERENBETZ, ROBERT, manufacturing executive; b. Rockville Centre, N.Y., Apr. 18, 1944; s. Raymond Robert Serenbetz and Mildred (Egner) Clapp; m. Karen Jeanne Jackson, Dec. 30, 1967; children: Todd, Gregg,

Kathryn. AB, Dartmouth Coll., 1966; MBA, Harvard U., 1968. Mktg. staff asst. to group product mgr. Colgate-Palmolive Co., N.Y.C., 1968-75; dir. mktg. Colgate-Palmolive Colombia, Cali, Colombia, 1975-77; v.p. mktg. Colgate-Palmolive Canada, Toronto, Ont., Can., 1977-81; v.p. mktg. western hemisphere Warner-Lambert Co., Morris Plains, N.J., 1981; pres. Warner-Lambert Can., Toronto, 1981-85; pres. Latin Am., Asia, Australia Warner-Lambert Co., Morris Plains, 1986-89; pres. Am. Chicle, Morris Plains, 1989-91; pres., COO DNA Plant Tech. Corp., Cinnaminson, N.J., 1991-92; pres., CEO DNA Plant Tech. Corp., Oakland, Calif., 1992-94; chmn., CEO DNA Plant Tech. Corp., Cinnaminson, N.J., 1994—; mem. adv. bd. Coun. Ams., N.Y.C., 1987-89; mem. steering com. Pharm. Mfrs. Assn., Washington, 1987-89; bd. dirs. Caribbean/Cen. Am. Com., Washington, 1989; mem. adv. bd. Coun. for Internat. Unity, N.Y.C., 1987-89. Bd. dirs. Notch Brook Resort Gen. Ptnrs. Condominium Assn., Stowe, Vt., 1988-94; active U.S. Postal Svc. Mktg. Adv. Bd., 1990—. Mem. Nat. Candy Wholesalers Assn. (bd. dirs. 1989-91), Morris County C. of C. (bd. dirs. 1989-91), Leadership Inc. (bd. dirs. Phila. br. 1993-94), Union League (Phila.), Wild Dunes Club (Isle of Palms, S.C.). Republican. Episcopalian. Avocations: golf, stamp collecting, photography, tennis. Office: DNA Plant Tech Corp 6701 San Pablo Ave Oakland CA 94608

SERENBETZ, WARREN LEWIS, financial management company executive; b. N.Y.C., Mar. 27, 1924; s. Lewis E. and Estelle (Weygand) S.; m. Thelma Randby, Apr. 10, 1948; children: Warren Lewis, Paul Halvor, Stuart Weygand, Clay Raymond. B.S., Columbia U., 1944, M.S., 1949. Cons. Emerson Engrs., N.Y.C., 1949-51; with Oliver Corp., 1951-53; with REA Express, 1953-68, sr. v.p., 1968-68; v.p., dir. REA Leasing Corp., 1961-68; chmn. exec. com., chief exec. officer Interpool, Ltd., 1968-86; pres., chief exec. officer Radcliff Group, Inc., 1986—; pres. Containerization and Intermodal Inst., 1986-87; bd. dirs. Containerization and Intermodal Inst., Interpool Ltd., Interpool Inc., Microtech Corp., Trac Lease Inc. Trustee St. Cabrini Nursing Home. Served to lt. (j.g.) USNR, World War II. Mem. Am. Mgmt. Pres. Assn., Larchmont Yacht Club, Univ. Club Larchmont, Union League Club. Presbyterian. Home: Hunter Hill West St Harrison NY 10528 Office: Radcliff Group Inc 695 West St Harrison NY 10528

SERENO, PAUL C., paleontologist, educator; b. 1958. Ph.D. in paleontology, Columbia U, NY. Asst. prof. U Chicago, 1987—. Recipient Player of the Yr., Tempo All-Professor Team, Chicago Tribune, 1993. Achievements include discovering Eoraptor, the earliest known dinosaur, in the Argentine foothills of the Andes mountains, and two new species of dinosaur, Afrovenator abakensis and a new type of sauropod, in the Saharan desert about 600 miles northeast of Niamey, Niger. Office: U Chgo Dept Organismal Biology/Anatomy 1027 E 57th St Chicago IL 60637-1508*

SERGEY, JOHN MICHAEL, JR., manufacturing company executive; b. Chgo., Nov. 17, 1942; s. John Michael and Helen Ann (Bruchan) S.; m. Sharon Lee Ourada (div. 1982); children: John Michael III, Elisabeth Ann, Mark William, Tanya Ruth; m. Pamela Lynne Murphy, Aug. 8, 1987; children: Brian M., Sarah L. BA in Bus., Northwestern U., 1968; MBA, U. Chgo., 1976. Mgr. rolled products A. M. Castle, Chgo., 1959-74; v.p. Dietzgen Corp., Chgo., 1974-78; dir. sales and mktg. Avery Label, Azusa, Calif., 1978-80; v.p., gen. mgr. Fasson Roll div. Avery, Painesville, Ohio, 1980-84; group v.p. Soabar Products Group div. Avery, Phila., 1984-87, Materials Group div. Avery, Painesville, 1987-89; pres., CEO GAF Materials Corp., Wayne, N.J., 1989—. Mem. Huntingdon Valley Country Club (Phila.), Cleve. Racquet Club, The Country Club (Pepper Pike, Ohio), Arcola Country Club (Paramus, N.J.), Indian Trail Club (Franklin Lakes, N.J.). Office: GAF Materials Corp 1361 Alps Rd Bldg 2-2 Wayne NJ 07470-3700

SERGI, THEODORE S., educational administrator. Assn. commr. Ednl. Programs and Svcs., Middletown, Conn. Office: Ednl Programs and Svcs Indusrial Park Rd Middletown CT 06457

SERKIN, PETER, pianist; b. N.Y.C., July 24, 1947; s. Rudolf and Irene (Busch) S. Student, Curtis Inst. Music, 1958-64. Instr. piano Mannes Coll. of Music, N.Y.C. Debut in, N.Y.C., 1959, appearances including with, Phila., Cleve., N.Y.C., London (Eng.), Zurich (Switzerland), Paris (France), Casals Festival orchs., recitals in, N.Y.C., London, Japan, maj. European and Am. cities; premiered works composed for him by Takemitsu, Berio, Lieberson; appearances including with benefit performances for pacifism, aid to victims of war; rec. artist for, RCA, ProArte, New World Records, CBS records, Boston Records. Recipient prize Premio Accademia Musicale Chigian Siena, 1983. Office: care Shirley Kirshbaum Assoc 711 W End Ave Apt 5KN New York NY 10025-6843 also: Mannes Coll Music 150 W 85th St New York NY 10024*

SERNA, DAVID C., lawyer; b. May 2, 1953; s. E.C. "Dave" and Barbara (Wray) S. BA, U. N.Mex., 1971; JD, Georgetown U., 1977; postgrad., U. Guadalajara, Mex. Bar: N.Mex. 1977, D.C. 1978. Prosecutor Dist. Atty.'s Office Bernalillo County, 1977-81; faculty criminal law Albuquerque Career Inst., 1981; pvt. practice law Law Offices of David C. Serna, Albuquerque. Vol. lawyer United Way of Greater Albuquerque. Mem. N.Mex. State Bar Assn. (past chair criminal law sect.), Nat. Bd. Trial Advocacy (diplomate, criminal def.). Nat. Hispanic Bar Assn., N.Mex.-Hispanic Bar Assn., Nat. Assn. Criminal Def. Lawyers, N.Mex. Criminal Def. Lawyers Assn. (chmn. controlled substances tax com., NORML nat. legal com., specialist criminal law N.Mex. bd. legal specialization). Office: 411 10th St SW Albuquerque NM 87102-2923

SERNA, JOE, JR., mayor; b. Stockton, Calif.; m. Isabel Serna; children: Phillip, Lisa. BA in Social Sci., Govt., Sacramento State Coll., 1966; postgrad., U. Calif., Davis. Vol. Peace Corps, Guatemala, 1966; aide advisor Lt.-Gov. Mervyn Dymally, 1975-77; prof. govt. Calif State U, Sacramento, 1969—; mayor City of Sacramento, 1992—. Mem. Sacramento City Coun. 5th Dist., 1981-92, law and legis. com., 1989-92, Housing & Devel. Commn., Sacramento, chmn. budget and fin. com., 1981-89, transp. and cmty. devel. com., 1989-92; dir. United Farmworkers Am.'s Support Com. in Sacramento County, 1970-75; co-trustee Crocker Art Mus. Assn.; founder Thursday Night Market, Mayor's Summer Reading Camp; mem. Sacramento Housing & Devel. Commn.; bd. dirs. Regional Transit. Office: Office of the Mayor 915 I St Sacramento CA 95814-2604*

SERNETT, RICHARD PATRICK, lawyer; b. Mason City, Iowa, Sept. 8, 1938; s. Edward Frank and Loretta M. (Cavanaugh) S.; m. Janet Ellen Ward, Apr. 20, 1963; children: Susan Ellen, Thomas Ward, Stephen Edward, Katherine Anne. BBA, U. Iowa, 1960, JD, 1963. Bar: Iowa 1963, Ill. 1965, U.S. Dist. Ct. (no. dist.) Ill. 1965, U.S. Supreme Ct. 1971. House counsel, asst. sec. Scott, Foresman & Co., Glenview, Ill., 1963-70; sec., legal officer Scott, Foresman & Co., Glenview, 1970-80; v.p., law sec. SFN Cos., Inc., Glenview, 1980-83, sr. v.p., sec., gen. counsel, 1983-85, exec. v.p., gen. counsel, 1985-87; pvt. practice Northbrook, Ill., 1988-90; v.p., gen. counsel Macmillan/McGraw-Hill Sch. Pub. Co., 1990-92; v.p. Bert Early Assoc., Chgo., 1992-93; ptnr. Sernett & Blake, Northfield, Ill., 1993—; mem. U.S. Dept. State Adv. Com. on Internat. Copyright, 1972-75. Chmn. bd. dirs. Iowa State U., Broadcasting Co., 1987-94. Mem. ABA (com. on program for revision copyright law 1971-72, com. on copyright legis. 1967-68, 69-70, chmn. copyright divsn. 1972-73), Am. Intellectual Property Law Assn., Am. Soc. Corp. Secs., Ill. Bar Assn. (chmn. copyright com. 1971-72), Chgo. Bar Assn., Patent Law Assn. Chgo. (bd. mgrs. 1979-82, chmn. copyright law com. 1972-73, 77-78), Copyright Soc. U.S.A. (trustee 1972-75, 77-80), North Shore Country Club (Glenview, Ill.), Eagle Ridge Country Club (Galena, Ill.), Wyndemere Golf and Country Club (Naples, Fla.), Met. Club Chgo. Home: 2579 Fairford Ln Northbrook IL 60062-8101 Office: Sernett & Blake 540 Frontage Rd Ste 2245 Northfield IL 60093-1250

SERNOFF, LOUIS R., lawyer; b. Sellersville, Pa., Dec. 23, 1940. BA, U. Pa., 1962, LLB, 1965. Bar: D.C. 1966. With Bur. Competition FTC, Washington, 1966-74, atty. advisor to Commr., 1974; ptnr. Baker & Hostetler, Washington. Mem. ABA, Fed. Bar Assn., D.C. Bar. Office: Baker & Hostetler Washington Sq 1050 Connecticut Ave NW Ste 1100 Washington DC 20036-5303

SEROKA, JAMES HENRY, social sciences educator, university administrator; b. Detroit, Mar. 5, 1950; s. Henry S. and Mary (Wyoral) S.; m.

Carolyn Marie White, June 27, 1970; children: Mihail, Maritsa. BA, U. Mich., 1970; MA, Mich. State U., 1972, PhD, 1976. Labor mkt. analyst U.S. Dept. of Labor, Washington, 1970-71; asst. prof. U.N.C. Greensboro, 1976-77, Appalachian State U., Boone, N.C., 1977-79, So. Ill. U., Carbondale, 1979-81; assoc. prof. So. Ill. U., 1981-87, prof., dir., 1987-88; prof., head div. humanities and social scis. Pa. State U., Erie, 1988-90; prof. U. North Fla., Jacksonville, 1990—, also dir. Ctr. for Local Govt. Adminstrn.; dir. Master of Pub. Adminstrn. Master Bus. Adminstrn. Ill. U., 1987-88, Rural and Small Town Adminstrn. Project, 1980-85; asst. dir. Appalachian Regional Bur. Govts., Boone, N.C., 1977-79; manpower planning analyst U.S. Dept. Labor, Washington, 1970-71; exchange prof. Fakultet Politickih Nauka, Univerzitet u Beogradu, Yugoslavia, 1986; sr. researcher Coun. for the Internat. Exchange Scholars Yugoslavia, 1980; mem. state adv. com. Gov.'s Rural Affairs Coun. for State of Ill., 1988. Co-author: Political Organizations in Social Yugoslavia, 1986 (Choice award 1987); editor Rural Public Adminstration, 1986; co-editor: Developed Socialism, 1982, Comparative Political Systems, 1990, Yugoslavia: The Failure of Democratic Transformation, 1992; contbr. numerous articles to profl. jours. Recipient Akademischer Austausch Dienst Lang. scholar Fed. Republic of Germany, 1988 and numerous other grants, traveling fellows. Mem. Am. Soc. Pub. Adminstrn. (so Ill. chpt. 1982-83), Nat. Civic League, Am. Polit. Sci. Assn., Internat. Polit. Sci. Assn., Midwest Polit. Sci. Assn., So. Polit. Sci. Assn., Southwestern Polit. Sci. Assn., Western Polit. Sci. Assn., Policy Studies Orgn., Acad. Polit. Sci., Rural Sociol. Assn., Internat. Studies Assn., Am. Assn. Advancement of Slavic Studies, Western Social Sci. Assn. Cmty. Devel. Soc. Office: U North Fla Ctr Local Govt Adminstn 4567 Saint Johns Bluff Rd S Jacksonville FL 32224-6606

SEROTA, JAMES IAN, lawyer; b. Chgo., Oct. 20, 1946; s. Louis Henry and Phyllis Estelle (Horner) S.; m. Susan Perlstadt, May 7, 1972; children: Daniel Louis, Jonathan Mark. AB, Washington U., St. Louis, 1968; JD cum laude, Northwestern U., 1971. Bar: Ill. 1971, U.S. Dist. Ct. (no. dist.) Ill. 1972, D.C. 1978, U.S. Supreme Ct. 1978, U.S Ct. Appeals (D.C. cir.) 1978, U.S. Dist. Ct. (D.C. dist.), U.S Ct. Claims 1980, N.Y. 1981, U.S. Dist. Ct. (so. dist.) N.Y. 1981, (ea. dist.) N.Y. 1981, U.S. Ct. Appeals (2d cir.) 1983. Trial atty. Antitrust div. U.S. Dept. Justice, Washington, 1971-77; assoc. Bell, Boyd & Lloyd, Washington, 1977-81; of counsel Milman & Shwergold, N.Y.C., 1981-82; ptnr. Werner, Kennedy & French, N.Y.C., 1982-85, Levitsky & Serota, 1985-86, Huber, Lawrence & Abell, N.Y.C., 1987—. Recipient Spl. Achievement award U.S. Dept. Justice, 1976. Mem. ABA (chmn. ins. industry com. 1987—), N.Y. State Bar Assn., Assn. of Bar of City of N.Y. (antitrust and trade regulations com. 1988—), Fed. Bar Council. Contbr. articles to profl. jours. Editor Law Rev. Northwestern U. Office: Huber Lawrence & Abell 99 Park Ave New York NY 10016

SEROTA, NICHOLAS ANDREW, art gallery director; b. Apr. 27, 1946. BA, Cambridge (Eng.) U., 1968; MA, Courtauld Inst. Art, London, 1970. Regional art officer, organizer exhibitions Arts Council Gr. Britain, 1970-73; dir. Mus. Modern Art, Oxford, Eng., 1973-76, Whitechapel Art Gallery, London, 1976-88, Tate Gallery, London, 1988—; mem. visual arts adv. com. Brit. Coun., 1976—, chmn., 1992—; mem. adv. com. Carnegie Internat. Pitts., 1985, 88. Trustee Pub. Art Devel. Trust, 1983-87, Architecture Found., 1991—. Office: Tate Gallery, Millbank, London SW1P 4RG, England

SEROTA, SUSAN PERLSTADT, lawyer; b. Chgo., Sept. 10, 1945; d. Sidney Morris and Mildred (Penn) Perlstadt; m. James Ian Serota, May 7, 1972; children: Daniel Louis, Jonathan Mark. AB, U. Mich., 1967; JD, NYU, 1971. Bar: Ill. 1971, D.C. 1972, N.Y. 1981, U.S. Dist. Ct. (no. dist.) Ill. 1971, U.S. Dist. Ct. (so. dist.) N.Y. 1981, U.S. Dist. Ct. (ea. dist.) N.Y. 1985, U.S. Ct. Claims 1972, U.S. Tax Ct. 1972, U.S. Ct. Appeals (D.C. cir.) 1972. Assoc. Gottlieb & Schwartz, Chgo., 1971-72, Silverstein & Mullens, Washington, 1972-75, Cahill Gordon & Reindel, N.Y.C., 1975-82; assoc. Winthrop Stimson, Putnam & Roberts, N.Y.C., 1982, ptnr., 1983—; adj. prof. Sch. Law, Georgetown U., Washington, 1974-75; mem. faculty Practicing Law Inst., N.Y.C., 1983—. Assoc. editor Exec. Compensation Jour., 1973-75; dep. editor Tax Mgmt., Estate and Gift Taxation and Exec. Compensation, 1972-75; mem. editorial adv. bd. Benefits Law Jour., 1988—, Tax Mgmt. Compensation Jour., 1993—; mem. bd. editors ERISA and Benefits Law Jour., 1992—; contbr. articles to profl. jours. Mem. ABA (chmn. joint com. employee benefits 1988-89, chair com. employee benefits taxation sect. 1991-92, coun. mem. taxation sect. 1994—), Internat. Pension and Employee Benefits Lawyers Assn. (co-chair 1993—), N.Y. State Bar Assn. (exec. com. tax sect. 1988-92), Am. Bar Retirement Funds (dir. 1994—). Democrat. Office: Winthrop Stimson Putnam & Roberts One Battery Park Pla New York NY 10004-1490

SEROW, WILLIAM JOHN, economics educator; b. N.Y.C., Apr. 8, 1946; s. William John and Dorothea (Goyette) S.; m. Elizabeth Goetz, Aug. 24, 1968; 1 child, Erika. BA, Boston Coll., 1967; MA, Duke U., 1970, PhD, 1972. Rsch. dir. Univ. Va., Charlottesville, 1970-81; prof., dir. Fla. State U., Tallahassee, 1981—. Editor: Handbook of International Migration, 1990; author: Population Aging in the United States, 1990. Capt. U.S. Army, 1967-73. Recipient grants Fla. Health Care Cost Containment Bd., 1988-90, Nat. Instn. Aging, 1983-89, Nat. Inst. Mental Health, 1984-86. Mem. Internat. Union for Scientific Study of Population, Population Assn. Am., Am. and So. Econ. Assns., So. Demographic Assn. (pres. 1986-87), So. Regional Sci. Assn. (pres. 1982-83), Gerontol. Soc. Am. Avocations: railroads, Sherlock Holmes, baseball rsch. Office: Ctr for Study of Population 654 Bellamy Bldg Tallahassee FL 32306

SERPAN, ROGER L., cement and concrete company executive; b. 1939; married. BS, Colo. State U., 1962. With Am. Cement Amcord, 1965-74; v.p. ops. Hercules Cement, Amcord-Hercules, 1974-79; v.p. Riverside Cement Amcord-Riverside, 1979-80; with Gifford-Hill & Co. Inc., Dallas, 1965—, v.p. ops., 1980-85; v.p., gen. mgr. Gifford-Hill & Co. Inc., Diamond Bar, Calif., 1985-88; pres., chief oper. officer Gifford-Hill & Co. Inc., Dallas, 1988—, also dir. Capt. U.S. Army, 1962-64. Office: Gifford-Hill & Co Inc 2515 Mckinney Ave Dallas TX 75201-1908

SERRA, RICHARD, sculptor; b. San Francisco, Nov. 2, 1939. Student, U. Calif., Berkeley; BA, U. Calif., Santa Barbara; BFA, MFA, Yale U. One-man shows include Richard Hines Gallery, Seattle, 1979, Venice Biennale, 1981, Pace Gallery, Leo Castelli Gallery, 1987, Bonnefantenmuseum, Maastricht, 1990, Pace Gallery, 1992; exhbns. include Stedelijk Mus., Amsterdam, 1969, Kunsthalle, Bern, Switzerland, 1969, Solomon R. Guggenheim Mus., N.Y.C., 1969, Pasadena (Calif.) Art Mus., 1970, Leo Castelli Gallery, N.Y.C., 1970, 72, 74, 82, 84, ACE Gallery, L.A., 1970, 72, 74, Whitney Mus. Am. Art, N.Y.C., 1973, Akira Ikeda Gallery, Nagoya, Japan, 1982, Margo Levin Gallery, 1984, Visual Arts Mus., 1985, Mus. Modern Art, N.Y.C., 1986; group shows include Tony Shafrazi Gallery, 1991-92, Pace Gallery, 1992; represented in permanent collections: Mus. Modern Art, N.Y.C., Whitney Mus. Am. Art, N.Y.C., Guggenheim Mus., N.Y.C., Pasadena Mus. Art, L.A. County Mus. Art, Art Gallery Ont., Toronto, Stedelijk Mus.; also filmmaker. Office: 173 Duane St New York NY 10013 also: Gagosian Gallery 980 Madison Ave New York NY 10021

SERRA-BADUE, DANIEL FRANCISCO, artist, educator; b. Santiago de Cuba, Sept. 8, 1914; came to U.S., 1962; s. Daniel Serra and Eloisa Badue; m. Aida Betancourt, Mar. 8, 1944; 1 dau., Aida Victoria. Licenciate in Law, U. Barcelona, 1936; LL.D., U. Havana, 1938, Dr. in Social, Polit. and Econ. Scis., 1949; M.F.A. Nat. Sch. Fine Arts, Havana, 1943. Prof. Sch. Fine Arts, Santiago de Cuba, 1945-60, Nat. Sch. Fine Arts, Havana, 1960-62; lectr. Columbia U., N.Y.C., 1962-63; instr. Bklyn. Mus. Art Sch., N.Y.C., 1962-83; prof. St. Peter's Coll., Jersey City, 1967—; asst. dir. culture Ministry Edn., Havana, 1959-60. Exhibited over 40 one-man shows and over 250 group shows. Bd. dirs. Cintas Found., N.Y.C. Recipient Pa. Acad. prize, 1941; recipient Bienal Hispano Americana prize, 1954; Guggenheim Found. fellow, 1938, 39; Cintas Found. fellow, 1963, 64. Mem. AAUP, Coll. Art Assn. Am. Home: 15 W 72nd St #10T New York NY 10023 Office: St Peter's Coll 2641 Kennedy Blvd Jersey City NJ 07306

SERRANI, THOM, management consultant, former mayor; b. Glens Falls, N.Y., Nov. 5, 1947; s. Italo N. and Florence Rosemary (LaPointe) S.; m. Beth Burgeson, June 24, 1978. B.A. in Liberal Arts, Sacred Heart U., Bridgeport, Conn.; 1970; postgrad., Fairfield U., 1970-72. Mem. Stamford

Bd. Reps., Conn., 1973-75; mem. Conn. Ho. of Reps., 1975-81, Conn. Senate, 1981-84; mayor City of Stamford, Conn., 1983-91; bus. cons. Ludlow Assocs., Stamford, 1991—; mem. Nat. Conf. State Legislators, 1975-83, vice chmn. transp. com., 1981-83. Mem. Springdale Vol. Fire Co., Stamford, 1973—; apptd. mem. Gov.'s Task Force on Safety in Pub. Spaces, Hartford, 1986, Gov.'s Fire Marshall Tng. Council, Hartford, 1986; chmn. Met. Planning Orgn., Conn., 1986; vice chmn. Stamford Econ. Assistance Corp., Conn., 1986; del. Dem. Nat. Conv., N.Y., 1976, San Francisco, 1984; chmn. bd. (ex officio) Stamford Ctr. Arts. Recipient legis. award State Firemen's Assn., Conn., 1976, Community Svc. award Sacred Heart U., 1984, Outstanding Svc. award Easter Seal Rehab. Ctr., 1987, Equal Opportunity award NAACP, 1989, Aid for Retarded Recognition award, Disting. Community Svc. award B'nai Brith, 1988, Pitney Bowes Foreman's Club Merit award, 1987; named Legislator of Yr., Conn. Caucus of Dems., 1980, Downtown Man of Yr., 1985. Mem. Piedmont Assocs., Glenbrook Athletic Assn. Avocations: cross country skiing, construction, gardening. Home: 56 Hickory Way Stamford CT 06907-1308 Office: Ludlow Assocs Corp Ctr 700 Canal St Stamford CT 06902

SERRANO, JOSE E., congressman; b. Mayaguez, P.R., Oct. 24, 1943; s. Jose E. and Hipolita (Soto) S.; m. Mary Serrano; children: Lisa Marie, Jose Marco, Justine, Jonathan, Benjamin. With Mfrs. Hanover Trust Co., 1961-69; mem. Bd. Edn. N.Y., 1969-74; former N.Y. State Assemblyman Albany, from 1975; mem. 102nd-104th Congresses from 18th (now 16th) N. Y. dist.N.Y., Washington, D.C., 1991—; mem. appropriations com., subcom. fgn. ops., export financing and related programs, subcom. labor, health, human svcs. and edn., 1993-94, mem. subcom. constitution, judiciary com.; chmn. Congl. Hispanic Caucus, 1993-94. Roman Catholic. Office: 2342 Rayburn Hob Washington DC 20515 also: 890 Grand Concourse Bronx NY 10451-2828

SERRIE, HENDRICK, anthropology and international business educator; b. Jersey City, July 2, 1937; s. Hendrick and Elois (Edge) S.; m. Gretchen Tipler Ihde, Sept. 3, 1959; children: Karim Jonathan, Keir Ethan. BA with honors, U. Wis., 1960; MA, Cornell U., 1964; PhD with distinction, Northwestern U., 1976. Dir. Solar Energy Field Project, Oaxaca, Mex., 1961-62; instr. U. Aleppo, Syria, 1963-64; asst. prof. Beloit (Wis.) Coll., 1964-69, Calif. State U., Northridge, 1969-70, Purdue U., West Lafayette, Ind., 1970-72, New Coll./U. South Fla., Sarasota, 1972-77; tchr. Pine View Sch., Sarasota, 1978; prof. anthropology, internat. bus. Eckerd Coll., St. Petersburg, Fla., 1978—; dir. internat. bus. overseas programs Eckerd Coll., 1981—; sr. rsch. assoc., Human Resources Inst., St. Petersburg, 1988—. Author, editor: Family, Kinship, and Ethnic Identity Among the Overseas Chinese, 1985, Anthropology and International Business, 1986, What Can Multinationals Do for Peasants, 1994; writer, dir. films: Technological Innovation, 1962, Something New Under the Sun, 1963; contbr. articles to Wall Street Jour. and Wall Street Jour. Europe. Tchr. Sunday sch., North United Methodist Ch., Sarasota, 1977—. Exxon scholar, So. Ctr. for Internat. Issues, Atlanta, 1980-81; Presdl. fellow Am. Grad. Sch. Internat. Mgmt., 1991; recipient Leavy award, Freedoms Found., Valley Forge, Pa., 1989. Fellow Am. Anthropol. Assn., Soc. Applied Anthropology; mem. So. Ctr. Internat. Issues, Acad. Internat. Bus., Tampa Bay Internat. Trade Coun., Internat. Soc. Intercultural Edn., Tng. and Rsch. Democrat. Avocations: singing, drawing, beach walking, cycling, sailing. Home: 636 Mecca Dr Sarasota FL 34234-2713 Office: Eckerd Coll Dept Internat Bus Saint Petersburg FL 33733

SERRIN, JAMES BURTON, mathematics educator; b. Chgo., Nov. 1, 1926; s. James B. and Helen Elizabeth (Wingate) S.; m. Barbara West, Sept. 6, 1952; children: Martha Helen Stack, Elizabeth Ruth, Janet Louise Sucha. Student, Northwestern U., 1944-46; B.A., Western Mich. U., 1947; M.A., Ind. U., Ph.D., 1951; D.Sc., U. Sussex, 1972; DSc in Engring., U. Ferrara, Italy, 1992; DSC in Math., U. Padova, Italy, 1992. With MIT, Cambridge, 1952-54; mem. faculty U. Minn., Mpls., 1955—, prof. math., 1959—, Regents prof., 1968—, head Sch. Math., 1964-65; Vis. prof. U. Chgo., 1964, 75, Johns Hopkins, 1966, Sussex U., 1967-68, 72, 76, U. Naples, 1979, U. Modena, 1988, Ga. Inst. of Tech., 1990. Author: Mathematical Principles of Classical Fluid Mechanics, 1957. Mem. Met. Airport Sound Abatement Council, Mpls., 1969—. Recipient Disting. Alumni award Ind. U., 1979. Fellow AAAS; mem. NAS, Am. Math. Soc. (G.D. Birkhoff prize 1973), Math. Assn. Am., Soc. for Natural Philosophy (pres. 1969-70). Home: 4422 Dupont Ave S Minneapolis MN 55409-1739

SERRITELLA, JAMES ANTHONY, lawyer; b. Chgo., July 8, 1942; s. Anthony and Angela (Deleonardis) S.; m. Ruby Ann Amoroso, Oct. 3, 1981. B.A., SUNY-S.I., 1965, Pontifical Gregorian U., Rome, 1966; postgrad., DePaul U., 1966-67; M.A., U. Chgo., 1968, J.D. 1971. Bar: Ill. 1971, U.S. Supreme Ct. 1976, U.S. Tax Ct. 1985. Ptnr. Kirkland & Ellis, Chgo., 1978; ptnr. Reuben & Proctor, Chgo., 1978-86, Mayer, Brown & Platt, Chgo., 1986—; lectr. in field. Contbr. articles to profl. jours. Mem. exec. bd. govt. rels. com. United Way of Chgo., 1979-84; bd. dirs. Child Care Assn. Ill., 1975-79, Lyric Opera Guild, 1979-84; v.p. Comprehensive Community Svcs. of Met. Chgo., 1976-81; chmn. adv. bd. DePaul U. Coll. Law Ctr. Ch./State Studies, 1982—, mem. dean's vis. com., 1982—; trustee Mundelein Coll., 1982-86, St. Xavier Coll., St. Mary of the Lake Sem., 1982-83, Sta. WTTW Chgo. Pub. TV, 1978-81, Loretto Hosp., 1989-91; mem. geriatrics/gerontology steering com. McGaw Med. Ctr. Northwestern U., 1981-82; mem. bd. advisors Alzheimer's Ctr. Rush-Presbyn.-St. Luke's Med. Ctr., 1990—; founder, chmn. bd. Chgo. Ctr. for Peace Studies, 1990—; mem. adv. coun. Charitable Trust div. Ill. Atty. Gen., 1991—; cons. Union of Bulgarian Founds., 1992, Internat. Acad. for Freedom of Religion and Belief, Budapest, Hungary, 1992; active Ill. State Hist. Soc. Coun. for Ill. History, 1994—. Fellow Am. Bar Found.; mem. ABA, FBA, NCCJ (adv. com. on ch., state and taxation), Am. Assn. homes for Aging, Nat. Health Lawyers Assn., Ill. State Bar Assn. (bd. govs., spl. com. on jud. redistricting), Ill. Bar Found. (charter), Chgo. Bar Assn. (com. on evaluation of jud. candidates), Cath. Lawyers Guild (bd. govs.), Canon Law Soc. Am. (active mem.), Diocesan Attys. Assn. (exec. com.), Nat. Cath. Cemetery Conf., Cath. Health Assn., The Park Ridge Ctr., The Chgo. Club, Econ. Club, Tavern Club. Office: Mayer Brown & Platt 190 S La Salle St Chicago IL 60603-3410

SERRITELLA, WILLIAM DAVID, lawyer; b. Chgo., May 16, 1946; s. William V. and Josephine Dolores (Scalise) S. J.D., U. Ill., Champaign, 1971. Bar: Ill. 1971, U.S. Dist. Ct. (no. and cen. dists.) Ill. 1972, U.S. Ct. Appeals (7th cir.) 1974, U.S. Supreme Ct. 1979. Law clk. U.S. Dist. Ct., Danville, Ill., 1971-72; ptnr. Ross & Hardies, Chgo., 1972—; arbitrator Am. Arbitration Assn. Mem. ABA, Ill. Bar Assn., Chgo. Bar Assn., Nat. Assn. R.R. Trial Counsel (Ill.), Soc. Trial Lawyers, Defense Rsch. Inst., Legal Club, Trial Lawyers Club (Chicago). Office: Ross & Hardies 150 N Michigan Ave Ste 2500 Chicago IL 60601-7567

SERTICH, TONY, artistic director; b. Detroit, Jan. 23, 1953; s. Tony and Mary (Bacha) S.; m. Kathleen Sertich, Nov. 12, 1989; children: Nicholas Owen, Eleanor Mary. BA in Theatre Mgmt. Percussionist, 1972-78; asst. box office mgr. Nederlander Theatrical Orgn., 1979-84; dir. nat. touring prodns. Children's Theatre Co., Mpls., 1985-89; mng. dir. touring theatre Nat. Theatre of Deaf, 1990-91; exec. dir. League of Chgo. Theatres., 1991—. Home: 427 Laurel Elk Grove Village IL 60007

SERVAAS, BEURT RICHARD, corporate executive; b. Indpls., May 7, 1919; s. Beurt Hans and Lela Etta (Neff) S.; m. Cory Jane Synhorst, Jan. 7, 1950; children: Eric, Kristin, Joan, Paul, Amy. Student, U. Mex., Mexico City, 1938-39; AB, Ind. U., 1940, MD, 1970; postgrad., Purdue U., 1941; D Bus. Mgmt., Ind. Inst. Tech.; LHD (hon.), Butler U. Agt. CIA, China, 1946; v.p. constrn. Vestar Corp., N.Y.C., 1948; founder, chief exec. officer No. Vernon Forge, Inc. Rev. Pub. Co., ServAas Labs., Indpls., 1949—; chmn. bd. ServAas, Inc., Indpls. and affiliated cos. Curtis Pub. Co., Forge Mexicana, Edgerton Tool, Dependable Engring., ServAas Mgmt., ServAas Rubber, Premier, Indpls. Rubber Co., Bridgeport Brass Co.; bd. dirs. Bank One Ind. Pres. City-County Coun., Indpls.; chmn. Ind. Toxic Chem. Higher Edn.; chmn. Kirksville Coll. Osteopathic Medicine; bd. dirs. Coll. Univ. Corp., Ind. Pub. Health Found., Robert Schuller Ministries; past bd. dirs. Indt State Bd. Health, Nat. Fgn. Rels. Commn. With USNR, 1941-45. Decorated Bronze Star; recipient Horatio Alger award, 1980. Mem. NAM,

Am. Acad. Achievement (Golden Plate award 1973), Assn. Am. Med. Colls., Ind. C. of C., Indpls. C. of C, Marion County Hist. Soc., Ind. Hist. Soc., Newcomen Soc. N.Am., U.S. Naval Res. Assn., World Future Soc., Am. Legion, Columbia Club, Econ. Club, Indpls. Athletic Club, Indpls. Press Club, Meridian Hills Country Club, Phi Delta Kappa. Presbyterian. Home: 2525 W 44th St Indianapolis IN 46208-3249 Office: Office of the City County Coun 241 City-County Bldg 200 E Washington St Indianapolis IN 46204-3307

SERVAN-SCHREIBER, JEAN-JACQUES, engineer, author; b. Paris, Feb. 13, 1924; s. Emile and Denise (Bresard) Servan-S.; grad. Ecole Polytechnique, Paris, 1947; children: David, Emile, Franklin, Edouard. Sr. writer, fgn. affairs editor Le Monde, Paris, 1948-53; Groupe Expres, mags. L'Express, 1953-73; mem. nat. Parliament from Nancy; pres. Radical Party; pres. Lorraine region 1970-79; founder, 1979, chmn. Groupe de Paris (Europe, Japan, Arabia); chmn. World Center for Informatics and Human Resources, Paris, 1982-85; chmn. internat. com. Carnegie-Mellon U., Pitts., 1985—. Served as fighter pilot Free French Forces, World War II. Decorated Cross of Mil. Valor. Author: Lieutenant in Algeria, 1957, The American Challenge, 1967, The Radical Manifesto, 1971, The World Challenge, 1981, Passions I, 1991, Les Fossoyeurs, 1993.

SERVEDIO, DOMINICK MICHAEL, engineering executive; b. N.Y.C., Aug. 7, 1940; s. Daniel and Margaret (Ingenito) S.; m. Patricia L. Filatro, July 26, 1969; children: Dominique, Daniel. BEE, NYU, 1962; MBA, St. John's U., 1972. Registered profl. engr., N.H., Mass. Engr. in tng. N.Y. Cen. R.R., N.Y.C., 1962-63, engr., 1965-67; elec. engr. Citizen Utility Co., N.Y.C., 1967-68; project engr. L.I. R.R., N.Y.C., 1968-73; asst. dir., supervising engr. Met. Transp. Authority, N.Y.C., 1973-77; from v.p. to pres., chief operating officer Seelye Stevenson Value & Knecht, N.Y.C., 1977—, also dir.; exec. v.p. STV Group, Pottstown, Pa. Mem. Columbus Citizens Found., Inc., N.Y.C., 1990, N.J. Alliance for Action, Edison, 1991; active Greater N.Y. March of Dimes, 1991, Greater N.Y. Couns. Boy Scouts Am., 1991. 1st lt. U.S. Army, 1963-65. Mem. NSPE, Soc. Am. Mil. Engrs., N.Y. R.R. Club Inc., Soc. for Mktg. Profl. Svcs., Moles. Avocations: golfing, skiing, reading. Office: STV/Seelye Stevenson & Knecht 225 Park Ave S New York NY 10003-1604*

SERVISON, ROGER THEODORE, investment executive; b. Columbus, Ohio, June 6, 1945; s. Theodore Calvin and Hilda Augusta (Longmack) S.; m. Kristin Landsteiner, Jan. 8, 1972. BA, U. Iowa, 1967; MBA, Harvard U., 1972. Chmn. Tax Man, Inc., Cambridge, Mass., 1970-72; v.p. Continental Investment Corp., Boston, 1972-75, Phoenix Investment Counsel, Boston, 1975-76; mng. dir. Fidelity Investments, Boston, 1976—; bd. dirs. Tax Man, Cambridge, Boston Fin. Group, Longwood Covered Coats, Brookline. Dir. First Night, Inc., Boston, 1985. Mem. Longwood Cricket Club, Sippican Club, Federal Club, City Club, Piney Point Beach Club. Avocations: art, antiques, tennis, aerobics.

SERVODIDIO, PAT ANTHONY, broadcast executive; b. Yonkers, N.Y., Nov. 9, 1937; s. Pasquale and Catherine (Verdisco) S.; m. Ulla I. Schalien, May 4, 1968; children: Christian, Alexa. BS, Fordham U., 1959; postgrad., St. John's U., N.Y.C., 1960-63. Asst. to bus. mgr. Sta. WCBS-TV, N.Y.C., 1960-64; account exec. Sta. WTNH-TV, New Haven, 1964-66; account exec., N.Y. sales mgr. RKO TV Reps., N.Y.C., 1967-74; v.p., N.Y. sales mgr. Sta. WOR-TV, N.Y.C., 1974-79, v.p., gen. sales mgr., 1979-81; v.p., gen. mgr. Sta. WNAC-TV, Boston, 1981-82; pres. RKO TV, N.Y.C., 1982-87; pres. RKO Gen., Inc., N.Y.C., 1987-91, also bd. dirs.; v.p., gen. mgr. Sta. WKYC-TV, Cleve., 1991-92; pres. Multimedia Broadcasting Co., Cin., 1992-94; broadcast cons., 1995—. Bd. regents St. Peter's Coll., 1983—; mem. com. future financing Rutgers U., New Brunswick, N.J., 1983-85; dir. TV bur. Advt. Bd., 1993—; bd. dirs. Internat. Radio and TV Found., 1983-93, Assn. for Maximum Svc. TV, Inc., 1993—. With U.S. Army, 1959-62. Office: Multimedia Broadcasting Co 140 W 9th St Cincinnati OH 45202-1905

SERWATKA, WALTER DENNIS, publishing executive; b. Irvington, N.J., July 19, 1937; s. Walter F. and Grace R. (Sheehan) S.; m. Beverly M. Farrell, Aug. 10, 1963 (div. Feb. 1988); children—David, Nora, Nancy. BBA in Acctg., Upsala U., 1959; MBA in Fin., Fairleigh Dickinson U., 1966; postgrad. in bus., Harvard U., 1978, Columbia U., 1979, Stanford U., 1985. With treas't dept. WESTVACO, N.Y.C., 1964-68; dir. fin. analysis Random House Co., N.Y.C., 1968-72; with McGraw-Hill Info. Systems Co., 1972-83; contr. Sweet's div. McGraw-Hill, Inc., N.Y.C., 1972-73, dir. profit planning, 1973-75, asst. contr., 1975-76, sr. v.p.-contr., 1976-79, group v.p. real estate info. svcs., 1979-83, sr. v.p. group mfg. and circulation svcs., 1985, exec. v.p., chief fin. officer, 1985-88, exec. v.p. ops., 1989—; exec. v.p. fin. and svcs. McGraw-Hill Publs. Co., N.Y.C., 1983-84; pres. McGraw-Hill Info. Svcs., N.Y.C., 1988-89. Trustee Upsala Coll., East Orange, N.J. Served with U.S. Army, 1959-62. Mem. Fin. Exec. Inst., Mag. Pubs. Assn., Am. Inst. Accts., Planning Execs. Inst., Pvt. Sector Council. Office: McGraw-Hill Inc 1221 Ave Of The Americas New York NY 10020-1001

SERWER, ALAN MICHAEL, lawyer; b. Detroit, Aug. 31, 1944; s. Bernard Jacob and Marian (Borin) S.; m. Laurel Kathryn Robbert, June 6, 1968; children: David Matthew, Karen Anne. BA in Econs., U. Mich., 1966; JD, Northwestern U., 1969. Bar: Ill. 1969, D.C. 1980, U.S. Dist. Ct. (no. dist.) Ill. 1970, U.S. Ct. Appeals (7th cir.) 1979, U.S. Supreme Ct. 1979, U.S. Ct. Appeals (6th cir.) 1982, U.S. Ct. Appeals (5th cir.) 1983, U.S. Ct. Appeals (11th cir.) 1984, U.S. Ct. Appeals (9th cir.) 1986. Trial atty. U.S. Dept. Labor, Chgo., 1969-78, counsel safety and health, 1978-79; assoc. Haley, Bader & Potts, Chgo., 1979-82, ptnr., 1983-87; ptnr. Bell, Boyd & Lloyd, Chgo., 1987—. Mem. Ill. Bar Assn., Chgo. Bar Assn., Assn. Trial Lawyers Am., Fed. Bar Assn. (recipient Million Gordon award 1977). Home: 233 Woodland Rd Highland Park IL 60035-5052 Office: Bell Boyd & Lloyd 70 W Madison St Ste 3200 Chicago IL 60602-4284

SESNO, FRANK, executive editor; married; 3 children. BA in Am. History, Middlebury Coll. Dir., reporter Sta. WCFR, Springfield, Vt.; with Voice of Am.; nat. corr. AP Radio; corr. White House CNN, Washington, 1984-90, anchor chair, 1991—, co-anchor The Internat. Hour, host Late Edition. Recipient First Place Reporting of Econs. Unity awards in Media, Spl. Jury award Best of Festival Worldfest-Houston Film Festival, Joan Shorenstein Barone award, Cable ACE award Nat. Acad. Cable Programming, Houston Internat. Film Festival award, Ben Grauer award for Best Spot News Reporting Overseas Press Club, Best Spot News Reporting award AP Broadcast, Nat. Press Club award. Office: CNN Am Inc Washington Bur 820 First St NE Washington DC 20002

SESONSKE, ALEXANDER, nuclear and chemical engineer; b. Gloversville, N.Y., June 20, 1921; s. Abraham and Esther (Kreitzer) S.; m. Marjorie Ann Mach, Apr. 17, 1952; children—Michael Jan, Jana Louise. B.Chem. Engring., Rensselaer Poly. Inst., 1942; M.S., U. Rochester, 1947; Ph.D., U. Del., 1950. Engr. Chem. Constrn. Corp., N.Y.C., 1942; chem. engr. Manhattan Project, 1943-45, Columbia-So. Chem. Corp., 1945-46; staff Los Alamos Sci. Lab., 1950-54, 60-61, 1961-63; faculty Purdue U., Lafayette, Ind., 1954; prof. nuclear and chem. engring. Purdue U., 1959-86, prof. emeritus, 1986—, asst. chmn. dept. nuclear engring., 1966-73; Cons. Oak Ridge Nat. Lab., 1963-67, Electric Power Research Inst., 1974; mem. rev. com. Argonne (Ill.) Nat. Lab., 1965-67, 75-81; ind. cons. 1986—. Author: (with Samuel Glasstone) Nuclear Reactor Engineering, 1963, 4th edit., 1994, Nuclear Power Plant Design Analysis, 1973; mem. editorial bd. Advances in Nuclear Sci. and Tech., 1972—; contbr. numerous articles to profl. jours. Recipient Wall of Fame award U. Del., 1988. Fellow Am. Nuclear Soc. (Arthur H. Compton award 1987); mem. Am. Inst. Chem. Engrs., Am. Soc. Engring. Edn., Sigma Xi, Omega Chi Epsilon. Research on nuclear fuel mgmt., liquid metal heat transfer and nuclear reactor engring. Home and Office: 16408 Felice Dr San Diego CA 92128-2804

SESSAMEN, DONALD WILLIAM, communications company executive; b. Whitpain Twp., Pa., Sept. 3, 1932; s. Guy Raymond and Sylvia Marion (Harlan) S.; m. Sandra Roberta MacFarland, Apr. 2, 1954 (div. Aug. 1972); children: Victoria Leigh, Deborah Reneé, Pamela Suzanne, Guy Raymond II; m. Alice Catherine Cusumano, Nov. 10, 1974. Student, Glassboro State U., 1964-65. Various positions-plant, engring., mktg. N.J. Bell Telephone Co., 1954-69; v.p., gen. mgr. Princeton (N.J.) Timesharing Services Inc., 1970-72;

western region v.p. Telecommunications Systems of Am., Oklahoma City, 1973-75; cen. region ops. mgr. So. Pacific Communications Co., McLean, Va., 1975-79; nat. ops. mgr. So. Pacific Communications Co., Burlingame, Calif., 1979-80; v.p. ops. Sprint Communications, Burlingame, 1980-82, sr. v.p. planning and bus. devel., 1982-83; sr. v.p. ops. Allnet Communication Services Inc., Birmingham, Mich., 1983-88, exec. v.p., 1988-89; pres., chief operating officer FiberTel, Inc., Columbus, Ohio, 1989—; mem. telecommunications adv. bd. U. Colo., Boulder, 1981—. Chmn. Cape May (N.J.) County Young Republicans, 1965; pres. Stone Harbor (N.J.) Lions Club, 1966; bd. dirs. Am. Speech-Lang.-Hearing Assn., Palo Alto, Calif., 1982-84, Am. Social Health Assn. Served to sgt. major USNG. Republican. Methodist. Home: 5605 Upper Ridge Way Auburn CA 95602-9248 Office: ALC Communications Corp 30300 Telegraph Rd Franklin MI 48025-4507

SESSION, WILLIAM TERRELL, lawyer; b. Kansas City, Mo., Oct. 26, 1952; s. Goldstein and Ruby (Sanders) S.; m. Linda Moore, Aug. 9, 1977 (div. 1978). BS, Northwest Mo. State U., 1973; MBA, U. Mo., 1974, JD, 1977. Bar: Mo. 1978, U.S. Dist. Ct. (we. dist.) Mo. 1978, U.S. Ct. Appeals (8th cir.) 1983, U.S. Ct. Appeals (6th cir.) 1986, U.S. Dist. Ct. (no. dist.) Mich. 1986, U.S. Dist. Ct. (no. dist.) Ohio 1986. Law clk. to presiding justice 16th Jud. Cir. Ct., Kansas City, 1977-78; ptnr. Linde, Thomson, Langworthy et al, Kansas City, 1978-89; of counsel Polsinelli, White, Vardeman & Shalton, Kansas City, 1989—. Bd. dirs. Habitat for Humanity, Kansas City; active Big Bros. Kansas City. Mem. Mo. Bar Assn., Kansas City Met. Bar Assn. Home: 3526 Harrison St Kansas City MO 64109-2904 Office: Polsinelli White Vardeman & Shalton 4705 Central St Kansas City MO 64112-1522

SESSIONS, JEFFERSON BEAUREGARD, III, lawyer; b. Selma, Ala., Dec. 24, 1946; s. Jefferson Beauregard and Abbie (Powe) S.; m. Mary Montgomery Blackshear, Aug. 9, 1969; children: Mary Abigail, Ruth Blackshear, Samuel Turner. B.A., Huntingdon Coll., Montgomery, Ala., 1969; J.D., U. Ala., 1973. Bar: Ala. 1973. Assoc. Guin, Bouldin & Porch, Russellville, Ala., 1973-75; asst. U.S. atty. U.S. Dept. Justice, Mobile, Ala., 1975-77, U.S. atty., 1981-93; assoc., ptnr. Stockman & Bedsole Attys., Mobile, Ala., 1977-81; ptnr. Stockman, Bedsole & Sessions, Mobile, 1993-95; atty. gen. State of Ala., 1995—. Am. Speech-Lang.-Hearing Assn. Served as chmn. adminstrv. bd. Ashland Pl. United Meth. Ch., Mobile, 1982. Capt. USAR, 1975-85. Mem. ABA, Ala. Bar Assn., Mobile Bar Assn., Omicron Delta Kappa. Home: 16 S Lafayette St Mobile AL 36604-1714

SESSIONS, JUDITH ANN, librarian, university library dean; b. Lubbock, Tex., Dec. 16, 1947; d. Earl Alva and Anna (Mayer) S. BA cum laude, Cen. Fla. U., 1970; MLS, Fla. State U., 1971; postgrad., Am. U., 1980, George Washington U., 1983. Head libr. U. S.C., Salkehatchie, 1974-77; dir. Libr. and Learing Resources Ctr. Mt. Vernon Coll., Washington, 1977-82; planning and systems libr. George Washington U., Washington, 1981-82, asst. univ. libr. for adminstrn. svcs., acting head tech. svcs., 1982-84; univ. libr. Calif. State U., Chico, 1984-88; univ. libr., dean of libr. Miami U., Oxford, Ohio, 1988—; cons. Space Planning, S.C., 1976, DataPhase Implementation, Bowling Green U., 1982, TV News Study Ctr., George Washington U., 1981; asst. prof. Dept. Child Devel., Mt. Vernon Coll., 1978-81; mem., lectr. U.S.-China Libr. Exch. Del., 1986, 91; lectr., presenter in field. Contbr. articles, book revs. to profl. jours. Trustee Christ Hosp., Cin., 1990-94, Hamilton YMCA, Deaconess Gamble Rsch. Ctr., Cin., 1990-94. Recipient award for outstanding contbn. D.C. Libr. Assn., 1979; rsch. grantee Mt. Vernon Coll., 1980; recipient Fulbright-Hayes Summer Travel fellowship to Czechoslovakia, 1991. Mem. ALA (Olofson award 1978, councillor-at-large policy making group 1981-94, coun. com. on coms. 1983-84, intellectual freedom com. 1984-88, directions and program rev. com. 1989-91, fin. and audit subcom. 1989-90, mem. exec. bd. 1989-94), Assn. Coll. and Rsch. Librs. (editorial bd. Coll. and Rsch. Librs. jour. 1979-84, nominatins and appointments com. 1983-85, faculty status com. 1984-86), Libr. and Info. Tech. Assn. (chair legis. and regulation com. 1980-81), Libr. Adminstrn. and Mgmt. Assn. (bd. dirs. libr. orgn. and mgmt. sect. 1985-87), Calif. Inst. Librs. (v.p., pres. elect 1987-88), Mid-Atlantic Regional Libr. Fedn. (mem. exec. bd. 1982-84), Jr. Mems. Round Table (pres. 1981-82), Intellectual Freedom Round Table (sec. 1984-85), Freedom to Read Found. (trustee 1984-88, v.p 1985-86, treas. 1986-87, pres. 1987-88), Rotary, Beta Phi Mu. Home: 45 Waters Way Hamilton OH 45013-6324 Office: Miami U Edgar W King Oxford OH 45056

SESSIONS, ROBERT PAUL, former college president and administrator, retired educator, writer; b. Hardy, Ark., Oct. 5, 1926; s. Adolphus Wann and Mattie Orel (Gibson) Jernigan; adopted son Loys Rutherford S.; m. Martha Rae Rutledge, 1950 (div. 1957); children: Laura Elizabeth Sessions Stepp, Teresa Rae Sessions Kramer; m. Julia Margaret Anderson, Dec. 26, 1960; children: Kathryn Grace, Sarah Ruth. A.B., So. Meth. U., 1948, Th.M., 1950; Ph.D., Boston U., 1968. Ordained to ministry Meth. Ch., 1950. Pastor St. John's Meth. Ch., Van Buren, Ark., 1950-56, 1st Meth. Ch., Booneville, Ark., 1956-62, East Braintree Meth. Ch., Mass., 1962-67; asst. prof. sociology and religion W.Va. Wesleyan Coll., Buckhannan, 1967-70; prof., dept. chmn. East Tenn. State U., Johnson City, 1970-81; pres. Southwestern Coll., Winfield, Kans., 1981-84; dean Grad. Sch., dir. institutional planning Kearney State Coll., Nebr., 1988-92; cons. W.Va. Dept. Edn., Charleston, 1967-70, Tenn. Com. for the Humanities, Nashville, 1974, McCormick Theol. Sem., Chgo., 1976-77. Author: The Heart of the Bible, 1976; editor: Great Lakes Bulletin, 1945-46; co-editor: Updating Intergroup Education in Public Schools, 1970; contbr. articles to mags., religious jours. Bd. dirs. Broadside TV, Johnson City, Tenn., 1974-76; trustee Richard Young Psychiat. Hosp., Kearney, Nebr., 1985-88, chmn. 1987-88. Served with USN, 1944-46. Human Relations Inst. grantee, 1968; Updating Interethnic Edn. grantee, 1969. Mem. Am. Sociol. Assn., So. Sociol. Soc., Soc. for the Study of Social Problems, Soc. of Christian Ethics, Religious Research Assn., Phi Kappa Phi, Alpha Kappa Delta, Pi Gamma Mu, Phi Delta Kappa. Democrat. Lodges: Rotary Masons.

SESSIONS, WILLIAM LAD, philosophy educator, administrator; b. Somerville, N.J., Dec. 3, 1943; s. William George and Alice Edna (Billhardt) S.; m. Vicki Darlene Thompson, Aug. 28, 1965; children: Allistair Lee, Laura Anne. BA magna cum laude, U. Colo., 1965; MA in Comparative Study of Religion, Union Theol. Sem., N.Y.C., 1967; postgrad., Oxford (Eng.) U., 1967-68; PhD, Yale U., 1971; postdoctoral studies, Stanford U., 1976, Harvard U., 1977-78. Teaching fellow Yale U., 1969; instr. U. Conn., Waterbury, 1970-71; asst. prof. philosophy Washington and Lee U., 1971-77, assoc. prof., 1977-83, instr. So. Sem., 1972, vis. prof. St. Olaf Coll., 1985-86, assoc. dean Coll. Washington and Lee U., 1992-95, acting dean 1995—. Author: The Concept of Faith, 1994; contbr. articles to religious and philos. jours. Ruling elder Lexington (Va.) Presbyn. Ch., 1983-89, tchr. Sunday sch., 1984-95. Glenn grantee Washington and Lee U., 1975—, Babcock Found. grantee, 1976, NEH grantee, 1977, 83, 86, Mellon Found. grantee, 1978-79, Mellon East Asian Studies grantee, 1990. Mem. Am. Philos. Assn., Va. Philos. Assn., Soc. for Philosophy of Religion (exec. coun. 1988-94, v.p. 1991, pres. 1992), Soc. Christian Philosophers (steering com. ea. region 1986-90, 92—, exec. com. 1987-90), Phi Beta Kappa (exec. com. Va. chpt. 1986-94, v.p 1989-91, pres. 1991-93). Office: Washington & Lee U Office of Dean Lexington VA 24450

SESSIONS, WILLIAM STEELE, former government official; b. Fort Smith, Ark., May 27, 1930; s. Will Anderson and Edith A. (Steele) S.; m. Alice Lewis, Oct. 5, 1952; children: William Lewis, Mark Gregory, Peter Anderson, Sara Anne. BA, Baylor U., 1956, JD, 1958; hon. degree, John C. Marshall Law Sch., St. Mary's U. Sch. of Law, Dickinson Sch. of Law, Flager Coll., Davis & Elkins Coll. Bar: Tex. 1959. Ptnr. McGregor & Sessions, Waco, Tex., 1959-61; assoc. Tirey, McLaughlin, Gorin & Tirey, Waco, 1961-63; ptnr. Haley, Fulbright, Winniford, Sessions & Bice, Waco, 1963-69; chief govt. ops sect. criminal divsn. U.S. Dept. Justice, Washington, 1969-71; atty. U.S. Dist. Ct. (we. dist.) Tex., San Antonio, 1971-74, dist. judge, 1974-80, chief judge, 1980-87; dir. FBI, Washington, 1987-93; ptnr. Sessions, Sessions, Sklencar and Warburton, San Antonio; bd. dirs. Fed. Jud. Ctr., Washington, chmn. bench book com., 1981; (honorary) bd. dir. MLK, Jr. Fed. Holiday Corp., 1993—. Contbr. articles to profl. jours. Commr. Dr. Martin Luther King Jr. Fed. Holicy Commn., 1991-93, 94—. Lt. USAF, 1951-55; capt. USAFR,. Recipient Rosewood Gavel award St. Mary's U. Sch. Law, San Antonio, 1982, Disting. Alumni award Baylor U., Golden Plate award Am. Acad. Achievement, 1988, Law Enforcement

Leadership award Assn. Fed. Investigators, 1989, medal of honor DAR, 1989, Disting. Eagle Scout award Boy Scouts Am., 1990, Person of Yr. award Am. Soc. for Indsl. Security, 1990, Magna Charta award Baronial Order of Magna Charta, 1990; named Lawyer of Yr., Baylor Law Sch., 1988, Father of Yr., Nat. Fathers Day Com., 1988, Ellis Island Congl. Medal of Honor, 1992. Mem. ABA, Jud. Conf. U.S. (com. on ct. adminstrn., chmn. jud. improvements subcom. 1983-85, ad hoc com. on automation to subcom., 1984-87, mem. ad hoc ct. reporter com. 1984-87), San Antonio Bar Assn. (bd. dirs. 1973-74), Fed. Bar Assn. (pres. San Antonio sect. 1974), Am. Judicature Soc. (exec. com. 1982-84), Dist. Judges Assn. of 5th Cir. (pres. 1982-83), State Bar of Tex. (chmn. com. to develop procedures for cert. state law questions to Supreme Ct. by Fed. Cts. 1983-85), Waco McLennan County Bar Assn. (pres. 1968), San Antonio Inns of Cts. XX (pres. 1986). Republican. Methodist. Avocations: hiking, climbing, canoeing. Office: 3920 Argyle Ter NW Washington DC 20011-5329 also: Sessions Sessions et al 30th Fl Weston Ctr 112 E Pecan San Antonio TX 75208

SESSLE, BARRY JOHN, university administrator, researcher; b. Sydney, New South Wales, Australia, May 28, 1941; immigrated to Can., 1971; s. Frederick George and Sadie Isobel (Lawson) S.; m. Mary Baldwin; children from previous marriage: Erica Jane, Claire Marie. B.D.S., Sydney U., New South Wales, 1963, M.D.S., 1965, B.Sc., 1965; Ph.D., U. New South Wales, 1969. Scholar Dental Found. Sydney U., 1963-64; teaching fellow U. New South Wales, 1965-68; vis. assoc. U.S. Nat. Inst. Dental Research, Bethesda, Md., 1968-70; assoc. prof. U. Toronto Dental Sch., Ont., Can., 1971-76, prof., 1976-85, chmn. div. biol. scis., 1978-84, assoc. dean research, 1985-90, dean, 1990—; mem. com. on dental scis. Can. Med. Research Council, Ottawa, 1979-82. Author: The Neural Basis of Oral and Facial Function, 1978; editor: Mastication and Swallowing, 1976, Oro-facial Pain and Neuromuscular Dysfunction, 1985, Effects of Injury of Trigeminal and Spinal Samotosensory Systems, 1987, Trigeminal Neuralgia: Current Concepts Regarding Pathogenesis and Treatment, 1991, Temporomandibular Joint and Masticatory Muscle Disorders, 1994, Temporomandibular Disorders and Related Pain Conditions, 1995; mem. editorial adv. bd. Arch. Oral Biol. Jour., 1988—; mem. editorial adv. bd. panel Pain Jour., 1986-90, assoc. editor, 1990-93; mem. editorial bd. Dysphagia Jour., 1990—; contbr. articles to profl. jours. Recipient Tchr. award Can. Fund for Dental Edn.; grantee Canadian Med. Research Council, 1971—, NIH, 1974—. Mem. Internat. Assn. Study Pain (sec. Can. chpt. 1982-87, mem. coun. 1993—), Soc. Neurosci. (pres. South Ont. chpt. 1982-83), Internat. Assn. Dental Rsch. (pres. Can. divsn. 1977-78, sec.-treas. 1976-79, pres. neurosci. group 1985-86, pres. 1994-95, Oral Sci. award 1976, Pindborg ORal Biol. prize 1994), Internat. Union Physiol. Sci. (sec. oral physiology commn. 1983—). Office: Faculty Dentistry U Toronto, 124 Edward St, Toronto, ON Canada M5G 1G6

SESSLER, ANDREW MARIENHOFF, physicist; b. Bklyn., Dec. 11, 1928; s. David and Mary (Baron) S.; m. Gladys Lerner, Sept. 23, 1951 (div. Dec. 1994); children: Daniel Ira, Jonathan Lawrence, Ruth. BA in Math. cum laude, Harvard U., 1949; MA in Theoretical Physics, Columbia U., 1951, PhD in Theoretical Physics, 1953. NSF fellow Cornell U., N.Y., 1953-54; asst. prof. Ohio State U., Columbus, 1954, assoc. prof., 1960; on leave Midwestern Univs. Research, 1955-56; vis. physicist Lawrence Rediation Lab., 1959-60, Niels Bohr Inst., Copenhagen, summer 1961; researcher theoretical physics U. Calif. Lawrence Berkeley Lab., Berkeley, 1961-73, researcher energy and environment, 1971-73, dir., 1973-80; sr. scientist plasma physics, 1980—; U.S. advisor Panjab U. Physics Inst., Chandigarh, India; mem. U.S.-India Coop. Program for Improvement Sci. Edn. in India, 1966, high energy physics adv. panel to U.S. AEC, 1969-72, adv. com. Lawrence Hall Sci., 1974-78; chmn. Stanford Synchrotron Radiation Project Sci. Policy Bd., 1974-77, EPRI Advanced Fuels Adv. Com., 1978-81, BNL External Adv. Com. on Isabelle, 1980-82; mem. sci. pol. bd. Stanford Synchrotron Radiation Lab., 1991-92; LJ. Haworth dist. scientist Brookhaven Nat. Lab., 1991—. Mem. editorial bd. Nuclear Instruments and Methods, 1969—; correspondent Comments on Modern Physics, 1969-71; contbr. articles in field to profl. jours. Mem. hon. adv. bd. Inst. Advanced Phys. Studies, LaJolla Internat. Sch. Physics, 1991—; mem. Superconducting Super Collider Sci. Policy Com., 1991-94. Recipient E.O. Lawrence award U.S. Atomic Energy Commn., 1970, U.S. Particle Accelerator Sch. prize, 1988; fellow Japan Soc. for Promotion Sci. at KEK, 1985. Fellow AAAS (nominating com. 1984-87), Am. Phys. Soc. (chmn. com. internat. freedom scientist 1982, study of directed energy weapons panel 1985-87, chmn. panel pub. affairs 1988, chmn. div. physics of beams 1990, chmn. com. applications of physics 1993); mem. NAS, IEEE, Fedn. Am. Scientists Coun. (vice chmn. 1987-88, chmn. 1988-92), N.Y. Acad. Sci., Assoc. Univ. Inc. (bd. dirs. 1991-94). Home: 225 Clifton St Apt 313 Oakland CA 94618-1468 Office: U Calif Lawrence Berkeley Labb 1 Cyclotron Rd M/S 71-259 Berkeley CA 94720

SESSOMS, ALLEN LEE, academic administrator, former diplomat, physicist; b. N.Y.C., Nov. 17, 1946; s. Albert Earl and Lottie Beatrice (Leff) S.; m. Csilla Manette von Csiky, Apr. 18, 1990; children: Manon Elizabeth, Stephanie Csilla. BS, Union Coll., Schenectady, N.Y., 1968; PhD, Yale U., 1972. Sci. assoc. CERN, Geneva, Switzerland, 1973-78; asst. prof. physics Harvard U., Cambridge, Mass., 1974-81; sr. tech. advisor OES, State Dept., Washington, 1980-82; dir. Office Nuclear Tech. & Safeguards, State Dept., Washington, 1982-87; counselor for sci. and tech. U.S. Embassy, Paris, 1987-89; polit. minister, counselor U.S. Embassy, Mexico City, 1989-91, dep. chief of mission, 1991-93; exec. v.p., v.p. for acad. affairs U. Mass. Sys., Boston, 1993-95; pres. CUNY Queens Coll., Flushing, N.Y., 1995—; mem. adv. com. U.S. Sec. Energy. Contbr. articles to profl. jours. Adv. com. mem. U.S. Sec. of Energy. Ford Found. travel/study grantee, 1973-74; Alfred P. Sloan Found. fellow, 1977-81. Mem. AAAS, Am. Phys. Soc., N.Y. Acad. Sci., Cosmos Club. Office: Pres Office Queens Coll CUNY 65-30 Kissena Blvd Flushing NY 11367-1597

SESSOMS, STUART MCGUIRE, physician, educator, retired insurance company executive; b. Autryville, N.C., July 16, 1921; s. Edwin Tate and Lillian Olive (Howard) S.; m. Thelma Ernestine Catil, June 21, 1944; children: Stuart McGuire, Cristi Kay. B.S., U. N.C., 1943; M.D., Med. Coll. Va., 1946; postgrad., Johns Hopkins U. Diplomate: Am. Bd. Internal Medicine. Intern U.S. Marine Hosp., Balt., 1946-47; resident internal medicine U.S. Marine Hosp., 1947-50, asst. chief med. service, charge med. outpatient dept., 1950-52; asst. resident medicine Meml. Center Cancer and Allied Diseases, N.Y.C., 1952-53; with NIH, Bethesda, Md., 1953-68; mem. clin. medicine, surgery Nat. Cancer Inst., 1953-54, acting chief gen. medicine, 1954, asst. dir., 1958, asso. dir. collaborative research, 1961-62; chief cancer chemotherapy Nat. Service Center, 1958-62; asst. dir. clin. center NIH, 1955-57, dep. dir., 1962-68; clin. instr. medicine George Washington U., 1953-54; asso. dean, prof. medicine Duke Sch. Medicine, Durham, 1968-75; dir. Duke U. Hosp., 1968-75, prof. health adminstrn., 1973-75; sr. v.p. Blue Cross and Blue Shield of N.C., 1976-87. Contbr. articles to profl. jours. Active PTA. Recipient Distinguished Service award U.S. Jr. C. of C., 1957. Mem. AMA, Assn. Mil. Surgeons U.S., Am. Hosp. Assn., N.C. hosp. assns., Am. Pub. Health Assn., N.Y. Acad. Sci., Phi Delta Chi, Rho Chi, Alpha Kappa Kappa. Presbyterian. Home: 3432 Dover Rd Durham NC 27707-4520

SESSOMS, WALTER WOODROW, telecommunications executive; b. Darlington, S.C., Jan. 14, 1934; s. Frank Darlington and Maggie (Garrison) S.; m. HArriet Floyd, June 14, 1957; children: Lee, Kay. BA, Wofford Coll., 1956. Asst. engr. So. Bell, Columbia, S.C., 1956-64; forecast supr. So. Bell, Greenville, S.C., 1964-65; mgr. pub. rels. So. Bell, Spartanburg, S.C., 1965-66; dist. engr. So. Bell, Florence, S.C., 1967-69; gen. mktg. mgr. So. Bell, Charlotte, N.C., 1969-75; v.p. So. Bell, Miami, Fla., 1975-79; v.p. So. Bell, Atlanta, 1979-89, sr. v.p., 1989-91; fin. supr. AT&T, N.Y.C., 1969-73; pres. svcs. group BellSouth Telecomm. Inc., Atlanta, 1991—; practitioner, lectr. U. Ga., Athens, 1984—. Trustee Ga. Bd. Edn., Atlanta, 1989—; chmn. bd. trustees Wofford Coll., Spartanburg, 1990-91; chmn. bd. dirs. Metro Atlanta chpt. Salvation Army, 1990—; chmn. Atlanta Partnership Bus. and Edn., 1990-91; mem. Ga. Edn. 2000, 1991—. 1st lt. U.S. Army, 1957-59. Recipient U.S. Fed. Govt. Pres. Outstanding Svc. award, 1974. Mem. Telephone Pioneers of Am. (sr. vice pres., 1995), Ga. C. of C. (bd. dirs. 1991-92), Presdl. Exec. Interexch. Assn., Commerce Club, Ashford Club, Rotary. Methodist. Home: 5995 River Chase Cir NW Atlanta GA 30328-3562 Office: BellSouth Telecomm 675 W Peachtree St NW Rm 4502 Atlanta GA 30308-1952

SESTINI, VIRGIL ANDREW, biology educator; b. Las Vegas, Nov. 24, 1936; s. Santi and Merceda Francesca (Borla) S. BS in Edn., U. Nev., 1959; postgrad., Oreg. State U., 1963-64; MNS, U. Idaho, 1965; postgrad., Ariz. State U., 1967, No. Ariz. U., 1969; cert. tchr.; Nev. Tchr. biology Rancho High Sch., 1960-76; sci. chmn., tchr. biology Bonanza High Sch., Las Vegas, 1976-90; ret., 1990; co-founder, curator exhibits Meadows Mus. Nat. History, 1993-94; part time tchr. Meadows Sch., 1987-94; ret., 1994; edn. specialist, cell biologist SAGE Rsch., Las Vegas, 1993. Served with USAR, 1959-65. Recipient Rotary Internat. Honor Tchr. award, 1965, Region VIII Outstanding Biology Tchr. award, 1970, Nev. Outstanding Biology Tchr. award Nat. Assn. Biology Tchrs., 1970, Nat. Assn. Sci. Tchrs., Am. Gas Assn. Sci. Teaching Achievement Recognition award, 1976, 1980, Gustov Ohaus award, 1980, Presdl. Honor Sci. Tchr. award, 1983; Excellence in Edn. award Nev. Dept. Edn., 1983; Presdl. award excellence in math. and sci. teaching, 1984, Celebration of Excellence award Nev. Com. on Excellence in Edn., 1986, Hall of Fame award Clark County Sch. Dist., 1988, Excellence in Edn. award, Clark County Sch. Dist., 1987, 88, Spl. Edn. award Clark County Sch. Dist., 1988, NSEA Mini-grants, 1988, 89, 92, World Decoration of Excellence medallion World Inst. Achievement, 1989, Cert. Spl. Congl. Recognition, 1989, Senatorial Recognition , 1989, minigrant Jr. League Las Vegas, 1989, Excellence in Edn. award, Clark Country Sch. Dist., 1989; named Nev. Educator of Yr., Milken Family Found./Nev. State Dept. Edn., 1989; grantee Nev. State Bd. Edn., 1988, 89, Nev. State Edn. Assn., 1988-89. Author: Lab Investigations For High School Honors Biology, 1989, Microbiology: A Manual for High School Biology, 1992, Laboratory Investigations in Microbiology, 1992; co-author: A Biology Lab Manual For Cooperative Learning, 1989, Metrics and Science Methods: A Manual of Lab Experiments for Home Schoolers, 1990, Experimental Designs in Biology I: Botany and Zoology, 1993, Designs in Biology: A Lab Manual, 1993, Integrated Science Lab Manual, 1994; contbr. articles to profl. jours. Mem. AAAS, NEA, Nat. Assn. Taxidermists, Nat. Sci. Tchrs. Assn. (life, Nev. State chpt. 1968-70), Nat. Assn. Biology Tchrs. (life, OBTA dir. Nev. State 1991—), Am. Soc. Microbiology, Coun. for Exceptional Children, Am. Biographic Inst. (rsch. bd. advisors 1988), Nat. Audubon Assn., Nat. Sci. Suprs. Assn., Am. Inst. Biol. Scis., So. Nev. Scale Modlers (coord. Modeloberfest, 1995). Avocations: scale models, military figures, scale model circus, photography, chess.

SESTRIC, ANTHONY JAMES, lawyer; b. St. Louis, June 27, 1940; s. Anton and Marie (Gasparovic) S.; student, Georgetown U., 1958-62; JD, Mo. U., 1965; m. Carol F. Bowman, Nov. 24, 1966; children: Laura Antonette, Holly Nicole, Michael Anthony. Bar: Mo. 1965, U.S. Ct. Appeals (8th cir.) 1965, U.S. Dist. Ct. Mo. 1966, U.S. Tax Ct. 1969, U.S. Supreme Ct. 1970, U.S. Ct. Appeals (7th cir.) 1984, U.S. Dist. Ct. (no. dist.) Tex. 1985, U.S. Claims Ct. 1986. U.S. Dist. Ct. Ill., 1994. Law clk. U.S. Dist. Ct., St. Louis, 1965-66; ptnr. firm Sestric, McGhee & Miller, St. Louis, 1966-77; spl. asst. to Mo. atty. gen., St. Louis, 1968; ptnr. Fordyce and Mayne, 1977-78, Sestric & Garvey, St. Louis, 1978—; hearing officer St. Louis Met. Police Dept.; active Fed. Jud. Selection Commn., 1993. Contbr. articles to profl. jours. Mem. exec. com. Nat. Caucus of State Bar Leaders, 1987-90; mem. Fed. Judicial Commn., 1993, mem. St. Louis Air Pollution Bd. Appeals and Varience Rev., 1974-83, chmn., 1968-73; mem. St. Louis Airport Commn., 1975-76; dist. vice chmn. Boy Scouts Am., 1970-76; bd. dirs. Full Achievement, Inc., 1970-77; bd. dirs. Legal Aid Soc. of St. Louis, 1976-77, Law Library Assn. St. Louis, 1976-78; v.p. bd. St. Elizabeth Acad., 1985-86; mem. bd. dirs. Thomas Dunn Memls., 1995—; mem. U.S. Judicial Selections Commn., 1993—. Mem. ABA (state chmn. judiciary com. 1973-75, cir. chmn. com. condemnation, zoning and property use 1975-77, standing com. bar activities 1982-88), Nat. Conf. Bar Pres.'s (exec. coun. 1987-90), Mo. Bar (vice chmn. young lawyers sect. 1973-76, bd. govs. 1974-77), Bar Assn. Met. St. Louis (chmn. young lawyers sect. 1974-75, exec. com. 1974-83, 94-95, pres. 1981-82). Home: 3967 Holly Hills Blvd Saint Louis MO 63116-3135 Office: Sestric & Garvey 22 Morgan St Saint Louis MO 63102-2558

SETAPEN, JAMES ANTHONY, orchestra conductor; b. N.Y.C., Nov. 8, 1948; s. Fred Albert and Agatha Marguerite (Di Lascio) S.; m. Carol Susan Feinblatt, Sept. 2, 1979; children: Ilana Michelle, Adam Michael. MusB, Eastman Sch. Music, Rochester, N.Y., 1970; MusM, Cleve. Inst. Mus., 1975. Asst. condr. Omaha Symphony Orch., 1975-76; prin. condr. Cleve. Opera Theater, 1976-78; condr. U. Ala. Symphony, Tuscaloosa, 1976-78; asst. condr. Oakland (Calif.) Symphony Orch., 1978-80; Exxon Arts endowment condr. Denver Symphony Orch., 1980-83, assoc. condr., 1983-88; music dir., condr. Amarillo (Tex.) Symphony Orch., 1988—. Contbr. articles to profl. jours. With U.S. Army, 1970-73. Recipient Cert. of Appreciation Gov. Roy Romer of Colo., 1988. Mem. Condrs. Guild (bd. dirs.). Office: Amarillo Symphony Orch PO Box 2552 Amarillo TX 79105-2552

SETENCICH, ELI JOHN, columnist; b. Sacramento, Apr. 10, 1924; s. Joko Ilija and Jovanka (Ljcsovic) S.; m. Elizabeth Jackson (div.); m. Yvonne Dillon, Sept. 4, 1965; children: Stephen, Amy Lynn. BA in Journalism, U. Calif., Berkeley, 1952. Reporter Walnut Creek (Calif.) Sun, 1952-54, KFRE radio-TV, Fresno, Calif., 1954-61; polit. writer Fresno Bee, 1961-80, columnist, 1980—. Author: Fresno, California's Heartland, 1993. Capt. USAF, 1942-45, ETO. Avocations: tennis, cooking, travel. Office: The Fresno Bee 1626 E St Fresno CA 93706

SETH, OLIVER, federal judge; b. Albuquerque, May 30, 1915; s. Julien Orem and Bernice (Grefe) S.; m. Jean MacGillivray, Sept. 25, 1946; children: Sandra Bernice, Laurel Jean. A.B. Stanford U., 1937; LL.B. Yale U., 1940. Bar: N.Mex. 1940. Practice law Santa Fe, 1940, 46-62; judge U.S. Ct. Appeals 10th Circuit, 1962—, chief judge from 1976, now senior judge; dir. Santa Fe Nat. Bank, 1949-62; chmn. legal com. N.Mex. Oil and Gas Assn., 1956-59, mem. regulatory practices com., 1960-62; counsel N.Mex. Cattlegrowers Assn., 1950-62, N.Mex. Bankers Assn., 1952-62; govt. appeal agent SSS, 1948-52. Mem. bd. regents Mus. of N.Mex., 1956-60; Bd. dirs. Boys Club, Santa Fe, 1948-49, New Mex. Land Resources Assn., 1956-60, Ghost Ranch Mus., 1962—; mng. bd. Sch. Am. Research, 1950— Served from pvt. to maj. AUS, 1940-45, ETO. Decorated Croix de Guerre (France). Mem. Santa Fe C. of C. (dir.), N.Mex., Santa Fe County bar assns., Phi Beta Kappa. Presbyterian. Office: US Ct Appeals 10th Circuit PO Drawer I Santa Fe NM 87504*

SETH, VIKRAM, writer; b. Calcutta, India, June 20, 1952; s. Premnath and Leila S. BA, Corpus Christi Coll., 1975, MA, 1978; MA, Stanford U., 1977; attended, Nanjing U., China, 1982. Sr. editor Stanford U. Press, Calif., 1985-86. Author: Mappings, 1980, From Heaven Lake: Travels Through Sinkiang and Tibet, 1983 (Thomas Cook Travel Book award 1983), The Humble Administrator's Garden, 1985 (Commonwealth Poetry Prize Asian Region 1985), The Golden Gate, 1986 (New Voice award Quality Paperback Book Club 1986, Commonwealth Poetry Prize Asian Region 1986), All You Who Sleep Tonight, 1990, A Suitable Boy: A Novel, 1993, Three Chinese Poets, 1993, Beastly Tales from Here and There, 1994, Arion and the Dolphin, 1995. Ingram Merrill fellow, 1985-86, Guggenheim fellow, 1986-87. Office: c/o HarperCollins Pubs Inc 10 E 53rd St New York NY 10022-5244*

SETHI, SHYAM SUNDER, management consultant; b. Rawalpindi, Pakistan, July 11, 1942; s. Balraj and Shakuntala (Sawhney) S.; m. Kiran Nair, Oct. 17, 1972; children: Seema, Shana. B.E. in Mech. Engring., Birla Inst. Tech., Ranchi, India, 1964; M.S.I.E., U. Wis., 1970. Cert. mgmt. cons. V.p. Drake Sheahan/Stewart Dougall, N.Y.C., 1970-80; pres., ptnr. Distbn. Mgmt. Assocs., Inc., Princeton, N.J., 1980—; cons. in logistics, inventory mgmt., ops. for maj. indsl. cos. and retailers, Europe, S.Am. and U.S.; spkr. internat. logistics conf. Contbr. articles to profl. jours. Pres. N.J. chpt. Coun. Logistics Mgmt., 1987-88, N.J. chpt. Inst. Mgmt. Consultants, 1987-88. Mem. Yacht Assn. India. Hindu. Avocations: tennis, sailing. Home: 4 Haelig Ct Bridgewater NJ 08807-2377 Office: Distbn Mgmt Assocs Inc 22 Wall St Princeton NJ 08540-1513

SETHNA, BEHERUZ NARIMAN, college president, marketing/management educator; b. Bombay, July 31, 1948; came to U.S., 1973; s. Nariman Dhanjishaw and Mithu Nariman (Mistry) S.; m. Madhavi Kaji, May 25, 1974; children: Anita B., Shaun B. B in Tech. with honors, Indian Inst. Tech., Bombay, 1971; MBA, Indian Inst. Mgmt., Ahmedabad, 1973; MPhil, Columbia U., 1975, PhD in Bus., 1976; cert., Ind. U., 1986, Harvard U. Inst. Educ. Mgmt., 1991. Engring. and mgmt. trainee various corps., Bombay,

1968-69, 70-72; case writer, trainee Clarion Advt., Bombay, 1973; project mgr., cons. Lever Bros. Co., N.Y.C., 1974-76; prof., chair mktg. and mgmt. info. systems Clarkson U., Potsdam, N.Y., 1976-89, dir. grad. programs, 1978-80; mktg., rsch. and strategic planning mgr. Procter & Gamble (India)/Richardson Hindustan (Vicks), Bombay and Westport, Conn., 1980-81; interim exec. v.p. acad. and student affairs; interim exec. v.p. ASA; dean Coll. of Bus. and chief academic officer Lamar (Tex.) U., 1989-94, Gulf States Utilities prof. bus., 1991-94; pres. West Ga. Coll., Carrollton, 1994—; mem. adv. coun. SUNY-Canton (N.Y.) Coll., 1975-89; cons. in field. Author: Research Methods in Marketing, 1984; contbr. articles to profl. jours. Scoutmaster Boy Scouts Am., Potsdam, 1987-89, pack com. chair, den leader, 1987-89; mem. Ant. Task Force for Lebanon, 1988—; leader Girl Scouts U.S., Beaumont, 1989—. Recipient Instrl. Innovation award Decision Scis. Inst., 1984, 85, 86, 87, 88, 89, Pres.'s Scout Gold Cord, Boy Scouts Am., 1966, Minority Achiever's award Role Model award, 1991, Dean's Leadership award Acad. of Bus. Adminstrn., 1993; Fulbright scholar U.S. Info. Agy., 1986-87; U.S. Dept. Energy grantee, 1980, IBM Corp. grantee, 1984, AT&T grantee 1985. Mem. Decision Scis. Inst., Rotary (polio plus edn. chair). Avocations: family, scouting. Home: 1903 Maple St Carrollton GA 30117 Home: 1903 Maple St Carrollton GA 30117 Office: Office of Pres West Ga Coll Carrollton GA 30118-4500

SETHNESS, CHARLES OLIN, international financial official; b. Evanston, Ill., Feb. 24, 1941; s. Charles Olin and Alison Louise (Burge) S.; 1 son, Peter Worcester; m. Geraldine Greene, June 25, 1977; stepchildren: John, Carla, Sarah Houseman. A.B., Princeton U., 1963; M.B.A. with high distinction (Baker scholar), Harvard U., 1966. Sr. credit analyst Am. Nat. Bank & Trust Co., Chgo., 1963-64; research asst. Harvard Bus. Sch., 1966-67; assoc. Morgan Stanley & Co., N.Y.C., 1967-71; v.p. Morgan Stanley & Co., 1972, mng. dir., 1975-81; mgr. Morgan & Cie Internat., S.A., Paris, 1971-73; U.S. exec. dir. World Bank; and spl. asst. to sec. treasury Washington, 1973-75; assoc. dean for external relations Harvard U. Bus. Sch., Boston, 1981-85; asst. sec. treasury for domestic fin. Dept. Treasury, Washington, 1985-88; dir. capital markets dept. Internat. Fin. Corp., 1988-89; chief fin. officer Inter-Am. Devel. Bank, 1990—. Home: 6219 Garnett Dr Bethesda MD 20815-6617 Office: Inter-Am Devel Bank 1300 New York Ave NW Washington DC 20577-0001

SETLOW, JANE KELLOCK, biophysicist; b. N.Y.C., Dec. 17, 1919; d. Harold A. and Alberta (Thompson) Kellock; m. Richard Setlow, June 6, 1941; children—Peter, Michael, Katherine, Charles. B.A., Swarthmore Coll., 1940; Ph.D. in Biophysics, Yale U., 1959. With dept. radiology Yale U., 1959-60; with biology div. Oak Ridge Nat. Lab., 1960-74; biophysicist Brookhaven Nat. Lab., Upton, N.Y., 1974—; mem. recombinant DNA molecule program adv. com. NIH, chmn., 1978-80. Author articles; mem. editorial bd. jours. Predoctoral fellow USPHS, 1957-59; postdoctoral fellow, 1960-62. Mem. Biophys. Soc. (pres. 1977-78), Am. Soc. Microbiology. Democrat. Home: 57 Valentine Rd Shoreham NY 11786-1243 Office: Biology Dept Brookhaven Nat Lab Upton NY 11973

SETLOW, RICHARD BURTON, biophysicist; b. N.Y.C., Jan. 19, 1921; s. Charles Meyer and Elsie (Hurwitz) S.; children: Peter, Michael, Katherine, Charles; m. Neva Delihas, Mar. 3, 1989. AB, Swarthmore Coll., 1941; PhD, Yale U., 1947; DSc, U. Toronto, 1985; MD, U. Essen, 1993. Assoc. prof. Yale U., 1956-61; biophysicist Oak Ridge (Tenn.) Nat. Lab., 1961-74, sci. dir. biophysics and cell physiology, 1969-74; dir. U. Tenn.-Oak Ridge Grad. Sch. Biomed. Scis., 1972-74; sr. biophysicist Brookhaven Nat. Lab., Upton, N.Y., 1974—, chmn. biology dept., 1979-87, assoc. dir. life scis., 1985—; prof. biomed. scis. U. Tenn., 1967-74; adj. prof. biochemistry SUNY, Stony Brook, 1975—. Author: (with E.C. Pollard) Molecular Biophysics, 1962; editor: (with P.C. Hanawalt) Molecular Mechanisms for Repair of DNA, 1975. Recipient Finsen medal Internat. Assn. Photobiology, 1980, Enrico Fermi award U.S. Dept. Energy, 1988. Mem. NAS, Am. Acad. Arts and Scis., Biophys. Soc. (pres. 1969-70), Internat. Com. Photobiology (pres. 1972-76), Radiation Rsch. Soc., Am. Soc. Photobiology, Am. Soc. Biochemistry and Molecular Biology, Am. Soc. Cancer Rsch., Environ. Mutagen Soc., 11th Internat. Congress on Photobiology (hon. pres. 1992), Phi Beta Kappa. Home: 4 Beachland Ave East Quogue NY 11942-4941 Office: Brookhaven Nat Lab Dept Biology Upton NY 11973

SETO, JOSEPH TOBEY, virologist, educator; b. Tacoma, Aug. 3, 1924; s. Toraichi and Kiyo Morita Seto; m. Grace K. Nakano, Aug. 9, 1959; children: Susan L., Steven F. BS, U. Minn., 1949; MS, U. Wis., 1955, PhD, 1957. Postdoctoral fellow UCLA, 1958-59; asst. prof. San Francisco State U., 1959-60; prof. microbiology Calif. State U., L.A., 1960-88, prof. emeritus, 1988; cons. U.S. Naval Biology Lab., Oakland, Calif., 1959-61; vis. prof. Inst. Virology, Giessen, Fed. Republic Germany, 1965-66, 72-73, 79-80, 86-87, NATO sr. scientist, 1972, WHO Exchange Worker, 1972. Sgt. U.S. Army, 1945-46. United Health Found. fellow, 1965; recipient Humboldt Found. award 1972, 86, Humboldt Found. medal 1991. Fellow Am. Soc. Microbiology; mem. AAAS, Microscopy Soc. Am., Sigma Xi. Office: Calif State U Dept Microbiology Los Angeles CA 90032-8201

SETO, WILLIAM RODERICK, public accounting company executive; b. N.Y.C., July 2, 1954; s. James and Dorothy (Tsang) S. BS, U. Pa., 1976; JD, Cornell Law Sch., 1979. Bar: N.Y. 1980; CPA. Ptnr. Ernst & Young, Atlanta; S.E. area dir. internat. tax, 1986-88; Ernst & Young, Atlanta, 1988—; lectr. in field. Mem. editl. bd. Atlanta Internat. Mag., 1992-94. Mem. ABA, AICPAs, N.Y. Bar Assn., Soc. Internat. Bus. Fellows, Leadership Atlanta, Internat. Fiscal Assn., FSC/DISC Tax Assn. (bd. advisors). Office: Ernst & Young 2800 Nations Bank Plz 600 Peachtree St Atlanta GA 30308

SETON, CHARLES B., lawyer; b. Bridgeport, Conn., Oct. 1, 1910; s. Charles Hillison and Stella (Rosen) Shapiro; m. Suzanne Alexia Maimin, Mar. 7, 1948; children: Pam Elinor Seton Lorenzo, Charles B. B.A., Yale U., 1931, LL.B., 1934. Bar: N.Y. 1934. Pvt. practice N.Y., 1934-55, Larchmont, N.Y., 1955—; assoc. firm Rosenman, Goldmark, Colin & Kaye (and predecessors), 1935-51; partner Rosen & Seton, 1955-58, 74-79, Rosen, Seton & Sarbin, 1958-74; sec. Ziff-Davis Pub. Co., 1974-77, gen. counsel, 1958-79; sec. Ziff Corp., 1976-77; ann. guest lectr. Advanced Copyright Seminar, N.Y. U. Law Sch., 1953-76, Practising Law Inst., 1955-74; past chmn. bd. trustees Fed. Bar Coun.; mem. Consular Law Soc., 1959-91. Participating author: The Business and Law of Music, 1965, Internat. Music Industry Conference, 1969; contbr. articles to profl. jours. Vice pres., founding dir. Music for Westchester, Inc., 1962-75, Arthur Judson Found., Inc., 1959—, founding trustee Copyright Soc. U.S., v.p., chmn. Copyright Luncheon Circle (co-chmn., 1952-82). Lt. comdr. USNR, 1942-45. Mem. ABA, Westchester County Bar Assn. (profl. econs. com.), assoc. at Bar of City of N.Y., Guadalcanal Campaign Vets. (N.Y. state rep. 1987-92), Mory's Club, Yale Club, Victory Svcs. Club. Home: 33 W Putnam Ave Greenwich CT 06830-5328 Office: Seton Law Office Ste 403 Larchmont NY 10538-3031

SETON, FENMORE ROGER, manufacturing company executive, civic worker; b. Bridgeport, Conn., Nov. 27, 1917; m. Phyllis Winifred Zimmerman, Apr. 5, 1942; 1 child, Diana Seton Adams Wakerley. BA in English, Yale U., 1938; EdM, So. Conn. State Coll./Yale U., 1956; LLD (hon.), U. New Haven, 1990; DHL (hon.), Albertus Magnus Coll., 1994. Asst. prof. air sci. and tactics Yale U., New Haven, 1952-56; pres., chief exec. officer Seton Name Plate Co., 1946-81; pres. Nat. Assn. Metal Etchers, Washington, 1968-69, Internat. Mktg. Device Assn., Chgo., 1973-74, mfrs. div. New Haven C. of C., 1974-79; chmn. Am. Nat. Standards Com. A13, N.Y.C., 1972-82. Apptd. Pres.'s Com. on Employment of People With Disabilities, Washington, 1973—; world pres. Rehab. Internat., World Secretariat in N.Y.C., 1988-92; bd. govs. U. New Haven, 1979—; treas. Save the Children Fedn., Westport, Conn., 1984-88; assoc. fellow Calhoun Coll. Yale U., 1976—. Recipient Citation of Honor Sec. HEW, Washington, 1976, Preminger medallion People-To-People program Com. for Handicapped, Washington, 1988, Elm and Ivy award Yale U., 1985, Pub. Svc.award Social Security Adminstrn., 1992, Yale medal Pres. Yale U. on behalf of Bd. Govs. Assn. Yale Alumni, 1992, Disting. Svc. award Pres. of U.S. 1992. Fellow Inst. Dirs. (U.K.); mem. Cercle de l'Union Interallié (Paris), Explorers Club (N.Y.C.), Circumnavigators Club (N.Y.C.), Elizabethan Club (New Haven), Mory's Assn. (New Haven), New Haven Country Club. Republican. Home: 2 Old Orchard Rd North Haven CT 06473-3022

SETRAKIAN, BERGE, lawyer; b. Beirut, Lebanon, Apr. 14, 1949; came to U.S. 1976; s. Hemayak and Arminee S.; m. Vera L. Nazarian, Nov. 22, 1975; children: Ani, Lara. Diplome d'Etudes de Doctorat, U. Lyons, France, 1973; Diplome d'Etudes de Doctorat Droit Compare, F.I.E.D.C., Strasbourg, France, 1974; Licence en Droit Francais, U. St. Joseph, Beirut, 1972, Licence en Droit Libanais, 1972. Bar: Beirut 1972, N.Y. 1983. Assoc. Tyan & Setrakian, Beirut, 1972-76; ptnr. Whitman & Ransom, N.Y.C., 1976-93, Whitman, Breed, Abbott & Morgan, N.Y.C., 1993—; bd. dirs. Bank Audi (Calif.), 1987—, Bank Audi (USA), 1991; fgn. law cons., N.Y., 1978. Bd. dirs., v.p., sec. Armenian Gen. Benevolent Union, N.Y.C., 1977—; pres. Worldwide Youth orgns., 1978—; bd. dirs. Armenian Assy. of Am., Washington, 1978-87; mem. Am. Task Force for Lebanon, 1988—; bd. dirs. Am. U. Armenia, 1992—. Mem. ABA, N.Y. Bar Assn., Beirut Bar Assn., U.K. Law Soc., Am. Fgn. Law Assn., Englewood Field Club. Office: Whitman Breed Abbott Morgan 200 Park Ave New York NY 10166-0001

SETSER, CAROLE SUE, food science educator; b. Warrenton, Mo., Aug. 26, 1940; d. Wesley August and Mary Elizabeth (Meine) Schulze; m. Donald Wayne Setser, June 2, 1969; children: Bradley Wayne, Kirk Wesley, Brett Donald. BS, U. Mo., 1962; MS, Cornell U., 1964; PhD, Kans. State U., 1971. Grad. asst. Cornell U., Ithaca, N.Y., 1962-64; instr. Kans. State U., Manhattan, 1964-72, asst. prof., 1974-81, assoc. prof., 1981-86, prof., 1986—. Recipient Rsch. Excellence award Coll. of Human Ecology, Manhattan, 1990. Mem. Am. Assn.Cereal Chemists (assoc. editor 1989-93), Inst. Food Techs. (chmn. sensory evaluation divsn. edn. com. 1989-92, continuing edn. com. 1992—, other offices), Kappa Omicron Nu (Excellence for Rsch. award 1987), Sigma Xi, Phi Upsilon Omicron, Gamma Sigma Delta, Phi Tau Sigma. Office: Kansas State U Justin Hall Dept Foods Nutrition Manhattan KS 66506

SETSER, DONALD WAYNE, chemistry educator; b. Great Bend, Kans., Jan. 2, 1935; s. Leo Wayne and Velma Irene (Hewitt) S.; m. Carole Sue Schulze, June 2, 1969; children: Bradley Wayne, Kirk Wesley, Brett Donald. BS, Kans. State U., 1956, MS, 1958; PhD, U. Wash., 1961. Asst. prof. Kans. State U., Manhattan, 1963-66, assoc. prof., 1966-68, prof. chemistry, 1968—, Alumni Disting. prof. chemistry, 1984—; vis. prof. U. Grenoble, France, 1981, 84, 87, 91. Editor Reactive Intermediates, 1976; contbr. 240 articles to profl. jours. Recipient Rank prize electro-optics divsn., 1992. Fellow Am. Phys. Soc.; mem. Am. Chem. Soc. (Midwest award St. Louis sect. 1984), British Chem. Soc. Home: 414 Wickham Rd Manhattan KS 66502-3751 Office: Kans State U Dept Of Chemistry Manhattan KS 66506

SETTIPANI, FRANK G., news correspondent; b. Bklyn., July 18, 1948; s. Gaspare and Marion (Caronna) S.; m. Laura A. Czachor, Aug. 21, 1982; children: Cara, Paul. BA in Polit. Sci., Bklyn. Coll., 1968. Reporter UPI, N.Y.C., 1969-70; anchor, reporter Sta. WHLI Radio, L.I., N.Y., 1970-74, Sta. WNEW Radio, N.Y.C., 1975-80; anchor Sta. WGBB-Radio, L.I., 1974-75, Sta. WINS Radio, N.Y.C., 1980-81; reporter Dow Jones, N.Y.C., 1981; corr. CBS News, N.Y.C., 1982—. Trustee N.J. Ctr. for Outreach and Svcs. for Autism Cmty., Ewing, 1991-94. Recipient Champion-Tuck Econ. award for radio reporting Dartmouth Coll., 1984. Mem. AFTRA, TV and Radio Working Press Assn. Roman Catholic. Avocation: advocacy for handicapped and developmentally disabled. Office: CBS News 524 West 57th St New York NY 10019

SETTLE, MARY LEE, author; b. Charleston, W.Va., July 29, 1918; d. Joseph Edward and Rachel (Tompkins) S.; m. Rodney Weathersbee, 1939 (div. 1946); 1 child, Christopher Weathersbee; m. Douglas Newton, 1946 (div. 1956); m. William Littleton Tazewell, Sept. 2, 1978. Student, Sweet Briar Coll., 1936-38. Asst. editor Harper's Bazaar, 1945; Eng. corres. Flair, 1950-51; editor Am. Heritage, 1961—; assoc. prof. Bard Coll., Annandale-on-Hudson, N.Y., 1965-76; vis. lectr. Iowa Writer's Workshop, 1976, U. Va., 1978. Author: The Love Eaters, 1954, The Kiss of Kin, 1955, O Beulah Land, 1956, Know Nothing, 1960 (pub. as Pride's Promise, 1976), Fight Night on a Sweet Saturday, 1964, (play) Juana La Loca, 1965, All the Brave Promises: Memories of Aircraft Woman 2nd Class 2146391, 1966, The Story of Flight, 1967, The Clam Shell, 1971, The Scopes Trial: The State of Tennessee vs. John Thomas Scopes, 1972, Prisons, 1973, Blood Tie, 1977 (Nat. Book award 1978), The Scapegoat, 1980, The Killing Ground, 1982 (Janet Heidinger Kafka Prize in fiction 1983), Water World, 1984, Celebration, 1986, Maugham, 1987, The Search for Beulah Land, 1988, Charley Bland, 1989, Turkish Reflections, 1991, Choices, 1995; (with Raymond W. Settle) War Drums and Wagon Wheels: The Story of Russell, Majors, and Waddell, 1966, Saddles and Spurs: The Pony Express Saga, 1972. Served with Womens Aux., RAF, 1942-43. Recipient Merrill Found. award, 1975, Academy award in literature Am. Academy Arts and Letters, 1994; John Simon Guggenheim fellow, 1958, 60. Democrat. Founder PEN/Faulkner award, 1980. Office: care Farrar Straus & Giroux 19 Union Sq W New York NY 10003-3304*

SETTLES, F. STAN, JR., manufacturing executive, educator; b. Denver, Oct. 3, 1938; s. Frank S. and Dorothy Marie (Johnson) S.; m. Evelyn Brown, June 10, 1961; children: Frank S. III, Richard, Charles, Michael. BS in Prodn. Tech., Indsl. Engring., LeTourneau Coll., Longview, Tex., 1962; MS in Indsl. Engring., Ariz. State U., 1967, PhD in Indsl. Engring., 1969. Sr. systems analyst AiResearch Mfg. Co., Phoenix, 1968-70, project mgr., 1970-74, mgr. operational planning 1974-80; mgr. indsl. engrs. Garrett Pneumatic Systems, Phoenix, 1980-83; mgr. indsl. mfg. engring. Garrett Turbine Engring. Co., Phoenix, 1983-85; v.p. mfg. ops. AiResearch Mfg. Co., Torrance, Calif., 1985-87; dir. indsl. mfg. engring. The Garrett Corp., Phoenix, 1987-88; dir. planning Garrett Engine Div., Phoenix, 1988-92; asst. dir. White House Office of Sci. and Tech. Policy, 1992-93; program dir. NSF, 1992-94; prof., chmn. indsl. and systems engring. dept. U. So. Calif., L.A., 1994—; faculty assoc. Ariz. State U., Tempe, 1974-85, 90-92, rsch. prof., 1992-94. Mem. sch. bd. Tempe Elem. Sch. Dist., 1978-84; mem. YMCA Indian Guides, nat. chief, 1978-79. Fellow Inst. Indsl. Engrs. (pres. 1987-88, Ops. Rsch. award 1980); mem. Nat. Acad. Engrs., Soc. Mfg. Engrs. (sr.), Inst. Mgmt. Sci. (sr.), Am. Soc. Quality Control, Quality and Productivity Mgmt. Assn. Republican. Presbyterian. Home: 1750 E Ocean Blvd #713 Long Beach CA 90802-6019 Office: Univ So Calif Dept Indsl and System Engring Los Angeles CA 90089-0193

SETZER, HERBERT JOHN, chemical engineer; b. N.Y.C., Oct. 23, 1928; s. Leo and Barbara (Hafner) S. m. Elizabeth Bernadette Curran, May 30, 1957; children: Stephen Lawrence, Robert Drew, John Herbert, Brian Edmund. BChemE, CUNY, 1951; MChemE, NYU, 1958. Engr. U.S. Army Ordnance Corps Redstone Arsenal, Huntsville, Ala., 1955-57; rsch. asst. NYU, 1958-61; rsch. engr. Internat. Fuel Cells (joint venture United Techs. Corp., Hartford, Conn. and Toshiba Corp., Tokyo), 1962-92; vis. lectr. Am. Tech. Inst., Conn., 1993—. Holder 21 U.S. patents chem. processing and hydrogen generation, other patents in Can., Europe, Africa, Asia, Australia; contbr. tech. papers in field to publs. Chmn. troop com. Long Rivers coun. Boy Scouts Am. 1973-81. With U.S. Army, 1951-56. Recipient Mason award, NYU, 1962, Spl. award United Techs. Corp., 1980. Mem. Catalyst Soc. New Eng., Sigma Xi, Elks. Roman Catholic. Office: 17 Virginia Dr Ellington CT 06029-3432

SETZER, KIRK, religious leader. Pres. Amana (Iowa) Ch. Soc. Office: Amana Church Society Amana IA 52203

SETZLER, EDWARD ALLAN, lawyer; b. Kansas City, Mo., Nov. 3, 1933; s. Edward A. and Margaret (Parshall) S.; m. Helga E. Friedemann, May 20, 1972; children: Christina, Ingrid, Kirstin. BA, U. Kans., 1955; JD, U. Wis. 1962. Bar: Mo. 1962, U.S. Tax Ct. 1962. Assoc. Spencer, Fane, Britt & Browne, Kansas City, 1962-67, ptnr., 1968—; mng. ptnr., 1974-77, 78-82, chmn. trust and estate sect., 1974—; lectr. U. Mo. and Kansas City Sch. Law Continuing Edn. programs, 1983-95; mem. Jackson County Probate Manual com., 1988—; Mo. State rep. Joint Editl. Bd./Uniform Probate Code, 1989—. Co-author: Missouri Estate Administration, 1984, supplements, 1985-93; co-author, co-editor, reviewer Missouri Estate Planning, 1986, supplements, 1987-93; contbg. editor: A Will Is Not The Way -- The Living Trust Alternative, 1988; contbg. editor: Understanding Living Trusts, 1990, expanded edit., 1994; bd. editors Wis. State Rev., 1961-62. Admitted: bd. govs. bd. dirs Am. Royal, 1982—; mem. planned giving com., bus. coun. Nelson Atkins Mus. Art, 1984—; mem. deferred giving com. Children's

Mercy Hosp., 1991—; mem. Kansas City Estate Planning Symposium Com., 1984-92, chmn., 1991. Fellow Am. Coll. Trust and Estate Counsel (state chmn. 1992—); mem. ABA, Mo. Bar Assn. (lectr., vice chmn. probate and estate planning com. 1994—), Lawyers Assn. Kansas City, Kansas City Met. Bar Assn. (lectr., chmn. probate and trust 1979, 92, vice chmn. 1983-85, 91, legis. rev. com. 1991—), Estate Planning Soc. Kansas City (co-founder 1965, pres. 1983-84, dir. 1984-85, mem. social com. 1968—), Order of Coif, Sigma Chi, Phi Delta Phi. Office: Spencer Fane Britt & Browne 1000 Walnut St Ste 1400 Kansas City MO 64106-2140

SETZLER, WILLIAM EDWARD, chemical company executive; b. Bklyn., Dec. 20, 1926; s. William Edward and Gertrude A. (Seyer) S.; m. Dorothy C. Kress, Dec. 2, 1950 (dec. Mar. 1987); children: William John, Heather A.; m. Lenore Kelly, July 13, 1991. B of Chem. Engring., Cooper Union, 1950; MS in Liberal Studies, Columbia U., 1993. V.p. ops. Argus Chem. Corp., N.Y.C., 1950-66; v.p. engring., then group v.p. Witco Chem. Corp. (now Witco Corp.), N.Y.C., 1966-75, exec. v.p., 1975-90, ret., 1990, also bd. dirs.; chmn. and CEO Faimount Chem. Inc., 1993—. Author and patentee in field. Served with USAAF, 1945-46. Mem. Am. Inst. Chem. Engrs., Soap and Detergent Assn. (bd. dirs.). Home: 3921 Lincoln St Seaford NY 11783-2115

SEUNG, THOMAS KAEHAO, philosophy educator; b. Jungju, Korea, Sept. 20, 1930; m. Kwihwan Hahn, May 29, 1965; children: Hyunjune Sebastian, Kwonjune Justin, Haesue Florence. BA, Yale U., 1958, MA, 1961, PhD, 1965. Instr. Yale U., 1963-65; asst. prof. Fordham U., 1965-66; mem. faculty dept. philosophy U. Tex., Austin, 1966—; prof. in philosophy U. Tex., 1972—, prof. in govt., 1985—, prof. in law, 1993—, Jesse H. Jones prof. liberal arts, 1987—. Author: The Fragile Leaves of the Sibyl, 1962, Kant's Transcendental Logic, 1969, Cultural Thematics, 1976, Structuralism and Hermeneutics, 1982, Semiotics and Thematics, 1982, Intuition and Construction, 1993, Kant's Platonic Revolution, 1994, Plato Rediscovered, 1995. Served as officer Korean Army, 1950-53. Recipient Wilbur Lucius Cross medal Yale Grad. Sch. Alumni Assn., 1988; Soc. Religion in Higher Edn. fellow, 1969-70; Am. Council Learned Soc. fellow, 1970-71; NEH fellow, 1977-78. Office: U Tex Dept Philosophy Austin TX 78712

SEVCENKO, IHOR, history and literature educator; b. Radosc, Poland, Feb. 10, 1922; came to U.S., 1949, naturalized, 1957; s. Ivan and Maria (Cherniatynska) S.; m. Oksana Draj-Xmara, Apr., 1945 (div. 1953); m. Margaret M. Bentley, July 16, 1953 (div. 1966); m. Nancy Patterson, June 18, 1966; children: Catherine, Elisabeth. Dr.Phil., Charles U., Prague, Czechoslovakia, 1945; Doct. en Phil. et Lettres, U. Louvain, Belgium, 1949; PhD (hon.), U. Cologne, Germany, 1994. Fellow in Byzantinology Dumbarton Oaks, 1949-50, dir. studies, 1966, prof. Byzantine history and lit., 1965-75, sr. research assoc., 1975—; lectr. Byzantine and ancient history U. Calif., Berkeley, 1950-51; fellow Byzantinology and Slavic lit., research program USSR, 1951-52; instr., then asst. prof. Slavic langs. and lit. U. Mich., 1953-57; mem. faculty Columbia U., 1957-72, prof., 1962-65, adj. prof., 1965-72; vis. prof. Harvard U., 1973-74, prof., 1974-92, emeritus, 1992; vis. fellow All Souls Coll., Oxford U., 1979-80, Wolfson Coll., Oxford U., 1987, 93; vis. mem. Princeton Inst. for Advanced Study, 1956; vis. prof. Munich U., 1959, Coll. de France, spring 1985, Cologne U., fall 1992; freas., acting treas., bd. dirs. Am. Rsch. Inst. in Turkey, 1964-66, 67, 75—; assoc. dir. Harvard Ukrainian Rsch. Inst., 1973-89, acting dir., 1977, 85-86; chmn. Nat. Com. Byzantine Studies, 1966-77; mem. Internat. Com. for Greek Paleography, 1983—. Author: Etudes sur la polémique entre Théodore Métochite et Nicéphore Choumnos, 1962, Society and Intellectual Life in Late Byzantium, 1981, Ideology, Letters and Culture in the Byzantine World, 1982, Byzantium and the Slavs in Letters and Culture, 1991; co-author: Der Serbische Psalter, 1978, Life of St. Nicholas of Sion, 1984; contbr. articles to profl. jours. Guggenheim fellow, 1963, Humboldt-Forschungspreistraeger, 1985. Fellow Mediaeval Acad. Am., Brit. Acad. (corr.); mem. Am. Philos. Soc., Am. Acad. Arts and Scis., Ukrainian Acad. Arts and Scis., Scientific Sevčenko Soc., Société des Bollandistes Belgium (adj.), Accademia di Palermo (fgn.), Internat. Assn. Byzantine Studies (v.p. 1976-86, pres. 1986—), Christian Archeological Soc. of Athens (hon.), Austrian Acad. Sci. (corr.), Accademia Internazionale of Naples (fgn.), Acad. Sci. Ukrainian SSR (fgn.); Phi Beta Kappa (hon.). Clubs: Cosmos (Washington); Harvard (N.Y.C.). Office: Harvard Univ 319 Boylston Hall Cambridge MA 02138

SEVER, TOM, labor union administrator; b. West Newton, Pa., Aug. 13, 1935; widowed; children: Margaret, Josephine, Thomas, Paul. Student, St. Vincent Coll., Latrobe, Pa. Trustee local 30 Internat. Brotherhood Teamsters, Jeanette, Pa., 1973-75, bus. agt. local 30, 1979-91, pres. local 30, 1985—; gen. sec.-treas. Internat. Brotherhood Teamsters, Washington, 1992—. Mem. VFW, NRA, Eagles, Moose. Avocations: hunting, fishing. Office: Int Brotherhood Teamsters 25 Louisiana Ave NW Washington DC 20001

SEVERA, GORDON L., utility executive; b. Clarkson, Nebr., Feb. 15, 1930; s. Rudolph G. and Olga (Indra) S.; m. Dorothy Jacqueline Smith, Feb. 23, 1952; children: Susan, Dan, Siri Lyn and Sara Jane (twins). B.S. in Bus. Adminstrn. cum laude, U. Nebr., Omaha, 1951. With HNG/Internorth (name now EnRon Corp.), Omaha, 1951-86; pres. Nat. Gas Group, 1977-81, sr. v.p. gas ops., 1981-83; sr. v.p. Petroleum and Chem. Group, 1983-85, exec. v.p., chief of staff, 1985-86; ret., 1986. Home: 9950 Devonshire Rd Omaha NE 68114-3852 Office: 2223 Dodge St Omaha NE 68102-1228

SEVERANCE, CHRISTOPHER CHURCHILL, museum director; b. Sydney, N.S., Can., Aug. 12, 1943; s. Glenwood and Freda (Braye) S. BA, Univ. Kings Coll., 1965; BE, Dalhousie U., 1966; MA, St. Mary's U., 1972. Tchr. King's Coll., N.S., 1966-70; dir. Miners Mus., Glace Bay, N.S., 1971-74; curator London (Ont.) Historical Mus., 1974-88; gen. mgr. London Regional Art and Historical Mus., 1988-91; exec. dir. Prince Edward Island Mus. & Heritage Found., Charlottetown, 1991—. Home: 145 Bunbury Rd, Charlottetown, PE Canada C1A 7G9 Office: Museum & Heritage Foundation, 2 Kent St, Charlottetown, PE Canada C1A 1M6

SEVERINGHAUS, NELSON, JR., mining company executive; b. Gainesville, Ga., Aug. 27, 1929; s. Nelson and Josephine (Thompson) S.; m. Virginia Terry Severinghaus, Aug. 31, 1952; 1 child, Virginia S. BS in Mining Engring., U. Ariz., 1951. Engr. Cities Svc., Ducktown, Tenn., 1954-55; engr./mgr. Ga. Marble Co., Tate, Ga., 1955-65; officer/pres. Ga. Marble Co., Atlanta, 1965-76; pres. Franklin Indsl. Minerals, Nashville, 1976—; pres., chief oper. officer Franklin Industries, Inc., Nashville, 1992—; lectr. in field. Author: Filler Minerals, 1983; patentee in field. 1st lt. U.S. Army, 1951-54. Mem. AIME (pres. 1984), Soc. Mining Engrs. (pres. 1980), Nat. Stone Assn. (bd. dirs. 1976-92), Atlanta Athletic Club, Cumberland Club, Belle Meade Club. Republican. Methodist. Avocations: boating, reading, photography.

SEVERINO, ROBERTO, foreign language educator, academic administration executive; b. Catania, Italy, July 19, 1940; s. Giuseppe and Alba (Scroppo) S. Student, State U. Catania, Italy, 1960-62; BA, Columbia Union Coll., 1967; MA, U. Ill., 1969, PhD, 1973. Head acct., pers. dir. Industria Nazionale Apparecchiature Scientifiche, Milan, 1961-63; teaching asst., lang. lab. supv. Columbia Union Coll., Takoma Park, Md., 1965-67; grad. teaching asst. U. Ill., Urbana, 1967-70, coord. Corr. Sch., 1971-73; instr. dept. French and Italian U. Mass., Amherst, 1971-73; prof. dept. Italian Georgetown U., Washington, 1973—, acting chmn., 1987, chmn. dept., 1988—; pres., co-founder Nat. Inst. Contemporary Italian Studies, 1986—; pres. Am. U. of Rome, 1990-93; lit. dir. Georgetown U. Elec. Text Repository, Italian Archive, 1988—, Ultramarina, 1992—; mem. adv. bd. Nat. Italian Am. Found. Nat. Christopher Columbus 1992 Celebration; mem. U.S. delegation to 1st Conf. on Italian lang. and culture in U.S., 1987; lectr., speaker in field. Author: Le soluzioni immaginarie, 1985, The Signs and Sounds of Italian, 1985, A carte scoperte, 1990, Presente imperfetto ed altri tempi, 1992, The Battle for Humanism, 1994, A Dumas: Mariano Stabile Sindaco di Palermo, 1994; co-author: Periscopio, 1986, International Nuclear Agreements Multilingual Glossary, 1988, United Nations Organization Multilingual Glossary, 1988, Regularizing the Irregular Italian Verb, 1990; translator; The Next 6000 Days by Saverio Avveduto, 1987; editor: (serials) Segni, 1985-88, Hispano-Italic Studies, 1976, 79; guest editor: Forum Italicum, 1989; mem. editorial bd. Educazione Comparata, 1993—; contbr. articles to profl. jours. Trustee Joel Nafuma Refugee Ctr., Rome, 1993—.

Rsch. grantee Interuniversity Ctr. European Studies, 1977; recipient Accademia Internazionale di Lettere, Scienze, Arti medal, 1983, Internat. Poetry prize, 1986, Gold Cross Cavaliere dell'Ordine al Merito della Reppublica Italiana, 1983, Gold medal Italian Ministries of Univs. and Sci. Rsch., 1988, Marranzano d'Argento prize, 1989, Gold Commander class Cross al Merito della Reppublica Italiana, 1990, Governor U. Vicennial Disting. Svc. medal, 1994. Mem. MLA, So. Atlantic Modern Lang. Assn., Nat. Assn. Secondary Sch. Prins. (mem. sch. partnerships internat. Italian adv. coun. 1988—), Italian Am. Cultural Found., Italian Cultural Soc. (pres. 1979-81, 83-85, Outstanding Svc. award 1983, chmn. acad. policy com. 1981—), Assn. Internationale Critiques Literaires and Associazione Italiana Critici Letterari, Greater Washington Assn. Tchrs. Fgn. Langs. (mem. award selection com. 1983-85), Manuscript Soc., Renaissance Soc. Am., Circolo Culturale Italiano (hon.), Am. Club (Rome), Touring Club Italiano (hon.), Gamma Kappa Alpha (v.p. 1990—, sec.-treas. and chpt. advisor 1985-90), World Jurist Assn. Ctr. Assocs. (U.S. pres. 1993—), Associazione Internazionale del Diritto e dell'Arte (v.p. 1994—). Home: 4949 Quebec St NW Washington DC 20016 Office: Georgetown U Dept Italian 37th and O Sts NW Washington DC 20057

SEVERINSEN, DOC (CARL H. SEVERINSEN), conductor, musician; b. Arlington, Oreg., July 7, 1927; m. Emily Marshall, 1980; children—Nancy, Judy, Cindy, Robin, Allen. Ptnr. Severinsen-Akwright Co.; pops condr. The Phoenix (Ariz.) Symphony Orchestra. Mem., Ted Fio Rito Band, 1945, Charlie Barnet Band, 1947-49, then with, Tommy Dorsey, Benny Goodman, Norro Morales, Vaughn Monroe; soloist network band: Steven Allen Show, NBC-TV, 1954-55; mem., NBC Orch. Tonight Show, 1962-67 , music dir., 1967-92 ; past host of: NBC-TV show The Midnight Special; recs., RCA Records, including; albums: Brass Roots, 1971, Facets, 1988, The Tonight Show Band, Night Journey. Address: care Thomas Cassidy Inc 0366 Horseshoe Dr Basalt CO 81621 also: c/o William Morris Agency 151 El Camino Dr Beverly Hills CA 90212 also: The Phoenix Symphony Orch Symphony Hall 2498 3707 N Seventh St Phoenix AZ 85014*

SEVERINSON, KENNETH J., athletic and electronic equipment manufacturing executive. Chmn., chief exec. officer AMF Inc., White Plains, N.Y., 1985—, also dir.; pres., former chief oper. officer Minstar Inc., Mpls., also bd. dirs.; pres., CEO Marimar Marine Corp., Pulaski, Wis., 1991—; pres., CEO, dir. Genmar Industries, Inc., Mpls., 1994—. Address: Minstar Inc 100 S 5th St Minneapolis MN 55402*

SEVERNS, PENNY L., state legislator; b. Decatur, Ill., Jan. 21, 1952. BS in Polit. Sci. and Internat. Relations, So. Ill. U., 1974. Spl. asst. to adminstr. AID, Washington, 1977-79; city councilwoman Decatur, from 1983; mem. 51st dist. Ill. State Senate, 1987—, chief budget negotiator for Senate Dems., 1993—, minority spokesperson appropriations com., 1994—. Office: Ill State Senate State Capitol Springfield IL 62706

SEVERO, RICHARD, writer; b. Newburgh, N.Y., Nov. 22, 1932; s. Thomas and Mary Theresa (Farina) S.; m. Emöke Edith de Papp, Apr. 7, 1961. B.A., Colgate U., 1954; postgrad., NYU Inst. Fine Arts, 1955-56, Columbia U. Sch. Architecture and Urban Planning, 1964-65. News asst. CBS, N.Y.C., 1954-55; reporter Poughkeepsie (N.Y.) New Yorker, 1956-57, A.P., Newark, 1957-61, N.Y. Herald Tribune, 1961-63; writer TV news CBS, N.Y.C., 1963-66; reporter Washington Post, 1966-68; investigative reporter N.Y. Times, N.Y.C., 1968-71; fgn. corr. N.Y. Times, Mex., C. Am. and Caribbean, 1971-73; investigative and environ. reporter N.Y. Times, 1973-77, sci. and environ. reporter, 1979—; assoc. Seminar on the City, Columbia U., 1966-69; vis. lectr. Am. culture Vassar Coll., 1985—; bd. dirs. Colgate U. Alumni Corp., 1988-92. Author: Lisa H., 1985; (with Lewis Milford) The Wages of War, 1989 (Am. Legion Nat. Comdr.'s award 1990); contbr. articles to mags. Poynter fellow-in-residence Vassar Coll., 1974 75; CBS News fellow, 1964-65; Recipient Front Page award Washington-Balt. Newspaper Guild, 1967; Journalistic award H.A.V.E.N., 1969; Schaeffer Gold Typewriter award N.Y. Newspaper Reporters Assn., 1969; Page One award Newspaper Guild of N.Y., 1970; hon. mention Mike Berger award Columbia U., 1970; Leone di San Marco award Italian Heritage and Culture Com., 1982; George Polk Meml. award L.I. U. Sch. Journalism, 1975; Hudson River Fisherman's Assn. award, 1976; Mike Berger award Columbia U., 1976; James Wright Brown award Deadline Club, Sigma Delta Chi, N.Y.C., 1976; Feature award N.Y. Press Club, 1977; Page One award Newspaper Guild N.Y., 1977, 82; Media award Am. Cancer Soc., 1977; hon. mention Heywood Broun Meml. award Am. Newspaper Guild, 1977; Penney-Mo. Newspaper award U. Mo. Sch. Journalism, 1978; Media award Agt. Orange Victims Internat., 1982; Page One award N.Y. Newspaper Guild, 1982; Gift of Life award N.Y. Blood Ctr., 1991, Spl. Writing award Soc. of the Silurians, 1992. Home: 81 Balmville Rd Newburgh NY 12550-1917

SEVERS, CHARLES A., III, lawyer; b. N.Y.C., Sept. 16, 1942; s. Charles A. and Gertrude (O'Neill) S.; m. Regina Ferrone, Sept. 4, 1965; children: Charles A. IV, Cornelius Forsythe, Rudyard Pimpernel, Olivia Consuelo. BA, Georgetown U., 1964, JD, 1967. Bar: N.Y. 1968, D.C. 1985. Ptnr. Dewey Ballantine, N.Y.C., 1967—; lectr. various continuing legal edn. programs. Contbr. articles to profl. jours. Fellow Am. Coll. Probate Counsel; mem. ABA, N.Y. State Bar Assn., Assn. of Bar of City of N.Y., D.C. Bar Assn., Union Club, Downtown Assn. Home: 1095 Park Ave New York NY 10128-1154 Office: Dewey Ballantine 1301 Ave Of The Americas New York NY 10019-6092

SEVERS, WALTER BRUCE, pharmacology educator, researcher; b. Pitts., June 10, 1938; s. Walter Bruce and Pauline Marie (Sever) S.; m. Anne Elizabeth Daniels, Apr. 25, 1970; children—Mary, Jane, Steven, William, Katherine. B.S., U. Pitts., 1960, M.S., 1963, Ph.D., 1965. Postdoctoral fellow NIH, Bethesda, Md., 1966-68; asst. prof. pharmacology Coll. Medicine, Pa. State U., Hershey, 1968-71, assoc. prof., 1971-77, prof., 1977—; ad hoc grant cons. NIH, U.S. Army, NSF. Mem. editorial bd. Am. Jour. Physiology, 1978—, Pharmacology, 1978—. Contbr. numerous articles, chpts., revs. to profl. pubs. Recipient Disting. Alumnus award U. Pitts., 1978, I.M. Setchenov medal Acad. Med. Sci. USSR, 1983, Blue medal for sci. Acad. Med. Sci., Bulgaria, Medal for Sci. U. Belgrade; NASA grantee, 1976—. Mem. Am. Physiol. Soc., Am. Soc. Pharmacology and Exptl. Therapeutics, Soc. for Neurosci., Pavlovian Soc. Am., Sigma Xi (pres. Pa. State U. chpt. 1981-82). Republican. Roman Catholic. Lodge: Kiwanis (pres. Hershey area 1980, bd. dirs.). Avocations: reading; camping; hiking; fishing. Home: 1011 Grubb Rd Palmyra PA 17078-3510 Office: Pa State U Coll Medicine Dept Pharmacology 850 University Dr Hershey PA 17033

SEVERSON, ROGER ALLAN, bank executive; b. Thief River Falls, Minn., Sept. 2, 1932; s. Alfred Gerhard and Esther Olga (Landro) S.; m. Beverly Diane Hays, Aug. 30, 1953; children: Eric Hays, Holle Diane. BS, U. Minn., 1954. Group v.p. First Nat. Bank, Mpls., 1952-73; pres. FBS Fin., Inc., Mpls., 1974-77; exec. v.p. F&M Savs. Bank, Mpls., 1977-82; sr. v.p. First Nat. Bank, St. Paul, 1983-85; exec. v.p. Shelard Nat. Bank, Mpls., 1985-86, TCF Bank Savs., Mpls., 1986-92; ret.; mem. Robert Morris Assocs., 1980-92; trustee Heitman Mortgage Investors, Chgo., 1970-71, Mass. Mut. Mortgage Realty Investors, Springfield, 1972-85. Vice chmn. bd. of trustees The Am. Luth. Ch., Mpls., 1976-81; trustee Children's Health Ctr., Mpls., 1971-72; bd. dirs. Goodwill Industries, Mpls., 1967-70. Fellow Versterheim Mus.; mem. Ethics in Pub. Policy Ctr. Ctr. for Am. Experiment, Sons of Norway. Home: 8321 Essex Rd Chanhassen MN 55317-8705

SEVERY, LAWRENCE JAMES, psychologist, educator; b. Detroit, Mar. 30, 1943; m. Linda Andrea Anstensen, Aug. 20, 1966; children: Beth Andrea, Lisa Ellen. BS in Psychology, Wayne State U., 1965; MA in Psychology, U. Colo., 1970, PhD in Psychology, 1970. Rsch. asst. Inst. Behavioral Sci., U. Colo., Denver, 1968-69; predoctoral trainee Inst. Genetics and Behavior for Psychologists, U. Colo., Denver, 1969; asst. prof. psychology, sr. rsch. scientist Ark. Rehab. Rsch. and Tng. Ctr., U. Ark., 1970-71; various positions to prof., dept. psychology U. Fla., Gainesville, 1971—, R. David Thomas Endowed Legis. prof. psychology, 1988, assoc. dean for student affairs Coll. Liberal Arts and Scis., 1990—; rsch. fellow Inst. Population Studies, U. Exeter, Devon, Eng., 1982, sr. rsch. assoc. Behavioral Rsch. Inst., 1976-77, postdoctoral trainee, U. N.C. Population Ctr.'s summer inst., 1973 and others; cons. in field. Author: A Contemporary Introduction to Social Psychology, 1976, Advances in Population: Psychosocial Perspectives, Vol. 1 1993, Vol. 2, 1994; contbr. articles, book

chpts. and monographs to profl. publs. Recipient numerous grants in population and health fields. Fellow APA (numerous coms.); mem. Southeastern Psychol. Assn., Population Assn. Am. (psycho-social workshop program chmn. 1982, 92), Assn. Consumer Rsch., Internat. Assn. Applied Psychology. Home: 4242 SW 94th Dr Gainesville FL 32608 Office: Coll Liberal Arts & Scis U Fla Gainesville FL 32611

SEVETSON, DONALD JAMES, minister, church administrator; b. Oak Park, Ill., Oct. 4, 1933; s. Earl Winfred and Lillian Ione (Anderson) S.; m. Mary Louise Frank, Nov. 30, 1957; children: Philip Curtis, Andrea Lyle, Erika Linnea. BA, Macalester Coll., 1954; BDiv, Chgo. Theol. Sem. and U. Chgo., 1957. Ordained to ministry Congl. Ch., 1958. Minister Raymond Congl. Ch., Franksville, Wis., 1959-62; assoc. minister 1st Congl. Ch., Mpls., 1957-59, Dekalb, Ill., 1962-65, Appleton, Wis., 1965-69; minister Parkview United Ch. of Christ, White Bear Lake, Minn., 1969-73; assoc. conf. minister Minn. Conf. United Ch. of Christ, Mpls., 1973-80; conf. minister Ctrl. Pacific Conf. United Ch. of Christ, Portland, Oreg., 1980—; chairperson coun. conf. ministers United Ch. of Christ, Cleve., 1994—, chairperson, bd. dirs. office of comm., 1989-93. Author: The First Century, 1994. Chair Oreg. Holocaust Resource Ctr., Portland, 1989-91, bd. dirs., 1984-91, 94—; trustee Pacific U., Forest Grove, Oreg., 1989—. Mem. NAACP, Urban League, Chgo. Theol. Sem. Alumni Assn. (pres. 1962-64). Democrat. Avocations: long distance running, golf, historical research. Office: United Ch of Christ Ctrl Pacific Conf 0245 SW Bancroft St Ste E Portland OR 97201

SEVIER, ERNEST YOULE, lawyer; b. Sacramento, June 20, 1932; s. Ernest and Helen Faye (McDonald) S.; m. Constance McKenna, Apr. 12, 1969; children: Carolyn Stewart, Katherine Danielle. A.B., Stanford U., 1954, J.D., 1956. Bar: Calif. 1956, U.S. Supreme Ct. 1965. Asso. mem. firm Sedgwick, Detert, Moran & Arnold, San Francisco, 1958-62; mem. firm Severson & Werson, San Francisco, 1962—; mem. Commn. Non-lawyer Practice, 1992—. Served with USAAF, 1956-57. Fellow Am. Bar Found.; mem. ABA (chmn. tort and ins. practice sect. 1982-83, exec. coun. 1976-84, chmn. standing com. on assoc. comms. 1988-90, chmn. coord. com. on Outreach to Pub. 1989-90, chmn. standing com. on lawyers responsibility for client protection 1991-94, commn. on non-lawyer practice 1992—), Calif. Bar Assn., Internat. Assn. Def. Counsel, Fedn. Ins. and Corp. Counsel. Office: Severson & Werson 1 Embarcadero Ctr Ste 2500 San Francisco CA 94111-3714

SEVIK, MAURICE, engineer; b. Istanbul, Turkey, Mar. 19, 1923; s. Benjamin and Esther (Barzilai) S.; m. Jacqueline Delannoy, June 2, 1953; children: Michele, Martine. DIC, Imperial Coll. Sci. Tech., London, 1946; PhD, Pa. State U., 1963. Registered profl. engr., Ont. With Bristol Aircraft Corp., U.K., 1946-51; sr. structures engr. Avro Aircraft Ltd., Can., 1952-59; prof. aerospace engring., dir. Garfield Thomas Water Tunnel, Pa. State U., University Park, 1959-72; mem. assoc. tech. dir. ship signatures directorate David Taylor Rsch. Ctr., Bethesda, Md., 1972—; vis. prof. Cambridge (Eng.) U., 1970; cons. USAF Office Sci. Rsch. 1965. Contbr. articles to profl. jours. Fellow Churchill Coll., Cambridge U., 1970; recipient Gold Medal award The Am. Soc. of Naval Engrs., 1990, Disting. Alumni award Central Pa. chpt. Acoustical Soc. of Am., Charles B. Martell Tech. Excellence award Nat. Security Indsl. Assn., 1992. Fellow Acoustical Soc. Am., ASME, Sigma Xi; mem. Nat. Acad. Engring. Home: 7817 Horseshoe Ln Rockville MD 20854-3828 Office: David Taylor Rsch Ctr Bethesda MD 20084

SEVILLA, STANLEY, lawyer; b. Chi., Apr. 3, 1920; s. Isadore and Dienna (Levy) S.; m. Lois A. Howell, July 25, 1948; children: Stanley, Susan, Donald, Carol, Elizabeth. B.A. in Econs. with high honors, U. Cin., 1942; J.D., Harvard U., 1948. Bar: Calif. 1949. Since practiced in Los Angeles; assoc. Williamson, Hoge & Curry, 1948-50; mem. firm Axelrod, Sevilla and Ross, 1950-75, Stanley Sevilla (P.C.), 1975—; gen. counsel La.-Pacific Resources, Inc., 1970-90; bd. dirs. Caesars World, Inc. Served with USAAF, 1942-46. Mem. Los Angeles County Bar Assn., Beverly Hills Bar Assn., Phi Beta Kappa, Tau Kappa Alpha. Home: 16606 Merivale Ln Pacific Palisades CA 90272-2236 Office: PO Box 308 Pacific Palisades CA 90272-0308

SEVIN, EUGENE, engineer, consultant, educator; b. Chgo., Jan. 5, 1928; s. Sol and Rella (Yastrow) S.; m. Ruth H. Hirschson, June 12, 1951 (dec. Dec. 1989); children: Lori J. Sevin Gunther, Lynne M. Sevin Bossart, Lisa C.; m. Phyllis Robbins, Feb. 20, 1994. B.S. in M.E., Ill. Inst. Tech., 1949, Ph.D., 1958; M.S. in M.E., Calif. Inst. Tech. 1951. Research engr. Armour Research Found., Chgo., 1951-65; research dir. Research Inst. Ill. Inst. Tech., Chgo., 1965-69, adj. prof., 1967-70; cons. E. Sevin Assocs., Olympia Fields, Ill., 1969-70; prof., head dept. mech. engring. Ben Gurion U., Beer-Sheva, Israel, 1970-74; asst. to dep. dir. Def. Nuclear Agy., Washington, 1974-86; asst. dep. undersec. research and engring. Dept. Def., Washington, 1986-91; dep. dir. Missiles and Space Systems, Office Undersec. Def., Washington, 1992-94; cons. Lundhurst, Ohio, 1994—. Author: (with W.D. Pilkey) Optimum Shock and Vibration Isolation, 1971; contbr. papers to confs., articles to profl. jours.; monograph series. Mem. NAE, ASME, AIAA, Sigma Xi (Disting. lecture 1985), Tau Beta Pi, Pi Tau Sigma. Avocations: computer software development; handball. Home: 1782 Kenton Circle Lyndhurst OH 44124

SEVOLD, GORDON JAMES, savings and loan executive; b. Randall, Iowa, Sept. 26, 1926; s. Oscar Theodore and Elvira (Guest) S.; m. Nell Ruth Reeves, Jan. 7, 1978; children: Deborah, Louise, Robert. B.S., Drexel U., 1958. Controller, treas. Frank H. Fleer Corp., Phila., 1962-66; v.p. fin. plumbing products div. Borg Warner Co., Mansfield, Ohio, 1966-71; treas., chief fin. officer Centran Corp., Cleve., 1971-82; chmn. bd., pres. Investors Income Ins. Co., Dallas, 1975-82; exec. v.p. Am. Savs. and Loan Assn., Salt Lake City, 1982-85; chief fin. officer Northwestern region FSLIC Receivership, 1985-88; dep. dir. Ea. Region FSLIC Receivership, 1988-89; chief fin. officer FDIC, Atlanta, 1989-92; sr. acct. FDIC, Orlando, Fla., 1992-94; ret., 1994. Treas. Centran Polit. Action Com., 1975-79. Served with USAAF, 1944-45. Mem. Fin. Execs. Inst., Budget Execs. Inst. Republican. Club: Willow Creek Country. Home: 1808 Danbury Dr Sun City Center FL 33573-5251

SEVY, ROGER WARREN, retired pharmacology educator; b. Richfield, Utah, Nov. 6, 1923; s. Carl Spencer and Maude (Malmquist) S.; m. Barbara Florence Snetsinger, Aug. 16, 1948; children—Pamela Jane, Jonathan Carl. Student, Utah State U., 1941-43, Harvard, 1943-45; M.S., U. Vt., 1948; Ph.D., U. Ill., 1951, M.D., 1954. Asst. physiology U. Ill., 1948-51, instr., 1951-54; asst. prof. pharmacology Temple U., Phila., 1954-56, prof., 1956-89, chmn. dept., 1957-73, dean Sch. Medicine, 1973-79, prof. emeritus, 1989—. Served with AUS, 1943-45. Mem. Am. Soc. Pharmacology and Exptl. Therapeutics, Am. Physiol. Soc., Endocrine Soc., AAAS, Sigma Xi., Alpha Omega Alpha. Research on hypertension and cardiovascular pharmacology. Home: 242 Mather Rd Jenkintown PA 19046-3129 Office: Temple U 3420 N Broad St Philadelphia PA 19140-5104

SEWALL, TINGEY HAIG, banker; b. N.Y.C., Aug. 3, 1940; s. George Tingey and Mary (Bossidy) S.; m. Lucy M. Roosevelt, Oct. 10, 1964 (div. Sept. 1989); 1 child, Margaret Haig; m. Joan S. Law, Feb. 7, 1993. BA, Bowdoin Coll., 1962; grad. in banking, Rutgers U., 1974. Various positions State Street Bank & Trust Co., Boston, 1964-76, v.p., 1976-82; v.p. BankBank Norfolk, Dedham, Mass., 1982-84, sr. v.p., sr. lending officer, 1984-86, exec. v.p., sr. lending officer, 1986-90; exec. v.p. BayBank South, Dedham, 1990-91, BayBank, Burlington, Mass., 1991—. Bd. overseers Dana Farber Cancer Inst., Boston, 1984—; trustee FCD Edni. Svcs., Inc., Needham, Mass.—. Served to capt. USAR, 1960-64. Mem. Robert Morris Assocs. (sr. assoc., bd. dirs. 1987-89 New Eng. chpt.), Newcomen Soc. U.S., Union Boat Club (Boston), Mahkeenac Boating Club (Stockbridge, Mass.). Home: 11 Spindrift Ln Cohasset MA 02025

SEWALL, WILLIAM DANA, data processing manager; b. Boston, Jan. 17, 1948; s. Charles Hull Sewall and Mary (Butler) Spring; m. Lucinda Thames, Oct. 24, 1981; children: Rebecca, Alyssa, Holly, Madeline. BA, Dartmouth Coll., 1970; JD, Boston Coll., 1977. Bar: Mass. 1978, Calif. 1979. Tchr. Concord (N.H.) Sch. Dist., 1970-74; assoc. Csapler & Bok, Boston, 1977-81; gen. counsel LEF & C Corp., San Francisco, 1981-83; sr. v.p. technology Citicorp Bankers Leasing, Foster City, Calif., 1983—; also bd. dirs. Bankers Leasing, San Mateo. Editor Boston Coll. Law Rev., 1975-77. Mem. Am. Assn. Equipment Lessors (bd. dirs.). Avocations: gardening, sailing, jogging. Home: 25 Trace Ln Half Moon Bay CA 94019 Office: Citicorp Bankers Leasing 989 E Hillsdale Blvd Ste 300 Foster City CA 94404

SEWARD, GEORGE CHESTER, lawyer; b. Omaha, Aug. 4, 1910; s. George Francis and Ada Leona (Rugh) S.; m. Carroll Frances McKay, Dec. 12, 1936 (dec. 1991); children: Gordon Day, Patricia McKay (Mrs. Dryden G. Liddle), James Pickett, Deborah Carroll (Mrs. R. Thomas Coleman). Grad., Louisville Male High Sch., 1929; BA, U. Va., 1933, LLB, 1936. Bar: Va. 1935, N.Y., Ky., D.C., U.S. Supreme Ct. With Shearman & Sterling, N.Y.C., 1936-53, Seward & Kissel, N.Y.C., 1953- ; founder, hon. chmn. Internat. Capital Mkts Group of Internat. Fedn. Accts., Fedn. Internat. des Bourses de Valeurs, Internat. Bar Assn.; legal adv. com. N.Y. Stock Exch., 1984-87, trustee, Edwin Gould Found. for Children, N.Y. Geneal. and Biol. Soc. Author: Basic Corporate Practice, Seward and Related Families; coauthor: Model Business Corporation Act Annotated, We Remember Carroll. Trustee Arts and Scis. Coun. U.Va., 1983-93, pres., 1991-93. Elected to Louisville Male High Sch. Alumni Assn. Hall of Fame, 1991; named Ky. Col., 1993. Fellow Am. Bar Found. (chmn. model corp. acts com. 1956-65), N.Y. State Bar Found.; mem. Internat. Bar Assn. (hon. pres.-founder bus. law sect. 1969-74, hon. life pres.; lectr. series named in his honor, New Delhi, 1988, Lisbon, 1992, Budapest, 1993, Geneva 1994), ABA (chmn. bus. law sect. 1958-59, chmn. sect. com. corp. laws 1952-58, chmn. sect. banking com. 1960-61, mem. ho. of dels. 1959-60, 63-74, mem. joint com. with Am. Law Inst. on continuing legal edn. 1965-74), Athenaeum Lit. Assn. (Louisville), Down Town Assn. (N.Y.C.), Knickerbocker Club, N.Y. Yacht Club, University Club (Chgo.), Met. Club (Washington), Bohemian Club, Shelter Island Yacht Club, Gardiner's Bay Country Club, Greencroft Club (Charlottesville, Va.), Cum Laude Soc., Raven Soc., Order of Coif, Phi Beta Kappa Assocs. (pres. 1969-75), Phi Beta Kappa, Theta Chi, Delta Sigma Rho. Home: 48 Greenacres Ave Scarsdale NY 10583-1436 Office: Seward & Kissel One Battery Park Plz New York NY 10004 also: Internat Bar Assn, 2 Harewood Pl Hanover Square, London W1R 9HB, England

SEWARD, WILLIAM W(ARD), JR., author, educator; b. Surry, Va., Feb. 2, 1913; s. William Ward and Elizabeth (Gwaltney) S.; m. Virginia Leigh Widgeon, Dec. 27, 1941; children: Virginia R. Godwin, Leigh W. Huston. AB, U. Richmond, 1934, MA, 1935; grad. fellow, Duke U., 1938-39, 40-41. English tchr. pub. schs., 1935-38; instr. U. Richmond, 1939-40, summer 1944; head English dept. Greenbrier Mil. Sch., 1941-42; prof., head English dept. Tift Coll., 1942-45; faculty Old Dominion U., Norfolk, Va., 1945, 47— ; prof. Old Dominion U., 1957-77, prof. emeritus, 1977—, head dept. English, 1947-61; lectr. U. Va. extension div., 1952-54. Author: The Quarrels of Alexander Pope, 1935; editor: The Longer Thou Livest the More Fool Thou Art (W. Wager), 1939, Literature and War, 1943, Skirts of The Dead Night, 1950, Foreword to Descent of the White Bird (Barbara Whitney), 1955, Contrasts in Modern Writers, 1963, My Friend Ernest Hemingway, 1969; contbr. to book: The True Gen: An Intimate Portrait of Hemingway by those Who Knew Him (Denis Brian), 1988; mem. editorial bd.: Lyric Virginia Today, 1956; contbr. articles to profl. jours. Recipient Charles T. Norman medal for best grad. in English U. Richmond, 1934. Mem. Poetry Soc. Va. (pres. 1952-55), Poetry Soc. Am., Hemingway Soc., Internat. Mark Twain Soc. (hon.), Va. Writers Club (emeritus), Princess Anne Country Club, Virginia Beach Country Club, Phi Beta Kappa, Kappa Alpha, Pi Delta Epsilon. Methodist. Home: 701 Cavalier Dr Virginia Beach VA 23451-3837

SEWELL, BEN GARDNER, lawyer; b. Palestine, Tex., Mar. 23, 1911; s. Roy C. and Carrie (Gardner) S.; m. Elizabeth Hall, Nov. 14, 1947. B.A. Rice U., 1933; LL.B., U. Tex., 1936. Bar: Tex. 1936. Ptnr. Sewell & Riggs, Houston; mem. office gen. counsel War Prodn. Bd., Washington, 1942. Lt. comdr. USNR, 1942-46. Fellow Am. Coll. Trial Lawyers; mem. ABA, Am. Law Inst., Phi Beta Kappa, Order of Coif, Phi Delta Phi. Home: 115 Stablewood Ct Houston TX 77024-7046 Office: Sewell & Riggs Three Allen Ctr # 800 Houston TX 77002

SEWELL, BEVERLY JEAN, financial executive; b. Oklahoma City, July 10, 1942; d. Benjamin B. Bainbridge and Faith Marie (Mosier) Allision; m. Ralph Byron Sewell, Jan. 23, 1962; children: M. Timothy, Pamela J. Student, U. Okla., 1960-61, Jackson C.C., 1973-77; BA in Bus., Mesa Coll., 1982; cert., Coll. Fin. Planning, 1984, MS in Fin. Planning, 1994. Sole practice fin. planning Grand Junction, Colo., 1985-87; fin. planner, broker Interpacific Investors Services, Grand Junction, 1987-88; investment broker A.G. Edwards & Sons, Inc., Grand Junction, 1988-92, v.p., 1992—; MS in Fin. Planning, 1994. Mem. ctrl. com. Grand Junction Rep. Orgn., 1988; mem. Grand Junction Planning Commn., 1987-89; bd. dirs. Grand Junction Symphony, 1991-94, Downtown Devel. Authority, St. Mary's Hosp. Mem. Inst. Cert. Fin. Planners, Internat. Assn. Fin. Planning. Avocations: tennis, jogging. Home: 717 Wedge Dr Grand Junction CO 81506-1866 Office: A G Edwards & Sons Inc 501 Main St Grand Junction CO 81501-2607

SEWELL, CHARLES HASLETT, banker; b. Buford, Ga., Jan. 16, 1928; s. Grover C. and Jennie G. (Haslett) S.; m. Margaret Gillespie, Sept. 9, 1985; children: Anna E., William H., John L. B.A., Emory U. 1951. Econs. mgmt. cons. Rsch. and Cons. Corp., Atlanta, 1952-72; sr. v.p. Deposit Guaranty Nat. Bank, Jackson, Miss., 1972—, exec. v.p., 1974—; chmn, chief exec. officer Deposit Guaranty Mortgage Co., Jackson, Miss., 1976-91; cons. in field; chmn. Miss. Econ. Council, 1983—; chmn. Sml. Bus. Devel. Ctr. U. Miss, Oxford, 1979—. Contbr. articles to profl. jours. Trustee Miss. State Libr. Commn., 1983—; chmn. Miss. Com. for Humanities, 1983—; pres. Miss. Symphony Orch., 1988-89; chmn. Miss. internat. adv. bd. Emory U. Coll. Arts and Scis., 1992—; exec.-in-residence Else Sch. Mgmt., Millsaps Coll. Mem. University Club (Jackson). Republican. Presbyterian. Home: 25 Village Green Cir Jackson MS 39211-2927 Office: Millsaps Coll Grad Sch Mgmt Jackson MS 39210

SEWELL, DARREL LESLIE, art museum curator; b. Cushing, Okla., Dec. 21, 1939; s. William Leslie and Irma Lena (Upp) S.; B.A., U. Chgo., 1962, M.A., 1965. Instr. art history Ohio State U., 1966-67, U. Ill. Chgo. Circle, 1968-70; curator edn. Nat. Collection Fine Arts, 1970-73; curator Am. Art, Phila. Mus. Art, 1973-76; The Robert L. McNeil Jr. curator of Am. Art, 1976—; exhibitions: Pa.: Three Centuries of Am. Art, 1976, Reinstallation of Am. Galleries, 1977, The U. Pa.: Collector and Patron of Art, 1779-1979, 1979, Copley from Boston, 1980; Thomas Eakins: Artist of Phila., 1981-82, One Hundred Yrs. of Acquisitions, 1983, Benjamin West in Pa. Collections, 1986, Modern Jewelry, 1984-86; The Helen Drutt Collection, 1986-87, The Fairmount Waterworks, 1988, Henry O. Tanner, 1991. Author: Philadelphia: Three Centuries of American Art, 1976; Thomas Eakins, Artist of Philadelphia, 1982; Henry O. Tanner, 1991. Office: Phila Mus Art PO Box 7646 Philadelphia PA 19101-7646

SEWELL, DWIGHT A., state government official; b. Washburn, Maine, July 26, 1932; s. Thomas Nixon and Alice Emily (Chapman) S.; m. Jacqueline J. Jordan, Aug. 16, 1958; children: Donna Walker, Thomas, Jon. BS, U. Maine, 1954. County supv. Farmers Home Adminstrn., Ft. Fairfield, Maine, 1957-65; chief com. svc. Farmers Home Adminstrn., Orono, Maine, 1965-79, state dir., 1981-89; divsn. dir. Farmers Home Adminstrn., Washington, 1979-81; exec. dir. Maine Potato Bd., Presque Isle, 1989-90; exec. dir., chmn. bd. commn. Maine State Housing Authority, Augusta, 1990—. Capt. U.S. Army, 1957-64. Mem. Masons. Office: Maine State Housing Authority PO Box 2669 Augusta ME 04338-2669

SEWELL, ELIZABETH, author, English educator; b. Coonoor, India, Mar. 9, 1919; came to U.S., 1949; d. Robert Beresford Seymour and Dorothy (Dean) S. BA, Cambridge U., Eng., 1942, MA, 1945, PhD, 1949; LittD (hon.), Fordham U., N.Y.C., 1968, U. Notre Dame, 1984. Lectr. English Vassar Coll., Poughkeepsie, N.Y., 1951-52; vis. prof. Fordham U. 1954-55, 58-59, chair Bensalem Experimental Coll., 1967-69; lectr. Christian Gauss sem. Princeton U., N.J., 1957; vis. prof. English Bennett Coll., Greensboro, N.C., 1960-61, Tougaloo Coll., Miss., 1963-64; prof. English, Hunter Coll. CUNY, 1971-74; Rosenthal prof. humanities U. N.C., Greensboro, 1974-77. Author 4 novels, 1952, 55, 62, 95, 3 poetry collections, 1962, 68, 84 (nat. award AAAL 1981). Recipient Zoe Brockman Kincaid award N.C. Poetry Soc., 1985; fellow Howard Rsch., 1949-50, Sr. Simon, 1955-57, Ashley, 1959. Mem. Lewis Carroll Soc. N.Am., PEN Am. Ctr. Home: 854 W Bessemer Ave Greensboro NC 27408-8404

SEWELL, JOHN WILLIAMSON, research association executive; b. Cleve., Dec. 19, 1935; s. William and Hilda F. (Gaunt) S.; m. Maryann Strauss, July 19, 1958; children: Gregory J., Michael P. B.A., U. Rochester, 1957; M.A., NYU, 1967. Fgn. service officer Dept. State, 1961-68; asst. to dir. Bur. Intelligence Research, Dept. State, Washington, 1968-70; asst. to pres. Brookings Inst., Washington, 1970-71; v.p. Overseas Devel. Council, Washington, 1971-77; exec. v.p. Overseas Devel. Council, 1977-79, pres., 1980—; mem. Bretton Woods Com.; mem. Interaction, North-South Roundtable, Internat. Ctr. for Rsch. on Women, Internat. Adv. Group for 1995 World Summit for Social Devel.; spl. advisor to the adminstrn. UNDP. Author: U.S. Foreign Policy and the Third World Agenda, 1985-86; Growth, Exports, & Jobs in a Changing World Economy: Agenda 1988; co-editor: United States Budget for a New World Order, FY, 1992, Challenges and Priorities in the 1990s: An Alternative U.S. International Affairs Budget, FY, 1993; contbr. articles to jours. Mem. World Resources Inst., The Carter Ctr., Christian Children's Fund, The Kellogg Inst.; pres. Nat. Choral Found., 1969-75. With U.S. Army, 1958-60. Mem. Coun. on Fgn. Rels., Cosmos Club. Home: 7614 Morningside Dr NW Washington DC 20012-1557 Office: Overseas Devel Council Ste 500 1875 Massachusetts Ave NW Washington DC 20036-1804

SEWELL, PHYLLIS SHAPIRO, retail chain executive; b. Cin., Dec. 26, 1930; d. Louis and Mollye (Mark) Shapiro; m. Martin Sewell, Apr. 5, 1959; 1 child, Charles Steven. B.S. in Econs. with honors, Wellesley Coll., 1952. With Federated Dept. Stores, Inc., Cin., 1952-88, research dir. store ops., 1961-65, sr. research dir., 1965-70, operating v.p., research, 1970-75, corp. v.p., 1975-79, sr. v.p., research and planning, 1979-88; bd. dirs. Lee Enterprises Inc., Davenport, Iowa, Pitney Bowes Inc., U.S. Shoe Corp., SYSCO Corp. Bd. dirs. Nat. Cystic Fibrosis Found., Cin., 1963—; chmn. divsn. United Appeals, Cin., 1982; mem. bus. adv. coun. Sch. Bus. Adminstrn., Miami U., Oxford, Ohio, 1982-84; trustee Cin. Community Chest, 1984-94, Jewish Fedn., 1990-92, Jewish Hosp., 1990—. Named One of 100 Top Corp. Women Bus. Week mag., 1976; named Career Woman of Achievement YWCA, 1983; recipient Alumnae Achievement award Wellesley Coll., 1979, Disting. Cin. Bus. and Profl. Woman award, 1981; named to Ohio Women's Hall of Fame, 1982.

SEWELL, RICHARD HERBERT, historian, educator; b. Ann Arbor, Mich., Apr. 11, 1931; s. Herbert Mathieu and Anna Louise (Broene) S.; m. Natalie Paperno, Jan. 13, 1971; 1 child, Rebecca Elizabeth. A.B., U. Mich., 1953; M.A., Harvard U., 1954, Ph.D., 1962. Asst. prof. No. Ill. U., DeKalb, 1962-64; asst. prof. history U. Wis.-Madison, 1965-67, assoc. prof., 1967-74, prof, 1974—, chmn. dept. history, 1982-85; vis. lectr. U. Mich., Ann Arbor, 1964-65; adv. bd. Lincoln and Soldiers Inst., Gettysburg Coll., Pa., 1990—. Author: John P. Hale and the Politics of Abolition, 1965, Ballots for Freedom, 1976, A House Divided, 1988; mem. editorial bd. Revs. in Am. History, 1981—; contbr. articles to profl. jours. Served to lt. (j.g.) USNR, 1954-57. Mem. Soc. Civil War Historians, So. Hist. Assn., Hist. Soc. Wis., Phi Beta Kappa, Phi Kappa Phi. Avocation: whitewater rafting. Home: 2206 Van Hise Ave Madison WI 53705-3822 Office: U Wis Dept History 5109 Humanities Bldg Madison WI 53706

SEWELL, ROBERT DALTON, pediatrician; b. Newman, Calif., Apr. 28, 1950; s. James Dalton and Mary Louise (Hartwell) S.; m. Esther Madiedo, Oct. 26, 1975; children: Kevin, David. BA magna cum laude, Pacific Union Coll., 1972; MD, Loma Linda U., 1975. Diplomate Am. Bd. Pediatrics. Pediatric intern and resident White Meml. Med. Ctr., L.A., 1975-77; pediatric resident, chief resident Milton S. Hershey Med. Ctr., Pa. State U., Hershey, 1977-80; pediatrician Children's Med. Ctr. Asheville, N.C. 1980-81, Lincoln City Med. Ctr. P.C., Lincoln City, Oreg., 1982-95; examining physician C.A.R.E.S. Ctr. Emanuel Hosp. & Health Ctr., Portland, Oreg., 1988-90; prof. Loma Linda (Calif.) U. Sch. Medicine, 1995—; chmn. child protection team North Lincoln Hosp., Lincoln City, 1983-86, sec. med. staff, 1990-92, pres. med. staff., 1992-94; mem. Citzens' Rev. Bd. Lincoln County, Newport, Oreg., 1986—, Early Intervention adv. com., Newport, 1986-90. Mem. North Lincoln Local Sch. Com., Lincoln City, 1983-94, chmn., 1986-90; mem. bd. dirs. Lincoln Shelter & Svcs., Inc., Lincoln City, 1983-89, chmn., 1987-89; mem. North Lincoln div. Am. Heart Assn., Lincoln City, 1986-89, v.p. 1987-89; mem. Drug and Alcohol Task Force, Lincoln City, 1988; mem., 2d vice-chmn. Yr. 2000 Plan housing com. Lincoln City Planning Commn., 1987-88; mem. AIDS taskforce Lincoln County Sch. Dist., 1987—; mem. Lincoln County Children's Agenda Taskforce, 1988. Named Citizen of Yr. child protection com. Lincoln County, 1984, Man of Yr. Lincoln City C. of C., 1988. Mem. Am. Acad. Pediatrics (sect. on child abuse), Oreg. Pediatric Soc., Oreg. Med. Assn. (mem. med. rev. com. 1990-95, mem.-at-large med. staff sect. gov. bd. 1993-95), Lincoln County Med. Soc., Am. Profl. Soc. on the Abuse of Children (charter mem.), Nat. Assn. Counsel for Children, Internat. Soc. for the Prevention Child Abuse and Neglect, N.Am. Soc. for Pediatric and Adolescent Gynecology, Oreg. Profl. Soc. on the Abuse of Children (founding pres. 1992-94). Democrat. Seventh-day Adventist. Avocations: music, sports, boating, auto racing. Office: Lincoln City Med Ctr PC 2870 NE West Devils Lake Rd Lincoln City OR 97367-5199

SEWELL, WILLIAM HAMILTON, sociologist; b. Perrington, Mich., Nov. 27, 1909; s. Will H. and Lulu (Collar) S.; m. Elizabeth Shogren, June 13, 1936; children: Mary, William, Robert. A.B., Mich. State U., 1933, A.M., 1934, D.Sc. (hon.), 1973; Ph.D., U. Minn., 1939. Instr. U. Minn., 1934-37; asst. prof. sociology Okla. State U., 1937-38, assoc. prof., 1938-40, prof., 1940-44; prof. sociology, rural sociology U. Wis., 1946-64, Vilas research prof. sociology, 1964—, chmn. dept., 1951-53, chmn. social sci. research com., 1952-55, social sci. div., 1950-53, chmn. dept. sociology, 1958-63, univ. chancellor, 1967-68; vis. scholar Russell Sage Found., 1968-69; Walker-Ames vis. prof. U. Washington, 1954; vis. prof. U. Tex., 1941, U. P.R., 1949, Garrett Inst., 1950, Columbia U., 1952; Ford Found. vis. prof. Delhi, Bombay, Poona univs., 1956-57; cons. human resources Sec. War, Research and Devel. Bd., Dept. Def., 1946-54; cons. Nat. Inst. Mental Health, USPHS, 1957-80; chmn. behavioral scis. study sect., 1959-63; chmn. behavioral scis. tng. com. NIH, 1962-67, mem. metal health research adv. com., 1968-70; exec. com. behavorial sci. div. NRC, 1966-70; chmn. Nat. Commn. on Research, 1978-80; Trustee Chatham Coll., Am. Coll. Testing Program Reseach Inst., Nat. Opinion Research Center; bd. dirs. Social Sci. Research Council. Author: Construction and Standardization of a Scale for the Measurement of Farm Family Socioeconomic Status, 1941, (with others) Scandinavian Students on An American Campus, 1961, Attitudes and Facilitation in Status Attainment, 1972, Education, Occupation and Earnings: Achievement in the Early Career, 1975; co-editor: Uses of Sociology, 1967, Schooling and Achievement in American Society, 1976; assoc. editor: Am. Sociol. Rev, 1954-57, Sociometry, 1955-58, Human Resources, 1967-83, Sociology of Edn., 1983-87; contbr. articles, monographs on sociology to profl. jours. Served as lt. USNR, 1944-46. Recipient Outstanding Achievement award U. Minn., 1972, Disting. Rsch. award Am. Ednl. Rsch. Assn., 1975, Commonwealth award for disting. contbns. to sociology , 1983; fellow Center for Advanced Study in Behavioral Scis., 1959-60; rsch. fellow East-West Population Inst. Fellow AAAS (chmn. sect. 1975-76), Am. Sociol. Assn. (mem. social psychology sect. 1960-61, v.p. 1961-62, pres. 1970-71), Cooley-Mead award in social psychology 1988, Willard Waller award in sociology edn. 1990), Am. Acad. Arts and Scis., Am. Philos. Soc.; mem. NAS (chmn. social and polit. scis. sect. 1981-84), Am. Statis. Assn., Rural Sociol. Soc. (pres. 1955), Southwestern Sociol. Soc. (pres. 1941), Midwestern Sociol. Soc. (pres. 1954), Sociol. Rsch. Assn. (pres. 1954), Soc. Rsch. in Child Devel. Clubs: Blackhawk Country, University. Home: 1005 Merrill Springs Rd Madison WI 53705-1314

SEWELL, WINIFRED, pharmaceutical librarian; b. Newport, Wash., Aug. 12, 1917; d. Harold Arthur and Grace (Vickerman) S. BA, State Coll. Wash., Pullman, 1938; BS in LS, Columbia U. 1940; DSc (hon.), Phila. Coll. Pharmacy and Sci., 1979. Asst. Columbia U. Library, N.Y.C., 1938-42; asst. librarian Wellcome Research Labs., Tuckahoe, N.Y., 1942-43; librarian Wellcome Research Labs., 1943-46, Squibb Inst. Med. Research, 1946-61; subject heading specialist Nat. Library of Medicine, 1961-62, dep. chief bibliog. services div., 1962-65, head drug literature program, 1965-70; adj. asst. prof. U. Md. Sch. Pharmacy, 1970-86; lectr. U. Md. Coll. Libr. and Info. Svcs., 1969-92; cons. Nat. Health Planning Info. Ctr., 1975-81; instr. pharm. lit. and librarianship Columbia U., summer 1979; mem. com on modern methods for handling chem. info. Nat. Acad. Scis-NRC; mem. Martindale Databank Adv. Panel, 1981-82. Editor: Unlisted Drugs, 1949-

59, 62-64; author: Guide to Drug Information, 1976 (Ida and George Eliot award Med. Library Assn. 1977), (with Merle Harrison) Using MeSH for Effective Searching: a Programmed Guide, 1976, (with Sandra D. Teitelbaum) Micromanual for Casual Users of National Library of Medicine Databases, 1986, Reader in Medical Librarianship, 1973; editor: Health Affairs Series, Gale Info. Guides, 1971-80; mem. editorial bd.: Drug Info. Jour. Active Excerpta Medica adv. com., 1985-88. Mem. Am. Soc. for Info. Sci. (chmn. spl. interest group/classification research 1974-75), Med. Library Assn. (chmn. Rittenhouse award com. 1975-76, chmn. recert. com. 1979-80, chmn. public health and health adminstrn. sect. 1979-80, chmn. med. libraries edn. sect. 1981-82), Spl. Libraries Assn. (chmn. pharm. sect., sci.-tech. div. 1952-53, pres. 1960-61, publs. award sci. and tech. div. 1966), ALA, Drug Information Assn. (v.p. 1966-67, pres. 1970-71), Am. Assn. Colls. Pharmacy (chmn. libraries/ednl. resources sect. 1979-80, del. council on sects. adv. bd. 1980-83). Home and Office: 6513 76th Pl Cabin John MD 20818-1413

SEXSON, SANDRA GRIFFIN BISHOP, child psychiatrist, educator; b. Baldwyn, Miss., Sept. 16, 1945; d. Horace Omer Bishop and Correne Griffin; m. William R. Sexson, June 24, 1972; children: Kristen, Ryan. BS in Phys. Scis., Miss. State Coll. for Women, 1967; M.D., U. Miss., 1971. Intern in pediat. U. Miss. Sch. Medicine, Jackson, 1971-72; resident in gen. psychiatry U. Tex. Health Sci. Ctr., San Antonio, 1972-74; fellow in child devel. Child Devel. Clinic U. Hosp.-U. Miss., Jackson, 1974-75; fellow in child psychiatry, asst. in psychiatry Wash. U. Sch. Medicine, St. Louis, 1976-78; asst. prof. in pediats. psychiatry Wright State U., Dayton, Ohio, 1978-83, assoc. prof. psychiatry, 1983-84; asst. prof. child psychiatry Sch. Medicine, Emory U., Atlanta, 1984-93, assoc. prof. child psychiatry, 1993—, chief child psychiatry, 1994. Recipient Spl. Achievement award YWCA Salute to Career Women, 1984, Outstanding Mentor award Am. Acad. Child and Adolescent Psychiatry, 1990; named Ohio Outstanding Young Woman of Am., 1981. Mem. Am. Assn. Dirs. Psychiatry, Am. Acad. Child Psychiatry, Soc. Rsch. in Child Devel. (assoc. chair), Ga. Coun. Child and Adolescent Psychiatry (pres.). Office: Emory U Sch Medicine 2215 Ridgewood Dr NE Atlanta GA 30322

SEXTON, CAROL BURKE, financial institution executive; b. Chgo., Apr. 20, 1939; d. William Patrick and Katharine Marie (Nolan) Burke; m. Thomas W. Sexton Jr., June 30, 1962 (div. June 1976); children: Thomas W., J. Patrick, M. Elizabeth. BA, Barat Coll., 1961; cert. legal, Mallinckrodt Coll., 1974. Tchr. Roosevelt High Sch., Chgo., 1961-63, St. Joseph's Sch., Wilmette, Ill., 1975-80; dir. Jane Byrne Polit. Com., Chgo., 1980-81; mgr. Chgo. Merc. Exch., 1981-84, sr. dir. govt. and civic affairs, 1984-87, v.p. pub. affairs, 1987-94, sr. v.p. corp. rels., 1994—; mem. internat. trade an investment subcom. Chgo. Econ. Devel. Commn., 1989, 90. Bd. dirs. Chgo. Sister Cities, 1992—; chmn. Chgo.-Toronto Sister Cities Com., 1992—; bd. dirs. Ill. Ambs., 1991—, pres., 1994; bd. dirs., sec. Internat. Press Ctr., 1992—, chmn. bd., 1994. Mem. Exec.'s Club of Chgo. (bd. dirs.), Chgo. Conv. and Tourism Bur. (sec. 1989—, exec. com. 1987—, chmn. elect 1990, chmn. 1991-92), Chgo.-Toronto Sister Cities Internat. (chmn.), mem. Econ. club of Chgo. Roman Catholic. Avocations: books, gardening, travel, mountain hiking. Office: Chgo Merc Exch 30 S Wacker Dr Chicago IL 60606-7402

SEXTON, DONALD LEE, business administration educator; b. New Boston, Ohio, June 14, 1932; s. Benjamin Franklin and Virgie Marie (Jordan) S.; m. Levonne Bradley, June, 1954 (div. June 1964); 1 child, Rhonda Jane; m. Carol Ann Schwaller, Dec. 18, 1965; children: David Lee, Douglas Edward. BS in Math. and Physics, Wilmington Coll., 1959; MBA, Ohio State U., 1966, PhD in Mgmt., 1972. Indsl. engr. Detroit Steel Corp., Portsmouth, Ohio, 1959-61; sr. rsch. engr. Rockwell Internat., Columbus, Ohio, 1961-68; v.p. merchandising R.G. Barry Corp., Columbus, 1968-74; v.p., gen. mgr. Henri Fayette, Inc., Chgo., 1976; gen. mgr. M.H. Mfg. Co., Jackson, Miss., 1976-77; assoc. prof. Sangamon State U., Springfield, Ill., 1977-79; Caruth prof. entrepreneurship Baylor U., Waco, Tex., 1979-86; Davis prof. free enterprise Ohio State U., Columbus, 1986-94; dir. curriculum devel. Ctr. for Entrepreneurial Leadership Inc., Kauffman Found., Kansas City, Mo., 1994—; mem. adv. bd. SBA, Columbus, 1986-94; rsch. adv. bd. U. So. Calif., L.A., 1986-90. Co-author: Entrepreneurship Education, 1981, Experiences in Small Business, 1982, Starting A Business in Texas, 1983; co-editor: Encyclopedia of Entrepreneurship, 1981, Art and Science of Entrepreneurship, 1986, Women Owned Businesses, 1989, Entrepreneurship: Creativity and Growth, 1990, The State of the Art of Entrepreneurship, 1991. Served to staff sgt. USAF, 1951-55. Recipient Leavy Free Enterprise award Freedoms Found. Valley Forge, 1985, Cert. Appreciation SBA, Washington, 1984, 85, Outstanding Contbn. to Entrepreneurship Edn. award Assn. Coll. Entrepreneurs, 1991, Disting. Alumni award Wilmington Coll., 1993; named Adv. of Yr.-Innovation SBA, Dallas, 1982, 83, 84. Mem. Internat. Coun. for Small Bus. (sr. v.p. 1986), U.S. Assn. for Small Bus. (v.p. pub. rels. 1987), Acad. Mgmt. (chmn. entrepreneurship com. 1981, mem. adv. bd. 1984-85), Masons, Shriners, Eagles, Am. Legion, Alpha Tau Omega. Republican. Baptist. Avocation: golf. Home: 11006 W 127th Ter Overland Park KS 66213 Office: Kauffman Found 4900 Oak St Kansas City MO 64112

SEXTON, JOHN EDWARD, lawyer, educator; b. Bklyn., Sept. 29, 1942; s. John Edward and Catherine (Humann) S.; m. Lisa Ellen Goldberg; children: Jed, Katherine. B.A., Fordham U., 1963, Ph.D, 1978; J.D., Harvard U., 1979. Bar: N.Y. 1981, U.S. Supreme Ct. 1984. Prof. religion St. Francis Coll., Bklyn., 1965-75; law clk. U.S. Ct. Appeals, Washington, 1979, 80; law clk. U.S. Supreme Ct., Washington, 1980-81; prof. law NYU, N.Y.C., 1981—, dean law Sch., 1988—; dir. Washington Sq. Legal Services, N.Y.C., 1983—; Pub. Interest Law Found., N.Y.C., 1983-85. Author: A Managerial Model of the Supreme Court, 1985, Federal Jury Instructions-Civil, 1985, How Free Are We? A Study of the Constitution, 1985, Cases and Materials in Civil Procedure, 1988. Dir. Root-Tilden Scholarship Program, 1984-88. Home: 29 Washington Sq W New York NY 10011-9180 Office: NYU Law Sch 40 Washington Sq S New York NY 10012-1099

SEXTON, OWEN JAMES, vertebrate ecology educator, conservationist; b. Phila., July 11, 1926; s. Gordon and Elizabeth May (Evans) S.; m. Mildred Lewis Bloomsburg, Apr. 5, 1952; children: Kenneth, Jean, Ann, Carolyn. Student, Sampson Coll., 1947-48; BA, Oberlin Coll., 1951; MA, U. Mich., 1953, PhD, 1956. Sr. teaching fellow Washington U., St. Louis, 1955-56, instr., 1956-57, asst. prof., 1957-62, assoc. prof., 1962-68, prof. vertebrate ecology, 1968—; vis. prof. U. Mich. Biol. Sta., Pellston, 1975-83; cons. UNESCO, 1974-75; adj. curator St. Louis Sci. Ctr., 1986-88. Pres., bd. dirs. Mo. Prairie Found., Columbia, 1968—; pres. Wild Canid Survival and Research Ctr., St. Louis, 1971-73; sec. Conservancy Art Soc., 1972-73; bd. dirs. Creve Coeur Figure Skating Club, 1982-89; mem. membership com. U.S. Figure Skating Assn., 1987-90. NSF fellow, 1966-67; vis. research fellow U. New Eng., 1984. Fellow Herpetologists League; mem. Am. Soc. Icthyologists and Herpetologists, Ecol. Soc. Am., Soc. Study of Amphibians and Reptiles, Orgn. Tropical Studies (bd. dir. 1976-85). Democrat. Home: 13154 Greenbough Dr Saint Louis MO 63146-3622 Office: Washington Lindell & Skinker Dept Biology Saint Louis MO 63130

SEXTON, RICHARD, lawyer, diversified manufacturing company executive; b. Madison, Wis., 1929; s. Joseph Cantwell and Eleanor Carr (Kenny) S.; m. Joan Fleming, 1957; children: Molly, Joseph, Lucy, Michael, Ann, Katherine. Student, Amherst Coll., 1947-49; B.S., U. Wis., 1951; LL.B. Yale U., 1958. Bar: N.Y. 1959, U.S. Supreme Ct. 1968. Assoc. firm Sullivan & Cromwell, N.Y.C., 1958-64; with SCM Corp., N.Y.C., 1964-86; asst. counsel SCM Corp., 1964-67; dir. gen. counsel Smith-Corona Marchant div., 1967-72, v.p., gen. counsel parent co., 1972-86, sec., 1977-86. Bd. dirs. Commonweal Mag. Bd. dirs. Advocates for Children of N.Y.C. Served to lt. (j.g.) USNR, 1951-55. Mem. Assn. Bar N.Y.C., ABA. Club: Yale. Home: 532 3rd St Brooklyn NY 11215-3003 Office: 63 Wall St New York NY 10005-3001

SEXTON, RICHARD, school system administrator. Supt. schs. Diocese of Fresno, Calif. Office: Office Supt Schs 1510 N Fresno St Fresno CA 93703-3711

SEXTON, ROBERT FENIMORE, educational organization executive; b. Cin., Jan. 13, 1942; s. Claude Fenimore and Jane (Wisenall) S.; m. Pam Peyton Papka, Sept. 15, 1985; children: Rebecca, Robert B., Ouita Papka,

Paige Papka, Perry Papka. BA, Yale U., 1964; MA in History, U. Wash., Seattle, 1968, PhD in History, 1970; DHL (hon.), Berea Coll., 1990. Georgetown Coll., Ky., 1993. Asst. prof. history Murray (Ky.) State U., 1968-70; dir. Office Acad. Programs, Commonwealth of Ky., Frankfort, 1970-73; assoc. dean, exec. dir. Office Exptl. Edn. U. Ky., Lexington, 1973-80; dep. exec. dir. Ky. Coun. Higher Edn., Frankfort, 1980-83; exec. dir. Prichard Com. for Acad. Excellence, Lexington, 1983—; founder, pres. Ky. Ctr. Pub. Issues, Lexington, 1988—; vis. scholar Harvard U., Cambridge, Mass., 1992, 94; chair Nat. Ctr. for Internships, Washington, 1973-80, Coalition for Alternatives in Post Secondary Edn., Washington, 1977-80; bd. dirs. Editl. Projects in Edn., Ky. Long Term Policy Rsch. Ctr., Coun. Advancement Exptl. Learning, 1976-80; adv. bd. Consortium for Prodn. in Schs., 1992—. Pub. The Ky. Jour., 1988—; editor book series: Public Papers of Governors of Kentucky, 1973-86; author reports in field. Co-chair Carnegie Ctr. for Literacy, Lexington, 1990-93; mem. Gov.'s Task Force on Health Care, Frankfort, 1992—; bd. dirs. Ky. Inst. Edn. Rsch. Fund for Improvement in Postsecondary Edn., 1993—; chair Bluegrass Edn. Work Coun., Lexington, 1978-80; founder, mem. steering com. Gov.'s Scholars Program, Frankfort, 1983-85. Recipient Charles A. Dana award for pioneering achievement, 1994. Mem. Am. Assn. Higher Edn. (bd. dirs. 1979-83). Democrat. Avocations: fishing, travel. Office: Prichard Com Acad Excell 167 W Main St Ste 310 Lexington KY 40507

SEXTON, THOMAS JOHN, science administrator, research physiologist; b. Mt. Holly, N.J., Aug. 11, 1942; married, 1964; 3 children. BS, Delaware Valley Coll., 1964; MS, U. NH., 1966; PhD in Dairy Sci., Pa. State U., 1972. Rsch. asst. U. N.H., 1964-66, U. Conn., 1966-67; rsch. assoc. Pa. State U., 1967-71; rsch. physiologist USDA, 1971-83, rsch. leader, 1983-88, dir. Livestock & Poultry Sci. Inst., Agr. Rsch. Svc., 1988—; vis. prof. Auburn U., Ala., 1984—. Mem. Poultry Sci. Assn. (Rsch. award 1982), World's Poultry Sci. Assn., Soc. Cryobiology, Sigma Xi. Achievements include research on critical problems that limit the reproductive efficiency of the avian male, cryogenic preservation of semen, artificial insemination and isolation of female gamete. Office: USDA Agr Rsch Ctr Livestock & Poultry Sci Inst B-200 Beltsville Beltsville MD 20705*

SEXTON, WILLIAM COTTRELL, journalist; b. Balt., Sept. 22, 1928; s. Hardigg and Grace Dean (Cottrell) S.; m. Bonnie Stone, Dec. 18, 1976; 1 child, Paul Norman. Student, U. N.C, 1946-47. With UPI, 1948-62, mgr. N.Y. bur., 1959-62; assoc. dir. Am. Press Inst., Columbia U., 1963-66; mng. editor Louisville Courier Jour., 1966-67; mng. editor, then editor World Book Sci. Service, 1967-69; editor Publishers-Hall Syndicate, N.Y.C., 1969-70; with Newsday, Inc. Melville, N.Y., 1970-91, asst. to editor, 1972-73, assoc. editor, 1973-86, Asia bur., Peking, 1979-83, Asia bur., Tokyo, 1986-89, diplomatic corr., N.Y.C., 1989-91, editorial columnist, 1983-86; dir. Ford Found. seminar for African newspaper execs., 1965; vice chmn. N.Y. State Fair Trial Free Press Conf., 1977-79, mem., 1984-87. Pres. Richmond Hist. Soc., 1991—, Bershire Bach Soc., 1993-94; sec. Boston Symphony Assn. Vols. Tanglewood, 1992-94. Served with AUS, 1951-52. Mem. Coun. Fgn. Rels., Am. Radio Relay League. Home: 105 West Rd Richmond MA 01254-9392

SEYBERT, JOANNA, judge; b. Bklyn., Sept. 18, 1946; married; 1 child. BA, U. Cin., 1967; JD, St. John's U., 1971. Bar: N.Y. 1972, U.S. Dist. Ct. (ea. and so. dists.) N.Y. 1973, U.S. Ct. Appeals (2d cir.) 1973. Trial staff atty. Legal Aid Soc., N.Y.C., 1971-73; sr. staff atty. Legal Aid Soc., Mineola, N.Y., 1976-80; sr. trial atty. Fed. Defender Svc., Bklyn., 1973-75; bur. chief Nassau County Atty's Office, Mineola, 1980-87; judge Nassau County Dist. Ct., Hempstead, N.Y., 1987-92, Nassau County Ct., Mineola, 1992-94, U.S. Dist. Ct. (ea. dist.) N.Y., Bklyn., 1994—. Past mem. environ. bd. Town of Oyster Bay; mem. Rep. com. Nassau County, 1979-87. Recipient Norman F. Lent award Criminal Cts. Bar Assn., 1991. Mem. ABA, N.Y. State Bar Assn., Bar Assn. Nassau County, Nassau County Women's Bar Assn., Theodore Roosevelt Inns of Ct., Fed. Judges Assn., Nassau Lawyer's Assn. (past pres.). Office: 2 Uniondale Ave Uniondale NY 11553

SEYFERTH, DIETMAR, chemist, educator; b. Chemnitz, Germany, Jan. 11, 1929; came to U.S., 1933; s. Herbert C. and Elisabeth (Schuchardt) S.; m. Helena A. McCoy, Aug. 25, 1956; children—Eric Steven, Karl Dietmar, Elisabeth Mary. B.A. summa cum laude, U. Buffalo, 1951, M.A., 1953; Ph.D., Harvard, 1955; Dr. honoris causa, U. Aix-Marseille, 1979, Paul Sabatier Univ., Toulouse, France, 1992. Fulbright scholar Tech. Hochschule, Munich, Germany, 1954-55; postdoctoral fellow Harvard U., 1956-57; faculty MIT, 1957—, prof. chemistry, 1965—, Robert T. Haslam and Bradley Dewey prof., 1983—; cons. to industry, 1957—. Author: Annual Surveys of Organometallic Chemistry, 3 vols, 1965, 66, 67; regional editor: Jour. Organometallic Chemistry, 1963-81; coordinating editor revs. and survey sects., 1964-81; editor: Organometallics, 1981—; contbr. research papers to profl. lit. Recipient Disting. Alumnus award U. Buffalo, 1964, Alexander von Humboldt Found. sr. award, 1984, Clifford C. Furnas Meml. award SUNY-Buffalo, 1987; Guggenheim fellow, 1968. Fellow AAAS, Am. Inst. Chemists, Inst. Materials, Am. Acad. Arts and Scis.; mem. Am. Chem. Soc. (frederic Stanley Kipping award in organsilicon chemistry 1972, disting. svc. award advancement inorganic chemistry 1981), Materials Rsch. Soc., Am. Ceramic Soc., Royal Soc. Chemistry, Gesellschaft Deutscher Chemiker, German Acad. Scientists-Leopoldina, Phi Beta Kappa, Sigma Xi. Office: MIT 77 Massachusetts Ave Rm 4-382 Cambridge MA 02139-3594

SEYFFARTH, LINDA JEAN WILCOX, corporate executive, controller; b. Montour Falls, N.Y., May 10, 1948; d. Maurice Roscoe and Theodora (Van Tassell) Wilcox; m. P. Tomlin Agnew, June 29, 1991; 1 child by previous marriage, Kristin. BA magna cum laude, Syracuse (N.Y.) U., 1970; MBA with honors, NYU, 1977. Programmer Prudential Ins. Co., Newark, 1970-73; with Hoffmann-La Roche Inc., Nutley, N.J., 1973—, corp. controller, 1985-88, v.p., contr., 1989-95; v.p. fin. Roche Labs., 1995—. Bd. dirs., treas. St. Barnabas Burn Found., West Orange, N.J., Glen Ridge (N.J.) Ednl. Found., Ind.Coll. Fund, Summit, N.J. Mem. Nat. Assn. Accts., Fin. Execs. Inst., Leadership N.J., Phi Beta Kappa, Beta Gamma Sigma. Office: Hoffmann-LaRoche Inc 340 Kingsland St 340 Kingsland St Nutley NJ 07110-1150

SEYMORE, JAMES W., JR., magazine editor. Mng. editor Entertainment Weekly, N.Y.C. Office: Entertainment Weekly 1675 Broadway New York NY 10019-5820

SEYMOUR, ARTHUR HALLOCK, retired newspaper editor; b. Des Moines, Oct. 22, 1928; s. Forrest Wilson and Pearl Bernice (Yeager) S.; m. Ann Adele Ulness, Aug. 19, 1977; children—Forrest Wilson, Macy Yeager, Andrew Hallock. B.A., Harvard U., 1952. Reporter AP, Cheyenne, Wyo., 1952-53, Denver, 1953-55; mem. staff Mpls. Star and Tribune, 1955-90, bus. news editor, 1965-70, asst. news editor, 1970-72, news editor, 1972-78, dep. mng. editor, 1978-90, ret. Served with USMCR, 1946-49. Home: 29562 Orchard Rd Red Wing MN 55066-6164

SEYMOUR, BRIAN RICHARD, mathematics educator, researcher; b. Chesterfield, Derby, Eng., Sept. 25, 1944; came to U.S., 1968, Can., 1973; s. Douglas and Hilda (Ball) S.; m. Rosemary Jane Pembleton, Sept. 23, 1943; children—Mark, Jane, Richard. B.Sc. with honors, U. Manchester, 1965; Ph.D., U. Nottingham, 1968. Asst. prof. Lehigh U., 1969-70, N.Y. U., 1970-73, U. B.C., 1973-76; assoc. prof. U. B.C., 1976-81, Vancouver, Can., prof. math., 1981—, dir. inst. applied math, 1986-93; vis. prof. Ctr. Water Rsch. U. Western Australia, 1993-94. Contbr. research papers to profl. jours. Sci. Research Council sr. research fellow Oxford U., 1978; Killam sr. fellow Killam Trust, Monash U., 1984. Mem. Can. Applied Math. Soc., Soc. Indsl. & Applied Math. Avocation: field hockey. Office: U BC, 222-1984 Mathematics Rd, Vancouver, BC Canada V6T 1Z2

SEYMOUR, DALE GILBERT, publisher, author, speaker, consultant; b. Hugo, Colo., Sept. 30, 1931; s. Earl Daniel and Alice Edna (Andersen) S.; m. Linda Lou Horn, June 9, 1953 (div. Sept. 1969); children: Luanne, Douglas, Jill; m. Margo Lee Draper, Dec. 27, 1974. BS, U. Colo., 1953, MA, 1961; postgrad., Calif. State U., Hayward, San Jose State U. Tchr., coach Bayard (Nebr.) Pub. Schs., 1953-54, Longmont (Colo.) High Sch., 1956-62; tchr. Palo Alto (Calif.) Unified Sch. Dist., 1962-69; founder, pub., CEO, Creative Publs., Palo Alto, 1968-79; pub. Dale Seymour Publs., Palo Alto, 1979—, CEO, 1979-92; cons., author, speaker, 1994—; speaker over 600 state, nat.

and internat. tchr. confs., 1968—; instr. East Tenn. State U., U. Hawaii; chmn. math. dept. Jordan Jr. High Sch., Palo Alto, 1963-69, assoc. math. curriculum, 1965-69; mem. addendum com. Calif. Math. Framework, 1979-80; mem. Calif. Model Curriculum Standards Com., 1984. Author, co-author numerous supplemental math. books and publs., 1965—; designer over 100 ednl. products, 1968—. 1st lt. C.E., U.S. Army, 1954-56. Mem. Nat. Coun. Tchrs. Math. (curriculum and evaluation standards commn. 1987-88), Nat. Coun. Suprs. Math. (Glen Gilbert award 1993).

SEYMOUR, HARLAN FRANCIS, healthcare industry executive; b. East Saint Louis, Mo., Jan. 25, 1950; s. Harlan Edward and Agnes Wilhelmina (Noakes) S.; m. Ellen Katheleen Schmitt, Aug. 17, 1973; children: Melissa Ann, Harlan Francis Jr. BA in Math., U. Mo., 1973; MBA, Keller Grad. Sch. Mgmt., 1980. Corp. v.p Statis. Tabulating Corp., Chgo., 1973-80; dist. mgr. Datacorp, Chgo., 1980-83; exec. v.p. 1st Fin. Mgmt. Corp., Atlanta, 1983-94; pres., CEO 1st Health Svcs. Corp., Richmond, Va., 1989-94; exec. v.p., COO Trigon Blue Cross/Blue Shield, Richmond, 1994—; mem. mgmt. info. systems adv. bd. U. Ga., Athens, 1986, 87, Va. Commonwealth Univ., 1991—; bd. dirs. J. Sargeant Reynolds Community Coll., 1991—. V.p. St. Joseph's Home and Sch., Marietta, Ga., 1987—. Mem. Nat. Assn. Bank Servicers, Bank Mktg. Assn., Richmond Metro C. of C., Fin. Mgrs. Soc. Roman Catholic. Avocations: sailing, tennis, jogging. Home: 12106 Country Hills Ct Glen Allen VA 23060-5347 Office: Trigon Blue Cross/Blue Shield 7130 Glen Forest Dr Richmond VA 23226

SEYMOUR, JANE, actress; b. Hillingdon, Middlesex, Eng., Feb. 15, 1951; came to U.S., 1976; d. John Benjamin and Mieke Frankenberg; m. David Flynn, July 18, 1981 (div. 1991); 2 children; m. James Keach, May 15, 1993. Student, Arts Ednl. Sch., London. Appeared in films Oh What A Lovely War, 1968, The Only Way, 1968, Young Winston, 1969, Live and Let Die, 1971, Sinbad and the Eye of the Tiger, 1973, Somewhere in Time, 1979, Oh Heavenly Dog, 1979, Lassiter, 1984, Head Office, Scarlet Pimpernel, Haunting Passion, Dark Mirror, Obsessed with a Married Woman, Killer on Board, The Tunnel, 1988, The French Revolution; TV films include Frankenstein, The True Story, 1972, Captains and The Kings, 1976 (Emmy nomination), 7th Avenue, 1976, The Awakening Land, 1977, The Four Feathers, 1977, Battlestar Galactica, Dallas Cowboy Cheerleaders, 1979, Our Mutual Friend, PBS, Eng., 1975, Jamaica Inn, 1982, Sun Also Rises, 1984, Crossings, 1986, Keys to Freedom, Angel of Death, 1990, Praying Mantis, 1993; A Passion for Justice: The Hazel Brannon Smith Story, 1994; Broadway appearances include Amadeus, 1980-81, I Remember You, 1992, Matters of the Heart, 1991, Sunstroke, 1992, Praying Mantis, 1993, Heidi, 1993; TV mini-series include East of Eden, 1980, The Richest Man in the World, 1988 (Emmy award), The Woman He Loved, 1988, Jack the Ripper, 1988, War and Remembrance, 1988, 89; host PBS documentary, Japan, 1988; TV series: Dr. Quinn: Medicine Woman, 1993— (Emmy nomination, Lead Actress - Drama, 1994); author: Jane Seymour's Guide to Romantic Living, 1986. Named Hon. Citizen of Ill., Gov. Thompson, 1977. Mem. Screen Actors Guild, AFTRA, Actors Equity, Brit. Equity. Office: Metropolitan Talent Agency 4526 Wilshire Blvd Los Angeles CA 90010*

SEYMOUR, JON, federal government official. Asst. sec. Dept. Transp., Washington, 1986—. Office: Dept Transp Adminstrn 400 7th St SW Washington DC 20590-0001

SEYMOUR, MCNEIL VERNAM, lawyer; b. St. Paul, Dec. 21, 1934; s. McNeil Vernam and Katherine Grace (Klein) S.; children—Margaret, McNeil Vernam, James, Benjamin; m. Mary Katherine Velner, May 15, 1993. A.B., Princeton U. 1957; J.D., U. Chgo., 1960. Bar: Minn. 1960, U.S. Dist. Ct. Minn. 1960. Mem. Seymour & Seymour, St. Paul, 1960-71; mem. firm Briggs & Morgan, St. Paul, 1971—, ptnr., 1976—. Trustee Oakland Cemetery Assn.; pres., treas. White Bear Unitarian Ch., 1964-65; sec., bd. dirs. Ramsey County Law Library, 1972-76. Served with U.S. Army, 1960-62. Mem. Ramsey County Bar Assn., Minn. Bar Assn. Republican. Unitarian. Clubs: Somerset Country Club. Home: 886 S Highview Cir Mendota Hts MN 55118-3686 Offices: Briggs & Morgan 2200 1st Nat Bank Bldg Saint Paul MN 55101

SEYMOUR, MICHAEL, production designer. Prodn. designer: (films) Gumshoe, 1971, Theatre of Blood, 1973, Rosebud, 1975, Alien, 1979 (Academy award nomination best art direction 1979), Eureka, 1984, The Bride, 1985, Mr. Destiny, 1990, (with Benjamin Fernandez) Revenge, 1990, (with Hector Romero, Jr.) Gunmen, 1992, (with Thomas Wilkins) The Thing Called Love, 1993, Beverly Hills Cop III, 1994. Office: Judy Marks Agency 650 N Bronson Ave Ste 148 Los Angeles CA 90004*

SEYMOUR, RICHARD KELLOGG, linguist, educator; b. Hinsdale, Ill., June 21, 1930; s. William and Katharine (Fifield) S.; m. Nancy Ann Nutt, June 23, 1951; children: Michael Bradley, William David. B.A., U. Mich., 1951, M.A., 1952; cert., U. Tübingen, Tübingen, Germany, 1953; Ph.D., U. Pa., 1956, postgrad. linguistics, 1957. Asst. instr. U. Pa., 1952-55; instr. Princeton U., 1954-58; linguist NDEA Summer Inst., 1963; asst. prof. Duke U., 1958-63, asso. prof., 1963-67, endowment fellow, 1966; prof., chmn. dept. European langs. and lit. U. Hawaii, Honolulu, 1967-75, prof., 1977-95; ret., 1995; dean Coll. Langs., Linguistics and Lit. U. Hawaii, Honolulu, 1981-95; prof. German dept. Pa. State U., University Park, 1975-77; vis. prof. Cologne (Germany) U., 1974. Author: A Bibliography of Word Formation in the Germanic Languages, 1968; assoc. editor Unterrichtspraxis, 1969-80; editor Am. Jour. Germanic Linguistics and Lit., 1989—; contbr. articles to profl. jours. Princeton Research Council grantee, 1958; Am. Council Learned Socs. grantee, 1957; Fulbright travel award, 1981. Mem. Linguistic Soc. Am., Internat. Linguistic Assn., Am. Dialect Soc., Am. Assn. Tchrs. German, MLA, S. Atlantic MLA (exec. sec. 1962-67), Delta Phi Alpha (nat. sec.-treas. 1968—). Congregationalist (bd. deacons, sec. 1970-71).

SEYMOUR, STEPHANIE KULP, federal judge; b. Battle Creek, Mich., Oct. 16, 1940; d. Francis Bruce and Frances Cecelia (Bria) Kulp; m. R. Thomas Seymour, June 10, 1972; children: Bart, Bria, Sara, Anna. BA magna cum laude, Smith Coll., 1962; JD, Harvard U., 1965. Bar: Okla. 1965. Practice Boston, 1965-66, Tulsa, 1966-67, Houston, 1968-69; assoc. Doerner, Stuart, Saunders, Daniel & Anderson, Tulsa, 1971-75, ptnr., 1975-79; judge U.S. Ct. Appeals (10th cir.) Okla., Tulsa, 1979—, now chief justice; assoc. bar examiner Okla. Bar Assn., 1973-79; trustee Tulsa County Law Library, 1977-78; mem. U.S. Jud. Conf. Com. Defender Svcs., 1985-91, chmn., 1987-91. Mem. various task forces Tulsa Human Rights Commn., 1972-76, legal adv. panel Tulsa Task Force Battered Women, 1971-77. Mem. Am. Bar Assn., Okla. Bar Assn., Tulsa County Bar Assn., Phi Beta Kappa. Office: US Courthouse 333 West 4th St Rm 4-562 Tulsa OK 74103

SEYMOUR, THADDEUS, English educator; b. N.Y.C., June 29, 1928; s. Whitney North and Lola Virginia (Vickers) S.; m. Polly Gnagy, Nov. 20, 1948; children—Elizabeth Halsey, Thaddeus, Samuel Whitney, Mary Duffie, Abigail Comfort. A.B., U. Calif., 1950; M.A., U. N.C., 1951, Ph.D., 1955; D.H.L. (hon.), Wilkes Coll., 1968; LL.D. (hon.), Butler U., 1971, Ind. State U., 1976; LLD (hon.), Wabash Coll., 1984, U. Cen. Fla., 1990, Stetson U., 1990; DHL (hon.), Rollins Coll., 1990. Mem. faculty Dartmouth Coll., 1954-69, prof. English, dean coll., 1959-69; pres. Wabash Coll., Crawfordsville, Ind., 1969-78; pres. Rollins Coll., Winter Park, Fla., 1978-90, prof. English, 1978—; pres. Ind. Conf. Higher Edn., 1977; v.p. Assoc. Colls. Ind., 1978; vice-chmn. Fla. Ind. Colls. Fund. Past mem. Ind. Bicentennial Commn.; del. N.H. Republican Conv., 1958, 64; vice-chmn. N.H. Rep. Com., 1967-68; trustee Park-Tudor Sch., 1970-78, Bach Festival Soc.; chmn. Fla. selection com. Rhodes Scholarship Trust, 1983-88. Mem. Nat. Rowing Found. (dir.), Ring 219 (charter), Internat. Brotherhood Magicians, Ind. Colls. and Univs. Fla. (sec.), Fla. Assn. Colls. and Univs., Century Assn., Omicron Delta Kappa. Home: 1350 College Pt Winter Park FL 32789-5700

SFAT, MICHAEL RUDOLPH, biochemical engineer; b. Timisoara, Romania, Oct. 28, 1921; came to U.S., 1924; s. Peter and Emilia (Iovin) S.; m. Jane Buckridge, Nov. 24, 1948; children: Gail Buckridge Sergent, Mary Anne Bauer. B Chem. Engring., Cornell U., 1943, M Chem. Engring., 1947; postgrad., Princeton U., 1949-50. Registered profl. engr., Wis. Rsch. assoc. Cornell U., Ithaca, N.Y., 1943-44; asst. microbiologist Merck & Co., Inc., Rahway, N.J., 1947-51, sr. microbiologist, 1951-52; dir. devel. pilot plant Pabst Brewing Co., Milw., 1952-54; rsch. dir. Rahr Malting Co., Manitowoc, Wis., 1954-58, coord. R&D, 1958-60, v.p. R&D, 1960-69; pres. Bio-Tech.

Resources, Manitowoc, 1962-89, pres. emeritus, 1989—; mem. Gov.'s Counl on Biotech., Wis., 1990. Contbr. articles to profl. jours.; patentee in field. 2nd lt. U.S. Army, 1944-46. Recipient Schwarz prize for brewing tech., 1966, Disting. Svc. award Coll. Engring., U. Wis., 1993. Fellow Nat. Acad. Engring., Am. Acad. Microbiology, Am. Inst. Med. and Biol. Engrs.; mem. Am. Chem. Soc., Am. Inst. Chem. Engrs., Am. Soc. Brewing Chemists (pres. 1974-75), Am. Soc. Microbiology, Inst. Food Technologists, Master Brewers Assn. Am., Soc. Indsl. Microbiology, Manitowoc-Two Rivers C. of C. (dir. 1970-78), Branch River Country Club (dir. 1972-78), Elks. Republican. Presbyterian. Avocations: golf, tennis, skiing, windsurfing, barn restoration. Home: 1030 W Crescent Dr Manitowoc WI 54220 Office: Bio-Technical Resources 1035 S 7th St Manitowoc WI 54220

SFEKAS, STEPHEN JAMES, lawyer, educator; b. Balt., Feb. 12, 1947; s. James Stephen and Lee (Mesologites) S.; m. Joanne Lorraine Murphy, May 27, 1973; children: James Stephen, Andrew Edward Stephen, Christina Marie. BS in Fgn. Svc., Georgetown U., 1968; MA (Danforth fellow, Woodrow Wilson fellow) Yale U., 1972; JD, Georgetown U., 1973. Bar: Md. 1973, U.S. Dist. Ct. Md. 1974, U.S. Ct. Appeals (4th cir.) 1974. Law clk. U.S. Dist. Ct., Balt., 1973-74; assoc. firm Frank, Bernstein, Conaway & Goldman, Balt., 1974-75; asst. atty. gen. State of Md., Balt., 1975-81; assoc. firm Tydings & Rosenberg, Balt., 1981-82, ptnr., 1983-86, with firm Miles & Stockbridge, 1986-90; ptnr. Weinberg & Green, 1991—; instr. legal writing Community Coll. Balt., 1976-79; instr. legal ethics Goucher Coll., Balt., 1979; adj. prof. adminstrv. law U. Md., Balt., 1981-93, adj. prof. health care law, sch. law, 1993—. Editor Georgetown Law Jour., 1972-73; contbr. articles to legal publs. Bd. dirs. Md. region NCCJ, 1981-89, co-chmn. Md. region, 1986-89; mem. Piraeus Sister City Com., City of Balt., 1983-89; mem. parish council Greek Orthodox Cathedral of Annunciation, Balt., 1981-84; mem. internat. com. Balt. region ARC, 1984-85; mem. adv. com. on bread for the world, Dept. Ch. and Soc., Greek Orthodox Archdiocese N. and S.Am., 1984—; pres. Greek Orthodox Counseling and Social Services of Balt., 1984-88; bd. dirs. Orthodox Christian Laity, 1990—, Cen. Md. Ecumenical Coun., 1991—; mem. bylaw com. Girl Scouts of Cen. Md., 1989-91. WHO fellow, London, 1979. Fellow Soc. for Values in Higher Edn.; mem. ABA (Grant Morris fellow 1979, forum com. on health law), Md. Bar Assn., Bar Assn. Balt. City, Nat. Health Lawyers Assn., Am. Soc. Hosp. Attys. Democrat. Office: Weinberg & Green 100 S Charles St Baltimore MD 21201-2720

SFIKAS, PETER MICHAEL, lawyer, educator; b. Gary, Ind., Aug. 9, 1937; s. Michael E. and Helen (Thureanos) S.; m. Freida Platon, Apr. 24, 1966; children—Ellen M., Pamela C., Sandra N. BS, Ind. U., 1959; JD, Northwestern U., 1962. Bar: Ill. 1962, U.S. Dist. Ct. (no. dist.) Ill. 1963, U.S. Ct. Appeals (7th cir.) 1963, U.S. Supreme Ct. 1970, U.S. Ct. Appeals (9th cir.) 1976, U.S. Ct. Appeals (3d cir.) 1981, U.S. Ct. Appeals (D.C. cir.) 1984, U.S. Dist. Ct. (cen. dist.) Ill. 1988. Atty. Legal Aid Bur., United Charities Chgo., 1962-63; sr. ptnr. Peterson & Ross, Chgo., 1970—; prosecutor Village of LaGrange Park, Ill., 1969-74; mem. rules com. Ill. Supreme Ct., 1975—; arbitrator Nat. Panel Arbitrators, 1972—; adj. prof. Loyola U. Sch. Law, 1978—; guest lectr. U. Ill. Coll. Dentistry, 1988—; lectr. 23d ann. corp. counsel inst. Northwestern U. Sch. Law, 1984. Contbr. articles to profl. jours. Mem. Ill. steering com. Ct. Watching Project, LWV, 1975-77; pres. Holy Apostles Greek Orthodox Ch. Parish Coun., 1987-89; co-pres. Oak Sch. PTO, 1989-90; mem. com. to select sch. supr., dist. 86, DuPage County, Ill., 1993-94. Recipient Chgo. Bar Found. Maurice Weigle award 1973. Fellow Am. Bar Found., Am. Coll. Trial Lawyers, Chgo. Bar Found. (life); mem. ABA (editor in chief Forum Law Jour. sect. ins., negligence and compensation law 1972-76), Ill. Bar Found. (bd. dirs.), Northwestern U. Law Alumni Assn. (1st v.p. 1985-86, pres. 1986-87, Svc. award 1990), Ill. State Bar Assn. (bd. govs. 1970-76, chmn. antitrust law sect. coun. 1986-87), Chgo. Bar Assn. (editl. bd. Chgo. Bar Record 1973-84), Bar Assn. 7th Fed. Cir., Ill. Trial Inst. Continuing Legal Edn. (chmn. profl. antitrust problems program 1976, author program on counseling corps., antitrust and trade regulation), Legal Club Chgo. (sec.-treas, 1984-86, v.p. 1989-90, pres. 1990-91), Law Club. Office: Peterson & Ross 200 E Randolph Dr Ste 7300 Chicago IL 60601-6401

SGANGA, JOHN B., furniture holding company executive; b. Bronx, N.Y., Nov. 21, 1931; s. Charles and Marie (Crusco) S.; B.S. in Acctg. cum laude, Bklyn. Coll., 1961; postgrad. Bernard Baruch Coll.; m. Evelyn Joan Battilana, Jan. 19, 1957; children: Mark, John B. Jr., Matthew. Systems analyst DIVCO, Wayne, N.Y., 1965-67; mgr. mgmt. cons. services Coopers & Lybrand, C.P.A.s N.Y.C., 1967-74; sr. v.p. fin. and adminstrn. Aurora Products Co. subs. RJR Nabisco, West Hempstead, N.Y., 1974-79; controller Gt. Lakes Carbon Corp., N.Y.C., 1979-80, v.p., 1980-81, sr. v.p. fin., CFO, 1981-86; v.p. Cunard Line, Ltd., N.Y.C., 1988; exec. v.p., CFO Consolidated Furniture Corp. (formerly Mobasco Corp.), Wilmington, Del., 1989—, also bd. dirs. Served with USNR, 1950-54. Mem. Inst. Cert. Mgmt. Cons. (a founder), Inst. Mgmt. Accts., Fin. Execs. Inst. (past chmn. com. M.I.S.). Clubs: Treas.'s, Brookside Racquet and Swim. Contbr. articles to jours. in field; editl. adv. to Financial Management mag. Home: 255 Davidson Ave Ramsey NJ 07446-1003 Office: Consolidated Furniture Corp One Commerce Ctr 1201 N Orange St Ste 790 Wilmington DE 19801

SGRO, JOSEPH ANTHONY, psychologist, educator; b. New Haven, Conn., Nov. 22, 1937; s. Fred and Tullia (Franceseoni) S.; m. Beverly Ann Huston, Feb. 1, 1964; children: Anthony, Jennifer. BA, Trinity Coll., 1959; MS, Lehigh U., 1961; PhD, Tex. Christian U., 1966. Asst. prof. Old Dominion U., Norfolk, Va., 1965-67; asst. prof. Va. Poly. Inst. & State U., Blacksburg, 1967-71, assoc. prof., 1971-79, prof., 1979—; dept. head psychology, 1982—; mem. exec. bd., sec.-treas. coun. grad. dept. psychology, 1990-92, chmn., 1992-93; vice-chmn. Va. Bd. Psychologists Examiners, Richmond, 1970-75. Editor: Virginia Tech Symposium on Applied Behavioral Science, 1980. Mem. Am. Psychol. Assn., Am. Psychol. Soc., Psychonomic Soc., Southeastern Psychol. Assn. (chmn. assn. heads depts. psychology 1987-89), Ea. Psychol. Assn., Soc. for Philosophy & Psychology, Va. Psychol. Assn. (pres. 1974-76), Omicron Delta Kappa, Psi Chi, Sigma Xi. Avocations: golf, cooking. Home: 4185 Pearman Rd Blacksburg VA 24060-8549 Office: Va Poly Inst & State U Dept Psychology Blacksburg VA 24061

SGROI, MARIO, publishing executive. With Calgary Sun and Toronto Sun, 1970-90; pres., dir. Fla. Sun Publs., Inc., Bradenton, 1991—. Office: Fla Sun Publs Inc 717 1st St Bradenton FL 34208-1947

SHAAR, H. ERIK, academic administrator. V.p. acad. affairs Shippensburg U. of Pa., until 1986; pres. Lake Superior State U., Sault Sainte Marie, Mich., 1986-92, Minot (N.D.) Stte U., 1992—. Office: Minot State U Office of Pres Minot ND 58701

SHABAZ, JOHN C., federal judge; b. West Allis, Wis., June 25, 1931; s. Cyrus D. and Harriet T. Shabaz; children: Scott J., Jeffrey J., Emily D., John D. Student, U. Wis., 1949-53; LLB, Marquette U., 1957. Pvt. practice law West Allis, Wis., 1957-81; mem. Wis. Assembly, 1965-71; judge U.S. Dist. Ct. (we. dist.) Wis., 1981—. With U.S. Army, 1954-56. Office: US Dist Ct PO Box 591 Madison WI 53701-0591

SHABAZZ, AIYSHA MUSLIMAH, social work administrator; b. Columbia, S.C., Aug. 9, 1942; d. Jerry James Gadson and Edna Louise (Bellinger) Gadson Smalls; m. Abdullah Muslim Shabazz, July 28; children: Ain, Wali. BA, Fed. City Coll., Washington, 1973; MSW with honors, U. S.C., 1994; postgrad, 1994-95. Cert. child protective svcs. investigator, S.C.; adoption investigator, S.C.; lic. social worker and ACBSW; cert. AIDS instr. ARC; lic. notary pub., S.C. Social work asst. Family Service Ctr., Washington, 1966-68; admission counselor Washington Tech. Inst. Washington, 1968-70; program dir. Park Motor Community Ctr., Washington, 1970-75; adminstrv. asst. Neighborhood Planning Council, Washington, 1974-75; substitue tchr. D.C. Pub. Sch. System, Washington, 1974-75; substitute tchr. Dist. 1 Pub. Schs., Columbia, 1977; home sch. program dir. Community Care, Inc., Columbia, 1977-81; monitor summer program U.S.C., Columbia, 1982; program dir. Dept. Social Services, Columbia, 1984—, case auditor, 1987-88, social worker supr., 1988—; writer Acad. of Bacholu-Social Workers Exam, 1991; speaker in field. Bd. dirs. Frederick Douglas Inst., Washington, 1968-69; pres. Park Motor Resident Coun., Washington, 1972-75; expert witness Family Ct.; bd. dirs. Coun. on Child Abuse and Neglect;

adv. com., v.p. Benedict Coll. Sch. Social Work, S.C. Protection and Advocacy Handicapped Children; vol. AIDS instr. ARC, 1994. Mem. NASW (bd. dirs. 1993-95), S.C. Child Abuse and Neglect Task Force, AIDS Task Force (chmn. 1987-89). Democrat. Office: Dept Social Services 3220 Two Notch Rd Columbia SC 29204-2826

SHABICA, CHARLES WRIGHT, earth science educator; b. Elizabeth, N.J., Jan. 3, 1943; s. Anthony Charles and Eleanor (Wright) S.; m. Susan Ewing, Dec. 30, 1967; children: Jonathan, Andrew, Dana. BA in Geology, Brown U., 1965; PhD, U. Chgo., 1971. Prof. earth sci. Northeastern Ill. U., Chgo., 1971—; disting. prof., 1991; pres. Shabica & Assocs., Inc., Northfield, Ill., 1985—; chmn. bd. dirs. Aesti Corp.; rsch. collaborator Nat. Park Svc., 1978-82, 89—; adj. prof. Coll. V.I., St. Thomas, 1980; Kellogg fellow Northeastern Ill. U., 1979—; chmn. Task Force on Lake Michigan, Chgo., 1986-89; mem. Chgo. Shoreline Protection Commn., 1987-88; cons. Shedd Aquarium, Chgo., 1991; mem. Ft. Sheridan Commn., 1989-90. Commr., packmaster Boy Scots Am., Winnetka, Ill., 1984-87. Coop. Inst. for Limnology and Ecosystems Rsch. Lab. fellow. Mem. Am. Shore and Beach Assn., Internat. Assn. for Gt. Lakes Rsch., Sigma Xi. Home: 326 Ridge Ave Winnetka IL 60093 Office: 345 Walnut St Northfield IL 60093

SHACHAR, AVISHAI, lawyer; b. Bklyn., Oct. 29, 1953; s. Zeev and Natasha (Kisler) S.; m. Orly Eylan, Sept. 6, 1977; children: Carmel, Tal. LLB, Tel-Aviv U., 1980; SJD, Harvard U., 1984. Bar: Israel 1983, N.Y. 1984. With Prof. Yuval Levi Law Offices, Tel-Aviv, 1979-80, Herzog, Fox, Neeman & Co., Tel-Aviv, 1980-81; assoc Davis, Polk & Wardwell, N.Y.C., 1984-86, ptnr., 1987—. Recipient acad. award Yad Avi Ha-Yeshuv, Israel, 1982. Mem. ABA, Internat. Fiscal Assn., Israeli Bar Assn. Office: Davis Polk & Wardwell PO Box 912 New York NY 10268-0912

SHACK, WILLIAM ALFRED, anthropology educator, researcher, consultant; b. Chgo., Apr. 19, 1923; s. William and Emma (McAvoy) S.; m. Dorothy Nash, Sept. 1, 1960; 1 child, Hailu A. B.A.E., Sch. of the Art Inst., Chgo., 1955; M.A., U. Chgo., 1957; Ph.D., London Sch. Econs., 1961. Asst. prof. sociology and anthropology Northeastern Ill. State Coll., Chgo., 1961-62; asst. prof. sociology Haile Sellassie I Univ., Addis Ababa, Ethiopia, 1962-65; assoc. prof. anthropology U. Ill., Chgo., 1966-70; prof. anthropology U. Calif.-Berkeley, 1970-91, dean, grad. div., 1979-85. Author: The Gurage, 1966, The Central Ethiopians, 1974; co-author: Gods and Heroes, 1974; co-editor: Strangers in African Societies, 1979. Trustee, bd. dirs. World Affairs Council of No. Calif., San Francisco. Served with USCG, 1943-46; PTO. Fellow AAAS, Calif. Acad. Scis. (trustee, v.p. 1993), Am. Anthrop. Assn., Royal Anthrop. Inst. (pres. N.Am. com. 1983-86), Internat. African Inst. (econ. coun. 1984-90; mem. club 1985-87, chmn. 1987—; Chevalier l'Ordre Nationale du Merite 1987), Athenaeum (London); mem. Faculty Club U. Calif.-Berkeley (pres. 1991-94). Avocation: vintage motor racing. Home: 2597 Hilgard Ave Berkeley CA 94709-1104 Office: U Calif-Berkeley Dept Anthropology 232 Kroeber Hall Berkeley CA 94720

SHACKELFORD, BARTON WARREN, retired utility executive; b. San Francisco, Oct. 12, 1920; s. Frank Harris and Amelia Louse (Schilling) S.; m. Charlaine Mae Livingston, July 24, 1949; children: Frank, Joan, Linda, Ann. B.S. in Civil Engring, U. Calif., Berkeley, 1941. Jr. engr. Todd-Calif. Shipbldg. Corp., 1941-44; with Pacific Gas & Electric Co., 1946-85; sr. v.p., then exec. v.p. Pacific Gas & Electric Co., San Francisco, 1976-79; pres. Pacific Gas & Electric Co., 1979-85; Bd. dirs. Harding Assocs., Inc., Calif. Energy Co. Inc. Office: Pacific Gas & Electric Co 123 Mission St PO Box 770000 Mail Code H17 San Francisco CA 94177

SHACKELFORD, GEORGE GREEN, historian; b. Orange, Va., Dec. 17, 1920; s. Virginius Randolph and Peachy Gascoigne (Lyne) S.; m. Grace Howard McConnell, June 9, 1962. B.A., U. Va., 1943, M.A., 1948, Ph.D., 1955; postgrad., Columbia U., 1949-51; cert., Attingham, Eng., 1957. Asst. prof. history Birmingham (Ala.) So. Coll., 1948-49; rsch. fellow Va. Hist. Soc., Richmond, 1951-53; instr. Va. Poly. Inst. and State U., Blacksburg, 1954-55; asst. prof. history Va. Poly. Inst. and State U., 1955-58, assoc prof., 1958-68, prof., 1968-90, prof. emeritus, 1990—; cons. hist. mgmt. Westmoreland Davis Meml. Found., Leesburg, Va., 1967-73, 77-81. Author: George Wythe Randolph and the Confederate Elite, 1988, Jefferson's Adoptive Son: William Short, 1993, Jefferson's Travels in Europe, 1995; editor: Monticello Assn. Collected Papers Vol I., 1965, Vol II, 1984; co-editor Va. Social Sci. Jour., 1967-68; contbr. articles to profl. jours. Mem. Va. Commn. on Bicentennial of The U.S. Constitution, 1987-92. Lt. USNR, 1943-49. Recipient award Va. soc. Am. Inst. Architects for Hist. Preservation, 1985. Mem. Am. Hist. Assn., English Speaking Union (pres. S.W. Va. br. 1979), Nat. Trust for Hist. Preservation (bd. advisors 1976-79), Assn. Inst. Early Am. History and Culture, Attingham Assocs., Assn. Preservation Va. Antiquities (bd. dirs. 1960-64, 67-77), Monticello Assn. (pres. 1969-71), Soc. Hist. Assn., Va. Hist. Assn., Soc. Archtl. History, Farmington Country Club, Univ. Club (Blacksburg). Democrat. Episcopalian. Home and Office: Westminster Canterbury 250 Pantops Mount Rd 55 Charlottesville VA 22901

SHADBOLT, DOUGLAS, architecture educator, administrator; b. Victoria, B.C., Can., Apr. 18, 1925; s. Edmund and Alice Mary Maude (Healy) S.; m. Sidney Osborne Craig, June 29, 1960; stepchildren: James Osborne Craig, Catherine Shand Craig. B. Arch., U. Oreg., 1957; D. Eng. (hon.), N.S. Tech. Coll., 1969, Carleton U., 1982. Archtl. asst. Montreal, Que., Can., Ottawa, Ont., Vancouver, B.C., Victoria, B.C., Seattle, Boston, 1942-58; lectr. U. Oreg., 1955-57; asst. prof. McGill U., Montreal, 1958-60, assoc prof., 1960-61; prof., dir. Sch. Architecture N.S. Tech. Coll., Halifax, Can., 1961-68; prof., dir. Sch. Architecture Carleton U., Ottawa, 1968-77, dir. Archtl. Research Group, 1977-79; prof., dir. Sch. Architecture, U. B.C., Vancouver, 1979-90, prof. emeritus, 1990—; pvt. practice cons. architect, 1961—. Recipient Disting. Prof. award Assn. Collegiate Sch. Architecture, 1987. Fellow Royal Archtl. Inst. Can. (Gold medal 1992); mem. Archtl. Inst. B.C.

SHADDOCK, CARROLL SIDNEY, lawyer; b. Beaumont, Tex., July 7, 1940; s. Carroll Bitting Jr. and Hulda Martha (Gaertner) S.; m. Dorothea Schulze, Nov. 30, 1963; children: Carroll Christian, Peter Eric, Matthew Nolan. BA, Rice U., 1962; JD, Yale U., 1965. Ptnr. Liddell, Sapp, Zivley, Hill & LaBoon L.L.P., Houston, 1967—. Chmn. Scenic Am., Washington, 1985-92, Scenic Tex., 1992—, Trees for Houston, 1982—; Billboards Limited, Houston, 1982-92. Republican. Lutheran. Avocations: church music, golf, travel. Home: 1715 South Blvd Houston TX 77098-5419 Office: Liddell Sapp Zivley Hill & LaBoon LLP 3400 Tex Commerce Towers Houston TX 77002

SHADDOCK, WILLIAM EDWARD, JR., lawyer; b. Lake Charles, La., Jan. 18, 1938; s. William Edward Shaddock and Edith (Burton) Plauche; m. Winifred Craig Gorham, Aug. 2, 1958; children: Stephen Gorham, Mary Craig, Nancy Edith. BS, La. State U., 1960, JD, 1963. Bar: La. 1963, U.S. Dist. Ct. (we. dist.) La. 1964, U.S. Supreme Ct. 1968, U.S. Ct. Appeals (5th cir.) 1981. Assoc. Plauche & Stockwell, Lake Charles, La., 1963-66; ptnr. Stockwell, Sievert, Viccellio, Clements & Shaddock, Lake Charles, 1966—. Fellow Am. Coll. Trusts and Estates Counsel (state chmn. 1994—). Republican. Methodist. Avocations: fishing, hunting, photography. Office: Stockwell Sievert Viccellio Clements & Shaddock PO Box 2900 One Lakeside Plz 4th Fl Lake Charles LA 70602

SHADE, THOMAS L., agricultural products executive. Chmn., ceo Moorman Manufacturing Co., Quincy, Ill. Office: Moorman Mfg Co 1000 N 30th St Quincy IL 62301-3428

SHADEGG, JOHN B., congressman; b. Phoenix, Oct. 22, 1950; s. Stephen and Eugenia Shadegg; m. Shirley Shadegg; children: Courtney, Stephen. BA, U. Ariz., 1972, JD, 1975. Advisor U.S. Sentencing Commn.; spl. asst. atty. gen. State of Ariz., 1983-90; spl. counsel Ariz. Ho. Rep. Caucus, 1991-92; pvt. practice; mem. 104th Congress from 4th Ariz. dist., 1995—, mem. various coms., asst. whip; mem. Victims Bill of Rights Task Force, 1989-90; mem. Fiscal Accountability and Reform Efforts Com., 1991-92; counsel Arizonian's for Wildlife Conservation, 1992; chmn. Proposition 108-Two-Thirds Tax Limitation Initiative, 1992. Rep. Party Ballot Security Chmn., 1982; active Corbin for Atty. Gen., 1982-86; Rep. Precinct committeeman; chmn. Ariz. Rep. Caucus, 1985-87; chmn. Ariz. Lawyers for Bush-Quayle,

---

1988; mem. steering com., surrogate spkr. Jon Kyl for Congress, 1988-92; former pres. Crime Victim Found.; founding dir. Goldwater Inst. Pub. Policy; chmn. Ariz. Juvenile Justice Adv. Coun.; mem. adv. bd. Salvation Army; mem. vestry Christ Ch. of Ascension, 1989-91; mem. class II Valley Leadership; bd. dirs. Ariz. State U. Law Sch. Office: US House Reps 503 Cannon House Office Bldg Washington DC 20515-0304*

SHADER, RICHARD IRWIN, psychiatrist, educator; b. Mt. Vernon, N.Y., May 27, 1935; s. Myer and Beatrice (Epstein) S.; m. Aline Brown, Sept. 21, 1958; children: Laurel Beth, Jennifer Robin, Robert Andrew. Student, Harvard U., 1952-56; M.D., NYU, 1960; grad., Boston Psychoanalytic Inst., 1970. Diplomate Am. Bd. Psychiatry and Neurology (dir. 1977-84, treas. 1982-83, pres. 1984). Intern Greenwich Hosp., Conn., 1960-61; resident in psychiatry Mass. Mental Health Ctr., Boston, 1961-62, 64-65, NIMH, Bethesda, Md., 1962-64; asso. prof. psychiatry Harvard Med. Sch., 1970-79; prof. dept. psychiatry Tufts U. Med. Sch., Boston, 1979—, chmn. dept., 1979-91; psychiatrist in chief New Eng. Med. Ctr. Hosp., Boston, 1979-91; prof. pharmacology Tufts U. Med. Sch., Boston, 1989—, chmn. dept. pharmacology and exptl. therapeutics, 1991-93; clin. prof. psychiatry Tufts U. Sch. Dental Medicine, 1985—; dir. tng. and edn. Mass. Mental Health Ctr., 1975-77; dir. Psychopharmacology Rsch. Lab., 1968-79, Continung Edn. Mass. Mental Health, 1977-79; dir. Am. Bd. Emergency Medicine, 1980-90, mem. exec. com., 1984-90; mem. clin. affairs coun. for Mental Health and Behavioral Scis. Svcs., VA, Washington, 1985-86; mem. psychiatry test com. Nat. Bd. Med. Examiners, 1987-93, chmn., 1991-93, mem. Step I com. 1993—; mem. Nat. adv. com. VA Cooperative Studies Program, 1987-88; mem. Nat. Adv. Mental Health Coun., 1984-87; mem. med. and sci. adv. bd. Alzheimer's Disease & Related Disorders Assn., 1988-94; mem. nat. sci. coun. Am. Fedn. Aging Rsch., 1995—. Author: (with A. DiMascio) Psychotropic Drug Side Effects, 1970, (with D.J. Greenblatt) Benzodiazepines in Clinical Practice, 1974, Manual of Psychiatric Therapeutics, 1975, 2d edit. 1994; editor: Psychiatric Complications of Medical Drugs, 1972, (with A. DiMascio) Clinical Handbook of Psychopharmacology, 1970, (with D.J. Greenblatt) Pharmacokinetics in Clinical Practice, 1985, (with A. DiMascio) Butyrophenones in Psychiatry, 1972; MAOI Therapy, 1988; (with J.P. Tupin and D.S. Harnett) Handbook of Clinical Psychopharmacology, 1988; (with others) Drug Interactions in Psychiatry, 1989, Clinical Manual of Chemical Dependence, 1991; editor in chief Jour. Clin. Psychopharmacology, 1980—. Bd. dirs. Med. Found., Inc., 1980-87. Served with USPHS, 1962-64. Joseph J Michaels merit scholar, 1968-69; fellow Ctr. for Advanced Study in Behavioral Scis., Stanford, Calif., 1990-91; recipient Seymour Vestermark award Am. Psychiat. Assn., 1988, 90. Mem. AMA, Mass. Med. Soc., Am. Coll. Neuropsychopharmacology (v.p. 1984, pres. 1990), Am. Soc. Clin. Pharmacology and Therapeutics, Am. Assn. Chairmen Depts. Psychiatry (pres. 1985-86), Am. Soc. Pharmacology and Exptl. Therapeutics. Democrat. Jewish. Office: Tufts U Sch Medicine 136 Harrison Ave Boston MA 02111-1800

SHADID, RANDEL COY, lawyer; b. Dallas, Sept. 28, 1947; s. Coy Constant and Jimmie Lee (Burrow) S.; m. Mitzie Jane Standlee Shadid, Aug. 8, 1970 (dec.); children: Jerame Scott, Jerod Ryan. BBA, U. Okla., 1969, JD, 1972. Bar: Okla. 1973, U.S. Dist. Ct. (we. dist.) Okla. 1973. Researcher Okla. Employment Security Commn., Oklahoma City, 1969-72; pvt. practice Edmond, Okla., 1973—; adj. prof. Cen. State U., Edmond, 1975-78. Mayor pro tem Edmond City Coun., 1979—, mayor 1991-95. Mem. Okla. County Bar Assn., Edmond C. of C. (pres. 1984, Citizen of Yr. 1986)), Ambucs, Rotary (treas. 1978), Delta Theta Phi, Delta Sigma Pi, Omicron Delta Kappa, Beta Gamma Sigma. Avocations: tennis, skiing, fishing, gardening, art & antique collecting. Home: 507 Timberdale Ter Edmond OK 73034-4215 Office: 19 N Broadway St # 100 Edmond OK 73034-3732

SHADLE, DONNA A. FRANCIS, elementary education educator; b. Canton, Ohio, Oct. 29, 1944; d. Gerald W. and Virginia M. (Kerker) Francis; m. Joseph E. Shadle, Apr. 24, 1965; children: Joseph, Paul, Ann, Mary. Student, Walsh Coll., 1964; BS in Edn., Kent State U., 1980, MS in Edn., 1989. Cert. early childhood, kindergarten, elementary edn., Ohio. Tchr. grade 4 St. Joseph's Elem., Canton, Ohio, 1964-65; dir., administr. Community Pre-sch., Canton, 1969-79; substitute tchr., K-8 Diocese of Youngstown, Canton, 1965-80; tchr. kindergarten St. Paul's Elem., North Canton, Ohio, 1980—; reading pubs. cons.; tchr. rep. Home & Sch. Assn., North Canton, 1985; tech. com., 1992—; dir. drama Ctrl. Cath. H.S., Canton, 1987—; workshop presenter various ednl. conventions, 1989—; adv. bd. ADD Partnership of Ohio, North Canton, 1992—; invited to participate in various dept. projects Ohio State Dept. Edn.; cons. Sadlier Pub. editor, pub. (newsletter) KinderKindlings, 1989—, pub. cons., 1994. Troop Leader Girl Scouts Am., North Canton, 1977-93; dir. Mime Easter drama, North Canton, 1983-89; vol. United Way, March of Dimes, Heart Fund Canton, Canton, 1965—. Recipient spl. recognition award for Ohio Tchr. of Yr. Ashland Oil, 1989. Mem. ASCD, Assn. Childhood Edn. Internat., Nat. Assn. Edn. Young Children, Nat. Cath. Ednl. Assn., Ohio Assn. Edn. Young Children, Canton Area Assn. Edn. Young Children. Home: 5544 Frazer NW North Canton OH 44720 Office: St Pauls Elem Sch 303 S Main North Canton OH 44720

SHADOAN, GEORGE WOODSON, lawyer; b. Galesburg, Ill., July 4, 1933; s. William Parker and Hortense (Lewis) S.; m. June Faith Spiegelman, May 16, 1969; 1 child, Jesse; 1 stepchild, Jenny Ducaud. B.S., U. Ky., 1958, LL.B., 1960; LL.M., Georgetown U., 1961. Bar: Ky., 1960, D.C. 1960, Md. 1963. Ptnr. Shadoan and Michael, P.A., Rockville, Md.; prof. law Georgetown U. Law Ctr., 1962-66. Author, editor: Law and Tactics in Federal Criminal Cases, 1964; Maryland Tort Damages, 1983, 85, 90, 94. Named Lawyer of Yr., Assn. Plaintiffs Trial Attys. of D.C., 1974. Fellow Am. Bar Found., Am. Bd. Trial Advocates, Am. Bd. Profl. Liability Attys.; mem. ATLA (gov. 1982-85), Md. Bar Assn., D.C. Bar Assn. (Young Lawyer of Yr. award 1963), Inner Circle of Advocates (pres. 1983-85), Trial Lawyers Pub. Justice (pres. 1984, Pub. Justice award 1994), Md. Trial Lawyers Assn. (pres. 1978-79), Internat. Soc. Barristers (chmn. Md. State Bar Assn. civil pattern jury instructions subcom.), Internat. Acad. Trial Lawyers, Am. Law Inst. Home: 4445 29th St NW Washington DC 20008-2307 Office: 108 Park Ave Rockville MD 20850-2619

SHADUR, MILTON I., judge; b. St. Paul, June 25, 1924; s. Harris and Mary (Kaplan) S.; m. Eleanor Pilka, Mar. 30, 1946; children: Robert, Karen, Beth. B.S., U. Chgo., 1943, J.D. cum laude, 1949. Bar: Ill. 1949, U.S. Supreme Ct. 1957. Pvt. practice practice Chgo., 1949-80; assoc. Devoe & Brussell, 1949-51; ptnr. Shadur, Krupp & Miller and predecessor firms, 1951-80; assoc. U.S. Dist. Ct. (no. dist.) Ill., Chgo., 1980—; commr. Ill. Supreme Ct. Character and Fitness, 1961-72, chmn., 1971; gen. counsel Ill. Jud. Inquiry Bd., 1975-80. Editor-in-chief: U. Chgo. Law Rev., 1948-49. Chmn. visiting com. U. Chgo. Law Sch., 1971-76, mem. vis. com., 1989-92; bd. dirs. Legal Assistance Found. Chgo., 1972-78; trustee Village of Glencoe, 1969-74, Ravinia Festival Assn., 1976-93, exec. com. 1983-93, vice chmn. 1989-93, life trustee, 1994—. Lt. (j.g.) USNR, 1943-46. Fellow Am. Bar Found.; mem. ABA (spl. com. on youth edn. for citizenship 1975-79), Ill. State Bar Assn. (joint com. on rules of jud. conduct 1974), Chgo. Bar Assn. (chmn. legis. com. 1963-65, jud. com. 1970-71, profl. ethics com. 1975-76, sec. 1967-69), Chgo. Council Lawyers, Order of Coif. Office: US Dist Ct 219 S Dearborn St Chicago IL 60606-7206

SHADUR, ROBERT H., lawyer; b. Chgo., June 17, 1947. Upper 2d degree, U. Birmingham, Eng., 1968; BA magna cum laude, UCLA, 1969; JD, U. Chgo., 1972. Bar: Ill. 1973. Ptnr. Winston & Strawn, Chgo. Mem. ABA, Ill. State Bar Assn., Chgo. Bar Assn., Phi Beta Kappa. Office: Shadur & Assocs 333 W Wacker Dr Ste 1650 Chicago IL 60606-1614

SHADWELL, WENDY JOAN, curator, writer; b. N.Y.C., Feb. 5, 1942; d. Howard and Phyllis Lilian (Jenner) S. BA with honors, Mary Washington Coll., 1963; postgrad. dept. art and archeology Columbia U., 1963-66. Curator Middendorf Collection, N.Y.C., 1966-73; cons. N.Y. Hist. Soc., N.Y.C., 1971-73, asst. editor, 1973-74, curator of prints, 1974—. Author: American Printmaking: The First 150 Years, 1969; Prized Prints, 1986. Contbr. articles to profl. jours. Sec. collections com. S.I. Hist. Soc., 1983—; v.p. Friends of Alice Austen House, S.I., 1983-85. Mem. Print Council Am., Am. Hist. Print Collectors Soc. (1st v.p.), Archivists Round Table, N.Am. Print Conf., Grolier Club, Phi Beta Kappa. Republican. Episcopalian. Office: NY Hist Soc 170 Central Park W New York NY 10024-5102

SHAEFFER, CHARLES WAYNE, investment counselor; b. Bridgeton, Pa., Dec. 12, 1910; s. Bartram Augustus and Carolyn I. (Morton) S.; m. Ruth S. Smyser, Oct. 2, 1937; children—Charles Wayne, Ann B. (Mrs. Clark F. MacKenzie), Julia P. B.A., Pa. State U., 1933; M.B.A., Harvard, 1935; LL.D., Loyola Coll., 1974. Investment counselor Mackubin Legg & Co., Balt., 1935-37; with T. Rowe Price Assos., Inc. (formerly T. Rowe Price & Assos., Inc.), Balt., 1938—; chmn. bd. T. Rowe Price Assos., Inc. (formerly T. Rowe Price & Assos., Inc.), 1966-76, pres., 1963-74, cons., 1976—; pres. T. Rowe Price Growth Stock Fund, Inc., 1968-74, chmn. bd., 1974-76; chmn. bd. Rowe Price New Income Fund, 1973—; dir. Rowe Price New Horizons Fund, Inc., 1966—, Rowe Price New Era Fund, Inc., Rowe Price Prime Res. Fund; trustee Monumental Properties Trust; lectr. investment mgmt. Balt. Coll. Commerce, 1938-70, Johns Hopkins, 1960-72. Trustee Pa. State U., Franklin Sq. Hosp.; bd. mgrs. Bryn Mawr Sch., U. Balt.; bd. dirs. Md. chpt. Nature Conservancy; chmn. bd. dirs. Md. Shock-Trauma Found. Recipient Distinguished Alumni award Pa. State U. Coll. Bus. Adminstrn., 1971-72. Mem. Investment Counsel Assn. Am. (pres. 1970-73, gov. 1965—), No-Load Mut. Fund Assn. (pres. 1972-75), Investment Co. Inst. (gov. 1968—, chmn. 1975-76), Alpha Sigma Phi, Pi Gamma Mu, Delta Sigma Pi. Episcopalian. Clubs: Maryland (Balt.), L'Hirodelle (Balt.), Merchants (Balt.), Center (Balt.), Elkridge (Balt.); Green Spring Valley Hunt (Garrison, Md.); Laurel Fish and Game Assn. (York, Pa.), Lafayette (York, Pa.); Seaview Country (Absecon, N.J.); Farmington Country (Charlottesville, Va.). Home: 603 Brightwood Club Dr Lutherville Timonium MD 21093-3632 Office: 100 E Pratt St Baltimore MD 21202-1009

SHAEVSKY, MARK, lawyer; b. Harbin, Manchuria, China, Dec. 2, 1935; came to U.S., 1938, naturalized, 1944; s. Tolio and Rae (Weinstein) S.; m. Lois Ann Levi, Aug. 2, 1964; children: Thomas Lyle, Lawrence Keith. Student, Wayne State U., 1952-53; BA with highest distinction, U. Mich., 1956, JD with highest distinction, 1959. Bar: Mich. 1959. Law clerk to presiding judge U.S. Dist. Ct., Detroit, 1960-61; assoc. Honigman Miller Schwartz & Cohn, Detroit, 1961-64; ptnr. Honigman, Miller, Schwartz & Cohn, Detroit, 1965-69, sr. ptnr., 1969—; instr. law Wayne State U. Law Sch.; Detroit, 1961-64; sec., gen. counsel Pulte Home Corp., Bloomfield Hills, Mich., 1974-94; comml. arbitrator Am. Arbitration Assn., Detroit, 1977-88; bd. dirs. First Fed. Mich. Corp., Detroit, First Fed. of Mich., Detroit. Contbr. Wayne State U. Law Rev., U. Mich. Law Rev., 1957-59, asst. editor, 1958-59. Dir. Detroit Mens Orgn. of Rehab. through Tng., 1969-79; mem. exec. bd. Am. Jewish Com., Detroit, 1965-74; trustee Jewish Vocat. Svcs., Detroit, 1973-76; sec., dir. Am. Friends Hebrew Univ., Detroit, 1976-84; mem. capital needs com. Jewish Welfare Fedn., Detroit, 1986—. With U.S. Army, 1959-60. Burton Abstract fellow, 1959. Mem. ABA, Mich. Bar Assn., Franklin Hills Country Club, Order of the Coif, Phi Beta Kappa. Home: The Hills of Lone Pine 4750 N Chipping Gln Bloomfield Hills MI 48302-2390 Office: Honigman Miller Schwartz & Cohn 2290 First National Bldg Detroit MI 48226

SHAFER, DALLAS EUGENE, psychology gerontology educator, minister; b. Holyoke, Colo., Jan. 26, 1936; s. Howard C. and Mary M. (Legg) S.; m. Opal Iline Bruner, Aug. 22, 1954; children: Kim, Jana, Amy. BA, Nebr. Christian, 1958; postgrad., U. Colo., Colorado Springs, 1968-72, U. So. Calif., L.A., 1973; PhD, Walden U., 1978. Cert. clin. pastoral counseling; ordained to ministry Christian Ch., 1958. Minister Christian Ch., Colorado Springs, 1960-62, Julesburg, Colo., 1962-67; instr. of honors program U. Colo., Colorado Springs, 1974, 75; instr. psychology-gerontology Coll. of St. Francis, Colorado Springs, 1982, 84, 93; adj. grad. prof. U. Colo., Colorado Springs, 1992—; sr. minister counseling Christian Ch., Security, Colo., 1967-93; prof. psychology/gerontology Pikes Peak C.C., Colorado Springs, 1969—, dept. chair psychology/gerontology, 1969-92, pres. faculty assn., 1992-94; vice chair devel. team Westley White Rehab. Ctr., Julesburg, 1966-67; trainer-cons. Pikes Peak Hospice, Colorado Springs, 1980-81; cons. St. Thomas Moore Hospice, Canon City, Colo., 1982, Sante Christo Hospice, Pueblo, Colo., 1983-84; chair Regional Easter Sunrise Svc., Garden of the Gods, Colo. Springs, 1993-94; trainer for grief teams in U.S. mil. pers., Hawaii, Japan, 1994. Author: Approaches to Palliative Care, 1978, 92, Delphi-80-Study of Ministry, 1981; contbr. articles to Christian Standard. Sr. min. counseling Christian Ch. Security, 1967-93; bd. dirs. Colo. State Bd. Examiner for Nursing Home, Denver, 1977-83, chmn., 1981-83; moderator Conf. on Prevention of Violence-Sch. Dist. #3, Security, 1992. Mem. Colo. Edn. Assn. (mem. higher edn. com. 1992-94). Avocations: cross country skiing, hi country 4 wheeling, antiques. Office: Pikes Peak CC 5675 S Academy Blvd Colorado Springs CO 80906-5422

SHAFER, ERIC CHRISTOPHER, minister; b. Hanover, Pa., Apr. 10, 1950; s. B Henry and Doris M. (Von Bergen) S.; m. Kristi L. Owens, Nov. 24, 1973. BA, Muhlenberg Coll., 1972; MDiv, Hamma Sch. Theology, 1976. Ordained to ministry Luth. Ch. Am., 1976. Pastor Holy Trinity Meml. Luth. Ch., Catasauqua, Pa., 1976-83; asst. to Bishop Northeastern Pa. Synod, Wescosville, Pa., 1983-92; staff commn. for fin. support Evang. Luth. Ch. in Am., Chgo., 1988-92, asst. dir. dept. for comm., 1992-93, dir. dept. for comm., 1993—; del. 5th Assembly Luth. World Fedn., Evian, France, 1970; trustee Muhlenberg Coll., Allentown, Pa., 1972-83. Contbf. editor The Lutheran mag., 1989-92; exec. producer TV series One in spirit, 1990-91. Bd. dirs. Luth. Film Assocs., 1993—; bd. govs. Religious Pub. Rels. Coun., Inc., 1993—; treas. dept. comm. Nat. Coun. Chs., 1994—. Democrat. Avocations: running, computers, photography, travel. Office: Evang Luth Ch in Am 8765 W Higgins Rd Chicago IL 60631

SHAFER, EVERETT EARL, business administration educator; b. Oelwein, Iowa, Apr. 19, 1925; s. Paul Emerson and Maude Blanche (Lovell) S.; m. Kathryn Elaine Rose, Sept. 4, 1949. B.S., Iowa State U., 1948; J.D., U. Iowa, 1951; M.B.A., U. Chgo., 1960. Bar: Iowa bar 1951, Ill. bar 1952. Mem. legal staff Motorola, Inc., Chgo., 1951-54; fin. adminstr. Motorola Fin. Corp., Chgo., 1954-60; asst. treas., credit mgr. Motorola Consumer Products, Inc., Chgo., 1960-68; assoc. prof. bus. adminstrn. Buena Vista Coll., Storm Lake, Iowa, 1968-72; chmn. faculty senate Buena Vista Coll., 1970-71; treas. Admiral Corp., Chgo., 1972-74; asst. treas. Addressograph Multigraph Corp., Chgo., 1975-76; pres., treas. Addressograph Multigraph Finance Corp., 1976-80; prof. bus. adminstrn. Buena Vista Coll., Storm Lake, Iowa, 1980-92, ret., 1992. Trustee Upper Iowa U. Served with USAAF, 1943-45. Decorated D.F.C., Air medal; recipient Outstanding Tchr. award Buena Vista Coll., 1972. Methodist. Home: 314 Forest Dr Bellevue NE 68005-2044 Office: Buena Vista Coll Storm Lake IA 50588

SHAFER, J. M., utility administrator; b. Worland, Wyo., Feb. 21, 1944; s. Melvin N. and Iva Bernice (Shaffer) S.; m. Michele Marie Burnell, Sept. 6, 1964; children: Kimberly Dru, John Tyler. AS, Casper Jr. Coll., 1964; BS, U. Wyo., 1966. Registered profl. engr., Wyo. Elec. engr. So. Calif. Edison Co., San Bernardino, 1966-67; elec. engr. U.S. Bur. Reclamation, Casper, Wyo., 1967-75, Lakewood, Colo., 1975-77; West Slope area mgr. U.S. Bur. Reclamation, Loveland, Colo., 1977-78; dir. div. engring. Western Area Power Adminstrn., Loveland, 1978-81, asst. area mgr., 1981-84, dep. area mgr., 1984-88; dep. adminstr. Southwestern Power Adminstrn., Tulsa, 1988, adminstr., 1988-94; adminstr. Western Area Power Adminstrn., Lakewood, Colo., 1994—. Chmn. Combined Fed. Campaign, 1988, 89, 93; bd. trustees Electric Power Rsch. Inst., 1995. Mem. Wyo. Soc. Profl. Engrs., S.W. Power Pool (bd. dirs. 1989-94, mem. exec. com. 1993, 94, rep. nat. electric reliability coun. 1994, 95), Optimists Club (v.p. Windsor, Colo. chpt. 1985-86, pres. 1986-87). Methodist. Office: Western Area Power Adminstrn PO Box 3402 1627 Cole Blvd Golden CO 80401

SHAFER, JEFFREY RICHARD, federal official; b. Lake Forest, Ill., Sept. 10, 1944; s. William McKinley and Betty (Schuchert) S.; m. Mary Louise Terenzio, Sept. 7, 1968; 2 children. AB cum laude, Princeton U., 1966; MPhil, Yale U., 1972, PhD, 1976. Economist internat. fin. divsn. bd. govs. Fed. Res. System, 1977-78, dep. assoc. dir., 1978-81; sr. internat. staff economist Pres.'s Coun. Econ. Advisers, 1977-78; v.p. rsch. function Fed. Res. Bank N.Y., 1981-84; dep. dir. econs. dept. Orgn. Econ. Cooperation and Devel., 1984-93; asst. sec. internat. affairs Dept. of Treasury, Washington, 1993—. 1st lt. U.S. Army, 1966-68, Vietnam, capt. USAR. Decorated Bronze Star with oak leaf cluster. Office: Asst Sec for Internat Affairs 15th & Pennsylvania Ave Washington DC 20220

SHAFER, R. DONALD, church official; b. May 22, 1936; married; children: Bernice Elaine Worley, Bruce Eric. BA, Messiah Coll., 1958; BDiv, Ea.

Bapt. Sem., 1962; D of Ministry, Fuller Sch. Theology, 1979. Assoc. pastor Brethren in Christ Ch., Elizabethtown, Pa., 1957-59, pastor, 1959-65; dir. Christian edn. Brethren in Christ Ch., 1964-72, bishop Midwest and Pacific regional confs., 1972-84, moderator, 1976-78, 82-84, adminstrv. dir. bd. Brotherhood concerns, 1992-94, gen. sec., 1984—; tchr. Mennonite Sch. Discipleship, Lancaster, Pa., summer 1980, Azusa (Calif.) Pacific Sch. Theology, Evang. Sch. Theology, Myerstown, Pa., Mennonite Bib., Fresno, Calif., winters 1980-92, Brethren in Christ Ch., 1983—; facilitator women in leadership seminar Grantham Brethren in Christ Ch., 1993; leader numerous seminars on Christian edn., ch. growth, worship and conflict mgmt., 1972—. Bd. trustees Messiah Coll., Grantham, 1972—; mem. U.S. and internat. Mennonite Cen. Com., 1984—; gen. conf. gen. sec., mem. gen. conf. bd. of adminstrn. Brethren in Christ Ch., 1984—; sec. Coun. Moderators & Secs., 1989-94; mem. Messiah Coll. Presdl. Search Com., 1993. Avocations: hiking, golf, camping, sports, reading. Office: Brethren in Christ Ch PO Box 290 431 Grantham Rd Grantham PA 17027-0290

SHAFER, RAYMOND PHILIP, lawyer, business executive; b. New Castle, Pa., Mar. 5, 1917; s. David Philip and Mina Belle (Miller) S.; m. Jane Harris Davies, July 5, 1941; children: Diane Elizabeth, Raymond Philip, Jane Ellen. AB cum laude, Allegheny Coll., 1938, LLD, 1963; LLB, Yale, 1941; numerous hon. LLD degrees. Bar: N.Y., Pa. Asso. firm Winthrop, Stimson, Putnam & Roberts, N.Y.C.; practice law Meadville, Pa., 1945-63; counsel Shafer, Swick, Bailey, Irwin and Stack; dist. atty. Crawford County, 1948-56; mem. Pa. Senate from 50th Dist., 1959-63; lt. gov. Pa., 1963-67; gov. Commonwealth Pa., 1967-71; vis. prof. U. Pa., 1973—; counselor to pres. of U.S., 1975-77; ptnr., sr. counselor Coopers & Lybrand, 1977-88; former pres. and chmn. bd. trustees Allegheny Coll., Meadville, Pa. Chmn. Nat. Commn. on Marijuana and Drug Abuse; chmn. Nat. Com. U.S.-China Rels.; chmn. Nat. Coun. on Pub. Svc.; world bd. govs. USO; mem. adv. bd. Am. Enterprise Inst.; active charitable, cmty. drives; bd. dirs., vice chmn. Atlantic Coun. U.S., Am.-China Soc.; trustee Cleve. Clinic Found., Freedoms Found. With USNR, 1942-45, PTO. Recipient Gold Medal award Soc. Family of Man, 1972, numerous humanitarian and civic awards. Mem. ABA, Pa. Bar Assn., Crawford County Bar Assn. (pres. 1961-63), Council Fgn. Relations, Phi Beta Kappa, Phi Kappa Psi. Republican. Club: Mason (33 deg.). Office: Dunaway & Cross 1146 19th St NW Washington DC 20036-3703 *One makes a living by what one gets. One makes a life by what one gives.*

SHAFER, ROBERT TINSLEY, JR., judge; b. Cin., Sept. 11, 1929; s. Robert Tinsley and Grace Elizabeth (Welsh) S.; m. Barbara Jean Hough, Dec. 27, 1950; children: Richard Hough, Janet Lee Shafer Davis, Charles Welsh. BA, Coll. of Wooster, 1951; JD, U. Cin., 1956. Bar: Fla. 1956, U.S. Ct. Appeals (5th cir.) 1963, U.S. Dist. Ct. (so. dist.) Fla. 1961, U.S. Supreme Ct. 1965. Asst. trust officer 1st Nat. Bank, Ft. Myers, Fla., 1956-57; ptnr. Henderson, Franklin, Starnes & Holt, P.A., Ft. Myers, 1957-77; cir. judge 20th Jud. Cir. State of Fla., Ft. Myers 1977-92, chief cir. judge, 1985-89, sr. judge, 1992—. Contbr. article to Corp. Law, 1955-56 (Goldsmith Corp. Law prize, 1956). Elder Covenant Presbyn. Ch., 1982-85; mem. jud. commn. Fla. Presbyn. Synod, 1960-63; chmn. Lee County chpt. Red Cross, Ft. Myers, 1963. 2nd lt. USMCR, 1951-53, PTO, Korea. Mem. ABA, Fla. Conf. Cir. Judges (exec. com. 1986-88), Fla. Bar Assn. (bd. govs. Jr. Bar sect. 1961-64), Lee County Bar Assn. (pres. 1968), Am. Judges Assn., Am. Judicature Soc., Nat. Conf. Met. Cts. Republican. Avocations: running races, bicycle racing, bicycle touring, travel, reading. Home: 2704 Shriver Dr Fort Myers FL 33901-5931

SHAFFER, ALFRED GARFIELD TERRY, service organization executive; b. Sunbury, Pa., Jan. 5, 1939; d. Alfred G. and Betty Marjorie (Vogel) S.; m. Nancy Jane Dawson, Aug. 29, 1976. BS, Susquehanna U., 1961. Cert. tchr., Pa. Tchr., Danville Sch. Dist. (Pa.), 1962-69; mgr. club service Kiwanis Internat., Chgo., 1969-74, dir. program devel., 1974-81, dir. program services, Indpls., 1982-85, dir. spl. services, 1985-87, asst. sec. for spl. svcs., 1987-88, asst. to internat. sec., 1988-94, internat. sec. 1994—; corp. affairs cons. Nat. Easter Seal Soc., Chgo., 1981-82; adminstr. Circle K Internat., Chgo., 1982; mem. Pres.'s Com. on Employment of Handicapped, 1983-86. Chmn. adv. council 70001 Ltd., Indpls., 1984-86. Recipient Gold Key of Svc., Pa. Dist. Key Clubs, 1964. Lutheran. Mem. Ind. Assn. Event Profls., Indpls. Athletic Club, 500 Festival Assocs., Kiwanis (pres. Selinsgrove, Pa. 1964, lt. gov. Pa. 1966-67, pres. Chgo. 1970-72, sec. Northwest Indpls. 1983-86, 91-92, Outstanding Svc. award 1981, Kiwanian of Yr. 1966, 85). Home: 5688 Broadway St Indianapolis IN 46220-3073 Office: Kiwanis International 3636 Woodview Terrace Indianapolis IN 46268-1168

SHAFFER, BERNARD WILLIAM, mechanical and aerospace engineering educator; b. N.Y.C., Aug. 7, 1924; s. Abraham and Eva (Ellinsky) S.; m. Florence Solow, Feb. 23, 1947 (dec. Oct. 29, 1980); children: Janet Ilene, Roberta Franceen. B in Mech. Engring., CCNY, 1944; MS in Mech. Engring., Case Inst. Tech., 1947; PhD, Brown U., 1951. Registered profl. engr., N.Y., R.I. Aero. rsch. scientist Flight Propulsion Rsch. NACA (now NASA), Cleve., 1944-47; spl. lectr. applied mechanics Case Inst. Tech., Cleve., 1946-47; rsch. assoc., grad. div. applied math. and engring., instr. Brown U., Providence, 1947-50; asst. prof. mech. engring. NYU, N.Y.C., 1950-53, assoc. prof., 1953-58, prof., project dir. rsch. div., 1958-73; prof. dept. mech. and aerospace engring. Poly. U., Bklyn. and Farmingdale, N.Y. 1973-93; prof. emeritus Poly. U., Bklyn. and Farmingdale, 1993—; cons. in field; mem. adv. coun. Coll. Aeros., N.Y.C., 1982—; vis. rsch. prof. mech. engring. Fla. Atlantic U., Boca Raton, 1992, Disting. vis. rsch. prof., 1993—. Contbr. articles to profl. jours. Bd. dirs. Harbor Hills Civic Assn., Great Neck, N.Y., 1968-71. With USAAF, 1944-47. Recipient various govt. grants. Fellow ASME (Richards Meml. award 1968), AIAA (assoc.); mem. Sigma Xi, Tau Beta Pi, Pi Tau Sigma. Avocations: golf, swimming. Home and Office: 18 Old Field Ln Great Neck NY 11020-1265

SHAFFER, CAROLYN LEE (CARI SHAFFER), staffing service executive; b. Denver, June 3, 1944; d. Richard Michael, Sr. and Joyce Adele (Carnahan) Knoll; m. Charles Larry Shaffer, Dec. 11, 1965; 1 child, Kelly Michael. Student, So. Oreg. Coll., 1962-64, U. Nev., 1964-78. Free lance sec. Colorado Springs, Colo., 1977-80; mgr. Accel Temporaries Colorado Springs, 1980-82, MG Temps div. Marshall Group, Colorado Springs, 1982-84; owner, mgr. Add Staff, Inc., Colorado Springs, 1984—. Bd. dirs. Tech. Research Assocs., Colorado Springs, 1971-73, Better Bus. Bur., 1988—, Mt. Bell Fed. Credit Union, 1989—. Spl. events chmn. London county unit Am. Cancer Soc., Sterling, Va., 1975-77; speaker for Goodwill, Colorado Springs, 1980—, Wagon Wheel council Girl Scouts U.S., Colorado Springs, 1980—, Jr. Achievement, Colorado Springs, 1980—, U. Colo., 1984—, Pikes Peak Community Coll., 1984—, Blair Jr. Coll., 1984—, Pikes Peak Inst., 1984. Mem. Internat. Personnel Women (v.p. 1982-83), Colorado Springs Personnel Women (pres. 1983—), Adminstrv. Mgmt. Soc. (salary survey chmn. 1982), Am. Soc. For Tng. and Devel., Amigos de Ser, Colorado Springs C. of C. (life mem., chmn. ambassador club, chamber vice chmn. exec. com. 1985-86, Ambassador of Yr. award 1984, exec. com. 1986). Recipient Woman of the Year award 1988. Republican. Roman Catholic. Club: Little People of Am. (Colorado Springs). Office: Add Staff Inc 2118 Hollow Brook Dr Colorado Springs CO 80918-1444

SHAFFER, DAVID, psychiatrist; b. Johannesburg, South Africa, Apr. 20, 1936; s. Isaac and Joyce (Freedman) S.; m. Serena Jessica Millington, Sept. 17, 1966 (div. Dec. 1983); children—Joseph, Samuel; m. Anna Wintour, Sept. 1984; children: Charles, Kate. Student, Internat. Sch. Geneva, 1952-55; M.D., U. London, 1961-62. House physician Univ. Coll. Hosp., London, 1962; sr. house officer Hosp. for Sick Children, London, 1963-64; lectr. pediatrics Univ. Coll. Hosp. Med. Sch., London, 1964-65; registrar Maudsley Hosp., 1965-67; Von Ameringen fellow in pediatric neurology and child devel. Yale U. Med. Sch., New Haven, 1967-68; registrar Maudsley Hosp., London, 1968-69; sr. lectr. psychiatry Inst. Psychiatry London, 1972-73; sr. registrar Maudsley Hosp., 1974-77; cons. child psychiatry Kings Coll. Hosp. London, 1977; dir. dept. child psychiatry N.Y. State Psychiat. Inst., N.Y.C.; dir. div. pediatric psychiatry Babies Hosp., Columbia Presbyn. Med. Ctr., N.Y.C.; prof. psychiatry and pediatrics Columbia U. Coll. Physicians and Surgeons, N.Y.C.; Irving Philips prof. child psychiatry Columbia U. Coll. Phys. and Surgs., N.Y.C., 1987—; mem. Sec.'s Commn. on Youth Suicide Prevention; gov. N.Y. State Commn. on Youth Suicide Prevention; bd. dirs. Am. Suicide Found.; pres. Soc. for Rsch. in Child and Adolescent Psychopathology, 1990-91; co-chmn. Child Disorders DSM-IV Work Group. Editor 5 books; contbr. articles to profl. jours. Recipient numerous rsch.

grants on suicide, diagnosis, and neuropsychiatry from NIMH and Ctrs. for Disease Control, 1977-94. Fellow Royal Coll. Psychiatrists (examiner 1976, acad. sec. 1975-77), Assn. Child Psychology and Psychiatry London (life treas. 1974-77); mem. Am. Acad. Child and Adolescent Psychiatry, Am. Psychiat. Assn., Royal Coll. Physicians; mem. Am. Acad. Child Psychiatrists (program com. 1981-85), Soc. Profs. Child Psychiatry, Travellers Club (London). Club: Travellers (London). Office: 722 W 168th St New York NY 10032-2603

SHAFFER, DAVID H., publishing company executive; b. Ottawa, Ohio, Dec. 18, 1942; s. William and Louise (Borer) S.; m. Janelle Meeker, Sept. 15, 1978; children: David Randolph, Deborah Lynn, Melinda Kay, Rebecca Ann, Thomas Joseph, Steven Michael, Amanda Rae. MBA, Northwestern U., 1983. With N.W. Airlines, Govt. The Bahamas, Ea. Airlines, USN, to 1974, Official Airline Guides Inc., Oak Brook, Ill., 1974—; account mgr. airline mktg. Official Airlines Guides Inc., Oak Brook, Ill., 1974-79, gen. mktg. mgr., 1979-80, v.p., 1980-83, sr. v.p. electronic pub., 1983-85, exec. v.p., 1985-86, pres., 1986—; exec. vice chmn.; group v.p. Macmillan Inc., New York, 1989; exec. v.p., 1989-90, pres., 1990-91; chief operating officer Maxwell Communication Corp. PLC, Greenwich, Conn., 1991—, chmn., 1992—; also bd. dirs. Macmillan Inc., N.Y.C., Maxwell Communications Corp plc, 1989—; vice chmn. Thomas Cook Travel USA, 1988—; bd. dirs. Northwestern Transp. Ctr., Molecular Design Ltd., Maxwell Data Mgmt. Ltd., Inst. of Certified Travel Agents; pres., bd. dirs. Travel Easy Publs. Mem. Travel Industry Assn. (bd. dirs.), Inst. Cert. Travel Agts. Office: Macmillan Inc 65 Railroad Ave Greenwich CT 06830-6302

SHAFFER, DONALD S., retail executive; b. Philippi, W.Va., Mar. 22, 1943; m. Leslie Stalker; 1 child. AA, Potomac State Coll.; BS in Acctg., W.Va. U. Mgmt. trainee Sears, Roebuck and Co., USA, 1968-70; pers. mgr. Sears, Roebuck and Co., USA, Washington, 1970-72, Landover, Md., 1972-73; asst. store mgr. Sears, Roebuck and Co., USA, Washington, 1973-75, soft lines mdse. mgr., 1975-78; zone oper. mgr. Sears, Roebuck and Co., USA, Watertown, N.Y., 1978-81; zone mgr. Sears, Roebuck and Co., USA, Albany, N.Y., 1981-82; store mgr. Sears, Roebuck and Co., USA, New Brunswick, N.J., 1982-83; with planning dept. nat. hdqs. Sears, Roebuck and Co., USA, Chgo., 1983-86; regional mgr. Sears, Roebuck and Co., USA, Hawaii, 1986-87; v.p. field sales ops. Sears Can. Inc., Detroit, 1987; v.p. field sales ops. and real estate Sears Can. Inc., 1988; regional gen. mgr. Sears, Roebuck and Co., USA, Detroit, 1989; nat. bus. mgr. womens apparel, accessories nat. hdqs. Sears, Roebuck and Co., USA, Chgo., 1989-90; nat. mdse. mgr. furniture Sears, Roebuck and Co., USA, 1990-93; exec. v.p., COO Sears Can. Inc. Toronto, Ont., 1993—; pres., CEO Sears Can. Inc.; bd. dirs. Sears Acceptance Co., Conf. Bd. Can., Bus. Coun. on Nat. Issues. Bd. govs. Jr. Achievement Can. 1st lt. U.S. Army, 1965-67. Office: Sears Can Inc, 222 Jarvis St, Toronto, ON Canada M5B 2B8

SHAFFER, DOROTHY BROWNE, retired mathematician, educator; b. Vienna, Austria, Feb. 12, 1923; d. Hermann and Steffy (Hermann) Browne; arrived U.S. 1940; m. Lloyd Hamilton Shaffer, July 25, 1943 (dec. 1978); children: Deborah Lee, Diana Louise, Dorothy Leslie. AB, Bryn Mawr Coll., 1943; MA, Harvard U., 1945, PhD, 1962. Mathematician, MIT, Cambridge, 1945-47; tchg. fellow, research asso., Harvard U., Cambridge, 1947-48; asso. mathematician Cornell Aeronautical Lab, Buffalo, N.Y., 1952-56; mathematician Dunlap & Assoc., Stamford, Conn., 1958-60; lectr. grad. engring. U. of Conn. at Stamford, 1962; prof. math Fairfield (Conn.) U., 1963-92, prof. emeritus, 1992—; vis. prof. Imperial Coll. Sci. and Tech., London, fall 1978, U. Md., College Park, spring 1981; vis. prof. U. Calif.-San Diego, summer 1981; vis. scholar, 1986; NSF faculty fellow IBM-T.J. Watson Research Center, Yorktown Heights, N.Y., 1979. Contbr. numerous papers in math. analysis. Mem. Am. Math. Soc., Math. Assn. of Am., Assn. for Women in Math., London Math. Soc. Achievement include patent in Viscosity Stabilized Solar Pond. Home: 156 Intervale Rd Stamford CT 06905-1311 Office: Fairfield U Dept Math & Computer Sci Fairfield CT 06430

SHAFFER, GAIL S., state government official; b. Kingston, N.Y., Aug. 1, 1948; d. Robert E. and Marion (Gallagher) S. BA summa cum laude, Elmira Coll., 1970; student, U. Paris, 1968-69. Editor Sam Har Press, 1972-76; legal asst. Rahrnas Law Firm, 1973-76; spl. asst. to commr. N.Y. State Environ. Conservation, 1977-79; exec. dir. N.Y. State Rural Affairs Council, 1979-80; mem. N.Y. State Assembly, 1981-83; sec. state State of N.Y., Albany, 1983—. Mem. N.Y. State Dem. Com., 1976—; chair Yonkers Emergency Fin. Control Bd., 1985—. Mem. Women Execs. in State Govt., N.Y. State Assn. Women Officeholders (pres.). Presbyterian. Office: Sec of State NY 162 Washington Ave Albany NY 12210-2304

SHAFFER, JAMES BURGESS, communications executive; b. Boston, May 6, 1945; s. Robert Howard and Marjorie Jane (Fitch) S.; m. Lynn Elliott Eitzen, June 3, 1967; children: Derek Bruce, Ryan Brooke. B.S. in Mech. Engring. Purdue U., 1967; M.B.A., Ind. U., 1969. Staff engr. Aerospace Research Applications Center, Bloomington, Ind., 1967-69; ops. analyst Mpls. Star & Tribune Co., 1970-71, research planning analyst, 1972-73, research planning mgr., 1974, dir. acctg., 1975-77; pres., pub. Stromberg Publs., Inc. subs., Ellicott City, Md., 1977-79; sr. v.p., assoc. pub. Buffalo Courier-Express Co., Inc. subs., 1979-82; v.p., chief fin. officer L.A. Times, 1983-84, v.p. fin. and planning, 1985-89; exec. v.p. The Sun-Times Co., 1989-91; pres., chief exec. officer Guy Gannett COmmunications, Portland, Maine, 1991—; vice-chmn. bd. dirs. Better Bus. Bur. Western N.Y., 1980. Trustee Wildwood Sch., Santa Monica, Calif., 1987; mem. bd. trustees Portland (maine) Symphony, 1993—; bd. dirs. Maine Coalition Excellence in Edn., 1993—, Conv. & Visitors Bur., 1993—. Home: 35 Foreside Rd Cumberland ME 04110 Office: Guy Gannett Comm Box 15277 1 City Ctr Portland ME 04112-5277

SHAFFER, JAY CHRISTOPHER, lawyer; b. Brookville, Pa., Sept. 18, 1947; s. John Rienard and Laverne (Berding) S.; m. Janice Rita McKenney, May 24, 1972; 1 child, Justin. BA, Ohio State U., 1969; JD, Harvard U. 1974. Bar: Ohio 1974, U.S. Supreme Ct. 1978. Atty. office gen. counsel FTC, Washington, 1974-77; counsel subcom. on oversight, interstate and fgn. com. U.S. Ho. of Reps., Washington, 1977-79; atty. antitrust div. U.S. Dept. of Justice, Washington, 1979-82, dep. dir. policy planning antitrust div. 1982-84, chief legal adv. unit antitrust div., 1984-86; dep. dir. bur. competition FTC, Washington, 1986-88; dep. gen. counsel Office of Gen. Counsel FTC, Washington, 1988—. Served to capt. U.S. Army, 1970-72, Korea. Mem. ABA, Fed. Bar Assn. Home: 7016 Leewood Forest Dr Springfield VA 22151-3930 Office: FTC Rm 564 Washington DC 20580

SHAFFER, JEROME ARTHUR, philosophy educator; b. N.Y.C., Apr. 2, 1929; s. Joseph and Beatrice (Leibowitz) S.; m. Olivia Anne Connery, Sept. 3, 1960 (div. 1985); children: Diana, David; m. Eliana Bar-shalom, Aug. 7, 1994. BA, Cornell U., 1950; PhD, Princeton U., 1952. Prof. philosophy Swarthmore (Pa.) Coll., 1955-67; prof. U. Conn., Storrs, 1967-94, prof. emeritus, 1994—, head dept. philosophy, 1976-94; exec. sec. Council Philos. Studies, 1965-72. Author: The Philosophy of Mind, 1968, Violence, 1970, Reality, Knowledge, and Value, 1971; contbr. articles to profl. jours. Served with U.S. Army, 1953-55. Fulbright fellow, 1952-53, fellow Ctr. for Advanced Study Behavioral Scis., 1963-64, NEH sr. fellow, 1973-74, Cambridge Clare Hall vis. fellow, 1987. Mem. Am. Philos. Assn., Phi Beta Kappa, Phi Kappa Phi. Home: 90 Pine Lake Dr Coventry CT 06238-1718 Office: U Conn Dept Philosophy # U-54 Storrs CT 06268

SHAFFER, LOUIS RICHARD, engineering research administrator, civil engineering educator; b. Sharon, Pa., Feb. 28, 1955; m. 1955; 3 children. BS, Carnegie-Mellon U., 1950; MS, U. Ill., 1957, PhD in Syss. Civil Engring., 1961. Asst. to master mechanic Nat. Castings Co., Pa., 1950-52; asst. to dir. engring. Sharon (Pa.) Steel Corp., 1953-54; instr. civil engring. U. Ill., Urbana, 1955-61, from asst. prof. to assoc. prof., 1961-65, prof. civil engring., 1965—; tech. dir. constrn. engring. rsch. lab. U.S. Army, 1969—; asst. dir. Tech. Direction Constrn. Engring. Rsch. Lab. U.S. Army, 1969-70, dep. dir., 1970-76; coord. Internat. Working Commn. on Orgn. and Mgmt. Constrn., 1974—; chmn. U.S. Nat. Com. Internat. Coun. Bldg. Rsch., 1977-83. Mem. Am. Soc. Civil Engrs. (chmn. tech. coun. rsch. 1976-77, Walter L. Hubaer rsch. prize, 1967, Constrn. Mgmt. award, 1978, Constrn. Rsch. award, 1987), Soc. Am. Mil. Engrs. Rsch. modern constrn. mgmt. with

emphasis on tech. innovation to increase productivity of mgmt. on all levels. Office: 2203 Pond St Urbana IL 61801*

SHAFFER, MICHAEL L., transportation company executive; b. Eldorado, Ill., Dec. 28, 1945; s. L.E. Jim Shaffer and Berniece (Belva) Andrews; m. Mary Elaine Charboneau, Jan. 30, 1970; children: Michelle, James. Dispatcher Atlas Van Lines, Inc., Long Beach, Calif., 1969-73; ops. mgr. Atlas Van Lines, Inc., Hyattsville, Md., 1973-75, Evansville, Ind., 1975-80; asst. v.p. Atlas Van Lines, Inc., 1980-84; v.p. gen mgr. Atlas Van Lines Texas, Austin, 1983-84; v.p. ops. Atlas Van Lines, Inc., Evansville, 1984-88; sr. v.p. Atlas Van Lines, Inc., 1988-90; pres. U.S. Transp. Group, 1991—. With U.S. Army, 1963-65, Vietnam. Roman Catholic. Home: 3599 Crossgate Ct Newburgh IN 47630-9661 Office: Atlas Van Lines Inc 1212 Saint George Rd Evansville IN 47711-2336

SHAFFER, OREN GEORGE, manufacturing company executive; b. Sharpsville, Pa., Aug. 13, 1942; s. Oren G. and Alice Marie (Miller) S.; m. Evelyne Soussan, Oct. 2, 1965; children: Kathleen R., Oren O. BSBA, U. Calif., Berkeley, 1968; MS, MIT, 1985. Mem. internal tng. squad Goodyear Tire and Rubber Co., Akron, Ohio, 1968-69, asst. comptr., 1983-84, v.p., treas., 1985-87, exec. v.p., chief fin. officer, 1987—; mem. fin. staff Goodyear SA, Diegem, Belgium, 1969-70, fin. mgr. Benelux, 1970-75; chief fin. officer Goodyear France, Paris, 1975-80, pres., 1981-83; chief fin. officer Goodyear Tyre and Rubber Co., Wolverhampton, Eng., 1980-81. bd. dirs. Akron Priority Corp., pres. 1987. Mem. Nat. Assn. Accts., Fin. Execs. Inst., Officer's Conf. Group. Clubs: Firestone Country, Portage Country (Akron). Home: 2229 Stockbridge Rd Akron OH 44313-4544 Office: Goodyear Tire & Rubber Co 1144 E Market St Akron OH 44316-0002

SHAFFER, PAUL, musician, bandleader; b. Thunder Bay, Ont., Can., Nov. 28, 1949; m. Cathy Vasapoli; 1 child, Victoria Lily. Mem. band Fabulous Fugitives, Thunder Bay, 1964-68; keyboardist NBC's Saturday Night Live, 1975-80; musical dir. Blues Bros. Band, 1978-79; leader, keyboardist The World's Most Dangerous Band NBC's Late Night with David Letterman, 1982-1993; music director The Late Show with David Letterman (CBS), 1993—. Mus. dir. (Toronto, Ont. prodn.) Godspell, 1972; musician: (N.Y.C. prodn.) The Magic Show, 1974, (Gilda Radner's mus. revue, also co-composer) Live in New York, 1979, (off-Broadway prodn.) Leader of the Pack, 1984; rec. artist, keyboardist: (with Barry Manilow) This One's For You, 1976, (with National Lampoon) Good-Bye Pop, 1976, (with the Jeff Healey Band) Feel This, 1977, (Blues Bros.) Briefcase Full of Blues, 1978, Made in America, 1980, (with Jaon Armatrading) Me Myself, 1980, (with Nina Hagen) Nunsexmonkrock, 1980, (with Diana Ross) Silk Electric, 1981, (with Yoko Ono) It's Alright, 1982, (Honey Drippers) The Honey Drippers, 1985, (film soundtrack) The Karate Kid II, 1986, (with Dion, Ben E. King, Bobby Womack and Wilson Pickett) Coast to Coast, 1991, (with Blues Traveler) Save His Soul, 1993, (with the Party Boys of Rock 'n' Roll) The World's Most Dangerous Party, 1993; regular mem. cast (TV series) A Year at the Top, 1977; film appearances include This Is Spinal Tap, 1984; solo album Coast to Coast, 1999 (2 Grammy nominations). Office: Late Show w/ David Letterman CBS 530 W 57th St New York NY 10019*

SHAFFER, PAUL E., banker; b. Rockford, Ohio, Aug. 3, 1926; s. Randall J. and Zelah V. (Alspaugh) S.; m. Dorothy L. Schumm, June 26, 1951; children: Paula Kay, Patti Lee. Grad., U. Wis. Sch. Banking, 1954; cert., Am. Inst. Banking; DHL (hon.), Purdue U., 1985. With Rockford Nat. Bank, 1945-48; asst. nat. bank examiner Treasury Dept., 1948-52; with Ft. Wayne (Ind.) Nat. Bank, 1952—, exec. v.p., 1965-68, pres., 1968-85, chmn., CEO, 1970-92, chmn. emeritus, 1991-93, chmn. emeritus, also bd. dirs.; bd. dirs. Old First Nat. Bank, Bluffton, Ind., Lincoln-Life Improved Housing, Inc., MESC Holdings, Inc. (Magnavox). Pres. Downtown Fort Wayne Assn., 1965, Credit Bur., Fort Wayne, 1962, Jr. Achievement, 1967-69; treas. Fort Wayne Better Bus. Bur., 1968, Ind.-Purdue Devel. Fund; mem. regional adv. com. Comptroller Currency, 1968-70; commr. Ft. Wayne Conv. and Tourism Authority.; past bd. dirs. Fort Wayne Conv. Bur., Fort Wayne Philharmonic Orch., Parkview Meml. Hosp.; bd. dirs. Caylor-Nickel Hosp., Ft. Wayne campus Ind. U., Ind.-Purdue Found., Taxpayers Research Assn.; past bd. dirs. United Community Services, chmn. drive, 1970-71; past bd. dirs. Fort Wayne YMCA, v.p., 1964-67; bd. adviser Ind. U.-Purdue U., Ft. Wayne; mem. fin. adv. bd. Luth. Social Services; bd. govs. Assn. Colls. Ind.; chmn. vol. com. U.S. Savs. Bonds, Allen County, Ind., numerous other civic activities. Served with USAAF, 1945. Mem. Am. Inst. Banking (past pres. Fort Wayne chpt.), Am. Bankers Assn. (governing council 1978-79), Ind. Bankers Assn. (past pres., bd. dirs.), Fort Wayne C. of C. (past v.p., bd. dirs.), Ind. C. of C. (state dir.), Rotary, Ft. Wayne Country Club, Summit Club, Quest Club, Ft. Wayne Press Club, Mad Anthonys Club, Pine Valley Country Club, Sycamore Hills Country Club, Masons, Shriners. Home: 11132 Carnoustie Ln Fort Wayne IN 46804 Office: Ft Wayne Nat Corp 110 W Berry St Fort Wayne IN 46802-2304

SHAFFER, PETER LEVIN, playwright; b. Liverpool, Eng., May 15, 1926; s. Jack and Reka (Fredman) S. BA, Cambridge U., Eng., 1950. Conscript coal mines, Eng., 1944-47; with N.Y. Pub. Libr., N.Y.C., 1951-54, Bosey & Hawkes, London, 1954-55; lit. critic Truth, 1956-57; music critic Time and Tide, 1961-62. Author: (plays) Five Finger Exercise, 1958 (Evening Standard Drama award 1958, N.Y. Drama Critics Circle award 1960), The Private Ear, 1962, The Public Eye, 1962, The Merry Rooster's Panto, 1963, The Royal Hunt of the Sun, 1964, Black Comedy, 1965, The White Liars, 1967, The Battle of Shrivings, 1970, Equus, 1973 (Best Play Tony award 1975, Outer Critics Circle Best Play award 1975, N.Y. Drama Critics Circle Best Play award 1975), Amadeus, 1979 (Evening Standard Drama award 1979, London Drama Critics award 1979, Best Play Tony award 1980, Plays and Players Best Play award 1980), Yonadab, 1985, Lettice and Lovage, 1987 (Evening Standard Drama award 1988), The Gift of the Gorgon, 1992; (screenplays) Follow Me!, 1971, Equus, 1977 (Acad. award nominee for best screenplay adaptation 1977), Amadeus, 1984 (Acad. award for best screenplay adaptation 1984); (TV plays) The Salt Land, 1955, Balance of Terror, 1957; (radio plays) The Prodigal Father, 1955, Whom Do I Have the Honor of Addressing?, 1989; (novels with Anthony Shaffer) The Woman in the Wardrobe, 1951, How Doth the Little Crocodile?, 1952, Withered Murder, 1955. Decorated comdr. Order Brit. Empire; recipient Hamburg Shakespeare prize, 1987, William Inge award for disting. achievement in Am. theatre, 1992. Fellow Royal Soc. Lt. (London chpt.). Address: 173 Riverside Dr New York NY 10024

SHAFFER, RICHARD JAMES, lawyer, former manufacturing company executive; b. Pe Ell, Wash., Jan. 26, 1931; s. Richard Humphrys and Laura Rose (Faas) S.; m. Donna M. Smith, May 13, 1956; children: Leslie Lauren Shaffer and Stephanie Jane Athenton. B.A., U. Wash.; LL.B., Southwestern U. Bar: Calif. Vice pres., gen. counsel, sec. NI, Inc., Long Beach, Calif., 1974-89; gen. counsel Masco Bldg. Products Corp., Long Beach, 1985-89; pvt. practice Huntington Beach, Calif., 1989—; mem. ltd. liability co. drafting com. and task force Calif. State Bar, 1992-94; lectr. on ltd. liability cos. Trustee Ocean View Sch. Dist., 1965-73, pres., 1966, 73; mem. fin. adv. com. Orange Coast Coll., 1966; mem. Long Beach Local Devel. Corp., 1978-89, Calif. Senate Commn. on Corp. Governance, Shareholders' Rights and Securities Transactions, 1986—, chmn. drafting com. ltd. liability co. act for senate com., 1993-94. Mem. ABA, Nat. Assn. Securities Dealers (bd. arbitrators), Calif. Bar Assn. (exec. com. corp. law dept. com. bus. sect. 1981-88, mem. drafting com. ltd. liability co. act), Orange County Bar Assn., Huntington Harbour Yacht Club, Wanderlust Skiers of Huntington Harbour, Huntington Harbour Ski Club. Office: 17111 Beach Blvd Ste 103 Huntington Beach CA 92647-5999

SHAFFER, RUSSELL K., advertising agency executive; b. N.Y.C., Apr. 12, 1933; s. Russell Parl and Alice (Cole) S.; m. Leslie Van Nostrand, July 28, 1956; children—Cole Van Nostrand, Wendel L., Daniel W., Russell W. A.B., Brown U., 1954; M.B.A., Harvard U., 1958. 'Account exec. McCann-Erickson, N.Y.C., 1958-62; account supr. Grey Advt., N.Y.C., 1962-66; exec. v.p. Richard K. Manoff, Inc., N.Y.C., 1966-71; pres. Richard K. Manoff, Inc., 1971-77, also dir.; pres. David H. Mann, Inc., 1977-80; exec. v.p. F.W. Free Inc. (now Laurance, Charles & Free, Inc.), N.Y.C., 1980-86; sr. v.p. SSC&B, N.Y.C., 1986—. Served to lt. USNR, 1954-56. Home: 2 Richards Ave Norwalk CT 06854-2318 Office: One Dag Hammarskjold Pla New York NY 10017

SHAFFER, THOMAS LINDSAY, law educator; b. Billings, Mont., Apr. 4, 1934; s. Cecil Burdette and Margaret Jeanne (Parker) S.; m. Nancy Jane Lehr, Mar. 19, 1954; children: Thomas, Francis, Joseph, Daniel, Brian, Mary, Andrew, Edward. B.A., U. Albuquerque, 1958; J.D., U. Notre Dame, 1961; LL.D., St. Mary's U., 1983. Bar: Ind. 1961. Assoc. Barnes, Hickam, Pantzer, & Boyd, Indpls., 1961-63; prof. law U. Notre Dame, Ind., 1963-80, assoc. dean, 1969-71, dean, 1971-75, Robert and Marion Short prof., 1988—; supervising atty. Notre Dame Legal Aid Clinic, 1991—; prof. law Washington and Lee U., 1980-87, Robert E.R. Huntley prof. law, 1987-88; vis. prof. UCLA, 1970-71, U. Va., 1975-76, U. Maine, 1982, 87, Boston Coll., 1992; dir. Cornerstone Found.; mem. Ind. Constl. Revision Commn., 1969-70, Ind. Trust Code Study Commn., 1968-71; reporter Ind. Jud. Conf., 1963, 67; mem. adv. com. on rules U.S. Ct. Appeals, 1977-79. Author: Death, Property, and Lawyers, 1970, The Planning and Drafting of Wills and Trusts, 1972, 3d edit., 1991, Legal Interviewing and Counseling, 1976, 2d edit., 1987, On Being a Christian and a Lawyer, 1981, American Legal Ethics, 1985, Faith and the Professions, 1987, American Lawyers and Their Communities, 1991; co-author: Lawyers, Law Students, and People, 1977, Cases in Legal Interviewing and Counseling, 1980, Property Cases, Materials and Problems, 1992, Lawyers, Clients, and Moral Responsibility, 1994; co-editor: The Mentally Retarded Citizen and the Law, 1976; contbr. articles to legal jours. Served with USAF, 1953-57. Frances Lewis scholar Washington and Lee U., 1979; recipient Emil Brown Found. Preventive Law prize, 1966, Presdl. citation U. Notre Dame, 1975, St. Thomas More award St. Mary's U., 1983, Law medal Gonzaga U., 1991, Jour. Law and Religion award, 1993. Mem. Ind. State Bar Assn., Soc. Christian Ethics, Jewish Law Assn. Roman Catholic. Home: 1865 Champlain Blvd Niles MI 49120-8935 Office: U Notre Dame Law Sch Notre Dame IN 46556

SHAFFNER, PATRICK NOEL, architectural engineering executive; b. Burlington, N.C., Nov. 1, 1939; s. Samuel Hubert and Martha Jane (Noel) Shaffner; m. Patricia Anne Anders, June 12, 1961; children: Scott Anders, Kimberly Page, Melissa Hope. BS, Va. Poly. and State U., 1961. Registered profl. engr., Va. and others. Structural engr. Hayes, Seay, Mattern & Mattern, Roanoke, Va., 1963-68; sr. structural engr. Sherertz & Franklin, Roanoke, 1968-72; ptnr. Sherertz, Franklin, Crawford, Shaffner, Roanoke, 1972-87; pres., chief exec. officer Sherertz, Franklin, Crawford, Shaffner, Inc., Roanoke, 1988—. Bd. dirs. Va. Found. for Arch., Mill Mt. Theatre, Va. Tech. Coll. Engring. Com. 100; chmn. Am. Heart Assn., ARC. Capt. Corps Engrs., U.S. Army, 1961-63. Paul Harris fellow. Fellow ASCE; mem. AIA (assoc.), Soc. Am. Mil. Engrs., Roanoke Regional C. of C. (Small Bus. Person of Yr. 1991), Rotary (pres. Roanoke club 1986). Republican. Baptist. Lodge: Rotary (Roanoke) (pres. 1986). Home: 2635 Turnberry Rd Salem VA 24153-7483 Office: Sherertz Franklin 305 S Jefferson St Roanoke VA 24011-2000

SHAFRAN, HANK, public relations agency executive; b. Boston, Nov. 13, 1945; s. Milton and Pauline (Hoffman) S.; m. Jane D. Shafran, Aug. 11, 1969 (div. Apr. 1982); children: Michael, Debra; m. Antoinette M. Delisi, July 26, 1987. BS, Boston U., 1968. Account exec. Burson-Marsteller, N.Y.C., 1968-71; exec. asst. to dir. Gov.'s Com. on Criminal Justice, Boston, 1971-77; dir. communications Computer Libr. Systems Inc., Newton, Mass., 1977-78; dir. pub. rels. Arnold & Co., Boston, 1983-84; exec. v.p., ptnr. Cone Comms., Boston, 1984-91; comms. and pub. rels. cons., 1991—. Sec. Ronald McDonald House, Brookline, Mass., 1979—. Mem. Counselors Acad. Pub. Rels. Soc. Am., Pub. Rels. Soc. Am. (v.p. Boston chpt.), New Eng. Broadcasting Assn., Advt. Club of Greater Boston, Publicity Club of New Eng. Democrat. Jewish. Avocation: music.

SHAFRITZ, DAVID ANDREW, physician, research scientist; b. Phila., Oct. 5, 1940; s. Saul and Ethel (Kohn) S.; m. Sharon C. Klemow, Aug. 16, 1964; children: Gregory S., Adam B., Keith M. AB in Chemistry with honors, U. Pa., 1962, MD, 1966. Diplomate Nat. Bd. Med. Examiners, Am. Bd. Internal Medicine. Intern, then asst. resident U. Md. Hosp., Balt., 1966-68; rsch. assoc. NIH, Bethesda, Md., 1968-71; clin. and rsch. fellow Mass. Gen. Hosp., Boston, 1971-73; instr. Harvard Med. Sch., Boston, 1971-73, asst. prof. medicine, 1973; asst. prof. medicine and cell biology Albert Einstein Coll. Medicine, Yeshiva U., Bronx, N.Y., 1973-76, assoc. prof., 1976-81, prof. medicine and cell biology, 1981—, dir. Marion Bessin Liver Rsch. Ctr., 1985—, Herman Lapota prof. liver disease rsch., 1992—; cons. Integrated Genetics Inc., Framingham, Mass., 1981-86, Immuno, Vienna, Austria, 1986-91, Innovir, Inc., N.Y.C., 1991—, Eugenetech Internat., Inc., Ramsey, N.J., 1991-93; temp. advisor WHO, Geneva, 1983; mem. Nat. Com. for Clin. Lab. Standards, Villanova, Pa., 1983—; mem. sci. adv. bd. com. liver cancer program Inst. for Cancer Rsch., Fox Chase and Phila., 1987—; mem. rev. panel C, study sect. Nat. Inst. Diabetes and Digestive Kidney Diseases, 1988-92, chmn. 1991-92; mem. cen. coordination com. Liver Tissue Procurement and Distbn. System, 1986—; mem. NIH Metabolic Pathology Study Sect., 1995—. Co-author: The Liver: Biology and Pathobiology, 1982, 3rd edit., 1993, Hepatobiliary Diseases, 1991; assoc. editor Hepatology, 1981-86; mem. editl. bd. Jour. Med. Virology, 1982-93, Hepatology, 1990—, Jour. Virology, 1992—; contbr. numerous rsch. articles and revs. to profl. publs.; contbr. chpts. to books; patentee in field. Trustee Westchester Jewish Ctr., Mamaroneck, N.Y., 1980-86. Lt. comdr. USPHS, 1968-71. Recipient Merck award U. Pa., 1962, Morton McCutcheon Meml. Rsch. prize Sch. Medicine, 1966, Career Scientist award Irma T. Hirschl Trust, N.Y.C., 1974-79; European Molecular Biology Orgn. fellow, 1978; recipient Rsch. Career Devel. award NIH, 1975-80, spl. rsch. fellow, 1971-73, rsch. grantee, 1974—. Mem. Am. Assn. for Study of Liver Diseases, Internat. Assn. for Study of Liver, Am. Gastroenterol. Assn., Am. Soc. Biochemistry and Molecular Biology, Am. Soc. Clin. Investigation, Assn. Am. Physicians, N.Y. Acad. Scis., Harvey Soc., Interurban Clin. Club. Democrat. Jewish. Avocations: jogging, tennis. Home: 4 Pheasant Run Larchmont NY 10538-3423 Office: Yeshiva U Albert Einstein Coll Med Marion Bessin Liver Rsch Ctr 1300 Morris Park Ave Bronx NY 10461-1926

SHAFTMAN, FREDRICK KRISCH, telephone communication executive, lawyer; b. Roanoke, Va., Apr. 9, 1948; s. Sydney and Rosalie (Krisch) S.; m. Diane Hasson, Dec. 27, 1970; children: Stephanie, Emily. BSBA, U. Ala. 1970, JD, 1973. Bar: Va. 1973. Gen. counsel Bell South Communication Systems (formerly Universal Communication Systems, Inc.), Roanoke, 1973-74, v.p., gen. counsel, 1974-79, pres., 1979-84, chief exec. officer, 1984—, also bd. dirs.; v.p. Am. Motor Inns, Inc. Bd. dirs. United Way of Roanoke Valley, Roanoke Mill Mountain Zoo; trustee North Cross Country Day Sch., Roanoke, Roanoke Valley Sci. Mus., Roanoke Valley Red Cross. Recipient Pres.'s Disting. Service award N.Am. Telecommunication Assn., 1985, Achievement award United Jewish Assn., 1989. Mem. N.Am. Telephone Assn. (bd. dirs.), Western Va. Better Bus. Bur. (bd. dirs.), ABA, Va. State Bar Assn. Lodge: Rotary. Office: Bellsouth Comm Systems 1936 Blue Hills Dr NE Roanoke VA 24012-0455

SHAFTO, ROBERT AUSTIN, insurance company executive; b. Council Bluffs, Iowa, Sept. 15, 1935; s. Glen Granville and Blanche (Radigan) S.; m. Jeanette DeFino, Dec. 17, 1954; children: Robert, Dennis, Teri, Shari, Michael. BS in Actuarial Sci., Drake U., Des Moines, 1959. Mgr. computer svcs. Guarantee Mut. Life Ins. Co., Omaha, 1959-65; v.p. Beta div. Electronic Data Systems, Dallas, 1965-71; from 2d v.p. to v.p. for computer systems devel. and info. svcs. New England Mutual Life Ins. Co., Boston, 1972-75, sr. v.p. policy holder and computer svcs., 1975-81, adminstrv. v.p., 1981-82, exec. v.p individual ins. ops., 1982-86, exec. v.p. ins. and employee benefits ops., 1986-88, pres. ins. and personal fin. svcs., 1988-90, pres., chief oper. officer, 1990-92, pres., CEO, 1992-93, pres., CEO, chmn., 1993—, also bd. dirs.; bd. dirs., pres. New Eng. Variable Life, Fleet Bank of Mass., Am. Coun. Life Ins. Bd. overseers Children's Hosp., Boston, 1989—; mem. corp. Dana Farber Cancer Inst., Northwestern U.; bd. dirs. United Way of Mass; trustee Am. Coll. Mem. Greater Boston C. of C. (bd. dirs.). Roman Catholic. Avocations: tennis, golf, scuba diving, jogging. Office: New Eng Mut Life Ins Co 501 Boylston St Boston MA 02116-3706*

SHAGAN, STEVE, screenwriter, novelist, film producer; b. N.Y.C., Oct. 25, 1927; s. Barnet Harry and Rachel (Rosenzweig) S.; m. Elizabeth Leslie Florance, Nov. 18, 1956; 1 son, Robert William. Grad. high sch. Film technician Consol. Film, Inc., N.Y.C., 1952-56, RCA, Cape Canaveral, Fla., 1956-59; asst. to publicity dir. Paramount Pictures, Hollywood, Calif., 1962-63. Producer: TV series Tarzan, 1966; producer, writer movies for TV,

Universal and CBS, Hollywood, Calif., 1968-70; writer original screenplay: Save the Tiger, Paramount Studios, 1972 (Writers Guild award, Acad. award nominee 1973); also producer film; author screenplay: City of Angels (produced as movie Hustle), 1975, novel, screenplay The Formula, 1979; screenplay Voyage of the Damned, 1976 (Acad. award Nomination); writer, producer: film The Formula, MGM, 1980; author novels: Save the Tiger, 1972, City of Angels, 1975, The Formula, 1979, The Circle, 1982, The Discovery, 1985, Vendetta, 1986, Pillars of Fire, 1989, A Cast of Thousands, 1993. Served with USCG, 1944-46. Mem. Writers Guild Am. (bd. dirs. West chpt. 1978-82). Office: care Michael Mesnick CPA 11300 W Olympic Blvd Los Angeles CA 90064-1637

SHAH, BIPIN CHANDRA, banker; b. Bombay, July 23, 1938; s. Manilal and Keshar Shah; m. Fay Shah, 1962 (div. 1985); m. Ellen T. Dever, Sept. 20, 1985; children: Nelie, Sarah Lynn, Genevieve. BA, Baldwin-Wallace Coll., 1962; MA, U. Pa., 1965. Pres. Vertex Systems, Inc., King of Prussia, Pa., 1970-74; sr. v.p. Fed. Res. Bank, Phila., Pa., 1974-78, Am. Express, N.Y.C., 1979-80; exec. v.p. Phila. Nat. Bank, 1980-84; exec. v.p. CoreStates Fin. Corp., Phila., 1984-86, vice chmn., 1986-89, COO, 1990-91; pres., CEO Transaction Processing Inc., Phila., 1991—; bd. dirs. VISA, USA, San Matteo, Calif., Franklin Inst., Phila., Phila. Internat. Bank, N.Y.C., U.S. Pro Indoor Tennis, Phila.; chmn. bd. dirs. CoreStates Bank Del., Wilmington. Fund raiser Phila. Indoor Tennis, 1985-88. Mem. Union League. Republican. Avocations: reading, golf, tennis, fishing. Office: Transaction Processing Inc 2 Penn Ctr Plz Ste 312 Philadelphia PA 19102

SHAH, HARESH C., civil engineering educator; b. Godhra, Gujarat, India, Aug. 7, 1937; s. Chandulal M. and Rama Shah; m. Mary-Joan Dersjant, Dec. 27, 1965; children: Hemant, Mihir. BEngring., U. Poona, 1959; MSCE, Stanford U., 1960, PhD, 1963. From instr. to assoc. prof. U. Pa., Phila., 1962-68; assoc. prof. civil engring. Stanford (Calif.) U., 1968-73, prof., 1973—, chmn. dept. civil engring., 1985-94, John A. Blume prof. engring., 1988-91, Obayashi prof. engring., 1991—, dir. Stanford Ctr. for Risk Analysis, 1987-94; dir. Stanford Ctr. for Risk Analysis; bd. dirs. Stanford Mgmt. Group, Inc., Risk Mgmt. Software, Inc.; cons. in field. Author 1 book; contbr. over 250 articles to profl. jours. Mem. ASCE, Am. Concrete Inst., Earthquake Engring. Rsch. Inst., Seismol. Soc. Am., Sigma Xi, Tau Beta Pi. Avocations: hiking, climbing, travel. Office: Stanford U Dept Civil Engring Stanford CA 94305

SHAH, JAGDEEP, physicist, researcher; b. Surat, India, Sept. 3, 1942; came to U.S., 1962; s. Chandrawadan C. and Kusum C. (Choksi) S.; m. Shobhana J. Bhatt, Apr. 16, 1967; children: Roopak, Raina. BSc, U. Bombay, 1962; PhD, MIT, 1967. Mem. tech. staff AT&T Bell Labs., Holmdel, N.J., 1967-84, disting. mem. tech. staff, 1985—; gen. chmn. Internat. Conf. on Quantum Electronics, 1994. Editor: Hot Electrons in Semiconductor Nanostructure Physics and Application, 1992. Named Humboldt sr. U.S. rsch. scientist Humboldt Found., Germany, 1990. Fellow Am. Phys. Soc., Optical Soc. Am. Office: Crawfords Corner Rd Holmdel NJ 07733

SHAH, MANU HIRACHAND, civil and structural engineer; b. Bardoli, Gujrat, India, May 14, 1936; came to U.S., 1959; s. Hirachand N. and Gulabben H. Shah; m. Ila M. Shah, Dec. 14, 1962; children: Paras, Pamuna, Punam. BE Civil, Victoria Jubilee Tech. Inst., Bombay, 1958; MS Structural, U. Ill., 1960. Registered structural engr., Ill.; registered profl. engr., 16 states. Design engr. Patel Engring., Bombay, 1958-59; project engr. Skidmore Owings & Merril, Chgo., 1960-73, Alfred Benesch & Co., Chgo., 1974-75; owner, pres. Shah Engring., Inc., Chgo., 1976—; pres. Chgo. Archtl. Assistance Ctr., 1985, bd. dirs., 1976-85. Mem. Zoning Bd. of Appeal, Village of Oak Brook, 1992—; pres. India Assn. Met. Chgo., 1965. Mem. ASCE, NSPE, Am. Concrete Inst. (bd. dirs. Chgo. chpt. 1984-85), Structural Engrs. Assn. Ill. (bd. dirs. 1982-85), Jain Soc. (coord. Chgo. 1986-887), Jain Social Group (pres. Chgo. 1986-87), Midwest Club (Oak Brook) (trustee, chmn. archtl. com. 1986-90, 1993—), Toastmasters (mem. Speakers Forum 1976-77). Achievements include constrn. inspection of Kennedy Expressway and Lake Shore Dr., design and constrn. mgmt. of Metra's Kensington Yard facility, design of improvements on CTA Lake St. and North Main Line, rehab. of high rise bldg. at Cabrini Green. Home: 1510 Midwest Club Pky Oak Brook IL 60521-2521 Office: Shah Engring Inc 1 E IBM Plz Ste 3200 Chicago IL 60611-3604

SHAH, RAMESH KESHAVLAL, automotive company executive; b. Bombay, India, Sept. 23, 1941; came to U.S., 1963; s. Keshavlal M. and Hiraben K. (Kothari) S.; m. Rekha R. Maniar, Jan. 22, 1968; children: Nilay R., Nirav R. BME, Gujarat U., Ahmedabad, Gujarat, 1963; MS, Stanford U., 1964, ME, 1970, PhD in Mech. Engring., 1972. Project engr. Air Preheater Co., Wellsville, N.Y., 1964-66, Avco-Lycoming, Charleston, S.C., 1968-69; rsch. engr. Delphi Harrison Thermal Systems GM, Lockport, N.Y., 1971-75; staff engr. Harrison Radiator Div., GM, Lockport, N.Y., 1976-83, staff devel. engr., 1983-88, sr. staff rsch. scientist, 1989—; tchr. short courses, presenter keynote lectrs., seminars on heat exchanger design at various univs. and rsch. insts. in U.S., India, Can., U.K., Turkey, Yugoslavia, Fed. Republic of Germany, People's Republic of China, Japan, Australia, Argentina, Brazil, Portugal, Czechoslovakia, Hungary, Taiwan, South Korea, Israel, Belgium, Sweden, Lithuania, Russia, Greece, Italy, Malta, Singapore, Ukraine. Author: (with A.L. London) Laminar Flow Forced Convection in Ducts, Suppl. 1 to Advances in Heat Transfer, 1978; editor: (with S. Kakac and A.E. Bergles) Low Reynolds Number Flow Heat Exchangers, 1983, (with S. Kakac and W. Aung) Handbook of Single-Phase Convective Heat Transfer, 1987, (with E.C. Subbarao and R.A. Mashelkar) Heat Transfer Equipment Design, 1988, (with E.N. Ganic and K.T. Yang) Experimental Heat Transfer, Fluid Mechanics and Thermodynamics, 1988, (with A.D. Kraus and D.E. Metzger) Compact Heat Exchangers: A Festschrift for Professor A.L. London, 1990, (with H. Md. Roshan, V.M.K. Sastri and K.A. Padmanabhan) Thermomechanical Aspects of Manufacturing and Materials Processing, 1991, (with J.F. Keffer and E.N. Ganic) Experimental Heat Transfer, Fluid Mechanics and Thermodynamics, 1991, (with A. Hashemi) Aerospace Heat Exchanger Technology, 1993, (with M.D. Kelleher, K.R. Sreenivasan and Y. Joshi) Experimental Heat Transfer, Fluid Mechanics and Thermodynamics, 1993, (with S.P. Sukhatme, V. Venkat Raj, and V.M.K. Sastri) Heat and Mass Transfer, 1994; editor 12 symposium vols.; founding co-editor, editor-in-chief Exptl. Thermal and Fluid Sci., 1987—; tech. papers reviewer ASME Jour. Heat Transfer, Internat. Jour. Heat and Mass Transfer, Jour. Numerical Heat Transfer, AIChE Jour., ASME Jour. Fluids Engring., Heat Transfer Engring. Jour., numerous engring. jours. NSF grantee (7) 1981-90; NATO grantee (4) 1980-87; UN grantee 85-86, 88-89. Fellow ASME (Region III Tech. Achievement award 1979, Valued Svc. award 1986, 87, 50th Anniversary award of Heat Transfer Div. 1988, Charles Russ Richards Meml. award 1989); mem. Soc. Automotive Engrs., Indian Soc. Heat and Mass Transfer (life), Associacao Brasileira de Ciencias Mechanicas, Niagara Frontier Assn. R and D Dirs. Jain. Avocations: travel, reading, bridge. Office: GM Delphi Harrison Thermal Syss. Lockport NY 14094-1896

SHAH, SURENDRA POONAMCHAND, engineering educator, researcher; b. Bombay, Aug. 30, 1936; s. Poonamchand C. and Maniben (Modi) S.; m. Dorothie Crispell, June 9, 1962; children: Daniel S., Byron C. BE, B.V.M. Coll. Engring., India, 1959; MS, Lehigh U., 1960; PhD, Cornell U., 1965. Asst. prof. U. Ill., Chgo., 1966-69, assoc. prof., 1969-73, prof., 1973-81; prof. civil engring Northwestern U., Evanston, Ill., 1981—, dir. Ctr. for Concrete and Geomaterials, 1987—; dir. NSF Sci. and Tech. Ctr. for Advanced Cement-Based Materials Northwestern U., 1989—, Walter P. Murphy prof. of engring., 1992—; cons. govt. agys. and industry, U.S.A., UN, France, Switzerland, People's Republic of China, Denmark, The Netherlands; vis. prof. MIT, 1969, Delft U., The Netherlands, 1976, Denmark Tech. U., 1984, LCPC, Paris, 1986, U. Sidney, Australia, 1987; NATO vis. sci. Turkey, 1992. Co-author: Fiber Reinforced Cement Composites, 1992, High Performance Concrete and Applications, 1994; contbr. more than 350 articles to profl. jours.; editor 12 books; mem. editl. bds. 4 internat. jours.; editor-in-chief Jour. Advancement Based Materials. Recipient Thompson award ASTM, Phila., 1983, Disting. U.S. Vis. Scientist award Alexander von Humboldt Found., 1989, Swedish Concrete award, Stockholm, 1993. Fellow Am. Concrete Inst. (chmn. tech. com., Anderson award 1989), Internat. Union Testing and Rsch. Labs. Materials and Structures (chmn. tech. com. 1989—, Gold medal 1980); mem. ASCE (past chmn. tech. com., mem. exec. com.).

Home: 921 Isabella St Evanston IL 60201-1773 Office: Northwestern U Tech Inst Rm A130 2145 Sheridan Rd Evanston IL 60208-0002

SHAHEEN, MICHAEL EDMUND, JR., lawyer, government official; b. Boston, Aug. 5, 1940; s. Michael Edmund and Dorothy Wallace (Cameron) S.; m. Polly Adair Dammann, Sept. 11, 1976; children: Michael Edmund, Timothy Andrew. B.A., Yale U., 1962; LL.B., Vanderbilt U., 1965. Bar: Tenn. 1968. Dir. ann. capital support fund, instr. physics Memphis Univ. Sch., 1965-66; law clk. Judge Robert M. McRae, Jr., Memphis, 1966-68; individual practice law Tenn., Miss., 1968-73; dep. chief voting and public accomodations sect. Dept. Justice, Washington, 1973-74, dep. chief fed. programs sect., civil rights div., 1974-75; counsel to Atty. Gen. for Intelligence, 1975; spl. adv. to atty. gen., counsel, dir. Office Profl. Responsibility, 1975—; mayor, Como, Miss., 1970-73; pres. Como Resources, Inc., 1971-72; mcpl. judge, Como, 1970-73; chmn. Como Indsl. Devel. Commn., 1970-73. Mem. Phi Delta Phi, Zeta Psi. Office: Dept Justice 10th Constitution Ave NE Washington DC 20530-0001

SHAHIN, THOMAS JOHN, dry cleaning wholesale supply company executive; b. Buffalo, July 30, 1943; s. Thomas Mark and Marie (Colletto) S.; m. Laraine Edna Clements, Feb. 25, 1967; 1 child, Lori Lynn. BSBA, Calif. State U., L.A., 1966. Asst. v.p. stock brokerage div. United Calif. Bank, L.A., 1969-76; v.p., gen. mgr., treas. Newhouse Splty. Co. Inc., Santa Ana, Calif., 1976—, also bd. dirs. Patentee belt buckle. Officer USN, 1966-69, Vietnam. Mem. Textile Care Allied Trade Assn., Laundry and Drycleaners Suppliers, Internat. Fabricare Inst., Internat. Drycleaners Congress, Calif. Fabricare Inst., Beta Gamma Sigma. Republican. Roman Catholic. Avocations: new product research, reading, travel, golf, tennis. Office: Newhouse Splty Co Inc 2619 Oak St Santa Ana CA 92707-3720

SHAH-JAHAN, M. M., economist; b. Dhaka, Bangladesh, June 30, 1943; came to U.S., 1975; s. M.M. Serajul Hoq and Ayesha A. Khaton; m. Mahmuda Khatun, Aug. 15, 1972; children: Al M., Nydia. BA in Bus., Dacca U., 1963, MA in Bus., Head; MA in Econs., Georgetown U., 1982; PhD in Econs., Georgetown-Pacific Western U., 1987. Asst. prof. adn. dept. Dacca Coll., 1965-75; sec. gen. prof. staff coun., 1971-75; audit supr. Marriott Corp., Arlington, Va., 1975-81; economist Potomac Electric Power Co., Washington, 1981—; cons. economist World Bank, Washington, 1988—. Author: (with M.R. Khan) Principles of Income Tax, 1970, Principles of Banking, 1974, An Econometric Forecasting Model, 1987, Jordan: A Macroeconomic Projection, 1988, U.S. Macroeconomic Outlook, 1989, The Open Economy Macro Model for Policy and Planning in the Developing Economies, 1993, Twenty-five Year Macroeconomic Outlook for Bangladesh, 1994. Govt. of Pakistan scholar, 1964. Mem. Am. Econ. Assn., Soc. Govt. Economists, Arlington Swimming Club, Nat Economists Club. Democrat. Islam. Avocations: tennis, swimming, movies, travel, photography. Home: 1223 S Buchanan St Arlington VA 22204-3407 Office: Potomac Electric Power Co 1900 Pennsylvania Ave NW Washington DC 20068

SHAIMAN, MARC, composer, arranger, orchestrator; b. Newark, Oct. 22, 1959; s. William Robert and Claire (Goldfein) S. Composer (films) Misery, City Slickers, The Addams Family, Father of the Bride, Sister Act, A Few Good Men, Mr. Saturday Night, Sleepless in Seattle (Academy Award nomination for best song), A Wink and a Smile, City Slickers II, Heart and Souls, Addams Family Values, North, Speechless, (Broadway and off Broadway shows) Bette Midler's Divine Madness, Harry Connick Jr. in Concert, Peter Allen in Concert, Leader of the Pack, Legends with Mary Martin and Carol Channing; record producer, arranger Bette Midler's Thighs and Whispers, Divine Madness, Beaches, When Harry Met Sally, We Are in Love, Some Peoples Lives; producer various concerts by artists including Barbara Streisand, Billy Crystal, Barry Manilow, Luther Vandross, Raquel Welch; film music adaptations, supervision include When Harry Met Sally, Beaches, Scenes from a Mall, For the Boys; composer, arranger (TV shows) Saturday Night Live, various Acad., Grammy, and Emmy awards shows, (HBO spls.) Martin Short, Robin Williams, Bette Midler, Billy Crystal; actor (films) Broadcast News, Hot Shots. Avocation: Kelly Bush Pub Rels 2047 Glencoe Way Los Angeles CA 90068 also: The Kraft-Benjamin Agency 8491 Sunset Blvd Ste 492 West Hollywood CA 90069

SHAIN, HAROLD, magazine publisher. Publisher Newsweek, N.Y.C. Office: Newsweek Inc The Washington Post Co 251 W 57th St New York NY 10019*

SHAIN, IRVING, retired chemical company executive and university chancellor; b. Seattle, Jan. 2, 1926; s. Samuel and Selma (Blockoff) S.; m. Mildred Ruth Udell, Aug. 31, 1947; children—Kathryn A., Steven T., John R., Paul S. B.S. in Chemistry, U. Wash., 1949, Ph.D. in Chemistry, 1952. From instr. to prof. U. Wis., Madison, 1952-75, vice chancellor, 1970-75, chancellor, 1977-86; provost, v.p. acad. affairs U. Wash., Seattle, 1975-77; v.p. Olin Corp., Stamford, Conn., 1987-92, ret., 1992; mem. tech. adv. bd. Johnson Controls, Inc., Milw., 1980—; bd. dirs. Olin Corp., Stamford, Conn., 1982—; trustee Univ. Rsch. Park, Inc., Madison, pres., 1984-86, v.p., 1987—; mem. Nat. Commn. on Superconductivity, 1989-90. Contbr. articles on electroanalytical chemistry to profl. jours. Bd. dirs. Madison Gen. Hosp., 1972-75; v.p. Madison Cmty. Found., 1984-86. Served with U.S. Army, 1943-46, PTO. Fellow AAAS; mem. Am. Chem. Soc., Electrochem. Soc., Internat. Soc. Electrochemistry, Conn. Acad. Sci. and Engring., Phi Beta Kappa, Sigma Xi, Phi Kappa Phi. Home: 2820 Marshall Ct # 8 Madison WI 53705-2270 Office: Univ Wis Univ Rsch Park 610 Walnut St Madison WI 53705-2336

SHAINE, THEODORE HARRIS, advertising agency executive; b. N.Y.C., Apr. 8, 1947; s. Bernard Leonard and Edna (Zeman) S. B.F.A., Pratt Inst., Bklyn., 1968. Art dir. Doyle Dane Bernbach, N.Y.C., 1968-73; art supr. Carl Ally, N.Y.C., 1973-75; creative supr. Young & Rubicam, N.Y.C., 1975-77; sr. v.p. Marschalk Co., N.Y.C., 1977-79; assoc. creative dir. Della Femina, Travisano, N.Y.C., 1979-81; sr. v.p. Doyle Dane Bernbach, N.Y.C., 1981-86, Ammirati & Puris, N.Y.C., 1986-90; exec. v.p., creative dir. Hill Holiday, Boston, 1990-92; exec. v.p. BBDO, N.Y.C., 1992—; advt. cons. to V.P. George Bush 1988 Presdl. campaign; instr. Pratt Inst., Bklyn., 1979-80; lectr., instr. Sch. Visual Arts, N.Y.C., 1973-77; lectr. One Club for Art and Copy N.Y.C. 1983. Poster design represented in collection Mus. Modern Art N.Y. Named to Clio Hall of Fame, 1977, 78; recipient One Show Gold award, One Club, 1974, 83, Art Dirs. Show Gold award, 1973, Gold Lion award Cannes Film Festival, 1989. Home: PO Box 632 Montauk NY 11954-0502 Office: BBDO NY 1285 Avenue Of The Americas New York NY 10019-6028

SHAINESS, NATALIE, psychiatrist, educator; b. N.Y.C., Dec. 2, 1915; d. Jack and Clara (Levy-Hart) S.; div.; children: David Spiegel, Ann Spiegel. BA in Chemistry, NYU, 1936; MD, Va. Commonwealth U., 1939. Diplomate in psychiatry; cert. in psychoanalysis. Pvt. practice N.Y.C., 1955—; faculty William Alanson White Inst. Psychiatry, Psychoanalysis, N.Y.C., 1961-81; asst. clin. prof. psychiatry N.Y. Sch. Psychiatry, N.Y.C., 1964-67; teaching analyst N.Y. Med. Academie, 1966-67; faculty, psychiatry Columbia U. Coll. Physicians and Surgeons, N.Y.C., 1966-80; faculty, supervising analyst L.I. Inst. Psychoanalysis, N.Y., 1980—; invited participant 1st and 2nd Internat. Conf. on Abortion, 1967, 68; research project on menstruation. Editorial bd. Jour. of the Am. Women's Med. Assn., 1985—; author: Sweet Suffering: Woman as Victim, 1984; contbr. over 100 articles to profl. jours. and over 90 profl. book revs. Mem. Physicians for Social Responsibility, Nuclear Freeze, several other anti-nuclear orgns. Fellow Am. Acad. Psychoanalysis (former trustee, organizer several panels), Am. Psychiat. Assn. (life mem.; organizer several panels), N.Y. Acad. Medicine (hon.), Soc. Med. Psychoanalysts (honored for keen erudition, lively imagination and professionalism 1993, councillor); mem. Assn. for Advancement of Psychotherapy, Women's Med. Assn. N.Y.C. (fin. assistance com., 1st Pres.'s award 1990). Avocations: music, the arts. Home and Office: 140 E 83rd St New York NY 10028-1924

SHAINMAN, IRWIN, music educator, musician; b. N.Y.C., June 27, 1921; s. Samuel and Gussie (Pollack) S.; m. Bernice Cohen, Aug. 29, 1948; children—Joan, Jack. B.A., Pomona Coll., 1943; M.A., Columbia, 1948; Premier Prix, Conservatoire Nat. de Musique de Paris, France, 1950. Prof. music, curator Paul Whiteman collection Williams Coll., Williamstown, Mass., 1948-91, prof. emeritus, 1991—; chmn. music dept., 1971-77, dean faculty, 1972-73, coordinator performing arts, 1973-76, Class of 1955 prof. music, 1980-91; tchr. extension U. Mass., 1952-55, Mass. State Coll., North Adams, 1957, also Bennington Coll. Composer's Conf. and Chamber Music Center; cons. advanced placement program Coll. Entrance Exam. Bd., 1969-75; mem. edn. com. Saratoga Performing Arts Center, 1967-68; pres. Williamstown Theatre Found., 1972-77, South Mountain Concert Assn., 1980—. Condr., Berkshire Symphony, 1950-65, also Williams Coll. band, brass ensemble and woodwind ensemble, 1st trumpet, Albany (N.Y.) Symphony Orch., 1960-65, Vt. Symphony Orch., 1954-58; contbr. articles to profl. jours.; columnist: Berkshire Eagle; author: Avoiding Cultural Default and Other Essays, 1991. Mem. merit aid panel Mass. Arts Council, 1984. Served with AUS, 1942-45. Decorated Purple Heart, Combat Inf. badge.; N.Y. Philharmonic scholar, 1934-35; Recipient Danforth Found. Tchrs. award, 1957-58. Mem. Am. Musicological Soc., Coll. Music Assn., Music Critics Assn. Home: 88 Baxter Rd Williamstown MA 01267-2111

SHAIR, DAVID IRA, human resources executive; b. N.Y.C., May 1, 1921; s. Henry and Jessie (Brinn) S.; m. Hortense Spitz, Oct. 18, 1947. BA, CUNY, 1940; MBA, NYU, 1950. Assoc. Benj. Werne Assocs., N.Y.C., 1952-70; dir. labor relations London Records, Inc., N.Y.C., 1970-80; v.p. personnel Carl Fischer, Inc., N.Y.C., 1980-92; mgmt. cons., freelance writer, 1993—. Author various articles on personnel and labor relations. Served with inf. U.S. Army, 1942-45, ETO. Decorated Purple Heart. Mem. Soc. Adminstrv. Mgmt. (v.p. 1986-87, exec. v.p. 1987-90), Indsl. Rels. Rsch. Assn., Soc. Human Resource Mgmt. Assn. Jewish. Avocation: photography. Home: 6 Peter Cooper Rd New York NY 10010-6701 also: 7 Rosemaries Ln PO Box 3099 East Hampton NY 11937

SHAKESPEARE, FRANK, ambassador; b. N.Y.C., Apr. 9, 1925; s. Francis Joseph and Frances (Hughes) S.; m. Deborah Anne Spaeth, Oct. 9, 1954; children: Mark, Andrea, Fredricka. BS, Holy Cross Coll., 1947; D.Eng. (hon.), Colo. Sch. Mines, 1975; DCS (hon.), Pace U., 1979; LLD (hon.), Del. Law Sch., 1980, Sacred Heart U., 1985, U. Dallas, 1987, Pepperdine U., 1990, Nichols Coll., 1991, Marquette U., 1993. Formerly pres. CBS-TV Services; exec. v.p. CBS-TV Stas.; dir. USIA, 1969-73; exec. v.p. Westinghouse Electric Corp., 1973-75; pres. RKO Gen. Inc., N.Y.C., 1975-85, vice chmn., 1983-85; U.S. ambassador to Portugal Lisbon, 1985-87; U.S. ambassador to The Holy See Vatican City, 1987-89. Chmn. Heritage Found., 1975-85, dir., 1989—; chmn. Radio Free Europe/Radio Liberty, Inc., 1976-85; dir. Bradley Founhd., 1989—. Served to lt. (j.g.) USNR, 1945-46. Club: Union League. Home: 303 Coast Blvd La Jolla CA 92037-4630

SHAKLAN, ALLEN YALE, broadcast executive; b. Newark, July 10, 1945; s. David George and Esther (Sweet) S.; m. Marlene Sokoloff, July 11, 1968; children: Steven, Daniel. AB, Rutgers U., Newark, 1967, JD, 1969; LLM, NYU, 1974. Bar: N.Y., D.C. Atty. FTC, N.Y.C., 1969-71, CBS, N.Y.C., 1971-84; v.p., asst. to pres. CBS TV, N.Y.C., 1984-86, v.p. programming, news adminstrn. and sta. services, 1986-88; v.p., gen. mgr. Sta. WCIX-TV, Miami, Fla., 1989—. Mem. Nat Assn. TV Programming Execs., Fla. Assn. Broadcasters. Office: WCIX-TV 8900 NW 18th Ter Miami FL 33172-2696

SHAKNO, ROBERT JULIAN, hospital administrator; b. Amsterdam, Holland, Aug. 15, 1937; came to U.S. 1939, naturalized, 1944; s. Rudy C. and Gertrude (Loeb) S.; m. Elka Linda Baum, June 10, 1962; children: Steven Lee, Deborah Sue. B.B.A. (scholar 1955), So. Methodist U., 1959; M.H.A., Washington U., St. Louis, 1961. Adminstrv. asst. Mt. Sinai Hosp., Chgo., 1961-63; assoc. adminstr. Tex. Inst. Rehab. and Research, Houston, 1963-65; asst. adminstr. Michael Reese Hosp., Chgo., 1965-70; v.p., hosp. dir. Michael Reese Hosp., 1970-73; assoc. exec. dir. Cook County Hosp., Chgo., 1973-75; pres. Hackensack Med. Center, N.J., 1975-85, Mt. Sinai Med. Ctr., Cleve., 1985—; oper. trustee, sec. LAurelwood Hosp., Willoughby, Ohio; clin. instr. Washington U., St. Louis, U. Chgo., Northwestern U., Columbia U.; bd. dirs. Ohio Hosp. Ins. Co. Mem. editorial bd. Mgmt. Series, Am. Coll. Healthcare Execs. Mem. Leadership Cleve.; bd. dirs. Premier Hosp. Alliance, chmn., 1994—; bd. dirs. The New Cleve. Inc., Univ. Circle Inc., Cleve., Cleve. Sight Ctr.; chmn. social svcs. div. United Jewish Appeal, Cleve., 1987-88, chmn. health cabinet, 1990, gen. co-chmn., 1990—; chmn. Hosp. Pacesetter campaign United Way, chmn. health svcs. portfolio, 1988-89, oversight commn., 1992-93. Served to 1st lt. USAR, 1960-66. Named Young Adminstr. of Yr., Washington U., 1968. Fellow Am. Coll. Hosp. Adminstrs.; mem. Am. Hosp. Assn. (coun. urban hosps., del. coun. on met. hosps., rep. regional policy bd.), Washington U. Alumni Assn. (past pres.), Greater Cleve. Hosp. Assn. (bd. dirs.), Ohio Hosp. Assn. (bd. dirs.), Cleve. Sight Ctr. (trustee, bd. dirs.), Sigma Alpha Mu (past pres.). Home: 32050 Meadow Lark Way Pepper Pike OH 44124-5508 Office: Mt Sinai Med Ctr 1 Mount Sinai Dr Cleveland OH 44106-4198

SHAKOW, DAVID JOSEPH, law educator; b. 1945. BA, Harvard U., 1967, JD, 1970; LLM, NYU, 1976. Bar: N.Y. 1971. Law clk. to Hon. William H. Hastie Phila., 1970-71; assoc. Davis, Polk & Wardwell, N.Y.C., 1971-77; atty. adviser Office Tax Legis. Counsel U.S. Treasury, D.C., 1977-79; assoc. tax legis counsel, 1979-80, dep. tax legis. counsel, 1980-81; assoc. prof. U. Pa., Phila., 1981-87, prof. law, 1987—. Author: The Taxation of Corporation and Their Shareholders, 1991. Office: U Pa Law Sch 3400 Chestnut St Philadelphia PA 19104-6204

SHALALA, DONNA EDNA, federal official, political scientist, educator, university chancellor; b. Cleve., Feb. 14, 1941; d. James Abraham and Edna (Smith) S. AB, Western Coll., 1962; MSSC, Syracuse U., 1968, PhD, 1970; 16 hon degrees, 1981-91. Vol. Peace Corps, Iran, 1962-64; asst. to dir. met. studies program Syracuse U., 1965-69; instr. asst. to dean Syracuse U. (Maxwell Grad. Sch.), 1969-70; asst. prof. polit. sci. CUNY, 1970-72; assoc. prof. politics and edn. Tchrs. Coll. Columbia U., 1972-79; asst. sec. for policy devel. and research HUD, Washington, 1977-80; prof. polit. sci., pres. Hunter Coll., CUNY, 1980-88; prof. polit. sci., chancellor U. Wis., Madison, 1988-93; Sec. Dept. of Health and Human Services, Washington, 1993—. Author: Neighborhood Governance, 1971, The City and the Constitution, 1972, The Property Tax and the Voters, 1973, The Decentralization Approach, 1974. Bd. govs. Am. Stock Exch., 1981-87; trustee TIAA, 1985-89, Com. Econ. Devel., 1981-93; bd. dirs. Inst Internat. Econs., 1981-93, Children's Def. Found, 1980-93, Am. Ditchley Found., 1981-93, Spencer Found., 1988-93, M&I Bank of Madison, 1991-93, NCAA Found., 1991; mem. Trilateral Commn., 1988-93, Knight Commn. on Intercollegiate Sports, 1990-93; trustee Brookings Inst., 1989-93. Ohio Newspaper Women's scholar, 1958, Western Coll. Trustee scholar, 1958-62; Carnegie fellow, 1966-68; Nat. Acad. Edn. Spencer fellow, 1972-73; Guggenheim fellow, 1975-76; recipient Disting. Svc. medal Columbia U. Tchrs. Coll., 1989. Mem. Am. Polit. Sci. Assn., Am Soc. Pub. Adminstrn. Nat. Acad. Pub. Adminstrn., Coun. Fgn. Rels., Nat. Acad. Edn. Office: Dept Health and Human Svcs Office of Sec 200 Independence Ave SW Rm 615F Washington DC 20201-0004

SHALAM, JOHN JOSEPH, car stereo and cellular telephone company executive; b. Alexandria, Egypt, Dec. 10, 1933; came to U.S., 1948, naturalized, 1973; s. Murad Joseph and Vicky (Harari) S.; m. Jane Bishop, Mar. 9, 1970; children—Ari M., David M., Marc J. Student, pvt. schs. From exec. trainee to trader U.K. dept. Continental Grain Co., N.Y.C., 1955-58; v.p. Lynn Supply Co., N.Y.C., 1958-61; pres. Custom Imports, Inc., N.Y.C., 1961-63, Audiovox Corp., Hauppauge, N.Y., 1963—. Mem. Ben Franklin Soc., U. pa. Alumnae Assn., Glen Oaks Country Club, Penn Club N.Y., Old Westbury Horsemen's Found. (pres.), Wharton Sch. Club L.I. and N.Y., Chevalier, Confrerie de la Chaine des Rotisseurs. Republican. Jewish. Office: Audiovox Corp 150 Marcus Blvd Hauppauge NY 11788-3723

SHALES, THOMAS WILLIAM, writer, journalist, television and film critic; b. Elgin, Ill., Nov. 3, 1953; s. Clyde LeRoy and Hulda Louise (Reko) S. BA, Am. U., 1973. Entertainment editor Washington Examiner, 1968-71; arts reporter Washington Post, 1971-77, TV editor and chief TV critic, 1977—; film critic, modular arts service Nat. Public Radio, 1970-79, film critic, Morning Edit., 1979—; adj. prof. Am. U., 1978; syndicated columnist On the Air, Washington Post Writers Group, 1979—. Author: The American Film Heritage, 1972, On the Air!, 1982, Legends, 1989. Recipient Disting. Alumnus award Am. U., 1978. Recipient Pulitzer Prize, 1988. Office: Washington Post Co 1150 15th St NW Washington DC 20071-0002

SHALHOUB, MICHAEL See SHARIF, OMAR

SHALIKASHVILI, JOHN MALCHASE, military career officer; b. Warsaw, Poland, June 27, 1936; s. Dimitri and Maria (Rediger) S.; m. Gunhild Bartsch, Apr. 18, 1963 (dec. May 1965); m. Joan E. Zimpleman, Dec. 27, 1966; 1 child, Brant. BSME, Bradley U., 1958; MA in Internat. Affairs, George Washington U., 1970. Enlisted U.S. Army, 1958, advanced through grades to gen., 1991, various troop and staff assignments Alaska, U.S., Fed. Republic of Germany, Vietnam, Korea, 1959-75; battalion comdr. 9th infantry div. U.S. Army, Ft. Lewis, Wash., 1975-77; asst. chief of staff ops. So. European Task Froce U.S. Army, Vicenza, Italy, 1978-79; cmdr. div. arty., 1st Armored Div. U.S. Army, Nuernberg, Fed. Republic of Germany, 1979-81; chief., politico-mil div. U.S. Army, Washington, 1981-84; asst. div. comdr. 1st. Armored div. U.S. Army, Nuernberg, Fed. Republic of Germany, 1984-86; dir. strategy, plans, policy U.S. Army, Washington, 1986-87; comdg. gen. 9th inf. div. Ft. Lewis, Wash., 1987-89; dep. comdr.-in-chief Hdqrs. USAREUR and 7th Army, Heidelberg, Fed. Republic of Germany, 1989-91; asst. to chmn. Joint Chiefs of Staff, Washington, 1991-92; Supreme Allied Commdr. Europe, Commdr.-in-Chief US Forces Europe, 1992-93; chmn. Joint Chiefs of Staff, 1993—. Home: 6 Grant Ave Arlington VA 22211-1204

SHALITA, ALAN REMI, dermatologist; b. Bkln., Mar. 22, 1936; s. Harry and Celia; m. Simone Lea Baum, Sept. 4, 1960; children: Judith and Deborah (twins). AB, Brown U., 1957; BS, U. Brussels, 1960; MD, Bowman Gray Sch. Medicine, 1964; DSc (hon.), L.I. U., 1990. Intern Beth Israel Hosp., N.Y.C., 1964-65; resident dept. dermatology NYU Med. Ctr., 1967-68; NIH tng. grant fellow dept. dermatology Med. Ctr. NYU, 1968-70, instr. dermatology Med. Ctr., 1970-71, asst. prof. Med. Ctr., 1971-73; asst. prof. dermatology Columbia U., N.Y.C., 1973-75; assoc. prof. medicine, head div. dermatology SUNY Downstate Med. Ctr., Bklyn., 1975-79; prof. medicine, head div. dermatology SUNY Downstate Med. Ctr., 1979-80; prof. and chmn. dept. dermatology Med. Ctr. SUNY Downstate Med. Ctr., Bklyn., 1980—; asst. dean Downstate Med. Ctr. SUNY, 1977-83, acting dean Queen's campus Downstate Med. Ctr., 1983-84; assoc. dean clin. affairs SUNY Health Sci. Ctr., Bklyn., 1989-92; assoc. provost for clin. affairs, 1992-93; assoc. v.p. clin. affairs SUNY Health Sci. Ctr., Bklyn., 1993—; asst. attending in dermatology Univ. Hosp., N.Y.C., 1970-73, Bellevue Hosp. Ctr., 1970-73, Manhattan VA Hosp., 1971-73, Presbyn. Hosp., 1973-75; mem. med. bd. Kings County Hosp. Ctr.; cons. dermatology Bklyn. VA Hosp., 1975—; chief dermatology Brookdale Med. Ctr., 1977-90; chief dermatology Univ. Hosp. of Bklyn., 1975—; chief dermatology Kings County Hosp. of Bklyn., 1975—, acting med. dir., 1989-92; med. dir. Univ. Hosp. of Bklyn., 1992—. Pres. Temple Shaaray Tefila, N.Y.C., 1982-86, chmn. bd. trustees, 1987—. Lt. M.C. USNR, 1965-67. Recipient Torch of Liberty award Anti-Defamation League, 1987, Surg. and Pediatric awards Beth Israel Hosp., N.Y.C., 1965; spl. fellow NIH, 1970-73. Mem. AMA, ACP, AAAS, Am. Acad. Dermatology (bd. dirs. 1983-87, v.p. 1995—), Soc. Investigative Dermatology, Dermatology Found. (past trustee), Am. Dermatol. Assn., N.Y. Acad. Scis., Am. Soc. Dermatol. Surgery (past bd. dirs.), Internat. Soc. Tropical Dermatology, N.Y. State Med. Soc., Soc. Cosmetic Chemists, N.Y. Acad. Medicine, Dermatol. Soc. Greater N.Y. (pres. 1980-81), N.Y. State Dermatol. Soc., Assn. Profs. Dermatology (sec.-treas. 1988-94, pres.-elect 1994—), N.Y. Dermatol. Soc. (pres. 1989-90). Republican. Home: 70 E 77th St New York NY 10021-1811 Office: 450 Clarkson Ave Brooklyn NY 11203-2012

SHALKOP, ROBERT LEROY, retired museum consultant; b. Milford, Conn., July 30, 1922; s. Bertram Leroy and Dorothy Jane (Boardman) S.; m. Antoinette Joan Benkowsky, Dec. 7, 1963; 1 son, Andrew Goforth. Student, Maryville (Tenn.) Coll., 1940-42; M.A., U. Chgo., 1949; postgrad., Sorbonne, 1951-52. Dir. Rahr Civic Center, Manitowoc, Wis., 1953-56, Everhart Mus., Scranton, Pa., 1956-62, Brooks Meml. Art Gallery, Memphis, 1962-64; assoc. dir. Colorado Springs (Colo.) Fine Arts Center, also curator Taylor Mus., 1964-71; dir. Anchorage Mus. History and Art, 1972-87; pvt. practice mus. cons. Salisbury, N.C., 1987-94; archaeologist Smithsonian Instn., 1948, 50, Am. Found. Study Man, 1951, U. Wash., 1953, State U. Idaho, 1960. Author: Wooden Saints, the Santos of New Mexico, 1967, A Comparative View of Spanish Colonial Sculpture, 1968, Arroyo Hondo, the Folk Art of a New Mexican Village, 1969, A Comparative View of Spanish Colonial Painting, 1970, A Show of Color: 100 Years of Painting in the Pike's Peak Region, 1971, Russian Orthodox Art in Alaska, 1973, Sydney Laurence, an Alaskan Impressionist, 1975, Eustace Ziegler, 1977, Contemporary Native Art of Alaska, 1979, Henry Wood Elliott, 1982; Editor: An Introduction to the Native Art of Alaska, 1972; assoc. editor: Exploration in Alaska, 1980. Served with USAAF, 1942-45. Mem. Am. Assn. Museums, Internat. Council Museums. Home and Office: 309 W Marsh St Salisbury NC 28144-5345

SHALOWITZ, ERWIN EMMANUEL, civil engineer; b. Washington, Feb. 13, 1924; s. Aaron Louis and Pearl (Myer) S.; m. Elaine Mildred Langerman, June 29, 1952; children—Ann Janet, Aliza Beth, Jonathan Avram. Student, U. Pa., U. Notre Dame, 1944-45; B.C.E., George Washington U., 1947, postgrad., 1948-49; grad. soil mechanics, Cath. U., 1951; M.A. in Pub. Adminstrn. (fellow U.S. Civil Service Commn.), Am. U., 1954. Registered profl. engr., Washington. Engr. Klemitt Engring. Co., N.Y.C., 1947; with cons. firm Whitman, Requardt & Assos., Balt., 1947-48; chief structural research engr., head def. research sect., project officer and tech. adviser for atomic tests Bur. Yards and Docks, Dept. Navy, Washington, 1948-59; supervisory gen. engr. spl. asst. for protective constrn. programs, project mgr. for bldg. systems, chief research br., chief mgmt. information, chief contracting procedures and support, chief contract evaluation and analysis, Pub. Bldgs. Service, Gen. Services Adminstrn., Washington, 1959—; chmn. fed. exec. tng. program U.S. Civil Service Commn., 1950; fallout shelter analyst Dept. (def.; chmn. GSA Fire Safety Com., GSA Fallout Protection Com., GSA Bldg. Evaluation Com.; mem. Interagy Com. on Housing Rsch. and Bldg. Tech.; mem. Nat. Evaluation Bd. Architect-Engr. Selections; mem. standing com. on procurement policy Nat. Acad. Sci. Bldg. Research Adv. Bd. and Interagency Com. on Procurement Curriculum Rev.; coordinator pub. bldgs. design and constrn. Small Bus. Program and Minority Enterprise and Minority Subcontracting Programs. Contbr. articles profl. jours. Served to engring. officer USNR, 1944-46. Recipient Commendable Svc. award GSA, 1968, Outstanding Performance recognition, 1976, 77, 79, 83, 87, 93, 94, Superior Accomplishment award, 1995, cash award, 1977, 79, 83-95; Engr. Alumni Achievement award George Washington U., 1985. Fellow ASCE, Am. Biog. Inst.; mem. Soc. Advancement Mgmt., Am. Biog. Inst. (nat. bd. advisors), Soc. Am. Mil. Engrs., Sigma Tau, Pi Sigma Alpha. Jewish. Home: 5603 Huntington Pky Bethesda MD 20814-1132 Office: 19th and F Sts NW Washington DC 20405 PRINCIPLES: Look beyond the material for lasting values and meaning, optimize managerial effectiveness by creating an objective and challenging climate in an organization, delve into the underlying causes of problem areas for meaningful solutions, and persevere in spite of obstacles. IDEAS: Cultural pluralism; the intrinsic potential of each individual; and love, appreciation, and support of one's family as indispensable for real accomplishment. GOALS: To attain the highest level of professional accomplishment within my capabilities and to continue to have a rich, happy, and fulfilling family life. STANDARDS OF CONDUCT: To be fair, consistent, and straightforward; and to avoid over-reacting.

SHALWITZ, HOWARD, theater director, actor; b. Buffalo, Apr. 12, 1952; s. Fred and Shirley (Brotz) S. BA, Wesleyan U., Middletown, Conn., 1974; MAT, Brown U., 1975. Founder, artistic dir., dir. Woolly Mammoth Theatre Co., Washington, 1980—; on-site evaluator for theater program Nat. Endowment Arts, Washington, 1986—; v.p. Helen Hayes Awards, Washington, 1987—. Co-author: New Theatres for Washington, D.C., 1986. Mem. Actors Equity Assn., League Washington Theatres (pres. 1984-86). Avocations: golf, swimming. Office: Woolly Mammoth Theatre Co 1401 Church St NW Washington DC 20005-1903

SHAM, LU JEU, physics educator; b. Hong Kong, Apr. 28, 1938; s. T.S. and Cecilia Maria (Siu) Shen; m. Georgina Bien, Apr. 25, 1965; children: Kevin Shen, Alisa Shen. GCE, Portsmouth Coll., Eng., 1957; BS, Imperial Coll., London U., Eng., 1960; PhD in Physics, Cambridge U., Eng., 1963. Asst. rsch. physicist U. Calif. at San Diego, La Jolla, 1963-66, assoc. prof., 1968-76, prof., 1975—, dean div. natural scis., 1985-89; asst. prof. physics U. Calif. at Irvine, 1966-67; rsch. physicist IBM Corp., Yorktown Heights, N.Y., 1974-75; reader Queen Mary Coll., U. London, 1967-68. Assoc. editor Physics Letters A., 1992—; contbr. sci. papers to profl. jours. Recipient Churchill Coll. studentship, Eng., 1960-63, Sr. U.S. Scientist award

SHAMANSKY, ROBERT NORTON, lawyer; b. Columbus, Ohio, Apr. 18, 1927; s. Harry Solomon and Sarah (Greenberg) S. BA Polit. Sci. cum laude, Ohio State U., 1947; JD, Harvard U., 1950. Bar: Ohio 1950, U.S. Supreme Ct. 1963. Ptnr. Feibel, Feibel, Shamansky & Rogovin, Columbus, 1954-81; mem. U.S. House Reps., Washington, 1981-83; ptnr. Guren, Merritt, Sogg & Cohen, Columbus, Ohio, 1981-84; of counsel Bensch, Friedlander, Coplan & Aronoff, Columbus, Ohio, 1984-93, 1993; mem. Nat. Security Edn. Bd., 1994—; pres., founder Legal Aid and Defender Soc., Columbus, 1955-58; spkr. in field. Contbr. articles to newspapers. Mem. Rickenbacker Port Authority, Franklin County, Ohio, 1983-86; chmn. Indsl. Tech. and Enterprise adv. bd. State Ohio, Columbus, 1983-89. With U.S. Army, 1950-52. Mem. ABA, Ohio State Bar Assn. (chmn. legal ethics and profl. conduct com. 1970-73), Columbus Bar Assn., Columbus Housing Ptnrship, Inc. (sec. 1985-91), Coun. Ethics in Econs. (bd. dirs. 1983-93), Phi Beta Kappa. Democrat. Jewish. Avocations: fgn., domestic travel, pub. policy. Home: 560 S 3rd St Columbus OH 43215-5722 Office: Benesch Friedlander Coplan & Aronoff 88 E Broad St Columbus OH 43215-3506

SHAMASH, YACOV, dean, electrical engineering educator; b. Iraq, Jan. 12, 1950; m. Linda Shamash, June 21, 1976; children: Aharon, Hela. BSEE, Imperial Coll., London, 1970; PhD in Control Systems, Imperial Coll., 1973. Postdoctoral fellow in elec. engring. Tel-Aviv U., 1973-75, from lectr. elec. engring. to sr. lectr. elec. engring., 1975-78; prof. elec. engring. Fla. Atlantic U., Boca Raton, 1977-85; prof., chair dept. elec. engring. dept. Wash. State U., Pullman, 1985-92; dean engring. SUNY, Stony Brook, 1992—; bd. dirs. KeyTronics, Spokane, Wash., 1990—; vis. asst. prof. U. Pa., Phila., 1976-77. Contbr. over 100 articles to profl. jours., book chpts. Fellow IEEE (sr.). Office: SUNY Coll Engring & Applied Sci Stony Brook NY 11790-2200

SHAMASK, RONALDUS, fashion designer; b. Amsterdam, The Netherlands, Nov. 24, 1945. Window display artist Melbourne, Australia, 1963-66; fashion illustrator The Times and The Observer, London, 1967-68; freelance stage set, costume designer for ballet, opera, Company of Man Buffalo, 1968-71; freelance interior and clothing designer N.Y.C., 1971-77; founder, ptnr. Moss Shamask Fashion Co., N.Y.C., 1978—; founder Moss Boutique, N.Y.C., 1979—; contbr. design packing Revlon Cosmetics and Fragrances, 1993; launched cosmetic line, Fire & Ice Fragrance, Revlon, 1993—. Exhibit at MIT, 1982. Recipient Coty Fashion award, 1981; Fil d'Or award Conf. Internat. du Lin, 1982. Office: Moss Shamask 39 West 37th St New York NY 10018

SHAMBAUGH, GEORGE ELMER, III, internist; b. Boston, Dec. 21, 1931; s. George Elmer and Marietta Susan (Moss) S.; m. Katharine Margaret Matthews, Dec. 29, 1956 (dec.); children: George, Benjamin, Daniel, James, Elizabeth; m. Martha Repp Davis, Jan. 3, 1987. B.A., Oberlin Coll., 1954; M.D., Cornell U., 1958. Diplomate Am. Bd. Internal Medicine. Gen. med. intern Denver Gen. Hosp., 1958-59; research fellow physiologic chemistry U. Wis.-Madison, 1968-69; asst. prof. medicine Northwestern U. Med. Sch., Chgo., 1969-74, assoc. prof., 1974-81, prof., 1981—; mem. Ctr. for Endocrinology, Metabolism and Molecular Medicine, 1969—; chief endocrinology and metabolism VA Lakeside Med. Ctr., Chgo., 1974—; attending physician Northwestern Meml. Hosp., Chgo., 1969—. Contbr. articles to text books and profl. jours. Served with M.C., U.S. Army, 1959-67. NIH spl. postdoctoral fellow, 1967-69; Schweppe Found. fellow, 1972-75. Fellow ACP; mem. Am. Fedn. Clin. Rsch., Sci. Rsch. Soc., am. Endocrine Soc., Am. Thyroid Assn., Am. Inst. Nutrition, Am. Soc. Clin. Nutrition, Am. Physiol. Soc., Ctrl. Soc. Clin. Rsch., Inst. Medicine Chgo., Taipei Internat. Med. Soc. (mem. 1960), N.Y. Acad. Sci., Euro Diabetes Assn., Am. Men and Women of Sci., Sigma Xi, Nu Sigma Nu. Home: 530 S Stone Ave La Grange IL 60525-2720 Office: Northwestern Med Faculty Found Inc 303 E Ohio St Fl 460 Chicago IL 60611-3301 also: VA Lakeside Med Ctr 333 E Huron St Chicago IL 60611-3004

SHAMBUREK, ROLAND HOWARD, physician; b. Adell, Wis., June 7, 1928; s. William and Catherine (Illig) S.; m. Gladys Irene Gibbons, June 21, 1952; children: Steven J., Robert D., Daniel J. BS, U. Wis., 1950, MD, 1953; MPH, Harvard U., 1960. Diplomate: Am. Bd. Preventive Medicine. Commd. 1st lt. M.C., U.S. Army, 1953, advanced through grades to col., 1968; intern St. Joseph's Hosp., Marshfield, Wis., 1953-54; grad. U.S Naval Sch. of Aviation Medicine, Pensacola, Fla., 1957; resident in preventive medicine USAF Sch. Aerospace Medicine, Brooks AFB, 1960-63; service in Europe, 1955-56, 63-66; comdr. 67th EVAC Hosp., Vietnam, 1970-71, U.S. Army Med. Pers. Support Agy., 1975-77; ret., 1977; exec. v.p. Aerospace Med. Assn., 1977-79; clin. practice Pentagon Health Clinic, Washington, 1981-85; med. researcher Office of Army Surgeon Gen., 1985-87. Contbr. papers in field. Decorated Legion of Merit with oak leaf cluster, Commendation medal, Meritorious Service medal. Mem. AMA (del. 1978), Assn. Mil. Surgeons (John Shaw Billings award 1968), Am. Coll. Preventive Medicine (v.p. 1968-69), Aerospace Med. Assn. (v.p. 1968-69), Soc. Med. Cons. Armed Forces, Soc. U.S. Army Flight Surgeons, Soc. NASA Flight Surgeons, Internat. Acad. Aviation and Space Medicine, Internat. Health Soc. Address: 3700 Moss Dr Annandale VA 22003-1915

SHAMES, HENRY JOSEPH, lawyer; b. Milw., Jan. 20, 1921; s. Aron and Jennie (Greenberg) S.; m. Beverly Cleveland Van Wert, June 9, 1972; children: Stephen H., Suzanne Shames Sattelmeyer, Sarah Shames Phillips, Diana Shames Strandberg. A.B., U. Chgo., 1942; J.D., Harvard U., 1948. Bar: Ill. 1949, Calif. 1962. Mem. firm Arvey, Hodes & Mantynband, Chgo., 1949-61; partner Pacht, Ross, Warne, Bernhard & Sears, Los Angeles, 1962-75, Grossman & Shames, Los Angeles, 1975-83, Rosenfeld, Parnell & Shames Inc., Los Angeles, 1984-86; counsel Patterson, Belknap, Webb and Tyler, Los Angeles, 1986-87; chmn. bd. Switzer Center, Los Angeles, 1966-73. Served with USNR, 1943-46. Mem. Assn. Bus. Trial Lawyers (bd. govs. 1973-76, v.p. 1973-76), Calif. State Bar Assn., So. Def. Counsel, Los Angeles County Bar Assn., Phi Beta Kappa. Home: 4906 La Ramada Dr Santa Barbara CA 93111-1518 Office: 1875 Century Park E Los Angeles CA 90067-2501

SHAMES, IRVING HERMAN, engineering educator; b. Oct. 31, 1923; married; 2 children. BSME, Northeastern U., 1948; MS in Applied Mechanics, Harvard U., 1949; PhD in Applied Mechanics, U. Md., 1953. Instr. U. Md., College Park, 1949-53, asst. prof. mech. engring., 1953-55; asst. prof. Stevens Inst. Tech., Hoboken, N.J., 1955-57; prof., chmn. dept. engring. sci. Pratt Inst., Bklyn., 1957-62, acting chmn. dept. physics, 1960-61; prof., chmn. div. interdisciplinary studies and research Sch. Engring. SUNY, Buffalo, 1962-70, faculty prof. engring., applied sci., 1970-73, 79—, prof., chmn. dept. engring. scis., aerospace engring. and nuclear engring., 1973-83, disting. teaching prof., 1980—; lectr. Naval Ordnance Lab, 1952-55; vis. prof. materials dept. Technion, Israel, 1969, mech. engring. dept., 1976; Disting. vis. prof. George Washington U. 1993. Author: Engineering Mechanics: Statics, 1959, 3d rev. edit., 1980, Engineering Mechanics: Dynamics, 1959, 3d rev. edit., 1980, Mechanics of Fluids, 1962, rev. edit., 1982, 3d edit., 1992, Mechanics of Deformable Solids, 1964, (with C. Dym) Solid Mechanics- A Variational Approach, 1973, Introduction to Statics, 1971 Introduction to Solid Mechanics, 1975, (with C. Dym) Energy and Finite Elements in Structural Mechanics, 1985, (with F. Cozzarelli) Elastic and Inelastic Stress Analysis, 1992; editor McGraw-Hill Series in Advanced Engineering; contbr. numerous articles to profl. jours.; several books translated in Portuguese, Spanish, Japanese, Korean, Chinese, Arabic. Mem. Sigma Xi, Tau Beta Pi, Phi Eta Sigma, Pi Tau Sigma, Golden Key. Home: 1113 Fairview Ct Silver Spring MD 20910

SHAMMAS, NAZIH KHEIRALLAH, environmental engineering educator, consultant; b. Homs, Syria, Feb. 18, 1939; came to U.S., 1991; s. Kheirallah Hanna and Nazha Murad (Hamwi) S.; m. Norma Massouh, July 28, 1966; children: Sarmed Erick, Samer Sam. Engring. degree with distinction, Am. U., Beirut, Lebanon, 1962; MS in Sanitary Engring., U. N.C., 1965; PhD in Civil Engring., U. Mich., 1971. Instr. Civil Engring. Am. U., Beirut, Lebanon, 1965-68; asst. prof. Civil Engring. Am. U., Beirut, 1972-76; teaching fellow U. Mich., Ann Arbor, 1968-71; asst. prof. Civil Engring. King Saud U., Riyadh, Saudi Arabia, 1976-78; assoc. prof. King Saud U.,

Riyadh, 1978-91; prof. Environ. Engring. Lenox (Mass.) Inst. Water Tech., 1991-92, dean edn., 1992-93; prof. Sr. U., 1994—; cons., ptnr. Cons. and Rsch. Engrs., Beirut, 1973-76; advisor, cons. Riyadh Water and Sanitary Drainage Authority, 1979-83, Ar-Riyadh Devel. Authority, 1977—, Associated Consulting Engring. Team, 1994—. Co-author: Environmental Sanitation, 1988, Wastewater Engineering, 1988; contbr. over 30 articles to profl. jours. and confs. Recipient Excellence in Teaching awards King Saud U., 1981, 84; U. Mich. block grantee, 1968-70. Mem. ASCE, Water Environ. Fedn., Am. Water Works Assn., European Water Pollution Control Assn., Internat. Assn. Water Quality, Assn. Environ. Engring. Profs. Achievements include research on biological and physicochemical remediation processes, math. modeling of nitrification process, water and wastewater mgmt. in developing countries, water conservation, wastewater treatment and reuse, appropriate tech. for developing countries, multidisciplinary studies in environmental management and planning. Home: 63 Leona Dr Pittsfield MA 01201

SHAMOO, ADIL ELIAS, biochemist, biophysicist, educator; b. Baghdad, Iraq, Aug. 1, 1941; came to U.S., 1964, naturalized, 1973; s. Elias M. and Mariam T. (Mansour) S.; m. Joan Hutchison, Dec. 16, 1967; children: Abraheem, Zachary, Jessica. B.Sc. in Physics, U. Baghdad, 1962; M.S. in Physics (grad. fellow), U. Louisville, 1966; Ph.D. in Biophysics, CUNY, 1970. Instr. engring. physics Speed Sch., U. Louisville, 1965-68; asst. prof. physiology City U. N.Y., 1971-73; guest worker Lab. Biophysics and Neurochemistry, NIH, Bethesda, Md., 1972-73; asst. prof. radiation biology and biophysics U. Rochester, 1973-75; guest prof. Max-Planck Inst. Biophysics, Frankfurt, West Germany, 1977-78; assoc. prof. radiation biology and biophysics U. Rochester, 1975-79; prof., chmn. dept. biol. chemistry U. Md., Balt., 1979-82, head membrane biochemistry research lab., 1982—; cons. div. biol. scis. Kodak Co., Rochester, 1976-77; NIH tng. fellow U. Louisville, 1967; investigator Am. Heart Assn., 1976-79; Neurosci. Rsch. Program fellow, Boulder, Colo., summer 1977; pres. Sci. Profls. Inc.; chmn. symposia, various coms. in field; mem. organizing coms. workshops in field. Editor: (with M.W. Miller) Membrane Toxicity, 1977, Carriers and Channels in Biological Systems, 1975, Carriers and Channels in Biological Systems-Transport Proteins, 1980, Regulation of Calcium Transport Across Muscle Membranes, 1985, Principles of Research Data Audit, (with R. Verna) Biotechnology Today; editor-in-chief Membrane Biochemistry, 1977-93, Accountability in Research: Policies and Quality Assurance, 1988—; mem. edit. bd. Molecular and Cellular Biochemistry, 1987-94, Quality Assurance: Good Practice Regulation and Law, 1991—; contbr. articles and abstracts to profl. jours. Bd. dirs. Alliance for Mentally Ill of Md., 1990-93, Friends Med. Rsch. Ctr., Inc., 1994-97; mem. rsch. monitoring com. Nat. Alliance for Mentally Ill, bd. dris. 1994-97; pres. faculty senate U. of Md. at Balt., 1993-94. Recipient Advocacy award Mental Health Assn. Md., 1994, Disting. Svc. award Alliance for Mentally Ill of Md., 1994. Mem. AAAS, AAUP (chpt. sec. 1971-72), Basic Sci. Council of Am. Heart Assn., Am. Soc. Biol. Chemists and Mol. Biol., Am. Coll. Sports Medicine, Am. Assn. Physics Tchrs., Am. Physiol. Soc., Biophys. Soc. (Cole Membrane Award Com. 1983-84, chmn. biophysics subgroup 1982-83, council 1986-89), Membrane Biophys. Group (chmn. 1982-83, sec.-treas. 1983-85, co-chmn. U.S. bioenergetics group 1979-80), Md. Acad. Scis. (chmn. com. programs and exhbns. 1986-87, sci. council 1985-89), N.Y. Acad. Scis., Coun. of Biology (editor 1989—), Soc. Quality Assurance. Achievements include patents for liquid scintillators. Office: 108 N Greene St Baltimore MD 21201-1503

SHAMOS, MORRIS HERBERT, physicist educator; b. Cleve., Sept. 1, 1917; s. Max and Lillian (Wasser) S.; m. Marion Jean Cahn, Nov. 26, 1942; 1 son, Michael Ian. AB, NYU, 1941, MS, 1943, PhD, 1948; postgrad., MIT, 1941-42. Faculty NYU, 1942—, prof. physics, 1959-83, prof. emeritus, 1983—; chmn. dept. Washington Sq. Coll., 1957-70; sr. v.p. research and devel. Technicon Corp., 1970-75, chief sci. officer, 1975-83, also dir., prin. sci. cons., 1983-92; pres. M.H. Shamos & Assocs., 1983—; chmn. Protein Databases, Inc., 1985-90, Sci. Imaging Corp., 1985-88; Med. Mktg. Internat., 1992-94; dir. Anagen Ltd., 1989-92, Nat. Assn. for Sci. Tech. & Soc., 1990-91, Anagen Holdings, Ltd., 1992—, Xsirius, Inc., 1993—; chmn. Med. Mktg. Internat., 1992-94; Coms. pvt. industry; cons. Armament Center, USAF, 1955-57, Tung-Sol Electric, Inc., 1949-65, Office Pub. Information, UN, 1958, NBC, 1957-67, AEC, 1957-70, N.Y. Eye and Ear Infirmary, 1961-64, 79—, L.I. Jewish Hosp., 1962—, N.Y.C. Health Dept., 1961-70, Technicon Instruments Corp., 1964-70, U.S. Office Edn., 1964-72. Author: Great Experiments in Physics, 1959, The Myth of Scientific Literacy, 1995; co-editor: Recent Advances in Science, 1956, Industrial and Safety Problems of Nuclear Technology, 1950; cons. editor Addison-Wesley Pub. Co., 1965-69; adv. bd. Jour. Coll. Sci. Teaching, 1971-80, Clin. Lab. Guide, Am. Chem. Soc., 1972-76. Dir. tng., N.Y.C. Office Civil Def., 1950-54; subscribing mem. N.Y. Philharmonic Soc.; mem. adv. council Pace U., 1971—; N.Y. Poly. Inst., 1980—; trustee Hackley Sch., 1971-80, Westchester Arts Council. Poly. U. fellow. Fellow N.Y. Acad. Scis. (past chmn. phys. sci., bd. govs 1977-83, rec. sec. 1978-80, v.p 1980-81, pres. 1982), AAAS; mem. IEEE, AAUP, AFTRA, NSTA (pres. 1967), Am. Chem. Soc., Nat. Assn. Edn. Broadcasters, Am. Phys. Soc., Assn. Physics Tchrs. Britain, Chemist's Club, Am. Assn. Clin. Chemists, Cosmos Club, Phi Beta Kappa, Sigma Xi, Pi Mu Epsilon, Sigma Pi Sigma. Clubs: Cosmos, Chemists. Spl. research atomic and nuclear physics, biophysics. Home: 3515 Henry Hudson Pky Bronx NY 10463-1326

SHAMUS, M. ANNETTE, nursing administrator; b. Coaldale, Pa., July 14, 1936; d. Charles P. and Anne M. (Barry) Menconi; m. Michael J. Shamus, Feb. 15, 1958; children: Michael, Ann, Megan. Diploma, Chestnut Hill Hosp., 1957; BSN cum laude, Marymount U., 1984, MSN in Adminstrn., 1988. RN, Va. Emergency nurse Arlington (Va.) Hosp., evening supr., clin. dir., v.p. nursing div. Harris Trust scholar, Va. Orgn. Nurse Execs. scholar; Johnson & Johnson-Wharton fellow. Mem. Am. Orgn. Nurse Execs., ANA, Va. Nurse's Assn., Eta Alpha chpt. Sigma Theta Tau. Home: 2311 N Underwood St Arlington VA 22205-1950 Office: Arlington Hosp 1701 N George Mason Dr Arlington VA 22205-3698

SHAN, ROBERT KUOCHENG, biology educator; b. Gaoan, Jiangxi, China, Nov. 9, 1927; came to U.S., 1963; m. Lily Yikhwei Chenshan, Sept. 7, 1963; 1 child, Tony Donguang. BS, Taiwan Normal U., 1956; MS, U. B.C., Vancouver, Can., 1962; PhD, Ind. U., 1967. Instr. Taiwan U., Taipei, 1956-59; teaching fellow, rsch. fellow U. B.C., 1959-62; teaching fellow Dalhousie U., Halifax, N.S., Can., 1962-63; rsch. fellow Ind. U., Bloomington, 1963-67, rsch. assoc., 1967-69; asst. prof. biology Fairmont (W.Va.) State Coll., 1969-72, assoc. prof., 1972-75, prof., 1975—. Mem. Am. Inst. Biol. Scis., Ecol. Soc. Am., Am. Soc. Limnology and Oceanography, Sigma Xi. Office: Fairmont State Coll Fairmont WV 26554

SHANAHAN, EDMOND MICHAEL, savings and loan executive; b. Omaha, Oct. 20, 1926; s. Jeremiah H. and Agnes (Corcoran) S.; m. Elizabeth Rover, Apr. 26, 1952 (dec. Mar. 1994); children: Michael, Mary Elizabeth, Thomas, Terrence (dec.). B. Econs., St. Mary's Coll., Winona, Minn.; M.B.A., U. Chgo., 1965. Customer rels. and employee tng. ofcl. Peoples Gas Light & Coke Co., Chgo., 1949-59; instr. DePaul U. Evening Sch., 1957-59; v.p. savs. and advt. Bell Fed. Savs. & Loan Assn., Chgo., 1959-79, pres., COO, dir., 1979-84, pres., CEO, dir., 1984-93, chmn. bd., 1993— Served with USNR. Mem. Rolling Green Country Club. Office: Bell Bancorp 79 W Monroe St Chicago IL 60603-4901

SHANAHAN, EUGENE MILES, flow measurement instrumentation company executive; b. Great Falls, Mont., Sept. 18, 1946; s. Raymond Eugene and Marie Marjorie (Graham) S.; m. Beverly Ann Braaten, Sept. 8, 1967; children—Bret Allen, Shaun Eugene, Shae Erin. B.S. in Mech. Engring., Mont. State U., 1968; M.S., Mont. State U., 1969; M.B.A., Portland State U., 1976. Registered profl. engr., Oreg. Mech. engr. Tektronix, Beaverton, Oreg., 1968-71; mech. engr. Shell Oil Co., Martinez, Calif., 1967; chief mech. project engr. Mears Controls, Beaverton, 1971-76; mktg. mgr. Mears Controls, 1976-79; v.p., gen. mgr. Eaton Corp., Beaverton, 1979-87; pres. Dieterich Standard (a Dover Co.), Boulder, Colo., 1987—. Served with N.G., 1969-75. NSF trainee, 1969. Mem. ASME, Instrumentation Soc. Am., Tau Beta Pi, Phi Kappa Phi, Pi Tau Sigma. Home: 8417 Sawtooth Ln Niwot CO 80503-7281 Office: Dieterich Standard PO Box 9000 Boulder CO 80301-9000

SHANAHAN, MICHAEL FRANCIS, manufacturing executive, hockey team executive; b. St. Louis, Oct. 29, 1939; m. Mary Ann Barrett; children: Megan Elizabeth, Michael Francis Jr., Maureen Patricia. BS in Commerce, St. Louis U.; postgrad., Wash. U., St. Louis; LHD (hon.), St. Louis Rabbinical Coll., 1987. With McDonnell Douglas Automation Co., St. Louis, 1962-73, sales mgr.; 1969-71, br. mgr., 1971-72, mktg. dir. cen. region, 1972-73; mktg. v.p. Numerical Control Inc., St. Louis, 1973-74, pres., 1974-79; v.p. Cleve. Pneumatic Co. (formerly Numerical Control Inc.), St. Louis, 1979-82; chmn., chief exec. officer Engineered Air Systems Inc., St. Louis, 1982—; chmn. St. Louis Blues Hockey Team; bd. dirs. Engineered Air Systems Inc. (chmn.), St. Louis Blues Hockey Inc. (chmn.); adv. com. Nat. Hockey League; mem. U.S. Senatorial Bus. Adv. Bd.; bd. dirs. Capital Bank and Trust of Clayton, The Graphic Arts Ctr. Inc., Kilo Rsch. Found. (vice chmn.). Bd. dirs. Am. Heart Assn., St. Louis Ambassadors, Catholic Charities of St. Louis, Galway Sister City Com., The Backstoppers, Christmas in St. Louis Found.; nat. bd. dirs. Boys Hope; bd. trustees, pres. coun. St. Louis U.; adv. bd. Safe Kids; hon. bd. Paraquad; hon. chmn. Small Bus. Week in St. Louis, 1989; hon. co-chmn. Veteran's Day Observance and Parade, 1989; co-chairperson AMC Cancer Rsch. Ctr. Community Svc. award. Named St. Louis Ambassador of Yr., 1986, Olivette Businessman of Yr., 1987, St. Louis Bus. Leader of Yr. Coll. Bus. Adminstrn., So. Ill. U. at Carbendale, 1987, Outstanding Philanthropist St. Louis chpt. Nat. Soc. Fund Raising Execs., 1987; recipient Spirit of Life award City of Hope Labor Mgmt., 1987, St. Louis U. Alumni Merit award, 1987, Meritorious Svc. to Sports award MS Soc., 1987, Presdl. Sports award Maryville Coll., 1987, Sales Exec. of Yr. award Sales and Mktg. Execs. of Met. St. Louis, 1988, St. Louis Port Coun.'s Mgmt. Man of the Yr. award Greater St. Louis Area and Vicinity Port Council, Maritime Trades Dept., AFL-CIO, 1989. Mem. Alzeimer's Disease and Related Disorders Assn. (hon.), St. Louis Counts, Hawthorn Found., St. Louis Club, Mo. Athletic Club, Old Warson Country Club, Norwood Hills Country Club. Office: Engineered Air Systems Inc 1270 N Price Rd Saint Louis MO 63132-2316

SHANAHAN, ROBERT B., banker; b. Buffalo, Jan. 8, 1928; s. Bart J. and Florence (Dietrich) S.; m. Janet I. Mulholland, Feb. 6, 1954; children: Maureen Shanahan DeRose, Timothy, Karin Halpern, Molly Healy, Colleen Collins, Mark, Ellen Becker. BS in Econs., U. Pa., 1951. New bus. rep. Assocs. Discount Corp., Buffalo, 1951-55; pres. Universal Time Plan, Inc., Buffalo, 1956-67; v.p. Norstar Bank, Buffalo, 1967-69, sr. v.p., 1969-72, exec. v.p., dir., 1972-91; dir. Eastern States Bankcard Assn., Lake Success, N.Y., Chase Fed. Bank, Miami, Fla. Contbg. author: The Bankers Handbook, 1978; mem. adv. coun. Banking Mag., 1978-84; contbr. articles to profl. jours. Pres. Multiple Sclerosis Assn. Western N.Y., Buffalo, 1982-86; trustee Theodore Roosevelt Inaugural Site, Inc., Buffalo, 1983—; pres. Buffalo Council on World Affairs, 1984-86; chmn. Catholic Charities Buffalo, 1986-87, 89-90. Served with U.S. Army, 1944-46. Decorated Knight of Holy Sepulchre Order, 1991; recipient Past Pres.'s award Multiple Sclerosis Assn., 1985. Mem. Am. Bankers Assn. (bd. dirs. 1977-84, chmn. installment lending divsn. 1978-79, edn., policy and devel. coun. 1983-84, Eagle award 1978), N.Y. State Bankers Assn. (mem. exec. com. consumer divsn. 1988-90), Buffalo Area C. of C., U. Pa. Club Western N.Y. (bd. dirs.), Buffalo Club, Cherry Hill Club (Ridgeway, Ont., Can.) (pres. 1992-93). Republican. Roman Catholic. Home: 42 Dorset Dr Buffalo NY 14223-1917

SHANAHAN, THOMAS J., lawyer; b. Buffalo, June 23, 1932; s. Bart J. and Florence E. (Dietrich) S.; m. Theresa K. Conroy, May 5, 1958; children: Thomas, Kevin, John, Susan, Brian. BS, Canisius Coll., 1954; JD, U. Buffalo, 1961. Assoc. Falk, Twelvetrees, Johnston and Seimer, Buffalo, 1961-62; counsel NASA, Cleve., 1962-64; counsel Tops Markets Inc., Buffalo, 1964-70, gen. counsel, 1970—. Served to 1st lt. USMC, 1957-60. Mem. N.Y. State Bar Assn., Am. Soc. Corp. Secs. Republican. Roman Catholic. Home: 87 Old Spring Ln Buffalo NY 14221-2107 Office: Tops Markets Inc 60 Dingens St Buffalo NY 14206-2308

SHANAHAN, THOMAS M., judge; b. Omaha, May 5, 1934; m. Jane Estelle Lodge, Aug. 4, 1956; children: Catherine Anne Shanahan Trofholz, Thomas M. Jr., Mary Elizabeth, Timothy F. A.B. magna cum laude, U. Notre Dame, 1956; J.D., Georgetown U., 1959. Bar: Nebr., Wyo. Mem. McGinley, Lane, Mueller, Shanahan, O'Donnell & Merritt, Ogallala, Nebr.; assoc. justice Nebr. Supreme Ct., Lincoln, 1983-93; judge U.S. Dist. Ct. Nebr., Omaha, 1993—. Office: US Dist Ct PO Box 457 Omaha NE 68101

SHANAHAN, WILLIAM STEPHEN, consumer products company executive; b. Cin., Apr. 15, 1940; s. William Stephen and Dorothea (Murken) S.; children: Kimberly, Michael Erika, Alejandra. B.A., Dartmouth Coll., 1962; postgrad., U. Calif.-Berkeley, 1962-63, Internat. Christian U., Tokyo, 1963-64, U. Philippines-Manila, 1964-65. Pres., gen. mgr. Colgate-Palmolive Co., Sao Paulo, Brazil, 1972-76; v.p. mktg. services div. Colgate U.S.A. Colgate-Palmolive Co., N.Y.C., 1976-78, v.p. western hemisphere, group v.p., sr. exec. v.p. ops., until 1989, now chief oper. officer, 1989—; pres., chief exec. officer Helena Rubinstein, N.Y.C., 1978-80. Office: Mennen Co 191 E Hanover Ave Morristown NJ 07960

SHANARD, GEORGE HARRIS, retired state senator, entrepreneur; b. Bridgewater, S.D., July 30, 1926; s. Jacob Harris Shanard and Martha Elizabeth Findahl; m. Iris Lorraine Achenbach, June 22, 1952 (div. Jan. 1983); children: George III, Laurie, Kari, Heidi; m. Neva Jean Bartlett, Mar. 10, 1984. BSBA, U. S.D., 1950. Sec.-treas. Shanard, Inc., Bridgewater, 1951-64, pres., 1964-84; chmn. Shanard, Inc., Mitchell, S.D., 1984—, Ramkota, Inc.; majority leader S.D. Senate, 1988-92; bd. dirs Regency Inns, Kelly Inns, Ltd. With USN, 1944-46, PTO. Named Alumnus of Yr. U. S.D., 1968. Mem. Am. Legion (Comdr. Bridgewater 1956-57), Masons, Shriners, Jesters. Avocations: hunting, fishing, golf. Home: PO Box 1023 Mitchell SD 57301-1540 Office: PO Box 1023 Mitchell SD 57301-7023 also: Shanard Inc N Riverside Rd Mitchell SD 57301

SHANAS, BERT Z., public relations executive, journalist; b. N.Y.C., June 2, 1944; s. Maurice S. and Anne (Stracovsky) S.; divorced; children—Elona, David, Gary. B.A. in Polit. Sci., Hunter Coll., 1965; M.A. in Media Studies, New Sch. for Social Research, 1977. Editor, reporter edn. and travel N.Y. Daily News, N.Y.C., 1965-86; dir. communications United Fedn. Tchrs., N.Y.C., 1986—; travel cons. Learning Annex, N.Y.C., 1984—; adj. prof. journalism NYU, N.Y.C., 1975—, Hunter Coll., N.Y.C., 1984—. Contbr. articles to profl. jours., newspapers, and mags. Served with USN, 1966-68. Recipient Freedom Found. award, 1967, Soc. of Silurians award, 1974, Soc. Am. Travel Writers award, 1985; named to Hunter Coll. Hall of Fame, 1980. Mem. Pub. Rels. Soc. Am. (winner Big Apple award Pub. Rels. 1990), Soc. Am. Travel Writers, N.Y. Travel Writers Assn., N.Y. Press Club, Edn. Writers Assn. (First prize 1967, 78). Avocation: theatre.

SHANAS, ETHEL, sociology educator; b. Chgo., Sept. 6, 1914; d. Alex and Rebecca (Rich) S.; m. Lester J. Perlman, May 17, 1940; 1 child, Michael Stephen. AB, U. Chgo., 1935, AM, 1937, PhD, 1949; LHD (hon.), Hunter Coll., N.Y.C., 1985. Instr. human devel. U. Chgo., 1947-52, rsch. assoc. prof., 1961-65; sr. rsch. analyst City of Chgo., 1952-53; sr. study dir. Nat. Opinion Rsch. Ctr., Chgo., 1956-61; prof. sociology U. Ill., Chgo., 1965-82, prof. emerita, 1982—; vice chmn. expert com. on aging UN, 1974; mem. com. on aging NRC, Washington, 1978-82, panel on statistics for an aging population, 1984-86; mem. U.S. Com. on Vital and Health Stats., Washington, 1976-79. Author: The Health of Older People, 1962; (with others) Old People in Three Industrial Societies, 1968; editor: (with others) Handbook of Aging and the Social Sciences, 1976, 2d edit., 1985. Bd. govs. Chgo. Heart Assn., 1972-80; mem. adv. council on aging City of Chgo., 1972-78. Keston lectr. U. So. Calif., 1975; recipient Burgess award Nat. Council on Family Relations, 1978; Disting. Chgo. Gerontologist award Assn. for Gerontology in Higher Edn., 1988. Fellow Gerontol. Soc. Am. (pres. 1974-75, Kleemeier award 1977, Brookdale award 1981), Am. Sociol. Assn. (chmn. sect. on aging 1985-86 Disting. Scholar award, 1987); mem. Midwest Sociol. Soc. (pres. 1980-81), Inst. Medicine of Nat. Acad. Scis. (sr. mem.). Home: 222 Main St Evanston IL 60202-2467 Office: U Ill Chgo Dept Sociology M/C 312 4112 Behavioral Sci Bldg Chicago IL 60607-7140

SHANDLING, GARRY, comedian, scriptwriter, actor; b. Chgo., Nov. 29, 1949; s. Irving and Muriel S. Grad., U. Ariz. TV screenwriter: Sanford and Son, Welcome Back Kotter, Three's Company; guest host The Tonight Show, 1986-88; host Emmy Awards 1987, 88, Grammy Awards 1990, 91, 92; writer, prodr. Garry Shandling: Alone in Las Vegas, 1984; exec. prodr., writer It's Garry Shandling's Show 25th Anniversary Special, 1986, It's Garry Shandling's Show, 1986-90 (Ace award best comedy series 1989, 90, Ace award best actor in a comedy seires 1990), Garry Shandling: Stand-Up, 1991, The Larry Sanders Show, 1992— (CableAce award, Writing in a Comedy Series, 1994); actor: (film) Love Affair, 1994, Mixed Nuts, 1994. Office: Brillstein/Grey 9200 W Sunset Blvd Ste 428 Los Angeles CA 90069-3506

SHANDS, COURTNEY, JR., lawyer; b. St. Louis, Mar. 17, 1929; s. Courtney and Elizabeth W. (Jones) S.; m. Frances Jean Schellfeffer, Aug. 9, 1952 (div. 1976); children: Courtney III, E.F. Berkley, Elizabeth V.; m. Nancy Bliss Lewis, Oct. 25, 1980. AB, Washington U., St. Louis, 1951; LLB, Harvard U., 1954. Assoc. Thompson and Mitchell, St. Louis, 1954-62, ptnr. Thompson, Walther and Shewmaker, St. Louis, 1962-69, Kohn, Shands, Elbert, Gianoulakis & Giljum, St. Louis, 1970—. Trustee Frank G. and Florence V. Bohle Scholarship Found., Edward Chase Garvey Meml. Found., L.F. Jones Charitable Trust, 1958-60; bd. dirs. St. Louis Fund, 1972—, Law Libr. St. Louis, 1988—, Hope Ednl. & Rsch. Found, 1989—, Citizenship Edn. Clearing House, St. Louis, 1985-87, pres. 1986-87, Mark Twain Summer Inst., St. Louis, 1968-89, pres., 1974-79; Andrews Acad., 1989—, v.p., 1989—; pres. com. Goldwater for Pres., Met. St. Louis, 1964, Ea. Mo. chpt. ACLU, 1966-69, nat. bd. dirs. 1969-72. Mem. ABA, Mo. Bar Integrated, Bar Assn. of Met. St. Louis, Selden Soc., Law Libr. Assn., Noonday Club, Racquet CLub, St. Louis Club. Republican. Episcopalian. Home: 507 S Taylor Ave Saint Louis MO 63122-4458 Office: Kohn Shands Elbert 1 Mercantile Ctr Fl 24 Saint Louis MO 63101-1643

SHANDS, HENRY LEE, plant geneticist, administrator; b. Madison, Wis., Aug. 30, 1935; s. Ruebush George and Elizabeth (Henry) S.; m. Catherine Miller, Nov. 20, 1962; children: Deborah A. Jeanne A., James L. BS, U. Wis., 1957; MS, Purdue U., 1961, PhD, 1963. NSF fellow Swedish Seed Assn., Svalov, 1962-63; asst. prof. Purdue U., West Lafayette, Ind., 1963-66, asst. prof. botany and plant pathology, 1965-66; rsch. agronomist, leader ea. wheat project Dekalb Hybrid Wheat, Inc., Lafayette, 1966-79; rsch. agronomist, dir. sunflower rsch. Dekalb-Pfizer Genetics and predecessor firms, Glyndon, Minn., 1979-86; nat. program leader for plant germplasm USDA Agrl. Rsch. Svc., Beltsville, Md., 1986-92, assoc. dep. adminstr. for genetic resources, 1992—; mem. AID Project, Minas Gerais, Brazil, 1963-65. 1st lt. U.S. Army, 1957-59. Recipient 1st Victor M. Bendelow Meml. Lectr. award U. Man., 1992. Fellow AAAS, Am. Soc. Agronomy, Crop Sci. Soc. Am. (Frank N. Meyer medal for plant genetic resources 1992); Am. Genetic Assn., Genetics Soc. Can., Am. Phytopath. Soc. Office: USDA-ARS Bldg 005 BARC-W Beltsville MD 20705-2350

SHANDS, WILLIAM RIDLEY, JR., lawyer; b. Richmond, Va., Nov. 23, 1929; s. William Ridley and Josephine (Winston) S.; m. Lynneth Williams, May 31, 1958; children: William Tyler, Laura Sawyer. B.A., Hampden-Sydney Coll., 1952; LL.B., U. Va., 1958. Bar: Va. 1958. Atty., assoc. firm Christian, Barton, Epps, Brent & Chappell, Richmond, 1958-61; counsel The Life Ins. Co. of Va., Richmond, 1961-66; asst. gen. counsel The Life Ins. Co. of Va., 1966-68, asso. gen. counsel, 1968-71, gen. counsel, 1971-73, v.p., gen. counsel, 1973-78, sr. v.p., gen. counsel, 1978-79; sr. v.p. law and public affairs Continental Fin. Services Co., Richmond, 1980-85; sr. v.p., sec. Life Ins. Co. Va., Richmond, 1985-88; counsel Sands, Anderson, Marks & Miller, Richmond, 1988—. Chmn. Eastern Appeal Bd. Selective Svc. System, 1969; pres., chmn. bd. dirs. Trinity Episcopal High Sch., 1971-72; bd. dirs. Richmond Area Heart Assn., 1965-71, Southampton Cotillion, 1970-72; vestryman St. Michael's Episc. Ch., 1965-68, sr. warden, 1968. Served with AUS, 1952-55, Philippines. Mem. Va. Bar Assn., Richmond Bar Assn., Assn. Life Ins. Counsel (pres. 1987-88), Am. Coun. Life Ins. (chmn. legal sect. 1982-83), Va. Assn. Life Underwriters, Commonwealth Club, Country Club Va. Home: 3811 Darby Dr Midlothian VA 23113-1318 Office: Sands Anderson Marks & Miller 801 E Main St # 1998 Richmond VA 23219-2901

SHANE, JOHN MARDER, endocrinologist; b. Kansas City, Mo., Oct. 5, 1942; s. Henry Kamsler and Ruth (Marder) S.; m. Eileen Goodart, June 18, 1967; children: Robert M., Edward G. BS, U. Okla., 1964, MD, 1967. Diplomate Am. Bd. Ob-Gyn., Am. Bd. Reproductive Endocrinology. Resident Harvard Med. Schs., Boston, 1970-73, fellowship, 1973-75, instr.; 1970-75, asst. prof., 1975-78; pvt. practice Tulsa, 1978—; lectr., cons. Tutorial Svcs. Internat., England, 1984—; bd. dirs. St. Francies G.I.F.T. Lab., Tulsa; cons. to preimplantation genetics project Chapman Genetics Inst., Children's Med. Ctr., Tulsa. Author: CIBA Symposium Infertility: Diagnosis and Treatment; contbr. articles to profl. jours. and publs. Mem. Tulsa Garden Ctr., 1988—; bd. dirs. Temple Israel, Tulsa, 1985-86. Captain USAF, 1967-69. Recipient Annual award Boston Obstet. Soc., 1977. Mem. ACS, Tulsa Gynecol. Soc. (past pres. 1986-87), Soc. Reproductive Endocrinologists, Tulsa bonsai Soc. (bd. dirs. 1988—), Am. Coll. Ob-Gyn. (v.p. 1971-92, pres. New England Jr. divsn. 1972-73), Am. Bonsai Soc. (nat. bd. dirs.), Chanie des Rotisseurs (l'Ordre Mondial, Tulsa v.p.), Southside Rotary of Tulsa (bd. dirs.), Nat. Arboretum (nat. bd. dirs.). Republican. Jewish. Avocations: bonsai, collector oriental arts. Office: 6465 S Yale Ave Tulsa OK 74136-7805

SHANE, PETER MILO, law educator, lawyer; b. Oceanside, N.Y., July 12, 1952; s. Albert and Ann (Semanoff) S.; m. Martha Elisabeth Chamallas, June 27, 1981; 1 child, Elisabeth Ann. AB, Harvard U., 1974; JD, Yale U., 1977. Bar: N.Y. 1978, U.S. Ct. Appeals (5th cir.) 1978, D.C. 1979, U.S. Ct. Appeals (8th cir.) 1983, U.S. Supreme Ct. 1984. Law clk. to judge U.S. Ct. Appeals (5th cir.), New Orleans, 1977-78; atty., advisor office of legal counsel, U.S. Dept. Justice, Washington, 1978-81; asst. gen. counsel Office of Mgmt. and Budget, Washington, D.C., 1981; assoc. prof. law U. Iowa, Iowa City, 1981-85, prof., 1985-94; dean, prof. law U. Pitts., 1994—; adj. lectr. Am. U., Washington, D.C., 1979-80; vis. prof. law Duke U., Durham, N.C., 1986; cons. U.S. Dept. Edn., Washington, D.C., 1980, MacArthur Justice Found., Chgo., 1987, adminstrv. conf. U.S., 1991, pub. mem. 1995—; cons. Nat. Commn. Jud. Discipline and Removal, 1992-93; cooperating atty. Iowa Civil Liberties Union, Des Moines, 1982-94, bd. dirs., 1987-89. Author: (with H.H. Bruff) The Law of Presidential Power: Cases and Materials, 1988, (with J. Mashaw and R. Merrill) Administrative Law: The American Public Law System, 1992. Mem. Dem. con. committee Johnson County, Iowa, 1982-88. Old Gold Summer fellow U. Iowa, 1981-84, Mellon Found fellow, 1982. Mem. ABA (coun. sect. adminstrv. law and regulatory practice 1993—, chmn. com. on govt. orgn. and separation of powers 1987-91), Assn. Am. Law Schs. (chair adminstrv. law 1990, chair remedies 1992). Jewish. Office: U Pitts Sch Law Pittsburgh PA 15260

SHANE, RITA, opera singer; b. N.Y.C.; d. Julius J. and Rebekah (Milner) S.; m. Daniel F. Tritter, June 22, 1958; 1 child, Michael Shane. BA, Barnard Coll., 1958; postgrad., Santa Fe Opera Apprentice Program, 1962-63, Hunter Opera Assn., 1962-64; pvt. study with, Beverly Peck Johnson, Elizabeth Schwartzkopf, Bliss Hebert. Prof. voice Manhattan Sch. of Music, 1993—; prof. voice Eastman Sch. Music Rochester U., 1989—; pvt. teaching, N.Y.C., 1978—. Performer with numerous opera cos., including profl. debut, Chattanooga Opera, 1964, Met. Opera, San Francisco Opera, N.Y.C. Opera, Chgo. Lyric Opera, San Diego Opera, Santa Fe Opera, Teatro alla Scala, Milan, Italy, Bavarian State Opera, Netherlands Nat. Opera, Geneva Opera, Vienna State Opera, Phila., New Orleans, Balt. Opera, Opera du Rhin, Strasbourg, Scottish Opera, Teatro Reggio, Turin, Opera Metropolitana, Caracas, Portland Opera, Minn. Opera, also others; world premiere Miss Havisham's Fire, Argento; Am. premieres include Reimann-Lear, Schat-Houdini, Henze-Elegy for Young Lovers; participant festivals, including Mozart Festival, Lincoln Center, N.Y.C., Munich Festival, Aspen Festival, Handel Soc., Vienna Festival, Salzburg Festival, Munich Festival, Perugia Festival, Festival Canada, Glyndebourne Festival, performed with orchs. including Santa Cecilia, Rome, Austrian Radio, London Philharmn., Louisville, Cin., Cleve., Phila., RAI, Naples, Denver, Milw., Israel Philharm., rec. artist, RCA, Columbia, Louisville, Turnabout labels, also radio and TV. Recipient Martha Baird Rockefeller award, William Matheus Sullivan award. Mem. Am. Guild Mus. Artists, Screen Actors Guild. Office: care Daniel F Tritter 545 5th Ave New York NY 10017-3609

SHANE, RONALD, financial company executive; b. Chgo., May 9, 1953. A.A., Miami Dade Jr. Coll., 1972; B.A., Fla. Internat. U., 1974. Pres. Trans Leasing of Fla., Ft. Lauderdale, 1976-77; co-founder, pres. Assoc.

Leasing Internat. Corp., Ft. Lauderdale, 1977—; v.p., dir. Assoc. Fin. Internat. Corp., Ft. Lauderdale, 1977—; Assoc. Mortgage Internat. Corp., Ft. Lauderdale, 1980—. Contbr. articles to fin. trade jours. Sec., mem. bd. dirs. Manors of Inverrary CondoAssn., Lauderhill, Fla., 1971, 72; mem. archtl. com. San Simeon Homeowners Assn., Boca Raton, Fla., 1984—. Recipient Personalities of Am. award, 1986. Mem. Internat. Machine Tool Assn. (assoc.), Graphic Arts and Printing Soc. (assoc.), Radiol. Soc. N.Am. (assoc.), Roll Royce Owners Cub Club, Antique Automobile Club, Classic Car Club, Riviera Owners Club, Fraternal Order of Police (assoc. Nat. Grand Lodge, chartered), Woodlands Country Club (Tamarac, Fla., jr. mem.). Avocations: collecting and restoring classic cars, power boating, golf, travel. Office: Assoc Leasing Internat Corp 1489 W Palmetto Park Rd Ste 475 Boca Raton FL 33486-3326

SHANEFIELD, DANIEL JAY, ceramics engineering educator; b. Orange, N.J., Apr. 29, 1930; s. Benjamin and Nan (Leichter) S.; m. Elizabeth Davis, June 28, 1964; children: Alison, Douglas. BS in Chemistry, Yale U., 1952; PhD in Chemistry, Rutgers U., 1962. Sr. project engr. ITT Group, Nutley, N.J., 1962-67; sr. mem. tech. staff AT&T Bell Labs., Princeton, N.J., 1967-86; disting. prof. Rutgers U., New Brunswick, N.J., 1986—; adv. panel NSF, 1990—; course dir. Ctr. for Profl. Advancement, U.S. and The Netherlands, 1993—; cons. in field; presenter at profl. confs. Author: Organic Additives for Ceramics Processing, 1995; co-author: Defects in Gold Plating, 1981; contbr. 4 chpts. to tech. books, numerous articles to profl. jours.; co-inventor 17 patents; assoc. editor Jour. Am. Ceramic Soc., 1987—. With U.S. Army, 1952-54, Korea. Fellow Am. Inst. Chemists, Am. Ceramic Soc. (Best Paper award); mem. IEEE (chmn. standards com. 1984—), Am. Chem. Soc. Republican. Avocations: modifying sports cars, writing audio, stereo articles. Home: 119 Jefferson Rd Princeton NJ 08540-3373 Office: Rutgers U Ceramics Engring Dept PO Box 909 Piscataway NJ 08855-0909

SHANER, JOHN WESLEY, physicist; b. Arlington, Mass., June 3, 1942. BS, MIT, 1964; PhD in Physics, U. Calif., Berkeley, 1969. Assoc. instr. physics U. Utah, 1970-72; group leader exp physics Lawrence Livermore Lab., 1972-78; group leader Shockwave Physics Los Alamos (N.Mex.) Nat. Lab., 1978—. Resident Ernest Orlando Lawrence Meml. award U.S. Dept. Energy, 1993. Fellow Am. Phys. Soc.; mem. Internat. Orgn. High Pressure Sci. and Tech. (treas. 1985-88). Home: 152 Piedra Loop Los Alamos NM 87544*

SHANEYFELT, PATRICIA THARIN, elementary education educator; b. Dunedin, Fla., Apr. 12, 1954; d. Robert M. and Ruth (Black) Tharin; m. James L. Shanyfelt, Dec. 28, 1973 (div. 1983); children: Daniel J., Randall D. AA with honors, St. Petersburg Jr. Coll., 1974; BA, U. South Fla., 1986. Second and third grade tchr. Cross Bayou Elem. & Deaf Edn., Pinellas Park, Fla., 1986-90; second and fourth grade tchr. Garrison Jones Elem. Sch., Dunedin, Fla., 1990—. Author: Heart Connections, The Character Factory. Recipient Fla. State Teaching Econs. award, 1989, 91, 2nd Place award Pinellas County Econs. Fair, 1989, 1st Place award Nat. Awards Program Teaching Econs., 1990, 92; named Cross Bayou's Tchr. of Yr., 1990, Garrison Jones Tchr. of Yr., 1992. Democrat. Episcopalian. Avocations: swimming, boating, camping. Home: 238 Garden Cir S Dunedin FL 34698-7544 Office: Garrison-Jones Elem Sch Palm Harbor FL 34683

SHANGE, NTOZAKE (PAULETTE WILLIAMS), playwright, poet; b. Trenton, N.J., Oct. 18, 1948; d. Paul T. and Eloise Williams; m. David Murray, July 4, 1977 (div.); 1 child: Savannah. BA in Am. Studies cum laude, Barnard Coll., 1970; MA in Am. Studies, U. So. Calif., 1973. mem. faculty Sonoma State U., 1973-75, Mills Coll., 1975, CCNY, 1975, Douglass Coll., 1978; lectr. in field. Author: (plays) for colored girls who have considered suicide/when the rainbow is enuf, 1975 (Obie award for best play 1977, Outer Critics Circle award for best play 1977, Audelco award 1977, Tony award nomination for best play 1977, Grammy award nomination for best spoken word rec. 1977), Melissa and Smith, 1976, A Photograph: A Study of Cruelty, 1977, (with Thulani Nkabinde and Jessica Hagedorn) Where the Mississippi Meets the Amazon, 1977, Boogie Woogie Landscapes, 1978, From Okra to Greens, 1978, Spell #7: A Geechee Quick Magic Trance Manual, 1979, Black and White Two Dimensional Planes, 1979, Mouths, 1981, A Photograph: Lovers in Motion, 1981, Three For a Full Moon, 1982, Bocas, 1982, Three Views of Mt. Fuji, 1987; (adaptations) Mother Courage and Her Children (Brecht), 1980 (Obie award for best play 1981), Educating Rita, 1982; (operetta) Carrie, 1981; (novels) Sassafrass, 1976, Sassafrass, Cypress and Indigo, 1982, Betsey Brown, 1985, Liliana: Resurrection of the Daughter, 1994; (poems) Natural Disasters and Other Festive Occasions, 1977, Nappy Edges, 1978, Three Pieces, 1981 (L.A. Book prize for poetry 1981), A Daughter's Geography, 1983, From Okra to Greens, 1984, The Love Space Demands, 1991, I Live in Music, 1994; (nonfiction) See No Evil: Prefaces, Essays and Accounts 1976-1983, 1984, Ridin' the Moon in Texas: Word Paintings, 1987; contbr. poetry, essays and short stories to numerous mags. and anthologies, including Third World Women, Chgo. Rev., Am. Rag, Sojourner, Womansports; actress: For Colored Girls Who Have Considered Suicide/When the Rainbow is Enuf, 1976, Where the Mississippi Meets the Amazon, 1977; dir.: The Mighty Gents, 1979, A Photograph: A Study in Cruelty, 1979, The Issue, 1979, The Spirit of Sojourner Truth, 1979; writer: An Evening with Diana Ross: The Big Event, 1977 (Emmy award nomination 1977); performing mem.: Sounds in Motion Dance Co.; performed in various jazz/poetry collaborations; dancer with Third World Collective, Raymond Sawyer's Afro-American Dance Co., Sound in Motion, West Coast Dance Works; founder, dancer For Colored Girls Who Have Considered Suicide. Recipient Frank Silvera Writer's Workshop award, 1978, Excellence award College U., 1981, Taos World Poetry Heavyweight Champion, 1992, 93, 94; NDEA fellow, 1973, Guggenheim fellow, 1981. Mem. Actors Equity, Nat. Acad. TV Arts and Scis., Acad. Am. Poets, Dramatist's Guild, PEN Am Center, Poets and Writer's, Inc., N.Y. Feminist Art Guild. Office: care St Martins Press 175 Fifth Ave New York NY 10010*

SHANGRAW, CLARENCE FRANK, museum official; b. Burlington, Vt., Aug. 9, 1935; s. Eugene and Hazel Bernice (Fuller) S.; m. Sylvia Chen, Dec. 23, 1961 (dec.); children—Lea Lihsia, Lin Ethan. Grad., Yale U. Inst. Far Eastern Langs., 1955; A.B. with high honors, U. Calif.-, Berkeley, 1963, M.A., 1965. Tchr. U. Calif.-, Berkeley, 1964-65; art research asst. M.H. de Young Mus., 1965; asst. curator Avery Brundage Collection, 1966-68; sr. curator Asian art Asian Art Mus. San Francisco, 1968-85, acting dir., chief curator, 1985, chief curator, 1986-89, dep. dir., chief curator, 1989-92, chief curator emeritus, 1992; dir. Tsui Mus. Art, Hong Kong, 1992-93; Asian art cons., 1993—; adj. prof. Sch. Mus. Studies John F. Kennedy U., 1980—. Author: Origins of Chinese Ceramics, 1978, Masterworks of Ming: 15th Century Chinese Blue and White Porcelains, 1985, Marvels of Medieval China: Those Lustrous Song and Yuan Lacquers, 1986; co-author: Chinese Blue and White Porcelains from the Voyages of Drake and Cermeno Found at Drakes Bay, California, 1982; editor: Legacy of Chenghua, Hong Kong, 1993; contbr. sect.: Chinese, Japanese and Korean Sculptures in the Avery Brundage Collection, 1974, 5,000 Years of Korean Art, 1979, The Art of Japan: Masterworks in the Asian Art Mus. of San Francisco, 1991, Vol. I, Tsui Museum of Art: Early Chinese Ceramics, Reflections on Early Chinese Ceramics, 1992; contbr.: catalog Treasures from the Shanghai Museum: 6, 000 Years of Chinese Art, 1983, Looking at Asian Art Patronage, 1989, Beauty, Wealth, and Power: Jewels and Ornaments of Asia, 1992, Some Reflections on the Beginnings of China's Ceramic Traditions, 1993; contbr. numerous articles to profl. jours. Served with USAF, 1954-58. Mem. Am. Assn. Mus., Internat. Council Mus., Oriental Ceramics Soc. London, Am. Inst. Archaeology, Assn. Asian Studies. Republican. Conglist. Home: 5517 Diamond Heights Blvd San Francisco CA 94131-2642 Office: Asian Art Mus Golden Gate Park San Francisco CA 94118

SHANK, CHARLES VERNON, science administrator, educator; b. Mt. Holly, N.J., July 12, 1943; s. Augustus Jacob and Lillian (Peterson) S.; m. Brenda Buckhold, June 16, 1969. BS, U. Calif., Berkeley, 1965, MS, PhD, 1969. Mem. tech. staff AT&T Bell Labs., Holmdel, N.J., 1969-76, head quantum physics and electronics dept., 1976-83, dir. Electronics Rsch. Lab., 1983-89; dir. Lawrence Berkeley Lab., faculty mem. chemistry, physics, elec. engring. and computer scis. U. Calif., Berkeley, 1989—. Numerous patents in field. Recipient E. Longstreth medal Franklin Inst., Phila., 1982, Morris E. Leeds award IEEE, 1982, David Sarnoff award IEEE, 1989. R.W. Wood prize. Fellow AAAS, Am. Phys. Soc., Optical Soc. Am. (R. W. Wood prize

1981); mem. NAS, NAE, Am. Acad. Arts and Scis. Home: 9 Ajax Pl Berkeley CA 94708-2119 Office: U Calif Lawrence Berkeley Lab 1 Cyclotron Rd Berkeley CA 94720-0001

SHANK, CLARE BROWN WILLIAMS, political leader; b. Syracuse, N.Y., Sept. 19, 1909; d. Curtiss Crofoot and Clara Irene (Shoudy) Brown; m. Frank E. Williams, Feb. 18, 1940 (dec. Feb. 1957); m. Seth Carl Shank, Dec. 28, 1963 (dec. Jan. 1977). B in Oral English, Syracuse U., 1931. Tchr., 1931-33, merchandising exec., 1933-42; Pinellas County mem. Rep. State Com., 1954-58; life mem. Pinellas County Rep. Exec. Com.; exec. com. Fla. Rep. Com., 1954-64; Fla. committeewoman Rep. Nat. Com., 1956-64, mem. exec. com., 1956-64, asst. chmn. and dir. women's activities, 1958-64; alt., mem. arrangements com., major speaker Rep. Nat. Conv., Chgo., 1960; alt., program and arrangement coms. Rep. Nat. Conv., 1964. Pres. St. Petersburg Women's Rep. Club, 1955-57; Mem. Def. Adv. Com. on Women in Services, 1959-65; trustee St. Petersburg Housing Authority, 1976-81. Recipient George Arents medal Syracuse U., 1959; citation for patriotic civilian service 5th U.S. Army and Dept. Def.; 1st woman to preside over any part of nat. polit. conv., Rep. Nat. Conv., Chgo., 1960. Mem. AAUW, DAR, Gen. Fedn. Women's Clubs, Colonial Dames 17th Century, Fla. Fedn. Women's Clubs (dist. pres. 1976-78), Women's Club (St. Petersburg, pres. 1974-76, Yacht Club, Lakewood Country Club (St. Petersburg). Methodist. Home: 939 Beach Dr NE Apt 409 Saint Petersburg FL 33701-2009

SHANK, FRED ROSS, federal agency administrator; b. Harrisonburg, Va., Oct. 11, 1940; m. Peggy Anne Westbrook, June 1967; children: Virginia Anne, Fred Ross III. BS in Agriculture, U. Ky., 1962, MS in Nutrition, 1964; PhD, U. Md., 1969. Dep. dir. Office Nutrition and Food Sci. FDA, Washington, 1979-86, dir. Office Phys. Sci., 1986-87, dep. dir. Ctr. for Food SAfety and Applied Nutrition, 1987-89, dir., 1989—. Fellow Inst. Food Technologists; mem. Am. Assn. Cereal Chemists, Am. Inst. Nutrition, Am. Soc. for Clin. Nutrition, Assn. Food and Drug Ofcls. Home: 2621 Steeplechase Dr Reston VA 22091-2130 Office: FDA Ctr Food Safety and Applied Nutrition 200 C St SW Washington DC 20204-0001

SHANK, MAURICE EDWIN, aerospace engineering executive, consultant; b. N.Y.C., Apr. 22, 1921; s. Edwin A. and Viola (Lewis) S.; m. Virginia Lee King, Sept. 25, 1948; children: Christopher K., Hilary L. Shank-Kuhl, Diana L. Boehm. B.S. in Mech. Engring., Carnegie-Mellon U., 1942; D.Sc., MIT, 1949. Registered profl. engr., Mass. Assoc. prof. mech. engring. MIT, Cambridge, 1949-60; with Pratt & Whitney, East Hartford, Conn., 1960-87, dir. engine design and structures engring., 1980-81, dir. engring. tech., 1981-85, dir. engring. tech. assessment, 1985-86; v.p. Pratt Whitney of China, Inc., East Hartford, 1986-87; pvt. exec. cons. to industry and govt., 1987—; cons. editor McGraw-Hill Book Co., N.Y.C., 1960-80; adv. com. to mechanics div. Nat. Bur. Standards, Washington, 1964-69; vis. com. dept. mech. engring. Carnegie-Mellon U., Pitts., 1968-78; corp. vis. coms. depts. materials sci. and engring., dept. aeros. and astronautics MIT, 1968-74, 79-92; mem. rsch. and tech. adv. coun. com. on aero. propulsion NASA, Washington, 1973-77, mem. aero. adv. com., 1978-86; mem. aero. and space engring. bd. NRC, 1989-92; lectr. in field. Contbr. articles to profl. jours. Served to maj. U.S. Army, 1942-46. Fellow AIAA, ASME, AIME, Am. Soc. Metals; mem. Nat. Acad. Engring., Conn. Acad. Sci. and Engring. Episcopalian. Club: Cosmos. Avocations: boating; fishing.

SHANK, ROBERT ELY, physician, preventive medicine educator emeritus; b. Louisville, Sept. 2, 1914; s. Oliver Orlando and Isabel Thompson (Ely) S.; m. Eleanor Caswell, July 29, 1942; children: Jane, Robert Oliver, Bruce. A.B., Westminster Coll., 1935; M.D., Washington U., 1939. Diplomate: Am. Bd. Nutrition. Intern, house physician Barnes Hosp., 1939-41; asst. resident physician, asst. in research Hosp. Rockefeller Inst. Med. Research, 1941-46; research asso. div. nutrition and physiology Pub. Health Research Inst. City N.Y., 1946-48; prof. preventive medicine Washington U. Sch. Medicine, 1948-55, Danforth prof. preventive medicine, 1955-83, prof. emeritus preventive medicine, 1983—; Cutter lectr. preventive medicine Harvard, 1964; Mem. food and nutrition bd. NRC, 1949-69; spl. cons. nutrition USPHS, 1949-53; chmn. adv. bd. health and hosps., St. Louis County, 1949-54; med. adv. bd. St. Louis Vis. Nurses Assn., 1950-86; mem. com. food and nutrition nat. adv. bd. health services A.R.C., 1950-53; mem. adv. com. metabolism Office Surgeon Gen., 1956-60, mem. adv. com. on nutrition, 1964-72; mem. Am. Bd. Nutrition, 1955-64, sec., treas., 1958-64; mem. Nat. Bd. Med. Examiners, 1957-58; co-dir. nutrition survey NIH, Peru, 1959, N.E. Brazil, 1963; mem. sci. adv. bd. Nat. Vitamin Found., 1958-61; mem. nutrition study sect. NIH, 1964-68, chmn. sect., 1966-68; mem. gastroenterology and nutrition tng. com., 1968-69, mem. nat. adv. child health and human devel. council, 1969-73; mem. clin. application and prevention adv. com. Nat. Heart, Lung and Blood Inst., 1976-80. Author sects. in med. textbooks, sci. papers relating to nutritional, metabolic disorders.; Asso. editor: Nutrition Revs, 1948-58; editorial adv. bd.: Nutrition Today, 1966-76, Hepatology, 1980-85. Served as lt. comdr. M.C. USNR, 1942-46. Recipient Alumni Achievement award Westminster Coll., 1970, Alumni Faculty award Washington U., 1989. Fellow Am. Pub. Health Assn. (governing council 1955-56), Am. Inst. Nutrition; mem. N.Y. Acad. Scis., Harvey Soc., Am. Soc. Biol. Chemists, Soc. Exptl. Biology and Medicine (council 1952-54), Central Soc. Clin. Research, Am. Soc. Clin. Investigation, Assn. Tchrs. Preventive Medicine (v.p. 1955-57, pres. 1957-58), A.M.A. (council on foods and nutrition 1960-69, chmn. 1963-66), Gerontological Soc., Assn. Am. Physicians, Am. Soc. Clin. Nutrition (council 1963-65, pres. 1967-68), Am. Dietetic Assn. (hon.), Am. Soc. for Study Liver Diseases (council 1963-66, pres. 1966), Am. Heart Assn. (chmn. nutrition com. 1973-76, award of merit 1981) Sigma Xi, Alpha Omega Alpha. Presbyterian. Home: 1325 Wilton Ln Saint Louis MO 63122-6940 Office: Wash U Sch Medicine 4566 Scott Ave Saint Louis MO 63110-1095

SHANK, RUSSELL, librarian, educator; b. Spokane, Wash., Sept. 2, 1925; s. Harry and Sadie S.; m. Doris Louise Hempfer, Nov. 9, 1951 (div.); children: Susan Marie, Peter Michael, Judith Louise. B.S., U. Wash., 1946, B.A., 1949; M.B.A., U. Wis., 1952; Dr.L.S., Columbia U., 1966. Reference libr. U. Wash., Seattle, 1949; asst. engring. libr. U. Wis.-Madison, 1949-52; chief pers. Milw. Pub. Libr., 1952; engring.-phys. scis. libr. Columbia U., N.Y.C., 1953-59; sr. lectr. Columbia U., 1964-66, assoc. prof., 1966-67; asst. univ. libr. U. Calif.-Berkeley, 1959-64; dir. sci. libr. N.Y. Met. Reference and Rsch. 1966-68; dir. libr. Smithsonian Inst., Washington, 1967-77; univ. libr. prof. UCLA, 1977-89, asst. vice chancellor for libr. and info. svcs. planning, 1989-91, univ. libr., prof. emeritus, 1991—; cons. Indonesian Inst. Sci., 1970; bd. cons. Pahlavi Nat. Library, Iran, 1975-76; pres. U.S. Book Exchange, 1975; bd. trustees Freedom to Read Found., 1989—. Trustee OCLC, Inc., 1978-84, 87, chmn., 1984; mem. library del. People's Republic of China, 1979; bd. dirs. Am. Council on Edn., 1980-81. Served with USNR, 1943-46. Recipient Disting. Alumnus award U. Wash. Sch. Librarianship, 1968, Role of Honor award Freedom to Read Found., 1990, Disting. Alumnus award Columbia U. Sch. Libr. Sci., 1992; fellow Coun. on Libr. Resources, 1973-74. Fellow AAAS; mem. ALA (pres. 1978-79, coun. 1961-65, 74-82, exec. bd. 1975-83, chmn. internat. rels. com. 1980-83, pres. info. sci. and automation div. 1968-69), Assn. Coll. and Rsch. Librs. (pres. 1972-73, Hugh Atkinson award 1990), Assn. Rsch. Librs. (bd. dirs. 1974-77). Home: 12919 Montana Ave Apt 101 Los Angeles CA 90049-4843 *Intellectual freedom is the paramount human right. It is the American's premier heritage. Without it the claim to democracy is a sham. Should the principles of our society fade or perish, the survival of this freedom alone would justify the nation's experience. The freedom to think, to read, and to speak will be our enduring monument. Their diffusion throughout the world must be our unending crusade.*

SHANK, STEPHEN GEORGE, lawyer, toy manufacturing executive; b. Tulsa, Dec. 6, 1943; s. Louis Warren and Lillian Margaret Shank; m. Judith Frances Thompson, July 17, 1966; children: Susan, Mary. BA, U. Iowa, 1965; MA (Woodrow Wilson fellow), Fletchers Sch., Tufts U., 1966; JD, Harvard U., 1972. Bar: Minn. 1972. Ptnr. Dorsey, Marquart, Windhorst, West & Halladay, Mpls., 1972-74, 78-79, Dorsey, Windhorst, Hannaford, Whitney & Halladay, Mpls., 1978-79; gen. counsel Tonka Corp., Hopkins, Minn., 1974-78, sec., 1974-79, pres., chief exec. officer, 1979-88; chmn., chief exec. officer Tonka Corp., Minnetonka, Minn., 1988—, also bd. dirs.; asst. prof. law William Mitchell Coll. Law, 1974-77; bd. dirs. Nat Computer Systems, Inc., Eden Prairie, Minn. Assoc. editor: Harvard Law Rev., 1971-

72. Bd. dirs. Loring-Nicollet-Bethlehem Center, Mpls., 1977, Walker Art Ctr., 1989—; bd. govs. Meth. Hosp., 1982-85; trustee Mpls. Soc. Fine Arts, 1986-87, Minn. Med. Found., 1986-87; chmn. Vanguard A div., Mpls. United Way Campaign, 1986. With U.S. Army, 1966-69. Decorated D.S.M. Mem. ABA, Minn. State Bar Assn., Nat. Assn. Mfrs. (bd. dirs. 1985, 87—), Toy Mfrs. Am. (vice-chmn. 1983, adv. com. 1983-84, chmn. 1984). Home: 330 Peavey Ln Wayzata MN 55391-1525 Office: Tonka Corp 200 Narragansett Park Dr Pawtucket RI 02861-4338

SHANK, WESLEY IVAN, retired architect, educator; b. San Francisco, Mar. 1, 1927; s. Ivan Wesley and Lenore (Futernick) S.; m. Georgene Morrison, Aug. 13, 1949; children: Jennifer Jean Casstevens, Matthew Wyatt, Edmund George. BA, U. Calif., Berkeley, 1951; MArch, McGill U., Montreal, Que., Can., 1965. Draftsman, architect various archtl. and engring. firms, San Francisco Bay area, 1951-63; prof. architecture Iowa State U., Ames, 1964-92, prof. emeritus, 1993—; architect, archtl. historian Hist. Am. Bldg. Survey, Nat. Pk. Svc., various locations, 1967-84; mem. nominations rev. com. Iowa Nat. Register Hist. Places, 1973-86, 94—. Author, compiler: The Iowa Catalog: Historic American Buildings Survey, 1979. Mem. AIA, Soc. Archtl. Historians. Democrat. Episcopalian.

SHANK, WILLIAM O., lawyer; b. Hamilton, Ohio, Jan. 11, 1924; s. Horace Cooper and Bonnie (Winn) S.; m. Shirleen Allison, June 25, 1949; children—Allison Kay, Kristin Elizabeth. B.A., Miami U., Oxford, O., 1947; J.D., Yale, 1950. Bar: Ohio, Ill. bars, also U.S. Supreme Ct. bar. Pvt. practice Hamilton, Ohio, 1951-55; assoc. Lord, Bissell & Brook, 1955-58; atty. Chemetron Corp., 1958-60, sr. atty., 1960-61, gen. atty., asst. sec., 1961-71, sec., gen. counsel, 1971-78; v.p., gen. counsel, sec. Walgreen Co., Deerfield, Ill., 1978-89; ptnr. Burditt & Radzius, Chartered, Chgo., 1989—; exec. v.p. Internat. Bus. Resources, Inc., Chgo., 1993—; mem. bus. adv. coun. Miami U., Oxford, Ohio, 1975—. Bd. dirs. coun. for Community Svcs. Met. Chgo., 1973-77; trustee Libr. Internat. Rels., 1971-78; bd. dirs. Chgo. Civic Fedn., 1984-89, Walgreen Drug Stores Hist. Found., 1990—, Walgreen Alumni Assn., 1992—; mem. Chgo. Crime Commn., 1985-89. 1st lt. pilot 8th Air Force, USAAF, WWII, ETO. Fellow Am. Bar Found (life); mem. ABA, Ill. Bar Assn., Chgo. Bar Assn. (chmn. com. on corp. law depts. 1971-72, 89-90), Am. Corp. Secs. (pres. Chgo. regional group 1983-84, nat. bd. dirs. 1984-87), Yale U. Law Sch. Assn. (pres. Ill. Alumni, formerly exec. com. New Haven), Walgreen Alumni Assn. (pres. 1992-94), Legal Club (pres. 1979-80), Law Club, Univ. Club, Econ. Club, Yale Club of Chgo., Omicron Delta Kappa, Phi Delta Kappa, Sigma Chi. Home: 755 S Shore Dr Crystal Lake IL 60014-5530 Office: Burditt & Radzius Chartered 333 W Wacker Dr Ste 2600 Chicago IL 60606-1227

SHANKEL, GERALD MARVIN, association executive; b. Alma, Mich., Jan. 1, 1943; s. Marvin A. Shankel and Ruth E. (Walworth) Heppner; m. Lois M. Herzberg, June 22, 1963; children: Cheryl A., Jill M., Steven G. BA, Alma Coll., 1965; MBA, U. Mich., 1966. Auditor Ernst & Ernst, Detroit, 1966-68; mng. dir. fin. and adminstrn. Soc. Mfg. Engrs., Dearborn, Mich., 1968-87; assoc. exec. dir. fin. and adminstrn. ASME, N.Y.C., 1988-92; exec. dir. Nat. Assn. Corrosion Engrs. Internat., Houston, 1992—; bd. dirs. Greater Houston (Tex.) Visitors & Conv. Bur., 1994—. Mem. Am. Soc. Assn. Execs. (cert. assn. exec.), Coun. Engring. and Sci. Soc. Execs. (treas. 1978-86). Avocations: swimming, reading, traveling. Home: 3414 Cinco Lakes Dr Katy TX 77450 Office: NACE Internat 1440 S Creek Dr Houston TX 77084

SHANKER, ALBERT, labor union official; b. N.Y.C., Sept. 14, 1928; s. Morris and Mamie S.; m. Edith Gerber, 1960; children: Carl, Adam, Jennie, Michael. B.A., U. Ill., 1949; postgrad., Columbia U.; Dr. Pedagogy (hon.), R.I. Coll., 1980; D.H.L. (hon.), CUNY Grad. Sch., 1983, Adelphi U., 1985; LL.D., U. Rochester, 1985. Tchr. elementary schs., jr. high sch. math. pub. schs. N.Y.C., 1952-59; pres. United Fedn. Tchrs., N.Y.C., 1964-86, Am. Fedn. Tchrs., Washington, 1974—; founding pres. Edn. Internat.; v.p. AFL-CIO, Washington, 1973—; chair dept. profl. employees, chmn. bd. AFL-CIO; exec. v.p. N.Y. State United Tchrs., 1972-78; v.p. N.Y. State AFL-CIO, 1973—; mem. N.Y.C. Cen. Labor Coun.; sec. Jewish Labor Com., 1965—; assoc. Univ. Seminar on Labor Columbia U.; hon. vice chmn. Am. Trade Union Coun. for Histadrut; mem. exec. com. Workers Def. League; mem. edn. ; mem. group Nat. Bd. Profl. Teaching Standards, 1986—; mem. Edn. Commn. of States, 1974—; 20th Century Fund; mem. labor adv. com. U.S. Holocaust Mus.; tchr. Hunter Coll., Harvard Grad. Sch. Edn.; scholar-in residence U. Chgo., Claremont Coll., UCLA; elected Ind. Sector Bd., 1990. Columnist (weekly) Where We Stand; contbr. articles to profl. and popular publs. Mem. labor com. Boy Scouts Am., 1969; bd. dirs. A. Philip Randolph Inst., 1965—, Internat. Rescue Com., 1973—, Com. for the Free World, 1980—; mem. internat. adv. com. for Def. of Soviet Polit. Prisoners, 1980—; mem. internat. adv. council Population Inst., 1976—; mem. Trilateral Commn.. Recipient Disting. Svc. medal Columbia U. Tchrs. Coll., Annual Labor Mgmt. award The Work Am. Inst. 1990. Mem. Nat. Acad. Edn., Nat. Bd. Profl. Teaching Standards. Democrat. Jewish. Avocations: reading, music, gardening, gourmet cooking. Office: Am Fedn Tchrs 555 New Jersey Ave NW Washington DC 20001-2029

SHANKER, MORRIS GERALD, lawyer, educator; b. Cleve., Aug. 23, 1926; s. Hyman and Anna (Kaplan) S.; m. Bernice Jacobs, Dec. 16, 1956; children: Chari, Jaymie Ann. BSEE, Purdue U., 1948; MBA, JD, U. Mich., 1952. Bar: Ohio 1952. Assoc. Grossman, Schlesinger & Carter, Cleve., 1952-61; prof. law Case Western Res. U., Cleve., 1961—, acting dean Law Sch., 1972—, John Home Kapp prof. law, 1975—; vis. prof. law U. Mich., 1964, U. Calif., Berkeley, 1966, Wayne State U., 1969, U. London, 1971, 87; cons., asst. reporter adv. com. on bankruptcy rules U.S. Supreme Ct., 1965-68, mem. com., 1969-77; mem. Nat. Bankruptcy Conf., 1966—; comml. and labor arbitrator; spl. master R.R. reorgn. procedures; lectr. comml. and bankruptcy law throughout U.S., Can. and U.K., 1961—. Contbr. articles to profl. jours. With USNR, 1944-46. Mem. ABA, Ohio Bar Assn., Cleve. Bar Assn., Am. Law Inst., Nat. Bankruptcy Conf., Order of Coif, Tau Beta Pi, Eta Kappa Nu. Home: 15712 Chadbourne Rd Cleveland OH 44120-3334 Office: Sch Law Case Western Res U Cleveland OH 44106

SHANKLIN, DOUGLAS RADFORD, physician; b. Camden, N.J., Nov. 25, 1930; s. John Ferguson and Muriel (Morgan) S.; student Wilson Tchrs. Coll., 1949; A.B. in Chemistry, Syracuse U., 1952; M.D., SUNY, Syracuse, 1955; m. Virginia McClure, Apr. 7, 1956; children—Elizabeth, Leigh, Lois Virginia, John Carter, Eleanor. Intern in pathology Duke U., 1955-56, resident, 1958; resident in pathology SUNY, Syracuse, 1958-60; practice medicine specializing in pathology, Gainesville, Fla., 1960-67, 78-83; mem. faculty U. Fla., 1960-67; prof. pathology, ob-gyn U. Chgo., 1967-78; pathologist-in-chief Chgo. Lying-In Hosp., 1967-78; prof. dept. pathology U. Tenn.-Memphis, 1983—, prof. obstetrics, 1986—, vice chmn. dept. pathology, 1983-90; vis. prof. U. Okla., 1967, Duke U., Mich. State U., 1969, Leeds U., Dundee U., Karolinska, 1974, Leeds U., 1978, 85, Emory U., 1980, London U., Edinburgh U., 1981, 85, U. Brit. Coll., 1987; jr. investigator Marine Biol. Lab., Woods Hole, Mass., 1951-54, sr. investigator 1966—, mem. corp., 1970—; parliamentarian, 1990-93; mem. Marine Resources Adv. Com., 1988-90, mem. election com., 1994-95; chmn. nat. adv. com. W-I-C evaluation U.S. Dept. Agr., 1979-86; lectr. Coll. Law U. Fla., 1963-67, 77-83; cons. Pan Am. Health Orgn., 1973-89; sr. cons. Santa Fe Found., 1976-79, exec. dir., 1979-83; course dir. Center Continuing Edn. U. Chgo., 1980-82. Trustee Coll. Light Opera Co., Falmouth, Mass., 1970—, Hippodrome Theatre, Gainesville, 1973-83, Opera Memphis, 1989-92. With M.C., USNR, 1956-58. Recipient Best Basic Sci. Teaching award U. Fla., 1967; named freeman citizen of Glasgow, 1981. Fellow Royal Soc. Medicine (London); mem. AAAS, Am. Soc. Exptl. Pathology, Am. Soc. Molecular Marine Biology and Biotech., Soc. Pediat. Rsch., Internat. Acad. Pathologists, So. Soc. Pediatric Research, So. Med. Assn., N.Y. Acad. Scis., Am. Coll. Ob-Gyn, Physicians Social Responsibility, Internat. Physicians for Prevention Nuclear War, Coll. Physicians and Surgeons Costa Rica, Pediatric Pathology Club (sec.-treas. 1970-75, pres. 1981-82), Phi Beta Kappa, Sigma Xi. Author: Syllabus for Study of Gynecologic-Obstetric-Pediatric Disease, 1961, Diseases of Woman, Pregnancy, Child, 1964, Maternal Nutrition and Child Health, 1979, 2nd edit., 1995, Tumors of Placenta and Umbilical Cord, 1990; editor: Interscience Devel. Disorders, 1971-80; assoc. editor Jour. Reproductive Medicine, 1968-70, 79-85, editor in chief, 1970-75;

contbr. articles to profl. jours. Home: 1238 NW 18th Ter Gainesville FL 32605-5370 Office: 134 Grove Park Cir Memphis TN 38117-3115

SHANKLIN, RICHARD VAIR, III, mechanical engineer; b. Bklyn., Feb. 12, 1937; s. Richard Vair and Sue Hall (Morfit) S.; m. Margaret Krogstad Courtney, July 3, 1981; children by previous marriage: Carolyn Dennett Shanklin Payne, Anne Landon Scott Weaver. B.S.M.E., Duke U., 1959; M.S., U. Tenn., 1965, Ph.D., 1971. Engring. asst. Phillips Petroleum Co. Tex., 1959-60; assoc. engr. Boeing Co., Seattle, 1960-62; design engr. Aro Inc., Arnold Air Force Sta., Tenn., 1962-64; chief engr. J.B. Dicks & Assos., Inc., Tullahoma, Tenn., 1967-70; assoc. prof. mech. engring. technology Nashville State Tech. Inst., 1971-72; asst. prof. U. Tenn., Tullahoma, 1972-73; sr. scientist Systems Research Labs., Dayton, Ohio, 1973-75; asst. dir. MHD div. ERDA, Washington, 1975-77; sr. staff engr. Energy Systems Group, TRW Inc., Morgantown, W.Va., 1977-78; dir. MHD div. Dept. Energy, Washington, 1978-79; mgr. combustion programs Energy Systems Group, TRW, Inc., Redondo Beach, Calif., 1979-80; asst. ops. mgr. for process devel. Energy Systems Group, TRW, Inc., McLean, Va., 1980-82; project officer U.S. Synthetic Fuels Corp., Washington, 1982-86; cons. to industry, 1986-89; dir. planning and facility transition BDM Fed., Inc., McLean, Va., 1989—. Author papers and reports in field. Recipient Spl. Achievement awards ERDA, 1976, 77, Cosmos Club Washington, Sigma Xi. Episcopalian. Home: 6206 Hardy Dr Mc Lean VA 22101-3113

SHANKS, DAVID, publishing executive. Pres. Berkley Pub. Co., N.Y.C. Office: Berkley Pub Group 200 Madison Ave New York NY 10016

SHANKS, EUGENE B., JR., banker. BA, Vanderbilt U., 1969; MA, PhD, Stanford U., 1972. V.p. Bankers Trust Co., N.Y.C., 1977-82, sr. v.p., 1992—, exec. v.p., 1984-86, mng. dir., 1986-92, exec. v.p., 1987-91, pres., dir., 1992—. Office: Bankers Trust NY Corp 280 Park Ave New York NY 10017-1216

SHANKS, GERALD ROBERT, insurance company executive; b. Knox, Ind., Dec. 12, 1942; s. Robert William and Beatrice (Lane) S.; m. Carol Sue Turner, Aug. 14, 1965. AB, Ind. U., 1965. CPCU. Claims adjuster Fireman's Fund, Indpls., 1965-70; claims supr. Fireman's Fund, Chgo., 1970-76; claims mgr. Fireman's Fund, Pitts., 1977-79; in human resources CNA, Chgo., 1980-82; recruiter Don Howard Pers., Chgo., 1982-83; asst. claims mgr. Fireman's Fund, Boston, 1983-84; claims mgr. Fireman's Fund, Detroit, 1984-85; v.p. claims, bd. dirs. Interstate Nat. Corp. subs. Fireman's Fund, Chgo., 1985-92, sr. v.p., 1992—; bd. dirs. Geo. F. Brown and Sons, Chgo., Interstate Nat. Corp., Chgo. Ins. Co. and Interstate Indemnity Co., Interstate Fire and Casualty Co. Mem. Fedn. Ins. and Corp. Coun., Excess & Surplus Lines Assn., Soc. CPCU's, Union League Club of Chgo., Exec. Club of Chgo., Innsbrook Country Club (Merrillville, Ind.), Ky. Col. Republican. Methodist. Avocations: golf, horses. Home: 1919 W 64th Pl Merrillville IN 46410 Office: Interstate Nat Corp 55 E Monroe Chicago IL 60603

SHANKS, HERSHEL, editor, writer; b. Sharon, Pa., Mar. 8, 1930; s. Martin and Mildred (Freedman) S.; m. Judith Alexander Weil, Feb. 20, 1966; children: Elizabeth Jean, Julia Emily. B.A., Haverford (Pa.) Coll., 1952; M.A., Columbia, 1953; LL.B., Harvard, 1956. Bar: D.C. 1956. Trial atty. Dept. Justice, 1956-59; pvt. practice Washington, 1959-88; ptnr. Glassie Pewett, Beebe & Shanks, 1984-88; editor Bibl. Archaeology Rev., Washington, 1975—; pres. Bibl. Archaeology Soc., 1974—, Jewish Ednl. Ventures Inc., 1987—. Author: The Art and Craft of Judging, 1968, The City of David, 1973, Judaism in Stone, 1979; also articles; co-editor: Recent Archaeology in the Land of Israel, 1984; editor Ancient Israel, A Short History, 1988, Christianity and Rabbinic Judaism, 1992, Understanding the Dead Sea Scrolls, 1992, Jerusalem—An Archaeological Biography, 1995, Bible Rev., 1985—; editor Moment mag., 1987—. Mem. ABA, D.C. Bar Assn., Am. Schs. Oriental Rsch., Nat. Press Club, Phi Beta Kappa. Home: 5208 38th St NW Washington DC 20015-1812 Office: Bibl Archaeology Soc Ste 300 4710 41st NW Washington DC 20016 *I try to take time to identify what is important in my life, to focus on that and ignore the rest when it conflicts. It takes conscious effort not to dissipate energy on activities and attitudes that don't matter in the big picture of my priorities. Free to concentrate on what I value most, I try to accomplish something each day in a regular, habitual way.*

SHANKS, ROBERT BRUCE, lawyer; b. Gallipolis, Ohio, Jan. 2, 1950; s. William and Kathryn (Morrow) S.; m. Margaret Elizabeth McCloskey, Sept. 15, 1984; children: Bruce, Brennan, Grace. AB, Brown U., 1972; JD, U. Va., 1975. Bar: D.C. 1977, U.S. Dist. Ct. D.C. 1977, U.S. Ct. Appeals (D.C. cir.) 1977, U.S. Supreme Ct. 1981. Law clk. to hon. judge Edward A. Tamm U.S. Ct. Appeals (D.C. cir.), 1975-76; law clk. to assoc. justice William J. Brennan Jr. U.S. Supreme Ct., 1976-77; assoc. Steptoe and Johnson, Washington, 1977-78, Latham and Watkins, Washington, 1978-81; dep. asst. atty. gen. Dept. Justice, Washington, 1981-84; v.p., gen. counsel Overseas Pvt. Investment Corp., 1984-87; ptnr. Sidley & Austin, Washington, 1987-91, Latham & Watkins, Washington, 1991—; adj. prof. Sch. Law Georgetown U., Washington, 1982-85. Contbr. articles to profl. jours. Mem. ABA (chmn. com.), D.C. Bar Assn. (steering com. 1986-87), Washington Fgn. Law Soc. (bd. govs.) Internat. Law Inst. (bd. dirs.), Order of Coif, Phi Beta Kappa. Avocations: skiing, running, sailing. Office: Latham & Watkins 10th & Penn Ave NW Washington DC 20008

SHANLEY, ELLEN, costume curator; b. Astoria, N.Y., Aug. 27, 1958; d. Edward and Anne (Doheny) S. A in Fashion Design, FIT, 1978; BA, Empire State Coll. Freelance designer and stylist N.Y.C., 1980-81; curatorial asst. Mus. at FIT, N.Y.C., 1981-93, curator of costumes, 1993—; part-time freelance exhbn. and design stylist, N.Y.C., Europe and Japan. Vol. N.Y. Cares, N.Y.C., 1992-94. Mem. Costume Soc. Am., The Fashion Group. Muslim. Office: Mus at FIT Rm E-201 227 W 27th St New York NY 10001-5992

SHANLEY, JOHN PATRICK, screenwriter; b. N.Y., Oct. 13, 1950; m. Jayne Haynes (div.). Playwright: Ketchup, 1980, Rockaway, 1982, Welcome to the Moon, 1982, Danny and the Deep Blue Sea, 1984, Savage in Limbo, 1985, the dreamer examines his pillow: A Heterosexual Homily, 1985, Women of Manhattan, 1986, All for Charity, 1987, Italian-American Reconciliation, 1988, The Big Funk, 1990, Beggars in the House of Plenty, 1991, four dogs and a bone, 1993; screenwriter: Moonstruck, 1987 (Academy award best original screenplay 1987, Writers Guild of Am. award 1987), Five Corners, 1988 (Special Jury prize Barcelona Film Festival 1989), The January Man, 1989, Alive, 1993, We're Back!: A Dinosaur's Story, 1993; screenwriter, dir.: Joe Versus the Volcano, 1990; appeared in film Crossing Delancey, 1988. Office: care William Morris Agy 151 S El Camino Dr Beverly Hills CA 90212-2775*

SHANLEY, WILLIAM C., III, sugar company executive; b. N.Y.C., Aug. 22, 1925; s. William Carlton and Molly (Kelly) S.; m. Grace Ross, May 1, 1954; children: Sharon, William, Thomas, Lynn, Timothy, Patrick. BSEE, Cornell U., 1946; MSChemE, Columbia U., 1949. Chem. engr., asst. supt. Amstar Sugar Corp., Bklyn., 1949-53; asst. to refinery mgr. Amstar Sugar Corp., Bklyn. and Phila., 1954-57; mgr. ind. sales and sales mgr. Amstar Sugar Corp., N.Y.C. and Balt., 1957-61; dir. sales Amstar Sugar Corp., Balt. and N.Y.C., 1961-68; gen. sales mgr. Amstar Sugar Corp., N.Y.C., 1968-69, asst. v.p., v.p. sugar sales div., 1969-76, exec. v.p., 1976-79, pres., 1979-88, pres., chief exec. officer, 1989—; Chmn. bd. dirs. Mineral Mining Corp., Kershaw, S.C., The Sugar Assn.; bd. dirs. East NY Savs. Bank, N.Y.C., First Empire State Corp. Buffalo. Lt. (j.g.) USNR, 1943-46. Mem. Sales Exec. Club N.Y., Sugar Club N.Y., Blooming Grove Hunting and Fishing Club, Woodway Country Club. Avocations: tennis, golf, hunting, fishing, squash. Office: Amstar Sugar Corp 1251 Ave Of The Americas New York NY 10020-1104

SHANMAN, JAMES ALAN, lawyer; b. Cin., Aug. 1, 1942; s. Jerome D. and Mildred Louise (Bloch) S.; m. Marilyn Louise Glassman, June 11, 1972; 1 child, Ellen Joan. BS, U. Pa., 1963; JD, Yale U., 1966. Bar: N.Y. 1967, U.S. Ct. Mil. Appeals 1971, U.S. Supreme Ct. 1971, U.S. Ct. Appeals (2d cir.) 1972, U.S. Dist. Ct. (so. and ea. dists.) N.Y. 1972, U.S. Ct. Internat.

Trade 1976, U.S. Ct. Appeals (fed. cir.) 1987, U.S. Dist. Ct. (ea. dist.) Mich. 1989. Assoc. Cahill Gordon & Reindel, N.Y.C., 1971-74, Freeman, Meade, Wasserman, Sharfman & Schneider, N.Y.C., 1974-76; mem. Sharfman, Shanman, Poret & Siviglia, P.C., N.Y.C., 1976-95; ptnr. Camhy Karlinsky & Stein LLP, N.Y.C., 1995—; speaker on reins. law topics. Capt. USAF, 1966-71. Mem. ABA, N.Y. State Bar Assn., Assn. of Bar of City of N.Y. (com. ins. law 1985-88, 90-92, com. profl. liability ins. 1988-92, com. on assn. ins. plans 1989—), Am. Arbitration Assn. (comml. panel arbitrators). Office: Camhy Karlinsky & Stein 1740 Broadway New York NY 10019-4315

SHANNAHAN, JOHN HENRY KELLY, energy consultant; b. Sparrows Point, Md., Nov. 1, 1913; s. John Henry Kelly and Beulah Williams (Day) S.; m. Mary Reynolds Kline, Apr. 22, 1939; children: John H.K., James R., Jennifer K. (Mrs. Bernard R. Koerner, Jr.). AB, Princeton U., 1934; postgrad., U. Mich., 1954. Sr. elec. program Mass. Inst. Tech., 1959; Comml. mgr. Ind.-Mich. Electric Co., 1955-59; asst. v.p. Am. Electric Power Service Corp., 1959-61; asst. to pres. Kans. Power & Light Co., 1961-63; v.p., exec. dir. Electric Heating Assn., 1964-72; pres. Electric Energy Assn., 1972-75; sr. v.p. Edison Electric Inst., N.Y.C., 1975—; cons. energy matters, 1975-80. Trustee Suttons Bay Congl. Ch. Maj. F.A., AUS, 1942-45, ETO. Decorated Bronze Star with oak leaf cluster; recipient Trend Maker award Elec. Info. Publs. Inc., 1967. Presbyterian (elder). Club: Marines Memorial (San Francisco), Suttons Bay Rotary. Home: 2393 N Lake Leelanau Dr Lake Leelanau MI 49653-9707

SHANNAHAN, WILLIAM PAUL, lawyer; b. Detroit, Mich., Nov. 21, 1934; s. William and Jean (Boyle) S.; m. Saracia L. Price, Sept. 24, 1983; children: MeglynAnne, Michael-Padraic. AB, U. Detroit, 1956; JD, Georgetown U., 1958. Bar: D.C. 1958, Mich. 1958, Calif. 1962. Ptnr. Higgs, Fletcher & Mack, La Jolla, Calif., 1967-81, Aylward, Kintz, et al.2, La Jolla, Calif., 1981-87, pvt. practice, La Jolla, Calif., 1987—. with U.S. Army, 1959-60. Democrat. Roman Catholic. Office: 1200 Prospect St Ste 425 La Jolla CA 92037-3608

SHANNON, ALBERT JOSEPH, educator; b. Pitts., Apr. 12, 1949; s. William Park and Dorothea B. (Brown) S.; m. Mary Jean Boblick, May 22, 1971; children: Erica Lynne, Sean Paul. BA summa cum laude, Marquette U., 1971; MEd, Boston U., 1972; PhD, Marquette U., 1978; grad. mgmt. devel. program Harvard U., 1989. Tchr. reading North Div. High Sch., Milw., 1972-76; reading cons. sch. dists. Wis., 1976-78; mem. faculty St. Mary's Coll., Notre Dame, Ind., 1978-83, asst. prof. dept. edn., 1978-83; assoc. prof. Sch. Edn., Rider U., Lawrenceville, N.J., 1983-86; chmn. dept. edn., dir. grad. edn. St. Joseph's U., Phila., 1986-88, chmn., grad. dir. edn. and health svcs., 1988-92; v.p. acad. affairs St. Joseph's Coll., Rensellaer, 1992-93, pres. 1993—; cons. on reading edn., 1978—; cons. computer edn., N.J. Contbr. articles to profl. jours. Recipient Outstanding Secondary Teaching award, 1975; Nat. Endowment for Humanities fellow Middlebury Coll., 1987-88, Am. Coun. on Edn. fellow U. Pa., 1990-91; named Sagamore of the Wabash, 1995. Mem. ACE, Ind. Coll. Found. (dir.), Phi Beta Kappa, Phi Delta Kappa. Roman Catholic. Home: 215 E Thompson St Rensselaer IN 47978-3133 Office: St Joseph's Coll Box 869 Rensselaer IN 47978

SHANNON, CLAUDE ELWOOD, mathematician, educator; b. Gaylord, Mich., Apr. 30, 1916; s. Claude Elwood and Mabel Catherine (Wolf) S.; m. Mary Elizabeth Moore, Mar. 27, 1949; children: Robert James, Andrew Moore, Margarita Catherine. BS, U. Mich., 1936, DSc, 1961; MS, PhD in Math., MIT, 1940; MS (hon.), Yale U., 1954; DSc, Princeton U., 1962, U. Edinburgh, Scotland, 1964, U. Pitts., 1964, Northwestern U., Evanston, Ill., 1970, Oxford (Eng.) U., 1978, East Anglia U., 1982, Carnegie Mellon U., 1984, Tufts U., 1987; DSc (hon.), U. Pa., 1991. Staff Carnegie Instn., Washington, 1939, Bolles fellow, 1939-40; Nat. Research fellow Princeton U., N.J., 1940; cons. Nat. Def. Research Com., 1941; research mathematician Bell Telephone Labs., 1941-72; vis. prof. elec. communications MIT, 1956, prof. communications scis. and math., 1957—, Donner prof. sci., 1958-78, prof. emeritus, 1978—; vis. fellow All Souls Coll., Oxford, 1978; Vanuxem lectr. Princeton U., 1958; Steinmetz lectr., Schenectady, 1962; Gibbs lectr. Am. Math. Soc., 1965; Shannon lectr. IEEE, 1973; Chichele Lectr. Oxford U., 1978. Author: Mathematical Theory on Communication, 1949; editor: (with J. McCarthy) Automata Studies, 1956, Collected Papers, 1993; contbr. papers on math. subjects to profl. jours. Recipient AIEE award, 1940, Morris Liebmann Meml. award, 1949, Stuart Ballantine medal Franklin Inst. Phila., 1955, Research Corp. award, 1956, Mervin J. Kelly award AIEE, 1962, medal of honor IEEE, 1966, Harvey prize Am. Soc. for Technion, 1972, Eduard Rhein prize, 1991; medal of honor Rice U., 1962, Nat. Medal Sci., 1966, Golden Plate award, 1967, Jacquard award, 1978, Harold Pender award, 1978, John Fritz award, 1983, Audio Engring. Soc. Gold medal, 1985, Kyoto prize Basic Sci., 1985, Marquis Achievement award, 1985, Lord Found. award, 1989; fellow Ctr. Advanced Study Behavioral Scis., Stanford, Calif., 1957-58. Fellow IEEE; mem. Am. Acad. Arts. and Scis., Nat. Acad. Scis., Leopoldina Acad.; Royal Netherlands Acad. Arts & Scis., Nat. Acad. Engring., Am. Philos. Soc., Royal Irish Acad., Royal Soc. of London, Tau Beta Pi, Sigma Xi, Phi Kappa Phi. Home: 5 Cambridge St Winchester MA 01890-3703

SHANNON, DAVID THOMAS, academic administrator; b. Richmond, Va., Sept. 26, 1933; s. Charlie Lee and Phyllis (Gary) S.; m. Shannon P. Averett, June 15, 1957; children—Vernitia Averett, Davine Belinda S. Sparks, David Thomas Jr. B.A., VA. Union U., 1954, B.D., 1957; S.T.M., Oberlin Grad. Sch. Theology, 1959; D. Min., Vanderbilt U., 1974; D.D. (hon.), U. Richmond, 1983; Ph.D., U. Pitts., 1975; LHD (hon.), Interdenominational Theol. Ctr., 1992; LLD (hon.), Tuskegee U., 1993. Pastor Fair Oaks (Va.) Bapt. Ch., 1954-57; student pastor Antioch Bapt. Ch., Cleve., 1957-59; grad. asst. Oberlin (Ohio) Grad. Sch. Theology, 1958-59; univ. pastor Va. Union U., Richmond, 1960-61, lectr. humanities and history, 1959-69; pastor Ebenezer Bapt. Ch., Richmond, 1960-69; eastern dir. Christian Higher Edn. Services Am. Bapt. Bd. Edn. and Publ., Valley Forge, Pa., 1969-71; vis. prof. St. Mary's Sem. Urban Tng. Program, Cleve., 1969-72; assoc. prof. religion and dir. minority studies Bucknell U., Lewisburg, Pa., 1971-72; dean faculty Pitts. Theol. Sem., 1972-79; Bibl. scholar Hartford (Conn.) Sem. Found., 1979; pres. Va. Union U., Richmond, 1979-85; vice pres. for acad. services, dean faculty Interdenominational Theol. Ctr., Atlanta, 1985-91; pres. Andover Newton Theol. Sch., Newton Centre, Mass., 1991-94, Allen U, Columbia, S.C., 1994—; co-chmn. internat. dialogue Secretariat of Roman Catholic Ch. Bapt., Rome and Washington, 1985-90; co-chmn. task force on witnessing apostolic faith World Council of Chs., Geneva, 1989—; mem. faith and order commn. Nat. Council of Chs., N.Y.C., 1984; mem. commn. on doctrine and inter-ch. cooperation Bapt. World Alliance, Washington, 1980—; active Faith and Order Commn. World Coun. Chs. Author: Studies in the Life and Works of Paul, 1961, Old Testament Experience of Faith, 1977; co-editor: (with G. Wilmore) Black Witness to the Apostolic Faith, 1985; contbr. articles to profl. jours., chpts. to books. Life mem. NAACP, N.Y., 1950. Recipient Nat. Clergy award Opportunities Industrialization Ctrs. Am., 1993; named Man of Yr. NCCJ, 1981. Mem. Am. Assn. Higher Edn., Am. Acad. Religion, Soc. for Study of Black Religion, Soc. Bibl. Lit., Newton Rotary Club, Alpha Kappa Mu, Phi Beta Sigma, Theta Phi. Home: 3072 Pivilion Towers Circle Columbia SC 29201 Office: Allen U 1530 Harden St Columbia SC 29204

SHANNON, DONALD HAWKINS, retired newspaperman; b. Auburn, Wash., Feb. 1, 1923; s. Ernest Victor and Fern (McConville) S.; m. Sally van Deurs, June 13, 1952; children—John McConville, Susanna Shepard. B.A., Stanford, 1944; postgrad., Law Sch. 1946-47. Reporter Brazil Herald, Rio de Janeiro, 1947-48, U.P.I., London, Eng., 1949-51, Western Reporters, Washington, 1951-53; mem. staff Los Angeles Times, 1954-92; bur. chief Los Angeles Times, Paris, France, 1962-65, Africa, 1965-66, Tokyo, Japan, 1966-71; bur. chief UN, N.Y.C., 1971-75, UN (Washington bur.), 1975-92. Served with AUS, 1944-46, PTO. Mem. Phi Gamma Delta. Clubs: Federal City (Washington), City Tavern (Washington); Overseas Press (N.Y.C.); Foreign Correspondents (Tokyo). Address: 1068 30th St NW Washington DC 20007

SHANNON, EDFRED L., JR., gas and oil drilling company executive; b. 1926; (married). B.S., U. Calif., Berkeley, 1951. Petroleum engr. Union Oil Co. of Calif., 1951-53; with Santa Fe Internat. Corp., Alhambra, 1953—, v.p., 1960-63, chmn., from 1963, chief exec. officer. Pres. from 1986, also dir. Office: Santa Fe Internat Corp Box 4000 1000 S Fremont Ave Alhambra CA 91802

SHANNON, EDGAR FINLEY, JR., English language educator; b. Lexington, Va., June 4, 1918; s. Edgar Finley and Eleanor (Duncan) S.; m. Eleanor H. Bosworth, Feb. 11, 1956; children—Eleanor, Elizabeth, Lois, Susan, Virginia. A.B., Washington and Lee U., 1939, Litt.D., 1959; A.M., Duke U., 1941, Harvard U., 1947; Rhodes scholar, Merton Coll., Oxford, 1947-50; D.Phil., Oxford U., 1949; LL.D., Rhodes Coll., 1960, Duke U., 1964, Hampden-Sydney Coll., 1971; H.H.D., Wake Forest U., 1964; D.H.L., Thomas Jefferson U., Phila., 1967, U. Hartford, 1981, Ohio State U., 1981; Litt.D., Centre Coll., 1968, Coll. William and Mary, 1973; L.H.D., Bridgewater Coll., 1970. Assoc. prof. naval. sci. and tactics Harvard U., 1946, instr. English, 1950-52, asst. prof. English, 1952-56; assoc. prof. English U. Va., Charlottesville, 1956-59; prof. English U. Va., 1959-74, pres., 1959-74, pres. emeritus, 1988—, Commonwealth prof. English, 1974-86, Linden Kent Meml. prof. English, 1986-88, prof. emeritus, 1988—; chmn. dept. English, 1980-81; mem. state and dist. selection coms. Rhodes scholars; pres. Council So. Univs., 1962-64, 71-72; pres. State Univs. Assn., 1963-64; exec. com. Nat. Assn. State Univs. and Land-Grant Colls., 1964-67, chmn. exec. com., 1966-67, pres., 1965-66; mem. So. Regional Edn. Bd., 1963-71; bd. govs. Nat. Commn. on Accrediting, 1961-67; mem. U.S. Nat. Commn. for UNESCO, 1966-67, Pres.'s Commn. on CIA Activities within U.S., 1975. Author: Tennyson and the Reviewers, 1952; editor: (with Cecil Y. Lang) The Letters of Alfred, Lord Tennyson, vol.I, 1981, vol. II, 1987, vol. III, 1990; contbr. articles to various jours. Bd. visitors U.S. Naval Acad., 1962-64, USAF Acad., 1965-67; bd. cons. Nat. War Coll., 1968-71; bd. dirs. Am. Council on Edn., 1967-70, vice chmn., 1971-72; trustee Thomas Jefferson Meml. Found., 1973-88, hon. trustee, 1988—, pres., 1980-83, chmn. 1987-88; trustee Washington and Lee U., 1973-85, Darlington Sch., 1966-76, Mariners Mus., 1966-75, Colonial Williamsburg Found., 1975-88; chmn. Va. Found. Humanities and Pub. Policy, 1973-79; v.p. Oceanic Edn. Found., 1968-83; bd. adminstrs. Va. Inst. Marine Sci., 1963-71; hon. v.p. Tennyson Soc., 1960—; mem. council White Burkett Miller Center for Pub. Affairs, 1975—; mem. Gov. Va.'s Task Force on Sci. and Tech., 1982-83. Served from midshipman to lt. comdr. USNR, 1941-46; capt. Res. ret. Decorated Bronze Star, Meritorious Service medal; Distinguished Eagle Scout, 1973; named Va. Cultural Laureate, 1987; recipient Distinguished Service award Va. State C. of C., 1969, Medallion of Honor Virginians of Md., 1964; Thomas Jefferson award U. Va., 1965; Algernon Sydney Sullivan award Washington and Lee U., 1939; Algernon Sydney Sullivan award U. Va., 1975; Jackson Davis award Va. chpt. AAUP, 1977, Disting. Alumnus award Darlington Sch., 1986; Guggenheim fellow, 1953-54; Fulbright research fellow Eng., 1953-54. Mem. MLA, Assn. Va. Colls. (pres. 1969-70), Raven Soc., Signet Soc., Jefferson Soc., Soc. Cin., Am. Soc. Order of St. John of Jerusalem, Phi Beta Kappa (senator 1967-85, vis. scholar 1976-77, v.p. 1976-79, pres. 1979-82, chmn. Coun. Nominating Com. 1988-94), Omicron Delta Kappa (Laurel Crowned Cir. award 1980), Phi Eta Sigma, Beta Theta Pi, Century Assn. Club, University Club (N.Y.C.). Presbyterian. Home: 250 Pantops Mountain Rd # 3 Charlottesville VA 22901-8600

SHANNON, GEORGE WARD, JR., museum director, anthropologist, archaeologist; b. Landstuhl, Germany, Sept. 25, 1954; s. George Ward Sr. and Frances Ada (Terrell) S.; m. Faye Joy Grimsby; children: Benjamin (dec.), George Ward III. BA in Anthropology, U. Alaska, 1976; MA in Anthropology, Fla. Atlantic U., 1979; PhD in Anthropology, Mich. State U., 1987. Exec. dir. Northlake Mus. & Nature Ctr., Mandeville, La., 1988-89; curator La. State Mus., New Orleans, 1988-89; br. dir. La. State Mus., Shreveport, 1989-91; exec. dir., CAO La. State Exhibit Mus., Shreveport, 1991—. Mem. Rotary. Presbyterian. Avocations: hunting, fishing. Office: La State Exhibit Mus PO Box 38356 3015 Greenwood Rd Shreveport LA 71139

SHANNON, IRIS REED, nursing educator; b. Chgo.; d. Ira Paul and Iola Sophia (Williams) S.; m. Robert Alwood Shannon, Aug. 21, 1953. BS in Nursing, Fisk U.-Meharry Med. Coll., 1948; MA, U. Chgo., 1954; PhD, U. Ill., Chgo., 1987; D in Pub. Svc. (hon.), Elmhurst Coll., 1993. Staff nurse Chgo. Bd. Health, 1948-50; instr. pub. health nursing Meharry Med. Coll., Nashville, 1951-56; tchr.-nurse, health coordinator child devel. Head Start, Chgo. Bd. Edn., 1957-66; dir. community nursing Mile Sq. Neighborhood Health Center, Presbyn.-St. Luke's Hosp., Chgo., 1966-69; co-dir. nurse assoc. programs Rush Presbyn.-St. Luke's Hosp., Chgo., 1971-76; chairperson community nursing Rush U., Chgo., 1972-77; acting chairperson Rush U., 1988-90; asst. prof. pub. health nursing U. Ill., 1971-74; assoc. prof. community nursing Rush U., 1974—; adj. faculty Sch. Public Health, U. N.C., 1977-85; mem. profl. adv. bd. Vis. Nurse Assn. Chgo., 1973-75; cons. Video Nursing, Inc.; mem. profl. adv. com. Mile Sq. Home Health Unit, Chgo., 1975-77; mem. Nat. Adv. Council on Nurse Tng., HEW, 1978-81; Mem. Nat. Task Force on Credentialing in Nursing, 1979-82; mem. Chgo. regional com. Ill. White House Conf. on Children, 1979-80. Recipient award of merit Ill. Public Health Assn., 1979, Outstanding Achievement award YWCA of Met. Chgo., 1988, Disting. Svc. award Chgo. chpt. Meharry Alumni, 1989, Lowenberg Chair of Excellence in nursing Memphis State U., 1993; Rockefeller fellow, 1953-54. Fellow Am. Pub. Health Assn. (chmn. pub. health nursing sect. 1977-79, governing coun. 1980-82, exec. bd. 1985-87, pres. 1988-89), Royal Soc. Health (hon. 1989), Am. Acad. Nursing; mem. Am. Nurses Assn., Inst. Medicine of Nat. Acad. Scis., Delta Sigma Theta, Sigma Theta Tau.

SHANNON, JAMES PATRICK, foundation consultant, retired food company executive; b. South St. Paul, Minn., Feb. 16, 1921; s. Patrick Joseph and Mary Alice (McAuliffe) S.; m. Ruth Church Wilkinson, Aug. 2, 1969. B.A. in Classics, Coll. St. Thomas, St. Paul, 1941; M.A. in English, U. Minn., 1951; Ph.D., Yale U., 1955; J.D., U. N.Mex., 1973; LL.D., U. Notre Dame, 1964, Macalester Coll., 1964, Lora Coll., 1964, DePaul U., 1965, St. Mary's Coll., 1965, Carleton Coll., 1965, Creighton U., 1966, Northland Coll., Ashland, Wis., 1979, William Mitchell Coll. Law, 1980; Litt.D., Seton Hall, 1965, Coe Coll., Cedar Rapids, Iowa, 1966, U. Minn., 1966; J.U.D., Lawrence U., 1969. Ordained priest Roman Catholic Ch., 1946; asst. prof. history Coll. St. Thomas, 1954-56, pres., 1956-66; aux. bishop Archdiocese of St. Paul, 1965-68; pastor St. Helna Parish, Mpls., 1966-68; tutor Greek St. John's Coll., Santa Fe, 1969-70; v.p. St. John's Coll., 1969-70; mem. firm Sutin, Thayer & Browne, Albuquerque, Santa Fe, 1973-74; exec. dir. Mpls. Found., 1974-78; v.p. Gen. Mills, Inc., 1980-88; columnist, writer, found. cons., 1970-79, 88—; dir. Midwest Importers, Inc. Author: Catholic Colonization on the Western Frontier, 1957. Bd. dirs. James H. Hill Libr., St. Paul, 1985-94, Inst. Ecumenical and Cultural Rsch., Collegeville, Minn., 1985-93, chmn., 1990—; bd. dirs. Ind. Sector, D.C., 1988-94, N.Mex. Cmty. Found., 1991—; Gen. Svc. Found., 1991-94; coun. Conf. Bd., 1982-88; chmn. Rhodes Scholarship Selection Com. for Upper Midwest Selection Com., 1976-86; chmn. exec. found., Washington, 1984-85; vice chmn. Found. Ctr., N.Y.C.; sr. cons. Coun. on Founds. Mem. D.C. Bar Assn., N.Mex. Bar Assn., Minn. Bar Assn., Mpls. Club (bd. govs. 1989—), pres. 1994-95). Democrat. Address: PO Box 112 Wayzata MN 55391-0112

SHANNON, JOHN SANFORD, railway executive, lawyer; b. Tampa, Fla., Feb. 8, 1931; s. George Thomas and Ruth Evangeline (Garrett) S.; m. Elizabeth Howe, Sept. 22, 1962; children: Scott Howe, Elizabeth Garrett, Sandra Denison. AB, Roanoke Coll., 1952; JD, U. Va., 1955. Bar: Va. 1955. Assoc. Hunton Williams Gay Powell & Gibson, Richmond, Va., 1955-56; solicitor Norfolk & Western Ry., Roanoke, Va., 1956-60, asst. gen. solicitor, 1960-64, gen. atty., 1964-68, gen. solicitor, 1965-68, gen. counsel, 1968-69, v.p. law, 1969-80, v.p. law, 1980-82; exec. v.p. law Norfolk (Va.) So. Corp., 1982—; bd. dirs. Norfolk So. Ry. Co., Pocahontas Land Corp., Va. Holding Corp.; Norfolk and Western Ry. Co. Editor-in-chief: Va. Law Rev, 1954-55. Chancellor Episcopal Diocese Southwestern Va., 1974-82; pres. bd. trustees North Cross Sch., Roanoke, 1973-82; trustee, past chmn. exec. com. Roanoke Coll., Salem, Va.; bd. dirs. Legal Aid Soc., Roanoke Valley, 1969-80, pres., 1970-79; trustee Chrysler Mus., Norfolk, 1982-94, Norfolk Acad., 1987—. Mem. ABA, Va. Bar Assn., Norfolk and Portsmouth Bar Assn., Shenandoah Club, Roanoke Country Club, Norfolk Yacht and Country Club, Harbor Club, Met. Club (Washington), Order of Coif, Sigma Xi, Omicron Delta Kappa, Phi Delta Phi. Home: 7633 Argyle Ave Norfolk VA 23505-1701 Office: Norfolk So Corp 3 Commercial Pl Norfolk VA 23510-2191

SHANNON, LYLE WILLIAM, sociology educator; b. Storm Lake, Iowa, Sept. 19, 1920; s. Bert Book and Amy Irene (Sivits) S.; m. Magdaline W. Shannon, Feb. 27, 1943; children: Mary Shannon Will, Robert William, John

Thomas, Susan Michelle. BA, Cornell Coll., Mount Vernon, Iowa, 1942; MA, U. Wash., 1947, PhD, 1951. Acting instr. U. Wash., 1950-52; mem. faculty dept. sociology U. Wis., Madison, 1952-62; assoc. prof., 1958-62; prof. sociology U. Iowa, Iowa City, 1962—, chmn. dept. sociology and anthropology, 1962-70, dir. Iowa Urban Community Research Ctr., 1970—, prof. emeritus, 1991—; vis. prof. Portland State U., Wayne State U., U. Wyo., U. Colo. Author: Underdeveloped Areas, 1957, Minority Migrants in the Urban Community, 1973, Criminal Career Continuity: Its Social Context, 1988, Changing Patterns of Delinquency and Crime: A Longitudinal Study in Racine, 1991, Developing Areas, 1995, Socks and Cretin: Two Democats Helping Bill with the Presidency, 1995; editor: Social Ecology of the Community series, 1974-76. With USNR, 1942-46. Mem. AAAS, Am. Sociol. Assn., Midwest Sociol. Soc., Urban Affairs Assn., Population Assn. Am., Soc. Applied Anthropology, Am. Soc. Criminology, Phi Beta Kappa. Democrat. Lodge: Kiwanis. Home: River Heights Iowa City IA 52240 Office: U Iowa Iowa Urban Community Rsch Ctr 170W Seashore Hall Iowa City IA 52242-1401

SHANNON, MARGARET ANNE, lawyer; b. Detroit, July 6, 1945; d. Johannes Jacob and Vera Marie (Spade) Van De Graaf; m. Robert Selby Shannon, Feb. 4, 1967. Student Brown U., 1963-65; B.A. in History, Wayne State U., 1966, J.D., 1973. Bar: Mich. 1973. Housing aide City of Detroit, 1967-68; employment supr. Sinai Hosp., Detroit, 1968-69; assoc. gen. counsel regulatory affairs Blue Cross Blue Shield of Mich., Detroit, 1969-80; ptnr. Honigman Miller Schwartz and Cohn, Detroit, 1980—. Nat. Merit scholar, 1963-66. Mem. Detroit Bar Assn., Mich. State Bar (chmn. health care com. 1991, 92), Nat. Health Lawyers Assn., ABA (vice chmn. pub. regulation of ins. law com. 1981-82), U. Liggett Sch. Alumni (bd. govs.). Home: 825 Park Ln Grosse Pointe MI 48230-1852 Office: Honigman Miller Schwartz and Cohn 2290 First National Bldg Detroit MI 48226

SHANNON, MARGARET T., nursing administrator, educator; b. New Haven, June 23, 1939; d. Michael Joseph and Ellen (McNamara) S. MS in Chemistry, St. Louis U., 1967; BSN, Northwestern State U. of La., Nachitoches, 1978; MN, La. State U., New Orleans, 1981; PhD., U. New Orleans, 1987. Staff nurse Touro Infirmary, New Orleans; instr. nursing Touro Infirmary Sch. Nursing, New Orleans; asst. prof. nursing La. State U. Med. Ctr., New Orleans; dean divsn. nursing Our Lady of Holy Cross Coll., New Orleans. Co-author: (with B.A. Wilson) Giovani & Hayes Drugs and Nursing Implications, 8th edit., 1995, Giovani & Hayes Nurses' Drug Guide, 1995. Mem. ANA, NLN, La. League for Nursing, La. State Nurses Assn., Sigma Theta Tau, Phi Kappa Phi, Phi Delta Kappa.

SHANNON, MICHAEL EDWARD, specialty chemical company executive; b. Evanston, Ill., Nov. 21, 1936; s. Edward Francis and Mildred Veronica (Oliver) S.; m. A. Laura McGrath, July 4, 1964; children: Claire Oliver Mary, Kathryn Ann Elizabeth. BA, U. Notre Dame, 1958; MBA, Stanford U., 1960. With Continental Oil Co., Houston, 1960-62; with Gulf Oil Corp., 1962-75, asst. treas., 1970-75; treas. Gulf Oil Co. U.S., Houston, 1970-72, Gulf Oil Co.-Ea. Hemisphere, London, 1972-75; treas. Republic Steel Corp., Cleve., 1975-84, v.p., 1978-82, exec. v.p., 1982-84; exec. v.p., chief fin. officer Ecolab Inc., St. Paul, 1984, chief fin. and adminstrv. officer, 1984-90; pres. ChemLawn Svcs. Corp., Columbus, Ohio, 1988-90; chief fin. officer Ecolab Inc., 1990-92; pres. Residential Svcs. Group, 1990-92, vice chmn., chief fin. and adminstrv. officer, 1992—; bd. dirs. Ecolab Inc., St. Paul. Bd. dirs. Minn. Pub. Radio, St. Paul, Minn. Orchestral Assn., Mpls., chair-elect. Mem. Fin. Execs. Inst., Nat. Assn. Mfrs. (bd. dirs.), Univ. Club, Rolling Rock Club, Mpls. Club, Minikahada Club, Minn. Club. Roman Catholic. Office: Ecolab Inc Ecolab Ctr Saint Paul MN 55102

SHANNON, PETER MICHAEL, JR., lawyer; b. Chgo., Oct. 13, 1928; s. Peter Michael Sr. and Marian (Burke) S.; m. Anne M. Mueller, April 3, 1969; children: Peter III, Stephen, Heather, Eamon. BA, St. Mary of the Lake, Mundelein, Ill., 1949, MA, 1952, STL, 1953; JCL, Gregorian U., Rome, 1958; JD, U. Calif., Berkeley, 1971. Bar: Calif. 1972, D.C. 1972, Ill. 1988, U.S. Dist. Ct. Md. 1972, U.S. Dist. Ct. D.C. 1972, U.S. Dist. Ct. (no. dist.) Ill. 1988, U.S. Ct. Appeals (1st, 2d, 3d, 4th, 5th, 6th, 7th, 8th, 9th and 10th cirs.) 1972-75, U.S. Supreme Ct. 1975. Supervisory atty. litigation U.S. Dept. of Justice, Washington, 1971-75; ptnr. Shannon, et al, Washington, 1980-82, Keck, Mahin & Cate, Chgo., 1982—; sr. appellate atty. ICC, Washington, 1975-77, dir. enforcement, 1977-80. Author: Energy and Transportation Implications of Ratemaking Policy Concerning Sources of Energy, 1980, Disposition of Real Estate by Religious Institutions, 1987, The Dual Approach of Civil Law Courts to Ecclestical Related Disputes, 1988. Mem. ABA (chmn. transp. com., adminstrv. law and regulatory practice sect. 1984-87, council mem., 1988-91), Am. Acad. Hosp. Attys., Assn. Transp. Practitioners, Canon Law Soc. (pres. 1965-66). Office: Keck Mahin & Cate 77 W Wacker Dr Ste 4900 Chicago IL 60601-1693

SHANNON, ROBERT RENNIE, optical sciences center administrator, educator; b. Mt. Vernon, N.Y., Oct. 3, 1932; s. Howard A. and Harriebell (Rennie) S.; m. Helen Lang, Feb. 13, 1954; children: Elizabeth, Barbara, Jennifer, Amy, John, Robert. B.S., U. Rochester, 1954, M.A., 1957. Dir. Optics Lab., ITEK Corp., Lexington, Mass., 1959-69; prof. Optical Scis. Ctr., U. Ariz., 1969—, dir., 1983-92, prof. emeritus, 1992—; cons. Lawrence Livermore Lab., 1980-90; trustee Aerospace Corp., 1985-94; mem. Air Force Sci. Adv. Bd., 1986-90; mem. NRC Commn. on Next Generation Currency, 1992-94; mem. com. on def. space tech. Air Force Studies Bd., 1989-93, Hubble Telescope recovery panel, 1990; bd. dirs. Precision Optics Corp., Schott Glass Techs. Editor: Applied Optics and Optical Engineering, Vol. 7, 1980, Vol. 8, 1981, Vol. 9, 1983, Vol. 10, 1987, Vol. 11, 1992. Fellow Optical Soc. Am. (pres. 1985, mem. engring. coun. 1989-91), Soc. Photo-Optical Instrumentation Engrs. (pres. 1979-80, recipient Goddard award 1982); mem. NAE, Tucson Soaring Club (past pres.), Sigma Xi. Home: 7040 E Taos Pl Tucson AZ 85715-3344 Office: U Ariz Optical Scis Ctr Tucson AZ 85721

SHANNON, STEPHEN QUINBY, JR., broadcasting and human resources executive; b. July 29, 1968; s. Stephen Quinby and Elsie Elaine (Vetter) S.; m. Laurine Shannon, July 29, 1968; children: Debbie Lynn, Stephen Quinby, Kathleen Elaine, Logan Michelle. BS, U. Ariz., 1956. Promotion mgr. Sta. KPHO-TV-Radio, Phoenix, 1956-61; adminstrv. mgr. Meredith Broadcasting, Omaha, 1961-62; dir. pub. rels. Sta. WHEN-TV-Radio, Syracuse, N.Y., 1962-63; v.p., gen. mgr. Meredith-Avco, Inc., 1964-69; adminstrv. mgr. Meredith Broadcasting, N.Y.C. and Omaha, 1969-72; gen. mgr. Sta. KCMO-KCEZ, v.p. broadcasting group Meredith Broadcasting, Kansas City, Mo., 1975-83; v.p. staff ops. Broadcasting Group Meredith Broadcasting, Kansas City, 1984-85; v.p., gen. mgr. Sta. WOW/KEZO, Omaha, 1972-75; exec. v.p. Sunbelt Communications, Colorado Springs, Colo., 1985-86; v.p.-radio Palmer Communications, Inc., Ft.Myers, Fla., 1986-90; gen. mgr. Sta. WHO/KLYF, Des Moines, 1986-88; mng. dir. Exec. Group Inc., Boca Raton, Fla., 1991-93; sr. cons. EnterChange, Inc., Boca Raton, Fla., 1993-94; broadcast and human resource cons. Quinby Skylur, Inc., 1994—. Bd. dirs. Urban League of Greater Kansas City, 1979-83, Boca Forum Palm Beach County; bd. dirs., treas. Pers. Assn. Palm Beach County; mem. exec. com. Rep. Party of Palm Beach County; mem. Boca Raton Men's Rep. Club. Recipient Bernard Powell Community Service award of C. of C. Greater Kansas City, 1981. Mem. Fla. Assn. Broadcasters, Employment Mgrs. Assn. U.S.A., Soc. Human Resource Mgmt., Rotary (bd. dirs. Boca Raton Club). Home: 3825 Sabal Lakes Rd Delray Beach FL 33445-1214

SHANNON, THOMAS ALFRED, association executive; b. Milw., Jan. 2, 1932; s. John Elwood and Eleanor Ann (Mitchell) S.; m. Barbara Ann Weidner, June 26, 1954; children: Thomas Alfred, Paul J., Suzanne L., Terrence D. BS, U. Wis, 1954; JD, U. Minn., 1961. Bar: Minn. 1961, Calif. 1963, U.S. Supreme Ct. 1965, D.C. 1977, Va. 1984; Life cert. as sch. adminstr., Calif.; cert. assoc. exec. Am. Soc. Assn. Execs. Practiced law Mpls., 1961-62; schs. atty. San Diego City Schs., 1962-73; dept. suppt. gen. counsel, 1973-77; exec. dir. Nat. Sch. Bds. Assn., Washington, 1977—; adj. prof. law and edn. U. San Diego; vis. prof. edn. U. Va.; adv. mem. Edn. Commn. of States; prof. Nat. Acad. Sch. Execs., 1971—; legal counsel Am. Assn. Sch. Adminstrs., 1973-77. Exec. pub. The American School Board Jour, 1977—, Exec. Educator, 1978—; Sch. Bd. News, 1981—. Chmn. San Diego County Juvenile Justice Commn., 1973-74; mem. nat. coun. Boy Scouts Am., 1979—; bd. dirs. Found. for Teaching Econ., San Francisco, 1993—. With USN, 1954-59. Mem. VFW (life), Am. Bar Assn. (chmn.

com. public edn. 1978-82), Nat. Orgn. on Legal Problems of Edn. (pres. 1973), Nat. Sch. Bds. Assn. (chmn. council sch. attys. 1967-69). Home: 3811 26th St N Arlington VA 22207-5241 Office: NSBA 1680 Duke St Alexandria VA 22314-3455

SHANNON, THOMAS FREDERIC, German language educator; b. Cambridge, Mass., Mar. 16, 1948; m. Christine D. Höner. BA in German summa cum laude, Boston Coll., 1969; MA in German Lit., SUNY, Albany, 1973; MA in Theoretical Linguistics, Ind. U., 1975, PhD in Germanic Linguistics, 1982. Instr. in German Boston Coll., 1969-70; teaching fellow in German SUNY, Albany, 1971-73; univ. fellow Ind. U., Bloomington, 1973-74, assoc. instr., 1974-76, 1979-80; acting asst. prof. in Germanic linguistics U. Calif., Berkeley, 1980-82, asst. prof., 1982-87, assoc. prof., 1987-94, prof., 1994—, dir. lang. lab., 1989-92, assoc. dir. Berkeley Lang. Ctr., 1994-95; co-organizer Berkeley Confs. on Dutch Lang. & Lit., 1987, 89, 91, 93, 95; econs., presenter, speaker in field. Contbr. articles to profl. jours. With USAR, 1970-76. Grantee U. Calif.-Berkeley, 1983-84, 94-95, Am. Coun. Learned Socs., 1987, Internat. Assn. Netherlandic Studies, 1988, 91, 94, Fulbright Found., 1979; NDEA fellow, 1969; Fulbright rsch./lectr. grantee Rijksuniversiteit Groningen, Netherlands, 1992-93. Mem. MLA (exec. com. discussion group in Germanic philology 1989-94, discussion group for Netherlandic Studies 1995—, divsn. on lang. change 1995), Am. Assn. Netherlandic Studies (exec. com. 1988—, editor newsletter 1989—, series editor publs. 1994—), Am. Assn. Tchrs. German, Assn. Computers and Humanities, Internat. Assn. Netherlandic Studies, Internat. Assn. Germanstik, Internat. Soc. Hist. Linguistics, Linguistic Soc. Am., Netherlands Am. U. League, Philol. Assn. Pacific Coast, European Linguistic Soc., Soc. Germanic Philology (v.p. 1991-92, 95—), Alpha Sigma Nu. Home: 770 Rose Dr Benicia CA 94510-3709 Office: U Calif Dept German 5317 Dwinelle Hall Berkeley CA 94720-3243

SHANNON, WILLIAM NORMAN, III, marketing and international business educator, food service executive; b. Chgo., Nov. 20, 1937; s. William Norman Jr. and Lee (Lewis) S.; m. Bernice Urbanowicz, July 14, 1962; children: Kathleen Kelly, Colleen Patricia, Kerrie Ann. BS in Indsl. Mgmt., Carnegie Inst. Tech., 1959; MBA in Mktg. Mgmt., U. Toledo, 1963. Sales engr. Westinghouse Electric Co., Detroit, 1959-64; regional mgr. Toledo Scale, Chgo., 1964-70; v.p. J. Lloyd Johnson Assoc., Northbrook, Ill., 1970-72; mgr. spl. projects Hobart Mfg., Troy, Ohio, 1972-74; corp. v.p. mktg. Berkel, Inc., La Porte, Ind., 1974-79; gen. mgr. Berkel Products, Ltd., Toronto, Can., 1975-78; chmn. Avant Industries, Inc., Wheeling, Ill., 1979-81; chmn., pres. Hacienda Mexican Restaurants, South Bend, Ind., 1978—; chmn. Ziker Shannon Corp., South Bend, 1982-88, Hacienda Franchising Group, Inc., South Bend, Ind., 1987—; assoc. prof. mktg. and internat. bus. St. Mary's Coll., Notre Dame, Ind., 1982—; chmn. Hacienda Franchise Group, Inc., 1987—, Hacienda Mex. Restaurants Mgmt., Inc., 1994—; mem. London program faculty, 1986, 89, 92, 94, coord. internat. bus. curriculum, 1989—, mktg. curriculum, 1983, 88, 95—; advisor Coun. Internat. Bus. Devel., Notre Dame, 1991—; mng. dir. Alden & Torch Lake Railway, 1995—. Co-author: Laboratory Computers, 1971; columnist small bus. Bus. Digest mag., 1988—; bd. editors Jour. Bus. and Indsl. Mktg., 1986—; mem. bd. editorial advisors South Bend Tribune Business Weekly, 1990—; contbr. articles to profl. jours. V.p. mktg. Jr. Achievement, South Bend, Ind., 1987-90; pres. Small Bus. Devel. Coun., South Bend, 1987-90; bd. dirs. Ind. Small Bus. Coun., Indpls., 1986—, Mental Health Assn., South Bend, 1987-90; Michiana World Trade Orgn., Internat. Bus. Edn., 1989-91; Entrepreneurs Alliance Ind., 1988-92, Nat. Small Bus. United, Washington, 1989-92, Women's Bus. Initiative, 1986-90, dir. ednl. confs., 1986-90; chmn. bd. trustees, Holy Cross Coll., Notre Dame, Ind., 1987—, chmn. edn. com., 1993—; chmn. St. Joseph County Higher Edn. Coun., 1988-91, Nat. Coun. Small Bus., Washington, 1988—; Midwest region adv. coun. U.S. SBA, 1988-91; at-large mem. U.S. Govt. Adv. Coun. on Small Bus., Washington, 1988-90, 1994—, chmn. Bus. and Econ. Devel. com., 1988-90, 1994—; vice chmn. Internat. Trade Com., 1994—; mem. nat. adv. coun. Women's Network for Entrepreneur Tng., 1991—; mem., vice chmn. State of Ind. Enterprise Zone Bd., 1991—; elected del. White House Conf. Small Bus., Washington, 1986; bd. dirs. Ind. Small Bus. Devel. Ctrs. Adv. Bd. Named Small Bus. Person of the Yr., City of South Bend, 1987, Small Bus. Advocate of the Yr., State of Ind., 1987, Ind. Entrepreneur Advocate of the Yr., 1988. Mem. Am. Mktg. Assn. (chmn. Mich./Ind. chpt., pres. 1985-86), U.S. Assn. Small Bus. and Entrepreneurship (nat. v.p. for entrepreneurship edn. 1991-92, nat. v.p. entrepreneurship devel. 1992—), Ind. Inst. New Bus. Ventures (mktg. faculty 1987-91), Michiana Investment Network (vice chmn. 1988-91), SBA (adminstrn. adv. coun. 1988—, contbg. editor Our Town Michiana mag. 1988-91), U.S.C. of C., Nat. Coun. Small Bus. (Washington), South Bend C of C. (bd. dirs. 1987—, vice chmn. membership 1993—), Assn. for Bus. Communications (co-chmn. Internat. Conf. 1986), Univ. Club Notre Dame (vice chmn.), Shamrock Club Notre Dame (exec. dir., trustee 1993—), Rotary. Roman Catholic. Home: 2920 S Twyckenham Dr South Bend IN 46614-2116 Office: Saint Mary's Coll Dept Bus Adminstrn Eco Notre Dame IN 46556 *Enjoy good fortune resulting from LUCK, an acronym for (L) Learning how to (U)Use your talents with genuine (C) Concern on how your (K) Knowlege can benefit others.*

SHANSBY, JOHN GARY, investment banker; b. Seattle, Aug. 25, 1937; s. John Jay and Jule E. (Boyer) S.; m. Joyce Ann Dunsmore, June 21, 1959 (div.); children: Sheri Lee, Kimberly Ann, Jay Thomas; m. Barbara Anderson De Meo, Jan. 1, 1983 (div.); m. Jane Robinson Dettner, May 1, 1990. B.A., U. Wash., 1959. Sales exec. Colgate-Palmolive Co., N.Y.C., 1959-67; subs. pres. Am. Home Products Corp., N.Y.C., 1968-71; v.p. Clorox Co., Oakland, Calif., 1972-73; ptnr. Booz, Allen & Hamilton, San Francisco, 1974-75; chmn. bd., chief exec. officer, dir. Shaklee Corp., San Francisco, 1975-86; mng. gen. ptnr. The Shansby Group, San Francisco, 1986—. Chmn. Calif. State Commn. for Rev. of Master Plan Higher Edn.; founder J. Gary Shansby chair mktg. strtegy U. Calif., Berkeley; trustee Calif. State U. Mem. San Francisco C. of C. (past pres.), Villa Traverna Club, Silverado Country Club, Lincoln Club of No. Calif., Pennask Lake Fishing Club (B.C.), St. Francis Yacht Club, Sky Club of N.Y.C., Sigma Nu. Republican. Office: The Shansby Group 250 Montgomery St San Francisco CA 94104-3401

SHANSTROM, JACK D., federal judge; b. Hewitt, Minn., Nov. 30, 1932; s. Harold A. and Willian (Wendorf) S.; m. June 22, 1957; children: Scott S., Susan K. BA in Law, U. Mont., 1956, BS in Bus., 1957, LLB, 1957. Atty. Park County, Livingston, Mont., 1960-65; judge 6th Jud. Dist. Livingston, 1965-82; U.S. magistrate Billings, Mont., 1983-90, U.S. Dist. judge, 1990—. Capt. USAF, 1957-60. Office: US Dist Ct PO Box 985 Billings MT 59103-0985

SHAO, OTIS HUNG-I, corporate executive, educator; b. Shanghai, China, July 18, 1923; came to U.S., 1949, naturalized, 1956; s. Ming Sun and Hannah (Chen) S.; m. Marie Sheng, Apr. 2, 1955. B.A., St. John's U., 1946; M.A., U. Colo., 1950; Ph.D., Brown U., 1957. From instr. to prof. polit. sci. Moravian Coll., Bethlehem, Pa., 1954-62; provost, then prof. polit. sci. Fla. Presbyn. Coll., St. Petersburg, 1962-68; prof. internat. politics, dean (Grad. Sch., U. Pacific), 1968-74; dir. Pub. Affairs Inst., 1969-74; provost Callison Coll., 1974-76; dean faculty, v.p. Occidental Coll., 1976-78; asso. exec. dir. sr. commn. Western Assn. Schs. and Colls., 1978-80; v.p., dean Hawaii Loa Coll., 1980-85; pres. Sheng Shao Enterprises Calif., 1985-92; CEO, chmn. D.S. Capital Internat., Calif., 1993-94; Mem. grad. students relations com. Council Grad. Schs. U.S. 1970-73; mem. exec. council undergrad. assessment program Ednl. Testing Service, 1978-80. Contbr. articles to profl. jours. Chmn. bd. dirs. Fgn. Policy Assn. Lehigh Valley, 1961-62; bd. dirs. World Affairs Council, San Joaquin County, 1969-77; trustee Inst. Med. Scis., Pacific Med. Center, San Francisco, 1968-72, optical scis. group of Prof. and Pub. Service Found., 1969-72; Resident fellow Harkness House, Brown U., 1953-54, Danforth Asso., 1958-85. Recipient Distinguished Service award Fgn. Policy Assn. Lehigh Valley, 1962. Mem. AAUP (pres. Fla. Presbyn. Coll. chpt. 1965-66), Am. Assn. Higher Edn., Rho Psi, Tau Kappa Epsilon. Democrat. Presbyn. Home: 6218 Embarcadero Dr Stockton CA 95219-3824

SHAO, SHIU, financial executive; b. Taipei, Taiwan, Rep. of China, Nov. 13, 1951; came to U.S., 1975; s. Chi-Ching and Tintz (Yu) S.; m. Misara Chan. B.S. in Physics, Chan Yuan U., 1973; M.B.A. in Fin., U. Pitts., 1977. Programmer analyst Standard Brands, Inc., Burlingame, Calif., 1977-78;

acctg. analyst Watkins Johnson Co., Palo Alto, Calif., 1978-81; controller Oromeccanica Inc., Burbank, Calif., 1981-82; v.p. fin., chief fin. officer Oroamerica, Inc., Burbank, 1982—; dir. Am. Internat. Chain Co., Emex Corp. Author: Financial Credit Line Tie to Commodity Index for Precious Metals Industries, 1982. Jr. Achievement advisor, Santa Clara County, Calif., 1979. Served to 2d lt. Chinese Marine Corps, 1973-75. Mem. Nat. Assn. Accts. Home: 250 W Fairview Ave Apt 308 Glendale CA 91202-2952 Office: Oroamerica Inc 443 N Varney St Burbank CA 91502-1733

SHAPAZIAN, ROBERT MICHAEL, publishing executive; b. Fresno, Calif., Nov. 3, 1942; s. Ara Michael and Margaret (Azhderian) S. BA, U. Calif., 1964; AM, Harvard U., 1965, PhD in Renaissance English and Fine Arts, 1970. Design assoc. Arthur Elrod Assocs., L.A., 1971-73; v.p. El Mar Corp, Fresno, Calif., 1973-87; dir., art dir. The Lapis Press, Venice, Calif., 1987—; mem. photographic forum San Francisco Mus. Art, 1982-85, Mus. Modern Art, N.Y.C., 1985; mem. photographic ocm. Met. Mus. ARt, N.Y.C., 1994; assoc. Gagosian Gallery, N.Y.C. Author: Metaphorics of Artificiality, 1970, Maurice Tabard, 1985; editor: Surrealists Look at Art, 1991 (AIGA award 1991, N.Y. Art Dirs. award 1991), A Witch, 1992 (AIGA award 1992, N.Y. Art Dirs. award 1992, L.A. Art Dirs. award 1992), Pacific Wall (AIGA award 1993), Albucius (We. Art Dirs. award 1993, N.Y. Art Dirs. award 1994). Bd. dirs. Big Brothers/Big Sisters, Fresno, Calif., 1980-82, Film Forum, L.A., 1984-86. Recipient Individual Achievement award Literary Market Place, N.Y.C., 1992, 20 awards for art direction and design; named Chevalier in Order of Arts and Letters, Govt. of France. Mem. Harvard Club (N.Y.C.). Avocations: twentieth century art, illustrated books, experimental photography. Office: The Lapis Press 589 N Venice Blvd Venice CA 90291

SHAPELL, NATHAN, financial and real estate executive; b. Poland, Mar. 6, 1922; s. Benjamin and Hela S.; m. Lilly Szenes, July 17, 1948; children: Vera Shapell Guerin, Benjamin (dec.). Co-founder Shapell Industries, Inc., Beverly Hills, Calif., 1955; now chmn. bd. Shapell Industries, Inc.; mem. adv. bd. Union Bank, Beverly Hills; mem. residential bldgs. adv. com. Calif. Energy Resources Conservation and Devel. Commn.; speaker in field. Mem. Calif. Commn. Govt. Reform, 1978; Atty. Gen. Calif. Adv. Council, Dist. Atty. Los Angeles County Adv. Council; chmn. Calif. Govt. Commn. Orgn. and Economy, 1975—, Gov.'s Task Force on Affordable Housing, 1980—; mem. adv. council Pres.'s Commn. on the Holocaust, 1979; pres. Am. Acad. Achievement, 1975—; mem. deans council UCLA Sch. Architecture and Urban Planning, 1976—. Author: Witness to the Truth, 1974. Trustee U. Santa Clara, Calif., 1976—; bd. councillors U. So. Calif. Med. Sch., 1973—. Recipient Golden Plate award Am. Acad. Achievement, 1974, Fin. World award, 1977. Jewish. Club: Hillcrest Country (Los Angeles). Prisoner in Auschwitz, 1943-45. Address: Shapell Industries Inc 8383 Wilshire Blvd Ste 700 Beverly Hills CA 90211-2406

SHAPER, STEPHEN JAY, finance company executive; b. Houston, Oct. 7, 1936; s. Charles Harry and Ruth (L.) S.; m. Sue Z. Shaper, June 6, 1959; children: Peter, Park, Page, Penn. BS, Rice U., 1958; MBA, U. Harvard, 1960. Mfg. engr. Tex. Instruments, Houston, 1960-61; pres. El Patio Products Corp., Houston, 1961-87; chmn. Seville Industries, Ft. Worth, 1982-87; chief oper. officer TeleCheck Internat., Inc., Houston, 1987—, also bd. dirs.; bd. dirs. Trussway Inc., Houston, CDP Corp., Dallas, Brooks, Collier Architects, Houston, Assoc. Bldg. Svcs., Houston. Bd. dirs. Rice U.; chmn. Rice Fund Coun., Hsouton, 1989-90. Capt. U.S. Army, 1961. Mem. Breakfast Club Houston, Houston Racquet Club, April Sound Country Club. Avocations: handball, jogging, skiing, bridge. Home: 325 Ripple Creek Dr Houston TX 77024-6931 Office: TeleCheck Internat 5251 Westheimer # 1000 Houston TX 77056

SHAPERE, DUDLEY, philosophy educator; b. Harlingen, Tex., May 27, 1928; s. Dudley and Corinne (Pupkin) S.; m. Hannah Hardgrave; children—Hannah Elizabeth, Christine Ann; children by previous marriage: Alfred Dudley, Catherine Lucretia. B.A., Harvard U., 1949, M.A., 1955, Ph.D., 1957. Instr. philosophy Ohio State U., 1957-60; asst. prof. U. Chgo., 1960-65, asso. prof., 1965-67, prof., 1967-72, mem. com. on evolutionary biology, 1969-72, chmn. undergrad. program in history and philosophy of sci., 1966-72, chmn. com. on conceptual founds. sci., 1970-72; prof. U. Ill., Urbana, 1972-75; chmn. program in history and philosophy of sci. U. Ill., 1972-75; prof. U. Md., College Park, 1975-84; Z. Smith Reynolds prof. philosophy and history of sci. Wake Forest U., 1984—; mem. com. on history and philosophy of sci. U. Md., 1975-84; chmn. program in history and philosophy of sci. U. Md., 1983-84; vis. prof. Rockefeller U., 1965-66, Harvard U., 1968; mem. Inst. Advanced Study, Princeton, N.J., 1978-79, 81; spl. cons. (program dir.) program in history and philosophy of sci. NSF, 1966-75; Sigma Xi nat. bicentennial lectr., 1974-77. Author: Philosophical Problems of Natural Science, 1965, Galileo: A Philosophical Study, 1974, Reason and the Search for Knowledge, 1984; editorial bd.: Philosophy of Sci., Studies in History and Philosophy of Sci.; rev. bd.: Philosophy Research Archives; contbr. articles to profl. jours. Served with AUS, 1950-52. Recipient Quantrell award for excellence in undergrad. teaching U. Chgo., 1968; Disting. Scholar-Tchr. award U. Md., 1979-80. Fellow AAAS (sec. sec. 1972); mem. APA, Philosophy of Sci. Assn., History of Sci. Soc., Am. Philos. Assn., Acad. Internat. de Philosophie des Scis. Home: 3125 Turkey Hill Ct Winston Salem NC 27106 Office: Wake Forest U PO Box 7229 Winston Salem NC 27109-7229

SHAPERO, HAROLD (SAMUEL), composer, pianist, educator; b. Lynn, Mass., Apr. 29, 1920; m. Esther Geller, 1945. Attended, Malkin Conservatory, Boston, 1936-37; studied composition with Ernst Krenek, 1937, studied piano with Eleanor Kerr; studied composition with Walter Piston, Harvard U., 1938-41; studied composition with Paul Hindemith, Berkshire Music Ctr., Tanglewood, Mass., 1970; studied composition with Nadia Boulanger, Longy Sch., 1942-43. Founding prof. music dept. Brandeis U., Waltham, Mass., 1952-85. Compositions include: (symphonies/orchestral) Nine-Minute Overture, 1940 (Am. Prix de Rome 1941), Serenade in D for string orch., 1945, Symphony for Classical Orch., 1947, The Travellers Overture, Sinfonia in C, 1948, Concerto for Orch., 1950, Credo, 1955, Lyric Dances, 1955, Partita in C. for piano and small orch., 1960, On Green Mountain, 1981; (chamber/instrumental) String Trio, 1938, Three Pieces for Three Pieces, 1939, Sonata for trumpet and piano, 1940, Sonata for piano, 1941, String Quartet, 1941, Sonata for violin and piano, 1942, Three Amateur Sonatas for piano, 1944, Variations in C for piano, 1947, Sonata in F for piano, 1948, American Variations for piano, 1950, On Green Mountain for jazz group, 1957, Three Improvisations in B for piano and synthesizer, 1968, Three Studies in C# for piano and synthesizer, 1969, Four Pieces in B flat for piano and synthesizer, 1970; (vocal/choral) Four Baritone Songs for voice, piano and cummings, 1942, Two Psalms, 1952, Hebrew Cantata, 1954, Two Hebrew Songs, 1973. Nuameline fellow, 1942, Guggenheim fellow, 1947, 48, Fulbright fellow, 1948; recipient Arthur George Knight prize, 1938, 40, Gershwin prize, 1946, Bearns prize, 1946. Office: Brandeis U Dept Music 415 South St Waltham MA 02254*

SHAPERO, SANFORD MARVIN, hospital executive, rabbi; b. Cin., Mar. 4, 1929; s. David Theodore and Leah Freda (Adler) S.; m. Evelyn Leavitt, Jan. 24, 1982. BA, U. Dayton, 1950; BHL, Hebrew Union Coll., 1952, MHL, 1955, DHL, 1959, DD (hon.), 1981. Rabbi Elmira, N.Y., 1957-59; Bridgeport, Conn., 1959-64, Beverly Hills, Calif., 1964-68; exec. v.p. Alliance Med. Industries, Straford, Conn., 1968-69; v.p. N.Am. Biologicals, Miami, 1969-72; regional dir., nat. dir. gerontology Union Am. Hebrew Coll., Miami, 1972-79; pres., chief exec. officer City of Hope, L.A., 1979—. Contbr. articles to profl. jours. Lt. (j.g.) USNR, 1955-57. Mem. CCAR, Nat. Adv. Coun. on Aging, Rotary (bd. dirs. 1987—). Avocations: private flying, anthropology, travel, classical music, biking. Office: City of Hope Nat Med Ctr 1500 E Duarte Rd Duarte CA 91010-3011

SHAPEY, RALPH, composer, conductor, educator; b. Phila., Mar. 12, 1921; s. Max and Lillian (Paul) S.; m. Vera Shapiro, Oct. 28, 1957; 1 child, Max Klement; m. Elsa Charlston, Oct. 12, 1985. Student violin with Emanuel Zetlin; composition with, Stefan Wolpe. Prof. music U. Chgo., 1964-85, Disting. prof., 1985-91; ret., 1991; vis. prof. Queens Coll., 1973; chmn. admissions com. MacDowell Colony. Dir. Contemporary Chamber Players, Chgo., ret. 1994; cond., music dir. Phila. Nat. Youth Adminstrs. Symphony Orch., 1938-42; guest condr., Phila. Symphony Orch. at Robin Hood Dell, 1942 (winner Phila. Finds Contest); condr. 1st performance saxophone quartet by Wolpe, McMillan Theatre, N.Y.C., 1950, repeat performance, Times Hall, N.Y.C., 1950; condr. clarinet concerto, N.Y. Philharmonic Chamber Soc., 1955, Internat. Soc. Contemporary Music, N.Y.C., 1961, 62, Phila., 1961-63, Fromm Found. Concert, N.Y.C., 1962; guest condr., London Symphony Orch. for BBC, mus. dir. orch. and chorus, U. Pa., 1963-64, mus. dir., Contemporary Chamber Players, U. Chgo., 1964—; Composer: Challenge-The Family of Man, for symphony orchestra, 1955, Mutations, for piano, 1956, Duo for Viola and Piano, 1957, Ontogeny for symphony orchestra, 1958, Form for piano, 1959, Rituals for symphony orchestra, 1959, Dimensions for soprano and 23 instruments, 1960, Incantations for soprano and 10 instruments, 1961, Convocation for chamber group, 1962, Birthday Piece for piano, 1962, Brass Quintet, 1963, String Quartet VI, 1963, VII, Sonance for carillon, 1964, Configurations for Flute and Piano, Praise, oratorio, Variations for piano, O Jerusalem, for soprano and flute, Songs of Eros, for soprano, orch. and tape, Covenant for Soprano, 16 players and tape, 1977, 21 Variations for Piano, 1978, Song of Songs 1, 1979, II, 1980, III, 1980, Evocation for cello, piano and percussion, 1979, Evocation III for viola and piano, 1981, Fanfare for 2 trumpets, horn, trombone and tuba, Concerto Grosso for woodwind quintet, 1981, Songs for Soprano and Piano, 1982, Passacaglia for Piano, 1982, Double Concerto for Violin, Cello and Orchestra, 1983, Discourse II for Violin, Clarinet, Cello, and Piano, 1983, Fantasy for Violin and Piano, 1983, Mann duo for Violin and Viola, 1983, Songs for Soprano and Four Instruments, 1984, Gottlieb Duo for Piano and Percussion, 1984, Variations for Organ, 1985, Duo Variations for Violin and Cello, 1985, Psalm I for Soprano and Piano, 1985, Psalm II for Baritone and Piano, 1986, Duo Variations for violin and cello, 1985, Soli for percussion, 1985, Kroslish Sonata for cello and piano, 1985, Symphonie Concertante for symphony orch. (commd. Phila. Orch.), 1986, Songs of Love (I am My Beloved's) for baritone and piano, 1986, Songs of Love (And My Beloved is Mine) for baritone and piano, 1986, Concerto for piano and string orch., 1986, In Memorium for soprano, baritone and 9 players, 1987, Theme and Variations for harpsicord, 1987, Concertante #II for alto saxophone and 14 players, 1987, Songs of Joy for soprano and piano, 1987, Variations on a Cantus for piano, 1987, Kroslish Sonate for cello and piano, 1987, Concertante #1 for trumpet and 13 players, 1987, Variations for Viola and 9 Players, 1987, 2 For 1 Solo for Snare Drum, 1988, Concerto Fantastique for Symphony Orch., 1989, Chgo. Symphony Orch., Intermezzo for Dulceme & piano/Celesta, 1990, Duo for 6 Winds, Two Players, 1991, Centennial Celebration for soprano, mezzo soprano, tenor, baritone and 12 players, 1991, Movement of Varied Moments for Two-flute and vibraphone, 1991, Trio 1992 for violin, cello, piano, 1992, Trio Concertant for Violin, Piano and Percussion, 1992, Inventions for Clarinet and Percussion, 1992, Dinosaur Annex for Violin, Vibraphone & Marimba/Glock, 1993, String Quartet VIII, Naumberg, 1993, Constellations for Bang on the Can All-Stars, 1993, Rhapsody for Cello and Piano, 1993, Evocations # IV for Violin, Cello, Piano & Percussion, others: Recs. include: Music for a 20th Century Violinist, Fromm Variation: 31 Variations for Piano, 1973, Three for Six, 1980, 21 Variations for Piano. Served with AUS, 1942-45. Mac Arthur fellow, 1982, Inst. of Arts and Letters fellow, 1989; grantee Italian govt., 1959-60; recipient Creative Arts award Brandeis U., 1962, Nat. Found. Arts and Letters award, 1966, Norlin Found. award, 1978, 1st prize Friedheim award, 1990, Fromm award Outstanding contbn. 20th century Music, 1993. Mem. ASCAP, AAAL, Am. Acad. Arts and Scis., Internat. Soc. Contemporary Music (dir.). Office: U Chgo Dept Music 5845 S Ellis Ave Chicago IL 60637-1404 *My credo: Great art is a miracle! The music must speak for itself.*

SHAPIRA, DAVID S., food chain executive; b. 1942; married. B.A. Oberlin Coll., 1964; M.A., Stanford U., 1966. V.p. Giant Eagle, Inc. (formerly Giant Eagle Markets, Inc.), Pitts., 1974-81, pres., from 1981, chief exec. officer, also bd. dirs.; CEO Phar-Mor Inc., Youngstown, chmn. bd. Office: Giant Eagle Inc 101 Kappa Dr Pittsburgh PA 15238-2809 Office: Tamarkin Company PO Box 1588 Youngstown OH 44501*

SHAPIRO, ALAN B., secondary education educator; b. Phila., Feb. 22, 1958; s. Harry and Claire (Jonis) S.; m. Risa E. Bader, June 18, 1989; 1 child, Rachel Elizabeth. BS, Pa. State U., 1984. Tchr. Hillsborough County Schs., Tampa, Fla., 1986-88, Pinellas County Schs., Largo, Fla., 1988—; environmental educator Boyd Hill Nature Park, St. Petersburg, Fla., summers 1990—. Bd. dirs. Friends of Boyd Hill, St. Petersburg, 1992-93; mem. com. Greenthumb Festival, St. Petersburg, 1993. Recipient 4th pl. Trash Rappin State of Fla., 1991, award Sharing Successes in Environ. Edn., 1993. 1st pl. Pres. Environ. Youth, Pres. of U.S., 1991. Avocations: birdwatching, backpacking. Office: Boca Ciega High Sch 924 58th St S Largo FL 34646

SHAPIRO, ALVIN PHILIP, physician, educator; b. Nashville, Dec. 28, 1920; s. Samuel and Mollie (Levine) S.; m. Ruth Thomson, 1951; children: Debra, David. A.B., Cornell U., 1941; M.D., L.I. Coll. Medicine, Bklyn., 1944. Diplomate Nat. Bd. Med. Examiners; cert. Am. Bd. Internal Medicine. Intern L.I. Coll. Hosp., Bklyn., 1944-45; asst. resident internal medicine Goldwater Meml. Hosp., N.Y.C., 1945-46; asst. resident psychiatry L.I. Coll. Hosp. and Kings County Hosp., 1947-48; practice acad. medicine specializing in internal medicine Cin., 1948-51, Dallas, 1951-56, Pitts., 1956—; research fellow Cin. Gen. Hosp., 1948-49; med. teaching fellow Commonwealth Fund Psychosomatic Program, 1949-51, attending physician, 1949-51; attending physician Parkland, VA hosps., Dallas, 1951-56, Presbyn.-Univ. Hosp., Pitts., 1957-61; sr. staff Presbyn.-Univ. Hosp., 1962—; attending physician VA Hosp., Pitts., 1960-66; cons. VA Hosp., 1967—; attending physician Shadyside Hosp., 1986—; co-dir. hypertension-renal clinic Falk Clinic U. Pitts., 1956-65, dir. hypertension clinic, 1965-86; instr. dept. internal medicine U. Cin. Coll. Medicine, 1949-51; asst. prof. Southwestern Med. Sch., U. Tex., 1951-56; asst. prof. depts. clin. sci. and medicine U. Pitts. Sch. Medicine, 1956-60, assoc. prof. dept. medicine, 1960-67, prof., 1967-93, prof. emeritus, 1993—; dir. psychosomatic program dept. medicine, 1960-71, interim chief renal sect., 1962-63, chief clin. pharmacology-hypertension sect., 1960-71, assoc. dean acad. affairs, 1971-75, vice-chmn. dept. medicine, 1975-79, interim chmn. dept. medicine, 1977-79; dir. Internal Medicine Residency program, Shadyside Hosp., 1986-93; cons. AMA Council on Drugs, 1959, Med. Letter of Drugs and Therapy, 1960; Fulbright vis. prof. U. Utrecht, The Netherlands, 1968; chmn. spl. projects study com. Nat. Heart Inst., 1970, chmn. policy adv. bd. nat. hypertension study, 1972-82. Author: (with S.O. Waife) Clinical Evolution of New Drugs, 1959, Hypertension-Current Management, 1963, 77, Hypertension in Renal Disease, 1969, Pharmacologic Mechanisms in Control of Hypertension, 1971; assoc. editor: Psychosomatic Medicine, 1963-92; assoc. editor Integrative Physiol. and Behavioral Sci., 1990; contbr. articles to profl. jours. Served as capt. M.C. AUS, 1946-47. Co-recipient Albert Lasker spl. pub. health award, 1980. Fellow ACP (Laureate award for teaching excellence Pa. chpt. 1988), AAAS (elected 1989); mem. Am. Fedn. Clin. Rsch., Am. Psychosomatic Soc. (sec.-treas. 1969-73, pres. 1975), AMA, Am. Heart Assn. (med. adv. bd. coun. high blood pressure, coun. on circulation, coun. on epidemiology), Pa. County Med. Soc., Allegheny County Med. Soc., N.Y. Acad. Sci., Am. Diabetes Assn., Am. Soc. Clin. Investigation, Soc. for Exptl. Biology and Medicine, Am. Soc. for Pharmacology and Exptl. Therapeutics, Cen. Soc. Clin. Rsch., Internat. Soc. Hypertension, Acad. Behavioral Medicine (coun. 1986, pres. 1987), Alpha Omega Alpha. Achievements include research in hypertension and related diseases and in behavioral sciences. Office: Shadyside Hosp Pittsburgh PA 15232

SHAPIRO, AMY ROSEMARIE, film studio executive; b. Stamford, Conn., Dec. 31, 1949; d. Salem Seeley and Edith Geraldine (Herwitz) S. BA, Goucher Coll., Towson, Md., 1971. Asst. to dir. Manpower Adminstrn. U.S. Dept. Labor, Washington, 1971-73; editorial asst. Distbn. Codes, Inc., Washington, 1973-75; asst. to v.p. Pay-TV dept. Universal Pictures, Inc., N.Y.C., 1976-80; adminstr. Pay-TV div. Universal Pictures, Inc., Los Angeles, 1980-82; dir. sales Pay-TV div. Universal Pictures Inc., Los Angeles, 1983-84; v.p. sales Pay-TV div. Mca Home Entertainment Group, Los Angeles, 1985-87, v.p. adminstrn. and new mktg. devel., 1988-90; pres. Niche In Time Ent. and Yma Prodn. and Distribution Co., 1991—. Coordinator Udall Presdl. Campaign, Weston, Conn., 1976; mem. Dem. Town Com., Weston, Conn., 1976-77; vol. coordinator Gary Hart Presdl. Campaign, Los Angeles, 1984. Recipient Case Study award Cable TV Adminstrn. and Mktg. Soc., 1988. Democrat. Jewish. Avocations: skiing, reading, sailing. Home: 4401 Sepulveda Blvd Sherman Oaks CA 91403 Office: Yma Prodn & Distribution 4401 Sepulveda Blvd Sherman Oaks CA 91403-3900

SHAPIRO, ARTHUR MAURICE, biology educator; b. Balt., Jan. 6, 1946; s. Bernard Robert and Rose (Pogach) S.; m. Adrienne Ruth Austin, Aug. 3, 1969; children: Austin Warren, Alexa Katherine Rose. BA, U. Pa., 1966; PhD, Cornell U., 1970. Asst. prof. CUNY, 1970-71; asst. prof. U. Calif. Davis, 1972-75, assoc. prof., 1975-80, prof., 1980-84, prof. zoology, 1984—, vice chmn. dept., 1984-93. Research on Lepidoptera, 1982; contbr. over 200 articles to profl. jours. Grantee NSF, 1977-79, 84-87, 93—, Nat. Geog. Soc. 1976-82, 87-89, 94. Fellow AAAS, Explorers Club, Royal Entomol. Soc. London, Calif. Acad. Scis.; mem. Soc. Study of Evolution, Lepidopterists' Soc. (v.p. 1974-76, exec. council 1976-79). Avocations: Andean exploration, photography, botany, polit. sci. Office: U Calif Dept Ecology & Evolution Storer Hall Davis CA 95616

SHAPIRO, ASCHER HERMAN, mechanical engineer, educator, consultant; b. Bklyn., May 20, 1916; s. Bernard and Jennie (Kaplan) S.; m. Sylvia Charm, Dec. 24, 1939 (div. 1959); children: Peter Mark, Martha Ann, Bennett Mary; m. Regina Julia Lee, June 4, 1961 (div. 1972); m. Kathleen Larke Crawford, Sept. 6, 1985. Student, CCNY, 1932-35; S.B., MIT, 1938, Sc.D., 1946; D.Sc. (honoris causa), Salford U., Eng., 1978, Technion-Israel Inst. Tech., 1985. Asst. mech. engring. MIT, 1938-40, faculty, 1940—, prof. mech. engring., 1952—, prof. charge fluid mechanics div., mech. engring. dept., 1954-65, Ford prof. engring., 1962-75, chmn. faculty, 1964-65, head dept. mech. engring., 1965-74, inst. prof., 1975-86, inst. prof. emeritus, sr. lectr., 1986—; vis. prof. applied thermodynamics U. Cambridge, Eng., 1955-56; Akroyd Stuart Meml. lectr. Nottingham (Eng.) U., 1956; editor Acad. Press, Inc., 1962-65; cons. United Aircraft Corp., M.W. Kellogg Co., Arthur D. Little, Inc., Hardie-Tynes Mfg. Co., Carbon & Carbide Chems. Corp., Oak Ridge, Rohm & Haas Co., Ultrasonic Corp., Jackson & Moreland (Engrs.), Stone & Webster, Bendix Aviation, Oak Ridge Nat. Lab., Acushnet Processing Co., Kennecott Copper Co., Welch Sci., Sargent-Welch, Bird Machine Co., Organogenesis, Inc.; others; served on sub-coms. on turbines, internal flow, compressors and turbines NACA; mem. Lexington Project to study and report on nuclear powered flight to AEC, summer 1948; dir. Project Dynamo to study and report to AEC on technol. and econs. nuclear power for civilian use, 1953, Lamp Wick study Office Naval Research, 1955; mem. tech. adv. panel aeronautics Dept. Def.; cons. ops. evaluation group Navy Dept.; sci. adv. bd. USAF, 1964-66; founder, mem. Nat. Com. for Fluid Mechanics Films, 1962—, chmn., 1962-65, 71—; chmn. com. on ednl. films Commn. on Engring. Edn., 1967-71; dir. lab. for devel. power plants for use in torpedoes Navy Dept., 1943-45; mem. ad hoc med. devices com. FDA, HEW, 1970-72; mem. com. Nat. Council for Research and Devel., Israel, 1971—; mem. com. sci. and pub. policy Nat. Acad. Scis., 1970-74. Author: The Dynamics and Thermodynamics of Compressible Fluid Flow, vol. 1, 1953, vol. 2, 1954 (with Chinese tranls.), Shape and Flow, 1961 (Japanese, Italian, German and Spanish transls.); also 3 ednl. films, 39 videotape lecture series: Fluid Dynamics, 1984; contbr. 125 articles to scientific jours.; editorial bd.: Jour. Applied Mechanics, 1955-56; editorial com.: Ann. Rev. Fluid Mechanics, 1967-71; mem. editorial bd.: MIT Press, 1977-87, chmn., 1982-87. Mem. Town Meeting Arlington, Mass.; chmn. 1st Mass. chpt. Atlantic Union Com., 1951-52, mem. council, 1954—; bd. govs. Technion, Israel Inst. Tech., 1968-89. Recipient Naval Ordnance Devel. award, 1945; joint certificate outstanding contbn. War and Navy depts., 1947; Richards Meml. award ASME, 1960; Worcester Reed Warner medal, 1965; Fluids Engring. award, 1981; Townsend Harris medal Coll. City N.Y., 1978. Fellow AIAA, Am. Acad. Arts and Scis. (councillor 1967-71), ASME; mem. Am. Sci. Films Assn., Nat. Acad. Scis. (com. on sci. and pub. policy 1973-77), Nat. Acad. Engring. (adv. com. on edn. 1985-89), Am. Inst. Med. and Biol. Engring. (founding fellow), Biomed. Engring. Soc. (charter mem. 1968), AAAS, Am. Soc. Engring. Edn. (Lamme medal 1977), MIT Faculty Club, Cavendish Club (Brookline, Mass.), Sigma Xi, Tau Beta Pi, Pi Tau Sigma. Patentee fluid metering equipment, combustion chamber, propulsion apparatus, gas turbine aux., magnetic disc, magnetic disc storage device, vacuum pump, low-density wind tunnel, recipe calculator, decanter centrifuges. Home: 111 Perkins St Apt 86 Jamaica Plain MA 02130-4321

SHAPIRO, BABE, artist; b. Newark, N.J., May 4, 1937; d. George and Sarah (Kay) S. B.A., N.J. State Tchrs. Coll., 1952; M.A., Hunter Coll., 1958. dir. Mount Royal Grad. Sch. Painting, Md. Inst. Coll. Art, Balt., 1974—. One-man shows: Stable Gallery, N.Y.C., 1962-69, Gertrude Kasle Gallery, Detroit, 1971, 73, 75, A.M. Sachs Gallery, N.Y.C., 1971, 73, 75, 77, 80, Paula Allen Gallery, N.Y.C., 1986, Md. Art Place, Balt., 1990, Irving Gallery, Palm Beach, Fla., 1993; group shows include: Newark Mus., 1958, 65, Pa. Acad. Fine Arts, 1962, Phila. Mus. Art, 1965, N.J. State Mus., Trenton, 1965, Cin. Mus. Art, 1966, Flint (Mich.) Inst. Art, 1969, Balt. Mus. Art, 1970, U. Md. Art Gallery, 1971, Colorado Springs Fine Arts Mus., 1972, Tex. Tech. U., 1974, Philbrook Art Center, Tulsa, 1975, Carnegie Inst., 1975, Anita Shapolsky Gallery, N.Y.C., 1994; represented in permanent collections, Albright Knox Gallery, Buffalo, N.Y., Cooper Hewitt Mus., N.Y.C., Corcoran Gallery Art, Washington, Newark Mus., Scottish Nat. Gallery Modern Art, Edinburgh, Balt. Mus. Art, Storm King Art Ctr., Mountainville, N.Y., numerous others. Ford Found. grantee, 1966. Address: 31 Walker St New York NY 10013-3595

SHAPIRO, BARRY ROBERT, lawyer; b. Bklyn., Apr. 10, 1947; s. Sam and Jean (Moak) S.; m. Marjorie Spiegelman, Dec. 24, 1968; children: Andrew, Daniel. Ba, Hofstra U., 1968; JD, Columbia U., 1973. Bar: N.Y., U.S. Dist. Ct. (so. dist.) N.Y., U.S. Ct. Appeals (2d cir.). Assoc. Shereff, Friedman et al, N.Y.C., 1973-74; v.p., gen. counsel Avis, Inc., Garden City, N.Y., 1974-83; ptnr. Farrell, Fritz, Caemmerer, Cleary, Barnosky & Armentano P.C., Uniondale, N.Y., 1983-88; sr. ptnr. Rivkin, Radler & Kremes, 1988—. Contbr. article to profl. jours. Chmn. bd. dirs. L.I. Philharmonic, Melville, N.Y., 1986—; bd. dirs. L.I. Coalition Fair Broadcasting, 1989—, Inst. Cmty. Devel., 1992-94, New Ctr. Wholistic Health Edn. Rsch., 1992—. Mem. ABA, N.Y. State Bar Assn., Nassau County Bar Assn. (lectr. 1985-86, 93), Hofstra Club (Hempstead, N.Y.). Avocations: sports, music. Office: Rivkin Radler & Kremer EAB Plz Uniondale NY 11556

SHAPIRO, BENNETT MICHAELS, biochemist, educator; b. Phila., July 14, 1939; s. Simon and Sara (Michaels) S.; m. Fredericka Foster, Mar. 13, 1982; children: Lisa, Lise, Jonathan. BS, Dickinson Coll., 1960; MD, Jefferson Med. Coll., 1964. Research assoc. NHLI, NIH, 1965-68, med. officer, 1970-71; vis. scientist Inst. Pasteur, Paris, 1968-70; from assoc. prof. to full prof. biochemistry U. Wash., 1971-90, chmn. biochemistry dept., 1985-90; exec. v.p. for worldwide basic rsch. Merck Rsch. Labs., Rahway, N.J., 1990—. Contbr. articles to profl. jour. Served as surgeon USPHS, 1968-70. John S. Guggenheim fellow, 1982; Japan Soc. for Promotion Sci., 1984. Mem. Am. Soc. Biol. Chemists, Am. Soc. Cell Biology, Am. Soc. Devel. Biology, Phi Beta Kappa, Alpha Omega Alpha. Office: Merck Rsch Labs PO Box 2000 Rahway NJ 07065-0900

SHAPIRO, BETH JANET, librarian; b. Newton, Mass., July 18, 1946; d. Harold H. and Marilyn Ann (Katz) S.; m. Russell Carl Barnes, May 15, 1987; children: Gabrielle Alexandra Barnes. BS in Sociology, Mich. State U., 1968, MA in Sociology, 1971; MLS, Western Mich. U., 1974; PhD in Sociology, Mich. State U., 1981. Urban affairs bibliographer Mich. State U. Libs., East Lansing, 1974-76, urban policy and planning librarian, 1976-79, social sci. coord., 1979-81, asst. dir., 1981-85, assoc. dir., 1985-87, deputy dir., 1987-90; univ. libr. Rice U., Houston, 1991—; mem. rsch. librs. adv. com. Online Coll. Libr. Ctr., Inc., 1992—; bd. dirs. Ctr. for Rsch. Librs., 1994—. Editor: Selection of Library Materials in the Humanities, Social Sciences. and Sciences., 1985, Selection of Library Materials in Applied and Interdisciplinary Fields, 1987. Mem. Ingham County Equal Opportunity Com., Mason, Mich., 1974-75, Lansing Com. on Affirmative Action, 1976-78, Capital City Revitalization Task Force, Lansing, 1986; mem. Mich. Consumers Coun., Lansing, 1982-88, chmn., 1987-88; bd. dirs. Interracial Family Alliance of Houston, 1993—. Grantee Coun. on Libr. Resources, 1978, 83, 93. Mem. ALA (councilor 1991-95), N.Am. Soc. for Sociology Sport. Office: Rice University Fondren Library MS44 6100 Main St Houston TX 77005

SHAPIRO, BURTON LEONARD, experimental pathologist, geneticist, educator; b. N.Y.C., Mar. 29, 1934; s. Nat Lazarus and Fay Rebecca (Gartenhouse) S.; m. Eileen Roman, Aug. 11, 1958; children—Norah Leah, Anne Rachael, Carla Faye. Student, Tufts U., 1951-54; D.D.S., NYU, 1958; M.S., U. Minn., 1962, Ph.D., 1966. Faculty U. Minn. Sch. Dentistry, Mpls., 1962—; assoc. prof. div. oral pathology U. Minn. Sch. Dentistry, 1966-70,

prof., chmn. div. oral biology, 1970-79, prof., chmn. dept. oral biology, 1979-88, prof. dept. oral pathology and genetics, 1979-88, dir. grad. studies, mem. grad. faculty genetics, 1966—, prof. dept. oral sci., 1988—, mem. grad. faculty pathobiology, 1979; prof. dept. lab. medicine and pathology U. Minn. Sch. Medicine, 1985—, mem. Human Genetics Inst., 1988—, univ. senator, 1968-72, 88-93; also mem. med. staff U. Minn. Health Scis. Center; exec. com. Grad. Sch. U. Minn., chmn. health scis. policy rev. council, chmn. univ. faculty consultative com., 1988-92; chmn. univ. fin. and planning com. Grad. Sch. U. Minn., 1988; hon. research fellow Galton Lab. dept. human genetics Univ. Coll., London, 1974; spl. vis. prof. Japanese Ministry Edn., Sci. and Culture, 1983. Mem. adv. editorial bd.: Jour. Dental Research, 1971—; Contbr. articles to profl. jours. Served to lt. USNR, 1958-60. Am. Cancer Soc. postdoctoral fellow, 1960-62; advanced fellow, 1965-68; named Century Club Prof. of Yr., 1988. Fellow Am. Acad. Oral Pathology, AAAS; mem. Internat. Assn. Dental Research (councilor 1969), Am. Soc. Human Genetics, Craniofacial Biology Soc. (pres. 1972), Sigma Xi, Omicron Kappa Upsilon. Home: 148 Nina St # 2 Saint Paul MN 55102-2160 Office: U Minn Sch Dentistry Dept Oral Sci Minneapolis MN 55455

SHAPIRO, CARL, economics educator and consultant; b. Austin, Tex., Mar. 20, 1955; s. Sherman and Ellen S.; m. Dawn Boyer, Apr. 16, 1978; children: Eva, Benjamin. BS, MIT, 1976, PhD, 1981; MA, U. Calif., 1977. Prof. econs. and consult. U. Calif., Berkeley, 1990—; dep. asst. atty. gen. (designate) 1995—. Assoc. editor: Rand Jour. Econs., 1984-85, Quarterly Jour. Econs., 1984-87; co-editor: Jour. Econ. Perspectives, 1986-93, editor, 1993—. NSF grantee 1982, 84, 86, 88, 91; Sloan Found. fellow, 1984. Mem. Am. Econ. Assn., Econometric Soc. Avocations: frisbee, camping, bicycling. Office: U Calif Haas Sch Bus 350 Barrows Hall Berkeley CA 94720

SHAPIRO, CHERYL BETH, lawyer; b. Neptune, N.J., July 11, 1962; d. Bernard D. and Marcia K. (Goldstein) S.; m. David B. Lebowitz, Nov. 22, 1992. BA, George Washington U., 1983; JD, Widener U., 1986. Bar: Pa. 1986, N.J. 1986. Law clk. Samuel Shevlin, Phila., 1986; coord. planning & devel. Goldco Devel. C., Lakewood, N.J., 1986-87; law clk. Ct. Common Pleas, Phila., 1988-89; corp. atty. CSS Inds., Inc., Phila., 1989—. Pa. Bar Assn., Phila. Bar Assn., Phi Delta Phi. Avocations: theatre, travel. Office: CSS Inds Inc 1845 Walnut St Ste 800 Philadelphia PA 19103

SHAPIRO, DAVID, artist, art historian; b. N.Y.C., Aug. 28, 1916; s. Jacob and Ida (Katz) S.; m. Cecile Peyser, June 18, 1944; children: Deborah Jane, Anna Roberta. Student, Ednl. Alliance Art Sch., 1933-35, Am. Artists Sch., 1936-39. Instr. Smith Coll., 1946-47, Bklyn. Coll., summer, 1947; asst. prof. art U. B.C., 1947-49; mem. faculty dept. art Hofstra U., 1961-81, prof. emeritus, 1981—; prof. fine art New Coll., 1972-81; prof. fine art, artist-in-residence U. Belgrade, Yugoslavia, 1981; vis. critic Vt. Studio Ctr., Johnson, Vt., 1990. Author: Social Realism: Art as a Weapon, 1973, Abstract Expressionism: A Critical Record, 1989; one-man shows include Ganso Gallery, N.Y.C., 1955, Milch Gallery, N.Y.C., 1958, 61, 63, Galleria Dell'Orso, Milan, 1971, Tweed Art Mus., Duluth, Minn, 1978, U. Belgrade Gallery, 1981; 50 yr. retrospective T.W. Wood Art Gallery, Vt. Coll. Arts Ctr., 1987; represented in permanent collections Bklyn. Mus., Met. Mus., Libr. Congress, Nat. Mus., Smithsonian Instn., Phila. Mus. Art. Fulbright grantee, 1951-52, 52-53; MacDowell fellow, 1976; Tamarind fellow, 1976; Nat. Endowment Arts, grantee, 1978; Fulbright grantee, 1980-81. Mem. Soc. Am. Graphic Artists (pres. 1968-70), Coll. Art Assn. Home: RR 1 Box 77 Cavendish VT 05142-9730 *My work and my family are the main interests in my life. Both make it very worthwhile.*

SHAPIRO, DAVID ISRAEL, lawyer; b. Bklyn., June 17, 1928; s. Louis Raymond and Rae (Remin) S.; m. Carolyn M. Foy, Feb. 3, 1980; children by previous marriage: Steven, Claudia, Anthony, James, Miles. Student, U. Wis., 1944-45, Bklyn. Coll., 1946; LL.B., Bklyn. Law Sch., 1949. Bar: N.Y. State bar 1949, U.S. Supreme Ct. bar 1955, D.C. bar 1958. Partner firm Dickstein, Shapiro & Morin (and predecessor firms), Washington, 1953—; sr. partner Dickstein, Shapiro & Morin (and predecessor firms), 1973—. Served with USNR, 1944-46. Mem. Am. Bar Assn., A.C.L.U. Democrat. Home: 10650 Gunston Rd Lorton VA 22079-3915 Office: Dickstein Shapiro & Morin 2101 L St NW Washington DC 20037-1526

SHAPIRO, DAVID LOUIS, lawyer, educator; b. N.Y.C., Oct. 12, 1932; s. Louis and Sara (Grabelsky) S.; m. Jane Wilkins Bennett, June 19, 1954; 1 child, Lynn Mayson. Grad., Horace Mann Sch., 1950; A.B. magna cum laude, Harvard U., 1954, LL.B. summa cum laude, 1957. Bar: D.C. 1957, Mass. 1964. Assoc. atty. firm Covington & Burling, Washington, 1957-62; law clk. Supreme Ct. Justice John M. Harlan, 1962-63; faculty Harvard Law Sch., 1963—, prof. law, 1966—, William Nelson Cromwell prof. law, 1984—, assoc. dean, 1971-76; dep. solicitor gen. U.S. Dept. Justice, 1988-91; mem. labor arbitration and comml. arbitration panels Am. Arbitration Assn., 1966-89; reporter, adv. com. on fair trial and free press ABA, 1965-68. Author: (with others) The Federal Courts and the Federal System, 1973, 2d edit., 1988, Federalism: A Dialogue, 1995; editor: The Evolution of a Judicial Philosophy: Selected Opinions of Justice John M. Harlan, 1969; directing editor University Casebook Series, 1980—; contbr. articles to profl. jours. Mem. Am. Law Inst. (asst. reporter study of div. of jurisdiction 1963-65, reporter Restatement of Judgments 2d 1970-74). Home: 17 Wendell St Cambridge MA 02138-1816 Office: Law Sch Harvard U Cambridge MA 02138

SHAPIRO, DEBBIE LYNN (LYNN SHAPIRO), singer, actress, dancer; b. Santa Monica, Calif., Sept. 29; d. Morton Harold and Anne (Lipsman) S.; m. Beau Gravitte, Sept. 21, 1986. Appeared in Broadway shows including Jerome Robbins' (Tony award 1989, N.Y. Women Stopper award 1989), Zorba, Blues in the Night, Perfectly Frank (Drama Desk nomination); (Broadway debut) They're Playing our Song; Annie Get Your Gun, Spotlight, Swing, King's Tapestry, Berlin to Broadway, Gentleman Prefer Blondes, Mack and Mabel; TV shows include Broadway Plays Washington, CBS Cable Songwriters Series, Trial and Error; TV appearances Pat Sajak, Merv Griffin Show; recs. include Mack and Mabel in Concert; Zorba (with Anthony Quinn), The Songs of Stephen Sondheim, The Songs of N.Y., Jerome Robbins Broadway, They're Playing Song, The First Nudie Musical; nightclubs acts include Sands Hotel, Atlantic City, Harrah's, Atlantic City, Freddy's Supper Club, N.Y.C., Rainbow and Stars, Rockefellar Ctr., N.Y.C., Les Mouches, N.Y.C., The St. Regis Hotel, N.Y.C., others. •

SHAPIRO, EDWARD ROBERT, psychiatrist, educator, psychoanalyst; b. Boston, Sept. 13, 1941; s. Jacob and Ruth (Yankelovich) S.; m. Donna Elmendorf; 1 child from previous marriage, Jacob Matthew; 1 stepchild, Zachary. BA magna cum laude, Yale U., 1962; MA in Anthropology, Stanford U., 1966; MD, Harvard U., 1968. Diplomate Am. Bd. Psychiatry and Neurology. Intern in medicine Beth Israel Hosp., Boston, 1968-69; resident in psychiatry Mass. Mental Health Ctr., Boston, 1969-72, chief resident in psychiatry, 1971-72; clin. assoc. NIMH, Bethesda, Md., 1972-74; dir. Adolescent and Family Treatment and Study Ctr. McLean Hosp., Belmont, Mass., 1974-89; dir. Psychosocial Tng. and Consultation, 1989-91; bd. dirs. Ctr. for Study of Groups and Social Systems, Boston, 1983-90; bd. dirs. A.K. Rice Inst., Washington, 1983-90; dir. Nat. Group Rels. Conf., 1989-91; faculty mem. Boston Psychoanalytic Inst., 1978—; assoc. clin. prof. psychiatry Harvard Med. Sch., Boston, 1982—; med. dir. The Austen Riggs Ctr., Stockbridge, Mass., 1991—. Co-author: (with A.W. Carr) Lost in Familiar Places: Creating New Connections Between the Individual and Society, 1991; mem. editorial bd. Jour. Adolescence, 1977-82, Psychiatry, 1988—; assoc. editor Jour. Adolescence, 1982-84; contbr. articles to profl. jours. With USPHS, 1972-74. Recipient Isenberg Teaching award McLean Hosp., 1980, Rsch. prize for Family Therapy and Rsch., 1984, Felix and Helen Deutsch Sci. prize Boston Psychoanalytic Inst., 1980. Fellow Am. Psychiat. Assn., Am. Psychoanalytic Assn., Am. Family Therapy Assn., Am. Coll. Psychoanalysts, A.K. Rice Inst.; mem. Yale Russian Chorus, Group for the Advanced Study of Psychiatry. Avocation: music. Office: The Austen Riggs Ctr PO Box 962 25 Main St Stockbridge MA 01262-0962

SHAPIRO, ELI, business consultant, educator, economist; b. Bklyn., June 13, 1916; s. Samuel and Pauline (Kushel) S.; m. Beatrice Ferbend, Jan. 18, 1946; 1 child, Laura J. A.B., Bklyn. Coll., 1936; A.M., Columbia U., 1937, Ph.D., 1939. Instr. Bklyn. Coll., 1936-41; rsch. assoc. Nat. Bur. Econ. Rsch., 1938-39; cons. Nat. Bur. Econ. Research, 1939-42; mem. rsch. staff

Nat. Bur. Econ. Rsch., 1955-62; asst. prof. fin. U. Chgo., 1946-47, asso. prof., 1948-52, prof., 1952; prof. fin. Mass. Inst. Tech., 1952-61; assoc. dean Mass. Inst. Tech. (Sch. Indsl. Mgmt.), 1954-58, Alfred P. Sloan prof. mgmt., 1976-84, Alfred P. Sloan prof. emeritus, 1984—; prof. fin. Harvard Bus. Sch., 1962-72, Sylvan C. Coleman prof. fin. mgmt., 1968-72; chmn. fin. com., dir. Travelers Ins. Cos., Hartford, Conn., 1971-78; vice chmn. bd., dir. Travelers Ins. Cos., 1976-78; chmn. bd. Mass. Co., 1971-72; pres. Nat. Bur. Econ. Research, 1982-84; chmn. bd. Fed. Home Loan Bank Boston, 1970-89; econ. analyst div. monetary rsch. U.S. Dept. Treasury, 1941-42; economist rsch. div. OPA, 1941-42; staff cons. Com. Econ. Devel., 1950-51, mem. rsch. adv. com., 1943-44, 69—; project dir., 1966-69; cons. to sec. treasury; mem. enforcement commn. WSB, 1952-53; cons. Inst. Def. Analyses; dep. dir. Rsch. Com. on Money and Credit, 1959-61. Author: (with others) Personal Finance Industry and Its Credit Standards, 1939, (with Steiner) Money and Banking, 1941, Development of Wisconsin Credit Union Movement, 1947, Money and Banking, 1953, (with others), 1958, (with D. Meiselman) Measurement of Corporate Sources and Uses of Funds, 1964, (with others) Money and Banking, 1969, (with Wolf) The Role of Private Placement in Corporate Finance, 1972; Editor: (with W.L. White) Capital for Productivity and Growth, 1977. Served from ensign to lt. USNR, 1942-46. Recipient Econ. Dept. award Bklyn. Coll., 1936, Honors Day award for distinguished alumni, 1949. Fellow Am. Acad. Arts and Scis.; mem. Nat. Bur. Econ. Research (pres.), Am. Econ. Assn., Council Fgn. Relations, Am. Fin. Assn. Home and Office: 180 Beacon St Boston MA 02116-1455

SHAPIRO, ELLEN MARIE, graphic design company executive, writer; b. L.A., June 26, 1948; d. Leon e. and Elizabeth (Nussbaum) S.; m. Jerry Miller, Oct. 10, 1980 (div. 1986); 1 child, Alex Miller. BA, UCLA, 1970. Art dir. UCLA Alumni and Devel. Ctr., 1970-72; sr. designer Lubalin Smith Carnase, Inc., N.Y.C., 1972-74; art dir. Barton-Gillet Co., N.Y.C., 1974-76; ptnr. Design Concern, N.Y.C., 1976-78; pres. Shapiro Design Assocs. Inc., N.Y.C., 1978—, Shapiro Communications, Inc., 1992—; mem. faculty dept. communication design, Parsons Sch. Design, N.Y.C., 1986—; judge design and advt. shows, U.S. and Can. Art dir., Upper & Lower Case, 1988; author: Clients and Designers, 1989. Recipient over 60 awards from profl. orgns. Mem. Am. Inst. Graphic Arts (N.Y. chpt. 1987-89), N.Y. Art Dirs. Club (Gold and Silver awards), N.Y. Type Dirs. Club. Avocations: cooking, gardening, swimming. Office: Shapiro Design Assocs Inc 10 E 40th St New York NY 10016-0200

SHAPIRO, FRED DAVID, lawyer; b. Cleve., Nov. 10, 1926; s. Isadore R. and Lottie (Turetsky) S.; m. Helen Solomon, Sept. 5, 1948; children—Gary N., Ira R., Diane S. B.A. cum laude, Ohio State U., 1949; LL.B., Harvard U., 1954. Bar: Ohio 1954. Since practiced in Cleve.; sr. partner firm Shapiro, Turoff & Belkin, 1976-94; prin. Fred D. Shapiro Co., L.P.A., 1994—. Served with USNR, 1945-46. Mem. Ohio Bar Assn., Greater Cleve. Bar Assn., Cuyahoga County Bar Assn., The Rowfant Club, Phi Beta Kappa. Jewish. Home: 29226 S Woodland Rd Cleveland OH 44124-5737

SHAPIRO, FRED LOUIS, physician, educator; b. Mpls., Aug. 18, 1934; s. Ralph Samuel and Dora (Cohn) S.; m. Merle Sandra Rosenzweig, June 23, 1957; children: Wendy Judith, Richard Scott. BA magna cum laude, U. Minn., 1958, BS, 1961, MD, 1961. Intern Hennepin County Med. Ctr., Mpls., 1961-62, resident in internal medicine, 1962-65, instr., 1965-68, chief nephrology, 1965-84; med. dir. Regional Kidney Disease Program, 1966-84; asst. prof. U. Minn., Mpls., 1968-71, assoc. prof., 1971-75, prof., 1975—; pres. Hennepin Faculty Assocs., 1983—. Contbr. articles to profl. jours. With USNR, 1953-55. Mem. Am. Soc. Nephrology, Am. Soc. Artificial Internal Organs, Nat. Kidney Found., Mpls. Soc. Internal Medicine, Phi Beta Kappa, Sigma Xi, Alpha Omega Alpha. Home: 3490 Fairway Ln Minnetonka MN 55305-4451 Office: Hennepin Facility Assocs 600 HFA Bldg 914 S 8th St Minneapolis MN 55404

SHAPIRO, GARY MICHAEL, philosophy educator; b. St. Paul, June 17, 1941; s. Irving H. and Florence Beverly (Gleckman) S.; m. Anne Goll, 1961 (div. 1966); 1 child, Marya Suzanne; m. Lynne Margolies, 1968 (div. 1991); children: David Benjamin, Rachel Shulamith. B.A. magna cum laude, Columbia U., 1963, Ph.D., 1970; postgrad., Yale U., 1963-64. Instr. Columbia U., N.Y.C., 1967-70; asst. prof. U. Kans., Lawrence, 1970-75, assoc. prof., 1975-81, prof., 1981-91; prof. philosophy, Tucker Boatwright prof. in humanities U. Richmond, Va., 1991—. Author: Nietzschean Narratives, 1989, Alcyone, 1991, Earthwards: Robert Smithson and Art after Babel, 1995; editor: After the Future, 1990; mem. editl. adv. bd. Philosophy and Literature, 1982—, Contemporary Studies in Philosophy and Literature, Jour. History of Philosophy; co-editor: Hermeneutics: Questions & Prospects, 1984; contbr. articles to profl. jours. Woodrow Wilson fellow. Am. Coun. Learned Socs. fellow, 1978, U. Calif., Irvine Sch. of Criticism and Theory fellow, 1976; sr. rsch. fellow Wesleyan U. Ctr. for the Humanities, 1985, Nat. Humanities Ctr. fellow, 1993-94. Mem. Internat. Assn. for Philosophy and Lit. (exec. com. 1984-89), N. Am. Nietzsche Soc. (exec. com. 1983-89), Am. Philo. Assn. (com. on lectrs. philosophy and research 1985-88), Phi Beta Kappa. Office: U Richmond Dept Philosophy Richmond VA 23173

SHAPIRO, GEORGE HOWARD, lawyer; b. St. Louis, Nov. 10, 1936; s. Isadore T. and Alice (Schucart) S.; m. Mary Kenney Leonard, 1977 (div. 1994); 1 child, Ellen Leonard. B.A., Harvard U., 1958, LL.B., 1961; postgrad., London Sch. Econs., 1961-62. Bar: Ga. 1960, D.C. 1963. Atty. U.S. Dept. Labor, Washington, 1962-63; assoc. Arent Fox Kintner Plotkin & Kahn, Washington, 1963-69, ptnr., 1970—. Co-author: 'Cable Speech' The Case for First Amendment Protection, 1983; editor: New Program Opportunities in the Electronic Media, 1983, Current Developments in CATV, 1981. Served with USAR, 1962-68. Frank Knox Meml. fellow Harvard U., 1961-62. Mem. D.C. Bar Assn., Fed. Communications Bar Assn., Fed. Bar Assn. (dep. chmn. communications law com. 1970-71), ABA (vice chmn. cable TV com. 1982-83). Democrat. Jewish. Avocation: skiing. Home: 3249-D Sutton Pl NW Washington DC 20016-3507 Office: Arent Fox Kintner Plotkin & Kahn 1050 Connecticut Ave NW Washington DC 20036-5339

SHAPIRO, GEORGE M., lawyer; b. N.Y.C., Dec. 7, 1919; s. Samuel N. and Sarah (Milstein) S.; m. Rita V. Lubin, Mar. 29, 1942; children: Karen Shapiro Spector, Sanford. BS, LIU, 1939; LL.B. (Kent scholar), Columbia U., 1942; LL.D. (hon.), L.I. U., 1986. Bar: N.Y. 1942. Mem. staff gov. N.Y., 1945-51, counsel to gov., 1951-54; ptnr. Proskauer, Rose Goetz & Mendelsohn, N.Y.C., 1955—, mem. exec. com., mng. ptnr., 1974-84, co-chmn. corp. dept., 1980-90; pres. Edmond de Rothschild Found., 1964-92; dir. Bank of Calif., 1973-84; counsel, majority leader N.Y. Senate, 1955-59; counsel N.Y. Constl. Revision Commn., 1960-61. Chmn. council State U. Coll. Medicine, N.Y., 1955-71; mem. Gov.'s Com. Reapportionment, 1964, Mayor's Com. Jud. Selection, 1966-69; chmn. Park Ave. Synagogue, 1973-81; mem. Coun. on Fgn. Rels., 1974-92. Served with USAAF, 1943-45. Club: Harmonie. Home: 1160 Park Ave New York NY 10128-1212 Office: Proskauer Rose Goetz & Mendelsohn 1585 Broadway New York NY 10036-8200

SHAPIRO, GILBERT LAWRENCE, orthopedist; b. Lewiston, Maine, June 14, 1931; s. Samuel and Freda (Meyer) S.; m. Frima Lee Goldman, Aug. 28, 1955; children: Beth S. Lewyckyi, Karen S. Goldaber, Ruth A. BA, Dartmouth Coll., 1953; MD, Tufts U., 1957. Diplomate Am. Bd. Orthopaedic Surgery. Pvt. practice orthopaedic surgery New Bedford, Mass., 1963—. Bd. dirs. NBIS Savings Bank, New Bedford, 1982—; trustee St. Luke's Hosp., New Bedford, 1989—; pres. bd. trustees Pilgrim Healthcare (HMO), Norwell, Md., 1991—; Old Dartmouth Hist. Soc. (whaling mus.), New Bedford, 1991—. Mem. ACS, Am. Acad. Orthopaedic Surgeons, New England Orthopaedic Soc. (pres. 1988-90), Ea. Orthopaedic Soc. Office: 84 Grape St New Bedford MA 02740 also: New Bedford Whaling Mus 18 Johnny Cake Hill New Bedford MA 02740

SHAPIRO, GLENN ALAN, marketing executive, consultant; b. Bklyn., Apr. 4, 1953; s. Abraham L. and Roslyn Shapiro; m. Judy Lynn Levine, Nov. 7, 1976; children: Valerie, Jamie. BA in Econs., NYU, 1974, JD, MBA in Mktg. & Finance, 1977. Bar: N.Y. 1977. Mgr., administr. dir. mktg. card divsn. Am. Express, N.Y.C., 1976-78; dir. advt. Am. Express Travel Related Svcs., N.Y.C., 1978-80, v.p. bus. devel. commn. divsn., 1980-83; v.p. mkt. planning, direct mktg. Am. Mgmt. Assn., N.Y.C., 1983-85; dir. direct mktg. Prodigy divsn., IBM/Sears Co., N.Y., 1985-87; sr. v.p. mktg. Family Shopping Network, White Plains, 1987-88; sr. v.p. subscription mktg. Bur. Bus.

Practive divsn. Prentice Hall-Simon and Schuster, Waterford, Conn., 1988-93; v.p. mktg. market data retrieval Dun & Bradstreet, Shelton, Conn., 1994—; prof. Direct Mktg. New Sch., N.Y.C. 1982-83; dir., cons. Ad Net Corp., Lebanon, Ohio 1984—. Recipient Founder's Day award for Acad. Excellence N.Y.U., 1974. Mem. N.Y. State Bar Assn., Direct Mktg. Assn. Avocations: racquetball, skiing, sailing. Home: 21 Mackinnon Pl East Lyme CT 06333-1534 Office: Dun & Bradstreet Market Data Retrieval 16 Progress Dr Shelton CT 06484

SHAPIRO, HAROLD DAVID, lawyer, educator; b. Chgo., Apr. 15, 1927; s. Charles B. and Celia (Nierenberg) S.; m. Beatrice Cahn, June 6, 1950; children: Matthew D., Michael Ann, Nicholas J. BS, Northwestern U., 1949; JD, Northwestern U., Chgo., 1952. Adminstrv. asst. State of Ill. Dept. Fin., Springfield, 1952; assoc. Sonnenschein Nath & Rosenthal, Chgo., 1953-59; ptnr. Sonnenschein Nath & Rosenthal, 1959—; Edward A. Harriman adj. prof. law Northwestern U., Chgo., 1970—; sec., bd. dirs. West Side Affordable Housing, Inc., West Side Village, Inc. Trustee, mem. exec. com., sec. Jr. Achievement of Chgo.; bd. dirs. Schwab Rehab. Ctr., Chgo.; pres. Northwestern U. Law Alumni Assn., Chgo., 1984-85. Served with Seabees, USNR, 1945-50, PTO. Recipient Merit award Northwestern U., 1988. Mem. Ill. Bar Assn., ABA, Chgo. Bar Assn., Chgo. Council Lawyers, Legal Club of Chgo. (pres.), Law Club of Chgo., Order of Coif, Wigmore Key, Standard Club, Met. Club, Cliff Dwellers, Chicago Club, Lake Shore Country Club. Democrat. Jewish. Home: 34 Linden Ave Wilmette IL 60091-2837 Office: Sonnenschein Nath & Rosenthal 8000 Sears Tower 233 S Wacker Dr Chicago IL 60606

SHAPIRO, HAROLD TAFLER, university president, economist; b. Montreal, Que., Can., June 8, 1935; s. Maxwell and Mary (Tafler) S.; m. Vivian Bernice Rapoport, May 19, 1957; children: Anne, Marilyn, Janet, Karen. BComm, McGill U., Montreal, 1956; PhD in Econs. (Harold Helm fellow, Harold Dodds sr. fellow), Princeton U., 1964. Asst. prof. econs. U. Mich., 1964-67, assoc. prof., 1967-70, prof., 1970-76, chmn. dept. econs., 1974-77, prof. econs. and pub. affairs, from 1977, v.p. acad. affairs, 1977-79, pres., 1980-87; research adv. Bank Can., 1965-72; prof. econ. and pub. affairs, pres. Princeton U., 1988—; bd. dirs. Dow Chem.; trustee Univs. Rsch. Assn., 1988—; mem. exec. com. Assn. Am. Univs., 1985-89, N.J. Commn. on Sci. and Tech., 1988-91; mem. Pres.'s Coun. Advisors on Sci. and Tech., 1990-92; chmn. com. on employer-based health benefits Inst. Medicine, 1991. Trustee Alfred P. Sloan Found., 1980—, Interlochen Ctr. for Arts, 1988—, U. Pa. Med. Ctr., 1992—; dir. Am. Coun. Edn., 1989-92; chmn. Spl. Presdl. Com., The Research Libraries Group, 1980-91; mem. Gov.'s High Tech. Task Force, Mich., 1980-87; mem. Gov.'s Commn. on Jobs and Econ. Devel. (Mich.), 1983-87; mem. Carnegie Commn. on Coll. Retirement, 1984-86. Recipient Lt. Gov.'s medal in commerce McGill U., 1956. Fellow Am. Acad. Arts and Scis., Mich. Soc. Fellows (dir.); mem. Inst. Medicine of NAS, Am. Philos. Soc., Nat. Bur. Econ. Rsch. (bd. dirs.). Office: Princeton U 1 Nassau Hall Princeton NJ 08544*

SHAPIRO, HARRY DEAN, lawyer; b. Louisville, June 21, 1940; s. Herman Shapiro and Toby (Spector) Levy; m. Linda Siegel, Dec. 19, 1970; 1 child, Deborah Anne. BS, U. Louisville, 1962, JD, 1964. Bar: Ky. 1964, D.C. 1968, Md. 1970. Trial and appellate atty. U.S. Dept. Justice, Washington, 1964-70; assoc. Venable, Baetjer & Howard, Balt., 1970-74, ptnr., 1975-87; sr. ptnr., head of tax practice Weinberg & Green, Balt., 1987—; chmn. corp. dept., 1993-95; transaction group coord., 1995—. Author: Federal Tax Liens, 1981; contbr. articles to profl. jours. Mem. Md. State Bd. Edn., 1990—; v.p. Assoc. Jewish Charities of Balt., Inc. 1991-94; vice chmn. The Assoc. Jewish Cmty. Fedn. Balt. 1987-89, asst. treas., 1989-91, mem. exec. com., 1993—; trustee Sinai Hops., Balt., 1987-90; trustee, counsel Balt. Mus. Art, 1984—, sec., 1985-92, v.p., sec., 1992-94, v.p., 1994—; dir., chmn. Joint Budgeting Coun., 1993—, Coun. Jewish Fedns. Capt. USAR, 1967-70. Mem. ABA (tax sect.), Md. State Bar Assn., Ky. Bar Assn., D.C. Bar Assn., Md. Club, Center Club. Home: 7903 7 Mile Ln Baltimore MD 21208-4306 Office: Weinberg & Green 100 S Charles St Baltimore MD 21201-2725 *Our country is at a crossroads in its history, and it is becoming clear that a sea change is necessary. Basic reforms must occur in our governmental and educational structures. The question is whether we have the intelligence to reject the cries for bigger government and more taxes to solve these problems when fundamental action is required.*

SHAPIRO, HARVEY, poet; b. Chgo., Jan. 27, 1924; s. Jacob J. and Dorothy (Cohen) S.; m. Edna Lewis Kaufman, July 23, 1953; children—Saul, Dan. B.A., Yale U., 1947; M.A., Columbia U., 1948. Instr. English Cornell U., 1949-50, 51-52; creative writing fellow Bard Coll., 1950-51; mem. editorial staff Commentary, New Yorker, 1955-57; editorial staff N.Y. Times mag., N.Y.C., 1957; asst. editor N.Y. Times mag., 1964-75; editor N.Y. Times Book Rev., 1975-83; dep. editor N.Y. Times Mag., 1983—. Author: The Eye, 1953, The Book and Other Poems, 1955, Mountain, Fire, Thornbush, 1961, Battle Report, 1966, This World, 1971, Lauds, 1975, Nightsounds, 1978, The Light Holds, 1984, National Cold Storage Company, 1988, A Day's Portion, 1994. Served with USAAF, World War II. Decorated D.F.C., Air medal with 3 oak leaf clusters.; Rockefeller Found. grantee in poetry, 1967. Club: Elizabethan (New Haven), Century (N.Y.). Office: NY Times 229 W 43rd St New York NY 10036-3913

SHAPIRO, HOWARD ALAN, lawyer; b. Albany, N.Y., May 12, 1932; s. Ralph and Estelle (Warshak) S.; m. Eleanor Siegel, June 20, 1954; children: David Todd, Andrew Neil, Diane Graser. A.B. magna cum laude, Harvard U., 1953, LL.B. magna cum laude, 1956. Bar: N.Y. 1956. Assoc. Proskauer Rose Goetz & Mendelsohn, N.Y.C., 1956-65, ptnr., 1965—; lectr. Practicing Law Inst., 1971-79. Editor Harvard Law Rev., 1954-56, note editor, 1955-56. Mem. Assn. of Bar of City of N.Y. (com. on corp. law 1971-74, com. on banking law 1978-81, 86-89), N.Y. State Bar Assn., ABA, N.Y. County Lawyers' Assn. Home: 140 E 72nd St New York NY 10021-4243 Office: Proskauer Rose et al 1585 Broadway New York NY 10036-8200

SHAPIRO, HOWIE, newspaper editor. Cultural arts editor The Phila. Inquirer. Office: The Philadelphia Inquirer 400 N Broad St Philadelphia PA 19130*

SHAPIRO, IRVING S., medical think-tank executive. Chmn. of the trustees The Howard Hughes Medical Inst., Bethesda, Md. Office: The Howard Hughes Med Inst 6701 Rockledge Dr Bethesda MD 20817

SHAPIRO, IRVING SAUL, lawyer; b. Mpls., July 15, 1916; s. Sam I. and Freda (Lane) S.; m. Charlotte Farsht, Mar. 1, 1942; children: Stuart Lane, Elizabeth Irene. B.S., U. Minn., 1939, LL.B., 1941. Bar: Minn. 1941, Del. 1958. Atty. criminal div. Dept. Justice, 1943-51; with E.I. du Pont de Nemours & Co., Inc., 1951-81, v.p., 1970-73, vice chmn. bd., 1973, chmn., chief exec. officer, 1974-81, also dir., chmn. exec. com., chmn. pub. affairs com., until 1981; ptnr. firm Skadden, Arps, Slate, Meagher & Flom, N.Y., 1981-89, of counsel, 1990; bd. dirs. AEA Investors Inc., J.P. Morgan Fla. Fed. Savs. Bank. Chmn. bd. trustees Howard Hughes Med. Inst., Ohmicron Corp., Pediat. Scvs. of Am. Inc., Sola Internat. Inc. Office: Skadden Arps Slate Meagher & Flom 1 Rodney Sq Wilmington DE 19801

SHAPIRO, IRWIN IRA, physicist, educator; b. N.Y.C., N.Y., Oct. 10, 1929; s. Samuel and Esther (Feinberg) S.; m. Marian Helen Kaplun, Dec. 20, 1959; children: Steven, Nancy. A.B., Cornell U., 1950; A.M., Harvard U., 1951, Ph.D., 1955. Mem. staff Lincoln Lab. MIT, Lexington, 1954-70; Sherman Fairchild Distinguished scholar Calif. Inst. Tech., 1974; Morris Loeb lectr. physics Harvard, 1975; prof. geophysics and physics MIT, 1967-80, Schlumberger prof., 1980-84; Paine prof. practical astronomy, prof. physics Harvard U., 1982—; sr. scientist Smithsonian Astrophys. Obs., 1982—; dir. Harvard-Smithsonian Ctr. for Astrophysics, 1983—; cons. NSF, NASA. Contbr. articles to profl. jours. Recipient Albert A. Michelson medal Franklin Inst., 1975, award in phys. and math. scis. N.Y. Acad. Scis., 1982; Guggenheim fellow, 1982. Fellow AAAS, Am. Geophys. Union (Charles A. Whitten medal 1991, William Bowie medal 1993), Am. Phys. Soc.; mem. Am. Acad. Arts and Scis., Nat. Acad. Scis. (Benjamin Aprhorp Gould prize 1979), Am. Astron. Soc. (Dannie Heineman award 1983, Dirk Brouwer award 1987), Internat. Astron. Union, Phi Beta Kappa, Sigma Xi, Phi Kappa Phi. Home: 17 Lantern Ln Lexington MA 02173-6029 Office: Smithsonian Astrophysical Obs 60 Garden St Cambridge MA 02138-1596*

SHAPIRO, ISAAC, lawyer; b. Tokyo, Jan. 5, 1931; s. Constantine and Lydia (Chernetzky) S.; m. Jacqueline M. Weiss, Sept. 16, 1956; children: Tobias, Alexandra, Natasha. A.B., Columbia U., 1954, LL.B., 1956; postgrad., Inst. de Droit Compare, U. Paris, 1956-57. Bar: N.Y. 1957, U.S. Supreme Ct. 1971, Paris 1991. Assoc. Milbank, Tweed, Hadley & McCloy, N.Y.C., 1956-65, ptnr., 1966-86; resident ptnr. Milbank, Tweed, Hadley & McCloy, Tokyo, 1977-79; ptnr. Skadden Arps Slate Meagher and Flom, N.Y.C., 1986—; teaching fellow comparative law NYU, 1959-61; lectr. Soviet law, 1961-67; adj. asst. prof. NYU, 1967-69, adj. assoc. prof., 1969-71, 74-75; bd. dirs. Bank of Tokyo Trust Co., N.Y.C., Carl Zeiss, Inc., Thornwood, N.Y., PRT Corp., N.Y.C. Author: (with Hazard and Maggs) The Soviet Legal System, 1969; author: Japan: The Risen Sun (in Japanese), 1982; editor: The Middle East Crisis-Prospects for Peace, 1969; contbr. articles to periodicals. Mem. Joint Com. U.S.-Japan Cultural and Ednl. Cooperation, Washington, 1972-78; mem. Japan-U.S. Friendship Commn., 1975-78; trustee Nat. Humanities Ctr., Triangle Park, N.C., 1976-89; trustee, v.p. Chamber Music Soc. Lincoln Ctr., 1980-86; trustee, pres. Isamu Noguchi Fedn., 1985—; trustee, chmn. Ise Cultural Fedn., 1984—; bd. dirs. Bus. Coun. for Internat. Understanding, 1989—, Nat. Com. for U.S.-China Rels., 1989—. Fulbright scholar, 1956-57. Mem. ABA, N.Y. State Bar Assn., Assn. Bar City N.Y., Japan Soc. (pres. N.Y. 1970-77), Coun. Fgn. Rels. Home: 6 rue Goethe, 75116 Paris France Offices: Skadden Arps Slate Meagher & Flom, 105, rue du faubourg St Honore, 75008 Paris France

SHAPIRO, ISADORE, materials scientist, consultant; b. Mpls., Apr. 25, 1916; s. Jacob and Bessie (Goldman) S.; m. Mae Hirsch, Sept. 4, 1938; children: Stanley Harris, Jerald Steven. BChemE. summa cum laude, U. Minn., 1938, PhD, 1944. Asst. instr. chemistry U. Minn., 1938-41, rsch. fellow, 1944-45; rsch. chemist E. I. duPont de Nemours and Co., Phila., 1946; head chem. lab. U.S. Naval Ordnance Test Sta., Pasadena, Calif., 1947-52; dir. rsch. lab. Olin-Mathieson Chem. Corp., 1952-59; head chemistry Hughes Tool Co., Aircraft div., Culver City, Calif., 1959-62; pres. Universal Chem. Systems Inc. 1962—, Aerospace Chem. Systems, Inc., 1964-66; dir. contract rsch. HITCO, Gardena, Calif., 1966-67; prin. scientist Douglas Aircraft Co. of McDonnell Douglas Corp., Santa Monica, Calif., 1967; prin. scientist McDonnell Douglas Astronautics Co., 1967-70; head materials and processes AiResearch Mfg. Co., Torrance, Calif., 1971-82, cons., 1982—; inaugurated dep. gov. Am. Biog. Inst. Rsch. Assn., 1988; dep. dir. gen. Internat. Biog. Ctr., 1989, Eng. Rater U.S. Civil Svc. Bd. Exam., 1948-52. Served 1st lt. AUS, 1941-44. Registered profl. engr., Calif. Fellow Am. Inst. Chemists, Am. Inst. Aeros and Astronautics (assoc.); mem. AAAS, Am. Ordnance Assn., Am. Chem. Soc., Soc. Rheology, Soc. Advancement Materials and Process Engring., Am. Inst. Physics, AIM, Am. Phys. Soc., N.Y. Acad. Sci., Am. Assn. Contamination Control, Am. Ceramic Soc., Nat. Inst. Ceramic Engrs., Am. Powder Metallurgy Inst., Internat. Plansee Soc. for Powder Metallurgy, Sigma Xi, Tau Beta Pi, Phi Lambda Upsilon. Author articles in tech. publs. Patentee, discoverer series of carborane compounds; created term carborane; formulator of universal compaction equation for powders (metals, ceramics, polymers, chemicals). Home: 5624 W 62nd St Los Angeles CA 90056-2009

SHAPIRO, IVAN, lawyer; b. N.Y.C., Nov. 11, 1928; s. Archie M. and Auguste (Reiff) S.; m. Florence Goodstein, June 24, 1951 (div. Oct. 1958); 1 child, Lisa J. Kubiske; m. Maria Schaffner, Sept. 16, 1960; 1 child, Alexandra. B.S.S., CCNY, 1948; J.D., Harvard U., 1951. Bar: N.Y. 1952. Assoc. Wien, Lane, Klein & Purcell, N.Y.C., 1954-59; ptnr. Wien, Lane & Klein, 1959-74, Greenbaum, Wolff & Ernst, N.Y.C., 1974-81, Willkie Farr & Gallagher, N.Y.C., 1981-91; lectr. Real Estate Inst., NYU Sch. Continuing Edn. N.Y.C., 1978-81. Author: Case Studies in Real Estate Finance, 1980; author pamphlets on ethical issues, 1973-80, articles on civil liberties issues, 1966-80. Trustee Ethical Culture Soc., N.Y.C., 1970—, pres., 1972-78, Ethical Culture Schs., N.Y., 1976-82; bd. visitors Grad. Sch., Univ. Ctr. CUNY, 1986—, vice chmn., 1992—; mem. Asia Watch Com. Human Rights Watch, 1990-95; bd. dirs., pres. Urban Pathways Inc. (formerly West Side Cluster Inc.), 1991-95; bd. dirs. Bklyn. Navy Yard Devel. Corp., 1991—; bd. dirs. Abortion Rights Assn. N.Y., 1970-71, Nat. Assn. for Repeal of Abortion Laws, 1971-74. Mem. ACLU (bd. dirs. N.Y. chpt. 1966-80, treas. 1989—), Assn. of Bar of City of N.Y., Phi Beta Kappa. Democrat. Office: 1 CitiCorp Ctr 153 E 53rd St New York NY 10022-4677

SHAPIRO, JAMES EDWARD, judge; b. Chgo., May 28, 1930; s. Ben Edward and Rose (Slate) S.; m. Rhea Kahn, Dec. 28, 1958; children—Jeffrey Scott, Steven Mark. B.S., U. Wis., 1951; J.D., Harvard U., 1954. Bar: Wis. 1956, U.S. Dist. Ct. (ea. dist.) Wis. 1956, U.S. Ct. Appeals (7th cir.) 1962, U.S. Supreme Ct. 1971. Sole practice, Milw., 1956-57; resident house counsel Nat. Presto Industries, Eau Claire, Wis., 1957-60; ptnr. Bratt & Shapiro, Milw., 1960-64; sole practice, Milw., 1964-74; ptnr. Frank, Hiller & Shapiro, Milw., 1974-82; judge U.S. Bankruptcy Ct., Milw., 1982—; mem. Bayside Bd. Appeals, Wis., 1969-77; Milw. county ct. commr., 1969-78; dir. Milw. Legal Aid Soc., 1969-77. Served to 1st lt. U.S. Army, 1954-56. Mem. State Bar Assn. Wis. (chmn. bankruptcy, insolvency, creditors rights sect.), Milw. Bar Assn. (past chmn., past vice chmn. bankruptcy sect.). Jewish. Office: US Courthouse 140 Fed Bldg 517 E Wis Ave Milwaukee WI 53202

SHAPIRO, JEREMY FRANK, management educator; b. Durham, N.C., May 21, 1939; s. Lester and Jean (Morris) S.; m. Martha Jane Heigham, Jan. 5, 1980; children: Alexander, Lara, Nicholas. B.M.E., Cornell U., 1962, M.I.E., 1963; Ph.D., Stanford U., 1967. Asst. prof. Sloan Sch. Mgmt., MIT, Cambridge, 1966-69, assoc. prof., 1969-75, prof., 1975—; co-dir. Ops. Research Ctr., 1977—; sr. research assoc. Nat. Bur. Econ. Research, Cambridge, 1972-77; ptnr., chmn. bd. Resource Mgmt. Systems, Boston, 1979—; co-dir. Ops. Research Ctr., MIT, 1977-86; ptnr., chmn. bd. Resource Mgmt. Systems, Cambridge, 1979—. Author: Mathematical Programming: Structures and Algorithms, 1979. Mem. Nat. Acad. Scis. panel on energy conservation, 1985-86. Mem. Ops. Research Soc. Am., Inst. Mgmt. Sci., Math. Programming Soc. Home: 226 Commonwealth Ave Boston MA 02116-2530 Office: MIT Operations Rsch Ctr Cambridge MA 02139

SHAPIRO, JEROME GERSON, lawyer; b. N.Y.C., May 12, 1924; s. Joseph Louis and Beatrice Rebecca S.; m. Marjorie Kemble Mackay, Dec. 31, 1959; children—Jeffrey Kemble, Jill Dara, Eric Paul. A.B. summa cum laude, NYU, 1946; LL.B. magna cum laude, Harvard U., 1948. Bar: N.Y. State bar 1949, U.S. Supreme Ct. bar 1955. Asso. mem. firm Hughes Hubbard & Reed, N.Y.C., 1949-51, 52-57; spl. asst. atty. gen., sr. asst. counsel N.Y. State Crime Commn., 1951-52; ptnr. firm Hughes Hubbard & Reed, N.Y.C., 1957-95; chmn. Hughes Hubbard & Reed, 1975-90; consul, 1995—; prof. law N.Y. Law Sch., 1951-53. Vice chmn. trustees James W. Johnson Community Centers, Inc., N.Y.C., 1975-78; trustee Lawyers Com. for Civil Rights Under Law, 1976—. Served with AUS, 1943-45. Decorated Purple Heart, Bronze Star. Fellow Am. Coll. Trial Lawyers; mem. Assn. of Bar of City of N.Y. (exec. com. 1967-73), Am. Bar Found. (rsch. com.), Harvard Club, Phi Beta Kappa. Jewish. Office: Hughes Hubbard & Reed 1 Battery Park Plz New York NY 10004

SHAPIRO, JEROME HERBERT, radiologist, educator; b. Cleve., Aug. 5, 1924; s. Louis and Rose (Hamburger) S.; m. Amy Elizabeth Alderman, June 16, 1948 (dec. Jan. 1991); children: Nancy Lee, Mathew Paul, Wendy Jane, Deborah Gail; m. Meredith Pearlstein, Dec. 16, 1993. Student, Western Res. U., 1942-44; M.D., Yale U., 1948. Intern Mt. Sinai Hosp., Cleve., 1948-49; resident radiology Montefiore Hosp., N.Y.C., 1949-52; fellow X-ray diagnosis Meml. Center, N.Y.C., 1952; attending radiologist Montefiore Hosp., 1952-63; assoc. clin. prof. radiology N.Y. U., 1960-63; prof. radiology Boston U. Sch. Medicine, 1963—, chmn. dept. radiology, 1963-92; dir. radiology Boston City, Univ. hosps., 1963-92; Lectr. radiology Harvard, Tufts med. schs., 1963—. Sr. author: Cardiac Calcifications, 1963; Contbr. numerous articles to profl. jours. Vice pres. Wellesley (Mass.) Symphony Orch., 1980-82, pres., 1982-86. Fellow Am. Coll. Radiology (chancellor 1973-79, 89-90, v.p. 1980-81, pres. 1989-90, gold medal 1992), Coun. Med. Splty. Socs. (pres. 1992-93); mem. AMA, Radiol. Soc. N.Am., Am. Roentgen Ray Soc. (pres. 1974-75), Assn. Univ. Radiologists, Am. Soc. Neuroradiology, Mass. Radiol. Soc. (pres temple 1968-72). Jewish (pres. temple 1968-72). Home: 416 Commonwealth Ave # 608 Boston MA 02215-2811 Office: Univ Hosp Dept Radiology 88 E Newton St Boston MA 02118-2308

SHAPIRO, JOE, lawyer, entertainment company executive. BA, U. Pa., 1968; JD, Harvard U., 1971. Bar: N.Y. 1972, Calif. 1980. Assoc. Donovan,

Leisure, Newton & Irvine, 1971-79, ptnr., 1979-85; sr. v.p., gen. counsel Walt Disney Co., Burbank, Calif., 1985—. Office: Walt Disney Co Corp Legal Dept 500 S Buena Vista St Burbank CA 91521-0001

SHAPIRO, JOEL ELIAS, artist; b. N.Y.C., Sept. 27, 1941; s. Joseph and Anna (Lewis) S.; m. Ellen Phelan; 1 dau., Ivy Bess. B.A., NYU, 1964, M.A., 1969. One-person shows include Paula Cooper Gallery, N.Y.C., 14 shows 1970-89, 90-92, Inst. Art and Urban Resources, N.Y.C., 1973, Mus. Contemporary Art, Chgo., 1976, Albright-Knox Art Gallery, Buffalo, 1977, Gallery M. Bochum, W. Ger., 1977, Galerie Mukai, Tokyo, 1980, 81, 88, Asher/Faure, L.A., 1980, 89, Whitechapel Gallery, London, 1980, Hans Lange, Krefeld, W. Ger., 1980, Moderna Museet, Stockholm, 1980, Brown U., 1980, Ackland Art Mus., Chapel Hill, N.C., 1981, Contemporary Arts Ctr., Cin., 1981, Israel Mus., Jerusalem, 1981, Portland Ctr. Visual Arts, Oreg., 1982, Whitney Mus. Am. Art, N.Y.C., 1982, Galerie Aronowitsch, Stockholm, 1983, Delahunty Gallery, Dallas, 1983, Donald Young Gallery, Chgo., 1984, Stedelijk Mus., Amsterdam, 1985, Kunstmuseum, Dusseldorf, 1985, Staatliche Kunsthalle, Baden-Baden, 1985, Seattle Art Mus., 1986, Galerie Daniel Templon, Paris, 1986, 88, The John and Mable Ringling Mus., Sarasota, 1986, John Berggruen Gallery, San Francisco, Hirshhorn Mus. and Sculpture Garden, Washington, 1987, Hans Strelow, Dusseldorf, Germany, 1988, Toledo Mus. Art, 1989, Waddington Gallery, London, 1989, Museet I Varberg, Sweden, 1990, Balt. Art Mus., 1990, Des Moines Art Ctr., 1991, Ctr. for Fine Arts, Miami, 1991, IVAM Centre Julio Gonazlez, Valencia, Spain, 1990, Ctr. for the Fine Arts, Miami, 1991, Asher-Faure, L.A., 1991, Gallery Mukai, Tokyo, 1991, John Berggruen Gallery, San Francisco, 1991, Pace Gallery, 1993, Galerie Karsten Greve, Cologne, Germany, 1993, Gallery Seomi, Seoul, 1994, Glerie Aronowitsch, Stockholm, 1995, Karsten Greve, Paris, 1995, Pace Gallery, N.Y., 1995; numerous group exhibits; permanent collections and commns. include Mus. Modern Art, N.Y.C., Whitney Mus. Art, N.Y.C., Walker Art Center, Mpls., Met. Mus. Art, N.Y.C., Albright Knox Art Gallery, Buffalo, Detroit Inst. Art, Stedelijk Mus., Amsterdam, Moderna Museet, Stockholm, Dallas Mus. Art, Centre Pompidou, Paris, Nat. Gallery Art, Washington, Brit. Mus., London, Bkln. Mus., Cocoran Gallery, Washington, Fogg Art Mus. at Harvard U., Cambridge, Mass., High Mus. Art, Atlanta, Hirshhorn Mus. and Sculpture Garden at Smithsonian Instn., Washington, Israel Mus., Jerusalem, Kunsthaus Zürich, Switzerland, Mus. Contemporary Art, L.A., Mus. Fine Arts, Boston, Mus. Modern Art, Friuli, Italy, Parrish Art Mus., Southampton, N.Y., Phila. Mus. Art, Tate Gallery, London, commissions include Cigna Corp., Phila., 1983-84, Fukuoka (Japan) Sogo Bank, 1988, Creative Artists Agy., L.A., 1988-89, Kawamura Meml. Mus. Art, Chiba, Japan, 1988-89, Govt. Svc. Adminstrn., L.A., 1988-90, Hood Mus. Art at Dartmouth Coll., Hanover, N.H., 1989-90, U.S. Holocaust Meml. Mus., Washington, 1993, Sony Music Entertainment, N.Y.C., 1994-95, Friedrichstadt Passagen, Berlin, 1994-95; represented by Pace Gallery, N.Y.C., Cleve. Mus. Art, N.C. Mus. Art, Raleigh, Des Moines Art Ctr., Pace Gallery, N.Y.C. Recipient Nat. Endowment for Arts award, 1975, Brandeis award, 1984, Skowhegan medal, 1986, Award of Merit, Am. Acad. and Inst. of Arts and Letters, 1990. Mem. Swedish Royal Acad. Art. Office: care Pace Gallery 32 57th St New York NY 10022

SHAPIRO, JUDITH R., anthropology educator, university official; b. N.Y.C., Jan. 24, 1942. Student Ecole des Haute Etudes Initiat d'Etudes Politiques, Paris, 1961-62; BA, Brandeis U., 1963; PhD, Columbia U., 1972. Asst. prof. U. Chgo., 1970-75; postdoctoral fellow U. Calif.-Berkeley, 1974-75; Rosalyn R. Schwartz lectr., asst. prof. anthropology Bryn Mawr Coll., Pa., 1975-78, assoc. prof. 1978-85, prof., 1985—, chmn. dept., 1982-85, acting dean undergrad coll., 1985-86, provost, 1986-94; pres. Barnard Coll., N.Y., 1994—; contbr. articles to profl. jours., chpts. to books. Fellow Woodrow Wilson Found., 1963-64, Columbia U., 1964-65, NEH Younger Humanist, 1974-75, Am. Coun. Learned Socs., 1981-82, Ctr. for Advanced Study in the Behavioral Scis., 1989; grantee NSF summer field tng., 1965, Ford Found. 1966, NIMH, 1974-75, Social Sci. Rsch. Coun., 1974-75. Mem. Phila. Anthrop. Soc. (pres. 1983), Am. Ethnol. Soc. (nominations com . 1983-84, pres. elect 1984-85, pres. 1985-86), Am. Anthrop. Assn. (ethics com. 1976-79, bd. dirs. 1984-86, exec. com. 1985-86), Social Sci. Rsch. Coun. (com. social sci personnel 1977-80), Women's Forum, Phi Beta Kappa, Sigma Xi. Office: Barnard Coll Office of the Pres 3009 Broadway New York NY 10027-6598

SHAPIRO, KARL JAY, poet, former educator; b. Balt., Nov. 10, 1913; s. Joseph and Sarah (Omanski) S.; m. Evalyn Katz, Mar. 25, 1945 (div. Jan. 1967); children: Katharine, John J., Elizabeth (dec. Jan. 1993); m. Teri Kovach, July 31, 1967 (dec. July 1982); m. Sophie Wilkins, Apr. 25, 1985. Student Johns Hopkins U., 1937-39. Cons. poetry Library of Congress, 1946-47; assoc. prof. writing Johns Hopkins U., 1947-50; editor Poetry: A Magazine of Verse, 1950-56; prof. English U. Nebr., Lincoln, 1956-66, U. Ill. Circle Campus, Chgo., 1966-68, U. Calif. at Davis, 1968-85; now ret. Author: Poems, 1935, New and Selected Poems, 1940-46, Person, Place and Thing, 1942, The Place of Love, 1942, V-Letter and Other Poems, 1944, Essay on Rime, 1945, Trial of a Poet, 1947, Bibliography of Modern Prosody, 1948, Poems, 1942-53, 1953, Beyond Criticism, 1953, Poems of a Jew, 1958, In Defense of Ignorance, 1960, (with James E. Miller, Jr. and Bernice Slote) Start with the Sun, 1960, Prose Keys to Modern Poetry, 1962, The Bourgeois Poet, 1964, A Prosody Handbook, 1964, (with Robert Beum) Selected Poems, 1968, To Abolish Children, 1968, White-Haired Lover, 1968, The Poetry Wreck, Selected Essays 1950-70, 1975, Adult Bookstore, 1976, Love & War, Art & God, 1984, Collected Poems 1940-1978, 1978, New and Selected Poems, 1968 and 1987, The Younger Son, 1988, Reports of My Death, 1990, The Old Horsefly, 1993; (novel) Edsel, 1971; (film) Karl Shapiro's America, 1976. Served with AUS, 1941-45. Recipient Jeanette S. Davis prize, 1942, Levinson prize, 1943, Contemporary Poetry prize, 1943, Pulitzer prize for poetry, 1945, Shelley Meml. prize, 1945, Bollingen prize for poetry, 1969, Robert Kirsch award L.A. Times, 1989, Charity Randall citation, 1990; grantee Am. Acad. Arts and Letters, 1944; fellow Kenyon Sch. Letters, 1956, 57, Guggenheim fellow, 1953-54, fellow Libr. of Congress. Mem. PEN, Nat. Acad. Arts and Letters, Am. Acad. Arts and Scis.

SHAPIRO, LARRY JAY, pediatrician, scientist, educator; b. Chgo., July 6, 1946; s. Philip and Phyllis (Krause) S.; m. Carol-Ann Uetake; children: Jennifer, Jessica, Brian. A.B., Washington U., St. Louis, 1968, M.D., 1971. Diplomate Am. Bd. Pediatrics, Am. Bd. Med. Examiners, Am. Bd. Med. Genetics. Intern St. Louis Children's Hosp., 1971-72, resident, 1971-73; research assoc. NIH, Bethesda, Md., 1973-75; asst. prof. Sch. Medicine, UCLA, 1975-79, assoc. prof., 1979-83, prof. pediatrics and biol. chemistry, 1983-91; investigator Howard Hughes Med. Inst., 1987-91; prof., chmn. dept. pediat. U. Calif.-San Francisco Sch. Medicine, 1991—, chief pediat. svcs. U. Calif. San Francisco Med. Ctr., 1991—. Contbr. numerous articles to profl. publs. Served to lt. comdr. USPHS, 1973-75. Fellow AAAS, Am. Acad. Pediatrics (E. Mead Johnson award in research 1982); mem. Soc. Pediatric Research (council 1984-87, pres. 1991-92), Western Soc. for Pediatric Research (council 1983-87, Ross award in research 1981, pres. 1989-90), Soc. for Inherited Metabolic Disease (council 1983-88, pres. 1986-87), Assn. Am. Physicians, Inst. Medicine, Nat. Acad. Scis., Am. Soc. Human Genetics (council 1985-88), Am. Soc. Clin. Investigation, Am. Pediatric Soc. Office: Univ of California Third Ave & Parnassus San Francisco CA 94143

SHAPIRO, LEE TOBEY, planetarium administrator, astronomer; b. Chgo., Dec. 12, 1943; s. Sydney Harold and Ruth Iva (Levin) S.; m. Linda Susan Goldman, Aug. 16, 1970; children: Steven Robert, Aaron Edward. BS in Physics, Carnegie Inst. Tech., 1966; MS in Astronomy, Northwestern U., 1968, PhD, 1974. Lectr. Adler Planetarium, Chgo., 1967-74; asst. prof. astronomy Mich. State U., East Lansing, 1974-79, assoc. prof., 1979-82; bd. dirs. Abrams Planetarium, 1974-82, Morehead Planetarium U. N.C.-Chapel Hill, 1982—, adj. assoc. prof., 1983—; vis. prof. Duke U., Durham, N.C., summers 1987-89, 93-94. Fellow Royal Astron. Soc.; mem. Am. Astron. Soc., Am. Assn. Mus., Astronomical Soc. of the Pacific, Internat. Planetarium Soc., Great Lakes Planetarium Assn. (pres. 1980). Jewish. Office: Morehead Planetarium # 3480 U of NC Chapel Hill NC 27599-3480

SHAPIRO, LEO J., social researcher; b. N.Y.C., July 8, 1921; m. Virginia L. Johnson, Feb. 9, 1952; children: David, Erik, Owen, Amy. BA, U. Chgo., 1942, PhD, 1952. Survey specialist Fed. Govt. Agy., Washington, 1941-45, Sci. Rsch. Assn., Chgo., 1948-52; prin., founder Leo J. Shapiro and Assocs., Chgo., 1952-91; pres. Greenhouse, Inc. 1991—; bd. dirs. Circle Fine Art,

Chgo. Mem. vis. com. bd. trustees U. Chgo. Fellow U. Chgo., 1949. Fellow Social Sci. Research Council; mem. Am. Mktg. Assn., Am. Assn. Pub. Opinion Research, Am. Sociol. Assn., AAAA, Phi Beta Kappa.

SHAPIRO, LUCILLE, molecular biology educator; b. N.Y.C., July 16, 1940; d. Philip and Yetta (Stein) Cohen; m. Roy Shapiro, Jan. 23, 1960 (div. 1977); 1 child, Peter; m. Harley H. McAdams, July 28, 1978; stepchildren: Paul, Heather. BA, Bklyn. Coll., 1961; PhD, Albert Einstein Coll. Medicine, 1966. Asst. prof. Albert Einstein Coll. Medicine, N.Y.C., 1967-72, assoc. prof., 1972-77, Kramer prof., chmn. dept. molecular biology, 1977-86, dir. biol. scis. div., 1981-86; Eugene Higgins prof., chmn. dept. microbiology, Coll. Physicians and Surgeons Columbia U., N.Y.C., 1986-89; Joseph D. Grant prof., chmn. dept. devel. biology Sch. Medicine, Stanford U., 1989—; bd. dirs. Silicon Graphics; bd. sci. counselors NIH, Washington, 1980-84, DeWitt Stetten disting. lectr., 1989; bd. sci. advisors G.D. Searle Co., Skokie, Ill., 1984-86; sci. adv. bd. Mass. Gen. Hosp., 1990-93, SmithKline Beecham, 1993—; bd. trustees Scientists Inst. for Pub. Info., 1990-94; lectr. Harvey Soc., 1993; commencement address, U. Calif. Berkeley, 1994. Editor: Microbiol. Devel., 1984; mem. editorial bd. Jour. Bacteriology, 1978-86, Trends in Genetics, 1987—, Genes and Development, 1987-91, Cell Regulation, 1990-92, Molecular Biology of the Cell, 1992—, Molecular Microbiology, 1991—, Current Opinion on Genetics and Devel., 1991—; contbr. articles to profl. jours. Mem. sci. bd. Helen Hay Whitney Found., N.Y.C., 1986—; co-chmn. adv. bd. NSF Biology Directorate, 1988-89; vis. com., bd. overseers Harvard U., Cambridge, Mass. 1987-90; mem. sci. bd. Whitehead Inst., MIT, Boston, 1988-93; mem. sci. rev. bd. Howard Hughes Med. Inst., 1990-94, Cancer Ctr. of Mass. Gen. Hosp., Boston, 1994; mem. Presidio Coun. City of San Francisco, 1991-94; mem. Pres. Coun. U. Calif., 1993—. Recipient Hirschl Career Scientist award, 1976, Spirit of Achievement award, 1978, Excellence in Sci. award Fedn. Am. Socs. Exptl. Biology, 1994; Jane Coffin Child fellow, 1966. Fellow AAAS, Am. Acad. Arts and Scis., Am. Acad. Microbiology; mem. NAS, Inst. Medicine of NAS, Am. Soc. Biochemistry and Molecular Biology (nominating com. 1982, 87, coun. 1990—), Am. Heart Assn. (sci. adv. bd. 1984-87). Avocation: watercolor painting. Office: Stanford U Sch Medicine Beckman Ctr Dept Devel Biology Stanford CA 94305

SHAPIRO, LYNDA P., biology educator, director; b. Bklyn., June 11, 1938; d. Nathan and Evelyn (Zetler) S. BA, U. Ark., 1960, MS, 1963; postgrad., Columbia U., 1966-67; PhD, Duke U., 1974. Instr. biology La. State U., 1963-66; rsch. teaching asst. Columbia U., N.Y.C., 1967-68; tech. assoc. med. ctr. Duke U., 1968-69; postdoctoral investigator Woods Hole Oceanographic Inst., 1975-75, asst. scientist, 1975-79; rsch. scientist Bigelow Lab. for Ocean Scis., 1979-90; prof. biology, dir. Inst. Marine Biology U. Oregon, Charleston, 1990—; commr. South Slough Nat. Estuarine Rsch. Reserve, 1990—; invited speaker various workshops, symposiums. Contbr. articles to profl. jours. Woodrow Wilson fellow. Mem. AAAS, PSA, TOS, Am. Soc. Limnology and Oceanography, Phi Sigma. Achievements include research in ecology, biogeography and physiology of marine phytoplankton; distributions of ultraphytoplankton species, effects of environmental factors on those distributions, and effects of those distributions on the various marine environments; predation on ultraplankton by pelagic protists. Office: Univ Oreg Oreg Inst Marine Biology Charleston OR 97420

SHAPIRO, MARK HOWARD, physicist, educator, academic dean, consultant; b. Boston, Apr. 18, 1940; s. Louis and Sara Ann (Diamond) S.; m. Anita Rae Lavine, June 8, 1961; children: David Gregory, Diane Elaine, Lisa Michelle. A.B. with honors, U. Calif., Berkeley, 1962; M.S. (NSF coop. fellow), U. Pa., 1963, Ph.D., 1966. Research fellow Kellogg Radiation Lab., Calif. Inst. Tech., Pasadena, 1966-68; vis. assoc. Kellogg Radiation Lab. Calif. Inst. Tech., 1976—; research assoc. Nuclear Structure Research Lab. U. Rochester (N.Y.), 1968-70; mem. faculty Calif. State U., Fullerton, 1970—, prof. physics, 1978—, acting assoc. dean Sch. Math., Sci. and Engring., 1985-86, acting dir. Office Faculty Research and Devel., 1986-87, chmn. physics dept., 1989—; dir. tchr. enhancement program NSF, Washington, 1987-88; tour speaker Am. Chem. Soc., 1983-85. Contbr. over 125 articles to profl. jours. Pres. Pasadena Young Democrats, 1967-68; mem. pub. info. and edn. com. Calif. Task Force on Earthquake Preparedness, 1981-85; bd. dirs. Calif. State U. Fullerton Found., 1982-85. Grantee Research Corp., 1971-74, Calif. Inst. Tech., 1977-78, U.S. Geol. Survey, 1978-85, Digital Equipment Corp., 1982, NSF, 1985-87, 90—. Mem. AAAS, Am. Phys. Soc., Am. Assn. Physics Tchrs. (profl. concerns com. 1990-93, chmn. 1991-93), Am. Geophys. Union, N.Y. Acad. Scis., Materials Rsch. Soc., Coun. on Undergrad. Rsch. (physics/astronomy councillor 1993—). Achievements include research in experimental nuclear physics, experimental nuclear astrophysics, geophysics and atomic collisions in solids. Office: Calif State Univ Physics Dept Fullerton CA 92634

SHAPIRO, MARTIN, law educator; b. 1933. B.A., UCLA, 1955; Ph.D., Harvard U., 1961. Instr. polit. sci. Harvard U., Cambridge, Mass., 1960-62; prof. Harvard U., 1971-74; asst. prof. Stanford U., Calif., 1962-65; assoc. prof. U. Calif.-Irvine, 1965-70, prof., 1970; prof. polit. sci. U. Calif.-Berkeley, 1971, prof. law, 1977—; prof. U. Calif.-San Diego, 1974-77. Author: Law and Politics in the Supreme Court, 1964, Freedom of Speech, The Supreme Court and Judicial Review, 1966, Supreme Court and Administrative Agencies, 1968, Courts, 1981, Who Guards the Guardians, 1987. Mem. Law and Soc. Assn. (trustee 1992—), Western Polit. Sci. Assn. (pres. 1978), Am. Acad. Arts and Scis., Am. Polit. Sci. Assn. (v.p. 1988). Office: U Calif Law Sch 225 Boalt Hall Berkeley CA 94720

SHAPIRO, MARVIN LINCOLN, communications company executive; b. Erie, Pa., Feb. 12, 1923; s. Hyman and Flora (Burstein) S.; m. B. Gertrude Berkman, Oct. 25, 1946; children: Susan Jo, Barbara Ann, Jonathan David. BS, Syracuse U., 1948; postgrad., Williams Coll., 1966, Columbia U., 1975. Account exec. WSYR, Syracuse, 1948-50; account exec. sta. WCAU-TV, Phila., 1950-55; nat. sales mgr. sta. WCAU-TV, 1956-58; account exec. CBS TV spot sales, Chgo., 1955-56, N.Y.C., 1958-60; with TV Advt. Reps., Inc., N.Y.C., 1961-66; exec. v.p. TV Advt. Reps., Inc., 1965-66, pres., 1968-69, dir., vice chmn., 1969-77, chmn., 1978; pres. Radio Advt. Reps., Inc., N.Y.C., 1966-68; dir., vice chmn. Radio Advt. Reps., Inc., 1969-77; exec. v.p., COO, pres. sta. group Westinghouse Broadcasting Co., Inc., N.Y.C., 1969-77; sr. v.p. Westinghouse Broadcasting Co., Inc., 1978-83, also dir., 1969-83; pres., dir. Foxwood Comm. Inc., N.Y.C., 1983—; mng. dir. Veronis, Suhler & Assocs., N.Y.C., 1983—; pres., dir. Farragut Comm., Inc., Yakima, Wash., 1992—; Columbia Empire Broadcasting Corp., Yakima, 1992—; dir. Queen City Broadcasting, Inc., N.Y.C., 1989-92, Galway Corp., Dublin, 1990-92; dir. Garden State Cablevision, Inc., N.Y.C., 1989—, Kansas Broadcasting System, Inc., Wichita, 1993-94, dir Burbach Broadcasting Co., 1994—; chmn. bd. Micro-Relay, Inc., 1974-83; chmn. bd., pres. CATV Enterprises, Inc., 1970-83. Boxing official Pa. Athletic Comm., 1952-55; Bd. dirs. TV Bur. Advt., 1974-81, chmn., 1977-79; bd. dirs. Radio Advt. Bur., 1970-77; With USAAF, 1942-45. Decorated Air medal with 9 oak leaf clusters; recipient Communications Alumni award Syracuse U., 1960. Mem. Internat. Radio and TV Soc., DAV, Alpha Epsilon Rho (hon.). Clubs: Long Ridge (Stamford). Home: 26 Foxwood Rd Stamford CT 06903-2207 Office: Foxwood Communications Inc 866 United Nations Plz New York NY 10017

SHAPIRO, MARVIN SEYMOUR, lawyer; b. N.Y.C., Oct. 26, 1936; s. Benjamin and Sally (Book) S.; m. Natalie Kover, July 12, 1959; children: Donna, Meryl. AB, Columbia U., 1957, LLB, 1959. Bar: D.C. 1959, Calif. 1962. Atty. appellate sect. Civil Div. U.S. Dept. Justice, Washington, 1959-61; ptnr. Irell & Manella, L.A., 1962—; mng. ptnr., 1992—; lectr. U. So. Calif. Tax Inst., Calif. Continuing Edn. of the Bar, Practising Law Inst. Articles editor Columbia Law Rev., 1958-59. V.p. Jewish Fedn. Coun., L.A., 1985—, bd. dirs.; treas. Alan Cranston Campaign, 1974, 80, 86; chmn. credentials com. Dem. Nat. Com., 1972-76. Mem. L.A. County Bar Assn., Beverly Hills Barristers (pres. 1970). Avocations: travel, golf. Home: 432 N Cliffwood Ave Los Angeles CA 90049-2620 Office: Irell & Manella 1800 Avenue Of The Stars Los Angeles CA 90067

SHAPIRO, MATTHEW DAVID, economist; b. Mpls., Apr. 11, 1958; s. Irving and Janet (Reinstein) S.; m. Susan L. Garetz, Oct. 21, 1989. BA summa cum laude, Yale U., 1979, MA, 1979; PhD, MIT, 1984. Jr. staff economist Coun. Econ. Advisers, Washington, 1979-80, sr. economist 1993-94; from asst. prof. to assoc. prof. Yale U., New Haven, 1984-95; prof. U.

Mich., Ann Arbor, 1995—; rschr. Nat. Bur. Econ. Rsch., Cambridge, 1986—. Bd. editors Am. Econ. Rev., 1993—; contbr. articles to profl. jours. Olin fellow Nat. Bur. Econ. Rsch., Cambridge, 1986-87, Alfred P. Sloan fellow Sloan Found., 1991-93. Mem. Am. Econ. Assn., Econometric Soc., Phi Beta Kappa. Office: U Mich Dept Econs 611 Tappan Ann Arbor MI 48109-1220

SHAPIRO, MAURICE MANDEL, astrophysicist; b. Jerusalem, Israel, Nov. 13, 1915; came to U.S., 1921; s. Asher and Miriam R. (Grunbaum) S.; m. Inez Weinfield, Feb. 8, 1942 (dec. Oct. 1964); children: Joel Nevin, Elana Shapiro Ashley Naktin, Raquel Tamar Shapiro Kislinger. S. U. Chgo., 1936, M.S., 1940, Ph.D., 1942. Instr. physics and math. Chgo. City Colls., 1937-41; chmn. dept. phys. and biol. scis. Austin Coll., 1938-41; instr. math. Gary Coll., 1942; physicist Dept. Navy, 1942-44; lectr. physics and math. George Washington U., 1943-44; group leader, mem. coordinating council of lab. Los Alamos Sci. Lab., U. Calif., 1944-46; sr. physicist, lectr. Oak Ridge Nat. Lab., Union Carbon and Carbide Corp., 1946-49; cons. div. nuc. energy for propulsion aircraft Fairchild Engine & Aircraft Corp., 1948-49; head cosmic ray br. nucleonics div. U.S. Naval Research Lab., Washington, 1949-65, supt. nucleonics div., 1953-65, chief scientist Lab. for Cosmic Ray Physics, 1965-82, apptd. to chair of cosmic ray physics, 1966-82, chief scientist emeritus, 1982—; lectr. U. Md., 1949-50, 52—, assoc. prof., 1950-51, vis. prof. physics and astronomy, 1986—; vis. prof. physics and astronomy U. Iowa, 1981-84; vis. prof. astrophysics U. Bonn, 1982-84; vis. scientist Max Planck Inst. für Astrophysik, W. Ger., 1984-85; cons. Argonne Nat. Lab., 1949; cons. panel on cosmic rays U.S. nat. com. IGY; lectr. physics and engring. Nuclear Products-Erco div. ACF Industries, Inc., 1956-58; lectr. E. Fermi Internat. Sch. Physics, Varenna, Italy, 1962; vis. prof. Weizmann Inst. Sci., Rehovoth, Israel, 1962-63, Inst. Math. Scis., Madras, India, 1971; Inst. Astronomy and Geophysics Nat. U. Mex., 1976; vis. prof. physics and astronomy Northwestern U., Evanston, Ill., 1978; cons. space rsch. in astronomy Space Sci. Bd., Nat. Acad. Scis., 1965; cons. Office Space Scis., NASA, 1965-66, 89; prin. investigator Gemini S-9 Cosmic Ray Expts., NASA, 1964-69, Skylab, 1967-76, Long Duration Exposure Facility, 1977—; mem. Groupe de Travail de Biologie Spatiale, Council of Europe, 1970—; mem. steering com. DUMAND Consortium, 1976—, mem. exec. com., 1979-82, mem. sci. adv. com., 1982—; lectr. Summer Space Inst., Deutsche Physikalische Gesellschaft, 1972; dir. Internat. Sch. Cosmic-Ray Astrophysics, Ettore Majorana Centre Sci. Culture, Erice, Italy, 1977—, also sr. corr., 1977—; chmn. U.S. IGY com. on interdisciplinary research, mem. nuclear emulsion panel space sci. bd.; Nat. Acad. Scis., 1959—; chief U.S. rep., steering com. Internat. Coop. Emulsion Flights for Cosmic Ray Research; cons. CREI Atomics, 1959—; vis. com. Bartol Research Found., Franklin Inst., 1967-74; mem. U.S organizing com. 13th and 19th Internat. Confs. on Cosmic Rays; mem. sci. adv. com. Internat. Confs. on Nuclear Photography and Solid State Detectors, 1966—; mem. Com. of Honor for Einstein Centennial, Acad. Naz. Lincei, 1977; mem. Internat. Organizing com. Tex. Symposia on Relativistic Astrophysics, 1976—; Regents lectr. U. Calif. Riverside, 1985; Edison lectr. Naval Rsch. Lab award, 1990; Victor Hess Meml. lectr., Rome, 1995. Mem. editorial bd. Astrophysics and Space Sci., 1968-75; assoc. editor: Phys. Rev. Letters, 1977-84; editor (NATO) ASI Series on Cosmic-Ray Astrophysics; contbr. to Am. Inst. Handbook of Physics, various encys. Mem. exec. bd. Cong. Beth Chai, Washington, 1987—; trustee Nat. Capital Astronomers, Washington, 1989—; mem. internat. panel Chernobyl World Lab., 1988. Recipient Disting. Civilian Svc. avrad Dept. Navy, 1967, medal of honor Soc. for Encouragement au Progrés, 1978, publs. award Naval Rsch. Lab., 1970, 74, 76, Dir.'s Spl. award, 1974, Sr. U.S. Scientist award Alexander von Humboldt Found., 1982, Profl. Achievement citation U. Chgo., 1992. Fellow Am. Phys. Soc. (chmn. organizing com. div. cosmic physics, chmn. 1971-72, com. on publs. 1977-79), AAAS, Washington Acad. Scis. (past com. chmn., Disting. Career in Scis. award, 1993); mem. Am. Astron. Soc. (exec. com. div. high-energy astrophysics 1978—, chmn. 1982), Philos. Soc. Washington (past pres.), Am. Technion Soc. (Washington bd.), Assn. Los Alamos Scientists (past chmn.), Assn. Oak Ridge Engrs. and Scientists (past chmn.), Fedn. Am. Scientists (past mem. exec. com., nat. council), Internat. Astron. Union (organizing com. commn. on high-energy astrophysics), Phi Beta Kappa, Sigma Xi (Edison lectr. 1990). Club: Cosmos (Washington). Achievements include patents in field; discovery of first definitive evidence for production of cosmic ray secondaries in the interstellar medium; research in cosmic radiation, composition, origin, propagation, and nuclear transformations; in high-energy astrophysics; in particles and fields; in nuclear physics, neutron physics and fission reactors; in hydrodynamics and gamma-ray and neutrino astronomy. Office: 205 S Yoakum Pky Ste 1514 Alexandria VA 22304-3838

SHAPIRO, MEL, playwright, director, drama educator; b. Bklyn., Dec. 16, 1935; s. Benjamin Shapiro and Lillian (Lazarus) Bestul; m. Jeanne Elizabeth Shapiro, Feb. 23, 1963; children: Joshua, Benjamin. BFA, Carnegie-Mellon U., 1961, MFA, 1961. Resident dir. Arena Stage, Washington, 1963-65; producing dir. Tyrone Guthrie Theater, Mpls., 1968-70; master tchr. drama NYU, N.Y.C., 1970-80; guest dir. Lincoln Ctr. Repertory, N.Y.C., 1970; dir. N.Y. Shakespeare Festival, N.Y.C., 1971-77; prof. Carnegie Mellon U., Pitts., 1980-90, head. dept., 1980-87; bd. dirs. Pitts. Pub. Theater, 1982—; head acting UCLA Sch. Theater, Film and TV, 1990—; founder Onstage Co., L.A., 1993. Dir. N.Y.C. prodns. The House of Blue Leaves, 1970, Bosoms and Neglect, 1978; co-adaptor mus. Two Gentlemen of Verona, 1971 (Tony award); author: (plays) The Price of Admissions, 1984 (Drama-Logue mag. award), The Lay of the Land (Joseph Kesselring award 1990), A Life of Crime, 1993. With U.S. Army, 1955-57. Recipient N.Y. Drama Critics award, 1971, 72, Obie award Village Voice, 1972, Drama Desk award, 1973, Drama-logue award, 1993. Mem. Soc. Stage Dirs. and Choreographers (founder, editor The Jour. 1978). Office: UCLA Sch Theatre Film & TV 405 Hilgard Ave Los Angeles CA 90024-1722

SHAPIRO, MICHAEL, supermarket corporate officer; b. N.Y.C., Mar. 3, 1942; s. Jack and Celia (Schwartzbaum) S.; m. Sara Louise Ress, Mar. 22, 1964; children: Jeffrey, Lisa, Kenneth. B.S., CCNY, 1962. CPA, N.Y., N.J. Acct. Sidney Kaminsky & Co., N.Y.C., 1964-68; supr. Hurdman Cranston, Penney & Co. (C.P.A.s), N.Y.C., 1968-71; with Mayfair Super Markets Inc., Elizabeth, N.J., 1971-87; v.p. fin. and adminstrn. Mayfair Super Markets Inc., 1978-80, sr. v.p. fin. and adminstrn., 1980-84, exec. v.p. fin. and corp. devel., 1986-87, also dir.; self employed ins. cons., 1988-89; v.p. Fin. Fidelity Land Devel. Corp., Chatham, N.J., 1989-92; v.p. fin. and ops. Apex One Inc., Piscataway, N.J., 1992-94; sr. v.p., CFO, treas. Foodarama Supermarkets, Inc., Freehold, N.J., 1994—. Mem. AICPA, N.Y. State Soc. CPAs. Office: Foodarama Supermarkets Inc 922 Hwy 33 Bldg 6 Ste 1 Freehold NJ 07728

SHAPIRO, MICHAEL EDWARD, museum administrator, curator, art historian; b. N.Y.C., Nov. 15, 1949; s. Edward Aaron and Sylvia (Fishman) S.; m. Elizabeth Harvey, 1977; 2 children. BA, Hamilton Coll., 1972; MA, Williams Coll., 1976, Harvard U., 1978; PhD, Harvard U., 1981. Mgr. asst. prof. dept. art history Duke U., Durham, N.C., 1980-84; curator 19th-20th century art St. Louis Art Mus., 1984-92, chief curator, 1987-92; dir. Los Angeles County Mus. Art, 1992-93; dir. mus. programs Chief Curator High Mus. Art, Atlanta, 1994—. Author: Bronze Casting and American Sculpture, 1985; contbg. author: Frederic Remington: The Masterworks, 1988, George Caleb Bingham, 1990.

SHAPIRO, MICHAEL HENRY, government executive; b. Bayonne, N.J., Sept. 23, 1948; s. William and Sophie (Slotkin) S. BS, Lehigh U., 1970; MS, Harvard U., 1972, PhD, 1976. Assoc. prof. Harvard U., Cambridge, Mass., 1976-82, analyst, 1980-81, br. chief, 1981-83, dir. econs. and tech. divsn., 1983-89; dep. asst. adminstr., air and radiation EPA, Washington, 1989-93; dir. Office of Solid Waste, Washington, 1993—. Office: EPA 401 M St SW # 5301 Washington DC 20460-0001

SHAPIRO, MURRAY, structural engineer; b. N.Y.C., July 5, 1925; s. Samuel and Fannie (Korman) S.; m. Florence Morrison, June 16, 1951; children: Fred Richard, Alan Neil. BCE, CCNY, 1947. Registered profl. engr., N.Y., N.J., Pa., Md., Ga., N.C., Mass., Conn. Steel detailer Knopf & Amron, N.Y.C., 1947-48; asst. engr. N.Y.C. Bd. Transp., 1948-50; designer James Ruderman cons. engrs., N.Y.C., 1950-53, sr. engr., 1953-58, assoc., 1958-65; jr. ptnr. Office of James Ruderman, N.Y.C., 1965-66, sr. ptnr., 1966—. Structural designer many highrise office buildings, including GM Bldg., N.Y.C., Pan Am Bldg., N.Y.C., also schs., apartment houses, theaters.

With U.S. Army, 1943-45, ETO. Decorated Purple Heart, Bronze Star. Mem. N.Y. Cons. Engrs. Assn. (trustee 1972-77, sec. 1974-76), Am. Concrete Inst., N.Y. Acad. Scis., Glen Head Country Club. Republican. Jewish. Home: 170 West End Ave 15D New York NY 10023 Office: Office of James Ruderman 15 W 36th St New York NY 10018-7910

SHAPIRO, MYRA STEIN, poet; b. Bronx, N.Y., May 21, 1932; d. David M. and Ida Betty (Leader) Stein; m. Harold M. Shapiro, Feb. 15, 1953; children: Karen S., Judith M. BA, U. Tenn., 1968; MA in English, Middlebury Coll., 1973; MFA, Vt. Coll., 1993. reader, Internat. Women's Day, Jefferson Market Libr., N.Y.C., 1989; reading performance Midday Muse Series, Folger Shakespeare Libr., Washington, 1983, NEA Hunter Mus., Chattanooga, 1988, Bower's Mus., Santa Ana, Calif., 1986, 88. Author: (poetry) The Ohio Review, 1989, Education for Peace, 1988, Kalliope, 1988, Ploughshares, 1990-91, The Harvard Review, 1994. Recipient Dylan Thomas Poetry award, The New Sch., N.Y.C., 1981, The MacDowell Colony Fellowship, The MacDowell Colony, Peterborough, N.H., 1985, 87. Mem. Poetry Soc. Am., Poets House (bd. dirs.). Office: 111 4th Ave Apt 12I New York NY 10003-5240

SHAPIRO, NORMA SONDRA LEVY, federal judge; b. Phila., July 27, 1928; d. Bert and Jane (Kotkin) Levy; m. Bernard Shapiro, Aug. 21, 1949; children: Finley, Neil, Aaron. BA in Polit. Theory with honors, U. Mich., 1948; JD magna cum laude, U. Pa., 1951. Bar: Pa. 1952, U.S. Supreme Ct. 1978. Law clk. to presiding judge Pa. Supreme Ct., 1951-52; instr. U. Pa. Law Sch., 1951-52, 55-56; assoc. Dechert Price & Rhoads, Phila., 1956-58, 67-73; ptnr. Dechert Price & Rhoads, 1973-78; judge U.S. Dist. Ct. (ea. dist.) Pa., 1978—; assoc. trustee U. Pa. Law Sch., 1978-93; former trustee Women's Law Project, Albert Einstein Med. Ctr.; v.p. Jewish Pub. Soc.; trustee Fedn. Jewish Agys., 1980-83; mem. lawyers adv. panel Pa. Gov.'s Commn. on Status of Women, 1974; legal adv. regional Coun. Child Psychiatry, bd. dirs. Women Judges' Fund for Justice. Guest editor: Shingle, 1972. Mem. Lower Merion County (Pa.) Bd. Sch. Dirs., 1968-77, pres., 1977, v.p., 1976; v.p. Jewish Community Relations Council of Greater Phila., 1975-77; chmn. legal affairs com., 1978; pres. Belmont Hills Home and Sch. Assn., Lower Merion Twp.; legis. chmn. Lower Merion Sch. Dist. Intersch. Council; mem. Task Force on Mental Health of Children and Youth of Pa.; treas., chmn. edn. com. Human Relations Council, Lower Merion; v.p., parliamentarian Nes Ami Penn Valley Congregation, Lower Merion Twp. Named Woman of Yr., Oxford Circle Jewish Community Center, 1979, Woman of Distinction, Golden Slipper Club, 1979; Gowen fellow, 1954-55; recipient Hannah G. Solomon award Nat. Coun. Jewish Women, 1992. Mem. Am. Law Inst., Am. Bar Found., ABA (ho. dels. 1990—, coun./chmn. conf. fed. judges 1986-87, vice-chmn. com. law and mental health sect. family law), Pa. Bar Assn. (ho. of dels. 1979-81), Phila. Bar Assn. (chmn. com. women's rights 1972, 74-75, chmn. bd. govs. 1977-78, chmn. pub. rels. com. 1978), Fed. Bar Assn. (Bill of Rights award 1991), Nat. Assn. Women Lawyers, Phila. Trial Lawyers Assn., Am. Judicature Soc., Phila., Nat. Assn. Women Judges, Fellowship Commn., Order of Coif (chpt. pres. 1973-75), Tau Epsilon Rho, Jurisprudence. Office: US Dist Courthouse Independence Mall West 601 Market St Rm 10614 Philadelphia PA 19106-1723

SHAPIRO, NORMAN RICHARD, Romance languages and literatures educator; b. Boston, Nov. 1, 1930; s. Harry Alexander and Eva (Goldberg) S. B.A., Harvard U., 1951, M.A., 1952, Ph.D., 1958; diplôme de Langue et Lettres Françaises, Université d'Aix-Marseille, 1956; M.A. (hon.), Wesleyan U., 1972. Instr. French Amherst Coll., 1958-60; asst. prof. romance langs. and lits. Wesleyan U., 1960-65, assoc. prof., 1965-71, prof., 1971—. Editor: Echos, 1965, Palabres, 1973; translator, editor: Négritude, 1971; translator: Four Farces by Georges Feydeau, 1970, Comedy of Eros, 1971, Kamouraska by Anne Hébert, 1973, Virginie, or the Dawning of the World by Joseph Majault, 1974, The Camp of The Saints by Jean Raspail, 1975, Feydeau, First to Last, 1982, Fables from Old French: Aesop's Beasts and Bumpkins, 1983, A Fitting Confusion by Georges Feydeau, 1985, The Pregnant Pause, or Love's Labor Lost, By Georges Feydeau, 1987, The Brazilian by Henri Meilhac and Ludovic Halévy, 1987, A Slap in the Farce by Eugène Labiche, 1988, A Matter of Wife and Death by Eugène Labiche, 1988, Fifty Fables of La Fontaine, 1988, The Fabulists French: Verse Fables of Nine Centuries, 1992, La Fontaine's Bawdy: Of Libertines, Louts and Lechers, 1992; composer: Three Songs, 1961; contbr. articles, transls. and revs. to profl. jours. Mem. African Studies Assn., Am. Assn. Tchrs. French, Universala Esperanto-Asocio, Esperanto League N.Am., Judezmo Soc., Am. Lit. Transl. Assn. (Disting. Translation award 1992), Dramatists Guild, Beast Fable Soc. (editorial bd. Bestia), Signet Soc. of Harvard, Delta Kappa Epsilon. Jewish. Home: 214 High St Middletown CT 06457-3242

SHAPIRO, PERRY, economics educator; b. Los Angeles, Jan. 15, 1941; s. Abraham and Ann (Warshaw) S.; m. Jody Silverstein, June 25, 1994; children: Elizabeth Naomi, Samuel Robert, Sarah Gertrud. BA in Econs., U. Calif.-Berkeley, 1962, PhD in Econs., 1968. Postdoctoral fellow in urban econs. Washington U., St. Louis, 1967-68; lectr. London Sch. Econs., 1968-69; asst. prof. econs. U. Calif.-Santa Barbara, 1969-74, assoc. prof., 1974-78, prof., 1978—, chair dept. econs., 1987-93; vis. prof. U. Mich., Ann Arbor, 1979-80; vis. scholar Federalism Rsch. Ctr. Australian Nat. U., 1992, adj. prof. Rsch. Sch. Social Scis., 1994—. Author: An Analytical Framework for Regional Policy, 1970. Vis. scholar U.S. Bur. Labor Stats., Washington, 1975-76; grantee NSF, 1979—, Nat. Inst. Justice, 1980-85; Fulbright sr. rsch. scholar Australia Nat. U., 1990-91. Mem. Am. Econs. Assn., Econometric Soc., Nat. Tax Assn. Office: U of Calif Dept Econs Santa Barbara CA 93016

SHAPIRO, RAYMOND L., lawyer; b. N.Y.C., Aug. 1, 1934; s. Alexander and Sadye (Morrison) S.; m. Judith Manis, Dec. 23, 1956; children: Joel, Todd, Lisa. BS, Temple U., 1956, LLB, 1959. Ptnr. Wexler, Weisman, Forman & Shapiro, Phila., 1959-84, Blank, Rome, Comisky & McCauley, Phila., 1984—. Author: Dunlap-Hanna Pa. Forms, 1963-83, Pa. Civil Practice Handbook, 1973-83; contbg.-author: Business Workouts Manual. Trustee Phila. Fedn. Jewish Agys., 1979—, treas., 1984-87, v.p., 1987-90; pres. Jewish Pub. Group, 1992—. Fellow Am. Coll. Bankruptcy (bd. dirs.); mem. ABA, Pa. Bar Assn., Phila. Bar Assn., Locust Club (bd. dirs. 1990). Office: Blank Rome Comisky & McCauley 4 Penn Center Plz 10-13 Fl 4 Philadelphia PA 19103-2599

SHAPIRO, RICHARD CHARLES, sales and marketing executive; b. Bklyn., May 28, 1936; s. Isidore and Sylvia (Rappaport) S.; m. Marilyn Joyce Bialy, Feb. 17, 1957 (div. 1974); children: Joseph, Scott; m. Francine L. Shaw, Sept. 19, 1975. BS in Edn., Golden State U., 1978, MBA, 1981; PhD in Bus. Adminstrn., Honolulu U., 1987. Lic. real estate broker, Ill. Affiliate Effective Motivation Assocs./Success Motivation inst., Bethpage, N.Y., 1965-69; v.p. sales Field Enterprises, Chgo., 1962-78; pres., CEO Snack-In, Inc., Detroit, 1978-82; sr. ptnr. Directions Growth and Strategy Cons., Chgo., 1982—; v.p. domestic & internat. mktg. & sales Ency., oper. officer Ency. Brit.-Compton's Learning Co., 1991-93; pres., bd. dirs.; assoc. editor Media technics Pub. Assn., Lake Forest, 1988; instr. planning Life Underwriter Tng. Coun., L.I., 1965-66; bd. dirs. nat. Video Libr.; speaker on mktg., sales and leadership. Author various self-improvement cassettes; contbr. articles to profl. jours. Active Explorers, high schs., youth clubs, 1965-74; founder, pres. Abundance and Goodwill Soc., 1968—. Served with USAF, 1957-60. Recipient Leadership award Am. Sales Masters, 1968; named Sales/Mktg. Execs. Leadership Recruiter/Trainer of Decade award. Mem. Salesmen With a Purpose, Chgo. Computer Soc., Effective Motivation Assocs. Avocations: wild-water rafting, white-water canoeing, camping, tennis, writing.

SHAPIRO, RICHARD GERALD, retired department store executive, consultant; b. N.Y.C., Apr. 24, 1924; s. David and Sophie (Hayflich) S.; m. Lila Eig, July 22, 1951; children—Judith, Amy, Donald. B.A., U. Mich., 1946; M.B.A., Harvard, 1948. With Lord & Taylor, N.Y.C., 1948-64; v.p. Lord & Taylor, 1959-63, Air v.p. 1963-64; also mem. advr. bd.; pres. Wm. Filene's Sons Co., Boston, 1965-68; chief exec. officer, chmn. bd. Wm. Filene's Sons Co., 1968-73; pres. Gimbel Bros. Corp., N.Y.C., 1973-76; v.p. W.R. Grace & Co., pres. sporting goods div., 1977-79, pres. splty. store div., 1979-84; pres. Richard Shapiro Assocs., 1979—; sr. v.p. Montgomery Ward, Inc., 1986-88; bd. dirs. Assoc. Merchandising Corp., Nitrotec Corp., Capital Market Fund; retail chmn. Greater N.Y. Fund, 1963; chmn. merc. div. Mass. Bay United Fund, 1967. Mem. corp. Simmons Coll., Boston Mus. Fine Arts (permanent); bd. dirs. Mass. Mchts.; bd. dirs Family Counseling and

Guidance Centers, 1969-72, v.p.; 1970; trustee Brandeis U. Served with AUS, 1942-46. Mem. Harvard Bus. Sch. Assn. (gov.). Home: 10019 Gable Manor Ct Potomac MD 20854

SHAPIRO, RICHARD STANLEY, physician; b. Moline, Ill., June 11, 1925; s. Herbert and Esther Dian (Grant) S.; BS, St. Ambrose Coll., 1947; BS in Pharmacy, U. Iowa, 1951, MS in Preventive Medicine and Environ. Health, 1951, M.D., 1957; m. Arlene Blum, June 12, 1949; children: Michele Pamela, Bruce Grant, Gary Lawrence; m. Merry Lou Cook, Oct. 11, 1971. Pharmacist, Rock Island, Ill., 1951-53; research asst. U. Iowa Coll. Medicine, Iowa City, 1950-51, 53-57; practice medicine specializing in allergy, Beverly Hills, Calif., 1958-62, Lynwood, Calif., 1962—; attending physician Good Hope Found. Allergy Clinic, Los Angeles, 1958-62, Cedars of Lebanon Hosp., Hollywood, Calif., 1959-68, U. So. Calif.-Los Angeles County Med. Center, 1962—; physician St. Francis Hosp., Lynwood, 1962—; assoc. clin. prof. medicine U. So. Calif., 1978-84, emeritus, 1984—. Bd. dirs. Westside Jewish Community Center, 1961-65, Camp JCA, 1964-65. Served with USNR, 1943-45; PTO. Diplomate Am. Bd. Allergy and Immunology. Fellow Am. Geriatric Soc., Am. Coll. Allergy, Am. Assn. Clin. Immunology and Allergy; mem. Am. Soc. Tropical Medicine and Hygiene, Am. Acad. Allergy, Los Angeles Allergy Soc., AMA, Calif., Los Angeles County med. assns., West Coast Allergy, Am. Heart Assn., Sierra Club, Sigma Xi. Jewish. Mason; mem. B'nai B'rith. Contbr. articles to profl. jours. Office: 8301 E Florence Ave Ste 104 Downey CA 90240-3946

SHAPIRO, ROBERT ALAN, retail executive; b. Denver, Dec. 24, 1946; s. George and Ruth Bearnice (Horn) S.; m. Jan Laurelle Tilker, Nov. 8, 1980; children: Aaron Phillip, Michael Samuel. BA, U. Denver, 1968; student, Northwestern U. Law Sch, 1968-70. V.p. Draper and Kramer, Inc., Chgo., 1970-73; asst. v.p. Urban Investment & Devel. Co., Chgo., 1973-75; dir. real estate The Limited, Columbus, Ohio, 1975-78; pres. Robert A. Shapiro & Assocs., Chgo., 1978-85; sr. v.p., corp. ops. asst. sec. County Seat Stores, Inc., Dallas, 1985—; lectr. Northwestern U., Evanston, Ill., Ohio State U., Columbus, 1976-78; mem. retail adv. bd. Shopping Ctr. World mag. Mem. Internat. Coun. Shopping Ctrs. (tenant com. 1975-78), Nat. Retail Fedn. (splty. store task force com.). Jewish. Avocations: swimming, reading, skiing. Office: County Seat Stores 17950 Preston Rd Dallas TX 75252-5793

SHAPIRO, ROBERT B., manufacturing executive; b. N.Y.C., Aug. 4, 1938; s. Moses and Lilly (Langsam) S.; m. Basia Gordon, Mar. 27, 1964; children: James Gordon, Nina Rachel. A.B., Harvard U., 1959; LL.B., Columbia U., 1962. Bar: N.Y. 1963. Assoc. in law Columbia U., 1962-63; atty. firm Poletti Freidin Prashker Feldman & Gartner, N.Y.C., 1963-67; spl. asst. to gen. counsel and underwear. U.S. Dept. Transp., Washington, 1967-69; assoc. prof. law Northeastern U., Boston, 1969-71; asst. prof. law U. Wis., Madison, 1971-72; v.p., gen. counsel Gen. Instrument Corp., N.Y.C., 1972-79, G.D. Searle & Co., Skokie, Ill., 1979-82; pres. NutraSweet Group div. G.D. Searle & Co., Skokie, Ill., 1982-85; chmn., pres., chief exec. officer Nutra Sweet Co. subs. Monsanto, Skokie, Ill., 1985-95, also bd. dirs; now chmn., pres. Monsanto Co., St. Louis, 1995—. Mem. Mass. Gov.'s Transp. Task Force, 1970-71; mem. com. on procedure CAB, 1975-76; mem. bus. adv. com. White House Domestic Policy Rev. on Indsl. Innovation, 1978-79; Nat. Bd.. Trustees Boys Clubs of Am. Recipient John R. Miller award as outstanding corporate mktg. exec., 1984; Outstanding Achievement award Sales and Mktg. Mgmt. Mag., 1984. Mem. Am. Bar Assn. (vice chmn. com. on corp. counsel 1981-82), U.S.C. of C. (council on antitrust policy 1981-82), N.Y. State Bar Assn. Office: Monsanto Co 800 N Lindburgh Blvd Saint Louis MO 63167

SHAPIRO, ROBERT FRANK, investment banking company executive; b. St. Louis, Dec. 19, 1934; s. Eugene J. and Clara (Katz) S.; m. Anna Marie Susman, Dec. 21, 1960; children: Albert Andrew, Robert Jr., Jeanne Savitt. Grad., St. Louis Country Day Sch., 1952; BA, Yale U., 1956. Assoc. Lehman Bros., N.Y.C., 1956-67, ptnr., 1967-73, dir., sr. mng. dir., 1970-73; ptnr. Wertheim & Co., 1974-77; exec. v.p. Wertheim & Co., Inc., N.Y.C., 1974-75, pres., 1975-86; co-chmn. Wertheim Schroder & Co., Inc., 1986-87; chmn. RFS and Assocs., Inc., N.Y.C., 1988—, New Street Capital Corp., 1992-94; bd. dirs. TJX Cos., Inc., The Burnham Fund, Am. Bldgs. Co.; ind. gen. ptnr. Equitable Capital Ptnrs.; chmn. nominating com. N.Y. Stock Exch., 1980, mem. regulatory adv. com., 1988—, surveillance com., 1989—; bd. govs. Am. Stock Exch., 1970-76. Trustee Lenox Hill Hosp., Skowhegan; mem. gov. bd. Yale U. Art Gallery, New Haven, 1993—. Mem. Securities Industry Assn. (chmn. 1985, Bond Club N.Y. (pres. 1987-88, Yale Culb, Rockefeller Ctr. Club, Century Country Club. Office: RFS & Assocs 375 Park Ave Ste 2602 New York NY 10152-0001

SHAPIRO, ROBERT LESLIE, lawyer; b. Plainfield, N.J., Sept. 2, 1942; m. Linell Thomas, Mar. 7, 1970; children: Brent Edward, Grant Thomas. BS in Fin., UCLA, 1965; JD, Loyola U., L.A., 1968. Bar: Calif. 1969, U.S. Ct. Appeals (9th cir.) 1972, U.S. Dist. Ct. (cen., no & so. dists.) Calif. 1982. Dep. dist. atty. Office of Dist. Atty., L.A., 1969-72; sole practice L.A., 1972-87, 88—; of counsel Bushkin, Gaims, Gaines, Jonas, L.A., 1987-88. Recipient Am. Jurisprudence award Bancroft Whitney, 1969. Mem. Nat. Assn. Criminal Def. Lawyers, Calif. Attys. for Criminal Justice, Trial Lawyers for Pub. Justice (founder 1982), Century City Bar Assn. (Best Criminal Def. Atty. 1993). Office: 2121 Ave of Stars 19th Fl Los Angeles CA 90067

SHAPIRO, ROBYN SUE, lawyer, educator; b. Mpls., July 19, 1952; d. Walter David and Judith Rae (Sweet) S.; m. Charles Howard Barr, June 27, 1976; children: Tania Shapiro-Barr, Jeremy Shapiro-Barr, Michael Shapiro-Barr. BA summa cum laude, U. Mich., 1974; JD, Harvard U. 1977. Bar: D.C. 1977, Wis. 1979. Assoc. Foley & Lardner, Washington, 1977-79; ptnr. Barr & Shapiro, Menomonee Falls, Wis., 1980-87; assoc. Quarles & Brady, Milw., 1987-92; ptnr. Michael Best & Friedrich, Milw., 1992—; adj. asst. prof. law Marquette U., Milw., 1979-83; assoc. dir. bioethics ctr. Med. Coll. Wis., Milw. 1982-85, dir., 1985—; asst. prof. bioethics Med. Coll. Wis., 1984-89, assoc. prof. bioethics, 1989—; dir. Wis. Ethics Com. Network, 1987—; bd. mem. Wis. Health Decisions, 1990-93. Editorial bd. mem: Cambridge Quarterly, 1991—, HEC Forum, 1988-91; contbr. articles to profl. jours. Mem. ethics com. St. Luke's Hosp., Milw., 1983—, Elmbrook Meml. Hosp., Milw., 1983-86, Community Meml. Hosp., Menomonee Falls, 1984—, Sinai Samaritan Hosp., Milw., 1986—, Milw. County Med. Complex, 1985—, Froedtert Meml. Luth. Hosp., 1985—; mem. subcom. organ transplantation Wis. Health Policy Coun., Madison, Wis., 1984, bioethics com., 1986—; mem. com. study on bioethics Wis. Legis. Coun., Madison, 1984-85; bd. dirs. Jewish Home and Care Ctr., 1994—, chair ethics com., 1994—; chair Bayside Ethics Bd., 1994—. James B. Angell scholar, 1971-72. Mem. ABA (forum com. health law, individual rights and responsibilities sec., health rights com. chair 1994—, mem. coordinating com. on bioethics and the law), Nat. Health Lawyers Assn., Am. Soc. Law & Medicine, Am. Hosp. Assn. (bioethics tech. panel 1991-94, spl. com. HIV & practitioners 1991-93) Wis. Bar Assn. (coun. Wis. health law sect. 1984-87, chair health law sect. 1988-89, individual rights sect. coun. 1987-90), Assn. Women Lawyers, ACLU, Wis. Found. (Atty. of Yr. 1988), Milw. Acad. Medicine (coun. 1992—, chair bioethics com. 1992—), Milw. AIDS Coalition (steering com. 1988-91), Internat. Bioethics Assn. (chair task force on ethics coms.), Phi Beta Kappa, others. Home: 9474 N Broadmoor Rd Milwaukee WI 53217-1309 Office: Med Coll Wis Bioethics Ctr 8701 W Watertown Plank Rd Milwaukee WI 53226-3548

SHAPIRO, SAM, health care analyst, biostatistician; b. N.Y.C., Feb. 12, 1914; married, 1938; 2 children. BS, Bklyn. Coll., 1933. Chief natality analysis br. Nat. Office Vital Stats., USPHS, 1947-54; sr. study dir. Nat. Opinion Rsch. Ctr., 1954-55; assoc. dir. div. rsch. and stats. Health Ins. Plan Greater N.Y., 1955-59, v.p., dir., 1959-73; dir. Health Svc. R & D Ctr., Balt., 1973-83; prof. health policy and mgmt. Johns Hopkins Sch. Hygiene and Pub. Health, Balt., 1973-85; emeritus prof. Johns Hopkins Sch. Hygiene and Pub. Health, 1985—; lectr. in pub. health Columbia U. Sch. Pub. Health and Adminstrv. Medicine, 1961-80; adj. prof. medicine Mt. Sinai Sch. Medicine, N.Y.C., 1972-78. Recipient prize GM Cancer Rsch. Found., 1988, Disting. Achievement award Am. Soc. Preventive Oncology, 1985. Fellow AAAS, APHA, Am. Statis. Assn., Am. Coll. Radiology (hon.); mem. Inst. Medicine, Assn. for Health Svcs. Rsch. (Disting. Career in Health Svcs. Rsch. award

1985). Office: Johns Hopkins U Sch Hygiene and Pub Health 624 N Broadway Baltimore MD 21205-1901

SHAPIRO, SAMUEL BERNARD, management consultant; b. Chgo., Nov. 15, 1909; s. Bernard and Ida (Schwartz) S.; m. Mary Heller, Dec. 24, 1933; children: Judith Shapiro DeGraff, Richard B. B.S., U. Chgo., 1935. Asst. to mgr. Greater Chgo. Safety Council, 1928-33; exec. sec. Authorized Ford Dealers Assn., 1933-38; mgr. Chgo. Automobile Trade Assn. and Chgo. Auto Shows, 1938-43; chief research and planning, automobile rationing br. (OPA), 1943; exec. dir. Linen Supply Assn. Am., 1946-75; pres. Samuel B. Shapiro Cons. Inc., 1975—; v.p. Seminars, Speakers, Travel, Inc. Washington, 1976-82; Sr. v.p., treas., dir. Am. Soc. Assn. Execs., 1958-62, pres., 1962-63; chmn. bd. trustees CAE-ASAE, 1972; pres. Assn. Execs. Forum Chgo., 1956-57; chmn. exec. operating council Insts. Orgn. Mgmt., Mich. State U., 1957; mem. exec. adv. council Fla. Atlantic U., 1974-84. Co-author: textbook Association Management, 1958, Forward Planning, 1969, Future Perspectives, 1985, Handbook for Corporate Directors, 1985; author: The Whys of Association Executive Success (and Failure), 1977, Before and After Retirement, 1978, Financial Incentives for Association Executives, 1983, From the Past Comes the Future, 1986, Coming of Age of the Association Profession, 1987; mem. adv. bd.: Adult Edn. mag, 1956-58; contbr. articles and monographs to profl. lit.; lectr. in field. Served with AUS, 1943-45. Recipient Key award Cert. Assn. Exec.-Am. Soc. Assn. Execs., 1960. Mem. ACLU, Am. Soc. Assn. Execs. (1st hon. mem. 1988), Internat. Soc. Gen. Semantics (charter mem., v.p. 1969-82), Am. Vets. Com., Phi Beta Kappa. Home: 5945 N Bay Rd Miami Beach FL 33140-2037

SHAPIRO, SANDER WOLF, lawyer; b. St. Louis, Sept. 24, 1929; s. Robert and Bess (Fisher) S.; m. Lottie F. Frankel, Aug. 14, 1955; children: Julie A. Shapiro Schechter, Susan B. Shapiro Schmitz. BA, Rice U., 1951; postgrad., Columbia U., 1951-52; JD, U. Tex., 1954. Atty. tax div. Dept. Justice, Washington, 1955-57; atty. advisor U.S. Tax Ct., Washington, 1957-58; ptnr. Clark, Thomas, Winters & Shapiro, Austin, Tex., 1958-84; sr. ptnr. Shapiro, Edens & Cook, Austin, 1984-91; of counsel Jenkens & Gilchrist, P.C., Austin, 1991—; adj. prof. law U. Tex., 1975—; lectr. in tax field. Author, editor Tex. Franchise Earned Surplus and Tax, 1985—, Family Solutions to Family Concerns, 1991—, A Walk Through Form 706, 1991—; co-editor Tex. Tax Svc., 1986-94. Bd. dirs. Austin Symphony Orch. Soc., 1974—, fin. v.p., 1980-95; bd. dirs. U. Tex. Coll. Fine Arts Adv. Coun., 1987-95, pres., 1991-94; bd. dirs. Capital of Tex. Pub. Telecomm. Coun., 1988—, pres., 1994—; bd. dirs. Ronald McDonald House of Ctr. Tex., Austin, 1990—, pres., 1994—; bd. dirs. Capital Met. Transit Authority, 1988-91, chair, 1990; bd. dirs. Austin Cmty. Found., 1985-92, pres., 1991. Sander W. Shapiro Presdl. Scholarship in Law at U. Tex. endowed in his honor by Jenkens & Gilchrist, 1992. Fellow Am. Bar Found. (life), Am. Coll. Trust and Estate Counsel, Am. Coll. Tax Counsel, Tex. Bar Found. (sustaining life); mem. ABA, State Bar Assn. Tex., Am. Law Inst., Internat. Acad. Estate and Trust Law (academician), Nat. Assn. State Bar Tax Sects. (bd. dirs., sec.-treas. 1995), Tex. Law Rev. Assn. (pres. 1992-93). Avocations: reading, music, golf. Office: Jenkens & Gilchrist 600 Congress Ave Ste 2200 Austin TX 78701

SHAPIRO, SANDOR SOLOMON, hematologist; b. Bklyn., July 26, 1933. BA, Harvard U., 1954, MD, 1957. Intern Harvard med. svc. Boston City Hosp., 1957-58, asst. resident, 1960-61; asst. surgeon divsn. biol. std. NIH, USPHS, 1958-60; NIH spl. fellow MIT, 1961-64; from instr. to assoc. prof. Cardeza found. Jefferson Med. Coll., Phila., 1964-72, prof. medicine, 1972—, assoc. dir., 1978-85, dir., 1985—; mem. hematology study sect. NIH, 1972-76, 78-79; mem. med. adv. coun. Nat. Hemophilia Found., 1973-75; chmn. Pa. State Hemophilia Adv. Com., 1974-76. Mem. Am. Soc. Clin. Investigation, Am. Soc. Hematology, Am. Assn. Immunologists, Assn. Am. Physicians, Internat. Soc. Thrombosis and Hemostasis. Achievements include research in hemostasis and thrombosis, prothrombin metabolism, hemophilia, lupus anticoagulants, endothelial cells. Office: Thomas Jefferson U Cardeza Found Hematologic Rsch 1015 Walnut St Philadelphia PA 19107

SHAPIRO, SANDRA, lawyer; b. Providence, Oct. 17, 1944; d. Emil and Sarah (Cohen) S. AB magna cum laude, Bryn Mawr Coll., Pa., 1966; LLB magna cum laude, U. Pa., 1969. Bar: Mass. 1970, U.S. Dist. Ct. Mass. 1971, U.S. Ct. Appeals (1st cir.) 1972, U.S. Supreme Ct. 1980. Law clk. U.S. Ct. Appeals (1st cir.), Boston, 1969-70; assoc. Foley, Hoag & Eliot, Boston, 1970-75, ptnr., 1976—; bd. dirs. Mass. Govt. Land Bank; mem. Bd. Bar Overseers Mass. Supreme Judicial Ct., 1988-92, Gender Bias Study Com., 1986-89. Contbr. articles to profl. jours. Bd. dirs. Patriots' Trail coun. Girl Scouts U.S., 1994—; mem. bd. overseers Boston Lyric Opera, 1993—; bd. overseers New Eng. Conservatory of Music, 1995—. Woodrow Wilson fellow, 1966. Mem. ABA (ethics, professionalism and pub. edn. com. 1994—), Women's Bar Assn. of Mass. (prs. 1985-86), New Eng. Women in Real Estate, Nat. Women's Law Ctr. Network, Mass. Bar Assn. (chmn. real property sect. coun., com. on profl. ethics), Boston Bar Assn. (mem. coun.), U. Pa. Law Sch. Alumni Assn. (bd. mgrs. 1990—), Order of Coif, Boston Club. Office: Foley Hoag & Eliot 1 Post Office Sq Boston MA 02109-2170

SHAPIRO, SIDNEY, physicist, educator; b. Boston, Dec. 4, 1931; s. Samuel and Sadie (Aberblatt) S.; m. Janice Ann Yeutter, May 14, 1960; children—Sara Ruth, Johanna Sue. AB, Harvard U., 1953, AM, 1955, PhD, 1959. Physicist, also group leader Arthur D. Little, Inc., 1959-64; mem. tech. staff Bell Telephone Labs., Inc., 1964-67; assoc. prof. elec. engring. U. Rochester, N.Y., 1967-73, prof., 1973-93, prof. emeritus, 1994—, chmn. dept. elec. engring., 1980-89; assoc. dean U. Rochester (Coll. Engring. and Applied Sci.), 1974-79; vis. prof. Physics Lab I, Tech. U. Denmark, 1972-73. Contbr. articles to profl. publs. Fellow IEEE. Democrat. Jewish. Pioneer exptl. confirmation AC Josephson effect in superconducting tunneling. Home: 220 Parkwood Ave Rochester NY 14620-3406 Office: U Rochester Dept Elec Engring Rochester NY 14627

SHAPIRO, STANLEY, materials scientist; b. Bklyn., Jan. 3, 1937; s. George Israel and Dora (Richman) S.; m. Janet Esther Skolnick, Aug. 24, 1958; children: Shari Lynne, David Elliot, Jill Diane. BSChemE, CCNY, 1960; MS in Engring. Sci., Rensselaer Poly. Inst., Troy, N.Y., 1964; PhD in Metallurgy and Materials Sci., Lehigh U., 1966. Rsch. engr. Pratt & Whitney Aircraft Co., 1960-61; rsch. scientist United Aircraft Corp., 1961-64; instr. asst. Lehigh U., 1964-66; rsch. scientist, supr. metals rsch. lab. Olin Metals Rsch., New Haven, 1966-79; pres. Revere Rsch. Inc. subs. Revere Copper & Brass, Inc., Edison, N.J., 1979-84; v.p. R & D Nat. Can Corp., Des Plaines, Ill., 1984-87; v.p. R & D ops. Am. Nat. Can Co., Barrington, Ill., 1987-89; cons. Mergers & Acquisitions, Skokie, Ill., 1989-93; corp. contr. Metamor Techs. Ltd., Chgo., 1993-94; chief fin. officer Metamor Techs., Ltd., Chgo., 1994—. Patentee in field. Mem. AAAS, ASTM, Metall. Soc., Am. Soc. Metals, Am. Mgmt. Assn., Electron Microscopy Soc., Inst. Metals, Sci. Research Soc., N.Y. Acad. Scis., Packaging Inst., Inst. Food Technologists, Research Dirs. Chgo., Indsl. Research Inst., Sigma Xi. Achievements include 30 patents in field. Office: One N Franklin Chicago IL 60606

SHAPIRO, STEPHEN MICHAEL, lawyer; b. Chgo., May 3, 1946; s. Samuel H. and Dorothy A. (D'Andrea) S.; m. Joan H. Gately, Oct. 30, 1982; children: Dorothy Henderson, Michael Clifford. BA magna cum laude, Yale U., 1968, JD, 1971. Bar: Ill. 1971, Calif. 1972, D.C. 1991, U.S. Dist. Ct. (no. dist. trial bar) Ill. 1992, U.S. Ct. Appeals (all cirs.), U.S. Supreme Ct. 1975. Law clk. U.S. Ct. Appeals (9th cir.), San Francisco, 1971-72; ptnr., head appellate practice Mayer, Brown & Platt, Chgo., 1972-78, 83—; asst. to solicitor gen. U.S. Dept. Justice, Washington, 1978-80, dep. solicitor gen., 1981-82. Co-author: Supreme Court Practice, 1993; contbr. articles to profl. jours. Mem. Am. Law Inst., Supreme Ct. Hist. Soc., Product Liability Adv. Found. (trustee), Phi Beta Kappa. Republican. Jewish. Office: Mayer Brown & Platt 190 S La Salle St Chicago IL 60603-3410

SHAPIRO, STEPHEN RICHARD, retired air force officer, physician; b. Bklyn., Dec. 30, 1934; s. George Daniel and Bertha Brinna (Bazerman) S.; m. Myrna Farber, May 28, 1960; children: David C., Robert S., Marc E. BA, Bklyn. Coll., 1956; MD, SUNY Downstate Med. Ctr., 1960. Diplomate Am. Bd. Internal Medicine, Am. Bd. Allergy and Immunology, Am. Bd. Med. Mgmt. Commd. 2nd lt. USAF, 1960, advanced through grades to brig. gen., 1987; intern, then resident and fellow Walter Reed Gen. Hosp., Washington, 1960-65; asst. chief allergy Wilford Hall USAF Med. Ctr., San

Antonio, 1965-73; chief clin. svc. Ramstein (Germany) Clinic, 1973-74; chief divsn. clin. medicine Hdqrs. USAFE/SG, Ramstein, 1974-76; comdr. USAF Hosp. RAF, Upper Heyford, Eng., 1976-80; dep. surgeon Hdqrs. AFSC/SG, Andrews AFB, Md., 1980-82; surgeon Hdqrs. AFRES/SG, Robins AFB, Ga., 1982-84; command surgeon Hdqrs. AFSC/SG, Andrews AFB, Md., 1984-87; comdr. Malcolm Grow USAF Med. Ctr., Andrews AFB, 1987-89; command surgeon Hdqrs. AFLC/SG, Wright-Patterson AFB, Ohio, 1989-92, Hdqrs. AFMC, 1991-92; chief of staff VA Outpatient Clinic, El Paso, Tex., 1992—. Fellow Aerospace Med. Assn. (assoc.); mem. Am. Coll. Physician Execs., Am. Acad. Allergy and Immunology, Air Force Soc. Flight Surgeons, Air Force Soc. Physicians, Alpha Omega Alpha. Jewish. Avocations: gardening, reading, travel. Office: 5919 Brook Hollow Dr El Paso TX 79925-1810

SHAPIRO, STUART CHARLES, computer scientist, educator; b. N.Y.C., Dec. 30, 1944; s. Louis M. and Bertha (Rubinstein) S.; m. Caren Dee Knight, July 16, 1972. BS, MIT, 1966; MS, U. Wis., 1968, PhD, 1971. Lectr. computer scis. dept. U. Wis., Madison, 1971; vis. asst. prof. Ind. U., Bloomington, 1971-72, asst. prof., 1972-77, assoc. prof., 1977-78; asst. prof. SUNY, Buffalo, 1977-78, assoc. prof., 1978-83, prof., 1983—, chmn., 1984-90; cons. Calspan UB Rsch. Ctr., Buffalo; rsch. scientist Nat. Ctr. for Geographic Info. and Analysis, 1989—. Author: Techniques of Artificial Intelligence, 1979, LISP: An Interactive Approach, 1986, Common Lisp: An Interactive Approach, 1992; editor: Encyclopedia of Artificial Intelligence, 1987, paperback edit., 1990, 2d edit., 1992; contbr. articles to profl. jours. Grantee NSF, 1971—; recipient numerous grants for computer sci. research, 1971—. Fellow Am. Assn. Artificial Intelligence; mem. IEEE (sr.), Assn. Computing Machinery (chmn. spl. interest group on artificial intelligence 1991-95), Assn. Computational Linguistics, Cognitive Sci. Soc., Sigma Xi. Home: 142 Viscount Dr Buffalo NY 14221-1770 Office: SUNY at Buffalo Dept of Computer Sci 226 Bell Hall Buffalo NY 14261

SHAPIRO, SUMNER, retired naval officer, business executive; b. Nashua, N.H., Jan. 13, 1926; s. Maurice David and Hannah (Goodman) S.; m. Eleanor S. Hymen, June 14, 1949; children: Martha, Steven, Susan. B.S., U.S. Naval Acad., 1949; M.S., George Washington U., 1966; postgrad., Naval War Coll., 1966, U.S. Army Inst. Advanced Soviet and Eastern European Studies, 1961. Commd. ensign U.S. Navy, 1949; advanced through grades to rear adm.; asst. naval attache U.S. Navy (Am. embassy), Moscow, 1963-65; dep. asst. chief of staff for intelligence U.S. Naval Forces Europe, London, 1967-69; comdg. officer Naval Intelligence Processing System Support Activity, Washington, 1969-72; asst. chief staff for intelligence U.S. Atlantic Command and U.S. Atlantic Fleet, Norfolk, Va., 1972-76; dep. dir. naval intelligence, 1976-77; comdr. Naval Intelligence Command, Washington, 1977-78; dir. naval intelligence Washington, 1978-82; ret., 1982; v.p. for advanced planning BDM Internat., 1983-89; pres. The Sumner Group Inc., 1989—. Pres. Naval Intelligence Found. Decorated D.S.M., Legion of Merit and others., Nat. Intelligence D.S.M., Netherlands Order Orange-Nassau, Brazil Order Naval Merit, French Nat. Order Merit, others. Mem. U.S. Naval Inst., Assn. Former Intelligence Officers (v.p.), Nat. Mil. intelligence Assn., Nat. Security Industries Assn., U.S. Naval Acad. Alumni Assn., Naval Submarine League.

SHAPIRO, THEODORE, psychiatrist, educator; b. N.Y.C., Feb. 26, 1932; s. Herman Alexander and Nettie (Rosenblatt) S.; m. Joan May Itkin, June 26, 1955; children: Susan, Alexander Herman. BA, Wesleyan U., 1953; MD, Cornell U., 1957. Diplomate Am. Bd. Psychiatry and Neurology, Am. Bd. Child Psychiatry, Am. Psychoanalytic Assn. Intern Montefiore Hosp., N.Y.C., 1957-58; resident in psychiatry NYU-Bellevue Hosp., 1958-61, rsch. assoc. child psychiatry, 1961-65; instr. to prof. NYU Sch. Medicine, 1960-76; prof. psychiatry and pediatrics Cornell U. Med. Coll., N.Y.C., 1976—; asst. lectr. N.Y. Psychoanalytic Inst., N.Y.C., 1970-86, tng. and supervising analyst, 1986—; cons. Alcohol, Drug Abuse and Mental Health Adminstrn., WHO, Washington, Geneva, Copenhagen, 1980-82; Am. Acad. Child and Adolescent Psychiatry, Washington; chair com. on stewardship Task Force Future, 1980-82, acad. sec., 1981-83, chair work group on sci. issues, 1988-89, chair com. editorship and stewardship of jour., 1984-86, 90-92; participant in APA bilateral exch. in Eastern Europe, 1992. Author: Clinical Psycholinguistics, 1979; co-editor: Infant Psychiatry, 1976; editor: Psychoanalysis and Contemporary Science, 1976, Structure in Psychoanalysis, 1991, Affect: Psychoanalytic Perspectives, 1992; editor Jour. Am. Psychoanalytic Assn. 1984-93; book rev. editor Internat. Jour. Psychoanalysis, 1993—; co-editor Research in Psychoanalysis, 1995; contbr. articles to profl. jours. Recipient Sandor Rado lectureship Columbia Psychoanalytic Clinic, 1991, Prager lectureship George Washington U. Sch. Medicine; NIMH residency tng. grantee, 1976-86; recipient Wilfred C. Hulse N.Y. Coun. Child Psychiatry, 1982, Harry Bakwin Meml. NYU, 1982, Maurice Laufer lectureship E.P. Bradley Hosp., 1982. Fellow Am. Acad. Child Psychiatry (sec. 1981-83), Am. Psychiat. Assn.; mem. Soc. Profs. Child Psychiatry (chmn. com. on edn. 1982—), Group for Advancement of Psychiatry (chmn. com. on child psychiatry 1985-90), Am. Bd. Psychiatry & Neurology (com. on child and adolescent psychiatry 1987-93, chmn. 1992-93), N.Y. Psychoanalytic Soc. Jewish. Office: Cornell U Med Coll Payne Whitney Clinic Box 147 525 E 68th St New York NY 10021-4873

SHAPIRO, VICTOR LENARD, mathematician; b. Chgo., Oct. 16, 1924; s. Joseph E. and Anna (Grossman) S.; m. Florence Gilman, Mar. 21, 1948; children—Pamela Sue Shapiro Baer, Laura Fern Shapiro Young, Charles R., Arthur G. B.S., U. Chgo., 1947, M.S., 1949, Ph.D., 1952. Mem. faculty Rutgers U., 1952-60, prof. math., 1959-60; mem. Inst. Advanced Studies, Princeton, N.J., 1953-55, 58-59; mem. faculty U. Oreg., Eugene, 1960-64; prof. math. U. Calif., Riverside, 1964—; faculty research lectr. U. Calif., 1978. Author: Topics in Fourier and Geometric Analysis, 1961, also articles. Served with AUS, 1943-46. NSF postdoctoral fellow, 1954-55. Mem. Am. Math. Soc., Math. Assn. Am., Am. Soc. Indsl. and Applied Math. Office: Math Dept U Calif Riverside Riverside CA 92521

SHAPLEY, LLOYD STOWELL, mathematics and economics educator; b. Cambridge, Mass., June 2, 1923; s. Harlow and Martha (Betz) S.; m. Marian Ludolph, Aug. 19, 1955; children—Peter, Christopher. A.B., Harvard U., 1948; Ph.D., Princeton U., 1953; PhD (hon.), Hebrew U., Jerusalem, 1986. Mathematician Rand Corp., Santa Monica, Calif., 1948-50; 54-81; prof. depts. math. and econs. UCLA, 1981—; instr. Princeton U., 1952-54; sr. research fellow Calif. Inst. Tech., 1955-56; fellow Inst. Advanced Studies, Hebrew U., Jerusalem, 1979-80; mem. faculty Rand Grad. Inst. for Policy Studies, 1970-86. Author: (with S. Karlin) Geometry of Moment Spaces, 1953, (with R. Aumann) Values of Non-Atomic Games, 1974; editor: (with others) Advances in Game Theory, 1964; mem. editorial bd. Internat. Jour. Game Theory, 1970—, Math. Programming, 1971-80, Jour. Math. Econs, 1973—, Math. Ops. Research, 1975—, Games and Econ. Behavior, 1988—. Served with AC U.S. Army, 1943-45. Decorated Bronze Star. Fellow Econometric Soc., Am. Acad. Arts and Scis.; mem. Nat. Acad. Scis., Ops. Research Soc. Am., Am. Math. Soc., Math. Programming Soc. Research in game theory, math., econs., polit. sci. Office: UCLA Dept Math Los Angeles CA 90024

SHAPLEY, ROBERT MARTIN, neurophysiology and perception educator; b. N.Y.C., Oct. 7, 1944; s. Benjamin and Florence Edith (Rosenthal) S.; m. Laurie Rose Sigal, July 31, 1966; children: Nina Claire, Alice Eve. AB, Harvard U., 1965; PhD, Rockefeller U., 1970. Postdoctoral fellow Northwester U., Evanston, 1970-71, Cambridge U., Eng., 1971-72; asst. prof. Rockefeller U., N.Y.C., 1972-76, assoc. prof., 1976-87; prof. neural sci. NYU, N.Y.C., 1987—, sponsor prof. for sci., 1992—, dir. Ctr. for Neural Sci., 1991-94; chmn. Visual Scis. B, Study Sect., Bethesda, Md., 1990-92. Assoc. editor Jour. Gen. Physiology, 1983—, Visual Neurosci., 1988-91; sensory editor Exptl. Brain Rsch. (Hamburg Fed. Republic Germany), 1990—; editor Contrast Sensitivity, 1993; contbr. articles to profl. jours. Recipient Career Devel. award NIH, 1977-82; Helen Hay Whitney Found. fellow, 1970-72; John and Catherine MacArthur Found. fellow, 1986. Mem. Assn. for Rsch. in Vision and Ophthalmology, Soc. for Neurosci. Jewish. Avocations: tennis, squash, history of art. Home: 1 Washington Square Vlg New York NY 10012-1601 Office: NYU Ctr for Neural Sci 4 Washington Pl New York NY 10003-6621

SHAPO, HELENE S., law educator; b. N.Y.C., June 5, 1938; d. Benjamin Martin and Gertrude (Kahaner) Seidner; m. Marshall S. Shapo, June 21, 1959; children: Benjamin Mitchell, Nathaniel Saul. BA, Smith Coll., 1959; MA in Teaching, Harvard U., 1960; JD, U. Va., 1976. Bar: Va. 1976, U.S. Dist. Ct. (we. dist.) Va. 1977, Ill. 1993. Tchr. Dade County, Miami, Fla., 1960-64; assoc. Robert Musselman & Assocs., Charlottesville, Va., 1976-77; law clk. to presiding justice U.S. Dist. Ct. Va., Charlottesville, 1977-78; asst. prof. law Northwestern U., Chgo., 1978-81, assoc. prof. law, 1981-83, prof. law, 1983—; instr. Sweet Briar Coll., Va., 1976-77, U. Va., Charlottesville, 1976-78; mem. com. law sch. admissions council/testing and devel., 1983—; cons. in field. Mem. ABA, Va. Bar Assn., Assn. of Am. Law Schs. (sect. chairperson 1985—), Women's Bar Assn. Chgo. Office: Northwestern U Sch Law 357 E Chicago Ave Chicago IL 60611-3008

SHAPO, MARSHALL SCHAMBELAN, lawyer, educator; b. Phila., Oct. 1, 1936; s. Mitchell and Norma (Schambelan) S.; m. Helene Shirley Seidner, June 21, 1959; children: Benjamin, Nathaniel. AB summa cum laude, U. Miami, 1958, JD magna cum laude, 1964; AM, Harvard U., 1961, SJD, 1974. Bar: Fla. 1964, Va. 1977. Copy editor, writer Miami (Fla.) News, 1958-59; instr. history U. Miami, 1960-61; asst. prof. law U. Tex., 1965-67, assoc. prof., 1967-69, prof., 1969-70; prof. law U. Va., 1970-78, Joseph M. Hartfield prof., 1976-78; Frederic P. Vose prof. Northwestern U. Sch. Law, Chgo., 1978—; of counsel Sonnenschein, Nath & Rosenthal, Chgo., 1991—; vis. prof. Juristisches Seminar U. Gottingen (Fed. Republic Germany), 1976; cons. on med. malpractice and tort law reform U.S. Dept. Justice, 1978-79; mem. panel on food safety Inst. Medicine, NAS, 1978-79; vis. fellow Centre for Socio-legal Studies, Wolfson Coll., Oxford, vis. fellow of Coll., 1975, Wolfson Coll., Cambridge, 1992; mem. Ctr. for Advanced Studies, U. Va., 1976-77; cons. Pres.'s Commn. for Study of Ethical Problems in Medicine and Biomed. and Behavioral Rsch., 1980-81; reporter Spl. Com. on Tort Liability System Am. Bar Assn., 1980-84; del. leader People to People Citizen Amb. program delegation to East Asia Tort and Ins. Law, 1986; lectr. appellate judges' seminars ABA, 1977, 83, 90; reporter symposium on legal and sci. perspectives on causation, 1990; advisor Restatement of the Law, Third, Torts: Products Liability, 1992—. Author: Towards a Jurisprudence of Injury, 1984; Tort and Compensation Law, 1976, The Duty to Act: Tort Law, Power and Public Policy, 1978, A Nation of Guinea Pigs, 1979, Products Liability, 1980, Public Regulation of Dangerous Products, 1980, The Law of Products Liability, 1987, Tort and Injury Law, 1990, The Law of Products Liability, 2 vols., 3d edit., 1994, supplements, 1991, 92, 93, Products Liability and the Search for Justice, 1993; (with Page Keeton) Products and the Consumer: Deceptive Practices, 1972, Products and the Consumer: Defective and Dangerous Products, 1970; editorial bd.: Jour. Consumer Policy, 1980-88, Products Liability Law Jour.; author: A Representational Theory of Consumer Protection: Doctrine, Function and Legal Liability for Product Disappointment, 1974; mem. adv. bd. Loyola Consumer Law Reporter; contbr. articles to legal and med. jours. NEH sr. fellow, 1974-75. Mem. Am. Law Inst., Am. Assn. Law Schs. (chmn. torts compensation systems sect. 1983-84, torts round table coun. 1970). Home: 1910 Orrington Ave Evanston IL 60201-2910 Office: Northwestern U Sch Law 357 E Chicago Ave Chicago IL 60611-3008

SHAPOFF, STEPHEN H., financial executive; b. N.Y.C., Nov. 1, 1944; s. Barney and Freda Shapoff; m. Andrea Dorin, May 30, 1967; 1 child, Matthew F. BBA, Pace U., 1967. CPA, N.Y. With audit dept. Ernst & Young, N.Y.C., 1967-72; asst. controller Seeburg Industries, Inc., 1972-74, 1967-72; with Estee Lauder, Inc., N.Y.C., 1974-78; controller Coleco Industries, Inc., Hartford, Conn., 1978-79; sr. v.p. fin. Ivy Hill Corp. subs. of Time Warner Inc., N.Y.C., Conn., 1979-85; exec. v.p. Ivy Hill Corp. subs. Time Warner Communications Inc., N.Y.C., 1985—; adj. asst. prof. Pace U., N.Y.C., 1971—. Mem. AICPA, Fin. Exec. Inst. (pres. L.I. chpt. 1988, 92-94, chair nat. membership com.), N.Y. Soc. CPAs, Nat. Assn. Accts. Office: Ivy Hill Corp 375 Hudson St New York NY 10014

SHAPPIRIO, DAVID GORDON, biologist, educator; b. Washington, June 18, 1930; s. Sol and Rebecca (Porton) S.; m. Elvera M. Bamber, July 8, 1953; children: Susan, Mark. B.S. with distinction in Chemistry, U. Mich., 1951; A.M., Harvard U., 1953, Ph.D. in Biology, 1955. NSF postdoctoral fellow in biochemistry Cambridge U., Eng., 1955-56; research fellow in physiology Am. Cancer Soc.-NRC, U. Louvain, Belgium, 1956-57; mem. faculty U. Mich., Ann Arbor, 1957—, prof. zool. and biology, 1967—, Arthur F. Thurnau prof., 1989—; assoc. chmn. div. biol. scis. U. Mich., 1976-83, acting chmn., 1978, 79, 80, 82, 83, coordinator NSF undergrad. sci. edn. program, 1962-67, dir. honors program Coll. Lit. Sci. and Arts, 1983-91; vis. lectr. Am. Inst. Biol. Scis., 1966-68; reviewer, cons. to pubs. on textbook devel.; reviewer grant proposals NSF, NIH, mem. program site visit teams. Author research on biochemistry and phisiology growth, devel., dormancy; invited speaker, rsch. symposia of nat. and internat. orgns. in field. Recipient Disting. Teaching award U. Mich., 1967, Excellence in Edn. award, 1991, Bausch & Lomb Sci. award, 1974; Lalor Found fellow, 1953-55; Danforth Found. assoc. Fellow AAAS; mem. Am. Inst. Biol. Scis. (vis. lectr. 1966-68), Am. Soc. Cell Biology, Biochem. Soc., Entomol. Soc. Am., Am. Soc. Zoologists, Royal Entomol. Soc., Lepidopterists Soc., Soc. Exptl. Biology, Soc. Gen. Physiologists, Assn. Biol. Lab. Edn., Xerces Soc., Phi Beta Kappa. Office: U Mich Dept Biology 3065 Natural Sci Bldg Ann Arbor MI 48109-1048

SHARBAUGH, THOMAS J., lawyer; b. Mar. 7, 1952. BS, Pa. State U., 1973; JD, U. Mich., 1976. Bar: Pa. 1976. Ptnr. Morgan, Lewis & Bockius, Phila. Office: Morgan Lewis & Bockius 2000 One Logan Sq Philadelphia PA 19103

SHARBEL, JEAN M., editor; b. Lansford, Pa.; d. Joseph and Star (Nemr) Sharbel. BA in Journalism, Hunter Coll., N.Y.C. Editorial dir., v.p. Dauntless Books, N.Y.C., 1962-75; editor romance mags., True Confessions Mag., Macfadden Holdings, Inc., N.Y.C., 1976-92; freelance editor fiction and nonfiction books, 1989—. Home: 165 E 66th St New York NY 10021-6132

SHARBONEAU, LORNA ROSINA, artist, educator, writer; b. Spokane, Wash., Apr. 5, 1935; d. Stephen Charles Martin and Midgie Montana (Hartzel) Barton; m. Thomas Edward Sharboneau, Jan. 22, 1970; children: Curtis, Carmen, Chet, Cra, Joseph. Student, Delta Coll., 1983—; studies with Steve Lesnick, Las Vegas, Nev.; studies with Bette Myers/Zimmerman, Phoenix and Bonners Ferry, Idaho. Prin. Sharboneau's Art Gallery, Spokane, 1977-80; tchr. art Mitchell's Art Gallery, Spokane, 1978-79; art therapist Vellencino Sch. Dist., Calif., 1981-83; indl. artist Lind, Wash., 1948—; dir., producer, stage designer Ch. of Jesus Christ of LDS, San Jose, Sonora, Modesto, Calif., 1978 (1st. place road show San Jose); dir. Sharboneau's Art Show, Spokane, 1979, Hands On-Yr. of the Child; platform spkr., poet, fundraiser, libr., 1984-87; assts., apprentice to Prof. Rowland Cheney, Delta Coll. Arts, Stockton, Calif., 1985, 86, 87; demonstrated drip oil technique, Bonners Ferry, Idaho, Spokane, Wash., Stockton, Calif., Delta Coll. Author, illustrator: Through the Eyes of the Turtle Tree, The One-Armed Christmas Tree, The Price of Freedom, William Will, Bill Can, Song of the Turtle Tree, Chet's Ottle-Bottle: The Unbreakable Bottle, One Drop of Water and a Grain of Sand; poet; prolific artist completed over 3000 paintings and drawings, displayed works in galleries through western states; featured in Magnolia News, Seattle, Delta Coll. Impact, Stockton, Calif., Stockton Record, Union Democrat, Sonora, Calif., Lincoln Center Chronicle, Stockton, Calif., Spokesman Rev., Spokane, Wash., Modesto (Calif) Bee, Angels Camp, Calif., Union Democrat, Sonora, Calif., New-Letter, Ch. of Jesus Christ of L.D.S 1st ward, Sonora; artist mixed media, oil, drip oil works, sculptures, pastel, watercolor; illustrations pen and ink, acrylic; sculpter bronze, lost wax method, ceramic art, soap stone, eggtempra, original techniques. Dir., programmer, fundraiser Shelter Their Sorrows, Sonora, Calif., 1989-92, vol. Community Action Agency and Homeless Shelter. Recipient Golden Rule award J.C. Penny, 1991, Recognition award Pres. George Bush, cert. Spl. Congl. Recognition Congressman Richard H. Lehman, 3rd Pl. Best Show East Valley Artists/Pala Show, 1973, 74, 75, 3d Pl. Artist of Yr., 1974, Valley Fair, Santa Clara, Calif., 1974, 1st and 2d Pl. Spokane County Fair, 1978, 3 honorable mentions, 4 premiums, 1979, 3 1st Pl., 3 2d Pl., 2 3d Pl., honorable mention Calaveras County Fair/Angels Camp, Calif., 1983, 1st and 3d Pl. Unitarian Art Festival, Stockton, Calif., 1984, 2nd Pl., 1985, 3d Pl., 1986, 1st Pl. Lodi Art Ann., 1985, 3d Pl., 1986, 1st Pl., 1987, 1st Pl., 1988, honorable mention SJCAC Junque Art Show, Stockton, 1985, 1st Pl. Central Art League, Modesto, 1986, 88; 3d Pl. Camilla Art Show, San Jose, Calif., 1974; 1st, 2d, and 3d Pl., Spokane County Fair, 1978; 4 honorable mentions, Mother Lode

Art Show, 1991, 2 hon. mentions, Sonora, Calif., 1993; homeless shelter kitchen named in her honor, Sonora. Mem. Cen. Sierra Arts Coun., Mother Lode Artists Assn., Internat. Platform Assn. (Judges Choice conv. arts competition 1993), The Planetary Soc. Mem. Ch. of Jesus Christ of LDS. Avocations: mathematics, astronomy, baseball, archeology. Home and Studio: 400 Mono Way Sonora CA 95370-5235 Office: Internat Platform Assn PO Box 250 Winnetka IL 60093-0250

SHARER, JOHN DANIEL, lawyer; b. Bklyn., Sept. 19, 1950; s. Albert Robert and Alda Loretta (Tapiro) S.; m. Kathleen Gail Donaldson, Feb. 14, 1981; 1 child, Stephanie Erin. AB, Dartmouth Coll., Hanover, N.H., 1972; JD, U. Pa., 1975. Bar: Pa. 1975, N.J. 1975, D.C. 1976, N.Y. 1989, Va. 1994. Law clk. Superior Ct. Pa., Hon. Edmund B. Spaeth, Jr., Phila., 1975-76; assoc. Sutherland, Asbill & Brennan, Washington, 1976-82, ptnr., 1982-94; counsel Christian, Barton, Epps, Brent & Chappell, Richmond, Va., 1994—. Bd. dirs. Wakefield Sch. Marshall, Va., 1990-94; mem. enrollment com. Dartmouth Club of Ctrl. Va. Mem. Phi Beta Kappa. Republican. Avocations: classical piano, computers, dogs. Home: 12317 Northlake Ct Richmond VA 23233-6635

SHARETT, ALAN RICHARD, lawyer, environmental mediator and arbitrator, educator; b. Hammond, Ind., Apr. 15, 1943; s. Henry S. and Frances (Givel) Smulevitz; children: Lauren Ruth, Charles Daniel; m. Cherie Ann Vick, Oct. 15, 1993. Student Ind. U., 1962-65; J.D., DePaul U., 1968; advanced postgrad. legal edn. U. Mich. and U. Chgo., 1970-71. Bar: N.Y. 1975, Ind. 1969, U.S. Ct. Appeals (2d cir.) 1975, U.S. Ct. Appeals (7th cir.) 1974, U.S. Supreme Ct. 1973. Assoc. Call, Call, Borns & Theodoros, Gary, Ind., 1969-71; judge protem Gary City Ct., 1970-71; environ. dist. atty. 31st Jud. Cir., Lake County, Ind., 1971-75; counsel Dunes Nat. Lakeshore Group, 1971-75; mem. Cohan, Cohan & Smulevitz, 1971-75; town atty., Independence Hill, Ind., 1974-75; judge pro tem Superior Ct., Lake County, Ind., 1971-75; professorial dir. NYU Pub. Liability Inst., N.Y.C., 1975-76; speaker, guest lectr., adj. faculty ATLA, Purdue U., N.Y. U., Ind. U., De Paul U., Valparaiso U., St. Joseph Coll., U. Miami; Coll. paralegal instr., 1970-89; adj. faculty prof. constl. law Union Inst., Miami, Cin., 1990-92; adj. prof. environ. litigation and alternative dispute resolution Ward Stone Coll., Miami, 1994; guest prof. internat. environ. law Dept. Internat. and Comparative Law, U. Miami, 1992—; mem. adv. panel, seminar speaker on internat. issues Interamerican Dialogue on Water Mgmt., 1993; gen. counsel Marjory Stoneman Douglas Friends of Everglades, 1992-93; asst. atty. gen., chair fed. and constnl. practice, N.Y. State, N.Y.C., 1976-78; pvt. practice, Flushing, N.Y., 1980-82, Miami Beach, Fla., 1988—, lead trial counsel, chmn. lawyers panel for No. Ind., ACLU, 1969-71; liaison trial counsel Lake County and Ind. State Health Depts. and Atty. Gen., 1971-75; mem. Nat. Dist. Attys. Assn., 1972-75, mem. environ. protection com.; pres. ESI Group, Nat. Environ. Responsibility Cons, Inc. Editor in chief DePaul U. The Summons, 1967-68; mem. staff DePaul Law Rev., 1968; contbr. articles to profl. jours. Mem. coalition Fla. Save Our Everglades Program. Recipient Honors award in forensic litigation Law-Sci. Acad. Am., 1967. Mem. ABA (nat. article editor law student div. 1967-68, nat. com. environ. litigation, com. fed. procedure, com. toxic torts, hazardous substances and environ. law, com. energy resources law, com. internat. environ. law, com. internat. litigation, environ. interest group, ABA section natural resources, energy and environ. law, judge negotiation competition championship round, law student divsn. midyear meeting 1995), Am. Arbitration Assn., Soc. Profls. in Dispute Resolution, Assn. of Bar of City of N.Y., N.Y. County Lawyers Assn. (com. on fed. cts. 1977-82), Am. Judicature Soc., ATLA (nat. coms. toxic, environ. and pharm. torts, environ. litigation), Environ. Law Inst., Am. Immigration Lawyers Assn., Ill. State Bar Assn. (staff editor 1967-68), N.Y. State Bar Assn. (environ. law sect., family law sect.), Ind. State Bar Assn. (environ. law sect., internat. law sect., trial practice sect.), Nat. Fla. Assn. Environ. Profls., Greater Miami C. of C. (coms. on environ. awareness, environ. econs., biomedical exch., planning and zoning growth mgmt., internat. econ. devel., bus. and industry econ. devel., govtl. affairs, ins., internat. banking, Europe/Pacific rim), Am. Acad. Poets. Office: ESI Group Nat Environ Responsibility Cons Inc 6800 SW 40th St Ste 458 Miami FL 33155-3708

SHARF, STEPHAN, automotive company executive; b. Berlin, Dec. 30, 1920; came to U.S., 1947; s. Wilhelm and Martha (Schwartz) S.; m. Rita Schantzer, June 17, 1951. Degree in Mech. Engring., Tech. U., Berlin, Fed. Republic Germany, 1947. Tool and die maker Buerk Tool & Die Co., Buffalo, 1947-50; foreman Ford Motor Co., 1950-53; gen. foreman Ford Motor Co., Chgo., 1953-58; with Chrysler Corp., Detroit, 1958-86, master mechanic Twinsburg stamping plant, 1958-63, mfg. engring. mgr., 1963-66, mrg. prodn. Twinsburg stamping plant, 1966-68, plant mgr. Warren stamping plant, 1968-70, plant mgr. Sterling stamping plant, 1970-72, gen. plants mgr. stamping, 1972-78, v.p. Engine and Casting div., 1978-80, v.p. Power Train div., 1980-81, exec. v.p., mfg., dir., 1981-85, exec. v.p. internat., 1985-86, also bd. dirs.; pres. SICA Corp., Troy, Mich., 1986—; bd. dirs. Medar, Inc., Gecamex Tech., Can., Channel 56 Pub. TV. Bd. dirs. Jr. Achievement, Detroit council Boy Scouts Am.; trustee, v.p. Oakland U. Mem. Soc. Auto Engrs., Detroit Engring. Soc. Club: Wabeek Country. Home: 966 Adams Castle Dr Bloomfield Hills MI 48304-3713 Office: SICA Corp PO Box 623 Troy MI 48099-0623

SHARFSTEIN, STEVEN SAMUEL, health care executive, medical director; b. N.Y.C., July 2, 1942; s. Sidney J. and Beverly (Zevie) S.; m. Margaret Shiling, June 13, 1965; children: Joshua, Daniel, Sarah. BA magna cum laude, Dartmouth Coll., 1964; MD, Albert Einstein Coll. Medicine, 1968; MPA, Harvard U., 1973. Diplomate Nat. Bd. Med. Examiners. Intern in pediatrics Bronx (N.Y.) Mcpl. Hosp. Ctr., 1968-69; jr. resident Mass. Mental Health Ctr., Boston, 1969-70, sr. resident, 1970-71, chief resident, 1971-72; dir. mental health svcs. Brookside Park Family Life Ctr., Jamaica Plain, Mass., 1972-73; adj. asst. to dir. Office Planning & Evaluation Nat. Inst. Mental Health, 1973-74, dir. program analysis and evaluation Office Program Devel. and Analysis, 1974-76, dir. divsn. mental health svc. programs, 1976-80, attending psychiatrist clin. ctr., 1980-82, assoc. dir. behavioral medicine, 1980-82; dep. med. dir. Am. Psychiat. Assn., 1983-86; exec. v.p., COO, med. dir. The Sheppard & Enoch Pratt Hosp., Balt., 1986-91, pres., CEO, med. dir., 1992—; lectr. in psychiatry Johns Hopkins U., Balt., 1987—; professorial lectr. in psychiatry dept. psychiatry Georgetown U., Washington, 1991—; clin. prof. U. Md., College Park, 1986—; cons. Neighborhood Employment Ctr. and Barbara Street Welfare Office, 1970-71, Allegheny County Mental Health/Retardation Bd., Pitts., 1973-74; examiner Am. Bd. Psychiatry and Neurology, 1979—; active Gov. Adv. Coun. on Mental Hygiene, 1987—, Inst. Medicine Bd. on Biobehavioral Scis. & Mental Disorders, 1993—. Co-author: Madness and Government: Who Cares for the Mentally Ill, 1983, Maintaining and Improving Psychiatric Insurance Coverage: An Annotated Bibliography, 1983, Coverage for Mental and Nervous Disorders, 1983, Health Insurance and Psychiatric Care, 1984; author chpts. to books; co-editor: Neighborhood Psychiatry, 1977, The New Economics and Psychiatric Care, 1985, Prospective Payment & Psychiatric Care, 1988; assoc. editor Am. Jour Psychiatry, 1993; mem. ednl. adv. bd. Cmty. Mental Health Jour., 1980—; mem. editl. bd. Jour. Mental Health Adminstrn., 1989—, Relapse, 1993; contbr. articles to profl. jours. Served with USPHS, 1970-73. Recipient Andrew Edison prize in govt. Dartmouth Coll., 1964; Harry C. Solomon prize Harvard U. Med. Sch., 1974; Adminstr.'s award for meritorious achievemnt Alcohol, Drug Abuse and Mental Health Adminstrn., 1980; Sr. Exec. Service Bonus award, 1981. Fellow Am. Psychiat. Assn. (mem. commn. on stds. and third party payments 1976-82, chmn. budget com. 1987-90, chmn. com. on managed care 1990—, sec. 1991—), Am. Coll. Psychiatrists (mem. pubs. com. 1984-87, mem. budget com. 1987-89, chair Dean award com. 1990—), Am. Orthopsychiat. Assn., Am. Coll. Mental Health Adminstrn.; mem. AMA, AAAS, Am. Assn. Gen. Hosp. Psychiatrists, Am. Assn. Psychiat. Adminstrs. (Significant Contbns. in adminstrn. award 1987), Am. Psychosomatic Soc., Washington Psychiat. Soc. (mem. coun. 1982—, Outstanding Svc. award 1984), Md. Assn. Private Practicing Psychiatrists, Md. Psychiat. Soc., Balt.-Washington Soc. for Psychoanalysis (affiliate), Washington Psychoanalytic Soc. (hon.), Med. Soc. D.C. Office: Sheppard and Enoch Pratt Hosp 6501 N Charles St Baltimore MD 21204-6819

SHARIF, OMAR (MICHAEL SHALHOUB), actor; b. Alexandria, Egypt, Apr. 10, 1932; s. Joseph and Claire (Saada) Shalhoub; m. Faten Hamama, Feb. 5, 1955; 1 child, Tarek. Attended, Victoria Coll., Cairo. Appeared in numerous Egyptian, French and Am. films including (debut) Ciel d' enfer,

1953, The Mamluks, The Blazing Sun, Goha, Lawrence of Arabia, 1962 (Golden Globe award for best supporting actor), Behold a Pale Horse, 1964, The Fall of the Roman Empire, 1964, Genghis Khan, 1965, The Yellow Rolls Royce, 1965, Doctor Zhivago, 1966 (Golden Globe award best actor), Night of the Generals, 1967, More Than a Miracle, 1967, Funny Girl, 1968, Mayerling, 1969, Che!, 1969, MacKenna's Gold, 1969, The Appointment, 1969, The Horsemen, 1970, The Last Valley, 1971, The Burglars, 1972, The Tamarind Seed, 1974, The Mysterious Island of Captain Nemo, 1974, Juggernaut, 1974, Funny Lady, 1975, Crime and Passion, 1975, Ace Up The Sleeve, The Pink Panther Stikes Again, The Right To Love, Ashanti, 1979, Bloodline, 1979, Oh Heavenly Dog, 1980, The Baltimore Bullet, 1980, Green Ice, Chanel Solitaire, Top Secret, 1984, The Rainbow, 1989, Mountains of the Moon, 1990, Journey of Love, 1990; TV appearances include S*H*E*, Pleasure Palace, The Far Pavillion, Mrs. 'arris Goes to Paris, 1992, (miniseries) Peter the Great, 1986, Anastasia: The Mystery of Anna, 1986, Grand Larceny, Omar Sharif Returns to Egypt, The Mysteries of the Pyramids (host). Author: The Eternal Male, 1977; author syndicated columns on bridge. Office: William Morris Agy care Ames Cushing 151 S El Camino Dr Beverly Hills CA 90212-2704*

SHARIFY, NASSER, librarian, educator, author; b. Tehran, Iran, Sept. 23, 1925; came to U.S., 1953, naturalized, 1972; s. Ebrahim and Eshrat (Saghafy) S.; m. Homayoun Taslimy, June 14, 1950 (div. 1978); children: Sharareh, Shahab. Licencie es Lettres, U. Tehran, 1947; M.S., Columbia U., 1954, Dr. L.S., 1958. Editorial staff Teheran jours. Rah-e Now, Jahan-e Now, Saba, Jonb ua Jush, 1943-51; translator, announcer All India Radio, 1948-49; librarian, dep. dir. Library of Parliament Iran, Tehran, 1949-53; cataloger Library of Congress, 1954-55; program asst. libraries devel. sect. UNESCO, Paris, 1959-61; acting chief servicing sect. Dept. Edn., 1962-63; dir. gen. Ministry Edn., Tehran, 1961-62; asst. prof. library and info. scis. and internat. edn. U. Pitts., 1963-66; founder, dir. Internat. Library Info. Center, 1964-66; vis. lectr. SUNY Albany Sch. Library Sci., summer, 1966; dir. internat. librarianship and documentation, internat studies and world affairs SUNY, Oyster Bay, 1966-68; dean, prof. grad. sch. library and info sci. Pratt Inst., Bklyn., 1968-87, chmn. inst. research council, 1971-89, disting. prof., dean emeritus sch. computer, info. and library scis., 1987-89, dean emeritus, 1987—; pres. B.E.L.T., Inc., internat. planning cons., 1981—; Dir. Grad. Library Tng. Program, UNESCO Mission, Nat. Tchrs. Coll., Tehran, 1960; Iran's Ofcl. del. to UNESCO Conf. Ednl. Pubs., Geneva, 1961, SE Asia Edn. Secs. Conf., Murree, Pakistan, 1961, Internation Conf., on Cataloging Prins., Paris, 1961, CENTO Libr. Devel. Conf., Ankara, Turkey, 1962; chmn. standing com. for preparation reading materials for new literates UNESCO, Tehran, 1961-62; mem. U.S. AID Mission, Turkey, Pakistan, 1966; dir. Conf. on Internat. Responsibility Coll. and Univ. Librarians, Oyster Bay, 1967; U.S. del. 33d Conf. and Internat. Congress on Documentation, Tokyo, 1967; ALA del. UN Conf. on Non-Govtl. Orgn., 1969; cons. U.S. AID, Conf. on Book Devel., 1967; mem. adv. bd. Ency. Libr. and Info. Scis., 1969—; chmn. Pre-Am. Library Assn. Conf. Inst. on Internat. Libr. Manpower, Edn. and Placement in N.Am., Detroit, 1970; mem. Am. del. Internat. Fedn. Libr. Assn. Conf., Liverpool, Eng., 1971, Budapest, 1972, Grenoble, France, 1973, Washington, 1974, Brussels, 1977, Montreal, 1982, Chgo., 1985; bldg. cons. Learning Resources Center, Nat. Tchrs. Coll., Iran, 1972-73, cons. campus planning, 1972-73; UNESCO cons. missions to plan and evaluate Nat. Sch. Info. Sci., Morocco, 1973-74, 79-81, 89; cons. U.S. Info. Agy., Morocco, 1991; chmn. Conf. on Orgn. and Control of Info for Islamic Research, 1982; chmn. bd. cons. to Nat. U. Iran, 1974-75, Pahlavi Nat. Library of Iran, 1975-77; speaker Symposium Internat. sur l' information Economique, Casablanca, Morocco, 1990. Author: cataloging of Persian works Including Rules for Transliteration Entry and Description, 1959, Book Production, Importation and Distribution in Iran, Pakistan and Turkey, 1966; Beyond the National Frontiers: The International Dimension of Changing Library Education for a Changing World, 1973; The Pahlavi National Library of the Future, 17 vols., 1976, other books; contbr. to Ency. of Library and Info. Sci., 1969, ALA World Ency. Library and Info. Services, 1980, 86, library jours., 1973—, Bookmark, 1972, Remembering Rangathan: A Sentimental Reflection, 1992; contbr. poetry to various jours. and anthologies, 1947-51, 67, 91-93 lyrics to Iranian motion pictures and recs., 1948-52; works on display at Archievies of Hoover Inst. on War Revolution and Peace, Stanford U.; Contbr. to: film script for motion picture Morad, 1951-52. Trustee Bklyn. Public Library, 1970-82; pres. Maurice F. Tauber Found., 1981—. Recipient Taj (crown) medal and citation for disting. svc. Mohammad Reza Shah Pahlavi, Shah of Iran, 1978, Kaula Gold medal and citation for disting. svc. to internat. librarianship, 1985; named for Annual Nasser Sharify Lecture Series, Sch. of Computer Info. and Libr. Scis., Pratt Inst., 1988—; writings by and about Naser Sharify are preserved at Archives of Hoover Instn. on wars, revolutions and peace., Stanford U., Stanford, Calif. Mem. ALA (chmn. com. equivalencies and reciprocity 1966-71, mem. Pakistan and Middle East Resource panels, internat. library edn. com., mem. com. internat. library schs. div. library edn. 1968-72, coordinator country resources panels, internat. library edn. com. library edn. div. 1973-78), N.Y. Library Assn. (dir. library edn. sect. 1969-72), Pub. Library Assn. (task force on internat. relations 1981-86), Am. Assn. Library Schs. (chmn. govtl. relations com., 1984-88), Am. Soc. Info. for Sci., Spl. Librarian Assn., Internat. Fedn. Library Assns. (adv. group library edn. 1971-73, v.p. library schs. sect. 1973-77). Home: 252 Jericho Tpke Westbury NY 11590-1213 Office: Pratt Inst Sch Info and Libr Sci 200 Willoughby Ave # 4 Brooklyn NY 11205-3899 *If I am asked to wash a car, I try to make it spotless. If I am to write a book, I try to make it faultless. But it seems that I always find spots on the shining surface of the car, and faults in many well-written pages of the book. This gives me another reason to live for another day.*

SHARIR, YACOV, artistic director, choreographer; b. Casablanca, Morocco, Aug. 22, 1940; came to U.S., 1978; s. Simon and Rene Sharir. Student, Jerusalem Acad. Music, 1962-65, Bat-Sheva Dance Co. Sch., 1965-67; grad., Jerusalem Besalel Acad. F.A., 1966. Instr. Bat-Sheva Dance Co., 1966-74; ballet instr. Israeli Ballet Co. & Kibbutz Dance Co., 1970-73; founder, artistic dir. Am. Deaf Dance Co., Austin, Tex., 1977-82, Sharir Dance Co., Austin, 1982—; sr. lectr. U. Tex., Austin, 1977—; faculty dance Jerusalem Rubin Acad. Music & Dance, 1988—; arts fellow for dance & virtual reality project Banff Ctr. For the Arts, 1992-94; choreographer over 70 pieces for various dance companies. Choreographer Homage to Jerome Robbins, Mechanical Doll, Quadroped, Right to Left, others. Choreography fellow NEA, 1989, 89-90.. Avocations: ceramics, sculpting, gardening. Home: 5406 Mount Bonnell Austin TX 78731 Office: U Tex Dept Theatre & Drama Austin TX 78712

SHARITS, DEAN PAUL, motion picture company executive; b. Mankato, Minn., Feb. 6, 1944; s. Loran Ross and June Banita (Timmann) S.; m. Patricia Ann Taylor, June 14, 1966 (div. 1973); 1 child, James Dean; m. Adela Zamora, July 23, 1988. AS in Engring., L.A. Trade Tech., 1974; BS in Bus., Calif. State U., Northridge, 1979; MBA, Mankato State U., 1980. Prodn. mgr. Walt Disney Imagineering, Glendale, Calif., 1980-84; gen. mgr. Recreation Entertainment Comml., Burbank, Calif., 1984-85; pres., CEO Apogee Prodns., Inc., Van Nuys, Calif., 1985-90; sr. v.p. Landmark Entertainment Group, L.A., 1990-92; pres., CEO Gold Springs Enterprises, Inc., San Diego, 1992-93; exec. v.p. Scenic Techs., Las Vegas, 1994—; dir. Internat. Kinetics Corp., Altadena, Calif., 1990—, Concerned Calif. for Motion Pictures and TV, Hollywood, Calif., 1986-88; cons. Technifex, Inc., Sun Valley, Calif., 1989-91, Water Entertainment Techs., Universal City, Calif., 1989-91. Contbr. articles to profl. jours. With USN, 1961-65. Republican. Avocations: tennis, skiing, running. Home: 7808 Riviera Beach Dr Las Vegas NV 89123 Office: Scenic Techs 4170 W Harmon Las Vegas NV 89123

SHARKEY, VINCENT JOSEPH, lawyer; b. Newport, R.I., May 25, 1944; s. Vincent Joseph and Dorothy (Auvil) S.; m. Joyce Toomey, Dec. 27, 1969; children: Alison, Christina, John, Julia. BA in Econs., Yale U., 1966; JD, U. Va., 1971. Bar: N.J. 1971, U.S. Ct. Appeals (3d cir.) 1985. Asst. prosecutor Bergen County Prosecutor's Office, Hackensack, N.J., 1971-72; pvt. practice, Bergen County, 1972-75; ptnr. Riker, Danzig, Scherer, Hyland & Perretti, Morristown, N.J., 1975—. Lt. U.S. Army, 1966-68. Mem. ABA, N.J. Bar Assn., Bergen County Bar Assn., Yale U. Alumni Assn. (pres. Bergen County chpt. 1986-88). Office: Riker Danzig Scherer 1 Speedwell Ave Morristown NJ 07962-1981

SHARLACH, JEFFREY ROY, marketing company executive; b. Stamford, Conn., June 11, 1953; s. Lester Herbert and Elaine Ruth (Roven) S. BS in

Journalism, Northwestern U., 1974; JD, NYU, 1977. Bar: Conn. 1977, D.C. 1978. Client service mgr. Burson-Marsteller div. Young and Rubicam, N.Y.C., 1982-85; v.p., dir. creative services Carl Byoir & Assocs. div. Foote, Cone, Belding Communications, Inc., N.Y.C., 1985-86; co-founder, dir., exec. v.p. Advanced Mktg. Tech. Corp. (Amtech), N.Y.C., 1986-87; co-founder, dir., pres. The Dext Corp., N.Y.C., 1987—; pvt. practice law Danbury, Conn., 1986—. Mem. Greater Gotham Bus. Council, 1981—. Recipient Silver award Internat. TV and Film Awards, 1978, 79, Silver Anvil award Pub. Relations Soc. of Am., 1980, 82. Mem. ABA, Conn. Bar Assn., D.C. Bar Assn., Bar Assn. of City of N.Y., Writers Guild of Am., Nat. Acad. of TV Arts and Scis., N.Y. Advt. and Communications Network (founding mem.).

SHARMA, BHU DEV, mathematics educator, researcher; b. Bijnor, North, India, June 21, 1938; came to U.S., 1987; s. Janki Prasad and Shanti Devi Sharma; m. Kusum Lata, July 9, 1959; children: Ritu, Swati, Harsh. Student, Govt. Inter Coll., Bijnor, 1951, Govt. Inter Coll., Moradabad, India, 1953; BS, Agra U., India, 1955, MS, 1957; PhD, Delhi U., 1971. Lectr. in math. NAS Coll., Agra U., Meerut, 1957-63; head maths. dept. Mcpl. Coll., Agra U., Mussoorie, India, 1963-64; head math. dept. Vaish Coll., Agra U., Shamli, India, 1964-66; lectr. in math. U. Delhi, 1966-72, reader in math., 1972-79; prof. math. U. W.I., St. Augustine, Trinidad, 1979-88; prof. math. Xavier U., New Orleans, 1988—, chair dept. math., 1994—; vis. postdoctoral fellow Colo. State U., Ft. Collins, 1976; vis. prof. U. Santa Caterina, Florianapolis, Brazil, 1985, U. P.R., Rio Piedras, 1982, 85, 89, U. Bielefeld, Germany, 1991, Chinese Acad. Scis., Inst. Systems Scis.. Beijing;. Chief editor: Jour. Combinatories Info. and System Sci., 1976—; editor-in-chief: Vishva-Vivek mag.; adv. editor: Jour. Info. and Optimization Sci., 1979-94; editor: Caribbean Jour. of Math., 1981—, Jour. Ramanu. Trustee Hindu Temple Soc. of Greater New Orleans, 1992-94. Mem. Am. Math. Soc., Math. Assn. Am., Indian Math. Soc. (life), Soc. Indian Academics in Am. (nat. rep. 1993-94), Hindu Ednl. and Religious Soc. Am., Inc. (pres.), Calcutta Math. Soc. (life), Operational Rsch. Soc. (life), Forum for Interdisciplinary Math. (life, pres. 1987-91), Hindi Nidhi (Trinidad chmn. acad. com. 1986-88, v.p. 1988-89), Lokenath Divine Fellowship La. (pres. 1995—). Hindu. Office: Xavier U La 7325 Palmetto St New Orleans LA 70125-1056

SHARMA, BRAHAMA DATTA, chemistry educator; b. Sampla, Punjab, India, June 5, 1931; naturalized Am. citizen; s. Des Raj and Kesara Devi (Pathak) S.; m. Millicent M. Hewitt, Dec. 22, 1956; children: Nalanda V. Sharma Bowman, Renuka D. BS with honors, U. Delhi, India, 1949, MS, 1951; PhD, U. So. Calif., 1961. Chemist Govt. Opium Factory, Ghazipur, India, 1951-52; lab. assoc., sci. asst. Nat. Chem. Lab., Poona, India, 1952-55; lab. assoc. U. So. Calif., L.A., 1955-61; research fellow Calif. Inst. Tech., Pasadena, 1961-65; asst. prof. chemistry U. Nev., Reno, 1963-64, Oreg. State U., Corvallis, 1965-70; asst. prof. chemistry Calif. State U., Northridge, 1973-75, assoc. prof., 1975-76; prof. L.A. Pierce Coll., Woodland Hills, Calif., 1976—; part-time assoc. prof. chemistry Calif. State U., L.A., 1973-85, prof., 1985—; vis. assoc. Calif. Inst. Tech., 1979, 82; pres. L.A. Pierce Coll. Senate, 1981-82, chmn. profl. and acad. stds., 1989-92. Contbr. articles to profl. jours. Grantee E.I. duPont de Nemours, L.A., 1961, Am. Chem. Soc. Petroleum Rsch. Fund, Washington, 1965-69, NSF, Washington, 1967-69. Mem. AAAS, Royal Soc. Chemistry (chartered chemist), Am. Crystallography Assn., Am. Inst. Parliamentarians (sec., adminstr., lt. gov. Region VII), Nat. Assn. Parliamentarians, Calif. State Assn. Parliamentarians (pub. rels. chmn., statewide edn. chmn. So. area, pres. Calif. Sigma unit), Sigma Xi. Avocations: playing bridge, reading, history, classical music, crystal models. Office: Los Angeles Pierce Coll Woodland Hills CA 91371

SHARMA, RAGHU NANDAN, technical corporation executive, electronic design engineer; b. Dist. Montgomery, Pakistan, Mar. 28, 1938; came to U.S., 1963; s. Shambhu Dutt and Ladwati (Devi) S.; m. Kaushalya Devi, Feb. 18, 1963 (div.); m. Patricia Jean Buchholz; children—Janel Kumari, Mathew Raghu, Adrienne Devi. B.S. in Physics with honors, U. Delhi, 1957; D.I.I.Sc., Indian Inst. Sci., Bangalore, 1960, M.Engring., 1962; Ph.D. in Elec. Engring., U. Minn., 1969. Founder, pres. Multi-Tech Systems, Mpls., 1971-74, pres., New Brighton, Minn., 1977—, dir., 1971—; staff engr. Warner Swasey Co., Mpls., 1974-76; with Anderson-Cornelius Co., Eden Prairie, Minn., 1976-77. Designer all modems sold by Multi-Tech Systems. NSF scholar, 1969, postdoctoral fellow, 1970. Hindu. Home: 16 Evergreen Rd Saint Paul MN 55127-2004 Office: Multi-Tech Systems Inc 82 2nd Ave SE New Brighton MN 55112-7815*

SHARMA, SANTOSH DEVRAJ, obstetrician and gynecologist, educator; b. Kenya, Feb. 24, 1934; came to U.S., Jan. 1972; d. Devraj Chananram and Lakshmi (Devi) S. BS, MB, B.J. Medical Sch., Pune, India, 1960. House surgeon Sasson Hosp., Poona, India, 1960-61; resident in ob-gyn. various hospitals, England, 1961-67; house officer Maelor Gen. Hosp., Wrexham, U.K., 1961-62; asst. prof. ob-gyn. Howard U. Med. Sch., Washington, 1972-74; assoc. prof. John A. Burns Sch. Med., Honolulu, 1974-78, prof., 1978 —. Fellow Royal Coll. Ob-Gyn., Am. Coll. Ob-Gyn. Avocations: travel, photography, environmental protection. Office: 1319 Punahou St Rm 824 Honolulu HI 96826-1032

SHARMA, SUSHIL CHANDRA, hospital administrator; b. Feb. 2, 1956; s. Chandra Dhar and Sushila Sharma; m. Heena Sharma, Feb. 19, 1988; children: Shefali, Sangita. MBA in Fin., Gannon U., 1978, MS in Health Adminstrn., 1981; cert. Sch. Pub. Health Exec. Program, Harvard U., 1988. Internal auditor Hamot Med. Ctr., Erie, Pa., 1977-80; contr. and dir. fin. Community Health Services Crawford County, Meadville, Pa., 1980-82; dir. fin. Jamestown (N.Y.) Gen. Hosp., 1982-83; dir. fin. and ops. Buffalo Columbus Hosp., 1983-85, pres., CEO, 1985-94; pres., CEO Buffalo Healthcare Corp., 1994—; bd. dirs. Mountainview Nursing Rehab. Ctr., Duncannon, Pa.; mem. corp. Blue Cross Western N.Y., Buffalo, 1984—; developer Preventive Health Svcs. Wellness Wagon, 1985—. Mem. Congress U.S., 1987, N.Y. State senator, 1987. Recipient resolution Erie County, 1987, City of Buffalo, 1987, Hispanics United of Buffalo Community Svc. award, Community Svc. award Kiwanis Internat., 1990, Community Svc. award West Side Sportsmen's Assn., 1990; named Up and Comer, Modern Healthcare Mag., 1990; New Diagnostic and Treatment Ctr. at Buffalo Columbus Hosp. named in his honor. Mem. Western N.Y. Hosp. Assn. (govt. relations com. 1986—), Am. Hosp. Assn. Ambulatory Soc., Am. Coll. Health Execs., Statue of Liberty Found., Pres. Assn., Village Glen Club (Williamsville, N.Y), Waterfront Club, Rotary (civic affairs com. Buffalo 1987—). Avocations: tennis, racquetball, jogging, walking, reading. Office: Buffalo Columbus Hosp 300 Niagara St Buffalo NY 14201-2135

SHARMAN, RICHARD LEE, telecommunications executive, consultant; b. Warren, Pa., Oct. 23, 1932; s. Scott Albert Sr. and Viola Lena Marie (Kittner) S.; m. Diane Lee Van Patten, Nov. 3, 1973; children: Daria Lee, Deedra Lee; children by previous marriage, Suzanne Annette, Cynthia Lee. BS in Engring. Physics, U. Toledo, 1959; MS in Elec. Engring., Cornell U., 1961. Project engr. advanced electronics ctr. GE, Syracuse, N.Y., 1965-68, mgr. infrared and optics, electronics lab., 1965-68; mgr. info. networks info. systems div. GE, Bethesda, Md., 1968-73; mgr. comml. analysis Xerox Corp., Rochester, N.Y., 1973-78; mgr. mktg. systems Xerox Corp., Rochester, 1978-80; v.p. bus. sector GTE Corp., Stamford, Conn., 1980-84; v.p. mktg. GTE Mobilnet Inc., Houston, 1984-87, gen. mgr. Tex. region, 1987-90; v.p. ops. GTE Mobilnet Inc. Hdqrs., Houston, 1990-92; pres., COO Guidry Group, Houston, 1992-93; pres., owner Mgmt. Consulting Svcs. Co., The Woodlands, Texas, 1993—; pres., founder Mgmt. Consulting Svcs., The Woodlands, Tex., 1993—; bd. dirs. Cellular Communications Corp., Irvine, Calif., 1985-87. Contbr. articles to profl. jours. Bd. dirs. Houston unit ARC. With USCG, 1951-54. Exec. mem. Am. Mktg. Assn., Houston C. of C. (mem. Region Mobility com.), Houston Grand Opera (patron 1990—), Tau Beta Pi, Forum Club (Houston). Republican. Episcopalian. Avocation: photography. Home and Office: 26 Fernglen Dr The Woodlands TX 77380

SHARMAN, WILLIAM, professional basketball team executive; b. Abilene, Tex., May 25, 1926; m. Joyce Sharman; children by previous marriage: Jerry, Nancy, Janice, Tom. Student, U. So. Calif. Basketball player Washington Capitols, 1950-51, Boston Celtics, 1951-61; coach Los Angeles/Utah Stars, 1968-71; coach Los Angeles Lakers, 1971-76, gen. mgr., 1976-82, pres., 1982-88, spl. cons., 1991—. Author: Sharman on Basketball Shooting, 1965. Named to Nat. Basketball Assn. All Star First Team, 1956-59, 2d Team,

1953, 55, 60, All League Team, 7 times; named Coach of Year Nat. Basketball Assn., 1972, Naismith Basketball Hall of Fame, 1976. Home: 4511 Roma Ct Marina Del Rey CA 90292 Office: Los Angeles Lakers PO Box 10 3900 W Manchester Blvd Inglewood CA 90306*

SHARON, NATHAN, biochemist; b. Brisk, Poland, Nov. 4, 1925; arrived in Israel, 1934; m. Rachel Itzikson, 1948; children: Esther, Osnat. MS, Hebrew U., Jerusalem, 1950, PhD, 1953; Dr. (hon.), U. Rene Descartes, Paris, 1990. Rsch. asst. Agrl. Rsch Sta., Rehovot, Israel, 1949-53; rsch. asst. dept. biophysics Weizmann Inst. Sci., Rehovot, Israel, 1954-57, rsch. assoc. dept. biophysics, 1957-60, sr. scientist dept. biophysics, 1960-65, assoc. prof. dept. biophysics, 1965-68, prof. dept. biophysics, 1968—; vis. scientist numerous univs. and colls. Author: Complex Carbohydrates: Their Chemistry, Biosynthesis and Functions, 1975; co-editor: Biotechnological Applications of Proteins and Enzymes, 1977, The Lectins: Properties, Functions and Applications in Biology and Medicine, 1986; co-author: Lectins, 1989; contbr. over 400 articles to profl. jours. Recipient Laundau prize Mifal Hapyis, Israel, 1973, Weizmann prize in exact scis. City of Tel Aviv, 1977, Olitzki prize Israel Soc. Microbiology, 1989, Datta lectureship award Fedn. European Biochem. Socs., 1987, Bijvoet medal Utrecht U., 1989, Israel Prize in Biomedical and Medical Research, 1994. Mem. Am. Chem. Soc., Biochem. Soc. Eng., Am. Soc. Biol. Chemists (hon.), European Molecular Biology Orgn., Israel Acad. Scis. and Humanities, Internat. Sci. Writers Assn., Israel Biochem. Soc. (pres. 1969-70), Soc. for Complex Carbohydrates, Fedn. European Biochem. Socs. (chmn. 1980-81), Internat. Glycoconjugate Orgn. (pres. 1989-91). Avocation: swimming. Home: 77 Mishmeret, Afeka Tel Aviv 69012, Israel Office: Weizmann Inst Sci, Dept Biophysics, Rehovot 76100, Israel

SHARP, AARON JOHN, botanist, educator; b. Plain City, Ohio, July 29, 1904; s. Prentice Daniel and Maude Katharine (Herriott) S.; m. Cora Evelyn Bunch, July 25, 1929; children: Rosa Elizabeth, Maude Katharine, Mary Martha (dec.), Fred Prentice, Jennie Lou. AB, Ohio Wesleyan U., 1927, DSc, 1952; MS, U. Okla., 1929; PhD, Ohio State U., 1938. Instr. botany U. Tenn., Knoxville, 1929-37, asst. prof., 1937-40, assoc. prof., 1940-46, prof., 1946-65, Disting. Service prof., 1965-74, prof. emeritus, 1974—; curator herbarium, 1949-68, assoc. curator herbarium, 1968—, head dept. botany, 1951-61; assoc. editor The Bryologist, 1938-42, 45-53, acting editor, 1943-44; assoc. editor Castanea, 1947-66; trustee Highlands (N.C.) Biol. Lab., 1934-38, 48-64, bd. mgrs., 1946-52; Cecil Billington lectr. Cranbook Inst. Sci., 1947; sec. sect. Inter-Am. Conf. on Conservation of Renewable Natural Resources, Denver, 1948; vis. prof. Stanford U., 1951, U. Mich. Biol. Sta., 1954-57, 59-64, U. Minn. Biol. Sta., 1971, U. Mont. Biol. Sta., 1972, Nat. U. Taiwan, 1965, Instituto Universitario Pedagógico Experimental, Maracay, Venezuela, 1976, U. Va. Biol. Sta., 1980; mem. staff Hattori (Japan) Bot. Lab., 1956—; vis. lectr. Am. Inst. Biol. Scis., 1967-70; mem. nat. adv. bd. Ministry of Ecology, 1975-81; cons. Time-Life Books, 1975, Brit. Broadcasting Corp., 1984, Nat. Geog. Books, 1985; hon. curatorship in the Inst. of Systematic Botany of the N.Y. Bot. Garden, 1994; hon. life mem. Save-the-Redwoods League, 1995. Assoc. editor: Hattori Bot. Jour., Nichinan, Japan, 1961—; contbr. articles to sci. jours. and Ency. Britanica. Bd. dirs. Nature Conservancy, 1955-61, Gt. Smoky Mountains Nat. Hist. Assn., 1979-81. Decorated officer Order of Rising Sun (Japan); Guggenheim Found. fellow, 1944-46; recipient Merit award Tenn. Environ. Edn. Assn., 1991, Disting. Achievement award Ohio Wesleyan U., 1992, Eloise Payne Luquer medal Garden Club Am., 1983, Appreciation cert. Great Smoky Mountains Nat. Park, 1994. Fellow AAAS (v.p. 1963), Linnean Soc. London; mem. AAUP, New Eng. Bot. Club, Internat. Soc. Phytomorphologists, Internat. Assn. Plant Taxonomy, So. Appalachian Bot. Club (pres. 1946-47), Sullivant Moss Soc. (pres. 1935), Am. Bryol. and Lichen. Soc., Am. Fern Soc., Bot. Soc. Am. (editorial com. 1948-53, treas. 1957-62, v.p. 1963, pres. 1965, Merit award 1972), Soc. for Study Evolution, Soc. Botánica de México (hon.), Soc. Mexicana de Historia Natural, Tenn. Acad. Sci. (exec. com. 1943-44, v.p. 1952, pres. 1953), Am. Soc. Plant Taxonomists (pres. 1961), Assn. Southeastern Biologists (v.p. 1956, Meritorious Tchr. award 1972, Bartholomew award 1989), Ecol. Soc. Am. (v.p. 1958-59), Torrey Bot. Club, Nature Conservancy (gov. 1955-61), Am. Soc. Naturalists, Bot. Brit. Bryol. Soc., Internat. Soc. Tropical Ecology, Internat. Phycolog. Soc., Am. Assn. Biology Tchrs., Phycolnog. Soc. India, Phycolog. Soc. Am., Systematics Assn., Am. Assn. Stratigraphic Palynol., Soc. Latino-Americano de Briologia (hon.), Tenn. Nat. Plant Soc. (hon.), Gt. Smoky Mountains Conservation Assn., (bd. dirs. 1960—), U. Tenn. Arboretum Soc. (bd. dirs. 1979—), Explorers Club, Phi Beta Kappa, Phi Kappa Phi, Sigma Xi, Phi Sigma, Phi Epsilon Phi, Sigma Delta Pi. Home: 1105 Tobler Rd Knoxville TN 37919-8164 Office: U Tenn Dept Botany Knoxville TN 37996 *The Universe is so constructed that for every error committed someone must pay a penalty now or in the future.*

SHARP, ALLEN, chief federal judge; b. Washington, D.C., Feb. 11, 1932; s. Robert Lee and Frances Louise (Williams) S.; children: Crystal Catholyn, Scarlet Frances. Student, Ind. State U., 1950-53; AB, George Washington U., 1954; JD, Ind. U., 1957; MA, Butler U., 1986. Bar: Ind. 1957. Practiced in Williamsport, 1957-68; judge Ct. of Appeals Ind., 1969-73; judge U.S. Dist. Ct. (no. dist.) Ind., South Bend, 1973—, now chief judge. Bd. advisers Milligan (Tenn.) Coll. Served to JAG USAFR. Mem. Ind. Judges Assn., Blue Key, Phi Delta Kappa, Pi Gamma Mu, Tau Kappa Alpha. Republican. Mem. Christian Ch. Club: Mason. Office: US Dist Ct 124 Fed Bldg 204 S Main St South Bend IN 46601-2122

SHARP, ANNE CATHERINE, artist, educator; b. Red Bank, N.J., Nov. 1, 1943; d. Elmer Eugene and Ethel Violet (Hunter) S. BFA, Pratt Inst., 1965; MFA (teaching fellow 1972), Bklyn. Coll., 1973. tchr. art Sch. Visual Arts, 1978-89, NYU, 1978, SUNY, Purchase, 1983, Pratt Manhattan Ctr., N.Y.C., 1982-84, Parsons Sch. Design, N.Y.C., 1984-90, Visual Arts Ctr. of Alaska, Anchorage, 1991, Anchorage Mus. Hist. and Art, 1991, 93, 94, 95, U. Alaska, Anchorage, 1994, 95. One-person shows Pace Editions, N.Y.C., Ten/Downtown, N.Y.C., Katonah (N.Y.) Gallery, 1974, Contemporary Gallery, Dallas, 1975, Art in a Public Space, N.Y.C., 1979, Eatontown Hist. Mus., N.J., 1980, N.Y. Pub. Library Epiphany Br., 1988, Books and Co., N.Y., 1989, The Kendall Gallery, N.Y.C., 1990, Alaska Pacific U., Carr-Gottstein Gallery, Anchorage, 1993, Internat. Gallery Contemporary Art, Anchorage, 1993, Art Think Tank Gallery, N.Y.C., 1994, U.S. Geol. Survey, Reston, Va., 1994, Stonington Gallery, Anchorage, 1990; group shows include Arnot Art Mus., Elmira, N.Y., 1975, Bronx Mus., 1975, Mus. Modern Art, N.Y.C., 1975-76, Nat. Arts Club, N.Y.C., 1979, Calif. Mus. Photography, Riverside, 1983-92, Jack Tilton Gallery, N.Y.C., 1983, Lincoln Ctr., N.Y.C., 1983, Cabo Frio Print Biennale, Brazil, 1983, Pratt Graphic Ctr., N.Y.C., 1984, State Mus. N.Y., Albany, 1984, Kenkeleba Gallery, N.Y.C., 1985, Hempstead Harbor Art Assn., Glen Cove, N.Y., 1985, Mus. Modern Art, Weddel, Fed. Republic of Germany, 1985, Kenkeleba Gallery, N.Y.C., 1985, Paper Art Exhbn. Internat. Mus. Contemporary Art, Bahia, Brazil, 1986, Mus. Salon-de-Provence, France, 1987, Mus. Contemporary Art, Sao Paulo, Brazil, 1985-86, Salon de Provence, France, 1987, Adirondack Lakes Ctr. for Arts, Blue Mountain Lake, N.Y., 1987, Kendall Gallery, N.Y.C., 1988, Exhibition Ctr. Parsons Sch. Design, N.Y.C., 1989, F.M.K. Gallery, Budapest, Hungary, 1989, Galerie des Kulturbundes Schwarzenberg, German Dem. Republic, Q Sen Do Gallery, Kobe, Japan, 1989, Anchorage (Alaska) Mus. History and Art, 1990-91, U. Alaska, Anchorage, 1990, 91, Coos Art Mus., Coos Bay, Oreg., 1990, Spaceship Earth, Mus. Internat. de Neu Art, Vancouver, Can., 1990, Councourse Gallery, Emily Carr Coll. Art and Design, 1990, Nat. Mus. Women in the Arts, Washington, 1991, Visual Arts Ctr. Alaska, 1991, 92, Nomad Mus., Lisbon, Portugal, 1991, Mus. Ostdeutsche Gallery, Regensberg, Germany, 1991, Mcpl. Mus. Cesley Krumlov (So. Bohemia) CSFK, Czechoslovakia, 1991, Böltmiche Dörter Exhbn. Hochstrass 8, Munich, 1992, BBC-TV, Great Britain, U.K., Sta. WXXI-TV, Rochester, N.Y., 1992-93, Site 250 Gallery Contemporary Art, Fairbanks, Alaska, 1993, The Rochester (N.Y.) Mus. and Sci. Ctr.. 1990-94, Anchorage Mus. History and Art, 1994, Space Arc: The Archives of Mankind, Time Capsule in Earth Orbit, Hughes Comm., Divec TV Satellite Launch, 1994, Stonington Gallery, Anchorage, 1994; represented in permanent collections Smithsonian Instn., Nat. Air and Space Mus., Washington, Albright Knox Gallery, Buffalo, St. Vincent's Hosp, N.Y.C., N.Y. Pub. Libr. N.Y.C., U.S. Geol. Survey, Reston, Va., White House (Reagan, Bush adminstrns.), Site 250 Gallery Contemporary Art, Fairbanks, Anchorage (Alaska) Mus. History and Art, others; Moon Shot series to commemorate moon landing, 1970-76, Cloud Structures of the Universe Painting series, 1980-86, Am. Landscape series, 1987-89, Thoughtlines, fall 1986, Swimming in the Mainstream with Her, U. Va., Charlottesville; author: Artist's Book - Travel Dreams U.S.A., 1989, Artworld-Welt Der Kunst, Synchronicity, 1989—, Art Think Tank: Projects in Art and Ecology, 1990—, The Alaska Series, 1990—, Potraits in the Wilderness, 1990—. Sponsor IDITOROD Trail Com., Libby Riddles. Artist-in-residence grantee Va. Center for Creative Arts, 1974, Artpark, Lewiston, N.Y., 1980, Vt. Studio Colony, 1989; recipient Pippin award Our Town, N.Y.C. 1984. Mem. Nat. Space Soc., Nat. Mus. Women in Arts, Alaska Natural History Assn., Alaska Photography Ctr., Pratt Inst. Alumni Assn., Mus. Modern Art, Internat. Assn. for Astron. Artists, The Planetary Soc., Internat. Assn. Near-Death Studies, Art and Sci. Collaborations, The Internat. Gallery of Contemporary Art. Address: PO Box 100480 Anchorage AK 99510-0480 *As an active painter I explore the mysteries of the 20th century space adventure in my American landscapes, painted directly from nature and in planetary landscapes, fantastic pictures of the cosmos. I believe it is in the reconciliation between inner and outer experience, through a personal sense of humor and use of universal symbols that a mystical or cosmic harmony can be expressed in art.*

SHARP, BERT LAVON, retired education educator, retired university dean; b. Philadelphia, Miss., Nov. 4, 1926; s. Bert L. and Louie (McBeath) S.; m. Mary Warren, Dec. 24, 1948; children—Kenneth, Richard. B.S., Miss. Coll., Clinton, 1949; M.Ed., U. Fla., Gainesville, 1953, D.Ed., 1960. Tchr., dir. guidance Miss. and Fla., 1945-55; dir. ednl. research Pinellas County, Fla., 1955-56; dir. secondary curriculum and ednl. services, 1958-61; assoc. prof., chmn. counselor edn. Auburn (Ala.) U., 1961-63; mem. faculty U. Fla., Gainesville, 1956-58, prof. edn., 1963-85, prof. emeritus, 1985—, dean Coll. Edn., 1968-78, dean emeritus, 1978—; cons. in field. Contbr. articles to profl. jours. Mem. Am. Assn. Colls. Tchr. Edn. (dir. 1973-76, exec. com. 1974-76, 78-81, pres. 1979), Assn. Colls. Schs. Edn. in State Univs. and Land-Grant Colls. (pres. 1976), Am. Personnel and Guidance Assn., Am. Assn. Counselor Edn. and Supervision, Fla. Council Deans, Am. Sch. Counselor Assn., Assn. Deans Edn. Land Grant Coll. and State Univs., Fla. Council Tchrs. Edn., Am. Assn. Sch. Adminstrs., Gov. Fla. Council Tchr. Edn. Centers, Internat. Council for Edn. of Tchrs. (bd. dirs. 1980—), Phi Kappa Phi, Phi Delta Kappa, Alpha Kappa Delta. Home: Richland Pl Apt 115 500 Elmington Ave Nashville TN 37205-2518

SHARP, DANIEL ASHER, foundation executive, corporate consultant; b. San Francisco, Mar. 29, 1932; s. Joseph C. and Miriam (Asher) S.; m. Jacqueline Borda, 1967 (div. 1975); 1 son, Benjamin Daniel; m. Revelle Pergament Allen, 1989. B.A., U. Calif.-Berkeley, 1954; J.D., Harvard U., 1959. Bar: Calif. 1959. Dep. atty. gen. State of Calif., San Francisco, 1959-61; with U.S. Peace Corps, 1961-68; asst. dir. internat. programs U.S. Peace Corps, Washington, 1961-62; assoc. dir. U.S. Peace Corps, Cuzco, Peru, 1962-64; acting dir. Peace Corps, La Paz, Bolivia, 1964; creator, dir. Staff Tng. Ctr. Peace Corps, Washington, 1965-68; dir. div. edn. resources U.S. Peace Corps, 1966; dir. edn. and Latin Am. programs, asst. dir. Adlai Stevenson Inst. Internat. Affairs, U. Chgo., 1968-70; dir. tng. ITT, Latin Am., 1970-72; mgr. mgmt. devel. ITT World Hdqrs., N.Y.C, 1973; with Xerox Corp., 1973-88; dir. human resources devel. Xerox Corp. (Xerox LatinAm. group), 1973-75, chmn. overhead value analysis task force, 1975-76; dir. ops. support Xerox Corp. (Xerox Latinam. group), 1976, dir. Inter-Am. affairs, 1977-79; dir. internat. affairs Xerox Corp. Hdqrs., 1979-85, dir. internat. and pub. affairs, 1985-87, internat. cons., 1988-93, sr. internat. advisor InterMatrix Group, 1990—; pres. Am. Assembly Columbia U., 1987—; adj. prof. internat. and pub. affairs Columbia U., 1991—; faculty Aspen Inst., 1995—; cons. U.S. Dept. State, fgn. govts., corps., founds.; mem. U.S. del. to UN Econ. and Social Coun., Geneva, 1961; mem. U.S. del. to OAS, San Juan, 1986; negotiated 6 treaties U.S. Govt.; U.S. rep. Internat. Conf. on Vol. Programs, The Hague, Netherlands, 1961; mem. outside bd. adv. coun. Macmillan Ltd. (U.K.), 1982; rep. U.S. bus. cmty. nat. task force on Europe Bus. and Industry Adv. Com., regional trade blocs, Paris, 1989. Editor: United States Foreign Policy and Peru, 1972, Los Estados Unidos y La Revolucion Peruaña, 1972, U.S. editor European Business Journal, 1988—; contbr. articles to N.Y. Times, Wall St. Jour., Internat. Herald Tribune, and chapters in several books. Chmn. adv. bd. Coun. of Ams., 1978-85; bd. dirs. Overseas Devel. Coun., 1980—, Internat. Ctr. of N.Y., 1980-88, Fund for Multinat. Mgmt. Edn., 1979-85, Accion, 1980-88, World Press Inst., 1986-89, Forum for World Affairs, 1987-95, Stamford Symphony, 1987-91; bd. advs. Landegger Program in Internat. Bus. Diplomacy, Sch. Fgn. Svc., Georgetown U., 1981-92, Econ. Growth Ctr., Yale U., 1987, Consortium on Competitiveness and Coop., U. Calif., 1987-90, Fletcher Sch. Law and Diplomacy, 1984-89; bd. visitors Duke U. Inst. of Policy Scis. and Pub. Affairs, 1988-91; mem. U.S./Mex. Bus. Coun., 1981-87. Served with U.S. Army, 1954-55; capt. Res. Recipient Medalla de Oro y Diploma de Honor del Consejo Provincial del Cuzco, 1963, Manchester Leadership award, 1992; Woodrow Wilson fellow Princeton, N.J., 1981-85. Mem. State Bar Calif., Coun. on Fgn. Rels., Mid-Atlantic Club (bd. dirs.). Home: 94 Campbell Dr Stamford CT 06903-4032 Office: Am Assembly Columbia U 475 Riverside Dr Ste 456 New York NY 10115

SHARP, DONALD EUGENE, bank consultant; b. Chgo., Nov. 4, 1929; s. Arthur Eugene and Alma (Melchior) S.; m. Phyllis Stevens, Sept. 11, 1954; 1 child, John Stevens. BA in Polit. Sci., Denison U., 1952; MA in History, Columbia U., 1959. Cert. econ. developer. With Chem. Bank, 1962-86, V.p. regular credit com., 1976-86; v.p. N.Y. Job Devel. Authority, 1986-91; lending cons. Community Mutual Savings Bank, 1992—; bd. dirs. Networld, Inc. Contbr. articles to profl. jours. Trustee Village of Bronxville, N.Y., 1989-91. Sgt. U.S. Army, 1952-54, Korea. Mem. Am. Econ. Devel. Coun. (bd. dirs.), Northeastern Indsl. Devel. Assn., Acad. Polit. Sci., Shenorock Shore Club, Skytop Club. Democrat. Episcopalian. Home: 66 Avon Rd Bronxville NY 10708-1721 Office: Community Mutual Savings Bank 10 Bank St White Plains NY 10606

SHARP, DOUGLAS ANDREW, secondary school educator; b. Austin, Tex., July 19, 1945; s. Jack Weston and Jean Ernestine (Beeman) S.; m. Marylin Gene Martin, Jan. 20, 1977. BA in Math., Tex. A&M U., 1967, MS in Math., 1970, postgrad., 1969-71; EdD, La Salle U., Mandville, La., 1993. Teaching fellow dept. math. Tex. A&M U., College Station, 1967-71; chmn. math. dept., asst. coach/coach athletics dept. Southfield Sch., Shreveport, La., 1972-73; coach athletics dept. St. John's Sch., Houston, 1975, chmn. math. dept., 1981-93, master teaching chair math., 1987-89; disting. vis. lectr. U. Houston, 1989-90, adj. prof., 1990. Contbr. articles to profl. jours. Recipient Excellence in Teaching award Fin. Dept. U. Houston, 1993, Outstanding Tchr. award Tandy Technol. Scholars, 1993-94. Mem. Am. Math. Soc., Am. Soc. Composer Authors and Pubs., Am. Statistical Assn., Math. Assn. Am. (Edyth May Sliffe award 1991), Calculus and Elem. Analysis Tchrs. Houston, Nat. Coun. Tchrs.Math. Office: St John's Sch 2401 Claremont St Houston TX 77019-5897

SHARP, EDGAR E., diversified corporation executive; b. 1933; married. BS, Mississippi State U., 1955. With Aluminum Co. Am., 1955-61, Raytheon Co., 1961-62, Textron Inc., 1962-69, Keene Corp., 1969-72; former v.p., then pres. Tilling Thomas Inc., Stamford, Conn.; pres., chief exec. officer BTR Inc. (subs BTR plc, London), Stamford, Conn.; chief oper. officer BTR Indsl. Group, Weston, Mass. Office: BTR Inc 1000 1 Main Pl Stamford CT 06902-3845 also: BTR Indsl Group Riverside Office Park 9 Riverside Rd Weston MA 02193

SHARP, GEORGE KENDALL, federal judge; b. Chgo., Dec. 30, 1934; s. Edward S. and Florence S.; m. Mary Bray; children: Florence Kendall, Julia Manger. BA, Yale U., 1957; JD, U. Va., 1963. Bar: Fla. 1963. Atty. Sharp, Johnston & Brown, Vero Beach, Fla., 1963-78; pub. defender 19th Cir. Ct., Vero Beach, Vero beach, 1963-78; bd. atty. Indian River County, Fla., 1968-78; Fla. circuit judge 19th Cir., 1978-83; judge U.S. Dist. Ct. (mid. dist.) Fla., Orlando, 1983—. Office: US Dist Ct 635 US Courthouse 80 N Hughey Ave Orlando FL 32801-0231

SHARP, GLENN (SKIP SHARP), vocational education administrator; b. Stroud, Okla., Nov. 19, 1938; s. Charles W. and Adeline M. (Jenisch) S.; m. Sherry Caroline Waddle, Aug. 29, 1959; children: Stephanie, Patricia, Nancy, Christopher. BS, Emporia State U., 1960, MS, 1966. Bus. educator Windthorst High Sch., Spearville, Kans., 1960-64; Bus. educator Northwest Kans. Area Vocat. Tech. Sch., Goodland, 1964-66, asst. dir., 1966—. Commr. Goodland City Commn., 1986-87; mem. state Scholar Com.,

Topeka, 1984-85; county chmn. Am. Cancer Soc., Sherman County, Kans., 1981-82; bloodmobile chmn. ARC, Sherman County, 1978-80; cubmaster Boy Scouts Am., Goodland, 1976— (Silver Beaver award 1992, Award of Merit 1989, James E. West Fellowship 1995); bd. dirs. N.W.K. Regional Med. Ctr., 1993—. Recipient Outstanding Svc. award Kans. Jaycees, 1972, Silver Beaver award Boys Scouts Am., 1992, award of Merit, 1989; named Employee of Yr. Goodland C. of C., 1988. Mem. Nat. Assn. Fin. Aid (bd. dirs. 1988-91, Nat. Leadership award 1995), Am. Vocat. Assn. (life), Rocky Mountain Assn. Fin. Aid (pres., bd. dirs. 1985-91, Disting. Svc. awards 1985, 87, Hall of Fame 1992), Kans. Vocat. Assn. (life), Kans. Assn. Fin. Adminstrs. (pres., bd. dirs. 1983-93, Outstanding Svc. award 1986), Meritorious Achievement award 1995), Kiwanis (pres. 1968-69, 92-93, Outstanding Kiwanian 1968, 94, Phi Delta Kappa (pres. 1983-84, Outstanding Educator 1985-86, Svc. Key 1991). Democrat. Christian. Avocations: camping, collecting, grandchildren, travel. Home: 702 Walnut St Goodland KS 67735-2048

SHARP, JANE ELLYN, operations executive; b. Chgo., Jan. 5, 1934; d. Truman V. and Mildred L. (Sweitzer) Lasswell; m. David H. Sharp, July 24, 1965 (div. Aug. 1979); children: Michelle Lynn, Lisa Elizabeth. BBA, Coll. Santa Fe, 1985, MBA, 1988. Adminstrv. asst. San Diego State U., 1956-58; dir. classified personnel Grossmont (Calif.) Union High Sch. and Jr. Coll. Dist., 1959-62; legal asst. Stockly & Boone, Attys., Los Alamos, N.Mex., 1974-75; with adminstrn. Los Alamos (N.Mex.) Nat. Lab., 1976-78, pub. rels. specialist, 1978-81, asst. group leader, 1981-82, dep. group leader, 1982-83, asst. div. leader, 1983-84, office dir. protocol, 1984-89, dep. assoc. dir. for ops., 1989—. Mem. adv. bd. Youth Working for Youth, Los Alamos, 1985—; mem. Adults Working for Youth, Los Alamos, Santa Fe Rail Link Task Force, 1987-90, Los Alamos Community Devel. Com., 1989—; bd. dirs. Los Alamos Econ. Devel. Corp., 1989—, Los Alamos United Way, 1992—. Recipient Woman at Work award Coun. on Working Women, 1984. Mem. Tri Area Assn. for Econ. Devel., Los Alamos Nat. Lab. Community Coun. (rep. exec. bd. 1986—), Los Alamos C. of C. (bd. dirs. 1991—). Democrat. Avocations: music, hiking, sewing, reading, aerobics. Office: Los Alamos Nat Lab PO Box 1663 Los Alamos NM 87544-0600

SHARP, JOANN M., county official; b. Lynn, Mass., Sept. 30, 1942; d. Joseph M. and Theresa S. (Angelone) Foti; m. John S. Sharp, May 8, 1970; children: Jocelyn, Jacqueline, Joanna, Julianne. Selectman Northborough, Mass., 1986-92, chmn. bd. selectmen, 1990-91; commr. Worcester (Mass.) County, 1992—. Chmn. Northborough to Feed the Hungry, 1987-91, Rep. town com., 1991-92. Mem. Jr. Women's Club (hon.). Roman Catholic. Avocations: politics, books, cooking, singing, travel. Home: Box 132 51 Cherry St Northborough MA 01532 Office: Worcester Cnty Commrs Courthouse 2 Main St Worcester MA 01608

SHARP, JOEL H., JR., lawyer; b. Salem, Ohio, Aug. 25, 1935. BS, Yale U., 1957; LLB, Stanford U., 1960. Bar: Calif. 1961, Fla. 1964. Ptnr. Baker & Hostetler, Orlando, Fla. Fellow Am. Coll. Trust and Estate Coun., Am. Coll. Tax Coun.; mem. ABA (vice chmn. corp. com., tax sect. 1984-86, chmn. 1986-88), State Bar Calif., Fla. Bar (mem. exec. coun. tax sect. 1965—, chmn. 1976-77, mem. bd. govs. 1975-79), Orange County Bar Assn. (mem. exec. coun. 1967-74, pres. 1972-73). Office: Baker & Hostetler Sun-Bank Ctr 200 S Orange Ave Ste 2300 Orlando FL 32802-3432

SHARP, JOHN MALCOLM, JR., geology educator; b. St. Paul, Mar. 11, 1944. BGeoE, U. Minn., 1967; MS, PhD., U. Ill., 1974. Civil engring. officer USAF, 1967-71; with geology dept. U. Mo., Columbia, 1974-82; Chevron Centennial prof. geology U. Tex., Austin, 1982—. Alexander von Humbolt fellow 1981-83. Fellow Geol. Soc. Am. (O.E. Meinzer award 1979); mem. Phi Kappa Phi, Sigma Xi, Tau Beta Pi. Office: U Tex Dept Geol Scis Austin TX 78712-1101

SHARP, MITCHELL WILLIAM, adviser to prime minister; b. Winnipeg, Man., Can., May 11, 1911; s. Thomas and Elizabeth (Little) S.; m. Daisy Boyd, Apr. 23, 1938 (dec.); 1 son, Noel; m. Jeannette Dugal, Apr. 14, 1976. B.A., U. Man., 1934, LL.D. (hon.), 1965; postgrad., London Sch. Econs., 1937-38; hon. Dr. Social Sci., U. Ottawa, 1970; LL.D. (hon.), U. Western Ont., 1977. Statistician Sanford Evans Statis. Service, 1926-36; economist James Richardson & Sons Ltd., 1936-42; officer Canadian Dept. Fin., Ottawa, 1942-51; dir. econ. policy div. Canadian Dept. Fin., 1947-51; assoc. dep. minister Canadian Dept. Trade and Commerce, 1951-57, dep. minister, 1957-58; v.p. Brazilian Traction, Toronto, Can., 1958-62; mem. Can. Ho. of Commons, from 1963; minister trade and commerce, 1963-65, minister fin., 1965-68, sec. state external affairs, 1968-74, pres. Privy Council, house leader, 1974-76, resigned, 1978; commr. No. Pipeline Agy., 1978-88. Decorated officer Order of Can. Address: 33 Monkland Ave, Ottawa, ON Canada K1S 1Y8

SHARP, PAUL DAVID, institute administrator; b. Youngstown, Ohio, Nov. 3, 1940; s. Robert Henderson and Kathryn (Tadsen)S.; m. Carole G. Graff, Sept. 16, 1967; children: David Allen, Kathryn Elizabeth. BA cum laude, Kenyon Coll., Gambier, Ohio, 1962; MPA, Auburn U., 1974. Commd. 2d lt. USAF, 1962, advanced through grades to col., 1983, intelligence officer, 1962-80; comdr. Detachment 1, 7450th Intelligence Squadron USAF, Neubruecke, Germany, 1980-83; comdr. 480th Reconnaissance Tech. Group USAF, Langley AFB, Va., 1983-85, dir. intelligence systems HQ Tactical Air Command, 1985-86, dep. chief intelligence Tactical Air Command, 1986-88; mgr. operational intelligence group Battelle Meml. Inst., Columbus, Ohio, 1988-89, mgr. fgn. tech. assessment group, 1989-91, mgr. intelligence projects/programs, 1991-92, v.p. bus. devel. fgn. sci. and tech., 1992—; mem. student career coun. Kenyon Coll., Columbus, 1992-95. Trustee Brandywine Assn., Yorktown, Va., 1987, Chase Assn., Powell, Ohio, 1991. Decorated Legion of Merit, Meritorious Svc. medals. Mem. Nat. Mil. Intelligence Assn., Armed Forces Communications and Electronics Assn., Air Force Assn., Sigma Pi (pres. Lambda chpt. 1961-62). Republican. Episcopalian. Avocations: golf, woodworking, photography, music. Office: Battelle Meml Inst 505 King Ave Columbus OH 43201

SHARP, PAUL FREDERICK, former university president, educational consultant; b. Kirksville, Mo., Jan. 19, 1918; s. Frederick J. and L. Blanche (Phares) S.; m. Rosella Ann Anderson, June 19, 1939; children: William, Kathryn, Paul Trevor. AB, Phillips U., 1939; PhD, U. Minn., 1947; LLD (hon.), Tex. Christian U., 1961, Austin Coll., 1978, Drake U., 1980; LHD (hon.), Buena Vista Coll., 1967, U. Nev., Towson State U., 1980; LittD (hon.), Limestone Coll., 1971; HHD, Okla. Christian U. Sci. & Arts, 1992. Instr. U. Minn., 1942, 46-47, vis. lectr., 1948; asso. prof. Am. history Iowa State U., 1947-54; prof. Am. history, dir. Am. Instns. program U. Wis., 1954-57, vis. lectr., 1953; vis. lectr. San Francisco State Coll., 1950, U. Oreg., 1955; Fulbright lectr. Am. Instns., univs. Melbourne, Sydney, 1952; pres. Hiram Coll., 1957-64; chancellor U. N.C., Chapel Hill, 1964-66; pres. Drake U., Des Moines, 1966-71; pres. U. Okla., Norman, 1971-78, pres. emeritus, Regents' prof., 1978-88, pres. emeritus, Regents' prof. emeritus, 1988—; disting. prof. history U. Sci. and Arts, Okla., 1990—; dir. Am. Coun. on Edn. Insts. for Coll. and Univ. Presidents, 1977-79; vis. lectr. Harvard U. Bus. Sch. summer session, 1970-72. Author: Agrarian Revolt in Western Canada, 1948, Old Orchard Farm, Story of an Iowa Boyhood, 1952, Whoop-Up Country, Canadian American West, 1955; coms. author: Heritage of Midwest, 1958; Editor: Documents of Freedom, 1957; Contbr. articles to profl. jours. U.S. Navy Liaison Officer, 1943-46, His Majesty's Australian Ship. Minn. Hist. Soc. grantee, 1947, 48, Social Sci. Research Council grantee, 1949, 51; Ford Faculty fellow, 1954, Guggenheim fellow, 1957; recipient Iowa State U. Alumni Fund award, 1952, award of merit Am. Assn. State and Local History, 1955, Silver Spur award Western Writers Am., 1955, Fulbright award to Australia, 1952, Outstanding Achievement award U. Minn., 1975, Outstanding Achievement award Phillips U., Outstanding Achievement award U. Okla. Mem. Phi Beta Kappa, Phi Kappa Phi, Phi Delta Kappa, Pi Gamma Mu, Phi Alpha Theta. Mem. Disciples of Christ Ch. Home: 701 Mockingbird Ln Norman OK 73071-4829 Office: U Okla 630 Parrington Oval Rm 105 Norman OK 73069-8813

SHARP, PHILLIP ALLEN, academic administrator, biologist, educator; b. Ky., June 6, 1944; s. Joseph Walter and Katherin (Colvin) S.; m. Ann Christine Holcombe, Aug. 29, 1964; children: Christine Alynn, Sarah Katherin, Helena Holcombe. BA, Union Coll., Barbourville, Ky., 1966, LHD (hon.), 1991; PhD, U. Ill., 1969. NIH postdoctoral fellow Calif. Inst.

Tech., 1969-71; sr. research investigator Cold Spring Harbor (N.Y.) Lab., 1972-74; assoc. prof. MIT, Cambridge, 1974-79, prof. biology, 1979—, head dept. biology, 1991—, dir. Ctr. Cancer Rsch., 1985-91; Co-founder, mem. sci. bd., dir. BIOGEN, 1978—; mem. editl. bd. Cell, 1974-95, Jour. Virology, 1974-86, Molecular and Cellular Biology, 1974-85. Co-recipient Nobel Prize in Physiology or Medicine, 1993; recipient awards Am. Cancer Soc., 1974-79, awards Eli Lilly, 1980, awards Nat. Acad. Sci./U.S. Steel Found., 1980, Howard Ricketts award U. Chgo., 1985, Alfred P. Sloan Jr. prize Gen. Motors Research Found., 1986, award Gairdner Found. Internat., 1986, award N.Y. Acad. Scis., 1986, Louisa Horwitz prize, 1988, Albert Lasker Basic Med. Rsch. award, 1988, Dickson prize U. Pitts., 1990; awarded Class of '41 chair, 1986-87, John D. MacArthur chair, 1987-92, Salvador E. Luria chair, 1992—. Fellow AAAS; mem. Am. Chem. Soc., Am. Soc. Microbiology, NAS (councilor 1986), Am. Acad. Arts and Scis, European Molecular Biology Orgn. (assoc.), Am. Soc. Biochemistry and Molecular Biology (elected mem. coun.), Am. Philos. Soc. (elected mem.), Inst. of Medicine of NAS (elected mem.). Home: 36 Fairmont Ave Newton MA 02158-2212 Office: MIT Ctr for Cancer Rsch 40 Ames St Rm E17 529B Cambridge MA 02139-4307

SHARP, RICHARD L., retail company executive; b. Washington, Apr. 12, 1947. Student, U. Va., 1965-66, Coll. of William and Mary, 1968-70. Programmer Group Health Inc., Washington, 1970-75; founder, pres. Applied Systems Corp., Washington, 1975-81; with Circuit City Stores, Inc., Richmond, Va., 1982—, exec. v.p. 1982-84, pres., 1984-86, pres., CEO 1986-94, chmn. pres., CEO, 1994—; bd. dirs. S&K Famous Brands, Inc., Flextronics Internat., Dominion Resources, Inc., Va. Power Co. With USAF, 1967-70. Office: Circuit City Stores Inc 9950 Mayland Dr Richmond VA 23233-1464

SHARP, ROBERT PHILLIP, geology educator, researcher; b. Oxnard, Calif., June 24, 1911; s. Julian Hebner Sharp and Alice Sharp Darling; m. Jean Prescott Todd, Sept. 7, 1938; adopted children—Kristin Todd, Bruce Todd. B.S., Calif. Inst. Tech., Pasadena, 1934, M.S., 1935; M.A., Harvard U., Cambridge, Mass., 1936, Ph.D., 1938. Asst. prof. U. Ill., Urbana, 1938-43; prof. U. Minn., Mpls., 1946-47; prof. Calif. Inst. Tech., Pasadena, 1947-79, chmn., 1952-67, prof. emeritus, 1979—. Author: Glaciers, 1960, Field Guide-Southern California, 1972, Field Guide-Coastal Southern California, 1978, Living Ice-Understanding Glaciers and Glaciation, 1988, (with A.F. Glazner) Geology Under Foot in Southern California, 1993. Served to capt. USAF, 1943-46. Recipient Exceptional Sci. Achievement medal NASA, 1971, Nat. Medal Sci., 1989, Charles P. Daly medal Am. Geog. Soc., 1991; Robert P. Sharp professorship Calif. Inst. Tech., 1978. Fellow Geol. Soc. Am. (councillor, Kirk Bryan award 1964, Penrose medal 1977), Am. Geophys. Union; hon. fellow Internat. Glaciological Soc.; mem. NAS. Republican. Avocations: flyfishing, snorkeling, camping. Home: 1901 Gibraltar Rd Santa Barbara CA 93105-2326 Office: Calif Inst Tech 1200 E California Blvd Pasadena CA 91125

SHARP, ROBERT WEIMER, lawyer; b. Cleve., Feb. 12, 1917; s. Isaac Walter and Ruth (Weimer) S.; m. Norine Wines, Nov. 13, 1948; children: Kathleen L. Sharp Samuel, Pamela J. Sharp Adamson, Janet E. Sharp Schoon, Andrea S. Sharp Bobak, Gail N. Sharp Henderson. A.B. magna cum laude, Oberlin Coll., 1939; LL.B., Harvard U., 1942. Bar: Ohio 1944. Practiced in Cleve; ptnr. Gallagher, Sharp, Fulton & Norman and predecessors, 1958-92; pres. Bulkley Bldg. Co., 1966-70. Trustee emeritus St. Luke's Hosp. Assn.; trustee emeritus Ohio East Area United Meth. Found., 1974—, sec., 1967-74, 83-86, pres., 1974-80; trustee Ohio divsn. Am. Cancer Soc. Served with USNR, 1942-46. Mem. ABA, Ohio Bar Assn., Cleve. Bar Assn., Phi Beta Kappa. Republican. Methodist. Home: 3090 Fairmount Blvd Cleveland OH 44118-4129 Office: Gallagher Sharp Fulton & Norman 600 Bulkley Bldg Cleveland OH 44115

SHARP, RONALD ALAN, English literature educator, author; b. Cleve., Oct. 19, 1945; s. Jack Trier and Florence (Tenenbaum) S.; m. Inese Brutans, June 22, 1968; children: Andrew Janis, James Michael. BA, Kalamazoo Coll., 1967; MA, U. Mich., 1968; PhD, U. Va., 1974. Instr. in English Western Mich. U., Kalamazoo, 1968-70; instr. Kenyon Coll., Gambier, Ohio, 1970-72, asst. prof. English, 1974-78, assoc. prof., 1978-85; prof. Kenyon Coll., 1985-90, John Crowe Ransom prof. English, 1990—, chmn. dept. English, 1984-86, co-editor Kenyon Rev., 1978-82; dir. Keats Bicentennial Conf., Harvard U., 1995. Author: Keats, Skepticism and the Religion of Beauty, 1979, Friendship and Literature: Spirit and Form. 1986; translator: Teatro Breve (Garcia Lorca), 1979, editor (with Eudora Welty) The Norton Book of Friendship, 1991, (with Nathan Scott) Reading George Steiner, 1994; contbr. articles to profl. jours. Recipient award for editl. excellence Ohioana Assn., 1980; fellow Nat. Humanities Ctr., 1981, 86, NEH, 1981, 84-87, 93, 94, Ford Found., 1971, Mellon Found., 1980, Danforth Found., 1971, English Speaking Union, 1973, Am. Coun. Learned Socs., 1986. Mem. MLA, NEH (chmn's. adv. group humanities edn. 1987), Wordsworth-Coleridge Assn., Keats-Shelley Assn. Jewish. Home: 11671 Kenyon Rd Mount Vernon OH 43050-9207 Office: Kenyon Coll Dept English Gambier OH 43022

SHARP, WALTER LEN, secondary educator; b. Norfolk, Va., Nov. 26, 1943; s. Thomas Leonard and Mary Josephine (Messick) S.; m. Melodie Lynn Lambert, July 1, 1967; children: Lara, Ryan. BS in Secondary Edn., Old Dominion U., 1967; MS in Sci. Edn., Syracuse U., 1971; cert. advanced study in adminstrn., SUNY, Brockport, 1980. Cert. permanent earth sci. and biology tchr., supervision, adminstrn., N.Y. Dir. swimming and gymnasium Boys Clubs Norfolk, 1962-67; tchr. sci. Norfolk City Schs., 1967-69; tchr. earth sci. West Genesee Cen. Schs., Camillus, N.Y., 1969-72; tchr. sci., chmn. dept. Virginia Beach (Va.) City Schs., 1972-76; tchr. earth sci. Liverpool (N.Y.) Cen. Schs., 1976—; regent's wrtier N.Y. State Edn. Dept., Albany, 1988, 89, 90; mem. N.Y. new Compact for Learning, Albany, 1991—; mem. earth sci. statement com. Am. Geol. Union, Washington, 1992; mem. NSTA for high schs. and tours; sci. tchr.; manuscript renew and task force on exemplary programs; earthquake cons.; writer N. Leer SUNY, Buffalo; writer NSTA/NASA Student Act. Book. Author slide and script program Natural History of Central New York, 1987; contbg. writer AGU/FEMA National Earthquake Curriculum Guide, 1993. Contbr., advisor World Resources Inst., Washington, 1992. Recipient Tchr. Field award Earthwatch, Alaska, 1987, Excellence in Sci. Teaching award Prentice Hall/Stanys, 1988; Close-Up Found. fellow, 1993, Sci-Mat fellow, 1993, NSF grantee, numerous tchr. enhancements grants. Mem. NSTA (STANYS liaison, 1994-96, Newmast award 1987, award for Innovations in H.S. Tchg. of Sci. 1993), Nat. Earth Sci. Tchrs. Assn. (pres. 1992-94, Disting. Svc. award 1993), Nat. Assn. Geol. Tchrs. (ea. sect. Outstanding Earth Sci. Tchr. award 1988), Sci. Tchrs. Assn. N.Y. (pres. 1991-92, Disting. svc. award 1988), Am. Fedn. Tchrs., Greenpeace, Optimists, Phi Delta Kappa (Tchr. of Yr. award 1990). Baptist. Avocations: travel, photography, collecting fossils, writing, sports. Home: 2731 Rolling Hills Rd Camillus NY 13031 Office: Liverpool High Sch HSE 5 Wetzel Rd Liverpool NY 13090

SHARPE, CHARLES RICHARD, retail company executive; b. St. Catharines, Ont. Can., Feb. 11, 1925; s. James Walter and Anna B. (Clark) S.; m. Marjorie Agnes Pepler, Apr. 22, 1954; children: Lisette, David, Catherine, Sarah. BA in Bus. Adminstrn. with honors, U. Western Ont., 1950. Trainee Simpsons-Sears, Ltd. (now Sears Can., Inc.), Toronto, Ont., 1950-52, buyer, 1952-55, buying supr., 1955-62, gen. mdse. mgr., 1962-70, v.p. merchandising, 1970-79, chmn., chief exec. officer, dir., 1989—, dir., 1989—; bd. dirs. Sears Can. Inc., Sears Acceptance Co. Inc., BCE Inc., Bell Can., Can. Imperial Bank Commerce, Mediacom Inc., Noranda Forest Inc., Omers Realty Corp. Bd. dirs. Sir Edmund Hillary Found., Wellesley Hosp.; mem. adv. coun. Sch. Bus. Adminstrn., U. Western Ont. With RCAF, 1943-46,92, (hon. col. 436T squadron). Mem. Toronto Club, York Club, Univ. Club, Toronto Golf Club. Anglican. Home: 759 Cardinal Pl, Mississauga, ON Canada L5J 2R8 Office: Sears Can Inc, 222 Jarvis St, Toronto, ON Canada M5B 2B8

SHARPE, DANIEL ROGER, lawyer; b. Detroit, Mar. 13, 1948; s. Roger Holdsworth and Dorothy Jane Donner S.; m. Jane Paula Marinsky, Aug. 25, 1972; children: Leah, Rebecca, Anna. BA, U. Rochester, 1970; JD, Ohio State U., 1975. Bar: N.Y. 1976, U.S. Dist. Ct. 1976, U.S. Tax Ct. 1978. Assoc. Hodgson, Russ, Andrews, Woods & Goodyear, Buffalo, 1975-79, ptnr., 1980—; instr. Canisius Coll., Buffalo, 1987, 91; pres. N.Y. Employee

Benefits Conf., Syracuse, N.Y., 1988-90. Author: (with others) Individual Retirement Plans, 1988, (with others) Taxation of Distributions from Qualified Plans, 1991. Bd. dirs., tax cons. Allentown Assn., Inc., Buffalo, 1977-78; tax cons. Parkside Community Assn., Inc., Buffalo, 1980; bd. dirs. Concerned Eccumenical Ministry of Upper West Side, Inc., Buffalo, 1993-95. Mem. ABA (mem. tax sect., mem. employee benefits com. 1989-95). Office: Hodgson Russ Andrews Woods & Goodyear 1800 One M & T Plz Buffalo NY 14203-2391

SHARPE, DONALD EDWARD, lawyer; b. Edmonton, Alta., Can., Oct. 24, 1937; came to U.S., 1945; s. Eldon Durwood Sharpe and Bertha Evelyn (Johnston) Skinner; m. JoAnn Firth; children: Jennifer, William, Gregory. BA, U. Md., 1960, LLB, 1963. Bar: Md. 1963, U.S. Dist. Ct. Md. 1964, U.S. Ct. Appeals (4th cir.) 1964, U.S. Dist. Ct. D.C. 1981. Law clk. to presiding judges U.S. Dist. Ct. Md., Balt., 1963-64; assoc Piper & Marbury, Balt., 1964-67, 69-71, ptnr., 1971—; asst. U.S. atty. U.S. Atty.'s Office, Balt., 1967-69. Recent Decisions editor Md. Law Rev., 1963. Mem. ABA (chmn. products-torts and ins. practice sect. 1985-86, membership com. 1988-89, task force on selection and performance standards of counsel 1988-89), Order of Coif. Democrat. Presbyterian. Avocations: golf, volleyball, woodworking, gardening, fishing. Office: Piper & Marbury 36 S Charles St Baltimore MD 21201-3020

SHARPE, HENRY DEXTER, JR., manufacturing company executive; b. Providence, May 5, 1923; s. Henry Dexter and Mary Elizabeth (Evans) S.; m. Peggy Plumer Boyd, Aug. 1, 1953; children: Henry Dexter, Douglas, Sarah. Grad., Brown U., Providence, 1945. With Brown & Sharpe Mfg. Co., Providence, 1946—, v.p., 1950-51, pres., 1951-76, chmn., chief exec. officer, 1976-80, chmn., 1980—; bd. dirs., mem. exec. com. Providence Jour. Co.; vice chancellor Brown U., 1986-87. Bd. dirs. R.I. Pub. Expenditure Coun.; trustee, fellow Brown U.; trustee Coll. of the Atlantic, 1992— L.t. (j.g.) USNR, 1943-46. Mem. Am. Soc. Tool Engrs., Nat. Machine Tool Builders Assn. (pres. 1969-70), ASME, Machinery and Allied Products Inst. (ret. mem. exec. com.). Office: Pojac Point Rd North Kingstown RI 02852-1031

SHARPE, JAMES SHELBY, lawyer; b. Ft. Worth, Sept. 11, 1940; s. James Henry and Wanzel (Vanderbilt) S.; m. Martha Moudy Holland, June 9, 1962; children: Marthanne Freeman, Caren Roark, Stephen. BA, U. Tex., 1962, JD, 1965. Bar: Tex. 1964, U.S. Dist. Ct. (no. dist.) Tex. 1966, U.S. Dist. Ct. (ea. dist.) Tex. 1993, U.S. Ct. Appeals (5th and 6th cirs.) 1982, U.S. Ct. Appeals (fed. cir.) 1983, U.S. Ct. Appeals 10th cir.) 1992, U.S. Supreme Ct. 1972. Briefing atty. for chief justice Supreme Ct. of Tex., Austin, 1965-66; ptnr. Brown, Herman, Scott Dean, Miles, Ft. Worth, 1966-84, Gandy Michener Swindle Whitaker & Pratt, Ft. Worth, 1984-87; shareholder Sharpe & Spurlock, Ft. Worth, 1988—; adj. prof. polit. sci. Tex. Christian U., Ft. Worth, 1969-79, Dallas Bapt. U., 1987, 1992—; gen. counsel USA-Radio Network, Internat. Christian Media, Denton Pub. Co. Pres. Ft. Worth-Tarrant County Jr. Bar, 1969-70, bd. dirs. 1968, sec., 1968, v.p. 1968-69; head marshal USA-USSR Track and Field Championships, Ft. Worth, USA-USSR Jr. Track and Field Championships, Austin, Tex. Relays, Austin, 1963—, NCAA Nat. Track and Field Championships, 1976, 80, 85, 92, S.W. Conf. Indoor Track and Field Championships, 1987— Olympic Festival, San Antonio, 1993, Colorado Springs, 1995; 11-time head marshal S.W. Conf. Track and Field Championships. USA/Mobil Track Championships, 1994, 95, USA Nat. Jr. Track Championship, 1994, 95. Mem. ABA, State Bar of Tex. (dist. 7-A grievance com. 1983-85, com. adminstrn. of justice 1985-92, com on ct. rules 1992—, chmn. 1992-93, 93-94). Baptist. Home: 8304 Crosswind Dr Fort Worth TX 76179-3003 Office: Sharpe & Spurlock 500 Throckmorton St Ste 2400 Fort Worth TX 76102-3811

SHARPE, JEAN ELIZABETH, lawyer; b. Kingston, Jamaica; came to U.S., 1958; d. John Anthony and Maisie Viola (Chang) Wright; m. a. John Fowle, Sept. 14, 1980; children: Amelia, Anastasia. AB, Barnard Coll., 1973; JD, NYU, 1977. Bar: N.Y. 1978, U.S. Dist. Ct. (ea. and so. dists.) N.Y. 1978. Adminstrv. asst. Office of the Mayor, N.Y.C., 1967-69; asst. to producer Stockbridge Prodns., N.Y.C., 1969-71; rsch. asst. Frederick O'R Hayes, N.Y.C., 1971-72; program officer Fund for City N.Y., 1972-73; assoc. Marshall, Bratter, Greene, Allison & Tucker, N.Y.C., 1977-79; pres. Vosko Assocs Ltd., N.Y.C., 1979-85; assoc. gen. coun. Brooke Mgmt. Inc., N.Y.C., 1985-87, gen. counsel, 1987-90; exec. v.p., gen. counsel Brooke Group Ltd., N.Y.C., 1990-93; also bd. dirs. Brooke Group Ltd. Author: Transition of Mayoral Adminstration-Addiction Services Agency, 1972. Mem. ABA, N.Y. State Bar Assn., Assn. of Bar of City of N.Y. Buddhist. Office: Brooke Group Ltd 135 E 57th St New York NY 10022-3219

SHARPE, KEITH YOUNT, lawyer; b. Hiddenite, N.C., July 11, 1930; s. Ruel Yount and Eileen Lois (Lackey) S.; m. Margaret Joyce Land, Aug. 27, 1955; children: Jonathan, Matthew, Leonora, Felicia. A.B., Duke U., 1952; J.D., Wake Forest U., 1957, M.B.A., 1982. Bar: N.C. 1957. Practiced law Winston-Salem, N.C., 1957-62, 82-94; asst. solicitor Mcpl. Ct. of Winston-Salem, 1958-60; with Pilot Freight Carriers Inc., Winston-Salem, 1962-82; sr. v.p. Pilot Freight Carriers Inc., 1967-76, v.p., 1976-82; also dir.; v.p., dir. Comml. Automotive Co., 1967-76, Terminal Warehouse Corp., 1967-82, bd. govs. So. Motor Carriers Rate Conf., 1977-81. Served with inf. U.S. Army, 1952-54. Mem. ABA, N.C. Bar Assn., Assn. Transp. Practitioners, Phi Alpha Delta, Theta Chi. Democrat. Episcopalian. Home: Box 4191 Asheville NC 28805-1260

SHARPE, MYRON EMANUEL, publisher, editor, writer; b. Chester, Pa., Sept. 10, 1928; s. Abraham Maxwell and Emma (Friedman) S.; m. Jacqueline Steiner, 1959 (div.); children: Susanna, Matthew; m. Carole S. Brafman, 1983; children: Elizabeth, Hannah. B.A., Swarthmore Coll., 1950; M.A., U. Mich., 1951, postgrad., 1951-54. Pres. Modern Factors Corp., Phila., 1957; founder, chmn. bd., pres. M.E. Sharpe, Inc. (Pub.), Armonk, N.Y., 1958—, writer, editor, 1955—; founder, exec. dir. Com. to Save the Life of Henry Spetter, 1974; co-founder, coord. Initiative Com. for Nat. Econ. Planning, 1974-76; co-founder, pres. M.E. Sharpe, Ltd. (Arts and Antiques), New Canaan, Conn., 1981-83. Author: John Kenneth Galbraith and the Lower Economics, 1973. Chmn. Pro Arte Chamber Music Soc. of Conn., 1982-83; pres. Waveny Chamber Music Soc., 1987—; econ. advisor to Senator Birch Bayh for presdl. campaign, 1975. Office: M E Sharpe Inc 80 Business Park Dr Armonk NY 10504-1710

SHARPE, RICHARD SAMUEL, architectural company executive; b. New Haven, Conn., Aug. 7, 1930; s. Herman and Betty (Silberman) S.; m. Anne Johnson; children: Peter, Andrew, Rebecca. BArch, U. Pa., 1953; postgrad., U. Liverpool, Eng., 1953-54. Registered architect, Conn., N.Y., R.I., Mass. Prin. Richard Sharpe Assocs. P.C., Norwich, Conn., 1957—; v.p. Pan-Am. Fedn. Architects, 1972-78. Bd. dirs. Conn. Humanities council, 1974-78; pres. Conn. Habitat, 1978-79; pres. Thames River Devel. Corp., 1982-83. Recipient Ann. award Producers Council, 1974-78, Ann. Craft award Slater Mus., Norwich, 1986, spl. citation AIA, 1978. Fellow Am. Inst. Archs.; mem. Conn. Soc. Archs. (v.p. 1963, pres. 1966), Hist. Dist. Conn. (com. chmn.), S.E. Conn. Grievance Comm., Rotary. Avocations: wood pottery, photography, pre-Columbian art collecting, sailing. Office: Richard Sharpe Assocs PC 30 Connecticut Ave Norwich CT 06360-1502

SHARPE, ROBERT F., SR., writer, lecturer, educator, consultant, publisher; b. Florence, Ala., Sept. 8, 1926; s. Thomas Leslie and Lida (Gammill) S.; m. Jane A. Sharpe, Dec. 28, 1948; children: Susan, Robert Jr., Paul, Timothy. BS, Memphis State U., 1957. Life ins. agt. Pilot Life Ins. Co., Greensboro, N.C., 1950-54; agt., supr. Vol. Life Ins. Co., Chattanooga, 1954; agt. Crown Life Ins. Co., Toronto, Can., 1954-59; sec. stewardship Good News Broadcasting Assn., Lincoln, Nebr., 1959-63; chmn., founder Robert F. Sharpe & Co. Inc., Memphis, 1963-92, sr. cons., 1992-95; exec. dir. Reformed Presbyn. Fedn., St. Louis, 1963-65; founder, exec. dir. The Nat. Planned Giving Inst., 1967—, The Nat. Planned Giving Assn., 1985. Author: The Planned Giving Idea Book, Before You Give Another Dime, 27 Plus Ways to Increase Giving to Your Church; pub. monthly newsletter Give and Take; contbr. articles to publs. Bd. trustees Ch. Health Ctr., Memphis, Endowment Assn. Coll. William and Mary, Williamsburg, Va.; pres. Memphis Mus. Inc., 1994-95. With USN, 1944-47, PTO. Recipient Disting. Svc. award Memphis State U., 1970. Mem. Soc. Entrepreneurs. Methodist. Avocation: sailing. Office: 5050 Poplar Ave Fl 7 Memphis TN 38157-0101

SHARPE, ROBERT FRANCIS, equipment manufacturing company executive; b. Buffalo, Mar. 29, 1921; s. Bertram Francis and Agnes (Coppinger) S.; m. Audrey Rembe, July 10, 1943; 1 son, Robert Francis. B.S. in Chem. Engring, Rensselaer Poly. Inst., 1942. With Duriron Co., 1946—; mgr. pump sales Duriron Co., Dayton, 1955-58; dir. research, devel. Duriron Co., 1958-63, v.p. plastics ops., 1963-65, exec. v.p., 1967-68, pres., chief operating officer, 1968-69, pres., 1969-76, chief exec. officer, 1969-79, chmn. bd., 1978-83. Served with USAAF, 1943-46. Mem. Am. Inst. Chem. Engrs., Hydraulic Inst. Home: 15520 Whitney Ln Naples FL 33963 also: PO Box 8820 Dayton OH 45401-8820

SHARPE, ROCHELLE PHYLLIS, journalist; b. Gary, Ind., Apr. 27, 1956; d. Norman Nathaniel and Shirley (Kaplan) S. BA, Yale U., 1978. Reporter Concord (N.H.) Monitor, 1979-81; statehouse rep. Wilmington News Jour., Dover, Del., 1981-85; statehouse corr. Gannett News Svc., Albany, N.Y., 1985; nat. reporter Gannett News Svc., Washington, 1986-93; staff reporter social issues The Wall St. Jour., Washington, 1993—. Contbr. articles to profl. jours. Recipient Pulitzer prize for series in child abuse, Columbia U., 1991. Home: 2500 Q St NW #315 Washington DC 20007 Office: Wall St Jour Washington Bur 1025 Connecticut Ave NW Ste 800 Washington DC 20036

SHARPE, ROLAND LEONARD, retired engineering company executive, earthquake and structural engineering consultant; b. Shakopee, Minn., Dec. 18, 1923; s. Alfred Leonard and Ruth Helen (Carter) S.; m. Jane Esther Steele, Dec. 28, 1946; children: Douglas Rolfe, Deborah Lynn, Sheryl Anne. BS in Civil Engring., U. Mich., 1947, MSE, 1949. Registered civil engr. and structural engr., Calif. Designer, Cummins & Barnard, Inc., Ann Arbor, Mich., 1947-48; instr. engring U. Mich., 1948-50; exec. v.p. John A. Blume & Assocs., engrs., San Francisco, 1950-73; chmn., founder Engring. Decision Analysis Co., Inc., Cupertino, 1974-87; cons. earthquake engr., 1987—; mng. dir. EDAC, GmbH, Frankfurt, Germany, 1974-82; dir. EDAC; pres. Calif. Devel. & Engring. Co., Inc., Las Vegas, Nev., 1973-81; mem. nat. earthquake hazard reduction program adv. com. overviewing Fed. Emergency Mgmt. Agy., U.S. Geol. Survey, NSF and Nat. Inst. Stds. and Tech., 1990-93. Author: (with J. Blume, E.G. Kost) Earthquake Engineering for Nuclear Facilities, 1971. Mem. Planning Commn., Palo Alto, 1955-60; mng. dir. Applied Tech. Coun., Palo Alto, 1973-83; dir. Earthquake Engring. Rsch. Inst., 1972-75, now mem.; project dir., editor Tentative Provisions for Devel. of Seismic Regulations for Buildings, 1978; tech. mgr., contbr., editor Data Processing Facilities: Guidelines for Earthquake Hazard Mitigation, 1987. Served with USMC, 1942-46. Author, co-author over 200 engring. papers and reports; author: (with others) Seismic Safety Guide, 1995; contbr. chpts. book. Fellow ASCE (hon. mem., chmn. dynamic effects com., 1978-80, exec. com. structural div. 1980-84, 89-93, chmn. 1983, mgmt. group B 1989-93, Earnest O. Howard award 1994); mem. Japan Structural Cons. Assn. (hon. mem. 1992), Structural Engrs. Assn. Calif. (dir. 1971-73, chmn. seismology com. 1972-74), Structural Engrs. No. Calif. (dir. 1969-71, life mem.), Am. Concrete Inst. (life). Recipient citation for contbn. to constrn. industry Engring. News Record, 1978-79, 86-87; chmn. U.S. Joint Com. on Earthquake Engring., 1982-88. Home: 10320 Rolly Rd Los Altos CA 94024-6520 *Personal philosophy: One's conduct should be beyond reproach both morally and ethically and I should serve each of my clients to the best of my ability.*

SHARPE, SHANNON, professional football player; b. Chgo., June 26, 1968. Student, Savannah State U. Tight end Denver Broncos, 1990—; player AFC Championship game, 1991. Named to Pro Bowl Team, 1992, 93, Sporting News NFL All-Pro Team, 1993. Office: Denver Broncos 13655 E Broncos Pkwy Englewood CO 80112*

SHARPE, STERLING, professional football player; b. Chgo., Apr. 6, 1965. BA, U.S.C., 1987. With Green Bay Packers, 1988-95. Named to Sporting News Coll. All-Am., 1987; named receiving leader NFL, 1989, 92, wide receiver All-Pro Team NFL, 1989. Played in Pro Bowl, 1989, 90, 92; named to Pro Bowl, 1993. *

SHARPE, WILLIAM FORSYTH, economics educator; b. Cambridge, Mass., June 16, 1934; s. Russell Thornley Sharpe and Evelyn Forsyth (Jillson) Maloy; m. Roberta Ruth Branton, July 2, 1954 (div. Feb. 1986); children: Deborah Ann, Jonathan Forsyth; m. Kathryn Dorothy Peck, Apr. 5, 1986. AB, UCLA, 1955, MA, 1956, PhD, 1961. Economist Rand Corp., 1957-61; asst. prof. econs. U. Wash., 1961-63, assoc. prof., 1963-67, prof., 1967-68; prof. U. Calif., Irvine, 1968-70; Timken prof. fin. Stanford U., 1970-89, Timken prof. emeritus, 1989-92; prin. William F. Sharpe Assocs., 1986-92; prof.fin. Stanford U., 1993—; STANCO 25 prof. of fin., 1995—. Author: The Economics of Computers, 1969, Portfolio Theory and Capital Markets, 1970; co-author: Fundamentals of Investments, 1989, 2d edit., 1993, Investments, 5th edit., 1995. With U.S. Army, 1956-57. Recipient Graham and Dodd award Fin Analysts' Fedn., 1972, '73, '86-88. Nicholas Molodovsky award, 1989. Nobel prize in econ. scis., 1990. Mem. Am. Fin. Assn. (v.p. 1979, pres. 1980), Western Fin. Assn. (Enduring Contbn. award 1989), Ea. Fin. Assn. (Disting. Scholar award 1991), Am. Econ. Assn., Phi Beta Kappa.

SHARPE, WILLIAM NORMAN, JR., mechanical engineer, educator; b. Chatham County, N.C., Apr. 15, 1938; s. William Norman and Margaret Horne (Womble) S.; m. Margaret Ellen Strowd, Aug. 21, 1959; children: William N., J. Ashley. BS, N.C. State U., 1960, MS, 1961; PhD, Johns Hopkins U., 1966. Registered profl. engr., Mich., La., Md. Assoc. prof. Mich. State U., East Lansing, 1970-75, prof., 1975-78; prof., chmn. dept. mech. engring. La. State U., Baton Rouge, 1978-83; prof., dept. mech. engring. Johns Hopkins U., Balt., 1983—, Decker prof. mech. engring., 1985—. Recipient Alexander von Humboldt award, Fed. Republic Germany, 1989. Fellow ASME (Nadai award 1993), Soc. Exptl. Mechanics (Tatnall award, exec. bd. 1979-81, pres. 1984-85); mem. ASTM, Am. Soc. Engring. Edn. Home: 220 Ridgewood Rd Baltimore MD 21210-2539 Office: Johns Hopkins U Dept Mech Engring Latrobe Hall Rm 127 Baltimore MD 21218

SHARPLES, D. KENT, college administrator; b. Swanton, Ohio, May 26, 1943; s. Morrill and Doris Elizabeth (Saeger) S.; m. Linda Mancini Sharples; children: Dawn, Steven. BS, Bowling Green State U., 1965, MEd, 1966; PhD in Ednl. Adminstrn., Ohio U., 1973. Tchr. Maumee (Ohio) Jr. High Sch., 1966-67; instr. dept. engring. graphics Coll. Engring. and Tech., Athens, Ohio, 1967-73; project dir. S.C. State Bd. for Tech. and Comprehensive Edn., West Columbia, 1973-76; v.p. for edn., dean of instrn. Tri-County Tech. Coll., Pendleton, S.C., 1976-80; pres. Horry-Georgetown Tech Coll., Conway, S.C., 1980—. Mem. Am. Assn. Community and Jr. Colls. (chair small/rural coll. commn. 1983-87, bd. dirs. 1987), Assn. Community Colls Trustees, So. Assn. of Cols. and Schs., Council for Occupational Edn. Am. Tech. Edn. Assn., Myrtle Beach C. of C. Episcopalian. Lodge: Rotary. Office: Horry-Georgetown Tech Coll PO Box 1966 Highway 501 Conway SC 29526

SHARPLES, WINSTON SINGLETON, automobile importer and distributor; b. Springfield, Mass., Oct. 24, 1932; s. Winston Singleton and Carmela (Parrino) S.; m. Jeanette Williams, July 1961 (div. Apr. 1981); children: John, Hadley, Gillian; m. Ruth Emily Lissak, June 26, 1981. BA, Harvard Coll., 1953; postgrad. drama, Yale U., 1956-57; MFA, Carnegie Mellon U., 1959; postgrad., Univ. Md., 1978-80. Freelance writer, 1959—; producer, dir. Mon. Valley Playhouse, Charleroi, Pa., 1959, Robin Hood Theater, Arden, Del., 1960-61; pres., film and music editor Synchro-Sound Inc., N.Y.C., 1961-71; prof. CUNY, 1969-74, Temple Univ., Phila., 1974-76, U. Md., College Park, 1978-79; adminstr. film preservation and documentation Am. Film Inst., Washington, 1976-78; prof. Howard Univ., Washington, 1978-80; pres. Cantab Motors, Ltd., Round Hill, Va., 1984—. Author: (with others) A Primer for Film-Making, 1971—; supr. Am. Film Inst. Catalog of Feature Films, 1960-69, 77; editor, music editor films and cartoons; contbr. articles to profl. jours. and mags. With U.S. Army, 1953-56. Nat. Endowment for the Humanities grantee, 1977. Mem. ASCAP, Archeol. Soc. Va., Am. Studies Assn., Univ. Film Assn. (v.p. 1975-76), Soc. for Cinema Studies, Soc. Automotive Engrs., Washington Automotive Press Assn., Morgan Car Club, Land Rover Owners Assn. Va., British Automobile Mfrs Assn., Harvard Club (N.Y.C.). Democrat. Avocations: forestry, archeology. Home: RR 1 Box 537A Round Hill VA 22141-9310 Office: Cantab Motors Ltd Valley Indsl Park 12 E Richardson Ln Purcellville VA 22132-3500

SHARPLESS, JOSEPH BENJAMIN, former county official; b. Takoma Park, Md., Feb. 4, 1933; s. William Raiford and Julia Maude (Rouse) S.; m. Nancy Kathleen Steffen, July 28, 1962 (dec. Feb. 1988); 1 child, Carole Marie. BA, Earlham Coll., 1955; MS, Pa. State U., 1960. Instr. recreation Montgomery County Recreation Dept., Rockville, Md., 1957-58; from program supr. to dir. Recreation and Parks Dept., Livingston, N.J., 1959-70; chief recreation svc. Md.-Nat. Capital Park and Planning Commn. Prince George's County, Riverdale, Md., 1970-77, parks and recreation div. chief, 1977-95; ret., 1995—. Contbr. articles to profl. jours. V.p. Montpelier Cmty. Assn., South Laurel, Md., 1983-84, pres., 1985; mem. Md. Sports Adv. Com., 1988-92; Md. State Games Commr., 1986-91; bd. regents, instr. Sch. Sports Mgmt. N.C. State U., 1989-92; nat. volleyball chmn. AAU, 1966-69, 72, volleyball chmn. N.J. chpt., 1961-70, volleyball chmn. Potomac Valley chpt., 1971-73; mem. volleyball games staff 1996 Olympic Games, Atlanta; dir. volleyball Spl. Olympics Internat., 1994—. Mem. U.S. Volleyball Assn. (bd. dirs. 1973—, mem. exec. com. 1976-80, 85-89, 92—, v.p. 1973-90, regional commr. 1965-78, nat. ofcl. 1967—, exec. cons. 1989-91, corp. sec. 1992—, mng. editor pubs. 1994—, numerous awards), Nat. Intercollegiate Soccer Ofcls. Assn. (sec. 1966-68, 1968-70), Nat. Recreation and Parks Assn. (disting. svc. award, Mid-Atlantic fellow), Am. Park & Recreation Soc. (bd. dirs. 1977-97, nat. coun., coun. affiliate pres.), N.J. Recreation and Parks Assn. (pres. 1967), Md. Recreation and Park Assn. (v.p. 1975-77, pres. 1977-78, named mem. of yr. 1975, citation 1985), Ret. Life Profl., N.J. Soccer Ofcls. Assn. (sec. 1966-70), National Capitol Area Bd. Volleybal Ofcls. (sec. 1985-89). Republican. Mem. Soc. of Friends. Home: 8754 Oxwell Ln Laurel MD 20708-2469

SHARPLESS, K. BARRY, chemist; b. Phila., Apr. 28, 1941; m. Jan Dueser, Apr. 28, 1965; children: Hannah, William, Isaac. BA, Dartmouth Coll., 1963; PhD, Stanford U., 1968. Postdoctoral assoc. Harvard U.; postdoctoral assoc. Stanford U., to 1970, faculty dept. chemistry, 1977-80; faculty MIT, Cambridge, 1970—; prof. chemistry, 1975-77, 80-90; prof. chemistry Scripps Rsch. Inst., La Jolla, Calif., 1990—. Recipient Paul Janssen Prize for Creativity in Organic Suntheisis, Rolf Sammet prize vis. lectureship Johann W. Goethe Univ., Frankfurt, Fed. Republic Germany, 1988, Chem. Pioneer award Am. Inst. Chemists, 1988, Prelog Medal Eidenössische Technische Hochschuee, Zurich, 1988, Scheele medal and prize Swedish Acad. Pharm. Scis.; A.P. Sloan fellow, Guggenheim fellow, 1987-88; Camille and Henry Dreyfus Tchr. scholar. Fellow AAAS, Am. Acad. Arts and Scis.; mem. NAS, Am. Chem. Soc. (Creative Work in Synthetic Organic Chemistry award 1983, Arthur C. Cope scholar's award 1986, Harrison Howe award Rochester chpt. 1987, Remsen award Md. sect. 1989). Office: Scripps Rsch Inst CVN-2 10666 N Torrey Pines Rd La Jolla CA 92037-1027

SHARPLESS, RICHARD KENNEDY, lawyer; b. Springdale, Pa., Mar. 30, 1911; s. Charles Thomas and Luella Lincoln (Kennedy) S.; m. Eleanor Ridgway Crowther, Mar. 4, 1946; m. Nancy Jean Sleight, July 23, 1948; children: Kendall Deborah, Richard Kennedy, Lincoln Kennedy. AB, Boston U., 1932; LLB, Harvard U., 1935, JD, 1969. Bar: Pa. 1936, Calif. 1947, Hawaii 1949. With firm Dalzell, McFall & Pringle, Pitts., 1936-42; mem. legal sect. trust dept. Bank of Am., Los Angeles, 1946-48; atty. Office Dist. Engr., Honolulu, 1948-49; with Office Atty. Gen., T.H., 1949-55, atty. gen., 1956-57; mem. Lewis, Saunders & Sharpless (and predecessor firm), 1957-68; mng. dir. City and County of Honolulu, 1968-72, 75-78, corp. counsel, 1973-75, 78-80; of counsel firm Case, Kay & Lynch, Honolulu, 1980-81. Mem. Planning Commn. City and County of Honolulu, 1966-68, chmn., 1968; asst. to Town Atty. of Chapel Hill, 1984-93; bd. dirs. United Way, 1982-85, Pub. Sch. Found., 1984-89, Village Cos. Found., 1987-89; mem. exec. com. PTA Thrift Show, 1986-90. Capt. C.E., AUS, 1942-46. Mem. Bar Assn. Hawaii (pres. 1960-61), Chapel Hill-Carrboro C. of C. (dir. 1984-86), SAR (pres. Hawaii 1961), Kiwanis. Episcopalian. Home: 134 Berry Patch Ln Chapel Hill NC 27514

SHARROW, MARILYN JANE, library administrator; bd. Oakland, Calif.; d. Charles L. and H. Evelyn S.; m. Lawrence J. Davis. BS in Design, U. Mich., 1967, MALS, 1969. Librarian Detroit Pub. Libr., 1968-70; head fine arts dept. Syracuse (N.Y.) U. Libr., 1970-73; dir. libr. Roseville (Mich.) Pub. Libr., 1973-75; asst. dir. libr. U. Wash., 1975-77, assoc. dir. libr., 1978-79; dir. libraries U. Man., Winnipeg, Can., 1979-82; chief libr. U. Toronto, Can., 1982-85; univ. libr. U. Calif., Davis, 1985—. Recipient Woman of Yr. in Mgmt. award Winnipeg YWCA, 1982; named Woman of Distinction, U. Calif. Faculty Women's Rsch. Group, 1985. Mem. ALA, Assn. Rsch. Libris. (bd. dirs., v.p., pres-elect 1989-90, pres. 1990-91, chair sci. tech. work group 1994—, rsch. collections com. 1993—), Online Computer Libr. Ctr.-Rsch. Libris. Adv. Com. (vice chmn. 1992-93, chair 1993-94). Office: U Calif Shields Lib Davis CA 95616

SHARTLE, KEITH ROBERT, producer. BA, UCLA, 1974. Purchasing agt. Profl. Photosystems Corp., 1970, v.p. gen. mgr. retail and photo supply div.; with client rels. and contracts, photography and film editing depts. Dream Quest Images, Simi Valley, Calif., 1982, bus. mgr., 1987, exec. producer Film divsn., 1987-94, pres. Film Group, 1994—. Exec. producer of visual effects for films including The Abyss, Total Recall, Scrooged, Short Circuit 2, Big Business, The Lost Boys, Crimson Tide; overseer prodn. of effects for more than 80 feature films and 30 TV episodes and movies, numerous film attractions worldwide theme parks. Office: Dream Quest Images 2635 Park Center Dr Simi Valley CA 93065-6212

SHARWELL, WILLIAM GAY, retired university president and company executive; b. Newark, July 26, 1920; s. William G. Sharwell and Lillian Kenny; m. Jacqueline Larocque, Oct. 22, 1960; children: William L., Paul L. BS, Seton Hall U., 1941, DBA (hon.), 1980; MBA, NYU, 1950, Harvard U., 1952; DCS, Harvard U., 1960; LLD (hon.), Pace U., 1979. V.p., comptr. N.Y. Tel., N.Y.C., 1967-68, exec. v.p. ops., 1968-70; sr. v.p. AT&T, N.Y.C., 1976-84; pres. Pace U., N.Y.C., 1984-90; ret., 1990; bd. dirs. U.S. Life Corp., N.Y.C., U.S. Life Ins. Co., N.Y.C., Am. Biogenetic Scis., Inc., Copiague, N.Y., Associated Solo Artists; gen. ptnr. Equitable Capital Ptnrs., L.P. Mem. editorial bd. Ency. of Profl. Mgmt., 1978. Bd. dirs. Internat. House, NOW/Legal Def. Edn. Fund, N.Y.C., 1978—; trustee Coll. New Rochelle (N.Y.). Mem. Harvard Club (N.Y.C.). Avocations: tennis, kite flying, video editing.

SHASTEEN, DONALD EUGENE, government official; b. Englewood, Colo., Dec. 3, 1928; s. George Donald and Frances True (Meyers) S.; m. Shirley Mae Johnson, Aug. 8, 1954; children: Jon Randolph, Ron Winston, Sherilyn Sue. B.A. in Journalism, U. Colo., 1950. Reporter Omaha World-Herald, Des Moines, 1954-58, Lincoln, Nebr., 1958-66; exec. asst. to Senator Carl T. Curtis of Nebr., Washington, 1966-73, adminstrv. asst., 1973-78; adminstrv. asst. to Sen. Gordon J. Humphrey, 1979-80; with transition group Senate Republican Conf., 1980; dep. under sec. for legislation and intergovtl. affairs Dept. Labor, 1981-83, dep. asst. sec. for vets. employment, 1983-85, asst. sec. for vets. employment and tng., 1985-89; chmn. exec. com. Am. World Svcs., Inc.; v.p. Cocke & Phillips, Inc. Rep. nominee for U.S. Senate Nebr., 1978. Served with U.S. Army, 1951-52. Mem. Am. Legion, VFW, Am. Vets., Disabled Am. Vets., Phi Delta Theta. Republican. Lutheran.

SHASTID, JON BARTON, wine company executive; b. Hannibal, Mo., Nov. 21, 1914; s. Jon Shepherd and Mary (Barton) S.; m. Natalie Kiliani, Dec. 16, 1944; children—Lucinda, Jon G.H., Victoria A., Thomas Bartwyn. Bar: Calif. bar 1959; C.P.A., Calif., Kans. Pub. accountant Dodge City, Kans., 1938-42; v.p. finance Johnson Bronze Co., New Castle, Pa., 1946-54; exec. v.p., treas. E. & J. Gallo Winery, Modesto, Calif., 1954-88; pres. Gallo Wine Co. of La. at New Orleans, 1960-89. City councilman, Modesto, 1961-69. Served to capt. USAAF, 1942-46. Mem. State Bar of Calif., Am. Bar Assn., Calif. Soc. C.P.A.'s. Home and Office: PO Box 3808 Modesto CA 95352-3808

SHATIN, JUDITH, music composing educator; b. Boston, Nov. 11, 1949; d. Leo and Harriet Evelyn (Sommer) S.; m. Michael Kubovy, June 28, 1992. AB, Douglass, Coll., 1971; MM, Julliard Sch., 1974; PhD, Princeton U., 1979. Asst. prof. U. Va., Charlottesville, 1979-85, assoc. prof., 1985-92, prof., 1992—; dir. Va. Ctr. Computer Music, 1988—. Composer (piano concerto) Passion of St. Cecilia, 1985, (soprano and tape) Three Summers Heat, 1989 (Barlow Found. Commn.), Piping the Earth (commd. by Women's Philharmonic), 1990, Stringing the Bow (commd. Va. Chamber Orchestra), 1992, COAL, 1994. Nat. Endowment for the Arts Composer fellow, 1980, 85, 89, 92; recipient award Va. Commn. for the Arts, 1989, 90. Mem. Am. Music Ctr., Am. Women Composers (pres. 1989-93). Avocations: swimming, yoga, hiking.

SHATKIN, AARON JEFFREY, biochemistry educator; b. Providence, July 18, 1934; s. Morris and Doris S.; m. Joan A. Lynch, Nov. 30, 1957; 1 son, Gregory Martin. A.B., Bowdoin Coll., 1956, D.Sc. (hon.), 1979; Ph.D., Rockefeller Inst., 1961. Sr. asst. scientist NIH, Bethesda, Md., 1961-63; research chemist NIH, 1963-68; vis. scientist Salk Inst., La Jolla, Calif., 1968-69; assoc. mem. dept. cell biology Roche Inst. Molecular Biology, Nutley, N.J., 1968-73; full mem. Roche Inst. Molecular Biology, 1973-77, head molecular virology lab., 1977-86, head dept. cell biology, 1983-86; dir. N.J. Ctr. Advanced Biotech. Medicine, 1986—; prof. molecular genetics UMDNJ, 1986—; univ. prof. molecular biology Rutgers U., New Brunswick, N.J., 1986—; adj. prof. cell biology Rockefeller U.; vis. prof. molecular biology Princeton U. Mem. editl. bd. Jour. Virology, 1968-82, Archives of Biochemistry and Biophysics, 1972-82, Virology, 1973-76, Comprehensive Virology, 1974-82, Jour. Biol. Chemistry, 1977-83, 94—; editor Advances Virus Research, 1983—, Jour. Virology, 1973-77; editor-in-chief Molecular and Cellular Biology, 1980-90. Served with USPHS, 1961-63. Recipient U.S. Steel Found. prize in molecular biology, 1977, N.J. Sci. and Tech. Pride award, 1989, Thomas Edison Sci. award State of N.J., 1991; Rockefeller fellow, 1956-61. Fellow Am. Acad. Microbiology, N.Y. Acad. Scis.; mem. NAS, AAAS, Am. Soc. Microbiology, Am. Soc. Biol. Chemists, Am. Soc. Virology, Am. Chem. Soc., Am. Soc. Cell Biology, Harvey Soc. Home: 1381 Rahway Rd Scotch Plains NJ 07076-3452 Office: Ctr Advanced Biotech and Medicine 679 Hoes Ln Piscataway NJ 08854-5638

SHATNER, WILLIAM, actor; b. Montreal, Que., Can., Mar. 22, 1931; s. Joseph and Anne S.; m. Gloria Rand, Aug. 12, 1956 (div. Mar. 1969); m. Marcy Lafferty, Oct. 20, 1973; 3 daus. B.A., McGill U., 1952. Stage debut, 1952; appeared Montreal Playhouse, summers 1952, 53; played juvenile roles Canadian Repertory Theatre, Ottawa, 1952-53, 53-54; appeared Stratford Shakespeare Festival, Ont., 1954-56; Broadway appearances include Tamburlaine the Great, 1956, The World of Suzie Wong, 1958, A Shot in the Dark, 1961; films include The Brothers Karamazov, 1958, The Explosive Generation, 1961, Judgement at Nuremburg, 1961, The Intruder, 1962, The Outrage, 1964, Dead of Night, 1974, The Devil's Rain, 1975, Star Trek, 1979, The Kidnapping of the President, 1979, Star Trek: The Wrath of Khan, 1982, Star Trek III: The Search for Spock, 1984, Star Trek IV: The Voyage Home, 1986, (director) Star Trek V: The Final Frontier, 1989, Star Trek VI: The Undiscovered Country, 1991, National Lampoon's Loaded Weapon, 1992, Star Trek: Generations, 1994; also TV movies and appearances on The Andersonville Trial, The Bastard, 1978, Disaster on the Coastliner, 1979, Secrets of a Married Man, 1984, North Beach and Rawhide, 1985, Columbo, 1993; star of TV show Star Trek, 1966-69, animated series, 1973-75; TV series Barbary Coast, 1975-76, The Babysitter, 1979, T.J. Hooker; host (TV series) Rescue 911, CBS, 1989—; dir. TV movie TekWar; author: (novels) TekWar, 1989, TekLords, 1991, TekLab, 1991, Tek Vengeance, 1992, Tek Secret, 1993, (memoirs) Star Trek Memories, 1993, Star Trek Movie Memories, 1994. Recipient Tyrone Guthrie award, 1956, Theatre World award, 1958. Mem. Actors Equity Assn., AFTRA, Screen Actors Guild, Dirs. Guild. Address: care of Lemli Prodns 760 N LaCienega Blvd Los Angeles CA 90069*

SHATTO, GLORIA MCDERMITH, college administrator, economist; b. Houston, Oct. 11, 1931; d. Ken E. and Gertrude (Osborne) McDermith; m. Robert J. Shatto, Mar. 19, 1953; children: David Paul, Donald Patrick. BA with honors in Econs., Rice U., 1954, PhD (fellow), 1966. Mkt. rsch. Humble Oil & Refining Co., Houston, 1954-55; tchr. pub. sch. C.Z., 1955-56; tchr. Houston Ind. Sch. Dist., 1956-60; asst. prof. econs. U. Houston, 1965-69, assoc. prof., 1969-72; prof. econs., assoc. dean Coll. Indsl. Mgmt., Ga. Inst. Tech. Atlanta, 1973-77; George R. Brown prof. bus. Trinity U., San Antonio, 1977-79; pres. Berry Coll., Mt. Berry, Ga., 1980—; small bus. adv. com. U.S. Treasury, 1977-81; trustee Joint Coun. Econ. Edn., 1985-88; dir. Ga. Power Co., Kmart Corp., So. Co., Becton Dickinson and Co., Tex. Instruments, Inc. Contbr. articles to profl. jours.; Editor: Employment of the Middle-Aged, 1972; mem. editorial bd.: Ednl. Record, 1980-82. Mem. Tex. Gov.'s Commn. on Status of Women, 1970-72, Gov.'s Commn. on Economy and Efficiency in State Govt., 1991, State Ethics Com., 1995—; trustee Ga. Tech. Rsch. Inst., 1977, Berry Coll., Ga., 1975-79, Ga. Forestry Commn., 1987-95; mem. Ga. Gov.'s Commn. on Status of Women, 1975; mem. commn. on women in higher edn. Am. Council on Edn., 1980-82, chmn., 1982; mem. Ga. Study Com. on Public Higher Edn. Fin., 1981-82; v.p. Ga. Found Ind. Colls., 1981, pres., 1982, 94; mem. adv. bd. to Sch. Bus. Adminstrn., Temple U., Phila., 1981-83; mem. Study Com. on Ednl. Processes, So. Assn. Colls. and Schs., 1981-82, Ga. United Meth. Commn. on Higher Edn. and Campus Ministry, 1981-82; trustee Redmond Park Hosp., Rome, Ga., 1981-87, 1st United Meth. Ch., 1986-89. Recipient Disting. Alumni award Rice U., 1987; OAS fellow, summer 1968. Mem. Royal Econ. Assn., Am. Econ. Assn., So. Econ. Assn., Southwestern Econ. Assn. (pres. 1976-77), Am. Fin. Assn. (nominating com. 1976), Southwestern Social Scis. Assn., Fin. Execs. Inst. (chmn Atlanta edn. com. 1976-77, mem. com. on profl. devel. 1981), AAUW (area rep. 1967-68, Tex. chmn. legis. program 1970-71, mem. internat. fellowships-awards com. 1970-76, chmn. 1974-76), Ga. Newcomen Soc. (chmn. 1991—), Newcomen Soc. U.S. (trustee), Phi Beta Kappa, Phi Kappa Phi, Omicron Delta Epsilon. Office: Berry Coll Office of the President 39 Mt Berry Sta Mount Berry GA 30149-0039

SHATTUCK, CATHIE ANN, lawyer, former government official; b. Salt Lake City, July 18, 1945; d. Robert Ashley S. and Lillian Culp (Shattuck). B.A., U. Nebr., 1967, J.D., 1970. Bar: Nebr. 1970, U.S. Dist. Ct. Nebr. 1970, Colo. 1971, U.S. Dist. Ct. Colo. 1971, U.S. Supreme Ct. 1974, U.S. Ct. Appeals (10th cir.) 1977, U.S. Dist. Ct. D.C. 1984, U.S. Ct. Appeals (D.C. cir.) 1984. V.p., gen. mgr. Shattuck Farms, Hastings, Nebr., 1967-70; asst. project dir. atty. Colo. Civil Rights Commn., Denver, 1970-72; trial atty. Equal Employment Opportunity Commn., Denver, 1973-77; vice chmn. Equal Employment Opportunity Commn., Washington, 1982-84; pvt. practice law Denver, 1977-81; mem. Fgn. Svc. Bd., Washington, 1982-84, Presdl. Personnel Task Force, Washington, 1982-84; ptnr. Epstein, Becker & Green, L.A. and Washington, 1984—; lectr. Colo. Continuing Legal Edn. Author: Employer's Guide to Controlling Sexual Harrassment, 1992; mem. editorial bd. The Practical Litigator, 1988—. Bd. dirs. KGNU Pub. Radio, Boulder, Colo., 1979, Denver Exchange, 1980-81, YWCA Met. Denver, 1979-81. Recipient Nebr. Young Career Woman Bus. and Profl. Women, 1967; recipient Outstanding Nebraskan Daily Nebraskan, Lincoln, 1967. Mem. ABA (mgmt. chair labor and employment law sect. com. on immigration law 1988-90, mgmt. chair com. on legis. devels. 1990-93), Nebr. Bar Assn., Colo. Bar Assn., Colo. Women's Bar Assn., D.C. Bar Assn., Nat. Women's Coalition, Delta Sigma Rho, Tau Kappa Alpha, Pi Sigma Alpha, Alpha Xi Delta, Denver Club.

SHATTUCK, GEORGE CLEMENT, lawyer; b. Syracuse, N.Y., Sept. 2, 1927; s. Frank M. and Genevieve Mary (Hannon) S.; m. Sheila Eagan, Sept. 21, 1957 (div. 1985); children: Edward, George, Frank, Mark, Patrick; m. Carla A. Amussen, June 19, 1987; 1 child, Morgan. BS in Mgmt., Syracuse U., 1950, JD, 1953. Bar: N.Y. 1954, U.S. Supreme Ct. 1973. Ptnr., estate planning splty. practice Bond Schoeneck & King Law Firm, Syracuse, 1954—. Author: Oneida Land Claims, 1991, Estate Planning for the Small Business Owner, 1993. Mem. Syracuse Bd. Edn., 1968-75. Roman Catholic. Avocations: writing, reading history and philosophy, fishing, biking. Home: 5158 W Lake Rd Cazenovia NY 13035-9633 Office: Bond Schoeneck & King One Lincoln Ctr Syracuse NY 13202

SHATTUCK, JOHN H. F., federal official; m. Ellen Hume; 4 children. BA magna cum laude, Yale U., JD; MA with 1st-class honors, Cambridge U., Eng. Law clk. to Hon. Edward Weinfeld U.S. Dist. Ct. (so. dist.) N.Y., 1970-71; nat. counsel ACLU, 1971-77, dir. Washington office, 1977-84; v.p. govt., community and pub. affairs Harvard U., 1984-93, sr. assoc. sci. tech. and pub. policy program John F. Kennedy sch. govt., 1984-93; asst. sec. of state bur. human rights and humanitarian affairs Dept. of State, Washington, 1993—; lectr. Harvard U.; vis. lectr. Princeton U. Editor Yale U. Law Jour.; contbr. articles to profl. jours. Recipient H.L. Mencken award Free Press Assn., Pub. Svc. award Yale U., Roger Baldwin medal. Mem. Leadership Conf. Civil Rights (mem. exec. com.). Office: Dept of State Office of the Secretary 2201 C St NW Washington DC 20520-0004

SHATTUCK, MAYO ADAMS, III, investment banking executive; b. Boston, Oct. 7, 1954; s. Mayo Adams, Jr. and Jane (Bergwall) S.; m. Jennifer Whithed Budge, June 18, 1977; children: Mayo Adams IV, Kathleen Elizabeth. BA, Williams Coll., 1976; MBA, Stanford U., 1980. Analyst Morgan Guaranty Trust Co., N.Y.C., 1976-78; mgr. Bain & Co., Menlo Park, Calif., 1980-83; v.p. to mng. dir. and head of corp. fin. Alex Brown & Sons, San Francisco, 1985-91; pres. and COO Alex Brown & Sons, Balt., 1991—; bd. dirs. Alex Brown, Inc., Balt., Constellation Holdings Inc. subs. Balt. Gas and Electric. Trustee Gilman Sch., Wellness Cmty., Balt., 1991—; chmn. bd. dirs. Columbus Ctr., Balt., 1992—; adv. dir. U. Md., Balt., 1992—. Mem. Am. Bus. Conf. Avocations: tennis, golf. Office: Alex Brown & Sons 135 E Baltimore St Baltimore MD 21202-1607

SHATTUCK, ROGER WHITNEY, author, educator; b. N.Y.C., Aug. 20, 1923; s. Howard Francis and Elizabeth (Colt) S.; m. Nora Ewing White, Aug. 20, 1949; children—Tari Elizabeth, Marc Ewing, Patricia Colt, Eileen Shepard. Grad., St. Paul's Sch., Concord, N.H., 1941; B.A., Yale, 1947; Doctorat honoris causa, U. Orléans, France, 1990. Information officer UNESCO, Paris, France, 1947-48; asst. editor Harcourt, Brace & Co., 1949-50; mem. Soc. Fellows, Harvard, 1950-53, instr. French, 1953-56; faculty U. Tex., Austin, 1956-71; prof. English, French U. Tex., 1968-71, chmn. dept. French and Italian, 1968-71; Commonwealth prof. French U. Va., Charlottesville, 1974-88; univ. prof., prof. modern fgn. langs. Boston U., 1988—; mem. adv. bd. Nat. Translation Center, 1964-69, chmn., 1966-69; provediteur gen. Coll. de Pataphysique, Paris, 1961—; Fulbright prof. U. Dakar, Senegal, 1984-85. Author: The Banquet Years, 1958; poems Half Tame, 1964; Proust's Binoculars, 1963, Marcel Proust, 1974 (Nat. Book award 1975), The Forbidden Experiment, 1980, The Innocent Eye, 1984; editor or co-editor: Selected Writings of Guillaume Appollinaire, 1950, Mount Analogue, (Rene Daumal), 1959, The Craft and Context of Translation (with William Arrowsmith), 1961, Selected works of Alfred Jarry, 1965, Occasions by Paul Valéry, 1970; mem. editorial bd.: PMLA, 1977-78. Served to capt. USAAF, 1942-45. Decorated Ordre Palmes Academiques (France).; Guggenheim fellow, 1958-59; Fulbright research fellow, 1958-59; Am. Council Learned Socs. research fellow, 1969-70. Fellow Am. Acad. Arts and Scis. Office: Boston U Univ Profs Program 745 Commonwealth Ave Boston MA 02215-1401

SHATTUCK, SCOTT HARLAN, performing company executive; b. Denver, Aug. 23, 1960; s. Harlan Louis Jr. and Gloria Mae (Evick) S. BA, Colo. State U., 1983; MFA, U. Tex., Austin, 1988. Prodn. stage mgr. Colo. Shakespeare Festival, Boulder, Colo., 1983-84; prodn. asst. Denver (Colo.) Center Theatre Co., 1983-85; dir. prodn. Tex. Shakespeare Festival, Kilgore, 1988-92; asst. prof. dramatic arts Dickinson Coll., Carlisle, Pa., 1988-92, chair dramatic arts, 1991-92; producing dir. Jean Cocteau Repertory, N.Y.C., 1992-94, artistic dir., 1994—; bd. advisers Theatre Insight, Austin, 1989-92; cons. Region VII Edn. Svc. Ctr., K ilgore, 1989—; artistic assoc. Vortex Repertory Co., Austin, Tex., 1991—; adj. asst. prof., Marymount Manhattan Coll., N.Y.C., 1993—. Mem. Assn. Theatre in Higher Edn., East Cen. Theatre Conf., Theatre Assn. Pa., Theatre Comm. Group. Democrat. Office: Jean Cocteau Repertory 330 Bowery New York NY 10012-2400

SHATZ, STEPHEN SIDNEY, mathematician, educator; b. Bklyn., Apr. 27, 1937; s. Nathan and Agusta S.; children: Geoffrey, Adria. A.B., Harvard U., 1957, A.M., 1958, Ph.D., 1962; A.M. (hon.), U. Pa., 1971. Instr. Stanford U., 1962-63, acting asst. prof., 1963-64; asst. prof. U. Pa., Phila., 1964-67; assoc. prof. U. Pa., 1967-69, prof. math., 1969—, chmn. dept. math., 1983-86; vis. prof. U. Pisa, 1966-67. Author: Profinite Groups, Arithmetic and Geometry, 1972; contbr. articles to profl. jours. Mem. Am. Math. Soc. (editor Trans. 1975-78, mem. council 1975-80). Office: U Pa Dept Math Philadelphia PA 19104-6395

SHATZKIN, LEONARD, publishing consultant; b. Warsaw, Poland, July 16, 1919; came to U.S., 1920, naturalized, 1922; s. Isaac and Helen (Feiman) S.; m. Eleanor Oshry, Aug. 4, 1940; children: Michael, Karen, Nancy. Student, CCNY, 1935-38; B.S., Carnegie Inst. Tech., 1941. Prodn. mgr. House Beautiful Mag., N.Y.C., 1941-43; research scientist Manhattan Project, N.Y.C., 1943-45; prodn. mgr. Viking Press, N.Y.C., 1945-50; asst. to dir. mfg. Doubleday & Co., N.Y.C., 1950-55; dir. research Doubleday & Co., 1955-60; v.p. Crowell-Collier Macmillan Co., N.Y.C., 1960-63; dir. mfg. McGraw-Hill Book Co., N.Y.C., 1963-68; v.p. McGraw-Hill Book Co., 1968-70; pres. Planned Prodn., N.Y.C., 1970-78, Two Continents Pub. Group, Ltd., N.Y.C., 1972-78; prin. Shatzkin & Co. (Cons.), Croton-on-Hudson, N.Y., 1979—; instr. div. gen. studies NYU, 1948-53; bd. dirs. Yates Industries, 1965-72; instr. Pratt Inst., 1971-72; cons. George Banta Co., Avon Industries, Macmillan Co., Orbis Books, Doubleday & Co., Grove Press, St. Martin's Press, Thomas Nelson, Grolier, Inc., CBS Internat., Dodd Mead, N.Y. Bot. Garden, Pahlavi Nat. Libr., Teheran, Iran., Ford Found., Gen. Mills, USIA, Raben & Sjogren, Stockholm, Sweden, Nat. Endowment for Arts, John Wiley & Sons, Ediouro Pub. Co., Rio de Janeiro, Curio Bookstore, Rio de Janeiro, Internat. Trademark Assn., N.Y.; cons. to Christian Lit. Assn. of Malawi, Internat. Exec. Svc. Corps re-book distbn. in Russia. Editor and translator: The Stars Bear Witness, 1947; author: In Cold Type, 1982; contbr.: articles to Publishers Weekly, others. Mem. Am. Inst. Graphic Arts (treas. 1952-59), Trade Book Clinic, Christian Literature Assn., Publishers Round Table, Tamiment Inst., Amnesty Internat. Mem. Democratic Socialists of Am. Patentee field of book binding. Home: 132 Old Post Rd N Croton On Hudson NY 10520-1934

SHAUB, HAROLD ARTHUR, food products executive; b. Lancaster County, Pa., Nov. 28, 1915; s. Arthur and Clara (Cramer) S.; m. Eileen Bair, Aug. 5, 1939; children: John A., Carole Sue Shaub Hoffman, Lynn E. Shaub Benton. BS in Commerce, Drexel U., 1939. Indsl. engr. Talon, Inc., 1941-42; gen. supt. Camden (N.J.) plant, then other supervisory positions Campbell Soup Co., Camden and Chgo., 1942-57; sr. v.p., frozen food ops. and Can. and Pepperdige Farm subs. Campbell Soup Co., Camden, 1968-69, exec. v.p., 1969, pres., chief exec. officer, 1972-80; v.p., gen. mgr. Campbell Soup Co. Ltd. (subs. Campbell Soup Co.), Toronto, Ont., Can., 1957-58, pres., 1961-66; pres. Pepperidge Farm, Inc. (subs. Campbell Soup Co.), Norwalk, Conn. and internat. ops., 1966-68; bd. dirs. United Med. Corp.; former mem. internat. adv. council Can. Imperial Bank Commerce, Toronto; former mem. industries adv. com. Advt. Council and The Conf. Bd.; food mfg. industry chmn. U.S. Indsl. Payroll Savs. Com., 1976, 77; former bd. dirs. Exxon Corp., R. H. Macy & Co., Inc., Scott Paper Co., Campbell Soup Co. Trustee Drexel U., Coriell Inst. Med. Rsch.; former trustee Valley Forge Mil. Acad. and Jr. Coll.; bd. dirs. Citizens Crime Commn. Phila., 1987—; former mem. bd. mgrs. Franklin Inst. Phila. Named Bus. Leader of the Yr. Drexel U., 1973. Office: 25 Chestnut St Ste 108 Haddonfield NJ 08033

SHAUD, JOHN ALBERT, association executive, former air force officer; b. Cleve., Dec. 15, 1933; s. Albert Grant and Helen Katherine (Meek) S.; m. Janelle Marie Ohlenbusch, July 19, 1958; children: Patricia, James, Katherine. BS, U.S. Mil. Acad., 1956; MS, George Washington U., 1967; PhD, Ohio State U., 1971. Commd. 2d lt. USAF, 1956, advanced through grades to gen., 1988; pilot B-47, B-52, RF-4C USAF, Ariz., Ohio, Thailand, Vietnam, 1957-71; mem. faculty Air Command and Staff Coll., Montgomery, Ala., 1971-73; student, rsch. assoc. Nat. War Coll., Washington, 1973-74; dep. comdr. for ops., vice wing comdr. 449 Bomb Wing, Kinross, Mich., 1974-75; staff officer plans and ops. USAF Hdqrs., Pentagon, Washington, 1975-78; wing comdr. 92 Bomb Wing, Spokane, Wash., 1978-80; air div. comdr. 47th/57th Air Div., Wash. and N.D., 1980-81; dep. dir., dir. plans, plans and ops. USAF Hdqrs., Pentagon, 1981-85; dep. chief of staff, pers. Hdqrs., Pentagon, 1985-86; comdr. Air Tng. Command, San Antonio, 1986-88; chief of staff Supreme Hdqrs. Allied Powers Europe (SHAPE), Mons, Belgium, 1988-91; ret., 1991; dir. Air Force Aid Soc., Arlington, 1991—. Decorated Def. D.S.M., Air Force D.S.M. with one oak leaf cluster, DFC, Legion of Merit with one oak leaf cluster, Air medal with 5 oak leaf clusters. Mem. Air Force Assn., Order of Daedalians, Mil. Order of Carabao, Beta Gamma Sigma, Alpha Tau Omega. Lutheran. Office: Air Force Aid Soc 1745 Jefferson Davis Hwy Ste 202 Arlington VA 22202

SHAUGHNESSY, THOMAS WILLIAM, librarian, consultant; b. Pitts., May 3, 1938; s. Martin T. and LaVerne (O'Brien) S.; m. Marlene D. Reuben, Aug. 11, 1968; 1 child, Mark Andrew. AB, St. Vincent Coll., 1961; MLS, U. Pitts., 1964; PhD, Rutgers U., 1970. Asst. dean Rutgers U., New Brunswick, N.J., 1969-71; libr. dir. Rutgers-Newark, 1971-74; assoc. dean U.

So. Calif., L.A., 1974-78; asst. libr. dir. U. Houston, 1978-82; libr. dir. U. Mo.-Columbia, 1982-89; univ. libr. and dir. U. Minn., Mpls.-St. Paul, 1989—; rsch. dir. Chgo. Pub. Libr. Survey, 1968-69; cons U. Tulsa Libr., 1982-83; adv. com. OCLC Rsch. Librs., 1988—. Author: (with Lowell A. Martin) Library Response to Urban Change, 1969, Developing Leadership Skills: A Source Book for Librarians, 1990. U.S. Office Edn. grantee Rutgers U., 1971; fellow Coun. Libr. Resources, 1973, sr. fellow, 1985. Mem. ALA, Assn. Coll. and Rsch. Librs., Assn. Rsch. Librs. (cons. tng. fellow 1981, bd. dirs. 1989-92), Minn. Libr. Assn., Beta Phi Mu. Home: 5705 Wycliffe Rd Minneapolis MN 55436-2264 Office: U Minn Wilson Libr Minneapolis MN 55455-0414

SHAULL, RICHARD, theologian, educator; b. Felton, Pa., Nov. 24, 1919; s. Millard and Anna (Brenneman) S.; m. Mildred Miller, May 17, 1941 (div. May 1975); children: Madelyn, Wendy; m. Nancy Johns, Apr. 14, 1981. B.A., Elizabethtown Coll., 1938, D.D., 1958; B.Th., Princeton Theol. Sem., 1941, Th.M., 1946, Th.D., 1959. Ordained to ministry Presbyn. Ch., 1941; pastor in Wink, Tex., 1941-42; missionary in Colombia, 1942-50, U. Brazil, 1952-62; prof. ch. history Campinas (Brazil) Presbyn. Sem., 1952-60; v.p. Mackenzie Inst., São Paulo, Brazil, 1960-62; prof. ecumenics Princeton Theol. Sem., 1962-80, prof. emeritus, 1980—; vis. internat. programs, 1960—; chmn. N.Am. Congress Latin Am., 1966-89, World Student Christian Fedn., 1968-73; acad. dir. Instituto Pastoral Hispano, N.Y.C., 1983-89. Author: Encounter with Revolution, 1955, (with Carl Oglesby) Containment and Change, 1967, (with Gustavo Gutierrez) Liberation and Change, 1977, Heralds of a New Reformation, 1984, Naming the Idols, 1988, The Reformation and Liberation Theology, 1991, also 3 books in Portuguese. Home and Office: 46 Morgan Cir Swarthmore PA 19081-2214

SHAVELL, STEVEN, law educator; b. 1946. AB, U. Mich., 1968; PhD, MIT, 1973. Asst. prof. Harvard U., Cambridge, Mass., 1974-79, 80-82, assoc. prof., 1979-80, prof., 1982—. Office: Harvard U Law Sch Cambridge MA 02138

SHAVELSON, MELVILLE, writer, theatrical producer and director; b. N.Y.C., Apr. 1, 1917; s. Joseph and Hilda (Shalson) S.; m. Lucille T. Myers, Nov. 2, 1938; children: Richard, Carol-Lynne. AB, Cornell U., 1937. Author: How to Make a Jewish Movie, 1970, Lualda, 1975, The Great Houdinis, 1976, The Eleventh Commandment, 1977, Ike, 1979, Don't Shoot, It's Only Me, 1990; writer Bob Hope Pepsodent Show, NBC radio, 1938-43; screenwriter The Princess and the Pirate, 1944, Wonder Man, 1944, Room for One More, 1951, I'll See You in My Dreams, 1952; screenwriter, dir. The Seven Little Foys, 1954, Beau James, 1956, Houseboat, 1957, The Five Pennies, 1958, It Started in Naples, 1959, On the Double, 1960, Yours, Mine and Ours, 1968, The War Between Men and Women, 1972, The Legend of Valentino, 1975, Deceptions, 1985; screenwriter, dir., producer The Pigeon That Took Rome, 1962, A New Kind of Love, 1963, Cast a Giant Shadow, 1966, Mixed Company, 1974, The Great Houdinis, 1976, Ike, 1979; dir. The Other Woman, 1983; creator TV shows including Danny Thomas Show, ABC-TV, 1953, My World—and Welcome To It, NBC-TV, 1969; author Broadway mus. Jimmy, 1969. Recipient Screen Writers Guild award, 1959, Christopher award, 1959, Sylvania TV award, 1953, Acad. Award nominations (screenplay), 1955, 58, Screen Writers Ann. award nominations (screenplay), 1952 (2), 58, 59, 62, 68, 72, 75, Screen Writers award (best written Am. mus.), 1959, Award of Merit United Jewish Appeal, 1966. Mem. Dirs. Guild Am., Writers Guild Am. (exec. bd. dirs 1960-75, 78, pres. screen writers br. 1967, pres. found. 1975—), Acad. Motion Picture Arts and Scis. (mem. bd. govs.), Writer Guild Am. West (pres. 1969-70, 79-81, 85-87, Valentine Davies award 1979, Laurel award 1984), Sigma Delta Chi. Home and Office: 11947 Sunshine Ter Studio City CA 91604-3708

SHAVER, CARL HUTCHENS, retail company executive; b. Richland, Oreg., June 10, 1913; s. Charles Jacob and Minne (Mary) S.; m. Georgia Bruce, Oct. 17, 1934 (dec. Apr. 1980); children—Carl B., Dennis G.; m. Laura Frazier, Aug. 12, 1983. Student N.W. Nazarene Coll., Nampa, Idaho, 1931-32. Clk., Stockwells, Nampa, 1935-36, mgr., Donnelly, Idaho, 1936-41; mgr. Shavers, Donnelly and New Meadows, Idaho, 1941-53; pres. Shaver's Inc., Boise, Idaho, 1953-80, chmn. bd., 1980—; pres. Boise Wholesale Drygoods Co., Inc., 1953-77; chmn. bd. Citizens Nat. Bank, Boise, 1981—; vice-chmn. Associated Food Stores, also bd. dirs.; bd. dirs., v.p. Shore Club Lodge Inc., McCall, Idaho. Bd. dirs. United First Meth. Ch., Boise, 1968-74. Named Small Businessman of Yr., State of Idaho, 1973; recipient Disting. Citizen award Idaho Daily Statesman, 1984. Mem. Nat. Assn. Textile and Apparel Wholesalers (bd. dirs. 1962-74, pres. 1974-76), Idaho Retailers (pres. 1951), Greater Boise C. of C. (bd. dirs. 1965-71). Republican. Clubs: Hillcrest Country, Arld (bd. dirs. 1959-60). Lodges: Masons, Shriners. Home: 3100 Crescent Rim Dr Apt 401 Boise ID 83706-2868 Office: Shavers Inc 705 S 8th PO Box 7278 Boise ID 83707-1278 other: Associated Food Stores Inc 3100 Cresent Rim Dr Boise ID 83706

SHAVER, DANIEL P., law educator, civilian military employee; b. 1958; m. 1981; 3 children. BS, U.S. Mil. Acad., West Point, 1980; JD magna cum laude, Washington and Lee U., 1986; LLM, U. Va., 1993. Bar: Va., U.S. Supreme Ct. Field artillery officer 24th Infantry Divsn. Artillery, Ft. Stewart, Ga., 1980-83; trial counsel Office of Staff Judge Advocate, Ft. Dix, N.J., 1986-87, chief of justice, sr. trial counsel, 1987-88, environ. and adminstrv. law atty., 1988-89; sr. def. counsel Ft. Dix office U.S. Army Trial Def. Svc., 1989-90; instr. The Judge Advocate Gen.'s Sch., U.S. Army, Charlottesville, Va., 1990-91, asst. prof. law, 1991—. Editor: (jours.) The Army Lawyer, 1990-91, The Regimental Reporter, 1990—, Mil. Law Rev., 1991—. Decorated Army Achievement medal 1982, Army Commendation medal 1983, 90; recipient Steinheimer award Comml. Law, 1986. Mem. Omicron Delta Kappa, Order Coif. Office: Military Law Review USAR Judge Advocate Gen's Sch Charlottesville VA 22903

SHAVER, JAMES PORTER, education educator, university dean; b. Wadena, Minn., Oct. 19, 1933. BA magna cum laude, U. Wash., Seattle, 1955; MA in Teaching, Harvard U., 1957, EdD, 1961. Instr. Grad. Sch. Edn., Harvard U., 1961-62; assoc. prof., dir. Social Studies Curriculum Ctr., Ohio State U., Columbus, 1964-65; mem. faculty Utah State U. Coll. Edn., Logan, 1962-64, prof., 1965—, chmn. Bur. Rsch. Scis. 1965-93, assoc. dean rsch., 1978-93, acting dean Sch. Grad. Studies, 1990-91, 92-93, dean, 1993—; mem. Commn. Youth Edn. for Citizenship, ABA, 1975-81; mem. info. task force Am. Hist. Assn.-Am. Polit. Sci. Assn. Project '87, 1981-84; tech. advisor Nat. Ctr. on Effective Secondary Schs., 1988-91; mem. adv. bd. program in civic and moral edn. Inst. for Philosophy and Pub. Policy, U. Md., 1992—; mem. steering com. Nat. Assessment Ednl. Progress Civics Consensus Project, 1995-96. Co-author: Teaching Public Issues in the High School, 1966, 2d edit., 1974, Facing Value Decisions: Rationale-building For Teachers, 1976, 2d edit., 1982; editor: Building Rationales for Citizenship Education, 1977, Handbook of Research on Social Studies Teaching and Learning, 1991; co-editor: Democracy, Pluralism, and the Social Studies, 1968; also others. Mem. AAAS, AAUP, Nat. Coun. Social Studies (pres. 1976), Am. Ednl. Rsch. Assn. Home: PO Box 176 Hyrum UT 84319-0176 Office: Utah State U Main 132 Logan UT 84322-0900

SHAVER, JESSE MILTON, JR., manufacturing company executive; b. Nashville, Nov. 16, 1919; s. Jesse M. and Daisy (Rule) S.; m. Ludmila B. Tilton, Aug. 26, 1992; children: Jesse Milton III, John Warren. B.S. in Engring, Purdue U., 1942; M.B.A., U. Chgo., 1955. Mgmt. cons. Booz, Allen & Hamilton, 1952-58; div. mgr. Wells-Gardner Electronics Corp., 1958-62; exec. v.p. Am. Air Filter Co., Inc., Louisville, 1962-67; pres., chief operating officer Am. Air Filter Co., Inc., 1967, chmn. bd., exec. chief exec. officer, 1968-80; exec. v.p. Allis-Chalmers Corp., 1978-81, cons., 1981-85; pres. JMS Corp., 1985—; also dir. Bd. dirs. Air Conditioning and Refrigeration Inst., pres., 1972. Served to maj. F.A. AUS, 1942-47, ETO. Decorated Bronze Star medal. Mem. IEEE, ASHRAE, Sigma Chi, Beta Gamma Sigma. Episcopalian. Clubs: Economic (Chgo.), University (Chgo.); Louisville Country (Louisville), Pendennis (Louisville); Metropolitan (N.Y.C.). Home: 37 Brownsboro Hill Rd Louisville KY 40207-2009 Office: JMS Corp Starks Bldg Ste 854 455 S 4th St Louisville KY 40202-2510

SHAVER, KELLY G., psychology educator; b. Highland Park, Ill., Oct. 30, 1941. BS, U. Wash., 1963, MS, 1965; PhD, Duke U., 1969. Teaching asst. U. Wash., 1963-64, rsch. asst., 1964-65; rsch. asst. Duke U., 1965-68; asst. prof. Coll. William and Mary, Williamsburg, Va., 1968-73, assoc. prof.,

1973-82, prof., 1982—, rsch. dir. Tech. Entrepreneurship Ctr., 1989-90; dir. social and devel. psychology program divsn. behavioral and neural scis. NSF, 1977-79; chair Hampton-Roads Innovation and Tech. Edn. Consortium, 1990—; mem. adv. com. Va. Assembly on Adult Corrections, 1983-84; mem. oversight review com. programs in cognitive sci. divsn. behavioral and neural scis. NSF, 1984, mem. adv. panel social psychology divsn. social scis., 1973-75, mem. presdl. young investigator awards review panel divsn. behavioral and neural scis., 1989, mem. review panel undergrad. faculty enhancement program divsn. undergrad. sci., engring. and math. edn., 1990, mem. rsch. tng. groups adv. panel for biol., behavioral and social scis., 1991, mem. rsch. experiences undergrads. adv. panel for biol., behavioral and social scis., 1991, mem. adv. panel undergrad. course and curriculum devel. program divsn. undergrad. sci., engring., and math. edn. directorate for edn. and human resources, 1992, mem. small bus. innovation rsch. adv. panel, decision risk and mgmt. scis. program divsn. social and econ. sci., 1992, rep. to interagy. panel for rsch. adolescence, 1977-79, leader behavioral and neural scis. review panel, 1980, mem. adv. panel social and devel. psychology divsn. behavioral and neural scis., 1982; cons. Commonwealth Fund, 1986; lectr. Kendon Smith meml. lectrs. U. N.C., Greensboro, 1988; ad-hoc reviewer behavioral scis. rsch. review com. Nat. Inst. Mental, 1990; ad-hoc reviewer rsch. review com. on human devel., Nat. Insts. Health, 1990, human devel. and aging spl. study sect., 1990, 91, 92; chair social scis. review panel La. Ednl. Quality Support Fund, Bd. Regents, 1991, 92; lectr. psychology seminar series Coll. Charleston, 1982; mem. program review com. dept. psychology Bucknell U., 1982; mem. editorial bd. Entrepreneurship and Regional Devel., 1992—, Entrepreneurship: Theory and Practice, 1989-92, Jour. Personality, 1983-87, Jour. Applied Social Psychology, 1983—, Jour. Personality and Social Psychology, 1977-88; proposal reviewer various orgns.; outside evaluator various colls. and univs.; presenter in field. Author: An Introduction to Attribution Processes, 1975, Principles of Social Psychology, 1977, Attribution of Blame: Causality, Responsibility, and Blameworthiness, 1985, (with E. Stotland and S. Sherman) Empathy and Birth Order: Some Experimental Explorations, 1971, (with R.M. Tarpy) Psychology, 1993; author: (with others) New Directions in Attribution Research, 1981, Life Crises and Experiences of Loss in Adulthood, 1992; contbr. 30 articles to profl. jours. Mem. Am. Psychol. Soc., Am. Psychology-Law Soc., Va. Bd. Lic. Examiners (registered social psychologist), Ea. Psychol. Assn. (program com. 1991—), Capital Area Social Psychology Assn., Acad. Mgmt., Soc. Exptl. Social Psychology, Soc. Psychol. Study Social Issues, Soc. Advancement Social Psychology (steering com. 1984-85), Richmond Venture Capital Club (bd. dirs.), Small Bus. Devel. Ctr. Grater Hampton Rds. (bd. dirs.). Office: Coll William and Mary Williamsburg VA 23187-8795

SHAVIRO, DANIEL NATHAN, law educator; b. N.Y.C., May 11, 1957; s. Sol and Frieda (Wachs) S.; m. Patricia Diane Ludwig, Sept. 11, 1988. AB, Princeton U., 1978; JD, Yale U., 1981. Bar: D.C. 1981. Assoc. Caplan & Drysdale, Chartered, Washington, 1981-84; legislation atty. Joint Com. on Taxation U.S. Congress, Washington, 1984-87; asst. prof. law U. Chgo., 1987—; spl. cons. Tax Mgmt. Adv. Bd., Washington, 1987—. Author: Passive Loss Rules, 1988, The Political Economy of Budget Deficits, 1995; contbr. articles to profl. jours. Mem. ABA. Avocations: arts, sports, politics. Office: NYU Law Sch 40 Washington Sq S New York NY 10012

SHAVIV, EDDIE, marketing and sales executive; b. Suceava, Romania, Oct. 24, 1940; s. Friedrich and Paula (Eidinger) Scherzer; m. Emanuela Drach, July 7, 1968; children: Bernard Daniel, Enid Naomi. MSME, Poly. Inst. Bucharest, Romania, 1962; MBA with distinction, N.Y. Inst. Tech., 1988. Engring. mgr. Malaxa Engine Factory, Bucharest, 1962-73, Savkel, Tel Aviv, Israel, 1973-78; plant mgr. Sivaro, Carmiel, Israel, 1978-80; engring. mgr. Tadiran Batteries, Rehovoth, Israel, 1980-84; mktg. & sales mgr. Tadiran Batteries, Port Washington, N.Y., 1984-90; nat. accounts mgr. Varta Batteries Inc., Elmsford, N.Y., 1990—; dir. nat. accounts OEM sales and mktg., 1992—, dir. OEM sales and mktg., 1988-90. Patentee for water pumps, rechargeable batteries; contbr. articles to profl. jours. Sgt. Israeli Def. Forces, 1975-80. Recipient Galil War award Israeli Def. Forces, 1979. Mem. Delta Mu Delta Nat. Honor Soc. Jewish. Home: 57 Netto Ln Plainview NY 11803-3129 Office: Varta Batteries 300 Executive Blvd Elmsford NY 10523

SHAW, ALAN ROGER, financial executive, educator; b. Bklyn., July 7, 1938; s. Sewall S. and Vera (Dimmick) S.; children: Stephen S., Todd J., Bradley C.; married 2d, Mary Elizabeth Hogg, May 30, 1987. Student, Susquehanna U., 1957, Adelphi U., 1963-66. Analyst Harris Upham & Co., N.Y.C., 1958-71; asst. v.p. 1971-73, v.p. 1973-75; 1st v.p. Smith, Barney, Harris, Upham & Co., N.Y.C., 1975-80; sr. v.p., mng. dir. Smith Barney, N.Y.C., 1980—; lectr. N.Y. Inst. Fin., 1966—. Mem. Market Technicians Assn. (pres. 1974), N.Y. Soc. Security Analysts, Securities Industry Assn. Inst. (trustee 1986-92), Southward Ho Country Club, Unqua Corinthian Yacht Club (commodore 1988-90). Home: 87 Wagstaff Ln West Islip NY 11795-5206 also: 322 W 57th St New York NY 10019 also: 2123 Fisher Island Dr Fisher Island FL 33109-0052 Office: Smith Barney Inc 388 Greenwich St New York NY 10013

SHAW, ANGUS ROBERTSON, III, minister; b. Charlotte, N.C., Oct. 7, 1932; s. Angus Robertson Jr. and Claudia (Morrison) S.; m. Carolyn Farmer, Aug. 14, 1965; children: Karen, Rob. BA, Bob Jones U., 1955; MDiv, Columbia Theol. Sem., 1958, DMin, 1989; DD (hon.), King Coll., 1965. Asst. pastor 1st Presbyn. Ch., Pulaski, Va., 1956-62; pastor Seagle Meml. Ch., Pulaski, 1956-62, Royal Oak Ch. Marion, Va., 1962-69; sr. pastor 1st Presbyn. Ch., Dothan, Ala., 1969-78, Johnson City, Tenn., 1978—; chmn. bd. Salvation Army, Johnson City, Tenn., 1986-92; Trustee Lees-McRae Coll., Banner Elk, N.C., 1979-84; chmn. ch. coll. coun. Montreat (N.C.)-Anderson Coll., 1980; chmn. ann. fund King Coll., Briston, Tenn., 1985-86; bd. trustees Tusculum Coll., 1993—, chair coun. on ch. rels., 1992; bd. dirs. United Way, 1991—. Mem. Watauga Mental Health Assn. (bd. dirs. 1990—), chair 1992-93), Kiwanis (pres. 1990-91), Soc. Theta Pi. Home: 1013 Somerset Dr Johnson City TN 37604-2919 Office: 1st Presbyn Ch 105 S Boone St Johnson City TN 37604-6262

SHAW, ARTIE, musician, writer, lecturer; b. N.Y.C., May 23, 1910; s. Harry and Sarah Shaw; m. Margaret Allen; m. Lana Turner; m. Elizabeth Kern; 1 son, Steven Kern; m. Ava Gardner (div. Oct. 1946); m. Kathleen Winsor, (ct. 28, 1946; 1 son, Jonathan; m. Evelyn Keyes, 1957 (div. June 1985). Extension work in lit., Columbia U.; MusD (hon.), U. Nebr., 1938, LittD (hon.); LHD (hon.), Calif. Luth. U., 1987. Former owner firm Shooters Service and Dewey (gun mfrs.); pres. Artixo Prodns., Ltd. (film distbn. co.); lectr. colls. and univs.; ann. lectr. U. Calif., Santa Barbara, Oxnard Coll., Camarillo, Calif. Orch. leader, 1936-54; appeared in motion pictures Dancing Coed, Second Chorus; also engaged in film, theatrical prodn.; producer Broadway mus. The Great Gatsby; recipient Downbeat award best Am. swing band, Esquire Mag. Poll award as favorite band of armed services, Hall of Fame award for rec. Begin the Beguine; Stardust, Nat. Acad. Rec. Arts and Scis. 1977); condr., composer numerous songs and orchestral works including Concerto for Clarinet; author: A Clarinet Method; The Trouble with Cinderella; I Love You, I Hate You, Drop Dead! Three Variations on a Theme; The Best of Intentions, and Other Stories, 1989. Former mem. exec. council, bd. Hollywood Ind. Citizens Com. Arts, Scis. and Professions. Served with USNR, 1942-44. Recipient Presdl. award Am. Soc. Mus. Arrangers, 1990. Subject of film: Artie Shaw: Time is All You've Got (Acad. award Best Feature-length Documentary 1986). I'm still trying to figure life out and will let you know when, as, or if I ever do. But don't hold your breath; I imagine it'll take some 80 years more for me to find an answer.

SHAW, BERNARD, television journalist; b. Chgo., 1940; m. Linda Shaw; children: Anil, Amar. Corr. Washington bur. CBS News, 1971-77; Ing. corr., bur. chief ABC News, 1977-80; anchor Cable News Network, Washington, 1980—. Served with USMC. recipient, Cable Ace award: Best Newscaster, 1994. Office: CNN 820 1st St NE Washington DC 20002-4205

SHAW, BONITA LYNN, school administrator; b. Eau Claire, Wis., Jan. 4, 1944; d. Orrin Emil and Jennie (Eide) Indrebo; m. Robert Terry Shaw, Oct. 4, 1962; children: Chad Robert, Brooke Erin. BS in Spl. Edn., U. Wis., Eau Claire, 1968, MS in Spl. Edn., 1973; edn. specialist, U. Wis., Superior, 1992. Cert. tchr., adminstr., Wis. Tchr. spl. edn. Bullock Creek Jr.-Sr. High Sch.,

Midland, Mich., 1968-69, Wausau (Wis.) Sch. Dist., 1970-71; tchr. Hayward (Wis.) Elem. Sch., 1969-70, Chippewa Falls (Wis.) Sch. Dist., 1971-89; asst. prin. South Mid. Sch., Eau Claire, 1989—; tchr. summer sch. program, gifted and talented program, U. Wis., Eau Claire, 1975; presenter at profl. confs. Author handbook for student tchr. in spl. edn. Mem. ASCD, Wis. Assn. Mid. Level. Edn., Assn. Wis. Secondary Adminstrs., Nat. Assn. Secondary Sch. Adminstrs., Nat. Mid. Sch. Assn. Avocations: hunting, golf, refinishing antiques, reading. Home: 2884 Green View Dr Eau Claire WI 54703 Office: South Mid Sch 2115 Mitscher Ave Eau Claire WI 54701

SHAW, BREWSTER HOPKINSON, JR., astronaut; b. Cass City, Mich., May 16, 1945; m. Kathleen Mueller; children: Brewster H. III, Jessica Hollis, Brandon Robert. BS in Engring. Mechanics, U. Wis., 1968, MS in Engring. Mechanics, 1969. Commd. USAF, 1969, advanced through grades to col.; student pilot Craig AFB, Ala., 1970; assigned to F-100 replacement tng. unit Luke AFB, Ariz., 1970-71; served as F-100 combat fighter pilot, 352d Tactical Fighter Squadron Phan Rang Air Base, Republic of Vietnam, 1971; assigned to F-4 Replacement Tng. Unit George AFB, Calif., 1971; served with 25th Tactical Fighter Squadron Ubon Republic Thailand AFB; F-4 flight instr. 20th Tactical Fighter Tng. Squadron George AFB, Calif., 1973; student USAF Test Pilot Sch., Edwards AFB, Calif., 1975-76, instr., operational test pilot 6512th Test Squadron, 1977-78; astronaut NASA, 1978—, mem. support crew and Entry CAPCOM for STS-3 and STS-4, head Orbiter fleet, astronaut office liaison with Dept. Def., staff mem. Roger's Presdl. Commn. investigating STS 51-1, Challenger accident, pilot STS-9/Spacelab-1, 1983; spacecraft comdr. STS-61B, 1985, STS-28, 1989, completing total of 534 hours in space; dep. dir. Space Shuttle Ops. Kennedy Space Ctr., Fla. 1989-93, dir. Space Shuttle Ops., 1993—, chmn. Mission Mgmt. Team, 1989—. Decorated DFC with 7 oak leaf clusters, Def. Superior Svc. medal, Def. Meritorious Svc. medal, Air medal with 20 oak leaf clusters, Cross of Gallantry Republic Vietnam, NASA Space Flight medals, 1983, 85, 89, numerous other mil. and NASA awards; recipient Flight Achievement award Am. Astronautical Soc., 1983, Nat. Space award VFW, 1984. Avocations: running, skiing, flying, hunting. Office: care JF Kennedy Space Ctr NASA Orlando FL 32899

SHAW, BRYAN P. H., retired investment company executive; b. Kwongtung, China, Aug. 16, 1921; came to U.S., 1947, naturalized, 1962; s. Ying-Chow (Chung-ching) and Sui-ming (Soo) S.; m. Linda L.T. Tan, Apr. 4, 1953 (dec. 1976). B.A., St. John's U., Shanghai, China, 1946; M.A., Fordham U., 1955. Vice pres., treas. Counselled Funds Distbr. Inc., N.Y.C., 1959-61, also dir.; sec., treas. Axe Sci. Mgmt. Co., Inc., Tarrytown, N.Y., 1960-74; treas. Axe Sci. Corp., Tarrytown, 1960-74, Axe-Houghton Found., Tarrytown, 1968-70, Axe-Houghton Income Fund, Inc., Tarrytown, 1968-86, Axe-Houghton Fund B, Inc., Tarrytown, 1969-86, Axe-Houghton Stock Fund, Inc., Tarrytown, 1970-86, Axe-Houghton Money Market Fund, Inc., Tarrytown, 1982-86; v.p. Axe-Houghton Mgmt., Inc., Tarrytown, 1977-86. Clubs: Fordham U. (Bronx); Fordham U. Wall Street (N.Y.C.). Home: Coral Ridge Towers S 3333 NE 34th St Apt 819 Fort Lauderdale FL 33308

SHAW, BRYCE ROBERT, author; b. Mansfield, Pa., Feb. 22, 1930; s. Wilford Walter and Genevieve (Cox) S.; m. Sally Ruth Prutsman, June 29, 1952; children: David Bryce, Jody Lynn McMillin, Erin Suzanne Hunsinger. AB, Muhlenberg Coll., Allentown, Pa., 1952; MA, U. Mich., 1953, postgrad., 1959-64. Cert. secondary edn. tchr. Teaching fellow U. Mich., Ann Arbor, 1953-55; math. analyst Willow Run Rsch. Ctr., Ypsilanti, Mich., 1954-59; tchr. math. Mt. Morris (Mich.) Bd. Edn., 1959-60, Flint (Mich.) Bd. Edn., 1960-64; lectr. math. U. Mich, Flint, 1961-68; coord. math. Flint Bd. Edn., 1964-75, dir. math. and computer systems, 1975-77; author in residence Houghton Mifflin Co., Boston, 1977-81, sr. author, 1970—; rsch. mathematician sch. dists., univs., Houghton Mifflin, others, Flint, Boston, L.A., 1961—; math. cons. sch. bds., state edn. depts., univs., U.S., Can., Mex., 1965—, Am. Sch. Found., Mexico City, 1965-68; lectr. edn. Ea. Mich. U., Ypsilanti, 1964-67; lectr. math. Nat. and Regional Math. Couns., Mich. State U., East Lansing, 1965-67; chmn. math. dept. Flint Bd. Edn., 1960-64; lectr. math. curriculum Flint Bd. Edn., 1960-80; lectr. math. curriculum devel. bds. edn., sch. math. staffs. Author: (textbooks) General Math I, 2d edit., 1979, Mathematics Plus, 1980, Fundamentals of Mathematics, 2d edit., 1986, Personalized Computational Skills Program, Vol. I, 1980, vol. II, 1981, Personalized Computational Skills Program--Skills and Applications, 1982, Personalized Computational Skills Program: Module A, B, C, D, E, and F, 3d edit., 1982, Mathematics Plus!, 1982, Computer Math Program, Computational Skills Program, 1988, Brush-Up: Mathematics Program, 1995; contbr. articles to profl. jours. Recipient Internat. Man of Yr. award, 1991-92, Key of Success: Profl. Performance Achievement Rsch. and Notable Author award, Biographical Hon. award in Math.; named Disting. Lectr. Coll. Mathematicians. Mem. Math. Assn. Am., Nat. Coun. Tchrs. Math., Textbook Authors Assn., Phi Delta Kappa, Omicron Delta Kappa, Alpha Kappa Alpha. Avocations: music, chess. Home and Office: PO Box 531 Venice FL 34284-0531

SHAW, CAROLE, editor, publisher; b. Bklyn., Jan. 22, 1936; d. Sam and Betty (Neckin) Bergenthal; m. Ray Shaw, Dec. 27, 1957; children: Lori Eve Cohen, Victoria Shaw Locknar. BA, Hunter Coll., 1962. Singer Capitol Records, Hilton Records, Rama Records, Verve Records, 1952-65; TV appearances Ed Sullivan, Steve Allen, Jack Paar, George Gobel Show, 1957; owner The People's Choice, L.A., 1975-79; founder, editor-in-chief Big Beautiful Woman mag., Beverly Hills, Calif., 1979—; creator Carole Shaw and BBW label clothing line for large-size women. Author: Come Out, Come Out Wherever You Are, 1982. Avocations: piano, painting, swimming, travel. Office: BBW Mag PO Box K-298 Tarzana CA 91356

SHAW, CHARLES ALEXANDER, judge; b. Jackson, Tenn., Dec. 31, 1944; s. Alvis and Sarah (Weddle) S.; m. Kathleen Ingram, Aug. 17, 1969; 1 child, Bryan Ingram. BA, Harris Stowe State Coll., 1966; MBA, U. Mo., 1971; JD, Cath. U. Am., 1974. Bar: D.C. 1975, Mo. 1975, U.S. Ct. Appeals (8th and D.C. cirs.) 1975, U.S. Dist. Ct. (ea. dist.) Mo. 1976, U.S. Ct. Appeals (6th and 7th cirs.) 1976. Tchr. St. Louis Pub. Schs., 1966-69, D.C. Pub. Schs., Washington, 1969-71; law clk. U.S. Dept. Justice, Washington, 1972-73; law clk. NLRB, Washington, 1973-74, atty., 1974-76; assoc. Lashly, Caruthers, Theis, Rava & Hamel, St. Louis, 1976-80, asst. U.S. atty., 1980-87; judge Mo. Cir. Ct., St. Louis, 1987-94, asst. presiding judge, 1993-94; judge U.S. Dist. Ct., St. Louis, 1994—; hearing officer Office of the Mayor, Washington, 1973-74; instr. U. Mo., St. Louis, 1980-81. Mem. state bd. dirs. United Negro Coll. Fund, St. Louis, 1979-83; trustee St. Louis Art Mus., 1979-82, 89-93; bd. dirs. Arts and Edn. Coun., 1992-93, Metro Golf Assn. Landmarks Assn., St. Louis, 1980-82. Danforth Found. fellow, 1978-79; Cath. U. Am. scholar, 1971-74. Mem. D.C. Bar Assn., Mo. Bar Assn., Mound City Bar Assn., Bar Assn. Metro. St. Louis, Harris-Stowe State Coll. Alumni Assn. (bd. dirs., Disting. Alumni 1988), Phi Alpha Delta (Svc. award 1973-74). Avocations: golf, tennis. Home: 4426 Westminster Pl Saint Louis MO 63108-1813 Office: 1114 Market St Saint Louis MO 63101-2043

SHAW, CHARLES RAYMOND, journalist; b. Phila., Feb. 2, 1951; s. Charles Raymond Sr. and Dorothy Blanche (Buckman) S.; m. Francine Ruth Pennock, Jan. 14, 1983. BS in Journalism, Temple U., 1972; MS in Journalism, Columbia U., 1973. Staff writer Intelligencer Jour., Lancaster, Pa., 1973-83, asst. news editor, 1983-88, news editor, 1988—. Office: Lancaster Newspapers Inc Intelligencer Jour 8 W King St Lancaster PA 17603-3824

SHAW, DAVID ALLEN, magazine publisher; b. Lafayette, Ind., Oct. 24, 1959; s. Stanley Allen and Patricia (Ford) S.; m. Marjorie E.L. Shaw, Jan. 1, 1982 (div.); m. Rene Sue Redfield, Sept. 26, 1992; 1 child, Gwendolyn Violet. BA with honors, U. Calif., Irvine, 1981; cert., Mgmt. Action Program, 1988; cert. Pub. Mgmt. Inst., Kellogg Grad. Sch. Mgmt., 1989. Mng. editor Brentwood Pub. Corp., L.A., 1981-82, Hester Communications, Irvine, 1982-84; editor east coast HBJ Publs., N.Y.C., 1985-86; dir. market rsch. HBJ Publs., Irvine, 1986-88; pub. Edgell Communications, Irvine, 1988-91; pub. dir. Edgell Communications (name changed to Advanstar Comms., 1992), Irvine, 1991-93; group v.p. Advanstar Comm., Santa Ana, 1993-94, group v.p., 1994—; awards chmn. N.Y. Bus. Press Editors, 1985-86. Contbr. articles to profl. jours. Mem. Am. Bus. Press, World Futurists Soc., Western Publs. Assn. (17 Maggie nominations, 1 Maggie award), Video Software Dealers Assn. Democrat. Avocations: scuba diving, travel,

fishkeeping, writing, editing. Office: Advanstar Comm 201 Sandpointe Ave Ste 600 Santa Ana CA 92707

SHAW, DAVID ELLIOT, financial executive; b. Chgo., Mar. 29, 1951; s. Charles B. Jr. and Marilyn (Baron) S. BA, U. Calif., San Diego, 1972; MS, Stanford U., 1975, PhD, 1980. Pres. Stanford Systems Corp., Palo Alto, Calif., 1976-79; assoc. prof. Columbia U., N.Y.C., 1980-86; v.p. Morgan Stanley & Co., N.Y.C., 1986-88; chmn. D.E. Shaw & Co., N.Y.C., 1988—; contbr. articles to profl. jours. Chmn. N.Y.C. Mayor's Panel on Tech. and Fin., 1987, White House Panel Ednl. Tech., 1995—; mem. N.Y.C. Partnership Subcom. on Tech. and Fin., 1987; appted. Pres.'s com. adv. sci. and tech., 1994—; Mem. Am. Fin. Assn., N. Y. Acad. Scis. (bd. govs. 1993). Democrat. Jewish.

SHAW, DAVID LYLE, journalist, author; b. Dayton, Ohio, Jan. 4, 1943; s. Harry and Lillian (Walton) S.; m. Alice Louise Eck, Apr. 11, 1965 (div. Sept. 1974); m. Ellen Torgerson, July 17, 1979 (dec.); stepchildren: Christopher, Jordan; m. Lucy Stille, Apr. 14, 1988; 1 child, Lucas. BA in English, UCLA, 1965. Reporter Huntington Park Signal (Calif.), 1963-66, Long Beach Independent (Calif.), 1966-68; reporter L.A. Times, 1968-74, media critic, 1974—. Author: WILT: Just Like Any Other 7-Foot, Black Millionaire Who Lives Next Door, 1973, The Levy Caper, 1974, Journalism Today, 1977, Press Watch, 1984; contbr. numerous articles to mags. including Gentlemen's Quar., Esquire, TV Guide, New York. Recipient Mellet Fund Nat. award, 1983, PEN West award, 1990, Calif. Bar Assn. Gold Medallion, 1990, Pulitzer Prize for disting. criticism, 1991. Office: LA Times Times Mirror Sq Los Angeles CA 90012

SHAW, DAVID TAI-KO, electrical and computer engineering educator, university administrator; b. China, Mar. 13, 1938; came to U.S., 1960, naturalized, 1972; m. Katharine Lin-Yee Yang; children: Albert, Stanley. B.S.M.E., Nat. Taiwan U., Taipei, 1959; M.S. in Nuclear Engring., Purdue U., 1961, Ph.D., 1964. Asst. prof. div. interdisciplinary studies and research Sch. Engring., SUNY-Buffalo, 1964-67, assoc. prof. faculty engring. and applied scis., 1967-74, prof. elec. engring. and nuclear engring., aerospace and engring. sci., 1974-77, prof. elec. and computer engring., 1974—, dir. lab. for power and environ. studies, 1978—; exec. dir. N.Y. State Inst. on Superconductivity, 1987—; vis. prof. U. Paris, 1976-77; vis. scientist Centre d'Etudes Nucleairs de Fontenay-aux-Roses (France) Commissariat a L'Energie Atomique, 1976-77; vis. assoc. dept. environ. health engring. Calif. Inst. Tech., 1970-71; mem. U.S. del. French Commissariat a L'energie ATomique, 1974, U.S. del. Joint Nuclear Energy Agy. IAEA Internat. Liaison Group on Thermionic Elec. Power Generation, Paris, 1974; mem. U.S. vis. team USSR Acad. Scis.; Editor: Fundamentals of Aerosol Science, 1978, Recent Developments in Aerosol Science, 1978, Assessment of Airborne Radioactivity, 1978; editor-in-chief: Jour. Aerosol Sci. and Tech., 1982-93; contbr. numerous articles to profl. publs. Mem. IEEE, ASME, AAAS, Am. Assn. Aerosol Rsch. (pres. 1982-85, Assn. award 1984, Internat. Aerosol Fellow award 1994), Am. Nuclear Soc., Air Pollution Control Assn., Assn. Aerosol Rsch. (Germany), Sigma Xi, Sigma Pi Sigma. Office: SUNY-Buffalo NYS Inst Superconductivity 330 Boner Hall Buffalo NY 14260

SHAW, DEAN ALVIN, architect; b. El Paso, Tex., Jan. 22, 1954; s. Harold Alvin and Ann May (Glass) S.; m. Wendy June Hudgens, May 11, 1985; 1 child, Deanna Marie. BArch, Tex. Tech. U., 1979. Registered architect, Tex., Calif. Draftsman J.V. Scoggins Engring., Lubbock, Tex., 1978-79; intern R.S. Colley Architects, Corpus Christi, Tex., 1979-82; intern Campbell Taggart, Inc., Dallas, 1982-83, archtl. sec. leader, 1983, mgr. facilities design, 1983—. Chmn. youth edn. com. Wilshire Bapt. Ch., Dallas, 1990—. Named Best Citizen, Ozona Women's League, 1972, Outstanding Young Am., 1985. Mem. Constrn. Specifications Inst., AIA, Tex. Soc. of Architects, Nat. Coun. Archtl. Registration Bd.. Republican. Baptist. Avocations: photography, gardening, racquetball, softball, tennis. Office: Campbell Taggart Inc 6211 Lemmon Ave Dallas TX 75209-5788

SHAW, DENIS MARTIN, university dean, former geology educator; b. St. Annes, Eng., Aug. 20, 1923; emigrated to Can., 1948; s. Norman Wade and Alice Jane Sylvia (Shackleton) S.; m. Pauline Mitchell, Apr. 6, 1946 (div. 1975); children--Geoffrey, Gillian, Peter; m. Susan L. Evans, Apr. 9, 1976. BA, Emmanuel Coll., Cambridge, Eng., 1943, MA, 1948; Ph.D., U. Chgo., 1951. Lectr. McMaster U., Hamilton, Ont., Can., 1949-51; asst. prof. McMaster U., 1951-55, asso. prof., 1955-60, prof. geology, 1960-89, prof. emeritus, 1989—, chmn. dept., 1953-59, 62-66, dean grad. studies, 1978-84; assoc. prof. Ecole nationale supérieure de géologie appliquée, U. Nancy, France, 1959-60; invited prof. Inst. de Minéralogie, U. Genève, 1966-67. Exec. editor: Geochimica et Cosmochimica Acta, 1970-88; asso. editor: Handbook of Geochemistry, 1966—; Author: Masson Et Cie, 1964. Served with RAF, 1943-46. Fellow Royal Soc. Can. (W.G. Miller medal 1981); mem. Geol. Assn. Can., Geochem. Soc., Mineral. Assn. Can. (pres. 1964, Past Pres.' medal 1985), Am. Geophys. Union, AAAS. Address: McMaster U, Dept Geology, Hamilton, ON Canada L8S 4M1

SHAW, DONALD HARDY, lawyer; b. Oelwein, Iowa, June 1, 1922; s. John Hardy and Minnie (Brown) S.; m. Elizabeth Jean Orr, Aug. 16, 1946; children: Elizabeth Ann, Andrew Hardy, Anthony Orr. B.S., Harvard U., 1942; J.D., U. Iowa, 1948. Bar: Ill. 1949, Iowa 1948; cert. fin. planner 1983. With firm Sidley & Austin, Chgo., 1948-55; with Iowa-Ill. Gas & Electric Co., Davenport, Iowa, 1956-87; treas. Iowa-Ill. Gas & Electric Co., 1960-72, v.p. finance, 1973-87, also dir.; of counsel Walton, Creen, Curry and Robertson, Davenport, Iowa, 1987-88, Newport, Bell & Oxley, Davenport, 1989—. Mem. Iowa State Bd. Regents, 1969-81, Iowa State TV-Radio Com., 1976-81; trustee St. Luke's Hosp., Davenport, 1966-91. Served to capt. USAAF, 1942-45. Recipient Philo Sherman Bennett award, 1942. Mem. Iowa Bar Assn., Rock Island Arsenal Club, Outing Club, Harvard Club N.Y.C., Order of Coif, Delta Thata Phi. Democrat. Congregationalist. Home: 29 Hillcrest Ave Davenport IA 52803-3726 Office: Newport Bell & Oxley 246 W 3rd St Davenport IA 52801-1947

SHAW, DONALD LESLIE, Spanish language educator; b. Manchester, Eng., Feb. 11, 1930; s. Stephen Leslie and Lily (Hughes) S.; m. Maria Concetta Cristini, June 30, 1958; children: Andrew Leslie, Sylvia Maria Pierina. BA, U. Manchester, Eng., 1952, MA, 1953; PhD, U. Dublin, Ireland, 1960. Asst. lectr. U. Dublin, 1955-57; lectr. U. Glasgow, Scotland, 1957-64, U. Edinburgh, Scotland, 1964-69, sr. lectr., 1969-72, reader, prof. Spanish, 1972-86; prof. Spanish, U. Va., Charlottesville, 1986—; vis. prof. Brown U., Providence, 1967, U. Va., Charlottesville, 1983. Author: Historia de la Literatura Española, 1973, La Generación del 98, 1977, Nueva Narrativa Hispanoamericana, 1981, Alejo Carpentier, 1985, Borges' Narrative Strategies, 1992, Antonio Skármeta and the Post-Boom, 1994. Served with RAF, 1953-55. Avocation: cycling. Home: 1800 Jefferson Park Ave Charlottesville VA 22903-3554 Office: U Va 402 Cabell Hall Charlottesville VA 22903

SHAW, DORIS, creative marketing consultant; b. Richmond, Va., Sept. 12, 1921; d. Barnett H. and Cora (Wachsman) Garey; m. Sanford Maizel (div.); 1 child, Liza; m. Leo M. Shaw (div.). BA, Newark Sch. Fine & Indsl. Arts, 1941. Art dir. Frederick Loeser, Bklyn., 1941-49; art dir. Franklin Simon, N.Y.C., 1955-58, creative dir., 1958-61, v.p. sales promotion, 1961-72; v.p. sales promotion Saks Fifth Ave, N.Y.C., 1972-74, sr. v.p., sales promotion, 1974-76; sr. v.p. sales promotion Bloomingdales, 1976-77; editor in chief House Beautiful Mag., N.Y.C., 1977-78; sr. v.p., dir. sales promotion May Co., L.A., 1978-80; sr. v.p., sales promotion dir. Abraham & Straus, Bklyn, 1980-86, exec. v.p., mktg. and communications, 1987-88; creative mktg. cons. Abraham & Straus, Bklyn., 1988—; prin. Shaw Concepts, Palm Desert, Calif., 1989—. Mem. Nat. Retail Merchants Assn. (bd. dirs.), Retail Advt Council (bd. dirs.), The Fashion Group, Inc. (bd. dirs.), Am. Women's Econ. Devel. (bd. dirs.). Avocations: painting, graphic design, music, interior design. Office: Abraham & Strauss 420 Fulton St Brooklyn NY 11201

SHAW, E. CLAY, JR. (CLAY SHAW), congressman; b. Miami, FL, Apr. 19, 1939; s. E. Clay and Rita (Walker) S.; m. Emilie Costar, Aug. 22, 1960; children: Emilie, Jennifer, E. Clay, John C. B.S., Stetson U., 1961, J.D., 1966; M.B.A., U. Ala., 1963. Bar: Fla. 1967; CPA, Fla. Asst. city atty. City of Ft. Lauderdale, 1968, chief city pros., 1968-69, assoc. mcpl. judge, 1969-71, city commr., 1971-73, vice mayor, 1973-74, mayor, 1975-80; mem. 97th-

102nd Congresses from 15th Fla. dist., 1981—; mem. Ways and Means com. 97th-104th Congresses from 15th (now 22nd) Fla. dist.; chmn. Ways and Means subcom. on human resources; U.S. spl. ambassador to Papua New Guinea Independence; pres. U.S. Conf. Republican Mayors; mem. adv. and exec. bd. U.S. Conf. Mayors.; former chmn. mcpl. div. Ft. Lauderdale United Fund Campaign, 1971; former Young Rep. Club Broward County, Ft. Lauderdale Rep. Exec. Com.; past mem. exec. com. Rep. Nat. Com.; former mem. House Selects Com. Narcotics Abuse and Control; past bd. dirs. Broward County Traffic Assn.; mem judiciary com. Pub. Works and Transp. Bd. overseers Stetson Coll. Law. Home: 700 Coral Way Fort Lauderdale FL 33301-2532 Office: US Ho of Reps 2267 Rayburn Washington DC 20515-0922*

SHAW, EDGAR ALBERT GEORGE, research association executive; b. Middlesex, Eng., July 10, 1921; s. Albert and Lily (Hill) S.; m. Millicent Selina Chandler, Oct. 6, 1945; children: Jennifer, Kenneth. Student, U. London, 1938-40; BSc assoc., Royal Coll. Sci., 1948; PhD, Imperial Coll., London, 1950. Tech. officer U.K. Ministry Aircraft Prodn., London, 1940-44, Brit. Air Commn., Washington, 1944-46; asst. NRC, Can., Ottawa, Ont., 1950-53; assoc. NRC, Can., 1953-60, sr. research officer, 1960-74, prin. research officer, 1974-86, researcher emeritus, 1986—, head acoustics sect., 1975-85; Lectr. U. Ottawa, 1958-75; Mem. com. hearing, bioacoustics and biomechanics U.S. Nat. Acad. Scis., 1965—; mem. Internat. Commn. on Acoustics, Internat. Union Pure and Applied Physics, 1972-78, chmn., 1975-78, assoc., 1985-87; co-chmn. Internat. Commn. on the Biol. Effects of Noise, 1988-93, mem.-at-large, 1993—. Contbr. articles to profl. jours. Recipient Rayleigh medal Inst. of Acoustics, 1979. Fellow Acoustical Soc. Am. (councilman 1960-63, v.p. 1968-70, pres. 1973-74), Royal Soc. Can., Inst. Acoustics U.K.; mem. Inst. Physics (Eng.), Canadian Assn. Physicists. Presbyterian. Patentee in field. Home: 1391 Wesmar Dr, Ottawa, ON Canada KIH 7T4 Office: NRC, Inst Microstructural Scis, Ottawa, ON Canada K1A OR6

SHAW, ELEANOR JANE, newspaper editor; b. Columbus, Ohio, Mar. 23, 1949; d. Joseph Cannon and Wanda Jane (Campbell) S. BA, U. Del., 1971. With News-Jour. newspapers, Wilmington, Del., 1970-82, editor HEW desk, asst. met. editor, 1977-80, bus. editor, 1980-82; topics editor USA Today, 1982-83; asst. city editor The Miami Herald, 1983-85; projects editor The Sacramento Bee, 1985-87, news editor, 1987-91, news bus. editor, 1991-93, editor capitol bureau news, 1993—. Bd. dirs. Del. 4-H Found., 1978-83. Mem. Calif. Soc. Newspaper Editors (bd. dirs. 1990—), No. Calif. Wine Soc. (v.p. 1987-93, pres. 1993—). Office: The Sacramento Bee PO Box 15779 Sacramento CA 95852-0779

SHAW, GAYLORD, newspaper executive; b. El Reno, Okla., July 22, 1942; m. Judith Howard, 1960; children: Randall, Kristine, Kelly. Attended, Cameron Coll., 1960-62, U. Okla., 1962-64. Night police reporter Lawton (Okla.) Constitution Press, 1960-62; Okla. City bur. night editor, statehouse correspondent AP, 1962-66, Washington bur. night editor, investigative reporter, spl. assignment team editor, White House correspondent, 1966-75; asst. mng. editor to mng. editor/news Dallas Times Herald, 1981-83; editor-in-chief Shaw Comms. Inc., Charlotte, N.C., 1983-85; correspondent Washington, Denver L.A. Times, 1975-81, correspondent, projects coord. Washington bur., 1985-88; Washington bur. chief Newsday, 1988-95; sr. corr. for projects Newsday, Washington, 1995—. Recipient Pulitzer Prize Nat. Reporting, 1978, Disting. Svc. award for Washington correspondence Sigma Delta Chi/Soc. Profl. Journalists, 1978, Loeb award Disting. Bus. Reporting, 1978, Disting. Reporting award Merriman Smith/White House Correspondents Assn., 1974, Worth Bingham Disting. Reporting award, 1968, Washington Correspondence award Nat. Press Club, 1991. Home: 2815 Otsego Dr Herndon VA 22071-2444 Office: Washington Bureau Newsday Ste 1250 1001 Pennsylvania Ave NW Washington DC 20004-2505

SHAW, GEORGE BERNARD, consulting engineer, educator; b. Dayton, Ohio, Feb. 25, 1940; s. William E. and Edna E. (Hartley) S.; m. Carol M. Crawford, Aug. 6, 1966. A in Mech. Engring., U. Dayton, 1963, BCE, 1967, MSCE, 1971. Diplomate Am. Acad. Environ. Engrs.; registered profl. engr., Ohio, Va., Ind. Ky. Tenn., W.Va., Fla., Kans., Mich., N.C., Mo., Okla., Ill., Tex.; lic. profl. surveyor, Ohio. Asst. to chief engr. Northmont Engrs., Vandalia, Ohio, 1960-66; estimator Oberer Constrn., Dayton, 1966-67; sanitary engr. Alden E. Stilson & Assocs., Columbus, 1967-68; staff cons. Miami Conservancy Dist., Dayton, 1969-71; assoc. prof. civil and environ. engring. U. Dayton, 1967—; pres., CEO Shaw, Weiss & De Naples, Dayton, 1968—; pres., CEO GBS Environ., 1989—; chmn. Panterra Corp., 1990—. Contbr. articles to profl. jours. Mem. NSPE, ASCE, Am. Consulting Engrs. Coun., Soc. Am. Mil. Engrs., Water Environment Fedn., Inter-Am. Assn. Sanitary Engring., City of Dayton Environ. Adv. Bd., Am. Water Works Assn. Avocation: travel. Office: Shaw Weiss & De Naples PC 14 W 1st St Dayton OH 45402-1213

SHAW, GRACE GOODFRIEND (MRS. HERBERT FRANKLIN SHAW), publisher, editor; b. N.Y.C.; d. Henry Bernheim and Jane Elizabeth (Stone) Goodfriend; m. Herbert Franklin Shaw (dec. 1992); 1 son, Brandon Hibbs. Student, Bennington Coll.; BA magna cum laude, Fordham U., 1976, MS, 1991. Reporter Port Chester (N.Y.) Daily Item; editorial coordinator World Scope Ency., N.Y.C.; assoc. editor Clarence L. Barnhart, Inc. Bronxville, N.Y.; freelance-writer for reference books; editing supr. World Pub. Co., mng. editor, sr. editor; mng. editor Peter H. Wyden Co., N.Y.C., 1969-70; assoc. editor Dial Press, N.Y.C., 1971-72; sr. editor Dial Press, 1972, David McKay Co., N.Y.C., 1972-75, Grosset & Dunlap, 1975-79; chief editor Today Press (Grosset), 1977-79; sr. editor, coll. dept. Bobbs-Merrill, N.Y.C., mng. editor, exec. editor trade div., 1979-80; pub. Bobbs-Merrill, 1980-84; mng. editor Rawson Assocs. div. Macmillan Pub., 1985-91; pres. Grace Shaw Assocs., Scarsdale, N.Y., 1991—. Home and Office: 85 Lee Rd Scarsdale NY 10583-5212

SHAW, (FRANCIS) HAROLD, performing arts administrator; b. Hebron, N.Y., June 11, 1923. Student, Ithaca Coll., 1942, Columbia, 1944, N.Y. U. Extension, 1948. Former assoc. Hurok Concerts, Inc., N.Y.C.; chmn., owner Shaw Concerts, Inc., N.Y.C., 1969—; performing arts dir. Seattle World's Fair, 1961-62; former mgr. Nathan Milstein, Vladimir Horowitz, Dame Janet Baker, others; now mgr. Jessye Norman, Helen Donath, Jacqueline duPre, Wolfgang Holzmair, Jard van Nes, Mitsuko Uchida, Garrick Ohlsson, Shura Cherkassky, Horacio Gutiérrez, Julian Bream, John Williams, Elmar Oliveira, Kyoko Takezawa, Robert Shaw, Andrew Davis, and over 100 artists and attractions; exec. dir. President's Shakespeare Ann. Com., 1964. Dir. exec. staff, mem. performing arts com. Cultural Commn., N.Y.C., 1966; nat. chmn. Performing Arts Energy Commn., 1974; chmn. bd. trustees Am. Shakespdare Theatre, Stratford, Conn., 1974. With USAAF, 1942-43. Mem. Internat. Performing Arts Administrs., Am. Symphony Orch. League, Assn. Coll., Univ. and Community Arts Administrs., Actors Equity Assn., Am. Summer Stock Mgrs. Assn. (co-founder), Players Club, Bohemians, N.Y. Athletic Club, Phi Mu Allpha Sinfonia. Office: Shaw Concerts Inc 1900 Broadway 2nd FL New York NY 10023-7004

SHAW, HELEN LESTER ANDERSON, nutrition educator; b. Lexington, Ky., Oct. 18, 1936; d. Walter Southall and Elizabeth (Guyn) Anderson; m. Charles Van Shaw, Mar. 14, 1988. BS, U. Ky., 1958; MS, U. Wis., 1965, PhD, 1969. Registered dietitian. Dietitian Roanoke (Va.) Meml. Hosp., 1959-60, Santa Barbara (Calif.) Cottage Hosp., 1960-61; dietitian, unit mgr. U. Calif., Santa Barbara, 1961-63; rsch. asst., NIH fellow U. Wis., Madison, 1963-68; from asst. prof. to prof. U. Mo., Columbia, 1969-88, assoc. dean, prof., 1977-84; prof., chair dept. food and nutrition U. N.C., Greensboro, 1989-94, dean Sch. Human Environ. Scis., 1994—; cluster leader Food for 21st Century rsch. program U. Mo., 1985-88. Contbr. articles to rsch. publs. Elder 1st Presbyn. Ch., Columbia, 1975-89, Greensboro, 1992-94. Recipient Teaching award Home Econ. Alumni Assn., 1981, Gamma Sigma Delta 1984; rsch. grantee Nutrition Found., 1971-73, NIH, 1972-75, NSF, 1980-83. Mem. Am. Inst. Nutrition, Am. Bd. Nutrition, Am. Soc. for Clin. Nutrition, Am. Dietetic Assn., Am. Family and Consumer Sci. Assn., Soc. for Nutrition Edn., Sigma Xi, Phi Upsilon Omicron, Kappa Omicron Nu. Democrat. Avocations: tennis, barbershop singing.

SHAW, HENRY D., insurance company executive; b. Presque Isle, Maine, Nov. 20, 1933; s. Otis Edwin and Hanna Bera (Tweedie) S.; m. Mary A. Shaw, Nov. 24, 1965; children—Edward, Leslie. B.A., Bowdoin Coll., 1956.

With John Hancock Mut. Life Ins. Co., Boston, 1966—, asst. actuary, 1966-70, assoc. actuary, 1970-76, 2d v.p. actuarial, 1976-81, v.p. actuarial, 1981-82, v.p. underwriting, 1972-73, sr. v.p. underwriting, 1983—. Fellow Soc. Actuaries; mem. Am. Acad. Actuaries, Home Office Life Underwriters Assn., Inst. Home Office Underwriters. Home: 42 Woodridge Rd Wayland MA 01778-3621 Office: John Hancock Mut Life Ins Co PO Box 111 Boston MA 02117-0111

SHAW, HERBERT JOHN, physics educator emeritus; b. Seattle, June 2, 1918; s. Herbert John and Nell Grace (Cayley) S.; m. Francel Harper, Apr. 25, 1943; children: John Joseph, Kathleen, Karen. BA, U. Wash., 1941; MS, Stanford U., 1943, PhD, 1948. Test engr. GE, Schenectady, 1940-41; rsch. assoc. elec. engring. dept. Stanford (Calif.) U., 1948-50, rsch. assoc. Microwave Lab., 1950-57, sr. rsch. assoc., 1957-74, assoc. dir., 1968-77, adj. prof., 1974-83, rsch. prof. applied physics dept., 1983-88, prof. emeritus, 1989—; liaison scientist U.S. Office Naval Rsch., London, 1968-69; cons. to numerous electronics and optics cos. and govt. agys., 1950—. Fellow IEEE (Morris N. Liebmann Meml. award 1976, achievement award group on sonics and ultrasonics 1981); mem. NAE, Tau Beta Pi. Home: 719 Alvarado Row Stanford CA 94305-1037 Office: Stanford U Edward L. Ginzton Lab Stanford CA 94305

SHAW, IAN ALEXANDER, accountant, mining company executive; b. Toronto, Ont., Can., Feb. 28, 1940; m. JoAnne Millyard, Dec. 22, 1967; children: Julia, Martin, Laura. B.Comm., U. Toronto, 1964. Chartered acct. Deloitte Touche & Sells, Toronto, 1964-68; v.p. fin. A.G.F. Mgmt. Ltd., Toronto, 1968-75; treas. Sherritt Gordon Mines Ltd., Toronto, 1975-86; v.p., treas. Curragh Inc., Toronto, 1986-93; CFO Caribgold Resources, Inc., Metallica Resources, Inc. Office: Ste 905 Box 22, 26 Wellington St E, Toronto, ON Canada M5E 1S2

SHAW, JACK ALLEN, communications company executive; b. Auburn, Ind., Jan. 1, 1939; s. Marvin Dale and Vera Lucille (Harter) S.; m. Martha Sue Collins, Aug. 24, 1963; 1 child, Mark Allen. B.S.E.E., Purdue U., 1962, hon. doctorate Capitol Coll., 1994. Project engr. Hughes Aircraft Co., El Segundo, Calif., 1962-69; dir. program mgmt. ITT Space Communications, Ramsey, N.J., 1969-74; v.p., corp. devel. Digital Communications Corp., Gaithersburg, Md., 1974-78, exec. v.p., chief operating officer, Germantown, Md., 1978-81, pres. chief exec. officer, 1981-84, pres., chief exec. officer M/A-com Telecom. divsn., 1984-87; chmn., chief exec. officer Hughes Network Systems Inc., 1988—; chmn. also bd. dirs. 1978—, Hughes Network Systems Inc., Germantown, 1987—; bd. dirs. DCC Ltd., Milton Keyes, Eng., Hughes Software Systems, Pvt. Ltd., New Delhi; sr. v.p., mem. office of chmn. Hughes Electronics. Vice chmn. United Fund Campaign Montgomery County, 1982. Named Disting. Engring. Alumni Purdue U., 1994, Outstanding Electrical Engr. Purdue U., 1994. Mem. IEEE (sr.), Radio Club of Am.(honored 1993). Republican. Clubs: Lakewood Country, Aspen Hill Racquet. Home: 11504 Lake Potomac Dr Potomac MD 20854-1223 Office: Hughes Network Systems Inc 11717 Exploration Ln Germantown MD 20876-2700

SHAW, JAMES, church administrator. Exec. dir. Ministry to the Armed Forces Standing Committee of the Lutheran ChurchMO Synod International Ctr., St. Louis. Office: Lutheran Church 1333 S Kirkwood Rd Saint Louis MO 63122-7295

SHAW, JAMES, computer systems analyst; b. Salt Lake City, June 26, 1944; s. James Irvin and Cleo Lea (Bell) S. Student, San Antonio Coll., 1962-64; BA in History, St. Mary's U., San Antonio, 1966. With VA Automation Ctr., Austin, Tex., 1967—, sr. computer programmer analyst, 1984-87, supervisory computer programmer analyst, 1987-88, computer systems analyst, 1988-94, sr. computer systems analyst, 1994—. Mem. Smithsonian Institution, Planned Parenthood, Met. Mus. Art, Laguna Gloria Art Mus. Mem. Am. Assn. Individual Investors. Democrat. Home: 11500 Jollyville Rd # 1312 Austin TX 78759-4070 Office: VA Automation Ctr 1615 Woodward St Austin TX 78772-0001

SHAW, JAMES HEADON, nutritionist, educator; b. Sharon, Ont., Can., Jan. 1, 1918; came to U.S., 1939, naturalized, 1948; s. Merton and Myrtle (Foord) S.; m. Vera Gwendolyn Chapman, Dec. 18, 1943; children—Sandra Yvonne, James Stephen. BA, McMaster U., Hamilton, Ont., 1939; MS, U. Wis., 1941, PhD, 1943; AM (hon.), Harvard U., 1955. Postdoctoral research fellow U. Wis., 1943-45; mem. faculty Sch. Dental Medicine, Harvard U., 1945-84, prof. nutrition, 1965-84; prof. emeritus Harvard U., 1984—; immin. com. postdoctoral edn. Sch. Dental Medicine, Harvard U. (Sch. Dental Medicine), 1974-85; mem. com. dentistry, med. sci. div. NRC, 1953-62; mem. com. on dietary phosphates and dental caries Food and Nutrition Bd., 1958-63; mem. com. nutrition edn. schs. dentistry Internat. Union Nutritional Scis., 1967-69; panel 1V-2 advanced teaching nutrition White House Conf. Food, Nutrition and Health, 1969; panel to evaluate nat. caries program Nat. Inst. Dental Research, chmn. sub-panel on modifying diet, 1979. Author textbooks; contbr. articles to profl. publs.; asst. editor Nutrition Revs., 1946-49, contbg. editor, 1971-89. Recipient Rsch. Career award Nat. Inst. Dental Rsch., 1964-84; Shenstone scholar McMaster U., 1939, Wis. Rsch. Alumni Found. scholar, 1939-43. Fellow AAAS; mem. ADA (biochemistry test constrn. com. nat. bd. examiners 1964-70), Soc. Exptl. Biology and Medicine (editorial bd. procs. 1969-85), Internat. Assn. Dental Research, Am. Inst. Nutrition, Soc. Nutrition Edn. (charter), Sigma Xi, Omicron Kappa Upsilon (hon.). Office: Countway Libr Medicine Harvard Med Area Countway Libr Medicine Fl 4 Boston MA 02115

SHAW, JEANNE OSBORNE, editor, poet; b. Stone Mountain, Ga., June 1, 1920; d. Virgil Waite and Daisy Hampton (Scruggs) Osborne; m. Harry B. Shaw, Dec. 10, 1982; children: Robert Allan Gibbs, Marilyn Osborne Gibbs Barry. BA, Agnes Scott Coll., 1942. Mem. editorial staff Atlanta Constitution, 1942; feature writer New London (Conn.) Day, 1943; book reviewer Atlanta Constitution, 1940-42, Atlanta Jour., 1945-48; poetry editor Banner Press, Emory U., 1957-59; book editor Georgia Mag., Decatur, 1957-73. Pres., Newton class Druid Hills Bapt. Ch., 1973-74, dir. ch. tng., 1978-79. Recipient Internat. Narrative Poem award Poets and Patrons, Inc., Chgo., 1992, Robert Martin, Burke, Otto, In Praise of Poetry awards N.Y. Poetry Forum, 1973, 79, 81; Westbrook award Ky. Poetry Soc., 1976; Ariz. award, 1981, Ind. State Fedn. of Poetry Clubs award, Ala. State Poetry Soc. award, 1990, Nat. Fedn. State Poetry Socs. Mem. Ga. Writers Assn. (lit. achievement award 1971), Poetry Soc. Ga. (John Clare prize 1955, Katharine H. Strong prize 1975, Eunice Thomson prize 1976, Jimmy Williamson prize 1977, Capt. Frank Spencer prize 1985, 88, Conrad Aiken prize, 1987, 88, Sarah Cunningham prize 1989, 94, Soc. prize 1989, Lucy McEntire prize 1990, 94, Grace Schley Knight prize 1991, 93, Gerald Chan Sieg prize 1991, 95, Eunice Thompson prize 1992, Harriet Ross Colquitt prize 1994), Atlanta Writers Club (pres. 1949-50, named Aurelia Austin Writer of Year in poetry 1971, Wyatt award 1986, Light Verse award 1989, Edward Davin Vickers award, Light Verse award 1990, Daniel Whitehead Hicky award, F. Levering Neely award 1991, Poet Laureate's award 1993), Ga. State Poetry Soc. (Traditional award 1984, Cole and Ledford award 1986, Goreau award, 1987, 93, Melissa Henry award 1989, Charles and Virginia Dickson award 1990, Jo Ann Yeager Adkins award 1991, Poem About Atlanta award 1992, 14th Aniv. Free Verse award 1993), Phi Beta Kappa. Author: The Other Side of the Water (Author of Year in Poetry award Dixie Council of Authors and Journalists), 1970; Unravelling Yarn, 1979; co-author: Noel! Poems of Christmas, 1979; They Continued Steadfastly, History of Druid Hills Baptist Church, 1987; author: Faithbuilders, 1982-84; contbr. poems, pen and ink sketches to mags. Home: 809 Pinetree Dr Decatur GA 30030-2332

SHAW, JEROME, computer executive; b. 1926. BSEE, N.Mex. State U., 1950. V.p., sec. Volt Info. Scis. Inc., N.Y.C., until 1982, exec. v.p., 1982—; also sec., dir. Office: Volt Info Scis Inc 101 Park Ave New York NY 10178-0002

SHAW, JOHN ARTHUR, lawyer; b. San Antonio, June 6, 1922; s. Samuel Arthur and Ellen Agnes (Lawless) S.; m. Margaret Louise Strudell, June 9, 1951; children: John Richard, Barbara Ann, David William. Student, Loyola U., Chgo., 1940-41, U. N.C., 1943-44; LL.B, St. Louis U., 1948, J.D., 1969. Bar: Mo. 1948. Assoc. firm Pollock, Tenney & Dahman, St. Louis, 1948-51; atty. St. Louis Probate Ct., 1951-53; ptnr. firm Pollock, Ward, Klobasa & Shaw, St. Louis, 1953-63; gen. counsel Reliable Life Ins.

Co., Webster Groves, Mo., 1967-83, sr. v.p., 1969-80, sec., 1980-83, dir., 1968-83, also dir., officer, gen. counsel subs. cos., 1967-85. Contbg. author: Basic Estate Planning, 1957; editor: Missouri Probate Law and Practice, 1960. Bd. dirs. sec. Tatman Found., 1967-84; committeeman Boy Scouts Am., 1969-77; bd. dirs. Mo. Ins. Guaranty Assn., 1973-87, sec. 1983-87. Served as lt. AUS, 1943-46, ETO; maj. U.S. Army Res., (ret.). Mem. Mo. Bar, Met. St. Louis Bar Assn., Assn. Life Ins. Counsel, Ret. Officers Assn., Mil. Order of the World Wars, Alpha Sigma Nu, Delta Theta Phi. Club: Town and Country. Home and Office: 306 Luther Ln Saint Louis MO 63122-4647

SHAW, JOHN FIRTH, orchestra administrator; b. Chesterfield, U.K., June 28, 1948; s. Jack Firth and Mary Stuart (MacPherson) S.; m. Julia Valette Phillips, Dec. 29, 1973; children: Mary Valette, Mark Firth, Andrew Nicholas. Licentiate Royal Acad. Music, 1968; grad. Royal Schs. of Music, 1970. Freelance musician, 1966-70; prin. musician Calgary Philharm. Orch., 1970-77, asst. mgr., 1977-78, asst. gen. mgr., 1978-79, gen. mgr.; 1979-93; mng. dir. Hamilton Philharm. Orch. Bd. dirs. Calgary Philharm. Soc., 1974-77, Calgary Centre for Performing Arts, 1980-85, Choral Music Assn. Calgary, 1991-92; mem. adv. com. Mount Royal Coll. Conservatory of Music, 1990-93. Recipient Alta. Achievement award, 1991, Disting. Citizen Calgary award, 1993. Mem. Assn. Can. Orchs. (dir. 1982-84, 86—, pres. 1988-92, dir. 1992—). Home: 52 Markland St, Hamilton, ON Canada L8P 2J7 Office: 25 Main St W, Hamilton, ON Canada L8P 1H1

SHAW, JOHN FREDERICK, retired naval officer; b. Dallas, Oct. 14, 1938; s. John Frederick and Sarah E. (Crouch) S.; m. Janice Muren, July 14, 1962; children: Elizabeth Lee, Suzanne Michele. BS, U.S. Naval Acad., 1960; MS in Mgmt. with distinction, Naval Postgrad. Sch., Monterey, Calif., 1970; grad., Armed Forces Staff Coll., 1971. Commd. ensign USN, 1960, advanced through grades to rear adm., 1983; exec. officer USS Long Beach (CGN 9), 1978-79; comdg. officer USS Bainbridge (CGN 25), 1980-83; dir. guided missile destroyer 51, Arleigh Burke program Comdr. Naval Sea Systems Command, Washington, 1983-85, mgr. AEGIS shipbldg. program, 1985-87; comdr. Cruiser-Destroyer Group One, San Diego, 1987-88; dep. chief staff plans and policy Supreme Allied Comdr., Atlantic, Norfolk, Va., 1988-89, chief staff, 1989-91; ret., 1991; prof. joint mil. ops. Coll. Continuing Edn., Naval War Coll., San Diego, 1992-94; bd. advisors United Svc. Benefit Assn., Kansas City, Kans., 1987-93. Decorated Def. D.S.M., Legion of Merit with two gold stars, Meritorious Svc. medal with gold star, Navy Commendation medal with gold star. Mem. U.S. Naval Inst.(life), U.S. Naval Acad. Alumni Assn. (life, pres. Washington chpt. 1986). Avocations: golf, reading, economics.

SHAW, JOHN MALACH, federal judge; b. Beaumont, Tex., Nov. 14, 1931; s. John Virgil Shaw and Ethel (Malach) Newstadt; m. Glenda Ledoux, Nov. 10, 1970; children: John Lewis, Stacy Shaw Walpole. Student, Tulane U., 1949-50; B.S. with spl. attainments in Commerce, Washington and Lee U., 1953; LL.B., J.D., La. State U., 1956. Bar: La. 1956; U.S. Dist. Ct. (we. dist.) La. 1958, U.S. Ct. Appeals (5th cir.) 1966. Ptnr. firm Lewis and Lewis, Opelousas, La., 1958-79; U.S. dist. judge Western Dist. La., Opelousas, 1979—; now chief judge, 1991—; Govt. appeal agt. Local Bd. 60, La., 1965-72. Mem.: La. Law Rev, 1954-56; asso. editor, 1955-56; author articles, 1954-56. Served with U.S. Army, 1956-58. Recipient Presdl. cert. of appreciation for services as appeal agt. Mem. Fed. Judges Assn., Fifth Cir. Dist. Judges Assn. Democrat. Methodist. Club: Kiwanis. Office: 249 Federal Bldg 705 Jefferson St Lafayette LA 70501-6909

SHAW, JOHN W., lawyer; b. Mo., 1951. BA, U. Mo., 1973, MA, 1973, JD, 1977. Bar: Mo. 1977. Ptnr. Bryan Cave, Kansas City. Mem. ABA, Securities Industry Assn. (legal and compliance group), Mo. Bar, Def. Rsch. Inst. (chmn. firearms litigation subcom.), Order of Coif. Office: Bryan Cave 3300 One Kansas City Pl 1200 Main St Kansas City MO 64105-6914

SHAW, JOSEPH THOMAS, Slavic languages educator; b. Ashland City, Tenn., May 13, 1919; s. George Washington and Ruby Mae (Pace) S.; m. Betty Lee Ray, Oct. 30, 1942; children: David Matthew, Joseph Thomas, James William. A.B., U. Tenn., 1940, A.M., 1941; A.M., Harvard, 1947, Ph.D., 1950. Asst. prof. Slavic langs. Ind. U. 1949-55, assoc. prof., 1955-61; prof. Slavic langs. U. Wis. 1961-89, prof. emeritus, 1989—; chmn. dept. Slavic langs., 1962-68, 77-86, chmn. div. humanities, 1964-65, 72-73, assoc. dean Grad. Sch., 1965-68. Author: The Letters of Alexander Pushkin, 1963, Pushkin's Rhymes: A Dictionary, 1974, Baratynskii: A Dictionary of the Rhymes and a Concordance to the Poetry, 1975, Pushkin: A Concordance to the Poetry, 1985, American Association Teachers Slavic and East European Languages: The First Fifty Years 1941-91, 1991, Pushkin's Poetry of the Unexpected: The Nonrhymed Lines in the Rhymed Poetry and the Rhymed Lines in the Nonrhymed Poetry, 1994; editor: The Slavic and East European Jour, 1957-70; Contbr. articles to profl. jours. Served to capt. USNR, 1942-46, 51-53. Mem. Am. Assn. Tchrs. Slavic and East European Langs. (mem. exec. council 1953-70, 73-80, pres. 1973-74). Home: 4505 Mineral Point Rd Madison WI 53705-5071

SHAW, JULIUS C., carpet manufacturing company executive; b. 1929. Student, Ga. Inst. Tech. Supt. Crown Cotton Mills Inc., 1950-57; with Rocky Creek Mills, 1957-63; v.p., gen. mgr. Dan River Carpets, Danville, Va., 1965-67; pres. Sabre Carpets Inc. (merged into Shaw Industries), Dalton, Ga., 1967—; now chmn., dir. Shaw Industries, Dalton, Ga. Office: Shaw Industries Inc 616 E Walnut Ave Dalton GA 30721-4409

SHAW, (GEORGE) KENDALL, artist, educator; b. New Orleans, Mar. 30, 1924; s. George Kendall and Florence Gladys (Worner) S.; m. Frances Glenn Fort, Oct. 31, 1955. Student, Ga. Inst. Tech., 1944-46; B.S. in Chemistry, Tulane U., 1949, M.F.A. in Painting, 1959; postgrad., La. State U., 1950. instr. Columbia U., 1961-66, Hunter Coll., 1966-68, Parsons Sch. Design, N.Y.C., 1966-86, Lehman Coll., 1968-70, Bklyn. Mus. Art Sch., 1970-76. One-man shows include Columbia U., 1965, Bienville Gallery, New Orleans, 1968, Tibor de Nagy Gallery, N.Y.C., 1964, 65, 67, 68, Southampton Coll., 1969, John Bernard Myers Gallery, 1972, Alessandra Gallery, 1976, Lerner/Heller Gallery, N.Y.C., 1979, 81, 82, Bernice Steinbaum Gallery, N.Y.C., 1991, Artists Space, N.Y.C., 1992; group shows include P.S.I., N.Y.C., 1977, Gladstone-Villani Gallery, N.Y.C., 1978, Galerie Habermann, Cologne, 1979, Modern Art Gallery, Vienna, 1980, Jacksonville Art Mus. (Fla.), 1983, others; represented in permanent collections Peter Ludwig, Aachen, Bklyn. Mus., Albright-Knox Gallery, Buffalo, Mus. Contemporary Art, Nagaoka, Japan, Everson Mus., Syracuse, Chase Manhattan Bank, N.Y.C., Chem. Bank, N.Y.C., N.Y. U., N.Y.C. Served with USN, 1943-46. Mem. Coll. Art Assn., Artists Equity Assn. Democrat. Address: 458 Broome St New York NY 10013-2611

SHAW, KENNETH ALAN, university president; b. Granite City, Ill., Jan. 31, 1939; s. Kenneth W. and Clara H. (Lange) S.; m. Mary Ann Byrne, Aug. 18, 1962; children: Kenneth William, Susan Lynn, Sara Ann. BS, Ill. State U., 1961, DHL, 1987; EdM, U. Ill., 1963; PhD, Purdue U., 1966, EdD (hon.), 1990; DHL, Towson State, 1979, Ill. Coll., 1986. Tchr. history, counselor Rich Twp. High Sch., Park Forest, Ill., 1961-63; residence hall dir., instr. edn. Ill. State U., 1963-64; counselor Office Dean of Men, Purdue U., 1964-65, Office Dean of Men, Purdue U. (Office Student Loans), 1965-66; asst. to pres., lectr. sociology Ill. State U., 1966-69; v.p. acad. affair, dean Towson State U., Balt., 1969-76; pres. So. Ill. U., Edwardsville, 1977-79; chancellor So. Ill. U. System, Edwardsville, 1979-86; pres. U. Wis. System, Madison, 1986-91; chancellor Syracuse U., 1991—. Trustee CICU, Albany, N.Y., 1993—, Am. Coll. Testing, 1990—; bd. dirs. Unity Mutual Life Ins. Co., 1992—, Golden Key Nat. Honor Soc., 1992—, Syracuse (N.Y.) C. of C., 1991—, Met. Devel. Assn., 1991—; mem. adv. bd. U.S. Peace Corps. recipient Young Leader in Edn. award, 1980, Citizen of Yr. award, So. Ill. Inc., 1985, Silver Anniversary award NCAA, 1986, Coaches Silver Anniversary award Nat. Assn. of Basketball, 1986; named to Ill. Basketball Hall of Fame, 1983. Mem. Am. Assn. State Colls. and Univs. (external refs. com. 1986-88), Am. Coun. Edn. (com. on minorities in higher edn. 1987-91), Am. Social. Assn., Am. Higher Edn. Assn., State Higher Edn. Exec. Officers Assn., Phi Delta Kappa, Pi Gamma Mu. Office: Syracuse U Syracuse NY 13244-1100

SHAW, L. EDWARD, JR., lawyer; b. Elmira, N.Y., July 30, 1944; s. L. Edward and Virginia Anne (O'Leary) S.; m. Irene Ryan; children—Christopher, Hope, Hillary, Julia, Rory. B.A. in Econs., Georgetown U., Washington, 1966; J.D., Yale U., New Haven, 1969. Bar: N.Y. 1969. Assoc. Milbank, Tweed, Hadley & McCloy, N.Y.C., 1969-77, ptnr., 1977-83; sr. v.p., gen. counsel Chase Manhattan Corp., N.Y.C., 1983-85, exec. v.p., gen counsel, 1985—. Mem. Assn. Bar City N.Y., Winged Foot Golf Club, Phi Beta Kappa. Roman Catholic. Avocations: youth athletics; golf. Office: Chase Manhattan Corp 1 Chase Manhattan Plz 29th Fl New York NY 10081-0001*

SHAW, LEANDER JERRY, JR., state supreme court justice; b. Salem, Va., Sept. 6, 1930; s. Leander J. and Margaret S.; m. Vidya B. Lye. BA, W.Va. State Coll., 1952, LLD (hon.), 1986; JD, Howard U., 1957; PhD (hon.) in Pub. Affairs, Fla. Internat. U., 1990; LLD (hon.), Nova Law Sch. 1991, Washington & Lee Law Sch., 1991. Asst. prof. law Fla. A&M U., 1957-60; sole practice Jacksonville, Fla., 1960-69, 72-74; asst. pub. defender Fla., 1965-69; asst. state's atty. Fla., 1969-72; judge Fla. Indsl. Relations Commn., 1974-79, Fla. Ct. Appeals (1st dist.), 1979-83; justice Fla. Supreme Ct., Tallahassee, 1983—, chief justice, 1990-92. Office: Fla Supreme Ct Supreme Ct Bldg Tallahassee FL 32399

SHAW, LEONARD GLAZER, electrical engineering educator, consultant; b. Toledo, Aug. 15, 1934; s. A. Daniel and Mary (Glazer) S.; m. Susan Gail Weil, Dec. 24, 1961; children: Howard Benjamin, Mitchell Bruce, Jenny Louise. BSEE, U. Pa., 1956; MSEE, Stanford U., 1957, PhD, 1961. From asst. prof. to assoc. prof. Polytech. U., N.Y., Bklyn., 1960-1975, prof., 1975—, head dept. elec. engring. and computer sci., 1982-90, dean sch. elec. engring. and computer sci., 1990-94; vice provost for undergraduate studies, 1995—. vis. prof. Tech. U., Eindhoven, Netherlands, 1970, Ecole Nationale Superieure de Mecanique, Nantes, France, 1977; cons. Sperry Systems Mgmt. Div., Great Neck, N.Y.; mem. grant rev. panels NSF, 1986—. Author: (with others) Signal Processing, 1975. Contbr. articles to profl. jours. Research grantee NSF, 1973, 81. Fellow IEEE (various coms., editorial bd. 1961-92, editor-in-chief, IEEE Press 1988-93, gen. chmn. Conf. on Decision and Control, Dec. 1989, v.p. Fin. Control System Soc., 1992-93; mem. AAAS, Am. Soc. for Engring. Edn. Office: Polytech U Jacobs Coll Engring & Sci 6 Metrotech Ctr Brooklyn NY 11201-2990

SHAW, LILLIE MARIE KING, vocalist; b. Indpls., Nov. 27, 1915; d. Earl William and Bertha Louise (Groth) King; m. Philip Harlow Shaw, June 26, 1940. Student, Jordan Conservatory Music, Indpls., 1940-43; BA, Ariz. State U., 1959; MA, Denver U., 1962; pvt. vocal study, 1944-70. Educator, libr. Glendale (Ariz.) Schs., 1959-67; lectr. libr. sci. Ariz. State U., Tempe, 1962-68. Concertizing, oratorio, symphonic soloist, light opera, 1965-82; soloist First Ch. of Christ Scientist, Sun City West, Ariz., 1980—. Monthly lectr. Christian Women's Fellowship, Phoenix, 1989—; World Conf. del. Soc. of Friends, 1967. Mem. Nat. Soc. Arts and Letters (sec. 1990-94, nat. del. 1992), Am. Philatelic Assn. (life), Am. Topical Assn., Phoenix Philatelic Soc., Auditions Guild Ariz. (sec. 1989-92), Phoenix Opera League, Phoenix Symphony Guild (bd. mem. youth activities 1986—), Sigma Alpha Iota Alumnae (Phoenix chpt., life, treas. 1988-94, Sword of Honor 1972, Rose of Honor 1982, Rose of Dedication 1995). Republican. Avocations: philately, gardening. Home: 6802 N 37th Ave Phoenix AZ 85019-1103

SHAW, MARGERY WAYNE SCHLAMP, geneticist, physician, lawyer; b. Evansville, Ind., Feb. 15, 1923; d. Arthur George and Louise (Meyer) Schlamp; m. Charles Raymond Shaw, May 31, 1942 (div. Nov. 1972); 1 dau., Barbara Rae. Student, Hanover Coll., 1940-41; A.B. magna cum laude, U. Ala., 1945; M.A., Columbia U., 1946; postgrad., Cornell U., 1947-48; M.D. cum laude, U. Mich., 1957; J.D., U. Houston, 1973; D.Sc. (hon.), U. Evansville, 1977, U. So. Ind., 1986. Intern St. Joseph Mercy Hosp., Ann Arbor, Mich., 1957-58; practice medicine specializing in human genetics Ann Arbor, 1958-67; instr. dept. human genetics Med. Sch. U. Mich., 1958-61, asst. prof., 1961-66, assoc. prof., 1966-67; assoc. prof. dept. biology Grad. Sch. Biomed. Scis., U. Tex., Houston, 1967-69; prof. Grad. Sch. Biomed. Scis., U. Tex., 1969-88, dir. Med. Genetics Ctr., 1971-83, acting dean, 1976-78, prof. emeritus, 1988—; mem. genetics study sect. NIH, Bethesda, Md., 1966-70 mem. genetics tng. com., 1970-74, adv. com. to dir., 1979-82; chromosome studies astronauts NASA, 1970-71; mem. med. adv. bd. Nat. Genetics Found., 1972-88; rsch. adv. bd. Planned Parenthood, Houston, 1972-79; vis. scholar Yale Law Sch., 1974; Andrew D. White prof.-at-large Cornell U., 1982-88; vis. prof. U. Utah, 1983; adj. prof. U. Houston Law Ctr., 1988-89. Asso. editor: Am. Jour. Human Genetics, 1962-68; editorial bd.: Am. Jour. Med. Genetics, 1977-87, Am. Jour. Law and Medicine, 1977-88; contbr. articles to profl. jours. First aid instr. ARC, 1962-67; unit chmn. United Fund, 1966. Recipient Billings Silver medal AMA, 1966; Achievement award AAUW, 1970-71; Am. Jurisprudence award, 1973. Mem. Am. Soc. Human Genetics (past sec., dir., pres. 1982), Genetics Soc. Am. (sec. 1971-73, pres. 1977-78, Wilhelmene Key award 1977), Tissue Culture Assn. (trustee 1970-72), Environ. Mutagen Soc. (coun.), Am. Soc. Cell Biology, Am. Soc. Law Medicine (trustee 1980-88), Phi Beta Kappa, Alpha Omega Alpha. Home: 2617 Pine Tree Dr Evansville IN 47711-2117

SHAW, MARI GURSKY, lawyer; b. Chgo., 1947. BA, U. Ill., 1969; JD, U. Wis., 1973. Bar: Wis. 1973, Pa. 1973. Ptnr. Dechert Price & Rhoads, Phila.; chmn. Wilma Theater, 1991-93; chmn. adv. bd. Paly-Levy Gallery, Moore Coll. of Art, 1993—. Office: Dechert Price & Rhoads 4000 Bell Atlantic Tower 1717 Arch St Philadelphia PA 19103-2793

SHAW, MARY M., computer science educator; b. Washington, Sept. 30, 1943; d. Eldon Earl and Mary Lewis (Holman) Shaw; m. Roy R. Weil, Feb. 15, 1973. BA cum laude, Rice U., 1965; PhD, Carnegie Mellon U., Pitts., 1972. Asst. prof. to prof. computer sci. Carnegie Mellon U., Pitts., 1972—, assoc. dean computer sci. for profl. programs, 1992—, Alan J. Perlis chair computer sci.; chief scientist Software Engring. Inst., Carnegie Mellon U., Pitts., 1984-88; mem. Computer Sci. and Telecommunications Bd., NRC, Washington, 1986-93. Author: Fundamental Structures of Computer Science, 1981, The Carnegie Mellon Curriculum for Undergraduate Computer Science, 1985; contbr. articles to profl. jours. Recipient Warnier prize, 1993; named Woman of Achievement, YWCA of Greater Pitts., 1973. Fellow AAAS, IEEE (disting. lectr.); mem. Assn. for Computing Machinery (SIGPLAN exec. com. 1979-83, Recognition of Svc. award 1985 90), Sigma Xi. Office: Carnegie Mellon U Dept Computer Sci Pittsburgh PA 15213

SHAW, MELVIN PHILLIP, physicist, engineering educator, psychologist; b. Bklyn., Aug. 16, 1936; s. Harry and Yetta (Stutsky) S.; m. Carol Joan Phillips, Sept. 5, 1959 (div. Feb. 1987); children: Adam, Evan; m. Bernetta Berger, May 16, 1987. BS, Bklyn. Coll., 1959; MS, Case Western Res. U., 1963, PhD, 1965; MA, Ctr. for Humanistic Studies, 1988. Research scientist United Techs. Research Labs., E. Hartford, Conn., 1964-68, scientist-in-charge, 1966-70; prof. Wayne State U., Detroit, 1970—; adminstrv. dir. Assocs. of Birmingham/Kingswood Hosp., 1991-93; cons. Energy Conversion Devices, Troy, Mich., 1970-92. Co-author: The Gunn-Hilsum Effect, 1979, The Physics and Applications of Amorphous Semiconductors, 1988, The Physics of Instabilities in Solid State Electron Devices, 1992, Creativity and Affect, 1994. Fellow Am. Phys. Soc.; mem. IEEE (sr.), Am. Psychol. Assn. (assoc.). Avocations: cooking, walking, travel.

SHAW, MICHAEL, biologist, educator; b. Barbados, W.I., Feb. 11, 1924; s. Anthony and Myra (Perkins) S.; m. Jean Norah Berkinshaw, Oct. 16, 1948; children—Christopher A., Rosemary E., Nicholas R., and Barbara H. B. Sc., McGill U., 1946, M. Sc., 1947, Ph.D., 1949, D.Sc., 1975. Nat. Research Council Can. postdoctoral fellow Botany Sch., Cambridge U., 1949-50; Assoc. prof. biology U. Sask., 1950-54, prof., 1954-67, prof., head dept. biology, 1961-67; dean faculty agrl. sci., U. B.C., 1967-75, v.p. acad. devel., 1975-81, acad. v.p., provost 1981-83, univ. prof., 1983-89, univ. prof. emeritus, 1989—; mem. Sci. Council Can., 1976-82, Natural Scis. and Engring. Research Council Can., 1978-80. Contbr. articles to profl. jours. Recipient Queen's Silver Jubilee medal, 1977, gold medal Biol. Coun. Can., 1983. Fellow Royal Soc. Can. (Flavelle medal 1976), Can. Phytopath. Soc., Am. Phytopath. Soc., N.Y. Acad. Scis.; mem. Can. Bot. Assn., Can. Soc. Plant Physiologists (gold medal 1971), Am. Soc. Plant Physiologists. Home: 1792 Western Pky, Vancouver, BC Canada V6T 1V3 Office: U BC, Dept Plant Sci, Vancouver, BC Canada V6T 1Z4

SHAW, MICHAEL ALLAN, lawyer, mail order company executive; b. Evanston, Ill., July 14, 1940; s. Frank C. and Mabel I. (Peacock) S.; m. Genevieve Schrodt, Aug. 16, 1964; children: M. Ian, Trevor A. BA, Colo. State U., 1962; JD, U. Denver, 1965; MBA, DePaul U., 1969; postgrad., Columbia U., 1970. Bar: Ill. bar 1965. Practiced in Chgo., 1965-83; asst. counsel, staff asst. to v.p. traffic Jewel Cos., Inc., Melrose Park, Ill., 1965-71; corp. sec., asst. treas., house counsel Wieboldt Stores, Inc., Chgo., 1972-83; pvt. practice law Naperville, Ill., 1983-89; pres. Kingston Korner, Inc., Naperville, Ill., 1983—, Aztec Corp., Naperville, Ill., 1989—. Pres. Folk Era Prodns., producers folk music concert series, records, 1985—; editor Folk Music Editor, 1984; contbr. articles to legal jours. Mem. Village Planning Commn., Itasca, Ill., 1973-77; bd. dirs. Crimestoppers, Naperville, 1984—, chmn., 1988-94; session mem. Naperville Lumen Christi United Presbyn. Ch., 1984-85; chmn. bldg. fin. com. Naperville Presbyn. Ch., 1989-93. Mem. Fox Valley Folklore Soc. (bd. dirs. 1991—). Home: 6 S 230 Cohasset Rd Naperville IL 60540 Office: Aztec Corp 705 S Washington St Naperville IL 60540-6654

SHAW, MILTON CLAYTON, mechanical engineering educator; b. Phila., May 27, 1915; s. Milton Fredic and Nellie Edith (Clayton) S.; m. Mary Jane Greeninger, Sept. 6, 1939; children—Barbara Jane, Milton Stanley. B.S. in Mech. Engring., Drexel Inst. Tech., 1938; M.Eng. Sci., U. Cin., 1940, Sc.D., 1942; Dr. h.c., U. Louvain, Belgium, 1970. Research engr. Cin. Milling Machine Co., 1938-42; chief materials br. NACA, 1942-46; with Mass. Inst. Tech., 1946-61, prof. mech. engring., 1953-61, head materials processing div., 1952-61; prof., head dept. mech. engring. Carnegie Inst. Tech., Pitts., 1961-75; univ. prof. Carnegie Inst. Tech., 1974-77; prof. engring. Ariz. State U., Tempe, 1977—; Cons. indsl. cos.; lectr. in Europe, 1952; pres. Shaw Smith & Assos., Inc., Mass., 1951-61; Lucas prof. Birmingham (Eng.) U., 1961; Springer prof. U. Calif. at Berkeley, 1972; Distinguished guest prof. Ariz. State U., 1977; mem. Nat. Materials Adv. Bd., 1971-74; bd. dirs. Engring. Found., 1976, v.p. conf. com., 1976-78. Recipient Outstanding Research award Ariz. State U., 1981; Am. Machinist award, 1972; P. McKenna award, 1975; Guggenheim fellow, 1956; Fulbright lectr. Aachen T.H., Germany, 1957; OECD fellow to Europe, 1964—. Fellow Am. Acad. Arts and Scis., ASME (Hersey award 1967, Thurston lectr. 1971, Outstanding Engring. award 1975, ann. meeting theme organizer 1977, Gold medal 1985, hon. 1980), Am. Soc. Lubrication Engrs. (hon., nat. award 1964), Am. Soc. Metals (Wilson award 1971, fellow 1981); mem. Internat. Soc. Prodn. Engring. Research (pres. 1960-61, hon. mem. 1975), Am. Soc. for Engring. Edn. (G. Westinghouse award 1956), Soc. Mfg. Engrs. (hon. mem. 1970, Gold medal 1958, internat. edn. award 1980), Nat. Acad. Engring., Polish Acad. Sci., Am. Soc. Precision Engrs. (hon.). Home: 2625 E Southern Ave C 119 Tempe AZ 85282-7633 Address: Arizona State Univ Tempe AZ 85287-6106

SHAW, MILTON HERBERT, conglomerate executive; b. Phila., June 16, 1918; s. Milton Herbert and Ethel (Shane) S.; m. Rita P. Revins, Nov. 24, 1971. BS, U. Pa., 1949. cons. indsl. safety and workmen's compensation. Accountant Franklin Sugar Refinery, Phila., 1945-52; with Kaiser Metal Products, Inc., Bristol, Pa., 1952-61; mgr. ins. and taxes Kaiser Metal Products, Inc., 1955-61; with Kidde Consumer Durables Corp., Bala Cynwyd, Pa., 1961-88; asst. v.p. Kidde Consumer Durables Corp., 1968-88, dir. corp. svcs. and risk mgmt., 1977-88; cons. Indsl. Safety-Workmans Compensation, 1988; owner Golden Grain Goldens; co-owner Potpourri Promotions, Rita P. Shaw Porcelain Studio. Served with USNR, 1936-45. Mem.NRA, VFW, Nat. Wildlife Fedn., Sigma Kappa Phi. Home and Office: 2209 Blackhorse Dr Warrington PA 18976-2118

SHAW, MONTGOMERY THROOP, chemical engineering educator; b. Ithaca, N.Y., Sept. 11, 1943; s. Robert William and Charlotte (Throop) S.; m. Stephanie Habel, Sept. 5, 1966 (dec. 1989); 1 child, Steven Robert; m. Maripaz Nespral,June 25, 1994. BChemE, Cornell U., 1966, MS, 1966; MS, Princeton (N.J.) U., 1968, PhD, 1970. Engr., project scientist Union Carbide Corp., Bound Brook, N.J., 1970-76; assoc. prof. Dept. Chem. Engring., U. Conn., Storrs, 1973, prof.; 1983—; sabbatical prof. Sandia Nat. Labs., Albuquerque, 1983-84; adv. bd. Jour. of Applied Polymer Sci., 1984-89; vis. scientist DuPont Control Rsch., 1992-93. Co-author: Polymer-Polymer Miscibility, 1977, Computer Programs for Rheologists, 1994. Grantee Alcoa Found., 1985, Exxon Edn. Found., 1986. Mem. IEEE (assoc. editor transactions on elec. insulation), Soc. Rheology (sec. 1977-81), Am. Chem. Soc., Am. Phys. Soc. Achievements include patents on rheological measurement method and apparatus and low density microcellular foams. Office: U Conn IMS 97 S Eaglevile Rd Storrs Mansfield CT 06268-2502

SHAW, NANCY RIVARD, museum curator, art historian, educator; b. Saginaw, Mich.; d. Joseph H. and Jean M. (O'Boyle) Marcotte; m. Danny W. Shaw, Feb. 29, 1980; 1 stepchild, Christina Marie. BA magna cum laude, Oakland U., 1969; MA, Wayne State U., 1973. Asst. curator Am. art Detroit Inst. Arts, 1972-75, curator, 1975—; adj. prof. art and art history Wayne State U., Detroit, 1991—. Contbg. author: American Art in the Detroit Institute of Arts, 1991; contbr. articles to exhbn. catalogues and profl. jours. Mem. Wayne State U. Alumni Assn. Roman Catholic. Avocations: knitting, painting, golf. Office: Detroit Inst Arts 5200 Woodward Ave Detroit MI 48202-4094

SHAW, SIR NEIL MCGOWAN, sugar, cereal and starch refining company executive; b. Montreal, Que., Can., May 31, 1929; s. Harold LeRoy and Fabiola Marie (McGowan) S.; m. Frances Audrey Robinson, July 6, 1952; children: David, Michael, Cynthia, Andrea, Sonia; m. 2nd Elizabeth Mudge Massey, Sept. 15, 1985. Student, Lower Coll. Chmn., chief exec. Tate & Lyle plc, London, 1986-92, chmn., 1992-93, exec. chmn., 1993—; vice chmn. Redpath Industries Ltd., Toronto, 1981; bd. dirs. United Biscuits Holdings, plc, U.K., Alcantara, Portugal, Americare Corp., Toronto, 1983, World Sugar Rsch. Org., U.K., 1982, G.R. Amylum N.V., Belguim, 1982; vice chmn. A.E. Staley Mfg. Co., Decatur, 1988-91, dir., 1991—; bd. dirs. Can. Imperial Bank of Commerce, Toronto, Tate & Lyle Mgmt. and Fin. Ltd., Bermuda, Tunnel Refineries, London, M & G Investment Income Trust, Inst. of Dirs., mem. adv. com., 1991; chmn. Assn. of Lloyds Members, 1991-94, Tate & Lyle Holdings, London, 1981-91 ; mem. adv. coun. Prince's Youth Bus. Trust, 1990—; chmn. World Sugar Rsch. Orgn., 1994. Gov. Reddy Meml. Hosp., Montreal Gen. Hosp., World Econ. Forum, World Food Argo Forum; mem. adv. coun. Youth Enterprise Scheme, 1986; chmn. Anglo Can. Support Group Care, 1989; mem. Can. Meml. Found., 1989; mem. adv. coun. London Enterprise Agy., 1986; chmn. Bus. in Community, 1991-94; trustee Royal Botanic Gardens Kew Found., 1990—, chmn. Trustees and Friends Royal Botanic Gardens Kew, 1994; dir. Theatre Royal Windsor, 1991—. Named Knight Bachelor; honored at Queen of Eng. Birthday, 1994. Fellow Inst. Grocery Distbn.; mem. Food Assn. Can. Univs. Soc. Gt. Britain (adv. coun. 1989), Brit. N.Am. Com., Ptnrs. of the World, Brit. Inst. Mgmt. (companion 1981), Home-Start Consultancy (v.p.) Toronto Golf Club, Brooks Club, Toronto Club, Wentworth Golf Club, Taymouth Estate Golf Club (Scotland), Per Cent Club (joint chmn.). Avocations: skiing, golf, sailing. Office: Tate & Lyle PLC, Sugar Quay Lower Thames St, London EC3R 6DQ, England

SHAW, RANDALL FRANCIS, state legislator; b. Concord, N.H., Sept. 5, 1931; s. Joseph F. and Irma A. (Randall) S.; m. Margaret J. Geary, Dec. 23, 1942; children: Randall J., Joel T. BS, Franklin Pierce Coll., Rindge, N.H., 1983. Supervising field auditor U.S. PFO, Concord, 1965-75, supervising computer specialist, 1975-85; asst. U.S. Property and Fiscal Office, Concord, 1985-90; mem. N.H. Ho. of Reps., Concord, 1990—. Mem. N.H. Republican Com., Concord, 1994, Merrimack County Exec. Com., Concord, 1994. Served to lt. col. U.S. Army Res., 1954-86. Mem. Res. Officers Assn., Am. Legion, Masons. Home: 425 Deerpath Ln Pembroke NH 03275 Office: State Legislature State House Concord NH 03301

SHAW, RICHARD, artist; b. Hollywood, Calif., Sept. 12, 1941; s. Richard Blake and Catherine (Dexter) S.; m. Martha Helen Hall, Apr. 24, 1965; children: Alice, Virgil, Dexter, Whitney, Kate. Student, Orange Coast Coll., Costa Mesa, Calif., 1961-63; B.F.A., San Francisco Art Inst., 1965; postgrad., U. Calif., Davis, 1967-68. Instr. ceramics U. Calif., Berkeley, 1970, asst. prof. ceramics, 1987—; Instr. ceramics U. Wis., 1971. Exhibited in oneman shows, San Francisco Art Inst., 1967, Dilexi Gallery, San Francisco 1968, Quay Gallery, San Francisco, 1970, 71, 73, 75, E.G. Gallery, Kansas City, Mo., 1974, Braunstein/Quay Gallery, 1979, 81, 84, 86, 88, 90, 94, Michael Berger Gallery, Pitts., 1979, Alan Frumkin Gallery, 1970, 80, 86,

88, Newport Harbor Art Mus., Newport Beach, Calif., 1981, San Jose (Calif.) Mus. Art, 1981, Boise Gallery Art, 1982, Mendell Art Gallery, Can. 1982, Greenberg Gallery, St. Louis, 1982, Madison Art Ctr., 1982, Alta. (Can.) Coll. Art, 1982, Morgan Gallery, Kansas City, 1984, Asher/Faure Gallery, Los Angeles, 1985, Art Mus. of S. Tex., Corpus Christi, 1986, Huntsville Mus., Ala., 1986, Everson Mus. Art, Syracuse, N.Y., 1986, Tucson Mus. Art, 1986, Asher/Faure, Los Angeles, 1985, Scottsdale (Ariz.) Ctr. for Arts, 1986, Huntsville (Ala.) Mus. Art, 1986, Honolulu Contemporary Art. Ctr., 1987, Palm Springs Desert Mus., Calif., 1987, Tucson Mus. Art, 1987, Bergstrom-Mahler Mus., Neenah, Wis., 1987, Grand Rapids Art Mus., Mich., 1987, Foster/White Gallery, Seattle, 1987, Sierra Nev. Mus. Art, Reno, 1988, Univ. of Pacific, Stockton, Calif., 1988, U. Wis., Kenosha, 1989, Thomas Segal Gallery, Boston, 1989, Schneider Art Mus., 1990, 93, Braunstein Quay Gallery, 1990, 93, Palo Alto Cultural Ctr., 1990, Frumkin-Adams Gallery N.Y.C., 1990, Fullerton Mus. Ctr., Calif., 1990, 92, Helander Gallery, Palm Beach, Fla., 1992, Perimeter Gallery, Chgo., 1995; exhibited in group shows, Mus. Contemporary Crafts, N.Y.C., 1965, 66, 70, 71, Boston Soc. Arts and Crafts, 1966, Mus. West of Am. Craftsman's Council, San Francisco, 1966, Scripps Coll., Claremont, Calif., 1967, U. Sask., 1968, Smithsonian Instn., 1969, 76, San Francisco Art Inst., 1969, 71, 83, Oakland Mus., 1970, 79, 84, 85, 94, Bklyn. Mus., 1970, Whitney Mus. Am. Art, N,Y.C., 1970, 74, 76, 80, 81, USIA, 1972, Nat. Mus. Modern Art, Tokyo and Kyoto, 1971-72, U. Miami, Coral Gables, Fla., 1972, Evanston (Ill.) Art Center, 1972, 74, Victoria and Albert Mus., London, 1972, Calif. State U., Hayward, 1972, Stanford U. Art Gallery, 1972, San Francisco Mus. Art, 1972, 74, 82, David Stuart Gallery, Los Angeles, 1972, Emerson Mus. Art, Syracuse, N.Y., 1972, Sch. Arts and Crafts Soc., Portland, Oreg., 1973, 74, Kohler Art Center, Sheboygan, Wis., 1973, Balt. Mus. Art, 1974, Krannert Art Mus., Champaign, Ill., 1974, Phila. Coll. Art, 1974, Fendrick Gallery, Washington, 1975, Carborundum Mus., Niagara Falls, N.Y., 1975, San Diego Mus., 1975-80, U. Tex., Arlington, 1976, Campbell Mus., 1976, Contemporary Crafts Mus., 1976, Art Gallery U. Calif., Santa Barbara, 1976, Hopkins Art Center, Dartmouth, 1976-77, San Francisco Mus. Modern Art, 1976, Nat. Gallery Art, Washington, 1976, U. Calif., Fullerton, 1976, Laguna Beach (Calif.) Mus. Art, 1977, DeYoung Downtown Center, San Francisco, 1977, U. N.C., Chapel Hill, 1977, Grossmont Coll. Art Gallery, 1977, No. Ill. Art Gallery, DeKalb, Ill., 1977, Renwick Gallery, Washington, 1980-83, Iowa Mus. Art, U. Iowa, Iowa City, 1981, Am. Crafts Mus., N.Y.C., 1981, The Taft Mus., Ohio, 1983, Galerie Alain Blondel, Paris, 1983, Contemporary Arts Mus., Houston, 1983, Marcia Rodell Gallery, Los Angeles, 1983, U.S.A. Today Exhbn., Washington, 1983, Boise Gallery Art, 1983, Clay Studio, Phila., 1983, Heath Gallery, Atlanta, 1984, Santa Barbara Mus., 1984, Mus. Fine Arts, Boston, 1984, TransAm. Pyramid, San Francisco, 1985, San Francisco Mus. Art, 1984, Oakland Mus. Art, 1984, Mus. Fine Arts, Boston, 1984, 85, Esther Saks Gallery, Chgo., 1985, Columbus (Ohio) Mus. At, Marsha Mateyka Gallery, Washington, 1986, Los Angeles Mcpl. Art and Gallery, 1986, Am. Craft Mus., N.Y., 1986, Everson Mus., Syracuse , N.Y., 1987, Mus. Ceramica, Barcelona, Spain, 1987, Frumkin/Adams Gallery, N.Y., 1988, Philbrook Mus. Art, Tulsa, 1988, San Francisco Craft & Folk Art Mus., 1988, John Kohler Art Ctr., Wis., 1989, Braunstein/Quay Gallery Calif., 1990, 93, John Natsoulas Gallery, Calif., 1990, Coll. of North Calif. Art Redding Mus., 1991, Riverside Mus., Calif., 1991, Fine Arts Gallery U. Nevada, 1991, Howard Yezerski Gallery, Boston, 1991, Craft and Folk Art Mus., 1992, Joanne Rapp Gallery, Scottsdale, Ariz., 1994, San Francisco Art Inst., Curators Forum, Charlotte, N.C., numerous others; rep. permanent collections at, Oakland Mus., San Francisco Mus. Art, John Michael Kohler Arts Ctr., Sheboygan, Wis., Nat. Mus. Art, Tokyo, Levi-Strauss Co., San Francisco, Utah Mus. Fine Arts, Salt Lake City, Stedelijk Mus., Gemeentemusea, Amsterdam. Chmn. artists com. San Francisco Art Inst. Recipient Nat. Endowment Arts grants, 1970, 74. Mem. Internat. Soc. Ceramists, Geneva, Switzerland.

SHAW, RICHARD ALLAN, lawyer; b. Portland, Oreg., Oct. 14, 1937; s. Leland B. and Vena (Gaskill) S.; m. Jo-Ann O. Shaw, Mar. 23, 1959; 1 child, Kevin A. BS, U. Oreg., 1959, JD, 1962; LLM in Taxation, NYU, 1963. Bar: Oreg. 1962, Ariz. 1967, Calif. 1969. Assoc. Kramer, Roche, Burch, Streich & Cracchiolo, Phoenix, 1966-68, Hewitt & Greaves, San Diego, 1968-71; ptnr. Hewitt & Shaw, San Diego, 1972-77; pres., sr. mem. Shenas, Shaw & Spievak A.P.C., San Diego, 1978—; teaching fellow NYU Sch. Law, N.Y.C., 1962-63; disting. adj. prof. advanced bus. planning and advanced corporate tax problems U. San Diego Sch. Law, 1978—; founding incorporator, dir. San Diego County Bar Found., 1979; lectr. insts. and programs nationally. Editor Oreg. Law Rev., 1961-62, The Fed. Bar Jour., 1964-68, The Tax Lawyer, 1973-74, Jour. of S Corp. Taxation, 1988—; contbr. articles in field to profl. jours. Pres. San Diego County Boy Scouts, 1982-84; chmn. Washington-Lincoln Laurels for Leaders, San Diego, 1986-87; chmn. Corp. Fin. Coun., 1993-94; chmn. Eagle Scout Alumni Assn., 1978. Capt. JAGC, U.S. Army, 1963-66. Recipient Silver Beaver award Boy Scouts Am., San Diego, 1979, Silver Antelope award, 1982, Disting. Eagle Scout award, 1988. Fellow Am. Coll. Tax Counsel, ABA (chmn. tax. com. on S corps. 1974-76, coun. dir. taxation sect. 1988-94, vice-chmn. taxation sect. 1991-94); chair Taxation Taskforce White House Conf. on Small Bus.; mem. Oreg. State Bar, Ariz. State Bar, Calif. State Bar (chmn. taxation sect. 1981-82, V. Judson Klien award 1985), Western Region Tax Bar Assn. (chmn. 1988), San Diego County Bar Assn. (chmn. bus. law sect. 1974), Kiwanis (disting. past pres. 1985-86). Republican. Avocations: skiing, painting, stained glass. Office: Shenas Shaw & Spievak 701 B St Ste 2200 San Diego CA 92101-8106

SHAW, RICHARD FRANCIS, fisheries administrator, oceanography educator; b. Lawrence, Mass., Feb. 22, 1952; s. Alfred Edward and Florence Ann (Coleman) S.; m. Carolyn A. Rubino, Nov. 29, 1986; 1 child, Gregory Peter Nunzio. BA in Biology cum laude, Merrimac Coll., 1973; PhD in Oceanography, U. Maine, Orono, 1981. Rsch. assoc. IV Coastal Ecology and Fisheries Inst., Baton Rouge, 1981-85; asst. prof. dept. marine sci. La. State U., Baton Rouge, 1985-89, assoc. prof. dept. oceanography and coastal sci., 1989-95, prof., 1995—, interim dir. coastal fisheries inst., 1989-90, dir., 1990—; mem. plankton work group, S.E. area monitoring and assessment program subcom. Gulf States Marine Fisheries Commn., 1982—; mem. global climatic change, ecosystem monitoring and fishery mgmt. com. NOAA/Nat. Marine Fisheries Svc., 1987-90; mem. La. marine finfish tech. working group La. Dept. Wildlife and Fisheries, 1988—; mem. La. wetlands tech. adv. group La. State U., 1989-90; mem. tech. adv. com., coastal fisheries ecosystems, coastal ocean program NOAA, 1990—; mem. Gulf of Mex. program, living aquatic resources subcom. U.S. EPA, 1992—; rep. fish and wildlife resources sect. Nat. Assn. State Univs. and Land-Grant Colls., 1993—; reviewer oceanography programs. com. study rsch.-doctorate programs in U.S. Nat. Rsch. Coun., 1993—; program reviewer zoo-/icthtyoplankton rsch. Fla.'s Dept. Natural Resources, 1993—; internat. instr. program ecology, fisheries and oceanography of Gulf of Mex. U. Campeche and Nat. U. Mex., 1993; cons. in field. Reviewer Marine Biology, 1987—, Southwestern Naturalist, 1988—; N.Am. Jour. Fisheries Mgmt., 1992—; Aquaculture, 1993—, others; mem. editorial bd. Jour. Exptl. Marine Biology and Ecology, 1994—; contbr. articles to profl. jours. Recipient Rsch. Initiative and Support award NSF, 1979, 80; grantee U.S. Dept. Energy and La. Dept. Wildlife and Fisheries, 1981-83, La. Sea Grant, 1983—, La. Fisheries Initiative Program, 1984-85, La. Bd. Regent, 1984-86, 88-90, Marine Fisheries Initiative, 1986-92, La. Stimulus Excellence Rsch. Program, 1987-91, La. Dept. Wildlife and Fisheries, 1989—, La./Tex. Phys. Oceanography Program, 1991-94, U.S. AID, African-Am. Inst., 1993-94. Mem. Am. Fisheries Soc. (co-chmn., convener distbn. and transp. sect. Early Life History Symposium and 7th annual Larval Fish Conf. 1983), Am. Geophysical Union, Am. Soc. Ichthyologists and Herpetologists, Am. Soc. Limnology and Oceanography, La. Wildlife Biologists Assn., Southeastern Fishes Coun., Internat. Soc. Mangrove Ecosystems, Estuarine Rsch. Fedn. Office: La State U Coastal Fisheries Inst Wetland Resources Bldg Baton Rouge LA 70803

SHAW, RICHARD JOHN GILDROY, insurance executive; b. Southampton, Eng., June 7, 1936; s. Edward Philip and Mary Elizabeth (Tanner) S.; m. Yvonne Kathleen Maskell; 1 child, Rupert Henry Gildroy. Ins. assoc. J.H. Minet & Co., Ltd., London, 1955-67; asst. dir. H.J. Symons, London, 1967-70; dep. chmn. C.E. Heath & Co., Ins. Broking Ltd., London, 1970-79; chmn. C.E. Health & Co. Latin Am., Ltd., London, 1979-88; CEO Lowndes Lambert Group Ltd., London, 1979-88, chmn.; 1991—; dept. chmn., CEO Lowndes Lambert Group Holdings, London, 1979—; CEO Lowndes Lambert Group Holdings PLC, London, 1992—, chmn., 1993—; dir. Hill Sammich Group Plc; bd. dirs. Lowndes Lambert Group

Can. Ltd., Lowndes Lambert Group Australia Ltd., Lowndes Lambert France Sarl, Hill Samuel Group, PLC, 1979-88; pres. Lowndes Lambert Group Italy Spa; chmn. Lowndes Lambert Group Ltd., Lowndes Lambert Group Holdings plc. Mem. Portland (London), Sunningdale (Ascot, Eng.), Golf (Berkshire, Eng.), City of London Club, Carlton Club. Mem. Ch. of England. Avocations: golf, cricket, reading, yachting. Home: 18 Phillimore Gardens, W8 7QE London England Office: Lowndes Lambert Group Ltd, Friary Ct Crutched Friars, London EC3N 2NP, England

SHAW, RICHARD LESLIE, engineering company executive; b. Beaver, Pa., May 8, 1927; s. George L. and Marguerite (Clements) S.; m. Margaret Powell, Nov. 30, 1951; children: Leslie P. Sidney. BS, U. Pitts., 1950. Ordering corr. Westinghouse Elec. Corp., Beaver, 1950-52; with Michael Baker Jr. Inc., Beaver, 1952-73; pres. and chief exec. officer Michael Baker Corp., Beaver, 1984—; now chmn. bd. dirs. Michael Baker Corp.; mem. legis. com. Am. Pub. Transit Assn., Washington. Co-chmn. Beaver County Alliance of Southwestern Pa. Growth Alliance; bd. dirs. Profls. Coalition; pres., bd. dirs. United Way Beaver County, 1985-87. Served to sgt. U.S. Army, 1940-44. Mem. Pa. Cons. Engrs. Council (bd. dirs. 1987—), Engrs. Soc. Western Pa., Pa. SW Assn. (bd. dirs. 1978—), Beaver County Corp. Econ. Devel. (bd. dirs. 1985—), Corp. Owner/Operator Projects. Oak. Dist. 1984—). Republican. Presbyterian. Avocations: golf, reading. Home: 150 Wilson Ave Beaver PA 15009-2824 Office: Michael Baker Corp PO Box 12259 Pittsburgh PA 15231 also: Michael Baker Jr Inc PO Box 280 4301 Dutch Ridge Rd Beaver PA 15009*

SHAW, ROBERT E., carpeting company executive; b. Cartersville, GA, 1931. Pres., chief exec. officer Star Finishing Co. Inc. (merged into Shaw Industries Inc.), Dalton, Ga., until 1969; now pres., chief exec. officer Shaw Industries Inc., Dalton, Ga., 1969—, also bd. dirs., 1969—. Office: Shaw Industries Inc 616 E Walnut Ave Dalton GA 30721-4409

SHAW, ROBERT EUGENE, minister, administrator; b. Havre, Mt., Apr. 8, 1933; s. Harold Alvin and Lillian Martha (Kruse) S.; m. Marilyn Grace Smit, June 14, 1957; children—Rebecca Jean, Ann Elizabeth, Mark David, Peter Robert. B.A., Sioux Falls Coll., 1955; M.Div., Am. Baptist. Sem. of West, 1958; D.D. (hon.), Ottawa U., 1976, Judson Coll., 1984. Ordained to ministry Am. Bapt. Chs. U.S.A., 1958; pastor First Bapt. Ch., Webster City, Ia., 1958-63, Community Bapt. Ch., Topeka, Kans., 1963-68; sr. pastor Prairie Bapt. Ch., Prairie Village, Kans., 1968-78; pres. Ottawa U, Kans., 1978-83; exec. minister Am. Bapt. Chs. Mich., East Lansing, 1983—; mem. gen. bd. Am. Bapt. Chs. U.S.A., Valley Forge, Pa., 1972-80, nat. v.p., 1978-80; nat. v.p. Am. Bapt. Minister Council, Valley Forge, 1969-72, nat. pres., 1972-75; nat. chair Am. Bapt. Evang. Team, 1988—; mem. Internat. Commn. on Edn. and Evangelism, Bapt. World Alliance, 1990—; mem. nat. exec. com. Am. Bapt. Administrs. Colls. and Univs., 1980-82; bd. dirs. Kans. Ind. Colls. Assn., 1980-82. Trustee No. Bapt. Theol. Sem., Lombard, Ill., 1983—, Kalamazoo Coll., Mich., 1983—, Judson Coll, Elgin, Ill., 1983—; dir. Webster City C. of C., 1961-62, Ottawa C. of C., 1980-82. Office: Am Baptist Chs of Mich 4578 S Hagadorn Rd East Lansing MI 48823-5355

SHAW, ROBERT FLETCHER, retired civil engineer; b. Montreal, Que., Can., Feb. 16, 1910; s. John Fletcher and Edna Mary Baker (Anglin) S.; m. Johann Alexandra MacInnes, Dec. 24, 1935; 1 son, Robert Fletcher (dec.). B.C.E., McGill U., Montreal, 1933; D.Sc. (hon.), McGill U., 1985; Sc.D. (hon.), McMaster U., 1967, U. N.B., 1986; D.Eng. (hon.), Tech. U. of N.S., 1967. Registered profl. engr., Que. With Found. Co. Can. Ltd., Montreal, 1933-63; pres. Found. Co. Can. Ltd., 1962-63; dir., 1968-71; shipyard mgr. Found. Maritime Ltd., Pictou, N.S., 1943-45; on loan to Govt. Can. as v.p., chief engr. Def. Constrn. (1951) Ltd., 1951-52; on loan as mem. working party mil. airfields NATO, 1952; dep. commr. gen., also dir. Expo '67, Montreal, 1963-68; v.p. administrn. McGill U., 1968-71; chmn. bd., dir. Found. Can. Engring. Corp., 1968-71; dep. minister environment Govt. Can., 1971-75; pres., dir. Monenco Pipeline Cons. Ltd., 1975-78; adv. Nfld. Dept. Indsl. Devel., 1978-80; sr. cons. Montreal Engring. Co. Ltd., 1975-92; chmn. rsch. policy com. Ctr. Cold Ocean Resources Engring. Meml. U. Nfld., 1981-82. Bd. govs. McGill U., 1964-68; bd. govs. U. N.B., 1973-85, chmn., 1978-80; bd. govs. Montreal Gen. Hosp., 1963-94; pres. Can. Assn. Mentally Retarded, 1963-65; bd. dirs. Montreal Internat. Music Competition, 1967-87. Decorated companion Order Can., 1967; recipient Can. Centennial medal, 1967, citation Engring. News Record, 1967, Queen's Jubilee medal, 1977; named Hon. Chmn. Can. Engring. Centennial Bd., 1984-87. Fellow Engring. Inst. Can. (pres. 1975-76, Julian C. Smith award 1967, Keefer medal 1979), Can. Soc. Civil Engrs., fellow Can. Acad. of Engring, 1987—; mem. Order Engrs. Que. (pres. 1953), Can. Council Profl. Engrs. (v.p. 1954, gold medal 1979), Grads. Soc. McGill U. (pres. 1964-65, Gold medal 1968), Royal Montreal Golf. Home: Apt C29, 3980 Cote des Neiges Rd, Montreal, PQ Canada H3H 1W2 Exploding population is creating a heavy demand on the world's resources. If species man is to survive and improve, he must innovate, mass produce, provide the additional energy required, enhance the environment, and learn the value of interdependence. So far we are losing ground. The human reaction to these problems seems to be confrontation, conflict, fragmentation and increased social and economic nationalism. I hope that I have made a contribution to increasing productivity, better management and more interdependent action.

SHAW, ROBERT GILBERT, restaurant executive, senator; b. Erwin, N.C., Nov. 22, 1924; s. Robert Gilbert B. and Annie Elizabeth (Byrd) S.; m. Grace Lee Wilson, Jan. 29, 1951 (div. 1976); children: Ann Karlen, Barbara Jean; m. Linda Owens, May 22, 1982. AA, Campbell U., 1948; postgrad., U. N.C., 1948-50. Restauranteur, 1951—. County commr. County of Guilford, Greensboro, N.C., 1968-76; chair N.C. Rep. Ctrl. Com., Raleigh, 1975-77; minority leader N.C. Senate, Raleigh, 1984—; chair Guilford County Rep. Ctrl. Com., 1973-75; active Rep. Nat. Ctrl. Com., Washington, 1975-77. With U.S. Army, 1943-46. Named Legislator of Yr. Nat. Fedn. Wildlife, 1990. Mem. Elks (life, bd. govs. 1953—). Presbyterian. Avocations: fishing, hunting, politics. Home: 4901 Tower Rd Greensboro NC 27410 Office: NC Senate 1129 Legislative Bldg Raleigh NC 27611

SHAW, ROBERT LAWSON, symphony orchestra conductor; b. Red Bluff, Calif., Apr. 30, 1916; s. Shirley Richard and Nelle Mae (Lawson) S.; m. Maxine Farley, Oct. 15, 1939 (div. 1973); children: Johanna, Peter Thein, John Thaddeus; m. Caroline Sauls Hitz, Dec. 19, 1973; 1 child, Thomas Lawson. AB, Pomona Coll., 1938; hon. degree, Coll. of Wooster, 1951, Pomona Coll., 1953, St. Lawrence U., 1955, Mich. State U., 1960, Kenyon Coll., 1962, U. Alaska, 1963, Cleve. Inst. Music, 1966, Case Western Res. U., 1966, Emory U., 1967, Fla. State U., 1968, Westminster Choir Coll., 1975, U. Akron, 1976, Morehouse Coll., 1977, Oglethorpe U., 1977, Baldwin-Wallace Coll., 1980, Stetson U., 1983, New Eng. Conservatory, 1983, St. Olaf Coll., 1985, Duke U., 1988, Atlanta Coll. Art., 1988, Fla. So. Coll., 1989, Baylor U., 1990, Rhodes Coll., 1990, Johns Hopkins U., 1990, Eastman Sch. Music, 1991, State U. of N.Y., 1993, Ind. Univ., 1993, Boston U., 1994. Dir. choral music Juilliard Sch. Music, N.Y.C., 1945-48; founder, condr. Robert Shaw Chorale, 1948-65; condr. San Diego Symphony, 1953-57; music dir. Alaska Festival, Anchorage, 1956-75; assoc. condr., dir. choruses Cleve. Orch., 1956-67; condr., music dir. Atlanta Symphony Orch., 1967-88, music dir. emeritus and conductor laureate, 1988—; vis. prof. U. Tex, Austin, 1988. Dir. Fred Waring Glee Clubs, 1938-45; founder, condr. Collegiate Chorale, N.Y.C., 1941-60, choral dir.: Aquacades, 1942-43, Carmen Jones, 1943, Seven Lively Arts, 1944, Berkshire Music Ctr., Tanglewood, Mass., 1945-48; guest condr. numerous orchs. including Chgo. Symphony, Cin. Symphony, Minn. Orch., N.Y. Philharm., Phila. Orch., Boston Symphony, NBC Symphony, Dallas Symphony, others; recs. on RCA Victor, Telarc, Vox (Turnabout), Pro Arte and New World labels including (with Robert Shaw Chorale) Mass in B Minor by Bach (Grammy award 1961), Ceremony of Carols by Britten (Grammy award 1964), Handel's Messiah (Grammy award 1966), Gloria by Poulenc (Grammy award 1965), Symphony of Psalms by Stravinsky (Grammy award 1965), (with Atlanta Symphony) Pelleas et Melisande by Faure (Grammy award 1986), Requiem by Berlioz (2 Grammy awards 1986), Verdi Requiem, 1989 (2 Grammy awards, Gramaphone award), Rorem String Symphony, 1989 (Grammy award). Recipient ASCAP award 1976, 81, 86, Alice M. Ditson award Columbia U., 1955, Govs. award in the arts, Ga., 1973, 75, Disting. Svc. award Atlanta Boys Club, 1975, Nat. Fedn. Music Clubs award 1975, Samuel Simons Sanford medal Yale U., 1980, Am. Choral Dirs. Assn. award 1981, Martin Luther King Jr. award for artistic achievement, 1982, Fulton

County (Ga.) Arts Coun. award, 1985, Gold Baton award Am. Symphony Orch. League, 1988, George Peabody medal for outstanding contbn. to music in Am. Peabody Conservatory, 1990, Kennedy Ctr. Honors, 1991, Nat. Medal of Arts award White House, 1992, Theodore Thomas award Conductor's Guild, 1993; Guggenheim fellow, 1944, Ind. U. fellow, 1983; Housewright Eminent scholar Fla. State U., 1986; named Outstanding Am. Born Condr. of Yr., 1943, Musician of Yr. in Musical Am., 1992. Office: Atlanta Symphony Orch 1293 Peachtree St NE Atlanta GA 30309-3552*

SHAW, ROBERT T., life insurance holding company executive; b. McCrory, AR. Former pres. ICH Corp., Louisville; now chmn., chief exec. officer ICH Corp.; chmn. Bankers Life and Casualty Corp., Bankers Multiple Life Ins. Co., Cert. Life Ins. Co., Constitution Life Ins. Co., St. So. Life Ins. Co., Phila. Life Ins. Co., Southwestern Life Ins. Co., Wabash Life Ins. Co., Western Pioneer Life Ins. Co. Office: ICH Companies 100 Mallard Creek Rd Ste 400 Louisville KY 40207-5137

SHAW, ROBERT WILLIAM, JR., management consultant, venture capitalist; b. Ithaca, N.Y., Aug. 10, 1941; s. Robert William and Charlotte G. (Throop) S.; m. Anne P. Meads, Aug. 29, 1964; children: Mark Andrew, Christopher Matthew. B.E.P., Cornell U., 1964, M.S.E.E., Princeton U. Stanford U., 1968; M.P.A., Am. U., 1981. Postdoctoral fellow Cavendish Lab., Cambridge, Eng., 1968-69; mem. tech. staff Bell Telephone Labs., Murray Hill, N.J., 1969-72; with Booz Allen Hamilton, Bethesda, Md., 1972-83; sr. v.p. energy and environ. div. Booz Allen Hamilton, 1979-83, mem. operating council, 1981-83, also dir.; pres. Arete Ventures, Inc., 1983—, Utech Venture Capital Corp., 1985—; gen. ptnr. Utech Venture Capital Corp. Fund I, 1985—, Utech Venture Capital Corp. Fund II, 1988—, Utech Venture Capital Corp. I Parallel Fund L.P., 1988—, Utech Venture Capital Corp. II Parallel Fund, L.P., Rockville, Md., 1991—; v.p. Can. Energy and Environment Ventures, Inc., 1993—; mem. energy com. Aspen Inst. Humanistic Studies; chmn. bd. Superconductivity, Inc., Evergreen Solar, Inc.; bd. dirs. AstroPower Corp., Nanophace Tech. Corp., Shena, Inc. Contbr. articles to profl. jours. NASA trainee; Air Force Office Sci. Research fellow, 1968-69. Mem. AAAS, Am. Phys. Soc. (investment com.), Internat. Transactional Analysis Assn., Nat. Venture Capital Assn., Organizational Devel. Network, Assn. Humanistic Psychology, Sigma Xi, Tau Beta Pi, Phi Kappa Phi, Pi Alpha Alpha, Kappa Delta Rho. Home: 9405 Falls Bridge Ln Rockville MD 20854-3953 Office: 6110 Executive Blvd Ste 1040 Rockville MD 20852-3903

SHAW, RONALD AHREND, physician, educator; b. Toledo, July 20, 1946; s. Harold Michael and Eve Helen (Ganch) S.; m. Carol Ann Rapp, June 13, 1970; children: Robert, Benjamin, Daniel. BS, U. Toledo, 1968; MD, Washington U., 1972. Diplomate Am. Bd. Emergency Medicine. Intern, then resident in surgery St. Luke's Hosp., St. Louis, 1972-73, resident in surgery, 1973; mem. staff Bapt. Med. Ctr.-Montclair, Birmingham, Ala., 1976-81, chief emergency svc., 1979-81; assoc. dir. lifesaver flight ops. Caraway Meth. Med. Ctr., Birmingham, 1981-85; dir. emergency svc. sch. medicine U. Ala., 1985-89; asst. dir. emergency svc. R.I. Hosp., Providence, 1989—; cons. U. Tex., Houston, 1986, Bell Helicopter, Ft. Worth, 1986, Mutual Assurance, Birmingham, 1986-89, NYU, 1988-89, R.I. State Med. Examiners Office, 1991—, Fla. Dept. Health, EMS Office, 1991—; chmn. adv. bd. emergency svc. Ala. Dept. Pub. Health, 1986-89; med. dir. Emergency Med. Svcs. div. R.I. Dept. of Health, 1990—. Bd. dirs. MADD, Ala., 1986; mem. planning com. Youth Baseball, Vestavia Hills, Ala., 1986, 87; mem. disaster com. City of Birmingham, 1984-89; mem. 911 Commn., State of R.I., 1991—. Maj. USAF, 1973-76. Recipient Disting. Achievement award Birmingham Emergency Med. Svc., 1988. Fellow Am. Coll. Emergency Physicians (bd. dirs. Ala. chpt. 1984-89, steering com. EMS sect. 1991—); mem. AAAS, ACS (state com. on trauma, R.I. chpt. 1990—), N.Y. Acad. Sci., Med. Assn. Ala. (mem. coun. med. svc. 1985-86). Republican. Avocations: hunting, stamp and record collecting. Office: RI Hosp Dept Emergency Medicine 593 Eddy St Providence RI 02903-4923

SHAW, RONALD GORDON, manufacturing company executive; b. Phila., Sept. 17, 1938; s. Herbert B. and Henrietta (Green) Schurowitz; m. Phyllis E. Hollander, Nov. 29, 1959; children: Steven, Susan, Alan. Student, U. Miami, Fla., 1956-60. Mgr. nat. sales Bic Corp., Milford, Conn., 1961-75; pres. Pilot Pen Corp. of Am., Trumbull, Conn., 1975—; bd. assocs. U. Bridgeport, Conn., 1985—. Nat. commr. Anti-Defamation League, N.Y.C. 1986— (Torch of Liberty award 1984). Recipient Humanitarian award United Cerebral Palsy, 1986, Probus Club, 1985, 86, Am. Heritage award Anti-Defamation League, 1990. Mem. Office Products Mfrs. Assn. (bd. dirs. 1986—), Wholesale Stationers Assn. (v.p. 1987—). Avocations: swimming, tennis. Home: 5 Forest Glen Dr Woodbridge CT 06525-1420 Office: Pilot Pen Corp of Am 60 Commerce Dr Trumbull CT 06611-5403

SHAW, RUSSELL BURNHAM, association executive, author; b. Washington, May 19, 1935; s. Charles Burnham and Mary (Russell) S.; m. Carmen Hilda Carbon, July 19, 1958; children: Mary Hilda, Emily Anne, Janet, Charles, Elizabeth. BA, Georgetown U., 1956, MA, 1960. Staff writer Cath. Standard, Washington, 1956-57; reporter Nat. Cath. News Svc., 1957-66; dir. publs., pub. info. Nat. Cath. Ednl. Assn., 1966-69; dir. Nat. Cath. Office for Info., 1969-73; assoc. sec. for communication U.S. Cath. Conf., 1973-74, sec. for pub. affairs Nat. Conf. Cath. Bishops, 1975-87; dir. pub. info. KC, 1987—; consultor Pontifical Commn. for Social Communications, 1984-89. Author: The Dark Disciple, 1961, Abortion on Trial, 1968, Church and State, 1979, Choosing Well, 1982, Why We Need Confession, 1986, Renewal, 1986, Signs of the Times, 1986, Does Suffering Make Sense?, 1987, To Hunt, To Shoot, To Entertain, 1993, Understanding Your Rights, 1994; co-author: S.O.S. for Catholic Schools, 1970, Beyond the New Morality, 3d edit., 1988, Fulfillment in Christ, 1991, others; columnist monthly mag. Washington Report, 1966—. Mem. Pub. Rels. Soc. Am., Nat. Press Club, Phi Beta Kappa. Roman Catholic. Home: 2928 44th Pl NW Washington DC 20016-3555 Office: Knights of Columbus 1275 Pennsylvania Ave NW Washington DC 20004-2404

SHAW, RUSSELL CLYDE, lawyer; b. Cleve., Mar. 19, 1940; s. Clyde Leland and Ruth Arminta (Williams) S.; BS, Ohio State U., 1962; JD, Ohio State U., 1965; m. Jane Ann Mohler, Feb. 15, 1969 (div. 1988); children: Christopher Scott, Robin Nicole, Curtis Russell; m. Lynn Baird Breuer, Oct. 21, 1989; stepchildren: Heather Breuer, Matthew Breuer, Russell Breuer. Bar: Ohio 1965, U.S. Supreme Ct. 1968. Assoc., Thompson, Hine & Flory, Cleve., 1965, 69-74, ptnr., 1979-93, chmn. area specialty group, 1988-90; ptnr. Walter & Haverfield (formerly Walter, Haverfield, Buescher & Chockley), Cleve., 1993—, chmn. area specialty group, 1993—. Mem. Geauga United Way Svcs. Council, 1980-87, officer, 1982-87, chmn. (chief vol. officer), 1984-87; trustee United Way Svcs. of Cleve., 1983-88, assoc. v.p., 1986-88; trustee Cleve. Community Fund, 1986-88, Ohio Citizen's Council; trustee Ohio United Way, 1986—, v.p., 1987-90, chmn., 1990-92, mem. exec. com., 1990—; chmn. Ohio Citizen's Council Welfare Reform Task Force, 1987-90, mem. United Way of Am. Welfare Reform Task Force; mem. Ohio Adv. Coun. for the Aging, 1990—, vice chmn., 1992-93, chmn., 1993—; mem. Gov. Ohio's Ops. Improvement Task Force, 1991-93; Nat. Inst. for Responsible Fatherhood and Family Devel., 1990—, trustee, exec. com. mem. Fairmount Presbyn. Ch.; del. White House Conf. on Aging, Washington, 1995. Served to capt. AUS, 1965-69. Recipient Harvey H. Hebert Meml. award Delta Sigma Phi, 1989; named to Honorable Order of Ky. Cols. Commonwealth of Ky. Mem. ABA (employee benefits com. taxation sect.), Def. Rsch. Inst. (employee benefits com.), Fed. Bar Assn., Ohio Bar Assn., Nat. Lawyers Club, Internat. Found. Employee Benefit Plans, Employee Benefits Attys. Forum Cleve., Old English Sheepdog Club Am. (nat. officer 1972-74), Fedn. Ohio Dog Clubs (pres. 1978-82), Sugarbush Kennel Club (pres. 1975-78, 81—), Midwest Pension Conf., Delta Sigma Phi (nat. officer 1975—, nat. officer Found. 1978—, trustee Found. 1983—, Herbet Meml. award), Pres.'s (Ohio State U.) Presbyterian. Office: Walter & Haverfield 50 Public Sq 1300 Terminal Tower Cleveland OH 44113

SHAW, SALLYE BROWN, women's health nurse; b. Charlotte, N.C., Oct. 14, 1941; d. Robert Cotten III and Nannie Lee (Phillips) Brown; m. Phillip A. Shaw, III, July 19, 1986. BS, Queens Coll., Charlotte, 1964; M in Nursing, Emory U., Atlanta, 1967. Instr. nursing edn. Western Carolina Ctr., Morganton, N.C., 1964; staff nurse York Gen. Hosp., Rock Hill, S.C., 1965-66; assoc. prof. Fla. State U., Tallahassee, 1967-81; exec. dir. NAACOG, Washington, 1981-92; assoc. dir. collaborative practice ACOG,

1993—; cons. Edn. in Childbirth Assn., Tallahassee, 1972-74, Gadsden County Hosp., Ft. Walton, Fla., 1974-75, Fla. State U. Sch. of Nursing and Community Agys., Tallahassee, 1974-75, task force Common Course Numbering, State Fla. 1975-77; adv. panel Maternal-Child Core Competencies, 1986-88; adv. bd. ParentSource, Waltham, Mass., 1993-94, Vida Health Comm., 1989-91, Williams and Wilkins Pub., 1987-89; speaker in field. Contbr. articles to profl. jours. Vol. Telephone Pollsters, Alexandria, Va., 1990-93; pres. Presbyn. Women Westminster Ch., Alexandria, 1992-94. Mem. ANA, NAACOG (pres. 1977), Nat. League Nursing (bd. dirs. D.C. League 1986-87), Sigma Theta Tau (bd. dirs. Pi chpt. 1977-79), Am. Soc. Assn. Execs. Avocations: reading, piano/organ, needlework. Home: 3212 Old Dominion Blvd Alexandria VA 22305-1316 Office: ACOG 409 12th St SW Washington DC 20024-2188

SHAW, SAMUEL ERVINE, II, retired insurance company executive, consultant; b. Independence, Kans., Apr. 10, 1933; s. Samuel Ervine and Jessie Elizabeth (Guernsey) S.; m. Dale Foster Dorman, June 19, 1954; children: Samuel Ervine III, Christopher Atwood, Elizabeth Foster. BA, Harvard U., 1954; JD, Boston Coll., 1965. Bar: Mass. 1965, U.S. Supreme Ct. 1971; enrolled actuary 1976-93; cons. actuary, 1987. With John Hancock Mut. Life Ins. Co., Boston, 1955-87, group pension and ins. actuary, 2d v.p., 1979-85, v.p.; group ins. actuary, 1985-87; dir. Health Reins. Assn. Conn., Hartford, 1980-87; cons. Internat. Exec. Service Corps, Guayaquil, Ecuador, 1973, Jakarta, Indonesia, 1988, Perm, Russia, 1994, Pension Benefit Guaranty Corp., Washington, 1974-75, Nat. Hosp. Ins. Fund, Nairobi, Kenya, 1990. Mem. Brookline Hist. Commn. (Mass.), 1981-88, Brookline Retirement Bd., 1985-90; chmn. Brookline Com. on Town Govt. and Structure, 1975-79. Served to maj. USAF, 1954-57. Fellow Soc. Actuaries; mem. Am. Acad. Actuaries, Internat. Actuarial Assn., ABA, Mass. Bar Assn., Boston Bar Assn. Episcopalian. Home and Office: 131 Sewall Ave Brookline MA 02146-5314

SHAW, SCOTT ALAN, photojournalist; b. Danville, Ill., 1963. BS in Journalism, So. Ill. U., 1985. Formerly with The Comml. News, Danville; with The Paragould (Ark.) Daily Press, 1985-86; staff photographer The Odessa (Tex.) Am., 1986-89; with St. Louis Sun, 1989-90; now staff photographer The Plain Dealer, Cleve., 1994—. Recipient Pulitzer Prize for spot news photography, 1988. Office: The Plain Dealer 1801 Superior Ave Cleveland OH 44114

SHAW, STANLEY MINER, nuclear pharmacy scientist; b. Parkston, S.D., July 4, 1935; s. George Henry and Jensina (Thompson) S.; m. Excellda J. Watke, Aug. 13, 1961; children: Kimberly Kay, Renee Denise, Elena Aimee. BS, S.D. State U., 1957, MS, 1959; PhD, Purdue U., 1962. Instr. S.D. State U., 1960-62; asst. prof. bionucleonics Purdue U., West Lafayette, Ind., 1962-66; assoc. prof. Purdue U., 1966-71, prof. nuclear pharmacy, 1971—, head. Div. Nuclear Pharmacy, 1990—, acting head Sch. Health Scis., 1990-93; Mem. Bd. Pharm. Spltys., Splty. Council Nuclear Pharmacy, 1978-82. Contbr. sci. articles to profl. jours. Recipient Lederle Pharmacy faculty awards, 1962, 65, Parenteral Drug Assn. rsch. award, 1970, Henry Heine Outstanding Tchr. award Sch. Pharmacy Purdue U., 1989, 93, Disting. Alumnus award S.D. State U., 1991, Disting. Pharmacy Educator award AACP, 1994. Fellow Acad. Pharmacy Practice (chmn. sect. nuclear pharmacy 1979-80, historian 1981-85, mem.-at-large 1993-95, chair-elect 1995-96), Am. Soc. Hosp. Pharmacy; mem. Health Physics Soc., Am. Pharm. Assn. (ho. of dels. 1977, 79, 86, 92, Founders award nuclear pharmacy sect.), Sigma Xi, Phi Lambda Upsilon, Phi Lambda Sigma, Rho Chi. Assembly of God. Home: 610 Perry Ln West Lafayette IN 47906-9657 Office: Purdue U Sch Pharmacy West Lafayette IN 47907-1333

SHAW, STEVEN JOHN, retired marketing educator, academic administrator; b. Hamilton, N.Y., Nov. 16, 1918; s. Constantine J. and Agnes (Tilicki) S.; m. Aracelis Goberna, June 8, 1952. B.S., N.Y. State U., 1941; M.S in Retailing, N.Y. U., 1946, Ph.D., 1955. Instr. mktg. U. Miami, Coral Gables, Fla., 1948-52; asst. prof. Tulane U., New Orleans, 1954-55, U. Fla., Gainesville, 1955-57; assoc. prof., then prof. U. S.C., Columbia, 1957-89, Disting. prof. emeritus, 1989—, dir. dept. mktg., 1968-72; cons. Hoffman LaRoche, Nutley, N.J.; exec. dir. S.C.-Southwestern Colombia chpt. Ptnrs. of Ams., 1977-79, asst. exec. dir., 1987-91, also bd. dirs. Author: Salesmanship: Modern Viewpoints on Personal Communication, 1960, Marketing in Business Management, 1963, Cases in Marketing Management Strategy, 1971. Recipient N.Y. U. Founders Day award, 1956, Steven J. Shaw award for most scholarly article in Jour. Bus. Research. Mem. So. Marketing Assn. (pres. 1964), Beta Gamma Sigma (pres. 1965). Home and Office: 7600 Tryall Dr Hialeah FL 33015-2931

SHAW, TALBERT O., university president. BD, Andrews U., 1963; MA, U. Chgo., 1968, PhD, 1973. Dean of students Oakwood Coll., Huntsville, Ala., 1965-71; dean Howard U., Washington, 1971-76; dean Coll. Arts and Scis. Morgan State U., Balt., 1976-87; pres. Shaw U., Raleigh, N.C., 1987—. Office: Shaw U 118 E South St Raleigh NC 27601-2341

SHAW, THOMAS DOUGLAS, newspaper executive; b. Dixon, Ill., Jan. 2, 1948; s. Benjamin Douglas and Lucy Bates (Denny) S.; m. Tamsin Johanna Davis, May 9, 1971; children: Jesse Thomas, Benjamin Davis, John Peter Morgan, Katerine Johanna, Mary Alice Powell. BBA, Colo. Coll., 1970. Owner Dixon Cable TV, 1970-81; asst. gen. mgr. Dixon Telegraph, 1974-75, gen. mgr., 1975-86; chief ops. officer Shaw Newspapers, Dixon, 1986-93, pres., CEO, 1993—; owner Durango (Colo.) Stockman, 1976-87; bd. dirs. Amcore Bank Dixon. Bd. dirs., pres. Dixon Family YMCA, 1972-78; pres. Dixon Rural Fire Dist., 1972-76; pres. Katherine Shaw Bethea Hosp. Found., Dixon, 1985-86; bd. dirs. KSB Hosp., Dixon, 1979-85; Alternate del. Rep. Nat. Conv., Detroit, 1980, 84. Mem. Inland Daily Press Assn., Ill. Press Assn. Avocations: skiing, swimming, jogging. Home: 435 River Bluff Dr Dixon IL 61021-8767 Office: Shaw Newspaper 113 S Peoria Ave Dixon IL 61021-2900

SHAW, TIMOTHY MILTON, political science educator; b. Frimley, Surrey, Eng., Jan. 27, 1945; came to Can., 1971; s. Arnold J. and Margaret E. (Milton) S.; m. Jane L. Parpart, Sept. 2, 1983; children—Laura, Lee Parpart; m. Susan M. Sturt, July 8, 1967 (div. 1980); children—Benjamin, Amanda. B.A., Sussex U., Brighton, Eng., 1967; M.A., East Africa U., Kampala, Uganda, 1969; M.A., Princeton U., 1971, Ph.D., 1975. Teaching fellow Makerere U., Kampala, 1968-70; lectr. U. Zambia, Lusaka, 1973-74; assoc. prof. Carleton U., Ottawa, Ont., Can., 1978-79; sr. lectr. U. Ife, Nigeria, 1979-80; prof. polit. sci. Dalhousie U., Halifax, N.S., Can., 1971-73, 74-78, 80—; dir. Centre African Studies, Dalhousie U., Halifax, 1983-89, dir. Centre for Fgn. Policy Studies, Halifax, 1993; dir. Internat. Devel. Studies Program, 1986-89; dir. Pearson Inst., Halifax, 1985-87, Carrashaw Internat. Devel. Agy., 1994-95; cons. UN Econ. Commn. for Africa, Addis Ababa, Ethiopia, 1983-88; editor Macmillan Press Internat. Polit. Economy Series, London, 1984—. Author: Nigeria, 1988. Reformism and Revisionism in Africa's Political Economy in the 1990s, 1993; co-editor (with Julius Nyang'oro) Beyond Structural Adjustment in Africa, 1992, Corporatism in Africa, 1988, Political Economy of NICS, 1988, (with Larry A. Swatuk) The South at the End of the Twentieth Century, 1994, numerous others. mem. Waegwoltic club, Halifax, 1980—, New Democratic party, Halifax, 1984—, (with Julius E. Okolo) The Political Economy of Foreign Policy in ECOWAS. Research grantee Social Scis. & Humanities Research Council of Can., Africa, 1981—. Mem. Internat. Polit. Sci. Assn., Can. Assn. Devel. Studies (pres. 1993-94), Can. Assn. African Studies (pres. 1984-85), Internat. Studies Assn. Avocations: jogging; cooking; building; traveling. Home: 1143 Studley Ave, Halifax, NS Canada B3H 3R8 Office: Dalhousie University, Halifax, NS Canada B3H 4H6

SHAW, WARD ERIC, information company executive; b. Boston, Dec. 8, 1945; s. Erwin and Barbara (Ward) S.; m. Janet Seeley; children: Eric, Tucker; m. 2d Heather Cameron; 1 child, Geoffrey. AB, Hamilton Coll., 1967; SM, Simmons Coll., 1968; LLD (hon.), N. No. Colo., 1990. Asst. dir. Colby Coll. Libr., Waterville, Maine, 1968-72; assoc. dir. U. Denver Libr., 1972-78; exec. dir. Colo. Alliance of Rsch. Libr., Denver, 1978-88; ptnr., chmn. CEO Carl Corp., Denver, 1988—; cons. in field; mem. various bds. Author, editor various publs. Recipient Lita Gaylord award for excellence in libr. and info. tech. ALA, 1989. Home: 2202 S Milwaukee Denver CO 80210 Office: Carl Corp 3801 E Florida Denver CO 80210

SHAW, WILLIAM, diversified telecommunications company executive; b. 1924; married. BS, Bklyn. Coll. Mgr. Remington Rand Co., Inc., 1945-48; with Nat. Lead Industries, 1948-50; now chmn. bd., pres., chief exec. officer Volt Info. Scis., Inc., N.Y.C. Office: Volt Info Scis Inc 101 Park Ave New York NY 10178-0002

SHAW, WILLIAM FREDERICK, statistician; b. Bklyn., Feb. 24, 1920; s. Charles Peter and Josephine Veronica (Seusing) S.; m. Josephine Cannington Kerbey, Jan. 18, 1947; children—William Frederick, Teresa Anne. B.B.A., U. Miami, 1949; M.A., George Washington U., 1953; postgrad. studies in econometrics, math. and computer scis., U.S. Dept. Agr. Grad. Sch., 1964-74; Ph.D. (fellow), Walden U., 1977. Research asst. U. Miami, 1948-49; with Research and Stats. div. FHA, Washington, 1950-73; chief statistician Research and Stats. div. FHA, 1969—; chief statistician, dir. Advanced Statis. Analysis and Computer Applications Staff HUD, 1974-82, chief statistician, dir. housing stats. div., 1982-89, chief statistician, dir. info. systems div., 1990-91, chief statistician, dir. Office of Evaluation, 1991—; pres. Kerbey-Shaw Assos. Served with F.A. AUS, 1943-45. Decorated D.S.C., Silver Star and Bronze Star medals for heroism; recipient Superior Performance award HUD, 1977; named by Info. Resources Adminstrn. Council as Fed. Office Systems Profl. of Yr., 1983. Mem. AAAS, Am. Statis. Assn., Am. Risk and Ins. Assn., Western Finance Assn., Am. Real Estate and Urban Econ. Assn., So. Econ. Assn., Va. Assn. Economists, Am. Econ. Assn., Am. Finance Assn., Assn. Computing Machinery, Am. Ednl. Research Assn., N.Y. Acad. Scis., Nat. Assn. Rev. Appraisers and Mortgage Underwriters, Internat. Instn. Valuers, Manufactured Housing Appraisal Inst., So. Fin. Assn., Soc. of Cost Estimating and Analysis, Res. Officers Assn. U.S., 101st Airborne Div. Assn., Air Force Assn., Alpha Kappa Psi. Roman Catholic. Home: 6527 Byrnes Dr Mc Lean VA 22101-5227 Office: HUD 7th and D Sts SW Washington DC 20411

SHAW-COHEN, LORI EVE, magazine editor; b. Manhattan, N.Y., Apr. 22, 1959; d. Ray and Carole (Bergenthal) Shaw; m. Robert Mark Cohen, Sept. 20, 1981; children: Joshua Samuel, Drew Taylor, Logan Shaw. BA in Journalism, U. So. Calif., 1981. Editorial asst., writer BBW: Big Beautiful Woman Mag., Los Angeles, 1979-80; editorial asst., writer Intro Mag., Los Angeles, 1980-81; mng. editor 'Teen Mag., Los Angeles, 1981-86; writer, interviewer Stan Rosenfeld & Assocs. Pub. Relations, Los Angeles, 1980-81; cons. BBW: Big Beautiful Woman Mag., Los Angeles, 1981—, Media Research Group, Los Angeles, 1984; condr. seminars Women in Communication, Los Angeles, 1983, Pacific N.W. Writers Conf., Seattle, 1984. Patentee children's toy, 1971; lyricist for songs, 1977—; contbr. articles and poems to profl. jours. and mags. Avocations: travel; reading; photography; horseback riding. Office: BBW: Big Beautiful Woman Mag 19528 Ventura Blvd # 298 Tarzana CA 91356-2917

SHAWHAN, SAMUEL FRAZIER, JR., telecommunications executive; b. Lexington, Ky., Sept. 19, 1932; s. Samuel F. and Lucille (Holman) S.; m. Ruth Edwards, December 15, 1962; 1 child, Kevin F. BS, Syracuse U., 1955. Various mgmt. positions Gen. Tel. of Upstate N.Y., Johnstown, 1958-62, gen. sales adminstr., 1962-64; dist. mgr. Gen. Tel. of Upstate N.Y., Pulaski, 1964-66; nat. accounts adminstr. GTE Svc. Corp., N.Y.C., 1966-68; market devel. adminstr. GTE Communications Inc., 1968-71; div. mgr. Gen. Telephone of S.E., Dalton, Ga., 1971-75; dir. regulatory affairs GTE Svc. Corp., Washington, 1975-80, asst. v.p. regulatory affairs, 1980-84; v.p. govt. affairs GTE Corp., Washington, 1984—. Trustee Fed. City Coun., Washington. Mem. George Town Club, Internat. Club, Econ. Club of Washington. Presbyterian. Office: GTE Corp 1850 M St NW Ste 1200 Washington DC 20036-5803

SHAWL, S. NICOLE, counseling psychologist; b. South Amboy, N.J., July 26, 1940; d. Michael Joseph and Kathleen Shawl; life ptnr. Donna J. Talcott. BA, Georgian Court Coll., 1971; MA, Kean Coll. of N.J., Union, 1975; PhD, Calif. Coast U., Santa Ana, 1992; postgrad. Saybrook Inst., San Francisco; postgrad. studies in hypno-behavioral psychology, The Union Inst., Cin. Joined Sisters of Mercy, North Plainfield, N.J., 1958, left, 1966; N.J. cert. Substance Awareness Coord. Tchr. pub. and parochial schs., Monmouth & Ocean Counties, N.J., 1960-79; interviewer, pub. rels. mgr. ARC, Toms River, N.J., 1980; editor, writer Prentice-Hall, Englewood Cliffs, N.J., 1980; counselor, asst. dir. coll. program Georgian Court Coll., Lakewood, N.J., 1980—; adj. instr. UCLA, 1975-76; owner, pres. Auntie Nuke Enterprises. Mem. AAUW, ACLU, ACA, So. Poverty Law Ctr., Mercy Higher Edn. Colloquium Assn. Democrat. Avocations: singing opera., sailing, fishing and crabbing, gardening, carpentry. Office: Georgian Court Coll 900 Lakewood Ave Lakewood NJ 08701-2600

SHAWN, WALLACE, playwright, actor; b. N.Y.C., Nov. 12, 1943; s. William and Cecille (Lyon) S.. BA., Harvard U., 1965; MA, Oxford U., Eng., 1968, MA, 1975. Instr. English Indore Christian Coll., Madhya Pradesh, India, 1965-66; tchr. English, Latin, drama Ch. of Heavenly Rest Day Sch., N.Y.C., 1968-70; shipping clk. Laurie Love Ltd., N.Y.C., 1974-75; machine operator Hamilton Copy Ctr., N.Y.C., 1975-76. Author: (plays) Our Late Night, 1975 (Obie award for disting. playwriting 1975), Summer Evening, 1976, The Youth Hostel, 1976, Mr. Frivolous, 1976, (libretto) In the Dark, 1976, (trans.) The Mandrake, 1977, Marie and Bruce, 1980, The Hotel Play, 1981, Aunt Dan and Lemon, 1985; (monologue) The Fever, 1990 (Obie award for best play 1991); (screenplay) My Dinner with Andre, 1981; actor: (theatre) The Mandrake, 1977, The Master and Margarita, 1978, Chinchilla, 1979, The First Time, 1983, Ode to Napoleon Bonaparte, 1984, Aunt Dan and Lemon, 1985, The Fever, 1991; (films) Manhattan, 1979, Starting Over, 1979, All That Jazz, 1979, Simon, 1980, Atlantic City, 1981, My Dinner with Andre, 1981, A Little Sex, 1982, The First Time, 1983, Deal of the Century, 1983, Lovesick, 1983, Strange Invaders, 1983, Saigon-Year of the Cat, 1983, Crackers, 1984, The Hotel New Hampshire, 1984, The Bostonians, 1984, Micki and Maude, 1984, Heaven Help Us, 1985, Head Office, 1986, Radio Days, 1987, The Bedroom Window, 1987, Nice Girls Don't Explode, 1987, Prick Up Your Ears, 1987, The Princess Bride, 1987, The Moderns, 1988, She's Out of Control, 1989, Scenes From the Class Struggle in Beverly Hills, 1989, We're No Angels, 1989, Shadows and Fog, 1992, Mom and Dad Save the World, 1992, Nickel and Dime, 1992, The Cemetary Club, 1993, Un-Becoming Age, 1993, The Meteor Man, 1993, Vanya on 42nd Street, 1994, Mrs. Parker and the Vicious Circle, 1994, Canadian Bacon, 1995, Clueless, 1995; (TV) The Cosby Show, Taxi, How To Be Perfect In Three Days. Fulbright scholar, India, 1956-66. Office: care Rosenstone/Wender 3 E 48th St New York NY 10017-1027 Office: William Morris Agy 151 El Camino Dr Beverly Hills CA 90212*

SHAY, JOHN E., JR., college president; b. Rochester, N.Y., July 29, 1933; m. Patricia Kopacz; children: Maria, John, David. B.A., U. Fla., 1955; M.A., Tchrs. Coll., Columbia U., 1960; Ph.D. in Higher Edn., U. Mich., 1966. Asst. dir. student activities Harpur Coll., SUNY, 1960-62; dean men Marshall U., 1964-65, dean student affairs, 1965-67; dean student Coll. Holy Cross, 1967-71, v.p. student affairs, 1969-71; v.p. student affairs U. R.I., 1971-80; pres. Marygrove Coll., Detroit, 1980—; v.p. student pers. adminstr. W.Va. Coll. and Univs., 1966-67. Contbr. articles to profl. jours. Trustee Detroit Symphony Orch. Hall; bd. dirs. Sta. WTVS-Pub. TV, Detroit, Greater Detroit Interfaith Roundtable NCCJ. Mem. NAACP, Nat. Assn. Student Pers. Adminstrs. (edn. bd. 1967-70, region 1 v.p 1970-71), Mich. Colls. Found. (exec. com.), Nat. Assn. Ind. Colls. and Univs. (bd. dirs.), Assn. Ind. Coll. and Univs. Mich. (treas., exec. com.). Office: Marygrove Coll Office of the Pres 8425 W McNichols Rd Detroit MI 48221-2599

SHAY, ROSHANI CARI, political science educator; b. Milw., Oct. 5, 1942; d. Walter John and Dorothee May (Dahnke) O'Donnell; 1 child, Mark Sather. Student, Willamette U., 1960-63; BA, U. Oreg., 1968, MA, 1971, PhD, 1974. Adminstrv. asst. Dept. of Youth Svcs., Lubbock, Tex., 1963; teaching asst., instr. U. Oreg., Eugene, 1969-72; vis. asst. prof. Oreg. State U., Corvallis, 1973-74, Willamette U., Salem, Oreg., 1973-79, Lewis and Clark Coll., Portland, Oreg., 1976, 78; from asst. prof. to assoc. prof. Western Oreg. State Coll., Monmouth, 1979—, chair history, polit. sci., pub. adminstrn. dept., 1991-94; chair social sci. divsn., 1994—. Author: (with others) The People of Rajneeshpuram, 1990, Annual Yearbook on the Sociology of Religion, 1995, (simulation) European Unity Project, 1982. Cofounder, v.p., sec.-treas. Ind. Opportunities Unltd., Salem, 1986—; cofounder, sec. Inst. for Justice and Human Rights, San Francisco, 1988-94; bd. dirs. Oreg. UN Assn., Portland, 1982—, Salem UN Assn., 1982-91; v.p.,

---

pres., bd. dirs. Garten Found. for Disabled, Salem, 1989—; pres. Assn. Oreg. Faculties, 1989-91; mem. adv. bd. Connections Program for Disabled Deaf, Salem, 1989—; pres., bd. dirs. Model UN of the Far West, San Diego, 1981-84, 86-88; mem. Oreg. Women's Polit. Caucus. Danforth Found. fellow, 1968-74; named Woman of Achievement YWCA Tribute, Salem, 1990. Mem. Am. Fedn. Tchrs. (v.p. and legis. officer local 2278 1982-88), Western Polit. Sci. Assn., Communal Studies Assn., Mental Health Assn. Oreg., Oreg. Acad. Sci., Oreg. Internat. Coun., Phi Kappa Phi (hon.). Democrat. Avocations: volunteer work with multiply disabled deaf, reading, meditation. Home: 348 S Main St Falls City OR 97344-9763 Office: Western Oreg State Coll 345 Monmouth Ave N Monmouth OR 97361-1314

SHAYE, ROBERT KENNETH, cinema company executive; b. Detroit, Mar. 4, 1939; s. Max Mendle and Dorothy (Katz) S.; m. Eva G. Lindsten, 1970; children: Katja, Juno. B.B.A., U. Mich., 1960; postgrad., Sorbonne, 1961; J.D., Columbia U., 1964. Bar: N.Y. 1967. Chmn. of the bd. New Line Cinema Corp., N.Y.C., 1967—. mem. Gov. Adv. Bd. on Motion Pictures and TV. Recipient 1st prize Rosenthal competition Soc. Cinematologists, 1964; recipient cert. of merit Inst. Copyrights and Patents, U. Stockholm, 1966; Recipient award ASCAP/Nathan Burkan Meml. competition, 1964; Fulbright scholar, 1964-66. Mem. Motion Picture Pioneers (bd. dirs.). Club: Friar's (N.Y.C.). Office: New Line Cinema 116 N Robertson Blvd West Hollywood CA 90048-3103 also: New Line Cinema Corp 888 7th Ave New York NY 10106 *Life is a lot tougher than television watching in the '50's led me to believe.*

SHAYKIN, LEONARD P., investor; b. Chgo., Nov. 17, 1943; s. Lawrence L. and Rose (Yaker) S.; m. Norah Josephine Kan, June 26, 1966; children: Benjamin, Gabriel, Rebecca. BA, U. Chgo., 1965, MA, 1966, MBA, 1973; postgrad., U. Sussex, Brighton, Eng., 1970. Investment officer First Capital Corp., Chgo., 1970-74; asst. to chmn. Apeco Corp., Chgo., 1975-76; div. pres. Brown Mfg. Co., Woodstock, Ill., 1976-78; v.p. Citicorp Venture Capital, N.Y.C., 1978-79; v.p., dir. Citicorp Capital Investors, N.Y.C., 1979-82; mng. ptnr. Adler & Shaykin, N.Y.C., 1983—; bd. dirs. Addiction Recovery Corp. Waltham, Mass., GP Tech. Inc., Somerville, N.J., Joy Techs., Inc., Pitts., Best Products, Inc., Richmond, Folger-Adam Inc., Ill., Athena Ptnrs., Israel; chmn., bd. dirs. Peterson Outdoor Advt., Inc., Orlando, 1986-88, Chicago Sun-Times, 1986—; chmn., pres. N.Y. Venture Capital Forum, N.Y.C., 1983; chmn. USIL Investments, Israel. Chmn. Hebrew Arts Sch. and Merkin Concert Hall, N.Y.C., 1983-86. Avocations: sailing, skiing. Home: 101 Central Park W Apt 2F New York NY 10023-4204 Office: Bac Holdings Group Inc 375 Park Ave New York NY 10152-0001 also: Chgo Sun-Times Inc 401 N Wabash Ave Rm 110 Chicago IL 60611-3532

SHAYMAN, JAMES ALAN, nephrologist, educator; b. Chgo., June 14, 1954; s. Benjamin and Chernie (Abrams) S.; m. Deborah Berko, May 30, 1976; children: Rebecca Lynn, David Aaron. AB, Cornell U., 1976; MD, Washington U., St. Louis, 1980. Intern and resident Barnes Hosp., St. Louis, 1980-83; instr. Washington U., St. Louis, 1985-86; asst. prof. U. Mich., Ann Arbor, 1986-92, assoc. prof., 1992—. Mem. Am. Soc. Nephrology, Internat. Soc. Nephrology, Am. Diabetes Assn., Am. Soc. Clin. Investigation, Am. Physiol. Soc., Phi Beta Kappa, Phi Kappa Phi, Alpha Omega Alpha. Achievements include research in renal inositol phosphate metabolism and renal glycolipid metabolism. Office: U Mich Med Ctr 1500 E Med Ctr Dr Ann Arbor MI 48109

SHAYNE, ARNIE See SCHWARTZ, ARNOLD

SHAYNE, STANLEY H., lawyer. Ptnr. Baker & Hostetler, Columbus, Ohio. Office: Baker & Hostetler 65 E State St Columbus OH 43215-4213

SHAYS, CHRISTOPHER, congressman; b. Stamford, Conn., Oct. 18, 1945; m. Betsi deRaismes, 1968; 1 child. BA, Principia Coll.; MBA, MPA, NYU. Vol. U.S. Peace Corps, 1968-70; state rep. State of Conn. (Dist. 147), Stamford, 1974-87; mem. 100th-103rd Congresses from 4th Conn. Dist., Washington, 1987—. Republican. Office: House of Reps 1502 Longworth Bldg Washington DC 20515

SHAYS, RONA JOYCE, lawyer; b. N.Y.C., July 16, 1928; d. Samuel and Beatrice (Fleisher) Eskin; children: Douglas, Sharon; m. Henry C. Shays, Sept. 15, 1974. Student, U. Mich., 1944-47; LLB, Bklyn. Law Sch., 1950; MA, Columbia U., 1968. Bar: N.Y. 1950, U.S. Dist. Ct. (so. and ea. dists) N.Y. 1952. Law clk., assoc. Arthur Bardack, Esquire, Bklyn., 1947-51; assoc. Legal Aid Soc., Mineola, N.Y., 1951-52; legal asst. Mut. Life Ins. Co., N.Y.C., 1959-63; assoc. Hays, Sklar & Herzberg, N.Y.C., 1963-68; from assoc. to ptnr. Mitchell Salem Fisher & Shays, N.Y.C., 1968-76; ptnr. Sheresky, Kalman & Shays, N.Y.C., 1976-77, Shays Kemper, N.Y.C., 1977—. Named Matrimonial Law Arbitrator, Am. Acad. Matrimonial Lawyers, 1992. Fellow Am. Acad. Matrimonial Lawyers (sec. N.Y. state chpt. 1975-82, 90-91, v.p. N.Y. state chpt. 1984-85, 89-90, chair admissions com. N.Y. state chpt. 1986-91, counsel N.Y. state chpt. 1992-93, nat. co-chair interdisciplinary rels. com. 1990-94), Internat. Acad. Matrimonial Lawyers; mem. Assn. of Bar of City of N.Y. (matrimonial law com. 1982-85, 86-89, 92—), Nat. Forum on Mental Health and Family Law (co-chair 1990—), N.Y. State Interdisciplinary Forum on Mental Health and Family Law (co-chair 1986—). Office: Shays Kemper 276 5th Ave New York NY 10001-4509

SHEA, BERNARD CHARLES, retired pharmaceutical company executive; b. Bradford, Pa., Aug. 7, 1929; s. Bernard and Edna Catherine (Green) S.; m. Marilyn Rishell, Apr. 12, 1952; children—David Charles, Melissa Leone. BS in Biology, Holy Cross Coll., Worcester, Mass. Dir. mktg. Upjohn Co., Kalamazoo, Mich., 1954-80; pres. pharm. div. Pennwalt Corp., Rochester, N.Y., 1980-86; v.p. health div. Pennwalt Corp., Phila., 1986, sr. v.p. health div., 1987-88, sr. v.p. chemicals, 1988-89; group pres. Atochem N.Am., Inc., Phila., 1989-90, pharm. cons., 1990-93. Served to lt. (j.g.) USN, 1951-54, Korea.

SHEA, DANIEL BARTHOLOMEW, JR., English language educator, actor; b. Mpls., Oct. 29, 1936; s. Daniel Bartholomew and Dorothea (Lonergan) S.; m. Kathleen Anne Williams, June 3, 1978; children: Timothy, Matthew, Catherine, Daniel, Emily. B.A. summa cum laude, Coll. St. Thomas, 1958; M.A., Stanford U., 1962, Ph.D., 1966. Teaching asst. Stanford U., 1959-61; instr. to prof. English Washington U., St. Louis, 1962—; chmn. dept. Washington U., 1978-84; acting chair performing arts, prof. drama, 1995—; Fulbright-Hays lectr. Univs. of Caen and Nice, France, 1968-69; vis. fellow Clare Hall, U. Cambridge, Eng., 1984-85. Author: Spiritual Autobiography in Early America, 1968, 2d edit., 1988; editorial bd.: Early Am. Lit, 1972-74; sect. editor: Columbia Literary History of the United States; contbr. chpts. to books. Woodrow Wilson fellow, 1958; NEH summer grantee, 1971. Mem. MLA (del. gen. assembly 1977-78), AFTRA, Equity. Home: 6138 Kingsbury Blvd Saint Louis MO 63112-1102 Office: Washington Univ Dept of English Saint Louis MO 63130

SHEA, DAVID MICHAEL, state supreme court justice; b. Hartford, July 1, 1922; s. Michael Peter and Margaret (Agnes) S.; m. Rosemary Anne Sasseen, Apr. 28, 1956; children—Susan, Kathleen, Margaret, Rosemary, Christina, Michael, Maura, Julie. B.A., Wesleyan U., 1944; LL.B., Yale U., 1948. Bar: Conn. 1948. Assoc. Tunick & Ferriss, Greenwich, Conn., 1948-49; assoc. Bailey & Wechsler, Hartford, 1949-57; ptnr. Bailey, Wechsler & Shea, Hartford, 1957-65; judge Conn. Superior Ct., Hartford, 1966-81; justice Conn. Supreme Ct., Hartford, 1981-92, trial referee, 1992—. Served with U.S. Army, 1943-46. Democrat. Roman Catholic. Office: Conn Superior Ct 95 Washington St Hartford CT 06106

SHEA, DION WARREN JOSEPH, association executive; b. New London, Conn., June 10, 1937; s. Frank Steven and Violette Marie (Dion) S.; m. Elizabeth M. Siaba, Dec. 31, 1986; children from previous marriage: Dion Warren Joseph, Nancy Wallace. A.B., Sc.B. in Physics, Brown U., 1959; M.A. in Physics, Boston U., 1962; Ph.D., U. Colo., 1968. Mem. tech. staff RCA, 1959-62; asst. prof. physics Creighton U., 1967-68; NRC/Environ. Sci. Svcs. Adminstrn. fellow, rsch. assoc. Environ. Sci. Svcs. Adminstrn., Boulder, Colo., 1968-70; exec. dir. Soc. Physics Students, Am. Inst. Physics, 1970-87, mgr. edn. div., 1972-87; cons. ednl. and computer sytems, 1988—; dir. alumni affairs U.S. Merchant Marine Acad., Kings Point, N.Y., 1989-93;

---

assoc. dir. devel. CUNY Grad. Sch., 1993—. Author sci. articles. Fellow AAAS; mem. Am. Phys. Soc., Am. Assn. Physics Tchrs., Assn. Coll. Honor Socs. (exec. com. 1984-86), Am. Soc. Assn. Execs., N.Y. Soc. Assn. Execs., Nat. Soc. Fund Raising Execs. (greater N.Y. chpt.), Planned Giving Group Greater N.Y., Coun. Advancement and Support Edn., Sigma Xi, Sigma Pi Sigma, Sigma Chi, Huntington Bicycle Club, Appalachian Mountain Club, Port Dive Club (treas. 1980-83). Home: 1 Doone Dr Syosset NY 11791-6308 Office: Office of Devel Grad Sch and Univ Ctr CUNY 33 W 42d St New York NY 10036

SHEA, DONALD FRANCIS, state supreme court justice; b. Pawtucket, R.I., Sept. 14, 1925; s. Edward Leo and Lucy Rose (Read) S.; m. Ursula V. Rafferty, June 17, 1950; children: Donald Edward, Michaela Theresa, Christopher John, Sara Elizabeth, Ellen Marie. A.B., Providence Coll., 1950; J.D., Georgetown U., 1954. Bar: R.I. Trial atty. firm Boss, Conlan, Keenan, Bulman and Rice, Providence, 1955-72; assoc. justice Superior Ct. R.I., 1972-81, Supreme Ct. R.I., 1981—; part-time law instr. Roger Williams Coll., Bristol; mem. R.I. Ho. of Reps., 1960-68; exec. asst. to gov. R.I., 1968-72. Served with USNR, 1943-46. Mem. ABA, R.I. Bar Assn.

SHEA, DONALD RICHARD, political science educator; b. Mpls., July 15, 1926; s. John James and Marjorie (Jennings) S.; m. Mary Patricia Donovan, June 4, 1948; children: Barbara, John, Marjorie, Kathleen. B.A., U. Minn., 1947, M.A., 1949, Ph.D., 1953. Prof. polit. sci. U. Wis., Milw., 1949-89, prof. emeritus, 1989—, chmn. dept. polit. sci., 1957-61, dir. Inst. for World Affairs, 1960-63, spl. asst. to chancellor, 1962-64, adminstr. Peace Corps Tng. Center, 1962-69, dean Internat. Studies and Programs, 1963-70, dir. Ctr. for Latin America, 1976-89, dir. Inst. World Affairs, Summer Fgn. Student Seminar, 1962, 63, 71, 72; cons. Ford Found., 1966-68. Author: The Calvo Clause: A Problem of Inter-American and International Law and Diplomacy, 1955; editor: Business and Legal Aspects of Latin America Trade and Investment, 1976; sr. editor: Reference Manual on Doing Business in Latin America, 1979; co-editor: Mass Communication in the Americas: Focus on the New World Information and Communication Order, 1985; contbr. to Ency. Americana, The Univ. of Wis.-Milw.: A Hist. Profile, 1992. Bd. dirs. World Affairs Council Milw., Inst. World Affairs, Milw. Internat. Student's Center. Served with USNR, 1944-46. Doherty fellow for research in Latin Am., 1955-56; recipient Kiekhofer Meml. Teaching award, 1975. Mem. Am. Soc. for Internat. Law, Am. Polit. Sci. Assn., Latin Am. Studies Assn. Home: 3346 N Summit Ave Milwaukee WI 53211-2929

SHEA, DONALD WILLIAM, career officer; b. Butte, Mont., Apr. 15, 1936; s. Edward Joseph and Agnes C. (Stanton) S.. BA, Carroll Coll., 1958; BTh., St. Paul (Minn.) Sem., 1962; MA in Human Rels., U. Okla., 1984; MEd, L.I. U., 1975; MA in Pers. Mgmt., Cen. Mich. U., 1981. Ordained priest Roman Cath. Ch., 1962. Commd. 1st lt. U.S. Army, 1966, advanced through grades to maj. gen.; student Basic Chaplain Officer Sch., Ft. Hamilton, N.Y., 1966, Airborne Sch., Ft. Bragg, N.C., 1966; with 3d Brigade, 5th Inf. Div. Dept. of the Army, Ft. Carson, Colo., 1966; student spl. forces officer course Ft. Bragg, N.C., 1967; chaplain 10th Spl. Forces Group Dept. of the Army, Bad Toelz, Germany, 1967; chaplain 5th Spl. Forces Group Dept. of the Army, Vietnam, 1968; chaplain 1st Brigade, 7th Inf. Div. Dept. of the Army, Republic of Korea, 1969; chaplain 15th Field Arty. Group Dept. of the Army, Vietnam, 1970; chaplain 4th Bn., 10th Inf. Dept. of the Army, Panama, 1972; chaplain 2d Bn., 9th Inf. Div. Dept. of the Army, Ft. Lewis, Wash., 1975; chaplain 1st Brigade, 1st Armored Div. Dept. of the Army, Germany, 1977; student Command and Gen. Staff Coll., Ft. Leavenworth, Kans., 1978; div. chaplain 1st Armored Div. Dept. of the Army, Germany, 1978; with office Chief of Chaplains Dept. of the Army, Washington, 1979; student U.S. Army War Coll., Carlisle Barracks, Pa., 1984; chaplain VII Corps U.S. Army, Germany, 1984; staff chaplain U.S. Army Europe, 7th Army U.S. Army War Coll., Germany, 1986; exec. officer, chief of chaplains U.S. Army, Washington, 1989; dep. chief of chaplains U.S. Army War Coll., Washington, 1990-94; chief of chaplains U.S. Army, 1994—. Apptd. Domestic Prelate Pope John Paul II, 1992. Office: Chief of Chaplains US Army The Pentagon Washington DC 20310-2700

SHEA, EDWARD EMMETT, lawyer, educator, author; b. Detroit, May 29, 1932; s. Edward Francis and Margaret Kathleen (Downey) S.; m. Ann Marie Conley, Aug. 28, 1957; children: Michael, Maura, Ellen. AB, U. Detroit, 1954; JD, U. Mich., 1957. Bar: Mich. 1957, Fla. 1959, N.Y. 1961. Assoc. Simpson Thacher & Bartlett, N.Y.C., 1960-63, Dykema, Wheat, Spencer, Detroit, 1963-69, Cadwalader Wickersham & Taft, N.Y.C., 1969-71; v.p., gen. counsel, chmn. Reichhold Chems., White Plains, N.Y., 1971-81; adj. prof. Grad. Sch. Bus. Pace U., N.Y.C., 1982—; counsel, ptnr. Windels, Marx, Davies & Ives, 1982-84, ptnr., 1986—; sr. v.p., gen. counsel GAF Corp., 1984-86; sec. Peridot Chems., 1988—; lectr. N.Y. Inst. Fin., 1995—. Co-author: Acquisitions, Mergers, Sales, Buyouts and Takeovers, 1991; author: An Introduction to the U.S. Environmental Laws, 1995; editor: The Acquisitions Yearbook, 1991, 92, 93; contbr. articles to profl. jours. 1st lt. JAGC, USAF, 1957-60. Mem. N.Y. State Small Bus. Ctr. Program (adv.bd.), N.Y. Athletic Club, Chemist's Club. Office: Windels Marx Davies & Ives 156 W 56th St New York NY 10019-3800

SHEA, JAMES WILLIAM, lawyer; b. N.Y.C., July 10, 1936; s. William P. and Mildred E. (McCaffrey) S.; m. Ann Marie Byrne, June 6, 1964; children: James T., Kathleen A., Tracy A. BS, St. Peters Coll., 1957; JD, Fordham U., 1962; LLM in Taxation, NYU, 1965. Bar: N.Y. 1962, U.S. Dist. Ct. (so. and ea. dists.) N.Y. 1966, U.S. Supreme Ct. 1967. Revenue agent U.S. Treasury Dept., N.Y.C., 1961-63; tax atty. Kennecott Copper Corp., N.Y.C., 1963-67; tax counsel CBS Inc., N.Y.C., 1968-71; ptnr. Hunton & Williams and predecessor firm Conboy, Hewitt, O'Brien & Boardman, N.Y.C., 1971—; bd. dirs. Victory Van Lines Inc., N.Y.C. Rep. committeeman, Staten Island, N.Y., 1980; mem. adv. com. tax and fin. N.Y. State Charter Commn. City of S.I. Served to 1st lt. U.S. Army, 1957-61, to capt. USAR, 1962-72. Mem. ABA, N.Y. State Bar Assn. Republican. Roman Catholic. Club: Richmond County Country (Staten Island), 101 (sec. 1993—). Home: 399 Tysens Ln Staten Island NY 10306-2844 Office: Hunton & Williams 200 Park Ave New York NY 10166-0001

SHEA, JOHN J., catalog and retail company executive; b. Newark, NJ, 1938. BS, La Salle Coll., 1959; MBA, U. Pitts., 1960. With John Wanamaker, Phila., 1953-80; pres., chief exec. officer Spiegel, Inc., Hinsdale, Ill., 1981—, now also vice chmn. Office: Spiegel Inc 1515 W 22nd St Hinsdale IL 60521-2007

SHEA, JOSEPH F., aeronautical engineering educator. Prof. dept. aeronautics MIT, Cambridge, Mass. Fellow AIAA. Office: MIT Dept Aeronautics 77 Massachusetts Ave Cambridge MA 02139-4307*

SHEA, KEVIN MICHAEL, lawyer; b. Indpls., Dec. 23, 1951; s. James Louis and Elizabeth (Walker) S.; m. Marilyn Alkire, Nov. 27, 1985; children: Brendan Alkire, Maura Kathryn. BS, U. Colo., 1973; JD, U. Detroit, 1976. Bar: Colo. 1976, U.S. Dist. Ct. D.C. 1976, U.S. Ct. Appeals (10th cir. 1980), U.S. Supreme Ct. 1982. Dep. dist. atty. Boulder, Colo., 1976-79; shareholder, dir., assoc. Roath & Brega P.C, Denver, 1980-85; spl. counsel Holme Roberts & Owen, Denver, 1985-87, ptnr., 1987-94; ptnr. Ballard, Spahr, Andrews & Ingersoll, Denver, 1994—. Mem. ABA (vice chair environ. crime sect. 1991—), Colo. Bar Assn. (chair criminal law sect. 1990-91), Denver Country Club. Democrat. Avocation: ranching. Office: Ballard Spahr Andrews Inger 1225 17th St Ste 2300 Denver CO 80202

SHEA, MAURICE P., III, bank executive. Pres., chief exec. officer Key Bank of Southwestern N.Y., Chester. Office: Keycorp 1 Key Corp Pla PO Box 88 Albany NY 12201-0088

SHEA, ROBERT MCCONNELL, lawyer; b. North Adams, Mass., May 28, 1924; s. Edward Michael and Margaret Frances (McConnell) S.. AB cum laude, Harvard U., 1948, LLB, 1951; grad. sr. exec. program, MIT, 1962. Bar: Mass. 1951. With John Hancock Mut. Life Ins. Co., Boston, 1951-91, counsel, 1966-70, v.p., counsel, 1970-85; pvt. practice cons., 1986-91. Bd. trustees Lesbard Coll., Boston, 1976-88, sec., 1981-88. Served with U.S. Army, 1943-46. Decorated Bronze Star; recipient Labouré medal Labouré Coll., 1989. Mem. Am., Boston bar assns., Assn. Life Ins. Co., Am. Life

Ins. Assn., Health Ins. Assn. Am. Republican. Catholic. Club: Harvard. Home: 85 Grove St Apt 209 Wellesley MA 02181-7823

SHEA, ROBERT STANTON, retired academic administrator; b. Quincy, Mass., Oct. 15, 1928; s. Arthur Joseph and Isabella (Crowley) S.; m. Ruth Eva Summers, May 30, 1952; children: Robert S. Jr., Stephen D. BS in Math., Boston Coll., 1952; MBA, Calif. State U., Fullerton, 1969. CLU, Chartered Fin. Cons. Test equipment engr. Hughes Aircraft Co., El Segundo, Calif., 1952-56; rsch. engr., project engr. Rockwell Internat., Anaheim, Calif., 1956-70; acctg. systems analyst Safeguard Bus. Systems, Van Nuys, Calif., 1971-76; cons. Am. Grad. U., Covina, Calif., 1987-94; registered rep. Mut. of N.Y., Anaheim, Calif., 1987-94; fin. cons. Empcom Ins. Svcs., Inc., Long Beach, Calif., 1984-94, also bd. dirs.; dean Coll. of Bus. Adminstrn. Pacific States U., L.A., 1972-94; ret., 1994. Track and field official The Athletics Congress, L.A., 1958-88; mem. Anaheim East chpt. Rotary Internat., Anaheim, 1973-85, pres. 1980; patrol leader Boy Scouts Am., Anaheim, 1964-75. With USN, 1946-48. Recipient Merit award Rotary Internat., 1978, Award of Merit, The Athletics Congress, 1977. Mem. Beta Gamma Sigma. Republican. Roman Catholic. Avocations: bicycling, backpacking, fishing, electronics, amateur radio. Home: 43815 Pioneer Ave Hemet CA 92544

SHEA, STEPHEN MICHAEL, physician, educator; b. Galway, Ireland, Apr. 25, 1926; came to U.S., 1956, naturalized, 1966; s. Stephen and Margaret Mary (Cooke) S. B.Sc. in Anatomy and Pathology, Univ. Coll., Galway Nat. U. Ireland, 1948; M.B., B.Ch. in Medicine, 1950, M.Sc. in Pathology, 1951, M.D., 1959. Diplomate: Am. Bd. Pathology. Intern St. Vincent's Hosp., Dublin, Ireland, 1950-51; Dr. Keenan traveling scholar, dept. physiology Univ. Coll., London, 1951-53; asst. lectr. pharmacology Univ. Coll., Dublin, 1953-56; resident in pathology Mallory Inst. Pathology, Boston City Hosp., 1956-59, chief resident, 1958-59; asst. prof. pathology U. Toronto, Ont., Can., 1959-61; instr. Harvard U. Med. Sch., 1961-63, instr. math. biology, 1963-65, asso. in pathology, 1965-67, asst. prof. pathology, 1967-70, assoc. prof., 1970-73; assoc. pathologist Mass. Gen. Hosp. and Shriners Burns Inst., both Boston, 1972-73; prof. pathology Robert Wood Johnson Med. Sch., U.M.D.N.J., 1973—. Contbr. articles to profl. publs. Fellow Royal Coll. Pathologists (U.K.), Royal Coll. Physicians (Can.); mem. Am. Soc. Invest Pathologists, Internat. Acad. Pathology, Am. Soc. Cell Biology, Biophys. Soc., Soc. Math. Biology, Microcirculatory Soc., Harvard Club, Travellers Club, Harvard of Boston Club. Roman Catholic. Home: 1050 George St Apt 12L New Brunswick NJ 08901-1020 Office: UMDNJ-Robert Wood Johnson Med Sch Piscataway NJ 08854

SHEA, WALTER JAMES, labor union executive; b. Bklyn., Nov. 30, 1929; s. Walter Edmund and Madlyn (Baker) S.; m. Mary Ann Carr, Aug. 2, 1952; children: Michael, Kathleen, Sheila, Margaret, Patrick, Mary. A.B. in Edn., U. S.C., 1953. Claims adjuster, examiner Govt. Employees Ins. Co., Washington, 1956-57; research dept. asst. to dir. Eastern Conf. Teamsters, Washington, 1957-67; exec. asst. to gen. pres., v.p. Internat. Brotherhood of Teamsters, Chauffeurs, Warehousemen and Helpers of Am., 1967-92, chmn. Ea. Conf. Teamsters, 1991—; mem. Teamsters Nat. Freight Industry Negotiating Com., 1964-92; co-chmn. Nat. Automobile Negotiation Com., 1967-89; mem. exec .coun. AFL-CIO, 1990—, sec./treas. Dept. Transp. Trades, 1990—. Mem. Presdl. Commn. for Drunk Driving, 1982—; mem. Nat. Coal Council, Dept. Energy; mem. Quadular Forum, Georgetown U. Ctr. Strategic Studies; mem. Panama Canal Commn. Served to capt. USAF, 1954-56. Mem. Kappa Sigma. Democrat. Roman Catholic. Home: 498 Fawns Walk Annapolis MD 21401-5657

SHEA, WILLIAM RENE, historian, philosopher of science, educator; b. Gracefield, Que., Can., May 16, 1937; s. Herbert Clement and Jeanne (Lafreniere) S.; m. Evelyn Fischer, May 2, 1970; children—Herbert, Joan-Emma, Louisa, Cecilia, Michael. B.A., U. Ottawa, 1958; L.Ph., Gregorian U., Rome, 1959; L.Th., Gregorian U., 1963; Ph.D., Cambridge U., Eng., 1968. Assoc. prof. U. Ottawa, Ont., Can., 1968-73; fellow Harvard U., Cambridge, Mass., 1973-74; prof. history and philosophy of sci. McGill U., Montreal, 1974—; dir. d'etudes Ecole des Hautes Etudes, Paris, 1981-82; sec.-gen. Internat. Union of History and Philosophy of Sci., 1983-89, pres., 1990-93; mem. gen. com. Internat. Coun. of Sci. Union, Paris, 1983-89; cons. Killam Found., Ottawa, Ont., 1983-85; mem. McGill Centre for Medicine, Ethics and Law, 1990-95; Hydro Que. prof. environ. ethics, 1992—; vis. prof. U. Rome, 1992; dir. Inst. History of Sci., U. Louis Pasteur, Strasbourg, 1995—. Author: Galileo Intellectual Revolution, 1972, The Magic of Numbers and Motion, 1991; co-author: Galileo Florentine Residences, 1979; editor: Nature Mathematized, 1983, Otto Hahn and the Rise of Nuclear Physics, 1983, Revolutions in Science, 1988, Creativity in the Arts and Science, 1990, Persuading Science: The Art of Scientific Rhetoric, 1991, Interpreting the World, Science and Society, 1991, Energy Needs in the Year 2000: Ethical and Environmental Perspectives, 1994. Can. Coun. fellow, 1965-68, Can. Cultural Inst. fellow, Rome, 1973, Social Scis. and Humanities Rsch. Coun. Can., 1980-81, Inst. of Advanced Studies in Berlin fellow, 1988-89; recipient The Alexandre Koyre medal Internat. Acad. of History of Sci., 1993, Knight of the Order of Malta, 1993. Fellow Royal Soc. Can.; mem. History of Sci. Soc. (coun. 1973-76), European Sci. Found. (standing com. for humanities 1989-95), Can. Nat. Com. of History and Philosophy of Sci. (coun. 1982-93), Can. Philos. Assn., Internat. Acad. History of Sci. (ordinary), McGill Faculty Club. Home: 217 Berkely, Saint Lambert, PQ Canada J4P 3C9 Office: McGill U Dept Philosophy, 855 Sherbrooke St W, Montreal, PQ Canada H3A 2T7

SHEAHAN, JOHN BERNARD, economist, educator; b. Toledo, Sept. 11, 1923; s. Bernard William and Florence (Sheahan) S.; m. Denise Eugénie Morlino, Nov. 29, 1946; children: Yvette Marie, Bernard Eugene. BA, Stanford U., 1948; PhD, Harvard U., 1954. Econ. analyst Office Spl. Rep. in Europe, ECA, Paris, France, 1951-54; mem. faculty Williams Coll., 1954—; prof. econs. Williams Coll., Williamstown, Mass., 1966-94, prof. emeritus; mem. devel. adv. service Colombia adv. group Harvard, 1963-65; nat. research prof. Brookings Instn., 1959-60; vis. prof. El Colegio de México, Mexico City, 1970-71; Fulbright research scholar Institut de recherche économique et de planification, Université de Grenoble, France, 1974-75; vis. scholar Inst. Devel. Studies, U. Sussex, 1981-82; vis. fellow Ctr. for U.S.-Mexican Studies, U. Calif. at San Diego, 1991. Author: Promotion and Control of Industry in Postwar France, 1963, The Wage-Price Guideposts, 1967, An Introduction to the French Economy, 1969, Patterns of Development in Latin America, 1987, Conflict and Change in Mexican Economic Strategy, 1992. Mem. Presdl. Price Adv. Com., 1979-80. Mem. Am. Econ. Assn., Latin Am. Studies Assn., New England Coun. Latin Am. Studies (pres. 1989-90), Phi Beta Kappa. Home: Syndicate Rd Williamstown MA 01267 Office: Williams Coll Dept Econs Williamstown MA 01267

SHEAHAN, ROBERT EMMETT, lawyer, management employment and environment law consultant; b. Chgo., May 20, 1942; s. Robert Emmett and Lola Jean (Moore) S.; m. Pati Smith, Mar. 20, 1991. BA, Ill. Wesleyan U., 1964; JD, Duke U., 1967; MBA, U. Chgo., 1970. Bar: Ill. 1967, La. 1975, N.C. 1978. Vol. VISTA, N.Y.C., 1967-68; trial atty. NLRB, Milw. and New Orleans, 1970-75; ptnr. Jones, Walker, Waechter, Poitevent, Carrere & Denegre, New Orleans, 1975-78; pvt. practice, High Point, N.C., 1978—; bd. dirs. Inst. for Effective Mgmt., Bus. Publs. Inst. Author: Employees and Drug Abuse: An Employer's Handbook, The Encyclopedia of Drugs in the Workplace, Labor and Employment Law in North Carolina, 1991, Personnel and Employment Law in North Carolina, 1992, Desk Book of Labor and Employment Law for Healthcare Employers, 1995; contbg. author: The Developing Labor Law, 1975—; editor: The World of Personnel; contbg. editor: Employee Testing and the Law. Bd. dirs. High Point United Way, 1979-83; mem. congressional action com. High Point C. of C., chmn., 1991—. Mem. ABA, N.C. Bar Assn., High Point Bar Assn., Ill. Bar Assn., La. Bar Assn. Republican. Roman Catholic. Clubs: Sedgefield (N.C.) Country, String and Splinter (High Point), Bald Head (N.C.) Island Club. Home: 101 Bellwood Ct Jamestown NC 27282-9446 Office: Eastchester Office Ctr 603B Eastchester Dr High Point NC 27262-7634

SHEALY, CLYDE NORMAN, neurosurgeon; b. Columbia, S.C, Dec. 4, 1932; s. Clyde Lemuel and Palma Leona (Padget) S.; m. Mary-Charlotte Bayles, June 13, 1959; children: Brock Allison, Craig Norman, Laurel Elizabeth. B.S. in Medicine, Duke U., 1956, MD, 1956; PhD, Humanistic Psychology Inst., San Francisco, 1977; DSc (hon.), Ryodomaku Rsch. Inst.,

Kansas City, 1979. Intern Duke U. Hosp., Durham, N.C., 1956-57; resident in neurosurgery Mass. Gen. Hosp., Boston, 1958-63; sr. instr., then asst. prof. neurosurgery Western Res. U. Med. Sch., 1963-66; chief neurosurgery Gundersen Clinic, LaCrosse, Wis., 1966-71; assoc. clin. prof. neurosurgery U. Minn. Med. Sch., 1970-75; asst. clin. prof. U. Wis. Med. Sch., 1967-74; dir. Pain and Health Rehab. Center, S.C., LaCrosse, 1971-81; pres. Holos Insts. Health, 1981—; founder, dir. Shealy Pain and Health Rehab. Inst., Springfield, Mo.; clin. prof., prof. clin. research Forest Inst. Profl. Psychology; adj. prof. Columbia Pacific U. Author: Occult Medicine Can Save Your Life, 1975, The Pain Game, 1976, 90, Days to Self Health, 1977 (with Mary-Charlotte Shealy), To Parent or Not, 1981, Speedy Gourmet, 1985, AIDS: Pathway to Transformation, 1987, The Creation of Health, 1988, Third Party Rape: The Conspiracy to Rob You of Health Care, 1993, The Self-Healing Workbook, 1993; also articles. Served with USNR, 1956-63. Fellow ACS, Am. Coll. Preventive Medicine; mem. AMA, Am. Acad. Pain Medicine, Am. Acad. Pain Mgmt., Mo. State Med. Assn., Greene County Med. Soc., Harvey Cushing Soc., Am. Holistic Med. Assn. (founder, past pres., chmn. edn. com.), Am. Assn. Study Headache, Internat. Assn. Study Pain, Internat. Acad. Preventive Medicine, Phi Beta Kappa, Alpha Omega Alpha. Address: 1328 E Evergreen Springfield MO 65803 *Preventing illness is infinitely more important than treating it. My belief and practice has evolved from the treatment of illness to a major educational role. Most illnesses are the result of unhealthy habits. We need to teach people how to deal with those at all levels: physical, chemical, emotional, mental and spiritual.*

SHEALY, DAVID LEE, physicist, educator; b. Newberry, S.C., Sept. 16, 1944; s. William Elmer and Elizabeth (Plaxico) S.; m. Elaine Wohlford, June 17, 1969; children: Bridget McGill, David McElwee. BS, U. Ga., 1966, PhD, 1973. Prof., chmn. dept. physics, U. Ala., Birmingham, 1984—; cons. Motorola, Phoenix, 1978-84, Jet Propulsion Lab., Pasadena, Calif., 1980-82, Los Alamos Nat. Lab., 1989-91, NASA Marshall Space Flight Ctr., 1989—. Contbr. articles to profl. jours. Faculty fellow NASA, ASEE, 1980, 81; recipient Silver Quill and Publ. award Motorola, 1982, 83. Mem. IEEE (adminstrv. com., 1988-90, research paper award Ala. Sect. 1984), Am. Assn. Physics Tchrs., Am. Physical Soc., Optical Soc. Am. (fellow 1988), Material Rsch. Soc., N.Y. Acad. Sci. Republican. Avocation: running. Home: 2337 Morningstar Dr Birmingham AL 35216-2005 Office: U Ala-Birmingham Dept Physics CH-310 Birmingham AL 35294-1170

SHEALY, WALTER DIXON, III, banker; b. Charleston, S.C., Apr. 14, 1949; s. Walter Dixon Jr. and Celia Louise (Snipes) S.; m. Dottie Jean Cummings. BS, Presbyn. Coll., Clinton, S.C., 1971. V.p. Citizens and So. Nat. Bank, Atlanta, 1971-78; sr. v.p. Mortgage Guaranty Ins. Corp., Milw., 1978-84; sr. exec. v.p., chief mktg. officer CenTrust Mortgage Corp. subs. CenTrust Savs. Bank, Deerfield, Fla., 1984, now dir. mgmt., also bd. dirs.; sr. exec. v.p., dir. Capital Markets Group CenTrust Savs. Bank, Miami, Fla., 1984—, chmn. asset and liability mgmt. com., pres., 1988—; bd. dirs. Old Am. Ins. Co., Kansas City, Mo., Securnet Securities Corp., Phoenix. Author (with others): The MGIC Secondary Market Guide; contbr. articles to profl. jours. Mem. Fla. League Fin. Instns. (dist. dir.), Greater Miami C. of C. (bd. govs.), Blue Key Soc., Brickell Club. Presbyterian. Avocations: tennis, hunting, fishing, ranching. Office: CenTrust Savs Bank 100 SE 2nd St Miami FL 33131-2100

SHEAR, THEODORE LESLIE, JR., archaeologist, educator; b. Athens, Greece, May 1, 1938; s. Theodore Leslie and Josephine (Platner) S.; m. Ione Doris Mylonas, June 24, 1959; children: Julia Louise, Alexandra. AB summa cum laude, Princeton U., 1959, MA, 1963, PhD, 1966. Instr. Greek and Latin Bryn Mawr Coll., 1964-66, asst. prof., 1966-67; asst. prof. art and archaeology Princeton (N.J.) U., 1967-70, assoc. prof., 1970-79, chmn. program in classical archaeology, 1970-85, assoc. chmn. dept. art and archaeology, 1976-78, 82-83, prof. classical archaeology, 1979—; prof. archaeology Am. Sch. Classical Studies, Athens, 1988—; mem. mng. com. Am. Sch. Classical Studies, Athens, 1972—; mem. archaeol. expdns. to Greece and Italy, including Mycenae, 1953-54, 58, 62-63, 65-66, Eleusis, 1956, Perati, 1956, Corinth, 1960, Morgantina, Sicily, 1962; mem. Ancient Agora of Athens, 1955, 67, field dir., 1968-94; trustee William Alexander Procter Found., 1982-89, Princeton Jr. Sch., 1983—, pres., 1994—. Author: Kallias of Sphettos and the Revolt of Athens in 286 B.C., 1978; contbr. articles to profl. jours. White fellow Am. Sch. Classical Studies, 1959-60. Mem. Archaeol. Inst. Am., Am. Philol. Assn., Coll. Art Assn., Archaeol. Soc. Athens (hon.), Phi Beta Kappa. Republican. Episcopalian. Clubs: Century Assn. (N.Y.C.); Nassau (Princeton); Princeton (N.Y.C.); Hellenic Yacht (Piraeus, Greece). Home: 87 Library Pl Princeton NJ 08540-3015

SHEARER, CAROLYN JUANITA, secondary education educator; b. Heber Springs, Ark., May 20, 1944; d. James A. and Juanita Ruth (Wallace) S. BS, U. Colo., Boulder, 1966, MA, 1972. Cert. tchr., Colo. Tchr. Aurora (Colo.) Pub. Schs., reading resource tchr.; presenter writing process workshops. Author curriculum materials. Mem. PTA. Mem. NEA, ASCD, Colo. Edn. Assn., Aurora Edn. Assn. (bd. dirs., bargaining support team), Internat. Reading Assn., Colo. Reading Assn., Aurora Reading Assn. Pi Lambda Theta (v.p. Denver Metro chpt.). Democrat. Methodist. Office: West Mid Sch 10100 E 13th Ave Aurora CO 80010-3302

SHEARER, CHARLES LIVINGSTON, academic administrator; b. Louisville, Ky., Nov. 23, 1942; s. Guy Cooper and Kathryn (Aufenkamp) S.; m. Susan Pulling Shearer, Mar. 30, 1968; children: Todd A., Mark G., Scott B. BS, U. Ky., 1964, MA, 1967; MA, Mich. State U., 1973, PhD, 1981. Instr. Henderson (Ky.) Community Coll., 1967-69; asst. prof. Ferris State Coll., Big Rapids, Mich., 1969-71; grad. asst. Mich. State U., East Lansing, 1971-73; dir. mngmt. program Albion (Mich.) Coll., 1973-75, dir. ops., 1975-79; v.p. fin. Transylvania U., Lexington, Ky., 1979-83, pres., 1983—; bd. dirs. Ky. Utilities, Lexington. Bd. dirs. Lexington Philharmonic Soc., 1983-89; mem. adv. bd. Salvation Army, Lexington, 1983-87; mem. Henry Clay Meml. Found., Lexington, 1983-89. Capt. U.S. Army Nat. Guard, 1966-76. Named One of Outstanding Young Men in Am., 1978. Mem. Am. Econs. Assn., Lexington C. of C. (bd. dirs 1985—). Mem. Christian Ch. (Disciples of Christ). Lodge: Rotary.

SHEARER, CYNTHIA HODGE, lawyer; b. Midland, Mich., Sept. 18, 1950; d. John Austin Jr. and Mary Jean (Bale) Hodge; m. Richard L. Shearer, Aug. 26, 1978; children: Whitney Marie, James Michael. BA, Western Mich. U., 1972; JD, U. Denver, 1980. Bar: Colo. 1981, U.S. Dist. Ct. Colo. 1981. Assoc. Hall & Evans, Denver, 1980-83, Constantine, Anderson & Tobey, Denver, 1983-85; atty. Colo. Nat. Bank, Denver, 1985—. Mem. ABA, Colo. Bar Assn., Denver Bar Assn. Avocations: skiing, scuba diving, travel, gourmet cooking. Office: Colo Nat Bank 950 17th St Denver CO 80202

SHEARER, DEREK N., international studies educator, diplomat, administrator; b. L.A., Dec. 5, 1946; s. Lloyd and Marva (Peterson) S.; m. Ruth Y. Goldway, July 8, 1976; 1 child, Casey; stepchildren: Anthony, Julia. BA, Yale U., 1968; PhD, Union Grad. Sch., Yellow Springs, Ohio, 1977. Lectr. U. Calif., L.A., 1979-81; dir. internat. and pub. affairs ctr., prof. of pub. policy Occidental Coll., L.A., 1981-94; dep. under sec. U.S. Dept. Commerce, Washington, 1993; U.S. ambassador to Finland U.S. Dept. State, Washington, 1994—; fellow Econ. Strategy Inst., Washington, 1993; policy adv. to Presidential Candidate Bill Clinton, 1990-92. Co-author: A New Social Contract, 1984, Economic Democracy, 1980, Putting People First, 1992. Planning commr. City of Santa Monica (Calif.), 1984; bd. mem. Nat. Consumer Bank, Washington, 1991. Recipient Guggenheim Fellowship Guggenheim Found., 1984, U.S.-Japan Leadership fellow Japan Soc., 1991. Democrat. Avocations: baseball, tennis, travel, mysteries. Home: 12725 Sunset Blvd Los Angeles CA 90049

SHEARER, JOHN CLYDE, economics consultant, labor arbitrator, international manpower consultant; b. Phila., June 24, 1928; s. John Dwight and Edna Mildred (Moser) S.; m. Mary Ann Shafer, Apr. 30, 1955; children—John Peter, Rachel Alicia. Student, Cornell, 1945-46, 48-52; B.S., N.Y. State Sch. Indsl. and Labor Relations, 1952; postgrad., U. Manchester, Eng., 1952-53; A.M., Princeton, 1958, Ph.D., 1960. Adminstrv. asst. indsl. relations Union Carbide Metals Co., Marietta, Ohio, 1952-56; research asst. indsl. relations Princeton, 1957-60; asst. prof. econs. Grad. Sch. Indsl. Adminstrn. Carnegie Inst. Tech., Pitts., 1960-65; assoc. prof. econs. Pa. State

U., State College, 1965-67; prof. econs., dir. Manpower Research and Tng. Center Okla. State U., Stillwater, 1967-87, emeritus prof. econs., 1987—; prof., economist Latin Am. Inst. Econ. and and Social Planning, UN Econ. Commn. for Latin Am., Santiago, Chile, 1962-63; cons. OAS, UN, Ford Found., Inter-Am. Devel. Bank, Coun. Internat. Progress in Mgmt., ILO, AMA, others; mem. arbitration panels Fed. Mediation and Conciliation Svc., Am. Arbitration Assn., Employment Disputes Settlement Panel. Author: High-Level Manpower in Overseas Subsidiaries: Experience in Brazil and Mexico, 1960, La Importación y La Exportación de Los Recursos Humanos, 1964, (with Jacob Kaufman, Grant Farr) The Development and Utilization of Human Resources, 1967, Industrial Relations of American Corporations Abroad, 1967, (with Rafael Isaza) Employment and Unemployment in Colombia, 1969, Manpower Environments Confronting American Firms in Western Europe, 1970, Intra and International Movements of High-Level Human Resources, 1971, High-Level Human Resources in Economic Development, 1973, Arbitration and Changing Life Styles, 1974, Fact and Fiction Concerning Multinational Labor Relations, 1977, Dispute Settlement in the South, 1981, (with I.B. Helburn) Human Resources and Industrial Relations in China: A Time of Ferment, 1984, Reducing Cost of Arbitration Through Increasing the Parties' Options, 1985, Reinstatement without Back Pay: An Appropriate Remedy?, 1987; contbr. articles to profl. jours. Mem. for edn. Southwestern Regional Manpower Adv. Com. to Secs. Labor and HEW. Served with USMC, 1946-48. Fulbright fellow Eng., 1952-53; Owen D. Young fellow, 1956-57, 57-58; Ford Found. fellow, 1958-59. Mem. Am. Econ. Assn., So. Econ. Assn., Okla. Civil Liberties Union, Indsl. Relations Research Assn., Internat. Indsl. Rel. Assn., Soc. Internat. Devel., Nat. Acad. Arbitrators (bd. govs.), Am. Arbitration Assn., Soc. Profl. in Dispute Resolution. Home: 2020 N Crescent Dr Stillwater OK 74075-2801 also: RR 1 Box 2210 Mount Vernon ME 04352-9720

SHEARER, P. SCOTT, government relations professional; b. Clinton, Ill., Feb. 27, 1948; s. Lloyd Jr. and Pauline Lucille (Glosser) S.; m. Barbara Boston, July 3, 1981; children: Jason J., Carrie K. BS, U. Ill., 1970, MS, 1975. Asst. dir. cash mgmt. State Treas. Ill., Springfield, 1973-74, asst. chief fin. officer, 1974-77, chief fiscal officer, 1977-78; dir. vehicle svc. State of Ill., Springfield, 1978-81; legis. asst. Senator Dixon U.S. Senate, Washington, 1981-84; exec. dir. Nat. Corn Growers Assn., St. Louis, 1984-90; dir. govt. rels. Halfpenny, Hahn, Roche & Marchese, 1990-93; dir. legis. affairs Zeneca Inc., Washington, 1993; dep. asst. sec. congl. rels. USDA, 1993—; adv. com. Ill. Atty.'s Gen. Agr. Law, State of Ill., 1985-91, Dean Coll. Agr., U. Ill., 1989-90, U. Ill. Dept. Agrl. Econs., 1986-89. Del. Dem. Nat. Conv., 1978, Mo. Dem. State Conv., 1988, Va. Dem. State Conv., 1992, 93; mem. Police Bd. Commrs., Chesterfield, Mo., 1988-90; pres. Mo. River Dem. Club, 1987-89. Named to Hon. Order of Ky. Cols., 1990, Alpha Gamma Sigma nat. merit award, 1991. Mem. St. Louis Agr.-Bus. Club (sec.-treas. 1987-88, 2d v.p. 1988-89, v.p. 1989-90, pres. 1990), U. Ill. Alumni Assn., U. Ill. Coll. Agr. Alumni Assn. (dir. at large 1990), Ill. Group (chmn. 1993), Alpha Zeta. Methodist. Home: 2744 Clarkes Landing Dr Oakton VA 22124-1120 Office: Dept Agr 213-A Adminstrn Bldg 14th & Independence Ave Washington DC 20250

SHEARER, RICHARD EUGENE, industrial consultant; b. Connellsville, Pa., Dec. 30, 1919; s. H.D. and Florence (Prinkey) S.; m. Ruth Mansberger, June 16, 1944 (dec. Mar. 1993); children: Patricia (Mrs. Richard Wilson), Suzanne (Mrs. Terry Jones), Richard J.; m. Marilyn Likeness Erdman, May 7, 1994. A.B., Eastern Bapt. Coll. and Sem., Phila., 1943, D.D., 1953; B.D., New Brunswick Theol. Sem., 1945; M.A., Columbia, 1948, Ed.D., 1959; LL.D., Denison U., 1958; H.H.D., Bishop Coll., 1977. Ordained to ministry Bapt. Ch., 1943; minister Atlantic Highlands, N.J., 1943-45, New Brunswick, N.J., 1945-50; pres. Alderson-Broaddus Coll., Philippi, W.Va., 1951-83; ind. cons., 1983—; cons., interim dir. W.Va. Found. Ind. Colls.; prin. resdl. devel. Bridgeport, W.Va., 1983—; v.p., exec. dir. United Health Found., Clarksburg, W.Va., 1987—; pres. R. Shearer & Assocs., Philippi, W.Va., 1984; lectr. Mex. Pastor's Conf., summer 1955; past pres. W.Va. Found. Ind. Colls.; mem. commn. on Instnl. Funding, Am. Bapt. Chs., U.S.A.; coordinator (Central Europe Coll. Program); pres. Am. Bapt. Assn. Sch. and Coll. Adminstrs., 1977; mem. W.Va. Ednl. Found., W.Va. State Scholarship Commn. Bd. regents W.Va. Assn. Pvt. Colls.; bd. dirs. W.Va. Found. Independent Colls.; sr. min. Bridgeport (W.Va.) Bapt. Ch., 1988-93; bd. dirs. Eastern Bapt. Theol. Sem., Phila. Named Phi Delta Kappa Profl. Educator of Year, 1964. Mem. Am. Assn. Sch. Adminstrs., W.Va. Assn. Coll. and Univ. Presidents (sec. mem. exec. com. 1963—), Assn. Am. Colls. (commn. coll. and soc.), Kiwanis. Office: Alderson-Broaddus Coll RR 3 Box 27216 Philippi WV 26416-9803 *The joint impact of good religion and good education has been the dominant theme of my life and work. I feel that education is a powerful force which can be directed in either constructive or destructive directions. Good religion can assure that the power in education is constructive, and good education can assure that religion has depth.*

SHEARER, RONALD ALEXANDER, economics educator; b. Trail, C., Can., June 15, 1932; s. James Boyd and Mary Ann (Smith) S.; m. Renate Elizabeth Selig, Dec. 20, 1956 (dec.); children: Carl, Bruce. B.A., U. B.C., 1954; M.A., Ohio State U., 1955, Ph.D., 1959. Asst. prof. econs. U. Mich., 1958-62; economist Royal Commn. Banking and Finance, Toronto, 1962-63; mem. faculty U.B.C, Vancouver, 1963—; prof. econs. U. B.C., 1970—, head dept., 1972-76. Co-author: Money and Banking, 1975, The Economics of the Canadian Financial System, 1994; editor: Trade Liberalization and a Regional Economy, 1971. Mem. Am., Canadian econs. assns. Office: Univ BC, Dept Economics, Vancouver, BC Canada

SHEARER, VELMA MILLER, clergywoman; b. Hines, Minn., Jan. 2, 1921; d. Floyd and Mary (Ross) M.; m. Byron C. Shearer, Nov. 3, 1946; 1 child, Mary Jane. RN, Rockford (Ill.) Meml. Hosp., 1944; BFA, U. Dayton, Ohio, 1968; MDiv, United Theol. Sem., Dayton, 1984, DMin, 1987. Ordained to ministry Ch. of the Brethren, 1987. Staff nurse, supr. Castaner (P.R.) Gen. Hosp., 1945-47; staff nurse, oper. rm. supr. Dettmer Hosp., Troy, Ohio, 1954-58; nursing instr. Miami Valley Hosp., Dayton, 1970-72; clergy So. Ohio dist. Ch. of the Brethren, 1983—, Neighbors in Need, 1990—; field edn. supervisor Bethany Theol. Sem., Richmond, Ind., 1994—. Author: Nuc Radiation and Cancer, 1981; artist numerous paintings and drawings. Mem. nuclear study com. Ch. of the Brethren, So. Ohio, 1978-92; bd. dirs. Ohio Environ. Coun. Recipient Ann. Peace award Wright State U.; Ohio Humanities Coun. grantee, 1989-90. Mem. Internat. Assn. Women Ministers, Ohio Environ. Coun. (bd. dirs. 1994—). Home and Office: 124 Chestnut St Apt 210 Englewood OH 45322-1410

SHEARER, WILLIAM KENNEDY, lawyer, publisher; b. Marysville, Calif., Jan. 21, 1931; s. William and Eva (Kennedy) S.; m. Eileen Mary Knowland; Nov. 25, 1956; 1 child, Nancy Lorena. BA, San Diego State U., 1955; JD, Western State U., 1975. Bar: Calif. 1975, U.S. Dist. Ct. (so. dist.) Calif. 1975, U.S. Ct. Claims 1976, U.S. Supreme Ct. 1982, U.S. Ct. Appeals (fed. cir.) 1982, U.S. Ct. Appeals (9th cir.) 1983. Legis. asst. to Congressman James Utt, 1953, 55-56; exec dir. San Diego County Rep. Cen. Com., 1956-58; pub. Oceanside-Carlsbad Banner, Oceanside, Calif., 1958-63; adminstrv. asst. Assemblyman E.R. Barnes, Sacramento, Calif., 1963-65; polit. campaign cons. Banner Advt., San Diego, Los Angeles, 1964-75; atty. Duke, Gerstel, Shearer & Bregante, San Diego, 1975—. Pub. newsletters Calif. Statesman, 1962—, Legis. Survey, 1963—, Fgn. Policy Rev., 1972—, Am. Ind., 1974—. Rep. nominee for State Assembly, San Diego County, 1956, 58; state chmn. Am. Ind. Party, Calif., 1967-70, nat. chmn. 1968-71, 73-77; nat. vice chmn. U.S. Taxpayers Party, 1992—; Am. Ind. nominee for Gov., 1970; adv. com. Elections Com., Calif. Legislature, Sacramento, 1971-76; bd. dirs. San Diego Gilbert & Sullivan Co., 1984-90, pres. 1986-88, v.p., 1985-86, 88-90. With U.S. Army, 1953-55. Mem. ABA, Calif. Bar Assn., San Diego County Bar Assn. Avocations: ancient Near Eastern history, gardening, music. Home: 8160 Palm St Lemon Grove CA 91945-3028 Office: Duke Gerstel Shearer & Bregante 101 W Broadway Ste 600 San Diego CA 92101

SHEARER, WILLIAM THOMAS, pediatrician, educator; b. Detroit, Aug. 23, 1937. BS, U. Detroit, 1960; PhD, Wayne State U., 1966; MD, Washington U., St. Louis, 1970. Diplomate Am. Bd. Pediatrics, Am. Bd. Allergy & Immunology (chmn.), Nat. Bd. Med. Examiners; cert. in diagnostic lab. immunology. Post-doctoral fellow in biochemistry dept. chem. Indiana U., Bloomington, 1966-67; intern in pediatrics St. Louis Children's Hosp., 1970-71, resident in pediatrics, 1971-72, dir. divsn. allergy and immunology, 1974-

78; fellow in immunology in pediatrics Barnes Hosp., Washington U., St. Louis, 1972-74; spl. USPHA sci. rsch. fellow in medicine dept. medicine Washington U., 1972-74, assoc. prof., 1978, prof., 1978; prof. pediatrics and microimmunology Baylor Coll. Medicine, Houston, 1978—, dir. AIDS rsch. ctr., 1991—; head sect. allergy & immunology Tex. Children's Hosp., Houston, 1978—; mem. ACTU comm. adv. bd. Tex. Children's Hosp., 1991; ad hoc reviewer NIAID/NIH, Bethesda, 1991; chair Am. Bd. Allergy and Immunology, 1990—; dir. pediatric HIV/AIDS Clin. Rsch. Ctr., Houston, 1988—; chmn. exec. com. clin. trial intravenous gammaglobulin in HIV infected children NICHHD, Bethesda, mem. pediatric core com., pediatrics AIDS clin. trial group NIAID, 1989. Guest editor Seminar Pediatric Infectious Disease, 1990; editl. bd. Jour. of Allergy and Clin. Immunology, Clin. and Diagnositc Lab. Immunology; editor Pediatric Allergy and Immunology, Allergy and Immunology Training Program Dir., 1993; contbr. intro.: Allergy: Principles and Practice, 1992; contbr. articles to profl. jours. including New Eng. Jour. Medicine. AIDS cons. Houston Ind. Sch. Dist., 1986—; med. adv. Spring Branch Ind. Sch. Dist., Houston, 1987—; chmn. community HIV/AIDS adv. group Tex. Med. Ctr., 1991—. Recipient Rsch. Scholar award Cystic Fibrosis Found., 1974-77, Faculty Rsch. award Am. Cancer Soc., 1977-79, Myrtle Wreath award Hadassah, 1985, Spl. Recognition award Am. Acad. Allergy and Immunology, 1994. Mem. Am. Soc. Clin. Investigation, Am. Acad. Pediatrics (mem. exec. com. sect. allergy & immunology) 1991—). Achievements include research in half-matched T-cell-depleted bone marrow transplants, in membrane signal pathway of human B lymphcytes. Office: Tex Childrens Hosp A/I Svc 6621 Fannin St Houston TX 77030-2303

SHEARING, CLIFFORD DENNING, criminology and sociology educator; b. Durban, Natal, South Africa, Feb. 2, 1942; s. Cecil and Amy (Clifford) S.; children: Anthony Denning, Renée Anne. B Social Sci. in Psychology-and-Sociology, U. Natal, Durban, 1965, B Social Sci. in Sociology cum laude, 1967; MA in Sociology 1st class, U. Toronto, Ont., Can., 1968, PhD in Sociology, 1977. Assoc. Can. Inst. for Advanced Rsch., 1985-89; rsch. assoc. Ctr. Criminology U. Toronto, 1972-75, sr. rsch. assoc., 1976-83, coord. grad. studies, 1978-83, 89—, sr. fellow Woodsworth Coll., 1985—, assoc. prof. Ctr. Criminology, 1984-89, prof., 1989—, dir. Ctr. Criminology, 1993—, instr. Woodsworth Coll., 1976-81, assoc. prof., 1981-89, prof., 1989—, assoc. prof. dept. sociology, 1981-89, prof., 1989—; mem. bd. control Ctr. for Socio-Legal Studies, U. Natal, 1988-90, assoc. mem., 1990—; vis. rsch. prof. Cmty. Law Ctr., U. Western Cape, Cape Town, South Africa, 1991-93, dir., 1993—; vis. prof. faculty law U. Cape Town, 1992-93, vis. lectr., 1993—; assoc. Inst. Criminology, 1992-93; vis. fellow dept. law Rsch. Sch. Social Sci., Australia Nat. U., 1992; faculty advisor Can. Criminology Forum, 1979-83, reviewer, 1983-85; reviewer Can. Jour. Sociology, 1982—; Social Problems, 1982—, Law and Society Rev., 1983-85, Am. Bar Found. Rsch. Jour./Law and Social Inquiry, 1988—, Can. Jour. Criminology, 1988—, Criminology, 1989—, Jour. Contemporary Ethnography, 1990—, Law and Policy, 1991—; Economy and Society, 1995—; assoc. cons. Jour. Criminal Law and Criminology, 1991—; cons. Can. Police Coll., 1979-80, Met. Toronto Housing Authority, 1987-89, Toronto Transit Commn., 1987, Office Pub. Compaints Commr., Ont., 1986-87, Hoppo Valley Estates, Zimbabe, 1986, Ont. Waste Mgmt. Corp., 1986, Law Reform Commn. Can., 1979-80, 84-85, Nat. Mus. Can., 1983; advisor police powers project Can. Human Rights Found., 1983; advisor Commn. of Inquiry Concerning Activities of the Royal Can. Mounted Police, 1977-81; numerous others. Author: (with Hilstan L. Watts) Blood Donation: Attitudes and Motivation, 1966, (with Margaret B. Farnell) Private Security: An Examination of Canadian Statistics, 1961-71, (with Philip C. Stenning) Police Training in Ontario: An Evaluation of Recruit and Supervisory Course, 1980, (with Farnell and Stenning) Contract Security in Ontario, 1980, (with Michael Brogden) Policing for a New South Africa, 1993; editor Organizational Police Deviance: Its Structure and Control, 1981, -a-Cop: A Study of Police Mobilization, 1984; co-editor: Private Security and Private Justice: The Challenge of the 80's, 1983, Private Policing, 1987, Criminology: A Readers Guide, 1991; assoc. editor Can. Jour. Sociology, 1975-78, Critical Arts, 1986—; mem. editl. bd. Natal U. Law and Society Rev., 1985—, Policing and Society, 1988—, Jour. Regulatory Law and Practice, 1992—; contbr. articles and revs. to profl. jours., chpts. to books. Office: U Toronto, Ctr Criminology, 130 St George St Rm 8001, Toronto, ON Canada M5S 1A1

SHEARING, GEORGE ALBERT, pianist, composer; b. London, Aug. 13, 1919; came to U.S., 1947, naturalized, 1956; s. James Philip and Ellen Amelia (Brightman) S.; m. Beatrice Bayes, May 1, 1941 (div.); 1 dau., Wendy Ann; m. Eleanor Geffert. Student, Linden Lodge Sch. for Blind, London. V.p. Shearing Music Corp. Composer: Lullaby of Birdland, numerous other popular songs; recs. English Decca and Parlophone, Am. Savoy, London, MGM Capitol, Sheba Records, Concord Jazz; albums include: An Evening with George Shearing and Mel Torme, 1982, Top Drawer, 1983, An Evening at Charlie's, 1984, Grand Piano, 1985, An Elegant Evening, 1986, George Shearing and Barry Tuckwell Play the Music of Cole Porter, 1986, More Grand Piano, 1987, (with Marian McPartland) Alone Together, 1981, George Shearing and Dakota Stanton: In the Night, A Vintage Year, 1987, George Shearing and Hank Jones: The Spirit of 1761, 1989, In Dixieland with the Dixie Six, 1989, I Hear a Rhapsody: Live at the Blue Note, 1994, (with Brian Torff) On a Clear Day, 1993, On the Sunny Side of the Strip, 1993; appearances at: London Symphony Pops Concerts, 1986, 87, London Paladium, 1987, Concord Jazz Festival, Japan, 1987, Hong Kong Cultural Ctr., 1992. Bd. dirs. Guide Dogs for Blind, San Rafael, Hadley Sch. for Blind, Winnetka, Ill. Voted top English pianist, 1941-47; winner all Am. jazz polls, also many pvt. awards; recipient Golden Plate award Am. Acad. of Achievement, 1968. Mem. Broadcast Music Inc. Club: Bohemian (San Francisco). Office: care Joan Shulman, 103 Avenue Rd Ste 301, Toronto, ON Canada M5R 2G9*

SHEARON, FORREST BEDFORD, humanities educator; b. Bolivar, Tenn., Sept. 7, 1934; s. George W. and Carrie Mae (Shinault) S.; m. Jeannette Brooks, June 5, 1955 (div. 1972); children: Angelia J. Shearon Schulte, Michael F.; m. Lynn Britton, June 11, 1981. AB in History, Union U., 1956; postgrad., Northwestern U., 1962-63; MA in English, U. Louisville, 1965, PhD in English, 1973. English tchr. Halls (Tenn.) High Sch., 1956-58, Pleasure Ridge Park High Sch., Louisville, 1958-62, 63-65; asst. prof. English Ky. So. Coll., Louisville, 1965-68; instr. English U. Louisville, 1969-73; asst. prof., assoc. prof., prof. humanities Ea. Ky. U., Richmond, 1973—. Contbr. articles to profl. jours. Recipient Outstanding Grad. Student award U. Louisville, 1973; Ford Found. fellow, 1962-63, NEH fellow, 1979; Fulbright-Hays grantee, 1987. Mem. MLA, So. Humanities Coun. (sec. 1989—), Ky. Philological Assn. (exec. sec. 1983-84), South Atlantic MLA, South Asian Lit. Assn., Phi Kappa Phi. Democrat. Presbyterian. Avocations: travel, reading, writing. Home: 305 Summit St Richmond KY 40475-2133 Office: Ea Ky U Dept Humanities Case Annex 368 Richmond KY 40475-3140

SHEASGREEN, BETTY, interior designer, painter, sculptor; b. Thief River Falls, Minn., May 16, 1920; d. Harry Weiser and Genevieve (Schutt) Protzeller; m. Otto Frederick Stoehr, June 3, 1951 (div. June 1964); 1 child, Cynthia Jane Stoehr Arenander; m. Francis Barrett Sheasgreen, Nov. 28, 1978. AA, Stephens Coll., 1940; student, U. Minn., 1940-42, Maharishi Internat. U., 1989-90, Clatsop C.C., Astoria, Oreg., 1990—. Designer Conrae Interiors, Reno, Nev., 1963-65; owner, designer Studio West, Reno, 1965-75; interior designer McQueen's Interiors, Lahaina, Hawaii, 1975-82; owner Compass-Rose Travel Agy., Portland, Oreg., 1982-85; intl. artist Seaside, Oreg., 1990—; designer interiors condominium projects Maui, Hawaii. Interior designs include Middlefork Lodge, Harrah's Clubs. With USN, 1942-45. Mem. N.W. Watercolor Soc., Watercolor Soc. Oreg., Trails End Art Assn. (pres. 1992). Mem. Natural Law Party. Transcendental Meditationist. Avocations: painting, sculpting, aerobics, yoga. Home and Studio: PO Box 828 2460 Ocean Vista Dr Seaside OR 97138

SHEA-STONUM, MARILYN, judge; b. Anaconda, Mont., June 6, 1947. AB, U. Calif., Santa Cruz, 1969; JD, Case Western Res. U., 1975. Bar: Ohio 1975, Calif. 1976. Law clk. to Hon. Battisti U.S. Dist. Ct. (no. dist.), Ohio, 1975-76; ptnr. Jones, Day, Reavis & Pogue, Cleve., 1984-94; bankruptcy judge ea. divsn. U.S. Bankruptcy Ct. Ohio (no. dist.), Akron, 1984-94; bankruptcy judge U.S. Bankruptcy Ct. Ohio, Akron, 1994—. Office: US Bankruptcy Ct No Dist Ohio Ea Divsn 2 S Main St Ste 240 Akron OH 44308

SHECHTER, BEN-ZION, artist, illustrator; b. Tel Aviv, Aug. 7, 1940; s. Isaac and Elka (Demb) S.; m. Laura Judith Goldstein, Feb. 26, 1969; 1 child, Adam. B.F.A., Bezalel Acad. Fine Art, Jerusalem, 1966. Airplane mechanic Israeli aviation industry (Lod), 1961-62; free-lance comml. artist N.Y.C., 1966—, artist, illustrator, 1974—. Illustrator: Common Ground, 1980; one-man shows Martin Sumers Graphic, N.Y.C., 1983, Wustum Mus., Racine, Wis., 1982, Cayuga Community Coll., Auburn, N.Y., 1982, Suffolk County Community Coll., Selden, N.Y., 1984, Capricorn Gallery, Bethesda, Md., 1989, FDR Gallery, N.Y.C., 1993; exhibited in group shows U. Iowa Mus., 1983, Bklyn. Mus., 1980, 84, Minn. Mus. Art, St Paul, 1980, Elvchjem Mus., U. Wis.-Madison, 1983, Ark. Art Ctr., Little Rock, 1986, 92, Hunt Inst. (Carnegie Instn.), Pitts., 1988, Butlur Inst., Youngstown, Ohio, 1988, Kutztown (Pa.) U., 1989, Suffolk County C.C., Selden, N.Y., 1994; represented in permanent collections, Bklyn Mus., U. Iowa Mus., Boston Mus. Fine Art, Israel Mus., Jerusalem. Served with Israeli Air Force, 1958-61. City of Jerusalem scholar, 1963, 64; Israeli Ministry Edn. scholar, 1965, 66. Jewish. Home: 429 4th St Brooklyn NY 11215-2901

SHECHTER, LAURA JUDITH, artist; b. Bklyn., Aug. 26, 1944; d. Philip and Jeannette (Newmark) Goldstein; m. Ben-Zion Shechter, Feb. 26, 1969; 1 son, Adam. B.A. with honors in Art, Bklyn. Coll., 1965. Case worker Dept. Social Service, N.Y.C., 1965-73; artist N.Y.C., 1965—; lectr., 1978—; curator Forum Gallery, N.Y.C., 1978; tchr. Parson Sch. Design, N.Y.C., 1984, Nat. Acad. Design, N.Y.C., 1985-88, 94—. Exhibited one-woman shows Forum Gallery, N.Y.C., 1976, 80, 83, Greenville County Mus. of Art, (S.C.), 1982, Wustum Mus., Racine, Wis, 1982, Schoelkopf Gallery, N.Y.C., 1985, Staempfli Gallery, N.Y.C., 1987, 88, Rahr West Mus., Manitowoc Wis., U. Richmond, 1991, Perlow Gallery, N.Y.C., 1992, 94, Suffolk County C.C., N.Y., 1994; group shows include Akron Art Inst., 1974, Minn. Mus. Art, St. Paul, 1981, Pa. Acad. Art, Phila., 1982, Boston Mus., 1982, Bklyn. Mus., 1980, 84, Nat. Mus. Am. Art, Washington, 1985, San Francisco Mus. Modern Art, 1985, Huntsville Mus., Ala., 1987, Butler Inst., Youngstown, Ohio, 1987, 88, Ind. U. Art Mus., Bloomington, 1990, Spiva Art Mus., Joplin, Mo., 1991, Arkansas Art Ctr., 1992; represented in pub. collections including Boston Mus. Fine Art, Bklyn. Mus., Carnegie Inst., Indpls. Mus., Israel Mus., others. Recipient Creative Artist Pub. Service award N.Y. State, 1982. Mem. Artists Equity. Home: 429 4th St Brooklyn NY 11215 *I believe that my work is always slowly changing through hard and consistent effort. There was a strong idea that initiated this work. Although that idea has been completely altered, it still exists.*

SHECTER, HOWARD L., lawyer; b. Boston, May 13, 1943. AB, Harvard U., 1965; JD, U. Pa., 1968. Bar: Pa. 1968. Assoc. Morgan, Lewis & Bockius, Phila., 1968-73, ptnr., 1973—. Office: Morgan Lewis & Bockius 2000 One Logan Sq Philadelphia PA 19103

SHEDD, BEN ALVIN, film producer, director, production company executive; b. Stockton, Calif., Jan. 27, 1947; s. Robert Alvin and Beverly Joyce (Ganeles) S.; 1 child, Nara Noelva. B.A. in Radio-TV-Film, San Francisco State U., 1968; M.A. in Cinema, U. So. Calif., 1973. adj. prof. cinema U. So. Calif., 1979-89; faculty Calif. Inst. Arts, 1984-89, Dow Creativity Ctr., Northwood Inst., Mich., 1989; PNM endowed chair prof. media arts U N.Mex., 1989-90. Filmmaker Churchill Films, Los Angeles, 1971-73; producer, dir., writer: pub. TV sci. documentary series NOVA, Sta.WGBH-TV, Boston, 1973-76; film and videotape dir./producer, pres. public TV sci. documentary series, Shedd Prodns., Inc., Los Angeles, 1976—, Shedd Prodns., Inc.; dir., writer, editor: documentaries The Flight of the Gossamer Condor, 1976-78, Poetry for People Who Hate Poetry; film series, Steffens/Shedd Poetry Films, 1979; producer commls. Newby's Movies, Los Angeles, 1980; producer Calif. Dream Series, Sta. KOCE, Huntington Beach, 1981, The Homefront, U. So. Calif./PBS TV Spl., Los Angeles, 1982; songwriter Making the Music, TriStar Pictures, N.Y., 1984; producer, dir., co-writer, co-editor Seasons, Imax/Omnimax Film Sci. Mus. Minn./Graphic Films, 1985-87; dir. Dealing with Feelings About Nuclear Age Issues, 1988; dir., co-producer Tropical Rainforest, 1987-91. Served with USAR, 1969-75. Co-recipient Peabody award U. Ga. Sch. Journalism and Bd. Regents, 1974; Acad. award for best documentary short subject Acad. Motion Picture Arts and Scis., 1978; also numerous U.S. and internat. film festival awards. Mem. Acad. Motion Picture Arts and Scis., Acad. Magical Arts. Office: PO Box 4220 Albuquerque NM 87196-4220

SHEDD, DENNIS W., federal judge; b. 1953. BA, Wofford Coll., 1975; JD, U. S.C., 1978; M of Laws, Georgetown U., 1980. Bar: S.C. Mem. staff U.S. Senator Strom Thurmond, 1978-88; chief counsel U.S. Senate Jud. Com., Washington, 1985-86; of counsel Bethea, Jordan & Griffin, Columbia, S.C., 1988-90; pvt. practice, 1989-90; judge U.S. Dist. Ct. S.C., Greenville, 1990-91; adj. prof. law U.S.C., 1989-90. Mem. S.C. Bar Assn., Richland County Bar Assn., Phi Beta Kappa. Office: 1845 Assembly St Columbia SC 29201

SHEDD, DONALD POMROY, surgeon; b. New Haven, Aug. 4, 1922; s. Gale and Marion (Young) S.; m. Charlotte Newsom, Mar. 17, 1946; children: Carolyn, David, Ann, Laura. B.S., Yale U., 1944, M.D., 1946. Diplomate Am. Bd. Surgery. Intern Yale New Haven Hosp., 1946-47, asst. resident, resident, 1949-53; instr. surgery Yale U. Med Sch., New Haven, 1953-54, asst. prof., 1954-56, assoc. prof., 1956-67; chief dept. head and neck surgery Roswell Park Cancer Inst., Buffalo, 1967—. Co-editor: Surgical and Prosthetic Speech Rehabilitation, 1980, Head and Neck Cancer, 1985; contbr. numerous articles to profl. jours. Founding bd. dirs. Hospice Buffalo, Inc., 1973-83. Served to capt. U.S. Army, 1947-49. Mem. Soc. Univ. Surgeons, Soc. Surg. Oncology, New Eng. Surg. Soc., Soc. Head and Neck Surgeons (pres. 1976-77). Avocations: sailing; windsurfing; tennis. Home: 671 Lafayette Ave Buffalo NY 14222-1435 Office: Roswell Park Cancer Inst 666 Elm St Buffalo NY 14263-0001

SHEDLOCK, JAMES, library director, consultant; b. Detroit, Nov. 25, 1950. BA in English, U. Notre Dame, 1974; AM in LS, U. Mich., 1977. Reference and serials libr. St. Joseph Mercy Hosp., Pontiac, Mich., 1977-79; document delivery libr. Wayne State U. Med. Libr., Detroit, 1979-81; coord. online search svc. U. N.C. Health Scis. Libr., Chapel Hill, 1982-85; head pub. svcs. Med. Libr., Northwestern U., Chgo., 1985-88, assoc. dir., 1988-91, dir. Galter Health Scis. Libr., 1991—; cons. U.N. High Commr. for Refugees, Cyprus, 1993-94. Mem. ALA, Med. Libr. Assn., Am. Med. Informatics Assn., Assn. Acad. Health Scis. Libr. Dirs. (rep.), Acad. Health Info. Profls. (disting.). Offices: Northwestern U Galter Health Scis Libr 303 E Chicago Ave Chicago IL 60611-3008

SHEED, WILFRID JOHN JOSEPH, author; b. London, Eng., Dec. 27, 1930; came to U.S., 1947; s. Francis Joseph and Maisie (Ward) S.; m. Miriam Ungerer; children: Elizabeth, Francis, Marion. BA, Lincoln Coll., Oxford U., 1954, MA, 1957. Movie reviewer Jubilee mag., N.Y.C., 1959-61, assoc. editor 1959-66; drama critic, book editor Commonweal mag., N.Y.C., 1964-71; movie critic Esquire mag., N.Y.C., 1967-69; columnist N.Y. Times, 1971—; vis. prof. Princeton, 1970-71; judge, mem. editorial bd. Book of Month Club, 1972-88. Author: Joseph, 1958, A Middle Class Education, 1960, The Hack, 1963, Square's Progress, 1965, Office Politics, 1966 (Nat. Book award nomination 1966), The Blacking Factory and Pennsylvania Gothic: A Short Novel and a Long Story, 1968, Max Jamison, 1970 (Nat. Book award nomination 1971), The Morning After, 1971, People Will Always Be Kind, 1973, Three Mobs: Labor, Church and Mafia, 1974, Vanishing Species of America, 1974, Muhammad Ali: A Portrait in Words and Photographs, 1975, Transatlantic Blues, 1978, The Good Word and Other Words, 1978, Clare Boothe Luce, 1982, Frank and Maisie, 1985, The Boys of Winter, 1987, The Kennedy Legacy: A Generation Later, 1988, Essays in Disguise, 1989, Face of Baseball, 1990, My Life as a Fan, 1993, In Love with Daylight, 1995; editor: G.K. Chesterton's Essays and Poems, 1957, Sixteen Short Novels, 1986, Baseball and Lesser Sports, 1991; contbr. to periodicals including N.Y. Times Book Rev., Esquire, Sports Illustrated, Commonweal. Recipient Nat. Inst. and Am. Acad. award in literature, 1971; Guggenheim fellow, 1971-72. Mem. PEN, Authors Guild. Roman Catholic. Address: Sag Harbor NY 11963*

SHEEDER, ROBERT ELWOOD, lawyer; b. Ind., Pa., Apr. 8, 1951; s. Elwood B. and Alice (Poole) S.; m. Martha Ann Painter. BA, U. Va., 1973; JD, U. Mich., 1976. Bar: Tex. 1976, Pa. 1978, U.S. Dist. Ct. (we. dist.) Pa. 1980, U.S. Ct. Appeals (3d cir.) 1981, U.S. Dist. Ct. (no. dist.) Tex. 1985, U.S. Dist. Ct. (ea. dist.) Tex. 1986, U.S. Ct. Appeals (5th cir.) 1988, U.S.

Dist. Ct. (so. dist.) Tex. 1989, U.S. Dist. Ct. (we. dist.) Tex. 1991. Assoc. Reed, Smith, Shaw & McClay, Pitts., 1977-84; ptnr. Winstead, McGuire, Sechrest & Minick, Dallas, 1984-92; shareholder, sect. head labor group Jenkens & Gilchrist, Dallas, 1992—; lectr. labor law North Tex. State U., Denton, 1985, So. Meth. U., 1988-90. Editor-in-chief Tex. Labor Letter, 1994—. Mem. ABA (labor law sect.), Tex. Bar Assn. (cert. specialist in labor law 1985), Dallas Bar Assn. (labor law sect.), North Tex. Indsl. Resl. Rsch. Assn. (pres. 1992), City Club, Phi Beta Kappa, Phi Eta Sigma. Republican. Presbyterian. Clubs: Tex., City (Dallas). Home: 3331 Bryn Mawr Dallas TX Office: Jenkens & Gilchrist 1445 Ross Ave Ste 3200 Dallas TX 75201

SHEEDY, ALLY (ALEXANDRA ELIZABETH SHEEDY), actress; b. N.Y.C., June 13, 1962; d. John and Charlotte (Baum) S.; m. David Lansbury. Student, U. So. Calif. Past ballet dancer. Film debut in Bad Boys, 1983; other films include Wargames, 1983, Oxford Blues, 1984, The Breakfast Club, 1985, St. Elmo's Fire, 1985, Twice in a Lifetime, 1985, Short Circuit, 1986, Blue City, 1986, Maid to Order, 1987, Heart of Dixie, 1989, Betsy's Wedding, 1990, Only the Lonely, 1991, Home Alone II: Lost in New York, 1992, The Pickle, 1992, Man's Best Friend, 1993, Tattle Tale, 1993; TV films include The Best Little Girl in the World, 1981, The Day the Loving Stopped, 1981, The Violation of Sarah McDavid, 1981, Splendor in the Grass, 1981, Dead Lessons, 1983, We Are the Children, 1987, Fear, 1990, The Lost Capone, 1990, Lethal Exposure, 1993, Chantilly Lace, 1993, The Hauting of Sea Cliff Inn, 1994, Ultimate Betrayal, 1994, Parallel Lives, 1994; author (children's book) She Was Nice to Mice, 1975, (poetry) Yesterday I Saw the Sun, 1991. Address: care William Morris Agency 151 El Camino Beverly Hills CA 90212*

SHEEDY, PATRICK THOMAS, judge; b. Green Bay, Wis., Oct. 31, 1921; s. Earl P. and Elsie L. (Brauel) S.; m. Margaret P. Mulvaney, Sept. 6, 1952; children: Michael, Mary Kathleen, Pat Jr., Ann, Maureen. BS in Bus. Adminstrn., Marquette U., 1943, JD, 1948; LLM in Taxation, John Marshall Law Sch., 1972. Bar: Wis. 1948. Pvt. practice Milw., 1948-80; judge Wis. Cir. Ct., Milw., 1980-90; chief judge 1st Jud. Dist., Milw., 1990—. Past vice chmn. Archdiocesean Sch. Bd., Milw., chairperson, 1986—. Served to col. USAR, 1942-73. Decorated Legion of Merit. Mem. ABA (state del. 1983-85, 89-92, bd. govs. 1985-88), Wis. Bar Assn. (pres. 1974-75, bd. govs., exec. com.). Roman Catholic. Club: Exchange (pres.).

SHEEHAN, CHARLES VINCENT, investment banker; b. London, Dec. 19, 1930; came to U.S., 1931; s. Charles Vincent and Mary Margaret (Stokes) S.; m. Susan Ellen Rosar, May 5, 1962. BS, Georgetown U., 1952. Chief fin. officer Gen. Electric Co., Tokyo, Sydney, Australia and Sao Paulo, Brazil, 1962-64, 64-66, 67-71; staff exec. Gen. Electric Co., Fairfield, Conn., 1972-83, v.p. corp. exec. office, 1983-87; sr. v.p., chief fin. and adminstrn. officer Kidder, Peabody Group, Inc., N.Y.C., 1987-90; bd. dirs. Shawmut Nat. Trust Co. Chmn. Non-partisan Polit. Action Com. for Gen. Electric Co. employees, Fairfield, 1982-83. Served to lt. USN, 1952-54. Mem. Johns Island Club (Vero Beach, Fla.), Wildcat Cliffs Country Club (Highlands, N.C.). Republican. Roman Catholic. Avocations: golfing, surf fishing. Home: 884 Indian Ln Vero Beach FL 32963-1131

SHEEHAN, DEBORAH ANN, radio station and theater executive; b. Paterson, N.J., Mar. 29, 1953; d. John J. and Ruth (Badertscher) S.; m. Emidio S. Quattrocchi, Mar. 15, 1985; 1 child, Deirdre Emily Sheehan. B.A., William Paterson Coll., 1975. With radio Sta. WWDJ, Hackensack, N.J., 1980-83, Shadow Traffic, N.Y.C., 1981-83; dir. news, community affairs WPAT-AM/FM, N.Y.C., 1979—. Actress-tchr. Paterson Arts Ctr., 1975-79; host radio show Bus. Jour. N.J., 1984; host, producer radio show Debbie Sheehan mag., 1983; host FDU Focus, Cable Network N.J.; writer plays. Exec. dir., actress Learning Theater Co., Paterson, 1975—; sec. bd. dirs. YMCA Passaic Valley, Paterson, 1983-89; mem. N.J. Legal Bd., Montclair, N.J., 1984-86; mem. Paterson Edn. Found., 1984-89; bd. dirs. United Way Passaic Valley, Conn., 1985, chair allocations com., 1985-92. Recipient Edward R. Murrow Gold medal B'nai B'rith, 1983, finalist 1984-85; Gold medal Internat. Radio Festival, 1983; Best Reporter award Sigma Delta Chi, 1985-87, Personality Profile award local chpt., 1987, Best Pub. Service award, 1987; Best Feature award AP, 1985, 87; Angel Excellence award, Los Angeles, 1985, 87; Internat. Press Assn. fellow, Japan, 1985, New Zealand, 1988. Club: Zonta. Avocations: weaving; travel; acting. Office: WPAT-AM-FM 1396 Broad St Clifton NJ 07013-4222

SHEEHAN, DENNIS WILLIAM, lawyer, business executive; b. Springfield, Mass., Jan. 2, 1934; s. Timothy A. and H. Marjorie (Kelsey) S.; m. Elizabeth M. Hellyer, July 27, 1957; children: Dennis William, Catherine Elizabeth, John Edward. BS, U. Md., 1957; JD, Georgetown U., 1960, LLM, 1962. Bar: D.C., Md. 1960, Mo. 1970, Ohio 1977. Legal asst. to chmn. NLRB, Washington, 1960-61; trial atty. U.S. SEC, Washington, 1962-63; corp. atty. Martin Marietta, Balt., N.Y.C., 1963-64; v.p., gen. counsel, sec. Bunker Ramo Corp., Oak Brook, Ill., 1964-73; exec. v.p., gen. counsel, dir. Diversified Industries, Inc., St. Louis, 1973-75; v.p., gen. counsel, dir. N-ReN Corp., Cin., 1975-77; v.p., gen. counsel, sec., dir. AXIA Inc., Oak Brook, Ill., 1977-84, chmn., pres., chief exec. officer, 1984—; bd. dirs. Andamios Atlas, Mexico City, Compagnie Fischbein (S.A.), Brussels, Greenfield Industries, Augusta, Ga., Bliss & Laughlin Industries Inc., Chgo.; chmn. Allied Healthcare System, St. Louis, Flair Corp., Ocala, Fla. Bd. dirs. St. Margaret's Sch. Found., chmn. U.S. of C. Mgmt. Assn. Ill., Nat. Coun. on Crime and Delinquency. Mem. ABA, Mgmt. Assn. Ill., U.S. of C. (chmn.), Chgo. Club, St. Louis Club, Econ. Club Chgo., Met. Club Washington, Bankers Club Cin., Downtown Richmond Club, Met. Club Chgo., Univ. Club Balt., Phi Delta Pi, Sigma Alpha Phi, Delta Sigma Phi. Republican. Home: 450 Lexington Dr Lake Forest IL 60045-1563 Office: Axia Corp 2001 Spring Rd Ste 300 Hinsdale IL 60521-1879

SHEEHAN, DONALD THOMAS, university administrator; b. Winsted, Conn., Jan. 2, 1911; s. James J. and Louise (Coffey) S.; m. Betty Young, June 25, 1941; 1 son, Michael Terrence. Grad., Gilbert Sch., Winsted, 1931; B.S. in Edn, Syracuse U., 1935; student, Sch. Pub. Affairs, Am. U., 1936. Dir. health edn. D.C. Tb. Assn., 1937-39; dir. Washington office NCCJ, 1939-41; dir. Bur. Info. Nat. Cath. Welfare Conf., Washington, 1944-42; spl. cons. to U.S. Commr. Edn., 1946; staff mem. John Price Jones Co., Inc. (pub. relations cons.), 1946-51; cons. civil def. edn. program, asst. adminstr. charge vol. manpower FCDA, 1951-54, cons. vol. manpower, 1954—; dir. pub. relations U. Pa., 1954-76, sec. corp., 1975-76, sec., v.p. emeritus, 1976—; spl. lectr. pub. relations Drexel U., 1957-72; cons. Nat. Bd. Med. Examiners, 1964—, Coll. Physicians Phila., 1973—, Citizens' Action Com. to Fight Inflation, 1974-75, Wistar Inst. Anatomy and Biology, 1979, Univ. Mus., U. Pa., 1982—, Inst. Environ. Medicine, 1983—; Mem. adv. com. Nat. Trust for Hist. Preservation; cons. Am. Philos. Soc., 1983—. Served from 1st lt. to lt. col. USAAF, 1942-46. Decorated Bronze Star medal. Fellow Coll. Physicians Phila. (hon. assoc.).; mem. Public Relations Soc. Am., Pi Gamma Mu. Roman Catholic. Club: Nat. Press. Home: 201 W Evergreen Ave Apt 310 Philadelphia PA 19118

SHEEHAN, EDWARD JAMES, technical consultant, former government official; b. Johnstown, Pa., Dec. 31, 1935; s. Louis A. and Ethel F. (Schaefer) S.; m. Florence Ann Hartnett, June 17, 1958; children—Edward, James, John, William, Mary. B.S in Physics, St. Francis Coll., 1959; M.S. (Sloan fellow), Mass. Inst. Tech., 1972. Project engr. Electronics Command, Dept. Army, 1959-61, project team leader electro-optic equipment for tanks, 1961-63, project team leader electro-optic equipment for infantry, 1963-65, tech. area dir. electro-optic night vision equipment, 1965-73, assoc. lab. dir. for devel. engring., 1973-76; lab. dir. Night Vision Lab., Fort Belvoir, Va., 1976-79; founder, pres. Sheehan Assocs. Inc., Alexandria, Va., 1979-92; founder, CEO, chmn. Stardyne, Inc., Johnstown, 1992—; chmn. Nat. and Internat. Symposia for Electro-Optical Tech. and Applications; bd. dirs. Johnstown (Pa.) Corp. Recipient numerous awards including Meritorious Civilian Svc. award Dept. Army, Disting. Alumnus award in sci. St. Francis Coll., 1989; named Man of Yr., Combined Svc. Clubs, Johnstown, Pa., 1993. Home: 8502 Crestview Dr Fairfax VA 22031-2803

SHEEHAN, JAMES JOHN, historian, educator; b. San Francisco, May 31, 1937; s. James B. and Sally W. (Walsh) S.; m. 1960; 1 child, Michael L.; m. Margaret L. Anderson, Sept. 2, 1989. BA, Stanford U., 1958; MA, U. Calif., Berkeley, 1959, PhD, 1964. From asst. to assoc. prof. Northwest

U., Evanston, Ill., 1964-79; prof. Stanford (Calif.) U., 1979-86, chmn. dept., 1982-89, Dickason prof. in humanities, 1986—. Author: Lujo Brentano, 1966, German Liberalism, 1978, German History 1770-1866, 1989, Der Ausklang des alten Reiches, 1994; editor: The Boundaries of Humanity, 1991; contbr. articles to profl. jours. Fellow Am. Council Learned Socs., 1981-82, NEH, 1985-86, Wissenschaftskolleg Berlin. Fellow AAAS (Humboldt Rsch. prize 1995); mem. Am. Hist. Assn. (nominating com. 1979-81, chmn. conf. group on Ctrl. European history 1985-86). Office: Stanford U Dept of History Stanford CA 94305

SHEEHAN, JAMES PATRICK, media company executive; b. Jersey City, June 6, 1942; s. John Patrick and Helen Teresa (Woods) S.; m. Mary Ellen Finnell, July 1, 1967; children: James, Christopher. B.S. Seton Hall U., 1965; M.B.A. Wayne State U., 1973. Controller Otis Elevator Co. N.Am., Farmington, Conn., 1976-78; dir. mfg. Otis Elevator Co. N.Am., Yonkers, N.Y., 1978-80; v.p., controller Pratt & Whitney Aircraft, East Hartford, Conn., 1980-82; sr. v.p. A. H. Belo Corp., Dallas, 1982-84, chief fin. officer, 1984-86, pres., chief operating officer, 1987-93; ret., 1993; also dir. A. H. Belo Corp., ret., 1993. Mem. devel. bd. U. Tex.-Dallas, 1985—; bd. dirs. United Way, The Dallas Partnership, The Dallas Morning News Charities; trustee St. Paul Med. Ctr. Found. Served to Lt. (j.g.) USN, 1967-69, Vietnam. Mem. Am. Newspaper Pubs. Assn., So. Newspaper Pubs. Assn. Roman Catholic. Avocations: tennis; racquetball; golf; jogging.

SHEEHAN, JOHN FRANCIS, cytopathologist, educator; b. Portsmouth, N.H., July 28, 1906; s. John Thomas and Ellen Agnes (Lynes) S.; m. Grace Anne O'Neil, Aug. 3, 1935; 1 child, John Thomas. B.S., U. N.H., 1928, M.S., 1930; Ph.D., State U. Iowa, 1945; postgrad., McGill U., 1949. Grad. asst. U. N.H., 1928-30; instr. biology Creighton U., 1930-38, asst. prof., 1938-44, assoc. prof., 1944-49, chmn. biology dept., 1949-58, prof. biology, 1949-67, prof. pathology Sch. Medicine, 1967-88, prof. ob-gyn, 1975-88, prof. emeritus pathology and gynecology, 1988—; attending staff AMI St. Joseph Hosp.; dir. cytopathology St. Joseph Hosp., Omaha, 1978-82; dir. cytopathology emeritus St. Joseph Hosp., 1982—; prof. emeritus biology and pathology Creighton U., 1989. Recipient Golden Jubilee Svc. award Creighton U., 1981, Certificate award AAUP, 1988; Dept. Biology Creighton U. lecture hall named in his honor, 1984. Fellow Am. Soc. Colposcopy and Cervical Pathology; mem. AAUP, Am. Soc. Cytopathology, Internat. Coll. Surgeons (vice regent for Nebr. 1984), Am. Inst. Biol. Scis., Am. Micros. Soc., Am. Men and Women of Sci., Am. Soc. Clin. Pathologists, Nebr. Heart Assn., Nebr. Acad. Scis., Sigma Xi, Alpha Omega Alpha, Phi Sigma, Phi Kappa Theta, Alpha Sigma Nu, Phi Rho Sigma. Home: 7300 Graceland Dr Apt 307A Omaha NE 68134-4341 Office: St Joseph Hosp 601 N 30th St Omaha NE 68131-2197

SHEEHAN, LAWRENCE JAMES, lawyer; b. San Francisco, July 23, 1932. AB, Stanford U., 1957, LLB, 1959. Bar: Calif. 1960. Law clk. to chief judge U.S. Ct. Appeals 2d Cir., N.Y.C., 1959-60; assoc. O'Melveny & Myers, L.A., 1960-68, ptnr., 1969-94, of counsel, 1995—; bd. dirs. Am. Capital Mutual Funds, FPA Mutual Funds, TCW Convertible Securities Fund Inc., Source Capital, Inc. Mem. ABA, Los Angeles County Bar Assn., Calif. Bar Assn., Order of Coif. Office: O'Melveny & Myers 1999 Avenue Of The Stars Los Angeles CA 90067 also: O'Melveny & Myers 400 S Hope St Los Angeles CA 90071

SHEEHAN, LINDA SUZANNE, educational administrator; b. Dayton, Ohio, Aug. 1, 1950; d. Paul J. and Betty L. (Fowler) King; m. J. Scott Sheehan, Dec. 18, 1971. 1 child Amy Elizabeth. BS in Edn. with honors, Ohio State U., 1971; MEd, U. Tex., 1974; adminstrn. cert. Houston Bapt. U., 1983. Cert. tchr., Tex. Tchr. Upper Arlington Schs., Columbus, Ohio, 1971-72, Brown Sch., San Marcos, Tex., 1972-73, Comal Ind. Sch. Dist., New Braunfels, Tex., 1973-75, Alief Ind. Sch. Dist., Houston, 1975-79; asst. prin. Killough Mid. Sch., Houston, 1979-84; prin. Olle Mid. Sch., Houston, 1984-92, Holub Middle Sch., 1992—. Named Tchr. of Yr., Olle Mid. Sch., Houston, 1978. Mem. NEA, Nat. Mid. Sch. Assn., Nat. Assn. Secondary Sch. Prins., Tex. Assn. Secondary Sch. Prins., Tex. Mid. Sch. Assn. (dir. 1979-91, pres. 1991-92, state convention chair 1993-94), Houston Council Social Studies, Kappa Delta Pi (pres. 1984-85), Phi Delta Kappa. Roman Catholic. Home: 526 Nottingham Oaks Trl Houston TX 77079-6332 Office: Holub Mid Sch 9515 S Dairy Ashford Houston TX 77099

SHEEHAN, MICHAEL JARBOE, archbishop; b. Wichita, Kans., July 9, 1939; s. John Edward and Mildred (Jarboe) S. MST, Gregorian U., Rome, 1965; D of Canon Law, Lateran U., Rome, 1971. Ordained priest Roman Cath. Ch., 1964. Asst. gen. sec. Nat. Coun. Cath. Bishops, Washington, 1971-76; rector Holy Trinity Sem., Dallas, 1976-82; pastor Immaculate Conception Ch., Grand Prairie, Tex., 1982-83; bishop Diocese of Lubbock, Tex., 1983-93; archbishop Archdiocese of Santa Fe, Albuquerqe, N.Mex., 1993—; past chmn. Am. Bd. Cath. Missions, 1989-91; trustee Cath. Relief Svcs., 1992—. Contbr. articles to New Cath. Ency. Trustee St. Mary Hosp., Lubbock, 1983-89; bd. dirs. Tex. Conf. of Chs. Mem. Serra Club (chaplain 1983-93). Avocations: snow skiing, racquetball. Office: Archdiocese of Santa Fe 4000 Saint Joseph Pl NW Albuquerque NM 87120

SHEEHAN, MICHAEL TERRENCE, arts administrator, historian, consultant; b. Washington, Dec. 15, 1942; s. Donald Thomas and Betty (Young) S. BA, U. Pa., 1965, MA, 1968, PhD, 1974. House mgr. Annenberg Ctr., Phila., 1968-72; magr. Performing Arts Ctr. SUNY, Albany, 1972-76; mng. dir. Taconic Theatre Co., Spencertown, N.Y., 1973-77; exec. dir. Snug Harbor Cultural Ctr., N.Y.C., 1978-82; cons. Washington, 1984-87; pres. Oatlands Plantation, Leesburg, Va., 1987-89; dir. Woodrow Wilson House Nat. Trust for Historic Preserve, Washington 1989—. Bd. dirs. Albany League of Arts, 1972-77, Loudon County League of Arts, Leesburg, 1988-89; mem. Loudon County Tourism Bd., 1987-89; consortium officer Historic House Museums of Met. Washington, 1992—. Mem. Am. Assn. Mus., League Historic Am. Theatres, Nat. Press Club Washington, Nat. Trust Historic Preservation, Internat. Coun. Mus. Office: Woodrow Wilson House 2340 S St NW Washington DC 20008-4015

SHEEHAN, NEIL, reporter, scholarly writer; b. Holyoke, Mass., Oct. 27, 1936; s. Cornelius Joseph and Mary (O'Shea) S.; m. Susan Margulies, Mar. 30, 1965; children—Maria Gregory, Catherine Fair. AB cum laude, Harvard, 1958; LittD (hon.), Columbia Coll., Chgo., 1972; LHD (hon.), Am. Internat. Coll., 1990, U. Lowell, 1991. Vietnam Bur. chief U.P.I., Saigon, 1962-64; reporter N.Y. Times, N.Y.C., Djakarta, Saigon, Washington, 1964-72. Author: The Arnheiter Affair, 1972, A Bright Shining Lie: John Paul Vann and America in Vietnam, 1988 (Nat. Book award 1988, Pulitzer Prize for gen. non-fiction 1989, Robert F. Kennedy book award 1989, Vetty award Vietnam Vets. Ensemble Theatre Co. 1989, Spl. Achievement award Vietnam Vets. Am. 1989, Outstanding Investigative Reporting award Investigative Reporters and Editors, Inc. of U. Mo. Sch. Journalism 1989, Amb. award English-Speaking Union 1989, John F. Kennedy award, Holyoke, Mass 1989), After the War Was Over: Hanoi and Saigon, 1992, also articles and book revs. for popular mags.; contbr. to The Pentagon Papers, 1971. Served with AUS, 1959-62. Recipient Louis M. Lyons award for conscience and integrity in journalism, 1964, Silver medal Poor Richard Club, Phila., 1964, certificate of appreciation for best article on Asia Overseas Press Club Am., 1967, 1st Ann. Drew Pearson prize for excellence in investigative reporting, 1971, Columbia Journalism awards, 1972, 89, Sidney Hillman Found. awards, 1972, 88, Page One award Newspaper Guild N.Y., 1972, Distinguished Service award and Bronze medallion Sigma Delta Chi, 1972, citation of excellence Overseas Press Club, 1972, Literary Lion award N.Y. Pub. Libr., 1992; Guggenheim fellow, 1973-74; Adlai Stevenson fellow, 1973-75; Lehrman Inst. fellow, 1975-76; Rockefeller Found. fellow in humanities, 1976-77; Woodrow Wilson Internat. Center for Scholars fellow, 1979-80. Mem. Soc. Am. Historians, Am. Acad. Achievement. Obtained Pentagon Papers, 1971. Home: 4505 Klingle St NW Washington DC 20016-3580

SHEEHAN, PATTY, professional golfer. 4th ranked woman LPGA Tour, 1992; winner U.S. Women's Open, 1992, 94, LPGA Championship, 1983-84, 93. Inductee LPGA Hall of Fame, 1993, Sports Illustrated Sportsman of the Yr., 1987. Winner 31 LPGA Tournaments including Mazda Japan Classic, 1981, 88, Inamori Classic, 1982-83, 86, Orlando Lady Classic, 1982, Safeco Classic, 1982, 90, LPGA Corning Classic, 1983, LPGA Championship, 1983-84, 93, Henredon Classic, 1983-84, Elizabeth Arden Classic, 1984, McDonald's Kids Classic, 1984, 90, Sarasota Classic, 1985-86, 88, J&B

Scotch Pro AM, 1985, Konica San Jose Classic, 1986, Rochester Internat., 1989-90, 92, Jamaica Classic, 1990, Ping-Cellular One Championship, 1990, Orix Hawaiian Ladies Open, 1991, Jamie Farr Toledo Classic, 1992, U.S. Women's Open, 1992, 94. Office: LPGA 2570 Volusia Ave Ste B Daytona Beach FL 32114-7183*

SHEEHAN, ROBERT W., lawyer; b. New London, Conn., Aug. 16, 1945; s. Eugene Francis Sheehan and Lucille Irene (Izbicki) Heard; m. Pauline Orr Vietor, July 27, 1968; children: Margaret O., William B., Thomas V., Arthur W., Eliza F. BA, Yale U., 1967; JD cum laude, NYU, 1974. Bar: N.Y. 1975, U.S. Dist. Ct. (so. dist.) N.Y. 1975, U.S. Tax Ct. 1994. Assoc. Milbank, Tweed, Hadley & McCloy, N.Y.C., 1974-81; assoc., ptnr. Breed, Abbott & Morgan, N.Y.C., 1981-91; ptnr. Chadbourne & Parke, N.Y.C., 1991—. Pres. N.Y.C. Mission Soc., 1993. 1st. lt. U.S. Army, 1969-72. Fellow Am. Coll. Trust and Estate Counsel; mem. N.Y. State Bar Assn. (chmn. trusts & estate sect., com. charitable orgns. 1993—), Assn. of Bar of City of N.Y. (com. trusts, estates & surrogates cts. 1992—). Office: Chadbourne & Parke 30 Rockefeller Plz New York NY 10112

SHEEHAN, SUSAN, writer; b. Vienna, Austria, Aug. 24, 1937; came to U.S., 1941, naturalized, 1946; d. Charles and Kitty C. (Herrmann) Sachsel; m. Neil Sheehan, Mar. 30, 1965; children—Maria Gregory, Catherine Fair. BA (Durant scholar), Wellesley Coll., 1958; DHL (hon.), U. Lowell, 1991. Editorial researcher Esquire-Coronet, N.Y.C., 1959-60; free-lance writer N.Y.C., 1960-61; staff writer New Yorker mag., N.Y.C., 1961—. Author: Ten Vietnamese, 1967, A Welfare Mother, 1976, A Prison and a Prisoner, 1978, Is There No Place on Earth for Me?, 1982, Kate Quinton's Days, 1984, A Missing Plane, 1986, Life For Me Ain't Been No Crystal Stair, 1993; contbr. articles to various mags., including N.Y. Times Sunday Mag., Washington Post Sunday Mag., Harper's, Atlantic, New Republic, McCall's, Holiday, Boston Globe Sunday Mag., Life. Judge Robert F. Kennedy Journalism awards, 1980, 84; mem. lit. panel D.C. Commn. on Arts and Humanities, 1979-84; mem. pub. info. and edn. com. Nat. Mental Health Assn., 1982-83; mem. adv. com. on employment and crime Vera Inst. Justice, 1978-86; chair Pulitzer Prize nominating jury in gen. non-fiction for 1988, 1994, mem., 1991. Recipient Sidney Hillman Found. award, 1976, Gavel award ABA, 1978, Individual Reporting award Nat. Mental Health Assn., 1981, Pulitzer prize for gen. non-fiction, 1983, Feature Writing award N.Y. Press Club, 1984, Alumnae Assn. Achievement award Wellesley Coll., 1984, Carroll Kowal Journalism award NASW, 1993, Disting. Grad. award Hunter Coll. H.S., 1995, Pub. Awareness award Nat. Alliance for Mentally Ill, 1995; fellow Guggenheim Found., 1975-76, Woodrow Wilson Ctr. for Internat. Scholars, 1981. Mem. Soc. Am. Historians, Phi Beta Kappa, Authors Guild. Home: 4505 Klingle St NW Washington DC 20016-3580 Office: New Yorker Mag 20 W 43rd St New York NY 10036-7400

SHEEHY, EUGENE PAUL, retired librarian, author; b. Elbow Lake, Minn., Oct. 10, 1922; s. Thomas Joseph and Roxy Odessa (Vincent) S. B.A., St. John's U., Collegeville, Minn., 1950; M.A. in English, U. Minn., 1951, B.S. in L.S. 1952. Reference librarian Georgetown U., 1952-53; reference asst. Columbia U., 1953-65, head reference dept., 1965-87. Author: Joseph Conrad at Mid-Century, 1957, The Achievement of Marianne Moore, 1958, Yvor Winters, 1959, Frank Norris, 1959, Sherwood Anderson, 1960, Index to the Little Review, 1961, Index to Little Magazines, 1953-63, 5 vols., 1957-64, Guide to Reference Books, supplements 1-3 to 8th edit, 1968-72, Guide to Reference Books, 9th edit, 1976, 1st-2d Supplements, 1980-82, 10th edit., 1986, Bibliography of American Folk Art, 1987—. Served with USMC, 1942-46. Mem. ALA (Isadore Gilbert Mudge citation 1981). Roman Catholic. Home: 185 W End Ave New York NY 10023-5539

SHEEHY, GAIL HENION, author; b. Mamaroneck, N.Y., Nov. 27, 1937; d. Harold Merritt and Lillian Rainey (Paquin) Henion; m. Albert F. Sheehy, Aug. 20, 1960 (div. 1967); 1 dau., Maura; 1 adopted dau., Mohm; m. Clay Felker, Dec. 16, 1984. BS, U. Vt., 1958; fellow, Journalism Sch., Columbia U., 1970. Traveling home economist J.C. Penney & Co., 1958-60; fashion editor Rochester Democrat & Chronicle, 1961-63; feature writer N.Y. Herald Tribune, N.Y.C., 1963-66; contbg. editor New York mag., 1968-77. Contbr. to N.Y. Times Mag., Parade, New Republic, Washington Post; polit. contbg. editor Vanity Fair mag., 1988—; author: Lovesounds, 1970, Panthermania: The Clash of Black Against Black in One American City, 1971, Speed Is of the Essence, 1971, Hustling: Prostitution in Our Wide-Open Society, 1973, Passages: Predictable Crises of Adult Life, 1976, Pathfinders, 1981, Spirit of Survival, 1986, Character: America's Search for Leadership, 1988, Gorbachev: The Man Who Changed the World, 1990, The Silent Passage: Menopause, 1992, New Passages: Mapping Your Life Across Time, 1995; (plays) Maggie and Misha, 1991. Adv. bd. Women's Health Initiative, NIH; bd. dirs. Girls, Inc., Poets and Writers; eminent citizen's com. UN Internat. Conf. on Population and Devel., 1994. Recipient 4 Front Page awards Newswomen's Club N.Y., Nat. Mag. award Columbia U., 1973, Penney-Mo. Journalism award U. Mo., 1975, Anisfield-Wolf Book award, 1986, Best Mag. Writer award Washington Journalism Rev., 1991, N.Y. Pub. Libr. Literary Lion, 1992; Columbia U. fellow, 1970; Alicia Patterson Found. grantee, 1974. Mem. PEN, NOW, Authors Guild. *

SHEEHY, HOWARD SHERMAN, JR., minister; b. Denver, Mar. 19, 1934; s. Howard Sherman and Mildred Louise (Fishburn) S.; m. Thelma Florine Cline, Sept. 4, 1954; children: John Robert, Lisa Florine, Michael Howard. A.A., Graceland Coll., 1953; B.S., Central Mo. State Coll., 1955; M.S., U. Kans., 1960, postgrad. Ordained to ministry Reorganized Ch. of Jesus Christ of Latter-Day Sts., 1954. Youth dir. Reorganized Ch. Jesus Christ Latter-day Saints, Independence, Mo., 1960-64; pastor Des Moines, 1964-68; church supr. Haiti, 1968-70, Canada, 1970-74, Australia, 1970-75, N.Z., 1970-75, India, 1970-78, Japan, Korea, Republic of China, Philippines, 1976-78; mem. Council of Twelve Apostles, 1968-78, mem. 1st presidency, 1978—; mem. corp. body Outreach Internat., Restoration Trail Found. Editor-in-chief: Saints Herald. Mem. nat. Protestant com. on scouting Boy Scouts Am., 1964-66; trustee Independence Regional Health Ctr., 1979-88, 90-95. Lt. USNR, 1955-59. Mem. Pi Omega Pi, Phi Delta Kappa, Phi Kappa Phi. Republican. Home: 3403 S Crane St Independence MO 64055-2532 Office: The Auditorium The Temple PO Box 1059 Independence MO 64051-0559

SHEEHY, LEE EDWARD, lawyer; b. Des Moines, July 27, 1951; s. Edward Charles and Beverly (Roberts) S.; m. Linda J. Jadwin, Aug. 6, 1983. BA in Govt. cum laude, Harvard U., 1973; JD cum laude, U. Minn., 1977. Bar: Minn. 1977, U.S. Dist. Ct. Minn. 1977, U.S. Ct. Appeals (8th cir.) 1977, U.S. Supreme Ct. 1993. Investigator U.S. Senate Select Com. on Presdl. Campaign Activities, 1973-74; spl. asst. atty. gen. Office of Minn. Atty. Gen., 1977-80; assoc. Popham, Haik, Schnobrich & Doty, Ltd., 1980-83; ptnr. Popham, Haik, Schnobrich & Kaufman, Ltd., Mpls., 1983—, also bd. dirs.; chmn. fin. com. and budget com., mem. compensation com. Popham, Haik, Schnobrich & Kaufman, Ltd., Mpls. Contbr. articles to law jours. Chmn. Alan Page for Justice Com.; mem. nat. staff, cons. Carter-Mondale Campaign, 1976, Office of Advance, White House, 1977-79, Carter-Mondale Re-election Campaign, 1979-80, Mondale-Ferraro Presdl. Election Campaign, 1983-84; teaching asst. Upward Bound Poject, Hudson; Ohio; active numerous campaign and fundraising acctivities for local and statewide campaigns. Mem. ABA, Minn. State Bar Assn., Harvard Club of Minn. (past pres., chmn. schs. and scholarship com., mem. exec. com.). Office: Popham Haik Schnobrich 222 S 9th St Ste 3300 Minneapolis MN 55402-3398

SHEEHY, PAT MURPHY, artistic director. BA, George Washington U., 1960; postgrad., Catholic U., 1980. Founding mem. dir. Trinity Players, 1977-82; mgr. Source Theatre Co., Washington, 1984-86, mng. dir., 1986, producing artistic dir., 1986—; apptd., mem. major instns. panel, pers. com., commr.-convener visual arts panel D.C. Arts and Humanities Commn., 1984-87; chair D.C. Commn. on Arts, 1984-91; state rep. Nat. Assn. State Arts Agys., 1987-91, planning com., 1990; mem. steering com. 14th St. Arts Festival, 1992; mem. Mayor's Arts Task Force, 1978, Mayor's Adv. Task Force on Howard Theatre, 1989, Mayor's Cultural Transition Task Force, 1990, Mayor's Adv. Task Force on Lincoln Theatre, 1992-93, Mayor's Adv. Com. on Entertainment, 1993—; bd. dirs. Lincoln Theatre; presenter and panlist in field. Dir. (stage prodns.) Distant Fires, Lloyd's Prayer, Mud, Beirut, Time Remembered, Dust Conspiracy, Busboy (Best Dir. award 1985), The Father, Ivory Pawns, Many Moons, Madonna of the

Powder Room, Da, The Last Meeting of the Knights of the White Magnolia, The Bad Seed, Sherlock Holmes; asst. dir. (stage prodns.) K-2, The Ephemeral is Eternal; actress White Money, Dumb Stuff, True West, The Aunts, Beyond the Horizon, The Dining Room, Mirrors, And Miss Reardon Drinks a Little, The Mousetrap, Hands Across the Sea, Family Album. Chair spl. fundraising Rufus Phillips Congl. Campaign, Va., 1974; chair precinct fundraising ward 3 Marion Barry Mayoral Campaign, 1978; mem. exec. com. Cardozo-Shaw Neighborhood Com. Recipient Spl. Recognition award Mayor's Arts Awards, 1991, Washington Post award, 1993. Mem. League Washington Theatres (exec. com. 1989-91, chair advocacy com. 1989-91, pres. 1991-93), Cleve. Park Hist. Soc. (founding, bd. dirs. 1984-90). Home: 2941 Newark St NW Washington DC 20008-3339 Office: Source Theatre Co 1835 14th St NW Washington DC 20009-4425

SHEEHY, SIR PATRICK, tobacco and financial services executive; b. Sept. 2, 1930; s. Sir John Francis Sheehy and Jean Newton Simpson; m. Jill Patricia Tindall, 1964; 2 children. Grad., Ampleforth Coll., Yorkshire, Eng.; LHD (hon.), Va. Union U., 1985. Joined Brit.-Am. Tobacco Co., (BATCo) 1950, from mgmt. trainee to gen. mgr., Nigeria, Ghana, Ethiopia and W.I. 1950-62, mktg. advisor, London, 1962-67, gen. mgr., Holland, 1967-70, mem. group bd., 1970—, chmn. tobacco div. bd., N. Am. and Australia, 1975-76, dir. dep. chmn. B.A.T. Industries, 1976, vice chmn., 1981-82, chmn., 1982—, chmn. BATco, 1976-79, also bd. dirs. BAT Industries; dir. Brit. Petroleum Co. plc, 1984, Cluff Resources, 1992; mem. coun. internat. advisers Swiss Bank Corp., 1985; bd. dirs. The Spectator, 1988—. Chmn. South London Bus. Initiative, 1986—. Appointed chmn. Home Office Inquiry into Police Responsibilities and Rewards, 1992. 2d lt. Irish Guards, 1948-50. Mem. Confedn. Brit. Industry, Action Com. for Europe, European Round Table, Royal Inst. Internat. Affairs (coun. mem.). Avocations: golf, skiing, reading. Office: BAT Industries plc, Windsor House 50 Victoria St, London SW1H 0NL, England*

SHEEHY, THOMAS DANIEL, apparel and textile manufacturing company executive; b. Lawrence, Mass., Dec. 9, 1946; s. Bernard Agustine and Frances Patricia (Noone) S.; m. Brenda J. Hutchey; children: Christine Judith, Matthew Thomas. BSBA, Suffolk U., 1969, MBA, 1974. R & D engr. Malden Mills, Inc., 1970-71, prodn. control mgr., 1972-77; corp. mgr. Champion Products, Inc., Rochester, N.Y., 1977-80, mgr. prodn. and inventory mgmt., 1980-81, dir. mfg. resource planning, 1981-83, dir. mfg., 1984-85, v.p. mfg., 1985-86, v.p. ops., 1986-89, v.p. gen. mgr. retail, 1989-90, exec. v.p., 1990; pres., chief oper. officer Signal Apparel Co., Chattanooga, Tenn., 1991-93; pres. T.D. Sheehy Consulting, 1993—. Area chmn. Suffolk U. Alumni Fund, 1975-77. With U.S. Army, 1970-71. Mem. Am. Prodn. and Inventory Control Soc. (cert. practitioner inventory mgmt.). Home: 2020 Clematis Dr Hixson TN 37343-3510

SHEEKS, BILL F., minister; b. Kannapolis, N.C., Mar. 10, 1934; s. Harley Grady and Sadie Pauline (Pethel) S.; m. Eleanor Stout, May 31, 1958; children: Cheryl Stansky, Randy. AA, Lee Coll., 1954; BA, Catawba Coll., 1956; MA, Calif. Grad. Sch. Theology, 1978, DMin, 1979. Pastor Camp Greene Ch. of God, Charlotte, N.C., 1959-64, state youth dir., 1964-68; pastor Ch. of God, Burlington, N.C., 1968-70; state evangelism dir. Ch. of God, Charlotte, 1970-74; state overseer Ch. of God, Aiea, Hawaii, 1974-78, Decatur, Ill., 1978-82, Birmingham, Ala., 1982-86; asst. dir. evangelism and home missions Ch. of God, Cleveland, Tenn., 1986-90, dir. of evangelism and home ministries, 1990—; dir. N.C. State Bible Sch. Ch. of God, Charlotte, 1967-73, mem. N.C. Children's Home Bd., Kannapolis, 1968-72, N.C. State Coun., Charlotte, 1968-72. Author: The Growth of the Church of God: America's Oldest Pentecostal Church, 1979, How to Plant a Church of God, 1987, Winning Everyone, 1993; editor: Winning Kids, 1988. Named one of Outstanding Young Men Am., 1964. Avocation: walking. Home: 1165 Bramblewood Trl NW Cleveland TN 37311-4106 Office: Ch of God Internat Offices 2490 Keith St NW Cleveland TN 37311-1309

SHEELINE, PAUL CUSHING, hotel executive; b. Boston, June 6, 1921; s. Paul Daniel and Mary (Child) S.; m. Harriet White Moffat, May 23, 1948 (dec. 1962); children: Christopher White, William Emerson, Mary Child, Leonora Moffat; m. Sandra Dudley Wahl, July 24, 1965; 1 child, Abby Tucker. B.S., Harvard U., 1943, J.D. 1948. Bar: N.Y. 1949, D.C. 1986. Assoc. Sullivan & Cromwell, N.Y.C., 1948-51; with Lambert & Co., N.Y.C., 1954-65, gen. ptnr., 1958-65; chief fin. officer Intercontinental Hotels Corp., N.Y.C., 1966-71, pres., 1971-74, chief exec. officer, 1971-85, chmn. bd., 1972-87, cons., 1987-90; of counsel Verner, Liipfert, Bernhard, McPherson & Hand, Washington, 1986-93; bd. dirs. Resorts Internat., Inc., 1991-94; mem. Presdl. Bd. Advisors on Pvt. Sector Initiatives, Washington, 1987-89. Vice chmn. Community Service Soc. of N.Y., 1962-63; dir. Am. Assn. for UN, 1951-58; former mem. Harvard Overseers Com. to visit Center for Internat. Affairs and Dept. Romance Langs.; trustee East Woods Sch., Oyster Bay Cove, N.Y., 1959-68, Camargo Found., St. Luke's/Roosevelt Hosp. Ctr.; bd. dirs. Bus. Council for Internat. Understanding, 1975-88, Fgn. Policy Assn., 1981-90, Scientists' Inst. Pub. Info., 1984-91, Battle of Normandy Found., 1986-91. Served to capt. USAAF, 1942-46. Decorated Silver Star medal, French Legion of Honor, Croix de Guerre with palm, Moroccan Ouissam Alaouite. Mem. Council Fgn. Relations, Am.-Arab Assn. Commerce and Industry (chmn. bd. 1984-86), Phi Beta Kappa. Clubs: Cold Spring Harbor Beach; Harvard (N.Y.C.); Balsam Lake Anglers (N.Y.).

SHEEM, SANG KEUN, fiber optics engineering professional; b. Seoul, Korea, Mar. 20, 1944; s. Eung-Taek and Ki-Jik (Oh) S.; m. Susan Kim, Mar. 22, 1970; children: Edward J., Shana J. MS in Engring., U. Calif., 1973, PhD in Engring., 1975. Rsch. physicist U.S. Naval Rsch. Lab., Washington, 1976-81; mgr. Rockwell Internat., Dallas, 1981-86; mgr. sensor program Rockwell Internat., Dallas, 1982-86; cons. Kaptron Fiber Optic Co., Palo Alto, Calif., 1987-88, Amaco Rsch. Ctr., Naperville, Ill., 1986-87; pres. Berkeley Optics Co., Livermore, 1994—. Contbr. articles, referee to profl. jours. Mem. IEEE, Optical Soc. Am., Korean Scientist and Engr. Assn. (pres. No. Calif. chpt. 1990-91). Achievements include 15 patents in fiber optics and integrated optics. Office: Lawrence Livermore Nat Lab 7000 East Ave L-407 Livermore CA 94550

SHEEN, CHARLIE (CARLOS IRWIN ESTEVEZ), actor; b. L.A., Sept. 3, 1965; s. Ramon (Martin Sheen) and Janet Estevez. Appearances include (film) Grizzly II: The Predator, 1984, Red Dawn, 1984, The Boys Next Door, 1985, Ferris Bueller's Day Off, 1986, Lucas, 1986, Platoon, 1986, Wisdom, 1986, The Wraith, 1986, Wall Street, 1987, No Man's Land, 1987, Three for the Road, 1987, Eight Men Out, 1988, Young Guns, 1988, Major League, 1989, Tale of Two Sisters, 1989, Beverly Hills Brats, 1989, Never on Tuesday, 1989, Courage Mountain, 1990, Navy Seals, 1990, Men At Work, 1990, The Rookie, 1990, Cadence, 1990, Backtrack, 1990, Hot Shots!, 1990, National Lampoon's Loaded Weapon 1, 1993, Hot Shots: Part Deux, 1993, The Three Musketeers, 1993, The Chase, 1994, Major League 2, 1994, Terminal Velocity, 1994; (TV movies) Silence of the Heart, 1984, Out of the Darkness, 1985. Office: care William Morris Agency 151 El Camino Beverly Hills CA 90212*

SHEEN, MARTIN (RAMON ESTEVEZ), actor; b. Dayton, Ohio, Aug. 3, 1940; s. Francisco and Mary Ann (Phelan) Estevez; m. Janet Sheen, Dec. 23, 1961; children: Emilio, Ramon, Carlos, Renee. Grad. high sch. Made N.Y. stage debut as mem. Living Theatre in The Connection, 1959; Broadway debut in Never Live Over a Pretzel Factory, 1964; other stage appearances include The Subject Was Roses, 1964-66, The Wicked Crooks, 1967, Hamlet, 1967, Romeo and Juliet, 1968, Hello and Goodbye, 1969, The Happiness Cage, 1970, Death of a Salesman, 1975, Julius Caesar, 1988; film appearances include The Incident, 1967, The Subject Was Roses, 1968, Catch-22, 1970, No Drums, No Bugles, 1971, Rage, 1972, Badlands, 1973, The Legend of Earl Durand, 1974, The Cassandra Crossing, 1976, The Little Girl Who Lives Down the Lane, 1977, Apocalypse Now, 1979, The Final Countdown, 1980, Gandhi, 1982, That Championship Season, 1982, The King of Prussia, 1982, No Place to Hide, 1983, The Dead Zone, 1983, Man, Woman, and Child, 1983, Enigma, 1983, Eagle's Wing, 1983, Firestarter, 1984, The Believers, 1987, Wall Street, 1987, Siesta, 1987, Judgement in Berlin, 1988, Walking After Midnight, 1988, Da, 1988, Beverly Hills Brats, 1989, Cadence, 1991 (also dir.), JFK, 1991 (narrator), Hot Shots, Part Deux!, 1993 (cameo), Hear No Evil, 1993, Gettysburg, 1993; regular: TV series As the World Turns; TV movies and miniseries include Then Came Bronson, 1969,

The Subject Was Roses, 1969, Mongo's Back in Town, 1971, Welcome Home, Johnny Bristol, 1972, That Certain Summer, 1972, Catholics, 1973, The Execution of Private Slovik, 1974, The California Kid, 1974, The Story of Pretty Boy Floyd, 1974, The Missiles of October, 1974, Sweet Hostage, 1975, The Last Survivors, 1975, Blind Ambition, 1979, Taxi!!, 1978, The Long Road Home, 1980, Fly Away Home, 1981, Kennedy, 1982, Choices of the Heart, 1983, The Atlanta Child Murders, 1985, Consenting Adult, 1985, Out of Darkness, 1985, Shattered Spirits, 1986, Samaritan, 1986, News at Eleven, 1986, Conspiracy: The Trial of the Chicago 8, 1987, No Means No (exec. producer), Night Breaker, 1989; other TV appearances include Mannix, Murphy Brown (Emmy award, Guest Actor - Comedy Series, 1994). Roman Catholic. Office: Continental Film Group Park St Sharon PA 16146-3090

SHEEN, ROBERT TILTON, manufacturing company executive; b. Phila., Dec. 10, 1909; s. Milton Roy and Emma Elizabeth (Tilton) S.; m. Dorothy Martha Dillenbeck, June 25, 1932; children—James D., Roberta Alace (Mrs. R. Donald Peterson); m. Mary Regina Orban, Aug 17, 1951; 1 dau., Regina Elizabeth (Mrs. Brian C. Ridgway); m. Frieda Marie Van Riter, July 19, 1972. B.S. in Chem. Engring, Lehigh U., 1931, Chem Engr., 1936. Registered profl. engr., Pa., N.J., Ohio, Ill. Chem. engr. Swann Chem. Co., Anniston, Ala., 1931-32; tech. dir., then dir. cons. div. W.H. & L.D. Betz Co., 1932-43; co-founder Milton Roy Co., Phila and St. Petersburg, Fla. 1946; pres., chmn. bd. Milton Roy Co., 1947-68, chmn. bd., chief exec. officer, 1968-72, chmn. bd., 1972-74, dir., chmn. exec. com., 1975-89. Author: Robert T. Sheen-His-Story, 1991; contbr. articles to profl. jours. Pres. Jr. Achievement of St. Petersburg, 1965-66; chmn. Bayfront Med. Center, Inc., St. Petersburg, 1968-72, hon. chmn. campaign for New Times, 1984-86; mem. Fla. Gov.'s Council on Productivity and Council on Profl. Regulation, 1980-83; bd. dirs. United Fund S. Pinellas, Fla., 1972; trustee Eckerd Coll., St. Petersburg, 1959—, chmn. bd., 1974-77, mem. Acad. Sr. Profls. Eckerd Coll., 1983—; hon. trustee Sci. Center Pinellas County; mem. Fla. Com. on Aging, 1984-86; hon. bd. dirs. Fla. Council on Econ. Edn., 1984—; mem. council advisers Fla. State U., Tallahassee, 1975-82; former dir., chmn. health care com. Fla. Council of 100, 1969-77, chmn. human affairs com., 1978-82. Recipient Diamond Jubilee award U.S. CSC, 1958, Outstanding Citizen award, 1967, West Coast Fla. Engr. of Yr. award, 1968, Silver Medallion Brotherhood award NCCJ, 1977, Top Mgmt. award Soc. Mfg. Engrs., St. Petersburg, 1981, Monroe J. Rathbone Alumni Achievement award Lehigh U., 1989, Robert T. Sheen award for Vol. Leadership Bayfront Med. Ctr., 1993. Fellow Instrument Soc. Am. (pres. 1955-56); hon. mem. Am. Mgmt. Assn. (dir. 1962-67, 70-73, mem. exec. com. 1965-67, 70-73, life mem.); mem. Am. Chem. Soc., Am. Soc. Profl. Engrs., Am. Inst. Chem. Engrs., Suncoasters Inc. (named Mr. Sun 1969, pres. 1974-75), Newcomen Soc. N.Am. Patentee chem. pumps, chem. feed systems. Home: 672 Boca Ciega Point Blvd N Saint Petersburg FL 33708-2730

SHEER, BARBARA LEE, nursing educator; b. Riverside, N.J., Dec. 16, 1946; d. David J. and Edna (Maher) Phelan; m. George W. Sheer, Nov. 15, 1969; 1 child, Jeffrey B. Grad., Phila. Gen. Hosp. Sch. Nursing, 1967; BSN, U. Pa., 1971; PNP, Rutgers U., 1976; MSN, SUNY, Binghamton, 1981; DNSc, Widener U., 1989. Cert. family nurse practitioner ANA, CRNP, Pa. Instr. Coll. Misericordia, Dallas, Pa.; asst. prof. U. Scranton (Pa.); nurse practitioner Maternal Health Svcs., Wilkes Barre, Pa.; assoc. prof. Wilkes U., Wilkes Barre; asst. prof. U. Del.; coord. family nurse practitioner program U. Denver. Author: Nurse Practitioners: A Review of the Literature. Recipient Del. C. of C. Superstar Educator of Yr., 1994; Pub. Health Svcs. Policy fellow, 1992. Mem. ANA, Nat. Alliance of Nurse Practitioners (gov. body mem., chair 1994-95), Am. Acad. Nurse Practitioners (membership sec., pres., Outstanding Leadership and Svc. award 1994), Pa. Nurses Assn., Primary Health Care Nurse Practitioners of NEPA (coalition rep.), Sigma Theta Tau. Home: Box 374 Grouse Hill Dalton PA 18414 Office: U Del McDowell Hall Newark DE 19716

SHEERAN, MICHAEL JOHN LEO, priest, college administrator; b. N.Y.C., Jan. 24, 1940; s. Leo John and Glenna Marie (Wright) S. AB, St. Louis U., 1963, PhL, 1964, AM in Polit. Sci., 1967, AM in Theology, 1971, STL, 1971; PhD, Princeton U., 1977. Joined Soc. Jesus, 1957; ordained priest Roman Catholic Ch., 1970. Exec. editor Catholic Mind, N.Y.C., 1971-72; assoc. editor Am. mag., N.Y.C., 1971-72; assoc. chaplain Aquinas Inst., Princeton, N.J., 1972-75; asst. dean Regis Coll., Denver, 1975-77, dean of Coll., 1977-82, v.p. acad. affairs, 1982-92, acting pres., 1987-88, pres., 1993—; retreat dir., cons. on governance for religious communities, 1970—. Author: Beyond Majority Rule, 1984. Contbr. articles and editorials to publs. Trustee Rockhurst Coll., Kansas City, Mo., 1982-91, Creighton U., Omaha, 1985—, U. San Francisco, 1985-94, Loyola U., New Orleans, 1994—, Rocky Mountain Coll. of Art and Design, 1994—; active Mile High United Way, 1995—. Ford Found. scholar, 1963. Democrat. Home: 3333 Regis Blvd Denver CO 80221-1099 Office: Regis U 3333 Regis Blvd Denver CO 80221-1099

SHEERAN, THOMAS JOSEPH, education educator, consultant, judge; b. N.Y.C., Feb. 24, 1947; s. John Joseph and Dorothy (McAdams) S.; m. Maureen Elizabeth Flynn, June 27, 1970; children: Meaghan, Brendan. BS, Ithaca (N.Y.) Coll., 1968, MS, 1969; MEd, Niagara U., 1976; EdD, SUNY, Buffalo, 1976. Cert. tchr., N.Y. Teaching asst. Ithaca Coll., 1968-69; instr. Niagara U., Lewiston, N.Y., 1969-81, men's swimming coach, 1969-80, asst. prof., 1969—, women's swimming coach, 1969-74; prof., 1980—; chmn. dept. phys. edn. Niagara U., Lewiston, N.Y., 1980-82, chmn. dept. edn., 1988-91; tchr. Niagara U. Campus Sch., Lewiston, 1969-81; cons. various colls. and high schs., 1984-90. Mem. water safety com. ARC, Niagara Falls, N.Y., 1970-81; mem. planning bd. Town of Lewiston, 1982-84, zoning bd., 1986-92; mem. zoning Bd. Town Justice, 1992—. Fellow Am. Coll. Sports Medicine; mem. ASCD, Am. Alliance Health and Phys. Edn. (rsch. fellow), Assn. Tchr. of Edn., N.Y. Assn. Coll. Tchr. Edn. (pres. 1992-93), N.Y. Magistrates Assn., Niagara County Magistrates Assn., Niagara Falls Tchrs. Ctr. (policy bd. 1993—), N.Y. Assn. Coll. Tchr. Edn. (pres. 1992-93), Am. Assn. Coll. Tchrs. Edn. (state rep. 1992-93), Niagara Falls Country Club. Phi Delta Kappa, Pi Lambda Theta. Democrat. Roman Catholic. Avocations: golf, tennis. Home: 5230 Hewitt Pky Lewiston NY 14092-1923 Office: Niagara U Dept Edn Niagara Falls NY 14109

SHEERAN, WILLIAM JAMES, engineering executive; b. Saratoga Springs, N.Y., Nov. 29, 1938; s. James Joseph and Marjorie O. (Owen) S.; m. Mary Katherine Driscoll, July 31 1982; children: Michael, Jeffrey, Jacquelyn. BME magna cum laude, Syracuse U., 1960, MME, 1963, PhD, 1966. Various engring. positions Calspan Corp., Buffalo, 1966-74; mgr. fluid mechanics program R&D dept. GE Corp., Schenectady, N.Y., 1974-77, mgr. thermal br., 1977-80, mgr. liaison operation, 1980-84; gen. mgr. GE Elec. Distbn. and Control, Plainville, Conn., 1984-89; v.p. corp. engring., mfg. and sourcing GE Co., Fairfield, Conn., 1989-90; v.p. technology GE Appliances, Louisville, 1990-92; sr. v.p. engring. United Techs. Otis Elevator, Farmington, Conn., 1992—. Contbr. articles to profl. jours. Fellow ASME (assoc.), AIAA (assoc.); mem. Country Club of Farmington, Sigma Xi. Republican. Roman Catholic. Avocations: skiing, golf. Home: 99 Henley Way Avon CT 06001-4067 Office: United Techs Otis Elevators 10 Farm Springs Rd Farmington CT 06032-2568

SHEERIN, MAGGIE, small business owner, artist; b. Vernon, Tex., Sept. 22, 1940; d. Leslie L. and Sue Maxcy (Watters) Speir; m. James O. Davis, Sept. 14, 1957 (div.); m. Robert M. Sheerin, Jan. 3, 1967; children: James Maxcy, Cynthia Kathleen, John Malcolm. Owner Mag Ties, San Antonio, 1989—; bd. dirs. Tex. Bank North, San Antonio, 1982-85; founder, chmn. Winston Sch. of San Antonio, 1985—. Founding com. St. Mary's Hall Summer Arts, San Antonio, 1979-81; advisor Hugh O'Brien Youth Found., San Antonio, 1981; bd. dirs. Joffrey Workshop Com., 1982-83, Cancer Ctr. Coun., 1982-83, S.W. Found. Forum, 1971-76, Project ABC & ABC Alliance, 1983-84; bd. dirs., crusade chmn. Am. Cancer Soc., 1987-83; bd. dirs. Gallery of the McNay, 1992-94. Recipient Sword of Hope, Am. Cancer Soc., 1981, Golden Rule, J.C. Penney Co., 1985, Outstanding Svc. award Winston Sch., 1989, ABC Alliance, 1986, Profiles in Leadership, San Antonio, 1991. Mem. San Antonio Mus. Assn., San Antonio Art League, McNay Mus., N.Y. Drama League, Assn. of Children with Learning Disabilities, Am. Rsch. Ctr. in Egypt, Egypt Exploration Soc. (London), Harry's Bar London, Annabels London, Doubles N.Y., The Argyle. Republican. Avocations: egyptology, backgammon, bridge, reading, traveling to

ancient sites. Home and Office: Mag Ties 17 Auburn Pl San Antonio TX 78209-4739

SHEERR, DEIRDRE MCCRYSTAL, architectural firm executive. BA, Monmouth Coll., 1969; MArch, U. Colo., 1978; MA in Counseling Psychology, Antioch U., 1995. Registered architect, N.H., Colo. Computer systems and program analyst, 1970-75; pres. McCrystal Design & Devel., Inc., Denver, 1976-83; ptnr., head housing divsn. Sheerr & McCrystal, Inc., New London, N.H., 1983—; instr. passive solar design Denver Free U.; cons. solar and low income housing design Capitol Hill Architects and Planners; solar cons. Bros. Redevelopment, Inc. Prin. works include Lawrence Berkeley (Calif.) Lab., Solar Homestead, Boulder, Colo. (Nat. Passive Solar Design award HUD), 1515 South Pearl St., Curtis Pk. Face Block Renovation Project, Denver (Nat. Honor award AIA), St. Paul's Episcopal Ch. (Archtl. award Gov.'s Commn. Handicapped 1987). Mem. pres.'s adv. coun. Colby Sawyer Coll., 1987-91; mem. fundraising com. Ausbon Sargent Land Preservation Trust, 1989—, co-chair ski-a-thon, 1990—, trustee, 1991—, bd. dirs., 1992—; mem. affordable housing task force charrette for City of Laconia, N.H. Housing Authority, 1989; mem. bus. adv. coun. Town of New London, 1990—; life mem. Upper Valley Humane Soc.; active Nature Conservancy, Wilderness Soc., Greenpeace, Connecticut River Watershed Coun., Sierra Club, Nat. Audubon Soc. Recipient Main St. Comml. Beautification award New London Garden Club, Best Restoration of Yr. award Denver Mag., 1983, Heritage Concord Grand award 1994; Nat. Hist. Preservation grantee Sec. of Interior, 1980. Mem. AIA (bd. dirs. N.H. chpt. 1984-89, sec. 1985, pres.-elect 1986, pres. 1987, immediate past pres. 1988, mem. exec. bd. New Eng. regional coun. 1986-87, spkr. N.W. regional conf., Denver Housing Authority Law Income Housing Design co-winner 1976, Western Regional Merit award 1981, 11 awards for Excellence in Architecture N.H. chpt. 1983, 85, 86, 88, 90, 91, 92, 93, 94, Nat. Honor award 1983), Nat. Trust Hist. Preservation, Nat. Pks. and Conservation Assn., Homebuilder's Assn. N.H. (SAM Silver award), N.H. Hist. Soc., Boston Computer Soc., New London Hist. Soc., Urban Design Forum, Appalachian Mountain Club. Office: Sheerr & McCrystal Inc 177 Main St New London NH 03257-4550

SHEETS, HERMAN ERNEST, marine engineer; b. Dresden, Germany, Dec. 24, 1908; s. Arthur Chitz and Gertrude (Stern) S.; m. Norma Sams, Oct. 17, 1942 (dec. Dec. 1970); m. Paulann Hosler, May 29, 1982; children: Lawrence S., Michael R., Arne H., Diana E., Elizabeth J., Karn N. M.E., U. Dresden, 1934; Dr. Tech. Scis. in Applied Mechanics, U. Prague, Czechoslovakia, 1936. Engr. Prvni Brněnska Strojima, Brno, 1936-39; Chief engr. Chamberlin Research Corp., East Moline, Ill., 1939-42; mgr. research St. Paul Engring. & Mfg. Co., 1942- 44; project engr. Elliott Co., Jeannette, Pa., 1944-46; engring. mgr. Goodyear Aircraft Corp., Akron, Ohio, 1946-53; v.p. Electric Boat div. Gen. Dynamics Corp., Groton, Conn., 1953-69; v.p. engring. and research; prof. dept. ocean engring. U. R.I., Kingston, 1969-80, dept. chmn., 1971-79; dir. engring. Analysis and Tech., North Stonington, Conn., 1979-84; cons. engr. Groton, 1980—. Author numerous articles in field. Recipient citation sec. war. Fellow AIAA (asso.), ASME, AAAS; mem. N.Y. Acad. Scis., Nat. Acad. Engring., Soc. Naval Architects and Marine Engrs., Am. Soc. Naval Engrs., Marine Tech. Soc., Pi Tau Sigma. Home and Office: Mumford Cove 87 Neptune Dr Groton CT 06340

SHEETS, MICHAEL JAY, consumer products company executive; b. Seattle, Sept. 5, 1930; s. John William and Romaine Burnell (Little) S.; m. Niki K. Sarachan Singer, Feb. 24, 1973; children: Alexandra Burnell, Hilarie Maria, Romaine Kitty, Nicholas Simon Feramorz. BA, Stanford U., 1952; BBA, U. Wash., 1952; postgrad., Harvard U., 1981. Marketing plansman N. W. Ayer & Son, Phila., 1956-59; account exec. McCann-Erickson, Chgo., 1960-62; v.p. Gardner Advt. Co., St. Louis, 1962-68; v.p. marketing RJR Foods, N.Y.C., 1968-74; sr. v.p. marketing Warner Cable Corp., N.Y.C., 1974-75; pres. consumer products div. Airwick Industries, Carlstadt, N.J., 1975-80; pres., chief operating officer, dir. Airwick Industries, 1980-81; pres., chief exec. officer Airwick N.Am., Carlstadt, 1981-85; pres., CEO Airwick Industries, Inc., Wayne, N.J., 1985-90; pres., chief oper. officer French Culinary Inst., N.Y.C., 1994; prin. Schoenfeld, Chapman & Pearl Ventures, N.Y.C., 1994—; mem. mgmt. com. Ciba-Geigy Corp., Ardsley, N.Y., 1981-85; mem. exec. com. Reckitt & Colman Inc., Wayne, 1985-90; bd. dirs. Stern's Miracle-Gro, Inc., Port Washington, N.Y., Scott's Liquid Gold Inc., Denver. Served with counter intelligence corps., U.S. Army, 1952-55. Mem. N.Y. Soc. Libr., Union Club (N.Y.C.), Knickerbocker Country Club (Tenafly, N.J.), Kappa Sigma. Office: 462 Broadway New York NY 10013

SHEETZ, RICHARD LATRELLE, retired association executive; b. Macon, Mo., Aug. 10, 1906; s. Robert Karl and Lena M. (Fetter) S.; m. Aagot Velline, Aug. 12, 1939; children: Robert K., Susan S. Laitsch, Timothy R.; stepchildren: Ferne D. Holmes, Harold S. Austin, Geraldine M. Beck. A.B., Westminster Coll., 1928. Asst. sales mgr. Lowe and Campbell Athletic Goods Co., Kansas City, Mo., 1928-33; officer mgr., campaign asst. Kansas City Charities Fund, 1933-36; exec. dir. N.D. Community Chest, Fargo, 1936-39, Tex. Community Chest and Planning Council, Austin, 1939-43, Va. United Communities Fund, Norfolk, 1943-71; The Norfolk Found.-Community Trust, 1971-86; ret., 1986; pres. S.E. region Community Chests and Councils of Am., 1948-49, Va. Fedn., 1949-59; nat. bd. dirs. Community Chests and Councils of Am., 1953-59. Author: Savannah, Georgia, A Study of Community Organization, 1950. Named Mr. Citizen of his generation Norfolk Union Labor Council, 1971; recipient citation for outstanding service City of Norfolk, 1970, Golden Legion award Westminster Coll., 1978. Mem. Nat. Conf. Social Welfare, Beta Theta Pi. Club: Virginia. Home: 2545 Murray Ave Norfolk VA 23518-4521

SHEFFEL, IRVING EUGENE, psychiatric institution executive; b. Chgo., July 5, 1916; s. Joseph and Jennie (Leibson) S.; m. Beth Silver, Aug. 2, 1942; 1 dau., Anita (dec.). A.B., U. Chgo., 1939; M.P.A., Harvard U., 1946; LHD (hon.), Washburn U., 1987. Insp., wage and hour div. Dept. Labor, Chgo., 1940-41; mgmt. and budget analyst VA, Washington, 1946-48; budget analyst U.S. Bur. of Budget, Washington, 1948-49; controller, treas. Menninger Found., Topeka, 1949-73; v.p. Menninger Found., 1973-93, v.p. emeritus, 1993—; instr. Menninger Sch. Psychiatry. Bd. dirs. Washburn U. Art Center, 1969—, pres., 1971-73; treas. Karl Menninger lect. series, 1983—. Served to maj. U.S. Army, 1942-45. Fellow Assn. Mental Health Adminstrs. (charter); mem. Am. Soc. Public Adminstrn. (charter), Topeka Opera Soc. (treas 1985—). Jewish. Home: 1215 SW 29th Ter Topeka KS 66611-2192 Office: PO Box 829 Topeka KS 66601-0829

SHEFFIELD, DON B., wholesale distribution company executive; b. 1935. BS, U. Tex., 1958. With Geosource Inc., Houston, 1958—, various mgmt. positions, 1958-73, sr. v.p., 1973-76, exec. v.p. geophys. ops. western hemisphere, 1976-78, exec. v.p. geophys. ops. worldwide, 1978-79, pres. mgr. exploration services, 1979-80, pres. petroleum exploration group, 1980-81, v.p. service ops., 1981-82, pres., chief exec. officer, 1984—. Office: Geosource Inc 6909 Southwest Fwy Houston TX 77074-2105 Office: Gearhart Industries Inc 1100 Everman Pky Fort Worth TX 76140-4908

SHEFFIELD, GARY ANTONIAN, professional baseball player; b. Tampa, Fla., Nov. 18, 1968. Baseball player Milw. Brewers, 1986-92, San Diego Padres, 1992-93, Florida Marlins 1993—. mem. Nat. League All-Star Team, 1992-93; Sporting News Player of the Year, 1992; Sporting News All-Star Team, 1992; recipient Silver Slugger award, 1992; named Minor League Co-Player of the Yr. Sporting News, 1988, Comeback Player of Yr., Sporting News, 1992. Nat. Batting League Champion, 1992. Office: Florida Marlins 2269 NE 199th St Miami FL 33180*

SHEFFIELD, HORACE LINDSEY, JR., union official; b. Vienna, Ga., Feb. 22, 1916; s. Horace Lindsey and Georgie (Brown) S.; m. Joyce Richards; children: Corliss Sheffield Williams, Kathryn, Lavonne Sheffield Turner, Horace Lindsey III. Student, Detroit Inst. 1937-41, Wayne State U., 1941-42, 48; LL.D. Wayne State U., 1972, Maygrove Coll., 1989; student, UCLA, 1952. Joined United Auto Workers, Detroit, 1940; internat. rep. United Auto Workers, 1942-67, adminstrv. asst. to internat. v.p., 1967-74, adminstrv. asst. to pres., 1975-81; with Ford Motor Co., 1936—; columnist Mich. Chronicle weekly. Bd. dirs. A. Philip Randolph Inst.; mem. adv. bd. United Way; sr. adv. coun. Blue Cross/Blue Shield; mem. Nat. Coalition Black Trade Unionists; v.p. Trade Union Leadership Coun.; pres. emeritus Detroit Assn. Black Orgns.; pres. Detroit Coalition Black Trade

Unionists; coord. Citizens Coalition Against Crime, Alliance for a Safer, Greater Detroit; treas. Nat. Assn. Black Orgns. Recipient Ira W. Jayne Meml. medal Detroit NAACP, 1972, Liberty Bell award Mich. State Bar, 1964, U. Mich. Hon. Doctorate Degree. Mem. NAACP (Golden Heritage award), Kappa Alpha Psi. Episcopalian. Home: 2101 Bryanston Crescent St Detroit MI 48207-3883 Office: Detroit Office Black Orgns 12048 Grand River Detroit MI 48204-4126

SHEFFIELD, LESLIE FLOYD, retired agricultural educator; b. Orafino, Nebr., Apr. 13, 1925; s. Floyd L. and Edith A. (Presler) S.; BS with high distinction in Agronomy, U. Nebr., 1950, MS, 1964; postgrad. U. Minn., summer 1965; PhD, U. Nebr., 1971; m. Doris Fay Fenmore, Aug. 20, 1947; children: Larry Wayne, Linda Faye (Mrs. Bernard Eric Hempelman), Susan Elaine (Mrs. Randy Thorman). County extension agt. Lexington and Schuyler, Nebr., 1951-52; exec. sec. Nebr. Grain Improvement Assn., 1952-56; chief Nebr. Wheat Commn., Lincoln, 1956-59; exec. sec. Great Plains Wheat, Inc., market devel., Garden City, Kans., 1959-61; asst. to dean Coll. Agr., U. Nebr. at Lincoln, 1961-66, supt. North Platte Expt. Sta., 1966-71, asst. dir. Nebr. Coop. Extension Service, Nebr. Agrl. Expt. Sta., Lincoln, 1971-75, asst. to vice chancellor Inst. Agr. and Natural Resources, 1975-84, also extension farm mgmt. specialist and assoc. prof. agrl. econs., 1975-94; ret. U. Nebr., Lincoln, 1994. v.p. U. Nebr. Found., 1982-86; sec.-treas. Circle 4S-L Acres, Wallace, Nebr., 1973-87; cons. econs. of irrigation in N.D., Minn., S.D. and Brazil, 1975, 88, Sudan, Kuwait and Iran, 1976, People's Republic of China, 1977, 81, Can., 1977, 78, 79, 80, Mex., 1978, 79, Argentina, 1978, Hong Kong, 1981, Japan, 1981, Republic of South Africa, 1985, Argentina, Brazil and Paraguay, 1992, Australia, 1994, New Zealand, 1994. Author: Economic Impact of Irrigated Agriculture, 1985; author chpt. to book; editor: Procs. of Nebr. Water Resources and Irrigation Devel. for 1970's, 1972; contbg. editor Irrigation Age Mag., St. Paul, 1974-86; contbr. articles to various publs. With U.S. Army, 1944-46; ETO. Recipient Hon. State Farmer award Future Farmers Am., 1955, Hon. Chpt. Farmer award, North Platte chpt., 1973; fellowship grad. award Chgo. Bd. Trade, 1964, Agrl. Achievement award Ak-Sar-Ben, 1969, Citizen award U.S. Dept. Interior Bur. Reclamation, 1984; Pub. Svc. award for contbns. to Nebr. agr. Nebr. Agribus. Club, 1984, Ditch Rider award Four States Irrigation Coun., 1988, Disting. Svc. award Am. Soc. Farm Mgrs. & Rural Appraisers Nebr. chpt., 1993, Alumnus of Yr. award U. Nebr.-Lincoln Coll. Agr. & Natural Resources Alumni Assn., 1993, Headgate award Four States Irrigation Coun., 1995, Pioneer Irrigation award Nebr. Water Conf. Coun. and U. Nebr. Lincoln, 1995; NASA Rsch. grantee, 1972-77; inducted Nebr. Hall of Agrl. Achievement, 1988; named Irrigation Man of Yr. Irrigation Assn., Nebr. 1988. Mem. Am. Agrl. Econs. Assn., Am. Nat., Nebr. Water Resources Assns. (Pres.'s award 1979, award for Commitment to Irrigated Agriculture 1993), Nebr. Irrigation Assn., Nebr. Assn. Resource Dists., Am. Soc. Farm Mgrs. Rural Appraisers, Orgn. Profl. Employees of U.S. Dept. Agr., Lincoln C. of C. (chmn. agrl. com. 1974-77), Rotary (dir. 1965-66), Gamma Sigma Delta, Alpha Zeta (v.p. Nebr. agrl. rels. coun., 1993-94). Home: 3800 Loveland Dr Lincoln NE 68506-3842

SHEFFIELD, LEWIS GLOSSON, physiologist; b. Adel, Ga., Oct. 30, 1957; s. Eugene Davis and Martha Sue (Sinclair) S.; m. Mary Frances Tanner, July 18, 1980. MS, Clemson U., 1980; PhD, U. Mo., 1983. Rsch. asst. Clemson (S.C.) U., 1978-80, U. Mo., Columbia, 1980-83; postdoctoral assoc. Mich. State U., East Lansing, 1983-86; asst. prof. dairy sci. dept. U. Wis., Madison, 1986-91, assoc. prof., 1991—, dir. endocrinology-reproductive physiology program, 1990—. Contbr. articles to profl. jours. Recipient First award NIH, 1988. Mem. Am. Dairy Sci. Assn. (milk synthesis chair 1991-92), Com. on Mammary Gland Biology, Endocrine Soc., Sigma Xi. Achievements include demonstration that epidermal growth factor interacts with estrogen and progesterone to regulate mammary devel. and are working to understand the cellular and molecular basis of that interaction; that prolactin causes a decrease in epidermal growth factor-induced growth responses, which appears to be related to mammary gland differentiation. The molecular regulation of this response is also under investigation. Office: U Wis 960 Animal Scis Bldg 1675 Observatory Dr Madison WI 53706*

SHEFFIELD, RICHARD LEE, physicist; b. Dayton, Ohio, Sept. 22, 1950; s. Albert H. and Pauline E. (Schutte) S.; m. Antoinette M. Mals, Oct. 28, 1978; children: Nicole, Angela, Michael. BS, Wright State U., 1972; PhD, MIT, 1978. Staff mem. high energy high density physics Los Alamos (N.Mex.) Nat. Lab., 1978-82, staff mem. free electron laser tech., 1982-85, dep. group leader, 1985-89, group leader accelerator theory & free electron laser tech., 1989-93, prin. investigator advanced FEL initiative, 1990—; adj. prof. dept. physics Wright State U., Dayton, 1991—; advisor UV/FEL adv. panel Brookhaven (N.Y.) Nat. Lab., 1991—; Project Leader Advanced Accelevator Tech., 1994—; lectr. U.S. Accelerator Summer Sch., 1989. Editorial bd. Particle Accelerators, 1991—; patentee photoinjector, high brightness electron accelerators. Pres. Los Alamos United Way, 1981-84; vice chmn. Los Alamos County Planning and Zoning Commn., 1983-86, exec. coun. for divsn. of Beams and Particles. Recipient R&D 100 award R&D 100 Mag., 1988, Strategic Def. Tech. Achievements award Strategic Def. Preparedness Assn., 1989. Mem. Am. Phys. Soc., Sigma Pi Sigma.

SHEFLIN, MICHAEL JOHN EDWARD, transportation commissioner; b. Toronto, Ont., Can., Dec. 27, 1938; s. John Edward and Marguerite Christine (MacKinnon) S.; m. Elizabeth Anne Taylor, Apr. 19, 1965; children: Sydney Michelle Taylor, Siobahn Morgan Taylor. Diploma in engring., St. Francis Xavier U., Antigonish, N.S., 1959; B of Civil Engring., Tech. U. N.S., 1962; diploma, Banff Sch. Advanced Mgmt., Alta., 1972. Engr. USAF, Harmon AFB, 1962-65; town mgr. Town of Stephenville, Nfld., 1965-66; sr. engr. ops. City of St. Catharines, Ont., 1966-70; dir. engring. and works City of Halifax, N.S., 1970-75; transp. commr. Regional Municipality of Ottawa-Carleton, Ont., 1975—; gov. Internat. Pub. Works Fedn., Washington, 1989-92; eminent overseas speaker Instn. of Engrs., Canberra, Australia, 1989. Co-author: Management of Local Public Works, 1986; contbr. articles to jours. V.p. Liberal Party of Nfld., Stephenville, 1966; chmn. Econ. Affairs, Jaycees, Can., 1966, 67, Niagara Regional Sci. Fair, St. Catharines, 1969, United Way City of Halifax, 1973. Fellow Inst. Transp. Engrs. (Outstanding Svc. award 1991); mem. Internat. Fedn. of Mcpl. Engrs. (life mem. Oslo, 1st v.p. 1991-94, 2d v.p. 1985-88, pres.1988-94), Transp. Assn. Can. (v.p. 1988-91, treas. 1990-93, award of merit 1991, hon. life mem. Calgary), Inst. Mcpl. Engrs. (pres. 1976-77, hon. mem.), Am. Pub. Works Assn. (leader of yr. 1981). Avocations: history, traveling, walking. Home: 35 3d Ave, Ottawa, ON Canada K15 2J5 Office: Regional Municipality, 111 Lisgar St Cartier Sq, Ottawa, ON Canada K2P 2L7

SHEH, ROBERT BARDHYL, environmental management company executive; b. N.Y.C., July 29, 1939; s. Talat and Nedime (Karali) S.; m. Mary Cheney Fleming, Dec. 29, 1961; children—Andrea K., Jonathan C., Robert R., Elisabeth F., Theresa N. BS in Civil Engring, Rennselaer Poly. Inst., 1960; grad. program for Mgmt. Devel., Harvard U., 1974. With The Ralph M. Parsons Co., 1971—; sr. v.p. mgr. petroleum, chem., mining and metall. div. The Ralph M. Parsons Co., Pasadena, Calif., 1988, pres., 1989-92, also bd. dirs.; pres., CEO Internat. Tech. Corp., Torrance, Calif., 1992—; mem. adv. bd. Sch. Chem. Engr. U. Calif., Berkeley, 1986—; bd. dirs. Davidson Assocs. Bd. regents Marymount Internat. Sch., London, 1979; bd. trustees Harvey Mudd Coll., 1992—. With USNR, 1960-64. Mem. Calif. Club (L.A.), Annandale Golf Club (Pasadena), L.A. Country Club. Office: Internat Tech Corp 23456 Hawthorne Blvd Torrance CA 90505

SHEHAN, WAYNE CHARLES, lawyer; b. Miami, Fla., Nov. 25, 1944; s. Joseph L. Shehan and Louise A. Salloum; m. Sherrin M. Graham, May 21, 1981; children: Christopher, Kevin. BS, U. Detroit, 1966, JD, 1969. Bar: Mich. 1969. Prin. Wayne C. Shehan, P.C., St. Clair Shores, Mich., 1969—; prof. U. Detroit, 1969-70; mediator Macomb County Cir. Ct., Mt. Clemens, Mich., 1988—; lectr. People's Law Sch., St. Clair Shores, 1987—. Provost del. Macomb County Rep. Party, St. Clair Shores, 1974-80. Mem. State Bar Assn. Mich. (family law sect., estate planning sect., gen. practice sect.), Macomb County Bar Assn. (speakers bur.), Macomb County Trial Lawyers Assn. Avocations: skiing, tennis, ice skating, ice hockey. Office: 22420 Greater Mack Saint Clair Shores MI 48080

SHEHEEN, FRED ROUKOS, education association administrator; b. Camden, S.C., July 7, 1936; s. Austin M. and Lucile (Roukos) S.; m. Rose Maria Serio, Nov. 26, 1966; children: Maria, Vincent, Margaret Rose. AB

Polit. Sci., Duke U., 1958; postgrad., Harvard U., 1990; LLD (hon.), Claflin Coll., 1990; HHD, Lander Coll., 1992; AA honoris causa, Tech. Coll. Lowcountry, Beaufort, S.C., 1992. Bureau chief Charlotte (N.C.) Observer, Rock Hill, Columbia, S.C., 1958-63; press sec. to Gov. Donald Russell, Columbia, 1963-65; exec. asst. to Sen. Donald Russell, Washington, 1965-66; asst. to dir. S.C. State Devel. Bd., Columbia, 1967-68; v.p. & sec., pres. & publisher Banner Publishers Inc., Chronicle Publishers Inc., N.C., S.C., 1968-76; founder, pres., prin. owner Camden (S.C.) Co., 1976-87; commr. of higher edn. S.C. Commn. on Higher Edn., Columbia, 1987—; bd. dirs. S.C. Rsch. Authority, Columbia, 1983-86; mem. S.C. Commn. Human Affairs, 1971-72, S.C. Commn. Higher Edn., 1971-75, 79-86, (chmn. 1983-86), Edn. Improvement Act Selection com., 1983-86, Commn. Future S.C., Columbia, 1987-89. Contbr. chpt. to book, article to profl. jour. Pres. Kershaw County Mental Health Assn., Camden, S.C., 1971, 76; mem. S.C. Tuition Grants Commn., 1988—, Nat. Edn. Goals Panel task force Collegiate Attainment and Assessment, 1988—, S.C. Edn. Goals Panel, 1992—, So. Regional Coun. Coll. Bd., 1993—; adv. bd. Master Pub. Adminstrn. program U. S.C. Coll. Charleston, 1992—; trustee Springdale Sch., Camden, 1976-84, Boyland-Haven-Mather Acad., Camden, 1976-83, S.C. Gov's. Sch. Sci. and Mathematics, 1987—; bd. dirs. Kershaw County Cancer Soc. Recipient Sertoma Svc. to Mankind award Sertoma club, 1973; named Educator of Yr. S.C. Tech. Edn. Assn., 1990. Mem. State Higher Edn. Exec. Officers (exec. com. 1990—, Nat. Ctr. Edn. Statistics Network adv. com. 1990—), S.C. Agy. Dir's. Orgn. (pres. 1992). Roman Catholic. Avocations: racquetball, water sports, reading. Home: 2107 Washington Ln Camden SC 29020-1723 Office: SC Commn Higher Edn 1333 Main St Ste 200 Columbia SC 29201-3201

SHEINBAUM, GILBERT HAROLD, international management consultant; b. N.Y.C., Apr. 20, 1929; s. Herman and Selma (Klimberg) S.; m. Inger Fredebo Thomsen, Aug. 28, 1971; children: Neil, Britt. AB in History, NYU, 1950; postgrad., CUNY, 1954-55, New Sch. for Social Rsch., 1955-56. Various fgn. svc. posts Washington, Laos, France, Vietnam, 1957-68; polit. officer Am. Embassy, Copenhagen, 1968-72, U.S. Dept. of State, Washington, 1972-75; chargé d'affaires Am. Embassy, Antananarivo, Madagascar, 1975-77; dep. chief of mission Am. Embassy, Lilongwe, Malawi, 1977-79; Am. consul Am. Consulate, Cebu, Philippines, 1979-83; polit. counselor U.S. Mission to the UN, Geneva, 1983-86; dir. Colombo Plan (internat. orgn.), Colombo, Sri Lanka, 1986-91; assoc. Global Bus. Access, Ltd., Washington, 1991; cons. Nat. Security Edn. Program, Washington, 1992-95, Internat. Found. for Electoral Systems, Washington, 1995—; internat. observer Sri Lankan elections, 1993, 94. Author and editor articles on econ. devel. in Asia. Trustee George Keyt Cultural Found., Colombo, 1987-91; bd. chmn. Overseas Children's Sch., Colombo, 1987-90; commr. Boy Scouts Am., Geneva, 1984-86; stage mgr. Am. Light Opera Co., Washington, 1962-64. Served to 1st lt. U.S. Army, 1951-53. Recipient Award of Recognition, Mindanao State U., Marawi, Philippines, 1983. Mem. Am. Fgn. Svc. Assn., World Affairs Coun. of Washington DC, World Affairs Coun. of No. Calif., Asia Soc., Vietnamese-Am. C. of C. (bd. dirs. 1992—), Diplomatic and Consular Officers Ret. (treas.). Avocations: tennis, jogging, touring, reading. Home: 210 Patterson St Falls Church VA 22046 Office: Internat Found for Electoral Systems 1101 15th St NW Washington DC 20006

SHEINBERG, ISRAEL, computer company executive; b. Fort Worth, Apr. 15, 1932; s. Samuel I. and Pauline C. (Fram) S.; m. Betty S. Topletz, Aug. 19, 1962; children—Amy, Karen, David, Paula. B.S. in Physics, U. Tex., 1953; student, UCLA, 1957-58, Arlington (Tex.) State Coll., 1960, Southwestern Med. Sch., 1961. Electronic engr. Hughes Aircraft Co., 1956-60, Nat. Data Processing Corp., 1961; also exec. v.p. and gen. mgr. European ops. Recognition Equipment Inc., 1961-90; pvt. cons. to industry Dallas, 1990—; bd. dirs. Tex. Commerce Bank, Balchem Corp.; mem. adv. coun. of engring. found., adv. coun. for natural scis. U. Tex., Austin; speaker on image technology, optical character recognition and related subjects. Contbr. articles to profl. jours. With AUS, 1954-56. Inducted into Assn. for Work Process Improvement Hall of Fame. Mem. Optical Soc. Am., Am. Mgmt. Assn. Jewish (bd. dirs. synagogue). Home: 5706 Watson Cir Dallas TX 75225-1653 Office: Sheinberg Assocs 5706 Watson Cir Dallas TX 75225-1653

SHEINBERG, SIDNEY JAY, recreation and entertainment company executive; b. Corpus Christi, Tex., Jan. 14, 1935; s. Harry and Tillie (Grossman) S.; m. Lorraine Gottfried, Aug. 19, 1956; children: Jonathan J., William David. A.B., Columbia Coll., 1955; LL.B., Columbia U., 1958. Bar: Calif. 1958. Assoc. in law UCLA Sch. Law, 1958-59; with MCA, Inc., Universal City, Calif., 1959—, pres. TV div., 1971-74, corp. exec. v.p., 1969-73, corp. pres., chief operating officer, 1973—. Mem. Assn. Motion Picture and Television Producers (chmn. bd.). Office: Universal City Studios Inc 100 Universal City Plz Universal City CA 91608*

SHEINFELD, DAVID, composer; b. St. Louis, Sept. 20, 1906; s. Joseph and Feige (Sandler) S.; m. Dorothy Jaffe, Apr. 12, 1947; children: Daniel, Paul. MusB, Am. Conservatory Music, Chgo., 1929; studies with Ottorino Respighi, Santa Cecilia Acad., Rome, 1929-31. Violinist, arranger various radio programs, Chgo., 1934-40; violist Pitts. Symphony, 1944-45; violinist San Francisco Symphony, 1945-71; ind. composer, tchr. San Francisco, 1971—. Composer orchestral and chamber music works including Adagio and Allegro, 1947, Patterns, 1962, Dualities, 1981, Dreams and Fantasies, 1982; commd. to compose work for San Francisco Symphony Orch.'s 60th anniversary, 1971 (Recipient Norman Fromm award for chamber music composition 1979), 2d string quartet Kronos Quartet, 1990; compositions performed by symphony orchs. in San Francisco, Chgo., Pitts., Phila. Chamber Symphony, chamber music performed, numerous cities in U.S., Can., Eng. Recipient Composer's award AAAL, 1993, award Koussevitzky Music Found., 1993; NEA grantee for orch. work, 1987-88. Mem. Broadcast Music, Inc. Avocations: astronomy, physics. Home and Office: 1458 24th Ave San Francisco CA 94122-3312 *Respect for the rights of others; respect for our cultural achievements and ideals; respect for the art of music; these principles have guided my life.*

SHEINFELD, MYRON M., lawyer, educator; b. Mass., Mar. 18, 1930; s. Robert and Sadye (Rosenberg) S.; m. Christina Trzcinski, Mar. 30, 1985; children: Scott, Tom. BA, Tulane U., 1951; JD, U. Mich., 1954. Bar: Mich. 1954, Tex. 1956. Researcher Legis. Research Inst. U. Mich., 1954; asst. U.S. atty. So. Dist. Tex., 1958-60; law clk. U.S. Dist. Judge, 1960-61; ptnr. Strickland, Gordon & Sheinfeld, Houston, 1961-68, Sheinfeld, Maley & Kay, P.C., Houston, 1968—; adj. prof. law U. Tex.; cons. Meyer, Hendricks, Victor, Osborn & Maledon, Phoenix, 1990—; mem. Nat. Bankruptcy Conf.; chmn. Tex. Bankruptcy Adv. Commr.; bd. dirs. Nabors Industries, Third Ave. Value Fund, Inc., Am. Coll. Bankruptcy. Bd. editors Practical Lawyer; contbr. articles to profl. jours. With JAG U.S. Army, 1955-58. Fellow Am. Coll. Bankruptcy; mem. State Bar Tex., Houston Ctr. Club (bd. dirs.), Ramada Tejas Club, Phi Beta Kappa, Phi Sigma Alpha (Mich.). Office: Sheinfeld Maley & Kay PC 1001 Fannin Ste 3700 Houston TX 77002

SHEINGOLD, DANIEL H., electrical engineer; b. Boston, Sept. 26, 1928; s. Louis S. and Elsie (Frank) S.; m. Ann Silverman, Aug. 2, 1953 (dec. Feb. 1995); children: Mark J., Laura R. BSEE with distinction, Worcester Poly. Inst., 1948; MSEE, Columbia U., 1949. Engr. George A. Philbrick Rschs. Inc., Boston 1949-55, application engring. mgr., 1957-63; v.p. George A. Philbrick Researches, Inc., Dedham, Mass., 1964-67; staff cons. Teledyne Philbrick, Dedham, 1967-68; tech. mktg. mgr. Analog Devices, Inc., Norwood, Mass., 1969—. Editor: Analog-Digital Conversion Handbook, 1972, 3d edit., 1986, Nonlinear Circuits Handbook, 1974, Transducer Interfacing Handbook, 1980; editor Analog Dialogue jour., 1969—, others. With AUS, 1955-57. Fellow IEEE; mem. IEEE Instrumentation and Measurement Soc. (sec.-treas. 1976, v.p. 1977, pres. 1978), AAAS. Jewish. Avocations: music, walking, crosscountry skiing, reading. Office: Analog Devices Inc PO Box 9106 3 Technology Way Norwood MA 02062-9106

SHEININ, ROSE, biochemist, educator; b. Toronto, Ont., Can., May 18, 1930; d. Harry and Anne (Szyber) Shuber; BA, U. Toronto, 1951, MA (scholar), 1953, PhD in Biochemistry, 1956, L.H.D., 1985; DHL (hon.), Mt. St. Vincent U., 1985; DSc (hon.) Acadia U., 1987, DSc (hon.) U. Guelph, 1991; m. Joseph Sheinin, July 15, 1951; children—David Matthew Khazanov, Lisa Basya Judith, Rachel Sarah Rebecca. Demonstrator in bi-

ochemistry U. Toronto (Ont., Can.), 1951-53, asst. prof. microbiology, 1964-75, asst. prof. med. biophysics, 1967-75, prof. microbiology, 1975-90, prof. med. biophysics, 1978-90, assoc. prof. med. biophysics, 1975-78, chmn. microbiology and parasitology, 1975-82, vice dean Sch. Grad. Studies, 1984-89; vice-rector acad., Concordia U., Montreal, Que., Can., 1989-94, prof. dept. biology, 1989—; mem. Health Scis. Com.; vis. rsch. assoc. chem. microbiology, Cambridge U., 1956-57, Nat. Inst. Med. Rsch., London, 1957-58; rsch. assoc. fellow div. biol. research Ont. Cancer Inst., 1958-67; sci. officer cancer grants panel Med. Research Council Can.; mem. Can. Sci. Del. to People's Republic of China, 1973; mem. adv. com. Provincial Lottery Health Research Awards; mem. adv. com. on biotech. NRC Can., 1984-87; mem. Sci. Council Can., 1984-87; adv. com. on sci. and tech. CBC, 1980-85; mem. bd. dirs. Can. Bacterial Disease Network, 1989-94; vis. prof. biochemistry U. Alta., 1971. Nat. Cancer Inst. Can. fellow, 1953-56, 58-61; Brit. Empire Cancer Campaign fellow, 1956-58; Recipient Queen's Silver Jubilee medal, 1978, Woman of Distinction award Health and Edn., YWCA, 1988; Josiah Macy Jr. Faculty scholar, 1981-82; fellow Ligue Contre le Cancer, France, 1981-82, Massey Coll. U. Toronto, 1981—, resident sr. fellow, 1994—; hon. fellow Ryerson Polytech. U., 1993. Fellow Am. Acad. Microbiology, Royal Soc. Can. (chair women in scholarship com. 1990-93); mem. Can. Biochem. Soc. (pres. 1974-75), Can. Soc. Cell Biology (pres. 1975-76), Am. Soc. Virology, Am. Soc. Microbiologists, Canadian Assn. Women in Sci., Internat. Assn. Women Bioscientists, Sigma Xi Rsch. Soc., Scitech, Soc. Complex Carbohydrates, Toronto Biochem. and Biophys. Soc. (pres. 1960-70, council 1970-74). Assoc. editor Can. Jour. Biochemistry, 1968-71, Virology, 1969-72, Intervirology, 1974-85; editorial bd. Microbiol. Revs. 1977-80; author, co-author various publs. Office: U Toronto Massey Coll, 4 Devonshire Pl, Toronto, ON Canada M55 2E1

SHEINKMAN, JACK, union official, lawyer; b. N.Y.C., Dec. 6, 1926; s. Shaia and Bertha (Rosenkrantz) S.; m. Betty Francis Johnson, May 31, 1954; children: Michael, Joshua, Mark. B.S., Cornell U., 1948, LL.B., 1952; cert. in econs., Oxford U., 1949. Bar: N.Y. 1952. Atty. NLRB, Washington, 1952-53; atty. Amalgamated Clothing Workers Am., N.Y.C., 1953-58, gen. counsel, 1958-72, v.p. 1966-72, sec.-treas., 1972-76; sec.-treas. Amalgamated Clothing and Textile Workers Union, N.Y.C., 1976-87, pres., 1987-95, pres. emeritus, 1995—; chmn. bd. Amalgamated Bank of N.Y.; exec. coun., v.p. AFL-CIO, 1987-95, indsl. union dept.Internat. Textile, Garment and Leather Workers Fedn., Brussels, 1972-95. Dir. internat. rescue com. N.Y. Hist. Soc. ; commr. Martin L. King, Jr. Fed. Holiday Commn.; vice-chmn. Coun. Competitiveness United Housing Found.; bd. trustees Aspen Inst.; mem. Pres.'s Adv. Com. on Trade Policy Negotiations. Lt. (j.g.) USNR, 1944-46, PTO. Mem. Workers Def. League (dir.), Am. Arbitration Assn. (dir.), Coun. Fgn. Rels., UN Assn. U.S.A. (bd. govs.), Brit.-N.Am. Com (exec. com.), Can.-Am. Com. (exec. com.). Democrat. Jewish. Home: 52 W 76th St New York NY 10023-1517 Office: Amalgamated Bank NY 15 Union Sq W New York NY 10003

SHELANSKI, MICHAEL L., cell biologist, educator; b. Phila., Oct. 5, 1941; s. Herman Alder and Bessie B.; m. Vivien Brodkin, June 9, 1963; children: Howard, Samuel, Noah. Student, Oberlin Coll., 1959-61; M.D. (Life Ins. Med. Research Fund fellow), U. Chgo., 1966, Ph.D., 1967. Intern in pathology Albert Einstein Coll. Medicine, N.Y.C., 1967-68; fellow in neuropathology Albert Einstein Coll. Medicine, 1968-70, asst. prof. pathology, 1969-74; staff scientist NIH, Bethesda, Md., 1971-73; vis. scientist Inst. Pasteur, Paris, 1973-74; assoc. prof. neuropathology Harvard U., Cambridge, Mass., 1974-78; sr. research assoc., asst. neuropathologist Children's Hosp. Med. Center, Boston, 1974-78; prof., chmn. dept. pharmacology N.Y. U. Med. Center, N.Y.C., 1978-86; Delafield Prof., chmn. dept. pathology Coll. Physicians and Surgeons, Columbia U., N.Y.C., 1987—; dir. pathology services Presbyn. Hosp., N.Y.C., 1987—; mem. Neurology A study sect. NIH, 1974-78, Pharmacological Scis. study sect., 1986-90; mem. sci. and med. adv. bd. Alzheimer's Disease and Related Disorders Assn., 1985-92, sec., 1987-92, bd. dirs., 1991-92, mem. Zenith award panel, 1993—; chmn. overhead powerline adv. panel State of N.Y., 1981-87; dir. Alzheimer's disease rsch. ctr. Columbia U., 1989—; mem. Am. Cancer Soc. IRG Panel, 1989-93, sci. adv. bd. Dystonia Assn., Amyotrophic Lateral Sclerosis Assn. Mem. editl. bd. Jour. Neurochemistry, 1982-90, Jour. Neuropathology and Exptl. Neurology, 1983-85, Neuroscis., 1985—, Neurobiology of Aging, 1988-95, Lab. Investigation, 1989—, Brain Pathology, 1990-93. Served as sr. asst. surgeon USPHS, 1971-73. Guggenheim fellow, 1973-74. Mem. Am. Soc. Cell Biology, Am. Assn. Neuropathologists, Assn. Med. Coll. Pharmacologists, Am. Soc. Neurochemistry, Am. Assn. Physicians. Achievements include research on fibrous proteins of brain, aging of human brain, devel. neurobiology. Office: Columbia U Coll Physicians and Surgeons Dept Pathology 630 W 168th St New York NY 10032-3702

SHELBY, JAMES STANFORD, cardiovascular surgeon; b. Ringgold, La., June 15, 1934; s. Jesse Audrey and Mable (Martin) S.; BS in Liberal Arts La. Tech. U., 1956; MD, La. State U., 1958; m. Susan Rainey, July 15, 1967; children: Bryan Christian, Christopher Linden. Intern, Charity Hosp. La., New Orleans, 1958-59, resident surgery and thoracic surgery, 1959-65; fellow cardiovascular surgery Baylor U. Coll. Medicine, Houston, 1965-66; practice medicine specializing in cardiovascular surgery, Shreveport, La., 1967—; mem. staff Schumpert Med. Ctr., Highland Hosp., Willis-Knighton Med. Ctr.; assoc. prof. surgery La. State U. Sch. Medicine, Shreveport, 1967—. With M.C., AUS, 1961-62. Diplomate Am. Bd. Surgery, Am. Bd. Thoracic Surgery. Recipient Tower of Medallion award La. Tech. U., 1982. Mem. Am. Coll. Cardiology, AMA, Soc. Thoracic Surgeons, Am. Heart Assn., Southeastern Surg. Congress, So. Thoracic Surg. Assn. Home: 6003 E Ridge Dr Shreveport LA 71106-2425 Office: 2751 Virginia Ave Ste 3B Shreveport LA 71103-3941

SHELBY, JEROME, lawyer; b. N.Y.C., Mar. 17, 1930; s. Morris and Rose (Pollack) S.; m. Adrian Austin, Nov. 24, 1957; children: Karen A. Anderson, P. Austin. AB, NYU, 1950; LLB, Harvard U., 1953. Bar: D.C. 1953, N.Y. 1954. Assoc. Cadwalader, Wickersham & Taft, N.Y.C., 1953-63, ptnr., 1963-92, of counsel, 1993—; sr. v.p. Marine Transport Lines Inc., N.Y.C., 1958-74, also dir., 1989-92, adv. dir., 1993—; exec. v.p., dir. Energy Transp. Corp., N.Y.C., 1973—; dir. Astro Tankers Ltd. Mem. Assn. of Bar of City of N.Y. Clubs: Down Town Assn. (N.Y.C.); Montclair (N.J.) Golf; Palm Beach (Fla.) Polo. Home: 74 Highland Ave Montclair NJ 07042-1910 Office: Cadwalader Wickersham & Taft 100 Maiden Ln New York NY 10038-4892

SHELBY, RICHARD CRAIG, senator, former congressman; b. Birmingham, Ala., May 6, 1934; s. O.H. and Alice L. (Skinner) S.; m. Annette Nevin, June 11, 1960; children: Richard Craig, Claude Nevin. AB, U. Ala., 1957, LLB, 1963. Bar: Ala. 1961, D.C. 1979. Law clk. Supreme Ct. of Ala., 1961-62; practice law Tuscaloosa, Ala., 1963-79; prosecutor City of Tuscaloosa, 1964-70; spl. asst. atty. gen. State of Ala., 1969-70; U.S. magistrate No. Dist. of Ala., 1966-70; mem. Ala. State Senate, 1970-78, 96th-99th Congresses from 7th Ala. dist., 1979-87; mem. energy and commerce com., mem. vets. affairs com., U.S. senator from Ala., 1987—, mem. com. on appropriations, com. on banking, housing, and urban affairs, select com. on intelligence, spl. com. on aging. Active Boy Scouts Am.; pres. Tuscaloosa County Mental Health Assn., 1969-70; bd. govs. Nat. Legis. Conf., 1975-78. Mem. ABA, Ala. Bar Assn., Tuscaloosa County Bar Assn., D.C. Bar Assn., Exch. Club. Republican. Presbyterian. Home: 1414 High Forest Dr N Tuscaloosa AL 35406-2152 Office: US Senate 110 Hart Senate Bldg Washington DC 20510

SHELDON, BROOKE EARLE, librarian, educator; b. Lawrence, Mass., Aug. 29, 1931; d. Leonard Hadley and Elsie Ann (Southerl) Earle; m. George Duffield Sheldon, Mar. 28, 1955 (dec.); children: L. Scott, G. Stephen. B.A., Acadia U., 1952, D.C.L. (hon.), 1985; M.L.S., Simmons Coll., 1954; Ph.D., U. Pitts., 1977. Base librarian Ent AFB, Colorado Springs, Colo., 1955-57, U.S. Army, Germany, 1956-57; br. librarian Albuquerque Public Library, 1959-61; coordinator adult services Santa Fe Public Library, 1965-67; head library devel. N.Mex. State Library, Santa Fe, 1967-72; asst. dir. leadership tng. inst. U.S. Office Edn., Washington, 1971-73; head tech. svcs. and tng. Alaska State Library, Juneau, 1973-75; dean Sch. Library Info. Studies Tex. Woman's U., Denton, 1977-90; acting provost Library Info. Studies, U. Tex., Austin, 1991—. Author: Leaders in Libraries: Styles and Strategies for Success, 1991; contbr. articles to profl. jours. Bd. dirs.

Am. Libr. in Paris, 1992—. Recipient Alumni Achievement award Simmons Coll., 1983; Disting. Alumni award Sch. Library Info. Sci., U. Pitts., 1986. Mem. ALA (pres. 1983-84), Tex. Libr. Assn., Rotary Internat., Beta Phi Mu. Democrat. Episcopalian.

SHELDON, CHARLES HARVEY, political science educator; b. Jerome, Idaho, Aug. 2, 1929; s. Milo Francis and Martha Susan (McCorkle) S.; m. Patricia Ann Murphy, Dec. 31, 1970; children—Lee Ann, Christopher, Ross, Thomas. B.A., U. Wash., Seattle, 1952, M.A., 1957; Ph.D., U. Oreg., 1965. Instr. polit. sci. Boise (Idaho) Jr. Coll., 1958-61; asst. prof., chmn. dept., dir. Sch. Social Sci., U. Nev., Las Vegas, 1962-68; asso. prof., chmn. dept. Southampton (N.Y.) Coll., L.I. U., 1968-70; mem. faculty Wash. State U., Pullman, 1970—; prof. polit. sci. Wash. State U. 1974—, dir. div. govtl. studies and services, 1976, dept. chmn., 1993-94, Claudius O. and Mary W. Johnson disting. prof. polit. scis., 1994—. Author: The American Judicial Process: Models and Approaches, 1974, A Century of Judging: A Political History of the Washington Supreme Court, 1988, The Washington High Bench: A Biographical History of the State Supreme Court, 1992; co-author: Democracy at the Crossroads, 1978, Politicians, Judges and the People, 1980, Political Life in Washington, 1985, Government and Politics in the Evergreen State, 1992; editor: The Supreme Court: Politicians in Robes, 1969; co-editor: Postwar America: The Search for Identity, 1968, Government and Politics of Washington State, 1978; contbr. articles to profl. jours. and law revs. Served with AUS, 1952-55. Grantee Am. Philos. Soc., 1976; grantee Nat. Endowment Humanities, 1978; grantee NSF, 1982-83, 95. Mem. ACLU, Am. Polit. Sci. Assn., Am. Judicature Soc., Wash. State Com. Minority and Justice, Wash. State Hist. Soc., Western Polit. Sci. Assn., Law and Soc. Assn., U.S. Masters Swimming, Alpha Delta Phi. Nationally ranked masters swimmer, 1975-80, 85, 87. Address: SE 905th Spring St Pullman WA 99163

SHELDON, DAVID FREDERICK, museum director, headmaster; b. N.Y.C., Feb. 2, 1929; s. Seward Ross and Zue Mac (Bronaugh) S.; m. Judith West, June 18, 1954; children: Frederick William, Charles Seward, James Nias. A.B., Amherst Coll., 1951; M.B.A., Harvard U., 1953, M.A.T., 1958. Trainee, then account exec. McCann-Erickson Inc. (advt.), 1953-57; tchr. history and English Middlesex Sch., Concord, Mass., 1957-59; dir. admissions Middlesex Sch., 1961-64, headmaster, 1964-90; exec. dir. Shelburne (Vt.) Mus., 1990—; Pres. Sch. Scholarship Service, 1963-65. Trustee Charles River Sch., Dover, Mass., 1965-68, Carroll Sch., Lincoln, Mass., 1972—, Interalp, Princeton, N.J., 1973—, Ind. Schs. Coun. for Religion; mem. corp. Emerson Hosp., Concord, Mass., 1970—; mem. overseers vis. com. Harvard U., 1966—; exec. com. Ind. Schs. Found. Mass., 1981—; mem. commn. for ind. schs. New Eng. Assn. Schs. and Colls., 1985-88; exec. dir. Shelburne (Vt.) Mus. Mem. Headmasters Assn., New Eng. Assn. Schs. and Colls. (commn. ind. schs. 1985-88, overseas schs. 1985-88, pres. 1990-91). Episcopalian (vestryman). Address: Shelburne Museum PO Box 10 Shelburne VT 05482

SHELDON, ELEANOR HARRIET BERNERT, sociologist; b. Hartford, Conn., Mar. 19, 1920; d. M.G. and Fannie (Myers) Bernert; m. James Sheldon, Mar. 19, 1950 (div. 1960); children: James, John Anthony. A.A., Colby Jr. Coll., 1940; A.B., U. N.C., 1942; Ph.D., U. Chgo., 1949. Asst. demographer Office Population Rsch., Washington, 1942-43; social scientist USDA, Washington, 1943-45; assoc. dir. Chgo. Community Inventory, U. Chgo., 1947-50; social scientist Social Sci. Rsch. Coun., N.Y.C., 1950-51, rsch. grantee, 1953-55, pres., 1972-79; rsch. assoc. Bur. Applied Social Rsch. Columbia U., 1950-51, lectr. sociology, 1951-52, vis. prof., 1969-71; social scientist UN, N.Y.C., 1951-52; rsch. assoc., lectr. sociology UCLA, 1955-61; assoc. rsch. sociologist, lectr. Sch. Nursing U. Calif., 1957-61; sociologist, exec. assoc. Russell Sage Found., N.Y.C., 1961-72; vis. prof. U. Calif., Santa Barbara, 1971; dir. Equitable Life Assurance Soc., Mobil Corp., H.J. Heinz Co. Author: (with L. Wirth) Chicago Community Fact Book, 1949, America's Children, 1958, (with R.A. Glazier) Pupils and Schools in N.Y., 1965; editor: (with W.E. Moore) Indicators of Social Change, Concepts and Measurements, 1968, Family Economic Behavior, 1973; contbr. (with W.E. Moore) articles to profl. jours. Bd. dirs. Colby-Sawyer Coll., 1979-85, UN Rsch. Inst. for Social Devel., 1973-79; trustee Rockefeller Found., 1978-85, Nat. Opinion Rsch. Ctr., 1980-87, Inst. East-West Security Studies, 1984-88. William Rainey Harper fellow U. Chgo., 1945-47. Fellow Am. Acad. Arts and Scis., Am. Sociol. Assn., Am. Statis. Assn.; mem. AAAS, U. Chgo. Alumni Assn. (Profl. Achievement award), Sociol. Rsch. Assn. (pres. 1971-72), Coun. on Fgn. Rels., Am. Assn. Pub. Opinion Rsch., Ea. Sociol. Soc., Internat. Sociol. Assn., Internat. Union Sci. Study of Population, Population Assn. Am. (2d v.p. 1970-71), Inst. of Medicine (chmn. program com. 1976-77), Cosmopolitan Club. Home and Office: 630 Park Ave New York NY 10021-6544

SHELDON, ERIC, physics educator; b. Pilsen, Bohemia, Oct. 24, 1930; s. Robert Bernard and Martha (Martin) S.; m. Sheila Harper, July 8, 1959; 1 child, Adrian. B.Sc., London (Eng.) U., 1951, B.Sc. in Physics with honors, 1952, Ph.D., 1955, D.Sc., 1971. Chartered chemist; chartered physicist. Lectr., rsch. assoc. Acton Tech. Coll., London, 1952-55; assoc. physicist IBM Rsch. Lab., Switzerland, 1957-59; rsch. assoc. E.T.H., Zurich, Switzerland, 1959-62, lectr., 1962-64, prof., 1964-69; prof. physics and applied physics Lowell (Mass.) Technol. Inst. and U. Lowell, 1970-91, U. Mass. at Lowell, 1991—; honors dir., 1994—; Univ. prof. U. Lowell, 1985-88; vis. prof., NSF sr. fgn. sci. fellow U. Va., 1969-70; vis. prof. U. Nev., 1969-70, U. Oxford (Eng.), 1989. Author: (with R. Szostak and P. Marmier) Kernphysik I, 1960, Kernphysik II, 1961, (with P. Marmier) Physics of Nuclei and Particles, Vol. I, 1969, Vol. II, 1970; editor Procs. Internat. Conf. on Interactions of Neutrons with Nuclei, 1976; contbr. articles to books, encys. and profl. jours. Mem. Convocation London U., 1951—. Decorated Order of Merit (Poland). Fellow AAAS, Am. Phys. Soc. (chmn. New Eng. sect. 1985-86, mem. exec. com. 1983-87), Inst. Physics, Royal Soc. Chemistry, Royal Astron. Soc.; mem. Zurich Physical Soc. (life), Royal Instn. Gt. Britain, Am. Assn. Physics Tchrs., Mensa. Anglican/Episcopalian (lay reader). Office: U Mass at Lowell Dept Physics 1 University Ave Lowell MA 01854-2881 *The benefits of happiness in my work and throughout my life, of health, contentment, fulfillment and zest for living, impose an obligation to repay this good fortune in some measure through direct service to the world around me. And still the wonder remains: Life has given me so much more than I ever could contribute—inspiration and love from family and friends, the grace of beauty in the world around me, vivacity and the radiant miracle of laughter. For all that is gentle, peaceful, wise, goodwilled, compassionate, nobly inspiring and yet idealistic in this wondrous universe, I feel deep reverence, appreciation and profound gratitude.*

SHELDON, GARY, conductor, music director; b. Bay Shore, N.Y., Jan. 21, 1953. Student, Wash. U., St. Louis, 1972; BMus, Juilliard Sch. Music, 1974; diploma, Inst. Hautes Etudes Musicales, Montreux, Switzerland, 1975. Prin. condr. Opera Theater, Syracuse, 1976-77; asst. condr. Syracuse Symphony Orch., 1976-77, New Orleans Symphony Orch., 1977-80; assoc. condr. Columbus (Ohio) Symphony Orch., 1982-89; music dir. Lancaster (Ohio) Festival, 1988—; Marin Symphony Orch., San Rafael, Calif., 1990—. Composer: Variations on a Theme of Handel, 1984, Mississippi River (for documentary film Miss. River Mus.), Memphis; rec. performances include Beauty and the Beast (with Frank DiGiacomo), 1977, Ballet Class with Karen Hebert, 1982. Recipient New Orleans Music and Drama Found. award, 1982, 3d prize Rupert BBC Symphony Found., London, 1982, 4th prize Leopold Stokowski Conducting Competition, 1986. Mem. Am. Symphony Orch. League (youth orch. div. bd. dirs. 1980—). Office: Marin Symphony Orchestra Marin Center Aud 4340 Redwood Hwy San Rafael CA 94903*

SHELDON, GEORGE F., medical educator; b. Dec. 20, 1934; s. Richard Robert and Helen Irene (Zerzan) S.; m. Ruth Guy, Aug. 28, 1959; children: Anne Anderson, Elizabeth, Julia. BA, U. Kans., 1957, MD, 1961; postgrad., Mayo Clinic Grad. Sch., 1965. Resident surgery U. Calif., San Francisco, 1965-69; fellow in surg. biology Harvard Med. Sch. of Peter Bent Brigham Hosp., 1969-71; from asst. to full prof. U. Calif., 1971-82; Dr. Zack D. Owens Disting. prof. surgery, dept. chmn. U. N.C., Chapel Hill, 1984—; chmn. residency rev. com. accreditation Coun. for Grad. Med. Edn.; mem. Coun. Grad. Med. Edn. of Health and Human Svcs., 1986. With USPHS, 1962-64. Mem. ACS (regent 1983-92), Am. Bd. Surgery (chmn. 1989-90), Nat. Bd. Med. Examiners (test com. 1981-84), Am. Assn. Surgery of Trauma (pres. 1984), Am. Surg. Assn. (sec. 1989-94, pres. 1994-95), Inst. Medicine (sec. com. on employer based health ins. and tech. assessment edn. bds.),

Merit Rev. Bd. for Surgery Va. (chmn.). Office: U NC at Chapel Hill Dept Of Surgery Chapel Hill NC 27514

SHELDON, GILBERT IGNATIUS, clergyman; b. Cleve., Sept. 20, 1926; s. Ignatius Peter and Stephanie Josephine (Olszewski) S. Student, John Carroll U.; M.Div., St. Theol. Sem., 1970; D.Min., St. Mary Sem. and Ohio Consortium of Sems., 1974. Ordained priest Roman Cath. Ch., 1953, bishop, 1976. Assoc. pastor Cleve. Diocese, 1953-64, diocesan dir. propagation of faith, 1964-74; pastor, Episcopal vicar Lorain County, Ohio, 1974-76; aux. bishop Cleve., 1976—; vicar for Summit County, 1979-80, So. Region, 1980-92; bishop Steubenville, 1992—; bd. dirs. Soc. Propagation of Faith, 1968-74, Diocesan Presbyteral Coun.; instr. theology St. John Coll.; clergy adv. bd. econ. edn. Akron U.; mem. Bishop's Com. Latin Am.; bd. trustees St. Mary Seminary, Diocesan Health Ins. Adv. Bd., Cath. Charities Corp.; former mem. bd. trustees Borromeo Coll.; mem. acad. bd. St, Mary Seminary; bd. dirs. Bishops' Com. Latin Am., adminstrv. com. Nat. Conf. Cath. Bishops/ USCC, Nat. Adv. Coun., Bishops' Com. for Missions, Nat. Bd. Soc. for Propagation of Faith; bd. trustees Pontifical Coll. Josephinum. Mem. adv. bd. Internat. Chem. Workers; mem. econ. adv. bd. Akron U. Clergy; mem. Summit Mental Health Adv. Bd.; mem. Summit chpt. Nat. Cancer Soc.; mem. Goals for Greater Akron. Served with USAAF, 1944-45. Mem. Nat. Conf. Cath. Bishops (adminstrv. bd. 1985—), Am. Legion, Cath. War Vets., Knights of Columbus, Order of Alhambra., Rotary Club Akron and Steubenville. Club: K.C. Lodge: Rotary (Akron). Avocations: golf, astronomy, photography, history, travel. Office: 40 University Ave Akron OH 44308-1678*

SHELDON, HARVEY M., lawyer; b. Chgo., Dec. 7, 1942; s. Richard A. and Beatrice (Gutensky) S.; m. Gail Harrington; children: Paul (dec.), Timothy, Victoria. AB, Amherst Coll., 1965; JD, Harvard U., 1968. Bar: Ill. 1968, U.S. Ct. Appeals (7th and D.C. cirs.) 1978, U.S. Supreme Ct. 1980. Assoc. Schiff, Hardin & Waite, Chgo., 1968-70; asst. atty. gen. spl. prosecutions State of Ill., 1970-71, chief environ. control div., 1972-73; regional counsel U.S. EPA, 1973-74; ptnr. Nisen, Elliott & Meier, Chgo., 1974-85; ptnr. Coffield, Ungaretti, Harris & Slavin, Chgo., 1985-88; capital ptnr., head environ. law group McDermott, Will & Emery, Chgo., 1988—; pres. Harvey M. Sheldon P.C., 1993—; instr. environ. law and equity law John Marshall Law Sch., 1974-76; adj. prof. environ. law Loyola U., Chgo., 1983-90. Active Mayor's Task Force on Air Quality, 1978-82; spl. counsel Ill. Dept. Mines & Minerals, 1977-86; bd. dirs. Nature of Ill. Found.; bd. advisors The Environ. Counselor, 1988—. Mem. ABA, Ill. Bar Assn., Fed. Bar Assn. Chgo. Bar Assn., Air Pollution Control Assn., Environ. Law Inst. (assoc.), Chicagoland C. of C., (dir., chmn. environ. control com.), Chem. Indsl. Coun. of Ill. (assoc.), Ill. State C. of C. (environ. com.), Union Club (Chgo.). Republican. Catholic. to environ. law handbooks. Office: McDermott Will & Emery 227 W Monroe St Chicago IL 60606-5096

SHELDON, INGRID KRISTINA, mayor; b. Ann Arbor, Mich., Jan. 30, 1945; d. Henry Ragnvald and Virginia Schmidt (Clark) Blom; m. Clifford George Sheldon, June 18, 1966; children: Amy Elizabeth, William David. BS, Eastern Mich. U., 1966; MA, U. Mich., 1970. Cert. tchr., Mich. Tchr. Livonia (Mich.) Pub. Schs., 1966-67, Ann Arbor Pub. Schs., 1967-68; bookkeeper Huron Valley Tennis Club, Ann Arbor, 1978—; acct. F.A. Black Co., Ann Arbor, 1984-88; coun. mem. Ward II City of Ann Arbor, 1988-92, mayor, 1993—; chair Housing Bd. Appeals, Ann Arbor, 1988-91; del. S.E. Mich. Coun. of Govts., 1989. Mem. Ann Arbor Planning Commn., 1987—, Ann Arbor Hist. Found., 1985—, Huron Valley Child Guidance Clinic, Ann Arbor, 1984—, excellence com. Ann Arbor Pub. Schs. reorgn., 1985; treas. SOS Community Crisis Ctr., Ypsilanti, Mich., 1987—; precinct ward city vice-chair Ann Arbor Rep. City Com., 1978—. Recipient Community Svc. award Ann Arbor Jaycees, 1980; AAUW fellowship, 1982. Mem. Mich. Mcpl. League (del. 1989–), Ann Arbor Women's City Club (chair endowment com. 1989-90, fin. com. 1987-90, treas.), Rotary (dir.-elect Ann Arbor chpt.), Kappa Delta Pi, Alpha Omnicron Pi. Republican. Methodist. Avocation: musical theatre. Home: 1416 Folkstone Ct Ann Arbor MI 48105-2848

SHELDON, RICHARD ROBERT, Russian language and literature educator; b. July 12, 1932; s. Richard Robert and Helen Irene (Zerzan) S.; m. Karen Ryden Sears, Feb. 8, 1964; children: Katherine Palmer, John Ryden, Robert Charles, Rebecca Ann. BA, U. Kans., 1954; JD, U. Mich., 1960, MA, 1962; PhD, Mich. U., 1966. Chmn. Russian dept. Grinnell (Iowa) Coll., 1965-66; asst. prof. Dartmouth Coll., Hanover, N.H., 1966-70, assoc. prof., 1970-75, prof. Russian lang. and lit., 1975—, chmn. dept. 1970-81, 90—, formerly dir. fgn. studies programs, chmn. com. on orgn. and policy, com. on admissions, com. on diversity, com. on off-campus study, dean of humanities, 1984-89, acad. dir. alumni coll., 1990; vis. prof. U. Calif. Berkeley, 1968, Stanford (Calif.) U., 1974; cons. Coun. Internat. Ednl. Exchange, N.Y.C., 1967-83, Dept. Edn., Washington, 1979—, Cornell U. Press, Ithaca, N.Y., 1970—; sr. assoc. mem. St. Antony's Coll., Oxford, Eng., 1983-84. Translator: (author: (books by V. Shklovsky) A Sentimental Journey, 1970, Zoo or Letters Not About Love, 1971, Third Factory, 1977; compiler: Viktor Shklovsky: An International Bibliography of Works by and about Him, 1977; co-editor: Soviet Society and Culture, 1988; author articles, book revs., other transls. Chmn. bd. Norwich (Vt.) Day Care Ctr., 1980-83. Pfc. U.S. Army, 1955-57. Summerfield scholar, 1952-54; Nat. Def. Act fellow Dept. Edn., Washington, 1961-64, Alfred P. Lloyd fellow U. Mich., Ann Arbor, 1964-65, Ctr. Advanced Study fellow U. Ill., Urbana, 1969-70, Am. Coun. Learned Socs. fellow, 1970; Internat. Rsch. and Exchanges Bd. study grantee, USSR, 1964-65. Mem. Am. Assn. Advancement Slavic Studies, Am. Assn. Tchrs. Slavic and East European Langs., Coun. of Mem. Instns. (exec. com.), Phi Beta Kappa, Phi Alpha Theta, Phi Delta Theta (pres. 1953), Delta Sigma Rho. Democrat. Episcopalian. Home: 86 S Main St Hanover NH 03755-2029 Office: Dartmouth Coll Russian Dept 44 N College Hanover NH 03755-1801

SHELDON, SIDNEY, author; b. Chgo., Feb. 11, 1917; s. Otto and Natalie (Marcus) S.; m. Jorja Curtright, Mar. 28, 1951 (dec. 1985); 1 dau., Mary; m. Alexandra Kostoff, 1989. Ed., Northwestern U. Started as reader, Universal and 20th Century Fox Studios; author: novels The Naked Face, 1970, The Other Side of Midnight, 1975, A Stranger in the Mirror, 1976, Bloodline, 1977, Rage of Angels, 1980, Master of the Game, 1982, If Tomorrow Comes, 1985, Windmills of the Gods, 1987, The Sands of Time, 1988, Memories of Midnight, 1990, The Dooms Day Conspiracy, 1991, The Stars Shine Down, 1992, Nothing Lasts Forever, 1994; creator, writer, producer: Nancy, The Patty Duke Show, I Dream of Jeannie; created TV show Hart to Hart; author: plays including Roman Candle, Jackpot, Dream With Music, Alice in Arms, Redhead; writer: screenplays including Billy Rose's Jumbo, The Bachelor and the Bobby-Soxer, Easter Parade, Annie Get Your Gun; writer, dir.: screenplays including Dream Wife, Buster Keaton Story; writer: screenplays including Anything Goes, Never Too Young; recipient Acad. award for screenplay The Bachelor and the Bobby-Soxer 1947, Tony award for Redhead 1959, Writers Guild Am. Screen awards for Easter Parade, 1948, Annie Get Your Gun 1950, Edgar Allan Poe award Mystery Writers Am. for Naked Face, 1970. Served with USAAF, World War II. Address: care William Morrow & Co Press Rels 1350 Avenue Of The Americas New York NY 10019-4701

SHELDON, TED PRESTON, library director; b. Oak Park, Ill., July 5, 1942; s. Preston and Marjorie Sheldon; m. Beverly Stebel; children: Kathy, Mark. BA, Elmhurst (Ill.) Coll., 1964; MA, Ind. U., 1965, PhD, 1976; MLS, U. Ill., 1977. Asst. archivist U. Ill., Urbana, 1976-77; reference librarian U. Kans., Lawrence, 1977-79, head collection devel., 1979-81; assoc. dir. libraries SUNY, Binghamton, 1981-83; assoc. dir. libraries U. Mo., Kansas City, 1983-85, dir. libraries, 1985—; pres., bd. dirs. Mo. Libr. Network Corp.; bd. dirs. Axxess Info. Solutions, Inc. Author: Population Trends, 1976, Kans. Coll. Devel. Policy, 1978, History, Sources Social Science, 1985. Mem. ALA, Mus. Libr. Assn., Internat. Assn. Sound Archives, Assn. Recorded Sound Collection (mng. editor jour. 1988—). Office: U Mo Libraries 5100 Rockhill Rd Kansas City MO 64110-2446

SHELDON, TERRY EDWIN, lawyer, business consultant, advisor; b. Sacramento, June 22, 1945; s. Earl M. and Christine M. S.; m. Jan L. Winters, Aug. 26, 1966; children: Jeffrey, Tiffini, Melissa. BS magna cum laude, Abilene Christian U., 1967; JD, So. Meth. U., 1970. Bar: Calif. 1970. Assoc. Bronson, Bronson & McKinnon, San Francisco, 1970-74; gen.

counsel, also dir. Consol. Capital Cos., Emeryville, Calif., 1974-83, exec. v.p. chief oper. officer, 1984-85, cons., advisor, 1986-87; pres., trustee Consol. Capital Spl. Trust, 1980-85; exec. v.p., trustee Consol. Capital Realty Investors, 1975-85, Consol. Capital Income Trust, 1978-85, Consol. Capital Income Opportunity Trust, 1983-85, Consol. Capital Income Opportunity Trust 2, 1985; chmn. Nat. Syndication Forum (a div. of RESSI), 1981-82; real estate securities specialist RESSI; v.p.; prin. Alpha Venture Corp., Walnut Creek, Calif., 1987; bus. cons., 1988—. Chmn. bd. visitors adv. com. Coll. of Bus. Adminstrn. Abilene Christian U., 1990. Mem. ABA, Calif. Bar Assn., Nat. Assn. Securities Dealers (direct participation programs com., real estate com., standing adv. com. to bd. govs. 1980-83), Nat. Syndication Forum. Republican. Mem. Ch. of Christ.

SHELDON, THOMAS DONALD, academic administrator; b. Canastota, N.Y., July 15, 1920; s. Harry Ellsworth and Sadie Joyce (McNulty) S.; m. Helen Elizabeth Kyser, Aug. 29, 1941; children: Thomas, Paul, Edward, Patricia, Curtis, Roberta, Kevin. BS, Syracuse U., 1942, M.S., 1949, Ed.D., 1958; grad., USAF Air War Coll., 1972. Tchr. sci., coach Split Rock (N.Y.) High Sch., 1942-43; tchr. sci., coach, vice prin., prin. Minoa (N.Y.) High Sch., 1946-59; prin., asso. supt. Hempstead (N.Y.) High Sch., 1959-63; supt. schs. Hempstead Public Schs., 1963-68; supt. Balt. City Schs., 1968-71; dep. commr. N.Y. State Edn. Dept., Albany, 1971-77; pres. Utica Coll. of Syracuse U., 1977-82; interim pres. Mohawk Valley Community Coll., 1983; then interim pres. Onondaga Community Coll., 1984, now hon. pres. emeritus; prof. ednl. adminstrn. Syracuse U., N.Y., 1984-85; supt. Sewanhaka Central High Sch. Dist., 1985-86; interim pres. Munson-Williams-Proctor Inst., 1990-91; exec. dir. Syracuse U. Relations, N.Y.C., 1987-93; chmn. Edn. Profls. Internat., 1977—. Co-author and editor various N.Y. State Regents publs., 1971-76. Served with U.S. Army, 1943-46; served to col. USAF, 1961-62, Berlin; to brig. gen. Air N.G. 1955-76. First recipient Outstanding Grad. award Syracuse U. Sch. Edn., 1977; recipient Outstanding Md. Educator award Md. State Council PTA's, 1969; Disting. Am. Educator award Freedoms Found., 1966; Conspicuous Service medal N.Y. State Gov., 1976; N.Y.C. PSAL medal, 1978; named to Balt. Afro-Am. Honor Roll, 1970. Mem. N.Y. State PTA (hon. life), N.Y. State Coaches Assn. (pres. 1957), Am. Legion, Lions (hon. life), Phi Delta Kappa. Clubs: Lions (hon. life).

SHELDON, WILLIAM CHARLES, marketing professional; b. Muskegon, Mich., Apr. 20, 1943; s. John Pitt and Doris Augustus (Spafford) S.; m. Judith Ann Roughton; children: Elizabeth Ann, William Charles Jr. BA, Lakeland Coll., 1966. Sales rep. Ciba-Geigy Pharms., Summit, N.J., 1966-69, hosp. sales rep., 1970-73, dist. mgr., 1974-78, mgr. hosp. sales, 1979, dir. instl., 1980-81, product dir., 1982, exec. dir., portfolio mgmt., 1983, v.p. sales, 1984-85, sr. v.p. mktg., 1986—; bd. dirs. Biocine Co., Emeryville, Calif. Bd. dirs. Epilepsy Found. N.J.; trustee Overlook Hosp., Summit, N.J. Mem. Nat. Pharm. Council (bd. dirs. 1986). Avocations: travel, sports, reading, painting. Office: Ciba-Geigy Corp 556 Morris Ave Summit NJ 07901-1398

SHELDRICK, GEORGE MICHAEL, chemistry educator, crystallographer; b. Huddersfield, Great Britain, Nov. 17, 1942; s. George and Elizabeth S.; m. Katherine E. Herford, 1968; 4 children. Student, Huddersfield New Coll.; Jesus Coll., Cambridge. Lectr. Cambridge U., Eng., 1966-78; prof. inorganic chemistry U. Göttingen, Germany, 1978—; with Inst. Anorg. Chemie, Göttingen, Germany. Contbr. numerous articles to profl. jours. Recipient Meldola and Corday-Morgan medals Royal Soc. Chemistry, Leibniz prize Deutsche Forschungsgemeinschaft, A.L. Patterson award Am. Crystallographic Assn., 1993. Achievements include authorship of widely used computer programs for crystal structure determination. Office: Institut für Anorganische Chemie, Tammannstrasse 4, D-37077 Göttingen Germany

SHELESNYAK, MOSES CHAIM, biodynamicist, physiologist; b. Chgo., June 6, 1909; s. Jonas and Fay (Leavitt) S.; m. Roslyn Benjamin, Jan. 28, 1942 (dec. July 1987); children: Betty Jane (Mrs. Franz Sondheimer), Henry Lawrence (dec.). BA, U. Wis., 1930; PhD (U. fellow), Columbia, 1933; postgrad., Alliance Francaise, Paris, summer 1929, N.Y. Sch. Social Work, 1938-39. Instr. physiology, pharmacology Chgo. Med. Sch., 1935-36; lectr. human growth New Coll., Tchrs. Coll., Columbia, 1936-37; research asso. Mt. Sinai Hosp., N.Y.C., 1936-40; research asso. Friedsam fellow Beth Israel Hosp., N.Y.C., 1940-42; acting head biophysics br. U.S. Office Naval Research, Washington, 1946-47; head human ecology br. U.S. Office Naval Research, 1946-49; lectr. ecology Johns Hopkins U., 1949-50; dir. Arctic Inst. N.Am., Balt.-Washington, 1949-50; sr. scientist Weizmann Inst. Sci., Rehovoth, Israel, 1950-58; asso. prof. Weizmann Inst. Sci., 1958-59, prof., 1959, head dept. biodynamics, 1960-68; assoc. dir. Interdisciplinary Communications Program, Office Asst. Sec. Sci., Smithsonian Instn.-N.Y. Acad. Scis., 1967-68; exec. sec. Council Communication, 1968-72; dir. Interdisciplinary Communications Program, Smithsonian Instn., 1968-77, research assoc., 1977-94; dir. Internat. Program Population Analysis, 1972-77; pres., chmn. bd. Interdisciplinary Communication Assocs., 1969-84; vis. lectr. geography McGill U., 1948; vis. prof. Coll. de France, 1960; mem. bd. human ecology arid zones UNESCO, 1954-72; rsch. com. Internat. Planned Parenthood Fedn., 1959-72; selection and adv. com. Internat. Tng. Program Physiology Reprodn., Worcester, Mass., 1959-70; neuroendocrinology panel Interdisciplinary Brain Rsch. Orgn., 1961—; expert adv. panel WHO, 1965-70, more. Editor: Ovum Implantation, 1969, Growth of Population, 1969; co-editor: Frontiers in Teaching of Physiology: Computer Literacy and Simulation; editorial bd.: Contraception; contbr. articles to profl. jours. bd. dirs. Santa Ynez Valley Hosp., Solvang, Calif. Served to lt. comdr. USNR, 1942-46. Gen. Edn. Bd. fellow, 1936-38, Sir Simon Marks Fellow Birmingham (Eng.) U., 1957-58, univ. rsch. fellow, 1957-58. Fellow AAAS, Arctic Inst. N.Am., Eugenics Soc.; mem. Aerospace Med. Assn., AAUP, Israel, Am. chem. socs., Am. Inst. Biol. Sci., Am. Physiol. Soc. (dir. task force centennial commemorative com., exec. editor The Physiology Tchr. 1977-83, exec. editor hist. sect. The Physiologist 1979-83), Am. Polar Soc., Am. Soc. Study Sterility, Animal Behavior Soc., Arctic Circle, Biochem. Soc. Israel, Brit. Glaciological Soc., Ecol. Soc. Am., Endocrine Soc. Am., Endocrine Soc. Ireland, Internat. Soc. Drug Toxicity, History Sci. Soc., Inst. Aero. Scis., Soc. Exptl. Biology and Medicine, Israel Fertility Soc., Israel Soc. Exptl. Biology and Medicine, Israel Soc. Undersea Exploration, N.Y. Acad. Scis., Internat. Soc. Research in Reprodn. (founding), Soc. Internat. Devel., Soc. Research Child Devel., Soc. Gen. Systems Research, Am. Acad. Polit. and Social Sci., Acad. Polit. Scis., Population Assn. Am., World Future Soc., Acad. Medicine Washington, Soc. Study Reproduction, Sigma Xi; fgn. mem. La Sociedad Chilena d'Obstetricia y Ginecologia, Societa Italiana per il progresso della zootecnica, Societe Royale Belge de Gynecologie et d'Obstetrique. Clubs: Cosmos (Washington), Explorers (N.Y.C.). Home: 674 Chalk Hill Rd Solvang CA 93463-2007

SHELEY, DONALD RAY, JR., manufacturing company executive; b. Vincennes, Ind., May 20, 1942; s. Donald R. and Norma M. (Cardinel) S.; m. Pamela J. Petho, Jan. 6, 1968; children: Stephanie L., Anne E. AS in Bus. Adminstrn., Vincennes U., 1962; BS in Bus. and Fin., Ind. U., 1964; MBA, U. Chgo., 1971. Acct. Inland Steel Co., East Chicago, Ind., 1964-66, asst. supr. billing and services, 1966-68, supr. ops. acctg., 1968-71; fin. analyst FMC Corp., Chgo., 1971-74; controller petroleum equipment group, wellhead ops. FMC Corp., Houston, 1974-77; controller petroleum group Joy Mfg., Houston, 1977-80; asst. controller Cooper Industries Inc., Houston, 1980-81, dir. bus. analysis, 1981-86, controller, 1986-88, v.p., controller, 1988-94, v.p., controller ops., 1994—. Pres. Greenwood Residence Club Inc., Houston, 1979-80; treas. Greenwood Forest Fund Inc., Houston, 1983-87. Republican. Office: Cooper Industries Inc 1001 Fannin St Ste 4000 Houston TX 77002-6711

SHELKROT, ELLIOT LOUIS, librarian; b. Pitts., June 24, 1943; s. Max L. and Ruth (Abrams) S.; m. Evelyn C. Minick, Sept. 2, 1977; children: David, Daniel, Max, Benjamin L. B.A., Oberlin Coll. (Ohio), 1965; M.L.S., U. Pitts., 1966. Young adult librarian, br. head Free Library Phila., 1966-69; specialist community services, div. library devel. and services Md. Dept. Edn., 1969-76; interim Md. state librarian State Library of Pa., Harrisburg, 1980-87; pres., dir. The Free Library of Phila., 1987—; bd. dirs. Fellowship Commn., 1989—. Mem. York Sch. Bd., 1984-87; trustee Ctr. for Literacy, Phila. 1987—; mem. Mayor's Cultural Adv. Council, 1987—; bd. dirs. NCCJ, 1991—. Mem. ALA (coun. 1972-78, 83-91), intellectual freedom com. 1975-79, legis. com. 1989—), Pub. Library Assn. (goals, guidelines and

standards task force 1979-83, dir.-at-large new standards task force, v.p., pres. elect 1991—), Assn. State Library Agys. (dir. 1973-75), Assn. Specialized and Coop. Library Agys. (bd. dirs. 1984-86). Pa. Library Assn., Md. Library Assn. (chpt. councilor 1972-78), Chief Officers of State Library Agys. (exec. bd. 1983-84). Office: Free Library of Philadelphia Logan Square Philadelphia PA 19103-1116

SHELL, ART, professional football team coach; b. Charleston, S.C.; m. Janice Shell; 2 children. Student, Md. State Coll. Player L.A. Raiders, 1968-83, coach, 1983-89, head coach, 1989—. Inducted into Pro Football Hall of Fame, 1989; recipient, Jackie Robinson Award for Athletics (Ebony mag.), 1990; named N.F.L. Coach of Yr., 1991. Office: Los Angeles Raiders 332 Center St El Segundo CA 90245-4098*

SHELL, BILLY JOE, retired university president; b. Ecorse, Mich., Sept. 2, 1925; s. Millard Wootson and Flossie Mae (Evans) S.; m. Edythe Lorraine Roach, Dec. 25, 1948; children: Deborah Shell Wilkinson, Brian Jeffrey. B.S., Mich. State U., 1947, M.S., 1949, Ph.D., 1955. Registered profl. engr., Ariz., Miss., Tex. Faculty U. Ariz., 1949-53, Mich. State U., 1955; v.p., chief engr. San Xavier Rock & Sand Co., Tucson, 1956-66; asso. dean engring. Miss. State U., 1966-70, acting v.p. for research, 1969-70; dean engring. Calif. State Poly. U., Pomona, 1970-73, acting v.p. acad. affairs, 1971-72; pres. Northrop U., Inglewood, Calif., 1973-89, ret., 1989, also trustee; pres. Calif. Engring. Found., 1982-85; vice chmn. Ariz. Bd. Tech. Registration, 1965-66; chmn. Calif. Council for Pvt. Postsecondary Ednl. Instns. Mem. Environ. Quality Control Com., Los Angeles County, 1971; chmn. bd. dirs. Tucson Boys Chorus, 1965-66. Served with USMCR, 1943-45. Recipient Engr. of Year award So. chpt. Ariz. Soc. Profl. Engrs., 1965, Outstanding Service award, 1966, Educator of Year award Region VII, Soc. Mfg. Engrs., 1973; Skill, Integrity and Responsibility award Assn. Gen. Contractors Calif., 1975. Fellow ASCE, Inst. for Advancement Engring.; mem. NSPE, AAAS, AAUP, Calif. Soc. Profl. Engrs. (Outstanding Svc. award 1973, Edn. Achievement award 1975), Nat. Coun. Engring. Examiners, Am. Water Works Assn., Water Pollution Control Fedn., Am. Soc. Engring. Edn., Inglewood C. of C. (pres. 1986-87, bd. dirs.), Sigma Xi, Chi Epsilon, Sigma Pi Alpha, Sigma Delta Phi, Tau Beta Pi. Clubs: Mason, Rotarian. Home: 1182 Steele Dr Brea CA 92621-2233

SHELL, GLENN HARMEN, bank executive; b. Bklyn., Sept. 13, 1943; s. Joseph John and Grace (DeYoung) S.; m. Gail A. Lebowitz, Nov. 4, 1943; children: Douglas P., Theodore M., Courtney A. AB, Brown U., 1965; MBA, Washington U., St. Louis, 1967; postgrad., Columbia U., 1971. Asst. sec. Irving Trust Co. N.Y.C., 1967-69, asst. v.p., 1972-74, v.p., 1974-78, mgr., v.p., 1978-85; exec. v.p. Dauphin Deposit Bank and Trust Co., Harrisburg, Pa., 1985-87, pres., 1987—. Home: 116 Cottage Pl Ridgewood NJ 07450 Office: Citizens First Nat Bank 208 Harristown Rd Glen Rock NJ 07452

SHELL, KARL, economics educator; b. Paterson, N.J., May 10, 1938; s. Joseph J. and Grace (De Young) S.; m. Susan Witherow Schulze, Jan. 27, 1962; children: Stephanie Shell Read, Jason Anthony. AB in Math. with honors, Princeton U., 1960; PhD in Econs., Stanford U., 1965; MA (hon.), U. Pa., 1971. Asst. and assoc. prof. econ. MIT, Cambridge, 1964-68; assoc. prof. U. Pa., Phila., 1968-70, prof., 1970-87; Robert Julius Thorne Prof. Econs. Cornell U., Ithaca, N.Y., 1986—; vis. prof. Stanford U., Calif., 1972-73, Autonomous U. Barcelona, 1989, Bocconi Inst. Mgmt., Milan, Italy, 1990, U. Calif., San Diego, 1992; adj. prof. U. Paris, 1979-81, 91; rschr. CEPREMAP, Paris, 1977-78; dir. Ctr. for Analytic Rsch. in Econs. and the Social Scis., Phila., 1975-86; Ctr. for Analytic Econs., Ithaca, 1986-92; pvt. practice econ., Ithaca, 1964—. Co-author: Economic Theory of Price Indices, 1972; editor: Optimal Economic Growth, 1967, Jour. Econ. Theory, 1968—; co-editor: Investment and Finance, 1972, Hamiltonians, 1976, Economic Complexity, 1989. Woodrow Wilson Found. fellow, 1960-61, 63-64; Ford Found. faculty rsch. fellow, 1967-68; Guggenheim fellow, 1977, Ctr. for Advanced Study in Behavioral Sci. fellow, 1984; Fulbright scholar, Barcelona, Spain, 1989. Fellow Econometric Soc.; mem. Am. Econ. Assn., European Econ. Assn., Econ. Study Soc., Soc. for Promotion of Econ. Theory, Elm Club (Princeton), Princeton Club (N.Y.), Statler Club (Ithaca), Sigma Xi. Republican. Episcopalian. Home: 917 Wyckoff Rd Ithaca NY 14850-2130 Office: Cornell U Dept Econs 402 Uris Hall Ithaca NY 14853-7601

SHELL, KEVIN DUANE, human services researcher, psychologist; b. Caldwell, Idaho, Apr. 15, 1951; s. Leland Wayne and Allene Fern (Wigfield) S.; m. Cynthia Anne Ballinger, Nov. 22, 1979 (div. June 1987); m. Vicki Lynn Ades, June 24, 1989; children: Joseph Ades, Kari Ades, Benjamin Ades, Sam, Simon, Nicholas. BS in Psychology and Math., Albertson Coll. Idaho, 1973; MS in Quantitative Psychology, Purdue U., 1975, PhD in Ednl. Psychology, 1982. Presentence investigation specialist State Probation & Parole Dept., Caldwell, Idaho, 1971-73; teaching asst. Purdue U., West Lafayette, Ind., 1973-76, statis. program cons., 1974-80, rsch. assoc., 1976-82, applied measurement psychologist, 1982-83, manpower rschr., project coord. agrl. econ., 1983, applied measurement psychologist, 1983-84, manpower rschr., labor analyst, 1983—; co-devel., writer Interest Inventory, Purdue Interest Questionaire, 1987. Treas. 1st Ch. God, Lafayette, 1987-94; bd. dirs. Sycamore chpt. Girl Scouts U.S., Lafayette, 1988-91. Mem. Am. Soc. Engring. Edn., Am. Edn. Rsch. Assn., Four Sigma Soc. Independent. Fundamental Christian. Avocations: singing, vegetable gardening, investment analysis. Office: Purdue U Office Manpower Studies Knoy Hall West Lafayette IN 47907-1410

SHELL, MARY KATHERINE JAYNES HOSKING (MRS. JOSEPH C. SHELL) county official; b. Bakersfield, Calif., Feb. 9, 1927; d. Walter Charles and Mary Ellen (Young) Jaynes; student Bakersfield College, 1946-48; m. Richard Hosking Aug. 21, 1948 (div. 1968); children—Geoffrey Richard, Timothy William (dec.), Meredith Katherine (dec.); m. 2d, Joseph C. Shell, Jan. 8, 1970. Mem. editorial staff Bakersfield Californian, 1944-45; mem. editorial staff Bakersfield News Bull., 1965-68, mng. editor, 1969; polit. columnist Bakersfield Californian, 1971-80; mayor City of Bakersfield, 1980-84; supr. Kern County, 1984—. Founding pres. Bakersfield Jr. Woman's Club, 1954-55. Mem. Kern County Republican Central Com., 1956-60; founder, state sec. United Reps. Calif., 1963; mem. Calif. del. Rep. Nat. Conv., 1964. Club: Kern Press (founder 1967). Home: 2930 21st St Bakersfield CA 93301-3209 Office: Office Bd Suprs Adminstrv Ctr 1115 Truxtun Ave 5th Fl Bakersfield CA 93301

SHELL, OWEN G., JR., banker; b. Greenville, S.C., June 19, 1936; s. Owen and Katherine S.; m. Mary Ruth Trammell, Aug. 9, 1980; children: Katherine Sloan, Mary Carroll, Robert Owen, James Walker. B.S., U. S.C., 1960; post grad., Stonier Grad. Sch. Banking, 1971; grad., Advanced Mgmt. Program, Harvard U., 1979. Tech. supt. Deering-Milliken, Inc., 1962-63; v.p. Citizens & So. Nat. Bank S.C., Columbia, 1968-71; sr. v.p. Citizens & So. Nat. Bank S.C., 1971-74, exec. v.p., 1974-79; pres., dir. chief exec. officer First Am. Nat. Bank, Nashville, 1979-86; vice chmn. bd., dir. First Am. Corp., 1979-86; chmn., pres., chief exec. officer Sovran Bank/Tenn., Nashville, 1986-91; pres. Nations Bank of Tenn. (formerly Sovran Bank), Nashville, 1992—; chmn. NationsBank of Ky.; dir. Nashville br. Fed. Res. Bank of Atlanta. Adv. bd. INROADS/Nashville; active Leadership Nashville, Tenn. Performing Arts Found., Mid. Tenn. coun. Boy Scouts Am., Vanderbilt U. Owen Grad. Sch. Mgmt.; trustee Met. Nashville Pub. Edn.; bd. dirs. Tenn. Bus. Roundtable, Tenn. Tomorrow. Mem. Am. Res. City Bankers, Nashville Area C. of C., Kappa Alpha, Omicron Delta Kappa. Presbyterian. Clubs: Rotary, Cumberland, Belle Meade Country. Home: 4412 Chickering Ln Nashville TN 37215-4915

SHELLEDY, JAMES EDWIN, III, editor; b. Spencer, Iowa, Nov. 11, 1942; s. James E. Jr. and Patricia L. (Cornwall) S.; m. Susan Emily Thomas, Mar. 7, 1986; 1 child, Ian Whittaker. BA, Gonzaga U., 1966. Reporter Spkesman-Rev. Spokane, Wash., 1963-66; tchr. coach Kootenai High Sch., Harrison, Idaho, 1967-71; reporter AP, Boise, Idaho, 1971-72; reporter, editor Lewiston (Idaho) Morning Tribune, 1973-80; editor, pub. Idahonian, Moscow, Idaho, 1981-91, Daily News, Pullman, Wash., 1981-91; editor The Salt Lake Tribune, Salt Lake City, 1991—; juror Pulitzer Prize Com., Columbia U., 1987-88; dir. Investigative Reporters and Editors, 1978-82; bd. dirs. New Directions for News, 1989—, Newspaper Agy. Corp., 1994—; mem. AP audit com., N.Y.C., 1982-91. Dir. Idaho Parks Found., Boise,

1976-78, Idaho-Washington Symphony, Pullman, Wash., 1986-89; commr. Idaho Lottery Commn., Boise, 1990-91; adv. bd. Utah YWCA, 1992—. Roman Catholic. Avocations: golf, sailing. Office: The Salt Lake Tribune 143 S Main St Salt Lake City UT 84111-1917

SHELLER, JOHN WILLARD, lawyer; b. L.A., Oct. 29, 1950; s. Willard Newton and Barbara (Tremaine) S.; m. Mary Elizabeth Hodor, Aug. 9, 1975; children: Matthew John, James Henry. BA, Stanford U., 1972; JD, Loyola U., L.A., 1975. Bar: Calif. 1975. Ptnr. Haight, Brown & Bonesteel, Santa Monica, Calif., 1975—. Contbr. articles to profl. jours. Mem. Calif. State Bar Assn., Los Angeles County Bar Assn., So. Calif. Assn. Def. Counsel, Fedn. Ins. and Corp. Counsel, L.A. Country Club. Avocation: golf. Home: 15461 DePauw St Pacific Palisades CA 90272 Office: Haight Brown & Bonesteel PO Box 680 1620 26th St Santa Monica CA 90406-0680

SHELLEY, CAROLE AUGUSTA, actress; b. London, Aug. 16, 1939; came to U.S., 1964; d. Curtis and Deborah (Bloomstein) S.; m. Albert G. Woods, July 26, 1967 (dec.). Student, Arts Ednl. Sch., 1943-56, Prepatory Acad. Royal Acad. Dramatic Art, 1956-57; studies with Iris Warren. Studied with Iris Warren and Eileen Thorndike; Trustee Am. Shakespeare Theatre., 1974-82. Appeared in revues, films, West End comedies, including Mary Mary at the Globe Theatre; first appeared as Gwendolyn Pigeon in stage, film and TV versions of The Odd Couple, Absurd Person Singular; The Norman Conquests (L.A. Drama Critics Circle award 1975); appeared as Rosalind in As You Like It, as Regan in King Lear, as Neville in She Stoops to Conquer, Stratford, Ont., Can., 1972, as Mrs. Margery Pinchwife in The Country Wife, Am. Shakespeare Festival, Stratford, Conn., 1973, as Nora in A Doll's House, Goodman Theatre, Chgo., as Ann in Man and Superman, as Lena in Misalliance, Zita in Grand Hunt; appeared at Shaw Festival, 1977, 80, Stepping Out, 1986 (Tony nomination 1986), Broadway Bound, 1987-88; appeared in: The Play's the Thing, Bklyn. Acad. Music, 1978; played Eleanore in stage prodn. Lion in Winter, 1987; other stage appearances include Nat. Co. of The Royal Family (L.A. Drama Citics Circle award 1977), The Elephant Man (Outer Critics Circle award 1978-79 season, Tony award for best actress 1978-79 season), What the Butler Saw, 1989; appeared inaugural season, Robin Phillips Grand Theatre Co., London, Ont., Can., 1983-84, Broadway and Nat. Co. of Noises Off, 1985, Waltz of the Toreadors, 1986, Oh Coward, 1986-87 ; appeared as Kate in Broadway Bound by Neil Simon The Nat. Co. and L.A. Premiere, 1987-88; played Lettice in Lettice and Lovage Globe Theatre, London, 1989-90, Frosine in The Miser, 1990, Cabaret Verboten, 1991, The Destiny of Me, 1992-93, Later Life, 1993 (Outer Critics nominee), Richard II, 1994, London Suite, 1994, N.Y. Shakespeare Festival; films include: The Boston Strangler, The Odd Couple, The Super, 1990, Devlin, 1991, Quiz Show, 1993, The Road to Wellville, 1993; created: voice characters in Walt Disney films Robin Hood, The Aristocats. Recipient Obie Award for Twelve Dreams N.Y. Shakespeare Festival, 1982. Jewish. Office: care Duva-Flack Assocs Inc 200 W 57th St New York NY 10019-3211

SHELLEY, EDWARD HERMAN, JR., retired insurance company executive; b. Harrisburg, Pa., Oct. 14, 1919; s. E. Herman and Elizabeth (Workman) S.; m. Dorothy M. Treier, Feb. 14, 1942; children: David, Martha. A.B., Franklin and Marshall Coll., Lancaster, Pa., 1941. Office mgr. Nationwide Ins. Co., Harrisburg, Pa., 1941-50; head systems dept. Nationwide Ins. Co., Columbus, 1950-57, Agway, Ithaca, N.Y., 1958-60; v.p. data processing State Farm Ins. Co., Bloomington, Ill., 1960-83; adj. prof. sr. profls. Ill. State U.; bd. dirs. Bank One Bloomington/Normal. Bd. dirs. Project Oz, Bloomington, 1980; with Vol. Income Tax Assistance, 1987—. Served with AUS, 1944-46. Mem. Nat. Office Mgmt. Assn., Assn. for Computing Machinery, Life Office Mgmt. Assn. (mem. property and casualty systems com. 1981-83), Phi Sigma Kappa. Republican. Lutheran. Home: RR 2 Box 168 Lexington IL 61753-9548 Office: State Farm Ins Cos 1 State Farm Plz Bloomington IL 61701-4300

SHELLEY, ELBERT VERNELL, professional football player; b. Tyronza, Ark., Dec. 24, 1964. Student, Ark. State U. Cornerback Atlanta Falcons, 1987—. Named to Pro Bowl Team, 1992, 93. Office: Atlanta Falcons 2745 Burnett Rd Suwanee GA 30174*

SHELLEY, HERBERT CARL, lawyer; b. Stamford, Tex., Jan. 28, 1947; s. Carl B. and Lourena A. (Whitley) S.; m. Jerilyn S. Ray, Aug. 9, 1969; children: Megan, Caitlyn, Daniel. BA, Columbia Coll., 1969; JD, Vanderbilt U., 1972; LLM Internat. and Comparative Law magna cum laude, Vrije Universiteit Brussel, Brussels, Belgium, 1973. Bar: D.C. 1973, Md. 1985, U.S. Ct. Appeals (fed. cir.) 1981, U.S. Ct. Internat. Trade 1982, U.S. Supreme Ct. 1987. Atty./adv. U.S. Tariff Commn., Washington, 1973-74; Internat. trade specialist, asst. Office dir. Office Tariff Affairs U.S. Dept. Treasury, Washington, 1974-76; internat. trade negotiator Office Spl. Trade Reps., Geneva, Switzerland, 1976-79; ptnr. Plaia & Schaumberg, Washington, 1979-86, Howrey & Simon, Washington, 1986—. Mem. ABA, D.C. Bar Assn., Md. Bar Assn., City Club Washington. Avocations: skiing, golf, cooking, travel. Office: Howrey & Simon 1299 Pennsylvania Ave NW Washington DC 20004-2402

SHELLEY, JAMES HERBERT, lawyer, paper products company executive; b. Columbia, S.C., Oct. 12, 1943; s. William H. and Elizabeth G. (Garner) S.; m. Wayring Patricia Knight, Apr. 1, 1969; children—Joy Patricia, Susan Elizabeth. B.A. in English, U. of S.C., 1965, J.D., 1968. Bar: S.C. 1968. With Sonoco Products Co., Hartsville, S.C., 1969—, indsl. devel. coordinator, 1969-70, indsl. relations rep., 1970-71, dir. indsl. relations, 1971-78, corp. dir. indsl. relations and personnel, 1978-86, staff v.p. personnel and indsl. relations, 1986—; chmn. Sonopal. Bd. dirs. Pee Dee Mental Health, vice chmn., 1977-80; vice chmn. Hartsville YMCA project, 1983-86; bd. trustees S.C. Bus. & Indsl. Pol. Education Com. Served to sgt. 1st class USAR, 1968-73. Recipient Outstanding Drill Sgt. award, 1970. Mem. S.C. Bar Assn. (sec./treas. employment and labor law sect.), ABA (labor law sect.). Methodist. Clubs: Hartsville (S.C.) Country, Prestwood (Hartsville). Home: 219 Park Ave Hartsville SC 29550-3235 Office: Sonoco Products Co North 2nd St PO Box 160 Hartsville SC 29550

SHELLEY, JAMES LAMAR, lawyer; b. Joseph City, Ariz., Dec. 8, 1915; s. Thomas Heber and Eva (Tanner) S.; m. Virginia Rand, Nov. 21, 1942; children: Carol (Mrs. Danny Parker Boyle), Marlene (Mrs. J. Robert Tolman), Jana (Mrs. Gunn B. McKay), Mary (Mrs. Mark Hutchings), Gerald LaMar, James Rand. B.A., Ariz. State Coll., 1936; J.D., U. Ariz., 1949. Bar: Ariz. 1948. Asst. city atty. City of Mesa, Ariz., 1948-49, city atty., 1950-87; ptnr. Johnson & Shelley, Mesa, 1951-88; gen. counsel League Ariz. Cities and Towns, Phoenix, 1959—; ptnr. Shelley & Bethea, Mesa, 1988—. Adv. bd. Theodore Roosevelt coun. Boy Scouts Am., 1962-92, adv. coun. Grand Canyon coun., 1993—, Mesa Dist. chmn., 1967-68; v.p. Mesa United Fund, 1967-69, pres., 1970; pres. bd. mgmt. Mesa br. YMCA; pres. Mesa Christmas Basket Assn., Mesa Fine Arts Assn., 1978-80; mem. religious adv. com. Ariz. Dept. Corrections, 1981. Lt. USNR, 1942-45. Named Mesa Man of Year, 1965. Mem. Ariz. Acad., Nat. Inst. Mcpl. Law Officers (past pres.). Republican. Mem. Ch. of Jesus Christ of Latter-day Saints (former regional rep.). Clubs: Exchange (past pres.), Southside Dinner (past pres. Mesa). Home: 550 N Emerson St Mesa AZ 85201-5516 Office: Shelley & Bethea 1201 S Alma School Rd Ste 3400 Mesa AZ 85210-2077

SHELLEY, JOHN FLETCHER, lawyer; b. Des Moines, Oct. 7, 1943; s. John DeWane and Catherine Hilma (Fletcher) S.; m. Karan Antonette Early, Aug. 27, 1966 (div. 1994); children: Jack, Joseph. AB, Harvard U., 1965; LLB., Harvard U., 1968. Bar: Ohio 1968. Assoc., Squire, Sanders & Dempsey, Cleve., 1968, 72-78, ptnr., 1978—; practice area coord. Estates, Trusts, and Employee Benefits Practice Area, 1984-94. V.p., trustee Child Guidance Ctr. of Cleve., 1980-86; trustee Univ. Circle, Inc., 1988—. Trustee Cleve. Inst. Music, 1989—. With USNR, 1968-71. Mem. ABA, Bar Assn. Greater Cleve. (mem. coun. estate planning and probate sect.), Ohio State Bar Assn., Bar Assn., Union Club, Club at Key Ctr. Democrat. Home: 3283 Norwood Rd Cleveland OH 44122-3439 Office: Squire Sanders & Dempsey 4900 Society Ctr 127 Public Sq Cleveland OH 44114-1304

SHELLEY, WALTER BROWN, physician, educator; b. St. Paul, Feb. 6, 1917; s. Patrick K. and Alfaretta (Brown) S.; m. Marguerite H. Weber, 1942 (dec.); children: Peter B., Anne E. Kiselewich, Barbara A. (dec.); m. E. Dorinda Loeffel, 1980; children: Thomas R., Katharine D., William L. B.S.,

U. Minn., 1940, Ph.D., 1941, M.D., 1943; M.A. honoris causa, U. Pa., 1971; M.D. honoris causa, U. Uppsala, Sweden, 1977. Diplomate: Am. Bd. Dermatology (pres. 1968-69, dir. 1960-69). Instr. physiology U. Pa., Phila., 1946-47; asst. instr. dermatology and syphilology U. Pa., 1947-49, asst. prof. dermatology, 1950-53, assoc. prof., 1953-57, prof., 1957-80, chmn. dept., 1965-80; prof. dermatology U. Ill. Peoria Sch. Medicine, 1980-83; prof. medicine (dermatology) Med. Coll. Ohio, 1983—; instr. dermatology Dartmouth Coll., 1949-50; Regional cons. dermatology VA, 1955-59; mem. com. on cutaneous system NRC, 1955-59, Commn. Cutaneous Diseases, Armed Forces Epidemiological Bd., 1958-61, dep. dir., 1959-61; cons. dermatology Surgeon Gen. USAF, 1958-61, U.S. Army, 1958-61; mem. NRC, 1961-64. Author: (with Crissey) Classics in Clinical Dermatology, 1953, (with Pillsbury, Kligman) Dermatology, 1956, Cutaneous Medicine, 1961, (with Hurley) The Human Apocrine Sweat Gland in Health and Disease, 1960, (with Botelho and Brooks) The Endocrine Glands, 1969, Consultations in Dermatology with Walter B. Shelley, 1972, Consultations II 1974 (with Shelley) Advanced Dermatologic Therapy, 1987, Advanced Dermatologic Diagnosis, 1992, A Century of International Dermatological Congresses, 1992; mem. editorial bd.: Jour. Investigative Dermatology, 1961-64, Archives of Dermatology, 1961-62, Skin and Allergy News, 1970-93, Excerpta Medica Dermatologica, 1960—, Cutis, 1972—, Jour. Geriatric Dermatol, 1993; assoc. editor: Jour. Cutaneous Pathology, 1972-81; editorial cons.: Medcom, 1972—. Served as capt. M.C. AUS, 1944-46. Recipient Spl. award Soc. Cosmetic Chemists, 1955, Hellerstrom medal, 1971, Am. Med. Writers Assn. Best Med. Book award, 1973, Dohi medal, 1981, Rothman medal Soc. for Investigative Dermatology, 1987, Rose Hirschler award, 1990. Master A.C.P.; fellow Assn. Am. Physicians, St. John's Dermatol. Soc. London (hon.); mem. AMA (chmn. residency rev. com. for dermatology 1963-67, chmn. sect. dermatology 1969-71), Assn. Profs. Dermatology (pres. 1972-73), Pacific Dermatol. Assn. (hon.), Am. Dermatol. Assn. (hon., dir., pres. 1975-76), Soc. Investigative Dermatology (hon. pres. 1961-62), Am., Phila. physiol. socs., Brit. Dermatol. Soc. (hon.), Phila. Dermatol. Soc. (pres. 1960-61), Mich. Dermatol. Soc., (Gold medal 1992, hon. pres. 1971-72), Pa. Acad. Dermatology (pres. 1972-73), Am. Soc. for Dermatologic Surgery, , Noah Worcester Dermatological Soc., Royal Soc. Medicine; corr. mem. Nederlandse Vereniging Van Dermatologen, Israeli Dermatol. Assn., Finnish Soc. Dermatology, Swedish Dermatol. Soc., French Dermatologic Soc.; fgn. hon. mem. Danish Dermatol. Assn., Japanese Dermatol. Assn., Internat. Dermatol. Soc. S.Africa. Home: 21171 W River Rd Grand Rapids OH 43522-9703 Office: Med Coll Ohio PO Box 10008 3000 Arlington Ave Toledo OH 43614-2595

SHELLHASE, LESLIE JOHN, social work educator; b. Hardy, Nebr., Jan. 12, 1924; s. John Clayton and Sanna Belle (Muth) S.; m. Fern Eleanor Kleckner, June 8, 1948; children: Jeremy Clayton, Joel Kleckner. Student, U. Calif.-Berkeley, 1942-44; A.B. Midland Coll., 1947 M.S.W., U. Nebr., 1950; D.Social Work, Catholic U. Am., 1961. Lic. social worker, Ala. Parole supr. Child Welfare, Omaha, 1948-49; psychiat. social work intern Letterman Gen. Hosp. San Francisco, 1950-51; commd. 2d lt. U.S. Army, 1949, advanced through grades to lt. col., 1966; chief social worker (6th Inf. Div.), Ft. Ord, Calif., 1952-55; chief med. social worker Walter Reed Gen. Hosp. Washington, 1955-57, research investigator Walter Reed Inst. Research, 1957-63; head social work faculty Med. Field Service Sch., Ft. Sam Houston, Tex., 1963-66; chief sociologist U.S. Army, Washington, 1966-68; prof. Sch. Social Work, U. Ala., Tuscaloosa, 1968-89; prof. emeritus Sch. Social Work, U. Ala., 1989—; pvt. practice social work, 1968—; dir. tour, interpreter to surgeon gen. Belgium Armed Forces, 1961; lectr. Catholic U. Am., 1961-63, 66-68; research dir. Jewish Social Service Fedn., San Antonio, 1963-66; rep. to internat. social and behavioral scis. community Dept. Army, 1966-68; cons. Family Service Assn. Am., 1969—, Ala. Mental Health Dept., 1989—; mem. expert group on social welfare UN, 1975—; mem. Internat. Relations Forum, 1981—; research fellow U. Exeter, 1981-82; mem. social work tng. com. NIMH, 1983—; mem. Interfaith Com on AIDS, 1993; newscaster Radio Reading Svc., Ala. Pub. Broadcast, 1989—; condr. workshops; broadcaster PBS, 1989—; cons. on group psychotherapy Ala. Dept. Mental Health, 1989—. Author: The Group Life of the Schizophrenic Patient, 1961, Bibliography of Army Social Work, 1962; book rev. editor Social Perspectives, 1979-83; editorial reviewer Social Work Papers, mem. editorial bd., 1986—; editorial reviewer Mac Millan Press, 1990—, Families in Society, 1992—, Oxford U. Press, 1994; internat. editorial bd. Internat. Abstracts Social Sci.; contbr. articles on social and behavioral sci. to nat. and internat. profl. jours.; chpts. to books. Bd. dirs. Crisis Intervention Center; bd. dirs., chmn. Soc. for Crippled Children and Adults; chmn. bd. social ministry So. Dist. Lutheran Ch. Served with inf. U.S. Army, 1942-46. Decorated Legion of Merit, Bronze Star, Purple Heart; recipient letters of commendation from Pres., 1968, letters of commendation from Surgeon Gen., 1961. Fellow Am. Sociol. Assn.; mem. NASW (mem. nat. task force on ethics 1976-79, chmn 1976-77, dir. 1963-66), Coun. Social Work Edn., Nat. Conf. Social Welfare, Acad. Cert. Social Workers, Brit. Social. Assn., Brit. Assn. Social Workers, Ret. Officers Assn., So. Sociol. Soc., Blue Key. Democrat. Home: 3823 Somerset Pl Tuscaloosa AL 35405-5436 Office: PO Box 870314 Tuscaloosa AL 35487-0314

SHELLHORN, RUTH PATRICIA, landscape architect; b. L.A., Sept. 21, 1909; d. Arthur Lemon and Lodema (Gould) S.; m. Harry Alexander Kueser, Nov. 21, 1940. Student dept. landscape architecture, Oreg. State Coll., 1927-30; grad. landscape architecture program, Cornell U. Coll. Architecture, 1933. Pvt. practice landscape architecture, various cities Calif., 1933—; exec. cons. landscape architect Bullocks Stores, Calif., 1945-78, Fashion Sqs. Shopping Ctrs., Calif., 1958-78, Marlborough Sch., L.A., 1968—, El Camino Coll., Torrance, Calif., 1970-78, Harvard Sch., North Hollywood, Calif., 1974-90; cons. landscape architect, site planner Disneyland, Anaheim, Calif., 1955, U. Calif., Riverside Campus, 1956-64, numerous others, also numerous gardens and estates; landscape architect Torrance (Calif.) City Goals Com., 1969-70; cons. landscape architect City of Rolling Hills (Calif.) Community Assn., 1973-93. Contbr. articles to garden and profl. publs.; subject of Oct. 1967 issue Landscape Design & Constrn. mag. Named Woman of Year, Los Angeles Times, 1955, Woman of Year, South Pasadena-San Marino (Calif.) Bus. Profl. Women, 1955; recipient Charles Goodwin Sands medal, 1930-33, Landscape Architecture award of merit Calif. State Garden Clubs, 1984, 86, Horticulturist of the Yr. award So. Calif. Hort. Inst., numerous nat., state, local awards for excellence. Fellow Am. Soc. Landscape Architects (past pres. So. Calif. chpt.), Phi Kappa Phi, Kappa Kappa Gamma (Alumni Achievement award 1960). Projects subject of Oct. 1967 issue of Landscape Design and Constrn. Mag. Home and Office: 362 Camino De Las Colinas Redondo Beach CA 90277-6435 *Integrity, honesty, dependability, sincerity, dedication, and a willingness to give more than is expected in service, are the basic principles which have guided my career. Never losing sight of the importance of the individual, I have tried to create total environments of harmony and beauty to which each individual can relate in a very personal and pleasureable way, and for a little while, can find a calm oasis in a busy and demanding world.*

SHELLMAN, EDDIE J., ballet dancer, teacher, choreographer; b. Tampa, Fla., May 10, 1956; s. Eddie J. and Elizabeth (Coleman-Smith) Lucas. Ed., High Sch. Performing Arts, N.Y.C. Dancer Pepsie Bethel Jass Co., N.Y.C., 1972-73; dancer U.S. Terpsichore, N.Y. Sch. Ballet, N.Y.C., 1974-75; prin. dancer Dance Theatre Harlem, N.Y.C., 1975—, also choreographer; guest artist The Royal Ballet, London, Iowa U. Gala, Ballet New Eng. Performed in Internat. Ballet Festival of Havana, 1986. Recipient Key to City, Birmingham, Ala., 1981, Resolution, City of Balt., 1981. Club: 4 Sevens (N.Y.C.). Avocations: Photography; cars; swimming; refinishing wood furniture. Office: Dance Theatre Harlem 466 West 152nd St New York NY 10031*

SHELLMAN-LUCAS, ELIZABETH C., special education educator, researcher; b. Thomas County, Ga., Feb. 5, 1937; d. Herbert and Juanita (Coleman) Smith; m. John Lee Lucas, Jr. (div.); 1 child, Sandie Juanita Lucas Boyce; m. Eddie Joseph Shellman; 1 child, Eddie Joseph Shellman, Jr. MS in Edn., CUNY, 1990. Pvt. practice cosmetologist N.Y.C., 1959—; tchr. N.Y.C. Bd. of Edn. High Sch. Dist., 1984—. Vol. various community orgns.; citizen amb. del. People to People Internat., 1994. Mem. Coun. for Exceptional Children. Avocations: reading, music, dancing, jogging, languages.

SHELLOW, ROBERT, management service company executive, consultant; b. Milw., Sept. 22, 1929; s. Henry G. and Sadie (Myers) S.; m. Dorothea

Laadt, Aug. 30, 1963; children: Sarah Katherine, Leslie Suzzane. BA, Reed Coll., 1951; MA, U. Mich., 1952, PhD, 1956. Commd. USPHS, Bethesda, Md., 1955, advanced through grades to commdr., Psychol. U.S. Bureau Prisons, 1955-58; asst. dep. dir. Nat. Adv. Commn. on Civil Disorders, 1967-68; dir. pilot programs D.C. Dept. Pub. Safety, 1968-70; prof. Carnegie-Mellon U., Pitts., 1970-76; pres. IMAR Corp., Washington, 1978—; cons. in field; expert witness psychol. deterence, security negligence cases, state and fed. cts., 1978—; mng. dir. Cross-Continent Assocs., Ltd. 1993—. Author: Issues in Law Enforcement, 1976; contbr. numerous articles to profl. jours. USPHS fellow U. Mich., 1953. Fellow Am. Psychol. Assn. ; mem. Nat. Bus. Aircraft Assn., Internat. Assn. Profl. Security Cons. (v.p. 1987-89, pres. 1989-91), Sigma Xi. Avocations: sailing; automobile and boat restoration. Office: IMAR Corp PO Box 34528 Bethesda MD 20817-0528

SHELLY, CHRISTINE DEBORAH, foreign service officer; b. Pontiac, Mich., May 1, 1951; d. Chester Price and Margaret Alice (Neafie) S.; m. Jose Manuel San-Bento Menezes, July 19, 1987; 1 stepchild, Ana Ferreira San-Bento Menezes. BA cum laude, Vanderbilt U., 1973; MA, Tufts U., 1974, MA in Diplomacy, 1975. Fgn. affairs analyst Intelligence and Rsch. Bur. Dept. State, Washington, 1975-77, desk officer Near Eastern Affairs, 1977-79; fin. attache Am. Embassy Dept. State, Cairo, 1979-81; asst. v.p. BankAmerica Internat., N.Y.C., 1981-82; spl. asst. Near Eastern Affairs Dept. State, Washington, 1982-83; cons., polit. officer Am. Embassy Dept. State, Lisbon, Portugal, 1983-87; dep. econ. advisor U.S. Mission to NATO, Brussels, 1987-90, dep. cabinet dir. Sec. Gen., 1990-93; dep. spokesman, dep. asst. sec. pub. affairs Dept. State, Washington, 1993—. Avocation: equestrian. Office: Bur Pub Affairs Dept State 2201 C St NW Rm 6800 Washington DC 20520

SHELP, RONALD KENT, non-profit business and trade association executive, author, lecturer, consultant; b. Cartersville, Ga., Sept. 29, 1941; s. Clarence Harrison Mulkey and Willie Marion (Puckett) Shelp; m. Anna June Mueller, Feb. 14, 1982. A.B. cum laude, U. Ga., 1964; M.A., Johns Hopkins SAIS, Washington, 1966; postgrad., London Sch. Econs., 1981—. Asst. to U.S. Senator Richard Russell, Washington, 1964-66; exec. sec. Internat. Ins. Adv. Council, Washington, 1966-73; co-founder, exec. v.p. Art Enterprise Internat., Washington, 1970-72; asst. mgr. internat. div. U.S.C. of C., Washington, 1970-73; exec. sec. Assn. Am. C. of C. in Latin Am., Washington, 1969-73; v.p. Am. Internat. Group, N.Y.C., 1973-85; v.p., mem. pres.' operating com. Celanese Corp., N.Y.C., 1985-87; v.p. Hoechst Celanese Corp., 1987; pres., chief exec. officer N.Y.C. Partnership, 1987-93, N.Y. C. of C. and Industry, 1987-93; mem. exec. com. Burson-Marsteller, N.Y.C., 1994—; dir. Am. Internat. Underwriters Corp., N.Y.C., 1973-85, AIG Polit. Risk Inc., N.Y.C., 1981-85; cons. OECD, Paris, 1982, mem. U.S. del., 1978-85; chmn. U.S. Govt.-Services Ind. Adv. Com., Washington, 1980-85; adj. prof. internat. bus. and econs. NYU, N.Y.C., 1982-84. Co-author: Politics of Raw Material, 1979, Service Industries and Economic Development, 1984, Industrial Policy: Business and Politics in the United States and France, 1985, Revitalizing the U.S. Economy, 1986, Services in Transition: The Impact of Information Technology on the Service Sector, 1986, The Insurance Industry in Economic Development, 1986, Entrepreneurship: The Key to Economic Growth, 1986; author: Beyond Industrialization, 1981, 3d edit. in Japanese; Co-author: The U.S. Trade Deficit: Impact and Implication, 1985; contbr. articles to Foreign Policy, Wall Street Jour., N.Y. Times, Los Angeles Times, Boston Globe, Forbes, Christian Science Monitor, Jour. Social Econ. Studies, Across the Board, Financier, Georgetown Law Jour., Policy Options. Dir. Pan Am. Devel. Found., Washington, 1981-87, Johns Hopkins SAIS, Washington, 1982-89, 90-95, Internat. Peace Acad., N.Y.C., 1983-89; trade and econ. advisor Presdl. Campaign of Sen. Gary Hart, Washington, 1983-84, 86-87; adv. bd. Overseas Devel. Council, Washington, 1983-91, N.Y.C. Coun. on Econ. Edn., 1988—; bd. dirs. Citizens Budget Commn., N.Y.C. 1985-87, Fund for Modern Cts., N.Y.C. Indsl. Tech. Assistance Corp., 1987-89, Mus. American Folk Art, 1987-90, Corp. Fund for Dance 1987-91, Econ. Devel. Corp., 1988-93, Manhattan Theatre Club, 1992—, N.Y.C. Housing Partnership Devel. Co. vice chmn., 1992-94; chmn. World Environ. Ctr., 1987-88; mem. Mayor's Mgmt. Adv. Task Force, 1990-93, Mayor's Adv. Com. to Productivity, 1990-93, Mayor's Task Force on Telecommunications Network Reliability, 1990-93, N.Y. State Indsl. Cooperation Coun., 1989-93, N.Y. State Job Trng. Partnership Coun., 1989-94, N.Y. State Telecommunications Exchange, 1992-93, Mayor's Coun. of Econ. Advisors, 1992-93. With USAR, 1966-72. Recipient Crown Zerlerbach fellow, Johns Hopkins SAIS, 1964, Francis P. Bolton fellow, 1965. Mem. Coun. Fgn. Rels., Econ. Club N.Y., Explorers Club, Met. Club (Washington), Georgetown Club (Washington), Union League Club, Phi Beta Kappa. Democrat. Avocations: collecting primitive, folk and contemporary African American southern art, fly fishing, exploration, skiing, tennis. Home: 32 Washington Sq W New York NY 10011 Office: Burson-Marsteller 230 Park Ave S New York NY 10003

SHELTON, AUSTIN JAMES (SONNY SHELTON), territorial legislator; b. Yigo, Guam, June 30, 1949; s. Austin James and Amanda (Guzman) S.; m. Eleanore Connelly (div. 1984); children: Melinda Nadine, Madeline Anne; m. Gracialla Rose Shinohara, June 15, 1985; 1 child, Austin James III. G-rad. high sch., Agana, Guam. Businessman, 1978-86; senator 19th Guam Legislature, Agana, 1987—. Mem. Asian-Pacific Parliamentarian's Union (secretariat-gen. 1987-89), Assn. of Pacific Island Legislatures. Democrat. Roman Catholic. Home: PO Box 803 Agana GU 96910-0803 Office: PO Box CB-1 Agana GU 96910

SHELTON, DAVID HOWARD, economics educator; b. Winona, Miss., Nov. 30, 1928; s. Tuttle M. and Kate (Moss) S.; m. Margaret Murff, Feb. 4, 1951; children: David Keith, Sarah Katherine, Susan Esther. B.A., Millsaps Coll., 1951; M.A., Ohio State U., 1952, Ph.D., 1958. Instr. Ohio State U., 1958; asst. prof. U. Del., 1958-63, asso. prof., 1963-65; prof. U. N.C., Greensboro, 1965—, head dept. econs., bus. adminstrn., 1967-70, dean Sch. Bus. and Econs., 1970-83, head dept. econs., 1988-93; Cons. Joint Council on Econ. Edn., 1969-72, N.C. Dept. Pub. Instrn., 1970-73. Trustee N.C. Council on Econ. Edn., 1971—, chmn., 1971-75, pres., 1975-85. Served with USNR, 1946-48. M.D. Lincoln fellow, 1956-57; H.L. and Grace Doherty fellow, 1957. Mem. Beta Gamma Sigma, Omicron Delta Kappa, Kappa Sigma. Episcopalian. Home: 3609 Dogwood Dr Greensboro NC 27403-1010

SHELTON, DOROTHY DIEHL REES, lawyer; b. Manila, Sept. 16, 1935; came to U.S., 1945; d. William Walter John and Hedwig (Glienecke) Diehl; m. Charles W. Rees, Jr., June 15, 1957 (div. 1971); children: Jane Rees Stebbins, John B., Anne Rees Slack, Esq., David C., Esq.; m. Thomas C. Shelton, Mar. 4, 1977 (dec.). BA in Music, Stanford Univ., 1957; JD, Western State Univ. Coll. Law, 1976. Bar: Calif. 1977, U.S. Dist. Ct. (so. dist.) Calif. 1977. Pvt. practice, San Diego, 1977—. Mem. ABA, Calif. State Bar, Am. Trial Lawyers Assn., Calif. Trial Lawyers Assn., Calif. Attys. for Criminal Justice, San Diego County Bar Assn., San Diego Trial Lawyers Assn., Stanford U. Alumni Assn., Jr. League San Diego, Gt. Pyrenees Club Am., Dachshund Club Am., Nu Beta Epsilon. Roman Catholic. Avocations: gardening, reading, tennis, Great Pyrenees dogs. Office: 110 W C St Ste 918 San Diego CA 92101-3959

SHELTON, JOANNA REED, economist; b. Orange, Tex., Mar. 16, 1951; d. John Alexander and Winifred Irene (Gormley) S.; m. Richard David Erb, Mar. 22, 1980. BA, Duke U., 1974; MA, Johns Hopkins U., 1977. Researcher, writer Congl. Quarterly, Inc., Washington, 1974-75; internat. economist offices of internat. trade policy, internat. monetary affairs, office of the secretary U.S. Dept. Treas., Washington, 1978-83; sr. advisor on Japan Motorola, Inc., Washington, 1984; profl. staff mem., economist U.S. Ho. of Reps. Com. on Ways and Means, Washington, 1984-92; dep. asst. sec. trade policy and programs U.S. Dept. State, Washington, 1992—. Co-author: Subsidies in Internat. Trade, 1984; contbr. articles to profl. jours. Mem. adv. coun. Johns Hopkins U. Sch. of Advanced Internat. Studies, Washington, 1986-92; mem. adv. com. Fulbright Scholar selection for northeast Asia, Washington, 1989-91. Mem. Japan-Am. Soc. (trustee 1990-92), Cosmos Club of Washington. Avocations: tennis, horseback riding, flute. Office: Dept of State 2201 C St NW Rm 3831A Washington DC 20520

SHELTON, KARL MASON, management consultant; b. Lincolnton, N.C., June 8, 1933; s. Karl and Annie (Grace) S.; m. Deloris Hundley, May 8, 1954; children: Melanie Dwain, Leslie Elaine, Kevin Karl. Grad., Am. Inst.

Banking, 1960, Carolinas Sch. Banking, 1963, Stonier Grad. Sch. Banking, 1967. Vice pres. N.C. Nat. Bank, Charlotte, 1954-71; sr. v.p., treas. Seattle-First Nat. Bank, 1971-79; pres. Citizens Fidelity Corp., Louisville, 1979-82; exec. v.p. Southeast Bank, N.A., Miami, Fla., 1982-86; pres., chmn. bd. Shelton Mgmt. Services, Panama City, Fla., 1987-88, 89—; pres., chief operating officer Sec. Fed. Savs. Bank, Columbia, S.C., 1988-89. Contbg. editor: Bankers Handbook, 1978. Served with AUS, 1952-54. Methodist.

SHELTON, LARRY BRANDON, apparel company executive; b. Paducah, Ky., Aug. 4, 1934; s. Brandon and Annabelle (Jones) S.; m. Lura Jane Peyton, Aug. 26, 1955; children: Tracey Jean, Ted Peyton. BS in Commerce, Bowling Green Coll. Commerce, 1956; MA, Harvard Bus. Sch., 1977; grad. advanced mgmt. program, Harvard U., 1977. C.P.A., Tenn. With Genesco Inc., Nashville, 1956—; sr. internal auditor, 1961, spl. fin. asst. exec. dept., 1962-62, v.p. Eastern control office, 1962-69, v.p. central control, 1969, sec., 1973-75, vice chmn., 1975-77, exec. v.p., 1977-83, pres., chief oper. officer, 1988—; chief exec. officer Greif Cos. (Genesco's tailored clothing op.), Nashville, 1983—, also bd. dirs., 1986—; bd. dirs. Textile Clothing Tech. Corp., Footwear Distbrs. and Retailers Am. Mem. exec. bd. Mid. Tenn. Coun. Boy Scouts Am.; bd. dirs. devel. steering com. Western Ky. U. Mem. Am. Inst. C.P.A.s, Tenn. Soc. C.P.A.s, Nashville C. of C. Methodist. Office: Genesco Inc Genesco Pk Nashville TN 37217

SHELTON, MURIEL MOORE, religious education administrator; b. Freeport, N.Y., May 29, 1921; d. Samuel Talbott and Agnes Jerolean (Trigg) Payne; m. Ernest William Moore, May 29, 1944 (dec. Apr. 2, 1978); children: Diana Moore Williams, David E. Moore, Cathi Moore Mount, Douglas L. Moore; m. Malcolm Wendell Shelton, Aug. 9, 1987. AB, Eastern Nazarene Coll., 1942; MusM, U. Tex., 1966. Cert. educator gen. and choral music, English, Tex., Tenn., Ark., Kans. Music dir. Coll. Ave. United Meth. Ch., Manhattan, Kans., 1969-71, Cen. United Meth. Ch., Lawrence, Kans., 1971-75, First United Meth. Ch., Horton, Kans., 1975-78; dir. Christian edn. St. Mark's United Meth. Ch., Bethany, Okla., 1980—; chmn. bd. dirs. Northwest Food Pantry, Oklahoma City, 1987-88; rep. St. mark's United Meth. Ch. Labor Link Ctr., 1989—; lectr. in field. Contbr. articles to quar. mags.; author: Song of Joy, 1985, Promises of Good, 1989, Healing in His Wings, 1992. Mem. Christian Educators' Fellowship. Home: 6404 NW 35th St Bethany OK 73008-4136 Office: St Mark's United Meth Ch 8140 NW 36th St Bethany OK 73008-3500 A life for God is eternally significant.

SHELTON, O. L., state legislator; b. Greenwood, Miss., Feb. 6, 1946; s. Obie and Idell (McClung) S.; m. Linda Kay, July 21, 1980; children: Eric, Jaimal, Schron, Kiana. AB, Lincoln U., 1970. Youth specialist Mo. Ext. Svc., St. Louis, 1972-82. Committeeman 4th ward Dem. party, St. Louis 1988—; vice-chmn. Dem. Party; advisor Ville Area Neighborhood Housing Assn.; active Black Leadership Roundtable, Mary Rydar Homes, Williams Community Sch. Mem. Early Childcare Devel. Corp. Home: 1803A Cora Saint Louis MO 63113

SHELTON, RICHARD FOTTRELL, investment executive; b. Cebu, Philippines, May 23, 1929; s. Edward Mason and Emily (Fottrell) S.; m. Nan Dodson, 1955 (div. 1962); children: Leslie, Anita; m. Patricia Brooks, 1964 (dec. 1968); 1 dau., Celia; m. Sydney Walton, 1973; stepchildren: Suzanne, Peter, Jenny. A.B., Stanford U., 1950. Account exec. Merrill Lynch, Pierce Fenner & Smith, 1954-63; br. mgr., then regional partner Paine, Webber, Jackson & Curtis, Inc., San Francisco, 1963-71; sr. v.p., div. dir. Paine, Webber, Jackson & Curtis, Inc., 1972-82; asst. dir.; gen. ptnr., then sr. v.p. mng. dir. Hambrecht & Quist, 1982-85; pres. Calif. Investment Trust Fund Group, San Francisco, 1985—. Pres. bd. trustees Children's Cancer Research Inst., San Francisco, 1980-82, Katherine Burke Sch., 1976-78; pres. The Guardsmen, 1964-65; treas. bd. trustees Santa Catalina Sch. 1982-85; commr. Asian Art Mus., San Francisco, 1987—, Asian Art Mus. Found., 1987—. Served to 1st lt. USAF, 1950-54. Decorated Air medal with 2 oak leaf clusters. Mem. Burlingame Country Club (Hillsborough, Calif.), Pacific-Union Club, Bohemian Club, Kappa Sigma. Republican. Episcopalian. Office: 44 Montgomery St Ste 2100 San Francisco CA 94104

SHELTON, RICKY VAN, country music singer, songwriter; b. Danville, Va., Jan. 12, 1952; s. Jenks Dewitt and Julia Eloise (Simpson) S.; m. Bettye Witt, Aug. 4, 1986. Grad. high sch., Gretna, Va., 1970. Various pipefitting and constrn. jobs various cos., 1970-86; car salesman Alta Vista (Va.) Ford Co., 1972-74; plumber J.H. Cothran Plumbing Co., Alta Vista, Va., 1980-84; country music singer Columbia Records, Nashville, 1985—. Albums: Wild-Eyed Dream, 1987 Loving Proof, 1988, Ricky Van Shelton Sings Christmas, 1989, RVS III, 1990, Backroads, 1991, Don't Overlook Salvation, 1992, Greatest Hits Plus, 1992, A Bridge I Didn't Burn, 1993, Love and Honor, 1994. Recipient TNN/Music City News Awards Entertainer of the Yr., 1990, 91. Mem. Country Music Assn. (Horizon award 1988, Male Vocalist of Yr. 1989), Acad. County Music. Recipient Male Vocalist of Yr. award, Album of Yr. award Nashville Network Viewer's Choice, 1989. Avocations: farming, fishing, raising beefalo. Office: care Michael Campbell & Assocs 40 Music Sq E Nashville TN 37203-4323

SHELTON, ROBERT NEAL, physics educator, researcher; b. Phoenix, Oct. 5, 1948; s. Clark B. and Grace M. (McLaughlin) S.; m. Adrian Ann Millar, Aug. 30, 1969; children: Christian, Cameron, Stephanie. BS, Stanford U., 1970; MS, U. Calif., San Diego, 1973, PhD, 1975. Postdoctoral researcher U. Calif.-San Diego, La Jolla, 1975-76, asst. rsch. physicist, 1976-78; asst. prof. Iowa State U., Ames, 1978-81, assoc. prof., 1981-84, prof. physics, 1984-87; prof. physics, chmn. dept. U. Calif.-Davis, 1987-90, vice chancellor for rsch., 1990—. Contbr. over 200 articles to profl. jours. Mem. Am. Phys. Soc., Sigma Xi. Office: U Calif Dept Physics Davis CA 95616

SHELTON, SALLY ANGELA, political scientist, writer, educator, editor; b. San Antonio, Aug. 29, 1944; d. Harlan Bryan and Edith Angela (Pratka) S.; m. William Eagan Colby, Nov. 20, 1984. BA, U. Mo., 1966; student, Institut des Scis. Politiques, Paris, 1968; MA, John Hopkins U., 1968; PhD (hon.), Mt. St. Mary's Coll., Emmitsburg, Md., 1986. Legis. asst. Sen. Lloyd Bentsen, Washington, 1971-77; deputy asst. Sec. of State Dept. of State, Washington, 1977-79; U.S. Ambassador Eastern Caribbean U.S. Govt., Barbados, 1979-81; fellow Harvard U., Cambridge, Mass., 1981-82; v.p. Internat. Bus. Govt. Couns., Washington, 1982-84, Baultens Trust Co., Washington, 1984-86; Multinati, Banks & Corps. Multinati, Baults & Corps, Washington, 1986—; co-editor Global Assessment, Washington, 1988—; adj. prof. Georgetown U., Washington, 1989—; dir. Nat. Endowment for Democracy, Washington, Ctr. for Internat. Bus. Studies, Texas A & M U.; v.p. bd. dirs. Coun. of Am. Ambassadors, Washington; mem. Coun. Overseas Devel. Coun., Washington. Author: several articles including N.Y. Times, Washington Post, Los Angeles Times, and Jour. of Commerce. Dir. U.S. Com. of the U.N. Fund for Women, Washington, Atlantic Coun. of the U.S., Washington, 1989, Internat. Planned Parenthood Fedn./Western Hemisphere Region,. Recipient Fulbright fellowship John Hopkins U., 1968. Mem. Washington Inst. for Fgn. Affairs, Coun. on Fgn. Rels., NOW, Nat. Women's Pol. Coun., Fulbright Alumni Assn. Democrat. Roman Catholic. Home: 3028 Dent Pl NW Washington DC 20007-2915

SHELTON, SLOANE, actress; b. Hahira, Ga., Mar. 14, 1934; d. Clarence Duffie and Ruth Evangeline (Davis) S. Student, Berea Coll., 1955; honors diploma, Royal Acad. Dramatic Art, London, 1959. Mem. O'Neill Found., Waterford, Conn., 1981-83, 85, 89, 91, 94; mem. theater panel N.Y. State Coun. on the Arts, 1979-81. Producer: (with Kevin Brownlow and Norma Millay Ellis) (documentary film) Millay at Steepletop, 1976; appearances in Broadway plays include: I Never Sang for My Father, Sticks & Bones, The Runner Stumbles, The Shadow Box, Orpheus Descending, Passione, Open Admissions; films include: All That Jazz, All the President's Men, Tiger Warsaw, Running on Empty, Jacknife, Lean on Me. Pres. Berilla Kerr Found. Mem. Actors Equity Assn., Screen Actors Guild, Actors Fund Am., AFTRA. Democrat.

SHELTON, STEPHANI, broadcast journalist, consultant; b. Boston; d. Phil and Babette (Belloff) Saltman; m. Frank Herold. BS, Boston U. Reporter, news broadcaster Sta. WPAT, Paterson, N.J., 1972-73; corr. CBS News, N.Y.C., 1973-84; news corr. WWOR-TV, N.Y.C., 1984-88; corr., anchor Fin. News Network, N.Y.C., 1989-91; indl. broadcast journalist, producer, cons., 1991—; freelance reporter Sta. WPIX-TV, 1991—, Sta. WNBC-TV, 1993—; freelance radio documentary writer Westinghouse

Group W Broadcasting, N.Y.C., 1970-73. Recipient Peabody award, 1972, N.J. Best Spot News award AP, 1987, 88, N.J. Working Press award, 1992, 93, 94; Emmy nominee, 1994-95. Mem. Radio and TV Working Press Assn. (v.p. 19856), Soc. Profl. Journalists, RTNDA. Guiding principles: a questioning mind, a refusal to take no for an answer and the memory of 28 marathons whatever happens the important thing is to survive.

SHELTON, TURNER BLAIR, diplomat; b. Louisa County, Va., Dec. 3, 1915; s. David Rice and Lillie Blanche (Gibson) S.; m. Lesly Starr, Sept. 23, 1951. Student, U. Va., 1932-34, 36-40, U. Richmond, 1935-36. With Loew's, Inc., Washington, 1941-42; asst. to dir. Treasury Dept., Washington, 1942-46; asst. to exec. producer Monogram Studios, Hollywood, Calif., 1946-47; producer Eagle Lions Studios, Hollywood, 1948-49; assoc. producer motion picture T-Men Exec. Warner Bros. Studios, 1949-51; cons. State Dept. 1951-54; dep. asst. dir. U.S.I.A., 1954-55, asst. dir., 1955-61; spl. asst. Soviet and Eastern European Exchanges Staff, Bur. European Affairs, 1961; counselor of legation Budapest, Hungary, 1962-64; spl. asst. to asst. sec. state Washington, 1964-66; consul gen. Nassau, The Bahamas, 1966-70; U.S. ambassador to Nicaragua, 1970-75; Dept. State adviser to Pres., Naval War Coll., Newport, R.I., 1976—; del. meeting on post-war financing, Paris, France, 1945, negotiator for State Dept. portion of sci., tech., ednl. and cultural exchange agreement with U.S. and USSR, 1958, mem. U.S. del. which negotiated new agreement with USSR, 1959, which negotiated cultural agreement with Rumania, 1960. Recipient Distinguished Service award U.S.I.A., 1956; Unit award for valor Dept. State, 1973. Mem. Motion Picture Acad. Arts and Scis. Home: 1121 Tower Rd Beverly Hills CA 90210-2130

SHELTON, WAYNE VERNON, professional services and systems integration company executive; b. Mpls., Nov. 27, 1932; s. Olen George and Evelyn Ruth (Karpen) S.; m. Mary Kay Schwappach, Dec. 29, 1956; children: William David, Susan Evelyn. BS, U. Minn., 1954. Instr. U. Minn., Mpls., 1954-56; tchr. Mpls. Pub. Schs., 1956-57; mathematician Rand Corp., Santa Monica, Calif., 1957-62; sr. assoc. Planning Research Corp., Los Angeles, 1963-72; v.p. Planning Research Corp., McLean, Va., 1972-83, sr. v.p., 1983-85, pres., chief operating officer, 1985-87, chmn., pres. and chief exec. officer, 1987-90; v.p. Emhart Corp., Farmington, Conn., 1987-88; exec. v.p., pres. Emhart Info. and Electronics Systems, Towson, Md., 1988-90; v.p. Hughes Aircraft Co., 1990—; pres. Hughes Info. Systems, Reston, Va., 1994—; instr. data processing Santa Monica (Calif.) Coll., 1960-62; pres. Assn. Ind. Software Cos., McLean, 1970-71; bd. dirs. Profl. Svcs. Coun., Washington, 1972—, vice chmn., 1993-95; bd. dirs. Security Affairs Support Assn., Annapolis, Md., 1983-85, chmn., 1983-84. Bd. dirs. No. Va. Tech. Coun., 1992—. Mem. Armed Forces Comm. and Electronics Assn. (bd. dirs. 1987—, internat. v.p. 1994—), Navy League (life), Assn. U.S. Army, Air Force Assn., Nat. Security Indsl. Assn., Am. Electronics Assn. (bd. dirs. 1988-89, 93—). Republican. Avocations: gardening, personal investments, personal computers, running. Home: 8578 Brickyard Rd Rockville MD 20854-4833

SHELTON, WILLIAM EVERETT, university president; b. Batesville, Miss., Sept. 6, 1944; s. Loyd Taylor and Merle Golden (Barlow) S.; m. Sharon Nordengreen, Apr. 23, 1965; 1 child, William Bradley. BS, Memphis State U., 1967, MA, 1970; EdD, U. Miss., 1975. Tchr. Olive Branch (Miss.) High Sch., 1967-68; prin. Oakland (Tenn.) Elem. Sch., 1968-70; administr., instr. N.W. Miss. Jr. Coll., Senatobia, 1970-76; dean for student devel. Henderson State U., Arkadelphia, Ark., 1976-78, v.p. for higher edn., 1978-83; v.p. Kent (Ohio) State U., 1983-89; pres. Ea. Mich. U., Ypsilanti, 1989—. Vice chmn. Ohio Pub. TV, 1986-89. Mem. Am. Assn. for Higher Edn., Am. Assn. State Colls. and Univs., Kent Area C. of C. (pres. 1986). Avocations: flying, golf. Office: Ea Mich U 202 Welch Hall Ypsilanti MI 48197-2214

SHEMIN, BARRY L., insurance company executive; b. Bklyn., Dec. 17, 1942. AB magna cum laude, Brown U., 1963; MA, U. Mich., 1964. With John Hancock Mut. Life Ins. Co., Boston, 1968—, sr. v.p., corporate actuary; bd. dirs. John Hancock Property and Casualty Holding Co., Hancock Natural Resource Group. Bd. dirs. ARC of Mass. Bay. Fellow Soc. Actuaries; mem. Am. Acad. Actuaries, Internat. Actuarial Assn., Phi Beta Kappa, Sigma Xi. Club: Brown Univ. (Boston). Office: John Hancock Mut Life Ins Co PO Box 111 Boston MA 02117-0111

SHEN, BENJAMIN SHIH-PING, scientist, engineer, educator; b. Hangzhou, China, Sept. 14, 1931; s. Nai-cheng and Chen-chiu (Sun) S.; m. Lucia Elisabeth Simpson, 1971; children: William, Juliet. AB, Assumption Coll., Mass., 1954, ScD (hon.), 1972; AM in Physics, Clark U., 1956; DSc d'Etat in Physics, U. Paris, 1964; MA (hon.), U. Pa., 1971. Asst. prof. physics SUNY, Albany, 1956-59; assoc. prof. space sci. dept. aeros. and astronautics Engring. Sch., NYU, 1964-66; assoc. prof. U. Pa., Phila., 1966-68, prof., 1968-72, Reese W. Flower prof. astronomy and astrophysics, 1972—, assoc. provost, 1979-80, chmn. coun. grad. deans, 1979-81, provost, 1980-81, chmn. dept. astronomy and astrophysics, 1973-79, dir. Flower and Cook Obs., 1973-79, mem. Ctr. for Energy and Environment, 1976-93, chmn. roundtable on sci. industry and policy, 1976-92, prof. Sch. Engring. and Applied Sci., 1980-85; mem. U.S. Nat. Sci. Bd., 1990-94, chmn. U.S. sci. and engring. indicators, 1990-92, chmn. task force on sci. literacy, 1992-94; cons. GE, 1961-68, Office Tech. Assessment, U.S. Congress, 1977-78; sci. and tech. adviser Budget Com., U.S. Senate, 1976-77; mem. guest staff Brookhaven Nat. Lab., 1963-64, 65-70; chmn. commn. on pub. understanding of sci. N.Y. Acad. Scis., 1972-75; mem. adv. com. Mt. John Obs., New Zealand, 1978-84. Author: Nuclear Problems in Radiation Shielding in Space, 1963, Passage des Protons dans des Milieux Condensés, 1964; editor, co-author: High-Energy Nuclear Reactions in Astrophysics, 1967; co-editor, co-author: Spallation Nuclear Reactions and Their Applications, 1976; mem. editorial bd. Earth and Extraterrestrial Scis., 1974-78, assoc. editor, 1978-79; assoc. editor: Comments on Astrophysics, 1979-85; contbr. articles to profl. jours. Mem. Hayden Planetarium com. of bd. trustees Am. Mus. Natural History, 1978—; mem. sci. adv. bd. Children's TV Workshop, N.Y.C., 1977, 79—; former trustee ABA-AAAS Nat. Conf. Bd. Lawyers and Scientists, 1986-92; former trustee or bd. dirs. N.Y. Acad. Scis., University City Sci. Ctr. Rsch. Park, Phila., U. Pa. Rsch. Found., Morris Arboretum, Phila., Univ. Mus., Phila., Pa. Ballet Co. Decorated Ordre des Palmes Académiques (France); recipient Vermeil medal for sci. Soc. d'Encouragement au Progrès, France, 1978. Fellow Am. Phys. Soc., AAAS (com. on sci. engring. and pub. policy 1978-84, chmn. subcom on fed. research and devel. budget 1978-81), Royal Astron. Soc. (U.K.); mem. Internat. Astron. Union. Office: U Pa David Rittenhouse Lab Philadelphia PA 19104-6396

SHEN, CHIA THENG, former steamship company executive, religious institute official; b. Chekiang, China, Dec. 15, 1913; came to U.S., 1952, naturalized, 1964; s. Foo Sheng and Wen Ching (Hsai) S.; m. Woo Ju Chu, Apr. 21, 1940; children: Maria May Shen Sackton, Wilma Way Shen George, David Chuen-Tsing, Freda Foh. BEE, Chiao Tung U., 1937; LittD (hon.), St. John's U., 1973. With Central Elec. Mfg. Works, China, 1937-44; factory mgr. Central Elec. Mfg. Works, 1942-44; dep. coordinating dept. Nat. Resources Commn., Govt. of China, 1945-47; pres. China Trading and Indsl. Devel. Corp., Shanghai, 1947-49; mng. dir. China Trading & Indsl. Devel. Co. Ltd., Hong Kong, 1949-53; with TransAtlantic Financing Corp., 1954-62, pres., 1958-62; pres. Pan-Atlantic Devel. Corp., N.Y.C., 1955-70; with Marine Transport Lines Inc., N.Y.C., 1958-70; sr. v.p. Marine Transport Lines Inc., 1964-70; with Am. Steamship Co., Buffalo, 1967-80; chmn. bd., chief exec. officer Am. Steamship Co., 1971-80. Trustee Inst. Advanced Studies World Religions, N.Y., 1970—, chmn. bd., chief exec. officer, 1970-92, pres., 1970-84, 90—; trustee China Inst. in Am., N.Y.C., 1963-90, vice chmn., 1970-79, chmn., 1979-80, mem. exec. com., 1963-84; trustee, v.p. Buddhist Assn., U.S., N.Y.C., 1964—. Mem. Chinese Inst. Engring. Home and Office: RD 2 Rte 301 Carmel NY 10512-9802 To benefit all human beings and to work toward freeing them from fear is my goal. The collective wisdom of all world religions furnishes us the direction and means to achieve that goal. To introduce such wisdom into the daily life of mankind in general and America in particular, is therefore what I devote my energy to. To the extent that I succeed in this endeavor, I consider my life successful.

SHEN, JEROME TSENG YUNG, pediatrician; b. Shanghai, China, Aug. 5, 1918; came to U.S., 1947; s. John G.K. and Agnes (Yao) S.; m. Theresa D.S. Yao, Oct. 10, 1938; children: Jerome L., Elizabeth Burke, Frances Schuman, Li Poppen, Thomas. BS, St. John's U., Shanghai, 1942, MD,

1945; MS in Pediatrics, St. Louis U., 1949. Lic. physician, Mo.; diplomate Am. Bd. Pediatrics. Instr. dept. pediatrics St. Louis U. Sch. Medicine, 1949-52, sr. instr., 1952-60, asst. clin. prof., 1960-70, assoc. clin. prof., 1970-76, clin. prof., 1976-93, clin. prof. emeritus, 1994—; grad. fellow adolescent medicine Harvard Grad. Sch., Boston, 1958-59; vis. prof. Nat. Coll. Juvenile Ct. Judges, Reno, Nev., 1973, adj. prof. jud. adminstrn., 1981-82; cons. adolescent medicine St. Louis State Hosp. and Mo. Inst. Psychiatry, St. Louis, 1973-80; head dept. pediatrics St. Louis City Hosp., 1959-63; chief dept. pediatrics and outpatient dept. Scott Field Air Force Hosp., Belleville, Ill., 1956-58; chief dept. pediatrics St. Louis Labor Health Inst., 1967-90; sr. cons. adolescent clinic Cardinal Glennon Children's Hosp., St. Louis,1977-90; hon. staff Cardinal Glennon Children's Hosp., St. Mary's Health Ctr., St. John's Mercy Health Ctr.; emeritus staff Jewish Hosp. St. Louis, 1993; chmn., Expert Advisors Medicine and Pub. Health Rep. China (Taiwan), 1978; bd. dirs., mem. exec. com. Children's Lobby, Washington,1972; mem. planning com. Mo. State Conf. on Crime, Delinquency and System of Justice; mem. adv. com. Mo. Divsn. Family Svcs., 1973-80; pres. Bi-state Interagy. Coun. on Smoking and Health. 1971-74; Mo. del. to White house Conf. on Children and Youth, 1970; mem. Gov. Com. for Children and Youth, chmn. subcom. on health, 1972-81; chmn. Midwest Regional Conf. Smoking and Health, 1972. Author; editor: Clinical Practice of Adolescent Medicine, 1980, Spanish edit., 1983; editorial bd. Postgrad. Medicine, 1977-88; contbr. articles to profl. jours. Coord. Mother Teresa's Gift of Mary Ctr., St. Louis; founder, bd. dirs. past pres. Pro Life Citizens Polit. Action Com., St. Louis, 1986—; chmn. Mo. Task Force on Unwed Adolescent Sexual Activity and Pregnancy, Jefferson City, 1987; hon. mem. Nat. Coun. Juvenile and Family Ct. Judges, Reno, 1982—; bd. dirs. Birthright Counseling, St. Louis, Lakeside Ctr. St. Louis County, 1965—, St. Louis Archdiocesan Pro Life Com., 1974—, Mo. and Nat. Drs. for Life, 1980—; mem. Bd. of Health, City of University, 1974-80; chmn. Midwest Regional Conf. on Smoking and Health, 1972. Maj. USAF, 1956-58. Recipient Cardinal Carberry Pro Life award Archdiocese of St. Louis, 1978, Citation for Outstanding Achievement Senate State of Mo., Jefferson City, 1988, Svc. award St. Louis U. Fellow Am. Acad. Pediatrics (now emeritus; liaison rep. to various couns., mem. Nat. Com. on Youth 1970-76, com. on adolescence 1977-80, chmn. Mo. com. on youth 1969-70, co-chmn. youth and sch. com. 1971); mem. Soc. Adolescent Medicine (treas. 1973-75, chmn. pvt. practice com. 1969-75, historian 1982-90). Republican. Roman Catholic. Avocations: photography, insects, collection of miniatures, stamps, coins. Home: 7132 Kingsbury Blvd University City MO 63130

SHEN, LIANG CHI, electrical engineer, educator, researcher; b. China, Mar. 17, 1939; came to U.S., 1962; s. Kuang Huai and ting Chin (Yu) S.; m. Grace Liu, June 26, 1965; children: Michael, Eugene. BSEE, Nat. Taiwan U., Taipei, 1961; PhD, Harvard U., 1967. Registered profl. engr., Tex. Prof., chmn. electrical engring. dept. U. Houston, 1977-81, prof., dir. well logging lab., 1978—. Author: Applied Electromagnetism, 1987, 3d edit., 1995. Fellow IEEE (assoc. editor geosci. and remote sensing 1986—). Office: U Houston Dept Elec Engring Houston TX 77204

SHEN, MASON MING-SUN, medical center administrator; b. Shanghai, Jiang Su, China, Mar. 30, 1945; came to U.S., 1969; s. John Kaung-Hao and Mai-Chu (Sun) S.; m. Nancy Hsia-Hsian Shieh, Aug. 7, 1976; children: Teresa Tao-Yee, Darren Tao-Ru. BS in Chemistry, Taiwan Normal U., 1963-67; MS in Chemistry, S.D. State U. 1971; PhD in Biochemistry, Cornell U., 1977; MS in Chinese Medicine, China Acad., Taipei, Taiwan, 1982; OMD, San Francisco Coll Acupuncture, 1984; AMD (hon.), Asian Am. Acupuncture Coll., Sri Lanka, 1985; MD (Medicina Alternativa), Internat. U., Colombo, Sri Lanka, 1988, MD, 1988. Diplomate Nat. Commn. for Cert. of Accupuncturists; lic. acupuncturist. Rsch. assoc. Lawrence Livermore (Calif.) Lab., 1979-80; assoc. prof. Nat. Def. Med. Coll., Taipei, 1980-82; prof. Inst. of Chinese Medicine China Acad., Taipei, 1981-82, San Francisco Coll. Acupuncture, 1983-85; chief acupuncturist Acupuncture Ctr. of Livermore, Calif., 1982-93; prof. Acad. Chinese Culture & Health Scis., Oakland, Calif., 1985-86; chief acupuncturist Acupuncture Ctr. of Danville, Calif., 1985-89; dir. Pain & Stress Mgmt. Ctr., Danville, Calif., 1989-90; adminstr. Ea. Med. Ctr., Pleasanton, Calif.; chmn. adminstrn. subcom., 1991-92, acupuncture com. State of Calif., 1988-92. Contbr. articles to profl. jours. Rep. Rep. Party, Danville, 1988-93; bd. dirs. Asian Rep. Assembly, 1989—. 2d lt. Rep. of China Army, 1966-69. Recipient Nat. Rsch. Svc. award NIH, 1977. Mem. AAAOM, N.Y. Acad. Sci., Calif. Cert. Acupuncturists Assn. (bd. dirs. 1984-88, pres. 1984-85), Acupuncture Assn. Am. (bd. dirs. 1986-90, v.p. 1987-89), Am. Assn. Acupuncture and Oriental Medicine (bd. dirs. 1987-92, pres. 1989-90), Nat. Acupuncture Detoxification Assn. (cons. 1987—), Presdl. Round Table (presdl. adv. com.), Hong Kong and Kowloon Chinese Med. Assn. (hon. life pres. 1985). Republican. Avocations: travel, horse back riding, rifles. Home: 3240 Touriga Dr Pleasanton CA 94566 Office: Eastern Med Ctr 3510 Old Santa Rita Rd Ste D Pleasanton CA 94588-3466

SHEN, RONGER, artist, Qigong educator; b. Shanghai, China, Nov. 11, 1942; came to U.S., 1984; d. Jianping and Huijun (Peng) S.; m. Yi Wu, Dec. 31, 1965; 1 child, Yan Wu. BA, Nat. Nanjing Acad. Arts, 1961-65. Dir. arts and crafts dept. Jiangsu Light Industry Bur., Nanjing, 1965-79; dir. Jiangsu Acad. Arts and Crafts, 1982—; profl. painter Jiangsu Acad. Traditional Chinese Painting, 1979—; pres. Qigong Ctr., Inc., N.Y., 1989—; Qigong cons. to dept. orthopedics Mt. Sinai Sch. Medicine, N.Y.C., 1991—; N.J. Med. Ctr. Pain Mgmt. Ctr., Newark, 1992—; NIH approved rsch. project on Life Info. Pictures, Life Info. Rhythm and Qigong, 1993. Mem. Artists Assn. China (Jiangsu br.), Acad. Arts and Crafts China, Eastern Am. Qigong U.S. (chmn. 1991—). Home and Studio: 32-05 146th St Flushing NY 11354

SHEN, THEODORE PING, investment banker; b. N.Y.C., Feb. 18, 1945; s. Shih-Chang and Clara Grace (Low) S.; m. Carol Lee Wing, June 13, 1968; 1 child, Carla Patricia. B.A. in Econs., Yale U., 1966; M.B.A. in Fin., Harvard U., 1968. V.p.; securities analyst Donaldson, Lufkin & Jensette, N.Y.C., 1968-78; mng. dir. research Donaldson, Lufkin & Jenrette, N.Y.C., 1978-81, mng. dir. equities div., 1981-84, pres. DLJ Capital Markets Group, 1984-86, chmn. DLJ Capital Markets Group, 1986—; bd. dirs. Donaldson, Lufkin & Jenrette, Inc., N.Y.C., 1984—; bd. dirs. N.Y. Urban Coalition; chmn. bd. trustees The Packer Collegiate Inst., Bklyn.; trustee Phillips Exeter Acad. Mem. N.Y. Soc. Securities Analysts, The Bond Club of N.Y., Heights Casino Club (Brooklyn Heights, N.Y.). Office: Donaldson Lufkin & Jenrette Securities Corp 140 Broadway New York NY 10005-1101

SHEN, YUEN-RON, physics educator; b. Shanghai, China, Mar. 25, 1935; came to U.S.; s. BS, Nat. Taiwan U., 1956; MS, Stanford U., 1959; PhD, Harvard U., 1963. Rsch. asst. Hewlett-Packard Co., Palo Alto, Calif., 1959; rsch. fellow Harvard U., Cambridge, Mass., 1963-64; asst. prof. U. Calif., Berkeley, 1964-67, assoc. prof., 1967-70, full prof., 1970—; prin. investigator Lawrence Berkeley Lab., 1964—. Author: The Principles of Nonlinear Optics, 1984. Sloan fellow, 1966-68; recipient Guggenheim Found. fellowship, 1972-73, Charles Hard Townes award, 1986, Arthur L. Schawlow prize Am. Phys. Soc., 1992, Alexander von Humboldt award, 1984, Outstanding Rsch. award DOE-MRS Rsch., 1983, Sustained Outstanding Rsch. award, 1987. Fellow Am. Phys. Soc. (disting. traveling lectr. Laser Sci. Topical Group 1994—), Optical Soc. Am.; mem. AAAS, Academia Sinica. Achievements include research in solid state physics. Office: U Calif Berkeley Dept Physics Berkeley CA 94720

SHENEFIELD, JOHN HALE, lawyer; b. Toledo, Jan. 23, 1939; s. Hale Thurel and Norma (Bird) S.; m. Judy Simmons, June 16, 1984; children: Stephen Hale, Christopher Newcomb. AB, Harvard U., 1960, LLB, 1965. Bar: Va. 1966, D.C. 1966. Assoc. Hunton & Williams, Richmond, Va., 1965-77; dep. asst. atty. gen. antitrust Div. Dept. Justice, Washington, 1977; asst. atty. gen. Dept. Justice, 1977-79, assoc. atty. gen., 1979-81; assoc. Milbank, Tweed, Hadley & McCloy, 1981-86, Morgan, Lewis & Bockius, Washington, 1986—; assoc. prof. law U. Richmond, 1975; former law Georgetown Law Ctr. 1981-83; chmn. Nat. Commn. for Rev. Antitrust Law and Procedures, 1978-79. Co-author The Antitrust Laws - A Primer, 1993; contbr. articles on law to profl. jours. Va. Sec. Va. Dem. Com., 1970-72, treas., 1976-77; chmn. Richmond Dem. Party, 1975-77; bd. govs. St. Albans Sch., 1983-90, chmn. 1988-90; mem. chpt. Washington Cathedral, 1988—; pres. Nat. Cathedral Assn., 1993—; chmn. Va. Racing Commn., 1989—. 2d lt. U.S. Army, 1961-62; to capt. Res., 1965. Mem. ABA, Va. Bar Assn. Home:

220 Carrwood Rd Great Falls VA 22066-3721 Office: Morgan Lewis & Bockius 1800 M St NW 6th Fl Washington DC 20036

SHENG, BRIGHT, composer, pianist, conductor; b. Shanghai, China, Dec. 6, 1954; came to U.S., 1982; s. David K-Y and Alice D-J (Cheng) S. BMus, Shanghai Conservatory Music, 1982; M. Mus. Arts, CUNY, 1984; Dr. Mus. Arts, Columbia U., 1993. Pianist/timpanist Folk Dance & Music Theater, Chinhai Province, China, 1971-78; instr. Columbia U., N.Y.C., 1985-89; Baldwin pianist/artist, 1988—; composer-in-residence Lyric Opera of Chgo., 1989-92, Seattle Symphony, 1992—, LaJolla Chamber Music Summerfest, 1993, Santa Fe Chamber Music Festival, 1993; artistic dir. Wet Ink '93 Festival/San Francisco Symphony, 1993; artist-in-residence U. Wash. Seattle, 1994—; lectr. The Juilliard Sch., Peabody Conservatory, Princeton U., U. Chgo., U. Md., Northwestern U., Harvard U., others. Commns. and performances by N.Y. Philharmonic, Chgo. Symphony, Cleve. Orch., San Francisco Symphony, Seattle Symphony, Balt. Symphony, N.Y. Chamber Symphony, Honolulu Symphony Orch., Sinfonica dell'Accademia Nazionale di Santa Cecilia, Houston Symphony, Boston Symphony, Lyric Opera of Chgo., Houston Grand Opera, Chamber Music Soc. of Lincoln Ctr., Tanglewood Music Festival, Aspen Music Festival, Santa Fe Chamber Music Festival, LaJolla Chamber Music Summerfest, Seattle Chamber Music Festival, Seattle Internat. Music Festival, others; recordings include New World Records, Delos, Koch Internat. Recipient 1st prize Art Song Competition, Shanghai, 1979, 1st and 2d prizes chamber music composition competition, Shanghai, 1980, Am. Acad. and Inst. Arts and Letters, 1984, Alfred Knapp award Tanglewood Music Ctr., 1985; grantee The Mary Flagler Charitable Trust, 1987, Nat. Endowment of Arts, 1987, 90, 94, 95, Guggenheim Found., 1990, Naumberg Found., 1990, Rockefeller Found., 1991, Seattle Arts Commn., 1992. Home: 158-13 78 Rd Flushing NY 11366 Office: Seattle Symphony Seattle Center House 305 Harrison St 4th Fl Seattle WA 98109

SHENK, GEORGE H., lawyer; b. N.Y.C., Sept. 10, 1943; BA, Princeton U., 1965; M in Internat. Affairs, Columbia U., 1967; JD, Yale U., 1970. Bar: N.Y. 1971, Calif. 1985. Assoc. Coudert Bros., Paris, 1970, N.Y.C., 1970-73, Hong Kong, 1973-75, Tokyo, 1975-78, ptnr., N.Y.C., 1978-91, San Francisco, 1991—. Contbr. articles to publs. Bd. dirs. alumni council Columbia Sch. Internat. Affairs, N.Y.C., 1982-85, French-Am. C. of C. of San Francisco, 1991—, Internat. Ctr. N.Y.C., 1983-86. Mem. Bar Assn. City of N.Y., Calif. State Bar Assn., Council Fgn. Relations, San Francisco Tennis Club. Office: Heller Ehrman White & McAuliffe 333 Bush St San Francisco CA 94104

SHENK, JOHN CHRISTIAN, JR., retired savings bank executive; b. Evanston, Ill., May 7, 1926; s. John Christian and Anabel (Kroell) S.; m. Mary Elizabeth Strobel, July 18, 1950; children: John Christian III, Mary Elizabeth II. A.B., Wash. U., 1950; J.D., State U. Iowa, 1955. Bar: Iowa 1955. Practice in Davenport, 1955-61; v.p., gen. counsel First Trust and Savs. Bank, Davenport, 1961-62; gen. counsel First Fed. Savs. Bank of Iowa, Davenport, 1962-74; exec. v.p. First Fed. Savs. Bank of Iowa, 1965-74, pres., 1974-78, chmn., 1978 —, also dir.; chmn. Plains Spirit Fin. Corp., 1992—. Bd. dirs. United Community Services Scott County, Iowa, 1967-71, pres., 1970; bd. dirs. Jr. Achievement Scott County, 1963-65, pres., 1964, chmn. bd., 1965. Served with criminal investigation div. U.S. Army, World War II, Korea. Republican. Mem. of Reformed Ch. Home: 1730 Harmony Ct Bettendorf IA 52722-3101

SHENK, RICHARD LAWRENCE, real estate developer, photographer, artist; b. Columbus, Ohio, Jan. 26, 1940. BBA, Tulane U., 1961, U. of Va., 1961-62, Ohio State U., 1962-65. Plant mgr. S.A. Shenk Co., Columbia and U.S., 1962-65; v.p. Konter Corp., Cin., 1965-70; owner Richard L. Shenk Devel., Cin., 1970—; bd. dirs. Consol. Stores Corp., Columbus; co-founder Images Photographic Gallery, Cin., 1980; pres. Cmty. Improvement Corp., Springdale, Ohio, 1989-93; past. pres., bd. dirs., chmn. fin. com. Talbert House, Inc., Cin. Author: Different Way of Seeing, 1989. Mem. program com. People Working Cooperatively; mem. adv. bd. Judaic studies program U. Cin.; mem. bd. overseers Cin. Campus Hebrew Union Coll.; bd. dirs., chmn. fin. com. Jewish Home of Cin.; past campaign chmn., pres.-elect Jewish Fedn. of Cin.; bd. dirs. Adath Israel Synogogue. Mem. Greater Cin. C. of C., United Jewish Appeal (nat. vice chmn.), Rotary (past pres. Springdale chpt.). Home: 541 Hickory Hill Ln Cincinnati OH 45215-2604

SHENK, THOMAS EUGENE, molecular biology educator; b. Bklyn., Jan. 1, 1947; s. Eugene Richard and Helen Marie (Deffenbaugh) S.; m. Susan Mary Hillman, July 4, 1979; children—Christopher Thomas, Gregory Thomas. BS, U. Detroit, 1969; PhD, Rutgers U., 1973. Asst. prof. molecular biology U. Conn., Farmington, 1975-80; prof. molecular biology SUNY, Stony Brook, 1980-84; prof. molecular biology Princeton U., 1984—; Am. Cancer Soc. prof., 1986—. Co-editor: Enhancers and Eukaryotic Gene Expression, 1983. Mem. Am. Soc. Microbiology (Eli Lilly award 1982). Office: Princeton U Dept Molecular Biology Princeton NJ 08544-0001*

SHENK, WILLIS WEIDMAN, newspaper executive; b. Manheim, Pa., Nov. 2, 1915; s. John Horst and Amanda (Weidman) S.; m. Elsie Sherer, Aug. 31, 1940; 1 son, J. David. Acct. Raymond D. Shearer, Lancaster, Pa., 1937-39; sr. acct. Lancaster Newspapers, Inc., 1940-50, sec.-controller, 1950-61, v.p., sec., 1961-76, pres., 1977-83, chmn. bd., 1984—. Pres. United Way of Lancaster County, 1961; pres., bd. trustees Lancaster Country Day Sch., 1971-72; trustee Franklin and Marshall Coll., Lancaster, 1977-85; sec. Pequea Twp. Planning Commn., 1965-77. Mem. Nat. Assn. Accts., Pa. Inst. CPAs, Lancaster Country Club. Lutheran. Clubs: Hamilton, Masons. Office: Lancaster Newspapers Inc PO Box 1328 8 W King St Lancaster PA 17603-3824

SHENKAROW, BARRY L., professional hockey team executive. Pres., gov. Winnipeg (Man.) Jets (NHL), Can., 1983—. Office: Winnipeg Jets, 1661 Portage Ave 10th Fl, Winnipeg, MB Canada R3J 3T7

SHENKER, IRA RONALD, physician; b. N.Y.C., July 8, 1934; s. Morris and Rose (Wilner) S.; m. Caroline Cabin, June 22, 1958; children: Diane Amy, Mitchell Steven. B.S., U. Wis., 1955, M.D., 1958. Diplomate Am. Bd. Pediatrics. Intern, L.I. Jewish Med. Ctr., New Hyde Park, N.Y., 1958-59; resident pediat., 1959-61; resident pub. health Nassau County Health Dept., N.Y., 1961-62; coll. health physician Mt. Holyoke Coll., 1962-64; chief adolescent medicine L.I. Jewish Med. Ctr., 1965—; assoc. prof. pediat. SUNY-Stony Brook, 1979—; prof. pediat. Albert Enstein Coll. Medicine, 1989—. Author: Human Figure Drawings in Adolescence, 1972. Editor: Adolescent Medicine, 1981, Clinical Monographs in Pediatrics: Adolescent Medicine, 1994. Contbr. articles to profl. jours. Bd. dirs. Roslyn Sr. Citizens, N.Y., 1975-94. USPHS grantee, 1965-82. Fellow Am. Acad. Pediat.; mem. Queens Pediat. Soc. (pres. 1981-82), N.Y. Pediat. Soc., Nassau Pediat. Soc., Soc. for Adolescent Medicine (pres. 1986). Home: 5 Fairway Rd Roslyn Harbor NY 11576-1502 Address: 270-05 76th Ave New Hyde Park NY 11040 Office: Schneider Children's Hosp of LI Jewish Med Ctr New Hyde Park NY 11042

SHENKER, JOSEPH, college administrator; b. N.Y.C., Oct. 7, 1939; s. George and Isabelle (Schwartz) S.; m. Adrienne Green (div. 1979); children: Deborah, Karen; m. Susan Armiger, Jan. 2, 1988; childrenA Sarah Gabrielle, Jordan. BA in Psychology, Hunter Coll., 1962, MA in Econ., 1963; EdD in High Edn., Tchrs. Coll., 1969. Dean, community coll. affairs CUNY, 1967-69; acting pres. Kingsborough Community Coll., N.Y.C., 1969-70; chief negotiator for mgmt. CUNY, 1977; acting pres. Hunter Coll., N.Y.C., 1979-80; founding pres. LaGuardia Community Coll., N.Y.C., 1970-88; pres. Bank St. Coll. Edn., N.Y.C., 1988—; bd. dirs. Sch. & Bus. Alliance, N.Y.C.; ptnr. N.Y.C. Partnership, 1990—; chmn. Liberty Scholarship Adv. Com., Albany, N.Y., 1989—; co-chmn. Task Force on Early Childhood Edn., N.Y.C. 1989—, Agenda for Children Tomorrow, 1989—; chmn. Chancellor's Com. on U./Sch. Collaboratives, N.Y.C., 1988. Recipient Distinguished Alumni award Tchrs. Coll. Columbia U., N.Y.C., 1990. Mem. Princeton Club. Office: Bank Street Coll Edn 610 W 112th St New York NY 10025-1898

SHENKIR, WILLIAM GARY, business educator; b. Three Rivers, Tex., June 27, 1938; s. William and Lydia (Jancik) S.; m. Missy Smith, Jan 1, 1973. B.B.A., Tex. A & M U., 1960; postgrad. (Rockefeller Bros. Theol.

fellow), Drew U. Sem., 1960-61; M.B.A., U. Tex., 1962, Ph.D., 1964. Asst. prof. McIntire Sch. Commerce, U. Va., Charlottesville, 1967-69; assoc. prof. McIntire Sch. Commerce, U. Va., 1969-72, prof., 1972-73, dean, 1977-92; William Stamps Farish prof. McIntire Sch. Commerce U. Va., 1992—; project dir. Fin. Acctg. Standards Bd., Stamford, Conn., 1973-76; vis. prof. NYU Grad. Sch. Bus., N.Y.C., 1976-77; bd. dirs. 1st Union Nat. Bank Va., Roanoke. Editor: Carman Blough: His Professional Career and Accounting Thought, 1978; contbr. articles to profl. jours. Served to 1t. USAF, 1964-67. Mem. AICPA, Am. Acctg. Assn. (former v.p., acctg. edn. change commn.), Am. Assembly Collegiate Schs. of Bus. (former bd. dirs., pres. 1990-91), Fin. Execs. Inst., Va. Soc. CPAs, Boar's Head Sports Club, Raven Soc., Landfall Club, Phi Delta Kappa, Beta Gamma Sigma, Phi Kappa Phi. Presbyterian. Home: 420 Rookwood Dr Charlottesville VA 22903-4732

SHENNUM, ROBERT HERMAN, retired telephone company executive; b. Scobey, Mont., Apr. 12, 1922; s. Joseph M. and Nellie M. Shennum; m. Doris Postlewait; children: Sharon, Keith, Marsha Shennum Burns. B.S.E.E., Mont. State U., 1944, M.S.E.E., 1948, D. Eng. (hon.), 1963; Ph.D in Physics and Elec. Engring., Calif. Inst. Tech., 1954. Instr. engring. Mont. State U., Bozeman, 1946-50; rsch. assoc. engring. Calif. Inst. Tech., Pasadena, 1950-54; cons. Kelman Electric Co., Los Angeles, 1954; mem. tech. staff AT&T Bell Labs., Murray Hill, N.J., 1954-85; also dir. AT&T Bell Labs., Parsippany, N.J.; mem. adv. com. Internat. Telecommunications Energy Conf., 1974-87. Contbr. articles to profl. jours.; patentee pulse code modulation. Served to 1st lt. Signal Corps, U.S. Army, 1944-46, ETO. Recipient cert. of appreciation for patriotic services U.S. Army, 1975. Fellow IEEE (chmn. N.C. sect. 1973), Greensboro C. of C. (chmn. continuing edn. 1970-74). Republican. Home: 2888 Swan Hwy Bigfork MT 59911-6414

SHENOY, SUDHAKAR VENKATRAYA, computer software company executive; b. Kanhangad, India, Apr. 23, 1947; came to U.S., 1970; s. Konchady Venkatraya and Radha Bai Shenoy; m. Bina Sudhakar Prabhu; children: Sushma, Divya. BTech. with honors, Indian Inst. Tech., Bombay, India, 1970; MS, U. Conn., 1971, MBA, 1973. Tchr. U. Conn., Storrs, 1972-73; fin. mgr. Windsor (Conn.) Mfg. Co., 1973-78; sr. analyst, project mgr. Am. Mgmt. Systems, Arlington, Va., 1978-80; pres. Info. Mgmt. Cons., Inc., Falls Church, Va., 1981—. Office: Info Mgmt Cons Inc 7915 Westpark Dr Mc Lean VA 22102-4201

SHENTON, JAMES PATRICK, history educator; b. Passaic, N.J., Mar. 17, 1925; s. Walter Gardiner and Lillian (Spitzel) S. A.B., Columbia, 1949, M.A., 1950, Ph.D., 1954. Mem. faculty Columbia U., N.Y.C., 1951—; prof. Am. history, 1967—, departmental rep. history dept., 1963-69. Author: Robert John Walker, A Politician from Jackson to Lincoln, 1960, Reconstruction, The South After the War, 1963, A Historian's History of the United States, 1966, Melting Pot, 1971, These United States, 1978; lectr. edn. Sta. WNDT-TV, 1963-64. Served with AUS, 1943-46. Mem. Am. Hist. Assn., AAUP, Am. Cath. Hist. Assn. (bd. dirs. 1973—). Home: 80 Passaic Ave Passaic NJ 07055-4860 Office: Columbia U 324 Fayerweather Hall New York NY 10027

SHEON, AARON, art historian, educator; b. Toledo, Oct. 7, 1937; s. Benjamin William and Katherine (Rappoport) S.; m. Martine Bruel, Jan. 26, 1963 (div. 1986); children: Sandrine, Nicolas. B.A., U. Mich., 1959, M.A., 1960; M.F.A. (Wilson fellow), Princeton U., 1962, Ph.D., 1966; postgrad., U. Paris, 1962-63. Staff officer, dir. gen.'s cabinet UNESCO, Paris, 1963-66; asst. prof. U. Pitts., 1966-69, asso. prof., 1969-78, prof. art history, 1979—; acting chmn. dept. fine arts, 1969, 79-80; dir. univ. program U. Pitts., Rouen, France, 1974-75; vis. prof. Carnegie-Mellon U., 1981; Vis. exhbn. curator Mus. Art, Carnegie Inst., Pitts., 1977-81; program cons. Nat. Endowment Arts and Humanities, 1978-85; visual arts cons. Pa. Arts Council, 1981; vis. mem. Inst. for Advanced Study, Princeton, 1984-85. Author: The Gosman Collection, 1969, Monticelli, His Contemporaries, His Influence, 1978, Organic Vision, The Architecture of Peter Berndtson, 1980, Monticelli, 1986, Paul Guigou, 1987. Recipient Charles E. Merrill faculty award, 1968; Chancellor Bowman award, 1976; Honor award Pa. Soc. Architects, 1982; grantee Ford Found., 1967, NEH, 1979; Gould Arts Found. fellow, 1986. Mem. Coll. Art Assn., Société de l'histoire de l'art français, Am. Assn. of Mus. Office: U Pitts Dept Fine Arts Pittsburgh PA 15260

SHEPARD, ALAN BARTLETT, JR., astronaut, real estate developer; b. East Derry, N.H., Nov. 18, 1923; s. Alan Bartlett and Renza (Emerson) S.; m. Louise Brewer, Mar. 3, 1945; children: Laura, Juliana. Student, Admiral Farragut Acad., 1940; B.S., U.S. Naval Acad., 1944; grad., Naval War Coll., 1958; M.S. (hon.), Dartmouth Coll.; D.Sc. (hon.), Miami U. Commd. ensign USN, 1944, advanced through grades to rear adm., 1971, designated naval aviator, 1947; assigned destroyer U.S.S. Cogswell, Navy Test Pilot Sch., Pacific, World War II, Fighter Squadron 42, aircraft carriers in Mediterranean, 1947-49; with USN Test Pilot Sch., 1950-53, 55-57, took part in high altitude tests, expts. in test and devel. in-flight refueling system, carrier suitability trials of F2H3 Banshee; also trials angled carrier deck ops. officer Fighter Squadron 193, Moffett Field (Calif.), carrier U.S.S. Oriskany, Western Pacific, 1953-55; test pilot for F4D Skyray, 1955, F3H Demon, F8U Crusader, F11F Tigercat, 1956; project test pilot F5D Skylancer, 1956; instr. Naval Test Pilot Sch., 1957; aircraft readiness officer staff Comdr.-in-Chief, Atlantic Fleet, 1958-59; joined Project Mercury man in space program NASA, 1959; first Am. in space, May 5, 1961, chief of astronaut office, 1965-74, selected to command Apollo 14 Lunar Landing Mission, 1971, became 5th man to walk on moon, hit 1st lunar golf shot; pres. Seven Fourteen Enterprises, 1986, Windward Coors Co., Deer Park, Tex., 1974; presdl. appointee, del. 26th Gen. Assembly UN, 1971. Author: (with Deke Slayton) Moon Shot: The Inside Story of America's Race to the Moon, 1994. Decorated D.S.M., D.F.C., Presdl. unit citation, NASA Disting. Service medal, Congressional Medal of Honor, 1978; recipient Langley medal Smithsonian Instn., 1964. Fellow Soc. Exptl. Test Pilots; mem. Order Daedlians, Soc. Colonial Wars, Lions, Kiwanis, Rotary.

SHEPARD, D. C., wood products manufacturing company executive; b. 1924. BA, Yale U., 1953. With Menasha (Wis.) Corp., Neenah, Wis., 1945—, v.p., 1953-80, pres., chief exec. officer, 1980—, also bd. dirs. Served with USMC, 1943-46. Office: Menasha Corp 1645 Bergstrom Rd # 367 Neenah WI 54956-9766

SHEPARD, ELAINE ELIZABETH, writer, lecturer; b. Olney, Ill.; d. Thomas J. and Bernice E. (Shadle) S.; m. Terry D. Hunt, Apr. 16, 1938; m. George F. Hartman, Oct. 1, 1943 (div. June 1958). Covered nat. polit. convs. for Stas. WTTG-TV and WINS, Chgo., 1952, 1956; polit. reporter for NANA and WINS, Chgo. and Los Angeles, 1960; reporter Congo rebellion for N.Am. Newspaper Alliance and N.Y. Mirror, 1960-61; corr. covering Pres. Eisenhower's Middle East, Far East and S.Am. tour, 1959-60; Vietnam corr. MBS, 1965-66; granted interviews with Khrushchev, Castro, Tito, Chou En-lai, Nasser, Shah of Iran, King Hussein, King Faisel, Duvalier, Lumumba, Chiang-Kai-Shek, Nehru, Menzies, John F. Kennedy, Richard M. Nixon, others; mem. White House Press Corps accompanying Pres. Nixon to, Austria, Iran, Poland, Moscow, 1972. Film and theater actress, Hollywood, N.Y.C., Europe, 1939-50, cover girl, John Robert Powers, 1939-43, under contract to, RKO and Metro-Goldwyn-Mayer, 1940-45, guest commentator for, Voice of Am.; contbr.: feature articles to various mags., including N.Y. News Sunday Mag, 1953—; columnist, contbg. editor: feature articles to various mags., including Nat. Cath. Press, 1969-74; author: Forgive Us Our Press Passes, 1962, The Doom Pussy, 1967, The Doom Pussy II, 1991. Recipient 2 citations for participating in armed helicopter assaults with 145th Aviation Bn. Vietnam. Mem. Screen Actors Guild, AFTRA, Actors Equity. Club: Overseas Press (N.Y.). Home: 12 E 62nd St New York NY 10021-7218 *Happiness is the full use of your powers along lines of excellence in a life affording hope.*

SHEPARD, GEOFFREY CARROLL, insurance company executive; b. Santa Barbara, Calif., Nov. 7, 1944; s. James J. and Barbara (Hoose) S.; m. Saundra Gayle Carlton, Jan. 10, 1973; children: Jonathan Pettus, William Dabney. B.A., Whittier Coll., 1966; J.D., Harvard U., 1969. Bar: Mass. 1970, D.C. 1972, Pa. 1977, U.S. Supreme Ct. 1973. White House fellow, 1969-70; staff asst. to Pres. White House, 1970-72, assoc. dir. domestic couns., 1972-75; sr. assoc. Steptoe & Johnson, Washington, 1975-77; sr. v.p., assoc. gen. counsel CIGNA Corp., Phila., 1977-91; sr. v.p., gen. counsel, corp. sec.

Reliance Ins. Group, Phila., 1991-94; pres. comml. divsn. Karr Barth Assocs., Phila., 1994—; mem. pvt. security adv. coun. Dept. Justice, 1975-77. Adv. coun. on gen. govt. Rep. Nat. Com. 1977-78; Phila. Cmty. Leadership Seminar, 1978-79, exec. com. Boy Scouts Am., Phila., 1981-82; bd. dirs. Sacred Heart Med. Ctr., 1983-85, Swarthmore Presbyn. Ch., 1984-86, Wallingford Hills Civi Assn., 1983-85, Com. of 70, 1985-87, Acad. Natural Scis., Phila., 1987-93, Pub. Affairs Coun., Washington, 1986-89, Episc. Acad., 1987-90, exec. com. White House fellows reg. selection panel, 1987-93; exec. bd. Valley Forge coun. Boy Scouts Am., 1994—; prin. coun. Excellence in Govt., 1994—. Mem. ABA, Assn. for Ad. Life Underwriting, Pa. Bar Assn., Phila. Assn. of Life Underwriters, D.C. Bar Assn., White House Fellows Alumni Assn., Met. Club (Washington), Union League Club (Phila.), Harvard Club (N.Y.C.). Office: Karr Barth Assocs Inc Comml Divsn 40 Monument Rd Bala Cynwyd PA 19004

SHEPARD, HENRY BRADBURY, JR., lawyer; b. Exeter, N.H., Oct. 29, 1927; s. Henry Bradbury and Frances Gardner (Dudley) S.; m. Klaudia Ockert Steidle, July 26, 1958; children: Katherine Shepard Alexander, Emily Perry, Julia Bradbury. BA with honors, Yale U., 1949; postgrad., U. Goettingen, Germany, 1951-52; LLB with honors, Harvard U., 1957. Instr. Am. U. in Cairo (Egypt), 1949-51; asst. dir. Fridtjof Nansen Internat. Student House, Goettingen, Germany, 1951-52; instr. Interpreters Inst., Goettingen, Germany, 1951-52; assoc. Goodwin, Procter & Hoar, Boston, 1957-64, ptnr., 1964-93, counsel, 1994—; dir. Mass. Venture Capital Corp., Boston, 1973-88, The C.T. Main Corp., Boston, 1975-85, Neworld Bancorp, Inc., Boston, 1986-92, Neworld Bank, Boston, 1968-92. Author: Handbook of Recent Developments in Massachusetts Banking Law, 1983, Obligations and Liabilities of Bank Directors and Trustees, 1990. Trustee George R. Wallace Found., Boston, 1978—, N.H. Hist. Soc., Concord, 1991—; hon. trustee Deree-Pierce Coll., Athens, Greece, 1970—. With U.S. Army, 1952-54. Mem. ABA (chmn. subcom. on regulatory liaison mut. savs. banks 1980-85), Mass. Bar Assn., Boston Bar Assn., Greater Boston C. of C. (bd. dirs. 1974-80, pres. 1979-80), The Hamilton Trust (v.p. 1989, pres. 1990-91), New Bedford Yacht Club, The Country Club, Harvard Travellers Club, Phi Beta Kappa. Independent. Office: Goodwin Procter & Hoar Exch Pl Boston MA 02109

SHEPARD, JAMES EDWARD, physician; b. Laconia, N.H., Dec. 8, 1933; s. Robinson and Myra Ellen (Foster) S.; m. Sally-Jean Shupert, Oct. 4, 1958; children: Sandra Jean, Elizabeth Anne. BA, Wesleyan U., Middletown, Conn., 1955; MD, Cornell U., 1959. Diplomate Am. Bd. Nephrology, Am. Bd. Luteinal Medicine. Practice medicine specializing in luteinal medicine and nephrology Greenbrae, Calif., 1974—; chief medicine Marin (Calif.) Gen. Hosp., 1974-76; asst. clin. prof. medicine U. Calif., San Francisco, 1970—. Contbr. articles to profl. jours. Pres. Marin Heart Assn., 1969-71; active, founder Marin Kidney Assn., 1970-80; mem. San Francisco Graphic Arts Council, 1980-86. Fellow ACP; mem. Nat. Soc. Nephrology, Luteinational Soc. Nephrology, Calif. Acad. Medicine, Sigma Xi. Club: Mill Valley (Calif.) Tennis. Office: Drs Shepard Lambert Haveock Shepard 1000 S Eliseo Dr San Rafael CA 94904-2133

SHEPARD, JEAN HECK, publishing company consultant; b. N.Y.C., Feb. 2, 1930; d. Chester Reed and Anna S. (Charig) Heck; m. Lawrence Vaeth Hastings, Mar. 29, 1950 (div. 1953); 1 child, Lance Clifford Hastings; m. Daniel A. Shepard, July 26, 1954 (div. 1981); 1 child, Bradley Reed. BA, Barnard Coll., 1950; postgrad., Columbia U., 1952. Mem. sch. and libr. svc. Viking Press, N.Y.C., 1956-57; asst. dir. sch. and libr. promotion E.P. Dutton, N.Y.C., 1957-58; dir. advt. publicity and promotion Thomas Y. Crowell Co., N.Y.C., 1958-62; dir. advt. and promotion Charles Scribner's Sons, N.Y.C., 1962-67; cons. Stephen Greene Press, Brattleboro, Vt., 1970-73; mktg. mgr. A&W Publishers, N.Y.C., 1979-80, Franklin Watts Publ., N.Y.C., 1980-82; pub. mags., divsn. advt. & promotion mgr. McGraw Hill Book Co., N.Y.C., 1983-85; cons. Monitor Publ. Co., N.Y.C., 1988—. Author: Simple Family Favorites, 1971, Herb and Spice Sampler, 1972, Cook With Wine!, 1973, Earth Watch: Notes on a Restless Planet, 1973, Harvest Home Steak Cookbook, 1974, Fresh Fruits and Vegetables, 1974, Yankee Magazine, 1972. Mem. Authors Guild, Pub. Ad Club, Am. Libr. Assn., Women's Nat. Book Assn. Methodist. Avocations: the dance, reading, writing, travel, music. Home: 73 Kingswood Dr Bethel CT 06801 Office: The Shepard Agy Ste 3 Southeast Plaza Pawling Savs Bank Bldg Brewster NY 10509

SHEPARD, JON MAX, sociologist; b. Ashland, Ky., July 15, 1939; s. Maxwell Irwin and Mabel Louise S.; m. Virginia Kay Vogel, July 16, 1961; 1 son, Jon Mark. B.A., Georgetown (Ky.) Coll., 1961; M.A., U. Ky., 1963; Ph.D., Mich. State U., 1968. Rsch. assoc. MIT, 1968-69; from asst. prof. to prof. sociology U. Ky., 1969-78, prof. mgmt. and sociology, 1978-88; prof. mgmt. and sociology Va. Poly. Inst. and State U., Blacksburg, 1989—. Pamplin prof. mgmt. Author: Automation and Alienation, a Study of Office and Factory Workers, 1971, Organizational Issues in Industrial Society, 1972, (with H. Voss) Social Problems, 1978, Sociology, 1993; contbr. articles to profl. jours. Recipient Gt. Tchr. award U. Ky., 1978. Mem. Am. Acad. Mgmt., Am. Sociol. Assn. Home: 2821 Chelsea Ct Blacksburg VA 24060 Office: Va Poly Inst & State U Pamplin Hall Blacksburg VA 24061

SHEPARD, KATHRYN IRENE, public relations executive; b. Tooele, Utah, Jan. 6, 1956; d. James Lewis and Glenda Verleen (Slaughter) Clark; m. Mark L. Shepard, June 5, 1976. BA in History, Boise State U., 1980. On-air writer Sta. KTTV, Channel 11, L.A., 1982-85; publicity dir. Hollywood (Calif.) C. of C. 1985-87; pres. Kathy Shepard Pub. Rels., Burbank and Portland, 1987-93; dir. public relations Las Vegas Hilton; instr. pub. rels. ext. program UCLA, 1991-92. Contbr. articles to profl. publs. Mem. Publicity Club L.A. (pres. 1991-92, bd. dirs. 1987-91). Avocations: genealogy, film, travel. Office: Las Vegas Hilton PR Dept 3000 Paradise Rd Las Vegas NV 89109

SHEPARD, MIKKI MAUREEN ALLISON, personal care company executive; b. Queens, N.Y., May 12, 1951; d. George William and June Rita (Ferrary) S.; m. Tom C. Blankenheim, July 2, 1983; 1 child, Jeffrey Thomas. BA, U. Colo., 1982. Cert. real estate brokerage mgr. Employment counselor Centennial Personnel, Colorado Springs, Colo., 1977-78; ins. auditor Associated Ins. Utah, Colorado Springs, 1978-79; broker, co-owner TCB Realty and Investment Co., Inc., Colorado Springs, 1979-90; exec. NuSkin, Castles of Am., Inc., Colorado Springs, Colo., 1989—; speaker Nat. Assn. Realtors, Chgo., 1985—. Contbr. articles to Real Estate Today, Colo. Realtor News Communiqué, Gazette Telegraph. Pres. Christmas Unlimited, Colorado Springs, 1988, 89; campaign worker El Paso County Reps., Colorado Springs, 1977-78; mem. Realtors Polit. Action Com., Chgo., 1979—; mem. Profl. Women's Rep. Club, Colorado Springs, 1987. Served with USAF, 1970-74. Mem. Colo. Assn. Realtors (dir. 1988—), Colorado Springs Bd. Realtors (bd. dirs. 1981, 84, treas. 1985-86, sec. 1987-88, pres. 1989-90), Realtors Nat. Mktg. Inst., Women's Coun. Realtors (Colo. chpt. pres. 1989—, gov. 1990, Pikes Peak chpt. treas. 1984-85, pres. 1986-87, Woman of Yr. Pikes Peak chpt. 1986, Woman of the Yr. Colo. State chpt. 1990), Nat. Women's Coun. Realtors (leadership tng. grad. 1987, edn. chmn. 1987-88). Methodist. Avocations: writing, speaking. Office: Castles of Am Inc 3960 Weather Vane Dr Colorado Springs CO 80920

SHEPARD, PAUL HOWE, ecology educator, author, lecturer; b. Kansas City, Mo., July 12, 1925; s. Paul Howe and Clara (Grigsby) S.; m. Melba Wheatcroft, 1950 (div.); children: Kenton, Margaret, Jane; m. Florence Krall, 1988. A.B., U. Mo., 1949; M.S., Yale U., 1952, Ph.D., 1954. From instr. to asso. prof. biology and dir. Green Oaks, Knox Coll., 1954-64; lectr. biology Smith Coll., 1965-70; vis. prof. environ. perception Dartmouth Coll., 1971-73; Avery prof. natural philosophy and human ecology Pitzer Coll. and Claremont Grad. Sch., 1973-94, emeritus, 1994—; nat. lectr. Sigma Xi, 1984-86; NSF in-svc. inst. program dir., 1959. Author: Man in the Landscape: A Historic View of the Esthetics of Nature, 1967, 2d edit., 1990, The Subversive Science: Essays Toward an Ecology of Man, 1969, Environmental: Essays on the Planet as a Home, 1971, The Tender Carnivore and the Sacred Game, 1973, Thinking Animals, 1977, Nature and Madness, 1982, The Sacred Paw, The Bear in Nature, Myth and Literature, 1985, 2d edit., 1992; mem. editorial adv. bd. Landscape and Urban Planning. Served with AUS, 1943-46. Fulbright rsch. scholar Wellington, N.Z., 1961; Guggenheim fellow, 1969; USPHS grantee, 1962; fellow Rockefeller Found., 1977, Coun.

for Internat. Exch. Scholars, India, 1989; Disting. Vis. Lectr., India, 1985. Fellow Inst. Human Ecology. Home: PO Box 99 Bondurant WY 82922

SHEPARD, RANDALL TERRY, judge; b. Lafayette, Ind., Dec. 24, 1946; s. Richard Schilling and Dorothy Ione (Donlen) S.; m. Amy Wynne MacDonell, May 7, 1988. AB cum laude, Princeton U., 1969; JD, Yale U., 1972; LLM, U. Va., 1995; LLD (hon.), U. So. Ind., 1995. Bar: Ind. 1972, U.S. Dist. Ct. (so. dist.) Ind. 1972. Spl. asst. to under sec. U.S. Dept. Transp., Washington, 1972-74; exec. asst. to mayor City of Evansville, Ind., 1974-79; judge Vanderburgh Superior Ct., Evansville, 1980-85; assoc. justice Ind. Supreme Ct., Indpls., 1985-87, chief justice, 1987—; instr. U. Evansville, 1975-78. Author: Preservation Rules and Regulations, 1980; contbr. articles to profl. publs. Bd. advisors Nat. Trust for Hist. Preservation, 1980-87, chmn. bd. advisors, 1983-85, trustee, 1987—; dir. Hist. Landmarks Found. Ind., 1983—, chmn., 1989-92, hon. chmn., 1992—; chmn. State Student Assistance Commn. on Ind., 1981-85; chmn. Ind. Commn. on Bicentennial of U.S. Constn., 1986-91; vice chmn. Vanderburgh County Rep. Ctrl. Com., 1977-80. Recipient Friend of Media award Cardinal States chpt. Sigma Delta Chi, 1979, Disting. Svc. award Evansville Jaycees, 1982, Herbert Harley award Am. Judicature Soc., 1992. Mem. ABA (coun. mem. sect. on legal edn. 1991—, exec. com., and vice chmn. appellate judges conf. 1992—), Ind. Bar Assn., Ind. Judges Assn., Princeton Club (N.Y.), Capitol Hill Club (Washington), Columbia Club (Indpls.). Republican. Methodist. Home: 4057 N Meridian St Indianapolis IN 46208-4012 Office: Ind Supreme Ct 304 State House Indianapolis IN 46204-2213

SHEPARD, RAYMOND GUY, purchasing executive; b. Chicago Heights, Ill., June 10, 1942; s. Ewing Hugh and Anna (Luden) S.; m. Barbara Ellen Shepard, July 13, 1948; children: Gregory, Lauren. Student, So. Ill. U., 1964-68. Cost acct. Midland Screw, Chgo., 1968-71; purchasing agt. Harris Hub Co., Harvey, Ill., 1971-79; dir. purchasing Marvel Metal Co., Chgo., 1979-81; ptnr. Ather-Shepard Software Co., Columbus, Miss., 1986-88; divisional purchasing mgr. Ceco Bldgs. Divsn., Columbus, 1981-87; purchasing dir. Troxel Co., Moscow, Tenn., 1988—; del. mem. to Russia UN Indsl. Devel. Assn., N.Y.C., 1989, China The Citizen Amb. Program, Spokane, Wash., 1994. Author: (computer software) Real Estate Automation, 1990, Sales Automation, 1992. Tchr. Jr. Achievement, Moscow, 1990-91; bd. mem. ticket and seating Columbus Concert Assn., 1981-83, truss., 1983-86, v.p. membership drive, 1986-88; mem. pres. coun. So. Ill. U. Found., 1993-94. Recipient Humanitarian Svc. award Markham (Ill.) Sheltered Workshop, 1973, Community Svc. award Columbus Concert Assn., 1988, Capt. of Industry award Collierville (Tenn.) C. of C., 1989. Mem. Kiwanis (activities chmn. 1984-88), Civitan (activities chmn. 1981-84). Avocations: golf, travel, gardening. Home: 1210 Cotton Hill Ln Collierville TN 38017

SHEPARD, ROBERT CARLTON, English language educator; b. Akron, Ohio, Dec. 20, 1933; s. Robert and Mildred Lucille (Stewart) S.; m. Marjorie Alma Mackey, June 9, 1956; children: Robert Lincoln, Donald Ward. BA, U. Oreg., 1970, MA, 1971; postgrad., England, 1979, 1991. Prof. English Southwestern Oreg. C.C., Coos Bay, 1971-94, chair divsn. English, 1976-78, prof. emeritus, 1994—; liaison Oreg. Com. for Humanities, 1985-86; judge statewide writing contests Nat. Coun. Tchrs. English, Urbana, Ill., 1987-88; founder Willamette Valley Vineyards, Turner, Oreg., 1991; co-founder Willamette Valley Brewing Co., Portland, 1993, Breweries Across Am., Portland, 1994. Author, photographer, producer: (multi-image show) Christmas Fiestas of Oaxaca (Mexico), 1985; developer ednl. software, 1993—. With USMCR, 1954-58. Grad. Teaching fellow U. Oreg., 1970-71. Democrat. Avocations: bicycling, photography, music appreciation, world travel. Home: 3280 Sheridan Ave North Bend OR 97459-3043

SHEPARD, ROBERT M., lawyer, investment banker, engineer; b. Amityville, N.Y., Feb. 15, 1932; s. Sidney M. and Undine L. (Lehmann) Shapiro; m. Barbara S. Stannard, June 25, 1955 (div. 1980); children: Karen Michele Shepard Sweer, Daniel Robert; m. Joanne E. Devlin, May 16, 1981 (div. 1993). B.C.E., Cornell U., 1954; M.B.A., Hofstra Coll., 1960; LL.B., Yale U., 1963; LLM, NYU, 1968. Bar: N.Y. 1964; registered profl. engr., N.Y., Conn. Project engr. Lockwood Kessler & Bartlett, Syosset, N.Y., 1956-60; assoc. atty. Cravath, Swaine & Moore, N.Y.C. and Paris, 1963-70; gen. ptnr. Kuhn, Loeb & Co., N.Y.C., 1970-77; sr. v.p. Donaldson, Lufkin & Jenrette, N.Y.C., 1977-83; gen. ptnr. Donovan Leisure Newton & Irvine, N.Y.C., 1983-89, Adler & Shepard, N.Y.C., 1989-91, Shepard & van Essche, N.Y.C. 1991, Ballon Stoll Bader & Nadler, P.C., N.Y.C., 1992—. Note and comment editor: Yale Law Jour., 1962-63. Bd. dirs. N.Y. Grand Opera, 1987—. Recipient Fuertes Medal Cornell U., 1953. Mem. ABA, Am. N.Y. State Bar Assn., Pub. Power Assn., Nat. Assn. Bond Lawyers, Order of Coif, Tau Beta Pi, Chi Epsilon. Club: Union League. Home: 750 Park Ave Apt 12B New York NY 10021 Office: Ballon Stoll Bader & Nadler 1450 Broadway New York NY 10018-2201

SHEPARD, ROGER NEWLAND, psychologist, educator; b. Palo Alto, Calif., Jan. 30, 1929; s. Orson Cutler and Grace (Newland) S.; m. Barbaranne Bradley, Aug. 18, 1952; children: Newland Chenoweth, Todd David, Shenna Esther. B.A., Stanford U., 1951; Ph.D., Yale U., 1955; A.M. (hon.), Harvard U., 1966; ScD (hon.), Rutgers U., 1992. Rsch. assoc. Naval Research Lab., 1955-56; rsch. fellow Harvard, 1956-58; mem. tech. staff Bell Telephone Labs., 1958-66, dept. head, 1963-66; prof. psychology Harvard U., 1966-68, dir. psychol. labs., 1967-68; prof. psychology Stanford U., 1968—, Ray Lyman Wibur prof. social sci., 1989. Guggenheim fellow Center for Advanced Study in Behavioral Scis., 1971-72, N.Y. Acad. Scis. award, 1987. Fellow AAAS, Am. Psychol. Assn. (pres. exptl. div. 1980-81, Disting. Sci. Contbn. award 1976); mem. Am. Acad. Arts and Scis., Nat. Acad. Scis., Psychometric Soc. (pres. 1973-74), Psychonomic Soc., Soc. Exptl. Psychologists (Howard Crosby Warren medal 1981). Office: Stanford U Dept Psychology Bldg 420 Stanford CA 94305-2130*

SHEPARD, SAM (SHEPARD ROGERS), playwright, actor; b. Ft. Sheridan, Ill., Nov. 5, 1943; s. Samuel Shepard and Jane Elaine (Schook) Rogers; m. O-Lan Johnson Dark, Nov. 9, 1969 (div.); 1 son, Jesse Mojo; children with Jessica Lange: Hannah Jane, Samuel Walker. Student, Mt. San Antonio Jr. Coll., Walnut, Calif., 1961-62. Playwright-in-residence Magic Theatre, San Francisco. Author: (plays) Cowboys, 1964, The Rock Garden, 1964, 4-H Club, 1965, Up to Thursday, 1965, Dog, 1965, Rocking Chair, 1965, Chicago, 1965 (Obie award 1966), Icarus's Mother, 1965 (Obie award 1966), Fourteen Hundred Thousand, 1966, Red Cross, 1966 (Obie award 1966), Melodrama Play, 1966 (Obie award 1968), La Turista, 1967 (Obie award 1967) Cowboys #2, 1967, Forensic and the Navigators, 1967 (Obie award 1968), The Holy Ghostly, 1969, The Unseen Hand, 1969, Operation Sidewinder, 1970, Shaved Splits, 1970, Mad Dog Blues, 1971, Terminal, 1971, (with Patti Smith) Cowboy Mouth, 1971, Black Bog Beast Bait, 1971, The Tooth of Crime, 1972 (Obie award 1973), Blue Bitch, 1973, (with Megan Terry and Jean-Claude van Itallie) Nightwalk, 1973, Geography of a Horse Dreamer, 1974, Little Ocean, 1974, Action, 1974 (Obie award 1975), Killer's Head, 1974, Suicide in B-Flat, 1976, Angel City, 1976, Curse of the Starving Class, 1977 (Obie award 1977), Buried Child, 1978 (Pulitzer Prize in drama 1979, Obie award 1979), Tongues, 1979, Savage/ Love, 1979, Seduced, 1979, True West, 1981, Fool for Love, 1983 (Obie award 1984), Superstitions, 1983, The Sad Lament of Pecos Bill on the Eve of Killing his Wife, 1983, A Lie of the Mind, 1985 (New York Drama Critics' Circle award 1986), States of Shock, 1991, Simpatico, 1993; (collections of plays) Five Plays by Sam Shepard, 1967, The Unseen Hand and Other Plays, 1971, 2nd edit., 1986, Mad Dog Blues and Other Plays, 1972, The Tooth of Crime and Geography of a Horse Dreamer, 1974, Angel City, Curse of the Starving Class and Other Plays, 1976, Buried Child, Seduced, Suicide in B-Flat, 1979, Four Two-Act Plays by Sam Shepard, 1980, Chicago and Other Plays, 1981, Seven Plays, 1981, Fool for Love and The Sad Lament of Pecos Bill on the Eve of Killing his Wife, 1983, Fool For Love and Other Plays, 1984, The Unseen Hand and Other Plays, 1986; contbr. to Oh! Calcutta, 1976; (screenplays) Me and My Brother, 1967, (with Michelangelo Antonioni, Tonino Guerra, Fred Graham, and Clare Peploe) Zabriskie Point, 1970, (with Murray Mednick) Ringaleevio, 1971, (with others) Oh! Calcutta!, 1972, (with Bob Dylan) Renaldo and Clara, 1978, Paris, Texas, 1984 (Golden Palm award Cannes Film Festival 1984), Fool for Love, 1985; (other writings) Rolling Thunder Logbook, 1977, Hawk Moon: A Book of Short Stories, Poems and Monologues, 1981, Motel Chronicles, 1982; writer, dir.: (plays) Fool for Love, 1983, A Lie of the Mind, 1985, (screenplays) Far North, 1988, Silent Tongue, 1993; actor: (films) Renaldo

and Clara, 1978, Days of Heaven, 1978, Resurrection, 1980, Raggedy Man, 1981, Frances, 1982, The Right Stuff, 1983 (Academy award nomination best supporting actor 1984), Country, 1984, Fool for Love, 1985, Crimes of the Heart, 1986, Baby Boom, 1987, Steel Magnolias, 1989, Hot Spot, 1990, Bright Angel, 1991, Defenseless, 1991, Thunderheart, 1992, The Pelican Brief, 1993, Safe Passage, 1994, The Good Old Boys, 1995. Fellow U. Minn., 1966, Yale U., 1967; grantee Rockefeller Found., 1967, Guggenheim Found., 1968, 71; recipient Nat. Inst. and Am. Acad. Arts and Letters award for lit., 1974, Creative Arts award Brandeis U., 1975, Theater Hall of Fame, 1994. mem. Am. Acad. and Inst. of Arts and Letters, 92. Office: Internat Creative Mgmt 8942 Wilshire Blvd Beverly Hills CA 90211*

SHEPARD, STEPHEN BENJAMIN, journalist, magazine editor; b. N.Y.C., July 20, 1939; s. William and Ruth (Tanner) S.; m. Lynn Povich, Sept. 16, 1979; children—Sarah, Ned. B.S., CCNY, 1961; M.S., Columbia U., 1963. Reporter, editor, writer Business Week, N.Y.C., 1966-75; asst. prof., dir. Walter Bagehot fellowship program econs. and bus. journalism Columbia U., N.Y.C., 1975-76; sr. editor Newsweek, N.Y.C., 1976-81; editor Saturday Rev., N.Y.C., 1981-82; exec. editor Business Week mag., N.Y.C., 1982-84, editor in chief, 1984—. Mem. Am. Soc. Mag. Editors (v.p. 1990-92, pres. 1992-94), Coun. Fgn. Rels. Home: 322 Central Park W New York NY 10025-7629 Office: Business Week McGraw Hill Inc 1221 Ave Of The Americas New York NY 10020-1001

SHEPARD, THOMAS HILL, physician, educator; b. Milw., May 22, 1923; s. Francis Parker and Elizabeth Rhodes (Buchner) S.; m. Alice B. Kelly, June 24, 1946; children: Donna, Elizabeth, Ann. A.B., Amherst Coll., 1945; M.D., U. Rochester, 1948. Intern Strong Meml. Hosp., Rochester, N.Y., 1948-49; resident Strong Meml. Hosp., 1950-52, Albany (N.Y.) Med. Center, 1949-50; pediatric endocrine fellow Johns Hopkins Hosp., 1954-55; pediatrician U. Wash., Seattle, 1955-61; embryologist dept. anatomy U. Fla., 1961-62; teratologist U. Wash., 1961—, prof. pediatrics, head central lab. for human embryology, 1961-93, prof. emeritus, 1993—; research assoc. dept. embryology Carnegie Inst., 1962, U. Copenhagen, 1963; cons. NIH, FDA, EPA, 1971—; vis. prof. pediatrics U. Geneva, 1972, 73-74. Author: A Catalog of Teratogenic Agents, 1973, 8th edit., 1995; contbr. articles to profl. jours. Served with U.S. Army, 1946-48; Served with USAF, 1952-54. Mem. Teratology Soc. (hon. mem. 1993, pres. 1968), Western Soc. Pediatric Rsch. (pres. 1970), Am. Pediatric Soc., Acad. Pediatrics. Home: 3015 98th Ave NE Bellevue WA 98004-1818 Office: U Wash Sch Medicine Dept Pediatrics Seattle WA 98195

SHEPARD, THOMAS ROCKWELL, JR., publishing consultant; b. N.Y.C., Aug. 22, 1918; s. Thomas Rockwell and Marie (Dickinson) S.; m. Nancy Kruidenier, Sept. 20, 1941; children: Sue Shepard Jaques, Molly Shepard Richard, Amy S. Knight, Thomas Rockwell III. B.A., Amherst Coll., 1940. Asst. sales promotion mgr. Vick Chemical Co., 1940-41; with Look mag., N.Y.C., 1946-72; advt. sales mgr. Look mag., 1961-64, advt. dir., 1964-67, pub., 1967-72; cons. Cowles Communications, Inc.; pres. Inst. Outdoor Advt., 1974-76. Co-author: The Disaster Lobby, 1973; contbr. articles to various pubs. Pres. Greenwich Community Chest, 1964-65; chmn. Robert A. Taft Inst. Govt., 1978-81, Rep. Roundtable of Greenwich, 1981-85; bd. dirs. Advt. Coun., Lit. Vols. Am., 1989-91, Community Answers, 1988-91; chmn. Amherst Coll. Alumni Fund, 1986; mem. exec. com. alumni coun. Amherst Coll.; hon. pres. Soc. Amherst Coll. Alumni. Lt. comdr. USNR, 1941-45. Recipient George Washington honor medal for pub. address Freedoms Found., 1970, 73, Amherst Coll. medal for eminent svc., 1990. Republican. Clubs: Princeton (N.Y.C.); Bell Haven; Round Hill. Home: 44 Lismore Ln Greenwich CT 06831-3760

SHEPARD, THOMAS ROCKWELL, III, advertising sales executive; b. Greenwich, Conn., Apr. 21, 1951; s. Thomas Rockwell, Jr. and Nancy (Kruidenier) S.; m. Margaret O'Neal, Sept. 1, 1972; children—Amanda Marie, Thomas Rockwell IV, Brian Dickinson. B.A., Amherst Coll., Mass., 1973. Hockey player Calif. Golden Seals, Oakland, 1973-74; salesman Union Carbide Battery Products, N.Y.C., 1974-78; became mem. advt. sales staff Hearst Mags., N.Y.C., 1978, became advt. dir. Good Housekeeping mag., 1984; now pub. Redbook mag. Redbook mag. Clubs: Manursing (Rye, N.Y.) N.Y. Athletic (N.Y.C.). Office: Redbook Hearst Magazines 224 West 57th Street New York NY 10019*

SHEPARD, WILLIAM SETH, government official, diplomat; b. Boston, June 7, 1935; s. Robinson and Myra Ellen (Foster) S.; m. Lois Rosalie Burke, June 25, 1960; children—Stephanie Lee, Cynthia Robin, Warren Burke (dec.). A.B. cum laude, Wesleyan U., Middletown, Conn., 1957; J.D., Harvard U., Cambridge, Mass., 1961. Bar: N.H. 1961, U.S. Ct. Mil. Appeals 1962 U.S. Supreme Ct., 1970.. Aide to ambassadors Henry Cabot Lodge and Ellsworth Bunker U.S. embassy, Saigon, Vietnam, 1966-67; staff officer Exec. Secretariat Dept. of State, Washington, 1967-69; consul, polit. officer U.S. Embassy, Budapest, Hungary, 1970-73; desk officer Hungarian affairs Dept. State, Washington, 1973-75; desk officer Singapore and Malaysian affairs Dept. of State, Washington, 1975-77; dep. polit. counselor U.S. embassy, Athens, Greece, 1978-80; consul gen. consulate gen. U.S., Bordeaux, France, 1983-85; dir. office congressional affairs U.S. Arms Control and Disarmament Agy., 1987-89; cons. to the gen. counsel U.S. Dept. Agriculture, 1991-92; lectr. internat. law U. Singapore, 1965-66; CEO The Shepard Internat. Group, Inc., 1994—. Author: Family Law in the Civil Law System, 1961; also articles. Candidate for Rep. nomination 8th Md. Congl. Dist., 1985-86, Rep. nominee for Gov. of Md., 1990, candidate, 1994; del. Rep. Nat. Conv., 1992. Recipient Pro Libertate Hungariae Commemorative medallion, 1981; French Govt. teaching asst. and Fulbright travel grantee, 1957-58; Congl. fellow Am. Polit. Sci. Assn. and fgn. policy legis. asst. to Senator Robert Dole, 1982-83. Mem. Am. Fgn. Service Assn., SAR, Soc. Mayflower Desc., Gov. Bradford Compact, Soc. Desc. Colonial Govs. (chancellor gen. 1993-95), Soc. Desc. Colonial Wars; corr. mem. Montesquieu Acad. France. Republican. Unitarian. Clubs: City Tavern (Washington), Flagon and Trencher, Les Chevaliers de Bretvin, Ordre des Compagnons de Bordeaux, Connetable de Guyenne, La Jurade de St. Emilion, Bontemps Medoc et des Graves, Commanderie de Bordeaux (Washington), also others. Avocations: American history; vintage Bordeaux wines; rose cultivation. Home: 8602 Hidden Hill Ln Potomac MD 20854-4225

SHEPHARD, MARK SCOTT, civil and mechanical engineering educator; b. Buffalo, Oct. 27, 1951; s. William N. and Beatrice (Hass) S.; m. Sharon L. Nirschel, Nov. 25, 1972; children: Steven W., Kari L. BS, Clarkson U., 1974; PhD, Cornell U., 1979. Asst. prof. civil engring. and mech. engring. Rensselaer Poly. Inst., Troy, N.Y., 1979-84, assoc. prof., 1984-87, prof., 1988—, dir. Sci. Computation Rsch. Ctr., 1990—; Samuel A. and Elisabeth C. Johnson Jr. prof. engring., 1993—; assoc. dir. Rensselaer Design Rsch. Ctr., Troy, N.Y., 1980-90; vis. rsch. fellow GE Corp. R & D, Schenectady, 1985, cons., 1984-87; cons. GM Rsch. Lab., Detroit, 1980—, also other orgns.; mem. tech. adv. bd. Aries Tech., Lowell, Mass., 1987—. Mem. editorial bd. Internat. Jour. Numerical Methods in Engring., Engring. with Computers, Engring. Applications of Artificial Intelligence; contbr. articles to profl. jours., chpts. to books. Fellow AIAA (assoc.); mem. ASCE, ASME, Am. Soc. Engring. Edn., Am. Acad. Mechanics, Internat. Assn. for Computational Mechanics, U.S. Assn. for Computational Mechanics (sec.), Sigma Xi, Tau Beta Pi, Phi Kappa Phi. Home: RR 4 Box 11 Averill Park NY 12018 Office: Rensselaer Poly Inst II0 8th St Troy NY 12180-3590

SHEPHERD, ALAN J., construction executive, management consultant; b. Bklyn., Jan. 15, 1942; s. Morris Elijah and Jean (Birnbaum) Shapiro; children: Robin Elyse, Kevin Peter. B.S. in Mech. Engring., Mich. State U.; M.S. in Indsl. Engring., Wayne State U., 1966. Mgmt. trainee Chrysler Corp., Detroit, 1964-65, product engr., 1965-66; exec. v.p. Bruce Erts & Assocs., Southfield, Mich., 1966-70; pres. Creative Mgmt. Group Inc., Southfield, Mich., 1970-76, chmn. bd., 1976, pvt. cons., 1976-79; dir. planning and coordination Mgmt. Support Assocs., Tel Aviv, Israel, 1979-81, gen. mgr., 1981-82; mgmt. cons. MSA Consortium, Washington, 1982-83; regional mktg. dir. Hill Internat., Washington, 1983-84; mng. v.p. spl. projects CRS Sirrine, Inc., Washington, 1984-85; dir. advanced mgmt. program BDM Corp., McLean, Va., 1986-89; v.p. Hill Internat., Inc., Willingboro, N.J., 1989-90, AWD Techs, Inc., Rockville, Md., 1990-94; bd. dirs. Brown & Root, Inc., Washington; instr. Lawrence Inst. Tech., 1971, 73. Mem. Am. Inst. Indsl. Engrs., Project Mgmt. Inst., Soc. Am. Mil. Engrs. Office: AWD Techs Inc 15204 Omega Dr Ste 200 Rockville MD 20850-4601

SHEPHERD, CYBILL, actress, singer; b. Memphis, Feb. 18, 1950; d. William Jennings and Patty Shobe (Micci) S.; m. David Ford, Nov. 19, 1978 (div.); 1 child, Clementine; m. Bruce Oppenheim, March 1, 1987; children: Molly Ariel and Cyrus Zachariah (twins). Student, Hunter Coll., 1969, Coll. of New Rochelle, 1970, Washington Sq. Coll., NYU, 1971, U. So. Calif., 1972, NYU, 1973. Appeared in motion pictures Last Picture Show, 1971, The Heartbreak Kid, 1973, Daisy Miller, 1974, At Long Last Love, 1975, Taxi Driver, 1976, Special Delivery, 1976, Silver Bears, 1977, The Lady Vanishes, 1978, Earthright, 1980, The Return, 1986, Chances Are, 1988, Texasville, 1990, Alice, 1990, Once Upon a Crime, 1992, Married to It, 1993; star TV series The Yellow Rose, 1983-84, Moonlighting, 1985-89, Cybill, 1994—; TV films include A Guide for the Married Woman, 1978, Secrets of a Married Man, 1984, Seduced, 1985, The Long Hot Summer, 1985, Which Way Home, 1991, Memphis, 1992 (also co-writer, co-exec. prodr.), Stormy Weathers, 1992, Telling Secrets, 1993, There Was a Little Boy, 1993; record albums include Cybill Does It To Cole Porter, 1974, Cybill and Stan Getz, 1977, Vanilla with Phineas Newborn, Jr, 1978; appeared in stage plays A Shot in the Dark, 1977, Picnic, 1980, Vanities, 1981. Office: Rogers and Cowan 10000 Santa Monica Blvd Los Angeles CA 90067*

SHEPHERD, DANIEL MARSTON, executive recruiter; b. Madison, Ind., Apr. 8, 1939; s. Marston Vincent and Edith America (Brunson) S.; m. Bonnie Lynn Brawley, June 27, 1970 (div. Nov. 1987); children: Vincent, David, Christopher, Megan; m. Gail Lenore Sanborn, Oct. 3, 1989; children: Heather, Shannon. BS in Civil Engring., U. Ky., 1962; MBA, Harvard Bus. Sch., 1964. Mfg. and distbn. mgr. Procter & Gamble Co., Staten Island, N.Y., 1966-70; distbn. and ops. mgr. Mattel, Inc., Gardenia, Calif., 1970-73; gen. mgr., dir. ops. Fuqua Industries, Inc., Atlanta, 1973-76; v.p. product/ market mgmt. Masonite Corp., Chgo., 1976-78; v.p. Heidrick & Struggles, Chgo., 1978-82, Lamalie Assocs., Chgo., 1982-86; prin. Sweeney Shepherd Bueschel Provus Harbert & Mummert, Chgo., 1986-91, Shepherd Bueschel & Provus, Inc., Chgo., 1991—. Capt. U.S. Army, 1964-66. Decorated Army Commendation medal, 1966; recipient Am.'s Top 150 Recruiters award Harper Bus., N.Y.C., 1992. Mem. Assn. Exec. Search Cons., Inc., Union League Club, Harvard Bus. Sch. Club. Republican. Episcopalian. Avocations: coin and art collecting, skiing, baseball, food, wine. Home: 990 N Lake Shore Dr Apt 27E Chicago IL 60611-1345 Office: 1 S Wacker Dr Ste 2740 Chicago IL 60606-4617

SHEPHERD, FRANK ANDREW, lawyer; b. West Palm Beach, Fla, Dec. 11, 1946; s. Vernon Francis and Helen Veronica (Shaab) S.; children: Scott, Kristi, Sandra. BA, U. Fla., 1968; JD, U. Mich., 1972. Bar: Fla. 1972, D.C. 1975, U.S. Dists. Ct. (so., mid. and no. dists.) Fla., U.S. Ct. Appeals (5th and 11th cirs.), U.S. Supreme Ct. Assoc. Kimbrell & Hamann, P.A., Miami, Fla., 1972-90; with Popham, Haik, Schnobrich & Kaufman Ltd, Miami. Vice chmn. State Affairs Com., Miami, 1990-91. With U.S. Army Res., 1972-79. Mem. ABA, Dade County Bar Assn., Dade County Def. Bar Assn., Am. Jurisprudence Soc., Def. Rsch. Inst., U.S. Supreme Ct. Hist. Soc., Miami C. of C. Republican. Office: Popham Haik Schnobrich & Kaufman 4000 International Pl 100 SE 2nd St Miami FL 33131-2100

SHEPHERD, JAMES HAROLD, JR., hospital administrator, contruction executive; b. Atlanta, Jan. 26, 1951; s. James Harold and Alana (Smith) S. BBA in Fin., Mgmt., Bus. Law, U. Ga., 1973. Pres., treas. Shepherd Constrn. Co., Inc., Atlanta, 1974—; chmn., pres. bd. Shepherd Ctr. for Treatment of Spinal Injuries, Inc., Atlanta, 1980—; advisor Emory U. Rehab., Decatur, Ga., 1978-83; del. White House Conf. on Handicapped Indivuals, Washington; mem. Ga. Conf. of Handicapped Individuals, Atlanta. Bd. dirs. Ctr. for Rehab., Ga. Tech. U., Atlanta, 1981—, Goodwill Industries, Atlanta, 1980-82; mem. Ga. Gov. Coun. on Devel. Disabilities, Ga. State Health Planning and Devel. Task Force on Rehab. Svcs. Named One of Ten Outstanding Young Men in Am., U.S. Jaycees, 1985, One of Outstanding Young Persons of the World, Jaycee Internat., 1985. Mem. Young Pres. Orgn., Chi Phi. Home: 1600 Cave Rd NW Atlanta GA 30327-3122 Office: Shepherd Spinal Ctr Inc 2020 Peachtree Rd NW Atlanta GA 30309-1465

SHEPHERD, JOHN FREDERIC, lawyer; b. Oak Park, Ill., May 22, 1954; s. James Frederic Shepherd and Margaret Joanne (Crotchett) Woollen; children: Eliza Marion, Justine Catherine. AB magna cum laude, Dartmouth Coll., Hanover, N.H., 1976; JD, U. Denver, 1979. Bar: Colo. 1979, U.S. Dist. Ct. Colo. 1979, D.C. 1981, U.S. Dist. Ct. D.C. 1981, U.S. Ct. Appeals (10th cir.) 1981, U.S. Ct. Appeals (D.C. cir.) 1982, U.S. Ct. Appeals (9th cir.) 1990, U.S. Supreme Ct. 1984. Assoc. Holland & Hart, Denver, 1979-81; assoc. Holland & Hart, Washington, 1981-85, ptnr., 1985-87; ptnr. Holland & Hart, Denver, 1987—. Reporter Mineral Law Newsletter, 1985-92. Mem. 50 for Colo., Denver, 1989. Mem. ABA (chmn. pub. lands and land use com. 1991-93, mem. coun. for sect. of natural resources energy and environ. law 1993—), Rocky Mountain Oil and Gas Assn. (mem. pub. lands com. 1987—), Rocky Mountain Mineral Law Found. (mem. long-range planning com. 1988—, bd. trustees 1993—), Dartmouth Alumni Club (pres. Washington chpt. 1985-86), Denver Athletic Club. Avocations: flyfishing, basketball, running. Home: 848 Monroe St Denver CO 80206 Office: Holland & Hart 555 17th St Ste 3200 Denver CO 80202-3979

SHEPHERD, JOHN THOMPSON, physiologist; b. No. Ireland, May 21, 1919; s. William Frederick and Matilda (Thompson) S.; m. Helen Mary Johnston, July 28, 1945; children: Gillian Mary, Roger Frederick John; m. Marion G. Etzwiler, Apr. 22, 1989. Student, Campbell Coll., Belfast, No. Ireland, 1932-37; M.B., B.Ch., Queen's U., Belfast, 1945, M.Chir., 1948, M.D., 1951, D.Sc., 1956, D.Sc. (hon.), 1979; M.D. (hon.), U. Bologna, 1984, U. Gent, 1985. Lectr. physiology Queen's U., 1948-53, reader physiology, 1954-57; assoc. prof. physiology Mayo Found., 1957-62, prof. physiology, 1962—, chmn. dept. physiology and biophysics, 1966-74; bd. govs. Mayo Clinic, 1966-80; trustee Mayo Found., 1969-81, dir. research, 1969-77, dir. for edn., 1977-83, chmn. bd. devel., 1983-88; dean Mayo Med. Sch., 1977-83; assoc. dir. Gen. Rsch. Ctr. Mayo Clinic, Rochester, 1992-94. Author, editor: Physiology of the Circulation in Human Limbs in Health and Disease, 1963, Cardiac Function in Health and Disease, 1968, Veins and Their Control, 1975, Human Cardiovascular System, 1979, Handbook of Physiology. The Cardiovascular System Peripheral Circulation and Organ Blood Flow, 1983, Vascular Diseases in the Limbs, 1993, Nervous Control of the Heart, 1994; mem. editorial bd. Hypertension, 1973—; Am. Jour. Physiology, Am. Heart Jour., Microvascular Rsch.; cons. editor Circulation Rsch., 1982; editor-in-chief News in Physiol. Sci., 1988-94; contbr. over 590 sci. articles and 350 papers to profl. jours. Recipient NASA Skylab Achievement award, 1974, A. Ross McIntyre medal for achievement, 1991; Brit. Med. Assn. scholar, 1949-50, Fulbright scholar, 1953-54; Anglo-French Med. exchange bursar, 1957; Internat. Francqui chair, 1978; Einthoven lectr. 1981, Volhard lectr., 1990. Fellow Am. Coll. Cardiology (hon.), Royal Coll. Physicians (London), Royal Acad. Medicine (Belgium); mem. Am. Physiol. Soc. (Disting. Svc. award 1990), Louis Rapkine Assn., Central Soc. Clin. Research, Am. Heart Assn. (dir. 1968—, pres. 1975-76, chmn. vascular medicine and biology task force 1990, hon. fellow council clin. cardiology), Physiol. Soc. Gt. Brit., Med. Research Soc. London, Nat. Acad. Scis. (space sci. bd. 1973-74, chmn. com. space biology and medicine 1973), Assn. Am. Physicians, Internat. Union of Angiology (hon.), Rappaport Inst. Israel (sci. adv. bd.), Sigma Xi. Home: 600 4th St SW Rochester MN 55902-3291 Office: Mayo Clinic 1043 Plummer Bldg Rochester MN 55902

SHEPHERD, KAREN, congresswoman; b. Silver City, N.Mex., July 5, 1940; m. Vincent P. Shepherd. BA, U. Utah, 1962; MA, Brigham Young U., 1963. Former instr. Brigham Young U., Am. U., Cairo; former pres. Webster Pub. Co.; former adminstr. David Eccles Sch. Bus., U. Utah; former dir. Salt Lake County Social Svcs., Utah; former dir. continuing edn. Westminster Coll.; former mem. Utah Senate; mem. 103d Congress from 2d Utah dist., Washington, 1993-95; dir. social svcs. for Salt Lake County; dir. continuing edn. Westminster Coll.; founding mem. Utah Women's Polit. Caucus, Project 2000. Former mem. United Way, Pvt. Industry Coun.; former mem. adv. bd. U.S. West Grad. Sch. Social Work, Westminster Coll.; co-cha. Recipient Women in Bus. award U.S. Small Bus. Assn., Woman of Achievement award, Pathfinder award, 1st place award Nat. Am. Journalists. Fellow Inst. Politics Kennedy Sch Govt.; Salt Lake Area C. of C. (pub. rels. com.). Home: 1261 2nd Ave Salt Lake City UT 84103 Office: US Ho Reps 414 Cannon Washington DC 20515-4402

SHEPHERD, LINDA PACE, nurse, educator, administrator; b. Toxey, Ala., Jan. 18, 1951; Raymond Lee Pace and Zaylee (Sims) Harris; m. Darryl D. Shepherd, June 4, 1974; children—Darryl D. Jr., Michelle, Christopher. BS in Nursing, Dillard U., 1973; MS in Nursing, U. Ala., 1979. Instr. nursing Mobile Infirmary-Mobile Coll., Ala., 1974-80; dir., instr. S. D. Bishop State Jr. Coll., Mobile, 1980—. Mem. Nat. League Nursing, Am. Nurses Assn., Health Edn. Media Assn., NEA, So. Council on Collegiate Edn. for Nurses, Ala. Edn. Assn., Ala. Assn. Jr. Community Colls., Ala. State Nurses' Assn., Ala. League Nursing, Mobile County Nurses' Soc. Baptist. Club: Wives of Alpha (Mobile). Avocation: singing. Office: SD Bishop State Jr Coll Dept Nursing 351 N Broad St Mobile AL 36690

SHEPHERD, MARK, JR., retired electronics company executive; b. Dallas, Jan. 18, 1923; s. Mark and Louisa Florence (Daniell) S.; m. Mary Alice Murchland, Dec. 21, 1945; children: Debra Aline Shepherd Robinson, MaryKay Theresa Shepherd Welker, Marc Blaine. BSEE, So. Meth. U., 1942; MSEE, U. Ill., at Urbana, 1947. Registered profl. engr., Tex. With GE, 1942-43, Farnsworth TV and Radio Corp., 1947-48; with Tex. Instruments, Dallas, 1948-88, v.p., gen. mgr. semicondr.-components div., 1955-61, exec. v.p., chief operating officer, 1961-66, pres., chief operating officer, 1967-69, pres., chief exec. officer, 1969-76, chmn. bd. dirs., chief operating officer, 1976-84, chmn. bd. dirs., chief corp. officer, 1984-85, chmn., 1985-88; ret. Hon. trustee Com. for Econ. Devel.; trustee Am. Enterprise Inst. Pub. Policy Rsch.; councillor Conf. Bd.; mem. Bus. Coun. Lt. (j.g.) USNR, 1943-46. Fellow IEEE; mem. Soc. Exploration Geophysicists, Coun. on Fgn. Rels., Nat. Acad. Engring., Sigma Xi, Eta Kappa Nu.

SHEPHERD, PAUL H., elementary school educator; b. Salt Lake City, Sept. 6, 1955; s. Richard Lawrence and Janis (Hoskings) S.; m. Marlene Wade, Aug. 31, 1978; children: Janice, Faith, Matthew, Andrew, Luke, Christian. BS in Elem. Edn., U. Utah, 1981, MEd, 1985. Cert. elem. tchr., Utah. Printer Transamerica Film Svc., Salt Lake City, 1978-81; tchr. Granite Sch. Dist., Salt Lake City, 1981—; pres. Granite Fedn. Tchrs., 1985-87, treas., 1990-92. Active mem. State House of Reps., 1992-94; Bishop LDS Ch., West Jordan, Utah, 1988; mem. Oquivrh Shadows Community Coun., West Jordan, 1987; chmn. rels. com. Boy Scouts Am., 1972—. Recipient Outstanding Tchr. award Excel Found., 1985, Elem. Tchr. of Yr. award Utah Fedn. Tchrs., 1991. Mem. ASCD, Utah Assn Gifted Children. Democrat. Avocations: fishing, guitar. Home and Office: 6644 S 5095 W West Jordan UT 84084

SHEPHERD, R. F., retired bishop; b. July 15, 1926; s. Herbert George and Muriel (Grant) S.; m. Ann Alayne Dundas, 1952; 6 children. BA with honors, U. B.C., 1948; postgrad., King's Coll., London; DD (hon.), St. John's Coll., Winnipeg, 1988. Curate St. Stephen's, London, 1952-57; rector St. Paul's, Glanford, Ont., 1957-59, All Sts., Winnipeg, 1959-65; dean, rector All Sts. Cathedral, Edmonton, Alta., 1965-69, Christ Ch. Cathedral, Montreal, 1970-83; rector St. Matthias, Victoria, B.C., 1983-84; Anglican Bishop of B.C., 1985-92. Fellow Coll. of Preachers. Home: 110 Ensilwood Rd, Salt Spring Island, BC Canada V8K 1N1

SHEPHERD, ROBERT JAMES, plant pathology researcher, educator; b. Clinton, Okla., June 5, 1930; s. Lee Fines and Ruby (Gilleland) S.; m. Shirley Ann Stuby, Sept. 6, 1975 (div. Sept. 1976); children: Steven L., Eudora Deidre, David A.; m. Mary Ann Sall, Mar. 18, 1978. Student, U. Okla., 1948-50; BS, Okla. State U., 1954, MS, 1955; PhD, U. Wis., 1959. Asst. prof. U. Wis., Madison, 1959-61; asst. prof. U. Calif., Davis, 1961-66, assoc. prof., 1966-72, prof. plant pathology, 1972-84; prof. plant pathology U. Ky., Lexington, 1984—; chmn. plant virus subcom. Internat. Com. Taxonomy of Viruses, 1971-76; mem. sci. bd. Calgene Inc., Davis, 1980-85; cons. Ohio Bd. Regents, 1985-86. Editor Virology jour., 1971-73; contbr. articles and revs. to profl. jours. With U.S. Army, 1950-52, Korea. Fulbright scholar, Cambridge, Eng., 1955-56. Fellow Am. Phytopathol. Soc. (Ruth Allen award 1981); mem. NAS. Democrat. Avocations: bird watching, gardening. Office: Univ Ky Dept Of Plant Pathology Lexington KY 40546

SHEPHERD, STEPHEN BEERS, construction executive; b. Atlanta, Aug. 28, 1951; s. Dan Plunkett and Bertha Salisbury (Beers) S.; m. Eloise Fraser, May 7, 1977; children: Mary Alexander, Madeline McCall. BS, U. N.C. 1974. Pres. Shepherd Constrn. Co., Inc., Atlanta, 1979-81; v.p., sec., bd. dirs. Plant Improvement Co., Inc., Atlanta, 1981—. Active Leadership Atlanta, 1987—; treas., dir. corp. fund drive Shepherd Spinal Ctr. Jr. Com., Atlanta, 1987—. Mem. Associated Gen. Contractors Am. (mem. closely held bus. com. 1978—), Westminster Schs. Alumni Bd. (pres. 1982), The Atlanta Forum. Presbyterian. Office: Shepherd Construction Co Inc 1800 Briarcliff Rd NE Atlanta GA 30329-4096

SHEPHERD, STEWART ROBERT, lawyer; b. Chgo., Sept. 9, 1948; s. Stewart and LaVina Beatrice (Nereim) S.; m. Margaret Brownell Shoop, Aug. 14, 1970; children: Elisabeth Ashby, Megan Brownell, Blair Stewart. BA, Rockford Coll., 1970; JD, U. Chgo., 1973. Bar: Calif. 1973, U.S. Dist. Ct. (no. dist.) Calif. 1973, Ill. 1976, U.S. Dist. Ct. (no. dist.) Ill. 1976. Assoc. Heller, Ehrman, White & McAuliffe, San Francisco, 1973-75; assoc. Hopkins & Sutter, Chgo., 1975-79, ptnr., 1979—. Mem. ABA, Order of Coif, Phi Beta Kappa. Office: Hopkins & Sutter 3 1st National Plz Chicago IL 60602

SHEPLEY, HUGH, architect; b. Boston, Mar. 17, 1928; s. Henry Richardson and Anna Lowell (Gardiner) S.; m. Mary Waters Niles, Dec. 27, 1950; children: Hamilton Niles, Philip Foster. B.A., Harvard U., 1951; BArch., Boston Archtl. Ctr., 1958; postgrad., Mass. Inst. Tech., 1958-59. Mem. archtl. firm Shepley, Bulfinch, Richardson & Abbott, Boston, 1955-63; ptnr. Shepley, Bulfinch, Richardson & Abbott, 1963-91. Bd. dirs. Greater Boston Red Cross, 1967-73, mem. exec. com., 1968-69; bd. dirs. Cmty. Music Ctr., Boston, 1968-72, Boston Ctr. for Blind Children, 1979-87; trustee New Eng. Conservatory Music, 1978-83, overseer, 1983—; trustee Univ. Hosp., 1980—, mem. exec. com., 1981-92, vice chmn. bd. dirs., 1985-89, chmn. bd. dirs., 1989-92; trustee Am. Coll. of Greece, 1983-92, treas., 1986-88; trustee, sec. Rotch Travelling Scholarship, 1987-93, v.p., 1993—; mem. adv. coun. Boston U. Med. Ctr., 1990—, Corp. Old South Assn. 1993—; v.p. Manchester (Mass.) Hist. Soc., 1994—. Fellow AIA; mem. Mass. Assn. Architects (pres. 1972), Boston Soc. Architects (pres. 1974), Boston Archtl. Ctr. (pres. 1969-71). Republican. Episcopalian. Clubs: Tavern (Boston); Manchester Yacht (commodore 1985-87). Home: 18 Forster Rd Manchester MA 01944-1420 Office: S B R & A 40 Broad St Fl 6 Boston MA 02109-4305

SHEPP, ALLAN, chemist and physicist; b. N.Y.C., Apr. 2, 1928; s. Joseph and Eva (Kaplan) S.; m. Marion Russell Gray, Sept. 14, 1948; children: Russell Gray, Susan Anderson. BA, Oberlin Coll., 1948; PhD, Cornell U., 1953. Dir. rsch. Tech. Ops. Inc., Burlington, Mass., 1959-70; sr. scientist Polaroid Corp. Inc., Cambridge, Mass., 1970-85; dir. laser physics Avco Rsch. Lab., Textron Co., Everett, Mass., 1985-92; tech Triton Systems, Inc., Chelmsford, Mass., 1992—. Editor: Imaging Processes and Materials, 1989; contbr. articles to profl. jours. Mem. Soc. Imaging Sci. and Tech. (exec. v.p., treas., conf. v.p. 1970-90), Soc. Photog. Instrumentation Engrs., Am. Chem. Soc., Am. Def. Preparedness Assn. Office: Triton Systems Inc 114 Turnpike Rd Chelmsford MA 01824

SHEPP, BRYAN EUGENE, psychologist, educator; b. Cumberland, Md., Sept. 13, 1932; s. Bryan Evert and Dorothy Lorene (Stell) S.; m. June Lee Langeluttig, Jan. 31, 1953; children—Karen Suzanne, David Bryan. B.S., U. Md., 1954, M.S., 1956, Ph.D., 1960; M.S. (hon.), Brown U., 1966. Research prof. U. Conn., 1961-63; asst. prof. psychology George Peabody Coll., 1963-64; asst. prof. Brown U., 1964-66, assoc. prof., 1966-69, prof., 1969—; chmn. dept. psychology, 1983-88, assoc. dean of faculty, 1988-91, dean of faculty, 1991—; cons. in field; vis. scientist Oxford (Eng.) U., 1970. Contbr. numerous articles to profl. publs.; ad hoc editor for several psychol. jours. Served with USN, 1955-59. Decorated letter of commendation Sec. of Navy; USPHS postdoctoral fellow, 1959-61; Nat. Inst. Child Health and Human Devel. grantee, 1965—. Fellow Am. Psychol. Assn.; mem. Psychonomic Soc., AAAS, AAUP. Club: Univ. Office: 89 Waterman St Providence RI 02912-0001

SHEPP, LAWRENCE ALAN, mathematician, educator; b. Bklyn., Sept. 9, 1936; s. Benjamin and Francis (Stein) S.; m. Britt Louise Gunnarsdotter;

children: Steven Lawrence, Linda Louise, Eric Brian. BS in Applied MAth., Polytech. Inst. Bklyn., 1958; MA in Math., Princeton U., 1959, PhD in Math., 1961. Instr. U. Calif., Berkeley, 1962; mem. tech. staff AT&T Bell Labs., Murray Hill, N.J., 1962—; prof. Stanford (Calif.) U., 1980—. Recipient W.L. Putnam prize, 1958, Paul Levy prize, 1967, Disting. Scientist award IEEE Soc. Nuclear Sci. Soc., 1982. Fellow Inst. Math. Statistics; mem. NAS, Inst. Medicine, Am. Math. Soc., B'nai Brith. Avocations: chess, ping-pong, Russian language. Office: AT&T Bell Labs 600 Mountain Ave Rm 2c374 New Providence NJ 07974-2008

SHEPPARD, ALBERT PARKER, JR., mathematics educator; b. Griffin, Ga., June 6, 1936; s. Albert Parker and Cornelia (Cooper) S.; m. Judith Prosser, Sept. 9, 1957 (div. 1976); children: Albert Parker III, Frank Phillip; m. Eleanor C. Davis, Feb. 8, 1978 (dec. Oct. 1994); stepson: Phillip Hancock. B.S., Oglethorpe U., 1958; M.S., Emory U., 1959; Ph.D., Duke U., 1965. Sr. engr. Orlando (Fla.) rsch. div. Martin Marietta Co., 1960-63; physicist U.S. Army Rsch. Office, Durham, N.C., 1963-65; prin. rsch. engr., head spl. techniques br., electronics div. Ga. Inst. Tech., 1965-71, chief of chem. sci. lab., 1971-72, assoc. dean coll. engring., 1972-74, prof. elec. engring., 1972-89, assoc. v.p. for rsch., 1974-88, acting v.p. rsch., 1979-80, asst. to pres. info. tech., 1986, v.p. for interdisciplinary programs, 1988-89, acting v.p. info. tech., 1988-89; Charles and Mildred Jenkins prof. math. Fla. So. Coll., Lakeland, 1989—; mem. evening faculty DeKalb Coll., Clarkston, Ga., 1967-71; pres. Microwave and Electronics Cons., Lakeland, 1980—; cons. scholar IBM So. Area 8, 1990—. Contbr. articles to profl. jours. Inventor linear down-draft biomass gasifier. Trustee Southeastern Univs. Research Assocs., 1983-86. Recipient Disting. Alumni award Oglethorpe U., 1974; Woodrow Wilson fellow, 1959. Mem. IEEE (sr.), Am. Soc. Engring. Edn., Univ. Space Rsch. Assn. (vice chmn. coun. instns. 1980-81, chmn. 1981-82, trustee 1985-89, vice chmn. bd. dirs. 1986-87, chmn. 1987-88, chmn. engring. sci. coun. 1989-94), Ga. Tech. Rsch. Corp. (trustee), Maths. Assn. Am., Lone Palm Golf Club, Lakeland Yacht and Country Club, Sigma Xi, Sigma Pi Sigma, Kappa Mu Epsilon. Presbyterian. Home: 1240 Jefferson Dr Lakeland FL 33803-2300 Office: Fla So Coll Dept Math Lakeland FL 33801

SHEPPARD, CLAUDE-ARMAND, lawyer; b. Ghent, Belgium, May 26, 1935; m. Claudine Proutat; children—Jean-Pierre, Michel, Marie-Claude, Stephane, Annabelle. B.A., McGill U., 1955; B.C.L., 1958. Bar: Que. 1959. Partner firm Robinson, Sheppard & Shapiro, Montreal, 1965—; legal commentator for French and English radio and television networks in, Can.; lectr. various instns.; counsel various royal commns.; counsel to com. Canadian Ho. of Commons; legal supr. Que. Commn. of Inquiry Lang. Rights; dir. various orgns. and founds. Author: The Law of Languages in Canada, 1965, The Organization and Regulation of the Health and Social Welfare Professions in Quebec, 1970, Language Rights in Quebec, 1973, also numerous papers. Past pres. Canadian Civil Liberties Union; former mem. Canadian Adv. Council on Status of Women. Fellow C.B.A. Found. for Legal Rsch. Mem. ABA (assoc.), Can. Bar Assn., Internat. Inst. Comparative Linguistic Law (pres. 1987—), Que. Bar Found. (gov.), Found. André-Guerin (pres. 1991—), Found. Montreal 2000 (v.p. 1994—). Office: Robinson Sheppard & Shapiro, 800 Place Victoria Ste 4700, Montreal, PQ Canada H4Z 1H6

SHEPPARD, HAROLD LLOYD, gerontologist, educator; b. Balt., Apr. 1, 1922; s. Joseph and Anna Leslie (Levy) S.; m. Gloria Stefanowicz, July 27, 1986; children by previous marriages: Mark, Jenny. MA, U. Chgo., 1945; PhD, U. Wis., Madison, 1949. Assoc. prof. sociology Wayne State U., Detroit, 1947-59; rsch. and staff dir. spl. com. on aging U.S. Senate, Washington, 1959-61; asst. adminstr. area redevel. adminstrn. U.S. Dept. Commerce, Washington, 1961-63; staff social scientist W.E. Upjohn Inst. Employment Rsch., Washington, 1963-75; sr. rsch. fellow Am. Inst. Rsch., Washington, 1975-80; counselor on aging to Pres. Carter Washington, 1980-81; assoc. dir. Nat. Coun. on Aging, Washington, 1981-82; dir. Internat. Exchange Ctr. Gerontology U. South Fla., Tampa, 1983-91; prof. Dept. Gerontology U. South Fla., Tampa, 1983—; cons. U.S. Dept. Labor, Washington, Senate Com. on Unemployment and Poverty, Washington, ILO, Geneva, OECD, Paris. Author, editor: Towards an Industrial Gerontology, 1970; co-author: Where Have all the Robots Gone?, 1972, The Graying of Working America, 1979; editor: Poverty and Wealth in America, 1972, Future of Older Workers, 1990. Fulbright scholar, France, 1957-58. Fellow Gerontol. Soc. Am. Avocation: sailing.

SHEPPARD, JACK W., retired air force officer; b. Parkersburg, W.Va., Aug. 8, 1931; s. James Lee and Audrey Irene (Heiney) S.; m. Norma Ann Stutler, Sept. 4, 1953; children—Bradley, Gregory. B.A.C. U. Akron, Ohio, 1955; M.A. in Pub. Administrn., George Washington U., 1965. Commd. lt. U.S. Air Force, 1955, advanced through grades to maj. gen.; vice comdr. 60 Mil. Airlift Wing, USAF, Travis AFB, Calif., 1977-79; comdr. 1606 Air Base Wing, USAF, Kirtland AFB, N.Mex., 1979-81; dir. internat. staff Inter Am. Def. Bd., USAF, Washington, 1981-82; dep. chief staff for personnel USAF Mil. Airlift Command, Scott AFB, Ill., 1982-83, chief of staff, 1983-85; comdr. Twenty First Air Force, McGuire AFB, N.J., 1985-87; asst. dep. chief staff programs and resources Hdqrs. USAF, Washington, 1987-88, ret., 1988. Mem. Order of Daedalians, Air Force Assn., Airlift Assn., Theta Chi. Presbyterian. Home: PO Box 908 21 Beaver Ln Cedar Crest NM 87008-9433

SHEPPARD, JACQUELYN SMITH, school system founder and administrator; b. Perry, Ga., Feb. 21, 1943; d. Hiram Marshall and Minton Mae (Holland) Smith; m. Glenn L. Sheppard, Sept. 6, 1965; children: Glenn III, Krista, Trent. BA, Mercer U., 1964-65; postgrad. So. Bapt. Theol. Seminary, 1969. Tchr. social studies Dudley-Hughes Vocat. Sch., Macon, Ga., 1965; English tchr. Valdosta (Ga.) High Sch., 1965-67, Shirely High Sch., Louisville, 1967-68, Fern Creek High Sch., Louisville, 1968-69; Title I English tchr. Early County High Sch., Blakely, Ga., 1972-74; learning devel. tutor Springs Acad. and Learning Ctr., Conyers, Ga., 1979-86, founder, dir. Coll. Prep. and Tech. Prep. High Sch., 1989—. Contbr. articles to newspapers. Active counseling svc. for adolescents, Conyers, marital counseling svc., Conyers, 1980—. Mem. Internat. Prayer Ministries (co-founder). Avocations: travel, writing. Office: Springs Academic Learning Ctr 1516 Old Mcdonough Hwy SE Conyers GA 30207-5942

SHEPPARD, JOHN WILBUR, computer research scientist; b. Pitts., Aug. 21, 1961; s. Harry Reid and Mary Jane (Amon) S.; m. Justine Anne Pape, Oct. 29, 1988. BS, So. Meth. U., 1983; MS, Johns Hopkins U., 1989, postgrad., 1990—. Systems analyst Sheppard Internat., Inc., Hermitage, Pa., 1979-86; prin. tech. analyst ARINC Inc., Annapolis, Md., 1986—. Coauthor: System Test and Diagnosis, 1994; contbr. articles to profl. jours. Mem. YCMA, Hermitage, 1979-85, Md. Hall for the Creative Arts, Annapolis, 1988-90; pres. Univ. Chapel Campus Ministry, Dallas, 1982-83. Mem. IEEE, Am. Assn. for Artificial Intelligence, Mensa, Internat. Neural Network Soc., Internat. Assn. Knowledged Engrs., Soc. Logistics Engrs., Kappa Mu Epsilon. Republican. Lutheran. Achievements include U.S. and foreign patent pending for methods and apparatus for diagnostic testing; development of explanation-based learning approach for fault diagnosis. Home: 1203 Will-O-Brook Dr Pasadena MD 21122 Office: ARINC Inc 2551 Riva Rd Annapolis MD 21401-7435

SHEPPARD, LOUIS CLARKE, biomedical engineering educator; b. Pine Bluff, Ark., May 28, 1933; s. Ellis Allen and Louise (Clarke) S.; m. Nancy Louise Mayer, Feb. 8, 1958; children—David, Susan, Lisa. B.S. in Chem. Engring., U. Ark., 1957; Ph.D. in Elec. Engring., U. London, 1976. Registered profl. engr., Ala.; Tex. Devel. staff supr. Diamond Alkali Co., Deer Park, Tex., 1957-63; staff engr. IBM, Rochester, Minn., 1963-66; assoc. prof. surgery dept. U. Ala.-Birmingham, 1966-88, sr. scientist Cystic Fibrosis Research Ctr., 1981-87, prof., chmn. biomed. engring. dept., 1979-88; prof. phsiology and biophysics, asst. v.p. rsch. U. Tex., Galveston, 1988-90, assoc. v.p. bioengring. and biotech., 1990—, prof. biomed. engring., Austin; adj. prof. elec. engring. U. Houston; mem. med. adv. bd. Hewlett Packard, 1980-84; cons. IMED Corp., 1982-83, Oximetrix, 1982, 86-88, MiniMed, 1986-88; mem. sci. adv. bd. JJMI, 1992-94; dir. FBK Internat.; pres. S.E.A. Corp., 1984-94; mem. editorial bd. Med. Progress Through Tech., 1984-94, Springer-Verlag, Berlin; cons. Nat. Heart, Lung and Blood Inst. Bd. dirs. Birmingham Met. Devel. Bd. dirs. Universities Space Rsch. Assn., 1995—. Served with AUS, 1958-66. Recipient Ayerton Premium award IEE (U.K.), 1984. Recipient Disting. Alumnus citation, U. Ark., 1987, Lifetime

Achievement award M.D. Buyline, 1987. Fellow IEEE, Am. Inst. for Med. and Biol. Engring.; mem. Coll. Med. Informatics; mem. Brit. Computer Soc., Biomed. Engring. Soc. (dir.), IEEE, Am. Inst. Chem. Engrs., Am. Med. Informatics Assn., Acad. Med. Arts and Scis., Blue Key, Sigma Xi, Tau Beta Pi, Alpha Pi Mu, Eta Kappa Nu, Theta Tau. Club St. Andrews Soc. of Middle South, The Houstonian, The Yacht Club. Contbr. abstracts, chpts. to books, editorials; patentee method and system for estimation of arterial pressure. Home: 5 Broad Oaks Ln Houston TX 77056-1218 Office: U Tex Med Br 5 108 Adminstrn Bldg Galveston TX 77555-0133

SHEPPARD, POSY (MRS. JEREMIAH MILBANK), social worker; b. New Haven, Aug. 23, 1916; d. John Day and Rose Marie (Herrick) Jackson; m. John W. Sheppard, May 16, 1936 (dec. Apr. 1990); children: Sandra S. (Mrs. Allan Gray Rodgers), Gail G. (Mrs. Gail Bidwell), Lynn S. (Mrs. William Muir Manger), John W.; m. Jeremiah Milbank, May 4, 1991. Student, Vassar Coll. 1938. Vol. field cons. Conn. A.R.C., 1955-60; vice chmn. bd. govs. Am. Nat. Red Cross, 1962-66; rep. League Red Cross Socs. to UN, 1957-80, Am. Nat. Red Cross to com. internat. social welfare Nat. Social Welfare Assembly, 1957-61; chmn. Non-Govtl. Orgn. Com. for UNICEF, 1963-64, 71-73; chmn. Non-Govtl. Orgn. Com. exec. com. for Office Pub. Information, UN, 1964-66; pres. conf. non-govtl. orgns. in consultative status with UN Econ. and Social Council, 1966-69. Mem. Am. Soc. Polit. and Social Sci., Soc. Internat. Devel., Nat. Soc. Colonial Dames, Descs. Signers of Declaration Independence, Round Hill Club, River Club (N.Y.). Home: 535 Lake Ave Greenwich CT 06830

SHEPPARD, SCOTT, magazine publisher. Publisher Southern Living, Birmingham. Office: Southern Living 2100 Lakeshore Dr Birmingham AL 35209*

SHEPPARD, THOMAS FREDERICK, history educator; b. Indpls., June 5, 1935; s. Francis Sherman and Dorothy (White) S.; m. Donna Cox; children: Jocelyn, Allison. AB, Vanderbilt U., 1957; MA, U. Nebr., 1962; PhD, Johns Hopkins U., 1969. Instr. history Western Ky. State U., Bowling Green, 1962-65; asst. prof. Coll. William and Mary, Williamsburg, Va., 1969-71, assoc. prof., 1971-77, prof., 1977—; chmn. dept. history Coll. of William and Mary, 1975-81. Author: Lourmarin in the Eighteenth Century, 1971; contbr. numerous articles and book revs. to profl. publs. Capt. USMCR, 1957-65. Recipient Fellowship for Young Humanists award NEH, France, 1972-73. Office: Coll of William and Mary Dept History Williamsburg VA 23185

SHEPPARD, THOMAS RICHARD, lawyer; b. Pasadena, Calif., Aug. 8, 1934; s. James Carroll and Ruth Mary (Pashgian) S.; m. Arlene Clubb, June 23, 1956; children—Eileen Diana, Pamela Lynn, Thomas Richard. A.B., Stanford U., 1956; LL.B., Harvard U., 1961. Bar: Calif. bar 1962. Assoc. firm Sheppard, Mullin, Richter & Hampton, Los Angeles, 1961-66; ptnr. Sheppard, Mullin, Richter & Hampton, 1966—; dir. numerous small corps.; pres. Legal Aid Found. Los Angeles, 1973. Trustee Harold Lloyd Found., Los Angeles, 1971-87, Della Martin Found., 1979—. Served to lt. (j.g.) USN, 1956-58. Mem. Am. Bar Assn., State Bar Assn. Calif., Los Angeles County Bar Assn., Am. Law Inst., Am. Coll. Real Estate Lawyers, Beta Theta Pi. Club: Calif. (Los Angeles) (bd. dirs. 1985-87, sec. 1987). Home: 1680 Oak Grove Ave San Marino CA 91108-1109 Office: Sheppard Mullin Richter & Hampton 333 S Hope St Bldg 48 Los Angeles CA 90071-3003

SHEPPARD, WALTER LEE, JR., chemical engineer, consultant; b. Phila., June 23, 1911; s. Walter Lee and Martha Houston (Evans) S.; m. Dorothy Virginia Cosby Vanderslice, Oct. 17, 1942 (dec. Mar. 1947); m. Boudinot Atterbury Oberge Kendall, Mar. 24, 1953; stepchildren: Charles H. Kendall Jr., John Atterbury Kendall. BChem, Cornell U., 1932; MS, U. Pa., 1933. Registered profl. engr., Del., Calif.; diplomate Am. Acad. Environ. Engrs.; ordained deacon Liberal Cath. Ch., 1954, priest, 1955. Control chemist various cos., 1933-35; advt. writer N.W. Ayer & Son, 1936-37; asst. to editor The Houghton Line (E.F. Houghton Co.), 1937-38; salesman Atlas Mineral Products, 1938-48; plant mgr., cons. engr. Tanks & Linings, Ltd., Droitwich, Eng., 1948-49; sales engr., dist. mgr. ElectroChem. Engring. & Mfg., and successor cos., 1949-68; nat. accounts mgr., field sales mgr. Corrosion Engring. div. Pennwalt Corp., Phila., 1968-76; pres. C.C.R.M., Inc.; cons. on chemically resistant masonry, 1976—; profl. genealogist, 1936—. Author: Ancestry and Descendants of Thomas Stickney Evans and Sarah Ann Fifield, His Wife, 1940, Chemically Resistant Masonry, 1977, 2d edit., 1982, Ancestry of Edward Carleton and Ellen Newton, His Wife, 1978; author, editor: Corrosion and Chemical Resistant Masonry Materials Handbook, 1986; editor: Passengers and Ships Prior to 1684, 1965; successor editor: Ancestral Roots of 60 New England Colonists, 7th edit., 1992, Magna Charta Sureties 1215, 4th edit., 1991; contbg. editor Am. Genealogist, 1941-79, Nat. Geneal. Quar., 1961—; mem. pubds. com. Pa. Geneal. Mag., 1960-76; contbr. articles on corrosion resistant masonry constrn. to profl. jours. Dir. displaced persons camps UNRRA, also d.p. specialist, staff Chief of Mission, Vienna, Austria, 1945-46; founding trustee Bd. Cert. Genealogists, 1965-82, pres., 1969-78, chmn., 1978-79. Served to maj. U.S. Army, 1941-45, UNRRA, 1945-46; lt. col., Res., ret. 1960. Named Hon. Mem. Class of 1928 U.S. Naval Acad., 1976. Fellow Am. Soc. Genealogists (sec. 1958-61, 66-67, v.p. 1967-70, pres. 1970-73), Nat. Geneal. Soc., Pa. Geneal. Soc.; mem. ASTM (membership sec. 1975-83, C-3 com.), NSPE, Am. Acad. Environ. Engrs., Welcome Soc. (pres. 1969-76), Illegitimate Sons and Daus. of Kings and Queens of Britain (founder, sec. 1950-68, pres. 1968-88), Flagon and Trencher Soc. (co-founder, pres. 1967-73), Nat. Assn. Corrosion Engrs. (cert. competence in corrosion engring., chmn. Phila. sect. 1962), New Eng. Historic Geneal. Soc. (com. on Heraldry, 1991—), Nat. Geneal. Soc. Quar. (contbg. editor) Geneal. Soc. Pa., Soc. Genealogists (London), Yorkshire Archeol. Soc., Savoy Co., Gilbert and Sullivan Soc. (founder, pres. Phila. br. 1957-63), Sovereign Order St. John of Jerusalem, Mil. Order Fgn. Wars, Mayflower Descs., Order of Three Crusades, Order of the Crown of Charlemagne in Am. (3rd v.p. 1989—), Ret. Officers Assn., Phi Kappa Psi (nat. v.p. 1964-68, pres. 1968-70), Alpha Chi Sigma. Home and Office: 923 Old Manoa Rd Havertown PA 19083-2610

SHEPPARD, WILLIAM STEVENS, investment banker; b. Grand Rapids, Mich., Apr. 29, 1930; s. James Herbert and Emily Gilmore (Stevens) S.; m. Jane Steketee, 1956 (dec. 1975); children: Stevens C., Elizabeth W., Emily R.; m. Patricia Gillis Bloom, Dec. 2, 1978. B.A. in Econs, U. Va., 1953. Trainee J.P. Morgan & Co., Inc., N.Y.C., 1955-58; investment adv. Delafield & Delafield, N.Y.C., 1958-71; from salesman to sr. v.p. and dir. F.S. Smithers & Co., N.Y.C., 1971-76; sr. v.p., dir. successor Paine, Webber, Jackson & Curtis, Inc., 1976-81; pres., chief exec. officer, dir. Paine Webber Real Estate Securities Inc., 1980-85; mng. dir. Paine Webber Capital Markets, N.Y.C., 1985-88, Berkshire Capital Corp., N.Y.C., 1988—; chmn. bd. dirs. Ea. Bancorp. An editor: Ginny Mae Manual, 1979; contbr. to handbooks. Trustee, treas. Riot Relief Fund City N.Y., 1970—. Served to lt. USNR, 1953-55. Republican. Clubs: N.Y. Yacht; Country of Fairfield (Conn.); Pequot Yacht; Mashomack Fish and Game, North Haven Casino. Home: 405 Sasco Rd Southport CT 06490 Office: Berkshire Capital Corp 399 Park Ave 28th Fl New York NY 10022-4614

SHEPRO, RICHARD W., lawyer; b. Berwyn, Ill., May 9, 1953; s. Justice Warren and Inez Marjorie (McKillip); m. Lindsay Ellen Roberts, Sept. 5, 1981; children: Claire Willoughby, Warren Boyd. AB, Harvard U., 1975, JD., 1979; MSc, London Sch. Econs., Eng., 1976. Bar: Ill. 1979, Calif. 1981, U.S. Ct. Appeals (9th cir.) 1981, U.S. Dist. Ct. (no. dist.) Ill. 1982, U.S. Supreme Ct. 1993. Teaching fellow Harvard U., Cambridge, Mass., 1979; law clk. to chief judge U.S. Ct. Appeals (9th cir.), San Francisco, 1979-81; assoc. Mayer, Brown & Platt, Chgo., 1981-85, ptnr., 1986—; lectr. law U. Chgo., 1992—; staff mem. U.S. Senate Judiciary Com., 1979; spl. asst. atty. gen., Ill., 1981-82; corr. on bus. law The Fin. Times, London, 1986—. Coauthor: Bidders & Targets: Mergers and Acquisitions in the U.S., 1990; contbr. numerous articles to profl. jours. Del. Nat. Orgn. for Women Nat. Conv., 1980; bd. govs. The Kohl Children's Mus. Recipient U.S. Presdl. scholar Pres. of U.S., Washington, 1971, Greenman Prize Harvard U., 1975; named Harvard Law Rev. Supreme Ct. Editor, Harvard Law Rev. Assn., 1977-79; named to Am. Law Inst., 1993. Fellow Chgo. Bar Found.; mem. ABA, Chgo. Coun. Lawyers (bd. govs. 1986-89, chmn. election law com. 1987—), Chgo. Coun. Fgn. Rels., The Chgo. Ensemble (dir. and v.p.), Chgo. Club, LaSalle Club (dir. and mem. exec. com.), Les Nomades Club.

Home: 837 W Oakdale Ave Chicago IL 60657-5121 Office: Mayer Brown & Platt 190 S La Salle St Chicago IL 60603-3410

SHER, ALLAN L., retired brokerage company executive; b. Superior, Wis., Oct. 19, 1931; s. Robert Edward and Pearl (Wolpert) S.; m. Judy Biegel, June 17, 1962; children: Allison, Victoria, Robert. BA, Princeton U., 1953; grad. Advanced Mgmt. Program, Harvard U., 1975. With Merrill Lynch, Pierce, Fenner & Smith, N.Y.C., 1956-81, exec. v.p. services, 1976-79, exec. v.p. fin./adminstrn., 1979-81, also bd. dirs.; sr. v.p. Merrill Lynch & Co. Inc., 1980-81; pres. Wertheim Asset Mgmt. Svcs., Inc., 1981-83; ptnr. Wertheim and Co., 1981-83; vice chmn., bd. dirs. Drexel Lambert Inc., 1983-90; sr. v.p., bd. dirs. Kemper Securities Group, 1990, 1990-92; bd. dirs. Am. Stock Exch. Trustee Congregation Emanu-El, Scarsdale, N.Y. Served with U.S. Army, 1954-56. Democrat. Club: Century Country. Home: 20 Ocean Park Blvd Unit 12 Santa Monica CA 90405

SHER, LINDA ROSENBERG, lawyer; b. Chgo., May 16, 1938; d. Sidney and Rebecca Rosenberg; B.A., U. Chgo., 1959; LL.B., Yale U., 1962; m. Stanley O. Sher, Aug. 11, 1963; children—Jeremy Jay, Hellyn Sue. Admitted to D.C. bar, 1962; counsel constl. rights subcom. Senate Judiciary Com., 1962-64; atty. NLRB, 1964-77, asst. gen. counsel supreme ct. br., 1977-93, acting assoc. gen. counsel, 1994—. Office: NLRB 1099 14th St NW Washington DC 20570-0001

SHER, NORMAN, psychiatrist, child psychiatrist; b. Phila., Jan. 21, 1931; s. Max and Emma (Friedman) S.; widowed; children: Jonathan, Katherine. BA, Swarthmore Coll., 1952; MD, U. Chgo., 1956. Diplomate in psychiatry and child psychiatry Am. Bd. Psychiatry and Neurology. Intern Kings County Hosp., Bklyn., 1955-57, resident in psychiatry, 1957-58; sr. psychiatrist Manhattan State Hosp., N.Y.C., 1960-62; fellow in child psychiatry Bklyn. Psychiat. Ctrs., 1962-64; dir. child psychiatry Maimonides Med. Ctr., Bklyn., 1964-68, dir. child psychiat. tng., 1968-78, dir. gen. psychiat. tng., 1972-82; med. dir. Bensonhurst Mental Health Ctr., Bklyn., 1982-86; pvt. practice psychiatry and child psychiatry Bklyn., 1964—; pres. med. staff Maimonides Med. Ctr., 1979-80; clin. assoc. prof. SUNY Health Scis. Ctr. at Bklyn., 1966—. Contbr. articles to profl. jours. Mem. adv. bd. Zero Population Growth, Washington, 1986—. Capt. M.C. U.S. Army, 1958-60. Fellow Am. Psychiat. Soc., Am. Acad. Child and Adolescent Psychiatry, Am. Orthopsychiat. Soc., Bklyn. Psychiat. Soc. Democrat. Jewish. Avocations: reading, swimming, gardening, population growth. Home and Office: 2047 E 63d St Brooklyn NY 11204

SHER, PAUL PHILLIP, physician, pathologist; b. Bklyn., Oct. 25, 1939; s. Louis and Lottie (Kloner) S.; m. Joan E. Zeffren, June 9, 1964; children: Matthew, Andrew, Lawrence. BS cum laude, Hobart Coll., 1961; MD, Washington U., 1965. Diplomate Am. Bd. Pathology. Intern in pathology Columbia-Presbyn. Hosp., N.Y.C., 1965-66, resident in pathology, 1966-69; instr. pathology Columbia Presbyn. Hosp., N.Y.C., 1968-70; resident in pathology Englewood (N.J.) Hosp., 1969-70; dir. clin. chemistry Frances Delafeld Hosp., N.Y.C., 1970-71; dir. blood bank Bethesda Naval Hosp., Rockville, Md., 1971-72, dir. hematology, 1973; dir. clin. chemistry NYU Med. Ctr., Tisch Hosp., 1973, dir. clin. labs., 1980-93; clin. prof. pathology, prof. med. informatics Biomed. Info. Comm. Ctr. Oreg. Health Scis. U., Portland, 1993—. Editor Lab. Med.; contbr. articles, editorial, revs. to profl. jours.; Lt. comdr. USN, 1971-73. Fellow Coll. Am. Pathologists, Am. Soc. Clin. Pathologists, Explorer's Club.

SHERAK, THOMAS MITCHELL, motion picture company executive; b. Bklyn., June 22, 1945; s. Myer and Freida (Rosenthal) S.; m. Madeleine Frankfurter, Nov. 22, 1967; children: Barbra, Melissa, William. A.A. in Mktg., N.Y. Community Coll., Bklyn., 1965. Salesman Paramount Pictures, N.Y.C., Washington, St. Louis, 1970-74; booker film R/C Theatres, Balt., 1974-77; dist. film buyer Gen. Cinema, Cherry Hill, N.J., 1977-78; v.p. film Gen. Cinema, N.Y.C., 1978-82; v.p. head film buyer Gen. Cinema, Cherry Hill, N.J., 1982-83; pres. domestic distbn. and mktg. 20th Century-Fox Pictures, Beverly Hills, Calif., 1983-85, pres. domestic distbn., 1985—. Served with U.S. Army, 1967-69. Mem. Motion Picture Bookers Club (hon.), Motion Picture Pioneer, Will Rogers. Democrat. Home: 4041 Declaration Ave Calabasas CA 91302-5742 Office: 20th Century-Fox Film Corp 1211 Avenue Of The Americas New York NY 10036-8701 Office: PO Box 900 Beverly Hills CA 90213-0900

SHERBELL, RHODA, artist, sculptor; b. Bklyn.; d. Alexander and Syd (Steinberg) S.; m. Mervin Honig, Apr. 28, 1956; 1 child, Susan. Student, Art Students League, 1950-53, Bklyn. Mus. Art Sch., 1959-61; also; pvt. study art, Italy, France, Eng. 1956. cons., coun. mem. Emily Lowe Gallery, Hofstra U., Hempstead, N.Y., 1978, pres., 1989-81, instr., 1991—, life mem. bd. friends, pres. bd. trustees; tchr. instr. Mus. Modern Art, N.Y.C., 1959, NAD Art Sch., N.Y.C., 1985—, Art Students League, N.Y.C., 1980—. Exhibited one-woman shows Country Art Gallery, Locust Valley, N.Y., Bklyn. Mus. Art Sch., 1961, Adelphi Coll., A.C.A. Galleries, N.Y.C., 1967, Capricorn Galleries, Rehn Gallery, Washington, 1968, Huntington Hartford Mus., N.Y.C., 1969, Morris (N.J.) Mus. Arts and Scis., 1980, Bergen Mus. Arts and Scis., N.J., 1984, William Benton Mus., Conn., 1985, Palace Theatre of the Arts, Stamford, Conn., Bronx Mus. Arts, 1986, Hofstra Mus. Art, L.I., N.Y., 1989, 90, County Art Gallery, N.Y.C., 1990; one-woman retrospective at N.Y. Cultural Ctr., 1970, Nat. Arts Collection, Washington, 1970, Montclair Mus. of Art, 1976, Nat. Art Mus. of Sport, 1977, Jewish Mus. of N.Y.C., 1980, Black History Mus., 1981, Queens Mus., 1981, 82, Nat. Portrait Gallery, Washington, 1981, 82, Bronx Mus., N.Y., Bklyn. Mus., Mus. Modern Art, N.Y.C., Country Art Gallery, 1990, Port Washington Library, Nat. Mus. Am. Art, The Smithsonian Instn., 1982, Nat. Acad. Design, N.Y.C., 1984, 89, Castle Gallery Mus., N.Y.C., 1987, Emily Lowe Mus., N.Y.C., 1987, Heckshire Mus., N.Y.C., 1989, Islip Art Mus., N.Y.C., 1989, Gallery Emanuel, N.Y.C., 1993, Sundance Gallery, Bridgehampton, N.Y., CASTIRON Gallery SoHo Show, 1995, Nat. Acad. Design Exhibition, 1995, exhibited group shows Heckscher Mus., 1989, Downtown Gallery, N.Y.C., Maynard Walker Gallery, N.Y.C., F.A.R. Gallery, N.Y.C., Provincetown Art Assn., Detroit Inst. Art, Pa. Acad. Fine Arts, Bklyn. and L.I. Artists Show, Old Westbury Gardens Small Sculpture Show, Audubon Artists, NAD, Allied Artists, Heckscher Mus., Nat. Art Mus. Sports, Mus. Arts and Scis., L.A., Am. Mus. Natural History, Post of History Mus., 1987, 88, Caslte Gallery Mus., N.Y.C., 1987, Emiloy Lowe Gallery Mus., N.Y., 1987, Bronx Mus. Arts, 1987, Chgo. Hist. Soc., Mus. of Modern Art, N.Y.C., 1988, Sands Point Mus., L.I., NAD, Hofstra Mus., 1990, Nat. Mus. Sports Art, 1991, Indpls. Art Mus., Phoenix Mus. Art, Corcoran Mus. Art, Washington, IBM, N.Y.C., Fire House Gallery Mus. Nassau Cmty. Coll., L.I., 1992, Nat. Arts Club Ann. Exhbn., 1992, Sports in Art From Am. Mus. at IBM, N.Y.C., 1992, Nat. Sculpture Soc. and The Regina A Quick Ctr. for The Arts Fairfield U.Centennial Anniversary Exbn., 1993, Mus. Modern Art, N.Y.C., Nat. Sculpture Soc. 100 Anniversary Exhbn., 1993, Italy, 1994, Provincetown Assn. and Art Mus., 1993, Kyoto (Japan) Mus. Sculpture Guild, 1993, Nat. Sculpture Soc. Exhbn. in Italy, Lucca, 1994, Sculptures Guild, N.Y.C., 1994-95, Cline Gallery, Santa Fe, 1995; represented permanent collections, Stony Brook Hall of Fame, William Benton Mus. Art, Colby Coll. Mus., Oklahoma City Mus., Montclair (N.J.) Mus., Schonberg Library Black Studies, N.Y.C., Albany State Mus., Hofstra U., Bklyn. Mus., Colby Coll. Mus., Nat. Arts Collection, Nat. Portrait Gallery, Smithsonian Instn., Baseball Hall of Fame Cooperstown, N.Y., Nassau Community Coll., Hofstra U. Emily Lowe Gallery, Art Students League, Jewish Mus., Queens Mus., Black History Mus., Nassau County Mus., Stamford Mus. Art and Nature Ctr., Jericho Pub. Library, N.Y., African-Am. Mus., Hempstead, N.Y., 1988, Stamford (Conn.) Mus. Art and Scis., Silvermine Artists North East exhibition, 1989, Nassau Community Coll. Fire House Gallery Exbn., 1992, Nat. Portrait Gallery Smithsonian Instn.; also pvt. collections, TV shows, ABC, 1968, 81; ednl. TV spl. Rhoda Sherbell-Woman in Bronze, 1977; important works include Sed Ballerina, portraits of Aaron Copland (Bruce Stevenson Meml. Best Portrait award Nat. Arts Club 1989), Eleanor Roosevelt, Variations on a Theme (36 works of collaged sculpture), 1982-86; appeared numerous several TV shows; guest various radio programs; contbr. articles to newspapers, popular mags. and art jours. Council mem. Nassau County Mus., 1978, trustee, 1st v.p. council; asso. trustee Nat. Art Mus. of Sports, Inc., 1975—; cons., community liaison WNET Channel 13, cultural coordinator, 1975-83; host radio show Not for Artists Only, 1978-79; trustee Women's Boxing Fedn., 1978; mem. The Art

Comm of The City of New York, 1993. Recipient Gold medal Allied Artists of Am., 1989, Alfred G. B. Steel Meml. award Pa. Acad. Fine Arts, 1963-64; Helen F. Barnett prize NAD, 1965, Jersey City Mus. prize for sculpture, 1961, 1st prize sculpture Locust Valley Art Show, 1966, 67, Ann. Sculpture prize Jersey City Mus., Bank for Savs. 1st prize in sculpture, 1950, Ford Found. purchase award, 1964, 2 top sculpture awards Mainstreams 77, Cert. of Merit Salmagundi Club, 1978, prize for sculpture, 1980, 81, award for sculpture Knickerbocker Artists, 1980, 81, top prize for sculpture Hudson Valley Art Assn., 1981, Sawyer award NAD, 1985, Gold medal of honor Audubon Artists, 1985, 39th Ann. Silvermine Exhbn. award, Gold medal Allied Artists Am., 1990, Pres' award Nat arts Club N.Y.C.; MacDowell Colony fellow, 1976 Am. Acad. Arts and Letters and Nat. Arts and Letters grantee, 1960, Louis Comfort Tiffany Found. grantee, 1962, Ford Found. grantee, 1964, 67, also award; named one of top 5 finalist World Wide Competition to do Monument of Queen Catherine of England, 1991. Fellow Nat. Sculpture Soc.; mem. Sculpture Guild (dir.), Nat. Assn. Women Artists (Jeffery Childs Willis Meml. prize 1978), Allied Artists Soc. (dir., Gold medal 1990), Audubon Artists (Greta Kempton Walker prize 1965, Chaim Gross award, award for disting. contbr. to orgn. 1979, 80, Louis Weskeem award, dir.), Woman's Caucus for Art, Coll. Art Assn., Am. Inst. Conservation Historic and Artistic Works, N.Y. Soc. Women Artists, Artists Equity Assn. N.Y., Nat. Sculpture Soc. (E.N. Richard Meml. prize 1989), Internat. Platform Assn., Profl. Artists Guild L.I., Painters and Sculptors Soc. N.J. (Bertrum R. Hulmes Meml. award), Am. Watercolor Soc. (award for disting. contbr. to orgn.), Catharine Lorillard Wolfe Club (hon. mention 1968), Nat. Arts Club (N.Y.C., Stevenson Meml. award 1989, Pres. award 1992), NAD Design (Leila Gordon Sawyer prize 1989; The Dessle Green Prize 1993). Home: 64 Jane Ct Westbury NY 11590-1410

SHERBORNE, ROBERT, editor; b. Fairborn, Ohio, Mar. 26, 1950; s. Henry Hall and Lauramay (Rider) S.; m. Pamela Saunders, Apr. 16, 1988; children: Laura, Sophie. BS in Comms., U. Tenn., 1976. Reporter Clarksville (Tenn.) Leaf Chronicle, 1976, Tullahoma (Tenn.) News, 1976-77; reporter The Tennessean, Nashville, 1977-92, regional editor, 1993-94, special project editor, 1995—. Recipient Nat. Gold Mass Media award Nat. Conf. Christians & Jews, 1983; special citation Nat. Headliners award Press Club of Atlantic City, N.J., 1983. Office: The Tennessean 1100 Broadway Nashville TN 37202

SHERBOURNE, ARCHIBALD NORBERT, civil engineering educator; b. Bombay, India, July 8, 1929; s. Manekji and Sarah Agnes (Sherbourne) Bulsara; m. Jean Ducan Nicol, Aug. 15, 1959; children: Mary, Sarah, Jeffrey, Nicolas, Jonathan, Simon. B.Sc., U. London, 1953, D.Sc., 1970; B.S., Lehigh U., 1955, M.S., 1957; M.A., Cambridge U., 1959, Ph.D., 1960. Registered profl. engr., Ont.; chartered engr. U.K., European Engr. Mem. faculty U. Waterloo, Ont., Can., 1961—; prof. civil engring. U. Waterloo, 1963—; dean U. Waterloo (Faculty Engring.), 1966-74; dir. Sherbourne Consultants Ltd.; vis. prof. U. W.I., Trinidad, 1969-70, Nat. C.E. Lab., Lisbon, Portugal, 1970, Ecole Polytechnique Federale, Lausanne, Switzerland, 1975-77; DAAD vis. fellow, W. Ger., 1975, NATO sr. scientist fellow, vis. lectr., 1975-76; advisor-cons. Commonwealth Africa study group on tech. edn. in industry Commonwealth Secretariat London, 1978; Gledden vis. sr. fellow U. Western Australia, Perth, 1978; acad. adviser Centre for Sci. and Tech., Fed. U. Paraiba, Campina Grande, Brazil, 1979; prin. cons. acad. planning Faculty Engring., U. Victoria, B.C., Can., 1979-80; advisor Tata Sons Ltd., Bombay, 1980; vis. prof. civil engring. Mich. Technol. U., Houghton, 1980-81, 82-83, U. Melbourne, 1983; spl. cons. technol. edn. for developing countries Can. Internat. Devel. Agy.; vis. prof. ocean engring. Fla. Atlantic U., Boca Raton, 1985, archtl. engring. N.C. A & T State U., Greensboro, 1987; vis. prof. aerospace engring. I.I. Sci., Bangalore, India, 1990. Contbr. articles to profl. jours. OECD fellow Switzerland, 1964; recipient Engring. medal Assn. Profl. Engrs., Province Ont., 1975. Fellow Instn. Structural Engrs. (London), Royal Soc. Arts, Can. Soc. Civil Engring., Can. Acad. Engring.; mem. Internat. Assn. Bridge & Structural Engring. Home: 131 Keats Way Pl, Waterloo, ON Canada N2L 5H4 Office: U Waterloo Dept Civil Engring, Faculty Engring, Waterloo, ON Canada N2L 3G1

SHERBURNE, DONALD WYNNE, philosopher, educator; b. Proctor, Vt., Apr. 21, 1929; s. Hermon Kirk and Alma May (Bixby) S.; m. Elizabeth Statesir Darling, July 30, 1955; children:—Kevin Darling, Nancy Elizabeth, Lynne Darling. A.B., Middlebury Coll., 1951; B.A., Balliol Coll., Oxford U., 1953; M.A., Yale U., 1958, Ph.D., 1960. Instr. philosophy Yale, 1959-60; asst. prof. Vanderbilt U., Nashville, 1960-64, asso. prof., 1964-68, prof. philosophy, 1968-95, chmn. dept., 1973-80, 90-94, prof. emeritus, 1995; Cowling vis. prof. philosophy Carleton Coll., 1990; chmn. editorial adv. com. Vanderbilt U. Press, 1991-95. Author: A Whiteheadian Aesthetic, 1961, A Key to Whitehead's Process and Reality, 1966; editor: Soundings—An Interdisciplinary Jour, 1980-85; co-editor: Corrected Edition of Whitehead's Process and Reality, 1978. Troop leader Cub Scouts, 1965-67. Served with U.S. Army, 1954-56. Recipient Jeffrey Nordhaus award for excellence in teaching., 1984; Dutton fellow Oxford U., 1951-53; sr. fellow NEH, 1977-78. Mem. AAUP (pres. Vanderbilt chpt. 1966-67), Metaphys. Soc. Am. (governing coun. 1969-73, 86-90, pres.-elect 1992-93, pres. 1993-94), So. Soc. Philosophy and Psychology (governing coun. 1971-74, treas. 1974-77, pres.-elect 1977, pres. 1978, Jr. award for Excellence 1961), Am. Philos. Assn. (program com. 1982, com. on status and future of profession 1989-92, nominating com. 1994-95), Am. Soc. Aestheti cs, Phi Beta Kappa (pres. Vanderbilt chpt. 1975-77). Home: 3 Jefferson Ct S Saint Petersburg FL 33711

SHERCK, TIMOTHY C., lawyer; b. Hamilton, Ohoi, Feb. 27, 1949. BA with honors, Northwestern U., 1971; JD magna cum laude, Harvard U., 1974. Bar: Ill. 1975, U.S. Dist. Ct. (no. dist.) Ill., 1975, U.S. Tax Ct. 1977, U.S. Dist. Ct. (ea. dist.) Wis. 1977, U.S. Ct. Appeals (7th cir.) 1979. Ptnr. Mayer, Brown & Platt, Chgo. Contbr. articles to profl. jours. Mem. ABA, Chgo. Bar Assn., Phi Beta Kappa. Office: Mayer Brown & Platt 190 S La Salle St Chicago IL 60603-3410

SHERE, DENNIS, publishing executive; b. Cleve., Nov. 29, 1940; s. William and Susan (Luskay) S.; m. Maureen Jones, Sept. 4, 1965; children: Rebecca Lynn, David Matthew, Stephen Andrew. B.S. in Journalism, Ohio U., 1963, M.S. in Journalism, 1964. Staff writer Dayton (Ohio) Daily News, 1966-69; asst. prof. Sch. Journalism Bowling Green (Ohio) State U., 1969-70; fin. editor Detroit News, 1970-72, city editor, 1973-75; editor Dayton Jour. Herald, 1975-80; pub. Springfield (Ohio) Newspapers Inc., 1980-83, Dayton Newspapers, Inc., 1983-88; gen. mgr. Media Group Moody Bible Inst., 1989—. Served with AUS, 1964-66. Mem. Sigma Alpha Epsilon, Omicron Delta Kappa. Office: Moody Bible Inst 820 N La Salle Blvd Chicago IL 60610

SHERER, SAMUEL AYERS, lawyer, urban planning consultant; b. Warwick, N.Y., June 17, 1944; s. Ernest Thompson and Helen (Ayers) S.; m. Dewi Sudewinahidah, June 28, 1980. AB magna cum laude, Oberlin Coll., 1966; JD, Harvard U., 1970; M in City Planning, MIT, 1970. Bar: D.C. 1972, U.S. Supreme Ct. 1979. Atty., advisor HUD, Boston, 1970; sr. cons. McClaughry Assoc., Washington, 1970-71, 74-76; cons. Urban Inst., Washington, 1971-72; atty., urban planner IBRD Jakarta (Indonesia) Urban Devel. Study, 1972-74; atty., advisor Office Minority Bus. U.S. Dept. Commerce, Washington, 1976-77; prin. Topping & Sherer, Washington, 1977-90; pres. Sherer-Axelrod-Monacelli, Inc., Cambridge, Mass., 1978—; prin. The Washington Team, Inc., 1992—; bd. dirs. Optical Comm. Corp., PADCO, Inc., The Urban Agriculture Network; rep. Internat. Devel. Law Inst., Washington, 1983-90; sr. fellow Climate Inst., 1988—; cons. in field. Co-author: Urban Land Use in Egypt, 1977; editor: Important Laws and Regulations Regarding Land, Housing and Urban Development in the Arab Republic of Egypt, 1977, Important Laws and Regulations Regarding Land, Housing and Urban Development in the Hashemite Kingdom of Jordan, 1981. Bd. dirs. MIT Enterprise Forum of Washington-Balt., 1980-82; mem. D.C. Rep. Cent. Com., 1984-88; mem. nat. governing bd. Ripon Soc., Washington, 1977-83. Urban Studies fellow HUD, 1970. Mem. ABA, D.C. Bar Assn., Am. Planning Assn., Asia Soc., Phi Beta Kappa. Avocations: tennis, sailing. Home: 4600 Connecticut Ave NW Apt 205 Washington DC 20008-5702 Office: 316 Pennsylvania Ave SE # 202 Washington DC 20003-1146

SHERICK, JOHN MATTHEW (JACK SHERICK), technical services company executive; b. Butte, Mont., May 9, 1941; s. Mark William and Victoria (Bugni) S.; m. Diane Harriet Meyer, Dec. 28, 1963; children: Michael, Vicki, Heidi. BSChemE, Mont. State U., 1963; MBA, U. Idaho, 1970. ETR reactor engr. Phillips Petroleum Co., Idaho Falls, Idaho, 1963-66; ETR asst. shift supr. Idaho Nuclear Corp., Idaho Falls, 1966-71; ETR shift supr. Aerojet Nuclear Corp., Idaho Falls, 1971-76; ETR experiment br. mgr. EG&G Idaho Inc., Idaho Falls, 1976-79; mgr. projects and engring. div. Mtn. States Energy, Inc., Butte, 1979-83, pres., gen. mgr., 1983-92, sr. v.p., 1992—; also bd. dirs. Mtn. States Energy Inc., Butte; bd. dirs., v.p. MHD Devel. Corp., Butte; v.p. PLASMA Corp., Butte. Scoutmaster Boy Scouts Am., Butte, 1972—, pres., Mtn. States Coun.; bd. dirs. Jr. Achievement, Butte, 1984—; Butte-Silver Bow C. of C., 1986—; pres. 1990-91, Mont. ambassador, 1987—; loaned exec. Butte-Silver Bow United Way, 1983; pres. Butte High Athletic Coun., 1981-82; pres. Jr. Achievement, Butte, 1988. Recipient Disting. Eagle Scout award Boy Scouts Am., 1986. Mem. Am. Nuclear Soc., Mont. Coll. Mineral Sci. and Tech. Found. (bd. dirs. 1987—, pres. 1991-92), Butte Exch. Club. Roman Catholic. Home: 122 Rampart Dr Butte MT 59701-4326 Office: MSE Inc 122 Rampart Butte MT 59701

SHERIDAN, CHRISTOPHER FREDERICK, human resources executive; b. Syracuse, N.Y., June 7, 1953; s. Frederick John and Patricia Ann (McCormick) S.; m. Diane Marie Harman, Dec. 31, 1977; children: Ryan, Kelly. BS in Indsl. Relations, LeMoyne Coll., 1975. Employee rels. trainee Anaconda Co., Buffalo, 1975-76; employee rels. rep. Anaconda Co., Los Angeles, 1976-78; pers. mgr. HITCO, Gardena, Calif., 1978-80; labor rels. rep. Miller Brewing Co., Fulton, N.Y., 1980-82; labor rels. mgr. Miller Brewing Co., Los Angeles, 1982-90; employee rels. mgr. Ryder Distbn. Resources, Anaheim, Calif., 1990-91; dir. human resources Alta-Dena Cert. Dairy Inc., City of Industry, Calif., 1991—. Mem. Soc. Human Resources Mgmt., Am. Mgmt. Assn. Roman Catholic. Avocations: golf, basketball, reading, music. Office: Alta-Dena Cert Dairy Inc 17637 Valley Blvd La Puente CA 91744-5731

SHERIDAN, DIANE FRANCES, public policy facilitator; b. Wilmington, Del., Mar. 12, 1945; d. Robert Kooch and Eileen Elizabeth (Forrest) Bupp; m. Mark MacDonald Sheridan III, Dec. 7, 1968; 1 child, Elizabeth Anne. BA in English, U. Del., 1967. Tchr. English Newark (Del.) Sch. Dist., 1967-68, Lumberton (Tex.) Ind. Sch. Dist., 1969-71, Crown Point (Ind.) Sch. Dist., 1972-75; sr. assoc. The Keystone (Colo.) Ctr., 1986—; environ. policy facilitator Taylor Lake Village, Tex., 1986—; chair Keystone Siting Process Local Rev. Com. 1st v.p. LWV, Washington, 1992-94; sec. treas voters edn. fund, sec. treas. Nat. LWV, 1994; pres. LWV of Tex., 1987-91, chair edn. fund, 1987-91, bd. dirs., 1983-87; pres. LWV of the Bay Area, 1981-83; adv. com. Ctr. for Global Studies of Houston Advanced Rsch. Ctr., The Woodlands, Tex., 1991—; mem. U. Houston-Clear Lake Devel. Adv. Coun., 1989—, adv. com. Ctr. for Conflict Analysis and Mgmt., bd. advisors Environ. Inst.; mem. Bay Area Community Awareness and Emergency Response Local Emergency Planning Com., 1988-92; active Tex. House-Senate Select Com. on Urban Affairs' Regional Flooding Task Force, 1979-80, Congressman Mike Andrews Environ. Task Force, 1983-85, Gov.'s Task Force on Hazardous Waste Mgmt., 1984-85; dir. local PTAs, 1981-91; coord. Tex. Roundtable on Hazardous Waste, 1982-87; sec., v.p. Tex. Environ. Coalition, 1983-85; co-chair Tex. Risk Comm. Project, 1986-89. Mem. Soc. for Profls. in Dispute Resolution, Internat. Assn. for Pub. Participation Practitioners, Mortarboard, Pi Sigma Alpha, Kappa Delta Pi.

SHERIDAN, EILEEN, librarian; b. N.Y.C., Jan. 11, 1949; d. Edward John and Florence Veronica (Glennon) S. BA in English, U. Bridgeport, Conn., 1972; MLS, So. Conn. State U., 1974. Children's libr. I, Bridgeport Pub. Libr., 1974-80, children's libr. II, 1980-82, coord. youth svcs., 1982—. Pres. Sch. Vol. Assn., Bridgeport, 1987-89; bd. dirs. Action for Bridgeport Cmty. Devel., 1989-90; pres. Conn. Zool. Soc., 1989-91, v.p., 1991—. Recipient vol. award for contbn. to children Mt. Aery Bapt. Ch., 1988, Champion of Children award South End Cmty. Ctr., 1992. Mem. LWV. Avocations: writing, travel, reading. Home: 3300 Park Ave Unit 11 Bridgeport CT 06604 Office: Bridgeport Pub Libr 925 Broad St Bridgeport CT 06604

SHERIDAN, JAMES EDWARD, history educator; b. Wilmington, Del., July 15, 1922; s. Phillip Lambert and Ida Alverna (Green) S.; m. Sonia Landy, Sept. 27, 1947; 1 son, Jamy. B.S., U. Ill., 1949, M.A., 1950; Ph.D., U. Calif. at Berkeley, 1961. Lectr. Chinese history Stanford U., 1960; mem. faculty Northwestern U., 1961—, prof. history, 1968—, chmn. dept., 1969-74, assoc. dean Coll. Arts and Scis., 1985-89, prof. emeritus, 1992—. Author: Chinese Warlord: The Career of Feng Yu-hsiang, 1966, China: A Culture Area in Perspective, 1970, China in Disintegration: The Republican Era in Chinese History, 1912-1949, 1975; editor: The Transformation of Modern China series, 1975—. Served to ensign USN, 1941-46. Fulbright fellow France, 1950-51; Ford Found. fellow, 1958-60; grantee Am. Council Learned Socs.-Social Sci. Research Council, 1966-67, 71-72. Home: 80 Lyme Rd Apt 429 Hanover NH 03755-1236 Office: Northwestern Univ Dept History Evanston IL 60201

SHERIDAN, JAMES LESLIE, real estate developer; b. Butte, Mont., June 13, 1942; s. Leslie Meredith Sheridan and Sarajane (Murphey) Corette; m. Paula Sogard Sheridan, June 29, 1968; children: Paul, Chase, Philip. BS, U. Mont., 1965; MBA, Denver U., 1969. Controller Fairchild Camera & Instruments, Mountain View, Calif., 1969-70; asst. treas. Morrison Knudson, Boise, Idaho, 1970-71; mgr. F&S Constrn. Co., Butte, Mont., 1971-72; investment banker Dreyfuss & Co., N.Y.C., 1972-73; v.p. United Calif. Mortgage Co., San Francisco, 1973-78, Integrated Resources, San Francisco, 1978-79; ptnr. Trammell Crow Co., Dallas, 1979-87, Hamilton Ptnrs., Chgo., 1987—; mem. state com. Internat. Coun. Shopping Ctrs., Chgo., 1984. Chmn. Winnetka (Ill.) Design Review Bd., 1988—. Republican. Roman Catholic. Home: 639 Spruce St Winnetka IL 60093 Office: Hamilton Ptnrs 300 Park Blvd Itasca IL 60143

SHERIDAN, JIM, director, screenwriter; b. Dublin, Ireland, 1949. Student, Univ. Coll., Dublin, NYU. Dir., writer Lyric Theatre, Belfast, No. Ireland; artistic dir. Project Arts Theatre, 1976-80, N.Y. Irish Arts Ctr., 1982-87; founder Children's Theatre Co., Dublin, Ireland. Scripts include (plays) Mobile Homes, Spike in the First World War (Edinburgh Festival Fringe Best Play award 1983); (film) Into the West, 1993; screenwriter, dir.: My Left Foot, 1989 (Acad. award nomination best dir. 1989, Acad. award nomination best adapted screenplay 1989), The Field, 1990, In the Name of the Father, 1993 (Acad. award nomination best dir. 1993, Acad. award nomination best adapted screenplay 1993). Office: CAA 9830 Wilshire Blvd Beverly Hills CA 90212-1804

SHERIDAN, PATRICK MICHAEL, finance company executive; b. Grosse Pointe, Mich., Apr. 13, 1940; s. Paul Phillip and Frances Mary (Rohan) S.; m. Diane Lorraine Tressler, Nov. 14, 1986; children: Mary, Patrick, Kelly, Kevin, James. BBA, U. Notre Dame, 1962; MBA, U. Detroit, 1975. Acct. Peat, Marwick, Mitchell & Co., Detroit, 1962-72, audit mgr., 1969-72; exec. v.p. fin. Alexander Hamilton Life Ins. Co., Farmington, Mich., 1973-76; sr. v.p. ops. Sun Life Ins. Co. Am., Balt., 1976-78, exec. v.p., 1978-79; Chris Ins. Services, Inc., 1979-81; pres., chief exec. officer Am. Health & Life Ins. Co., Balt., 1981-85; chief exec. officer Gulf Ins. Co., 1985-86; sr. v.p., chief fin. officer Comml. Credit Co., 1985-86, sr. v.p. audit, 1987; exec. v.p., chief fin. officer The Associated Group, Indpls., 1987—. Rep. candidate for U.S. Congress, 1972; past pres. Charlesbrooke Cmty. Assn.; past v.p. Jr. Achievement of Met. Balt., 1984-85; bd. dirs. Goodwill Industries of Balt. 1986, bd. govs. 1994; bd. dirs. Family Svcs. Assn., 1994, Goodwill Industries of Indpls., 1994; mem. adv. coun. Clowes Meml. Hall. Capt. AUS, 1963-65. Recipient various Jaycee awards. Fellow Life Mgmt. Inst.; mem. Am. Mgmt. Assn. (pres.'s assn.), AICPAs, Mich. Assn. CPAs, Md. Assn. CPAs, Am. Soc. CLUs, U.S. Jaycees (treas. 1973-74), Mich. Jaycees (pres. 1971-72), Detroit Jaycees (pres. 1968-69), Balt. C. of C. (bd. dirs.), Mensa, Notre Dame Club, Skyline Club.

SHERIDAN, PHILP HENRY, pediatrician neurologist; b. Washington, June 29, 1950; s. Andrew James and Mildred Adele (Stohlman) S.; m. Margaret Mary Williams, Oct. 3, 1987; children: Gerard Andrew, Philip Henry, Kathleen Mary, Patrick Gerard, Mary Margaret Gerard. BS magna cum laude, Yale U., 1972; MD cum laude, Georgetown U., 1976. Diplomate

Am. Bd. Pediatrics, Am. Bd. Psychiatry and Neurology, Am. Bd. Qualification in Electroencephalography. Resident in pediatrics Children's Hosp. Phila., 1976-79; fellow in pediatric neurology Hosp. of U. Pa., Phila., 1979-82; med. staff fellow NIH, Bethesda, Md., 1982-84, neurologist, epilepsy br. Nat. Inst. Neurol. Disorders and Stroke, 1984—, health scientist adminstr., guest worker researcher, 1984-89, chief Devel. Neurology Br., NIH, 1989—, acting chief Epilepsy Br., 1994—; cons., lectr. Nat. Naval Med. Ctr., Bethesda, 1984—; med. dir. U.S. Pub. Health Svc. Contbr. articles on clin. and rsch. neurology to med. jours. Neurologist Div. Children's Splty. Svcs., Fairfax, Va., 1984—. Mem. Am. Acad. Neurology, Child Neurology Soc. (invited reviewer), Soc. for Neurosci., Alpha Omega Alpha. Roman Catholic. Current work: Planning and administering a comprehensive research program concerning epilepsy, pediatric neurology, developmental neurobiology, and neuromuscular disorders. Subspecialties: Neurology, Pediatrics. Office: NIH Fed Bldg Rm 8C10 Bethesda MD 20892

SHERIDAN, RICHARD BERT, economics educator; b. Emporia, Kans., Feb. 10, 1918; s. Bert and Olive Nancy (Davis) S.; m. Audrey Marion Porter, Oct. 18, 1952; children—Richard David, Margaret Anne. B.S., Emporia Kans. State U., 1940; M.S., U. Kans., 1947; Ph.D., London Sch. Econs. and Polit. Sci., 1951. Instr. to assoc. prof. U. Kans., Lawrence, 1947-62, prof. econs., 1963-88; emeritus prof. econs., 1988—; external examiner U. W.I., Kingston, Jamaica, 1964-74; vis. prof. Coll. V.I., St. Thomas, 1971, U. West Indies, St. Augustine, Trinidad, 1987. Author: Economic History of South Central Kansas, 1956, Chapters in Caribbean History, 1970, Sugar and Slavery, 1974, Doctors and Slaves, 1985; cons. editor: Jour. Caribbean History, 1971—; contbr. articles to profl. jours. Served to lt. USNR, 1942-46. Recipient Article award N.C. Bicentennial Contest, 1976, Article award Kans. State Hist. Soc., 1989; Fulbright scholar U. W.I., 1962-63; grantee NIH, Nat. Libr. Medicine, 1973. Fellow Royal Hist. Soc.; mem. Soc. for Human Econs., Assn. Caribbean History. Democrat. Congregationalist. Home: 1745 Louisiana St Lawrence KS 66044-4055 Office: U Kans Dept of Econ Lawrence KS 66045

SHERIDAN, SONIA LANDY, artist, retired art educator; b. Newark, Ohio, Apr. 10, 1925; d. Avrom Mendel and Goldie Cornelia (Hanon) Landy; m. James Edward Sheridan, Sept. 27, 1947; 1 son, Jamy. A.B., Hunter Coll., 1945; postgrad., Columbia U., 1946-48; M.F.A. with high honors, Calif. Coll. Arts and Crafts, 1961. Tchr. art public high schs. Calif., 1951-57; chmn. dept. art Taipei Am. Sch., Taiwan, 1957-59; instr. Calif. Coll. Arts and Crafts, 1960-61; asst. prof. art Sch. Art Inst. Chgo., 1961-67, assoc. prof., 1968-75, prof., 1976-80, prof. emeritus, 1980—; founder, head generative systems program, 1970-80; artist-in-residence 3M Corp., 1970, 76; cons. French Ministry of Culture, 1986; artist-in-residence Xerox Corp., 1981; lectr., univs., museums, art schs., workshops; lectr. Hungarian Acad. Scis. Symposium Collected Essays & Exhbn., Budapest, 1989. One-woman shows include Rosenberg Gallery, Chgo., 1966, Visual Studies Workshop, Rochester, N.Y., 1973, Iowa Mus. Art, Iowa City, 1976, Mus. Sci. Industry, Chgo., 1978; two-person show Mus. Modern Art, N.Y.C., 1974; exhibited in group shows at Print Ann, Boston Mus., 1963, Software, Jewish Mus., N.Y.C., 1969-70, Photography into Art, London, 1972-73, Photokino, Cologne, Germany, 1974, San Francisco Mus. Art, 1975, U. Mich. Mus. Art, 1978, Toledo Mus. Art, 1982-83, Mus. Modern Art, Paris, 1983, Siggraph, U.S., Japan, France, 1982, 83, Reina Sofia Mus., Madrid, Spain, 1986, Smithsonian Instn., 1990, Tokyo Met. Mus. Photography, 1991, Madrid City Cultural Ctr., 1992, Karl Ernst Osthaus Mus., Hagen, Germany, 1992, Circulo des Belles Artes, Madrid, 1992, Yale U. Art Gallery, 1995, Tokyo Intercom. Ctr., 1995, U. Montreal, 1995; represented in permanent collections Art Inst. Chgo., San Francisco Mus. Art, Mus. Sci. and Industry, Chgo., U. Iowa Mus. Art, Nat. Gallery Art, Ottawa, Can., Visual Studies Workshop, Rochester, Tokyo Met. Mus. Photography, U. Mich. Mus. Photography; author: Energized Artscience: Sonia Landy Sheridan, 1978; co-editor Leonardo jour.; contbr. articles, essay to profl. jours. Guggenheim fellow, 1973; Nat. Endowment for Arts workshop grantee 1974, pub. media grantee, 1976, artist grantee 1981; Union Ind. Colls. Art grantee 1975. Mem. ACLU, Coll. Art Assn., Internat. Soc. for Interdisciplinary Study of Symmetry.

SHERIDAN, THOMAS BROWN, mechanical engineering and applied psychology educator, researcher, consultant; b. Cin., Dec. 23, 1929; s. Mahlon Brinsley and Esther Anna (Brown) S.; m Rachel Briggs Rice, Aug. 1, 1953; children: Paul Rice, Richard Rice, David Rice, Margaret Lenore. BS, Purdue U., 1951; MS, UCLA, 1954; ScD, MIT, 1959; Dr. (hon.), Delft U. Tech., The Netherlands, 1991. Registered profl. engr., Mass. Asst. prof. mech. engring. MIT, Cambridge, 1959-65, assoc. prof., 1965-70, prof. 1970-78, prof. engring. and applied psychology, 1978-94, prof. aeronautics and astronautics, 1994—, Ford prof., 1995—; lectr. U. Calif., Berkeley, Stanford U., 1968; vis. prof. U. Delft, The Netherlands, 1972, Stanford U., 1989; chmn. com. human factors, mem. com. aircrew-vehicle interaction, com. on commercially developed space facility, com. on human factors in air traffic control, NRC; mem. adv. com. on applied phys., math. and biol. scis. NSF; mem. life scis. adv. com., study group on robotics, oversight com. flight telerobotic servicer NASA; mem. task force on appropriate tech. U.S. Congress Office Tech. Assessment; mem. study sect. accident prevention and injury control NIH; mem. Def. Sci. Bd. Task Force on Computers, Tng. and Gaming, Nuclear Regulatory Commn. on Nuclear Safety Research Review Com. Author: Telerobotics, Automation and Human Supervisory Control, 1992; co-author: Man Machine Systems, 1974; editor: (with others) Monitoring Behavior and Supervisory Control, 1976; assoc. editor Automatica, 1982—; mem. editorial adv. bd. Tech. Forecasting and Social Change, Computer Aided Design, Advanced Rototics, Robotics and Computer Integrated Mfg., Abstracts in Human-Computer Interaction; editor in chief Presence: Telerobots and Virtual Environments, 1991—. Served to 1st lt. USAF, 1951-53. Fellow IEEE (pres. Systems, Man and Cybernetics Soc. 1974-76, Centennial medal 1984, Norbert Wiener award 1993), Human Factors Soc. (Paul M. Fitts award 1977, pres. 1990-91); mem. Nat. Acad. Engring. Democrat. Member, The United Ch. of Christ. Office: MIT 77 Massachusetts Ave Cambridge MA 02139-3594

SHERIDAN, WILMA FROMAN, dean; b. Ashland, Oreg., Jan. 31, 1926; d. Carl Edwin and Mary Charlotte (Evans) Froman; m. Robert Jackson Sheridan, May 24, 1946; children: Sarah Ruth, Richard Carl, Scott Daniel. MusB, Willamette U., 1945; MusM in Edn., Lewis and Clark Coll., 1955; PhD, U. Oreg., 1979. Secondary choral music tchr. Ashland Pub. Schs., 1945-46; instr. in piano Wash. State U., Pullman, 1946-47; comml. tchr. Everett (Wash.) High Sch., 1949-50, Ashland High Sch., 1950-51; elem. music tchr. Portland (Oreg.) Pub. Schs., 1954-60; from instr. to prof. in music Portland State U., 1969-85, head music dept., 1980-85, dean Sch. Fine and Performing Arts, 1985—; instr. in music Lewis and Clark Coll., Portland, 1956-65. Composer, arranger various mus. works, including How Blest Are They, Christmas Bells; author: The Oregon Plan for Mainstreaming in Music, 1978. Bd. dirs. mem. music com. Ecumenical Ministries, Portland, 1965-68; bd. dirs. Portland Symphonic Choir, 1972-76, Community Music Ctr., Portland, 1984—. Mem. Music Educators Nat. Conf. (mem. nat. com. for handicapped learners 1978-81), Multhomah Athletic Club, Mu Phi Epsilon (chpt. Mem. of Yr. 1989, award for music therapy 1982, 85). Avocations: gardening, travel. Home: 2400 NW 92d Ave Portland OR 97220 Office: Portland State U PO Box 751 Portland OR 97207

SHERIFIS, MICHAEL ELEFTHERIOU, ambassador; b. Famagusta, Cyprus, Nov. 18, 1937; s. Eleftherios and Andriani (V.) S.; m. Rossella Franchini. Degree in law, U. Athens, 1959, degree in polit. and econ. scis., 1961. Diplomat various missions Paris, Cairo, Greece, N.Y.C., Washington, 1961-73; permanent rep. of Cyprus UN, Geneva, 1973-75; dir. polit. affairs and human rights Ministry of Fgn. Affairs, Nicosia, 1975-79; ambassador, dir. public affairs UN, N.Y.C., 1979-83; ambassador of Cyprus Belgrade, Yugoslavia, 1983-85, Moscow, 1985-89, Washington, 1989—. Contbr. articles to profl. jours. Mem. Polit. Analysis and Info. Systems, 1961—; mem. UN com of experts on human rights. Decorated Golden Cross of Phoenix, Greece, 1962, Grand Nat. Flag with Ribbon, Yugoslavia, 1985. Home: 1825 24th St NW Washington DC 20008-4031 Office: Embassy of Cyprus 2211 R St NW Washington DC 20008-4017

SHERIN, EDWIN, theatrical and film director, actor; b. Danville, Pa., Jan. 15, 1930; s. Joseph and Ruth (Berger) S.; m. Jane Alexander, Mar. 29, 1975;

children: Anthony J., Geoffrey B., Jonathan E.; 1 stepchild, Jason E. AB in History and Polit. Sci., Brown U., 1952. Acting tchr. Am. Theatre Wing, N.Y.C., 1962-64; acting tchr. Am. Theatre Tng. Inst. Southeastern Mass. U., South Dartmouth, 1974; Lucille Lortel Disting. guest artist U. Bridgeport (Conn.), 1980; dir. Sch. Theatre Arts Boston U., 1981; acting tchr. Okla. Summer Arts Inst., 1985-86, One on One, L.A., 1989, 90; exec. v.p. Altion Prodns., L.A., 1985-93; mem. nat. adv. for Mus. Am. Theatre; instr. Okla. Summer Arts Inst., guest dir. Calif. Inst. Arts. Actor with Houseman's troupe Phoenix Theatre, N.Y.C., 1957-58, actor N.Y. Shakespeare Festival, 1956-60; appeared as: Octavius Caesar in, Anthony and Cleopatra, 1958; appeared in Broadway plays Come Blow Your Horn, 1960, Desert Incident, 1961, Romulus, 1962, Face of a Hero, 1963; TV films Playhouse 90, 1956-58, Studio One, 1956-58, Omnibus, 1957-60, East Side/West Side, 1960; dir. Broadway plays including The Great White Hope, 1968, Glory Hallelujah, 1969, 6 RMS RIV VU, 1973, Find Your Way Home, Of Mice and Men, 1974, Red Devil Battery Sign, 1975, Sweet Bird of Youth, 1976, Eccentricities of a Nightingale, 1976, The First Monday in October, 1978, Goodbye Fidel, 1980, The Visit, 1992; assoc. producing dir. Washington's Arena Stage, 1964-68; dir. Cosi Fan Tutte, N.Y. City Opera Co., 1972, A Streetcar Named Desire, Piccadilly Theatre, London, 1973, Semmelweiss, Studio Arena Theatre, Buffalo, N.Y., 1978, Outrage, Kennedy Ctr., Washington, 1982; films including Valdez is Coming, 1970, My Old Man's Place, 1971; producing artistic dir. Showdown at Adobe Hotel, Semmelweiss, Hedda Gabler, Night Must Fall, A Streetcar Named Desire, Hartman Theatre, Stamford, Conn., 1980-85; dir. Chelsea Walls, Naked Angels, N.Y.C., 1990, TV programs Hill Street Blues, Moonlighting, WIOU, L.A. Law, Tour of Duty, MEN; co-exec. prodr. Law and Order, 1993-94, exec. prodr., 1994—. (TV films) The Father Clements Story, Lena, My 100 Children, Daughter of the Streets, Getting Even, A Marriage: Georgia O'Keeffe and Alfred Stieglitz, 1991. With USN, 1952-56, Korea. Recipient Outer Circle award, 1969; New Eng. Theatre award, 1969; Recipient N.Y. Drama Critics award, 1969, Drama Desk award, 1969, L.A. Drama Circle award, 1971, Recipient Tony nomination, 1974, London Evening Standard citation, 1973, Joseph Jefferson award, 1976, Buffalo drama award, 1978; New Eng. Theatre Conf. award; Ford Found. grantee, 1965-66. Mem. AFTRA, SAG, Actors Equity Assn., Dirs. Guild Am., Dramatists Guild, Soc. Stage Dirs. and Choreographers (v.p. 1970-80), Lincoln Soc., Phi Gamma Delta.

SHERK, KENNETH JOHN, lawyer; b. Ida Grove, Iowa, Feb. 27, 1933; s. John and Dorothy (Myers) Sherk; m. Virginia Kay Taylor, June 28, 1958; children: Karin Fulton, Katrina, Keith, Kyle. BSC, U. Iowa, 1955; JD, George Washington U., 1961. Bar: Ariz. 1962, U.S. Dist. Ct. Ariz. 1962, U.S. Ct. Appeals (9th cir.) 1966, U.S. Supreme Ct. Assoc. Moore & Romley, Phoenix, 1962-67, ptnr., 1967-79; ptnr. Romley & Sherk, Phoenix, 1979-85; dir. Fennemore Craig, Phoenix, 1985—. Served as 1st lt. U.S. Army, 1955-58, Korea. Recipient Profl. Achievement Svcs. award George Washington Law Assn., 1986, Ariz. Judges Assn., 1989, Disting. Svc. award Phoenix Assn. Def. Counsel, 1990. Fellow Am. Coll. Trial Lawyers, Am. Acad. Appellate Lawyers; mem. ABA (ho. of dels. 1990-93), Ariz. Bar Assn. (pres. 1985-86), State Bar of Ariz. (Mem. of Yr. award 1994), Maricopa Bar Assn. (pres. 1978-79). Republican. Congregational. Avocations: fishing, hiking, bicycling. Home: 1554 W Las Palmaritas Dr Phoenix AZ 85021-5429 Office: Fennemore Craig 2 N Central Ave Ste 2200 Phoenix AZ 85004-2390

SHERLINE, HAROLD ALBERT, adult education professional; b. Bklyn., July 8, 1925; s. Herman Milton and Margaret (Bisset) S.; m. Frances Aileen Mitchell, Aug. 3, 1956; children: Dixie Sherline McQuality, Lori Sherline Charles. BS, MEd, U. Ill., 1952; MEd, U Ill., 1959. Cert. tchr., adminstr., Ill. Tchr., coach Ea. Jr. High Sch., Silver Spring, Md., 1952-54; tchr., coach, adminstr. Williamsville (Ill.) High Sch., 1954-56; coach, dir. athletics Taylorville (Ill.) High Sch., 1956-62; tchr., coach Larkin High Sch., Elgin, Ill., 1962-67; dir. Mattoon (Ill.) Area Adult Edn. Ctr., 1967—; appointee State Adv. Coun. Adult, Vocat. and Tech. Edn., Ill., 1977-83; del. nat. forum Excellence in Edn., 1983. Coord. successful overrides of gov.'s veto of adult edn. funding, Ill., 1973, 88, 89, 90. Cpl. USMC, 1943-46, PTO. Recipient Nat. Literacy award Internat. Reading Assn./Ea. Ill. U., 1993, Cmty. Svc. award Phi Delta Kappa, 1993; named Adult Educator of Yr. Pub. Adult and Continuing Educators Assn. Ill., 1973; coach of teams in State Basketball Finals, 1959, State Cross-Country Finals, 1964. Mem. Ill. Adult and Continuing Educators Assn. (pres. 1990-91, Pres.'s award 1988), Am. Assn. Adult and Continuing Edn., Phi Delta Kappa (Cmty. Svc. award 1993). Avocations: reading, athletics, recreational activities, political activism. Office: Mattoon Area Adult Edn Ctr 1617 Lakeland Blvd Mattoon IL 61938-5915

SHERLOCK, JOHN MICHAEL, bishop; b. Regina, Sask., Can., Jan. 20, 1926; s. Joseph and Catherine S. Student, St. Augustine's Sem., Toronto, Ont., Can., 1950; student canon law, Catholic U. Am., 1950-52; LLD (hon.), U. Windsor, 1986; DD (hon.), Huron Coll., London, Ont., 1986. Ordained priest Roman Catholic Ch., 1950, bishop, 1974; asst. pastor St. Eugene's, Hamilton, Ont., 1952-59, St. Augustine's; Dundas, Ont., 1959-63, Cathedral Christ the King, Hamilton, also Guelph and Maryhill, Ont., 1950-52; pastor St. Charles Ch., Hamilton, 1963-74; aux. bishop London, Ont., 1974-78; bishop, 1978—; chaplain Univ. Newman Club, McMaster U., Hamilton, 1963-66; pres. Canadian Conf. Cath. Bishops, 1983-85, liaison with U. Chaplains Can. and Pres. Cath. Coll. and Univs.; chmn. social affairs com. commn. Ont. Conf. Cath. Bishops, edn. commn., family life com.; adv. judge for the Regional Marriage Truban, 1954-72. Mem. Wentworth County Roman Cath. Separate Sch. Bd., 1964-74, chmn., 1972-73. Address: Chancery Office, 1070 Waterloo St, London, ON Canada N6A 3Y2

SHERMA, JOSEPH, chemistry educator. Prof. dept. chemistry Lafayette Coll., Easton, Pa. Recipient ACS award for research at an undergraduate institution Am. Chem. Soc., 1995. Office: Lafayette College Dept Chemistry Easton PA 18042-1798*

SHERMAN, ALAN ROBERT, psychologist, educator; b. N.Y.C., Nov. 18, 1942; s. David R. and Goldie (Wax) S.; m. Llana Helene Tobias, Aug. 14, 1966 (div. 1989); children: Jonathan Colbert, Relissa Anne. BA, Columbia U., 1964; MS, Yale U., 1966, PhD, 1969. Lic. psychologist, Calif. Faculty psychology U. Calif., Santa Barbara, 1969—; clin. psychologist in pvt. practice Santa Barbara, 1981—; cons. in field. Author: Behavior Modification, 1973; contbr. articles to profl. jours. and chpts. in books. Pres. Santa Barbara Mental Health Assn., 1978, 84-85, 91, Mountain View Sch. Site Coun., Santa Barbara, 1978-84. NIMH predoctoral rsch. fellow, 1964-69; recipient Vol. of Yr. award Santa Barbara Mental Health Assn., 1979, Teaching Excellence awards Delta Delta Delta, Chi Omega, Gamma Phi Beta, Santa Barbara; several grants. Fellow Behavior Therapy and Rsch. Soc.; mem. APA, AAUP (chpt. pres. 1978-79), Calif. Psychol. Assn., Assn. for Advancement of Behavior Therapy, Santa Barbara County Psychol. Assn. (pres. 1985), Phi Beta Kappa (chpt. pres. 1977-78), Sigma Xi, Psi Chi (chpt. faculty advisor, 1979—). Office: Univ of Calif Dept Psychology Santa Barbara CA 93106-9660

SHERMAN, ARLENE, television producer; b. Washington, Sept. 12, 1947; d. Burton H. and Ann M. (Butt) S. BFA, NYU, 1970. Free lance film editor U.S., France, Eng., 1970-78; prodn. coordinator Children's TV Workshop, N.Y.C., 1978-81, assoc. producer, 1981-85, producer, 1985—; exec. producer PBS primetime spl. Sesame St. Jam, 1994; assoc. dir. TV programs, 1985—. Producer TV series Sesame St., 1988 (Emmy award); dir. film The Machine, 1970 (Cannes Film Festival award 1970). Recipient Emmy for Producing Sesame St., 1990, 91, 92, 94; nominee Emmy for Sesame St. Jam. Mem. Am. Film Inst., Nat. Acad. TV Arts and Scis., Dirs. Guild Am. Avocations: photography, anthropology, collage. Office: Children's TV Workshop 1 Lincoln Plz New York NY 10023-7170

SHERMAN, CHARLES DANIEL, JR., surgeon; b. Avon Park, Fla., Oct. 5, 1920; s. Charles Daniel and Mary Alice (Oliver) S.; m. Jean Riebling, Aug. 13, 1943; children: Rachel, Charles Daniel, Edward. B.S., U. Fla., 1942; M.D., Johns Hopkins U., 1945. Diplomate: Am. Bd. Surgery. Intern Duke U. Hosp., Durham, N.C., 1945-46; resident U. Rochester Med. Center, 1948-52, instr., 1952-56, asst. prof., 1956-64, clin. assoc. prof. surgery, 1964-70, clin. prof., 1970—; fellow Meml. Center for Cancer, 1951; practice medicine specializing in cancer surgery Rochester, 1953—; mem. staff Highland Hosp., Rochester, N.Y.; v.p. Redd Labs., Clearwater, Fla., 1961-70; advisor N.Y. State Bur. Cancer Control, 1964-75; sec.-treas. Monroe County Health

Planning Coun., 1967-69; mem. Monroe County Bd. Health, 1966-78; advisor to WHO, 1971; mem. advisory com. Nat. Cancer Insts.; dir. Internat. Union Against Cancer Project to Survey Cancer Edn. in Latin Am., 1976, Asia, 1977; mem. hosp. adv. com. to Joint Com. on Accreditation of Hosps., 1980-88; organizer WHO/Internat. Union Against Cancer European Congress on Cancer Edn., 1981; mem. Accreditation Council for Continuing Med. Edn., 1983-89, vice chmn. 1988, chmn., 1989; organizer Coordinating Coun. on Cancer Edn. in Latin Am., 1986, in Asian-Pacific region, 1987; chmn. Coordinating Coun. for Cancer Edn. in Europe, 1987—; bd. dirs. Nat. Resident Matching Plan, 1988—, treas., 1989—; mem. organizing com. Internat. Med. Scholar Program, 1987-89; keynote speaker Internat. Cancer Congress, 1992; lectr. in field. Author: Clinical Concepts in Cancer Management, 1976; co-author: Clinical Oncology, 1974; editor, pub.: Directory of U.S. Oncologists, 1983—; editor: (with others) Programmed Instruction in Medical Education; Newsletter in Cancer, 1968-80; chmn. editorial bd. for 2d , 3d and 4th edits. Clinical Oncology (monograph): (with others) Internat. Union against Cancer, 1978-86; mem. editorial bd. Jour. Cancer Edn., 1984—, Greek Jour. Continuing Med. Edn., 1986—; participant movie on esophogeal reconstrn., 1957; producer exhibits on cancer treatment and cancer edn.; co-contbr. articles to profl. jours. Mem. adv. com. on Continuing Edn. in Oncology of the European Community, 1993; advisor European Sch. Oncology, European Med. Student Assn.; mem. internat. adv. com. Asian Pacific Cancer Congress, Beijing, 1991, Bangkok, 1993, Singapore, 1995, Malaysia, 1996. Fulbright fellow Mendoza, Argentina, 1963; recipient Health Edn. award N.Y. State Pub. Health Assn., 1973; cert. of merit. Rochester Acad. Medicine, 1982. Mem. ACS, AMA (N.Y. state del. to Ho. of Dels., coun. on med. edn. 1983-92, com. on med. liability 1984-85, com. on fgn. grads. 1984, com. on cancer 1970-74, exec. com. 1989-90), Am. Radium Soc., Soc. Head and Neck Surgeons, Royal Soc. Medicine, Am. Assn. Cancer Edn. (pres. 1975-76), Am. Fedn. Clin. Oncologic Socs. (bd. govs. 1974-77), N.Y. State Med. Soc. (councillor 1973-79, asst. treas. 1980-83, treas. 1983-85, v.p. 1986, pres.-elect 1987, pres. 1988-89, trustee 1990—, chair trustees 1994-95, liaison com. on med. edn. 1992—), N.Y. Acad. Sci., N.Y. State Cancer Programs Assn. (pres. 1970-71, chmn. UICC prof. edn. program 1986-94, exec. coun. 1986-94), Internat. Union Against Cancer (chmn. profl. edn. program), Monroe County Med. Soc. (pres. 1965, Edward Mott Moore award 1978), Monroe County Cancer and Leukemia Assn. (pres. 1962-66), European Assn. Cancer Edn. (bd. dirs. 1987—), Soc. Surg. Oncology (chmn. residents award com. 1963-66), Am. Soc. Preventive Oncology, U.S. Squash Rackets Assn. (dir. 1963-65), Argentine Anti-Smoking Union (hon.), Blue Key Soc., Phi Beta Kappa, Alpha Phi Omega. Home: 127 Southern Pky Rochester NY 14618-1052

SHERMAN, CHARLES EDWIN, broadcasting executive, educator; b. Phila., Mar. 20, 1934; s. Abe and Rae (Ginsberg) S.; m. Elaine Landsburg, Sept. 11, 1960; children: Jean, Eric, David. BS, Temple U., Phila., 1960, MA, 1962; PhD, Wayne State U., Detroit, 1967. Announcer, program producer Sta. WHAT, Phila., 1957-62; mem. prodn. staff Sta. WFIL-TV, Phila., 1961; grad. asst. Temple U., 1960-62; TV producer-dir., prodn. supr. Wayne State U., 1962-64, instr. dept. speech, 1964-66, asst. to dir. div. mass communication, 1966-67; asst. prof. dept. speech U. Wis., 1967-70, assoc. prof. dept. communication arts, assoc. chmn., 1970-73, assoc. prof., acting chmn., 1974, prof., assoc. chmn. dept. communication arts, 1974-75; prof., chmn. dept. telecommunications Ind. U., Bloomington, 1975-79, adj. prof. telecommunications, 1980—; pres., gen. mgr. WTRF-TV, Wheeling, W.Va., 1979-84, WHOI-TV, Peoria, Ill., 1984-88; sr. v.p. TV Nat. Assn. of Broadcasters, Washington, 1988—; cons. Forward Communications, Inc., Wausau, Wis., 1974-79; mem. CBS Network TV Affiliates Bd., 1982-84, ABC Network TV Affiliates Bd., 1986-88; bd. dirs. Bank of Wheeling, Nat. Assn. TV Program Execs. Ednl. Found., 1986—, Accreditating Council on Edn. in Journalism and Mass Communication, 1986—; chmn. Task Force on Citizens Rights and Access, Wis. Commn. on Cable TV, 1973; vice chmn. W.Va. Ednl. Broadcasting Authority, 1980-85. Contbr. articles on broadcasting to profl. jours. Bd. dirs. Upper Ohio Valley United Way, 1979-85, Heart of Ill. United Way, 1986-88, Peoria Human Services Ctr., 1986-88; bd. dirs., mem. exec. com. Wheeling Devel. Corel., 1980-85; trustee Ohio Valley Med. Ctr., 1980-85. With U.S. Army, 1955-57. Recipient Communications award Temple U., 1960, Sigma Delta Chi award Temple U., 1960, Disting. Service award in broadcasting Wayne State U., 1966. Mem. Speech Communication Assn., Broadcast Edn. Assn. (chmn. Internat. Seminar 1974, chmn. Internat. Interest Group 1974, dir., sec., treas. 1983-85, chmn. 1985-86), Nat. Assn. Ednl. Broadcasters, Nat. Assn. Broadcasters (chmn. rsch. com.), Wheeling C. of C. (bd. dirs. 1979-85), Alpha Epsilon Rho, Sigma Delta Chi. Jewish. Office: Nat Assn Broadcasters 1771 N St NW Washington DC 20036-2805

SHERMAN, CINDY, artist; b. Glen Ridge, N.J., 1954. Student, State Univ. Coll. Buffalo, 1972-76. One-woman exhbns. include Hallwalls Gallery, Buffalo, 1976, 77, Contemporary Arts Mus., Houston, 1980, The Kitchen, N.Y., 1980, Metro Pictures, N.Y., 1980, 83, Saman Gallery, Genoa, 1981, Young/Hoffman Gallery, Chgo., 1981, Chantal Crousel Gallery, Paris, 1982, Stedelijk Mus., Amsterdam, 1982, St. Louis Art Mus., 1983, Fine Arts Ctr. Gallery, SUNY-Stony Brook, 1983, Rhona Hoffman Gallery, Chgo., 1983, Douglas Drake Gallery, Kansas City, 1983, 84, Seibu Gallery Contemporary Art, Tokyo, 1984, Akron Art Mus., 1984, Linda Cathcart Gallery, Santa Monica, Calif., 1992, Museo de Monterrey, Mex., 1992; group exhbns. include Albright-Knox Art Gallery, Buffalo, 1975, Artists Space, N.Y., 1978, Max Protetch Gallery, N.Y., 1979, Castelli Graphics, N.Y., 1980, Lisson Gallery, London, 1980, Centre Pompidou, Paris, 1981; NIT, 1981, Renaissance Soc. U. Chgo., 1982, Metro Pictures, N.Y., 1982, La Ciennale de Venezia, Venice, Italy, 1982, Documenta 7, Kassel, West Germany, 1982, Chantall Crousel Gallery, Paris, 1982, San Francisco Mus. Modern Art, 1982, Inst. Contemporary Art, London, 1982, Grey Art Gallery, N.Y., 1982, Inst. Contemporary Art, Phila., 1982, Young Hoffman Gallery, Chgo., 1983, Hirshhorn Gallery, Washington, 1983, 1983, Whitney Mus. Am. Art, N.Y., 1983, 85, 91; represented in permanent collections Mus. Fine Arts, Houston, Albright/Knox Art Gallery, Buffalo, Dallas Mus. Fine Arts, Mus. Boymansvan Beuningen, Rotterdam, Akron Art Mus., Ohio, Mus. Modern Art, N.Y.C., Walker Art Ctr., Mpls., Tate Gallery, London, Rose Art Mus., Brandeis U., Centre Pompidou, Paris, Stedelijk Mus., Amsterdam, Met. Mus. Art, N.Y., St. Louis Art Mus., San Francisco Mus. Modern Art. Office: care Metro Pictures 150 Greene St New York NY 10012-3202

SHERMAN, DEMING ELIOT, lawyer; b. Providence, July 22, 1943; s. Edwin Fisk and Martha Amy (Parkhurst) S.; m. Jane Catherine Bauer, Dec. 20, 1966; children: Melissa Jane, Nicholas Deming. BA, Amherst (Mass.) Coll., 1965; JD, U. Chgo., 1968. Bar: R.I. 1968, U.S. Dist. Ct. R.I. 1970, U.S. Supreme Ct. 1974, Mass. 1985, U.S. Dist. Ct. Mass. 1985. Ptnr. Edwards & Angell, Providence, 1969—, mng. ptnr., 1986-94. Trustee First Night Providence, 1988-93, pres., 1991-93, R.I. Philharmonic Orch., 1993—; v.p. Providence Preservation Soc., 1994—; mem. R.I. Com. Jud. Tenure and Discipline, 1992—; bd. dirs. Providence YMCA, 1975-85, Blackstone Park Improvement Assn., Providence, 1980—, R.I. Commodore, New England Legal Found., 1994—, Nopes Island Conservation Assn., 1992—; corporator R.I. Hosp., 1989—. Fellow R.I. Bar Found.; mem. ABA, R.I. Bar Assn., Amherst Alumni Assn. R.I. (pres. 1980-91), Greater Providence C. of C. (bd. dirs. 1991-94). Home: 254 Irving Ave Providence RI 02906-5544 Office: Edwards & Angell 2700 Hospital Trust Towers Providence RI 02903

SHERMAN, EDWARD FRANCIS, lawyer, educator; b. El Paso, Tex., July 5, 1937; s. Raphael Eugene and Mary (Stedmon) S.; m. Alice Theresa Hammer, Feb. 23, 1963; children—Edward F. Jr., Paul. AB, Georgetown U., 1959; MA, U. Tex.-El Paso, 1962, 67; LLB, Harvard U., 1962. SJD, 1981. Bar: Tex. 1962, Ind. 1976. Aide to gov. Nev., state govt. fellow, Carson City, 1962; law clk. to U.S. dist. judge Western dist. Tex., El Paso, 1963; ptnr. firm Mayfield, Broaddus & Perrenot, El Paso, 1963-65; teaching fellow Harvard Law Sch., Cambridge, Mass., 1967-69; prof. Ind. U. Sch. Law, Bloomington, 1969-77; Fulbright prof. Trinity Coll., Dublin, 1973-74; vis. prof. U. London, 1989; Edward Clark Centennial prof. law, U. Tex., Austin, 1977—; of counsel Baker & McKenzie, 1993—; counsel Tex. County Jail Litigation, 1978-85; bd. dirs. officer Travis County Dispute Resolution Ctr., Austin, 1985-88; chmn. bd. dirs. Tex. Ctr. Pub. Policy Dispute Resolution, 1993-94; mem. arbitrator panel, course dir. Internat. Ctrs. for Arbitration. Capt. U.S. Army, 1965-67, lt. col. Res., 1970-90. Fulbright lectr. in law Trinity Coll., Dublin, Ireland, 1973-74. Fellow Tex. Bar Found.; mem. ABA (reporter ABA civil justice improvements project 1993, offer of judgement task force, 1995), Am. Arbitration Assn. (arbitrator panel), AAUP (gen. counsel 1986-88), Am. Law Inst., Tex. State Bar Assn. (alternative dispute resolution com. 1985—, chair Pattern Jury Charge Com. 1983-94), Tex. Civil Liberties Union (gen. counsel 1985-91). Co-author: The Military in American Society, 1979, Complex Litigation, 1985, 2d edit., 1992, Processes of Dispute Resolution, 1989, Civil Procedure: A Modern Approach, 1989, 2nd edit., 1995, Rau & Sherman's Texas ADR and Arbitration Statutes, 1994. Home: 2622 Wooldridge Dr Austin TX 78703-2538 Office: U Tex Sch Law 727 E 26th St Austin TX 78705-3224

SHERMAN, ELAINE C., gourmet foods company executive, educator; b. Chgo., Aug. 1, 1938; d. Arthur E. and Sylvia (Miller) Friedman; m. Arthur J. Spiegel, Jan. 1989; children: Steven J., David P., Jaime A. Student, Northwestern U., 1956-58; diploma in cake decorating, Wilton Sch. Profl. Cake Decorating, 1973; diploma, Dumas Pere, L'école de la Cuisine Française. Tchr. cooking and adult edn. Maine, Oakton, Niles Adult and Continuing Edn. Program, Park Ridge, Ill., 1972-82; corp. officer The Complete Cook, Glenview, Ill., 1976-82, Madame Chocolate, Glenview, 1983-87; food columnist Chgo. Sun Times, 1985-87; dir. mktg. Sue Ling Gin, Chgo., 1987-88; co-owner Critical Eye, Chgo., 1988—; v.p., dir. merchandising, gen. mgr. Foodstuffs, Inc., Evanston, Ill., 1990-91, food cons. mgmt. and mktg., 1991—. Author: Madame Chocolate's Book of Divine Indulgences, 1984 (nominated Tastemaker award 1984). Bd. dirs. Chgo. Fund on Aging and Disability, 1989—; co-chmn. Meals on Wheels, 1989-90, 91. Mem. Les Dames D'Escoffier (founding pres.), Women's Foodservice Network (pres.), Confrerie de la Chaine Des Rotisseurs (vice conselliere gastronomique), Am. Inst. Wine and Food (bd. dirs.). Home and Office: 1728 Wildberry Dr # D Glenview IL 60025-1748

SHERMAN, ELLIOT MARK, lawyer; b. Brookline, Mass., Aug. 6, 1952; s. Daniel and Elizabeth (Bromfield) S. B.A., U. Mass., 1974; JD, Western New England Coll., 1977. Bar: Mass. 1977, U.S. Dist. Ct. Mass. 1977, U.S. Tax Ct. 1981. Ptnr. Burns and Levinson, Boston, 1977—. Mem. Mass. Bar Assn. (coun. 1993—, family law sect.), Norfolk County Bar Assn. (exec. coun. 1992-93), Mass. Acad. Trial Attys., Assn. Trial Lawyers Am. Democrat. Avocations: sailing, skiing, carpentry, scuba diving. Office: Burns & Levinson 125 Summer St Boston MA 02110-1624

SHERMAN, EUGENE JAY, marketing executive, economist; b. N.Y.C., Jan. 10, 1935; s. Samuel and Sarah (Lavinsky) S.; m. Mary Eileen Van, Apr. 22, 1966; 1 child, Rebecca. BA, CCNY, 1956; MBA, NYU, 1959, postgrad., 1959-63. Economist Fed. Res. Bank N.Y., 1959-62, Chase Manhattan Bank, N.Y.C., 1962-65; v.p. Bank of N.Y., N.Y.C., 1965-72; sr. v.p., exec. dir., dir. research Merrill Lynch and Co., N.Y.C., 1972-78; v.p., chief economist, mgr.internat. investment Internat. Gold Corp., N.Y.C., 1980-86; sr. v.p., chief economist Fed. Home Loan Bank N.Y., 1986-93; sr. v.p., dir. rsch. M.A. Schapiro & Co., Inc., N.Y.C., 1993—; gold cons., N.Y.C., 1986—. Author: Gold Investment: Theory and Application, 1986; contbr. articles to profl. jours. Mem. Money Marketeers (pres. 1971-72, honored fellow 1987), Downtown Economist Club (chmn. 1988-89), Forecasters (winner 1986), Treasury Securities Luncheon (pres. 1995—), Nat. Assn. Bus. Econs., N.Y. Assn. Bus. Econs. Avocations: mountaineering, performing arts. Home: 115 E 9th St New York NY 10003-5414

SHERMAN, GEORGE M., manufacturing company executive; b. N.Y.C., Aug. 6, 1941; s. Joseph B. and Fredericka (Hand) S.; m. Betsy Rae Bicknell, Nov. 26, 1966; children: Jonathan, David, Michael, Matthew. B.S., L.I.U. 1963; M.B.A., U. Louisville, 1971. Product gen. mgr. Gen. Electric Co., Bridgeport, Conn., 1966-79; pres. Weed Eater div. Emersen Electric Co., Houston, 1979-80; pres. Skil Corp. div. Emerson Electric Co., Chgo., 1980-82; group v.p. U.S. power tools group Black & Decker Corp., Balt., 1985, sr. v.p., pres. power tools group, from 1986, then exec. v.p., pres. power tools group, until 1990; now chief exec. officer Danaher Corp, Washington, D.C., 1990—; mem. adv. bd. Nat. Home Ctr. Show, Chgo., 1987; bd. dirs. D.I.Y. Research Inst., Lincolnshire, Ill., 1988. Bd. dirs. Ctr. Stage, Balt., 1988. Served with U.S. Army, 1964-66. Mem. Am. Mgmt. Assn. (mem. gen. mgmt. council 1988). Clubs: Center (Balt.); Hillendale Country (Phoenix, Md.). Avocations: flying, skiing, scuba diving, racquetball, golf. Office: Danaher Corporation 1250 24th St NW Ste 800 Washington DC 20037-1124

SHERMAN, GERALD, financial estate planner, nuclear physicist; b. Bklyn., Sept. 7, 1938; s. Saul and Claire S.; m. Annette Ellen Drasin, Aug. 29, 1965; children: Rochelle Heidi, Sondra Nicole. BA in Physics, UCLA, 1960, MS in Nuclear Physics, 1962; PhD in Physics, Columbia Pacific U. 1985. Cert. Nat. Assn. Securities Dealers, Series 6, Investment Co. Products/Variable Contracts, registered rep.; lic. in securities and health and life ins. Calif. Physics instr., lower divsn. Lab. UCLA, 1960-62, physics instr. upper divsn. nuclear physics, 1961-62; nuclear ion engine rocket physicist Rocketdyne, Canoga Park, Calif., 1961; scientist Advanced Tech. Co., L.A., 1965-66; physicist, principle investigator Northrop Space Sci. Lab., Hawthorne, Calif., 1966-70; pres. Sherman Ins. Agy., Inc., L.A., 1970-84; pres., CEO Sherman Fin. Svcs., Inc., Thousand Oaks, Calif., 1984—; cons. TRW, 1970; speaker scientific seminars for NASA, U.S. Air Force, Lockheed; speaker fin. seminars, 1972—. Author: Microwave Phenomenological Theory of Superconductivity, 1965, Superconductive Antennas, 1966. Recipient Atomic Energy Commn. award Am. Electronics, 1960, Top Prodr. Nationwide award U.S. Life Ins. Co. Calif., 1978, Leading Disability Prodr. Nationwide award Chubb Life Ins. Co. Am., 1983-85, 90, Leading Combined Life and Disability Prodr. award Chubb, 1987, Leading Combined Disability and Life Ins. Producer award Chubb, 1989, Internat. Life and Health Ins. awards Chubb Corp./Summit Club Calif., 1979, 88, 89, 92, 94, Hawaii, 1982, 92, 94, Italy, 1983, 93, Greece, 1984, Bermuda, 1985, 72, 88, England, 1985, Scotland, 1985, Mex., 1986, Monaco 1987, Switzerland, 1987, Hong Kong, 1988, Thailand, 1988, France, 1989, Africa, 1989, Puerto Rico, 1990, 95, Ariz., 1991, Australia, 1992, Fla., 1993, Austria, 1994; PhD Rsch. fellow UCLA, 1962-64. Mem. Calif. Assn. Life Underwriters, Westlake Art Guild, UCLA Physics Honor Soc. (v.p. 1959, exec. v.p. 1960), Sigma Pi Sigma. Avocations: landscape artist; played trumphet and drums, 1956-59, USAF ROTC marching band; arranger and composer of music; planetary astrophotography. One of the first to design the NASA crystal experiment for astronauts; originated and performed first superconductive non-destructive test to determine aircraft alloy strength; created concept and experimentally performed the first superconductive short antenna for very low frequency communication. Office: Sherman Financial Svcs Inc 2158 Calle Riscoso Thousand Oaks CA 91362-1141

SHERMAN, GORDON RAE, computer science educator; b. Menomenee, Mich., Feb. 24, 1928; s. Gordon E. and Myrtle H. (Evenson) S.; m. Lois E. Miller, July 3, 1951; children—Karen Rae, Gordon Thorstein. BS, Iowa State U., 1953; M.S., Stanford U., 1954; Ph.D., Purdue U., 1960. Instr. math. and research assoc. Statis and Computational Lab., Purdue U., Lafayette Ind., 1956-60; dir. Computing Ctr., U. Tenn., Knoxville, 1960—, prof. computer sci., 1960—; program dir. techniques and systems Office of Computing Activities, NSF, 1971-72; chmn. membership com. EDUCOM Council, 1983-85. Served with USAF, 1946-49, 50-51. Recipient Chancellor's citation U. Tenn., 1983; NSF grantee, 1974. Fellow Brit. Computer Soc.; mem. Am. Statis. Assn., Assn. for Computing Machinery, Dta Processing Mgmt. Assn. (internat. computer sci. Man of Yr. award S.E. Region VIII, 1973; Profl. of Yr. Region VIII 1979), Ops. Research Soc. Am., Soc. for Indsl. and Applied Math., Sigma Xi, Phi Kappa Phi. Republican. Lutheran. Contbr. articles on computer sci. to profl. jours. Home: 301 Cheshire Dr Apt 105 Knoxville TN 37919-5849 Office: U Tenn 209 Stokely Mgmt Ctr Knoxville TN 37996

SHERMAN, IRWIN WILLIAM, biological sciences educator, university official; b. N.Y.C., Feb. 12, 1933; s. Morris and Anna (Ezaak) S.; m. Vilia Gay Turner, Aug. 25, 1966; children: Jonathan Turner, Alexa Joy. BS, CCNY, 1954; MS, Northwestern U., 1959, PhD, 1960. Asst. prof. U. Calif. Riverside, 1962-67, assoc. prof., 1967-70, prof. biology, 1970—, chmn. biology dept., 1974-79, dean Coll. Natural and Agrl. Scis., div. agrl. expt. sta., 1981-88, exec. vice chancellor, 1993-94; instr. marine biol. lab. Woods Hole, Mass., 1963-68; mem. study sect. tropical medicine NIH, 1970-73; cons. Agy. Internat. Devel., 1978—; mem. ad hoc study group U.S. Army, 1975-78. Author: (book) The Invertebrates: Function and Form, 1976, Biology: A Human Approach, 1989. Mem. steering com. World Health Orgn., 1978-87. Served with U.S. Army, 1954-56. USPHS fellow Rockefeller Inst., 1960-62, Guggenheim fellow, 1967, NIH/Nat. Inst. Med. Rsch. fellow 1973-74, Walter and Eliza Hall Inst. for Med. Rsch. fellow, 1986; Wellcome Trust

lectr. Brit. Soc. Parasitology, 1987, Scripps Rsch. Inst. fellow 1991. Mem. AAAS, Am. Soc. Tropical Medicine and Hygiene, Soc. Protozoology, Soc. Parasitology, Sigma Xi. Democrat. Jewish. Avocations: painting, reading. Office: Univ of Calif-Riverside Dept Biology Riverside CA 92521

SHERMAN, JEFFREY BARRY, retail executive; b. Passaic, N.J., June 25, 1948; s. Maxwell and Elinor (Richman) S.; m. Karin Lynn Swann, May 1, 1971; children—Erik, Brett, Peter, Kristin. B.S. in Econs., CCNY, 1971; M.B.A., NYU, 1975. With Bloomingdale's, N.Y.C., 1971—; v.p. merchandising Bloomingdale's, 1982-83, sr. v.p., 1983-85, exec. v.p., 1985—, now pres. Avocations: skiing; sailing. Office: Bloomingdale's 59th St & Lexington New York NY 10022*

SHERMAN, JOHN CLINTON, geography educator; b. Toronto, Ont., Can., May 3, 1916; s. Harold C. and Grace (Ubbes) S.; m. Helen Jean Loyd, Mar. 15, 1941; children: Constance Sherman Newell, John Harold (dec.), Mary Helen (Mrs. Stephen Wood), Barbara Lillian (Mrs. David Graves). B.A., U. Mich., 1937; M.A., Clark U., 1942; Ph.D., U. Wash., 1947. Mem faculty U. Wash., Seattle, 1942—; prof. geography U. Wash., 1963-86, prof. emeritus, 1986—, chmn. dept., 1963-73; Mem. sub-com. on geography adv. to U.S. Geol. Survey space programs for earth observation Nat. Acad. Sci-NRC, 1965—. Author: Atlas of a Single ERTS Image, 1975, (with others) Atlas of Marine Use for the North Pacific; Adv. co-editor: (with others) Oxford Regional Economic Atlas of U.S. and Can, 1967; visual and tactile map of met. Washington, tactile atlas of The Mall, Washington. Mem. Wash. State Bd. on Geog. Names. Mem. Assn. Am. Geographers, Assn. Pacific Coast Geographers, Internat. Cartographic Assn. (mem. U.S. com.). Research and publs. on maps for the blind, maps and graphics for partially seeing children. Home: 7424 55th Ave NE Seattle WA 98115-6220

SHERMAN, JOHN FOORD, biomedical consultant; b. Oneonta, N.Y., Sept. 4, 1919; s. Henry C. and Ruth (Foord) S.; m. Betsy Deane Murray, Feb. 8, 1944; children: Betsy Deane, Mary Ann. B.S., Albany Coll. Pharmacy of Union U., 1949, D.Sc., 1970; Ph.D., Yale U., 1953. With NIH, 1953-74; assoc. dir. extramural programs Nat. Inst. Neurol. Diseases and Blindness, 1961-62, Nat. Inst. Arthritis and Metabolic Disease, 1962-63; assoc. dir. for extramural programs Office Dir. NIH, 1964-68, dep. dir., 1968-74; v.p. Assn. Am. Med. Colls., Washington, 1974-91, exec. v.p., 1987-91, spl. cons., 1991-94; mem. bd. advisors Am. Bd. Internal Medicine, 1991—; sr. advisor Rsch!Am., 1994—. Asst. surgeon gen. USPHS, 1964-68; spl. rsch. chemotherapy and neuropharmacology; mem. panel on data and studies NRC, 1976-87; mem. biomed. libr. rev. com. NIH; bd. dirs. Spinal Cord Injury Edn. and Tng. Found., 1986-92, Musculoskeletal Transplant Found., 1987—. With U.S. Army, 1941-46. Decorated Bronze Star; recipient Meritorious Svc. award USPHS, 1965, Disting. Svc. award HEW, 1971, Sec.'s Spl. Citation award, 1973, award Nat. Civil Service League, 1973, Disting. Alumnus award Union U.-Pharmacy Coll. Coun., 1974, Lifetime Achievement award Nat. Assn. for Biomed. Rsch., 1990. Fellow AAAS; mem. Inst. Medicine NAS, Cosmos Club, Sigma Xi. Congregationalist.

SHERMAN, JOSEPH HOWARD, clergyman; b. Marion, S.C., June 14, 1923; s. Samuel and Alma (Cannon) S.; m. Daisy Lee Littles; children: Joseph Howard Jr., Beatrice Sherman Boone. D.D. (hon.), Trinity Hall Coll.; LL.D. (hon.), New Haven Theol. Appointed Jurisdictional Bishop of N.C., 2d Jurisdiction, 1963. Founder, pastor Pentecostal Temple Ch. of God in Christ, Charlotte, N.C.; pres. N.C. Youth Dept.; dist. supt. N.C. Jurisdiction, Wadesboro; chmn. Council of Bishops, Memphis, 1976—; pres. C. H. Mason System of Bible Colls., Charlotte, N.C., 1975; mem. Nat. Hymnal Com. Author: (book) Weapons of the Righteous; (phamplet) Witchcraft, The Work of the Devil; (album) Peace That Only Christ Can Give; editor The Mighty Voice That Crieth mag. pres., founder J. Howard Sherman Scholarship Fund, Charlotte, 1974—; bd. dirs. C. H. Mason Scholarship Found., Memphis, Saints Ctr.; mem. NAACP, Charlotte, Hiring of the Handicapped, Charlotte, 1984, Ch. of God in Christ Hosp. Fund; mem. grievance com. Housing Authority, Charlotte, 1983, 84; mem. steering com. Democratic Governorship, N.C., 1984. Named Knight of Queen City, Charlotte, 1976, hon. citizen City of Balt., 1981, hon. atty. gen. N.C., 1983; J.H. Sherman Day named in his honor, Charlotte, 1980-84. Mem. Ministerial Alliance (sec. Charlotte chpt. 1983—). Office: The Church of God in Christ PO Box 329 Charlotte NC 28201

SHERMAN, JOSEPH OWEN, pediatric surgeon; b. Chgo., Aug. 15, 1936; s. Joseph Owen and Mary Elizabeth (Kelly) S.; m. June Marie Martin, Mar. 16, 1963; children: Brian William, Lee Ann. Student, U. Ill., 1955-58; BS, Northwestern U., 1959, MD, 1962. Diplomate Am. Bd. Surgery, Am. Bd. Pediatric Surgery; lic. physician, Ill. Rotating intern Passavant Meml. Hosp., Chgo., 1963-64; resident in gen. surgery VA Rsch. Hosp., Chgo., 1964-65, 67-68; Am. Cancer Soc. clin. fellow Northwestern U. Med. Sch., Chgo., 1965-66; resident in pediatric surgery Children's Meml. Hosp., Chgo. 1966, 68-69; resident in thoracic surgery Mcpl. Tb San., Chgo., 1967; from instr. to assoc. prof. surgery Northwestern U. Med. Sch., 1967-86, prof. clin. surgery, 1986—; emeritus staff dept. surgery Children's Meml. Hosp., 1995—, Evanston (Ill.) Hosp., 1995—. Contbr. articles to profl. jours. Served with Ill. Army N.G., 1953-69, Ill. Air N.G., 1966-67. Fellow ACS, Am. Acad. Pediatrics, Inst. of Medicine of Chgo.; mem. AMA, Am. Pediatric Surg. Assn., Assn. for Acad. Surgery, Ctrl. Surg. Assn., Chgo. Med. Soc., Chgo. Surg. Soc., Ill. Pediatric Surg. Assn., Ill. State Med. Soc. Avocations: photography, computer programing, indoor and outdoor gardening.

SHERMAN, JUDITH DOROTHY, producer, recording company owner, recording engineer; b. Cleve., Nov. 12, 1942; d. William Paul and Laverne (Spoerke) Luekens; m. Kenneth Sherman, Aug. 1, 1964 (div. Aug. 1972); m. Max Wilcox, Jan. 1, 1981 (div. Jan. 1988); m. Curtis Macomber, Apr. 29, 1988. BA, Valparaiso U., 1964; MFA, SUNY-Buffalo, 1971. Rec. engr. Edward at the Moog, N.Y.C., 1971-72; producer-music dir. WBAI-FM, N.Y.C., 1972-76; owner-producer Judith Sherman Prodns., N.Y.C., 1976—; rec. engr. Marlboro (Vt.) Music Festival, 1976-94; adminstrv. dir. La Musica di Asolo, Sarasota, Fla., 1986-88; vocalist Steve Reich and Musicians, 1971-72. Recipient Corp. Pub. Broadcasting award, 1976, two Grammy award nominations, 1991, Grammy award, Classical Prodr. of Yr., 1993, Grammy award nominations, 1994. Mem. NAFE, Chamber Music Am., NARAS. Democrat. Home and Office: 645 W 239th St Apt 6F Bronx NY 10463-1277

SHERMAN, KENNETH, oceanographer; b. Boston, Oct. 6, 1932. BS, Suffolk U., 1954, DSc (hon.), 1979; MS, U. R.I., 1960; DSc, Morski Inst. Ryback, 1978. Instr. conservation edn. Mass. Audubon Soc., 1954-55; fishery aide U.S. Bur. Commn. Fisheries, Mass., 1955-56; fishery rsch. biologist zooplankton ecology U.S. Bur. Commn. Fisheries, Hawaii, 1960-63, Maine, 1963-71; tchr. high sch. Mass., 1959-60; coord. marine resources monitoring assessing and prediction program U.S. Dept. Commerce, NOAA, Nat. Marine Fisheries Svc., 1971-73; chief resource assessment divsn. U.S. Dept. Commerce, NOAA, Nat. Marine Fisheries Svc., Washington, 1973-75; lab. dir., chief marine ecosystems br. U.S. Dept. Commerce, NOAA, Nat. Marine Fisheries Svc., Narragansett, R.I., 1975—; mem. biol. oceanographic com. Internat. Coun. Exploration Sea, 1972-87; U.S. project officer Plankton Sorting Ctr., Szczecin, Poland, 1973—; adj. prof. grad. sch. oceanography U. R.I., 1980—. Co-editor: Food Chains Yields, Models, & Management of Large Marine Ecosystems, 1991, Large Marine Ecosystems: Patterns, Processes & Yields, 1990, Biomass Yields & Geography of Large Marine Ecosystems, 1989, Variability & Management of Large Marine Ecosystems, 1986. Mem. AAAS, Am. Soc. Limnology and Oceanography, Ecol. Soc. Am., Am. Soc. Zoology, Am. Soc. Ichthyology and Herpetology. Office: Nat Marine Fisheries Svc NE Fisheries Sci Ctr 28 Tarzwell Dr Narragansett RI 02882*

SHERMAN, LOUIS ALLEN, biologist, researcher; b. Chgo., Dec. 16, 1943; s. Stanley E. and Sarah R. Sherman; m. Debra Meddoff, June 15, 1969; children: Daniel, Jeff. BS in Physics, U. Chgo., 1965, PhD in Biophysics, 1970. Postdoctoral fellow Cornell U., Ithaca, N.Y., 1970-72; asst. prof. U. Mo., Columbia, 1972-78, assoc. prof., 1978-83, prof., 1983-88, dir. biol. scis., 1985-88; prof., head dept. biol. scis. Purdue U., West Lafayette, Ind., 1989—.

SHERMAN, MARTIN NMI, entomologist; b. Newark, Nov. 21, 1920; s. Louis and Anna (Norkin) S.; m. Ruth Goldsmith, Sept. 25, 1943 (div. Nov. 1975); children: Laurel Deborah Sherman Englehart, Susan Leslie Sherman Kitakis. B.S., Rutgers U., 1941, M.S., 1943; Ph.D., Cornell U., 1948. Research fellow in entomology Rutgers U., 1941-43; research asst. Cornell U., 1945-48; entomologist Beech-Nut Packing Co., Rochester, N.Y., 1948-49; mem. faculty U. Hawaii, Honolulu, 1949—; prof. entomology U. Hawaii, 1958-86, prof. emeritus entomology, 1986—; Fulbright scholar U. Tokyo, 1956-57, Royal Vet. and Agrl. Coll. of Denmark, 1966; vis. prof. Rutgers U., 1973. Editorial bd.: Pacific Sci, 1962-66, Jour. Med. Entomology, 1968-72. Served to 1st lt. USAAF, 1943-45. Fellow Am. Inst. Chemists; mem. Entomol. Soc. Am. (gov. bd. 1974-77, pres. Pacific br. 1970), Am. Chem. Soc., Soc. Toxicology, Soc. Environ. Toxicology and Chemistry, Am. Registry Profl. Entomologists, Japanese Soc. Applied Entomology and Zoology, Hawaiian Entomology Soc. (pres. 1969-70), Internat. Soc. for Study Xenobiotics, Sigma Xi, Delta Phi Alpha, Phi Kappa Phi, Gamma Sigma Delta. Club: Torch. Address: 1121 Koloa St Honolulu HI 96816-5103

SHERMAN, MARY ANGUS, public library administrator; b. Lawton, Okla., Jan. 3, 1937; d. Donald Adelbert and Mabel (Felkner) Angus; m. Donald Neil Sherman, Feb. 8, 1958; children: Elizabeth Sherman Cunningham, Donald Neil II. BS in Home Econs., U. Okla., 1958, MLS, 1969. Br. head Pioneer Libr. System, Purcell, Okla., 1966-76; regional libr. Pioneer Libr. System, Norman, Okla., 1976-78, asst. dir., 1978-80, dir., 1987—. Named one of Distinguished Alumni Sch. Home Econs., U. Okla., 1980. Mem. ALA (councilor 1988—, planning and budget assembly 1990-91, internat. rels. com. 1992—), Pub. Libr. Assn. (divsn. of ALA, pres. pub. policy for pub. librs. section 1995—), AAUW (pres. Okla. chpt. 1975-77, nat. bd. dirs. 1983-87, S.W. cen. region dir. 1983-85, v.p. nat. membership 1985-87, Woman of the Yr. Purcell chpt. 1982), Okla. Libr. Assn. (pres. 1982-83, interlibrary cooperation com. 1993—, chair 1994-95, Disting. Svc. award 1986), Norman C. of C. bd. dirs. 1988—, pres. 1994-95), Altrusa Internat., Rotary (program chair 1991-92, bd. dirs. 1993—, pres. 1995—, Paul Harris fellow), Norman Assistance League Club (cmty. assoc.), Norman, Okla. Sisters City Com., 1994—, Delta Gamma Mothers (pres. 1978-79), Kappa Alpha Theta (pres. Alpha Omicron House Corp. 1984-87, nat. dir. house corps. 1987-88), Beta Phi Mu, Phi Beta Kappa. Democrat. Methodist. Office: Pioneer Libr System 225 N Webster Ave Norman OK 73069-7133

SHERMAN, MAX RAY, lawyer, academic executive, former state senator; b. Viola, Ark., Jan. 19, 1935; s. Ernest and Eva (Davenport) S.; m. Gene Alice Wienbroer, July 29, 1961; children: Lynn Ray, Holly Ruth. BA in History, Baylor U., 1957, LLD (hon.), 1978; JD with honors, U. Tex., 1960. Ptnr. Gibson, Ochsner and Adkins, Amarillo, Tex., 1960-77; Tex. State Senator, 1971-77; pres. West Tex. State U., Canyon, 1977-82; spl. counsel to Tex. gov. State of Tex., Austin, 1983; dean Lyndon B. Johnson Sch. Pub. Affairs, Austin, 1983—; Mem. exec. com. So. Regional Edn. Bd., 1986-87. Contbr. articles to law revs. Served to capt. USAR, 1960-64. Named One of Ten Best Legislators, Tex. Monthly, 1973, 75, 77. Mem. ABA, Tex. Bar Assn., Nat. Assn. Schs. of Pub. Affairs and Adminstrs. (exec. counc. 1983-87, 88—, pres. 1988-89), Nat. Acad. Pub. Adminstrn., Assn. for Pub. Policy Analysis and Mgmt. (exec. com. 1983-86), Nat. Commn. State and Local Pub. Svc. Democrat. Presbyterian. Avocations: racquetball, tennis. Office: Univ Tex LBJ Sch Pub Affairs Drawer Y Univ Sta Austin TX 78713-8925

SHERMAN, MONA DIANE, school system administrator; b. N.Y.C., Aug. 28, 1941; d. Hyman and Lillian (Baker) Ginsberg; m. Richard H. Sherman, May 9, 1964; children: Holly Baker, Andrew Hunter. BS, Hunter Coll., CUNY, 1962; MS, CUNY, 1965. Cert. elem. tchr., K-12 reading endorsement specialist, ESL tchr., elem. adminstrn. and supervision, instrnl. supervision, spl. edn. learning disabilities and neurologically impaired edn., Ind. Elem. tchr. N.Y.C. Pub. Schs., 1962-77; team leader Tchr. Corps Potsdam (N.Y.) State Coll., SUNY, 1977-79; dir. Tchr. Ctr., Sch. City of Hammond, Ind., 1979-87; lab. coord. PALS, Gary (Ind.) Sch. Corp., 1987-93, mentor, 1988—, facilitator of staff devel., 1993—; instr. Tex. Instrument Computer Co., Lubbock, 1983-84, Performance Learning System, Emerson, N.J., 1984—; cons. in classroom discipline and computer instrn. Gary Staff Devel. Ctr., 1987—; mentor Urban Tchr. Edn. program Ind. U. N.W., Gary, 1991—; chair sch. improvement team, tchr. of yr. com., 1993-94; mem. Gary Tech. Com., Gary Distance Learning Com. Mem. Lake Area United Way Lit. Coalition NW Ind., 1990, Gary Reading Textbook Adoption Com.; sec. Martin Luther King Jr. Acad. PTSA, mem. sch. improvement team. Recipient Recognition NW Ind. Forum, 1988, Tchr. of Yr. award Merrillville (Ind.) Lions Club, 1988, Outstanding Tchr. of Yr. award Inland Ryerson, East Chicago, Ind., 1989. Mem. Ind. Reading Assn., Gary Reading Assn., Phi Delta Kappa, Delta Kappa Gamma. Avocations: theatre, crafts, tennis. Home: 1112 Fran Lin Pky Munster IN 46321-3607

SHERMAN, NORMAN MARK, advertising agency executive; b. N.Y.C., June 19, 1948; s. Sol and Rhoda (Kaplan) S.; m. Michelle Petnov, Jan. 8, 1978; 1 child, Michael Isaac. BA, U. Buffalo, 1970; MBA, Columbia U., 1972. Cert. tchr., N.Y. Product mgr. RCA Records, N.Y.C., 1972-73; dir. mktg. Shelter Records, N.Y.C., 1973-74; account exec. Rosenfeld Sirowitz & Lawson, N.Y.C., 1974-76; account exec. Benton & Bowles, N.Y.C., 1976-78, v.p. account supr., 1978-81, sr. v.p., mgmt. supr., 1981-84; exec. v.p., dir. account mgmt. Avrett, Free & Ginsberg, N.Y.C., 1984-85; sr. v.p., group account dir. D'arcy, Masius, Benton & Bowles, 1985-93, mgn. dir., 1993—; also bd. dirs. Home: 330 W 72nd St New York NY 10023 Office: D'Arcy Masius Benton & Bowles 1675 Broadway New York NY 10019-5865

SHERMAN, RANDOLPH S., lawyer; b. New Rochelle, N.Y., Nov. 19, 1944; s. Julius and Selma (Goldstein) S.; m. Joan E. Lauterbach, May 28, 1967; children: Elissa, Stephanie. BS in Indsl. Labor, Cornell U., 1966; JD, NYU, 1969. Bar: N.Y. 1970, U.S. Ct. Appeals (2d cir.) 1980, U.S. Ct. Appeals (3d cir.) 1983, U.S. Ct. Appeals (4th cir.) 1994, U.S. Ct. Appeals (8th cir.) 1986, U.S. Supreme Ct. 1984. Ptnr. Kaye Scholer, Fierman, Hays & Handler, N.Y.C., 1969—. Mem. ABA (antitrust sect., litigation sect.), U.S. Trademark Assn., N.Y.C. Bar Assn. Office: Kaye Scholer Fierman Hays & Handler 425 Park Ave New York NY 10022-3506

SHERMAN, RICHARD BEATTY, history educator; b. Somerville, Mass., Nov. 16, 1929; s. James Beatty and Hilda Louise (Ford) S.; m. Hanni Fey, June 13, 1952; children: Linda Caroline, Alan Theodore. AB, Harvard U., 1951, PhD, 1959; MA, U. Pa., 1952. Instr. history Pa. State U., State College, 1957-60; asst. prof. Coll. of William and Mary, Williamsburg, Va., 1960-65, assoc. prof., 1965-70, prof. 1970-87, chancellor prof., 1987-92, Pullen prof., 1992-94, prof. emeritus, 1994—; Fulbright prof. Am. history U. Stockholm, 1966-67. Served with U.S. Army, 1952-54. Am. Philos. Soc. grantee, 1964, 66; faculty research grantee, Coll. of William and Mary, 1962, 63, 65, 80, 87. Mem. AAUP, Am. Hist. Assn., Assn. Am. Historians, Phi Beta Kappa. Democrat. Author: The Negro and the City, 1970; The Republican Party and Black America, 1973, The Case of Odell Waller, 1992; co-author: The College of William and Mary: A History, 1993; contbr. articles to profl. jours. Home: 205 Matoaka Ct Williamsburg VA 23185-2810 Office: Coll William and Mary Dept History Williamsburg VA 23185

SHERMAN, RICHARD H., education educator; b. Yonkers, N.Y., Jan. 5, 1941; m. Mona D. Sherman, May 9, 1964; children: Holly Baker, Andrew Hunter. BA, Hunter Coll., 1962; MA, Iowa U., 1965; MS, Queens Coll., 1970; EdD, Yeshiva U., 1977. Cert. tchr., Ind., Ill., N.Y. Asst. prof. edn. SUNY, Potsdam; instr. Herbert H. Lehman Coll., CUNY; asst. prof. edn. Purdue U., Hammond, Ind.; assoc. dean Ind. Vocat. Tech. Coll., Gary; chmn., assoc. prof. Calumet Coll. St. Joseph, Whiting, Ind.; edn. dir. Mus. Broadcast Communications, Chgo.; dir. Zarem/Golde ORT TECH Inst. Chgo.; workshop leader; presenter and speaker in field. Author, playwright, poet, critic. Bd. dirs. Jewish Fedn. N.W. Ind.; chmn. events "Walk for Israel", Lake Area United Way, v.p. mobilization and resources devel, needs and assessment priorities com., chmn. section campaign; active Lake County chpt. ARC, N.W. Ind. Film Commn. Recipient N.W. Ind. Forum Svc.

Recognition award, Jewish Fedn. N.W. Ind. Young Leadership award, Harlem Arts Svc. award. Mem. Internat. Reading Assn.; Am. Assn. Theatre Critics, Dramatists Guild, Ind. Reading Coun., Ind. Reading Profs. (treas.), Hammond Reading Coun. (pres.), Ind. State Coun., N.W. Ind. Arts Assn. (subcom.), Rotary Club, Sigma Tau Delta, Phi Delta Kappa.

SHERMAN, ROBERT B(ERNARD), composer, lyricist, screenwriter; b. N.Y.C., Dec. 19, 1925; s. Al and Rosa (Dancis) S.; student UCLA, 1943; BA, Bard Coll., 1949; MusD (hon.) Lincoln U., 1990; m. Joyce Ruth Sasner, Sept. 27, 1953; children: Laurie Shane, Jeffrey Craig, Andrea Tracy, Robert Jason. Popular songwriter, 1950-60, including Tall Paul, Pineapple Princess, You're Sixteen (Gold Record); songwriter Walt Disney Prodns., Beverly Hills, Calif., 1960-68, for 29 films including The Parent Trap, 1961, Summer Magic, 1963, Mary Poppins, 1964, That Darn Cat, 1965, Winnie The Pooh, 1965, Jungle Book, 1967, Bedknobs and Broomsticks, 1971; co-composer song It's A Small World, theme of Disneyland and Walt Disney World, Fla.; composer, lyricist United Artists, Beverly Hills, 1969—, songs for film Chitty, Chitty, Bang, Bang, 1969, Snoopy, Come Home!, 1972; song score Charlotte's Web, 1972; composer for Walt Disney's Wonderful World of Color, TV, 1961—; co-producer NBC-TV spl. Goldilocks, 1970; v.p. Musi-Classics, Inc.; co-producer, composer, lyricist stage musical Victory Canteen, 1971; composer-lyricist Broadway show Over Here, 1975; screenplay and song score Tom Sawyer, United Artists, 1972, Huckleberry Finn, 1974, The Slipper and the Rose, 1977, The Magic of Lassie, 1978. Served with inf. AUS, 1943-45; ETO. Decorated Purple Heart; recipient 2 Acad. awards best score for Mary Poppins, 1964, best song for Chim Chim Cheree, 1964, Grammy award, 1965; Christopher medal, 1965, 74; nine Acad. award nominations; Acad. award nomination for song score Bedknobs and Broomsticks, 1971, for best song The Age of Not Believing, 1971, others; 16 golden, 4 platinum and one diamond record album, 1965-83; first prize best composer song score Tom Sawyer, Moscow Film Festival, 1973, B.M.I. Pioneer award, 1977; Golden Cassette awards for Mary Poppins, Jungle Book, Bed Knobs and Broomsticks, 1983, Mouscar award Disney Studios, Disney Legend award, 1990, BMI Richard Kirk Achievment award, 1991. Mem. Acad. Motion Picture Arts and Scis. (exec. bd. music br. 12 yrs.), AFTRA, Nat. Acad. Rec. Arts and Scis., Composers and Lyricists Guild (exec. bd.), Writers Guild Am., Dramatists Guild, Authors League. Office: 9030 Harratt St West Hollywood CA 90069-3858

SHERMAN, ROGER, economics educator; b. Jamestown, N.Y., Sept. 10, 1930; s. Claire Blanchard and Margaret Gertrude (Burke) S.; m. Charlotte Ann Murphy, Apr. 4, 1953; children:—Claire Randall, Thomas Allen. B.S. in Math., Grove City Coll., 1952; M.B.A. in Fin., Harvard U., 1959; M.S. in Econs., Carnegie-Mellon U., 1965, Ph.D., 1966. Mgr. mfg. control IBM Corp., N.Y.C., 1956-62; asst. prof., assoc. prof., prof. U. Va., Charlottesville, 1965-72, Brown Forman prof. econs., 1982—, chmn. dept. econs., 1982-90; vis. scholar Oxford U., 1987, Sydney U., 1988. Author: Oligopoly: An Empirical Approach, 1972, The Economics of Industry, 1974, Antitrust Policies and Issues, 1978, The Regulation of Monopoly, 1989; editor: Perspectives on Postal Service Issues, 1980; contbr. articles to profl. jours. Bd. dirs. McGuffey Art Ctr., Charlottesville, 1984-92. Lt. USNR, 1953-62. U. Bristol fellow, 1968-69; Fulbright lectr., Madrid, 1972; Sci. Ctr. Berlinfellow, 1975, 79, 80; Rockefeller Found. Vis. scholar, 1985. Mem. Am. Econ. Assn., Royal Econ. Soc., Econometric Soc. Home: 500 Court Square #807 Charlottesville VA 22902 Office: U Va Rouss Hall Charlottesville VA 22903-3288

SHERMAN, ROGER TALBOT, surgeon, educator; b. Chgo., Sept. 30, 1923; s. Joseph Bright and Alice Elizabeth (Baur) S.; m. Ruth Kathryn Thieman, Aug. 23, 1952; children: Nann, Alice, Nina, John, Julie. A.B., Kenyon Coll., 1946; M.D., U. Cin., 1948. Diplomate Am. Bd. Surgery (mem.). Intern, fellow in pathology St. Luke's Hosp., Chgo., 1948-50; resident in surgery Cin. Gen. Hosp., 1950-56; chief dept. exptl. surgery Walter Reed Army Med. Center, 1956-59; asst. prof. to prof. surgery U. Tenn., Memphis, 1959-72; prof., chmn. dept. surgery U. South Fla., Tampa, 1972-82; prof. surgery Emory U. Sch. Medicine, Atlanta, 1983-93; chief surgery Grady Meml. Hosp., Atlanta, 1983-92; attending surgeon Atlanta VA Hosp., Decatur, Ga., 1993—; Whitaker prof. surgery Emory U. Sch. Medicine, Atlanta, 1994—; dir. surg. edn. Piedmont Hosp., Atlanta, 1994—; cons. Walter Reed Army Med. Center. Mem. editorial bd. Am. Surgeon, 1970-91, Jour. Trauma, 1970-93; contbr. articles to profl. jours., chpts. to books. Served to maj. M.C. AUS, 1956-59. Recipient Golden Apple Tchr. of the Yr. award, 1972, Williams Disting. Teaching award Emory U., 1984, Curtis P. Artz award, 1988. Fellow ACS (gov.); mem. Am. Assn. Surgery of Trauma (pres. 1979), Am. Surg. Assn., So. Surg. Assn., Southeastern Surg. Congress (pres. 1985), Internat. Surg. Soc., Soc. Surgery of Alimentary Tract, Am. Burn Assn., Shock Soc., Am. Trauma Soc., Sigma Xi, Psi Upsilon, Alpha Omega Alpha. Home: 1170 Woods Cir NE Atlanta GA 30324-2736 Office: Piedmont Hospital Department of Surgery 1984 Peachtree Rd NW Atlanta GA 30309-1231 *Surgery. The opening, exploration and repair of the living human body is an awesome responsibility afforded to only a few. To be privileged to be counted among those is a high honor, surpassed only by being trusted to teach others this demanding, and marvelous craft.*

SHERMAN, RON, photographer; b. Cleve., May 10, 1942; s. Hyman B. and Sheryl D. Sherman; m. Myra LeBell, Aug. 16, 1969; children: Scott Neal, Jonathan Harris, Hannah Beth. BFA in illustrative photography, Rochester Inst. Tech., 1964; MA in photographic commn., Syracuse U., 1971. Staff photographer Gannett Newspapers (Democrat, Chronicle and Times Union), Rochester, N.Y., 1961-64, U. Fla., Gainesville, 1964-66; photo-officer, military intelligence unit U.S. Army-Signal Corps, Vietnam, 1967-68; staff photographer Milw. Journal, Wis., 1969; photographer Syracuse U., Syracuse, N.Y., 1969-71; prin. Ron Sherman Photographer, Atlanta, 1971—, Computer Aided Photography, Inc., Atlanta, 1991—; adv. comml. photography Gwinett Tech. Inst., Lawrenceville, Ga., 1983—; cons. ABC TV, Alcoa, AT&T, CBS Sports, The Coca-Cola Co., Eastman Kodak, Ford Motor Co., IBM, TRW, Atlanta Com. for the Olympic Games, Bell-South, Southern Bell, Atlanta Gas Light Co., Nat. Hockey League, Sonat, Gen. Mills, Ga. Power, Southern Co., Phoenix Comms. Pub. works in Life, Time, Newsweek, Inside Sports, Business Week, Forbes, Reader's Digest, Ford Times, America Illustrated, Medical World News, New York Times, U.S. News and World Report, Venture; pub. works in Atlanta calendar, 1994, 95—; Atlanta photos used to illustrate Peter Max's Super Bowl XXVIII poster, (hard cover book) Greater North Fulton. 1st Lt. U.S. Army 1968-69, Vietnam. Mem. Nat. Press Photographers Assn., Am. Soc. Media Photographers (pres. Atlanta chpt. 1980-81). Avocations: gardening, reading, classical and jazz music. Office: PO Box 28656 Atlanta GA 30358

SHERMAN, SAUL LAWRENCE, lawyer, government official; b. N.Y.C., Sept. 5, 1926; s. Louis and Hannah Jean (Auerbach) S.; m. Carol Esberg, Nov. 12, 1964 (dec. 1972); children: Kate M., William Benjamin; m. Judith Shonkoff, June 5, 1977. Grad., Fieldston Sch., 1943; S.B. magna cum laude, Harvard U., 1946, J.D. cum laude, 1949. Bar: N.Y. 1949, D.C. 1964, also U.S. courts. With U.S. Fgn. Service, Frankfurt, Germany, 1949-51, London, 1951-52; assoc. Lord, Day & Lord, N.Y.C., 1952-62; ptnr. Rivkin Sherman & Levy (and predecessor firms), N.Y.C., 1962-84; Schnader, Harrison, Segal & Lewis, N.Y.C., 1984-87; pvt. practice law N.Y.C., 1988—; of counsel Moldover, Hertz, Cooper and Gidaly, N.Y.C., 1990—; adj. prof. law Cardozo Sch. Law, N.Y.C.; exec. sec. U.S. affiliate Internat. Commn. Jurists, 1962-66; U.S. mem. Bd. Validation German Dollar Bonds, 1962—; adviser multilateral trade agreements U.S. Dept. Commerce, 1978-80; mem. U.S. Trade Rep. industry adv. com., 1980-86; mem. com. on trade regulation Internat. C. of C., Paris, 1979—; mem. U.S.-Can. NAFTA Binational Arbitration Panels, 1992—; lectr. internat. trade to profl. and bus. groups. Co-author: Commentary on the GATT Customs Valuation Code, 2d edit., 1988; contbr. articles to profl. jours. Served with USNR, 1944-45. Mem. ABA, Am. Soc. Internat. Law, N.Y. State Bar Assn. (exec. com., internat. law and practice sect.), Assn. Bar City N.Y. (com. internat. trade 1984-90, chmn. 1987-90, coun. internat. affairs 1985-92, com. nat. security and arms control 1992-93), Customs and Internat. Trade Bar Assn. (bd. dirs. 1972-81), Am. Assn. Exporters and Importers (bd. dirs. 1974-88, 94—, trade policy com., chmn. com. U.S.-Can. free trade agreement, chmn. customs valuation com.), Phi Beta Kappa (1st marshal Harvard). Home: PO Box 820 Water Mill NY 11976-0820 Office: 750 3d Ave New York NY 10017

SHERMAN, SAUL S., manufacturing company executive; b. 1917. BA, U. Chgo., 1939. Profl. football player Chgo. Bears, 1939-40; pres., treas. Emerson Machinery Corp., 1937-66; with Davis & Thompson Corp., 1948—; pres. Am. Eagle Corp. merged Allied Products Corp., 1962-65; with Allied Products Corp., 1963—, chmn. bd. dirs., 1973—. Office: 21 Internat Holdings 375 Park Ave fl 11 New York NY 10152 also: Knoll Internat Holdings Inc 153 E 53rd St New York NY 10022-4611

SHERMAN, SIGNE LIDFELDT, securities analyst, former research chemist; b. Rochester, N.Y., Nov. 11, 1913; d. Carl Leonard Broström and Herta Elvira Maria (Thern) Lidfeldt; m. Joseph V. Sherman, Nov. 18, 1944 (dec. Oct. 1984). BA, U. Rochester, 1935, MS, 1937. Chief chemist Lab. Indsl. Medicine and Toxicology Eastman Kodak Co., Rochester, 1937-43; chief rsch. chemist Chesebrough-Pond's Inc., Clinton, Conn., 1943-44; ptnr. Joseph V. Sherman Cons., N.Y.C., 1944-84; investment strategist Signe L. Sherman Cons., Troy, Mont., 1984—. Author: The New Fibers, 1946. Fellow Am. Inst. Chemists; mem. AAAS, AAUW (life), Am. Chem. Soc., Am. Econ. Assn., Am. Assn. Ind. Investors (life), Fedn. Am. Scientists (life), Union Concerned Scientists (life), Western Econ. Assn. Internat., Earthquake Engring. Rsch. Inst., Nat. Ctr. for Earthquake Engring. Rsch., N.Y. Acad. Scis. (life), Internat. Platform Assn., Cabinet View Country Club. Office: Signe L Sherman Cons Angel Island 648 Halo Dr Troy MT 59935-9415

SHERMAN, STUART, physician; b. New York, N.Y., Feb. 21, 1955; s. Sol and Rhoda (Kaplan) S.; m. Leslie Jane Derus, Oct. 5, 1991; 1 child, Matthew Sherman. BA, SUNY, Binghampton, 1977; MD, Washington U., St. Louis, 1982. Diplomate Am. Bd. Internal Medicine. Resident in internal medicine U. Pitts., 1982-85, rsch. fellow, 1985-86; gastroenterology fellow Sch. of Medicine UCLA, 1986-89; therapeutic endoscopy fellow Sch. Medicine Ind. U., 1989-90; asst. prof. medicine and pancreaticobiliary endoscopy UCLA, 1990-92, Ind. U., 1992—; cons. Bard Interventional Products Adv. Panel, Tewksbury, Mass., 1994—. Contbr. articles to profl. jours. Recipient Glaxo Award for excellence in gastroenterology Midwest Am. Fedn. Clin. Rsch., 1993, Young Scholars Rsch. award World Congress of Gastroenterology, L.A., 1994. Mem. ACP, Am. Coll. Gastroenterology, Am. Soc. for Gastrointestinal Endoscopy, Am. Gastroent. Assn. Avocations: traveling, skiing, tennis, golf. Office: Ind U Med Ctr 550 N Univ Blvd Ste 2300 Indianapolis IN 46202-5000

SHERMAN, SUSAN ELIZABETH, nursing administrator; b. Salem, Mass., July 12, 1945; d. Frederick Lewis and Dorothy Emily (Field) S.; children: Jennifer Rosenberg, Sarah Rosenberg. Grad., R.I. Hosp. Sch. Nursing, Providence, 1966; BSN, U.R.I., 1969; MA, NYU, 1971. Instr. Hunter Coll., N.Y.C.; asst. prof. Bronx (N.Y.) Community Coll.; cons. Nat. League for Nursing, N.Y.C.; head dept. nursing Community Coll. Phila.; project adminstr. Cmty. Coll. Nursing Partnership, 1990-94. Mem. Am. Soc. on Aging, Am. Gerontol. Soc. in Higher Edn., Independence Found. (sec./treas.), Nat. Assn. of C.C., Orgn. for the Advancement of ADN, Sigma Theta Tau. Office: Community Coll Phila 1700 Spring Gardens St Philadelphia PA 19130-3991

SHERMAN, SUZETTE, interior design consultant; b. Detroit, June 9, 1954; d. Roger and Susan Joan (Gilomen) S.; m. Peter Stathis, July 23, 1988. Student, Calif. Coll. Arts and Crafts, 1974-76, U. Cin., 1978-82. Interior designer Gerber-Built, Inc., N.Y.C., 1982-83, Walker Group/CNI, N.Y.C., 1983-86; free lance interior designer Cold Spring, N.Y., 1986—; free lance cons. Environ. Def. Fund, N.Y.C., 1988—; cons. exhbn. Mcpl. Art Soc., N.Y.C., 1990. Judge competition Metropolis mag., N.Y.C., 1991; chairperson tree bd. Village of Cold Spring, 1991, mem. hist. bd., 1991; mem. waste reduction group Greenpeace, N.Y.C., 1988. NEA grantee, 1992. Mem. Indsl. Designers Soc. Am. (seminar organizer 1989-91, editor newsletter 1989, Kudos award 1990, 91), Heritage Rose Soc. Avocation: gardening. Home and Office: 2208 Saint James St # 2 Philadelphia PA 19103-5502

SHERMAN, TARA S., writer; b. Houston, Dec. 24, 1945; d. Dale and Judith (Larson) Sultzbaugh; m. Robin Sherman, Dec. 31, 1965 (div. Apr. 1980); children: Rebecca, Stephanie, Hazel. BA in English, U. Tex., El Paso, 1967. adj. prof. creative writing U. Tex., Dallas, 1979-84; cons. Werik, Inc., Dallas, 1990—. Author: (children's books) Rebecca Finds a Cat, 1977, Little Big Socks, 1977, Rebecca Gets a Christmas Tree, 1978, Tara and Rebecca, 1979, Tara Moves In, 1980, Tara Gets a Ring, 1981, Tara and the Fish, 1982, Tara and Brian, 1983, Stephanie Moves In, 1984, Tracey Bumps Her Head, 1985, Tracey Falls Asleep, 1986, Greg-Chuck Takes a Nap, 1986, Sharon Goes to New York, 1986, Stephanie Goes to Disney World, 1987, Hazel Catches a Cold, 1988, Rock and Bowl, 1989, Harriet the Tiger, 1990, Rebecca's Spots, 1991, Elyse Takes a Break, 1992, Kevin Gets Away, 1993, Sam Says So, 1993; (novels) Better Nate Than Lever, 1987, Time's Fun When You're Havin' Flies, 1990; contbr. stories to literary jours. Vol. Project Literacy, Dallas, 1990-94. Mem. ASCAP. Presbyterian. Office: Werik Inc 13405 Floyd Circle Ste 100 Dallas TX 75243-1515

SHERMAN, WENDY RUTH, federal agency administrator; b. Balt., June 7, 1949; m. Bruce Edward Stokes; 1 child, Sarah Renee. BA, Boston U., 1971; MSW, U. Md., 1976. Former chief of staff Senator Barbara Mikulski; spl. sec. for children and youth State of Md., 1987, dir. Office Child Welfare; dir. Washington ops. Dukakis for Pres., 1987-88; dir. Campaign '88 Dem. Nat. Com., Washington, 1988; polit. and pub. policy cons. Ctr. Nat. Policy Foreman and Heidepriem, Washington, 1988-91; ptnr. Doak, Shrum, Harris, Sherman, Washington, 1991-93; asst. sec. state legis. affairs Dept. State, Washington, 1993—. Office: Dept State Bur Legis Affairs 2201 C St NW Washington DC 20520-0001

SHERMAN, WILLIAM COURTNEY, foreign service officer; b. Edmonton, Ky., Sept. 27, 1923; s. George Frederick and Katherine Courtney (Kinnaird) S.; m. Mary Jane Hazelip, Apr. 28, 1945; children—Katherine Courtney, John Justin, Roger Woodson. AB, U. Louisville, 1946; student, U. Colo., 1945. Okla. A&M Coll., 1945-46, Nat. War Coll., 1967-68. With Mil. Govt., in Korea, 1946-48; ECA mission to Korea, 1948-50; joined Fgn. Service, Dept. State, 1951; vice consul Yokohama, Japan, 1952-54; 3d sec. embassy Tokyo, Japan, 1954-56; assigned State Dept., 1956-60; 1st sec. embassy Rome, Italy, 1960-65; spl. asst. to dep. under sec. state for adminstrn., 1966-67; consul gen. Kobe-Osaka, Japan, 1968-70; counselor for polit. affairs Am. embassy, Tokyo, 1970-73; minister-counselor, dep. chief mission Am. embassy, 1977-81; dir. for Japanese affairs State Dept., Washington, 1977-77; dep. U.S. rep. (with rank of amb.) UN Security Coun., 1981-84; dep. asst. sec. state for East Asian and Pacific Affairs, 1984-86; diplomat in residence Sch. Advanced Internat. Studies, Johns Hopkins U., 1986-94, sr. advisor Reischaver Ctr., 1994—. Served to lt. (j.g.) USNR, 1943-46, 50-51. Mem. Omicron Delta Kappa. Home and Office: 1702 Beaver Cir Reston VA 22090-4407

SHERMAN, ZACHARY, civil and aerospace engineer, consultant; b. N.Y.C., Oct. 26, 1922; s. Harry and Minnie (Schulsinger) S.; m. Bertha Leikin, Mar. 23, 1947; children: Gene Victor, Carol Beth. BCE, CCNY, 1943; MCE, Polytech. U. N.Y., Bklyn., 1953, PhD in Civil Engring. & Mechanics, 1969; MME, Stevens Inst. Tech., 1968. Registered profl. engr., N.Y., N.J. Stress analyst Gen. Dynamics, San Diego, 1943-45; sr. stress analyst Republic Aviation, Farmingdale, N.Y., 1945-47, 59-62; prof. civil engring. U. Miss., Oxford, 1954-59; lectr. civil engring. Stevens Inst. Tech., Hoboken, N.J., 1962-67, CUNY, 1967-69; assoc. prof. aerospace engring. Pa. State U., State College, 1969-73; prin. Dr. Zachary Sherman Cons. Engrs., Long Beach, N.Y., 1973—; aerospace engr. FAA, N.Y.C., 1980-86; designated engr. rep., FAA. Contbr. articles to profl. jours. NSF grantee, 1972. Fellow ASCE; mem. AIAA (v.p. Western Conn. chpt. 1977-78), N.Y. Acad. Scis., Sigma Xi. Achievements include development of beam/beam-column deck suspension bridge, prestressed aircraft wing. Home and Office: 25 Neptune Blvd Apt 7H Long Beach NY 11561-4657

SHERR, LYNN BETH, TV news correspondent; b. Phila., Mar. 4, 1942; d. Louis and Shirley (Rosenfeld) S.; m. Lawrence B. Hilford, Jan. 11, 1980. B.A., Wellesley Coll., 1963. Writer, editor Conde Nast Publications, N.Y.C., 1963-65; writer, reporter AP, N.Y.C., 1966-72; corre. Sta. WCBS-TV News, N.Y.C., 1972-74; anchor, corre. Pub. Broadcasting System, N.Y.C., 1975-77; nat. corre. ABC News, N.Y.C., 1977—. Author: (with Jurate Kazickas) The Liberated Woman's Appointment Calendar, 1971-82,

The American Woman's Gazetteer, 1976, Susan B. Anthony Slept Here, 1994, Failure is Impossible: Susan B. Anthony in Her Own Words, 1995. Recipient Ohio State award Ohio State U., 1976; recipient spl. commendation Am. Women in Radio & TV, 1979, Emmy for Post Election Spl., 1980, numerous others. Office: 20/20 147 Columbus Ave Fl 10 New York NY 10023-5900

SHERRATT, GERALD ROBERT, college president; b. Los Angeles, Nov. 6, 1931; s. Lowell Heyborne and Elva Genevieve (Lamb) S. B.S. in Edn., Utah State U., 1953, M.S. in Edn. Adminstrn., 1954; Ph.D. in Adminstrn. Higher Edn., Mich. State U., 1975. Staff assoc. U. Utah, Salt Lake City, 1961-62; dir. high sch. relations Utah State U., Logan, 1962-64, asst. to pres., 1964-77, v.p. for univ. relations, 1977-81; pres. So. Utah U., Cedar City, 1982—; dir. Honeyville Grain Inc., Utah; mem. council pres. Utah System Higher Edn., 1982—; chmn. bd. Utah Summer Games, Cedar City, 1984—; chmn. pres.'s council Rocky Mountain Athletic Conf., Denver, 1984-85. Author hist. pageant: The West: America's Odyssey, 1973 (George Washington Honor medal 1973). Chmn. Festival of Art. West, Logan, Utah, 1972-91; chmn. bd. Utah Shakespearean Festival, Cedar City, 1982-86; chmn. bd. dirs. Salt Lake City Branch of the Federal Reserve Bank of San Francisco. Served to 1st lt. USAF, 1954-57. Recipient Editing award Indsl. Editors Assn., 1962, Robins award Utah State U., 1967, Disting. Alumnus award Utah State U., 1974, So. Utah U., 1991, Total Citizen award Cedar City C. of C., 1993; named to Utah Tourism Hall of Fame, 1989. Mem. Am. Assn. State Colls. and Univs., Cache C. of C. (bd. dirs. 1980-82), Phi Kappa Phi, Phi Delta Kappa, Sigma Nu (regent 1976-78). Mem. LDS Ch. Lodge: Rotary. Home: 331 W 200 S Cedar City UT 84720-3101 Office: So Utah U 351 W Center St Cedar City UT 84720-2498

SHERRELL, JOHN BRADFORD, lawyer; b. Indpls., Jan. 27, 1951; s. Carl and Mary Jean (Bell) S.; m. Sherry Naomi Calhoun, Apr. 28, 1974; children: David Alan, Corinne Elizabeth. BA, Yale U., 1973; JD, U. Mich., 1977. Bar: Calif. 1977. Ptnr. Latham & Watkins, Los Angeles, 1977—. Dep. gen. counsel to Ind. Commn. on L.A. Police Dept. Mem. ABA, Calif. Bar Assn. (co-chair real estate fin. subsect. of real property sec. 1990-92), L.A. County Bar Assn. (barrister's exec. com. 1978-80, bd. trustees 1991-93). Office: Latham & Watkins Ste 800 1900 Avenue Of The Stars Los Angeles CA 90067-4503

SHERRER, CHARLES DAVID, college dean, clergyman; b. Marion, Ohio, Sept. 21, 1935; s. Harold D. and Catherine E. (Fye) S. A.B., U. Notre Dame, 1958, M.A., 1965; S.T.L., Gregorian U., 1962; Ph.D., U. N.C., 1969. Ordained priest Roman Cath. Ch., 1961. Instr. English U. Portland, Oreg., 1963-64, asst. prof., 1969-74, prof., 1990—, chmn. dept., 1970-74, dean Grad. Sch., 1982-87, mem. Bd. Regents, 1986-87, acad. v.p., 1987—; pres. King's Coll., Wilkes Barre, Pa., 1974-81; bd. trustees Stonehill Coll., 1992—; dir. studies Holy Cross Fathers, Ind. Province, 1979-88. Office: U Portland Office of Acad Vice Pres Portland OR 97203

SHERRICK, DANIEL NOAH, real estate broker; b. Greenup, Ill., Mar. 28, 1929; s. Conrad Donovan and Helen Lorene (Neeley) S.; m. Dora Ann Moore, Aug. 11, 1957; children: Renata Ann Sherrick McBride, Sherrie Dee Sherrick Sierra. B.S. in Edn., Eastern Ill. U., Charleston, 1956. Owner Midwest Ins. Agy., Greenup, 1956-60; supt. agys. Midwest Life Ins. Co., Lincoln, Nebr., 1960-62; asst. v.p. Gulf Life Ins. Co., Jacksonville, Fla., 1962-71; pres. Bank of Carbondale, Ill., 1971-74, Prescription Learning Corp., Springfield, Ill., 1974-76; exec. v.p. Imperial Industries, Inc., Miami Lakes, Fla., 1976-88, pres., chief exec. officer, 1988-90; broker, salesman Coldwell Banker Residential Real Estate, 1990-91, 93—; pres., bd. dirs. Palmer State Bank, Taylorville, Ill., 1991-93; broker-salesman Coldwell Banker Hunter Realty, 1993—. Pres. Alderman Park Civic Assn., Jacksonville, 1968, Heritage Hills Home Owners Assn., Carbondale, 1973. With USAF, 1948-52. Mem. Am. Legion, Greater Sebring C. of C., VFW, Internat. Torch Club, Masons, Elks. Presbyterian. Home: 6228 Aquavista Dr Sebring FL 33870-7409 Office: Coldwell Banker Hunter Realty 2617 US 27 S Sebring FL 33870

SHERRIFFS, RONALD EVERETT, communications and film educator; b. Salem, Oreg., Apr. 10, 1934; s. Robert William and Margaret Kathleen (Tutt) S.; m. Mary Lona West, July 9, 1960; children: Ellen, Matthew. BA, San Jose State U., 1955, MA, 1957; PhD, U. So. Calif., 1964. Instr. theater Mich. State U., East Lansing, 1960-61; asst. prof. broadcasting Tex. Tech U., Lubbock, 1964-65; asst. prof. speech U. Oreg., Eugene, 1965-70, assoc. prof., 1970-79, prof. telecommunications and film, 1979-92, chmn. dept. speech, 1978-84, 88-90, prof. journalism and comm., 1993—. Author: (with others) Speech Communication via Radio and TV, 1971, TV Lighting Handbook, 1977, Small Format TV Production., 1985, 3d edit., Video Field Production and Editing, 1994; producer, dir. TV programs, 1965—. Mem. Oreg. Pub. Broadcasting Policy Adv. Bd., 1980-88. Served to lt. comdr. USNR, 1957-68, PTO. Faculty enrichment program grantee Can., 1984, 91. Mem. Speech Communication Assn. Am., AAUP, Western States Communication Assn. Clubs: Oreg. Track; McKenzie Flyshers (Eugene). Office: U Oreg Eugene OR 97403

SHERRILL, ANITA AILEEN, elementary school educator, consultant, educational system administrator; b. Visalia, Calif., Jan. 8, 1942; d. Oscar Lawrence Sherrill and Opal Gertrude (Brock) Smith; children: Theresa St. Pierre, Janine Wilson, Cary Sherrill. BS, Minot State U., 1970; MA, Ball State U., 1974; EdD, U. So. Calif., 1986. Cert. elem. tchr. Victor. Dept. Def., Tripoli, Libya, 1964-67; tchr., cons. U.S. Dependent Schs. Europe, Zaragoza, Spain, 1970-75, Spangdahlem, Germany, 1975-81, Bad Kreuznach, Germany, 1981-90; curriculum coord., edn. specialist U.S. Dependent Schs. Europe, Wiesbaden, Germany, 1990—. Office: Dept of Def Dependent Schs Postfach 6200 Weisbade APO AE 09196

SHERRILL, GLADYS MARIE, elementary education educator; b. Little Rock, Sept. 8, 1940; d. Henry and Elcano Sherrill. BS in Edn., Ctrl. State U., Wilberforce, Ohio, 1963; MA in Edn., St. John Coll., Cleve., 1975. Tchr. Cleve. City Schs., 1963-70, Detroit City Schs., 1970-71; edn. dir. Head Start, Cleve., 1972-73; elem. tchr. Cleve. City Schs., 1973—. Mem. NEA (Black caucus, peace and justice caucus, fine arts com.), Ohio Edn. Assn., Zeta Pi Beta, Phi Delta Kappa. Republican. Mem. Unity Ch. Home: 1701 E 12th St Cleveland OH 44114-3237

SHERRILL, H. VIRGIL, securities company executive, manufacturing company executive; b. Long Beach, Calif., 1920. Grad., Yale U., 1942, JD, 1948. Sr. dir. Prudential Securities, N.Y.C. Office: Prudential Securites 199 Water St 34th Fl New York NY 10038-3500

SHERRILL, JOSEPH HARLAN, JR., tobacco company executive; b. Winston-Salem, N.C., Mar. 27, 1941; s. Joseph Harlan and Mary Isabelle (Sink) S.; m. Camilla Dize Mathews, July 1, 1967 (div. 1987); children: Kathryn Elizabeth, James Harlan; m. Cunthia Lynn Maull, May 24, 1982. BA in Psychology, Guilford Coll., 1964; MBA, Columbia U., 1966. Various sales and mtg. positions R. J. Reynolds, Winston-Salem, 1967-75, dir. mktg. rsch., 1975-78; pres., gen. mgr. R. J. Reynolds P.R., San Juan, 1978-81; pres., CEO R. J. Reynolds Asia Pacific, Hong Kong, 1981-84, pres., 1989—; pres., CEO R. J. Reynolds do Brazil, Rio De Janeiro, 1984-88; sr. v.p. mktg. R. J. Reynolds Internat., London, 1988-89; bd. dirs. R. J. Reynolds Tobacco Internat. (Asia/Pacific), Inc., Hong Kong, Mr. J. Reynolds Tobacco Co. (H.K.), Ltd., Hong Kong, RJR Nabisco China Ltd., Hong Kong, R. J. Reynolds Berhad, Kuala Lumpur, R. J. Reynolds Tobacco Co. Sdn. Bhd., Kuala Lumpur, R. J. Reynolds Tobacco (Taiwan) Inc., Taipei, China-Am. Cigarette Co. Ltd., Xiamen, Savers Life, Winston-Salem, N.C. Sgt. USMCR. Avocations: tennis, scuba diving, hiking. Office: RJ Reynolds Asia Pacific HD, 10 Harbour Rd, Hong Kong Hong Kong

SHERRILL, THOMAS BECK, financial planner, state legislator; b. Atlanta, Sept. 30, 1946; s. Elie Beck and Vena Edele (Thomas) S.; m. Dianne Hutchins, Sept. 3, 1966; children: Alison, Jessica. BA, Ga. State U., 1968; MA, U. Va., 1970. CFP. Chartered life underwriter Conn. Mut. Life, Atlanta, 1975-84; pres. Sherrill & Hutchins Fin. Advisory, Inc., Atlanta, 1984—; mem. Ga. Ho. of Reps., Atlanta, 1991—. Mem. adminstrv. bd. Oak Grove United Meth. Ch., Atlanta, 1993-94. Capt. U.S. Army, 1971-75. Recipient Guardian of Bus. award Nat. Fedn. Ind. Businesses, Atlanta, 1992,

94, achievement award Alzheimer's Assn., Atlanta, 1992, outstanding legislator award Coun. on Aging, Atlanta, 1992, 94, leadership in govt. award Common Cause, Atlanta, 1993, legislative svc. award Assn. County Commissioners of Ga., 1994, legislative award Ga. Gerontology Soc., 1994; named Policymaker of Yr., Atlanta Alliance on Devel. Disabilities, 1995, Lawmaker of Yr., Ga. chpt. Autism Soc., 1995. Mem. Inst. CFPs, Internat. Assn. for Fin. Planning (past v.p.), Echo Ridge Recreation Club, Atlanta Hist. Soc., Omicron Delta Kappa. Democrat. Avocations: Civil War history, tennis, reading.

SHERRILL, THOMAS BOYKIN, III, newspaper publishing executive; b. Tampa, Fla., Nov. 19, 1930; s. Thomas Boykin Jr. and Mary Emma (Addison) S.; m. Sandra Louise Evans, Dec. 27, 1969; children: Thomas Glenn, Stephen Addison. Circulation dir. Tampa (Fla.) Tribune, 1962-67, Sarasota (Fla.) Herald-Tribune, 1967-75; v.p. circulation The Dispatch Printing Co., Columbus, Ohio, 1975-78, v.p. mktg., 1978—, bd. dirs., 1977—; v.p., bd. dirs. Ohio Mag. Inc., Columbus, 1979—. Chmn. bd. dirs. Salvation Army, BBB, past chmn. of bd.; bd. dirs. Cen. Ohio Ctr. Econ. Edn., 1978—; v.p. trustee Columbus Dispatch Charities; exec. bd. dirs. Simon Kenton coun. Boy Scouts Am.; past pres. Wesley Glen United Meth. Retirement Home; pres.'s adv. bd. Meth. Theol. Sch.; chmn. adminstrv. coun. N.W. United Meth. Ch., Upper Arlington, Ohio. With USN, 1951-56. Recipient Disting. Svc. award Editor and Pub. Mag., 1978; named hon. pres. Troy State U., 1979, hon. Ky. Col., 1980, hon. lt. col. aide-to-camp to Gov. State of Ala., 1984. Mem. Internat. Circulation Mgrs. Assn. (pres. 1975, Pres's. award 1989), Internat. Newspaper Mktg. Assn., Ohio Newspaper Assn. (bd. dirs., pres. 1986-88, Pres.'s award 1990), So. Circulation Mgrs. Assn. (pres. 1967-68, C.W. Bevinger Meml. award 1972), Audit Bur. Circulations (bd. dirs. 1980-90), Am. Advt. Fedn., Navy League, Ohio Newspapers Found., Ohio Circulation Mgrs. Assn (Pres.' award 1989), Columbus Area C. of C., SAR, Internat. Platform Assn., Columbus Met. Club, Athletic Club of Columbus, Muirfield Village Country Club, Kiwanis (pres. 1982). Republican. Home: 5215 Hampton Ln Columbus OH 43220-2270 Office: Columbus Dispatch 34 S 3rd St Columbus OH 43215-4241

SHERROD, BLACKIE, newspaper sports columnist. Sports columnist Dallas Morning News. Office: Dallas Morning News Communications Ctr 508 Young St Dallas TX 75265

SHERROD, LONNIE RAY, foundation administrator, researcher, psychologist; b. Knoxville, Tenn., Sept. 7, 1950; s. Raymond O. and Jane L. (Lambdin) S.; m. Barbara A. Cornblatt, Jan. 31, 1981; 1 child, Sara Raye. BS, Duke U., 1972; MA, U. Rochester, N.Y., 1974, Yale U., 1976; PhD, Yale U., 1978. Rsch. assoc. Yale U., New Haven, 1978; staff assoc. Social Sci. Rsch. Coun., N.Y.C., 1979-85; sr. program assoc. William T. Grant Found., N.Y.C., 1986-89, v.p. programs, 1990-94; exec. v.p. 1995—; asst. dean grad. faculty New Sch. for Social Rsch., N.Y.C., 1986-89; mem. adj. faculty psychology dept. NYU, N.Y.C., 1980-85, grad. faculty, 1986-91. Co-author: Infant Social Cognition, 1981; contbr. articles to profl. jours.; assoc. editor: Human Nature, 1989-91. Mem. program coms. Grantmakers of Children and Youth, 1990, N.Y. Regional Assn. of Grantmakers, 1991-94; evaluation com. Nat. Found. Collaboration on Violence Prevention, 1994—; mem. adv. bd. Ctr. Study of Child and Adolescent Devel., Pa. State U., 1992—; bd. dirs. Life Trends, Inc., 1992—, Timber Trails Comty. Assn., 1992—, v.p., 1994—. Mem. APA (co-chair internat. com. 1994—), Am. Psychol. Soc., Soc. Study of Social Biology (sec., treas. N.Y.C. chpt. 1984-90), Internat. Soc. for Study of Behavior Devel., Soc. Rsch. on Adolescence, Soc. for Rsch. in Child Devel. (mem. com. on pub. policy, pub. info. and child devel., chmn. 1993—; chmn. subcom. on pub. 1992-94). Office: William T Grant Found 515 Madison Ave New York NY 10022-5403

SHERRY, GEORGE LEON, political science educator; b. Lodz, Poland, Jan. 5, 1924; came to U.S., 1939, naturalized 1945; s. Leon G. and Henrietta (Mess) S.; m. Doris H. Harf, Mar. 6, 1947; 1 child, Vivien Gail Sherry Greenberg. BA summa cum laude, CCNY, 1944; MA, Columbia U., 1951, MA, cert. Russian Inst., 1955, PhM, 1959. Reporter, radio news writer The N.Y. Times, N.Y.C., 1944-46; editor, interpreter, then sr. interpreter UN N.Y.C., 1946-59, from polit. officer to dir. and dep. to under sec.-gen. for spl. polit. affairs, 1959-84; polit. advisor to missions Congo, Cyprus, India and Pakistan, 1962-66; asst. sec.-gen. for spl. polit. affairs UN (office in charge peacekeeping forces which won Nobel Peace Prize, 1988), N.Y.C., 1984-85; Stuart Chevalier prof. diplomacy and world affairs Occidental Coll., Los Angeles, 1985—; dir. Occidental at-the-UN program, 1985—; U.S. del. staff Dartmouth Soviet-Am. confs., 1961—; assoc. seminar on problem of peace Columbia U., N.Y.C.; cons. UN dept. peacekeeping ops., 1992, 93; leader UN tech. mission to Ga., 1993; UN envoy to follow Russian elections, 1993; advisor Internat. Peace Acad., 1993—. Author: The United Nations Reborn: Conflict Control in the Post-Cold War World, 1990; editorial adv. bd. Polit. Sci. Quar., N.Y.C., 1973-89; contbr. articles and revs. to profl. jours. Recipient Townsend Harris medal CCNY, 1993; UN Inst. for Tng. and Rsch. sr. fellow, 1985-93. Mem. Coun. on Fgn. Rels., Internat. Studies Assn., Phi Beta Kappa. Democrat. Avocations: piano playing; skiing; sailing. Home: 185 E 85th St Apt 3-c New York NY 10028-2172

SHERRY, HENRY IVAN, marketing consultant; b. Chgo., Aug. 10, 1930; s. Emmanuel H. and Dorothy Harriet (Rose) S.; B.S. in Bus. Adminstrn., U. Ala., 1952; m. Maxine Rae Gould, Aug. 7, 1955; children—Dale Sara, Michael Jay. Account exec. Jones, Frankel Co., Chgo., 1954-60; account exec., account supr., v.p. group supr. Edward H. Weiss & Co., Chgo., 1960-66; v.p., account supr., sr. mgmt. officer Interpub. Group of Cos.-McCann Erickson, Inc., Atlanta, dir. Communications Counselors Network, 1966-69; sr. v.p., dir., exec. policy com. The Marchalk Co., Atlanta, N.Y.C., 1969-71; pres. Henry Sherry Assocs., Inc., Atlanta, 1971-88; chmn. Sherry & Bellows, Inc., Atlanta 1988-91; pres. Sherry & Mitchell Inc., 1991—. Mem. assoc. bd. Mt. Sinai Hosp., 1965-66; chmn. pub. info. United Way, 1970; dir. The Temple, 1982—; mem. exec. com. Coverdell for Congress, 1976. Served with U.S. Army, 1952-54. Club: Standard (dir. 1967-68, 84-86). Office: Sherry & Mitchell Inc 1100 Circle 75 Pkwy St 800 Atlanta GA 30339

SHERRY, PAUL HENRY, minister, religious organization administrator; b. Tamaqua, Pa., Dec. 25, 1933; s. Paul Edward and Mary Elizabeth (Stein) S.; m. Mary Louise Thornburg, June 4, 1957; children: Mary Elizabeth, Paul David. BA, Franklin and Marshall Coll., 1955; ThM, Union Theol. Sem., N.Y.C., 1958, PhD, 1969; hon. doctorate, Ursinus Coll., 1981, Elmhurst Coll., 1990, Defiance Coll., 1991, Lakeland Coll., Sheboygan, Wis., 1991; postgrad., Reformed Theological Acad., Debrecen, Hungary, 1994, United Theol. Sem. Twin Cities, 1995. Ordained to ministry United Ch. of Christ, 1958. Pastor St. Matthew United Ch. of Christ, Kenhorst, Pa., 1958-61, Community United Ch. of Christ, Hasbrouck Heights, N.J., 1961-65; mem. staff United Ch. Bd. Homeland Ministry, N.Y.C., 1965-82; exec. dir. Community Renewal Soc., Chgo., 1983-89; pres. United Ch. of Christ, Cleve., 1989—; mem. gen. bd. Nat. Coun. Chs., N.Y.C., 1989—; mem. cen. com. World Coun. Chs., Geneva, 1991—, del. 7th Assembly, Canberra, Australia, 1991; bd. dirs. Ind. Sector, Washington, 1991—. Editor: The Riverside Preachers; editor Jour. Current Social Issues, 1968-80; contbr. numerous articles to religious jours.; host weekly radio programs local sta., 1974-78, 84-85, 93—. Mem. Soc. Christian Ethics. Democrat. Avocations: reading, hiking, cultural events. Home: 13400 Shaker Blvd Cleveland OH 44120-1589 Office: United Ch of Christ 700 Prospect Ave E Cleveland OH 44115-1131

SHERRY, ROBERT JOSEPH, lawyer; b. East Liverpool, Ohio, Dec. 22, 1957; s. Arthur William Jr. and Lillian Ann (Gebauer) S.; m. Ruth Gail Tiger, May 21, 1983. BA cum laude, Dickinson Coll., 1979; JD, Am. U., 1982. Bar: DC 1982, U.S. Ct. Appeals (D.C. cir.) 1983; U.S. Dist. Ct. (D.C. cir.) U.S. Ct. Claims 1985. Law clk. presiding justice U.S. Ct. of Appeals (D.C. cir.), Washington, 1982-83; atty McKenna, Conner & Cuneo, Washington, 1983—. Contbr. articles to profl. jours. Mem. ABA, (antitrust sect. and pub. contracts sects. 1983—; comml. products services com. 1984), D.C. Bar Assn. Democrat. Roman Catholic. Avocation: amateur hockey. Home: 4301 Massachusetts Ave NW Washington DC 20016-5545 Office: McKenna Conner & Cuneo 1575 Eye St NW Washington DC 20005

SHERRY, SUZANNA, law educator; b. N.Y.C., Mar. 29, 1954; d. Leonard Isaac and Bernice (Cohen) S. AB cum laude, Middlebury Coll., 1976; JD cum laude, U. Chgo., 1979. Bar: D.C. 1980. Law clk. U.S. Ct. Appeals (5th cir.), Montgomery, Ala., 1979-80; assoc. Miller, Cassidy, Larroca & Lewin,

Washington, 1980-82; assoc. prof. U. Minn. Law Sch., Mpls., 1982-88, prof., 1988—. Author (with others): A History of the American Constitution, 1989; contbr. numerous articles to law revs. Mem. D.C. Bar Assn., Am. Law Inst. Office: Univ Minn Law Sch 229 19th Ave S Minneapolis MN 55455-0400

SHERTZER, BRUCE ELDON, education educator; b. Bloomfield, Ind., Jan. 11, 1928; s. Edwin Franklin and Lois Belle S.; m. Carol Mae Rice, Nov. 24, 1948; children: Sarah Ann, Mark Eldon. Ed.D., 1958. Tchr., counselor Martinsville (Ind.) High Sch., 1952-56; dir. div. guidance Ind. Dept. Pub. Instrn., 1956-58; assoc. dir. project guidance of superior students North Central Assn. Coll. and Secondary Sch., 1958-60; asst. prof. Purdue U., 1960—, assoc. prof., 1964, now prof., head dept. ednl. studies, 1989—; vis. prof. ednl. psychology U. Hawaii, 1967; Fulbright sr. lectr., Reading, Eng., 1967-68; vis. prof. U. So. Calif. Overseas Grad. Program, 1975, 82; chmn. Nat. Adv. Council for Career Edn., 1976. Author: Career Exploration and Planning 1973, 2d edit., 1976, Fundamentals of Counseling, 3d edit., 1980, Fundamentals of Guidance, 4th edit., 1981, Individual Appraisal, 1979, Career Planning, 3d edit., 1985, also articles. Chmn. bd. trustees Found. Am. Assn. of Counseling and Devel., 1986-87. With AUS, 1946-47. Mem. Am. Counseling Assn. (pres. 1973-74, Disting. Profl. Svc. award 1986). Home: 1620 Western Dr West Lafayette IN 47906-2236 Office: Purdue U Liberal Arts Edn Bldg West Lafayette IN 47907

SHERVA, DENNIS G., investment company executive; b. Mpls., Dec. 3, 1942; s. Garfield Theodore and Dorothy Genevive (Oberlander) S.; m. Cathleen Marybeth Tischer, Oct. 15, 1965. B.A., U. Minn., 1964; M.A., Wayne State U., 1965. Chartered fin. analyst. Fin. analyst 1st Nat. Bank, Mpls., 1965-67; fin. analyst Honeywell, Inc., Mpls., 1967; v.p. Smith, Barney & Co., N.Y.C., 1967-71, Baker, Weeks & Co., N.Y.C., 1971-77; mng. dir. Morgan Stanley & Co., Inc., N.Y.C., 1977—; bd. dirs. Morgan Stanley Ventures, San Francisco, Morgan Stanley Venture Capital, N.Y.C., Morgan Stanley Asset Mgmt. Inc., N.Y.C. Recipient All-Am. Research Team 1st place award Instl. Investor Mag., 1979, 81, 83, 84, 85, 87. Mem. Nat. Assn. Securities Dealers (instl. com. 1985—), N.Y. Athletic Club, Torrington Country Club. Home: 791 Park Ave New York NY 10021-3551 Office: Morgan Stanley & Co Inc 1221 Ave Of The Americas New York NY 10020-1001

SHERVHEIM, LLOYD OLIVER, insurance company executive, lawyer; b. Kensington, Minn., June 22, 1928; s. Lewis and Ruth Amanda (Thronson) S.; m. Ruth Elaine Rhodes, Oct. 29, 1950; children: Daniel, Anne, Heidi, Garold, Robette, Shanna, Bryce. Student, Gustavus Adolphus Coll., 1948-50, U. Minn., 1950-52; B.S., William Mitchell Coll. Law, 1958, LL.B., 1958. Bar: Minn. 1959. Supr., asst. to corp. sec. Investors Diversified Services, Inc., 1952-59; legal counsel Investors Syndicate Life Ins. Co., Mpls., 1959-66; gen. counsel Western Life Ins. Co., St. Paul, 1966-72; corporate sec. St. Paul Cos., Inc., 1969-82, chief legal officer, 1972-78, v.p. legal affairs, 1978-85, sr. v.p. law, corporate sec., 1985-89; corporate sec. St. Paul Fire and Marine Ins. Co., 1969-82; dir. St. Paul Ins. Co., Tex., St. Paul Surplus Lines Ins. Co., Ill. Charter patron Minn. Theatre Co., 1958; mem. Lake Elmo City Council, 1970-78; past chmn. protection open space task force Met. Open Space Adv. Bd., 1969-70; trustee William Mitchell Coll. Law, 1981-92, vice chmn., 1983-86, chmn., 1986-89; dir. Minn. Citizens Council on Crime and Justice, 1986-89. With U.S. Army, 1946-48. Mem. ABA, Minn. Bar Assn. (chmn. ins. com. 1964-65, gov. 1980-81), Fed. Bar Assn. (pres. Minn. chpt. 1978-79), Ramsey County Bar Assn. (ethics com. 1978-80), Assn. Life Ins. Counsel, Am. Soc. Corp. Secs., Am. Life Conv. (v.p. Minn. chpt. 1969-71), Am. Judicature Soc., Corp. Counsel Assn. Minn. (dir., pres. 1979-80), Pool and Yacht Club (St. Paul). Lutheran (chmn. bd. trustees). Home and Office: 3065 Klondike Ave N Lake Elmo MN 55042-9717

SHERWIN, BYRON LEE, religion educator, college official; b. N.Y.C., Feb. 18, 1946; s. Sidney and Jean Sylvia (Rabinowitz) S.; m. Judith Rita Schwartz, Dec. 24, 1972; 1 child, Jason Samuel. BS, Columbia U., N.Y.C., 1966; B of Hebrew Lit., Jewish Theol. Sem. of Am., 1966, M of Hebrew Lit., 1968; MA, NYU, 1969; PhD, U. Chgo., 1978. Ordained rabbi, 1970. Prof. Jewish philosophy and mysticism Spertus Coll. Judaica, Chgo., 1970—, v.p. acad. affairs, 1984—. Author: Judaism, 1978, Encountering the Holocaust, 1979, Abraham Joshua Heschel, 1979, Garden of the Generations, 1981, Jerzy Kosinski: Literary Alarm Clock, 1981, Mystical Theology and Social Dissent, 1982, The Golem Legend, 1985, Contents and Contexts, 1987, Thank God, 1989, In Partnership with God: Contemporary Jewish Law and Ethics, 1990, No Religion Is an Island, 1991, Toward a Jewish Theology, 1991, How To Be a Jew: Ethical Teachings of Judaism, 1992, The Theological Heritage of Polish Jews, 1995, also articles. Mem. Midwest Jewish Studies Assn. (pres.), Am. Philos. Assn., Assn. for Jewish Studies, Rabbinical Assembly, Am. Acad. Religion, Religious Ednl. Assn. Republican. Avocations: cooking, book collecting. Office: Spertus Coll Judaica 618 S Michigan Ave Chicago IL 60605-1901

SHERWIN, JAMES TERRY, lawyer, window covering company executive; b. N.Y.C., Oct. 25, 1933; s. Oscar and Stella (Zins) S.; m. Judith Johnson, June 21, 1955 (div. Apr. 1984); children—Miranda, Alison, Galen; m. Hiroko Inouye, June 15, 1985. BA, Columbia U., 1953, LLB (Stone scholar), 1956. Bar: N.Y. 1956, U.S. Supreme Ct. 1963. Assoc. Kaye, Scholer, Fierman, Hays & Handler, N.Y.C., 1957-60; with GAF Corp., N.Y.C., 1960-83, 84—, asso. counsel, gen. mgr. European ops., 1969-71, group v.p. photography, 1971-74, exec. v.p. fin. and adminstrn., legal and investment svcs., 1974-83; vice chmn., chief adminstrv. officer GAF Corp., Wayne, N.J., 1984-90; exec. v.p. chief fin. officer Triangle Industries, Inc., 1983-84, Hunter-Douglas N.V., 1991—; exec. v.p., CFO. Bd. dirs. Internat. Rescue Com., chmn. exec. com.; v.p. to 1990. Lt. comdr. USCGR, 1956-57. U.S. intercollegiate chess champion, 1951-53, N.Y. State champion, 1951, U.S. speed champion, 1956-57, 59-60, internat. master. Mem. Am. Chess Found. (pres., bd. dirs. to 1990), Marshall (N.Y.) Chess Club (pres. 1967-69, gov. to 1990), Phi Beta Kappa. Home: Stegenhöhe 24, CH 6048 Horw Switzerland Office: Hunter Douglas Mgmt AG, Adligenswilerstrasse 37, 6006 Lucerne Switzerland

SHERWIN, MICHAEL DENNIS, government official; b. Decorah, Iowa, Dec. 29, 1939; m. Diann May, Feb. 6, 1965; children: Catherine, Jennifer, Carolyn, Elizabeth. B.A., Coll. St. Thomas, 1962. Intelligence analyst CIA, Washington, 1963-66; copy editor St. Paul Pioneer Press, 1966-67; personnel mgr. Office Personnel Mgmt. U.S. Civil Service Commn., Washington, 1967-79; dir. human resources CAB, Washington, 1977-81, mng. dir., 1981-84; dir. mgmt. systems FAA, Washington, 1985-91, dep. asst. adminstr. for info. tech., 1991-92, dir. civil aviation security program mgmt., 1992-93; dep. asst. adminstr. USAID, Washington, 1993—. Recipient Commrs. award U.S. CSC 1978, Adminstr's Spl. Achievement award for EEO, FAA, 1986, Meritorious Svc. award Sec. of Transp., 1990, Top 100 award Fed. Computer Week, 1990. Roman Catholic. Office: FAA AID 320 21st St NW Washington DC 20523-0002

SHERWOOD, AARON WILEY, aerodynamics educator; b. St. Louis, Jan. 13, 1915; s. Charles Vliet and Amelia Pauline (Kappler) S.; m. Helene M. Gysin, 1944; children—Susan Helene, Mark Wiley. M.E., Rensselaer Poly. Inst., 1935; M.S., U. Md., 1943. Exptl. engr. Wallace & Tiernan Co., Inc., 1936-38; devel. engr. Assoc. Engring., 1938-39; layout engr. Glenn L. Martin Co., 1939-40; instr. U. Md., 1940-44; aero. project engr. David Taylor Model Basin, 1944-46, prof. aerodynamics, 1946—, acting head dept. aero. engring., 1950-58, head dept. aerospace engring., 1958-67, prof. dept. aerospace engring., 1967-77; in charge wind tunnel lab. Glenn L. Martin Inst. Tech., 1946-55; owner, engring. cons. Aerolab. Author: Aerodynamics, 1946. Fellow ASME (chmn. Washington sect. 1954-55); mem. Am. Inst. Aeros and Astronautics (sect. chmn.), Am. Soc. Engring. Edn., Sigma Xi, Tau Beta Pi, Phi Kappa Phi, Phi Kappa Tau. Home: 3411 Chatham Rd Hyattsville MD 20783-1852 Office: Aerolab 9580 Washington Blvd N Laurel MD 20723-1372 *Instead of carefully planned progress toward some firm fixed goals, I advocate frequent modifications of both goals and access routes according to current circumstances. One should follow one's interests, tempered only by the needs of his associates and by firm ethical standards —a sort of intelligent muddling along.*

SHERWOOD, ALLEN JOSEPH, lawyer; b. Salt Lake City, Sept. 26, 1909; s. Charles Samuel and Sarah (Abramson) Shapiro; m. Edith Ziff, Jan. 19, 1941; children—Mary (Mrs. John Marshall), Arthur Lawrence. Student, UCLA, 1927-30; AB, U. So. Calif., 1933, LLB, 1933. Bar: Calif. 1933, U.S. Supreme Ct. 1944. Pvt. practice law L.A., 1933-54, Beverly Hills, 1954—; legal counsel Internat. Family Planning Rsch. Assn., Inc., 1970-76; bd. dirs. Family Planning Ctrs. Greater L.A., Inc., 1968-84, pres., 1973-76. Mem. editorial bd. So. Calif. Law Rev., 1932-33. Contbr. articles to profl. jours. Mem. Calif. Atty. Gen.'s Vol. Adv. Coun. and its legis. subcom., 1972-78. Mem. Med.-Legal Soc. So. Calif. (bd. dirs. 1966-74), ABA, L.A. County Bar Assn., Beverly Hills Bar Assn., State Bar of Calif., Am. Arbitration Assn. (nat. panel arbitrators 1965—), Order of Coif, Tau Delta Phi, Brentwood Country Club (L.A.), Masons. Home: 575 Moreno Ave Los Angeles CA 90049-4840 Office: 12424 Wilshire Blvd Bldg 900 Los Angeles CA 90025-1043

SHERWOOD, ARTHUR LAWRENCE, lawyer; b. L.A., Jan. 25, 1943; s. Allen Joseph and Edith (Ziff) S.; m. Frances Merele, May 1, 1970; children: David, Chester. BA magna cum laude, U. Calif.-Berkeley, 1964; MS, U. Chgo., 1965; JD cum laude, Harvard U., 1968. Bar: Calif. 1969, US. dist. cts. (cen. dist.) Calif. 1968 (no. dist.) Calif. 1971 (so. dist.) Calif. 1973 (ea. dist.) Calif. 1973, U.S. Ct. Appeals (9th cir.) 1973, U.S. Ct. Appeals (D.C. cir.) 1991, U.S. Supreme Ct., 1980. Instr. UCLA Law Sch., 1968-69; assoc. Gibson, Dunn & Crutcher, Los Angeles, 1968-75, ptnr., 1975—; judge pro tem Los Angeles Mcpl. and Superior Ct., 1980—; instr. law, UCLA, 1968-69, arbitrator N.Y. Stock Exchange, Nat. Futures Assn. Co-author: Civil Procedure During Trial, 1984, 95, Civil Procedure Before Trial, 1990, contbr articles to profl. jours. NASA fellow U. Chgo., 1964-65; chmn. Far Ea. Art Coun., L.A. County Mus. Art, 1992—. Mem. ABA, L.A. County Bar Assn., Calif. Bar Assn., Phi Beta Kappa. Republican. Avocations include: art, 18th century Am. history. Office: Gibson Dunn & Crutcher 333 S Grand Ave Fl 45 Los Angeles CA 90071-1504

SHERWOOD, ARTHUR MORLEY, lawyer; b. Buffalo, Oct. 3, 1939; s. Frederick T. and Neva E. (Merrill) S.; m. Karen H. Hilstad, Apr. 2, 1964; children: Laurel Ann, Carolyn Margaret. BA, Harvard U., 1961; JD, U. Mich., 1964. Bar: Mich. 1965, N.Y. 1967, U.S. Supreme Ct. 1989. Law clk. to Hon. Ralph M. Freeman U.S. Dist. Ct. (ea. dist.) Mich., Detroit, 1964-66; pntr. Phillips, Lytle, Hitchcock, Blaine & Huber, Buffalo, 1971—. Contbr. articles to Trusts and Estates, N.Y. State Bar Jour. and N.Y. Tax Svc. Asst. chancellor Episcopal Diocese of Western N.Y., 1982—; mem. adv. com. N.Y. State Legislature on N.Y. Estates, Powers and Trusts Law, Surrogate's Ct. Procedure. Fellow Am. Coll. Trust and Estate Counsel, N.Y. Bar Found.; mem. N.Y. State Bar Assn. (chairperson trusts and estates law sect. 1987). Home: 3770 Windover Dr Hamburg NY 14075-6322 Office: Phillips Lytle Hitchcock Blaine & Huber 3400 Marine Midland Ctr Buffalo NY 14203-2887

SHERWOOD, LINDA KATHLEEN, lawyer; b. Houston, May 11, 1947; d. Mack Hayes and Dorothy Clare (Sullender) D.; m. Don Curtis Sherwood, Nov. 28, 1981; children: Matthew Curtis, Patrick Hayes, Andrew Wade. BS in Home Econs., U. Tex., 1969, JD, 1972. Bar: Calif. 1972, Tex. 1972, U.S. Dist. Ct. (cen. dist.) Calif. 1973, U.S. Ct. Appeals (9th cir.) 1973. From assoc. to ptnr. Latham & Watkins, L.A., 1972—, mng. ptnr., 1988—. Mem. ABA, Los Angeles Bar Assn., Women Lawyers Los Angeles. Episcopalian. Office: Latham & Watkins 633 W Fifth St Ste 4000 Los Angeles CA 90071

SHERWOOD, (PETER) LOUIS, retail executive; b. London, Oct. 27, 1941; came to U.S., 1979; s. Peter and Mervyn (De Toll) S.; m. Nicole Dina, Aug. 22, 1970; children: Christopher, Anne, Isabelle. BA, Oxford U., 1963, MA, 1966; MBA, Stanford U., 1965. Fin. planning officer Morgan Grenfell & Co. Ltd., London, 1965-68; gen. mgr. Melias Ltd., Welwyn Garden City, Eng., 1969-72; dir. Anglo-Continental Investment & Fin. Co. Ltd., London, 1973-79; chmn., chief exec. officer Maidenhead Investments, London, 1977-79; sr. v.p. Grand Union Co., Elmwood Park, N.J., 1979-85; pres. Gt. Atlantic & Pacific Tea Co. Inc., Montvale, N.J., 1985-88; chmn., chief exec. officer Gateway Foodmarkets, Bristol, Eng., 1988-89; chmn. Airedale Holdings plc, Keighley, Yorkshire, Eng., 1990-92, HTV Group plc, Cardiff, Wales, 1991—, New Look plc, Weymouth, Dorset, 1994—. Harkness fellow Stanford U., 1965.

SHERWOOD, LOUIS MAIER, physician, scientist, pharmaceutical company executive; b. N.Y.C., Mar. 1, 1937; s. Arthur Joseph and Blanche (Burger) S.; m. Judith Brimberg, Mar. 27, 1966; children: Jennifer Beth, Arieh David. AB with honors, Johns Hopkins U., 1957; MD with honors, Columbia U., 1961. Diplomate Am. Bd. Internal Medicine, Subsplty. Bd. in Endocrinology and Metabolism. Intern Presbyn. Hosp., N.Y.C., 1961-62, asst. resident in medicine, 1962-63; clin. assoc. research fellow Nat. Heart Inst., NIH, Bethesda, Md., 1963-66; NIH trainee endocrinology and metabolism Coll. Physicians and Surgeons, Columbia U., N.Y.C., 1966-68; assoc. medicine Beth Israel Hosp. and Harvard Med. Sch., Boston, 1968-69; chief endocrinology Beth Israel Hosp., 1968-72; asst. prof. medicine Harvard U., 1969-71, assoc. prof., 1971-72; physician-in-chief, chmn. dept. medicine Michael Reese Hosp. and Med. Ctr., Chgo., 1972-80; prof. medicine, div. biol. scis. Pritzker Sch. Medicine, U. Chgo., 1972-80; Ted and Florence Baumritter prof. medicine and biochemistry Albert Einstein Coll. Medicine, 1980-88, vis. prof. medicine, 1989—, chmn. dept. medicine, 1980-87; physician-in-chief Montefiore Hosp. and Med. Ctr., N.Y.C., 1980-87; adj. prof. medicine U. Pa., 1993—; sr. v.p. med. and sci. affairs Merck, Sharp & Dohme Internat., 1987-89; exec. v.p. worldwide devel. Merck, Sharp & Dohme Rsch. Labs., 1989-92, sr. v.p. U.S. Med. and Sci. Affairs Merck Human Health, 1992—; bd. dirs. Physicians and Surgeons Corp., Michael Reese Med. Ctr., 1973-80, Barren Found., 1974-80; Josiah Macy Jr. Found. fellow and vis. scientist Weizmann Inst., Israel, 1978-79; assoc. mem. bd. on subcom. endocrinology and metabolism Am. Bd. Internal Medicine, 1977-83. Editor: Beth Israel seminars New Eng. Jour. Medicine, 1968-71; mem. editorial bd. Endocrinology, 1969-73; assoc. editor Metabolism, 1970-85, Gen. Medicine B Study Sect., NIH, 1975-79; mem. editorial bd. Yr. in Endocrinology, 1976-86, Calcified Tissue Internat., 1978-80, Internal Medicine Alert, 1979-89; contbr. numerous articles on endocrinology, protein hormones, calcium metabolism and ectopic proteins to jours. Trustee Michael Reese Med. Ctr., 1974-77; mem. vis. council CUNY Med. Sch., 1986—; mem. alumni council Columbia Coll. Physicians and Surgeons, 1986—. Served as surgeon USPHS, 1963-66. Recipient Joseph Mather Smith prize for outstanding alumni research Coll. Physicians and Surgeons, Columbia U., 1972, Sr. Class Teaching award U. Chgo., 1976, 77; grantee USPHS, 1968-88. Fellow ACP (Outstanding Contbn. to Internal Medicine award 1987); mem. AAAS, Am. Fedn. Clin. Rsch. (bd. dirs. Found. 1989-92, Spl. Recognition award 1992), Am. Inst. Chemists, Am. Soc. Biol. Chemists, Am. Soc. Clin. Investigation (pres. 1982-83), Assn. Am. Physicians, Endocrine Soc., Am. Physicians Fellowship for Medicine in Israel (pres. 1993—), N.Y. Acad. Medicine (bd. dirs. 1991-94), Am. Soc. Hypertension (bd. dirs. 1992—), Mass. Med. Soc., Ctrl. Soc. Clin. Rsch., Assn. Program Dirs. Internal Medicine (coun. 1979-85, pres. 1983-84), Assn. Profs. Medicine, Chgo. Soc. Internal Medicine, Assn. Prof. Med. Industry Roundtable, Interurban Clin. Club, Phi Beta Kappa, Alpha Omega Alpha. Achievements include research in protein and polypeptide hormones: structure, function and regulation of secretion; molecular studies of hormone biosynthesis; clinical pharmacology, new drug development and outcomes research. Office: Merck & Co US Human Health Sumneytown Pike West Point PA 19486 *To be a successful leader, you must be willing to surround yourself with outstanding individuals, to give them your full support and enjoy their growth.*

SHERWOOD, ROBERT PETERSEN, retired sociology educator; b. Black Diamond, Wash., May 17, 1932; s. James Brazier and Zina (Petersen) S.; m. Merlene Burningham, Nov. 21, 1951; children: Robert Lawrence, Richard William, Rolene, RaNae. BS, U. Utah, 1956, MS, 1957; EdD, U. Calif., Berkeley, 1965. Tchr. Arden-Carmichael Sch. Dist., Carmichael, Calif., 1957-59; vice prin. jr. high Arden-Carmichael Sch. Dist., 1960-61, prin. jr. high 1962-65; v.p., prin. San Juan Unified Sch. Dist., Sacramento, 1966-70; assoc. prof. Calif. State U., Sacramento, 1966-71; dir. outreach progs. Am. River Coll., Sacramento, 1971-73; acting assoc. dean of instrn. Am. River Coll., 1973-74, prof. sociology, 1970-92, chmn. sociology/anthropology dept., 1980-86, retired, 1992; pres. acad. senate Am. River Coll., 1990-91. With USN, 1953-55. Recipient Merit Recognition award, Boy Scouts Am.,

1989. Mem. NEA, Calif. Tchrs. Assn., Faculty Assn. Calif. Community Colls., Western Assn. Schs. and Colls., Calif. Fedn. Coll. Profs., Phi Delta Kappa (life). Mem. LDS Ch. Avocations: reading, writing, woodworking, travel. Home: 4053 Esperanza Dr Sacramento CA 95864-3069

SHERZER, HARVEY GERALD, lawyer; b. Phila., May 19, 1944; s. Leon and Rose (Levin) S.; m. Susan Bell, Mar. 28, 1971; children: Sheri Ann, David Lloyd. BA, Temple U., 1965; JD with honors, George Washington U., 1968. Bar: D.C. 1970, U.S. Ct. Appeals (D.C. cir.) 1970, U.S. Ct. Fed. Claims 1970, U.S. Ct. Appeals (fed. cir.) 1970, U.S. Supreme Ct. 1974. Law clk. to trial judges U.S. Ct. Fed. Claims, Washington, 1968-69; law clk. to chief judge U.S. Ct. Appeals for Fed. Cir., Washington, 1969-70; assoc. Sellers, Conner & Cuneo, Washington, 1970-75, ptnr., 1975-80; ptnr. McKenna, Conner & Cuneo, Washington, 1980-82, Pettit & Martin, Washington, 1982-85, Howrey & Simon, Washington, 1985—. Contbr. articles to profl. jours. Office: Howrey & Simon 1299 Pennsylvania Ave NW Washington DC 20004-2400

SHESTACK, ALAN, museum administrator; b. N.Y.C., June 23, 1938; s. David and Sylvia P. (Saffran) S.; m. Nancy Jane Davidson, Sept. 24, 1967. BA, Wesleyan U., 1961, DFA (hon.), 1978; MA, Harvard U., 1963. Mus. curator graphic art Nat. Gallery Art, Washington, 1965-67; assoc. curator prints and drawings Yale Art Gallery, New Haven, 1967-68; curator prints and drawings Yale Art Gallery, 1968-71, dir., 1971-85; adj. prof. history of art Yale U., 1971-85; dir. Mpls. Inst. Art, 1985-87, Boston Mus. Fine Arts, 1987-93; dep. dir. Nat. Gallery of Art, Washington, 1994—; mem. adv. com. Art Mus., Princeton, 1972-75; mem. vis. com. Harvard Univ. Art Mus., 1990—; mus. panel Nat. Endowment for the Arts, 1974-77; mem. com. prints and illustrated books Mus. Modern Art, N.Y.C., 1972—; mem. Fed. Arts and Artifacts Indemnification Panel, 1979-83. Author: Fifteenth Century Engravings of Northern Europe, 1967, The Engravings of Martin Schongauer, 1968, Master LCZ and Master WB, 1971, Exhibitions Organized and Catalogued: Master E.S, 1967, The Danube School, 1969, Hans Baldung Grien, Prints and Drawings, 1981; contbr. articles to profl. jours. Woodrow Wilson fellow Harvard U., 1963, David E. Finley fellow, 1963-65. Mem. Print Coun. Am. (bd. dirs., v.p. 1970-71), Coll. Art Assn. (bd. dirs. 1972-76), Am. Assn. Mus., Am. Fedn. Arts (trustee 1981-94), Alpha Delta Phi, Phi Beta Kappa. Office: Nat Gallery of Art Washington DC 20565

SHESTACK, JEROME JOSEPH, lawyer; b. Atlantic City, N.J., Feb. 11, 1925; s. Isidore and Olga (Shankman) S.; m. Marciarose Schleifer, Jan. 28, 1951; children: Jonathan Michael, Jennifer. A.B., U. Pa., 1944; LL.B., Harvard U., 1949. Bar: Ill. 1950, Pa. 1952. Teaching fellow Northwestern U. Law Sch., Chgo., 1949-50; assoc. prof. law, faculty editor La. State Law Sch., Baton Rouge, 1950-52; dep. city solicitor City of Phila., 1952, 1st dep. solicitor, 1952-55; ptnr. Schnader, Harrison, Segal & Lewis, Phila. and Washington, 1956-91, Wolf, Block, Schorr & Solis-Cohen, Phila., 1991—; adj. prof. law U Pa., 1956; U.S. amb. to UN Human Rights Commn., 1979-80; U.S. del. to ECOSOC, UN, 1980; sr. U.S. del. to Helsinki Accords Conf., 1979-80; mem. U.S. Commn. on Improving Effectiveness of UN, 1989—; chmn . Internat. League Human Rights, 1973—, U.S. del. to CSCE Conf., Moscow, 1991; bd. dirs., sec. Internat. Comm. Jurists Assn.; founder, chmn. Lawyers Com. Internat. Human Rights, 1978-80, Jacob Blaustein Inst. Human Rights, 1988-92; mem. nat. adv. com. legal svcs. OEO, 1965-72; bd. dirs., exec. com. Laywers Com. Civil Rights. Editor: (with others) Rights of Americans, 1971, Human Rights, 1979, International Human Rights, 1985, Bill of Rights: A Bicentennial View, 1991, Understanding Human Rights, 1992, Thomas Jefferson; Lawyer, 1993, Abraham Lincoln, Circuit Lawyer, 1994. Mem. exec. com. Nat. Legal Aid and Defender Assn., 1970-80; trustee Eleanor and Franklin Roosevelt Inst., 1986—; bd. govs. Tel Aviv U., 1983—; v.p. Am. Jewish Com., 1984-89; chmn. bd. dirs. Am. Poetry Ctr., 1976-91; trustee Free Libr. Phila, vice chmn., 1989—. With USNR, 1943-46. Rubin fellow Columbia U. Law Sch., 1984; hon. fellow U. Pa. Law Sch., 1980. Fellow Am. Bar Found.; mem. ABA (ho. of dels. 1971-73, 77—, mem. jud. com. 1985-90, bd. govs. 1992—, chmn. program com. 1994-95, exec. com. 1994-95), Pa. Bar Assn. (bd. govs.), Internat. Bar Assn. (chmn. com. on human rights), Am. Soc. Internat. Law (exec. com.), Am. Law Inst., Am. Coll. Trial Lawyers, Am. Acad. Appellate Lawyers, Order of Coif. Home: Parkway House 2201 Pennsylvania Ave Philadelphia PA 19130-3513 Office: Wolf Block Schorr & Solis-Cohen Packard Bldg 12th Fl SE Corner 15th & Chestnut Sts Philadelphia PA 19102-2678

SHESTACK, MELVIN BERNARD, editor, author, filmmaker, television producer; b. Bklyn., Aug. 18, 1931; s. David and Sylvia Pearl (Saffran) S.; m. Jessica Gifford, Feb. 13, 1965; 1 dau., Victoria J.; 1 dau. by previous marriage, Lisa F. A.B., U. So. Calif., 1953; postgrad., U. Rochester, N.Y. U., New Sch. Social Research. Assoc. editor Sat. Eve. Post, 1965-67; staff producer CBS-TV News, 1967-69; asso. producer Sta. WOR-TV, 1970; exec. editor True mag., N.Y.C., 1971-75, editor-in-chief, 1975; editor In The Know mag., N.Y.C., 1975—; exec. dir. Ponca Inter. Am. Studies, 1976-80; exec. editor Antelope Classics, Empire Editors, 1977—; v.p., dir. spl. projects Montcalm Pub. Co., 1980-85; pres. Gifford-Shestack Assocs., 1985-89; exec. v.p., dir. creative devel. Gt. Western Entertainment Corp., N.Y.C., 1989—. Producer, writer: (documentary) The Forgotten American, 1967, Changing Health Care, 1986; dir., producer: (PBS series) America's Challenge, 1990; author: The Country Music Encyclopedia, 1974; co-author: (filmscript) The Soul, 1978, Secrets of Success, 1980, "How'm I Doing?": The Wit and Wisdom of Ed Koch, 1981, New Country Encyclopedia, 1993, (screenplay) 5 Rooms, 1992; pub. Fresh Ayer, 1994; contbr. articles to profl. publs. Served with AUS, 1953-55. Recipient Brown-Nickerson award for best religious radio program, 1967. Mem. Pi Lambda Phi. Home: 4 Great Jones St New York NY 10012-1134 Office: Centuri Internat Prodns 825 8th Ave New York NY 10019-7416

SHETH, JAGDISH NANCHAND, business administration educator; b. Rangoon, Burma, Sept. 3, 1938; came to U.S., 1961, naturalized, 1975; s. Nanchand Jivraj and Diwaliben Sheth; m. Madhuri Ratilal Shah, Dec. 22, 1962; children—Reshma J., Raju J. B.Com. with honors, U. Madras, 1960; M.B.A., U. Pitts., 1962; Ph.D., 1966. Research assoc., asst. prof. Grad. Sch. Bus., Columbia U., 1963-65; asst. prof. M.I.T., 1966-68, Columbia U., 1966-69; asso. prof. bus. adminstrn. U. Ill., Urbana, 1969-71; acting head dept. U. Ill., 1970-72, prof. and research prof., 1971-73, I.B.A. Disting. prof. and research prof., 1973-79, Walter H. Stellner Disting. prof. and research prof., 1979-83; Robert E Brooker Disting. prof. mktg. and research U. So. Calif. Los Angeles, 1983-91; Charles H. Kellstadt prof. mktg. Emory U. Atlanta, 1991—; founder, dir. Ctr. for Telecommunications Mgmt. U. So. Calif. 1983—, Ctr. Relationship Mktg. Emory U.; vis. prof. Indian Inst. Mgmt., 1969; vis. lectr. Internat. Mktg. Inst., Harvard U., 1969; Albert Frey vis. prof. mktg. U. Pitts., 1974; condr. seminars for industry and govt.; cons. to industry. Author: (with John A. Howard) The Theory of Buyer Behavior, 1969, (with S.P. Sethi) Multinational Business Operations: Advanced Readings, 4 vols, 1973, (with A. Woodside and P. Bennett) Consumer and Industrial Buying Behavior, 1977, (with Bruce Newman): A Theory of Political Choice Behavior, 1986; (with Dennis Garrett) Marketing Theory, 1986; (with S. Ram) Bringing Innovation to Market; (with Gary Frazier) Theories of Marketing Practice; (with Milind Lele) The Customer is Key; editor: Models of Buyer Behavior, 1974, (with Peter L. Wright) Marketing Analysis for Societal Problems, 1974, Multivariable Methods for Market and Survey Research, 1977, Winning Back Your Market, 1984, (with David Gardener and Dennis Garrett) Marketing Theory: Evolution and Evaluation, 1988, also (with Abdol Reza and Goli Eslghi) 9 vols. on global bus., 1989-90, (with Bruce Newman and Barbara Gross) Consumption Values and Choice Behavior, 1990; series editor Research in Marketing, 1978—, Research in Consumer Behavior, 1984—; contbr. articles profl. jours. Recipient Viktor Mataja medal Austrian Rsch. Soc., 1976, Mktg. Educator award Sales and Mktg. Execs. Internat., 1991; Mgmt. Program for Execs. fellow, S & H Green Stamps fellow, 1963-64. Fellow APA; mem. Am. Mktg. Assn. (P.D. Converse award 1992), Acad. Mktg. Sci. (Mktg. Educator award 1989). Home: 1626 Mason Mill Rd NE Atlanta GA 30329-4133

SHETTLES, LANDRUM BREWER, obstetrician-gynecologist; b. Pontotoc, Miss., Nov. 21, 1909; s. Basil Manly and Sue (Mounce) S.; m. Priscilla Elinor Schmidt, Dec. 18, 1948; children—Susan Flora, Frances Louise, Lana Brewer, Landrum Brewer, David Ernest, Harold Manly and Alice Annmarie (twins). B.A., Miss. Coll., 1933, D.Sc. (hon.), 1966; M.S. (fellow 1933-34), U. N.M., 1934; Ph.D., Johns Hopkins, 1937, M.D., 1943.

Diplomate: Am. Bd. Obstetrics and Gynecology, N. Am. sect. obstetrics and gynecology Pan Am. Med. Assn. Instr. biology Miss. Coll., 1932-33; biologist U.S. Bur. Fisheries, 1934; instr. biology Johns Hopkins, 1934-37, research fellow, 1937-38; research fellow Nat. Com. Maternal Health, N.Y.C., 1938-43; intern Johns Hopkins Hosp., 1943-44; resident Columbia-Presbyn. Med. Center, N.Y.C., 1947-51; attending obstetrican-gynecologist Columbia-Presbyn. Med. Center, 1951-73, Doctors, Polyclinic and Flower-Fifth Av hosps., N.Y.C., 1974-75; chief obstetrican-gynecologist Gifford Meml. Hosp., Randolph, Vt., 1975-81, Star Clinic, Las Vegas, Nev., 1981-82, Oasis Clinic, Las Vegas, Nev., 1982-85; attending gynecologist-obstetrican Women's Hosp., Las Vegas, Nev., 1981-94, Sunrise Hosp. and Med. Ctr., 1994—; Markle Found. scholar Columbia Coll. Phys. and Surg., 1951-56; assoc. prof. clin. obstetrics-gynecology Coll. Phys. and Surg., Columbia, 1951-73; individual practice, N.Y.C., 1951-73; dir. research N.Y. Fertility Research Found., 1974-75; Anglo-Am. lectr. Royal Coll. Obstetricians and Gynecologists, London, Eng., 1959; Research cons. Office Naval Research, Am. embassy, London, 1951-52. Author: Ovum Humanum, 1960, Your Baby's Sex, Now You Can Choose, 1970, From Conception to Birth, 1971, Choose Your Baby's Sex, 1976, The Rites of Life: The Scientific Evidence of Life Before Birth, 1983, How to Choose Your Baby's Sex, 1984, 89; also numerous articles. Served to maj., M.C. AUS, 1944-46. Editorial bd. Infertility. Recipient Ortho medal and award Am. Soc. Study Fertility, Sterility and Allied Subjects, 1960, Order of the Golden Arrow award Miss. Coll., 1993, Disting. Alumnus award Miss. Coll., 1993. Fellow ACS, AAAS, Am. Coll. Obstetricians and Gynecologists, World Med. Assn., Royal Soc. of Health (London), Royal Soc. Medicine (London); mem. AMA, Am. Soc. Zoologists, Am. Physiol. Soc., Soc. Exptl. Biology and Medicine, Vt. Med. Soc., Soc. U. Gynecologists, N.Y. Obstet. Soc., Harvey Soc., Wisdom Soc., N.Y. State Med. Assn., N.Y. County Nev. Med. Assn., Clarke County Med. Assn., 50 Yr. Club of Miss. Coll., 50 Yr. Club of Johns Hopkins U., 50 Year Club of Vt. State Med. Soc., 25 Yr. Club of Columbia-Presbyn. Med. Ctr., Phi Beta Kappa, Sigma Xi, Omicron Delta Kappa, Gamma Alpha. Spl. research fishries biology, physiology, human reprodn., fertility and sterility, hemorrhagic disease in newborn infants, sperm biology; discovered, identified male and female producing sperms; achieved gamete intrafallopian transfer, 1978; human in vitro fertilization, 1951. Home and Office: 2209 Pardee Pl Las Vegas NV 89104-3424

SHETTY, MULKI RADHAKRISHNA, oncologist, consultant; b. Hiriadka, Karnataka, India, July 10, 1940; came to U.S., 1974; s. Mulki Sunderram and Kusumavati Shetty. MBBS, Stanley Med. Coll., Madras, 1964; DTM, U. Liverpool, Eng., 1968; LMCC, Med. Coun., Can., 1975. House surgeon and physician Bombay Hosp., 1965-66; sr. house officer Manor Pk. Hosp., Bristol, Eng., 1966-67, Torbay Hosp., 1967-68, St. Lukes Hosp., Huddersfield, 1969-70; sr. resident Gen. Hosp. Meml. U., New Foundland, 1971-72; intern Ottawa Gen. Hosp., 1972-73; fellow in chemotherapy Ont. Cancer Found., Ottawa, Can., 1973-74; fellow in clin. oncology U. Fla., Gainesville, 1974-75; attending oncologist N.W. Community Hosp., Arlington Heights, Ill., 1975—; cons. N.W. Community Hosp., 1975—. Author: Lung Cancer, 1980, Recent Advances in Chemotherapy, 1985; contbr. numerous articles to profl. jours.; coined new word, calcifectomy. Recipient Cert. for Outstanding Svc., Am Cancer Soc., 1982. Fellow Royal Soc. Medicine; mem. Internat. Assn. for Study of Lung Cancer, Chgo. Med. Soc. Hindu. Office: NW Community Hosp 800 W Central Rd Arlington Heights IL 60005-2392

SHEVACK, BRETT DAVID, advertising agency executive; b. N.Y.C., Mar. 2, 1950; s. Paul Irwin and Joan Bernice (Abrams) S. BFA, Pratt Inst., 1971. Asst. art. dir. Benton & Bowles, N.Y.C., 1972-73; art dir. Daniel & Charles Assocs., N.Y.C., 1973-75, creative dir., 1976-83; art dir. Young & Rubicam, N.Y.C., 1975-76; pres. LCF&S, N.Y.C., 1983-85, Calvillo, Shevack & Ptnrs., N.Y.C., 1985-88, Partners & Shevack, N.Y.C., 1988—. Avocation: running. Office: Partners & Shevack 1350 Ave Of The Americas New York NY 10019-4701

SHEVEL, WILBERT LEE, information systems executive; b. Monessen, Pa., Oct. 26, 1932; s. Wilbert Lee and Lillian Marie (Palomaki) S.; m. Faye Elizabeth Johnston, Aug. 20, 1954; children: Lynn, Laurel, Kathleen, Amy. BSEE, Carnegie-Mellon U., 1954, MSEE, 1955, PhDEE, 1956. With IBM Corp., White Plains, N.Y., 1956-73; v.p. consumer electronics Motorola Corp., Franklin Park, Ill., 1973-74; v.p. gen. mgr. home electronics Rockwell Internat., Schaumburg, Ill., 1974-76; pres., chief exec. officer OMEX Inc., Santa Clara, Calif., 1976-80, Barrington Inc., San Jose, Calif., 1980-82; sr. v.p. corp. ops. Burroughs Corp., Detroit, 1982-84; v.p. systems and tech. Unisys (formerly Systems Devel. Corp.) div. Burroughs Corp., McLean, Va., 1984-88; pres Paramax Def. Systems Can., 1988-92; v.p. corp. info. systems Unisys Corp., 1992-94; mng. dir. EIM, San Deigo, 1994—. Patentee in field. Mem. adv. bd. Carnegie Mellon U. Sch. Computer Sci., 1988—. 1st lt. U.S. Army, 1957. Fellow IEEE. Office: EIM 16776 Bernardo Ctr Dr 110-B San Diego CA 92128

SHEVIN, ROBERT LEWIS, lawyer; b. Miami, Fla., Jan. 19, 1934; s. Aaron and Pauline (Bott) S.; m. Myrna Bressack, Jan. 27, 1957; children: Laura Dawn, Hilary Beth, Harry Alan. BA, U. Fla., 1955; JD magna cum laude, U. Miami, 1957. Bar: Fla. 1957, U.S. Dist. Ct. (so. and mid. dists.) Fla. 1963, U.S. Supreme Ct. 1971, U.S. Ct. Appeals (5th cir.) 1971, U.S. Dist. Ct. (no. dist.) Fla. Ptnr. Shevin, Goodman and Holtzman, 1957-67, Shevin and Shevin, 1967-70; mem. Fla. Ho. of Reps., 1963-65, chmn. interim com. on crime and law enforcement, 1965; mem. Fla. State Senate, 1966-70, chmn. select com. to investigate organized crime and law enforcemnt, 1967, mem. interim study com. on urban affairs, 1968; atty. gen. State of Fla., 1971-79; ptnr. Sparber, Shevin, Rosen, Shapo & Heilbronner, Miami, 1979-87, Stroock & Stroock & Lavan, Miami, 1988—; mem. Fla. Tax Reform Commn., 1968, Fla. Constl. Revision Commn., 1978; city atty. City of Miami Beach, Fla., 1979-80. Chmn. Housing Fin. Authority Dade County, Fla., 1980—, Fla. State Athletic Commn., 1984-87; mem. exec. com. Miami Citizens Against Crime; bd. dirs. Fla. Citizens Against Crime, 1985—; pres. Fla. Senate's Sunshine Adv. Com., 1988; chmn. Ptnrs. for Safe Neighborhoods, 1994; vis. com. U. Miami Law Sch. Recipient Allen Morris award, 1969, Intergovtl. award HUD, 1969, Conservationist of Yr. awards Fla. Wildlife Fedn., 1973, Audubon Soc., 1974, Furtherance of Justice award Fla. Prosecuting Attys. Assn., 1974, Disting. Svc. award Fla. Sheriff's Assn., 1976, Peace award State of Israel, 1977; named one of 10 Most Valuable Mems. Fla. Legislature Capital Press Corps, 1965. Mem. ABA, Internat. Bar Assn., Fla. Bar Assn., Dade County Bar Assn., Am. Trial Lawyers Assn., Am. Judicare Soc., Nat. Assn. Attys. Gen. (chmn. So. region 1981), Iron Arrow, Fla. Blue Key, Sertoma, Phi Delta Phi, Pi Lambda Phi, Phi Kappa Phi, Omicron Delta Kappa. Democrat. Jewish. Home: 7171 SW 56th St Miami FL 33155 Office: Stroock & Stroock & Lavan 33rd Fl 200 S Biscayne Blvd Miami FL 33131

SHEWARD, RICHARD S., judge; b. Jackson, Ohio, May 21, 1944; s. D.J. and M.A. (Rapp) S.; m. Kathryn L. Wagner, Sept. 26, 1975; children—Carrin E., Alison M. B.B.A., Ohio U., 1967; J.D., Capital U., 1974. Bar: Ohio 1974, U.S. Dist. Ct. (so. dist.) Ohio 1975, U.S. Supreme Ct. 1978. Asst. pros. atty. Franklin County (Ohio), 1974-76; ptnr. Sheward & Weiner, Columbus, Ohio, 1976-87; judge Franklin County Mcpl. Ct., 1987-91, Franklin County Ct. Common Pleas, 1991-93, presiding judge, 1993—; instr. real estate law Columbus Tech. Inst., 1977-80. Mem. Upper Arlington (Ohio) Civic Assn.; mem. Franklin County Republican Central Com., 1983-87. Served with U.S. Army, 1968-71. Decorated Bronze Star, Air medal. Mem. ABA, Ohio Bar Assn., Columbus Bar Assn. (common pleas ct., chmn. criminal law com. 1985-86, 86-87), Franklin County Trial Lawyers Assn. (pres. 1984-85), Am. Arbitration Assn. (labor panel), Franklin County Pros. Atty. Alumni Assn. (chmn. 1979-87). Methodist. Clubs: Buckeye Rep. (pres. 1981), Touchdown, Agonis, Charity Newsies. Lodge: Masons (32 deg.). Home: 2090 Cheltenham Rd Columbus OH 43220-4343 Office: Franklin County Common Pleas Ct 373 S High St # 22 Columbus OH 43215-4591

SHEWMAKER, JACK CLIFFORD, retired retail executive, rancher, consultant; b. Buffalo, Mar. 14, 1938; s. Clifford Verl and Pansy Louise (Brackley) S.; m. Melba June Prosser, Mar. 16, 1958; children: Daniel, Shari Shewmaker Steiger, Emily Shewmaker Loyd. Student, Ga. Tech. Inst.; hon. doctorate, S.W. Baptist U., 1985. Dist. mgr. Wal-Mart Stores, Inc., Bentonville, Ark., 1970-73, v.p. security, 1973-74, v.p store ops., 1974-76, exec. v.p., 1976-78, pres., chief operating officer, 1978-84, vice-chmn., chief fin. officer, 1984-88, ret., 1988, also bd. dirs.; owner, operator Jac's Ranch,

Bentonville, Ark., 1983—; cons. Edgars, South Africa, IMRA, Washington, Lowe's Cos., Inc., North Wilkesboro, N.C., Wal-Mart Stores, Inc., Bentonville, Ark., Big W Discount Stores, Sydney, Australia, ALH Australia & Pacific, Dunlop, Melbourne, Australia, Snape, Portugal, Big C, Bangkok, Thailand. Contbr. articles to bus. jours. Vice chmn., bd. trustees Drury Coll., Springfield, Mo.; chmn. Students in Free Enterprise, Inc., Springfield, Mo., 1985-88, bd. dirs., 1985—. Named Discount Retailer of Yr., 1981; Retailer of Yr., Mass Market Retailer mag., 1985. Republican. Baptist. Avocations: hunting, fishing, skiing. Address: Jac's Ranch Rte 4 Box 313 10054 E Hwy 72 Bentonville AR 72712

SHEWMAKER, KENNETH EARL, history educator; b. L.A., June 26, 1936; s. James Virgil and Jeanette M. (Greenberg) S.; m. Elisabeth L. Spalteholz, June 12, 1960; children: Richard Glenn, Nancy Jeanette. BS, Concordia Tchrs. Coll., 1960; MA, U. Calif., Berkeley, 1961; PhD, Northwestern U., 1966. Instr. Northwestern U., Evanston, Ill., 1965-66; asst. prof. Coll. William and Mary, Williamsburg, Va., 1966-67; from asst. prof. to assoc. prof. Dartmouth Coll., Hanover, N.H., 1967-78, prof. history, 1978—, acting chair dept. history, 1985-86, chmn. dept. history, 1986-89. Author: Americans and Chinese Communists, 1927-45: A Persuading Encounter, 1971 (Stuart L. Bernath prize 1972); editor: Papers of Daniel Webster, Diplomatic Papers, Vol. 1, 1841-1843, 1983, Vol. 2, 1850-1852, 1987, Daniel Webster, The Completest Man, 1990; contbr. articles to profl. jours. Mem. Am. Hist. Assn., N.H. Hist. Soc., Orgn. Am. Historians, Soc. Historians Am. Fgn. Rels. Lutheran. Avocations: fly fishing, fly tying. Office: Dartmouth College Dept History Hanover NH 03755

SHEWMON, PAUL GRIFFITH, metallurgical engineer, educator; b. Rochelle, Ill., Apr. 18, 1930; s. Joe Allen and Mildred Elizabeth (Griffith) S.; m. Dorothy E. Bond, Aug. 30, 1952; children: David A., Joan E. (dec.), Andrew B. B.S. in Metall. Engring. U. Ill., 1952; M.S., Carnegie Mellon U., 1954, Ph.D., 1955. Staff Westinghouse Research Lab., Pitts., 1955-58; prof. metall. engring. Carnegie Mellon U., Pitts., 1958-67; assoc. dir. metal div., 1967-69; assoc. dir. metal div. Exptl. Breeder Reactor II Project, Argonne Nat. Lab., 1969-70, dir. material sci. div., 1971-73; dir. div. materials research NSF, 1973-75; prof. Ohio State U., 1976—, head dept., 1976-83; mem. adv. com. on reactor safeguards U.S. Nuclear Regulatory Commn., 1977—. Author: Diffusion in Metals, 1963, Phase Transformations, 1969. Dow fellow, 1952-55; NSF sci. faculty fellow, 1963-64; recipient Disting. Alumnus award U. Ill. Engring. Coll., 1981, Disting. Scholar award Ohio State U., 1984. Fellow Am. Soc. Metals (Howe medal 1977), AAAS, The Metall. Soc.-AIME (Rossiter Raymond award 1959, Noble award 1959, Mathewson Gold medal 1982, V. Humboldt Sr. Scientist award 1984), Am. Nuclear Soc.; mem. Nat. Acad. Engrs., Tau Beta Pi, Sigma Xi. Home: 2477 Lytham Rd Columbus OH 43220-4672 Office: Ohio State Univ Dept Metall Sci & Engring 116 W 19th Ave Columbus OH 43210

SHI, FENG SHENG, mathematician; b. Shanghai, China, Sept. 28, 1935; came to U.S., 1990; s. Jing Long and Xu Wenzheng Shi; m. Dorothy Shi, May 30, 1992. Degree of engr., 1957. Prof. math. and physics U. Industry, Shanghai, 1961-64; ship designer Govt. of China, Shanghai, 1964; rschr., business liaison Hong Kong of U.S.A. Liaison for Bus. Investment; owner, editor Pendulum Math. Jour. in Libr. of Congress; trustee, founder, dir. Chinese Math. Students Orgn., Miami, Fla., 1993—; dir. Chinese Internat. Math. Students Orgn., 1994—. Author: (math. solutions) Exist, 1991 (Libr. of Congress), Solving the Fermat Problem and Goldbach's Conjecture, 1993. Recipient Son of Yr. award Son's & Daughter's Found., 1990. Mem. All Nations (trustee, bd. dirs. 1990-93, Internat. Man of Yr. 1991). Home and Office: 1000 8th St N Saint Petersburg FL 33701

SHIBATA, SHOJI, pharmacology educator, researcher; b. Kyoto, Japan, Nov. 12, 1927; came to U.S., 1963; s. Shuzo and Tetsu Shibata; m. May 1958; children: Toshiyuki, Eri. MD, Nara (Japan) Med. Coll., 1952; PhD, Kyoto U., 1957. Instr. pharmacology Kyoto U. Med. Sch., 1957-60, U. So. Calif., Los Angeles, 1960-62; assoc. prof. Kyoto Coll. Pharmacy, 1962-63; instr. U. Miss., Jackson, 1963-64, asst. prof., 1964-66; assoc. prof. U. Hawaii, Honolulu, 1967-69, prof., 1970—. Author: Recent Developments in Cardiac Muscle Pharmacology, 1982, Factors Influencing Vascular Reactivity, 1977, Basic Methods of Pharmacology, 1981, Vascular Neuroeffector Mechanisms; 4th Internat. Symposium, 1983, recent advances in Ca Channels and Ca antagonist, 1990; editor Jour. Cardiovascular Pharmacology, Cardiovascular Drug Rev., Meeting Reports Cardiovascular. Fellow Japanese Dept. of Edn., 1954-57, Can. Heart Assn., 1978; sr. fellow Japanese Acad. Scis. Assn. Mem. Am. Physiology Soc., Am. Soc. Pharmaxology and Exptl. Therapy, Microcirculatory Soc., Internat. Soc. Heart Rsch. Home: 3338 Keahi St Honolulu HI 96822-1206 Office: U Hawaii Sch Medicine 1960 E West Rd Honolulu HI 96822-2319

SHIBLEY, GAIL ROSE, state legislator; b. North Bend, Oreg., Apr. 7, 1958; d. Lyle Donald and Rosemarie Elizabeth (Duban) S.; life ptnr. Kelly Sue Rogers. BA, U. Oreg., 1980. Congrl. aide U.S. rep. Jim Weaver U.S. Ho. Reps., Washington and Eugene, Wash., 1980-86; acct. exec. Ryan, Hutchins, Southwick, Portland, 1987-90; program mgr. City of Portland, Oreg., 1990—; mem. Oreg. Ho. Reps., Portland, 1991—; mem. Multi County Community Action Com., Portland, 1992—, Gov.'s Coun. DUII, Portland, 1992—, Breast and Cervical Cancer Coalition, Portland, 1992—. Dem. precinct leader, Multnomah County, Oreg., 1991—; fundraiser, mem. Right of Privacy, Oreg., 1985—; mem. Gay and Lesbian Victory Fund, 1992—; trustee No On 13 Com., Oreg., 1994—; bd. dirs. Neighborhood Partnership Fund, Portland, 1994. Recipient Legis. Excellence award Multnomah County Community Action Agy., 1991, Nan Wood Honeyman award Oreg. Women's Polit. Caucus, 1991, Torch award Human Rights Campaign Fund, 1992; named to Legis. Honor Roll Oreg. Environ. Coun., 1991. Fellow Am. Leadership Forum, 1994-95, Oreg. Women's Polit. Caucus, Oreg. Hist. Soc., City Club Portland. Democrat. Avocations: running, tennis, scuba. Home: PO Box 6805 Portland OR 97228 Office: Oreg Ho of Reps H-395 State Capitol Salem OR 97310

SHIDELER, ROSS PATRICK, foreign language and comparative literature educator, author, translator, poet; b. Denver, Apr. 12, 1936. B.A., San Francisco State U., 1958; M.A., U. Stockholm, 1963; Ph.D., U. Calif., Berkeley, 1968. Instr. in comparative lit. U. Calif., Berkeley, 1967-68; asst. prof. English Hunter Coll. N.Y.C., 1968-69; asst. prof. Scandinavian lang. and comparative lit. UCLA, 1969-73, assoc. prof., 1973-79, prof., 1979—; chmn. program in comparative lit., 1979-86, 92—. Author: (monograph) Voices Under The Ground: Themes and Images in the Poetry of Gunnar Ekelof, 1973, Per Olov Enquist-A Critical Study, 1984; translator: (play) The Night of the Tribades (Per Olov Enquist), 1977, The Hour of the Lynx, 1990 (Per Olov Enquist), 1990; U.S. assoc. editor Swedish Book Rev., 1984— Fellow NDFL, 1964; fellow NDEA, 1965; Fulbright-Hays fellow, 1966-67. Mem. MLA (exec. com. divsn. Scandinavian Langs. and Lits. 1993—), Soc. for Advancement Scandinavian Studies (exec. coun. 1985-89), Am. Comparative Lit. Assn., Assn. Depts. and Programs Comparative Lit. (exec. com. 1993-94, 94—). Office: UCLA Program In Comparative Los Angeles CA 90024

SHIDELER, SHIRLEY ANN WILLIAMS, lawyer; b. Mishawaka, Ind., July 9, 1930; d. William Harmon and Lois Wilma (Koch) Williams; 1 dau., Gail Shideler Frye. LLB, Ind. U., 1964. Bar: Ind. 1964. Legal sec. Barnes, Hickam, Pantzer & Boyd, Indpls., 1953-63; assoc. Barnes & Thornburg, 1964-70, ptnr., 1971-92, of counsel, 1993—. Participant fund drives Indpls. Symphony, 1968-81, Indpls. Mus. Art, 1969-79, Marion County Libr. Restoration, 1985-88, Goodwill Industries, 1988-89; bd. dirs. bus. unit gals Indpls. Mus. Art, 1973-80; bd. dirs. Indpls. Legal Aid Soc., 1982-93, Community Hosp. Found., Cen. Newspapers Found. Fellow Am. Coll. Trust and Estate Counsel; mem. ABA, Ind. Bar Assn. (sec. 1975-76, chmn. probate, trust and real property sect. 1982), Nat. Conf. Bar Founds. (trustee 1988-94), Indpls. Bar Assn. (bd. mgrs. 1968-72, v.p. charge affairs 1972), Ind. Bar Found. (bd. mgrs. 1980-92, sec. 1981-82, treas. 1981-86, v.p. 1986-88, pres. 1988-90), Indpls. Bar Found. (bd. mgrs. 1970-82, sec. 1977-79, Estate Planning Coun., Women's Rotary (pres. Indpls. club 1969-71, dir. 1968-79). Home: 2224-C Boston Ct Indianapolis IN 46208 Office: Barnes & Thornburg 1313 Mchts Bank Bldg 11 S Meridian St Indianapolis IN 46204-3506

SHIEBER, STUART MERRILL, natural sciences educator; b. St. Louis, Apr. 27, 1959; s. William and Hortense (Rader) S.; m. Cassia Wyner, June 19, 1993. AB in Applied Math. summa cum laude, Harvard U., 1981; PhD in Computer Sci., Stanford U., 1989. Rsch. fellow Ctr. for Study of Lang. and Info., Stanford U., 1983-89; rsch. computer scientist Artificial Intelligence Ctr., SRI Internat., 1981-89; asst. prof. computer sci. Harvard U., Cambridge, Mass., 1989-93, John L. Loeb assoc. prof. natural scis., 1993—; founder Cartesian Products, Inc., 1991; vis. prof. U. Calif., Santa Cruz, summer 1991; founder, organizer The Computation and Lang. E-Print Archive. Author: An Introduction to Unification-Based Approaches to Grammar, 1986, Spanish transl., 1989, French transl., 1990; Constraint-Based Grammar Formalisms, 1992; (with Fernando C.N. Pereira) Prolog and Natural-Language Analysis, 1987, Italian transl., 1992; editor: (with Peter Sells and Thomas Wasow) Foundational Issues in Natural Language Processing, 1991; contbr. numerous articles to profl. jours.; mem. editl. bd. Computational Linguistics, 1990-93, Jour. Artificial Intelligence Rsch., 1993—. Named Presdl. Young Investigator, 1991-93; Presdl. Faculty fellow, 1993—. Mem. Assn. Computational Linguistics (mem. exec. com. 1993—), Phi Beta Kappa. Office: Harvard Univ Cambridge MA 02138

SHIEH, JOHN TING-CHUNG, economics educator; b. China. BS, Chunghsing U., Taiwan, 1956; MS, Kans. State U., 1960; MA, U. Calif., Riverside, 1970; D in Bus. Adminstrn., U. So. Calif., 1981. Asst. prof. Northwestern State Coll., Alva., 1964-67; asst. prof. econs. Calif. State Poly. U., Pomona, 1967-70, assoc. prof., 1970-81, prof., chmn. dept. econs., 1982-85, prof., 1981—; prof., dir. Inst. Mainland China Studies, Nat. Dong-hua U., Hwalian, Taiwan, 1995—; cons. to small bus., So. Calif., Taiwan, 1975—; vis. prof. Tax Inst., U. So. Calif., L.A., 1977-84, U. Calif., Irvine, 1978-79, U. So. Calif., 1978-81, UCLA, 1983—. Rsch., publs. in field. NSF fellow, 1965, 66, 67, 73; fellow seminars in econs. and math. U. Wyo., summer 1972. Mem. Am. Econ. Assn., Omicron Delta Epsilon, Omega Rho. Home: 10556 Ilona Ave Los Angeles CA 90064 Office: Calif State Poly U Dept Econs Pomona CA 91768 also: Inst Mainland China Studies, Nat Dong-hua U, Hwalian Taiwan

SHIEKMAN, LAURENCE ZEID, lawyer; b. Phila., Feb. 13, 1947; s. Morton and Roberta (Zeid) S.; m. Marjorie Kershbaum, Dec. 25, 1970; children: Wendy K., Thomas K. BS in Econs., U. Pa., 1968, JD, 1971. Bar: Pa. 1971. Law clk. to Hon. A. Leon Higginbotham, Jr. U.S. Dist. Ct. (ea. dist.) Pa., 1971-73; asst. prof. Fla. State U. Coll. Law, Tallahassee, 1973-75; assoc. Pepper, Hamilton & Scheetz, Phila., 1975-78, ptnr., 1978—. Chmn. 20th Yr. reunion com. U. Pa. Law Sch., Phila., 1990. Mem. ABA, Pa. Bar Assn., Phila. Bar Assn. Office: Pepper Hamilton & Scheetz 3000 Two Logan Sq 18th & Arch Sts Philadelphia PA 19103-2799

SHIELDS, ALLAN EDWIN, writer, photographer, retired educator; b. Columbus, Ohio, July 3, 1919; s. Richard Edwin and Eloessa (Smith) S.; m. Bernice Clark, Aug. 2, 1941; children—Allan Oakley, Richard Minter, Larry Michael, Catherine Marie. A.B., U. Calif.-Berkeley, 1941; M.A., U. So. Calif., 1947, Ph.D., 1951. Prof. philosophy San Diego State U., 1949-68, 70-78; emeritus prof. San Diego State Coll., 1978—; dean Coll. Humanities and Fine Arts U. No. Iowa, 1968-70; owner, pub. Jerseydale Ranch Press, 1992—; seasonal ranger naturalist Nat. Park Service, Yosemite Nat. Park, 1955-60; freelance writer, photographer, 1978—; violinist-violist, frequent recitalist; mem., sometime concertmaster Merced Symphony Orch., Calif., 1979-91; founder, with wife, Jerseydale Ranch Press, 1992. Author: Guide to Tuolumne Meadows Trails, 1960, rev. edit., 1973, (with Herbert Searles) A Bibliography of the Works of F.C.S. Schiller, 1969, (with Richard Shields) Tuolumne Profile: Yosemite, 1967, (novella) The Tragedy of Tenaya, 1974, new version 1992, A Bibliography of Bibliographies in Aesthetics, 1974, (poetry) A Horse in the House, 1985, Mariposa Now and Then, 1993, Tuffy, An Angel Hid in a Cloud, 1994, What Animals Taught Me, 1995, also numerous poems and articles; editor: A Yosemite Adventure in 1863, 1992, Wild Bill Neely and the Pagan Brothers' Golden Goat Winery, 1993, The Song of Sonora, 1993, O.S.S.: One Sad Sack--Pvt. Neely Disciplines the Military, 1994, A Yosemite Naturalist's Odyssey, 1994, Wilderness Treks by Foot, Canoe and Adobe Rocket, and Father's Far-Flung Fables, 1995; pub. various profl. jours. Bd. dirs. San Diego Symphony. Served with USAAF, 1942-45. Mudd fellow in philosophy U. So. Calif., 1948-49. Mem. Am. Soc. for Aesthetics (trustee), Phi Beta Kappa, Phi Kappa Phi, Phi Mu Alpha Sinfonia (hon.). Home: 6506 Jerseydale Rd Mariposa CA 95338-9638 *My greatest satisfactions have come with tasks completed to the best of my abilities. Whether raising children, building a building, nurturing a marriage, learning the violin, or writing, all have inherent standards demanding recognition. Though there is always joy in the process of doing, joy can be transformed into satisfaction only in completion evaluated against the standards of worth for that kind of undertaking.*

SHIELDS, BROOKE CHRISTA CAMILLE, actress, model; b. N.Y.C., May 31, 1965; d. Francis A. and Teri (Schmon) S. BA, Princeton U., 1987. Model for Ivory Soap commls. starting in 1966, later for Calvin Klein jeans and Colgate toothpaste commls.; actress: (films) Alice, Sweet Alice, 1975, Pretty Baby, 1977, King of the Gypsies, 1978, Wanda Nevada, 1978, Just You and Me Kid, 1978, Blue Lagoon, 1979, Endless Love, 1980, Sahara, 1983, Backstreet Strays, 1989, Brenda Starr, 1992, Seventh Floor, 1993, Running Wild, 1993, Freaked, 1993; (TV movies) The Prince of Central Park, 1977, After the Fall, Wet Gold, I Can Make You Love Me: The Stalking of Laura Black, 1993, (TV shows) The Tonight Show, Bob Hope spls., The Diamond Trap, 1988; appeared on Broadway in Grease, 1994. Office: Christa Inc Ste 630 2300 West Sahara Blvd 18 Las Vegas NV 89102

SHIELDS, CAROL ANN, writer, educator; b. Oak Park, Ill., June 2, 1935; came to Can., 1957, naturalized, 1974; d. Robert Elmer and Inez Adelle (Sellgren) Warner; m. Donald Hugh Shields, July 20, 1957; children: John, Anne, Catherine, Margaret, Sara. B.A., Hanover Coll., 1957; M.A., U. Ottawa, Ont., Can., 1975. Editorial asst. Can. Slavonic Papers, Ottawa, 1972-74; lectr. U. Ottawa, 1976-77, U. B.C., Vancouver, Can., 1978-80; assoc. prof. U. Man., Winnipeg, Can., 1980—. Author: (poems) Others, 1972, Intersect, 1974, Coming to Canada, 1991; (novels) Small Ceremonies, 1976, The Box Garden, 1977, Happenstance, 1980, A Fairly Conventional Woman, 1982, Various Miracles, 1985, Swann: A Mystery, 1987, The Orange Fish, 1989, The Republic of Love, 1992, The Stone Diaries, 1993 (Nat. Book Critics Circle award for fiction 1994, Pulitzer Prize for fiction 1995); (play) Women Waiting, 1973, Departures and Arrivals, 1974, Thirteen Hands, 1993, (with Catherine Shields) Fashion Power Guilt. Grantee Can. Council, 1973, 76, 78, 86, Man. Arts Council, 1984, 85; recipient prize CBC, 1983, 84, Nat. Mag. award, 1985, Arthur Ellis award, 1987, Can. Book Sellers'award 1994, Manitoba Book of the Yr., 1994, Marian Engel award Writers' Devel. Trust, 1990, Gov. Gen.'s award Can. Coun., 1993. Mem. PEN, Writers Union Can., Writers Guild Man., Jane Austen Soc., N.Am. Can. Coun. Bd. Quaker. Home: 701 237 Wellington Crescent, Winnipeg, MB Canada R3M 0A1 Office: care Bella Pomer Agency Inc, 22 Shallmar Blvd Penthouse 2, Toronto, ON Canada M5N 2Z8

SHIELDS, H. RICHARD, tax consultant,business executive; m. Frances Augenstein; 1 dau., Eileen. A.B., Bklyn. Coll.; LL.B., J.D., NYU; M.B.A., Harvard U. Bar: N.Y. bar 1940. Corp. practice law, 1940-60; secs. Forbes Realty Corp., 1960-70; exec. v.p. Forbes Industries, Ltd., 1965-70; exec. v.p. Am. Diversified Industries Corp., 1964-66, pres., chmn. bd., 1966-76; exec. v.p. Daily Mirror, Sunday Mirror, N.Y.C.; chmn., chief exec. officer, dir. TTC Industries (also subs. Armstrong Glass Mfg. Corp.), Erwin, Tenn., 1970-76; pres. dir. Euro Industries, Ltd.; and dir.; pres., chief exec. officer, dir. Dairene Industries, Ltd. 1971-80; tax cons. Regal Cons., Ltd, Great Neck, N.Y., 1974-85; dir. Blue Ribbon Mktg. Corp.; govt. appeal agt. U.S. Selective Service; mem. N.Y. State Commn. on Human Rights; former arbitrator Civil Ct., N.Y.C. Served to maj. USAAF, 1942-46, CBI. Decorated Commendation medal, Legion of Merit, China War Meml. medal. Mem. Am. Inst. Mgmt., Nat. Assn. Accts., Nat. Tax Assn. (com. fed. taxation), Tax Inst. Am., Tax Execs. Inst., Nat. Assn. Corp. Dirs., Assn. Bar City N.Y. (legis. com.). Club: Harvard.

SHIELDS, JAMES JOSEPH, JR., educator, educational administrator, author; b. Phila., Feb. 11, 1935; s. James Joseph and Lena Josephine (Dyer) S. BS in Polit. Sci., Saint Joseph's U., 1956; EdM, Temple U., 1959; EdD, Columbia U., 1963. Asst. to dir., internat. studies Tchrs. Coll., Columbia U., N.Y.C., 1961; researcher, Tchrs. for East Africa Program Tchrs. Coll.,

Columbia U., N.Y.C. and Kampala, Uganda, 1961-62; asst. prof. history and philosophy of edn. SUNY, New Paltz, 1962-64; asst. prof. comparative and politics of edn. CUNY, 1964-69; assoc. prof. comparative and politics of edn. CUNY, N.Y.C., 1969-75, prof. comparative and politics of edn., 1975—, head, Sch. Adminstrn. Program, 1983-85, chair, dept. social and psychol. founds., 1988-90, dir., Japan Initiative Com., 1986—; cons. Inst. for Ednl. Devel., N.Y.C., 1968-71, Equitable Life Ins. Co. N.Y.C., 1961; vis. rsch. prof. Tokyo Met. U., 1986—; vis. prof. Tchrs. Coll., Columbia U., 1965-67, 93-95; mem. evaluation bd. Nat. Coun. on Accreditation of Tchr. Edn., Washington, 1970-75; assoc. Columbia U., Univ. Seminar on Modern Japan, N.Y.C., 1987—, chair, 1990-91. Author: Education in Community Development: Its Function in Technical Assistance, 1967; editor: Problems and Prospects in International Education, 1968, Foundations of Education: Dissenting Views, 1974, Japanese Schooling: Patterns of Socialization Equality and Political Control, 1989 (nominated for Books on Japan award), rev. edit. 1993; author numerous book chpts., monographs and book reviews; contbr. numerous articles to profl. jours. Mem. Pub. Edn. Assn. Task Force on a Reconstructed Ednl. Sys., N.Y.C., 1977-78, Pub. Edn. Assn. Task Force on Tchr. Selection, N.Y.C., 1981; mem. N.Y. Urban Coalition, 1982-84, Alumni Coun., Tchrs. Coll. Columbia U., 1993—. With USAR, 1959-59. Grantee Japan-U.S. Friendship Commn., 1986-89, The City Coll., Provost, 1988-89, 89-90, Rsch. Found. CUNY, 1980-81, N.Y. State Edn. Dept., 1969-72, SUNY Rsch. Found., 1964; Fulbright travel grantee, 1964, Japan Found. Ctr. for Global Partnership, 1994, The U.S.-Japan Found., 1994-95; recipient Higher Edn. award Holy Family Coll., Phila., 1990, Wyo. Gov.'s Youth Coun. award, 1974, Ann. Gertrude Langsam Ednl. Reconstrn. award Adelphi U., 1992; postdoctoral fellow Yale U., New Haven, 1967-68. Mem. Am. Ednl. Studies Assn. (pres. 1973-74, exec. coun. 1970-75), Carnegie Coun. on Ethics and Internat. Affairs, Comparative and Internat. Edn. Soc. (N.E. region conf. coord. 1984, bd. dirs. 1992—), Japan Soc. of N.Y., Internat. House of Japan, Soc. for Ednl. Reconstruction (exec. com. 1973—), Am. Ednl. Rsch. Assn. Avocations: collecting Long Island painters (1850-1950), travel, gardening. Home: 562 W End Ave Apt 4D New York NY 10024-2718 Office: CUNY 138th St and Convent Ave New York NY 10031

SHIELDS, JERRY ALLEN, ophthalmologist, educator; b. Pride Station, Ky., June 9, 1937; s. Fendell Harris and Beulah Etta (Williams) S.; m. Carol Lally, Oct. 26, 1985; children: Jerry, Patrick, William, Margaret, John. BA, Murray State U., 1960; MD, U. Mich., 1964. Diplomate Am. Bd. Ophtalmology. Intern Denver Gen. Hosp., 1964-65; resident in ophthalmology Wills Eye Hosp., Phila., 1967-70, fellowship in retina, 1970, fellowship in pathology, 1971, dir. ocular oncology svc., 1973—; prof. ophthalmology Thomas Jefferson U. Hosp., Phila., 1980—. Author: Diagnosis and Management of Intraocular Tumors, 1983, Diagnosis and Management of Orbital Tumors, 1989, Intraocular Tumors: A Text and Atlas, 1991; contbr. articles to jours., chpts. to textbooks. Lt. MC, USN, 1965-67, Vietnam. Recipient Golden Apple award Sr. Residents Wills Eye Hosp., 1990; co-recipient award Brady Cancer Rsch. Inst., 1986. Mem. AMA, Am. Acad. Ophthalmology, Am. Assn. Rsch. Ophthalmology, Phila. Ophthalmic Club, Pa. Acad. Ophthalmology and Otolaryngology. Home: 617 Williamson Rd Bryn Mawr PA 19010 Office: Wills Eye Hosp Dept Oncology 9th & Walnut Sts Philadelphia PA 19107*

SHIELDS, JOAN E., chemistry educator; b. Oct. 11, 1934. AB, Regis Coll., 1956; MS, Tufts U., 1958; PhD, Boston Coll., 1966. Prof. Long Island U., Greenvale, N.Y., 1976—, chmn. dept. chemistry, 1976-81, 88—. Author: 2 books; pub. 34 papers. Postdoctoral fellow Max Planck Inst., Germany, 1966-67; Sarah Berliner fellow AAUW, 1974-75. Mem. ACS (chem. edn. divsn., organic chemistry divsn., mem. numerous coms., Outstanding Svc. award N.Y. sect. 1981), Sigma Xi. Office: Long Island U Dept of Chemistry C W Post Campus Greenvale NY 11548*

SHIELDS, JOHN CHARLES, American studies and African American studies and literature educator; b. Phoenix, Oct. 29, 1944; s. Granville Blaine and Elizabeth Merle (Hartgraves) S. BA, U. Tenn., Knoxville, 1967, MA in Coll. Teaching, 1969, PhD, 1978; EdS, George Peabody Coll., 1975. Tchr. English Sevier County High Sch., Sevierville, Tenn., 1967-68; head dept. English Battle Ground Acad., Franklin, Tenn., 1969-71; dir. academics Brentwood Acad., Nashville, 1971-73, Columbia (Tenn.) Mil. Acad., 1973-74; instr. U. Tenn., Knoxville, 1978-79; asst. prof. Ill. State U., Normal, 1979-86, assoc. prof. English, 1986-93, prof. English, 1993—; cons. Ency. Britannica, Oxford Companion to African Am. Lit., Norton Anthology African American Literature, others; project dir. conf. on Phillis Wheatley NEH, 1983-85; faculty advisor Native Am. Student Soc. Ill. State U., 1990—. Assoc. editor Style, DeKalb, Ill., 1988-90, guest editor, 1990—; editor: The Collected Works of Phillis Wheatley, 1988, paperback, 1989; adv. editor, contbr. Am. Nat. Biography, 20 vols., 1994—; contbr. articles to lit. jours. and chpts. to books; manuscript reviewer various presses and jours. Spokesperson for Native Am. citizens, 1990—. Ford Found. fellow, 1968-69, Soc. for Humanities fellow Cornell U., 1984-85, NEH fellow, 1983, 84, 89, 93, John. C. Hodges Teaching Excellence award, 1969. Mem. MLA, Am. Studies Assn., Melville Soc., Coll. Lang. Assn., Phi Mu Alpha Sinfonia, Alpha Phi Omega, Sigma Nu. Unitarian. Avocations: piano, singing, Native American culture, archaeology, rare book collecting. Home: 1566D Hunt Dr Normal IL 61761-2109 Office: Ill State Univ Normal IL 61761

SHIELDS, JOHN JOSEPH, computer manufacturing executive; b. Worcester, Mass., Aug. 31, 1938; s. John Joseph Jr. and Pauline Shields; m. Judith A. Morse, Sept. 1980; 6 children. Student, Worcester Poly. Inst., hon. degree, 1989; grad. mgmt. devel. progam, Harvard U. Field svc. engr. to v.p. field svc. tng. Digital Equipment Corp., Maynard and Stow, Mass., 1961-79, v.p. customer svcs., 1979-81, group v.p. sales, svcs., mktg. and internat., 1981-86; sr. v.p. Digital Equipment Corp., Stow, Mass., 1986—; bd. dirs. Ionics, Inc., Watertown, Mass. Trustee, chmn. acad. affairs com. Clark U., Worcester, Mass. Roman Catholic.

SHIELDS, LAWRENCE THORNTON, orthopedic surgeon; b. Boston, Oct. 2, 1935; s. George Leo and Catherine Elizabeth (Thornton) S.; AB, Harvard U., 1957; MD, Johns Hopkins U., 1961; m. Karen S. Kraus, Sept. 21, 1968; children: Elizabeth Coulter, Laura Thornton, Sarah Daly, Michael Lawrence. Intern, Barnes Hosp., Washington U., St. Louis, 1961-62, resident, 1962-63; resident orthopedic surgeon Children's Hosp. Med. Ctr., Boston, 1966-67, Mass. Gen. Hosp., Boston, 1967-68, Peter Bent Brigham, Robert Breck Brigham hosps., Boston, 1968-69; resident orthopedic surgeon Harvard Med. Sch., Boston, 1965-69, instr., 1969—; orthopedic surgeon Peter Bent Brigham & Women's Hosp., Children's hosps., 1969—, orthopedic surgeon Waltham (Mass.)-Weston Hosp. and Med. Ctr., 1969—, also chief orthopedic surgery, pres. med. staff; mem. Waltham-Weston Orthopedic Assos.; proprietor Boston Athenaeum; mem. staffs Hahnemann Hosp., Boston, Newton-Wellesley (Mass.) hosps.; cons. orthopedic surgeon VA Hosp., Boston; mem. faculty Harvard Med. Sch.; vis. scholar Cambridge U., 1987; bd. dirs. Wal-West Health Systems, 1986—; pres. Massachusetts Bay Investment Trust; dir. Waltham Investment Group. Bd. dirs. Mass. Acad. Emergency Med. Technicians, Waltham Boys' Club; bd. of overseers Boston Lyric Opera, 1993—; trustee, exec. com. Waltham-Weston Hosp. and Med. Ctr. Lt. M.C., USNR, 1963-65. Diplomate Am. Bd. Orthopedic Surgery. Fellow ACS, Am. Acad. Orthopedic Surgeons, Mass. Hist. Soc. Libr., Mass. Hist. Soc.; mem. N.Y. Acad. Scis., Royal Soc. Medicine, Mass. Orthopaedic Assn. (bd. dirs., sec. 1986—), New Eng. Orthopaedic Club, Boston Orthopedic Club, Charles River Dist. (treas., exec. com., pres. 1982-83) Mass. (councillor; v.p. 1982-83) med. socs., R. Austen Freeman Soc. (v.p.), Thomas B. Quigley Sports Medicine Soc., Titanic Hist. Soc., Boston Opera Assns. (bd. dirs.), Harvard Mus. Assn., Thoreau Soc., Emerson Soc., Trollope Soc. (founding mem., bd. dirs., London), Handel and Hayden Soc. (bd. overseers) Waltham Hist. Soc., St. Botolph Club (Boston), Les Amis d'Escoffier Soc., Harvard Club, Algonquin Club of Boston (bd. dirs., pres. 1990—), St. Crispin's Soc. Boston (founding mem., pres. 1991—), English Speaking Union (bd. dirs.), Union Club of Boston, St. Botolph Club of Boston, Boston Lyric Opera (bd. overseers 1993), Rotary, Pi Eta (Harvard). Contbr. articles to med. jours. Home: 9 Beverly Rd Newton MA 02161-1112 Office: 721 Huntington Ave Boston MA 02115-6016 also: 20 Hope Ave Ste 314 Waltham MA 02154

SHIELDS, MARLENE SUE, elementary school educator; b. Denver, Apr. 7, 1939; d. Morris and Rose (Sniderman) Goldberg; m. Charles H. Cohen,

Dec. 22, 1957 (dec.); children: Lee, Richard, Monica; m. Harlan Shields. BA magna cum laude, Met. State Coll., 1980; MA, U. No. Colo., 1986. Preschool tchr. Temple Emanuel, Denver, 1970-75; tchr. Kindergarten Temple Sinai, Denver, 1975-80; tchr. pre-Kindergarten St. Mary's Acad., Englewood, Colo., 1980-83; tchr. Beach Court Elem., Denver, 1983-86, Valverde Sch., Denver, 1984-85; tchr. third grade Brown Elem., Denver, 1985-86; tchr. learning disabilities Cowell Elem. Sch., Denver, 1986-87, Sabin Elem. Sch., Denver, 1987-88; tchr. second grade Sabin Elem., Denver, 1988—; mem. curriculum com. Denver Pub. Sch., 1989—, pers. subcom., 1991—. Mem. Colo. Copun. Internat. Reading Assn., Nat. Assn. for Young Children, Nat. Tchrs. Colo. Math.; Internat. Reading Assn., Carousel of Intervention, Delta Kappa Gamma (impact com.), PRIDE (lang. curriculum com., math. curriculum com., impact com., CDM rep. 1994-95). Home: 5800 Big Canon Dr Englewood CO 80111-3516

SHIELDS, PERRY, judge; b. Townsend, Tenn., Jan. 12, 1925; s. Fred David and Alice Elizabeth (Dorsey) S.; m. Bonnie Manning Davis, Nov. 1, 1951; children: Bailey Davis, Leslie, Beth. LLB, Duke U., 1950. Bar: Tenn. 1950, U.S. Ct. Appeals (6th cir.) 1973, U.S. Supreme Ct. 1981. Revenue agt. IRS, Knoxville, Tenn., 1950-52, tax atty. office chief counsel, Washington, Atlanta and Greensboro, N.C., 1952-56; sole practice, Knoxville, 1956-58, Chattanooga, 1958-60; ptnr. Stone & Bozeman, Knoxville, 1960-63, Ford & Shields, Knoxville, 1963-70, Shields, Rainwater & Humble, Knoxville, 1970-82; judge U.S. Tax Ct., Washington, 1982—; trustee Tenn. Fed. Tax Inst., 1963-64. Served with U.S. Army, 1943-45. Mem. Nat. Lawyers Club, Tenn. Bar Assn. (past chmn. tax sect.). Republican. Baptist. Club: LeConte (Knoxville). Home: 5506 Holston Dr Knoxville TN 37914-3823 Office: US Tax Ct 400 2nd St NW Washington DC 20217-0002

SHIELDS, ROBERT EMMET, merchant banker, lawyer; b. Ridley Park, Pa., May 18, 1942; s. Joseph Leonard and Kathryn J. (Walsh) S.; m. Mary Katherine Reid, July 22, 1967; children: Christopher D., David R., Kevin M., Kathleen. AB, Coll. Holy Cross, 1964; LLB cum laude, NYU, 1967. Bar: Pa. bar 1968. Mem. faculty Boalt Hall Sch. Law U. Calif., Berkeley, 1967-68; assoc. Drinker Biddle & Reath, Phila., 1968-74; ptnr. Drinker Biddle & Reath, 1974-94, dir., 1979-83, 85-94, head corp. and securities group, 1983-93, CFO, 1993-94; mng. dir., ptnr. Questor Gen. Ptnr., L.P., 1995—; mng. ptnr. Questor Ptnrs. Fund, L.P., 1995—; sec. Numar Corp., Wallquest Inc. Author: (with Eliot B. Thomas) Federal Securities Act Handbook, 4th edit, 1977; (with Robert H. Strouse) Securities Practice Handbook, 1987. Trustee Archmere Acad. Mem. ABA, Am. Law Inst., Pa. Bar Assn., Phila. Bar Assn. Club: Union League (Phila.). Home: 206 Atlee Rd Wayne PA 19087-3836 Office: Questor Mgmt Co 1100 Phila Nat Bank Bldg 1345 Chestnut St Philadelphia PA 19107

SHIELDS, THOMAS CHARLES, lawyer; b. Evergreen Park, Ill., Apr. 26, 1941; s. Thomas James and Adelaide (McElligott) S.; m. Nicoline M. Murphy, Sept. 14, 1974; children: Thomas James II, Nicoline Margaret, Suzanne Adelaide, Kerry Anne. AB, Georgetown U., 1963; JD cum laude, Northwestern U., 1966. Bar: Ill. 1966, U.S. Dist. Ct. (no. dist.) Ill. 1966, U.S. Ct. Appeals (7th cir.) 1966, U.S. Tax Ct. 1968, U.S. Supreme Ct. 1977. Assoc. Hopkins & Sutter, Chgo., 1966-73; ptnr. Hopkins & Sutter, 1973-93; ptnr., head health care law group Bell, Boyd & Lloyd, Chgo., 1994—; gen. counsel Cath. Health Assn. U.S., St. Louis, 1994—; mem. adv. bd. Health Law Inst. Loyola U. Sch. Law, Chgo., 1984-89, Health Law Inst. DePaul U. Sch. Law, Chgo., 1985—; lectr. Ill. Inst. Continuing Legal Edn., 1973; adv. com. Cath. Hosp. Assn., 1974. Contbr. articles to profl. pubs., chpt. to book; mng. editor Northwestern Law Rev., 1965-66. Bd. dirs. Cancer Rsch. Found., Chgo., 1987—, Chgo. Zool. Soc., Cath. Charities Chgo. Mem. Am. Acad. Hosp. Attys. (bd. dirs. 1983-91, pres. 1989-90), Am. Soc. Law and Medicine, Am. Hosp. Assn. (tax adv. group 1987-90), Ill. Bar Assn., Ill. Assn. HEalthcare Attys. (bd. dirs. 1983-89, pres. 1987-88), Chgo. Bar Assn., Univ. Club, Exec. club Chgo., Law Club Chgo., Mid-Am. Club Chgo., Order of Coif. Avocations: skiing, bicycling, golf, tennis. Office: Bell Boyd & Lloyd 3 First Nat Plz Ste 3200 Chicago IL 60602

SHIELDS, THOMAS WILLIAM, surgeon, educator; b. Ambridge, Pa., Aug. 17, 1922; s. John Jr. and Elizabeth (Flanagan) S.; m. Dorothea Ann Thomas, June 12, 1948; children: Thomas William, John Leland, Carol Ann. BA, Kenyon Coll., 1943, DSc (hon.), 1978; MD, Temple U., 1947. Resident surgery Northwestern U. Med. Sch., Chgo., 1949-55; prof. surgery Northwestern U. Med. Sch., 1968-92, prof. Emeritus of surgery, 1992—; practice medicine specializing in surgery Chgo., 1956—; chief of surgery VA Lakeside Hosp., Chgo., 1968-87; chief thoracic surgery VA Lakeside Med. Ctr., Chgo., 1987-90. Editor: General Thoracic Surgery, 1972, 4th edit., 1994, Bronchial Carcinoma, 1974, Mediastinal Surgery, 1991; assoc. editor Surgery, Gynecology and Obstetrics, Annals of Thoracic Surgery, 1993—; mem. editorial bd. Annals of Thoracic Surgery, Lung Cancer; contbr. articles to profl. jours. Served with U.S. Army, 1951-53. Mem. ACS, AMA, Am. Assn. for Thoracic Surgery, Soc. Thoracic Surgery, Central, Western Surg. Assns., Société Internationale de Chirurgie, Soc. for Surgery of Alimentary Tract, Internat. Assn. for Study Lung Cancer, Pan Pacific Surg. Assn., Phi Beta Kappa, Sigma Xi, Alpha Omega Alpha. Home: 1721 Jenks St Evanston IL 60201-1528 Office: 250 E Superior St Ste 201 Chicago IL 60611-2914

SHIELS, BARBARA L., lawyer. BA summa cum laude, Gustavus Adolphus Coll., 1977; JD cum laude, U. Minn., 1983. Bar: Minn., U.S. Dist. Ct. Minn., U.S. Ct. Appeals (8th cir.), U.S. Supreme Ct. Law clk. U.S. Atty.'s Office, Mpls., 1981-82; immigration law clk. Office Internat. Edn. U. Minn., Mpls., 1982-83; asst. univ. atty. Atty.'s Office U. Minn., Mpls., 1983-85, assoc. univ. atty., 1985—; law clk. Hennepin County Office of Pub. Defender, Mpls., summer 1982; panel mem. symposium on immigration reform and control act Internat. Inst. of Minn. and Mpls. C. of C., 1986; pub. speaker, presenter St. Olaf Coll., Northfield, Minn., 1985, Met. State U., St. Paul, Minn. and Twin Cities Acad. Network, Mpls., 1986-87, 8th Ann. Nat. Conf. on Law and Higher Edn., Clearwater Beach, Fla., 1987, 9th Ann. Internship Conf. Minn. Assn. for Field Experience Learning, Mpls., 1987. Mem. St. Anthony Park Assn.; vol. Loaves and Fishes; lector St. Lawrence Ch. U. Minn. scholar. Mem. ABA, Minn. Bar Assn., Hennepin County Bar Assn., Nat. Assn. Coll. and Univ. Attys. (presenter conf. for lawyers new to field of higher edn., reporter student affairs sect.), Minn. Women Lawyers, Nat. Assn. Fgn. Student Advisors. Home: 2120 Hoyt Ave W Saint Paul MN 55108-1315 Office: U Minn 100 Church St SE 320 Morrill Hall Minneapolis MN 55455

SHIELY, JOHN STEPHEN, company executive, lawyer; b. St. Paul, June 19, 1952; s. Vincent Robert and Mary Elizabeth (Hope) S.; m. Helen Jane Pauly, Aug. 29, 1981; children: Michael, Erin, Megan. BBA, U. Notre Dame, 1974; JD, Marquette U., 1977; M of Mgmt., Northwestern U., 1990. With Arthur Andersen & Co., Milw., 1977-79, Hughes Hubbard & Reed, Milw., 1979-83, Allen-Bradley Co., Milw., 1983-86, Rockwell Internat. Corp. Milw., 1985-86; with Briggs & Stratton Corp., Milw., 1986—, gen. counsel, 1986-90, v.p., gen. counsel, 1990-91, exec. v.p. adminstrn., 1991-94, pres., COO, 1994—. Dir., St. Charles, Inc., Milw., 1978—, Children's Hosp. of Wis., 1992—. Mem. Am. Corp. Counsel Assn. (past pres., bd. govs., Wis. chpt. 1984-94), Assn. for Corp. Growth (past pres., bd. dirs. Wis. chpt. 1988—). Office: Briggs & Stratton Corp PO Box 702 Milwaukee WI 53201-0702

SHIENTAG, FLORENCE PERLOW, lawyer; b. N.Y.C.; d. David and Ester (Germane) Perlow; m. Bernard L. Shientag, June 8, 1938. BS, NYU, 1940, LLB, 1933, JD, 1940. Bar: Fla. 1976, N.Y. Law aide Thomas E. Dewey, 1937; law sec. Mayor La Guardia, 1939-42; justice Domestic Relations Ct., 1941-42; mem. Tchrs. Retirement Bd., N.Y.C., 1942-46; asst. U.S. atty. So. dist. N.Y., 1943-53; cir. ct. mediator Fla. Supreme Ct., 1992; pvt. practice N.Y.C., 1994—; Palm Beach, Fla., 1994—; lectr. on internat. divorce; mem. Nat. Commn. on Wiretapping and Electronic Surveillance, 1973—, Task Force on Women in Cts. 1985-86; circuit ct. mediator Fla. Supreme Ct., 1992. Contbr. articles to profl. jours. Candidate N.Y. State Supreme Ct., 1954; bd. dirs. UN Devel. Corp., 1972-95; bd. dirs., assoc. treas. YM and YWHA.; hon. commr. commerce, N.Y.C. Mem. ABA, Fed. Bar Assn. (exec. com.), Internat. Bar Assn., N.Y. Women's Bar Assn. (pres., Life Time Achievement award 1994), N.Y. State Bar Assn., N.Y.C. Bar Assn. (chmn. law and art sect.), N.Y. County Lawyers Assn. (dir.), Nat. Assn. Women LAwyers (sec.). Home: 737 Park Ave New York NY 10021-4256 *Success is a product of self respect and hard work at what you do well.*

SHIER, GLORIA BULAN, mathematics educator; b. Philippines, Apr. 20, 1935; came to U.S., 1966.; d. Melecio Cauilan and Florentina (Cumagun) Bulan; m. Wayne Thomas Shier, May 31, 1969; children: John Thomas, Marie Teresita, Anna Christina. BS, U. Santo Tomas, Manila, Philippines, 1956; MA, U. Ill., 1968; PhD, U. Minn., 1986. Tchr. Cagayan (Philippines) Valley Coll., 1956-58, St. Paul Coll., Manila, Manila Div. City Schs., 1958-64; asst. prof. U. of East, Manila, 1961-66; rsch. asst. U. Ill., Urbana, 1968-69; instr. Miramar Community Coll., San Diego, 1974-75, Mesa Community Coll., San Diego, 1975-80, Lakewood Community Coll., St. Paul, 1984, U. Minn., Mpls., 1986-87, North Hennepin Community Coll., Brooklyn Park, Minn., 1987—; cons. PWS Kent Pub. Co., Boston, 1989—. Chairperson Filipino Am. Edn. Assn., San Diego, 1978-79. Fulbright scholar U.S. State Dept., U. Ill., 1966-70; fellow Nat. Sci. Found., Oberlin Coll., 1967; recipient Excellence in Teaching award UN Ednl. Scientific Cultural Organ., U. Philippines, 1960-62, Cert. Commendation award The Gov. of Minn., 1990, Outstanding Filipino in the Midwest Edn. Cat. award 1992, Cavite Assn. Mem. Am. Math. Soc., Math. Assn. Am., Phi Kappa Phi, Sigma Xi Rsch. Honor Soc., Nat. Coun. Tchrs. Math., Am. Math. Assn. for Two Yr. Colleges, Internat. Group for Psychology of Math. Edn. Minn. Coun. of Tchrs. Math., Minn. Math. Assn. of Two Yr. Colleges, Fil-Minnesotan Assn (bd.dirs. 1991—), Am. Statistical Assn. Roman Catholic. Avocation: piano. Home: 1715 Heritage Ln New Brighton MN 55112

SHIER, SHELLEY M., production company executive; b. Toronto, Mar. 15, 1957; d. Harry Shier and Rosaline (Cutler) Sonshine; m. Hank O'Neal, May 14, 1985. Student, H.B. Studio, N.Y.C., 1975-76, Stella Adler Conservatory, N.Y.C., 1976-80. Company mem., actor Soho Artists Theater, N.Y.C., 1976-81; casting dir. Lawrence Price Prodns., N.Y.C., 1981-82; pres. Hoss, Inc., N.Y.C., 1983—; v.p. Chiaroscuro Records, N.Y.C., 1987—; cons. Peter Martin Assocs., N.Y.C., 1983, Kloster Cruise Ltd., Miami, Fla., 1983—, Floating Jazz Festival, Big Bands At Sea, Rhythm & Blues Cruise, Dixieland At Sea, Oslo (Norway) Jazz Festival, 1986—, New Sch. for Social Rsch., N.Y.C., 1989—, Beacons In Jazz Awards Ceremony, A Tribute to the Music of Bob Wills and The Texas Playboys, Mardi Gras at Sea. Talent acquisition agt. Save the Children, N.Y.C., 1986, Tomorrow's Children, N.Y.C., 1990, Royal Caribbean Cruise Ltd., Miami, 1994—, Ultimate Caribbean Jazz Spectacular, Country Music Festival in the Caribbean, CUNARD N.Y.C., 1994—, Barcelona Olympics, NBC, 1992, others. Avocations: karate, photography, riding, fishing, weightlifting. Office: HOSS Inc 830 Broadway New York NY 10003-4827

SHIFF, ALAN HOWARD WILLIAM, judge; b. New Haven, June 2, 1934; s. Philip Robert and Harriet (Panikoff) S.; children: Daniel Stuart, Andrew Reuben; m. Carol Sweeterman Brumbaugh. BA, Yale U., 1957; LLB, U. Va., 1960. Bar: Conn. 1960, U.S. Dist. Ct. Conn. 1960, U.S.C. Appeals (2d cir.) 1969. Ptnr. Shiff, Shiff and Schancupp, New Haven, 1960-81; judge U.S. Bankruptcy Ct., Dist. Conn., Bridgeport, 1981—; spl. counsel Conn. Gen. Assembly Energy and Pub. Utilities Com., 1979-80; lectr. to various bar assns.Mem. Conn. Bar Assn., Administr. office of U.S. Cts. (adv. com. of bankruptcy judges 1984—, task force official on forms 1984-88, elected to serve 2nd cir. gov. Nat. Conf. Bankruptcy Judges, 1995—). Office: US Bankruptcy Court 915 Lafayette Blvd Bridgeport CT 06604-4706

SHIFFER, JAMES DAVID, utility executive; b. San Diego, Mar. 24, 1938; s. Kenneth Frederick and Thelma Lucille (Good) S.; m. Margaret Edith Rightmyer, Sept. 5, 1959 (div. July 1986); children: James II, Elizabeth Gonzales, Russell; m. Esther Zamora, Sept. 13, 1986; stepchildren: Bryan Boots, Jeremy Hellier, Marisol Boots. BS ChemE, Stanford U., 1960, MS ChemE, 1961. Registered profl. engr., Calif. Nuclear engr. Pacific Gas & Electric Co., Humboldt Bay Power Plant, Eureka, Calif., 1961-71; tech. mgr. Pacific Gas & Electric Co., Diablo Canyon Power Plant, Avila Beach, Calif., 1971-80; mgr. nuclear ops. Pacific Gas & Electric Co., San Francisco, 1980-84, v.p. nuclear power generation, 1984-90, sr. v.p. gen. mgr. nuclear power generation bus. unit, 1990-91, exec. v.p. elec. supply, nuclear power generation bus. units, 1991—, also bd. dirs; exec. v.p. Pacific Gas & Electric, San Francisco, 1994—; pres., CEO PG&E Enterprises, San Francisco, 1994—, also bd. dirs.; bd. dirs. Nuclear Energy Inst.; bd. control U.S Generating Co., U.S. Oper. Svcs. Co. Mem. AIChE, Commonwealth Club of Calif. (bd. govs.). Republican. Episcopalian. Avocations: golf, music. Home: 2550 Royal Oaks Dr Alamo CA 94507-2227 Office: Pacific Gas & Electric Co PO Box 770000 77 Beale St B32 San Francisco CA 94177

SHIFFMAN, BERNARD, mathematician, educator; b. N.Y.C., June 23, 1942; s. Max and Bella (Manel) S.; m. Doris Judith Yaffe, July 11, 1965; children: Jonathan, Daniel. BS, MIT, 1964; PhD (NSF fellow), U. Calif., Berkeley, 1968. C.L.E. Moore instr. MIT, 1968-70; asst. prof. math. Yale U., 1970-73; assoc. prof. Johns Hopkins U., Balt., 1973-77, prof., 1977—; chair dept. math., 1990-93; mem. Inst. Advanced Study, Princeton, N.J., fall 1975; series lectr. U. Kaiserslautern, West Germany, 1977, Inst. Math., Academia Sinica, Beijing, China, 1978, U. Paris VI, 1979, Nordic Summer Sch., Joensuu, Finland, 1981; mem. Inst. des Hautes Etudes Scientifiques, Bures-sur-Yvette, France, June 1979; vis. prof. U. Paris VI, 1981, 85, U. Grenoble, June 1992. Editor Forum Mathematicum, 1989—; assoc. editor Am. Jour. Math., 1990-92, editor, 1992-93, editor-in-chief, 1993—; researcher publs. in complex analysis. Hon. Woodrow Wilson fellow, 1964; Alfred P. Sloan rsch. fellow, 1973-75; recipient Woodrow Wilson Faculty Devel. award, 1979. Mem. Am. Math. Soc. Office: Johns Hopkins U Dept Math Baltimore MD 21218

SHIFFRIN, STEVEN H., law educator; b. 1941. BA, Loyola U., Chgo., 1963, JD, 1975; MA, Calif. State U., Northridge, 1964. Assoc. Irell & Manella, Los Angeles, 1976-77; acting prof. UCLA, 1977-81, prof., 1981-87; prof. Cornell U., Ithaca, N.Y., 1987—; vis. prof. Boston U., 1982-83, Mich. U., 1984. Office: Cornell U Law Sch Myron Taylor Hall Ithaca NY 14853

SHIH, BENEDICT CHESANG, investment company executive; b. Taipei, Taiwan, Jan. 3, 1935; s. Yun Ping and Chyu Ying (Shih) Chiu; m. Sophia Sufu Wu, Oct. 12, 1960; children: Vivian F. Shih Hauer, Peggy F., Phoebe F., Shih Sharp, Jonathan T. BA, Nat. Taiwan U., 1957. Pres. NOEC Corp., Taipei, 1973-78, chmn., CEO, 1995—; pres. KTT Corp., Irvine, Calif., 1983, Nat. Investment Corp., Taipei, 1983—, Nat. Investment Co. (U.S.) Corp., Issaquah, Wash., 1990—, Shih Corp., Issaquah, Wash., 1990—; cons. NCR Corp., Dayton, Ohio, 1979-83; ptnr. Blue Heron Assocs., Seabeck, Wash., 1989—; also bd. dirs. NOEC Corp., Taipei, Nat. Investment Corp., Taipei; bd. dirs. Shih Corp. Mem. TRW Credentials Svc., 1989—. Mem. Taiwan C. of C. of Seattle, Taiwan Chiaw Chi Country Club, Taiwan First Country Club, Taiwan Golf and Country Club, Bankers Club Taipei, Sahalee Country Club. Avocations: golf, travel, horseback riding, reading. Office: NIC (US) Corp 14800 SE 38th St Bellevue WA 98006-5727

SHIH, J. CHUNG-WEN, Chinese language educator; b. Nanking, China; came to U.S., 1948, naturalized, 1960; d. Cho-kiang and Chia-pu (Fang) S. B.A., St. John's U., Shanghai, 1945; M.A., Duke U., 1949, Ph.D., 1955. Asst. prof. English Kings Coll., N.Y., 1955-56; asst. prof. U. Bridgeport, Conn., 1956-60; postdoctoral fellow East Asian Studies Harvard, 1960-61; asst. prof. Chinese Stanford, 1961-64; assoc. prof. Chinese Pomona Coll. 1965-66; asso. prof. George Washington U., Washington, 1966-71, prof., chmn. dept. East Asian langs. and lit., 1971-93, prof. emeritus, 1993—, chmn. dept. East Asian langs. and lit., 1971-93, rsch. prof., 1994—. Author: Injustice to Tou O, 1972, the Golden Age of Chinese Drama: Yuan Tsa-chu, 1976, Return from Silence: China's Writers of the May Fourth Tradition, 1983. Bd. dirs. Sino-Am. Cultural Soc., Washington, 1971-80. AAUW fellow, 1964-65; Social Sci. Rsch. Coun. fellow, 1976-77; grantee NEH, 1979-80, 89-91, Annenberg/CPB Project, 1989-92; sr. scholars exchange program NAS, China, spring 1980. Mem. Asian Studies, Am. Council Fgn. Lang. Tchrs., Chinese Lang. Tchrs. Assn. (chmn. exec. bd. 1976-78). Home: 2500 Virginia Ave NW Washington DC 20037-1901 Office: George Washington U Dept East Asian Langs E Washington DC 20052

SHIH, JASON CHIA-HSING, biotechnology educator; b. Chien-Chen, Hunan, China, Oct. 8, 1939; came to U.S., 1969; m. Jane Chu-Huei Chien, Aug. 31, 1966; children: Giles C., Tim C. BS, Nat. Taiwan U., Taipei, 1963; MS, Nat. Taiwan U., 1966; PhD, Cornell U., 1973. Lectr. Tunghai U., Taichung, Taiwan, 1966-69; rsch. assst. Cornell U., Ithaca, N.Y., 1969-73; sr. rsch. assoc. Cornell U., Ithica, N.Y., 1975-76; rshc. assoc. U. Ill., Urbana, 1973-75; asst. prof. N.C. State U., Raleigh, 1976-80; assoc. prof. N.C. State

U., Raleigh, N.C., 1980-88, prof., 1988—; vis. fellow U. Coll. Cardiff, Wales, 1983; sci. advisor Shenyang Agrl. U., China, 1985—; vis. prof. Nat. Taiwan U., 1986, spl. advisor to the pres., 1994; vis. specialist UNDP, China, 1987-93; vis. prof. Bowman Gray Sch. Medicine, 1991. Patentee in field. Exec. com. mem. Triangle Area Chinese Am. Soc., Raleigh, 1979-82, pres. 1982-83, chmn. bd. 1992-93; coord. N.C. State U. exch. programs with China and Taiwan, 1985—; sci. exch. fellow to Spelderholt Poultry Rsch. Ctr., The Netherlands, USDA-Office of Internat. Coop. and Devel., 1994. Recipient numerous rsch. grants, 1977—; Pew Nat. fellow faculty scholar, 1990-91. Fellow Am. Heart Assn., Arteriosclerosis Rsch. Coun.; mem. Am. Instn. Nutrition (Travel award 1981, 89), Am. Soc. for Microbiology, Poultry Sci. Assn., Soc. Chinese Bioscientists in Am. (sec. and treas. 1985-86), Phi Kappa Phi, Sigma Iota Rho (J. Rigney award for Internat. Svc. 1994). Office: N C State U Dept Poultry Sci Raleigh NC 27695-7608

SHIH-CARDUCCI, JOAN CHIA-MO, cooking educator, biochemist, medical technologist; b. Rukuan, Chunghua, Republic of China, Dec. 21, 1933; came to U.S., 1955; d. Luke Chiang-hsi and Lien-chin (Chang) Shih; m. Kenneth M. Carducci, Sept. 30, 1960 (dec. July 1988); children: Suzanne R., Elizabeth M. BS in Chemistry, St. Mary Coll., Xavier, Kans., 1959; intern in med. tech., St. Mary's Hosp., Rochester, N.Y., 1960. Med. researcher Strong Meml. Hosp. (U. Rochester), 1960-61; pharm. chemist quality control Strasenburgh Labs., Rochester, 1961-62; cooking tchr. adult edn. Montgomery County Pub. Schs., Rockville, Md., 1973-79; cooking tchr. The Chinese Cookery Inc., Rockville, 1975-86; cooking tchr. The Chinese Cookery Inc., Silver Spring, Md., 1986—, pres., bd. dirs., 1975—; chemist NIH, Bethesda, 1987-94; analytical chemist NIH/WRAIR, Rockville, Md., 1994—. Author: The Chinese Cookery, 1981, Hunan Cuisine, 1984. Mem. Internat. Assn. Cooking Profls. Republican. Roman Catholic. Avocations: piano, music, dance, flowers, vegetables. Home and Office: The Chinese Cookery Inc 14209 Sturtevant Rd Silver Spring MD 20905-4448

SHIKLER, AARON, artist; b. Bklyn., Mar. 18, 1922; s. Frank and Annie (Blai) S.; m. Barbara Lurie, Oct. 4, 1947; children: Cathy M., Clifford M. B.F.A., B.S. in Edn; M.F.A., Tyler Sch. Fine Arts, Temple U., 1948; student, Barnes Found., Merion, Pa., 1941-43, Hans Hoffmann Sch., N.Y.C., 1949-51. One man shows, Davis Galleries, N.Y.C., 1953, 54, 56, 58, 60, 62, 64, 67, 71, 83, 84, Bklyn. Museum, 1971, Palace of Legion of Honor, San Francisco, 1971, Long Gallery, Houston, 1972, 76, 82, 85, Davis & Long Co., 1975, 79, Temple U., 1985, Claude Bernard Gallery, Paris, 1988, Davis & Langdale Co., 1987, 90, 93, Kunsthaus Bauler, Stuttgart, Germany; represented in permanent collections, Montclair (N.J.) Mus., Hofstra Mus. Art, L.I., Carnegie Inst., Pitts., Met. Mus. Art, Mint Mus. Art, Charlotte, N.C., Parrish Mus. Art, Southampton, L.I., N.A.D., Bklyn. Mus., Hirshorn Mus., Washington, Nat. Art Gallery, Wellington, N.Z., Nat. Gallery, Singapore, New Britain Mus. Am. Art, Sun Rise Mus., Charleston, W.Va., Sheldon Meml. Art Gallery, Lincoln, Nebr., Pa. State U. Gallery, Davis Galleries, 1987, Lyme Acad., 1986; executed: portraits Pres. and Mrs. John F. Kennedy for White House, Robert Lehman Pavilion at Met. Mus. Art, Henry F. duPont for Winterthur (Del.) Mus., Robert F. Kennedy for Dept. Justice, Washington, Sec. Carla Hills for HUD, Mrs. Lyndon B. Johnson for Johnson Library, Austin, Tex., Senator Mike Mansfield for U.S. Senate, Washington, Dr. Michael DeBakey for Baylor U., Pres.-Elect Ronald Reagan as Man of Yr. for Time mag., James M. Walton for Carnegie Inst., Pitts., Pres. Ronald Reagan and Mrs. Reagan for The White House, Andrew Heiskell for N.Y. Pub. Libr., William S. Paley for Mus. Broadcasting, Dr. Vartan Gregorian, N.Y. Pub. Libr., Dr. Manuel Koehane, Wesley Coll., Mass. Served with inf. AUS, 1943-46. Recipient Tiffany award, 1958; Dept. State grantee S.E. Asia and South Pacific, 1976; Temple U. Centennial fellow, 1985. Mem. NAD (Ranger award 1959, Proctor prize 1959, 60, Clarke prize 1961, Altman prize 1976). Club: Century Assn. Address: 44 W 77th St New York NY 10024-5150

SHILDNECK, BARBARA JEAN, accounting magazine editor; b. Waynesboro, Pa., Apr. 1, 1937; d. Barry Price and Helen Matilda (Armstrong) S. BA in English Lit., Wilson Coll., Chambersburg, Pa., 1959. With AICPA, N.Y.C., 1959—, jr. prodn. asst., 1959-62, sr. prodn. asst., 1962-66, editor The CPA, 1969-73, asst. editor to manuscript editor Jour. of Accountancy, 1966-79, from mng. editor to exec. editor, 1979—; editor Centennial issue AICPA, May, 1987; panelist edn. program video tapes in Can. and U.S.; lectr. in field. Contbr. articles to profl. jours. Recipient Gold Circle award Am. Soc. Assn. Execs., 1986, Bronze Ozzie for spl. issue Mag. Design and Prodn., May 1987, Soc. Nat. Assn. Publs. award, 1987, award of distinction Soc. Tech. Communication, 1987. Mem. NAFE, Am. Soc. Bus. Press Editors, Am. Acctg. Assn., Ocean Grove (N.J.) Civic League. Democrat. Avocations: drama, art, literature, writing, gardening, swimming. Office: Harborside Fin Ctr 201 Plaza Three Jersey City NJ 07311

SHILEPSKY, ARNOLD CHARLES, mathematics educator, computer consultant; b. Norwalk, Conn., Dec. 10, 1944; s. Morris Jacob and Rose (Pfeffer) S.; m. Carol Irene Carter, June 15, 1968; children: Lisa Ruth, Beth Carter. AB, Wesleyan U., Middletown, Conn., 1966; PhD, U. Wis., 1971. Asst. prof. Ark. State U., Jonesboro, 1971-74; asst. prof. Wells Coll., Aurora, N.Y., 1974-79, assoc. prof., 1979-85, prof., 1985—; Herbert E. Ives prof. of scis., 1985-91; cons. Digicomp Rsch. Corp., 1992-94. Pres. Community Devel. Fedn., Southwest Cayuga County, N.Y., 1987-92. Mem. Am. Math. Soc., Math. Assn. Am., Assn. for Women in Math., Assn. for Computer Machinery. Home: Main St # 295 Aurora NY 13026 Office: Wells Coll Aurora NY 13026

SHILL, VICTOR LAMAR, architect; b. Phoenix, July 6, 1933; s. Victor David and Olive (Nielsen) S.; m. Patsy Ann Nelson, Nov. 7, 1952; children: Michael, Wayne, Mark, Curt, Tracy. BArch, Ariz. State U., 1955. Registered architect, Ariz. Architect Kistner, Wright & Wright, Los Angeles, 1955-56, Horlbeck, Hickman & Assocs., Mesa, Ariz., 1956-63; pres. Shill, Judd, Richards & Johnson Architects, Inc., Mesa, 1963—. Prin. works include Mesa Police Bldg., Mesa Cts. Bldg., Dobson Jr. High Sch., Mesa (Lighting award 1981), Rhoder Jr. High Sch., Mesa (AIA award 1978), Ariz. State U. Student Health Bldg., Tempe, Ea. Ariz. Coll. Fine Arts Ctr., Thatcher, Shepherd Jr. High Sch., Brimhall Jr. High Sch., Dobson High Sch., Mohave High Sch., River Valley High Sch., over 100 ch. projects throughout Ariz. Mem. AIA. Republican. Mormon. Home: 2550 N Gilbert Rd Mesa AZ 85203-1304 Office: Shill Judd Richards & Johnson 1045 E Mckellips Rd Mesa AZ 85203-2624

SHILLESTAD, JOHN GARDNER, financial services company executive; b. Oak Park, Ill., Oct. 31, 1934; s. John Nelson and Isabel Blanche (Gardner) S.; m. Astri Cedervall; children—Christine C., Annette. B.B.A., Northwestern U., 1964, M.B.A., 1967. CLU; CPCU; ChFC. Mktg. dir. spl. plans CNA Ins., Chgo., 1958-66; asst. v.p Montgomery Ward Life, Chgo., 1966-69; pres., chief exec. officer Fort Dearborn Life Ins. Co., Chgo., 1969-79; sr. v.p. Hartford Life Cos., Conn., 1979-85, also bd. dirs., 1985-87; pres. JGS Fin. Svcs., Inc., 1987—; pres., chmn. bd., CEO, Columbian Mut. Life Ins. Co., Binghamton, N.Y., 1987—; chmn., CEO Columbian Life Ins. Co.; chmn. bd. dirs., CEO Washington Nat. Life N.Y. Mem. Bd. Edn., Dist. 30, Northbrook, Ill., 1976-79; bd. dirs. Salvation Army, Binghamton; mem. adv. bd. SUNY Sch. Mgmt., Binghamton, Kellogg Sch. Bus., Northwestern U. With U.S. Army, 1954-56. Mem. Sunset Ridge Club (Northfield, Ill.), Binghamton Country Club, City Club of Binghamton, Sky Club (N.Y.C.). Republican. Congregationalist. Home: 25 Virginia Ave Binghamton NY 13905-4305 Office: Columbia Mut Life Ins Co Vestal Pkwy E Binghamton NY 13802

SHILLING, A. GARY, economic consultant, investment advisor; b. Fremont, Ohio, May 25, 1937; s. Vaughn and Lettie E. (O'Harrow) S.; m. Margaret E. Bloete, Dec. 22, 1962; children: Geoffrey B., Andrew J., Stephen E., Jennifer E. AB in Physics magna cum laude, Amherst (Mass.) Coll., 1960; MA in Econs., Stanford (Calif.) U., 1962, PhD in Econs., 1965. Economist Standard Oil Co. (N.J.), N.Y.C., 1963-67; chief economist Merrill Lynch, Pierce, Fenner & Smith, N.Y.C., 1967-71; rsch. dir. Estabrook & Co., N.Y.C., 1971-72; sr. v.p., chief economist White, Weld & Co., N.Y.C., 1972-78; chmn., pres., dir. A Gary Shilling & Co., Inc., Springfield, N.J., 1978—; pres. Lakeview Econ. Svcs., Inc., Springfield, 1979—; owner Lakeview Svcs., Inc., Springfield, 1993—; bd. dirs. Nat. Life Vt., Montpelier, Am. Productivity and Quality Ctr., Houston; adv. dir. Austin (Tex.) Trust Co.; informal econ. advisor Former Pres. George Bush, 1978—; mem. Nat. Com. on Jobs

and Small Bus., 1986-87; dir. The Heartland Group of Mutual Funds, 1995—. Author: Is Inflation Ending? Are You Ready?, 1983, The World Has Definitely Changed: New Economic Forces and Their Implications for the Next Decade, 1986, After thr Crash: Recession or Depression? Investment and Business Strategies for a Deflationary World, 1988; creator bd. game The Deflation Game, 1989; columnist Forbes, S&P Credit Week, Nihon Keizai Shimbun Jour. Bd. dirs. Aim Packaging Inc., 1986-89, Henry H. Kessler Found., Inc., West Orange, N.J., 1988-95, Episcopal Ch. Found., N.Y.C., 1989—; chmn. Episcopal Evangelism Found., N.Y.C., 1988—; trustee Bates Coll., Lewiston, Maine, 1988-91, Kent Pl. Sch., Summit, N.J., 1983-89; bd. dirs. Geh Gen. Theol. Episcopal Sem., N.Y.C., 1988—, treas., 1994—; bd. dirs. N.J. Shakespeare Festival, Madison, 1988—, chmn., 1992—. Named Wall St. Top Economist, Instl. Investor Mag., 1975, 76, Top Commodity Trading Advisor, Futures Mag., 1993. Mem. Nat. Assn. Bus. Economists, N.Y. Soc. Security Analysts, Short Hills Club, Phi Beta Kappa, Sigma Xi. Republican. Episcopalian. Avocations: tennis, travel, gardening, hunting, fishing, beekeeping. Home: 33 Lakeview Ave Short Hills NJ 07078-2264 Office: A Gary Shilling & Co Inc 500 Morris Ave Springfield NJ 07081-1020

SHILLING, MARY EMILY, nursing administrator; b. Milford, Del., Aug. 25, 1931; d. Robert Edward and Mary Emma (Clifton) S. Diploma, Children's Hosp. Sch. Nursing, Boston, 1952; BSN, U. Va., 1966; MSN, U. Pa., 1968. Cert. nursing adminstr. Staff and head nurse Children's Hosp., Boston; assoc. adminstr., head nurse, supr. pediatrics Greenville (S.C.) Gen. Hosp.; assoc. adminstr. Greenville Meml. Hosp.; v.p. nursing and quality improvement Greenville Hosp. System, S.C.; past pres. S.C. State Bd. Nursing. Contbr. articles to profl. jours. Past bd. dirs., mem. nursing practice and standards com Nat. Coun. State Bds. Nursing; past mem. and chmn. S.C. Statewide Master Planning Com. for Nursing Edn. Mem. Am. Orgn. Nursing Execs., S.C. Orgn. Nursing Execs., Sigma Theta Tau. Home: 71 Briarview Cir Greenville SC 29615-2163

SHILLING, ROY BRYANT, JR., college president; b. Enville, Okla., Apr. 7, 1931; s. Roy Bryant and Lila M. (Prestage) S.; m. Margaret Riddle, Oct. 16, 1952; children: Roy Bryant III, Nancy Gale. BA, McMurry U., 1951, HHD, 1982; BD, So. Meth. U., 1957; MS, Ind. U., 1966, PhD, 1967. Presdl. asst. McMurry U., Abilene, Tex., 1959-61; asst. to pres. Tenn. Wesleyan Coll., 1961-64; asst. in devel. Ball State U., 1964-65; rsch. assoc. Ind. U., 1965-67; dir. planning and rsch. Baldwin Wallace Coll., 1967-68; exec. v.p. Southwestern U., 1968-69, pres., 1981—; pres. Hendrix Coll., 1969-81; mem. Nat. Commn. on United Meth. Higher Edn., 1975-77. Mem. Ark Arts and Humanities Coun., 1970-76, chmn., 1974-75; bd. dirs. Ark. Children's Hosp., 1981; mem. bd. higher edn. and ministry United Meth. Ch., 1972-80, mem. univ. senate, 1980-88, v.p. 1983-84, pres., 1984-88; chmn. Gulf dist. Rhodes Scholarship Selection Com., 1992, Ark. chmn., 1973-74, Tex. chmn., 1985-91; mem. Young Pres. Orgn., 1975-81; mem. bd. visitors Air U., 1991-94. Recipient Disting. Alumnus award McMurry U., 1980, Perkins Disting. Alumnus award So. Meth. U., 1987, Owen B. Sherrill award for leadership in econ. devel. Georgetown, 1988; named one of Top 100 Most Effective Coll. Pres. in Nation, Bowling Green State U./Exxon Edn. Found., 1988. Mem. North Cen. Assn. Colls. and Schs. (vice chmn., chmn.-elect 1980-81), Nat. Assn. Schs. and Colls. of United Meth. Ch. (v.p. 1975-76, pres. 1976-77), Nat. Coun. Ind. Colls. and Univs. (bd. dirs. 1972-76), Nat. Assn. Ind. Colls. and Univs. (bd. dirs 1988), So. U. Conf. (exec. com. 1974-78, 79-86, sec.-treas. 1979-86, v.p. 1991-92, pres. 1992-93), Am. Coun. Edn. (bd. dirs. 1989-91), Inst. for Humanities (bd. dirs. Salado, Tex., chpt. 1985-91, mem. internat. coun. advisors 1994—), Philos. Soc. Tex., Rotary, Masons, Alpha Chi, Phi Delta Kappa. Office: Southwestern U Georgetown TX 78626

SHILLINGLAW, GORDON, accounting educator, consultant, writer; b. Albany, N.Y., July 26, 1925; s. James McCombe and Margaret Blanche (Stephens) S.; m. Barbara Ann Cross, June 24, 1950; children—James McCombe, Laura Cross. A.B. magna cum laude, Brown U., 1945; M.S., U. Rochester, 1948; Ph.D., Harvard U., 1952. Asst. prof. Hamilton Coll., Clinton, N.Y., 1951-52; cons. assoc. Joel Dean Assocs., Yonkers, N.Y., 1952-55; asst. prof. MIT, Cambridge, 1955-61; assoc. prof. Columbia U., N.Y.C., 1961-66, prof. acctg., 1966-90, prof. emeritus, 1991—; vis. prof. Mgmt. Devel. Inst., Lausanne, Switzerland, 1964-65, 67-69; mem. U.S. Cost Acctg. Standards Bd., 1978-80, U.S. R.R. Acctg. Prin. Bd., 1985-87; trustee Scudder Latin Am. Fund, Scudder Pacific Opportunities Fund, Scudder Value Fund, Scudder Capital Growth Fund, Scudder Devel. Fund, Am. Assn. Ret. Persons Growth Trust, Insured Tax Free Income Trust, Money Market Trust; dir. Scudder Internat. Fund, Scudder Gold Fund; cons. in field. Author: Managerial Cost Accounting, 1961, 5th edit., 1982, Accounting: A Managment Approach, 1964, 9th edit., 1993, Financial Accounting: Concepts and Applications, 1989; contbr. articles to profl. jours. Mem. bd. advisors Fund Directions; bd. dirs., treas. Feris Found. Am., Stamford, Conn., 1970-94. Served with U.S. Navy. 1943-46. Recipient Disting. Teaching award Columbia U., 1970. Mem. Am. Acctg. Assn. (v.p. 1966-67), Inst. of Mgmt. Accts., Phi Beta Kappa, Beta Gamma Sigma. Avocations: tennis; travel; French and Italian language study. Home: 196 Villard Ave Hastings On Hudson NY 10706-1217 also: 109 Oakwood Dr Largo FL 34640

SHILLINGSBURG, MIRIAM JONES, English educator, academic administrator; b. Balt., Oct. 5, 1943; d. W. Elvin and Miriam (Reeves) Jones; BA. Mars Hill Coll., 1964; MA, U. S.C., 1966, PhD, 1969; m. Peter L. Shillingsburg, Nov. 21, 1967; children: Robert, George, John, Alice, Anne Carol. Asst. prof. Limestone Coll., Gaffney, S.C., 1969; asst. prof. Mississippi State (Miss.) U., 1970-75, assoc. prof., 1975-80, prof. English, 1980—; asst. to provost, 1987-88, assoc. v.p. for acad. affairs, 1988—; dir. summer sch., 1991—; vis. fellow Australian Def. Force Acad., 1989; Fulbright lectr. U. New South Wales, Duntroon, Australia, 1984-85. Nat. Endowment Humanities fellow in residence, Columbia U., 1976-77. New Sch. Study So. Lit., Nat. Acad. Advising Assn., South Atlantic Modern Lang. Assn., Australia-New Zealand Am. Studies Assn., Phi Kappa Phi. Author: Mark Twain in Australasia, 1988; editor: Conquest of Granada, 1988; mem. editorial bd. Works of W.M. Thackeray; assoc. editor Miss. Quarterly; contbr. articles to profl. jours. and mags.

SHILLINGSBURG, PETER LEROY, English language educator; b. Palmira, Colombia, Mar. 24, 1943; s. William and Florence (Wright) S.; m. Miriam Jones, Nov. 21, 1967; children: Robert, George, John, Alice, Anne. BA, U. S.C., 1966, MA, 1967, PhD, 1970. Asst. research archivist S.C. Dept. of Archives, Columbia, 1969; asst. prof. English Miss. State U., Mississippi State, 1970-73; assoc. prof. English Mississippi State U., 1973-78, prof. English, 1978—; vis. prof. English Royal Mil. Coll., Duntroon, Australia, 1984, Australian Def. Force Acad., 1989. Author: Scholarly Editing in the Computer Age, 1986, Pegasus in Harness: Victorian Publishing and W.M. Thackeray, 1992; editor: (England) Thackeray) edit. Norton crit. edit. Vanity Fair, 1994. Rsch. grantee NEH, 1978-82, 88-90, 93; Guggenheim fellow, 1982. Mem. MLA (coord. Ctr. for Scholarly Edits. 1975-76, chmn. 1982-84, 92-94), Soc. for Textual Scholarship (bd. dirs. 1982—, book rev. editor 1991—). Avocation: collecting books. Office: Mississippi State U Dept English Mississippi Station MS 39765

SHILS, EDWARD B., management educator, lawyer; b. Phila., May 29, 1915; s. Benjamin and Dinah (Berkowitz) S.; m. Shirley Seigle, July 31, 1942; children: Ronnie Lois, Nancy Ellen, Edward Barry. BS in Econs., U. Pa., 1936, MA in Polit. Sci., 1937, PhD, 1940, JD, 1986, LLM, 1990; LLD, Phila. Coll. Textiles and Sci., 1975; PhD (hon.), Tel-Aviv U., Israel, 1990. Bar: Pa. 1988, U.S. Dist. Ct. (ea. dist.) Phila. 1988. Research assoc. Pa. Economy League, 1938-42; cons. job classification and wage adminstrn. Phila. City Council, 1942-43; chief coordination and planning VA, Phila., 1947-48; cons. tchr. salary schedules Phila. Bd. Pub. Edn., 1949-50; dir. pub. edn. survey Greater Phila. Movement, 1950-51; sr. dept. head U.S. Wage Stabilization Bd., Phila., 1951; methods cons. Budget Office Gov. Pa., 1951-55; cons. Phila. County Med. Soc., 1955-56; chmn. social sci. dept. Community Coll., Temple U., Phila., grad. lectr. pub. adminstrn., 1948-56; mem. faculty Wharton Sch. U. Pa., Phila., 1956—, prof. mgmt., chmn. mgmt dept., 1968-76, George W. Taylor prof. emeritus entrepreneurial studies, 1979—, prof. emeritus polit. sci., 1985—, dir. Wharton Entrepreneurial Ctr., 1973-86, dir. emeritus, 1986—; judicial adminstr. U. Pa., 1986-90; prt. practice law Phila., 1988—; of counsel Sarner and Assocs., Phila.; Disting. prof. entrepreneurial studies Tel Aviv U., 1991—; pers. cons. Phila. Bd. Pub. Edn.,

1946-75, Phila. Psychiat. Ctr., 1971-76, Am. Bd. Internal Medicine, 1973-77, Girard Coll., 1974, Dental Mfrs. Am., 1952—; cons. Royal Coll. Physicians and Surgeons Can., 1977-80; cons. on sports and econs., major league baseball, football, hockey and basketball, 1985-91; cons. labor rels. Phila. Pub. Sch. Dist., 1951-68; cons. econ. Phila. New Conv. Ctr., 1988-90; mgmt. advisor to Phila. Dist. Atty., 1992-93. Author: Finances and Financial Administration of Philadelphia's Public Schools 1923-1939, 1940, Automation and Industrial Relations, 1963, Teachers, Administrators and Collective Bargaining, 1968, Industrial Peacemaker: George W. Taylor's Contribution to Collective Bargaining, 1979; co-editor: Frontiers of Entrepreneurship Research, 1985. V.p. Fedn. Jewish Agys. for Phila., 1976-84, Life Trust fed. Jewish Agys., 1990—; pres. Jewish Publs. Soc. Am., 1978-81, Hon. pres. 1982; Life trustee, hon. chmn. trustee com. on edn. Phila. Coll. Textiles and Sci.; chmn. bd., hon. pres. Pathway Sch., Jeffersonville, Pa., 1970-84; pres. Philadelphians for Good Govt., 1991-93, hon. pres., 1992—. Served as officer Signal Corps U.S. Army, 1943-46. Honored with a chair in his name at U. Pa. Law Sch., The Edward B. Shils Professorship in Arbitration and Alternative Dispute Resolution, 1991. Mem. Union League fla., Faculty Club U. Pa. (pres. 1966-69, 87-92), Green Valley Country Club (Plymouth, Pa.), Masons (32 degree). Home: 335 S Woodbine Ave Narberth PA 19072-1525 Office: U Pa Wharton Sch Philadelphia PA 19104 also: 123 S Broad St Philadelphia PA 19109-1029

SHILS, MAURICE EDWARD, physician, educator; b. Atlantic City, Dec. 31, 1914; s. Samuel L. and Sarah (Harris) S.; m. Cylia Finkiel, Feb. 19, 1939 (dec. Sept. 1987); children: Loraine J., Jonathan R.; m. Betty Ann Bell, Sept. 24, 1988. BA, Johns Hopkins U., 1937, ScD, 1940; MD, NYU, 1958. Intern joint program Cornell divsn. Bellevue Hosp. and Meml. Hosp., N.Y.C., 1958-59; fellow in physiology Meml. Hosp., 1959-60; instr., asst. prof. nutrition Sch. Pub. Health Columbia U., N.Y.C., 1944-54; instr. biochemistry Sch. Hygiene Johns Hopkins U., Balt., 1940-42; head Ctrl. Metabolic Lab. Sloan Kettering Inst., N.Y.C., 1960-72; from asst. to assoc. attending physician Meml. Hosp., N.Y.C., 1962-72, attending physician, 1972-85; asst. prof. biochem. Sloan-Kettering divsn. Med. Coll. Cornell U., N.Y.C., 1959-62, from asst. prof. to prof. medicine Med. Coll., 1962-85, prof. emeritus, 1985—; adj. prof. nutrition dept. pub. health scis. Bowman Gray Sch. Medicine, Winston-Salem, N.C., 1989-94, cons., 1994—. Author, co-editor: Modern Nutrition in Health and Disease, 8th edit., 1994; contbr. more than 200 rsch. and review articles to profl. jours. Fellow Am. Inst. Nutrition, Am. Coll. Physicians, N.Y. Acad. Medicine (Acad. Plaque award 1987); mem. AMA (chmn. nutrition adv. group 1974-77, Goldberger award 1983), Am. Soc. Clin. Nutrition (pres. 1985-86, Excellence in Med. Sch. award 1994), Am. Bd. Nutrition, Phi Beta Kappa, Alpha Omega Alpha.

SHIM, SANG KOO, state mental health official; b. Tokyo, Japan, Oct. 1, 1942; came to U.S., 1968; s. Sang Taek and Kum Ryon (Bae) S.; m. Jae Hee Lee, July 12, 1972; children: Tammy, David. BS, Seoul Nat. U., Korea, 1967; MBA, No. Ill. U., 1970; MS, U. Wis., 1975. CPA, Ill., cert. govt. fin. mgr., Assn. Govt. Accts. Acct Vaughn Mfg. Co., Chgo., 1970-72, Stewart-Warner Corp., Chgo., 1972-73; fin. cons. Cen. Acctg. Assn., New Baden, Ill., 1977-79; auditor Ill. Dept. Mental Health, Springfield, 1980-82, CFO, 1983—. Treas. Korean Assn. Greater St. Louis, 1982. Mem. Ill. CPA Soc., Assn. Govt. Accts. (cert. govt. fin. mgr.), Korean-Am. C. of C. (v.p. Greater St. Louis chpt. 1994-95). Home: 5 Settlers Ln Springfield IL 62707-9645 Office: Ill Dept Mental Health Bur Fin Svcs 401 S Spring St Springfield IL 62706-0002

SHIMADA, TOSHIYUKI, orchestra conductor, music director; b. Tokyo, Dec. 23, 1951; came to U.S., 1966; s. Ron and Matsue Shimada; m. Eva Virsik, 1987; 1 child, Matias. MusB, Calif. State U., Northridge, 1977. Dir. music, condr. Youth Musicians Found. Debut Orch., L.A., 1978-81; assoc. condr. Houston Symphony Orch., 1981-86; dir. mus., condr. Rice U. Symphony Orch., Houston, 1982-85, Nassau (N.Y.) Symphony Orch., 1987-88, Portland (Maine) Symphony Orch., 1986—; artist cons. Tex. Inst. for Aesthetic Study, Houston, 1984-86; artist in residence U. So. Maine, Portland, 1986-88. Trustee Japan Am. Soc. Maine, Portland, 1990-91. Recipient Condrs. award Young Musicians Found., 1977; finalist Herbert von Karajan Competition, Berlin, 1979; Toshiyuki Shimada Day proclaimed by City of Houston, 1986. Office: Portland Symphony Orch 30 Myrtle St Portland ME 04101-4991*

SHIMANSKI, CHARLES STUART, organization executive; b. Madison, Wis., Jan. 17, 1957; s. Stuart Thomas and Gloria Mae (Schindler) S.; m. Christiane Leitinger, May 30, 1992. BA in Econs., U. Wis., 1980. Float control mgr. United Bank of Denver, 1980-84; cash mgr. Oppenheimer, Denver, 1985-86, project mgr. office automation, 1987-93; sys. cons. Darlington Asset Mgmt., Geneva, 1986-87; exec. dir. Am. Alpine Club, Golden, Colo., 1993—; lectr. U. Colo., Boulder, U. Denver, Arapahoe C.C., Sierra Club, Denver Pub. Schs., Jefferson County Pub. Schs., Boy Scouts Am., Wilderness Med. Soc., Nat. Park Svcs., Nat. Ski Patrol, Nat. Forest Svc., Mountain Rescue Assn., Colo. Search and Rescue Bd., Colo. Mountain Club, Internat. Alpine Sch., also mountaineering outfitters and corps.; tech. cons., including Rescue 911, CBS, Unsolved Mysteries, NBC, Women of Valor, ABC, Tour de France, CBS, Emergency Call; published over 300 photographs in areas of alpine mountaineering, mountain rescue, med.-evacuation helicopter rescue, avalanche safety and rescue; EMT, State of Colo., 1985—; dir. Avalanche Awareness Week, Colo. Search and Rescue Bd., 1988-93, instr. Breckenridge Avalanche Sch., 1988—; mem. Alpine Rescue Team, Evergreen, Colo., 1983—, tng. and pub. rels. dir., 1991-92, pres., 1988-89, bd. dirs. 1987-91, dir. fund raising, 1987-89, sec., 1987-88. Author: Helicopters in Search and Rescue Operations—Basic, 1993, Intermediate, 1993, AVALANCHE!!!, 1993, General Back-Country Safety, 1993. Mem. Am. Assn. Avalanche Profls., Mountain Rescue Asssn (vice chmn., tng. dir. Rocky Mountain region 1989-92, chmn. 1992-94, nat. exec. officer 1992-94, chmn. edn. com. 1994—), Wilderness Med. Soc., Emergency Med. Svcs. Assn. Colo., Am. Alpine Club, Colo. Mountain Club. Avocations: mountain climbing, including peaks in France, Italy, Switzerland, Canada and U.S., photography. Office: Am Alpine Club 710 10th St Ste 100 Golden CO 80401

SHIMBERG, STEVEN JAY, lawyer; b. N.Y.C., Mar. 11, 1953; s. Lester Bernard and Bernyce (Zeff) S. BA in Psychology magna cum laude, SUNY, Buffalo, 1975; JD, Duke U., 1978. Bar: D.C. 1978, U.S Dist Ct. (fed. dist.) 1978, U.S. Ct. Appeals (D.C. cir.) 1979, (9th cir.) 1981. Trial atty. land and nat. resources divsn. Dept. Justice, 1978-81; spl. assist. U.S. Atty. Gen. No. Calif., Ea. Dist. N.Y., N.J., Ariz., 1981-91; majority counsel Senate Com. on Environment and Public Works, Washington, 1981-87, minority counsel, 1987-88, minority chief counsel, 1989-91, minority staff dir., chief counsel, 1991-95, majority staff dir., chief coun., 1995—; U.S. del. 4th meeting Conv. Internat. Trade in Endangered Species of Fauna and Flora, Botswana, 1982; adv. to U.S. del., Montreal Protocol on Substances that Deplete Ozone Layer, London amendments, Geneva, Vienna, Montreal, Nairobi, London, 1986-90, UN Conf. on Environment and Devel., Rio de Janeiro, 1992; orgn. of tropical studies program Interdependence: Econ. Devel. and Environ. Concerns in Tropical Countries, Costa Rica, 1988; rapporteur Interparliamentary Conf. Global Environment Working Group on Ozone Depletion, Washington, 1990. Contbr. articles to profl. jours. Fund raiser Nat. Multiple Sclerosis Soc., Washington, 1992—. Mem. D.C. Bar Assn. Avocations: long distance bicycling, photography, hiking. Home: 4407 38th St NW Washington DC 20016-2201 Office: US Senate Com on Environ Pub Works Washington DC 20510

SHIMELMAN, SUSAN FROMM, state administrator; b. N.Y.C., May 5, 1942; m. Myer M. Shimelman, Aug. 14, 1965; children: Wendy, Amy. BA, McGill U., Montreal, 1964; MS, Columbia U., 1970. Fellow Harvard U., Cambridge, Mass., 1964-65; Can. coun. fellow McGill U., Montreal, 1965-68; asst. dir. Yale-New Haven Hosp., 1970-80; exec. dir. New Haven Jewish Fedn., 1980-90; undersec. Office Policy and Mgmt., State of Conn., Hartford, 1991-94, sec., 1994—; chair Prison and Jail Overcrowding Commn., Hartford, 1990—; Health Care State Conn., Hartford, 1992—, Exec. Com. Info. and Tech., Hartford, 1994, vice chair chmty. Econ. Devel. Council, Hartford, 1994. Bd. dirs. Fedn. United Way, New Haven, 1970-94; alt. N.E. Regional Compact, N.J. and Conn. 1991-94; active A Conn. Party, Hartford, 1990-94. Recipient Pres. award New Haven Jewish Fedn.; 1990; named Powerful Woman of Vision, YWCA, 1988. Democrat. Home: 11

Forest Trl Woodbridge CT 06525 Office: State of Conn Office Policy and Mgmt 80 Washington St Hartford CT 06106

SHIMER, DANIEL LEWIS, corporate executive; b. San Angelo, Tex., July 30, 1944; s. Lewis V. and Mary A. (Slick) S.; married. BS in Acctg. and Mktg., Ind. U., 1972; postgrad., Loyola U., New Orleans, 1977. CPA. Sr. acct. Peat, Marwick, Mitchell & Co., Indpls., 1973-75; asst. treas. LTV Corp., Dallas, 1975-79; v.p. fin. Stoller Chem. Co., Houston, 1979-81; v.p., CFO Petro-Silver, Inc., Denver, 1981-83; v.p., treas. FoxMeyer Corp., Denver, 1983-86; v.p., treas., sec. CoastAmerica Corp., Denver, 1986-88; exec. v.p. Bard & Co., Denver, 1989-90; pres. nat accounts divsn. I Can't Believe It's Yogurt/ Brice Foods, Inc., Dallas, 1991-93; exec. v.p., CFO COREStaff Inc., Houston, 1994—. Mem. AICPA, Nat. Assn. Corp. Treas. Roman Catholic. Avocations: sailing, carpentry, snow skiing, camping, fishing. Home: 11 Duncannon Ct Dallas TX 75225-1809

SHIMER, ZACHARY, lawyer; b. Bklyn., Sept. 13, 1933; s. Nathan and Ida (Antonowsky) S.; m. Susan Rosenthal, Feb. 26, 1961; children—Jennifer Shimer Piper, Robert Jay. A.B., UCLA, 1955, LL.B., 1960. Bar: Calif. N.Y. Atty. Antitrust div. U.S. Dept. Justice, Washington, 1960-62; assoc. firm Chadbourne, Parke, Whiteside & Wolff (now Chadbourne & Parke), N.Y.C., 1962-70, ptnr., 1970—. Contbr. articles to profl. jours. Served with U.S. Army, 1955-57. Mem. State Bar of Calif., Assn. Bar City of N.Y., ABA, Order of Coif. Democrat. Jewish. Office: Chadbourne & Parke 30 Rockefeller Plz New York NY 10112-0127

SHIMIZU, TAISUKE, bank executive; b. Osaka, Japan, Apr. 8, 1936; m. Tomoko Shimizu; children: Yumi, Toru, Megumi. BF, U. Tokyo. With Bank Tokyo, 1959-85, gen. mgr. Brussels office, 1982, gen. mgr. Europe and Africa div., 1984-85; exec. v.p., chief fin. officer Calif. First Bank, San Francisco, 1985-87; gen. mgr. overseas div. Bank Tokyo, 1987-88; vice chmn., dir. Calif. First Bank, Union Bank, San Francisco, 1988-90; pres., chief exec. officer Union Bank, San Francisco, 1990—. Office: Union Bank 350 California St San Francisco CA 94104-1402

SHIMIZU, YOSHIAKI, art historian, educator; b. Tokyo, Feb. 27, 1936; came to U.S., 1953, U.S. resident, 1976; s. Mamoru and Michiko (Hayasaka) S.; children: Karen Akiko Marie, Kenneth Cuyler Norio, Katherine Kimie, Kei Robert. BA, Harvard U., 1963; MA, U. Kans., 1968; MFA, Princeton U., 1971, PhD, 1974. Asst. prof. dept. art and archaeology Princeton (N.J.) U., 1973-75, prof., 1984—, chmn. dept. art and archaeology, 1990-92, Marquand prof. art & archaeology, 1992—; asst. prof. U. Calif., Berkeley, 1975-78, assoc. prof., 1978-79; curator Japanese art Freer Gallery, Smithsonian Instn., Washington, 1979-84; guest curator Nat. Gallery Art, Washington, 1982-89; guest prof. U. of Heidelberg, 1993; mem. art adv. com. Japan Soc. Gallery, 1984—, adv. com. The Asia Soc. Galleries, N.Y.C., 1992—; vis. fellow dept. Comparative Culture Sophia U., Tokyo, 1993. Author: (with Suzan Nelson) Genji: The World of a Prince, 1982; (with John M. Rosenfield) Masters of Japanese Calligraphy, 1984; editor: (with Carolyn Wheelwright) Japanese Ink Paintings, 1976; author, editor: Japan: The Shaping of Daimyo Culture 1185-1858, 1988; mem. editorial bd. Archives of Asian Art, 1979—. Adv. bd. Asian Art, Smithsonian Inst., 1985-93; mem. vis. com. Arthur M. Sackler Gallery, Washington, 1984—. Smithsonian Inst. fellow, 1967; Social Sci. Research Council-Am. Council of Learned Socs. fellow, 1977-78. Mem. Coll. Art Assn. (bd. dirs. 1987—), Japan Art History Assn., Japan Soc. N.Y., Ctr. for the Study of Japanese Woodblock Prints (mem. internat. adv. bd. 1983—). Home: 171 Nassau St Princeton NJ 08544-2003 Office: Dept Art & Archaeology Princeton U Princeton NJ 08540

SHIMM, MELVIN GERALD, law educator; b. 1926; s. Joseph George and Sadie Rosalie (Rosenblatt) S.; m. Cynia Brown, Aug. 15, 1948; children: David Stuart, Jonathan Evan. AB, Columbia U., 1947; LLB, Yale U., 1950. Bar: N.Y. 1950. Assoc., Cahill, Gordon, Zachry & Reindel, N.Y.C., 1950-51; atty. Wage Stblzn. Bd., Washington, 1951-52; Bigelow fellow U. Chgo., 1952-53; asst. prof. Duke U. Law Sch., Durham, N.C., 1953-56, assoc. prof., 1956-59, prof., 1959—, assoc. dean, 1978-83; vis. prof. NYU, 1957, U. So. Calif., 1965, U. Mich., Ann Arbor, 1973, U. Tex.-Austin, 1976; chmn. Durham (N.C.) Bd. Adjustment, 1966-70; dir. Assn. Am. Law Schs. Orientation Program in Am. Law, 1968-70, Duke Inst. in Transnat. Law, 1987-92; cons. The Brookings Instn., 1965-67; mem. N.C. Gen. Statutes Commn., 1984-88. Bd. dirs., vice-chmn. Lucy Daniels Found., 1989—; pres. Beth El Congregation, Durham, N.C., 1967-70, 1975-78. Lt. U.S. Army. 1943-46. Mem. Order of Coif, Phi Beta Kappa. Editor-in-chief Law & Contemporary Problems, 1964; Legal Edn., Am. Editor Jour. Bus. Law; editor Yale Law Jour. Office: Duke U Sch Law PO Box 90360 Durham NC 27708-0360

SHIMODA, JERRY YASUTAKA, national historic park administrator; b. Haleiwa, Hawaii, Mar. 21, 1930; s. Tamotsu and Sasai Shimoda; m. Clara H. Segawa, Aug. 7, 1954; children: Karen Marie K., Randall T., Shaun T., Teri Ellen H., Jacqueline Y., David Y. BA in Govt., U. Hawaii, 1952, MA in Far Ea. Area Studies, 1957; postgrad., St. Louis U., 1957-59. Historian Jefferson Nat. Expansion Meml. Nat. Hist. Site, St. Louis, 1957-60; chief historian, in charge hist. rsch. and visitor svcs. Saratoga Nat. Hist. Park, Stillwater, N.Y., 1960-66; chief historian Home of Franklin D. Roosevelt Nat. Hist. Site and Frederick Vanderbilt Nat. Hist. Site, Hyde Park, N.Y., 1966-69; instr. Nat. Park Svc. Stephen T. Mather Tng. Ctr., Harpers Ferry, W.Va., 1969-72; supt. Pu'uhonua o Honaunau (Hawaii) Nat. Hist. Park, 1972—, Puukohola Heiau Nat. Hist. Site, Honaunau, 1972—; lectr. environ. edn. Pa. State U., U. W.Va., Shepherd Coll., 1969-72; acting supr. Kaloko-Honokohau Nat. Hist. Park, 1988-90; instr. environ. edn., interpretive and basic instructing techniques U. Hawaii, Hilo, Kapiolani C.C.; U.S. del. U.S.-Japan Panel on Nat. Parks and Equivalent Res., 1968—, World Conf. on Marine Parks, Tokyo, 1975; Japanese translator U.S. Nat. Park Svc.; mem. internat. bd. dirs. Heritage Interpretation Internat.; numerous presentations at confs. and tng. courses. Author booklets on nat. parks, mgmt. and history; contbr. numerous articles to profl. publs., mags. and newspapers. Bd. dirs. Volcano Art Ctr.; mem. adv. com. Wailoa State Ctr.; mem. Hawaii Gov.'s Task Force on Ocean and Recreation; chmn. restoration com. St. Benedict's Ch., Honounau, 1982-95. Recipient spl. achievement award Nat. Park Svc., 1964, 68, 70, resolution W.Va. Senate, 1971, Hawaii Ho. of Reps., 1982, sec.'s cert. Dept. Interior, 1971, Exec. of Yr. award West Hawaii chpt. Profl. Secs. Internat., 1981, cert. Govt. of Japan, 1981, staff plaque Pu'uhonua o Honaunau Nat. Hist. Park, Puukohola Heiau Nat. Hist. Site and Kaloko-Honokohau Nat. Hist. Park, 1988, cert. Japan Nat. Parks Assn., 1989, cert. of appreciation South Kona Aloha Lions Club, 1990, also others. Mem. Hawaii Mus. Assn. (bd. dirs. 1988-92), Kona Hist. Soc. (bd. dirs. 1988-92), Big Island Ocean Recreation and Tourism Assn. (exec. com.), Kona Judo Club (pres. 1977—), Rotary (pres. Kona Nauka 1978-79, Paul Harris fellow 1991, Disting. Svc. award 1992). Avocations: writing, reading, travel, teaching. Office: Pu'uhonua o Honaunau Nat Hist Pk PO Box 129 Honaunau HI 96726-0129

SHIMOJI, SADAO, applied mathematics educator, engineer; b. Tokyo, Apr. 22, 1932; s. Keijo and Kiyo (Miyakuni) S.; m. Tamiko Matsumoto, Dec. 15, 1961; children: Yuichi, Atsushi. MS in Physics, Tokyo U., 1957; PhD in Physics, Osaka (Japan) U., 1966. Cert. engr. Engr. Mitsubishi Electric Corp., Amagasaki, Japan, 1957-65, group mgr., 1965-79, mgr., 1970-75; concurrent lectr. Inst. of Space Tech. and Scis., Tokyo U., 1972-74; sr. scientist Mitsubishi Electric Corp., Amagasaki, Japan, 1975-86; prof. Tokyo Engring. U., Hachioji, Japan, 1986—; mem. program sub-com. 9th, 10th, 13d. 14th ISTS, Tokyo, 1970-84. Co-author: AIAA Progress, Vol. 65, 1978; contbr. articles to Jour. Phys. Soc. Japan, Jour. AIAA, Japanese Jour. Applied Physics, Jour. Applied Physics. Mem. amentry. coun. Hachioji City, 1987—. Buddhist. Achievements include discovery of optimum F-value found for the statistical regression analysis of thermal-vacuum test data of artificial satellites; development of theory that the behavior of the Carreau viscosity model for the long spinning time in the spin coating process was clarified by the numerical method and an analytical model of the solvent evaporation of polymer solutions. Home: Kitanodai 3-28-8, Hachioji 192, Japan Office: Tokyo Engring U, Katakura 1404, Hachioji 192, Japan

SHIMOYAMA, HIDEO, construction company executive; b. 1943. Grad. Osaka (Japan) U.; attended, Mich. State U. With Kajima Constrn. Svcs., Japan, 1967-81, Kajima Internat., 1981-91; pres., COO Kajima Constrn.

Svcs., Englewood Cliffs, N.J., 1991—. Office: Kajima Constrn Svcs 900 Sylvan Ave Englewood Cliffs NJ 07632

SHIMP, ROBERT EVERETT, JR., university administrator, historian; b. Phila., Mar. 1, 1942; s. Robert Everett Sr. and Vivian (Myrtetus) S.; m. Marilyn Hopkins, Aug. 3, 1963; children: Gregory, Cecily, Jennifer. BA, Thiel Coll., 1964; MA, Ohio State U., 1965, PhD, 1970. Instr. history Ohio Wesleyan U., Delaware, Ohio, 1970-78, asst. prof., 1970-76, assoc. prof., 1976-82, prof. history, 1982-84, dir. off campus program, 1979-84; acad. dean Ky. Wesleyan Coll., Owensboro, 1984-88; provost, v.p. for acad. affairs Millikin U., Decatur, Ill., 1988-93; pres. McMurry U., Abilene, Tex., 1993—; vis. assoc. prof. Ohio State U., Columbus, summer 1978, Coll. of V.I., St. Croix, fall 1982; mem. Inst. for Ednl. Mgmt. Harvard U., 1985; reader and table leader European history AP, Princeton, N.J. 1976-83; dir. Newberry Libr. Program in the Humanities, Chgo., 1976-77. Contbr. articles to profl. jours. Mem. Leadership Owensboro, 1986-87; capt. drives United Way, Owensboro and Delaware, 1981-85, bd. dirs. Decatur and Abilene; trustee for Sears Retirement Systems and Abilene Higher Edn. Authority; bd. dirs. Abilene C. of C. Fellow Ohio State U., 1968, Newberry Libr., Chgo., 1976-77. Mem. Ohio Acad. History, Conf. on Brit. Studies, Kiwanis. Democrat. Methodist. Avocations: fishing, reading. Office: McMurry U Office of Pres PO Box 98 Abilene TX 79604-0098

SHIMPFKY, RICHARD LESTER, bishop; b. Albuquerque, Oct. 18, 1940; m. Jamel Shimpfky, 1966; children: Trevor, Allison, Joshua. Grad., U. Colo., 1963, Va. Theol. Seminary, 1970. Ordained to diaconate Episc. Ch., 1970. With William L. Philips Found., Richmond, Va., 1963-67; curate St. Peter's Ch., Arlington, 1970-72; vicar All Saints' Sharon Chapel, Alexandria, Va., 1972-73, rector, 1973-77; rector Christ Ch., Ridgewood, N.J., 1977-90; bishop Diocese El Camino Real, Monterey, Calif., 1990—. Avocations: reading, traveling. Office: Diocese of El Camino Real PO Box 1093 Monterey CA 93942-1093

SHINAGEL, MICHAEL, English literature educator; b. Vienna, Austria, Apr. 21, 1934; came to U.S., 1941; s. Emanuel and Lilly (Hillel) S.; m. Ann Birdsey Mitchell, Sept. 1, 1956 (div. 1970); children: Mark Mitchell, Victoria Stuart; m. Rosa Joanne Bonanno, Dec. 6, 1973 (div. 1993); m. Marjorie Lee North, May 26, 1995. A.B., Oberlin Coll., 1957; A.M., Harvard U., 1959, Ph.D., 1964. Teaching fellow Harvard U., Cambridge, Mass., 1958-59, tutor in English, 1962-64, assoc. dir. career office, 1959-64, dean continuing edn., 1975—, lectr. extension, 1976—, sr. lectr. English, 1983—, master Quincy House, 1986—; asst. prof. English, Cornell U., Ithaca, N.Y., 1964-67; prof., chmn. dept. English, Union Coll., Schenectady, 1967-75; bd. dirs. Harvard Coop. Soc., publ. Harvard Rev.; pres. bd. dirs. Ednl. Exch. Boston, 1982-87. Author: Defoe and Middle-class Gentility, 1968; co-author: (handbook) Summer Institutes in English, 1965; editor: Concordance to Poems of Swift, 1972, Critical Edition of Robinson Crusoe, 1975 (revised 1993); co-editor: Harvard Scholars in English (1890-1990), 1991. Served with U.S. Army, Korea. Woodrow Wilson fellow, 1957; NEH grantee, 1965. Mem. Nat. Univ. Continuing Edn. Assn., Assn. Continuing Higher Edn., Mass. Hist. Soc., Old South Meeting House, The Johnsonians, The Saturday Club, Harvard Faculty Club (pres. 1985-87), Phi Beta Kappa. Avocations: reading; cooking; music; tennis. Home: Master's Residence Quincy House 58 Plympton St Cambridge MA 02138-6609 Office: Harvard U Div Continuing Edn 51 Brattle St Cambridge MA 02138-3701

SHINBO, ROBERT, landscape architect; b. Seattle, June 20, 1948; s. Hachiro and May (Asai) S.; m. Sharron Chin, Feb. 25, 1968; 1 child, Roberta. B Landscape Architecture, U. Wash., 1971; M. Harvard U., 1973. Registered landscape architect Calif., Wash. Designer Sakuma James Peterson, Seattle, 1970-71; research asst. Harvard U., Cambridge, Mass., 1972-73; designer Sasaki Assocs., Watertown, Mass., 1973-76, SWA Group, Irvine, Calif., 1976-77; sr. assoc. Edaw Co., Newport Beach, Calif., 1977-78; prin. Robert Shinbo Assocs., Seattle, 1978—. Commr. Pike Place Market Hist. Commn., Seattle, 1988—; mem. King County Affordable Housing Task Force, 1986; fund-raiser U. Wash. Coll. Architecture and Urban Planning. Recipient Nat. award Program for Energy Innovation of Wash. State Energy Office, 1986. Mem. Am. Soc. Landscape Architects (pres. Wash. chpt. 1985, Merit award 1986), Urban Land Inst., Am. Planning Assn., Lambda Alpha. Office: Robrt Shinbo Assocs 89 Virginia St Seattle WA 98101-1012

SHINDELL, SIDNEY, medical educator, physician; b. New Haven, May 31, 1923; s. Benjamin Abraham and Freda (Mann) S.; m. Gloria Emhoff, June 17, 1945; children: Barbara, Roger, Lawrence, Judith. BS, Yale U., 1944; MD, L.I. Coll. Medicine, 1946; postgrad., Emory U., 1948-49; LLB, Geo. Washington U., 1951. Diplomate Am. Bd. Preventive Medicine, Am. Bd. Occupational Medicine. With USPHS, 1947-52; med. dir. Conn. Commn. on Chronically Ill and Aged, 1952-57, Am. Joint Distbn. Com. 1957-59; asst. prof. preventive medicine U. Pitts., 1960-65; dir. Hosp. Utilization project Western Pa., 1965-64; prof. dept. preventive medicine Med. Coll. Wis., Milw., 1966-93, chmn. dept., 1966-89, dir. office internat affairs, 1989-93, prof. emeritus, 1993—; exec. dir. Health Svc. Data of Wis., 1967-73; bd. sci. advisers Am. Coun. on Sci. and Health, 1978-87, 92—; mem. Nat. Adv. Com. on Occupational Safety and Health, U.S. Dept. Labor, 1982-84; cons. Caribbean Epidemiology Ctr. Pan. Am. Health Orgn./ WHO, 1988, field epidemiology tng. program, Thailand, 1989, Nat. Office Occupational and Environ. Medicine Royal Thai Ministry of Pub. Health, 1990—; mem. gov's white paper com. on health care reform, Wis., 1993; acad. cons. Faculties of Medicine, Padjadjaran U., Bandung, Airlangga U., Surabaya, Indonesia, 1993, 94; bd. dirs. Am. Coun. of Sci. and Health, 1987-89, chmn. 1989-92. Author: Statistics, Science and Sense, 1964, A Method of Hospital Utilization Review, 1966, The Law in Medical Practice, 1966, A Coursebook on Health Care Delivery, 1976; contbr. 120 articles to profl. jours. Mem. Sch. Bd. Fox Point-Bayside (Wis.), Sch. Dist., 1970-71; vice-chmn. Citizens' Adv. Com. Met. Problems, 1971-72; Bd. dirs. Med. Care Evaluation S.E. Wis., 1973-76. Served with AUS, 1943-46. Fellow Am. Coll. Preventive Medicine (bd. regents 1982-85), Am. Pub. health Assn., Am. Coll. Occupational and Environ. Medicine, Am. Coll. Legal Medicine; mem. Am. Assn. Health Data Systems (sec. 1972-73), Assn. Tchrs. Preventive Medicine (dir. 1973-74, pres. 1976-77), Assn. Occupational Health Profls. (pres. 1980-90), Am. Acad. Occupational Medicine, Aircraft Owners and Pilots Assn., Masons, CAP. Home: 929 N Astor St Milwaukee WI 53202-3490 Office: PO Box 26509 Milwaukee WI 53226-0509

SHINDLER, DONALD A., lawyer; b. New Orleans, Oct. 15, 1946; s. Alan and Isolene (Levy) S.; m. Laura Epstein, June 22, 1969; children: Jay, Susan. BSBA, Washington U., St. Louis, 1968; JD, Tulane U., 1971. Bar: La. 1971, U.S. Dist. Ct. (ea. dist.) La. 1971, U.S. Tax Ct. 1974, Ill. 1975, U.S. Dist. Ct. (no. dist.) Ill. 1975; CPA, La.; lic. real estate broker, Ill. Assoc. Pope, Ballard, Shepard & Fowle, Chgo., 1975-78; assoc. Rudnick & Wolfe, Chgo., 1978-81, ptnr., 1981—; seminar lectr. Chgo. Bar Assn., Ill. Inst. CLE, Profl. Edn. Sys., Inc., NACORE, Urban Land Inst., ACCA, 1980—. Contbr. articles on real estate to legal jours. Trustee Glencoe (Ill.) Pub. Libr., 1981-87, pres., 1986-87; alumni bd. govs. Washington U., 1992-93; mem. Glencoe Zoning Commn. Bd. Appeals, 1994—. Lt. JAGC, USNR, 1971-75. Mem. ABA, La. State Bar Assn., Chgo. Bar Assn. (com. chmn. 1979-80, 83-84, 90-94, editor-land trust seminars 1984—), Urban Land Inst. (mem. exec. com. Chgo. dist. coun.), Internat. Assn. Corp. Real Estate Execs., Internat. Assn. Attys. and Execs. in Corp. Real Estate, Union League Club (co-chairperson real estate group 1993—), Order of Coif, Beta Gamma Sigma, Omicron Delta Kappa. Home: 555 Greenwood Ave Glencoe IL 60022-1601 Office: Rudnick & Wolfe 203 N La Salle St Ste 1800 Chicago IL 60601-1293

SHINDLER, MERRILL KARSH, writer, radio personality; b. N.Y.C., July 2, 1948; s. Joseph and Miriam (Karsh) S. BA, CCNY, 1970; MFA, NYU, 1971. Entertainment editor San Francisco Bay Guardian, 1972-75; music editor Rolling Stone mag., San Francisco, 1976-79; film critic Los Angeles mag., 1979—; restaurant critic Los Angeles Examiner, 1979—; editor Zagat Los Angeles Restaurant Survey, 1986—; restaurant critic L.A. Reader, 1990—, Daily Breeze, 1990—, Daily News, 1990—. Author: Best Restaurants of L.A., 1989, Zagat L.A. Restaurant Survey, 1986—; writer (radio shows) Am. Top 40, 1979-89, Casey's Top 40, 1989—, Casey's Biggest Hits, 1990—, USA Top 20, 1990—, (tv shows) Am. Top 10, 1980—, Cinematractions, 1990—, USA Music Today, 1990—; radio show host Dining Out with Merrill Shindler, 1988—; contbr. Gault-Millau Best of Los

Angeles, 1988, Gault-Millau Best of Hong Kong, 1989; conbtr. articles to jours. Avocations: restaurants, cooking, jogging, travel.

SHINE, HENRY JOSEPH, chemistry educator; b. London, Jan. 4, 1923; s. Nathan and Esther (Lewkovich) S.; m. Sellie Schneider, June 14, 1953; children: Stephanie, Trevor Paul. B.Sc., London U., 1944, Ph.D., 1947. Research chemist Shell Oil Co., Eng., 1944; research chemist U.S. Rubber Co., Passaic, N.J., 1951-54; asst. prof. chemistry Tex. Tech U., Lubbock, 1954-57; asso. prof. Tex. Tech U., 1957-60, prof., 1960—, Paul Whitfield Horn prof., 1968—, chmn. dept., 1969-75. Author: Aromatic Rearrangements, 1967; conbtr. articles to profl. jours. Mem. Am. Chem. Soc. (exec. com. div. organic chemistry 1973-75, alt. councillor 1975-78, councillor 1978-80), Chem. Soc. London, AAAS (regional pres. 1979-80), Sigma Xi (pres. chpt. 1976-77), Phi Kappa Phi. Home: 4705 17th St Lubbock TX 79416-5707 Office: Dept Chemistry and Biochemistry Tex Tech U Lubbock TX 79409

SHINE, KENNETH IRWIN, cardiologist, educator; b. Worcester, Mass., 1935. Grad., Harvard Coll., 1957; MD, Harvard U., 1961. Diplomate Am. Bd. Internal Medicine. Intern Mass. Gen. Hosp., 1961-62, resident, 1962-63, 65-66, fellow in cardiology, 1966-68; surgeon USPHS, 1963-65; assoc. in medicine Beth Israel Hosp., Resont, Va., from 1969; instr. Harvard Med. Sch., from 1968; asst. prof. medicine UCLA Sch. Medicine, 1971-73, assoc. prof., 1973-77, prof., 1977-92; dir. CCU UCLA Sch. Medicine, Washington, 1971-75; chief div. cardiology UCLA Sch. Medicine, 1975-79, vice chmn. dept. medicine, 1979-81, exec. chmn., 1981-86, dean, 1986-92, provost for med. scis., 1991-92; pres. Inst. Medicine, Washington, 1992—. Mem. Am. Heart Assn. (pres. 1986, 87), Assn. Am. Med. Colls. (adminstrv. bd. coun. deans 1989-92, exec. bd. 1990-92, chmn. coun. deans 1991-92). Office: Institute of Medicine 2101 Constitution Ave NW Washington DC 20418*

SHINE, NEAL JAMES, newspaper editor; b. Grosse Pointe Farms, Mich., Sept. 14, 1930; s. Patrick Joseph and Mary Ellen (Conlon) S.; m. Phyllis Theresa Knowles, Jan. 24, 1953; children: Judith Ann, James Conlon, Susan Brigid, Thomas Patrick, Margaret Mary, Daniel Edward. BS in Journalism, U. Detroit, 1952; PhD (hon.), Cleary Coll., 1989. Mem. staff Detroit Free Press, 1950—, asst. city editor, 1963-65, city editor, 1965-71, mng. editor, 1971-82, sr. mng. editor, 1982-89, pub., 1990—. Host, moderator Detroit Week in Rev., Sta. WTVS-TV, 1981-89, host Neal Shine's Detroit, 1989-91. Trustee, vice chmn. bd. trustees Youth for Understanding, 1973-75, chmn., 1975-78; mem. bd. for student publs. U. Mich.; bd. dirs. Children's Hosp., Econ. Club Detroit, Detroit Renaissance, New Detroit, Inc., Detroit Symphony Orch., Detroit Inst. Arts, Detroit Hist. Soc., United Way of Southeastern Mich., Met. Detroit Conv. and Visitors Bur., Operation ABLE, Detroit Press Club Found. With U.S. Army, 1953-55. Inducted Mich. Journalism Hall of Fame, 1990. Mem. Am. Soc. Newspaper Editors, Am. Newspapers Pubs. Assn., Mich. Press Assn. (bd. dirs. 1990—), A.P. Mng. Editors, Sons of Whiskey Rebellion (comdr.-in-chief 1979—), Inc. Soc. Irish-Am. Lawyers, Detroit Press Club (charter, bd. govs. 1966-89, sec. 1967-68, v.p. 1969-71, pres. 1971-73). Home: 11009 Harbor Place Dr Saint Clair Shores MI 48080-1527 also: Rathclaire, Gen Delivery, Pointe aux Roches, ON Canada N0R 1N0 Office: Detroit Free Press 321 W Lafayette Blvd Detroit MI 48231

SHINEFIELD, HENRY ROBERT, pediatrician; b. Paterson, N.J., Oct. 11, 1925; s. Louis and Sarah (Kaplan) S.; m. Jacqueline Marilyn Walker; children: Jill, Michael, Kimberley Strome, Melissa Strome. B.A., Columbia U., 1945, M.D., 1948. Diplomate: Am. Bd. Pediatrics (examiner, 1975—, bd. dirs., 1979-84, v.p., 1981-84). Rotating intern Mt. Sinai Hosp., N.Y.C., 1948-49; pediatric intern Duke Hosp., Durham, N.C., 1949-50; asst. resident pediatrician N.Y. Hosp. (Cornell), 1950-51, pediatrician to outpatients, 1953-59, instr. in pediatrics, 1959-60, asst. prof., 1960-64, asso. prof., 1964-65, asst. attending pediatrician, 1959-63, asso. attending pediatrician, 1963-65; pediatrician to outpatients Children's Hosp., Oakland, Calif., 1951-53; chief of pediatrics Kaiser-Permanente Med. Center, San Francisco, 1965-89, chief emeritus, 1989—; co-dir. Kaiser-Permanente Pediat4ric Vaccine Study Ctr., San Francisco, 1984—; asso. clin. prof. pediatrics Sch. Medicine U. Calif., 1966-68, clin. prof. pediatrics, 1968—, clin. prof. dermatology, 1970—; asso. attending pediatrician Paterson (N.J.) Gen. Hosp., 1955-59; chief of pediatrics Kaiser Found. Hosp., San Francisco, 1965—; attending Moffitt Hosp., San Francisco, 1967—; practice medicine specializing in pediatrics Paterson, 1953-59; cons. San Francisco Gen. Hosp., 1967—, Childrens Hosp., San Francisco, 1970—, Mt. Zion Hosp., San Francisco, 1970—; mem. research grants rev. br. NIH, HEW, 1970-74; med. dir. USPHSR, 1969—; bd. dirs. San Francisco Peer Rev. Orgn., 1975-81, sec., exec. com., 1976-81; chmn. Calif. State Child Health Disability Bd., 1973-82; mem. Inst. of Medicine, Nat. Acad. Scis., 1980—; cons. Bur. Drugs FDA, 1970, NIH, HEW, 1974—. Editorial bds. Western Jour. of Medicine, 1968-80, American Jour. of Diseases of Children, 1970-82; conbtr. writings to profl. publs. Chmn. San Francisco Med. Adv. Com. Nat. Found. March of Dimes, 1969-80. Served with USPHS, 1951-53. Fellow Am. Acad. Pediatrics (com. of fetus and newborn 1969-76, mem. com. on drugs 1978-82); mem. AMA, Soc. Pediatric Research, Infectious Diseases Soc. Am., Western Pediatric Soc., Western Soc. Clin. Research, Am. Pediatric Soc., Phi Beta Kappa. Home: 2705 Larkin St San Francisco CA 94109-1117 Office: 2200 Ofarrell St San Francisco CA 94115-3357

SHINEMAN, EDWARD WILLIAM, JR., retired pharmaceutical executive; b. Canajoharie, N.Y., Apr. 9, 1915; s. Edward W. and Bertelle H. (Shubert) S.; m. H. Doris Thompson, Apr. 15, 1939; children: Edward T., Alan B. AB, Cornell U., 1937. With apparatus dept., acctg. dept. Gen. Electric Co., 1938-46, line auditor, 1942-46; with Beech-Nut, Inc. and predecessor cos., 1946-68, asst. treas., 1948-63, contr., 1959-63, treas., 1963-68; asst. sec.-treas. Squibb Corp., 1968-81; bd. dirs. Fenimore Asset Mgmt., Inc., Taconic Farms, Inc. Trustee, pres. Arkell Hall Found.; mem. emeritus coun. Cornell U. Mem. Fin. Execs. Inst., Inst. Mgmt. Accts. Republican. Home: 420 E 51st St Apt 14E New York NY 10022-8022

SHINER, JOSETTE SHEERAN, editor; b. Orange, N.J., June 12, 1954; d. James Joseph and Sarah Ann (Gallagher) Sheeran; m. Whitney Taylor Shiner, Nov. 10, 1984; children: Nicole Munier, Daniel John, Gabrielle. BA, U. Colo., 1976. Nat. desk editor N.Y. News World, 1977-80; Washington bur. chief N.Y. News World, 1977-80, corr. The White House, 1980-82; Capital life and mag. editor Washington Times, 1982-84, asst. mng. editor, 1984-85, dep. mng. editor, 1985-92, mng. editor, 1992—. Mem. Leadership Washington Alumni Assn., 1987-88, v.p. , 1988-89, alumni chmn., 1989-90. Recipient Atrium award U. Ga., 1984. Mem. White House Corrs. Assn., Am. News Womens Club, Nat. Press Club (newsmaker chmn. 1980-82; Meritorious Svc. award 1981, Vivian award 1981), Am. Soc. Newspaper Editors, Coun. Fgn. Rels., Sigma Delta Chi. Office: Washington Times 3600 New York Ave NE Washington DC 20002

SHINN, ALLEN MAYHEW, retired naval officer, business executive; b. Niles, Calif., June 6, 1908; s. Joseph Clark and Florence Maria (Mayhew) S.; m. Sevilla Hayden Shuey, June 20, 1936; children: Allen Mayhew, James Washburn, Jonathan Hayden. BS, US Naval Acad., 1932; grad., Nat. War Coll., 1953. Commd. officer USN, 1932, advanced through grades to vice adm.; served in battleships, 1932-36; naval aviator, 1937, served in various fleet aircraft squadrons, comdr. 3, also comdr. attack carrier air group, 1944-45; served on various staffs; comdr. 2 carriers USS Saipan, 1956, USS Forrestal, 1958; comdt. midshipmen U.S. Naval Acad., Annapolis, Md., 1956-58; comdr. Anti-Submarine Warfare Carrier Task Group, 1960-61, Attack Carrier Task Force, 1963-64; chief Bur. Naval Weapons, Washington, 1964-66; comdr. Naval Air Force Pacific Fleet, 1966-70; ret., 1970; chmn. bd. Harvard Industries, Inc., 1970-71, All-Am. Industries, 1973-78; pres., CEO Internat. Controls Corp., 1973-78, dir. 1973-79; dir. Loral Corp., 1973—; Pennzoil Co., 1970-94; bd. dirs. Navy Mut. Aid Assn., 1962-66; bd. mgrs. Navy Relief Soc., 1962-64; pres. Naval Acad. Athletic Assn., 1956-58, North Water St. Corp., Edgartown, Mass., 1948-50. Trustee Longfellow Sch. Boys, Bethesda, Md., 1950-53. Decorated D.S.M. Mem. Soc. Mayflower Descendants, Cosmos Club, N.Y. Yacht Club, Edgartown Yacht Club, Delta Tau Delta. Republican. Unitarian. Home: 3130 Roadrunner Dr Borrego Springs CA 92004

SHINN, CLINTON WESLEY, lawyer; b. Haworth, Okla., Mar. 7, 1947; s. Clinton Elmo and Mary Lucille (Dowdy) S.; m. Catherine Borne; children:

Laura Kathryn, Clinton Wesley, Timothy Daniel. BS, McNeese State U., 1969; JD, Tulane U., 1972; LLM, Harvard U., 1973. Bar: La. 1972, U.S. Dist. Ct. (ea. dist.) La. 1975, U.S. Dist. Ct. (we. dist.) La. 1980, U.S. Ct. Appeals (5th cir.) 1981, U.S. Ct. Appeals (11th cir.) 1982, U.S. Tax Ct. (1982). Asst. prof. law Tulane U., New Orleans, 1973-75; assoc. Stone, Pigman et al, New Orleans, 1975-78, ptnr., 1979—; faculty advisor, 1974-76, editor in chief Tulane Law Rev., 1971-72. Editor in chief Tulane Law Rev., 1971-72. Co-founder, bd. dirs. Childhood Cancer Families Network, 1987-90; co-founder Camp Challenge, 1988; team leader Campaign for Caring, Childrens Hosp., New Orleans, 1989-91; bd. dirs. Christ Episcopal Sch., Covington, 1988-91, chmn. long-range planning, 1990-91, exec. com., 1989-91, chmn. legal com., 1989-91, chmn. admissions/recruitment com., 1988-90, mem. headmaster search com., 1993; bd. dirs. Greater New Orleans YMCA, 1989—, exec. com., 1991—, asst. sec., 1994—, mem. fin. com. 1994—, active Indian Guides/Princesses; bd. dirs. West St. Tammany YMCA, 1987—, exec. com. 1988—, bd. dirs. Christwood, 1992—; bd. dirs. La. Air & Waste Mgmt. Assn., 1993—, chmn. corp. rels. com. 1992-93. Co-recipient Pals of the Yr. award Greater New Orleans YMCA Indian Guides/Princesses, 1987-88; named Vol. of Yr. West St. Tammany YMCA, 1990, 92. Mem. ABA, Nat. Assn. Securities Dealers (bd. arbitrators), Nat. Wildlife Fedn. (life), La. Bar Assn., La. Forestry Assn., New Orleans Bar Assn., New Orleans Estate Planning Coun., Assn. Employee Benefit Planners New Orleans, Assn. Henri Capitant, Air and Waste Mgmt. Assn., Order of Coif. Avocations: backpacking, gardening. Home: Dogwood Ridge Farm 20297 Brunning Rd Covington LA 70433-7579 Office: Stone Pigman Walther Wittman & Hutchinson 546 Carondelet St New Orleans LA 70130-3521 *In all things be firm but fair.*

SHINN, DAVID HAMILTON, diplomat; b. Yakima, Wash., June 9, 1940; s. Guy Wilson and Ada Louise (Gelvin) S.; m. Judy Karen Rolfe, Sept. 9, 1961; children: Steven Hamilton, Christopher Rolfe. AA, Yakima Valley Coll., 1960; BA, George Washington U., 1963, MA, 1964, PhD, 1980; cert. African studies, Northwestern U., Evanston, Ill., 1969. With U.S. State Dept., 1964—; rotational officer U.S. Embassy, Beirut, Lebanon, 1964-66; polit. officer Nairobi, Kenya, 1967-68; desk officer East African affairs Washington, 1969-72; polit. officer Dar es Salaam, Tanzania, 1972-74; dep. chief of mission Nouakchott, Mauritania, 1974-76, Office of Mayor, City of Seattle, 1977-78; dep. coord. state and local govt. U.S. Dept. State, Washington, 1978-81; dep. chief of mission Yaounde, Cameroon, 1981-83, Khartoum, Sudan, 1983-86; U.S. ambassador Ouagadougou, Burkina Faso, 1987-90; diplomat-in-residence Southern U., Baton Rouge, La., 1990-91; diplomat State Dept., Washington, 1991—. Recipient Superior Honor award State Dept., 1980, 85, 94, Alumnus of Yr. award Am. Assn. Cmty. Colls., 1994, Phi Theta Kappa, 1995. Mem. Internat. Studies Assn., Am. Fgn. Service Assn., Am. Philatelic Soc. Methodist. Avocations: philately, skiing, softball, tennis, volleyball. Office: US Dept State Washington DC 20520

SHINN, GEORGE, professional basketball executive; b. Kannapolis, N.C. Owner, pres. Charlotte (N.C.) Hornets; owner Charlotte Knights Baseball, Gastonia Rangers Baseball; owner real estate devel. co., printing bus., auto dealerships. Pres. Mecklenburg County coun. Boy Scouts Am. Recipient Horatio Alger award, 1975. Mem. Charlotte C. of C. (bd. dirs.). Office: Charlotte Hornets 1 Hive Dr Charlotte NC 28217*

SHINN, GEORGE LATIMER, investment banker, consultant, educator; b. Newark, Ohio, Mar. 12, 1923; s. Leon Powell and Bertha Florence (Latimer) S.; m. Clara LeBaron Sampson, May 21, 1949; children: Deborah, Amy, Martha, Sarah, Andrew. AB, Amherst Coll., 1948; LLD (hon.), Denison U., 1975, Amherst Coll., 1982; MA, Drew U., 1990, PhD, 1992. Trainee Merrill Lynch, Pierce, Fenner & Beane, 1948-49; various exec. positions Merrill Lynch, Pierce, Fenner & Beane (now Merrill Lynch, Pierce, Fenner & Smith Inc.), 1949-73, pres., 1973-75; also pres. Goodbody & Co., Inc., Merrill Lynch & Co., Inc., 1974-75; chmn. bd., chief exec. officer 1st Boston Corp., 1975-83; chmn. bd., chief exec. officer First Boston Inc., 1976-83, chmn. exec. com., 1982-88; investment banking consultant, 1990—; adj. prof. philosophy Drew U., Madison, N.J., 1992—; mem. exec. com. President's Pvt. Sector Survey on Cost Control, 1982-84; exec.-in-residence Columbia U. Grad. Sch. Bus., 1983-85; bd. dirs. N.Y. Times Co., CS 1st Boston, Kelso & Co., Phelps Dodge Inc., N.Y. Life Ins.; bd. govs. Am. Stock Exchange, 1970-74; bd. dirs. N.Y. Stock Exchange, 1977-83, vice chmn., 1981-83; bd. dirs., trustee Colonial Group Mut. Funds. Gen. chmn. United Hosp. Fund, N.Y.C., 1973-74; trustee Kent Pl. Sch., Summit, N.J., 1966-73, Carnegie Found. for Advancement Teaching, 1976-85, Pingry Sch., 1977-79, Lucille P. Markey Charitable Trust, 1985—, Rockefeller Family Office Trust, 1989—; trustee emeritus Amherst Coll., 1968-82, chmn. bd. trustees, 1973-80; bd. dirs. Rsch. Corp., 1975-86; trustee Arts Coun. Morris Area, 1978-91; bd. trustee Philharm. Symphony Soc. N.Y., 1983-91, Nat. Humanities Ctr., 1988-94. Capt. USMCR, 1943-52. Fellow Am. Acad. Arts and Scis., River Club, Century Assn., Morris County Golf Club. Office: CS First Boston 12 E 49th St New York NY 10017

SHINN, LINDA JANE, nurse, association executive; b. Ft. Wayne, Ind., Jan. 10, 1948; d. Richard Kenneth and Dorothy Elaine (Carrier) S. Nursing degree, Meml. Hosp., South Bend, Ind., 1965-68; B, Ind. U., Indpls., 1977; M, Ind. Cen. U., 1983. Staff nurse Meml. Hosp., South Bend, 1968, Robert Long Hosp., Indpls., 1969-70; dir. legis. and labor rels. program Ind. State Nurses Assn., Indpls., 1969-71, asst. exec. dir. 1971-73, assoc. exec. dir. 1973-80, exec. dir., 1980-83; div. dir. Am. Nurses' Assn., Kansas City, Mo., 1983-87, dep. exec. dir., 1987—; adj. instr. U. Kans., Kansas City, 1986-90. Contbg. author Networking for Nurses, 1983. Mem. Gov.'s Commn. on Status of Women, Indpls., 1975, Gov.'s Council on Sports Medicine, Indpls., 1980-82; mentor Purdue U., Lafayette, Ind., 1974-83, Avila Coll., Kansas City, Mo., 1986; 2d v.p. Spay-Neuter Services, Inc., Indpls.; mem. adv. group Nat. Disaster Med. System, Washington, 1985. Fellow Am. Soc. Assn. Execs. (cert. 1989); mem. ANA, Am. Mgmt. Assn., sigma Theta Tau, Epsilon Sigma Alpha. Avocations: swimming, reading, golf. Office: ANA 600 Maryland Ave SW Ste 100W Washington DC 20024-2520

SHINN, RICHARD RANDOLPH, former insurance executive, former stock exchange executive; b. Lakewood, N.J., Jan. 7, 1918; s. Clayton Randolph and Carrie (McGravey) S.; m. Mary Helen Shea, Nov. 8, 1941; children: Kathleen, Patricia, John; m. Marion Berenson Weitman, Nov. 30, 1985. B.S., Rider Coll., 1938. C.L.U., 1949. With Met. Life Ins. Co., 1939-83, 2d v.p., 1955-63, v.p., 1963-64, sr. v.p., 1964-66, exec. v.p., 1966-68, sr. exec. v.p., 1968- 69, pres., dir., 1969-83, chief exec. officer, 1973-83, chmn., 1980-83, ret., 1983; exec. vice chmn. NYSE, N.Y.C., 1986-91; chmn. Olympia & York USA, 1993; bd. dirs. Union Tex. Petroleum Co., Grey Advt. Bd. dirs. Lincoln Ctr. for the Performing Arts, Inc.; mem. Cardinal's Com. for the Laity. Mem. Met. Opera Assn., Knights of Malta. Clubs: The Blind Brook (Port Chester, N.Y.); Round Hill (Greenwich, Conn.); Riverside Yacht; Sky Club, Links (N.Y.C.); Gulfstream Golf (Fla.), Delray Yacht Club (Fla.). Home: 136 Parsonage Rd Greenwich CT 06830-3943 Office: MetLife Bldg 200 Park Ave Ste 5700 New York NY 10166-0005

SHINNAR, REUEL, chemical engineering educator, industrial consultant; b. Vienna, Austria, Sept. 15, 1923; came to U.S., 1962; s. Abraham Emil and Rosa (Storch) Bardfeld; m. Miryam Halpern, June 22, 1948; children—Shlomo, Meir. Diploma in Chem. Engring., Technion, Haifa, Israel, 1945, M.Sc. in Chem. Engring., 1954; Dr. Engring. Sci., Columbia U., 1957. Various position in chem. engring. Israel, 1945-58; adj. assoc. prof. Technion, Haifa, Israel, 1958-62; visiting research fellow Guggenheim Labs., Princeton (N.J.) U., 1962-64; prof. chem. engring. CCNY, 1964—, disting. prof., 1979—; Pinhas Naor lectr. Technion U., 1974; Wilhelm Meml. lectr. Princeton U., 1985, Kelly lectr. Purdue U., 1991; cons. to various oil and chem. cos. Contbr. numerous articles to profl. jours.; patentee in field. Fellow AICE (Founders award 1992, Alpha Chi Sigma award 1979), N.Y. Acad. Scis.; mem. AIAA, Am. Chem. Soc., Nat. Acad. Engring. Office: City Coll NY Dept Chem Engring 140th St and Convent Ave New York NY 10031

SHINNAR, SHLOMO, child neurologist, educator; b. Haifa, Israel, Nov. 11, 1950; s. Reuel and Miryam (Halpern) S.; m. Shoshana Ellen Cohen, Aug. 11, 1974; children: Ora Rivka, Aviva Batya, Avraham Ever. BA in Physics summa cum laude, Columbia Coll., 1971; PhD, Albert Einstein Coll. Medicine, 1977, MD, 1978. Diplomate Am. Bd. Pediatrics, Am. Bd. Psychiatry and Neurology. Intern, asst. resident in pediatrics, fellow Johns

Hopkins Hosp., Balt., 1978-80, asst. resident, resident in neurology, fellow, 1980-83; from asst. prof. neurology and pediatrics to prof. neurology and pediatrics Albert Einstein Coll. Medicine, Bronx, 1983—; asst. attending in neurology and pediatrics Albert Einstein Coll. Medicine, Bronx, N.Y., 1983—; assoc. attending in neurology and pediatrics Montefiore Med. Ctr., Bronx Mcpl. Hosp. Ctr., North Ctrl. Bronx. Hosp., 1989—; dir. CERC Seizure Clinic R.F. Kennedy Ctr., Bronx, 1983—; co-dir. Epilepsy Mgmt. Ctr. Montefiore Med. Ctr. Albert Einstein Coll. Medicine, Bronx, 1983-86, dir., 1986—; mem. adv. bd. Epilepsy Inst., N.Y.C., 1984—, instnl. rev. bd. protection of human subjects Montefiore Med. Ctr., Bronx, 1985—, vice-chmn., 1989—; adj. rsch. scientist Gertrude Sergievsky Ctr. Columbia Coll. Physicians and Surgeons, N.Y.C., 1985—, Sergievsky scholar, 1988—; cons. in field. Field editor (jour.) Epilepsy Advances, 1987-93; mem. founding editl. bd. (jour.) The Neurologist, 1993—; mem. editl. bd. Epilepsia, 1994—; conbtr. articles to profl. jours. N.Y. State Regents scholar, 1967-71; Martin and Emily L. Fisher fellow, 1991—. Fellow Am. Acad. Pediatrics; mem. Am. Epilepsy Soc. (profl. adv. bd., ednl. affairs com. so. N.Y. chpt. 1991—, chmn. childhood onset epilepsy com. 1993—, councillor 1992—, Rsch. Recognition award 1989), Am. Acad. Neurology, Child Neurology Soc., Eastern EEG Soc., Internat. Child Neurology Soc., Nat. Assn. Epilepsy Ctrs., Soc. for Pediatric Rsch., Am. Neurol. Assn. Office: Montefiore Med Ctr 111 E 210th St Bronx NY 10467-2401

SHINNERS, STANLEY MARVIN, electrical engineer; b. N.Y.C., May 9, 1933; s. Earl and Molly (Planter) S.; m. Doris Pinsker, Aug. 4, 1956; children: Sharon Rose Cooper, Walter Jay, Daniel Lawrence. BEE, CCNY, 1954; MS in Elect. Engring., Columbia U., 1959. Equipment engr. Western Electric Co., N.Y.C., 1953-54; staff engr. electronics div. Otis Elevator Co., Bklyn., 1954-56; project engr. Consol. Avionics Corp., Westbury, N.Y., 1956-58; sr. rsch. sect. head Unisys Corp. (name formerly Sperry Corp.), Great Neck, N.Y., 1958—; adj. prof. engring. The Cooper Union, N.Y.C., 1966—, N.Y. Inst. Tech., Old Westbury, N.Y., 1972-92, Poly. Inst. Bklyn., 1959-72. Author: Control System Design, 1964, Techniques of Systems Engineering, 1967, A Guide to Systems Engineering and Management, 1976, Modern Control System Theory and Application, 1978, Modern Control System Theory and Design, 1992. Recipient Career Achievement medal CCNY Alumni Assn., 1980. Fellow IEEE; mem. Am. Soc. for Engring. Edn., Eta Kappa Nu, Tau Beta Pi. Home: 28 Sagamore Way N Jericho NY 11753-2358

SHINOMIYA, YAEKO, librarian; b. San Francisco, Apr. 15, 1936; d. Masao and Toshiko (Mukai) Iwawaki; m. Kazuichi Shinomiya, Dec. 20, 1958; children: Coco, Ken C. BA, U. Calif. Berkeley, 1957, MLS, 1960. Tchr. San Francisco Unified Sch. Dist., 1957-59; libr. Contra Costa County Library, Pleasant Hill, Calif., 1960-63, Solano County Library, Vallejo, Calif., 1973-79; asst. libr. The Tribune, Oakland, Calif., 1979-83, chief libr., 1983—. Named. Calif. Congress PTA's children's libr. fellow, 1959. Mem. Spl. Libr. Assn., Phi Beta Kappa. Office: The Tribune 409 13th St Oakland CA 94612-2637

SHINOZUKA, MASANOBU, civil engineer, educator; b. Tokyo, Dec. 23, 1930; s. Akira and Kiyo S.; came to U.S., 1957, naturalized, 1971; B.S., Kyoto (Japan) U., 1953, M.S., 1955; Ph.D., Columbia U., 1960; m. Fujiko Sakamoto, Oct. 25, 1954; children—Rei, Naomi, Megumi. Rsch. asst. civil engring. Columbia U., N.Y.C., 1958-61, asst. prof., 1961-65, assoc. prof., 1965-69, prof., 1969-88, Renwick prof., 1977-88; prof. Princeton U., 1988—, Sollenberger prof. civil engring., 1989—, on leave 1990—; dir. Nat. Ctr. for Earthquake Engring. Rsch., SUNY, Buffalo, 1990—, vis. Capen prof. structural engring., dept. civil engring., 1990—; vis. scholar N.C. State U., Raleigh, 1967-68; pres. Modern Analysis Inc., Princeton, N.J., 1972—; co-chmn. 2d Internat. Conf. on Structural Safety and Reliability, 1978, 3d, 1981, 4th, 1985, 5th, 1989, also co-editor Proc. of 2d, 3d and 4th confs.; mem. steering com. U.S. Panel on Structural Control Rsch., 1990—; cons. in field. Editor: Probabilistic Engineering Mechanics, 1987—. Recipient Wessex Inst. Tech. medal, 1991; NSF grantee, 1968—. Mem. NAE, ASCE (Walter L. Huber prize 1972; State-of-the-Art of Civil Engring. award 1973, Alfred M. Freudenthal medal 1978, Nathan M. Newmark medal 1985, Moisseiff award, 1988, C. Martin Duke award 1991), ASME, AIAA, Japan Soc. Civil Engrs., Sigma Xi. Editor: Reliability Approach in Structural Engineering, 1975; co-editor Proc. ASCE Symposium on Probabilistic Methods in Structural Engring., 1981. Home: 15 Andrews Ln Princeton NJ 08540 Office: Princeton U E-209 Engineering Quad Princeton NJ 08544

SHIPLER, DAVID KARR, journalist, correspondent, author; b. Orange, N.J., Dec. 3, 1942; s. Guy Emery Jr. and Eleanor (Karr) S.; m. Deborah S. Isaacs, Sept. 17, 1966; children: Jonathan Robert, Laura Karr, Michael Edmund. AB, Dartmouth Coll., 1964; LittD (hon.), Middlebury Coll., 1988, Glassboro (N.J.) State Coll., 1988; AM (hon.), Dartmouth Coll., 1994. News clk. N.Y. Times, 1966-67, news summary writer, 1968, reporter met. staff, 1968-73, fgn. corr. Saigon bur., 1973-75, fgn. corr. Moscow Bur., 1975—, bur. chief Moscow Bur., 1977-79, chief Jerusalem bur., 1979-84, corr. Washington bur., 1985-87, chief diplomatic corr., 1987-88; sr. assoc. Carnegie Endowment for Internat. Peace, Washington, 1988-90; guest scholar Brookings Instn., 1984-85; adj. prof. Am. U. Sch. Internat. Svc., Washington, 1990; Ferris prof. journalism and pub. affairs, Princeton U., 1990-91; Woodrow Wilson vis. fellow, 1990—. Author: Russia: Broken Idols, Solemn Dreams, 1983 (Overseas Press Club award); author: Arab and Jew: Wounded Spirits in a Promised Land, 1986 (Pulitzer Prize for General Non-fiction, 1987), exec. producer, prin. writer, narrator documentary film made from book, 1989 (Alfred DuPont-Columbia U. award for Broadcast Journalism, 1990); conbtr. articles to New Yorker and other nat. mags. Mem. Dartmouth Coll. Bd. Trustees. With USNR, 1964-66. Recipient award for disting. reporting Soc. Silurians, 1971; award for disting. pub. affairs reporting Am. Polit. Scis. Assn., 1971; award N.Y. chpt. Sigma Delta Chi, 1973; co-recipient George Polk award, 1982. Mem. Human Rights Watch Middle East (adv. com.). Office: 4005 Thornapple St Bethesda MD 20815-5037 *I have been governed professionally by the conviction that an open society needs open examination of itself to survive. Defining problems, inspecting blemishes, probing wounds, and exposing injustice are the required pastimes of a free people. Nothing intelligent can come from ignorance. If information does not guarantee wisdom, it is at least a prerequisite, for the only wise course is through knowledge. To write about current affairs, then, is to play a small role in a great endeavor. It is to measure one's own performance continually against the highest standards of honesty, fairness, thoroughness, intelligence, to search every day for a bit of truth, then share it. These are the ingredients of happiness, for such a job involves a life of constant learning, perpetual self-education. It keeps a man whole.*

SHIPLEY, DAVID ELLIOTT, university dean, lawyer; b. Urbana, Ill., Oct. 3, 1950; s. James Ross and Dorothy Jean (Elliott) S.; m. Virginia Florence Coleman, May 24, 1980; 1 child, Shannon C. BA, Oberlin Coll., 1972; JD, U. Chgo., 1975. Bar: R.I. 1975. Assoc. Tillinghast, Collins & Graham, Providence, 1975-77; asst. prof. U. S.C. Sch. Law, Columbia, 1977-81, assoc. prof., 1981-85, prof., 1985-90, assoc. dean, 1989-90; dean U. Miss. Sch. Law, University, 1990-93, U. Ky. Coll. Law, Lexington, 1993—; vis. prof. Coll. William and Mary, Williamsburg, Va., 1983-84, Ohio State U. Coll. Law, Columbus, 1986-87. Author: South Carolina Administrative Law, 1983, 2d edit., 1989; co-author Copyright Law, 1992. Pres. Shandon Neighborhood Assn., Columbia, 1988-90. Named Prof. of Yr., U. S.C. Sch. Law, 1990, faculty scholar, 1989-90. Mem. ABA, R.I. Bar Assn., S.C. Bar Assn. (assoc.). Methodist. Avocations: running, yardwork, gardening, reading. Home: 827 Lakeshore Dr Lexington KY 40502-3125 Office: U Ky Coll Law Lexington KY 40506-0048

SHIPLEY, L. PARKS, JR., banker; b. Orange, N.J., Aug. 2, 1931; s. L. Parks and Emily Catherine (Herzog) S.; m. Micheline Genevieve Oltramare, Apr. 2, 1966; children—Christiane, Daniel, Alix. B.A., Yale U., 1953. Vol. Moral ReArmament, Europe, Africa, S.Am., 1954-64; participant in founding Up With People Inc., 1964-69; from internat. banking officer to v.p. Marine Midland Bank, N.Y.C., 1969-76; v.p. Irving Trust Co. N.Y.C., 1976-84, exec. v.p., 1984-89; exec. v.p. Bank of N.Y., N.Y.C., 1989-90; pres. Ultramar Assoc., Inc., N.Y.C., 1990-91, Ultramar Group, Inc., 1991-92; U.S. rep., bd. advisor Banco Credito Argentino; pres. Shipley Assocs.; bd. dirs. The Keimei Fund for Internat. Edn. Inc. Trustee Young Life, 1991; mem. adv. bd. Ams. Soc. Corp. Program. Mem. Brazilian Am. C. of C., Yale

Club, Baltusrol Golf Club, Nagelvoort County Adv. Bd. Home: 77 Bellevue Ave Summit NJ 07901-2007 Office: 630 Fifth Ave Ste 3170 New York NY 10111

SHIPLEY, LUCIA HELENE, retired chemical company executive; b. Boston, Oct. 26, 1920; d. Harry Jacob and Helen Merrill (Dillingham) Farrington; m. Charles Raymond Shipley, Oct. 11, 1941; children: Helen Merrill, Richard Charles. Student, Smith Coll., 1938-41. Chief exec. officer, treas. Shipley Co. Inc., Newton, Mass., 1957-92, also bd. dirs. Patentee for immersion tin, electroless copper. Recipient Winthrop Sears award Chem. Industry Assn., 1985, Semi award Semicon West, 1990. Mem. Garden Club (pres. 1954-56). Republican. Congregationalist. Avocations: gardening, shell collecting, dogs, cage birds.

SHIPLEY, MARILYN ELIZABETH, school system administrator; b. Cleve., May 19, 1942; d. Melvin James and Ethel Maude (Paddon) Bramley; m. Charles Hudson Shipley, Oct. 1, 1977. BA in Elem. Edn., Ariz. State U., 1965, MA in Elem. Edn., 1970; MS in Sch. Adminstrn., Calif. State U., 1975; EdD in Ednl. Mgmt., U. LaVerne, 1992. Elem. tchr. Garden Grove (Calif.) Unified Sch. Dist., 1965-69; elem. substitute tchr. Scottsdale (Ariz.) Pub. Sch., 1969-70; program asst. ESEA Title III project prolexia Riverside (Calif.) County Office Edn., 1970-75, coord. curriculum and instrn., 1975-89, coord./prin. spl. edn., 1987-89, coord./prin. pregnant minor-sch. age parents, 1989-92, coord. curriculum and staff devel., 1992—; cons. in field, 1973-89. Co-author: Lexilogs, Lexileits, 1974, also student study folders. Mem. Assn. Calif. Curriculum Developers, Assn. Calif. Sch. Adminstrs., Western Riverside County Assn. Sch. Mgrs. (bd. reps. 1989-91, pres. 1992—), Calif. Alliance Concerned With Sch. Age Parents (sec. 1992, state bd. dirs.). Republican. Methodist. Avocations: quilting, swimming, writing. Home: 3936 Mescale Rd Riverside CA 92504

SHIPLEY, SAMUEL LYNN, advertising and public relations executive; b. Marlborough, Mass., Nov. 14, 1929; s. Clifford Lynn and Esther (Jacobs) S.; m. Sue Finucan, Sept. 5, 1955; children—Jeffrey Lynn, Beth Ann, Amy. Student, Charles Morris Price Sch. Advt. and Journalism, U. N.H. 1948-50. Exec. dir. Democratic Party N.H., 1953-56; pres., chmn. Shipley Assos., Inc., Wilmington, Del., 1962—, internat. Toy Shows, Inc., 1977—; pres. Cable TV Advt. Inc., 1982—; dir. Del. Devel. Dept., Dover, 1965-69. Del. U.S. Constl. Council of Thirteen Original States, 1976—; nominee for U.S. Congress, 1976; pub. relations dir. Del. Democratic Com., 1964-68; chmn. Del. Dem. Com., 1982-90; bd. dirs. Blood Bank of Del.; pres. Del. Heritage Found., 1980—; bd. trustees Grand Opera House; former chair Dem. State Com. Served with U.S. Army, 1951-53. Recipient Freedoms Found. Honor medal, 1966, Outstanding Grad. award Charles Morris Price Sch., 1974. Mem. Am. Advt. Fedn., Wilmington Advt. Club. Clubs: Mason. (Wilmington), Masonic of Del. (Wilmington). Home: 1196 Paper Mill Rd Newark DE 19711-2924 Office: 1300 Pennsylvania Ave Wilmington DE 19806-4311 *The ingredients for success are good health, average intelligence, a giving spirit, positive thinking, good imagination, self-discipline, hard work, and persistence.*

SHIPLEY, TONY L(EE), software company executive; b. Elizabethton, Tenn., July 19, 1946; s. James A. and Edith J. (Crowder) S.; m. Lynda Anne Jenkins, Nov. 19, 1971; children: Blake Alan, Sarah Robyn. BS in Indsl. Engring., U. Tenn., 1969; MBA, U. Cin., 1975. Indsl. engr. Monsanto Co., Pensacola, Fla., 1969-72; mktg. mgr. SDRC, Cin., 1972-76; v.p. sales and mktg. Anatrol Corp., Cin., 1977-81; pres. Entek Sci. Corp., Cin., 1981—. Named Small Bus. Person of Yr., Greater Cin. C. of C., 1994. Mem. ASME (mem. exec. com.), Soc. Automotive Engrs., Vibration Inst. Republican. Club: Terrace Park (Ohio) Country. Avocations: golf, family activities. Home: 7 Laurelwood Milford OH 45150-9748 Office: Entek Sci Corp 4480 Lake Forest Dr Ste 316 Cincinnati OH 45242-3753

SHIPLEY, VERGIL ALAN, political science educator; b. Amber, Okla., June 25, 1922; s. Guy and Ida Jean (Grant) S.; m. Zannie May Manning, May 3, 1947; children—Douglass Manning, John Grant. B.A., U. Okla., 1947, M.A., 1948; postgrad., U. Tex., 1947; Ph.D., London (Eng.) Sch. Econs., 1950. Assoc. prof. poli. sci. Wichita State U., 1950-56; asst. prof. govt. U. Miami, Coral Gables, Fla., 1957-61; assoc. prof. U. Miami, 1962-68, prof. politics and pub. affairs, 1968-89, prof. emeritus, 1989—, chmn. dept., 1970-77; acting dean Sch. Bus. Adminstrs., 1968-69; Polit. election analyst WTVJ-CBS, 1962-84; cons. to study commnn. on local govt., 1971-72. Served to capt. AUS, 1942-46, ETO. Mem. Am. Polit. Sci. Assn., Am. Soc. Pub. Adminstrn., Phi Beta Kappa, Phi Eta Sigma, Pi Sigma Alpha, Beta Gamma Sigma (pres. U. Miami chpt. 1969), Delta Sigma Pi (faculty adviser 1968-76). Democrat. Home: 1127 Alberca St Miami FL 33134-2446 Office: U Miami Dept Politics Pub Affa Coral Gables FL 33124

SHIPLEY, WALTER VINCENT, banker; b. Newark, Nov. 2, 1935; s. L. Parks and Emily (Herzog) S.; m. Judith Ann Lyman, Sept. 14, 1957; children: Barbara, Allison, Pamela, Dorothy, John. Student, Williams Coll., 1954-56; BS, NYU, 1961. With Chem. Bank, N.Y.C., 1956—, pres., 1982-83, chmn. bd., 1983-91, pres., 1992-93, chmn., CEO, 1994—; Bd. dirs. Champion Internat. Corp., NYNEX Corp., Reader's Digest Assn., Inc. Bd. dirs. Lincoln Ctr. for Performing Arts Inc., Goodwill Industries Greater N.Y. Inc., United Way Am., United Way Tri-State; trustee NYU. Mem. The Bus. Coun., Bus Roundtable, Coun. Fgn. Rels., Trilateral Commn., Links, Augusta Nat. Golf Club, Baltusrol Golf Club (Springfield, N.J.). Office: Chem Banking Corp 270 Park Ave New York NY 10017-2036

SHIPMAN, CHARLES WILLIAM, chemical engineer; b. Phillipsburgh, N.J., Aug. 29, 1924; s. George Funk and Elizabeth (Johnston) S.; m. Louise Jean Hendrickson, Aug. 31, 1946; children—Nancy Ruth, Jane Louise, Robert Walter George. SB, MIT, 1948, SM, 1949, ScD, 1952. Instr. chem. engring. MIT, 1949-50, research assoc., 1955-58; asst. prof. U. Del., 1952-55; mem. faculty Worcester (Mass.) Poly. Inst., 1958-74, prof. chem. engring., 1964-74, dean grad. studies, 1971-74; engr. Cabot Corp., Billerica, Mass., 1974-87; mgr. Carbon Black R/D, 1980-86; cons., 1953-74, 1987—; bd. dirs. Knox Dist. Housing, Bar Harbor, Maine, 1988—, MDI Helpers, Bar Harbor, 1988-90, treas. 1989-90. Contbr. articles to profl. jours. Served with USMCR, 1944-46. Mem. Combustion Inst. (recipient Silver Combustion medal 1964, bd. dirs. 1978-90), Am. Chem. Soc., Am. Inst. Chem. Engrs., Sigma Xi, Alpha Chi Sigma, Chi Phi. Home and Office: PO Box 32 Prospect Harbor ME 04669-0032

SHIPMAN, DAVID NORVAL, healthcare consultant; b. Henderson, Tex., Aug. 1, 1939; s. Norval Stewart Shipman and Dixie Juinita (VanNastrum) Retherford; m. Helen Morgan Suggs, July 1, 1960; children: Jeffrey Brian, Kimberly Kaye. Student, So. Ill. U., 1958-59, Okla. Bapt. U., 1959-61. Cert. Fin. Planner, CLU. Agt. Mutual Benefit Life Ins. Co., Oklahoma City, 1960-68; ptnr. Med. Cons. Inc., Oklahoma City, 1968-70; supr. Mutual Benefit Life Ins. Co., Oklahoma City, 1970-72; gen. agt. Mutual Benefit Life Ins. Co., Wichita, Kans., 1972-79; v.p. Mutual Benefit Life Ins. Co., Kansas City, Mo., 1979-83; pres. Fin. Group Inc., Kansas City, 1983-84; cons. Physicians Fin. Analysis Corp. (now Integrated Strategies), Kansas City, 1984—; charter mem. practice support initiative Am. Acad. Family Practice; mem. doctor's adv. network AMA. Contbr. articles to profl. jours. Bd. dirs. Young Dems. Oklahoma City, 1959-62, River Festival, Wichita, 1973-79, founding dir. Wichita Wagonmasters, 1975-79, Fellowship Christian Athletes, Wichita, 1976-79, Historic Wichita Cowtown, 1977-79. Mem. Am. Soc. CLU's, Internat. Assn. Fin. Planning, Inst. Cert. Fin. Planners, Nat. Assn. Securities Dealers (registered rep. 1969—), Nat. Assn. Life Underwriters, Gen. Agts. and Mgrs. Assn. (pres., bd. dirs. 1973-80), Profl. Assn. Health Care Office Mgrs., Jaycees (bd. dirs. 1961-65), C. of C., Leawood Country Club. Republican. Baptist. Avocations: horses, tennis, fishing. Home: 8914 Cedar Dr Shawnee Mission KS 66207-2216 Office: 10100 Sante Fe Ste 101 Overland Park KS 66212

SHIPMAN, LYNN KAREN, lawyer; b. N.Y.C., Oct. 21, 1950; d. Charles B. and Henrietta J. (Karsh) S.; m. Lawrence J. Meyer, Aug. 25, 1975; children: Michael Shipman-Meyer, Bethany Shipman-Meyer. BA, SUNY, Stony Brook, 1972; JD, St. John's U., 1975; LLM in Taxation, NYU, 1979. Bar: N.J. 1977, Pa. 1980, N.Y. 1980, U.S. Dist. N.J. 1977, U.S. Tax Ct. 1980. Sr. tax editor Prentice-Hall, Inc., Englewood Cliffs, N.J., 1975-79; assoc. Krekstein, Wolfson & Krekstein, P.C., Phila., 1979-86, shareholder, officer, 1986-92, also bd. dirs.; of counsel LaBrum & Doak, Phila., 1993—;

lectr. Fed. Tax Conf., 1986, 29th Ann. Wharton Sch. Tax Conf., 1989; discussion leader, lectr. CPA socs., Mass., 1985-90, Va., 1988, Fla., 1988, 90, 91, Ky., 1990, Ill., 1991, N.C., 1991, AICPA, 1989. Converted AICPA course Coping with Problems in Pensions and Profit Sharing Plans to home study course. Trustee Tamarac Lakes Assn. Recipient Outstanding Instr. award Pa. Inst. CPAs for AICPA courses taught 1988-89. Mem. ABA (com. affiliated corp. and related entities tax sect. 1981-90), Phila. Bar Assn. (lectr. tax lecture series 1988, com. on employee benefits tax sect.). Office: LaBrum & Doak 1818 Market St Ste 2900 Philadelphia PA 19103-3629

SHIPP, ROGER LEE, finance company executive; b. Waverly, Iowa, July 7, 1948; s. Leo Ralph and Edna Ida (Leisinger) S.; m. Theresa Ann Kruth, Sept. 12, 1970; children—Gregory, Laura. B.A., Wartburg Coll., 1970; M.B.A., Ind. U., 1974. C.P.A., Ind. Sr. acct. Assocs. Fin. Services, South Bend, Ind., 1970-72; asst. comptroller Assocs. Capital Services, South Bend, Ind., 1972-75; area comptroller ITT Aetna Fin., Dallas, 1975-77; mgr. ops. analysis ITT Fin. Services, N.Y.C., 1977-80; sr. v.p., comptroller ITT Consumer Fin. Corp., Mpls., 1980—. Mem. Am. Inst. C.P.A.s, Fin. Execs. Inst. Republican. Roman Catholic. Avocation: boating. Home: 14251 Wedgeway Ct Eden Prairie MN 55346-3021 Office: ITT Consumer Fin Corp 605 Highway 169 N Minneapolis MN 55441-6456

SHIPP, TRAVIS, education educator, author; b. Waycross, Ga., Jan. 10, 1940; s. Travis and Pernia (Ellis) S.; m. Barbara Diane Blake, Oct. 9, 1964 (div. Mar 1980). BS in Engring., Auburn U., Auburn, Ala., 1962, MBA, 1971; EdD, U. Ga., 1974. Registered profl. engr. Dean Auburn U., Montgomery, Ala., 1971-72; prof. Marshall U., Huntington, Ind., 1974-77, Ind. U., Bloomington, 1977—; pres. Waycross Corp., Ga., 1973—; v.p. EAP, Inc., Ind., 1981-84. Author 3 non-fiction books, 9 novels, 12 short stories and over 40 articles. Served to maj. U.S. Army, 1962-70, Vietnam. Decorated DSC, Silver Star with 1 bronze oak leaf cluster, Bronze Star with V Device with 2 bronze oak leaves, Purple Heart with silver oak leaf cluster, DFC with 2 bronze oak leaves. Mem. Am. Assn. Adult and Continuing Edn. (controller 1979-81), Am. Soc. Tng. and Devel. CLub: Columbia. Avocation: sailing. Office: Ind U Sch Edn Social Work Bur Studies Adult Edn 902 W N Y Ave Indianapolis IN 46223

SHIPPEY, LYN, reading center director; b. Childress, Tex., Mar. 6, 1927; d. Robert Coke and Alta (Timmons) Elliott; m. James George Shippey, Mar. 29, 1947; children: James Robert, Deborah Shippey Meyer, Marilyn Shippey Buron. BS, U. Corpus Christi, 1963; MA in Edn., San Diego State U., 1977; EdD, U. San Diego, 1993. Cert. tchr., reading specialist, tchr. of learning handicapped, Calif. Substitute tchr. Dept. Edn., Guam, 1958-61; tchr. counselor Robstown Ind. Sch. Dist., Tex., 1964-65; elem. tchr. Cupertino Union Sch. Dist., Calif., 1965-68, tchr., secondary, 1968-71; dir. PIRK Reading Center, Poway, Calif., 1973—; cons., workshop presenter PIRK Reading Programs, Calif., Tex., 1974—. Author: Perceptual Integration Reading Kits, 1971, PIRK Reading Program, 1977, rev. 1987. Mem. Coun. for Exceptional Children, Alcala Soc. U. San Diego (scholar), Orton Dyslexia Soc., Learning Disabilities Assn., Coun. for Learning Disabilities. Avocations: photography, gardening, research. Office: PIRK Reading Center 16957 Cloudcroft Dr Poway CA 92064-1306

SHIPPEY, SANDRA LEE, lawyer; b. Casper, Wyo., June 24, 1957; d. Virgil Carr and Doris Louise (Conklin) McC.; m. Ojars Herberts Ozols, Sept. 2, 1978 (div.); children: Michael Ojars, Sara Ann, Brian Christopher; m. James Robert Shippey, Jan. 13, 1991. BA with distinction, U. Colo., 1978; JD magna cum laude, Boston U., 1982. Bar: Colo. 1982, U.S. Dist. Ct. Colo. 1985. Assoc. Cohen, Brame & Smith, Denver, 1983-84, Parcel, Meyer, Schwartz, Ruttum & Mauro, Denver, 1984-85, Mayer, Brown & Platt, Denver, 1985-87; counsel western ops. GE Capital Corp., San Diego, 1987-94; assoc. Page, Polin, Busch & Boatwright, San Diego, 1994—. Active Pop Warner football and cheerleading. Mem. Phi Beta Kappa, Phi Delta Phi. Republican. Mem. Ch. of Christ. Avocations: tennis, photography. Home: 11878 Glenhope Rd San Diego CA 92128-5002 Office: Page Polin Busch & Boatwright 350 W Ash St #900 San Diego CA 92101

SHIPTON, HAROLD WILLIAM, biomedical engineering educator, researcher; b. Birmingham, Eng., Sept. 29, 1920; came to U.S., 1957; Student, Shrewsbury (Eng.) Tech. Coll., 1938. Engr. Burden Neurol. Inst., Bristol, Eng., 1946-57; asst. prof. biomed. engring. U. Iowa, Iowa City, 1957-59, prof., 1959-79; prof. biomed. engring. Washington U., St. Louis, 1979-89, prof. emeritus, 1989—, chmn. dept., 1986-89, chmn. pro tem dept. elec. engring., 1986-87; mem. study sect. NIH, 1965-70. Assoc. editor Jour. EEG and Clin. Neurophysiology; contbr. articles to profl. jours. Served with RAAF, 1940-47. Grantee NIH, 1968-76. Fellow Am. EEG Soc. (hon.); mem. The EEG Soc. U.K. (hon.), Cen. Assn. EEG (pres. 1975). Unitarian. Avocation: literature; lic. pilot. Home: 4 N Kingshighway Blvd Saint Louis MO 63108-1358 Office: Washington U Dept of Biomed Engring 1 Brookings Dr Saint Louis MO 63130

SHIRA, ROBERT BRUCE, university administrator, oral surgery educator; b. Butler, Pa., Dec. 2, 1910; s. Thomas Plummer and Erla (Brown) S.; m. Anne Eileen Anderson, Mar. 27, 1933; children: Sharon Lu, Mary Ann, Linda Kay. Student, Bartlesville (Okla.) Jr. Coll., 1927-28; D.D.S., U. Mo., Kansas City, 1932; D.Sc., Georgetown U., 1976, Tufts U., 1979, U. Mo., Kansas City, 1992, U. Detroit, 1987. Diplomate: Am. Bd. Oral and Maxillofacial Surgery (pres. 1974-75). Pvt. practice dentistry Pawhuska, Okla., 1932-38; commd. 1st lt., Dental Corps U.S. Army, 1938, advanced through grades to maj. gen., 1967; chief oral surgery Walter Reed Gen. Hosp., 1954-64; dir. dental activities Walter Reed Army Med. Center, 1966-67; dental surgeon Europe, 1964-66; asst. surgeon gen., chief Army Dental Corps, 1967-71; ret., 1971; prof. oral surgery Tufts U., Boston, 1971-93; dean Sch. Dental Medicine, Tufts U., Boston, 1972-78; sr. v.p., provost Tufts U., Boston, 1979-82, asst. to pres., 1982-93; vis. prof. U. of Pacific, 1954-71, U. Pa., 1956-71; professional lectr. Georgetown U., 1955-71. Contbr.: chpts. Textbook of Oral Surgery, 1973, Management of Office Emergencies, 1979, Improving Dental Practice through Preventive Measures, 1965; contbr. articles to profl. jours. Decorated D.S.M., Legion of Merit with 2 oak leaf clusters, Army Commendation medal, Army Disting. Svc. medal, Army Disting. Svc. medal; recipient Sword of Hope award Am. Cancer Soc., 1959; named Man of Yr. U. Mo., Kansas City, 1960. Mem. ADA (pres. 1975-76, cons. Council on Therapeutics, Disting. Service award), Am. Assn. Oral and Maxillofacial Surgery (pres. 1965-66), Am. Acad. Oral Pathology. Republican. Presbyterian. Home: Ste 814 3310 N Leisure World Blvd Silver Spring MD 20906

SHIRAI, TAKESHI, physician; b. Tensin, Republic of China, May 14, 1928; s. Yasushi and Miyo S.; m. Katsuko Shirai, Aug. 6, 1962; children: Takamitsu Shirai, Ryoko Shirai. MD, Nippon Med. Coll., 1954; Dr.Med.Sci., Kyushu U., 1958. Med. diploma of Japan. Intern Kyushu U. Hosp., Fukuoka, 1954-55; resident Kyushu U Hosp., Fukuoka, 1955-58, clin. and rsch. asst., 1958-62, assoc., instr. of medicine, 1966-74; trainee in metabolism Dept. of Medicine, Coll. Med. U. of Vt., 1962-66; prof. of medicine Fukuoka Dental Coll., 1974-94; physician in chief Fukuoka Dental Coll. Hosp., 1974-94; dir. Libr. of Fukuoka Dental Coll., 1989-94; prof. emeritus, 1994—; prof. Seika Women's Jr. Coll., Fukuoka, 1994—; dir. rsch. Inst. Hara-Nurses Tng. Sch., Fukuoka, 1994—. Author: Medicine for Dentist, 1990; translator: The Kidney, 1987; contbr. articles to jours. including Minerva Nefrologica, Annals of Internal Medicine, Diabetologia. Mem. Japanese Soc. of Internal Medicine, Internat. Soc. of Nephrology, Japanese Soc. of Nephrology (disting. mem.), Japanese Soc. of Clin. Physiology (coun.), Sigma Xi. Home: Chuou-ku, 48-1-807 Josui Dori, Fukuoka 810, Japan Office: Seika Womens Jr Coll, 2-12-1 Minamihatiman-Cho, Hakata-Ku, Fukuoka 816, Japan Office: Hara Nurses Tng Sch, 6-40-7 Aoba Higahi-Ku, Fukuoka 813, Japan

SHIRBROUN, RICHARD ELMER, veterinarian, cattleman; b. Coon Rapids, Iowa, Oct. 22, 1929; s. Francis Clyde and Clara Mable (Bell) S.; m. Treva Margaret Teter (div.), Sept. 9, 1951; children: Randal Mark, Camille Leean, James Bradley; m. Wava Lynne Frank, Nov. 11, 1989. DVM, Iowa State U., 1952. Owner, vet. Shirbroun Vet. Med. Ctr., Coon Rapids, 1955—. Lt. USAF, 1952-55. Mem. AVMA (trustee 1982—), Am. Assn. Bovine Practitioners (bd. dirs. 1982—, Excellence Preventive Medicine award 1987), Am. Assn. Swine Practitioners, Iowa Vet. Med. Assn. (pres. 1981, Pres.'

award 1985), Soc. for Theriogenology, N.Am. Limousin Found. (founding mem. 1968), Nat. Cattlemen Assn., Iowa Cattlemen Assn., Am. Legion, Rotary (pres. Coon Rapids 1965). Republican. Methodist. Home and Office: Shirbroun Vet Med Ctr Route 3 Box 143 Coon Rapids IA 50058

SHIRE, DAVID LEE, composer; b. Buffalo, July 3, 1937; s. Irving Daniel and Esther Miriam (Sheinberg) S.; m. Talia Rose Coppola, Mar. 29, 1970 (div.); 1 child, Matthew Orlando; m. Didi Conn. Feb. 11, 1984; 1 child, Daniel Joshua. BA, Yale U., 1959. Film scores include The Conversation, 1974, The Taking of Pelham 1-2-3, 1974, Farewell, My Lovely, 1975, The Hindenburg, 1975, All the President's Men, 1977, Saturday Night Fever (adaptation and additional music), 1977, Norma Rae, 1979 (Acad. award for best original song It Goes Like It Goes), Only When I Laugh, 1981, The World According to Garp, 1982, Max Dugan Returns, 1983, 2010, 1984, Return to Oz, 1985, Short Circuit, 1986, 'Night, Mother, 1986, Vice Versa, 1988, Monkey Shines, 1988, Paris Trout, 1991, Bed and Breakfast, 1992, The Journey Inside (IMAX), 1993, One Night Stand, 1994; TV scores include Raid on Entebbe, 1977 (Emmy nomination), The Defection of Simas Kudirka, 1978 (Emmy nomination), Do You Remember Love?, 1985 (Emmy nomination), Promise, 1986, Echoes in the Darkness, 1987, The Women of Brewster Place, 1989, The Kennedys of Massachusetts, 1990 (Emmy nomination), Common Ground, 1990, Sarah Plain & Tall, 1991, Last Wish, 1992, Broadway Bound, 1992, Skylark, 1993, Remember, 1993, The Companion, 1994, My Brother's Keeper, 1995, Serving in Silence, 1995, The Heidi Chronicles, 1995, My Antonia, 1995, Reunion, 1995; theatre scores include The Sap of Life, 1961, Graham Crackers, 1962, The Unknown Soldier and His Wife, 1967, How Do You Do, I Love You, 1968, Love Match, 1970, Starting Here, Starting Now, 1977, Baby, 1983 (Tony nominee best mus. and best original score), Urban Blight, 1988, Closer Than Ever, 1989 (Outer Critics Circle award best off-Broadway musical and best score); composer Sonata for Cocktail Piano, 1965; recorded songs include Autumn, 1959, Starting Here, Starting Now, 1965, What About Today?, 1969, Manhattan Skyline, 1977, The Promise, 1978 (Acad. award nomination), It Goes Like It Goes, 1979 (Acad. award), With You I'm Born Again, 1979; albums include Saturday Night Fever, 1977 (Grammy award 1978), Starting Here, Starting Now, 1977 (Grammy nomination 1977), Baby, 1984, Return to Oz, 1985, Closer Than Ever, 1990, David Shire at The Movies, 1991. With Army N.G., 1960-66. Mem. Composers and Lyricists Guild Am., Am. Fedn. Musicians, Broadcast Music Inc., Acad. Motion Picture Arts and Scis., Nat. Acad. Rec. Arts and Scis., Nat. Acad. TV Arts and Scis. Jewish. Office: Savitsky Stain & Geibelson 1901 Ave Of The Stars Ste 1450 Los Angeles CA 90067

SHIRE, DONALD THOMAS, retired air products and chemicals executive, lawyer; b. Boston, Jan. 13, 1930; s. Thomas J. and Nellie M. S.; m. Anne Court Bither, Nov 21, 1953; children: Jennifer Anne, Andrew Carter, Daniel Orchard. B.S. in Bus. Adminstrn, Boston U., 1951, LL.B., 1953; postgrad., Harvard Bus. Sch., 1985. Atty. Air Products and Chems., Inc., 1957-64, sec., atty., 1964-75, sec., asst. gen. counsel, 1975-78, v.p. energy and materials, 1978-85, v.p. human resources, 1986-90, sr. v.p. human resources and adminstrn., 1990-91, sr. v.p. adminstrn., 1991-93; ret., 1993; also bd. dirs. Air Products and Chems., Inc.; chmn. Air Products Found., 1991-93; bd. dirs. Lehigh Valley 2000: A Bus. Edn. Partnership. Trustee Muhlenberg Coll., Lehigh Valley Hosp. Served to lt. USNR, 1954-57. Mem. Am. Arbitration Assn. Episcopalian. Home: 1310 N Main St Allentown PA 18104-2913 Office: Air Products and Chems Inc 7201 Hamilton Blvd Allentown PA 18195-1526

SHIRES, GEORGE THOMAS, surgeon, physician, educator; b. Waco, Tex., Nov. 22, 1925; s. George Thomas and Donna Mae (Smith) S.; m. Robbie Jo Martin, Nov. 27, 1948; children: Donna Blain, George Thomas III, Jo Ellen. MD, U. Tex., Dallas, 1948. Diplomate Am. Bd. Surgery (dir. 1968-74, chmn. 1972-74). Intern Mass. Meml. Hosp., Boston 1948-49; resident Parkland Meml. Hosp., Dallas 1950-53; mem. faculty U. Tex. Southwestern Med. Sch. at Dallas, 1953-74, assoc. prof. surgery, acting chmn. dept., 1960-61, prof. chmn. dept. 1961-74; surgeon in chief surg. services Parkland Meml. Hosp., 1960-74; prof., chmn. dept. surgery U. Wash. Sch. Medicine, Seattle, 1974-75; chief of service Harborview Med. Center, Seattle, Univ. Hosp., Seattle, 1974-75; chmn. dept. surgery N.Y. Hosp.-Cornell Univ. Med. Coll., 1975-91; dean and provost for med. affairs Cornell U. Med. Coll., 1987-91; prof., chmn. surgery Tex. Tech U., Lubbock, 1991-95; cons. to Surgeon Gen., Nat. Inst. Gen. Med. Sci., 1965—, Surgeon Gen. Army, 1965-75, Jamaica Hosp., 1978-91; mem. com. metabolism and trauma Nat. Acad. Sci./NRC, 1964-71, com. trauma, 1964-71; mem. rsch. program evaluation com., reviewer clin. investigation applications career devel. program VA, 1972-76; mem. gen. med. rsch. program projects com. NIH, 1965-69; mem. Surgery A study sect., 1970-74, chmn., 1976-78; mem. Nat. Adv. Gen. Med. Scis. Coun., 1980-84; cons. editorial bd. Jour. Trauma, 1968—. Mem. editl. bd. Year Book Med. Publs., 1970-92, Annals of Surgery, 1972—, Surg. Techniques Illustrated: An International Comparative Text, 1974-75, Am. Jour. Surgery, 1968—, Contemporary Surgery, 1973-89; assoc. editor-in-chief Infections in Surgery, 1981; mem. editl. coun. Jour. Clin. Surgery, 1980-82; editor Surgery, Gynecology and Obstetrics, 1982-93. Lt. M.C. USNR, 1949-50, 53-55. Life Ins. Med. Rsch. fellow, 1947. Mem. ACS (bd. regents 1971-82, chmn. bd. regents 1978-80, pres. 1981-82), AMA, Dallas Soc. Gen. Surgeons (pres.-elect, pres. 1972-74), Am. Assn. Surgery Trauma, Am. Surg. Assn. (sec. 1969-74, pres. 1980), Digestive Disease Found. (founding mem.), Halsted Soc., Internat. Soc. Burn Injuries, Internat. Surg. Soc. (sec. 1978-81, v.p. 1982-83, pres. U.S. chpt. 1984-85), Pan-Am. Med. Assn. (surgery council 1971—), Pan Pacific Surg. Assn., Soc. Clin. Surgery, Soc. Surgical Alimentary Tract, Soc. Surg. Chairmen (pres. 1972-74), Soc. Univ. Surgeons (chmn. publs. com. 1969-71), So. Surg. Assn., Surg. Biology Club (sec. 1968-70), Western Surg. Assn., Allen O. Whipple Surg. Soc., James IV Assn. Surgeons (bd. dirs. 1980-81, sec. 1981-87, pres. 1987-91), Alpha Omega Alpha, Alpha Pi Alpha, Phi Beta Pi. Office: Tex Tech U Med Coll Lubbock TX 79430

SHIRK, ANNADORA VESPER, English educator; b. Altoona, Pa., Aug. 9, 1918; d. Harry M. and Jessie (Birchfield) Spengler; m. Albert R. Vesper (dec.); m. Eugene L. Shirk, 1949; children: Albert, Thea. PhD in Rhetoric, Temple U., 1977. Instr. English, Albright Coll., Reading, Pa., 1946, asst. prof., 1949-66, assoc. prof., 1966-76, prof., 1976—, chmn. dept., 1978-82, faculty chmn., 1980-82; speaker, 1955—. Mem. Reading Sch. Bd., 1955-61. Named Coll. Prof. of Yr., Reading C. of C., 1980; Lindback fellow, 1978; recipient Beacon award (Outstanding Woman of Yr.), Berks Women's Network, 1991, Albright Alumni Citation for Disting. Svc., 1992, Thiel Coll. Disting. Alumni award, 1989. Mem. AAUW (pres. Reading, 1976-78). Republican. Methodist. Avocation: cello. Home: 1503 N 12th St Reading PA 19604 Office: Albright Coll Dept English 13th St Reading PA 19604

SHIRK, EVELYN URBAN, retired philosophy educator; b. Flushing, N.Y., Sept. 12, 1918; d. Amos Urban and Mary Jane (Welchans) S.; m. Justus Buchler, Feb. 20, 1943; 1 child, Katherine Urban. B.A., Wilson Coll., 1940; M.A., Columbia U., 1942, Ph.D., 1949. Instr. Bklyn Coll., 1942-48; asst. prof. Hofstra Coll., Hempstead, N.Y., 1949-53, assoc. prof., 1953-63; prof. Hofstra U. (formerly Hofstra Coll.), 1963-89, dept. chmn., 1980-89, ret. Hofstra U., 1989. Contbg. editor: Readings in Philosophy, 1946; Adventurous Idealism: The Philosophy of Alfred Lloyd, 1952; The Ethical Dimension, 1965; In Pursuit of Awareness, 1967, After the Stroke: Coping With America's Third Leading Cause of Death, 1991. Mem. Am. Philos. Assn., Soc. Advancement Am. Philosophy (program chmn. 1976, exec. com 1977-79), L.I. Philos. Soc. (exec. com.), AAUP, Phi Beta Kappa. Home: 3 Homestead Ave Garden City NY 11530-1002

SHIRK, RICHARD D., insurance company executive; b. 1946; married. With Equitable Life Assurance, N.Y.C., Houston, 1967-86; pres. so. region Equicor Inc., Nashville, Houston, 1987-90; with Cigna Corp., Houston, 1990-92; pres., CEO Blue Cross & Blue Shield of Ga., Atlanta, 1992—. Office: Blue Cross & Blue Shield of GA 3350 Peachtree Rd NE Atlanta GA 30326-1040

SHIRLEY, DAVID ARTHUR, chemistry educator, science administrator; b. North Conway, N.H., Mar. 30, 1934; m. Virginia Schultz, June 23, 1956 (dec. Mar. 1995); children: David N., Diane, Michael, Eric, Gail. BS, U. Maine, 1955, ScD (hon.), 1978; PhD in Chemistry, U. Calif.-Berkeley, 1959; D honoris causa, Free U. Berlin, 1987. With Lawrence Radiation Lab. (now

Lawrence Berkeley Lab.), U. Calif., Berkeley, 1958-92, assoc. dir., head materials and molecular research div., 1975-80, dir., 1980-89, lectr. chemistry, 1959-60, asst. prof., 1960-64, assoc. prof., 1964-67, prof., 1967-92, vice chmn. dept. chemistry, 1968-71, chmn. dept. chemistry, 1971-75; sr. v.p. rsch., dean grad. sch. Pa. State U., University Park, 1992—. Contbr. over 400 rsch. articles. NSF fellow, 1955-58, 66-67, 70; recipient Ernest O. Lawrence award AEC, 1972, Humboldt award (sr. U.S. scientist); listed by Sci. Citation Index as one of the world's 300 most cited scientists for work published during 1965-78. Fellow Am. Phys. Soc.; mem. Nat. Acad. Scis., Am. Chem. Soc., AAAS, Am. Acad. Arts and Scis., Sigma Xi, Tau Beta Pi, Sigma Pi Sigma, Phi Kappa Phi.

SHIRLEY, GEORGE PFEIFFER, lawyer, educational consultant; b. Algood, Tenn., Dec. 12, 1939; s. Howard Dunbar and Maryhils Lewis (Pfeiffer) S.; m. Mary Ann Clawson, May 24, 1958 (div.); m. Susan Hawkins, July 24, 1971 (div.); m. Laura Gail Salmonsen, Feb. 29, 1992; children: Kathleen Underwood, Bryan. BA, U. Denver, 1962, MA, 1963, JD, 1966. Tchr. various high schs., coll. and law schs., 1964—; adminstr. Pan Am Petrol, Denver, 1966-68; lobbyist Sacramento and Washington, 1968-72; lawyer, exec. dir. legal svcs. Calif., Fla. and Minn., 1972-83; pvt. ednl. cons. San Jose, Calif., 1986—; bd. dirs. Cal-Micro, Inc., San Jose, Am. Grinding Co., San Jose; lectr. various univs., 1986—. Campaign coord. Dem. Party, Sacramento, 1972. 1st lt. ROTC, USMC 1957-66. Mem. Internat. Platform Assn., Order of Coif, Pi Gamma Mu. Methodist. Avocation: baseball.

SHIRLEY, GLENN DEAN, writer; b. Payne County, Okla., Dec. 9, 1916; s. Ellis Dean and Effie Teresa (Knorr) S.; m. Carrie Mabel Jacob, 1946; children: Glenda Lea, Kenneth Ellis. Diploma, N.Y. Inst. Photography, 1941, Internat. Criminologist Sch., 1948, Delehanty Inst., 1949, Okla. Inst. Tech., 1950; LL.B., LaSalle U., Chgo., 1940. Capt., asst. chief Stillwater Police Dept., (Okla.), 1936-57; criminal dep. Payne County Sheriff's Office, 1957-59; asst. chief security Okla. State U., Stillwater, 1959-69; publs. specialist, asst. dir. Okla. State U. Press, 1969-79, ret., 1980; freelance writer Stillwater, 1980—; now hist. cons. Western Publs., pub. True West, Old West mags., Stillwater; lectr. in field. Author: books of western history and personalities, including Toughest of Them All, 1953; Six-Gun and Silver Star, 1955, Law West of Ft. Smith: A History of Frontier Justice in the Indian Territory, 1834-1896/1957, 8th edit., 1988, Pawnee Bill: A Biography of Gordon W. Lillie, 1958, 4th edit., 1981, rev. 1993, Buckskin and Spurs: A Gallery of Frontier Rogues and Heroes, 1958, Outlaw Queen, 1960, Heck Thomas, Frontier Marshal: The Story of a Real Gunfighter, 1962, rev. edit., 1981, Born to Kill, 1963, Henry Starr, Last of the Real Badmen, 1965, 2d edit., 1976, Buckskin Joe: The Unique and Vivid Memoirs of Edward Jonathan Hoyt, Hunter-Trapper, Scout, Soldier, Showman, Frontiersman and Friend of the Indians, 1840-1918, 1966, 2d edit., 1988, Shotgun for Hire: The Story of Deacon "Jim Miller", Killer of Pat Garrett, 1970, 2d edit., 1980, The Life of Texas Jack: Eight Years a Criminal—41 Years Trusting in God, 1973, Red Yesterdays, 1977, West of Hell's Fringe: Crime, Criminals and the Federal Peace officer in Oklahoma Territory 1889-1907, 1978, Temple Houston, Lawyer with a Gun, 1980, Belle Starr and Her Times: The Literature The Facts and The Legends, 1982, Guardian of the Law, The Life and Times of William Matthew Tilghman, 1988, Purple Sage, The Exploits, Adventures and Writings of Patrick Sylvester McGeeney, 1989, Hello, Sucker! The Story of Texas Guinan, 1989, Gunfight at Ingalls, Death of an Outlaw Town, 1990, They Outrobbed Them All, The Rise and Fall of the Vicious Martins, 1992, The Fighting Marlows, Men Who Wouldn't be Lynched, 1994, Marauders of the Indian Nations: The Bill Cokk Gang and Cherokee Bill, 1994; contbr. numerous short stories, novelettes and factual articles to Western pulps, fact-detective and men's mags. and gen. markets, to anthologies; former contbg. editor: Westerner, Old Trails, Oklahoma Monthly; collector: Western Americana. Recipient Okla. Literary Endeavor award, 1960, Am.'s Star award U.S. Marshal Svc., 1989, Profl. Writing award U. Okla., 1990; inducted into Okla. Journalism Hall of Fame, 1981, Okla. Profl. Writers Hall of Fame, 1992;. Mem. Okla. Writers Fedn. (past pres., life mem.), Indian Ter. Posse Westerners (past pres.), Western Writers Am., Western History Assn., Nat. Assn. Outlaw and Lawman History, Oklahoma Heritage Assn., Inst. Great Plains, Assocs. Western History Collections (trustee), Okla. State Hist. Soc., Kans. State Hist. Soc., Mont. State Hist. Soc. Address: PO Box 824 Stillwater OK 74076-0824

SHIRLEY, ROBERT CLARK, university president, strategic planning consultant, educator; b. Jacksonville, Tex., July 1, 1943; s. James Cullen and Mary Jim (Clark) S.; m. Terrie Thomas, June 17, 1967; children: Robin, Deron. B.B.A., U. Houston, 1965, M.B.A., 1967; Ph.D., Northwestern U., 1972. Asst. dean faculties U. Houston, 1974-76; asst. to pres. SUNY-Albany, 1976-77, assoc. v.p. acad. affairs, 1977-79; assoc. prof. Central U. Iowa, Pella, 1979-81; prof. Trinity U., San Antonio, 1981-84; pres. U. So. Colo., Pueblo, 1984—; cons. on strategic planning and mgmt. to numerous colls. and univs. Author: Strategy and Policy Formation, 1981; contbr. articles to profl. publs. Mem. Pueblo Econ. Devel. Bd. Bill Laufman Meml. scholar U. Houston, 1965-66; Northwestern U. fellow, 1969-71; HEW research asst. grantee, 1971, 72; La. State U. Found. grantee, 1972, 73. Mem. Acad. Mgmt., Soc. Coll. and Univ. Planning, Pueblo C. of C. Presbyterian. Lodge: Rotary. Office: U So Colo 2200 Bonforte Blvd Pueblo CO 81001-4901

SHIRLEY, VIRGINIA LEE, advertising executive; b. Kankakee, Ill., Mar. 24, 1936; d. Glenn Lee and Virginia Helen (Ritter) S. Student, Northwestern U., 1960-61. With produn. control dept. Armour Pharm., Kankakee, 1954-58; exec. sec. Adolph Richman, Chgo., 1958-61; mgr. media dept. Don Kemper Co., Chgo., 1961-63, 65-69; exec. sec. Playboy mag., Chgo., 1964-65; exec. v.p. SMY Media Inc., Chgo., 1969—. Mem. Pla. Club. Home: 800 S Wells St Chicago IL 60607-4529 Office: SMY Media Inc 333 N Michigan Ave Chicago IL 60601-3901

SHIRLEY-QUIRK, JOHN, concert and opera singer; b. Liverpool, Eng., Aug. 28, 1931; came to U.S., 1990; s. Joseph Stanley and Amelia (Griffiths) S.-Q.; m. Patricia May Hastie, July 1955 (dec. Feb. 1981); children: Kate, Peter; m. Sara Van Horn Watkins, Dec. 29, 1981; children: Benjamin, Emily, Julia. BSc, Liverpool U., 1953, MusD (hon.), 1977; D Univ., Brunel U., 1981. Asst. lectr. Acton Tech. Coll., London, 1956-60; vicar choral St. Paul's Cathedral, London, 1960-61; profl. singer, 1960—; joint artistic dir. Aldeburgh Festival, 1981-84; mem. voice faculty Peabody Conservatory, Balt., 1991—; vis. artist Carnegie-Mellon U., Pitts., 1994—. Numerous recs. and 1st performances, especially works of Benjamin Britten. Mem. ct. Brunel U., 1977—. Flying officer RAF, 1952-55. Mem. Royal Acad. Music (hon.), Order of the British Empire (comdr. 1975).

SHIRPSER, CLARA, former Democratic national committeewoman; b. San Francisco, Aug. 25, 1901; d. Leo and Alexandra (Shragge) Garfinkle; m. Herman Rosenberg, 1921 (dec. 1938); 1 dau., Barbara (Mrs. Robert De Liban); m. Adolph Shirpser, Nov. 10, 1940 (dec. 1970); m. Nat Levy, Dec. 14, 1978 (dec. 1984). Student, U. Calif., 1919-21. Owner, mgr. retail bus. Berkeley, Calif., 1938-45; mem. Alameda County, Calif. State Dem. central coms., 1950-56; Mem. Dem. Nat. Com., 1952-56; vice chmn. nat. and Calif. Kefauver primary campaign for pres., 1952, 56; co-chmn. nat. exec. com. Stevenson-Kefauver Presdl. Campaign gen. election, 1956, del. to Dem. nat. conv., 1952, 56, 60; Dem. nominee for Assembly Calif. Legislature, 1950; Calif. Campaign Com. Brown for Gov., 1958; mem. Kennedy Presdl. Campaign Com., Kennedy Nat. Inaugural Com., 1960, 61; chmn. Alameda County Women for Johnson and Humphrey, 1964; mem. No. Calif. Com. Cranston for U.S. Senator Campaign, 1980, 85; active Congl. campaign, 1983; mem. Dem. Nat. Conv. Host Com., 1984; mem. Dianne Feinstein's Campaign Com. for mayor of San Francisco, 1984, Feinstein for Gov. Campaign Com., 1990—; mem. adv. com. No. Calif. Conf. on Substance Abuse and Family Issues, San Francisco U., 1987; mem. Roger Boas' campaign com. for Mayor of San Francisco, 1987. Subject oral history, Clara Shirpser - One Woman's Role in Democratic Politics- National, California and Local, 1950-73, in Bancroft Libr. U. Calif., Berkeley, 1975, and 16 univ. rsch. librs.; author: Behind the Scene in Politics-Memoirs of Clara Shirpser, 1981 (based on oral history), included in Libr. of Congress, Smithsonian Instn.; pub. American Lives Endowment. Mem. Merola Opera Ctr., San Francisco Opera, 1960-91; chmn. women's div. Herrick Meml. Hosp., Berkeley, 1956-74, hon. trustee, 1968-78; mem. franchise, taxation, charter amendment coms. Berkeley City Council, 1948-50, Alameda County Dem. Cen. Com., 1952-58; mem. Menninger Found., 1970-91; past

mem. nat. bd. Atlantic Union; chmn. Bldg. Fund East Bay Rehab. Center, Women's Div., 1958; mem. Gov.'s Adv. Com. to Calif. Consumers Counsel, 1959-67; pres. Arch Herrick Hosp. Guild, 1957-74; past bd. dirs. Calif. Heritage Council, Planned Parenthood San Francisco and Alameda Counties; chmn. viewpoints com. Center for Learning in Retirement, U. Calif. Extension Div., 1975-76; pres. League Women Voters Berkeley, 1948-49, Town Meeting chmn., 1949-50; mem. nat. bd. Women's Crusade for a Common Sense Economy, 1985.; bd. dirs. San Francisco Outlook, 1985-87; mem. U. Calif. Alliance, UN Assn. U.S.; San Francisco Edn. Childrens Fund, 1987, San Francisco Edn. Sch. Vols., 1988, ACLU, Common Cause, Nat. Council Jewish Women, 1991; past bd. dirs. World Affairs Coun. Home: Buena Vista Manor 399 Buena Vista Ave E San Francisco CA 94117-4170

SHIRTCLIFF, CHRISTINE FAY, healthcare facility executive; b. Greenfield, Mass.; d. Francis E. and Doris E. (Olsen) S.; 1 child, Danielle Elizabeth. BS in Pub. Health, U. Mass., 1973, MBA, 1987; MEd, Antioch U., 1978. Lic. nursing home adminstr., social worker. Health program rep. Fulton County Health Dept., Atlanta, 1973-74; home health aide supv. County Health Care, Greenfield, Mass., 1974-77; adminstrv. asst. Mary Lane Hosp., Ware, Mass., 1977-79, asst. exec. dir., 1979-85, exec. v.p., 1985—; founder, mem. steering com. We. Mass. Healthcare Mgrs. Group, 1983-86; active Mass. Rural Devel. Social Svcs. Subcom., 1986, Mass. Coun. Homemaker/Home Health Aide Svcs., 1976-85, bd. dirs., 1976-77, We. Mass. Health Planning Coun., 1974-78. Trustee Congl. Ch. in Belchertown, Mass., 1993—; mem. Belchertown Collaboration for Excellence in Edn., 1993; mem. blue ribbon com. on excellence in edn. Pioneer Valley Planning Commn. Fellow Am. Coll. Healthcare Execs.; mem. New England Women Healthcare Execs. Office: Mary Lane Hosp 85 South St Ware MA 01082-1697

SHIRVANI, HAMID, philosophy educator, university dean, critic; b. Tehran, Iran, Oct. 20, 1950; came to U.S., 1974, naturalized, 1986; s. Majid and Taji (Granpisheh) S. Diploma in architecture, Poly. of Cen. London, 1974; MArch, Pratt Inst., 1975; MS, Rensselaer Poly. Inst., 1977; MA, Harvard U., 1978, Princeton U., 1979; PhD, Princeton U., 1980. Project designer London Borough of Barnet, 1973-74; prin. Technokam Inc., Tehran and N.Y.C., 1975-77; asst. prof. architecture Pa. State U., 1979-82; prof., dir. grad. studies SUNY, Syracuse, 1982-85; prof., dir. Sch. Urban Planning and Devel., U. Louisville, 1985-86; prof. architecture and urban design U. Colo., Denver, 1986-92, dean Sch. of Architecture and Planning, 1986-91; prof. philosophy, dean Coll. Arts and Scis. U. Mass., Lowell, 1992—, prof. philosophy, dean Coll. Arts and Scis., 1992—; mem. vis. faculty So. Calif. Inst. Architecture, U. So. Calif.; vis. critic Harvard U., Yale U., Columbia U., Zhongshan U., Ball State U., Miss. State U., S.W. Mo. State U., Duke U., Mich. Technol. U., Wayne State U., U. Venice, U. Rome, Amsterdam Acad. Art, Chinese U. Hong Kong, So. China Inst. Tech., SUNY, Syracuse, U. N.C., U. Tex., Arlington, U. Ark., U. Waterloo, Ont., Can., U. Sydney, Australia, U. Wis., U. Pa. Author: Urban Design: A Comprehensive Reference, 1981, Urban Design Review, 1981, Urban Design Process, 1985, Beyond Public Architecture, 1990; editor Urban Design Rev., 1982-85, Urban Design and Preservation Quar., 1985-88; mem. editorial bd. Jour. Archtl. Edn., 1988-94, Avant Garde, 1988-93, Jour. Planning Edn. and Rsch., 1987-93, Art and Architecture, 1974-78, Jour. Am. Planning Assn., 1982-88. Recipient Gold Medal in Architecture and Urbanism, Faculty Honor award, Acad. Leadership award, Faculty Rsch. award. Fellow Royal Geog. Soc., Royal Soc. Arts; mem. MLA, Am. Studies Assn., Am. Soc. Aesthetics, Coun. Colls. Arts and Scis., Am. Soc. Landscape Architects (recognition award), Am. Inst. Cert. Planners, Am. Planning Assn. (chmn. urban design divsn. 1987-89, Disting. award 1984, Urban Design award 1985), Sigma Xi, Omicron Delta Epsilon, Tau Sigma Delta (Silver medal in archtl. edn. 1988), Tau Beta Pi, Sigma Lambda Alpha. Office: U Mass Office Dean Coll Arts-Scis Lowell MA 01854

SHISLER, ARDEN L., insurance and transportation company executive; b. 1941. Chmn. Nationwide Mut. Ins. Co., Columbus; also pres., CEO K&B Transport, Dalton, Ohio; also ptnr. Sweetwater Beef Farms, Dalton; v.p. Ohio Farm Bur., 1974-84; pres. Ohio Agriculture Mktg. Assn., 1982-84. Office: Nationwide Mut Ins Co 1 Nationwide Plz Columbus OH 43215*

SHISTER, JOSEPH, labor arbitrator, law educator; b. Montreal, Can., Nov. 27, 1917; came to U.S., 1939, naturalized, 1943; s. Eli Harry and Pearl (Millman) S.; m. Edna Louise Tuck, Dec. 28, 1941; children:—Neil Barry, Jayne Ellen, Gail Marilyn, Diane Marjorie. B.S., U. Montreal, 1939; M.A., Harvard, 1941, Ph.D., 1943. Instr. econs. Cornell U., 1942-43; research assoc. study trade-unionism Rockefeller Found., 1944-45; asst. prof. econs. Syracuse U., 1945-46; asst. prof. dir. research, labor and mgmt. center Yale U., 1946-49; mem. faculty SUNY, Buffalo, 1949-83; prof. SUNY, 1950-83, prof. emeritus indsl. relations, 1983—, chmn. dept. indsl. relations, 1950-78; vis. prof. Tufts U., Wesleyan U., Montreal U., 1949-55; moderator U. Buffalo Round Table of the Air, WBEN, WBEN-TV, WBEN-FM, 1952-72; labor arbitrator, 1944—; Cons. economist Nat. War Labor Bd., 1944; pub. mem. constrn. commn. Nat. Wage Stblzn. Bd., 1951-52; referee System Boards of Adjustment, 1959—; chmn. Presdl. Emergency Dispute Bd., 1961, 62, 64; spl. adviser labor legislation Gov. Conn., 1948-50; mem. social stratification com. Social Sci. Research Council, 1952-53; mem. N.Y. State Mediation Bd., 1966-69; spl. cons. N.Y. State Med. Bd., 1966-72; also spl. Mayor's Office Settlement Emergency Labor Disputes, 1959-70; spl. cons. Buffalo Full Employment Com., 1958-60; chmn. Erie County Grievance Bd., 1963-70; mem. N.Y. State Minimum Wage Bd. in Amusement and Recreation Industry, 1957-59, White House Conf. on Nat. Econ. Issues, 1962, White House Conf. on Indsl. World Ahead, 1972, Nat. Acad. Arbitrators, 1950—; arbitration panel Fed. Mediation and Conciliation Svc., 1952—, Am. Arbitration Assn., 1955—; mem. labor dispute panels various bds. and commns. Author: Economics of the Labor Market, rev. edit, 1956, Readings in Labor Economics and Industrial Relations, rev. edit, 1956; Co-author: Job Horizons, 1948, Conflict and Stability in Labor Relations, 1952; contbg. author: A Decade of Industrial Relations Research, 1958, Unions, Management and the Public, 1967, Problems de Planification, 1964, Economic Issues and Policies, 1965, Negotiation and Administration of Collective Bargaining Agreements, 1966, The Business World, 1967, Rights and Obligations of Parties Under Collective Agreements, 1967; Co-editor: Insight Into Labor Issues, 1948, Public Policy and Collective Bargaining, 1962; Contbr. articles to profl. jours. Served as pvt. AUS, 1943-44. Mem. Indsl. Rels. Rsch. Assn. (exec. bd. 1959-62), Phi Beta Kappa, Beta Gamma Sigma. Home: 2460 NW 15th St Delray Beach FL 33445-1359

SHIVE, PHILIP AUGUSTUS, architect; b. Luebo, Zaire, Apr. 14, 1938; came to U.S., 1955; s. Alexander M. and Jean B. (Setser) S.; m. Marilyn Ayce Miller, Aug. 3, 1968; children: Susannah, Heather. Student, Davidson Coll., 1956-58; BArch, N.C. State U., 1963; MArch, U. Pa., 1964. Registered architect, N.C., N.Y., Ga. Design architect I.M. Pei & Ptnrs., N.Y.C., 1964-68; ptnr. Gorman, Mixon & Shive, Atlanta, 1968-77; v.p. Wolf Assocs., Charlotte, 1977-83; v.p., dir. design J.N. Pease Assocs., Charlotte, 1983-88; pres. Shive/Bohm-NBBJ, Charlotte, 1988-91, Shive Assocs. Architects, Charlotte, 1991-95, Nix Mann Shive, 1995—. Mem. citizen's adv. com. Charlotte-Mecklenburg Planning Commn., 1985-87. Fellow AIA (Kamphoefner prize 1992, 27 design awards); mem. Nat. Am. Inst. Architects (urban design com.), N.C. Arts Coun. Design (arts planning com.), Charlotte City Club. Democrat. Presbyterian. Office: Shive Assocs Archs 1130 E 3d St Ste 200 Charlotte NC 28204

SHIVE, RICHARD BYRON, architect; b. Cleve., Jan. 16, 1933; s. Roy Allen and Mary Elizabeth (Thompson) S.; m. Patricia Butler, Aug. 28, 1954; children: Lisa Ann, Laura Mary, John Thompson, Nancy Butler. BS, Rensselaer Poly. Inst., Troy, N.Y., 1954; postgrad., Newark (N.J.) Coll. Engring., 1957, Rutgers U., 1960-63. Registered architect, N.J., N.Y., Pa., Vt.; lic. profl. planner, N.J. Field engr. Wigton-Abbott Corp., Plainfield, N.J., 1954-55, The Glenwal Co., Roselle Park, N.J., 1955; asst. supt. Wigton-Abbott Corp., Plainfield, 1955-57; archtl. draftsman Raymond B. Flatt, Architect, Bloomfield, N.J., 1957-58; chief draftsman Raymond B. Flatt, Architect, 1958-60; project architect Scrimenti/Swackhamer/Perantoni Architects, Somerville, N.J., 1960-66; assoc. Scrimenti/Swackhamer/Perantoni Architects, 1966-69; ptnr. Scrimenti, Shive, Spinelli, Perantoni Architects, Somerville, 1969-86, Shive/Spinelli/Perantoni & Assocs., Architects & Planners, Somerville, 1986—; adv. com. First Fidelity Bank,

Bound Brook, N.J., 1989-91; chmn. bd. Somerset Health Care Corp., 1987-91. Contbr. articles to profl. jours. Bd. dirs., exec. com. N.J. Hosp. Assn., Princeton, 1986-92, 93—; chmn. bd. trustees Somerset Med. Ctr., Somerville, 1973—; mem. Nat. Trust for Hist. Preservation; bd. dirs. Ctr. for Health Affairs, Inc., 1992—. Recipient award James F. Lincoln Arc Welding Found., 1973, President's award for outstanding svc. Rolling Hills coun. Girl Scouts U.S.A., 1988, Trustee of Yr. award N.J. Hosp. Assn., 1993, Outstanding Citizen of Yr. award Somerset County C. of C., 1993; Paul Harris fellow Bound Brook-Middlesex Rotary Club, 1993. Mem. AIA, ASTM, ASHRAE, ACI (chpt. bd. dirs. 1978-83), N.J. Soc. Architects, Illuminating Engring. Soc., Congress of Hosp. Trustees of Am. Hosp. Assn., Nat. Fire Protection Assn., Greater Somerset County C. of C. (v.p. 1985-86, 92—, Outstanding Citizen of Yr. award 1993), Rotary (pres. 1969-70, Paul Harris fellow 1993), Wash. Campground Assn. (pres. 1975-76, v.p. 1977-78, sec. 1978—), Chi Phi (sec. 1973). Republican. Congregationalist. Avocations: fishing, photography, skiing, canoeing, backpacking. Home: 1001 N Mountain Ave Bound Brook NJ 08805-1451 Office: Shive Spinelli Perantoni & Assocs PO Box 758 148 W End Ave Somerville NJ 08876-0758

SHIVELY, JOHN ADRIAN, pathologist; b. Rossville, Ind., Oct. 29, 1922; s. Henry Adam and Lucy (Gascho) S.; m. Lois Lorene Faris, Aug. 26, 1945; children—David A., Ann M., Theodore J., Janet S. B.A., Ind. U., 1944, M.D., 1946. Intern Phila. Gen. Hosp., 1946-47; resident internal medicine Clinic Hosp., Bluffton, Ind., 1949-50; resident pathology South Bend Med. Found., 1950-52; asst. prof. clin. pathology Ind. U. Sch. Medicine, 1954-57; assoc. prof. pathology U. Ky. Med. Sch., 1962-63; prof. pathology, chief clin. pathology U. Tex. M.D. Anderson Hosp., 1963-68; prof. pathology U. Mo. Med. Sch., 1968-71; prof. pathology, chmn. dept. U. Tenn. Coll. Medicine, 1971-76; vice chancellor for acad. affairs U. Tenn. Ctr. for Health Scis., 1976-82; med. dir. SmithKline Clin. Labs., Tampa, Fla., 1983-88; prof. pathology U.S. Fla. Coll. Medicine, 1988-93, assoc. dean, 1990-93, interim chmn. pathology, 1993-94; prof. emeritus, 1993—; pathologist-in-chief City of Memphis Hosps., 1971-76. Served with AUS, 1947-49. Mem. Am. Soc. Clin. Pathologists, Coll. Am. Pathologists, ACP, Am. Soc. Hematology, Am. Assn. Blood Banks (pres. 1967-68), Phi Beta Kappa, Sigma Xi, Alpha Omega Alpha. Research on platelet physiology. Office: 12901 N 30th St # 11 Tampa FL 33612-4799

SHIVELY, WILLIAM PHILLIPS, political scientist, educator; b. Altoona, Pa., Mar. 31, 1942; s. Arthur Willard and Ruth Phillips S.; m. Barbara Louise Shank, Aug. 29, 1964; children—Helen, David. B.A., Franklin and Marshall Coll., 1963; Ph.D., U. N.C., 1968. Mem. faculty U. Oreg., Eugene, 1967-68, Yale U., 1968-71; mem. faculty U. Minn., Mpls., 1971—; prof. polit. sci. U. Minn., 1979—, provost arts, scis. & engring., 1995—. Author: Craft of Political Research, 1974, rev. edit., 1989, Research Process in Political Science, 1985, Power and Choice, 1986, rev. edit., 1989, 4th edit., 1994, Comparative Governance, 1995, Cross-Level Inference, 1995; editor Am. Jour. Polit. Sci., 1977-79; contbr. articles on elections and voting to profl. jours. Home: 1572 Northrop St Saint Paul MN 55108-1322 Office: U Minn Dept Polit Sci Minneapolis MN 55455

SHIVERS, JANE, corporate communications executive, director; b. Georgetown, Tex., June 29, 1943; d. Marvin Bishop and Jewell (Petrey) Edwards; m. Harold E. Shivers; children: Clay Houston, Will Davis; m. Don Evans Hutcheson. BA, U. Md., 1965. Reseacher Amex Broadcasting Co., San Francisco, 1965-67; pub. info. officer Semester at Sea, Orange, Calif., 1967-69; dir. pub. rels. Atlanta Arts Alliance, 1974-78, RSVT, Atlanta, 1978-82; pres. Shivers Communications, Atlanta, 1982-84; exec. v.p., dir. Ketchum Pub. Rels., Atlanta, 1985—; pres. Midtown Bus. Assocs., Atlanta, 1987-91; bd. dirs. Crown Cryts, Inc. Trustee Alliance Theatre Co., Atlanta, 1980-93, Care, Internat., Atlanta, 1988-89; bd. dirs. Piedmont Park Conservancy, Emory Sch. Pub. Health. Recipient Mgmt. Woman Achievement award Women in Communication, Atlanta, 1984. Mem. Pub. Rels. Soc. Am. (bd. dirs.), Cen. Atlanta Progress Club, Commerce Club, Peachtree Club, Crown Crafts, Inc. (bd. dirs.). Episcopalian. Home: 238 15th St NE Atlanta GA 30309-3594 Office: Ketchum Pub Rels 999 Peachtree St NE Atlanta GA 30309-3964

SHIVLER, JAMES FLETCHER, JR., retired civil engineer; b. Clearwater, Fla., Feb. 17, 1918; s. James Fletcher and Frankie (Adams) S.; m. Katherine Lucille Howlett, Feb. 2, 1946; children: James Fletcher, Susan (Mrs. William J. Schilling). B.C.E., U. Fla., 1938, M.S., 1940. Registered profl. engr., Fla., Ga. Mem. engring. faculty U. Fla., 1940-41; with Reynolds, Smith & Hills Architects-Engrs.-Planners, Inc. (formerly Reynolds, Smith & Hills, architects and engrs.), Jacksonville, Fla., 1941-88, partner, 1950-69, pres., 1970-88, chmn. bd., 1983-88, ret.; ret., 1988; partner Lewis-Eaton Partnership (Architects-Engrs. & Planners), Jackson, Miss., 1969-88. Mem. Fla. Bd. Engr. Examiners, 1964-70, v.p., 1964-65, pres., 1965-70. Served to lt. j.g. USNR, 1943-46. Recipient Outstanding Service award Fla. Engring. Soc., 1971, Disting. Alumnus award U. Fla., 1972, citation for service to constrn. industry Engring. News Record, 1973. Fellow ASCE (pres. Fla. sect. 1952), Am. Cons. Engrs. Coun., Fla. Engring. Soc. (pres. 1960-61); mem. NSPE (pres. 1972-73, Meritorious Svc. award 1981), AM. Assn. Engring. Socs. (chmn. engring. affairs coun. 1982-83), Fla. C. of C. (dir.-at-large 1971-88), Jacksonville Area C. of C., Jacksonville Exchange Club, Univ. Club, Deerwood Club, Fla. Yacht Club, Tau Beta Pi. Presbyterian. Home: 8191 Hollyridge Rd Jacksonville FL 32256-7103

SHKLAR, GERALD, oral pathologist, periodontist, educator; b. Montreal, Que., Can., Dec. 2, 1924; came to U.S. 1950, naturalized, 1955; s. Louis and Ann (Schleifstein) S.; m. Judith Nisse, June 16, 1948 (dec. Sept. 18, 1992); children: David, Michael, Ruth; m. Diane Trickler, Mar. 6, 1994. B.S., McGill U., 1947, D.D.S., 1949; M.S., Tufts U., 1952; M.A. (hon.), Harvard U., 1971. Diplomate Am. Bd. Oral Pathology, Am. Bd. Periodontology. Asst. prof. oral pathology Tufts U. Sch. Dental Medicine, Boston, Mass., 1953-59; assoc. prof. Tufts U. Sch. Dental Medicine, 1960-61, prof., 1961-71, research prof. periodontology, 1961-71; lectr. in oral pathology, 1971—; Charles A. Brackett prof. oral pathology Harvard U. Sch. Dental Medicine, Boston, 1971—, head dept. oral medicine and oral pathology, 1971-93; sr. clin. investigator Forsyth Dental Ctr., Boston, 1994—; cons. oral pathology Children's Hosp. Med. Ctr., Brigham and Women's Hosp., Mass. Gen. Hosp. Author books, articles on oral diseases, oral cancer, exptl. pathology, exptl. oral cancer. Fellow Am. Acad. Dental Sci., AAAS, Am. Acad. Oral Pathology, Am. Coll. Dentists, Internat. Coll. Dentists; mem. ADA, Internat. Assn. Dental Rsch., Am. Acad. Periodontology, Am. Cancer Soc., Am. Assn. Cancer Rsch., Am. Assn. Cancer Edn., Am. Acad. Oral Medicine, Am. Acad. History Dentistry, History of Sci. Soc., Sigma Xi, Omicron Kappa Upsilon. Avocations: playing flute and harpsichord. Home: 7 Chauncy Ln Cambridge MA 02138-2401 Office: 188 Longwood Ave Boston MA 02115-5888

SHLAUDEMAN, HARRY WALTER, retired ambassador; b. L.A., May 17, 1926; s. Karl Whitman and Florence (Pixley) S.; m. Carol Jean Dickey, Aug. 7, 1948; children: Karl Frederick, Katherine Estelle, Harry Richard. BA, Stanford U., 1952. Joined U.S. Fgn. Svc., 1955; vice consul Barranquilla, Colombia, 1955-56; polit. officer Bogotá, Colombia, 1956-58; assigned lang. tng. Washington, 1958-59; consul Sofia, Bulgaria, 1960-62; chief polit. sect. Santo Domingo, Dominican Republic, 1962-64; officer charge Dominican Affairs State Dept., 1964-66; asst. dir. Office Caribbean Affairs, 1965-66; sr. seminar fgn. policy State Dept., 1966-67, spl. asst. to sec. state, 1967-69; dep. chief of mission Santiago, Chile, 1969-73; dep. asst. sec. state for Inter-Am. affairs Washington, 1973-75; amb. to Venezuela, 1975-76, asst. sec. state for Inter-Am affairs, 1976-77, amb. to Peru, 1977-80, amb. to Argentina, 1980-83; exec. dir. Nat. Bipartisan Commn. on Central Am., 1983-84; spl. amb. to Cen. Am., 1984-86; amb. to Brazil Brasilia, 1986-89; amb. to Nicaragua, 1990-92, ret., 1992. Served with USMCR, 1944-46. Recipient Disting. Honor award Dept. State, 1966, Pres. Disting. Svc. award, 1988, Pres. Medal Freedom, 1992. Mem. Am. Acad. Diplomacy, Bethesda Country Club, Phi Gamma Delta. Home: 3531 Winfield Ln NW Washington DC 20007

SHNAYERSON, ROBERT BEAHAN, editor; b. N.Y.C., Dec. 8, 1925; s. Charles and Madalene (Griffin) Beahan; m. Lydia Conde Todd, Dec. 23, 1950 (dec. Sept. 1973); children: Michael, Kate; m. Laurie Platt Winfrey, June 9, 1980; children: Maggie, Bonnie. AB, Dartmouth, 1950. Reporter N.Y. Daily News, 1946; reporter Life mag., N.Y.C., 1950-54; corr. Time-Life

News Svc., 1954-56; contbg. editor Time mag., 1957-59, edn. editor, 1959-64, law editor, 1964-67, sr. editor, 1967-71; editor-in-chief Harper's Mag., N.Y.C., 1971-76; editor, pub. Quest mag., N.Y.C., 1976-81, Technology mag., N.Y.C., 1981-82; editorial dir. Sci. Digest mag., 1986-87; editorial cons. Lear's mag., 1987-90; cons. in mag. field; sr. advisor Travel Holiday mag., 1989—. Author: Illustrated History of the Supreme Court, 1986; contbr. articles to various mags. With USNR, 1943-46. Home: 118 Riverside Dr New York NY 10024-3708

SHNEIDMAN, EDWIN S., psychologist, educator, thanatologist, suicidologist; b. York, Pa., May 13, 1918; s. Louis and Manya (Zukin) S.; m. Jeanne E. Keplinger, Oct. 1, 1944; children: David William, Jonathan Aaron, Paul Samuel, Robert James. A.B., UCLA, 1938, M.A., 1940; M.S., U. So. Calif., 1947, Ph.D., 1948. Diplomate: Am. Bd. Examiners Profl. Psychology (past v.p.). Clin. psychologist VA Center, Los Angeles, 1947-50; chief research VA Center, 1950-53; co-dir. Central Research Unit for Study Unpredicted Deaths, 1953-58; co-dir. Suicide Prevention Center, Los Angeles, 1958-66; chief Center Studies Suicide Prevention NIMH, Bethesda, Md., 1966-69; vis. prof. Harvard U., 1969; fellow Ctr. Advanced Study in Behavioral Scis., 1969-70; clin. assoc. Mass. Gen. Hosp., 1969, Karolinska Hosp., Stockholm, 1978; prof. med. psychology UCLA, 1970-75, prof. thanatology, 1975-88, emeritus, 1988—; vis. prof. Ben Gurion U. of Negev, Beersheva, 1983. Author: Deaths of Man, 1973, Voices of Death, 1980; Definition of Suicide, 1985, Suicide as Psychache, 1993; editor: Thematic Test Analysis, 1951; editor: (with N.L. Farberow) Clues to Suicide, 1957, The Cry for Help, 1961, Essays in Self-Destruction, 1967, (with M. Ortega) Aspects of Depression, 1969, On the Nature of Suicide, 1969, (with N.L. Farberow, L.E. Litman) Psychology of Suicide, 1970, Death and the College Student, 1972, Death: Current Perspectives, 1976, 80, 84, Suicidology: Contemporary Developments, 1976, Endeavors in Psychology: Selections From The Personology of Henry A. Murray, 1981, Suicide Thoughts and Reflections, 1981. Served to capt. USAAF, 1942-45. Recipient Harold M. Hildreth award Psychologists in Pub. Service, 1966; Louis I. Dublin award Am. Assn. Suicidology, 1969; Disting. Profl. Contbn. to Pub. Service award Am. Psychol. Assn., 1987. Mem. Am. Assn. Suicidology (founder, past pres.), Am. Psychol. Assn. (past div. pres.), Soc. Projective Techniques (past pres.), Melville Soc. Office: UCLA Neuropsychiat Inst 760 Westwood Plz Los Angeles CA 90024-8300

SHNEIDMAN, J. LEE, historian, educator; b. N.Y.C., June 20, 1929; s. Bernard Wolf and Fannia Abramova (Raskin) S.; m. Conalee Levine, Sept. 3, 1961; children—Philip, Jack. B.A., NYU, 1951, M.A., 1952; Ph.D., U. Wis., Madison, 1957. Lectr. CCNY, 1956-57, U. Md. Overseas, 1957-58; asst. prof. Fairleigh Dickinson U., 1958-62; prof. history Adelphi U., 1963—; chmn. seminar on hist., legal, and polit. thought Columbia U., 1985—. Author: Rise of the Aragonese-Catalan Empire, 2 vols, 1970, Spain and Franco, 1949-59, 1973, John F. Kennedy, 1974. Democratic N.Y. County committeeman, 1970—. Mem. Am. Hist. Assn., Medieval Acad. Am., Am. Philatel. Soc., Internat. Psychohist. Assn. (editor bull.), Rossica Soc., China Soc. Jewish. Home: 161 W 86th St New York NY 10024-3411 Office: History Dept Adelphi University Garden City NY 11530 Only by understanding from where we came can we understand where we are and where we are going.

SHNEOUR, ELIE ALEXIS, biochemist; b. Neuilly-sur-Seine, France, Dec. 11, 1925; came to U.S., 1941, naturalized, 1944; s. Zalman and Salomea (Landau) S.; m. Polly M. Henderson, 7 Sept. 1990; children from previous marriage: Mark Zalman, Alan Brewster. B.A., Bard Coll., 1947; DSc (hon.), Columbia U., 1969; M.A., U. Calif., Berkeley, 1955; Ph.D., UCLA, 1958. Teaching, research fellowship U. Calif., Berkeley, 1953-55, Am. Heart Assn. research fellow, 1958-62; teaching., research fellowship U. Calif., L.A., 1958; research fellow Nat. Cancer Inst., 1956-57; Am. Heart Assn. research fellow N.Y.U., 1958-59; research assoc. genetics Stanford U., 1962-65; assoc. prof. biology and neurosciences U. Utah, 1965-69; research neurochemist City of Hope Nat. Med. Ctr., Duarte, Calif., 1969-71; dir. rsch. Calbiochem., 1971-75; pres. Biosystems Insts., Inc., 1975—; dir. Biosystems Rsch. Inst., 1979—; mem. exec. com. Nat. Acad. Sci. Study Group on Biology and the Exploration of Mars, 1964; chmn. Western Regional coun. Rsch. in Basic Bioscis. for Manned Orbiting Missions, Am. Inst. Biol. Scis., NASA, 1966-69. Author: Extraterrestrial Life, 1965, (with Eric A. Ottesen) National Academy of Sciences, National Rsch. Coun., 1966, (with S. Moffat) Life Beyond the Earth, 1966, The Malnourished Mind, 1974; contbr. numerous articles to sci. and lay jours. Chmn. citizens adv. coun. San Diego Pub. Schs., 1971-72; mem. adv. coun. Cousteau Soc., 1977—; bd. dirs. Am.-Ukraine Trade Coun., 1991—, Lunar Power System Coalition, 1993—, Transinnova S.A. France, 1990—; chmn. sci. adv. bd. County of San Diego, 1995—; mem., bd. dirs. La Jolla Chamber Music Soc., 1994—. With U.S. Army, 1944-45. Recipient William Lockwood prize, 1947. Mem. IEEE, AAAS (hon. Soc. Calif. Skeptics soc. Pacific divsn. 1988-90), Am. Chem. Soc., N.Y. Acad. Scis., Am. Inst. Biol. Scis., Am. Soc. for Biochemistry and Molecular Biology (chmn. sci. advisors program 1973-75, mem. com. on pub. policy 1974-76, congl. liaison 1992—), Am. Soc. Neurochemistry (mem. coun. 1971-73), Soc. Neurosci., Internat. Soc. Neurochemistry, U.S.C. of C. (bd. dirs. 1993—), La Jolla Chamber Music Soc. (bd. dirs. 1994—), Sigma Xi, Phi Sigma. Office: Biosystems Insts Inc 700 Front St San Diego CA 92101-6009

SHNIDER, BRUCE JAY, lawyer; b. Lansing, Mich., Oct. 16, 1950; s. Harold A. and Raynor (Seidner) S.; m. Patricia Lynn Strandness, Dec. 28, 1973; 1 child, Ruth Strandness Shnider. AB magna cum laude, Dartmouth Coll., 1972; MPP, JD, Harvard U., 1977. Bar: Minn. 1977, U.S. Dist. Ct. Minn. 1977, U.S. Tax Ct., 1978, U.S. Ct. Appeals (8th cir.) 1980, U.S. Supreme Ct. 1981. Asst. to dir. Mich. Dept. Commerce, Lansing, 1972-73; law clk. United Mineworkers Am. Health/Retirement Funds, 1975; summer assoc. Robins, Davis & Lyon, Mpls., 1976; assoc. Dorsey & Whitney, Mpls., 1977-82, ptnr., 1983—; chmn. diversity com., 1990-93, chmn. tax practice group, 1994—; bd. dirs. Minn. Justice Found., Mpls., 1989-91. Mem. ABA, Minn. State Bar Assn., Hennepin County Bar Assn. Home: 1908 James Ave S Minneapolis MN 55403-2831 Office: Dorsey & Whitney 220 S 6th St Minneapolis MN 55402

SHNIDERMAN, HARRY LOUIS, lawyer; b. Erie, Pa., Sept. 26, 1916; s. Frank and Sophie (Barber) S.; m. Lenore Hyman, Nov. 29, 1942; children—Craig Mitchell, Neal Barber. A.B., U. Mich., 1938; LL.B., Harvard U., 1941. Bar: D.C. bar 1941, Pa. bar 1945, U.S. Supreme Ct. bar 1945. With litigation div. OPA, 1941-44; law clk. to Justice Rutledge, U.S. Supreme Ct., 1944-45; partner firm Covington & Burling, Washington, 1945—; lectr. Continuing Legal Edn. Programs, 1955—. Author: Price Discrimination in Perspective, 1977, 2d edit., 1987; Contbr. articles to profl. jours. Mem. ABA, D.C. Bar Assn., Harvard Law Sch. Assn., Phi Beta Kappa, Phi Kappa Phi, Delta Sigma Rho. Clubs: Harvard, City Tavern. Office: Covington & Burling PO Box 7566 1201 Pennsylvania Ave NW Washington DC 20044

SHNIER, ALAN, real estate executive; b. Emerson, Man., Can., June 11, 1928; m. Rhona Ostrove, Oct. 15, 1949. Chmn. bd. Met. Equities Ltd., Winnipeg, Man., 1975—; pres. S.W. United Holdings, Inc., United Fibre-Bond, Inc., United Woodframe, Inc. Office: Metropolitan Equities Ltd, 1175 Sherwin Rd, Winnipeg, MB Canada R3H 0V1

SHOAFF, THOMAS MITCHELL, lawyer; b. Ft. Wayne, Ind., Aug. 21, 1941; s. Harmon D. and Agnes H. (Hanna) S.; m. Eunice Swedberg, Feb. 7, 1970; children: Andrew, Nathaniel, Matthew-John. BA, Williams Coll., 1964; JD, Vanderbilt U., 1967. Bar: Ind. 1968. Assoc. Isham, Lincoln & Beale, Chgo., 1967-68; ptnr. Baker & Daniels, Ft. Wayne, Ind., 1968—; bd. dirs. Ft. Wayne Nat. Bank, Ft. Wayne Nat. Corp., Weaver Popcorn Co., Inc., Ft. Wayne, Dreibelbiss Title Co., Inc., Ft. Wayne, Am. Steel Investment Corp., Ft. Wayne. Bd. dirs. McMillen Found., Ft. Wayne, Wilson Found., Ft. Wayne. Mem. ABA, Allen County Bar Assn., Ind. State Bar Assn. Presbyterian. Avocations: golf, sailing. Office: Baker & Daniels Nat Bank Bldg 2400 Ft Wayne Fort Wayne IN 46802

SHOAI, ELINOR JOSEPHINE KELLY, elementary school educator; b. Atlanta, June 30, 1943; d. Neal Kelly and Kathryn Brown-Kelly; m. Morteza Shoai, Dec. 13, 1973; 1 child, Shirin Elma. AA, Merritt Coll, 1962; BA in Elem. Edn., San Francisco State U., 1964. Cert. elem. tchr., Calif. Elem. tchr. Oakland (Calif.) Pub. Schs., 1967-95. Founder, editor: The West

Oakland-Gryphon, 1981-82 (Marcus Foster award 1981-82). Grantee Marcus Foster Inst., 1982. Mem. Oakland Edn. Assn., Toastmasters (3 first place awards 1989-90). Democrat. Roman Catholic. Avocations: public speaking, writing children's books, gardening. Home: 707 33rd St Oakland CA 94609 Office: Prescott Elem Sch 920 Campbell St Oakland CA 94607

SHOBER, EDWARD WHARTON, bioscience company executive; b. Bryn Mawr, Pa., Nov. 16, 1926; s. Edward Wharton and Catherine Mather S.; m. Sandra Metcalf, May 27, 1978; children: Jorie, Edward, Paula. Student, Princeton U., 1950; DSc, Wilkes U., 1975. Pres., CEO Atec Corp., N.Y.C., 1957-71, Hahnemann Med. Coll., Phila., 1971-77; CEO, co-founder Gen. Arabian Medical, Riyadh, Saudi Arabia, 1978-88; chmn. Pioneer Biocis. Ltd., Malmesbury, Wiltshire, Eng., 1990—; chmn. Drexel, Hahnemann, Jefferson Med. Coll. Pa. Cancer Ctr., 1973-77. Author: Blood Lost, 1990, Royal Treachery, 1993. Dir. Old Phila. Devel. Corp., 1972-78, Bryn Mawr Hosp., Phila., 1965-72; hon. consul Nicaragua, Phila., 1960-75; dir. English Speaking Union, Newport, R.I., 1960-85. 1st lt. C.E. German mil., 1950-52. Office: Pioneer Biocis Ltd, PO Box 1545, Malmesbury Wiltshire SN16 9XX, England

SHOBERT, ERLE IRWIN, II, management consultant; b. DuBois, Pa., Nov. 19, 1913; s. Erle Irwin and Edna Mae (Gray) S.; m. Marjorie E. Sullivan, Apr. 6, 1939; children: Judith Ann (Mrs. Edward Marsden), Margaret (Mrs. William G. Hayes). AB summa cum laude, Susquehanna U., 1935, DSc, 1957; student, Georg August U., Goettingen, Germany, 1935-36; MA in Physics, Princeton, 1939. With Stackpole Carbon Co., St. Mary's, Pa., 1934-79, v.p. tech., 1971-79, cons., 1979—; bd. dirs. Chemcut Corp., State College, Pa., 1968-83, chmn., 1978-80, Tech. Adv. Contact Tech., Inc., 1990—; mem. materials adv. panel Pa. Dept. Commerce, 1972; indsl. and adv. com. Pa. State U., 1968-71; adv. com. Am. Carbon Conf., 1967-73; bd. dirs. Engrs. Joint Council, 1969-72; exec. standards council Am. Nat. Standards Inst., 1973, bd. dirs., 1974-76; bd. dirs. Kaul Land Co. Author 3 books, tech. papers. Pres. Elk County Soc. Crippled Children and Adults; pres. St. Mary's Youth Council.; pres., bd. dirs. Susquehanna U., 1978—, chmn. 1978-86; bd. dirs. Kaul Found., 1981—. Recipient Outstanding Alumni award Susquehanna U., 1969. Fellow ASTM (bd. dirs. 1966-74, pres. 1971-72), IEEE (Ragnar Holm Sci. Achievement award 1974, Armington Recognition award 1985, prize paper competition named in his honor, Outstanding Achievement award 1994); mem. Masons, Sigma Xi, Omicron Delta Kappa. Patentee carbon products, electronic materials and applications. Home: PO Box 343 Saint Marys PA 15857-0343 I am product of a Tom Sawyer youth and the scholarship and work opportunities of the American higher education system. My career was and continues to be with one organization, among people and work I liked and respected. My family, including my grandchildren and great grandchild, are my pride and joy. My wife and I try to repay some of the organizations and people who have helped us.

SHOCKLEY, EDWARD JULIAN, aerospace company executive; b. Augusta, Ga., Oct. 31, 1924; s. Julian P. and Margaret (Epps) S.; m. Dorothy Elizabeth Holley, Nov. 24, 1945; children: Edward J., Steven Holley. B.Aero. Engring., Ga. Inst. Tech., 1950; postgrad. (Sloan fellow), Stanford U. Grad. Sch. Bus., 1962-63. Flight test engr. Douglas Aircraft Co., 1950-53; with Lockheed-Ga. Co., 1953-80, dir. quality and safety, 1965-74, dir. mktg., 1974-78, v.p., 1978-80; pres. Lockheed Aircraft Service Co. div. Lockheed Corp., Burbank, Calif., 1980-86, sr. advisor to pres., 1986-87, ret., 1987; pres. Millimeter Wave Tech., Inc., Marietta, Ga., 1988-90, vice chmn. bd. dirs., 1991-92; dir. Aerosurge Mgmt. Cons., 1991-92; pres. Lockheed-Ga. Fed. Credit Union, 1971-74. Mem. bus. adv. coun. Ga. So. U.; mem. adv. coun. Sch. Bus. and Econs., Coll. of Charleston. Served with USN, 1941-46. Mem. Cherokee Town and Country Club. Republican. Methodist.

SHOCKLEY, JAMES THOMAS, physics educator; b. Topaz, Mo., Sept. 16, 1925; s. William Ervin and Minnie Catherine (Turnbull) S.; m. Joan Elsie Griess, June 17, 1950 (div. Aug. 1968); 1 child, John William; m. Betty Jean Truitt, July 8, 1989. BA, Calif. State U., Fresno, 1951, MA, 1953; postgrad., Claremont Grad. Sch., 1955; PhD, U. So. Calif., 1961. Cert. secondary tchr., Calif.; cert. community coll. tchr., Calif. Aerodynamicist N.Am. Aviation, Los Angeles, 1953; instr. Calif. State U., Fresno 1954-55, asst. prof. physics, 1956-63, instr. workshop in phys. sci. for elem. tchrs., 1961, credential advisor, supr. student teaching, 1956-86, assoc. prof., 1963-68, prof., 1968-90, prof. emeritus physics, 1990—; cons. Fresno County Schs., 1971, USAF, Fresno 1971, 72; validity cons. Commn. Tchr. Preparation and Licensing, San Francisco, 1977; instr. NSF Inst. for high sch. physics tchrs., 1962-63. Author: Physics and Astronomy for Liberal Arts Students, 1970; creator 7 Univ. Courses, 1958-85; textbook reviewer, 1965-77; contbr. articles to profl. jours. Active mem. Civil Def., Fresno, 1952; mem. City-Univ. Edn. Liaison Com., Fresno, 1963-64; judge Bullard High Sch. Sci. Fair, Fresno, 1964-66; sponsor Physics Club, Fresno, 1953-55. Recipient I Dare You award Danforth Found., Sanger, Calif., 1944, Tchr. grant Danforth Found., Fresno, 1958; Congress of Parents and Tchrs. scholar, San Diego, 1960. Mem. Am. Inst. Physics, Planetary Soc., Astron. Soc. Pacific, Aero Club, Phi Delta Kappa. Mem. Christian Ch. Avocations: flying, oil painting, internat. travel, reading, photography.

SHOCKLEY, THOMAS DEWEY, electrical engineering educator; b. Haynesville, La., Nov. 2, 1923; s. Thomas Dewey and Inez (Hudson) S.; m. Willie Belle Austin, Feb. 13, 1947; children: Dianne, Cecilia. B.S. in Elec. Engring, La. State U., 1950, M.S. in Elec. Engring, 1952; Ph.D., Ga. Inst. Tech., 1963. Instr. La. State U., 1950-53; aerophysics engr. Gen. Dynamics, 1953-56; research engr. asst. prof. Ga. Inst. Tech., 1956-63; assoc. prof. U. Ala., 1963-64; prof. U. Okla., 1964-67; prof., chmn. dept. elec. engring. Memphis State U., 1967-83; pres. SSC Inc., Germantown, Tenn., 1978—, chmn. bd., 1981—; system cons. ITT, Md. Co., State Farm Fire & Casualty Co., Aetna Ins. Cos., CNA Ins. Co. Mem. elec. code panel, Shelby County, Tenn., 1978-84; mem. Memphis-Shelby County Appeals Bd., 1984—. Served with AUS, 1942-46, 1950. Mem. IEEE (treas. Memphis sect. 1970-71, sec. 1971-72, vice chmn. 1972-73, chmn. 1973-74, Centennial medal 1984), Nat. Soc. Profl. Engrs., Tenn. Soc. Profl. Engrs., Nat. Fire Protection Assn. (com. 110), Sigma Xi (chpt. pres. 1969-71), Phi Kappa Phi (chpt. pres. 1973-74, 84-85). Home: 1526 Poplar Estate Pky Memphis TN 38138-1836 Office: SSC Inc Germantown TN 38138

SHOCKLEY, W. RAY, travel trade association executive; b. Apalachee, Ga., Aug. 19, 1924; s. Benjamin Arthur and Sophie Sarah (Harris) S.; m. Virginia Nell Davis, Sept. 21, 1946; children—Lisa Wray, David Wray, Jenifer Wray. B.A. in Journalism, U. Ga., 1956. News editor Athens (Ga.) Banner Herald and, Gainesville (Ga.) Daily Times, 1948; state news editor Augusta (Ga.) Chronicle, 1948-52; Sunday editor Atlanta Jour.-Constitution, 1952-54, 1954-56; field rep. pub. rels. Am. Textile Mfgs. Inst., Washington, 1956-58; asst. sec., treas. Am. Textile Mfgs. Inst. 1958-70, dep. exec. v.p., 1974-76, exec. v.p., 1976-84; exec. v.p. S.C. Textile Mfrs. Assn., Columbia, 1970-74; pres., chief oper. officer Am. Soc. Travel Agts., 1985-90; cons. pub. affairs, 1990-91; dir. industry and bus. affairs C. of C., Athens, 1991—. Served with USN, 1944-45, PTO. Mem. Am. Soc. Assn. Execs., Ga. Alumni Assn. (out-of-state v.p. 1967-69), Belle Haven Country Club (Alexandria, Va.), Athens C. of C. (dir. industry and small bus. affairs 1991—), Rotary (pres. Dilworth club 1964-65, Athens East 1991—). Methodist (treas. 1966-70). Home: 507 Cherokee Rd Winterville GA 30683-9566

SHOCKMAN, GERALD DAVID, microbiologist, educator; b. Mt. Clemens, Mich., Dec. 22, 1925; s. Solomon and Jennie (Madorsky) S.; m. Arlyne Taub, June 2, 1949; children—Joel, Deborah. B.S., Cornell U., 1947; Ph.D., Rutgers U., 1950; Docteur (hon.), U. Liege. 1991. Predoctoral fellow Rutgers U., 1947-50; research asso. U. Pa., 1950-51; research fellow, research asso. Inst. Cancer Research, Phila., 1951-60; asso. prof. Temple U. Sch. Medicine, Phila., 1960-66; prof. dept. microbiology and immunology Temple U. Sch. Medicine, 1966—, chmn. dept., 1974-90. Contbr. articles to profl. jours. Served with U.S. Army 1942-44. Recipient Research Career Devel. award NIH, 1965-70, Titular de la Chaire d'Actualité Scientifique U. Liège, Belgium, 1971-72; NRC fellow, 1954-55. Mem. Am. Soc. Biol. Chemists, Am. Acad. Microbiology, Am. Soc. Microbiology, AAAS, Sigma Xi. Home: 901 Rodman St Philadelphia PA 19147-1247 Office: Temple U Sch Medicine 3400 N Broad St Philadelphia PA 19140-5196

SHOCTOR, JOSEPH HARVEY, barrister, producer, civic worker; b. Edmonton, Alta., Can., Aug. 18, 1922. BA, LLB, U. Alta., 1946, LLD (hon.), 1981; diploma in theatre adminstrn. (hon.), Grant McEwan Coll., 1986. Named to Queens Counsel, 1960. Barrister, solicitor, sr. counsel Duncan & Craig, Edmonton, 1993—; bd. dirs. Saxony Investments, Inc., Desa Stores Ltd.; pres., exec. officer Harvey Holdings Ltd. Prodr. Broadway plays including Peter Pan, 1965, Henry, Sweet Henry, 1967, Billy, 1969, Hamlet, 1969; founder, pres., exec. producer, bldg. chmn., campaign chmn. Citadel Theater; producer Circle 8 Theatre, Civic Opera, Red Cross Entertainment; panelist pub. affairs talk show and sports forum. Active United Community Fund, 1968—; chmn. Downtown Devel. Corp., Edmonton, 1986; mem. Edmonton Jewish Welfare Bd.; past pres. Edmonton Jewish Community Council; past nat. sec. Federated Zionist Orgn.; past nat. v.p. United Israel Appeal, Inc.; past bd. dirs. Can. Council Jewish Welfare Funds; chmn. divsn. Brit. Commonwealth Games Found., 1978; bd. govs. Nat. Theatre Sch. of Can., officer Order of Can., 1986. Inducted into Cultural Hall of Fame, 1987; named Man of Hr., Sta. CFRN-TV, 1966, Citizen of Yr., B'nai B'rith, 1966, one of Twelve Top Albertans of the 70's, The Alberta Report, U. Alberta Alumni Wall of Recognition, 1995; recipient Performing Arts award City of Edmonton, 1972, Theatre Arts Achievement award Province of Alta., 1975, Prime Minister's medal State of Israel, 1978, Builder of Community award City of Edmonton, 1979, Queen's Silver Jubilee medal, 1977, City of Edmonton Silver Ribbon award, 1985, Great Canadian award, 1992, Commemorative medal for 125th Anniversary Canadian Confederation, 1992; The Shoctor Theatre named in his honor, 1976; Alta. Order of Excellence. Mem. Edmonton C. of C. Clubs: The Edmonton, The Centre, Eskimo Football (founder, past sec.-mgr.). Office: Duncan & Craig, 10060 Jasper Ave 2800, Edmonton, AB Canada T5J 3V9

SHOEMAKER, BILL (WILLIAM LEE SHOEMAKER), retired jockey, horse trainer; b. Fabens, Tex., Aug. 19, 1931; s. B. B. and Ruby (Call) S.; m. Cynthia Barnes, Mar. 7, 1978; 1 dau., Amanda Elisabeth. Jockey, 1949-90, ret., 1990, trainer, 1990—. Author: Stalking Horse, 1994. Winner Ky. Derby, 1955, 59, 65, 86, Belmont Stakes, 1957, 59, 62, 67, 75, Preakness Stakes, 1963, 67; ret. with 8,833 wins, including over 1000 Stakes wins. Office: Care Vincent Andrews Mgmt 315 S Beverly Dr Ste 216 Beverly Hills CA 90212-4310*

SHOEMAKER, CAROLYN SPELLMANN, planetary astronomer; b. Gallup, N.Mex., June 24, 1929; d. Leonard Robert and Hazel Adele (Arthur) Spellmann; m. Eugene Merle Shoemaker, Aug. 18, 1951; children: Christine Shoemaker Woodard, Patrick Gene, Linda Shoemaker Salazar. BA cum laude, Chico State Coll., 1949, MA, 1950; ScD (hon.), No. Ariz. U., 1990. Vis. scientist Br. astrogeology U.S. Geol. Survey, Flagstaff, Ariz., 1980—; rsch. asst. Calif. Inst. Tech., Pasadena, 1981-85; rsch. prof. astronomy No. Ariz. U., Flagstaff, 1989—; mem. staff Lowell Obs., Flagstaff, 1993—; guest observer Palomar Obs., Palomar Mountain, Calif., 1982-94. Co-recipient Rittenhouse medal Rittenhouse Astron. Soc., 1988, Scientists of the Yr. award ARCS Found., 1995; recipient Women of Distinction award Soroptimist Internat., 1994, Choice Champion award New Choices, 1995, 20th Anniversary Internat. Women's Yr. award Zonta Internat. and the Ninety-Nines, 1995; named Emmons lectr. C.O. Sci. Soc., 1995. Mem. Astron. Soc. Pacific, PEO Sisterhood. Achievements include discovery of 32 comets including Periodic Comet Shoemaker-Levy 9 which impacted Jupiter in July 1994, more than 500 asteroids including 41 Earth approachers and approximately 68 Mars crossers, meteorites at Veevers Crater, Australia and impactites at Wolfe Creek Crater. Home: RR 4 Box 998 Flagstaff AZ 86001 Office: Lowell Obs 1400 W Mars Hill Rd Flagstaff AZ 86001

SHOEMAKER, CYNTHIA CAVENAUGH JONES, academic director; b. Washington, Feb. 13, 1938; d. Robert LaTourrette and Herta (Wilson) Cavenaugh; m. Roger H. Jones, July 4, 1958 (div. Dec. 1984); children: Roger, Michael, Steve, Allison; m. Douglas B.G. Shoemaker, Oct. 21, 1989. BS in Human Ecology, Cornell U., 1959; MEd in Edn., U. Md., 1974, PhD in Edn., 1981, postgrad., 1987-91. Tchr. St. Raphael's Nursery Sch., Rockville, Md., 1971-72; sr. v.p. Home and Sch. Inst., 1972-75; exec. dir. Early Childhood Edn. Adminstrn. Inst., 1975-84; asst. to dean continuing edn. Cath. U., 1982; program dir. continuing edn. Montgomery Coll., 1983-84; assoc. dir. off-campus programs George Washington U., Washington, 1984—; parent-child presch. observation program tchr. Montgomery County (Md.) Pub. Schs., 1972-75; adj. prof. M.A. in Teaching Trinity Coll., Washington, 1974-78, asst. prof., 1978-84; adj. prof. Webster Coll., St. Louis, 1981; adj., assoc. prof. George Mason U., Fairfax, Va., 1989-95; speaker various meetings, confs. and workshops throughout U.S., 1970-94; exec. bd. Md. Coun. Staff Devel., 1987-89; chmn. Tri-County Staff Devel. Consortium, Charles County, St. Mary's County and Calvert Counties, Md.; program chmn. Assn. Fed. Info. Resource Mgmt., 1993-94; conf. chmn. AFFIRM/ SIGCAT, 1994, exec. v.p., 1995—. Author: (with Dorothy Rich) Success for Children Begins at Home, 1973, The Home New Educational Partnership, 1974, A Family Affair: Education, 1977, Leadership and the Use of Power in ECE Administration, 1980; Motivating Staff, Parents and Children, 1981, Home Learning Enablers and Other Helps, 1992, Administration and Management of Programs for Young Children, 1995; contbr. articles to profl. jours. Elder Rockville Presbyn. Ch. Grantee U.S. SBA, Montgomery C.C., 1983, 84, Md. State Dept Edn., Tri-County Staff Devel. Consortium, 1988; recipient nat. award Parent Coop. Preschs. Internat., 1970. Mem. ASCD, Nat. Assn. Edn. Young Children, Assn. Childhood Edn. Internat., assn. Fed. info. Resource Mgmt., Am. Soc.of Pub. Adminstrn. Presbyterian. Office: George Washington U 2231 Crystal Dr Ste 150 Arlington VA 22202 Helping children and adults develop to their full potential and helping east and west understand each other better are two very rewarding goals of my life.

SHOEMAKER, DAVID POWELL, chemist, educator; b. Kooskia, Idaho, May 12, 1920; s. Roy Hopkins and Sarah (Anderson) S.; m. Clara Brink, Aug. 5, 1955; 1 son, Robert Brink. B.A., Reed Coll., 1942; Ph.D., Calif. Inst. Tech., 1947. Research asst. Calif. Inst. Tech., 1943-45, NRC fellow, 1945-47, sr. research fellow, 1948-51; fellow John Simon Guggenheim Meml. Found. Inst. Theoretical Physics, Copenhagen, Denmark, 1947-48; asst. prof. chemistry Mass. Inst. Tech., Cambridge, 1951-56; assoc. prof. Mass. Inst. Tech., 1956-60; prof. MIT, 1960-70; prof. chemistry Oreg. State U., Corvallis, 1970-84, prof. emeritus, 1984—, chmn. dept. chemistry, 1970-81; vis. scientist Lab. Cristallographie, CNRS, Grenoble, France, 1965, 1978-79; vis. lectr. Kemisk Institut, Aarhus, Denmark, June 1979; cons. Exxon Co. U.S.A., Baton Rouge, 1957-86; sec.-treas. U.S.A. Nat. Com. for Crystallography, 1962-64, chmn.; Nat. mem. vis. com. chemistry dept. Brookhaven Nat. Lab., 1974-79; mem. evaluation panel material scis. div. Nat. Bur. Standards, 1977-79. Author: (with Carl W. Garland, Joseph W. Nibler) Experiments in Physical Chemistry, 1962, 67, 74, 81, 89; Am. co-editor: Acta Crystallographica, 1964-69. Recipient Howard Vollum Sci. and Tech. award Reed Coll., 1986. Fellow AAAS, Am. Phys. Soc.; mem. Am. Chem. Soc., Am. Crystallographic Assn. (pres. 1970), Am. Acad. Arts and Scis., Internat. Union Chrystallography (mem. exec. com. 1972-78), Phi Beta Kappa, Sigma Xi, Phi Lambda Upsilon, Phi Kappa Phi. Home: 3453 NW Hayes Ave Corvallis OR 97330-1729 Office: Oreg State U Dept Chemistry Corvallis OR 97331

SHOEMAKER, DON (DONALD CLEAVENGER SHOEMAKER), columnist; b. Montreal, Que., Can., Dec. 6, 1912; (parents Am. citizens); s. Richard Samuel and Alberta (Stone) S.; m. Lyal Reynolds, Oct. 30, 1937 (dec. July 1968); 1 child, Elizabeth; m. Suzanne Statler, Aug. 2, 1969; 1 child, Charlotte. AB, U. N.C., 1934; LittD (hon.), Hollywood Coll., 1970. Tel. editor Greensboro Record, N.C., 1934-37, Asheville Times, N.C., 1937-41; assoc. editor Asheville Citizen, 1941-47, editor, 1947-55; exec. dir. So. Edn. Reporting Serve, 1955-58; editor, editorial page The Miami Herald, 1958-62, editor, 1962-78; columnist Knight-Ridder Newspapers, 1978—. Editor: Henry George: Citizen of the World (by Anna George de Mille), 1950, Middle East Journey; The Case of the Lively Ghost, 1957, With All Deliberate Speed, 1957, Spanish Diary, 1974; contbr. to mags. and encys. Sec. Fla. World's Fair Authority; mem. Orange Bowl Com.; dir. Fla. Bicentennial Commn.; past vice chmn. Fla. Council of 100; chmn. N.C. Conf. Editorial Writers, 1951-52; pres. Buncombe County Community Chest, 1951; mem. Coun. on Fgn. Relations; chmn. Dade Coordinating Council, 1974-75; chmn. Fla. region NCCJ, also nat. trustee; trustee U. Miami, Mus. of Sci.; trustee United Way Dade County, pres., 1976, chmn. bd., 1977; dir., chief U.S. del. United Way Internat., Hong Kong, 1977; mem. Fla. Edn. Council, Fla. Task Force on Student Assessment; chmn. Fla. Profl. Tchr. Task Force, 1985-86. Recipient Silver medallion award NCCJ, 1970, medal of merit The Asheville

Sch., Diamond Jubilee award Nat. Jewish Hosp., 1974, Disting. Eagle Scout award, 1978; named to N.C. Journalism Hall of Fame, 1982. Mem. Inter-Am. Press Assn., Asociacion de Amigos del Pais (Guatemala), Internat. Press Inst., Am. Soc. Newspaper Editors, Order of Golden Fleece (U. N.C.), Newcomen Soc., Bath Club, Pi Kappa Alpha, Sigma Delta Chi. Episcopalian. Home and Office: 617 Sabal Palm Rd Bay Point Miami FL 33137

SHOEMAKER, ELEANOR BOGGS, television production company executive; b. Gulfport, Miss., Jan. 20, 1935; d. William Robertson and Bessie Eleanor (Ware) Boggs; m. D. Shoemaker, April 9, 1955 (div. 1987); children: Daniel W., William Boggs. Student in protocol, Southeastern U., 1952-53; student, George Washington U., Washington, 1953-56; BA in Communications and Polit. Sci. with honrs, Goucher Coll., 1981; postgrad.. Villanova U. Feature writer Washington Times Herald, 1951-54; dir. Patricia Stevens Modeling Agy., Washington, 1955-56; free-lance model Julius Garfinkel, Woodward & Lothrop, Washington, 1951-56; research analyst Balt. County Council, Towson, Md., 1980-81; feature news reporter Sta. WGCB-TV, Red Lion, Pa., 1980—; pub. speaker, protocol The Reliable Corp., Columbia, Md., 1982-86; media cons. The Enterprise Found., Columbia, Md., 1985-86; faculty, TV prodn. and communication St. Francis Prep Sch., Spring Grove, Pa., 1985-88; owner Windswept Prodns. Co., Felton, Pa., 1984—; mktg. svcs. coord. Yorktowne, Inc., Red Lion, Pa., 1993-95; mem. conservation bd. Pa. Parks and Recreation Soc., 1984—; prodr. The Pa. County TV Prodn., 1981; prodr., host Westar 4 Channel 9 half hour weekly news program Keystone Report. Prodr. The Pa. County TV Prodn., 1981, The Pa. County TV Prodn., 1981, documentary Human Rights: A Special Report, Sta. WGCB-TV, 1989; prodr., host Westar 4 Channel 9 half hour weekly news program Keystone Report, 1990. Bd. dirs. York (Pa.) County Parks and Recreation, 1972-87, YWCA, York, 1957-82, Hist. York, 1990—; mem. exec. com. York County Reps., 1972-82; accreditation adv. com. York Coll. of U.; instr. YWCA Women in Politics; founder, mem. Child Abuse Task Force, York, 1983—; mem. select com. Pa. Agrl. Zoning, 1988; mem. steering com. York Forum, 1989—; co-chmn. Cross Mill Restoration, 1987; mem. Displaced Homemaker's Bd., 1989—, pres., 1993—; bd. dirs. Hist. York, 1990—; founder, host Old Rose Tree Pony Club, 1967—; chair Spring Valley Hunt Pk. Task Force, 1972; master of fox hounds Mrs. Shoemaker's Hounds, 1969—; master of beagles Mrs. Shoemaker's Weybright Beagles, 1988—. Recipient pro bono child legal representation grant Pa. Bar Assn., 1983, Pa. Tree Farmer of Yr. award, 1987, Outstanding Achievement in Broadcasting award Am. Women in Radio and TV, 1992, Lay Person of Yr. award Pa. Recreation and Parks Assn. and Gov. Thornburg, 1982, Jefferson award, 1992, Matrix award Ctrl. Pa. Women in Comm., 1993, First pl. corp. video prodn. Ctrl. Pa. Women in Comm., 1993; selected journalist for Novosti Press USSR-U.S. Press Exch. program, 1989. Mem. Am. Polled Hereford Assn., York Area C. of C., York County C. of C. (publicity com. 1985—, agri. bus. com.), Masters of Foxhounds Assn. Episcopalian. Avocation: foxhunting, beagling. Home and Office: PO Box 167 Felton PA 17322-0167

SHOEMAKER, EUGENE MERLE, geologist; b. L.A., Apr. 28, 1928; s. George Estel and Muriel May (Scott) S.; m. Carolyn Jean Spellmann, Aug. 18, 1951; children: Christine Carol, Patrick Gene, Linda Susan. B.S., Calif. Inst. Tech., 1947, M.S. 1948; M.A., Princeton U., 1954, Ph.D., 1960; Sc.D., Ariz. State Coll., 1965, Temple U., 1967, U. Ariz., 1984. Geologist U.S. Geol. Survey, 1948-93, scientist emeritus, 1993—, exploration uranium deposits and investigation salt structures Colo. and Utah, 1948-50, regional investigations geochemistry, volcanology and structure Colorado Plateau, 1951-56, research on structure and mechanics of meteorite impact and nuclear explosion craters, 1957-60, with E.C.T. Chao, discovered coesite, Meteor Crater, Ariz., 1960, investigation structure and history of moon, 1960-73, established lunar geol. time scale, methods of geol. mapping of moon, 1960, application TV systems to investigation extraterrestrial geology, 1961—, geology and paleomagnetism, Colo. Plateau, 1969—, systematic search for planet-crossing asteroids and comets, 1973-94; with C.S. Shoemaker and D.H. Levy discovered Periodic Comet Shoemaker-Levy 9, 1993; Trojan asteroids U.S. Geol. Survey, 1985-94, geology of satellites of Jupiter, Saturn, Uranus and Neptune, 1978—, investigating role of large body impacts in evolution of life, 1981—; impact craters of Australia, 1983—; organized br. of astrogeology U.S. Geol. Survey, 1961; co-investigator TV expt. Project Ranger, 1961-65; chief scientist, center of astrogeology U.S. Geol. Survey, 1966-68; prin. investigator geol. field investigations in Apollo lunar landing, 1965-70; also television expt. Project Surveyor, 1963-68; prof. geology Calif. Inst. Tech., 1969-85, chmn. div. geol. and planetary scis., 1969-72; sci. team leader Clementine Mission to the Moon, 1993-94; staff mem. Lowell Observatory, Flagstaff, Ariz., 1993—. Recipient (with E.C.T. Chao) Wetherill medal Franklin Inst., 1965; Arthur S. Flemming award, 1966; NASA medal for exceptional sci. achievement, 1967; honor award for meritorious service U.S. Dept. Interior, 1973; Disting. Service award, 1980; Disting. Alumni award Calif. Inst. Tech., 1986, co-recipient Rittenhouse medal, 1988, Nat. Medal of Sci. President Bush, 1992. Mem. NAS, Internat. Astron. Union, Am. Acad. Arts and Scis., Geol. Soc. Am. (Day medal 1982, Gilbert award 1983), Mineral Soc. Am., Soc. Econ. Geologists, Geochem. Soc., Am. Assn. Petroleum Geologists, Am. Geophys. Union (Whipple award 1993), Am. Astron. Soc. (Kuiper prize 1984), Meteoritical Soc. (Barringer award 1984, Leonard medal 1985). Home: RR 4 Box 998 Flagstaff AZ 86001-9803 Office: US Geol Survey 2255 N Gemini Dr Flagstaff AZ 86001-1637

SHOEMAKER, FRANK CRAWFORD, physicist, educator; b. Ogden, Utah, Mar. 26, 1922; s. Roy Hopkins and Sarah Parker (Anderson) S.; m. Ruth Elizabeth Nelson, July 11, 1944; children—Barbara Elaine, Mary Frances. A.B., Whitman Coll., 1943, D.Sc. (hon.), 1978; Ph.D., U. Wis., 1949. Staff mem. Radiation Lab. MIT, 1943-45; instr. physics U. Wis., 1949-50; mem. faculty Princeton U., 1950-89, prof. physics, 1962-89, emeritus, 1989—; assoc. dir. Princeton U. Pa. Accelerator, 1962-66; vis. scientist Rutherford High Energy Lab., 1965-66; main accelerator sect. head Nat. Accelerator Lab., 1968-69; prin. investigator Dept. of Energy High Energy Physics Contract, 1972-85. Co-author proposal for 3 billion electron volt Princeton-Pa. Accelerator, 1955. Fellow Am. Phys. Soc.; mem. Phi Beta Kappa, Sigma Xi. Home: 361 Walnut Ln Princeton NJ 08540-3446

SHOEMAKER, GRADUS LAWRENCE, chemist, educator; b. Zeeland, Mich., Jan. 18, 1921; s. Corey and Hattie (Lubbers) S.; m. Florence Etta Wright, June 5, 1952; children—Robert Neil, Betty Lynn. A.B., Hope Coll., 1944; M.S., U. Ill., 1947, Ph.D., 1949. Mem. faculty U. Louisville, 1949—, prof. chemistry, 1955-88, prof. emeritus, 1988—, chmn. dept., 1963-64, 65-67, chmn. div. natural sci., 1967-79; mem. exec. bd. Covenant Housing, Inc., 1989—. Served as ensign USNR, 1944-45. Mem. Am. Chem. Soc. (councillor 1968-80), AAUP, Ky. Acad. Sci., Blue Key, Sigma Xi, Alpha Epsilon Delta, Phi Kappa Phi, Phi Lambda Upsilon. Presbyn. Home: 2815 Meadow Dr Louisville KY 40220-2406

SHOEMAKER, HAROLD LLOYD, infosystem specialist; b. Danville, Ky., Jan. 3, 1923; s. Eugene Clay and Amy (Wilson) S.; A.B., Berea Coll., 1944; postgrad. State U. Ia., 1943-44, George Washington U., 1949-50, N.Y. U., 1950-52; m. Dorothy M. Maddox, May 11, 1947 (dec. Feb. 1991). Research physicist State U. Ia., 1944-45, Frankford Arsenal, Pa., 1945-47; research engr. N.Am. Aviation, Los Angeles, 1947-49, Jacobs Instrument Co., Bethesda, 1949-50; asso. head systems devel. group The Teleregister Corp., N.Y.C., 1950-53; mgr. electronic equipment devel. sect., head planning for indsl. systems div. Hughes Aircraft Co., Los Angeles, 1953-58; dir. command and control systems lab. Bunker-Ramo Corp., Los Angeles, 1958-68, v.p. Data Systems, 1968-69, corp. dir. data processing, 1969-75; tech. staff R & D Assocs., Marina Del Rey, Calif., 1975-85; info. systems cons., 1985—. Served with AUS, 1945-46. Mem. IEEE. Patentee elec. digital computer. Home: PO Box 3385 Granada Hills CA 91394-0385

SHOEMAKER, INNIS HOWE, art museum curator; b. Reading, Pa.; d. William Erety and Jean (Miller) S. AB, Vassar Coll., 1964; MA, Columbia U., 1968, PhD, 1975. Curator Vassar Coll. Art. Gallery, Poughkeepsie, N.Y., 1965-68, 73-76; asst. dir. Ackland Art Mus., U. N.C., Chapel Hill, 1976-82, dir.; 1983-86; sr. curator prints, drawings and photographs Phila. Mus. Art, 1986—; fellow in art history Am. Acad. in Rome, 1971-73; adj. prof. U. N.C., Chapel Hill, 1983-86; bd. dirs. Conservation Ctr., Phila., 1987—; vis. com. Frances Lehman Lueb Art Ctr., Vassar Coll., 1993—. Co-author: The Engravings of Marcantonio Raimondi, 1981, Paul Cézanne: Two Sketchbooks, 1989. Mem. Coll. Art Assn. Am., Am. Assn. Mus., Print

Coun. Am. (bd. dirs. 1986-89), Conservation Ctr. for Art and Historic Artifacts, Phila. (bd. dirs. 1987—), Lehman Loeb Art Ctr., Vassar Coll. (vis. com. 1993—). Office: Phila Mus Art PO Box 7646 Philadelphia PA 19101-7646

SHOEMAKER, JOAN, mayor; b. Hartford, Conn., Feb. 20, 1935; d. Jean George and Olive Irene (Clifford) Hauet; m. Warner D. Dalton, Nov. 8, 1956 (div. Apr. 1960); children: Lori, Robert; m. Steven R. Shoemaker, Dec. 18, 1965; children: Mike, Marsi, Jennifer, Douglas. Mayor City of El Cajon, Calif., 1990—. Planning commr. City of El Cajon, 1979-83, councilwoman, 1983-90. Republican. LDS. Office: City of El Cajon 200 E Main St El Cajon CA 92020-3912

SHOEMAKER, ROBERT MORIN, retired army officer, county government official; b. Almont, Mich., Feb. 18, 1924; s. Uriah Beebe and Pomala (Morin) S.; m. Mary Alice Rickard, July 17, 1948. BS, U.S. Mil. Acad. 1946; postgrad., U.S. Army Command and Gen. Staff Coll., 1959, Army War Coll., 1967. Commd. 2d lt. U.S. Army, 1946, advanced through grades to gen., 1978, platoon leader, bn. staff officer, co. comdr. 18th Inf., Fed. Republic Germany, 1947-50; co. comdr., regtl. S2, S3, 23d Inf. U.S. Army, Republic of Korea, 1953-54; staff officer inf. br. DA U.S. Army, 1954-56; student, faculty officer U.S. Army Aviation Sch. U.S. Army, Ft. Rucker, Ala., 1959-62; project officer Army Concept Team U.S. Army, Vietnam, 1962-63; bn. comdr., asst. chief of staff, G-3, 11th Air Assault Div. U.S. Army, Ft. Benning, Ga., 1963-65; bn. cmdr., squadron comdr. 1st Cav. Div. U.S. Army, Vietnam, 1965-66; chief plans and programs Army Aviation DA U.S. Army, 1967-69; chief of staff, asst. div. comdr. 1st Cav. U.S. Army, Vietnam, 1969-70; dep. comdr., chief. of staff III Corps and Ft. Hood, Tex. U.S. Army, 1970; dept. comdr. MASSTER U.S. Army, Ft. Hood, Tex., 1971-72; comdr. 1st Cav. U.S. Army, 1973-75; comdr. III Corps U.S. Army, Ft. Hood, 1975-77; dep. comdr. FORSCOM U.S. Army, Ft. McPherson, Ga., 1977-78; comdr. U.S. Army Forces Command, 1978-82; ret., 1982; county commr. Bell County, Tex., 1987-94. Decorated D.S.M., Silver Star medal with oak leaf cluster, Legion of Merit, D.F.C., Bronze Star, Air medal with 48 oak leaf clusters, Army Commendation medal with oak leaf cluster, Croix de Guerre (France), Gallantry Cross with palm (Republic of Vietnam), RVN Honor medal 1st class. Home: Rte 4 RR 4 Box 4510 K Belton TX 76513-9415 Office: PO Box 768 Belton TX 76513-0768

SHOEMAKER, SYDNEY S., philosophy educator; b. Boise, Idaho, Sept. 29, 1931; s. Roy Hopkins and Sarah Parker (Anderson) S.; m. Molly McDonald, Oct. 1, 1960; 1 son, Peter William. B.A., Reed Coll., 1953; postgrad., Edinburgh Univ., Scotland, 1953-54; Ph.D., Cornell Univ., 1958. Instr. Ohio State Univ., Columbus, 1957-60; asst. prof. Cornell Univ., Ithaca, N.Y., 1961-64, assoc. prof., 1964-67, prof., 1970—, Susan Linn Sage prof. philosophy, 1978—; assoc. prof. Rockefeller Univ., N.Y.C., 1967-70; John Locke lectr. Oxford U., England, 1972; Josiah Royce lectr. Brown U., 1993. Author: Self-Knowledge and Self-Identity, 1963, Identity, Cause, and Mind, 1984; co-author: Personal Identity, 1984; co-editor: Knowledge and Mind, 1983, Philso. Rev., 1964—(intermittently); gen. editor: Cambridge Studies in Philosophy, 1982-90. Fulbright scholar Edinburgh, Scotland, 1953-54; Santayana fellow Harvard Univ., Cambridge, Mass., 1960-61; fellow Ctr. Advanced Study in Behavioral Scis., Stanford, Calif., 1973-74; Nat. Endowment for Humanities, 1980-81, Guggenheim Found., 1987-88, Nat. Humanities Ctr., 1987-88. Mem. AAUP, Am. Philos. Assn. (mem. exec. com. ea. div. 1977-80, v.p. 1992-93, pres. 1993-94). Home: 104 Northway Rd Ithaca NY 14850-2241 Office: Cornell Univ Dept Philosophy 218 Goldwin Smith Hall Ithaca NY 14853

SHOEMAKER, WILLIAM EDWARD, financial executive; b. Charleston, W.Va., Sept. 17, 1945; s. Robert Edward and Janet Elizabeth (Hogland) S. BBA, U. Notre Dame, 1967. Assoc. buyer Proctor & Gamble, Cin., 1971; gen. mgr. Eastwind Inc., Anchorage, 1972-73; pres., operator Golden Horn Lodge, Inc., Bristol Bay, Alaska, 1973-79; treas. Hawley Resource Group, Inc., Anchorage, 1979-88; treas., chief fin. officer Golden Zone Resources, Inc., Campbell, Calif., 1988-90; ptnr. Resort Mgmt. Corp., Anchorage, 1987-90; pres. Discovery Holdings, Inc., Ft. Lauderdale, Fla., 1991—; bd. dirs. Pacific Art & Design Cons., Inc. Bd. dirs. Anchorage Econ. Devel. Corp., 1988-90. Served to lt. (j.g.) USN, 1967-71. Mem. Quarter Deck Club (Anchorage). Republican. Avocations: boating, skiing, fishing. Home: 2301 Solar Plaza Dr Fort Lauderdale FL 33301

SHOEMATE, CHARLES RICHARD, food company executive; b. LaHarpe, Ill., Dec. 10, 1939; s. Richard Osborne and Mary Jane (Gillette) S.; m. Nancy Lee Gordon, Sept. 16, 1962; children: Steven, Jeffrey, Scott. BS, Western Ill. U., 1962; MBA, U. Chgo., 1973. Supr. Corn Products Co., Summit, Ill., 1962-72; comptroller Corn Products Unit of CPC Internat., Englewood Cliffs, N.J., 1972-74; plant mgr. Corn Products Unit of CPC Internat., Corpus Christi, Tex., 1974-76; v.p. ops. Corn Products Unit of CPC Internat., Englewood Cliffs, 1976-81; pres. Can. Starch Co., Montreal, Que., 1981-83; v.p. Corn Refining div. CPC Internat., Englewood Cliffs, 1983-86, pres., 1986-88; corp v.p. CPC Internat., Englewood Cliffs, 1983-88, pres., 1988—, chmn., chief exec. officer, 1990—. Office: CPC Internat Inc Box 8000 Internat Plz Englewood Cliffs NJ 07632

SHOEN, EDWARD JOSEPH, transportation and insurance companies executive; s. Leonard and Anna (Carty) S. MBA, Harvard U. Pres., chmn. Amerco Nev. Corp., Phoenix; pres. U-Haul Internat., Inc., Phoenix. Office: Amerco Nev Corp PO Box 21502 Phoenix AZ 85036-1502 also: Amerco 1325 Airmotive Way Reno NV 89502-3201*

SHOFF, PATRICIA ANN, lawyer; b. Colby, Kans., Sept. 27, 1948; d. Clarence O. and Clara C. (Ortbal) Shoff; m. Thomas E. Salsbery, Oct. 6, 1979; children: Emily Anne, Edward Philip. BA with honors, U. Iowa, 1970, JD with distinction, 1973. Bar: Iowa 1973, U.S Dist. Ct. (no. and so. dists.) Iowa 1974. Law clk. Supreme Ct. of Iowa, Des Moines, 1973-74; assoc. Thoma Schoenthal Davis, Hockenberg & Wine, Des Moines, 1974-79; ptnr., shareholder Davis, Hockenberg, Wine, Brown, Koehn & Shors, P.C., Des Moines, 1979—. Sec. bd. dirs. Iowa's Children and Families of Iowa, 1980-91, v.p 1981-82, pres. 1982-83, Very Spl. Arts Iowa, 1988—, sec. 1990, chair personnel com., 1990-92, pres. 1992, chair resource devel. com. 1992—; mem. Gov.'s Com. Child Abuse Prevention, 1982-92, chair 1987-92; pres. bd. govs. Greater Des Moines Leadership Inst., 1984-85; co-chair fundraising com. Hospice of Ctrl. Iowa, 1983-85; pub. rels. com. St. Augustin's Ch., 1986-87; exec. bd. Mid-Iowa Coun. Boy Scouts Am., 1988—, nominating com., 1989-91, Homestead bd. dirs., 1993, pres. elect, 1994. Mem. ABA (family law section, labor, employemnt law section), Iowa Law Sch. Gound (bd. dirs. 1992—), AAUW (juvenile justice com. 1974-76),Iowa State Bar Assn. (younr lawyers sect., family law com. 1979-81, mem. com. 1979-81, chair legal aid com. 1981-85, labor and employment law com. 1991-92, others), Iowa Supreme Ct. Bd. Law Examiners (vice chair 1991—, pres. 1994), Polk County Bar Assn. (treas. 1989-92, v.p. 1992-93, pres. elect 1993, award of Merit 1990), Women's Fedn. Lawyers, Greater Des Moines C. of C. Fedn. (bd. dirs. 1984-85, bur. econ. devel. com. 1985—, exec. call com. 1985—), Polk County Women Attys., Iowa Orgn. Women Attys., Greater Des Moines C. of C. Leadership Inst. (pres. bd. govs. 1984-85, alumni orgn. 1984—), Jr. League (adv. planning 1984-83, placement advisor 1986-87, grants com. 1988), Phi Delta Phi. Democrat. Roman Catholic. Office: Davis Hockenberg Wine Brown 2500 Fin Ctr 666 Walnut St Des Moines IA 50309-3904

SHOFSTAHL, ROBERT MAXWELL, savings and loan executive; b. New Orleans, Feb. 8, 1942; s. Maxwell Frederick and Ellen Anna (Falkenstein) S.; m. Lois Alice Berrigan, June 6, 1964; children: Tyson Brahm, Elisia Ellette, Christian Aric. BA cum laude (scholar) Tulane U., 1964; postgrad., 1966. Mgr. So. Bell-South Central Bell, New Orleans, Baton Rouge, Shreveport, 1964-71; asst. to pres. Pelican Homestead Savs. & Loan, Metairie, La., 1971-73, exec. v.p., 1973-77, dir., 1973-92, pres., CEO, 1978-92, pres., COO, dir. AmWest Savs. Assn., Bryan, Tex., 1992—; dir. Fed. Res. Bank of Atlanta, New Orleans br., 1986-88. Mem. Future of industry task force U.S. League, 1987-88; mem. 9th dist. FHLB Com. on Mgmt. Consignment Program, 1985; mem. last carousel fin. com. Friends of City Park, 1986-87; bd. dirs. Neighborhood Housing Services of New Orleans, 1978-81, treas., 1979-81; trustee St. Martin Episcopal Sch., 1981-87, treas., 1984, v.p., 1985-86, capital funds tri-chmn., 1984, headmaster search com., 1985, bd. visitors, 1989—; lectr. south grad. bus. sch. Loyola U., 1982—; mem. vis. com. Loyola U.

Bus. Sch., 1991-92; speaker ann. conv. Deans So. Bus. Adminstn. Assn., 1989; apptd. to gov's. Thrift Industry Adv. Coun., 1981-84; mem. adv. bd. New Orleans Opera Ball, 1984; inaugural pres. New Orleans Aquatics, 1988; panelist New Orleans: The Decade Ahead, 1989; hon. econ. devel. ambassador State of La., 1985; La. Newsmaker of Yr., USA Today, 1983. Mem. U.S. League Savs. Instns. (vice chmn. ad hoc fl. ins. com., 1976-77, chmn. ins. and protective com., 1979-80), La. League Savs. Instns. (ins. com. 1974, exec. com. 1980-81, 87-89, legis. com. 1983-84), League Homestead/Savs. and Loan Assn. Greater New Orleans (pres. 1973), Nat. Assn. Bus. Economists (panelist nat. policy suvey 1989-92), New Orleans Coun. Bus. Economists, Bryan-College Station C. of C. (mem. inner circle 1993—), Phi Beta Kappa, Phi Eta Sigma, Eta Sigma Phi. Episcopalian. Home: 324 Homestead Ave Metairie LA 70005 Office: AmWest Savs Assn 2800 S Texas Ave Bryan TX 77802

SHOGAN, ROBERT, news correspondent; b. N.Y.C., Sept. 12, 1930; s. Albert and Millie (Jacobs) S.; m. Ellen Shrewsbury, May 26, 1959; children: Cynthia Diane, Amelia Ford. B.A., Syracuse U., 1951; postgrad., U. Mich. Inst. Pub. Adminstrn., 1951, Columbia U. Grad. Faculty Polit. Sci., 1952. Reporter Detroit Free Press, 1956-59; telegraph editor Miami (Fla.) News, 1959-61; asst. editor Wall St. Jour., N.Y.C., 1961-65; evaluation officer Peace Corps, Washington, 1965-66; corr. Newsweek, Washington, 1966-73; nation polit. corr. Los Angeles Times, Washington, 1973—; profl.-in-residence Annenberg Sch. Communication, U. Pa., 1993. Author: Question of Judgement, 1972, Promises to Keep, 1977, None of the Above, 1982, The Riddle of Power, 1991, Hard Bargain, 1995; co-author: (with Tom Craig) The Detroit Race Riot, 1964. Served with U.S. Army, 1952-54. McCormick fellow Hoover Presdl. Libr., 1993; recipient 1st prize Feature Writing, Mich. AP, 1959, Disting. Reporting Pub. Affairs award Am. Polit. Sci. Assn., 1969. Mem. Phi Beta Kappa. Home: 3513 Raymond St Chevy Chase MD 20815 Office: 1875 I St NW Washington DC 20006-5409

SHOHET, JUDA LEON, electrical and computer engineering educator, researcher, high technology company executive; b. Chgo., June 26, 1937; s. Allan Sollman and Frannye Ina (Turner) S.; m. Amy Lenore Scherz, Sept. 5, 1969; children: Aaron, Lena, William. BS, Purdue U., 1958; MS, Carnegie Mellon U., 1960; PhD, Carnegie-Mellon U., 1961. Registered profl. engr., Wis. Asst. prof. Johns Hopkins U., Balt., 1961-66; assoc. prof. U. Wis., Madison, 1966-71, prof., 1971—, chmn. dept. elec. and computer engring., 1986-90, dir. Torsatron/Stellarator Lab., 1974—, dir. Engring. Rsch. Ctr. for Plasma-Aided Mfg., 1986—; pres. Omicron Tech., Inc. Madison, 1985—; cons. Hewlett-Packard Co., Abbott Labs, Trane Co., Oak Ridge Nat. Lab., McGraw-Edison Co., Princeton U., Los Alamos Sci. Lab., Nicolet Instruments, Lawrence Livermore Nat. Lab., Westinghouse Elec. Corp. Author: The Plasma State, 1971, Flux Coordinates and Magnetic Field Structure. 1991; contbr. over 100 articles to profl. jours; author over 350 conf. papers; patentee in field. Recipient Frederick Emmons Terman award Am. Soc. for Engring. Edn., 1978, John Yarborough Meml. medal British Vacuum Coun., 1993. Fellow IEEE (Centennial medal 1984, Richard F. Shea Disting. Mem. award 1992), Am. Phys. Soc.; mem. IEEE Nuclear and Plasma Scis. Soc. (pres. 1980-82, Merit award 1978, Plasma Sci. and Applications prize 1990). Avocations: skiing, sailing, hiking. Home: 1937 Arlington Pl Madison WI 53705-4001 Office: U Wis Dept Elec & Computer Engring 2414 Engring Bldg Madison WI 53706

SHOICHI, IDA, artist, printmaker, painter, sculptor; b. Kyoto, Japan, Sept. 13, 1941; came to U.S., 1970; s. Ida Kikuji and Ida Yukie. BA, Kyoto Mcpl. U. Art, MFA, BA (hon.). Cert. mus. curator. lectr. dept. sculpture, printmaking Kyoto Mcpl. U. Art, 1965-68, 70-72, Ohio State U., Columbus, 1974, Columbus Inst. Printmaking, 1974, SUNY, New Paltz, 1974, Kala Art Inst., Berkeley, Calif. 1979, San Francisco Art Inst., 1979, Art Inst. Chgo., 1980, U. Alta., 1981, Calif. Coll. Art and Craft, 1986, Whitman Coll., Walla Walla, Wash., 1989, Art Mus. Cin., 1989, others; panelist in field. Solo exhbns. include Gallery Azuchi, Osaka, Japan, 1966, Dragon, Inc., Paris, 1970, Gallery Crews, N.Y.C., 1970, Himezi Gallery, Tokyo, 1974, 75, 76, Gallery Coco, Kyoto, Japan, 1976, Tokyo Gallery, 1977, 79, 82, 86, 92, Suzuki Gallery, N.Y.C., 1979, San Francisco Art Inst., 1979, Yoh Art Gallery, Osaka, 1979, 80, 82, 83, 84, 87, 88, 90, 92, Mary Baskett Gallery, Cin., 1981, 90, Gallery Ueda, Tokyo, 1983, 85, 87, 88, 89, 90, 92, Gallery 24, Osaka, 1983, 86, Chgo. Art Fair, 1993, Suzuki Gallery, N.Y., 1993, Life Gallery TEN, Fukuoka, Japan, 1994, Gallery Ueda, Tokyo, 1994, Perimeter Gallery, Chgo., 1994, Gallery Mori, Tokyo, 1994, many others; innumerable group exhbns. Japan, Europe, U.S, 1966—, include Kyoto Mcpl. Mus. Art, Mcpl. Mus. Mod. Art, Paris, Nat. Mus. Modern Art, Tokyo, Kyoto, San Jose (Calif.) Mus. Art, Mus. Modern Art, Chgo.; exhbns. Internat. Biennale Prints and Drawings; represented in collections Nat. Libr., Paris, Victoria and Albert Mus., London, MOMA, N.Y.C., Swedish Art Assn., Osaka (Japan) Contemporary Art Ctr., Museo de Arte Contemporaneo, Ibiza, Spain, Mus. Modern Art, Krakow, Poland, L.A. County Mus. Art, Art Acad. Cin., Smithsonian Internat.-Arthur M. Sackler Gallery, Deutsch Bank AG, Frankfurt, Ger., Hara Mus. Contemporary Art, Tokyo, numerous others. Recipient Peter Millard prize 7th Brit. Internat. Print Biennale, Bradford, Eng., 1982, (with Robert Rauschenberg) Award for Excellence Internat. Cultural Exchange NEA, Washington, 1986, Grand Priz Suntory Prize Suntory Found., 1989, Aequo Prize 12th Internat. Print Biennale, Krakow, Poland, 1988, The Suntry Grand prize, 1989, others; French Govt. grantee, 1968, Japan Soc. N.Y.C. grantee, 1974, Asian Cultural Coun. grantee, N.Y.C., 1986, Hitachi Found. grantee, Washington, 1986, Centrum Found. grantee, Centennial Wash. State, 1989. Office: 4 5 2 Kagamishhi Okitayama, Kita-ku Kyoto 603, Japan also: 2924 Russell St Berkeley CA 94705-2334

SHOKEIR, MOHAMED HASSAN KAMEL, medical geneticist, educator; b. Mansoura, Egypt, July 2, 1938; emigrated to Can., 1969, naturalized, 1974; s. Hassan Sayed and Lolia Nora (Kira) S.; m. Donna Jean Nugent, Feb. 27, 1968; children: Marc Omar, Vanessa May. MB, BCh in Medicine and Surgery, Cairo U., 1960, ChD, 1963, ChD in Orthopedics, 1964; MS, U. Mich., 1965, PhD, 1969. Intern Cairo U. Hosps., 1960-61, resident, 1961-64; Fulbright rsch. scholar dept. human genetics U. Mich., 1964-69; asst. prof. pediatrics U. Sask., Saskatoon, 1969-71, assoc. prof., 1971-73, prof., 1977—, dir. div. med. genetics, 1975—, head dept. pediatrics, 1979—; head dept. pediatrics Saskatoon Dist. Health Bd., 1993—; head sect. clin. genetics U. Man., Winnipeg, 1973-75; mem. staffs Univ. Hosp., Saskatoon City Hosp., St. Paul's Hosp.; cons. Winnipeg Health Scis. Centre, Regina Gen. Hosp. Contbr. articles to profl publs. Mem. Acad. Freedom and Tenure Com., Ottawa, Ont., Can., 1980-90, Queen Elizabeth II scientist, 1969-75. Med. Rsch. Coun. grantee, 1970-79; Canadian Coll. Med. Geneticists Found. fellow, 1975—. Fellow Can. Coll. Med. Geneticists, Can. Soc. Clin. Investigation (councillor 1974-76), Can. Med. Assn. (chmn., mem. adv. com. 1987—; mem. Assn. Med. Sch. Pediatric Dept. Chairmen, Am. Canadian Univ. Dept. Chairmen, Am. Pediatric Soc., Soc. Pediatric Research, N.Y. Acad. Scis., Am. Geriatrics Soc., Am. Fedn. Clin. Research, Mid-Western Soc. Pediatric Research, Western Pediatric Soc., Am. Soc. Human Genetics, Genetics Soc. Am., Genetics Soc. Can., Am. Genetic Assn., Am. Pediatric Health Assn. Home: 108 Riel Crescent, Saskatoon, SK Canada S7J 2W6 Office: U Sask, Dept Pediatrics, Saskatoon, SK Canada S7N 0X0 *Never tried to imagine what the future will bring, found the present and its implications enough to occupy me. The overriding passions in my life have been the love of man and the pity for his suffering. I have come to accept the futility of eliminating bias, even prejudice—mine or others'; my hope now is to recognize it and shield one's actions from it. What the world needs is more tolerance. Always found praise a bit embarrassing, confusing and altogether inhibiting—the most lavish for the least deserved accomplishment. Always thought the world is, at best, approximate. I now realize that in life one cannot have all bases covered.*

SHOKUROV, VYACHESLAV VLADIMIROVICH, mathematics educator; b. Moscow, May 18, 1950; came to U.S., 1991; s. Valdimir Nicolaevich and Zinaida (Filippovna) S.; m. Svetlana Igorevna Slabnavich, July 21, 1981; children: Anton Vyacheslavovich, Svyatoslav Vyacheslavovich. Diploma with honors, Moscow State U., 1972, PhD, 1976; DSc, Math. Inst. Acad Sci, Moscow, 1985. Researcher All-Union Inst. Sci. and Tech. Info., Moscow, 1975-82; prof. Yaroslavl' (Russia) Pedagogical Inst. Ministry of Edn., 1982-91, Johns Hopkins U., Balt., 1991—; participant in Year of Algebraic Geometry, Inst. for Advanced Study, Princeton, N.J., 1981-82. Contbr. articles to profl. jours. Recipient scholarship Max Planck Inst., Bonn, Fed. Republic Germany, 1983, Inst. for Advanced Study, Princeton, N.J., 1990-91. Mem.

Moscow Math. Soc., Spl. Sci. Coun. on Algebra, Yaroslavl' (v.p. 1991—). Mem. Eastern Orthodox Ch. Avocations: music, sports. Office: Johns Hopkins U Baltimore MD 21218

SHOLDER, JASON ALLEN, medical products company executive; b. Boston, Dec. 13, 1944; s. Samuel and Muriel (Weiss) S.; 1 child from previous marriage, Adam; m. Nancy Kate Oyer, Dec. 20, 1992; 1 child, Rachel. BSEE, Northeastern U., Boston, 1967; MS in Physics, MIT, 1969. Sr. v.p. tech. Pacesetter, Inc., Sylmar, Calif., 1977—. Contbr. articles to profl. jours. Mem. N.Am. Soc. Pacing and Electrophysiology. Achievements include 56 patents in field of cardiac pacemakers. Office: Pacesetter Inc 15900 Valley View Ct Sylmar CA 91392

SHOLES, DAVID HENRY, lawyer, former state senator; b. Providence, June 1, 1943; s. Leonard and Anna S. BA, Brown U., 1965; JD, Boston U. 1968. Bar: R.I. 1968, Mass. 1968. Pvt. practice law, Providence and Warwick, R.I., 1969-72; sr. ptnr. Sholes & Sholes, Warwick, 1972—; former lectr. U. R.I. Extension; mem. R.I. State Senate, 1976-92, chmn. senate com. on health, edn. & welfare; state adv. com. U.S. Civil Rights Commn.; former mem. Def. Civil Preparedness Adv. Coun., Cranston Gen. Hosp. Mem. R.I. Bar Assn., R.I. Trial Lawyers Assn., Cranston Hist. Soc., Phi Alpha Delta. Democrat. Mem. Clubs: K.P., Masons, Kiwanis, Touro Fraternal Assn. (bd. dirs.). Home: 32 Mauran St Cranston RI 02910-1818 Office: 1375 Warwick Ave Warwick RI 02888-5032

SHON, FREDERICK JOHN, nuclear engineer; b. Pleasantville, N.Y., July 24, 1926; s. Frederick and Lucy (Stelz) S.; m. Dorothy Theresa Patterson, June 8, 1946; 1 son, Robert Frederick. BS, Columbia U., 1946; postgrad, Ohio State U., U. Calif., Berkeley. With Publicker Alcohol Co., Phila., 1946-47, Thermoid Co., Trenton, N.J., 1947-48, Mound Lab., Miamisburg, Ohio, 1948-51; radiation chemist Atomics Internat., Canoga Park, Calif., 1951-52; physicist, reactor ops. supr. Lawrence Radiation Lab., Livermore, Calif. 1952-61; chief exam br., div. licensing and regulations U.S. AEC, Washington, 1961-62, chief reactor safety br., div. operational safety, 1963-67, asst. dir. nuclear facilities, 1967-72; dep. chief adminstrv. judge-tech., vice-chmn. tech., atomic safety and licensing bd. panel U.S. Nuclear Regulatory Commn., Washington, 1972—; cons. various nuclear firms including Danish AEC, Risoe, Atomics Internat., Spanish AEC, IAEA; lect. nuclear engring. U. Calif., Berkeley, 1955-63. Mem. Am. Nuclear Soc., Tau Beta Pi. Home: 4212 Flower Valley Dr Rockville MD 20853-1808 Office: US Nuclear Regulatory Commn Washington DC 20555

SHONDELL, DONALD STUART, physical education educator; b. Fort Wayne, Ind., Jan. 1, 1929; s. Howard David and Elizabeth (Jones) S.; m. Betty Lou Hudson, Dec. 30, 1951; children: Steven, Kim, David, John. BS, Ball State U., 1952, MS, 1955; PED, Ind. U., 1970. Tchr. Brook (Ind.) High Sch., 1956-58; instr. Ball State U., Muncie, Ind., 1958—; pres. U.S. Volleyball Assn., Colorado Springs, Colo., 1979-80, v.p. 1972-80; ch mn. NCAA Volleyball Com., Overland, Kans. Author: Volleyball, 1970. Recipient Leader in Volleyball award, 1971, William Morgan Pres.'s award U.S. Volleyball Assn., 1981, Tachikara 600 Victory Club award, 1989, H.T. Friermood award U.S. Volleyball Assn., Outstanding Faculty Tchr. award Ball State U. 1980; named to Ball State Athletic Hall of Fame, 1984, Del. County Athletic Hall of Fame, 1987, Disting. Alumni award Ball State U., 1994; named outstanding alumnus Ball State Tchrs. Coll. Alumni Assn., 1980. Methodist. Avocations: racket sports, volleyball. Home: 4215 N Winthrop Rd Muncie IN 47304-2960 Office: Ball State U Muncie IN 47306

SHOOB, MARVIN H., federal judge; b. Walterboro, S.C., Feb. 23, 1923; s. Michael Louis and Lena (Steinberg) S.; m. Janice Paradies, Nov. 14, 1949; children: Michael, Wendy. J.D., U. Ga., 1948. Bar: Ga. 1948. Ptnr. Brown & Shoob, Atlanta, 1949-55; ptnr. Phillips, Johnson & Shoob, Atlanta, 1955-56, Shoob, McLain & Merritt, Atlanta, 1956-79; judge U.S. Dist. Ct., Atlanta, 1979—; chmn. Juvenile Ct. Com., 1974-70; mem. Ga. State Bar Grievance Tribunal, 1975-79; chmn. Ga. State Bar Fed. Legislation Com., 1977-79; guest lectr. Continuing Legal Edn., Athens, Ga., 1975-77. Democrat. 5th Dist. Democratic Exec. Com., 1974-76. Mem. Phi Eta Sigma, Phi Kappa Phi. Jewish. Office: US Dist Ct 1921 US Courthouse 75 Spring St SW Atlanta GA 30303

SHOOK, ANN JONES, lawyer; b. Canton, Ohio, Apr. 18, 1925; d. William M. and Lura (Pontius) Jones; m. Gene E. Shook Sr., Nov. 30, 1956; children: Scott, William, Gene Edwin Jr. AB, Wittenberg U., 1947; LLB, William McKinley Law Sch., 1955. Bar: Ohio 1956, U.S. Dist. Ct. (no. dist.) Ohio 1961, U.S. Ct. Appeals (6th cir.) 1981. Cost acct. Hoover Co., North Canton, Ohio, 1947-51; asst. sec. Stark County Prosecutor's Office, Canton, Ohio, 1951-53; ins. adjuster Traveler's Ins. Co., Canton, 1953-56; ptnr. Shook & Shook Law Firm, Toledo, 1958-62, North Olmsted, Ohio, 1962—. Mem. at large coun. Olmsted Community Ch., Olmsted Falls, Ohio, 1987-90; chmn. ways and means com. North Olmsted PTA, 1968; area chmn. United Way Appeal, North Olmsted, 1963; v.p. LWV, Toledo, 1960-62. Mem. Cleve. Bar Assn. Avocations: reading, boating, dancing, fitness.

SHOOK, LANGLEY R., lawyer; b. Alexandria, Va., Dec. 22, 1947. AB, U. Mich., 1969, JD magna cum laude, 1974. Bar: Ill. 1974, U.S. Dist. Ct. (no. dist.) Ill. 1974, U.S. Ct. Appeals (7th cir.) 1974, D.C. 1977, U.S. Dist. Ct. (D.C. dist.) 1977, U.S. Ct. Appeals (D.C. cir.) 1977. Ptnr. Sidley & Austin, Washington. Office: Sidley & Austin 1722 I St NW Washington DC 20006-3705

SHOOK, ROBERT LOUIS, insurance company executive, business writer; b. Apr. 7, 1938; m. Elinor Marks; children: Carrie, RJ, Michael. BSBA, Ohio State U., 1959. Chmn. bd. Shook Assocs. Corp.; co-founder, chmn. bd. Am. Exec. Corp., Am. Exec. Life Ins. Co.; Appearences on over 600 radio and TV talk shows, including CNN, The David Susskind Show, The Sally Jessy Raphael Show, The Today Show and others. Author: Winning Images, 1977, 2d edit., 1978, The Greatest Salespersons, 1978, 2d edit., 1980, The Entrepreneurs, 1980, The Real Estate People, 1980, The Chief Executive Officers, 1981, Why Didn't I Think of That!, 1982, The Shaklee Story, 1982, The Book of Why, 1983, Survivors: Living with Cancer, 1983, The Healing Family, 1984, The IBM Way...Insights into the World's Most Successful Marketing Organization, 1986, The Perfect Sales Presentation, 1986, Wheel of Fortune, 1987, Honda) An American Success Story, 1988, All You Need to Know About Patents, Copyrights and Trademarks, 1989, How to Close Every Sale, 1989, Turnaround: The New Ford Motor Company, 1990, The Wall Street Dictionary, 1990, Hardball: Subtle High-Pressure Selling Techniques That Work, 1990, The Book of Odds, 1991, America's Best Kept Secret, 1991, The Name of the Game is Life, 1992, The Winner's Circle, 1992, It's About Time, 1992, Franchising: The Business Strategy That Changed the World, 1993; co-author: How to be the Complete Professional Salesman, 1974, Total Commitment, 1975, Successful Telephone Selling in the 90's, 1990, Joe Gandolfo's How to Make Big Money Selling, 1984, The Greatest Sales Stories Ever Told, 1995, (with Mary Kay Ash) Women Who Want It All, 1995; contbg. editor: Success Mag., 1978-81. Bd. dirs., vice-chmn. Franklin County Am. Cancer Soc.; bd. dirs. Value City Dept. Stores; past trustee Columbus Opera. Home and Office: 261 S Columbia Ave Columbus OH 43209-1626

SHOOMAN, MARTIN LAWRENCE, electrical engineer, computer scientist, educator; b. Trenton, N.J., Feb. 24, 1934; s. Lou and Ada (Pearl) S.; m. Sylvia Rose Bashoff, Dec. 23, 1962; children: Andrew Michael, Alice Helen (Mrs. Mark Lebowitz). BS, MIT, 1956, MS, 1956; DEng, Poly. Inst. Bklyn., 1961. Test engr. GE Co., 1953-55; teaching fellow MIT, Cambridge, Mass., 1955-56, vis. assoc. prof. elec. engring., 1971; rsch. engr. Sperry Gyroscope Co., 1956-58; successively instr., asst. prof., assoc. prof. elec. engring. Poly. Inst. Bklyn., 1958-72; prof. elec. engring. and computer sci. Poly. U., 1973—; dir. computer sci. div., 1980-83; spl. lectr. IBM, Grumman Aerospace, Hazeltine Corp., U.S. Army, U. Calif., George Washington U., U. Md. Eng., France, Can., Israel, Belgium, Italy and others; cons. to govt. agys. and industry, including Bell Labs., NASA, GE, RCA; tech. chmn. IEEE Computer Soc. Symposium Software Reliability and Software Engring., 1973, 76, 79; gen. chmn., 1975, 85, chmn. com. software engring., 1975; prin. investigator Poly. U.; rsch. contracts with NASA, Office Naval Rsch., USAF, Dept. Transp., others. Author: Probabilistic Reliability, 1968, 2d edit. 1990, Software Engineering, 1983 (transl. Japanese and Chinese 1989), also chpts. in 6 textbooks, numerous rsch. papers and reports on reliability, safety,

computers, software and control systems. Fellow IEEE (spl. lectr., mem. adminstrv. com. reliability soc., software reliability tech. com., Best Tech. Paper on Reliability award, 1967, 71, 77, 83, Ann. Reliability award 1977, Best Paper on Software award 1977, mem. adv. bd. ann. reliability and maintainability symposium 1985—); Sigma Xi, Tau Beta Pi, Eta Kappa Nu. Home: 12 Broadfield Pl Glen Cove NY 11542-2004 Office: 6 Metrotech Ctr Brooklyn NY 11201-3840

SHOOP, DEBORAH, lawyer; b. Detroit, May 15, 1948; d. F. W. and E. M. Shoop; m. Charles John Bopp III, Jan. 31, 1982; 1 child, Charles John IV. BA, U. Mich., 1970, MLS, 1972; JD, Wayne State U., 1977. Bar: Mich. 1977, U.S. Dist. Ct. (ea. dist.) Mich. 1977, U.S. Ct. Appeals (6th cir.) 1980. Asst. v.p.; sr. counsel Alexander Hamilton Life Ins. Co. Am., Farmington Hills, Mich., 1979—; arbitrator Better Bus. Bur., Detroit, 1983—. Mem. ABA, Mich. Bar Assn. Home: 35684 Camden Ct Farmington Hl MI 48335-1214 Office: Alexander Hamilton Life Ins Co Am 33045 Hamilton Ct Farmington MI 48334-3358

SHOOTER, ERIC MANVERS, neurobiology educator, consultant; b. Mansfield, U.K., Apr. 18, 1924; came to U.S., 1964; s. Fred and Pattie (Johnson) S.; m. Elaine Staley Arnold, May 28, 1949; 1 child, Annette Elizabeth. BA, U. Cambridge, U.K., 1945, MA, 1949, PhD, 1950, ScD, 1986; DSc, U. London, 1964. Sr. scientist biochemistry Brewing Industry Rsch. Fedn., 1950-53; biochemistry lectr. Univ. Coll., London, 1953-63; assoc. prof. genetics Stanford U., 1963-68, prof. genetics and biochemistry, 1968-75, prof., chmn. neurobiology dept., 1975-87, prof. neurobiology, 1987—, chmn. Neurosci. PhD Program, 1972-82; assoc. Neurosci. Rsch. Program, N.Y.C., 1979-89; teaching staff Internat. Sch. Neurosci., Praglia, Italy, 1987-93; sr. cons. Markey Charitable Trust, Miami, Fla., 1985—; chair sci. adv. bd., and dir. Regeneron Pharm., Inc., Tarrytown, N.Y., 1988—. Assoc. editor: (book series) Ann. Rev. Neuroscis., 1984—; contbr. numerous articles to profl. jours. Recipient Wakeman award Duke U., 1988; Faculty scholar Josiah Macy Jr. Found., N.Y.C., 1974-75. Fellow AAS, The Royal Soc. (London), Am. Acad. Arts and Scis.; mem. Inst. Medicine NAS (fgn. assoc.), Biochem. Soc., Am. Assn. Biol. Chemists, Am. Soc. Neurochemistry, Soc. Neurosci., Internat. Soc. Neurochemistry, Internat. Brain Rsch. Orgn. Avocation: travel. Home: 370 Golden Oak Dr Portola Vally CA 94028-7757 Office: Stanford U Sch Medicine Dept Neurobiology Stanford CA 94305

SHOPE, ROBERT ELLIS, epidemiology educator; b. Princeton, N.J., Feb. 21, 1929; s. Richard Edwin Shope and Helen Madden (Ellis) Flemer; m. Virginia Elizabeth Barbour, Dec. 27, 1958; children—Peter, Steven, Deborah, Bonnie. B.A., Cornell U., 1951, M.D., 1954. Intern then resident Grace-New Haven Hosp., 1954-58; mem. staff Rockefeller Found., Belem, Brazil, 1959-65; dir. Belem Virus Lab., Brazil, 1963-65; from asst. to assoc. prof. epidemiology Yale Sch. Medicine, New Haven, 1965-75, prof., 1975-95; mem. faculty dept. pathology U. Tex. Med. Br., Galveston, 1995—; adv. bd. Gorgas Inst., Panema City, 1972-90; mem. WHO Expert Panel Arboviruses, Geneva, Switzerland, 1974—, U.S. del. U.S-Japan Coop. Med. Scis. Program, Washington, 1977—, Pan Am. Health Orgn. Commn. for Dengue, Washington, 1980—. Served to capt. U.S. Army, 1955-57, Southeast Asia. Fellow Am. Acad. Microbiology; mem. Am. Soc. Tropical Medicine and Hygiene (pres. 1980, Bailey K. Ashford award 1974, Walter Reed award 1993), Am. Soc. Virology, Am. Soc. Epidemiology, Infectious Diseases Soc. Am. Democrat. Office: U Tex Med Br Dept Pathology 11th and Texas Ave Galveston TX 77555-0609

SHOR, GEORGE G., JR., geophysicist, oceanographic administrator, engineer; b. N.Y.C., June 8, 1923; s. George Gershon and Dorothy (Williston); m. Elizabeth Louise Noble, June 11, 1950; children: Alexander Noble, Carolyn Elizabeth, Donald Williston. B.S., Calif. Inst. Tech., 1944, M.S., 1948, Ph.D., 1954. Joined Seismic Explorations, Inc., Houston, 1948; party chief Seismic Explorations, Inc., 1949-50; asst. research geophysicist to research geophysicist Scripps Inst. Oceanography, La Jolla, Calif., 1953-69; prof. marine geophysics Scripps Inst. Oceanography, 1969-90, prof. emeritus, 1990—, assoc. dir., 1968-91; mgr. Calif. Sea Grant program, 1969-73; Mem. NAS-NRC panel on Mohole site selection, 1959; com. on underwater telecommunications, 1968, USN Marine Geophys. Survey Liaison Council, 1965-67; spl. adv. to Com. for Coordination of Joint Prospecting for Mineral Resources in Asian Offshore Areas, 1976-91; chmn. ship scheduling panel Univ. Nat. Oceanographic Lab. Systems, 1987-89; sci. leader oceanographic expdns. to various parts of Pacific and Indian oceans, 1955-82. Served to lt. (j.g.) USNR, 1943-46; now comdr. USNR Ret. Fellow Geol. Soc. Am., Am. Geophys. Union; mem. Soc. Exploration Geophysicists, Scholia Club. Home: 2655 Ellentown Rd La Jolla CA 92037-1147

SHOR, SAMUEL WENDELL WILLISTON, naval engineer; b. N.Y.C., June 25, 1920; s. George Gershon and Dorothy (Williston) S.; m. Joan Bopp, June 21, 1958; children: Peter Williston, Molly Hathaway. Student, Harvard U., 1937-39; B.S., U.S. Naval Acad., 1942; Naval Engr., MIT, 1949; M.S. in Math., NYU, 1963. Commd. ensign U.S. Navy, 1942, advanced through grades to capt., 1962; served in cruisers Chicago, St. Louis, and Quincy, Pacific and Atlantic, 1942-46; assigned San Francisco Naval Shipyard, 1949-52, naval reactors br. AEC, 1952-53; AEC rep. for initial tests of submarines nuclear propulsion in U.S.S. Nautilus and U.S.S. Seawolf, 1953-57; AEC rep. for startup testing of Shippingport Atomic Power Sta., 1957-58; design supt., prodn. engring. officer N.Y. Naval Shipyard, 1958-63; dir. sonar systems office Naval Ship Systems Command, 1963-67, exec. dir. plans, 1967-69, dep. comdr. for engring., 1969-71; project mgr. electronic warfare Naval Electronic Systems Commd., 1971-73; with Bechtel Power Corp., San Francisco, 1973—. Author tech. papers. Mem. Soc. Naval Architects and Marine Engrs., Soc. Naval Engrs., Am. Math. Soc., Am. Phys. Soc., Sigma Xi. Home: 318 Montford Ave Mill Valley CA 94941-3313 Office: Bechtel Corp 50 Beale St San Francisco CA 94105-1895

SHORB, GARY SEYMOUR, hospital administrator; b. Memphis, Sept. 7, 1950; married. B, Clemson U., 1972; M, Memphis State U., 1985. Acting dir. Regional Med. Ctr., Memphis, 1984-87, pres., CEO, 1987-90; pres., CEO Meth. Hosps. of Memphis, 1990—. Contbr. articles to profl. jours. Home: 360 Bluff Ridge Cove Cordova TN 38018 Office: Meth Hosps Memphis 1265 Union Ave Memphis TN 38104

SHORE, HARVEY HARRIS, business educator; b. Cambridge, Mass., Apr. 14, 1940; s. Jacob and Freda Edna (Pearlman) S.; m. Roberta Ann Rogers, Jan. 29, 1967; children: Nina Ellen, Elissa Amy. BA cum laude, Harvard U., 1961; MS, MIT, 1963; DBA, Harvard U., 1966. Asst. prof. indsl. adminstrn. U. Conn., Storrs, 1966-72; assoc. prof. indsl. adminstrn. U. Conn., 1972-77; dir. Hartford MBA prog. U. Conn., Hartford, 1977-82; assoc. prof. mgmt. U. Conn., Storrs, 1982-95, assoc. prof. emeritus, 1995—. Contbr. articles to profl. jours.; editor Cubic Rev., 1975-78; author: Arts Administration and Management, 1987. Chmn. bus. adv. com. Tunxis Community Coll., Farmington, Conn., 1983-85; bd. dirs. Temple Beth Sholom, Manchester, Conn., 1987-90. Mem. Employee Assistance Soc. N.Am., Masons. Democrat. Jewish. Avocation: tennis. Office: U Conn 368 Fairfield Rd Storrs CT 06269

SHORE, HERBERT, writer, poet, educator; b. Phila., June 6, 1924; s. Meyer and Frances (Smiler) S.; m. Yen Lu Wong, Dec. 23, 1977; children: Norman Jon, Pia Ilyen Wong. Maya Iming Wong. B.A., U. Pa., 1942; postgrad., Columbia U., 1946-48, Dramatic Workship New Sch., 1946-48; postgrad. Stanford U., 1948-53; M.A., Stanford U., 1958; Ph.D., Internat. Coll., 1983. Writer, poet, dramatist and dramaturg, 1956—; dir. Council Tech. and Cultural Transformation, 1974-88; prof., assoc. dean Sch. of Theatre U. So. Calif., 1979-93; founding dir. TNR: The New Repertory, 1972—; cons. UNESCO, 1974—; provost Internat. Coll. 1983-86; writer-in-residence Blue Mountain Centre, 1985, 86; dir. plays for theatre and TV, author plays also cantatas; disting. vis. fellow La Trobe U., Australia, 1990; scholar in residence Eltham Coll., Australia, 1990; sr. rsch. scholar Ctr. for Multiethnic and Transnat. Studies, U. So. Calif., 1993—; fellow Mayiboye Ctr., South Africa, 1995; mentor global studies Immaculate Heart Coll. Ctr., 1993—. Author: Come Back Africa, 1970, Ashes Dark Antigone, 1972, Toward the World of Tomorrow, 1978, Cultural Policy, 1981, Cicada Images, Moulting, 1983, No Future Wrapped in Darkness, 1984; Seek to Be Human, 1985, Beginnings are Born in Memory, 1986, Shime, 1986, Trees Die Standing, 1987, And the Dogs Are Silent, 1988, Should the Grain Perish, 1989, Namashawala, Santa Claus and the Bagamoyo Cock, 1990, South

African Township Theatre, 1990, Southern Africa: A Dream Deferred, 1990, Apartheid's Waning and Dangerous Years, 1990, Sounds in the Wind, 1991, Exile from El Salvador, Terra Infirma, 1992; also articles, short stories, poems. Adv. council Internat. Symposium on Arts, Banff Centre, 1984—; exec. com. Internat. Inst. Audio-Visual Media, Vienna, 1985—; assoc. Ctr. for African Studies, Eduardo Mondlane U., 1988—. Served with USMC, 1943-46. Recipient Writers Digest prize for fiction, 1963, medal of Bagamoyo, Nat. Assembly, Mozambique, 1989; Herbert Shore Collection established in his honor Immaculate Heart Coll. Ctr., 1991, Mayiboye Ctr., South Africa, 1995; grantee Ford Found., 1978-78, Rockefeller Found., 1966-67, NEH, 1979—, Helen Wurlitzer Found., 1958-60, Social Sci. Rsch. Coun., 1967-68, African and Am. Univs. Program, 1964-65, Kate Maremont Found., 1959-60, Centro Mexicano de Escritores, 1958. Mem. PEN, Assn. Theatre Higher Edn., LMDA, USA West, Nat. Writers Union, Acad. Am. Poets, Soc. Writers and Poets, African Studies Assn. Office: U So Calif Ctr Multiethnic Transnat Studies Univ Park Ker 310 Los Angeles CA 90089-7724

SHORE, HOWARD LESLIE, composer; b. Toronto, Ontario, Canada, Oct. 18, 1946; s. Mac and Bernice (Ash) S.; m. Elizabeth Ann Cotnoir, Aug. 3, 1990; 1 child, Mae. Student, Berklee Sch. Music, 1965-67, Forest Hill Collegiate, Toronto, Ont., Can., 1961-64. Composer film scores including I Miss You, Hugs and Kisses, 1978, The Brood, 1979, Scanners, 1981, Videodrome, 1983, Places in the Heart, 1984, After Hours, 1985, Belizaire the Cajun, 1986, Fire With Fire, 1986, The Fly, 1986, Nadine, 1987, Heaven, 1987, Moving, 1988, Dead Ringers, 1988 (Genie award), Big, 1988, She-Devil, 1989, An Innocent Man, 1989, Postcards from the Edge, 1990, The Silence of the Lambs, 1990, A Kiss before Dying, 1991, Naked Lunch, 1991, Prelude to a Kiss, 1992, Single White Female, 1992, (TV score) Scales of Justice, 1990, Guilty as Sin, 1993, Sliver, 1993, M. Butterfly, 1993, Mrs. Doubtfire, 1993, Philadelphia, 1993, The Client, 1994, Ed Wood, 1994, Nobody's Fool, 1994; music dir. Saturday Night Live, 1975-80. Mem. ASCAP, Lighthouse (founding mem.). Home: Wee Wah Lodge Tuxedo Park NY 10987 Office: Prince in NY Music Corp Wee Wah Rd Tuxedo Park NY 10987-0836

SHORE, JAMES H(ENRY), psychiatrist; b. Winston-Salem, N.C., Apr. 6, 1940; s. James Henry and Ellen Elizabeth (Hayes) S.; m. Christine Lowenbach, Aug. 24, 1963; children—Ellen Ottilie, James Henry. M.D., Duke U., 1965. Diplomate Am. Bd. Psychiatry and Neurology. Intern U. Utah Med. Center, 1965-66; resident in psychiatry U. Wash., 1966-69; chief mental health office Portland (Oreg.) Area Indian Health Service, 1969-73; assoc. prof. psychiatry, dir. community psychiatry tng. program U. Oreg. Health Scis. Center, 1973-75, prof., chmn. dept. psychiatry, 1975-85; chmn. dept. psychiatry U. Colo. Health Scis. Ctr., Denver, 1985—; interim chancellor, 1992-93; dir. Colo. Psychiatry Hosp., 1985—; interim dir. U. Colo. Hosp., Denver, 1987-88; mem. exptl. and spl. edn. com. NIMH-Internal Rev. Group, 1976-80; cons. in field. Contbr. numerous articles to profl. publs. Mem. Various community bds. Served with USPHS, 1969-73. Decorated USPHS Commendation medal; various grants. Fellow Am. Psychiat. Assn., Am. Coll. Psychiatry; mem. Am. Assn. Chmn. Depts. Psychiatry (pres. 1989), Am. Bd. Psychiatry and Neurology (dir. 1987—, pres. 1994), Residency Rev. Com. for Psychiatry (chmn. 1991-92). Office: U Colo Health Scis Ctr PO Box C-249 4200 E 9th Ave Denver CO 80262-0001

SHORE, MILES FREDERICK, psychiatrist, educator; b. Chgo., May 26, 1929; s. Miles Victor and Margaret Elizabeth S.; m. Eleanor M. Gossard, July 4, 1953; children: Miles Paul, Rebecca Margaret, Susanna Gladys. BA, U. Chgo., 1948; AB, Harvard U., 1950, MD, 1954. Intern U. Ill. Research and Edn. Hosp., Chgo., 1954-55; resident in psychiatry Mass. Mental Health Center, Beth Israel Hosp., Boston, 1956-61; asst. prof. psychiatry Tufts U. Sch. Medicine, Medford, Mass., 1964-68; assoc. prof. Tufts U. Sch. Medicine, 1968-71, prof., 1971-75, prof. community health, 1972-75; founder, dir. Tufts Community Mental Health Center, 1968-74, asso. dean community affairs, 1972-75; mem. faculty Boston Psychoanalytic Inst., 1973—; Bullard prof. psychiatry Harvard Med. Sch., Boston, 1975—, dir. div. mental health systems, 1993—; supt. Mass. Mental Health Ctr., 1975-93; vis. fellow John F. Kennedy Sch. Govt. Harvard U., 1993—; dir. program for chronic mental illness Robert Wood Johnson Found., 1985-92. Mem. editorial bd. Hosp. and Community Psychiatry Jour., 1990; bd. editors Jour. of Interdisciplinary History, 1975, Psycho History Rev., 1978; column editor Harvard Rev. Psychiatry, 1993; contbr. articles to profl. jours. Bd. dirs. Federated Dorchester Neighborhood Houses, Boston, 1975-78, Med. Found., Boston, 1987—; mem. Blue Ribbon Commn., Mass. Dept. Mental Health, 1979-80. Capt. U.S. Army, 1956-58. Community Mental Health Center grantee, 1964-75. Fellow Am. Psychiat. Assn. (life, mem. joint commn. on pub. affairs, Adminstrv. Psychiatry award 1987), Am. Coll. Psychiatrists (chmn. fin. com. 1983-89, bd. regents 1988-90, 1st v.p. 1994, pres. elect 1995-96, Bowls award for svc. 1990, Arthur P. Noyes award 1994); mem. Boston Psychoanalytic Soc. and Inst. (chmn. bd. trustees 1970-73), Mass. Psychiat. Soc. (pres. 1970-71), Mass. Hosp. Assn. (trustee 1980-85), Am. Hosp. Assn. (governing coun. for mental health and psychiat. svcs. 1985-87, chmn. governing coun. for psychiat. and substance abuse svcs. 1992-93), Roxbury Clin. Record Club, Aesculapian Club, Mass. Hist. Soc. Office: JFK Sch Govt 79 JFK St Cambridge MA 02138

SHORE, RICHARD ARNOLD, mathematics educator; b. Boston, Aug. 18, 1946; s. Philip M. and Miriam (Krensky) S.; m. Naomi J. Spiller, Aug. 3, 1969; children—Deena A., Aviva R. B. Jewish Edn., Hebrew Coll., 1966; A.B., Harvard U., 1968; Ph.D., MIT, 1972. Instr. U. Chgo., 1972-74; asst. prof. Cornell U., Ithaca, N.Y., 1974-78, assoc. prof., 1978-83; prof. U. Ill.-Chgo., 1977; vis. assoc. prof. MIT, Cambridge, 1980; vis. prof. Hebrew U., Jerusalem, 1982-83; prof. math. Cornell U., Ithaca, 1983—; organizing com. Logic Yr. at MSRI, 1989-90, other internat. meetings. Author: (with A. Nerode) Logic for Applications; cons. editor Jour. Symbolic Logic, 1980-83, editor, 1984-93, coord. editor, 1989-91; editor: Recursion Theory: mng. editor: Bull. Symbolic Logic, 1993—; contbr. articles to profl. jours. V.p. for edn. Hillel Acad. Broome County, Binghamton, N.Y., 1985-89; treas. Beth David Synagogue, 1993—. NSF grantee, 1973—. Mem. Am. Math. Soc., Spl. Interest Group in Algorithms and Computation Theory, Assn. for Computing Machinery, Assn. for Symbolic Logic (coun. 1984—). Jewish. Home: 7 Avon Rd Binghamton NY 13905-4201 Office: Cornell U Dept Math White Hall Ithaca NY 14853

SHORE, STEPHEN, photographer; b. N.Y.C., Oct. 8, 1947; m. Ginger Cramer Seippel, 1980; 1 child, Nicholas; 1 stepchild, Alex Seippel. Student, Minor White, Workshop, 1970. Photographer, 1953—. One-man shows, Met. Mus. Art, N.Y.C., 1971, Light Gallery, N.Y.C., 1972, 73, 75, 77, 78, 80, Phoenix Gallery, San Francisco, 1975, Mus. Modern Art, N.Y.C., 1976, U. Akron, Ohio, 1978, Vision Gallery, Boston, 1978, La Photogaleria, Madrid, 1979, Ewing Gallery, Washington, 1979, Catskill Ctr. Photography, Woodstock, N.Y., 1980, Fraenkel Gallery, San Francisco, 1982, Mus. Arts and Scis., Daytona Beach, Fla., 1981, Polk Pub. Mus., 1982, ARCO Ctr. Visual Arts, Los Angeles, 1982, N. Mex. State U. Art Gallery, Las Cruces, 1982, Art Inst. Chgo., 1984, Pace/MacGill, N.Y.C., 1989; group shows include, Met. Mus. Art, N.Y.C., 1973, Internat. Mus. Photography, George Eastman Hosue, Rochester, N.Y., 1975, Documenta 6, Kassel, W. Ger., 1977, Art Inst. Chgo., 1977, 79, Mus. Modern Art, N.Y.C., 1978, Corcoran Gallery, Washington, 1979, Kunsthaus, Zurich, Switzerland, 1980, U. Ariz. Mus. Art, Tucson, 1981; represented in permanent collections, Met. Mus. Art, N.Y.C., Mus. Modern Art, N.Y.C., Internat. Mus. Photography, George Eastman House, Rochester, N.Y., Mus. Fine Arts, Boston, Library of Congress, Washington, Art Inst. Chgo., in Permanent collections, Ctr. Creative Photography, U. Ariz., Tucson, in permanent collections, Stedelijk Mus., Amsterdam, Netherlands, Neue Sammlung, Munich, W.Ger., Australian Nat. Gallery, Canberra; author: Andy Warhol, 1968, Uncommon Places, 1982, The Gardens at Giverny, 1983; portfolio 12 Photographs, 1976; contbr. articles to profl. jours. Grantee Nat. Endowment Arts, 1974, 79; Guggenheim fellow, 1975; Am. Acad. (Rome) spl. fellow, 1980. Office: Pace-McGill 11 E 57th St New York NY 10022-2514

SHORE, THOMAS SPENCER, JR., lawyer; b. Akron, Ohio, Jan. 1, 1939; s. T. Spencer and Harriet G. (Delicate) S.; m. Margaret F. Kudzma, Aug. 12, 1961; children—Thomas Spencer III, John Christopher, Daniel Andrew, Mary Margaret. B.A., Brown U., 1961; J.D., Northwestern U., 1964. Bar: Ohio 1964. Assoc. Taft, Stettinius and Hollister, Cin., 1964-69; asso. Rendigs, Fry, Kiely & Dennis, Cin., 1969-71; partner Rendigs, Fry, Kiely &

Dennis, 1972—; adj. asst. prof. Chase Law Sch., U. No. Ky. Bd. dirs. United Cerebral Palsy of Cin., 1978—; bd. dirs., sec. Boys Club Am., Cin.; trustee emeritus Family Svc. of Cin. Area; past pres. Vis. Nurse Assn. of Cin., hon. trustee. Mem. Cin. Bar Assn., Ohio Bar Assn., Am. Bar Assn. Clubs: Cin. Country, Cin. Tennis, Queen City, Webhanet. Home: 3224 Columbia Pky Cincinnati OH 45226-1042 Office: 900 Central Trust Tower Cincinnati OH 45202

SHORENSTEIN, ROSALIND GREENBERG, physician; b. N.Y.C., Jan. 14, 1947; d. Albert Samuel and Natalie Miriam (Sherman) Greenberg; m. Michael Lewis Shorenstein, June 18, 1967; children: Anna Irene, Claire Beth. BA in Chemistry, Wellesley Coll., 1968; MA in Biochemistry and Molecular Biology, Harvard U., 1970, PhD in Biochemistry and Molecular Biology, 1973; MD, Stanford U., 1976. Diplomate Am. Bd. Internal Medicine. Resident in internal medicine UCLA Med. Ctr., 1976-79; pvt. practice internal medicine Santa Cruz, Calif., 1979—; mem. dept. internal medicine Dominican Hosp., Santa Cruz, 1979—; co-dir. med. svcs. Health Enhancement & Lifestyle Planning Systems, Santa Cruz, 1983—. Contbr. articles to profl. journals. Dir. Santa Cruz Chamber Players, 1993-94, pres., bd. dirs., 1994—. Recipient Charlie Parkhurst award Santa Cruz Women's Commn., 1989; NSF fellow, 1968-72, Sarah Perry Wood Med. fellow Wellesley Coll., 1972-76. Mem. Am. Soc. Internal Medicine (del. 1994), Calif. Soc. Internal Medicine (trustee 1994—), Am. Med. Women's Assn. (Outstanding Svc. award 1987, br. #59 pres. 1986—), Calif. Med. Assn. (on women 1987-93), Santa Cruz County Med. Soc. (mem. bd. govs. 1993—), Phi Beta Kappa, Sigma Xi. Jewish. Office: 700 Frederick St Ste 103 Santa Cruz CA 95062-2239

SHORENSTEIN, WALTER HERBERT, commercial real estate development company executive; b. Glen Cove, N.Y., Feb. 23, 1915; m. Phyllis J. Finley, Aug. 8, 1945 (dec.); children: Joan (Dec.), Carole, Douglas. Student, Pa. State U., 1933-34, U. Pa., 1934-36; D Econs. (hon.), HanYang U., Seoul, 1988. With property sales mgmt. depts. Milton Meyer & Co., San Francisco, 1946-51, ptnr., 1951-60, owner, chmn. bd., 1960—; owner, chmn. bd. Shorenstein Group, San Francisco, Shorenstein Co., San Francisco, 1960—. Past chmn. bd. trustees Hastings Law Ctr., U. Calif., San Francisco; founding mem. exec. adv. com. Hubert H. Humphrey Inst. Pub. Affairs, U. Minn.; founder Joan Shorenstein Barone Ctr. on Press, Politics and Pub. Policy, Harvard U. Kennedy Sch. Govt.; past pres., hon. life bd. dirs. San Francisco Park and Recreation Commn.; chmn. Vietnam Orphans Airlift; bd. dirs. San Francisco Performing Arts Ctr.; trustee Asia Found.; fin. chmn. Dem. Nat. Conv., 1984; apptd. by Pres. Clinton to Nat. Svc. Commn., 1994, also numerous polit. activities. Maj. USAF, 1940-45. Named Leader of Tomorrow, Time mag., 1953, Calif. Dem. of Yr., 1985; recipient Nat. Brotherhood award NCCJ, 1982, Disting. Svc. award Dem. Nat. Com., 1983; Golden Plate award Am. Acad. Achievement. Mem. Calif. C. of C. (bd. dirs.), San Francisco C. of C. (past chmn. bd., life bd. dirs. Office: Shorenstein Co 555 California St Ste 4900 San Francisco CA 94111

SHORNEY, GEORGE HERBERT, publishing executive; b. Oak Park, Ill., Dec. 16, 1931; s. George Herbert and Mary (Wallace) S.; m. Nancy Leith, Aug. 27, 1955; children: Cynthia, Herbert, John, Scott. BA, Denison U., 1954. Office mgr. Hope Pub. Co., Carol Stream, Ill., 1958-61, v.p., 1961-70, pres., 1970-91, chmn., 1992—; bd. dirs. Gary-Wheaton (Ill.) Bank. Contbr. New Grove Dictionary of Music, 1989. Pres. West Suburban Choral Union, Wheaton, 1984-92, Ctrl. DuPage Hosp. bd. govs., Winfield, Ill., 1985—; mem. governing com. Chgo. Symphony Orch., 1986—; chmn. Wheaton Fire and Police Commrs., 1974-81, Wyndemere Retirement Community, Wheaton, Ill., 1989; chmn. bd. dirs. Healthcorp Affiliates, Naperville, Ill., 1982—; chmn. bd. trustees Westminster Choir Coll., Princeton, N.J., 1988-91. With USN, 1954-56. Mem. Ch. Music Pubs. Assn. (pres. 1986-87), Denison Univ. Alumni Soc. (pres. 1976-78), Univ. Club (Chgo.), Nat. Liberal Club (London). Democrat. Presbyterian. Home: 160 W Elm St Wheaton IL 60187-6428 Office: Hope Pub Co 380 S Main Pl Carol Stream IL 60188-2475

SHORNEY, MARGO KAY, art gallery owner; b. Great Falls, Mont., July 5, 1930; d. Angus Vaughn McIver and Loneta Eileen Kuhn; m. James Thomas Shorney, Apr. 17, 1954; 1 child, Blair Angus. Student, Coll. Edn., Great Falls, Mont., 1948-50, U. Denver, 1950-53. Owner, dir. Shorney Gallery Fine Art, Oklahoma City, 1976—; pres. Mont. Inst. of Arts, Great Falls, Mont., 1953-54, Okla. Art Gallery Owners Assn., Oklahoma City, 1981-82; lectr. Norman (Okla.) Art League, 1987-91; judge fine art Ponca City (Okla.) 12 An, Fine Arts, 1986, Edmond (Okla.) Art Assn. Art Expo, 1995; appraiser Globe Life, Oklahoma City. Works exhibited in group shows, various orgns., 1953-90. Mentor South Oklahoma City Coll., 1990; active Okla. Mus. Art, 1973-78. Mem. Nat. Assn. Women Bus. Owners, Okla. Sculpture Soc. (charter), Okla. Art Guild (bd. dirs. 1979-82, lectr. 1981, 82, 83, 92). Republican. Episcopalian. Avocations: swimming, figure skating, horseback riding, landscaping. Office: Shorney Gallery Fine Arts 6616 N Olie Oklahoma City OK 73116-7318

SHORS, CLAYTON MARION, cardiologist; b. Beemer, Nebr., June 10, 1925; s. Joseph Albert and Morva Edith (Clayton) S.; m. Arlene Towle, June 6, 1948; children—Susan Debra, Clayton Robert, Scott Towle. B.S., U. Nebr., 1950, M.D., 1952. Diplomate Am. Bd. Internal Medicine (subspecialty cardiovascular disease). Intern Detroit Receiving Hosp., 1952-53, resident, 1953-56; practice medicine specializing in cardiology Detroit; chief cardiology St. John Hosp., Detroit. Bd. dirs. Sedona Acad.; mem. Sedona 30. Served with U.S. Army, 1943-46. Fellow Am. Coll. Cardiology, Internat. Coll. Angiology, Am. Heart Assn. Council on Clin. Cardiology; mem. Alpha Omega Alpha. Home: 44 Rue De La Rose Sedona AZ 86336-5970 Office: 1785 W Us Highway 89A Sedona AZ 86336-5567

SHORT, ALEXANDER CAMPBELL, lawyer; b. Washington, July 26, 1940; s. Joseph Hudson and Beth (Campbell) S.; m. Patricia Graves Thompson, Aug. 24, 1968; children: Joseph Graves, Ashley Campbell, Justin Owen. BA, Amherst Coll., 1963; MA, U. Pa., 1968; JD, U. Va., 1972. Bar: Conn. 1972, Md. 1973. Field and site rep. U.S. Dept. of HUD, Phila., 1963-69; assoc. Reid & Riege P.C., Hartford, Conn., 1972-73, Piper & Marbury, Balt., 1973-79; assoc. Miles & Stockbridge, Balt., 1979-81, ptnr., 1981-94; pvt. practice Balt., 1994—; bd. dirs., pres. Handel Soc. adv. bd. to Handel Choir, Balt., 1983-87; pres. Handel Choir, Balt., 1987-88. Bd. dirs. Homeland Assn., Balt., 1984-85; mem. bd. of mgrs. Camp Dudley YMCA, 1991—. Mem. Md. Bar Assn. (real property planning and zoning sect., sec. 1982-84, chmn. elect 1984-86, chmn. 1986-88. Democrat. Presbyterian. Avocations: choral singing, scouting, gardening. Office: 200 E Pratt St Ste 800 Baltimore MD 21202

SHORT, BOBBY See SHORT, ROBERT WALTRIP

SHORT, BYRON ELLIOTT, engineering educator; b. Putnam, Tex., Dec. 29, 1901; s. Samuel W. and Florence Gertrude (Sublett) S.; m. Mary Jo Fitzgerald, June 1, 1937; children: Mary Aileen Short Gauntt, Byron Elliott Jr. B.S., U. Tex., 1926, M.S., 1930; M.M.E., Cornell U., 1936, Ph.D., 1939. Cadet engr. Tex Co., summers 1926-27, mech. engr., summers 1928-30; instr. U. Tex., 1926-29, asst. prof., 1929-36, charge heat-power, fluid mechanics lab., 1930-65, mech. engr., summers 1932-36, 40, asso. prof., 1936-39, prof. mech. engring., 1939-73, prof. emeritus, 1973—, chmn. dept., 1945-47, 51-53; acting dean U. Tex. (Coll. Engring.), 1948-49; teaching fellow Cornell, 1935-36; cons. Oak Ridge Nat. Lab., research participant, 1956, 57. Author: Flow, Measurement and Pumping of Fluids, 1934, Engineering Thermodynamics, (with H.L. Kent, B.F. Treat), 1953, Pressure Enthalpy Charts (with H.L. kent and H.A. Walls), 1970; assoc. editor Design Volume, Am. Soc. Refrigerating Engrs. Databook, 1953-55, editor, 1957; contbr. articles to engring. Fellow ASME (life; chmn. South Tex. sect. 1938-39, mem. heat transfer and power test code com.), ASHRAE (life); mem. SAR, Am. Soc. Engring. Edn., Huguenot Soc. Am. (state pres. 1983-85), Masons (33d degree SR & KT), Shriners, Sigma Xi, Tau Beta Pi, Phi Kappa Phi, Pi Tau Sigma. Baptist. Home: 502 E 32d St Austin TX 78705-3105 *As I look backward over the years relative to what I have done professionally and in home and civic life, I think of the men and women whom I admired and loved and thus influenced my life. An early admonition of my mother was "learn things while young before your mind becomes cluttered with non-essentials".*

SHORT, EARL DE GREY, JR., psychiatrist, consultant; b. Talladega, Ala., Jan. 11, 1933; s. Earl de Grey and Adeline Eugenia (McWilliams) S.; m. Martha Burt Rossiter, Oct. 12, 1963; children: Earl D III, Philip A., Catherine E., William R. BS, The Citadel, 1956; MD, Med. U. S.C., Charleston, 1959. Commd. 2d lt. USAR, 1956; entered active duty capt. U.S. Army, 1961, advanced through grades to col., 1976, ret., 1980; battalion surgeon 4th Armored BN, 8th Inf. div., Germany, 1961-62; resident psychiatry Walter Reed Army Med. Ctr., Washington, 1962-65; chief dept. psychiatry U.S. Army Hosp., Ft. Polk, La., 1965-68, U.S. Walson Army Hosp., Ft. Dix, N.J., 1968-70; student Command and Gen. Staff Coll., Ft. Leavenworth, Kans., 1970-71; divsn. surgeon, comdr. 2d Med. Bn., 2d Infantry divsn., Korea, 1971-72; chief psychiatry svc. Brooke Army Med. Ctr., Ft. Sam Houston, Tex., 1972-80; ret. U.S. Army, 1980; psychiatrist Mecklenburg County Mental Health Ctr., Charlotte, N.C., 1980-86, Carolinas Medical Ctr. for Mental Health, Charlotte, N.C., 1986—; psychiat. cons. Mecklenburg County, Charlotte, 1987—, Amethyst, Charlotte, 1993—. Founder Philip Alexander Short Meml. Scholarship Fund, Wingate (N.C.) Coll., 1988, Short Endowment Fund, Wingate Coll., 1991, Philip Alexander Short Meml. Fund, Elon Homes for Children, Elon Coll., N.C. Decorated Meritorious Svc. medal with 1 oak leaf cluster, U.S. Army, 1972, 80, Army Commendation medal with 1 oak leaf cluster, U.S. Army, 1968, 70; recipient All Am. award The Citadel, 1956. Mem. AMA, Am. Psychiat. Assn., N.C. Med. Soc., N.C. Psychiat. Assn., Charlotte Psychiat. Soc., Assn. Mil. Surgeons, Mecklenburg County Med. Soc., Ret. Officers Assn., Assn. Citadel Men, Am. Legion, Sons Am. Revolution, Nat. Assn. Uniformed Svcs., VFW. Republican. Presbyterian. Avocations: composing piano music, restoring ancestral homes, collecting stamps, books, and coins, genealogy. Office: P O Box 18773 Charlotte NC 28218

SHORT, ELIZABETH M., physician, educator, federal agency administrator; b. Boston, June 2, 1942; d. James Edward and Arlene Elizabeth (Mitchell) Meehan; m. Herbert M. Short, Sept. 2, 1963 (div. 1969); 1 child, Timothy Owen; m. Michael Allen Friedman, June 21, 1976; children: Lia Gabrielle, Hannah Ariel, Eleanor Elana. BA Philosophy magna cum laude, Mt. Holyoke Coll., 1963; MD cum laude, Yale U., 1968. Diplomate Am. Bd. Internal Medicine, Am. Bd. Med. Genetics. Intern, jr. resident internal medicine Yale New Haven Hosp., 1968-70; postdoctoral fellow in human genetics Yale Med. Sch., 1970-72; postdoctoral fellow in renal metabolism U. Calif., San Francisco, 1972-73; sr. resident in internal medicine Stanford (Calif.) Med. Sch., 1973-74, chief resident in internal medicine, 1974-75; staff physician Palo Alto Veterans Med. Ctr., Stanford, Calif., 1975-80; asst. prof. of medicine Stanford Med. Sch., 1975-83, asst. dean Student Affairs, 1978-80, assoc. dean Students Affairs/Medical Education, 1980-83; dir. biomed. rsch. and faculty devel. Assn. Am. Med. Colls., Washington, 1983-87; assoc. v.p. dir. dept. acad. affairs, 1983-87, dep. dir. biomedical rsch., 1987-88; dep. assoc. chief med. dir. for acad. affairs VA, Washington, 1988-92, assoc. chief medical dir. for acad. affairs, 1992—; vis. prof. Human Biology, Stanford U., 1983-86; resource allocation com. Veteran's Health Adminstrn., 1989-91; budget planning and policy review coun. 1991—; planning review com. Veterans Health Adminstrn., 1991—; chair resident work limit task force 1991—; managed care task force, 1993-94; co-chair com. status women Am. Fedn. Clin. Rsch., 1975-77; mem. numerous adminstrv. coms., Yale Med. Sch., Stanford U.; accreditation coun. grad. med. edn., 1988—; mem. public policy com. Am. Soc. Human Genetics, 1984—, chair, 1986-94; mem. White House Task Force on Health Care Reform, 1993. assoc. editor Clin. Rsch. Jour., 1976-79, editor elect, 1979-80, editor 1980-84; contbr. articles to profl. jours. Mem. nat. child health adv. coun. NIH, 1991—; mem. com. edn. and training Office Sci. and Tech. Policy, 1991—. Recipient Maclean Zoology award Mt. Holyoke Coll.; Munger scholar, Markle scholar, Sara Williston scholar Mt. Holyoke Coll., 1959-63, Yale Men in Medicine scholar, 1964-68; Bardwell Meml. Med. fellow, 1963. Mem. AAAS, Am. Soc. Human Genetics, Am. Fedn. Clin. Rsch. (bd. dirs 1973-83, editor 1978-83, nat. coun., exec. com., pub. policy com. 1977-87), Am. Assn. Women in Scis., Western Soc. Clin. Investigation, Calif. Acad. Medicine, Phi Beta Kappa, Alpha Omega Alpha. Home: 6807 Bradley Blvd Bethesda MD 20817-3004 Office: Dept Veterans Affairs Health Adminstrn Acad Affairs 810 Vermont Ave VHA 14 Washington DC 20420

SHORT, JANET MARIE, principal; b. Boston, Sept. 18, 1939; d. Robert Emmet and Getta Agnes (Mills) S. BS in Edn., Boston State Coll., 1962, MEd, 1967; LLD (hon.), Regis Coll., 1991. Tchr. Boston Pub. Schs., 1962-70, acting asst. dir. staff devel., 1970-71, tchr.-in-charge, 1971-75; prin. D.L. Barrett Sch., Boston, 1976-81; tchr. Boston Pub. Schs., 1981-82; prin. Maurice J. Tobin Sch., Boston, 1982—; lectr. in field. Adv. bd. DiMaiti Stuart Found., Boston, 1990—; adv. bd. Mission Hill and Camp Mission Posible, 1984-87; community adv. bd. Harvard Sch. Pub. Health, Boston, 1990—; adv. bd. Boston Against Drugs, 1990-94. Recipient Women of Achievement award Big Sister Assn. of Greater Boston, 1994, Thankful Recognition award Channel 5, Boston, 1987, Recognition award Boston Women's Mag., 1988, Pub. Svc. award Henry L. Shattuck, Bus. Mcpl. Bur. Rsch. award, 1988, Freedom's Found. Honor medal, 1990, Annual Excellence in Edn. award Alpha Gamma chpt. Pi Lambda Theta, 1993 and others; movie based on J.M. Short, "A Matter of Principal", 1990. Mem. ASCD, Mass. Middle Level Adminstrs. Assn., Boston Assn. Sch. Adminstrs. (exec. bd. 1984-93), Boston Middle Sch. Assn., Boston Elem. Prins. Assn., MESPA, Delta Kappa Gamma (chpt. pres. 1978-80). Roman Catholic. Avocations: travel, bowling, reading. Office: Maurice Tobin Sch 40 Smith St Roxbury MA 02120-2799

SHORT, JOEL BRADLEY, lawyer, consultant, software publisher; b. Birmingham, Ala., Dec. 27, 1941; s. Forrest Edwin and Laura Elizabeth (Bradley) S.; m. Georgianna Pohl, June 5, 1965 (div. Apr. 1973); m. Nancy Ann Harty, Dec. 17, 1977; children: Christopher Bradley, Matthew Douglas. BA, U. Colo., 1963, LLB, 1966, JD, 1968. Bar: Kans. 1966, U.S. Dist. Ct. Kans. 1966, U.S. Ct. Appeals (10th cir.) 1975, U.S. Supreme Ct. 1976. Ptnr. Short & Short, Attys., Fort Scott, Kans., 1966-77, Nugent & Short, Overland Park, Kans., 1977-83; pvt. practice J. Bradley Short & Assoc., Overland Park, Kans., 1983-91; ptnr. Short & Borth, Overland Park, Kans., 1991—; owner Bradley Software; mem. tech. adv. com. Kans. Jud. Coun., Topeka, 1991—. 1st lt. U.S. Army, 1967-73. Fellow Am. Acad. Matrimonial Lawyers; mem. Johnson County Bar Assn. (ethics and family law coms. 1983—). Avocation: sailing. Office: Short and Borth Attys 32/1111 Corporate Woods 9225 Indian Creek Pky Overland Park KS 66210-2009

SHORT, MARION PRISCILLA, neurologist; b. Milford, Del., June 12, 1951; d. Raymond Calistus and Barbara Anne (Ferguson) S.; m. Michael Peter Klein. BA, Bryn Mawr Coll., 1973; diploma, U. Edinburgh (Scotland), 1975; MD, Med. Coll. Pa., 1978. Diplomate Am. Bd. Psychiatry and Neurology, Am. Bd. Internal Medicine. Intern in internal medicine Hahnemann Med. Coll. Hosp., Phila., 1978-79; med. resident in internal medicine St. Lukes-Roosevelt Hosp., N.Y.C., 1979-81; neurology resident U. Pitts. Health Ctr., 1981-84; fellow in med. genetics Mt. Sinai Med. Ctr., N.Y.C., 1984-86; fellow in neurology Mass. Gen. Hosp., Boston, 1986-90, asst. neurologist, 1990—; asst. prof. dept. neurology Harvard Med. Sch., 1990—; cons. Spaulding Rehab. Hosp., Boston. Recipient Clin. Investigator Devel. award NIH, 1988-93. Mem. Am. Acad. Neurology, Am. Soc. for Human Genetics. Office: Mass Gen Hosp Dept Neuropathology Warren 329 MGH Fruit St Boston MA 02114

SHORT, MARTIN, actor, comedian; b. Mar. 26, 1951; s. Charles Patrick and Olive Short; m. Nancy Dolman; children: Katherine, Oliver, Henry. Degree in social work, McMaster U., 1972. Actor: (feature films) Three Amigos, 1986, Innerspace, 1987, Cross My Heart, 1987, Three Fugitives, 1989, The Big Picture, 1989, Pure Luck, 1991, Father of the Bride, 1991, Captain Ron, 1992, We're Back! A Dinosaur's Story, 1993 (voice), Clifford, 1994, The Pebble and the Penguin, 1995 (voice), Father of the Bride 2, 1995; (TV series) The Associates, 1979, I'm a Big Girl Now, 1980-81, SCTV Network 90, 1982-84, Saturday Night Live, 1985-86, The Completely Mental Misadventures of Ed Grimley, 1988-89 (voice), The Martin Short Show, 1994; (TV movies) The Family Man, 1979, Sunset Limousine, 1983, (TV spls.) Martin Short's Concert for the North Americas, 1985, Really Weird Tales, 1987, I, Martin Short Goes Hollywood, 1989; also numerous revues and cabaret appearances with Second City comedy troupe, 1977-78, appeared on Broadway in The Goodbye Girl, 1993. •

SHORT, RAY EVERETT, minister, sociology educator emeritus, author, lecturer; b. Coffeyville, Kans., Jan. 5, 1919; s. Franklin Marion and Jennie (Messersmith) S.; m. Jeannette Louise Stephens, June 12, 1954; children: Glenn Alan, Linda Louise, Kenneth Ray, Timothy Wesley, Karen Amy; 1 stepdau., Mary Jennings. AB, Willamette U., 1944; postgrad., U. Chgo., 1946; BD, Duke, 1948, PhD, 1961; postgrad., U. Idaho, 1950-51. Ordained to ministry Meth. Ch., 1946. Dir. Westminster Found., Duke, 1944-46; co-pastor Interracial Meth. Ch., Durham, N.C., 1947; asst. prof. religion, dir. chapel programs Fla. So. Coll., Lakeland, 1947-48; exec. dir. Fla. br. United World Federalists, 1948-51; dir. Intermountain Region, 1953-54, Wesley Found., U. Idaho, 1950-51; exec. dir. Student YMCA-YWCA, U. Denver, 1951-53; pastor Fairmont Meth. Ch., Lockport, Ill., 1954-56; grad. asst. sociology Duke, 1956-57; assoc. prof. religion, head divsn. religion and philosophy, chaplain Tenn. Wesleyan Coll., 1957-60; assoc. prof. sociology and religion, head dept. sociology U. Dubuque, Iowa, 1960-65, acting chmn. div. social sci., 1962-65; assoc. prof. sociology, head dept. sociology and anthropology U. Wis., Platteville, 1965-70, prof. sociology, 1966-87, prof. emeritus, 1987—; prof. sociology and anthropology Copenhagen Study Ctr. U. Wis., spring 1974, nat. lectr., 1975—; chmn. Peace and World Order divsn. North Iowa Meth. Conf., 1963-69; rep. U.S. Jr. C. of C in testimony before U.S. Senate Com. on Fgn. Rels., 1950; Midwest region rep. Nat. Coun. World Federalist Assn., 1964-73, pres. Midwest region, 1967-69, chmn. nat. coun., 1971-72, nat. v.p., 1991—; mem. spl. Wis. Conf. called with Pres's Commn. for Observance of 25th Anniversary of UN, 1970-87; mem. Wis. U. Meth. Bd. on Ch. and Soc., 1973-80, chmn. World Peace divsn., mem. exec. com., 1975-80. Author: Sex, Love or Infatuation: How Can I Really Know?, 1978, on videocassette, 1987, 2nd edit., 1990, Sex, Dating and Love: Questions Most Often Asked, 1984, 2nd edit., 1994; contbr. articles to profl. jours. Dem. candidate for Wis. 3rd Dist. Congl. Seat, 1970, 72; del. Dist. and State Convs., 1969-87, mem. state platform com., 1975-87; bd. dirs. Dubuque Salvation Army, 1961-65; mem. nat. bd. Am. Freedom Assn.; nat. v.p. Campaign for UN Reform, 1983-87, 1st v.p., 1989—; dir., founder Wis. Ann. High Sch. World Peace Study Program, 1975-87. Recipient NSF grant Anthropology Inst., Fairmont State Coll., W.Va., 1962. Fellow Am. Sociol. Assn.; mem. AAUP, Nat. Coun. on Family Rels., Fedn. Am. Scientists, Nat. United Meth. Men (mem. peace adv. task force 1990—). Home: 505 S Miller Ave Lafayette CO 80026-1545 *Nuclear and chemical weapons, crises of environments. While my life has largely been spent helping others have a better future, I now know we have to help assure that they have a future at all.*

SHORT, ROBERT HENRY, retired utility executive; b. Klamath Falls, Oreg., Oct. 15, 1924; s. Judge Haywood and Henrietta Luella (Lyon) S.; m. Ruby Madalyn Rice, Aug. 1, 1946; children—Robert L., Victoria (Mrs. Gregory Baum), Casey. BS in Journalism, U. Oreg., 1950; PhD in Humane Letters (hon.), Linfield Coll., 1984. City editor Klamath Falls Herald and News, 1950-52; dir. pub. rels. Water and Elec. Bd., Eugene, Oreg., 1952-55; mgr. pub. info. Portland Gen. Electric Co., Oreg., 1955-57, asst. to chmn., 1957-62, v.p., 1962-71, sr. v.p., 1971-73, exec. v.p., 1973-77, pres., 1977-80, chmn. bd., chief exec. officer, 1980-88, ret., 1989; bd. dir. First Interstate Bank of Oreg. Bd. dirs. Oreg. Ind. Colls. Found., Oreg. Health Sci. U.; trustee Oreg. Grad. Inst. With USNR, 1942-45. Mem. Portland Golf Club, Arlington Club. Home: 1210 SW 61st Ct Portland OR 97221-1504 Office: One SW Columbia St Ste 555 Portland OR 97258

SHORT, ROBERT WALTRIP (BOBBY SHORT), entertainer, author; b. Danville, Ill., Sept. 15, 1924; s. Rodman Jacob and Myrtle (Render) S. Grad. high sch. Singing pianist as child and after high sch.; appeared in night clubs in U.S. and abroad, concerts in maj. cities; regular cabaret performer N.Y.C.; recordings include: Krazy for Gershwin, Live at Cate Carlyle, Loves Cole Porter, Short Celebrates Rodgers and Hart, Guess Who's in Town, 1987, 50 From Bobby Short, 1987. Late Night At The Cafe Carlyle, 1992, (with the Alden-Barret Quinlet) Swing That Music, 1993; appeared in TV movie Roots, The Next Generation, 1979; appeared in motion picture Splash, 1984; appeared in Broadway prodns., 1956—; appeared at White House for Duke and Duchess of Windsor at request of Pres. Nixon, 1970; Author: Black and White Baby, 1971; also articles. Grammy nomination, Best Jazz Vocal for "Swing That Music" (with the Alden-Barrett Quintet), 1994. Mem. NAACP (life). Address: care Cafe Carlyle Madison Ave at 76th St New York NY 10021•

SHORT, THOMAS EDWARD, JR., educator; b. Pulaski, Tenn., Mar. 21, 1944; s. Thomas Edward Sr. and Elizabeth (Sims) S.; m. Marlene K. Martin, Mar. 20, 1971 (dec. July 1984); 1 child, Shikira R.; m. Sandra Renee Pikes, Oct. 7, 1986; children: Arnetta L. Abney, Shalonda Y. BS in Edn., Music, Wittenberg U., 1966; MEd, U. Md., 1984. Cert. tchr. Washington. Freelance musician Washington Met. Area, 1970-87; tchr. Washington Pub. Schs. System, 1971—, Washington Youth Orch. Program, 1973-77; minister Maple Springs Bapt. Ch., Capitol Hts., Md., 1987-90, 1990—; tchr. Maple Springs Bapt. Sem., Capitol Hts., Md., 1990—. With USN, 1966-70. First Black musician in U.S. Naval Acad. band. Home: PO Box 531335 Forestville MD 20753 Office: Browne Jr High Sch 21st Benning Rd NE Washington DC 20002

SHORTER, JAMES RUSSELL, JR., lawyer; b. N.Y.C., June 10, 1946; s. James Russell and Helen (Ibert) S. AB, Columbia Coll., 1968; JD, Harvard U., 1975; LLM in Taxation, NYU, 1979. Bar: N.Y. 1976, U.S. Dist. Ct. (so. and ea. dists.) N.Y. 1976, U.S. Tax Ct. 1987. Assoc. Thacher Proffitt & Wood, N.Y.C., 1975-84, ptnr., 1984—. Capt. USNR, 1968—. Mem. ABA (tax, bus. law sect.). Republican. Club: Harvard (N.Y.C.). Home: 345 E 80th St Apt 26C New York NY 10021-0671 Office: Thacher Proffitt & Wood 2 World Trade Ctr Fl 39 New York NY 10048-0002

SHORTER, WALTER WYATT, forest products executive; b. 1932; B.S. in Chemistry, Va. Mil. Inst., 1953; M.S. in Pulp and Paper Tech., U. Maine, 1957; married. With Union Camp Corp., 1957-78, v.p., resident mgr., until 1978; pres. Mac Millan Bloedel Inc., Pine Hill, Ala., 1978—; sr. v.p. Container Bd. and Packaging, Mac Millan Bloedel Ltd., 1989—, also bd. dirs.; bd. dirs. First Ala. Bank of Montgomery, First Ala. Bancshares, Inc., Jenkins Brick Co., U.K. Corrugated Ltd. Mem. Govs. Agrl. Emphasis com. Ala.; trustee Huntingdon Coll., Inst. Paper Sci. and Tech.; chmn. bd. trustees Paper Industry Mgmt. Assn.; treas. Leadership Ala.; past chmn. Ala. Alliance Bus. and Industry. Capt. USMC, 1953-58. Mem. Paper Industry Mgmt. Assn. (past pres., now trustee), Bus. Coun. Ala. (bd. dir.), Am. Paper Inst. (bd. dirs.), Ala. Coun. Econ. Edn. Office: MacMillan Bloedel Inc 272 Commerce St Montgomery AL 36104-2559

SHORTER, WAYNE, musician; b. Newark, Aug. 25, 1933. B.A., NYU, 1956. Played saxophone with Art Blakey, 1959-63, Miles Davis, 1964-70, Weather Report, 1970-86, Miles Davis Tribute Band, 1992; solo albums include: Schizophrenia, 1968, Supernova, 1970, Native Dancer, 1974, Native Dancer, 1975, Etcetera, 1981, Atlantis, 1986, Phantom Navigator, 1987, Joy Rider, 1988, Native Dancer, 1990, The All Seeing Eye, 1994. Served with U.S. Army, 1956-58. Winner numerous Down Beat mag. awards., 1970-77, named Best Soprano Sax, 1984, 85; co-recipient Grammy award for best jazz instrumental composition, 1987. Office: care Blue Note Records 1750 Vine St Los Angeles CA 90028-5247•

SHORTESS, EDWIN STEEVIN, marketing consultant; b. Cedar Rapids, Iowa, Oct. 31, 1920; s. Edwin Stephen and Rita (Clemente) S.; m. Jane Elizabeth Gallagher, Dec. 27, 1941 (div. Apr. 1970); children: E. Stephen, Richard J., Mark Andrew, Cathy Shortess Pool; m. Mary Francis Kerns, May 28, 1970; children: Dana Menshing, Emil Bartsche, Roger Bartsche, Lisa Bartsche, Vincent Bartsche, Kirsten Bartsche Chirico. Student, North Iowa U., 1938-39; BSEE, Chgo. Tech. Coll., 1942. Engring. rsch. analyst Douglas Aircraft Corp., El segundo, Calif., 1942-44; liaison engr. Martin Aircraft Corp., Omaha, 1944-45; chief engr. dir. Burlington (Iowa) Instrument co., 1945-53; adminstrv. engr. dir. Hickok Elec. Instrument Co., Clev., 1953-59; ea. sales mgr. Hickok Elec. Instrument Co., Paramus, N.J., 1960-65; v.p., gen. mgr. dir. Wacline, Dayton, Ohio, 1959-60; v.p., gen. mgr. Colo. Hickok, Grand Junction, 1965-69; pres. Shortess Rawson & Assocs., Kenilworth, N.J., 1969-86; mktg. cons. Shortess Rawson & Assocs., Allenwood, N.J., 1986—; bd. dirs. Federated Purchasers Inc., Kenilworth, N.J. Author: Design and Application of Electrical Industrial Instruments, 1964. Mem. Instrument Soc. Engrs. (sr.). Republican. Methodist. Avocations: golf, bridge. Home and Office: PO Box 152 Allenwood NJ 08720-0152

SHORTLIFFE, EDWARD HANCE, internist, medical information science educator; b. Edmonton, Alta., Can., Aug. 28, 1947; s. Ernest Carl and Elizabeth Joan (Rankin) S.; m. Linda Marie Dairiki, June 21, 1970; children: Lindsay Ann, Lauren Leigh. AB, Harvard U., 1970; PhD, Stanford U., 1975, MD, 1976. Diplomate Am. Bd. Internal Medicine. Trainee NIH, 1971-76; intern Mass. Gen. Hosp., Boston, 1976-77; resident Stanford Hosp., Palo Alto, Calif., 1977-79; asst. prof. medicine Stanford U. Sch. Medicine, Palo Alto, 1979-85, assoc. prof., 1985-90, prof., 1990—, chief div. gen. internal medicine, 1988—; pres. SCAMC, Inc. (Symposium on Computer Applications in Med. Care), Washington, 1988-89; assoc. chair medicine Primary Care, 1993—; bd. dirs. Smart Valley, Inc.; advisor Nat. Bd. Med. Examiners, Phila., 1987-93; mem. Nat. Fed. Networking Adv. Coun., NSF, 1991-93; mem. computer sci. and telecomm. bd. NRC, 1991—. Editor: Rule-Based Expert Systems, 1984, Readings in Medical Artificial Intelligence, 1984, Medical Informatics: Computer Applications in Health Care, 1990; developer several medical computer programs including MYCIN, 1976 (Grace M. Hopper award Assn. Computing Machinery). Recipient Young Investigator award Western Soc. Clin. Investigation, 1987, rsch. career award Nat. Libr. of Medicine, 1979-84; scholar Kaiser Family Found., 1983-88. Fellow Am. Assn. Artificial Intelligence, Am. Coll. Med. Informatics (pres. 1992-94); mem. Soc. for Med. Decisionmaking (pres. 1989-90), Inst. Medicine, Am. Soc. for Clin. Investigation, Am. Med. Informatics Assn., Assn. Am. Physicians, Am. Clin. and Climatol. Assn. Avocation: skiing. Office: Stanford U Sch Medicine Sect on Med Informatics 300 Pasteur Dr Stanford CA 94305

SHORTS, GARY K., newspaper publisher; b. Grove City, Pa., Feb. 26, 1951; s. Leonard and Sarah Maxine (Young) S.; m. Karen Healy; children: Steven A., Elizabeth H., Daniel C. BA in Journalism, Economics, Ohio Wesleyan U., 1973; MBA, U. Pa., 1975. Circulation dir. News Democrat, Belleville, Ill., 1977-80; mktg. dir. Oakland Press, Pontiac, Mich., 1981-83; v.p., gen. mgr. Times Pub. Co., Wichita Falls, Tex., 1983-85; v.p. mktg. Harte-Hanks Comms., San Antonio, 1985-86; pres. So. Calif. Newspapers, Inc., San Diego, 1986-87; pub., chief exec. officer The Morning Call, Allentown, Pa., 1987—; dir. Pa. Newspaper Pubs. Assn., treas. 1991-92, v.p. daily newspapers 1992-93, pres. 1993-94; dir. Lehigh County Indsl. Devel. Corp., Allentown Econ. Devel. Corp., sec. 1988—. Chmn. United Way, Allentown, 1991; trustee Cedarcrest Coll. Mem. Allentown-Lehigh County C. of C. Office: Morning Call PO Box 1260 101 N 6th St Allentown PA 18105*

SHORTZ, RICHARD ALAN, lawyer; b. Chgo., Mar. 11, 1945; s. Lyle A. and Wilma Warner (Wildes) S.; m. Jennifer A. Harrell; children: Eric, Heidi. BS, Ind. U., 1967; JD, Harvard U., 1970. Bar: Calif. 1971, U.S. Supreme Ct. 1980. Assoc. Gibson, Dunn & Crutcher, L.A., 1970-73; sr. v.p., gen. counsel, sec. Tosco Corp., L.A., 1973-83; ptnr. Jones, Day, Reavis & Pogue, L.A., 1983—. Mem. L.A. World Affairs Inst., 1983—, Town Hall L.A., 1983—. 2nd lt. U.S. Army, 1970-71. Mem. ABA, L.A. Bar Assn., Calif. Club, Beach Club (Santa Monica, Calif.), L.A. Country Club. Republican. Episcopalian. Home: 1343 Pavia Pl Pacific Palisades CA 90272-4047 Office: Jones Day Reavis & Pogue 555 W 5th St Ste 4600 Los Angeles CA 90013-1025

SHORTZ, WILL, puzzle editor; b. Crawfordsville, Ind., Aug. 26, 1952; s. Lyle A. and Wilma Warner (Wildes) S. AB, Ind. U., 1974; JD, U. Va., 1977. Editor Penny Press, Stamford, Conn., 1977-78; assoc. editor Games Mag., N.Y.C., 1978-82, sr. editor, 1982-89, editor, 1989-93; crossword editor N.Y. Times, N.Y.C., 1993—; founder, dir. Am. Crossword Puzzle Tournament, Stamford, Conn., 1978—, World Puzzle Team Championship, N.Y.C., 1992; puzzlemaster Weekend Edit. Sunday NPR, Washington, 1987—; U.S. team capt. Internat. Crossword Marathon, Brno, Czechoslovakia, 1989, Bjelovar, Yugoslavia, 1990, World Puzzle Championship, Brno, 1993, Cologne, 1994. Author: Brain Games, 1979, The American Quiz Book, 1979, Brain Games 2, 1980, The Bantam Great Masters Winning Crossword Puzzles, vol. 1-3, 1980, World Class Championship Crosswords, 1982, Brain Games 3, 1983, Games Mag. Book of Crossword Puzzles, 1985, American Championship Crosswords, 1990, Games Mag. Giant Book of Games, 1991, Will Shortz's Best Brain Busters, 1991, Games Mag. Best Pencil Puzzles, 1992, The World's Most Ornery Crosswords, vol. 1, 1992, Brain Twisters from the First World Puzzle Championships, 1993. Mem. Am. Cryptogram Assn., Authors Guild, Nat. Puzzlers' League (pres. 1977, 81, historian 1992—). Avocations: table tennis, book collecting. Office: NY Times 229 W 43rd St New York NY 10036-3913

SHORY, NASEEB LEIN, dentist, retired state official; b. Birmingham, Ala., Sept. 27, 1925; s. Lein George and Fomeyi (Buhana) S.; m. Mary Jo Howard, Sept. 8, 1951; children: Lawrence G., Richard L., Carl B., Celeste Marie. B.S., U. Ala., 1948; D.D.S., Loyola U., Chgo., 1952; M.P.H., U. Mich., 1962. Diplomate: Am. Bd. Dental Pub. Health. Pvt. practice dentistry Montgomery, Ala., 1952-60; dir. Bur. Dental Health, Ala. Dept. Pub. Health, 1961-68, 1983-88; assoc. clin. prof. Med. Coll. Ala., 1966-68; assoc. prof., head dept. community and preventive dentistry La. State U. Sch. Dentistry, 1968-70; prof., chmn. dept. community dentistry Loyola U. of New Orleans, 1968-70; lectr. Tulane U. Sch. Pub. Health and Tropical Medicine, 1968-70; prof., dir. div. health services Sch. Dental Medicine, So. Ill. U., Edwardsville, 1970-72; asst. to dean Sch. Dental Medicine, So. Ill. U., 1972-73, chmn. dept. health ecology, 1970-73; mem. Ala. Bd. Dental Scholarships, 1965-68, 73-87; dir. Ala. Smile Keeper Program, 1976-87; mem. Ala. State Health Advisory Commn., 1977-79; Pres. Profl. Men's Credit Assn., Montgomery, 1960-61; mem. Montgomery Community Council, 1960-61, Youth Adv. Council, Montgomery Police Dept., 1960-61. Served with AUS, 1943-45, ETO. Decorated Purple Heart; recipient Most Excellent Fellow award Ala. Dental Assn., 1968; D.G. Gill award Outstanding Contbn. to Pub. Health in Ala., 1982. Fellow Internat. Coll. Dentists (dep. regent for Ala. 1986-88, dist. V vice regent 1987-88); mem. ADA (chmn. nat. task force on prohibition confection sales in schs. 1978-79, mem. council dental health and health planning 1984-86; Council on Community Health, Hosps., Instns. and Med. Affairs 1986-88), Ill. Dental Assn., La. Dental Assn. (chmn. council on dental health 1969-70), Ala. Dental Assn. (ho. of dels., trustee), Am. Assn. Pub. Health Dentists, Assn. State and Territorial Dental Dirs. (pres. 1980-82, Outstanding Achievement award 1991), Ala. Pub. Health Assn. (pres. 1984-85), Council on Dental Health (state com. on pub. health 1988-92), Optimist Club (v.p. Perdido Bay chpt. 1991-92), Svc. Corps Ret. Execs. Home: 34090 Kathryn Dr Lillian AL 36549-9584

SHOSID, JOSEPH LEWIS, government official; b. Ft. Worth, Aug. 27, 1927; s. Samuel and Lilly Minna (Schneider) S.; children: Sharon Suzann, Steven Stanford; m. Linda D. Johnson, Oct. 8, 1994. BA, Tex. Christian U., 1950, MA, 1952; grad., Indsl. Coll. Armed Forces, Washington. Former exec. profl. baseball with L.A. (Bklyn.) Dodgers farm orgn.; bus. mgr. Ft. Worth Baseball Club, 1950-54; with various newspapers, radio & TV stas. as sportscasting and advt. exec.; pres. Advt. Unlimited, Inc., Ft. Worth, 1954-76; spl. asst. to U.S. Ho. of Reps. Speaker of Ho. Jim Wright 12th Dist. Tex., 1955-89; pres., chief exec. officer Shosid & Assocs., Ft. Worth and Washington, 1981—; chmn. Ft. Worth Airpower Coun., 1972-74; mem. adv. coun. Pres.'s Nat. Com. for Employer Support of Guard and Res., 1971—; spl. asst. to Vice Pres. Hubert H. Humphrey, 1966-69. Basketball and football ofcl. NCAA, 1953— including 13 football bowl games, 21 basketball playoffs, 21 Aloha Classics, 1989-90, Japan Classics, Osaka and Tokyo; liaison officer USAFE-Sports, Ramstein AB, Feb. Republic of Germany, 1964—. With AUS, WWII; maj. gen. USAF Ret. Decorated D.S.M., Air Force Legion of Merit, Exceptional Service award USAF, 1975. Mem. Air Force Assn. (past nat. pres. and chmn. bd., Nat. Man of Yr. 1963, Medal of Merit 1962, Exceptional Svc. Plaque 1971, life mem., nat. bd. dirs.), S.W. Basketball Ofcls. Assn. (past pres.), Congl. Staff Club, Aerospace Edn. Found. (Dolittle fellow), Ft. Worth C. of C., Res. Officers Assn., Am. Basketball Assn., Nat. Assn. Basketball Coaches, Fed. Internat. Basketball Assn., Naismith Basketball Hall of Fame, Am. Football Coaches Assn., Collegiate Sports Info. Dirs. Am., Atlantic Coast Football Ofcls. Assn. (life), Masons (32 degree), Shriners. Mem. Christian Ch. Home: 1612 Ems Rd W Fort Worth TX 76116-1828 *I had the good fortune of being schooled at an early age that a mind is a terrible thing to waste. And that every American has an obligation to serve his/her country in a constructive way, thus the*

inspiration for my interest in a military career. Parents who came to America from Lithuania, fleeing the Marxist Revolution didn't have to wait until post World War II to understand or be told about the "Soviet Threat." They saw it first hand. A major thesis of my life has been to be grateful that they had the great courage to immigrate to this great nation and thus allow me the freedom of thought and mind otherwise denied.

SHOSS, CYNTHIA RENÉE, lawyer; b. Cape Girardeau, Mo., Nov. 29, 1950; d. Milton and Carroll Jane (Duncan) S.; m. David Goodwin Watson, Apr. 13, 1986; 1 child, Lucy J. Watson. BA cum laude, Newcomb Coll., 1971; JD, Tulane U., 1974; LLM in Taxation, NYU, 1980. Bar: La. 1974, Mo. 1977, Ill. 1978, N.Y. 1990. Law clk. to assoc. and chief justices La. Supreme Ct., New Orleans, 1974-76; assoc. Stone, Pigman et al, New Orleans, 1976-77, Lewis & Rice, St. Louis, 1977-79, Curtis, Mallet-Prevost, et al, N.Y.C., 1980-82; ptnr. LeBoeuf, Lamb, Greene & MacRae, N.Y.C., 1982—; mng. ptnr. London office LeBoeuf, Lamb, Leiby & MacRae, N.Y.C., 1987-89; assoc. editor Tulane Law Rev., 1972-74; frequent speaker before profl. orgns. and assns. Contbr. articles to profl. jours. Mem. ABA, Internat. Tax Planning Assn., Am. Mgmt. Assn. (ins. and risk mgmt. coun.), Corp. Bar Westchester and Fairfield (pro bono steering com.), Tax. Rev., Lawyers Alliance N.Y. (vice chair, bd. dirs.). Office: LeBoeuf Lamb Greene & MacRae 125 W 55th St New York NY 10019-5369

SHOSTAKOVICH, MAXIM DMITRIYEVICH, symphonic conductor; b. Leningrad, USSR, May 10, 1938; came to U.S., 1981; s. Dmitri Dmitriyevich and Nina (Varzar) S.; 1 child, Dmitri; m. Marina Tisie; children: Maria, Maxim. Student, Leningrad Conservatory, 1961-62, Moscow Conservatory, 1963; DFA, U. Md., 1982. Asst. condr. Moscow Symphony Orch., 1963-66, Moscow State Symphony Orch., 1966-69; prin. condr., artistic dir. Orch. Radio and TV USSR, Moscow, 1971-81; mus. advisor Hartford Symphony Orch., Conn., 1985; prin. guest condr. Hong Kong Philharm., 1982—; music dir. New Orleans Symphony Orch., 1986-91; hon. music dir. La. Philharmonic Orch., 1993-94. Debut London Philharm. Orch., 1968; toured Can., U.S., Mex. with USSR State Symphony Orch., 1969; guest condr., Europe, N.Am., Japan and Australia; pianist including Piano Concerto No. 2; rec. father's ballet compositions including Bolt, The Age of Gold, suites, music for films Zoya, Pirogov with Bolshoi Theater Orch., Shostakovich Symphonies; recs. EMI, Philips, Chandos including Shostakovich's Violin Concerto No. 1, Shostakovich's Symphony No. 5, Suite on Verses of Michelangelo, 1971, 77, Piano Concerti Nos. 1 and 2 rec. with Philips Shostakovich's Cello Concerti, 1984. Recipient Outstanding Performance for Arts award Combo Fund Campaign, 1982. Mem. Concert Artists Guild, Great Artists Series NYU (exec. bd. Gallatin div. N.Y.C.). Home: 173 Black Rock Tpke West Redding CT 06896-2519 Office: care Columbia Artists Inc 165 W 57th St New York NY 10019-2201*

SHOTTS, DAVID ALLISON, manufacturing executive; b. Galesburg, Ill., Nov. 21, 1941; s. Samuel E. and Doris R. (Ray) S.; m. Judith Anne Buck, Apr. 15, 1960; children: Catherine, Alison Barker. BA in History and Polit. Sci., U. Ill., 1964. Group gen. mgr. Schlegel Corp., Rochester, N.Y., 1980-85; v.p. ops. ATCOR, Harvey, Ill., 1985-88; chief oper. officer Allied Tube & Conduit, Harvey, 1988—; chmn. Com. Pipe and Tube Imports, Washington, 1991. Mem. Soc. US Constn., Pres'. Coun. U. Ill. Major U.S. Army, 1964-68. Avocation: rose gardening. Office: Allied Tube & Conduit 16100 Lathrop Ave Harvey IL 60426-6082

SHOTTS, WAYNE J., nuclear scientist, federal agency administrator; b. Des Plaines, Ill., Mar. 20, 1945; s. Norman Russell Shotts and Winnifred Mae (Averill) Shotts Goeppinger; m. Melinda Maureen Antilla, June 24, 1967 (dec. Feb. 1975); children: Kenneth Wayne Shotts, Jeffrey Alan Shotts; m. Jacquelyn Francyle Willis, Aug. 11, 1979. BA in Physics, U. Calif., Santa Barbara, 1967; PhD, Cornell U., 1973. Rsch. physicist E.I. duPont deNemours & Co., Wilmington, Del., 1973-74; physicist U. Calif. Livermore, Calif., 1974—; physicist Lawrence Livermore Nat. Lab., Livermore, Calif., 1974-79, group leader, thermonuclear design divsn., 1979-85, divsn leader, nuclear chemistry, 1985-86, divsn. leader, prompt diagnostics, 1986-88, prin. dep. assoc. dir., military applications, 1988-92, prin. dep. assocs. dir. def. and nuclear techs., 1992—. Recipient Ernest Orlando Lawrence Meml. award U.S. Dept. Energy, Washington, 1990. Mem. Am. Phys. Soc., Am. Assn. Advancement Sci. Office: Lawrence Livermore Nat Lab PO Box 808 Livermore CA 94550

SHOTWELL, MALCOLM GREEN, minister; b. Brookneal, Va., Aug. 14, 1932; s. John Henry and Ada Mildred (Puckett) S.; m. LaVerne Brown, June 19, 1954; children: Donna (dec.), Paula. BA in Sociology, U. Richmond, 1954; MDiv, Colgate Rochester Div. Sch., 1957; D Ministry, Ea. Bapt. Theol. Sem., 1990; DD (hon.), Judson Coll., 1990. Ordained to ministry Am. Bapt. Ch. in U.S.A., 1957. Student asst. Greece Bapt. Ch., Rochester, N.Y., 1954-57; pastor 1st Bapt. Ch., Cuba, N.Y., 1957-62; sr. pastor 1st Bapt. Ch., Galesburg, Ill., 1962-71, Olean, N.Y., 1971-81; area minister Am. Bapt. Chs. of Pa. and Del., 1981-90; regional exec. minister Am. Bapt. Chs. of Great Rivers Region, Ill. and Mo., 1990—; mem. Midwest Commn. on Ministry, Am. Bapt. Chs. U.S.A., 1990—, mem. task force for So. Bapt.Am. Bapt. Chs. Relationships, 1990—. Author: Creative Programs for the Church Year, 1986, Renewing the Baptist Principle of Associations, 1990. Trustee No. Bapt. Theol. Sem., Lombard, Ill., 1993—, Judson Coll., Elgin, Ill., 1990—, mem. gen. bd. ABC, 1990—, mem. gen. exec. coun., 1990—; regional exec. ministers coun., 1990—; bd. dirs. Cen. Bapt. Theol. Sem., Kansas City, Kans., 1990—; sec. bd. dirs. Shurtleff Fund, Springfield, Ill., 1990—. Mem. Ministers Coun. Ill. and Mo. Office: Am Bapt Chs of Great Rivers 225 E Cook St Springfield IL 62704-2509

SHOUB, EARLE PHELPS, chemical engineer; b. Washington, July 19, 1915; m. Elda Robinson; children: Casey Louis, Heather Margaret Shoub Dills. BS in Chemistry, Poly. U., 1938, postgrad. 1938-39. Chemist, Hygrade Food Products Corp., N.Y.C., 1940-41, Nat. Bur. Standards, 1941-43; regional dir. U.S. Bur. Mines, 1943-62, chief divsn. Accident Prevention & Health, 1962-70; dep. dir. Appalachian Lab. Occupational Respiratory Diseases, Nat. Inst. Occupational Safety and Health, Morgantown, W.Va., 1970-77, dep. dir. div. safety research, 1977-79; mgr. occupational safety, indsl. environ. cons., safety products div. Am. Optical Corp., Southbridge, Mass., 1979; cons., 1979—; assoc. prof. dept. anesthesiology W.Va. U. Med. Center, Morgantown, 1977-82, prof. Coll. Mineral and Energy Resources, 1970-79. Recipient Disting. Service award Dept. Interior and Gold medal, 1959. Registered profl. engr.; cert. safety profl. Fellow Am. Inst. Chemists; mem. AIME, ASTM, NSPE, ANSI, Am. Indsl. Hygiene Assn., Vets. of Safety, Am. Soc. Safety Engrs., Nat. Fire Protection Assn., Am. Conf. Govtl. Indsl. Hygienists, Internat. Soc. Respiratory Protection (past pres., William H. Revoir award 1993), Am. Nat. Standards Inst., Sigma Xi. Methodist. Contbr. articles to profl. jours. and texts. Home: 5850 Meridian Rd Apt 202C Gibsonia PA 15044-9605

SHOULBERG, HARRY, artist; b. Phila., Oct. 25, 1903; s. Max and Tessie (Derfer) S.; m. Sylvia Hendler, June 1, 1931; 1 child, Ted. Student, Coll. City N.Y., 1931-35. Painter, serigrapher, 1931—; Dir. Studio Art Gallery, N.Y.C. Represented in numerous permanent collections including, Met. Mus., Carnegie Inst., San Francisco Mus., Smithsonian Instn., U.S. Army, Denver Pub. Schs., Brooks Meml. Art Gallery, U. Wis., N.Y.U., Denver Mus., Balt. Mus., Tel Aviv Mus., Ain Harod Mus., U. Oreg., Norfolk Mus. Arts and Scis., Butler Inst. Am. Art, Albrecht Gallery, St. Lawrence U., N.J. State Coll., Wichita State U., SUNY at Binghamton, Allerton Art Mus., Art Bank-U.S.A., Voorhees-Zimmerli Art Mus.; one-man exhbn. Salpeter Gallery, 1951, Hudson Guild, 1955, Carnegie Inst. Art, 1958, Harbor Gallery, 1968, Park Ave South Gallery, 1982, Nat. Acad. of Design, 1992, Broome St. Gallery, 1992; represented in Prize Prints of 20th Century, Allentown Art Mus., U.S. State Dept., Rutgers U.; appeared in Sta. TV WNET program Screenprinting: An American Art Form, 1989. Recipient 1st prize Am. Color Print Soc., 1st prize Guild Hall, Easthampton, N.Y., 1955, 1st prize Bronx, N.Y., purchase prize Nat. Serigraph Soc., Jane Phillips prize, 1956, Emily Lowe award, 1956, Jane Peterson prize Soc. N.J. Artists, 1956, Albert Kapp award Silvermine Artists, 1957, Grumbacher award N.J. Soc. Painters and Sculptors, 1963, Peterson medal of honor Audubon Artists, 1965, Talen's award N.J. Mus., 1966, M.J. Kaplan Meml. award Am. Soc. Contemporary Artists, 1967, Grumbacher prize, 1976, Erlanger Meml. award, 1980, prize Jersey City Mus., 1973, Patron of Arts award Bergen Community Mus., 1981, Dr. David Soletsky award Nat. Soc. Painters in

Casein and Acrylic, 1982, hon. mention Painters and Sculptors Soc., 1982, Binney and Smith award Am. Soc. Contemporary Artists, 1985; Elaine and James Hewitt award Audubon Artists, 1987, hon. mention, 1991. Mem. Nat. Serigraph Soc., Nat. Soc. of Painters in Casein, N.J. Soc. Painters and Sculptors (Pearl award 1979, Patron's award 1981), Bklyn. Soc. Artists, Artists Equity Assn., Audubon Artists, Artists League Am., League Present Day Artists, Artist Circle.

SHOULSON, BRUCE DOVE, lawyer; b. Phila., Feb. 12, 1940; s. I. Harry and Sonia (Rosen) S.; m. Robyn Winkler, June 16, 1963; children: Jeffrey S., Mark E., Adina L. AB, Columbia U., 1961; LLB, Harvard U., 1964. Bar: N.J. 1965, U.S. Dist. Ct. N.J. 1965, U.S. Ct. Appeals (3d cir.) 1967, U.S. Supreme Ct. 1977. Law sec. to hon. chief justice Joseph Weintraub N.J. Supreme Ct., Newark, 1964-65; assoc. Lowenstein, Sandler, Kohl, Fisher & Boylan, P.C., Newark, 1965-70; ptnr. Lowenstein, Sandler, Kohl, Fisher & Boylan, P.C., Roseland, N.J., 1970—. V.p. Daus. of Israel Geriatric Ctr., West Orange, N.J., 1988-90; pres., chair bd. Hebrew Youth Acad., West Caldwell, N.J., 1979-83; bd. dirs. Yeshiva U., N.Y.C., 1986—. Recipient Young Leadership award Jewish Community Fedn. of Met. N.J., 1977, Community Leadership award Agudath Israel of Am., 1983. Mem. ABA, N.J. Bar Assn., Essex County Bar Assn. Office: Lowenstein Sandler Kohl Fisher & Boylan PC 65 Livingston Ave Roseland NJ 07068-1725

SHOULTS, HAROLD E., social services administrator. Territorial commr., ctrl. ter. Salvation Army, Des Plaines, Ill. Office: Salvation Army 10 W Algonquin Rd Des Plaines IL 60016-6006

SHOUP, ANDREW JAMES, JR., oil company executive; b. Monroe, La., Mar. 26, 1935; s. Andrew James Sr. and Ruth (Landis) S.; m. Sue Cowles, Sept. 12, 1959; children: Catherine Shoup Collins, Andrew James III. BS in Petroleum Engring., La. State U., 1957; M in Indsl. Adminstrn., Yale U., 1959. Registered engr. Tex. Prodn. engr. Continental Oil Co., Houston, 1959-65; v.p. DeGolyer and MacNaughton, Dallas, 1965-74; chmn., chief exec. officer Sabine Corp., Dallas, 1974-89; pres. Pacific Enterprises Oil Co. U.S.A., Dallas, 1989-90; pres., chief exec. officer The Wiser Oil Co., Dallas, 1991—. 2nd lt. U.S. Army, 1959-60. Mem. Am. Petroleum Inst., Ind. Prodrs. Assn. Am., Soc. Petroleum Engrs. of AIME, Dallas Petroleum Club, Dallas Country Club. Avocations: skiing, jogging, tennis. Office: The Wiser Oil Co 8115 Preston Rd Ste 400 Dallas TX 75225

SHOUP, CARL SUMNER, retired economist; b. San Jose, Calif., Oct. 26, 1902; s. Paul and Rose (Wilson) S.; m. Ruth Snedden, Sept. 27, 1924; children: Dale, Paul Snedden, Donald Sumner (dec.). AB, Stanford U., 1924; PhD, Columbia U., 1930; PhD (hon.), U. Strasbourg, 1967. Mem. faculty Columbia U., 1928-71; dir. Internat. Econ. Integration Program and Capital Tax Project, 1962-64; Editor Bull. Nat. Tax Assn., 1931-35; staff mem. N.Y. State Spl. Tax Commrs., 1930-35; tax study U.S. Dept. Treasury, June-Sept. 1934, Aug.-Sept. 1937, asst. to sec. Treasury, Dec. 1937-Aug. 1938, research cons., 1943-46, 62-68; interregional adviser, tax reform planning UN, 1972-74; sr. Killam fellow Dalhousie U., 1974-75; staff Council of Econ. Advisers, 1946-49; dir. Twentieth Century Fund Survey of Taxation in U.S., 1935-37, Fiscal Survey of Venezuela, 1958, Shoup Tax Mission to Japan, 1949-50, Tax Mission to Liberia, 1969; co-dir. N.Y.C. finance study, 1950-52; pres. Internat. Inst. Pub. Finance, 1950-53; cons. Carnegie Ctr. for Transnat. Studies, 1976, Harvard Inst. for Internat. Devel., 1978-83, Venezuelan Fiscal Commn., 1980-83, Jamaica Tax Project, 1985, World Bank Value-Added Tax Study, 1986-87, Duke U. Tax Missions Study, 1987-88; vis. prof. Monash U., 1984. Author: The Sales Tax in France, 1930, (with E.R.A. Seligman) A Report on the Revenue System of Cuba, 1932, (with Robert M. Haig and others) The Sales Tax in the American States, 1934, (with Roy Blough and Mabel Newcomer) Facing the Tax Problem, 1937, (with Roswell Magill) The Fiscal System of Cuba, 1939, Federal Finances in the Coming Decade, 1941, Taxing to Prevent Inflation, 1943, Principles of National Income Analysis, 1947, (with others) Report on Japanese Taxation, 1949, (with others) The Fiscal System of Venezuela, 1959, Ricardo on Taxation, 1960,reprinted, 1992, The Tax System of Brazil, 1965, Federal Estate and Gift Taxes, 1966, Public Finance, 1969 (transl. into Japanese 1974, Spanish 1979), (with others) The Tax System of Liberia, 1970; Editor: Fiscal Harmonization in Common Markets, 1966. Decorated Order Sacred Treasure (Japan), Grand Cordon. Disting. fellow Am. Econ. Assn.; mem. Nat. Tax Assn. (pres. 1949-50, hon. mem.), Phi Beta Kappa. Address: 48 Heard Rd Center Sandwich NH 03227

SHOUP, CHARLES SAMUEL, JR., chemicals and materials executive; b. Nashville, Dec. 10, 1935; s. Charles Samuel and Leola Ruth (Turner) S.; m. Frances Carolyn DiCarlo, June 7, 1958; children: Mark Steven, Elizabeth Ann Shoup Kehoe, Margaret Carol Shoup Meyer. AB, Princeton U., 1957; MS, U. Tenn., 1961, PhD, 1962. Rsch. chemist Oak Ridge (Tenn.) Natl. Lab., 1962-67; mgr. special projects Union Carbide Corp., N.Y.C., 1967-68; mgr. planning and controls Bell and Howell Co., Lincolnwood, Ill., 1968; v.p. Bell and Howell Sch. Inc., Chgo., 1968-69; mgr. tech. planning Cabot Corp., Boston and Cambridge, Mass., 1969-70, dir. corp. rsch., Mass., 1970-73, gen. mgr. E-A-R div., 1973-87, v.p., Indpls., 1984-87; pres. Alphaflex Ind. Inc., Indpls., 1987-88, bd. dirs., 1988; pres. Cemkote Corp., Indpls., 1988—, also bd. dirs; chmn. bd. dirs. Blasterz Corp., Carmel, Ind., 1992—; bd. dir. Exec. Svc. Corps, Indpls., 1993—, mem. exec. com., 1994—. Contbr. articles to profl. jours.; patentee in field. Treas. Oak Ridge Community Arts Ctr., 1965-67; pres. Sherborn Edn. Found., 1974-76; chmn. Met. Div. United Way, 1982; bd. trustees, Ind. Safety Equipment Assn. 1978-81. Fellow Am. Inst. Chemists; mem. AAAS, Am. Chem. Soc., Noise Control Products and Materials Assn. (trustee 1977-87, pres. 1982-84), Sigma Xi. Presbyterian. Home: 13019 Andover Dr Carmel IN 46033-2419

SHOUP, HAROLD ARTHUR, advertising executive; b. Pontiac, Mich., Mar. 30, 1930; s. Claude Frank and Jessie Margaret (Forney) S.; m. Mary Ann Brinegar, May 31, 1958; children—Christopher Allen, Leslie Ann, Lisa Margaret. B.A., Mich. State U., 1952. With Babcock & Wilcox Co., N.Y.C., 1957-58, Barberton, Ohio, 1958-59; asso. account exec. Carr Liggett Advt., Cleve., 1959-60; account exec. Carr Liggett Advt., 1960-65, account suprv., 1965-66, asst. to pres., 1965-67, v.p. creative services, 1967-71, sr. v.p. and dir. client services, 1971-76, pres., 1976—, chmn. bd., chief exec. officer, 1978-88; exec. v.p. Am. Assn. Advt. Agys., Washington, 1989—; chmn. bd. dirs. Nat. Advt. Agy. Network; bd. dirs. Bus. Pub. Audit Inc. Vice-pres., mem. exec. bd. Cleve. council Boy Scouts Am. 1980-82; trustee Cleve. Ballet, 1985-88; trustee, vice chmn., mem. exec. com. Work in N.E. Ohio, 1982-87; mem. adv. bd. MADD. Served as 1st lt. USAF, 1952-56. Mem. Indsl. Mktg. Assn., Internat. Advt. Assn., Am. Assn. Advt. Agys. (sectreas., bd. dirs. 1982-82, chmn. Cleve. coun. 1981-82), Ctr. for Advt. History (Smithsonian adv. com.), The Media Inst. (trustee), Profl. in Advt. (treas., polit. action com.), Union of Cleve., Cleve. Advt. Club (bd. dirs. 1979—, v.p. 1980-81, pres. 1984-85), George Town, Nat. Press, Capitol Hill, Robert Trent Jones Gilf Club, Fauquier Springs Country Club. Republican. Presbyterian.

SHOUP, MICHAEL C., newspaper reporter, editor; b. Ringtown, Pa., July 17, 1940; s. Daniel George and Marie E (Fisher) S.; m. Mary Ellen Trimble, Jan. 2, 1965 (div. 1984); children: Rachael, Timothy; m. Mary Jo Crowley, July 22, 1988; stepchildren: David, Benjamin. BA, Moravian Coll., 1965; MS, Columbia U., 1966. Russian linguist intelligence svc. USAF, 1957-61; reporter, editor Phila. Bull., 1967-71; night city editor Phila. Inquirer, 1973, day city editor, 1974, mng. editor Phila. Inquirer Mag., 1975-79, travel editor, columnist, 1980—; travel columnist for Knight-Ridder newspapers, 1980—. Avocations: bicycling, running. Home: 2202 Wallace St Philadelphia PA 19130-3126 Office: Phila Inquirer 400 N Broad St Philadelphia PA 19130-4099

SHOUP, RONALD EDWARD, chemicals executive; b. Ft. Wayne, Ind. Dec. 24, 1951; s. Harold William and Roberta J. (Litherland) S.; m. Paula Jane Branham, Aug. 24, 1974; children: Jason Andrew, Sarah Jane. BS in Chemistry, Purdue U., 1974, BS in Math., 1974, PhD Analytical Chemistry, 1980. Rsch. chemist Bioanalytical Systems Inc., West Lafayette, Ind., 1980-83; v.p. rsch. Bioanalytical Systems Inc., 1983—; pres. BAS Analytics, West Lafayette, 1988—; mem. editorial bd. Elsevier Sci. Pub. Co., Amsterdam, Holland, 1989—. Editor: High Performance Liquid Chromatography Advances and Perspectives, vol. 4, 1986; editor Jour. Liquid Chromatography, 1983. Small Bus. Innovation Rsch. grantee NIH, 1982, 85.

Mem. Am. Chem. Soc., Am. Assn. for Pharm. Scis., Phi Beta Kappa, Phi Kappa Phi. Office: BAS Analytics 1205 Kent Ave West Lafayette IN 47906-1382

SHOUSHA, ANNETTE GENTRY, critical care nurse; b. Nashville, May 25, 1936; d. Thurman and Laura (Pugh) Gentry; m. Alfred Shousha, May 29, 1959; children: Mark André, Anne, Mary, Melanie. Diploma, St. Thomas Hosp., Nashville, 1957; student, Belmont Coll., Nashville, 1958, No. State U., Aberdeen, S.D., 1973; BSN, S.D. State U., 1985. Cert. coronary care. Instr. med. nursing Nashville Gen. Hosp., 1958-59, ob-gyn. nurse, 1959-60; insvc. educator Tri County Hosp., Ft. Oglethorpe, Ga., 1960-61; clin. mgr., office nurse Britton, S.D., 1962-90; med. nursing Nashville VA Hosp., 1990-92, gastrointestinal nurse, 1992-94, critical care nurse ICU, 1994—. Contbr. essays to S.D. Jour. Medicine. Del., S.D. Dem. Conv. Recipient Gov.'s Recognition award for outstanding vol. svc. Mem. ANA, AMA Aux. (state pres.), Nat. Hospice Assn., Nurses Orgn. VA, Donelson/Hermitage C. of C. Home: 2809 Lealto Ct Nashville TN 37214-1813

SHOWALTER, BUCK (WILLIAM NATHANIEL SHOWALTER, III), major league baseball team manager; b. DeFuniak Springs, Fla., May 23, 1956. Student, Chipola Jr. Coll., Fla., Miss. State U. Player various minor league teams N.Y. Yankee orgn., 1977-83, minor league coach, 1984, minor league mgr., 1985-89; coach N.Y. Yankees, 1990-91, mgr., 1992—. Named N.Y.-Pa. League Mgr. of Yr., 1985, Eastern League Mgr. of Yr., 1989, Am. League Mgr. of Yr., 1994. Office: NY Yankees Yankee Stadium E 161st St & River Ave Bronx NY 10451*

SHOWALTER, ELAINE, humanities educator; b. Cambridge, Mass., Jan. 21, 1941; married; 2 children. B.A., Bryn Mawr Coll., 1962; MA, Brandeis U., 1964; PhD in English, U. Calif., Davis, 1970. Teaching asst. English U. Calif., 1964-66, from instr. to assoc. prof., 1967-78; prof. English Rutgers U., from 1978; prof. English, Avalon Found. prof. humanities, Princeton (N.J.) U., 1984—; Avalon Found. prof. humanities Princeton (N.J.) U., 1987—; vis. prof. English and women's studies U. Del., 1976-77; vis. prof. Sch. Criticism and Theory, Dartmouth Coll., 1986; prof. Salzburg (Austria) Seminars, 1988; Clarendon lectr. Oxford (Eng.) U., 1989; vis. scholar Phi Beta Kappa, 1993-94; numerous radio and TV appearances. Author: A Literature of Their Own, 1977, The Female Malady, 1985, Sexual Anarchy, 1990, Sister's Choice, 1991; co-author: Hysteria Beyond Freud, 1993; editor: These Modern Women, 1978, The New Feminist Criticism, 1985, Alternative Alcott, 1987, Speaking of Gender, 1989, Modern American Women Writers, 1991, Daughters of Decadence, 1993; also articles and revs. Recipient Howard Behrman humanities award Princeton U., 1989; faculty rsch. coun. fellow Ruthers U., 1972-73, Guggenheim fellow, 1977-78, Rockefeller humanities fellow, 1981-82, fellow NEH, 1988-89. Mem. MLA. Office: Princeton U Dept of English Princeton NJ 08544

SHOWALTER, ENGLISH, JR., French language educator; b. Roanoke, Va., May 14, 1935; m. 1963; 2 children. B.A., Yale U., 1957, Ph.D. in French, 1964. Asst. prof. French Haverford Coll., 1961-64, U. Calif.-Davis, 1964-66, Princeton U., N.J., 1966-74; assoc. prof. Rutgers U., Camden, N.J., 1974-78; prof. Rutgers U., 1978-83, disting prof., 1985—; dir. MLA, N.Y.C., 1983-85. Author: The Evolution of the French Novel, 1641-1782, 1972, Voltaire et ses Amis, D'apres la Correspondance de Mme De Graffigny, 1975, Rousseau and Mme De Graffigny, 1978, Exiles and Strangers: A Reading of Camus's Exile and the Kingdom, 1984, Humanity and the Absurd: Camus' The Stranger, 1989, My Night at Maud's, 1993. Fellow NEH, 1977-78; Guggenheim fellow, 1982-83. Mem. MLA, Am. Assn. Tchrs. French, Am. Soc. 18th Century Studies, French Soc. 18th Century Studies. Office: Rutgers Univ French Dept Camden NJ 08102

SHOWALTER, ROBERT EARL, banker; b. Vienna, W.Va., Feb. 16, 1937; s. Clay and Edna Melinda (Mahaney) S.; m. Shirley Anita Tessmer, June 24, 1961; children: Brent Alan, Lynn Allison, Eric Michael, Dean Edward. BS, Marietta Coll., 1959; MBA, Case Western Res. U., 1964; postgrad. Advanced Mgmt. Program, Harvard U., 1983. Mgmt. trainee Republic Steel, Cleve., 1959-60; sr. v.p. Fed. Res. Bank, Cin., 1960-84; pres., CEO Commerce Nat. Bank, Lexington, Ky., 1984-90, Nat. City Bank, Toledo, 1990—; trustee Ohio Council Econ. Edn., 1980-83. Trustee Good Samaritan Hosp., Cin., 1979-85, Rotary Found., 1982-84, ARC, 1981-85, Cardinal Hill Hops., 1985-90, sec., 1989-90, Med. Coll. Ohio, 1991—; bd. dirs. United Way Bluegrass, 1985-90, campaign chmn., 1987, v.p., 1989. Named Disting. Alumnus, Marietta Coll., 1982. Mem. Am. Inst. Banking (bd. govs. Cleve. 1974-78), Thoroughbred of Am. Club, Toledo Club, Inverness Country Club. United Methodist. Home: 3707 Corey Rd Toledo OH 43615-1116 Office: Nat City Bank 405 Madison Ave Toledo OH 43604-1203

SHOWER, ROBERT WESLEY, financial executive; b. Harvey, Ill., Sept. 5, 1937; s. Glenn Wesley and Chrissie Irene (Ford) S.; m. Sandra Marie Stough, June 27, 1959; children: David Wesley, Lynece Marie. B.S., U. Tulsa, 1960; P.M.D., Harvard Business Sch., 1972. Sr. auditor Arthur Andersen & Co., Tulsa, 1960-64; with The Williams Cos., Tulsa, 1964-86; asst. v.p. The Williams Cos., 1968-69, v.p. adminstrn., 1969-71, v.p., treas., 1971, v.p. fin., 1971-73, sr. v.p. fin., 1973-77, exec. v.p. fin. and adminstrn., dir. 1977-86; mng. dir. Shearson, Lehman, Hutton, Dallas, 1986-90; v.p. fin. Ameriserv Food Co., Dallas, 1990-91; sr. v.p. fin., CFO Seagull Energy Co., Houston, 1992-93, exec. v.p., CFO, 1994—. Mem. Okla. Soc. CPAs, Bent Tree Country Club (Dallas), Lambda Chi Alpha, Delta Sigma Pi. Home: 17224 Village Ln Dallas TX 75248-6047 Office: Ste 1700 1001 Fannin Houston TX 77002

SHOWERS, RALPH MORRIS, electrical engineer educator; b. Plainfield, N.J., Aug. 7, 1918; s. Ralph W. and Angelina (Jackson) S.; m. Beatrice Anne Cicko, July 11, 1944; children—Virginia Ann, Janet Lynne, Carolin Joan. B.S., U. Pa., 1939, M.S., 1941, Ph.D., 1950. Lab. asst. Farnsworth Radio & Television, 1939-40; test engr. Gen. Electric Co., Phila., Schenectady, 1940-41; lab. asst. U. Pa., Phila., 1941-43, instr. elec. engring., 1942-43, research engr., lab. supr., 1943-45, asst. prof. elec. engring., 1945-53, prof., 1959-89, prof. emeritus, 1989—; v.p. Internat. Spl. Com. on Radio Interference, 1973-79, chmn., 1979-85; v.p. U.S. nat. com. Internat. Electrotech. Commn., 1975-94, chmn. accredited stds. com. C63, 1968—, chmn. com. of action adv. com. on electromagnetic compatibility, 1986-94; cons. Dept. Navy; cons. interference reduction panel R & D bd. Dept. Def., 1945; mem. spl. missin OSRD, Washington, 1945. Contbr. articles to profl. jours. Recipient Astin-Polk Internat. Standards medal Am. Nat. Standards Inst., 1991. Fellow IEEE (Charles Proteus Steinmetz award 1982, Centennial medal 1984, Standards medallion 1991); mem. EMC Soc. (life), Ops. Research Soc. Am., Am. Soc. Engring. Edn., Am. Nat. Standards Inst., AAUP, Sigma Xi. Home: 223 Oxford Rd Upper Darby PA 19083-3906 Office: U Pa Moore Sch Elec Engring Philadelphia PA 19104-6390

SHOWS, CLARENCE OLIVER, dentist; b. nr. Brantley, Ala., Oct. 17, 1920; s. John Oliver and Cora (Nichols) S.; student Wis. State Coll., 1946-47; DDS, Northwestern U., 1951; m. Rita Silverman Orenstein, Nov. 25, 1987; children from previous marriage: Toni Cherie, Kristin Clare Shows Ball, Bradley Scott, Gregory Norman, Jeffery Ryan. Individual practice dentistry, Valparaiso, Fla., 1951-53, Pensacola, 1953—. Mem. Pensacola Art Assn.; past pres. Escambia County unit Am. Cancer Soc., now bd. dirs. Fla. unit, also hon. life mem.; mem. Eagle Scout Bd. Rev., Escambia County; sec. Gulf Breeze Vol. Fire Dept. Served with USCG, 1939-46. Fellow Royal Soc. Health, Internat. Coll. Dentists, Internat. Acad. Gen. Dentistry, Am. Coll. Dentists; mem. Am. AAAS, ADA, Acad. Gen. Dentistry (master, past pres. Fla. unit), Internat. Orthodontic Assn., Internat. Acad. Preventive Medicine, Am. Orthodontic Soc., Gulf Breeze C. of C. (past pres.), Fla. Soc. Dentistry for Children (past pres.), Acad. Gen. Dentistry, Am. Profl. Practice Assn., L.D. Pankey Dental Found., Fedn. Dental Internat., Am. Assn. Clin. Hypnosis, Northwestern U. Alumni Assn., Navy League (life), G.V. Black Soc. (life), Pensacola Jr. Coll. Found. (life), Psi Omega. Presbyterian (elder). Clubs: Masons, Shriners, Jesters, Elks; Pensacola (past pres.), Exchange. Home: 519 Navy Cove Blvd Gulf Breeze FL 32561-4026 Office: 3090 W Navy Blvd Pensacola FL 32505-8024

SHOWS, WINNIE M., public relations company executive, professional speaker; b. L.A., Apr. 2, 1947; d. William Marion Arvin and Joan Catherine (Sperry) Wilson; m. George Albert Shows Mar. 18, 1967 (div. May 1980); 1 child, Sallie; m. Michael P. Florio, Jan. 1, 1990. BA in English, UCLA,

1969; MEd, Calif. State U., Long Beach, 1976. Tchr. St. Joseph High Sch., Lakewood, Calif., 1969-71; tchr. high sch. Irvine (Calif) Unified Sch. Dist., 1972-79; freelance writer, 1979-80; mgr. pub. rels. Forth, Inc., Hermosa Beach, Calif., 1980-81; account mgr., account supr., dir. mktg. Franson & Assoc., San Jose, Calif., 1981-84; v.p., pres. Smith & Shows, Menlo Park, Calif., 1984—. Author (newsletter) Smith & Shows Letter, 1989-94. Vol. Unity Palo Alto (Calif.) Cmty. Ch., 1989-94, Newcomers, Menlo Park, 1990-93, Kara, Palo Alto, 1991-94, Menlo Park Sch. Dist., 1993—. Named Woman of Vision, Career Action Ctr., 1994. Mem. Nat. Spkrs. Assn., Bus. Mktg. Assn. (program dir. 1985-87). Avocations: writing, reading, gardening. Office: Smith & Shows 535 Middlefield Rd Ste 200 Menlo Park CA 94025

SHPERLING, IRENA, internist; b. Tallin, USSR, Sept. 20, 1938; came to U.S., 1976; d. Ber Epstein and Maria Minkov; m. Betsalel R. Shperling, June 16, 1960; 1 child, Elena. MD, First Pavlov's Med. Inst., Leningrad, USSR, 1961. Diplomate Am. Bd. Internal Medicine. Med. dr. City Hosp., Leningrad, USSR, 1961-75; resident in internal medicine Winthrop U. Hosp. SUNY, 1977-80; gen. practice medicine Mineola, N.Y., 1980—. Mem. Am. Soc. Internal Medicine, N.Y. State Soc. Internal Medicine, Nassau County Soc. Internal Medicine, Am. Coll. Physicians, Am. Coll. Physicians, Nat. Assn. Female Execs. Avocations: art, travel, music. Office: Nassau Internists 134 Mineola Blvd Mineola NY 11501-3959

SHPILBERG, DAVID, management consultant, artificial intelligence researcher; b. Lima, Peru, Sept. 28, 1950; came to U.S., 1970; s. Salik and Rosa (Colcher) S.; m. Anita Vaidergorn, June 28, 1970; children: Patricia Elizabeth, Samuel Alexander, Tamara Selma. BS, M.I.T., 1972, MS, 1973, PhD, 1975. Prof. Sch. Mgmt. IESA, Caracas, Venezuela, 1975-79; pres. Sinergica, Caracas, 1979-83; ptnr. Coopers and Lybrand, N.Y.C., 1983—; vis. prof. Wharton Sch. Bus. U. Pa., Phila., 1979; adj. prof. Ga. State U., Atlanta, 1977-84; advisor UNESCO, Paris, 1985—. Atuhor: Statistical Decomposition Analysis, 1980, Seismic Risk, 1980; contbr. to profl. publs. Mem., bd. dirs. Bi-Cultural Day Sch., Stamford, Conn., 1986—. Grantee Factory Mutual Rsch. Corp., 1973, U.S. Geological Survey, 1982; recipient ANCLA award Venezuealan Ins. Assn., Caracas, 1979, rsch. honorarium Am. Risk and Ins. Assn., 1985, Literary Excellence award Assn. Cons. Mgmt. Engrs., 1987. Mem. Am. Assn. Artificial Intelligence, Inst. Mgmt. Sci., Ops. Rsch. Soc. Am., Assn. Computing Machinery, Internat. Ins. Soc. (chmn. program com. 1981), Sigma Xi. Jewish. Avocations: jogging, chess, travel, theatre, space. Home: 16 Hedge Brook Ln Stamford CT 06903-2029 Office: Coopers & Lybrand 1251 Ave Of The Americas New York NY 10020-1104

SHRADER, CHARLES REGINALD, historian; b. Nashville, July 3, 1943; s. Reginald Woodrow and Freda Olene (Presley) S.; m. Carole Anne Analore, Aug. 17, 1963; children: Peter Reginald, Sheila Lynne Shrader Bixby. BA cum laude, Vanderbilt U., 1964; MA History, Columbia U., 1970, M Phil, 1974, PhD History, 1976; Grad., U.S. Army Command/Gen. Staff, Coll., 1978, U.S. Army War Coll., 1982, NATO Def. Coll., 1984. Commd. 2d lt. U.S. Army, 1964, advanced through grades to lt. col., retired, 1987; asst. prof. history U.S. Mil. Acad., 1971-74; instr. European Div. U. Md., Pirmasens and Landstuhl, Germany, 1971-74; instr. U.S. Army Command and Gen. Staff Coll., 1977-80, U.S. Army War Coll., 1980-84; mem. staff NATO Def. Coll., Rome, 1984-85; independent historian, 1987—; exec. dir. Soc. for Mil. History, Carlisle, Pa., 1992—; adj. instr. Elizabethtown Coll., 1988-89, Penn State U.-Harrisburg, 1988-90; lectr. various Army svc. schs., CIA, U. Kans., U. Victoria/B.C., NATO Def. Coll. Mem. Carlisle Mcpl. Authority, 1993—. Mem. Army and Navy Club, Phi Kappa Psi, Phi Beta Kappa. Roman Catholic. Home and Office: 910 Forbes Rd Carlisle PA 17013

SHRADER, WILLIAM WHITNEY, radar consulting scientist; b. Foochow, China, Oct. 17, 1930; came to U.S.; s. Ralph Raymond and Elizabeth Talmadge (Hand) S.; m. Natalie Lucinda Hutchinson, July 21, 1984. BSEE, U. Mass., 1953; MSEE, Northeastern U., 1961. Rsch. engr. Boeing Airplane Co., Seattle, 1953-56; cons. scientist, tech. dir. numerous radar systems developed Raytheon Co., Wayland, Mass., 1956-1994; pvt. practice radar cons. Wayland, Ma., 1994—. Author: (with others) Radar Handbook, 1970, 2d edit., 1990; contbr. articles to profl. jours.; holder 10 U.S. patents, numerous fgn. patents. Fellow IEEE. Avocation: sports car rallying. Home and Office: 144 Harvard Rd Stow MA 01775-1070

SHRAUNER, BARBARA WAYNE ABRAHAM, electrical engineering educator; b. Morristown, N.J., June 21, 1934; d. Leonard Gladstone and Ruth Elizabeth (Thrasher) Abraham; m. James Ely Shrauner, 1956; children: Elizabeth Ann, Jay Arthur. BA cum laude, U. Colo., 1956; AM, Harvard U., 1957, PhD, 1962. Postdoctoral researcher U. Libre de Bruxelles, Brussels, 1962-64; postdoctoral researcher NASA-Ames Rsch. Ctr., Moffett Field, Calif., 1964-65; asst. prof. Washington U., St. Louis, 1966-69, assoc. prof., 1969-77, prof., 1977—; sabbatical Los Alamos (N.Mex.) Sci. Lab., 1975-76, Lawrence Berkeley Lab., Berkeley, Calif., 1985-86; cons. Los Alamos Nat. Lab., 1979, 84, NASA, Washington, 1980, Naval Surface Weapons Lab., Silver Spring, Md., 1984. Contbr. articles on transport in semiconductors, hidden symmetries of differential equations, plasma physics to profl. jours. Mem. IEEE, AAUP (local sec.-treas. 1980-82), Am. Phys. Soc. (div. plasma physics, exec. com. 1980-82), Am. Geophys. Union, Univ. Fusion Assn., Phi Beta Kappa, Eta Kappa Nu, Sigma Xi, Sigma Pi Sigma. Home: 7452 Stratford Ave Saint Louis MO 63130-4044 Office: Washington U Dept Elec Engring 1 Brookings Dr Saint Louis MO 63130-4862

SHREEVE, JEAN'NE MARIE, chemist, educator; b. Deer Lodge, Mont., July 2, 1933; d. Charles William and Maryfrances (Briggeman) S. BA, U. Mont., 1953, DSc (hon.), 1982; MS, U. Minn., 1956; PhD, U. Wash., 1961; NSF postdoctoral fellow, U. Cambridge, Eng., 1967-68. Asst. prof. chemistry U. Idaho, Moscow, 1961-65; assoc. prof. U. Idaho, 1965-67, prof., 1967-73, acting dept. chemistry, 1969-70, 1973, head dept., and prof., 1973-87, vice provost rsch. and grad. studies, prof. chemistry 1987—; Lucy W. Pickett lectr. Mt. Holyoke Coll., 1976, George H. Cady lectr. U. Wash., 1993; mem. Nat. Com. Standards in Higher Edn., 1965-67, 69-73. Mem. editl. bd. Jour. Fluorine Chemistry, 1970—, Jour. Heteroatom Chemistry, 1988—, Accounts Chem. Rsch., 1973-75, Inorganic Synthesis, 1976—; contbr. articles to sci. jours. Mem. bd. govs. Argonne (Ill.) Nat. Lab., 1992—. Recipient Disting. Alumni award U. Mont., 1970; named Hon. Alumnus, U. Idaho, 1972; recipient Outstanding Achievement award U. Minn., 1975, Sr. U.S. Scientist award Alexander Von Humboldt Found., 1978, Excellence in Teaching award Chem. Mfrs. Assn., 1980; U.S. hon. Ramsay fellow, 1967-68, Alfred P. Sloan fellow, 1970-72. Mem. AAAS (bd. dirs. 1991-95), AAUW (officer Moscow chpt. 1962-69), Am. Chem. Soc. (bd. dirs. 1985-93, chmn. fluorine divsn. 1979-81, Petroleum Rsch. Fund adv. bd. 1975-77, women chemists com. 1972-77, Fluorine award 1978, Garvan medal 1972, Harry and Carol Mosher award Santa Clara Valley sect. 1992), Phi Beta Kappa. Office: U Idaho Rsch Office 111 Morrill Hall Moscow ID 83843

SHREFFLER, GENEVIEVE, author; b. Kansas City, Kans., July 27, 1925; g. Raymond S. Gripkey and Genevieve Ruth O'Brien; m. S. Gordon Shreffler, Apr. 9, 1971; children: Steven Paul, Deborah Lynn, Rebekah Helena. BS in Polit. Sci., U. Ctrl. Okla., now postgrad. Designer Braille dress patterns Colorado Springs, Colo., 1966-69; pub. rels. dir. Okla. Women's Polit. Caucus, 1971-72; legis. intern Okla. State Legislature, 1976-77; ctrl. and ea. European specialist Internat. Trade Svcs., Oklahoma City, 1993—. Author: At the Edge, 1989; editor: Legends of Poland, 1990. Bd. dirs. Oklahoma City chpt. UN, 1988-89; founder, past pres. Polish-Am. Refugee Resettlement and Edn. Com., 1984—; active Freedoms Found. Valley Forge, Oklahoma City, 1990—; ex-officio mem. Ctrl. European Resettlement and Edn. Com., 1980-84, pres., 1984—; mem. Oklahoma City mayor's steering com. Internat. Sister City Program, 1993—; mem. internat. rels. comm. City of Scottsdale, Ariz., 1995—. Decorated Golden Cross of Merit (Poland), officer's cross Order of Poland Restituta; recipient Svc. award Rotary Internat. Club, 1984, Nat. Honor medal DAR, 1991. Mem. AAUW, Am. Bus. Women's Assn., Nat. Fedn. Press Women (Communicator of Achievement award Oklahoma City chpt.), European Acad. Arts, Scis. and Humanities (corr.), Alpha Chi. Home: 9815 N 100th Pl Scottsdale AZ 85258

SHREM, CHARLES JOSEPH, metals corporation executive; b. Cairo, May 9, 1930; came to U.S., 1959; s. Joseph C. and Paula (Cadranel) S.; m. Vivian L. Chalom, Jan. 30, 1955; children: Jeff, Leslie Allen. Degree in bus. and economy, Coll. Français, Cairo, 1951. Export mgr. Stanton Ironworks U.K., Middle East, 1950-57; comml. mgr. Soc. Sovibor, Paris, 1957-59; purchasing dir. Montanore, Inc., N.Y.C., 1959-65; exec. v.p Commonwealth Metal Corp., Englewood Cliffs, N.J., 1965-85, pres., chief exec. officer, 1985—. Bd. dirs. Adult Edn., Pequannock, N.J., 1970-80. Mem. U.S.C. of C. (econ. coun., exec. com. U.S. Polish Coun./U.S.C. of C.). Office: 560 Sylvan Ave Englewood Cliffs NJ 07632-3104

SHREVE, PEG, state legislator, retired elementary educator; b. Spencer, Va., July 23, 1927; d. Hubert Smith and Pearl (Looney) Adams; m. Don Franklin Shreve, June 17, 1950 (dec. Sept. 1970); children: Donna, Jennifer, John, Don. BA, Glenville State U., 1948. Cert. elem. tchr., W.Va. Reading tchr. Wood County Bd., Parkersburg, W.Va., 1948-50; elem. tchr. Mt. Solon, Va., 1950-52, Bridgewater, Va., 1952-53, Cody, Wyo., 1970-86; mem. Wyo. Ho. of Reps., 1983—, chmn. com. travel, recreation and wildlife, 1983-91, majority whip, 1992-94, speaker pro tem, 1995—. Mem. coun. Girl Scouts U.S.A., White Sulpher Springs, W.Va., 1962-65; co-chmn. Legis. Exec. Conf., Wyo., 1987; mem. Nat. Com. State Legislatures, 1982—. Named Legislator of Yr., Wyo. Outfitters Assn., 1989, Ofcl. of Yr., Wyo. Wildlife Assn., 1990, Alumna of Yr., Glenville State Coll., 1994. Mem. AAUW (exec. bd.), Nat. Women Legislators, Soroptimists (Women Helping Women award 1985), Beta Sigma Phi (Lady of Yr. award 1986). Republican. Presbyterian. Avocations: golf, walking, needlepoint, knitting, bridge. Home: PO Box 2257 Cody WY 82414-2257

SHREVE, SUSAN RICHARDS, author, English literature educator; b. Toledo, May 2, 1939; d. Robert Kennard and Helen (Greene) Richards; children—Porter, Elizabeth, Caleb, Kate. U. Pa., 1961; MA, U. Va., 1969. Prof. English lit. George Mason U., Fairfax, Va., 1976—; vis. prof. Columbia U., N.Y.C., 1982—; Princeton U., 1991, 92, 93. Author: (novels) A Fortunate Madness, 1974, A Woman Like That, 1977, Children of Power, 1979, Miracle Play, 1981, Dreaming of Heroes, 1984, Queen of Hearts, 1986, A Country of Strangers, 1989, Daughters of the New World, 1992, The Train Home, 1993, Skin Deep: Women & Race, 1995, The Visiting Physician, 1995; (children's books) The Nighmares of Geranium Street, 1977, Family Secrets, 1979, Loveletters, 1979, The Masquerade, 1980, The Bad Dreams of a Good Girl, 1981, The Revolution of Mary Leary, 1982, The Flunking of Joshua T. Bates, 1984, How I Saved the World on Purpose, 1985, Lucy Forever and Miss Rosetree, Shrinks, Inc., 1985, Joshua T. Bates In Charge, 1992, The Gift of the Girl Who Couldn't Hear, 1991, Wait for Me, 1992, Amy Dunn Quits School, 1993, Lucy Forever & the Stolen Baby, 1994, The Formerly Great Alexander Family, 1995, Zoe and Columbo, 1995. Recipient Jenny Moore award George Washington U., 1978; John Simon Guggenheim award in fiction, 1980; Nat. Endowment Arts fiction award, 1982. Mem. PEN/Faulkner Found. (pres.), Phi Beta Kappa.

SHRIBER, MAURICE NORDEN, research and manufacturing company executive; b. St. Louis, Oct. 24, 1943; s. Bernard and Yetta (Gitlin) S.; m. Nancy Jo Wood; children: Amy K., Rebecca D., Aaron L. BA, Washington U., St. Louis, 1965; MBA, St. Louis U., 1970. Sr. cons. Harbridge House, Boston, 1968-70; sr. staff analyst Office Sec. Def., Washington, 1970-78, dep. dir. material mgmt., 1978-79, chief aircraft systems div. Aviation Systems Command, St. Louis, 1979-80, staff dir. supply policy and programs, 1981-82, dir. supply mgmt. policy, 1982-84, dep. asst. sec. def. for spares program mgmt., 1984-85, dep. asst. sec. def. for logistics, 1985-87; corp. v.p. mfg. and logistics System Planning Corp., Rosslyn, Va., 1987-88, pres., corp. v.p., logistics div. mgr.; pres. System Planning Corp. Engring Svcs., Inc., Arlington, Va., 1988-91, COO, 1991-94, pres., 1994—. Assoc. author: Quantitative Analysis for Business and Economics, 1974. Served with U.S. Army, 1967-73. Recipient Presdl. Meritorious Rank award Office Personnel Mgmt., 1986, Disting. Civilian Service medal Dept. Def., 1987, Meritorius Civilian Svc. award U.S. Army.

SHRIBMAN, DAVID MARKS, editor; b. Salem, Mass., Mar. 2, 1954; m. Cynthia L. Skrzycki, Sept. 9, 1978; children: Elizabeth, Natalie. AB summa cum laude, Dartmouth Coll., 1976. Mem. city staff and Washington bur. Buffalo Evening News, 1977-80; mem. feature and nat. staff The Washington Star, 1980-81; with Washington bur. N.Y. Times, 1981-84; congl. reporter, nat. polit. corr. The Wall St. Jour., 1984-93; chief Washington bur., asst. mng. editor The Boston Globe, 1993—. Trustee Dartmouth Coll. James B. Reynolds scholar Jesus Coll.; recipient Pulitzer Prize for beat reporting, 1995. Mem. Phi Beta Kappa. Office: Globe Newspaper Co 1130 Connecticut Ave NW Washington DC 20036

SHRIER, ADAM LOUIS, investment firm executive; b. Warsaw, Poland, Mar. 26, 1938; came to U.S., 1943, naturalized, 1949; s. Henry Leon and Mathilda June (Czamanska) S.; m. Diane Kesler, June 10, 1961; children: Jonathan, Lydia, Catherine, David. B.S., Columbia U., 1959; M.S. (Whitney fellow), M.I.T., 1960; D.Engr. and Applied Sci. (NSF fellow), Yale U., 1965; postdoctoral visitor, U. Cambridge, Eng., 1965-66; J.D., Fordham U., 1976. With Esso Research & Engring. Co., Florham Park and Linden, N.J., 1963-65, 66-72; head. environ. scis. research area Esso Research & Engring. Co., 1969-72; coordinator pollution abatement activities, tanker dept. Exxon Internat. Co., N.Y.C., 1972-74; project mgr., energy systems Exxon Enterprises Inc., N.Y.C., 1974-75; gen. mgr. solar energy projects Exxon Enterprises Inc., 1975-77, pres. solar thermal systems div., 1977-81; corp. planning cons., sec. new bus. investments Exxon Corp., N.Y.C., 1981-82; div. mgr. supply and transp. Exxon Internat. Co., N.Y.C., 1983-86, mgr. policy and planning, 1986-88; mng. ptnr. Specialty Tech. Assocs., Washington, 1988—; adj. lectr. chem. egnring. Columbia U., N.Y.C., 1967-69; industry adv. bd. Internat. Energy Agy., 1984-88, Energy and Environ. Policy Ctr., Harvard U., 1986-88, Internat. Energy Program, Johns Hopkins U., 1987-88; sr. assoc. Global Bus. Forum, 1988—, Cambridge Energy Rsch. Assocs., 1988—. Patentee in field; contbr. articles to profl. jours. Mem. AIChE, Am. Inst. Energy Economists, Chemists' Club of N.Y., Cosmos Club (Washington), Sigma Xi, Tau Beta Pi, Phi Lambda Upsilon. Home: 4000 Cathedral Ave NW Washington DC 20016-5249

SHRIER, STEFAN, mathematician, educator; b. Mexico City, Nov. 7, 1942; s. Henry Leon Shrier and Mathilda June Czamanska; m. Helaine G. Elderkin, 1985. BS in Engring., Columbia U., 1964, MS in Ops. Rsch., 1966; PhD in Applied Math., Brown U., 1977. Chmn. computer sci. program Wellesley (Mass.) Coll., 1972-75; sr. engr. Booz, Allen and Hamilton, Bethesda, Md., 1977-79; dir. Latin Am. ops. SofTech, Inc., Springfield, Va., 1979-80; mem. rsch. staff Systems Planning Corp., Arlington, Va., 1980-83; tech. dir. Grumman-CTEC, Inc. subs. Grumman Data Systems, Inc. (absorbed by Grumman Data Systems, Inc. Jan. 1988), McLean, Va., 1983-85, dir. Lab. Machine Intelligence and Correlation, 1984-87, dir. R & D, 1985-87; asst. dir. tech. dept. Grumman Data Systems, Inc., McLean, Va., 1988-90, dep. dir. tech. dept. Washington ops., 1990-91; mem. tech. staff MRJ, Inc., Fairfax, Va., 1991—; professorial lectr. statistics George Washington U., 1981-84, adj. prof. stats., 1984-85; adj. prof. computer sci. George Mason U., 1985-87; sec. New Eng. Regional Computing Program, Cambridge, Mass., 1973-75. Contbr. articles to profl. jours. Fellow Washington Acad. Sci.; mem. Sigma Xi, Tau Beta Pi. Office: MRJ Inc 10560 Arrowhead Dr Fairfax VA 22030-7305

SHRINER, THOMAS L., JR., lawyer; b. Lafayette, Ind., Dec. 15, 1947; s. Thomas L. Sr. and Margaret (Kamstra); m. Donna L. Galchick, June 5, 1971; children: Thomas L. III, John H. , Joseph P., James A. AB, Ind. U., 1969, JD, 1972. Bar: Wis. 1972, U.S. Ct. Appeals (7th cir.) 1972, U.S. Dist. Ct. (ea. dist.) Wis. 1973, U.S. Dist. Ct. (we. dist.) Wis. 1977, U.S. Supreme Ct. 1978, U.S. Ct. Appeals (8th cir.) 1989, U.S. Ct. Appeals (fed. cir.) 1990. Law clk to Hon. John S. Hastings U.S. Ct. Appeals (7th cir.), Chgo., 1972-73; assoc. Foley & Lardner, Milwaukee, Wis., 1973-79, ptnr., 1979—. Contbr. articles to profl. jours. Fellow Am. Coll. Trial Lawyers; mem. 7th Cir. Bar Assn. (pres. 1993-94), Phi Beta Kappa. Republican. Roman Catholic. Office: Foley & Lardner 777 E Wisconsin Ave Milwaukee WI 53202-5302

SHRINSKY, JASON LEE, lawyer; b. Pitts., June 15, 1937; s. Abe and Sylvia S.; children: Jeffrey, Steven, Stacy. BA, U. Pitts., 1959; JD, George Washington U., 1962. Sr. ptnr. Shrinsky, Weitzman & Eisen, Washington,

1971-87; ptnr., exec. com. mem. Kaye, Scholer, Fierman, Hays & Handler, Washington, 1987—; mem. exec. com., 1993-97; panelist Paul Kagan Seminars on Radio and TV Acquisitions. Instl. Soc. Internat. Rsch.; atty.-advisor Complaints and Compliance Div. Broadcast Bur. FCC, Washington, 1961-64; bd. dirs. U.S. Com. Sports for Israel, Phila., FCC Bar Assn. Contbr. articles to Radio and Records mag., Broadcast Cable Fin. Jour. Presdl. del. Mt. Sinai transfer ceremonies, 1978; U.S. basketball chmn. 12th, 13th and 14th Maccabiah games, Israel; bd. dirs. Washington Hebrew Congregation, 1978-85. Mem. Internat. Radio and TV Soc., Nat. Broadcaster's Club (past pres.), U. Pitts. Alumni Assn. (bd. dirs.). Jewish. Office: Kaye Scholer Fierman 901 15th St NW Washington DC 20005-2327

SHRIVER, DONALD WOODS, JR., theology educator; b. Norfolk, Va., Dec. 20, 1927; s. Donald Woods and Gladys (Roberts) S.; m. Peggy Ann Leu, Aug. 9, 1953; children: Gregory Bruce, Margaret Ann, Timothy Donald. B.A., Davidson Coll., 1951; B.D., Union Theol. Sem. Va., 1955; S.T.M., Yale U., 1957; Ph.D. (Rockefeller Doctoral fellow), Harvard U., 1963; L.H.D. (hon.), Central Coll., 1970, Davidson Coll., 1984, Union Medal, Union Theol. Sem. Am., 1991; D.D. (hon.), Wagner Coll., 1978, Southwestern Coll., Memphis, 1983; LHD (hon.), Jewish Theol. Sem., 1991. Ordained to ministry Presbyterian Ch., 1955; pastor Linwood Presbyn. Ch., Gastonia, N.C., 1956-59; u. minister, prof. religion N.C. State U., Raleigh, 1963-72; dir. u. program on sci. and soc. N.C. State U., 1968-72; prof. ethics and soc. Emory U., Atlanta, 1972-75; William E. Dodge prof. applied Christianity Union Theol. Sem., N.Y.C., 1975—, pres. faculty, 1975-91; adj. prof. bus. ethics Sch. Bus. Adminstrn., Columbia U.; sr. fellow freedom forum Sch. Journalism, Columbia U., 1992-93; adj. prof. ethics, 1994—; lectr. Duke U., Va. State U., Ga. State U., numerous colls. and univs. in Can., Kenya, India, Japan and Korea. Author: How Do You Do and Why: An Introduction of Christian Ethics for Young People, 1966, Rich Man Poor Man: Christian Ethics for Modern Man Series, 1972, (with Dean D. Knudsen and John R. Earle) Spindles and Spires: A Restudy of Religion and Social Change in Gastonia, 1976, (with Karl A. Ostrom) Is There Hope for the City?, 1977, The Social Ethics of the Lord's Prayer, 1980, The Gospel, The Church, and Social Change, 1980, The Lord's Prayer: A Way of Life, 1983, An Ethic for Enemies: Forgiveness in Politics, 1995; co-author: Redeeming the City, 1989, Beyond Success: Corporations and Their Critics in the Nineties, 1991; editor: The Unsilent South, 1965, Medicine and Religion: Strategies of Care, 1979. Dir. Urban Policy Study N.C. State U., 1971-73; precinct chmn. Democratic Party, Raleigh, N.C., del. to nat. conv., 1968; mem. Mayor's Com. on Human Relations, Raleigh, 1967-71; chmn. Urban Policy Seminar, Center for Theology and Public Policy, 1978-82. Served with Signal Corps U.S. Army, 1946-47. Recipient The Union medal, Union Theol. Sem., 1991; Kent fellow in religion, 1959. Mem. Am. Soc. Christian Ethics (pres. 1979-80), Soc. for Values in Higher Edn., Soc. for Health and Human Values, Soc. for Sci. Study of Religion, AAAS, Am. Sociol. Assn., Am. Soc. Engring. Edn. (chmn. liberal arts div. 1972-73), United Christian Youth Movement of Nat. Council of Chs. (nat. chmn. 1951-53), Council on Fgn. Relations. Home: 440 Riverside Dr Apt 58 New York NY 10027-6828 Office: Union Theol Sem 3041 Broadway New York NY 10027-5710 *Modern people need to recover connections between memory and hope. The past we applaud pre-enacts the future we hope for, and the past we deplore forms our obligation, in the present, to make a different future. In a time when young people find it hard to envision a long human future, the connections of history and ethics are indispensable. The forging of such connections is my vocation as an educator.*

SHRIVER, DUWARD FELIX, chemistry educator, researcher, consultant; b. Glendale, Calif., Nov. 20, 1934; s. Duward Laurence and Josephine (Williamson) S.; m. Shirley Ann Clark; children: Justin Scott, Daniel Nathan. BS, U. Calif., Berkeley, 1958; PhD, U. Mich., 1961. From instr. to assoc. prof. chemistry Northwestern U., Evanston, Ill., 1961-70, prof., 1970-87, Morrison prof. of chemistry, 1987—, chmn. dept. chem., 1992-95; mem. Inorganic Syntheses Inc., 1974—, pres., 1982-85; vis. staff mem. Los Alamos (N.Mex.) Nat. Lab., 1976-85, cons., 1985-92; vis. prof. U. Tokyo, 1977, U. Wyo., 1978, U. Western Ont., Can., 1979. Author: The Manipulation of Air-Sensitive Compounds, 1969, edit., 1987; co-author: Inorganic Chemistry, 1990, 2d edit., 1994; editor in chief Inorganic Syntheses, Vol. 9, 1979; co-editor: The Chemistry of Metal Cluster Complexes, 1990, Inorganic Synthesis, 1979—, Advances in Inorganic Chemistry, 1986—, Jour. Coordination Chemistry, Inorganic Chimica Acta, 1988—, Chemistry of Materials, 1988-90, 92—, Jour. Cluster Sci., 1990—, Organometallics, 1993—; contbr. articles to profl. jours. Alfred P. Sloan fellow, 1967-69; fellow Japan Soc. Promotion of Sci. fellow, 1977; Guggenheim Found. fellow, 1983-84. Fellow AAAS; mem. Am. Chem. Soc. (Disting. Svc. in Inorganic Chemistry award 1987), Royal Soc. Chemistry London (Ludwig Mond lectr. 1989), Electrochem. Soc., Materials Rsch. Soc. (medal 1990). Home: 1100 Colfax St Evanston IL 60201-2611 Office: Northwestern U Dept Chemistry Evanston IL 60208

SHRIVER, EUNICE MARY KENNEDY (MRS. ROBERT SARGENT SHRIVER, JR.), civic worker; b. Brookline, Mass.; m. Robert Sargent Shriver, Jr., May 23, 1953; children: Robert Sargent III, Maria Owings, Timothy Perry, Mark Kennedy, Anthony Paul Kennedy. BS in Sociology, Stanford U., 1943; student, Manhattanville Coll. of Sacred Heart, LHD, 1963; LittD, U. Santa Clara, 1962; LHD, D'Youville Coll., 1962; LLD, Regis Coll., 1963; LHD, Newton Coll., 1973, Brescia Coll., 1974, Holy Cross Coll., 1979, Princeton U., 1979, Boston Coll., 1990; also hon. degrees, U. Vt., Albertus Magnus Coll., St. Mary's Coll. With spl. war problems div. State Dept. Washington, 1943-45; sec. Nat. Conf. on Prevention and Control juvenile Delinquency, Dept. of Justice, Washington, 1947-48; social worker Fed. Penitentiary for Women, Alderson, W.Va., 1950; exec. v.p. Joseph P. Kennedy, Jr. Found., 1956—; founder (1968) Spl. Olympics Internat.; social worker House of Good Shepherd, Chgo., also Juvenile Ct., Chgo., 1951-54; regional chmn. women's div. Community Fund-Red Cross Joint Appeal, Chgo., 1958; mem. Chgo. Commn. on Youth Welfare, 1959-62; cons. to Pres. John F. Kennedy's Panel on Mental Retardation, 1961; founder Community & Caring, Inc., 1986. Editor: "A Community of Caring", 1982, 85, "Growing Up Caring," 1990. co-chmn. women's com. Democratic Nat. Conv., Chgo., 1956. Decorated Legion of Honor; recipient Lasker award, Humanitarian award A.A.M.D., 1973, Nat. Vol. Service award, 1973, Phila. Civic Ballet award, 1973, Prix de la Couronne Française, 1974, Presdl. Medal of Freedom, 1984, named Lay person Year Religious Heritage Am. Office: care Joseph P Kennedy Jr 1350 New York Ave NW Ste 500 Washington DC 20005-4709

SHRIVER, GARNER EDWARD, lawyer, former congressman; b. Towanda, Kans., July 6, 1912; s. Edward Arthur and Olive (Glass) S.; m. Martha Jane Currier, June 4, 1941; children: Kay Kwon, David Garner, Linda Ann Breeding. A.B., U. Wichita, 1934; J.D., Washburn U., 1940; D. Pub. Service, Friends U., Wichita, 1970. Bar: Kans. 1940. Instr. English and speech South Haven (Kans.) High Sch., 1936-37; mem. firm Bryant, Cundiff, Shriver & Shanahan, Wichita, 1940-61; Mem. Kans. Ho. of Reps. from Sedgwick County, 1947-51; atty. Wichita Bd. Edn., 1951-60; mem. 87th-94th Congresses, 4th Kans. Dist.; Mem. Kansas Interstate Coop. Commn., 1953-55, Kans. Senate, 27th Dist., 1953-61; mem. Kan. Legis. Council, 1955-60; minority counsel Senate Vet. Affairs Com., 1975-80, gen. counsel, 1981-82; of counsel Johnson, Shriver & Kinzel, McPherson, Kans, 1983-86, Law Offices of David G. Shriver, McPherson, Kans., 1986—. Trustee Murdock Art Collection of Wichita Art Mus.; bd. dirs. Kans. Dialysis Assn., DeMolay Legion of Honor. Lt. USNR, World War II. Recipient U. Wichita Alumni Achievement award, 1961; recipient Washburn Alumni Disting. Service award, 1967. Mem. ABA, Kans. Bar Assn., Wichita Bar Assn., VFW, Am. Legion, Nat. Sorjourners, Masons (33d degree), Shriners. Republican. Methodist. Home: 15205 Timber Lake Cir Wichita KS 67230-9214 Office: Law Offices of David G Shriver 100 S Main St Mc Pherson KS 67460-4852

SHRIVER, MARIA OWINGS, news correspondent; b. Chgo., Nov. 6, 1955; d. Robert Sargent and Eunice Mary (Kennedy) S.; m. Arnold Schwarzenegger, Apr. 26, 1986; children: Katherine Eunice, Christina

Aurelia, Patrick. BA, Georgetown U. Coll. Am. Studies, Washington, 1977. News producer Sta. KYW-TV, 1977-78; producer Sta. WJZ-TV, 1978-80; nat. reporter PM Mag., 1981-83; news reporter CBS News, Los Angeles, 1983-85; news correspondent, co-anchor CBS Morning News, N.Y.C., 1985-86; co-host Sunday Today, NBC, 1987-90; anchor Main Street, NBC, 1987; co-anchor Yesterday, Today, and Tomorrow, NBC, 1989; anchor NBC Nightly News Weekend Edition, 1989-90, Cutting Edge with Maria Shriver, NBC, 1990, First Person with Maria Shriver, NBC, 1991—; co-anchor summer olympics, Seoul, Korea, 1988; substitute anchor NBC News at Sunrise, Today, NBC Nightly News with Tom Brokaw. Recipient Christopher award for "Fatal Addictions", 1990, Exceptional Merit Media award Nat. Women's Political Caucus. Democrat. Roman Catholic. Office: NBC News First Person with Maria Shriver 30 Rockefeller Plz New York NY 10112

SHRIVER, PAMELA HOWARD, professional tennis player; b. Balt., July 4, 1962. Profl. tennis player, 1979—; winner 21 career singles, 92 career doubles titles, 7 Australian Opens (with Martina Navratilova), 4 French Opens (with Navratilova), 5 Wimbledons (with Navratilova), 6 U.S. Opens, French Open mixed doubles (with Emilio Sanchez); mem. U.S. Fedn. Cup Team, 1986-87, 89, 92, U.S. Wightman Cup Team, 1978-81, 83, 85, 87. V.P. Internat. Tennis Hall of Fame; pres. of Women's Tennis Association, 1991, 92, 93. Recipient Gold medal 1988 Olympic Games in doubles (with Zina Garrison). Mem. Women's Tennis Assn. address: c/o PHS Ltd 2324 W Joppa Rd Ste 650 Lutherville Timonium MD 21093-4622

SHRIVER, PHILLIP RAYMOND, university president; b. Cleve., Aug. 16, 1922; s. Raymond Scott and Corinna Ruth (Smith) S.; m. Martha Damaris Nye, Apr. 15, 1944; children: Carolyn (Mrs. Richard Helwig), Susan (Mrs. Lester LaVine), Melinda (Mrs. David Williams), Darcy, Raymond Scott II. BA, Yale U., 1943; MA, Harvard U., 1946; PhD, Columbia U., 1954; LittD, U. Cin., 1966; LLD, Heidelberg Coll., 1966, Eastern Mich., 1972, Ohio State U., 1973; DH, McKendree Coll., 1973; DPS, Albion Coll., 1974; LHD, Central State U., 1976, No. Ky. State U., 1980, Miami U., 1984, U. Akron, 1988. Mem. faculty Kent (Ohio) State U., 1947-65, prof. Am. history, 1960-65; dean Coll. Arts and Scis., 1963-65; pres. Miami U., Oxford, Ohio, 1965-81; pres. emeritus, prof. Am. history Miami U., 1981—; pres. Ohio Coll. Assn., 1974-75; chmn. coun. pres.'s Mid-Am. Conf., 1971-77; chmn. Ohio Bicentennial Commn. for NW Ordinance and U.S. Constn., 1985-89, Ohio Tuition Trust Authority, 1989-92; chmn. coun. pres.'s Nat. Assn. State Univs. and Land Grant Colls., 1975-76, mem. exec. coun., 1976-78. Author: The Years of Youth, 1960, George A. Bowman: The Biography of an Educator, 1963, (with D.J. Breen) Ohio's Military Prisons of the Civil War, 1964, A Tour to New Connecticut: The Narrative of Henry Leavitt Ellsworth, 1985. Bd. dirs. Cin. Ctr. Sci. and Industry, 1965-70; trustee Ohio Coll. Library Center, 1968-74; chmn. bd. Univ. Regional Broadcasting, 1975-76, 78-79. Served to lt. (j.g.) USNR, 1943-46, PTO. Decorated Order of Merit Grand Duchy of Luxembourg, 1976; recipient Disting. Acad. Svc. award AAUP, 1965, Gov.'s award 1969, A.K. Morris award, 1974, Ohioana Career medal, 1987, Converse award, 1990, Award of Merit, Am. Assn. for State and Local History, 1993. Mem. Orgn. Am. Historians, Ohio Acad. History (pres. 1983-84, Disting. Svc. award 1991), Archaeol. Inst. Am., Ohio Hist. Soc. (trustee 1982-91, v.p. 1983-84, pres. 1984-86), Ohio Humanities Council, Am. Studies Assn., Mortar Board, Phi Beta Kappa, Omicron Delta Kappa, Phi Alpha Theta, Alpha Kappa Psi, Kappa Delta Pi, Phi Eta Sigma, Phi Kappa Phi, Kappa Kappa Psi, Alpha Lambda Delta, Beta Gamma Sigma, Sigma Delta Pi, Alpha Phi Omega, Delta Upsilon (Disting. Alumni Achievement award 1985). Presbyterian. Club: Rotary. Home: 5115 Bonham Rd Oxford OH 45056-1428 Office: Miami U Oxford OH 45056

SHRIVER, ROBERT SARGENT, JR., lawyer; b. Westminster, Md., Nov. 9, 1915; s. Robert Sargent and Hilda (Shriver) S.; m. Eunice Mary Kennedy, May 23, 1953; children: Robert Sargent III, Maria, Timothy, Mark Kennedy, Anthony Paul Kennedy. Student, Canterbury Sch.; B.A. cum laude, Yale U., 1938, LL.B., 1941; LL.D., St. Procopius Coll., 1959, Notre Dame U., DePaul U., Seton Hall Coll., 1961, St. Louis U., Kansas State U., Brandeis U., 1962, St. Michael's Coll., Vt., Fordham U., Boston Coll., Yale U., Duquesne U., N.Y.U., Wesleyan U.; D.C.L., U. Liberia, 1963, H.H.D., Salem Coll., 1963, Bowling Green State U.; L.H.D., Springfield (Mass.) Coll., 1963, U. Scranton, Providence Coll.; Dr. Polit. Sci., Chulalongkorn U., Bangkok, Thailand. Bar: N.Y. State 1941, Ill. 1959, U.S. Supreme Ct. 1969, D.C. 1971. With Winthrop, Stimson, Putnam & Roberts, 1940-41; asst. editor Newsweek 1945-46; assoc. Joseph P. Kennedy Enterprises, 1947-48; asst. gen. mgr. Merchandise Mart, Chgo., 1948-61; dir. Peace Corps., Washington, 1961-66, Office Econ. Opportunity, 1964-68; U.S. ambassador to France, 1968-70; spl. asst. to the Pres., 1965-68; sr. ptnr. law firm Fried, Frank, Harris, Shriver & Jacobson, N.Y.C., Washington, Los Angeles, London, Eng., 1971-86; of counsel Fried, Frank, Harris, Shriver & Jacobson, 1986—; pres. Spl. Olympics, Washington, 1986-90, chmn., 1990—, CEO, 1992—; mem. Am. Com. on East-West Accord, 1978—, Ams. for SALT, 1979—. Author: Point of the Lance, 1964. Pres. Chgo. Bd. Edn., 1955-60; mem.-at-large Nat. Coun. Boy Scouts Am.; pres. Cath. Interracial Coun. Chgo., 1955-60; chmn. Internat. Orgn. Patrons of Israel Mus., 1972-75, Democratic candidate for v.p., 1972, ran for Dem. presdl. election, 1976; bd. dirs. The Arms Control Assn., 1983—. Lt. comdr. USNR, 1940-45. Recipient Yale U. medal, 1957, Chgo. medal of merit, 1957, James J. Hoey award Cath. Interracial Coun. N.Y., 1958, Franklin D. Roosevelt Freedom from Want award, 1993, Presdl. Medal of Freedom, 1994; named Lay Churchman of Yr. Religious Heritage Am., 1963; recipient Golden Heart Presdl. award Philippines, 1964, Laetare medal U. Notre Dame, 1968. Mem. Yale U. Law Sch. Assn. (exec. com.), Navy League (life), Chgo. Council Fgn. Relations (dir.), Delta Kappa Epsilon. Roman Catholic. Clubs: Serra, Economic, Racquet, Executives (Chgo.); Onwentsia (Lake Forest, Ill.); Yale (N.Y.C.); University (Washington); Chevy Chase (Md.). Extensive world travel to visit Peace Corps projects, 1961-66. Office: Spl Olympics Internat 1325 G St NW Ste 500 Washington DC 20005-4709

SHRODER, TOM, newspaper editor. Exec. editor sunday "tropic" sec. The Miami Herald, Fla. Office: The Miami Herald Pub Co One Herald Plz Miami FL 33132-1693*

SHROFF, FIROZ SARDAR, merger and acquisition professional; b. Karachi, Pakistan, Feb. 27, 1950; s. Sardar Mohammad Shroff and Kulsum (Bano) Dhanji; m. Munira Firoz, Oct. 27, 1977; children: Khurram, Sara, Ally. Grad. high sch., Nairobi, Kenya. Apprentice, duty incharge Empire Investment Ltd., Nairobi, 1966-67; asst. mgr. to mgr. Trade Aids Inc., Karachi, 1967-69, asst. gen. mgr. 1969-72; gen. mgr. Canorient Overseas Distbrs. Ltd., London, 1972-74; dep. mng. dir. Sasi Ltd., Karachi, 1975-78; dir. internat. expansion Sasi Group Cos., Karachi, 1978-80, mng. dir., 1984—; dir. operation Key Internat. S.A., London, 1980-84; participant Nat. Book Devel. Council, Singapore, 1980, Arthur D. Little Mgmt. Edn. Inst. and Pakistan Mgmt., 1986; trustee Sasi Found., Karachi, 1985; developer bus. info. and rsch. ctr.; advisor/cons. various corp. bodies on takeover acquisition of bus. in U.S., U.K. and the Pacific; involved in group discussions on internat. bus. opportunities, contacts in fin. circles. Recipient Cert. Recognition Asia-Pacific Real Estate Congress, 1987. Mem. Pakistan Pubs. and Booksellers Assn. (copyright com. 1975-80), Internat. Real Estate Fedn., Assn. Builders and Developers (convenor 1985), Internat. Real Estate Inst. (chpt. head 1986), Inst. Dirs. Pakistan C. of C. and Industry, United Coop. Credit Soc. (bd. dirs. 1977-79), Property Cons. Soc., Internat. Airline Passengers Assn.

Muslim. Clubs: Karachi Golf; Def. Lodge: Rotary. Avocations: reading, travel. Office: Sasi House G/2, Block 9, KDA Scheme No 5, Main Clifton Rd, Khayaban-e-Iqbal Kehkashan Karachi Pakistan also: 306 No B North Dr Cohutta GA 30710

SHRONTZ, FRANK ANDERSON, airplane manufacturing executive; b. Boise, Idaho, Dec. 14, 1931; s. Thurlyn Howard and Florence Elizabeth (Anderson) S.; m. Harriet Ann Houghton, June 12, 1954; children: Craig Howard, Richard Whitaker, David Anderson. Student, George Washington U., 1953; LLB, U. Idaho, 1954; MBA, Harvard U., 1958; postgrad., Stanford U., 1969-70. Asst. contracts coordinator Boeing Co., Seattle, 1958-65, asst. dir. contract adminstrn., 1965-67, asst. to v.p. comml. airplane group, 1967-69, asst. dir. new airplane program, 1969-70, dir. comml. sales operations, 1970-73, v.p. planning and contracts, 1977-78; asst. sec. Dept. Air Force, Washington, 1973-76, Dept. Def., Washington, 1976-77; v.p.; gen. mgr. 707/727/737 div. Boeing Comml. Airplane Co., Seattle, 1978-82, v.p. sales and mktg., 1982-84; pres. Comml. Airplane Co. Boeing Div., Seattle, 1986—; pres., chief exec. officer The Boeing Co., Seattle, 1986—, chmn., chief exec. officer, 1988—; bd. dirs. Citicorp, Boise Cascade Corp., 3M Co.; mem. The Bus. Coun., 1987; vice chmn. New Am. Schs. Devel. Corp. Mem., bus. policy com. Bus. Roundtable; trustee Smithsonian Instn. 1st lt. AUS, 1954-56. Mem. Phi Alpha Delta, Beta Theta Pi. Clubs: Overlake Golf and Country, Columbia Tower. Office: Boeing Co PO Box 3707 Mail Stop 10-21 Seattle WA 98108-2207*

SHROPSHIRE, DONALD GRAY, hospital executive; b. Winston-Salem, N.C., Aug. 6, 1927; s. John Lee and Bess L. (Shouse) S.; m. Mary Ruth Bodenheimer, Aug. 19, 1950; children: Melanie Shropshire David, John Devin. B.S., U. N.C., 1950; Erickson fellow hosp. adminstrn., U. Chgo., 1958-59; LLD (hon.), U. Ariz., 1992; EdD (hon.), Tucson U., 1994. Personnel asst. Nat. Biscuit Co., Atlanta, 1950-52; asst. personnel mgr. Nat. Biscuit Co., Chgo., 1952-54; adminstr. Eastern State Hosp., Lexington, Ky., 1954-62; assoc. dir. U. Md. Hosp., Balt., 1962-67; adminstr. Tucson Med. Ctr., 1967-82, pres. 1982-92, pres. emeritus, 1992—; pres. Tucson Hosps. Med. Edn. Program, 1970-71, sec., 1971-86; pres. So. Ariz. Hosp. Council, 1968-69; bd. dirs. Ariz. Blue Cross, 1967-76, chmn. provider standards com., 1972-76; chmn. Healthways Inc., 1985-92; bd. dirs. 1st Interstate Bank Ariz., Tucson Electric Power Co. Bd. dirs. Health Planning Coun. Tucson, 1992, mem. exec. com., 1969-74; chmn. profl. divsn. United Way, Tucson, 1969-70, vice chmn. campaign, 1988, Ariz. Health Facilities Authority, 1992—, bd. dirs., 1992—; chmn. dietary svcs. com., vice chmn., 1988 Md. Hosp. Coun., 1966-67; bd. dirs. Ky. Hosp. Assn., 1961-62, chmn. coun. profl. proactice, 1960-61; past pres. Blue Grass Hosp. Coun.; trustee Assn. Western Hosps., 1974-81, pres., 1979-80; mem. accreditation Coun. for Continuing Med. Edn., 1982-87, chair, 1986; bd. govs. Pima C.C., 1970-76, sec., 1973-74, chmn., 1975-76, bd. dirs. Found., 1978-82, Ariz. Bd. Regents, 1982-90, sec., 1983-86, pres., 1987-88; mem. Tucson Airport Authority, 1987—, bd. dirs., 1990—; v.p. Tucson Econ. Devel. Corp., 1977-82; bd. dirs. Vol. Hosps. Am., 1977-88, treas., 1979-82; mem. Ariz. Adv. Health Coun. Dirs., 1976-78; bd. dirs. Tucson Tomorrow, 1983-87, Tucson Downtown Devel. Corp., 1988-95, Rincon Inst., 1992—, Sonoran Inst., 1992—; dir. Mus. No. Ariz., 1993—; nat. bd. advisors Coll. Bus. U. Ariz., 1992—, chmn. Dean's Bd. Fine Arts, 1992—; pres. Ariz. Coun. Econ. Edn., 1993—; vis. panel Sch. Health Adminstrn. & Policy Ariz. State U., 1990—. Named to Hon. Order Ky. Cols.; named Tucson Man of Yr. 1987; recipient Disting. Svc. award Anti-Defamation League B'nai B'rith, 1989. Mem. Am. Hosp. Assn. (nominating com. 1983-86, trustee 1975-78, ho. dels. 1972-78, chmn. coun. profl. svc. 1973-74, regional adv. bd. 1969-78, chmn. joint com. with NASW 1963-64, Disting. Svc. award 1989), Ariz. Hosp. Assn. (Salisbury award 1982, bd. dirs. 1967-72, pres. 1970-71), Ariz. C. of C. (bd. dirs. 1988-93), Assn. Am. Med. Colls. (mem. assembly 1974-77), Tucson C. of C. (bd. dirs. 1968-69), United Comml. Travelers, Nat. League for Nursing, Ariz. Town Hall (bd. dirs. 1982-92, chmn. 1990-92, treas. 1985), Pima County Acad. Decathlon Assn. (dir. 1983-85), Tucson Cmty. Coun. Rotary Club (pres. 1993-94), Pi Alpha Alpha. Baptist (ch. moderator, chmn. finance com., deacon, ch. sch. supt., trustee, bd. dirs. ch. found.). Home: 6734 N Chapultepec Circle Tucson AZ 85715 Office: Tucson Med Ctr Ste 202 2195 River Rd Tucson AZ 85718 *It seems important to put something back into life - for all we take from it.*

SHROPSHIRE, WALTER, JR., biophysicist emeritus, pastor; b. Washington, Sept. 4, 1932; s. Walter and Mary Virginia (Anderson) S.; m. Audrey Marie McConkey, June 28, 1958; children—Janet Marie, Susan Lynn, Edward Allen. BS in Physics, George Washington U., 1954, MS in Botany, 1956, PhD in Plant Physiology, 1958; MDiv summa cum laude, Wesley Theol. Sem., 1990; postdoctoral fellow biophysics, Calif. Inst. Tech., 1957-59. Ordained to ministry United Meth. Ch., 1977. Physicist Smithsonian Instn., Washington, 1959-63; asst. dir. Smithsonian Environ. Rsch. Ctr., Washington, 1963-86; Gast prof. U. Freiburg, Germany, 1968-69; biophysicist, dir. Omega Lab., Cabin John, Md., 1986—; professorial lectr. botany George Washington U., 1960-85; Gast prof. U. Zurich, Switzerland, 1985-86. Editor: Phytochrome, 1972, Joys of Research, 1981, Photomorphogenesis, Vol 16A, 16B, 1983, Photobiology, 1984-85; Contbr. articles to profl. jours. Pastor, Foundry United Meth. Ch., Washington, 1991—. Recipient Smithsonian Outstanding Performance award, 1967, Smithsonian Research award, 1968; NSF grantee, 1960-66. Fellow Explorers Club. Office: Omega Lab PO Box 189 Cabin John MD 20818-0189 *The world is an incredible place, rich with unexplored and unexplained interconnections between the biological and physical domains. I am fortunate to have been born when science has begun to unravel some of the mysteries of these interconnections and especially fortunate to have had teachers who shared their enthusiasm for learning. I also have benefited from mystical religious experiences of others and my own that enable me to work at the interface between science and religion. My belief is that the pursuit of both subjective and objective knowledge of ourselves and the universe we live in is necessary to enable humanity to develop to its fullest potential. This is an exciting pursuit I hope to continue to participate in a long time.*

SHRUM, GRANT ARTHUR, non-profit organization executive; b. Marquand, Mo., Apr. 9, 1926; s. Millerson R. and Emma Mae (Mathews) S.; m. Alma L. Stephens, Feb. 17, 1945; children: Janet, David, Peggy. BS, U. Mo., 1948. County extension agt. Univ. Mo., Columbia, 1948-53, state 4-H agt., 1953-54; sales rep. Standard Oil Co. Ind., Maryville, Mo., 1954-55; exec. dir. Nat. 4-H Found., Chevy Chase, Md., 1955-79; exec. v.p. Nat. 4-H Council, Chevy Chase, Md., 1979-82, pres., chief exec. officer, 1982—. Pres. Citizens Assn., Rockville, Md., 1975; bd. dirs. Council for Advancement Citizenship, Alexandria, Va., 1981-83. Served with USAF, 1944-46. Citation of Merit Univ. Mo., 1984, Nat. Friends of Extension award Epsilon Sigma Phi, 1985. Mem. Am. Soc. Assn. Execs., Ind. Sector., Nat. Assn. Ext. 4-H Agts. (bd. dirs. 1981-83, Disting. Service award 1980). Republican. Methodist. Club: Chicago. Home: 877 Errol Pky Apopka FL 32712-2601

SHTOHRYN, DMYTRO MICHAEL, librarian, educator; b. Zvyniach, Ukraine, Nov. 9, 1923; came to U.S., 1950; s. Mykhailo and Kateryna (Figol) S.; m. Eustachia Barwinska, Sept. 3, 1955; children: Bohdar O., Liudoslava V. Student, Ukrainian Free U., Munich, 1947-48, U. Minn., 1954; M.A. in Slavic Studies, U. Ottawa, Can., 1958, B.L.S., 1959, Ph.D. in Slavic Studies, 1970. Slavic cataloger, instr. library adminstrn. U. Ill., Urbana, Ottawa, 1959-60; Slavic cataloger, instr. library adminstrn. U. Ill., Urbana, 1960-64, head Slavic cataloging, assoc. prof., 1964-68, head Slavic cataloging, assoc. prof., 1968-91, head Slavic cataloging, prof., 1975-85, assoc. Slavic librarian, prof., 1985-95, prof. Ukrainian lit., 1991—; lectr. Ukrainian lit. U. Ill., 1975-91; vis. prof. Ukrainian lit. U. Ottawa, 1974; assoc. prof. Ukrainian lit. Ukrainian Cath. U., Rome, 1978—; prof. Ukrainian lit. Ukrainian Free U., Munich, 1983—, Ukrainian lang. and lit. U. Ill., 1991—; chmn. Ukrainian Research Program U. Ill., 1984—. Editor: Catalog of Publications of Ukrainian Academy of Sciences, 1966, Ukrainians in North America: A Biographical Directory, 1975; Author: Lubomyr R. Wynar: Bio-Bibliography, 1983, Oleh Kandyba-Olzhych: Bibliography, 1992; editor: Bull. Ukrainian Libr. Assn. Am., 1982-88; mem. editorial bd. Ukrainian Historian, 1985—, Ethnic Forum, 1985—, Crossroads, 1986—, Ukrainian Quar., 1993—. Counselor Boy Scouts Am., Champaign, Ill., 1967-85; bd. dirs. Ukrainian-Am. Found., Chgo., 1978-87. Recipient Grant Future Credit Union Toronto, 1956; recipient Grant U. Ill., 1977, 82, Silver medal Parliament of Can. Librarian, Ottawa, 1959, award Glorier Soc. Can., 1959. Fellow Shevchenko Sci. Soc. (exec. com.); mem. ALA (chmn. Slavic and East European sect. 1968-69), Ukrainian Libr. Assn. Am. (pres. 1970-74, 82-87), Ukrainian Acad. and Profl. Assn. (charter, sec. 1985-89, pres. 1989—), I. Franko Internat. Soc. (founding mem., pres. 1978-79, 81-82), Ukrainian-Am. Assn. Univ. Profs. (exec. com. 1981—), Ukrainian Hist. Assn. (exec. com. 1983—), Ukrainian Acad. Arts and Scis. in U.S. (exec. com. 1993—). Ukrainian Catholic. Home: 403 Park Lane Dr Champaign IL 61820-7729 Office: Dept Slavic Langs & Lits 3092 Fgn Langs Bldg 707 S Mathews Ave Urbana IL 61801-3607

SHU, CHI-WANG, mathematics educator, researcher; b. Beijing, People's Republic of China, Jan. 2, 1957; came to U.S., 1982, naturalized, 1993.; s. Kuang-Yao and Ding-Zhen (Shi) S.; m. Din-Sui Loh, May 1, 1984; 1 child, Hai-Shuo. BS, U. Sci. and Tech. of China, 1982; PhD, UCLA, 1986. Rsch. assoc. U. Minn., Mpls., 1986-87; asst. prof. applied math. Brown U., Providence, 1987-91, assoc. prof., 1992—; cons. ICASE, NASA Langley Rsch. Ctr., Hampton, Va., 1988—. Mem. editorial bd. Mathematics of Computation, SIAM Jour. Numerical Analysis, Jour. Computational Math., 1993—; contbr. articles to profl. jours. Grantee NSF, NASA, Army Rsch. Office; recipient NASA Pub. Svc. Group Achievement award for pioneer work in computational fluid dynamics, 1992. Mem. Am. Math. Soc., Soc. for Indsl. and Applied Math. Achievements include research in numerical solutions for discontinuous problems. Home: 135 Woodbury St Providence RI 02906-3511 Office: Brown U Div Applied Maths 182 George St Providence RI 02912-9056

SHU, FRANK HSIA-SAN, astronomy educator, researcher, author; b. Kunming, China, June 2, 1943; came to U.S. 1945; s. Shien-Siu and Irene I-Jen (Hsia) S.; m. Helen Chien-Ping Pu, June 22, 1968. B.S. in Physics, MIT, 1963; Ph.D. in Astronomy, Harvard U., 1968. Asst. prof. SUNY-Stony Brook, 1968-71, assoc. prof., 1971-73; assoc. prof. U. Calif.-Berkeley, 1973-76, prof. astronomy, 1976—, chmn. dept. astronomy, 1984—; research assoc. MIT, Cambridge, 1968, sr. research assoc., 1971; vis. scientist Kapteyn Astron. Lab., Groningen, The Netherlands, 1973; mem. Inst. Advanced Study, Princeton, N.J., 1982. Author: The Physical Universe, 1982; also numerous sci. and popular articles. Pamphlet writer McGovern Campaign, Suffolk County, N.Y., 1972. Recipient Bok prize Harvard U., 1972; Sloan research fellow, 1972-74. Mem. AAAS, Internat. Astron. Union, Am. Astron. Soc. (councilor 1982-85, Warner prize 1977), Astron. Soc. of Pacific (bd. dirs. 1985-86), Sigma Xi. Democrat. Avocations: chess; poker; bridge; sports; wine and food. Office: U Calif Dept Astronomy Berkeley CA 94720

SHUART, JAMES MARTIN, university president; b. College Point, N.Y., May 9, 1931; s. John and Barbara (Schmidt) S.; m. Marjorie Strunk, Apr. 5, 1953; children: James Raymond, William Arthur. BA, Hofstra U., 1953, MA, 1962; PhD, NYU, 1966. Group rep. Home Life Ins. Co., 1955-57; N.Y. Life Ins. Co., 1957-59; adminstr. Hofstra U., Hempstead, N.Y., 1959-70, asst. dir. admissions, asst. dean faculty, asst. pres., exec. dean student services, assoc. dean liberal arts scis., trustee, 1973-75; v.p. adminstrv. services Hofstra U., 1975-76, pres., 1976—; mem. higher edn. adv. com. N.Y. State Senate, 1979—; trustee Commn. on Ind. Colls. and Univs. N.Y. State, 1982-89, 92—, chmn., 1986-89; mem. Am. Coun. on Edn.'s Labor/Higher Edn. Coun., 1983-88, Am. Coun. on Edns. Commn. on Leadership Devel., 1987-92, Peat Marwick Higher Edn. Pres.' Adv. Com., 1988—; bd. dirs. Smith Barney World Funds, 1991—; European Am. Bank; chair Nassau County Property Tax Relief Commn.; co-chair N.Y. State Temporary Commn. for L.I. Tax Relief. Trustee Molloy Coll., 1973-77; mem. adv. bd. Adelphi U. Sch. Social Work, 1983-84; dep. county exec. Nassau County, 1973-75, commr. social svcs., 1971-73, chmn. L.I. Reg. Planning Bd., 1978-83, chmn., 1981-83; bd. dirs L.I. Assn., 1986-90; trustee Uniondale (N.Y.) Pub. Libr., 1967-78, L.I. Hosp. Planning Coun., 1971-75; pres. bd. dirs. Health Welfare Coun. Nassau County, 1971-80; chmn. Nassau Bd. Social Svcs., 1971-73; bd. dirs. Winthrop U. Hosp., 1979-86; mem. Nassau County Charter Revision Commn., 1993-94. Decorated officer Order of Orange Nassau (The Netherlands); recipient Founders Day award NYU, 1967, Alumnus of Yr. award Hofstra U., 1973, George M. Estabrook Disting. Svc. award Alumni Assn., 1974, Leadership in Govt. award C. W. Post Coll., L.I. U., 1978, Man of Yr. award Hempstead C. of C., 1978, L.I. Pers. and Guidance Assn. award, 1977, Lincoln Day award Syosset-Woodbury Rep. Club, 1981, L.I. Bus. Disting. Leadership award 1982, Joseph Giacalone award, 1986, Honor medal L.I.A., 1988, others; named to L.I. Hall of Fame, 1985. Home: 25 Cathedral Ave Garden City NY 11530-4412 Office: Hofstra U Office of Pres Hempstead NY 11550

SHUBART, DOROTHY LOUISE TEPFER, artist, educator; b. Ft. Collins, Colo., Mar. 1, 1923; d. Adam Christian and Rose Virginia (Ayers) Tepfer; m. Robert Franz Shubart, Apr. 22, 1950; children: Richard, Lorenne. Grad., Cleve. Inst. Art, 1944-46; AA, Colo. Women's Coll., 1944; grad., Cleve. Inst. Art, 1946; student, Western Res. U., 1947-48; BA, St. Thomas Aquinas Coll., 1974; MA, Coll. New Rochelle, 1978; grad., Cleve. Inst. Art. Art tchr. Denver Mus., 1942-44, Cleve. Recreation Dept., 1944-50; ind. artist, portrait painter Colo., Cleve., N.Y., and N.Mex., 1944—; adult edn. art tchr. Nanuet (N.Y.) Pub. Schs., 1950-65, Pearl River (N.Y.) Adult Edn., 1950-51; rec. sec. Van Houten Fields Assn., West Nyack, N.Y., 1969-74. Exhbns. include Hopper House, Rockland Ctr. for Arts, CWC, Cleve. Inst. Art, Coll. New Rochelle. Leader 4-H Club, Nanuet, 1960-80, Girl Scouts, Nanuet, 1961-68; mem. scholarship and gen. com. PTA, Nanuet, 1964-68; recording sec. Van Houten Fields Assn., West Nyack, N.Y., 1969-74; com. mem. Eldorado (Santa Fe) Cmty. Involvement Assn.-Arterial Rd. Planning Com., 1992-94; capt. Neighborhood Watch, local organizer Eldorado chpt.; worked for Jim Baca Gov.'s campaign, 1994. Gund scholar Cleve. Inst. Art, 1946. Mem. AAUW, NOW, Wilderness Club, El Dorado Arterial Road Planning Com., Delta Tau Kappa, Phi Delta Kappa. Democrat. Avocations: photography, bicycling, camping, tennis, walking. Home: 8 Hidalgo Ct Santa Fe NM 87505-8898

SHUBB, WILLIAM BARNET, lawyer; b. Oakland, Calif., May 28, 1938; s. Ben and Nellie Bernice (Fruechtenicht) S.; m. Sandra Ann Talarico, July 29, 1962; children: Alisa Marie, Carissa Ann, Victoria Ann. AB, U. Calif., Berkeley, 1960, JD, 1963. Bar: Calif., 1964, U.S. Ct. Internat. Trade 1981, U.S. Customs Ct. 1980, U.S. Ct. Appeals (9th cir.) 1964, U.S. Supreme Ct. 1972. Law clk. U.S. Dist. Ct., Sacramento, 1963-65; asst. U.S. atty., Sacramento, 1965-71; chief asst. U.S. atty. (ea. dist.) Calif., 1971-74; assoc. Diepenbrock, Wulff, Plant & Hannegan, Sacramento, 1974-77, ptnr., 1977-80, 81-90; U.S. atty. Eastern Dist. Calif., 1980-81; judge U.S. Dist. Ct. (ea. dist.) Calif., 1990—; chmn. com. drafting of local criminal rules U.S. Dist. Ct. (ea. dist.) Calif., 1974, mem. speedy trial planning com., 1974-80; lawyer rep. 9th Cir. U.S. Jud. Conf., 1975-78; mem. faculty Fed. Practice Inst., 1978-80; instr. McGeorge Sch. Law, U. Pacific, 1964-66. Mem. ABA, Fed. Bar Assn. (pres. Sacramento chpt. 1977), Calif. Bar Assn., Assn. Def. Counsel, Am. Bd. Trial Advs., Sacramento County Bar Council. Office: US Courthouse 650 Capitol Mall Sacramento CA 95814-4708

SHUBERT, GABRIELLE S., museum executive director; b. Phila., Apr. 28, 1955; d. Albert H. and Florence (Reiff) S. M in Art History, Oberlin Coll., 1977; M in Public Adminstrn., N.Y.U., 1989. Asst. to v.p./dir. of sales Columbia Artist Mgmt., N.Y.C., 1979-80; artist rep. Herbert Barrett Mgmt., N.Y.C., 1980-81; dir. sales Sheldon Soffer Mgmt., N.Y.C., 1981-87; dir. work study program The Parks Coun., N.Y.C., 1987-88; mgr. arts for transit Met. Transp. Authority, N.Y.C., 1988-91; exec. dir. N.Y. Transit Mus., N.Y.C., 1991—; guest lectr. N.Y.U., 1995, Yale U., New Haven, Conn., 1987; pub. art selection panel Dept. of Cultural Affairs N.Y.C., 1992. Chmn. Concerned Citizens Upper Broadway, N.Y.C., 1983-85. Fellow Mus. Mgmt. Inst. Getty Mus., Berkeley, Calif., 1995, Mayor's Leadership Inst., N.Y.C., 1995. Fellow Mcpl. Art Soc. Office: NY Transit Museum 130 Livingston St Rm 9001 Brooklyn NY 11201

SHUBERT, GUSTAVE HARRY, research executive, consultant, social scientist; b. Buffalo, Jan. 18, 1929; s. Gustave Henri and Ada Shubert (Smith) S.; m. Rhea Brickman, Mar. 29, 1952; children—Wendy J., David L. B.A., Yale U., 1948; M.A., NYU, 1951. Staff mem. Lincoln Lab., MIT, 1955-57; adminstr. systems engring. Hycon Eastern, Inc., Paris, 1957-59; with RAND Corp., Santa Monica, Calif., 1959—, corp. v.p. domestic programs, 1968-75, sr. corp. v.p. domestic programs, 1975-78, sr. corp. v.p., 1978-89, trustee, 1973-89, sr. fellow, corp. advisor and adv. trustee, 1989—;

founding dir. Inst. Civil Justice, 1979-87; dir. equities trust Neuberger & Berman, N.Y.C., 1989—; cons. Keene Corp., N.Y.C., 1990-92; pres. N.Y.C. Rand Inst., 1972-73, trustee, 1972-79; trustee Housing Allowance Offices Brown County, Wis. and South Bend, Ind., 1973-80; mem. adv. coun. Sch. Engring., Stanford U., 1976-79; mem. policy adv. com. clin. scholars program UCLA, 1975, 88; mem. adv. group evaluation and methodology divsn. GAO, 1986—; mem. adv. commn. on professionalism ABA, 1985-87; mem. Calif. jud. system com. Los Angeles County Bar Assn., 1984-85; mem. com. on evaluation of poverty rsch. NAS. Mem. history dept. adv. bd. Carnegie Mellon U., 1995—. With USAF, 1951-55. Decorated Air medal with 3 oak leaf clusters, Commendation medal. Mem. AAAS, Am. Judicature Soc. (bd. dirs. 1987-90), Inst. Strategic Studies (London) World Affairs Coun. (L.A. chpt.), Coun. of Fgn. Rels., Commonwealth Club of San Francisco, Town Hall Calif., Jonathan Club, Yale Club. Home: 13838 W Sunset Blvd Pacific Palisades CA 90272-4022 Office: RAND Corp 1700 Main St Santa Monica CA 90401-3208

SHUBERT, JOSEPH FRANCIS, librarian; b. Buffalo, Sept. 17, 1928; s. Joseph Francis and Lena M. (Kohn) S.; m. Dorothy Jean Whearty, Feb. 5, 1955 (div. Feb. 1980); children: Julia Ellen, Alan Joseph. BS, State U. Tchrs. Coll., Geneseo, N.Y., 1951; MA, U. Denver, 1957. Reference and extension librarian Nev. State Library, Carson City, 1951-57; library cons. Nev. State Library, 1957-59, state librarian, 1959-61; asst. dir. internat. relations office ALA, 1962-66; state librarian Ohio, 1966-77; state librarian, asst. commr. libraries N.Y. State Edn. Dept., 1977—, sec., treas. chief officer state Library Agys., 1973-76, chmn., 1976-78; mem. adv. council to U.S. Pub. Printer, 1974-77; adv. com. White House Conf. Library and Info. Services, 1977-79; bd. dirs. Capital Dist. Regional Info. Svc. Network, State U. Albany; trustee Ohio Coll. Library Center, 1976-78; mem. adv. com. Center for the Book, Library of Congress, 1979-82, mem. network adv. coun., 1981—; Disting. Alumnus lectr. U. Denver, 1979; mem. adv. coun. Sch. Library and Info. Sci., Pratt Inst., 1980—; bd. dirs. N.E. Document Conservation Center, 1980-82, treas. 1986-89, mem. 1989—; chmn. chief officers State Libraries in the NE, 1987-89; mem. design task force White House Conf. on Library and Info. Svcs., 1985. Editor: The Bookmark, 1987—; contbr. to numerous periodicals. Mem. adv. com. U. Wos. Inst. on Edn., Federally Funded Literacy Program, 1992-94. Recipient Hall of Fame award Ohio Libr. Assn., 1991, Exceptional Achievement award ALA Assn. Specialized and Coop. Library Agy. Assn., 1985, Disting. Pub. Service award SUNY-Albany, Nelson A. Rockefeller Coll. of Pub. Affairs and Policy, 1987; named Disting. Alumnus, SUNY-Geneseo, 1985. Mem. ALA, Nat. Ctr.for Ednl. Stats., Nat. Commn. on Librs. and Info. Svcs, Task Force on Pub. Libr. Stats. (adv. com. 1990—), Assn. of Specialized and Coop. Lit. Agys. (pres. 1988-89), Nev. Library Assn. (pres.), North Collins (Library Assn. (N.Y.), Meml. Library Assn., N.Y. Library Assn., Chief Officers State Library Agencies (chmn. 1977-78), Nev. Congress Parents and Tchrs., Kappa Delta Pi. Roman Catholic. Home: 494 Madison Ave Albany NY 12208-3601 Office: NY State Libr State Edn Dept 33 Cultural Edn Ctr # 10A Albany NY 12230

SHUBIK, MARTIN, economics educator; b. N.Y.C., Mar. 24, 1926; s. Joseph Louis and Sara S.; m. Julia Kahn, Aug. 11, 1970; 1 child, Claire Louise. B.A., U. Toronto, 1947, M.A., 1949; Ph.D., Princeton U., 1953. Research asst. Princeton U., 1950-53, research assoc., 1953-55; fellow Center for Advanced Study in Behavioral Scis., Palo Alto, Calif., 1955-56; cons. mgmt. consultation services Gen. Electric Co., 1956-60; adj. research prof. Pa. State U., 1957-59; vis. prof. econs. Yale U., New Haven, 1960-61; prof. econs. of orgn., dept. adminstrv. sci. Yale U., 1963-75, Seymour H. Knox prof. math. instl. econs., 1975—; bd. dirs. Equity Strategies, Third Ave. Fund; mem. staff T.J. Watson Rsch. Labs., IBM Corp., 1961-63; vis. prof. Escuela de Estudios Económicos U. Chile, Santiago, 1965, Inst. Advanced Studies, Vienna, Austria, 1968, 70, U. Melbourne, Australia, 1973; cons. Rand Corp., Santa Monica, Calif., 1963; dir. Cowles Found. for Rsch. In Econs., Yale U., 1973-76; mem. econs. bd. Santa Fe Inst., 1991—; cons. in field. Author or co-author: numerous books in field including The War Game, 1979, (with G. Brewer) The Aggressive Conservative Investor, 1979, (with M.J. Whitman) Market Structure and Behavior, 1980, (with R.E. Levitan) Game Theory in the Social Sciences, vol. 1, 1982, vol. 2, 1984; mem. editorial bd. Conflict Resolution; mem. editorial adv. bd. Internat. Studies Series; assoc. editor Mgmt. Sci, 1965-81; contbr. articles to profl. jours. Served to It. Royal Can. Navy. Recipient Lanchester prize, 1983; named hon. prof. U. Vienna. Fellow Econometric Soc., World Acad. Arts and Scis.; mem. Social Systems Inc. (chmn. bd. dirs. 1978), Am. Acad. Arts and Scis., Conn. Acad. Arts and Scis. Home: 140 Edgehill Rd New Haven CT 06517-4011 Office: 30 Hillhouse Ave New Haven CT 06511-3704

SHUBINSKI, RAYMOND, planetarium director; b. Pikeville, Ky., Apr. 27, 1951; s. Jacob and Claris (Justice) S.; m. Carol Weckwerth, Aug. 16, 1975; children: Jennifer Carol, Julie Anna. BA in Humanities, Mich. State U., 1975, MA in Communication Arts, 1982. Phys. sci. curator Lafayette (La.) Nat. History Mus. and Planetarium, 1977-79; curator Kelly Planetarium, Charlotte (N.C.) Nat. Mus., 1979-80; dir. Pink Palace Mus. Planetarium, Memphis, 1980-85, Flandrau Planetarium, U. Ariz., Tucson, 1985—. Contbr. articles to profl. mags. Assoc. mem. U. Ariz. Near East Ctr. Mem. Internat. Plaetarium Soc., Am. Assn. Mus., Nat. Assn. Watch and Clock Collectors. Avocations: photography, classical music, collecting books, bicycling, magic. Home: 1666 Maine St Quincy IL 62301-4265 Office: U Ariz Flandrau Planetarium Cherry at University Blvd Tucson AZ 85721

SHUCART, WILLIAM ARTHUR, neurosurgeon; b. St. Louis, Oct. 23, 1935; s. Frank M. and Beatrice S.; m. Laura Huber, Dec. 16, 1971. A.B., Washington U., 1957; M.D., U. Mo., 1961. Diplomate: Am. Bd. Neurol. Surgery. Intern U. Utah Hosp., Salt Lake City, 1961-62; resident surgery Peter Bent Brigham Hosp., Boston, 1963-64; resident neurosurgery Columbia-Presbyterian Hosp., N.Y.C., 1967-70; resident neurosurgery Hosp. for Sick Children, Toronto, ON, Can., 1976-71; mem. faculty dept. neurosurgery Tufts Med. Sch., Boston, 1971-76; assoc. prof. Tufts Med. Sch., 1976; neurosurgeon Tufts-New Eng. Med. Center, 1972-76, prof., chmn. dept. neurosurgery, 1981—; prof., chmn. dept. neurosurgery SUNY, Downstate Med. Center, Bklyn., 1976-81. Served with U.S. Army, 1964-67. Mem. A.C.S., Am. Assn. Neurol. Surgeons, Soc. Neurol. Surgeons. Home: 100 Meadowbrook Rd Weston MA 02193-2406 Office: New Eng Med Ctr PO Box 178 750 Washington St Boston MA 02111-1526●

SHUCHAT, ALAN HOWARD, mathematician, educator; b. Bklyn., Oct. 6, 1942; s. Morris M. and Molly (Kuris) S.; B.S., M.I.T., 1963; M.S., U. Mich., 1965, Ph.D., 1969; m. Alix E. Ginsburg; 1 child, Mark. Assoc. prof. math Wellesley (Mass.) Coll., 1974-83, prof., 1983—, chmn. dept., 1981-83; asst. prof. U. Toledo, 1968-71, Mt. Holyoke Coll. South Hadley, Mass., 1971-74. U.S. Dept. Transp. faculty fellow, 1981; NSF grantee, 1979-80. Mem. Am. Math. Soc., Math. Assn. Am., Ops. Research Soc. Am. Jewish. Research in functional analysis and operations research; curriculum devel. Office: Wellesley Coll Dept Math 106 Central St Wellesley MA 02181

SHUCK, JERRY MARK, surgeon, educator; b. Bucyrus, Ohio, Apr. 23, 1934; s. James Edwin and Pearl (Mark) S.; m. Linda Wayne, May 28, 1974; children: Jay Steven, Gail Ellen, Kimberly Ann, Lynn Meredith, Steven James. BS in Pharmacy, U. Cin., 1955, MD, 1959, DSc, 1966. Intern Colo. Gen. Hosp., Denver, 1959-60; resident in surgery U. Cin. Integrated Program, 1960-66; mem. faculty dept. surgery U. N.Mex., Albuquerque, 1968-80; prof. U. N.Mex., 1974-80; founder burn and trauma unit; Oliver H. Payne prof. dept. surgery, chmn. dept. Case-Western Res. U., Cleve., 1980—; interim v.p. for med. affairs; dir. surgery Univ. Hosps. Cleve., 1980—; cons. FDA, 1972-77. Contbr. articles to profl. jours. Served to capt. U.S. Army, 1966-68. Mem. ACS, Am. Surg. Assn., Am. Bd. Surgery (bd. dirs., chmn. 1993-94), Soc. Univ. Surgeons, Am. Assn. Surgery Trauma, Am. Trauma Soc. (founding mem.), Univ. Assn. Emergency Medicine (founding mem.), Am. Burn Assn. (founding mem.), We. Surg. Assn., Ctrl. Surg. Assn., Acad. Surgery, S.W. Surg. Assn., Cleve. Surg. Soc., Ohio Med. Assn., Acad. Medicine Cleve., Halsted Soc., Surg. Infection Soc. (founding mem.), B'nai B'rith, Pasteur Club, Jewish Community Ctr. Club, The Temple Club. Democrat. Jewish. Office: Case Western Res U 2074 Abington Rd Cleveland OH 44106-2602

SHUCK, ROBERT F., financial executive; s. Robert F. II and Gertrude (Lehr) S.; m. Page Downe, May 30, 1969; children: Robert F. IV, Hollister

A. BA in Acctg. with honors, S.E. Mo. Coll., 1959; MBA, Northwestern U., 1961. CPA, Ill.; cert. fin. planner. With Raymond James Fin., Inc., St. Petersburg, Fla., 1969—, vice chmn., 1991—; bd. dirs. RJ Comm., Inc. Trustee All Children's Hosp.; mem. long range devel. com. Fla. Coun. Econ. Edn.; mem. policy bd. Tampa Bay Partnership for Regional Econ. Devel.; mem. devel. found. St. Petersburg Jr. Coll.; stewardship chmn. Our Savior Luth. Ch., St. Petersburg. Mem. Securities Industry Assn. (sales and mktg. com.), Internat. Assn. for Fin. Planning (past bd. dirs.), Nat. Endowment for Fin. Edn. (trustee, mem. exec. com.). Office: Raymond James Fin 880 Carillon Pkwy Saint Petersburg FL 33716

SHUER, LAWRENCE MENDEL, neurosurgery educator; b. Toledo, Apr. 12, 1954; s. Bernard Benjamin and Estelle Rose (Drukker) S.; m. Paula Ann Elliott, Sept. 4, 1976; children: Jenna, Tammy, Nichole. BA with high distinction, U. Mich., 1975, MD cum laude, 1978. Diplomate Am. Bd. Neurol. Surgery, Nat. Bd. Med. Examiners. Fellow in neurology Inst. Neurology, London, 1979; intern in surgery Stanford (Calif.) U. Sch. Medicine, 1978-79, resident in neuropathology, 1980, resident in neurosurgery, 1980-84, clin. asst. prof. surgery and neurosurgery, 1984-90, assoc. prof., 1990—, acting chmn. dept. neurosurgery, 1992—; numerous presentations in field. Contbr. articles and abstracts to med. jours., chpts. to books. Recipient Kaiser tchr. award Stanford U., 1993; James B. Angell scholar. Mem. AMA, Am. Assn. Neurol. Surgeons, Congress Neurol. Surgeons, Western Neurosurg. Soc., Calif. Assn. Neurol. Surgeons (bd. dirs., treas. 1995—), Calif. Med. Assn., Am. Heart Assn. (fellow stroke coun.), Santa Clara County Med. Assn., San Francisco Neurol. Soc., Alpha Omega Alpha. Avocations: skiing, swimming, travel. Office: R155 Stanford U Med Ctr 300 Pasteur Dr Stanford CA 94305-5327

SHUEY, JOHN HENRY, diversified products company executive; b. Monroe, Mich., Mar. 14, 1946; s. John Henry and Bertha (Thomas) S.; children: Katherine, John Henry, John Joseph Satory. B.S. in Indsl. Engring., U. Mich., 1968, M.B.A., 1970. With Tex. Instruments Co., Dallas, 1970-74; asst. treas. The Trane Co., La Crosse, Wis., 1974-78, treas., 1978-81, v.p., treas., 1981-83, v.p. fin., chief fin. officer, 1983-86; also v.p., group exec. Am. Standard; sr. v.p. and chief fin. officer AM Internat. Inc., Chgo., 1986-91; exec. v.p. Amcast Indsl. Corp., Dayton, Ohio, 1991-93, pres., COO, 1993-95, pres., CEO, 1995—, also bd. dirs.; dir., chmn. audit com. State Bank of La Crosse, 1981-87. Bd. dirs. Pub. Expenditure Survey of Wis., La Crosse, 1980-83; bd. dirs., pres. Luth. Hosp. Found., 1983-87. Mem. Fin. Execs. Inst., Machinery and Allied Products Inst. Congregationalist. Office: Amcast Indsl Corp PO Box 98 Dayton OH 45401-0098 Also: Elkhart Products Corp 1255 Oak St Elkhart IN 46514-2277

SHUFF, LILY, artist, wood engraver; b. N.Y.C.; m. Martin Shir, May 12, 1950; children—Lewitt, Lawrence. B.A., M.A., Hunter Coll.; student, Art Students League, Bklyn., Acad. Fine Arts, N.Y. Sch. Social Research, Columbia U. Contbr. to: others. Artists U.S.A.; One-woman shows include, Argent Gallery, N.Y.C., 1947, 56, Van Dieman Lilenfeld Gallery, N.Y.C., 1948, 52, Giraudeau Gallery, Paris, 1951, Utica (N.Y.) Library Gallery, Cortland (N.Y.) Gallery, Mercersburg (Pa.) Acad., Thiel Coll., Greenville, Pa., Freemont (Mich.) Found., St. Vincent's Coll., Latrobe, Pa., 1960, State Coll., Conn., Purdue U., Inc., McPherson Coll., Kans., Regar Mus., Ala., Fairleigh Dickinson Coll., 1961, East Side Gallery, Erie (Pa.) Pub. Mus., Pack Meml. Mus., Asheville, N.C., State U. N.Y., U. N.D., Wesleyan U., S.D., Oreg. Coll., East Side Gallery, N.Y., 1962, 64, 66, others; exhibited in group shows, NAD, Whitney, Riverside, Bklyn., Jersey City museums, Nat. Print Show Library of Congress, Portland Mus. Arts, Nat. Sarasota Mus., Smithsonian Instn., also in, France, also in, Belgium, Holland, Switzerland, Can., Greece, Japan, Latin Am., India, S.A.M., Mex., Scotland, Eng., Israel; represented in permanent collections, Bat Yam Mus., Israel, Met. Mus., N.Y.C., Archives of Am. Art-Simthsonian Instn., Washington, Pakistan Consulato, James Fenimore Cooper High Sch., Robert Mueller, Paris, Mme. Germaine Richier, Paris, Yale U., Ga. Mus. Art, Am. Fedn. Art, Library of Congress, Monsieur Rene de Solier, Paris, Bezalel Nat. Mus., Jerusalem, Norfolk Mus., Neville Mus., Purdue U., Regar Mus., Dakota Wesleyan U., State U. N.Y., Baylor U., Mayville State Coll., St. Vincent Coll., Central Okla. Mus., Phila. Mus. Art, Baruch Coll., N.Y.C., Butler Mus. Am. Art, City Coll. N.Y., McPherson Coll., U. N.D., Rosenberg Library, Galveston, Tex., Erie (Pa.) Mus., Cleve. Mus. Art, East Islip Mus. Art.0-73, 75, 76, 77, prize in oil Knickerbocker Artists 1966, prize in oil Am. Soc. Contemporary Artists 1966, 67, 68, 70, Nat. Assn. Women Artists prize 1969, 70, 71, 75, 78, Silver medal for creative oil Audubon Artists 1979, cash award for oil Allied Artists Am. 1980, Ralph Fabri medal of merit Casein Soc., 1981, Pres.'s award Nat. Casein Soc., 1983, Gold medal Allied Artists Am., 1984, Shiva award for painting, 1984, prize for color woodcut L.I.U., 1986. Recipient prizes (oil) Bklyn. Soc. Artists, 1953, 56, 57, 60; N.J. Painters and Sculptors Soc., 1956, 68, 69, 70; (wood block print) Conn. Acad. Fine Art; 1st prize oil Caravan Gallery, 1957; (print) Nat. Assn. Women Artists, 1959; (casein) Argent Gallery, 1958; (print) Riverside Mus., 1959; Nat. Soc. Painters in Casein, 1963, 65, 66-67, 70-73, 75, 76, 77; Gold Medal of Honor Jersey City Mus., 1962; (oil) Knickerbocker Artists, 1966; (oil) Am. Soc. Contemporary Artists, 1966, 68, 70, 71, 75, 78; Silver medal for creative oil Allied Artists Am., 1980, Gold medal 1984; Ralph Fabri medal of merit Nat. Casein Soc., 1981, Pres.' award 1983; Shiva award for painting, 1984; prize for color woodcut L.I. U., 1986; hon. award Casein Soc., 1988, prize Casein Allied Artist, 1990, Oil prize SUNY, 1991, Oil prize Conn. Acad. Fine Arts, 1992, Oil prize L.I. Univ. Mem. Bklyn. Soc. Artists (dir., oil jury), N.Y. Soc. Woman Artists (dir., treas.), Nat. Assn. Woman Artists (dir., chmn. membership jury, oil jury, mem. adv. bd.), Nat. Soc. Casein Painters (sec.), Nat. Casein Soc. (oil jury Pres.'s award merit) (hon.), Artists Equity, Mus. Modern Art, Silvermine Guild Artists, Soc. Wash. Printmakers, Conn. Acad. Fine Arts, N.J. Painters and Sculptors Soc. (jury selection), Audubon Artists Assn. (Silver medal), Hunterdon County Art Center, Am. Soc. Contemporary Artists, Am. Color Print Soc., Physicians Wives League Greater N.Y. Club: Woman Pays. Address: 155 W 68th St Apt 212 New York NY 10023
I belong to an idealistic school that acclaims romanticism but accepts realities for study and style. Therefore, throughout my life I have held an optimistic view of mankind and of man's intellect.

SHUFORD, HARLEY FERGUSON, JR., furniture manufacturing executive; b. Norfolk, Va., Oct. 7, 1937; s. Harley Ferguson Sr. and Nancy (Pope) S.; m. Helgi Kuuskraa; children: Linda, David. BA, U. N.C., 1959. Engr. Century Furniture Co., Hickory, N.C., 1959-60, mgr. data processing, 1960-63, v.p. mfg., 1964-67, pres., 1967—; bd. dirs. First Union Bank of N.C., Charlotte; chmn. Shuford Inudstries, Inc., Hickory. Trustee Catawba Meml. Hosp., Hickory, 1971-77, chmn., 1977-81; pres. Catawba County C. of C., Hickory, 1976; bd. govs. U. N.C. System, Chapel Hill, 1975-83; bd. dirs. N.C. Citizens of Bus. and Industry, Raleigh, 1982—; chmn. N.C. Arts Coun., Raleigh, 1985-93. Mem. Am. Furniture Mfrs. Assn. (bd. dirs. 1968—, pres., chmn. 1980-82), Phi Beta Kappa. Republican. Mem. United Ch. of Christ. Office: Century Furniture Co PO Box 608 Hickory NC 28603-0608

SHUGART, ALAN F., electronic computing equipment company executive; b. L.A., Sept. 27, 1930. BS in Engring. and Physics, U. Redlands, 1951. Dir. engring. IBM, San Jose, Calif., 1952-69; v.p. Memorex Corp., Sunnyvale, Calif., 1969-73; pres. Shugart Assocs., 1973-78; chmn., chief exec. officer Seagate Tech., Scotts Valley, Calif., 1978—, also bd. dirs. Seagate Tech 920 Disc Dr Scotts Valley CA 95066-4544

SHUGART, CECIL GLENN, physics educator; b. Ennis, Tex., Oct. 13, 1930; s. Clifford Clarence and Ethel Hazel (Venable) S.; m. Theresa Lively, Aug. 26, 1955 (div. July 1981); children: David Neal, Peter Gregory; m. Anita Brumbelow, Dec. 14, 1985. Student, Navarro Coll., Corsicana, Tex., 1954-55; B.A., U. Tex. State U., 1957; M.A., U. Tex.-Austin, 1961, Ph.D., 1968. Research scientist Def. Research Lab., Austin, 1958-61; assoc. prof. IBM, San Jose, Calif., 1961-62; asst. prof., head dept. physics Hardin-Simmons U., Abilene, Tex., 1962-65; dir. Soc. Physics Students Am. Inst., N.Y.C., 1965-70; research assoc. U. Tex.-Austin, 1967-68; prof. physics, chmn. Northeast La. U., Monroe, 1970-77; prof. chmn. physics U. Memphis, 1977—; com. Tech. Legal Assocs., Memphis, 1978—. Author: (with Bedell and Genusa) Experiments for General Physics, 1975; co-author: (with Johnston) The Phenomena of Physics, 1982, Phenomenal Physics and Astronomy, 1991; editor: (with P. Barker) After Einstein, 1981, (with J. Payne) Scientists and Public Policy, 1982. Served with USAF, 1948-52. NSF fellow, 1966-67;

NSF grantee, 1974-75, 79-80. Fellow AAAS; mem. Am. Assn. Physics Tchrs., Am. Phys. Soc. (vice chmn. southeastern sect. 1982-83, sect. chmn. 1983-84, sect. sec., 1991—, sec. ea. region 1991—), Sigma Pi Sigma (pres. 1972-76). Republican. Methodist. Home: 3628 Beechollow Dr Memphis TN 38128-4272 Office: U Memphis Dept Physics Memphis TN 38152

SHUGART, HERMAN HENRY, environmental sciences educator, researcher; b. El Dorado, Ark., Jan. 19, 1944; s. Herman Henry and Katherine Luvois (Rich) S.; m. Ramona Jeanne Kozel, Aug. 27, 1966; children: Erika Christine, Stephanie Laurel. BS, U. Ark., 1966, MS, 1968; PhD, U. Ga., 1971. Research scientist Oak Ridge (Tenn.) Nat. Lab., 1971-84; asst. prof. U. Tenn., Knoxville, 1971-75, assoc. prof., 1975-82, prof., 1982-84; W.W. Corcoran prof. U. Va., Charlottesville, 1984—, chmn. dept. environ. sci., 1990-93. Author: Time Series Analysis, 1978, Systems Ecology, 1979, Forest Succession, 1981, A Theory of Forest Dynamics, 1984, A Systems Analysis of the Global Boreal Forest, 1992, Vegetation Dynamics and Global Change, 1993. Fellow AAAS; mem. Ecol. Soc. Am. (mem. editorial bd. 1981-83). Democrat. Unitarian/Universalist. Avocation: gardening. Home: 107 Cannon Pl Charlottesville VA 22901-2109 Office: Univ Va Dept Environ Sci Charlottesville VA 22903

SHUGART, HOWARD ALAN, physicist, educator; b. Orange, Calif., Sept. 21, 1931; s. Howard Ancil and Bertha Elizabeth (Henderson) S.; m. Elizabeth L. Hanson, Feb. 6, 1971. B.S., Calif. Inst. Tech., 1953; M.A., U. Calif.-Berkeley, 1955, Ph.D., 1957. Teaching asst. physics U. Calif.-Berkeley, 1953-56, assoc., 1957, lectr., 1957-58, acting asst. prof., 1958-59, asst. prof., 1959-63, assoc. prof., 1963-67, prof., 1967-93, prof. emeritus, 1993—, vice chmn., 1968-70, 79-87, 89—, acting chmn., summer 1979, 80, 81, 83, 84,87, atomic beam group leader Lawrence Berkeley Lab., 1965-79; Cons. Convair div. Gen. Dynamics Corp., 1960-61; mem. com. nuclear constants NRC, 1960-63. Recipient Donald Sterling Noyce prize for excellence in undergrad. tchg. U. Calif., 1988, Berkeley citation, 1993. Fellow Am. Phys. Soc. (acting sec. Pacific Coast 1961-64, exec. com. div. electron and atomic physics 1972-74), Nat. Speleological Soc. (vice-chmn. 1954-56); mem. Sigma Xi. Office: U Calif Dept Physics Berkeley CA 94720-7300

SHUGART, JILL, school system administrator; b. Dallas, July 15, 1940; d. Claude Ernest and Allie Merle (Hamilton) S. BA, Baylor U., 1962; MA, Tex. Woman's U., 1972, PhD, 1989. Middle sch. English tchr. Garland (Tex.) Ind. Sch. Dist., 1962-63, high sch. social studies tchr., 1963-76, high sch. asst. prin., 1976-79, dir. communications, 1979-82, asst. supt., 1982-85, supt., 1985—; mem. legis. coun. U. Interscholastic League, Tex., 1989—; chmn. Dist. III music com., Tex., 1989-95; adj. prof. Tex. Women's U., Denton, 1983; chmn. Region X ESC Adv. Coun., rep. to commr.'s supt.'s com., 1993-95. Gen. chmn. Boy Scouts Am. Scouting Night, Dallas, 1988-89; chmn. City of Garland Cmty. Rels. Coun., 1992; sec. Tex. Sch. Alliance, 1992-95; life mem. Tex. PTA. Named Outstanding Alumnus Tex. Women's U., Denton, 1986, Top 100 Educators to Watch, Executive Educator mag., 1985, Finalist as Outstanding Tex. Sch. Supt., 1990. Mem. Am. Assn. Sch. Adminstrs. (suburban sch. com. 1990-93), Tex. Assn. Sch. Adminstrs., Tex. Assn. for Supr. Curriculum Devel., Garland Adminstr. Assn. (pres. 1978-79), Nat. Tex. PTA. Republican. Baptist. Avocations: snow skiing, tennis. Office: Garland Ind Sch Dist 720 Stadium Dr Garland TX 75040-4616

SHUGHART, DONALD LOUIS, lawyer; b. Kansas City, Mo., Aug. 12, 1926; s. Henry M. and Dora M. (O'Leary) S.; m. Mary I. Shughart, July 25, 1953; children: Susan C. Shughart Hogsett, Nancy J. Goede. AB, U. Mo., Columbia, 1949, JD, 1951. Bar: Mo. 1951, U.S. Dist. Ct. (we. dist.) Mo. 1951, U.S. Tax Ct. 1979. With Shughart, Thomson & Kilroy, P.C., Kansas City, Mo., 1951—; v.p. K.C. Mack Sales & Service Inc., R.D. Mann Carpet Co.; mem. Mo. Motor Carriers Assn. Pub. Service Com. Bd. dirs. Rockhurst Coll.; mem. adv. bd. St. Joseph Hosp. Served with AC, U.S. Army, 1944-46. Mem. ABA, Kansas City Bar Assn., Lawyers Assn. Kansas City, Mo. Bar Assn. (chmn. corp. com. 1980-81, 82-83), Kansas City Bar Assn. (chmn. bus. orgns. com. 1990-91), Internat. Assn. Ins. Counsel, Am. Judicature Soc., Mo. Orgn. Def. Lawyers (pres. 1971-72), U. Mo. Law Soc., Univ. Club, Homestead Country Club, Brookfield Country Club, Phi Delta Phi. Republican. Roman Catholic.

SHUHLER, PHYLLIS MARIE, physician; b. Sellersville, Pa., Sept. 25, 1947; d. Raymond Harold and Catherine Cecilia (Virus) S.; m. John Howard Schwarz, Sept. 17, 1983; 1 child, Luke Alexander. BS in Chemistry, Chestnut Hill Coll., 1971; MD, Mich. State U., 1976; diploma of Tropical Medicine and Hygiene, U. London, 1980. Diplomate Am. Bd. Family Medicine. With Soc. Cath. Med. Missionaries, Phila., 1966-82; ward clk., nursing asst. Holy Family Hosp., Atlanta, 1971-72; resident in family practice Somerset Family Med. Residency Program, Somerville, N.J., 1976-79; physician East Coast Migrant Health Project, Newton Grove, N.C., 1980; physician, missionary SCMM, Diocese of Sunyani, Berekum, Ghana, West Africa, 1980-81; emergency rm. physician Northeast Emergency Med. Assn., Quakertown, Pa., 1981-82; founder, physician Family Health Care Ctr., Inc., Pennsburg, Pa., 1982-90; physician Lifequest Med. Group, Pennsburg, 1990-93; prvt. practice Pennsburg, 1993—. Fellow Royal Soc. Tropical Medicine and Hygiene; mem. Am. Acad. Family Practice, Am. Bd. Family Practice, Am. Med. Women Assn. Pa. Acad. Family Practice, Lehigh Valley Women Med. Assn. Roman Catholic. Avocations: guitar, reading, bicycling, hiking. Office: 101 W 7th St Ste 2C Pennsburg PA 18073

SHUKER, GREGORY BROWN, publishing and production company executive; b. Charleston, W.Va., Oct. 3, 1932; s. George and Florence (Brown) S.; m. Nancy Swift Frederick, June 9, 1956 (div. 1983); children: John Frederick, Allison Gregory, Frances Swift. B.S. in Journalism, Northwestern U., 1954. Corr. Life mag., 1959-60; producer Drew Assos., 1961-66, 73-78, Pub. Broadcast Lab., 1967-68; dir. programming CBS-EVR, 1969; program dir. Time-Life Video, RCA SelectaVision, 1970; exec. prod., v.p. Eden House Pub. Inc., N.Y.C., 1971—; exec. producer Playback Assos., Inc., 1972—; Communication for Edn. and Industry, 1981—; pres. GBS, Inc., media devel. group, 1991—; lectr. U. Mich. Sch. Comm., 1989-91; media devel. and mgmt. cons. Am. Flywheel Sys., Inc., 1992; dir. corp. TV CEO Seminard, 1993, CD-ROM Devel. Series, 1994-95; exec. prodr. Brazil-Imax Documentary and Comms. Devel. Group, 1995—; bd. dirs. The Loft Film and Theatre Ctr.; mng. dir. Tree-Free Print Out Devel. Group, 1995—. Producer: documentary films TV Crisis: Behind a Presidential Committment, 1963, The Chair, 1963 (Grand Prix Cannes), Faces of November, 1964 (1st prize Venice), Letters from Vietnam (ABC-TV), 1964, Free at Last, 1968 (1st prize Venice); exec. producer: documentary films TV What Do We Do Now? - The Need for Direction, 1976, Productivity Series, 1979-81, Corp. Media and HDTV Devel., 1984—; feature motion picture prodn., 1982—; producer, Aspira (AT&T), 1987, Lawrence of Arabia and Lowell Thomas, 1992, (TV series) Baltic Festival, 1994; line producer London-to-Peking, 1990; author: Learning by Television (Ford Found.), 1966. Served to lt. (j.g.) USNR, 1955-58. Mem. Deru, Sigma Delta Chi, Alpha Tau Omega, Kappa Tau Alpha. Clubs: Bronxville Field, Little Forum. Home and Office: 1 Cedar St Bronxville NY 10708 also: care NS Bienstock Inc 1740 Broadway New York NY 10019-4315 *God grant me the serenity to accept the things I cannot change, courage to change the things I can, and wisdom to know the difference.*

SHULA, DAVID D., professional football team coach; b. Lexington, Ky., May 28, 1959; s. Donald F. and Dorothy (Bartish) S.; m. Leslie Ann Maglathlin, June 5, 1982; children: Dan, Chris, Matt. BA, Dartmouth Coll., 1981. Pro football player Balt. Colts, 1981; asst. coach Miami (Fla.) Dolphins, 1982-89, Dallas Cowboys, Irving, 1989-91; asst. coach Cin. Bengals, 1991, head coach, 1991—. Mem. NFL Alumni Assn. Republican. Roman Catholic. Office: Cincinnati Bengals 200 Riverfront Stadium Cincinnati OH 45202*

SHULA, DON FRANCIS, professional football coach; b. Grand River, OH, Jan. 4, 1930; s. Dan and Mary (Miller) S.; children: David, Donna, Sharon, Anne, Michael; m. Mary Ann Shula. B.S., John Carroll U., Cleve., 1951, H.H.D. (hon.), 1972; M.A., Case Western Res. U., 1953; Sc.D. (hon.), Biscayne Coll., 1974. Profl. football player Cleve. Browns, 1951-52, Balt. Colts, 1953-56, Washington Redskins, 1957; asst. coach U. Va., 1958, U. Ky., 1959, Detroit Lions, 1960-62; head coach Baltimore Colts, 1963-69, Miami (Fla.) Dolphins, 1970—. Author: The Winning Edge, 1972. Fla. crusade chmn. Nat. Cancer Soc., 1975; co-chmn. Jerry Lewis March Against Dystrophy,

1975; nat. bd. dirs. Jesuit Program for Living and Learning, 1976; mem. nat. sports com. Multiple Schlerosis Soc., Muscular Dystrophy Assn.; bd. dirs. Heart Assn. Greater Miami; hon. chmn. Belen Jesuit Intercultural Fund Campaign To Build Schs.; established Don Shula Found., breast cancer rsch., 1991—; sponsor Don Shula Scholarship, 1978—. Coached 6 Superbowl teams, winning teams 1972, 73; recipient Coach of Yr. awards 1964, 66, 70, 71, 72, Coach of Decade Prof Football Hall of Fame, 1980, Pro Football's All-Time Winningest Coach, 1994, Brotherhood award Fla. region NCCJ, 1977, Light of Flames Leadership award Barry Coll., 1977, Concern award Cedars Med. Ctr., 1992, Solheim Lifetime Achievement award, 1992, Jim Thorpe award, 1993, Sportsman of Yr. Sports Illustrated, 1993, Horrigan award Pro Football Writers', 1994; named Balt. Colts Silver Anniversary Coach, 1977. Roman Catholic. Office: Miami Dolphins 7500 SW 30th St Davie FL 33314 *Success is never final; defeat is never fatal.*

SHULA, ROBERT JOSEPH, lawyer; b. South Bend, Ind., Dec. 10, 1936; s. Joseph Edward and Bertha Mona (Buckner) S.; m. Gaye Ann Martin, Oct. 8, 1978; children: Deirdre Regina, Robert Joseph II, Elizabeth Martin. BS in Mktg., Ind. U., 1958, JD, 1961. Bar: Ind. 1961; Diplomate Ind. Def. Trial Counsel. Ptnr. Bingham Summers Welsh & Spilman, Indpls., 1965-82, sr. ptnr., 1982-89; ptnr. Price & Shula, Indpls., 1989-91, Lowe Gray Steele & Hoffman, Indpls., 1991—; mem. faculty Nat. Inst. Trial Advocacy; guest lectr. Brit. Medicine and Law Soc., 1979, Ind. U. Sch. Law; medico-legal lectr. Ind. U. Schs. Medicine, Dentistry, and Nursing. Bd. dirs. Arts Insight, Indpls.; pres. Oriental Arts Soc., Indpls., 1975-79, Meridian Women's Clinic, Inc., Indpls.; trustee Indpls. Mus. Art, 1975-78, life trustee, 1984—; bd. dirs. Ind. Repertory Theatre, Indpls., 1982-92, chmn. bd., pres., 1985-89, pres. Repertory Soc., 1993—; v.p., bd. dirs. Flanner House of Indpls., Inc., 1977-88, chmn. 1988—; pres. Internat. Ctr. of Indpls., Inc., 1993—. Maj. JAGC, USAFR, 1961-65. Fellow Internat. Soc. Barristers; mem. ABA, Fed. Bar Assn., Ind. State Bar Assn., Indpls. Bar Assn., Am. Bd. Trial Advs., Am. Law Inst., Ind. Def. Lawyers Assn., Confrerie Chevaliers du Tastevin, Woodstock Country Club. Democrat. Episcopalian. Home: 4137 N Meridian St Indianapolis IN 46208-4014 Office: Lowe Gray Steele & Hoffman Bank One Ctr # 4600 111 Monument Cir Indianapolis IN 46204-5100

SHULER, ELLIE GIVAN, JR., heritage center administrator; b. Raleigh, N.C., Dec. 6, 1936; s. Ellie Givan and Berta (Williams) S.; m. Annette Fontaine Maury, Mar. 22, 1961; children—Ellie Givan III, Franklin Maury, Gray Hays. B.S.C.E., The Citadel, 1959; M.S. in Mgmt., Rensselaer Poly. Inst., 1967; grad., Squadron Officer Sch., Maxwell AFB, Ala., 1964; postgrad., Naval War Coll.; grad. command and staff course, Nat. War Coll., 1976; grad. cen. flight instr. course, Castle AFB, Calif. Engr. in ing., S.C. Commd. 2d lt. U.S. Air Force, 1959, advanced through grades to lt. gen., 1988, various positions and locations, 1959-68; F-4C pilot, asst. flight comdr. 558th Tactical Fighter Squadron U.S. Air Force, Cam Ranh Bay AFB, Republic of Vietnam, 1968-69; indsl. engr., then asst. dep. chief Engring. Mgmt. Div., Hdqrs. 2d Air Force U.S. Air Force, Barksdale AFB, La., 1969-71; asst. exec. officer to comdr. in chief U.S. Air Force in Europe, Lindsey Air Sta., West Germany, 1972-73; base civil engr., comdr. 86th Civil Engring. Squadron U.S. Air Force in Europe, Ramstein Air Base, Fed. Republic Germany, 1973-75; dir. ops. 3902d Air Base Wing, comdr. 3902d Ops. Squadron Offutt AFB, Nebr., 1976; dir. programs Office Dep. Chief of Staff for Engring. and Services SAC, Offutt AFB, Nebr., 1976-77, exec. to comdr. in chief, 1977-79; vice comdr., then comdr. 19th Bombardment Wing Robins AFB, Ga., 1979-80; comdr. 42d Bombardment Wing Loring AFB, Maine, 1980-81; comdr. 4th Air Div. F.E Warren AFB, Wyo., 1981-84; comdr. 3rd Air Div. SAC, Andersen AFB, Guam, 1984-86; asst. dep. then dep. chief of staff, ops. SAC Hqrs., Offutt AFB, Nebr., 1986-88; comdr. 8th Air Force SAC, Barksdale AFB, 1988-91; retired, 1991; chmn. bd., CEO 8th Air Force Heritage Ctr., 1993—. Bd. dirs. Longs Peak coun. Boy Scouts Am., 1983-84; trustee Falcon Found., USAF Acad. Decorated D.S.M. with oak leaf cluster, Legion of Merit with oak leaf cluster, D.F.C., Air medal with five oak leaf clusters, Air Force Commendation medal with oak leaf cluster. Mem. Soc. Am. Mil. Engrs. (chpt. pres. 1971), Am. Def. Preparedness Assn. (regional bd. dirs. 1981-84), Order of Dadaelians (hon. flight capt. 1981-85), Council on Am.'s Mil. Past, Mil. Order of World Wars, Tau Beta Pi. Republican. Episcopalian. Lodge: Kiwanis. Avocations: numismatics, golf, hunting, fishing, military history. Office: 675 Willow Way West Alexander City AL 35010-9555

SHULER, HOWARD L., superintendent. Supt. Auburn-Washburn U.S.D. 437, Topka, Kans. Recipient State Finalist for Nat. Supt. of Yr. award, 1993. Office: Auburn-Washburn USD 437 5928 SW 53rd St Topeka KS 66610-9423

SHULER, KURT EGON, chemist, educator; b. Nuremberg, Germany, July 10, 1922; came to U.S., 1937, naturalized, 1944; s. Louis and Donie (Wald) Schulherr; m. Beatrice Gwyn London, Nov. 11, 1944. B.S., Ga. Inst. Tech., 1942; Ph.D., Cath. U. Am., 1949; postdoctoral fellow, Johns Hopkins U., 1949-51. Sr. staff mem., asst. group supr., chem. physics group Applied Physics Lab., Johns Hopkins, 1951-55; supervisory phys. chemist Nat. Bur. Standards, 1955-58, cons. to dir., 1958-61, asst. dir. sr. research fellow, 1963-68; mem. research staff, sci. adviser to v.p. research Gen. Motors Corp., 1958; spl. asst. to dir. research Inst. Def. Analyses, 1961-63; vis. prof. chemistry U. Calif. at San Diego, La Jolla, 1966-67, prof. chemistry, 1968-91, prof. emeritus, 1991—, chmn. dept., 1968-70, 84-87; cons. to govt. and industry, 1956—; mem. Solvay Conf., 1962, 78; mem. adv. panel, chemistry div. NSF, 1973-75; assoc. Sotheby's, 1991—. Author, editor tech. books; assoc. editor Jour. Math. Physics, 1963-66; bd. editors: Jour. Statis. Physics, 1968-80; mem. adv. bd.: Chem. Engring. News, 1967-70; contbr. articles to profl. jours. Served with U.S. Army, 1944-46. Recipient Distinguished Service award Nat. Bur. Standards, 1959, Gold medal award Dept. Commerce, 1968; Solvay Found. fellow, 1975. Fellow Am. Inst. Chemists, AAAS, Am. Phys. Soc., Washington Acad. Sci.; mem. Am. Chem. Soc., Washington Philos. Soc. Club: Rancho Santa Fe Golf. Home: PO Box 1504 Rancho Santa Fe CA 92067-1504 Office: Univ Calif at San Diego Dept Chemistry La Jolla CA 92093

SHULER, MICHAEL LOUIS, biochemical engineering educator, consultant; b. Joliet, Ill., Jan. 2, 1947; s. Louis Dean and Mary Clara (Boylan) S.; m. Karen Joyce Beck, June 24, 1972; children: Andrew, Kristin, Eric, Katherine. BSChemE, U. Notre Dame, 1969; PhDChemE, U. Minn., 1973. Asst. prof. biochem. engring. Cornell U., Ithaca, N.Y., 1974-79, assoc. prof., 1979-83, prof., 1984-91; Samuel B. Eckert prof. chem. engring. Cornell U., Ithaca, 1992—; vis. scholar U. Wash., Seattle, 1980-81; vis. scientist U. Wis., Madison, 1988-89; bd. dirs. Phyton Catalytic Inc., Ithaca, N.Y. Editor 6 books; contbr. numerous articles to profl. jours. and chpts. to books. Bd. dirs., treas., sec., v.p. Advs. for the Handicapped, Ithaca, 1978-88; sec., bd. adv. Tompkins County Human Rights Commn., Ithaca, 1985-87; mem. adv. bd. Carnegie-Mellon Chem. Engring., Princeton U. Chem. Engring. Recipient Outstanding Paper award Am. Oil Chemist Soc., 1984, Coll. of Engring. Honor award U. Notre Dame, 1989. Fellow Am. Inst. Med. and Biol. Engrs. (founder, v.p. edn. com.); mem. NAE, AIChE (editor Biotech. Progress 1985-88, cons. editor jour. 1986—, mem. publ. com. 1988—, awards com. 1993—, chair Food Pharm. and Bioengring. divsn. 1994—, Food, Pharm., Energy and Bioengring. 1994, mem. adv. com. 1988—, Am. Chem. Soc. (M.J. Johnson award 1986), Am. Soc. Microbiology, Am. Soc. Pharmacognosy. Roman Catholic. Avocation: fishing. Office: Cornell U Dept Chem Engring 340 Olin Hall Ithaca NY 14853-5201

SHULER, SCOTT, civil engineer; b. Toledo, Ohio, July 28, 1952; m. Jan C. Schafer, May 26, 1979. BSCE, Purdue U., 1974, MSCE, 1976; PhD, Tex. A&M U., 1985. Registered profl. engr., Ariz., N.Mex., Tex., Fla. Grad. rsch. asst. Purdue U., West Lafayette, Ind., 1974-76; materials engr. Engrs. Testing Labs., Inc., 1976-80; rsch. engr. Civil Engring. Rsch. Facility U. N.Mex., Albuquerque, 1980-81; rsch. engr. Tex. Transp. Inst. Tex. A&M U., College Station, 1981-85; sr. rsch. engr. N.Mex. Engring. Rsch. Inst., Albuquerque, 1985-89; dir. rsch. The Asphalt Inst., Lexington, Ky., 1989—; chmn. subcom. A2DO2(4) on rubber in bituminous mixtures Transp. Rsch. Bd., mem. coms. A2D02, A3C05; chmn. task force 31-polymer modified asphalts AASHTO-ARTBA-AGC Joint Subcom. on New Materials; presenter numerous profl. meetings. Contbr. articles to profl. pubs. Mem. ASTM (vice-chmn. subcom. DO4.41 on emulsified asphalt specifications), Assn. Asphalt Paving Techs. Achievements include research on bituminous materials and bituminous concrete; on pavement design, evaluation and con-

struction techniques; and on portland concrete, portland cement, and flyash. Office: Asphalt Inst Research Park Dr Lexington KY 40512

SHULER-DONNER, LAUREN, film producer; b. Cleveland, OH. B.S. in Film & Broadcasting, Boston U., 1971. television films inlcude: Ameteur Night at the Dixie Bar and Grill, 1979; films include: Thank God It's Friday, 1978 (assoc. prodr.), Mr. Mom, 1983, Ladyhawke, 1985, St. Elmo's Fire, 1985, Pretty in Pink, 1986, Three Fugitives, 1989, Radio Flyer, 1992, Dave, 1993, Free Willy, 1993, The Favor, 1994. Office: Donner/Shuler-Donner Prodns Warner Bros 4000 Warner Blvd Burbank CA 91522

SHULEVITZ, URI, author, illustrator; b. Warsaw, Poland, Feb. 27, 1935; came to U.S., 1959, naturalized, 1965; s. Abraham and Szandla (Hermanstat) S. Student, Tel-Aviv Art Inst., 1953-55; Tchrs. Cert., Tchrs. Coll. Israel, 1956; student, Bklyn. Museum Art Sch., 1959-61. Instr. illustrating and writing children's books The New Sch., 1970-86; dir. illustrating and writing children's books Hartwick Coll., 1974-92. Author, illustrator: The Moon In My Room, 1963, One Monday Morning, 1967, Rain Rain Rivers, 1969, Oh What a Noise, 1971, The Magician, 1973, Dawn, 1974, The Treasure, 1978, (Caldecott honor Book 1979), The Strange and Exciting Adventures of Jeremiah Hush, 1986, Toddlecreek Post Office, 1990, The Secret Room, 1993; author: Writing with Pictures: How to Write and Illustrate Children's Books, 1985; illustrator: The Fool of the World and the Flying Ship, 1968 (Caldecott medal 1969), The Twelve Dancing Princesses, 1966, SOldier and Tsar in the Forest, 1972, The Touchstone, 1976, Hanukah Money, 1978, The Lost Kingdom of Karnica, 1979, The Golem, 1982, Lilith's Cave: Jewish Tales of the Supernatural, 1988, The Diamond Tree, 1991, The Golden Goose, 1995. Served with Israeli Army, 1956-59. Mem Authors Guild. Office: care Farrar Straus & Giroux Inc 19 Union Sq W New York NY 10003-3304

SHULGASSER, BARBARA, writer; b. Manhasset, N.Y., Apr. 10, 1954; d. Lew and Luba (Golante) S. Student, Sarah Lawrence Coll., 1973-74; BA magna cum laude, CUNY, 1977; MS, Columbia U., 1978. Feature writer Waterbury (Conn.) Rep., 1978-81; reporter, feature writer Chgo. Sun Times, 1981-84; film critic San Francisco Examiner, 1984—; freelance book critic N.Y. Times Book Rev., N.Y.C., 1983—; guest interviewer City Arts and Lectures U. San Francisco, 1990—. Co-author: (screenplay, with Robert Altman) Ready to Wear, 1994; freelance video columnist N.Y. Times Sunday Arts & Leisure, 1989, features for Vanity Fair, Glamour and Mirabella mags. Office: San Francisco Examiner 110 5th St San Francisco CA 94103-2918

SHULKIN, JEROME, lawyer; b. Stanley, N.D., May 2, 1929; s. Max and Sophia (Harris) S.; m. Jane Pearl Israel, Dec. 30, 1956, 1 child, Shellie Jo. BA, U. Minn, 1951; LLB, U. Wash., 1956. Bar: Wash. 1956, Oreg. 1957, U.S. Dist. Ct. (we. dist.) Wash. 1956, U.S. Dist. Ct. (ea. dist.) Wash. 1959, U.S. Dist. Ct. Oreg. 1960, U.S. Ct. Appeals (9th cir.) 1958, U.S. Supreme Ct. 1963. Law clk. Wash. Supreme Ct., Olympia, 1956-57; assoc. Miracle, Treadwell & Pruzan, Seattle, 1957-61, ptnr., 1961-68; ptnr. Casey, Pruzan, Kovarik & Shulkin, Seattle, 1968-76; sr. ptnr. Shulkin, Hutton & Bucknell Inc., P.S., Seattle, 1976-93, Shulkin, Hutton Inc., PS, Seattle, 1993—. Contbr. to law rev. Col. JAG U.S. Army, 1952-54, USAR, 1954-81, ret. Fellow Am. Coll. Bankruptcy; mem. Am. Bankruptcy Inst. (bd. dirs.), Am. Bankruptcy Bd. of Certification (bd. dirs.), Wash. State Bar Assn. (lectr. 1975—), Oreg. State Bar Assn. Democrat. Avocation: classic automobiles. Office: Shulkin Hutton Inc PS 1201 3rd Ave Ste 1900 Seattle WA 98101-3000

SHULKIN, JEROME ROBERT, insurance brokerage executive; b. Chgo., Mar. 13, 1929; s. Dave H. and Belle (Oland) S.; m. Audrey Claire Stearns, Dec. 30, 1941; children: Michael B., Marc A., Pamela J. Shulkin Ruzi. BA, BS, U. Nebr., 1950. Owner, mgr. Shulkin-Miller Agy., Denver, 1957-60, 1st Security Ins. Agy., Denver, 1960-85; exec. v.p. Rolliins Burdick Hunter Colo., Denver, 1985—. Capt. USAF, 1950-53. Home: 6550 E Colorado Dr Denver CO 80224-2202

SHULL, CLIFFORD G., physicist, educator; b. Pitts., Sept. 23, 1915; s.David H and Daisy I. (Bistline) H.; m. Martha-Nuel Summer, June 19, 1941; children—John C., Robert D., William F. B.S., Carnegie Inst. Tech., 1937; Ph.D., NYU, 1941. Research physicist Texas Co., 1941-46; chief physicist Oak Ridge Nat. Lab., 1946-55; prof. physics MIT, 1955-86, emeritus prof., 1986—; Chmn. vis. com. Brookhaven Nat. Lab., 1961-62; chmn. vis. com. Nat. Bur. Standard reactor, 1972-73; chmn. vis. com. solid state div. Oak Ridge Nat. Lab., 1974-75; chmn. vis. com. Nat. Small-Angle-Scattering Center, 1978-81. Contbr. articles to sci. jours. Recipient award of merit Alumni Assn. of Carnegie Mellon U., 1968, Humboldt Sr. U.S. Scientist award, 1979, Disting. Scientist award Gov. of Tenn., 1986, Gregori Aminoff prize, 1993, Ilja Frank prize, 1993, Nobel Prize in Physics, 1994. Fellow Am. Phys. Soc. (Buckley prize 1956, chmn. solid state physics div. 1962-63), A.A.A.S., Am. Acad. Arts and Scis., N.Y. Acad. Scis., Nat. Acad. Scis. (vice chmn. panel on neutron sci. 1977), mem. Am. Crystallographic Assn., Research Soc. Am., Sigma Xi, Tau Beta Pi, Phi Kappa Phi. Home: 4 Wingate Rd Lexington MA 02173

SHULL, HARRISON, chemist, educator; b. Princeton, N.J., Aug. 17, 1923; s. George Harrison and Mary (Nicholl) S.; m. Jeanne Louise Johnson, 1948 (div. 1962); children: James Robert, Kathy, George Harrison, Holly; m. Wil Joyce Bentley Long, 1962; children: Warren Michael Long, Jeffery Mark Long, Stanley Martin, Sarah Ellen. A.B., Princeton U., 1943; Ph.D., U. Calif. at Berkeley, 1948. Assoc. chemist U.S. Naval Research Lab., 1943-45; asst. prof. Iowa State U., 1949-54; mem. faculty Ind. U., 1955-79, research prof., 1961-79, dean Grad. Sch., 1965-72, vice chancellor for research and devel., 1972-76, dir. Research Computing Center, 1959-63, acting chmn. chemistry dept., 1965-66, acting dean arts and scis., 1969-70, acting dean faculties, 1974; mem. faculty, provost, v.p. acad. affairs Rensselaer Poly. Inst., 1979-82; chancellor U. Colo., Boulder, 1982-85; prof. dept. chemistry U. Colo. 1982-88; provost Naval Postgrad. Sch., 1988-95; vis. prof. Washington U., St. Louis, 1960, U. Colo., 1963; founder, supr. Quantum Chemistry Program Exchange, 1962-79; chmn. subcom. molecular structure and spectroscopy NRC, 1958-63; chmn. Fulbright selection com. chemistry, 1963-67; mem. adv. com. Office Sci. Personnel, 1957-60; chmn. First Gordon Research Conf. Theoretical Chemistry, 1962; mem. com. survey chemistry Nat. Acad. Sci., 1964-65; mem. adv. panel chemistry NSF, 1964-67; mem. adv. panel Office Computer Activities, 1967-70, cons. chem. information program, 1965-71, mem. adv. com. to research, 1974-76; mem. vis. com. chemistry Brookhaven Nat. Lab., 1967-70; mem. adv. com. Chem. Abstracts Service, 1971-74; provost, academic dean Naval Postgraduate Sch, Monterey, Calif.; dir. Storage Tech. Corp.; chief of Naval Ops. Exec. Panel, 1984-88. Assoc. editor: Jour. Chem. Physics, 1952-54; editorial adv. bd.: Spectrochimica Acta, 1957-63, Internat. Jour. Quantum Chemistry, 1967—, Proc. NAS, 1976-81; contbr. articles to profl. jours. Trustee Argonne U. Assn., 1970-75, Asso. Univs., Inc., 1973-76, U. Rsch. Assn., 1984-89, Inst. Defense Analysis, 1984—. Served as ensign USNR, 1945. NRC postdoctoral fellow phys. scis. U. Chgo., 1948-49; Guggenheim fellow U. Uppsala, 1954-55; NSF sr. postdoctoral fellow, 1968-69; Sloan research fellow, 1956-58. Fellow Am. Acad. Arts and Scis. (com. on sci. and education policy 1969-72, council, exec. com. 1971-74, chmn. Midwest Center 1976-79), Am. Phys. Soc.; mem. Nat. Acad. Scis. (com. on sci. and public policy 1969-72, council, exec. com. 1971-74, chmn. U.S.-USSR sci. policy subgroup for fundamental research 1973-81, naval studies bd. 1974-79, chmn. Commn. on Human Resources 1977-81, nominating com. 1978), Am. Chem. Soc., AAAS, Assn. Computing Machinery, Royal Swedish Acad. Scis. (fgn. mem.), Royal Acad. Arts and Scis. Uppsala (corr. mem.), Cosmos Club (Washington), Old Capital Club (Monterey), Phi Beta Kappa, Sigma Xi, Phi Lambda Upsilon. Office: Naval Postgrad Sch Provost 1 University Cir M12 Monterey CA 93943-5002

SHULL, RICHARD BRUCE, actor; b. Evanston, Ill., Feb. 24, 1929; s. Ulysses Homer and Zana Marie (Brown) S.; m. Margaret Ann Haddy, July 14, 1951 (div. 1956); m. Peggy Joan Barringer, June 9, 1957 (div. 1967); m. Marilyn Sandra Swartz, July 6, 1969 (div. 1985, remarried July 7, 1989). BA in Drama, State U. Iowa, 1950; AA in Humanities, Kemper Mil. Sch., 1986. exec. asst. producer Gordon W. Pollock Prodns., 1953-56; stage mgr. Hyde Park Playhouse, 1954-55; prodn. mgr. Kaufman Auditorium, N.Y.C. 1956; gen. mgr. Music Circle Theatre, Detroit, 1957; prodn. supr. Ford Motor Co. Am. Road Show, 1959; prodn. mgr. (film) Dana Prodns. Inc., 1959-60; dir.

Lake Luzerne Playhouse, 1962, 64, Showboat Dinner Theatre, 1968-69; art dir. (film) Tears are for Tomorrow, 1960. Freelance theatrical stage mgr. and dir., N.Y.C., 1950-70; appeared in plays, N.Y.C., including Each in His Own Way, 1950, Wake Up Darling, 1956, Minnie's Boys, 1970, Goodtime Charley (Tony nominee, Drama Desk nomination), 1975, Fools, 1981, Oh, Brother!, 1981, Desire Under the Elms, 1983, Fade the Game, 1984, The Marriage of Bette and Boo (Obie award), 1985, The Front Page, 1986, Opera Comique, 1987, Rough Crossing, 1990, One of the All-Time Greats, 1992, Ain't Broadway Grand, 1993, The Gig, 1994, Victor/Victoria, 1995, plays in L.A., including Mr. Ferris and The Model, 1967, The Tempest, 1989; film appearances include The Anderson Tapes and B.S., I Love You, 1970, Hail to the Chief and Such Good Friends, 1971, Slither and Ssssss, 1972, Cockfighter, 1974, The Fortune, The Black Bird and The Big Bus, 1975, The Pack, 1977, Lovesick, 1983, Spring Break, 1983, Unfaithfully Yours, 1984, Splash, 1984, Garbo Talks, 1984, My Blue Heaven, 1990, Tune in Tomorrow, 1990, Housesitter, 1992, For Love or Money, 1993, Trapped in Paradise, 1994, Café Society, 1995; appearances on TV include Your Hit Parade, 1950, Robert Montgomery Presents, 1950, Diana, 1973, Ironsides, 1975, Goodtimes, 1975, Holmes and YoYo, 1976, The Rockford Files, 1978, Ziegfeld, A Man and His Women, 1978, Studs Lonigan, 1979, Hart to Hart, 1979, Lou Grant, 1980, The Ropers, 1980, Alice, 1980, Nurse, 1981, Will There Really Be a Morning?, 1982, The Boy Who Loved Trolls, 1984, Keeping the Faith, 1984, Seize the Day, 1985, The Conan O'Brien Show, 1993; dir. Man Without a Shadow, 1958; author: motion picture story and screenplay Aroused, 1964, Pamela, Pamela You Are, 1967; program dir. Armed Forces Radio Sta. GYPSY; created AFKN Network program Concert in Jazz. Served with U.S. Army, 1951-53, Korea. Mem. AFTRA, Actors Equity Assn. (founding editorial bd., constl. tec. com. 1957), Screen Actors Guild, Acad. Motion Picture Arts and Scis., Episcopal Actors Guild (life), Actors Fund (life), SR, Soc. Colonial Wars, St. Nicholas Soc. (steward, bd. mgrs.), N.Y. Vet. Corps Artillery (councillor), Gen. Soc. War of 1812 (pres. N.Y. State soc.), colonial ORder Acorn, Sons of Union Vets. Civil War (treas, Tilden Camp), First Families Ohio, Soc. Ind. Pioneers, Pioneer Assn. State Wash., Sons Am. colonists (giv. N.Y. chpt.), Hon. Order Ky. Cols., Lambs Club (life), Players Club, Friars Club, Dutch Treat Club, Univ. Club (N.Y.C.), Sloane Club (London), Ends of the Earth, Pumpkin Papers Irregulars, Baker St. Irregulars. Democrat. Avocations: antique autos and railroading, animal protection. Office: Cheerieerie Ltd 130 W 42nd St # 2400 New York NY 10036-7802

SHULMAN, ARNOLD, judge, lawyer; b. Phila., Apr. 12, 1914; s. Edward Nathaniel and Anna (Leshner) S.; m. Mary Frances Johnson, Nov. 26, 1943; children: Diane Shulman Thompson, Warren Scott, Amy Lynn Shulman Haney. Student, Emory U., 1931; J.D., U. Ga., 1936. Bar: Ga. 1937. Mem. firm Shulman, Shulman, Bauer & Deitch (and predecessors), Atlanta, to 1977; judge Ga. Ct. Appeals, 1977-84, presiding judge, 1981-83, chief judge, 1983-84; of counsel Troutman, Sanders, Lockerman & Ashmore, Atlanta, 1984-87; appointed sr. appellate ct. judge, 1987—; chief judge settlement conf. div. Ct. Appeals Ga., 1989—; prof. Atlanta Law Sch., 1964-84; adj. prof. Ga. State U. Coll. Law, Atlanta. Author: (with Wiley H. Davis) Georgia Practice and Procedure, 1948, 3d edit., 1968, 4th edit, (with Warren S. Shulman), 1975; contbr. articles to legal jours. Chmn. DeKalb County (Ga.) Sch. Salary Commn., 1960-62, DeKalb County Sch. Study Commn., 1962-64; mem. Fulton County-Atlanta Ct. Study Commn., 1961-62. Served to capt. U.S. Army, 1941-46. Mem. ABA, Atlanta Bar Assn., Ga. State Bar, Lawyers Club (Atlanta). Home: 1527 September Chase Decatur GA 30033-1731 Office: 908 DeKalb County Courthouse Decatur GA 30030

SHULMAN, CAROLE KAREN, professional society administrator; b. Mpls., Nov. 25, 1940; d. Allen Eldon and Beulah Ovidia (Blomsness) Banbury; m. David Arthur Shulman, Mar. 26, 1962; children: Michael, Krista, Tracy, Robbyn. Student, Colo. Coll., 1958-61; California Coast U., 1983-84. Profl. instr. Rochester (Minn.) Figure Skating Club, 1962-84, dir. skating, 1964-79, cons., 1979—; exec. dir. Profl. Skaters Guild, Rochester, 1984—, master rating examiner, 1971—, world profl. judge, 1976, 79, 87-88. Editor Professional Skater mag., 1984—; producer U.S. Open Profl. Figure Skating Championships, 1987, 89. Pres. Rochester Arts Council, 1983. Named triple gold medalist, U.S. Figure Skating Assn., Colorado Springs, Colo, 1959, 63, Master Rated Coach Profl. Skaters Guild, 1970, Sr. Rated Coach in Dance Profl. Skaters Guild, 1970. Mem. Am. Harp Soc. Mem. Covenant ch. Avocations: harp, skiing. Office: Profl Skaters Guild Am PO Box 5904 Rochester MN 55903-5904

SHULMAN, HYMAN, food service executive; b. 1920. With Max Starks Delicatessen and Liquors, Roselle, N.J., 1942-43, 46-49; mgr. Bardy Farms Supply Market, Union, N.J., 1949-53; with West Essex Supermarkets Inc., Caldwell, N.J., 1953—, now chmn. bd. dirs.; asst. treas., bd. dirs. Twin County Grocers, Inc., 1983-84, sec., bd. dirs., 1984-89, vice chmn., bd. dirs., 1989—. Served U.S. Armed Forces, 1943-46. Office: Twin County Grocers Inc 145 Talmadge Rd Edison NJ 08817-2825

SHULMAN, LAWRENCE EDWARD, biomedical research administrator, rheumatologist; b. Boston, July 25, 1919; s. David Herman and Belle (Tishler) S.; m. Pauline K. Flint, July 19, 1946; 1 son, Lawrence E.; m. Reni Trudinger, Mar. 20, 1959; children: Kathryn Verena, Barbara Corina. A.B. Harvard U., 1941, postgrad., 1941-42; Ph.D., Yale U., 1945, M.D., 1949. Nat. Bd. Med. Examiners. Intern Johns Hopkins Hosp., 1949-50, resident and fellow in internal medicine, 1950-53; dir. connective tissue div. Johns Hopkins U., 1955-75, assoc. prof. medicine, 1964—; assoc. dir. div. arthritis, musculoskeletal and skin diseases NIH, Bethesda, Md., 1976-82, dir., 1982—; dir. Nat. Inst. Arthritis & Musculoskeletal & Skin Diseases NIH, 1986-94, dir. emeritus, 1994—; chmn. med. adminstrn. com. Arthritis Found., Atlanta, 1974-75, exec. com., 1972-77; dir. Lupus Found. Am.; med. adv. bd. United. Scleroderma Found., Watsonville, Calif., 1977-88; chair sci. group rheumatic diseases WHO, 1989. Discoverer: Eosinophilic Fasciitis, 1974, new med. sign friction rubs in scleroderma, 1961. Recipient Sr. Investigator award Arthritis Found., 1957-62, Disting. Svc. award, 1979, Heberden medal for rsch., London, 1975, Superior Svc. award USPHS, 1985, Spl. Recognition award Nat. Osteoporosis Found., 1991, Spl. award Am. Acad. Orthopaedic Surgeons, 1992, Presdl. citation for leadership Am. Acad. Dermatology, 1993, Leadership award Lupus Found. Am., 1994, Career Achievement award Am. Coll. Rheumatology, 1994; named W.R. Graham Meml. lectr., 1973, Cochrane Disting. lectr., 1993. Master Am. Rheumatism Assn. (pres. 1974-75); fellow ACP; mem. Soc. Clin. Trials, Pan-Am. League Against Rheumatism (pres. 1982-86), Am. Soc. for Bone and Mineral Rsch. (Outstanding Support of Rsch. award 1994), Soc. Investigative Dermatology. Home: 6302 Swords Way Bethesda MD 20817-3350 Office: NIH 9000 Rockville Pike Bldg 31 Bethesda MD 20892-0001

SHULMAN, MAX L, corporate executive; b. N.Y.C., Oct. 18, 1908; s. Jacob and Dora (Silverman) S.; m. Sylvia C. Weinstein, June 25, 1939; children: Lloyd J., Gail P. Student CCNY, 1924; LLB, Nat. U., Washington, 1930. Bar: D.C. 1930, N.Y. 1942. Chief exec. officer, J.W. Mays, Inc., Bklyn., 1953-63, chmn., 1963—; pres. Weinstein Enterprises, Inc., Carmel, N.Y., 1963—; pres. Weinstein Found. Inc., Carmel, 1963—. With U.S. Army, 1930, WWII; maj. USAR, ret. 1946. Decorated Army Commendation medal with oak leaf clusters. Mem. Harmonie Club, Rotary. Office: JW Mays Inc 9 Bond St Brooklyn NY 11201-5805

SHULMAN, ROBERT GERSON, biophysics educator; b. N.Y.C., Mar. 3, 1924; s. Joshua S. and Freda (Lipshay) S.; m. Saralee Deutsch, Aug., 1952 (dec. Oct. 1983); children: Joel, Mark, James; m. Stephanie S. Spangler, May 11, 1986. A.B., Columbia U., 1943, M.A., 1947, Ph.D., 1949. Research assoc. Columbia U. Radiation Lab., N.Y.C., 1949; AEC fellow in chemistry Calif. Inst. Tech., Pasadena, 1949-50; head semicondr. research sect. Hughes Aircraft Co., Culver City, Calif., 1950-53; mem. tech. staff Bell Labs., Murray Hill, N.J., 1953-66; head biophysics research dept. Bell Labs., 1966-79; prof. molecular biophysics and biochemistry Yale U., 1979—, dir. div. biol. scis., 1979-94, Sterling prof. molecular biophysics and biochemistry, 1994—; Rask Oersted lectr. U. Copenhagen, 1959; vis. prof. Ecole Normale Superieur, Paris, 1962; Appleton lectr. Brown U., 1965; vis. prof. physics U. Tokyo, 1965; Reilly lectr. U. Notre Dame, Ind., 1969; vis. prof. biophysics Princeton U., 1971-72; Regents lectr. UCLA, 1978. Guggenheim fellow in lab. molecular biology MRC Cambridge (Eng.) U., 1961-62; recipient Havinga medal Leiden U., 1983, Gold medal Soc. Magnetic Resonance in Medicine, 1984,. Mem. Nat. Acad. Scis., Inst. Medicine. Researcher spec-

troscopic techniques applied to physics, chemistry, biology. Office: Yale U MR Ctr Dept Molecular Bio PO Box 208043 New Haven CT 06520-8043*

SHULMAN, ROBERT JAY, physician; b. Newark; s. Irving Jack and Shirley (Weinstock) S.; 1 child, David Ian. BA, Emory U., 1972; MD, Chgo. Med. Sch., 1976. Asst. prof. pediatrics Baylor Coll. Medicine, Houston, 1982-89, assoc. prof. pediatrics, 1989—; dir. nutritional support team Tex. Children's Hosp., Houston, 1982—; mem. edit. bd. Jour. Pediatric Gastroenterology and Nutrition, 1994—. Author: Young Chef's Nutrition Guide and Cookbook, 1990, Keys to Child Nutrition, 1991, (with others) Principles and Practice of Pediatrics, 1994, Physiology of the Gastrointestinal Tract, 1994. Fellow Am. Acad. Pediatrics; mem. Am. Gastroenterological Soc., Am. Soc. Parenteral and Enteral Nutrition (pres. 1991-92), Am. Inst. Nutrition, N.Am. Soc. Pediatric Gastroenterology and Nutrition, Soc. Pediatric Rsch. Avocation: guitar. Office: Baylor Coll Medicine 1100 Bates St Houston TX 77030

SHULMAN, STEPHEN NEAL, lawyer; b. New Haven, Apr. 6, 1933; s. Harry and Rea (Karrel) S.; m. Sandra Paula Still, Aug. 14, 1954; children—Harry, Dean, John. B.A., Harvard, 1954; LL.B. cum laude, Yale, 1958. Bar: Conn. 1958, D.C. 1960. Indsl. relations Bendix Aviation Corp., 1954-55; law clk. to Justice Harlan, U.S. Supreme Ct., 1958-59; vis. asst. pro U. Mich. Law Sch., 1959; assoc. firm Covington & Burling, Washington, 1959-60; asst. U.S. atty. Washington, 1960-61; exec. asst. to sec. labor, 1961-62, dept asst. sec. of def., 1962-65; gen. counsel U.S. Air Force, 1965-66; chmn. Equal Employment Opportunity Commn., 1966-67; mem. Kane, Shulman & Schlei, Washington, 1967-70; mem. firm Cadwalader, Wickersham & Taft, N.Y.C., also Washington, 1971-95, Freedman, Levy, Kroll & Simonds, Washington, 1995—; vis. prof. mgmt. U. Okla., 1965-66. Co-author: The Law of Equal Employment Opportunity, 1990; editor in chief Yale Law Jour., 1957-58. Mem. Book and Gavel, Order of Coif, Cum Laude Soc., Phi Delta Delta. Home: 1332 Skipwith Rd Mc Lean VA 22101-1841 Office: Freedman Levy 1050 Connecticut Ave NW Washington DC 20036-5366

SHULMAN, YECHIEL, engineering educator; b. Tel Aviv, Jan. 28, 1930; came to the U.S., 1950; s. David and Rachel (Chonowski) S.; m. Ruth Danzig, June 29, 1950; children: Elinor D., Ron E., Orna L. BS in Aero. Engring., MIT, 1954, BS in Bus. and Engring. Adminstrn., 1954, MS in Aero. Engring., 1954, DSc Aero. and Astro., 1959; MBA, U. Chgo., 1973. Assoc. prof. mech. engring. Northwestern U., Evanston, Ill., 1959-67; v.p. adv. engring. Anocut, Inc., Elk Grove Vill., Ill., 1967-72; v.p. corp. devel. Alden Press, Elk Grove Vill., Ill., 1973-84; pres. MMT Environ., Inc., Shoreview, Minn., 1984-87; cons. Shulman Assocs., Mpls., 1982-89; prof., chair, mech. engring. dept. U. Minn., Mpls., 1989—, H. W. Sweatt chair in technol. leadership and dir. ctr. for devel. technol. leadership, 1989—; dir. grad. studies mgmt. and tech. program, 1990—. Mem. Am. Soc. Mech. Engrs., Inst. Indsl. Engrs. Office: U Minn 107 Lind Hall Minneapolis MN 55455

SHULTIS, ROBERT LYNN, finance educator, cost systems consultant, retired professional association executive; b. Kingston, N.Y., June 30, 1924; s. Albert H. and Dorothy Elizabeth (Jenkins) S.; m. Bernice Elizabeth Johnson, Jan. 20, 1946; 1 son, Robert Lee. BS, Columbia Univ. Sch. Bus., 1949, postgrad., 1949-51. Staff acct. Price Waterhouse, N.Y.C., 1949-52; credit mgr., controller Organon, Inc., West Orange, N.J., 1952-68; v.p., treas., chief fin. officer Arwood Corp., Rockleigh, N.J., 1968-72; v.p., controller Technicon, Tarrytown, N.Y., 1972-80; exec. dir. Inst. of Mgmt. Accts., Montvale, N.J., 1980-86; faculty, assoc. dir. Ctr. for Exec. Devel. Coll. William & Mary, Williamsburg, Va., 1987-91; instr. Rutgers U., 1964-74, Fairleigh Dickinson U., 1967-68; mem. Fin. Acctg. Standards Adv. Coun., 1981-86; cons. Acctg. and Cost Sys. design, 1990—; lectr. and seminar leader on controllership, activity-based costing, cost mgmt., cost sys. design, 1990—. Editor: Management Accountants' Handbook, and supplements, 1991-94. Mem. bd. advs. U. Fla. Sch. Accountancy, James Madison U. Sch. Accountancy; mem. fin. and budget com. Kingsmill Community Svcs. Assn. Served with USAF, 1943-45. Decorated Presdl. Unit Citation. Mem. AAUP, Fin. Execs. Inst., Assn. Systems Mgmt., Inst. of Mgmt. Accts., Am. Acctg. Assn., Ross Inst. Acctg. Rsch., Kingsmill Club, Beta Alpha Psi (adv. forum).

SHULTS, ROBERT LEE, real estate executive, airline executive; b. Helena, Ark., Feb. 23, 1936; s. Albert and Mary S.; m. Belinda Housley, Aug. 21, 1965; children: Catherine Ann, Robert L. BS in Acctg. magna cum laude, U. Ark.-Fayetteville, 1961. CPA, Ark. Mgr., Arthur Andersen & Co., Memphis, 1961-70; exec. v.p. Alltel Tel. Co., Little Rock, 1970-80; chmn. bd. Scheduled Skyways, Inc., Little Rock, 1980-88, chmn. bd., chief exec. officer, Fin. Ctr. Corp., Little Rock, 1980—, cons. Alltel Corp., Little Rock, 1980-90; chmn. bd., chief exec. Ranch Prop Inc., 1989—; chmn. bd. dir., chief exec. Fin. Ctr. Devel. Co., Air Midwest Inc.; past chmn. bd. Regional Airline Assn., Washington, 1984. Pres. bd. dirs. Ark. Children's Hosp., 1994—; bd. dirs., treas. Am. Cancer Soc., Ark., 1976-91, Inst. Pub. Utilities, Mich. State U., 1976-80; mem. Ark. Arts Ctr.; chmn. bd. trustees Trinity Cathedral, 1982-92, Fifty for Future Little Rock. With USMC, 1956-58. Recipient Pres.'s citation, U.S. Ind. Tel. Assn., 1978, 80. Mem. AICPA, Mo. Bd. Accts., Tenn. Bd. Accts., Met. Little Rock C. of C., Little Rock Club, The Capital Club, Summit Club, Little Rock Country Club, Rotary (bd. dirs. 1988-90). Episcopalian. Office: Fin Ctr Corp PO Box 56350 Little Rock AR 72215-6350

SHULTS, ROBERT LUTHER, JR., lawyer; b. Pine Bluff, Ark., Oct. 25, 1925; s. Robert Luther and Gay (Moseley) S.; m. Barbara Jo Taylor, Aug. 19, 1950; children—Steven Taylor, Elizabeth Gay. B.S. cum laude in Elec. Engring. La. State U., 1950; LL.B. cum laude, Harvard U., 1953; LL.D. (hon.), U. Ark., 1981. Bar: Ark. bar 1953. Assoc., ptnr. Wright, Lindsey, Jennings, Lester & Shults, Little Rock, 1953-65; ptnr. Lester and Shults, Little Rock, 1965-79, Shults, Ray & Kurrus, Little Rock, 1979—. Editor: Harvard Law Rev, 1952-53. Chmn. Little Rock Com. Fgn. Rels.; bd. dirs. Little Rock Ctrl. YMCA, Ark. chpt. Arthritis Found., Winrock Internat. Inst. for Agrl. Devel.; chmn. bd. Winthrop Rockefeller Found., Econ. Opportunity Agy. Pulaski County; trustee Winthrop Rockefeller Charitable Trust, Ark. Blue Cross-Blue Shield, Inc., Ark., Arts Ctr. 1st lt. AUS, 1943-46, ETO. Mem. ABA, Ark. Bar Assn. (chmn. legal edn. council 1963-66, chmn. exec. com. 1968-69), Am. Judicature Soc., Am. Inst. for Public Service (bd. of selectors), Nat. Audubon Soc. (dir. 1980-86), Sigma Chi, Tau Beta Pi, Omicron Delta Kappa. Democrat. Methodist. Clubs: Little Rock Country, Capital. Home: 11 Glenridge Rd Little Rock AR 72227 Office: Shults Ray & Kurrus 1600 Worthen Bank Bldg Little Rock AR 72201

SHULTZ, EDWARD JOSEPH, holdings company executive; b. Fostoria, Ohio, Aug. 29, 1944; s. Richard M. and Blanche M. (Lamberjack) S.; m. Joyce M. Schultz, Feb. 13, 1970; children—Jonathan, Eric, Nathan. B.S., Bowling Green State U. 1966. C.P.A., Ohio. Auditor, Dana Corp., Toledo, 1966-69, asst. treas., Hayes-Dana Corp., St. Catherines, Ont., Can., 1969-71, div. controller, Dana Corp., 1971-80, gen. mgr., Toledo, 1980-86, chmn., CEO Dana Credit Corp., Toledo, 1980—; pres. Dana Corp., Toledo, 1986—. Mem. Ohio Soc. C.P.A.s (dir. Ft. Wayne chpt. 1978-79), Fin. Execs. Inst., Equipment Leasing Assn. Republican. Roman Catholic. Office: Dana Corp PO Box 1000 Toledo OH 43697-1000

SHULTZ, GEORGE PRATT, former secretary of state, economics educator; b. N.Y.C., Dec. 13, 1920; s. Birl E. and Margaret Lennox (Pratt) S.; m. Helena M. O'Brien, Feb. 16, 1946; children: Margaret Ann Shultz Tilsworth, Kathleen Pratt Shultz Jorgensen, Peter Milton, Barbara Lennox Shultz White, Alexander George. BA in Econs., Princeton U., 1942; PhD in Indsl. Econs., MIT, 1949; hon. degrees, U. Notre Dame, Loyola U., U. Pa., U. Rochester, Princeton U., Carnegie-Mellon U., Baruch Coll., N.Y.C., Northwestern U., Yeshiva U., U. Tel Aviv, Technion-Israel Inst. Tech. Mem. faculty MIT., 1949-57; assoc. prof. indsl. relations MIT, 1955-57; prof. indsl. relations Grad. Sch. Bus., U. Chgo., 1957-68, dean sch. 1962-68; fellow Ctr. for Advanced Study in Behavioral Scis., 1968-69; U.S. sec. labor, 1969-70; dir. Office Mgmt. and Budget, 1970-72; U.S. sec. treasury, also asst. to Pres., 1972-74; chmn. Council on Econ. Policy, East-West Trade Policy com.; exec. v.p. Bechtel Corp., San Francisco, 1974-75, pres., 1975-77; vice chmn. Bechtel Corp., 1977-81; also dir., pres. Bechtel Group, Inc., 1981-82; prof. mgmt. and pub. policy Stanford U., 1974-82, prof. internat. econs.,

1989-91, prof. emeritus, 1991—; chmn. Pres. Reagan's Econ. Policy Adv. Bd., 1981-82; U.S. sec. of state, 1982-89; disting. fellow Hoover Instn., Stanford, 1989—; bd. dirs. Bechtel Group, Inc., Ziff-Davis Publishing Co.; mem. corp. adv. coun. GM, Gulfstream Aerospace Corp., AirTouch Comms.; chmn. J.P. Morgan Internat. Coun.; chmn. adv. coun. Inst. Internat. Studies, Gov.'s Econ. Policy Adv. Bd. State of Calif. Author: (with others) Pressures on Wage Decisions, 1951, (with Charles A. Myers) The Dynamics of a Labor Market, 1951, (with John R. Coleman) Labor Problems: Cases and Readings, 1953, (with T.L. Whisler) Management Organization and the Computer, 1960, (with Arnold R. Weber) Strategies for the Displaced Worker, 1966, (with Robert Z. Aliber) Guidelines, Informal Controls and the Market Place, 1966, (with Albert Rees) Workers and Wages in the Urban Labor Market, 1970, Leaders and Followers in an Age of Ambiguity, 1975, (with Kenneth W. Dam) Economic Policy Beyond the Headlines, 1977, Turmoil and Triumph: My Years as Secetary of State, 1993; also articles, chpts. in books, reports, and essays. Served to capt. USMCR, 1942-45. Mem. Am. Econ. Assn., Indsl. Relations Research Assn. (pres. 1968), Nat. Acad. Arbitrators. Office: Stanford U Hoover Instn Stanford CA 94305

SHULTZ, JOHN DAVID, lawyer; b. L.A., Oct. 9, 1939; s. Edward Patterson and Jane Elizabeth (Taylor) S.; m. Joanne Person, June 22, 1968; children: David Taylor, Steven Matthew. Student, Harvard Coll., 1960-61; BA, U. Ariz., 1964; JD, Boalt Hall, U. Calif., Berkeley, 1967. Bar: N.Y. 1968, Calif. 1978. Assoc. Cadwalader, Wickersham & Taft, N.Y.C., 1968-77; ptnr. Lawler, Felix & Hall, L.A., 1977-83, mem. exec. com., chmn. planning com., co-chmn. recruiting and hiring com.; ptnr. Morgan, Lewis & Bockius, L.A., 1983—, chmn. mgmt. com., mem. lateral entry com.; chmn. profl. evaluation com., chmn. bus. plan com., chmn. practice devel. com., chmn. recruiting com. Trustee St. Thomas Ch., N.Y.C., 1969-72, Shore Acres Point Corp., Mamaroneck, N.Y., 1975-77; mem. adv. bd. Internat. and Comparative Law Center, Southwestern Legal Found., 1981—; active Practicing Law Inst. Adv. Bd., Corp. and Securities Law, 1992—. Mem. ABA, Republican Nat. Com. Mem. Assn. Bar City N.Y., State Bar Calif., N.Y. State Bar Assn., Jonathan Club (L.A.), Phi Delta Phi, Sigma Chi. Episcopalian. Office: Morgan Lewis & Bockius 801 S Grand Ave Los Angeles CA 90017-3189

SHULTZ, LEILA MCREYNOLDS, botanist, educator; b. Bartlesville, Okla., Apr. 20, 1946; 1 child, Kirsten. BS, U. Tulsa, 1969; MA, U. Colo. 1975; PhD, Claremont Grad. Sch., 1983. Curator Intermountain Herbarium Utah State U., 1973-92; rschr. Harvard U., Cambridge, Mass., 1994—. Co-author: Atlas of the Vascular Plants of Utah, 1988; taxon editor: Flora of North America (12 vols.), 1987. Mem. Am. Bot. Soc. (systematics rep. 1988-90), Am. Soc. Plant Taxonomists (coun. 1990-92). Office: Harvard U Herbaria 22 Divinity Ave Cambridge MA 02138

SHULTZ, MARTHA JANE See DIETRICH, MARTHA JANE

SHULTZ, SILAS HAROLD, lawyer; b. Scribner, Nebr., Mar. 21, 1938; s. Harold Mohr and Arlene E. (Spath) S. BS, U. Pa., 1960; LLB, U. Ariz., 1966. Bar: Ariz. 1966, U.S. Supreme Ct. 1988, Colo. 1995; cert. specialist in personal injury and wrongful death, Ariz.; cert. civil trial specialist Nat. Bd. Trial Advocacy. Ptnr., dir. Fennermore, Craig, P.C, Phoenix, 1966-85; trial specialist Law Office of Richard Grand, Tucson, 1985-88; officer Shultz & Rollins, Ltd., Tucson, 1988—. 1st lt. U.S. Army Res., 1961-66. Mem. Am. Bd. Trial Advocates, Assn. Trial Lawyers Am. (Ariz. gov. 1994—), Ariz. Trial Lawyers Assn. Office: Shultz & Rollins Ltd 4280 N Campbell Ave Ste 214 Tucson AZ 85718-6585

SHULZE, FREDERICK BENNETT, music educator; b. Portland, Oreg., Aug. 25, 1935; s. Ivan Theodore and Eugenia Janet (Bennett) S.; m. Darlene Enid Nye, Sept. 4, 1965; children: Stephanie, Stephen. BM, Wheaton Coll., 1957; postgrad., U. Mich., 1957-58; MM, Northwestern U., 1963; DMA, U. Washington, 1970. Asst. prof. Cascade Coll., Portland, 1959-68; organist St. Stephen's Episcopal Ch., Seattle, 1968-69, 1st Presbyn. Ch., Seattle, 1969-70; prof. music Taylor U., Upland, Ind., 1970—; organist 1st Bapt. Ch., Muncie, Ind., 1971—. Composer hyms. Sec. Gideons Internat., Hartford City, 1990. Mem. Am. Guild Organists, Music Lib. Assn., Coll. Music Soc. Republican. Baptist. Avocations: reading, hiking, music. Home: PO Box 129 1014 S 1st St Upland IN 46989-9300 Office: Taylor U Music Dept 500 W Reade Ave Upland IN 46989

SHUMACKER, HARRIS B., JR., surgeon, educator, author; b. Laurel, Miss., May 20, 1908; s. Harris B. and Corinne (Teller) S.; m. Myrtle E. Landau, Dec. 1, 1933; children—Peter D., James N. B.S., U. Tenn., Chattanooga, 1927; A.M., Vanderbilt U., 1928; M.D., Johns Hopkins U., 1932; D.Sc. (hon.), Ind. U., 1985. Diplomate Am. Bd. Surgery, Am. Bd. Thoracic Surgery. Asst. in surgery Johns Hopkins U., 1932-35, instr., 1938-41, asst. prof., 1941-46; asst. in surgery Yale U., 1936-37, instr., 1937-38, assoc. prof., 1946-48; prof. surgery Ind. U., 1948-70, chmn. dept., 1948-68, Disting. prof., 1970-78, Disting. prof. emeritus, 1978—; prof., sr. advisor Uniformed Svcs. U. of Health Scis. Bethesda, Md., 1981-87, Disting. prof. surgery, 1988—; pres. Uniformed Svcs U. Assocs., 1987-88; hon. mem. surg. faculties in Peoples Republic of China, 1979—; dir. sect. cardiovascular-thoracic surgery St. Vincent Hosp., 1973-78, sr. surg. cons., 1978-81. Served from capt. to lt. col. M.C., U.S. Army, 1942-46; cons. surgeon gen., 1949-60. Recipient Roswell Park award, 1968, Medal of Honor, Evansville U., 1970, Disting. Alumus award U. Chattanooga, Curtis medal, 1970, Spl. Alumnus award Johns Hopkins U., 1973, Disting. Svc. award Am. Soc. Abdominal Surgery, letter of commendation Surgeon-Gen. 1987, Disting. Svc. medal Uniformed Svc. U. Health Scis., 1988, René Leriche prize Soc. Internat. de Chir., 1993. Fellow Royal Coll. Surgeons (hon.); mem. Am. Assn. Surgery of Trauma, Am. Surg. Assn. (1st v.p. 1961, sec. 1964-68), So. Surg. Assn., Central Surg. Assn., Pan-Pacific Surg. Assn. (trustee 1961-64, v.p., 1964-75, 78—, pres. 1975-78), AMA (chmn. sect. gen. surgery), Internat. Surg. Soc., Internat. Soc. Cardiovascular Surgeons (v.p. 1957-59, pres. N.Am. chpt. 1956-58), Soc. Clin. Surgery (pres. 1961-63), ACS (chmn. forum com. 1955-60, chmn. nat. TV com. 1964-68, Disting. Service award 1968), Soc. U. Surgeons (pres. 1951), Soc. for Vascular Surgery (pres. 1958-59), Am. Thoracic Surg. Assn., Soc. Thoracic Surgeons (hon.), Internat. Surg. Group (v.p. 1974-75, pres. 1975-76), Polish Surg. Assn. (hon.), Sociedad Cubana de Angiologia (hon.), Societa Italiana di Chirurgia (hon.), Internat. Surg. Group (hon.), Phi Beta Kappa, Sigma Xi, Alpha Omega Alpha.

SHUMAKER, JOHN WILLIAM, university president; b. Pitts., Aug. 21, 1942; s. Thomas E. Shumaker and Sara Jane (Giffn) Cobun; children: Timothy, Brian. BA, U. Pitts., 1964; MA, U. Pa., 1966, PhD, 1969; LLD hon., Briarwood Coll., 1989; EdD (hon.), Kyung Hee U., 1992. Asst. assoc. prof. classics Ohio State U., Columbus, 1969-77, asst. dean Coll. Humanities, 1971-72, acting chmn. dept. classics, 1972-73, assoc. dean Coll. Humanities, 1973-77; dean Coll. Humanities and Fine Art SUNY, Albany, 1977-83, v.p. rsch. and ednl. devel., 1983-85, v.p. academic planning and devel., 1985-87; pres. Cen. Conn. State U., New Britain, 1987—; exec. dir. Capital Dist. Humanities Program, Albany, 1978-83; trustee Nat. Commn. for Coop. Edn., Boston, 1987—, exec. com. 1993—. Bd. dirs. New Britain Gen. Hosp., 1988—, Hartford chpt. ARC, 1988-91, A.W. Stanley Found., New Britain, 1988-93, Fleet Bank Adv. Bd., 1993—, World Affairs Coun., Hartford, Conn., 1994—, New Britain Found. for Pub. Giving, 1994—. Mem. Internat. Assn. Univ. Pres. (exec. com. 1987—, vice chmn. N.Am. coun. 1990—), Internat. Assembly Coop. Edn., Am. Assn. State Colls. and Univs. (com. on internat. programs 1987-88, com. state reps. 1988-89, com. diversity 1993—), New Eng. Bd. Higher Edn. (bd. govs. 1990—), New Britain C. of C. (bd. dirs. 1988-89), Phi Beta Kappa. Avocation: swimming. Office: Cen Conn State U 1615 Stanley St New Britain CT 06053-2439

SHUMAN, DEANNE, dental hygienist, educator; b. Manhattan, Kans., June 7, 1953; d. Donald Gene and Sharlene (Cochran) S. BS in Dental Hygiene, Old Dominion U., 1974, MS, 1976, PhD in Urban Svcs., 1984—. With Old Dominion U., Norfolk, Va., 1975—; assoc. prof. Old Dominion U., Norfolk, 1983-89, prof., chairperson, 1989—. Contbr. articles to profl. jours. Team mem. Operation Smile, Norfolk, 1987. Mem. Am. Dental Hygienists Assn. (contbg. editor Chgo. 1986-90), Am. Assn. Dental Schs. (del. Chgo. 1987—), Internat. Assn. Dental Rsch., Profl. and Organizational Devel. Network in Higher Edn., Old Dominion U. Alumni Assn. (faculty liaison Norfolk chpt. 1987), Sigma Phi Alpha (sec. 1981—). Presbyterian. Office: Old Dominion U Sch Dental Hygiene Norfolk VA 23529-0499

SHUMAN, LARRY MYERS, soil chemist; b. Harrisburg, Pa., Apr. 3, 1944; s. Mark P. and Opal I. (Myers) Shuman; m. Catherine A. Yost, Mar. 21, 1970; children: Karen, Rebecca. BS, Pa. State U., 1966, MS, 1968, PhD, 1970. Asst. prof. soil chemistry U. Ga., Experiment, 1972-79, assoc. prof., 1979-91, prof., 1991—; USDA-OICD Exch. scientist to People's Republic of China, 1992. Co-editor, contbg. author Micronutrients in Agriculture, 1991; contbg. author: Zinc in Soils, 1979, Plant Environment Interactions, 1994; contbr. articles to profl. jours. Capt. M.S., U.S. Army, 1970-72. U.S. AID grantee, 1980-81, USDA-CSRS grantee, 1992-94. Mem. Am. Soc. Agronomy, Soil Sci. Soc. Am. (soil chemistry div. chair 1994, assoc. editor jour. 1986-91), Coun. Agrl. Sci. and Tech., Soc. Environ. Geochemistry and Health. Home: 447 Trice Rd Milner GA 30257-3427 Office: U Ga Ga Experiment Sta Griffin GA 30223-1797

SHUMAN, MARK SAMUEL, environmental and electroanalytical chemistry educator; b. Yakima, Wash., July 29, 1936; s. Samuel and Ardella (Martin) S.; children—Kim, Donna, Bryce. B.S., Wash. State U., 1959, Ph.D., U. Wis., 1966. Chemist Atlantic Research Corp., Alexandria, Va., 1960-62; asst. prof. chemistry Tex. Christian U., Ft. Worth, 1966-69; vis. prof. Whitman Coll., Walla Walla, Wash., 1969-70; asst. prof. environ. chemistry U. N.C., Chapel Hill, 1970-75; assoc. prof. U. N.C., 1975-80, prof, 1980-92, prof. emeritus, 1992—. Contbr. articles to profl. jours., chpts. to books. Served to capt. U.S. Army, 1960-61. EPA fellow, 1970. Mem. Am. Chem. Soc. Office: 6 Davie Ln Chapel Hill NC 27514-5909

SHUMAN, MICHAEL HARRISON, lawyer, policy analyst; b. N.Y.C., June 4, 1956; s. Jack Jacob and Bernadine Sydelle (Fine) S. AB, Stanford U., Palo Alto, Calif., 1979; JD, Stanford U., 1982. Bar: Calif. 1983, D.C. 1990. Intern NRDC, San Francisco, 1981-82; pres. Ctr. for Innovative Diplomacy, Irvine, Calif., 1982-91; fellow Inst. for Policy Studies, Washington, 1991-92, dir., 1992—. Author: Citizen Diplomats, 1987, Conditions of Peace, 1991, Technology for the Common Good, 1993, Security Without War, 1993, Towards A Global Village, 1994. Kellogg Found. fellow, 1987. Avocations: roller skating, moose paraphernalia, film making, juggling. Office: Inst Policy Studies 1601 Connecticut Ave NW Washington DC 20009-1035

SHUMAN, NICHOLAS ROMAN, journalist, educator; b. Chgo., June 30, 1921; s. Roman William and Pauline (Stasevich) S.; m. Marian Elaine Johnson, Feb. 23, 1952; children—Kristin Mary, Elizabeth Carol, Mark Nicholas. B.A., U. Ill., 1943. Writer Chgo. Jour. Commerce, 1938-46; mem. staff Herald-American, Chgo., 1946-51; asst. photo editor Herald-American, 1947-51; mem. staff Chgo. Daily News, 1951-78, fin. editor, 1961-65, asst. mng. editor, 1965-69, nat. and fgn. editor, 1969-77, chief editorial writer, 1977-78; editorial writer Chgo. Sun-Times, 1978-84; prof. journalism Columbia Coll., Chgo., 1984-92, cons., 1992—; columnist Chgo. Reporter, 1985-90; sr. editor World Book Ency., 1965-66; profl. instr. Medill Sch. Journalism, Northwestern U., 1954-61; freelance mag. writer, 1951—; TV commentator, 1958-61. Founding pres. Arlington Heights (Ill.) Human Relations Com., 1965. Served to 1st lt. AUS, 1943-46, ETO. Recipient awards Ill. AP, UPI, John Howard Assn., Inland Press Assn., Chgo. Newspaper Guild; nominated for Pulitzer prize 3 times. Mem. Alpha Kappa Lambda, Sigma Delta Chi. Home: 1001 W Clarendon Rd Arlington Heights IL 60004-4507 Office: Columbia Coll 600 S Michigan Ave Chicago IL 60605-1901

SHUMAN, R(OBERT) BAIRD, academic program director, writer, english educator, educational consultant; b. Paterson, N.J., June 20, 1929; s. George William and Elizabeth (Evans) S. A.B. (Trustees scholar), Lehigh U., 1951; M.Ed., Temple U., 1953; Ph.D. (Univ. scholar), U. Pa., 1961; cert. in philology, U. Vienna, Austria, 1954. Tchr. Phila. Pub. Schs., 1953-55; asst. instr. English U. Pa., 1955-57; instr. humanities Drexel U., Phila., 1957-59; asst. prof. San José (Calif.) State U., 1959-62; asst. prof. English Duke U., 1962-63, assoc. prof., 1963-66, prof. edn., 1966-77; prof. English, dir. English edn. U. Ill., Urbana-Champaign, 1977-85; dir. freshman rhetoric U. Ill., 1979-84, coord. Univ. Associates in Rhetoric Program, 1978-84, dir. devel., 1988-93, acting dir. Ctr. for Study of Writing, 1989-90, prof. emeritus, 1993—; vis. prof. Moore Inst. Art, 1958, Phila. Conservatory Music, 1958-59, Lynchburg Coll., 1965, King Faisal U., Saudi Arabia, 1978, 81, Bread Loaf Sch. English, Middlebury Coll., 1980, East Tenn. State U., Johnson City, 1980, Olivet Nazarene Coll., 1984, 86, 88, U. Tenn., Knoxville, 1987; cons. Edn. Testing Svc., 1970—, Am. Coll. Testing Svc., 1975-82; cons. in lang. and lit. Coll. Engring., U. Ill., 1980—; mem. William Inge Nat. Festival Com., 1989—. Author: Clifford Odets, 1962, Robert E. Sherwood, 1964, William Inge, 1965, rev. edit., 1989, Strategies in Teaching Reading: Secondary, 1978, (with Robert J. Krajewski) The Beginning Teacher: A Guide to Problem Solving, 1979, Elements of Early Reading Instruction, 1979, The First R: Strategies in Early Reading Instruction, 1987, rev. edit., 1989, Classroom Encounters: Problems, Case Studies, Solutions, 1989, (with Eric Hobson) Reading and Writing in High School, (with Denny T. Wolfe Jr.) Teaching English Through the Arts, 1990, Resources for Writers, 1992, American drama 1918-1960, 1992, Georgia O'Keeffe, 1993; editor: Nine Black Poets, 1968, An Eye for an Eye, 1969, A Galaxy of Black Writing, 1970, Creative Approaches to the Teaching of English: Secondary, 1974, Questions English Teachers Ask, 1977, Educational Drama for Today's Schools, 1978, Education in the 80's—English, 1980, The Clearing House: A Closer Look, 1984, 70th anniversary issue The Clearing House, 1995; exec. editor The Clearing House jour., 1976—; cons. editor Poet Lore, 1977-90, Cygnus, 1978—, Jour. Aesthetic Edn., 1978-82; contbg. editor Reading Horizons, 1975-85; editor quar. column Reading Horizons, 1975-85; editor Trends in English column Ednl. Leadership, 1989—. Active Nat. Trust Hist. Preservation. NEH researcher Trinity Coll., Dublin, Ireland, 1985. Mem. MLA, Nat. Coun. Tchrs. English (evaluator ERIC Clearing House, com. alt. careers for English profls.), Internat. Fedn. Tchrs. English, Internat. Coun. Edn. of Tchrs., Utah English Tchrs. Assn., Conf. English Edn. (exec. com. 1976-79), Internat. Reading Assn. (coord. symposium on cultural literacy, Queensland, Australia 1988), Internat. Assn. Univ. Profs. English, Nat. Soc. Study Edn., Am. Fedn. Tchrs., Union Profl. Employees (editor newsletter 1988-92, exec. com. 1988-92). Democrat. Home: PO Box 1706 Saint George UT 84771-1706 Office: U Ill 208 English Bldg 608 S Wright St Urbana IL 61801-3613 *An education that does not produce people who are vibrantly alive, intoxicated with the wonder of existence, has fallen short. Joy of learning is the fulcrum upon which the human equation is balanced.*

SHUMAN, SAMUEL IRVING, lawyer, law educator; b. Fall River, Mass., Aug. 7, 1925; s. Max and Fannie S.; m. Cynthia Webre, Mar. 25, 1990; children from previous marriage: Maxim Erric, Michael A. A.B., U. Pa., 1947, M.A., 1948, Ph.D., 1951; J.D., U. Mich., 1954; S.J.D., Harvard U., 1959. Bar: Mich. 1954, Tex. 1979. Research asst. Legis. Research Center, U. Mich., Ann Arbor, 1953-54; vis. prof. law Legis. Research Center, U. Mich., 1961; vis. prof. U. Rome, 1963-64; asst. prof. law Wayne State U., Detroit, 1954-55; assoc. prof. Wayne State U., 1955-56, prof., 1957-80; prof. dept. psychiatry Wayne State U. Med. Sch.; lectr. Internat. Faculty Comparative Law, Luxembourg, 1964; prof. forensic psychiatry, spl. counsel Lafayette Clinic, Mich. Dept. Mental Health; gen. counsel Mich. Psychiat. Assn., Epilepsy Center Mich. Author: Legal Positivism: Its Scope and Limitations, 1963, (with N.D. West) Introduction to American Law: Cases and Materials, 1971, Psychosurgery and the Medical Control of Violence: Autonomy and Deviance, 1977; editorial bd.: Am. Jour. Jurisprudence, 1969-79. Bd. dirs. Tex. Modern Art Found. Recipient Wayne State U. Bd. Govs. Faculty Recognition award, 1978; Probus Club award Disting. Acad. Achievement in Humanities, 1963; Fulbright fellow Italy, 1961; Rockefeller Found. grantee, 1959, 61; Fulbright travel grantee Germany, 1961; Wayne State U. research grantee, 1960-64; Internat. Research & Exchanges Bd. grantee, 1973. Mem. Am. Law Inst. (life). Office: Box D Camden ME 04843

SHUMAN, STANLEY S., investment banker; b. Cambridge, Mass., June 22, 1935; s. Saul A. and Sarah L. (Saxe) S.; m. Ruth H. Lande, 1967 (div 1979); children—David Lande, Michael Adam. B.A., Harvard U., Boston, 1956, J.D., 1959, M.B.A., 1961. Bar: Mass. 1959, N.Y. 1991. Exec. v.p., mng. dir. Allen & Co., Inc., N.Y.C., 1961—; bd. dirs. Bayou Steel Corp., Global Asset Mgmt. (USA), Inc., Hudson Gen. Corp., News Corp. Ltd., News Am. Holdings Inc., Sesac Inc. Mem. Fin. Control Bd., N.Y.C., 1977—; trustee The Dalton Sch.; 1977-84, hon. trustee, 1984—; class agt. Phillips Acad., Andover, Mass., 1972-90; pres. Wilwyck Sch., 1971-78; v.p.

exec. com. Jewish Guild for the Blind, 1973-80; trustee Jewish Publ. Soc., 1986-90, Channel 13 WNET, 1990—, Carnegie Hall, 1990—, N.Y. Law Sch., 1990—, The Markle Found., 1992—, Nat. Pub. Radio Found., 1992—; chmn. Nat. Econ. Devel. and Law Ctr., 1978-83; chmn. adv. bd. Inst. Policy Scis. and Pub. Affairs, Duke U., 1992—. Mem. ABA (comml. arbitration com., sect. corp. banking and bus. law 1974—). Clubs: Harvard (Boston); City Athletic, Quaker Ridge Golf, Harvard (N.Y.C.); East Hampton Tennis. Home: 17 E 73rd St New York NY 10021-3544 Office: Allen & Co Inc 711 5th Ave New York NY 10022-3109

SHUMANDINE, WILLIAM F., JR., banking executive; b. 1945. Attended, Hampden Sydney Coll., 1963-67. Various mgmt. positions Ctrl. Fidelity Bank, Richmond, Va., 1967—, now pres. Office: Ctrl Fidelity Bank 1021 E Cary St Richmond VA 23219-4000

SHUMATE, CHARLES ALBERT, retired dermatologist; b. San Francisco, Aug. 11, 1904; s. Thomas E. and Freda (Ortmann) S.; B.S., U. San Francisco, 1927, H.H.D., 1976; M.D., Creighton U., 1931. Pvt. practice dermatology, San Francisco, 1933-73, ret., 1973; asst. clin. prof. dermatology Stanford U., 1956-62; pres. E Clampus Vitus, Inc., 1963-64; hon. mem. staff St. Mary's Hosp. Mem. San Francisco Art Commn., 1964-67, Calif. Heritage Preservation Commn., 1963-67; regent Notre Dame Coll. at Belmont, 1965-78, trustee, 1977-93; pres. Conf. Calif. Hist. Socs., 1967; mem. San Francisco Landmarks Preservation Bd., 1967-78, pres., 1967-69; trustee St. Patrick's Coll. and Sem., 1970-86; dir. U.S. Catholic Hist. Soc., 1988—. Served as maj. USPHS, 1942-46. Decorated knight comdr. Order of Isabella (Spain); knight Order of the Holy Sepulchre, knight of St. Gregory, knight of Malta. Fellow Am. Acad. Dermatology; mem. U. San Francisco Alumni Assn. (pres. 1955), Calif. Book Club (pres. 1969-71), Calif. Hist. Soc. (trustee 1958-67, 68-78, pres. 1962-64), Soc. Calif. Pioneers (dir. 1979—). Clubs: Bohemian, Olympic, Roxburghe (pres. 1958-59) (San Francisco); Zamorano (Los Angeles). Author: Life of George Henry Goddard; The California of George Gordon, 1976, Jas. F. Curtis, Vigilante, 1988, Francisco Pacheco of Pacheco Pass, 1977; Life of Mariano Malarin, 1980; Boyhood Days: Y. Villegas Reminiscences of California 1850s, 1983, The Notorious I.C. Woods of the Adams Express, 1986, Rincon Hill and South Park, 1988, Captain A.A. Ritchie, Pioneer, 1991, Stormy Life of Major William Gouverneur Morris, 1993. Mem. St. Andrew Soc. (hon. mem.). Home: 1901 Scott St San Francisco CA 94115-2613 Office: 490 Post St San Francisco CA 94102-1401

SHUMATE, JOHN PAGE, diplomat; b. El Paso, Tex., Sept. 18, 1934; s. John Page and Elizabeth (McWilliams) S.; m. Caroline Taylor, June 16, 1978. BA in Polit. Sci., UCLA, 1956; MAin Internat. Rels., U. So. Calif., 1970. Counsellor of Embassy, U.S. Embassy, Quito, Ecuador, 1970-72; dir. exec. tng. Fgn. Service Inst., Washington, 1972-75; dir. U.K. Affairs, Dept. State., 1975-78, exec. dir. Bur. Ednl. and Cultural Affairs, 1978-80, exec. dir. Bur. Adminstrn., Washington, 1981-84; staff dir. Sec. of State's Adv. Panel on Overseas Security, 1984-85; exec. v.p., chief exec. officer Am. Fgn. Service Protective Assn., 1986—, Assn. Fed. Health Orgns. (chmn. bd. dirs. 1992—); co-pres. U.S.-Mexico Cultural Commn. com., 1978-80. Recipient Superior Honor award U.S. Dept. State., 1981; Phi Kappa Phi Cert. of Honor, 1970. Mem. Am. Fgn. Service Assn., Nat. Assn. Sr. Living Industries, Phi Kappa Phi. Clubs: Ft. Meyer Officers, Fgn. Service, Dacor Bacon House, Bethany West Tennis. Office: Am Fgn Svc Protective Assn 1716 N St NW Washington DC 20036-2907

SHUMATE, PAUL WILLIAM, JR., communications executive; b. Phila., July 15, 1941; s. Paul William and Ruth (Bailey) S.; m. Randi Atkins, June 20, 1964; 1 child, Angela Lynn. BS in Physics, Coll. of William & Mary, 1963; PhD in Physics, U. Va., 1968. Scientist Nat. Bur. of Standards, Washington, 1963-64; asst. prof. physics U. Va., Charlottesville, 1968-69; mem. tech. staff Bell Telephone Labs., Murray Hill, N.J., 1969-75, supr., 1975-84; dist. mgr. Bellcore, Morristown, N.J., 1984-86; div. mgr. Bellcore, Morristown, 1986-91, exec. dir., 1991—; lectr. and pub. in field; mem. optoelectronics study team Japanese Tech. Evaluation Ctr. NSF, 1994—. Editor-in-chief Photonics Tech. Letters, 1988-94, Trans. Mag., 1972-79, Lightwave Tech. Steering Com., 1992—; contbr. chpts. to books. Fellow IEEE (E.H. Armstrong award 1993, Telephony Fiber-in-the-Loop award 1993); mem. Optical Soc. Am., Lasers and Electro-Optics Soc. (v.p. publs.), Sigma Xi, Phi Beta Kappa. Office: Bellcore 445 South St Morristown NJ 07960-6454

SHUPACK, PAUL MARTIN, law educator; b. Bklyn., May 20, 1940; s. Ben and Florentina Marie (Leipniker) S.; m. Leslie Sloan, Dec. 23, 1989; stepchildren: Alexander Hoffert, Jason Hoffert. AB, Columbia U., 1961; postgrad., Harvard U., 1961-67; JD, U. Chgo., 1970. Bar: N.Y. 1971. Assoc. Cleary, Gottlieb, Steen & Hamilton, N.Y.C., 1970-77; asst. prof. Yeshiva U., N.Y.C., 1977-79, assoc. prof., 1980-84, prof., 1984—; vis. asst. prof. U. Chgo., 1979. Contbr. articles to profl. jours. Mem. Am. Law Inst., Assn. Bar City of N.Y. Home: 11 5th Ave Apt 3G New York NY 10003-4342 Office: Yeshiva U 55 5th Ave New York NY 10003-4301

SHUPP, FRANKLIN RICHARD, economist; b. Palmerton, Pa., Apr. 9, 1934; s. Floyd Edwin and Mona Elizabeth (Williams) S.; m. Carol Ann Edwards, Sept. 27, 1959; children: Diedre Elaine, Ruth Louise, Robert Seth. BS, Lafayette Coll., 1956; PhD, Princeton U., 1960. Asst. lectr. Edinburgh (Scotland) U., 1959-60; asst. prof. U. Ill., Urbana, 1960-64, assoc. prof., 1964-70, prof. econs., 1970—, chmn. dept. econs., 1986-89; Fulbright rsch. prof. U. Oslo, Norway, 1966-67; sr. economist bd. govs. FRS, Washington, 1970-71; vis. prof. U. York, Eng., 1973-74, U. Cambridge, Eng., 1981-82, U. Sydney, Australia, 1989-90, U. Beijing, Peoples U., China, 1992-93; cons. joint econ. com. U.S. Congress, Washington, 1978-80. Author monograph The Inflation Process, 1969-79, 1979; assoc. editor Jour. Econ. Dynamics and Control, 1979—; contbr. numerous articles to profl. jours., chpts. in books. Vis. fellow Wolfson Coll., Cambridge U., 1981, Gonville and Caius Coll., Cambridge U., 1982, U. Melbourne, Australia, 1990; recipient grants Ford Found., 1966, NSF, 1973, 79, Social Sci. Rsch. Coun., 1981, NAS, 1993. Mem. Soc. Econs. Dynamics and Control (sec.-treas. 1983-84, pres. 1984-86), Am. Econ. Assn., Royal Econ. Soc. Lutheran. Home: 507 W Vermont Ave Urbana IL 61801-4930 Office: U of Ill 193 Commerce W Champaign IL 61820

SHUR, GEORGE MICHAEL, lawyer; b. Portland, Maine, Nov. 10, 1942; m. Martha West, Nov. 14, 1970; children: Aaron, Rebecca. AB in Modern European History, Colby Coll.; JD, Boston U.; postgrad., Nat. Inst. for Trial Advocacy. Bar: Maine, 1968, U.S. Cist. Ct. Maine, 1968, U.S. Supreme Ct. 1980, U.S. Ct. Appeals (1st cir.) 1980, Ill. 1983, U.S. Dist. Ct. (no. dist.) Ill. 1983, U.S. Ct. Appeals (7th cir.) 1985. Assoc. Bernstein, Shur, Sawyer & Shur, 1968-72; ptnr. Bernstein, Shur, Sawyer & Nelson, Portland, Maine, 1972-83; univ. legal counsel, chief legal officer No. Ill. U., DeKalb, 1983—. Contbr. articles to profl. jours., chpts. to books. Mem. Cape Elizabeth (Maine) Town Dem. Com., del. State Dem. Conv., 1976-78, 80-82; mem. City of DeKalb Human Rels. Commn., 1985—, United Way Budget Com., 1972-77; faculty Nat. Small Craft Sch. ARC, summers 1963-70; bd. dirs. 1968-71; v.p. Children's Theatre of Maine, Inc., 1970-71, bd. dirs. 1968-72; pres. Portland Colby Alumni Club, 1979-82, Portland Players, Inc., 1972-74, bd. dirs. 1970-80, pres., Alumni Coun. Colby Coll., 1980-83; bd. dirs. Camp Fire Girls, 1969-72, ARC, Portland, 1968-72, DeKalb County Am. Cancer Soc., 1985—; bd. dirs., sec., mem. exec. com. Portland Boys' Club, 1977-83; asst. chmn. Bd. Zoning Appeals Town of Cape Elizabeth, Maine, 1978-83; mem. bd. trustees, exec. com. North Yarmouth Acad., 1980-83; mem. Dekalb Bd. of Edn., 1991—, v.p. 1992—. With USAR, 1968-76. Mem. ABA (local govt. law and legal edn. and admissions sects.), Maine State Bar Assn. (chmn. legal edn. and admissions com., bridging the gap program 1975-83, rep. commn. to examine bar admission process 1980-83), Ill. Bar Assn. (legal edn., admissions and competence com. 1984—), DeKalb County Bar Assn. (chmn. rev. model rules of profl. conduct com. 1984-85), Nat. Coll. and Univ. Attys. (chmn. attys. pres. elect 1987-88, chmn. ann. conf. program and 1st v.p. 1986-87, 2d v.p. 1985-86, exec. bd. 1974-78, 83-85, mid-winter Continuing Legal Edn. workshop 1979, program com. 1980-81, program com. ann. confs. 1985, rep. conf. of solicitors instns. higher edn. Dalhousie U. 1975, chmn. spl. conf. New Eng. Bd. Higher Ed. 1977, chmn. spl. conf. legal presentations Wakefield (Mass.) chpt. 1978, chmn. site selection com. 1981-82, 1st ann. mid-winter Continuing Legal Edn. workshop com. 1980, New Eng. membership sect. 1971-73, 76-81, student affairs sect. 1980—), Nat. Orgn. Legal Problems, Assn. Trial Lawyers Am., Maine Trial lawyers

Assn., Maine Econ. Soc. (charter mem., bd. dirs. 1980-83), Alpha Delta Phi. Home: 305 Forsythe Ln De Kalb IL 60115-2341 Office: No Ill U Lowden Hall Office Univ Legal Counsel De Kalb IL 60115-2880

SHUR, MICHAEL, electrical engineer, educator, consultant; b. Kamensk-Yralski, Sverdlovsk, USSR, Nov. 13, 1942; came to U.S., 1976; s. Saul and Anna (Katz) S.; m. Paulina Gimmelfarb, Sept. 25, 1966; children: Luba, Natasha. MS, Leningrad Elec. Tech. Inst., 1965; PhD, Ioffe Inst., Leningrad, 1967; DSc, Ioffe Inst., St. Petersburg, 1992; Hon. Doctorate, St. Petersburg State Tech. U., 1994. Scientist Ioffe Inst., 1965-75; asst. prof. Wayne State U., Detroit, 1976-77, Oakland U., Rochester, Mich., 1978; prof. U. Minn., Mpls., 1979-92; John Marshall Money prof. U. Va., Charlottesville, Va., 1989—; cons. Honeywell Corp., 1978-88, Xerox, 1986—; chair U.S. Commn. D Union Radio-Scientifique Internationale. Author 7 books; contbr. articles to profl. jours.; patentee in field. Fellow IEEE (assoc. editor IEEE Trans. 1990-93); mem. Am. Phys. Soc., Eta Kappa Nu, Tau Beta Pi. *When we were penniless refugees, the United States adopted me and my family with compassion and friendship, gave us work and citizenship. Our debt of gratitude to the American people who accepted us as their own we will be never able to repay.*

SHUR, WALTER, retired insurance company executive; b. N.Y.C., Feb. 1, 1929; m. Ruth Schram, Aug. 28, 1949; children: Robert, Richard, James. B.S., U. Tex., 1949, M.A., 1951; grad., Advanced Mgmt. Program, Harvard U., 1975. With N.Y. Life Ins. Co., N.Y.C., 1952—; asst. actuary 1956-59, asso. actuary, 1959-62, actuary, 1962-64, group actuary, 1964-65, 2d v.p., group actuary, 1965-69, v.p. in charge group ins., 1969-71, sr. v.p. in charge individual ins. ops., 1971-74, exec. v.p., 1974-81, exec. v.p., chief actuary, 1981-89, exec. v.p., 1989-91, exec. v.p., controller, 1991-92, exec. v.p., dir., 1992-94. Fellow Soc. Actuaries; mem. Am. Acad. Actuaries (exec. v.p. 1989-91, exec. v.p., contr. 1991-92, exec. v.p., dir. 1992-94). Office: NY Life Ins Co 51 Madison Ave New York NY 10010-1603

SHURE, MYRNA BETH, psychologist, educator; b. Chgo., Sept. 11, 1937; d. Sidney Natkin and Frances (Laufman) S.; student U. Colo., 1955; BS, U. Ill., 1959; MS, Cornell U., 1961, PhD, 1966. Asst. prof. U. R.I., head tchr. Nursery Sch., Kingston, 1961-62; asst. prof. Temple U., Phila., 1966-67, assoc. prof., 1967-68; instr. Hahneman Med. Coll., Phila., 1968-69, sr. instr. psychology, 1969-70, asst. prof., 1970-73, assoc. prof., 1973-80, prof., 1980—. NIMH research grantee, 1971-75, 77-79, 82-85, 87, 88-93. Recipient Lela Rowland Prevention award Nat. Mental Health Assn., 1982; . lic. psychologist, Pa. Fellow Am. Psychol. Assn. (Disting. Contbn. award div. community psychology 1984), Am. Psychol. Assn. (divsn. clin. psychology, child sect. 1994, Task Force on Prevention award 1987, Task Force on Model Programs award 1994); mem. Eastern Psychol. Assn., Soc. Research in Child Devel., Phila. Soc. Clin. Psychologists. Author: (with George Spivack) Social Adjustment of Young Children, 1974; (with George Spivack and Jerome Platt) The Problem Solving Approach to Adjustment, 1976; (with George Spivack) Problem Solving Techniques in Childrearing, 1978, (child curricula manual) I Can Problem Solve, 1992, (trade book) Raising a Thinking Child, 1994; mem. editl. bd. Jour. Applied Developmental Psychology; spl. cons. to The Puzzle Place PBS Children's TV Show.

SHURICK, EDWARD PALMES, television executive, rancher; b. Duluth, Minn., Dec. 15, 1912; s. Edward P. and Vera (Wheaton) S.; m. F(lossie) Dolores Pipes, Aug. 1, 1933; children—Patricia Annette (Mrs. Robert Dube), Sandra Sue Shurick Dryden, Linda Jean (Mrs. James Elsea), Edward P. III. Student, U. Minn., 1932-33; B.A. in Econs, U. Mo., 1946. Gen. sales mgr. Intermountain Network, Salt Lake City, 1937-41; advt. mgr. sta. KMBC, Kansas City, Mo., 1941-47; research mgr. Free & Peters, N.Y.C., 1947-49; v.p CBS TV, N.Y.C., 1949-57; exec. v.p. Blair TV, N.Y.C., 1957-62; chmn. treas. H-R TV, N.Y.C., 1962-76; dir. Seltel, Inc., N.Y.C.; v.p., owner Sta. KXXX-AM-FM, Colby, Kans., 1963-84; v.p. treas. H-R Rep. Cos., 1970-73; pres. S&S Enterprises, Charlottesville, Va., 1959-89, S & S Ranch Corp., Aspen, Colo., 1965-82; mem. bd. Chgo. Internat. Live Stock Expn., 1972-76. Author: First Quarter-Century of American Broadcasting, 1946. Pres. Shurick Rsch. Found., Bridgewater, 1959-72; v.p., originator Internat. Radio and TV Found., N.Y.C., 1964-73. Recipient Alumnus award U. Mo. at Kansas City, 1968; ordre du merit for contbns. to agr. Govt. France, 1970; Ordre du Charolais Francais, 1971. Mem. Internat. Radio and TV Soc. N.Y. (pres. 1967-69), Am. Internat. Charolais Assn. (pres. 1968-69), Colonial Charolais Breeders (dir. 1967-71), World Fedn. Charolais (pres. 1973-74), Broadcast Pioneers Assn., Am. Nat. Cattlemen's Assn. (tax com. 1968-76), Internat. Wine and Food Soc. (bd. dirs. 1985-88), Masons (32 degree), Shriners. Episcopalian (lay reader). Address: 1006 Fearrington Post Fearrington Village NC 27312 *The opportunity to succeed as a self-made person still exists in the United States today. This may seem hackneyed and out-of-date, but it isn't. Honesty, dedication, long hours of hard work with an average amount of luck will build a fortune from a few cents to a million dollars.*

SHURLEY, JAY TALMADGE, psychiatrist, medical educator, polar explorer, author; b. Sonora, Tex., Dec. 20, 1917; s. Ira L. and Jewell L. (Choate) S.; m. Helen Loos Lee, June 2, 1945; children: John Lawrence (dec.), Tom Henry, Guy Gibbs, Philip Sherwood; m. Emily Alexander Jackson, Jan. 4, 1964; 1 child, John Alexander; m. Erwina Bode Cornelison, Dec. 20, 1986. BA in Zoology, U. Tex.-Austin, 1940; MD, U. Tex. Med. Br., Galveston, 1942; candidate in psychoanalysis, Inst. of Phila. Assn. for Psychoanalysis, 1946-51. Diplomate Am. Bd. Psychiatry and Neurology. Intern. Ind. U.-Indpls. Med. Ctr., 1943; Rockefeller fellow in neuropsychiatry dept. mental and nervous disease Inst. for Mental Hygiene Pa. Hosp., Phila., 1944-47; dir. Markle Meml. Unit for Insulin Therapy dept. for mental and nervous disease Pa. Hosp., Phila., 1945-50; pvt. practice medicine specializing in psychiatry and psychoanalysis Phila., 1947-51, Austin, 1951-52; pvt. practice medicine specializing in psychiatry San Antonio, 1952-54, Chevy Chase, Md., 1955-57; pvt. practice medicine specializing in psychiatry, psychoanalysis and sleep disorders medicine Oklahoma City, 1978-90; acting chief lab. adult psychiat. investigation, clin. investigations NIMH, NIH, Bethesda, 1955-57; chief psychiatry service and mental hygiene clinic VA Hosp., Oklahoma City, 1957-62; sr. med. investigator in psychiatry, research service, dept. medicine and surgery VA, 1962-76; founder and dir. behavioral scis. labs VA Med. Ctr., Oklahoma City, 1962-78; med. dir. outpatient psychiatry clinics Okla. Meml. Hosp. and Clinics, Okla Health Scis. Ctr., Oklahoma City, 1978-81; sci. dir. Oklahoma Mental Health Research Inst., Oklahoma Dept. Mental Health, 1988-89; cons.-liaison in geropsychiatry O'Donoghue Rehab. Inst., Okla. Med. Ctr., 1990-91; med. dir. emeritus Willow View Mental Health Ctr., Oklahoma City, 1985-87; prof. psychiatry U. Okla., Oklahoma City, 1957-62, career research prof. psychiatry and behavioral scis., 1962-77, prof. psychiatry and behavioral scis. Coll. of Medicine and Grad. Coll., 1977-81; prof. emeritus psychiatry and behavioral scis. U. Okla. Coll. Medicine, Oklahoma City, 1981—; adj. prof. human ecology Coll. Health, U. Okla., 1967-81; mem. com. on polar research, chmn. panel on biology and medicine NAS/NRC, 1970-74; U.S. rep. Working Group on Biology XII Sci. Com. on Antarctic Research, Canberra and Melbourne, Australia, 1972; U.S. rep. Working Group on Human Biology and Medicine XIII Sci. Com. on Antarctic Research, Jackson Hole, Wyo., 1974; disting. vis. scientist Acad. Scis. USSR, Moscow and Leningrad, 1972; Centennial Yr. vis. prof. dept. psychol. medicine U. Otago, Dunedin, N.Z., 1975; mem. Health Rsch. Com., 1986-91, Okla. Ctr. for Sci. and Tech., Okla. Alzheimer Rsch. Adv. Coun., 1990-92. Editor: Relating Environment to Mental Health and Illness: The Eco-psychiatric Data Base, 1979, Symposium on Man on the South Polar Plateau, 1970; mem. editorial bd. Jour. Clin. Psycholgy, 1970-80; contbr. more than 100 articles to sci. pubns. Served as capt. M.C. U.S. Army, 1952-54. Recipient Antarctic Svc. medal NSF/NAS, 1970, Disting. Profl. Svc. award Okla. Psychol. Assn., 1972, Sustained Superior Achievement cert. VA, 1974, Disting. Psychiatrist award Mid-Continent Psychiat. Assn., 1986, Okla. Psychiat. Assn., 1990, Sealy Inc. prize Assn. Profl. Sleep Socs., 1991; Shurley Ridge, Pensacola Mountains Antarctica named in his honor. Fellow Am. Psychiat. Assn. (life), Am. Coll. Psychiatrists (life); mem. AMA, Oklahoma County Med. Assn., Okla. State Med. Assn. (life), Okla. Psychiat. Assn. (pres. 1968, chair ethics com. 1989-91), Faculty House Club, Sigma Xi, Alpha Omega Alpha, Alpha Epsilon Delta. Democrat. Mailing Address: 3816 S Lamar Blvd Apt 3619 Austin TX 78704-7960

SHURTLEFF, LEONARD GRANT, ambassador; b. Boston, June 4, 1940; s. Leonard Francis and Mary Frances (Cornish) S.; m. Christine Morrissette, Dec. 8, 1967. BA in History cum laude, Tufts U., 1962; student, Maxwell Sch., Syracuse, N.Y., 1962; student African Areas Studies, U. Chgo., 1969-70. With fgn. service Dept. State, 1962-95; fgn. service officer gen. Am. Embassy, Caracas, Venezuela, 1963-65; polit. officer Am. Embassy, Freetown, Sierra Leone, 1965-67; intelligence analyst Bur. Intelligence and Research, Dept. State, Washington, 1967-69; prin. officer U.S. Consulate, Douala, Cameroon, 1970-72; dep. chief of mission Am. Embassy, Nouakchott, Mauritania, 1972-74; spl. asst. to ambassador Am. Embassy, Bogota, Colombia, 1975-77; alt. dir. Office of Inter-African Affairs, Washington, 1977-79; dep. dir. Office Cen. Africa Affairs, Washington, 1979-81; dep. exec. dir. Bur. African Affairs, Washington, 1981-83; dep. chief of mission (minister counselor) Am. Embassy, Monrovia, Liberia, 1983-86; mem. Sr. Sem. on Nat. and Internat. Affairs, Dept. State, Washington, 1986-87; A.E. and P. Am. Embassy, Brazzaville, Peoples Republic of Congo, 1987-90; coord. for mgmt. projects Office Undersec. for Mgmt., Dept. State, Washington, 1990-93; dir. office regional affairs Bur. of African Affairs, Dept. State, Washington, 1993-94. Decorated Congolese Order of Merit; recipient Meritorious Honor award U.S. Dept. State, 1969, EEO award, 1983, Superior Honor award, 1986, Wilber J. Carr award, 1994. Mem. World Affairs Coun., U.S. Naval Inst., Am. Fgn. Svc. Assn., Western Front Assn. (bd. dirs.), Order of DeMolay, Alpha Tau Omega. Home: Washington DC 20015 Office: AF/RA Dept State Washington DC 20520-3430

SHURTLEFF, MALCOLM C., plant pathologist, consultant, educator, extension specialist; b. Fall River, Mass., June 24, 1922; s. Malcolm C. and Florence L. (Jewell) S.; m. Margaret E. Johnson, June 14, 1950; children: Robert Glen, Janet Lee, Mark Steven. BS in Biology, U. R.I., 1943; MS in Plant Pathology, U. Minn., 1950, PhD in Plant Pathology, 1953. Asst. plant pathologist Conn. Agrl. Expt. Sta., New Haven, 1942, R.I. Agrl. Expt. Sta., Kingston, 1943; asst. extension prof. U. R.I., Kingston, 1950-54; assoc. extension prof. Iowa State U., Ames, 1954-61; prof. plant pathology U. Ill., Champaign-Urbana, 1961-92, prof. emeritus, 1992—; cons., writer Urbana, 1992—. Author: How to Control Plant Diseases, 1962, 66 (Am. Garden Guild award 1962, 66), How to Control Lawn Diseases and Pests, 1973, How to Control Tree Diseases and Pests, 1975, Controlling Turfgrass Pests, 1987; editor-in-chief: Phytopathology News, 1966-69, Plant Disease, 1969-72; contbr. articles to encys.; contbr. numerous rsch., ext., mag. articles. Lt. (j.g.) USN, 1943-46, PTO. Recipient Disting. Svc. award U.S. Dept. Agriculture, Washington, 1986. Fellow Am. Phytopathological Soc. (councilor at large 1970-71, Excellence in Extension Plant Pathology award 1991); mem. Internat. Soc. Plant Pathology (chmn. extension com. 1975-80), Am. Phytopathological Soc. (mem. various coms.). Avocation: photography. Home: 2707 Holcomb Dr Urbana IL 61801-7724 Office: U Ill Dept Plant Pathology N-427 N Turner Hall Urbana IL 61801

SHURTLIFF, MARVIN KARL, lawyer; b. Idaho Falls, Idaho, Nov. 6, 1939; s. Noah Leon and Melba Dorothy (Hunting) S.; m. Peggy J. Griffin, Nov. 23, 1963; 1 dau., Jennifer Karyl. B.A., Idaho State Coll., 1962; J.D., U. Idaho, 1968. Bar: Idaho 1968. Tchr. pub. schs. Jefferson County, Idaho, 1964-65; atty. U.S. Dept. Justice, Washington, 1968-74; commr. Idaho Pub. Utilities Commn., 1974-75, pres., 1975-76; spl. asst., legal counsel Gov. of Idaho, Boise, 1977; U.S. atty. for Dist. of Idaho, Boise, 1977-81; practice law Boise, 1981—; mem. Idaho Ho. of Reps., 1962-64. Mem. Idaho State Bd. Edn., 1990-95. Mem. Idaho Bar Assn. Democrat. Home: 62 Horizon Dr Boise ID 83702-4419 Office: PO Box 1652 Boise ID 83701-1652

SHUSTER, BUD, congressman; b. Glassport, Pa., Jan. 23, 1932; s. Prather and Grace (Greinert) S.; m. Patricia Rommell, Aug. 27, 1955; children: Peg, Bill, Debbie, Bobby, Gia. B.S., U. Pitts., 1954; M.B.A., Duquesne U., 1960; Ph.D. in Econs. and Mgmt., Am. U., 1967. Nat. account mgr. Univac div. Sperry Rand, 1956, Univac div. Remington Rand Co. (name now Sperry Rand), 1956-60; dist. mgr. Western Pa. RCA, 1960-62; mgr. ops. RCA, Washington, 1962-65; v.p. EPD div. RCA, 1965-68; pres. computer terminal co., 1968-72; mem. 93rd-104th Congresses from 9th Pa. dist., Washington, D.C., 1973—; pres. 93d Congress Republican Freshman Class; chmn. Nat. Transp. Policy Study Commn., 1976; ranking mem. Pub. Works and Transp. com. Author: Believing in America, 1983. Del. Republican Nat. Conv., 1976, 80, 84, 88, 92; co-chair Energy, Environment & Transp. Platform Subcom.; sr. transp. advisor Bush-Quayle campaign; also mem. platform com.; chmn. Reagan-Bush Campaign in Western Pa.; sr. adviser to transition team for Dept. Transp., 1980-81; trustee J.F. Kennedy Ctr. for Performing Arts. Served with inf. and CIC AUS, 1954-56. Recipient Watchdog of Treasury award, Guardian of Small Bus. award, Golden Age Hall of Fame award. Mem. Pa. Soc., Chowder and Marching Soc., Phi Beta Kappa, Omicron Delta Kappa, Sigma Chi (Significant Sig award). Club: Capitol Hill. Office: US Ho of Reps 2188 Rayburn House Office B Washington DC 20515

SHUSTER, HERBERT VICTOR, corporate executive, consultant; b. Boston, June 12, 1924; s. Myron and Marion Ruth (Lewis) S.; m. Rosanne Feldman, June 22, 1952; children: Amy J., Mark W., James L. BS, MIT, 1949, MS, 1949, PhD, 1953. Tech. dir. Shockley & Poor Spice Co., Charlestown, Mass., 1953-55; pres. Herbert V. Shuster, Inc., Boston, 1955-80, chmn. bd., Quincy, Mass., 1980—. Patentee dilution bottle, 1985. 1st lt. USAAF, 1943-46. Mem. Am. Oil Chemists Soc., Inst. Food Technologists, Pvt. Label Mfrs. Assn., Sigma Xi, Phi Tau Sigma. Avocation: real estate. Office: Herbert V Shuster Inc 5 Hayward St Quincy MA 02171-2493

SHUSTER, ROBERT G., electronics company executive, consultant; b. N.Y.C., June 1, 1927; s. Robert Chandler and Therese G. (Giraud) m. Marianne B. Lynski, Apr. 20, 1970 (div. Jan. 1987); m. H. Elizabeth Young, May 20, 1989. BSEE, CCNY, 1948; MSEE, Columbia U., 1955, postgrad., 1959-64. Test engr. Elec. Testing Labs., N.Y.C., 1948-50; project leader Sperry Gyroscope Co., Great Neck, N.Y., 1950-59; project mgr. RCA Advanced Communications Lab., N.Y.C., 1959-67; prin. scientist Tracor, Inc., Rockville, Md., 1967-75, v.p. electronics systems div., 1975-87; pres. Tracor Tech. Resources, Inc., Rockville, Md., 1984-90, RGS Assocs., McLean, Va., 1990—; v.p. C-Cubed Corp., Alexandria, Va., 1990-93; pres. C-Cubed Corp., 1993—. Mem. IEEE (sr.), AAAS, N.Y. Acad. Scis. Avocations: photography, hiking. Office: C-Cubed Corp 5252 Cherokee Ave Alexandria VA 22312-2000

SHUSTERMAN, MURRAY H., lawyer; b. Solochov, Ukraine, Sept. 8, 1913; came to U.S., 1922; s. Herman Shusterman and Esther Tsiboushnik; m. Judith Weiner, Nov. 10, 1940; children: Robert, Richard, Ronald. BS with honors, Temple U., 1933, JD with honors, 1936; MA, U. Pa., 1940, PhD, 1942. Bar: Pa. U.S. Supreme Ct. 1961. Atty. Bur. Mcpl. Rsch., Phila., 1936-42, Reconstructive Fin. Corp., Phila., 1942-49; spl. trial counsel Small Bus. Adminstrn., Phila., 1949-51; dep. city solicitor Phila., 1951-63, ptnr. various law firms, 1951-68; sr. ptnr. Fox, Rothschild, O'Brien & Frankel, Phila., 1968—; vice chmn. bd. Stenton Pl. Assocs., Atlantic City, N.J., 1978—; chmn. bd. Forum Mgmt. Corp., Phila., 1980—; adj. prof. law Temple U., 1962-94; former dep. solicitor Phila.; counsel Commn. Human Rels. Phila., City Coun. (citation Merit). Past pres. Law Alum. Temple U., former chair Friends Ben Gurion U. (Phila. chpt.); former v.p. Phila. City Bd. Health; co-chmn. Nat. Conf. Christians and Jews (Phila.), sec. Fellowship Commn.; pres. Jewish Community Rels. Coun. Greater Phila., founder, 1st pres. Pa.; chair B'nai Brith Klutznick Mus., Internat. adv. coun., internat. bd. govs., pres. B'nai Brith World Ctr., Jerusalem, past pres. B'nai Brith Dist. 3; bd. overseers Gratz Coll.; bd. govs. Ben Gurion U., Beer Sheva, Israel; trustee Annenberg Rsch. Inst., 1980-93, Fedn. Jewish Agys.; hon. life trustee Temple U.; Anti-Defamation League B'nai Brith (life mem. commn., Met. award); sec. Ctr. Judaic Studies U. Pa., 1993—. Recipient Loyal Legion award Temple U., 1957, Disting. Svc. award Phila. Commn. Human Rels., 1963, Tower award State of Israel, 1969, Met. award Anti-Defamation League, 1981, Justice Louis D. Brandeis award Zionist Orgn. Am., 1985. Mem. ABA, Pa. Bar Assn., Phila. Bar Assn. (chair civil rights com.), Lawyer's Club, Law Found. (pres.), B'nai Brith Internat. (v.p., sr. mem.). Jewish. Avocations: reading, golf, bridge, music. Home: 1810 Hemlock Cir Abington PA 19001-4706 Office: Fox Rothschild O'Brien & Frankel 2000 Market St Fl 10 Philadelphia PA 19103-3231

SHUSTERMAN, NEAL DOUGLAS, author, screenwriter; b. N.Y.C., Nov. 12, 1962; s. Milton and Charlotte Ruth (Altman) S.; m. Elaine Gale Jones,

Jan. 31, 1987; children: Brendan, Jarrod. BA in Psychology and Drama, U. Calif., Irvine, 1985. Author, screenwriter, 1987—. Author: Guy Talk, 1987, The Shadow Club, 1988 (Children's Choice award Internat. Reading Assn. 1989), Dissidents, 1989, Speeding Bullet, 1991 (Best Book for Teens award N.Y. Pub. Libr.), Kid Heroes, 1991, What Daddy Did, 1991 (Best Book for Young Adults award ALA, Outstanding Work of Fiction award So. Calif. Coun. Lit. for Children and Young People, Children's Choice award and Young Adult Choice award Internat. Reading Assn., Pick of the List award ABA, Best Book for Teens award N.Y. Pub. Libr., Okla. Sequoyah award 1994), The Eyes of Kid Midas, 1992 (ALA Best Book for Reluctant Readers), Darkness Creeping, 1993, Piggyback Ninja, 1994, The Scorpion Shards, 1995, Darkness Creeping II, 1995; screenwriter: Time Scavengers, 1990, Double Dragon, 1992, Evolver, 1993, The Eyes of Kid Midas, 1993, Speeding Bullet, 1994; dir. Heart on a Chain, 1991 (Golden Eagle award CINE), What About the Sisters, 1993 (Golden Eagle award CINE), Games: How to Host a Teen Mystery, 1994. Mem. PEN, Writers Guild Am. West, Soc. Children's Book Writers. Avocations: swimming, tennis, storytelling. Office: PO Box 18516 Irvine CA 92713-8516

SHUTE, DAVID, retail executive, lawyer; b. Crystal, Mich., Feb. 6, 1931; s. Bert M. and Bessie M. (Gleason) S.; m. Lorna Mae Lesnick (div. Apr. 1976); children: David K., Douglas R.; m. Roxanne J. Decyk (div. June 1987); m. Gerri Hilt, May, 1989. BA, Princeton U., 1953; JD, U. Mich., 1959. Bar: Wis. 1959, D.C. 1971, Ill. 1981. Assoc., then ptnr. Foley & Lardner, Milw., 1959-81; sr. v.p., gen. counsel Seraco Enterprise Inc., Chgo., 1981, Coldwell Banker Real Estate Group, Chgo., 1982-84, Sears Consumer Fin. Corp., Lincolnshire, Ill., 1984-86; corp. gen. counsel Sears Roebuck and Co., Chgo., 1987—, v.p., 1987-88, sr. v.p., sec., gen. counsel, 1988—. Mem. adv. com. Corp. Counsel Ctr., Northwestern U. Sch. Law, Chgo., 1987—, mem. planning com. Corp. Counsel Inst., Chgo. Vol. Legal Svcs. Found., 1988; mem. lawyers com. Nat. Ctr. for State Cts., Washington, 1987; bd. trustees Library Internat. Rels., Chgo. Lt. (j.g.) USNR, 1953-56. Mem. ABA (com. on corp. law depts.), Ill. Bar Assn., Chgo. Bar Assn., Assn. Gen. Counsel, Am. Enterprise Inst. (mem. fin. svcs. adv. com.), The Law Club, Economic Club of Chgo., Saddle and Cycle Club, Metropolitan Club. Avocations: tennis, skiing, travel. Home: 1448 N Lake Shore Dr # 10C Chicago IL 60610-1625 Office: Sears Roebuck & Co 68th Floor Sears Tower Chicago IL 60684*

SHUTE, RICHARD EMIL, government official, engineer; b. Bklyn., May 1, 1938; s. William Leonard and Doris (Schlichting) S.; m. Linda Janan McElhiney, Mar. 7, 1960. B.S in Mech. Engring., U. Miami, 1960; M.B.A. Fla. State U., 1970. Registered profl. engr., Fla. Engr. Pratt and Whitney Aircraft, West Palm Beach, Fla., 1960-62, Gen. Dynamics Corp., San Diego, 1962-64; aerospace engr. NASA/Kennedy Space Ctr., Fla., 1964-71; dir. planning and evaluation Fla. Dept. Health and Human Services, Tallahassee, 1971-76; dir. office program devel. Office Human Devel., HHS, Washington, 1976-87; dir. office of mgmt. and info. systems U.S. Dept. Commerce, Washington, 1987-90; pres. Richard E. Shute and Assocs. Mgmt. Cons., 1990—. Recipient Superior Achievement award NASA, 1966; recipient Spl. Achievement award HHS, 1977, Sr. Exec. award HHS, 1982. Mem. SAE, Nat. Assn. Security Dealers (registered arbitrator).

SHUTER, BRUCE DONALD, lawyer; b. N.Y.C., Feb. 20, 1940; s. David C. and Lillian (Hermann) S.; m. Marsha Nan Ellen, Aug. 20, 1961 (div. 1989); children: David, Richard; m. Janis Lynn Klein, May 23, 1989. BA, Alfred U., 1961; JD, NYU, 1964. Bar: N.Y. 1964, Pa. 1971. Atty. Fed. Res. Bd., Washington, 1964-68, chief counsel divsn. supervision and regulation, 1968-70; assoc. Drinker Biddle & Reath, Phila., 1970-72, ptnr., chmn. banking dept., 1972—. Mem. Com. of Seventy, Phila., 1976-78. Mem. Pyramid Club of Phila., Wissahickon Skating Club (bd. dirs. 1992). Office: Drinker Biddle & Reath 1345 Chestnut St Fl 2100 Philadelphia PA 19107-3421

SHUTIAK, JAMES, management consultant; b. Saskatoon, Sask., Can., July 1, 1932; s. Nicholas and Anna (Zabaczinski) S. MBA, Simon Fraser U., 1977. Chartered acct.; cert. mgmt. cons., fraud examiner. Ptnr. Winspear, Higgins, Stevenson & Co. (C.A.), 1951-61; comptroller, treas. Wainwright Producers & Refiners, Calgary, Alta., Can., 1961-63; sec., treas. Peace River Oil Pipeline Co., Ltd., Calgary, 1963-69; asst. to treas., asst. treas. Columbia Cellulose Co., Ltd., Vancouver, 1969-71; mgmt. cons. J. Shutiak (C.A.), Vancouver, 1971-73; asst. gen. mgr., dep. chmn. Man. Devel. Corp., Winnipeg, 1973-75; treas. Alta. Gas Trunk Line Co., Ltd., Calgary, 1975-79, also v.p. oil and gas subs., 1977-79; v.p. fin., CFO CDC Oil & Gas Ltd., Calgary, 1979-80; pres. IES Consulting, a divsn. of IES Resources Ltd., Calgary, 1980—; pvt. mgmt. cons., 1980—. Mem. Inst. Chartered Accts. Alta., Inst. Cert. Mgmt. Cons. Alta., Assn. Cert. Fraud Examiners, Fin. Execs. Inst., Simon Fraser U. Alumni Assn., Calgary Petroleum Club. Home: Box 1 Site 17 RR 1, De Winton, AB Canada T0L 0X0

SHUTLER, KENNETH EUGENE, lawyer; b. Wichita, Kans., Mar. 27, 1938; s. Walter Kenneth and Charlene Belle (Swearingen) S.; m. Jean E. Rohner, June 24, 1967 (div.); children: Samantha Elizabeth, Whitney Anne. A.B., U. Pa., 1960; LL.B., Yale U., 1963. Bar: Pa. 1965, Calif. 1971. Practiced in Phila., 1965-68; assoc. Stradley, Ronon, Stevens & Young, Phila.; v.p. Shareholders Mgmt. Co., Los Angeles, 1968-72; v.p., gen. counsel Republic Corp., Los Angeles, 1972-78; sr. v.p., gen. counsel Nat. Med. Enterprises, Inc., Los Angeles, 1978-79; v.p. law div. Continental Aircraft Services, Inc., subs. Continental Airlines, 1979-81; v.p., gen. counsel Caesars World, Inc., 1981-83; ptnr. Troy & Gould, Los Angeles, 1983-91; exec. v.p., gen. counsel MGM Grand, Inc., Las Vegas, Calif. 1991-92, Las Vegas, Nev., 1993—; bd. dirs. MGM Grand, Inc. Bd. dirs. Constl. Rights Found., L.A. coun. Girl Scouts U.S.A., 1980-82, L.A. Chamber Orch., 1983-85; trustee Nev. Symphony Orch., 1993; alumni trustee, Pres.'s coun., U. Pa. Capt. U.S. Army, 1963-65. Mem. ABA, Calif. Bar Assn., L.A. County Bar Assn., Yale Alumni Assn. (schs. com.), U. Pa. Alumni Assn. (pres. So. Calif. 1971-72), Venice Squash Club, Bel-Air Bay Club, Ctr. Cts. Club, Beefeaters Club, Green Valley Athletic Club.

SHUTLER, MARY ELIZABETH, academic administrator; b. Oakland, Calif., Nov. 14, 1929; d. Hal Wilfred and Elizabeth Frances (Gimbel) Hall; m. Richard Shutler Jr., Sept. 8, 1951 (div. 1975); children: Kathryn Allice, John Hall, Richard Burnett. BA, U. Calif., Berkeley, 1951; MA, U. Ariz., 1958, PhD, 1967. Asst., assoc., full prof. anthropology, chmn. dept. San Diego State U., 1967-75; prof. anthropology, dept. chmn. Wash. State U., Pullman, 1975-80; dean Coll. Arts and Scis., prof. anthropology U. Alaska, Fairbanks, 1980-84; vice chancellor, dean of faculty, prof. anthropology U. Wis. Parkside, Kenosha, 1984-88; provost, v.p. for acad. affairs, prof. anthropology Calif. State U., L.A., 1988-94; provost West Coast U., L.A., 1994—; mem. core staff Lahav Rsch. Project, Miss. State U., 1975—. Co-author: Ocean Prehistory, 1975, Deer Creek Cave, 1964, Archaeological Survey of Southern Nevada, 1963, Stuart Rockshelter, 1962; contbr. articles to jours. in field. Mem. coun. Gamble House. Fellow Am. Anthropol. Assn.; mem. Soc. for Am. Archaeology, Am. Schs. for Oriental Rsch., Am. Coun. Edn., Am. Assn. for Higher Edn., Am. State Colls. and Univs., Delta Zeta. Republican. Roman Catholic. Avocations: travel, gardening, cats. Office: West Coast U 440 Shatto Pl Los Angeles CA 90020

SHUTT, FRANCES BARTON, special education educator; b. Pryor, Okla., Nov. 12, 1912; d. Edwin Harley and Bonnie (Heflin) Barton; m. John Paul Shutt, Dec. 24, 1932; children: Jon Edwin, Frances Paulette. BA, Northeastern Tchrs. U., 1941; MA, U. N.Mex., 1954, cert. in spl. edn., 1958. Classroom tchr. Pryor, Okla., 1932-40; classroom tchr. Albuquerque, 1941-55, homebound tchr. in spl. edn., 1955-72; substitute tchr. Las Cruces, N.Mex., 1973-75; ESL tchr. Las Cruces, N.Mex. Author: First Grade Guide, 1952. Mem. AAUW, 1962-68, Daus. of Nile, 1953; mission work in Japan, 1964, Samoa, 1972. Mem. N.Mex. Assn. Ednl. Retirees, Coun. for Exceptional Children (state pres. 1963-65), Order Eastern Star (worthy matron 1938), Pi Lambda Theta (pres. 1958-60), Alpha Delta Kappa (pres 1968-70), Delta Kappa Gamma (pres. 1986-88), Kappa Kappa Iota (pres. 1990-93). Democrat. Baptist. Home: PO Box 697 Mesilla Park NM 88047-0697

SHUTT, RALPH B., research physicist. Rsch. scientist Brookhaven Nat. Lab., Upton, N.Y. Recipient W.K.H. Panofsky prize Am. Phys. Soc., 1993. Office: Brookhaven National Laboratory Upton NY 11973*

SHUTZ, BYRON CHRISTOPHER, real estate executive; b. Kansas City, Mo., Feb. 16, 1928; s. Byron Theodore and Maxine (Christopher) S.; m. Marilyn Ann Tweedie, Mar. 30, 1957; children: Eleanor S. Gaines, Byron Christopher, Collin Reid, Allison S. Moskow, Lindley Anne Baile. A.B. in Econs, U. Kans., 1949. Ptnr. Herbert V. Jones & Co., Kansas City, Mo., 1953-72; pres. Herbert V. Jones Mortgage Corp., Kansas City, 1967-72, The Byron Shutz Co., Kansas City, 1973—; dir. 1st Am. Financial Corp., Rothschild's, Inc. Chmn. bd. trustees U. Kansas City, 1979-81; trustee Pembroke-Country Day Sch., 1974-77, Midwest Rsch. Inst., 1980-89; chmn. bd. govs. Kansas City Art Inst., 1960-62; chmn. bd. dirs. Ctr. for Bus. Innovation, Inc., 1985-87; bd. dirs. Kansas City Crime Commn. 1st lt. USAF, 1951-53. Mem. Mortgage Bankers Assn. Am. (bd. govs. 1966-74), Am. Inst. Real Estate Appraisers. Clubs: Kansas City Country, University, Mercury (pres. 1978-79); Fla. Yacht (Jacksonville), Ocean Reef (Key Largo, Fla.). Home: 1001 W 58th Ter Kansas City MO 64113-1159 Office: 800 W 47th St Kansas City MO 64112-1251

SHUTZE, VIRGIL COX, advertising executive; b. May 16, 1944; children from previous marriage: Trip, Alec; m. Suzanne Shutze. BA, U. of South, 1968. Copywriter Sears Roebuck & Co., 1967-69, Henderson Advt., Greenville, S.C., 1969-71; exec. v.p., creative dir. MacDonald & Little, Atlanta, 1971-85; pres. Hutcheson Shutze, Atlanta, 1985-90; chief creative officer BBDO South, Atlanta, 1990—, also chmn. bd. dirs. Recipient over 100 creative awards including Cannes Gold Lion, 1988, 2 Clios, Silver Pencil award Brit. Design Art Dirs. Assn. Office: BBDO Atlanta 3414 Peachtree Rd NE Atlanta GA 30326-1113

SHWARTZ, ROBERT N., lawyer; b. Bklyn., Apr. 20, 1950; s. Morton and Joyce (Rosenthal) S.; m. Susan J. Greenberg, Feb. 22, 1992. BA, Syracuse U., 1972; JD, Columbia U., 1975. Bar: N.Y. 1976, D.C., U.S. Dist. Ct. (so. and ea. dists.) N.Y., U.S. Dist. Ct. (ea. dist.) Mich., U.S. Ct. Appeals (2d and 3d cirs.). Clk. to Hon. Orrin G. Judd U.S. Dist. Ct. (ea. dist.) N.Y., Bklyn., 1975-76; assoc. Curtis, Mallet, Prevost, Colt & Mosle, N.Y.C., 1976-77; asst. U.S. atty. U.S. Dist. Ct. (so. dist.) N.Y., N.Y.C., 1977-83; assoc. Debevoise & Plimpton, N.Y.C., 1983-84, ptnr., 1985-87, 88—; assoc. ind. counsel, Iran-Contra Office Ind. Counsel, Washington, 1987-88. Contbr. articles to profl. jours. Office: Debevoise & Plimpton 875 3rd Ave New York NY 10022

SHYER, CHARLES RICHARD, screenwriter, film director; b. Los Angeles, Oct. 11, 1941; s. Melville Shyer and Lois Jones. Co-writer: (films) Goin' South, 1977, Housecalls, 1978; co-writer, prodr.: (film) Private Benjamin, 1980 (Acad. Award nominee for screenplay 1981, Best Original Comedy award Writers Guild 1980); co-writer, dir.: (films) Irreconcilable Differences, 1984, Baby Boom, 1987, Father of the Bride, 1991, I Love Trouble, 1994, Father of the Bride II, 1995. Mem. ASCAP, Acad. Motion Picture Arts and Scis., Writers Guild Am., Writers Guild Am. West, Dirs. Guild Am.

SHYER, JOHN D., lawyer; b. Nashville, May 4, 1956; s. Michael and Hilda (Wertheim) S.; m. Marsha Anne Gisser. May 7, 1989. AB, Princeton U., 1978; JD, Stanford U., 1981. Bar: N.Y. 1982, U.S. Ct. Appeals (2d cir.) 1983, U.S. Ct. Appeals (3d cir.) 1992. Assoc. Donovan, Leisure, Newton & Irvine, N.Y.C., 1981-85; assoc. Latham & Watkins, N.Y.C., 1985-89, ptnr., 1989—. Trustee Princeton (N.J.) Broadcasting Svc., 1985—. Mem. Assn. Bar City N.Y. Avocations: traveling, hiking, reading. Office: Latham & Watkins 885 3rd Ave Ste 1000 New York NY 10022-4834

SHYLLON, PRINCE E.N., lawyer, law educator; b. Freetown, Sierra Leone, Nov. 3, 1943; came to the U.S.; s. Henry W.O. and Lois (Johnson) S.; m. Millicent Boutchway, June 8, 1974; children: Nicky H., Selwyn A. BA in Economics, Shaw U., 1972; JD Sch. of Law, N.C. Ctrl. U., Durham, 1975. Bar: N.C. 1977, U.S. Dist. Ct. (ea. dist.) 1978, U.S. Ct. of Appeals (4th cir.), 1978. Ptnr. Shabica, Shyllon & Shyllon, Raleigh, N.C., 1977-79, Shyllon, Shyllon & Ratliff, Raleigh, N.C., 1979-85; prof. Bus. Law and Ins. Saint Augustines Coll., Raleigh, N.C., 1975-91; ptnr. Shyllon & Shyllon, Raleigh, N.C., 1986—; university counsel St. Augustines Coll., 1992—. Mem. ABA, N.C. Acad. of Trial Lawyers. Home: 1101 Athens Dr Raleigh NC 27606-2420 Office: Shyllon & Shyllon 4002 Barrett Dr Raleigh NC 27609-6604

SHYY, WEI, aerospace, mechanical engineering researcher and educator; b. Tainan, Taiwan, China, July 19, 1955; came to U.S. 1979; s. Chiang-Chen and June-Hua (Chao) S.; m. Yuchen Shih; children: Albert, Alice, Andrew Chang, Kevin Chang. BS, Tsin-Hua U., Taiwan, 1977; MSE, U. Mich., 1981, PhD, 1982. Postdoctoral rsch. scholar U. Mich., Ann Arbor, 1982-83; rsch. scientist GE Corp. Rsch. and Devel. Ctr., Schenectady, N.Y., 1983-88; faculty mem. of aeronautics and astronautics Nat. Cheng-Kung U., Taiwan, 1987; assoc. prof. aerospace engring., mechanics and engring. sci. U. Fla., Gainesville, 1988-92, prof. aerospace engring., mechanics and engring. sci., 1992—; co-founder, pres. SCRAM Tech., Inc.; cons. numerous govt., fed. agencies U.S., Taiwan; lectr. in field. Author: Computational Modeling for Fluid Flow and Interfacial Transport, 1994; co-author: Computational Fluid Dynamics with Moving Boundaries, 1995; editor: Recent Advances in Computational Fluid Dynamics, 1989; reviewer U.S. govt., other govts., indsl. labs., profl. jours.; contbr. numerous articles to profl. jours. Bd. advisors Am. Biog. Inst., 1991—. Recipient GE Rsch. and Devel. Ctr. 1986 Pubs. award, Chinese Soc. of Mech. Engrs. 1987 Rsch. Paper award, NASA/ASEE 1991 Cert. of Recognition. Fellow AIAA (assoc.); mem. ASME Combustion and Fuel Com. 1984 Hon. Paper award), Combustion Inst., APS, TMS, Consortium of Computational Fluid Dynamics for Propulsion. Achievements include research in computational fluid dynamics, combustion and propulsion, gravity-induced thermofluid transport processes, materials processing and solidification, microgravity sciences and engring. contributions to gas turbine, hydraulic turbine, high pressure lamp and electronic cooling. Office: U Fla Dept Aerospace Engring 231 Aero Bldg Gainesville FL 32611

SIART, WILLIAM ERIC BAXTER, banker; b. Los Angeles, Dec. 25, 1946; s. William Ernest and Barbara Vesta (McPherson) Baxter; m. Noelle Ellen Reid, Sept. 17, 1966; children—Shayne Allison, Tiffany Ann. B.A. in Econs., U. Santa Clara, 1968; M.B.A., U. Calif., Berkeley, 1969. With Bank of Am., 1969-78; v.p. corp. banking Bank of Am., Brussels, 1977-78; sr. v.p. charge mktg. Western Bancorp, Los Angeles, 1978-81; pres., chief operating officer First Interstate Bank of Nev. N.A., Reno, 1981-82; pres., chief exec. officer First Interstate Bank of Nev. N.A., 1982-84, chmn. bd., pres., chief exec. officer, 1984; formerly chmn., pres., chief exec. officer First Interstate Bank Calif., L.A., also bd. dirs.; pres. First Interstate Bancorp, L.A., 1990—, CEO, 1994—. Trustee U. Nev.-Reno Found.; bd. dirs. Sierra Arts Found. Mem. Am. Bankers Assn. (mem. govt. relations council), Reno-Sparks C. of C. (dir.). Republican. Roman Catholic. Office: First Interstate Bancorp 633 W 5th St Los Angeles CA 90017-3501

SIAS, JOHN B., multi-media company executive; b. 1927. A.B., Stanford U., 1949. Group v.p. Metromedia Inc., 1962-71; with Capital Cities Communications, 1971-93; pres. Fairchild Pubs. Inc., 1971-75, exec. v.p., pres. pub. div., 1975-85; pres. ABC-TV Network Group, N.Y.C., 1986-93; also former exec. v.p. Capital Cities/ABC Inc.(parent), N.Y.C., pres., ceo Chronicle Pub. Co., San Francisco, 1993—. Served with AUS, 1945-46. Office: Chronicle Pub Co 901 Mission St San Francisco CA 94103 also: Capital Cities/ABC Inc 24 E 51st St New York NY 10022*

SIAU, JOHN FINN, wood scientist, educator; b. Detroit, Mar. 30, 1921; s. Robert H. and Marguerite L. (Finn) S.; children: John E., Mary M. B.S., Mich. State Coll., 1943; M.S., SUNY, Syracuse, 1964; Ph.D., SUNY-Syracuse, 1968. Engr. Utah Radio Products, Huntington, Ind., 1946-48; design engr. vacuum tubes Gen. Electric Co., Schenectady, 1948-58; prof. physics Paul Smith's (N.Y.) Coll., 1958-66; prof. wood products engring. SUNY Coll. Environ. Sci. and Forestry, Syracuse, 1966-85, emeritus prof., 1985-93; adj. prof. wood physics VPI, State U., Blacksburg, Va., 1993—; vis. prof. U. Aberdeen, U.K., 1978, Tech. U., Zvolen, Slovakia, 1994. Author: Flow in Wood, 1971, Transport Processes in Wood, 1984; editor: Wood and Fiber Sci., 1994. Served with USNR, 1943-46. Recipient Wood award 2d pl. Forest Products Research Soc., 1968. Mem. Forest Products Research Soc., Internat. Assn. Wood Anatomists, Soc. Wood Sci. and Tech., Tau Beta Pi. Roman Catholic. Club: Adirondack Mountain. Home: 1005 Kabrich St

Blacksburg VA 24060-3239 Office: Brooks Forest Products Ctr Va Poly Inst and State U Blacksburg VA 24061

SIBBALD, JOHN RISTOW, management consultant; b. Lincoln, Nebr., June 20, 1936; s. Garth E.W. and Rachel (Wright) S.; BA, U. Nev., 1958; MA, U. Ill., 1964; m. Kathryn J. Costick ; children: Allison, John, Wright. Office mgr. Hewitt Assocs., Libertyville, Ill., 1964-66; coll. rels. mgr. Pfizer Inc., N.Y.C., 1966-69; pres., chief exec. officer Re-Con Systems, N.Y.C., 1969-70; v.p. Booz, Allen & Hamilton, N.Y.C., 1970-73, Chgo., 1973-75; pres., founder John Sibbald Assocs., Inc., Chgo., 1975; mem. Nat. Advisory Coun., Nat. Club Assn. Author: The Career Makers, 1990, 92, 94; contbr. articles to profl. jours. Served to capt. AUS, 1958-64. Mem. Mid-Day Club Chgo., St. Louis Club. Episcopalian. Office: 8725 W Higgins Rd Chicago IL 60631-2702

SIBIGTROTH, JOSEPH CLARENCE, insurance company executive; b. Mendota, Ill., Nov. 29, 1915; s. Joseph and Alma (Leifheit) S.; m. Marjorie Ward, June 12, 1941; children: Alan, Joan. B.A., U. Ill., 1939, M.S., 1940. With Met. Life Ins. Co., N.Y.C., 1940-52; adminstrv. asst. N.Y. Life Ins. Co., N.Y.C., 1952-54; exec. asst. N.Y. Life Ins. Co., 1954-56, asst. v.p., 1956-57, actuary, 1957-59, 2d v.p., actuary, 1959-66, v.p., actuary, 1966-71, sr. v.p., chief actuary, 1971-81; cons. actuary, 1981—; dir. life ins. co. Served to lt. USNR, 1942-45. Fellow Soc. Actuaries; mem. Am. Acad. Actuaries. Lutheran. Home: 1075 Avocet Rd Delray Beach FL 33444

SIBLEY, ALDEN KINGSLAND, former organization executive, retired army officer; b. Tuscaloosa, Ala., Jan. 3, 1911; s. Frederick Hubbard and Annabelle (Pearson) S.; m. Elvira Trowbridge, Nov. 15, 1945; 1 child, Frederick Drake. Student, U. Nev., 1928-29; BS, U.S. Mil. Acad., 1933; BA, Oxford U., Eng., 1936, BSc, 1936, MA, 1943; postgrad., Engr. Sch., Ft. Belvoir, Va., 1937-38; grad., Nat. War Coll., 1957; doctoral study nuclear physics, George Washington U., 1955—; DSc, Coll. Advanced Sci., Canaan, N.H., 1962. Registered profl. engr. Mass. Commd. 2d lt. U.S. Army, 1933, advanced through grades to maj. gen., 1961; condr. sci. expdn. around world, 1935; bn. comdr. 1st Bn., 5th Engr. Regt. Ft. Belvoir, Va., 1936; mil. aide to pres., White House, 1937-38; exec. officer constrn. Conchas Dam N.Mex., 1938; chief, inspection constrn. John Martin Dam Colo., 1939; exec. officer St. Lawrence Seaway and Power Project, 1940-41; dist. engr. African Engr. Dist. Cairo, 1942, asst. chief staff G-4 (logistics), Middle-East Theater Ops., 1942; comdg. officer Eritrea and Tripoli Base commands N. Africa, 1943; chief Army component Joint Brit.-U.S. Operations Planning Group Middle East, 1943; dep. chief staff Middle East Theater Operations, 1943; exec. officer, asst. chief staff G-4 (logistics), SHAEF London, 1943-44; chief SHAEF Mission to France, 1944-45, dep. asst. chief staff G-4, War Dept. Gen. Staff, 1945, mem. joint logistics com. Joint Chiefs Staff, 1946, chief theaters br. Gen. Staff Army, 1946-48, chief ops. planning group Office Chief Staff Army, 1949, mil. sec. Army Policy Council, Office Sec. Army, also spl. asst. under sec. army for politico-mil. affairs, 1950-52; chief, logistic plans br. SHAPE Paris, 1952-55; dir. ednl. devel., faculty Nat. War Coll., 1955-57; chief staff U.S. del. for negotiations Fed. Republic of Germany Bonn, 1956; chief staff Philippine Base Negotiations Manila, 1956; div. engr. U.S. Army Engr. Div. New Eng., 1957-60; dep. chief Mil. Assistance Adv. Group Saigon, Vietnam, 1960-61; dep. chief engrs. Washington, 1961-62; comdg. gen. U.S. Army Mobility Command Center Line, Mich., 1962-64; dep. chief staff logistics, acting chief of staff U.S. Army Europe Heidelberg, Germany, 1964-66; comdg. gen. XI U.S. Army Corps St. Louis, 1966-67; dep. comdg. gen. 5th U.S. Army Chgo., 1967-68; exec. asst. to chmn. bd. Champion Internat. Corp., N.Y.C., 1968-74, Econ. Devel. Council, N.Y.C., 1974-78. Contbr. articles to profl. publs.; exhibited original oil paintings, Grand Palais, Société des Independents, 1954. Mem. Rhodes Scholarship selection com., Europe, 1954, Mass., 1958, Mich., 1963, Mo., 1966; dir. World Affairs Council, Boston ; bd. dirs. Isabel O'Neil Found. Decorated D.S.M., Legion of Merit, Bronze Star, Army Commendation ribbon with oak leaf cluster U.S.; Medal of Honor 1st class Vietnam; Order Brit. Empire; comdr. Legion of Honor; Croix de Guerre with palm France; recipient Diamond Jubilee Anniversary medal ASME, 1956, Author's award Automotive Industries, 1963-64; Rhodes scholar Oxford U., 1936. Mem. AAAS, ASME, Am. Def. Preparedness Assn., Armed Forces Mgmt. Assn., Assn. U.S. Army (pres. N.Y. chpt. 1972-73), Am. Soc. French Legion of Honor (exec. v.p., dir., chmn. exec. com., 1968-82), Pilgrims U.S., S.A.R., Nat. Aviation Hall of Fame, Soc. Am. Mil. Engrs. (founding pres. Saigon chpt., nat. dir., pres. Boston chpt. 1958-59), Soc. Am. Rhodes Scholars, Nat. Inst. Social Scis. (dir.), Chevaliers du Tastevin (grand officier), Sigma Xi, Phi Kappa Phi. Clubs: Army-Navy (Washington), Marco Polo (N.Y.C.). Home: 969 Park Ave New York NY 10028-0322

SIBLEY, CELESTINE (MRS. JOHH C. STRONG), columnist, reporter; b. Holly, Fla., May 23, 1917; d. W.R. and Evelyn (Barber) S.; m. James W. Little (dec. 1953); children: James W., Susan Little Bazemore, Mary Little Vance; m. John C. Strong (dec. 1988). Attended, U. Fla., Spring Hill Coll.; LHD (hon.), Spring Hill Coll. Columnist, reporter Atlanta Constitution, 1941—; twice juror Pulitzer Pirze newspaper awards. Author: The Malignant Heart, 1957, Peachtree Street, U.S.A.: An Affectionate Portrait of Atlanta, 1963, (stories) Christmas in Georgia, 1964, A Place Called Sweet Apple, 1967, Dear Store: An Affectionate Portrait of Rich's, 1967, Especially at Christmas, 1969, Mothers are Always Special, 1970, The Sweet Apple Gardening Book, 1972, Day by Day with Celestine Sibley, 1975, Small Blessings, 1977, Ah, Sweet Mystery: A Kate Mulcay Novel of Suspense, 1991, Straight As an Arrow: A Kate Mulcay Mystery, 1992, Dire Happenings at Scratch Ankle, 1993, A Plague of Kinfolks, 1995, others. Bd. vis. Grady Hosp.; mem. adv. bd. Neighborhood Justice Ctr.; mem. literary panel Ga. Coun. Arts; head fund appeal Atlanta Area Svcs. for Blind. Recipient Literary Achievement award Ga. Writers Assn., 1964, 2 Recognition awards Dixie Coun. Authors and Journalists, 2 AP awards, Radio and TV Big Story award Pall Mall, 2 awards Ga. Conf. Social Work, Nat. Christopher award, Wesley Woods award, Ralph McGill award Lifetime Achievement in Journalism by Soc. Profl. Journalists, numerous others; named Woman of Yr. in Arts, Atlanta, 1956. Democrat. Presbyterian. Office: Atlanta Constitution Metro Desk 72 Marietta St NW Atlanta GA 30303-2804

SIBLEY, CHARLES GALD, biologist, educator; b. Fresno, Calif., Aug. 7, 1917; s. Charles Corydon and Ida (Gald) S.; m. Frances Louise Kelly, Feb. 7, 1942; children: Barbara Susanne, Dorothy Ellen, Carol Nadine. A.B., U. Calif.—Berkeley, 1940, Ph.D., 1948; M.A. (hon.), Yale U., 1965. Biologist USPHS, 1941-42; instr. zoology U. Kans., 1948-49; asst. prof. San Jose (Calif.) State Coll., 1949-53; assoc. prof. ornithology Cornell U., 1953-59, prof. zoology, 1959-65; prof. biology Yale U., 1965-86, prof. emeritus, 1986—, William Robertson Coe prof. ornithology, 1967-86, emeritus, 1986—; dir. div. vertebrate zoology, curator birds Peabody Mus., 1965-86, dir. mus., 1970-76; Dean's prof. sci., prof. biology San Francisco State U., 1986-92; cons. systematic biology, 1963-65; mem. adv. com. biol. medicine NSF, 1968—; exec. com. biol. agr. NRC, 1966-70. Co-author: (with Jon Ahlquist) Phylogeny and Classification of Birds, 1990, (with Burt Monroe) Distribution and Taxonomy of Birds of the World, 1990; mem. editorial bd. Jour. Molecular Evolution, 1983—, Molecular Biology and Evolution, 1986—. Served to lt. USNR, 1943-45. Guggenheim fellow, 1959-60. Fellow AAAS; mem. NAS (Daniel Giraud Elliot medal 1988), Soc. Study Evolution, Am. Soc. Naturalists, Soc. Systematic Biology, Am. Ornithologists' Union (pres. 1986-88, Brewster Meml. medal 1971), Royal Australian Ornithol. Union, Deutsche Ornithol. Gesellschaft, Internat. Ornithol. Congress (sec.-gen. 1962, pres. 20th congress 1986-90). Home: 433 Woodley Pl Santa Rosa CA 95409

SIBLEY, DAVID EMILE, oil company executive; b. New Orleans, Nov. 24, 1935; s. John Meares and Esther (Wagner) S.; m. Diane Winstel, Jan. 25, 1958; children: David E., Michael S., Gregory M., Michele W. BS in Geology, La. State U., 1957; postgrad., Columbia U., 1977. Exploitation engr. Shell Oil Co., New Orleans 1957-62; with La. Land & Exploration Co., 1962—; v.p., gen. mgr. La. Land & Exploration Co., Houston, 1980-82; v.p. La. Land & Exploration Co. New Orleans, 1982-85, sr. v.p. prodn., 1985—; bd. dirs. S.E. U.S. IPAA. Bd. trustees Multiple Sclerosis Soc., New Orleans, 1983—. Mem. Soc. Petroleum Engrs., Am. Assn. Petroleum Geologists, Soc. Profl. Well Log Analysts, Petroleum Club of New Orleans (pres. 1989). Republican. Roman Catholic. Avocations: golf, hunting, snow skiing. Home: 16 Pontet Canet Kenner LA 70065 Office: La Land & Exploration Co 909 Poydras St New Orleans LA 70112-1017

SIBLEY, DAVID MCADAMS, state senator, lawyer, oral surgeon; b. Waco, Tex., Nov. 23, 1947; s. J Dale and Marilyn (McAdams) S.; m. Pam Patterson, Dec. 19, 1970; children: Rachel Anne, David Jr., Jonathan Patterson. BA, Baylor U., 1970, DDS, 1974, MSD, 1976, JD, 1989. Oral and maxillofacial surgeon Waco, 1978-85, pvt. practice, 1990—; mem. Tex. State Senate, Austin, 1991—. Commr. Commn. on Excellence in Edn., Waco, 1984; councilman Waco City Coun., 1984-87; mayor City of Waco, 1987-88. Rsch. fellow Am. Cancer Soc., 1976. Republican. Baptist. Avocations: golf, youth sports, coaching. Home: 411 Woodfall Waco TX 76712 Office: 3600 Chateau Waco TX 76710

SIBLEY, HORACE HOLDEN, lawyer; b. Phila., Oct. 13, 1939; s. John Adams and Barbara (Thayer) S.; m. Beverly Bryan, Mar. 18, 1961; children: Clare, Holden, Eve. BA, Vanderbilt U., 1961; LLD, U. Ga., 1964; MBA, Ga. State U., 1971. Bar: Ga. 1964, U.S. Supreme Ct. 1975. Assoc. King and Spalding, Atlanta, 1968-72, ptnr., 1972—; chmn. Ga. Ctr. for Advanced Telecomm. Tech.; bd. dirs. So. Ctr. for Internat. Studies, Atlanta Com. for Dynamic Curves. Trustee, mem. exec. com. Agnes Scott Coll., Atlanta, 1977; adv. trustee Henrietta Egleston Hosp. for Children, Atlanta, 1974-77, trustee, mem. exec. com., 1977—, chmn. bd. dirs., 1983-90; mem. exec. com. Atlanta Organizing Com. Summer Olympics, 1989—; chmn. bd. dirs. Butler St. YMCA, Atlanta, 1981; past bd. dirs. United Way, Nat. Assn. of Childrens' Hosp. and various other charitable orgns.; participant Leadership Ga., 1978, Leadership Atlanta, 1973, Soc. Internat. Bus. Fellows, 1982—; elder Trinity Presbyn. Ch., 1969-73. Capt. inf. U.S. Army, 1965-68, Germany. Mem. ABA, Ga. Bar Assn., Atlanta Bar Assn., World Trade Club Atlanta (bd. dirs. 1988—), Japan-Am. Soc. (bd. dirs. 1981-87), Rotary, Blue Key Svc. Soc., Phi Kappa Phi, Omicron Delta Kappa. Democrat. Presbyterian. Avocations: tennis, running, fishing. Office: King & Spalding 191 Peachtree St NE Atlanta GA 30303-1740

SIBLEY, JAMES MALCOLM, retired lawyer; b. Atlanta, Aug. 5, 1919; s. John Adams and Nettie Whitaker (Cone) S.; m. Karen Norris, Apr. 6, 1942; children: Karen Mariea, James Malcolm Jr., Jack Norris, Elsa Alexandria Victoria, Quintus Whitaker. A.B., Princeton U., 1941; student, Woodrow Wilson Sch. Law, 1942, Harvard Law Sch., 1945-46. Bar: Ga. 1942. Assoc. King & Spalding, Atlanta, 1942-47, ptnr., 1947-91; bd. dirs. Rock-Tenn. Co., Summit Industries, Inc.; dir. emeritus Life Ins. Co. of Ga.; exec. com., mem. pub. affairs com. Coca-Cola Co., 1979-91; chmn. exec. com. John H. Harland Co., 1963-91; chmn. exec. com., mem. compensation com. Trust Co. of Ga., 1975-92; mem. exec. com., mem. compensation com. SunTrust Banks, Inc., 1985-92. Trustee Joseph B. Whitehead Found., Lettie Pate Evans Found., Emory U., A.G. Rhodes Home, Inc., Robert W. Woodruff Found., Inc. (formerly Trebor Found.), John H. and Wilhelmina D. Harland Charitable Found., Inc.; bd. dirs. Callaway Gardens Found. With USAF, 1942-45. Mem. ABA, Ga. Bar Assn., Atlanta Bar Assn., Am. Coll. Probate Counsel, Am. Bar Found., Am. Law Inst. Episcopalian. Clubs: Piedmont Driving, Commerce. Home: 63 Peachtree St NE Atlanta GA 30309-3556 also: King & Spalding 191 Peachtree St NE Atlanta GA 30303-1763

SIBLEY, MARK ANDERSON, ophthalmologist; b. Daytona Beach, Fla., Sept. 15, 1950; s. John Rheney and Alyce K. (McDonald) S.; m. Sue Ellen White, Jan. 27, 1978; children: Paul Anderson, Laura Katherine. AA, Daytona Beach Jr. Coll., 1970; BA, U. Fla., 1972; MD, Meharry Med. Coll., Nashville, 1976. Diplomate Nat. Bd. Med. Examiners, Am. Bd. Ophthalmology. Intern, Orlando Regional Med. Ctr., Fla., 1976-77; resident U. Ala., 1977-80; fellow Eye Found. Hosp., Birmingham, Ala., 1980; ophthalmologist Suncoast Med. Clinic, St. Petersburg, Fla., 1980-92; chief med. staff Sunbay Hosp., 1983-85, staff ophthalmologist, 1980—, bd. trustees, 1983-85; mem. staff Bayfront Hosp. 1980-89, St. Anthony's Hosp., 1980-89; asst. clin. prof. U. South Fla., Tampa, 1982—; team eye physician Tampa Bay Lightning profl. hockey team, 1994, St. Petersburg Kids and Kids Softball, 1990—. Contbr. articles to profl. jours. Med. advisor Fla. Soc. Prevent Blindness, Tampa, 1981—; bd. dirs., 1982—; mem. Physician Edn. Network, St. Petersburg, 1981—; founding mem. OPTIC Found., 1986—, vice chmn. bd. trustees, 1986—; founding mem. Fla. Diabetic Retinopathy Task Force, 1986—, steering com. 1986—, pub. rels., com., 1986—, exec. com., 1989—; bd. dirs. Am. Diabetes Assn., Pinellas County, Fla., 1982—; bd. dirs. Suncoast Med. Clinic, 1980-92, also mem. exec. com., 1984-86; founder, med. dir. bd. dirs. Fla. Eye Ctr; founding mem. sec. Fla. Eye Specialists Network, IPA, Inc., 1993; co-founder Tampa Bay Health Plan HMO, 1983, Mercantile Bank, 1987. Recipient Blue Key award U. Fla., 1970, Physician Recognition, AMA, 1982, 85, 88, 91. Fellow ACS, Am. Acad. Ophthalmology (alt. mem. bd. councillors 1987-89); mem. AMA, Fla. Soc. Ophthalmology (pub. rels. com. 1981-91, exec. com. 1985-91, sec.-treas. 1986, pres. elect 1987-88, pres. 1988-89, past pres. 1989-90, chmn. Nat. Eye Health Care Month 1984—, Fla. bd. medicine liaison com., Fla. ins. liaison com.), Am. Soc. Contemporary Ophthalmology (Cert. Advanced Studies award 1982, 85, 88), Fla. Med. Assn., Am. Cataract and Refractive Surgery, Am. Coll. Eye Surgeons, Am. Intraocular Implant Soc., Soc. Geriatric Ophthalmology (named to Wisdom Hall of Fame, Wisdom award of honor), Internat. Soc. Refractive Keratoplasty, Internat. Acad. Sports Vision, Out Patient Ophthalmalic Surgery Soc., St. Petersburg C. of C. Republican. Roman Catholic. Avocations: biking, fishing, coaching Little League, karate. Office: Fla Eye Ctr 1515 9th Ave N Saint Petersburg FL 33705-1224

SIBLEY, WILLIAM ARTHUR, academic administrator, physics educator, consultant; b. Ft. Worth, Nov. 22, 1932; s. William Franklin and Sada (Rasor) S.; m. Joyce Elaine Gregory, Dec. 21, 1957; children: William Timothy, Lauren Shawn, Stephen Marshall. B.S., U. Okla., 1956, M.S., 1958, Ph.D., 1960. Teaching and rsch. asst. U. Okla., 1956-60; postdoctoral rsch. in defect solid state Kernforschungsanlage Julich and Tech. U. Aachen, Germany, 1960-61; rsch. solid state div. Oak Ridge Nat. Lab., 1961-70; prof., head physics Okla. State U., Stillwater, 1970-76; dir. Sch. Phys. and Earth Scis. Okla. State U., 1976-78, asst. v.p. rsch., 1978-88; program dir. NSF, Washington, 1988-89; acting div. dir. Div. Materials Rsch., 1990; v.p. acad. affairs U. Ala.-Birmingham, 1990—; mem. solid state sci. com. NAS, 1977-83; bd. dirs. Oak Ridge Assoc. Univs., 1982-88, Coun. on Govt. Rels., 1987-93, Okla. Ctr. for Advancement Sci. and Tech., 1987-88; trustee and chmn. materials rsch. counsel Southeastern Univ. Rsch. Assn., 1992—. Contbr. articles to profl. jours. Pres. Stillwater Indsl. Found., 1985-86. Served to lt. AUS, 1951-53; maj. Res. 1953-60. Fellow Am. Phys. Soc.; mem. Rotary Internat., Omicron Delta Kappa, Sigma Xi, Sigma Pi Sigma, Pi Mu Epsilon. Baptist. Home: 422 Delcris Dr Birmingham AL 35226-1979 Office: U Ala Birmingham Office Academic Affairs Birmingham AL 35294

SIBLEY, WILLIAM AUSTIN, neurologist, educator; b. Miami, Okla., Jan. 25, 1925; s. William Austin and Erna Johanna (Quickert) S.; m. Joanne Shaw, Sept. 4, 1954; children: John, Mary Jane, Peter, Andrew. B.S., Yale U., 1945, M.D., 1948. Intern Univ. Hosp., Cleve., 1948-50; asst. resident neurologist Neurol. Inst. Presbyn. Hosp., N.Y.C, 1953-55; chief resident neurologist Neurol. Inst., Cleve., 1956-63; assoc. prof. Western Res. U., Cleve., 1956-63; assoc. prof. Western Res. U., 1963-67; prof. U. Ariz. Coll. Medicine, Tucson, 1967—, head dept. neurology, 1967-82. Chmn. therapy com. Internat. Fedn. Multiple Sclerosis Soc., 1986-92. Served to capt. M.C. USAF, 1951-53. Recipient LaFayette B. Mendel prize in physiol. chemistry Yale U., 1945. Mem. Am. Neurol. Assn. (v.p. 1979-80), Am. Acad. Neurology (v.p. 1985-87), Central Soc. for Neurol. Research (pres. 1968). Helped establish effectiveness of beta-interferon therapy in multiple sclerosis. Home: 2150 E Hampton St Tucson AZ 85719-3810 Office: 1501 N Campbell Ave Tucson AZ 85724-0001

SIBLEY, WILLIS ELBRIDGE, anthropology educator, consultant; b. Nashville, Feb. 22, 1930; s. Elbridge and Elizabeth Reynolds (LaBarre) S.; m. Barbara Jean Grant, June 9, 1956; children: Sheila Katherine, Anthony Grant, Michael David. B.A., Reed Coll., 1951; M.A., U. Chgo., 1953, Ph.D., 1958. Instr. sociology and anthropology Miami (Ohio) U., 1956-58; asst. prof. anthropology U. Utah, 1958-60; from asst. prof. to prof. anthropology Wash. State U., 1960-71; prof. anthropology Cleve. State U., 1971—; chmn. dept., 1971-77, Cleve. (City) faculty fellow, 1987, interim chmn., 1989-90, prof. emeritus, 1990—; sr. program analyst EPA, Washington, 1977-78; Govtl. fellow Am. Coun. on Edn., 1978; Rockefeller Found. vis. prof. anthropology U. Philippines, Quezon City, 1968-69; postdoctoral fellow in society and tech. Carnegie-Mellon U., 1981-82. Fulbright grantee, 1954-55, 64; NIMH grantee, 1959-61; NSF grantee, 1964-71; Nat. Acad. Scis.-NRC travel grantee, 1966; Office Edn., HEW research grantee, 1967. Fellow AAAS, Am. Anthropol. Assn. (treas. 1989-91, alt. dir. Renewable Natural Resources Found.), Soc. Applied Anthropology (sec. 1977-80, pres. 1981-82); mem. AAUP (treas. Wash. State U. chpt. 1962-63, v.p. 1963-64, pres. 1965-66, pres. Cleve. State U. chpt. 1979-80, treas. 1980-81, interim pres. 1989-90), ACLU (pres. Pullman chpt. 1963, 66), Anthropol. Soc. Washington, Ctrl. States Anthropol. Soc. (past mem. exec. bd., treas. 1986-89), Wash. Assn. Profl. Anthropologists, Philos. Club Cleve. Home: 1190 Cedar Ave Shady Side MD 20764-9513 Office: Cleve State U Dept Anthropology Cleveland OH 44115

SICES, DAVID, language educator, translator; b. N.Y.C., June 10, 1933; s. Harry and Henrietta (Finger) S.; m. Joan Picker, May 25, 1956 (div. 1961); children: Laura, Harry J. AB, Dartmouth Coll., 1954, MA (hon.), 1971; PhD, Yale U., 1962. Instr. Dartmouth Coll., Hanover, N.H., 1957-62, asst. prof., 1962-67, assoc. prof., 1967-71, prof. French and Italian, 1971-75; prof. emeritus, 1995—; cons. NEH, Washington, 1986—, Can. Arts Council, Ottawa, 1979; mem. screening com. French Govt. Assistantships, N.Y.C., 1978-83. Author: Harmony of Contracts, 1968, Theater of Solitude, 1974; co-author: French Idioms, 1991; co-reviser: 2001 French Idioms, 1982; co-editor, translator: Comedies of Machiavelli, 1985; translator: Comedies and Proverbs of Musset, 1994. Fulbright-Hays fellow, Paris, 1956-57, Fulbright-Hays summer seminar, Rome, 1966; fellow Am. Council Learned Socs., 1969-70; humanities devel. grant Dartmouth Coll., Hanover, 1976. Mem. AAUP, Am. Literary Translators Assn., Am. Assn. Tchrs. French, Am. Assn. Tchrs. Italian, Dante Soc. Am. Avocations: music, travel, photography.

SICHERL, PAVLE, economics educator, consultant; b. Ljubljana, Slovenia, Yugoslavia, Feb. 16, 1935; s. Janko and Ana (Debeljak) S.; m. Jana Milava Primc, Aug. 11, 1962; children: Igor, Borut. Diploma in Econs., U. Ljubljana, 1960; MA, Williams Coll., Williamstown, Mass., 1962; PhD, U. Ljubljana, 1967. Economist Yugoslav Inst. Econ. Rsch., Belgrade, 1962-66; Hallsworth rsch. fellow U. Manchester, Eng., 1966-67; dep. dir. Yugoslav Inst. Econ. Rsch., Belgrade, 1967-68, acting dir., 1968-69; macroecon. advisor Harvard Inst. Internat. Devel., Addis Abeba, Ethiopia, 1970-74; prof. econs. U. Ljubljana Law Sch., 1975—; vis. prof. Williams Coll., Williamstown, 1980; vis. fellow Yale U., New Haven, 1986-87; vis. scholar Centre for the Study of Public Policy, Strathclyde U., Glasgow and Centre for Econ. Performance, London Sch. Econs., 1992-93, Inst. World Econs., Kiel, 1992-93; mem. Fed. Coun. Econ. Advisors, Belgrade, 1980-84; cons. UN, World Bank, Washington, 1987, 92, OECD, 1991; chmn. Subcom. Commn. Econ. Reform, 1988; dir. Sicenter, Ljubljana, 1993—. Author: Capital as a Factor of Economic Growth, 1971, Personality of Public Enterprise, 1981, Methods of Measuring Disparity Between Men and Women, 1989, Slovenia Now, 1990, Integrating Comparisons Across Time and Space, 1993. Recipient Sr. Fulbright rsch. award Fulbright Commn., 1986. Mem. Internat. Assn. Rsch. Income and Wealth, Am. Econ. Assn., Slovenian Statis. Soc., Slovenian Econ. Assn. Avocation: chess. Home: Brajnikova 19, 61000 Ljubljana Slovenia Office: U Ljubljana Faculty Law, Kongresni trg 12, 61000 Ljubljana Slovenia

SICHERMAN, MARVIN ALLEN, lawyer; b. Cleve., Dec. 27, 1934; s. Harry and Malvina (Friedman) S.; m. Sue Kovacs, Aug. 18, 1957; children: Heidi Joyce, Steven Eric. B.A., Case Western Res. U., 1957, LL.B., 1960, J.D., 1968. Bar: Ohio 1960. Mng. prin. Dettelbach, Sicherman & Baumgart, Cleve., 1971—. Editorial bd.: Case-Western Res. Law Rev, 1958-60; Contbr. articles to legal jours. Mem. Beachwood (Ohio) Civic League, 1972—; mem. Beachwood Bd. Edn., 1978-86, pres., 1981, 85, v.p.; trustee Beachwood Arts Council, 1977-84. Mem. ABA, Ohio Bar Assn. (lectr. truth in lending 1969, lectr. bankruptcy 1972, 81, 84; Meritorious Service awards 1971, 77, 78, 79, 83, 84, 85, 86, 87), Cleve. Bar Assn. (lectr. practice and procedure clinic 1960-80, 82-87, chmn. bankruptcy ct. com. 1971-73), Jewish Chautauqua Soc., Tau Epsilon Rho, Zeta Beta Tau. Jewish (trustee Temple brotherhood 1968-76, sec. 1971-73). Home: 24500 Albert Ln Cleveland OH 44122-2302 Office: Dettelbach Sicherman & Baumgart 1100 Ohio Savings Plz Cleveland OH 44114

SICILIANO, ELIZABETH MARIE, secondary education educator; b. Mansfield, Ohio, Apr. 22, 1934; d. Samuel Sevario and Lucy (Sferro) S. BS in Edn., Ohio State U., 1957; MA in Edn., Ea. Mich. U., 1971; MFA, Bowling Green U., 1975. Cert. tchr., Mich. Instr. adult edn. The Toledo (Ohio) Mus. Art, 1972-81; tchr. art Monroe (Mich.) Pub. Schs., 1975—; workshop facilitator, presenter in field. Artist, working in oils, pastels and fabricating jewelry. Judge Monroe Bicentennial, Monroe Arts and Crafts League, other shows. Mem. NEA, Mich. Edn. Assn., Nat. Art Edn. Assn., Mich. Art Edn. Assn., Stratford Festival for the Arts, Toledo Craft Club, Toledo Fedn. Art Socs., Toledo Mus. Art. Avocations: swimming, skiing, classic cars, designing and creating jewelry, portraiture and landscape in oils. Home: 7179 Edinburgh Dr Lambertville MI 48144 Office: Monroe High Sch 901 Herr Rd Monroe MI 48161

SICILIANO, ROCCO CARMINE, institute executive; b. Salt Lake City, Mar. 4, 1922; s. Joseph Vincent and Mary (Arnone) S.; m. Marion Stiebel, Nov. 8, 1947; children: Loretta, A. Vincent, Fred R., John, Maria. B.A. with honors, U. Utah, 1944; LL.B., Georgetown U., 1948; LHD, Hebrew Union Coll. Bar: D.C. bar 1949. Legal asst. to bd. mem. NLRB, Washington, 1948-50; asst. sec.-treas. Procon Inc., Des Plaines, Ill., 1950-53; asst. sec. labor charge employment and manpower Dept. Labor, Washington, 1953-57; spl. asst. to Eisenhower for personnel mgmt., 1957-59; ptnr. Wilkinson, Cragun & Barker, 1959-69; pres. Pacific Maritime Assn., San Francisco, 1969-69; undersec. of commerce Washington, 1969-71; pres., chmn. bd., chief exec. officer Ticor, Los Angeles, 1971-84; chmn., exec. com. Ticor, 1984-85; of counsel Jones, Day, Reavis & Pogue, 1984-87; chmn. bd., chief exec. officer Am. Health Properties, Inc., 1987-88; chmn. Dwight D. Eisenhower World Affairs Inst., Washington, 1991—; chmn. Ctr. for Govtl. Studies, 1992—; commr. Calif. Citizens Budget Commn.; bd. dirs. United TV, Inc.; mem. Fed. Pay Bd., 1971-73; trustee J. Paul Getty Trust. Bd. dirs. Eisenhower Inst., L.A. Philharm. Assn.; past chmn. Calif. Bus. Roundtable; trustee Com. for Econ. Devel.; co-chmn. Calif. Commn. on Campaign Financing; bd. govs. Cedars-Sinai Med. Ctr. 1st lt. AUS, 1943-46, MTO, ETO. Decorated Bronze Star; Order of Merit (Italy). Mem. Nat. Acad. Pub. Adminstrn., Met. Club (Washington), Calif. Club (L.A.). Home: 612 N Rodeo Dr Beverly Hills CA 90210-3208 Office: 918 16th St NW Ste 501 Washington DC 20006-2902 also: PO Box 2249 Beverly Hills CA 90213-2249

SICK, WILLIAM NORMAN, JR., investment company executive; b. Houston, Apr. 20, 1935; s. William Norman and Gladys Phylena (Armstrong) S.; m. Stephanie Anne Williams, Sept. 14, 1963; children: Jill Melanie, David Louis. BA, Rice U., 1957, BSEE, 1958. With Tex. Instruments Inc., Dallas, Washington, Phila., 1958-70; pres. Tex. Instruments, Asia Ltd., Tokyo, 1971-74; asst. v.p. strategic devel., gen. mgr. Europe Tex. Instruments, Dallas, 1974-77; v.p. group mgr. materials and elec. products Tex. Instruments, Attleboro, Mass., 1977-80; v.p. group mgr. consumer products Tex. Instruments, 1980-82; semicondr. products group Tex. Instruments Inc., Dallas, 1982-86; exec. v.p. Asia Pacific Region Tex. Instruments, Inc., Dallas, 1987; bd. dirs. Tex. Instruments, Inc., 1985-87; CEO Am. Nat. Can Co., Chgo., 1988-89 also bd. dirs. Nat. Can Co., Chgo., 1988-89; mem. exec. com. Pechiney, Paris, 1989; bd. dirs. Pechiney Internat., 1989; vice, chmn. bd. dirs. Triangle Industries, N.Y.C., 1988; chmn., CEO Bus. Resources Internat., Winnetka, Ill., 1989—; bd. dirs. Power Trends, Batavia, Ill., ShipNet, Lisle, Ill., Aware, Cambridge, Mass., Metasolv, Dallas; guest lectr. Sophia U., Tokyo, 1973. Chmn. bd. trustees Shedd Aquarium, Chgo.; exec. com. adv. bd. Brown Sch. Engring., Rice U., 1983-94. Mem. IEEE, Japan-Am. Soc., Chgo. Comml. Internat. Soc., Exec. Club Chgo., Glenview Club, Sigma Xi, Tau Beta Pi, Sigma Tau. Episcopalian. Office: Bus Resources Internat PO Box 500 Winnetka IL 60093-0500

SICKELS, ROBERT JUDD, political science educator; b. Nyack, N.Y., June 26, 1931; s. Robert and Dorothy (Judd) S.; m. Alice Esterer; children: Stephen Judd, Wendy. B.A., U. Chgo., 1950, M.A., 1954; Ph.D., Johns Hopkins U., 1960. Asst. staff dir. Pres.'s Commn. on Registration and Voting Participation, Washington, 1963-64; assn. dir. exec. insts. U.S. CSC, Washington, 1964-65; asso. prof. polit. sci. Purdue U., West Lafayette, Ind.,

1965-68; assoc. prof. polit. sci. U. N.Mex., Albuquerque, 1968-73; prof. U. N.Mex., 1973-95; prof. emeritus U. N.Mex., Albuquerque, 1995—; chmn. dept. U. N.Mex., 1976-81. Author: Race, Marriage, and the Law, 1972, Presidential Transactions, 1974, The Presidency, 1980, John Paul Stevens and The Constitution: The Search for Balance, 1988; contbr. articles to profl. jours. Home: 1514 Harvard Ct NE Albuquerque NM 87106-3712

SICKELS, WILLIAM LOYD, secondary educator; b. Porterville, Calif., Mar. 26, 1936; s. Roy Ernest and Lula Mae (Weaver) S.; m. Donna Louise Eilers; 1 child, Alan Michael. AA, Porterville (Calif.) Coll., 1956; BA, San Jose (Calif.) State U., 1960, MA, 1965. Tchr. Redwood High Sch., Visalia, Calif., 1962-68; instr. Victor Valley Coll., Victorville, Calif., 1968-70; athletic dir., tchr. Tulare (Calif.) Western High Sch., 1970—. Pres. Sequoia Lake Conf. of YMCA's (pres. 1990-91, bd. dirs. 1982—). With U.S. Army, 1960-62. Named to Hall of Fame Visalia YMCA, 1990, Man of Yr., 1984. Fellow Y's Men Internat. (pres. 1985—), Calif. State Athletic Dirs. Assn. (v.p. 1984-94, Athletic Dir. of Yr. 1981, pres. 1995-96). Republican. Methodist. Avocations: back-packing, hiking. Home: 2723 W Country Ave Visalia CA 93277 Office: Tulare Western High Sch 824 W Maple Tulare CA 93274

SICURO, NATALE ANTHONY, academic administrator; b. Warren, Ohio, July 19, 1934; s. Gaetano and Antonette (Montecalvo) S.; m. Linda Lou Rockman, Aug. 3, 1957; children: Michael, Christine, Paul. BS, Kent State U., 1957, PhD, 1964; MS in Pub. Health, U. N.C., Chapel Hill, 1958. Tchr., coach, recreation adminstr. schs. in N.E. Ohio, 1958-62; instr., grad. asst., teaching fellow Kent State U., 1962-64; asst. supt. Geauga (Ohio) County schs., 1964-65; dir. program planning, asst. dean regional campuses Kent State U., 1965-68, 70-72, dean continuing edn., assoc. provost med. affairs, 1972-78; sr. cons., mgr. Peat, Marwick, Mitchell, Washington and L.A., 1968-70; pres. So. Oreg. State Coll., Ashland, 1979-86, Portland State U. 1986-88, Roger Williams U., Bristol, R.I., 1989-93, Roger Williams U. Sch. Law, Bristol, 1992-93; Jones Disting. Univ. prof. Jones Inst. for Ednl. Excellence Tchrs. Coll., Emporia (Kans.) State U., 1993-94; pres. SICURO Ednl. Cons., 1994—; pres. Ohio Council Continuing Edn., 1975-76; bd. dirs. So. Oreg. Coll. Found., 1979-86; state rep., chmn. fed. relations com. Am. Assn. State Colls. and Univs., 1979-86, bd. dirs. 1987-88, chmn.-elect, 1988; chmn. Govtl. Relations Commn., Am. Council on Edn., 1983-86; mem. council of presidents Nat. Assn. Intercollegiate Athletics; chmn. council of presidents Evergreen Conf.; co-chmn. council of presidents Columbia Football League; dir. Rogue Valley Physicians Service. Pres. United Way of Jackson County, Oreg., 1982; bd. dirs. Ashland YMCA, 1980-81, Ashland Indsl. Devel. Corp., 1982-85; mem. Jackson County Econ. Devel. Com., 1981-86, Am. Council on Edn., 1986-87. Mem. Nat. Challenges Commn. Higher Edn., Ashland Rotary, Bristol Rotary, Phi Delta Kappa, Phi Kappa Phi. Roman Catholic. Office: 77628 Woodhaven Dr S Palm Desert CA 92211

SIDAMON-ERISTOFF, ANNE PHIPPS, museum official; b. N.Y.C., Sept. 12, 1932; d. Howard and Harriet Dyer (Price) Phipps; m. Constantine Sidamon-Eristoff, June 29, 1957; children—Simon, Elizabeth, Andrew. B.A., Bryn Mawr Coll., 1954. Chmn., bd. dirs. Am. Mus. Natural History, N.Y.C.; dir.-at-large Black Rock Forest Consortium; trustee God Bless Am. Fund. Bd. dirs. Greenacre Found., Highland Farm (N.J.) Pub. Libr., N.Y. Cmty. Trust, Storm King Art Ctr., Mountainville, N.Y., Nat. Coun. World Wildlife Fund; former bd. dirs. Scenic Hudson, St. Bernard's Sch., N.Y.C., Mus. Modern Art, N.Y.C., Mus. Hudson Highlands, World Wildlife Fund. Home: 120 East End Ave New York NY 10028-7552

SIDAMON-ERISTOFF, CONSTANTINE, lawyer; b. N.Y.C., June 28, 1930; s. Simon C. and Anne Huntington (Tracy) Sidamon-E.; m. Anne Phipps, June 29, 1957; children: Simon, Elizabeth, Andrew. B.S.E. in Geol. Engring. Princeton U., 1952; LL.B., Columbia U., 1957. Clk., then assoc. firm Kelley Drye Newhall Maginnes & Warren, N.Y.C., 1957-64; individual practice law N.Y.C., 1964-65, 74-77; exec. asst. to Congressman John V. Lindsay, 1964-65; city coordinator Lindsay Mayoral Campaign, N.Y.C., 1965; asst. to mayor City of N.Y., 1966, commr. hwys., 1967-68, transp. adminstr., 1968-73; ptnr. Sidamon-Eristoff, Morrison, Warren, & Ecker, N.Y.C., 1978-83; counsel Morrison & de Roos, 1984-88; pvt. practice N.Y.C., 1988-89; regional adminstr. Region II EPA, N.Y.C., 1989-93; of counsel Patterson, Belknap, Webb & Tyler, N.Y.C., 1993—; mem. N.Y. State Met. Transp. Authority Bd., 1974-89; commr. N.Y. State Jud. Commn. on Minorities, 1987-91; mem. Gov.'s Coun. on Hudson River Valley Greenway, 1989; trustee United Mut. Savs. Bank, N.Y.C., 1979-82; trustee Phipps Houses, N.Y.C., 1974—, chmn. 1986—. Trustee Allaverdy Found., N.Y.C., 1962—; Am. Farm Sch., Thessaloniki, Greece, 1973-79, Carnegie Hall, N.Y.C., 1967-92, Millbrook (N.Y.) Sch., 1971-89, hon. trustee, 1989—, Orange County (N.Y.) Citizens Found., 1974-81, Am. the Beautiful Fund (Washington), 1985—; bd. dirs. Caramoor Center for Music and Arts, Katonah, N.Y., 1961-80, Tolstoy Found., Inc., N.Y.C., 1975—, chmn., 1979-89, 94—, Boyce Thompson Inst. for Plant Rsch., Ithaca, N.Y., 1994—; bd. dirs., mem. exec. com. Mid-Hudson Pattern for Progress, Poughkeepsie, N.Y., 1975-89, chmn., 1981-85; bd. dirs. Coun. on Mcpl. Performance, N.Y.C., 1979-87, chmn., 1979-83, vice chmn., 1986, 87, N.Y. State Republican committeeman, 1980-89. Served to 1st lt. arty. AUS, 1952-54, Korea. Decorated Bronze Star; recipient Honor award Kings County chpt. N.Y. State Soc. Profl. Engrs., 1969, Honor award Greater N.Y. coun. Girl Scouts U.S., 1973, Board Leadership award Coun. Mcpl. Performance, 1984, Transp. Man of Yr. award Greater N.Y. March of Dimes, 1985, Award of Excellence Mid-Hudson Pattern for Progress, 1990, Honor award Nat. and N.Y. Parks and Conservation Assn., 1992, Bronze medal USEPA, 1993. Mem. ABA, N.Y. State Bar Assn., Assn. of Bar of City of N.Y., N.Y. County Lawyers Assn., Kent Moot Ct., AIME, Phi Delta Phi, Delta Psi. Eastern Orthodox. Clubs: Century Assn. (N.Y.C.), Knickerbocker (N.Y.C.), Racquet and Tennis (N.Y.C.). Office: Patterson Belknap Webb & Tyler LLP 1133 Ave of the Americas New York NY 10036-6710

SIDDAYAO, CORAZÓN MORALES, economist, educator; b. Manila, July 26, 1932; came to U.S., 1968; d. Crispulo S. and Catalina T. (Morales) S. Cert. in elem. teaching, Philippine Normal Coll., 1951; BBA, U. East, Manila, 1962; MA in Econs., George Washington U., 1971, MPhil, 1975; PhD., Inst. de Français, 1989. Tchr. pub. schs. Manila, 1951-53; asst. pensions officer IMF, Washington, 1968-71; cons. economist Washington, 1971-75; rsch. assoc. Policy Studies in Sci. and Tech. George Washington U., Washington, 1971-72, teaching fellow dept. econs., 1972-75; natural gas specialist U.S. Fed. Energy Adminstrn., Washington, 1974-75; sr. rsch. economist, assoc. prof. Nat. S.E.A. Studies, Singapore, 1975-78; sr. rsch. fellow energy/economist East-West Ctr., 1978-81, acad. staff coord. energy and industrialization, 1981-86; vis. fellow London Sch. Econ., 1984-85; sr. energy economist in charge energy program Econ. Devel. Inst., World Bank, Washington, 1986-94, ret., 1994; affiliate prof., econs. U. Hawaii, 1979—; vis. prof. econs. U. Philippines, intermittently 1989—; vis. prof. U. Montpellier, France, 1992; cons. internat. orgns. and govts. Author: Increasing the Supply of Medical Personnel, 1973, The Offshore Petroleum Resources of Southeast Asia: Some Potential Conflicts and Related Economic Factors, 1978, Round Table Discussion on Asian and Multinational Corporations, 1978, The Supply of Petroleum Reserves in Southeast Asia: Economic Implications of Evolving Property Rights Arrangements, 1980, Critical Energy Issues in Asia and the Pacific: the Next Twenty Years, 1982, Criteria for Energy Pricing Policy, 1985, Energy Demand and Economic Growth, 1986; editor: Energy Policy and Planning series, 1990-92, Energy Investments and the Environment, 1993; co-editor: Investissements Energetiques et Environnement, 1993; co-editor (series) Energy Project Analysis for CIS Countries (Russian), 1993, Materiel Pedagogique sur la Politique d'Efficacité de l'Energie et d'Efficacité de l'Energie et l'Environnement, Energy Efficiency Policy and Environment, 1994; contbr. chpts. to books, articles to profl. jours. Grantee in field. Mem. Am. Econ. Assn., Internat. Assn. Energy Economists, Alliance Francaise, Omicron Delta Epsilon. Roman Catholic.

SIDDERS, PATRICK MICHAEL, financial executive; b. Duluth, Minn., Oct. 19, 1940; s. Blaine L. and Elizabeth M. (Murphy) S.; m. Barbara E. Powers, Aug. 31, 1963; children: Patrick Michael, Kevin, Jennifer. B.A. in Bus. Adminstrn, St. Benedict's Coll., Atchison, Kans., 1963; postgrad., U. Minn. Grad. Sch. Bus. Adminstrn. Investment analyst Prudential Ins. Co., 1964-68; v.p. corp. fin. Dain Bosworth, Inc., Mpls., 1968-73; v.p. fin., treas. Modern Merchandising Inc., Minnetonka, Minn., 1973-79, exec. v.p., acting chief operating officer, 1979-81; pres. Modern Merchandising, Minnetonka,

Minn., 1982-83; also dir. Modern Merchandising Inc., Minnetonka, Minn.; pres., chmn. and chief exec. officer Drag Spltys., Inc., Minnetonka, 1983-89, also dir.; chief fin. officer Salkin & Linoff, Mpls., 1989-90; sr. v.p., mng. dir. corp. fin. John G. Kinnard & Co., Mpls., 1990-94; exec. v.p. adminstrn., CFO, dir. Casino Magic Corp., Bay St. Louis, Miss., 1994—. Mem. Fin. Execs. Inst. Republican. Roman Catholic. Home: 7636 Tahiti Cir Diamondhead MS 39525-3476 Office: 711 Casino Magic Dr Bay Saint Louis MS 39520

SIDDON, THOMAS EDWARD, Canadian government official, environmental consultant; b. Drumheller, Alta., Can., Nov. 9, 1941; s. Ronald Victor and Gertrude Violet (Humfrey) S.; m. Patricia Audrey Yackimetz, Sept. 1, 1962; children—Charles, David, Robert, Elizabeth, Katherine. BSME with distinction, U. Alta., 1963; MS in Aerospace Engring., U. Toronto, 1965, PhD in Aerodyn Noise, 1968. Assoc. prof. mech. engring. U. B.C., 1968-79; mem. House of Commons, Ottawa, Ont., Can., 1978-93; minister of state for sci. and tech. House of Commons, Ottawa, Ont., 1984-85, minister of fisheries and oceans, 1985-90, minister Indian Affairs and Northern Devel., 1990-93, min. nat. def., 1993; mem. Queen's Privy Coun., 1984; founder acoustical engring. firm and audiometric testing bus.; acoustical cons., Can.; U.S.; mem. priorities and planning com., 1988-93, environment, fed.-provincial rels. com., human rels. com., cultural affairs com.; lectr. environ. law and land use Okanagan U. Coll.; pres. Bonaccord Consulting Group. Alderman Twp. of Richmond, B.C., 1975-77. Recipient Assn. Profl. Engrs. award, 1978. Fellow Acoustical Soc. Am. Anglican. Office: Box 118, Kaleden, BC Canada V0H 1K0

SIDELLS, ARTHUR F., architect; b. Warren, Ohio, July 4, 1907; s. Byron T. and Mabel Ellen (Luce) S.; m. June Marie Isaly, Nov. 5, 1932; children: Stephen A., Stuart F. BArch, Carnegie Inst. Tech, 1931. Registered architect, Ohio, Pa., Fla., Calif. Pvt. practice Menlo Park, Calif.; vis. lectr. Kent State U.; alumni counselor Carnegie-Mellon U.; mem. Ohio State Bd. Examiners of Architects, 1961-72, pres., 1965, 66, 71; mem. Nat. Coun. Archtl. Registration Bds., 1964-68, chmn. pub. rels. com., chmn. nominating com, exam. com.; mem. Nat. Architect Accrediting Bd., 1967-74, pres., 1972-73, past pres., 1973-74. Prin. works include W.D. Packard Music Hall, Trumbull Regional Campus, Kent State U., Warren Western Reserve High Sch., Riverview Housing for Elderly, St. Joseph Hosp., Second Nat. Bank and Office Tower, Union Savings & Trust Eastwood Br.; contbr. articles to profl. jours. Charter pres. Warren Jaycees, 1933, 1st v.p. Ohio Jaycees, 1937; pres. Warren Rotary Club, 1950, Warren Community Chest, 1950-52. Recipient Sch. Exhibit awards AASA Convs., 1956-61, Spl. citation Pub. Edn., Geneva, Award of Merit Ohio Prestressed Concrete Assn., 1970, Thomas Jefferson medal Nat. Architect Accrediting Bd., 1985; established (with Stephen A. Sidells and Stuart F. Sidells) Carnegie Tradition Scholarship, Carnegie-Mellon U., 1986; Arthur F. Sidells Collection accepted into architecture archives, Carnegie-Mellon U., 1987. Fellow AIA (Ea. Ohio chpt. Gold medal award 1983); mem. SAR, The Buckeye Club (life, pres. 1958). Office: Arthur F Sidells Architect 1330 University Dr Apt 64 Menlo Park CA 94025-4242

SIDER, E(ARL) MORRIS, English, history educator, archivist; b. Cheapside, Ont., Can., Nov. 20, 1928; s. Earl Morris and Elsie (Sheffer) S.; m. Leone Dearing, Aug. 11, 1951; children: Karen Redfearn, Donna Gable. AB, Upland (Calif.) Coll., 1952, ThB, 1953; MA, U. Western Ont., London, 1955; PhD, SUNY, Buffalo, 1966. Ordained to ministry, Brethren in Christ Ch., 1954. Prin. Niagara Christian Coll., Ft. Erie, Ont., 1956-58; prof. history and English lit. Messiah Coll., Grantham, Pa., 1963—; mem. pubs. bd. Brethren in Christ Ch., 1958-61, Bd. Adminstrn., 1984-90, Bd. for Ministry and Doctrine, 1984—; asst. moderator, 1986-88, archivist, 1979—; com. mem. Ea. Mennonite Coll. and Sem., Harrisonburg, Va., 1990—; exec. bd. mem. Conf. on Faith and History. Editor Brethren in Ch. History and Life Jour., Grantham, Pa., 1978—; cons. editor Mennonite Quar. Rev., Goshen, Ind., 1986—; author: Messiah College: A History, 1984, The Brethren in Christ in Canada, 1988, Nine Portraits, 1978, A Vision for Service, 1976, others; contbr. articles to profl. jours. Recipient Excellence in Teaching award, Messiah Coll., 1987, Teaching Excellence and Campus Leadership award Sear-Roebuck, 1991; named Alumnus of the Yr., Niagara Christian Coll., 1983; Can. Coun. fellow, 1958-59. Mem. Can. Hist. Assn., Brit. Hist. Assn., Am. Hist. Assn. Office: Messiah Coll Grantham PA 17027

SIDER, HARVEY RAY, minister, church administrator; b. Cheapside, Ont., Can., June 20, 1930; s. Earl M. and Elsie (Sheffer) S.; m. Erma Jean Heise, July 20, 1957; children: Cheryl Sider Giles, Steven. BA, Western U., Ont., 1957; BD, Winona Lake Sch. Theology, Inc., 1962. Ordained to ministry Brethren in Christ Ch., 1953; cert. tchr., Ont. Pastor Brethren in Christ Ch., Toronto, Ont., 1957-61; missionary, adminstr. missions dept. Brethren in Christ Ch., Bihar, India, 1962-74; pastor Brethren in Christ Ch., Stayner, Ont., 1974-76; pres. Niagara Christian Coll., Ft. Erie, Ont., 1976-78; bishop Brethren in Christ Ch., Can., 1978-90; moderator Brethren in Christ Ch., N.Am., 1990—. Office: Brethren Christ Ch PO Box 290 Grantham PA 17027-0290

SIDER, RONALD J., theology educator, author; b. Stevensville, Ont., Can., Sept. 17, 1939; m. Arbutus Lichti Sider, Aug. 19, 1961; children: Theodore Ronald, Michael Jay, Sonya Maria. BA with honors, Waterloo Luth. U., 1962; MA in History, Yale U., 1963, BD, 1967, PhD in History, 1969. Lectr., asst. prof., then assoc. prof. Messiah Coll., 1968-78, acting dir., dean, 1971-75; assoc. prof. theology Ea. Bapt. Theol. Sem., Wynnewood, Pa., 1978-84, prof. theology, 1984—; coord., chair, convenor workshops in field; coord. Internat. Consultation on Simple Lifestyle, London, 1980; lectr. in field. Editor: Preaching on Peace, 1982, Lifestyle in the Eighties: An Evangelical Commitment to Simple Life-Style, 1982, Living More Simply, 1980, Cry Justice: The Bible on Hunger and Poverty, 1988, 91; author: Christ and Violence, 1979, Karlstadt's Battle with Luther: Documents in a Liberal-Radical Debate, 1978, 82, Evangelism, 1985, Rich Christians in an Age of Hunger: A Biblical Study, 1977, rev. edit., 1984, 90, German edit., 1979, Dutch edit., 1980, Portuguese edit., 1984, Japanese edit., 1989, Korean edit., 1995, Andreas Bodenstein Von Karlstadt, 1974, (with Richard K. Taylor) Nuclear Holocaust and Christian Hope, 1982, English edit., 1984, (with Oliver O'Donovan) Peace and War: A Debate About Pacifism, 1985, (in chinese) Evangelical Faith and Social Ethics, 1986, Completely Pro-Life, 1987, (with Michael A. King) Preaching About Life in Threatening World, 1988, (with Kathleen Hayes), JustLife/88: A 1988 Election Study Guide for Justice, Life and Peace, 1988, Testing the Limits of Nonviolence, 1988, One-Sided Christianity? Uniting the Church to Heal a Lost and Broken World, 1993, Cup of Water, Bread of Life: Inspiring Stories About Overcoming Lopsided Christianity, 1994; editor, contbr.: The Chicago Declaration, 1974; contbr. numerous articles to profl. publs., chpts. to books. Head voter registration dr., New Haven, 1967; pres. Diamont St. Cmty. Ctr., 1986-91; exec. dir. Evangelicals for Social Action, 1987-92, pres., 1992—; exec. dir. Just Life, 1987-91, pres., 1991-94; bd. dirs. Bread for the World, 1978-84, Mennonite Ctrl. Com., 1978-80; co-chair Nat. Workshop on Race and Reconciliation, Atlanta, 1975. Malcolm Chase fellow, 1962-63, R.E. Darlin fellow, 1963-64, fellow Yale U., 1967-68, Inst. for Advanced Christian Studies, 1976. Mem. Am. Acad. Religion (mem. social action commn. 1975—). Mennonite. Home: 312 W Logan St Philadelphia PA 19144 Office: Ea Bapt Sem 6 Lancaster Ave Wynnewood PA 19096

SIDES, JAMES RALPH, aerospace executive; b. Carbon Hill, Ala., Apr. 17, 1936; s. James Beatty and Ruby (Kilpatrick) S.; m. Martha Sue Ryland, Nov. 1, 1955; children: James R. Jr., Christopher Kent, Patrick Ryland. BS in Chemistry, U. Ala., 1958. Chemist Thiokol Chem. Corp., Huntsville, Ala., 1958-60; chemist, group leader Amcel Propulsion Co. (subs. Celanese), Asheville, N.C., 1960-65; head process engring., chief mfg. and engring., project office mgr. Atlantic Rsch. Corp., Gainesville, Va., 1965-69, dir. engring., 1969, asst. dir. propulsion div., mgr. engring dept., 1970-78, asst. gen. mgr. propulsion div., dir. engring. dept., 1978-80, v.p., gen. mgr. propulsion div., 1980-85, sr. v.p. gen. mgr. propulsion div., 1985-87, group pres., 1987—; bd. dirs. Atlantic Rsch. Corp., Prince William County Higher Edn. Bd.; mem. exec. com. Bendix-Atlantic Inflator Co. Contbr. articles to profl. jours.; patentee in field. Mem. Dulles Airport Task Force, Va., 1987. Recipient Cert. of Commendation USAF, 1964. Fellow AIAA (assoc., Wyld Propulsion award, 1989); mem. Am. Defense Preparedness Assn. (chmn. missiles and astronautics), Va. Mfrs. Assn. (bd. dirs.), Air Force Assn., Assn.

U.S. Army, Field Artillery Assn., Navy League, Alpha Chi Sigma. Home: 11133 Tattersall Trl Oakton VA 22124-1927 Office: Atlantic Rsch Corp 1577 Spring Hill Rd 600 Vienna VA 22182

SIDES, KERMIT FRANKLIN, furniture manufacturing company executive; b. Lee County, Miss., Feb. 13, 1932; s. Robert Franklin and Francis Jet (Cox) S.; grad. high sch., Wheeler, Miss.; m. Edna E. Heavener, Aug. 1, 1953; children: Connie Ann, Timothy Franklin. Mfg. supr. Futorian Mfg. Co., New Albany and Okolona, Miss., 1953-69; v.p. mfg., gen. mgr. Action Industries, Verona, Miss., 1969-79; exec. v.p., sec., treas. PeopLounger Inc., Nettleton, Miss., 1979—, also dir. Indsl. chmn. Lee United Neighbors div. United Way, Tupelo, Miss., 1969-73; v.p., bd. dirs. Northeast Miss. Community Relations Assn.; co-founder PeopLoungers, 1979. Recipient award for Outstanding Contbn. to Appearance of City, 1981. Baptist. Home: 2637 St Andrews Dr Belden MS 38826-9535 Office: PO Drawer 429 Nettleton MS 38858

SIDES, LARRY EUGENE, advertising executive; b. Albany, Ga., Nov. 14, 1946; s. Robert N. and Florine (Stewart) S.; m. Kathy Ashworth, Aug. 13, 1950. BA in Radio and TV, U. Southwestern La., 1970, MS in Communications, 1975. News reporter Sta. KATC-TV, Lafayette, La., 1970-71; account exec. Herbert S. Benjamin Assocs., Lafayette, La., 1971-76; pres. Sides & Assocs., Lafayette, La., 1976—. Vice chmn. Crimestoppers, Lafayette, 1985; bd. dirs. Episcopal Sch. Acadiana, Lafayette, 1987; pres. Gateway Found., 1990; active Leadership La., 1989. Named one of Outstanding Young Men of Am., Lafayette Jaycees, 1976. Mem. Am. Assn. Advt. Agys. (pres. La. coun., 1989-90), Am. Soc. Hosp. Pub. Rels., Pub. Rels. Soc. Am., La. Assn. Advt. Agys., Pub. Rels. Assn. La., Acadiana Advt. Fedn., Lafayette C. of C. (pres. 1989, Entrepreneur of Yr. 1983), Sigma Nu (alumni pres. Lafayette chpt. 1977). Club: Beaver (pres. 1986, Outstanding Club Mem. award 1976). Home: 1015 W St Mary Blvd Lafayette LA 70506-3420 Office: 404 Eraste Landry Rd Lafayette LA 70506-2324

SIDEWATER, ARTHUR, retired retail executive, consultant; b. Phila., June 15, 1914; s. Iaasic and Fanny S.; m. Estelle Czarzasty; children—June, Jacalyn. Founder, sr. exec. v.p. Charming Shoppes, 1940-89. Avocation: Woodworking. Home: 44 Parkview Rd Cheltenham PA 19012-1428 Office: Charming Shoppes Inc 450 Winks Ln Bensalem PA 19020-5919

SIDEY, HUGH SWANSON, correspondent; b. Greenfield, Iowa, Sept. 3, 1927; s. Kenneth H. and Alice Margaret (Swanson) S.; m. Alice Anne Trowbridge, Dec. 5, 1953; children—Cynthia Anne, Sandra, Bettina, Edwin. B.S., Iowa State U., 1950. Reporter Adair County (Iowa) Free Press, 1950, The Nonpariel, Council Bluffs, Iowa, 1950-51, Omaha World-Herald, 1951-55, Life mag., 1955-58; corr. Time mag., 1958—; columnist Time mag., Life mag. (The Presidency), 1966—; chief Time mag. (Washington Bur.), 1969-78, Washington contbg. editor, 1978—. Author: John F. Kennedy, President, 1963, A Very Personal Presidency, Lyndon Johnson in the White House, 1966, These United States, 1975, Portrait of a President, 1975, The Presidency, 1991; co-author: 1,000 Ideas for Better News Pictures, 1956, The Memories, 1961—JFK—1963, 1973; contbr.: The Kennedy Circle. Served with AUS, 1945-46. Office: 1050 Connecticut Ave NW Washington DC 20036-5303

SIDHU, JAY S., banking executive. CEO Sovereign Bancorp, Wyomissing, Pa. Office: Sovereign Bancorp Inc 1130 Berkshire Blvd Wyomissing PA 19610-1200

SIDLE, ROY CARL, research hydrologist; b. Quakertown, Pa., Oct. 31, 1948; s. Carl G. and Isabel (Ziegler) S.; children: Shelley, Bradley. BS, U. Ariz., 1970, MS, 1972; PhD, Pa. State U., 1976. Hydrologist Wright Water Engrs., Denver, 1972; rsch. asst. Pa. State U., University Park, 1972-76; rsch. soil scientist USDA-ARS, Morgantown, W.Va., 1976-78; watershed extension specialist Oreg. State U., Corvallis, 1978-80; rsch. hydrologist Forest Svc., PNW Rsch. Sta., USDA, Juneau, 1980-86; project leader (hydrologist) Forest Svc., INT Rsch. Sta., USDA, Logan, Utah, 1986—; adj. prof. Utah State U., Logan, 1986—; symposium chmn. Am. Soc. Agronomy, Anaheim, Calif. and Las Vegas, Nev., 1982; vis. fellow Japanese Forestry and Forest Products Rsch. Inst., 1991. Sr. author: Hillslope Stability and Land Use, 1985; assoc. editor Jour. of Environ. Quality, 1990—; contbr. numerous articles to profl. jours. Grantee, Water Resources Rsch. Inst., Oreg. State U., 1979, USDA-Forest Svc., Portland, Oreg., 1979, Am. Geophys. Union, 1982, Am. Philos. Soc., 1982; recipient Cert. of Merit, Chief, USDA-Forest Svc., 1989. Mem. Am. Soc. Agronomy, Soil Sci. Soc. Am., Am. Geophys. Union, Am. Water Resources Assn., Internat. Soc. Soil Sci., Sigma Xi, Gamma Sigma Delta. Avocations: skiing, weight lifting, baseball card collecting, antique collecting, biking. Office: USDA Forest Svc INT Sta 860 N 1200 E Logan UT 84321-3648

SIDLIN, MURRY, conductor. Studies with Sergio Celibidache, Leon Barzin. Resident condr. Nat. Symphony, 1973-77; music dir., condr. Long Beach Symphony Orch., 1979-88; asst., condr. Balt. Symphony; condr.-in-residence Aspen Music Festival, Oreg. Symphony; artistic dir. San Diego Summer Pops; dir. conducting series Aspen Music Festival; guest condr. St. Louis Symphony, Boston Pops, Pitts. Symphony, Milw. and Utah Symphony, Atlanta Symphony, Omaha Symphony, San Diego Symphony, Oregon Symphony, Miami Symphony, N.J. Symphony, Houston Symphony, Long Beach Opera, Que. Symphony, San Antonio Orch. and Opera, Houston and San Francisco Symphonies; host (children's TV series) 'Music Is'. Office: San Diego Symphony Orch 1245 Seventh Ave San Diego CA 92101 also: Shaw Concerts Inc 3436 Springhill Rd Lafayette CA 94549

SIDMAN, ROBERT JOHN, lawyer; b. Cleve., Aug. 4, 1943; s. Charles Frances and Louise (Eckert) S.; m. Mary Mato, July 29, 1967; children: Christa Mary, Alicia Mary. BA, Benedictine Coll., 1965; JD, U. Notre Dame, 1968. Bar: Ohio 1968, U.S. Dist. Ct. (so. dist.) Ohio 1970, U.S. Ct. Appeals (6th cir.) 1971, U.S. Supreme Ct. 1971. Law clk. U.S. Dist. Ct. (so. dist.) Ohio, Columbus, 1968-70; assoc. Mayer, Tingley & Hurd, Columbus, 1970-75; judge Bankruptcy Ct. U.S. Dist. Ct. (so. dits.) Ohio, Columbus, 1975-82; ptnr. Vorys, Sater, Seymour & Pease, Columbus, 1982—; prof. Ohio State U. Law Sch., Columbus, 1984, 85, 86. Mem. Nat. Conf. Bankruptcy Judges (bd. dirs. 1981-82), Assn. Former Bankruptcy Judges (bd. dirs. 1983-89, treas. 1986-87, pres. 1988-89). Office: Vorys Sater Seymour & Pease PO Box 1008 52 E Gay St Columbus OH 43215-3161

SIDNEY, SYLVIA (SOPHIA KOSSOW), actress; b. N.Y.C., Aug. 8, 1910; d. Victor and Rebecca (Saperstein) Kossow; m. Bennett Alfred Cerf, 1935 (div.); m. Luther Adler, 1938 (div.); 1 child, Jacob L.; m. Carlton Alsop, 1945 (div.). Attended, N.Y.C. pub. schs., Theater Guild Sch., 1925. Made stage debut starring as Prunella at the Garrick theater, 1926; subsequent stage appearances include The Challenge of Youth, Washington, 1926, The Squall, N.Y.C., 1927, Crime, 1927, Mirrors, 1928, The Breaks, 1928, The Gods of the Lightning, 1928, Nice Women, N.Y.C., 1929, Cross-Roads, 1929, Many a Slip, 1930, Bad Girl, 1930, To Quito and Back, N.Y.C., 1937, Pygmalion, 1938, The Gentle People, N.Y.C., 1939, Accent on Youth, 1941, Angel Street, 1942, 64, Pygmalion, 1943, Joan of Lorraine, 1947, Kind Lady, 1948, The Two Mrs. Carrolls, 1949, Pygmalion, 1949, O Mistress Mine, 1949, Goodbye My Fancy, 1950, Anne of the Thousand Days, 1950, Innocents, Black Chiffon, 1951, The Gypsies Wore High Hats, 1952, The Fourposter, 1952, A Very Special Baby, 1956, Auntie Mame, 1958, Enter Laughing, 1963, Silver Cord, 1964, Kind Lady, 1964, Come Blow Your Horn, 1968-69, Vieux Carré, Sabrina Fair, Morning's at 7, 1981, Shadow Box, 1981, Come Along with Me, 1981; appearances in Nat. Repertory Theatre plays includes The Rivals, 1965-66, The Little Foxes, 1966, The Importance of Being Earnest, 1966, She Stoops to Conquer, 1968; film career began in 1930; movie appearances include Beetlejuice, Summer Wishes Winter Dreams (Acad. award nominee for best supporting actress), I Never Promised You A Rose Garden, Accent on Youth, 30 Day Princess, Behold My Wife, Sabotage, 1/3 of a Nation, Damien: Omen 2, Hammett, City Streets, An American Tragedy, Street Scene, Merrily We Go to Hell, Mary Burns, Fugitive, Madame Butterfly, Trail of the Lonesome Pine, Fury, You Only Live Once, Dead End, The Searching Wind, Love from a Stranger, Les Miserables, Used People; TV appearances include My Three Sons, Whiz Kids, Magnum PI, Trapper John, M.D.; TV movies include The Shadow Box, 1980, Raid on Entebbe, 1977, Snowbeast, 1977, Siege, 1978, A Small Killing, 1981, An Early Frost, André's Mother, 1990 (Golden Globe nominee); author: Sylvia Sidney's Needlepoint Book, 1968, The Sylvia Sidney Question and Answer Book on Needlepoint, 1975. Bd. dirs. Nat. Amyotrophic Lateral Sclerosis Found. Avocations: needlepoint, reading, watching TV. Office: care John Springer 130 E 67th St New York NY 10021-6136

SIDO, KEVIN RICHARD, lawyer; b. Alton, Ill., Nov. 22, 1951; s. Robert Frederick and Mary (Colligan) S.; m. Mary O'Neil, July 28, 1984. BA, U. Ill., 1972, JD, 1975. Bar: Ill. 1975, U.S. Dist. Ct. (no. dist.) Ill. 1975, U.S. Tax Ct. 1976, U.S. Ct. Appeals (7th cir.) 1977, U.S. Supreme Ct. 1979. Assoc. Hinshaw, Culbertson, Moelmann, Hoban & Fuller, Chgo., 1975-82, ptnr., 1982—; lectr. Ill. Inst. Continuing Legal Edn., 1977—. Contbr. articles to profl. jours. Bd. dirs. Lake Barrington Shores (Ill.) Homeowners Assn., 1979. Mem. ABA, Ill. Bar Assn., Chgo. Bar Assn., Def. Research Inst. (state chmn. No. Ill. 1988—), Ill. Def. Counsel Assn. (bd. dirs. 1982-83, 87—, editor 1984-87), Internat. Assn. Def. Counsel, Phi Beta Kappa. Avocations: photography, antiques. Office: Hinshaw and Culbertson 222 N La Salle St Ste 300 Chicago IL 60601-1081

SIDRAN, MIRIAM, retired physics educator, researcher; b. Washington, May 25, 1920; d. Morris Samson and Theresa Rena (Gottlieb) S. BA, Bklyn. Coll., 1942; MA, Columbia U., N.Y.C., 1949; PhD, NYU, 1956. Rsch. assoc. dept. physics NYU, N.Y.C., 1950-55, postdoctoral fellow, 1955-57; asst. prof. Staten Island Community Coll., Richmond, N.Y., 1957-59; rsch. scientist Grumman Aerospace Corp., Bethpage, N.Y., 1959-67; prof. N.Y. Inst. Tech., N.Y.C., 1967-72; NSF rsch. fellow Nat. Marine Fisheries Svc., Miami, Fla., 1971-72; assoc. prof. then prof. physics Baruch Coll., N.Y.C., 1972-89, chmn. dept. natural scis., 1983-89, prof. emerita, 1990—; v.p. Baruch chpt. Profl. Staff Congress, 1983-89. Contbr. numerous articles to profl. and govtl. publs., chpts. to books. N.Y. State Regents scholar, 1937-41; NSF summer fellow, Miami, 1970. Mem. N.Y. Acad. Scis., Am. Assn. Physics Tchrs. Avocations: French and Hebrew languages, music, bicycling. Home: 210 W 19th St Apt 5G New York NY 10011-4009

SIDRANSKY, HERSCHEL, pathologist; b. Pensacola, Fla., Oct. 17, 1925; s. Ely and Touba (Bear) S.; m. Evelyn Lipsitz, Aug. 18, 1952; children: Ellen, David Ira. B.S., Tulane U., 1948, M.D., 1953, M.S., 1958. Diplomate: Am. Bd. Pathology. Intern Charity Hosp. La., New Orleans, 1953-54; vis. asst. pathologist Charity Hosp. La., 1954-58; practice medicine, specializing in pathology Washington, 1977—; pathologist Nat. Cancer Inst., NIH, Bethesda, Md., 1958-61; instr. pathology Tulane U., 1954-58; prof. pathology U. Pitts., 1961-72; prof., chmn. dept. pathology U. South Fla., Tampa, 1972-77, George Washington U., 1977—; cons. VA Hosp. and Children's Hosp., Washington. Mem. editorial bd. Jour. Nutrition, 1973-77, Cancer Research, 1974-77, Human Pathology, 1979-91, Am. Jour. Clin. Nutrition, 1979-82, Am. Jour. Pathology, 1980-85, Jour. Exptl. Pathology, 1982—, Exptl. Molecular Pathology Jour., 1987—; contbr. articles to profl. jours. Served with AUS, 1944-46. Life Ins. Med. Research fellow, 1956-57; USPHS fellow, 1957-58, 67-68; NIH research grantee, 1961—. Mem. Am. Soc. for Investigative Pathology, Soc. Exptl. Biology and Medicine, Am. Assn. Cancer Rsch., Am. Inst. Nutrition, Am. Soc. Clin. Nutrition, U.S.-Can. Acad. Pathologists, Med. Mycology Soc. Ams., Reticuloendothelial Soc., Assn. Pathology Chmn., Intersoc. Com. on Pathology Info., Sigma Xi. Home: 5144 Macomb St NW Washington DC 20016-2612 Office: 2300 I St NW Washington DC 20037-2337

SIEBEL, MATHIAS PAUL, mechanical engineer; b. Witten, Germany, Mar. 6, 1924; came to U.S., 1957, naturalized, 1962; s. Franz and Marie-Luise S.; m. Katherine Elizabeth Jente, May 27, 1960. B.S. in Mech. Engring, U. Bristol, Eng., 1949, Ph.D., 1952. From research and devel. engr. to asst. plant mgr. Tube Investments Ltd., Birmingham, Eng., 1952-57; research asso. Columbia U., N.Y.C., 1958-59; mgr. pressure equipment Pall Corp., Glen Cove, N.Y., 1959-64; v.p. ops. RDI Co., Westbury, N.Y., 1964-65; dir. mfg. engring. lab., then mem. sci. staff Marshall Space Flight Center, NASA, Huntsville, Ala., 1965-79; mgr. NASA Michoud Assembly Facility, New Orleans, 1979-87, cons., 1987—; assoc. dean Coll. Engring. U. New Orleans, 1989-92. Author. Mem. Sigma Xi. Patentee in field. Home: 5204 Janice Ave Kenner LA 70065-3238

SIEBENBURGEN, DAVID A., airline company executive; b. Cin., Sept. 18, 1947; s. Joseph and Elsie (Diersing) S.; m. Marcia Altieri, Sept. 27, 1974, 1 child, Brian. BBA, Xavier U., 1972. CPA, Ohio. Acct. Arthur Andersen & Co., Ohio, Ohio, 1974—; pres., COO Comair, Inc., Cin., 1984—. Mem. St. James Ch., Cin., 1980— Community Chest, Cin. Republican. Roman Catholic. Office: Comair Inc PO Box 75021 Cincinnati OH 45275-0021

SIEBER, SUZANNE MAHONEY, sales executive; b. Pitts., Apr. 18, 1963; d. John Patrick and Naomi Ruth (O'Neil) M.; m. Richard M. Sieber, Dec. 29, 1990. BS in Elec. Engr., Pa. State U., 1985; MS in Indsl. Adminstrn., Carnegie Mellon U., Pitts., 1990. Project mgr. Otis Elevator Co., Pitts., 1986, svc. sales rep., 1986-89, new equipment sales rep., 1989—. Dir. Canevin High Sch. Musical, Pitts. 1987. Mem. Am. Mktg. Assn., Western Pa. Soc. Engrs., Pitts. Ski Club, Pa. State Alumni Assn., Delta Delta Delta Alumni Assn. Democrat. Roman Catholic. Avocations: skiing, reading, theater. Home: 1441 Pueblo Dr Pittsburgh PA 15228 Office: Otis Elevator Co 50 13th St Pittsburgh PA 15222-4298

SIEBERT, CALVIN D., economist, educator; b. Hillsboro, Kans., Feb. 11, 1934; s. Ira and Margaret (Everett) S.; m. Valerie Dawn Nanninga, Feb. 18, 1960; children—Douglas Erik, Derek Christopher. BA, U. Kans., 1958, MA, 1960; PhD in Econs., U. Calif., Berkeley, 1966. Asst. prof. econs. U. Iowa, 1965-68, assoc. prof., 1968-75, prof., 1975—, chmn. dept., 1969-71, 75-79; Rockefeller Found. vis. asso. prof. U. Philippines, 1971-72. Contbr. articles to profl. jours. With U.S. Army, 1954-56. Ford Found. grantee, 1964-65. Mem. Am. Econ. Assn., AAUP, Phi Beta Kappa. Home: 341 N 7th Ave Iowa City IA 52245-6003 Office: U Iowa Dept Econs W276 Pbab Iowa City IA 52242

SIEBERT, DIANE DOLORES, author, poet; b. Chgo., Mar. 18, 1948; m. Robert William Siebert, Sept. 21, 1969. RN. Author: Truck Song, 1984 (Notable Children's Book award ALA, 1984, Sch. Libr. Jour. one of Best Books 1984, Outstanding Children's Book award N.Y. Times Book Rev. 1984, Reading Rainbow Selection book 1991), Mojave, 1988 (Children's Editor's Choice 1988, Internat. Reading Assn. Tchrs.' Choice award 1989, others), Heartland, 1989 (award Nat. Coun. for Social Studies/Children's Book Coun. 1989, on John Burroughs List Nature Book for Young Readers 1989, award Ohio Farm Bur. Women 1991), Train Song, 1990 (Notable Children's Book award ALA, 1990, Redbook Mag. one of Top Ten Picture Books 1990, one of Best Books award Sch. Libr. Jour. 1990, others), Sierra, 1991 (Outstanding Sci. Trade Book for Children award Nat. Sci. Tchrs.' Assn. 1991, Notable Children's Trade Book in Field Social Studies award Nat. Coun. Social Studies 1991, Beatty award Calif. Libr. Assn. 1992), Plane Song, 1993 (Outstanding Sci. Trade Book for Children 1994, Platinum award Oppenheim Toy Portfolio). Avocations: environmental affairs, running, classical guitar, motorcycle, animals. Home: PO Box 758 Terrebonne OR 97760-0758

SIEBERT, KARL JOSEPH, food science educator, consultant; b. Harrisburg, Pa., Oct. 29, 1945; s. Christian Ludwig and Katharine (Springer) S.; m. Sui Ti Atienza, Mar. 14, 1970; children: Trina, Sabrina. BS in Biochemistry, Pa. State U., 1967, MS in Biochemistry, 1968, PhD in Biochemistry, 1970. Chemist Applied Sci. Labs, State College, Pa., 1968-70; rsch. assoc. Stroh Brewery Co., Detroit, 1971, head R & D sect., 1971-73, mgr R & D lab., 1973-82, dir. rsch., 1982-90; prof. Cornell U., Geneva, N.Y., 1990—, chmn. dept. food sci. and tech., 1990-95; also assoc. dir. Cornell Inst. Food Sci. Cornell U., Ithaca, 1990-95. Contbr. articles to profl. jours. Bd. visitors Oakland U. Biology Dept., Rochester, Mich., 1985-89; bd. dirs. Cornell Rsch. Found., 1990—, Geneva Concerts Inc., 1991—. Capt. USAR, 1967-75. Recipient Presdl. award Master Brewers Assn., 1986, 90. Fellow NSF; mem. Am. Chem. Soc. (divsn. agrl. and food chemistry), Master Brewer Assn. Ams., Am. Soc. Brewing Chemists (chmn. tech. com. 1986-88, mem. edit. bd. 1983-91), Inst. Food Technologists, Internat. Chemometrics Soc. (N.Am. chpt.). Avocations: computers, electronics. Home: 9 Parkway St Geneva NY 14456-9765 Office: NY State Agrl Expt Sta Cornell U Dept Food Sci Geneva NY 14456

SIEBERT, MURIEL, business executive, former state banking official; b. Cleve.; d. Irwin J. and Margaret Eunice (Roseman) Siebert; student Western Res. U., 1949-52; DCS (hon.), St. John's U., St. Bonaventure U., Molloy Coll., Adelphi U., St. Francis Coll., Mercy Coll., Coll. New Rochelle, St. Lawrence U., Manhattan Coll. Security analyst Bache & Co., 1954-57; analyst Utilities & Industries Mgmt. Corp., 1958, Shields & Co, 1959-60; partner Stearns & Co., 1961, Finkle & Co., 1962-65, Brimberg & Co., N.Y.C., 1965-67; individual mem. (first woman mem.) N.Y. Stock Exchange, 1967; chmn., pres. Muriel Siebert & Co., Inc., 1967-77; trustee Manhattan Savs. Bank, 1975-77; supt. banks, dept. banking State of N.Y., 1977-82; dir. Urban Devel. Corp., N.Y.C., 1977-82, Job Devel. Authority, N.Y.C., 1977-82, State of N.Y. Mortgage Agy., 1977-82; chmn., pres. Muriel Siebert & Co., Inc., 1983—; assoc. in mgmt. Simmons Coll.; mem. adv. com. Fin. Acctg. Standards Bd., 1981-84; guest lectr. numerous colls. Former mem. women's adv. com. Econ. Devel. Adminstrn., N.Y.C.; former trustee Manhattan Coll.; v.p., former mem. exec. com. Greater N.Y. Area council Boy Scouts Am.; mem. N.Y. State Econ. Devel. Bd., N.Y. Coun. Economy; bd. overseers NYU Sch. Bus., 1984-88; former bd. dirs. United Way of N.Y.C.; trustee Citizens Budget Commn., L.I. U.; mem. bus. com. Met. Mus., bus. com. of N.Y. State Bus. Coun.; active Women's Campaign Fund; bd. dirs. N.Y. Women's Agenda. Recipient Spirit of Achievement award Albert Einstein Coll. Medicine, 1977; Women's Equity Action League award, 1978; Outstanding Contbns. to Equal Opportunity for Women award Bus. Council of UN Decade for Women, 1979; Silver Beaver award Boy Scouts Am., 1981; Elizabeth Cutter Morrow award YWCA, 1983; Emily Roebling award Nat. Women's Hall of Fame, 1984; Entrepreneurial Excellence award White House Conf. on Small Bus., 1986; NOW Legal Def. and Edn. Fund award, 1981, Brotherhood award Nat. Conf. of Christians and Jews, 1989, Women on the Move award Anti-Defamation League, 1990, award Borough of Manhattan, 1991, Benjamin Botwinick prize Columbia Bus. Sch.'s, 1992, Women in Bus. Making History award Women's Bus. Coun. N.Y. C. of C., 1993, Disting. Woman of the Yr. award Greater N.Y. Boy Scouts of Am., 1993, Woman of the Yr. award Fin. Women's Assn. N.Y., 1994, Medal of Honor award Ellis Island, 1994, Bus. Philanthropist of the Yr. award So. Calif. Conf. for Women Bus. Owner's, 1990, Corning Excellence award N.Y.S. Bus. Coun., 1993, Star award N.Y. Women's Agenda, Established Siebert Entrepreneurial Philanthropic Plan, N.Y. Urban Coalition's Achievement award, 1994, Women of Distinction award Crohn's and Colitis Found., Entrepreneurial Leadership award Nat. Found. Teaching Entrepreneurship, 1994; inductee Nat. Woman's Hall of Fame, Seneca Falls, N.Y., 1994, Internat. Women's Forum Hall of Fame, 1994. Mem. Women's Forum (founding mem., pres.), Com. 200, Fin. Women's Assn. (Community Svc. award 1993), River Club, Doubles Club, Westchester County Club, West Palm Beach Polo and Country Club, Nat. Assn. Women Bus. Owners (Veuve Clicquot Bus. Women of Yr. award 1992, Lifetime Achievement award 1993), Econ. Club. Home: 435 E 52nd St New York NY 10022-6445 Office: Muriel Siebert & Co Inc 885 3rd Ave New York NY 10022-4834

SIEBERT, THOMAS L., ambassador to Sweden; b. Cleve., May 2, 1946; m. Deborah Simpson; 4 children. BA, Georgetown U., JD. Intern Rep. Robert E. Sweeney, 1965-66; vol. Senator Robert F. Kennedy, 1966-68; aide Senator Carl Hayden, 1968-70; assoc. Pittman, Lovett, Ford & Hennessey, Washington, 1971-78; ptnr. Lovett, Ford, Hennessey, Stambler & Siebert, 1978-87; of counsel Besozzi & Gavin, 1987-93, Besozzi, Gavin & Craven, Washington, 1993; U.S. amb. to Sweden, 1993—. Bd. Regents Cath. U.; bd. visitors St. John's Coll.; active U.S. Naval Acad. Midshipmen Program, Md. Hall for the Creative Arts. Mem. ABA, D.C. Bar, Fed. Comm. Bar Assn., Annapolis Assn. Office: Am Embassy, Strandvagen 101, S-115 89 Stockholm Sweden

SIEBERT, WILLIAM MCCONWAY, electrical engineering educator; b. Pitts., Nov. 19, 1925; s. Charles Theodore Jr. and Isabel (McConway) S.; m. Anne Decker, Sept. 10, 1949; children: Charles R. (dec.), Thomas McC., Peter W., Terry A., Theodore D. SB, MIT, 1943, ScD, 1952. Jr. engr. Westinghouse Rsch. Labs., 1946-47; group leader Lincoln Lab. MIT, Cambridge, Mass., 1953-55, mem. faculty, 1952—, prof. elec. engring., 1963—; cons. to govt. and industry, 1952—. With USNR, 1943-46. Fellow IEEE; mem. Acoustical Soc. Am., Sigma Xi, Tau Beta Pi, Eta Kappa Nu. Research in applications of communication theory to radar and biol. systems. Home: 100 Keyes Rd Unit 304 Concord MA 01742-1633 Office: MIT 77 Massachusetts Ave Cambridge MA 02139-3594

SIEBRAND, WILLEM, theoretical chemist, science editor; b. Ijsselmuiden, Overijsel, Netherlands, Aug. 12, 1932; came to Can., 1963; s. Gerrit and Pietje (Brienne) S.; m. Elisabeth Kroon, Dec. 20, 1962; children—Barbara, Saskia. B.Sc., U. Amsterdam, 1956, M.Sc., 1960, Ph.D., 1963. Asst. research officer Nat. Research Council Can., Ottawa, Ont., 1963-66, assoc. research officer, 1966-72, sr research officer, 1972-83, prin. rsch. officer, 1983—. Editor Can. Jour. Chemistry, 1985—; assoc. editor Jour. Chem. Physics, 1977-79; mem. editorial bd. Chem. Physics Letters, Amsterdam, 1971—, Jour. Raman Spectroscopy, London, 1974—; author numerous articles. Trustee E.W.R. Steacie meml. fund. Recipient of Henry Marshall Tory Medal, 1991, Royal Soc. Can. Fellow Royal Soc. Can. (Henry Marshall Tory medal 1991); mem. Am. Phys. Soc., (corr. mem.) Royal Dutch Soc. Arts and Scis., Can. Inst. Chemistry. Home: 752 Lonsdale Rd, Ottawa, ON Canada K1K 0K2 Office: NRC Canada, Steacie Inst for Molecular Scis, Ottawa, ON Canada K1A 0R6*

SIECKMANN, WALTER, industrial manufacturing and engineering company executive; b. Duesseldorf, Germany, June 7, 1931; came to U.S., 1958; s. Heinrich and Erna (Neschen) S.; M.S. in Metallurgy, Tech. Hochschule Aachen, 1958; m. Edith Erdelyi, July 28, 1956; children—Michael, Martin. Metallurgist, Crucible Steel Co., 1958-59; project engr., dir. vacuum process dept. Lectromelt Corp., 1959-65, pres., 1967-69; exec. v.p. Heraeus-Engelhard Co., 1965-67; sr. v.p. Pa. Engring. Corp., 1967-69, exec. v.p., chief operating officer, 1969—; group exec. v.p. NVF Co., Sharon Steel Corp., Pa. Engring. Corp., 1983—; chief operating officer, exec. v.p., dir. Birdsboro Corp.; v.p., dir. Alaska Gold Co.; dir. Chesapeake Ins. Co., Ltd.; sr. v.p. DWG Corp.; sr. v.p., dir. Evans Products Co., Mueller Brass Co.; dir. Salem Corp., Sharon Steel Corp. Birdsboro Corp. Mem. Am. Iron and Steel Inst. (dir.), Am. Iron and Steel Engrs., AIME. Clubs: Duquesne, Univ. (Pitts.); St. Clair Country (Upper St. Clair, Pa.); Edeworth (Sewickley, Pa.). Home: Treetop Mnr # 5 Sewickley PA 15143-9355 Office: NVF Co PO Box 4055 Pittsburgh PA 15201-0055 also: NVF Co Yorklyn Rd Yorklyn DE 19736

SIEDLE, ROBERT DOUGLAS, management consultant; b. Canton, Ohio, Aug. 8, 1932; m. Beverly Rose Scholl, Mar. 18, 1972 (div. Oct. 1983). BA in Econs., Hiram Coll., 1956; profl. cert. edn., Kent State/Western Res. Univ., 1963. Tchr., prin. Ohio secondary schs., 1957-65; salesman, area rep. visual products divsn. 3M Co., 1966-68; mgr. market devel. and tng. AV divsn. Bell & Howell, 1968-69; Chgo. br. mgr. info. systems divsn. 3M, 1969-72; mgr. edn. systems divsn. Audiotronics Corp., 1972-76; gen. mgr. Niles Entertainment/Wardway Films, 1977-80; pres. The Ultimate Image, Lakeland, Fla., 1985—. Producer: (films) New Dimensions in Learning II, 1969, District 65: The Exceptional Child, 1969, Career Exploration: Health, 1976, The Wide World of Work, 1976; author: Multisensory Learning: A Training Guide, 1973, Alphabet Zoo, 1973, The Quick Job Hunt Guide, 1991; author, producer, dir.: (multimedia rd. show) "Rap" With Students, 1975; producer, editor: (film) Stampin' Ground, 1977; author poetry appearing in books and mags., 1983—; appeared on nat. radio and TV programs in U.S. and Can. Named Internat. Man of Yr., Internat. Biog. Ctr., Cambridge, Eng., 1992-93, recipient Internat. Order of Merit, 1993. Fellow Am. Biog. Inst. (Man of Yr. and Most Admired Man of Decade 1993); mem. Am. Biog. Inst. Rsch. Assn. (dep. gov. life), U.S. Naval Aviation Mus. (life), U.S. Naval Inst. (life), World Future Soc., Internat. Platform Assn. Baptist. Office: The Ultimate Image PO Box 91388 Lakeland FL 33804-1388

SIEDLECKI, PETER ANTHONY, English educator; b. North Tonawanda, N.Y., May 19, 1938; s. Anthony Paul and Mary Barbara (Litwin) S.; m. Rose Mary Murphy, June 25, 1960 (div. 1978); children: Christopher, Gregory, Jeffrey, William; m. Lynnette Noreen Mende, Apr. 26, 1980; children: Peter Emmanuel Mende-Siedlecki. BA, Niagara (N.Y.) U., 1960, MA, 1966; PhD, SUNY, Buffalo, 1982. Tchr. English Lewiston-Porter Sr. High Sch., Youngstown, N.Y., 1960-64, Grand Island (N.Y.) Sr. High Sch., 1964-65; prof. English Rosary Hill Coll., Amherst, N.Y., 1965-74, Daemen Coll., Amherst, 1974—; prof. Am. Lit. Jagiellonian U., Krakow, Poland, 1982-84, Friedrich-Schiller U., Jena, 1988-89. Author numerous poetry in jours. and revs.; contbr. articles to profl. jours. Fulbright Sr. lectr., Council for Internat. Exchange of Scholars, 1982-84, 88-89. Mem. MLA, Fulbright Alumni Assn. Democrat. Home: 249 Winspear Ave Buffalo NY 14215-1035 Office: Daemen College 4380 Main St Buffalo NY 14226-3592

SIEDLER, ARTHUR JAMES, nutrition and food science educator; b. Milw., Mar. 17, 1927; s. Arthur William and Margaret (Stadler) S.; m. Doris Jean Northrop, Feb. 23, 1976; children: William, Nancy Siedler Wilhite, Sandra Siedler Lowman, Roxanne Rose Butler, Randy Rose. BS, U. Wis., 1951; MS, U. Chgo., 1956, PhD, 1959. Chief div. biochemistry and nutrition Am. Meat Inst. Found., Chgo., 1959-64; group leader Norwich (N.Y.) Pharmacal Co., 1964-65, chief physiology sect., 1965-69, chief biochemistry sect., 1969-72; acting dir. div. nutritional scis. U. Ill., Urbana, 1978-81, head dept. food sci., 1972-89, prof. food sci., internal medicine and nutritional scis., 1972-94, prof. emeritus, 1994—. With USCG, 1945-46, PTO. NIH research grantee, 1960-63; Nat. Livestock and Meat Bd. grantee, 1959-64. Mem. Inst. Food Technologists, Am. Chem. Soc., Am. Inst. Nutrition, Coun. for Agrl. Sci. and Tech., Eagles, Moose, Rotary, Sigma Xi. Patentee in field. Home: 8 Stanford Pl Champaign IL 61820-7620 Office: 382M Ag Eng Sci 1304 W Pennsylvania Ave Urbana IL 61801-4726

SIEFER, STUART B., architect; b. Detroit, Nov. 28, 1942; s. Louis and Esther (Ressler) S.; m. Nancy Ann Feldman, Apr. 23, 1967; children: Eric S., Jeremy M., Ted B. BA, Wayne State U., 1965; postgrad., U. Detroit, 1965-68; BArch, Ariz. State U., 1971. Registered architect, Ariz. Designer, draftsman various firms, Detroit, 1966-68; rschr. Detroit Bd. Edn., 1967; archtl. designer Peace Corps, Tegucigalpa, Honduras, 1968-70; designer, job capt. various firms, Phoenix, 1970-73; prin. Siefer Assocs., Tempe, Ariz., 1973—. Bd. dirs. Downtown Tempe Community, Inc., 1993—; vol. bd. mem. Tempe Ctr. for Habilitation, 1993—; mem. Ariz. Town Hall, Phoenix, 1993—. Recipient 11 design awards Tempe Beautification Com., 1975—, merit & Crescordia award Valley Forward Assn. AIA Ariz., 1988, 93, Beautification award City of Mesa, Ariz. Mem. AIA (pres. Rio Salado chpt.), Rio Salado Architecture Found. (exec. mem.), Tempe C. of C. (pres. 1992-93) Found. (founding bd. mem. 1995). Avocations: jogging, skiing, hiking, tennis.

SIEFERS, ROBERT GEORGE, banker; b. Pitts., Aug. 28, 1945; s. George Francis and Idella Alice (Eiler) S.; m. Janice Lynn Kirkpatrick, Mar. 25, 1970; children—Robert Scott, Jillian Stewart. B.A., Mt. Union Coll., 1967; M.B.A., Kent State U., 1971; J.D., Cleveland Marshall Law Sch., 1976. Security analyst Nat. City Bank, Cleve., 1971-76, v.p., investment rsch. dir., 1976-80, v.p. administrn. and rsch., 1980-82; sr. v.p. corp. planning Nat. City Corp., Cleve., 1982-85; sr. v.p. corp. banking Nat. City Bank, Cleve., 1985-86; pres., chief exec. officer Ohio Citizens Bank (affiliate Nat. City Corp.), Toledo, 1986-90; exec. v.p., chief fin. officer Nat. City Corp., Cleve., 1990—; bd. dirs. HCR Corp. Republican. Presbyterian Club: Chagrin Valley Country. Home: 10 Pebblebrook Ln Chagrin Falls OH 44022-2380 Office: Nat City Corp National City Ctr Cleveland OH 44022

SIEG, ALBERT LOUIS, photographic company executive; b. Chgo., Mar. 25, 1930; s. Albert Fredrick and Louise Augusta (Sieg) S.; m. Irma Alice Spencer, Sept. 3, 1955; children—Karen, Diane, Susan. B.S. in Chemistry, U. Ill., 1951; Ph.D. in Organic Chemistry, U. Rochester, 1954; P.M.D., Harvard Bus. Sch., 1971. Supr. emulsion Eastman Kodak Co., Rochester, N.Y., 1970-72, corp. mgr. instant., 1972-76, mgr. paper mgf., 1976-81, v.p., dir., 1981-84; pres. Kodak Japan K.K., Tokyo, 1984-89; pres., rep. dir. Eastman Kodak Japan, Tokyo, 1989-91, also bd. dirs.; pres., rep. dir. Eastman Chems. Japan Ltd., Tokyo, 1989-91; v.p., dir. strategic resources, sec. imaging bd. Eastman Kodak Co., Rochester, 1991-92, ret., 1992; prin., cons. Albert L. Sieg Assocs., Rochester, 1992—; bd. dirs. Kodak Japan Industries, Ltd.; sr. lectr. U. Bennett, Oliver Wight) Tokyo Chronicles, How, 1972; co-author (with S. Bennett, Oliver Wight) Tokyo Chronicles, 1994; inventor in field. Bd. dirs., chmn. corp. gifts Rochester Philharm. Orch., 1982-84; chmn. corp. gifts Internat. Mus. Photography at George Eastman House, 1993; pres. Reformation Luth. Ch., Rochester, 1978-83; bd. dirs. St. John's Home for the Aging, 1994—, St. John's Nursing Home, 1994—. Served with Med. Svc. Corps, U.S. Army, 1955-57. Recipient George Eastman Medal Kodak Camera Clubs, 1980; Kiwanis Club Chgo. fellow, U. Ill., 1947-51; Am. Cyanamide fellow, 1953-54. Fellow Am. Inst. Chemists, Photog. Soc. Am. (v.p. 1969-84, Harold Lloyd award 1978); mem. Am. Chem. Soc., Soc. Photog. Scientists and Engrs., AAAS, Rochester C. of C., Am. C. of C. in Japan (bd. govs. 1988-91, v.p. 1989-91), Internat. Stereoscopic Union (pres. 1993). Republican. Club: American (Tokyo); Fgn. Correspondence. Avocations: skiing; photography; gardening. Home and Office: 159 Hillhurst Ln Rochester NY 14617-1938

SIEGAL, ALLAN MARSHALL, newspaper editor; b. N.Y.C., May 1, 1940; s. Irving and Sylvia Norma (Wrubel) S.; m. Gretchen M-P. Leefmans, May 31, 1977; children—Anna Marianita, Peter Bert. Grad., NYU, 1962. With New York Times, 1960—, editor Pentagon Papers, 1971, asst. fgn. editor, 1971-76, asst. to exec. editor, 1976-77, news editor, 1977-87, asst. mng. editor, 1987—, founding editor nat. edit., 1980; tchr. journalism NYU, 1966, Columbia U., 1967-69; juror Pulitzer Prize Nominating Com., 1987-89. Mem. Century Assn., Am. Soc. Newspaper Editors. Office: NY Times Co 229 W 43rd St New York NY 10036-3913

SIEGAL, BURTON LEE, product designer, consultant, inventor; b. Chgo., Sept. 27, 1931; s. Norman A. and Sylvia (Vitz) S.; m. Rita Goran, Apr. 11, 1954; children: Norman, Laurence Scott. BS in Mech. Engring., U. Ill., 1953. Torpedo designer U.S. Naval Ordnance, Forest Park, Ill., 1953-54; chief engr. Gen. Aluminum Corp., Chgo., 1954-55; product designer Chgo. Aerial Industries, Melrose Park, Ill., 1955-58; chief designer Emil J. Paidar Co., Chgo., 1958-59; founder, pres. Budd Engring. Corp., Chgo., 1959—; dir. Dur-A-Case Corp., Chgo.; design cons. to numerous corps. Holder more than 114 patents in more than 32 fields including multimemory for power seats and electrified office panel sys.; contbr. articles to tech. publs. Mem. math., sci. and English adv. bds. Niles Twp. High Schs., Skokie, Ill., 1975-79; electronic cons. Chgo. Police Dept., 1964. Winner, Internat. Extrusion Design Competition, 1975; nominated Presdl. Medal Technology Sen. Paul Simon and Rep. Dan Rostenkowski, 1986; named Inventor of Yr. Patent Law Assn. Chgo., 1986. Mem. ASME, Soc. Plastics Engrs., Soc. Mfg. Engrs., No. Ill. Indsl. Assn., Inventor's Coun., Soc. Automotive Engrs., Pres.'s Assn. Ill., Ill. Mfg. Assn. Office: 8707 Skokie Blvd Skokie IL 60077-2269

SIEGAL, JACOB J., management and financial consultant; b. Phila., Apr. 4, 1929; s. Louis and Henrietta (Greenberg) S.; m. Dolores Berg, June 8, 1952; children: Marla, Karen, Leslie. B.S., Temple U., 1951, LL.B., 1954; postgrad., U. Chgo., 1973. Bar: Pa. 1955, Ill. 1973. With City of Phila., 1954-61, chief counselor, 1959-61, dep. city solicitor, 1958-61; pvt. practice law, partner firm Meltzer & Schiffrin, Phila., 1961-72; v.p., gen. counsel, dir. Bluebird Inc., Phila., 1972-74; exec. v.p Bluebird Inc., 1974-78, pres., 1978-79, chmn., chief exec. officer, 1979; chmn. bd. Armen Cadillac-Osmobile, Inc. Mem. Am. Bar Assn., Am. Soc. Corp. Secs., Am. Meat Inst. (dir., conv. speaker 1978). Home: 101 Cheswold Ln Haverford PA 19041-1865 Office: PO Box 193 Plymouth Meeting PA 19462-0193

SIEGAL, RITA GORAN, engineering company executive; b. Chgo., July 16, 1934; d. Leonard and Anabelle (Soloway) Goran; m. Burton L. Siegal, Apr. 11, 1954; children: Norman, Laurence Scott. Student, U. Ill., 1951-53; BA, DePaul U., 1956. Cert. elem. tchr., Ill. Tchr. Chgo. Public Schs., 1956-58; founder, chief exec. officer Budd Engring. Corp., Skokie, Ill., 1959—; founder, pres. Easy Living Products Co., Skokie, 1960—; pvt. practice in interior design, Chgo., 1968-73; dist. sales mgr. Super Girls, Skokie, 1976; lectr. Northwestern U., 1983; guest speaker nat. radio and TV, 1979—. Contbr. to profl. jours. Mem. adv. bd. Skokie High Schs., 1975-79; advisor Cub Scouts Skokie coun. Boy Scouts Am. 1975; bus. mgr. Nutrition for Optimal Health Assn., Winnetka, Ill., 1980-82, pres., 1982-84; v.p. med./profl., 1985-93; leader Great Books Found., 1972; founder Profit Plus Investment, 1970; bd. dirs. Noha, Internat. Recipient Cub Scout awards Boy Scouts Am., 1971-72, Nat. Charlotte Danstrom award Nat. Women of Achievement, 1988, Corp. Achievement award, 1988. Mem. North Shore Women in Mgmt. (pres. 1987-88), Presidents Assn. Ill. (bd. dirs. 1990-94, membership chairperson 1991-93), No. Ill. Indsl. Assn., Ill. Mfrs. Assn.,

Inventors Coun. Office: Budd Engring Corp 8707 Skokie Blvd Skokie IL 60077-2269

SIEGAN, BERNARD HERBERT, lawyer, educator; b. Chgo., July 28, 1924; s. David and Jeannette (Seitz) S.; m. Sharon Goldberg, June 15, 1952 (dec. Feb. 5, 1985). AA, Herzl. Jr. Coll., Chgo., 1943, 46; Student, Roosevelt Coll., Chgo., 1946-47; J.D., U. Chgo., 1949. Bar: Ill. 1950. Practiced in Chgo.; partner firm Siegan & Karlin, 1952-73; pres., sec. various small corps. and gen. partner in partnerships engaged in real estate ownership and devel., 1955-70; weekly columnist Freedom newspaper chain, other papers, 1974-79; cons. law and econs. program U. Chgo. Law Sch., 1970-73; adj. prof. law U. San Diego Law Sch., 1973-74, prof., 1974-75, Disting. prof., 1975—; adj. scholar Cato Inst., Washington, 1991—, Heritage Found., 1992—; cons. windfalls and wipeouts project HUD, 1973-74; cons. FTC, 1985-86, U.S. Justice Dept., dir. constl. bibliog. project, 1986-88; keynote speaker 5th Internat. Conf. on Urbanism, Porto Alegre, Brazil, 1989; nominated by Pres. Reagan to U.S. Ct. Appeals (9th cir.) Feb. 2, 1987, confirmation denied July 14, 1988 by party line vote Senate Judiciary Com. Author: Land Use Without Zoning, 1972, Other People's Property, 1976, Economic Liberties and the Constitution, 1980, The Supreme Court's Constitution: An Inquiry Into Judicial Review and Its Impact on Society, 1987, Drafting A Constitution for a Nation or Republic Emerging into Freedom, 1992, 2nd edit. 1994, Portuguese, Ukranian, Polish and Spanish edits., 1993; Editor: Planning without Prices, 1977, The Interaction of Economics and the Law, 1977, Regulation, Economics and the Law, 1979, Government, Regulation and the Economy, 1980. Mem. pres.-elect's Task Force on Housing, 1980-81; mem. Pres.'s Commn. on Housing, 1981-82; mem. Nat. Commn. on bicentennial of U.S. Constn., 1985-91; chmn. adv. com. Affordable Housing Conf., San Diego, 1985, Rights of Regulated Conf., Coronado, Calif., 1976; chmn. Conf. on the Taking Issue, 1976; mem. Houston Regional Urban Design Team, Study of Houston, 1990; mem. U.S. team Bulgarian Econ. Growth and Transition Project, 1990; mem. devel. bd. Mingei Internat. Mus. World Folk Art, 1981-84. Served with AUS, 1943-46. Research fellow law and econs. U. Chgo. Law Sch., 1968-69; Urban Land Inst. research fellow, 1976-86; recipient Leander J. Monks Meml. Fund award Inst. Humane Studies, 1972, George Washington medal Freedom Founds. at Valley Forge, 1981, Spl. award Liberal Inst. of Rio Grande do Sul, Porto Alegre, Brazil, 1989. Home: 6005 Camino De La Costa La Jolla CA 92037-6519

SIEGEL, ABRAHAM J., economics educator, academic administrator; b. N.Y.C., Nov. 6, 1922; s. Samuel J. and Dora (Drach) S.; m. Lillian Wakshull, Dec. 22, 1946; children: Emily Jean Siegel Stangle, Paul Howard, Barbara Ann Pugliese. B.A. summa cum laude, CCNY, 1943; M.A., Columbia U., 1949; Ph.D., U. Calif., Berkeley, 1961. Instr. dept. econs. CCNY, 1947-49; research economist Inst. Indsl. Relations, U. Calif., Berkeley, 1952-54; instr. dept. econs. M.I.T., Cambridge, 1954-56, asst. prof., 1956-59, assoc. prof., 1959-64, prof. dept. econs. Sloan Sch. Mgmt., 1964-93, assoc. dean Sloan Sch. Mgmt., 1967-80, dean, 1980-87, prof. emeritus, sr. lectr., 1993—; spl. lectr. Trade Union Program, Harvard U., 1961-64; vis. prof. Brandeis U., 1956-60; vis. prin. mem. div. Internat. Inst. Labour Studies, Internat. Labor Office, Geneva, 1964-65; asso. staff dir. Com. Econ. Devel., Study Group on Nat. Labor Policy, 1960-61; trustee, chmn. administrv. com. M.I.T. Retirement Plan for Staff Mems., 1970—. Co-author: Industrial Relations in the Pacific Coast Longshore Industry, 1956, The Public Interest in National Labor Policy, 1961, The Impact of Computers on Collective Bargaining, 1969, Unfinished Business: An Agenda for Labor, Management and the Public, 1978. Bd. dirs. Whitehead Inst. Biomed. Rsch., Analysis Group, Inc., Internat. Data Group; mem. adv. group Internat. Inst. for Applied Systems Analysis, Laxenburg, Austria; mem. Framingham Sch. Com., South Middlesex Regional Dist. Sch. Com., 1968-71. With USAF, 1943-46. Mem. Am. Econ. Assn., Indsl. Relations Research Assn., Nat. Acad. Arbitrators, Am. Arbitration Assn. (mem. various panels), Inst. Mgmt. Scis. Bus. Roundtable (exec. com.), Phi Beta Kappa. Clubs: Comml, St. Botolph's. Home: 112 Gardner Rd Brookline MA 02146-4537 Office: MIT Sloan Sch Mgmt 50 Memorial Dr Cambridge MA 02142-1347

SIEGEL, ALLEN GEORGE, lawyer; b. Chgo., May 19, 1934; s. David Harry and Jeanette (Morris) S.; m. Rochelle Robin, Mar. 12, 1961; children: Dina Robin, Jonathan Joseph. B.B.A., CCNY, 1957; LL.B. with distinction, Duke U., 1960. Bar: Fla. 1960, D.C. 1965. Pvt. practice law Jacksonville, Fla., 1960-62; field atty. NLRB, 1962-64; assoc. Arent, Fox, Kintner, Plotkin & Kahn, Washington, 1964-70, ptnr., 1970-80, sr. ptnr., 1980—; sr. lectr. in law Duke U., Durham, N.C., 1979—. Author: Confidential Supervisors Guide to Labor Relations, 1980, Confidential Supervisors Guide to Equal Employment, 1981; contbr. articles. Past pres. United Cerebral Palsy D.C.; founder David H. Siegel Meml. Scholarship Duke U. Sch. Law, bd. dirs. pvt. ajudication ctr., 1986—; mem. bd. regents Cath. U. Am., 1990—; founder Rabbi Seymour Siegel Meml. Mott Ct. Competition Duke U. Law Sch.; founder Leanard Siegel Meml. Scholarship, Phillip M. Siegel Meml. Scholarship; gen. counsel Jewish Social Svc. Agy. Washington, United Cerebral Palsy Assn. Washington and No. Va. Mordecai Soc. scholar. Mem. ABA, Fla. Bar, D.C. Bar Assn., Am. Judicature Soc., Univ. Club Washington, Internat. Club Washington, Order of Coif. Republican. Jewish. Home: 7505 Connecticut Ave Chevy Chase MD 20815-4925 Office: Washington Square 1050 Connecticut Ave NW Washington DC 20036-5339

SIEGEL, ARTHUR, corporate executive; b. N.Y.C., July 4, 1908; s. Louis and Helena (Kaufman) S.; m. Mirian Bierman, Sept. 3, 1939; children—Barbara Joan Siegel Frankfort, Louise Susan Siegel Riordan. B.S., N.Y. U., 1930. Vice pres. Congress Financial Corp., N.Y.C., 1963-68 v.p., dir. Commonwealth United Corp., Chgo., 1969—; pres., dir. Williams Electronics Inc., Chgo., 1969—; sr. v.p., dir. Seeburg Corp., Chgo., 1968—, Inland Credit Corp., N.Y.C., 1953-63; v.p., dir. Indsl. Equipment Credit Corp., N.Y., 1948-53. Home: 437 Golden Isles Dr Hallandale FL 33009-7556 Office: 1500 N Dayton St Chicago IL 60622-2522

SIEGEL, BARBARA Z(ENZ), biology research scientist, educator; b. Detroit, July 22, 1931; d. Joseph and Barbara (Justh) Zenz; m. Sanford Marvin Siegel, June 24, 1950 (dec. 1990); children: Stephanie Siegel Morgan, Andrea, Peter Mark, David Nathaniel. AB in Philosophy, U. Chgo., 1960; MA in Zoology, Columbia U., 1963; PhD in Biology, Yale U., 1966. Postdoctoral fellow Yale U., New Haven, 1966-67; dir. biology program U. Hawaii, Honolulu, 1967-72, sr. researcher Pacific Biomed. Research Ctr., 1975-87, interim dir. research adminstrn., dean grad. sch., 1979-82, dir. pesticide hazard assessment project, 1983-87, prof. microbiology and botany grad. dept. pub. health, 1986-89, assoc. dean sch. pub. health, 1989—, dean Sch. Pub. Health, 1992—; prof. pub. health sci. and environ./occupational health Pacific Biomed. Rsch. Ctr., 1989—; had environ./occupational health Pacific Biomed. Research Ctr., 1989—; co-chmn. radiation sub-com. Com. Space Research Hdqrs., Paris, 1975-82; vis. prof. Heidelberg (Fed. Republic of Germany), 1973, Weizmann Inst. Rehovot, Israel, 1986, vis. prof. Geology, Botany, U. Brit. Columbia, 1982; vis. scholar People's Republic of China, 1985; vis. colleague Nat. Research Council of Italy, Pisa, 1987—; sr. lectr. Fulbrights-Hays, Finland, 1988. Editor: Hawaii Energy Resource Overviews: Geothermal Development, 1980; contbr. numerous articles to profl. jours. Chmn. Gov.'s Panel on Pesticides, Honolulu, 1985; mem. Commn. on Pesticides, Honolyly, 1986-88; mem. Peace Inst., Honolulu, 1985—; chmn. Masunnaga Inst. for Peace, 1992; mem. univ. commn. on status of women Hawaii Assn. Women in Sci. and Faculty Women's Caucus, 1986; co-investigator U.S./Israel Bionat., 1988—. Fulbright-Hays scholar, Yugoslavia, 1972; Fulbright rsch. fellow USIS, Yugoslavia and Fed. Republic of Germany, 1972-73; scholar to Finland, 1988-89. Mem. Am. Chem. Soc., Internat. Chem. Ecology Assn., Hawaii Acad. Scis. (chair 1993—), Sigma Xi (Disting. Nat. lectr. 1994-95, Cloptin award for Disting. Community Svc.). Avocations: arts, travel, internat. coop. Home: 3119 Beaumont Woods Pl Honolulu HI 96822-1421 Office: U Hawaii Sch Pub Health Biomed 208 Honolulu HI 96822

SIEGEL, BETTY LENTZ, college president; b. Cumberland, Ky., Jan. 24, 1931; d. Carl N. and Vera (Hogg) Lentz; m. Joel H. Siegel, June 6; children: David Jonathan, Michael Jeremy. B.A., Wake Forest Coll., 1952; M.Ed., U. N.C., 1953; Ph.D., Fla. State U., 1961; postgrad., Ind. U., 1964-66; honorate, Miami U., 1985, Cumberland Coll., 1985, Ea. Ky. U., 1992. Asst. prof. Lenoir Rhyne Coll., Hickory, N.C., 1956-59; assoc. prof., 1961-64; asst. prof. U. Fla., Gainesville, 1967-70; assoc. prof. U. Fla., 1970-72, prof., 1973-

76, dean acad. affairs for continuing edn., 1972-76; dean Sch. Edn. and Psychology Western Carolina U., Cullowhee, N.C., 1976-81; pres. Kennesaw State Coll. Marietta, Ga., 1981—; bd. dirs. Atlanta Gas Light Co., Equifax Inc., Nat. Services Industries, Acordia Benefits of the South Inc.; cons. numerous sch. systems. Author: Problem Situations in Teaching, 1971; contbr. articles to profl. jours. Bd. dirs. United Way Atlanta, Ga. Acad. Children and Youth Profls., Ga. Partnership for Excellence in Edn., Ga. Coun. Econ. Edn., Northside Hosp. Found., Atlanta Ballet. Recipient Outstanding Tchr. award U. Fla., 1969; Mortar Bd. Woman of Yr. award U. Fla., 1973, Mortar Bd. Educator of Yr., Ga. State U., 1983, CASE award, 1986, Alumna of Yr. award Wake Forest U., 1987, "Grad Made Good" award Fla. State U. Alumni Assn, Omicron Delta Kappa, 1991, Spirit of Life award City of Hope, 1992, Woman of Achievement award Cobb Chamber YWCA, 1992; named One of 100 Most Influential People in State of Ga., Ga. Trend Mag., Outstanding Alumni, Fla. State U. Coll. Edn. Alumni Assn., 1992. Mem. ASCD, Am. Psychol. Assn., Am. Assn. State Colls. and Univs. (bd. dirs., chmn. 1990), Am. Coun. Edn. (bd. dirs., bd. advisors), Am. Inst. Mng. Diversity (bd. dirs.), Soc. Internat. Bus. Fellows, Internat. Alliance for Invitational Edn. (co-founder, co-dir.), Bus./Higher Edn. Forum (mem. exec. com.), Assn. Tchr. Educators' Commn. on Leadership in Interprofl. Edn. (task force on tchr. edn.), Cobb C. of C. (chair-elect 1995), Phi Alpha Theta, Pi Kappa Delta, Alpha Psi Omega, Kappa Delta Pi, Pi Lambda Theta, Phi Delta Kappa, Delta Kappa Gamma, Kiwanis (Atlanta chpt.). Baptist. Office: Kennesaw State Coll Office of the President PO Box 444 Marietta GA 30061-0444

SIEGEL, CAROLE ETHEL, mathematician; b. N.Y., Sept. 29, 1936; d. David and Helen (Mayer) Schore; m. Bertram Siegel, Aug. 18, 1957; children: Sharon, David. BA in Math., NYU, 1957, MS in Math., 1959, PhD in Math., 1963. With computer dept. Atomic Energy Commn., 1957-59; rsch. asst. Courant Inst. of Math. Sci., 1959-63; rsch. scientist dept. of engring. NYU, N.Y.C., 1963-64; rsch. math. Info. Scis. Div. Rockland Rsch. Inst., Orangeburg, N.Y., 1965-74; head Epidemiology and Health Svcs. Rsch. Lab Stat. Scis., Epidemiology Divsn./Nathan S. Kline Inst. Rsch., Orangeburg, N.Y., 1974—; rsch. prof. dept. psychiatry NYU, 1987—; dep. dir. WHO Collaborating Ctr., Nathan S. Kline Inst., 1987—; grant reviewer NIHM, 1988—. Editor: (with S. Fischer) Psychiatric Records in Mental Health Care, 1981; contbr. articles to profl. jours. Recipient grants NIMH, 1993—, 88-91, Nat. Ctr. for Health Svcs. Rsch., 1979-82, Nat. Inst. Alcohol Abuse, 1978-82. Mem. Assn. for Health Svcs. Rsch., Am. Soc. Clin. Pharmacology and Therapeutics, Assn. Women in Math., Am. Statis. Assn. Avocations: pottery, gardening, cooking. Office: Nathan S Kline Inst Orangeburg NY 10962

SIEGEL, DAVID DONALD, law educator; b. Bklyn., Oct. 18, 1931; s. Harry Wilbur and Ida Claire (Scharaga) S.; m. Rosemarie Ann Duffy, Dec. 21, 1969; children: Sheela Nell, Rachel Ann. B.A., CUNY, 1953; J.D., St. John's U., 1958; LL.M., NYU, 1964. Bar: N.Y. 1958. Law sec. to chief judge N.Y. Ct. Appeals, 1958-59; practiced law N.Y.C., 1960-62; asst. prof. law St. John's U., 1962-65, asso. prof., 1965-67, prof., 1967-72; vis. prof., 1972-84, McNiece prof., 1984-90; prof. Albany Law St., 1972-84, disting. prof., 1990—; vis. prof. NYU, 1967-70, 84-85, 88-89, SUNY, Buffalo, 1971-72, Cornell U., 1978, Hofstra U., 1980, Albany Law Sch., 1984-90; adv., cons. on procedure Am. Arbitration Assn.; mem. N.Y. adv. com. on civil practice, 1979—, chmn., 1979-81. Author: New York Practice, 1978, 2d edit., 1991, Conflict of Laws in a Nutshell, 1982, 2d edit., 1994, Practising Law Inst. Monograph on Fed. Jurisdiction and Practice, ann. commentaries N.Y. civil practice McKinney's Consolidated Laws and fed. jurisdiction and practice U.S. Code Annotated and Federal Rules Decisions; editor: N.Y. State Law Digest, 1977—, Siegel's Practice Rev., 1993—; draftsman Appellate Division Handbook, 1979, Court of Appeals Handbook, 1981, 2d edit., 1991. Served with U.S. Army, 1953-55. Mem. Am. Law Inst., ABA, N.Y. State Bar Assn., Assn. Bar City N.Y. Jewish. Office: Albany Law Sch 80 New Scotland Ave Albany NY 12208-3494

SIEGEL, FREDERIC RICHARD, geology educator; b. Chelsea, Mass., Feb. 8, 1932; s. Louis and Eva (Minsky) S.; m. Felisa Matilde Puszkin, Mar. 3, 1962; children—Gabriela Davina, Galia Dinah. BA, Harvard U., 1954; MS, U. Kans., 1958, PhD, 1961. Prof. titular Universidad Nacional de Tucuman, Argentina, 1961-63; head geochemistry div. Kans. Geol. Survey, Lawrence, 1963-65; assoc. prof. geochemistry George Washington U., Washington, 1965-69, prof., 1969—; dir. geochemistry program, 1965—, chmn. dept. geology, 1976-86; tech. cons. UN Devel. program, Havana, Cuba, 1980. Author: Applied Geochemistry, 1974, Geoquímica Aplicada, 1992; editor: Review of Research on Modern Problems in Geochemistry, 1979. Served with U.S. Army, 1954-56; ETO. Recipient Erasmus Haworth award Dept. Geology, U. Kans., 1958; Fulbright prof., 1970, Best Paper award Energy Minerals div. Am. Assn. Petroleum Geologists, 1989. Mem. Assn. Exploration Geochemists (councillor 1988-95), Soc. Econ. Paleontology and Mineralogists, Geochem. Soc., Internat. Assn. Geochemists and Cosmochemists, Soc. Mining Engrs., Inc. (editor geochemistry divsn. 1989-90), Soc. Environ. Geochemistry and Health. Jewish. Home: 4353 Yuma St NW Washington DC 20016-2027 Office: George Washington U 2029 G St NW Washington DC 20006-4211

SIEGEL, GEORGE HENRY, international business development consultant; b. Bklyn., Oct. 8, 1926; s. Samuel S. and Sara (Kaplan) S.; m. Lenore D. Greenberg, Oct. 28, 1951; children: Arthur B., Ellen S. B.S.E.E., CCNY, 1948; M.S. in Indsl. Engring, NYU, 1951. Registered profl. engr., N.Y. From engr. to gen. mgr. Gen. Electric Corp., Syracuse, Utica and Binghamton, N.Y., 1951-74; v.p., gen. mgr. flight systems div. Bendix Corp., Detroit, 1974-77, chief tech. officer, 1977-79, v.p., gen. mgr. diesel engine controls, 1979-82; v.p. group exec. Bendix Automation Co., Cleve., 1983-84; v.p. tech. Allied-Signal Internat., Morristown, N.J., 1984-90; pres. Point North Assocs., Inc., Madison, N.J., 1990—; v.p. Volt Tech. Svcs. Co., N.Y.C., 1991-93; invited guest lectr. UCLA, 1960-63. Bd. visitors Oakland U., Rochester, Mich., 1977-83. Served with AUS, 1944-46. Mem. IEEE (sr., sect. chmn. 1965), Soc. Automotive Engrs. Office: Point North Assocs Inc PO Box 907 Madison NJ 07940-0907

SIEGEL, HERBERT BERNARD, certified professional management consultant; b. N.Y.C., Mar. 10, 1934; s. Jacob and Clara Dora (Goldgeier) S.; m. Joan Miriam Goodkin, Nov. 6, 1955; children—Jeffrey Roy, Lori Robin, Amy Hope, Jonathan Stuart. Degree, N.Y. U., 1959, postgrad. in bus., 1960-63; postgrad. in bus., Harvard U., 1975; PhD candidate, Columbia Pacific U., 1995. With William Iselin & Co., Inc., N.Y.C., 1957-67; treas. Bates Mfg. Co., Inc., N.Y.C., 1968; pres. Emle Industries, Inc., N.Y.C., 1968-72; fed. trustee Interstate Stores, Inc., N.Y.C., 1973-78; pres. Nat. Silver Co., N.Y.C., 1973-78. F.B. Rogers Silver Co., N.Y.C., 1979-82; pres., chief exec. officer Quaker City Steel Co., 1980-86, Seal-Kap Packaging Co., N.Y.C., 1980-90, J. Ramsey Reese, Inc., Tarrytown, N.Y., 1980-87; exec. v.p. Deerhill Devel. Corp., 1980-87, Columbia Profl. Baseball Club, Inc., 1980-87; pres., chief exec. officer J.R. Reese Enterprises, Ltd., 1989-90, New Swissco, Inc., 1991; pres. T.P.C.C.-Brandon, Inc., 1991—; prin. officer Whitestone Cons. Group, Ltd., 1991—; trustee Dime Savs. Bank of Williamsburg, N.Y.C.; thesis examiner Grad. Sch. Banking, Rutgers U., 1963-64; lectr. Grad. Sch. Mgmt. and Orgn., Yale U.; bd. dirs. N.Y. Pacific Exch. Ltd., Silvergull Industries Inc. Author: A Trustee's View of Chapter Ten, 1981, Tomorrow's America, Made Today in the U.S.A., 1993, The Masquerade of Cost Cutting, 1995, The Entropy of Government Deficits, 1995. Bd. dirs. United Cerebral Palsy, Nassau, N.Y. Served with AUS, 1955-57. Mem. NYU Alumni Club, Turnaround Mgmt. Assn., Prime Raters Fin. Club (pres.), Am. Mensa Soc., Am. Consultants League. Home: 515 E Bay Dr Long Beach NY 11561-2409

SIEGEL, HOWARD JEROME, lawyer; b. Chgo., July 29, 1942; s. Leonard and Idele (Lehrner) S.; m. Diane L. Gerber; children: Sari D., Alison J., James G. BS, U. Ill., 1963; JD, Northwestern U., 1966. Bar: Ill. 1966, U.S. dist. Ct. (no. dist.) Ill. 1967. Assoc., Ancel, Stonesifer & Glink, Chgo., 1966-70; ptnr. Goldstine & Siegel, Summit, Ill., 1970-75; sole practice, Chgo., 1975-77; pres. Wexler, Siegel & Shaw, Ltd., Chgo., 1978-82; ptnr. Keck, Mahin & Cate, Chgo., 1982—; village atty. Willow Springs, Ill., 1973-75, Westhaven, Ill., 1973-75, Harwood Heights, Ill., 1967-70; ptnr. various corps. Mem. Deerfield Sch. Bd., Ill., 1978-80. Mem. ABA, Chgo. Bar Assn., Ill. Bar Assn., Internat. Council Shopping Ctrs., Urban Land Inst., Chgo. Real.Es-

tate Bd. Clubs: Standard (Chgo.); Ravisloe Country (Homewood, Ill.). Office: Keck Mahin & Cate 77 W Wacker Dr Ste 4900 Chicago IL 60601-1693

SIEGEL, IRA T., publishing executive; b. N.Y.C., Sept. 23, 1944; s. David Aaron and Rose (Minsky) S.; m. Sharon Ruth Sacks, Sept. 5, 1965. BS, NYU, 1965; MBA, L.I. U., 1968. Bus. mgr. Bothenheim Pub. Co., N.Y.C., 1965-72; corp. v.p. rsch. Cahners Pub. Co. div. Reed Pub. USA, Boston, 1972-86; pres., COO R.R. Bowker Pub. Co. div. Reed Pub. USA, New Providence, N.J., 1986-91; pres. Martindale-Hubbell div. Reed Pub. USA, New Providence, N.J., 1990-91, Reed Reference Pub. (includes R.R. Bowker Co., Martindale-Hubbell, Nat. Register Pub. Co., The Salesman's Guide, Marquis Who's Who), New Providence, N.J., 1991—; pres., CEO, 1993-95; pres. Lexis-Nexis, Dayton, Ohio, 1995—. Mem. Am. Mktg. Assn., Am. Mgmt. Assn., ALA, Am. Booksellers Assn., Info. Industry Assn. Office: Lexis-Nexis Mead Data Control PO Box 933 Dayton OH 45401

SIEGEL, JACK MORTON, retired biotechnology company executive; b. Sioux City, Iowa, June 11, 1922; s. Harry and Rose (Perlman) S.; m. Betty Virginia Collins, Feb. 22, 1946 (dec. Feb. 1986); children: Jennifer L. Mastricola, Marjorie G., Thomas A.; m. Dolores E. Williams Kinert, Dec. 20, 1991. BS in Chemistry, UCLA, 1944; PhD in Chemistry, Washington U., St. Louis, 1950. Chemist The Clinton Labs., Oak Ridge, Tenn., 1944-46; asst. prof. chemistry U. Ark. Sch. Medicine, Little Rock, 1950-55; chemist, v.p. P-L Biochems. Inc., Milw., 1955-82; v.p., gen. mgr. Pharmacia P-L Biochems. Inc., Milw., 1982-87, pres., 1987-89. Contbr. articles to profl. jours. Mem. AAAS, Am. Chem. Soc. Democrat. Jewish.

SIEGEL, JACK S., federal official; b. Long Branch, N.J., June 2, 1946; s. Joseph and Idene (Boss) S.; m. Shari Diane Goodman, June 12, 1971; children: Erica Robyn, Adam Michael. BSChemE, Worcester Poly. Inst., 1968; postgrad., George Washington U. Chem. engr. Dept. of the Navy, Indian Head, Md., 1968-71; supervisory chem. engr. EPA, Washington, 1971-76; asst. dir. for environ. planning and assessment U.S. Energy R & D Adminstrn., Washington, 1976-77; dir. office of environ. policy Dept. of Energy, Washington, 1977-83, dep. dir. for coal utilization, advanced combustion and gasification, 1983-84, dep. asst. sec. for coal tech., 1984—; fed. rep. to Nat. Coal Assn., 1986—; dir. tech. panel Innovative Control Tech. Adv. Panel, Washington, 1987-89; speaker in field. Mem. Am. Inst. Chem. Engrs., Washington Coal Club. Jewish. Avocations: exercise, racquetball. Office: Dept Energy Coal Tech 1000 Independence Ave SW Washington DC 20585-0001

SIEGEL, JEFFREY NORTON, lawyer; b. N.Y.C., Nov. 27, 1942; s. George Siegel and Rose (Friedman) Gerber; m. Judith Sharon Chused, June 11, 1966; children: Daniel, Linda. AB, Brown U., 1964; LLB, Harvard U., 1967. Bar: N.Y. 1968. Assoc., ptnr. Golenbock & Barell, N.Y.C., 1967-89; ptnr. Whitman & Ransom, N.Y.C., 1990-93, Shack & Siegel, P.C., N.Y.C., 1993—. Mem. bus. com. The Jewish Mus. Mem. ABA, Assn. Bar City N.Y. (com. securities regulation 1987-90, com. profl. responsibility 1979-84), Phi Beta Kappa. Home: 25 Valley Ln Chappaqua NY 10514-2005 Office: Shack & Siegel PC 530 5th Ave New York NY 10036-5101

SIEGEL, JOEL STEVEN, television news correspondent; b. Los Angeles, July 7, 1943; s. Robert and Libby (Kantor) S.; m. Jane Kessler, Nov. 21, 1976 (dec. 1982); m. Melissa Nina De Mayo, Aug. 27, 1985 (div.). BA, UCLA, 1965, postgrad., 1966-67. Copywriter, producer Carson & Roberts Advt., Los Angeles, 1967-72; freelance writer Rolling Stone mag., Los Angeles Times, others, 1967-77; news anchorman Sta. KMET-FM, Los Angeles, 1972; corr. Sta. WCBS-TV, N.Y.C., 1972-76; corr., film critic Sta. WABC-TV, N.Y.C., 1976—, Good Morning America, N.Y.C., 1980—. Author: (Broadway mus.) The First, 1981 (Tony award nomination 1981). Dir. voter registration drive SCLC/Dr. Martin Luther King, Macon, Ga., 1965; joke writer Robert F. Kennedy, 1968. Served with USAR, 1967-73. Recipient 5 Emmy awards, numerous nominations Nat. Acad. TV Arts and Scis. (N.Y. chpt.). Freedom award B'nai Brith/Anti-Defamation League, 1976. Mem. AFTRA, Dramatists Guild, Drama Desk. Democrat. Jewish. Office: Good Morning Am 147 Columbus Ave New York NY 10023-5900

SIEGEL, LAURENCE GORDON, conductor; b. N.Y.C., July 23, 1931; s. Jacob and Esther (Gordon) S.; m. Luz M. Morales, Oct. 15, 1959; 1 child, Carla. BA, CCNY, 1953; MusM, New Eng. Conservatory Music, 1955. Worked with Boris Goldovsky and Leonard Bernstein Berkshire Music Ctr.; Dr. Fritz Stiedry; condr. Orquesta Sinfonica del Salvador; Symphony of the Air, N.Y.C.; condr. Orquesta Sinfonica de Las Palmas, Spain, Manila Met. Philharm. Orch. and Opera Assn., Teatro Sperimentale di Spoleto (Italy), Belgrade (Yugoslavia) Symphony, Filharmonica de Stat Oradea (Romania), Honolulu Orch., Shreveport (La.) Festival Orch., Alexandria (Va.) Symphony, Jacksonville (Fla.) Symphony and Opera Co., 1975-85, Conn. Grand Opera Co.; music dir., condr. Puccini Festival Orch., Italy, Italy, 1984; condr. Orch. of the Radio Assn. Italiana, Milan, 1985-95; music dir. North Miami Beach (Fla.) Symphony, 1976—; recorded with various record labels including Audio Team, Miller Internat., Intercord Klassiche Discothek, CTA Records Co. Ltd., Golden Master Series, Stradivari Records, Germany, Pilz Records, Germany, Madacy, Can., Delta, Germany; cons. Miami Internat. Music Competition; music dir., condr. Festival of Continents, Key West, Fla., 1990; chief condr. Osaka (Japan) Opera, 1990; music dir. Panam. Sinfonica, Miami, 1991—; guest condr. Kensington Symphony, Calif., Orch. Sinfonia de Sao Paulo, Orch. Sinfonia de Paraguay, Asuncion, R.I.A. Milano Orch., Italy, 1994, 95. Condr. numerous operas including The Impressario, Cosi Fan Tutte, La Perchole, Don Pasquale, Faust, I Pagliacci, Samson and Dalila, Madame Butterfly, Tosca, La Boheme, Elisir D. Amore, Hansel and Gretl, La Traviata, Fledermaus, Otello, Rigoletto, Il Trovatore, Carmen, Ernani, Merry Widow, Lucia di Lammermoor; condr. albums Tschaikovsky with the New Philharm. Orch. London, Mozart Symphony 41, recs. with London Philharm., London Festival Orch., Royal Philharm. Recipient numerous citations and medals Country of Italy; named hon. Dr. of Music, London, Paris, Knight of Templar Order of Germany.

SIEGEL, LLOYD HARVEY, architect, real estate developer, consultant; b. N.Y.C., Nov. 27, 1928; s. Saul M. and Lillian (Bell) S.; m. Margot Kopsidas Phillips, Oct. 25, 1987. BArch., Princeton U., 1949; MArch., MIT, 1953. Registered architect, N.Y., N.J., Conn., Ohio, Ill., Mich. Designer Skidmore, Owings & Merrill, then I. M. Pei & Assocs., then Antonin Raymond, N.Y.C., 1955-60; assoc. Kelly & Gruzen, N.Y.C., 1960-66; dep. health services adminstr. City of N.Y., 1966-70; dep. exec. dir. health and hosps. governing commn. Cook County, Chgo., 1970-76; prin. L.H.S. Cons. in Health Planning, Facility Design & Mgmt., Washington, 1976—, Siegel & Schroeder, P.C., Chgo., 1983-87; dir. Office Architecture & Engring., VA, Washington, 1987-94; dir. Facilities Quality Office VA, Washington, 1994—; prin. Yacht Harbor Devel. Co., South Haven, Mich., 1983-88, Siegel & Schroeder Developers Inc., Chgo., 1984-88; mem. adv. coms. HEW; mem. pub. adv. panels GSA; mem. adv. com. Legislature State of Ill.; mem. fellowship evaluation com. AIA-Am. Hosp. Assn.; mem. tech. adv. com. to Northeastern Ill. Planning Commn.; chmn. Com. on Architecture for Health, 1984. Author: Hidden Asset? Interstitial Space, A Critical Evaluation, 1987; photography in permanent collections Met. Mus. Art, N.Y.C., Mus. Modern Art, N.Y.C., others; prin. works include N.Y. World's Fair Spanish Pavillion, N.Y.C. (N.Y. chpt. AIA award 1964), Williams Meml. Residence, Flushing, N.Y. (Queens C. of C. award 1964), Hebrew Home for Aged, Riverdale, N.Y. (Bronx C. of C. award 1966). Fulbright fellow Università di Roma, 1954, Politecnico di Milano, 1955. Fellow AIA; mem. Urban Land Inst., The Arts Club, Univ. Club. Avocations: micology, microphagy, oenology. Home: 3133 Connecticut Ave NW Washington DC 20008-5147 Office: VA 810 Vermont Ave NW Washington DC 20420

SIEGEL, LOUIS PENDLETON, forest products executive; b. Richmond, Va., Nov. 6, 1942; s. John Boschen Jr. and Francis Beale (Tyler) S.; m. Nancy Dicks Blanton, Apr. 10, 1974 (dec. July 1976); m. Nancy Northon, June 26, 1982; children: Kathryn Tyler. AB in Econs., Dartmouth Coll., 1967. Asst. cashier, security researcher First Nat. Citibank, N.Y.C., 1967-71; v.p. security rsch. Drexel Burnham Lambert, N.Y.C., 1971-79; with Potlatch Corp., San Francisco, 1979—, sr. v.p. fin. and adminstrn., 1989, group v.p. wood products and corp. planning, 1989-92, group v.p. pulp and paperboard and corp. planning 1992-93, exec. v.p. pulp-based ops. and corp. planning, 1993-94, pres., COO, 1994—; bd. dirs. San Francisco Fed. Corp. Pres., bd. dir. Bay Area Sci. Fair, San Francisco, 1989-90; bd. dirs. Bay Area

Coun. With USCG, 1964-65. Republican. Episcopalian. Avocations: golf, tennis, fishing. Office: Potlatch Corp 1 Maritime Plz San Francisco CA 94111-3404

SIEGEL, MARC MONROE, television and film producer, writer, director; b. N.Y.C., Dec. 8, 1916; s. Isaac and Annie N. (Natelson) S.; m. Anne Dorothy Fishman, Sept. 8, 1940; 1 son, Peter Kieve. B.A., Washington Sq. Coll., 1936; M.A., N.Y. U. Sch. Edn., 1938. Free-lance mag. writer, especially for: New Yorker mag, 1948-50; writer: Eternal Light radio series, NBC, N.Y.C., 1950-60; writer-dir-producer: Directions, ABC-TV, N.Y.C., 1961-78; exec. producer chief writer: Heritage: Civilization and the Jews, WNET, N.Y.C., 1978-84; author: feature screenplays A Child is Crying, 1961, The Young Adventurers, 1963; ABC News Bicentennial spls. Rendezvous With Freedom, 1973, The Right to Believe, 1975, The Will to Be Free, 1976; ABC News feature The Panama Canal, 1977 (Writers Guild award); (Recipient numerous awards, including: Edinburgh Film Festival award 1948, Venice Film Festival award 1962, Cannes Film Festival award 1964, Eternal Light award Jewish Theol. Sem. Am. 1969). Served with USAAF, 1943-45. Peabody award, 1979, 84; Gabriel award Nat. Assn. Catholic Broadcasters, 1979; Emmy award, 1984, Christopher award, 1984; also several awards Freedoms Found. Mem. Nat. Acad. TV Arts and Scis., Writers Guild Am. East (council 1972-73, 78-79, 84-88, awards 1959, 73, 78, 85, Jablow Meml. award 1988), Dirs. Guild Am. Democrat. Home: 75 Central Park W New York NY 10023-6011

SIEGEL, MARTIN JAY, lawyer, investment advisor; b. N.Y.C., Apr. 12, 1942; s. Barney and Ruth (Baer) S. BA in Econs., Mich. State U., 1963; JD, Bklyn. Law Sch., 1966; MBA in Fin., Fordham U., 1980. Served to col. U.S. Army, 1966—, commd. 2d lt., 1966; advanced through grades to col., 1991, ret., 1990; fin. advisor, pvt. practice law, N.Y.C., 1971—. Col. USAR, 1990—. Office: 150 Broadway Ste 1400 New York NY 10038

SIEGEL, MARVIN, newspaper editor; b. N.Y.C., June 23, 1935; s. Murray and Belle (Diamond) S.; 1 child, Joshua Murray. BA, U. Mich., 1957. Reporter The Record, Hackensack, N.J., 1957-59; free-lance writer Western Europe, 1960-62; reporter Fairchild Pubs., N.Y.C., 1962-63; editor The World Telegram, N.Y.C., 1963-66; copy editor The N.Y. Times, 1966-67, asst. met. editor, 1967-76, founding editor Weekend sect., 1976-82; founding editor World of N.Y., 1982-86; founding editor Edn. Life The N.Y. Times, 1986, dep. editor Week in Rev., 1987, culture news editor, 1988-92, dep. editor Book Rev., 1992-95; asst. to mng. editor, 1995—. Co-author: The World of New York, 1985, The New Yotk Times: Great Lives of the 20th Century, 1988; co-editor: The Seven Deadly Sins, 1994. Pfc. U.S. Army. Jewish. Office: NY Times Co 229 W 43d St New York NY 10036-3913

SIEGEL, MICHAEL ELLIOT, nuclear medicine physician, educator; b. N.Y.C., May 13, 1942; s. Benjamin and Rose (Gilbert) S.; m. Marsha Rose Snower, Mar. 20, 1966; children: Herrick Jove, Meridith Ann. A.B., Cornell U., 1964; M.D., Chgo. Med. Sch., 1968. Diplomate Nat. Bd. Med. Examiners. Intern Cedars-Sinai Med. Ctr., L.A., 1968-69; resident in radiology, 1969-70; NIH fellow in radiology Temple U. Med. Ctr., Phila., 1970-71; NIH fellow in nuclear medicine Johns Hopkins U. Sch. Medicine, Balt., 1971-73, asst. prof. radiology, 1972-76; assoc. prof. radiology, medicine U. So. Calif., L.A., 1976—; prof. radiology, 1989—, dir. div. nuclear medicine, 1982—; dir. Sch. Nuclear Medicine, L.A. County-U. So. Calif. Med. Ctr., 1976—; dir. div. nuclear medicine Kenneth Norris Cancer Hosp. and Rsch. Ctr., L.A., 1983—; dir. dept. nuclear medicine Orthopaedic Hosp., L.A., 1981—, Intercommunity Hosp., Covina, Calif., 1981—, U. So. Calif. Univ. Hosp., L.A., 1993—; cons. dept. nuclear medicine Rancho Los Amigos Hosp., Downey, Calif., 1976—. Author: Textbook of Nuclear Medicine, 1978, Vascular Surgery, 1983, 88, and numerous others textbooks; editor: Nuclear Cardiology, 1981, Vascular Disease: Nuclear Medicine, 1983. Mem. Maple Ctr., Beverly Hills. Served as maj. USAF, 1974-76. Recipient Outstanding Alumnus award Chgo. Med. Sch., 1991. Fellow Am. Coll. Nuclear Medicine (sci. investigator 1974, 76, nominations com. 1980, program com. 1983, bd. trustees 1993, disting. fellow, 1993, bd. reps., 1993—); mem. Soc. Nuclear Medicine (sci. exhbn. com. 1978-79, program com. 1979-80, Silver medal 1975), Calif. Med. Assn. (sci. adv. bd. 1987—), Radiol. Soc. N.Am., Soc. Nuclear Magnetic Resonance Imaging, Alpha Omega Alpha. Lodge: Friars So. Calif. Research on devel. of nuclear medicine techniques to: evaluate cardiovascular disease and diagnose and treat cancer, clinical utilization of video digital displays in nuclear medicine development; inventor pneumatic radiologic pressure system. Office: U So Calif Med Ctr PO Box 693 1200 N State St Los Angeles CA 90033

SIEGEL, MILTON P., health foundation executive, international executive, educator, management consultant; b. Des Moines, July 23, 1911; s. Barney and Sylvy (Levinson) S.; m. Rosalie Rosenberg, May 25, 1934 (dec. Jan. 1991); children: Betsy Lee, Larry (dec.), Sally (dec.). Dir. fin. and stats. Iowa Emergency Relief Adminstrn., also treas.; Iowa Rural Rehab. Adminstrn., 1933-35; regional fin. and bus. mgr. Farm Security Adminstrn., U.S. Dept. Agr., 1935-41, chief fiscal officer, 1942-44; asst. treas., dir. Office for Far East, UNRRA, 1944-45; asst. dir. fiscal br. prodn. and mktg. adminstrn. U.S. Dept. Agr., 1945-47; asst. dir.-gen. WHO, Geneva, 1947-71; prof. internat. health Sch. Pub. Health, U. Tex. Health Scis. Center, Houston, 1971-75, prof. internat. health, mgmt. and policy scis., 1988-89, prof. emeritus, 1989; health mgmt. cons. Imperial Govt. of Iran, Nat. Health Ins. Orgn., 1975-76; sr. cons. to adminstr. UN Devel. Program, 1976-77; chmn. bd. trustees Mgmt. Planning Systems Internat., Inc., 1977—; pres., chief exec. officer Fedn. World Health Founds, 1978—; mem. permanent scale contbns. commn. League Red Cross Socs., 1967-81; sr. mgmt. scientist Children's Nutrition Rsch. Ctr., Baylor Coll. Medicine, Houston, 1979-80; cons. Sch. Pub. Health, U. N.C., Chapel Hill, 1970, Carolina Population Ctr., 1970; vis. prof. Sch. Pub. Health, U. Mich., 1967; awarded acad. chair U. Tex. Health Sci. Ctr., Houston, 1984. Chmn. bd. trustees World Health Found., U.S.A., 1976-89. Recipient Sam Beber award, 1960. Mem. Am. Public Health Assn. Home: 2833 Sackett St Houston TX 77098-1125

SIEGEL, MORTON KALLOS, religious organization administrator, educational administrator; b. N.Y.C., Dec. 5, 1924; s. Samuel William and Esther (Sackin) S.; m. Pearl Fox, June 28, 1949; children: Deborah Siegel Eisenstadt, Daniel, Deenah Siegel Speiser. BA summa cum laude, Yeshiva U., 1945; MA in Philosophy and History, Columbia U., 1946, PhD, 1952. Ednl. dir. Laurelton Jewish Ctr., Queens, N.Y., 1945-49; ednl. dir., dir. educator placement United Synagogue Am., N.Y.C., 1949-51, dir. youth activities, 1953-64, exec. dir., 1970-75, ednl. dir., 1964-88, dir. regional and extension activities, 1988—; adj. asst. prof. Sch. Edn., NYU, 1971-76; lectr. in field. Contbr. numerous articles on pedagogy to profl. jours. Home: 43 Crossbow Ln Commack NY 11725-1214 Office: 155 Fifth Ave New York NY 10010-6811

SIEGEL, NATHANIEL HAROLD, sociology educator; b. Bklyn., May 17, 1929; s. Victor and Yetta (Kogel) S.; m. Annabelle Replansky, Mar. 3, 1958; children—Anthony, Jennifer. A.B., Bklyn. Coll., 1950; A.M., N.Y.U., 1952, Ph.D., 1956. Asst. prof. sociology Columbia, 1956-59; sociologist Hillside Hosp., Queens, N.Y., 1958-63; assoc. dir. behavioral research N.Y.C. Dept. Health, 1963-64; chief social sci. tng. sect. NIMH, 1964-67, cons., 1970—; prof. sociology Queens Coll., 1967-79; chmn. dept., 1967-70, v.p., dean faculty, 1970-74, provost, 1974-77, acting pres., 1977-78; sr. v.p. acad. affairs SUNY Purchase, 1979—. Served with M.C. AUS, 1950-51. Home: 8 Birchfield Rd Larchmont NY 10538-1505 Office: SUNY Purchase NY 10577

SIEGEL, NORMAN JOSEPH, pediatrician, educator; b. Houston, Mar. 8, 1943; m. Rise Joan Ross, Dec. 24, 1967; children: Andrew, Karen. BA, Tulane U., 1964; MA, U. Tex. Med. Br., Galveston, 1968, MD, 1968. Intern, then resident Yale-New Haven Hosp., 1968-70; fellow Sch. Medicine, Yale U., New Haven, 1970-72, asst. prof. pediatrics and medicine, 1972-76, assoc. prof., 1976-82, prof., 1982—, vice chmn. pediatrics, 1979—. Contbr. articles to profl. jours., chpts. to books. Grantee NIH, Am. Heart Assn., Hood Found. Mem. Am. Pediatric Soc. (sec.-treas. 1993—), Am. Soc. Pediatric Nephrology (pres. 1988-89), Nat. Kidney Found. (chmn. com. on pediatric nephrology and urology 1987-91, grantee, scientific adv. com. 1988-91), Soc. Pediatric Rsch. (membership sec. 1979-85), Nat. Bd. Med. Examiners (pediatric test com. 1993-95), Phi Beta Kappa, Mu Delta. Office:

Yale U Sch Medicine Dept Pediatrics 333 Cedar St PO Box 208064 New Haven CT 06520-8064

SIEGEL, RICHARD DAVID, lawyer, former government official; b. Lewistown, Pa., Oct. 13, 1939; s. Robert and Pearl Eleanor (Nieman) S.; m. Marjorie Esther Greenwald, Mar. 13, 1966; children—Andrew, Jonathan, Michele. B.A., U. Pa., 1960; J.D., Harvard U., 1963. Bar: Pa., D.C., U.S. Supreme Ct. Staff writer Phila. Inquirer, 1964-66; spl. asst. U.S. Rep. Richard Schweiker, Washington, 1966-69; legis. counsel U.S. Senator Richard Schweiker, Washington, 1969-71; assoc. minority counsel Senate Com. on Labor and Human Resources, Washington, 1971-73; sole practice Washington, 1978-79, mem. various firms, 1973-78, 80-81; dep. asst. sec. for natural resources and environment USDA, Washington, 1981-87; sole practice Washington, 1987—. Contbr. articles to profl. jours. Treas. Com. for Senator Schweiker, Washington, 1974; mem. nat. council Am. Israel Pub. Affairs Com., Washington, 1974-77; v.p. Tifereth Israel Congregation, Washington, 1980-82, 1993—; sec. treas, North Am.-Israel Horticultural Found., 1987—. Served with USCGR, 1963-64. Mem. Assn. Former Senate Aides, ABA, Pa. Bar Assn., Fed. Bar Assn., Soil and Water Conservation Soc. Republican. Jewish. Home: 3141 Aberfoyle Pl NW Washington DC 20015-2325 Office: 1400 16th St NW Washington DC 20036-2220

SIEGEL, ROBERT, heat transfer engineer; b. Cleve., July 10, 1927; s. Morris and Mollie (Binder) S.; m. Elaine Jane Jaffe, July 19, 1951; children: Stephen, Lawrence. BS, Case Inst. Tech., 1950, MS, 1951; ScD, MIT, 1953. Heat transfer engr. GE, Schenectady, N.Y., 1953-54; heat transfer analyst Knolls Atomic Power Lab., Schenectady, 1954-55; rsch. scientist NASA Lewis Rsch. Ctr., Cleve., 1955—; adj. prof. U. Toledo, 1981, 85, adj. prof. mech. engring. U. Akron (Ohio), 1987, adj. prof. mech. engring. Cleve. State U., 1989, 91; mem. adv. coun. U. Akron, 1989—. Author: Thermal Radiation Heat Transfer, 1972, 3d edit., 1992; tech. editor ASME, 1972-83, AIAA, 1986—; author numerous sci. papers. With U.S. Army, 1945-47. Recipient Exceptional Sci. Achievement medal NASA, 1986. Fellow ASME (Heat Transfer Meml. award 1970), AIAA (Thermophysics award 1993); mem. Sigma Xi, Tau Beta Pi. Jewish. Avocations: ballroom dancing, piano. Home: 3052 Warrington Rd Cleveland OH 44120-2425 Office: NASA Lewis Rsch Ctr 21000 Brookpark Rd Cleveland OH 44135-3191

SIEGEL, ROBERT CHARLES, broadcast journalist; b. N.Y.C., June 26, 1947; s. Joseph and Edith Ruth (Joffe) S.; m. Jane Claudia Schwartz, June 17, 1973; children: Erica Anne, Leah Harriet. BA, Columbia U., 1968, postgrad. sch. journalism, 1969-70. Newscaster Sta. WGLI, Babylon, N.Y., 1968-69; reporter, news dir. Sta. WRVR-FM, N.Y.C., 1971-76; assoc. producer, editor Nat. Pub. Radio, Washington, 1976-78, sr. editor, 1976-79, dir. news and info., 1983-87, host All Things Considered, 1987—; sr. editor Nat. Pub. Radio, London, 1979-83; host Ea. Europe: Breaking with the Past, The Learning Channel, Washington, 1990, Earth Scope, Arlington, Va., 1990-91. Editor: The NPR Interviews. Recipient DuPont-Columbia award Columbia U., 1984. Jewish. Avocations: reading, golf, baseball. Home: 1340 19th Rd S Arlington VA 22202-1637 Office: Nat Pub Radio All Things Considered 635 Massachussetts Ave NW Washington DC 20001

SIEGEL, ROBERT GORDON, lawyer; b. Harrisburg, Pa., Dec. 6, 1950; s. Hyman and Charlotte Siegel; m. Elaine Sorin, Aug. 13, 1972; children: Adam, Todd, Kate. BA, Wesleyan U., Middletown, Conn., 1972; MBA, Cornell U., 1975, JD, 1976. Bar: Conn. 1976, U.S. Dist. Ct. conn. 1976, U.S. Claims Ct. 1988, U.S. Tax Ct. 1985. Assoc. Day, Berry & Howard, Hartford, Conn., 1976-83, ptnr., 1983—. Dir. Literacy Vols., Hartford, 1980-86, Inroads Greater Hartford, 1993—; sec. Comm. affiliate Am. Diabetes Assn., Meriden, 1991-93. Mem. ABA, Conn. Bar Assn., Hartford County Bar Assn., Tax Club Hartford (pres. 1989-90). Office: Day Berry & Howard Cityplace Hartford CT 06103

SIEGEL, ROBERT TED, physicist; b. Springfield, Mass., June 10, 1928; s. Charles V.D. and Ida B. S.; m. Rebecca Weisberg, June 14, 1951; children: Carol D., Naomi L., Joan E., Jonathan D., Richard M. B.S., Carnegie-Mellon U., 1948, M.S., 1950, D.S., 1952. Research assoc. Carnegie Mellon U., 1952-57, asst. prof. physics, 1957-60, assoc. prof., 1960-63; prof. Coll. William and Mary, 1963—, W.F.C. Ferguson prof. physics, 1979—, dean grad. studies, 1965-67, dir. space radiation effects lab., 1967-79. Fellow Am. Phys. Soc.; mem. AAAS, AAUP. Jewish. Office: Coll William and Mary Physics Dept Williamsburg VA 23185

SIEGEL, SAMUEL, metals company executive; b. Elizabeth, N.J., Oct. 30, 1930; s. Morris and Anna (Fader) S.; m. Raenea Kershenbaum, Mar. 29, 1953; children: Daryl Lynn, Annie Roslyn. BBA, CUNY, 1952. CPA, N.Y., Ariz. Cost accountant Seaporcel Metals, Inc., Long Island City, N.Y., 1955-56; asst. to controller Deltown Foods, Inc., Yonkers, N.Y., 1956-57; sr. accountant DeLoitte & Touche, N.Y.C., 1957-61; vice chmn., chief fin. officer, treas., sec. dir. Nucor Corp., Charlotte, N.C., 1961—. Mem. AICPA, Am. Soc. Corp. Secs., Fin. Execs. Inst. Home: 3421 Windbluff Dr Charlotte NC 28277-9850 Office: Nucor Corp 2100 Rexford Rd Charlotte NC 28211

SIEGEL, SHELDON C., physician; b. Mpls., Jan. 30, 1922; s. Carl S.; m. Priscilla Rikess, Mar. 3, 1946; children—Linda, Nancy. A.A., Va. Jr. Coll., 1940; B.A., B.S., U. Minn., 1942, M.D., 1945. Intern U. Minn. Hosp., 1946, resident in pediatrics, 1947-48; fellow in pediatric allergy Rochester, N.Y., 1949-50; practice medicine specializing in pediatric allergy and pediatrics St. Paul, 1950-52, San Antonio, 1952-54, Los Angeles, 1954—; clin. instr. pediatrics U. Rochester, 1949-50, U. Minn., 1951-52; asst. prof. pediatrics U. Tex., 1952-54; asst. clin. prof. U. Calif. at Los Angeles Med. Sch., 1955, clin. assoc. prof., 1957-62, clin. prof., 1963—, co-chief pediatric allergy clinic, 1957—; mem. staff Harbor Gen. Hosp., Torrance, Calif., Daniel Freeman Hosp., Inglewood, Calif., Centinela Valley Community Hosp., Inglewood, Hawthorne (Calif.) Community Hosp. Editorial bd.: Jour. Allergy, 1973-75; contbr. articles to med. jours. Fellow Am. Acad. Allergy (pres. 1974), Am. Coll. Allergists. Am. Acad. Pediatrics; mem. AMA, Allergy Found. Am. (pres. 1976), Calif., Los Angeles County med. assns., Los Angeles Pediatric Soc., Calif., Los Angeles socs. allergy, Western Pediatric Research Soc., Am. Bd. Med. Specialists, Sigma Xi. Office: 11620 Wilshire Blvd Los Angeles CA 90025-1708

SIEGEL, SID, composer, lyricist; b. Chgo., Jan. 20, 1927; s. Michael and Rose (Wolfson) S.; m. Carrie Patricia Zeigler, May 18, 1952; children: David, Jodi, Mark. BMus in Composition, Roosevelt Coll., Chgo., 1950. Composer-lyricist for local TV shows, nightclub performers and popular songs, also commls. for radio and TV, nightclub shows; composer-lyricist, arranger, condr. for radio and TV commls., films, slide presentations, industry shows.; (Recipient numerous awards for music for commls. and films including Cindy Indsl. Film Producers Am. and Capa Chgo. Audio-Visual Producers Assn.). With USNR, 1945-46. Mem. ASCAP, Am. Fedn. Musicians. Address: 326 Satinwood Ct N Buffalo Grove IL 60089

SIEGEL, STANLEY, lawyer, educator; b. N.Y.C., Mar. 2, 1941; s. David Aaron and Rose (Minsky) S.; m. Karina Haum, July 20, 1986. B.S. summa cum laude, NYU, 1960; J.D. magna cum laude, Harvard U., 1963. Bar: N.Y. 1963, D.C. 1964, Mich. 1970, Calif. 1976; CPA, Md. Atty. Office Sec. of Air Force, 1963-66; asst. prof. law U. Mich., Ann Arbor, 1966-69, assoc. prof., 1969-71, prof., 1971-74; ptnr. Honigman, Miller, Schwartz & Cohn, Detroit, 1974-76; prof. law UCLA, 1976-86; prof. law NYU, 1986—, assoc. dean, 1987-89; vis. prof. Stanford Law Sch., 1973, Ctrl. European U., Budapest, 1993—; fellow Max-Planck Inst., Hamburg, 1988; cons. reogrn. U.S. Postal Svc., 1969-71; exec. sec. Mich. Law Revision Commn., 1973; mem. bd. examiners AICPA, 1980-83. Author: (with Schulman and Moscow) Michigan Business Corporations, 1979, (with Conard and Knauss) Enterprise Organization, 4th edit., 1987, (with D. Siegel) Accounting and Financial Disclosure: A Guide to Basic Concepts, 1983. Served to capt. USAF, 1963-66. Mem. ABA, D.C. Bar Assn., Calif. Bar Assn., Assn. of Bar of City of N.Y., Am. Law Inst., AICPA. Office: NYU Law Sch 40 Washington Sq S New York NY 10012-1099

SIEGEL, THOMAS LOUIS, lawyer; b. N.Y.C., Oct. 7, 1939; s. Jack M. and Helen S. (Simpson) S.; m. Ruth L. Rosenthal, June 23, 1963; children: Peter, Karen. B.A., Rutgers U., 1961; J.D., Cornell U., 1964. Bar: N.Y. 1964, D.C. 1967, Tex. 1982. Atty. advisor Office of Gen. Counsel, FHA,

Washington, 1968; assoc. mem. firm Arent, Fox, Kintner, Plotkin & Kahn, Washington, 1968-70; gen. counsel Group Health Assn., Inc., 1970-74; ptnr. Diuguid, Siegel & Kennelly, Washington, 1974-80; gen. counsel, div. fed. law and regulation Am. Hosp. Assn., 1980—; pvt. practice Dallas, 1982—; legal counsel St. Paul Hosp., Dallas; legal cons. div. organizational devel. HEW, 1974-80. Pres. bd. trustees St. Luke's House, Bethesda, Md. Served with USAF, 1965-67. Mem. N.Y. State Bar Assn., Tex. Bar Assn., Bar Assn. D.C., Dallas Bar Assn., Nat. Health Lawyers Assn., Rutgers, Cornell U. alumni assns. Home: 3739 Waldorf Dr Dallas TX 75229-3937 Office: 4100 Mcewen Rd Ste 285 Dallas TX 75244-5100

SIEGELMAN, DON EUGENE, state official; b. Mobil, Ala., Feb. 24, 1946; m. Lori Allen; c. Dana, Joseph. B.A. U. Ala.; J.D., Georgetown U., 1972; postgrad., Oxford U., Eng., 1972-73. Bar: Ala. 1972. Sec. of state State of Ala., Montgomery, 1979-87, atty. gen., 1987-94; lt. gov. State of Ala., 1994—. Office: Office of Lt Gov Ala State House Ste 725 Montgomery AL 36130

SIEGER, CHARLES, librarian; b. Fountain Hill, Pa., Dec. 9, 1944; s. Charles Franklin and Kathryn (Farny) S.; m. Deborah Day Malone, May 13, 1972; children: C. Alexander, Meredith Kathryn. BA History, Wesleyan U., 1969; student, Duke U., 1969-71; MS Libr. Sci., UNC, 1979. Reference, U.S. Documents libr. Fairleigh Dickinson U., Rutherford, N.J., 1980-83, asst. dir. tech. svcs., 1983-85, assoc. dir., 1985-92, dir., 1992-94; dir. Lyndhurst (N.J.) Free Pub. Libr., 1994—. Contbr. articles to World Book ency., legal jours; contbr. chpts. to books. Coach, vice pres., then pres. Lyndhurst Youth Soccer Club; treas. Minolta Suburban Youth Soccer League; mem. parent adv. com. Lyndhurst High Sch.; vice-commr. Lipton Youth League. With U.S. Army, 1966-68, Vietnam. Mem. ALA, Am. Soc. Info. Sci., Govt. Documents Roundtable, Documents Assn. N.J. Inc. Avocation: soccer. Home: 227 Tontine Ave Lyndhurst NJ 07071-1819 Office: Lyndhurst Free Pub Libr 355 Valley Brook Ave Lyndhurst NJ 07071

SIEGER, CHARLES MARTIN, architect; b. N.Y.C., Oct. 8, 1946; s. Don J. and Lillian LoPrince; m. Joanna Gray, June 30, 1989; children by previous marriage: Lisa, Stacy. Student, Ecoles D'Art Americaines, Fontainebleau, France, 1968; BArch, U. Fla., 1969; MArch, U. Pa., 1970. Registered architect, Fla., Tex., N.Y., N.C., S.C., Va. Prin. Sieger Archtl. Partnership, Miami, Fla., 1972—; lectr. U. Miami, 1979, U. Fla., 1980, 81. Fellow AIA (bd. dirs. Miami chpt. 1976, sec. 1977, v.p. 1978, pres. 1979, state dir. 1980-82); mem. Nat. Assn. Home Builders, Advance Club (v.p. 1975), Fla. Assn. AIA's. Republican. Avocation: sailing. Office: Sieger Archtl Partnership 9300 SW 87th Ave Ste 6 Miami FL 33176-2413

SIEGERT, BARBARA (MARIE), health care administrator; b. Boston, May 22, 1935; d. Salvatore Mario and Mary Kathleen (Wagner) Tartaglia; m. Herbert C. Siegert (dec. Apr. 1974); children: Carolyn Marie, Herbert Christian Jr. Diploma, Newton-Wellesley (Mass.) Hosp. Sch. Nursing, 1956; MEd, Antioch U., 1980. Diplomate Am. Bd. Med. Psychotherapists. Supr. nursing Hogan Regional Ctr., Hathorne, Mass., 1974-78; community mental health nursing advisor Cape Ann area office Dept. Mental Health, Beverly, Mass., 1978-79; dir. case mgmt. Dept. Mental Health, Beverly, 1979-87, dir. case mgmt. north shore area office, 1988-91; dir. case mgmt. Dept. Mental Health-north shore area-Lynn (Mass.) site, Lynn, Mass., 1991-92; mem. interdisciplinary faculty, profl. cons. com., lecture staff clin. pastoral counseling program Danvers State Hosp./Hogan/Berry Regional Ctrs., Hathorne, Mass., 1982-86; nursing edn. adv. com. North Shore Community Coll., Beverly, 1983-91; tng. staff Balter Inst., Ipswich, Mass., 1987-88. Mem. Internat. Cultural Diploma Honor, 1989—. Recipient Spl. Recognition award Lexington (Mass.) Pub. Schs., 1973, Peter Torci award Lexington Friends of Children in Spl. Edn., 1974; named Internat. Biog. Roll. of Honor, 1989—. Fellow Am. Biog. Inst. (life, Woman of Yr. 1990); mem. World Inst. Achievement. Home: 63 Willow Rd # B Boxford MA 01921-1218

SIEGFRIED, DAVID CHARLES, lawyer; b. N.Y.C., Feb. 15, 1942; s. Charles Albert and Marjorie Claire (Young) S.; m. Meri Stephanie Smith; children: Karin Elisabeth, Christine Elise. AB summa cum laude, Princeton U., 1964; JD, Harvard U., 1967. Bar: N.Y. 1970. Assoc. Milbank, Tweed, Hadley & McCloy, N.Y.C., 1968-76, ptnr., 1977-79, 83-85, 88—; resident ptnr. Milbank, Tweed, Hadley & McCloy, Hong Kong and Singapore, 1979-83, 85-88; bd. dirs. PALS; speaker at confs. and seminars. Served to 1st lt. USAR, 1967-74. Mem. ABA, Am. Soc. Internat. Law, Brazilian Am. C. of C. (bd. dirs.), Internat. Bar Assn., N.Y. State Bar Assn., Assn. Bar City N.Y., Millburn-Short Hills Hist. Soc. (v.p.). Congregationalist. Clubs: Princeton (New York), Short Hills (N.J.), Am. (Hong Kong/Singapore), Tanglin (Singapore), Cricket. Avocations: running, tennis, historic reading. Home: 30 Western Dr Short Hills NJ 07078-3230

SIEGFRIED, TOM, newspaper editor. Sci. editor Dallas Morning News. Office: The Dallas Morning News Communications Ctr PO Box 655237 Dallas TX 75265-5237*

SIEGLER, MARK, internist, educator; b. N.Y.C., June 20, 1941; s. Abraham J. and Florence (Sternlieb) S.; m. Anna Elizabeth Hollinger, June 4, 1967; children:Dillan, Alison, Richard, Jessica. AB with honors, Princeton U., 1963; MD, U. Chgo., 1967. Diplomate Am. Bd. Internal Medicine. Resident, chief resident internal medicine U. Chgo., 1967-71; hon. sr. registrar in medicine Royal Postgrad. Med. Sch., London, 1971-72; asst. prof. medicine U. Chgo., 1972-78, assoc. prof. medicine, 1979-85, acting dir. div. gen. internal medicine, 1983-85, dir. Ctr. Clin. Med. Ethics, 1984—, prof. medicine, 1985—, dir. nat. leadership tng. program in clin. med. ethics, 1986—; vis. asst. prof. medicine U. Wis., Madison, 1977; vis. assoc. prof. medicine U. Va., Charlottesville, 1981-82. Co-author: Clinical Ethics, 1981, 3rd edit., 1992, An Annotated Bibliography of Medical Ethics, 1988, Institutional Protocols for Decisions about Life-Sustaining Treatment, 1988; co-editor: Changing Values in Medicine, 1985, Medical Innovations and Bad Outcomes, 1987; mem. editl. bd. Am. Jour. Medicine, 1979-94, Archives Internal Medicine, 1979-90, Bibliography of Bioethics, Jour. Med. Philosophy, 1978-89, Humane Medicine, Jour. Clin. Ethics; contbr. articles to profl. publs. Bd. govrs. Josephson Inst. for Advancement of Ethics, L.A., 1986-92. Grantee Andrew W. Mellon Found., Henry J. Kaiser Family Found., Pew Charitable Trusts, Field Found. Ill., Ira De Camp Found.; Phi Beta Kappa vis. scholar, 1991-92, others. Fellow ACP (mem. human rights com., mem. ethics com. 1985-90), Hastings Ctr.; mem. ACS (mem. ethics com. 1991—), Assn. Am. Physicians, Am. Geriat. Soc. (mem. ethics com. 1988-90), Chgo. Clin. Ethics Program (pres. 1989-90). Office: Univ Chgo MC 6098 MacLean Ctr Clin Med Ethics 5841 S Maryland Ave Chicago IL 60637-1463

SIEGLER, THOMAS EDMUND, investment banking executive; b. Bklyn., Oct. 12, 1934; s. John G. and Edna (Trill) S.; m. Mary V., July 7, 1956; children—Christopher, John, Mary, Therese, Ellen, James. B.B.A., St. John's U., 1959; M.B.A., NYU, 1966. Fin. analyst Exxon Corp., N.Y.C., 1952-66; sr. v.p. sec. Donaldson, Lufkin & Jenrette, Inc., N.Y.C., 1966—; arbitrator Nat. Assn. of Securities Dealers, N.Y.C. Mem. Am. Soc. Corp. Secs., Nat. Assn. Securities Dealers. Republican. Roman Catholic. Lodge: K.C. Avocations: cabinetry; running. Home: 39 Wildwood Dr Huntington Station NY 11746-6040 Office: Donaldson Lufkin & Jenrette Inc 140 Broadway New York NY 10005-1276

SIEGMAN, ANTHONY EDWARD, electrical engineer, educator; b. Detroit, Nov. 23, 1931; s. Orra Leslie and Helen Salome (Winnie) S.; (married). AB summa cum laude, Harvard U., 1952; MS, UCLA, 1954; PhD, Stanford U., 1957. Mem. faculty Stanford (Calif.) U., 1957—, assoc. prof. elec. engring., 1960-65, prof., 1965—; dir. Edward L. Ginzton Lab., 1978-83; cons. Lawrence Livermore Labs., Coherent Inc., GTE; mem. Air Force Sci. Adv. Bd.; vis. prof. Harvard U. 1965. Author: Microwave Solid State Masers, 1964, An Introduction to Lasers and Masers, 1970, Lasers, 1986; contbr. over 200 articles to profl. jours. Recipient Schawlow award Laser Inst. Am., 1991; Guggenheim fellow IBM Rsch. Lab., Zurich, 1969-70; Alexander von Humboldt Found. sr. scientist Max Planck Inst. Quantum Optics, Garching, Fed. Republic Germany, 1984-85. Fellow AAAS, IEEE (W.R.G. Baker award 1971, J.J. Ebers award 1977), Am. Phys. Soc. Laser Inst. Am., Optical Soc. Am. (R.W. Wood prize 1980), IEEE Laser Electro-Optics Soc. (Quantum Electronics award 1989), Am. Acad. Arts and Scis.;

mem. NAS, NAE, AAUP, Phi Beta Kappa, Sigma Xi. Patentee microwave and optical devices and lasers, including the unstable optical resonator. Office: Stanford U Ginzton Lab Mc 4085 Stanford CA 94305-4055*

SIEGMAN, HENRY, association executive; b. Germany, Dec. 12, 1930; came to U.S., 1942, naturalized, 1948; s. Mendel and Sara (Scharf) S.; m. Selma Goldberger, Nov. 8, 1953 (div.); children: Bonnie, Debra, Alan; m. Miriam Cantor, Aug. 11, 1981. Rabbi, Torah Vodaath Sem., N.Y.C., 1951; B.A., New Sch. Social Research, 1961, postgrad., 1961-64. Nat. dir. community activities div. Union Orthodox Jewish Congregations Am., 1953-59; exec. sec. Am. Assn. Middle East Studies, 1959-64; dir. internat. affairs Nat. Community Relations Adv. Council, N.Y.C., 1964-65; exec. v.p. Synagogue Council Am., N.Y.C., 1965-78; exec. dir. Am. Jewish Congress, N.Y.C., 1978—; guest lectr. U. Ill., Columbia, Williams Coll.; an organizer White House Conf. Civil Rights, 1967; nat. vice chmn. Religion in Am. Life, 1966—; exec. com. Interreligious Com. on Peace, 1966—; chmn. Interreligious Com. Gen. Secs. (Nat. Council Chs.-U.S. Cath. Conf.-Synagogue Council Am.), 1973. Editor: Middle East Studies, 1959-64; Contbr. articles to profl. jours. Steering com., exec. com. Nat. Urban Coalition. Served to 1st lt., chaplain AUS, 1952-54. Decorated Bronze Star; designated Disting. Am. by Pres. U.S., 1970. Mem. AAUP, Council on Fgn. Relations, Nat. Conf. Jewish Communal Service, Assn. Jewish Community Relations Workers. Home: 685 W End Ave New York NY 10025-6819 Office: Am Jewish Cong 15 E 84th St New York NY 10028-0458

SIEGMAN, MARION JOYCE, physiology educator; b. Bklyn., Sept. 7, 1933; d. c. Joseph and Helen (Wasserman) S. BA, Tulane U., 1954; PhD, SUNY, Bklyn., 1966. Instr. physiology Med. Coll. Thomas Jefferson U., Phila., 1967-68, asst. prof., 1971-77, prof., 1977—; mem. physiology study sect. NIH. Editor: Regulation and Contraction of Smooth Muscle, 1987. Recipient award for excellence in rsch. and teaching Burlington No. Found., 1986, award for excellence in teaching Lindback Found., 1987, Outstanding Alumna award, Newcomb Coll./Tulane U., 1990, grantee NIH, 1967—. Mem. Am. Physiol. Soc., Biophys. Soc., Soc. Gen. Physiologists, Physiol. Soc. Phila. (pres. 1972-73). Avocation: photography. Office: Jefferson Med Coll 1020 Locust St Philadelphia PA 19107-6799

SIEHL, RICHARD W., lawyer; b. Dayton, Ohio, Sept. 12, 1952. BA magna cum laude, Miami U., 1974; JD, U. Ill., 1977. Bar: Ohio 1977, Fla. 1979, W. Va. 1987. Asst. prosecuting atty. Franklin County, 1977-78; minority counsel Ohio House Reps., 1979-80; dep. dir. Ohio Dept. Adminstrv. Svcs., 1980-82; ptnr. Baker & Hostetler, Columbus, Ohio; chmn. Firmwide Healthcare Practice Group. Mem. ABA, Columbus Bar Assn. (chmn. Health law com.), Am. Acad. Hosp. Attys., Nat. Health Lawyers Assn., Soc. Ohio Hosp. Attys., Phi Beta Kappa, Phi Kappa Phi, Phi Delta Phi. Office: Baker & Hostetler 65 E State St Columbus OH 43215-4213

SIEKERT, ROBERT GEORGE, neurologist; b. Milw., July 23, 1924; s. Hugo Paul and Elisa (Kraus) S.; m. Mary Jane Evans, Feb. 17, 1951; children: Robert G. Jr., John E., Friedrich P. BS, Northwestern U., 1945, MS, 1947, MD, 1948. Cert. Am. Bd. Psychiatry and Neurology. Instr. anatomy U. Pa., Phila., 1948-49; fellow neurology Mayo Found., Rochester, Minn., 1950-54; cons. Mayo Clinic, Rochester, 1954-91, head neurology sect., 1966-76, bd. govs., 1973-80, prof. neurology med. sch., 1969—; chmn. Internat. Stroke Conf. Am. Heart Assn., 1976-80. Editor Mayo Clinic Procs., 1982-86; cons. editor Jour. Stroke, 1992—; contbr. articles to profl. jours. Trustee Mayo Found., Rochester, 1973-81. Served to lt. j.g. M.C., USNR, 1950-52. Recipient Disting. Achievement award Am. Heart Assn., 1984, Merit award, 1989, Robert G. Siekert Young Investigator award Am. Heart Assn., 1986. Fellow Am. Coll. Physicians; mem. Am. Neurol. Assn., Northwestern U. Med. Sch. Alumni Assn. (Service award 1983), Swiss Neurol. Soc. (corr.), Alpha Omega Alpha. Avocation: philately. Office: Mayo Clinic 200 1st St SW Rochester MN 55905-0001

SIEKEVITZ, PHILIP, biology educator; b. Phila., Feb. 25, 1918; s. Joseph and Tillie (Kaplan) S.; m. Rebecca Burstein, Aug. 7, 1949; children: Ruth, Miriam. BS in Biology, Phila. Coll. Pharmacy and Scis., 1942, PhD (hon.), 1972; PhD in Biochemistry, U. Calif., Berkeley, 1949; PhD (hon.), U. Stockholm, 1974. USPHS fellow Mass. Gen. Hosp., 1949-51; fellow oncology McArdle Lab., U. Wis., 1951-54; mem. faculty Rockefeller U. 1954-88, prof. cell biology, until 1988, ret.; mem. molecular biology panel NSF, 1964-67; panel Internat. Cell Research Orgn., 1963-79; bd. dirs., trans., chmn. Scientists Com. Pub. Information N.Y., 1962-80; bd. dirs. N.Y. Univs. Com., 1965-70; council Am. Fedn. Scientists, 1967-68. Author: (with A. Loewy, J. Menninger, J. Gallant) Cell Structure and Function, 3d edit, 1991; editor: Jour. Cell Biology, 1962-65, Jour. Cellular Physiology, 1970—, Biosci., Jour. Exptl. Zoology, 1969-73, Biochim. Biophysica Acta; mem. editorial bd.: Jour. Cell Sci., Jour. Molecular Brain Rsch. Served with USAAF, 1942-45. Mem. Am. Soc. Biol. Chemists, Am. Soc. Cell Biology (pres. 1966-67), Soc. Neurosci., AAAS, Am. Acad. Arts and Scis., Am. Inst. Biol. Scientists, N.Y. Acad. Scis. (hon. life, governing bd. 1973-79, pres. 1976), Nat. Acad. Scis., Sigma Xi. Office: Rockefeller U Dept Cell Biology 1230 York Ave New York NY 10021-6341

SIEKMAN, THOMAS CLEMENT, lawyer; b. Somerville, Mass., Sept. 22, 1941; s. Aloysius C. and Estelle M. (Forte) S.; m. Claire Dorgan, Oct. 15, 1966; children: Michael T., James T., Amy K. BS in Engring., Merrimack Coll., 1963; JD, Villanova U., 1966. Bar: Mass. 1966, U.S. Dist. Ct. Mass. 1969. Patent atty. Bethlehem (Pa.) Steel, 1966-68, Mohawk Data Scis., Stoneham, Mass., 1968-72, Chittick, Thompson & Pfund, Boston, Mass., 1972-73; from patent atty. to v.p. and gen. counsel Digital Equipment Corp., Maynard, Mass., 1973—; bd. dirs. N.E. chpt. Am. Corp. Coun. Assn., Ashland, Mass., Associated Industries Mass., Boston; mem. legal quality coun. Conf. Bd. Trustee Mass. Taxpayers Found. Mem. ABA, Am. Soc. Corp. Secs., Internat. Bar Assn., Law Coun. Mfrs.' Alliance for Productivity & Innovation. Avocations: squash, skiing. Home: 73 Edgewater Dr Needham MA 02192 Office: Digital Equipment Corp 111 Powder Mill Rd Maynard MA 01754-1482

SIEKMANN, DONALD CHARLES, accountant; b. St. Louis, July 2, 1938; s. Elmer Charles and Mabel Louise (Blue) S.; m. Linda Lee Knowles, Sept. 10, 1966; 1 child, Brian Charles. BS, Washington U., St. Louis, 1960. CPA, Ohio, Ga. Regional mng. ptnr. Arthur Andersen & Co., Cin., 1960—. Columnist Cin. Enquirer, 1983-86, Gannett News Services, 1983-86; editor "Tax Clinic" column Tax Advisor mag., 1974-75. Mem. bd. Cin. Zool. Soc., 1985-88; officer, bd. dirs. Cin. Found. for Pub. TV, 1984-88, Cin. Symphony Orch., 1973-85, Cin. Ballet Co., 1973-88, Cin. Theatrical Assn., Jewish Hosp., 1993—, Cin. Assn. for Performing Arts, 1992—, Cin. United Way, 1992—, Atlanta Opera, 1989-92, Atlanta Symphony Orch., 1989-92, Atlanta Ctr. Puppetry Arts, 1988-92, Cin. Nature Ctr., 1993-94. Mem. AICPA, Ohio Soc. CPAs, Cin. Country Club (trustee 1983-88), Optimists Club (pres. Queen City chpt. 1986). Lutheran. Club: Cin. Country (trustee 1983-88). Home: 5495 Waring Dr Cincinnati OH 45243 Office: Arthur Andersen & Co 425 Walnut St Ste 1500 Cincinnati OH 45202-1801

SIELICKI-KORCZAK, BORIS ZDZISLAW, political educator, investigative consultant; b. Wilno, Lithuania, Poland, Feb. 11, 1939; came to U.S., 1980; s. Wiltold and Antonina (Arciszewski) Sielicki-Korczak; m. Barbara Maria Kaniewski, May 29, 1971; children: Robert, Sandra. MSC, Warsaw U., 1964, Kunstindustriskole, Copenhagen, 1971; PhD, Basel (Switzerland) U., 1973. Pres. Impolex Ltd., Copenhagen, 1970-79; field operative Europe CIA, 1983-90; pres., educator Anti-Soviet Rsch. Ctr., McLean, Va., 1981-84; export dir. Worldwide Investment Ltd., Arlington, Va., 1985-87; pres. Amexim Internat. Co. Ltd., Arlington, 1986-89, BK & Assocs., Arlington, 1990—; pres. R.R. Internat. Ltd., Copenhagen, 1983-89; mng. dir. Securitas Inc., Arlington, 1986-87; multiple appearance on U.S. and fgn. TV shows as expert on terrorism, USSR and Russian intelligence and its ops. Author: A Man From Atlantis, 1976; designer anti-drug poster. Dir. Nat. Lyric Opera Co., Washington, 1981-91. Republican. Avocations: chess, classic music, travel, art, history. Office: Boris S de Korczak Inc PO Box 7091 Arlington VA 22207-0091

SIEMER, DEANNE CLEMENCE, lawyer; b. Buffalo, Dec. 25, 1940; d. Edward D. and Dorothy J. (Helsdon) S.; m. Howard P. Willens; 1 child, Jason L. BA, George Washington U., 1962; LLB, Harvard U., 1968. Bar: N.Y. 1968, D.C. 1969, Md. 1972, Trust Ter. 1976. Economist Office of

Mgmt. and Budget, Washington, 1964-67; assoc., then ptnr. Wilmer, Cutler & Pickering, Washington, 1968-90; ptnr. Pillsbury, Madison & Sutro, Washington, 1990—; gen. counsel U.S. Dept. of Def., Washington, 1977-79; spl. asst. to sec. U.S. Dept. of Energy, Washington, 1979-80. Author: Tangible Evidence, 1984, 2d edit., 1989, Understanding Modern Ethical Standards, 1985, Manual on Litigation Support Databases, 1986, supplement, 1992. Mem. Lawyers Com. for Civil Rights, Washington, 1973—; mediator D.C. Superior Ct., Washington, 1986—, U.S. Ct. Appeals, Washington, 1988—; chair Nat. Inst. Trial Advocacy, Am. Law Inst., 1995—. Recipient Citation Air Force Assn., 1977, Dist. Pub. Service medal Sec. of Def., 1979, Commendation Pres. of U.S. 1981. Mem. ABA, ATLA, D.C. Bar Assn., No. Marianas Bar Assn., Womens Bar Assn. Episcopalian. Office: Pillsbury Madison & Sutro 1667 K St NW Washington DC 20006-1605

SIEMER, FRED HAROLD, securities analyst; b. Mt. Vernon, N.Y., Apr. 3, 1937; s. Fred Henry and Doris Sophie (Peymann) S.; m. Barbara Jean Behrmann, May 20, 1960 (div. 1980); children: Carolyn Doris Baird, Charles Frederick, Janet Ann Bruno; m. Mary Brittain Brown, Aug. 20, 1981. BA in Chemistry, Colgate U., Hamilton, N.Y., 1958; MBA, Fairleigh Dickinson U., Rutherford, N.J., 1970. Cert. fin. analyst. Mgr. rsch. planning Allied Chem. Corp., Morristown, N.J., 1962-69; mgr. econ. evaluation BASF Corp., Parsippany, N.J., 1969-72; chems. analyst Prudential Ins. Co., Newark, 1972-74; v.p. rsch. F.Eberstadt & Co., Inc., N.Y.C., 1974-80, Smith Barney Harris Upham, N.Y.C., 1980-85; pres. F.H. Siemer & Co., Inc., N.Y.C., 1985-93, F. H. Siemer & Co., Inc., N.Y.C., 1993—. Editor: Chemical Research For Wall St.; contbr. articles to profl. jours. With U.S. Army, 1959-62. Mem. Am. Chem. Soc., N.Y. Soc. Securities Analysts, Assn. for Investment Mgmt. and Rsch., Chem. Analysts of N.Y. and Chem. Specialists of N.Y., Chem. Mktg. Rsch. Assn., Chem. Mktg. Rsch. and Econs. Grp., Soc. de Chemie Indsl. Avocations: reading, walking, tennis, music. Office: F H Siemer & CoInc 500 E 83rd St New York NY 10028-7247

SIEMER, PAUL JENNINGS, public relations executive; b. St. Louis, Jan. 24, 1946; s. Robert Vincent and Pauline Mary (Nece) S.; m. Susan MacDonald Arnott, Aug. 26, 1967. Student, U. Notre Dame, 1964-67. Reporter South Bend Tribune, Ind., 1967-69; reporter St. Louis Globe-Democrat, 1969-76; account exec. Fleishman-Hillard Inc., St. Louis, 1976-79, v.p., sr. ptnr., 1979-84, exec. v.p., sr. ptnr., 1984—. Mem. Pub. Relations Soc. Am. Roman Catholic. Club: St. Louis Press. Home: 2961 Hatherly Dr Saint Louis MO 63121-4551

SIENER, WILLIAM HAROLD, museum director, historian, consultant; b. Silver Creek, N.Y., Feb. 24, 1945; s. Harold Edwin and Christian (Dovesmith) S.; m. Estelle Minervino, Dec. 27, 1968; children: Alison Louise, Christian Dovesmith, Geoffrey David. AB, U. Rochester, 1967; MAT, U. Chgo., 1970; MA, U. Southampton, Eng., 1973; PhD, College William & Mary, 1982. Cert. social studies tchr. N.Y. Tchr. Cen. YMCA High Sch., Chgo., 1968-71; dir. youth svcs. City of Niagara Falls (N.Y.) Youth Bd., 1973; historian Gloucester County (Va.) Hist. Bicentennial Com., 1976; exec. dir. Wyo. Hist. and Geol. Soc., Wilkes-Barre, Pa., 1976-82; curator of history Rochester (N.Y.) Mus. and Sci. Ctr., 1982-86; exec. dir. Buffalo and Erie County (N.Y.) Hist. Soc., 1986—; curator various gallery exhibits, 1976—; mem. adv. bds. Pa. State Hist. Records, 1982, Documentary Heritage Program, Buffalo, 1986-92; adj. assoc. prof. dept. History Buffalo State Coll. 1987—; historian County of Erie, Buffalo, 1988—; cons. Arts Devel. Svcs., Buffalo, 1983, OAS, The Bahamas, 1984, 85, St. Lucia, 1985, 89; mem. Buffalo Preservation Bd., 1986-91; speaker N.Y. Speakers in the Humanities program N.Y. Coun. Humanities, 1992—. Author: (brochure) Silent Sentinel of the Shallow Seas, 1988; (catalog) The Lake Erie Shore: Views from Across the Border; co-author: (exhibit catalog) Children and Their Samplers, 1790-1850, 1983; co-editor: (manuscript guide) A Guide to Gloucester County Virginia, Historical Manuscripts, 1650-1865, 1976.; book and exhibit reviewer profl. jours., 1981—. Active Buffalo Preservation Bd., 1986-91, Leadership Buffalo, 1991; clk. of session Westminster Presbyn. Ch., Buffalo, 1991-92, Choir of Men & Boys St. Paul's Episc. Cathedral, Buffalo, 1993—; del. People to People Citizen Amb. Program Exchange to Russia, 1993; mem. adv. bd. Shakespeare in Delaware Park, Inc., Buffalo, 1993—; trustee Cmty. Music Sch., Buffalo, 1993—; mem. N.Y. Commr. of Edn.'s Task Force on the Future of Mus. in N.Y. State, 1994—. Mem. Am. Assn. Mus. (panel mem. 1985), Mid-Atlantic Assn. Mus. (chmn. internat. com. 1987-88), Am. Assn. for State and Local History, Nat. Trust for Hist. Preservation, Inst. Early Am. History and Culture (assoc.), Mid-Atlantic Assn. Mus's (vice-chmn. small mus. com. 1981-82, panel mem. 1982), Rotary. Democrat. Avocations: travel, camping, swimming, music, photography. Home: 264 Middlesex Rd Buffalo NY 14216-3118 Office: Buffalo/Erie County Hist Soc 25 Nottingham Ct Buffalo NY 14216-3119

SIENKIEWICZ, JOHN CASIMIR, insurance company executive; b. Doylestown, Pa., Oct. 8, 1933; s. Casimir Anthony and Jane (Patten) S.; B.A., Princeton U., 1955; m. Patricia Davis, May 12, 1956; children—Mark Patton, Peter Casimir. Partner, Hutchinson, Rivinus & Co., ins. brokers, Phila., 1957-69; with Alexander & Alexander Services Inc., ins. brokers, Phila., 1969—, sr. v.p., dir., 1971—; pres., chief exec. officer Alex & Alex Internat., 1976-86. Served to lt. USNR, 1955-57. Clubs: Gulph Mills Golf, Racquet, Princeton (Phila.); Bedens Brook (Princeton); Pine Valley Golf (Clementon, N.J.); River (N.Y.C.); Sunningdale Golf (Eng.). Avocations: golf, reading, tennis. Home: 55 Winfield Rd Princeton NJ 08540-2431 Office: Alexander & Alexander Svcs 1211 Ave Of The Americas New York NY 10036-8701

SIEPI, CESARE, opera singer; b. Milan, Italy, Feb. 10, 1923. Operatic debut in Rigoletto, Schio, 1941, Il Nabucco, LaScala Opera, Milan, 1946, Don Carlo, Met. Opera, N.Y.C., 1950; soloist debut in, Carnegie Hall, N.Y.C., 1951; sang in Mozart and Verdi requiems, Edinburgh Festival, Albert Hall, London; leading bass at, Salzburg Festival, LaScala, Milan; appeared in: play Bravo Giovanni, 1962; appeared: play Vienna Staatsoper; made many opera recordings for, London Records. (Winner Nat. Singing Competition, Florence 1941, recipient Italy's Orfeo award 1956). Operatic debut, Rigoletto, Schio, at age of 18. Home: 12095 Brookfield Club Dr Roswell GA 30075-1261 Office: c/o SA Gorlinsky Ltd, 33 Dover St, London W1X 4NJ, England

SIEPMANN, JOERN ILJA, chemistry educator; b. Cologne, Germany, June 28, 1964; came to U.S., 1993; m. Silke Schmid, Mar. 22, 1990; 1 child, Tim Christoph. PhD, Cambridge (Eng.) U., 1992. Postdoctoral fellow IBM Zurich Rsch. Lab.; Rüschlikon, Switzerland, 1991-92, Koninklijke/Shell Lab., Amsterdam, The Netherlands, 1992-93; rsch. assoc. U. Pa., Phila., 1993-94; asst. prof. chemistry U. Minn., Mpls., 1994—. Recipient Dreyfus New Faculty award Dreyfus Found., 1994. Mem. AIChE, Am. Chem. Soc. Achievements include research on configurational bias Monte Carlo of complex fluids. Office: U Minn Dept Chemistry 207 Pleasant St SE Minneapolis MN 55455-0431

SIERACKI, ALOYSIUS ALFRED, religious organization administrator; b. Chgo., Nov. 5, 1929; s. Peter Paul and Mary Ann (Kroll) S. BS in Chem. Engring., Ill. Inst. Tech., 1951; cert. in theology, Whitefriars Hall, Washington, 1960, MS in Math., U. Notre Dame, 1962. Ordained priest Roman Cath. Ch., 1959. Secondary sch. tchr. Mt. Carmel High Sch., Chgo., 1960-67; instr. chemistry and math. Mt. Carmel Coll., Niagara Falls, Ont., Can., 1967-68; instr. math. Marquette U., Milw., 1968-75; assoc. pastor St. Agnes Parish, Phoenix, 1975-81; provincial dir. lay Carmelites in U.S. and Can. Aylesford Carmelite Ctr., Darien, Ill., 1981—; chmn. Lay Carmelite Commn., 1987—. Author: Songs for God, 1990; editor: Carmel's Call, 10th edit., 1991; editor Aylesford Carmelite Newsletter, 1984—; contbr. articles to profl. jours. With U.S. Army, 1951-53. Democrat. Avocations: walking, poetry. Office: Aylesford Carmelite Ctr 8501 Bailey Rd Darien IL 60561-8417

SIERCK, ALEXANDER WENTWORTH, lawyer; b. N.Y.C., Dec. 15, 1940; s. Herbert Wentworth and Phebe Ann (Steers) S.; m. Susan Stephanie Arthur, Aug. 29, 1964; children: Carsten Wentworth, Alexander Arthur, Sarah Stephanie. BA, U. Va., 1962, JD, 1965. Bar: N.Y. 1965, D.C. 1968. Assoc. Wald Harkrader & Ross, Washington, 1968-74, ptnr., 1974-78; chmn. trade policy Antitrust div. U.S. Dept. Justice, Washington, 1978-80; ptnr. Beveridge & Diamond, Washington, 1980-92, Cameron & Hornbostel,

Washington, 1992—. Office: Cameron & Hornbostel 818 Connecticut Ave NW Ste 700 Washington DC 20006-2702

SIERLES, FREDERICK STEPHEN, psychiatrist, educator; b. Bklyn., Nov. 9, 1942; s. Samuel and Elizabeth (Meiselman) S.; m. Laurene Harriet Cohn, Oct. 25, 1970 (div. Aug. 1990); children: Hannah Beth, Joshua Caleb. AB, Columbia U., 1963; MD, Chgo. Med. Sch., 1967. Diplomate Am. Bd. Psychiatry and Neurology. Intern Cook County Hosp., Chgo., 1967-68; resident in psychiatry Mt. Sinai Hosp., N.Y.C., 1968-69, Chgo. Med. Sch., 1969-71, chief resident, 1970-71; staff psychiatrist U.S Reynolds Army Hosp., Ft. Sill, Okla., 1971-73; assoc. attending psychiatrist Mt. Sinai Hosp., Chgo., 1973-74; instr. psychiatry Chgo. Med. Sch., North Chicago, 1973-74, dir. undergrad. edn. in psychiatry, 1974-94, asst. prof., 1974-78, assoc. prof., 1978-88, prof., Finch U. Health Scis, Chgo. Med. Sch., 1988—, vice chmn., 1990-94, acting chmn., 1994—, chmn. ednl. affairs com., 1983-85, 86—, chmn. univ. tenure com. 1983-84, 88-94; cons. psychiatry Cook County Hosp., 1974-79, St. Mary of Nazareth Hosp., 1979-84, Great Lakes Naval Hosp., 1987-90, Jackson Park Hosp., 1987-89, Mt. Sinai Hosp., 1988—; chief Mental Health Clinic, North Chicago VA Hosp., 1982-85, chief psychiatry svc., 1983-85. Author: (with others) General Hospital Psychiatry, 1985, Behavioral Science for the Boreds, 1987, rev. 2d edit., 1989, rev. 3rd edit., 1993; editor: Clinical Behavioral Science, 1982, Behavioral Science for Medical Students, 1992; contbr. articles to profl. jours. Coach Glenview (Ill.) Youth Baseball, 1987-89, mgr., 1990 (age 10-12 Glenview World Series winner 1990), Glenview Tennis Club, 1986-90 (3.5 Men's Doubles League winner 1989-90). Maj., M.C., U.S. Army, 1971-73. Recipient Ganser Meml. award Mt. Sinai Hosp., 1970, Nancy C. Roeske award, 1991, Lawrence R. Medoff award, 1993; named Prof. of Yr. Chgo. Med. Sch., 1977, 80, 83, Disting. Alumnus, 1993; N.Y. State Regents scholar, 1959-63; NIMH grantee, 1974-83, Chgo. Med. Sch. grantee, 1974-83. Fellow Am. Psychiat. Assn. (coun. edn. & career devel. 1993—); mem. Am. Coll. Psychiatrists, Ill. Psychiat. Soc. (fellowship com. 1985—), Columbia Coll. Alumni Secondary Schs. Com., Assn. Dirs. Med. Student Edn. in Psychiatry (exec. council 1985—, chmn. program com. 1987-88, treas. 1989-91, pres. elect 1991-93, pres. 1993—), Nat. Assn. VA Physicians (sec.-treas. North Chgo. chpt. 1984-85), Sigma Xi, Alpha Omega Alpha, Phi Epsilon Pi. Office: Finch U Health Sci Chgo Med Sch 3333 Green Bay Rd North Chicago IL 60064-3095

SIERRA, ROBERTO, composer, music educator; b. Vega Baja, P.R., Oct. 9, 1953. Grad., P.R. Conservatory of Music, U. P.R., 1976; postgrad., Royal Coll. Music, London, U. London, 1976-78, Inst. Sonology, Utrecht, The Netherlands, 1978; studied with Gyorgy Ligeti, Hamberg (Germany) Hochschule for Music, 1979-82. Asst. dir. cultural activities dept. U. P.R., 1983-85, dir., 1985-86, dean of studies, 1986-87; chancellor P.R. Conservatory of Music, 1987—; prof. composition Cornell U., Ithaca, N.Y., 1992—; composer-in-residence Milw. Symphony Orch., 1989-92. Compositions include: (orchestral) Jubilo, 1985, Cuatro ensayos orquestales, 1986, Glosas for piano and orch., 1987, Deascargo, 1988, Sasima, 1990; (chamber) Tiempo Muerto for string quartet, 1978, Salsa on the C String for cello and piano, 1981, Seis piezas fáciles for two violins, 1982, Bongo-O for percussion, 1982, Salsa for wind quintet, 1983, Cinco bocetos for clarinet, 1984, Concierto Nocturnal for harsichord, flute, clarinet, oboe, violin and cello, 1985, Memorias Tropicales for string quartet, 1985, El sueño de Antonia for clarinet and percussion, 1985, Toccata y Lamento for guitar, 1987, Essays for wind quintet, 1987, Mano a Mano for two percussionists, 1987, Introducción y Descarga for piano, brass quintet and percussion, 1988, Tributo for harp, flute, clarinet and string quartet, 1988; (piano) Descarga en sol, 1981; (stage) El Mensajero de Plata for chamber opera, 1984, El Contemplado for ballet, 1987; (harpsichord) Tres Miniaturas, 1982, Con Salsa, 1984; (vocal) Cantos populares for chorus, 1983, Doña Rosita, 1985, Invocaciones, 1986, Glosa a la sombra, 1987; also, Entre terceras for 2 synthesizers and computer, 1988. Office: Conservatorio de Musica de PR Apt 41227, Minillas Station Santurce San Juan PR 00940 also: care Sandra Elm 411 W 21st St New York NY 10011*

SIERRA, RUBEN ANGEL GARCIA, professional baseball player; b. Rio Piedras, P.R., Oct. 6, 1965. Grad. high sch., Rio Piedras, P.R. Baseball player Tex. Rangers, 1982-92, Oakland Athletics, 1992—. Named Am. League Player of Yr., Sporting News, 1989, recipient Silver Slugger award, 1989; named to All-Star team, 1989, 91-92, 94; Am. League RBI Leader, 1989. Office: Oakland-Alameda County Coliseum 7000 Coliseum Way Oakland CA 94621-1945*

SIESS, CHESTER PAUL, civil engineering educator; b. Alexandria, La., July 28, 1916; s. Leo C. and Adele (Liebreich) S.; m. Helen Kranson, Oct. 5, 1941; 1 dau., Judith Ann. B.S., La. State U., 1936; M.S., U. Ill., 1939, Ph.D., 1948. Party chief La. Hwy. Commn., 1936-37; research asst. U. Ill., 1937-39; soil engr. Chgo. Subway Project, 1939-41; engr., draftsman N.Y.C. R.R. Co., 1941; mem. faculty U. Ill., 1941—, prof. civil engring., 1955-78, emeritus, head dept. civil engring., 1973-78; mem. adv. com. on reactor safeguards Nuclear Regulatory Commn., 1968-92, chmn., 1972. Recipient award Concrete Reinforcing Steel Inst., 1956, Alumni Honor award for disting. service in engring. U. Ill., 1985, Disting. Service award NRC, 1987; named to Engring. Hall of Distinction, La. State U., 1979. Mem. ASCE (hon. mem., Rsch. prize 1956, Howard medal 1968, Reese award 1970), Nat. Acad. Engring., Am. Concrete Inst. (pres. 1974—, Wason medal 1949, Turner medal 1964, hon. mem.). Reinforced Concrete Rsch. coun. (chmn. 1968-80, Baose award 1974), Internat. Assn. Bridge and Structural Engring., Sigma Xi, Tau Beta Pi, Phi Kappa Phi, Omicron Delta Kappa, Gamma Alpha, Chi Epsilon (chap. hon., nat. hon.). Research in reinforced and prestressed concrete structures and hwy. bridges. Home: 401 Burwash Dr Savoy IL 61874-9599 Office: Newmark Lab 205 N Mathews Ave Urbana IL 61801-2350

SIEVER, RAYMOND, geology educator; b. Chgo., Sept. 14, 1923; s. Leo and Lillie (Katz) S.; m. Doris Fisher, Mar. 31, 1945; children—Larry Joseph, Michael David. B.S., U. Chgo., 1943, M.S., 1947, Ph.D., 1950; M.A. (hon.), Harvard U., 1960. With Ill. Geol. Survey, 1943-44, 47-56, geologist, 1953-56; research assoc. NSF sr. postdoctoral fellow Harvard U., 1956-57, mem. faculty, 1957—, prof. geology, 1965-94, prof. geology emeritus, 1994—, chmn. dept. geol. scis., 1968-71, 76-81; assoc. geology Woods Hole (Mass.) Oceanographic Instn., 1957-65; cons. to industry and govt., 1957—. Author: (with others) Geology of Sandstones, 1965, Sand and Sandstone, 1972, 2d edit., 1987, Earth, 4th edit. 1986, Planet Earth, 1974, Energy and Environment, 1978, Sand, 1988, Understanding Earth, 1994; also numerous articles, papers. Served with USAAF, 1944-46. Recipient Pres.'s award Am. Assn. Petroleum Geologists, 1952. Fellow AAAS, Am. Acad. Arts and Scis., Geol. Soc. Am.; mem. Geochem. Soc. (pres. organic geochemistry group 1965), Am. Geophys. Union, Soc. Sedimentary Geology (Best Paper awards 1957, 91, hon. 1990). Home: 38 Avon St Cambridge MA 02138-1525 Office: Harvard U Dept Earth and Planetary Scis Cambridge MA 02138

SIEVERS, ALBERT JOHN, III, physics educator; b. Oakland, Calif., June 28, 1933; s. Albert John and Martha (McDowell) S.; m. Betsy Floy Ross, Feb. 6, 1959; children: Karla Jean, John Charles, Martha Caroline, Sylvia Jane. B.A., U. Calif.-Berkeley, 1958, Ph.D., 1962. Machinist, Varian Assocs., Palo Alto, Calif., 1951-58; research assoc. Cornell U., 1962-64, asst. prof. physics, 1964-67, assoc. prof., 1967-71, prof., 1971—; cons. Lockheed Rsch. Coun., 1969—, GM Corp., 1978—; lectr. NATO Summer Sch., Italy, 1966, Holland, 1968; E.L. Nichols chair Cornell U., 1992—. Contbr. editorial bd.: Solar Energy Materials. Named Alexander von Humboldt sr. scientist, 1985; NSF sr. postdoctoral fellow, 1970-71, Erskine fellow U. Canterbury, New Zealand, 1976, 93. Fellow Optical Soc. Am., Am. Phys. Soc. (Frank Isakson prize 1988); mem. AAAS, N.Y. Acad. Scis., Sierra Club., Phi Beta Kappa, Sigma Xi. Research far infrared spectroscopy of solids. Home: 115 Winston Dr Ithaca NY 14850-1935

SIEVERS, ROBERT H., wholesale distributing company executive; b. San Francisco, Nov. 2, 1941; s. Howard H. and Minnie A. (Sommers) S.; m. Maureen; children: Kirk Robert, Allison Jill, Julie Paige, Jennifer Lori. B.A. in Finance, Calif. State U., 1968. C.P.A., Calif. Audit mgr. Hurdman and Cranston, San Francisco, 1968-76; treas. Falstaff Brewing Corp., San Francisco, 1976-77, also dir.; v.p. fin. Capital Film Labs., Washington, 1977-81; also v.p. fin. Forman Bros. Inc., and Forman Distbg. Co. of Va., Inc. Wholesale Distbrs., 1981—. Mem. AICPA, Calif. Soc. CPAs, D.C. Inst.

CPAs. Home: 5522 Southwick St Bethesda MD 20817-3544 Office: 4235 Sheriff Rd NE Washington DC 20019-3795

SIEVERTS, FRANK ARNE, government official; b. Frankfurt, Fed. Republic Germany, June 19, 1933; s. Helmut J. and Cecile M. (Behrendt) S.; m. Jane Woodbridge, Dec. 31, 1957 (div.); children: Lisa, Michael; m. Sue Hubbell, Feb. 13, 1988; 1 stepchild, Brian. BA, Swarthmore Coll., 1955; M in Philosophy (Rhodes Scholar), Balliol Coll. Oxford U., 1957; postgrad., Nuffield Coll., 1957-59. News corr. Time mag., London and Washington, 1959-60; legis. asst. U.S. Senator Washington, 1960-62; with Dept. of State, Washington, 1962-86, spl. asst. to ambassador at large Averell Harriman, 1966-68, adviser on prisoner of war matters to U.S. delegation to Vietnam peace talks, spl. asst. to dep. sec. of state for prisoner of war matters, 1969-75, dep. asst. sec. for prisoner of war and missing in action matters, 1976—, dep. asst. sec. for refugee and migration affairs, 1978—; minister-counselor for humanitarian affairs U.S. Mission, Geneva, 1980—; spl. asst. for refugee programs, 1982-86; spokesman for Com. on Fgn. Relations U.S. Senate, 1987—; mem. advance team for release Am. prisoners of war, Hanoi, 1973. Editorial bd.: The Am. Oxonian. Mem. U.S. delegation to 20th Internat. Conf. Red Cross, Vienna, 1965, 21st Conf., Istanbul, 1969, 22d Conf., Tehran, 1973; chmn. 23d Conf., Bucharest, 1977, 24th Conf., Manila, 1981, 25th Conf., Geneva, 1986; U.S. del. Diplomatic Conf. on Humanitarian Law in Armed Conflicts, Geneva, 1974-77, to exec. com. of UN High Commn. for Refugees, 1978, 79, 80; staff dir. Indochinese Refugee panel, 1986. Mem. Am. Assn. Rhodes Scholars (bd. dirs.). Office: US Senate Com On Fgn Relations Washington DC 20510

SIEWIOREK, DANIEL PAUL, computer science educator, researcher; b. Cleve., June 2, 1946; s. Frank Stanley and Lena Mae (Pozum) S.; m. Karon Diane Walker, Aug. 5, 1972; children: Nora Ann, Gail Marie. B.S. in Elec. Engring., U. Mich., 1968; M.S. in Elec. Engring., Stanford U., 1969, Ph.D. in Elec. Engring., 1972. Asst. prof. computer sci. and elec. engring. Carnegie-Mellon U., Pitts., 1972-76, assoc. prof., 1976-79, prof., 1979—, Buhl prof., 1994—; cons. Digital Equipment Corp., Maynard, Mass., United Techs., Hartford, Conn., Systems Tech. Devel., Reston, Va. Author: (with H. Stone) Introduction to Computer Organization and Data Structures, 1975, (with Bell and Newell) Computer Structures: Principles and Examples, 1982, (with Swarz) The Theory and Practice of Reliable System Design, 1982, (with Barbacci) The Design and Analysis of Instruction Set Processors, 1982, (with Gehringer and Segall) Parallel Processing: The Cm* Experience, 1987, (with Birmingham and Gupta) Automating the Design of Computer Systems: The Micon Project, 1992, (with Koopman) The Architecture of Supercomputers: Titan, A Case Study, 1992, (with Swarz) Reliable Computer Systems: Design and Reliability, 1992. John Huntington Found. scholar, 1964; Jonathan Logan scholar, 1964-68; Tektronix fellow, 1968; recipient Frederick Emmons Terman award Am. Soc. Engring. Edn., 1983; Eckert-Mauchly award IEEE/ACM, 1988. Fellow IEEE (bmm. tech. com. on fault tolerant computing 1981-83, disting. lectr. 1981, disting. visitor 1981-82), Assn. Computing Machinery (dir. spl. interest group on computer architecture 1974-78); mem. Marine Tech. Soc., Sigma Xi, Tau Beta Pi, Eta Kappa Nu. Home: 1259 Bellerock St Pittsburgh PA 15217-1230 Office: Carnegie-Mellon U Sch Computer Sci Pittsburgh PA 15213

SIFFERT, ROBERT SPENCER, orthopedic surgeon; b. N.Y.C., June 16, 1918; s. Oscar and Sadye (Rusoff) S.; m. Miriam Sand, June 29, 1941; children: Joan, Helen. A.B. with honors in Biology, NYU, 1939, M.D., 1943. Diplomate: Am. Bd. Orthopaedic Surgery, Nat. Bd. Med. Examiners. Intern Kings County Hosp., Bklyn., 1943; resident orthopaedic surgery Mt. Sinai Hosp., N.Y.C., 1946-49, fellow pathology, 1949-52, mem. staff, 1949—, dir. orthopaedic surgery, orthopaedic surgeon in chief, 1960-86, Lasker/Siffert Disting. Svc. prof., 1986—; practice medicine specializing in orthopaedic surgery N.Y.C., 1949—; dir. dept. orthopaedics City Hosp., Elmhurst, 1965-86; sr. orthopaedic cons. N.Y.C. Dept. Health, 1952-60; attending orthopaedic surgeon Blythedale Children's Hosp., Valhalla, N.Y., 1960-86, cons., 1986-90; prof., chmn. dept orthopaedics Mt. Sinai Sch. Medicine, 1966-86, Dr. Robert K. Lippmann prof. orthopedics, 1983-86, acting chmn. 1993-94. Contbr. articles to profl. jours. Mem. adv. bd. CARE-MEDICO, 1972-83, bd. dirs., 1981-83, chmn., 1981-83; bd. dirs. CARE, 1983-90; adv. bd. Orthopaedics Overseas, 1981-93; bd. dirs., mem. profl. adv. com. Easter Seal Soc. for Crippled Children and Adults, 1st v.p., 1977-79. Capt. USAAF, 1944-46, CBI. Decorated 4 Battle Stars; recipient annual award medicine N.Y. Pub. Health Assn., 1958, annual award medicine N.Y. Philanthropic League, 1959, Richman award for humanism in medicine Mt. Sinai Sch. Medicine, 1989. Fellow ACS, Am. Pub. Health Assn.; mem. Am. Orthopaedic Assn., Am. Acad. Orthopaedic Surgery (chmn. com. care handicapped child), Assn. Bone and Joint Surgeons, Internat. Soc. Orthopaedic Surgery and Traumatology, Internat. Skeletal Soc., Orthopaedic Research Soc., N.Y. Acad. Medicine (fellow orthopaedic sect. 1952, sec. 1962-63, chmn. 1963-64), N.Y. State Med. Soc. (chmn. orthopaedic sect. 1967-68), Century Assn. (N.Y.C.), Phi Beta Kappa, Alpha Omega Alpha. Office: 955 5th Ave New York NY 10021-1738

SIFNEOS, PETER EMANUEL, psychiatrist; b. Greece, Oct. 22, 1920; came to U.S., 1941, naturalized, 1944; s. Demitrios Z. and Mary E. (Lucas) S.; divorced; children: Ann L., Peter G., Jean C. B.Sc., Sorbonne, 1940; M.D., Harvard U., 1946. Diplomate: Am. Bd. Psychiatry. Intern Boston City Hosp., 1946-47; resident in psychiatry McLean Hosp., Belmont, Mass., 1950-52; chief resident Mass. Gen. Hosp., Boston, 1952-53; mem. staff, chief psychiat. clinic Mass. Gen. Hosp., 1954-68; fellow Harvard U. Sch. Public Health, 1953-54; mem. faculty Harvard U. Med. Sch., 1952—; prof. psychiatry, 1973-91, prof. emeritus, 1991—; staff, assoc. dir. psychiatry dept. Beth Israel Hosp., Boston, 1968—. Author: Ascent from Chaos, 1964, Short-Term Psychotherapy and Emotional Crisis, 1972, Short-Term Dynamic Psychotherapy and Emotional Crisis, 1972, Short-Term Dynamic Psychotherapy Evaluation and Technique, 1979, 2d edit., 1987, Short-Term Anxiety Provoking Psychotherapy, 1992; editor-in-chief Psychotherapy and Psychosomatics, 1974-91; also 117 articles. Served with AUS, 1944-46, 47-50. Fellow Am. Psychiat. Assn. (life); mem. AMA, Internat. Fedn. Med. Psychotherapy (v.p. 1976-88, bd. dirs. 1988—), Am. Psychosomatic Soc., Boston Psychoanalytic Soc. (life), Hellenic Psychosomatic Soc. (hon.), Italian Psychosomatic Soc. (hon.). Democrat. Home and Office: 59 Common St Belmont MA 02178 *The principles which helped me most have been a belief in good education, a fierce sense of non-conformity, a strong sense of independence, an admiration of creativity and new ideas, a love of writing, teaching, reading, classic music, traveling to lecture and conduct workshops, seminars all over North and South America and Europe, swimming, and luck in being healthy.*

SIFTON, CHARLES PROCTOR, federal judge; b. N.Y.C., Mar. 18, 1935; s. Paul F. and Claire G. S.; m. Susan Scott Rowland, May 20, 1986; children: Samuel, Tobias, John. A.B., Harvard U., 1957; LL.B., Columbia U., 1961. Bar: N.Y. 1961. Assoc. Cadwalader, Wickersham & Taft, 1961-62, 64-66; staff atty. U.S. Senate Fgn. Rels. Com., 1962-63; asst. U.S. atty. N.Y.C., 1966-69; ptnr. LeBoeuf, Lamb, Leiby and MacRae, N.Y.C., 1969-77; judge U.S. Dist. Ct. (ea. dist.) N.Y., Bklyn., 1977—. Mem. Bar Assn. City of N.Y. Office: US Dist Ct US Courthouse 225 Cadman Plz E Brooklyn NY 11201-1876

SIFTON, DAVID WHITTIER, magazine editor; b. N.Y.C., Sept. 12, 1940; s. David William and Dorothy (Whittier) S. B.A., Trinity Coll., Hartford, Conn., 1962; M.A., Stanford U., 1967. Editor Inside Edn., N.Y. State Edn. Dept., 1968-70; adminstrv. editor Med. Econs., Oradell, N.J., 1970-72; editor Drug Topics, Oradell, 1972-75; editor in chief Current Prescribing, Oradell, 1975-78, RN mag., Oradell, 1978-83; dir. spl. editorial projects Med. Econs. Co., 1983-90; mgr. PDR Devel., Oradell, 1990—; founder Physicians' Desk Reference on CD-ROM, PDR's Drug Interactions and Side Effects Index, PDR's Indications Index, Pocket PDR (handheld electronic database), The PDR Family Guide to Prescription Drugs, The PDR Family Guide to Women's Health, The PDR Family Guide to Nutrition and Health. Served to 1st lt. USAF, 1963-66. Decorated Air Force Commendation medal; grantee Ford Found., 1967. Mem. Am. Bus. Press (chmn. editorial com. 1975-76). Republican. Episcopalian. Office: Med Econs Co Inc 5 Paragon Dr Montvale NJ 07645-1725

SIFTON, ELISABETH, book publisher; b. N.Y.C., Jan. 13, 1939; d. Reinhold and Ursula (Keppel-Compton) Niebuhr; m. Charles P. Sifton, 1962

(div. 1984); children: Peter Samuel, Charles Tobias, John Paul Gustav. B.A. magna cum laude, Radcliffe Coll., Cambridge, Mass., 1960; postgrad., U. Paris, 1960-61. Asst. to dep. asst. sec. of state U.S. Dept. of State, Washington, 1961-62; editorial asst., assoc. editor, editor, sr. editor Frederick A. Praeger Pubs., N.Y.C., 1962-68; editor, sr. editor, editor-in-chief The Viking Press, N.Y.C., 1969-83; v.p., pub. Elisabeth Sifton Books, Viking Penguin, N.Y.C., 1984-87; exec. v.p. Alfred A. Knopf, Inc., N.Y.C., 1987-92; sr. v.p. Farrar, Straus & Giroux, 1993—; pub. Hill & Wang, 1993—. Fulbright fellow, 1960-61. Democrat. Episcopalian. Home: 15 Claremont Ave New York NY 10027 Office: Farrar Straus & Giroux 19 Union Sq W New York NY 10003-3304

SIFTON, MICHAEL CLIFFORD, broadcaster, publisher; b. Toronto, Ont., Can., Jan. 21, 1931; s. Clifford and Doris Margaret (Greene) S.; m. Heather Ann McLean, Sept. 8, 1956; children: Clifford McLean, Michael Gregory, Derek Andrew. Student, U. Western Ont., 1950-54. Pres. Armadale Co. Ltd., Armadale Enterprises Ltd., Regina Leader-Post Ltd., Armadale Pubs. Ltd. (Saskatoon Star-Phoenix), Taber Times, Dauphin Herald, Yorkton This Week, Armadale Communications Ltd., Toronto Airways Ltd., Sta. CKOC/K-103 FM, Hamilton; chmn. Highland Chev-Olds Cadillac Ltd., Armadale Proprieties Ltd. Served to lt. with Can. mil. Named hon. col. 411th Air Res. Squadron, 1975; recipient Can. Forces Decoration. Mem. Can. Assn. Family Enterprise, Toronto Art Gallery, Can. Daily Newspaper Assn., Can. Assn. Airport Execs., Am. Newspapers Pubs. Assn., Royal Winter Fair (com. mem.), Toronto Club, Toronto and North York Hunt Club, Toronto Polo Club (pres.), Saskatoon Club, Can. Club, Empire Club, Order of Can. Mem. Anglican Ch. of Canada. Avocations: polo, flying, riding, skiing, water sports. Office: The Leader Post, Victoria Ave & Park St, Regina, SK Canada S4P 3G4

SIFTON, PATRICIA ANNE, library educator; b. London, Ont., Can., Nov. 23, 1929; d. Francis Wilbur Moore and Bessie Irene (O'Brien) Wood; m. Douglas Clare Dodge Sifton, Jan. 12, 1953 (div. 1980); children: Pamela, Julie, Noel, Eric, Todd. BA, U. W. Ont., Can., 1952; MLS, U. W. Ont., 1971. Tchr. Oxford County Sch. Bd., Woodstock, Ont., Can., 1969-75; merchandising mgr. Scholars Choice Ltd., Stratford, Ont., Can., 1975-78; instr. Fanshawe Coll., London, Ont., Can., 1978-80; program head U. Coll. Fraser Valley, Abbotsford, B.C., 1980—. Author: DDC 20, 1989, Biblio-Bytes, 1992. Mem. Can. Libr. Assn., B.C. Libr. Assn. Home: 2152 Dolphin Crescent, Clearbrook, BC Canada V3T 3T1 Office: Univ Coll Fraser Valley, 33844 King Rd RR 2, Abbotsford, BC Canada V2S 4N2

SIGAL, ISRAEL MICHAEL, mathematics educator; b. Kiev, Ukraine, Aug. 31, 1945; came to U.S., 1978; s. Moshe I. and Eva (Guz) S.; m. Brenda Lynn Tipper, Mar. 21, 1993; children: Alexander, Daniel. BA, Gorky (Russia) U., 1968; PhD, Tel-Aviv U., 1976. Postdoctoral fellow Swiss Inst. Tech., Zürichand, Switzerland, 1976-78; asst. prof. Princeton (N.J.) U., 1978-81; R.H. Revson sr. scientist Weizmann Inst., Rehovot, Israel, 1981-85; prof. U. Calif., Irvine, 1984-90, U. Toronto, Ont., Can., 1985—; invited spkr. various confs. in field. Editor Revs. Math. Physics, 1991—, Duke Math. Jour., 1991—, Internat. Rsch. Notices, 1991—; contbr. articles to profl. and sci. publs. I.W. Killam Rsch. fellow I.W. Killam Found., 1989-91; Recipient of John L. SyngeAwd., 1993, Royal Soc. Can. Fellow Royal Soc. Can. (John L. Synge award 1993). Office: U Toronto Dept Math, 100 St George St, Toronto, ON Canada M5S 1A1

SIGAL, MICHAEL STEPHEN, lawyer; b. Chgo., July 9, 1942; s. Carl I. and Evelyn (Wallack) S.; m. Kass M. Flaherty, May 16, 1971; 1 child, Sarah Caroline. BS, U. Wis.-Madison, 1964; JD, U. Chgo., 1967. Bar: Ill. 1967, U.S. Dist. Ct. (no. dist.) Ill. 1967. Assoc. firm Sidley & Austin and predecessor firm, Chgo., 1967-73, ptnr., 1973—. Mem. U. Chgo. Law Rev., 1965. Bd. dirs. EMRE Diagnostic Services, Inc., affiliate Michael Reese Hosp., Chgo., 1982-91, The Mary Meyer Sch., Chgo., 1986-87. Mem. ABA, Chgo. Bar Assn., Phi Beta Kappa, Phi Kappa Phi, Phi Eta Sigma. Jewish. Clubs: Law, Monroe (Chgo.); Mill Creek Hunt (St. dist. 1992—, Wadsworth, Ill.). Home: 2180 Wilmot Rd Bannockburn IL 60015-1556 Office: Sidley & Austin 1 First Nat Plz Chicago IL 60603

SIGALL, HAROLD FRED, psychology educator; b. N.Y.C., June 29, 1943; s. Walter and Regine (Goldenberg) S.; m. Brenda Ann Alpert, Aug. 8, 1965; children: Elana, Jennifer, Emily. BS, CUNY, 1964; PhD, U. Tex., 1968. Asst. prof. psychology U. Rochester, N.Y., 1968-72; assoc. prof. U. Md. College Park, 1972-78, prof., 1978—; dir. grad. program in social psychology; consulting editor Journal of Applied Social psychology, 1992—; cons. social research and decision making to numerous orgns., lectr. Smithsonian Inst., Washington, 1984, 85. Editor Personality and Social Psychology Bull., 1977-81; contbr. numerous articles to profl. jours. Bd. dirs. Columbia (Md.) Jewish Congregation, 1985-87, Howard County (Md.) Jewish Cmty. Soc., Columbia, 1986-87; mem. Human Rights Commn., Howard County, 1994-95. NDEA fellow, 1967-68, Danforth Found. fellow, 1970-71. Fellow Am. Psychol. Assn., Am. Psychol. Soc.; mem. Soc. Exptl. Social Psychology. Democrat. Home: 5060 Castlemoor Dr Columbia MD 21044-1454 Office: U of Md Dept Psychology College Park MD 20742

SIGALOS, GEORGE PETER, corporate executive; b. Chgo., Mar. 24, 1964; s. Peter George and Stella (Pantel) S. BA, Am. U., 1986. Journalist AP, Washington, 1987; press aide U.S. Dept. Commerce, Washington, 1987-89, U.S. Dept. Treas., Washington, 1989-91; assoc. editor American Banker-Bond Buyer, Washington, 1991-93; chief assoc., cons. Sigalos Assocs., Chgo., 1993—. Editor Ctrl. Bank Watch, 1991-92, Holding Co. Watch, 1991-92; newspaper writer Chgo. Spectator, 1993. Chpt. pres. Young Ams. for Freedom, Chgo., 1993—; mem. Presdl. trust Rep. Nat. Com., 1992—; guest del. Rep. Nat. Conv., Houston, 1992. Mem. Soc. Profl. Journalists, U.S. Treas. Dept. Hist. Assn., The Masonry. Avocations: tennis, art, guitar, driving sports cars. Home: 786 Lenox Rd Glen Ellyn IL 60137-3964

SIGALOW, STEVEN E., lawyer; b. Akron, Ohio, May 12, 1950. BA, Ohio State U., 1972; JD, Case Western Reserve U., 1975. Bar: Ohio 1975. Ptnr. Jones, Day, Reavis & Pogue, Cleve. Mem. Phi Beta Kappa, Order of Coif. Office: Jones Day Reavis & Pogue 901 Lakeside Ave E Cleveland OH 44114-1190

SIGBAND, NORMAN BRUCE, management communication educator; b. Chgo., June 27, 1920; s. Max and Bessie S.; m. Joan C. Lyons, Aug. 3, 1944; children: Robin, Shelley, Betsy. BA, U. Chgo., 1940, MA, 1941, PhD, 1954; LHD (hon.), DePaul U., 1986. Asst. prof. bus. communication De Paul U. 1946-50, assoc. prof., 1950-54, prof., 1954-65; prof. mgmt. communication U. So. Calif., 1965—, chmn. dept. mktg., 1970-72; assoc. dean U. So. Calif. (Sch. Bus.), 1975-80, Disting. prof. emeritus, 1990—; Disting. Centennial lectr. U. Tex., Austin, 1986; cons. to industry; speaker, condr. workshops, seminars in field; Scholar in Residence, Va. Commonwealth U., 1987, DePaul U., 1988; Disting. emeritus prof. U. So. Calif., 1989,. Author: books, including Practical Communication for Everyday Use, 25th printing, 1954, Effective Report Writing for Business, Industry and Government, 1960, Communication for Management, 1970, Communicacion Para Directivos, 1972, Management Communication for Decision Making, 1972, Communication for Management and Business, 1976, Communication for Managers, 6th edit., 1994, Communicating in Business, 1987, 3d edit., 1989, Patient-Pharmacist Consultation: A Communication Skills Approach, 1993, Communication for Pharmacists and Other Health Professionals, 1995; (movies) Communication Barriers and Gateways, 2d edit., 1993 Listening: A Key to Problem Solving (award winner), 2d edit., 1993, The Grapevine, The Power of a Minute, 1992; gen. editor: books, including Harcourt Brace Jovanovich Bus. Series; contbr. numerous articles to profl. jours., mags. Served to capt. AUS, 1942-46, ETO. Decorated Bronze Star; recipient Excellence in Teaching award U. So. Calif., 1975, Dean's award, 1972, Outstanding Educator award, 1973, Disting. Emeritus award, 1989. Fellow Am. Bus. Communication Assn. (pres. 1964-65); mem. Internat. Communication Assn., Acad. Mgmt., Anti-Defamation League, Hadassah Assocs., Blue Key, Phi Kappa Phi, Alpha Kappa Psi, Beta Gamma Sigma. Democrat. Jewish. Home: 3109 Dona Susana Dr Studio City CA 91604-4355 Office: U So Calif Health Sci Campus 1985 Zonal Ave Los Angeles CA 90033-1058

SIGEL, MARSHALL ELLIOT, financial consultant; b. Hartford, Conn., Nov. 25, 1941; s. Paul and Bessie (Somer) S. BS in Econs., U. Pa., 1963; JD,

U. Miami, 1982, LLM in Taxation, 1983. Exec. v.p. Advo-System div. KMS Industries, Inc., Hartford, 1963-69, pres., 1969-72; pres. Ad-Type Corp., Hartford, 1963-69, Ad-Lists, Inc., Hartford, 1963-69; fin. cons. Hartford, 1972-83, Boca Raton, Fla., 1987—; pvt. practice law, 1983-87. Bd. dirs. Wharton Sch. Club of South Fla.; mem. citizen's bd. U. Miami. Mem. FOPA, World Pres.' Orgn., citizens bd. U. Miami, Boca West Club, 100 Club of So. Palm Beach County. Home and Office: PO Box 273408 Boca Raton FL 33427-3408

SIGETY, CHARLES EDWARD, lawyer, medical products executive; b. N.Y.C., Oct. 10, 1922; s. Charles and Anna (Toth) S.; m. Katharine K. Snell, July 17, 1948; children: Charles, Katharine, Robert, Cornelius, Elizabeth. BS, Columbia U., 1944; MBA, Harvard U., 1947; LLB, Yale U., 1951; LHD (hon.), Cazenovia Coll., 1994. Bar: N.Y. 1952, D.C. 1958. With Bankers Trust Co., 1939-42; instr. adminstrv. engring. Pratt Inst., 1948; instr. econs. Yale U., 1948-50; vis. lectr. acctg. Sch. Gen. Studies Columbia U., N.Y.C., 1948-50, 52; rapporteur com. fed. taxation for U.S. coun. Internat. C. of C., 1952-53; asst. to com. fed. taxation Am. Inst. Accts., 1950-53; with Compton Advt. Agy., N.Y.C., 1954; vis. lectr. law Yale U., 1952; pvt. practice law N.Y.C., 1952-67; pres., dir. Video Vittles, Inc., N.Y.C., 1953-67; dep. commr. FHA, 1955-57; of counsel Javits and Javits, 1959-60; 1st asst. atty. gen. N.Y., 1958-59; dir., mem. exec. com. Gotham Bank, N.Y.C., 1961-63; dir. N.Y. State Housing Fin. Agy., 1962-63; chmn. Met. Ski Slopes, Inc., N.Y.C., 1962-65; pres., exec. adminstr. Florence Nightingale Health Ctr., N.Y.C., 1965-85; chmn. bd. Profl. Med. Products, Inc., Greenwood, S.C., 1982—; dir. Schaerer AG, Wabern, Switzerland, 1982-88; professorial lectr. Sch. Architecture, Pratt Inst., N.Y.C., 1962-66; mem. Sigety Assocs., cons. in housing mortgage financing and urban renewal, 1957-67; ho. cons. Govt. of Peru, 1956; mem. missions to Hungary, Poland, Fed. Republic Germany, Malta, Czechoslovakia, Russia, Israel, Overseas Pvt. Investment Corp., 1990-92; owner, operator Peppermill Farms, Pipersville, Pa., 1956—. Bd. dirs., sec., v.p., treas. Nat. Coun. Health Ctrs., 1969-85; bd. dirs. Am.-Hungarian Found., 1974-76, Pritikin Rsch. Found., 1991—, Stratford Arms Condo Assn., 1992-93, Global Econ. Action Inst., 1993—; trustee Cazenovia (N.Y.) Coll., 1981—; del. White House Conf. on Aging, 1971, White House Conf. on Mgmt. Tng. and Market Econs. Edn. in Cen. and Ea. Europe, 1991; bd. visitors Lander Coll., U. S.C., Greenwood, 1982-84; mem. fin. com. World Games, Santa Clara, 1981, London, 1985, Karlsruhe, 1989, The Hague, 1993, Confrerie des Chevaliers du Tastevin, Confrerie de la Chaine des Rotisseurs, Wine and Food Soc., Wednesday 10. Baker scholar Harvard U., 1947; recipient Pres.'s medallion Cazenovia Coll., 1990. Mem. Harvard Bus. Sch. Assn. (exec. coun. 1966-69, area chmn. 1967-69), Townsend Harris Alumni Assn. (bd. dirs. 1993—), Yale Club (N.Y.C.), Harvard Bus. Sch. Club (N.Y.C., pres. 1964-65, chmn. 1965-66, bd. dirs. 1964-70), Harvard Club (N.Y.C.), Met. Club (Washington), Alpha Kappa Psi, Phi Delta Phi. Presbyterian. Home: Peppermill Farms 7155 Old Easton Rd Box 156 Pipersville PA 18947 Office: Profl Med Products PO Box 3288 Greenwood SC 29648-3288

SIGGINS, JACK ARTHUR, librarian; b. Arp, Tex., July 11, 1938; s. Wilbur McCulla and Dayle Marie (Hensley) S.; m. Maureen Ellen Sullivan, Sept. 1, 1984. B.A., Princeton U., 1960; postgrad. law, U. Va., 1961-62; M.A., Am. U., 1967, U. Chgo., 1969. Research analyst Library of Congress, Washington, 1965-66; Librarian Far Eastern Library, U. Chgo., 1968-70; head East Asia Coll. U. Md., College Park, 1970-75, asst. dir. libraries, 1975-77, assoc. dir. libraries, 1977-82; dep. univ. librarian Yale U., New Haven, 1982-92; pvt. practice orgnl. cons. New Haven, 1993-94; univ. libr. George Washington U., Washington, 1995—; cons. Boston Coll. 1994, U. Mo., 1994, Harvard U., 1994, Nat. Libr. of Australia, 1993, Ctrl. Mich. U., 1993, Tulane U., 1993; advisor Md. Dept. Edn., Balt., 1978-82; mem. adv. com. Sch. Libr. Sci. So. Conn. State U., New Haven, 1981-88; vis. com. Princeton U. Libr., 1987—. Contbr. articles to profl. jours. Served with U.S. Army, 1961-64, Japan. Far Eastern Studies fellow Ford Found., 1966; Title II fellow U. Chgo., 1967-70; fellow Davenport Coll., Yale U., 1983-92. Mem. ALA (univ. libr. standards com. 1985-88), Beta Phi Mu. Club: Princeton (N.Y.C.). Office: George Washington U Gelman Libr Washington DC 20052

SIGHOLTZ, SARA O'MEARA, non-profit organization executive; b. Knoxville, Tenn.; m. Robert Sigholtz; children: John; stepchildren: Taryn, Whitney. Attended, Briarcliff Jr. Coll.; BA, The Sorbonne, Paris. Cofounder, chmn. bd., CEO CHILDHELP USA/Internat. (formerly Children's Village USA), Woodland Hills, Calif., 1974—. Bd. dirs. Internat. Soc. Prevention Child Abuse and Neglect, Children to Children, Inc.; hon. com. mem. Learning Disabilities Found., Inc.; mem. Mayor's adv. bd., Defense for Children Internat., Nat. Soc. Prevention Cruelty to Children, World Affairs Coun.; adv. bd. mem. Ednl. Film Co.; bd. dirs. Internat. Alliance on Child Abuse and Neglect; sustaining mem. Spastic Children's League, past pres.; mem., past recording sec. Assistance League So. Calif. Recipient Cross of Merit, Knightly Order of St. Brigitte, 1967, Victor M. Carter Diamond award Japan-Am. Soc., 1970, Dame Cross of Merit of Order of St. John of Denmark, 1980, Official Seal of 34th Gov. Calif., 1981, Woman of Achievement award Career Guild, 1982, Women Making History award Nat. Fedn. Bus. Profl. Women's Clubs, 1983, Disting. Am. award for svc., 1984, Humanitarian award Nat. Frat. Eagles, 1984, Nat. Recognition award outstanding leadership Am. Heritage Found., 1986, Notable Am. award svc. to Calif., 1986, Dove of Peace award Pacific Southwest and Ctrl. Pacific Regions B'nai B'rith, 1987, Paul Harris fellow award Rotary Found., 1989, Love and Help the Children award, 1990, Presdl. award, 1990, Hubert Humphrey award Touchdown Club Washington, 1994, numerous others. Mem. SAG, AFTRA, Victory Awards (exec. com.), Am. Biographical Inst. (nat. bd. advisors), Alpha Delta Kappa (hon.). Office: Childhelp USA 6463 Independence Ave Woodland Hills CA 91370

SIGINER, DENNIS AYDENIZ, mechanical engineering educator, researcher; b. Ankara, Turkey, July 10, 1943; came to U.S., 1976; s. Kazim Siginer and Emine Turkoz. BS, MS with honors, Tech. U. Istanbul, 1966, ScD, 1971; PhD, U. Minn., 1982. Rsch. assoc. U. Minn., Mpls., 1976-80; asst. prof. U. Ala., Tuscaloosa, 1981-83; assoc. prof. Auburn (Ala.) U., 1984-92, prof. mech. engring., 1992—; organizer, chmn. several internat. and nat. confs.; invited speaker to several countries, fgn. and nat. instns., internat. and nat. meetings; reviewer NSF, Internat. Sci. Found., Jour. Non-Newtonian Fluid Mechanics, Jour. Engring. Sci., Rheologica Acta, Jour. Fluids and Structures, Jour. Fluids Engring., Jour. Heat Transfer, Jour. Dynamic Systems Measurement and Ctrl., Jour. Applied Mechanics, book revs. for pubs. Editor 11 books on devels. in non-Newtonian flows, electrorheol. fluids and fluid mechanics phenomena in microgravity; editor procs. of 1st East-West Conf. on advances in structured and nonstationary continua, Moscow, 1993; author 4 books; contbr. more than 100 articles to profl. jours. Recipient three univ. teaching awards; Summer Faculty fellow NASA. Fellow Sci. and Tech. Rsch. Coun. Turkey; mem. ASME (Svc. award 1993), Am. Soc. for Engring. Edn. (rsch. award 1992), Soc. Rheology, Am. Acad. Mechs., Am. Inst. Physics, Soc. of Engring. Sci., N.Y. Acad. Sci., Sigma Xi, Pi Tau Sigma (hon.). Home: 3809 Flintwood Ln Opelika AL 36801 Office: Auburn U Dept Mech Engring Auburn AL 36849-5341

SIGLER, ANDREW CLARK, forest products company executive; b. Bklyn., Sept. 25, 1931; s. Andrew J. and Eleanor (Nicholas) S.; m. Margaret Romefelt, June 16, 1956; children: Andrew Clark, Patricia, Elizabeth. A.B., Dartmouth, 1953; M.B.A., Amos Tuck Sch., 1956. With Champion Papers Co., Hamilton, Ohio, 1957-72, corp. exec. v.p., 1972-74, pres., CEO, 1974-79, chmn., CEO, 1979—; pres. Champion Papers div. Champion Internat. Corp., 1972, exec. v.p., dir. parent co., 1972-74; pres., chief exec. officer, Stamford, Conn., 1974-79, chmn. bd., chief exec. officer, 1979—; dir. Bristol-Myers Squibb Co., Chem. Bank, Gen. Electric Co. Trustee Dartmouth Coll. Served from 2d lt. to 1st lt. USMCR, 1953-55. Office: Champion Internat Corp 1 Champion Plz Stamford CT 06921-6000*

SIGLER, JAY ADRIAN, political scientist, educator; b. Paterson, N.J., June 21, 1933; s. Benjamin and Lucille (Pakula) S.; m. Janet Barndt, May 5, 1984; children: Niall, Ian. B.A. with honors, Rutgers U., 1954, J.D. (Law Alumni scholar), 1957, M.A. (fellow), 1960, Ph.D., 1962. Asst. prof. polit. sci. Kent (Ohio) State U., 1961-63, U. Vt., Burlington, 1963-64; instr. dept. polit. sci. Rutgers U., Camden, N.J., 1960-61; asso. prof. Rutgers U., 1965-70, prof., 1970-73, Disting. profl. polit. sci., chmn. dept., 1973—; dir. Grad. Program in Public Policy, 1979—, asso. dean, 1970-71. Author: An Introduction to the Legal System, 1968, Double Jeopardy, 1969, The Conservative Tradition in American Thought, 1969, Courts and Public Policy, 1970, El Pensamiento Conservador en los Estados Unidos, 1971, Contemporary American Government, 1972, The Performance of American Government, 1972, American Rights Policies, 1975, The Legal Sources of Public Policy, 1977, Understanding Criminal Law, 1981, Minority Rights, 1983, International Handbook of Race and Race Relations, 1987, Interactive Compliance, 1988, Corporate Lawbreaking and Interactive Compliance, 1991; contbr. articles to profl. jours. Mcpl. chmn. Democratic Party, Haddonfield, N.J., 1968-70; mem. Camden County Dem. Com., 1968-71. Served with U.S. Army, 1957-58. Recipient Lindback award for disting. teaching, 1981; Rutgers Research fellow, 1973-74; Eagleton fellow, 1978-79; Am. Polit. Sci. Assn. Project 87 fellow, 1979; Nat. Endowment for Humanities summer fellow, 1979; Warren Sussman Disting. Teaching award, 1995. Mem. AAUP, Law and Soc. Assn., Policy Studies Orgn., Nat. Assn. Schs. Public Affairs and Adminstrn., Am. Polit. Sci. Assn. Club: Rutgers Faculty. Home: Box 1932 Edgartown MA 02539 Office: Rutgers U Grad Program Pub Policy 311 N 5th St Camden NJ 08102-1205 *The contemplation of the limits of a life, of the mixture of luck and planning for more luck, is a source of balance and calm. Discovering that a few persons mean more than any things is the hard and painful part.*

SIGLER, LEROY WALTER, banker, lawyer, entrepreneur; b. Racine, Wis., Aug. 3, 1926; s. LeRoy I. and Ruth Ann (Wacynski) S.; m. Joanne I. Nash, June 20, 1947 (dec. Jan. 7, 1966); m. Sylvia L. Schmidt, Sept. 20, 1969; children: Suzanne Sigler Herbster, Cynthia Sigler Whittaker, Lee Scott, Robb Nash, Paul Grant. B.B.A., U. Wis., 1952, J.D., 1952. Bar: Wis. 1952, Ohio 1967. Corp. counsel, asst. sec. J.W. Butler Paper Co., 1952-66, Butler Paper Co., 1952-66; asst. mgr. law dept. Nekoosa Edwards Paper Co., 1952-66; asst. sec., gen. counsel Seilon, Inc., 1966-68, v.p., sec., gen. counsel, 1968-70, pres., gen. counsel, dir., 1970-79; pres., gen. counsel, dir. Bancorp. Leasing, 1973-79, Thomson Internat. Co., Thomson Veracruz S.A., Thomson-Poole, Inc., Inmobilaria Elda S.A., 1971-79, Air-Way Sanitizor, Inc., 1972-79; various positions including pres., vice chmn., dir., sec., gen. counsel Nev. Nat. Bank, 1969-76; v.p., sec. gen., counsel, dir. Nev. Nat. Bancorp., 1969-76; sec., gen. counsel Lamb Enterprises, Inc., Lamb Communications, Inc., 1970-79; chmn., dir. Greenwood's Bancorp., Inc., 1976-81; pres., dir. Nekoosa Port Edwards Bancorp., Inc., 1979—, Nekoosa Port Edwards State Bank, 1980-95; chmn., CEO, dir. Nekoosa Port Edwards State Bank, 1995—; bd. dirs. Gross Common Carrier, Inc., Opollo, Lou-Ques Corp., Broadline Leasing, Freightline. Chmn. fund drive South Wood County United Fund; co-chmn. Community Planning Commn.; pres. Port Edwards Water Utility, Tri City Airways, Village of Port Edwards;pres., dir. Riverview Hosp., Riverview Manor; dir. Tri City Health Care, Inc., Advanced Med. Equipment, Inc.; chmn. South Wood County Airport Commn.; mem. parish council, fin. com., treas. Sacred Heart Ch., sec., bd. dirs. Sacred Heart Parish Found., Inc., Riverview Health Care Found., 1995; chmn. Nekoosa Bus. Council, 1981-82; chmn. Nekoosa Indsl. Devel., 1983-86. Served with AUS, 1945-47. Mem. Wisconsin Rapids C. of C. (dir. 1960-66, 81-83, Spl. Citizen award 1964), Tri-City Bar Assn. (pres.), 7th Circuit Bar Assn. (v.p.), Toastmasters Club (v.p.), Phi Delta Phi. Lodges: Elk (exalted ruler, trustee), Rotary. Home: PO Box 86 Nekoosa WI 54457-0086 Office: 405 Market St Nekoosa WI 54457-0009 *Play all games possible. Play by the rules. Play to win.*

SIGLER, PAUL BENJAMIN, molecular biology educator, protein crystallographer; b. Richmond, Va., Feb. 19, 1934; s. George and Florence (Kaminsky) S.; m. Althea Jo Martin, Oct. 2, 1958; children:—Jennifer, Michele, Jonathan, Deborah, Rebecca. A.B. in Chemistry summa cum laude, Princeton U., 1955; M.D., Columbia U., 1959; Ph.D. in Biochemistry, Cambridge U., 1967. Intern and resident dept. medicine Columbia-Presbyn. Med. Ctr., N.Y.C., 1959-61; research assoc. NIAMD, 1961-63, staff Lab. Molecular Biology, 1963-64; vis. fellow MRC Lab. Molecular Biology, Cambridge, Eng., 1964-67; assoc. prof. biophysics U. Chgo., 1967-73, prof. biophysics and theoretical biology, 1973-84, prof. biochemistry and molecular biology, 1984-88; prof. molecular biophysics and biochemistry Yale U., New Haven, 1989—; investigator Howard Hughes Med. Inst., 1989. Served with USPHS, 1961-64. Recipient Research Career Devel. award USPHS, 1971-75; Guggenheim fellow, 1974; Katzir fellow, 1975. Fellow Am. Acad. Arts and Scis.; mem. NAS, Am. Crystallographic Assn. Jewish. Avocations: painting; bicycling. Office: Yale U HHMI 154BCMM 295 Congress Ave New Haven CT 06519-1418

SIGLER, WILLIAM FRANKLIN, environmental consultant; b. LeRoy, Ill., Feb. 17, 1909; s. John A. and Bettie (Homan) S.; m. Margaret Eleanor Brotherton, July 3, 1936; children: Elinor Jo, John William. BS, Iowa State U., 1940, MS, 1941, PhD, 1947; postdoctoral studies, UCLA, 1963. Conservationist Soil Conservation Svc., Ill., 1935-37; cons. Cen. Engring. Co., Davenport, Iowa, 1940-41; rsch. assoc. Iowa State U., 1941-42; 1945-47; asst. prof. wildlife sci. Utah State U., 1947-50, prof., head dept., 1950-74; pres. W.F. Sigler & Assocs. Inc., 1974-86; cons. U.S. Surgeon Gen., 1963-67, FAO, Argentina, 1968. Author: Theory and Method of Fish Life History Investigations, 1952, Wildlife Law Enforcement, 1956, 4th edit., 1995, Fishes of Utah, 1963, (with R.R. Miller) Fishes of the Great Basin, 1987, (with J.W. Sigler) Fishery Management: Theory and Application, 1990, Fishes of Utah: A Natural History Review, 1995; contbr. nuermous articles to profl. jours. Mem. Utah Water Pollution Control Bd., 1957-65, chmn., 1963-65. Lt. (j.g.) USNR, World War II. Named Wildlife Conservationist of Yr., Nat. Wildlife Fedn., 1970, Outstanding Educator of Yr., 1971; recipient Disting. Svc. cert of recognition Iowa Coop. Wildlife Rsch. Unit, 1982, Alumni Achievement award Coll. Natural Resources Utah State U., 1987.Coll. Natural Resources Utah State U., . Fellow AAAS, Internat. Acad. Fishery Scientists; mem. AAUP, Ecol. Soc. Am., Wildlife Soc. (hon.), Am. Fisheries Soc. (award of merit Bonneville chpt. 1990), Outdoor Writers Am., Sigma Xi, Phi Kappa Phi. Home: 309 E 2nd D S D Logan UT 84321

SIGMON, DANIEL RAY, foundation administrator; b. Orangeburg, S.C., Sept. 15, 1949; s. Carment Ray and Freida Marion (Stoudenmire) S.; m. Cheryl Mahaffey, Dec. 31, 1976; children: Ashley W. Truluck, Elizabeth Wakefield, Caroline Christine. BE, U. S.C., 1971, MA, 1992. Tchr. Calhoun County Sch. Dist., St. Matthews, S.C., 1971-72; hist. sites supt. S.C. Dept. Parks, Recreation & Tourism, Columbia, S.C., 1972-73; staff historian S.C. Dept. Parks, Recreation & Tourism, 1973-85; exec. dir. Hist. Camden (S.C.), 1985-87; dir. Alexander Homesite & History Mus., Charlotte, N.C., 1987-88; exec. dir. Hist. Columbia Found., Columbia, 1988—. Author: Huntington Beach State Park; A Visitor's Guide, 1984, Hampton Plantation; Visitor's Guide, 1983; editor: A Guide to Historic Sites in Camden, S.C., 1985. Mem. Columbia Action Coun., 1989—, Cultural Coun. Richland and Lexington County, Columbia, 1989—; bd. dirs. Sunrise Found., 1992—; mem. county commn. Palmetto Project Discovery '92, 1992-93. Mem. Nat. Trust Hist. Preservation, Am. Assn. State and Local History, S.C. Confedn. Local Hist. Socs. (exec. coun. 1991—), S.C. Fedn. Mus. (pres. 1994-96), Palmetto Trust Hist. Preservation (exec. com. 1991—). Methodist. Avocations: gardening, backpacking, canoeing, camping, traveling. Office: Hist Columbia Found 1601 Richland St Columbia SC 29201-2633

SIGMON, JOYCE ELIZABETH, association executive; b. Stanley, N.C., Oct. 4, 1935; d. Rome Alfred and Pearl Elizabeth (Beal) S. BS, U. N.C. 1971; MA, Loyola U., 1980. Cert. dental asst., assn. exec. Dental asst. Dr. Paul A. Stroup, Jr., Charlotte, N.C., 1953-63; instr. Wayne Tech. Inst., Goldsboro, N.C., 1963-65, Ctrl. Piedmont Community Coll., Charlotte, 1965-69; dir. Dental Assisting Edn. ADA, Chgo., 1971-85, asst. sec. Coun. Prosthetics Svcs., 1985-87, mgr. Office Quality Assurance, 1987-80, exec. dir. Aux., 1990-92; dir. adminstrv. activities Am. Acad. of Implant Dentistry, Chgo., 1993—; exec. sec. Am. Bd. of Oral Implantology/Implant Dentistry, 1993—. Deacon 4th Presbyn. Ch., 1973-77, elder, 1975-77, 88-91, trustee, 1991-94; moderator Presbyn. Women in 4th Ch., 1987-91. Mem. Am. Soc. Assn. Execs., Chgo. Soc. Assn. Execs. (chair CAE com. 1991-92), Am. Dental Assts. Assn., N.C. Dental Assts. (pres. 1968-69), Charlotte Dental Assts. Soc. Presbyterian. Home: 260 E Chestnut St Chicago IL 60611 Office: Am Acad Implant Dentistry 211 E Chicago Ave Chicago IL 60611

SIGMOND, ROBERT M., medical educator; b. Seattle, June 18, 1920; s. Harry and Alice (Gottfeld) S.; m. Barbara, June 29, 1941; children: Alison, Laurence. B.A., Pa. State Coll., 1941, M.A., 1942. Research assoc. Gov.'s Commn. on Hosp. Facilities, Standards and Orgn., Phila., 1945-46, Hosp.

Council Phila., 1946-50; asst. to v.p. Albert Einstein Med. Center, Phila., 1950-55; exec. v.p. for planning Albert Einstein Med. Center, 1968-70, exec. v.p., 1971-75, recipient trustee medal, 1975; dir. fiscal studies Nat. Commn. Financing of Hosp. Care, Chgo., 1952-54; exec. dir. Hosp. Coun. Western Pa., Pitts., 1955-64, Hosp. Planning Assn., Allegheny County, Pitts., 1964-68; dir. Cmty. Programs for Affordable Health Care, Chgo., 1981-85; cons. Blue Cross Assn. and Blue Cross of Greater Phila., 1976-77; adviser on hosp. affairs Blue Cross Blue Shield Assn., Chgo., 1977—; scholar-in-residence Sch. Bus. Adminstrn. Temple U., 1985—; past adj. prof. Robert F. Wagner Grad. Sch. of Pub. Policy, chmn. nat. steering com. hosp. cmty. benefit stds. program NYU, 1988-94; past adv. panel on cost effectiveness Congl. Office of Tech. Assessment; past cons. com. cmty. health care coun. on med. svcs. AMA, Social Security Adminstrn., Pa. Gov.'s Hosp. Study Commns., USPHS, OEO, Pitts. Found., U. Mich. Study of Hosp. and Med. Econs., hosp. utilization project Calif. Dept. Health; expert Office Assn. Sec. of Health, HEW. Author: Methods of Making Experimental Inferences 2d edit, 1945; (with Thomas Kinser) The Hospital-Blue Cross Plan Relationship, 1976; numerous monographs for profl. jours. Chmn. nat. adv. com. Johnson Found. Community Hosp. Med. Staff Group Practice Program; trustee Dorothy Rider Pool Health Care Trust, Allentown, Pa., Integrated Mental Health Inc., Rochester, N.Y. Recipient 1st C. Rufus Rorem award, 1986; Edwin L. Crosby fellow Nuffield Provincial Hosps. Trust, London, 1976. Fellow Am. Pub. Health Assn. (mem. editorial bd. jour.); mem. Am. Hosp. Assn. (hon.), Am. Coll. Healthcare Execs. (Dean Conley award 1969), Forum for Healthcare Planning (award of merit 1984), Soc. Hosp. Planning (Corning award 1981), Internat. Hosp. Fedn., Hosp. Assn. Pa.(Disting. Svc. award 1992), Boondocks Med. Soc. Home: 2912 Carlton House 1801 John F Kennedy Blvd Philadelphia PA 19103-1731

SIGMUND, PAUL EUGENE, political science educator; b. Phila., Jan. 14, 1929; s. Paul Eugene and Marie (Ramsey) S.; m. Barbara Rowena Boggs, Jan. 25, 1964 (dec. 1990); children—Paul Eugene, David, Stephen. AB, Georgetown U., 1950; AB Fulbright scholar, U. Durham, Eng., 1950-51; M.A., Harvard, 1954, Ph.D., 1959; postgrad., U. Paris, France, U. Heidelberg, U. Cologne, Germany, 1955-56. Teaching fellow Harvard, 1953-55, 58-59, instr., 1959-63; assoc. prof. politics Princeton, 1963-70, prof. politics, 1970—. Author: Nicholas of Cusa and Medieval Political Thought, 1963, (with Reinhold Niebuhr) The Democratic Experience, 1969, Natural Law in Political Thought, 1971, 81, The Overthrow of Allende and the Politics of Chile, 1977, Multinationals in Latin America: The Politics of Nationalization, 1980, Liberation Theology at the Crossroads: Democracy or Revolution?, 1990, paperback, 92, The United States and Democracy in Chile, 1993; editor: The Ideologies of the Developing Nations, 1963, 67, 72, Models of Political Change in Latin America, 1970, (with Pedro Aspe) The Political Economy of Income Distribution in Mexico, 1983, Poder, Sociedad y Estado en USA, 1985; assoc. editor: World Politics; translator: The Military and the State in Latin America (A. Rouquié), 1987, St. Thomas Aquinas, On Politics and Ethics, 1988, Nicholas of Cusa, The Catholic Concordance, 1991. Served to 1st lt. USAF, 1956-57. Mem. Am. Polit. Sci. Assn., Latin Am. Studies Assn., Phi Beta Kappa. Home: 8 Evelyn Pl Princeton NJ 08540-3818

SIGNER, ETHAN ROYAL, biology educator; b. Bklyn., Apr. 3, 1937; s. Isador and Elca (Rothstein) S.; m. Laura Karp; 1 child, Jasper K.; children by previous marriage: Kira R., Rachel L. BS, Yale U., 1958; PhD, MIT, 1963. Postdoctoral fellow Med. Rsch. Coun. Lab. Molecular Biology, Cambridge, Eng., 1962-64, Institut Pasteur, Paris, 1964-66; asst. prof. microbiology MIT, Cambridge, 1966-68, assoc. prof. microbiology, 1968-72; vis. prof. genetics Harvard Med. Sch., Boston, 1986-87; prof. biology MIT, Cambridge, 1972-95; mem. sci. adv. bd. Plant Resources Venture Fund, Boston, 1981-89, Safer, Inc., Wellesley, Mass., 1987-90, Angencis, Inc., Cambridge, 1981-88; teaching award MIT Grad. Studnet Coun., 1976; Philips disting. visitor Heverford Coll., 1978; disting. Martin vis. lectr. microbiology U. Calif., San Francisco, 1982; vis. prof. biochemistry U. Paris, 1992, 93; co-founder Pharm. Peptides, Inc., 1994, CEO, 1994—. Co-author: The Genie in the Computer, 1982; assoc. editor Virology, 1969-76; contbr. sci. articles to profl. jours. Marion and Jasper Whiting Found. fellow, 1988, NATO, Am. Cancer Soc., Jane Coffin Childs Fund fellow, 1962-66; rsch. fellow NIH, NSF, Am. Cancer Soc., U.S. Dept. Energy, U.S. Agr., 1966—; recipient Career Devel. award USPHS, 1969-72, Charles E. Reed Faculty Initiatives award 1990. Mem. AAAS, Am. Soc. Microbiology, Genetics Soc. Am., Internat. Soc. Plant Molecular Biology, Am. Soc. Plant Physiologists, Am. Soc. Molecular Plant-Microbe Interactions, N.Y. Acad. Scis. Office: MIT Rm 68-625 77 Massachusetts Ave Cambridge MA 02139-4307

SIGNOROVITCH, DENNIS JAMES, communications executive; b. Norristown, Pa., July 23, 1945; s. James and Regina S.; m. Susan E. McLaughlin, 1968; children: James Edward, Sarah Elizabeth. BS in Fgn. Svc., Georgetown U., 1967; MA, Old Dominion U., 1972; postgrad., U. Toledo, 1972. Instr. U. Toledo, 1972-77; writer/editor Doehler Jarvis div. NL Industries, Toledo, 1977-78; mgr. pub. rels. Eltra Corp., N.Y.C., 1979, mgr. planning, 1980; spl. assignment staff Allied Corp., Morristown, N.J., 1981; dir. pub. affairs Eltra Corp., Morristown, 1981-82; dir. pub. affairs Allied Info. Systems, Trumbull, Conn., 1982-83, dir. pub. affairs indsl. and tech. sector, 1983-86, dir. corp. communications, 1986-90, staff v.p. communications, 1990-92; v.p. pub. affairs AlliedSignal Aerospace, Torrance, Calif., 1992—. With U.S. Army, 1967-70. Decorated Bronze Star with oak leaf cluster. Mem. Torrance C. of C. (bd. dirs. 1993), The Conf. Bd. (corp. comm. coun. 1991), Vol. Ctr. of South Bay (bd. dirs. 1994), L.A. Music Ctr. Unified Fund (aerospace com. mem. 1992, 93). Office: Allied Signal Aerospace 2525 W 190th St Torrance CA 90504-6061

SIGONA, RALPH JOHN, international business consultant; b. Pozzallo, Italy, Apr. 10, 1929; s. Francesco and Rosaria Sigona; m. Barbara Bertino, June 28, 1963; 1 child, Frank. BS in Bus., NYU, 1962; MS, U. Bari, Italy, 1964. Mktg. dir. Italian Trade Commn., N.Y.C., 1968-75; internat. bus. cons., pres. RJS Assocs, Ft. Lee, N.J., 1976—; prof. internat. mgmt. and mktg. NYU, 1984—. Mem. The Statue of Liberty Ellis Island Found., 1985—. Mem. Nat. Italian-Am. Found., Italian-Am. Forum, Am. Soc. Internat. Execs., NYU Alumni Assn., Coun. of 1000. Home: 1575 Center Ave Fort Lee NJ 07024-4644

SIGULER, GEORGE WILLIAM, financial services executive; b. Cleve., Apr. 26, 1947; s. John Frederick and Helen Alice (Popp) S.; m. Pamela Ann Mallon, Oct. 31, 1981; children: George William Jr., Emily Ann, Charles Arthur, Mary Elizabeth. AB, Amherst Coll., 1970; MBA, Harvard U., 1972. Ptnr. Harvard Mgmt. Co., Boston, 1974-83; chief of staff HHS, Washington, 1983-84; exec. v.p. Monarch Capital Corp., Springfield, Mass., 1984-87; vice chmn. dir. Monarch Capital Corp., Springfield, 1987-91; pres. Associated Capital Investor, San Francisco, 1990-91; mng. dir. Mitchell Hutchins Instl. Investors, Inc., N.Y.C., 1991—; assoc. treas. Harvard U., 1973-88; bd. dirs. Bus. Mortgage Investors, Venture Lending and Leasing, Inc., Russia Ptnrs., L.P., Allied Capital Corp., Washington, Nova Care, King of Prussia, Pa., Healthcare Capital, Inc., Great Neck, N.Y. Mem. vis. com. Harvard U. Med. Sch., Boston, 1986—; mem. nat. adv. com. on community health resources HHS, Washington, 1985-90; trustee Perkins Sch. for Blind, Watertown, Mass., 1976-83, New Eng. Aquarium, 1989-91. Recipient Disting. Svc. award HHS, 1984. Republican. Presbyterian. Office: Mitchell Hutchins Instl Investors Inc 1285 Ave of the Americas New York NY 10019

SIGURDSON, ERIK D., oil industry executive; b. Winnipeg, Man., Canada, 1952. Graduated, U. Manitoba, Winnipeg, 1973; CBA, McMaster U., 1976. Exec. v.p. Clark Oil & Refining Corp., St. Louis. Office: Clark Oil & Refining Corp 8182 Maryland Ave Saint Louis MO 63114

SIGURDSSON, HARALDUR, oceanography educator, researcher; b. Stykkisholmur, Snaefellsnes Iceland, May 31, 1939; came to U.S., 1974; s. Sigurdur and Anna (Oddsdottir) Steinthorsson; m. Jean Marie Bloom; children: Bergljot, Ashildur. BSc in Geology, Queen's U., Belfast, Northern Ireland, 1965; PhD in Geology, Durham (Eng.) U., 1970. Geologist Univ. Rsch. Inst., Reykjavik, Iceland, 1965-67; volcanologist U. West Indies, St. Augustine, Trinidad and Tobago, 1970-74; assoc. prof. oceanography U. R.I., Kingston, 1974-80, prof., 1980—; cons. U.S. State Dept., 1979, 84, 86. Editor Bull. Volcanology; assoc. editor Jour. Geophys. Rsch.; contbr. over 100 articles to sci. jours., popular sci. jours. including Nat. History mag. Recipient Excellence award U. R.I., 1993; 20 rsch. grants NSF, 5 rsch.

grants Nat. Geog. Soc., 4 rsch. grants NASA, also grantee Iceland Rsch. Coun. Fellow Icelandic Acad. Sci., Explorers Club; mem. Am. Geophys. Union, Internat. Assn. Volcanology and Chemistry of Earth's Interior, Glaciological Soc. Iceland. Avocations: sailing, mountaineering, art. Office: U RI Oceanography Dept S Ferry Rd Narragansett RI 02882-1197*

SIH, CHARLES JOHN, pharmaceutical chemistry educator; b. Shanghai, China, Sept. 11, 1933; s. Paul Kwang-Tsien and Teresa (Dong) S.; m. Catherine Elizabeth Hsu, July 11, 1959; children—Shirley, Gilbert, Ronald. A.B. in Biology, Caroll Coll., 1953; M.S. in Bacteriology, Mont. State Coll., 1955; Ph.D. in Bacteriology, U. Wis., 1958. Sr. research microbial biochemist Squibb Inst. for Med. Research, New Brunswick, N.J., 1958-60; mem. faculty U. Wis.-Madison, 1960—, Frederick B. Power prof. pharm. chemistry, 1978, Hilldare prof., 1987—. Recipient 1st Ernest Volwiler award, 1977; Roussel prize, 1980, Am. Pharm. Assoc. award 1987. Mem. Am. Chem. Soc., Soc. Am. Biol. Chemists, Acad. Pharm. Scis., Soc. Am. Microbiologists. Home: 6322 Landfall Dr Madison WI 53705-4309

SIHLER, WILLIAM WOODING, finance educator; b. Seattle, Nov. 17, 1937; s. William and Helen Alice (Wooding) S.; m. Mary Elizabeth Unwin, Aug. 21, 1963; children: Edward Wooding, Jennifer Mary. A.B. summa cum laude in Govt. (Sheldon traveling fellow), Harvard U., 1959, MBA with high distinction, 1962, DBA, 1965. Instr., asst. prof. Harvard U. Bus. Sch., 1964-67; asso. prof. Darden Grad. Bus. Sch., U. Va., Charlottesville, 1967-72; prof. Darden Grad. Bus. Sch., U. Va., 1972-76, A.J. Morris prof., 1976-84; R.E. Trzcinski prof., 1984—; dir. D.B.A. Program, 1971-73, assoc. dean acad. affairs, 1972-77; exec. dir. BAFT/Ctr. for Internat. Banking Studies, 1977-91; bd. dirs. Curtiss-Wright Corp.; pres. Southeastern Cons. Group, Ltd. Co-author: Financial Management: Text and Cases, 2d edit., 1991, The Troubled Money Business, 1992, Financial Service Organizations: Cases in Strategic Management, 1993, Cases in Applied Corporate Finance, 1994; editor: Classics in Commercial Bank Lending, vol. 1, 1981, vol. 2, 1985; contbr. articles to mgmt. publs. and anthologies of readings. Class sec. Harvard M.B.A. Class, 1962, Case Western Res. U., mem. vis. com. Sch. Mgmt., 1976-86, bd. overseers, 1980-86. Recipient DeL. K. Jay prize Harvard U., Disting. Prof. award U. Va. Alumni Assn., 1982; C.J. Bonaparte scholar Harvard U. Mem. Fin. Mgmt. Assn., Am. Econ. Assn., Am. Fin. Assn., Eastern Fin. Assn., Univ. Club (N.Y.C.), Harvard Club (N.Y.C.), Phi Beta Kappa, Beta Gamma Sigma. Home: 202 Sturbridge Rd Charlottesville VA 22901-2116 Office: PO Box 6550 Charlottesville VA 22906-6550

SIIMESTÖ, ORVO KALERVO, financial executive; b. Helsinki, Finland, Aug. 3, 1943; s. Idor and Ilma (Hukka) S.; m. Marja-Liisa Vehviläinen, May 30, 1964; children: Satu Kristiina, Katja Maarit. MBA, Helsinki Sch. Bus. Adminstrn., 1969. Dir. fin. Kone Oy, Hyvinkää, Finland, 1975-83; v.p. fin. Oy Wilhelm Schauman AB, Helsinki, 1983-88, A. Ahlstrom Corp., Helsinki, 1988—. Avocations: sailing, cross-country skiing, volleyball. Office: A Ahlstrom Corp, Eteläesplanadi 14, 00130 Helsinki Finland

SIIROLA, JEFFREY JOHN, chemical engineer; b. Patuxent River, Md., July 17, 1945; s. Arthur Raymond and Nancy Ellen (Harris) S.; m. Sharon Ann Atwood, Apr. 24, 1971; childen: John Daniel, Jennifer Ann. BS in Chem. Engring., U. Utah, 1967; PhD, U. Wis., 1970. Sr. rsch. assoc. Eastman Chem. Co., Kingsport, Tenn., 1972—; trustee CACHE Corp., Austin, Tex., 1983-. Co-author: Process Synthesis, 1973. Active Kingsport C. of C. Recycling, 1988—; Appalachian tr. maintenance Eastman Hiking Club, Kingsport, 1973—. With U.S. Army, 1970-72. Mem. AIChE (A.E. Marshall award 1967, Computing Practice award 1991, CAST divsn. programming chair 1988—), Am. Chem. Soc., Assn. for Computing Machinery, Am. Soc. for Engring. Edn., Nat. Acad. Engring., Am. Assn. for Artificial Intelligence. Achievements include development of the AIDES chem. process flowsheet invention program. Home: 2517 Wildwood Dr Kingsport TN 37660 Office: Eastman Chem Co PO Box 1972 Kingsport TN 37662-5150

SIKER, EPHRAIM S., anesthesiologist; b. Port Chester, N.Y., Mar. 24, 1926; s. Samuel S. and Adele (Weiser) S.; m. m . Eileen Mary Bohnel, Aug. 5, 1951; children—Kathleen Ellen, Jeffrey Stephen, David Allan, Paul William, Richard Francis. Student, Duke U., 1943-45; M.D., N.Y.U. 1949. Diplomate: Am. Bd. Anesthesiology (dir. 1971—, sec.-treas. 1974-82, pres. 1982-83) Nat. Bd. Med. Examiners. Intern Grasslands Hosp., Valhalla, N.Y., 1949-50, resident in anesthesia, 1950; resident dept. anesthesiology Mercy Hosp., Pitts., 1952-53; assoc. dir. dept. Mercy Hosp., 1955-62, chmn., 1962-92; practice medicine, specializing in anesthesiology Pitts., 1954—; pres. Pitts. Anesthesia Assocs., Ltd., 1967-89; dir. anesthesia services Central Med. Ctr., Pitts., 1973-89; courtesy staff St. Clair Meml. Hosp., Pitts., 1954-89, St. Margaret Meml. Hosp., 1962—; clin. prof. dept. anesthesiology U. Pitts. Sch. Medicine, 1968—; mem. exec. com. Am. Bd. Med. Spltys., 1978-81; Exchange cons. Welsh Nat. Sch. Medicine, Cardiff, 1955-56; mem. Pa. Gov.'s Commn. on Profl. Liability Ins., 1968-70; mem. adv. panel U.S Pharmacopeia, 1970-76; mem. Am. acupuncture anesthesia study group of Nat. Acad. Scis. to Peoples Republic China, 1974; mem. adv. com. on splty. and geog. distbn. of physicians Inst. Medicine, Nat. Acad. Scis., 1974-76; trustee Ednl. Council for Fgn. Med. Grads., 1980-82, Mercy Hosp. Found., 1983—; bd. dirs., sec. Anesthesia Patient Safety Found., 1985-89, mem. exec. com., 1985-1992, exec. dir., 1992—. Author: (with F.F. Foldes) Narcotics and Narcotic Antagonists, 1964; sect. on narcotic: (with F.F. Foldes) numerous other publs. in med. lit. Ency. Brittanica. Served to lt. M.C. USNR, 1950-52. USPHS postdoctoral research fellow, 1954; hon. fellow faculty anaesthetists Royal Coll. Surgeons, Eng., 1974; hon. fellow faculty anesthetists Coll. Medicine South Africa, 1983; recipient Hippocratic award Mercy Hosp., 1982. Fellow Royal Coll. Surgeons Ireland, Faculty Anaesthetists (hon. 1988); mem. Am. Soc. Anesthesiologists (pres. 1973—, bd. dirs. Disting. Svc. award 1984), AMA (alt. del. 1962), Pa. Med. Soc., Allegheny County Med. Soc., Pa. Soc. Anesthesiologists (pres. 1965, Disting. Svc. award 1986), Royal Soc. Medicine (Eng.), Pitts. Acad. Medicine, Am. Coll. Anesthesiologists (bd. govs. 1969-71), World Fedn. Anesthesiologists (chmn. exec. com. 1980-84, v.p. 1984-88), Assn. Anesthesia Program Dirs. (pres. 1988-89). Developed Siker Laryngoscope, 1956. Home: 185 Crestvue Manor Dr Pittsburgh PA 15228-1814 Office: 1400 Locust St Pittsburgh PA 15219-5166 *If you have to tell someone who you are, then you probably aren't. People are measured by more than their deeds, and such estimations are frequently made on the basis of their inter-personal relationships. While achievement and effort usually bear a linear relationship to each other, the impact that the achiever has on society depends upon the impact he makes on individuals.*

SIKES, ALFRED C., communications executive; b. Cape Girardeau, Mo., Dec. 16, 1939; s. William Kendall and Marcia (Weber) S.; m. Martha Pagenkopf, Aug. 19, 1961; children: Deborah Sue, Christine Louise, Marcia Cay. AB, Westminster Coll., 1961; LLB, U. Mo., 1964. Asst. atty. gen. Senator John Danforth, State of Mo., Jefferson City, 1970-72; campaign mgr. Bond for Gov. Com., Jefferson City, 1972; dir. gov.-elect transition staff Bond for Gov. Com., Jefferson City, 1972; dir. dept. community and consumer affairs State of Mo., Jefferson City, 1973-76; exec. v.p. Mahaffey Enterprises, Springfield, Mo., 1977-78; pres., CEO Sikes & Assocs., Springfield, Mo., 1978-86; asst. sec. nat. telecom. and info. adminstrn. U.S. Dept. Commerce, Washington, 1986-89; chmn. FCC, Washington, 1989—; contbr. articles to profl. jours. Pres. Springfield Coun. Chs., 1984. Recipient Alumni Achievement award Westminster Coll., 1987. Mem. Mo. Bar Assn., Orgn. Mo. Jaycees (pres. 1968-69), U.S. Jaycees (v.p. 1969-70), Orgn. Internat. Jaycees (legal counsel 1971-72). Republican. Methodist. Avocations: fishing, hunting, skiing, sailing. Home: 5907 Aberdeen Rd Bethesda MD 20817-3805 Office: FCC 1919 M St NW Washington DC 20554-0002

SIKORA, JAMES ROBERT, educational business administrator; b. Sacramento, July 8, 1945; s. George Robert and Marian Frances (Fears) S.; m. Marie Lynore Nyarady, June 22, 1968. BEE, U. Santa Clara, 1967; postgrad., U. Calif.-Santa Cruz, 1979-. Electronic engr. GTE-Sylvania, Santa Cruz, 1967-69; systems analyst GTE-Sylvania, 1969-71; sr. support analyst GTE-Sylvania, Mt. View, Calif., 1971-73; bus. systems coordinator Santa Clara County Office Edn., San Jose, Calif., 1973-76; dir. dist. payroll, personnel svcs. Santa Clara County Office Edn., 1976-85, dir. dist. bus. svcs., 1985—; cons. records mgmt. County Santa Clara, San Jose, 1982; v. chair Edn. Mandated Cost Network Exec. Bd., 1991—; mem. Schs. Fin. Svcs. subcom. 1987-94. Author, co-editor Howdy Rowdy Memorial, 1979. Sponsor San Jose/Cleveland Ballet, Santa Cruz County Symphony, Dixieland Monterey, Monterey Bay Aquarium Patrons Circle, Long Marine Lab., San Jose Repertory Theater, Ctr. Photographic Arts, Napa Valley Wine Libr., Fiat Lux Soc., U. Calif. Santa Cruz; mem. Team Shakespeare, Shakespeare Santa Cruz, Omni Found. Mem. Pub. Agy. Risk Mgmt. Assn., Am. Diabetes Assn., Calif. Assn. Sch. Bus. Ofcls. (subsect. pres. 1984-85, sect. bd. dirs. 1987-93, sect. pres. 1991-92, state bd. dirs. 1991-92, state legis. com. 1989—, state strategic planning com. 1994), Norwegian Elkhound Assn. (pres. 1977-79), Wine Investigation for Novices and Oenephiles, Amnesty Internat., Calif. Trout, Calif. State Parks Found., Am. Dog Owners Assn., Sierra Club (life). Libertarian. Roman Catholic. Avocations: photography, travel, gardening, fishing, snorkelling. Home: 400 Coon Heights Rd Ben Lomond CA 95005 Office: Santa Clara County Office Edn MC 252 100 Skyport Dr San Jose CA 95110

SIKORA, JANE ANN, secondary education educator, reference librarian; b. Joniskelis, Lithuania, Nov. 19, 1941; came to U.S., 1950; d. Casimir and Elizabeth (Jarasunaite) Vaisvila; m. Leon Sikora, July 31, 1967; children: Diane, Julie. BA, St. Francis Coll., Loretto, Pa., 1964; MLS, Rutgers U., 1969. Cert. secondary tchr. English, secondary tchr. French, media specialist, profl. libr., elem. edn. tchr., N.J. Tchr. Jr. High Sch. # 1, Trenton, N.J., 1964-69; libr. North Burlington County Regional Jr. Sr. High Sch., Columbus, N.J., 1969-83, tchr., 1983—; reference librar. Mercer County Libr., Lawrenceville, N.J., 1983—. Mem. NEA, N.J. Edn. Assn., Burlington County Tchrs. Assn. Roman Catholic. Home: 83 N Post Rd Lawrenceville NJ 08648 Office: N Burlington Co Reg Jr Sr High Sch Mansfield Rd Columbus NJ 08022

SIKORA, RICHARD INNES, philosophy educator; b. Boston, July 6, 1927; s. Frank E. and Frances (Small) S.; m. Dorothy Daniel, Apr. 25, 1953; 1 child, Anne. A.B. in Philosophy cum laude, Harvard U., 1950; Ph.D. in Philosophy, U. Calif.-Berkeley, 1962. Instr. U. Oreg., Eugene, 1959-60; vis. asst. prof. Whitman Coll., Walla Walla, Wash., 1960-61; asst prof. philosophy U. B.C., Vancouver, Can., 1964-76; asso. prof. U. B.C., 1976-82, prof., 1982—. Editor: (with others) Obligations to Future Generations, 1978; contbr. articles to profl. jours. Served with USCG, 1945-46. Can. Council grantee, 1981-82. Mem. Am. Philosophy Assn., Can. Philosophy Assn. Avocations: classical music; art collecting. Home: 2307 Perkins Ln W Seattle WA 98199 Office: U BC Dept Philosophy, 204-2075 Westbrook Mall, Vancouver, BC Canada V6T 1Z2

SIKORA, STEPHEN THEODORE, publisher; b. Ukiah, Calif., Sept. 17, 1943; s. John Paul and Florence Anholm (Smith) S.; m. Kathleen Faye Hagemeyer, Aug. 5, 1967 (div. Aug. 1987); children: Benjamin, Anna. BA, U. Calif., Berkeley, 1966; MA, San Francisco State U., 1974. Tchr. Nevada County Sch. Dist., North San Juan, Calif., 1969-71; carpenter, contractor pvt. practice, Calif., 1974-82; publisher pvt. practice, Albany, Calif., 1982—. Editor/publisher (mag.) The Letter Exchange, 1982—. Sgt. U.S. Army, 1966-68. Mem. Phi Beta Kappa. Avocations: homeric Greek studies, bicycling. Office: The Letter Exch PO Box 6218 Albany CA 94706

SIKOROVSKY, EUGENE FRANK, retired lawyer; b. Jackson, Mich., Nov. 27, 1927; s. Frank Joseph and Betty Dorothy (Malik) S.; m. Patricia O'Byrne, July 11, 1953; children: Paul, Charles, Catherine, Elizabeth, Emily. B.S. in Elec. Engring, U. Mich., 1948; LL.B., Harvard U., 1951. Bar: N.Y. 1952, Va. 1970, Ill. 1978. Assoc. predecessor firms Cahill, Gordon & Reindel, 1954-63, ptnr., 1964-68; v.p., gen. counsel, dir. Reynolds Metals Co., Richmond, Va., 1969-76; gen. counsel Gould Inc., Rolling Meadows, Ill., 1977-79; v.p. Gould Inc., 1977-81; dep. gen. counsel Bell & Howell Co., Skokie, Ill., 1981-83; v.p. Bell & Howell Co., Chgo., 1983-88, gen. counsel, 1983-92, sec., 1984-92, sr. v.p., dir., 1988-92. Served to lt. USNR, 1951-54. Mem. ABA, Va. Bar Assn., Ill. State Bar Assn., Assn. of Bar of City of N.Y., Tau Beta Pi, Eta Kappa Nu, Phi Eta Sigma, Phi Delta Theta. Episcopalian. Home: 31 Pembroke Dr Lake Forest IL 60045-2147

SIKORSKI, JAMES ALAN, research chemist; b. Stevens Point, Wis., Nov. 9, 1948; s. John Paul and Florence Lucille (Wierzba) S.; m. Jeanne Delaney, Apr. 15, 1968 (div. 1975); 1 child, Christine René; m. Georgina Weber, Nov. 19, 1977. BS, Northeast La. State Coll., 1970; MS, Purdue U., 1976, PhD, 1981. With Monsanto Agrl. Co., St. Louis, 1976-91, sci. fellow, 1987-91; sci. fellow Monsanto Corp. Rsch., St. Louis, 1991-93, G.D. Searle R&D, St. Louis, 1994—; instr. organic/med. chemistry St. Louis Community Coll., 1977-78; invited speaker tech. presentations and sems. Contbr. chpts. to books, rev. articles, symposia-in-print and articles to profl. jours.; patentee and co-patentee in field. Mem. AAAS, Am. Chem. Soc., Internat. Soc. Heterocyclic Chemistry, Sigma Xi. Avocations: hiking, canoeing, skiing, photography, snorkeling. Office: GD Searle R&D 700 Chesterfield Pky N Saint Louis MO 63198

SILAK, CATHY R., judge; b. Astoria, N.Y., May 25, 1950. BA, NYU, 1971; M in City Planning, Harvard U., 1973; JD, U. Calif., 1976. Bar: Calif. 1977, U.S. Dist. Ct. (no. dist.) Calif. 1977, D.C. 1979, U.S. Ct. Appeals (D.C. cir.) 1979, U.S. Dist. Ct. (so. dist.) N.Y. 1980, Idaho 1983, U.S. Dist. Ct. Idaho 1983, U.S. Ct. Appeals (2nd cir.) 1983, U.S. Ct. Appeals (9th cir.) 1985. Law clk. to Hon. William W. Schwarzer U.S. Dist. Ct. (no dist.), Calif., 1976-77; pvt. practice San Francisco, 1977-79, Washington, 1979-80; asst. U.S. atty. So. Dist. of N.Y., 1980-83; spl. asst. U.S. atty. Dist. of Idaho, 1983-84; pvt. practice Boise, Idaho, 1984-90; judge Idaho Ct. Appeals, 1990-93; justice Idaho Supreme Ct., Boise, 1993—; assoc. gen. counsel Morrison Knudsen Corp., 1989-90; mem. fairness com. Idaho Supreme Ct. and Gov.'s Task Force on Alternative Dispute Resolution; instr. and lectr. in field. Assoc. note and comment editor Calif. Law Rev., 1975-76. Land use planner Mass. Dept. Natural Resources, 1973; founder Idaho Coalition for Adult Literacy; bd. dirs. Literacy Lab., Inc. Recipient Joyce Stein award Boise YWCA, 1992. Fellow Idaho Law Found (ann., lectr.); mem. ABA (nat. conf. state trial judges jud. adminstrn. divsn.), Nat. Assn. Women Judges, Idaho State Bar (corp./securities sect., instr.). Office: PO Box 83720 Boise ID 83720-0101

SILAS, CECIL JESSE, retired petroleum company executive; b. Miami, Fla., Apr. 15, 1932; s. David Edward and Hilda Videll (Carver) S.; m. Theodosea Hejda, Nov. 27, 1965; children: Karla, Peter, Michael, James. BSChemE, Ga. Inst. Tech., Atlanta, 1953. With Phillips Petroleum Co., Bartlesville, Okla., 1953-94; pres. Europe-Africa, Brussels and London Phillips Petroleum Co., 1968-74; mng. dir. natural resource group Europe/Africa Phillips Petroleum Co., London, 1974-76; v.p. gas and gas liquids div. natural resources group Phillips Petroleum Co., Bartlesville, 1976-78, sr. v.p. natural resources group, 1978-80, exec. v.p. exploration and prodn., minerals, gas and gas liquids, 1980-82, pres., chief operating officer, 1982-85, chmn., CEO, 1985-94; bd. dirs. Milliken & Co. Bd. dirs. Jr. Achievement, Reader's digest Assocs., Inc., bd. dirs. of Halliburton Co. COMSAT Corp, Boys/Girls Clubs Am., Atlanta, Frank Phillips Found., Bartlesville, Okla.; parton councillor Atlantic Coun. of the U.S.; bd. dirs. Ethics Resource Ctr., Inc., Okla. Found. for Excellence; trustee Frank Phillips Found.; active Trilateral Commn. Served to 1st lt. Chem. Corps, AUS, 1954-56. Decorated comdr. Order St. Olaf (Norway); inducted into Ga. Inst. Tech. Athletic Hall of Fame, 1959, recipient Former Scholar-Athlete Total Person award, 1988; inducted into Okla. Bus. Hall of Fame, 1989; named CEO of Yr., Internat. TV Assn., 1987. Mem. Conf. Bd., Am. Petroleum Inst., U.S.C. of C. (past chmn. bd. dirs.), Bartlesville Area C. of C., Okla. State C. of C. and Industry, 25 Yr. Club, Phi Delta Theta. Avocations: fishing, golf, hunting. Office: PO Box 2127 Bartlesville OK 74005

SILBAJORIS, FRANK RIMVYDAS, Slavic languages educator; b. Kretinga, Lithuania, Jan. 6, 1926; came to U.S., 1949; s. Pranas and Elzbieta (Bagdanaviciute) S.; m. Milda Zamzickaite, Aug. 31, 1955; children: Victoria, Alex. BA, Antioch Coll., 1953; MA, Columbia U., 1955; PhD, Columbia U., 1962; D Philology (hon.), Latvian Acad. Scis., Riga, 1991. Instr. to asst. prof. Oberlin Coll., Ohio, 1957-63; assoc. prof. Ohio State U., Columbus, 1963-67, prof. Slavic langs., 1967-91, chmn. dept., 1986-89, prof. emeritus, 1992—; cons. NEH, 1978-79, exchange fellow, USSR, 1977-79; dir. NEH summer seminars, 1975, 77, 83, 84, 86, 88. Author: Russian Versification: The Theories of Trediakovskij, Lomonosov and Kantemir,1 968, Perfection of Exile: Fourteen Contemporary Lithuanian Writers, 1970, Tolstoy's Aesthetics and His Art, 1991; editor: The Architecture of Reading, 1976, Mind Against the Wall, 1983; contbr. articles to profl. jours. Cons., lectr., organizer cultural events Lithuanian-Am. Community Orgn., 1949—. Antioch

Coll. scholar, 1950-53; fellow John Hay Whitney Found., 1953-54, Ford Found., 1954-56, Woodrow Wilson Ctr., 1984, IREX, USSR, 1963-64. Mem. Inst. Lithuanian Studies (pres. 1977-82), Assn. Advancement Baltic Studies (pres. 1973-74), Am. Assn. Tchrs. Slavic and East European Langs., Am. Assn. Advancement Slavic Studies, Assn. Russian-Am. Scholars. Avocations: photography; bicycling; swimming; travel. Home: 4082 Ruxton Ln Columbus OH 43220-4046 Office: Ohio State U Dept Slavic Langs Columbus OH 43210

SILBAUGH, RUDY LAMONT, state legislator; b. Viroqua, Wis., Sept. 10, 1930; s. Clarabelle Larson Silbaugh; m. Janet Berdine Nysather, June 3, 1950; children: Mark David, Gary Steven, Laurie Margit. Grad. high sch., Stoughton, Wis., 1948. Floor covering installer Slinde Floorcovering, Stoughton, 1949-65; owner U&S Floorcovering & Furniture, Stoughton, 1965-89; state rep. Wis. Legislature, Madison, 1990—. Alderman Stoughton City Coun., 1978-90. Named Friend of Agr. Wis. Farm Bur., 1992, 94, Guardian of Sml. Bus. Nat. Fedn. Ind. Bus., 1992, 93, Friend of Life award Wis. Collegians for Life, 1992. Mem. AARP, Am. Legis. Exch. Coun., Toastmasters, Gideons, Lions (pres. 1993). Republican. Avocation: woodworking. Home: 115 E Wilson St Stoughton WI 53589-1443 Office: Wis State Legislature Wis State Capitol # 10 East Madison WI 53702

SILBER, JOHN ROBERT, university president; b. San Antonio, Aug. 15, 1926; s. Paul G. and Jewell (Joslin) S.; m. Kathryn Underwood, July 12, 1947; children: David Joslin, Mary Rachel, Judith Karen, Kathryn Alexandra, Martha Claire, Laura Ruth, Caroline Jocasta. B.A. summa cum laude, Trinity U., 1947; postgrad., Northwestern U., summer 1944, Yale Div. Sch., 1947-48, U. Tex. Sch. Law, 1948-49; M.A., Yale, 1952, Ph.D. 1956; L.H.D., Kalamazoo Coll., 1970, many others. Instr. dept. philosophy Yale U., 1952-55; asst. prof. U. Tex., Austin, 1955-59, asso. prof., 1959-62, prof. philosophy, 1962-70, chmn. dept. philosophy, 1962-67, Univ. prof. arts and letters, 1967-70, chmn. (Comparative Studies Program), 1967, dean (Coll. Arts and Scis.), 1967-70; Univ. prof., prof. philosophy and law Boston U., 1971—, pres., 1971—; vis. prof. U. Bonn, 1960; fellow Kings Coll. U. London, 1963-64. Author: The Ethical Significance of Kant's Religion, 1960, Straight Shooting: What's Wrong With America and How to Fix It, 1989; editor: Religion Within the Limits of Reason Alone, 1960, Works in Continental Philosophy, 1967—; assoc. editor: Kant-Studien, 1968—; Contbr. to profl. jours. Chmn. Tex. Soc. to Abolish Capital Punishment, 1960-69; mem. Nat. Common. United Methodist Higher Edn., 1974-77; exec. bd. Nat. Humanities Inst., 1975-78; trustee Coll. St. Scholastica, 1973-85, U. Denver, 1985-89, WGBH Ednl. Found., 1971—, Adelphi U., 1989—; bd. visitors Air U., 1974-80; bd. dirs. Greater Boston Council Boy Scouts Am., 1981-93, v.p. finance 1981-93, Silver Beaver award 1989, Nat. Humanities Faculty, 1968-73, Nat. Captioning Inst., 1985—; bd. advisors Matchette Found., 1971—; mem. Nat. Bipartisan Commn. on Central Am., 1983-84, Presdl. Adv. Bd. Radio Bradcasting to Cuba, 1985-92; adv. bd. Schurman Library of Am. Hist., Ruprecht-Karl U., Heidelberg, 1986—, Jamestown Found., 1989—; mem. def. policy bd. U.S. Dept. of Def., 1987-90; mem. internat council advisors Inst. for Humanities at Salado, 1988—; bd. dirs. New Eng. Holocaust Meml. Com., 1989—, Brit. Inst. of U.S., 1989—; Dem. gubernatorial candidate of Mass., 1990; bd. dirs. NE Savings Bank, 1988—; v.p. U.S. Strategic Inst., bd. dirs. Ams. Medical Progress, 1992—, chmn. 1994—; bd. advisors Nat. Assn. Scholars, U.S. Surgical Corp, 1994—. Recipient E. Harris Harbison award for disting. teaching Danforth Found., 1966, Wilbur Lucius Cross medal Yale Grad. Sch., 1971, Outstanding Civilian Service medal U.S. Army, 1985, Disting. Pub. Svc. award Anti-Defamation League of B'nai B'rith, 1989, Horatio Alger award, 1992, Am.-Swiss Friendship award, 1991; Fulbright Research fellow Germany, 1959-60; Guggenheim fellow Eng., 1963-64; decorated with Knight Comdr.'s Cross with Star of Order of Merit Fed. Republic of Germany, 1983; commandeur Nat. Order of Arts and Letters (France), 1985; recipient Israel Peace medal, 1985, Ehrenmedaille, U. Heidelberg, 1986, White House Small Bus. award for Entrepreneurial Excellence, 1986, Cross of Paideia, Greek Orthodox Archdiocese of North & South Am., 1988. Fellow Royal Soc. Arts; mem. Am. Philos. Assn., Am. Soc. Polit. and Legal Philosophy, Royal Inst. Philosophy, Am. Assn. Higher Edn., Nat. Assn. Ind. Colls. and Univs. (dir. 1976-81), Phi Beta Kappa. Office: Boston U 147 Bay State Rd Boston MA 02215-1789

SILBER, JUDY G., dermatologist; b. Newark, July 26, 1953. MD, SUNY, Bklyn., 1978. Intern Brookdale Med. Ctr., Bklyn., 1978-79; resident in dermatology Kings County Hosp., Bklyn., 1979-82; pvt. practice dermatology; affiliated with Meadowlands Med. Ctr., Secaucus, N.J. Fellow Am. Acad. Dermatology; mem. AMA, N.J. Med. Soc. Office: 992 Clifton Ave Clifton NJ 07013

SILBER, NORMAN JULES, lawyer; b. Tampa, Fla., Apr. 18, 1945; s. Abe and Mildred (Hirsch) S.; m. Linda Geraldine Hirsch, June 10, 1979; 1 child, Michael Hirsch. BA, Tulane U., 1967, JD, 1969; postgrad. in bus. adminstrn. NYU, 1970-72. Bar: Fla. 1970, U.S. Dist. Ct. (so. dist. Fla.) 1975, U.S. Tax Ct. 1975, U.S. Ct. Appeals (5th cir.) 1975, U.S. Ct. Appeals (11th cir.) 1981. With legal dept. Fiduciary Trust Co. N.Y., N.Y.C., 1969-72, asst. trust officer, 1971-72; exec. v.p. I.R.E. Fin. Corp., Miami, Fla., 1972-76; mng. atty. Norman J. Silber, P.A., Miami, 1973-85; ptnr. McDermott, Will & Emery, 1985—. Mem. ABA, Fla. Bar (chmn. 11th jud. cir. grievance com. I 1982-84), Dade County Bar Assn., Am. Judicature Soc., Assn. Trial Lawyers Am., Acad. Fla. Trial Lawyers. Republican. Jewish. Home: 1232 Palermo Ave Miami FL 33134-6327 Office: McDermott Will & Emery 201 S Biscayne Blvd Miami FL 33131

SILBER, WILLIAM L., finance educator; b. Yonkers, N.Y., Nov. 26, 1942; s. Joseph F. and Pauline (Rothstein) S.; m. Lillian Frank, Jan. 26, 1964; children: Jonathan Mark, Daniel Jay, Tammy Beth. BA, Yeshiva Coll., 1963; MA, Princeton U., 1966, PhD, 1966. Sr. economist Pres.'s Coun. of Econ. Advisors, Washington, 1970-71; prof. NYU, 1966-90; sr. v.p. Lehman Bros., Kuhn, Loeb, N.Y.C., 1987; Gitlow prof. of fin. NYU, 1990—; mem. Commodity Exch., N.Y.C., 1984—, N.Y. Mercantile Exch., 1986-90, N.Y. Cotton Exch., 1987—; N.Y. Stock Exch. Options Div., 1984-87; cons. Standard & Poors Corp., N.Y.C., 1986—, Odyssey Ptnrs., N.Y.C., 1988—, U.S. Senate Budget Com., Washington, 1975; advisor Fed. Res. Bank, N.Y.C., 1978-80, 1990—. Author: Principles of Money, Banking and Finance, 1973, 7th rev. edit., 1991, Money, 1970, 4th rev. edit., 1977, Portfolio Behavior, 1970; editor: Financial Options, 1990; assoc. editor Rev. of Econ. and Stats. jour., 1973—. Trustee Soc. of Bus., Yeshiva U., N.Y.C., 1987—; investment com. Social Sci. Rsch. Coun., N.Y.C., 1980-83; acad. adv. coun. Fed. Res. Bank N.Y., 1990. Mem. Am. Econ. Assn., Am. Fin. Assn. Avocation: collecting antique phonographs. Home: 1048 E 9th St Brooklyn NY 11230-4108 Office: NYU 44 W 4th St New York NY 10012-1126

SILBERBERG, DONALD H., neurologist; b. Washington, Mar. 2, 1934; s. William Aaron and Leslie Frances (Stone) S.; m. Marilyn Alice Damsky, June 7, 1959; children—Mark, Alan. M.D., U. Mich., 1958; M.A. (hon.), U. Pa., 1971. Intern Mt. Sinai Hosp., N.Y.C., 1958-59; clin. assoc. in neurology NIH, Bethesda, Md., 1959-61; Fulbright scholar Nat. Hosp., London, 1961-62; NINDB spl. fellow in neuro-ophthalmology Washington U., St. Louis, 1962-63; assoc. neurology U. Pa., 1963-65, asst. prof., 1965-67, assoc. prof., 1967-71, prof., 1971-73, acting chmn. dept., 1973-74, prof., vice chmn. neurology, 1974-82, chmn., 1982-94, assoc. dean internat. programs, 1994—; inpatient staff Hosp. U. Pa.; cons. Children's Hosp., both Phila. Contbr. articles to profl. jours., abstracts, chpts. in books. Recipient grants in study of multiple sclerosis. Mem. Am. Acad. Neurology, Am. Assn. Neuropathologists, Am. Neurol. Assn., Am. Soc. Neurochemistry, Assn. Rsch. in Nervous and Mental Disease, Coll. Physicians Phila., Internat. Brain Rsch. Orgn., Internat. Soc. Devel. Neuroscis., Internat. Soc. Neurochemistry, John Morgan Soc. U. Pa. (pres. 1974-75), N.Y. Acad. Scis., Nat. Multiple Sclerosis Soc. (chmn. med. adv. bd.), Assn. Univ. Profs. Neurology (pres.-elect 1993), Phila. Neurol. Soc. (pres. 1978-79), Soc. Neurosci., Alpha Omega Alpha. Office: Hosp U Pa Dept Neurology 3400 Spruce St Philadelphia PA 19104

SILBERBERG, INGA, dermatologist; b. Kassel, Germany, Sept. 16, 1934; came to U.S., 1938; d. Willi and Erna (Rosenbaum) S.; m. Herbert M. Sinakin, Feb. 16, 1969; 1 child, William Elias. BA, Hunter Coll., 1955; MD, SUNY, 1959; MS in Dermatology, NYU, 1965. Diplomate Am. Bd.

Dermatologists, 1964. Instr., clin. dermatology NYU Med. Ctr., N.Y.C., 1963-65, clin. asst. prof., 1965-66, asst. prof. dermatology, 1966-71, clin. assoc. prof. dermatology, 1971-76; cons., dermatology Newcomb Hosp., Vineland, N.J., 1977—. cons. dermatology. Jonas Salk scholar, City of N.Y., 1955-59, Henry Silver award, Dermatologic Soc. Greater N.Y., 1962, 65, Dermatology Found. Discovery award, 1993. Fellow Am. Acad. Dermatology; mem. AMA. Jewish. Avocation: bicycling.

SILBERBERG, RICHARD HOWARD, lawyer; b. N.Y.C., Feb. 20, 1951. BA, U. Wis., 1972; JD, NYU, 1975. Bar: N.Y. 1976, U.S. Dist. Ct. (so. and ea. dists.) N.Y. 1976, U.S. Ct. Appeals (2d cir.) 1983, U.S. Ct. Appeals (3d cir.) 1991, U.S. Ct. Internat. Trade 1983, U.S. Supreme Ct. 1994. Assoc. Delson & Gordon, N.Y.C., 1975-83, ptnr., 1983-87; ptnr. Dorsey & Whitney, N.Y.C., 1994—; mng. ptnr., 1994—; mem. panel arbitrators U.S. Dist. Ct. for Ea. Dist. N.Y., 1987—; mem. panel mediators U.S. Dist. Ct. for So. Dist. N.Y., 1992—; trustee Lawyers Com. for Civil Rights under Law, 1992—. Mem. Am. Arbitration Assn. (panel of arbitrators 1988—). Office: Dorsey & Whitney 350 Park Ave New York NY 10022-6022

SILBERFARB, PETER MICHAEL, psychiatrist, educator; b. Jersey City, Oct. 28, 1938; m. Anne Wagner, 1962; children: Benjamin, Leah S. BS, Bucknell U., 1960; postgrad., NYU, 1960-61; MD, Hahnemann Coll., 1965; MA (hon.), Dartmouth Coll., 1986. Diplomate Nat. Bd. Med. Examiners, Am. Bd. Psychiatry and Neurology (sr. examiner 1985-90, bd. dirs. 1991—). Intern Hahnemann Med. Coll. Hosp., Phila., 1965-66; resident in internal medicine Dartmouth Affiliated Hosps., Hanover, N.H., 1966-68, resident in internal medicine and psychiatry, 1968-69, psychiatry resident, 1971-72, chief resident in psychiatry, 1972-73; instr. in psychiatry Med. Sch., Dartmouth Coll., Hanover, 1972-73, asst. prof. of psychiatry, 1973-77, assoc. prof. clin. psychiatry, assoc. prof. clin. medicine, 1977-80, dir. grad. edn. and residency tng., 1978-86, assoc. prof. psychiatry, assoc. prof. medicine, 1980-82, prof. psychiatry, assoc. prof. medicine, 1982-85, dir. tng. and edn., 1984—, prof. psychiatry, prof. medicine, 1986—, chmn. dept. psychiatry, 1986—, Raymond Sobel prof. psychiatry, 1993; cons. psychiatrist Mary Hitchcock Meml. Hosp., Hanover, 1973—; dir. psychiat. in-patient svc. Dartmouth-Hitchcock Med. Ctr., 1973-75, dir. cancer psychiatry program Norris Cotton Cancer Ctr., 1975—, acting dir. psychiatry consultation svc., 1977-79, assoc. dir. cancer control Norris Ctr., 1981-86; sec. psychiatry com. Cancer and Leukemia Group B, 1976-79, vice chmn., 1979—; mem. grant rev. com. for cancer control Nat. Cancer Inst., 1979, 80, mem. spl. grant rev. com., 1981, 82, 85, cons. to bd. sci. counselors, 1982, mem. cancer control grant rev. com., 1986-90; vice chmn. adv. com. for psychosocial and behavioral rsch. Am. Cancer Soc., 1982-88, chmn., 1988-89; cons. collaborative ctr. for cancer pain relief WHO, Milan, 1985; mem. accreditation coun. for grad. med. edn. Appeals Bd. for Psychiatry, Chgo., 1983, specialist site visitor, 1985-90, mem. residency rev. com. for psychiatry, 1991—; prin. investigator in field. Author chpts. to books; mem. editl. bd. Jour. Psychosocial Oncology, 1983—, Internat. Jour. Psychiatry in Medicine, 1986-90, Contemporary Psychiatry, 1987-91, Psychooncology, 1991—; referee numerous manuscripts; contbr. articles to profl. jours. Surgeon USPHS, 1969-71. Fellow Am. Psychiat. Assn. (cons. to task force on treatment if psychiat. disorders 1989), Am. Coll. Psychiatrists; mem. AMA, Am. Soc. Psychiat. Oncology/AIDS, Am. Soc. Clin. Oncology, Am. Assn. Dirs. Psychiat. Residency Tng. (mem. curriculum com. 1979-88, mem. task force on med. students and residents, chmn. com. regional dirs. 1984-88, mem. exec. com. 1984-88), Am. Psychosomatic Soc., N.H. Psychiat. Soc. (chmn. membership com. 1974-76, chmn. continuing edn. com. 1977-79), N.H. Med. Soc., Assn. Rsch. in Nervous and Mental Disease, Assn. Acad. Psychiatry, Benjamin Rush Soc. Home: Bragg Hill Norwich VT 05055 Office: Dartmouth Coll Med Sch Dept Psychiatry Lebanon NH 03756-0001

SILBERG, JAY ELIOT, lawyer; b. N.Y.C., Apr. 5, 1941; s. Arnold and Lillian (Liberman) S.; m. Ruth Vogel, June 22, 1975; children: Eric, Karen, Joanne. BA cum laude, Amherst Coll., 1963; LLB, Harvard U., 1966. Bar: N.J. 1966, U.S. Dist. Ct. N.J. 1966, U.S. Ct. Appeals (D.C. cir.) 1970, U.S. Ct. Appeals (7th cir.) 1982, U.S. Supreme Ct. 1983, U.S. Ct. Appeals (6th cir.) 1986. Atty. Office Gen. Counsel AEC, Washington, 1966-69; assoc. Shaw, Pittman, Potts & Trowbridge, Washington, 1969-72, ptnr., 1973—. Mem. Assn. of Bar of City of N.Y. (chmn. nuclear tech. and law com. 1988-91). Republican. Jewish. Home: 6109 Neilwood Dr Rockville MD 20852-3706 Office: Shaw Pittman Potts & Trowbridge 2300 N St NW Washington DC 20037-1122

SILBERGELD, ARTHUR F., lawyer; b. St. Louis, June 1, 1942; s. David and Sabina (Silbergeld) S.; m. Carol Ann Schwartz, May 1, 1970; children: Diana Lauren, Julia Kay. BA, U. Mich., 1968; M City Planning, U. Pa., 1971; JD, Temple U., 1975. Bar: N.Y. 1976, Calif. 1978, D.C. 1983, U.S. Ct. Appeals (2d, 9th and D.C. cirs.). Assoc. Vladeck, Elias, Vladeck & Lewis, N.Y.C., 1975-77; field atty. NLRB, Los Angeles, 1977-78; ptnr., head employment law practice group McKenna, Conner & Cuneo, L.A., 1978-89; ptnr., head labor and employment law practice group Graham & James, L.A., 1990—; instr. extension divsn. UCLA, 1981-89. Author: Doing Business in California: An Employment Law Handbook, 1989, Advising California Employers, 1990, 91, 93 supplements; contbr. articles to profl. jours. Founding mem. L.A. Mus. Contemporary Art; mem. Mus. Modern Art, N.Y., Art Inst. Chgo.; bd. dirs. Bay Cities unit Am. Cancer Soc., Calif., 1981-85, Jewish Family Svc. L.A., 1981-85, So. Calif. Employment Round Table, 1990—. Mem. ABA (com. on devel. law under NLRA 1975—), L.A. County Bar Assn. (exec. bd. labor law sect. 1984—). Office: Graham & James 801 S Figueroa St Fl 14 Los Angeles CA 90017-2573

SILBERGELD, ELLEN KOVNER, environmental epidemiologist and toxicologist; b. Washington, July 29, 1945; d. Joseph and Mary (Gion) Kovner; m. Alan Mark Silbergeld, 1969; children: Sophia, Nicholas. AB, Vassar Coll., 1967; PhD, Johns Hopkins U., 1972. Kennedy fellow Johns Hopkins Med. Sch., Balt., 1974-75; scientist NIH, Bethesda, Md., 1975-81; chief toxics scientist Environ. Def. Fund, Washington, 1982-90; prof. epidemiology, toxicology and pharmacology U.Md., Balt., 1990—, affil. prof. environ. law, 1990—; adj. prof. Johns Hopkins Med. Insts., 1990—; guest scientist NIH, 1982-84; mem. sci. adv. bd. EPA, 1983-89, 94—, Dept. Energy, 1994—; mem. bd. on environ. sci. and toxicology NAS-NRC, 1983-89, mem. com. geosci. environment, 1994—; mem. bd. sci. counselors Nat. Inst. Environ. Health Scis., 1987-93; cons. Oil and Chem. Atomic Workers, 1970, NSF, 1974-75, OECD, 1987—. Mem. editl. bd. Neurotoxicology, 1981-86, Neurobehavioral Toxicology, 1979-87, Am. Jour. Indsl. Medicine, 1980—, Hazardous Waste, 1985—, Archives Environ. Health, 1986—; mem. editl. bd. Environ. Rsch., 1983—; editor-in-chief, 1994—; contbr. articles to profl. jours. Mem. Homewood Friends Meeting. Recipient Wolman award Md. Pub. Health Assn., 1991, Barsky award APHA, 1992, Md. Gov. Excellence citation, 1990, 93; Fulbright fellow, London, 1967, Woodrow Wilson and Danforth fellow, 1967; NAS arch. fellow, Yugoslavia, 1976; MacArthur Found. fellow, 1993; Baldwin scholar Coll. Notre Dame. Mem. AAAS, Am. Soc. Pharmacology and Exptl. Therapeutics, Soc. for Occupational and Environ. Health (sec.-treas. 1983-85, pres. 1987-89), Soc. Toxicology, Soc. for Neurosci., Am. Pub. Health Assn., Collegium Ramazzini, Phi Beta Kappa. Office: U Md Med Sch Dept Epid Prev Medicine Howard Hall 104 Baltimore MD 21201

SILBERGELD, SAM, psychiatrist; b. Wengrov, Poland, Mar. 1, 1918; came to U.S., 1923; s. Hyman and Frieda (Orenstein) S.; m. Mae Ann Driscoll, June 22, 1952; children: Sandra Sue, Daniel Lance, Janet Joy, Nancy Ann. AA, Blackburn Coll., 1938; BS, U. Chgo., 1939; PhD in Chemistry, U. Ill., 1943; MD, Duke U., 1955. Cert. specialist in psychiatry, Md. Instr. biochemistry Mayo Found., Rochester, Minn., 1942-44; instr., asst. prof. chemistry U. Ill., Chgo., 1945-46, 46-52; med. officer U.S. Pub. Health Svcs., Bethesda, Md., 1956-88; staff asst. to dir. Div. Biologic Standards, NIH, Bethesda, 1956-59; rsch. grants specialist Div. Gen. Med. Sci., NIH, Bethesda, 1959-60; chief gen. clin. rsch. NIH, Bethesda, 1960-64; various rsch. positions NIMH, Md., 1964-81; staff psychiatrist, adminstr. geriatric program St. Elizabeth Hosp., Washington, 1981-87; staff psychiatrist Sheppard & Enoch Pratt Hosp., 1988-89; clin. prof. dept. psychiatry Uniformed Svcs. of the Health Scis. Sch. of Medicine, Bethesda, 1982—; adj. prof. U. Md., College Park, 1979-87, part-time instr. dept. health edn., 1992—. Contbr. numerous articles to profl. jours. Mem. vis. com. in scis. Blackburn Coll., Carlinville, Ill., 1986, trustee, 1987—; ad hoc mem. Eagle

Scout Review Bd., Bethesda, 1987—; chmn. Boy Scout Troop Com., Kensington, Md., 1973-80. Recipient Leadership Citation, Blackburn U., 1989, Editor's Choice award for outstanding achievement in poetry Nat. Libr. of Poetry, 1974; rsch. grantee Stanford Sch. Medicine Dept. Psychiatry, 1966-67. Mem. AMA, AAAS, Am. Chem. Soc., Am. Psychiat. Assn., Am. Psychosomatic Soc., N.Y. Acad. Scis., Md. Psychiat. Soc. (mem. quality revue com., peer revue com. 1991—). Avocations: mountaineering, tennis, ping pong, basketball. Home: Box 377 10704 Clermont Ave Garrett Park MD 20896

SILBERMAN, ALAN HARVEY, lawyer; b. Chgo., Oct. 22, 1940; s. Milton J. and Mollie E. (Hymanson) S.; m. Margaret Judith Auslander, Nov. 17, 1968; children: Elena, Mark. BA with distinction, Northwestern U., 1961; LLB, Yale U., 1964. Bar: Ill., 1964, U.S. Dist. Ct. (no. dist.) Ill., 1966, U.S. Ct. Appeals (7th cir.) 1970, (5th and 9th cir.) 1977, (D.C. cir.) 1979, (4th cir.) 1980, (11th cir.) 1981, (3rd cir.) 1982, (8th and 10th cirs.) 1993, U.S. Supreme Ct. 1978. Law clk. U.S. Dist. Ct., Chgo., 1964-66; assoc. Sonnenschein Nath & Rosenthal, Chgo., 1964-71, ptnr., 1972—; mem. antitrust adv. bd. Bur. Nat. Affairs, Washington, 1985—. Contbr. articles to profl. jours. Bd. dirs., v.p., sec. Camp Ramah in Wisc., Inc., Chgo., 1966-86, pres. 1986-94; bd. dirs. Nat. Ramah Commn., Inc. of Jewish Theol. Sem. Am., N.Y.C., 1970—, v.p. 1986-94, pres., 1994—. Mem. Ill. State Bar Assn. (chmn. antitrust sect. 1975-76), ABA (chmn. antitrust sect. FTC com. 1981-83, chmn. nat. insts. 1983-85, mem. coun. antitrust sect. 1985-88, fin. officer, 1988-90, sect. del. ho. of dels. 1990-92, chair elect 1992-93, chair 1993-94). Home: 430 Oakdale Ave Glencoe IL 60022-2113 Office: Sonnenschein Nath 233 S Wacker Dr Ste 8000 Chicago IL 60606-6404

SILBERMAN, CHARLES ELIOT, magazine editor, author; b. Des Moines, Jan. 31, 1925; s. Seppy I. and Cel (Levy) S.; m. Arlene Propper, Sept. 12, 1948; children—David, Richard, Jeffrey, Steven. A.B., Columbia, 1946, postgrad. in econs, 1946-49; L.H.D. (hon.), Kenyon Coll., 1972. Tutor econs. Coll. City N.Y., 1946-48; instr. econs. Columbia, 1948-53, lectr. econs., 1955-66; asso. editor Fortune mag., 1953-60, mem. bd. editors, 1961-71; dir. Study Law and Justice, 1972-79, dir. The Study of Jewish Life, 1979-85; Mem. joint commn. on juvenile justice standards Am. Bar Assn.; dir. Carnegie Corp. Study Edn. Educators, 1966-69. Co-author: Markets of the Sixties, 1960; author: Crisis in Black and White, 1964, The Myths of Automation, 1966, Crisis in the Classroom, 1970, The Open Classroom Reader, 1973, Criminal Violence, Criminal Justice, 1978, A Certain People, 1985; contbr. to various jours. Bd. dirs. Found. for Informed Med. Decision Making, West End Synagogue; bd. govs. Reconstructionist Rabbinical Coll.; mem. exec. bd. N.Y. chpt. Am. Jewish Com. Lt. (j.g.) USNR, 1943-46. Field Found. fellow, 1971-72. Fellow Nat. Assn. Bus. Economists. Home and Office: 10 W 66th St New York NY 10023

SILBERMAN, H. LEE, public relations executive; b. Newark, Apr. 26, 1919; s. Louis and Anna (Horel) S.; m. Ruth Irene Rapp, June 5, 1948; children: Richard Lyle, Gregory Alan, Todd Walter. B.A., U. Wis., 1940. Radio continuity writer Radio Sta. WTAQ, Green Bay, Wis., 1940-41; reporter Bayonne (N.J.) Times, 1941-42; sales exec. War Assets Adminstrn., Chgo., 1946-47; copy editor Acme Newspictures, Chgo., 1947; reporter, editorial writer Wichita (Kans.) Eagle, 1948-55; reporter Wall St. Jour., N.Y.C., 1955-57; banking editor Wall St. Jour., 1957-68; 1st v.p., dir. corporate relations Shearson-Hamill & Co., N.Y.C., 1968-74; N.Y. corr. Economist of London, 1966-72; contbg. editor Finance mag., 1970-74, editor in chief, 1974-76; v.p., dir. Fin. Services Group, Carl Boyir & Assos., Inc., N.Y.C., 1976-78, sr. v.p., 1978-80, exec. v.p., 1981-86; sr. counselor Hill & Knowlton, Inc., N.Y.C., 1986-93, sr. v.p., 1993—. Contbr. articles to profl. jours. Served to capt. C.E. AUS, 1942-46. Recipient Loeb Mag. award U. Conn., 1965; Loeb Achievement award for distinguished writing on fin. Gerald M. Loeb Found., 1968. Mem. Soc. Profl. Journalists, Pub. Rels. Soc. Am., Soc. Silurians, N.Y. Fin. Writers Assn., Deadline Club N.Y., Overseas Press Club, Zeta Beta Tau. Republican. Home: 80 Miller Rd Morristown NJ 07960-5237 Office: 420 Lexington Ave New York NY 10017-0002

SILBERMAN, JAMES HENRY, editor, publisher; b. Boston, Mar. 21, 1927; s. Henry R. and Dorothy (Conrad) S.; m. Selma Shapiro, Aug. 26, 1986; children by previous marriage: Michael, Ellen. A.B., Harvard U., 1950. Asst. to pub. Writer, Inc., 1950-51; asst. to advt. mgr. Little, Brown & Co., 1951-53; publicity dir. Dial Press, Inc., 1953-55, editor, 1954-55, exec. editor, 1955-59, v.p., editor-in-chief, 1959-63; editor The Dial, 1959-62; sr. editor Random House, Inc., N.Y.C., 1963-65, exec. editor, 1965-66, exec. editor, v.p., 1966-68, v.p., editor in chief, 1968-76, also pub., 1975-76; pres., editor-in-chief Summit Books div. Simon & Schuster, 1976-91; v.p., sr. editor Little Brown & Co., N.Y.C., 1991—; judge First Novel, Am. Book Awards, 1982; mem. adv. com. George Polk Meml. Awards, 1980—. Served as pfc. AUS, World War II. Mem. PEN, Assn. Am. Pubs. (Freedom to Read com. 1971-80, Freedom to Pub. com. 1982), Book Table, Pubs. Lunch Club, Corp. of Yaddo (bd. dirs. 1987—, exec. com. 1989—). Clubs: Harvard (N.Y.C.) Century Assn. Home: 315 E 70th St New York NY 10021-8657 Office: Little Brown & Co Inc 1271 Avenue Of The Americas New York NY 10020-1300

SILBERMAN, JOHN ALAN, lawyer; b. Balt., Sept. 20, 1951; s. Ronnie A. and Dovera (Gogel) S. BA, Northwestern U., 1973; JD, Harvard U., 1976. Bar: N.Y. 1977, U.S. Dist. Ct. (so. and ea. dists.) N.Y. 1977. Assoc. Paul, Weiss, Rifkind, Wharton & Garrison, N.Y.C., 1976-84, ptnr., 1985—. Bd. dirs. Coun. on Econ. Priorities, N.Y.C., 1986-90, Young Audiences, N.Y.C., 1988-90. Office: Paul Weiss Rifkind Wharton & Garrison 1285 Ave Of The Americas New York NY 10019-6064

SILBERMAN, LAURENCE HIRSCH, federal judge; b. York, Pa., Oct. 12, 1935; s. William and Anna (Hirsch) S.; m. Rosalie G. Gaull, Apr. 28, 1957; children: Robert Stephen, Katherine DeBoer Balaban, Anne Gaull. AB, Dartmouth Coll., 1957; LLB, Harvard U., 1961. Bar: Hawaii 1962, D.C. 1973. Assoc. Moore, Torkildson & Rice and Quinn & Moore, Honolulu, 1961-64; ptnr. Moore, Silberman & Schulze, Honolulu, 1964-67; atty. appellate div. gen. counsel's office NLRB, Washington, 1967-69; solicitor of labor U.S. Dept. Labor, Washington, 1969-70, undersec. labor, 1970-73; ptnr. Steptoe & Johnson, Washington, 1973-74; dep. atty. gen. U.S. Washington, 1974-75; ambassador to Yugoslavia, 1975-77; mng. ptnr. Morrison & Foerster, Washington, 1978-79, 83-85; exec. v.p. Crocker Nat. Bank, San Francisco, 1979-83; judge U.S. Ct. Appeals (D.C. cir.), Washington, 1985—; lectr. labor law and legis. U. Hawaii, 1962-63; adj. prof. adminstrv. law Georgetown U., Washington, 1987-94, NYU, 1995—; Pres.' spl. envoy on ILO affairs, 1976; mem. gen. adv. com. on Arms Control and Disarmament, 1981-85; mem. Def. Policy Bd., 1981-85; vice chmn. State Dept.'s Commn. on Security and Econ. Assistance, 1983-84. Bd. dirs. Com. on Present Danger, 1978-85, Inst. for Ednl. Affairs, 1981-85; vice chmn. advisory council on gen. govt. Rep. Nat. Com., 1977-80. Served with AUS, 1957-58. Am. Enterprise Inst. sr. fellow, 1977-78, vis. fellow 1978-85. Mem. U.S. Jud. Conf. Com. on Ct. Adminstrn. and Case Mgmt., Coun. on Fgn. Rels.

SILBERMAN, LINDA JOY, legal educator; b. 1944. B.A., U. Mich., 1965, J.D., 1968. Bar: Ill. 1969. Fulbright scholar U. London, 1968-69; assoc. Sonnenschein, Levinson, Carlin, Nath & Rosenthal, 1969-71; asst. prof. law NYU, 1971-74, assoc. prof., 1974-77, prof., 1977—; cons. Mem. Order of Coif, Inst. Jud. Adminstrn. (dir. lay judges project). Author: Non-Attorney Justice in the United States, 1979; (with Foster & Freed) Family Law: Cases and Materials, 1977; contbr. articles to legal jours. Office: NYU Law Sch 40 Washington Sq S New York NY 10012-1005

SILBERMAN, ROBERT A. S., lawyer; b. Lebanon, Pa., Mar. 4, 1945; s. Henry T. and Genevieve (Mensh) S.; m. Nancy D. Netzer, Nov. 10, 1974. BA, Yale U., 1967; JD, Harvard U., 1970. Bar: Mass. 1970, Pa. 1984. Assoc. Csaplar & Bok, Boston, 1970-78, ptnr., 1978-90; ptnr. Gaston & Snow, Boston, 1990-91, Edwards & Angell, Boston, 1991—. Mem. citizens rev. com. United Way Massachusetts Bay, Boston, 1981-89; dir. All Newton (Mass.) Music Sch., 1994—. Mem. ABA (vice chmn. health law com. sect. bus. law 1992—), Internat. Bar Assn., Boston Bar Assn., Nat. Health Lawyers Assn., Phi Beta Kappa. Office: Edwards & Angell 101 Federal St Boston MA 02110

SILBERMAN, ROSALIE GAULL, federal official; b. Jackson, Miss., Mar. 31, 1937; d. Samuel and Alice (Berkowitz) Gaull; m. Laurence H. Silberman.

Apr. 28, 1957; children: Katherine, Anne, Robert. BA, Smith Coll., 1958. Tchr., 1967-72; with Natl. Adv. Coun. on Edn. of Disadvantaged Children, 1973-75; bd. dirs. Widening Horizons, 1973-75; dir. comm., press sec. Sen. Robert Packwood, 1977-79; exec. dir., sec., treas. New Coalition for Econ. and Social Change, 1981-83; dir. pub. rels. San Franciso Conservatory of Music, 1982-83; spl. asst. Commr. Mimi Weyforth Dawson FCC, 1983-84; with EEOC, 1984-86, vice chmn., 1986-94, now commr. Office: EEOC Office of Commr 1801 L St NW Washington DC 20507-0002

SILBERSACK, MARK LOUIS, lawyer; b. Cin., Dec. 27, 1946; s. Joseph Leo and Rhoda Marie (Hinkler) S.; m. Ruth Ann Schwalbe, Sept. 7, 1985. AB, Boston Coll., 1968; JD, U. Chgo., 1971. Bar: Ohio 1971, U.S. Dist. Ct. (so. dist.) Ohio 1973, U.S. Ct. Appeals (6th cir.) 1974, U.S. Supreme Ct. 1975. Atty. Dinsmore & Shohl, Cin., 1971—; lectr. Ohio CLE Inst., Columbus, 1981-91. Co-author: Managed Care: The PPO Experience, 1990, Information Sharing Among Health Care Providers, 1994. V.p. Cin. Cmty. Chest, 1985-89, chmn. bd. dirs., 1994—; v.p. Ohio United Way, Columbus, 1989—; pres. Hyde Park Neighborhood Coun., Cin., 1989-91, Hyde Park Ctr. for Older Adults, 1989-91; mem. Cin. Bd. Health, 1991—. Mem. ABA, Ohio State Bar Assn., Cin. Bar Assn., Fed. Bar Assn., Bankers Club, Hyde Park Golf And County Club. Republican. Roman Catholic. Avocations: reading, travel, theater. Home: 3465 Forestoak Ct Cincinnati OH 45208-1842 Office: Dinsmore & Shohl 1900 Chemed Ctr 255 E Fifth St Cincinnati OH 45202

SILBERSTEIN, ALAN MARK, banker; b. Munich, Dec. 22, 1947; came to U.S., 1949; s. Leon and Rose (Rosenblatt) S.; m. Carol Krongold, Aug. 30, 1970; children: Eric, Adam, Meredith. BS in Engring., Columbia U., 1969; MBA, Harvard U., 1972. Design engr. Ford Motor Co., Dearborn, Mich., 1969-70; budget analyst N.Y.C. Bur. of Budget, 1972-74; various positions Chem. Bank, N.Y.C., 1974-88, exec. v.p., head Consumer Banking Group, 1990-92; exec. v.p. and dir. of retail banking Midlantic Corp., Edison, N.J., 1992—; bd. dirs. N.Y. Switch Corp., 1990-92, Cirrus System, Inc., 1991. Trustee Tenafly Bd. Edn., N.J., 1983-86, Yeshiva U. Sy Syms Sch. Bus., 1989—; mem. consumer adv. coun. Fed. Res. Bd., 1989-91; bd. dirs. N.Y. State Tree Consortium Inc., 1990-92; mem. exec. Bergen County N.J. Boy Scouts Am., 1992—, exec. v.p.b fin., 1995. Mem. Am. Bankers Assn. (chmn. retail banking exec. com. 1992—), Harvard Bus. Sch. Club N.Y. (sec. 1981-85, bd. dirs. 1982-83, 85-88). Office: Midlantic Corp PO Box 600 Edison NJ 08818

SILBERT, ALVIN JAY, secondary physics educator; b. N.Y.C., Feb. 16, 1945; s. Bertram W. and Kay (Tepper) S.; m. Linda P. Bress, Aug. 14, 1966; children: Brian R., Cheryl J. BA, SUNY, New Paltz, 1965; MS, Yeshiva U., 1969; EdD, Columbia U., 1977. Cert. tchr. physics and math., N.Y. Tchr. math. Ramapo Pub. Schs., Spring Valley, N.Y., 1965-66, Woodlands High Sch. Summer Sch., Greenburgh, N.Y., 1970-73; owner, dir. Silbert Tutoring & Guidance Svc., Mahopac, N.Y., 1968—; owner, pub., author Silbert & Bress Publs., Mahopac, 1976—; tchr. physics Lakeland High Sch., Shrub Oak, N.Y., 1966—; adj. prof. adj. math. Mercy Coll., Yorktown, N.Y., 1985-86; leader gifted program Silbert Tutoring & Guidance, Mahopac, 1989—. Author: Creative Thinking Workbooks, 1976, Divergent Style Lab Program, 1977, Understanding People Storybooks, 1978, (life skills programs) Stong Kids Program, 1991, Stong Kids Early Childhood Program, 1993, Passport to Emotionally and Social Strong Kids, 1995. V.p. Temple Beth Shalom, Mahopac, 1982-84, pres., 1984-86, 91-92, pres. bd. edn., 1982-84. Recipient Fed. award United Jewish Appeal, 1983. Mem. Orton Dyslexia Soc. Avocations: running, bicycling, photography, furniture making. Office: Silbert & Bress Inc PO Box 68 Mahopac NY 10541-0068

SILBERT, LINDA BRESS, educational counselor, therapist; b. New Rochelle, N.Y., Sept. 14, 1944; d. Abram H. and Ann (Dreizen) Bress; m. Alvin Jay Silbert, Aug. 14, 1966; children: Brian R., Cheryl J. BS, SUNY, New Paltz, 1966; MS, We. Conn. State U., Danbury, 1989; PhD in Ednl. Adminstrn., Walden U., Mpls., 1993. Cert. in sch. counseling and elem. edn., N.Y. Children's writer Phone Programs, N.Y.C., 1984-86; owner, pub. Silbert & Bress, Inc., Mahopac, N.Y., 1976—, children's author, 1976—; owner, dir. Silbert Tutoring and Guidance Svc., Mahopac, 1968—; part-time prin. Temple Beth Shalom Hebrew Sch., Mahopac, 1985—; leader parent workshops Silbert Tutoring and Guidance, 1985—, leader gifted program, 1989; cons. Mahopac Ctrl. Sch. Dist., 1983-84; cons. developer Author in Your Sch. program, 1983-87. Author: Creative Thinking Workbooks, 1976, Understanding People Storybooks, 1978, (lifeskills programs) Stong Kids Program, 1991, Stong Kids Early Childhood Programs, 1993, Passport to Emotionally and Socially Strong Kids, 1995. Membership chair Temple Beth Shalom, Mahopac, 1980-85. Recipient Gabriel Schonfeld award for educator excellence Bd. of Jewish Edn. of Greater N.Y., 1991. Mem. Am. Counseling Assn., Orton Dyslexia Soc., Am. Mental Health Counselors Assn., United Jewish Fedn. (award 1983). Avocations: dancing, painting. Office: Silbert & Bress Inc PO Box 68 Mahopac NY 10541-0068

SILBEY, JOEL HENRY, history educator; b. Bklyn., Aug. 16, 1933; s. Sidney and Estelle (Mintzer) S.; m. Rosemary Johnson, Aug. 13, 1959; children: Victoria, David. BA, Bklyn. Coll., 1955; MA, U. Iowa, 1956, PhD, 1963. Asst. prof. San Francisco State Coll., 1960-64, U. Md., College Park, 1965-66; asst. prof. Am. History Cornell U., Ithaca, N.Y., 1966-67, assoc. prof., 1967-68, prof., 1968-86, Pres. White prof. history, 1986—; vis. asst. prof. history U. Pitts., 1964-65. Author: The Shrine of Party, 1967, The Transformation of American Politics, 1968, A Respectable Minority: The Democratic Party in the Civil War Era, 1977, The Partisan Imperative: The Dynamics of American Politics before the Civil War, 1985, The American Political Nation, 1838-1893, 1991; editor: (with others) Voters, Parties and Elections, 1972, American Political Behavior, 1984, The History of American Electoral Behavior, 1978; editor-in-chief: Encyclopedia of the American legislative System, 1993; editorial cons. numerous publs.; contbr. numerous articles to profl. jours. Am. Philos. Soc. fellow, 1969-70; NSF fellow, 1970-74; NEH fellow, 1980-81; vis. fellow Ctr. for Advanced Study in the Behavioral Scis., 1985-86; vis. scholar Russell Sage Found., 1988-89; John Simon Guggenheim Meml. fellow, 1989-90. Mem. Am. Hist. Assn. (program com. 1977), Orgn. Am. Historians (chmn. program com. 1983), So. Hist. Assn., Social Sci. History Assn. (co-chmn. membership com., mem. exec. com). Home: 105 Judd Falls Rd Ithaca NY 14850-2715 Office: Cornell U 452 Mcgraw Hall Ithaca NY 14853-4601

SILBEY, ROBERT JAMES, chemistry educator, researcher; b. N.Y.C., Oct. 19, 1940; s. Sidney Richard and Estelle (Mintzer) S.; m. Susan Sorkin, June 24, 1962; children: Jessica, Anna. BS, CUNY Bklyn. Coll., 1961; PhD, U. Chgo., 1965. Asst. prof. MIT, Cambridge, 1966-76, prof., 1976—; chmn. dept. chemistry; vis. prof. U. Utrecht, The Netherlands, 1972-73, U. Grenoble, France, 1983; cons. Exxon Rsch., Clinton, N.J., 1984—. Author: Physical Chemistry, 1991; editor: Conjugated Polymers, 1991; contbr. articles to profl. jours. Recipient Alexander von Humboldt Found. Sr. Scientist award, 1989, Max Planck award, 1992; Alfred P. Sloan fellow, 1968, John S. Guggenheim fellow, 1972; Dreyfus Found. Tchr.-Scholar grantee, 1969. Fellow AAAS, Am. Acad. Arts and Scis., Am. Phys. Soc. Avocations: swimming, sailing. Office: MIT Dept Chemistry 77 Massachusetts Ave Cambridge MA 02139

SILBURN, ELAINE GWENDOLYN, banker; b. Denver, June 3, 1937; d. Russell Edwin and Genevieve (Johnson) Seay; m. David L. Silburn, June 16, 1957; children: Carla Anne, James Russell. ABA in Bus. Adminstrn., U. Denver, 1957; student Northwestern U., 1960, U. Okla., 1981. Trust officer United Bank of Denver, 1957-65; personal banker, personal banking officer, asst. v.p., v.p. United Bank of Skyline, Denver, 1978-83, sr. v.p., 1983-89, dir., 1984-89; v.p. exec. banking United Bank of Denver, 1989—; v.p. Historic Denver, Inc., bd. dirs., 1988—. Vol. Denver Pub. Schs.; alumni fund campaign U. Denver, Channel 6 Pub. TV Auction, Am. Cancer Soc.; mem. major gifts fund com. Denver Symphony Orch., 1984-87; adv. bd. Mile High United Way, 1985; del. Rep. county and state assemblies. Recipient Women of Achievement award YWCA, 1985, 87. Mem. Mental Health Assn. Colo., Leadership Denver Assn., Denver C of C., Cultural Affairs Task Force, Gamma Phi Beta, Sweet Adelines Club (High Country chpt., pres. 1977). Episcopalian. Home: 3119 S Akron Ct Denver CO 80231-6413 Office: Norwest Bank Denver Private Banking Dept 8684 1740 Broadway Denver CO 80274-0002

SILBY, DONALD WAYNE, investment executive, entrepreneur; b. Charles City, Iowa, July 20, 1948; s. Bernard and Rita (Grad) S.; m. Joana Johnston Silby, Nov. 11, 1988 (div. Mar. 1994); 1 child, Georgina. BSE, U. Pa., 1970; JD, Georgetown U., 1975. Chmn. Calvert Group Funds, Washington, 1976-85; pres. Calvert Social Investment Fund, Washington, 1982—; sr. ptnr. Calvert Social Venture Ptnrs., Bethesda, Md., 1989—; dir. Acacia Mut. Life Ins. Co., Washington. Bd. dirs. Calif. Sch. Profl. Psychology, 1986-92; mem. bd. Inst. East-West Studies, 1994—. Recipient hon. award Interfaith Ctr. Corp. Responsibility, N.Y.C., 1990. Mem. Am. Assn. Higher Edn. (bd. dirs. 1986—92), Bus. Execs. Nat. Security (bd. dirs. 1986-89), Social Venture Network (bd. dirs., co-founder 1987-90), Social Investment Forum. Buddhist. Home and Office: 1715 18th St NW Washington DC 20009-2507

SILCOTT, JAMES, principal; b. Balt., Sept. 15, 1956; s. Thomas Braden and Janet Ann (Kreis) S.; m. Mary Beth Wirth, Sept. 6, 1980; children: Lauren, Bethany, Thomas. BS, Ohio State U., 1979, MA, 1985; postgrad., U. Dayton, 1992—. Cert. secondary English supr., elem. prin. middle sch. prin., secondary prin., asst. supt. Tchr. Bishop Watterson High Sch., Columbus, Ohio, 1979-89, chair drama dept., 1983-89, dir. activities, 1988-89; prin., tchr. Latin St. Timothy elem. sch., Columbus, 1989—; initiator student council, sch. newspaper, sch. recycling program St. Timothy Sch., Columbus, Japanese intern program, 1990, middle sch. leadership tng. program; tchr., adv. com. Columbus State C. C., 1991—; mem. Diocesan com. rewrite teacher supervision standards, 1992, Diocesan com. for tchr. lay-off provisions, 1993; espeaker in field. Contbr. articles to newspapers. Vol. Charity Newsies, Columbus,1990—; mem. fin. com. St. Timothy Parish. Recipient Nat. Sch. Excellence award U.S. Dept. Edn., Washington, 1989. Mem. Prin. Assn. Catholic Elem. Sch. (treas. 1990-92, exec. bd. 1990—), Phi Lambda Theta. Democrat. Roman Catholic. Avocations: swimming, poetry, drama, cycling. Home: 47 E Beaumont Rd Columbus OH 43214-2101 Office: St Timothy Sch 1070 Thomas Ln Columbus OH 43220-5047

SILCOX, JOHN, physicist, educator; b. Saltash, Cornwall, Eng., May 26, 1935; came to U.S., 1961; s. Arthur Leonard and Janet (Jones) S.; m. Heather Phyllis Penhale, Apr. 9, 1960; children: Heather Jane, Allison Tamar, Laurie Elizabeth. BSc, Bristol (Eng.) U., 1957; PhD, Cambridge (Eng.) U., 1961. Asst. prof. Cornell U., Ithaca, N.Y., 1961-64, assoc. prof., 1964-70, prof., 1970-88, David E. Burr prof. engring., 1988—; mem. solid state scis. com. NRC, Washington, 1978-82; mem. materials rsch. adv. com. NSF, Washington, 1985-91; John E. Dorn lectr. Northwestern U., 1985. Contbr. articles to profl. jours. J. S Guggenheim Found. fellow Paris, 1967-68. Mem. Am. Phys. Soc. (chmn. materials physics div. 1988-89), Electron Microscopy Soc. Am. (pres. 1979-80). Office: Cornell U 235 Clark Hall Ithaca NY 14853-2501

SILECCHIA, JEROME A., mechanical engineer; b. Bklyn., Oct. 25, 1941; s. Charles and Concetta (Yorio) S.; m. Collette Ambrico, June 27, 1964; children: Suzanne, Charles, Jerome. BME, Villanova U., 1963; MBA, Baruch Sch. Bus., 1973. Registered profl. engr., N.Y., N.J.; cert. plant engr., real property adminstr. Design engr. The Austin Co., N.Y.C., 1963-64, Worthington Corp., Harrison, N.J., 1964-67, York Div. of Borg Warner Corp, N.Y.C., 1967-69; mgr. H.K. Porter/Marlo Coil Div., N.Y.C., 1969-74; exec. v.p. engr. Nat. Engring. Maintenance Co., Inc., N.Y.C., 1974-93; pres. ServiceForce, Inc., 1993—; adj. lectr. NYU, 1990—. Contbr. articles to profl. jours. Mem. NSPE, Am. Inst. Plant Engrs., Am. Soc. Heating, Refrigeration and Air Conditioning Engrs., Soc. Real Property Adminstrs. Roman Catholic. Home: 92 Riverside Dr Rockville Centre NY 11570-5821

SILEN, WILLIAM, physician, surgery educator; b. San Francisco, Sept. 13, 1927; s. Dave and Rose (Miller) S.; m. Ruth Heppner, July 13, 1947; children: Stephen, Deborah, Mark. BA, U. Calif., Berkeley, 1946; MD, U. Calif., San Francisco, 1949; MA (hon.), Harvard U., 1966. Diplomate Am. Bd. Surgery. Intern U. Calif., San Francisco, 1949-50, asst. resident gen. surgery, 1950-56, chief resident gen. surgery, 1956-57; asst. chief surgery Denver VA Hosp., 1957-59, chief surgery, 1959-60; asst. chief surgery San Francisco Gen. Hosp., 1960-61; chief surgery, 1961-66; surgeon-in-chief Beth Israel Hosp., Boston, 1966—; instr. surgery, asst. prof. surgery U. Colo. Med. Sch., Denver, 1957-60; asst. prof. then assoc. prof. surgery U. Calif. Sch. Medicine, San Francisco, 1960-66; prof. surgery Harvard Med. Sch., Boston, 1966—, Johnson and Johnson prof. surgery, 1975—; dir. Harvard Digestive Diseases Ctr. NIH, Bethesda, Md., 1984. Author: Cope's Early Diagnosis of the Acute Abdomen, 1979, Conservative Management of Breast Cancer, 1983. With USAF, 1950-52. Mem. AMA, ACS, Soc. Univ. Surgeons, H.C. Naffziger Surg. Soc., Phi Beta Kappa. Avocation: bonsai cultivation. Office: Beth Israel Hosp 330 Brookline Ave Boston MA 02215-5400

SILER, EUGENE EDWARD, JR., federal judge; b. Williamsburg, Ky., Oct. 19, 1936; s. Eugene Edward and Lowell (Jones) S.; m. Christy Dyanne Minnich, Oct. 18, 1969; children—Eugene Edward, Adam Troy. B.A. cum laude, Vanderbilt U., 1958; LL.B., U. Va., 1963; LL.M., Georgetown U., 1964. Bar: Ky. 1963, Va. 1963, D.C. 1963. Individual practice law Williamsburg, 1964-65; atty. Whitley County, Ky., 1965-70; U.S. atty. Eastern Dist. Ky., Lexington, 1970-75; judge U.S. Dist. Ct., Eastern and Western Dists., Ky., 1975-91; chief judge Eastern Dist., Ky., 1984-91; judge U.S. Ct. Appeals (6th cir.), 1991—. Campaign co-chmn. Congressman Tim L. Carter, 1966, 5th Congl. Dist.; campaign co-chmn. U.S. Senator J.S. Cooper, 1966; trustee Cumberland Coll., Williamsburg, 1965-73, 80-88; 1st v.p. Ky. Bapt. Convention, 1986-87; bd. dirs. Bapt. Healthcare Systems Inc., 1990—. Served with USN, 1958-60, with Res. 1960-83. E. Barrett Prettyman fellow, 1963-64; recipient medal Freedom's Found., 1968. Mem. Fed. Bar Assn., Ky. Bar Assn., D.C. Bar Assn., Va. State Bar. Republican. Baptist. Home: PO Box 129 Williamsburg KY 40769-0129 Office: US Ct Appeals 1380 W 5th St London KY 40741

SILER, WALTER ORLANDO, JR., retired business executive; b. Atascadero, Calif., May 21, 1920; s. Walter Orlando and Hylda Ruth Martyn (Jackson) S.; m. Carolyn Louise Townsend, 1978; children by previous marriage: Robert Eugene, Barbara Ellen, Susan Jane,Donald Walter, David Brian. B.S., U. So. Calif., 1941. C.P.A., Calif. Partner Arthur Andersen & Co. (C.P.A.'s), Phoenix, 1950-61; pres., treas., dir. Bargain City, U.S.A., Inc., Phila., 1962; treas., dir. Getty Oil Co. Los Angeles, 1963-67; v.p. Getty Oil Co., 1966-67, asst. controller, 1968-70; controller Fluor Corp., Los Angeles, 1970-72; gen. mgr. Saudi Arabian ops. Whittaker Corp., 1972-73; bus. mgr. Northrop Aircraft Div., Taif, Saudi Arabia, 1973-74; v.p. fin. Fluor Arabia Ltd., Dhahran, Saudi Arabia, 1974-77; mgr. accounting The Ralph M. Parsons Co., Pasadena, Calif., 1977-78; v.p., treas., sec. Parsons Constructors Inc., Pasadena, 1978-85; treas., dir. Mission Corp., 1963-68; treas. Mission Devel. Co., 1963-67; dir. Skelly Oil Co., 1963-68. Served to maj. USAAF, 1941-46. Mem. AICPA, Fin. Execs. Inst. (bd. dirs. L.A. chpt. 1990-93), Calif. Soc. CPAs, Univ. Club of Pasadena (bd. govs. 1990-91), Town Hall Calif. (L.A.), Sigma Nu, Phi Kappa Phi, Beta Gamma Sigma, Beta Alpha Psi. Republican. Home: 703 N Stoneman Ave Apt G Alhambra CA 91801-1410

SILER-KHODR, THERESA MARIE, biochemistry educator; b. Pomona, Calif., June 17, 1947; d. Joseph Horace and Anna Marie (Ary) Siler; m. Gabriel Shukri, Jan. 26, 1974; children: Tanya Ann Khodr, Christina Emilie Knodr, Zeina Gabriella Khodr. BA in Chemistry, Immaculate Heart Coll., L.A., 1968; Phd in Biochemistry, U. Hawaii, 1971. Cert. profl. chemist, Am. Chem. Soc. Nuclear medicine technician St. Vincent's Hosp., L.A., 1968; NIH predoctoral fellow dept biochemistry and biophysics U. Hawaii, Honolulu, 1968-70, predoctoral Ford Found. fellow, 1970, postdoctoral Ford Found. fellow dept. anatomy andreproductive biology; 1971; chief adenohypophyseal hormone sect. InterSci. Inst., L.A., 1972; asst. rsch. biologist dept. reproductive medicine U. Calif. San Diego 1972-74; asst. prof. dept. ob-gyn. Am. Univ. Beirut Hosp. 1974-76; with U. Tex. Health Sci. Ctr., San Antonio, 1976—, assoc. prof. dept. ob-gyn, 1979-86, prof., 1986—; participant preceptor tng. programs including AID program for Internat. Edn. in Gynecology and Obstetrics, Dept. Ob-Gyn., Am. Univ. Beirut Hosp. 1974-76, Reproductive Endocrinology Fellowship Program, Health Sci. Ctr., U. Tex., 1987—; cons. rev. bd. for NIH Intramural Grants, S.W. Biomed. Rsch. Found., 1985-87; extramural reviewer Med. Rsch. Coun. Can., 1985, 86, 87, NICHD, 1985, NSF, 1981; presenter profl. confs. including XI World Congress of Gynecology and Obstetrics, West Berlin, 1985, 1stInternat. Meeting on Human Fetal Membranes, London, Ont., Can. 1986. Contbg. author:

Radioimmunoassay Methods, 1971, Biorhythm in Human Reproduction, 1973, Advances in the Biosciences 15, 1975, Physiology and Pathophysiology of Reproduction, 1979, Clinics in Perinatology, 1983, Neonatal and Fetal Medicine, 1989, others; contbr. numerous articles to profl. publs.; mem. editorial bd. Jour. Endocrinological Investigation, 1978-83, Endocrinology, 1987—; ad hoc reviewer Obstetrics and Gynecology, 1982, Psychoneuroendocrinology, 1983, 84, 85, Neuroendocrinology, 1985,86, Placenta, 1987,88. Recipient Wyeth award The Pacific Coast Fertility Soc., 1972, 79, 80, Purdue Frederick Pres.'s award Congress for Am. Coll. Ob-Gyn., 1972, 1st prize Armed Forces Congress of Ob-Gyn., 1971; rsch. grantee Syntex Labs., U. Tex. Health Sci. Ctr., 1980-85, WHO, Am. U. Beirut Hosp., 1975-76, co-investigator, preceptor or cons. many other rsch. grants. Mem. AAAS, NIH (mem. reproductive endocrinology study sect. 1986-89, rsch. grantee, 1980, 84, 82-86, 88-92), The Endocrine Soc. (chairperson fetal and neonatal endocrinology session of 65th soc. session 1983, mem. women's caucus), Soc. for Study of Reprodn., Soc. for Gynecologic Investigation, Am. Endocrine Soc., Assn. Profs. of Gynecology and Obstetrics, U. Tex. Health Sci. Ctr. Women's Faculty Assn., Sigma Xi. Office: Univ Tex Health Sci Ctr 7703 Floyd Curl Dr San Antonio TX 78284-6200

SILETS, HARVEY MARVIN, lawyer; b. Chgo., Aug. 25, 1931; s. Joseph Lazarus and Sylvia (Dubner) S.; m. Elaine L. Gordon, June 25, 1961; children: Hayden Leigh, Jonathan Lazarus (dec.), Alexandra Rose. BS cum laude, DePaul U., 1952; JD (Frederick Leicke scholar), U. Mich., 1955. Bar: Ill. 1955, U.S. Dist. Ct. (no. dist.) Ill. 1955, N.Y. 1956, U.S. Tax Ct. 1957, U.S. Ct. Mil. Appeals 1957, U.S. Ct. Appeals (7th cir.) 1958, U.S. Supreme Ct. 1959, U.S. Ct. Appeals (6th cir.) 1965, U.S. Ct. Appeals (2d cir.) 1971, U.S. Ct. Appeals (5th cir.) 1972, U.S. Ct. Appeals (11th cir.) 1981. Assoc. Paul, Weiss, Rifkind, Wharton & Garrison, N.Y.C., 1955-56; asst. atty. U.S. Dist. Ct. (no. dist.) Ill., 1958-60; chief tax atty. U.S. atty. No. Dist. Ill., Chgo., 1960-62; ptnr. Harris, Burman & Silets, Chgo., 1962-79, Silets & Martin, Ltd., Chgo., 1979-92; asst. advance tng. program IRS, U. Mich., 1952-53; law lectr. advance fed. taxation John Marshall Law Sch., 1962-66; adj. prof. taxation Chgo.-Kent Coll. Law, 1985—; gen. counsel Nat. Treasury Employees Union, 1968-92; mem. adv. com. tax litigation U.S. Dept. Justice, 1979-82; mem. Tax Reform Com., State of Ill., 1982-83; mem. Speedy Trial Act Planning Group U.S. Dist. Ct. (no. dist.) Ill. 1976-79; mem. civil justice reform act adv. com. U.S. Dist. Ct. (no. dist.) Ill., 1991—; lectr. in field. Contbr. articles to profl. jours. Trustee Latin Sch., Chgo., 1970-76; active Chgo. Crime Commn., 1975-93, Govv.'s Commn. Reform Tax Laws, Ill., 1982-83. With AUS, 1956-58. Fellow Am. Coll. Trial Lawyers (chmn. com. on fed. rules of criminal procedure 1982-91, fed. rules of evidence com. 1988-93, mem. judiciary com., Upstate Ill. com. chmn. 1990-91), Am. Coll. Tax Counsel, Internat. Acad. Trial Lawyers; mem. ABA (active various coms.), Bar Assn. 7th Fed. Cir. (chmn. com. criminal law and procedure 1972-82, bd. govs. 1983-86, sec. 1986-88, v.p. 1989-90, pres. 1990-91), Fed. Bar Assn. (bd. dirs. 1977-78, v.p. 1976-77, sec. 1975-76, treas. 1974-75, active various coms.), Chgo. Bar Assn. (tax com. 1958-66, com. devel. law 1966-72, 78—, com. fed. taxation 1968—, com. evaluation candidates 1978-80, exec. com. tax sect. 1994—), Am. Bd. Criminal Def. Lawyers, Chgo. Soc. Trial Lawyers, Decalogue Soc. Lawyers, Bar Assn. N.Y. City, Nat. Assn. Criminal Def. Lawyers, Standard Club, Cliff Dwellers Club, Chgo. Club, Phi Alpha delta, Pi Gamma Mu. Office: Katten Muchin & Zavis 525 W Monroe St Ste 1600 Chicago IL 60661

SILFEN, DAVID M., investment banker; b. N.Y.C., Nov. 30, 1945; s. Herman and Esther (Weiss) S.; m. Lyn Gordon, June 12, 1971; 1 son, Adam. B.A., U. Pa., 1966; M.B.A., Columbia U., 1968. Assoc. Goldman Sachs & Co., N.Y.C., 1968-74, v.p., 1974-78, ptnr., 1978—. Office: Goldman Sachs & Co 85 Broad St New York NY 10004-2434

SILFVAST, WILLIAM T., laser physics educator, consultant; b. Salt Lake City, June 7, 1937; s. Andrew William and Dorothy Phyllis (Hobba) S.; m. Susan Carol Denton, Sept. 19, 1959; children: Scott William, Robert Denton, Stacey Marie. BS in Physics, BS in Math., U. Utah, 1961, PhD in Physics, 1965. Rsch. assoc. U. Utah, Salt Lake City, 1965-66; NATO postdoctoral fellow Oxford (Eng.) U., 1966-67; mem. tech. staff Bell Labs., Holmdel, N.J., 1967-82; Guggenheim fellow Stanford (Calif.) U., 1982-83; disting. mem. tech. staff AT&T Bell Labs., Holmdel, 1983-89; prof. physics and elec. engring. U. Cen. Fla., Orlando, 1990-94, chair dept. physics, 1994—. Contbr. numerous articles to sci. jours.; numerous patents relating to lasers. Trustee 1st Presbyn. Ch., Matawan, N.J., 1979-82, 88-89; chmn. bd. trustees Monmouth County Arts Coun., Red Bank, N.J., 1987-88. Fellow IEEE (assoc. editor IEEE Jour. Quantum Elecs. 1986-91), Optical Soc. Am. (chmn. tech. coun. 1988-89), Am. Phys. Soc. Avocations: writing, golf, tennis, skiing, automobile restoration. Office: U Cen Fla CREOL 12424 Research Pky Orlando FL 32826-3249

SILHAVY, THOMAS JOSEPH, molecular biology educator; b. Wauseon, Ohio, Jan. 13, 1948; s. W.J. and Helen (Batdorf) S.; Daileen K. Stutzman, June 27, 1969; children—Marc Thomas, Ned Thomas. B.S. in Pharmacy, Ferris State Coll., 1971; A.M. in Biochemistry, Harvard U., 1974, Ph.D. in Biochemistry, 1975; D.S., Ferris State Coll, 1982. Instr. Harvard U. Med Sch., Boston, 1978-79; head genetics sect. Nat. Cancer Inst., Frederick, MD., 1979-81, dir. genetics, 1981-84; instr. Advanced Bacterial Genetics, Cold Spring Harbor, N.Y., 1981-85; prof. molecular biology Princeton U., 1984—. Co-author: Experiments with Gene Fusions, 1984, The Power of Bacterial Genetics: A Literature-based Course, 1992; contbr. over 100 articles to profl. jours. Patentee in field. Recipient Advanced Tech. Achievement award Litton, 1982, Wellcom vis. professorship in microbiol. scis., 1990, Pres.'s award for disting. teaching, 1993; Jane Coffin Childs fellow, 1975-77, Med. Rsch. Found. fellow, 1978-79. Fellow Am. Soc. Microbiology; mem. AAAS, Am. Soc. Biol. Chemists, Am. Soc. Cell Biology. Home: 22 Van Doren Way Belle Mead NJ 08502-5508 Office: Princeton U Dept Molecular Biology Princeton NJ 08544

SILINS, INTS M., ambassador; b. Riga, Latvia, Mar. 25, 1942; m. Elizabeth Louise Adolphson, 1976; children: Kate, Matthew, Lucas, Nicholas. BA with honors in Philosophy, Princeton U., 1965; postgrad., U. Coll., London. With Washington Star; sr. advisor State Dept., Duc Thanh, Mekong Delta, Vietnam, 1970-71; exec. secretariat State Dept., Washington, 1975-76, Romania desk officer, 1976-78; amb. aide U.S. Embassy, Saigon, Vietnam, 1971-73; econ., comml. officer U.S. Embassy, Bucharest, Romania, 1973-75; polit. officer U.S. Embassy, Port au Prince, Haiti, 1978-80; polit. counselor U.S. Embassy, Stockholm, 1983-86; chargé d'affaires U.S. Embassy, Riga, Latvia, 1991-92, U.S. Amb., 1992—; dep. prin. officer U.S. Consulate Gen., Leningrad, USSR, 1981-83; fellow Ctr. Internat. Affairs Harvard U., Cambridge, Mass., 1986-87; U.S. consul gen. Strasbourg, France, 1989-91. Recipient Valor award Dept. State, 1980, Meritorious Honor award Dept. State, 1985, Superior Honor award, 1988, 92. Office: US Embassy Riga, 7 Raina Blvd, Riga 1050, Latvia

SILIPIGNI, ALFREDO, opera conductor; b. Atlantic City, Apr. 9, 1931; s. Alfredo and Elisabeth (Calhoun) S.; m. Gloria Rose DiBenedetto, Apr. 11, 1953; children: Marisa, Elisabetta Luisa, Afredo Roberto. Student, Westminster Choir Coll., 1948, Juilliard Sch. Music, 1953; HHD (hon.), Kean Coll., N.J., 1978. Prin. condr., gen. dir., artistic dir. N.J. State Opera, Newark, 1965—; founder Young Artist Program, 1969—; guest lectr. Glassboro (N.J.) State Coll. Carnegie Hall debut with NBC Symphony Orch., 1956; condr. NBC Symphony, Boston, Bklyn. and Conn. operas, Newark Symphony; guest condr. Vienna State Opera, 1976, Grand Liceo di Barcelona, Spain, 1976, London, 1977, also numerous cos. Eng., Venezuela, France, Italy, Mex. and Can. with frequent appearances at L'Opera de Montreal; made recs. fo Zaza by Leoncavallo, 'Adriana Lecouvrer' by Cilea; prin. guest condr. and advisor Bellas Artes, Mex., 1993-94. Recipient Centennial medal St. Peter's Coll., 1972, Disting. Svc. to Culture award City of San Remo, Columbia Found. award, Boys Town of Italy award, Music award N.J. Edn. Assn., 1988. Office: NJ State Opera 1020 Broad St Newark NJ 07102-2400

SILJAK, DRAGOSLAV D., engineering educator; b. Belgrade, Yugoslavia, Sept. 10, 1933; came to U.S. 1964, naturalized; s. Dobrilo T. and Ljubica Z. (Zivanovic) S.; m. Dragana T. Todorovic, Sept. 28, 1967; children—Ana, Matija. BSEE, U. Belgrade, 1958, MSEE, 1961, ScD, 1963. Docent prof. U. Belgrade, 1963-64; assoc. prof. U. Santa Clara, Calif., 1964-70; prof.

engring. U. Santa Clara, 1970-84, B. and M. Swig Univ. chair, 1984—. Author: Nonlinear Systems, 1969, Large Scale Systems, 1978, Decentralized Control of Complex Systems, 1991. Disting. prof. Fulbright Found., 1984. Fellow IEEE; mem. Serbian Acad. Scis. and Arts (hon.). Mem. Christian Ch. Office: U Santa Clara The Alemeda Santa Clara CA 95053

SILK, ALVIN JOHN, business educator; b. Winnipeg, Manitoba, Can., Dec. 31, 1935; came to U.S. 1959, naturalized, 1975; s. John Edward and Bertha Lena (Kirton) S.; m. Diane D. Wilson; children: Jonathan, Andrea, Stephanie. BA, U. Western Ont., 1959; MBA, Northwestern U., 1960, PhD, 1968. Asst. prof. mgmt. UCLA, 1963-66; asst. prof. Chgo. 1966-68; from assoc. prof. to prof. Sloan Sch. Mgmt., MIT, Cambridge, 1968-88; dep. dean MIT Sloan Sch. Mgmt., Cambridge, 1981-87; Lincoln Filene prof. Grad. Sch. Bus. Adminstrn. Harvard U., Boston, 1988—; vis. rsch. fellow Mktg. Sci. Inst., Cambridge, Mass., 1970-71, trustee, 1984—; Ford Found. vis. prof. European Inst. for Advanced Studies in Mgmt., Brussels, 1975-76, Harvard Bus. Sch., 1987—; bd. dirs. BayFunds, Cambridge, Mass., Reed and Barton, Inc., Taunton, Mass. Co-editor: Behavioral and Management Science in Marketing, 1978; assoc. editor: Management Science, 1969-77; mem. editorial bd.; Jour. Marketing Research, 1969-73, Jour. Marketing, 1978-81, Marketing Science, 1980-93; author, co-author numerous articles to profl. jours. Mem. Am. Mktg. Assn. (O'Dell award 1983), Am. Statis. Assn., Assn. for Consumer Rsch., Econometric Soc., Inst. for Mgmt. Scis. (Achievement award 1982, 83), Psychometric Soc., Beta Gamma Sigma, Zeta Psi. Home: 327 Commonwealth Ave Boston MA 02115 Office: Harvard U Grad Sch Bus Adminstrn Soldiers Field Rd Allston MA 02134-1805

SILK, ELEANA S., librarian; b. Detroit, Aug. 10, 1951; d. John and Helen (Kavenski) S. BS in Zoology, Mich. State U., 1972; BS in Geology, George Washington U., 1979; MDiv, St. Vladimir's Sem., 1986, MA in Religious Edn., 1988; MLS, Columbia U., 1989. Asst. libr. St. Vladimir's Sem., Crestwood, N.Y., 1985-90, libr., 1990—; mem. history and archives commn., bicentennial commn. Orthodox Ch. in Am., Syosset, N.Y., 1989—. Editor: The Legacy of St. Vladimir, 1989; contbr. articles to religious jours. Mem. ALA, N.Y. Area Theol. Libr. Assn., Oral History Assn., Fellowship Orthodox Stewards, Orthodox Theol. Soc. Am., Federated Russian Orthodox Clubs (chpt. pres. 1978-80, gov. 1981-82). Office: St Vladimir's Sem 575 Scarsdale Rd Tuckahoe NY 10707-1659

SILK, FREDERICK C.Z., consumer products company executive; b. Pretoria, Transvaal, South Africa, July 29, 1934; arrived in Canada, 1964; s. Frederick Charles and Edythe D'Olier (Ziervogel) S.; m. Margaret Colbourne, May 12, 1962; children: Michael, Alison, Jennifer. BS, Rhodes U., Grahamstown, Republic South Africa, 1954; cert. acctg. theory, U. Witwatersrand, Johannesburg, Republic South Africa, 1957. Acct., cons. Deloitte, Plender, Haskins & Sells, Johannesburg, London and N.Y.C., 1954-64; mgmt. cons. P.S. Ross & Ptnrs, Montreal, Que, Can., 1964-68; v.p. fin. and adminstrn. J&P Coats (Can.) Ltd., Montreal, 1968-74; treas. Standard Brands, Ltd., Montreal, 1974-75; asst. treas. Standard Brands, Inc., N.Y.C., 1975-78; treas. Harlequin Enterprises, Ltd., Toronto, Ont., Can., 1978-82; v.p., treas. Nabisco Brands, Ltd., Toronto, 1982—. Fellow Inst. Chartered Accts. (Eng., Wales), Inst. Chartered Accts. (South Africa), Fin. Execs. Inst., Soc. Internat. Treas. Avocations: music, choral music, Gilbert and Sullivan operettas. Office: RJR Nabisco Securities Ltd, POB 188 Ste 1550 Royal Bank Plaza N, Toronto, ON Canada M5J 2J4 also: Nabisco Brands Ltd, 10 Park Lawn Rd, Etobicoke, ON Canada M8Y 3H8 also: RJR Macdonald Inc, 1 First Canadian Pl Ste 6000 POB 111, Toronto, ON Canada M5X 1E8

SILK, GEORGE, photographer; b. Levin, New Zealand, Nov. 17, 1916; s. Arthur and Constance (Naylor) S.; m. Margery G. Schieber, Nov. 28, 1947; children—Stuart, Georgiana B., Shelley G. Ed., New Zealand schs. With photographic store in New Zealand, 1935-39; ofcl. photographer Australian Inf. Forces in, Middle East, 1940-42, New Guinea, 1942-43; photographer Life mag., 1943-73; corr. in Life mag., ETO, 1944-45, PTO, 1945, China, 1946, N.Y.C., 1947-73; free lance photographer, 1973—. Pictures in color sect. 1959 annual Ency. Brit.; photographs in Fine Arts exhibit, 1962, 63. Recipient gold medal Art Dirs. Club, 1961; Photographer of Year award Ency. Brit., 1960; Am. Soc. Mag. Photographers Meml. award, 1962; Photographer of Year awards Nat. Press Photographers Assn., U. Mo., World Book, 1960, 62, 63, 64; Brehm Meml. award Rochester Inst. Tech., 1966. Home: Owenoke Park Westport CT 06880-6851

SILK, JOSEPH IVOR, astronomy educator; b. London, Dec. 3, 1942; came to U.S., 1964; s. Philip and Sylvia Silk; m. Margaret Wendy Kuhn, Aug. 11, 1968; children: Timothy William, Jonathan Charles. MA, Cambridge (Eng.) U., 1963; PhD, Harvard U., 1968. Research fellow Cambridge U., 1968-69, Princeton (N.J.) U., 1969-70; asst. prof. astronomy U. Calif., Berkeley, 1970-73, assoc. prof., 1973-78, prof., 1978—; chercheur associé Institut d'Astrophysique, Paris, 1982-83. Author: The Big Bang, 1980; co-author: The Left Hand of Creation, 1983. Recipient First prize Gravity Research Found., 1975, Bowdoin prize Harvard U., 1968, Bok prize Harvard U., 1970; fellow Sloan Found., 1972-74, Guggenheim Found., 1975-76, Inst. Advanced Study, 1975-76. Fellow AAAS, Royal Astron. Soc.; mem. Internat. Astron. Union, Am. Astron. Soc. Avocations: skiing, sailing. Office: U Calif Dept Astronomy Berkeley CA 94720

SILKENAT, JAMES ROBERT, lawyer; b. Salina, Kans., Aug. 2, 1947; s. Ernest E. and Mildred R. (Iman) S.; children: David Andrew, Katherine Anne. BA, Drury Coll., 1969; JD, U. Chgo., 1972; LLM, NYU, 1978. Bar: N.Y. 1973, D.C. 1980. Assoc. Cravath, Swaine & Moore, N.Y.C., 1972-80; counsel Internat. Fin. Corp., Washington, 1980-86; ptnr. Morgan, Lewis & Bockius, N.Y.C., 1986-89, Morrison & Foerster, N.Y.C., 1989-92, Winthrop, Stimson, Putnam & Roberts, N.Y.C., 1992—; chmn. Council N.Y. Law Assocs., 1978-79, Lawyers Com. Internat. Human Rights, 1978-80. Editor ABA Guide to Fng. Law Firms, Moscow Conf. on Law Bilateral Econ. Rels., ABA Guide to Internat. Bus. Negotiations; contbr. over 70 articles on law and pub. policy to profl. jours. Served to capt. U.S. Army, 1972-73. Fellow NEH, 1977, U.S. Dept. State, 1981. Fellow Am. Bar Found.; mem. ABA (chmn. internat. law and practice sect. 1989-90, chmn. sect. officer's conf. 1990-92, mem. ho. of dels. 1989—, bd. govs. 1994—). Office: Winthrop Stimson Putnam & Roberts One Battery Park Plz New York NY 10004

SILKETT, ROBERT TILLSON, food business consultant; b. Columbia, Mo., Nov. 12, 1929; s. Ross Jacob and Marion Dorchester (Tillson) S.; m. Sally Forrest Lash. Dec. 23, 1954; children—Robert Tillson, Elizabeth L. B.A., Duke U., 1951; M.B.A. with distinction, Wharton Grad. Sch., U. Pa., 1956. With mktg. dept. Anderson Clayton Co., 1956-58; with Gen. Foods Corp., 1958-78, group exec. corp. mktg. and sales, 1976-78; chmn. bd., chief exec. officer Reckitt & Colman N.A., Rochester, N.Y., also R.T. French Co., 1978-86; exec. v.p., dir. Curtice-Burns Foods, Rochester, 1986-90; owner, pres. The RTS Group, Rochester, 1990—. Past bd. dirs. Rochester United Way, Rochester Mus.; mem. exec. bd. Wharton Grad. Sch., Rochester council Boy Scouts Am. Served to lt. USNR, 1951-54. Mem. Wharton Grad. Sch. Alumni Assn. (past chmn.), Beta Gamma Sigma. Republican. Episcopalian. Clubs: Rochester Country, Wilton Riding (past pres.); Wharton M.B.A. (N.Y.C.) (past dir.), Mid Ocean (Bermuda), Key Largo Anglers, Card Sound (Key Largo).

SILLARS, MALCOLM OSGOOD, communications educator; b. Union City, N.J., Feb. 12, 1928; s. Malcolm Osgood and Dorothy Edna (Browning) S.; m. Charlotte Jane Grimm, June 1, 1948; children—Paul Louis, Bruce Malcolm, Alan Leslie. B.A., U. Redlands, 1948, M.A., 1949; PhD, U. Iowa, 1955. Asst. prof. communication Iowa State U., Ames, 1949-53; asst. prof. Calif. State U., Los Angeles, 1954-56; prof., dean Calif. State U., Northridge, 1956-71; pres. Calif. State U., 1969-70; prof. U Mass., Amherst, 1971-74; prof. communication U. Utah, Salt Lake City, 1974—; dean humanities U. Utah, 1974-81. Author: Speech: Content and Communications, 6th edit, 1991, Argumentation and Critical Decision Making, 3rd edit., 1993, Messages, Meanings, 1st edit, 1994; contbr. articles to profl. jours. Recipient Silver Beaver award Boy Scouts Am. Mem. Speech Communication Assn. (pres.), Western Speech Communication Assn. (pres.), AAUP, ACLU. Democrat. Home: 3508 Eastoaks Dr Salt Lake City UT 84124-3811 Office: U Utah Dept Communication Salt Lake City UT 84112

SILLECK, HARRY GARRISON, lawyer; b. Putnam Valley, N.Y., Mar. 19, 1921; s. Harry Garrison and Bertha May (Barrett) S.; m. June Baird, Mar. 4, 1977. B.A., Union Coll., 1940; LL.B., Columbia U., 1943. Bar: N.Y. 1944, U.S. Supreme Ct. 1966, U.S. Ct. Appeals (2d cir.) 1966 (6th cir.) 1976. Assoc. Dorr Hand Whittaker & Watson, N.Y.C., 1945-55, ptnr., 1955-63; ptnr. Mudge Rose Guthrie Alexander & Ferdon. N.Y.C., 1963-86; of counsel Mudge Rose Guthrie Alexander & Ferdon, 1986—, chmn. 1978-85. Served to 1st lt. AC, U.S. Army, 1943-45, ETO. Mem. Phi Beta Kappa. Home: 131 E 69th St New York NY 10021-5158 Office: Mudge Rose Guthrie Alexander & Ferdon 180 Maiden Ln New York NY 10038-4925

SILLIMAN, RICHARD GEORGE, retired lawyer, retired farm machinery company executive; b. Elgin, Ill., Aug. 11, 1922; s. Charles B. and Mabel Ellen (Winegar) S.; m. Mary L. Yost, June 12, 1945; children—Martha Jane, Charles R. B.A. in History, Cornell Coll. Mt. Vernon, Iowa, 1946; J.D., Northwestern U, 1949. Bar: Ill. 1949. Atty. various U.S. agys., Chgo., 1949-52; atty. asst. sec. Elgin Nat. Watch Co., Ill., 1952-59, sec., gen. atty., 1959-62; asst. gen. counsel Deere & Co., Moline, Ill., 1962-75, assoc. gen. counsel, 1975-82, sec., assoc. gen. counsel, 1982-87. Mem. editorial bd. Ill. Law Rev., 1948-49. Contbr. articles to profl. jours. Past pres., hon. dir. Quad-City Symphony Orch., Moline and Davenport, Iowa, 1968-87; bd. dirs., trustee Upper Rock Island County YMCA, Moline, 1965-87; bd. dirs. Police-Fire Commn., Elgin, 1957-61; bd. dirs., sec. Elgin YMCA, 1955. Served with USN, 1943-46. Mem. ABA, Ill. State Bar Assn. (past chmn. com. on corp. law dept.), Short Hills Country Club (Moline), Union League (Chgo.). Avocations: golf, music, sailing. Home: 4817 6th St Ct East Moline IL 61244

SILLIN, LELAN FLOR, JR., retired utility executive; b. Tampa, Fla., Apr. 19, 1918; s. Lelan Flor and Ruth (Berry) S.; m. Joan Outhwaite, Sept. 26, 1942; children: Lelan Flor, John Outhwaite, Andrew Borden, William Berry. AB with distinction, U. Mich., 1940, JD, 1942; LLD (hon.), Wesleyan U., 1969. Bar: N.Y. 1946. With Gould & Wilkie, N.Y.C., 1945-51; with Central Hudson Gas & Electric Corp., Poughkeepsie, N.Y., 1951-68, v.p., asst. gen. mgr., 1955-60, pres., 1960-68, chief exec. officer, 1964-67, also trustee; pres. Northeast Utilities, Hartford, Conn., 1968-70, chmn. bd., 1970-83, chief exec. officer, chmn. bd., 1968-83, also trustee; chmn. bd. Conn. Yankee Atomic Power Co., 1971-83, Northeast Energy, 1970-83; former chmn., dir. Fuel Cell User Group; bd. dirs. BNFL, Inc., Urenco, Inc., Waterbury Rep & Am.; past chmn. nat. power survey exec. adv. com. FPC, 1965-72; dir. Inst. Nuclear Power Ops., 1979-85, chmn., 1982-84. Former mem. steering com. Nat. Urban Coalition; former mem. Pres.'s Adv. Com. Environ. Quality; former bd. dirs. Nat. Office Social Responsibility, New Eng. Council; trustee emeritus Edwin Gould Found. for Children, Woodrow Wilson Nat. Fellowship Found., New Eng. Natural Resources Ctr.; trustee emeritus Wesleyan U., former vice-chmn. bd. trustees; past mem. adv. com. White House Conf. on Balanced Nat. Growth and Econ. Devel.; past mem. Pub. Com. on Mental Health; former mem. Am. Arbitration Assn.; former bd. dirs. Conn. Bus. and Industry Assn.; trustee emeritus Vassar Bros. Hosp., Poughkeepsie. Served to maj. USMCR, 1942-45. Recipient Raymond E. Baldwin medal Wesleyan U., 1986, Oliver Townsend award Atomic Indsl. Forum, 1986. Former mem. Conf. Bd. (sr.). Clubs: Hartford; Dauntless (Essex, Conn.); Century Association, University (N.Y.C.). Office: NE Utilities Millstone Nuclear Power Sta Tng Ctr Box 128 Waterford CT 06385

SILLIPHANT, STIRLING DALE, motion picture writer, producer, novelist; b. Detroit, Jan. 16, 1918; s. Leigh Lemuel Silliphant and Ethel May (Noaker) Wellershaus; m. Tiana Du Long, July 4, 1974; children: Stirling, Dayle, Loren (dec.). BA magna cum laude, U. So. Calif., Los Angeles, 1938. Publicity dir. 20th Century-Fox, N.Y.C., 1946-53; screenwriter, independent producer various studios in Hollywood, 1953—. Screenwriter: (films) Huk, Nightfall, Damn Citizen, Lineup, Village of the Damned, The Slender Thread, In The Heat of the Night, 1968 (Oscar award for best screenplay, Edgar Allen Poe award Mystery Writers Am., Golden Globe award Fgn. Press Assn.), Charly, 1969 (Golden Globe award Fgn. Press Assn.), The New Centurions, 1972, The Poseidon Adventure, 1972 (Writer of Yr. award Nat. Theater Owners Am.), Shaft, 1972 (Image award NAACP), Liberation of Lord Byron Jones, 1973, Murphy's War, 1974, The Towering Inferno, 1974 (Writer of Yr. award Nat. Theater Owners Am.), The Killer Elite, 1975, The Enforcer, 1976, Telefon, 1977, The Swarm, Circle of Iron, When Time Ran Out, Over the Top; prin. writer: (TV series) Naked City, 1960, Route 66, 1960; contbg. writer (TV series) The Chrysler Theater, Alfred Hitchcock Presents, Gen. Elec. Theater, Alcoa-Goodyear Theater; writer: (TV films) Pearl, 1978, Fly Away Home, 1981, Space, 1985, Mussolini, 1986, The Three Kings, 1987; novelist: Maracaibo, 1953, rev. edit., 1987, The Slender Thread, 1971, Pearl, 1980, (John Locke Adventures) Steel Tiger, 1985, Bronze Bell, 1986, Silver Star, 1987. Served to lt. (j.g.) USN, 1943-46. Mem. Writers Guild Am. West, Mystery Writers Assn., Authors League, Phi Beta Kappa. Avocations: ocean sailing, karate, traveling. Office: c/o Abramson & Co 15250 Ventura Blvd # 403 Sherman Oaks CA 91403

SILLMAN, ARNOLD JOEL, physiologist, educator; b. N.Y.C., Oct. 10, 1940; s. Philip and Anne L. (Pearlman) S.; m. Jean Fletcher Van Keuren, Sept. 26, 1969; children—Andrea Jose, Diana Van Keuren. A.B., U. Calif.-Los Angeles, 1963, M.A., 1965, Ph.D., 1968. Asst. prof. U. Calif.-Los Angeles, 1969-73, Davis, 1975-78, assoc. prof., 1978-85, prof. 1985—; asst. prof. U. Pitts., 1973-75. Contbr. articles to profl. jours. USPHS trainee, UCLA, 1966-67; fellow NSF, 1967-68, Fight for Sight, Inc., 1968-69. Mem. Am. Physiol. Soc.; Soc. Gen. Physiologists, Am. Soc. Zoologists, Assn. Research in Vision and Ophthalmology, AAAS, N.Y. Acad. Sci. Jewish. Home: 1140 Los Robles St Davis CA 95616-4927 Office: U Calif Dept Animal Physiology Davis CA 95616

SILLMAN, HERBERT PHILLIP, accounting firm executive; b. Detroit, July 18, 1927; s. David and Phyllis (Sumter) S.; m. Maurine R. Shapiro, Mar. 16, 1952; children: Marcie, David, Jonathon. B.S., UCLA, 1949. With Harold Gilbert & Co. (C.P.A.s), Detroit, 1951-54; pnr. Sillman, Kleiman & Thal, Detroit, 1954-69; mng. partner J.K. Lasser & Co. Detroit, 1969-77; assoc. mng. ptnr. internat. Touche Ross & Co., N.Y.C., 1985-89; assoc. mng. ptnr. Internat. Deloitte & Touche, Birmingham, Mich., 1989-91; prin. Sillman Enterprises, Bloomfield Hills, Mich., 1991—; bd. dirs. Offitbank, N.Y.C., CAPX, Miami, Fla.. Mem. Oak Park Sch. Dist. Bd. Edn., 1963-71, v.p., 1965-67, pres., 1967-69; mem. Oakland County Intermediate Bd. Edn., 1964-70, v.p., 1966-68, pres., 1968-70; mem. edn. com., mem. exec. com., 1st vice chmn. Southeastern Mich. Council Govt., 1969-70; mem. citizens assembly United Community Services Met. Detroit, 1978—, mem. budget com., 1977-79; mem. budget com. Oakland County Planning Com., 1976-79; bd. dirs. Mich. Colls. Found., 1979-85, Mich. League for Human Services, 1977-80, Jewish Family Service, pres., 1970-73; bd. dirs. Jewish Welfare Fedn., 1972-79, mem. exec. com., 1977-79; bd. dirs. Alvin Ailey Dance Found., 1985-90. Served with USNR, 1945-46. Mem. AICPA (chmn. com. on relations with internat. confs. accts. 1975-77), Mich. Assn. CPAs (chmn. audit com. 1976-77, com. on ins. and pensions 1970-74). Home: 425 Harmon St Birmingham MI 48009-1348 Office: Sillman Enterprises 6421 Inkster Rd Ste 200 Bloomfield Hills MI 48301-1307

SILLOWAY, BENTON, JR., food products executive; b. Mpls., Aug. 13, 1941; s. Benton and Shirley (Aygarn) S.; m. Leslie Sprague Patton, Sept. 7, 1963; children: Devin, Darby, Torey. BA, Middlebury Coll., 1963; MBA, Columbia U., 1965. Brand mgr. Procter & Gamble, Cin., 1965-70; v.p. Pepsico, Inc., Purchase, N.Y., 1970-80; sr. v.p. Hardee's Food Systems, Inc., Rocky Mount, N.C., 1980-82; pres. Silloway & Co., Rocky Mount, 1982-86; gen. mgr., chief exec. officer Haagen-Dazs Shoppe Co., Teaneck, N.J., 1987-89; pres., CEO Penguin's Pl., Inc., Thousand Oaks, Calif., 1990-92; pres. Silloway & Co, Wilmington, N.C., 1992—. Republican. Home and Office: 2229 Mason Point Pl Wilmington NC 28405-5276

SILLS, BEVERLY (MRS. PETER B. GREENOUGH), opera company director, coloratura soprano; b. Bklyn., May 25, 1929; d. Morris and Sonia (Bahn) Silverman; m. Peter B. Greenough, 1956; children: Meredith, Peter B.; stepchildren: Lindley, Nancy, Diana. Grad. pub. schs.; student voice, Estelle Leibling; student piano, Paolo Gallico; student stagecraft, Desire Defrere; hon. doctorates, Harvard U., NYU, New Eng. Conservatory, Temple U. Gen. dir. N.Y.C. Opera, 1979-1989; pres. N.Y.C. Opera Bd., 1989-90; mng. dir. Met. Opera, N.Y.C., 1991-94; chairwoman Lincoln Ctr.,

N.Y.C., 1994—; Bd. dirs. Am. Express, Macy's, Time/Warner Comm., Met. Opera; cons. Nat. Coun. on Arts. Radio debut as Bubbles Silverman on Uncle Bob'sRainbow House, 1932; appeared on Major Bowes Capitol Family Hour, 1934-41, on Our Gal Sunday; toured with Shubert Tours, Charles Wagner Opera Co., 1950, 51; operatic debut Phila. Civic Opera, 1947; debut, N.Y.C. Opera Co. as Rosalinda in Die Fledermaus, 1955; debut San Francisco Opera, 1953; debut La Scala, Milan as Pamira in Siege of Corinth, 1969, Royal Opera, Covent Garden in Lucia di Lammermoor, London, 1971, Met. Opera, N.Y.C., 1975, Vienna State Opera, 1967, Teatro Fenice in La Traviata, Venice; appeared Teatro Colon, Buenos Aires; recital debut Paris, 1971, London Symphony Orch., 1971; appeared throughout U.S., Europe, S. Am. including Boston Symphony, Tanglewood Festival, 1968, 69, Robin Hood Dell, Phila., 1969; title roles in: Don Pasquale, Norma, Ballad of Baby Doe, Thais, Traviata, Anna Bolena, Maria Stuarda, Lucia de Lammermoor, Barber of Seville, Manon, Louise, Tales of Hoffmann, Daughter of the Regiment, The Magic Flute, Elizabeth in Roberto Devereaux, I Puritana, Julius Caesar, Suor Angelica, Il Tabarro, G. Schicchi, Faust, La Loca, Merry Widow, Turk in Italy, Rigoletto, I Capuleti e I Montecchi, Lucrezia Borgia, Ariodante, Le Coq D'Or, others; recordings include The Art of Beverly Sills, Welcome to Vienna, Great Scores (with Placido Domingo); ret. from opera and concert stage, 1980; numerous TV spls; author: Bubbles-A Self-Portrait, 1976, autobiography Beverly, 1987. Chmn. bd. March of Dimes, nat. chmn. Mothers' March on Birth Defects; chmn. Lincoln Ctr. Recipient Handel medallion, 1973, Pearl S. Buck Women's award, 1979, Emmy award for Profiles in Music, 1976, Emmy award for Lifestyles with Beverly Sills, 1978, Medal of Freedom, 1980, Kennedy Ctr. honors. Office: care Edgar Vincent 157 W 57th St New York NY 10019-2210

SILLS, DAVID LAWRENCE, retired sociologist; b. N.Y.C., Aug. 24, 1920; s. R. Malcolm and Charlotte Noyes (Babcock) S.; m. Yole Laura Granata, Feb. 18, 1948; 1 son, Gregory Lawrence. BA, Dartmouth Coll., 1942; MA, Yale U., 1948; PhD, Columbia U., 1956. Research analyst pub. opinion and sociol. research div. Allied Occupation of Japan, 1947-50; research asso. Bur. Applied Social Research Columbia U., 1952-61, acting dir., 1961-62, dir. research, 1962; expert UN Tech. Assistance Orgn., Bombay, India, 1960-61; editor Crowell Collier and Macmillan, N.Y.C., 1962-67; assoc. dir. demographic div. Population Council, N.Y.C., 1968-70; dir. Population Council, 1970-72; exec. assoc. Social Sci. Research Council, N.Y.C., 1973-88, exec. assoc. emeritus, 1988—; fellow Ctr. for Advanced Study in Behavioral Scis., Stanford, Calif., 1967-68; vis. scholar Russell Sage Found., 1973. Editor: International Encyclopedia of the Social Sciences, 17 vols., 1968; editor (with Robert K. Merton): Social Science Quotations: Who Said What, Where and When, 1992. Served with U.S. Army, 1942-46. Mem. Am. Assn. Pub. Opinion Rsch., Am. Sociol. Assn., Sociol. Rsch. Assn. Democrat. Episcopalian. Home: PO Box 303 Rowayton CT 06853-0303

SILLS, HILARY H., public relations executive; b. Chgo., Feb. 24, 1947. Cert. in EEC Studies, U. Brussels, 1968; BA in History, Hollis Coll., 1969. With staff of William Whitehurst U.S. Ho. Reps.; with The Daily Bond Buyer, GE; dir. energy and environment Govt. Rsch. Group, 1975-87, v.p., 1988-89; sr. cons. Pub. Affairs Comm. Mgmt., 1987-88; v.p. Hill & Knowlton, 1989-91; sr. prin. Capitoline Internat. Group, 1991—. former contbg. editor Economist Intelligence Unit. Mem. Women in Govt. Rels. Office: Capitoline Internat Group Ltd 1615 L St NW # 1150 Washington DC 20036-5610

SILVA, BENEDICTO ALVES DE CASTRO, surgeon, educator; b. Salvador, Bahia, Brazil, June 26, 1927; s. Octacilio Alves de Castro and Nathercia Crusoé Silva; m. Maria Guanaes, Dec. 20, 1958; children: Catia Maria, Marta Maria, Gloria Maria. Degree, Bahia U., Salvador, 1952. Asst. prof. faculty odontology Bahia U., 1962-72, adj. prof. faculty odontology, 1972—, maxillar buco surgeon, 1962—; maxillar buco surgeon Santa Izabel Hosp., Salvador, 1953-72, Hosp. Martagão Gesteira, Salvador, 1958-60; coord. Bahia Oral Cancer Ctr., Salvador, 1988—; coord. Oncology Ctr.-Mouth-Bahia, Salvador, 1988—. Author: Patients of High Risk, 1988; contbr. chpt. to book: Phamacology, 1980. Pres. Bahia Dental Coun., Salvador, 1981-85. Officer Brazilian Army, 1944-45. Mem. Brit. Assn. Oral Maxillar Surgery (assoc.), Bahia Dental Acad., Pierre Fuchard Acad. (medal 1990), Minas Gerais Dental Acad. (medal 1990), Brazilian Soc. Cancer, European Sch. Oncology, Bahia Acad. Odontology (pres. 1985—). Home: Padre Daniel Lisboa # 5-A, 40 285-560 Salvador Brazil Office: Med Ctr Graça, Humberton de Campos St # 11, 40150 Salvador Brazil

SILVA, EUGENE JOSEPH, lawyer; b. Gloucester, Mass., May 23, 1942; s. Edward Joseph and Rose (Lebre) S.; m. Nancy Blue-Pearson, Jan. 8, 1972; children: Eugene Joseph II, Michael Joseph. BS with honors, Maine Maritime Acad., 1964; JD, U. Notre Dame, 1972. Bar: Calif. 1972, U.S. Dist. Ct. (so. and cen. dists.) Calif. 1972, Tex. 1977, U.S. Dist. Ct. (so. and ea. dists.) Tex. 1978, U.S. Ct. Appeals (5th, 2d and 11th cirs.) 1978, U.S. Supreme Ct. 1981; lic. Master Mariner. Assoc. Luce, Forward, Hamilton & Scripps, San Diego, 1972-77; assoc. Vinson & Elkins, Houston, 1977-79, ptnr., 1980—. Bd. dirs. Cabrillo Festival Inc., San Diego, 1974-77, San Jose Clinic Inc., 1990—, pres., 1993-95. Lt. USN, 1967-69. Decorated knight Equestrian Order of Holy Sepulchre of Jerusalem; recipient Outstanding Alumni award Maine Maritime Acad., 1990. Mem. Houston Bar Assn., Calif. Bar Assn. Tex. Bar Assn., Internat. Bar Assn., Grays Inn U. Notre Dame Sch. Law (pres. 1970-72), Southeastern Admiralty Law Inst., Maritime Law Assn. U.S. (proctor in admiralty 1974—), Portuguese Union Calif. (bd. dirs. 1973-74), Portuguese Am. League San Diego (pres. 1974-75), Portuguese Am. Leadership Coun. U.S., Asia-Pacific Lawyers Assn., Notre Dame Club (pres. San Diego chpt. 1976-77), Houston Yacht Club, Houston Tr. Club, The Naval Club (London). Roman Catholic. Home: 8 Smithdale Estates Houston TX 77024-6600 Office: Vinson & Elkins 2500 First City Tower 1001 Fannin Houston TX 77002-6760

SILVA, FELIPE, former tobacco company executive; b. Cienfuegos, Cuba, Feb. 27, 1919; came to U.S., 1960, naturalized, 1968; s. Felipe and Hortensia (Cardenas) S.; m. Dolores Alvarez, Feb. 3, 1945; children: Ana, Felipe Rafael, Maria Dolores, Lourdes. Student, U. Mich., 1936-38; D. Law, U. Havana, 1942, Public Acct., 1943. Pres. Tabacalera Cubana S.A., 1949-60; spl. sales rep. ACC div. Am. Tobacco Co., St. Petersburg, Fla., 1960-62; mgr. P.R. br. ACC div. Am. Tobacco Co., San Juan, 1963-67; export mgr. Am. Tobacco Co. div. Am. Brands, Inc., N.Y.C., 1968-78; pres. Am. Cigar div. Am. Brands, Inc., 1979-80, pres., chief exec. officer Am. Cigar div., 1981-83, chmn., chief exec. officer cigar div., 1983-84. Mem. U. Mich. Alumni Assn. Roman Catholic. Lodge: Rotary. Home: 600 Grapetree Dr Apt 7bs Miami FL 33149-2703

SILVA, JOHN PHILIP COSTA, newspaper editor; b. Providence, Jan. 19, 1951; s. Silvano Costa and Florence Josephine (Russo) S.; m. Deborah Helen Radovsky, May 8, 1977; children: Daniel David, Matthew Philip. BA in Journalism, U. R.I., 1973. Staff writer Providence Jour.-Bull., 1973-79; staff writer Miami (Fla.) News, 1979-81, asst. city editor, 1981-82; spl. corr. The Wall St. Jour., Miami, 1980-81; city editor Lexington (Ky.) Herald-Leader, 1982-84; night city editor L.A. Herald Examiner, 1984-85, assignment editor, 1985-87; asst. mng. editor Ariz. Daily Star, Tucson, 1987—. Recipient 1st place for spot news UPI Newspapers New Eng., 1977. Mem. Nat. Assn. Hispanic Journalists, Investigative Reporters and Editors Assn. Avocations: writing, historical research. Home: 9433 N Albatross Dr Tucson AZ 85741-5126 Office: Ariz Daily Star 4850 S Park Ave Tucson AZ 85714-1637

SILVA, JOSEPH DONALD, English language educator; b. Lowell, Mass., Jan. 19, 1935; s. Joseph Maria and Edna (Talbot) S.; m. Lucy Niles, June 22, 1957; children: Joseph Alden, Maria Margriet, Paul Frederic, Amanda Elizabeth. BA, U. N.H., 1957, MA, 1965. Instr. U. N.H. Durham, 1963-66, asst. prof., 1966-72, assoc. prof., 1972-85, prof., 1985—; chmn. N.E. Regional Conf. on English, 1977-79. Author: A Bibliography on the Madeira Islands, 1987. Pastor New Castle (N.H.) Congl. Ch., 1967—; moderator Rockingham (N.H.) Assn. United Ch. of Christ, 1987-89. 1st lt. U.S. Army, 1958. Mem. AAUP (chmn. Durham chpt. 1983-84), Nat. Coun. Tchrs. English, Conf. Coll. Composition and Communication. Avocations: travel, photography, hiking, swimming, gardening. Home: 55 Main St New Castle NH 03854-0132

SILVA, OMEGA LOGAN, physician; b. Washington, Dec. 14, 1936; d. Louis Jasper and Ruth (Dickerson) Logan; m. C. Francis A. Silva, Oct. 25, 1958 (div. 1981); 1 child, Frances Cecile; m. Harold Bryant Webb, Nov. 28, 1982. Grad., Howard U., Washington, 1958, MD, 1967. Bio-chemist NIH, Bethesda, Md., 1958-63; asst. chief endocrinology Vets. Affairs Med. Ctr., Washington, 1967—; assoc. prof. George Washington U., Washington, 1975-91, prof. 1991—; prof. Howard U., Washington, 1977—. Author: (with others) Endocrinology, 1990; contbr. articles to profl. jours. Charter mem. Nat. Mus. of Women in the Arts, Washington, 1986; health cons. River Pk. Mutual Homes, Inc., Washington, 1987; vol. Career Day Chillum Elem. Sch., Career Week, George Washington U., Washington, 1988; trustee Howard U., 1991—. Fellow ACP (Best Sci. Presentation award 1974); mem. Am. Chem. Soc., Am. Med. Women's Assn. (br. I v.p. 1986-87, pres. 1987-88, anti-smoking task force 1989—, chair govtl. affairs nominations com. 1992), Howard U. Med. Alumni (pres. 1983-88), Alpha Omega Alpha. Avocations: dress and hat design, furniture design, home contruction. Office: Veterans Affairs Med Ctr 50 Irving St NW Washington DC 20422-0002

SILVA-RUÍZ, SERGIO ANDRÉS, biochemist; b. San Juan, P.R., Jan. 12, 1944; s. Sergio A. and América (Ruíz) Silva-Izquierdo; m. Iris M. Piñero, Dec. 28, 1973; children: Maite Ira, Javier Juan, Siris Anya. BS in Chemistry, U. P.R., Rio Piedras, 1965, MS in Biochemistry, 1977, PhD, 1978. Scientist Schering-Plough, Manati, P.R., 1978-79; sr. scientist, 1979-82; mgr. R & D lab. Schering Corp., Manati, P.R., 1982-85; sr. scientist Schering Manati, Inc., Manati, P.R., 1986-91; mgr. fermentation plant Schering-Plough Products, Manati, P.R., 1991-93, plant mgr. antibiotics, 1993—; mem. adv. com. for biotech. Bachelors Degree, U. P.R., Rio Piedras, 1986-87; adv. bd. U. P.R. Minority Rsch. Ctr. for Excellence, Mayaquez, P.R., 1991—; mem. program com. Am. Soc. Microbiology Biotech. Conf., 1991; mem. planning com. Am. Soc. Microbiology Conf. on Water Quality in Western Hemisphere, P.R., 1992-93; mem. adv. bd. berkeley lawrence lab. Jackson State U., system science consortium Ana Méndez U., 1994—. Pres. Sci. Rev. Com. Arecibo's Edn. Region, Dept. Edn., 1992-93. Recipient Dept. Def. fellowship, 1973-74, Merck Manual, U. P.R. Med Scis. Campus, 1978. Mem. AAAS (Caribbean Div. pres. 1992-93, coun. mem. 1993-94), Parenteral Drug Assn. (v.p. P.R. chpt. 1991-93), Sociedad Microbiólogos de P.R. (pres. 1982-83), Am. Soc. for Microbiology (mem. coun. 1983-85), Am. Soc. Quality Control, N.Y. Acad. Sci., Sigma Xi. Home: RR6 B9228 Rio Piedras PR 00928 Office: Schering-Plough Products PO Box 486 Manati PR 00674-0486

SILVEIRA, AUGUSTINE, JR., chemistry educator; b. Mattapoisett, Mass., July 17, 1934; s. Augustine and Mildred (Lewis) S.; m. Beverly Ann Washburn, Aug. 20, 1960; children: Linda Ann, Karen Louise. BS, U. Mass., Dartmouth, 1957, ScD (hon.), 1975; PhD., U. Mass. Amherst, 1962. Research chemist Acushnet Process Co., Mass., 1957-58; instr. U. Mass., 1960-62; asst. prof. Rutgers U., 1962-63; assoc. prof. SUNY, Oswego, 1963-64, prof., 1964-67, prof., chmn. dept. chemistry, 1967—, disting. teaching prof., 1976—; Am. Council on Edn. fellow U. Calif., Irvine, 1969-70, vis. prof., 1976-77, 83-84, 91; vis. prof. Calif. State U., Long Beach, 1976-77; cons. to edn. and industry; guest lectr.; evaluator SUNY Grad. Programs, 1968—, Patent Policy Bd., 1971; mem. commn. higher edn. Middle States Assn., 1971—; mem. alumni adv. council U. Mass., 1971-75; mem. N.Y. State Bd. Optometry, 1981-91. Contbr. articles to profl. jours. SUNY faculty exch. scholar, 1981—; Pres.'s rsch. award SUNY, 1983, rsch. grantee; recipient N.Y. State/United Univ. Professions Excellence award, 1990; named to Fairhaven H.S. Hall of Fame Lifetime Achiever award, 1995. Fellow Am. Inst. Chemists; mem. AAUP (v.p. 1965-66), Am. Chem. Soc. (dist. rep., Syracuse sect. award 1988), Sigma Xi (pres. 1972-73, 78-79), Delta Kappa Phi, Alpha Kappa Phi. Home: 2021 Benson Ave Minetto NY 13115-9999 Office: SUNY Oswego Chemistry Dept Oswego NY 13126

SILVEIRA, MILTON ANTHONY, aerospace engineering executive; b. Mattapoisett, Mass., May 4, 1929; s. Antone and Carolinda (Avila) S.; children by previous marriage: Leland R., Douglas S., Carolyn M., Robert S.; m. B. Jane Rogers, June 20, 1992. BS, U. Vt., 1951, MS, 1961, PhD (hon.), 1977; postgrad., U. Va., Va. Poly Inst., U. Houston. Research intern Langley AFB, Hampton, Va., 1951; chief engring. U.S. Army, St. Louis, 1951-54; engring. officer 8th U.S. Army, Korea; acting head loads br. NASA, Hampton, 1955-63; project mgr. Manned Spacecraft Ctr. NASA, Houston, 1963-67, various engring. positions, dep. mgr. orbiter project Johnson Space Ctr., 1967-81; asst. to dep. adminstr. NASA, Washington, 1981-83, chief engr., 1983-86; v.p. advance requirements and analysis, Washington ops. Ford Aerospace and Communications Corp., Arlington, Va., 1987-90; pres. SEL, McLean, Va., 1990—. Mem. AIAA. Home: 7213 Evans Mill Rd Mc Lean VA 22101-3420 Office: SEL PO Box 843 Mc Lean VA 22101-0843

SILVER, CHARLES MORTON, communications company executive; b. New Haven, Sept. 22, 1929; s. Sam and Rose (Fischman) S.; m. Rose Charek, Mar. 27, 1960; children—Ronni Ellen, Suzanne Paula, Steven Mitchell. B.S., U. Conn., 1954. With Arthur Andersen & Co., N.Y.C., 1954-61, ITT, N.Y.C., 1961-88; ret. as v.p. and assoc. treas. ITT, 1988. Served with U.S. Army, 1947-48, 50-51. Mem. AICPA, Roxbury Swim and Tennis Club. Home: 51 Akbar Rd Stamford CT 06902-1401 also: PO Box 420275 Summerland Key FL 33042-0275

SILVER, DANIEL B., lawyer; b. Phila., Aug. 14, 1941; s. Samuel and Marjorie (Epstein) S.; m. Sybil F. Michelson, Jan. 20, 1963; children—Abigail Ruth, Rachel Ann, Alexander Joseph. A.B., U. Calif., Berkeley, 1961; M.A., Harvard U., 1965, Ph.D., 1967, LL.B., 1968. Bar: D.C. 1968, U.S. Ct. Appeals (D.C. cir.) 1975, U.S. Supreme Ct. 1975. Assoc. Cleary, Gottlieb, Steen & Hamilton, Washington, 1968-70, 73-76, Brussels, Belgium, 1973-76, ptnr., Washington, 1976-78, 81-83, 85—, Brussels, 1983-85; gen. counsel NSA, Washington, 1978-79, CIA, Washington, 1979-81; adj. prof. Georgetown U. Law Ctr., 1981-83, 89-92, 94; disting. vis. from prac., 1993. Trustee The Textile Mus. Recipient Exceptional Civilian Service award NSA, 1979; Disting. Intelligence medal CIA, 1981. Mem. ABA (sects. antitrust law, pub. contract law, internat. law), Security Affairs Support Assn. (gen. counsel 1982-91), Coun. for Excellence in Govt. (prin.), Coun. Fgn. Rels. Democrat. Jewish. Author: (with P. Fabrega) Illness and Shamanistic Curing in Zinacantan, 1975. Office: Cleary Gottlieb Steen & Hamilton 1752 N St NW Washington DC 20036-2806

SILVER, DAVID, financial executive, lawyer; b. N.Y.C., Jan. 27, 1931; s. Sol and Fannie (Stein) S.; m. Meryl Young, Sept. 14, 1952 (dec.); children: Daniel, Matthew, Joshua; m. Ann Schwartz, June 4, 1993. B.A., CCNY, 1953; LL.B. cum laude, Harvard U., 1958. Bar: N.Y. 1958, D.C. 1979. Pvt. practice law N.Y.C., 1960-61; spl. counsel SEC, Washington, 1961-65; gen. counsel Investors Planning Corp., N.Y.C., 1965-66; asst. counsel Investment Co. Inst., Washington, 1966-69, gen. counsel, 1969-77, pres., 1977-91; cons. securities regulation Govt. of India, 1964; pres. ICI Mut. Ins. Co., 1987—; lectr. Law Sch., Boston U., 1995—. Served with U.S. Army, 1953-55. Mem. Fed. Bar Assn. (exec. council securities com., past chmn. investment com.). Home: 9410 Brooke Dr Bethesda MD 20817 Office: ICI 1600 M St NW Ste 600 Washington DC 20036

SILVER, DAVID MAYER, former university official; b. West Pittston, Pa., July 16, 1915; s. Morris Jacob and Flora (Mayer) S.; m. Anita Rose Cohen, May 10, 1942; children: Gregory, Terence. AB magna cum laude, Butler U., 1937; AM, U. Ill., 1938, PhD, 1940; LittD (hon.), Butler U., 1990. Mem. faculty Butler U., 1940-85, prof. history, 1954-85, dean Coll. Liberal Arts and Scis., 1963-83, assoc. v.p. grad. studies and research, 1983-85; cons.-evaluator North Ctrl. Assn., 1974-85, mem. commn. higher edn., 1981-85. Author: Lincoln's Supreme Court, 1956, also articles. Pres. Indpls. Bd. Pub. Safety, 1956-63; mem. youth study com. Ohio Valley Council of Hebrew Congregations, 1963-65; Research dir. Ind. Democratic Central Com., 1944; Dem. nominee Ind. Legislature, 1944; Dem. candidate for Indpls. City Council, 1955; Bd. dirs. Indpls. Jewish Social Services, 1953-56. Recipient medal Butler U. Alumni Assn., 1987; U. Ill. scholar history, 1938, fellow, 1938-40; Butler U. faculty fellow, 1950-51. Mem. AAUP, Am. Hist. Assn., Orgn. Am. Historians, Supreme Ct. Hist. Soc., Ind. Hist. Soc., Ind. Conf. Acad. Deans (chmn. 1972), Ind. CLU, B'nai B'rith, Phi Beta Kappa, Phi Kappa Phi, Phi Eta Sigma, Sigma Alpha Mu. Jewish (dep. dirs, chmn. Hebrew congregation). Club: Broadmoor Country. Home: 8230 N Illinois St Indianapolis IN 46260-2943

SILVER, DONALD, surgeon, educator; b. N.Y.C., Oct. 19, 1929; s. Herman and Cecilia (Meyer) S.; m. Helen Elizabeth Harnden, Aug. 9, 1958; children: Elizabeth Tyler, Donald Meyer, Stephanie Davies, William Paige. AB, Duke U., 1950, BS in Medicine, MD, 1955. Diplomate Am. Bd. Surgery, Am. Bd. Gen. Vascular Surgery, Am. Bd. Thoracic Surgery. Intern Duke Med. Ctr., 1955-56, asst. resident, 1958-63, resident, 1963-64; mem. faculty Duke Med. Sch., 1964-75, prof. surgery, 1972-75; cons. Watts Hosp., Durham, 1965-75, VA Hosp., Durham, 1970-75; chief surgery VA Hosp., 1968-70; prof. surgery, chmn. dept. U. Mo. VA Med. Ctr., Columbia, 1975—; cons. Harry S. Truman Hosp., Columbia, 1975—; mem. bd. sci. advisers Cancer Research Center, Columbia, 1975—; mem. surg. study sect. A NIH. Contbr. articles to med. jours., chpts. to books; editorial bds.; Jour. Vascular Surgery, Postgrad. Gen. Surgery, Vascular Surgery. Served with USAF, 1956-58. James IV Surg. traveler, 1977. Fellow ACS (gov. 1994—), Deryl Hart Soc.; mem. AMA, AAAS, Mo. Med. Assn., Boone County Med. Soc., Internat. Cardiovascular Soc., Soc. Univ. Surgeons, Am. Heart Assn. (Mo. affiliate rsch. com.), Soc. Surgery Alimentary Tract, Assn. Acad. Surgery, So. Thoracic Surg. Assn., Internat. Soc. Surgery, Soc. Vascular Surgery, Am. Assn. Thoracic Surgery, Am. Surg. Assn., Ctrl. Surg. Assn. (pres.-elect 1990-9, pres. 1991-92), Western Surg. Assn., Midwestern Vascular Surg. Soc. (pres. 1984-85), Ctrl. Surg. Assn. Found. (treas. 1992-93, 2d v.p. 1993-94, 1st v.p. 1994-95, pres. 1955—). Home: 1050 Covered Bridge Rd Columbia MO 65203-9569 Office: U Mo Med Ctr Dept Surgery # M580 Columbia MO 65212

SILVER, GEORGE ALBERT, physician, educator; b. Phila., Dec. 23, 1913; s. Morris M. and Sara (Tutelman) S.; m. Mitzi Blieden, June 5, 1937; children—James David, Jane, Judith Ellen. B.A., U. Pa., Phila., 1934; M.D., Jefferson Med. Coll., Phila., 1938; M.P.H., Johns Hopkins U., Balt., 1948; M.A. (hon.), Yale U., New Haven, 1969. Diplomate Am. Bd. Preventive Medicine. Asst. demonstrator Jefferson Med. Coll., Phila., 1939-42; health officer Balt. City Health Dept., 1948-51; asst. prof. Johns Hopkins U., Balt., 1948-51; chief div. social medicine Montefiore Hosp., N.Y.C., 1951-65; assoc. prof. health adminstrn. Columbia U., N.Y.C., 1952-59; prof. social medicine Albert Einstein Coll. Medicine, N.Y.C., 1959-65; dep. asst. sec. health and sci. affairs HEW, Washington, 1965-68; health exec. Nat. Urban Coalition, Washington, 1968-71; prof. pub. health Yale U., New Haven, 1969-84, emeritus prof. pub. health, 1984—. Author: Family Medical Care, 1963; Spy in the House of Medicine, 1974; Child Health: America's Future, 1978. Served to maj. M.C., U.S. Army, 1942-46. Recipient Superior Svc. award HEW, 1966; named to Soc. of Scholars, Johns Hopkins U., 1993; fellow Branford Coll., Yale U. Fellow APHA (assoc. editor jour. 1993—), Nat. Acad. Social Ins., N.Y. Acad. Medicine, Inst. Medicine; mem. NAS (sr.), Elizabethan Club, Sigma Xi. Democrat. Jewish. Home: 590 Ellsworth Ave New Haven CT 06511-1636 Office: Yale U 89 Trumbull St New Haven CT 06511-3723

SILVER, HARRY R., lawyer; b. Phila., Aug. 8, 1946; s. Jerome Benjamin Silver and Josephine Sandler (Steinberg) Furr; m. Jessica Dunsay, Nov. 23, 1972; children: Gregory, Alexander. BA, Temple U., 1968; JD, Columbia U., 1971. Bar: N.Y. 1972, D.C. 1973, U.S. Dist. Ct. D.C., U.S. Ct. Claims, U.S. Ct. Appeals (1st, 4th, 5th, 7th, 8th, 9th, 10th, fed. and D.C. cirs.), U.S. Supreme Ct. Law clk. to presiding justice U.S. Ct. Appeals (2d cir.), N.Y.C., 1971-72; assoc. Arent, Fox, Kintner, Plotkin & Kahn, Washington, 1972-74; atty. U.S. Dept. Justice, Washington, 1974-77, U.S. Dept. Energy, Washington, 1977-78; assoc. Akin, Gump, Strauss, Hauer & Feld, Washington, 1978-81, ptnr., 1981-88; ptnr. Oppenheimer, Wolff & Donelly, Washington, 1988-91, Davis Wright Tremaine, Washington, 1991-94, Ober, Kaler, Grimes & Shriver, Washington, 1994—. Mem. ABA, Fed. Bar Assn. Avocations: running, music, travel. Home: 6829 Wilson Ln Bethesda MD 20817-4948 Office: Ober Kaler Grimes & Shriver 1401 H St NW Ste 500 Washington DC 20005-2110

SILVER, HORACE WARD MARTIN TAVARES, composer, pianist; b. Norwalk, Conn., Sept. 2, 1928; s. John and Gertrude (Edmounds) S. Ed. pub. schs., Norwalk. Pres. Ecaroh Music, Inc., N.Y.C. from 1955. Leader, Horace Silver Quintet, 1955—; Composer: Senor Blues, 1956, Doodlin', 1956, The Preacher, 1956, Nica's Dream, 1956, Lonely Woman, 1956, Home Cookin', 1956, Enchantment, 1956, Cookin' at the Continental, 1957, Moon Rays, 1957, Souville, 1957, Sister Sadie, 1959, Come on Home, 1959, Peace, 1959, Finger Poppin, 1959, Blowin' the Blues Away, 1959, Strollin', 1960, Filthy McNasty, 1961, The Tokyo Blues, 1962, Silver's Serenade, 1963, Song For My Father, 1965, 89, Que Pasa, 1965; albums include Six Pieces of Silver, 1956, 86, Horace Silver and the Jazz Messengers, 1985, Serenade to a Soul Sister, 1986, The Best of Horace Silver, 1988, Volume 2, 1989, Horace Silver Trio, 1989, Song for my Father, 1989, The Cape Verdean Blues, 1989, Doin the Thing, 1989, Silver's Blues, 1989, Horace-Scope, 1990, It's Got To Be Funky, 1993. Recipient Budweiser Mus. Excellence award, 1958, Silver Record award Blue Note Records, 1959, Citizen Call Entertainment award, 1960. Mem. A.S.C.A.P., Am. Fedn. Musicians. Office: Bridge Agy 8 S Oxford St Brooklyn NY 11217-1305 also: Blue Note Records 810 7th Ave Fl 4 New York NY 10019-5818*

SILVER, JOAN MICKLIN, film director, screenwriter; b. Omaha, May 24, 1935; d. Maurice David and Doris (Shoshone) Micklin; m. Raphael D. Silver, June 28, 1956; children: Dina, Marisa, Claudia. BA, Sarah Lawrence Coll., 1956. Writer, dir. (movies) Hester Street, 1975 (Writers Guild best screenplay nomination), Chilly Scenes of Winter, 1981, (TV film PBS) Bernice Bobs Her Hair starring Shelly Du Vall, 1975; dir. (TV films HBO) Finnegan, Begin Again with Robert Preston and Mary Tyler Moore, Parole Board, A Private Matter with Sissy Spacek and Aidan Quinn (films) Between the Lines, 1976, Crossing Delancey with Amy Irving, 1988, Loverboy, 1989, Stepkids, 1991; dir. stage plays and musicals including Album, Maybe I'm Doing It Wrong, Off-Broadway prodn. A...My Name is Alice; prod. On The Yard. Office: Silverfilm Prodns Inc 477 Madison Ave New York NY 10022-5802

SILVER, JOEL, producer. Film producer: The Warriors, 1979, Xanadu, 1980, 48 Hours, 1982, Jekyll & Hyde...Together Again, 1982, Streets of Fire, 1984, Brewster's Millions, 1985, Weird Science, 1985, Commando, 1985, Jumpin' Jack Flash, 1986, Lethal Weapon, 1986, Predator, 1987, Action Jackson, 1988, Die Hard, 1988, Lethal Weapon 2, 1989, Roadhouse, 1989, Ford Fairlane, 1990, Die Hard 2, 1990, Predator 2, 1990, Hudson Hawk, 1991, Ricochet, 1991, The Last Boy Scout, 1991, Lethal Weapon 3, 1992, Demolition Man, 1993, Richie Rich, 1994, Demon Knight, 1994. Office: Silver Pictures 4000 Warner Blvd Burbank CA 91522-0001*

SILVER, JONATHAN, lawyer; b. N.Y.C., June 30, 1953; s. Philip K. and Lillian (Schadlow) S.; m. Ellen Johnson, May 14, 1982. BA, SUNY, Albany, 1974; JD, SUNY, Buffalo, 1978. Bar: N.Y. 1979, U.S. Dist Ct. (ea. and so. dists.) N.Y. 1981. Staff atty. N.Y. State Dept. Social Svcs., Albany, 1978-79; of counsel N.Y. State Assembly Edn. Com., Albany, 1979-80; assoc. Garaufis & Kerson, Bayside, N.Y., 1980-82; pvt. practice, Forest Hills, N.Y., 1982—. Trustee Flushing Lawyers Charitable Trust. Mem. ABA, Queens County Bar Assn., Assn. of Bar of City of N.Y., N.Y. State Trial Lawyers Assn., Flushing Lawyers Club. Avocations: golf, softball, classical music, Chinese cooking. Home: 8624 Eton St Jamaica NY 11432-2409 Office: 80-02 Kew Gardens Rd Kew Gardens NY 11415

SILVER, JONATHAN MOSES, government official; b. Cleve., Sept. 3, 1957; s. Daniel Jeremy and Adele Francis (Zeidman) S. BA with honors, Harvard U., 1979; C.E.P., Inst. Polit. Studies, Paris, 1980; postgrad. Grad. Inst. Internat. Studies. U. Geneva, 1981-82. Asst. to exec. v.p. Manpower Demonstration Rsch. Corp., N.Y.C., 1980-81; asst. polit. dir. John Glenn Presdl. Campaign, Washington, 1983-84; assoc. Mckinsey and Co., N.Y.C., 1984-88; COO Tucker Comm., Inc., Cross River, N.Y., 1988-90; exec. v.p. John Blair Comm. Inc., N.Y.C., 1990-91; COO, mng. dir. Tiger Mgmt. Inc., N.Y.C., 1991-92; asst. dep. sec. U.S. Dept. Commerce, Washington, 1992—; chmn. Weybridge Holdings, Inc., N.Y.C., 1992—; trustee Jonathan M. Silver Found., N.Y.C. 1993—; ptnr. HS Ptnrs., N.Y.C., 1993—, visiting com. grad. faculty The New Sch. Bd. Harvard Coll. fellow, Cambridge, Mass., 1975-78, John Harvard fellow, 1979, Rotary grad. fellow, Paris, 1979, Fulbright grad. fellow, Swiss Univ. Exchange Grant, 1982. Jewish. Home: 2800 R St NW Washington DC 20007 Office: US Dept of the Interior 14th and Constitution NW Washington DC 20240

SILVER, LAWRENCE ALAN, marketing executive; b. New Haven, Sept. 5, 1943; s. Herman B. and Marcia (Azersky) S.; m. Deena Rae Rosenberg, Feb. 26, 1967; children: Cheryl Ann, Elyse Stephanie, Marc Aaron. BJ, Boston U., 1965, MS, 1966. Reporter New Haven Register, 1958-66; dir. pub. rels. Spear & Staff, Inc., Babson Park, Mass., 1966-70; pres. Silver Assocs. Pub. Rels. & Advt., Holliston, Mass., 1971-82; pres. RJ Communication, Inc., St. Petersburg, Fla., 1982—; sr. v.p., dir. mktg. Raymond James & Assocs., Inc., St. Petersburg, 1982—; v.p. investor relations Raymond James Fin., Inc., St. Petersburg, 1983—; chmn. Raymond James Fin. Mktg. Com., St. Petersburg, 1984—; coord. quality svcs. Raymond James Fin., St. Petersburg. 1989—; instr. journalism Framingham (Mass.) State Coll., 1974-80. Mem. Holliston Bylaw Study Com., 1978-82, U. Tampa Ctr. Quality Steering Com., 1993—; founding pres. Temple Beth Torah, Holliston, 1972-73; bd. dirs. Temple Ahavat Shalom Men's Club, Palm Harbor, 1983-84; trustee Temple Ahavat Shalom, 1985-86, Am. Stage Theatre, St. Petersburg, 1994—; pres. Temple Ahavat Shalom Brotherhood, 1985-86; founding bd. dirs. Jewish Community Ctr. of Greater Framingham, 1969-72; mem. Fla. Edn. and Industry Coalition, 1988-95, St. Petersburg Jr. Coll. Community Outreach program, 1988-89; mem. Fla. Sch. Adv. Coun., 1990-93; mem. adv. coun. Clearwater Jr. League, 1993—, sch. adv. coun. Tarpon Springs High Sch., 1988-93. With U.S. Army, 1967-69. Mem. Securities Industry Assn. (Pub. Rels. Advt. Roundtable 1986-90, Mktg. Roundtable 1988—, sales and mktg. com. 1991—, editor Marketshare 1994—), Boston U. Nat. Alumni Coun. Assoc. editor Venture Capital Jour., 1978-82. Home: 90 Greenhaven Cir Oldsmar FL 34677 Office: Raymond James & Assocs 880 Carillon Pky Saint Petersburg FL 33716

SILVER, MALCOLM DAVID, pathologist, educator; b. Adelaide, South Australia. Apr. 29, 1933; s. Peter Bertram and Stella Louisa (Riley) S.; m. Meredith May Galloway, Jan. 19, 1957; children: Stuart Faulkner, Claire Eleanor, Caryl Louise. M.D., U. Adelaide; Ph.D., McGill U. Diplomate: Am. Bd. Pathology. Resident med. officer Royal Adelaide Hosp., 1957-58; resident in pathology Royal Victoria Hosp.-Pathol. Inst., McGill U., Montreal, Que., Can., 1958-63; research fellow dept. exptl. pathology John Curtin Sch. Med. Research, Australian Nat. U., Canberra, 1963-65; asst. prof. pathology U. Toronto, 1965-68, assoc. prof., 1968-74, prof., 1974-79, prof., chmn. dept. pathology, 1985—; staff pathologist Toronto Gen. Hosp., 1965-72, sr. staff pathologist, 1972-79; prof., chmn. dept. pathology U. Western Ont., London, Ont., Can., 1979-85; chief pathology Univ. Hosp., London, 1979-85; pathologist in chief Toronto Gen. Hosp., 1985-89; pathologist in chief The Toronto Hosp. (Toronto Gen. and Toronto Western Divs.), 1989-91, sr. staff pathologist, 1991—. Edtl. bd. Jour. Cardiovascular Pathology, Modern Pathology, Jour. Long-Term Effects of Med. Implants; contbr. articles to profl. jours. Fellow Royal Coll. Pathologists of Australia, Royal Coll. Physicians and Surgeons Can.; mem. Can. Assn. Pathologists (chmn. membership com. 1975-77), Ont. Assn. Pathologists, Am. Soc. Investigative Pathology, Internat. Acad. Pathology, Can. Med. Assn., Ont. Med. Assn., Can. Cardiovascular Soc., Am. Heart Assn., AAAS. Office: U Toronto Dept Pathology, 100 College St, Toronto, ON Canada M5G 1L5

SILVER, MARY WILCOX, oceanography educator; b. San Francisco, July 13, 1941; d. Philip E. and Mary C. (Kartes) Wilcox; children: Monica, Joel. BA in Zoology, U. Calif., Berkeley, 1963; PhD in Oceanography, U. Calif., La Jolla, 1971. Asst. prof. biology San Francisco State U., 1971-72; prof. marine sci. U. Calif., Santa Cruz, 1972—, chmn. dept., 1983-89, 92—. Contbr. numerous articles on biol. oceanography to profl. jours. Grantee NSF, 1979—; recipient Bigelow medal, 1992. Mem. AAAS, Am. Soc. Limnology and Oceanography, Am. Phycological Soc. Office: U Calif Dept Marine Sci Santa Cruz CA 95064

SILVER, MICHAEL, school superintendent; b. Landsberg, Germany, Jan. 30, 1948; came to U.S., 1949; s. Norman and Esther Silver; m. Beverley Ann Moss, May 16, 1971; children: Sabina, Joseph. AB, Washington U., 1970, MEd, 1973, PhD, 1982. Cert. supt. Mo., Wash. Tchr. Normandy Sch. Dist., St. Louis, 1970-72; tchr. Parkway Sch. Dist., St. Louis, 1972-75, asst. prin., 1976-79, adminstrv. asst., 1979-83, asst. to supt., 1983-84, asst. supt., 1984-86; supt. South Ctrl. Sch. Dist., Seattle, 1986—; bd. dirs. Cities in Schs., Seattle; mem. adv. bd. Sta. KCTS, Seattle, 1990—; vis. exec. Seattle U. Sch. Edn., 1995. Author: Values Education, 1976, Facing Issues of Life and Death, 1976. Pres. SeaTac Task Force, Seattle, 1989; bd. dirs. Anti-Defamation League, Seattle, 1987—; mem. City of Tukwila (Wash.) 2000 Com., 1988-90. Recipient A Plus award Wash. Coun. Econ. Edn., 1992; named Exec. Educator, 100 Exec. Educator Mag., 1985; I/D/E/A fellow Charles F. Kettering Found., 1978, 88, Title VI fellow Washington U., 1971-73. Mem. Am. Assn. Sch. Adminstrs., Assn. Supervision and Curriculum Devel., Wash. Assn. Sch. Adminstrs. (mem. chpt., pres. 1989-90), King County Supts. (chmn. adv. com. 1989-90), Southcenter Rotary Club, Southwest King County C. of C., Phi Delta Kappa. Home: 14127 SE 50th St Bellevue WA 98006 Office: South Central SD 406 4640 S 144th St Seattle WA 98168

SILVER, MORRIS, economist, educator; b. N.Y.C., July 9, 1931; s. Julius and Lilly S.; m. Sondra P. Hartman, Jan. 26, 1958; children: Gerald David, Ronald Alan. B.A., CCNY, 1958; Ph.D. (Earhart Found. fellow, Ford Found. fellow), Columbia U., 1964. Mem. faculty City Coll. CUNY, 1964—, assoc. prof. econs., 1968—, prof., 1972—, chmn. dept., 1969—; research assoc. Nat. Bur. Econ. Research, 1967-71; cons crime deterrence and offender career Hudson Inst., 1974, Nat. Center for Health Services Research, 1970—. Author: (with R.D. Auster) The State as a Firm, 1979, Affluence, Altruism, and Atrophy: The Decline of Welfare States, 1980, Prophets and Markets: The Political Economy of Ancient Israel, 1983, Enterprise and the Scope of the Firm, 1984, Economic Structures of the Ancient Near East, 1985, Foundations of Economic Justice, 1989, Taking Ancient Mythology Economically, 1992, Economic Structures of Antiquity, 1995. Served with AUS, 1953-55. Mem. Am. Econ. Assn. Jewish. Office: Dept Econs City Coll 133 D St New York NY 10031

SILVER, PAUL, architect; b. N.Y.C., July 6, 1937; s. David and Rose Lily (Kirszencwajg) S.; m. Joan Marie D'Onofrio, Sept. 29, 1938; children: Susan Elizabeth, Michael Scott. B.Arch. summa cum laude, Pratt Inst., 1960. Registered architect in 17 states, including Mich., N.Y., Washington. Designer Eero Saarinen, Birmingham, Mich., 1960-62; ptnr. The Gruzen Partnership, N.Y.C., 1962-86; sr. ptnr. Silver & Ziskind, N.Y.C., 1986—; instr. Delehanty Inst., N.Y.C., 1965-67; instr. architecture CUNY, 1970-80, adj. prof., 1974-80; adviser N.Y. Community Coll., N.Y.C., 1975-80; expert witness on constl. criteria for justice facility design. Designer: Murry Bergstrum High Sch., N.Y.C., 1976 (Design award Met. Brick Council 1976), Ramsey County Detention Ctr., St. Paul, 1978 (AIA Honor 1978), Oak Park Heights Correctional Facility, Minn., 1980 (Am. Correctional Assn. Design 1980); developer photodrafting, 1995. Recipient Alumni Pratt Inst., 1981; Fulbright scholar, 1960. Fellow AIA; mem. Am. Arbitration Assn. (panel arbitrators), Am. Correctional Assn., Portland Cement Assn. (dir. 1978-80), Architects for Justice (dir. 1978—). Home: 101 Manor Dr White Plains NY 10603-1923 Office: Silver & Ziskind Architects 233 Park Ave S New York NY 10003

SILVER, PAUL ALLEN, lawyer; b. Providence, Mar. 1, 1950; s. Caroll M. and Gail (Arkin) S.; m. Katherine C. Haspel, June 22, 1975; children: Andrew Haspel, Nathaniel Haspel. AB, Harvard U., 1972; JD, Boston U., 1975. Bar: R.I. 1975, U.S. Dist. Ct. R.I. 1975, Mass. 1985. Assoc. firm Hinckley, Allen, Salisbury & Parsons, Providence, 1975-81; ptnr. Hinckley, Allen & Snyder, Providence, 1981—; faculty MS in Taxation Program, Bryant Coll., North Smithfield, R.I., 1982. Author: Cheap Eats, 1972, 2d edit., 73, 3d edit., 75. Bd. dirs. Travelers Aid Soc. of R.I., Providence, 1983-89; pres., 1986-89; bd. dirs. Ronald McDonald House, 1987—; Camp Ruggles, 1991—; active Planned Giving Coun. of R.I. Mem. ABA, R.I. Bar Assn., Estate Planning Coun. of R.I., Moses Brown Sch. Alumni Assn. (bd. dirs. 1984—), Internat. Assn. Fin. Planning (bd. dirs. R.I. chpt. 1986—). Jewish. Avocations: finance, business. Home: 310 Olney St Providence RI 02906-2326 Office: Hinckley Allen & Snyder 1500 Fleet Ctr Providence RI 02903

SILVER, PAUL ROBERT, marketing executive, consultant; b. Balt., Mar. 15, 1931; s. Harry and Frieda (Rosengarten) S.; m. Natalie Nessa Nechamkin, May 17, 1957; children: Geri Ellen, Steven Marc, Lawrence Alan. BA, U. Md., 1949; BS, U. Balt., 1958; postgrad., Eckerd Coll., 1984. Pres., CEO Sterling Prodns. Inc., Balt., 1950-51; advt. mgr. Hecht Co., Washington, 1951-53; pres., CEO Artists & Models, Inc., Washington and

Balt., 1974-76, The Charles Agy. Inc., Washington and Balt., 1955-80, The Golden Triangle Agy., Clearwater, Fla., 1980-82; COO Bridgman Assocs. Inc., Annapolis, Md., 1985-86; dir. promotions Internat. Beverage Expn., Washington, 1986; pres., CEO Prasco Inc., Tampa and Miami, Fla., and Balt., 1982—; cons. Lewis and Ptnrs., Inc., San Francisco, Corp. Vision Inc., L.A., Computer Response Inc., Balt., Themes and Schemes Inc., Dunedin, Fla. and San Diego, 1984—; J&B Mgmt. Co., 1991, Alberee Products, Inc., 1992; v.p. Coupon Am., Bel Air, Md., 1987-88; dir. mktg. Miles Homes, Inc., Cheshire, Conn., 1993; CEO Universal Industries, Inc., 1994—. Active in Radio Free Asia, 1972, Pinellas County Heart Savers, Clearwater, 1981; campaign mgr. for candidates for Balt. City Coun., U.S. Senate and U.S. Congress, 1968, 88, Fla. Commr. Agr., 1990. With U.S. Army, 1953-55, 72. Democrat. Jewish. Avocations: writing, art. Office: Prasco Inc PO Box 7667 Seminole FL 34645

SILVER, PHILIP WARNOCK, Spanish language educator; b. Bryn Mawr, Pa., Nov. 12, 1932; married; 3 children. B.A., Haverford Coll., 1954; M.A., Middlebury Coll., 1955, Princeton U., 1960; Ph.D., Princeton U., 1963. Instr. Spanish Rutgers U., N.J., 1961-63; asst. prof. Oberlin Coll., 1963-66; assoc. prof. dept. Spanish and Portuguese Columbia U., N.Y.C., 1967-71, vis. prof., 1971-72, prof. dept. Spanish and Portuguese, 1972—, chmn. dept. Spanish and Portuguese, from 1973. Author: (transl.) Unamuno: A Philosophy of Tragedy, 1962; Et in Arcadia ego: A Study of the Poetry of Luis Cernuda, 1965; Ortega As Phenomenologist, 1978. Samuel S. Fels fellow Princeton U., 1960-61; Guggenheim fellow, 1966. Mem. MLA, Am. Transl. Assn.,. Office: Columbia U Dept Spanish and Portuguese 612 W 116th St New York NY 10027-7009

SILVER, R. PHILIP, metal products executive; b. 1942. Grad., U. Mo., 1967. With Amour & Co., Atlanta, 1967-68, Boise Cascade Corp., Idaho, 1968-75; exec. v.p. Fla. Gas Co., Orlando, Fla., 1975-80; pres. Continental Can, Norwalk, Conn., 1980-87; pres., treas. Silgan Corp., Stamford, Conn., 1987—. Office: Silgan Corp 4 Landmark Sq Stamford CT 06901

SILVER, RALPH DAVID, distilling company director; b. Chgo., Apr. 19, 1924; s. Morris J. and Amelia (Abrams) S.; m. Lois Reich, Feb. 4, 1951; children: Jay, Cappy. B.S., U. Chgo., 1943; postgrad., Northwestern U., 1946-48; J.D., DePaul U., 1952. Bar: Ill. bar 1952. Staff accountant David Himmelblau & Co. (C.P.A.'s), 1946-48; internal revenue agt. U.S. Dept. Treasury, 1948-51; practice in Chgo., 1952-55; atty. Lawrence J. West, 1952-55; fin. cons., bd. dirs. Barton Inc., Chgo., 1955-92; bd. dirs. Stone Fin. Corp., Stone Fin. II Corp., 1992-95; arbitrator N.Y. State Exch., Cir. Ct. of Cook County, Ill., Nat. Assn. Securities Dealers. Bd. dirs., pres. Silver Found. Lt. (j.g.) USNR, 1943-46. Mem. ABA, Chgo. Bar Assn., AICPA. Club: Green Acres Country. Home: 1124 Old Elm Ln Glencoe IL 60022-1235

SILVER, RICHARD ABRAHAM, hospital administrator; b. Boston, Nov. 21, 1922; s. Samuel and Sylvia Lena S.; A.B., Boston U., 1943; LL.B., George Washington U., 1955, M.S.P.A., 1966; m. Janice Backer Lavien, June 10, 1948; children—Gary Neil, Ronald Howard, Scott Hugh. Personnel asst. VA, Boston, 1946-50; personnel officer VA, Washington, 1950-71; asst. dir. VA Med. Ctr., East Orange, N.J., 1973-74; dir. VA Med. Ctr., Northampton, Mass., 1974-76, VA Med. Ctr., Brockton, Mass., 1976-79, James A. Haley VA Hosp., Tampa, Fla., 1979—; lectr. U. S.Fla. Sch. Medicine, 1979—. Bd. dirs. Nat. Fedn. Temple Brotherhoods. Served as capt. U.S. Army, 1943-46. Mem. Am. Hosp. Assn., Am. Coll. Hosp. Adminstrs., Assn. Am. Med. Colls. (mem. council teaching hosps.), Fla. Gulf Health Systems Agy. (bd. dirs.), Phi Beta Kappa, Alpha Epsilon Pi. Jewish. Office: James A Haley Vets Hosp 13000 Bruce B Downs Blvd Tampa FL 33612-4745

SILVER, RICHARD TOBIAS, physician, educator; b. Jan. 18, 1929; m. Barbara Silver; 1 son, Adam Bennett. Diploma, A.B., Cornell U., 1950, M.D., 1953. Diplomate: Nat. Bd. Med. Examiners, Am. Bd. Internal Medicine, Am. Bd. Clin. Oncology. Intern N.Y. Hosp.-Cornell Med. Ctr., N.Y.C., 1953-54, asst. resident in medicine, 1956-57, resident in hematology, 1957-58; clin. assoc. gen. medicine br. Nat. Cancer Inst., NIH, Bethesda, Md., 1954-56; instr. in medicine Cornell U. Med. Coll., N.Y.C., 1955-58, instr. medicine, 1958-62, clin. asst. prof., 1962-67, clin. assoc. prof., 1967-73, clin. prof., 1973—; pres. N.Y. State Soc. Med. Oncologists and Hematologists, 1991—; asst. attending physician N.Y. Hosp., 1964-67, assoc. attending physician, 1967-73, attending physician, 1973—; asst. vis. physician 2d Cornell Med. div. Bellevue Hosp., N.Y.C., 1963-66; vis. Fulbright prof. U. Bahia Sch. Medicine, Brazil, 1958-59; vis. prof. Hershey Hosp.-Pa. State Hosp., 1976, Mayo Clinic, 1977, Upstate Med. Ctr., Binghamton, N.Y., 1977, Med. Coll. Va., 1979, Med. Sch. Colubia U., 1982, N.J. Coll. Medicine, New Brunswick, 1983, Meml. Med. Ctr. U. Ga., 1984, 86; invited lectr. Med. Coll. Shanghai and Zhengchow, 1979, VIII Brazilian Hematology Congress, Salvador, 1981, 14th Internat. Congress Chemotherapy, Kyoto, Japan, 1985, XI Brazilian Congress of Cancerology, Florianapolis, Santa Catarina, 1987, 2d Internat. Conf. CML, Bologna, Italy, 1992; mem. rev. bd. NIH, Nat. Cancer Inst.; cons. Cancer Chemotherapy Investigative Rev. Bd., 1980, clin. trials com., 1979-81; mem. Cornell U. COuncil, 1987—. Author: Morphology of the Blood and Marrow in Clinical Practice, 1970; co-author: (with R.D. Lauper, C.I. Jarowski) A Synopsis of Cancer Chemotherapy, 1977, ed edit., 1987; editor, contbr.: Topics in Cancer, 1982; contbr. chpts. to books and articles to profl. jours.; to nat. and internat. profl. confs., seminars and workshops in medicine. Fellow ACP; mem. N.Y. State Soc. Med. Hematologists and Oncologists (pres. 1991—), Cornell U. Med. Coll. Alumni Assn. (pres. 1973-76, sr. advisor 1976—), Am. Soc. Clin. Oncology, Internat. Soc. Hematology, Am. Soc. Hematology, N.Y. Soc. Study of Blood, N.Y. County Med. Soc., N.Y. State Med. Soc. Oncologists and Hematologists (pres. 1991-93), Harvey Soc., Am. Fedn. Clin. Rsch., Am. Assn. Cancer Rsch., Explorers Club (bd. dirs., chmn. sci. adv. com. 1987), Sigma Xi. Office: NY Hosp Cornell Med Ctr 525 E 68th St New York NY 10021-4873 also: 1440 York Ave New York NY 10021

SILVER, RON, actor, director; b. N.Y.C., July 2, 1946; s. Irving Roy and May (Zimelman) S.; m. Lynne Miller, Dec. 24, 1975. BA, U. Buffalo; MA, St. John's U., Taiwan. Appeared in (stage prodns.) Kaspar, Public Insult, 1971, El Grande de Coca-Cola, 1972, 75, Lotta, 1973, More Than You Deserve, 1973, Awake and Sing, 1976, Angel City, 1977, In the Boom Boom Room, 1979, Gorilla, 1983, Friends, 1983-84, Hurly Burly, 1984-85, Social Security, 1986, Hunting Cockroaches, 1987, Speed-the-Plow (Tony and Drama Desk awards), 1988, 92, Broken Glass, 1994, (films) Tunnelvision, 1976, Semi-Tough, 1977, Silent Rage, 1982, Best Friends, 1982, Lovesick, 1982, The Entity, Silkwood, 1983, The Goodbye People, 1984, Garbo Talks, 1984, Eat and Run, 1985, Enemies a Love Story, 1989, Blue Steel, 1990, Reversal of Fortune, 1990, Married to It, 1992, Time Cop, 1994; (TV) Rhoda, 1976-78, The Mac Davis Show, 1976, The Billionaire Boys Club (Emmy nomination), 1986, Hill Street Blues, Wiseguy, 1988, Fellow Traveller, 1990, Forgotten Prisoners: From the Amnesty Files, 1991, Blindside, 1992, Lifepod (also dir.), 1993, The Good Policeman (also exec. producer), 1994, A Woman of Independent Means, 1995. Recipient Israel Cultural award. Mem. AFTRA, SAG, Actors' Equity Assn. (pres.), Actors Studio, Actors Fund (trustee), Acad. Motion Picture Arts and Scis., The Creative Coalition (founder, pres.), Coun. on Fgn. Rels., Coun. Woodrow Wilson Internat. Ctr. for Scholars. Office: ICM care Sam Cohn 40 W 57th St New York NY 10019-4001 also: Actors Equity Assn 165 W 46th St New York NY 10036-2501

SILVER, SAMUEL MANUEL, rabbi, author; b. Wilmington, Del., June 7, 1912; s. Adolph David and Adela (Hacker) S.; m. Elaine Shapiro, Feb. 9, 1953; children: Lee, Joshua, Barry, Noah, Daniel. B.A., U. Del., 1933; M.H.L., Hebrew Union Coll., 1940, D.D., 1965. Ordained rabbi, 1940; dir. Hillel Found., U. Md., 1940-42; asst. rabbi in Cleve., 1946-52; rabbi Temple Sinai, Stamford, Conn., 1959-77, Jewish Community Center of Lee County, Cape Coral, Fla., 1977-79, Temple Sinai of South Palm Beach County, Fla., 1979—; Sec. Temple of Understanding, Greenwich, Conn., 1969; v.p. Stamford-Darien Council of Chs. and Synagogues; exec. bd. Fellowship in Prayer, 1970—; pres. Rabbinical Assn. South Palm Beach County, 1980-82. Author: (with Rabbi M.M. Applebaum) Sermonettes for Young People, 1964, How To Enjoy This Moment, 1967, Explaining Judaism to Jews and Christians, 1971, When You Speak English You Often Speak Hebrew, 1973, Mixed Marriage Between Jew and Christian, 1977, Speak to the Children of

Israel, 1977; Editor: Am. Judaism, 1952-59, The Quotable American Rabbis, 1967; columnist Nat. Jewish Post, 1955—. Served as chaplain AUS, 1942-46. Mem. Central Conf. Am. Rabbis (nat. exec. bd. 1954-56), Jewish War Vets (chaplain 1966-70), Assn. Jewish Chaplains U.S. (pres. 1959-62), Stamford-Darien Ministers League (pres. 1961-62), Zionist Orgn. Am. (pres. Southeast region 1984—), Alpha Epsilon Pi. Home and Office: 2475 W Atlantic Ave Delray Beach FL 33445-4425 *The greatest of all miracles is that we need not be tomorrow what we are today but that we can improve if we make use of the potential implanted within us by God.*

SILVER, SHEILA JANE, composer, music educator; b. Seattle, Oct. 3, 1946; d. Robert Eugene and Fannie (Horowitz) S.; m. John Feldman, Dec. 11, 1988. BA, U. Calif., Berkeley, 1968; postgrad., Hochschule fur Musik, Stuttgart, Fed. Republic Germany, 1969-71; MFA, Brandeis U., 1972, PhD, 1974. Assoc. prof. music SUNY, Stony Brook, 1979—. Composer classical works for orch., string orch., opera, chamber orch., string quartet, various instruments, also vocal and choral compositions and feature film scores. Radcliffe Inst. fellow, 1977-78, Koussevitzky fellow, 1972; recipient Composer award Am. Inst. and Acad. Arts and Letters, 1986, Prix de Rome, Am. Acad. in Rome, 1978-79, CARY Trust Recording award, 1995; winner Nat. Composers' Competition, Internat. Soc. Contemporary Music., 1981-82, winner competition Indpls. Symphony Orch., 1977, IV Internat. Wettbewerb fur Komponistinnen, 1976; Nat. Endorsment for the Arts Composer fellow, 1995. Mem. Fellows of Am. Acad., Am. Music Ctr., N.Y. Women Composers. Jewish. Home and Office: 68-37 Dartmouth St Forest Hills NY 11375

SILVER, SHELDON, lawyer, state legislator; b. N.Y.C., Feb. 13, 1944; s. Nathan and Frieda (Bearman) S.; m. Rosa Mandelkern, June 25, 1967; children: Edward, Janine, Michelle, Esther. BA, Yeshiva U., 1965; JD, Bklyn. Coll., 1968. Bar: N.Y. 1969, U.S. Dist. Ct. (so. and ea. dists.) N.Y. 1970. Assoc. Schechter & Schwartz, N.Y.C., 1968-71; law sec. to Judge Francis Pecora N.Y.C., 1971-76; ptnr. Agri, Bilder & Silver, N.Y.C., 1976-81; pvt. practice N.Y.C., 1981—; mem. N.Y. State Assembly, 1977—, chmn. ways and means com., 1992, speaker, 1994. Vice pres. Bialystoker Synagogue, Young Israel Synagogue. Named Man of Yr., Harry S. Truman Dem. Club, 1977, United Jewish Appeals, 1983, also others. Democrat. Office: 270 Broadway Ste 1800 New York NY 10007-2306

SILVER, STEVE, producer, director, writer; b. San Francisco, Feb. 6, 1944; s. Louis J. and Claire (Bencich) S. BA in Graphic Design, San Jose State U., Calif., 1969. Asst. art dir. Harold and Maude film, 1970; assoc. dir. plays Am. Conservatory Theatre, San Francisco, 1971-72; producer, dir., writer, designer, orginator Beach Blanket Babylon, San Francisco, 1974—; dir. musical event honoring Queen Elizabeth and Prince Philip's visit to San Francisco, 1986; curator de Young mus. exhibit Beach Blanket Babylon costumes and hats., San Francisco, 1988. Funded pediatric playroom Children's Hosp., San Francisco, 1983, Child Devel. Ctr. Parent's Pl., San Francisco, 1987, Aids Outreach program Open Hand, San Francisco, 1987, AIDS rsch. grant U. Calif. San Francisco Med. Ctr., 1988. Named Most Outstanding Musical Prodn., Bay Area Theatre Critics, San Francisco, 1979, Most Outstanding Dir. Musical, 1979, Most Outstanding Costume Designer, 1979, dir. Most Outstanding Achievment, DramaLogue, 1980, prodn. Most Outstanding Achievment, 1980; recipient John L. Wasserman Meml. award for outstanding contbrn. to entertainment, 1985, Paine Knickerbocker award for Excellence, Bay Area Theatre Critics, 1985; cited by Sonoma (Calif.) League for Hist. Preservation, 1986, others. Mem. Dramatists Guild. Avocation: painting. Home and Office: 678 Green St San Francisco CA 94133-3802

SILVER, WILLIAM ROBERT, corporate finance executive; b. Oakland, Calif., Mar. 31, 1947; s. Vernon Lowell and Barbara Jean (Zaniboni) S.; m. Joan Ellen Pagani, July 29, 1973. B.S. in Elec. Engring., U. Calif.-Davis, 1970, M.S. in Mgmt. Stanford U., 1987. With sales dept., then area sales mgr. Nuclear Energy div. Gen. Electric Co., San Jose, Calif., 1970-78; western regional mgr. Bankers Leasing & Fin. Corp. sub. Citicorp, San Mateo, Calif., 1978-79, v.p. mktg., 1979-82, sr. v.p. fin., dir., 1982-83, exec. v.p. fin. and mktg. dir., 1983-90, pres., 1990—. Served with Army N.G., 1970-76. Mem. Am. Assn. Equipment Lessors, Pacific Coast Elec. Assn., Am. Gas Assn. Republican. Roman Catholic. Office: Bankers Leasing & Fin Corp 2655 Campus Dr Ste 200 San Mateo CA 94403-2521

SILVERA, ISAAC FRANKLIN, physics educator; b. San Diego, Mar. 25, 1937; s. Albert and Victoria (Nahem) S.; m. Lili Jean Wong, June 3, 1961; children: Michelle, Janine, Cherie, Christopher. BA, U. Calif., Berkeley, 1959, PhD, 1965. Postdoctoral fellow Centre National de la Recherche Scientifique, Grenoble, France, 1965-66; tech. staff Rockwell Internat., Thousand Lakes, Calif., 1966-71; prof. physics U. Amsterdam, The Netherlands, 1971-82, Harvard U., Cambridge, Mass., 1982—. Contbr. over 200 articles to profl. jours. Recipient Hewlett Packard Europhysics award European Physical Soc., 1983. Fellow Am. Phys. Soc., AAAS. Office: Harvard Univ Dept Of Physics Cambridge MA 02138

SILVERBERG, DAVID S., financial consultant; b. Oelwein, Iowa, Mar. 3, 1936; s. Harold and Rose (Fishman) S.; m. Mary Ellen Silverberg, July 20, 1988; children: Laura, Sara, Stanley. Student, U. Minn., 1954-57; LUTC, Life Underwriter Coll., Sioux City, Iowa, 1976; CFP, Coll. Fin. Planning, Denver, 1979. With U.S. Army, 1963-68; fin. cons. Smith Barney, Sioux City, 1978—; instr. Western Iowa Tech. Coll., Sioux City, 1980-87, Inst. of Banking, Sioux City, 1990. Treas Sioux City Symphony, 1991-94; v.p. Sioux City Jewish Fedn., 1991-94, Sioux City Jewish Cemetery Assn., 1990—; bd. dirs. Job Tng. Partnership Act, Sioux City, 1990—. Recipient Young Leadership award Sioux City Jewish Fedn., 1984. mem. Internat. Assn. Fin. Planners, Landmark Lodge AF&AM, Scottish Rite (32nd degree), Shriners, Sioux City Country Club. Avocations: golf, fish. Home: 26 W 45th St Sioux City IA 51104 Office: Smith Barney 600 4th St Sioux City IA 51101

SILVERBERG, LEWIS HENRY, management consultant; b. L.A., Nov. 1, 1934; s. Milton Henry and Marjorie Vella (Coates) S.; m. Amelia Francis Backstrom, June, 9, 1959 (div. 1979); children: Stephen, Richard, Donna; m. Alice Ellen Deakins, Mar. 9, 1979. BA, Pomona Coll., 1955; JD, UCLA, 1958. Bar: Calif. 1959, U.S. Supreme Ct. 1966. Pvt. practice San Diego, 1959-89; exec. v.p., dir. Liquor Barn, Inc., San Diego, 1989-93; bus. cons. San Diego, 1993—; referee Calif. inheritance tax and probate, 1972-88. Trustee San Diego Zool. Soc.; active various pub., charitable and ednl. orgns. Republican. Office: PO Box 90947 San Diego CA 92169

SILVERBERG, MICHAEL JOEL, lawyer; b. Rochester, N.Y., Aug. 12, 1932; s. Goodman and Minnie (Krovetz) S.; m. Charlotte Goldman, June 19, 1955; children: Mark, Daniel. BA, U. Rochester, 1954; JD, Columbia U., 1957. Bar: N.Y. 1958, U.S. Dist. Ct. (so. dist.) N.Y. 1965, U.S. Dist. Ct. (ea. dist.) N.Y. 1990, U.S. Ct. Appeals (2d cir.) 1975, U.S. Supreme Ct. 1967. Instr. Columbia U. Law Sch., N.Y.C., 1957-58; assoc. Phillips, Nizer, Benjamin, Krim & Ballon, N.Y.C., 1960-67, ptnr., 1967—; bd. dirs. AMI/FAMI, N.Y. Mem. exec. bd. N.Y. chpt. Am. Jewish Com. Fulbright scholar U. Strasbourg, France, 1958-59. Mem. ABA, N.Y. State Bar Assn. (com. on internat. litigation), Assn. Bar City N.Y. Home: 205 West End Ave New York NY 10023-4804 Office: Phillips Nizer Benjamin Krim & Ballon 31 W 52nd St New York NY 10019-6118

SILVERBERG, ROBERT, author; b. N.Y.C., Mar. 15, 1935; s. Michael and Helen (Baim) S.; m. Barbara Brown, 1956; m. Karen Haber, 1987. B.A., Columbia U., 1956. Author: novels Thorns, 1967, The Masks of Time, 1968, Hawksbill Station, 1968, Nightwings, 1969, To Live Again, 1969, Tower of Glass, 1970, The World Inside, 1971, Son of Man, 1971, A Time of Changes, 1971, Dying Inside, 1972, The Book of Skulls, 1972, Born With the Dead, 1974, Shadrach in the Furnace, 1976, Lord Valentine's Castle, 1980, Majipoor Chronicles, 1982, Lord of Darkness, 1983, Valentine Pontifex, 1983, Gilgamesh the King, 1984, Tom O'Bedlam, 1985, Star of Gypsies, 1986, At Winter's End, 1988, To the Land of the Living, 1989, The New Springtime, 1990, (with Isaac Asimov) Nightfall, 1990, The Face of the Waters, 1991, (with Isaac Asimov) The Ugly Little Boy, 1992, Kingdoms of the Wall, 1993, (with Isaac Asimov) The Positronic Man, 1993, Hot Sky at Midnight, 1994, Mountains of Majipoor, 1995; non-fiction The Face of the Lost Cities and Vanished Civilizations, 1962, The Great Wall of China, 1965, The Old Ones: Indians of the American Southwest, 1965, Scientists and Scoundrels: A Book of Hoaxes, 1965, The Auk, the Dodo and the Oryx, 1966, The Morning of Mankind: Prehistoric Man in Europe, 1967, Mound Builders of Ancient America: The Archaeology of a Myth, 1968, If I Forget Thee, O Jerusalem: American Jews and the State of Israel, 1970, The Pueblo Revolt, 1970, The Realm of Prester John, 1971. Recipient Hugo award World Sci. Fiction Conv., 1956, 69, 87, 90; Nebula award Sci. Fiction Writers Am., 1970, 72, 75, 86. Mem. Sci. Fiction Writers Am. (pres. 1967-68). Address: PO Box 13160 Oakland CA 94661-0160

SILVERBERG, STUART OWEN, obstetrician, gynecologist; b. Denver, Oct. 14, 1931; s. Edward M. and Sara (Morris) S.; BA, U. Colo., 1952, MD, 1955; m. Joan E. Snyderman, June 19, 1954 (div. Apr. 1970); children: Debra Sue Owen, Eric Owen, Alan Kent; m. 2d, Kay Ellen Conklin, Oct. 18, 1970 (div. Apr. 1982); 1 son, Cris S.; m. 3d, Sandra Kay Miller, Jan., 1983. Intern Women's Hosp. Phila., 1955-56; resident Kings County Hosp., Bklyn., 1958-62; practice medicine specializing in obstetrics and gynecology, Denver, 1962—; mem. staff Rose Med. Ctr., N. Suburban Med. Ctr., U. Hosp., St. Anthony Hosp.; med. exec. bd., chmn. dept. obstetrics and gynecology, 1976-77, 86-87, dir. Laser Ctr., 1994-95; clin. instr. U. Colo. Sch. Medicine, Denver, 1962-72, asst. clin. prof., 1972-88, assoc. clin. prof., 1989—, dir. gynecol. endoscopy and laser surgery, 1988-90; v.p. Productos Alimenticos, La Ponderosa, S.A.; dir., chmn. bd. Wicker Works Video Prodns., Inc., 1983-91; cons. Ft. Logan Mental Health Ctr., Denver, 1964-70; mem. Gov.'s Panel Mental Retardation, 1966; med. adv. bd. Colo. Planned Parenthood, 1966-68, Am. Med. Ctr., Spivak, Colo., 1967-70. Mem. Colo. Emergency Resources Bd., Denver, 1965—. Served to maj. AUS, 1956-58; Germany. Diplomate Am. Bd. Obstetrics and Gynecology, Am. Bd. Laser Surgery. Fellow Am. Coll. Obstetricians and Gynecologists, Am. Soc. Laser Medicine and Surgery, ACS; mem. Am. Internat. fertility socs., Colo. Gynecologists and Obstetricians Soc., Hellman Obstet. and Gynecol. Soc., Colo. Med. Soc. (bd. dirs. 1987-95, speaker of the house 1989—), Clear Creek Valley Med. Soc. (trustee 1978, 80, 87, 93—, pres. 1995), Phi Sigma Delta, AMA, Flying Physicians Assn., Aircraft Owners and Pilots Assn., Nu Sigma Nu, Alpha Epsilon Delta. Jewish. Mem. editorial rev. bd. Colo. Women's Mag.; editor in chief First Image, Physicians Video Jour., 1984-86. Office: 8300 N Alcott St Ste 301 Westminster CO 80030

SILVERMAN, AL, editor; b. Lynn, Mass., Apr. 12, 1926; s. Henry and Minnie (Damsky) S.; m. Rosa Magaro, Sept. 9, 1951; children: Thomas, Brian, Matthew. B.S., Boston U., 1949, Litt.D., 1986. Assoc. editor Sport mag., 1951-52; sports editor True mag., 1952-54; asst. editor Argosy mag., 1954-55; free-lance mag. writer, contbr. Saturday Evening Post, Coronet, Pageant, This Week, Am. Weekly, Am. Heritage, Saturday Review, others, 1955-60; editor-in-chief Saga mag., Impact mag., Sport Library, Sport mag., 1960-72; exec. v.p., editorial dir. Book-of-the-Month Club, 1972—, pres., chief operating officer, 1981—, chmn., chief exec. office, 1985-88; v.p., contbg. editor Viking Penguin, 1989-92; sr. v.p., pub., editor in chief, 1992—. Author: Warren Spahn, 1961, Best from Sport, 1961, (with Phil Rizzuto) The Miracle New York Yankees, 1962, The World of Sport, 1962, Mickey Mantle, Master Yankee, 1963, World Series Heroes, 1964, (with Paul Hornung) Football and the Single Man, 1965, The Specialist in Pro Football, 1966, Sports Titans of the 20th Century, 1968, (with Frank Robinson) My Life is Baseball, 1968, More Sport Titans of the 20th Century, 1969, Joe DiMaggio, The Golden Year, 1969, I Am Third, (with Gale Sayers), 1970, Foster and Laurie, 1974; editor: The Book of the Month, 1986; co-editor: The 20th Century Treasury of Sports, 1992. Mem. Authors Guild. Home: 15 Woods Way White Plains NY 10605-5446 Office: Penguin US 375 Hudson St New York NY 10014-3658

SILVERMAN, ALAN, accounting firm partner; b. London, May 10, 1938; s. Michael and Hannah (Israel) S.; m. Helene Shaw, Nov. 22, 1959 (dec. Mar. 1984); 1 child, Simon Joel. BSc, U. London, 1959. Mathematician Nuclear Power Group, Knutsford, Eng., 1959-60; tchr. London County Council, 1960-61; salesman Diehl Machine Co., London, 1961-63; with mktg. support IBM, London, 1963-66, San Francisco, 1966-68; tng. instr. IBM, L.A., 1968-69; mktg. mgr. IBM, San Francisco, 1970-73, dir. litigation analysis, 1973-80; ptnr. Coopers & Lybrand, San Francisco, 1980—; vis. lectr. U. London, 1960-65, Hastings Coll. Law U. Calif., San Francisco, 1986—. Author: Attorney Client Privilege and the Work Product Doctrine, 1983; editor: Construction Litigation, 1986. Dir. San Francisco Hearing and Speech Ctr., 1984-87. Mem. ABA (assoc.), Am. Arbitration Assn. (panel of arbitrators 1986—), Inst. Mgmt. Cons., Calif. CPA Soc. (hon., com. on litigation services). Avocations: running, cycling, gardening. Office: Coopers & Lybrand 333 Market St San Francisco CA 94105-2102

SILVERMAN, (ALAN) JARED, state agency administrator, lawyer; b. N.Y.C., Mar. 10, 1943; s. Benjamin and Beatrice (Klein) S.; m. Sharon Frances Malamud, Feb. 4, 1968 (dec. Feb. 1986); 1 child, Matthew Austin; m. Pamela Rener Mestman, Nov. 16, 1986; 1 child, Helen Audrey; 1 stepchild, Samuel Asher Mestman. BS in Indsl. Engring., Columbia U., 1963, MS in Ops. Rsch., 1965; JD, NYU, 1970, LLM in Internat. Legal Studies, 1975. Bar: N.J., N.Y., D.C. Mem. info. sys. staff Western Electric Co., 1963-69; asst. dir. ops. planning Am. Stock Exch., 1969-71; assoc. Huber Magill Lawrence & Farrell, 1971-75; sr. atty. law dept. AT&T Co., 1975-90; pvt. practice, 1990-91; bur. chief N.J. Bur. of Securities, Newark, 1991—. Mem. N.Am. Securities Administrs. Assn. (fed. legis. com., internat. enforcement com., action group on problem brokers, chair spl. project abuses of computer bull. bds.). Office: Bur Securities PO Box 47029 153 Halsey St Newark NJ 07102-2825

SILVERMAN, ALBERT A., retired lawyer, manufacturing company executive; b. Copenhagen, Oct. 14, 1908; came to U.S., 1909, naturalized, 1921; s. Louis and Anna (Mendelsohn) S.; m. Gertrude Adelman, 1929 (div. 1934); 1 child, Violet (Mrs. Robert Blumenthal); m. Florence Cohen, Aug. 5, 1939 (dec. 1966); m. Francie Siefert, Oct. 1, 1975. Student, Northwestern U., 1929-34; AA, Cen. YMCA Coll., Chgo., 1936; JD, Loyola U., Chgo. 1940. Bar: Ill. 1940, Wis. 1959, U.S. Supreme Ct. 1960. With Cen. Republic Bank & Trust Co., Chgo., 1926-32; sec.-treas. Cen.-Ill. Co., 1932-42; sec. Republic Drill & Tool Co., 1942-44; asst. to treas. Hansen Glove Corp., Milw., 1944-45; v.p. Vilter Mfg. Corp., Milw., 1945-49, pres., 1949-88, 89-92, chmn., chief exec. officer, 1970-92, chmn. emeritus, 1992—; bd. dirs., pres. Vilter Found., Inc.; mem. council Marquette U. Engring. Sch., 1974—. Council, Med. Coll. Wis.; former bd. dirs. Milw. Housing Assistance Corp.; bd. dirs. Albert J. and Flora H. Ellinger Found., 1974—. Named Man of Yr. Milw. chief, 1974, Antonio R. Rizzuto Gold Medal award Unico Nat., Community Svc. award, VFW, 1989, award Wis. Reg. Bd. NCCJ, 1989; honored by VFW for community svc., 1988. Mem. ABA, ASHRAE, Wis. Bar Assn., Milw. Bar Assn., Chgo. Bar Assn., Am. Zool Soc., Loyola U. Alumni Assn. (hon.), Milw. Athletic Club, Wis. Club, Univ. Club of Milw., Tripoli Country Club, Milw. Athletic Club, Milw. Press Club (Knight of Bohemia award 1979, Headliner award 1981, NCJ award 1989), Masons (past master Milw. Harmony Lodge 1961, 32 deg.), Shriners, Beta Gamma Sigma (hon.). Jewish. Office: 2405 W Dean Rd River Hills WI 53217-2008 *As we go through life, we experience good and bad times, tragedies and happiness, successes and failures. Sometimes we are even handed lemons. Problems are opportunities, and with lemons one can make lemonade.*

SILVERMAN, ALBERT JACK, psychiatrist, educator; b. Montreal, Que., Can., Jan. 27, 1925; came to U.S., 1950, naturalized, 1955; s. Norman and Molly (Cohen) S.; m. Halina Weinthal, June 22, 1947; children: Barry Evan, Marcy Lynn. BSc., McGill U., 1947, M.D., C.M., 1949; grad., Washington Psychoanalytic Inst., 1964. Diplomate: Am. Bd. Psychiatry and Neurology. Intern Jewish Gen. Hosp., Montreal, 1949-50; resident psychiatry Colo. U. Med. Center, 1950-53, instr., 1953; from assoc. to assoc. prof. psychiatry Duke Med. Center, 1953-63; prof. psychiatry, chmn. dept. Rutgers U. Med. Sch., 1964-70; prof. psychiatry U. Mich. Med. Sch., Ann Arbor, 1970-90, prof. emeritus, 1990—; chmn. dept. U. Mich. Med. Sch., 1970-81; cons. Dept. of Def., 1974—; mem. biol. scis. tng. rev. com. NIMH, 1964-69, chmn., 1968-69; mem. rsch. scientist devel. award com., 1970-75, chmn., 1973-75; mem. merit rev. bd. in behavioral scis. VA, 1975-78, chmn., 1976-78; bd. mgrs. N.J. Neuropsychiat. Inst., 1965-69; trustee N.J. Fund Rsch. and Devel. Nervous and Mental Diseases, 1965-67; bd. dirs. N.J. Mental Health Assn., 1964-69; mem. behavioral scis. com. Nat. Bd. Med. Examiners, 1978-82, chmn. 1984-87, mem. comprehensive com., 1986-93, task force for

nervous system, 1989-91; chmn. task force on Cons. Liaison Psychiat., 1991-92. Cons. editor: Psychophysiology, 1970-74, Psychosomatic Medicine, 1972-87; Contbr. articles in field. Served as capt. M.C. USAF, 1955-57. Fellow Am. Coll. Psychiatry (charter), Am. Psychiat. Assn. (chmn. coun. on med. edn. 1970-75, chair task force on DSM III ednl. materials 1979-81), Am. Acad. Psychoanalysis, Am. Coll. Neuropsychopharmacology; mem. Am. Psychosomatic Soc. (coun. 1964-68, 70-74, pres. 1976-77, mem. vis. scholar com. 1992—, co-chair program com. 1992-93), N.J. Psychoanalytic Soc. (trustee 1968-70), Assn. Research Nervous and Mental Diseases, N.J. Neuropsychiat. Assn. (council 1966-69), Group Advancement Psychiatry (chmn. com. psychopathology 1968-74), Soc. Psychophys. Research, Soc. Biol. Psychiatry, Mich. Psychiat. Soc. (council 1975-77). Home: 19 Regent Dr Ann Arbor MI 48104-1738 Office: Mental Health Rsch Inst 205 Zina Pitcher Pl Ann Arbor MI 48109-0720

SILVERMAN, ALVIN MICHAELS, public relations consultant; b. Louisville, 1912; s. Alvin and May (Michaels) S.; m. Phyllis Hazel, Nov. 22, 1936; children: Lora (Mrs. A. Gene Samburg), Jane (Mrs. Carl Culos). Student, Adelbert Coll., Western Res. U., 1930-32. With Cleve. Plain Dealer, 1930-65, beginning as sportswriter, successively schs. editor, city hall reporter, state house corr., Columbus, editorial columnist, day city editor, 1930-57, chief Washington bur., 1957-65; pres., chief exec. officer Pearl-Silverman Agy. (pub. relations consultants), Washington, 1965—; dir. Tiffin Amusement Co., Ellet Co., Bklyn. Devel. Corp. Author: The American Newspaper, 1965. Trustee Ctr. to Protect Workers' Rights. Mem. White House Corrs. Assn., Ohio Legis. Corrs. Assn., Nat. Press Club, Press Club of Ohio, Woodmont Country Club (Rockville, Md.), Gridiron Club (Washington), Fed. City Club, Sigma Delta Chi, Zeta Beta Tau. Home: 4100 Cathedral Ave NW Washington DC 20016-3584 Office: 1125 17th St NW Washington DC 20036-4707

SILVERMAN, ARNOLD, physician; b. N.Y.C., Feb. 15, 1933; s. Sol and Gertrude (Cohen) S.; m. Bonnie J. Fenson, Aug. 28, 1955; children: Jeffrey R., Paul A., David E. BA, U. Colo., 1954, M.A., 1957, M.D., 1961. Diplomate: Am. Bd. Pediatrics. Intern Colo. Gen. Hosp., Denver, 1961-62; resident in pediatrics U. Minn. Hosp., Mpls., 1962-64; fellow in pediatric gastroenterology U. Colo. Med. Center, Denver, 1964-65; mem. faculty U. Colo. Med. Center, 1965—, assoc. prof. pediatrics, 1975-80; prof. U. Colo. Med. Ctr. (Health Sci. Ctr.), 1980-93, prof. emeritus, 1994—; dir. grad. edn. Denver Children's Hosp., 1967-75, chief gastroenterology svc., 1967-75; dir. pediatric svc. Denver Gen. Hosp., 1975-92; cons. Surgeon Gen., Fitzsimons Army Med. Hosp., 1976—; mem. Nat. Commn. Digestive Diseases, 1979-80. Author: (with C.C. Roy and D. Alagille) Pediatric Clinic Gastroenterology, 4th edit., 1995. Mem. Am. Acad. Pediatrics, Am. Gastroenterology Assn., Am. Pediatric Soc., Am. Gastroenterology Assn., N.Am. Soc. Pediatric Gastroenterology, Am. Assn. Study Liver Disease, Denver Med. Soc., Alpha Omega Alpha. Jewish. Home: 3335 S Newport St Denver CO 80224-2823

SILVERMAN, ARNOLD BARRY, lawyer; b. Sept. 1, 1937; s. Frank and Lillian Lena (Linder) S.; m. Susan L. Levin, Aug. 7, 1960; children: Michael Eric, Lee Oren. B Engring. Sci., Johns Hopkins U., 1959; LLB cum laude, U. Pitts., 1962. Bar: U.S. Dist. Ct. (we. dist.) Pa. 1963, Pa. 1964, U.S. Patent and Trademark Office 1965, U.S. Supreme Ct. 1967. Can. Patent Office 1968, U.S. Ct. Claims 1975, U.S. Ct. Appeals (3d cir.) 1982, U.S. Ct. Appeals (fed. cir.) 1985. Patent atty. Alcoa, New Kensington, Pa., 1962-67, 68-74, sr. patent atty., 1972-76; ptnr. Price and Silverman, Pitts., 1967-68; v.p., gen. patent counsel Joy Mfg. Co., Pitts., 1976-80; ptnr. Murray Silverman & Keck, Pitts., 1980-81, Buell, Blenko, Ziesenheim & Beck, Pitts., 1984; ptnr. intellectual property sect. Eckert, Seamans, Cherin & Mellott, Pitts., 1984—, chmn., 1992—; spl. asst. atty. gen. State of W.Va., 1985—; spl. counsel patents U. Pitts., 1975—; speaker on patents, trademarks, copyright, computer law; nat. panel of arbiters Am. Arbitration Assn., 1987—. Contbr. articles to profl. jours. on intellectual property, computer and pub. law. Mem. Churchill CSC (Pa.), 1967-90, chmn., 1975-90; mem. Pitts. law com. Anti-Defamation League, 1981—, regional adv. bd., 1982—, ch-chmn. Pitts. region ann. dinner, 1983, mem. chmn. by-laws com., 1983; bd. govs. Slippery Rock U. Found., 1985-91; Pitts. steering com. MIT Enterprise Forum, 1986-87. With U.S. Army, 1963-64. Recipient Am. Spirit Honor medal, Ft. Knox, 1963,. Mem. ABA, ASME, Allegheny County Bar Assn. (chmn. pub. rels. com. 1978-80, vice-chmn. intellectual property sect. 1981-83 chmn.), Pitts. Patent Law Assn. (chmn. pub. rels. com., 1968-69, chmn. patent laws com., 1970-72, chmn. nominating com., 1973, chmn. legis. action com., 1972-75, bd. mgrs. 1974-88, newsletter editor 1974-88, sec.-treas. 1976-84, v.p. 1984-85, pres. 1985-86, pub. rels. com. 1994—), Am. Intellectual Property Law Assn. (membership com. 1985-88, mem. pub. rels. com., 1994—), U.S. Trademark Assn. (chmn. task force on advt. agys. 1981, membership com. 1987-89), D.C. Bar Assn., Pa. Bar Assn., Assn. Corp. Patent Counsel (emeritus 1980—), Nat. Assn. Coll. and Univ. Attys., Am. Chem. Soc., Licensing Execs. Soc. (co-chair Pitts. 1994—), Brit. Inst. Chartered Patent Agts. (fgn. mem.), Johns Hopkins U. Alumni Assn. (chmn. publicity com. 1963-66, exec. com. 1966-87, v.p. 1969-70, pres. 1971-72, nat. alumni coun. 1989-92), Lic. Exec. Soc. (co-chmn. Pitts. chpt. 1994—), U. Pitts. Gen. Alumni Assn., U. Pitts. Law Alumni Assn. (bd. dirs. 1992—), Robert Bruce Assn. Law Fellows (life), Golden Panthers, Stratford Cmty. Assn. (v.p. 1966-67, gov. 1966-70, pres. 1967-68), Mensa (fellow, lawyers in Mensa 1978—, nat. assoc. counsel patents and trademarks copyrights 1980-82, inventors' spl. interest group 1980-86), Intertel (treas. Pitts. Forum 1983—), Duquesne Club, Order of Coif, Tau Epsilon Rho, Psi Chi. Republican. Jewish. Home: 2019 High Point Dr Murrysville PA 15668-8515 Office: 600 Grant St 42d Fl Pittsburgh PA 15219 *Welcome challenge and perform all tasks with enthusiasm, in a moral manner and to the very best of your ability.*

SILVERMAN, ARTHUR CHARLES, lawyer; b. Lewiston, Maine, June 13, 1938; s. Louis A. and Frances Edith (Brownstone) S.; BS. in Elec. Engring., BS in Indsl. Mgmt., MIT, 1961; JD, Columbia U., 1964; m. Donna Linda Zolov, June 18, 1961; children: Leonard Stephen, Daniel Edward. Bar: N.Y. 1965, U.S. Supreme Ct. 1971. Engr., engring. asst. Gen. Electric Co., Pittsfield, Mass. and Phila., 1958-62; assoc. Baer & Marks, N.Y.C., 1965-68; assoc. Golenbock and Barell, N.Y.C., 1968-72, ptnr., 1972-89, Reid & Priest, N.Y.C., 1989—. Sec. Lehrer McGovern Bovis, Inc. 1979—, Sec. Noris Inc., 1988—, treas., trustee Ramaz Sch., 1977-84, vice chmn., 1984-85, 86-88, chmn., 1988-92; bd. govs. MIT Hillel Found., 1979-84; mem. Bd. Jewish Edn. of City of N.Y., 1981-84; mem. exec. com. Nat. Jewish Ctr. for Learning and Leadership, 1984-90. Mem. IEEE, ABA, NSPE, N.Y. State Bar Assn., Fed. Bar Council, Assn. Bar City N.Y., N.Y. Soc. Architects, Internat. Bar Assn., Inter-Pacific Bar Assn., Constrn. Mgmt. Inst., Bldg. Futures Coun. (mem. Operating Com.), Masons. Republican. Home: 200 E 74th St New York NY 10021 Office: Reid & Priest 40 W 57th St New York NY 10019-4001

SILVERMAN, BRUCE GARY, advertising executive; b. N.Y.C., Feb. 16, 1945; s. Edward E. and Lillian (Brill) S.; children: Jennifer, Matthew. BA, Adelphi U., 1965; JD, Albany Law Sch., 1967. Sr. v.p., exec. creative dir. Ogilvy & Mather Inc., N.Y.C., 1967-80; exec. v.p., exec. creative dir. Bozell & Jacobs Inc., Dallas, 1981-83, Batten, Barton, Durstine & Osborn Inc., L.A., 1984-85; exec. v.p., creative dir. Asher/Gould Advt. Inc., L.A., 1986-89, pres., chief creative officer, 1989—. v.p., bd. dirs. Los Angeles Children's Mus., 1984-88; Community Resource Devel. com. Starbright Pavillion Found., 1993. Mem. Acad. TV Arts and Scis. Home: 3168 Dona Mema Pl Studio City CA 91604-4264 Office: Asher/Gould Advt Inc 5900 Wilshire Blvd Los Angeles CA 90036-5013

SILVERMAN, BURTON PHILIP, artist; b. Bklyn., June 11, 1928; s. Morris Daniel and Anne (Firstenberg) S.; m. Claire Guss, June 12, 1969; children: Robert Arthur, Karen Lila. BA, Columbia Coll., 1949. Freelance illustrator Life, Fortune, Esquire, Time, Newsweek, Sports Illus., New York, The New Yorkers mags., 1959—; instr. Ash. Visual Arts, N.Y.C., 1964-67. Co-author: Abel, 1968, A Portfolio of Drawings, 1968; author: Painting People, 1977, Breaking the Rules of Watercolor, 1983; contbr. articles and drawings to profl. jours.; one-man exhbns. include Davis Gallery, N.Y.C. 1956, 58, 62, Kenmore Galleries, Phila., 1963, 67, 70, FAR Gallery, N.Y.C., 1965, 70, 75, 77 Genesis Gallery, N.Y.C., 1979, Sindin Galleries, N.Y.C., 1983, Capricorn Galleries, Bethesda, Md., 1979, 91, Gallery 52, South Orange, N.J., 1967, 70, 77, Harbor Gallery, L.I., 1971, 74, U. Utah, 1967, Doll and Richards, Boston, 1980, Grand Central Galleries, N.Y.C., 1988,

Cudahy's Gallery, N.Y.C., 1990, Joseph Keifer, Inc., N.Y.C., 1993; group exhbns. include Butler Inst. Am. Art, Youngstown, Ohio, 1954-71, 74, 76, 79, 88, 90, 93, NAD, N.Y.C., 1958-95, Am. Watercolor Soc., N.Y.C., 1978-82, 84-87, 89-91, 95, Pa. Acad. Fine Art, 1949, New Britain (Conn.) Mus. Am. Art, 1964, Wadsworth Atheneum, Hartford, Conn., 1961, Am. Acad. Arts and Letters, 1967, 74, 76, 79, N.Y. Hist. Soc., 1976, Pa. State Mus. Art, Portsmouth (Va.) Mus. Art, 1976, 79, 80, 82 (Purchase prize, 1979, 82), Mexico City Mus. Art, 1990, Nat. Portrait Gallery, Washington, 1993, Hofstra Mus., N.Y.C., 1993, South Bend (Ind.) Mus. Art, 1994, Old Forge (N.Y.) Mus. and Gallery, 1994. With AUS, 1951-53. Named to Hall of Fame, Soc. of Illustrators, N.Y., 1990, Pastel Soc. Am. 1992. Mem. NAD (numerous awards and prizes including Joseph Isidor Gold medal 1992, Ranger Purchase prize 1962, 84, Benjamin Altman figure prize 1969), Am. Watercolor Soc. (numerous awards and prizes including Gold medal 1979, Silver medal 1984, 95, annuals). Home and Studio: 324 W 71 St New York NY 10023 *In art I am wary of things too facile, or appealing. My painting is rooted in a realist tradition that is equally concerned with objective facts and subjective realities. It is a visual language that allows me to explore the tensions and ambiguities engendered by this dual aspect of human experience. Art is my life and my life is in my art.*

SILVERMAN, FRED, television producer; b. N.Y.C., 1937. Student, Syracuse U.; M in TV and Theatre Arts, Ohio State U. With Sta. WGN-TV, Chgo.; then Sta. WPIX-TV, N.Y.C.; then dir. daytime programs CBS-TV, N.Y.C., v.p. programs, 1970-75; pres. ABC Entertainment, N.Y.C., 1975-78; pres., chief exec. officer NBC-TV, N.Y.C., 1978; now pres. Fred Silverman Co., L.A.; co-founder Pierce/Silverman TV Prodn. Co., 1989. Exec. producer TV series Perry Mason Movies, Matlock, In the Heat of the Night, Jake and the Fatman, Father Dowling Mysteries, Diagnosis Murder Starring Dick Van Dyck. Office: care The Fred Silverman Co In the Heat of the Night 9211 Hazelbrand Rd NE Covington GA 30209-2715

SILVERMAN, FREDERIC NOAH, physician; b. Syracuse, N.Y., June 6, 1914; s. Max and Sophia S.; m. Carolyn R. Weber, Jan. 14, 1945. A.B., Syracuse U., 1935, M.D., 1939. Intern Yale U., 1939-40; resident in pediatrics Johns Hopkins U., Balt., 1940-41; fellow in pediatric pathology Columbia U., N.Y.C., 1941-42; in pediatric radiology Babies Hosp., N.Y.C., 1945-47; dir. dept. radiology Children's Hosp., Cin., 1947-75; asst. prof. to prof. radiology and pediatrics U. Cin., 1947-76; prof. clin. radiology and pediatrics Stanford (Calif.) U., 1976-79, emeritus, 1979—; ad hoc cons. HEW, NAS. Chief editor Caffey's Pediatric X-Ray Diagnosis, 1978—; mem. editorial bd. pediatric and radiol. jours.; contbr. articles to profl. jours. With AUS, 1942-46, South West Pacific area. Decorated Combat Ned. Badge; recipient medal Centre Antoine Bélère, Paris, 1981, Gold medal Assn. Univ. Radiologists, 1993. Mem. Am. Acad. Pediatrics, Am. Pediatric Soc., Pediatric Research (past v.p.), Soc. for Pediatric Radiology (past pres., Gold medal 1988); hon. mem. Am. Roentgen Ray Soc., European Soc. Pediatric Radiology, Spanish Radiology Soc., El Salvador Pediatrics Soc., Chilean Radiol. Soc., regional radiol. socs. Home: 850 Webster St Apt 735 Palo Alto CA 94301-2838 Office: Dept Radiology Stanford U Med Center Stanford CA 94305

SILVERMAN, GEORGE ALAN, broadcasting executive; b. Boston, Aug. 27, 1946; s. Sam and Ann S.; m. Sunnie Gozansky, Sept. 1, 1968; children—Rebecca, Marjorie, Jennifer. B.B.A. in Mktg, U. Miami, Fla., 1969. Gen. sales mgr. CBS, Sta. WEEI-FM, Boston, 1972-75; pres. Sunshine Group Broadcasting, Portland, Maine, 1977—; instr. mktg. Husson Coll., Bangor, Maine. Bd. dirs. Greater Portland Landmarks, Gulf of Marine Aquarium, 1979-80; mem. Greater Portland Arts Council; bd. dirs. Multiple Sclerosis Soc. Mem. Greater Portland Radio Broadcasters Assn. (past pres.), New Eng. Broadcast Assn., Maine Assn. Broadcasters. Home: 98 Carroll St Portland ME 04102-3526 Office: Sunshine Group Broadcasting 1555 Islington St Portsmouth NH 03801-4215

SILVERMAN, HARVEY FOX, engineering educator, dean. BS with Honors in Engring., Trinity Coll., 1963, BSE, 1966; ScM, Brown U., 1968, PhD, 1971. Rsch. assoc. Gerber Sci. Instrument Co., Hartford, Conn., 1964-66; various rsch. and mgmt. positions T.J. Watson Rsch. Ctr. IBM, Yorktown Heights, N.Y., 1970-80; prof. engring. Brown U., Providence, R.I., 1980-91, dir. undergrad. engring. program, 1988-90, dean engring., 1991—; cons. submarine signal divsn. Raytheon Co., Portsmouth, R.I., 1968. Contbr. articles to profl. jours. Grantee IBM 1981-85, Analog Devices, 1982-87, GLAK 1982, AMP, 1984-85, Tektronix, 1985, US West, 1988; IBM fellow 1984-87, Metrabyte, 1992. Achievements include research in home designed networks of processing nodes, each of which has a high-speed RISC host coupled to a large, reconfigurable system, general C functions, time-varying speech analysis, talker independent connected-speech recognition algorithms and systems, and non-linear optimization. Office: Brown U Divsn Engring 182 Hope St Rumford RI 02916-1610

SILVERMAN, HENRY JACOB, history educator; b. New Haven, Feb. 22, 1934; s. Morris Samuel and Ethel (Ullman) S.; m. Ann Beryl Snyder, Apr. 12, 1957; children—Edwin Stodel, Emily Davies. B.A. (Univ. scholar) Yale U., 1955, M.A., 1956; M.A. (Ford Found. fellow); postgrad., Stanford U., 1959-60; Ph.D., U. Pa., 1963. Fgn. service officer Dept. States, 1961-63; bibliographer Am. history Library of Congress, Washington, 1963-64; assoc. prof. Am. thought and lang. Mich. State U., East Lansing, 1964-68, assoc. prof., 1968-71, prof., 1971-89, prof. history, 1988—, chmn. dept. Am. thought and lang., 1977-87, sec. for acad. governance, 1989-95; chmn. dept. history Mich. State U., 1995—. Author: American Radical Thought, 1970. Fulbright scholar, Munich, 1956-57; Danforth Found. Assoc., 1969-73; Nat. Endowment for Humanities/U. Iowa grantee, 1979. Mem. AAUP (mem. exec. bd. Mich. State U. chpt. 1975-77), ACLU (mem. Laxing exec. bd., 1975-78, v.p. 1991—, Mich. exec. bd. 1993—), Am. Hist. Assn., Am. Studies Assn., Orgn. Am. Historians. Home: 1099 Woodwind Trl Haslett MI 48840-8978 Office: Mich State U Dept History East Lansing MI 48823

SILVERMAN, HENRY RICHARD, diversified business executive, lawyer; b. N.Y.C., Aug. 2, 1940; s. Herbert Robert and Roslyn (Moskowitz) S.; m. Susan H. Herson, June 13, 1965 (div. Jan. 1977); children: Robin Lynn, Deborah Leigh; m. Nancy Ann Kraner, Jan. 22, 1978; 1 child, Catherine Anne. Grad. cum laude, Hackley Sch., Tarrytown, N.Y., 1957; B.A. with honors, Williams Coll., 1961; LL.B., U. Pa., 1964; postgrad. in corp. fin. and taxation, NYU, 1965. Bar: N.Y. 1965, U.S. Tax Ct. 1965, U.S. Ct. Appeals (2d cir.) 1965. Practice law, 1965-66; with White, Weld & Co, beginning 1966; then gen. ptnr. Oppenheimer & Co., until 1970; pres., chief exec. officer ITI Corp., 1970-72; founder, pres. Trans-York Securities Corp., 1972; exec. v.p., chmn. exec. com. Ladenburg, Thalmann & Co., 1973; pres., chief exec. officer Vavasseur Am. Ltd., subs. U.K. mcht. bank, 1974-75; gen. ptnr. Brisbane Ptnrs., 1976-77; prin. various investment groups, 1977—; Silverman Energy Co., N.Y.C., 1977—; NBC Channel 20, Springfield, Ill., 1977-83, ABC Channel 9, Syracuse, N.Y., 1977-81; prin., dir. Delta Queen Steamboat Co., New Orleans, 1977-86; also prin. outdoor advt., music pub., motion picture prodn., radio broadcasting & hardware mfg. cos.; pres., chief exec. officer Reliance Capital Corp., subs. Reliance Group Holdings, Inc., N.Y.C., 1982—; sr. v.p. bus. devel. Reliance Group Holdings, Inc., N.Y.C., 1982-90; chmn., chief exec. officer Days Inns Am., Inc., Atlanta, 1984-89; also dir.; pres., chief exec. officer Telemundo Group, Inc., N.Y.C., 1986-90; gen. ptnr. Blackstone Group, N.Y.C., 1990-91; chmn., CEO Hospitality Franchise Systems Inc., N.Y.C., 1990—; bd. dirs. N.Y. Univ. Mus., N.Y.C., 1987—. Served to lt. USNR, 1965-73. Republican. Jewish. Club: Harmonie (N.Y.C.). Avocation: tennis. Office: 712 Fifth Ave 41st Flr New York NY 10019*

SILVERMAN, HERBERT R., corporate financial executive; b. N.Y.C., June 10, 1914; s. Jacob and Minnie (Stein) S.; m. Roslyn Moskowitz, Dec. 17, 1933 (dec. Dec. 1965); children: Karen Silverman Mayers, Henry; m. Nadia Gray, Oct. 17, 1967 (dec. June 1994). BS, NYU, 1932; JD, St. Lawrence U., 1935. Bar: N.Y. bar 1935. Organizer, pres. Centaur Credit Corp. (merged with James Talcott, Inc. of N.Y.), 1945; v.p. James Talcott, Inc., 1944-46, exec. v.p., 1956-58, dir., 1956-75, pres., 1958-64, chmn. bd., chief exec. officer, 1961-73; chmn., chief exec. officer Talcott Nat. Corp., 1968-73, also chmn. exec. com., dir., 1968-75; pres. Nat. Comml. Fin. Conf., 1948-52, chmn., 1952-58; bd. dir. Baer-Am. Banking Corp., Painters Fund, Inc., Selected Sectors Fund, Inc.; sr. advisor Bank Julius Baer; adj. prof. fin. NYU Coll. Bus. and Pub. Adminstrn., 1973—; trustee med. ctr., vice chmn.

bd. NYU. Named Man of Yr. banking and finance Phi Alpha Kappa; recipient Golden Medallion for humanitarian services B'nai B'rith, Adam Gallatin award NYU, 1978. Mem. ABA, N.Y. Bar Assn. N.Y. Univ. Alumni Fedn. (pres. 1958-60), Phi Alpha Kappa, Iota Theta. Clubs: Harmonie (N.Y.C.); Navesink Country (Middletown, N.J.); N.Y. Univ. (past pres.). Home: 150 Central Park South New York NY 10019

SILVERMAN, IRA NORTON, news producer; b. Bklyn., May 17, 1935; s. Joseph and Mildred (Axelrod) S.; m. Elizabeth Parsons Aspray, June 16, 1979; children by previous marriage: Gary, Bruce; stepchildren: Elizabeth, Aime, Alison. AB, Columbia U., 1957. Newspaper, mag. and book editor, 1957-67; producer, writer NBC News, 1967-79; sr. producer spl. projects NBC Nightly News, Washington, 1979—. Co-author: The Pleasant Avenue Connection, 1976. Recipient Nat. Headliner award, 1977, 78, 81, 87, Alfred I. DuPont-Columbia U. award, 1983-84, 85-86, Emmy award for news and documentary, 1985, 87, award Overseas Press Club Am., 1987, 90, George Polk award L.I. U., 1988, Excellence in TV award Channels mag., 1990, George Foster Peabody award U. Ga., 1991, Citation for Excellence Overseas Press Club, 1992. Avocation: climbing. Office: NBC News 4001 Nebraska Ave NW Washington DC 20016-2733

SILVERMAN, JEFFREY STUART, manufacturing executive; b. N.Y.C., Nov. 25, 1945; s. Harry T. and Roberta S.; m. Pamela Silverman (div.); children: Jason S., Amanda P.; m. Joy Silverman; children: Evan M., Jessica Jaye. BS in Fin., L.I. U., 1967. Mem. N.Y. Stock Exchange, 1968-72; pres. Basil Cable, 1975-82, Silba Enterprises, N.Y.C., 1975-82; chmn. bd. dirs., CEO Ply-Gem Industries, N.Y.C., 1982—. Office: Ply-Gem Industries Inc 777 3rd Ave Fl 30 New York NY 10017-1301*

SILVERMAN, JERALD, veterinarian, academic administrator; b. Bklyn., Mar. 23, 1942; s. Herbert Louis and Martha (Bernstein) S.; m. Sara Kay Zwerling, Dec. 17, 1967 (div.); children: Adam, Daniel. BS, Cornell U., Ithaca, N.Y., 1964, DVM, 1966; MPS, New Sch. for Social Research, N.Y.C., 1986. Diplomate Am. Coll. Lab. Animal Medicine. Clin. veterinarian Humane Soc. N.Y., N.Y.C., 1966-67, L.I. Pet Hosp., Bklyn., 1967-69, Rockland Vet. Med. Ctr., Pearl River, N.Y., 1969-75; dir. research animal facility Am. Health Found., Valhalla, N.Y., 1975-85; assoc. dir. lab. animal resources Ohio State U., Columbus, 1985—; assoc. prof. veterinary preventive medicine Ohio State U., 1985—; cons. Revlon Health Care Group, Tuckahoe, N.Y., 1980-85, Avon Products, Suffern, N.Y., 1982-88, Eugene Tech. Internat., Allendale, N.J., 1984—, Am. Health Found., Valhalla, 1985-87. Contbr. articles to profl. jours. Recipient cancer research grants. Mem. AVMA, Am. Assn. Cancer Research, Am. Assn. Lab. Animal Sci., Am. Coll. Lab. Animal Medicine, Vet. Cancer Soc. Avocations: birdwatching, stamp collecting, track and field. Office: Ohio State U 6089 Godown Rd Columbus OH 43235-7555

SILVERMAN, JONATHAN, actor; b. L.A., Aug. 5, 1966; s. Hillel Emanuel and Devora (Halaban) S. Student, U. So. Calif. Appearances include (films) Girls Just Want to Have Fun, 1985, Brighton Beach Memoirs, 1986, Caddyshack II, 1988, Stealing Home, 1988, Weekend at Bernie's, 1989, Class Action, 1991, Little Sister, 1992, Age Isn't Everything, 1992, Weekend at Bernie's II, 1993, Little Big League, 1994, Teresa's Tattoo, 1994, Two Guys Talking About Two Girls, 1994; (TV movies) Traveling Man, 1989, For Richer, For Poorer, 1992, Broadway Bound, 1992, 12:01, 1993, Hands That See, 1994; (TV series) Gimme a Break!, 1985-87, The Single Guy, 1995—; (plays) Brighton Beach Memoirs, Biloxi Blues, Broadway Bound (Helen Hays award 1988), The Illusion (Drama Lounge award 1990), Pay or Play (Drama League award), Sticks and Stones, 1994. Co-founder Artists for a Free South Africa, L.A., 1989—. Mem. Young Artists United (hon. N.Y. and L.A. chpt. 1990, 91). *

SILVERMAN, JOSEPH, chemistry educator, scientist; b. N.Y.C., Nov. 5, 1922; s. Jakob and Mary (Chechick) S.; m. Joan Aline Jacks, Jan. 14, 1951; children: Joshua Henry, David Avrom. B.A., Bklyn. Coll., 1944; A.M., Columbia U., 1948, Ph.D., 1951. Head research dept. Walter Kidde (nuclear labs.), Garden City, N.Y., 1952-54; v.p., tech. dir. RAI Research Corp., L.I. City, N.Y., 1954-59; assoc. prof. chemistry State U. N.Y., Stony Brook, 1959-60; prof. dept. materials and nuclear engring. U. Md., College Park, 1960-92, prof. emeritus, 1992—; cons. Danish AEC, Indsl. Research Inst., Japan, Boris Kidric Inst., Yugoslavia, Bechtel Co., GPU Nuclear Corp., GE, IAEA, Vienna; disting. vis. prof. Tokyo U., 1974; gen. chmn. 2d Internat. Meeting on Radiation Processing, Miami, Fla., 1978, 3d Tokyo, 1980, hon. chmn. 6th, Ottawa, 1987; trustee Washington Inst. Values in Pub. Policy, 1981-87. Editor: Internat. Jour. Applied Radiation and Isotopes, 1973-78, Internat. Jour. Radiation Engring. 1970-73, Trans. 1st Internat. Meetings on Radiation Processing, 1977, 2d, 1979, 3d, 1981; mem. editorial adv. bd.: Radiation Physics and Chemistry, 1978—. Served with AUS, 1944-46. Recipient Founders award 6th Internat. Mtg. on Radiation Processing, 1987, Centennial medal U. Md. Coll. Engring., 1994; Rsch. fellow Brookhaven Nat. Lab., 1949-51; Guggenheim fellow, 1966-67. Fellow Nordic Soc. Radiation Chemistry and Tech., Am. Phys. Soc.; Am. Nuclear Soc. (Radiation Industry award 1975); mem. Am. Chem. Soc., Sigma Xi. Home: 320 Sisson St Silver Spring MD 20902-3149 Office: U Md Dept Materials and Nuclear College Park MD 20742-2115

SILVERMAN, JOSEPH HILLEL, mathematics educator; b. N.Y.C., Mar. 27, 1955; s. Harry and Shirley (Seiner) S.; m. Susan Leslie Greenhaus, June 13, 1976; children: Deborah, Daniel, Jonathan. ScB, Brown U., 1977; MA, Harvard U., 1979, PhD, 1982. Moore instr. MIT, Cambridge, 1982-86; assoc. prof. Boston U., 1986-88; assoc. prof. math. Brown U., Providence, 1988-91, prof., 1991—. Author: Arithmetic of Elliptic Curves, 1986; editor: Arithmetic Geometry, 1987, Rational Points or Elliptic Curves, 1992. Fellow NSF, 1983-86, Sloan fellow Sloan Found., 1987. Mem. Am. Math. Soc. Avocation: bridge. Office: Brown U Dept Math 79 Waterman St Providence RI 02912-9079

SILVERMAN, KENNETH EUGENE, English educator, writer; b. N.Y.C., Feb. 5, 1936; s. Gustave and Bessie (Goldberg) S.; children: Willa Zahava, Ethan Leigh. B.A., Columbia U., 1956, M.A., 1958, Ph.D., 1964. Instr. English U. Wyo., Laramie, 1958-59; preceptor in English Columbia U., N.Y.C., 1962-64; prof. English, co-dir. The Biography Seminar NYU, N.Y.C., 1964—; adv. council Inst. Early Am. History and Culture 1984-87. Author: Timothy Dwight, 1969, A Cultural History of the American Revolution, 1976, The Life and Times of Cotton Mather, 1984, Edgar A. Poe: Mournful and Never-ending Remembrance, 1991; editor: anthology Colonial American Poetry, 1968; compiler: Selected Letters of Cotton Mather, 1976; mem. editorial bd.: Early Am Lit., 1969-72, 77-80, William and Mary Quar., 1984-87, Am. Lit. 1987-90. Recipient Bancroft prize in Am. history, 1985, Pulitzer Prize for biography, 1985, Edgar Allan Poe award Mystery Writers Am., 1992; grantee Bicentennial award NEH, 1972-74, Am. Philos. Soc., 1986, Am. Coun. Learned Socs., 1986; Guggenheim fellow, 1989-90. Mem. MLA (chmn. Early Am. lit. group 1975), Soc. Am. Historians, Am. Antiquarian Soc., PEN Am. Ctr., Authors Guild, Soc. Am. Magicians,. Jewish. Office: NYU Dept English 19 University Pl New York NY 10003-4501

SILVERMAN, LEONARD M., university dean, electrical engineering educator. B.S., Columbia U., 1962, M.S., 1963, Ph.D., 1966. Prof. elec. engring. U. So. Calif., Los Angeles, dean sch. engring. Mem. Nat. Acad. Engring. Office: U So Calif Sch Engring University Pk Los Angeles CA 90089-1450

SILVERMAN, MARYLIN A., advertising agency executive; b. N.Y.C., Mar. 15, 1941; d. Morris George and Sophie (Betesh) Adler; m. Joseph Elias Silverman, May 30, 1965; children: Lisa, Jennifer. BA, Ind. U.-Bloomington, 1962; student Baruch Grad. Sch. Bus., CUNY, 1963-65. Research analyst Compton Advt., N.Y.C., 1962-63; account research supr. Foote, Cone & Belding, N.Y.C., 1963-68; self-employed market research cons., N.Y.C., 1968-78; research group head Ogilvy & Mather, Inc., N.Y.C., 1978-82; sr. v.p., assoc. research dir. Backer Spielvogel Bates, Inc., N.Y.C., 1982-88, exec. dir. strategic planning and internat. rsch., 1989-91, exec. v.p. strategic planning Bates Worldwide, 1991—; cons. Am. Assoc. Advt. Agys., Boys Clubs Am., N.Y.C.; bd. dirs. Women At Risk. Co-author: Marketing Review, 1980. Mem. exec. council Washington Sq. Park Council, 1969-74; mem. exec. bd. Friends Sem. PTA, N.Y.C., 1980-82, Advt. Rsch. Found.,

Children's Research Council Devel. Com.; bd. dirs. Women At Risk. Mem. Am. Mktg. Assn. (chair Effie awards), Women in Communications, Am. Assn. Advt. Agys. (research com.), Grenwich Ho. Potters and Sculptors Assn. Office: Bates Worldwide 405 Lexington Ave New York NY 10174-0094

SILVERMAN, MERVYN F., health science association administrator, consultant. BS cum laude, Washington and Lee U., 1960; MD, Tulane U., 1964; MPH, Harvard U., 1969. Diplomate Am. Bd. Preventive Medicine. Physician Peace Corps, Thailand, 1965-67; regional med. dir. East Asia and the Pacific Peace Corps, Washington, 1967-68; spl. asst. to commr. FDA, Washington, 1969-70; dir. Office of Consumer Affairs, 1970-72; dir. health Wichita (Kans.)-Sedgwick County Dept. Health, 1972-77; med. dir. Planned Parenthood Kans., Wichita, 1976-77; dir. health Dept. Health, San Francisco, 1977-85; health care cons. Mervyn F. Silverman & Assocs., Inc., 1985—; dir. AIDS health svcs. program Robert Wood Johnson Found., 1986-92; pres., nat. spokesperson Am. Found. for AIDS Rsch., 1986—, also bd. dirs.; resident physician Sta. KPIX-TV, San Francisco, 1979-85; dir., prodr., host weekly health program Sta. KMPX Radio, 1980-82; sr. tech. advisor Acad. Ednl. Devel.-AIDSCOM, 1990-92; advisor to pres. Pan Am. AIDS Found., 1991-93, advisor to mayor of San Juan, Puerto Rico, 1991-93; former med. advisor to bd. dirs. Golden Gate chpt. ARC, San Francisco; past vice chmn. Adv. Health Coun., State of Calif.; former assoc. clin. prof. Wichita State U.; assoc. clin. prof. U. Hawaii; adj. assoc. prof. Sch. Pub. Health and Tropical Medicine Tulane U.; adj. prof. Inst. Health Policy Studies, Sch. Medicine, U. Calif., San Francisco; mem. nat. adv. coun. Harvard AIDS Inst.; spkr., presenter in field. Author: (with others) Humanistic Perspectives in Medical Ethics, 1972, What to Do About AIDS, 1986, AIDS and Patient Management: Legal, Ethical and Social Issues, 1986, AIDS: Facts and Issues, 1986, AIDS in Children, Adolescents and Heterosexual Adults: An Interdisciplinary Approach to Prevention, 1988, others; contbg. and consulting editor Modern Medicine Publs., Mpls., 1970-75; contbg. editor Healthline, 1983-85; contbr. articles to profl. jours. Bd. dirs. vice-chmn. U.S.-China Ednl. Inst. Recipient Award for Courageous Leadership, San Francisco Found., Award of Excellence, KAIROS Support for Care Givers, Civic Achievement award Bay Area Non-Partisan Alliance; Wear Found. fellow Wichita State U.; adj. scholar Kans. Newman Coll. Mem. APHA, AMA, Calif. Med. Assn., San Francisco Med. Soc., Omicron Delta Kappa, Delta Omega. Address: 119 Frederick St San Francisco CA 94117*

SILVERMAN, MICHAEL, manufacturing company executive; b. Poland, May 9, 1913; arrived in U.S., 1920; m. Frances Setnor, Aug. 26, 1945; children: Leslie, Evan. Cutting rm. mgr. Rockland (Mass) Sportswear, 1938-58; owner Garmet Cutting Svc., Brockton, Mass., 1958-70; cons. Boston, 1970-73; cutting rm. mgr. Recent Mfg., Miami, 1973-85. Author: The New Breakthrough in Plaid Cutting, 1990, Marker Making Manual, 1955; inventor plaid matching device. Avocations: playing in poker tournament, gag writing (New Yorker, Jay Leno show).

SILVERMAN, MOSES, lawyer; b. Bklyn., Mar. 3, 1948; s. Bernard and Anne Silverman; m. Betty B. Robbins, Jan. 19, 1980; children: Benjamin, Rachel. AB, Colby Coll., 1969; JD, NYU, 1973. Bar: N.Y. 1974, U.S. Dist. Ct. (so. and ea. dists.) N.Y. 1974, U.S. Ct. Appeals (2d cir.) 1974, U.S. Ct. Appeals (D.C. cir.) 1977, U.S. Supreme Ct. 1977, U.S. Ct. Appeals (3d cir.) Appeals (fed. cir.) 1985, U.S. Ct. Appeals (11th cir.), 1986 - . Assoc. Paul, Weiss, Rifkind, Wharton & Garrison, N.Y.C., 1973-81, ptnr., 1981—. Vol. U.S. Peace Corps, Istanbul, Turkey, 1969-70. Mem. ABA, Assn. of Bar of City of N.Y. Home: 1036 Park Ave New York NY 10028-0971 Office: Paul Weiss Rifkind Wharton & Garrison 1285 Ave Of The Americas New York NY 10019-6028

SILVERMAN, PAUL HYMAN, parasitologist, former university official; b. Mpls., Oct. 8, 1924; s. Adolph and Libbie (Idlekope) S.; m. Nancy Josephs, May 20, 1945; children: Daniel Joseph, Claire. Student, U. Minn., 1942-43, 46-47; B.S., Roosevelt U., 1949; M.S. in Biology, Northwestern U., 1951; Ph.D. in Parasitology, U. Liverpool, Eng., 1955, D.Sc., 1968. Research fellow Malaria Research Sta., Hebrew U., Israel, 1951-53; research fellow dept. entomology and parasitology Sch. Tropical Medicine, U. Liverpool, 1953-56; sr. sci. officer dept. parasitology Moredun Inst., Edinburgh, Scotland, 1956-59; head dept. immunoparasitology Allen & Hanbury, Ltd., Ware, Eng., 1960-62; prof. zoology and veterinary pathology and hygiene U. Ill., Urbana, 1963-72; chmn. and head dept. zoology U. Ill., 1963-68; sr. staff mem. Center for Zoonoses Research, 1964; prof. biology, head div. natural scis. Colo. Women's Coll., Denver, 1970-71; prof., chmn. dept. biology, v.p., assoc. provost for rsch. U. N.Mex., 1972-77; provost for research and grad. studies SUNY, Central Adminstrn., Albany, 1977-79; pres. Research Found., SUNY, Albany, 1979-80, U. Maine, Orono, 1980-84; fellow bio. and med. div. Lawrence Berkeley Lab., U. Calif. Berkeley, 1984-86, acting div. head, 1986-87; adj. prof. med. parasitology Sch. Pub. Health U. Calif.-Berkeley, 1986, assoc. lab. dir. for life scis., dir. Donner Lab., 1987-90, dir. Systemwide Biotech. Rsch. and Edn. Program, 1989-90; dir. Beckman's Scientific Affairs, Fullerton, Calif., 1990-93; assoc. chancellor Ctr. for Health Scis., adj. prof. medicine U. Calif., Irvine, 1993—; cons., Commn. Colls. and Univs., North Central Assn. Colls. and Secondary Schs., 1964—; chmn. Commn. on Instns. Higher Edn., 1974-76; Fulbright prof. zoology Australian Nat. U., Canberra, 1969; adjoint prof. biology U. Colo., Boulder, 1970-72; examiner for Western Assn. Schs. and Colls., Accrediting Commn. for Sr. Colls. and Univs., Calif., 1972—; mem. bd. Nat. Council on Postsecondary Accreditation, Washington, 1975-77; faculty apointee Sandia Corp., Dept. Energy, Albuquerque, 1974-81; project dir. research in malaria immunology and vaccination AID, 1965-76; project dir. research in Helminth immunity USPHS, NIH, 1964-72; sr. cons. to Ministry Edn. and Culture, Brasilia, Brazil, 1975—; cons. to U.S. Senator George Mitchell, Maine; adv. on malaria immunology WHO, Geneva, 1967; bd. dirs. Inhalation Toxicology Research Inst., Lovelace Biomed. and Environ. Research Inst., Albuquerque, 1977-84; mem. N.Y. State Gov.'s High Tech. Opportunities Task Force; chmn. research and rev. com. N.Y. State Sci. and Tech. Found.; mem. pres.'s council New Eng. Land Grant Univs.; mem. policies and issues com. Nat. Assn. State Univs. and Land Grant Colls.; bd. advs. Lovelace-Bataan Med. Center, Albuquerque, 1974-77; adv. com. U.S. Army Command and Gen. Staff Coll., Ft. Leavenworth, Kans., 1983-84. Contbr. articles to profl. jours. Chmn. Maine Gov.'s Econ. Devel. Conf.; chmn. research rev. com. N.Y. State Sci. and Tech. Found. Fellow Royal Soc. Tropical Medicine and Hygiene, N.Mex. Acad. Sci.; mem. AAAS, Am. Soc. Parasitologists, Am. Soc. Tropical Medicine and Hygiene, Am. Soc. Immunologists, Brit. Soc. Parasitology (council), Brit. Soc. Immunologists, Soc. Gen. Microbiology, Soc. Protozoologists, Am. Soc. Zoologists, Human Genome Orgn., Am. Inst. Biol. Scis., Sigma Xi, N.Y. Soc. Tropical Medicine, World Acad. Art and Sci., B'nai B'rith, Sigma Xi, Phi Kappa Phi. Office: Univ Calif 501 Administration Bldg Irvine CA 92717

SILVERMAN, RICHARD BRUCE, chemist, biochemist, educator; b. Phila., May 12, 1946; s. Philip and S. Ruth (Simon) S.; m. Barbara Jean Kesner, Jan. 9, 1983; children: Matthew, Margaret, Philip. BS, Pa. State U., 1968; MA, Harvard U., 1972, PhD, 1974. Postdoctoral fellow Brandeis U., Waltham, Mass., 1974-76; asst. prof. Northwestern U., Evanston, Ill., 1976-82, assoc. prof., 1982-86, prof., 1986—, mem. Inst. for Neurosci., 1990—; cons. Procter and Gamble Co., Cin., 1984, Abbott Labs, North Chicago, 1987, Searle R&D, St. Louis, 1988-90, DuPont, 1991, Dow, 1991, Leytig, Voit & Mayer law offices, 1992-93, DowElanco, 1993—, G.D. Searle, 1995—; mem. adv. panel NIH, Bethesda, Md., 1981, 83, 85, 87-91; expert analyst CHEMTRACTS. Mem. editorial bd. Jour. Enzyme Inhibition, 1988—, Archives Biochemistry and Biophysics, 1993—, Jour. Medicinal Chemistry, 1995—, Archiv der Pharmazie-Pharmaceutical and Medicinal Chemistry, 1995—; contbr. articles to profl. jours.; patentee in field. Served with U.S. Army, 1969-71. Mem. adv. bd. Ill. Math. and Sci. Acad., 1988. Recipient Career Devel. award USPHS, 1982-87; DuPont Young Faculty fellow, 1976, Alfred P. Sloan Found. fellow, 1981-85; grantee various govt. and pvt. insts., 1976—. Fellow AAAS, Am. Inst. Chemists; mem. Am. Chem. Soc. (nat. elected nominating com. div. biol. chemistry, treas. divsn. biol. chemistry 1993—), Am. Soc. Biochem. Molecular Biology. Avocations: tennis, family interactions. Office: Northwestern U Dept Chemistry 2145 Sheridan Rd Evanston IL 60208-3113

SILVERMAN, ROBERT JOSEPH, lawyer; b. Mpls., Apr. 4, 1942; s. Maurice and Toby (Goldstein) S.; 1 child, Adam Graham-Silverman; m. Suzanne M. Brown; 1 child, Thomas B. BA, U. Minn., 1964, JD, 1967. Bar: Minn. 1967. Assoc. Dorsey & Whitney, Mpls., 1967-72, ptnr., 1972—; lectr. William Mitchell Coll. Law, St. Paul, 1977-78, Hamline Law Sch., St. Paul, 1990—, Minn. Continuing Legal Edn., Mpls, 1985—. Dir. Courage Ctr., Golden Valley, Minn., 1978-84, 85-95, v.p., 1983-86, pres., 1988-89. With USAR, 1967-73. Mem. ABA, Minn. Bar Assn., Hennepin County Bar Assn. Jewish. Office: Dorsey & Whitney 220 S 6th St Minneapolis MN 55402-4500

SILVERMAN, SAMUEL JOSHUA, lawyer; b. Odessa, Russia, Sept. 25, 1908; came to U.S., 1913; s. Benjamin and Ida (Kagarlitzky) S.; m. Claire Gfroerer, Aug. 21, 1941. Student, NYU, 1925; A.B., Columbia U., 1928, LL.B., 1930. Bar: N.Y. With firm Gilman & Unger, 1930-32, Engelhard, Pollak, Pitcher, Stern & Clarke, 1932-35; asst. corp. counsel N.Y.C. 1938-40; partner firm Paul, Weiss, Rifkind, Wharton & Garrison, N.Y.C., 1946-62; of counsel Paul, Weiss, Rifkind, Wharton & Garrison, 1985—; assoc. justice N.Y. Supreme Ct., 1963-66, 71-75; surrogate N.Y. County, 1967-70; assoc. justice appellate div. N.Y. Supreme Ct., 1976-84, spl. master appellate div., 1st dept., 1985-90, mem., spl. counsel, disciplinary com. 1st judicial dept., 1986—, chmn. adv. com. on judicial ethics, 1987—; lectr. Nat. Coll. State Trial Judges, Boulder, Colo., 1966. Bd. dirs. Univ. Settlement, N.Y.C., 1960-74. Fellow Am. Coll. Trial Lawyers; mem. Assn. Bar City N.Y., Am. Law Inst., N.Y. County Lawyers Assn. Democrat. Home: 210 E 68th St New York NY 10021 Office: 1285 Ave Of The Americas New York NY 10019-6064

SILVERMAN, STANLEY WAYNE, chemical company executive; b. Phila., June 18, 1947; s. Sidney and Ruth (Epstein) S.; m. Ellen J. Seligsohn, June 10, 1970; children: Robert, Eric. BSChemE, Drexel U., 1969, MBA, 1974; postgrad., Harvard U., 1989. Process engr. Atlantic Richfield Co., Phila., 1969-71, PQ Corp., Phila., 1971-74; mgr. oper. planning PQ Corp., Valley Forge, Pa., 1974-76, product mgr., 1976-80, mktg. mgr., 1980-82; nat. sales mgr. PQ Corp., Valley Forge, 1982-84; pres. Nat. Silicates Ltd. subs. PQ Corp., Toronto, Ont., Can., 1984-87; pres. indl. chem. group PQ Corp., Valley Forge, 1987-90, exec. v.p., chief oper. officer, 1990—. Mem. Am. Chem. Soc., Chem. Mktg. Rsch. Assn., Drexel U. Coll. Engring. Adv. Coun., World Affairs Coun. Greater Valley Forge and Phila. Avocations: sailing, jogging, polit. sci. Office: PQ Corp 1200 W Swedesford Rd Berwyn PA 19312

SILVERMAN, STEPHEN MEREDITH, journalist, screenwriter, producer; b. L.A., Nov. 22, 1951; s. Raymond and Shirley (Garfein) S. BA, U. Calif., Irvine, 1973; MS, Columbia U., 1975. Editor-in-chief Coast Mag., L.A., 1975-77; chief entertainment writer N.Y. Post, 1977-88; film critic New Woman Mag., 1986-88; editor-in-chief Hollywood Mag., L.A., 1989-90; adj. prof. Hunter Coll., N.Y.C., 1978, Marymount Manhattan, 1979, Columbia U., 1995; juror Internat. film festivals, Berlin, Edinburgh, 1991. Author: Public Spectacles, 1981, The Fox That Got Away: The Last Days of the Zanuck Dynasty, 1988, David Lean, 1989, Where There's a Will: Who Inherited What and Why, 1991; TV scripwriter: Hot On The Trail: The Search for Love, Sex and Romance in the Old West and the New, TBS, 1993; theatrical librettist/prodr.: Makin' Whoopee! The Love Lyrics of Gus Kahn, 1995. Avocation: global exploring. Office: 30 Lincoln Plz New York NY 10023-7122

SILVERMAN, SYDEL FINFER, anthropologist; b. Chgo., May 20, 1933; d. Joseph and Elizabeth (Bassman) Finfer; m. Mel Silverman, Dec. 27, 1953 (wid. Sept. 1966); children: Eve Rachel, Julie Beth; m. Eric R. Wolf, Mar. 18, 1972. MA, U. Chgo., 1957; PhD, Columbia U., 1963. From lectr. to prof. anthropology Queens Coll., CUNY, Flushing, 1963-75; prof., exec. officer PhD program anthropology Grad. Sch. CUNY, N.Y.C., 1975-86, acting dean of Grad. Sch., 1982-83; pres. Wenner-Gren Found. for Anthropol. Rsch., N.Y.C., 1987—; bd. dirs. Social Sci. Rsch. Coun., N.Y.C., 1984-87. Author: Three Bells of Civilization, 1975; editor: Totems and Teachers, 1981, Inquiry and Debate in the Human Sciences, 1992, Preserving the Anthropological Record, 1995; contbr. articles to profl. jours. Recipient fellowship Am. Coun. Learned Socs., 1986, NEH, 1973-74, NIH, 1960-63, NSF, 1959; grantee Am. Phil. Soc., 1985. Jewish. Office: Wenner-Gren Found 220 Fifth Ave New York NY 10001-7708

SILVERS, EILEEN S., lawyer; b. N.Y.C., Sept. 21, 1948; d. Sidney and Ethel Lynne (Starobin) Swertloff; children: Steven Jay, Sharron Roth. B.A. magna cum laude, SUNY-Buffalo, 1970; J.D., Columbia U., 1975. Bar: N.Y. 1977, U.S. Tax Ct. 1981, U.S. Ct. Claims 1983, D.C., 1984. Assoc., Paul, Weiss, Rifkind, Wharton & Garrison, N.Y.C., 1975-83, ptnr., 1983-94; v.p. taxes Bristol-Myers Squibb Co., N.Y.C., 1994—. Mem. ABA (tax sect. mem. of coms. on Fgn. Activities of U.S. Taxpayers and U.S. Activities of Foreigners and Tax Treaties 1986—), N.Y. State Bar Assn. (chmn. personal income com. tax sect. 1983-85, exec. com. 1982-85, 1990-91), D.C. Bar Assn. Home: 20 Mountain Peak Rd Chappaqua NY 10514-2110 Office: Bristol-Myers Squibb Co 345 Park Ave New York NY 10154-0037

SILVERS, GERALD THOMAS, publishing executive; b. Cin., Aug. 26, 1937; s. Steve Allen and Tina Mae (Roberts) S.; m. Ann Gregory Woodward, July 25, 1964. BA, U. Ky., 1960. Asst. research svcs. mgr. Cin. Enquirer, 1963-72, research svcs. dir. 1972-74, research dir., 1974-90, v.p. mktg. svcs., 1990-94, v.p. market devel., 1994—. Mem. Ky. Devel. Coun., Lexington, 1986—; trustee Neediest Kids of All, 1991—. 1st lt. U.S. Army, 1960-62. Recipient Thomas H. Copeland award of merit, 1991. Mem. U. Ky. Alumni Assn. Cin. Chpt. (pres. 1985), Newspaper Research Council (pres. 1985,86), Internat. Newspaper Market Assn., Am. Mktg. Assn. Presbyterian. Home: 229 Watch Hill Rd Covington KY 41011-1822 Office: Cin Enquirer 312 Elm St Cincinnati OH 45202

SILVERS, ROBERT BENJAMIN, editor; b. Mineola, N.Y., Dec. 31, 1929; s. James J. and Rose (Roden) S. A.B., U. Chgo., 1947; grad., Ecole des Sci. Politiques, Paris, France, 1956. Press sec. to Gov. Bowles of Conn.; 1950; mem. editorial bd. Paris Rev., 1954—; assoc. editor Harper's mag., 1959-63; co-founder, co-editor N.Y. Rev. Books, 1963—. Editor: Writing in America, 1960, Hidden Histories of Science, 1995; co-editor: The First Anthology: 30 Years of The New York Review of Books 1963-93; translator: La Gangrene, 1961; mem. editorial com. Rivista dei Libri, Italy, 1991—. Bd. dirs. Am. Ditchley Found., 1993—. With AUS, 1952-53. Named Chevalier de l'Ordre Nat. du Merite, France, 1988—. Mem. Coun. Fgn. Rels, Century Assn. Club (N.Y.C.), Coffee House Club (N.Y.C.). Office: NY Rev of Books 250 W 57th St New York NY 10107-0001

SILVERS, SALLY, choreographer, performing company executive; b. Greeneville, Tenn., June 19, 1952; d. Herbert Ralston and Sara Elizabeth (Buchanan) S.; life ptnr. Bruce Erroll Andrews. BA in Dance and Polit. Sci., Antioch Coll., 1975. Artistic dir. Sally Silvers & Dancers, N.Y.C., 1980—; mem. faculty Leicester Poly., 1986, 87, 89, summer choreography project Bennington Coll., 1988-92, Chisenhale Dance Space, London, 1989, 91, Am. Dance Festival, Durham, N.C., 1990, 92; guest tchr. European Dance Devel. Ctr., Arnhem, The Netherlands, 1992—. Choreographer: Politics of the Body Microscope of Conduct, 1980, Social Movement, 1981, Connective Tissue, 1981, Less Time You Know Praxis, 1981, Don't No Do And This, 1981, Lack of Entrepreneurial Thrift, 1982, Celluloid Sally and Mr. E, 1982, Mutate, 1982, Being Red Enough, 1982, Disgusting, 1982, Bedtime at the Reformatory, 1982, Eat the Rich, 1982, They Can't Get It in the Shopping Cart, 1982, Blazing Forceps, 1982, And Find Out Why, 1983, Tips for Totalizers, 1983, Choose Your Weapons, 1984, And Find Out Why, 1984, Extend the Wish for Entire, 1985, No Better Way, 1985, Every All Which is Not Us, 1986, Swaps Ego Say So, 1986, Be Careful Now, You Know Squar Melts in Water, 1987, Fact Confected, 1987, Both, Both, 1987, Tizzy Boost, 1988, Moebius, 1988, Whatever Ever, 1989, Get Tough, Sports and Dithertissement, 1989, Flap, 1989, Swan's Crayon, 1989, Fanfare Tripwire, 1990, Harry Meets Sally, 1990, Along the Skid Mark of Recorded History, 1990, Matinee Double-You, 1991, Grand Guignol, 1991, Dash Dash Slang Plural Plus, 1992, The Bubble Cut, 1992, Vigilant Gossage, 1992, Oops Fact, 1992, Small Room, 1993, Exwhyzee, 1993, Elegy, 1993, Now That It Is Now, 1994, Give Em Enough Rope, 1994, Swoon Noir, 1994, Radio Rouge, 1995, Braceletizing, 1995, Hush Comet, 1995m Bite the Pillow, 1995 and others; filmmaker: Little Lieutenant, 1993 (Silver award N.Y. Dance on Camera

Festival; co-author: Resurgant New Writings By Women, 1992; contbr. articles to profl. jours. Grantee Nat. Endowment Arts, 1987, 89, 90, 91, Jerome Found., 1993, Meet the Composer fellow Nat. Endowment Arts, 1988-91; Guggenheim Found. fellow, 1988. Mem. Segue Found. (bd. dirs. Segue Performance Space 1992—), n.Y. Found. Arts. Avocations: reading, writing, art events, costume design. Home: 303 E 8th St # 4F New York NY 10009

SILVERS, WILLYS KENT, geneticist; b. N.Y.C., Jan. 12, 1929; s. Lewis Julian and Miriam Elizabeth (Rosenzweig) S.; m. Abigail M. Adams, Sept. 29, 1956; children: Deborah Elizabeth, Willys Kent. BA, Johns Hopkins U., 1950; PhD, U. Chgo., 1954. Assoc. staff scientist Jackson Lab., Bar Harbor, Maine, 1956-57; assoc. mem. Wistar Inst., Phila., 1957-65; mem. faculty U. Pa. Med. Sch., 1965—; prof. genetics, 1967—; mem. allergy and immunology study sect. NIH, 1962-66, adv. bd. primate rsch. ctrs., 1968-71, com. cancer immunobiology Nat. Cancer Inst., 1974-78, bd. sci. overseers Jackson Lab., Bar Harbor, 1980-89. Author: The Immunobiology of Transplantation, 1971, The Coat Colors of Mice: A Model for Mammalian Gene Action and Interaction, 1979; mem. editorial bd. Transplantation, 1963-71, Jour. Exptl. Zoology, 1965-70, 81-86, Jour. Immunology, 1973-77, Jour. Reticuloendothelial Soc., 1974-77; contbr. articles to profl. jours. Mem. Am. Genetic Assn. (coun. 1980-83, pres. 1983). Home: 210 Millcreek Rd Ardmore PA 19003-1506 Office: U Pa Dept Genetics Sch Medicine Philadelphia PA 19104

SILVERSTEIN, ARTHUR MATTHEW, ophthalmic immunologist, educator, historian; b. N.Y.C., Aug. 6, 1928; s. Sol and Beatrice (Pearl) S.; m. Frances Swimmer, 1950; children—Alison, Mark, Judith. A.B., Ohio State U., 1948, M.Sc., 1951; Ph.D., Rensselaer Poly. Inst., 1954; D.Sc. (hon.), U. Granada, Spain, 1986. Research asst. Sloan Kettering Inst., N.Y.C., 1948-49; biochemist N.Y. Health Research Lab., N.Y.C., 1949-52; sr. biochemist N.Y. Health Research Lab., Albany, 1952-54; chief immunobiology Armed Forces Inst. Pathology, Washington, 1956-64; assoc. prof. Johns Hopkins Sch. Medicine, Balt., 1964-67; prof. Johns Hopkins Sch. Medicine, 1967-89, prof. emeritus, 1989—; cons. NIH, 1963-77. Author: Pure Politics and Impure Science: The Swine Flu Affair, 1981, A History of Immunology, 1989; mem. editorial bd. various sci. jours.; contbr. articles to profl. jours. Served to 1st lt. U.S. Army, 1954-56. Recipient Doyne Meml. medal Oxford Ophthal. Congress, Eng., 1974, Endowed Professorship Ind. Order Odd Fellows, 1964-89; Congl. Sci. fellow Fedn. Am. Socs. Exptl. Biology, 1975-76. Mem. AAAS, Am. Assn. Immunologists, Brit. Soc. Immunology, Assn. Research in Vision and Ophthalmology (trustee 1984-87, pres. 1988), Phi Beta Kappa, Sigma Xi. Home: 2011 Skyline Rd Baltimore MD 21204-6442 Office: Johns Hopkins Inst History Medicine 1900 E Monument St Baltimore MD 21205-2113

SILVERSTEIN, BARBARA ANN, conductor, artistic director; b. Phila., July 24, 1947; d. Charles and Selma (Brenner) S.; m. Bernard J. Taylor II, Aug. 19, 1978. Student Bennington Coll., 1965-67; B.Mus., Phila. Coll. Performing Arts, 1970. Assoc. music dir. Suburban Opera Co., Chester, Pa., 1967-75; asst. condr. Toledo Opera Assn., 1975-76; asst. condr., coach Curtis Inst. Music, Phila., 1973-77; asst. condr. Phila. Lyric Opera, 1971-74, Des Moines Opera Festival, Indianola, Iowa, 1974-78; music dir., condr. Savoy Co., Phila., 1977-80, Miss. Opera, Jackson, 1979-82; artistic dir., condr. Pa. Opera Theater, Phila., 1976-93; guest condr. Anchorage Opera, 1982, Opera Del., Wilmington, 1981, 83, Utah Festival Opera Co., 1993—, Lyric Opera of Kansas City, 1995—. Recipient Alumni award U. of Arts, 1989, Wash. H.S., 1991, Greater Phila. Mem. Am. Fedn. Musicians, Music Fund Soc., Pa. Council on the Arts (adv. panel 1987-90) OPERA Am. (bd. dirs. 1987-93, exec. com. 1988-93). Jewish. Avocations: scuba diving; reading.

SILVERSTEIN, HOWARD ALAN, investment banker; b. N.Y.C., Dec. 31, 1947; s. Samuel and Eleanor Lucille (Lehder) S.; m. Judith R. Goldstein, Aug. 17, 1969 (div. Sept. 1987); children: Rebecca Jill, Kathryn Elizabeth; m. Ruthann Mary Pritchard, Feb. 6, 1988 (div. Aug. 1990); m. Patricia Bleznak, Jan. 24, 1993. B.S. magna cum laude, U. Pa., 1969; postgrad., London Sch. Econs., 1969-70; M.B.A. with high distinction, Harvard U., 1972. With Goldman, Sachs & Co., N.Y.C., 1972—, v.p. investment banking div., 1976-80, gen. ptnr., 1980-94; ltd. ptnr., sr. dir., 1994—; co-head Fin. Instns. Group, N.Y.C., 1987-92, head, 1992-94; past bd. dirs. Hook-SupeRx Inc., Cin., PSWW, Inc., Salt Lake City, Trinity Paper and Plastics Corp., N.Y.C., Underwriters Re Corp., Woodland Hills, Calif.; mem. task force on conceptual framework for fin. acctg. and reporting Fin. Acctg. Stds. Bd., 1978-81; trustee Beth Israel Med. Ctr., N.Y.C., 1995—. Trustee Beth Israel Med. Ctr., N.Y.C., 1995—. Thouron British-Am. exchange fellow, 1969; Loeb Rhoades fellow, 1971; Baker scholar, 1972. Mem. Beta Gamma Sigma. Club: India House (N.Y.C.). Office: Goldman Sachs & Co 85 Broad St New York NY 10004-2434

SILVERSTEIN, JOSEPH HARRY, musician; b. Detroit, Mar. 21, 1932; s. Bernard and Ida (Katz) S.; m. Adrienne Shufro, Apr. 27; children—Bernice, Deborah, Marc. Student Curtis Inst. Music, 1945-50; hon. doctoral degrees Tufts U., 1971, Rhode Island U., 1980, Boston Coll., 1981, New Eng. Conservatory, 1986. Violinist, Houston Symphony Orch., Phila. Orch.; concertmaster Denver Symphony Orch., Boston Symphony Orch.; formerly chmn. string dept. New Eng. Conservatory Music; also chmn. faculty Berkshire Music Sch.; mem. faculty Boston U. Sch. Music, Yale U. Sch. Music; music dir. Boston Symphony Chamber Players, Boston U. Symphony Orch., Chautauqua (N.Y.) Instn., 1987—; interim music dir. Toledo Symphony Orch.; prin. guest condr. Balt. Symphony Orch., 1981; condr. Utah Symphony; mus. dir. Worcester Orch., Mass., until 1987. Recipient Silver medal Queen Elizabeth of Belgium Internat. contest, 1959, Naumberg found. award, 1960; named one of ten outstanding young men, Boston C. of C., 1962. Fellow Am. Acad. Arts and Scis. Office: care Utah Symphony Orch 123 W South Temple Salt Lake City UT 84101-1403*

SILVERSTEIN, LOUIS, art director, designer, editor; b. Bklyn., Oct. 10, 1919; s. Hyman and Yetta (Brodsky) S.; m. Helen Abby Becker, May 23, 1951; children: Jamie Richard (dec.), Anne Leith. B.F.A., Pratt Inst., Bkyln., 1940; M.A. credit, Inst. of Design, Chgo., 1948-50. Art. dir. Denhard & Stewart Advt., N.Y.C., 1942-43, 46-47; art. dir. Amerika (Russian lang. mag. distbn. USSR), Dept. State Publs., N.Y.C., 1947-48; promotion art dir. N.Y. Times, N.Y.C., 1952-67, corporate art dir., 1967-85, asst. mng. editor, 1969-85; cons. art director N.Y.C., 1985—; designer, cons. various newspapers, mags., U.S. and fgn. lectr. Am. Press Inst., Reston, Va., 1978-85; tchr. Sch. Visual Arts, N.Y.C., 1958-59; lectr. in field; bd. dirs. Am. Inst. Graphic Arts, N.Y.C., 1958-59, Soc. Publ. Designers, 1976-78; cons. Toronto Star, 1988—; founder Louis Silverstein Design Assn.; lectr. Ctr. Ind. Journalism, Prague, Czechoslovakia, 1991. Co-author: America's Taste, 1961; editor, art dir.: The Earth Times, 1993-; exhibited in group shows and galleries, 1951—, Am. Fedn. of Arts, 1963, USIA Exhbn., USSR, 1964; designer film strips Am. Fedn. Labor, 1950-52; one man shows include Cooper Union, 1988, U. Montreal, 1988, Walker Art Ctr., Mpls.; author: Newspaper Design for the Times, 1989, for The Hill, 1994; editor: the Earth Times, 1994. Served with USAF, 1943-46. Recipient Spl. Gold award N.Y. Times Op-Ed Page, N.Y. Art Dirs. Club, 1972, Hall of Fame, 1984, Gold Medal Lifetime Achievement award Soc. Publ. Designers, N.Y.C., 1984, Am. Inst. Graphic Arts Design Leadership award, Spl. medal for best design of Am. publs., 1989, Pulitzer prize nominee, 1984, 94, numerous awards Art Dir. Clubs, other profl. groups. Mem. Alliance Graphique Internationale, N.Y. Art Dirs. Club (bd. dirs. 1978-80, 82-84, 86—), Soc. Newspaper Design, Am. Abstract Artists. Jewish. Avocations: tennis; amateur poker. Home: 36 Highland Rd Southampton NY 11968-3612

SILVERSTEIN, SAMUEL CHARLES, cellular biology and physiology educator, researcher; b. N.Y.C., Feb. 11, 1937; s. Paul Robert and Jeanette (Kamen) S.; m. Jo Ann Kleinman, Apr. 2, 1967; children: David Paul, Jennifer Kate. A.B., Dartmouth Coll., 1958; M.D., Albert Einstein Coll. Medicine, 1963. Intern in medicine U. Colo. Med. Center, 1963-64; postdoctoral fellow dept. cell biology Rockefeller U., 1964-67, asst. prof. cellular physiology and immunology, 1968-71, assoc. prof., physician, 1972—; John Dalton prof. physiology Columbia U. Coll. Physicians and Surgeons, N.Y.C., 1983—, chmn. dept., 1983—; asst. resident in medicine Mass. Gen. Hosp., Boston, 1967-68; established investigator Am. Heart Assn., 1972-77; mem. sci. adv. com. Damon Runyon-Walter Winchell Cancer Fund, 1975-79, bd. dirs. cancer rsch. found.; mem. sci. adv. com.

N.Y. Blood Ctr.; cons. Nat. Inst. Allergy and Infectious Diseases, 1977-78, Nat. Inst. Gen. Med. Scis., 1985-89, Am. Heart Assn., 1986-89; mem. coun. Am. Soc. Cell Biology, 1988-92; chmn. Gordon Conf. Lysosomes, 1982; founder, dir. Columbia U. Summer Rsch. Program for Sci. Tchrs.; bd. dirs. Rsch. Am.; adv. coun. to dir. Nat. Inst. Allergy and Infectious Diseases, 1995—. Editor: Transport of Macromolecules in Cellular Systems, 1979; chmn. edtl. bd. Jour. Cell Biology, 1979-82, editor, 1978-89; contbr. articles on sci. policy and mountaineering to mags. Helen Hay Whitney fellow, 1964-67; John Simon Guggenheim fellow, 1994; recipient John Oliver LaGorce medal Nat. Geog. Soc., 1967, Marie Bonazinga Rsch. award, 1984, Soc. Leukocyte Biology, Disting. Alumnus award Albert Einstein Coll. Medicine, 1987. Fellow AAAS, Am. Soc. Microbiology; mem. Am. Soc. Cell Biology, Am. Soc. Clin. Investigation, Am. Assn. Immunologists, Infectious Diseases Soc. Am., Am. Soc. Biological Chemists, Am. Physiological Soc., Practitioners Soc. N.Y., Fedn. Am. Socs. for Exptl. Biology (bd. dirs. 1991—, v.p. 1993-94, pres. 1994-95). Clubs: Am. Alpine (dir. 1963-64, 69-74), Sierra, Explorers. Rsch. and numerous publs. on virology, cell biology, immunology. Home: 110 Riverside Dr New York NY 10024 Office: Columbia U Coll Physicians & Surgeons 630 W 168th St New York NY 10032-3702

SILVERSTEIN, SHELBY (SHEL SILVERSTEIN), author, cartoonist, composer, folksinger; b. Chgo., 1932; 1 daughter. Former corr., cartoonist Stars and Stripes, Pacific area; now cartoonist, writer Playboy Mag., Chgo., 1956—. Author: (books) Now Here's My Plan, 1960, Lafcadio, the Lion Who Shot Back, 1963, Uncle Shelby's ABZ Book, 1961, Giraffe and a Half, The Giving Tree, 1964, A Playboy's Teevee Jeebies, 1963, More Playboy's Teevee Jeebies, 1965, L'Arbe au Grand Coeur, 1973, Now Here's My Plan, 1976, Uncle Shelby's Zoo: Don't Bump the Glump, Where the Sidewalk Ends, 1974, The Missing Piece, 1976, The Missing Piece Meets the Big O, 1981, A Light in the Attic, 1981; co-author: Yhings Change, 1988, The Best American Short Plays 1992-1993: The Theatre Annual Since 1937, 1993; (drawings) Different Dances, 1979, Who Wants a Cheap Rhinoceros, 1964, Uncle Shelby's ABZ, 1985; plays: The Lady or the Tiger, 1981; composer: Comin' After Jinny, Boa Constrictor, A Boy Named Sue, One's On the Way, The Unicorn, So Good to So Bad, Yes, Mr. Rogers, Conch Train Robbery, Freakin' at the Freakers Ball, Where the Side Walk Ends; albums include: Dirty Feet, 1968, Ned Kelly, 1970, Freakin' at the Freakers' Ball, 1972, Sloppy Seconds, 1972, Dr. Hook, 1972, Bobby Bare Sings Lullabys, Legends and Lies, 1973, Drain My Brain, 1980; appeared in film: Who is Harry Kellerman and Why is He Saying Those Terrible Things About Me?, 1971. AUS Japan, Korea, 1950s. Office: Harper Collins Pubs Inc 10 E 53rd St New York NY 10022-5244*

SILVERSTONE, DAVID, advertising executive; b. N.Y.C., Sept. 21, 1932; s. Max and Rose (Orliansky) S.; m. Caroline A. Hill, June 14, 1963; children: Eva Hilary, Joshua David. Grad., Queens Coll., 1954; postgrad., Columbia U., Baruch Sch., UCLA. Sr. research analyst McCann-Erickson Inc., N.Y.C., 1956-63, mgr. media research, 1963-68, v.p., dir. mktg., Dataplan, 1968, supr. mktg. devel., 1972-74, mgr. mktg. planning and research, 1974-77, dir. research, 1977-80, sr. v.p., dir. mktg. planning, 1978-81; founder, dir. Media Info. Svcs., 1969-72; mem. Advt. Agy. Rsch. Dirs. Coun., 1977-82; mem. Queens Coll. Corp. Adv. Bd., 1986—, adj. prof., 1990—. Author: (with D.E. Sexton, Jr.) Understanding the Computer, Marketing Managers Handbook, 1973; contbr. papers and articles for U.S. and fgn. trade and profl. publs.; devel. pioneer system for defining TV mktg. areas, 1968, quantitative rsch. methodology for measuring consumer need states, 1975; participant in devel. industry's 1st computer models for media planning optimization and simulation of consumer media exposure, 1964, consumer lang. of product perceptions, 1978, worldwide study electronic mktg., 1981, global brand tracking system, 1989. Bd. dirs. United Way of Larchmont, 1974-77, Castle Gallery Coll. of New Rochelle, 1984-92; mem. adv. coun. Sch. Gen. Studies, Columbia U., 1991—. Developer of pioneer system for defining television marketing areas (1968), measuring consumer need states (1975), consumer language of product benefits (1978), global studies of business to business marketing (1981) and consumer products (1988). Home: 22 Glenn Rd Larchmont NY 10538-1543

SILVERSTONE, HARRIS J., chemistry educator; b. N.Y.C., Sept. 18, 1939; s. Sidney M. and Estelle (Cohen) S.; m. Ruth C. Federman, 1960; children: Robert, Aron, Nancy, Murray. AB, Harvard U., 1960; PhD, Calif. Inst. Tech., 1964. Asst. prof. Johns Hopkins U., Balt., 1965-68, assoc. prof., 1968-71, prof., 1971—. Contbr. articles to profl. jours. NSF Postdoctoral fellow Yale U., 1964. Mem. Am. Phys. Soc., Am. Chem. Soc., Internat. Soc. Theoretical Chem. Physics. Office: Johns Hopkins U 3400 N Charles St Baltimore MD 21218-2685

SILVERSTONE, LEON MARTIN, pedodontist, cariologist, neuroscientist, educator, researcher; b. London, May 21, 1939; came to U.S., 1976; s. Jack Stanley and Sadie (Osen) S.; m. Susan Petyan, Dec. 20, 1964; children: Samantha, Frances, Mark. Student, Queen Mary Coll., London, 1958-59; L.D.S., U. Leeds, U.K., 1963, B.Ch.D., 1964, D.D.Sc., 1971; L.D.S., Royal Coll. Surgeons, Eng., 1964; Ph.D., U. Bristol, Eng., 1967; postgrad., U. London, 1969-76. House surgeon Leeds Dental Hosp., Eng., 1963-64; research fellow Med. Research Council Unit, Bristol Dental Sch., 1964-67; lectr. in dental surgery U. Bristol, 1967-68; sr. lectr. child dental health Med. Coll., Royal London Hosp., 1969-75; reader in preventive and pediatric dentistry Med. Coll., London Hosp., 1975-76; cons. Royal London Hosp., 1973-76; vis. Lasby prof. Dental Sch. U. Minn., Mpls., 1974-75; prof., head div. cariology Dows Inst. Dental Research, Coll. Dentistry, U. Iowa, Iowa City, 1976-82; assoc. dean for research Dental Sch. U. Colo. Health Scis. Ctr., Denver, 1982-89; dir. Oral Scis. Research Inst. U. Colo. Health Scis. Ctr., 1986-89; biomed. cons., 1990; v.p. R & D The Synaptic Corp., La Jolla, Calif., 1990—; vis. Nicholaysen prof. U. Oslo, 1972; cons. Pan Am. Health Orgn., 1973-85, dental rsch. Va, 1978-85; mem. study sect. and program adv. com. NIH-Nat. Inst. Dental Rsch., 1976-84, chmn. subcom. on dental caries, 1982-83, chmn. program adv. com., 1983-84. Mem. editorial bd. Caries Rsch., 1976-86; contbr. chpts. to books, articles in field to profl. publs. Recipient A.B. Bofors prize in child dental health, 1971, ORCA-ROLEX rsch. prize, 1973, Disting. award in child dental health, 1981; NIH/Nat. Inst. Dental Rsch. grantee, 1976-89. Mem. European Orgn. Caries Research (mem. bd., sci. councillor 1971-83, pres. 1977-79), Internat. Assn. Dental Research (pres. cariology group 1982-83, Disting. Scientist award 1984), Am. Assn. Dental Research (pres. cariology group chpt. 1982-83, chmn. publs. com. 1985-86), Brit. Dental Assn., Internat. Assn. Dentistry for Children (exec. com. 1972-79, jour. editor 1971-79), AAAS, Soc. Exptl. Biology and Medicine, Space Medicine Com., AAUP, Am. Acad. Pedodontics, Omega Kappa Upsilon, Sigma Xi. Office: PO Box 1362 La Jolla CA 92038-1362

SILVERTHORN, ROBERT STERNER, JR., lawyer; b. Oklahoma City, Dec. 22, 1948; s. Robert Sterner and Marilyn I. Silverthorn; m. Mary Russell Cofer, June 26, 1982; children: Robert Sterner III, Christine Elizabeth. BA, Dickinson Coll., 1969; JD, U. Louisville, 1971; postgrad., Nat. Def. U., 1988, U.S. Army War Coll., 1989, 93. Bar: Ky. 1975, U.S. Dist. Ct. (we. dist.) Ky. 1975, U.S. Tax Ct. 1975, U.S. Dist. Ct. (ea. dist.) Ky. 1980, U.S. Dist. Ct. (so. dist.) Tex. 1981, U.S. Dist. Ct. (no. dist.) Ohio 1983, U.S. Dist. Ct. (so. dist.) Ind. 1993, U.S. Supreme Ct. 1983. Pvt. practice, Louisville, 1975; assoc. Pallo White & O'Conner, Louisville, 1975-76, Hargadon Lenihan & Harbolt, Louisville, 1976-82; ptnr. White Diamond & Silverthorn, Louisville, 1982-83; of counsel Nutt & Mayer, Louisville, 1983-91; mng. ptnr. Morris, Silverthorn & Dutton, Louisville, 1991-92, Silverhorn Law Offices, 1993—; commd. 2d lt. U.S. Army, 1970, advanced through grades to col., 1991, comdr. 1st Brigade 100th Divsn., 1993—; bd. dirs. Energy Buyers Svc. Corp., Houston, 1980-85, 92-93, Maroco Leasing, Inc., Louisville; repeat guest radio talk show Ask the Lawyers Sta. WHAS. Pres. Windhurst Acres Homeowners Assn., St. Matthews, Ky., 1981-85. Bd. dirs. Boy Scouts of Am. Cherokee Dist. Decorated Meritorious Svc. medal with 2 oak leaf clusters, Bronze Star with 1 oak leaf cluster, Air medal, Army Commendation medal with 3 oak leaf clusters, Army Achievement medal; recipient Constl. Book award U. Louisville, 1975. Mem. ABA (vice chair litigation, tort ins., litigation com. gen. practice sect.), Ky. Bar Assn., Louisville Bar Assn., Ky. Acad. Trial Attys., Res. Officers Assn., Assn. of Century (pres. 1993—), Assn. U.S. Army, chmn. Louisville Armed Forces Day com. 1986-88, Louisville Area C. of C. (mil. affairs com.), Hurstbourne Country Club, Jefferson Club, Club of Jeffersontown, Ky., Masons, Rotary (pres. 1995—), Delta Theta Phi (dean), Sigma Chi. Methodist. Home: 10400 Edgewater Rd

Louisville KY 40223-3733 Office: Silverthorn Law Offices 455 S 4th Ave Ste 1200 Louisville KY 40202-2512

SILVERTHORNE, MICHAEL JAMES, classics educator; b. Bristol, Eng., Dec. 20, 1941; emigrated to Can., 1966; s. Frederick J. and Freda (Fox) S.; m. Ann Frances O'Malley, Aug. 6, 1966; children: Christopher, Stephen, Katherine. B.A., Oxford U., 1964, B.Litt., 1966, M.A., 1967, D.Phil., 1973. Lectr. McGill U., Montreal, 1966-68; asst. prof. McGill U., 1968-74, assoc. prof. dept. classics, 1974—, chmn. dept., 1981-86, 88-91, 94—. Can. Council fellow, 1969-73; Social Sci. and Humanities Research Council Can. grantee, 1980-83, 92-95. Mem. Classical Assn. Can. (sec. 1991-95), Conf. Social and Polit. Thought. Office: McGill U Classics Dept, 855 Sherbrooke St W, Montreal, PQ Canada H3A 2T7

SILVESTER, PETER PEET, electrical engineer, educator, consultant; b. Jan. 25, 1935; m. Elizabeth Placek. B.S. in Elec. Engring., Carnegie-Mellon U., 1956; M.A.Sc. in Elec. Engring., U. Toronto, 1958; Ph.D. in Elec. Engring., McGill U., 1964. Registered profl. engr., Que. Asst. prof. elec. engring. McGill U., Montreal, Que., Can., 1962-67, assoc. prof., 1967-71, prof., 1971—; fellow commoner Trinity Coll., Cambridge, 198-89. Author: Modern Electromagnetic Fields, 1968, Finite Elements for Electrical Engineers, 1983, 2d edit., 1990, The Unix System Guidebook, 1984, 2d edit., 1988, Computer-Aided Design in Magnetics, 1986, Computer Engineering, 1989, Data Structures for Engineering Software, 1993, Finite Elements for Wave Electromagnetics, 1994. Fellow IEEE, Instn. of Elec. Engrs., Royal Soc. Can.; mem. ACM, N.Y. Acad. Scis. (life). Home: 363 Olivier Ave, Westmount, PQ Canada H3Z 2C8 Office: McGill U, 3480 University St, Montreal, PQ Canada H3A 2A7 also: 76 Lexham Gardens, London W8 5JB, England

SILVESTRI, ALAN ANTHONY, film composer; b. N.Y.C., Mar. 26, 1950; s. Louis and Elizabeth (Clarke) S.; m. Sandra Dee Shue; children: Alexandra, Joseph, James. PhD in Music (hon.), Berklee Coll. Music, Boston, 1995. Film scores include The Doberman Gang, 1972, The Amazing Dobermans, Las Vegas Lady, 1976, Romancing the Stone, 1984, Par ou t'es rentre? On t'as vu sortir, 1984, Fandango, 1984, Cat's Eye, 1984, Back to the Future, 1985 (Grammy award nominations best instrumental composition and best album of original score for a motion picutre, 1985), Summer Rental, 1985, Clan of the Cave Bear, 1986, The Delta Force, 1986, American Anthem, 1986, Flight of the Navigator, 1986, No Mercy, 1986, Critical Condition, 1987, Outrageous Fortune, 1987, Predator, 1987, Overboard, 1987, Who Framed Roger Rabbit?, 1988 (Grammy award nominations best instrumental composition and best album of original score for a motion picutre, 1988), My Stepmother Is an Alien, 1988, Mac and Me, 1988, She's Out of Control, 1989, Downtown, 1989, The Abyss, 1989, Back to the Future II, 1989, Back to the Future III, 1990, Young Guns II, 1990, Predator II, 1990, Soapdish, 1991, Dutch, 1991, Ricohet, 1991, Shattered, 1991, Father of the Bride, 1991, Ferngully: The Last Rainforest, 1992, Death Becomes Her, 1992, Stop! Or My Mom Will Shoot, 1992, The Bodyguard, 1992, Cop and a Half, 1993, Sidekicks, 1993, Super Mario Bros., 1993, Judgment Night, 1993, Grumpy Old Men, 1993, Clean Slate, 1994, I Love Trouble, 1994, Blown Away, 1994, Forrest Gump, 1994 (Academy award nomination best original score 1994, Grammy award nomination best instrumental performance 1994, Golden Globe award nomination best original score 1994), Richie Rich, 1994, The Quick and the Dead, 1994; TV themes include CHiPs, 1978-83, Manimal, 1983. Recipient ACE award Nat. Acad. Cable Programming for Tales from the Crypt - All Through the House, 1990, Saturn award Acad. Arts and Sci. for fantasy and horror film, 1987. Mem. Nat. Acad. Recording Arts and Scis., Acad. Motion Picture Arts and Scis.

SILVESTRI, PHILIP SALVATORE, lawyer; b. San Francisco, Nov. 10, 1944; s. Philip and Olga (Difilipo) S.; m. Dianne Loveland, June 22, 1968; children: Lauren, Steven, Karin. BA, U. San Francisco, 1966, JD, 1969. Bar: Calif. 1969; cert. family law specialist State Bar Calif. Assoc. Goth, Dennis & Aaron, Redwood City, Calif., 1969-84; ptnr. Goth, Aaron & Silvestri, Redwood City, 1984-87, Goth & Silvestri, A.P.C., Redwood City, 1987—. With N.G., 1969-75. Republican. Avocations: weight training, running. Office: Goth & Silvestri APC 1000 Marshall St Ste B Redwood City CA 94063

SILVESTRO, CLEMENT MARIO, museum director, historian; b. New Haven, Sept. 9, 1924; s. Joseph and Rose (Griego) S.; m. Betty C. Mack, June 26, 1950; 1 dau., Elizabeth J. Silvestro Casner. B.S., Central Conn. State Coll., 1949; M.S., U. Wis., 1951; Ph.D., 1959. Asst. to dir. Wis. Hist. Soc., 1956-57; dir. Am. Assn. State and Local History, 1957-64; editor History News, 1957-64; assoc. dir. Chgo. Hist. Soc., 1964-65, dir., 1965-74, sec., 1970-74; dir. Mus. of Our Nat. Heritage, Lexington, Mass., 1974-92; mem. exec. com. Am. Assn. Museums, 1965-71, v.p. 1966-71; vis. lectr. Northeastern U., 1983-85. Co-author: A Decade of Collecting: Maps, 1985. Mem. Chgo. Archtl. and Landmark Com., 1968-74; mem. Ill. Historic Sites Adv. Council, 1970-74, U.S. ICOM, Nat. Com., 1970-74; chmn. Pres.'s Adv. Council on Historic Preservation, 1974-77; mem. adv. bd. Eleutherian Mills-Hagley Found., 1973-76; U.S. rep. to UNESCO Internat. Adv. Com. to Safeguard City of Venice, 1975; trustee U.S. Capitol Hist. Soc.; trustee, pres. Fruitlands Mus., 1982-85. Served with USAAF, 1943-45. Decorated Air medal with oak leaf clusters. Mem. Am. Assn. Mus., Orgn. Am Historians (chmn. hist. sites com. 1973-78), Chgo. Hist. Soc., Colonial Soc. Mass., Bostonian Soc., Mass. Hist. Soc. (resident), Union Club Boston, Masons. Home: PO Box 502638 Saint Thomas VI 00805-2638 also: PO Box 119 Hancock ME 04640

SILVESTRO, JOHN PAT, hospital administrator; b. July 6, 1946; married; 2 children. BS in Biology, St. John's U., Jamaica, N.Y., 1967; MS in Bacteriology, Wagner Coll., S.I., N.Y., 1970; MS in Health Care Adminstrn., Columbia U., 1973. Lic. nursing home adminstr., N.Y. Asst. adminstr. Bklyn. Hosp. at Bklyn./Caledonia Med. Ctr., 1973-76; assoc. adminstr. Long Beach (N.Y.) Meml. Hosp., 1976-82; assoc. exec. dir. City Hosp. Ctr. at Elmhurst, N.Y., 1982-87; v.p. St. Francis Hosp., Roslyn, N.Y., 1987—. Bd. dirs. Nassau-Suffolk chpt. Am. Heart Assn., chmn. N.Y. State human resources com. Fellow Am. Coll. Healthcare Execs.; mem. Am. Hosp. Assn., Nassau-Suffolk Health Care Assocs., Alumni Assn. Columbia U. Sch. Pub. Health. Home: 15 Langley Ln Old Westbury NY 11568 Office: St Francis Hospital 100 Port Washington Blvd Roslyn NY 11576

SILVEY, ANITA LYNNE, editor; b. Bridgeport, Conn., Sept. 3, 1947; d. John Oscar and Juanita Lucille (McKitrick) S.; m. Bill Clark, 1988. BS in Edn., Ind. U., 1965-69; MA in Comm. Arts, U. Wis., 1970. Editorial asst. children's book dept. Little Brown and Co., Boston, 1970-71; asst. editor Horn Book Mag., Boston, 1975-76; mng. editor, founder New Boston Rev., 1975-76; mktg. mgr. children's books, libr. svcs. mgr. trade divsn. Houghton Mifflin, Boston, 1976-84; editor-in-chief Horn Book Mag., Boston, 1985—. Editor: Children's Books and Their Creators, 1995; contbr. articles to profl. jours. Named one of 70 Women Who Have Made a Difference, Women's Nat. Book Assn., 1987. Mem. ALA (chmn. children's librs., Laura Ingalls Wilder award 1987-89), Internat. Reading Assn. (mem. IRA Book award com. 1985-87), Assn. Am. Pubs. (libr. com.), New England Round Table (chmn. 1978-79). Office: Horn Book Mag 11 Beacon St Boston MA 02108-3001

SILVIUS, DONALD JOE, educational consultant; b. Kingman, Kans., July 30, 1932; s. Henry Edgar and Gladys Mae (Beaty) S.; m. Jean Anne Able, Aug. 30, 1951; children: Laurie Dawn Silvius Gustin, Steven Craig, Jonathan Mark, Brian James. Student So. Calif. Coll., 1949-52; AA, Bakersfield Coll., 1962; BA, Fresno State Coll., 1963, MA, 1968. Radio/TV announcer, musician, music arranger and copyist, life ins. underwriter, other positions, 1953-62; jr. high sch. English tchr., elem. and jr. high counselor, child welfare, attendance and guidance supr., supr. pupil personnel svcs. Standard Sch. Dist., Oildale, Calif., 1963-92; ret. 1992; edn., guidance and computer cons., 1992—; tchr. counseling/guidance and spl. edn. various colls. Recipient Standard PTA-Hon. Service award, Bakersfield "Up With People" Appreciation award, Golden Apple Service award Standard Sch. Dist. Tchrs. Assn., Innovations award Calif. Tchrs. Assn., Hon. Service award Kern chpt.

Calif. Assn. Sch. Psychologists, Outstanding Ednl. Leader award West Kern chpt. Assn. Calif. Sch. Adminstrs., 1977-78, 7th Dist. PTA-Silver Service award, Continuing Service award Highland-Wingland PTA, Outstanding Community Service for Developmentally Disabled award. Mem. NEA, Calif. Tchrs. Assn., North of the River C. of C., Calif. Assn. Supervision of Child Welfare and Attendance, Assn. Calif. Sch. Adminstrs., Am. Assn. Curriculum Devel., Am. Assn. Counseling and Devel., ACES, ASCD, AMECD, ARVIC, Mental Health Assn. (Calif. exec. bd.), Assn. Kern County, Mensa, PTA, Calif. Assn. Counseling and Devel., CACES, CACAE, CAMECD, CARVIC, Oildale Lions Club, Phi Delta Kappa

SILVOSO, JOSEPH ANTON, accounting educator; b. Benld, Ill., Sept. 15, 1917; s. Biagio and Camilla (Audo) S.; m. Wilda Lucille Miller, Nov. 16, 1942; children: Joseph A., Gerald R. EdB, Ill. State U., 1941; AM, U. Mo., 1947, PhD, 1951. CPA, Mo., Kans. Instr. U. Mo., 1947-48, 50-51; asst. U. Ill., 1948-49; staff acct/ Deloitte Touche (and predecessor, CPAs), Kansas City, Mo., 1951-55; ednl. dir. Deloitte Touche (and predecessor, CPAs), Detroit, 1956; assoc. prof. accountancy U. Mo., Columbia, 1955-58, prof., 1958-88, prof. emeritus, 1988—, sesquicentennial prof. accountancy, 1990—, Peat Marwick Mitchell prof. profl. acctg., 1978-88, chmn. dept. accountancy, 1964-75; dir. Sch. Accountancy, 1975-79; cons. in field, 1956-94. Author: Auditing, 1965, Illustrative Auditing, 1965, Audit Case, 1966. Chmn. Joint Adv. Council Accounting, 1962-64. Served with USAAF, 1942-45. Recipient Shutz Teaching award U. Mo., 1985; Fedn. Sch. Accountancy Faculty Award of Merit renamed FSA Joseph A. Silvoso Faculty Award of Merit in his honor, 1989; established chairs in the sch. of accountancy, specifically the KPMG Peat Marwick/Joseph A. Silvoso Disting. prof., 1992, The Price Waterhouse/Joseph A. Silvoso Disting. prof., 1993, The Joseph A. Silvoso Disting. dir., 1993, The Arthur Andersen/Joseph A. Silvoso Disting. prof., 1994. Mem. Am. Acctg. Assn. (chmn. membership com. Mo. 1956-58, nat. chmn. accounting careers com. 1961-63, sec. treas. 1971-73, pres.-elect 1979-80, pres. 1980-81), Am. Inst. C.P.A.s (contbg. editor jour. 1958-61, editorial bd. 1970-72, mem. council 1981-86, bd. dirs. 1983-86, Outstanding Acctg. Educator award 1986, Disting. Service award 1986, nominations com. 1988-89), Mo. Soc. C.P.A.s (chmn. acctg. careers com. 1966-67, dir., sec. ednl. found. 1968-70, bd. dirs. 1983-86, Max Myers Disting. Service Award 1984), Central States Conf. C.P.A.s (treas. 1975, sec. 1976, v.p. 1977, pres. 1978), Fedn. Schs. Accountancy (dir. 1977-78, v.p./pres.-elect 1981-82, pres. 1982-83), Nat. Assn. Accts., Inst. Internal Auditors, Fin. Exec. Inst., Midwest Econs. Assn., Delta Sigma Pi, Beta Gamma Sigma, Alpha Pi Zeta, Beta Alpha Psi (named Nat. Acad. Accountant of Yr. 1977). Methodist. Avocations: exercise, reading, gardening. Home: 818 Greenwood Ct Columbia MO 65203-2841 Office: U Mo 312 Sch Accountancy Columbia MO 65211

SILYE, JIM, member of Canadian House of Commons. M.P. Ho. of Commons, Ottawa, Ont., Can.; caucus coord. Reform Party, Can. Office: Hoise of Commons, 111 Wellington St PO Box 1103, Ottawa, ON Canada K1A 0A6*

SIM, CRAIG STEPHEN, investment banker; b. Bklyn., Apr. 23, 1942; s. William Henry Craig and Lenore (Overton) S.; m. Susan Hart; children: Brandon Craig William, Stephanie Brooke. BA, Gettysburg Coll., 1965. Account exec. Francis I. duPont & Co., N.Y.C., 1969-72; v.p. E.F. Hutton & Co., N.Y.C., 1972-75; sr. v.p. Donaldson, Lufkin & Jenrette, N.Y.C., 1975-83; exec. v.p. Shearson Am. Express, N.Y.C., 1983-84; mng. dir. Donaldson, Lufkin & Jenrette, N.Y.C., 1984—. Served to capt. USMC, 1965-69. Mem. Bond Club N.Y. (gov. 19779-80, 84-85, 90-93), Lawrence Beach Club, The Leash, India House, St. Andrew's Soc. (N.Y.C.), L.I. Wyandanch Club, Seawanhaka Corinthian Yacht Club, Army and Navy Club (Washington). Office: Donaldson Lufkin & Jenrette Securities Corp 140 Broadway Fl 34 New York NY 10005-1101

SIM, ROBERT WILSON, accountant; b. Three Rivers, Quebec, Can., June 10, 1944; came to U.S., 1955; s. James Wilson and Winnifred May (Stephenson) S.; m. Maureen Ann McCune, Mar. 28, 1970; children: Patricia Marie, Catherine Ann, Jennifer May. BSBA, U. Fla., 1966. CPA, Fla., Mo. Staff acct. Arnold and Co., Sarasota, Fla., 1964-66; audit supr. Ernst and Ernst, Atlanta, 1968-74; audit mgr. Tornwall, Lang and Lee, St. Petersburg, Fla., 1974-76; ptnr. Grant Thornton, St. Petersburg, Fla., 1976-80, Kansas City, Mo., 1980-85, Miami/Ft. Lauderdale, Fla., 1985-90; owner, practitioner Robert W. Sim, CPA, Hollywood, Fla., 1990—. Treas. Mental Health Assn. Pinellas County, Inc., St. Petersburg, 1976-80; sec./treas. Suncoast Rotary Club St. Petersburg, 1976-80; organizer Chinese/Am. Soc. Kansas City, 1983-85. With U.S. Army, 1966-68. Recipient Cert. of Appreciation, St. Petersburg C. of C., 1975, Univ. Fla., 1992; plaque CPA Club Miami, 1990, Youth Orch. Fla., 1992. Mem. Fla. Inst. CPAs (chmn. com. on Univ. Fla. Acctg. Conf. 1993), Women in Distress of Broward County, Inc. (fund raising com. 1992, vol. cons. 1975-80), Miami Fin. Group. Republican. Presbyterian. Avocations: golf, travel/camping, weight lifting, car buff, spectator sports. Office: Robert W Sim CPA 6565 Taft St Ste 211 Hollywood FL 33024

SIMAAN, MARWAN A., electrical engineering educator; b. July 23, 1946; m. Rita Simaan. MSEE, U. Pitts., 1970; PhD in Elec. Engring., U. Ill., 1972. Registered profl. engr., Pa. Rsch. engr. Shell Devel. Co., Houston, 1974-76; assoc. prof. elec. engring. U. Pitts., 1976-85, prof., 1985-89, Bell of Pa./Bell Atlantic prof., 1989—, chmn. dept. elec. engring., 1991—; cons. Gulf Rsch. and Tech., Pitts., 1979-85, ALCOA, Pitts., 1986-89. Editor: Vertical Seismic Profiles, 1984, Two-dimensional Transforms, 1985, Artificial Intelligence in Petroleum Exploration, 1989, Expert Systems in Exploration, 1991, (series) Advances in Geophysical Signal Processing; co-editor jour. Multidimensional Systems and Signal Processing; contbr. over 200 articles on signal processing and control to profl. jours. Grantee NSF, ONR, Ben Franklin, Gulf, ALCOA. Fellow IEEE (Best Paper award 1985); mem. Soc. Exploration Geophysics, Am. Assn. Artificial Intelligence, Eta Kappa Nu, Sigma Xi (Best Paper award ALCOA chpt. 1988). Achievements include patent in application of signal processing technology in aluminum manufacturing. Office: Univ Pitts Dept Elec Engring Pittsburgh PA 15261

SIMANDLE, JEROME B., federal judge; b. Binghamton, N.Y., Apr. 29, 1949; s. Paul R. Sr. and Mary F. Simandle; married; children: Roy C., Liza Jane. BSE magna cum laude, Princeton U., 1971; JD, U. Pa., 1976; diploma in Social Scis., U. Stockholm, 1974-75. Bar: Pa. 1977, N.J. 1978. Law clk. to Hon. John F. Gerry U.S. Dist. Ct., N.J., 1976-78; asst. U.S. atty. Dist. N.J., 1978-83; U.S. magistrate judge U.S. Dist. Ct., N.J., 1983-92, judge, 1992—. Internat. grad. fellow Rotary Found., 1974-75. Fellow Am. Bar Found.; mem. ABA, N.J. Bar Assn., U.S. Dist. Ct. N.J. (lawyers adv com. 1984—) Jud. Conf. U.S. (ct. adminstrn. case mgmt. com. 1991—), Camden Inn of Ct. (master 1987—, program chmn. 1990-93). Office: US Dist Ct US Courthouse One John F Gerry Plz Camden NJ 08101-0888

SIMBRO, WILLIAM CHARLES, journalist; b. Eldon, Iowa, Mar. 9, 1933; s. Elmer Leroy and Miriam Edna (Sheldon) S.; m. Shirley Jo Taylor Hunt, Jan. 18, 1976 (div. Apr. 1990); children: Robert Paul, David William. BA, William Penn Coll., 1956; MDiv, Garrett-Evang. Theol. Sem., 1961; postgrad., U. Iowa, 1958-59, 65-66. Ordained to ministry Meth. Ch., 1962. Pastor Ainsworth (Iowa) Meth. Ch., 1960-64, Coralville (Iowa) Meth. Ch., 1964-66; reporter Cedar Rapids (Iowa) Gazette, 1966-67; chief Cedar Rapids bur. The Des Moines Register, 1967-76, religion writer, 1976—; cons. Rockefeller Found., N.Y.C., 1980. Contbr. articles to profl. jours. Bd. dirs. Moingona coun. Girl Scouts U.S., 1994—. Recipient Faith and Freedom award Religious Heritage Am., 1990. Mem. Religion Newswriters Assn. (treas. 1980-82, Supple Meml. award 1978). Avocations: power walking, traveling, radio reading to the blind. Office: The Des Moines Register 715 Locust St Des Moines IA 50309-3724

SIMCHAK, MATTHEW STEPHEN, lawyer; b. Washington, Sept. 29, 1947; s. Matt Szymczak and Morag (MacLeod) Simchak; m. Jane Flues, Aug. 28, 1971; children: Thomas, Philip, Stephen. BA in History, Trinity Coll., 1969; JD, U. Va., 1972. Bar: D.C. 1973, Mass. 1985. Assoc. Sellers, Conner & Cuneo, Washington, 1972-74; from assoc. to ptnr. Pettit & Martin, San Francisco and Washington, 1974-84; ptnr. Ropes & Gray, Boston and Washington, 1984-93, Wiley, Rein & Fielding, Washington, 1993—; instr. govt. contract law continuing legal edn. program D.C. Bar, 1984; advisor Fed. Contracts Report Bur. Nat. Affairs, 1984-93. Trustee, chmn. St.

Albans Sch., Washington, 1978-83, 92—, chmn. capital campaign, 1993—; fundraiser for Al Gore, 1983, 88, 94; mem. Clinton/Gore Transition, 1992-93; mem. Chpt. of Protestant Episcopal Cathedral Found. D.C. Mem. ABA (pub. contract sect., editor-in-chief Pub. Contract Law Jour., 1982-94), D.C. Bar Assn. (steering com. 1983—). Democrat. Episcopalian. Club: Metropolitan (Washington). Home: 3719 Morrison St NW Washington DC 20015-1733 Office: Wiley Rein & Fielding 1776 K St NW Washington DC 20006-2304

SIMCHES, SEYMOUR OLIVER, language educator; b. Boston, Sept. 22, 1919; s. Meyer and Rebecca (Nadell) S.; m. Marcia Harriet Goldberg, Sept. 13, 1953; children: Judith Ellen, Jonathan David. A.B., Boston U., 1941; M.A., Harvard U., 1942, Ph.D., 1950. Teaching fellow Romance langs. Harvard U., 1947-50; resident tutor Adams Ho., Harvard, 1947-53; instr. Harvard U., 1950-53; asst. prof. Amherst Coll., 1953-54; mem. faculty Tufts U., 1954-90, chmn. dept. Romance langs. 1958-70, John Wade prof. modern langs., 1962-90, John Wade prof. emeritus, 1990—, co-founder, bd. dirs. Tufts Exptl. Coll., 1964-68; dir. Tufts Coll. Within, 1971-74, Center for European Studies, 1978-83; founding dir. Tufts European Center, 1983—; Mem. Mass. Adv. Com. Fgn. Langs., 1961—; cons. U.S. Office Edn., 1964; dir. Fgn. Lang. Insts., NDEA, 1960-62, 65; mem. bd. examiners advanced placement Coll. Entrance Exam. Bd., 1968—; mem. Mass. Adv. Bd. Non-Traditional Edn. Author: (with H.H. Golden) Modern French Literature and Language: A Bibliography of Homage Studies, 1956, Modern Iberian Literature and Language: A Bibliography of Homage Studies, 1958, Modern Italian Literature and Language: A Bibliography of Homage Studies, 1958, Le Romantisme et le Gout Esthetique du XVIIIème Siecle, 1964, The Theatre of Jacinto Grau, The Mythic Quest in Ionesco's Plays. Served with USAAF, 1942-46. Decorated Medaille Aero., chevalier officier and commandeur Palmes Academiques (France); Sheldon traveling fellow Harvard, 1949. Mem. New Eng. Modern Lang. Assn. (chmn. Eastern Mass. 1955-56), Am. Assn. Tchrs. French (pres. Boston 1958-60), NE Conf. Fgn. Lang. Tchrs. (vice chmn. 1964-65), Modern Lang. Assn., AAUP, Renaissance Soc. Am., Phi Beta Kappa, Phi Sigma Iota (hon.). Home: 5 Burbank Rd Medford MA 02155-2928

SIMCOX, CRAIG DENNIS, aeronautical engineer; b. Iowa Falls, Iowa, Sept. 18, 1939; s. Clair Mock and Alice Mae (Shane) S.; m. Molly A. H. Simcox, Aug. 4, 1961; 1 child, Vichi Rae Simcox Smokoff. BS in Aero. Engring., Iowa State U., 1962; MS in Aero. and Astro., Stanford U., 1965; PhD, Purdue U., 1969; postgrad., Columbia U., 1981. Research scientist Ames Research Ctr., NASA, Moffett Field, Calif., 1962-65; instr., cons. Purdue U., West Lafayette, Ind., 1965-68; research mgr. Boeing Comml. Airplanes Co., Renton, Wash., 1969-75; lab. mgr. Boeing Comml. Airplanes Co., Seattle, 1975-85; chief engr. Boeing Comml. Airplanes Co., Everett, Wash., 1985-90; dir. customer svcs. Boeing Comml. Airplanes Co., Seattle, 1990—; chmn. numerous nat. and internat. confs. Assoc. editor Tech. Periodic Jur. Aircraft, 1978-87; contbr. articles to profl. jours. V.p. Somerset Assn., Bellevue, Wash., 1978-80; v.p. civic affairs Boeing Mgmt. Assn., Seattle, 1986-88; pres. Eidelweiss Assn., Bellevue, Wash., 1991-92. Fellow AIAA (chmn. 1976-77, dep. dir. 1978-84, sec. aircraft design tech. com. 1988-91). Mem. Christian Ch. Avocations: skiing, golf, photography, music, boating. Home: 4640 132d Ave SE Bellevue WA 98006 Office: Boeing Comml Airplanes Co PO Box 3707 Seattle WA 98124-2207

SIME, DONALD RAE, business administration educator; b. Los Angeles, July 20, 1926; s. Chester I. and Gaynal (Ramage) S.; m. Patricia Evelyn Hawes, Sept. 4, 1949; children: Julia, Paul, Jill. B.A., Pepperdine Coll., 1949, MA, 1951; BD, Princeton Sem., 1954; PhD, U. Chgo., 1962. Prof. religion Harding Grad. Sch. Harding Coll., 1954-66; prof. dept. religion and psychology Pepperdine Coll., 1966-68, chmn. dept. bus. adminstrn., 1968-69; dean Sch. Bus. and Mgmt. Pepperdine U., 1969-78, v.p., 1973-81, prof., 1978—; cons. orgnl. devel., affirmative action programs Webco, Page Group, Los Angeles Cons. Group, Conceptual Consultants. Contbr. articles to bus. and religious publs. Served with USNR, 1944-46. Home: 20166 Village 20 Camarillo CA 93012-7506

SIMECKA, BETTY JEAN, convention and visitors bureau executive; b. Topeka, Apr. 15, 1935; d. William Bryan and Regina Marie (Rezac) S.; m. Alex Pappas, Jan. 15, 1956 (div. Apr. 1983); 1 child, Alex William. Student, Butler County Community Coll., 1983-85. Freelance writer and photographer L.A., also St. Marys, Kans., 1969-77; co-owner Creative Enterprises, El Dorado, Kans., 1977-83; coord. excursions into history Butler County Community Coll., El Dorado, 1983-84; dir. Hutchinson (Kans.) Conv. & Visitors Bur., 1984-85; dir. mktg. div. Exec. Mgmt., Inc., Wichita, 1985-87; exec. dir. Topeka Conv. and Visitors Bur., 1987-91, pres., chief exec. officer, 1991—; dir. promotion El Dorado Thunderboat Races, 1977-78. Contbr. articles to jours. and mags.; columnist St. Marys Star, 1973-79. Pres. El Dorado Art Assn., 1984; chmn. Santa Fe Trail Bike Assn., Kans., 1988-90; co-dir. St. Marys Summer Track Festival, 1973-81; chmn. spl. events Mulvane Art Mus., 1990, sec., 1991-92, membership chmn., 1993-94; bd. dirs. Topeka Civic Theater, 1991—, co-chmn. spl. events, 1992; Kans. chmn. Russian Festival Com., 1992-93; vice chmn. Kans. Film Commn., 1993-94, chmn., 1994; bd. dirs. Kans. Expoctr. Adv. Bd. Recipient Gov.'s Tourism award, 1993. Mem. Nat. Tour Assn., Sales and Mktg. Execs. (bd. dirs. 1991-92), Internat. Assn. Conv. and Visitors Burs. (co-chmn. rural tourism com. 1994—), Am. Soc. Assn. Execs., Travel Industry Assn. Kans. (membership chmn. 1988-89, sec. 1990, pres. 1991-92, Outstanding Merit award 1994), St. Marys C. of C. (pres. 1975), I-70 (v.p. 1989, pres. 1990), Optimists (social sec. Topeka chpt. 1988-89). Republican. Methodist. AAU record for 100-yard dash, 1974.

SIMERAL, WILLIAM GOODRICH, retired chemical company executive; b. Portland, Oreg., May 22, 1926; s. Claire Cornelius and Geneva B. (Goodrich) S.; m. Elizabeth Louise Ross, June 25, 1949; children: Linda Simeral McGregor, Karen Simeral Schousen, William Goodrich Jr., John David. B.S. in Physics, Franklin and Marshall Coll., Lancaster, Pa., 1948; Ph.D. in Physics, U. Mich., 1953. With E.I. duPont de Nemours and Co., Inc., 1953-87; v.p., gen. mgr. plastics dept. E.I. duPont de Nemours and Co., Inc., Wilmington, Del., 1974-76; v.p., gen. mgr. plastic products and resins dept. E.I. duPont de Nemours and Co., Inc., 1976-77, sr. v.p., dir., mem. exec. com., 1977-81, exec. v.p./dir., mem. exec. com., 1981-87; vice chmn. bd., chief operating officer Conoco Inc., 1984-85. Trustee Franklin and Marshall Coll., 1977—, chmn. bd., 1991-94; trustee, bd. dirs. Wilmington Med. Ctr., 1978-93, chmn. bd., 1982-86; bd. dirs. YMCA Wilmington and New Castle County, 1978-81. Mem. Chem. Mfrs. Assn. (vice chmn. bd. 1980-81, chmn. exec. com. 1981-82, chmn. bd. 1982-83), Am. Phys. Soc., Phi Beta Kappa, Sigma Xi, Wilmington Country Club, Quail Creek Country Club, The Club Pelican Bay.

SIMES, DIMITRI KONSTANTIN, international affairs expert and educator; b. Moscow, Oct. 17, 1947; came to U.S., 1973; s. Konstantin M. and Dina (Kaminsky) S.; m. Anastasia Ryurikov, May 27, 1993. MA, Moscow State U., 1969; PhD, Inst. World Economy and Internat. Relations, Moscow, 1972. Sr. research fellow Ctr. for Strategic and Internat. Studies, Washington, 1973-76, dir. Soviet studies, 1976-80; prof. Soviet studies, exec. dir. Soviet and East European research program Sch. Advanced Internat. Studies, Johns Hopkins U., Washington, 1980-83, lectr., 1983-90; sr. assoc. Carnegie Endowment for Internat. Peace, Washington, 1983-94; pres. Nixon Ctr. for Peace and Freedom, Washington, 1994—; vis. prof. polit. sci. U. Calif., Berkeley, 1982; adj. prof. govt. Columbia U., N.Y.C., 1985, 92; cons. CBS News, N.Y.C., 1985-87, NBC News, 1987—; mem. adv. bd. Ctr. for War, Peace and News Media, N.Y.C., 1986—; commentator Voice of Am., 1990—. Author: Detente and Conflict: Soviet Succession: Leadership in Transition, 1978; columnist Christian Sci. Monitor, Boston, 1983-87, L.A. Times Syndicate, 1987-89, Newsday, 1991—; Moscow News, 1993—; contbr. articles to newspapers and jours. Vice chmn. Fund for Democracy and Devel. Mem. Council on Fgn. Relations, Ctr. for Nat. Policy (nat. adv. bd.). Office: Nixon Ctr Peace and Freedom 1620 Eye St NW Ste 900 Washington DC 20006

SIMIC, CHARLES, English language educator, poet; b. Beograd, Yugoslavia, May 9, 1938; came to U.S., 1954, naturalized, 1971; s. George and Helen (Matijevich) S.; m. Helen Dubin, Oct. 1964; children: Anna, Philip. B.A., NYU, 1967. Editorial asst. Aperture, Quar. of Photography,

N.Y.C., 1966-69; prof. English Calif. State U., Hayward, 1970-73, U. N.H., Durham, 1973—; vis. tchr. Boston U., spring 1975, Columbia U., fall 1979. Author: poems What the Grass Says, 1967, Somewhere Among us a Stone is Taking Notes, 1969, Dismantling the Silence, 1971, White, 1972, Return to a Place Lit by a Glass of Milk, 1974, Biography and a Lament, 1976, Charon's Cosmology, 1977, Classic Ballroom Dances, 1980, Austerities, 1982, Weather Forecast for Utopia and Vicinity, 1983, Selected Poems, 1985, Unending Blues, 1986, The World Doesn't End, 1989 (Pulitzer Prize for poetry 1990), The Book of Gods and Devils, 1990, Hotel Insomnia, 1992, A Wedding in Hell, 1994; prose The Uncertain Certainty, 1985, Wonderful Words, Silent Truth, 1990, The Unemployed Fortune Teller; translator, editor: (with C.W. Truesdale) poems Fire Gardens, 1970, (with Mark Strand) Another Republic, 1976, (with others) Selected Poems of Tomaz Salamun, 1987, RollCall of Mirrors, 1987; translator: Four Modern Yugoslav Poets, 1970, (with P. Kastmiler) Atlantis, 1983; contbr. poems to mags. and anthologies. Served with U.S. Army, 1961-63. Recipient PEN Internat. award for translation, 1970, 80, Edgar Allan Poe award Am. Acad. Poets, 1975, Nat. Inst. Arts and Letters and AAAL award, 1976, Harriet Monroe poetry award U. Chgo., 1980, DiCastignola award Poetry Soc. Am., 1980, Pulitzer prize for poetry, 1990; Guggenheim fellow, 1972-73; Nat. Endowment for Arts fellow, 1974-75, 79-80; Fulbright Travelling fellow, 1982, Ingram Merrill fellow, 1983-84; Mac Arthur fellow, 1984-89. Home: PO Box 192 Strafford NH 03884-0192 Office: U NH Dept English PO Box 192 Strafford NH 03884-0192

SIMINI, JOSEPH PETER, accountant, financial consultant, author, former educator; b. Buffalo, Feb. 15, 1921; s. Paul and Ida (Martino) S.; B.S., St. Bonaventure U., 1940, B.B.A., 1949; M.B.A., U. Calif.-Berkeley, 1957; D.B.A., Western Colo. U., 1981; m. Marcelline McDermott, Oct. 4, 1968. Insp. naval material Bur. Ordnance, Buffalo and Rochester, N.Y., 1941-44; mgr. Paul Simini Bakery, Buffalo, 1946-48; internal auditor DiGiorgio (Fruit) Corp., San Francisco, 1950-51; tax accountant Price Waterhouse & Co., San Francisco, 1953; sr. accountant Richard L. Hanlin, C.P.A., San Francisco, 1953-54; prof. accounting U. San Francisco, 1954-79, emeritus prof., 1983—; mem. rev. bd. Calif. Bd. Accountancy, 1964-68. Mem. council com. Boy Scouts Am., Buffalo, San Francisco, 1942-65, Scouters Key, San Francisco council; bd. dirs. Nat. Italian Am. Found., Washington, 1979—. Served to ensign USNR, 1944-46. Recipient Bacon-McLaughlin medal St. Bonaventure U., 1940, Laurel Key, 1940; Outstanding Tchr. award Coll. Bus. Adminstrn., U. San Francisco, 1973; Disting. Tchr. award U. San Francisco, 1975, Joseph Peter Simini award, 1977. Crown Zellerbach Found. fellow, 1968-69; Gold Medal Associazione Piemontese nel Mondo, Turin, Italy, 1984; decorated Knight Order of Merit, Republic of Italy, 1982. CPA, Calif. Mem. Am. Inst. C.P.A.s, Calif. Soc. C.P.A.s (past chmn. ednl. standards, student relations com. San Francisco chpt.), Inst. of Mgmt. Accts. (past pres. San Francisco chpt.), Am. Acctg. Assn., Am. Mgmt. Assn. (lectr. 1968-78), Am. Arbitration Assn. (comml. arbitrator), Delta Sigma Pi (past pres. San Francisco alumni club), Beta Gamma Sigma. Roman Catholic. Clubs: Serra (past pres. Golden Gate chpt.), Il Cenacolo (past pres.), Toastmasters (past pres. Magic Word). Lodges: K.C., Rotary. Author: Accounting Made Simple, 1967, 2d rev. edit., 1987, Cost Accounting Concepts for Nonfinancial Executives, 1976, Become Wealthy! Using Tax Savings and Real Estate Investments, 1982, Balance Sheet Basics for the Nonfinancial Managers, 1989, Petals of the Rose, 1990, Wealth-Building Basics Letter, 1990. Tech. editor, Accounting Essentials, 1972. Patentee Dial-A-Trig and Verbum Est card game. Home: 977 Duncan St San Francisco CA 94131-1800 Office: PO Box 31420 San Francisco CA 94131-0420 *Personal philosophy: You can succeed! but you must program yourself for success and know what you want.*

SIMIS, THEODORE LUCKEY, investment banker, information technology executive; b. N.Y.C., June 17, 1924; s. Theodore William Ernest and Helen (Luckey) S.; m. Laura Cushman Ingraham, Sept. 8, 1946; children—Nancy Simis Ricca, Theodore Steven, Karen Simis Woods, June Simis Sobocinski. B.S., NYU, 1950, M.B.A., 1952. With Bell System, 1941-79; various positions to officer level with N.Y. Telephone Co., N.J. Telephone Co., and AT&T; v.p. Warner Amex Cable Co., 1980-81; sr. v.p. E.F. Hutton, Sarasota, Fla., 1982-87; vice chmn., bd. dirs. XMX Corp., Burlington, Mass., 1986—; pres. Pvt. Transatlantic Telecommunication System Inc., McLean, Va., 1987-89; chmn. Value Added Network System, Inc., Sarasota, Fla., 1990-91; dir. Liebenzell Mission, Schooleys Mountain, N.J.; vis. Nieman fellow Harvard U., 1977. Mem. Republican Nat. Com., 1981—. 1st lt. U.S. Army, 1942-53, ETO. Mem. N.Y. Acad. Scis., U.S. C. of C., NYU Club. Lutheran. Home: 6025 Manasota Key Rd Englewood FL 34223-9251

SIMITIS, SPIROS, legal educator; b. Athens, Greece, Oct. 19, 1934; s. George and Fanny (Christopoulo) S.; m. Ilse Grubrich, Aug. 3, 1963. JD, U. Marburg, Fed. Republic Germany, 1956. Assoc. prof. U. Frankfurt, Fed. Republic Germany, 1963; prof. U. Frankfurt, 1969, U. Giessen, Fed. Republic Germany, 1964-69; vis. prof. London Sch. Econs., U. Calif.-Berkeley, 1976, U. Pa., 1980, U. Strasbourg, France, 1987-88, Paris, 1990—, Yale U., New Haven, Conn., 1981—; sec. gen. Internat. Civil Status Commn., 1966-80; chmn. Data Protection Experts Com. of the Coun. of Europe, Strasbourg, 1982-86, Hesse Data Protect commr., 1975-91; mem. rsch. coun. European Univ. Inst. Contbr. numerous articles to legal publs. Mem. German Lawyers Assn. (bd. dirs. 1970-82), German Coun. Pvt. Internat. Law. Office: Johann Wolfgang Goethe U, Senckenberganlage 31 Postfach, 111932 60054 Frankfurt am Main Germany

SIMKIN, PETER ANTHONY, physician, educator; b. Morgantown, W.Va., Nov. 22, 1935; s. William Edward and Ruth Helen (Commons) S.; m. Penelope Hart Payson, Aug. 9, 1958; children—Andrew, Caroline, Mary, Elizabeth. B.A., Swarthmore Coll., 1957; M.D., U. Pa., 1961. Intern N.C. Meml. Hosp., Chapel Hill, 1961-62; resident N.C. Meml. Hosp., 1962-63, Univ. Hosps. Cleve., 1965-66; fellow in medicine U. Wash., Seattle, 1966-69; asst. prof. U. Wash., 1969-74, asso. prof., 1974-84, prof., 1984—. Mem. editorial bd.: Arthritis and Rheumatism, 1981-85, BIMR Rheumatology 1980-84; contbr. articles to profl. jours. Mem. Arthritis Wash. chpt. Arthritis Found., 1974-90, chmn. med. and sci. com., 1974-78. Served with U.S. Army, 1963-65. Fellow Am. Coll. Rheumatology; mem. Western Soc. Clin. Research, Am. Fedn. Clin. Investigation, Orthopaedic Research Soc. Quaker. Office: Dept Medicine RG-28 U Wash Seattle WA 98195

SIMKO, JAN, foreign language and English literature educator; b. Zlaté Moravce, Slovakia, Oct. 30, 1920; came to U.S., 1967; s. Simon Simko and Terezia Simkova; m. Libusa Safarikova, Dec. 20, 1950 (div. 1970); children: Jan, Vladimir (dec.). Diploma in English, U. Bratislava, 1942, Diploma in German, 1943, PhD in English, 1944; MPhil, U. London, 1967. Tchr. English and German various bus. schs., 1942-45; asst. depts. English and German U. Bratislava, 1945-46; instr. English Economn U., 1946-47; mem. faculty U. Bratislava, 1950-68, from asst. prof. to assoc. prof. English, 1957-68; prof. English Rio Grande Coll., Ohio, 1968-75; vis. prof. English, scholar-in-residence W.Va. U., Parkersburg, 1989-90; instr. Shakespear Georgetown U., 1982-84; instr. Slovak, Fgn. Svc. Inst., Washington, 1974; examiner critical langs. program Kent (Ohio) State U., 1974-91; feature writer Voice of America, 1983-94; numerous publications. Editor: Lectures in the Circle of Modern Philology, 2 vols., 1965-66; author 3 textbooks, 2 bilingual dictionaries, 1 monograph, numerous articles. With inf. Czecho-Slovak Army, 1946. Brit. Coun. grantee, 1947-49; Folger Shakespeare Libr./ U.S. Dept. State, 1967-68; Internat. Rsch. and Exch. Bd. grantee, 1982, others. Mem. MLA, Slovak Studies Assn., Met. Opera Guild, Soc. for Scis. and Arts, Shakespeare Theatre Guild, Nat. Symphony Orch. Assn. (Washington). Roman Catholic. Avocations: classical music, opera, theatre, fine arts, hiking, swimming. Home: 1356 E Capitol St NE Washington DC 20003

SIMMEL, MARIANNE LENORE, graphic designer; b. Jena, Germany; d. Hans E. and Else R. (Rapp) S. A.B., Smith Coll., 1943; A.M., Harvard U., 1945, PhD, 1949. Diplomate Am. Bd. Examiners Profl. Psychology. Intern psychology Worchester (Mass.) State Hosp., 1943; research asst. Neurol. Lab., Boston Dispensary, Tufts Coll. Med. Sch., Boston, 1943-45; instr. psychology Cambridge (Mass.) Jr. Coll., 1945-46; vol. asst. neurol. unit Childrens Hosp., Harvard Med. Sch., 1945-46; instr. psychology Hofstra Coll., 1946-48; vis. lectr. dept. psychology Wellesley Coll., 1948-49; from instr. to clin. assoc. prof. psychology dept. psychiatry Coll. Medicine, U. Ill., 1950-58; psychophysiologist, head psychol. lab. Ill. State Psychopathic Inst., Chgo., 1952-58; asst. dir. Ill. State Psychopathic Inst., 1952-55; vis. lectr.

med. psychology Duke Med. Sch., 1958-59; spl. research fellow USPHS, NIMH, 1959-61, 69-70; asst. psychologist in neurosurgery Mass. Gen. Hosp., 1959-61, from 63; research assoc. dept. psychology Brandeis U., 1959-61, from assoc. prof. to prof., 1963-78, adj. prof., from 1978, prof. emeritus psychology, 1987—; research assoc. in neurology Mt. Sinai Hosp., N.Y.C., 1961-67; now graphic designer. Contbr. articles to profl. jours.; Editor: The Reach of Mind: Essays in Memory of Kurt Goldstein, 1968. Recipient Research award Am. Rehab. Counseling Assn., 1964. Fellow Am. Psychol. Assn.; mem. Eastern Psychol. Assn., Psychonomic Soc., AAUP, Am. Soc. Aesthetics, Phi Beta Kappa, Sigma Xi. Home: PO Box 562 North Eastham MA 02651-0562 *Methodology is the last refuge of a sterile mind.*

SIMMERMAN, GARY F., bank executive; b. Salem, N.J., July 24, 1934; married; three children. Student, Sch. Pub. Relations N.J. Bankers Assn., Princeton, 1960, U. Va., 1965. Bookkeeping teller Cumberland Nat. Bank (merged with United Jersey Bank), Bridgeton, N.J., 1953-62, asst. cashier to mgr. Installment Loan Dept., 1962-68, v.p., 1968-72, exec. v.p., 1972, pres., chief exec. officer, 1973-86, chmn., pres. and chief exec. officer, 1986; pres., chief exec. officer Cumberland and SW brs. United Jersey Bank, Bridgeton and Cherry Hill, N.J., 1986, United Jersey Bank/South N. Am., Cherry Hill, 1986—. Mem. Exec. Adv. Council Rutgers U., 1987—; bd. dirs. West Jersey Hosp. Found., 1987, Bridgeton Hosp. Assn. Named Bridgeton Outstanding Young Man Bridgeton City Council, 1965, Citizen of Yr. Holly Shores Girl Scout Council, 1987, recipient John A. Cowan Meml. award Nat. Conf. Christians and Jews Bridgeton chpt., 1975, Liberty Bell award Cumberland County Bar Assn., 1982. Mem. Am. Bankers Assn. (banking advisor 1985—), N.J. Bankers Assn. (mem. legis. com. 1985—), South Jersey C. of C. (bd. dirs. 1987—), Bridgeton C. of C. Democrat. Baptist. Avocation: tennis. Office: United Jersey Bank South 1800 Chapel Ave W Cherry Hill NJ 08002-4602

SIMMERMON, JAMES EVERETT, credit bureau executive; b. Arnold, Pa., Mar. 23, 1926; s. Joseph C. and Melba J. (McGeary) S.; m. Lois Bowden, Apr. 19, 1952; children: James, Thomas, John, Lisa, William. BS in Bus. Adminstrn, Ashland (Ohio) U., 1949. Chmn. Collection Service Ctr., New Kensington, Pa., 1955—; mem. adv. bd. Associated Credit Bus., Houston, 1965-73, bd. dirs., 1984—; bd. dirs. Consumer Credit Counseling Svc. of Western Pa., 1975—; vice chmn. Citizens Gen. Enterprises Inc., 1986—. Trustee Ashland (Ohio) U., 1986—; bd. dirs. Citzens Gen. Hosp., New Kensington, Pa., 1972—. With USNR, 1944-46. Mem. Rotary Club of Fox Chapel (past dist. gov. dist 7300, 1982-83). Clubs: Oakmont Country. Home: 302 Fox Chapel Rd Apt 316 Pittsburgh PA 15238-2337

SIMMONDS, JAMES GORDON, mathematician, educator; b. Washington, July 26, 1935; s. James H. and Elisabeth (Welch) S.; m. Monique van den Eynde; children: Robin, Katherine. S.B in Aero. Engring, MIT, 1958, S.M., 1958, Ph.D. in Math, 1965. Aerospace technologist NASA, Langley AFB, 1958; prof. applied math. U. Va., Charlottesville, 1966—. Contbr. articles to sci. jours. Served with USAF, 1959-62. NATO fellow, 1972; NSF grantee, 1972—. Mem. Math. Assn. Am., Am. Soc. Mechanics, ASME, Soc. for Natural Philosophy, Delta Psi. Home: 2116 Morris Rd Charlottesville VA 22903-1723 Office: U Va Inst Applied Math and Mech Thornton Hall Charlottesville VA 22903-2442

SIMMONDS, RAE NICHOLS, musician, educator; b. Lynn, Mass., Feb. 25, 1919; d. Raymond Edward and Abbie Iola (Spinney) Nichols; m. Carter Fillebrown, Jr., June 27, 1941 (div. May 15, 1971); children: Douglas C. (dec.), Richard A., Mary L., Donald E.; m. Ronald John Simmonds, Oct. 9, 1971. AA, Westbrook Coll., Portland, Maine, 1981; B in Music Performance, U. Maine, 1984; MS in Edn., U. So. Maine, 1989; PhD in Edn., Walden U., 1994. Founder, dir. Studio of Music/Children's Studio of Drama, Portsmouth, N.H., 1964-71, Studio of Music, Bromley, Eng., 1971-73, Bromley Children's Theatre, 1971-73, Oughterard Children's Theatre, County Galway, Ireland, 1973-74, Studio of Music, Portland, Maine, 1977—; resident playwright Children's Theatre of Maine, Portland, 1979-81; organist/choir dir. Stevens Ave. Congl. Ch., Portland, 1987—; cons./educator on musical tng. for disabled vets. VA, Portsmouth, N.H., 1966-69; show pianist and organist, mainland U.S.A., 1953-59, Hawaii, 1959-62, Rae Nichols Trio, 1962—; field advisor grad. program Vt. Coll. Norwich U., 1995. Author/composer children's musical: Shamrock Road, 1980 (Blue Stocking award 1980), Glooscap, 1980; author/composer original scripts and music: Cinderella, If I Were a Princess, Beauty and the Beast, Baba Yaga - a Russian Folk Tale, The Journey - Musical Bible Story, The Perfect Gift - a Christmas Legend; original stories set to music include: Heidi, A Little Princess, Tom Sawyer, Jungle Book; compositions include: London Jazz Suite, Bitter Suite, Jazz Suite for Trio, Sea Dream, others. Recipient Am. Theatre Wing Svc. award, 1944, Pease AFB Svc. Club award, 1967, Bumpus award Westbrook Coll., 1980; Nat. Endowment for Arts grantee, 1969-70; Women's Lit. scholar, 1980, Westbrook scholar, 1980-81, Nason scholar, 1983; Kelaniya U. (Colombo, Sri Lanka) rsch. fellow, 1985-86. Mem. Musicians Assn. of Hawaii, Internat. League of Women Composers, Music Tchrs. of Maine, Am. Guild of Organists, Music Tchrs. Nat. Assn., Delta Omicron, Phi Kappa Phi. Democrat. Episcopalian. Avocations: travel, philately. Home: Back Bay Tower 401 Cumberland Ave Apt 1004 Portland ME 04101-2875

SIMMONS, ADELE SMITH, foundation president, former educator; b. Lake Forest, Ill., June 21, 1941; d. Hermon Dunlap and Ellen T. (Thorne) Smith; m. John L. Simmons; children—Ian, Erica, Kevin. BA in Social Studies with honors, Radcliffe Coll., 1963; PhD, Oxford U., Eng., 1969; LHD (hon.), Lake Forest Coll., 1976, Amherst Coll., 1977, Franklin Pierce Coll., 1978, U. Mass., 1978, Alverno Coll., 1982, Marlboro Coll., 1987, Smith Coll., 1988, Mt. Holyoke Coll., 1989, Am. U., 1992, Tufts U., 1994. Asst. prof. Tufts U., Boston, 1969-72; dean Jackson Coll. Medford, Mass., 1970-72; asst. prof. history, dean student affairs Princeton U., N.J., 1972-77; pres. Hampshire Coll., Amherst, Mass., 1977-89, John D. and Catherine T. MacArthur Found., Chgo., 1989—; bd. dirs. Marsh & McLennan, N.Y.C., 1st Chgo. Corp., Synergos, Union of Concerned Scientists; cons. Ford. Found., Stockholm Internat. Peace Rsch. Inst., Radcliffe Coll.; former corr. in Mauritius and Tunisia for N.Y. Times, The Economist; high level adv. bd. UN, 1993—. Co-author: (with Freeman, Dunkle, Blau) Exploitation from 9 to 5: Twentieth Century Fund Task Force Report on Working Women, 1975; author: Modern Mauritius, 1982; contbr. articles on edn. and pub. policy in The N.Y. Times, Christian Sci. Monitor, The Bulletin of Atomic Scientist, Harper's, The Atlantic Monthly and others. Commr. Pres.'s Commn. on World Hunger, Washington, 1978-80, Pres.'s Commn. on Environ. Quality, 1991-92; mem. Commn. Global Governance; trustee Carnegie Found. for Advancement Teaching, 1978-86; trustee Union Concerned Scientists, 1983—; chair Mayor Richard Daily's Youth Devel. Task Force, 1993—. Fellow Am. Acad. Arts and Scis.; mem. Phi Beta Kappa. Office: MacArthur Found 140 S Dearborn St Ste 1100 Chicago IL 60603-5206

SIMMONS, ALAN JAY, electrical engineer, consultant; b. N.Y.C., Oct. 14, 1924; s. George and Cherry (Danzig) S.; m. Mary Marcella Bachhuber, April 12, 1947; children, G. David, Peter A., Michael A.; Philip E., Paul I. BS in Physics and Chemistry, Harvard U., 1945; MSEE, MIT, 1948; PhDEE, U. Md., 1957. Electronic scientist Naval Rsch. Lab., Washington, 1948-57; dir. rsch. TRG Inc., Boston, 1957-65; div. mgr. TRG div. Control Data Corp., Boston, 1965-71; group leader MIT Lincoln Lab., Lexington, 1971-87; cons. Winchester, Mass., 1987—. Contbr. articles to profl. jours.; patentee in field. Mem. Town Dem. Com., Winchester, Mass., 1963. Lt. (j.g.) USN, 1943-46. Fellow IEEE (life); mem. AAAS (life), Antennas and Propagation Soc. (pres. 1986). Avocations: gardening, hiking, tennis, travel. Home and Office: PO Box 207 Center Sandwich NH 03227-0207

SIMMONS, ALAN JOHN, philosophy educator; b. Dover, N.J., May 4, 1950; s. Alan Gleason and Jessie May (Ahrens) S.; m. Jean Claire Dreyfus, Mar. 26, 1969 (div. Aug. 1982); 1 child, Shawn Kathleen Simmons; m. Nancy Ellen Schauber, May 30, 1987. AB summa cum laude, Princeton U., 1972; MA, Cornell U., 1975, PhD, 1977. Asst. prof. philosophy U. Va., Charlottesville, 1976-81, assoc. prof. philosophy, 1981-89, prof. philosophy, 1989—; vis. asst. prof. philosophy Johns Hopkins U., Balt., 1981; cons. FBI, Quantico, Va., 1982-88; vis. Prof. Philosophy U. Hawaii, Manoa, 1990. Author: Moral Principles and Political Obligations, 1979, The Lockean Theory of Rights, 1992, On the Edge of Anarchy, 1993; editor: International

Ethics, 1985, Punishment, 1995; contbr. articles to profl. jours.; editor Philosophy and Pub. Affairs, 1982—. NEH fellow, 1987-88. Mem. Am. Soc. Polit. Legal Philosophy, N. Am. Soc. Social Philosophy (exec. bd. 1983-84), Va. Philosophical Assn., Am. Philosophical Assn., Phi Beta Kappa, Ctr. Advanced Studies. Office: U Va Dept Philosophy 521 Cabell Hall Charlottesville VA 22903-3125

SIMMONS, BILL, newsman; b. Little Rock, Ark., Sept. 23, 1941; s. William F. and Pauline (Hollenberger) S.; m. Jane, Dec. 27, 1962; children: Theodosia Jane, William Tobias. Newsman AP, Little Rock, Ark., 1962-90, chief of bur., 1990—. Author (short stories) Hunter, Negro; also poems. Named Journalist of Yr., U. Ark., Little Rock, 1983. Home: 13803 Alexander Rd Alexander AR 72002 Office: AP Ste 100 10802 Executive Center Dr Little Rock AR 72211

SIMMONS, CAROLINE THOMPSON, civic worker; b. Denver, Aug. 22, 1910; d. Huston and Caroline Margaret (Cordes) Thompson; m. John Farr Simmons, Nov. 11, 1936; children: John Farr (dec.), Huston T., Malcolm M. (dec.). AB, Bryn Mawr Coll., 1931; MA (hon.), Amherst Coll. Chmn. women's com. Corcoran Gallery Art, 1965-66; vice chmn. women's com. Smithsonian Assos., 1969-71; pres. Decatur House Council, 1963-71; mem. bd. Nat. Theatre, 1979-80; trustee Washington Opera, 1955-65; bd. dirs. Fgn. Student Svc. Coun., 1956-79; mem. Washington Home Bd., 1955-60; bd. dirs. Smithsonian Friends of Music, 1977-79; commr. Nat. Mus. Am. Art, 1979-89; mem. Folger com. Folger Shakespeare Libr., 1979-86, trustee emeritus, 1986—; mem. Washington bd. Am. Mus. in Britain, 1970—; bd. dirs. Found. Preservation of Historic Georgetown, 1975-89; trustee Marpat Found., 1987—, Amherst Coll., 1979-81, Dacor-Bacon House Found., Phillips Collection, 1990—, Georgetown Presbyn. Ch., 1989-91; v.p. internat. coun. Mus. Modern Art, N.Y.C., 1964-90, emeritus trustee; bd. dirs. Alliance Francaise. Recipient award for eminent svc. Folger Shakespeare Libr., 1986. Mem. Soc. Women Geographers, Sulgrave Club, Chevy Chase Club. Address: 1508 Dumbarton Rock Ct NW Washington DC 20007-3048

SIMMONS, CHARLES, author; b. N.Y.C., Aug. 17, 1924; s. Charles and Mary (Landrigan) S.; m. Helen Elizabeth Fitzgerald, Feb. 8, 1947 (div.); children: Deirdre, Maud; m. Nancy Nicholas, Sept. 17, 1977 (div.). A.B., Columbia U., 1948. Picture editor Unicorn Press, N.Y.C., 1948-51; mem. staff N.Y. Times, 1951-84, asst. book rev. editor, 1963-84; exec. editor Memories mag., 1988-90; editor-at-large Travel Holiday, 1991-93; contbg. editor Penthouse, 1991-92; author/editor Wordworks, 1993—; vis. writer Am. Acad. in Rome, 1981; regents' lectr. U. Calif. at Santa Barbara, 1981; adj. prof. Sch. Arts, Columbia U., 1981. Author: Powdered Eggs, 1964 (William Faulkner award notable 1st novel), An Old-Fashioned Darling, 1971, Wrinkles, 1978, The Belles Lettres Papers, 1987, also stories, articles lit. criticism; editor: (with Nona Balakian) The Creative Present: Notes on Contemporary American Fiction, 1963, (with Alexander Coleman) All There Is to Know: Readings from the Illustrious 11th Edition of Encyclopaedia Britannica, 1994. Served with AUS, 1943-46. Home: 221 W 82d St New York NY 10024

SIMMONS, CLYDE, professional football player; b. Lanes, S.C., Aug. 4, 1964. Student, Western Carolina. Former defensive end Phila. Eagles, 1986-94; with Ariz. Cardinals, 1994—. Named NFL All-Pro team defensive end, The Sporting News, 1991. Played in Pro Bowl, 1991, 92. Office: Ariz Cardinals PO Box 888 Phoenix AZ 85001-0888*

SIMMONS, DAMIAN, secondary education educator. Teacher Barrington H.S., Barrington, Ill. Recipient Innovative Teaching Grants Program, Am. Assn. of Physics Teachers, 1992. Office: Barrington High Sch 616 Main St Barrington IL 60010

SIMMONS, DAN, science fiction writer; b. 1948. Author: Song of Kali, 1985 (World Fantasy award for best first novel 1985), Phases of Gravity, 1989, Hyperion, 1989 (Hugo award for best novel 1989), The Fall of Hyperion, 1989, Carrion Comfort, 1990 (Bram Stoker award 1990), Prayers to Broken Stones, 1990, Summer of Night, 1991, Children of the Night, 1992, The Hollow Man, 1992, Summer Sketches, 1992, Lovedeath, 1993, Pele's Fire, 1994. Office: care Warner Books Inc 1271 Avenue of the Americas New York NY 10020-1300*

SIMMONS, DEIDRE WARNER, performing company executive; b. Easton, Pa., May 11, 1955; d. Francis Joseph and Irene Carol (Burd) Mooney; m. Robert D. Jacobson, June 27, 1981 (div. Mar. 1989); m. William Richard Simmons, Aug. 18, 1990; children: Caitlin Dawn, Abigail Patricia, Samantha Irene. BA in Music, Montclair State Coll., 1978. Music tchr. Warren Hills Regional Sch., Washington, N.J., 1978-80; devel. dir. N.J. Shakespeare Festival, Madison 1981-83; dir. contbns. Parent Found., Lancaster, Pa., 1983-86; exec. dir. Fulton Opera House, Lancaster, 1986—; capital campaign counsel, 1990—. Vice chmn. bd. dirs. Ind. Eye, Lancaster, 1986-89; mem. adv. com. Lancaster Cultural Coun., 1988—. Mem. Theatre Communications Group, League Hist. Theatres. Avocations: piano, singing. Office: Fulton Opera House 12 N Prince St PO Box 1865 Lancaster PA 17603

SIMMONS, EDWIN HOWARD, marine corps officer, historian; b. Paulsboro, N.J., Aug. 25, 1921; s. Edwin Lonsdale and Nettie Emma (Vankirk) S.; m. Frances Bliss, Apr. 25, 1962; children: Edwin Howard, Clarke Vankirk, Bliss, Courtney. B.A., Lehigh U., 1942; M.A., Ohio State U., 1955; postgrad., Amphibious Warfare Sch., 1949-50, Nat. War Coll., 1966-67. Commd. 2d lt. USMC, 1942, advanced through grades to brig. gen., 1967; asst. prof. NROTC, Ohio State U., 1952-55; with Hdqrs. Marine Corps, 1955- 59; naval attache Dominican Republic, 1959-60; with Hdqrs. Marine Corps and Joint Staff, 1962-65, 3d Marine Div., 1965-66, 1st Marine Div., Vietnam, 1970-71; dep. fiscal dir. Marine Corps, 1967-70; dir. Marine Corps history and museums USMC Hdqrs., Arlington, Va., 1971—; pres. Am. Mil. Inst., 1979; v.p. U.S. Commn. Mil. History, 1979-83, exec. v.p. Marine Corps Hist. Found., 1979-88, pres. Coun. Am.'s Mil. Past, 1991—. Author: The United States Marines, 1974, Marines, 1987; Mng. editor: Marine Corps Gazette, 1946-49; sr. editor: Publs. Group, Marine Corps Schs., 1960-61; Contbr. to numerous books, encys., mags., jours. and annuals. Decorated D.S.M., Silver Star, Legion of Merit with two gold stars, Bronze Star with gold star, Meritorious Service medal, Navy Commendation medal, Purple Heart; knight Nat. Order of Vietnam, Vietnamese Cross of Gallantry with 2 palms and silver star; recipient Centennial Disting. Grad. medallion Ohio State U., 1970. Fellow Co. Mil. Historians; mem. Am. Soc. Mil. Comptrollers (nat. v.p. 1967-69, pres. 1969-70), Nat. War Coll. Alumni Assn. (v.p. 1969-70, 74-75), Phi Beta Kappa, Omicron Delta Kappa, Phi Sigma Kappa. Home: 9020 Charles Augustine Dr Alexandria VA 22308-2822 Office: USMC Mus MC Hist Ctr Navy Yard Bldg 160 Washington DC 20374-0580

SIMMONS, ELROY, JR., retired utility executive; b. Johnstown, Pa., Sept. 23, 1928; s. Elroy and Hazel Maria (Shomo) S. BS in Bus. Adminstrn., U. Pitts., 1951. With Pa. Electric Co., Johnstown, 1953, system treasury asst., 1969-71, system coordinator, treasury services, 1971-74, asst. treas., 1974-79, sec., treas., 1979-90; ret., 1990. Bd. dirs. Community Arts Ctr. of Cambria County, 1987—. With CIC, U.S. Army, 1951-53. Mem. Pa. Electric Assn. (customer relations com. 1965-69), Nat. Corp. Cash Mgmt. Assn., Nat. Assn. Accts., Nat. Assn. Corp. Treas. Republican. Methodist. Home: 1023 Hillside Trl Johnstown PA 15905-1234

SIMMONS, EMORY G., mycologist; b. Ind., Apr. 12, 1920. AB, Wabash Coll., 1941; AM, DePauw U., 1946; PhD in Botany, U. Mich., 1950; DSc in Microbiology (hon.), Kasetsart U., Thailand, 1988. Instr. bacteriology & botany DePauw U., Greencastle, Ind., 1946-47; asst. prof. botany Dartmouth Coll., Hanover, N.H., 1950-53; mycologist U.S. Army Natick Labs., 1953-58, head mycology lab., 1958-74; prin. investor Devel. Ctr. Cult Collection of Fungi, 1974-87; prof. botany U. Mass., Amherst, 1974-77, prof. microbiology, 1977-87, ret., 1987; chmn. adv. com. fungi Am. Type Cult Collection; U.S. rep. Expert Group on Fungus Taxonomy, Org. Econ. Coop. & Devel.; Rsch. fellow Sec. Army, Thailand, Indonesia, 1968-69; adj. prof. U. R.I., 1972-74; mem. exec. bd. U.S Fedn. Cult Collections, 1974-76, pres., 1976-78; pres., chmn. bd. dirs. Second Internat. Mycology Congregation, Inc., 1975-78; mem. adv. com. cult collections UN Environ. Program/UNESCO/In-

ternat. Cell Rsch. Orgn., 1977—. Mem AAAS, Mycological Soc. Am. (sec.-treas. 1963-65, v.p. 1966, pres. 1968, Disting. Mycologist award 1990), Brit. Mycological Soc., Internat. Assn. Plant Taxonomists. Achievements include research in taxonomic mycology, taxonomy of Fungi imperfecti, taxonomy and cultural characteristics of Ascomycetes. Office: 717 Thornwood Rd Crawfordsville IN 47933*

SIMMONS, GENE, musician; b. Haifa, Israel, Aug. 25, 1949; came to U.S., 1958, naturalized, 1963; A.B.A., Sullivan Coll., SUNY, 1970; B.A., Richmond Coll., CUNY, 1972. Singer, songwriter, actor, 1970—; founder, 1973 thereafter mem. group Kiss. Albums include: Alive, 1975, Kiss-The Originals, 1976, Destroyer, 1976, Rock & Roll Over, 1976, Love Gun, 1977, Alive II, 1977, Double Platinum, 1978, Gene Simmons, 1978, Dynasty, 1979, Unmasked, 1980, Music From the Elder, 1981, Creatures of the Night, 1982, Lick It Up, 1983, Animalize, 1984, Kiss, 1974, Hotter Than Hell, 1974, Dressed to Kill, 1975, Beth, 1976, I Was Made for Lovin' You, 1979, Asylum, 1985, Crazy Nights, 1987, Hot In The Shade, 1989, Smashes, Thrashes and Hits, 1989, Revenge, 1992; film appearance in Kiss-Attack of the Phantom, 1978, Runaway, 1984-85. Winner 16 Gold Record Albums, 12 Platinum Record Albums, 2 Gold Single Records. Mem. Am. Fedn. Musicians, AFTRA, ASCAP. Inventor of Axe bass guitar, 1980. Office: care Polygram Records Inc Worldwide Pla 825 8th Ave New York NY 10019-7416 *Listen to everyone around you, but do only what you believe.*

SIMMONS, GEORGE FINLAY, mathematics educator; b. Austin, Tex., Mar. 3, 1925; s. George Finlay and Armede Victoria (Hatcher) S.; m. Hope Bridgeford, Sept. 11, 1954; 1 child, Nancy Bingham. BS, Caltech, 1946; MS, U. Chgo., 1948; PhD, Yale U., 1957. Instr. U. Chgo., 1947-50, U. Maine, Orono, 1950-52, Yale U., New Haven, 1952-56; asst. prof. U. R.I., Kingston, 1956-58, Williams College, Williamstown, Mass., 1958-62; assoc. prof. math. Colo. Coll., Colorado Springs, 1962-65, prof., 1965-90, prof. emeritus, 1990—. Author: Introduction Topology and Modern Analysis, 1962, Differential Equations, 1972, 2d edit., 1991, Precalculus Mathematics in a Nutshell, 1981, Calculus with Analytic Geometry, 1985, 2d edit., 1995, Calculus Gems: Brief Lives and Memorable Mathematics, 1992. Mem. Math. Assn. Am. Avocations: travel, cooking, trout fishing, billiards. Home: 1401 Wood Ave Colorado Springs CO 80907-7348 Office: Colorado College Colorado Springs CO 80903

SIMMONS, GLENN REUBEN, management executive; b. Golden, Tex., Jan. 23, 1928; s. Reuben Leon and Fairess (Clark) S.; B.S., E. Tex. State U., 1950; postgrad. Tex. Christian U.; m. Diane Gee Callaway, Dec. 6, 1975; children—Susan, Martha, D'Andra. Mgmt. positions LTV Corp., 1949-69; v.p. Contran Corp. and affiliates, 1969-80; pres. Nat. City Lines and affiliates, Dallas, 1980-84; pres., chief exec. officer Keystone Consol. Industries, Inc., Dallas, 1982-84, also dir.; chmn., chief exec. officer, dir. Keycon Industries, Inc., 1984—; dir. LLC Corp. Served with U.S. Army, 1946-47. Mem. Am. Iron and Steel Inst. (dir.). Office: Valhi Inc 5430 Lyndon B Johnson Fwy Dallas TX 75240-2601

SIMMONS, HARDWICK, investment banker; b. Balt., June 8, 1940; s. Edward Ball and Margaret (Hardwick) S.; m. Sarah Bradlee Dolan, Sept. 9, 1962; children—Elizabeth, Huntington, Benjamin. B.A., Harvard U., 1962, M.B.A., 1966. With Shearson Lehman Bros. Inc., 1966—; regional officer Shearson Lehman Bros. Inc., New Eng., 1972-75; vice chmn., dir. Shearson Lehman Hutton Inc. (formerly Shearson Lehman Bros. Inc.), N.Y.C., 1975-90; chief exec. officer Prudential Securities Inc., N.Y.C., 1990—; dir. Chgo. Bd. Options Exchange. Served with USMCR, 1959-60. Mem. Bond Club N.Y.C. Republican. Office: Prudential Securities 1 Seaport Plz New York NY 10038

SIMMONS, HAROLD C., sugar company executive; b. 1931. BA, MA, U. Tex., 1952. Investigator U.S. Civil Service, Dallas, 1952-55; book examiner Fed. Deposit Ins. Corp., Dallas, 1955-56; loan officer Republican Nat. Bank, Dallas, 1956-61; with Amalgamated Sugar Corp., Dallas, 1961—; chmn., chief exec. officer, also bd. dirs. Amalgamated Sugar Corp., Ogden, Utah; pres., chief exec. officer, dir. Contran Corp., Dallas; chmn., dir. NL Industries Inc., Houston, 1961—; chmn., chief exec. officer, dir. Valhi, Inc., Dallas; chmn. Nat. City Lines, Dallas. Office: Valhi Inc Three Lincoln Centre 5430 LBJ Frwy Ste 1700 Dallas TX 75240-2697 Office: Amalgamated Sugar Co PO Box 1520 Ogden UT 84402-1520 also: NL Industries Inc 300 N Sam Houston Pkwy E Houston TX 77032*

SIMMONS, HARRIS H., banker; b. Salt Lake City, June 25, 1954; s. Roy William and Elizabeth (Ellison) S. BA in Econs., U. Utah, 1977; MBA, Harvard U., 1980. Comml. loan officer Allied Bancshares, Houston, 1980-81; asst. v.p. Zions Bancorp, Salt Lake City, 1981, fin. v.p., 1981-82; sr. v.p. fin. Zions Utah Bancorp, Salt Lake City, 1982-83, exec. v.p., sec., treas., 1984-86, pres., 1986—; pres. Zions Mortgage Co., 1987—; CEO Zions Bancorp, Salt Lake City, 1990—; pres., CEO Zions 1st Nat. Bank, 1990—; bd. dirs. Questar, Inc., Salt Lake City, Entrada Industries, Inc., Salt Lake City, Keystone Commn., Salt Lake City, S.F.I., Inc., Salt Lake City, Zions 1st Nat. Bank, Salt Lake City, Nat. Bank Ariz., Tucson, Nev. State Bank, Las Vegas. bd. dirs. United Way, Salt Lake City, 1983-89; bd. dirs. Utah Symphony, 1986—, vice chmn., 1990—; Salt Lake C.C., 1991-94; v.p. fin. Great Salt Lake coun. Boy Scouts Am., 1991—; co-chair Greater Salt Lake Shelter-the-Homeless Com., 1986-89. Mem. Utah Bankers Assn. (bd. dirs. 1987—, chmn. 1990-91), Salt Lake Area C. of C. (bd. dirs. 1991—), Phi Beta Kappa. Mem. LDS Ch. Office: Zions Bancorp 1380 Kennecott Building Bldg Salt Lake City UT 84133-1102

SIMMONS, HOWARD ENSIGN, JR., chemist, research administrator; b. Norfolk, Va., June 17, 1929; s. Howard Ensign and Marie Magdalene (Weidenhammer) S.; m. Elizabeth Anne Warren, Sept. 1, 1951; children: Howard Ensign III, John W. BS in Chemistry, MIT, 1951, PhD in Organic Chemistry, 1954; DSc (hon.), Rensselaer Poly. Inst., 1987. Mem. rsch. staff cen. rsch. and devel. dept. E.I. du Pont de Nemours & Co., Wilmington, Del., 1954-59, rsch. supr., 1959-70, assoc. dir. 1970-74, dir. rsch., 1974-79, dir., 1979-83, v.p., 1983-90, v.p., sr. sci. advisor, 1990—; adj. prof. chemistry U. Del., 1974—; Sloan vis. prof. Harvard U., 1968; Kharasch vis. prof. U. Chgo., 1978; mem. Nat. Sci. Bd., 1990. Author: (with R.E. Merrifield) Topological Methods in Chemistry, 1989. Trustee Gordon Rsch. Confs., 1974-77; elected trustee U. Del., 1994. Recipient Chandler medal Columbia U., 1991, Nat. medal of sci. NSF, 1992, Priestley medal, 1994. Fellow N.Y. Acad. Scis., Am. Acad. Arts and Scis.; mem. NAS, AAAS, Soc. Chem. Industry, Am. Chem. Soc., Indsl. Rsch. Inst., Nat. Sci. Bd., Am. Philos. Soc., Delta Kappa Epsilon. Home: PO Box 3874 Wilmington DE 19807-0874 Office: E I du Pont de Nemours & Co 1007 N Market St Wilmington DE 19898

SIMMONS, J. GERALD, management consultant; b. Atlanta, Sept. 17, 1929; s. Joseph D. and Nell (Ray) S.; m. Barbara McNeeley, Apr. 24, 1955 (dec.). BBA, U. Miami, 1956; student advanced mgmt. program, Harvard U., 1969. With IBM Corp., 1956-71; dir. mktg. Data Processing div. IBM Corp., White Plains, N.Y., 1969-71; v.p., gen. mgr. dept. and specialty store div. Revlon Inc., N.Y.C., 1971-73; v.p. mktg. Wiltek Inc., Norwalk, Conn., 1973-76; pres. Handy HRM Corp., N.Y.C., 1976—. With U.S. Army, 1951-54. Mem. Greenwich (Conn.) Country Club. Avocations: tennis, squash, golf. Office: Handy HRM Corp 250 Park Ave New York NY 10177-0074

SIMMONS, JAMES F., textiles executive; b. 1944. BA, Ga. Inst. Tech., 1966, MA, 1967. With Celanese Fibers Mktg. Co., Charlotte, N.C., 1968-90, Celanese Tech. Fibers, Chgo., 1968-90, Hoechst Celanese Textile Fibers Group, N.Y.C., 1968-90; v.p., gen. mgr. Hoechst Celanese Chem. Group, Dallas, 1990—. Office: Hoechst Celanese Chem Group 1601 Lyndon B Johnson Fwy Dallas TX 75234

SIMMONS, JEAN, actress; b. London, Jan. 31, 1929; d. Charles and Winifred Ada (Lovel) S.; m. Stewart Granger, Dec. 20, 1950 (div. June 1960); 1 dau., Tracy; m. Richard Brooks, Nov. 1, 1960; 1 dau., Kate. Ed., Orange Hill Sch., Burnt Oak, London. Motion picture actress, appearing in English and Am. films including Great Expectations, 1946, Black Narcissus, 1947, Hamlet, 1948 (Acad. award nomination), Adam and Evelyn, 1949, The Actress, 1953, Young Bess, 1953, Guys and Dolls, 1956, The Big Country, 1958, Home Before Dark, 1958, Spartacus, 1960, Elmer Gantry, 1960, The

Grass Is Greener, 1960, All the Way Home, 1963, Rough Night in Jericho, 1967, Divorce American Style, 1967, The Happy Ending, 1969 (Acad. award nomination), The Dawning, 1989; also theatre appearance A Little Night Music, Phila. and on tour, 1974; appeared in: TV mini-series The Dain Curse, 1978, A Small Killing, 1981, Valley of the Dolls, 1981, The Thornbirds, 1983 (Emmy award), North and South, 1985, North and South Book II, 1986; TV film: December Flower, 1987, The Legend of Lost Loves, 1988, Great Expectations, 1989; guest TV series Murder She Wrote, 1989, In the Heat of the Night, 1993; TV series Dark Shadows, 1991. Office: care Geoffrey Barr 9400 Readcrest Dr Beverly Hills CA 90210-2552 Office: Susan Smith & Assocs 121 N San Vicente Blvd Beverly Hills CA 90211-2303*

SIMMONS, JEAN ELIZABETH MARGARET (MRS. GLEN R. SIMMONS), chemistry educator; b. Cleve., Jan. 20, 1914; d. Frank Charles and Sarah Anne (Johnston) Saurwein; m. Glen R. Simmons, Nov. 14, 1935; children: Sally Anne, (Frank) Charles, James Fraser. B.A., Western Reserve U., 1933; Ph.D. (Stieglitz fellow 1935-37), U. Chgo., 1938. Faculty Barat Coll., Lake Forest, Ill., 1938-58; prof., chmn. dept chemistry Barat Coll., 1948-58; faculty Upsala Coll., East Orange, N.J., 1959—; prof. Upsala Coll. 1963-84, prof. emeritus, 1984—, chmn. dept. chemistry, 1965-71, 74, 76-81, chmn. sci. curriculum study, Luth. Ch. Am. grantee, 1965-68, chmn. div natural scis. Evang. Hosp. Sch. Nursing, Chgo., 1943-46; lectr. sci. topics; participant various White House Confs. Contbr. articles to publs. in field. Troop leader Girl Scouts U.S.A., Wheaton, Ill., 1952-58, neighborhood chmn., 1956-57, dist. chmn., DuPage County, 1958; chmn. U. Chgo. Alumni Fund Dr., Wheaton, 1957, 58, Princeton, N.J., 1964, 65; mem. nursing adv. com. East Orange (N.J.) Gen. Hosp., 1963-73; pres. Virginia Gildersleeve Internat. Fund, 1975-81, bd. dirs., 1969-83, chmn. nominating com., 1985-87, oral history com., 1981. Recipient Lindback Found. award for disting. teaching, 1964; vis. fellow Princeton U., 1977. Fellow Am. Inst. Chemists, AAAS (council 1969-71); mem. Am. Chem. Soc., AAUW (br. treas. 1960-62, chmn. sci. topic 1963-65, state v.p. program 1964, nat. sci. topic implementation chmn. 1965, 66, state dir. 1967-68, 71-72, state pres. 1968-70, 50 Yr. Cert. 1989), Fedn. Orgns. Profl. Women (nat. pres. 1974-75), Internat. Fedn. Univ. Women (alt. del. for U.S. at conf. 1968, 77, 83, del. conf. 1974, ofcl. observer UN Conf. Vienna 1979, Nairobi 1981, convenor membership com. 1980-84, adv. bd. 1980—, oral history com. 1990), AAUP (charter, past chpt. pres.), Phi Beta Kappa (pres. North Jersey alumni assn. 1973-74), Sigma Xi, Sigma Delta Epsilon (nat. pres. 1970-71, dir. 1972-78, edn. liaison 1978-87, chmn. nom. 1986-87, hon. award sci. edn. 1989). Episcopalian. Home: 40 Balsam Ln Princeton NJ 08540-5327

SIMMONS, JENNINGS (JAY), aerospace engineer. BSME, Tenn. Tech. Inst., 1956; cert. in bus., UCLA, 1967. Dir. spacelab program McDonnell Douglas Aerospace, Huntsville, Ala. Recipient Space Sys. award AIAA, 1994. Office: McDonnell Douglas Aerospace Mail Stop 33 E 2 689 Discovery Dr Huntsville AL 35806*

SIMMONS, JESSE DOYLE, minister, educator; b. South Boston, Va., Sept. 3, 1926; s. Heyward Benjamin and Elizabeth (Smith) S.; m. Lois Virginia Ingram, Oct. 12, 1947; children: Nova Lee Norman, Debra S. Sturkie, Virginia S. Miller, Jesse D. Jr. BTh, Holmes Theol. Sem, Greenville, S.C., 1954, B Sacred Lit., 1977; DD (hon.), Holmes Theol. Sem., Greenville, S.C., 1970; EdB, Wade Hampton Coll., Florence, S.C., 1956; DRE (hon.), Agape Christian U., 1994. Ordained to ministry Internat. Pentecostal Holiness Ch., 1952. Evangelist Internat. Pentecostal Holiness Ch., Lake City, S.C., 1950-54; pastor Internat. Pentecostal Holiness Ch., Columbia, S.C., 1954-75; dir. world missions and evangelism S.C. conf. Internat. Pentecostal Holiness Ch., 1975-82; supt. S.C. Conf. Internat. Pentecostal Holiness Ch., Lake City, 1982-85; asst. gen. supt., div. evangelism, ch. loan fund, dept. armed forces Internat. Pentecostal Holiness Ch., Oklahoma City, 1985-89; vice chmn., dir. world missions dept. chaplains' ministries Internat. Pentecostal Holiness Ch. of S.C. Conf., Oklahoma City, 1989-93; chmn. bd. trustees Holmes Coll. of the Bible, 1979—; gen. exec. bd. Gen. Bd. Administrn. Internat. Pentecostal Holiness Ch., Oklahoma City, 1985—; mem. bd. adminstrn. Nat. Assn. Evangelicals, Wheaton, Ill., 1990—, Pentecostal Fellowship N.Am., 1990—. Exec. editor Witnes, 1985-89, Worldorama, 1989—, Keynotes, 1989—. State constable, S.C., 1976; notary publ., S.C., 1982; trustee Holmes Coll. Bible, Greenville, S.C., 1979—. With U.S. Army, 1944-46, PTO. Mem. Am. Legion. Republican. Home: 8117 W Willow Creek Blvd Oklahoma City OK 73162-2018 Office: Pentecostal Holiness Ch PO Box 12609 Oklahoma City OK 73157-2609 *While much of society place great emphasis on self, independence and personal fulfillment, we would do well to remember that a fulfilled life is a life lived out for others, interdependent and challenging others to fulfillment.*

SIMMONS, JOHN DEREK, investment banker; b. Essex, Eng., July 17, 1931; came to U.S., 1952; s. Simon Leonard and Eve (Smart) S.; m. Rosalind Wellish, Mar. 5, 1961; children: Peter Lawrence, Sharon Leslie. BS, Columbia, 1956; MBA, Rutgers U., 1959; postgrad. NYU, 1959-62.Chief cost acct. Airborne Accessories, Hillside, N.J., 1952-57; sr. cost analyst Curtiss-Wright Corp., Wood Ridge, N.J., 1957; sr. fin. analyst internat. group Ford Motor Co., Jersey City, N.J., 1958-60; rsch. assoc. Nat. Assn. Accts., N.Y.C., 1960-64; asst. to v.p. fin. Air Reduction Co., Inc., 1965-67; mgr. corp. planning Anaconda Wire & Cable Co., N.Y.C., 1968; ind. fin. cons., 1968-71; assoc. cons. Rogers, Slade and Hill, Inc., N.Y.C., 1969-71; v.p., security analyst, economist Moore & Schley, Cameron & Co. (name now changed to Fourteen Rsch. Corp.), 1972-81; v.p., security analyst Merrill Lynch Capital Markets, N.Y.C., 1981-88; security analyst Arnhold and S. Bleichroeder, Inc., N.Y.C., 1988-89; v.p., security analyst, corp. fin. specialist Smith Barney, Harris Upham & Co., Inc., N.Y.C., 1989-90; sr. cons. Carl Byoir & Assocs., N.Y.C., 1991-94; assoc. mng. dir. Commonwealth Assocs., N.Y.C., 1994—; lectr. profl. socs. and confs.; lectr. econs., mgmt., polit. sci. Rutgers U., 1957-64. Contbr. articles on econs. of underdeveloped nations, polit. sci., mgmt., fin. to U.S. and fgn. publs. Served to 1st lt. Brit. Army, 1950-52. Granted personal coat of Arms By Queen Elizabeth II: manorial Lord of Ash., Suffolk, Eng. Mem. Am. Econ. Assn., Royal Econ. Soc., N.Y. Soc. Security Analysts, KT, Knight Templar Sovereign Mil. Order of Temple of Jerusalem. Home: 360 E 72nd St New York NY 10021-4753 Office: Commonwealth Assocs 733 Third Ave New York NY 10017

SIMMONS, JOHN KAUL, accounting educator; b. Beloit, Kans., July 12, 1938; s. Fred Cole and Bernice Eva (Kaul) S.; m. Gail Ruth Parrish, Aug. 22, 1959; children: Kauleen Kaye, Laura Elizabeth. B.S., Kans. State U., 1960; M.B.A., U. Denver, 1961; Ph.D., Ohio State U., 1967. C.P.A., Kans. Instr. Ohio State U., Columbus, 1961-63; accountant Peat, Marwick, Mitchell & Co., Columbus, 1963-64; asst. prof. U. Minn., Mpls., 1965-69; asso. prof. U. Minn., 1969-73, prof., 1973-74; prof., chmn. dept. accounting U. Fla., Gainesville, 1974-77; dir. Sch. Accounting U. Fla., 1977-80, KPMG Peat Marwick prof. Sch. Acctg., 1980—; Cons. NASA Manned Spacecraft Center, 1968; mem. written profl. exam. com. Fla. Bd. Accountancy, 1975-77. Contbr. articles to profl. jours. Bd. dirs. Fla. Athletic Assn., 1975-77. Co-recipient award for outstanding contbn. to accounting lit. Am. Inst. C.P.A.s, 1969. Mem. Am. Accounting Assn. (sec./treas. 1977-79, chmn. nat. meeting program 1984, pres.-elect 1988-89, pres. 1989-90), AICPA (practice subcom., bd. examiners 1983-87, chmn. practice analysis task force 1987-88, Outstanding Educator award 1991), Fla. Inst. CPAs (Outstanding Educator award 1989), Fedn. Schs. Accounting (sec./treas. 78, pres. 1980, Faculty Merit award 1987), Commn. on Profl. Acctg. Edn. 1982-83, Nat. Assn. State Bds. Accountancy (CPA exam. rev. bd. 1979-82, chmn. 1982), Internat. Qualifications Appraisal Bd., Beta Alpha Psi (Acct. of Yr. in Edn. award 1991), Beta Gamma Sigma, Alpha Kappa Psi, Sigma Chi. Home: 5242 River Park Villa Dr Saint Augustine FL 32092-1402 Office: U Fla Sch Acctg Gainesville FL 32611

SIMMONS, JOHN WESLEY, oil company executive; b. Chester, Pa., Aug. 25, 1918; s. J. William and Sara (Riley) S.; m. Maricia Murdoch, Dec. 16, 1943; children: John Wesley III, Jay William. BSME, Drexel U., 1943. Pres., gen. mgr. Atlantic Refining Co., Brazil, 1959-62; gen. mgr. internat. mktg. Atlantic Refining Co., Phila., 1962-66; v.p. internat. div. Atlantic Richfield Co., Phila. and N.Y.C., 1966-72, L.A., 1981—; pres. ARCO Petroleum Products Co., L.A., 1972-81; bd. dirs. Jacobs Enging. Group, Inc., Calif., Western Waste Industries, Calif., Verdugo Hills Hosp., Glendale, Calif. Capt. U.S. Army, 1943-46. Mem. Am. Petroleum Inst., Town Hall

Calif., Newcomen Soc. N.Am., Calif. Club, Annandale Country Club, Pauma Valley Club. Republican. Episcopalian. Home: 384 Meadow Grove St La Canada Flintridge CA 91011-3525

SIMMONS, JOSEPH JACOB, III, federal commissioner; b. Muskogee, Okla., Mar. 26, 1925; s. Jacob, Jr. and Eva (Flowers) S.; m. Bernice Elizabeth Miller, Jan. 30, 1947; children: Jacob IV, Mary Agnes, Bernice, Jacolyn, Eva Frances. Student, U. Detroit, 1942-44, 46-47; B.S. in Geol. Engring., St. Louis U., 1949; LLD (hon.), Madonna U., 1991. Registered profl. engr., Okla. V.p., sec.-treas., geologist Simmons Royalty Co., Muskogee, 1949-61; regional oil and gas mobilization specialist U.S. Dept. of the Interior, Battle Creek, Mich., 1961-62; domestic petroleum production specialist Office of Oil and Gas U.S. Dept. of the Interior, Washington, 1962-66, asst. dir. Office of Oil and Gas, 1966-68, dep. adminstr. Oil Import Adminstrn., 1968-69, adminstr. Oil Import Adminstrn., 1969-70, Under Sec., 1983-84; v.p. govt. relations Amerada Hess Corp., N.Y.C., 1970-82; commr. ICC, Washington; vice chmn. ICC, 1986, 89, 93; mem. fuel oil mktg. adv. com. Dept. Energy, 1978-82; commr. Pres.'s Commn. on Exec. Exchange, 1970-81; commr. Statue of Liberty Ellis Island Commn., 1983-88, bd. dirs. Found., 1984-86; mem. NAS Bd. of Earth Scis. and Resources, 1984—; mem. adv. bd. Dept. of Interior Outer Continental Shelf, 1984—. Youth dir. NAACP, 1950-55; candidate Okla. Ho. of Reps., 1956, City Council, 1956; trustee Madonna Coll., Livonia, Mich., 1969-76, Morehouse Sch. Medicine, Atlanta, 1990—. Served with USAAF, 1944-46. Recipient Alumni Merit award St. Louis U., 1968, Spl. Act of Service award Dept. Interior, 1963, Outstanding Performance award, 1968, Disting. Service award, 1970. Mem. Am. Assn. Petroleum Geologists (Pub. Service award 1984), Soc. Petroleum Engrs., AIME.

SIMMONS, JOSEPH THOMAS, accountant, educator; b. Forest Lake, Minn., Jan. 23, 1936; s. Roland Thomas and Erma (Rabe) S.; m. Winola Ann Zwald, Aug. 18, 1962 (div.); children: Thomas E, Kevin M. BS in Bus. and Econs., Morningside Coll., 1964; MBA, U. S.D., 1965; PhD in Bus., U. Nebr., 1974. CPA, S.D. Prof. acctg. and fin. U.S.D., Vermillion, 1966-69, 75—, dir. Sch. Bus., 1975—; prof. U. Nebr., Lincoln, 1969-71, U. Man., Winnipeg, Can., 1971-75; prin. Simmons and Assocs. Mgmt. Cons., Rapid City, S.D., 1981—; pvt. practice acctg. Rapid City, 1982—; pres. Simmons Profl. Fin. Planning, Vermillion, 1983—; bd. dirs. Powerhouse Computers, Sioux Falls, N.D., v.p. fin., 1992-93; bd. dirs. MDU Resources Inc., Bismarck, N.D., RE/spec, Rapid City, Gro-Tech, Rapid City; vis. prof. U. Warsaw, Poland, 1994. Served with U.S. Army, 1958-60. Mem. AICPA, Am. Acctg. Assn., Fin. Mgmt. Assn., S.D. Soc. CPA's. Republican. Methodist. Home and Office: Ponderosa Acres Lot 2 Burbank SD 57010

SIMMONS, LEE GUYTON, JR., zoological park director; b. Tucson, Feb. 20, 1938; s. Lee Guyton and Dorothy Esther (Taylor) S.; m. Marie Annette Geim, Sept. 6, 1959; children: Lee Guyton, Heather, Heidi. Student, Cen. State Coll.; DVM, Okla. State U. Resident veterinarian Columbus Zoo Powell, Ohio, 1963-66; resident veterinarian Henry Doorly Zoo, Omaha, dir.; research cons. VA Hosp.; assoc. veterinarian U. Nebr. Med. Ctr., Omaha; assoc. clin. prof. Creighton U. Sch. Dentistry. Contbr. articles to profl. jours. Bd. dirs. Nebr. State Mus., Lincoln. Served with USAR. Recipient Nat. Idealism award City of Hope, 1979; named Man of Yr., Lions Club, 1978. Fellow AVMA, Am. Assn. Zool. Veterinarians (pres.), Am. Assn. Zool. Parks, Nebr. Vet. Med. Assn. (Veterinarian of Yr. 1979). Lodge: Rotary. Office: Office of the Director Henry Doorly Zoo 3701 S 10th St Omaha NE 68107-2200*

SIMMONS, LEE HOWARD, book publishing company executive; b. N.Y.C., Aug. 17, 1935; s. Lee H. and Frances (Goodell) S.; m. Barbara E. Beck, Sept. 6, 1961; children: Christopher, Elizabeth. A.B., Duke U., 1958; M.A., NYU, 1960. Sales mgr. The Orion Press, N.Y.C., 1959-60; advt. mgr. Doubleday & Co., N.Y.C., 1960-61; account exec. Franklin Spier, N.Y.C., 1961-68, v.p., 1968-78, pres., 1978-86; exec. v.p., assoc. pub. Arbor House Pub. Co., N.Y.C., 1986-88; pres. Lee Simmons Assocs. Inc., Port Washington, N.Y., 1988—; chmn. Olivion Press, N.Y.C., 1977-82, N.Y. is Book Country, N.Y.C., 1986-87. Treas. Port Washington Estates Assn., 1975-78. Episcopalian. Home: 40 Richards Rd Port Washington NY 11050-3416 Office: Lee Simmons Assocs Inc 4 Boylston St Port Washington NY 11050

SIMMONS, LYNDA MERRILL MILLS, educational administrator; b. Salt Lake City, Aug. 31, 1940; d. Alanson Soper and Madeline Helene (Merrill) Mills; m. Mark Carl Simmons, Nov. 17, 1962; children: Lisa Lynn Simmons Morley, William Mark, Jennifer Louise, Robert Thomas. BS, U. Utah, 1961, MS, 1983. Cert. sch. adminstr., Utah. Tchr. Wasatch Jr. H.S./Granite Dist., Salt Lake City, 1961-64, Altamont (Utah) H.S./Duchesne Dist., 1964-66; tchr. spl. edn. Park City (Utah) H.S., 1971-73; resource tchr. Eisenhower Jr. H.S., Salt Lake City, 1979-88; tchr. specialist Granite Sch. Dist., Salt Lake City, 1985-90; asst. prin. Bennion Jr. H.S., Salt Lake City, 1990-93; prin. Hartvigsen Sch., Salt Lake City, 1993—; adj. prof. spl. edn. U. Utah, Salt Lake City, 1985—; mentor tchr. Utah Mentor Tchr. Acad., Salt Lake City, 1987—, Utah Prin. Acad., 1994-95; co-chair Utah Spl. Educators for Computer Tech., Salt Lake City, 1988-90; mem. adv. com. on handicapped Utah State Office Edn., 1990-93; presenter at confs. Author: Setting Up Effective Secondary Resource Program, 1985; contbr. articles to profl. publs. Dist. chmn. Heart Fund, Cancer Dr., Summit Park, Utah, 1970-82; cub pack leader Park City area Boy Scouts Am., 1976-80; bd. dirs. Jr. League Salt Lake City, 1977-80; cookie chmn. Park City area Girl Scouts U.S., 1981; dist. chmn. March of Dimes, 1982—. Recipient Amb. award Salt Lake Conv. and Vis. Bur., 1993. Mem. Nat. Assn. Secondary Sch. Prins., Park City Young Women's Mut. (pres. 1989-93, family history coms 1993—), Women's Athenaeum (v.p. 1990-93, pres. 1994—), Coun. for Exceptional Children (pres. Salt Lake chpt. 1989-90, pres. Utah Fedn. 1991-93, Spl. Educator of Yr. Utah Fedn. 1995), Granite Assn. Sch. Adminstrs. (sec.-treas. 1992-94). Mem. LDS Ch. Avocations: reading, cooking, writing, sports, handiwork. Office: Hartrigsen Sch 350 E 3605 S Salt Lake City UT 84115

SIMMONS, MARVIN GENE, geophysics educator; b. Dallas, May 15, 1929; s. Burt H. and Mable (Marshall) S.; divorced; children—Jon Eric, Debra Lynn, Sandra Kay, Pamela Jean. B.S., Tex. Agrl. and Mech. Coll., 1949; M.S., So. Methodist U., 1958; Ph.D., Harvard U., 1962. Petroleum engr. Humble Oil Co., 1949-51; propr. gravel business, 1953-58; asst. prof. So. Meth. U., 1962-65; prof. geophysics MIT, 1965-89, prof. emeritus, 1989—; prin. Hager-Richter Geoscience Inc., 1989—; Cons. NASA, 1965-72; chief scientist NASA (Manned Spacecraft Center), Houston, 1969-71; cons. on siting of nuclear facilities; sec. Internat. Heat Flow Com., 1967-71; chmn. com. drilling for sci. purposes Nat. Acad. Scis., 1965; Mem. geophysics panel NSF. Served with USAF, 1951-53. NSF postdoctoral fellow, 1961-62. Fellow Geol. Soc. Am., Am. Geophys. Union; mem. ASTM (com. C-18 on dimension stone 1986—), Boston Geol. Soc. (pres. 1967-68), Soc. Exploration Geophysicists, Sigma Xi, Tau Beta Pi. Research on physical properties of materials, lunar exploration, marine geophysics, temperature of earth, regional geophysics, engineering geology and geophysics. Home: 180 N Policy St Salem NH 03079-1916 Office: 8 Industrial Way Unit D10 Salem NH 03079-2837

SIMMONS, MERLE EDWIN, foreign language educator; b. Kansas City, Kans., Sept. 27, 1918; s. Walter Earl and Mabel Sophronia (Shoemaker) S.; m. Concepcion Rojas, Sept. 8, 1948; children: Martha Irene Simmons Hunt, Mary Alice Simmons Roberts. A.B., U. Kans., 1939, M.A., 1941; teaching fellow, Harvard U., 1946-47; Ph.D., U. Mich., 1952. Mem. faculty Ind. U., Bloomington, 1942—; prof. Spanish Ind. U., 1962-83, prof. emeritus, 1983—; dir. grad. studies dept. Spanish and Portuguese, 1967-76, chmn. dept., 1976-81. Author: The Mexican Corrido, 1957, A Bibliography of the Romance and Related Forms in Spanish America, 1963, Folklore Bibliography for 1974, 1977, for 1975, 1979, for 1976, 1981, Santiago F. Puglia, An Early Philadelphia Propagandist for Spanish American Independence, 1977, U.S. Political Ideas in Spanish America Before 1830: A Bibliographic Study, 1977, Los escritos de Juan Pablo Viscardo y Guzmán, 1983, Obra completa de Juan Pablo Viscardo y Guzmán, 1988, La Revolución Norteamericana y la Independencia de Hispanoamérica, 1992, also articles. Decorated Gran Oficial of the Order of the Sun (Peru); grantee Am. Philos. Soc., 1955, 76; grantee Am. Coun. Learned Socs., 1962. Mem. AAUP, Am. Folklore Soc., Am. Assn. Tchrs. Spanish and Portuguese, Conf. Latin Am. History, MLA, Midwest MLA, Midwest Assn. Latin Am. Studies, Nat. Acad. History of

Venezuela (corr.), Phi Beta Kappa, Phi Sigma Iota. Home: 4233 Saratoga Dr Bloomington IN 47408-3196 Office: Ind U Ballantine Hall # 857 Bloomington IN 47405

SIMMONS, MIRIAM QUINN, state legislator; b. Jackson, Miss., Mar. 28, 1928; d. Charles Buford and Viola (Hamill) Quinn; m. Willie Wronal Simmons, July 10, 1952; children: Dick, Sue, Wronal. BS, Miss. U. for Women, 1949. Tchr. Columbia (Miss.) City Schs., 1949-51, 53-54, literacy coord., 1986-87; home demonstration agt. Coop. Extension Svc., Bay Springs, Miss., 1951-52; tchr. Marion County Schs., Columbia, 1952-53, 54-55, Columbia Tng. Sch., 1961-63, Columbia Acad., 1970-73; rep. Miss. Ho. of Reps., Jackson, 1988—; adv. bd. Magnolia Fed. Bank for Savs; trustee State Inst. Higher Learning, Jackson, 1972-84; dir. Miss. Authority for Ednl. TV, Jackson, 1976-88. Named Marion County Outstanding Citizen Columbia Jr. Aux., 1981. Mem. Miss. Fedn. Women's Clubs, Bus. and Profl. Women's Club, Hilltop Garden Club, Delta Kappa Gamma. Democrat. Methodist. Home: 45 Old Highway 98 E Columbia MS 39429-8172

SIMMONS, PAUL ALLEN, retired federal judge; b. Monongahela, Pa., Aug. 31, 1921; s. Perry C. and Lilly D. (Allen) S.; m. Gwendolyn O. Gladden, Sept. 2, 1950; children—Paul A., Gwendolyn Dale, Anne Marie. B.A., U. Pitts., 1946; J.D., Harvard U., 1949. Mem. faculty, prof. law S.C. State Coll. Law, 1949-52; prof. law N.C. Central U., 1952-56; pvt. practice law Monongahela, 1956-73; judge Ct. of Common Pleas, Washington County, Pa., 1973-78; sr. judge U.S. Dist. Ct. (we. dist.) Pa., Pitts., 1978-91; ret., 1991. Mem. Pa. Human Relations Commn., 1963-68; mem. Pa. Minor Jud. Edn. Bd., 1970-86, Washington County Redevel. Authority, 1970-73. Mem. Pa. Bar Assn., N.C. Bar Assn., Am. Bar Assn., Washington County Bar Assn., Pa. Bar Assn., Am. Judicature Soc., NAACP. Democrat. Mem. African Meth. Episcopal Ch. Clubs: Masons, Elks.

SIMMONS, PETER, urban planning educator; b. N.Y.C., July 19, 1931; s. Michael L. and Mary A. S.; m. Ruth J. Tanfield, Jan. 28, 1951; children: Sam, Lizzard. A.B., U. Calif., Berkeley, 1953, LL.B., 1956; postgrad. (Alvord fellow), U. Wis., 1956-58. Prof. SUNY, Buffalo, 1963-67; mem. faculty Ohio State U., 1967-75, U. Ill., 1972, Case Western Res. U., 1974-75; prof. law and urban planning Rutgers U. Coll. Law, Newark, 1975—, dean, 1975-93; prof. Rutgers U., 1993—. Contbr. articles to profl. jours. Mem. Ohio Housing Commn., 1972-74; commr. Ohio Reclamation Rev. Bd., 1974-75; chmn. N.J. Criminal Disposition Commn., 1983-84; mem. N.J. Law Revision Commn., 1987—. Mem. Am. Planning Assn., Urban Land Inst., Am. Law Inst., AAUP (nat. council 1973-75). Office: Rutgers U Law Sch 15 Washington St Newark NJ 07102-3105

SIMMONS, RALPH OLIVER, physics educator; b. Kensington, Kans., Feb. 19, 1928; s. Fred Charles and Nellie (Douglass) S.; m. Janet Lee Lull, Aug. 31, 1952; children: Katherine Ann, Bradley Alan, Jill Christine, Joy Diane. B.A., U. Kans., 1950; B.A. (Rhodes scholar), Oxford U., 1953; Ph.D., U. Ill., 1957. Research assoc. U. Ill., Urbana, 1957-59, faculty physics, 1959—, assoc. prof., 1961-65, prof. physics, 1965—, head physics dept., 1970-86; vis. scientist Ctr. for Study Nuclear Energy, Mol, Belgium, 1965; mem. governing bd. Internat. Symposia on Thermal Expansion, 1970-88; cons. Argonne Nat. Lab., 1978-86, Los Alamos Nat. Lab., 1983-84; chmn. Office of Phys. Scis., NRC, 1978-81; mem. Assembly of Math. and Phys. Scis., 1978-81, Geophysics Rsch. Bd., 1978-81; trustee Argonne Univs. Assn., 1979-83. Mem. internat. adv. bd.: Jour. Physics C (Solid State Physics), 1971-76; mem. editorial bd.: Physical Review B, 1978-81. Recipient Sr. U.S. Scientist Rsch. award Alexander von Humboldt Found., 1992; sr. postdoctoral fellow NSF, 1965. Fellow Am. Phys. Soc. (vice chmn., chmn divsn. solid state physics 1975-77, coun. 1988), AAAS (chmn. sect. B Physics 1985-86); mem. Am. Crystallographic Assn., Am. Assn. Physics Tchrs., Materials Rsch. Soc., Phi Beta Kappa, Sigma Xi, Pi Mu Epsilon. Research on atomic defects in solids, neutron and x-ray scattering, quantum solids, molecular crystals, crystal dynamics, radiation damage. Home: 1005 Foothill Dr Champaign IL 61821-5622

SIMMONS, RAYMOND HEDELIUS, JR., lawyer; b. Salinas, Calif., May 27, 1958; s. Raymond Hedelius and Antoinette (Lynch) S. BA magna cum laude, U. Calif., San Diego, 1979; JD magna cum laude, U. Calif., San Francisco, 1982. Bar: Calif. 1982, U.S. Dist. Ct. (no. dist.) Calif. 1982, Ga. 1987. Assoc. Farella, Braun & Martel, San Francisco, 1982-85; atty., v.p. Barnett-Range Corp., Atlanta, 1985-86; counsel Nationwide Capital Corp. subs. HomeFed. Bank, Atlanta, 1986, HomeFed. Bank, San Diego, 1987-90; gen. counsel, sr. v.p., sec. ITT Fed. Bank, San Francisco, 1990—; also ITT Residential Capital Corp., ITT Residential Capital Servicing Corp., San Francisco. Mem. ABA, Calif. Bar Assn., Ga. Bar Assn., Calif. Scholarship Fedn. (life), Order of Coif, Thurston Soc. Home: 1055 California St Apt 7 San Francisco CA 94108 Office: ITT Fed Bank One Market Pl 1600 Stuart Tower San Francisco CA 94105

SIMMONS, RICHARD DE LACEY, mass media executive; b. Cambridge, Mass., Dec. 30, 1934; s. Ernest J. and Winifred (McNamara) S.; m. Mary DeWitt Bleecker, May 20, 1961; children: Christopher DeWitt, Robin Bleecker. Grad., 1951; AB, Harvard Coll., 1955; LLB, Columbia U., 1958. Bar: N.Y. 1959. V.p., gen. counsel Dun & Bradstreet Corp., N.Y.C., 1969-73, exec. v.p., 1976-79, vice chmn., 1979-81; vice chmn. Moody's Investors Svc., N.Y.C., 1973-75; pres. Dun & Bradstreet, Inc., N.Y.C., 1975; pres., chief oper. officer Washington Post Co., Washington, 1981-91; pres. Internat. Herald Tribune, Paris, 1989—; bd. dirs. The Washington Post Co., J.P. Morgan & Co., Inc., Morgan Guaranty Trust Co. of N.Y., Union Pacific Corp.; equity adv. bd. GE Investment Corp. Mem. coun. White Burkett Miller Ctr. Pub. Affairs, U. Va. Office: Internat Herald Tribune 1150 15th St NW Washington DC 20071-0001

SIMMONS, RICHARD MILTON TEAGLE, physical fitness specialist, television personality; b. New Orleans, July 12, 1948. With Coty Cosmetics, beginning 1971; maitre d' Derrick's, Los Angeles; founder Ruffage and the Anatomy Asylum, Beverly Hills, Calif., from 1975; star The Richard Simmons Show, from 1980; owner nationwide chain of exercise salons; author: (with Suzy Kalter) Never-Say-Diet Book, 1980, Never-Say-Diet Cookbook, 1982, Richard Simmons' Better Body Book, 1983, Reach for Fitness, 1986, Richard Simmons' Never Give Up: Inspirations, Reflections, Stories of Hope, 1993; column Simmons Says, Soap Opera Digest, from 1981; contbr. articles to various publs.; album Reach, 1982; videos Sweatin' to the Oldies, Sweatin' to the Oldies II, Sweatin' to the Oldies III; appeared numerous commls., Italy, until 1971; guest numerous talk shows including Merv Griffin, Mike Douglas, Phil Donahue, Charlie Rose, AM Los Angeles; Real People; cameo appearances: General Hospital, from 1979, All Star Salute to Mother's Day, 1981; appeared in movies: Satyricon, 1969, The Crowns, 1970. Office: care Anatomy Asylum 9306 Santa Monica Blvd Beverly Hills CA 90210

SIMMONS, RICHARD P., steel company executive; b. 1931; married. Grad. MIT, 1953. With Titanium Metals Corp. Am., 1957-59, Republic Steel 1959-68; with Allegheny Ludlum Steel Corp., Pitts., 1960—, chief exec. officer, 1980—, chmn., 1986—; also dir. Allegheny Ludlum Corp. (formerly Allegheny Ludlum Steel Corp.), Pitts., formerly also pres. Office: 1000 6th PPG pl Pittsburgh PA 15222

SIMMONS, ROBERT RUHL, state legislator, educator; b. N.Y.C., Feb. 11, 1943; s. Charles Herbert Jr. and Roxane Page (Ruhl) S.; m. Edith Heidi Paffard, June 22, 1974; children: Jane Adams, Robert Waldo Ruhl. BA, Haverford Coll., 1965; MPA, Harvard U., 1979. Ops. officer CIA, Washington, 1969-79; legis. assist. U.S. Senator John H. Chafee, Washington, 1979-81; staff dir. intelligence com. U.S. Senate, Washington, 1981-85; vis. lectr. Yale U., New Haven, Conn., 1985—; mem. Conn. Gen. Assembly, Hartford, 1991—. Contbr. articles to profl. jours. Chmn. Rep. Town Com., Stonington, Conn., 1988-92. Bd. Police Commrs., Stonington, 1986-88. 1st lt. U.S. Army, 1965-68, Vietnam; Col. USAR. Decorated Bronze Star with 1 oak leaf cluster, Army Commendation medal with 1 oak leaf cluster, Vietnam Svc. medal with four campaign stars, Nat. Def. medal, Army Res. Achievement medal. Republican. Episcopalian. Avocations: Chinese art, forestry. Home: 268 N Main St Stonington CT 06378-2910 Office: Legislative Office Bldg The Capital Ste 4200 Hartford CT 06106

SIMMONS, ROY, JR., university athletic coach. Head coach lacrosse team Syracuse U. Orangemen, 1971—. Coached team to Divsn. IA Lacrosse Championship, 1983, 88-90, 93. Office: Syracuse Univ Syracuse NY 13244*

SIMMONS, ROY WILLIAM, banker; b. Portland, Oreg., Jan. 24, 1916; s. Henry Clay and Ida (Mudd) S.; m. Elizabeth Ellison, Oct. 28, 1938; children—Julia Simmons Watkins, Matthew R., Laurence E., Elizabeth Jane Simmons Hoke, Harris H., David E. Asst. cashier First Nat. Bank Layton, Utah, 1944-49; Utah bank commr., 1949-51; exec. v.p. Bank of Utah, Ogden, 1951-53; pres. Lockhart Co., Salt Lake City, 1953-64, Zion's First Nat. Bank, Salt Lake City, 1964-81; chmn. bd. Zion's First Nat. Bank, 1965—; chmn., CEO Zion's Bancorp, 1965-91, chmn. bd., 1991—; chmn. bd. Zion's Savs. & Loan Assn., 1961-69; pres. Lockhart Co., 1964-87; bd. dirs. Beneficial Life Ins. Co., Mountain Fuel Supply Co., Ellison Ranching Co. Chmn. Utah Bus. Devel. Corp., 1969-80; Mem. Utah State Bd. Regents, 1969-81. Mem. Salt Lake City C. of C. (treas. 1964-65), Sigma Pi. Republican. Mem. Ch. of Jesus Christ of Latter Day Saints. Home: 817 E Crestwood Rd Kaysville UT 84037-1712 Office: Zions Bancorp 1000 Kennecott Bldg Salt Lake City UT 84133

SIMMONS, RUSSELL, recording industry executive; b. Hollis, N.Y., 1957; s. Daniel S. Attended, CCNY. Co-founder, owner Def Jam Records, N.Y.C., 1985—; owner Rush Artist Mgmt.; chmn. Rush Comms.; owner 6 record labels. Co-prodr. films Krush Groove, 1985, Tougher Than Leather, 1988; dir. music videos; HBO appearance Russell Simmons Def Comedy Jam; mgmt. co. represents Public Enemy, LL Cool J, others. Office: Def Jam Records 652 Broadway New York NY 10012-2316*

SIMMONS, S. DALLAS, university president; b. Ahoskie, N.C., Jan. 28, 1940; s. Yvonne Martin; m. Mary A. Simmons, Feb. 10, 1963; children: S. Dallas Jr., Kristie Lynn. BS, N.C. Cen. U., 1962, MS, 1967; PhD, Duke U., 1977. Asst. prof. bus. adminstrn. N.C. Cen. U., Durham, 1967-71, asst. to chancellor, 1971-77, vice chancellor for univ. relations, 1977-81; pres. St. Paul's Coll., Lawrenceville, Va., 1981-85, Va. Union Univ. Richmond, 1985—; faculty cons. IBM, Research Triangle Park, N.C., 1968-71; cons. for edn. devel. officers Nat. Lab. for Higher Edn., Durham, 1972-73; staff asst. to Pres., White House Advance Office, Washington, 1975-76; univ. fed. liaison officer Moton Coll. Service Bur., Washington, 1972-80; mem. competency testing commn. N.C. Bd. Edn., 1977-81; bd. dirs., mem. loan com., mem. planning com. Pace Am. Bank, Lawrenceville, 1984-85. Bd. dirs. N.C. Mus. Life and Sci., Durham, 1972-75, Volunteer Services Bur, Inc., Durham, 1972-77, Va. Poly. Inst. and State U., 1982-83; mem. Durham Civic/Conv. Ctr. Commn., 1972-73, U.S./Zululand Ednl. Found.; 1985; trustee, mem. exec. and pers. com. N.C. Cen. U., 1983-85; active various coms. United Negro Coll. Fund; mem. exec. bd. John B. McLendon Found., Inc., 1985. Named one of Outstanding Young Men Am., 1972, Citizen of Yr. Omega Psi Phi, 1983-84, Bus. Assoc. of Yr. Am. Bus. Women's Assn., 1984. Mem. Assn. Episc. Colls. (pres.-elect), Cen. Intercollegiate Athletic Assn. (exec. com. 1981—, bd. dirs. 1981—), Nat. Assn. for Equal Opportunity in Higher Edn. (bd. dirs., chmn. leadership awards com. 1984-85), Am. Mgmt. Assn., Data Processing Mgmt. Assn. (cen. Carolina chpt.), Am. Assn. Sch. Adminstrs., Am. Assn. Univ. Adminstrs., Kappa Alpha Psi (Kappa of Month Dec. 1981), Sigma Pi Phi (alpha beta boulé). African Methodist Episcopalian. Club: Downtown. Lodges: Masons (32 degree), Shriners, Kiwanis, Optimists. Home: 1200 W Graham Rd Richmond VA 23220-1409 Office: Va Union U 1500 N Lombardy St Richmond VA 23220-1711

SIMMONS, SAMUEL LEE, corporate executive; b. St. Louis, Dec. 27, 1929; s. David Mayo and Mayme Pearle (Looney) S.; m. Joan Miller, Oct. 8, 1959; children—Lesley, Samuel Lee. B.A. with honors, Principia Coll., 1951; J.D. cum laude, Harvard U., 1957. Bar: N.Y. 1958. Atty. Standard Oil Co. N.J., N.Y.C., 1957-59; firm Arthur, Dry & Dole, N.Y.C., 1959-63; with ITT, 1963-75; staff counsel, gen. counsel ITT Credit Corp., 1963-67; v.p. parent co., gen. counsel European hdqrs. Europe Inc., Brussels, Belgium, 1967-75; v.p., gen. counsel Revlon Inc., N.Y.C., 1975-76; sr. v.p., gen. counsel Revlon Inc., 1976-86, dir., 1976-85, corp. sec., 1979-81; sr. v.p., dir. corp. devel. ITT Corp., 1987—. Served with U.S. Army, 1952-54. Office: ITT Corp 1330 Ave Of The Americas New York NY 10019-5422

SIMMONS, SYLVIA JEANNE QUARLES (MRS. HERBERT G. SIMMONS, JR.), university administrator, educator; b. Boston, May 8, 1935; d. Lorenzo Christopher and Margaret Mary (Thomas) Quarles; B.A., Manhattanville Coll., 1957; M.Ed., Boston Coll., 1962, PhD, 1990, DHL (hon.) St. Joseph's Coll., 1994; m. Herbert G. Simmons, Jr., Oct. 26, 1957; children: Stephen, Alison, Lisa. Montessori tchr. Charles River Park Nursery Sch., Boston, 1970-76; registrar Boston Coll. Sch. Mgmt., Chestnut Hill, Mass., 1966-70; dir. fin. aid Radcliffe Coll., Cambridge, Mass., 1970-75, assoc. dean admissions and fin. aid, 1972-75, assoc. dean admissions, fin. aid and women's edn., 1975; assoc. dean admissions and fin. aid Harvard and Radcliffe, from 1975; assoc. v.p. for acad. affairs, central administrn. U. Mass., Boston, 1976-79, spl. asst. to chancellor, 1979; v.p. field services Am. Student Assistance, 1982-84, sr. v.p., 1984-93, exec. v.p. 1993—; mem. faculty Harvard U., 1970-77; cons. Mass. Bd. Higher Edn., 1973-77. Bd. dirs. Rivers Country Day Sch., Weston, Mass., Simon's Rock Coll., Great Barrington, Mass., Wayland (Mass.) Fair Housing, Cambridge Mental Health Assn., Family Service Greater Boston, Concerts in Black and White, Mass. Higher Edn. Assistance Corp.; chmn. bd. dirs. North Shore Community Coll., 1986-88, mem. bd. dirs., 1985—; trustee and alumnae bd. dirs. Manhattanville Coll., 1986—. Mem. adv. com. Upward Bound, Chestnut Hill Boston Coll., 1972-74, Women in Politics Johm McCormack Inst., 1994—; Camp Chimney Corners, Becket, Mass., 1971-75; bd. dirs. Am. Cancer Soc., Mass., 1987-89, Boston Coll., 1990—, Merrimack Coll., 1992—, Mass. Found. for the Humanities, 1990-92, Mass. Bay United Way, 1990-94, Grimes King Found., 1992—, St. Elizabeta's Hosp., 1991; overseer Mt. Ida Coll., 1990—. Recipient Educator of the Year award Boston and Vicinity Club, 1989; named One of Ten Outstanding Young Leaders, Boston Jr. C. of C., 1971, Sojourner's Daughters: 25 African women who have made a difference, 1991; recipient Bicentennial medal Boston Coll., 1976; Achievement award Greater Boston YMCA, 1977, Human Rights award Mass. Tchrs. Assn., 1988, Pres' award Mass Ednl. Opportunity Assn., 1988. Mem. Women in Politics, Nat. (exec. council 1973-75), Eastern (1st v.p. 1973) assns. financial aid officers, Coll. Scholarship Service Council, Links, (pres. local chpt. 1967-69), Nat. Inst. Fin. Aid Adminstrs. (dir. 1975-77), Jack and Jill Am. (pres. Newton chpt. 1972-74, Delta Sigma Theta, Delta Kappa Gamma (pres. 1988-90). Club: Manhattanville (pres. Boston 1966-68). Home: 3 Dean Rd Wayland MA 01778-5007 Office: 330 Stuart St Boston MA 02116-5229

SIMMONS, TED CONRAD, writer; b. Seattle, Sept. 1, 1916; s. Conrad and Clara Evelyn (Beaudry) S.; m. Dorothy Pauline Maltese, June 1, 1942; children: lynn, Juliet. Student U. Wash., 1938-41, UCLA and Los Angeles State U., 1952-54, Oxford (Eng.) U., 1980. Drama critic Seattle Daily Times, 1942; indsl. writer, reporter-editor L.A. Daily News, 1948-51; contbr. Steel, Western Metals, Western Industry, 1951—; past poetry dir. Watts Writers Workshop; instr. Westside Poetry Center; asst. dir. Pacific Coast Writers Conf., Calif. State Coll. Los Angeles. Served with USAAF, 1942-46. Author: (poetry) Deadended, 1966; (novel) Middlearth, 1975; (drama) Greenhouse, 1977, Durable Chaucer, 1978, Rabelais and other plays, 1980, Dickeybird, 1981 (nominated TCG Plays-in-Progress award 1985), Alice and Eve, 1983, Deja Vu, Deja Vu, 1986, The Box, 1987, Ingrid Superstar, 1988, Three Quarks for Mr. Marks, 1989, Ingrid: Skier on the Slopes of Stromboli, 1990, A Midsummer's Hamlet, 1991, Hamlet Nintendo, After Hours, Dueling Banjoes, Viva el Presidente, Climate of the Sun, 1992, Nude Descending Jacob's Ladder, 1993, Almost an Opera, 1994, Landscape with Inverted Tree and Fred Astaire Dancing, 1995, O.J. Othello, Fast Track; writer short story, radio verse; book reviewer Los Angeles Times; contbr. poetry to The Am. Poet, Prairie Wings, Antioch Rev. Award Two Anthology; editor: Venice Poetry Company Presents, 1972. Grantee Art Commn. King County, 1993.

SIMMONS, VAUGHAN PIPPEN, medical consultant; b. Balt., Nov. 19, 1922; s. Harry S. and Sarah Jane (Pippen) S.; m. Marguerite Carolyn Massino, Dec. 27, 1947 (dec. 1990); children: Malynda Sarah, Jefferson Vaughan. Student, Ill. Inst. Tech., 1943-44; B.S., U. Chgo., 1947, M.D., 1949. Diplomate Am. Bd. Life Ins. Medicine. From instr. to asst. prof. Marquette U. Sch. Medicine, Milw., 1950-56; asst. med. dir. Northwestern Mut. Life Ins. Co., Milw., 1956-60; med. dir. Fidelity Mut. Life Ins. Co.,

Phila., 1961-73, v.p.; 1968-73; v.p., med. dir. Colonial Penn Life Ins. Co., Phila., 1973-84; vis. lectr. ins. medicine Temple U. Sch. Medicine, Phila. 1966-84; asst. prof. anatomy Jefferson Med. Coll., Phila., 1977-88, hon. asst. prof. anatomy, 1988—. Patentee in field (3); contbr. articles to profl. jours. Mem. ofcl. bd. St. Luke United Methodist Ch., Bryn Mawr, Pa., 1963-83, chmn. commn. membership and evangelism, 1963-71, trustee, 1968-83. Served with M.C., U.S. Army, 1943-45, as lt. (j.g.) USNR, 1952-54; Korea. Fellow Coll. Physicians Phila. (chmn. sect. pub. health 1967-68, chmn. sect. ins. medicine 1970-72, planning com. 1981-82, adv. bd. Francis C. Wood Inst. History of Medicine 1984-88), Milw. Acad. Medicine, Am. Geriatrics Soc., N.Y. Acad. Medicine; mem. Assn. Life Ins. Med. Dirs. Am. (founding editor Ins. Medicine 1969-71, exec. council 1970-73, publs. com. 1967-75), Am. Life Ins. Assn. (sec. med. sect. 1974-77), Pa. Hist. Soc., Am. Assn. Automotive Medicine (dir. 1980-83), Am. Legion, Sigma Xi, Alpha Kappa Kappa. Clubs: Union League (bd. dirs. 1982-85, v.p. 1985-86), Sketch (Phila.). Avocations: photography, amateur radio; drawing; painting. Home: 4665 S Landings Dr Fort Myers FL 33919-4683

SIMMONS, WILLIAM, physicist, aerospace research executive; b. Chgo., Apr. 24, 1932; s. Walter Garfield and Edna Dean (Winch) S.; m. Barbara Millet Haury, Oct. 4, 1954; children: Sheryl Lee, Cynthia Jane, Shelly Jean. BA in Physics, Carleton Coll., 1953; MS in Physics, U. Ill., 1955, PhD in Physics, 1960. Mem. tech. staff Space Tech. Labs., Redondo Beach, Calif., 1960-62; sr. rsch. scientist Gen. Tech., Torrance, Calif., 1962; sr. rsch. scientist TRW, Redondo Beach, 1962-71, dir. rsch., 1984-89, chief engr. spl. projects assigned to Lawrence Livermore (Calif.) Labs., 1989-92; engring. mgr. Lawrence Livermore Labs., 1972-84, rsch. reviewer, 1985-89; prof. engring. UCLA, 1968-72; tech. panel mem. U. Calif., Berkeley, 1985; tech. reviewer Dept. Energy, Washington, 1986—, mem. rev. com., 1987—. Editor, reviewer 2 books, 1982, 83; contbr. numerous articles to profl. jours. 10 patents in electro-optics devices. Named Disting. Engine. Prof. of Yr. UCLA, 1972, one of Top 100 Innovators in U.S.A. Sci. Digest, 1986; George F. Baker Found. scholar Carleton Coll., 1949-53. Mem. IEEE (sr., gen. chmn. symposia 1988, 89, Simon Ramo Major medal 1987), Laser Inst. Am., Laser Engring. and Optical Soc., Am. Phys. Soc., Soc. of Photographic and Instrumentation Engrs., U.S. Chess Club, Phi Beta Kappa, Sigma Xi. Republican. Avocations: chess, table tennis, bridge. Office: Systems Solutions 1621 W 25th St Ste 231 San Pedro CA 90732-4300

SIMMS, ARTHUR BENJAMIN, management consultant, financier; b. Atlanta, Sept. 20, 1921; s. Arthur B. and Eva (Hurt) S.; m. Jane Laurice Griffin, Nov. 7, 1953; children: Arthur Benjamin IV, Jane Griffin, Anne Woodruff. Grad., Darlington Sch., 1938; student, Ga. Inst. Tech., 1939-40; B.S., U. Pa., 1942; M.B.A., Harvard, 1947. Bus. cons. Elec. Bond & Share Co., N.Y.C. 1947-50; pres. A. B. Simms & Assos. (mgmt. cons.), Atlanta, 1950—; prof. bus. adminstrn. Ga. State U., 1951-52; pres., chmn. bd. Peachtree House, Inc., 1957-65, S. & L. Corp., 1959-62, 1st Atlanta Investment Corp., 1960-65, Consol. Equities Corp., Atlanta, 1965—; chmn. Realty Capital Corp., 1967—; Growth Realty, Inc., 1961-65, Bayshore Towers, Inc., Tampa, Fla., 1961—, Atlanta Towers, Inc., 1961-65; hon. bd. dirs. Atlanta and Edgewood St. Railway Co. Trustee Pop Warner Little Scholars, Inc.; bd. dirs. Lay Involvement for Evangelism, Atlanta, 1978—. Served from ensign to lt. USNR, 1942-46, ETO. Mem. Am. Mktg. Assn., Atlanta Apt. Assn. (dir. 1964-65), Nat. Assn. Small Bus. Investment Cos. (gov. 1963), So. Regional Assn. Small Bus. Investment Cos. (pres. 1963), Am. Mgmt. Assn., Atlanta C. of C., A.I.M. (mem. pres.'s council), Newcomen Soc. N.Am. (Ga. com.), Soc. Colonial Wars, Sigma Alpha Epsilon (past dir.). Presbyn. (deacon, elder). Clubs: Kiwanian. (Atlanta), Breakfast (Atlanta), Harvard Bus. Sch. (Atlanta) (past dir.), Piedmont Driving (Atlanta), Capital City (Atlanta); Harvard (N.Y.C.). Home: 2637 Peachtree Rd NE Atlanta GA 30305-3607 Office: 1280 W Peachtree St NW Atlanta GA 30309-3420

SIMMS, CHARLES AVERILL, environmental management company executive; b. Hundred, W.Va., Apr. 12, 1937; s. Charles R. and Ada Faith (Devine) S.; m. Linda Magalis, June 24, 1961; children: Brian M., Eric C. BSBA, W.Va. U., 1959. Cert. internal auditor, Md. Jr. acct. Potomac Edison Co., Hagerstown, Md., 1960-61; internal auditor Potomac Edison Co., Hagerstown, 1961-66, supr. internal audits, 1966-69; constrn. audit mgr. Eastalco Aluminum Co., Frederick, Md., 1969-71, gen. acctg. mgr., 1971-73, exec. asst. to pres., 1973-74; contr. Teledyne Nat., Cockeysville, Md., 1974-77, dir. fin. and adminstrn., Northridge, Calif., 1977-79, v.p. ops., Timonium, Md., 1979-83; pres. Nat. Ecology, Inc., Timonium, 1983-89; pres., chief exec. officer Rescon Inc., Balt., 1989-93; chmn. exec. com., bd. dirs. Am. Ecology Corp., Houston, 1984-94. 1st lt. U.S. Army, 1959-67. Mem. Solid Waste Assn. N.Am., Shriners (Cumberland, Md.). Republican. Home: 3241 Sharp Rd Glenwood MD 21738 Office: Md Environ Svc 10320 York Rd Cockeysville Hunt Valley MD 21030

SIMMS, ELLENESE BROOKS, civic leader, retired school system administrator; b. New Orleans, Sept. 10, 1939; d. Annias and Ellen (Lyons) Brooks; m. Clarence Joseph Simms, June 16, 1960 (div. June 1967); 1 child, Stacy René; m. Melvin Simms, Apr. 27, 1968; 1 adopted child, Darrell Dean; 1 child, Christel Melvanesia. BA, Dillard U., 1962; MEd, Loyola U., New Orleans, 1976. Elem. tchr. New Orleans Pub. Schs., 1962-76, prin. Helen S. Edwards Elem. Sch., 1976-86, prin. Robert Russa Moton Elem. Sch., 1986-92, adminstr. for consol. programs, 1992—; mem. ednl. task force La. Dept. Edn., 1975-76; sec.-treas. Golden Svcs. Inc., exec. dir. 1990—; pres. Profl. Assn. Creative Educators, ednl. cons., 1982—; coord. Orleans Parish schs. area So. Assn. Colls. and Schs., 1982-93; designer, implementer year round sch. pilot project Orleans Parish Schs., 1989-92; mem. internat. curriculum devel. seminar in Cameroon, U. New Orleans, 1983. Mem. Brechtel Park Adv. Bd., 1984—; Mayor's Algiers Task Force Com., 1984-85; mem. ednl. cmty. adv. bd. Fla./Desire, 1977—; founder, v.p. Holly Park Civic Assn., pres., 1973-76; co-founder, past sec. Algiers-Gretna br. NAACP, 1990; co-chmn. Citizens Adv. Com. for Minority Participation, 1989; commr. Regional Transit Authority, 1991—; chmn. bd. commrs., 1991-94; founder Greater New Orleans Regional Transit Task Force, 1990, Transit Task Force for Civil Rights, 1993. Recipient area chmn. citation New Orleans Sickle Cell Anemia Found., Inc., 1979, Leadership and Svc. award La. Assn. Sch. Execs., 1982, Outstanding Educator award Negro Bus. and Profl. Women's Club New Orleans, 1988, Outstanding Svc. award Prins. Assn. New Orleans Pub. Schs., 1992, New Orleans City Coun., 1992, Woman of Distinction award Austin Met. Bus. Resource Ctr., 1993, Gov.'s award State of La., 1994, cert. of appreciation Nat. Coun. Negro Women, 1994; also others. Mem. Am. Pub. Transit Assn. (v.p. human resources 1992—, co-chmn. diversity coun. 1992—, mem. transit 2000 commn. oversight com. 1992), Nat. Assn. for Year Round Edn. (bd. dirs. 1991—), Ind. Women's Orgn., La. PTA (hon. state life), Delta Sigma Theta (life, Vol. Svc. award New Orleans Alumnae chpt. 1977),. Baptist. Avocations: cooking, crafts. Home: 3701 Mansfield Ave New Orleans LA 70131 Office: Regional Transit Authority 6700 Plaza Dr New Orleans LA 70127-2641

SIMMS, LOWELLE, synod executive; b. Sterling, Colo., June 16, 1931; s. Griffin L. and Irene O. (Geer) S.; m. Lois A. Streeter, Aug. 8, 1959. BA, Park Coll., 1953; MDiv, Union Theol. Sem., 1956. Ordained min. Presbyn. Ch., 1956. Pastor East Trenton Presbyn. Ch., Trenton, N.J., 1957-61, Calvary Presbyn. Ch., Phila., 1961-66; min. of mission First, North, Westminster Chs., Kalamazoo, Mich., 1966-80; assoc. exec. Presbytery of Scoto Valley, Columbus, Ohio, 1969-80; adminstr. interims Presbytery and Synods Presbyterian Ch., 1980-83; synod exec. Synod of the Covenant, Columbus. Avocation: photography. Office: Synod of the Covenant 6172 Busch Blvd Ste 3000 Columbus OH 43229

SIMMS, MARIA ESTER, health services administrator; b. Bahia Blanca, Argentina; came to U.S., 1963; d. Jose and Esther (Guays) Barberio Esandi; m. Michael Simms, July 15, 1973 (Aug. 1993); children: Michelle Bonnie Lee Carla, Michael London Valentine, Matthew Brandon. Degree medicine, Facultad del Centenario, Rosario, Argentina, 1962; Physician Asst. Cert. (hon.), U. So. Calif., 1977. Medical diplomate. Pres. Midtown Svcs. Inc., L.A., 1973—. Chmn. bd. dirs. Am.'s Film Inst., Washington. Fellow Am. Acad. Physicians' Assts.; mem. Bus. for Law Enforcement (northeast divsn.), Physicians for Social Responsibility, Mercy Crusade Inc., Internat. Found. for Survival Rsch., Noetic Scis. Soc., Inst. Noetic Scis., So. Calif. Alliance for Survival, Supreme Emblem Club of U.S., Order Eastern Star, Flying Samaritans, Shriners. Avocations: coin collecting, designing, writing, oil painting, flying.

SIMMS, MARIA KAY, publishing and computer services executive; b. Princeton, Ill., Nov. 18, 1940; d. Frank B. and Anna (Haurberg) S.; m. Neil F. Michelsen, Oct. 2, 1987 (dec. 1990); children: Shannon Sullivan Stillings, Molly A. Sullivan, Elizabeth Maria Jossick. BFA, Ill. Wesleyan U., 1962. Cert. cons. profl. astrologer; ordained min. L.A. Cmty. Ch. of Religious Sci. Art tchr. elem. and jr. high pub. schs., Dundee, Northbrook, Ill., 1962-65; high sch. art tchr. Danbury, Conn., 1975-76; self employed gallery painter various cities, 1962-77, free-lance commnl. illustrator, 1972-74, 86-87; shop, gallery, café owner Conn., 1976-79; art dir. ACS Pubs., Inc., San Diego, Calif., 1987-90; pres. Astro Comm. Svcs., Inc. (formerly ACS Pubs.), San Diego, 1990—; conf. lectr. United Astrology Congress, Washington, 1992, Am. Fedn. Astrologers Internat. Conv., Chgo., 1992. Author: Twelve Wings of the Eagle, 1988, Dial Detective, 1989; co-author: Search for the Christmas Star, 1989, Circle of the Cosmic Muse, 1994, Your Magical Child, 1994; contbr. numerous articles to mags. High priestess Cir. of the Cosmic Muse; chairperson pub. outreach focus group Wiccan Ind. Network. Recipient numerous art awards. Mem. Nat. Assn. Women Bus. Owners, Nat. Coun. Geocosmic Rsch. Inc. (dir., pubs. dir. 1981-92, editor jour. 1984-92), Am. Fedn. Astrologers, Internat. Soc. Astrol. Rsch., New Age Pubs. Assn. Office: Astro Comm Svcs Inc 5521 Ruffin Rd San Diego CA 92123

SIMMS, PHILLIP, sports commentator, former professional football player; b. Lebanon, Ky., Nov. 3, 1956. Student, Morehead State U. Quarterback N.Y. Giants, NFL, 1979-94; sports commentator ESPN, Prime Time Monday, 1994—. Named to Pro Bowl Team, 1985, 86, 93; recipient Pro Bowl Player of Game award, 1986, MVP award Super Bowl XXI, 1987. Appeared on NFL Championship Team, 1986. Office: ESPN ESPN Plz Bristol CT 06010

SIMMS, SUSAN FAYE, nursing administrator; b. Bklyn., Nov. 25, 1939; d. Sol and Freda (Leventhal) Simms. Diploma in Nursing, Jewish Hosp. Bklyn. Sch. Nursing, 1956-59; BSN, Tchrs. Coll., Columbia U. N.Y.C., 1964; M. Profl. Svcs. in Health Care Adminstrn., C. W. Post Coll., Long Island U., Greenvale, N.Y., 1975-77. Cons. Norman Jaspan Assocs., N.Y.C., 1968-69; asst./dir. nursing Peninsula Hosp. Ctr., Queens, N.Y., 1969-72; asst. dir. nursing Kingsbrook Jewish Med. Ctr., Bklyn., 1973-76, assoc. dir. nursing, 1976-77; asst. prof. St. Francis Coll., Bklyn., 1976-77; v.p. nursing Arlington Hosp., Va., 1977-87; asst. adminstr. nursing Fresno (Calif.) Community Hosp., 1987-90; prin. Veritas Cons. Group, Madera, Calif., 1990—; DON Biggsburg (Calif.) Dist. Hosp.; asst. prof. U. Phoenix, Sacramento Campus; cons. nursing edn. State Bd. Higher Edn. Ga., 1979; mem. govs. adv. com. Medicare and Medicaid, Va., 1982; adj. prof. George Mason U., Annandale, Va., 1980-81. Mem. Com. of 100, Arlington, Va., 1977-79; chmn. curriculum adv. com. nursing program No. Va. Community Coll., 1980—. Capt. USAF, 1964-66. Regents scholar N.Y. State U., 1956, 60. Named Honoree Va. div. AAUW, 1985. Mem. ANA, Va. Nurses Assn. (lobbyist 1984; pres. 1984—), Nat. League Nursing, Nat. Forum Adminstrs. Nursing Service, Va. Assn. Nursing Execs. (bd. dirs.), Am. Assn. Nurse Execs. Republican. Jewish. Club: Great Dane Rescue League (v.p. 1981-84) (Vienna, Va.). Avocations: cooking; traveling; gardening; writing.

SIMMS, THOMAS HASKELL, chief of police; b. Yuma, Ariz., Sept. 3, 1945; s. Jessie Lee and Mary Elizabeth (Servos) S.; m. Oct. 12, 1966 (div. July 1981); m. Virginia Lee David, Mar. 26, 1988; children: Thomas Haskell Jr., Julie Marie. BA, St. Mary's Coll., Moraga, Calif., 1981; MA, Calif. Poly., Pomona, 1991. Officer Mountain View (Calif.) Police Dept., 1972-76; police sgt. East Bay Parks, Oakland, Calif., 1976-79; police lt. Town of Moraga, Calif., 1979-84, chief police, 1984-87; chief police City of Piedmont, Calif., 1987-91; chief of police City of Roseville, Calif., 1991—. Bd. dirs. Piedmont coun. Boy Scouts Am., 1988-89. Maj. U.S. Army, 1967-71, Vietnam. Mem. Calif. Chiefs Police Assn., Calif. Peace Officers Assn., Rotary, Kiwanis (pres. Moraga 1982-83, Kiwanian of Yr. award 1983). Presbyterian. Avocations: hiking, photography, travel, golf. Office: Roseville Police Dept 311 Vernon St Roseville CA 95678-2634

SIMOKAITIS, FRANK JOSEPH, air force officer, lawyer; b. St. Louis, Dec. 12, 1922; s. Frank and Constance (Ladish) S.; m. Mary Jane Feeny; children: Frank, Peggy, Mary. Student, Washington U., St. Louis, 1945-47; LL.B., St. Louis U., 1950, J.D., 1970. Bar: U.S. Supreme Ct. U.S 1950, Mo. 1950, also other fed. cts. 1950. Commd. 2d lt. USAAF, 1943; advanced through grades to maj. gen. USAF, 1973; plans and ops. officer Hdqrs. Pacific Air Force, 1960-63; staff officer Hdqrs. USAF, Washington, 1963-69; exec. asst. to sec. air force Hdqrs. USAF, 1969-73; comdt. Air Force Inst. Tech., 1973-78; dir. Dept. Def. affairs Hdqrs. NASA, Washington, 1978-83, cons., 1983—. Bd. dirs. Dayton Club. ARC, Greater Miami chpt., arbitrator Better Bus. Bur. Decorated D.S.M., Legion of Merit, Air medal with 4 oak leaf clusters, Air Force Commendation medal. Mem. Miami Air Force Assn. (bd. dirs.), Navy League (v.p. U.S. Miami coun.), Bolling AFB Officers Club. Home: 3100 S Manchester St Falls Church VA 22044-2711

SIMON, ALBERT, physicist, engineer, educator; b. N.Y.C., Dec. 27, 1924; s. Emanuel D. and Sarah (Leitner) S.; m. Harriet E. Rubinstein, Aug. 17, 1947 (dec. June 1970); children: Richard, Janet, David; m. Rita Shiffman, June 11, 1972. B.S., CCNY, 1947; Ph.D., U. Rochester, 1950. Registered profl. engr., N.Y. State. Physicist Oak Ridge Nat. Lab., 1950-54, asso. dir. neutron physics div., 1954-61; head plasma physics div. Gen. Atomic Co., San Diego, 1961-66; prof. dept. mech. engring. U. Rochester, N.Y., 1966—; prof. physics U. Rochester, 1968—, chmn. dept. mech. engring., 1977-84; mem. Inst. for Advanced Study, Princeton, 1974-75; sr. vis. fellow U.K. Sci. Research Council, Oxford U., 1975. Author: An Introduction to Thermonuclear Research, 1959; contbr. to: Ency. Americana, 1964, 74; Editor: Advances in Plasma Physics, 1967—. With USN, 1944-46. Recipient Univ. Mentor award, 1988-89; John Simon Guggenheim fellow, 1964-65. Fellow Am. Phys. Soc. (chmn. plasma physics div. 1963-64); mem. ASME, ASEE (chmn. nuclear engring. div. 1985-86). Home: 263 Ashley Dr Rochester NY 14620-3327

SIMON, ARTHUR, pharmacologist, research laboratory executive; b. Bklyn., June 1, 1942; s. Harry and Ann S.; m. Sandra Goldberg, July 10, 1966; children—Brett David, Kira Denise. B.S. in Biology, Phila. Coll. Pharmacy and Sci., 1965; M.S. cum laude, Fairleigh Dickinson U., 1969; Ph.D. in Pharmacology (NIH fellow), U. Cin., 1972. Lab. technician La Wall and Harrisson Research Lab., Phila., 1962-63; research asst. toxicology dept. Wyeth Labs., Paoli, Pa., 1965-66; research assoc. pharmacology dept. Warner Lambert Research Inst., Morris Plains, N.J., 1966-69; research investigator Squibb Inst. for Med. Research, Princeton, N.J., 1972-74; sr. cardiovascular pharmacologist USV Pharm. Corp., Tuckahoe, N.Y., 1974-76; dir. cardiovascular clin. research Bristol Myers Co. Internat. Div., 1974-82; pres., chief exec. officer Research Testing Labs., Inc., Great Neck, N.Y., 1982—. Mem. Dermal Clin. Evaluation Soc., Drug Info. Assn., Assocs. Clin. Pharmacologist, Regulatory Affairs Profl. Soc., Internat. Assn. Dental Rsch., Am. Assn. Dental Rsch. Internat. Dental Rsch. Home: 52 Tamarack Ln Pomona NY 10970-2012 Office: Rsch Testing Labs Inc 255 Great Neck Rd Great Neck NY 11021-3314

SIMON, BARRY, mathematician, physicist, educator; b. Bklyn., Apr. 16, 1946; s. Hy and Minnie (Landa) S.; m. Martha Katzin, Jan. 24, 1971; children: Rivka, Benjamin, Zvi, Aryeh, Chana. B.A., Harvard U., 1966; Ph.D., Princeton U., 1970. Instr. depts. math. and physics Princeton U., N.J., 1969-70, asst. prof., 1970-72, assoc. prof., 1971-76, prof., 1976-81; prof. math. and theoretical physics Calif. Inst. Tech., Pasadena, 1981—, IBM prof. math. and theoretical physics, 1984—. Author 9 books in field; contbr. articles to profl. jours.; editor: Wadsworth Advanced Mathematics Book Series, 1980—, Mathematical Notes Series, 1980—; assoc. editor Jour. Operator Theory, 1979, Communications in Math. Physics, 1979—, Duke Math. Jour., 1980-90. Recipient medal Internat. Acad. Atomic and Molecular Sci., 1981, Stampacchia prize, 1982. Fellow Am. Phys. Soc.; mem. Am. Math. Soc. (council 1976-78, program com. for nat. meetings 1980-82). Office: Calif Inst Tech 1201 E California Blvd Pasadena CA 91125-0001

SIMON, BARRY PHILIP, lawyer; b. Paterson, N.J., Nov. 22, 1942; s. Alfred Louis and Rhoda (Tapper) S.; m. Hinda Bookstaber, Feb. 9, 1964; children: Alan, John, Eric. BA, Princeton U., 1964; LLB, Yale U., 1967. Bar: N.Y. 1965, Tex. 1986. Assoc. atty. Hughes Hubbard & Reed, N.Y.C., 1967-69, Sullivan & Cromwell, N.Y.C., 1969-72, Shea & Gould, N.Y.C.,

1972-73; v.p., gen. counsel Teleprompter Corp., N.Y.C., 1973-82; v.p., sec., gen. counsel Continental Airlines, L.A. and Houston, 1982-86; v.p. in-charge internat. div. Continental Airlines, Houston, 1987-90; sr. v.p. legal affairs, gen. counsel, sec. Continental Airlines, 1990-92; sr. v.p. Tex. Air Corp., 1986-87; sr. v.p. legal affairs, gen. counsel, sec. Ea. Airlines, Miami, 1987-90; exec. v.p., gen. counsel GAF Corp., Wayne, N.J., 1993—. Mem. copyright com. Nat. Cable TV Assn., Washington, 1974-76, mem. utilities com., 1973-82. Recipient Class of 1888 Lit. prize Princeton U., 1961. Mem. Montclair Golf Club, Houston Racquet Club. Home: 3435 Westheimer # 1604 Houston TX 77027

SIMON, BERNECE KERN, social work educator; b. Denver, Nov. 27, 1914; d. Maurice Meyer and Jennie (Bloch) Kern; m. Marvin L. Simon, Feb. 26, 1939; 1 dau., Anne Elizabeth. B.A., U. Chgo., 1936, M.A., 1942. Social worker Jewish Children's Bur. Chgo., 1938-40, U. Chgo. Hosps. and Clinics, 1940-44; mem. faculty U. Chgo., 1944-81, instr., 1944-48, asst. prof., 1948-60, prof. social casework, 1960—, Samuel Deutsch prof. Sch. Social Service Adminstrn., 1960-81, emeritus, 1981—. Mem. bd. editors 17th Edit. Ency. Social Work, 1975-77, Social Svc. Rev., 1975—; bd. editors: Social Work, 1978-82, book rev. editor, 1982-87; cons. editor Journal of Social Work Education, 1991—; contbr. articles to profl. jours., book chpts., monographs. Mem. Council Social Work Edn. (mem. nat. bd., sec. 1972-74), Nat. Assn. Social Workers, Acad. Cert. Social Workers, Nat. Acads. Practice: Social Work. Office: U Chgo Sch Social Service Adminstrn 969 E 60th St Chicago IL 60637

SIMON, CARLY, singer, composer, author; b. N.Y.C., June 25, 1945; d. Richard S.; m. James Taylor, 1972 (div. 1983); children: Sarah Maria, Benjamin Simon; m. James Hart, Dec. 23, 1987. Studied with Pete Seeger. Singer, composer, rec. artist, 1971—. Appeared in film No Nukes, 1980; albums include Carly Simon, 1971, Anticipation, 1972, No Secrets, 1973, Hotcakes, 1974, Playing Possum, 1975, The Best of Carly Simon, 1975, Another Passenger, 1976, Boys in the Trees, 1978, Spy, 1979, Come Upstairs, 1980, Torch, 1981, Hello Big Man, 1983, Spoiled Girl, 1985, Coming Around Again, 1987, Greatest Hits Live, 1988, My Romance, 1990, Have You Seen Me Lately?, 1990, Carly Simon, This Is My Life, 1992, Letters Never Sent, 1994; single records: Nobody Does It Better, 1977, Let the River Run, 1988 (Academy award best original song, 1989), (with Frank Sinatra) In the Wee Small Hours of the Morning, 1993; recipient Grammy award as best new artist 1971; TV appearance: Carly in Concert: My Romance, 1990; author: Amy the Dancing Bear, 1988, The Boy of the Bells, 1990, The Fisherman's Song, 1991, The Nightime Chauffeur, 1993; created opera Romulus Hunt, 1993. *

SIMON, CAROLINE K(LEIN), lawyer; b. N.Y.C.; d. David and Julia (Feist) Klein; m. Leopold King Simon (dec. 1952); children: Lee, Cathy Simon Silver (Mrs. Sidney Prince); m. Irving W. Halpern, 1953 (dec.). Student Columbia U.; LL.B., NYU; L.H.D. (hon.), Jewish Inst. Religion, Hebrew Union Coll., 1966. Bar: N.Y., U.S. Dist. Ct. (so. dist.) N.Y., U.S. Supreme Ct. Gen. practice, N.Y.C.; of counsel Kaplan Kilsheimer; sec. of state State of N.Y., 1959-63; judge N.Y. State Ct. Claims, 1963-71. Mem. spl. legis. com. on ct. reorgn. N.Y. State Senate; formerly chmn. subcom. on the jury N.Y. Appellate Divs. 1st and 2d Depts.; mem. com. on discrimination in employment N.Y. State War Coun., 1943-45; commr. State Workmen's Compensation Bd., 1944-45, State Commn. Against Discrimination, 1945-55, State Youth Commn., 1956-59; legal adviser U.S. del. UN Human Rights Commn., 1958; mem. White House Confs. on Children, 1950, 60; bd. dirs., exec. com. Com. on Modern Cts., Fund for Modern Cts.; mem. med. malpractice mediation panel 1st Jud. Dept.; adv. coun. Nat. Ctr. for State Cts.; past chmn. bd. trustees, past mem. exec. com. Nat. Coun. on Crime and Delinquency, also mem. nat. adv. coun.; hon. bd. trustees, past chmn. com. on social affairs and pub. responsibility Jewish Bd. Family and Children's Svcs.; life mem. exec. bd., mem. adminstrv. com. and bd. govs. Am. Jewish Com.; mem. Nat. Jewish Welfare Bd.; chmn., trustee, former pres. Fedn. Employment and Guidance Svc.; past bd. dirs., v.p. Willkie House; bd. dirs. USO of N.Y.; former bd. dirs., asst. treas. Freedom House, also exec. com. and counsel to bd.; trustee N.Y. County Lawyers Found.; hon. bd. dirs. Manhattan chpt. Brandeis U. Nat. Women's Com.; hon. v.p. Nat. Assn. Women Artists, Inc.; trustee U.J.A., Fedn. Jewish Philanthropies; former mem. Legacy com. Temple Emanu-El; candidate of Republican Party for pres. City Coun. of N.Y., 1957; Contbr. to books; contbr. articles on govt., law, social problems to publs. including N.Y. Times Mag., Jour. of Living, legal jours. Recipient Presdl. citation NYU, 1962. Outstanding Citizenship award Am. Heritage Found., 1961, citation and testimonial, Mass. Com. on Caths. Protestants and Jews, 1960. Bond Between Us Award for outstanding svc. to Israel, 1960, citation and testimonial dinner Assn. for Help of Retarded Children, 1960, Ann. Brotherhood award Temple Emanu-El, N.Y.C. 1961, Woman of Achievement award Fedn. Jewish Women's Orgns., Salute to Women award, 1962; named Woman of Achievement, Women's Internat. Exposition, 1957, Woman of Yr., Beth Israel Hosp. Sch. Nursing, 1960, Woman of History N.Y. State, 1980; named to Hall of Fame Mt. Vernon High Sch. (N.Y.), 1981. Mem. ABA (sect. jud. adminstrn., alt. del. to Internat. Bar Assn. 1966), N.Y. State Bar Assn. (sec. jud. adminstrn., former chmn. adminstrv. law com., currently mem. cts. and community com., com. on profl. issues and standards, com. on election law), N.Y. State Bar Assn. Found., N.Y. County Lawyers Assn. (life, coms. judiciary, forum, spl. com. profl. ethics, former mem. bd. dirs., coun.), Assn. Bar City N.Y. (com. on profl. responsibility, joint com. on fee concilliation, sr. vol. lawyers com.), World Habeus Corpus (exec. com.), Nat. Assn. Spl. Ct. Judges, Nat. Ctr. for State Cts. (adv. coun.), Judges for Arbitration and Mediation, Am. Arbitration Assn. (comml. law com. sect.), Delta Kappa Gamma (internat. hon.). Home: 685 3rd Ave New York NY 10017-4024 Office: 685 3rd Ave 26th FL New York NY 10017-4024

SIMON, CATHY JENSEN, architect; b. Los Angeles, Sept. 30, 1943; d. Bernard Everett and Bitten Hanne (Smith) S.; m. Michael Palmer, Nov. 23, 1972; 1 child, Sarah Marina. B.A. Wellesley Coll., 1965; M. Arch., Harvard U., 1969. Registered architect, Calif. 1974, N.Y. 1988, Mass. 1988. Architect Cambridge 7 Assocs., Mass., 1968-69, Building Systems Devel., San Francisco, 1970-72, Mackinlay Winnacker McNeil, Oakland, Calif., 1973-74; prin. Marquis Assocs., San Francisco, 1974-85; prin. Simon Martin-Vegue Winkelstein Moris, 1985—; sr. lectr. architecture U. Calif., Berkeley, 1982-85, vis. lectr., 1973-82; teaching coordinator Women's Sch. Planning and Arch., Santa Cruz, Calif., 1976; speaker ALA Nat. Conv., 1992, Les Grandes Bibliotheques de L'Avenir, Paris, 1991. Prin. works include Yerba Buena Gardens Retail and Entertainment Complex, San Francisco, Mus. N.Mex. Master Plan, Santa Fe, San Francisco Ballet Pavilion, Lick Wilmerding High Sch. Master Plan, San Francisco, Bothell Br. Campus, Bothell, Wash., San Francisco New Main Libr., Oceanside Water Pollution Control Project, San Francisco, Newport Beach (Calif.) Ctrl. Libr., Coll. 8 U. Calif., Santa Cruz, Olin Humanities Bldg. Bard Coll., N.Y., San Francisco Day Sch., Fremont (Calif.) Main Libr., Peter J. Shields Libr. U. Calif., Davis, Elena Baskin Visual Art Studios U. Calif., Santa Cruz, Primate Discovery Ctr., San Francisco Zoo, Braun Music Ctr., Stanford U. The Premier, La Jolla Colony, La Jolla, Calif. Mem. exec. com. San Francisco Mus. Modern Art; active Leadership Commn. Design Industry; mem. tech. assistance com., San Francisco Redevel. Agy., San Francisco, 1982—; mem. adv. panel Calif. Bd. Archtl. Examiners; bd. dirs. Golden Gate Nat. Park Assn. Recipient Calif. Preservation award Chambord Apartments, 1984, Adaptive Re-use award Engr. Offices, Am. Soc. Interior Designer, 1982, Commodore Sloat Sch. Honor award Nat. Sch. Bds. Assocs., 1980, Marcus Foster Mid. Sch. Honor award East Bay AIA, 1980; NEA grantee 1983. Mem. Orgn. Women Architects (founding 1972), San Francisco chpt. AIA, AIA (jury mem. nat. honor awards 1980, Los Angeles chpt. awards jury 1984). Home: 265 Jersey St San Francisco CA 94114-3822 Office: Simon Martin-Vegue Winkelstein Moris 501 2nd St # 701 San Francisco CA 94107-1431

SIMON, DAVID, principal. Dean Manhattan Sch. Music, 1970-79; prin. Balt. Sch. Arts. Recipient Blue Ribbon Sch. Award 1990-91. Office: Balt Sch for Arts 712 Cathedral St Baltimore MD 21201-5210

SIMON, DAVID HAROLD, retired public relations executive; b. Washington, Dec. 3, 1930; s. Isaac B. and Marjorie S. (Felstiner) S.; m. Ruth Lurie, Mar. 2, 1962; children: Rachel, Jessie. BEE, Cornell U., 1954. Mktg. engr. Sylvania Elec. Products, Inc., Boston, 1957-58; advt. mgr. Sylvania Elec. Products, Inc., Mountain View, Calif., 1958-60; regional sales engr. Sylvania Elec. Products, Inc., L.A., 1960-63; mgr. advt. and pub. rels. Electronic Splty. Co., L.A., 1963-66; corp. dir. advt. and pub. rels. Teledyne, Inc., L.A., 1966-67; pres. Simon/Pub. Rels., Inc., L.A., 1967-91. Contbr. articles on pub. rels. to various publs. Res. dep. sheriff L.A. Sheriff's Dept., 1973—; mem. L.A. Olympic Citizens' Adv. Commn., 1980-84; commr. City of L.A. Cultural Affairs Commn., 1987-92, pres., 1990-92; trustee Calif. Chamber Symphony, 1981-84; mem., founder L.A. Philharmonic, 1984—; mem. Philharmonic Men's Com., 1986—; bd. dirs. L.A. Mozart Orch., Odyssey Theater, L.A., 1992—. With USN, 1954-57. Named Res. Dep. Sheriff of Yr., L.A. Sheriff's Dept., 1994. Fellow Pub. Rels. Soc. Am. (bd. mem. L.A. chpt.); mem. Nat. Assn. Sci. Writers, Nat. Assn. Corp. Dirs. (founding pres. L.A. chpt.), Opera Buffs Inc. (bd. dirs. 1986-87), Mensa. Home: 13025 Weddington St Van Nuys CA 91401-6160

SIMON, DAVID SIDNEY, consumer goods manufacturing executive; b. Cleve., Feb. 5, 1941; s. Edwin and Dena (Katz) S.; m. Evelyn Wendy Kulber, Jan. 27, 1963; children: Eric Marc, Todd Alan. BS in Mgmt. Sci., Case Inst. Tech., 1963; MBA, Wharton Sch. U. Pa., 1965. Sr. fin. advisor Mobil Oil Corp., N.Y.C., 1965-69; asst. treas. Dart Industries, Los Angeles, 1969-81, Dart and Kraft Inc., Northbrook, Ill., 1981-82; exec. v.p. fin. and adminstrn. Dart and Kraft Fin. Corp., Northbrook, 1982-86; v.p., treas. Premark Internat. Inc., Deerfield, Ill., 1986-92; instr. Lake Forest Grad. Sch. Mgmt. Mem. Fin. Exec. Inst. (chmn. North Shore Luncheon group 1985-86), Econ. Club Chgo., Nat. Vehicle Leasing Assn. (dir. at large 1985-86). Republican. Club: Ravinia Green Country (Deerfield). Avocations: investments, tennis. Office: Premark Internat Inc 1717 Deerfield Rd Deerfield IL 60015-3978

SIMON, DOLPH B(ERTRAM) H(IRST), lawyer, jewelry company executive; b. Dallas, Mar. 20, 1933; s. Bertram H. and Leta P. S.; m. Nancy Carlson, Dec. 2, 1972; children: Debbie, Dolph, Terri, Beau, Lindsey, Carey. B.B.A. U. Tex., 1954, J.D., 1958. Bar: Tex. 1957. Atty. SEC, Washington, 1962-64; asso. Turner, Atwood, Meer & Francis, Dallas, 1964-67; partner Meer, Chandler, Simon & Bates, Dallas, 1967-70, Tobolowsky & Schlinger, Dallas, 1970-78; sr. v.p., sec., gen counsel Zale Corp., Dallas, 1978—. Served with USAF, 1955-57. Mem. ABA, State Bar Tex., Dallas Bar Assn. Jewish. Office: 901 W Walnut Hill Ln Irving TX 75038-1001

SIMON, DONALD JOHN, financial planner, insurance and investment broker; b. Chgo., July 16, 1947; s. Nicholas J. and Alice R. (Vaughan) S.; 1 child, Joshua K. BSBA, Oglethorpe U., 1969. CFP, CLU. Sales rep. D. W. Shaw, Inc., Berlin, N.J., 1969-74; owner Simon Fin. Co., Greenbelt, Md., 1975—; pres. Video Inventory Sys., Inc., McLean, Va. Bd. dirs. Orphans Found. of Am., Washington, 1994—. Mem. Nat. Assn. Life Underwriters, Inst. CFPs. Avocations: music, tennis. Home: 12600 Eastbourne Dr Silver Spring MD 20904

SIMON, ECKEHARD (PETER), foreign language educator; b. Schneidemühl, Germany, Jan. 5, 1939; came to U.S., 1955, naturalized, 1960; s. Herbert and Doris (Keiler) S.; m. Eileen Higginbottom, Dec. 19, 1959; children: Anders, Conrad (dec.), Matthew, Frederick. A.B., Columbia U., 1960; A.M., Harvard U., 1961, Ph.D., 1964. Instr., German Harvard U., Cambridge, Mass., 1964-65; asst. prof. Harvard U., 1965-69, asso. prof., 1969-71, prof., 1971—, head tutor and lang. coordinator, 1965-76, chmn. dept. German, 1976-82, 85-86, chmn. com. on medieval studies, 1992-95. Author: Neidhart von Reuental: Geschichte der Forschung und Bibliographie, 1968, Neidhart von Reuental, 1975, The Türkenkalender (1454) Attributed to Gutenberg and the Strasbourg Lunation Tracts, 1988; editor: The Theatre of Medieval Europe, New Research in Early Drama, 1991; mem. editorial adv. bd.: Dictionary of the Middle Ages, 1982-89; contbr. articles to profl. jours. Woodrow Wilson fellow, 1960-61; NEH Younger Scholar fellow, 1968-69; research fellow, 1977-78; Guggenheim fellow, 1968-69; Fulbright fellow U. Cologne, 1983. Mem. MLA, Am. Assn. Tchrs. German, Medieval Acad. Am. (asst. editor Speculum 1981-94, book review editor 1994—). Home: 11 Hayes Ave Lexington MA 02173-3521 Office: Harvard U Boylston Hall Cambridge MA 02138-6531

SIMON, ERIC JACOB, neurochemist, educator; b. Wiesbaden, Germany, June 2, 1924; came to U.S., 1938, naturalized, 1945; s. Joseph and Paula (Meyer) S.; m. Irene M. Ronis, Aug. 9, 1947; children: Martin A., Faye Ruth, Lawrence D. BS, Case Inst. Tech., Cleve., 1944; M.S., U. Chgo., 1947, Ph.D., 1951; hon. doctorate, U. René Descartes, Paris, 1982. Postdoctoral trainee in biochemistry Columbia U. Coll. Physicians and Surgeons, 1951-53; lectr. in chemistry CCNY, 1952-59; research assoc. Cornell U. Med. Coll., 1953-59; asst. prof. medicine NYU Med. Center, 1959-64, assoc. prof. exptl. medicine, 1964-72, prof. exptl. medicine, 1972-80, prof. psychiatry and pharmacology, 1980—; Harry Williams Meml. lectr. Dept. Pharmacology Emory U., Atlanta, 1986; mem. initial rev. com. Nat. Inst. Drug Abuse, 1976-80, chmn. 1979-80, mem. Nat. Adv. Coun. on Drug Abuse, 1989-92; Sterling-Winthrop lectr. Albany Med. Coll., 1977; vis. prof. Coll. de France, Paris, 1990. Trustee Teaneck (N.J.) Bd. Edn., 1975-79. Served with U.S. Army, 1944-46. Recipient Rsch. Pace Setter award Nat. Inst. Drug Abuse, 1977, Louis and Bert Freedman Found. award N.Y. Acad. Scis., 1980, Nathan B. Eddy Meml. award Com. on Problems of Drug Dependence, Lexington, Ky., 1983, Alumni Profl. Achievement award U. Chgo., 1986; Health Rsch. Coun. N.Y.C. career scientist, 1959-75. Fellow AAAS, N.Y. Acad. Scis. (trustee 1986-89); mem. Am. Soc. Biol. Chemists, Am. Soc. Neurochemistry, Am. Soc. Pharmacology, Internat. Soc. Neurochemistry, Am. Chem. Soc., Sigma Xi. Lodge: B'nai B'rith. Research, publs. on opiate receptors, endorphins, biochemistry of analgesic action, vitamin E metabolism, acyl-coenzyme A synthesis. Office: 550 1st Ave New York NY 10016-6481

SIMON, ERNEST ROBERT, physician, business executive; b. Karlsruhe, Germany, June 24, 1929; came to U.S., 1938, naturalized, 1944; s. Frederick David and Hedwig (Michel) S.; m. Eve Renee Maier, June 28, 1953; children: Carol, Lori, Renee. Student, U. Calif., Berkeley, 1947-50; M.D. cum laude, Harvard U., 1954. Intern Boston City Hosp., II and IV Med. Services (Harvard), Mass., 1954-55; resident Stanford U. Hosps., 1955-56; clin. asso. NIH, 1956-58; Helen Hay Whitney research fellow in biochemistry Bethesda, Md., 1958-59; hematology research fellow U. Wash. Sch. Medicine, Seattle, 1959-61; asst. prof. medicine U. Wash. Sch. Medicine, 1961-63; mem. faculty U. N.Mex. Sch. Medicine, Albuquerque, 1963-74; prof. medicine U. N.Mex. Sch. Medicine, 1969-74; dir. div. blood diseases and research Heart and Lung Inst., NIH, Bethesda, Md., 1973-76; dep. dir. div. blood and blood products Bur. Biologics FDA, Bethesda, 1976-80; exec. v.p. med. affairs Blood Systems, Inc., Scottsdale, Ariz., 1981—; prof. medicine George Washington U. Sch. Medicine, Washington, 1973-81; clin. prof. medicine U. N.Mex. Sch. Medicine, Albuquerque, 1982—; U.S.A. coordinator U.S.A.-USSR Health Exchange in Blood Transfusion, 1973-76; Mem. hematology study sect. NIH, 1966-70; cons. Nat. Blood Resources Program, also; rep. for implementation nat. blood policy, 1973-76; State Dept. observer to Council Europe com. of specialists on blood transfusion and immunohematology, 1975-80; edn. leader Soviet-Am. Conf. on Blood Services, 1984—; co-chmn. Nat. Conf. on AIDS, Ethics and the Blood Supply. Author: Red Cell Manual, 3d edit, 1966; Mem. editorial bd.: Transfusion, 1967-72, Am. Jour. Physiology, 1968-70, Jour. of Applied Physiology, 1968-70; Contbr. articles to profl. jours. Served as sr. asst. surgeon USPHS, 1956-58; med. dir. 1973-81. Fellow ACP; mem. Am. Soc. Clin. Investigation, Am. Assn. Blood Banks (Morten-Grove-Rasmussen Meml. award 1993), Blood Sys. (John B. Alexer Meml. award 1995), Internat. Soc. Blood Transfusion, Western Soc. Clin. Rsch. (councilor), Am. Soc. Hematology, Phi Beta Kappa, Alpha Omega Alpha. Home: 5325 N 41st St Phoenix AZ 85018-1605 Office: 6210 E Oak St Scottsdale AZ 85252-1867

SIMON, EVELYN, lawyer; b. N.Y.C., May 13, 1943; d. Joseph and Adele (Holzschlag) Berkman; m. Frederick Simon, Aug. 18, 1963; children: Amy Jocelyn, Marcie Ann. AB in Physics, Barnard Coll., 1963; MS in Physics, U. Pitts., 1964; JD, Wayne State U., 1978; LLB, Monash U., Melbourne, Australia, 1980. Bar: Mich. 1980, Victoria (Australia 1981. Supr. engring. Chrysler Corp., Detroit, 1964-72; edn. and profl. mgr. Engring. Soc. Detroit, 1972-78; solicitor Arthur Robinson & Co., Melbourne, 1980-81; sr. atty. Ford Motor Co., Detroit, 1981-89; assoc. gen. counsel Sheller-Globe Corp., Detroit, 1989-90; v.p. planning, gen. counsel United Techs. Automotive Inc., Dearborn, Mich., 1991-94, v.p. bus. devel. and legal affairs, 1995—. Mem. ABA, Mich. Bar Assn. Office: United Tecs Automotive Inc 5200 Auto Club Dr Dearborn MI 48126

SIMON, GREGORY, advisor to the Vice President; b. Blytheville, Ark., Nov. 18, 1951; s. Michael F. and Marcella (Kallie) S.; m. Jennifer Lee Marberg, Dec. 21, 1978 (div. Mar. 1982); m. Margo Lynn Reid, Sept. 5, 1988; children: Michael Reid Simon, Kallile Speice Simon. Student, U. Wien, Vienna, 1971-72; BA, U. Ark., 1973; JD, U. Wash., 1983. Bar: Wash. 1983. Press sec. Barry Commoner for Pres., Flushing, N.Y., 1980; law clk. Riddell, Williams et al, Seattle, 1982; atty. Roberts & Shefelman, Seattle, 1983-85; counsel, staff dir. Investigation and Oversight subcom. House Com. on Sci., Washington, 1985-91; legis. dir. Senator Al Gore, Washington, 1991-93; chief domestic policy advisor Vice Pres. Al Gore, Washington, 1993—. Named Outstanding Oralist, N.W. Round, Jessup Internat. Law Competition, 1983; European Cmty. Visitors Program fellow, Brussels, Strasbourg, London, Rome, Madrid, 1989. Office: Vice President Old Executive Ofc Bldg Washington DC 20501

SIMON, HAROLD, radiologist; b. Trenton, N.J., May 13, 1930; s. John and Rae B. (Gilinsky) S.; m. Jane L. Ludwig, Feb. 25, 1956; children—Steven Gregg, John Gregory. M.D., Duke U., 1955. Diplomate Am. Bd. Radiology, Am. Bd. Nuclear Medicine. Intern U.S. Naval Hosp., Chelsea, Mass., 1955-56; med. officer U.S. Navy, Newport, R.I., 1956-58; resident in radiology Mass. Gen. Hosp., Boston, 1958-61, Oak Ridge Inst. Nuclear Medicine, 1959; instr. radiology Med. Sch., Tufts U., Boston, 1961-63; clin. asst. prof. radiology Med. Sch., Tufts U., 1965, assoc. clin. prof., 1971-77, clin. prof. radiology, 1977—; practice medicine specializing in radiology and nuclear medicine Newton Lower Falls, Mass., 1963—; mem. staff Newton Wellesley Hosp., Newton, Mass.; assoc. chief radiology Newton Wellesley Hosp., 1977—, radiologist-in-chief, 1987—; dir. Sch. Nuclear Med. Tech.; bd. dirs. Grove Bank for Savs.; bd. dirs., mem. CRC com., mem. audit com. Grove Bank; bd. dirs., treas. Newell Physicians, Inc., 1986-93; bd. overseers Newell Health Corp. Contbr. articles to med. jours. Served with USNR, 1955-58. Fellow Am. Coll. Radiology; mem. Radiol. Soc. N.Am., Am. Roentgen Ray Soc., New Eng. Roentgen Ray Soc., Mass. Med. Soc. (mem. ins. com.), Mass. Radiology Soc., Pinebrook Country Club (pres. 1982-85), Belmont Country Club, Presdl. Country Club, Phi Beta Kappa, Phi Eta Sigma. Office: Newton-Wellesley Hosp Radiology Dept 2014 Washington St Newton MA 02162-1699

SIMON, HERBERT, professional basketball team executive; b. Bronx. Grad., CCNY. With Albert Frankel Co., Indpls., 1959; co-founder Melvin Simon and Assocs., Inc., Indpls., 1959—, pres., 1973—; owner Ind. Pacers (Nat. Basketball Assn.), Indpls., 1983—. Office: Ind Pacers Market Sq Arena 300 E Market St Indianapolis IN 46204-2603*

SIMON, HERBERT A(LEXANDER), social scientist; b. Milwaukee, Wisc., June 15, 1916; s. Arthur and Edna (Merkel) S.; m. Dorothea Pye, Dec. 25, 1937; children: Katherine S. Frank, Peter Arthur, Barbara. AB, U. Chgo., 1936, PhD, 1943, LLD (hon.), 1964; DSc (hon.), Case Inst. Tech., 1963, Yale U., 1963, Marquette U., 1981, Columbia U., 1983, Gustavus Adolphus U., 1984, Mich. Tech. U., 1988, Carnegie-Mellon U., 1990; Fil. Dr. (hon.), Lund U., Sweden, 1968; LLD (hon.), McGill U., Montreal, Que., Can., 1970, U. Mich., 1978, U. Pitts., 1979, U. Paul Valery, France, 1984, Harvard U., 1990; Dr. Econ. Sci. (hon.), Erasmus U. Rotterdam, Netherlands, 1973, Duquesne U., 1988; DSc (hon.), LHD (hon.), Ill. Inst. Tech., 1988; D in Polit. Sci. (hon.), U. Pavia, Italy, 1988; D in Psychology (hon.), U. Rome, 1993. Rsch. asst. U. Chgo., 1936-38; staff mem. Internat. City Mgrs.' Assn.; also asst. editor Pub. Mgmt. and Municipal Year Book, 1938-39; dir. adminstrv. measurement studies Bur. Pub. Adminstrn., U. Calif., 1939-42; asst. prof. polit. sci. Ill. Inst. Tech., 1942-45, assoc. prof., 1945-47, prof., 1947-49; also chmn. dept. polit. and social sci., 1946-49; prof. adminstrn. and psychology Carnegie Mellon U., Pitts., 1949-65; Richard King Mellon univ. prof. computer scis. and psychology Carnegie-Mellon U., Pitts., 1965—; head dept. indsl. mgmt. Carnegie Mellon U., 1949-60; assoc. dean Grad. Sch. Indsl. Adminstrn., 1957-73, trustee, 1972-93; emeritus trustee, 1993—; cons. to Internat. City Mgrs. Assn., 1942-49, U.S. Bur. Budget, 1946-49, U.S. Census Bur., 1947, Cowles Found. for Research in Econs., 1947-60; cons. and acting dir. Mgmt. Engring. br. Econ. Cooperation Adminstrn., 1948; Ford Distinguished lectr. N.Y. U., 1959; Vanuxem lectr. Princeton, 1961; William James lectr. Harvard, 1963, Sigma Xi lectr., 1964, 76-78, 86; Harris lectr. Northwestern U., 1967; Karl Taylor Compton lectr. MIT, 1968; Wolfgang Koehler lectr. Dartmouth, 1975; Katz-Newcomb lectr. U. Mich., 1976; Carl Hovland lectr. Yale, 1976; Ueno lectr., Tokyo, 1977; Gaither lectr. U. Calif., Berkeley, 1980; Camp lectr. Stanford U., 1982; Gannon lectr. Fordham U., 1982; Oates vis. fellow Princeton U., 1982; Marschak lectr. UCLA, 1983; Auguste Comte lectr. London Sch. Econs., 1987; Lee Kuan Yew lectr. U. Singapore, 1989, Hitchcock lectr. U. Calif., Berkeley, 1990, lectr. U. Roma Sapienza, 1993, Mattioli lectr. Bocconi U., Milan, 1993; hon. prof. Tianjin (China) U., 1980, Beijing (China) U., 1986; hon. research scientist Inst. Psychology, Chinese Acad. Scis., 1985; chmn. bd. dirs. Social Sci. Research Council, 1961-65; chmn. div. behavioral scis. NRC, 1968-70; mem. President's Sci. Adv. Com., 1968-72; trustee Carnegie Inst., Pitts., 1987-93, hon. trustee, 1993—; cons. bus. and govtl. orgns. Author or co-author books relating to field, including Administrative Behavior, 1947, 3d edit., 1976, Public Administration, 1950, with new Introduction, 1992, Models of Man, 1956, rev. edit., 1991, Organizations, 1958, with new Introduction, 1993, New Science of Management Decision, 1960, rev. edit., 1977, The Shape of Automation, 1965, The Sciences of the Artificial, 1968, 2d edit., 1981, Human Problem Solving, 1972, Skew Distributions and Business Firm Sizes, 1976, Models of Discovery, 1977, Models of Thought, Vol. I, 1979, Vol. II, 1989, Models of Bounded Rationality, 1982, Reason in Human Affairs, 1983, Protocol Analysis, 1984,with new Introduction, 1993, Scientific Discovery, 1987, Models of My Life, 1991. Chmn. Pa. Gov.'s Milk Inquiry Com., 1964-65. Recipient adminsts. award Am. Coll. Hosp. Adminstrs., 1957, Frederick Mosher award Am. Soc. Pub. Adminstrn., 1974, Alfred Nobel Meml. prize in econ. scis., 1978, Dow-Jones award, 1983, scholarly contbns. award Acad. Mgmt., 1983, Nat. Medal of Sci., 1986, Pender award U. Pa., 1987, Fiorino d'Oro City of Florence, Italy, 1988, Am. Psychol. Found. Gold medal, 1988, award for excellence in the scis. Gov. of Pa., 1990. Fellow AAAS, Am. Assn. Artificial Intelligence, Am. Ecn. Assn. (disting., Ely lectr. 1977), Econometric Soc., APA (disting. sci. contbn. award 1969, lifetime contbn. award 1993, William James fellow), Am. Sociol. Soc., Inst. Mgmt. Scis. (life, v.p. 1954, Von Neumann theory award 1988), Brit. Psychol. Assn. (hon.); mem. IEEE (hon.), Jewish Acad. Arts & Scis., Am. Polit. Sci. Assn. (James Madison award 1984), Am. Soc. Pub. Adminstrv. (Dwight Waldo award 1995), Internat. Joint Conf. Artificial Intelligence (rsch. excellence award 1995), Assn. Computing Machinery (A.M. Turing award 1975), NAS (com. on sci. and pub. policy 1967-69, 82-90, chmn. air quality control 1974, chmn. com. behavioral scis. NSF 1975-76, coun. 1978-81, 83-86, chmn. com scholarly comm. with PRC 1987-83, co-chmn. com. behavioral sci. in prevention of nuclear war 1986-90), Cognitive Sci. Soc., Soc. Exptl. Psychologists, Am. Philos Soc., Royal Soc. Letters (Lund) (fgn. mem.), Orgnl. Sci. Soc. (Japan, hon.), Yugoslav Acad. Scis. (fgn.), Indonesian Economists Assn. (hon.), Univ. Club. Pitts., Phi Beta Kappa, Sigma Xi (Procter prize 1980). Democrat. Unitarian. Office: Carnegie Mellon U Dept Psychology Schenley Park Pittsburgh PA 15213

SIMON, H(UEY) PAUL, lawyer; b. Lafayette, La., Oct. 19, 1923; s. Jules and Ida (Rogere) S.; m. Carolyn Perkins, Aug. 6, 1949; 1 child, John Clark. B.S., U. Southwestern La., 1943; J.D., Tulane U., 1947. Bar: La. 1947; CPA, La. 1947. Pvt. practice New Orleans, 1947—; asst. prof. advanced acctg. and taxation U. Southwestern La., 1944-45; staff acct. Haskins & Sells, New Orleans, 1945-53, prin., 1953-57; ptnr. law firm Deutsch, Kerrigan & Stiles, 1957-79; founding sr. ptnr. law firm Simon, Peraigne, Smith & Redfearn, 1979—; bd. adv. editors Tulane Law Rev., 1992—. Author: Community Property and Liability for Funeral Expenses of Deceased Spouse, 1946, Income Tax Deductibility of Attorney's Fees in Action in Boundary, 1946, Fair Labor Standards Act and Employee's Waiver of Liquidated Damages, 1946, Louisiana Income Tax Law, 1956, Changes Effected by the Louisiana Trust Code, 1965, Gifts to Minors and the Parent's Obligation of Support, 1968; co-author: Deductions—Business or Hobby, 1975, Role of Attorney in IRS Tax Return Examination, 1978; assoc. editor: The Louisiana CPA, 1956-60; mem. bd. editors Tulane Law Rev., 1945-46, adv. bd. editors, 1992—; estates, gifts and trusts editor The Tax Times, 1986-87. Bd. dirs., mem. fin. com. World Trade Ctr., 1985-86;

mem. New Orleans Met. Crime Commn., Coun. for a Better La., New Orleans Met. Area Com., Bur. Govtl. Rsch., Pub. Affairs Rsch. Coun.; co-chmn. NYU Tax Conf., New Orleans, 1976; mem. dean's coun. Tulane U. Law Sch. Mem. AICPA, ABA (tax sect. com. ct. procedure 1958—), La. Bar Assn. (com. on legislation and adminstrv. practice 1966-70), New Orleans Bar Assn., Internat. Bar Assn. (com. on securities issues and trading 1970-88), Am. Judicature Soc., Soc. La. CPAs, New Orleans Assn. Notaries, Tulane Alumni Assn., New Orleans C. of C. (coun. 1952-66), Tulane Tax Inst. (program com. 1960—), New Orleans Bd. Trade, Internat. House (bd. dirs. 1976-79, 82-85), Internat. Platform Assn., Petroleum Club, Press Club, New Orleans Country Club, Phi Delta Phi (past pres. New Orleans chpt.), Sigma Pi Alpha. Roman Catholic. Home: 6075 Canal Blvd New Orleans LA 70124-2936 Office: 30th Fl Energy Ctr New Orleans LA 70163 *Developing and maintaining consistency and constancy in feeling and showing genuine respect towards others nourish and stimulate an individual to become day by day a better person. Whether alone or in the presence of others, one who daily abides by the guidance and rules he would advocate to others invariably finds the greatest reward of all—true respect for one's self.*

SIMON, JACK AARON, geologist, former state official; b. Champaign, Ill., June 17, 1919; s. Abraham and Lenore (Levy) S. B.A., U. Ill., 1941, M.S., 1946; postgrad., Northwestern U., 1947-49, D.Sc. (hon.), 1981. Tech. and research asst. Ill. State Geol. Survey, Urbana, 1937-42; asst. to assoc. geologist Ill. State Geol. Survey, 1945-53, geologist, head, coal sect., 1953-67, prin. geologist, 1967-74, asst. chief, 1973-74, chief, 1974-81, prin. scientist, 1981-83; occasional cons.; asso. prof. dept. metallurgy and mining engring. U. Ill., 1967-74, prof., 1974-77, 80-85, adj. prof. dept. geology, 1979-86. Served with F.A. AUS, 1942-43, F.A., USAAF, 1943-45. Decorated Air medal with 4 oak leaf clusters; recipient Disting. Svc. award So. Ill. U., Edwardsville, 1982, Coal Day award So. Ill. U., Carbondale, 1982, Alumni Achievement award dept. geology, 1994. Fellow AAAS (sect. E chmn. 1980), Geol. Soc. Am. (chmn. coal geology div. 1962-63, Gilbert H. Cady award 1975, mem. council and exec. com. 1979-81); mem. Am. Assn. Petroleum Geologists (ea. sect. Gordon M. Wood Jr. Meml. award 1991), AIME (chmn. Midwest coal sect. 1966, Percy W. Nicholls award 1981), Am. Inst. Profl. Geologists (v.p. 1973), Am. Mining Congress, Assn. Am. State Geologists (hon.), Ill. Mining Inst. (hon. life; exec. sec.-treas. 1963-68, v.p. 1980-81, pres. 1981-82), Ill. Soc. Coal Preparation Engrs. and Chemists, Ill. Geol. Soc., Ill. Acad. Sci., Soc. Econ. Geologists (councillor 1982-84), B'nai Brith, Sigma Xi. Club: Exchange (Urbana) (pres. 1969). Home: 502 W Oregon St Urbana IL 61801-4044

SIMON, JACQUELINE ALBERT, political scientist, journalist; b. N.Y.C.; d. Louis and Rose (Axelroad) Albert; m. Pierre Simon; children: Lisette, Orville. BA cum laude, NYU, MA, 1972, PhD, 1977. Adj. asst. prof. Southampton Coll., 1977-79; mng. editor Point of Contact, N.Y.C., 1975-76; assoc. editor, U.S. bur. chief Politique Internationale, Paris, 1979—; sr. rsch. assoc. Inst. French Studies, NYU, 1980—, asst. prof. govt., 1982-83; assoc. Inst. on the Media for War and Peace; frequent appearances French TV and radio. Contbg. editor Harper's, 1984-92; contbr. numerous articles to French mags., revs., books on internat. affairs. Bd. dirs. Fresh Air Fund, 1984—. Mem. Ams. for Dem. Action, Overseas Press (bd. govs.), Phi Beta Kappa. Home: 988 Fifth Ave New York NY 10021-0143

SIMON, JAMES LOWELL, lawyer; b. Princeton, Ill., Nov. 8, 1944; s. K. Lowell and Elizabeth Ann (Unholz) S.; m. Deborah Ann Wolf, Dec. 27, 1966; children: Heather Lyn, Brandon James. Student, U. Ill., 1962-63, JD with honors, 1975; BSEE magna cum laude, Bradley U., 1967. Bar: Fla. 1975, U.S. Dist. Ct. (mid. dist.) Fla. 1976, U.S. Ct. Appeals (11th cir.) 1981, U.S. Patent Office 1983. Engr. Pan Am. World Airways, Cape Kennedy, Fla., 1967-68; assoc. Akerman, Senterfitt & Eidson, Orlando, Fla., 1975-80; ptnr. Bogin, Munns, Munns & Simon, Orlando, 1980-87, Holland & Knight, 1987—. With Seminole County Sch. Adv. Coun., Fla., 1981-88, chmn., 1982, 83; with Forest City Local Sch. Adv. Com., Altamonte Springs, Fla., 1981-84, Code Enforcement Bd., Altamonte Springs, 1983-84, Cen. Bus. Dist. Study com., Altamonte Springs, 1983-85, Rep. Coun. of '76, Seminole County, 1982-87; mem. Seminole County Libr. Adv. Bd., 1989-92, sec., 1990, pres., 1991, Seminole County Citizens for Quality Edn., 1990-92; mem. Seminole County Sch. Dist. Strategic Planning Com., 1991—, Class '91 Leadership Orlando; bd. dirs. Found. for Seminole County Pub. Schs., Inc., 1992—, chmn., 1993-94; bd. dirs. Greater Seminole C. of C., 1993. Capt. USAF, 1968-72. Mem. ABA, Orange County Bar Assn. (jud. rels. com. 1982-83, fee arbitration com. 1983—), Greater Orlando C. of C., Seminole County Bar Assn. (trial lawyers sect. 1993-94), Phi Kappa Phi, Tau Beta Pi, Sigma Tau, Eta Kappa Nu. Republican. Mormon. Home: 620 Longmeadow Ct Longwood FL 32779-2632 Office: Holland & Knight 200 S Orange Ave Ste 2600 PO Box 1526 Orlando FL 32802

SIMON, JEANNE HURLEY, federal commissioner; m. Paul Simon; 2 children. BA, Barat Coll.; JD, Northwestern U. Legis. analyst Nat. Adv. Coun. Women's Ednl. Programs; govtl. rels. rep. Ill. Atty. Gen. Neil Hartigan; mem. Ill. Gen. Assembly; chair Nat. Commn. Librs. and Info. Sci., Washington, 1993—; cons. women's initiative Am. Assn. Ret. Persons, Nat. Security Archive, Emeritus Found.; mem. adv. com. White Ho. Conf. Libr. and Info. Svcs., 1979. Mem. ALA, AAUW, LWV, Il. Bar Assn., Women's Bar Assn. Ill., D.C. Bar Assn., Women's Nat. Dem. Club. Office: Nat Comm on Libraries 1110 Vermont Ave NW Ste 820 Washington DC 20005-3522

SIMON, JIMMY LOUIS, pediatrician, educator; b. San Francisco, Dec. 27, 1930; s. Sylvain L. and Hilda M. (Netter) S.; m. Marilyn S. Wachter, June 21, 1953; children: Kent, Nancy. A.B., U. Calif.-Berkeley, 1952; M.D., U. Calif.-Berkeley, San Francisco, 1955. Diplomate Am. Bd. Pediatrics. Intern U. Calif., San Francisco, 1955-56; resident Grace-New Haven Hosp., 1956-57; sr. asst. resident Boston Children's Hosp., 1957-58; instr., asst. prof. pediatrics U. Okla., Oklahoma City, 1960-64; assoc. prof. U. Tex. Med. Br., Galveston, 1966-72; prof. pediatrics U. Tex. Med. Br., 1972-74; prof., chmn. pediatrics Bowman Gray Sch. Medicine, Wake Forest U., Winston-Salem, N.C., 1974—. Served with USAF, 1958-60. Mem. Am. Pediatric Soc., Am. Acad. Pediatrics, So. Soc. Pediatric Rsch., Am. Bd. Pediatrics, Ambulatory Pediatric Assn., Alpha Omega Alpha. Office: Bowman Gray Sch Med Dept Pediatrics Medical Center Blvd Winston Salem NC 27157

SIMON, JOANNA, singer; b. N.Y.C., Oct. 20, 1940; d. Richard Leo and Andrea S.; m. Gerald R. Walker, Dec. 4, 1976. B.A., Sarah Lawrence Coll. Appeared with maj. opera cos. in U.S. and Europe, including cos. of, Washington, Seattle, Balt., Phila.; mem., N.Y.C. Opera, appeared with: Salzburg (Austria) Festival, and Teatro Colon, Buenos Aires, Argentina, regular appearances as guest soloist with maj. U.S. orchs., including N.Y. Philharmonic, Chgo. Symphony, Boston Symphony, Phila. Orch. Office: care NYC Opera New York State Theatre 20 Lincoln Ctr New York NY 10023*

SIMON, JOHN BERN, lawyer; b. Cleve., Aug. 8, 1942; s. Seymour Frank and Roslyn (Schultz) S.; children: Lindsey Helaine, Douglas Banning. BS, U. Wis., 1964; JD, DePaul U., 1967. Bar: Ill. 1967. Ill. asst. atty. U.S. Justice Dept., Chgo., 1967-70, dep. chief civil div., 1970-71, chief civil div., 1971-74; spl. counsel to dir. Ill. Dept. Pub. Aid, Chgo., 1974-75; legal cons. to Commn. on Rev. of Nat. Policy Toward Gambling, Chgo., 1975-76; ptnr. firm Friedman & Koven, 1975-85, mem. exec. com., 1983-85; ptnr. firm Jenner & Block, 1986—; spl. cons. to administr. DEA Dept. Justice, 1976-77; counsel to Gov.'s Revenue Study Commn. on Legalized Gambling, 1977-78; spl. counsel Ill. Racing Bd., 1979-80; lectr. tng. seminars and confs.; instr. U.S. Atty. Gen.'s Advocacy Inst., Washington, 1974; lectr. Nat. Conf. Organized Crime, Washington, 1975, Dade County Inst. Organized Crime, Ft. Lauderdale, Fla., 1976; faculty Cornell Inst. Organized Crime, Ithaca, N.Y., 1976, judge Minor Moot Ct. competition Northwestern U., 1971-73; mem. law coun. DePaul U., 1974-83, pres. law alumni bd., 1984-85, chmn., 1975-79; adj. prof. DePaul U. Coll. Law, 1977, 81; faculty Practising Law Inst., Chgo., 1984. Contbr. articles to profl. jours. Bd. dirs. Community Film Workshop of Chgo., 1977-90; bd. dirs. Friends of Glencoe Parks, 1977-78, sec., 1978-79; mem. nominating com. Glencoe Sch. Bd., 1978-81, chmn. rules com., 1980-81; pres. Glencoe Hist. Soc., 1979-82; mem. Glencoe Zoning Bd. Appeals, Zoning Comm., Sign Bd. Appeals, 1981-86, chmn., 1984-86; mem. Ill. Inaugural Com., 1979, 83, 87; bd. dirs., mem. exec. com. Chgo. World's Fair Authority, 1983-85; mem. Chancery div. task force Spl. Commn. on

Adminstrn. of Justice in Cook County, 1985—; trustee De Paul U., 1990—; chair phys. plant and property com., 1992-94; commr. Ill. Racing Bd. 1990—; gen. trustee Lincoln Acad. Ill., 1993—. Recipient Bankcroft-Whitney Am. Jurisprudence award, 1965, 66, Judge Learned Hend Human Rels. award Am. Jewish Com., 1994. Mem. ABA (com. on liaison with the judiciary 1983—), Fed. Bar Assn. (fed. civil procedure com. 1979—, chmn. 1985-86, bd. mgrs. 1987-89, chmn. house com. 1989-90, treas. 1990-91, 2d v.p. 1991-92, 1st v.p. 1992-93, pres. 1993-94), Ill. Police Assn., Ill. Sheriffs Assn., U.S. Treasury Agts. Assn., DePaul U. Alumni Assn. (pres. 1985-87, chmn. spl. gifts com. campaign for DePaul, chmn. Simon Commn. 1989-91, nat. chair for ann. giving 1991-94), Standard Club. Office: Jenner & Block One IBM Plz Chicago IL 60611

SIMON, JOHN GERALD, law educator; b. N.Y.C., Sept. 19, 1928; s. Robert Alfred and Madeleine (Marshall) S.; m. Claire Aloise Bising, June 14, 1958; 1 son, John Kirby. Grad., Ethical Culture Schs., 1946; A.B., Harvard U., 1950; LL.B., Yale U., 1953; LLD (hon.), Ind. U., 1989. Bar: N.Y. 1953. Asst. to gen. counsel Office Sec. Army, 1956-58; with firm Paul, Weiss, Rifkind, Wharton & Garrison, N.Y.C., 1958-62; mem. faculty Yale Law Sch., 1962—, prof. law, 1967-76, Augustus Lines prof. law, 1976—, dep. dean, 1985-90, acting dean, 1991; dir., co-chmn. program on non-profit orgns. Yale U., 1977-88. Author: (with Powers and Gunnemann) The Ethical Investor, 1972. Pres. Taconic Found., 1967—; trustee, sec. Potomac Inst., 1961-93; mem. grad. bd. Harvard Crimson, 1950—; chmn. bd. dirs. Coop. Assistance Fund, 1970-76, vice chmn., 1977—; mem. governing coun. Rockefeller Archives Ctr., 1982-86; trustee The Found. Ctr., 1983-92. 1st lt. U.S. Army, 1953-56. Recipient Certificate of Achievement Dept. Army, 1956. Mem. Phi Beta Kappa. Office: Yale U Law Sch New Haven CT 06520

SIMON, JOHN IVAN, film and drama critic; b. Subotica, Yugoslavia, May 12, 1925; came to U.S., 1941; s. Joseph and Margaret (Reves) Simmon. AB, Harvard U., 1946, AM, 1948, PhD, 1959. Teaching fellow Harvard U., Cambridge, Mass., 1950-53; instr. U. Wash., 1953-54, MIT, Cambridge, 1954-55; asst. prof. Bard Coll., Annandale-on-Hudson, N.Y., 1957-59; assoc. editor Mid-Century Book Soc., 1959-61; drama critic The Hudson Rev., 1960-80, Theatre Arts Mag., 1962, Sta. WNET-TV, 1963, Commonweal, 1967-68; drama and film critic The New Leader, 1962-73, 75-77, cultural critic, 1974—; drama critic New York mag., 1968-75, 77—, film critic, 1975-77; film critic Esquire mag., 1973-75, Nat. Rev., 1978—; lang. critic Esquire mag., 1977-79; guest prof. U. Pitts.; lectr. in field. Author: Acid Test, 1963, Private Screenings, 1967, Movies into Film, 1971, Ingmar Bergman Directs, 1972, Uneasy Stages, 1976, Singularities, 1976, Paradigms Lost: Reflections on Literacy and its Decline, 1980, Reverse Angle: A Decade of American Films, 1982, Something to Declare: Twelve Years of Films from Abroad, 1983, The Sheep from the Goats: Selected Literary Essays, 1989; editor: Film 67/68, (with Richard Schickel) Fourteen for Now, 1969. With USAF, 1944-45. Recipient George Polk Meml. award in film criticism, 1968, George Jean Nathan award for dramatic criticism, 1969-70, Lit. award AAAL, 1976; Fulbright fellow U. Paris, 1949-50. Mem. PEN, N.Y. Drama Critics Circle, N.Y. Film Critics Circle. Office: New York Mag 755 2d Ave New York NY 10017

SIMON, JOHN P., lawyer; b. Chgo., Feb. 5, 1953. AB summa cum laude, UCLA, 1973, JD, 1976. Bar: Calif. 1976, Ill. 1983. Ptnr. Sidley & Austin, Chgo. Office: Sidley & Austin 1 First Nat Plz Chicago IL 60603

SIMON, JOHN ROGER, lawyer; b. Los Angeles, Sept. 16, 1939; s. Abram Robert and Rosema (Finsterwald) S.; m. Mary Ellen Bartlett; children: David, Gregory, Whitney, Andrew, Kate. B.S., U. Calif.-Berkeley, 1961, LL.B., 1964. Bar: Calif. 1965, U.S. Dist. Ct. (cen. dist.) Calif. 1965. Assoc. Keatinge and Sterling, Los Angeles, 1964-65; sole practice, Palm Springs, Calif., 1965-66; assoc. Schlesinger, Schlecht & McCullough, Palm Springs, 1966-68, Fine & Pope, Los Angeles, 1968-70, Cox, Castle & Nicholson, Los Angeles, 1970-72; ptnr. Cox, Castle & Nicholson, Los Angeles and Newport Beach, Calif., 1973-86; ptnr. Sheppard, Mullin, Richter & Hampton, Newport Beach, 1986—. Mem. Pacific Club. Contbr. articles to legal jours. Office: Sheppard Mullin Richter Hampton 4695 MacArthur Ct 7th Fl Newport Beach CA 92660

SIMON, JOSEPH PATRICK, food services executive; b. Phila., Nov. 9, 1932; s. Joseph Patrick and Elizabeth Gertrude (McLaughlin) S.; m. Vera Cornelia Steiner, Sept. 15, 1956; children: Joseph Walter, Walter Joseph, Leslie Vera, Ernest William. B.S., Cornell U., 1955. With Slater Systems, 1955-59; with ARA Services, Inc., Phila., 1959-72; regional v.p. ARA Services, Inc., 1964-66, area v.p., 1966-68, group v.p. and sr. v.p., 1968-70, pres. community and school food service div., 1970-71, gen. mgr., pres. internat. ops., 1971-72; v.p., gen. mgr. airline services div. Dobbs Houses Inc., Memphis, 1972-73; group v.p. Service Systems Corp., Buffalo, 1973-79; pres. Service Systems Corp., 1980-85, also nat. dir.; group v.p. P.J. Schmitt subs. Loblaw Ltd., 1984, sr. v.p., 1985-88, also bd. dirs., 1986, 87. Dist. chmn. Detroit United Fund, 1966-67, Nat. Alliance of Businessmen, 1969; mem. adv. bd. McComb Jr. Coll.; mem. council Cornell U., 1980-83; chmn. bd. Sheehan Emergency Hosp., Buffalo, 1984-85; trustee D'Youville Coll.; bd. dirs. United Fund, BUffalo, 1981-82. Served as 1st lt. U.S. Army, 1955-56. Mem. Assn. Food Svc. Mgmt. (dir.), Nat. Automatic Merchandising Assn. (dir.), Buffalo C. of C. (dir. 1982-84), Cornell Hotel Soc. Mich. (pres.), Memphis Athletic Club, Detroit Athletic Club, Buffalo Club, Park County Club, The Meadows Country Club, Zeta Psi. Episcopalian. Home: 4422 Whisperwood Sarasota FL 34235-6924

SIMON, JULIAN LINCOLN, economics educator; b. Newark, Feb. 12, 1932; s. Philip Mordechai and Mae (Goodstein) S.; m. Rita Mintz James, June 25, 1961; children: David Meyer, Judith Debs, Daniel Hillel. BA, Harvard U., 1953; MBA, U. Chgo., 1960, PhD, 1961. Advt. copywriter William Douglas McAdams Inc., N.Y.C., 1956; with sale promotion Ziff-Davis Pub. Co., N.Y.C., 1957-61; owner Julian Simon Assocs., Newark, 1961-63; prof. econs., mktg. and advt. U. Ill., Urbana, from 1963; now prof. mgmt. U. Md., College Park, 1983—; prof. Hebrew U., Jerusalem, 1968, 70-71, 74-75. Author: How to Start and Operate a Mail-Order Business, 1965, 4th edit., 1986, Basic Research Methods in Social Science, 1969, 3d edit.; 1985; (with Herman H. Fussler) Patterns of Use of Books in Large Research Libraries, 1969; Issues in the Economics of Advertising, 1970, The Management of Advertising, 1971, The Effects of Income on Fertility, 1974, Applied Managerial Economics, 1975, The Economics of Population Growth, 1977, The Ultimate Resource, 1981, Theory of Population and Economic Growth, 1986, Effort, Opportunity, and Wealth, 1987, The Economic Consequences of Immigration, 1989, Population Matters: People, Resources, Environment and Immigration, 1990; editor: Research in Population Economics, Vol. I, 1978, Vol. II (with Julie daVanzo), 1978, Vol. III (with Peter Lindert), Vol. IV (with Peter Lindert), 1982, (with Herman Kahn) The Resourceful Earth: A Response to the Global 2000 Report, 1984. Served to lt. (j.g.) USN, 1953-56. Mem. Am. Statis. Assn., Am. Econ. Assn., Pop Assn. Am., Population Assn. Am. Jewish. Home: 110 Primrose St Bethesda MD 20815-3325 Office: U Md Dept Mgmt College Park MD 20742

SIMON, JUSTIN DANIEL, lawyer; b. Chgo., Oct. 9, 1947. BA magna cum laude, Brandeis U., 1969; JD cum laude, Harvard U., 1972. Bar: Mass. 1972, D.C. 1973, U.S. Ct. Appeals D.C. 1973, U.S. Dist. Ct. D.C. 1974, U.S. Dist. Ct. Md. 1977, U.S. Supreme Ct. 1977, U.S. Ct. Appeals (4th cir.) 1982, U.S. Dist. Ct. Mass. 1984. Asst. U.S. atty. U.S. Dept. Justice, Washington, 1972-75; assoc. Dickstein, Shapiro & Morin, Washington, 1975-78, ptnr., 1978—; instr. NITA, Washington, 1979—; mem. exec. com. Am. Inn of Ct., Washington 1988—. Co-author: Guide to White Collar Crime, 1986; contbg. author: Lawyers Desk Book on White Collar Crime, 1991; contbr. articles to profl. jours. Mem. ABA (chmn. subcom. Non-Grand Jury Subpoenas, chmn. subcom. of witnesses in Congr. Inv. 1987-88), Harvard Law Sch. Assn. Avocations: soccer coach, skiing. Office: Dickstein Shapiro & Morin 2101 L St NW Washington DC 20037-1594

SIMON, KAREN JORDAN, retail executive; b. Bridgeport, Conn., Feb. 11, 1953; d. John Francis and Mary (Kirlik) J.; m. James Lawrence Simon, Aug. 12, 1977. BA, So. Conn. U., 1974. Asst. buyer Gimbels Dept. Store, Bridgeport, Conn., 1970-77; buyer Foremost Dist./McKesson June Foods Co., Secaucus, N.J., 1977-79; gen. mgr. Charrette Corp., Woburn, Mass.,

1979-80; dir. purchasing Cumberland Farms Inc., Canton, Mass., 1980-88; corp. v.p. Dairy Mart Inc., Enfield, Conn., 1988-90; sr. v.p. Circle K Corp., Phoenix, 1990-92; pres. FISCO Farm and Home Stores, Stockton, Calif., 1993—. Mem. Nat. Assn. Convenience Stores (exec. coun. 1990-92), Ariz. Retailers Assn. (bd. dirs. 1991-92). Office: FISCO 4554 Qantas Ln Ste 1 Stockton CA 95206-3985

SIMON, KARLA WEBER, law educator; b. New Haven, May 30, 1947; d. Frederick Tyler and Irene Marianne (Schoening) S. BA, Western Coll., Oxford, Ohio, 1969; JD, Duke U., 1972; LLM in Taxation, NYU, 1976. Bar: N.C. 1972, U.S. Dist. Ct. (mid. dist.) N.C. 1973, U.S. Ct. Appeals (4th cir.) 1974. Ptnr. Hobbet & Simon, Durham, N.C., 1972-76; rsch. fellow Yale U. Law Sch., New Haven, 1976-78; prof. U. San Diego Sch. Law, 1984-89, coord. L.A. grad. tax program, 1988-88; prof. Cath. U. Am. Sch. Law, Washington, 1989—; instr. U. Fla. Coll. Law, Gainesville, 1975; adj. asst. prof. Benjamin Cardozo Sch. Law, Yeshiva U., N.Y.C., 1977-78; vis. prof. UCLA Sch. Law, 1982-84; cons. O'Melveny & Myers, Washington, 1988—; exec. dir. Am. Tax Policy Inst., Washington, 1990—. Mem. ABA (chmn. com. on teaching taxation 1990—, vice chmn. tax procedure com. sect. adminstrv. law 1989—), Am. Coll. Tax Counsel, Am. Law Inst. Democrat. Avocations: running, collecting art and antiques. Home: 2137 R St NW 1410 Hopkins St NW Washington DC 20008 Office: Cath U Am Sch Law 620 Michigan Ave NE Washington DC 20064-0001

SIMON, KENNETH MARK, lawyer; b. Pitts., Apr. 25, 1952; s. Harvey and Jean (Busis) S.; m. Janet Hahn, June 24, 1979; children: Eliza, Jessica, Zachary. BA, U. Pitts., 1974; JD, Georgetown U., 1977. Bar: D.C. 1977. Assoc. Dickstein, Shapiro & Morin, Washington, 1977-85, ptnr., 1985—; mem. exec. com. Dickstein, Shapiro & Morin, Washington, 1992—; sec. Ocean State Power, Burrillville, R.I., 1989—. Gen. counsel Conservation Internat., Washington, 1988-93. Mem. Fed. Energy Bar (com. on cogeneration and ind. power, vice-chmn. 1989-90, chmn. 1990-91), D.C. Bar Assn. (sect. on environment, energy and natural resources energy com., chmn. energy com. 1988-90), Electric Generation Assn. (gen. counsel 1992—). Democrat. Office: Dickstein Shapiro Morin 2101 L St NW Washington DC 20037

SIMON, LEE WILL, astronomer; b. Evanston, Ill., Feb. 18, 1940; s. Clarence Turkle and Dorothy Elizabeth (Will) S.; m. Mary Jo Welsh, Feb. 19, 1966; children: John, Dan, Steve. B.A., Northwestern U., 1962, M.S., 1964, Ph.D. in Astronomy, 1972. Staff astronomer, program supr. Adler Planetarium, Chgo., 1969-77; dir. Morrison Planetarium, Calif. Acad. Scis., San Francisco, 1977-83, astronomer, 1983-84. Mem. Am. Astron. Soc., Sigma Xi. Roman Catholic. Home and Office: 245 San Marin Dr Novato CA 94945-1220

SIMON, LEONARD SAMUEL, banker; b. N.Y.C., Oct. 28, 1936; s. Nathaniel and Lena (Pasternack) S.; m. Marion Appel, Sept. 1, 1957; children: Andrew, Jonathan. B.S., MIT, 1958; M.S., Columbia U., 1959, Ph.D., 1963. Mem. faculty Grad. Sch. Mgmt., U. Rochester, 1962-79, prof., 1974-79; v.p. Community Savs. Bank, Rochester, N.Y., 1969-74; sr. v.p. Community Savs. Bank, 1974-77, exec. v.p., 1977-83; exec. v.p. Rochester Community Sav. Bank, 1983-84, chmn., chief exec. officer, 1984—; chmn. Telephone Computing Svc. Corp., 1974-79; trustee Tchrs. Ins. Annuity Assn. Editor-in-chief, founding editor: Interfaces, 1970-76; Author books and articles in field. Chmn. Rochester-Monroe County chpt. ARC, Rochester Area Ednl. TV Assn., Career Devel. Svcs. of Rochester; past trustee Ctr. for Govt. Rsch.; mem. Urban Policy Conf., Brookings Instn., 1972-73, 64th Am. Assembly. Ford Found. grantee, 1964; recipient MIT Corp. Leadership award, 1987. Mem. Community Bankers Assn. N.Y. State (bd. dirs.), Savs. and Community Bankers Am., Genesee Valley Club, Beta Gamma Sigma. Office: Rochester Community Savs Bank 235 E Main St Rochester NY 14604

SIMON, LOTHAR, publishing company executive; b. Wuppertal, Germany, Sept. 17, 1938; came to U.S., 1961, naturalized, 1973; s. Fritz and Erna (Backhaus) S.; m. Jeannine Rechtman, Oct. 30, 1964; 1 child, Charles. Mgr. book dept. Franz Bader Book Shop and Globe Book Shop, Washington, 1961-66; sales mgr. Humanities Press Inc., N.Y.C., 1966-73; pres. Longman Inc., N.Y.C., 1973-81; pub. cons., 1981-82; pres., chief exec. officer Sheridan House, Inc., Dobbs Ferry, N.Y., 1982—. Mem. Assn. Am. Pubs. Democrat. Club: Town (Scarsdale, N.Y.). Office: Sheridan House Inc 145 Palisade St Dobbs Ferry NY 10522-1617

SIMON, MARK, architect; b. N.Y.C., Sept. 5, 1946; s. Sidney Simon and Joan (Lewisohn) Crowell; m. Penelope Bellamy, June 22, 1980; children: Jessica Rabe, Thomas Jefferson. BA, Brandeis U., 1968; MArch, Yale U., 1972. Registered architect, N.Y., N.J., Mass., Conn., R.I., Va. Drafter Lewis Assocs., New Haven, 1972-73, Warren Platner Architects, New Haven, 1973-74; project mgr. Chas. W. Moore Assocs., Essex, Conn., 1974-75; project mgr. Moore Grover Harper, Essex, Conn., 1975-78, ptnr., 1978-84; ptnr. Centerbrook Architects, Essex, Conn., 1984—; vis. critic Carnegie Mellon U., Pitts., 1979, Yale U., New Haven, 1979-82, 85-87, N.C. State U., Raleigh, 1982-83, U. Md., 1989-90, Harvard U., 1990. Contbr. articles to profl. jours. Recipient Record House award Archtl. Record, 1978, 79, 85, award Am. Wood Coun., 1983, 86, 90, 93, Builder's Choice award Builder mag., 1985, 87, 90, Product Design award Inst. of Bus. Designers, 1993. Fellow AIA (chmn. com. on design 1982, Excellence award 1980, Jour. Drawing award 1982, Design award 1982, 2 Golf awards L.I. chpt. 1984, VA Design award 1994); mem. Conn. Soc. Architects (bd. dirs. 1985-86, Honor award 1978, 88, 89, 90, Unbuilt Projects Honor award 1990, 92). Office: Centerbrook Architects & Planners PO Box 955 Essex CT 06426

SIMON, MARTIN STANLEY, commodity marketing company executive, economist; b. St. Louis, Sept. 6, 1926; s. Elmer Ellis and Bessye Marion (Werner) S.; m. Rita Edith Scheinhorn, June 18, 1950; children: Deborah, Richard. B.B.A., CCNY, 1949; M.A., NYU, 1953. Econ. statistician Indsl. Commodity Corp., N.Y.C., 1949-52; agrl. econ. statistician Dept. Agr., Washington, 1952-58; commodity analyst Connell Rice & Sugar Co., Inc., Westfield, N.J., 1958-62, asst. to pres., 1962-67; v.p., 1967-74; sr. v.p. Connell Rice & Sugar Co., Inc. (now The Connell Co.), Westfield, N.J., 1974—; cons. AID, Jamaica, 1963; mem. Rice Insp. Industry Adv. Com., Washington, 1971-72; adv. U.S. Del. to UN FAO Intergovtl. Meetings on Rice, 1981. Served with U.S. Army, 1944-46, ETO. Recipient Class of 1920 award for merit in econ. stats. CCNY, 1949. Mem. Am. Econ. Assn., Rice Millers Assn. (chmn. legis. options working group 1984-86, govt. programs com. 1986-87, chmn. PL480 subcom. 1988-90), Nat. Economists Club. Office: The Connell Co 45 Cardinal Dr Westfield NJ 07090-1019

SIMON, MARVIN KENNETH, electrical engineer, consultant; b. N.Y.C., Sept. 10, 1939; s. Sidney and Belle (Cone) S.; m. Anita Joyce Sauerhof; children: Brette, Jeffrey. BEE, CCNY, 1960; MSEE, Princeton U., 1961; PhD, NYU, 1966. Mem. tech. staff Bell Telephone Labs., Holmdel, N.J., 1961-63, 66-68; sr. rsch. engr. Jet Propulsion Lab., Pasadena, Calif., 1968—; adj. prof. Calif. Inst. Tech., Pasadena, 1986-87, 88-90. Author: Telecommunications Systems Engineering, 1973, Phase-Locked Loops and Their Application, 1978, reprinted 1991, Spread Spectrum Communications, Vols. I, II, III, 1984, Introduction to Trellis - Coded Modulation with Application, 1990, Digital Communication Techniques, Vol. I: Signal Design and Detection, 1994, Spread Spectrum Communications Handbook, 1994; also. numerous articles; patentee in field. Recipient NASA Exptl. Svc. medal, 1979, NASA Exptl. Engring. Achievement medal, 1995. Fellow IEEE (Bicentennial medal 1984), Inst. for Advancement Engring. Avocation: computer games. Office: Jet Propulsion Lab Mail Stop 161-228 4800 Oak Grove Dr Pasadena CA 91109-8001

SIMON, MELVIN, real estate developer, professional basketball executive; b. Oct. 21, 1926; s. Max and Mae Simon; m. Bren Burns, Sept. 14, 1972; children: Deborah, Cynthia, Tamme, David, Max. Bs in Acctg., CCNY, 1949, M in Bus., Real Estate, 1983; PhD (hon.), Butler U., 1986, Ind. U., 1991. Leasing agt. Albert Frankel Co., Indpls., 1955-60; pres. Melvin Simon & Assocs., Indpls., 1960-73, chmn. bd., 1973—; co-owner Ind. Pacers, Indpls., 1983—; mem. adv. bd. Wharton's Real Estate, Phila., 1986—. Mem. adv. bd. dean's council Ind. U., Bloomington; bd. dirs. United Cerebral Palsy, Indpls., Muscular Dystrophy Assn., Indpls., Jewish Welfare

Found., Indpls.; trustee Urban Land Inst., Internat. Council Shopping Ctrs. Recipient Horatio Alger award Boy's Club Indpls., 1986; named Man of Yr., Jewish Welfare Found., 1980. Democrat. Jewish.

SIMON, MELVIN I., molecular biologist, educator; b. N.Y.C., Feb. 8, 1937; s. Hyman and Sarah (Liebman) S.; m. Linda, Jan. 7, 1959; children—Joshua, David, Rachel. B.S., CCNY, 1959; Ph.D., Brandeis U., 1963. Postdoctoral fellow Princeton U., N.J., 1963-65; prof. biology U. Calif.-San Diego, La Jolla, 1965-82, Calif. Inst. Tech., Pasadena, 1982—; pres., dir. Agouron Inst., La Jolla, 1980—. Contbr. articles to profl. jours. Mem. Nat. Acad. Scis. (Selman A. Waksman microbiology award 1991), Am. Soc. Microbiology.

SIMON, MICHAEL ALEXANDER, photographer, educator; b. Budapest, Hungary, June 20, 1936; came to U.S., 1957, naturalized, 1962; s. Miklos and Magda (Schreiber) Stern; m. Carol Susan Winters, Jan. 21, 1961; children: Amy Catherine, Nicholas Andrew. Student, Budapest Tech. U., 1954-56, Pa. State U., 1957-58; MFA in Photography, Rochester Inst. Tech., 1986. Propr. Michael Simon Studio, N.Y.C., 1966-68; mem. faculty Beloit (Wis.) Coll., 1968—, asst. prof. dept. art, 1971-76, chmn. dept. art and art history, 1984—, assoc. prof., 1976-85, prof., 1985—; curator photography Theodore Lyman Wright Art Center, 1980—. Free-lance photographer, 1958-66, artist-in-residence, Nat. Park Service, Mus. Div., Harpers Ferry, W.Va., 1971, vis. artist, U. Del., Newark, 1974, Sch. of Art Inst. Chgo., 1978; numerous one-man shows of photography, 1964—, latest being, Wright Art Center, Beloit, 1977, 78, Mpls. Inst. Arts, 1979, U. Rochester, 1985; group shows include, Gallery 38A, Beloit Coll., 1974, U. Iowa, Iowa City, 1975, Columbia Coll. Gallery, Chgo., 1975, Mpls. Inst. Arts, 1976, Evanston (Ill.) Art Center, 1978, Purdue U., Lafayette, Ind., 1978, Kohler Art Center, Sheboygan, Wis., 1979, Madison Art Ctr., (Wis.), 1983; represented in permanent collections, Mus. Modern Art, N.Y.C., U. Kans., Lawrence, Mpls. Inst. Arts, Sheldon Meml. Art Gallery, Lincoln, Nebr.; Author: (with Dennis Moore) First Lessons in Black and White Photography, 1978; contbr. numerous articles on Hungarian photography to profl. pubs. Wis. Arts Bd. fellow, 1980; Nat. Endowment for Arts grantee, 1980; Mellon Fund. grantee, 1977. Mem. Soc. for Photog. Edn. (chmn. nat. bd. 1979-81, chmn. Midwest region 1973-76), Szechenyi Soc. of Hungary. Research on history of Hungarian photography, the photographic snapshot. Office: Beloit Coll Dept Art Beloit WI 53511

SIMON, MICHAEL PAUL, general contractor, realtor; b. Madison, Wis., Sept. 23, 1941; s. Michael Francis and Ferne Doris (DeBower) S.; m. Sharon Lee Hackbart, Aug. 31, 1963; children: René M., Michael V. BS in Bldg. Constrn., Bradley U., 1964. Designer, estimator Michael F. Simon Builders, Inc., Waunakee, Wis., 1964-67, v.p., 1967-73, pres., 1973—. Commentator, St. John's Cath. Ch., Waunakee, 1975—. Named Bus. Man of Yr., Waunakee C. of C., 1980, One of Top Dane County Execs., Madison Mag. Poll, 1994. Mem. Nat. Assn. Home Builders. (bd. dirs. 1985—), Wis. Builders Assn. (bd. dirs. 1980-85, membership chair 1981), Madison Area Builders Assn. (pres. 1980, chair arbitration com. 1992-94, Builder of Yr. 1980), Waunakee Rotary. Roman Catholic. Avocations: boating, golf, travel.

SIMON, MORDECAI, religious association administrator, clergyman; b. St. Louis, July 19, 1925; s. Abraham M. and Rose (Solomon) S.; m. Maxine R. Abrams, July 4, 1954; children: Ora, Eve, Avrom. BA, St. Louis U., 1947; MA, Washington U., St. Louis, 1952; MHL, Rabbi, Jewish Theol. Sem. Am., N.Y.C., 1952, DD (hon.), 1977. Ordained rabbi, 1952. Rabbi in Mpls., 1952-56, Waterloo, Iowa, 1956-63; exec. dir. Chgo. Bd. Rabbis, 1963-80, exec. v.p., 1980—; nat. chaplain Jewish War Vets., 1977-78. Host: weekly TV program What's Nu?, Sta. WGN-TV, 1973-92. Mem. Jewish Community Rels. Coun., Jewish United Fund.; mem. nat. council Joint Distbn. Com., Religious Leaders Com. With AUS, 1943-46. Recipient citation Jewish War Vets., 1967, citation Boy Scouts Am., 1966, 74, 88, citation Chgo. chpt. Am. Jewish Congress, 1973, citation Chgo. Conf. Jewish Women's Orgns., 1973, citation Chgo. Bd. Rabbis, 1973, Rabbinical Service award of Appreciation Jewish Theol. Sem. Am., 1988, Raoul Wallenberg Humanitarian award, 1989. Mem. Rabbinical Assembly, Coun. Religious Leaders Met. Chgo. Home: 621 County Line Rd Highland Park IL 60035-5220 Office: 1 S Franklin St Chicago IL 60606-4609

SIMON, NEIL, playwright, television writer; b. N.Y.C., July 4, 1927; s. Irving and Mamie Simon; m. Joan Balm, Sept. 30, 1953 (dec.); m. Marsha Mason, 1973 (div.); m. Diane Lander, 1987. Student, NYU, 1946; LLD (hon.), Hofstra U., 1981, Williams Coll., 1984. Author materials for Tamiment (Pa.) revues, 1952-53; author: (with brother Danny) sketches Catch a Star, 1955, (with brother Danny) for New Faces of '56; book for musicals Little Me, 1962, Sweet Charity, 1966 (Evening Standard Drama award 1967), Promises, Promises, 1968 (Tony award nomination 1969), They're Playing Our Song, 1979, Little Me (Tony award nomination 1963 version, rev. version), 1982, The Goodbye Girl, 1993; plays include Come Blow Your Horn, 1961, Barefoot in the Park, 1963 (Tony award nomination 1963), The Odd Couple, 1965 (Tony award 1965), The Star-Spangled Girl, 1966, Plaza Suite, 1968 (Tony award nomination 1968), Last of the Red Hot Lovers, 1969 (Tony award nomination 1970), The Gingerbread Lady, 1970, The Prisoner of Second Avenue, 1971 (Tony award nomination 1972), The Sunshine Boys, 1972, The Good Doctor, 1973, God's Favorite, 1974, California Suite, 1976, Chapter Two, 1977, I Ought to be in Pictures, 1980, Fools, 1981, Brighton Beach Memoirs, 1983, Biloxi Blues, 1985 (Tony award for Best Playwright 1985, Best Play 1985), The Odd Couple (female version), 1985, Broadway Bound, 1986 (Tony award nomination 1987), Rumors, 1988, Lost in Yonkers, 1991 (Pulitzer Prize for drama 1991, Tony award Best Play 1991), Jake's Women, 1992, Laughter on the 23rd Floor, 1993, London Suite, 1995; wrote screenplays adapted from own plays: Barefoot in the Park, 1967, The Odd Couple, 1968, Plaza Suite, 1971, Last of the Red Hot Lovers, 1972, The Prisoner of Second Avenue, 1975, The Sunshine Boys, 1975, California Suite, 1978, Chapter Two, 1979, Only When I Laugh (adapted from play The Gingerbread Lady), 1981, I Ought to be in Pictures, 1982, Brighton Beach Memoirs, 1986, Biloxi Blues, 1988, Broadway Bound, 1992 (TV motion picture), Lost in Yonkers, 1993; other screenplays include After the Fox, 1966, The Out-of-Towners, 1970, The Heartbreak Kid, 1973, Murder by Death, 1976, The Goodbye Girl, 1977, The Cheap Detective, 1978, Seems Like Old Times, 1980, Max Dugan Returns, 1983, The Lonely Guy (adaptation), 1984, The Sluggers Wife, 1984, The Marrying Man, 1991; other motion pictures based on his stage plays: Come Blow Your Horn, 1963, Sweet Charity, 1969, The Star-Spangled Girl, 1971; wrote for TV shows: The Phil Silver Arrow Show, 1958, The Tallulah Bankhead Show, 1951, The Sid Caesar Show, 1956-57 (Emmy award 1956-57), Phil Silvers Show, 1958-59 (Emmy award 1958-59), Garry Moore Show, 1959-60; also NBC spl. The Trouble with People, 1972. Served to cpl. USAAF, 1945-46. Recipient Sam S. Shubert award 1968, Writers Guild screen awards, 1968, 70, 75, Writers Guild Laurel award, 1979. Mem. Dramatists Guild, Writers Guild Am. (3 award 1979, screen awards 1968, 70, 75). Address: care A DaSilva 502 Park Ave New York NY 10022

SIMON, NORMA PLAVNICK, psychologist; b. Washington, Sept. 20, 1930; d. Mark and Mary Plavnick; m. Robert G. Simon, Dec. 18, 1949; children: Mark Allan, Susan. BA, NYU, 1953, cert. in psychoanalysis, 1977; MA, Columbia U., 1953, EdD, 1968. Diplomate Am. Bd. Profl. Psychology, 1988. Psychologist Queens Coll. Counseling Ctr., Flushing, N.Y., 1968-70, asst. dir., 1970-76, dir. 1976; gen. practice psychology N.Y.C., 1976—; faculty, supr. New Hope Guild, Bklyn., 1976—, dir. child and adolescent tng. prog., 1988—; adj. prof. clin. psychology Columbia U., N.Y.C., 1986—; supr. NYU Postdoctoral Prog. in Psychoanalysis, 1988—. Author: (with Robert G. Simon): Choosing a College Major: Social Science, 1981; mem. editorial bd. The Counseling Psychologist jour., 1986-89. Vice chairperson N.Y. State Bd. for Psychology State Edn. Dept., Albany, 1978-82, chairperson, 1982-88; bd. dirs. Pelham (N.Y.) Guidance Coun., 1980-83; pres.-elect Assn. State and Provincial Psychology Bds., 1990, pres., 1991. Recipient Karl Heiser award, 1993. Fellow APA (mem. bd. profl. affairs 1987-89, editorial bd. 1991-93, mem. ethics com. 1995-98, John Black award 1994). Nat. Acads. of Practice (elected disting. practitioner). Office: 500A E 87th St # 5A New York NY 10128-7626

SIMON, PAUL, musician, composer; b. Newark, Oct. 13, 1941; s. Louis and Belle S.; m. Peggy Harper (div.); 1 son, Harper; m. Carrie Fisher (div.);

m. Edie Brickell, 1992; 1 child, Adrian Edward. B.A., Queens Coll.; postgrad., Bklyn. Law Sch. With mus. group Simon and Garfunkel, 1964-71; soloist, 1972—; songs recorded with Garfunkel include Mrs. Robinson (Grammy award), The Boxer, Bridge Over Troubled Water (Grammy award); albums with Garfunkel include Wednesday Morning 3 A.M, 1964, Sounds of Silence, 1966, Parsley, Sage, Rosemary and Thyme, 1966, The Graduate (soundtrack), 1968 (Grammy award), Bookends, 1968, Bridge over Troubled Waters, 1970 (Grammy award), Simon and Garfunkel's Greatest Hits, 1972, Concert in the Park, 1982; solo albums include Paul Simon, 1972, There Goes Rhymin' Simon, 1973, Live Rhymin', 1975, Still Crazy After All These Years, 1975 (Grammy award), Greatest Hits, Etc., 1977, One-Trick Pony, 1980, Hearts and Bones, 1983, Graceland, 1986 (Grammy award 1986, 87), Negotiations and Love Songs 1971-86, 1989, Paul Simon: Solo, 1990, The Rhythm of the Saints, 1990, 1964-93, 1993; concerts include Central Park, 1991, Born at the Right Time tour, Johannesburg, South Africa, 1992, series with Art Garfunkel, Paramount, 1993; appeared in films Annie Hall, 1977, One-Trick Pony, 1980; appeared in Showtime prodn. Paul Simon's Graceland: The African Concert, 1987; author: At the Zoo, 1991. Recipient Emmy award for Paul Simon Spl., NBC-TV, 1977; inducted into the Rock & Roll Hall of Fame, 1990. *

SIMON, PAUL, senator, educator, author; b. Eugene, Oreg., Nov. 29, 1928; s. Martin Paul and Ruth (Troemel) S.; m. Jeanne Hurley, Apr. 21, 1960; children: Sheila, Martin. Student, U. Oreg. 1945-46, Dana Coll., Blair, Nebr., 1946-48; 39 hon. doctorates. Pub. Troy (Ill.) Tribune and 14 other So. Ill. weeklies, 1948-66; mem. Ill. Ho. of Reps., 1955-63, Ill. Senate, 1963-69; lt. gov. Ill., 1969-73; fellow John F. Kennedy Sch. Govt., Harvard U., 1972-73; founded pub. affairs reporting program Sangamon State U., Springfield, Ill., 1972-73; mem. 94th-98th Congresses from 22d and 24th Dists. 94th-98th Congresses from 24th and 22d Dists. Ill., Ill., 1975-85; U.S. Senator from Ill. 1985—; U.S. presdl. candidate, 1987-88. Author: Lovejoy: Martyr to Freedom, 1964, Lincoln's Preparation for Greatness, 1965, A Hungry World, 1966, You Want to Change the World, So Change It, 1971, The Tongue-Tied American, 1980, The Once and Future Democrats, 1982, The Glass House, Politics and Morality in The Nation's Capitol, 1984, Beginnings, 1986, Let's Put America Back to Work, 1986, Winners and Losers, 1989; (with Jeanne Hurley Simon) Protestant-Catholic Marriages Can Succeed, 1967; (with Arthur Simon) The Politics of World Hunger, 1973, Advice and Consent, 1992, Freedom's Champion: Elijah Lovejoy, 1994. With CIC, AUS, 1951-53. Recipient Am. Polit. Sci. Assn. award, 1957; named Best Legislator by Ind. Voters of Ill., 7 times. Mem. Luth. Human Rels. Assn., Am. Legion, VFW, NAACP, Urban League. Democrat. Lutheran. Office: US Senate 462 Dirksen Senate Bldg Washington DC 20510

SIMON, RALPH, rabbi; b. Newark, Oct. 19, 1906; s. Isaac and Yetta (Biddleman) S.; m. Kelsey Hoffer, June 30, 1931; children—Matthew, Tamar (Mrs. Tamar Hoffs), Jonathan Carmi. B.A., Coll. City N.Y., 1927; M. in Hebrew Lit, Jewish Theol. Sem., 1931; M.A., Columbia, 1943; postgrad., Oriental Inst. U. Chgo., 1944-47; D.D., Jewish Theol. Sem., 1964; D.H.L., Spertus Coll. Judaica, 1972. Ordained rabbi, 1931. Rabbi Congregation Rodef Sholom, Johnstown, Pa., 1931-36, Jewish Center, Jackson Heights, N.Y., 1937-43, Congregation Rodfei Zedek, Chgo., 1943—; dir. Jewish Fedn. Met. Chgo., 1949-61; founder Camp Ramah, Conover, Wis., 1947; Pres. Chgo. Bd. Rabbis, 1952-54, Chgo. Council Rabbinical Assembly, 1943-45, Council Hyde Park and Kenwood Churches and Synagogues, 1956; mem. Ill. Bd. Mental Health Commrs., 1957-67, Chgo. Commn. on Human Resources, 1958-71; gen. chmn. Combined Jewish Appeal Met. Chgo., 1967, Bonds for Israel Campaign Greater Chgo., 1965-66; v.p. Rabbinical Assembly Am., 1966-67, pres., 1968-69; v.p. Bur. for Careers in Jewish Service, 1969-70; bd. dirs. World Council Synagogues, 1974—. Author: Challenges and Responses-Messages for the High Holy Day Period, 1985. Editorial writer: Sentinal Mag, 1976—. Recipient Julius Rosenwald award Jewish Fedn. Met. Chgo., 1991; named Man of Yr., Israel Bonds, 1976; named to Sr. Citizens Hall of Fame, 1979; Jewish Theol. Sem. created professorship, Ralph Simon chair in Jewish Ethics and Mysticism, 1959. Clubs: Standard (Chgo.), Idlewild Country (Chgo.). Home: 5000 S East End Ave Chicago IL 60615-3140 Office: 5200 S Hyde Park Blvd Chicago IL 60615-4298

SIMON, RALPH E., electronics executive; b. Passaic, N.J., Oct. 20, 1930; s. Paul and Sophie (Epstein) S.; m. Elena Schiffman, June 22, 1952; children: Richard L., David P., Michael A. BA, Princeton U., 1952; PhD, Cornell U., 1959. Mem. tech. staff RCA Labs., Princeton, N.J., 1958-67, dir., 1967-69; mgr. RCA Electronic Components, Lancaster, Pa., 1969-75; v.p. RCA Solid State Div., Lancaster, Pa., 1975-80; v.p. optoelectronics div. Gen. Instrument Corp., Palo Alto, Calif., 1980-84; pres. Lytel Inc., Somerville, N.J., 1984-87; pres., CEO QT Optoelectronics, Sunnyvale, Calif., 1989—; dir. Xsirius Scientific, Inc., Marina Del Rey, Calif., 1988-91, Applied Electron Corp., Santa Clara, Calif., 1987—. pres., mem. Lawrence Twp. Bd. Edn., Lawrenceville, N.J., 1964-69, Community Action Grou., 1967-69. Recipient UK Zworykin prize IEEE, 1973. Office: QT Optoelectronics 610 N Mary Ave Sunnyvale CA 94086-2906

SIMON, RICHARD A., insurance company executive; b. Morris, Ill., July 14, 1938; s. Alex and Lillian S.; m. Doris L. Kaulfuss, Apr. 29, 1961; children: Robert, Jon. Student, U. Ill. Br. mgr. CNA Ins., N.Y.C., 1960-77; from sr. v.p. to pres. svc. group Continental Ins., 1977-87; chmn. and chief exec. officer GAB Bus. Svcs., Inc., Parsippany, N.J., 1987—; pres., chief exec. officer SGS N. Am., Inc., Parsippany, N.J., 1992—; bd. dirs. SGS N.Am., Inc. Mem. Kappa Sigma. Avocations: tennis, golf, reading, movies. Office: SGS N Am Inc 9 Campus Dr Parsippany NJ 07054-4408

SIMON, RITA JAMES, legal educator; b. N.Y.C., Nov. 26, 1931; m. Julian L. Simon; children: David, Judith, Daniel. BA in Sociology, U. Wis., 1952; postgrad. in sociology, Cornell U., 1952-54; PhD in Sociology, U. Chgo., 1957. Prof., head sociology dept. U. Ill., Urbana, 1968-70, prof. sociology Coll. Law, 1971-74, dir. law and soc. program, 1975-80, prof. sociology, law and communications, 1968-83; prof. law Washington Coll. Law, Am. U., Washington, 1983—; dean Sch. Justice, 1983-89, prof. pub. affairs, law, 1989—; vis. prof. Hebrew U., Jerusalem, 1970-71, prof. law and sociology, 1975-80. Author: The Jury and the Defense of Insanity, 1967, Women and Crime, 1975, Transracial Adoptees and Their Families, 1987, The Insanity Defense, 1988, The Crimes Women Commit, The Punishments They Receive, 1991, Adoption Race and Identity, 1992, Women's Movements in America: Their Successes, Disappointments and Aspirations, 1991, The Ambivalent Welcome: Immigration Public Opinion and Print Media, 1993, Rabbis, Lawyers, Immigrants, Thieves: Women's Roles in Society, 1993. Named Guggenheim fellow, 1967-68. Mem. Law and Soc. Assn. (trustee 1986-89). Avocation: running. Office: Am U Sch Pub Affairs Washington DC 20016

SIMON, ROBERT G., lawyer; b. N.Y.C., Feb. 21, 1927; s. Monroe and Claire S. S.; m. Norma Plavnick, Dec. 18, 1949; children: Mark A., Susan. B.A., Cornell U., 1947; LL.B., J.D., Georgetown U., 1950; LL.M., N.Y. U., 1961. Bar: D.C. 1950, N.Y. 1951, U.S. Supreme Ct. 1955. Assoc. firms in N.Y.C., 1950-52; legal sec. to judge U.S. Dist. Ct. So. Dist. N.Y., 1953-58; assoc. Jaffe & Wachtell, N.Y.C., 1958-61; legal adv. TV series The Verdict Is Yours, 1958-60; successively dir. bus. affairs, v.p., sr. v.p., mgr. bus. affairs dept. McCann-Erickson, Inc., N.Y.C., 1961-80; sr. broadcast atty. The Interpublic Group of Cos., N.Y.C., 1980—; adj. faculty Manhattan Community Coll., 1967, Baruch Coll., 1968, CCNY, 1968, New Sch. Social Research, 1972-73; speaker in field. Author: (with Norma Simon) Choosing a College Major: The Social Sciences, 1981; contbr. articles to profl. jours. Dem.-Liberal candidate for county clk. Westchester County, N.Y., 1952; chmn. Narcotics Guidance Coun., Pelham, N.Y., 1973; mem. Nat. Media Coun. on Disability, 1986—; bd. dirs., gen. counsel Nat. Challenge Com. on Disability, 1986-88; adv. bd. The Caption Ctr. WGBH Found., 1987—. With USAAF, 1944-46. Mem. NATAS (chpt. gov. 1972-85, treas. 1976-81, 1st v.p. 1981-83, pres. 1983-85, nat. trustee 1981-85), N.Y. County Lawyers Assn. (com. on comms. and entertainment law 1990-94), Am. Assn. Advt. Agys. (com. on broadcast adminstrn. policy 1985-93). Home: 2 Garden Pl Pelham NY 10803-3207

SIMON, ROGER, newspaper columnist, author; b. Chgo., Mar. 29, 1948; s. Sheldon and Pauline (Odess) S.; m. Marcia Kramer, May 15, 1977. B.A., U. Ill., 1970. Reporter City News Bur. Chgo., 1970; columnist Waukegan News-Sun, Ill., 1970-72, Chgo. Sun-Times, 1972-84, Balt. Sun, 1984—; work

syndicated by Creators Syndicate; columnist Regardie's mag., Washington, 1986-91; nationally syndicated columnist Balt. Sun, Balt., 1984—. Author: Simon Says: The Best of Roger Simon, 1985, Road Show, 1990; contbr. freelance articles to Playboy mag., TV Guide, N.Y. Times Review of Books. Recipient Page One award Chgo. Newspaper Guild, 1972, 74, 75, 77, 78, 79, 82, 1st place award for public service UPI, 1974, 80, 82, 83, Silver Gavel award ABA, 1975, 76, 79, Nat. Merit award Assn. Trial Lawyers Am., 1975, 76, Disting. Reporter award Inland Daily Press Assn., 1975, 1st place award for column AP, 1976, 77, 78, 80, Peter Lisagor award, 1980, 82, 83, Distinguished Writing award for commentary Am. Soc. Newspaper Editors, 1984, 86, 2nd place, 1993, Washington-Balt. Newspaper Guild award, 1986, 87, 92, Front Page award for commentary Washington-Balt. Newspaper Guild, 1986, 87, 92, Nat. Headliner award for outstanding column, 1987, 89, 2nd place, 1992; work included in Best Newspaper Writing 1984, 86, 93. Mem. U. Ill. Alumni Assn., Pres.' Council. Office: Baltimore Sun 1627 K St NW Washington DC 20006-1702

SIMON, ROGER LICHTENBERG, writer; b. N.Y.C., Nov. 22, 1943; s. Norman and Ruth Elaine (Lichtenberg) S.; m. Dyanne Asimow, June 10, 1965 (div. May 1981); children: Raphael, Jesse. BA, Dartmouth U., 1964; MFA, Yale U., 1970. U.S. rep. Internat. Mystery Writers meetings in Mex., Italy, Spain and USSR. Author: Heir, 1968, The Mama Tass Manifesto, 1970, Wild Turkey, 1973, The Big Fix, 1974 (Mystery Writers of Am. Spl. award, John Creasy award of Crime Writers Gt. Britain), Peking Duck, 1978, California Roll, 1985, The Straight Man, 1986, Raising the Dead, 1988 (1st detective novel pub. in Soviet Union); screenwriter (films) The Big Fix, 1979, Bustin' Loose, 1980, My Man Adam, 1985, Enemies: A Love Story, 1988 (nominated Acad. award 1990), (with Paul Mazurksy) Scenes From a Mall, 1991. Mem. Internat. Assn. Crime Writers (1st N.Am. pres.), Writers Guild Am. (past bd. dirs.) PEN Ctr. USA West (pres.).

SIMON, RONALD CHARLES, curator; b. Phila., Feb. 23, 1951; s. Samuel Charles and Emily (Luzenberg) S. BA, Dickinson Coll., 1973; postgrad., Brit. Film and TV Inst., Stirling, Scotland, 1973, Columbia U., 1973-75. Researcher NBC, N.Y.C., 1974-77; mgr. media prodn. 1st Boston Corp., N.Y.C., 1978-78; curator TV, Mus. TV and Radio, N.Y.C., 1979—; adj. prof. Hunter Coll., CUNY, 1987—, Columbia U., N.Y.C., 1991—; cons., lectr. to mus. and colls., including Smithsonian Instn., Whitney Mus. Am. Art, NYU, Cooper Hewitt Mus., 1985—. Exhbns. curated include: The Television of Dennis Potter, Witness to History, Jack Benny: The Radio and Television Work. Mem. NATAS (panelist and juror for numerous awards 1985—, editorial bd. TV Quar. 1987—), Internat. Radio and TV Soc. Home: 141 E 17th St New York NY 10003-3422 Office: Television & Radio 25 W 52d St New York NY 10019

SIMON, RONALD I., financial consultant; b. Cairo, Nov. 4, 1938; came to U.S., 1942; s. David and Helene (Zilkha) S.; m. Anne Faith Hartman, June 19, 1960; children: Cheryl, Eric, Daniel. BA, Harvard U., 1960; MA, Columbia U., 1962, PhD, 1968. V.p. Harpers Internat., N.Y.C., 1959-62; fin. analyst Ameracce Corp., N.Y.C., 1965-66; v.p. Am. Foresight Inc., Phila., 1966-67; asst. to pres. Avco Corp., Greenwich, Conn., 1967-70; exec. v.p. Avco Community Developers Inc., La Jolla, Calif., 1970-73; pres. Ronald I. Simon Inc., La Jolla, 1973—; Delta Data Systems Corp., Phila., 1980-81; exec. v.p. Towner Petroleum Corp., Houston, 1983-85; mng. dir., chief fin. officer The Henley Group Inc., La Jolla, 1986-90; pvt. practice fin. cons. La Jolla, 1990—; chmn. Sonant Corp., San Diego; bd. dirs. Craig Corp., L.A., Reading Co., Phila. Bd. dirs. San Diego Opera Co., 1988-90; bd. dirs. Mandeville Art Gallery U. Calif., San Diego. Ford Found. fellow, 1963-65; recipient Ann. award Nat. Comml. Fin. Conf., 1963. Mem. University Club (N.Y.C.). Office: 1020 Prospect St Ste 410C La Jolla CA 92037-4148

SIMON, SEYMOUR, lawyer, former state supreme court justice; b. Chgo., Aug. 10, 1915; s. Ben and Gertrude (Rusky) S.; m. Roslyn Schultz Biel, May 26, 1954; children: John B., Nancy Simon Cooper, Anthony Biel. B.S., Northwestern U., 1935, J.D., 1938; LL.D. (hon.), John Marshall Law Sch., 1982, North Park Coll., 1986, Northwestern U., 1987. Bar: Ill. 1938. Spl. atty. Dept. Justice, 1938-42; practice law Chgo., 1946-74; judge Ill. Appellate Ct., Chgo., 1974-80; presiding justice Ill. Appellate Ct. (1st Dist., 3d Div.), 1977, 79; justice Ill. Supreme Ct., 1980-88; ptnr. Rudnick & Wolfe, Chgo., 1988—; former chmn. Ill. Low-Level Radioactive Waste Disposal Facility Siting Commn.; former dir. Nat. Gen. Corp., Bantam Books, Grosset & Dunlap, Inc., Ct. & Am. Ins. Corp. Mem. Cook County Bd. Commrs., 1961-66, pres., 1962-66; pres. Cook County Forest Preserve Dist., 1962-66; mem. Pub. Bldg. Commn., City Chgo., 1962-67; Alderman 40th ward, Chgo., 1955-61, 67-74; Democratic ward committeeman, 1960-74; bd. dirs. Schwab Rehab. Hosp., 1961-71, Swedish Covenant Hosp., 1969-75. Served with USNR, 1942-45. Decorated Legion of Merit; recipient citation for disting. svc. North Park Coll., Chgo., 1967, 9th Ann. Pub. Svc. award Tau Epsilon Rho, 1963, Alumni award of merit Northwestern U., 1982, Hubert L. Will award Am. Vets. Com., 1983, award of merit Decalogue Soc. Lawyers, 1986, Freedom award John Marshall Law Sch., 1987, Judge Learned Hand award Am. Jewish Com., 1994; named to Sr. Citizen's Hall of Fame, City of Chgo., 1989, Hall of Fame Jewish Cmty. Ctrs. Chgo., 1989. Mem. ABA, Ill. Bar Assn., Chgo. Bar Assn., Chgo. Hist. Soc., Decalogue Soc. Lawyers (Merit award 1986), Izaak Walton League, Chgo. Hort. Soc., Comml. Club Chgo., Standard Club, Variety Club, Order of Coif; Phi Beta Kappa, Phi Beta Kappa Assocs. Home: 1555 N Astor St Chicago IL 60610-1613 Office: Rudnick & Wolfe 203 N La Salle St Ste 1800 Chicago IL 60601-1210

SIMON, SHELDON WEISS, political science educator; b. St. Paul, Jan. 31, 1937; s. Blair S. and Jennie M. (Dim) S.; m. Charlann Lilwin Scheid, Apr. 27, 1962; 1 child, Alex Russell. BA summa cum laude, U. Minn., 1958, PhD, 1964; MPA, Princeton U., 1960; postgrad. U. Geneva, 1962-63. Asst. prof., then prof. U. Ky., 1966-75; prof. polit. sci. Ariz. State U., 1975—, chmn. dept., 1975-79, dir. Ctr. Asian Studies, 1980-88; vis. prof. George Washington U., 1965, U. B.C. Can., 1972-73, 79-80, Carleton U., 1976, Monterey Inst. Internat. Studies, 1991, Am. Grad. Sch. Internat. Mgmt., 1991-92; cons. USIA Rsch. Analysis Corp., Am. Enterprise Inst. Pub. Policy Rsch., Hoover Instn., Orkand Corp., Nat. Bur. Asian Rsch. Author: Asian Neutralism and U.S. Policy, 1975, The ASEAN States and Regional Security, 1982, The Future of Asian-Pacific Security Collaboration, 1988; editor: The Military and Security in the Third World, 1978, East Asian Security in the Post-Cold War Era, 1993; also others; contbr. articles to profl. jours., chpts. to books. Mem. Com. Fgn. Relations, Phoenix, 1976—; bd. dirs. Phoenix Little Theater, 1976-79. Grantee Am. Enterprise Inst., 1974, Earhart Found., 1979, 81, 82, 84, 88, U.S. Inst. Peace, 1994—; Hoover Instn. fellow, 1980, 85. Mem. Am. Polit. Sci. Assn., Assn. Asian Studies, Internat. Studies Assn. (profl. ethics com. 1987-91, v.p. 1991-93), Asia Soc. (contemporary affairs com. 1987—), U.S. Coun. for Asia-Pacific Security, Phi Beta Kappa. Democrat. Jewish. Avocations: acting, singing, tennis. Home: 5630 S Rocky Point Rd Tempe AZ 85283-2134 Office: Ariz State U Polit Sci Dept Tempe AZ 85287

SIMON, STEVE, public relations executive. CEO S&S Pub. Rels., Inc. Office: S & S Public Relations Inc 400 Skokie Blvd 200 Northbrook IL 60062*

SIMON, WILLIAM, biomathematician, educator; b. Pitts., May 27, 1929; m. Maxine Check, June 27, 1965; children: Robert, Steven, Alan. B.S. in Physics, Carnegie Inst. Tech., 1950; M.A. in Applied Physics, Harvard U., 1952, Ph.D., 1958. Staff physicist Comstock & Wescott, Inc. (consultant engrs.), Cambridge, Mass., 1951-53; head instruments sect. Spencer Kennedy Lab., Boston, 1953-57; sr. systems engr. Nat. Radio Co., Malden, Mass., 1957-59; chief physicist Image Instruments, Inc., Newton Lower Falls, Mass., 1959-60; mem. staff M.I.T. Lincoln Lab. and Center for Computer Tech. in Biomed. Scis., 1961-64; research asso. dept. physiology, dir. biomed. tech. cons. group Harvard U. Med. Sch., 1964-68; asso. prof., head div. biomath. U. Rochester Sch. Medicine and Dentistry, 1968-77, prof., head div. biomath., 1977-82, prof. biophysics, 1982—; prof. med. info., 1989; vis. assoc. prof. dept. elec. engring. MIT, 1974-75. Author: Mathematical Techniques for Physiology and Medicine, 1972, Mathematical Techniques for Biology and Medicine, 1977; contbr. articles to profl. jours. Office: U Rochester Box BPHYS Rochester NY 14642

SIMON, WILLIAM EDWARD, investment banker, former secretary of treasury; b. Paterson, N.J., Nov. 27, 1927; m. Carol Girard, Sept. 9, 1950;

children: William Edward Jr., John Peter, Mary Beth Simon Streep, Carol Leigh Simon Porges, Aimee Simon Bloom, Julie Ann Simon Munro, Johanna Katrina. BA in Govt. and Law, Lafayette Coll., 1952, LLD (hon.), 1973; other hon. degrees include LLD, Pepperdine U., 1975, Manhattanville Coll., 1978, Washington U., 1980, Boston U., 1980, Washington Coll., 1984, Rider Coll., 1984, Seton Hall U., 1984, Fairleigh Dickinson U., 1984, Rutgers U., 1985, U. Rochester, 1985; D of Civil Law, Jacksonville U., 1976; Scriptural Degree, Israel Torah Rsch. Inst., Jerusalem, 1976; Doctor Philosophiae honoris causa, Tel Aviv U., 1976; DSc, New Eng. Coll., 1977; HHD, Springfield U., 1986; D of Econs., Hanyang U., Seoul, Republic of Korea, 1988. With Union Securities Co., N.Y.C., 1952-57, asst. v.p.; mgr. mcpl. trading dept., 1955-57; v.p. Weeden & Co., N.Y.C., 1957-64; joined Salomon Bros. & Hutzler, N.Y.C., 1964; sr. ptnr., mem. exec. com. Salomon Bros. N.Y.C., 1964-73; dep. sec. Dept. Treasury, Washington, 1973-74; administr. Fed. Energy Office, Washington, 1973-74; sec. of the treasury, 1974-77; sr. cons. Booz Allen & Hamilton Inc., 1977-79; sr. advisor Blyth Eastman Dillon & Co. Inc., 1977-80; dep. chmn. Olayan Investments Co. Establishment, 1980-82; chmn. Crescent Diversified Ltd., 1980-82, Wesray Corp., 1981-86, Wesray Capital Corp., 1984-86; chmn. emeritus Wesray Corp., Wesray Capital Corp., 1987; currently chmn., pres. William E. Simon & Sons, Morristown, N.J.; co-chmn. WSGP Internat. Inc., L.A.; chmn. William E. Simon Found., Inc.; bd. dirs. Pompano Pk. Realty, Inc., Castleton, Inc.; former cons. W.R. Grace & Co., Brazilinvest, Allstate Ins. Co., Calvin Bullock Ltd., Johnson & Johnson; mem. pub. rev. bd. Arthur Andersen & Co.; past chmn. World Trade Bancorp.; lectr. numerous schs. including Harvard Bus. Sch., U. Mich., Georgetown U., Boston U., U. Chgo., Columbia U., Lafayette Coll., U. Notre Dame, Oxford U., USAF Acad., U.S. Mil. Acad., L.I. U., Washington U., St. Louis, Princeton U., Erasmus U., Rotterdam, The Netherlands, U. Rochester, Susquehanna U., Fairleigh Dickerson U.; lectr. confs., round tables, panels, corps., mem. adv. bd. Classics of Liberty Libr., Corp. for Devel. and Commerce, The Papers of Albert Gallatin. Author: A Time for Truth, 1978, A Time For Action, 1980; mem. editorial adv. bd. Gryphon Editions Inc., The Washington Times. Pres. John M. Olin Found., Richard Nixon Presdl. Libr. and Birthplace Found.; chmn. investment com. USAF Acad., USAF Acad. Academic Devel. Fund; former pres. and treas. U.S. Olympic Com., now mem. bd. adminstrs., fin. com.; mem. budget and fin. com., trustee Heritage Found.; trustee The Animal Med. Ctr., Nat. Investors Hall of Fame, Boston U.; hon. trustee Adelphi U., Newark Boys Chorus Sch.; trustee emeritus Lafayette Coll.; trustee, mem. investment com., mem. exec. adv. coun., trustee Simon Sch., U. Rochester; chmn. bd. trustees U.S. Olympic Found.; bd. dirs. Sequoia Inst., World Cup '94 Organizing Com., Kissinger Assocs., Nat. Football Found. and Hall of Fame Inc., dir. emeritus, Cath. Big Bros., Citizens Against Govt. Waste, Space Studies Inst., Boys Harbor Inc., Internat. Found. for Edn. and Self Help, Citizens Network for Fgn. Affairs, Atlantic Coun. of U.S., Target; bd. dirs., co-chmn. endowment com. Covenant House; hon. dir. The Gerald R. Ford Found.; bd. advisors Cath. League for Religious and Civil Rights; mem. nat. coun. trustees Freedoms Found. at Valley Forge; mem. adv. bd. Jesse Owens Found., sec./treas.; mem. bd. overseers Hoover Instn. on War, Revolution and Peace, Stanford U., Exec. Coun. on Fgn. Diplomacy; mem. adv. bd. Am. rep. Pacific Security Rsch. Inst., Sydney, Australia, U. So. Calif. Sch. Bus. Adminstrn., Nat. Ethnic Coalition of Orgns.; trustee Newark Acad., mem. nominating com.; mem. adv. bd., life mem. S.A.I.L., Inc.-Am. Tall Ship Syndicate, Pvt. Sector Initiatives Found., Women's Sports Found., U.S. Assn. Blind Athletes, Caths. Committed to Support the Pope, The Acton Inst., Ctr. for Internat. Mgmt. Edn., U. Dallas, Ctr. for Christianity and the Common Good; mem. nat. adv. bd. Sudden Infant Death Syndrome Alliance; hon. bd. govs. Tel Aviv U.; bd. dirs. U. Limerick Found.; mem. bd. advisors William J. Casey chair geopolit. studies John M. Ashbrook Ctr. Pub. Affairs; mem. fed. adv. bd. Commn. for Preservation of Treasury Bldg.; mem. Inaugural adv. bd. Gene Autry Western Heritage Mus.; mem. adv. coun. Consumer Alert; mem. internat. adv. coun. Internat. Ctr. for the Disabled; mem. com. Cardinal's Com. of the Laity; bd. govs. Hugh O'Brian Youth Fedn.; bd. govs., mem. fin. investment coms., spl. com. on hosp. environ., mem. internat. adv. bd. N.Y. Hosp.; bd. govs. Ronald Reagan Presdl. Found.; mem. Amb. John D. J. Moore Scholarship Fund, Univ. Coll., Dublin, Ireland, Pres.'s Com. on Arts and Humanities; mem. com. for restoration John B. Kelly Jr. Meml. Boathouse; mem. vis. com. Marine Scis. Rsch. Ctr., SUNY, Stony Brook; mem. internat. councillors Ctr. for Strategic and Internat. Studies; mem. hon. com. Women's Econ. Round Table; mem. exec. com. The Bretton Woods Com.; mem. policy coun. The Tax Found.; mem. of coun. Templeton Coll.; prin. Coun. for Excellence in Govt.; mem. exec. coun. Daytop Village, Inc.; mem. nat. steering com. Jefferson Energy Found.; mem. internat. com. Miles Jesu Internat. Com. for Human Dignity; mem. nat. planning bd. Morality in Media Inc.; mem. chmn.'s coun. Nat. Coun. on Alcoholism and Drug Dependence Inc.; mem. diplomatic coun. People to People Sports Com. Inc.; hon. chmn. Inst. Ednl. Affairs; hon. chmn. fund raising campaign Morris Ctr. YMCA; hon. co-chmn. Liberty Pk. Found.; Suffolk County Vietnam Vets. Meml. Commn., U.S. Fitness Acad. Campaign, Nat. Fitness Found.; mem. adv. coun. William J. Donovan Meml. Found. Inc. Served with inf. U.S. Army, 1946-48. Decorated Order of the Nile (Egypt); recipient Investment Bankers Assn. Am. award, 1970, Small Bus. Administrn. citation, 1971, 2d ann. Youth Services award Wall St. div. B'nai B'rith, 1971, Outstanding Service to His Country award Port Authority N.Y., 1973, Merit award Securities Industry Assn., 1973, Outstanding Citizen of N.J. award Advt. Club N.J., 1974, Financial World award, 1974, Good Scout award Boy Scouts Am., 1974, Exec. Govt. award OIC Govt. Relations Service, 1974, Outstanding Citizen of Yr. award, 1974, U.S. Indsl. Payroll Savs. award, 1974, Civic Leadership award Am. Jewish Com., 1975, Dean's citation Am. U., 1975, Trustees medal Fairleigh Dickenson U., 1975, Gold medal Nat. Inst. Social Scis., 1975, Am. Eagle award Nat. Invest in Am. Coun., 1975, Achievement award Newark Acad. Alumni Assn., 1975, Bicentennial award U.S. Citizen's Congress, 1975, Young Americans For Freedom citation, 1975, Am. Inst. for Pub. Service award, 1976, Bus. in Pub. Affairs award C. of C. of Md., 1976, Flame of Truth award Fund for Higher Edn. in Israel, 1976, Disting. Achievements award Money Marketers of NYU, 1976, Pa. Soc. medal, 1976, NYU Coll. Bus. med. Pub. Adminstrn. medal, 1976, Govt. Service award Pub. Relations Soc. Am., 1976, Carnauba Palm award S.C. Johnson and Son Inc., 1976, proclamation Pub. Relations Soc. Am., 1976, Pres.'s award for outstanding achievement, 1976, Econ. Forum citation Chapman Coll., 1977, Alexander Hamilton award Dept. Treasury, 1977, Am. Legion award, 1977, Brotherhood award NCCJ, 1977, Outstanding Achievement award Freedoms Found. at Valley Forge, 1978, Order of Anthony Wayne citation Valley Forge Mil. Acad. and Jr. Coll., 1978, Disting. Patriot award SAR, 1979, George Washington Kidd award Lafayette Coll. Alumni Assn., 1979, George Washington Honor medal Valley Forge Freedom Found., 1979, Eastside Conservative Club, 1980, Service Above Self award, Easton Rotary Club, 1980, Charles Edison Meml. award, Leadership award Columbia Bus. Sch., 1982, Cath. Big Bros. of Yr. award Lotus Club, 1982, Hall of Fame award Tri-County Scholarship, 1983, Disting. Service award The Liberty Bowl, 1983, Jesse Owens Internat. Amateur Athletic award, 1984, Reed K. Swenson Leadership award Nat. Jr. Coll. Athletic Assn., 1984, Gov.'s Com. on Scholastic Achievement award, 1985, Golden Medallion award Internat. Swimming Hall of Fame, 1985, Internat. Exec. of Yr. award Am. Grad. Sch. Internat. Mgmt., 1985, Humanitarian award Am. Sportscaster Assn., 1985, Man of Yr. award Morristown Rotary Club, 1986, Disting. Citizen award Greater N.Y. council Boy Scouts Am., 1986, Sportsman of Yr. award All-Am. Collegiate Golf Found., 1986, Golden Plate award Am. Acad. Achievement, 1986, Societe d'Honneur award Lafayette Coll., 1986, Kriendler award Marine Corps Sch., 1986, Reunion Alumni Achievement award Newark Acad., 1986, Disting. Service award Cons. Engrs. Council N.J., 1987, Charles McCaffree award Coll. Swimming Coaches Assn. Am. Inc., 1987, Covenant House award, 1988, 1st Ann. award Mid-Atlantic Legal Found., 1988, Pres.'s medal Adelphi U., 1989, Entrepreneur of Yr. award Henry Bloch Sch. Bus. and Pub. Adminstrn., U. Mo., Kansas City, 1989, Jesse Owens Internat. award U.S. Olympic Com., 1990, Ellis Island Medal of Honor award, 1990, Club of Champions Gold medal Cath. Youth Orgn. of Archdiocese N.Y., 1991; named to l'Ordre Olympique by le Comité Internat. Olympique, 1987, U.S. Olympic Com. Hall of Fame, 1991. Mem. Coun. on Fgn. Rels., The Soc. of Friendly Sons of St. Patrick, Pilgrims of U.S., Nat. Fedn. State high Sch. Assns. (chmn. bd. emeritus), Mont Pelerin Soc., Asia Soc. (former trustee), Explorers Club (bd. dirs. 1994), Assn. N.J. Rifle and Pistol Club, Am. Assn. Master Knights of Sovereign Milit. Order of Malta (exec. com.), Villa Taverna Soc. Clubs: Alfalfa (Washington); Balboa Bay (Calif.); Maidstone Inc., Sheriff's Jury Inc., Links, Brook Forum, N.Y. Yacht, Bond of N.Y., Mcpl. Bond of N.Y., N.Y. Athletic (N.Y.C., Man of Yr. 1984); Com-

monwealth of Calif. (San Francisco); Lyford Cay (Nassau, Bahamas); Mendham Valley Gun (N.J.); Country Club of Colo. (Colorado Springs); Gulf Stream Golf (Fla.); Rolling Rock (Ligonier, Pa.); Waialae Country, Oahu Country (Honolulu); Maui Country; Morris County Golf (N.J.); Robert Trent Jones Internat. Golf (founding bd. dirs.). Numerous scholarships and endowments established. Office: William E. Simon & Sons Inc 310 South St Morristown NJ 07960-7301

SIMON, WILLIAM H., legal educator; b. 1947. AB, Princeton, 1969; JD, Harvard U., 1974. Bar: Mass. 1974. Assoc. Foley, Hoag & Eliot, Boston, 1974-77; staff atty. legal svcs. inst. Harvard U., 1979-81; asst. prof. Stanford U., 1981-84, assoc. prof., 1984-85, prof., 1985—. Office: Stanford Law Sch Nathan Abbott Way Stanford CA 94305

SIMONDS, JOHN EDWARD, newspaper editor; b. Boston, July 4, 1935; s. Alvin E. and Rose Angeline (Rankin) S.; m. Rose B. Muller, Nov. 16, 1968; children—Maximillian P., Malia G.; children by previous marriage—Rachel F., John B. B.A., Bowdoin Coll., 1957. Reporter Daily Tribune, Seymour, Ind., 1957-58, UPI, Columbus, Ohio, 1958-60; reporter, asst. city editor Providence Jour. Bull., 1960-65, Washington Evening Star, 1965-66; corr. Gannett News Svc., Washington, 1966-75; mng. editor Honolulu Star Bull., 1975-80, exec. editor, 1980-87, sr. editor, editorial page editor, 1987-93; exec. Hawaii Newspaper Agy., Honolulu, 1993—. Served with U.S. Army, 1958. Mem. Am. Soc. Newspaper Editors, AP Mng. Editors, Soc. Profl. Journalists, Nat. Conf. Editorial Writers. Home: 5316 Nehu Pl Honolulu HI 96821-1942 Office: Hawaii Newspaper Agy 605 Kapiolani Blvd Honolulu HI 96813

SIMONDS, JOHN ORMSBEE, landscape architect; b. Jamestown, N.D., Mar. 11, 1913; s. Guy Wallace and Marguerite Lois (Ormsbee) S.; m. Marjorie C. Todd, May 1, 1943; children: Taye Anne, John Todd, Polly Jean, Leslie Brook. BS, Mich. State U., 1935, DSc hon.; MLandscape Architecture (Eugene Dodd medal), Harvard U., 1939. Landscape architect Mich. Dept. Parks, 1935-36; ptnr. Simonds and Simonds, Pitts., 1939-70, Collins, Simonds and Simonds, Washington, 1952-70; ptnr. The Environ. Planning and Design Partnership, Pitts., also Miami Lakes, 1970-82, emeritus, 1983—; cons. Dept. Pks., Collier County, Fla., 1986-90, Land and Nature Trust, Lexington, Ky., 1987-92, SW Fla. Water Mgmt. Dist., 1987-89; lectr., vis. critic urban and regional planning Carnegie-Mellon U., 1955-67; vis. critic Grad. Sch. Planning, also Sch. Architecture, Yale, 1961-62; Cons. Chgo. Cen. Area Com., 1962, Allegheny County Dept. Regional Pks., 1961-74; U.S. cons. community planning Inter-Am. Housing and Planning Ctr., Bogota, Colombia, 1960-61; mem. jury Am. Acad. Rome, 1963, 65, 66, 69; mem. Nat. Adv. Com. on Hwy. Beautification; chmn. panel on pks. and open space White House Conf. on Natural Beauty; mem. Interprofl. Commn. on Environ. Design, Joint Com. on Nat. Capital; mem. urban hwy. adv. bd. U.S. Bur. Pub. Rds., 1965-68; mem. landscape architecture adv. panel U.S. C.E., 1968-71, Pres.'s Task Force on Resources and Environ., 1968-70; mem. design adv. panel Operation Breakthrough, HUD, 1970-71; mem. Mid-Atlantic regional adv. bd. Nat. Park Svc., 1976-78; assoc. trustee U. Pa., 1962-66, mem. bd. fine arts, 1962-66; chmn. joint com. planning Carnegie-Mellon U. and U. Pitts., 1959-60; overseer's vis. com. Harvard Grad. Sch. Design, 1962-68, exec. coun. alumni assn., 1960-63; adv. com. Sch. Design, N.C. State U., 1965-67; mem. Fla. Gov.'s Task Force on Natural Resources, 1979-80, Chgo. Bot. Garden 25th Anniversary, 1991, keynote address, 1991, Internat. Fedn. Landscape Architects, Seoul, Korea, 1992; speaker keynote address Internat. Congress Urban Green, Geneva, 1986. Author: Landscape Architecture, the Shaping of Man's Natural Environment, 1961, rev. edit., 1983, Earthscape, a Manual of Environmental Planning, 1978, revised edit. 1986, Garden Cities 21, Creating a Livable Urban Environment, 1994; editor: Virginia's Common Wealth, 1965, The Freeway in the City, 1968; contbr. sect. on urban design Ency. Architecture, 1990, sect. on landscape architecture Ency. Urban Planning, 1980. Maj. works include master plans for Chgo. Bot. Garden, (with others) Mellon Sq., Pitts., (with others) Miami Lakes New Town, Va. I-66 Corridor, Fairfax and Arlington counties, Va., Pelican Bay Community, Fla., Weston New Town, Fla. Bd. dirs. Hubbard Ednl. Trust, 1974—; bd. govs. Pitts. Plan for Arts. Recipient citation Top Men of Year Engring. News-Record, 1973; Charles L. Hutchinson medal Chgo. Hort. Soc., John R. Bracken medal Dept. Landscape Architecture, Pa. State U., 1985, Sigma Lambda Alpha award Coun. Educators in Landscape Architecture, 1979. Fellow Am. Soc. Landscape Architects (mem. exec. com. 1959-67, pres. 1963-65, pres. Found. 1966-68, recipient medal 1973), Royal Soc. Arts (Gt. Britain); mem. NAD (assoc.), Archtl. League N.Y., Royal Town Planning Inst. (hon. corr.); hon. assoc. Pa. chpt. AIA, Harvard-Yale-Princeton Club. Presbyterian (ruling elder). Home: 17 Penhurst Rd Pittsburgh PA 15202-1023 Office: The Loft 17 Penhurst Rd Pittsburgh PA 15202 *Perhaps the most important lesson in life is to learn to address oneself with intensity to each person, object and event. One may be with friends without awareness of either friend or friendship, live with family as an almost stranger, partake of food and drink without savor, pass burgeoning tree, splashing stream, or splendid view without appreciation . . . unless one learns to address all powers of perception-first consciously, and then by habit, to the subject at hand. Only thus may each experience be made rich and rewarding, and life, the sum of experience, be lived to the full.*

SIMONDS, MARSHALL, lawyer; b. Boston, Sept. 17, 1930; s. Sidney Lawrence and Evelyn (Peterson) S.; m. Katharine Blewett, May 9, 1969; children: Robert Bradley, Joshua Lawrence. BA, Princeton U., 1952; LLB, Harvard U., 1955. Bar: Mass. 1955. Since practiced in Boston; ptnr. Goodwin, Procter & Hoar, Boston, 1965—; counsel Mass. Crime Commn., 1963-65; spl. asst. atty. gen. Commonwealth of Mass., 1964-66; dir. Dynatech Corp., 1960-85, Data Packaging Corp., 1972-79; trustee Middlesex Instn. Savs., 1974-79. Moderator of Carlisle, Mass., 1967—; trustee Trustees for Reservations, 1972-78; bd. dirs. South Boston Neighborhood House, 1972-78. Served with USMCR, 1955. Fellow Am. Coll. Trial Lawyers, Am. Bar Found., Mass. Bar Found.; mem. ABA, Mass. Bar Assn., Boston Bar Assn. (coun. 1980-82), New Eng. Legal Found. (dir.), Franklin Flaschner Jud. Inst. (acad. com.), Am. Kennel Club (del.), Labrador Retriever Club (bd. dirs.), Harvard Club (Boston), Orthopedic Found. for Animals (bd. dirs.). Address: Bliss Hill Rd Morrisville VT 05661

SIMONDS, PEGGY MUÑOZ, writer, lecturer, retired literature educator; b. New Rochelle, N.Y., Feb. 29, 1928; d. Francisco Javier Muñoz and Julia Pinckney Dunham; m. Roger Tyrrell Simonds, Nov. 21, 1956; children: Robin Pinckney, Martha Muñoz. BA in English, U. Del., 1949; MA in Creative Writing/Latin Am. Studies, U. of the Americas, Mexico City, 1956; PhD in Lit. and History of Art, Am. U., 1975. Journalist, arts critic Mexico City, 1949-55; tchr. English U. of the Ams., Mexico City, 1953-55; lectr. Greek drama Norfolk (Conn.) Music Sch. of Yale U., summer 1955; lectr. English Montgomery (Md.) Coll., 1966-88, prof. emerita, 1988—; ind. scholar, 1988—; lectr. and presenter in field. Author: Myth, Emblem, and Music in Shakespeare's "Cymbeline": An Iconographic Reconstruction, 1992, A Critical Guide to Iconographic Research in English Renaissance Literature, 1995; contbr. numerous articles to profl. jours. Recipient U. Del. Press award, 1990; NEH fellow, 1982. Mem. MLA, Shakespeare Assn. Am., Internat. Shakespeare Assn., Renaissance Soc. Am., Southeastern Renaissance Soc., Internat. Soc. for the Classical Tradition, Phi Kappa Phi. Home and Office: 5406 Beech Ave Bethesda MD 20814

SIMONDS, STEPHEN PAIGE, former state legislator; b. Franconia, N.H., Nov. 25, 1924; s. Stephen Moses and Gertrude Martha (Jesseman) S.; m. Judith Cole, Sept. 13, 1952; children: Scott, Mark, Laura, Jane. BA, U. N.H., 1948; MA in Social Svcs. Adminstrn., U. Chgo., 1953. Caseworker N.H. Dept. Pub. Welfare, Woodsville, 1950-51; dist. supr. N.H. Dept. Pub. Welfare, Conway and Woodsville, 1953-56; field supr. Conn. Dept. Welfare, Hartford, 1958-60; dir. social welfare Maine Dept. Health and Welfare, Augusta, 1960-67; commr. Assisted Payments Adminstrn. HEW, Washington, 1967-69; commr. Community Svcs. Adminstrn., 1969-71; founder, dir. Human Svcs. Devel. Inst., U. So. Maine, Portland, 1971-86; dir. Office Internat. Programs, 1986-92; mem. Maine Ho. of Reps., Augusta, 1990-94, mem. human resources com., edn. com. Past pres. Cmty. Counseling Ctr. Recipient Disting. Svc. award World Affairs Coun. Maine, 1991; Fulbright scholar, Eng., 1957-58. Mem. Ptnrs. of Ams., Chinese and Am. Friendship Assn. (a founder). Democrat. Avocations: flying, boating, canoeing, gardening. Home: 18 Brentwood Rd Cape Elizabeth ME 04107

SIMONE, ALBERT JOSEPH, academic administrator; b. Boston, Dec. 16, 1935; s. Edward and Mary (DiGiovanni) S.; m. Carolie Roberta Menko, Nov. 7, 1959; children: Edward, Karen, Debra, Laura. BA, Tufts U., 1957; PhD, MIT, 1962. Lectr. Coll. Bus. Adminstrn., Northeastern U., Boston, 1958-59; instr. econs. MIT and Tufts U., Boston, 1959-60; asst. prof. Northeastern U., Tufts U., 1960-63; assoc. prof. Coll. Bus. Adminstrn. Boston Coll., 1963-66, prof., dir. quantitative mgmt. program Coll. Bus. Adminstrn.,, 1966-68; prof. head dept. quantitative analysis Coll. Bus. Adminstrn. U. Cin., 1968-72, dean Coll. Bus. Adminstrn., 1972-83; v.p. acad. affairs U. Hawaii, Honolulu, 1983-84, acting pres., 1984-85; pres. U. Hawaii System, Honolulu, 1985-92; chancellor U. Hawaii at Manoa, 1985-92; pres. Rochester (N.Y.) Inst. Tech., 1992—; served on, chaired numerous univ. coms.; program chmn. 1970 Nat. Conf. of Am. Prodn. and Inventory Control Soc.; mem. accreditation com. Am. Assembly Collegiate Schs. Bus., 1978-83, visits to U. Ky., Carnegie-Mellon U., 1982; session chmn. various profl. confs.; cons. statis. forecasting, prodn. scheduling and sample design models various co. including Cin. Gas & Electric Co., Cin. Milacron, Kroger Co.; econ. and mgmt. cons. Atty. Gen.'s Office, State of Mass.; mem. council econ. advisors to Gov., Commonwealth of Mass. Author: Matematica Finita Con Aplicaciones A Las Ciencias Administrativas, 1969, Foundations of Contemporary Mathematics with Applications in the Social and Management Sciences, 1967, Probability: An Introduction with Applications, 1967; (with L. Kattsoff) Finite Mathematics with Applications in the Social and Management Sciences, 1965, (with R. Wessel and E. Willett) Statistics as Applied to Economics and Business, 1965; also articles. Bd. dirs. Greater Rochester Visitors Assn., Inc., Marine Midland Bank, N.A., Rochester/So. Region, United Way of Greater Rochester, Vis. Nurse Svc. of Rochester and Monroe County, Inc., High Tech. of Rochester; chmn. United Way Vol. Resources Divsn. Steering Com. Fellow of grad. sch. U. Cin.; named Prof. of Yr., Delta Sigma Pi, Alpha Theta chpt. U. Cin., 1972. Fellow Am. Inst. Decision Scis. (v.p. publs. 1969-70, v.p. and student liaison 1972, pres 1974-75; founding editor and editor-in-chief jour. 1970-72; Disting. Service award 1972); mem. Acad. of Mgmt., Am. Econ. Assn., Am. Inst. Indsl. Engrs., Am. Prodn. and Inventory Control Soc., Am. Statis. Assn., Assn. Computing Machinery, Econometric Soc., Fin. Execs. Inst., Inst. Mgmt. Sci., Ops. Research Soc. Am., Phi Beta Kappa, Beta Gamma Sigma. Mem. Univs. Rsch. Assn., Assn. of Ind. Tech. Univs., RIT Rsch. Corp. (chmn., bd. dirs.), Nat. Commn. for Coop. Edn., N.Y. Commn. for Ind. Coll. and Univs., Rochester Area Coll. Consortium. Office: RIT George Eastman Bldg Two Lomb Meml Dr Rochester NY 14623-5604

SIMONE, BEVERLY SUE, academic administrator; b. Evansville, Ind., Aug. 11, 1946; d. Lloyd C. and Edna Margaret (Steckler) Miller; 1 child, Andrella Christina Acheson-Rupert. BA in Speech and Theatre, Butler U., 1969; MS in Edn. and Communications, Ind. U., 1973, EdD in Adult Edn., 1986. Co-owner, mgr. Tres Bien Catering, Indpls., 1969-71; instr. communications Ind. Vocat. Tech. Coll., Indpls., 1970-72, dir. learning resources, 1972-75, chair div. gen. edn., 1975-79, dir. external svcs., 1979-80; v.p. community and govtl. rels. Milw. Area Tech. Coll., 1980-85, provost, 1985-87; pres. Western Wis. Tech. Coll., La Crosse, 1987-89; pres., chief exec. officer Madison Area Tech. Coll., 1989—; Nat. bd. dirs. Am. Family Ins. Mem. Milw. Jr. League, 1980-94, past v.p.; mem. Madison Jr. League, 1994—; bd. dirs. United Way Dane County, Madison, Wis., 1991, Am. Players Theatre, Madison Cmty. Found. Recipient Nat. Recognition award Am. Coun. Edn., 1981, 85, 86, Outstanding Alumnus award Ind. U. Sch. Edn., 1993; named Woman of Achievement La Crosse Regional Bus. Assn., 1988. Mem. Am. Assn. Community and Jr. Colls. (chair 1992-93, chair elect 1991-92, bd. dirs. 1989-94, Futures Commn.), Am. Assn. Women in Community and Jr. Colls. (pres. 1985-87), Am. Coun. on Edn. (bd. dirs.), Assn. C.C. Trustees (adv. mem. 1985-87), Internat. Women's Forum, Greater Madison C. of C. (bd. dirs.), Tempo, Vantage Point, Rotary. Office: Madison Area Tech Coll 3550 Anderson St Madison WI 53704-2520

SIMONE, JOSEPH R., lawyer; b. N.Y.C., Jan. 7, 1949; m. Virginia E. Simone, May 29, 1971; m. Jacquelyn, Robert. BA cum laude, Queens Coll., 1971; LLM in Taxation, NYU, 1977; JD cum laude, Fordham U., 1974. Bar: N.Y. 1975, U.S. Dist. Ct. (so. dist.) N.Y. 1975, U.S. Ct. Appeals (2d cir.) 1975. Ptnr. Patterson, Belknap, Webb & Tyler, N.Y.C., 1982-88, Schulte, Roth & Zabel, N.Y.C., 1988—. Author: (textbook) Pension Answer Book, 1990, 5th edit.; editorial advisor Jour. of Pension Planning. Mem. Am. Arbitration Assn. (panel on multiemployer pension plans, employee benefits law adv. com, co-chair symposium employee benefits), Phi Beta Kappa. Office: Schulte Roth & Zabel 900 3rd Ave New York NY 10022-4728

SIMONE, THOMAS B., distribution company executive; b. Chgo., Mar. 27, 1942; s. Manuel C. and Clara M. (Costa) S.; m. Shirley A. Zak, Oct. 24, 1964; children: Ann Marie, Jennifer, Kathleen. BS, De Paul U., Chgo., 1964, MBA, 1970. Corp. budget mgr. Keebler Co., Elmhurst, Ill., 1971-72, dir. prodn. planning, 1972-73; budget dir. McK Drug Co., San Francisco, 1973-76, v.p., controller, 1976-79; dir. bus. analysis McKesson Corp., San Francisco, 1979-81, v.p., controller, 1981-90; exec. v.p., chief fin. officer PCS Inc. (subs. McKesson Corp.), 1989-90; v.p. fin. McKesson Corp., San Francisco, 1990-91; pres. McKesson Drug Co. (subs. McKesson Corp.), San Francisco, 1991—; bd. dirs. NADRO S.A. de C.V., Mexico City. Bd. dirs. Bay Area Crisis Nursery, Ind. Colls. No. Calif., McKesson Found. Inc. Served with U.S. Army, 1964-66. Mem. Fin. Exec.'s Inst. Roman Catholic. Club: World Trade (San Francisco). Avocations: investments, tennis, music. Office: McKesson Corp One Post St San Francisco CA 94104

SIMONEAU, NORMAND J., hospital administrator; b. Sherbrooke, Que., Can., Apr. 23, 1932; s. Ernest and Jeanne (Leclerc) S.; m. Huguette Poirier, Feb. 15, 1958; children: Diane, Louise, Jacques. B.A., St. Charles Coll., 1954; L.Sc.Com., U. Montreal, 1957. Chartered acct. Treas. City Hall, Sherbrooke, Que., Can., 1959-64; exec. dir. Sta.-CHLT-TV, Sherbrooke, QUE, Can. 1964-70, U. Sherbrooke Med. ctr., Que., Can., 1970—. Bd. dirs. Que. Hosp. Assn., Can., 1983-87, pres. teaching hosp. div., 1982-86; dir. U. Sherbrooke, Que. Can., 1974-76. Mem. Exec. Dirs. Assn. (dir. 1983-86). Home: 469 Liege St, Sherbrooke, PQ Canada J1J 2N1 Office: Centre Hospitalier Universitaire, 3001 12th Ave N, Fleurimont, PQ Canada J1H 5N4

SIMONET, JOHN THOMAS, banker; b. Stillwater, Minn., Aug. 11, 1926; s. Joseph S. and Helen (Martin) S.; m. Helen Kennedy, Sept. 8, 1951; children: William T., Joseph K., Mary, Michelle, Anne. B.B.A., U. Minn., 1948, LL.B., 1951. With First Nat. Bank, St. Paul, 1951-72; cashier First Nat. Bank, 1958-60, v.p., 1960-71; exec. v.p. First Trust Co., St. Paul, 1972-74; pres. First Trust Co., 1974-85, chief adminstrv. officer, 1974-81, chief exec. officer, 1981-85, ret., 1985; asst. treas. Port Authority St. Paul, 1966-71; bd. dirs. First Trust, St. Paul, Carondelet Life Care Corp., Donovan Cos. Inc., Mairs and Power Funds, Inc. Mem. lay adv. bd. exec. com. St. Joseph's Hosp., St. Paul, 1965-70, trustee, 1971-82, chmn. bd. trustees, 1976-79; pres. adv. bd. Catholic Social Service St. Paul, 1968-70; chmn. Archbishop's Appeal Com., 1970; exec. bd. dirs. St. Paul Council Arts and Scis., 1967-69; trustee St. Paul Sem., 1969-92, Tozer Found., 1981—; bd. dirs. United Way, St. Paul, 1976-82, pres., 1980-81; mem. governing bd. St. Paul Found., 1979-85; bd. dirs. Mairs and Power Growth Fund, Mairs and Power Income Fund, 1992—. Served with USNR, 1944-46, 53-55. Club: St. Paul Athletic (treas. 1966-68).

SIMONETT, JOHN E., state supreme court justice; b. Mankato, Minn., July 12, 1924; m. Doris Bogut; 6 children. BA, St. John's U., 1948; LLB, U. Minn., 1951. Pvt. practice law Little Falls, Minn., 1951-80; assoc. justice Supreme Ct. of Minn., St. Paul, 1980—. Office: Minn Supreme Ct 423 Minnesota Jud Ctr 25 Constitution Ave Saint Paul MN 55155-1500

SIMONIAN, JOHN S., lawyer; s. Samuel and Mary Simonian. BA, U. R.I.; JD, Boston U. Bar: R.I., U.S. Dist. Ct. R.I. state rep. R.I. Ho. of Reps., Providence, 1991—, dep. majority leader, 1993—, chmn. commn. on criminal justice, 1993—, mem. house com. on fin., 1993—, joint com. on veteran's affairs, 1991—. Democrat. Apostolic. Home: 70 Preston Dr Cranston RI 02910-1825

SIMONIAN, SIMON JOHN, surgeon, scientist, educator; b. Antioch, French Ter., Mar. Apr. 20, 1932; came to U.S., 1965, naturalized, 1976.; s. John Simon and Marie Cecile (Tomboulian) S.; m. Arpi Ani Yeghiayan, July 11, 1965; children: Leonard Armen, Charles Haig, Andrew Hovig. MD, U.

London, 1957; BA in Animal Physiology, St. Edmund Hall, U. Oxford, Eng., 1964; MA in Animal Physiology, U. Oxford, Eng., 1969; MSc, Harvard U., 1967, Sc.D., 1969. Diplomate Am. Bd. Surgery. Rsch. asst. immunology unit Lister Inst. Preventive Medicine, Elstree, Essex, U.K., 1952; intern Univ. Coll. Hosp., London, 1957; intern Edinburgh (Scotland) Royal Infirmary, 1957-58, resident, 1961-62; clin. clk. Nat. Hosp. London, 1958; resident Edinburgh Western Gen. Hosp., 1958-59, City Hosp., Edinburgh, Birmingham Accident and Burns Hosp., U. Birmingham, Eng., 1959-60; demonstrator dept. anatomy Edinburgh U., 1960-61; rsch. fellow in pathology lab. chem. pathology Harvard U., Boston, 1965-68; trainee NIH Harvard U., 1967; instr. immunology Harvard Med. Sch., Boston, 1966-70; instr., assoc. in surgery Harvard Med. Sch., 1968-70, surg. dir. course on transplantation, biology and medicine, 1968-70; vis. prof. Harvard Med. Sch., Mass. Gen. Hosp., Brigham and Womens Hosp., New Eng. Deaconess Hosp., 1982; dir. transplantation immunology unit, asst. in surgery Brigham and Womens Hosp., Boston, 1968-70; resident in surgery Boston City Hosp., 1970-74; attending surgeon in transplantation and gen. surgery services U. Chgo. Med. Ctr., 1974-77; asst. prof. surgery, mem. com. immunology U. Chgo., 1974-77; head div. renal transplantation Hahnemann U. Sch. Medicine and Hosp., 1978-87, prof. surgery, 1978-88, chmn. Transplantation Com., 1983-88, chmn. quality assurance of surgery com., 1986-88; dept. surgery coord. with joint commn. for accreditation of hosps. Hahnemann U. Sch. Medicine, 1986; chief and chmn. dept. surgery St. John Hosp. and Med. Ctr., Detroit, 1988-89, chmn. credentials com. of surgery and oper. rm. com., 1988-89, assoc. v.p. for med. affairs, 1989-90; pres., CEO Vein Inst. of Met. Washington, Inc., 1990—; assoc. Fairfax Hosp., Falls Church, Va., 1990-92, active faculty, 1992—; clin. assoc. prof. surgery Georgetown U. Sch. Medicine, Washington, 1992-95, clin. prof. surgery, 1995—; lectr. in field; vis. prof. Vanderbilt U., 1968, Cedars-Sinai Med. Ctr., UCLA, 1977, Aldenbrooke's Hosp., Cambridge U., 1977, Karolinska Inst., 1977, Huddinge Hosp., U. Stockholm, 1977, Med. Coll. Pa. and Hosp., 1980, 81, 85, Grad. Hosp., U. Pa., 1981, 85, U. Athens, 1981, Univ. Coll. Hosp., U. London, 1981, VA Hosp., Tufts U., 1982, John Radcliffe Hosp., Oxford U., 1982, Western Gen. Hosp., U. Edinburgh, 1982, U. Yerevan (Armenia) Sch. Biol. Scis., 1995; cons. Michael Reese Hosp., Chgo., 1976-77; cons. in gen. surgery City of Phila., 1986-88; cons. vascular surgery Coll. Podiatry, Phila., 1986-88; chief med. team support for US presdl. visits to Detroit, 1988, 89; vis. surgeon Inst. Vein Disease, Mich., 1989-90; vis. scientist Argonne (Ill.) Nat. Lab., 1969, 74-77; guest lectr., panelist Eight Internat. Congress of Nephrology, Athens, Greece, 1981, 1st Congress Internat. Soc. Edn. and Rsch. in Vascular Disease, San Diego, bd. dirs. 1992, 4th Internat. Dialogue Transition to Global Soc., U. Md., College Park, 1995; chmn. session 5th Armenian Medical World Congress, Paris France, 1992, 11th World Congress Internat. Union of Phlebology, Montreal, 1992, 22nd World Congress Internat. Soc. for Cardiovasc. Surgery, Kyoto, Japan, 1995, 6th Annual Congress N.Am. Soc. of Phlebology, Lake Buona Vista, Fla., 1993, sec., bd. dirs. Woodrock Inc., 1992-93; eminent scholar, external assessor U. Zambia, Lusaka, Zambia, 1994; chmn. panel, session chmn., panel co-chmn., guest lectr., panelist 17th World Congress Internat. Union Angiology, London, 1995; chmn. panel, adv. bd. 12th World Congress Union Internationale phlebologie, London, 1995. Co-author: Manual of Vascular Access Procedures, 1987; cons. to editorial bdateline: Issues in Transplantation, 1985-87; mem. editorial bd. Phila. Medicine, 1988, Transplantation Proc., 1987—, Jour. Transplantation Abstracts, 1968-70; reviewer New England Jour. Medicine, 1993—, Jour. Am. Med. Assn., 1993, Jour. Oncology and Dermatologic Surgery, 1993; contbr. articles to profl. jours. and books; appeared in med. movie Giving. Co-founder Armenian Youth Soc., Eng., 1953, pres., 1953-54; Armenian Studies program U. Chgo., 1975; bd. govs. Friends Sch., London, 1964-65; Mass. del., co-founder Armenian Assembly, Washington, 1970-74; trustee, fellow, co-founder Entry into Manhood of Armenian Youth at Age 13, 1981 (nominating com. 1995—); co-founder Armenian Am. Health Assn. of Greater Washington, 1992, mem. pharmaceuticals com., 1992—, chmn. nominating com. 1993; mem. Am. Friends of St. Edmund Hall, U. Oxford, 1992—; Am. Friends for St. Edmund Hall, U. Oxford, 1995, U.S. Campaign for St. Edmund Hall, U. Oxford, 1995—; nominating com. mem. Rep. Presdl. Task Force; mem. St. Mary's Armenian Apostolic Ch., Washington, guest preacher 1994, 95; mem. Am. Friends Am. U. Armenia, Yerevan, 1994; bd. dirs. Arlington (Va.) Symphony Orch., 1992; mem. regional com. U.S. Campaign for Univ. Oxford, 1993; bd. dirs. First We. Found. Inc., 1994; active amphitheatre endowment fund Boston City Hosp., 1994. Nairn scholar, 1949-52; Middlesex scholar, 1952-57; recipient Suckling prize, 1956, Brit. Med. Research Council award, 1962-64, Alt prize, 1973, Thompson award, 1974-77, Johnson award, 1975-77, Presdl. Medal of Merit, 1982, Kabakjian award Armenian Student Assn. Am., 1986; named outstanding new citizen of Citizenship Coun. of Met. Chgo. and Dept. Justice, Washington, 1976-77, Jonathan E. Rhoads ann. orator, 1984; co-endowed The John and Marie J. Simonian Award, St. Nerces Sem., 1981, John R. Pfeifer, MD, Rsch. Award, Providence Hosp., Southfield, Mich., 1992; endowed the Dennis Knight prize Royal Acad. Music, London, 1991; endowed The Marie J. Simonian Prize, Georgetown U. Med. Sch., 1991 (prize com. 1991—); established The John N.D. Kelly Prize in Med. Studies St. Edmund Hall, U. Oxford, 1992, The Simon J. and Arpi A. Simonian Prize for scholastic excellence for doctoral candidates, Harvard U., 1992; recognized for philanthropy to Hahnemann U. by placques in med. sch. and hosp. lobbies., Simon and Arpi Simonian room Sch. of Humanities and Scis. U. Yerevan, Armenia, 1994, plaque in Cyrus Vesuna Auditorium and Conf. Ctr., Fairfax Hosp., Falls Church, Va., 1995; grantee U.S. Govt., industry cos., founds. Fellow Royal Coll. Surgeons Edinburgh, ACS (Phila., Mich. and Washington chpts.), Phila. Acad. Surgery (Jonathan E. Rhoads ann. orator 1984—, Samuel D. Gross prize com. 1988, councillor 1988); mem. AAAS, AMA (mem. jour. rev. 1993), AAUP, Royal Coll. Surgeons of Eng., Royal Coll. Physicians of London Licentiates, Nat. Assn. Armenian Studies and Rsch., Armenian Gen. Benevolent Union (pres.' club 1990—, rep. Midatlantic region, 1994), Knights of Vartan, Am. Armenian Med. Assn. (co-founder 1972, treas. 1972-74), Brit. Med. Assn., Immunology Club Boston, Cancer Rsch. Assn. Boston, Physicians for Social Responsibility, Am. Pub. Health Assn., Assn. for Study of Med. Edn., Armenian Med. and Dental Assn. Greater Phila. (co-founder 1983, pres. 1983-85, Outreach award 1986), Assn. Acad. Surgery, Transplantation Soc. (mem. membership com. 1980-82), Am. Fedn. Clin. Research, N.Y. Acad. Scis., Am. Soc. Transplant Surgeons (co-founding mem. 1974, chmn. immunosuppression study com. 1974-77, membership com. 1985-87), Am. Venous Forum, Assn. of Ill. Transplant Surgeons, Chgo. Assn. Immunologists, Chgo. Soc. Gastroenterology, Phila. Acad. Scis. (co-chmn. membership com. 1980-88, guest lectr. 1982), Greater Delaware Valley Soc. Transplant Surgeons (councillor 1978-80, 85-88, pres. elect 1980-82, pres. 1982-85), Phila. County Med. Soc. (rep. City Ctr. br. 1981-83, pres. 1984, bd. dirs. 1985-87, chmn. long range planning com. 1986-88), Pa. MeSamuel Hahnemann Surg. Soc., Am. Technion Soc., Am. Soc. Artificial Internal Organs, European Soc. Organ Transplant, Oxford and Cambridge Soc. of Phila. and Washington, Internat. Cardiovascular Soc. (N.Am. chpt.), N. Am. Soc. Phlebology (curriculum devel. projects com. 1992—, faculty 1993, 94, 95), End Stage Renal Disease Network 24 (mem. med. rev. bd. 1980-82, 86-87), Am. Coll. Physician Execs., Detroit Acad. Surgery, Detroit Surgical Assn., Transplantation Soc. Mich., Organ Procurement Agy. Mich. (adv. bd. 1988-89), Wayne County Med. Soc., Mich. State Med. Soc., Fairfax County Med. Soc., Med. Soc. Va., Met. Vascular Conf., Soc. Brigham Surg. Alumni, Greater Washington Telecomm. Assn. (pres.'s club 1994), Chesapeake Vascular Soc., Oxford Soc. Washington, Harvard Club (Phila. and Washington), Med. Club (Phila.), U. Chgo. Club (Washington), Bethesda Monthly Meeting, Sigma Xi. Mem. Soc. of Friends. Office: 3301 Woodburn Rd Annandale VA 22003-1229

SIMONNARD, MICHEL ANDRÉ, manufacturing executive; b. Amiens, France, Mar. 25, 1933; came to U.S., 1988; s. Marcel and Marthe (Catoire) S.; m. Axelle Note, May 26, 1988; 1 child, Alexia. Diploma in Engring., Ecole Polytechnique, Paris, 1956; MS, MIT, 1959. Cons. engr. SEMA-METRA, Paris, 1959-62; divisional dir. GRACE, Paris, 1963-65; mng. dir. aluminum sales PECHINEY GROUP, Paris, 1966-67, mng. dir. Cebal div. 1968-74, mng. dir. Ugine Aciers div., 1975-76, group v.p. nuclear fuel and spl. products div., 1977-82, group v.p. internat. trade div., 1981-84, sr. v.p. human resources and communications depts., 1985-86, exec. v.p. supervising human resources and regional affairs, 1987; exec. v.p. supervising Turbine Components div., gen. N.Am. Pechiney Group, Greenwich, Conn., 1988—. Office: Pechiney Corp 475 Steamboat Rd Greenwich CT 06830-7144

SIMONS, ALBERT, III, lawyer; b. Charleston, S.C., Nov. 22, 1950; s. Albert Jr. and Caroline Pinckney (Mitchell) S.; m. Theodora Bonnell Wilbur, Jan. 28, 1970; 1 child, Albert IV. BA, U. Va., 1972, JD, 1976. Bar: S.C. 1977, N.Y. 1978. Assoc. Brown, Wood, Ivey, Mitchell & Petty (now Brown & Wood), N.Y.C., 1977-84; ptnr. Orrick, Herrington & Sutcliffe, N.Y.C., 1984—. Sgt. S.C. Air Nat. Guard, 1972-73. Mem. S.C. Bar Assn., N.Y. State Bar Assn. Office: Orrick Herrington & Sutcliffe 599 Lexington Ave New York NY 10022

SIMONS, BARBARA M., lawyer; b. N.Y.C., Feb. 7, 1929; d. Samuel A. and Minnie (Mankes) Malitz; m. Morton L. Simons, Sept. 2, 1951; 1 child, Claudia. BA, U. Mich., 1950, JD, 1952. Bar: N.Y. 1953, U.S. Supreme Ct. 1963, U.S. Ct. Appeals (D.C. cir.) 1971, (5th cir.) 1992, (1st cir.) 1994. Ptnr. Simons & Simons, Washington, 1962—. Mem. Forest Hills Citizens Assn., Washington, Clean Air Project; past pres. D.C. chpt. U. Mich. Alumnae, Washington. Alumnae scholar U. Mich., 1946-50. Mem. Washington Coun. Lawyers, Women's Legal Def. Fund, Phi Beta Kappa, Phi Kappa Phi, Alpha Lambda Delta. Office: Simons & Simons 5025 Linnean Ave NW Washington DC 20008-2042

SIMONS, CHARLES EARL, JR., federal judge; b. Johnston, S.C., Aug. 17, 1916; s. Charles Earl Sr. and Frances (Rhoden) S.; m. Jean Knapp, Oct. 18, 1941 (dec. 1991); children: Charles Earl III, Paul Knapp, Richard Brewster, Jean Brewster Smith; m. Gail Shaw, Feb. 27, 1992. AB, U. S.C., 1937, LLB cum laude, 1939. Bar: S.C. 1939. Ptnr. Lybrand & Simons, Aiken, S.C., 1939-50, Thurmond, Lybrand and Simons, Aiken, 1950-54, Lybrand, Simons & Rich, Aiken, 1954-64; mem. S.C. Ho. of Reps., 1942, 47-48, 61-64; mem. ways and means com., 1947-48, 61-64; judge U.S. Dist. Ct. S.C., Aiken, 1964—, chief judge, 1980-86; sr. status, 1987—; mem. S.C. Constl. Revision Com., 1948, Bd. Discipline and Grievance, S.C. Bar, 1958-61, Ethics Adv. Panel, 1981-87; jud. rep. 4th cir. dist. Jud. Conf. U.S., 1973-79; chmn. subom. on fed. jurisdiction of Com. on Ct. Adminstrn., 1986-87. Mem. Chief Met. Dist. Judges Conf., 1980-89, chmn., 1986-89; bd. dirs. S.C. Athletic Hall of Fame; mem. Jud. Conf. Commn. on Jud. Br., 1988-92. With USN, World War II. Recipient Algernon Sidney Sullivan award, 1937, 64. Mem ABA, S.C. Bar Assn. (Outstanding com. mem.), Am. Law Inst., Am. Legion, U. S.C. Alumni Assn. (past pres. 1964), S.C. Golf Assn., Aiken Bus. Men's Club (past pres.), Palmetto Golf Club (pres 1984—), Kiwanis (past pres.), Rotary. Home: PO Box 2185 Aiken SC 29802-2185 Office: US Dist Ct SC Charles E Simons Jr Fed Courthouse PO Box 2185 Aiken SC 29802-2185

SIMONS, DOLPH COLLINS, JR., newspaper publisher; b. Lawrence, Kans., Mar. 11, 1930; s. Dolph Collins and Marie (Nelson) S.; m. Pamela Counseller, Feb. 7, 1952; children: Pamela, Linda, Dolph Collins, Dan. A.B., U. Kans., 1951; LL.D. (hon.), Colby Coll., 1972. Reporter Lawrence Jour.-World, 1953, asso. pub., 1957, pub., 1962—, editor, 1978—, pres., 1969—; reporter The Times, London, 1956, Johannesburg (South Africa) Star, 1958; pres. World Co.; mgr. WorldWest; bd. dirs. Commerce Bancshares, Kansas City, Mo.; mem. Pulitzer Awards Jury, 1977, 78, 80, 81. Trustee, past pres. William Allen White Found.; trustee Midwest Rsch. Inst., Menninger Found., Nat. Parks and Conservation Assn., The Kans. Nature Conservancy; former mem. governing bd. Children's Mercy Hosp., Kansas City, Mo.; trustee, chmn. U. Kans. Endowment Assn.; past bd. dirs. Greater Kansas City Community Found. Served to capt. USMRC, 1951-53. Recipient Elijah Parish Lovejoy award, 1972; Fred Ellsworth award for significant service to U. Kans., 1976; Disting. Service citation, 1980. Mem. Newspaper Advt. Bur. (past dir.), Am. Soc. Newspaper Editors, Inland Daily Press Assn. (past dir.), Kans. Press Assn. (past pres., dir.), AP (past dir.), Am. Newspaper Pubs. Assn. (past pres., past nat. sec.), Lawrence C. of C. (past pres., dir.), U. Kans. Alumni Assn. (past pres., dir.), Sigma Delta Chi, Phi Delta Theta. Republican. Episcopalian. Clubs: Lawrence Country, Kansas City Country, Kansas City River. Lodges: Masons, Rotary. Home: 2425 Vermont St Lawrence KS 66046-4761 Office: 609 New Hampshire St Lawrence KS 66044-2243

SIMONS, ELIZABETH R(EIMAN), biochemist, educator; b. Vienna, Austria, Sept. 1, 1929; came to U.S., 1941, naturalized; 1948; d. William and Erna Engle (Weisselberg) Reiman; B.Ch.E., Cooper Union, N.Y.C., 1950; M.S., Yale U., 1951, Ph.D., 1954; m. Harold Lee Simons, Aug. 12, 1951; children—Leslie Ann Mulert, Robert David. Research chemist Tech. Operations, Arlington, Mass., 1953-54; instr. chemistry Wellesley (Mass.) Coll., 1954-57; rsch. asst. Children's Hosp. Med. Center and Cancer Rsch. Found., Boston, 1957-59, rsch. assoc. pathology, 1959-62; research assoc. Harvard Med. Sch., 1962-66, lectr. biol. chemistry, 1966-72; tutor biochemical scis. Harvard Coll., 1971-94 (ret.); assoc. prof. biochemistry Boston U., 1972-78, prof., 1978—. Contbr. articles to profl. jours. Grantee in field. Mem. AAAS, Am. Chem. Soc., Am Heart Assn., Am. Soc. Biol. Chemists, Am. Soc. Cell Biology, Am. Soc. Hematology, Assn. Women in Sci., Biophys. Soc., Internat. Soc. Thrombosis and Hemostasis, N.Y. Acad. Sci., Sigma Xi. Office: Boston U Sch Medicine 80 E Concord St Roxbury MA 02118-2394

SIMONS, GALE GENE, nuclear engineering educator, university administrator; b. Kingman, Kans., Sept. 25, 1939; s. Robert Earl and Laura V. (Swartz) S.; m. Barbara Irene Rinkel, July 2, 1966; 1 child, Curtis Dean. BS, Kans. State U., 1962, MS, PhD, 1968. Engr. Argonne Nat. Lab., Idaho Falls, Idaho, 1968-77, mgr. fast source reactor, head exptl. support group, 1972-77; prof. nuclear engring. Kans. State U., Manhattan, 1977—, assoc. dean for rsch., dir. rsch. coun. Coll. Engring., 1988—, bd. dirs. Rsch. Found., 1988—, Presdl. lectr., 1983—, career counselor, 1984—; cons. to pvt. and fed. agys., 1983—; bd. dirs. Kans. Tech. Enterprise Corp., Topeka; mem. Kans. Gov.'s Energy Policy Com., Topeka, 1992—; numerous presentations in field; reviewer proposals fed. agys. Contbr. over 100 articles to sci. jours.; patentee radiation dosimeter. Expert witness State of Kans., Topeka, 1986. Fellow AEC, 1964-67; numerous grants from fed. agys., 1979—. Mem. AAAS, IEEE, Am. Nuclear Soc., Health Physics Soc., Am. Soc. for Engring. Edn., Masons, Rotary, Phi Kappa Phi, Tau Beta Pi, Pi Mu Epsilon. Home: 2395 Grandview Ter Manhattan KS 66502-3729 Office: Kans State U Durland Hall Rm 148 Manhattan KS 66506

SIMONS, GORDON DONALD, JR., statistician; b. Kansas City, Mo., Dec. 26, 1938; s. Gordon Donald and Delora (Kellogg) S.; m. Karen Janell Lee, Aug. 31, 1962; children: Delora Ann Simons Denney, Sylvia Kay Simons Holmes, Melinda Lee. BA in Math, U. Minn., 1960, MA in Math, 1964, PhD in Stats., 1966. Research asso. dept. stats. Stanford U., 1966-68; asst. prof. stats. U. N.C., Chapel Hill, 1968-71; asso. prof. U. N.C., 1971-75, prof., 1975—, chmn. dept. stats., 1976-81, 93—. Air Force Office Sci. Research grantee, 1968, 72-75; NSF grantee, 1969-71, 75-92. Mem. Inst. Math. Stats., Am. Statis. Assn. (asso. editor jour. 1971-76), Am. Sci. Affiliation. Presbyterian. Office: U NC 315 Phillips Hall Chapel Hill NC 27599

SIMONS, HELEN, school psychologist, psychotherapist; b. Chgo., Feb. 13, 1930; d. Leo and Sarah (Shrayer) Pomper; m. Broudy Simons, May 20, 1956 (May 1972); children: Larry, Sheri. BA in Biol., Lake Forest Coll., 1951; MA in Clin. Psychology, Roosevelt U., 1972; D of Psychology, Ill. Sch. Profl. Psychology, 1980. Intern Cook County Hosp., Chgo., 1979-80; pvt. practice psychotherapist Chgo., 1980—; sch. psychologist Chgo. Bd. Edn., 1974-79, 80—. Contbr. articles on psychotherapy of A.D.D. children to profl. jours. Mem. APA, Internat. Coun. Psychologists, Nat. Sch. Psychologists Assn., Midwestern Psychol. Assn., Mental Health Assn. Ill., Ill. Psychol. Assn., Ill. Sch. Psychologists Assn., Chgo. Psychol. Assn., Chgo. Sch. Psychol. Assn. Avocations: music, dancing, reading. Home: 6145 N Sheridan Rd Apt 29D Chicago IL 60660-2864 Office: Brennemann Sch 4251 N Clarendon Ave Chicago IL 60613-1593

SIMONS, JOHN H., electronics manufacturing company executive; b. Quebec City, Que., Can., May 11, 1939; s. Herbert A. and Catherine M. (Martin) S.; children—Christopher, Jonathan, Laura. B.E.E., McGill U., Montreal, 1961, M.E.E., 1963, Diploma in Mgmt., 1974, M.B.A., 1977. Registered profl. engr. Program mgr. Can. Marconi Co., Montreal, Que., 1969-74, gen. mgr., 1974-76, div. mgr., 1976-77, v.p., 1972-82, group v.p., 1982, exec. v.p., 1982-89, pres., chief exec. officer, 1989—; del. 5th Commonwealth Study Conf., 1980—. Mem. Order of Engrs. Que., Aerospace Industries Assn. Can. (bd. dirs. 1979—, chmn. 1981-82), Montreal Badminton and Squash Club. Home: 3514 Ave du Musee, Montreal, PQ Canada H3G 2C7 Office: Can Marconi Co, 2442 Trenton Ave, Montreal, PQ Canada H3P 1Y9

SIMONS, KENT COBB, mutual fund executive; b. Detroit, May 13, 1935; s. Orton Webster and Lucile (Cobb) S.; m. Patricia Doyle, Mar. 4, 1962 (div. 1977); children: Tracey, Kevin, Kim, David, Amy; m. Sally Waddell, Jan. 13, 1979; stepchildren: Tom Manuel, Betsy Manuel. BA, Princeton U., 1957, chartered fin. analyst. Mgmt. trainee Proctor & Gamble Co., S.I., N.Y., 1957-58; analyst Bankers Trust, N.Y.C., 1961-66; securities analyst Lionel Eady Co., N.Y.C., 1966-68; portfolio mgr. Anchor Corp., Elizabeth, N.J., 1968-73; instl. sale portfolio mgr. Neuberger & Berman, N.Y.C., 1973-80, portfolio mgr., 1980-84, pres. Guardian Mut. Fund, 1984—. Author (plays) Curse of Greed, 1970; (with others) Knights and Dames, 1971, Who's Afraid of George III, 1972, Making Whoopee, 1973. Served with U.S. Army, 1959-62. Avocations: reading, photography, travel, biking. Home: Pleasantville Rd New Vernon NJ 07976 Office: Neuberger & Berman 605 3rd Ave New York NY 10158-0001

SIMONS, LAWRENCE BROOK, lawyer; b. N.Y.C., Oct. 19, 1924; s. Harry A. and Marion B. (Brook) S.; m. Annalou Kadin, Aug. 24, 1947; children: Barbara Flexner, Kenneth. Student, Duke U., 1941-43, 46-47; JD, Columbia U., 1949. Bar: N.Y. 1949, D.C. 1984, U.S. Dist. Ct. (so. dist.) N.Y. 1949, U.S. Supreme Ct. 1987. Assoc. Spring & Eastman, N.Y.C., 1949-53; v.p. gen. mgr. Caribe Knitting Mills, San Juan, P.R., 1953-58; pres. LBS Constrn. Co. Inc., S.I., N.Y., 1958-77; asst. sec. housing FHA commn. HUD, Washington, 1977-81; ptnr. Powell, Goldstein, Frazier & Murphy, Washington, 1981—; mem. Task Force on Quality of Life, Dept. of Def., 1995. Trustee Bayley Seton Hosp., S.I., 1981-90, NHP Found., Inc., 1991—; chmn. bd. dirs. N.Y. State Urban Devel. Corp., 1975-77, Nat. Housing Conf., 1981—, Pa. Ave. Devel. Corp., 1981-87; mem. Nat. Housing Task Force, 1988, Nat. Housing Trust, 1990—; trustee Affordable Housing Found., 1990-92, Ctr. for Democracy, 1990—; pres., bd. dirs. Ctr. for Housing Policy, 1992—. With U.S. Army, 1943-46, ETO. Named Man of Yr. Nat. Housing Conf., Washington, 1985. Mem. ABA, Nat. Assn. Home Builders, Richmond County C. of C., Army Navy C. of C., Sea Pines Country Club, Lambda Alpha. Democrat. Jewish. Avocation: golf. Home: 5610 Wisconsin Ave Bethesda MD 20815-4415 Office: Powell Goldstein Frazier Murphy 1001 Pennsylvania Ave NW Washington DC 20004-2505

SIMONS, LEONARD NORMAN RASHALL, advertising executive; b. Youngstown, Ohio, July 24, 1904; s. William Rashall and Minna (Williams) S.; m. Harriette Lieberman, Jan. 21, 1930 (dec. Sept. 1986); children: Mary Lou Zieve, Susan. LLD (hon.), Wayne State U., 1957; LHD (hon.), Hebrew Union Coll.-Jewish Inst. Religion, 1964, Marygrove Coll., Detroit, 1986. Ptnr. Simons-Michelson Co. Investments, Troy, Mich., 1929—; v.p. Simons Michelson Zieve Advt. Agy., Inc., Troy, 1977—; former vis. lectr. N.Y. U. Adv. dir. U.S. Treasury for War Bonds, Mich., 1941-45; past pres. Wayne State U. Press, Temple Beth El, Bloomfield Hills, Mich.; pres. emeritus Detroit Hist. Commn.; past chmn. bd. Mich. Cancer Found.; past chmn. United Negro Coll. Fund Mich.; Bd. dirs., former v.p. Jewish Fedn. Detroit; bd. dirs. Jewish Nat. Fund Mich., Nat. Found. Infantile Paralysis S.E. Mich. (former chmn.), Sinai Hosp. (former v.p.), Jewish Home for Aged (past chmn. bd.), NCCJ (brotherhood chmn. 1952), Greater Detroit Interfaith Round Table Christians and Jews. Fellow Brandeis U.; Decorated Chevalier dans l'Ordre Nationale du Merite France; recipient Prime Minister's medal State of Israel; LNS Forest given in Israel Jewish Nat. Fund; Press bldg. named in his honor Wayne State U., Detroit; recipient Butzel award Jewish Fedn. Detroit; Hon. Alum award U. Detroit. Mem. Am. Jewish Hist. Soc. (hon. dir.), Detroit Hist. Soc. (hon. dir.), Phi Beta Kappa (hon.), Zeta Beta Tau. (hon.). Clubs: Franklin Hills Country (past pres.), Adcraft. Lodge: Masons. Home: Apt 1002-03 16300 W Nine Mile Rd Southfield MI 48075-5983 Office: Simons Michelson Zieve Inc 900 Wilshire Dr Troy MI 48084-1628

SIMONS, LEWIS MARTIN, journalist; b. Paterson, N.J., Jan. 9, 1939; s. Abram and Goldie (Fleisher) S.; m. Carol Lenore Seiderman, Feb. 5, 1965; children: Justine, Rebecca, Adam P.D. BA, NYU, 1962; MS, Columbia U., 1964. Corr. AP, Kuala Lumpur, Singapore, Saigon, Denver, 1965-70, Washington Post, Bangkok, New Delhi, 1971-82; bur. chief Knight-Ridder Newspapers, Tokyo, 1982—. Author: Worth Dying For, 1987. With USMC, 1962-64. Recipient Grand prize and Investigative Reporting award Am. Newspaper Guild, 1981, Citation for Excellence, Overseas Press Club Am., 1983, Jessie Meriton White award Friends World Coll., 1986, Investigative Reporters and Editors award U. Mo., 1986, Award of Excellence, World Affairs Coun., 1984, 86, 89, 92, Pulitzer Prize, 1986, George Polk award, 1985, Malcolm S. Forbes award Overseas Press Club Am., 1986, 92, Gerald Loeb award UCLA, 1993; Edward R. Murrow fellow Coun. of Fgn. Rels., 1970-71. Mem. Fgn. Corrs. Club Japan (bd. dirs. 1991-92, pres., 1993-94). Office: Knight-Ridder Newspapers, 14th Fl Kioicho Bldg 3-12 Kioicho, Chiyoda-ku Tokyo 102, Japan

SIMONS, LYNN OSBORN, state education official; b. Havre, Mont., June 1, 1934; d. Robert Blair and Dorothy (Briggs) Osborn; BA, U. Colo., 1956; postgrad. U. Wyo., 1958-60; m. John Powell Simons, Jan. 19, 1957; children: Clayton Osborn, William Blair. Tchr., Midvale (Utah) Jr. High Sch., 1956-57, Sweetwater County Sch. Dist. 1, Rock Springs, Wyo., 1957-58, U. Wyo., Laramie, 1959-61, Natrona County Sch. Dist. 1, Casper, Wyo., 1963-64; credit mgr. Gallery 323, Casper, 1972-77; Wyo. state supt. public instrn., Cheyenne, 1979-91; sec.'s regional rep. region VIII U.S. Dept. Edn., Denver, 1993—; mem. State Bds. Charities and Reform, Land Commrs., Farm Loan, 1979-91; mem. State Commns. Capitol Bldg., Liquor, 1979-91; Ex-officio mem. bd. trustees U. Wyo., 1979-91; ex-officio mem. Wyo. Community Coll. Commn., 1979-91; mem. steering com. Edn. Commn. of the States, 1988-90; mem. State Bd. Edn., 1971-77, chmn., 1976-77; advisor Nat. Trust for Hist. Preservation, 1980-86. Mem. LWV (pres. 1970-71). Democrat. Episcopalian. Office: US Dept Edn 1244 Speer Blvd Ste 310 Denver CO 80204-3582

SIMONS, RICHARD DUNCAN, judge; b. Niagara Falls, N.Y., Mar. 23, 1927; s. William Taylor and Sybil Irene (Swick) S.; m. Muriel E. Genung, June 9, 1951 (dec. 1992); m. Esther Turkington Tremblay, May 21, 1994; children: Ross T., Scott R., Katherine E., Linda A. A.B., Colgate U., 1949; LL.B., U. Mich., 1952; LLD (hon.), Albany Law Sch., 1983. Bar: N.Y. 1952. Pvt. practice law Rome, N.Y., 1952-63; asst. corp. counsel City of Rome, 1955-58, corp. counsel, 1960-63; justice 5th jud. dist. N.Y. Supreme Ct., 1964-83, assoc. justice appellate div. 3d dept., 1971-72, assoc. justice appellate div. 4th dept., 1973-82; assoc. judge N.Y. Ct. Appeals, 1983—, acting chief judge, 1992-93; mem. Law Sch. Admission Svcs., Bar Passage Study Com. Editorial staff: N.Y. Pattern Jury Instructions, 1979-83. Chmn. Republican City Com., 1958-62; vice chmn. Oneida County Rep. Com., 1958-62; bd. mgrs. Rome Hosp. and Murphy Meml. Hosp., 1953. Served with USN, World War II. NEH fellow U. Va. Law Sch., 1979. Fellow Am. Bar Found., N.Y. State Bar Found.; mem. ABA, N.Y. State Bar Assn., Oneida County Bar Assn., Rome Bar Assn., Am. Law Inst., Inst. Jud. Adminstrn. Home: 1410 N George St Rome NY 13440-2704 Office: NY Ct Appeals Hall 20 Eagle St Albany NY 12207-1004

SIMONS, STEPHEN, mathematics educator, researcher; b. London, Aug. 11, 1938; came to U.S., 1965; s. Jack Isidore Simons and Ethel Esther (Littman) Harris; m. Jacqueline Mania Berchadsky, Aug. 13, 1963; 1 son, Mark. BA, Cambridge U., Eng., 1959, PhD, 1962. Instr. U. B.C., Vancouver, Can., 1962-63; asst. prof. U. BC, Vancouver, Can., 1964-65; asst. prof. U. Calif., Santa Barbara, 1965-67, assoc. prof., 1967-73, prof., 1973—, chmn. dept., 1975-77, 88-89; trustee Math. Scis. Rsch. Inst., Berkeley, Calif., 1988-94. Peterhouse tech. fellow, Cambridge U., 1963-64. Mem. Am. Math. Soc., The Inst. Mgmt. Scis. Office: Univ Calif Dept Math Santa Barbara CA 93106

SIMONS, STEVEN J(AY), lawyer; b. Akron, Ohio, Oct. 30, 1946; s. Alex and Bella Simons; m. Harriet Fishman, Aug. 29, 1971; children: Sara, Rebecca, David. Ba, Harvard U., 1969, JD, 1972. Bar: Ohio 1972, Mass. 1975. Assoc. Squire, Sanders & Dempsey, Cleve., 1972-74; assoc. Ropes & Gray, Boston, 1974-81, ptnr., 1981—. Mem. Wellesley (Mass.) Town Meeting, 1983-94. Rotary Internat. fellow, 1969. Mem. ABA, Mass. Bar Assn., Nat. Assn. Bond Lawyers. Office: Ropes & Gray One International Pl Boston MA 02110-2624

SIMONS, THOMAS W., JR., ambassador; b. Crosby, Minn., Sept. 4, 1938; married; 2 children. BA, Yale U., 1958; MA, Harvard U., 1959, PhD, 1963. Joined Fgn. Svc., Dept. State, 1964; sec. del., tech. sec. U.S. Del. to 6th round trade negotiation in GATT, 1967-68; consular officer Am. Embassy, Warsaw, Poland, 1969-71; polit. officer Dept. State, Washington, 1971-72; Coun. on Fgn. Rels. fellow Hoover Instn., Stanford, Calif., 1972-74; internat. rels. officer Bur. Politico-Mil. Affairs, 1974-75, mem. policy planning staff, 1975-77; chief external reporting unit, polit. sect. Am. Embassy, Moscow, 1977-79; dep. chief of mission Am. Embassy, Bucharest, Romania, 1979-81; counselor for polit. affairs Am. Embassy, London, 1981-85; dir. for Soviet Union affairs Dept. State, 1985-86; mem. Sr. Seminar in Fgn. Policy, 1986-89; dep. asst. sec. for European and Can. affairs Dept. State, 1989-90; diplomat-in-residence, vis. scholar, adj. prof. history Brown U., Providence, 1990—. Office: Brown U Providence RI 02912

SIMONSON, BRUCE MILLER, geologist, educator; b. Washington, May 13, 1950; s. Roy Walter and Susan (Miller) S.; m. Sue Mareske, June 28, 1974; children: Joseph Walter, Sonja Anne, Maya Beth. BA with high honors, Wesleyan U., Middletown, Conn., 1972; PhD, Johns Hopkins U., 1982. Field mapper Nat. Geog. Inst. Honduras, 1973-74; instr. dept. geology Oberlin (Ohio) Coll., 1979-81, asst. prof., 1982-85, assoc. prof., 1986-88, prof., 1989—, chmn. dept. geology, 1986-89, 93—; adj. faculty Case We. Res. U., Cleve., 1983—; vis. scientist Geol. Survey, We. Australia, summers, 1985-87, 89, 93; tchr. U.S. Geol. Survey, Reston, Va., 1985, 93; vis. prof. U.S. Geol. Survey, Denver, Colo., 1992-93. Contbr. articles to profl. jours. Grantee Nat. Geog. Soc., 1986-89, 93-94, NSF, 1977-79, 84, 91-94, Rsch. Corp., 1983, Petroleum Rsch. Fund, 1982-84. Mem. Geol. Soc. Am., Internat. Assn. Sedimentologists, No. Ohio Geol. Soc., Soc. for Sedimentary Geology (sec. Gt. Lakes sect. 1986-90), Sigma Xi. Office: Oberlin Coll Dept Geology Oberlin OH 44074-1044

SIMONSON, DAVID C., retired newspaper association executive; b. N.Y.C., May 9, 1927; s. Simon and Rebecca (Coolman) S.; m. Lois E. Sneider, Nov. 1, 1952; children: Peter, Eric, John Frederick. BA, Hamilton Coll., 1948; postgrad., U. Vt., 1949, Art Student League of N.Y., 1949. Copywriter Forwell & Mart Advt., N.Y.C., 1949-50; reporter, editor Croton-Cortlandt News, Croton, N.Y., 1950-52; gen. mgr. Colony Publs., N.Y.C., 1952-54; editor, mgr. County Press Newspapers, Croton, 1955-59; promotion dir. Amcrete Corp., Peekskill, N.Y., 1959-60; various positions in mgmt. Patent Trader, Mt. Kisco, N.Y., 1960-72, pub., 1972-77; pres./pub. Pioneer Press Newspapers, Wilmette, Ill., 1977-86; exec. v.p., chief exec. officer Nat. Newspaper Assn., Washington, 1987-92; retired, 1992; bd. dirs. Christian Herald Assn., Chappaqua, N.Y.; lectr. Medill Sch. Journalism, Meridian House, U.S.A., numerous state press assns.; media cons.; seminar leader Eastern Europe for World Press Freedom Com.; cons. to Slovenian publs. for U.S. Info. Agy., 1993-94, cons. to Slovakian publs. for U.S. Info. Agy., 1995; cons. to African publs. for UNESCO, 1955; participant Freedom Forum Roundtables. Chmn. planning bd. Town of Croton-on-Hudson, N.Y., 1962-67, trustee, 1967, mayor, 1969. With USNR, 1945-46. Mem. Suburban Newspapers Am. (pres. 1984-85, bd. dirs. 1980-84), Ill. Press Assn (bd. dirs. 1980-84, 1st v.p. 1986), N.Y. Press Assn. (bd. dirs. 1966-76, 1st v.p. 1976), Nat. Newspaper Assn. (bd. dirs. 1985-86), Cook County Pubs. Assn. (pres. 1983-84). Avocations: painting, cartooning. Home: 1805 28th St S Arlington VA 22202-1536

SIMONSON, JOHN ALEXANDER, banking executive; b. Port Huron, Mich., July 22, 1945; s. Fred Alexander and Harriet (Woolfolk) S.; m. Juleen Marie Sheridan, June 18, 1971 (div. 1991); children: Laura E., Anne M. AB, U. Mich., 1967; MBA, Mich. State U., 1968. Exec. v.p., treas. Key Corp., Inc., Cleve., 1992—. Home: 225 Westwind Dr #49 Avon Lake OH 44012 Office: Soc Nat Bank 127 Pub Sq Cleveland OH 44114

SIMONSON, LEE STUART, broadcast company executive; b. Balt., July 3, 1948; s. Theodore and Sara (Silver) S.; m. Nancy Paula Levin, Mar. 25, 1973; children: Laura Todd, Michael Theodore. BA, U. Md., 1970. Acct. exec. WGMS-AM-FM (subs. RKO Gen.), Washington, 1971-73, retail sales mgr., 1973-76; sales mgr. WFYR-FM (subs. RKO Gen.), Chgo., 1976-80; v.p., gen. mgr. WRKS-FM (subs. RKO Gen.), N.Y.C., 1980-84, WOR-AM (subs. RKO Gen.), N.Y.C., 1984-88; vice chmn., COO, owner radio stas. Broadcasting Ptnrs., Inc., N.Y.C., 1988—. Bd. dirs. N.Y.C. chpt. March of Dimes, 1982—, Radio Advt. Bur., 1994—, IRTS Found., 1995—. With USAR, 1970-76. Jewish. Avocations: baseball, reading, tennis, symphony, films. Office: 20th Fl 1120 Ave of The Americas New York NY 10036

SIMONSON, MARGARET, newspaper publishing executive. V.p. employee rels. Chgo. Tribune. Office: Chgo Tribune Co 435 N Michigan Ave Chicago IL 60611*

SIMONSON, TED, principal. Prin. Los Gatos (Calif.) High Sch. Recipient Blue Ribbon Sch. award, 1990-91. Office: Los Gatos High Sch 20 High School Ct Los Gatos CA 95032-6917

SIMONT, MARC, artist; b. Paris, France, Nov. 23, 1915; came to U.S., 1927, naturalized, 1936; s. Josep and Dolors (Basté) S.; m. Sara Dalton, Apr. 7, 1945; 1 son, Marc Dalton. Attended, Academie Julian, Academie Ranson, André Lhote Sch., all Paris, 1932-35, NAD, N.Y.C., 1936. Asst. to Ezra Winter on Jefferson Wing mural Library of Congress, 1940; author, illustrator 9 children's books, 1939—; illustrator 80 books; author, illustrator: Opera Soufflé, 1950, Polly's Oats, 1951, The Lovely Summer, 1952, (with Red Smith) How to Get to First Base, 1952, Mimi, 1955, The Plumber Out of the Sea, 1955, The Contest at Paca, 1959, How Come Elephants?, 1965, Afternoon in Spain, 1965, A Childs' Eye View of the World, 1972; translator, illustrator The Lieutenant Colonel and The Gypsy, 1971; translator Ibrahim, 1989. Recipient Caldecott honor, 1950, Caldecott award, 1957, citation merit Soc. Illustrators, 1965; Tiffany Found. fellow, 1937. Mem. Am. Vets. Com., Authors Guild. Home: 336 Town St West Cornwall CT 06796-1304

SIMONTON, ROBERT BENNET, lawyer; b. N.Y.C., Feb. 23, 1933; s. Theodore E. and Beulah H. (Hulsebus) S.; m. Tanya Wood, Aug. 24, 1957; children: Sheri, Robert B. Jr., Scott S. Student Amherst Coll., 1950-52; BS in Engring., Columbia U., 1954; LLB, Syracuse U., 1959. Bar: N.Y. 1959. Patent agt., atty. Theodore E. Simonton, Cazenovia, N.Y., 1956-60; assoc. Hancock, Dorr, Ryan and Shove, Syracuse, N.Y., 1960-64; staff atty. Bristol-Myers Co., Syracuse, 1967, counsel, 1967-71, v.p., counsel Bristol Labs., 1971-74; v.p., sec., gen. counsel Crouse Hinds Co., Syracuse, 1974-75; staff atty. Sterling Drug Inc., N.Y.C., 1975-78, sec., asst. gen. counsel, 1978-88; small bus. cons., 1988—; adj. prof. U. Bridgeport (Conn.) Law Sch., 1988-90; trustee Syracuse Savs. Bank, 1973-76. Bd. govs. Citizens' Found., Syracuse, 1969-70; bd. dirs. Urban League of Syracuse, 1967-72, pres., 1967-71, chmn., 1971-72; bd. visitors Syracuse U. Coll. Law, 1968—; bd. dirs. Graham Windham, also sec., 1986-88, Goodwill Industries Coastal Empire, 1992—, treas., 1993-95; treas. Landings Assn. Inc., 1994—; bd. trustees Manlius Pub. Hill Sch., 1962-75, chmn., 1971-74. Served with U.S. Army, 1954-56. Recipient Justinian Honor Soc. award Syracuse U. Coll. Law, 1959.

SIMOPOULOS, ARTEMIS PANAGEOTIS, physician, educator; b. Kampos-Avias, Greece, Apr. 3, 1933; came to U.S. 1949, naturalized 1955; d. Panageotis L. and Nena P. (Konteas) S.; m. Alan Lee Pinkerson, Jan. 10, 1957; children: Daphne, Lee, Alexandra. B.A., Barnard Coll., 1952; M.D., Boston U., 1956. Diplomate Am. Bd. Pediatrics. Pediatric intern Kings County Hosp., Bklyn., 1956-57; resident Kings County Hosp., 1957-58; fellow in hematology Children's Hosp., Washington, 1960-61, asst. chief resident in pediatrics, 1961-62, mem. acad. staff, 1962-67, assoc. staff in pediatric nursery service, 1967-71; spl. lectr. pediatrics Ewha Woman's U. Sch. Medicine, Seoul, Korea, 1958-59; asst. prof. pediatrics George Washington U. Sch. Medicine, 1962-67, clin. asst. prof., 1967-71; dir. nurseries George Washington U. Hosp., 1965-67; staff pediatrician Nat. Heart and Lung Inst., NIH, 1968-71, cons. endocrinology dr., 1971-78; with div. med. scis. Nat. Acad. Scis., NRC, Washington, 1971-74; exec. sec. Nat. Acad. Scis., NRC, 1974-76, exec. dir. bd. maternal, child and family health research, 1974-76; cons. to dir. Nat. Inst. Child Health and Human Devel., NIH, Bethesda, Md, 1976-77; chief devel. biology and nutrition br., ctrs. for research for mothers and children Nat. Inst. Child Health and Human Devel., NIH, 1977; vice chmn. and exec. sec. nutrition coordinating com. NIH, 1977-78; cons. nutrition and health to spl. asst. to the Pres. for Consumer Affairs The White House, Washington, 1978-81; chmn. nutrition coordinating com. office of the dir. NIH, 1978-86; dir. divsn. nutritional sci. Internat. Life Sci. Inst. Rsch. Found., Washington, 1986-88; dir. Ctr. for

Genetics, Nutrition and Health, Washington, 1989-90, pres., 1990—; co-chmn., exec. sec. joint subcom. Human Nutrition Rsch., Office Sci. and Tech. Policy, Exec. Office of the Pres., 1979-83; vis. prof. Harokopio U., Athens, 1994-95. Editor World Rev. Nutrition and Dietetics, 1989—; contbg. editor Nutrition Revs., 1979—; mem. editorial bd. Jour. Nutrition, Growth, and Cancer, 1982—; Internat. Jour. Vitamin and Nutrition Research, 1986—, n=3 News, 1986-90, Annals Nutrition and Metabolism, 1991—, Food Revs. Internat., 1994—; cons. editor Nutrition Research, 1983—, Annals Internal Medicine, 1984—, Jour. AMA, 1985—, Food Reviews Internat., 1994—; contbr. articles in endocrinology, genetics, nutrition and fitness, omega-3 fatty acids, and obesity to profl. jours. Recipient 1st Presdl. award for studies in field of obesity and weight control Columbia-Presbyn. Med. Ctr., 1993, Outstanding Achievement award promoting nutrition and fitness and positive health Greek Govt., 1992; NIH grantee, 1960-61. Fellow Am. Acad. Pediatrics, Am. Coll. Nutrition; mem. Soc. Pediatric Rsch., Endocrine Soc., Maternity Ctr. Assn. (rsch. adv. com.), Am. Pediatric Soc., Am. Inst. Nutrition, Am. Soc. Clin. Nutrition, Am. Assn. for World Health (v.p. 1981-90, asst. treas. 1981-90, nat. chmn. for World Health Day 1982—, vice chmn. bd. 1991-92, chmn. pgm. com. 1993—), bd. dirs. 1993—), D.C. Med. Soc., N.Am. Assn. for Study Obesity, Internat. Life Scis. Inst. (trustee 1982-88, exec. com. 1982-85, trustee Nutrition Found. 1985-87), Internat. Soc. Study of Fatty Acids and Lipids (sec., treas. 1991-94, 95—). Greek Orthodox. Home: 4330 Klingle St NW Washington DC 20016-3577 Office: Ctr Genetics Nutrition and Health 2001 S St NW #530 Washington DC 20009

SIMOWITZ, LEE H., lawyer; b. Augusta, Ga., Sept. 7, 1946. BA cum laude, Harvard U., 1968; JD, Yale U., 1972. Bar: D.C. 1973. Law clk. to Hon. Harold H. Greene, chief judge Superior Ct., Washington, 1972-73; asst. to dir. bur. consumer protection FTC, Washington, 1975-76; atty.-adviser Calvin J. Collier, chmn. FTC, 1976-77; ptnr. Baker & Hostetler, Washington. Mem. ABA (antitrust law sect., public utility law sect.), D.C. Bar. Office: Baker & Hostetler Ste 1100 1050 Connecticut Ave NW Washington DC 20036-5304

SIMPICH, WILLIAM MORRIS, public affairs consultant; b. Washington, Sept. 24, 1924; s. Frederick and Margaret (Edwards) S.; m. Margaret Pearson Hunter, Sept. 9, 1950; children: William Morris, Margaret Edwards, John Hunter, Joseph Pearson. Student, George Washington U., 1942-43; BS, U.S. Naval Acad., 1946. Assoc. Ivy Lee & T.J. Ross (name later changed to T.J. Ross & Assocs., Inc.), N.Y.C., 1949-51, 54-63, v.p., 1964, sec., treas., 1965-84, sr. v.p., 1977-84, ret. as exec. v.p., 1984, also bd. dirs. With U.S. Navy, 1946-49, 51-53. Episcopalian. Home: 1021 Church Rd Lusby MD 20657-2636

SIMPKIN, LAWRENCE JAMES, utilities executive; b. Sault Ste Marie, Mich., Jan. 1, 1933; s. Fred Bernard and Helen Clara (Goetz) S.; m. Agnes Diane L'Huillier, Sept. 3, 1960; children: Lawrence J., Lynn Marie, Dawn Catherine. B.S. in Elec. Engring. Mich. Technol. Inst., 1954; M.S., Wayne State U., 1965. Registered profl. engr., Mich. Engr. Detroit Edison Co., 1957-61, supr. engring. instrumentation, 1961-69, dir. elec. div., 1969-72, dir. engring. research, 1972-75, dir. tech. systems planning, 1975-76, gen. dir. div. services, 1976-82, dir. outage mgmt., 1982-84, dir. nuclear engring., 1985-87, gen. dir. generation engring., 1987—; lectr. Lawrence Inst. Tech., 1965-72; adj. prof. U. Mich., 1974. Contbr. articles to profl. jours. Served to capt. USAF, 1954-57. Mem. IEEE, Engring. Soc. Detroit, Sigma Xi. Home: 22016 Clover Ln Novi MI 48375-5112 Office: 2000 2nd Ave Detroit MI 48226-1203

SIMPKINS, ANNE EDDLEMAN, interior designer; b. Charlotte, N.C., July 9, 1950; d. Alton B. and Melba (Ketner) Eddleman; m. Jesse E. Simpkins, June 23, 1973. BA in Home Econs., Appalachian State U., Boone, N.C., 1972; postgrad., U. Tenn., 1982. Decorating cons. J.C. Penney's, Knoxville, Tenn., 1972-76, Decorating Den, Knoxville, 1976-80; interior designer Vaughan Furniture, Knoxville, 1981-85; pres., interior designer Living Interiors, Inc., Knoxville, 1985—. Contbr. articles to profl. publs. Com. mem., showhouse designer Symphony League, Knoxville, 1989, 90. Recipient Designer's Choice award Mar. of Dimes, 1989, 2d Place People's Choice award Mar. of Dimes, 1989. Mem. Interior Design Soc. (nat. pres. 1990-92), East Tenn. Interior Design Soc. (pres. 1986-88, bd. dirs.), Toastmasters (pres. 1988, award 1989, 90, 92). Avocations: historic homes, writing. Office: Living Interiors Inc 6326 Papermill Rd # 6B Knoxville TN 37919-4810

SIMPKINS, CHARLES, Olympic athlete, track and field. Olympic triple jumper Barcelona, Spain, 1992. Recipient Triple Jump Silver medal Olympics, Barcelona, 1992. Office: US Olympic Com 1750 E Boulder St Colorado Springs CO 80909-5746*

SIMPLOT, JOHN R., agribusiness executive; b. Dubuque, Iowa, Jan. 4, 1909; m. Esther Becker; children: Richard, Don, Scott, Gay Simplot Otter. Founder, chmn. J.R. Simplot Co., Boise, Idaho, 1941—; bd. dirs. Micron Technology, First Security Corp., Continental Life and Accident Co., Morrison-Knudsen, Inc. Former chmn. bd. trustees Coll. Idaho. Avocations: skiing, horseback riding, hunting, fishing. Pioneer in commercial frozen french fries. Office: J R Simplot Co PO Box 27 1 Capitol Ctr Boise ID 83707

SIMPSON, A. W. B., law educator; b. 1931. Fellow Oxford U., Eng., 1955-72; prof. U. Kent, Canterbury, Eng., 1972-84, U. Chgo., 1984-87, U. Mich., Ann Arbor, 1987—. Office: U Mich Law Sch 625 S State St Ann Arbor MI 48109-1215

SIMPSON, ALAN KOOI, senator; b. Cody, Wyo., Sept. 2, 1931; s. Milward Lee and Lorna (Kooi) S.; m. Ann Schroll, June 21, 1954; children—William Lloyd, Colin Mackenzie, Susan Lorna. BS, U. Wyo., 1954, JD, 1958; LLD (hon.), Calif. Western Sch. of Law, 1983, Colo. Coll., 1986, Notre Dame U., 1987; JD (hon.), Am. U., 1989. Bar: Wyo. 1958, U.S. Supreme Ct. 1964. Asst. atty. gen. State of Wyo., 1959; city atty. City of Cody, 1959-69; partner firm Simpson, Kepler, and Simpson, Cody, Wyo., 1959-78; mem. Wyo. Ho. of Reps., 1964-77, majority whip, 1973-75, majority floor leader, 1975-77, speaker pro tem, 1977; legis. participant Eagleton Inst. Politics, Rutgers U., 1971; mem. U.S. Senate from Wyo., 1978—, asst. majority leader, 1985-87, asst. minority leader, 1987-95, chmn. vets. affairs com., chmn. fin. subcom. on Social Security and Family Policy, chmn. subcom. on immigration and refugee policy; mem. Sen. Rep. Policy Com. Spec. Com. on Aging; guest lectr. London exchange program Regent's Coll., London, 1987. Formerly v.p., trustee N.W. C.C. Powell, Wyo., 1968-76; trustee Buffalo Bill Hist. Ctr., Cody, Grand Teton Music Festival; del. Nat. Triennial Episcopal Ch. Conv., 1973, 76. With U.S. Army, 1954-56. Recipient Nat. Assn. Land Grant Colls. Centennial Alum award U. Wyo., 1987, Lifetime Svc. award Vietnam Vets. Am., 1993. Mem. Wyo. Bar Assn., Park County Bar Assn., Fifth Jud. Dist. Bar Assn., Am. Bar Assn., Assn. Trial Lawyers Am., U. Wyo. Alumni Assn. (pres. 1962, 63, Disting. Alumnus award 1985), VFW (life), Am. Legion, Amvets. (Silver Helmet award). Lodges: Eagles, Elks, Masons (33 deg.), Shriners, Rotary (pres. local club 1972-73). Office: US Senate 105 Dirksen Senate Bldg Washington DC 20510-5002*

SIMPSON, ALLYSON BILICH, lawyer; b. Pasadena, Calif., Feb. 5, 1951; d. John Joseph and Barbaran Rita (Bessolo) Bilich; m. Roland Gilbert Simpson, Aug. 11, 1979; children: Megan Elise, Erin Marie, Brian Patrick. BS, U. So. Calif., L.A., 1973, JD, 1976. Bar: Calif. 1976. Staff atty. Gen. Telephone Co., Thousand Oaks, Calif., 1978-79; group staff atty., dir. legis. compliance Pacific Mut. Life Ins. Co., Newport Beach, Calif., 1980-86; corp. counsel and sec. Amicare Ins. Co., Beverly Hills, Calif., 1986; assoc. Leboeuf, Lamb, Leiby & MacRae, L.A., 1986-87; from assoc. to ptnr. Musick, Peeler & Garrett, L.A., 1988-94; ptnr. Sonnenschein Nath & Rosenthal, L.A., 1994—; vis. pro. bus. law U. So. Calif., L.A., 1981. Trustee St. Anne's Maternity Home Found., L.A., 1991—; bd. dirs. St. Anne's Maternity Home, L.A., 1993—. Mem. Western Pension & Benefits Conf., Conf. of Ins. Counsel. Republican. Roman Catholic. Avocations: music, reading, family. Office: Sonnenschein Nath & Rosenthal 601 S Figueroa St Ste 1500 Los Angeles CA 90017

SIMPSON, ANDREA LYNN, energy communications executive; b. Altadena, Calif., Feb. 10, 1948; d. Kenneth James and Barbara Faries Simpson; m. John R. Myrdal, Dec. 13, 1986; 1 child, Christopher Ryan Myrdal. BA, U. So. Calif., 1969, MS, 1983; postgrad. U. Colo., Boulder Sch. Bank Mktg., 1977. Asst. cashier United Calif. Bank, L.A., 1969-73; asst. v.p. mktg. 1st Hawaiian Bank, Honolulu, 1973-78; v.p. corp. comm. BHP Hawaii, Inc. (formerly Pacific Resources, Inc.), Honolulu, 1978—. Bd. dirs. Arts Coun. Hawaii, 1977-81, Hawaii Heart Assn., 1978-83, Coun. Pacific Girl Scouts U.S., 1982-85, Child and Family Svcs., 1984-86, Honolulu Symphony Soc., 1985-91, Sta. KHPR Hawaii Pub. Radio, 1988-92, Kapiolani Found., 1990-95, Hanahauoli Sch., 1991—; bd. dirs., 2nd. v.p. Girl Scout Coun. Hawaii, 1994—; trustee Hawaii Loa Coll., 1984-86, Kapiolani Women's and Children's Hosp., 1988—, Hawaii Sch. For Girls at LaPietra, 1989-91, Kapiolani Med. Ctr. at Pali Momi, 1994—; commr. Hawaii State Commn. on Status of Women, 1985-87, State Sesquecentennial of Pub. Schs. Commn., 1990-91; bd. dirs. Hawaii Strategic Devel. Corp., 1991—, Hawaii Children's Mus., 1994—, Pacific Asian Affairs Coun., 1994—; adv. dir. Hawaii Kids at Work, 1991—, Hawaii Mothers Against Drunk Driving, 1992—. Named Panhellenic Woman of Yr. Hawaii, 1979, Outstanding Woman in Bus. Hawaii YWCA, 1980, Outstanding Young Woman of Hawaii Girl Scouts Coun. of the Pacific, 1985, 86, Hawaii Legis., 1980. Mem. Am. Mktg. Assn., Pub. Rels. Soc. Am. (bd. dirs. Honolulu chpt. 1984-86, Silver Anvil award 1984, Pub. Rels. Profl. Yr. 1991), Pub. Utilities Communicators Assn. (Communicator of Yr. 1984), Honolulu Advt. Fedn. (Advt. Woman of Yr. 1984), U. So. Calif. Alumni Assn. (bd. dirs. Hawaii 1981-83), Outrigger Canoe Club, Pacific Club, Kaneohe Yacht Club, Rotary (pub. rels. chmn. 1988—, Honolulu chpt.), Alpha Phi (past pres., dir. Hawaii), Hawaii Jaycees (Outstanding Young Person of Hawaii 1978). Office: BHP Hawaii Inc 733 Bishop St Ste 2700 Honolulu HI 96813-4025

SIMPSON, BERYL BRINTNALL, botany educator; b. Dallas, Apr. 28, 1942; d. Edward Everett and Barbara Frances (Brintnall) S.; children: Jonathan, Meghan. AB, Radcliffe Coll., 1964; MA, Harvard U., 1968, PhD, 1968. Rsch. fellow Arnold Arboretum/Gray Herbarium, Cambridge, Mass., 1969-71; curator Smithsonian Instn., Washington, 1971-78; prof. U. Tex., Austin, 1978—; chmn. U.S. Com. to IUBS, 1985-88; co-pres. Internat. Congress Systematic and Evolutionary Biology, 1980-85. Author: Economic Botany, 1994; editor: Mesquite, 1977; contbr. over 100 articles and notes to profl. jours. Recipient Greenman award Mo. Bot. Garden, 1970. Fellow AAAS, Am. Acad. Arts and Sci.; mem. Soc. for Study Evolution (coun. 1975-80, pres. 1985-86), Bot. Soc. Am. (pres. 1990-91, Merit award, 1992), Bot. Soc. Washington (v.p. 1975), Am. Soc. Plant Taxonomists (pres. 1994, Cooley award), Am. Inst. Biol. Scis. (bd. dirs. 1993—), U.S.-Mex. Found. for Sci. (bd. govs.). Office: Dept Botany BIO 308 U Tex Austin TX 78713

SIMPSON, CAROLE ESTELLE, broadcast journalist; b. Chgo., Dec. 7, 1940; d. Lytle Ray and Doretha Viola (Wilbon) S.; m. James Edward Marshall, Sept. 3, 1966; children: Mallika Joy, Adam. BA in Journalism, U. Mich., 1962; postgrad., U. Iowa, 1964-65. News reporter WCFL Radio, Chgo., 1965-68; reporter/anchorwoman WBBM Radio, Chgo., 1968-70; TV news reporter WMAQ-TV, Chgo., 1970-74; NBC news network corr. Midwest Bur., transferred to Washington, from 1974; anchorwoman World News Saturday, Washington, 1988-93, World News Sunday, Washington, 1993—; instr. journalism Tuskegee Inst., Ala., 1962-64; faculty Medill Sch. Journalism, Northwestern U., 1972-74; moderator 1992 Town Mtg. Presdl. Debate. Recipient med. journalism award AMA, Emmy award, Dupont award, Milestone in Broadcasting award Nat. Commn. on Working Women, Disting. Journalist award U. Mo., Star award Am. Women in Radio and TV, Journalist of Yr. award Nat. Assn. Black Journalists, 1992; named Outstanding Woman in Comm., YWCA Met. Chgo., 1974; named to U. Iowa Comm. Hall of Fame; established several coll. scholarships for women and minorities in broadcast journalism. Mem. Internat. Women's Media Found. (bd. of RFK Journalism awards), NAS (mem. of bd. of children and families), Radio TV News Dirs. Found. (trustee), Radio-TV Corrs. Assn. Washington. Office: ABC News Washington Bureau 1717 DeSales St NW Washington DC 20036

SIMPSON, CHARLES EDMOND, crop science educator; b. Winters, Tex., Aug. 19, 1940; s. Robert Charles and Rosalie Helen Simpson; m. Lynann Kruse, Aug. 29, 1964; children: Melissa E. Heatley, Shay L. BS in Agrl. Edn., Tex. A&M U., 1963, MS in Plant Breeding, 1966, PhD in Plant Breeding, 1967. From asst. prof. to assoc. prof. Tex. Agrl. Exptl. Sta., Tex. A&M U., Stephenville, 1967-84, prof., 1984—. Contbr. 5 chpts. to books, articles to profl. jours. Mem. Am. Soc. Agronomy, Am. Peanut Rsch. & Edn. Soc. (pres. 1991-92), Am. Phytopathol. Soc., Coun. on Agrl. Sci. & Tech. Diversity, Crop Sci. Soc. Am. (Frank N. Meyer medal 1993). Lutheran. Avocation: peanut germplasm preservation and collection. Office: Tex A&M U Tex Agrl Exptl Sta PO Box 292 Stephenville TX 76401

SIMPSON, CHARLES R., III, federal judge; b. Cleve., July 8, 1945; s. Charles Ralph and Anne Marie (Markel) S.; married; 3 children. BA, U. Louisville, 1967, JD, 1970. Bar: Ky. 1970, U.S. Dist. Ct. (we. dist.) Ky. 1971, U.S. Cir. Ct. (6th cir.) 1985. With Rubin, Trautwein & Mays, Louisville, 1971-75, Levin, Yussman & Simpson, Louisville, 1975-77; judge U.S. Dist. Ct. (we. dist.) Ky., Louisville, 1986—; ret. practice Louisville, 1977-86; part-time staff counsel Jefferson County Judge/Exec., 1978-84; adminstr. Jefferson County Alcoholic Beverage Control, 1983-84; city clk. City of Rolling Fields, 1985-86. Roman Catholic. Office: We Dist Ct Ky 247 US Courthouse 601 W Broadway Louisville KY 40202

SIMPSON, DALE ARTHUR, healthcare executive. BA, U. Ky., 1988; MHA, Xavier U., 1975. Adminstrv. resident Borgess Hosp., Kalamazoo, 1974-75; adminstr. Huron Meml. Hosp., Bad Axe, Mich., 1975-77; v.p. Ingalls Meml. Hosp., Harvey, Ill., 1977-79; exec. dir. Alexian Bros. Health Mgmt., Elk Grove Village, Ill., 1979-82, Alice Peck Day meml. hosp., Lebanon, N.H., 1982-85; corp. v.p The Hitchcock Alliance, Hanover, N.H., 1982-85; dir. healthcare mktg. Adden Furniture, Inc., Lowell, Mass., 1985-88; exec. v.p., chief oper. officer Cmty. Med. Ctr., Scranton, Pa., 1988-91, Marathon, Inc., Providence, 1992—. Bd. dirs. Hope House, Inc., 1979-82; mem. Ea. Regional Coun. on Alcohol and Drug Abuse, 1979-82; trustee Carter Cmty. Assn., 1982-85, Alcohol Referral Ctr., Rutland, Vt., 1982-85; pres. bd. dirs. Support Ctr. of R.I.; bd. dirs., mem. exec. com. Drug and Alcohol Treatment Assn. Fellow Am. Coll. Healthcare Execs.; mem. Am. Hosp. Assn., Assn. Univ. Programs in Health Adminstrn., Xavier U. Alumni Assn. Home: Marathon Inc 215 New Meadow Rd Barrington RI 02806 Office: Marathon Inc 131 Wayland Ave Providence RI 02906

SIMPSON, DANIEL H., ambassador; b. Wheeling, W.Va., July 9, 1939; married; 4 children. BA, Yale U., 1961; cert. in African studies, Northwestern U., 1973. Joined Fgn. Svc., U.S. Dept. State, Washington, 1966—, staff asst. Bur. Security and Consular Affairs, 1966-67, speech writer for asst. sec. state for African affairs, 1968, desk officer for Rhodesia, Botswana, Lesotho, and Swaziland, 1973-74; tng. officer USIA, Washington, 1967-68; polit., econ. and consular officer Am. Embassy, Bujumbura, Burundi, 1968-70; polit. officer Am. Embassy, Pretoria, Republic South Africa, 1970-72; dep. chief mission Am. Embassy, Beirut, until 1989; amb. to Cen. African Republic, Bangui, 1989-93; dep. comdr. Army War Coll., Carlisle, Pa., 1993-94; ambassador to Somalia Mogadishu, 1994—. Home and Office: 4204 Franklin St Bellaire OH 43906

SIMPSON, DANIEL REID, lawyer; b. Glen Alpine, N.C., Feb. 20, 1927; s. James R. and Margaret Ethel (Newton) S.; m. Mary Alice Leonard, Feb. 25, 1930; children: Mary Simpson Beyer, Ethel B. Simpson Todd, James R. II. BS, Wake Forest U., 1949, LLB, 1951. Bar: N.C. 1951, U.S. Dist. Ct. (we. dist.) N.C. 1951, U.S. Ct. Appeals (4th and 5th cirs.) 1980. Dir. First Union Nat. Bank, Morganton, N.C. mem. N.C. Ho. of Reps., 1959-65; now mem. N.C. Senate, mem. N.C. Hwy. Oversight Commn.; mem. oversight com. N.C. Dept. of Corrections; hon. mem. bd. dirs. N.C. Restaurant Assns.; del. Rep. Nat. Conv., 1968, 76, mem. N.C. Rep. Exec. Com.; mem. South Eastern Interstate Forest Fire Protection Compact Adv. Com. Served with AUS, 1943-45, PTO. Mem. N.C. Bar Assn., Burke County Bar Assn. Baptist. Club: Masons. Office: Simpson Aycock PA 204 E Mcdowell St Morganton NC 28655-3545 also: PO Drawer 1329 Morganton NC 28655

SIMPSON, DAVID WILLIAM, artist, educator; b. Pasadena, Calif., Jan. 20, 1928; s. Frederick and Mary Adeline (White) S.; m. Dolores D. Debus,

July 30, 1954; 1 stepchild, Gregory C. Vose; 1 child, Lisa C. B.F.A., Calif. Sch. Fine Arts, 1956; M.A., San Francisco State Coll., 1958. Instr. art Am. River Jr. Coll., Sacramento, 1958-60, Contra Costa Jr. Coll., San Pablo, Calif., 1960-65; prof. art U. Calif., Berkeley, 1967-91, prof. emeritus, 1991—. Exhibited in one-man shows including Robert Elkon Gallery, N.Y.C., 1961, 63, 64, San Francisco Mus. Art, 1967, Henri Gallery, Washington, 1968, Oakland Museum, 1978, Modernism, San Francisco, 1980-81, 84, 86, Sheldon Meml. Art Gallery, Lincoln, Nebr., 1990, Mincher/Wilcox Gallery, San Francisco, 1991, 92, 93, Angles Gallery, Santa Monica, Calif., 1991, 92, 94, Bemis Found., Omaha, Nebr., 1991, Anthony Ralph Gallery, N.Y.C., 1992, John Berggruen Gallery, San Francisco, 1994; group shows including Mus. Modern Art, N.Y.C., 1963, Carnegie Internat., Pitts., 1961-62, 66-67, Los Angeles Mus. Art, 1964, U. Ill., 1969, Expo '70, Osaka, Japan, 1970, Josly Art Mus., Omaha, 1970, John Berggruen Gallery, San Francisco, 1979, Janus Gallery, L.A., 1980, Gallery Show, Tokyo, 1984, Koplin Gallery, L.A., 1987, Angles Gallery, Santa Monica, 1988, 90, John GoodGallery, N.Y., 1992, John Berggruen Gallery, San Francisco, 1993; represented in permanent collections including, Phila. Mus. Art, Nat. Collection Fine Arts, Washington, Seattle Art Mus., La Jolla (Calif.) Mus. Art, Mus. Modern Art, N.Y.C., San Francisco Mus. Art, Oakland (Calif.) Mus., Panza Collection, Italy, Laguna Art Mus., Laguna Beach, Calif., Univ. Art Mus., Berkeley, Calif. Home: 565 Vistamont St Berkeley CA 94708 Office: U Calif Art Dept Berkeley CA 94720

SIMPSON, DENNIS ARDEN, lighting contracting company executive; b. Monroe, N.C., July 10, 1944; s. Arden L. and Lola M. Simpson; children from previous marriage: Anthony Dennis, Legare Catherine; m. Peggy Lee Kay, Oct. 22, 1983; 1 child, Andrew Dennis. AB in Econs., U. N.C., 1967. Trainee Jordan Marsh, Miami, Fla., 1966-67; with planning dept. Burlington Industries, Reidsville, N.C., 1967-69; with scheduling dept. Burlington Industries, N.Y.C., 1969-71; ops. mgr. Unifi/Summerfield, Rocky Mt., N.C., 1971-75; pres., CEO East Industries, Rocky Mt., 1974-88, Dennis A. Simpson, Inc., Rocky Mt., 1988—. Mem. Illuminating Engring. Soc., Assn. Energy Engrs., Benvenue Country Club. Republican. Baptist. Avocations: tennis, boating. Office: 1114 Instrument Dr PO Box 8526 Rocky Mount NC 27804

SIMPSON, DON, film producer; b. Anchorage, AK, Oct. 29, 1945. Prod. exec. Paramount, 1975-77, v.p prod., 1977-80, sr. v.p prod., 1980-83; co-founder Don Simpson/Jerry Bruckheimer Prods., 1983—. Prodns. include (with Jerry Bruckheimer) Flashdance, 1983, Beverly Hills Cop, 1984, Thief of Hearts, 1984, Top Gun, 1986, Beverly Hill Cop II, 1987, Days of Thunder, 1990, The Ref, 1994, Bad Boys, 1995, Crimson Tide, 1995, Dangerous Minds, 1995; film writer Aloha Bobby and Rose, 1975, Cannonball, 1976. Office: Don Simpson/Jerry Bruckheimer Films Hollywood Pics Animation 1B 500 S Buena Vista St Burbank CA 91521-0001

SIMPSON, FREDERICK JAMES, retired research administrator; b. Regina, Sask., Can., June 8, 1922; s. Ralph James and Lillian Mary (Anderson) S.; m. Margaret Christine Mengen, May 28, 1947; children: Christine Louise, Steven James, Leslie Coleen, Ralph Edwin, David Glen. B.Sc., U. Alta., Can., 1944, M.Sc. in Agr., 1946; Ph.D. in Bacteriology, U. Wis., 1952. With Nat. Research Council Can., 1946-84; asst. dir. Atlantic Research Lab., Halifax, N.S., 1970-73; dir. Atlantic Research Lab., 1973-84; sci. cons., 1985-90; vis. scientist U. Ill., Urbana, 1955-56, vis. prof., 1964; mem. exec. council Atlantic Provinces Interuniv. Com. on Scis., 1976-79, chmn., 1981-84; pres. Fed. Inst. Mgmt., Halifax, 1981-82. Contbr. numerous articles to profl. jours. Decorated Queen's Silver Anniversary medal. Fellow Royal Soc. of Arts (London); mem. Can. Soc. Microbiologists (hon., sec.-treas. 1969-70, v.p. 1971-72, pres. 1972-73), Nova Scotian Inst. Sci. (v.p. 1975-76, pres. 1977-78), Internat. Phycological Soc., Aquaculture Assn. Can., Sigma Xi. Mem. United Ch. of Canada.

SIMPSON, JACK WARD, computer company executive; b. Central City, Ky., Aug. 16, 1941; s. Grainger I. Simpson and Helen Marion Ward; m. Carolyn Sue Mushin, Sept. 1963; children—Jack Ward Jr., Christopher Wade, Brandon Ashley. B.S., U. Ky., 1963, M.S. in Elec. Engring., 1965. With IBM Corp., Lexington, U. Ky., 1963-70; mgr. advanced tech. Austin, Tex., 1970-72, mgr. lab., 1973-75, mgr. plans and controls, 1975-76, product mgr. office products, 1976-78, systems mgr. entry office systems, 1978-82, lab. dir. communications product div., 1982; pres. Mead Data Cen., Dayton, Ohio, 1982—, also bd. dirs.; chmn. bd. MicroMedex, Inc., 1986—. Patentee in field (6). Trustee Southwestern Ohio Council for Higher Edn., 1983-85; mem. adv. bd. Mead Found. Recipient 2 Outstanding Invention awards IBM Corp., 1970-75. Mem. IEEE, Info. Industry Assn. (bd. dirs. 1985-). Republican. Baptist. Avocations: running; racquetball; skiing; music; hiking. Home: 807 George Wythe Commons Dayton OH 45459-2940 Office: Mead Data Cen 9443 Springboro Pike Miamisburg OH 45342-4425

SIMPSON, JOANNE MALKUS, meteorologist; b. Boston, Mar. 23, 1923; d. Russell and Virginia (Vaughan) Gerould; m. Robert H. Simpson, Jan. 6, 1965; children by previous marriage: David Starr Malkus, Steven Willem Malkus, Karen Elizabeth Malkus. B.S., U. Chgo., 1943, M.S., 1945, Ph.D., 1949; D.Sc. (hon.), SUNY, Albany, 1991. Instr. physics and meteorology Ill. Inst. Tech., 1946-49, asst. prof., 1949-51; meteorologist Woods Hole Oceanographic Instn., 1951-61; prof. meteorology UCLA, 1961-65; dir. exptl. meteorology lab. NOAA, Dept. Commerce, Washington, 1965-74; prof. environ. scis. U. Va., Charlottesville, 1974-76; W.W. Corcoran prof. environ. scis. U. Va., 1976-81; head Severe Storms br. Goddard Lab. Atmospheres, NASA, Greenbelt, Md., 1981-88, chief scientist for meteorology, 1988—; Goddard sr. fellow, earth scis. dir. Goddard Space Flight Ctr., NASA, 1988—; project scientist tropical rainfall measuring mission, 1986—; mem. Bd. on Atmospheric Scis. and Climate, NRC/NAS, 1990-93, Bd. on Geophys. and Environ. Data, 1993—. Author: (with Herbert Riehl) Cloud Structure and Distributions Over the Tropical Pacific Ocean; assoc. editor: Revs. Geophysics and Space Physics, 1964-72, 75-77; contbr. articles to profl. jours. Mem. Fla. Gov.'s Environ. Coordinating Coun., 1971-74. Recipient Disting. Authorship award NOAA, 1969, Silver medal Dept. Commerce, 1967, Gold medal, 1972, Vincent J. Schaefer award Weather Modification Assn., 1979, Cmty. Headliner award Women in Comm., 1973, Profl. Achievement award U. Chgo. Alumni Assn., 1975, 92, Lifetime Achievement award Women in Sci. Engring., 1990, Exceptional Sci. Achievement award NASA, 1982, William Nordberg award NASA, 1994; named Woman of Yr. L.A. Times, 1963; Guggenheim fellow, 1954-55, Goddard Sr. fellow, 1988—. '. Home: 540 N St SW Washington DC 20024-4557 Office: NASA Goddard Space Flight Ctr Earth Scis Dir Greenbelt MD 20771

SIMPSON, JOHN ALEXANDER, physicist; b. Portland, Oreg., Nov. 3, 1916; s. John A. and Janet (B) S.; m. Elizabeth Alice Hilts, Nov. 30, 1946 (div. Sept. 1977); children: Mary Ann, John Alexander; m. Elizabeth Scott Johnson, Aug. 23, 1980. A.B., Reed Coll., 1940, D.Sc. (hon.), 1981; M.S., NYU, 1942, Ph.D., 1943. Research assoc. OSRD, 1941-42; sci. group leader Manhattan Project, 1943-46; instr. U. Chgo, 1945-47, asst. prof., 1947-49, assoc. prof., 1949-54, chmn. com. on biophysics, 1951; prof. physics, dept. physics and Fermi Inst. Nuclear Studies, 1954- 68, Edward L. Ryerson Disting. Service prof. physics, 1968-74, Arthur H. Compton Disting. Service prof. physics, 1974-87, Arthur H. Compton Disting. prof. emeritus, 1987—; also dir. Enrico Fermi Inst., 1973-78; Mem. Internat. Com. IGY; chmn. bd. Ednl. Found. Nuclear Sci.; mem. tech. panel cosmic rays NRC; mem. Internat. Commn. Cosmic Radiation, 1962—; mem. astronomy missions bd. NASA, 1968; vis. assoc. physics Calif. Inst. Tech.; vis. scholar U. Calif. Berkeley; founder Lab. Astrophysics and Space Research in Enrico Fermi Inst., 1962, Space Sci. Working Group, Washington, 1982. Bd. overseers, vis. com. astronomy Harvard; mem. Pres. Ford's Sci. Adv. Group on Sci. Problems, 1975-76; life trustee Adler Planetarium, 1977—. Recipient medal for exceptional sci. achievement NASA, Quantrell award for excellence in teaching, Gagarin medal Nat. Soviet Socialists Rep. Acad. of Scis., Cospar award UN Com. on Space Rsch., 1990; fellow Ctr. Policy Study, U. Chgo., Guggenheim fellow, 1972, 84-85; Nora and Edward Ryerson lectr., 1986; A. H. Compton Centennial lectr., 1992. Fellow Am. Acad. Arts and Scis., Am. Geophys. Union (Parker lectr. 1992), Am. Phys. Soc. (chmn. cosmic physics div. 1970-71); mem. NAS (mem. space sci. bd., Henryk Arctowski medal and premium 1993), Internat. Union Pure and Applied Physics (pres. cosmic ray commn. 1963-67), Atomic Scientists Chgo. (chmn. 1945-46, bd. bull. 1945—, pres. bull. bd. sponsors 1993—), Am. Astron. Soc. (Bruno Rossi prize 1991),

Internat. Acad. Astronautics, Smithsonian Inst. (Martin Marietta chair in history of space sci. 1987-88, Glennan, Webb, Seamans Group 1986—), Phi Beta Kappa, Sigma Xi. Achievements include research in nuclear radiation and instrumentation, also origin of cosmic radiation, solar physics, magnetospheric physics, high energy astrophys. problems, and acceleration and isotopic and elemental composition of charged particles in space; prin. investigator for 33 expts. in earth satellites and deep space probes, also 1st probes to Mercury, Mars, Jupiter and Saturn, fly by at Venus, 9 planetary encounters, comet dust expts. on the 2 Vega spacecraft to Halley's comet, 1986; Ulysses space craft experiments over poles of the sun, 1990—, Pioneer 10 space craft outside solar system. Office: Fermi Inst 5630 S Ellis Ave Chicago IL 60637-1433*

SIMPSON, JOHN JOSEPH, physics educator, researcher; b. North Bay, Ont., Can., May 26, 1939; s. John William and Teresa (Hagarty) S.; m. Marianne Cornelia Van der Veen, July 5, 1968; children: J. James R., Sarah J. BSc, U. Toronto, Ont., 1961, MA, 1962; PhD, U. Oxford, U.K., 1966. Rsch. assoc. U. Oxford, U.K., 1965-66, Weizmann Inst., Rehovot, Israel, 1966-68, U. Toronto, Can., 1968-69; asst. prof. U. Guelph, Ont., 1969-73, assoc. prof., 1973-80, prof., 1980—; vis. rsch. fellow Max Planck Inst., Heidelberg, Fed. Republic Germany, 1973, Niels Bohr Inst., Copenhagen, 1975-76; sci. assoc. CERN, Geneva, Switzerland, 1982-83. Fellow Royal Soc. Can. (Rutherford Meml. medal 1985), Can. Assn. Physicists. Office: U Guelph, Dept Physics, Guelph, ON Canada N1G 2W1

SIMPSON, JOHN MATHES, newspaper editor; b. Madison, Wis., Jan. 7, 1948; s. Robert C. and Mary (Mathes) S.; m. Carol Flaker, July 2, 1977; children: Kate, Alexis. BA, SUNY, Binghamton, 1969. Reporter, editor Sun-Bulletin, Binghamton, 1970-76; mng. editor Ithaca (N.Y.) Jour., 1976-78; mng. editor, exec. editor Pacific Daily News, Agana, Guam, 1978-83; internat. mng. editor USA Today, Washington, 1984-86, 88—, spl. projects mng. editor, 1986-87; dir. corp. projects Gannett Internat., Washington, 1987-88. Dir. World Press Freedom Com. Mem. Am. Soc. Newspaper Editors, Inter Am. Press Assn. (bd. dirs.), Nat. Press Club. Office: USA Today Internat 1000 Wilson Blvd Arlington VA 22229-0001

SIMPSON, JOHN NOEL, hospital administrator; b. Durham, N.C., Feb. 27, 1936; s. William Hays and Lucile (McNab) S.; A.B., Duke U., 1957; M.H.A., Med. Coll. Va., 1959; m. Virginia Marshall, June 27, 1959; children: John Noel, William M. Asst. adminstr. Riverside Hosp., Newport News, Va., 1962-65, assoc. adminstr., 1965-70; assoc. adminstr. Richmond (Va.) Meml. Hosp., 1970-74, sr. v.p., adminstr., 1974-77, exec. v.p., 1977-80, pres., 1980-85; pres. Health Corp. Va., 1985—; preceptor Sch. Health Adminstrn., Duke U. and Med. Coll. Va., Washington U., St. Louis; bd. dirs. Sun Health, Inc./Sun Alliance, 1979-92, vice chmn., 1984, chmn., 1985-87; vice-chmn. Med./Bus. Coalition, 1981-83; participant Leadership Met. Richmond; bd. dirs. Ctrl. Va. Health Sys. Agy., 1980-84, Richmond chpt. ARC, 1980-83; mem. Va. Bd. Med. Assistance, 1980-84; mem. joint subcom. studying Va.'s med. malpractice laws divsn. legal svcs. Gen. Assembly of Comm. of Va., 1984; chmn. Va. Health Network, 1989-91; chmn. Hanover Bus. Coun., 1994-95; mem. Gov.'s Regional Econ. Devel. Adv. Coun., 1994-95. Served with Med. Service Corps, U.S. Army, 1959-62. Fellow Am. Coll. Healthcare Execs. (Council of Regents 1976-82, Edgar C. Hayhow award 1976, bd. govs. 1990-94); mem. Am. Hosp. Assn. (chmn. RPBIII 1994—, del. 1989-93, mem. bd. trustees 1994—, Va. Hosp. Assn. (dir. 1974—, chmn.-elect, chmn. 1984-85), Va. Ins. Reciprocal (chmn. 1977-79), Met. Richmond C. of C. (bd. dirs.). Republican. Presbyterian. Home: 9127 Carterham Rd Richmond VA 23229-7752 Office: Health Corp of Va 1300 Westwood Ave Richmond VA 23227

SIMPSON, JOHN W., lawyer; b. Pitts. Sept. 29, 1922; s. John E. and Gail (White) S.; m. Virginia S. Simpson, June 16, 1951; children—Thomas, William, Cynthia. B.A., U. Rochester, 1944; LL.B., Harvard U., 1948. Atty. CAB, Washington, 1949-51; atty. Western Air Lines, Los Angeles, 1952-67; assoc. Koteen & Burt, Washington, 1967-81, Kelley, Drye & Warren, Washington, 1981—. Served to 1st lt. U.S.Army, 1943-45, ETO. Presbyterian. Home: 3617 Halcyon Ter Falls Church VA 22044-1308 Office: Kelley Drye & Warren 2300 M St NW Washington DC 20037-1434

SIMPSON, JOHN WISTAR, energy consultant, former manufacturing company executive; b. Glenn Springs, S.C., Sept. 25, 1914; s. Richard Caspar and Mary (Berkeley) S.; m. Esther Slattery, Jan. 17, 1948; children: John Wistar, Carter B. Patricia A., Barbara J. Student, Wofford Coll., 1932-33, DSc, 1972; BS, U.S. Naval Acad., 1937; MS, U. Pitts., 1941; DSc (hon.), Seton Hill Coll., 1970. With Westinghouse Electric Corp., 1937-77; mgr. Navy and Marine switchboard engring., switchgear div., on leave as mgr. nuclear engring. Daniels pile group, Oak Ridge Nat. Lab., successively as Westinghouse Electric Corp. (Bettis Atomic Power div.), 1949-58; v.p. Westinghouse Electric Corp.; gen. mgr. Westinghouse Electric Corp. (Bettis atomic power lab.), 1958-59, v.p., gen. mgr. atomic power divs., 1959-62, v.p. engring. and research, 1962-63, v.p. electric utility group, 1963-69, pres. power systems, corp. exec. v.p., dir., 1971-77; chmn. bd. Internat. Energy Assocs. Ltd.; pres. Simpson Bus. Services, Inc., 1980-86; v.p. Sea Pines Assocs., Hilton Head Island, S.C., 1989-91, also bd. dirs.; PRIME bd. dirs. Sea Pines Real Estate Cos., Hilton Head Island, S.C., 1987-91; pvt. energy cons.; mem. adv. bd. Lawrence Livermore Nat. Lab. Fusion, 1975-88; mem. Naval Tech. Mission to Japan, 1945; del. 1st Internat. Conf. on Peaceful Uses Atomic Energy, Geneva, Switzerland, 1955, Conf. on Peaceful Uses Atomic Energy (2d Internat. Conf.), 1958; chmn. Atomic Indsl. Forum, 1974-75; mem. energy research adv. bd. Dept. Energy, 1981-83; chmn. com. on outlook for fusion hybrid and tritium breeding fusion reactors NRC; mem. sci. adv. bd. Notre Dame, 1974-86. Author: Nuclear Power from Underseas to Outer Space, 1994. Mem. governing bd. Nat. Coun. Chs., 1979-81; trustee Seton Hall Coll., 1969-76, Point Park Coll., 1973—, Wofford Coll., 1973-87. Recipient Navy cert. of merit for civilian service in World War II, Gold medal for advancement of research Am. Soc. Metals. Fellow IEEE (Edison medal 1971), ASME (hon., George Westinghouse gold medal 1975), Am. Nuclear Soc. (pres. 1973); mem. Nat. Acad. Engring., Franklin INst. (Newcomen Gold medal). Clubs: Rolling Rock (Ligonier, Pa.); Melrose; Bear Creek Golf, Sea Pines (Hilton Head, S.C.). Home and Office: 36 E Beach Lagoon Rd Hilton Head Island SC 29928-5714 The guiding principles of my career have been to work in an area I considered to be of major importance, to have the most competent people working for me, to know enough technically that I could properly evaluate performance and, as far as possible, always make my position clear to all.

SIMPSON, JULIETTE RICH, elementary educator; b. Bainbridge, Ga., Jan. 9, 1944; d. Robert Lloyd Jr. and Juliette (Lane) Rich; m. Ralph Felward Simpson, Aug. 13, 1966; children: Juliette, Elena. AB in Elem. Edn., Wesleyan Coll., 1966. 2d grade tchr. Bibb County Sch. System, Macon, Ga., 1966-69; title I tchr. Tift County Sch. System, Tifton, Ga., 1974-77, 3d grade tchr., 1977—; mem. sci. curriculum writing com. Tift County Bd. Edn., Tifton, 1989-90, mem. lang. arts curriculum writing com., 1990-91, mem. social studies curriculum writing com., 1991-92. Alt. del. Nat. Rep. Conv., 1994—; co-pres. Tifton Cir Bar Assn., 1990-91; active Annie Belle Clark Sch. PTO; v.p. Tifton Choral Soc., 1994-95, chmn. Tift Co. Reps., 1995. Mem. Profl. Assn. Ga. Educators, Internat. Reading Assn., Tift County Found. for Ednl. Excellence (Outstanding Tchr. award), Ga. Coun. for Social Scis. Dogwood Garden Club. Republican. Presbyterian. Home: 1020 N College Ave Tifton GA 31794-3942 Office: Annie Belle Clark Sch 506 W 12th St Tifton GA 31794-3999

SIMPSON, KENNETH WARREN, army officer; b. Chgo., Feb. 29, 1944; s. Francis Simpson and Ramona Jean (Robinson) Krusinski; m. Susan Carlene Bywater, Mar. 9, 1962; children: Michael Scott, Katherine Diane Simpson Swetlow. BA, Calif. State U., San Bernardino, 1971; MA, Cen. Mich. U., 1977. Commd. 2d lt. U.S. Army, 1963, advanced through grades to brig. gen., 1990; comdr. 1st Bn., 37th F.A., Ft. Richardson, Alaska, 1980-82; br. chief F.A. Br., Alexandria, Va., 1982-84; student Nat. War Coll., Washington, D.C., 1984-85; comdr. 7th Inf. Div. Arty., Ft. Ord, Calif., 1986-88; comdt. U.S. Army Sergents Maj. Acad., Ft. Bliss, Tex., 1988-90; vice dir. Joint Staff, J7, Washington, 1990-91; asst. chmn. comdr. 7th Inf. Div., Ft. Ord, 1991—. Mem. Assn. U.S. Army, U.S. F.A. Assn. Home: 5 Bayonet Dr Fort Ord CA 93941 Office: Hdqrs 7th Inf Div Fort Ord CA 93941

SIMPSON, LAURA KAY, lawyer; b. Kansas City, Mo., Jan. 30, 1960; d. William Gene Simpson and Joanne Reid Sellers. BA in Bus. Adminstrn. and Psychology, Wm. Jewell Coll., 1982; JD, U. Mo., Kansas City, 1985. Bar: Kans. 1985, U.S. Dist. Ct. Kans. 1985, U.S. Ct. Appeals (10th cir.) 1986, Mo. 1987. Assoc. Wallace, Saunders, Austin, Brown & Enochs, Overland Park, Kans., 1985-87; claims counsel Employers Reinsurance Corp., Overland Park, 1987-88; corp. counsel Payless Cashways Inc., Kansas City, Mo., 1988-90, sr. corp. counsel, 1990—. Mem. Greater Kans. City Women's Bar Assn. (Mo.), Kans. City (Mo.) Bar Assn., Kans. Bar Assn., Mo. Bar Assn. Avocations: antiques, theatre. Office: Payless Cashways Inc 2300 Main 3748 State Ave Kansas City KS 66102-3831

SIMPSON, LINDA ANN, lawyer; b. Yonkers, N.Y., Aug. 29, 1954; d. Arthur James Jr. and Marian (Stevens) S.; m. John Riche Ettinger, Apr. 19, 1986; children: Katharine Simpson, John Tyler. AB, Princeton U., 1976; JD, U. Va., 1979. Bar: N.Y. 1979. Assoc. Davis Polk & Wardwell, N.Y.C., 1979-86, ptnr., 1987—. Mem. ABA. Republican. Presbyterian. Office: Davis Polk & Wardwell PO Box 912 New York NY 10268-0912

SIMPSON, LOUIS A., insurance company executive; b. Chgo., Dec. 23, 1936; s. Irving and Lillian (Rubin) S.; m. Margaret Rowley, Dec. 16, 1959; children: Irving, Kenneth, Edward. Student, Northwestern U., 1954-55; BA, Ohio Wesleyan U., 1958; AM, Princeton U., 1960. Instr. econs. Princeton U., 1961-62; assoc. ptnr. Stein Roe & Farnham, Chgo., 1962-69; v.p. Shareholders Mgmt., Los Angeles, 1969-70; sr. v.p., exec. v.p., pres. Western Asset Mgmt., Los Angeles, 1970-79; vice chmn. bd. Geico Corp., Washington, 1979-93, pres., chief exec. officer capital ops., 1993—; bd. dirs. Potomac Capital Investment, Solomon, Inc.. Bd. dirs. Potomac Electric Power, 1990—, Children's Hosp. Nat. Med. Ctr., 1980—. Woodrow Wilson fellow, 1958. Mem. Washington Soc. Ins. Analysts (bd. dirs. 1981-84), Columbia Country Club, Calif. Club, L.A. Country Club, Arts Club Chgo., Princeton Club N.Y., City Club Washington. Episcopalian. Office: Geico Corp 1 Geico Plz Washington DC 20076

SIMPSON, LOUIS ASTON MARANTZ, English educator, author; b. Jamaica, W.I., Mar. 27, 1923; s. Aston and Rosalind (Marantz) S.; m. Jeanne Claire Rogers, 1949 (div. 1954); 1 child, Louis Matthew; m. Dorothy Mildred Roochvarg, 1955 (div. 1979); children: Anne Borovoi, Anthony Rolf; m. Miriam Butensky Bachner, 1985. Higher studies. certificate, Munro Coll., Jamaica, 1939; B.S., Columbia U., 1948, A.M., 1950, Ph.D., 1959; D.H.L., Eastern Mich. U., 1977; DLitt, Hampden Sydney Coll., 1990. Editor Bobbs-Merrill Pub. Co., N.Y.C., 1950-55; instr. Columbia U., 1955-59; prof. English U. Calif., Berkeley, 1959-67; prof. English SUNY, Stony Brook, 1967-91, Disting. prof., 1991—. Author: poems The Arrivistes, 1949, Good News of Death, 1955, A Dream of Governors, 1959, At the End of the Open Road, 1963 (Pulitzer Prize for poetry 1964), Selected Poems, 1965, Adventures of the Letter I, 1971, Searching for the Ox, 1976, Caviare at the Funeral, 1980, The Best Hour of the Night, 1983, People Live Here: Selected Poems 1949-1983, 1983, Collected Poems, 1988, In the Room We Share, 1990, Wei Wei and Other Friends, 1990, Jamaica Poems, 1993; prose Riverside Drive, 1962, James Hogg: A Critical Study, 1962, North of Jamaica, 1972, Three on the Tower: The Lives and Works of Ezra Pound, T.S. Eliot and William Carlos Williams, 1975, A Revolution in Taste: Studies of Dylan Thomas, Allen Ginsberg, Sylvia Plath and Robert Lowell, 1978, A Company of Poets, 1981, The Character of the Poet, 1986, Selected Prose, 1989, Ships Going into the Blue, 1994, The King My Father's Wreck, 1995; editor: The New Poets of England and America, 1957, An Introduction to Poetry, 1967. Served with AUS, 1943-45. Decorated Purple Heart, Bronze Star with oak leaf cluster; Hudson Rev. fellow, 1957, Guggenheim fellow, 1962, 70; Am. Coun. Learned Socs. grantee, 1963; recipient Prix de Rome, 1957, Millay award, 1960, Distinguished Alumnus award Columbia U., 1960, medal for excellence Columbia U., 1965; American Acad. of Arts and Letters award in literature, 1976; Centenary medal Inst. of Jamaica, 1980, Jewish Book Coun. award for poetry, 1981, Elmer Holmes Bobst award, 1987. Fellow Am. Acad. in Rome. Home: 186 Old Field Rd Setauket NY 11733-1636

SIMPSON, MARY MICHAEL, priest, psychotherapist; b. Evansville, Ind., Dec. 1; d. Link Wilson and Mary Garrett (Price) S. B.A., B.S., Tex. Women's U., 1946; grad. N.Y. Tng. Sch. for Deaconesses, 1949; grad., Westchester Inst. Tng. in Psychoanalysis and Psychotherapy, 1976; S.T.M., Gen. Theol. Sem., 1982. Missionary Holy Cross Mission, Bolahun, Liberia, 1950-52; mem. Order of St. Helena, 1952—; acad. head Margaret Hall Sch., Versailles, Ky., 1958-61; sister in charge Convent of St. Helena, Bolahan, 1962-67, novice dir., 1968-74; pastoral counselor on staff Cathedral St. John the Divine, N.Y.C, 1974-87, canon residentiary, canon counselor, 1977-87, hon. canon, 1988—; ordained priest Episcopal Ch., 1977; cons. psychotherapist Union Theol. Sem., 1980-83; dir. Cathedral Counseling Service, 1975-87; priest-in-charge St. John's Ch. Wilmot, New Rochelle, N.Y., 1987-88; pvt. practice psychoanalyst, 1974—; Bd. dirs. Westchester Inst. Tng. in Psychoanalysis and Psychotherapy, 1982-84; trustee Council on Internat. and Pub. Affairs, 1983-87; interim pastor St. Michael's Ch., Manhattan, 1992-94; cons. Diocese of N.Y., 1992—. Mem. Nat. Assn. Advancement of Psychoanalysis, N.Y. State Assn. Practicing Psychotherapists, N.Y. Soc. Clin. Psychologists. Author: The Ordination of Women in the American Episcopal Church: the Present Situation, 1981; contbg. author: Yes to Women Priests, 1978. Home and Office: 151 E 31st St Apt 8H New York NY 10016-9502

SIMPSON, MICHAEL, metals service center executive; b. Albany, N.Y., Dec. 10, 1938; s. John McLaren Simpson and Constance (Hasler) Ames; B.A., U. Mich., 1965, M.B.A., 1966; m. Barbara Ann Bodtke, Jan. 5, 1963; children: Leslie Simpson Wikstrom, Elizabeth McLaren. Product mgr. Armour & Co., Chgo., 1966-68; with A. M. Castle & Co., Franklin Park, Ill., 1968—, pres. Hy-Alloy Steels Co. div., 1974-79, v.p. Midwestern region, 1977-79, chmn. bd., 1979—, dir., 1972—. Trustee, Rush-Presbyterian St. Luke's Med. Center, Chgo., 1978—, exec. com., 1980—, vice-chmn., 1991—; trustee Oldfields Sch., Glencoe, Md., 1982-87. Served in USMC, 1957-58. Mem. Steel Service Center Inst. (chmn. exec. com. 1982-84, exec. com. 1981-94). Republican. Episcopalian. Clubs: Shore Acres; Onwentsia; Racquet of Chicago. Office: A M Castle & Co 3400 N Wolf Rd Franklin Park IL 60131-1319

SIMPSON, MICHAEL KEVIN, college president, political science educator; b. Bellafonte, Pa., Apr. 22, 1949; s. Robert Paul and Helen Elisabeth (Popso) S.; m. Carol Anne Martin, June 27, 1970; children: Jennifer Lyn, Robert Manton. BA, Fordham Coll., 1970; MA, Tufts U., 1974, MA in Law and Diplomacy, 1976, PhD, 1976; MBA, Syracuse U., 1983. Instr. Newbury Jr. Coll., Boston, 1976-77; asst. prof. then prof. polit. sci. Utica (N.Y.) Coll. of Syracuse U., 1976—, v.p., 1987-88, pres., 1988—; Fulbright lectr. Univ. Nancy II, France, 1981-82; vis. prof. Syracuse U. Program in Strasbourg, 1981-82, 85-87; resident dir. Internat. Programs, Strasbourg, 1985-87; trustee Savs. Bank of Utica. Contbr. articles to profl. jours. Mem. exec. com. Land of Oneidas Coun. Boy Scouts Am.; dir. United Way of Greater Utica, 1987, mem. campaign cabinet, exec. com; congl. appointment Leadership Coun., N.E./Midwest Inst., 1989; chmn. Health and Hosp. Coun., 1989-90; joint hosp. bd., Mohawk Valley Network. Comdr. USNR ret. Decorated Def. Meritorious Svc. Medal, 1987; recipient Grad. Alumni award Syracuse U. Sch. Mgmt., 1983, Disting. Teaching award Utica Coll., 1983. Mem. Internat. Studies Assn., Naval Res. Assn., Rotary (bd. dirs. Utica club 1988—, v.p. 1991-92, pres., 1992), Phi Beta Kappa. Democrat. Home: 22 Ironwood Rd New Hartford NY 13413-3904 Office: Syracuse U Utica Coll 1600 Burrstone Rd Utica NY 13502

SIMPSON, MICHAEL MARCIAL, science specialist, consultant; b. Honolulu, Sept. 24, 1954; s. Marcial Tolentino and Beatrice (Martin) S. AB in Biol. Scis., U. Calif., Berkeley, 1976; MS in Biol. Scis., U. San Francisco, 1977; MS in Energy and Resources, U. Calif., Berkeley, 1979; PhD in Environ. Scis. and Engring., UCLA, 1986. Assoc. researcher NASA, Moffett Field, Calif., 1973; radio program host, producer Sta. KUSF-FM, San Francisco, 1976-78; rsch. asst. Lawrence Berkeley Lab., Berkeley, Calif., 1977-79; rsch. assoc. UCLA/US Dept. Energy, 1979-81; congl. fellow, environ. health U.S. Congress, Washington, 1981-82; head, biomed. policy sect. and specialist in life scis. U.S. Congl. Rsch. Svc., Washington, 1982—; adv. bd. Banbury Ctr., Cold Spring Harbor, N.Y., 1985—; adj. faculty The Washington Ctr., 1992—. Contbr. articles to profl. jours. Values clarification educator, Alexandria, Va., 1985—. Fellow AAAS (Named Congl. Sci.

fellow 1981-82); mem. Washington Acad. Sci., Library of Congress Profl. Assn., UCLA in Washington (exec. steering com. 1986-92). Avocations: photography, bicycle touring, short story writing, travel. Office: US Congl Rsch Svc CRS-SPR-LM413 Washington DC 20540-7490

SIMPSON, MURRAY, engineer, consultant; b. N.Y.C., July 27, 1921; s. George and Sonia (Vernov) S.; m. Ethel Gladstein, June 29, 1947; children: Anne Simpson Everett, David, Mindy, Jonathan. BEE, CCNY, 1942; MEE, Polytech. Inst. of N.Y., 1952. Engr. Internat. Tel.&Tel., N.Y.C., 1942-44; sr. engr. Raytheon Co., Waltham, Mass., 1946-48; sect. mgr. Fairchild Guided Missiles div., Farmingdale, N.Y., 1948-50; v.p. Maxson Elec. Co., N.Y.C., 1950-62; pres. SEDCO Systems Inc. subs. Raytheon Co., Melville, N.Y., 1963-86; cons. M. Simpson Assocs., West Hempstead, N.Y., 1986—; former chmn. bd. dirs. Radyne Corp. Contbr. articles to profl. jours. former bd. dirs. United Way of L.I., N.Y., 1984-87. Served to lt. (j.g.) USNR, 1944-46, PTO. Fellow IEEE (chmn. L.I. sect. 1963-64); mem. Anchorage Yacht Club, Inverrary Country Club. Clubs: Anchorage Yacht, Inverrary Country. Avocations: boating, skiing, golf, tennis.

SIMPSON, O. J. (ORENTHAL JAMES SIMPSON), former professional football player, actor, sports commentator; b. San Francisco, July 9, 1947; s. Jimmie and Eunice (Durton) S.; m. Marguerite Whitley, June 24, 1967 (div.); children: Arnelle, Jason; m. Nicole Brown, 1985 (div. 1992); children: Sydney, Justin. Student, U. So. Calif.; grad., City Coll. San Francisco. Halfback Buffalo Bills, 1969-78, San Francisco 49'ers, 1978-79; sports commentator ABC Sports, 1979-86; analyst ABC Monday Night Football broadcasts, 1984-1985; co-host NBC Sports NFL Live. Motion picture appearances include The Towering Inferno, 1974, The Cassandra Crossing, 1977, Killer Force, 1976, Capricorn One, 1978, Firepower, 1979, Hambone & Hillie, 1984, The Naked Gun, 1988, The Naked Gun 2 1/2: The Smell of Fear, 1991, The Naked Gun 33 1/3: The Final Insult, 1994; TV films include A Killing Affair, 1977, Goldie and the Boxer, 1979, The Golden Moment: An Olympic Love Story, 1980, Student Exchange, Cocaine and Blue Eyes; co-host "NFL" Live on NBC, 1990—; author: I Want to Tell You, 1995. Recipient Heisman trophy N.Y. Downtown Athletic Club, 1968; voted Coll. Player of Decade ABC Sports, 1970; named to Am. Football League All-Star Team, 1970, ProBowl Team, 1972, 73, 74, 75, 76; named Nat. Football League Player of Decade Pro Football Monthly, 1979; inducted into Pro Football Hall of Fame, 1985; mem. world record 440 yard relay team (38.6 seconds), 1967; former record holder for most yards rushing gained in a season, most yards rushing gained in a game.

SIMPSON, PAMELA HEMENWAY, art historian, educator; b. Omaha, Sept. 8, 1946; d. Myrle E. and Leone K. (Cook) Hemenway; m. Henry H. Simpson III, Apr. 4, 1970; 1 child, Peter Stuart Hay. BA, Gettysburg Coll., 1968; MA, U. Mo., 1970; PhD, U. Del., 1974. Instr. art history Pa. State Extension Campus, Media, 1973, Washington and Lee U., Lexington, Va., 1973-74; asst. prof. Washington and Lee U., Lexington, 1974-79, assoc. prof., 1979-85, prof. art history, 1985—, Ernest Williams prof., 1993, chair art dept., 1987—, assoc. dean of coll., 1981-86; chair co-edn. steering com. Washington and Lee Univ., Lexington, 1984-86; cons., head county survey Va. Hist. Landmarks Commn., Richmond, 1977-81. Author: Architecture of Historic Lexington, 1977 (Am. Assn. for State and Local History award 1977); book reviewer Women's Art Jour., columnist, 1990—; contbr. articles to profl. jours. Officer Rockbridge Hist. Soc., Lexington, 1980—, Rockbridge Valley Nat. Orgn. for Women, Rockbridge County, Va., 1984—, Historic Lexington (Va.) Found., 1987—; founder, officer Rockbridge Area Coalition Against Sexual Assault, Lexington, 1990—. Grantee Nat. Endowment for Arts, 1974, NEH, 1975, 77, Glenn, Washington and Lee U., 1980-81, 91; NEH Summer Inst. scholar, 1989; Hagley-Winterthur Mus. fellow, 1991. Mem. Southeastern Soc. Archtl. Historians (bd. dirs. 1990-94, v.p. 1993-94, pres. 1994-95), Soc. Archtl. Historians, Coll. Art Assn., Vernacular Architecture Forum (bd. dirs. 1982-84, 2d v.p. 1988-91), southeastern Coll. Art Conf. (pres. 1986-90, 2d v.p. 1994—, editor rev. 1979-82). Democrat. Episcopalian. Avocations: painting, reading mysteries. Office: Washington & Lee Univ Dupont Hall Lexington VA 24450

SIMPSON, RICHARD KENDALL, JR., surgeon, physician, researcher; b. Atlanta, Sept. 10, 1953; s. Richard Kendall and Juliet Hodges (Rowsey) S.; m. Martha Anne Baucom, Sept. 22, 1984. BA, Coker Coll., 1975; PhD, Med. U. S.C., 1980, MD, 1982; postgrad. Warnborough Coll., Oxford, Eng., 1974. Diplomate Nat. Bd. Med. Examiners, Am. Bd. Neurosurgery. Teaching asst. dept. physiology Med. U. S.C., Charleston, 1976-80, research assoc., 1980-83, intern neurology, 1982-83; resident neurosurgery dept. neurosurgery Baylor Coll. Medicine, Houston, 1983-89, asst. prof., 1989—; cons. Spinal Cord Injury Research, Charleston, S.C., 1980-83. Author: Peripheral Nerve Fiber Group and Spinal Corp Pathway Contributions to the Somatosensory Evoked Potential, 1980. Recipient Clin. Neurology Rsch. award, 1983, Physician Recognition award, 1986, Mayfield award, 1989, Minora Suzuki award, 1989, Young Alumni award, 1990, William H. Sweet award, 1994; ACS scholar, 1986; ACS Faculty fellow, 1994, Watson fellow Coker Coll., 1974. Mem. AMA, Am. Pain Soc., Am. Acad. Clin. Neurophysicians, Am. Acad. Pain Med., Tex. Med. Found., Soc. Neurosci., Houston Neurol. Soc., Sigma Xi, Alpha Omega Alpha, Houston Neurol. Soc. Episcopalian. Home: 14314 River Forest Dr Houston TX 77079-7417 Office: Baylor Coll Med Dept Neurosurgery 1 Baylor Plz Houston TX 77030-3411*

SIMPSON, RICHARD LEE, sociologist, educator; b. Washington, Feb. 2, 1929; s. Donald Dake and Lottie (Lee) S.; m. Ida Ann Harper, July 10, 1955; children: Robert Donald, Frank Daniel. A.B., U. N.C., 1950, Ph.D., 1956; M.A., Cornell U., 1952. Instr. Pa. State U., University Park, 1956-57; asst. prof. sociology Northwestern U., Evanston, Ill., 1957-58; asst. prof. U. N. C., Chapel Hill, 1958-61, assoc. prof. sociology, 1961-65; prof. U. N. C., Chapel Hill, 1965-80, Kenan prof. sociology, 1980—; acting dir. Inst. Research Social Sci., Chapel Hill, 1966-67. Author numerous research papers, articles and book chpts. in field; editor: Social Forces, 1969-72, 83—; co-editor Research in Sociology of Work, 1981—. Mem. Am. Sociol. Assn., So. Sociol. Soc. (pres. 1971-72), Sociol. Research Assn. Methodist. Home: 604 Brookview Dr Chapel Hill NC 27514-1406 Office: Univ NC Dept Sociology Cb 3210 Hamilton Hall Chapel Hill NC 27599

SIMPSON, ROBERT EDWARD, economist, consultant; b. Chgo., July 7, 1917; s. James Albert and Mabel Grace (Farrell) S.; m. Anna Margareta Nelson, May 22, 1954; children: Karen Anne, Heather Margot, John Frederick II. A.B., Amherst Coll., 1938; student, Nat. Inst. Pub. Affairs, 1939; M.A., George Washington U., 1964. Student U.S. Central Statis. Bd., 1938-39; economist U.S. Nat. Resources Com., 1939-40; personnel work Office Sec. of War, 1941; economist civilian supply div. WPB, 1941-42; econ., adminstrv. work Nat. Housing Adminstrn., 1946-47; asst. dir. European div., later dept. asst. dir. for econ. affairs Office Internat. Trade U.S. Dept. Commerce, 1947-53; dir. Office Econ. Affairs, Bur. Fgn. Commerce, 1953-61, Office Regional Econs., Bur. Internat. Commerce, 1961-70, Office Internat. Comml. Relations, 1970-73; counsellor for econ. and comml. affairs Am. Embassy, Canberra, Australia, 1973-77; dir. Office Country Affairs, U.S. Dept. Commerce, Washington, 1978-79; cons. economist, 1980—; mem. pub. adv. com. Met. Washington Council of Govts., 1987-88; assigned Nat. War Coll., Washington, 1961-62. Mem. U.S. dels. to various internat. confs., 1948-79; bd. examiners for U.S. Fgn. Svc.; mem. gov. bd. Common Cause, Md., 1985-88, v.p. 1987-88; v.p. Montgomery County Civic Fedn., 1985—; mem. Montgomery County Econ. Adv. Coun., 1989—; treas. Montgomery County Citizens PAC, 1993—. Comdr. USNR, 1942-46, PTO, ETO. Decorated Bronze Star. Mem. Nat. Economists Club, Phi Beta Kappa, Delta Tau Delta, Kappa Theta. Office: PO Box 386 Glen Echo MD 20812-0386

SIMPSON, ROBERT GLENN, lawyer; b. Seattle, June 27, 1932; s. Harold Vernon and Anna Rondeau (McCabe) S.; m. Josephine Anne Heald, June 7, 1959; children: Jenifer Jane, Thomas Glenn, Mary Elizabeth. BS, U. Oreg., 1954; LLB, Willamette U., 1959. Bar: Oreg. 1959. Assoc. William B. Adams Law Office, Portland, Oreg., 1959-67; ptnr. Adams McLaughlin & Simpson, Portland, 1967-70, Schwabe Williamson & Wyatt, Portland, 1970—. Trustee, sec. Legacy Good Samaritan Hosp. & Med. Ctr., Portland, 1983-89, mem. cmty. bd., 1989—; trustee, chancellor Episcopal Diocese of Oreg., Portland, 1988—. Mem. Oreg. Bar Assn. (exec. com. health law sect. 1987-90), Am. Acad. Trial Attys. (program com. 1987-88), Oreg. Soc. Hosp. Attys. (pres. 1977-78, legis. com. 1989), Multnomah Athletic Club,

Univ. Club, City Club. Home: 13345 SW Iron Mountain Blvd Portland OR 97219-9306 Office: Schwabe Williamson & Wyatt 1211 SW 5th Ave Portland OR 97204-3795

SIMPSON, R(OBERT) SMITH, author, retired diplomat; b. Arlington County Va., Nov. 9, 1906; s. Hendree Paine and Edith Lydia (Smith) S.; m. Henriette S. Lanniée, Nov. 7, 1934; children: Margaret Lanniée Simpson Maurin-Stunkard, Zélia Tinsley. B.S., U. Va., 1927, M.S., 1928; LL.B, Cornell U., 1931; postgrad., Columbia U., 1931-32. Spl. labor adviser, exec. NRA, 1933-34; trade. assn. exec., adminstrv. agt. Asphalt, Shingle and Roofing Code Authority, 1934-35; instr., then asst. prof. bus. law U. Pa., 1935-44; spl. adviser Pa. Unemployment Relief and Assistance Commn., co-drafter Pa. Unemployment Compensation Act, 1936; adviser N.J. Civil Service Commn., 1939; adv. unemployment compensation and relief joint Pa. State Commn., 1939-42; asst. dir. fgn. div. recruitment and manning orgn. War Shipping Adminstrn., 1942-43; with Dept. State, 1943-62, 65-66; consul gen. Mozambique, 1954-57; adv. African affairs Dept. Labor, 1958-60, dir. office country programs, 1960-61; dep. examiner bd. fgn. service examiners Dept. State, 1961-62, cons., 1965-66; lectr. Georgetown U., 1973, research prof. diplomacy, 1974-77; del. and/or mem. numerous nat. and internat. meetings; founding mem., bd. dirs. Inst. Study Diplomacy, Georgetown U., Washington, 1978-94, emeritus founding mem., 1995—. Author: Anatomy of the State Department, 1967, The Crisis in American Diplomacy, 1980, Some Perspectives on the Study of Diplomacy, 1986, Education in Diplomacy, 1987; editor: Belgium in Transition, 1946, Resources and Needs of American Diplomacy, 1968; Instruction in Diplomacy: The Liberal Arts Approach, 1972. Annual diplomacy debate named in his honor Univ. Va. Mem. Am. Fgn. Svc. Assn., Consular Officers Assn., Assn. for Diplomatic Studies and Tng., Inst. for Study of Diplomacy (Georgetown U., founding, bd. dirs.), Jefferson Lit. and Debating Soc. (U. Va., assoc.), Raven Soc., Phi Beta Kappa, Phi Sigma Kappa. Presbyterian. Address: # 41 250 Pantops Mountain Rd Charlottesville VA 22901 *I can remember standing on a slope of the Arlington National Cemetery as a teenager one Christmas Day, down apiece from the broken mast of the battleship Maine and, as I laid a wreath on the grave of an ancestor, vowing to do whatever I could the rest of my life for good will and peace among men. From that day, this has been my consuming objective. The broken mast of the Maine has been a kind of compass needle by which my private and diplomatic life has been guided.*

SIMPSON, RUSSELL GORDON, lawyer, mayor, consultant; b. Springfield, Mass., May 22, 1927; s. Archer Roberts and Maude Ethel (Gordon) S.; m. Bickley S. Flower, Sept. 11, 1954; children: Barbara G., Elisabeth Pires-Fernandes, Helen Blair. B.A., Yale U., 1951; J.D., Boston U., 1956; postgrad., Parker Sch. Internat. Law, 1962. Bar: Mass. 1956, U.S. Dist. Ct. (fed. dist.) Mass. 1957, U.S. Ct. Appeals (2d cir.) 1958, U.S. Supreme Ct. 1980. Advt. mgr. Burden Bryant Co., Springfield, 1951-53; assoc. Goodwin, Procter & Hoar, Boston, 1956-64, ptnr., 1965-87, of counsel, 1987—; sr. advisor to pres. The Experiment in Internat. Living, Brattleboro, Vt. 1988-89, exec. v.p. 1989-90, sr. v.p. 1990-91, trustee, 1991—; exec. com., 1994—; counselor to not-for-profit orgns., 1991—; mayor Jupiter Island, Fla., 1993—; dir. number of bus. corps., 1965-87; hon. consul New Eng. of Bolivia, 1958-82; mem. spl. com. to revise Mass. Corrupt Practices Act, 1961-62; dir., exec. com. Cmty. Found. Palm Beach and Martin Counties, West Palm Beach, Fla., 1994—. Author: The Lawyer's Basic Corporate Practice Manual, 1971, rev. edit., 1978, 84, 87. Bd. overseers Boston U. Sch. Mgmt., 1969-74; mem. exec. com. Sch. Law Boston U., 1978-90; mem. Mass. Rep. Com., 1959-67, exec. com., 1959-67, chmn., 1962-67; del. Rep. Nat. Conv., 1964, exec. dir. Mass. Del. Rep. Nat. Conv., 1968; state convs., 1960, 62, 64, 66, 67, 70; mem. Milton, Mass. Town Mtg., 1978-87; mem. Milton Town Warrant Com., 1976-80, chmn., 1978-80; adv. com. ambulatory care svc. Beth Israel Hosp., 1969-71; bd. dirs. Greater Boston Arts Found., Inc., 1983-87; Milton Hosp., Mass., 1983-86; Met. Boston Area Planning Coun., 1969-75; mem. adv. com. Mass. Mediation Svc., 1986-87; elected mayor of local municipality, 1993, 95—; counselor various non-profit orgns. including Save the Children, World Learning, German Marshall Fund, Rockefeller Bros. Found., 1991—. Named Outstanding Young Man of Greater Boston, 1963. Fellow Am. Bar Found., Mass. Bar Found.; mem. Mass. Bar Assn. (chmn. banking and bus. law sect. 1980-83, bd. dels., exec. com. 1983-87, v.p 1985-87), ABA (corp. banking and bus. law sect., com. on law firms, co-chmn. com. on law firm governance, panel on corp. law ednl. programs). Home: 101 Harbor Way Box 1106 Hobe Sound FL 33475

SIMPSON, STEVEN QUENTIN, physician, researcher; b. Miami, Okla., Aug. 17, 1957; s. Dallas James and Carolyn Sue (Moberly) S.; m. Pamela Janette Nicklaus, May 20, 1989; children: Nathan Edward, Andrew Dallas. BS, Baker U., 1979; MD, U. Kans., 1983. Diplomate Am. Bd. Internal Medicine, Am. Bd. Pulmonary Disease, Am. Bd. Critical Care Medicine; cert. Nat. Inst. Occupational Safety and Health. Intern in internal medicine Kans. U. Med. Ctr., Kansas City, 1983-84, resident in internal medicine, 1984-86; fellow in pulmonary and critical care medicine Rush-Presbyn. St. Luke's Med. Ctr., Chgo., 1986-89, instr. medicine Divsn. Pulmonary and Critical Care Medicine, 1986-89, asst. prof. Divsn. Pulmonary and Critical Care Medicine, 1989-90; asst. prof. Divsn. Pulmonary and Critical Care Medicine U. N.Mex., 1990—; attending physician Rush-Presbyn. St. Luke's Med. Ctr., Chgo., 1989-90, U. N.Mex. Hosp., Albuquerque, 1990—; adj. scientist Inhalation Toxicology Rsch. Inst., Lovelace Biomed. and Environ. Rsch. Inst., Albuquerque, 1991—; consulting physician Miner's Colfax Med. Ctr., Raton, N.Mex., 1990—, dir. Cardiopulmonary Outreach Program and Black Lung Clinic, 1992—; attending physician Albuquerque VA Med. Ctr., 1992—, dir. med. ICU, 1993—; presenter 19th Ann. Am. Thoracic Soc. Lung Disease Symposium, N.Mex., 1991, 94, U. N.Mex., 1993, Soc. of Critical Care Medicine, 1994. Author: (with others) The Physiologic and Pathologic Effects of Cytokines, 1990; contbr. articles to profl. jours. Grantee Chgo. Lung Assn., 1989-91, Am. Lung Assn., 1991-93, Miner's Colfax Med. Ctr., 1992—, N.Mex. Dept. Health, 1993-94. Mem. AAAS, ACP (Cecile Lehman Mayer Rsch. award finalist 1988, 92, Alfred Soffer Rsch. award 1992, DuPont Young Investigator award 1993), Am. Coll. Chest Physicians, Am. Thoracic Soc. (sec.-treas. N.Mex. chpt. 1994-95), Am. Fedn. for Clin. Rsch., N.Y. Acad. Scis., Soc. Critical Care Medicine, Blue Key Nat. Honor Soc., Alpha Delta Sigma. Avocations: writing prose, guitar, hiking. Office: U N Mex Dept Med Pulmonary Divsn 2211 Lomas Blvd NE # 5-ACC Albuquerque NM 87131-5271

SIMPSON, THOMAS WILLIAM, physician; b. Winston-Salem, N.C., Jan. 24, 1918; s. Thomas William Sr. and Sara Elizabeth (McGee) S.; m. Doris McElroy Cullings, June 2, 1941; children: Lucia Elisabeth Simpson Shen. BS with honors, Southwestern (Rhodes), 1940; MD, John Hopkins, 1943. Diplomate Am. Bd. Internal Medicine. Med. resident Vets. Adminstrn., Columbia, S.C., 1947-49; med. faculty Wake Forest Univ., Winston-Salem, N.C., 1949-66; med. officer Panama Canal Zone, Coco Solo, 1966-67; med. faculty U. Hawaii, Honolulu, 1967-70; med. faculty Johns Hopkins U., Balt., 1970-83, faculty emeritus, 1983—; health dir. Va. Health Dept.; chief med. cons. U. Hawaii, Okinawa, 1967-70; trop med. cons. DOD, 1967-70; resident coord. Johns Hopkins CMRT, Calcutta, India, 1970-72, acting dir., 1973-74. Author: (with others) Hunter's Tropical Medicine, 1984; contbr. articles to profl. jours. Oral fluid therapy cholera, Johns Hopkins U., 1971-72, health status migrant workers, Del Marva, 1983-85. Lt. USN, 1943-47. Recipient Commendation N.C. Health Dept., 1966, Va. Mental Hygiene Dept., 1988. Fellow ACP (coms.), Royal Soc. Tropical Medicine and Hygiene; mem. Am. Ornithologists Union, Am. Soc. Tropical Medicine and Hygiene (coms.). Democrat. Presbyterian. Achievements include incrimination of pigs as important amplifying host of Japanese encephalitis, restoration of Okinawan health care system after WW2, crucial early field trial of oral fluid therapy for cholera in West Bengal, improvement of health care for Haitian and Hispanic migrant farm workers. Office: Johns Hopkins Instn 615 N Wolfe St Baltimore MD 21205

SIMPSON, VI, state senator; b. Los Angeles, Mar. 18, 1946; d. Lloyd M. and Helen (Chacon) Sentman; m. William D. McCarty; children—Jason, Kristina. attended Ind. U. Sch. of Law, Indpls. Asst. to chmn. Com. on Status of Women, Calif., 1974-75; dir. pub. affairs Calif. Parks and Recreation Soc., Sacramento, 1975-77; county auditor Monroe County, Ind., 1980-84; mem. Ind. Senate, 1984—; exec. dir. Heritage Edn. Found., Indpls., 1989—. Editor: Equal Rights Monitor mag., 1974-76. Syndicated newspaper columnist Know Your Rights, 1975-76. Named Freshman Democrat Senator of Yr., Ind. broadcasters Assn. 1985, Legis. of Yr., Ind. State Employees Assn., 1985, various Legis. awards Sierra Club, Ind. Wildlife Fedn., Isaac

Walton League, Ind. Parks and Recreation Assn. Mem. NAACP, AAUW. Methodist. Avocations: gardening, cooking. Office: Heritage Edn Found 7821 W Morris St Indianapolis IN 46231

SIMPSON, VINSON RALEIGH, manufacturing company executive; b. Chgo., Aug. 9, 1928; s. Vinson Raleigh and Elsie (Passeger) S.; m. Elizabeth Caroline Matte, Sept. 9, 1950; children: Kathleen Simpson Jackson, Nancy Simpson Ignacio, James Morgan. S.B. in Chem. Engring, Mass. Inst. Tech., 1950; M.B.A., Ind. U., 1955. With Trane Co., LaCrosse, Wis., 1950-75, mgr. mktg. services, 1957-64, mgr. dealer devel., 1964-66; mng. dir. Trane Ltd., Edinburgh, Scotland, 1966; v.p. internat. Trane Co., LaCrosse, Wis., 1967, exec. v.p., 1968-70; exec. v.p., gen. mgr. comml. air conditioning div., 1970-73, pres., 1973-75; pres. Simpson and Co., La Crosse, 1975-76; pres., chief operating officer Marathon Electric Mfg. Corp., Wausau, Wis., 1976-80; chmn., pres., chief exec. officer Marion Body Works, Inc., Wis., 1980-93, chmn., 1993—; bd. dirs. Clintonville Area Found. Regional chmn. edn. coun. MIT; trustee Northland Coll.; bd. dirs., v.p Fox Valley Tech. Coll. Found.; past pres., bd. dirs. Wausau Area Jr. Achievement; mem. Marion Minutemen, Adv. Team, U. Wis. Served with USAF, 1951-53. Decorated Korean War Commendation ribbon. Mem. Fire Apparatus Mfrs., Nat. Truck Equipment Assn. (pres. divsn. van body mfrs.), Kappa Kappa Sigma, Alpha Tau Omega, Beta Gamma Sigma (mem. dirs. table), Am. Legion. Congregationalist. Lodges: Masons, Shriners, Jesters, Rotary (past. pres. Marion club, Paul Harris fellow). Avocations: running, handball, snorkeling, water skiing, cross country skiing. Home: 171 Fairway Dr Clintonville WI 54929-1071 Office: Marion Body Works Inc 211 W Ramsdell PO Box 500 Marion WI 54950-0500

SIMPSON, W. M., career officer administrator. Dir. U.S. Coast Gurard Research and Development Ctr., Groton, Conn. Office: US Coast Guard Rsch & Devel Ctr 1082 Shennecossett Groton CT 06340

SIMPSON, WILLIAM ARTHUR, insurance company executive; b. Oakland, Calif., Feb. 2, 1939; s. Arthur Earl and Pauline (Mikalasic) S.; m. Nancy Ellen Simpson, Mar. 31, 1962; children—Sharon Elizabeth, Shelley Pauline. B.S., U. Calif.-Berkeley, 1961; postgrad. Exec. Mgmt. Program, Columbia U. C.L.U. V.p mktg. Countrywide Life, L.A., 1973-76; v.p agy. Occidental Life of Calif., L.A., 1976-79; pres., CEO Vol. State Life, Chattanooga, 1979-83; exec. v.p. Transam. Occidental Life Ins. Co., L.A., 1983-86, pres., 1986-88, pres., CEO, 1988-90, also bd. dirs.; dir. USLIFE Corp., N.Y.C., 1990—; pres., CEO All Am. Life Ins. Co., Pasadena, Calif., 1990-94, USLIFE Life Ins. div. USLIFE Corp., 1994; pres., CEO USLIFE Corp. 1995—, mem. Office of Chmn., 1995—. Pres. Chattanooga coun. Boy Scouts Am., 1982, bd. dirs., L.A., 1983, v.p., 1983-85, vice-chmn L.A. area, 1989, chmn., 1989; pres. bd. councillors L.A. County Am. Cancer Soc.; trustee Verdugo Hills Hosp. Found. 1st lt. U.S. Army, 1961-64. Mem. Am. Soc. CLUs, Life Ins. Mktg. and Rsch. Assn. (bd. dirs. 1986-89). Republican. Presbyterian. Lodge: Rotary. Avocations: golf; skiing. Office: USLIFE Corp 125 Maiden Ln New York NY 10038

SIMPSON, WILLIAM KELLY, curator, Egyptologist, educator; b. N.Y.C., Jan. 3, 1928; s. Kenneth Farrand and Helen L.K. (Porter) S.; m. Marilyn E. Milton, June 19, 1953; children: Laura Knickerbacker Simpson Thorn, Abby Rockefeller Simpson Mydland. B.A., Yale U., 1947, M.A., 1948, Ph.D., 1954. Asst. in Egyptian Art Met. Mus. Art, 1948-54; rsch. fellow Center Middle East Studies, Harvard U., 1957-58; mem. faculty Yale U., New Haven, 1958—; prof. Egyptology Yale U., 1965—, chmn. dept. Near Eastern langs., 1966-69; curator Egyptian and ancient Near Eastern art Mus. Fine Arts, Boston, 1970-86; ltd. partner Kin and Co., 1967-69; ltd. ptnr. Venrock, 1970—; dir. editor of papers Penn-Yale Archaeol. Expdn. to Egypt, 1966—; mem. adv. council fgn. currency program Smithsonian Instn., 1966-69. Author: Papyrus Reisner I-Records of a Building Project, 1963, Hekanefer and the Dynastic Material from Toshka, 1963, Papyrus Reisner II-Accounts of the Dockyard Workshop, 1965, Papyrus Reisner III: Records of a Building Project in the Early Twelfth Dynasty, 1969, The Terrace of the Great god at Abydos, 1974, The Mastabas of Qar and Idu, 1976, The Offering Chapel of Sekhem-ankh-ptah, 1976, The Offering Chapel of Kayemnofret in the Museum of Fine Arts Boston, 1992, The Insanbes Material from the Pennsylvania-Yale Excavations at Abydos, 1995, (with others) The Ancient Near East, A History, 1971, The Literature of Ancient Egypt, 1972, The Mastaba of Queen Mersyankh III, 1974. Trustee Am. Sch. Classical Studies, Athens, Am. U. in Cairo; mem. internat. council Mus. Modern Art, N.Y.C.; pres. Wrexham Found., 1965-67. Fulbright fellow Egypt, 1955-57; Guggenheim fellow, 1965. Mem. Am. Oriental Soc., Am. Philos. Soc., Archaeol. Inst. Am., Internat. Assn. Egyptologists, Egypt Exploration Soc., Soc. française d'egyptologie, German Archaeol. Inst., Foundation egyptologique Reine Elisabeth. Clubs: Century (N.Y.C.), Met. Opera (N.Y.C.), University (N.Y.C.), Union (N.Y.C.), River (N.Y.C.); Union Boat (Boston); Bedford (N.Y.); Golf and Tennis. Home: 129 Katonah Woods Rd Katonah NY 10536-9532

SIMPSON, WILLIAM STEWART, retired psychiatrist, sex therapist; b. Edmonton, Alta., Can., Apr. 11, 1924; came to U.S., 1950, naturalized, 1963; s. William Edward And Ethel Lillian (Stewart) S.; m. Eleanor Elizabeth Whitbread, June 17, 1950; children—David Kenneth, Ian Stewart, James William, Bert Edward. B.Sc., U. Alta., 1946, M.D., 1948. Diplomate Am. Bd. Psychiatry and Neurology, Am. Bd. Sexology. Rotating intern U. Alta. Hosp., 1948-49, resident in internal medicine, 1949-50; resident in psychiatry Topeka State Hosp., 1950-53, cons., 1967-68, asst. sect. chief, 1953-54, clin. dir., 1954-59, 68-72; fellow Menninger Sch. Psychiatry, Topeka, 1950-53; sect. chief C.F. Menninger Meml. Hosp., 1959-66, dir. edn., 1963-66; assoc. dir. Menninger Sch. Psychiatry, 1966-68; dir. field services Menninger Found., 1972-74, sr. staff psychiatrist adult outpatient dept., 1977-84, assoc. dir. adult outpatient dept., 1984-88; dir. Ctr. for Sexual Health, 1986-92; dir. Psychopharmacotherapy Clinic Menninger Clinic, 1989-90; chief psychiatry service, residency tng. program Topeka VA Hosp., 1974-77; dir. Midwest Impotence Ctr., Kansas City, Mo., 1988-91; mem. faculty Menninger Sch. Psychiatry, 1953-92, Ann. Seminar Inst. on Alcoholism, U. Wis., 1973-74; guest lectr. sex therapy Chinese Med. Assn., Rep. of China, 1985, Med. Sch. Tokai (Japan) U., 1985, dept. psychology U. Warsaw, Poland, 1987; cons. Osawatomie State Hosp., 1954-68, Colmery-O'Neill VA Hosp., 1983-92; mem. staff Stormont-Vail Hosp., Topeka, St. Francis Hosp., Topeka, Kans. Rehab. Hosp., Topeka, 1988-92; cons. in sex therapy Colmery-O'Neill VA Hosp., Topeka, 1983-92. Assoc. editor Bull. Menninger Clinic, 1963-70; cons. editor Jour. Med. Aspects of Human Sexuality, 1991-92. Bd. dirs. Topeka Civic Symphony Soc., 1953-55, Topeka People to People Council, 1963-66; ruling elder local Presbyn. ch., 1960—; mem. Kans. Citizens' Adv. Com. on Alcoholism, 1973-78; co-founder Topeka affiliate Nat. Council on Alcoholism, 1964, pres., bd. dirs., 1964, bd. dirs. N.Y.C., 1967, v.p., 1971-73, pres., 1973-75, mem. exec. com., 1967. Recipient Bronze Key award, Topeka affiliate Nat. Council on Alcoholism; 1972, Silver Key award, 1975, Outstanding Achievement award U. Alta. Med. Alumni Assn., 1975. Fellow Am. Psychiat. Assn. (life); mem. Topeka Inst. Psychoanalysis (cert.), Am. Assn. Sex Educators, Counselors and Therapists (cert. sex therapist, sex educator, supr.), Am. Psychoanalytic Assn. (cert.), AMA, Kans. Psychiat. Soc., Kans. Med. Soc., Shawnee County Med. Soc., Topeka Psychoanalytic Soc., Menninger Sch. Psychiatry Alumni Assn. (pres. 1979-80), Soc. for Sci. Study of Sex, Soc. for Sex Therapy and Research, Am. Assn. Sex Educators, Counselors and Therapists, Phi Delta Theta (Phi of Yr. award Kansas State chpt. 1964). Democrat. Presbyterian. Club: Saturday Night Literary (pres. 1990-91). Lodge: Rotary. Avocations: reading, classical music, photography, travel, masters swimming. Home: 834 SW Buchanan St Topeka KS 66606-1428 Office: Menninger Found PO Box 829 Topeka KS 66601-0829

SIMS, ARMITA B., principal. Prin. Beeber Mid. Sch., Phila. Office: Beeber Middle Sch 59th & Malvern Ave Philadelphia PA 19131

SIMS, BENNETT JONES, minister, educator; b. Greenfield, Mass., Aug. 9, 1920; s. Lewis Raymond and Sarah Cosette (Jones) S.; children: Laura (Mrs. John P. Boucher), Grayson, David. AB, Baker U., 1943, LHD (hon.), 1985; postgrad., Princeton Theol. Sem. 1946-47; B.D., Va. Theol. Sem., 1949, D.D., 1966; D.D., U. of South, 1972; Merrill fellow, Harvard U., 1964-65; postgrad., Cath. U., 1969-71. Ordained to ministry Episc. Ch. as deacon, 1949, priest, 1950. Rector Ch. of Redeemer, Balt., 1951-64; dir. continuing edn. Va. Theol. Sem., 1966-72; bishop of Atlanta, 1972-83; vis. prof. theology Emory U., Atlanta, 1980-88, pres. Inst. for Servant Leadership, 1988—;

priest-in-charge St. Alban's Ch., Tokyo, 1962, 69. Trustee U. of South. With USNR, 1943-46. Named Young Man of Yr. Balt. C. of C., 1953; Disting. Alumnus of Yr., Baker U., 1972. Office: Inst Servant Leadership Hendersonville NC 28793

SIMS, BILL, state senator, business executive; b. Jan. 27, 1932. Grad. Tex. A&M U. Mem. Tex. Senate, mem. edn., intergovtl. rels., natural resources coms., vice chmn. subcom. energy. Democrat. Office: Tex Senate PO Box 12068 Austin TX 78711-2068

SIMS, DOUG, bank executive; b. 1946. Grad., U. Ill., Carbondale, 1968. With St. Louis Bank for Cooperatives, St. Louis, 1969-84; exec. v.p. Farm Credit Banks of St. Louis, 1984-86, pres., 1986-88; pres. Nat. Bank for Cooperatives, Englewood, Colo., 1988-93; CEO CoBank, Englewood, 1994—. Office: CoBank 5500 S Quebec St Englewood CO 80111

SIMS, EDWARD HOWELL, editor, publisher; b. Orangeburg, S.C., May 29, 1923; s. Hugo Sheridan and Jesse Lucile (Howell) S.; m. Frances Dell Hartt, Jan. 5, 1946; m. Martha Lurene Bass, July 18, 1960; children—Edward H., Robert; m. Bente Thorlund Christensen, Oct. 4, 1969; children—Edward Christian, Frederik. A.B., Wofford Coll., 1943; postgrad., Emory U., 1946-47. Mng. editor Orangeburg Times and Democrat, 1946, editor, 1952—; Washington corr., founder Washington bur. for number S.C. dailies, 1947; dir. Sims Pub. Co., Orangeburg. Columnist: Looking South From Washington, 1948—; Washington Bur. chief: Editor's Copy syndicate, 1950-52; editor-pub., 1952—; radio news analyst: The News of The Week In Washington, 1951—; Author: American Aces, 1958, Greatest Fighter Missions, 1962, The Fighter Pilots, 1967, Fighter Tactics 1914-70, 1972, Aces Over the Oceans, 1987; contbr. articles to publs. White House corr. covering Pres.'s confs., 1948—; mem. Senate and House press galleries, 1947—; Am. consul Munich, Germany, 1963-65; cons. Exec. Office of White House, 1966-67; consul gen. Zurich, 1992; apptd. mem. Commn. to Preserve Am. Heritage Abroad, 1987. Served to 1st lt. USAF, World War II. Recipient Young Man of the Year award S.C. Jr. C. of C., 1959. Mem. White House Corrs. Assn., Am. Legion, V.F.W. Methodist. Clubs: Rotary, Nat. Press; Metropolitan (Washington); R.A.F. (London). Home: 3803 Pin Oaks St Sarasota FL 34232-1241 also: Box 400 Fairview NC 28730 Office: PO Box 532 Orangeburg SC 29116-0532

SIMS, EVERETT MARTIN, publishing company executive; b. Morristown, N.J., June 27, 1920; s. Walter Leonard and Amy Ethel (Coleman) S. B.A., Drew U., Madison, N.J., 1941; M.A., Harvard U., 1947. Dir. project planning div. Prentice-Hall, Inc., Englewood Cliffs, N.J., 1950-60; asst. v.p. Prentice-Hall, Inc., 1956-60; with Harcourt Brace Jovanovich, Inc., N.Y.C., 1960-82; v.p. Harcourt Brace Jovanovich, Inc., 1970-80, v.p., 1980-82; dir. coll. dept., 1970-82; pres. Media Systems Corp., 1974-77, chmn., 1977-81; pres. Telamon Enterprises, Inc., 1982—. Served with USAAF, 1942-45; Served with USAF, 1950-51, ETO. Decorated Air medal Croix de Guerre, (France). Home and Office: 180 Sebonac Rd Southampton NY 11968-2727

SIMS, EZRA, composer; b. Birmingham, Ala., Jan. 16, 1928; s. Ezra G. and Kathryn W. (Wallace) S. B.A, Birmingham So. Coll., 1947; postgrad., Birmingham Conservatory Music, 1945-48; MusB in Composition, Yale U. Sch. Music, 1952; MA in Composition, Mills Coll., 1956. Librarian Harvard Music Library, Cambridge, Mass., 1958-62, 65-74; music dir. New Eng. Dinosaur Dance Theatre, Boston, 1968-78; instr. theory New Eng. Conservatory Music, Boston, 1976-78; instr. microtonal theory Mozarteum, Salzburg, 1992-93; freelance composer Cambridge, 1974—; dir. Dinosaur Annex Music Ensemble, Cambridge, pres. 1977-81; guest composer 23d Ann. Contemporary Music Festival, Ill. Wesleyan U., 1977; lectr. various colls. including Warwick U., Cleve. Inst. Music, Internat. Christian U., Westport Friends of Music, Schlumberger-Doll Rsch., Webster U., Mozarteum, Northwestern U., Hochschule für Musik, Hamburg. Composer over 100 works, predominantly microtonal music for various mediums including Chamber Cantata on Chinese Poems, 1954, Mass, 1955, Two Folk Songs, 1958, String Quartet, 1959, Sieben-Spencer Lieder, 1960, Sonate Concertanti, 1961, Third Quartet, 1962, Buchelin for Lyon, 1962, Cantata III, 1963, Octet for Strings, 1964, In Memoriam Alice Hawthorne, 1967, Antimatter: Three Dances for Toby, 1968, A Frank Overture: Four Dented Interludes and Coda, 1969, Pastorale, 1970, Clement Wenceslaus Lothaire Nepomucene, Prince Mettermich (1773-1859), In Memoriam, 1970, Real Toads, 1970, Interlope, 1971, Tango Variations, 1971, Museum Piece, 1972, Where the Wild Things Are, 1973, String Quartet #2 1962, 1974, After Lyle or Untitled, 1975, When the Angels Blow Their Trumpets, 1976, Celebration of Dead Ladies, 1976, Elegie-nach Rilke, 1976, Collage XIII, 1977, Aeneas on the Saxophone, 1977, Come Away, 1978, Midorigaoka, 1978, 5 Songs, 1979, -And, As I Was Saying..., 1979, Two for One, 1980, Sextet, 1981, All Done From Memory, 1980, Phenomena, 1981, Solo After Sextet, 1981, Quartet, 1982, Pictures for an Institution, 1983, Tune and Variations, 1983, Brief Elegies, 1983, String Quartet #4, 1984, The Conversions, 1985, Wedding Winds, 1986, Quintet, 1987, Chase, 1987, Solo in four movements, 1987, AEDM in memoriam, 1988, Flight, 1989, Night Piece: IN Girum Imus nocte et Consuminur Igni, 1989, Concert Piece, 1990, Duo, 1992, Invocation, 1992, Stanzas, 1995; contbr. articles to profl. jours. Served as pvt. U.S. Army, 1952-54. Recipient Composers Forum award, 1959, Koussevitzky Found. commn., 1983, Am. Acad. Arts and Letters award, 1985; grantee Cambridge Arts Coun., 1975, 76, Martha Baird Rockefeller Found., 1977; fellow Guggenheim Found., 1962, Nat. Endowment for Arts, 1976, 78, Mass. Artists Found., 1979, Fulbright Sr. Scholar, 1992. Mem. Am. Composers Alliance, Broadcast Music, Inc. Home and Office: 1168 Massachusetts Ave Cambridge MA 02138-5205

SIMS, HENRY P., management educator. Prof. mgmt. U. Md., College Park. Author: The Thinking Organization: Dynamics of Organizational Social Cognition, 1986, Super Leadership: Leading Others to Lead Themselves, 1989, The New Government Paradigm: Social Learning and Cognition in Organizations, 1992, Business Without Bosses: How Self-Managing Teams Are Building High-Performance Companies, 1993. Office: U Md Dept Mgmt College Park MD 20742-0001*

SIMS, J. TAYLOR, academic administrator. Acting pres. Cleve. State U., sr. v.p. Office: Cleveland State University Office of Development E 24th and Euclid Ave Cleveland OH 44115

SIMS, JAMES HYLBERT, English educator, former university administrator; b. Orlando, Fla., Oct. 29, 1924; s. James W. and Anna L. (Hylbert) S.; m. Ruth Elizabeth Gray, Jan. 3, 1944; children: James W., Timothy C., Suzannah C. Andrew, John M. BA in English, History and Psychology, U. Fla., 1949, MA in English, 1950, PhD in English Lit., 1959. Lic. comml. pilot FAA. Instr. English Tenn. Temple Coll., 1950-51; pres., instr. English Tri-State Bapt. Coll., Evansville, Ind., 1951-54; instr. English U. Fla., Gainesville, 1955-57, 58-59; prof. English, chmn. dept. Tift Coll., Forsyth, Ga., 1959-61, Austin Peay State U., Clarksville, Tenn., 1961-66; prof. U. Okla., Norman, 1966-76; prof. English and dean Coll. Liberal Arts U. So. Miss., Hattiesburg, 1976-82, v.p. acad. affairs, 1982-89, Disting. prof. U. So. Miss., 1989—; Clyde Kilby lectr. Wheaton (Ill.) Coll., 1991-92, Charles G. Smith lectr. in English Baylor U., 1994. Author: Biblical Allusions in Shakespeare's Comedies, 1960, The Bible in Milton's Epics, 1962, Dramatic Uses of Biblical Allusions in Marlowe and Shakespeare, 1966, Milton and Scriptural Tradition: The Bible Into Poetry, 1984, A Comparative Literary Study of Daniel and Revelation: Shaping the End, 1994; contbr. chpts. to books; contbr. numerous articles on lit. criticism and lit. history to scholarly jours.; assoc. editor: Seventeenth-Century News, 1968—. Bd. dirs. Baptist Faith Missions, Internat. Bd. Jewish Missions. Served with USN, 1943-46. Fellow Southeastern Inst. Medieval and Renaissance Studies, 1965-66, NEH, summer 1974, NEH-Huntington Libr., 1973, 78-79; recipient Regents' Superior Tchg. award U. Okla., 1968. Mem. MLA, Milton Soc. Am. (pres. 1976), South Atlantic MLA, South Ctrl. MLA, South Ctrl. Renaissance Conf. (pres. 1983—), Conf. Christianity and Lit. (chmn. South Ctrl. 1981-82, 87-88, nat. pres. 1990-92), Rotary. Democrat. Baptist. Home: 3103 Delwood Dr Hattiesburg MS 39401-7214 Office: U So Miss English Dept Hattiesburg MS 39406

SIMS, JAMES LARRY, hospital administrator, healthcare consultant; b. Birmingham, Ala., Feb. 16, 1936; s. James Alexander and Elsie Lee (Coleman) S.; m. Sandra Anne Hanzel, July 25, 1981. AB, Birmingham

Southern, 1958; cert., U. Ala., 1970. Diplomate Am. Acad. Med. Adminstrs. Sgt. USAF res. Fellow Am. Acad. Med. Adminstrs., Royal Soc. Health, Am. Coll. Healthcare Execs.; mem. Fla. Hosp. Personnel Dirs. Assn. (pres. 1964-65), South Fla. Hosp. Personnel Dirs. Assn. (pres. 1967-68), Fla. Hosp. Pub. Rels. Assn. (pres. 1970-71), South Fla. Pub. Rels. Coun. (pres. 1963-64). Democrat. Methodist. Home: 2250 Shady Pl Las Cruces NM 88005 Office: Mt Sinai Med Cntr 4302 Alton Rd Miami FL 33140

SIMS, JOE, lawyer; b. Phoenix, Sept. 29, 1944; s. Joe and Pauline Jane (Saunders) S.; m. Robin Ann Reed, Jan. 30, 1965; 1 child, Shannon Dane. BS in Fin., Ariz. State U., 1967, JD, 1970. Bar: Ariz. 1970, U.S. Supreme Ct. 1975, D.C 1978. Trial atty. antitrust div. Dept. Justice, Washington, 1970-73; spl. asst. to asst. atty. gen., 1973-75; dep. asst. atty. gen. for policy planning and legislation, 1975-77, dep. asst. atty. gen. for regulatory matters and fgn. commerce, 1977-78; mem. firm Jones, Day, Reavis & Pogue, Washington, 1978-79; ptnr. Jones, Day, Reavis & Pogue, 1979—; resident fellow Am. Enterprise Inst. for Pub. Policy Rsch., Washington, 1978-79, vis. fellow, 1979-81; prin. Coun. for Excellence in Govt. Contbr. various articles to prof. jours. Mem. ABA (chmn. antitrust law sect. one com. 1987-90, bus. law sect. antitrust law com. 1988-91, antitrust law civil practice and procedure com. 1990-91), Am. Law Inst., D.C. Bar Assn., City Club Washington, Tournament Players Club (Potomac, Md.), Firestone Country Club (Akron, Ohio), Collection River Plantation (Hilton Head Island, S.C.). Republican. Home: 10100 New London Dr Potomac MD 20854-4849 Office: Jones Day Reavis & Pogue 1450 G St NW Ste 600 Washington DC 20005-2088

SIMS, JOHN ROGERS, JR., lawyer; b. Red Star, W.Va., Apr. 10, 1924; s. John Rogers and Myrtle (Hutchison) S.; m. Geraldine L. Bucklew, Oct. 8, 1966; children: John Rogers III, Joyce Rebecca. B.S. in Commerce, U. Va., 1950, LL.B., 1952. Assoc. firm Dow, Lohnes & Albertson, Washington, 1953-57; gen. counsel D.C. Transit System, Inc., Washington, 1957-65; individual practice law Washington, 1965-68; partner firm Wrape and Hernly, Arlington, Va., 1968-71, Sims, Walker & Steinfeld (and predecessor firm), Washington, 1972-95; pvt. practice Great Falls, Va., 1995—; Chmn. bd. dirs. John Sims Assocs., Inc., Purnell Bros. Transport, Ltd., 1981-91; co-founder, bd. dirs., gen. counsel A Presdl. Classroom for Young Ams., Inc., chmn. bd. dirs., 1979-83; dir., v.p., gen. counsel, sec. SunWorld Internat. Airways, Inc., 1984-88. Vice chmn. Falls Church (Va.) Planning Commn., 1958-64; pres. Falls Church Republican Party, 1961-62; bd. dirs. Heart Assn. No. Va., Inc., pres., 1963-64; bd. dirs., v.p., gen. counsel Commonwealth Doctors Hosp., Fairfax, Va., 1967-74. Served with Armed Forces, 1943-45. Mem. ABA, W.Va. Bar Assn., D.C. Bar Assn., State Bar Va., Motor Carrier Lawyers Assn. (transp. law, logistics and policy com., nat. pres. 1971-72), Va. Trial Lawyers Assn., Rotary, Masons (Shriner), Washington Golf and Country Club, Farmington Country Club (Charlottesville, Va.). Presbyterian. Home: 815 Nethercliffe Hall Rd Great Falls VA 22066-2719 also: 1 Sawmill Creek Dr Nellysford VA 22958

SIMS, JOHN WILLIAM, lawyer; b. Vicksburg, Miss., Mar. 25, 1917; s. John Ernest and Helen Ross (Moore) S.; m. Marie Elise Hebert, Sept. 28, 1940; 1 dau., Helen Moore. B.A., Tulane U., 1937, LL.B., 1939. Bar: La. 1939. Of counsel Phelps Dunbar; mem. permanent adv. bd. and planning com. Tulane U. Admiralty Law Inst., 1966—, chmn., 1985-91; adj. prof. law Tulane Law Sch., 1981—; chmn. USCG-Lower Mississippi River Waterways Safety Adv. Com., 1983-93. Assoc. editor Am. Maritime Cases, 1974—; mem. editorial bd. Lloyd's Maritime and Comml. Law Quar., 1984-92; mem. bd. adv. editors Tulane Law Rev., 1985-93, Maritime Advisor-Ct. Case Digest, 1985—; contbr. articles to profl. jours. Trustee Gulf South Rsch. Inst., 1965-68, Children's Hosp., 1975-78; bd. dirs. Coun. for Better La., Bur. Govt. Rsch., 1973-84, USCG Found., 1986-91, La. World Expn., Inc., 1980-84, World Trade Ctr., 1985—; bd. dirs., v.p. New Orleans Opera Assn., 1974-93; mem. men's adv. bd. Christian Woman's Exch. Lt USCGR, 1942-45. Named Rex, King of Carnival Mardi Gras, New Orleans, 1981; recipient Disting. Pub. Service award Dept. Transp. U.S. Coast Guard, 1985. Fellow Am. Coll. Trial Lawyers; mem. Am. La. (past sec.-treas.), New Orleans Bar assns., Maritime Law Assn. U.S. (2d v.p. 1976-78, 1st v.p. 1978-80, pres. 1980-82, com. Supreme Ct. admiralty rules 1963-69, com. limitation of liability 1963—, com. Comite Maritime Internat. 1965-80, com. uniformity admiralty law 1975-92, com. liquified natural gas transp. 1978-80, del. Comite Maritime Internat. conv. N.Y.C. 1965, Rio de Janeiro, 1977, Montreal, 1981, adv. cons. Hamburg 1974, titular mem. Comite Maritime Internat. 1979—, del. Comite Maritime Internat. Lisbon Conv., 1985), SAR, Soc. Colonial Wars, Order of Coif, Phi Beta Kappa, Omicron Delta Kappa, Phi Delta Theta, Phi Delta Phi. Clubs: Boston, Louisiana. Office: Texaco Ctr 400 Poydras St Fl 30 New Orleans LA 70130-3245

SIMS, KEITH, professional football player; b. Balt., June 17, 1967. BS in Indsl. Tech., Iowa State U. Guard Miami Dolphins, 1990—; player AFC Championship Game, 1992. Named to Pro Bowl Team, 1993. Office: Miami Dolphins 2269 NW 199 St Miami FL 33169*

SIMS, KENT OTWAY, economist; b. Chickasha, Okla., Nov. 2, 1940; s. Jesse Otway and Mable Vela (Bear) S.; m. Jeanette McCollum, June 9, 1961; children: Marketa, Adam. B.A., U. Colo., 1963, Ph.D., 1966. registered investment advisor. Economist Urban Renewal Authority, Denver, 1965-66, U.S. Dept. State mission to Pakistan, 1966-69; economist Fed. Res. Bank of San Francisco, 1969-71, asst. v.p., 1971-72, v.p., dir. research, 1972-74, sr. v.p., 1974-82, exec. v.p., chief fin. officer, 1982-85; fin. advisor, investment mgr., mgmt. cons. Theodore R. Seton, 1985-86; ptnr. C&K Partnership, 1987-89; pres. Her Equal Share, Inc., 1986-89, San Francisco Econ. Devel. Corp., 1988-91; dir. econ. planning and devel. Mayor's Office, San Francisco, 1992-93, San Francisco Redevel. Agy., 1993—. Bd. govs. Econ. Lit. Coun. Calif., Long Beach, 1983-88; trustee Strybing Arboretum Soc. Golden Gate Park, San Francisco, 1993—; bd. dirs. Jewish Community Mus., San Francisco, 1986-93, Design Coun. San Francisco Bay Area, 1989-90, Career Resources Devel. Ctr., 1991-92; adv. bd. St. Lukes Hosp., San Francisco, 1988—. Mem. Am. Econs. Assn., Nat. Audubon Soc. Am. Clubs: Sierra.

SIMS, LARRY KYLE, secondary school educator; b. Ft. Worth, Dec. 28, 1944; s. Kyle G. and Gladys (Holloway) S.; m. Stephenie Chandler, Aug. 30, 1968; children: Alan Dean (dec.), Roy B. BBA, Howard Payne, Brownwood, Tex., 1969; MEd, Colo. State U., 1975. Cert. tchr., Tex., Wyo.; lic. real estate broker, Tex., Wyo. Coord. Breckenridge (Tex.) High Sch., 1970-74; multi-occupations coord. Lander (Wyo.) Valley High Sch., 1974-76; diversified occupations coord. Riverton (Wyo.) Career Ctr., 1977-79; mktg. edn. coord., tech. prep. coord. Stephenville (Tex.) High Sch., 1986—, tech prep coord., 1994—. Author: Little Spotted Moo, 1991. Mem. Am. Vocat. Assn., Nat. Mktg. Educators, Tex. Vocat. Assn. Consortium, Mktg. Educators Tex. (state pres. 1989-90). Baptist. Avocations: snow skiing, gold hunting, photography. Home: PO Box 1606 Stephenville TX 76401 Office: Stephenville High Sch 726 N Clinton St Stephenville TX 76401

SIMS, MARTHA J., library director; b. Portsmouth, Va., Oct. 29, 1946; m. Hunter Sims; children: Hunter, Clara. BA in English, Mary Baldwin Coll.; MS in Libr. Sci., U. N.C.; MA in Pub. Adminstrn., Old Dominion U. Reference asst. U. N.C., Chapel Hill, 1968-69; libr. art and music dept. Richmond Pub. Libr., 1969-71; br. libr. Virginia Beach Pub. Libr., 1971-74, asst. dir., 1974-76, dir., 1976—; mem. adv. bd. New Va. Review, 1980-90. Contbr. articles to profl. jours. Bd. dirs. Va. Beach Arts Ctr., 1971-82, treas., 1974-75; mem. Va. Beach Bicentennial Commn., 1975-76, Jr. League Norfolk, Virginia Beach, 1976-82; sec. Tidewater Area Libr. Dir.'s Coun., 1984-85; bd. dirs. Boys Club Norfolk/Virginia Beach, 1986-90, Literacy Action South Hampton Roads, 1988—, Va. Ctr. for the Book, 1987—, Va. Literacy Found., 1989—; mem. steering com. Virginia Beach Roundtable, 1988-92; census chairperson Mayor's Complete Count Com. 1990, 1989-90; lead agt. region 12 literacy coord. com. State Office Adult Literacy, 1989-92; trustee, sec. Va. Beach Pub. Libr. Endowment Found., 1982—; mem. adv. bd. Tidewater Literacy Coun., 1984—; tchr. Sunday sch. 1st Presbyn. Ch., 1988—; mem. steering com. Adult Literacy Lab, Adult Lng. Ctr. Va. Beach Pub. Schs., 1989—; keel divsn. leader United Way, 1991-92; bd. trustees Norfolk Acad., 1991—; keel club chairperson United Way, Virginia Beach, 1992-93; vice chmn. United Way, Virginia Beach, 1995. Mem. ALA, Am. Soc. Pub. Adminstrs., Southeastern Libr. Assn., Va. Libr. Assn. (sec. 1976-78, legis. com. 1979-85, local arrangements 1982 conv. 1981-82, chmn. pub. libr. sect. 1982-84, state libr. bd. liaison com. 1984-88). Home: 1160 Cedar

Point Dr Virginia Beach VA 23451 Office: Municipal Ctr Virginia Beach VA 23456

SIMS, PAUL KIBLER, geologist; b. Newton, Ill., Sept. 8, 1918; s. Dorris Lee and Vere (Kibler) S.; m. Dolores Carsell Thomas, Sept. 15, 1940; children: Thomas Courtney, Charlotte Ann. AB, U. Ill., 1940, MS, 1942; PhD, Princeton, 1950. Spl. asst. geologist Ill. Geol. Survey, 1942-43; geologist U.S. Geol. Survey, 1943-61; prof. geology, dir. Minn. Geol. survey U. Minn., 1961-73; research geologist U.S. Geol. Survey, 1973—; pres. Econ. Geology Pub. Co., 1979—; Bd. dirs. North Star Research and Devel. Inst., Mpls., 1966-73. Co-editor: Geology of Minnesota, 1972, 75th anniversary vo.. Economic Geology, 1981. Adviser Minn. Outdoor Recreation Resources Commn., 1963-67. Served with USNR, 1943-46. Recipient Meritorious Service award U.S. Dept. Interior, 1984; Goldich medal Inst. on Lake Superior Geology, 1985, Disting. Svc. award U.S. Dept. Interior, 1991. Fellow Geol. Soc. Am., Soc. Econ. Geologists (councilor 1965-68, pres. 1975, Ralph W. Marsden award medal 1989); mem. Internat. Assn. on Genesis of Ore Deposits, Internat. Union Geol. Sci. (subcom. Precambrian stratigraphy, sec. 1976-84), Assn. Am. State Geologists (hon.), Colo. Sci. Soc. (hon.). Research geology metalliferous ore deposits Colo., Minn., Wis., N.J., Ariz., Wash., also early evolution earth's crust in N.Am. Home: 1315 Overhill Rd Golden CO 80401-4238

SIMS, RICHARD LEE, hospital administrator; b. Columbus, Ohio, Jan. 6, 1929; s. Dorwin Delos and Christine Anna (Hanstein) S.; m. Marilyn Lou Atkinson, June 2, 1951; children: John Christopher, Steven Paul. B.S., Ohio State U., 1951. Pres. Doctors Hosp. Found., Columbus; preceptor faculty Ohio State U. Coll. Health Care Adminstrn.; past chmn. hosp. council Franklin County; past chmn. Hosp. Shared Svc. Inc.; chmn. Found. Osteo Health Svcs., 1989-93. Past pres. Franklin County chpt. ARC; past chmn. 1st Comty. Village Bd.; past chmn. governing bd. 1st Comty. Ch. With Med. Svc. AUS, 1953-56; maj. Ohio N.G., 1956-74. Recipient Distinguished Service award Columbus Jr. C. of C., 1960-63. Fellow Am. Coll. Healthcare Execs., Am. Coll. Osteo. Healthcare Execs.; mem. Am. Osteo. Hosp. Assn. (chmn. 1988), Ohio Trade Assn. Execs. (past pres.), Ohio Hosp. Assn. (past chmn. bd.), Ohio Osteo. Hosp. Assn. (past pres.), Am. Legion (past post comdr.), Sigma Chi. Clubs: University, Rotary (pres. 1978-79), Columbus. Home: 1180 Kenbrook Hills Dr Columbus OH 43220-4941 Office: 1100 Dennison Ave Columbus OH 43201-3262

SIMS, ROBERT BARRY, lawyer; b. N.Y.C., Aug. 20, 1942; s. Irving Zach and Laura (Levine) S.; m. Roberta Jane Donner, Nov. 17, 1973; children: Alexandra Lauren, Amanda Morgan. AB, Franklin and Marshall Coll., 1964; JD, George Washington U., 1967; MBA, NYU, 1969. Bar: N.Y. 1968, D.C. 1969, U.S. Dist. Ct. D.C. 1969, U.S. Dist. Ct. (so. and ea. dists.) N.Y. 1970, U.S. Dist. Ct. Conn 1978, U.S. Ct. Appeals (2d and D.C. cir.) 1969, U.S. Ct. Claims 1977, U.S. Ct. Customs and Patent Appeals 1978, U.S. Supreme Ct. 1979, Conn. 1980, U.S. Ct. Internat. Trade 1981. Assoc. firm Cahill, Gordon & Reindel, N.Y.C., 1967-69, Whitman & Ransom, N.Y.C., 1969-72; asst. counsel Gen. Signal Corp., N.Y.C., Stamford, Conn., 1972-76; v.p., sec., gen. counsel Raymark Corp. (formerly Raybestos-Manhattan, Inc.), Trumbull, Conn., 1976-82; assoc. gen. counsel Lever Bros. Co., N.Y.C., 1983; asst. to pres., corp. counsel Math. Applications Group, Inc., Elmsford, N.Y., 1984; sr. v.p., sec., gen. counsel Summagraphics Corp., Seymour, Conn., 1984—. Mem. ABA, N.Y. State Bar Assn., Assn. Bar City N.Y., D.C. Bar Assn., Conn. Bar Assn., Coporate Bar Assn. Office: Summargraphics Corp 8500 Cameron Rd Austin TX 78754

SIMS, ROBERT BELL, professional society administrator, public affairs official, newspaper publisher; b. Alamo, Tenn., Nov. 26, 1934; s. Robert Leslie and Lucille (Bell) S.; m. Patricia June Lytton, June 25, 1961; children—Jacqueline, James, Carolyn, William. B.A. Union U., Jackson, Tenn., 1956; postgrad., U. Sydney, Australia, 1957; M.A. in Polit. Sci., U. Wis., Madison, 1971, M.A. in Journalism, 1971; Grad., Nat. War Coll. Reporter Jackson Sun, Tenn., 1955-56; dir. pub. relations Union U., Jackson, 1958; commd. ensign USN, 1958, served to capt., 1984; spl. asst. to Pres., dir. pub. affairs NSC, Washington, 1982-83; spl. asst. to Pres., dep. press sec. for fgn. affairs The White House, Washington, 1983-85; asst. sec. def. pub. affairs Dept. of Def., Washington, 1985-87; v.p. communications Nat. Geographic Soc., Washington, 1987-89, sr. v.p., 1989—; owner, pub. The Crockett Times, Alamo, Tenn., 1974—. Author: Pentagon Reporters, 1983. Mem. bd. visitors U. Tenn. Coll. Arts and Scis., 1992—; bd. dirs. Mag. Pubs. Assn., 1992—, Travel Industry Assn. Decorated Legion of Merit; Rotary Internat. Found. fellow, 1957; recipient Disting. Service award Union U., 1985. Mem. Sigma Delta Chi. Republican. Lodge: Masons. Home: 2701 O St NW Washington DC 20007 Office: Nat Geog Soc Washington DC 20036

SIMS, ROBERT JOHN, financial planner; b. Phila., Mar. 18, 1926; s. Stanley Joseph and Marie (Kendrick) S.; m. Gloria MacCarter, Nov. 27, 1965; children: Lisa Byrne, Dana Hospodar, Ernest, William, Peter, Moira. Student, Temple U., 1947-51; MSFS, CLU, ChFC, Am. Coll., Bryn Mawr, Pa., 1957; CFP, Coll. Fin. Planning, Denver. With Provident Mut. Life Ins., Phila., 1947-56, Aetna Life Ins., Phila., 1956-58, Mut. of N.Y., Phila., 1958-68; pres. Fin-Plan Investments, Inc., Wayne, Pa., 1960—, Fin-Plan Cons., Inc., Wayne, 1960—, Fin-Plan, Inc., Wayne, 1960—; mem. Fin. Coun. Archdiocese of Phila., investment com., trustee Lay Employees Pension Plan. Trustee Notre Dame Acad. Bd., Radnor, Pa., United Fund; past pres. Phila. Jaycees, past nat. dir. U.S. Jaycees; bd. dirs. Gwynedd Mercy Coll., Phila.; active Big Bros.; mem. adv. bd. St. Charles Borremmeo Sem.; past pres., active Cath. Philopatrian Lit. Inst. With U.S. mil., 1944-46. Mem. Internat. Assn. Fin. Planners (founding pres. Delaware Valley chpt.), Inst. CFPs, Am. Soc. CLU, Phila. Estate Planning Coun., Phila. Assn. Life Underwriters, Golden Key Soc., Union League Phila., Overbrook Golf Club (Radnor), Phila. Country Club. Republican. Roman Catholic. Avocation: golf. Home: 219 Orchard Way Saint Davids PA 19087 Office: Fin-Plan Group 531 E Lancaster Ave Wayne PA 19087

SIMS, WILLIAM RILEY, JR., design and facility management educator, consultant; b. Gulfport, Miss., Dec. 17, 1938; s. William Riley and Hallie Pauline (Mills) S.; m. Jean Lee Booth, June 17, 1962; 1 child, Hallie Jean. B.Arch., U. N.Mex., 1963; M.Arch., M.C.P., U. Pa., 1965; Ph.D., MIT, 1973. Cert. facility mgr. Internat. Facility Mgmt. Assn., 1993. Planner, urban designer Phila. City Planning Commn., 1964; planner, urban designer Wallace McHarg Assocs., Phila., 1965; lectr. dep. city and regional planning U. Calif., Berkeley, 1966-68; asst. prof. dept. urban planning U. Wash., Seattle, 1970-73; assoc. prof. dept. city and regional planning Ohio State U., Columbus, 1973-80; prof., chmn. dept. design and environ. analysis Cornell U., Ithaca, N.Y., 1980—, co-dir. Internat. Facility Mgmt. program, 1989-93; co-dir. Workplace Studies Program, 1993—; cons. Capitol S. Community Redevel. Assn., Columbus, Ohio, 1978-80; prin. Orbit-II Study, Ithaca, 1984—, Becker-Sims Assocs. (formerly Facility Rsch. Assocs.), Ithaca, 1984—. Author: Neighborhoods, 1975; (with others) Taos Adobes, 1965; editor (jour.) Design Guidelines from Post Occupancy Evaluation, 1980; contbr. articles to profl. jours.; mem. publs. bd. Jour. Interior Design Edn. and Research, 1986-89. Trustee Columbus Landmarks Found., 1978-80; mem. bldgs. and properties com. Cornell U. Trustees. Fulbright scholar U.S. Inst. Internat. Edn., Norway, 1965-66; Mellon faculty fellow U. Wash., 1969, Ford faculty fellow Ohio State U., 1974. Mem. ASTM (chmn. assessing bldg. performance 1988-92), Internat. Facility Mgrs. Assn. (bd. dirs. 1984-87, cert. and accreditation task forces 1989—), Environ. Design Rsch. Assn., Assn. for Study of Man and Environ. Rels. (editl. bd. 1978-86), Am. Assn. Housing Educators (editl. bd. 1978-82). Home: 735 Ridge Rd Lansing NY 14882-8805 Office: Cornell U Dept Design & Environ Analysis Ithaca NY 14853-4401

SIMS, WILSON, lawyer; b. Nashville, Dec. 24, 1924; s. Cecil and Grace (Wilson) S.; m. Linda Bell, Aug. 12, 1948; children: Linda Rickman, Suzanne, Wilson. B.A., U. N.C., 1946; J.D., Vanderbilt U., 1948. Bar: Tenn. 1948. Since practiced in Nashville; ptnr. Bass, Berry & Sims, 1948—; gen. counsel, dir. Baird Ward Printing Co., Tenn., 1950-76, Southeastern Capital Corp., 1955-60, Martha White Foods, Synercon Corp., 1968-76, Forrest Life Ins. Co., 1972-75, Charter Co., 1983-84, The Bailey Co., Kenworth of Tenn., Inc. Chmn. Tenn. Commn. for Human Devel., 1970, Tenn. Commn. on Continuing Legal Edn., 1986-90; mem. Tenn. Gen. Assembly, 1959; bd. dirs. Nashville YMCA, United Cerebal Palsy, Kidney

Found., McKendree Village; trustee Meharry Med. Coll., Webb Sch., Bell Buckle, Tenn.; adv. bd. Jr. League; mem. bd. visitors U. N.C. 1st lt. USMCR, 1942-45, 50-52. Fellow Am. Bar Found. (life), Nashville Bar Found.; mem. ABA, Tenn. Bar Assn. (past speaker ho. of dels., past pres.), Nashville Bar Assn. (past pres., dir., Pub. Svc. award), Tenn. Bar Found. (past chmn.), Am. Judicature Soc., Am. Acad. Polit. Sci., Vanderbilt U. Law Alumni Assn. (past pres., Disting. Alumnus award), Nashville C. of C. (2 terms bd. govs.), Belle Meade Country (bd. dirs.), Wade Hampton Golf Club. Methodist. Home: 22 Foxhall Close Nashville TN 37215-1862 Office: Bass Berry & Sims 2700 First Am Ctr Nashville TN 37238

SIMSON, GARY JOSEPH, legal educator; b. Newark, Mar. 18, 1950; s. Marvin and Mildred (Silberg) S.; m. Rosalind Slivka, Aug. 15, 1971; children: Nathaniel, Jennie Anne. BA, Yale Coll., 1971; JD, Yale U., 1974. Bar: Conn. 1974, N.Y. 1980. Law clk. to judge U.S. Ct. Appeals 2d Cir., 1974-75; asst. prof. law, U. Tex., 1975-77, prof. law, 1977-80; vis. prof. law Cornell U., Ithaca, N.Y., 1979-80, prof. law, 1980—; vis. prof. law U. Calif., Berkeley, 1986; chair adv. bd. law casebook series Carolina Acad. Press. Author: Issues and Perspectives in Conflict of Laws, 1985, 2d edit., 1991. Mem. ABA, ACLU, Phi Beta Kappa. Contbr. articles to legal publs. Office: Cornell U Law Sch Myron Taylor Hall Ithaca NY 14853

SIMSON, JO ANNE, anatomy and cell biology educator; b. Chgo., Nov. 19, 1936; d. Kenneth Brown and Helen Marjorie (Pascoe) Valentine; m. Arnold Simson, June 1961 (div.); 1 child, Maria; m. Michael Smith, Nov. 10, 1971 (div.); children: Elizabeth Smith, Briana Smith. BA, Kalamazoo Coll., 1959; MS, U. Mich., 1961; PhD, SUNY, Syracuse, 1969. Postdoctoral fellow Temple U. Health Sci. Ctr., Phila., 1968-70; asst. prof. Med. U. S.C., Charleston, 1970-76, assoc. prof., 1976-83, prof. anatomy and cell biology, 1983—; featured in Smithsonian exhibit, Sci. in Am. Life, 1994— Author short stories and poems; contbr. articles to profl. jours. Active adult edn. Unitarian Ch., Charleston, 1973-75, social action, 1990-92. Grantee NSF, 1959-60; grantee NIH, 1966-67, 72-87, 91—, postdoctoral fellow, 1968-70. Mem. Am. Assn. Anatomists, Am. Soc. Cell Biology, Histochem. Soc. (sec. 1979-82, exec. coun. 1985-89), Fogarty Internat. Fellowship Bioctr. (Basel, Switzerland 1987-88), Amnesty Internat. (newsletter editor Group 168 1982-86), Phi Beta Kappa. Home: 1760 Pittsford Cir Charleston SC 29412-4110 Office: Med U SC Anatomy 171 Ashley Ave Charleston SC 29425-0001

SINAI, ALLEN LEO, economist, educator; b. Detroit, Apr. 4, 1939; s. Joseph and Betty Paula (Feinberg) S.; m. Lee Davis Etsten, June 23, 1963; children—Lauren Beth, Todd Michael. AB, U. Mich., 1961; MA, Northwestern U., 1966, PhD, 1969. Asst. prof. to assoc. prof. econs. U. Ill.-Chgo., 1966-75; chmn. fin. info. group, chief fin. economist Data Resources, Lexington, Mass., 1971-83; chief economist, mng. dir. Lehman Bros. and Shearson Lehman Bros. Inc., N.Y.C., 1983-87; chief economist, exec. v.p. The Boston Co. Inc., 1988-93; pres., CEO The Boston Co. Econ. Advisors Inc., Boston and N.Y.C., 1988-93, Econ. Advisors, Inc., 1993—; mng. dir., chief global economist Lehman Bros., N.Y.C., 1993—; cons. Laural Cons., Lexington and Evanston, Ill., 1966; vis. assoc. prof. econs. and fin. MIT, Cambridge, 1977-78; adj. prof. econs. Boston U., 1977-78, 81-83, NYU, 1984-88; adj. prof. econs. and fin. Lemberg Sch., Brandeis U., 1988—; vis. faculty Sloan Sch., MIT, 1989-91. Contbr. articles to profl. jours. and books. Mem. reducing the fed. budget deficit task force Roosevelt Ctr., Washington, 1984; bd. govs. Com. on Developing Am. Capitalism, 1984—, chmn., 1990—; bd. economists Time Mag., 1991—. Recipient Alumnus Merit award Northwestern U., 1985. Fellow Ea. Econs. Assn. (v.p. 1988-89, pres. 1990-91, Otto Eckstein prize 1988); mem. Am. Econ. Assn., Western Econ. Assn. (exec. com.). Jewish. Avocations: tennis; skiing. Home: 16 Holmes Rd Lexington MA 02173-1917 Office: Econ Advisors Inc 260 Franklin 15th Fl Boston MA 02209

SINANIAN, LORIS R., financial consultant, deacon; b. N.Y.C., Oct. 23, 1931; s. John and Araksi (Ozanian) S.; m. Peggy Gavin, July 18, 1959; children: Arlene, Linda, Claire, Stephen. B of Mech. Engring., NYU, 1952; grad. bus., UCLA, 1967. Ordained permanent deacon Roman Cath. Ch., 1989. Dir. reentry systems TRW Systems Group, Redondo Beach, Calif., 1963-72; v.p. devel., v.p. mktg. Nat. Distbn. Svcs. (subs. Eastern Airlines), Atlanta, 1972-73; exec. v.p. Credit Data of Southeast (now TRW Credit Data), Atlanta, 1973-80; pres. LRS Assocs., Atlanta, 1980-84; fin. cons. The Robinson-Humphrey Co., Atlanta, 1984—; founder-pres. and exec. dir. Faith Enrichment Inst., Atlanta, 1987—, Cath. Family Forum, Atlanta, 1992—; dir. Formation, Archdiocese of Atlanta, 1994, Fellowship of Cath. Scholars, 1994. Contbr. (newspaper) The Money Manager, Ga., 1985—. Vice pres. United Reps. Calif., 1964-71; active Rep. Ctrl. Com., 1966-68; formation dir. Archdiocese of Atlanta. Lt. USAF, 1952-54. Home: 90 River Court Pkwy Atlanta GA 30328

SINATRA, FRANK (FRANCIS ALBERT SINATRA), singer, actor; b. Hoboken, N.J., Dec. 12, 1915; s. Anthony and Natalie (Garaventi) S.; m. Nancy Barbato, Feb. 4, 1939 (div.); children: Nancy, Frank Wayne, Christine; m. Ava Gardner (div.); m. Mia Farrow, 1966 (div.); m. Barbara Marx, 1976. Student, Demarest High Sch., Hoboken, Drake Inst.; hon. doctorate, Stevens Inst. Tech., Hoboken, 1985. Sang with sch. band and helped form sch. glee club; worked after sch. on news truck of Jersey Observer; copy boy on graduation with sports div. covering coll. sports events (won first prize on Maj. Bowes Amateur Hour, touring with co. for 3 months); sustaining programs on 4 radio stas. and in Rustic Cabin, N.J., toured with Harry James Band, then Tommy Dorsey's, solo night club and concert appearances; starred on radio program Lucky Strike Hit Parade; appeared in motion pictures From Here to Eternity (Acad. award as best supporting actor 1953), Las Vegas Nights, 1946, Ship Ahoy, 1942, Miracle of the Bells, 1948, Kissing Bandit, 1949, Take Me Out to the Ball Game, 1949, Higher and Higher, 1942, Step Lively, 1944, Anchors Aweigh, 1945, It Happened in Brooklyn, 1947, Guys and Dolls, 1956, Not as a Stranger, 1955, The Tender Trap, 1955, The Man With the Golden Arm, 1955, Johnny Concho, 1956, The Pride and the Passion, 1957, Pal Joey, 1957, Some Came Running, 1959, Never So Few, 1960, Can-Can, 1960, Oceans 11, 1960, Pepe, 1960, The Devil at 4 O'Clock, 1961, The Manchurian Candidate, 1962, Come Blow Your Horn, 1963, Robin and the Seven Hoods, 1963, None But the Brave, 1964, Assault on a Queen, 1965, Von Ryan's Express, 1966, Tony Rome, 1966, Lady in Cement, 1967, The Detective, 1968, Dirty Dingus McGee, 1970, Who Framed Roger Rabbit (voice), 1988; actor, producer motion picture The First Deadly Sin, 1980, TV movie Contract on Cherry Street, 1977; hit songs include Night and Day, 1943, Nancy, 1945, Young at Heart, 1954, Love and Marriage, 1955, The Tender Trap, 1955, How Little We Know, 1956, Chicago, 1957, All the Way, 1957, High Hopes, 1959, It Was a Very Good Year, 1965, Strangers in the Night, 1966, My Way, 1969, (with Nancy Sinatra) Somethin Stupid, 1969; albums include Songs for Swingin' Lovers, 1956, Come Dance With Me, 1959, Come Fly With Me, 1962, September of My Years (Grammy award for best album), 1965, Moonlight 1966, Greatest Hits, 1968, My Way, 1969, Greatest Hits, Volume 2, 1970, L.A. is My Lady, 1984, Duets, 1993, Duets II, 1994; author: A Man and His Art, 1990. Recipient Sylvania TV award, Grammy awards for album of yr., 1959, 65, 66, best vocalist, 1959, 65, 66, rec. of yr., 1966, Peabody and Emmy awards, 1965, Jean Hersholt award Acad. Motion Picture Arts and Scis., 1971, Golden Apple award as male star of yr. Hollywood Women's Press Club, 1977, Humanitarian award Variety Clubs Internat., 1980, Cross of Sci. and the Arts, Austria, 1984, Presdl. Medal of Freedom, 1985, Kennedy Ctr. honor, 1986, Life Achievement award NAACP, 1987, Grammy Lifetime Achievement award, 1994. Club: Friars (abbot). Office: care Thomas Cassidy Inc 0366 Horseshoe Dr Basalt CO 81621 also: care Sinatra Enterprises 5757 Wilshire Blvd 240 Los Angeles CA 90036*

SINAY, HERSHEL DAVID, publisher; b. Chgo., Mar. 15, 1938; s. Irving Paul and Gertrude (Drucker) S. BA, U. So. Calif., 1960. Telecommunications and Cinema account exec. Wall St. Jour., L.A., 1961-63; account exec. R.J. Friedman Assocs., L.A., 1963-66; dir. sales Performing Arts Mag., L.A., 1966-72; pub. East, West Network, L.A., 1972-79, 85-87; pres., pub. Calif. Bus. Mag., L.A., 1979-85; pub., editor-in-chief Ranch & Coast Mag., DelMar, Calif., 1987-88; pub. Am. Film. Mag., L.A., 1988-91; pres., owner Project Mktg. Custom Publ. Specialists Pubs. of the Am. Film Inst. Life Achievement Award Annual, 1991—; Pubs. of Am. Cinema Editors Tribute Program, 1993—. Recipient Billboard Music awards Tribute Book, 1993, 1st Ann. Thurgood Marshall Lifetime Achievement award tribute Book,

NAACP Legal Def. and Ednl. Fund, 1993, 32 Maggie awards Western Pub. Assn., 1979-93. Mem. Am. Film Inst., L.A. Advt. Club. Avocations: yachting, jogging, gardening. Office: 810 S Hauser Blvd Los Angeles CA 90036-4726

SINAY, JOSEPH, retail executive; b. Chgo., Dec. 5, 1920; s. Hyman and Ella S.; m. Ruth Milman, Mar. 7, 1961; 1 dau., Elise Sinay Spilker. Student, Herzl Jr. Coll., 1939. Gen. mgr. Fanchon & Marco Theatres, Los Angeles, 1943-54; v.p. founder Interstate United, Chgo., 1953-56; partner Josam Investment Co., Los Angeles, 1956—; chmn. bd., pres., chief exec. officer R B Industries Inc., L.A., 1956-89, now cons. Bd. dirs. Am. Acad. Dramatic Arts; pres. Variety Clubs Internat., 1985-87; gen. chmn. United Jewish Welfare L.A., 1976; pres. We. region Am. Friends Hebrew U., 1980; Calif. fin. chmn. Muskie for Pres., 1972; trustee Idyllwild Arts Found., 1968-73; bd. dirs. Constl. Rights Found., 1973-78. Mem. Nat. Home Furnishing Assn. Jewish. Office: Josam Investment Co 1801 Century Park E Los Angeles CA 90067-2302

SINAY, RUTH DORIS, psychologist; b. Bklyn., Feb. 5, 1920; d. Maurice Howard and Marion Gertrude (Heller) Milman; m. Joseph Sinay, Mar. 7, 1961; 1 child, Frederick Allen Schiff. AA, Santa Monica City Coll., 1953; BA in Psychology cum laude, U. So. Calif., 1956, PhD, 1967. Tchr. pub. schs., Hawthorne, Calif., 1957-58; fashion model, instr. Rita LaRoy Fashion Modeling Sch., Beverly Hills, Calif., 1958-61; instr. psychology U. So. Calif. Sch. Medicine, Los Angeles, 1967-71, dir. child and adolescent psychol. tng. program, 1969—, acting dir. child and adolescent psychol. services, 1969-70, dir., 1971—, asst. clin. prof., 1971-79, assoc. clin. prof., 1979—; assoc. clin. prof. psychology Fuller Theol. Sem., Pasadena, Calif., 1969—; cons. in field. Author: (with H. Slucki and N. Tiber) The Really Easy Reader Game, 1974; contbr. articles to profl. jours. Mem. Los Angeles Mayor's Com. on Youth and Aging, 1974-75; chmn. Take A Giant Step, Los Angeles, 1977; active United Jewish Fund drives; alt. del. Muskie for Pres., 1972. Recipient Judas Magnos award Hebrew U., Jerusalem, Israel, 1977. Mem. Am. Psychol. Assn., Western Psychol. Assn., Calif. State Psychol. Assn. (sec. 1975-78), Los Angeles County Psychol. Assn., Psychologists in Pub. Service (sec. 1969-70), Pi Lambda Theta. Club: Los Angeles Variety. Home: 1000 Elden Way Beverly Hills CA 90210-2805 Office: 1937 Hospital Pl Los Angeles CA 90033-1073

SINCLAIR, ALASTAIR JAMES, geology educator; b. Hamilton, Ont., Can., Aug. 1, 1935; s. Burton Leslie and Grace (Isherwood) S.; m. Elizabeth Mary Sylvia Hill, June 13, 1964; children: Alison Trevena, Fiona Tamsin. BS, U. Toronto, 1957, MS, 1958; PhD, U. B.C., 1964. Asst. prof. U. Wash., Seattle, 1962-64; asst. prof. U. B.C., Vancouver, 1964-68, assoc. prof., 1968-74, prof., 1974—, head dept. geol. scis., 1985-90, dir. Geol. Engring., 1979-80, 81-82, 92—; pres. Sinclair Cons. Ltd., Vancouver, 1980—; bd. dirs. FSS Internat., Vancouver. Contbr. numerous articles to profl. jours. Killam Sr. fellow, 1990-91. Fellow Geol. Assn. Can. (treas. mineral deposits divsn. 1978-89), Soc. Econ. Geologists; mem. Assn. Profl. Engrs. B.C., Internat. Assn. Math. Geologists, Assn. Exploration Geochemists, Can. Inst. Mining, Metallurgy and Petroleum (life, Robert Elver award 1991), Geol. Soc. Brazil (hon. mem. sci.-tech. commn. geochemistry 1982), Brazilian Geochem. Soc. (hon. 1987). Avocations: classical music, skiing. Home: 2972 W 44th Ave, Vancouver, BC Canada V6N 3K4 Office: U BC, Dept Geological Sciences, Vancouver, BC Canada V6T 1Z4

SINCLAIR, CAROLE, publisher, editor, author; b. Haddonfield, N.J., May 13, 1942; d. Earl Walter and Ruth (Sinclair) Dunham; 1 child, Wendy. Student, U. Florence, Italy, 1963; BA in Polit. Sci., Bucknell U, 1964. Advt. copywriter BBD&O Advertising, N.Y.C., 1966-67; sales promotion mgr. Macmillan Pub. Co., N.Y.C., 1967-71; mktg. mgr. Doubleday & Co., Inc., N.Y.C., 1972-74, promotion dir., 1974-76, advt. mgr., sales and promotion, chmn. mktg. com., 1976-80; v.p. mktg., editorial dir. Davis Pubs., N.Y.C., 1980-83; founder, pub., editorial dir., sr. v.p. Sylvia Porter's Personal Fin. Mag., N.Y.C., 1983-90; pres. The Sylvia Porter Orgn., Inc., N.Y.C., 1980-91; founder, pres. Sinclair Media Inc., N.Y.C., 1990—; mktg. dir. Denver Pub. Inst., summers 1975-78; lectr. Columbia U. Bus. Sch. and Sch. of Journalism, 1976; host nationally syndicated TV show, Sylvia Porter's Money Tips, syndicated daily radio show, Sylvia Porter's Personal Fin. Report, audio cassette series on fin. topics. Author: Keys for Women Starting and Owning a Business, 1991, Keys to Women's Basic Professional Needs, 1991, When Women Retire, 1992; contbg. editor Pushcart Prize, 1977; contbr. The Business of Publishing, 1980. Renaissance Art Program fellow, Florence, Italy, 1963; White House intern, 1962. Mem. Women's Forum, Intercorp. Communications Group, Mag. Pubs.' Assn., Advt. Women in N.Y., Spence Sch. Parent's League. Presbyterian. Club: Pubs. Lunch. Avocation: boating.

SINCLAIR, DAISY, advertising executive, casting director; b. Perth Amboy, N.J., Mar. 22, 1941; d. James Patrick and Margaret Mary (McAniff) Nieland; m. James Pratt Sinclair, May 25, 1978; children: Duncan, Gibbons. BA, Caldwell Coll., 1962. Jr. copywriter Young & Rubican, N.Y.C., 1962-64; various positions in casting dept. Ogilvy & Mather, N.Y.C., 1964-90, sr. v.p., dir. casting, 1990—. Mem. Am. Assn. Advt. (talent agt. com. 1972—), Drama League N.Y. (3d v.p. 1982—), The Knickerbocker Greys (v.p.), Edgartown Yacht Club, Chapaquoit Yacht Club, The Tuxedo Club. Republican. Episcopalian. Avocations: opera, theater, sailing, skiing. Home: 4 E 95th St New York NY 10128-0705 Office: Ogilvy & Mather Advt Worldwide Plz 309 W 49th St New York NY 10019-7316

SINCLAIR, DORIS PAULA GIMMESON, nurse, educational administrator; b. Troy, Ohio, Dec. 5, 1932; d. Dwight Paul and Florence Mable (Oller) Gimmeson; m. Robert A. Sinclair, Sr., May 16, 1956; children: Elizabeth Ann Sinclair Biggan, Robert A., Mary Ruth, Sinclair Lonnerghan. Cert., Trinity U., San Antonio, 1955; diploma Baptist Meml. Hosp. Sch. Nursing, 1955; BSN cum laude, Incarnate Word Coll., San Antonio, 1968; MSN, U. Tex.-San Antonio, 1974. RN, Tex. Office nurse for pvt. practitioner, San Antonio, 1955-57, 59-62; staff nurse Bapt. Meml. Hosp., San Antonio, 1957-59, 63-64; instr. maternal child care nursing Bapt. Meml. Hosp. Sch. Nursing, San Antonio, 1962-63, 68-71, instr. clin. nursing, 1964-66; asst. dir. Bapt. Meml. Hosp. System Sch. Nursing, San Antonio, 1971-72, acting dir., 1972-74, dir., 1974-86, retired, 1986-87, pub. sch. nurse, 1987-88; dir. Bapt. Meml. Hosp. System Sch. Profl. Nursing, San Antonio, 1988—; mem. Bd. Vocat. Nurse Examiners, State of Tex., Austin, 1978-81; accreditation visitor So. Assn. Colls. and Schs., 1981-82; mem. coordinating bd., nursing edn. adv. com., Tex. Coll. and Univ. System, Austin, 1982-83. Coord., Explorer Scout Post 634, San Antonio, 1983-86; adv. bd. nurse career program Chicano Health Policy Devel., Inc., San Antonio, 1983-86. Recipient Nurse of Yr. award Baptist Meml. Hosp. System, 1973. Mem. Nat. League Nursing (accreditation visitor 1982-86, alt. accreditation bd. rev. 1991-93), Tex. League Nursing, Am. Hosp. Assn. Assembly Hosp. Schs. Nursing (nominating com. 1976-78, program com. 1979-80, chmn. program com. 1980-81), Council Deans and Dirs. of Schs. of Profl. Nursing for State of Tex. (chairperson 1978-79), Tex. Higher Edn. Co-ordinating Bd. (nursing adv. com. 1989-90), Am. Hosp. Assn. Inst. for Hosp. Clin. Nursing Edn. (gov. coun. 1990-92), Bapt. Meml. Hosp. System Sch. Nursing Alumni Assn., Sigma Theta Tau. Methodist. Clubs: San Antonio Coll. Faculty Wives, Ladies Oriental Shrine N. Am., Bapt. Meml. Hosp. System Lamplighter Assn. Avocations: gourmet cooking; ceramics; swimming. Office: Bapt Meml Hosp System Sch Profl Nursing 111 Dallas St San Antonio TX 78205-1201

SINCLAIR, GLENN BRUCE, mechanical engineering educator, researcher; b. Auckland, New Zealand, Mar. 7, 1946; came to U.S. 1969; s. Alan John and Piri (Vincent) S.; m. Della Jane Sutton, Dec. 23, 1972; children—Heidi Lee, Heather Ann, Hillary Colleen, Christopher Alan. B.Sc., U. Auckland, 1967, B.E., 1969; Ph.D., Calif. Inst. Tech., 1972. J. Willard Gibbs instr. mech. engring. Yale U., New Haven, 1972-74; lectr. U. Auckland, 1974-77; asst. prof. Carnegie-Mellon U., Pitts., 1977-80, assoc. prof., 1980-82, prof., 1982—, head, 1986-92; vis. prof. Cambridge U., Eng., 1981; research scientist Dept. Sci. and Indsl. Research, Wellington, New Zealand, 1968-69; summer prof. Pratt & Whitney, Hartford, Conn., 1978, Aircraft Corp., West Palm Beach, Fla., 1979; cons. in field. Contbr. articles to profl. jours. Fulbright scholar, 1969-72. Mem. Am. Acad. Mechanics. Office: Carnegie-Mellon Univ Dept Mech Engring 5000 Forbes Ave Pittsburgh PA 15213-3890

SINCLAIR, JAMES BURTON, plant pathology educator, consultant; b. Chgo., Dec. 21, 1927; s. James Lawrence Sinclair and Helen Marie (Thompson) Owens. BSc, Lawrence U., 1951; PhD, U. Wis., 1955. Grad. rsch. asst. U. Wis., Madison, 1951-55, grad. rsch. assoc., 1955-56; from asst. prof. to assoc. prof. La. State U., Baton Rouge, 1956-65, prof., 1965-68, adminstrv. asst. to chancellor, 1966-68; prof. U. Ill., Urbana, 1968—, dir. nat. soybean rsch. lab., 1992—. Co-author: Basic Plant Pathology Methods, 1985, Principles of Seed Pathology, 1987, Anatomy and Physiology of Diseased Plants, 1991; contbr. articles to profl. jours. Sgt. U.S. Army, 1946-47. Recipient Soybean Rsch. Recognition award Am. Soybean Assn., 1983, Prodn. Rsch. award, 1989, Paul A. Funk award, 1984, Disting. Svc. award USDA, 1988, Disting. Svc. award Phytopathol. Soc. (north cttl. divsn.), 1991, Rsch. award Land of Lincoln Soybean Assn., 1992. Fellow Am. Phytopathological Soc.; mem. Ill. Crop Improvement Assn. (hon.), Rotary (chmn. internat. com. Savoy chpt. 1990-91, v.p. 1991-93, pres. 1993-94). Home: 408 Arbours Dr Savoy IL 61874-9752 Office: U Ill Dept Plant Pathology 1102 S Goodwin Ave Urbana IL 61801-4709

SINCLAIR, JOSEPH SAMUELS, broadcasting company executive, retail merchant; b. Narragansett, R.I., June 14, 1922; s. James and Bertha (Samuels) S.; m. Betty Virginia Hintz, Feb. 16, 1946 (dec. 1968); children: Sherry Murr, Lani Patricia, Jodie Carol; m. Rosalyn K. Dwares, Oct. 24, 1969; children: Sara Ellen Sinclair, Steven Dwares. Student, Williams Coll., 1940-41; BS, U.S. Naval Acad., 1945; DBA (hon.), Johnson and Wales Coll., 1976. Commd. ensign USN, 1945, advanced through grades to lt. (j.g.), resigned, 1947; asst. to program mgr. Sta. WJAR-TV, Providence, 1949-57, mgr., 1957-60; dir. Outlet Co., 1955-58, mem. exec. com., 1958-60, v.p., 1960, pres., 1960-68, chmn. bd. dirs., 1968-84; pres. Sinclair Communications, Sinclair Assn., Sinclair Ventures, Providence, 1984—. Mem. pres.'s council Providence Coll.; trustee R.I. Council Econ. Edn., U. R.I. Found.; mem. adv. bd. Salve Regina Coll. Served as lt. (s.g.) USNR, 1950-52. Decorated Italian Star Solidarity; recipient R.I. Advt. Silver medal, 1968. Mem. Navy League R.I., Naval War Coll. Found., Nat. Assn. Broadcasters (dir.), R.I. Assn. Broadcasters (v.p.), TV Pioneers, Internat. Radio and TV Soc., World Bus. Coun., R.I. Commodores (adm.), Wellington Country Club, Sports Car Am., Cat Cay Club, Nat. Broadcasters, R.I. 100 (pres.), Point Judith Country Club, Dunes Club, Aurora Club, Palm Beach Polo and Country Club, Wellington Club. Home and Office: 170 Westminster St Providence RI 02903-2101

SINCLAIR, KENT, law educator; b. San Diego, July 8, 1946; s. Kent and Ruth Melva (Wilson) S.; m. Kathryn Sinning; children: K. Scott, Keith A. AB, U. Calif., 1968, JD, 1971. Bar: Calif. 1972, U.S. Dist. Ct. (so. dist.) N.Y. 1972, U.S. Ct. Appeals (2d cir.) 1972, N.Y. 1973, Va. 1986, U.S. Supreme Ct. 1990. Law clk. to judge James Browning U.S. Ct. Appeals 9th Cir., San Francisco, 1971-72; chief staff atty. U.S. Ct. Appeals 9th Cir., 1972; atty. Shearman & Sterling, N.Y.C., 1972-77; judge-magistrate U.S. Dist. Ct. So. Dist., N.Y.C., 1977-83; prof. law U. Va., Charlottesville, Va., 1983-89; prof. law, assoc. dean U. Va., 1989-93; spl. master U.S. Dist. Ct. SDN.Y., 1983-88; dep. spl. master Supreme Ct. U.S., 1989—; reporter decisions Supreme Ct. Va., Richmond, 1985—; dir. Va. Judges Inst., Charlottesville, 1984—. Author: Federal Civil Practice, 1992, Virginia Civil Procedure, 1993, Practice Before Federal Magistrates, 1984, Moore's Federal Practice, 1984, The Trial Handbook, 1989. Edn. dir. Va. State Bar, 1983-89, mem. Mem. Am. Law Inst., Va. Bar Assn. Avocation: computers. Office: U Va Sch Law 580 Massie Rd Charlottesville VA 22903-1789

SINCLAIR, ROBERT J., automotive executive. Pres. Saab-Scania of Am Inc., Orange, Conn. Office: Saab-Scania Am Inc Saab Dr PO Box 697 Orange CT 06477-4011

SINCLAIR, ROLF MALCOLM, physicist; b. N.Y.C., Aug. 15, 1929; s. Nathan and Elizabeth (Stout) S.; m. Margaret Lee Andrews, June 13, 1959 (div. 1978); children: Elizabeth Ann, Andrew Caisley; m. Allyn J. Miner, July 29, 1991. B.S., Calif. Inst. Tech., 1949; M.A. (Reade scholar), Rice U., 1951, Ph.D. (Inst. fellow), 1954. Physicist, Westinghouse Research Labs., 1953-56; vis. scientist U. Hamburg, Germany, 1956-57, U. Paris, 1957-58, U.K. Atomic Energy Authority, Culham Lab., Eng., 1965-66; research physicist Princeton U., 1958-69; program dir. NSF, Washington, 1969—; mem. Solstice Project, 1978-91; NSF rep. U.S. Solar Eclipse Expdn. to India, 1980, Amundsen-Scott South Pole Sta., 1995; Disting. vis. prof. N.Mex. State U., 1985; vis. prof. No. Ariz. U., 1986; vis. sci. Los Alamos Nat. Lab., 1988-89, guest scientist, 1989—; cons. to industry, 1960-69. Fellow Am. Phys. Soc. (panel pub. affairs 1976-77, nominating com. 1988-90), AAAS (sec. physics sect. 1972—, mem. coun. 1972-73, nominating com. 1982-83), Sigma Xi. Research and publs. on physics, archaeoastronomy, tech. and instrumentation. Home: 7508 Tarrytown Rd Chevy Chase MD 20815-6027 Office: Nat Sci Found Physics Divsn 4201 Wilson Blvd Arlington VA 22230

SINCLAIR, SARA VORIS, health facility administrator, nurse; b. Kansas City, Mo., Apr. 13, 1942; d. Franklin Defenbaugh and Inez Estelle (Figenbaum) Voris; m. James W. Sinclair, June 13, 1964; children: Thomas James, Elizabeth Kathleen, Joan Sara. BSN, UCLA, 1965. RN, Utah; lic. health care facility adminstr.; cert. health care adminstr. Staff nurse UCLA Med. Ctr. Hosp., 1964-65; charge nurse Boulder (Colo.) Meml. Hosp., 1966, Boulder (Colo.) Manor Nursing Home, 1974-75, Four Seasons Nursing Home, Joliet, Ill., 1975-76; dir. nursing Home Health Agy of Olympia Fields, Joliet, Ill., 1977-79; dir. nursing Sunshine Terr. Found., Inc., Logan, Utah, 1980, asst. adminstr., 1980-81, adminstr., 1981-93; dir. divsn. health systems improvement Utah Dept. Health, Salt Lake City, 1993—; mem. long term care profl. and tech. adv. com. Joint Commn. on Accreditation Healthcare Orgns., Chgo., 1987-91, chmn., 1990-91; mem. adj. clin. faculty Weber State U., Ogden, Utah; moderator radio program Healthwise, Sta. KUSU-RM, 1985-93; spkr. Nat. Coun. Aging, 1993, Alzheimer's Disease Assn. Ann. Conf., 1993; chmn. dept. Health Ethics Instnl. Rev. Bd., 1995—; rep. Congressman James V. Hansen White House Conf. on Aging, 1995; presenter in field. Contbg. author: Associate Degree Nursing and The Nursing Home, 1988. Mem. dean's adv. coun. Coll. Bus. Utah State U., Logan, 1989-91, mem. presdl. search com., 1991-92; chmn., co-founder Cache Cmty. Health Coun., Logan, 1985; chmn. bd. Hospice of Cache Valley, Logan, 1986; mem. Utah State Adv. Coun. on Aging, 1986—; apptd. chmn. Utah Health Facilities Com., 1989—; mem. Utah Adv. Coun. on Aging, 1987—; chmn. Bear River Dist. Adv. Coun. on Aging, 1989-91; chmn. health and human svcs. subcom. Cache 2010, 1992-93; chair ethics com. Utah Dept. Health, 1995—; rep. White House Conf. on Aging, 1995. Recipient Disting. Svc. award Utah State U., 1989. Fellow Am. Coll. Health Care Adminstrs. (presenter 1992-93, 95, v.p. Utah chpt. 1992-94, convocation and edn. coms. 1992-94, region IX vice gov. 1994—); mem. Am. Healthcare Assn. (non-proprietary v.p. 1986-87, region v.p. 1987-89, presenter workshop conv. 1990-93, presenter ann. convocation 1995, exec. com. 1993—), Am. Coll. Health Care Adminstrs. (vice gov. region 9 1994—), Utah Health Care Assn. (pres. 1983-85, treas. 1991-93, Disting. Svc. award 1991), Utah Gerontol. Soc. (bd. dirs. 1992-95, —, chmn. nominating com. 1993-94), Cache C. of C. (pres. 1991), Logal Bus. and Profl. Women's Club (pres. 1989, Woman of Achieve,ent award 1982, Woman of Yr. 1982), Rotary (Logan chpt., chair cmty. svc. com. 1989-90). Avocations: walking, reading. Office: Utah Dept Health Divsn Health Systems Improvement 288 N 1460 W Salt Lake City UT 84114-2851

SINCLAIR, VIRGIL LEE, JR., lawyer, writer; b. Canton, Ohio, Nov. 10, 1951; s. Virgil Lee and Thelma Irene (Dunlap) S.; m. Judy Ann Montgomery, May 26, 1969 (div. Mar. 1980); children: Kelly, Shannon. BA, Kent State U., 1973; JD, U. Akron, 1976; postgrad. Case Western Res. U., 1979. Adminstr. Stark County Prosecutor's Office, Canton, 1974-76; mem. faculty Walsh Coll., Canton, 1976-78; asst. pros. atty. Stark County, Canton, 1976-77; ptnr. Amerman Burt Jones Co. LPA, Canton, 1976-91, Buckingham, Doolittle and Burroughs Co., L.P.A., Canton, 1991—; judge Stark County Common Pleas Ct., 1995—; legal adviser Mayor's Office, City of North Canton, Ohio, 1978-79; referee Stark County Family Ct., Canton, 1981, Canton Mcpl. Ct., 1991—; spl. referee Canton Mcpl. Ct., 1985-86. Author: Law Enforcement Officers' Guide to Juvenile Law, 1975, Lay Manual of Juvenile Law, 1976; editor U. Akron Law Rev.; contbr. to Ohio Family Law, 1983, also articles to profl. jours. Mem. North Canton Planning Comm., 1979-82; bd. mgrs. North Canton YMCA, 1994—, Camp Tippecanoe, Ohio, 1981—; profl. adviser Parents Without Partners, 1980—; spl. dep. Stark County Sheriff Dept., 1983—; trustee Palace Theatre Assn.,

Canton, 1982—. Recipient Disting. Service award U.S. Jaycees, 1984. Mem. ABA, Ohio Bar Assn., Stark County Bar Assn. (lectr. 1984), Ohio Trial Lawyers Assn., Assn. Trial Lawyers Am., Nat. Dist. Attys. Assn., Delta Theta Phi (bailiff 1976; nat. key winner 1975-76), Jaycees. Republican. Methodist. Lodge: Elks, Eagles.

SINCLAIR, WARREN KEITH, radiation biophysicist, organization executive, consultant; b. Dunedin, New Zealand, Mar. 9, 1924; came to U.S., 1954; naturalized, 1959; s. Ernest W. and Jessie E. (Craig) S.; m. Elizabeth J. Edwards, Mar. 19, 1948; children: Bruce W., Roslyn E. Munn. B.Sc., U. Otago, N.Z., 1944, M.Sc., 1945; Ph.D., U. London, 1950. Cert. Am. Bd. Health Physics. Radiol. physicist U. Otago, 1945-47; radiol. physicist U. London Royal Marsden Hosp., 1947-54; chmn. dept. physics, prof. U. Tex. M.D. Anderson Hosp., 1954-60; sr. biophysicist Argonne (Ill.) Nat. Lab., 1960-85, div. dir., 1970-74, assoc. lab. dir., 1974-81; prof. radiation biology U. Chgo., 1964-85, prof. emeritus, 1985—; mem. Internat. Commn. on Radiation Units and Measurements, 1969-85, Internat. Commn. on Radiol. Protection, 1977—; alt. del. UN Sci. Com. on Effects of Atomic Radiation, 1979—; mem. Nat. Council on Radiation Protection and Measurements, 1967-91; pres. Nat. Council on Radiation Proteciton and Measurements, 1977-91; hon. mem., pres. emeritus Nat. Council on Radiation Protection and Measurements, 1991—, L.S. Taylor lectr., 1993; H.M. Parker lectr., Battelle Fedn.; mem. expert panel WHO; sec. gen. 5th Internat. Congress Radiation Rsch., 1974; chmn. bd. on radiation effects rsch. NSA-Nat. Rsch. Coun., 1992—; cons. in field. Author: Radiation Research: Biomedical, Chemical and Physical Perspectives, 1975; Contbr. numerous articles to profl. jours., also chpts. to books. Served with N.Z. Army, 1942-43. Nat. New Zealand scholar, 1942-45. Fellow Inst. Physics; mem. Am. Assn. Physicists in Medicine (pres. 1961-62, Coolidge award 1986), Radiation Research Soc. (council 1964-67, pres. 1978-79, Failla award 1987), Brit. Inst. Radiology (council 1953-54), Internat. Assn. Radiation Research (council 1966-70, 76-83), Radiol. Soc. N.Am., Biophys. Soc., Soc. Nuclear Medicine, Bioelectromagnetics Soc., Health Physics Soc., Soc. Risk Analysis, Hosp. Physicists Assn. Clubs: Innominates (U. Chgo.); Cosmos (Washington). Home: 2900 Ascott Ln Olney MD 20832-2626 Office: 7910 Woodmont Ave Ste 800 Bethesda MD 20814-3015

SINCLAIR, WILLIAM DONALD, church official, fundraising consultant, political activist; b. L.A., Dec. 27, 1924; s. Arthur Livingston and Lillian May (Holt) S.; m. Barbara Jean Hughes, Aug. 9, 1952; children: Paul Scott, Victoria Sharon. BA cum laude, St. Martin's Coll., Olympia, Wash., 1975; postgrad. Emory U., 1978-79. Commd. 2d lt. USAAF, 1944, advanced through grades to col. USAF, 1970; served as pilot and navigator in Italy, Korea, Vietnam and Japan; ret., 1975; bus. adminstr. First United Methodist Ch., Colorado Springs, Colo., 1976-85; bus. adminstr. Village Seven Presbyn. Ch., 1985-87; bus. adminstr. Sunrise United Meth. Ch., 1987-89; vice-chmn. council fin. and adminstrn. Rocky Mountain conf. United Meth. Ch., U.S.A., 1979-83. Bd. dirs. Chins-Up Colorado Springs, 1983—; chmn. bd. dirs Pikes Peak Performing Arts Ctr., 1985-92; pres. Pioneers Mus. Found., 1985—; Rep. candidate for Colo. State Chmn., 1992-93. Decorated Legion of Merit with oak leaf cluster, D.F.C., Air medal with 6 oak leaf cluster, Dept. Def. Meritorious Service medal, Vietnam Cross of Gallantry with Palms. Fellow Nat. Assn. Ch. Bus. Adminstrs. (nat. dir., regional v.p., v.p. 1983-85, pres. 1985-87; Ch. Bus. Adminstr. of Yr. award 1983), Colo. Assn. Ch. Bus. Adminstrs. (past pres.), United Meth. Assn. Ch. Bus. Adminstrs. (nat. sec. 1978-81), Christian Ministries Mgmt. Assn. (dir. 1983-85), USAF Acad. Athletic Assn. Clubs: Colorado Springs Country, Garden of the Gods, Met. (Denver), Winter Night Club. Lodge: Rotary (pres. Downtown Colorado Springs club 1985-86), Order of Daedalians. Home: 3007 Chelton Dr Colorado Springs CO 80909-1008 Ten words of two letters each, spoken by a black clergyman during the civil rights crusade of the 60s, are my guide to the future: "If it is to be, it is up to me." Only with this in mind can change occur.

SINCOFF, MICHAEL Z., human resources and marketing professional; b. Washington, D.C., June 28, 1943; s. Murray P. and Anna F. (Jaffe) S. m. Kathleen M. Dunham, Oct. 9, 1983. B.A. U. Md., 1964, MA, 1966; PhD, Purdue U., 1969. Instr. U. Tenn., Knoxville, 1968; asst. prof. Ohio U., Athens, 1969-74, dir. Ctr. for Comm. Studies, 1969-76, assoc. prof., 1974-76; vis. prof. U. Minn., St. Paul, 1974; dir. personnel devel. Celanese Corp., N.Y., 1976-79; dir. employee comm. The Mead Corp., Dayton, Ohio, 1979-81, dir. edn., tng., 1981-83; assoc. dean Sch. of Bus. Adminstrn. Georgetown U., Washington, 1983-84; v.p. human resources ADVO-System, Inc., Hartford, 1984-87; v.p. human resources, corp. officer DIMAC Direct Inc. (formerly Direct Mail Corp. Am.), St. Louis, 1987-88; sr. v.p. human resources and adminstrn., corp. officer, sec., asst. treas., exec. com. DIMAC Corp. (parent of DIMAC Direct Inc.), St. Louis, 1988—. Author, editor human resources sect. Am. Mgmt. Assn. Mgmt. Handbook, 3d edit., 1994; author approximately 50 books and articles; mem. edtl. adv. bd. Jour. Applied Comm. Rsch., 1991—. Life mem. Internat. Comm. Assn. (bus. mgr.-exec. sec. 1969-73, fin. com. 1982-85); mem. Am. Mgmt. Assn. (human resources coun. 1990—), Direct Mktg. Assn., Printing Industries of Am. (employer resources group 1989—).

SINDELAR, WILLIAM FRANCIS, surgeon, researcher; b. Cleve., Mar. 13, 1945; s. William Frank and Josephine Ann (Storkan) S.; m. Aleta Beth Merkel, May 8, 1982 (div. July 7, 1987). A.B., Western Res. U., 1967; M.A., Case Western Res. U., 1968, Ph.D., 1970, M.D., 1971. Diplomate Am. Bd. Surgery. Instr. Marine Biol. Lab., Woods Hole, Mass., 1966-67; fellow in biology Western Res. U., Cleve., 1966-67; fellow in surgery Johns Hopkins U., Balt., 1971-73; clin. assoc. Nat. Cancer Inst., Bethesda, Md., 1973-75, sr. investigator, 1977—; fellow in surgery U. Md., Balt., 1975-77, cons. in surgery, 1980-91. Contbr. articles to profl. jours., chpts. to books. NSF grantee; NIH grantee; recipient President's Scholar award Western Res. U., 1967, Thwing Throphy Leadership award Western Res. U., 1967, J.D. Lane Research award USPHS Profl. Assn., 1983, Brian Bednarz Lectureship Worcester Meml. Hosp., 1983, Curtis Lectureship Dartmouth Med. Sch., 1990. Fellow ACS, Internat. Coll. Surgeons; mem. AAAS, Am. Assn. Cancer Research, Am. Fedn. for Clin. Rsch., Am. Pancreatic Assn., Am. Radium Soc., Am. Soc. Cell Biology, Am. Soc. Clin. Oncology, Am. Soc. for Microbiology, Assn. Acad. Surgery, Assn. Mil. Surgeons of U.S., Commn. Officers Assn. of USPHS, Internat. Assn. Pancreatology, Internat. Hepatobiliary Pancreatic Assn., Internat. Photodynamic Assn., Johns Hopkins Med. and Surg. Assn., N.Y. Acad. Scis., Pancreas Club, Res. Officers Assn. of U.S., Soc. Surgery of Alimentary Tract, Soc. Surgical Oncology, Soc. Univ. Surgeons, Southeastern Surg. Congress, So. Assn. for Oncology, So. Med. Assn., Univ. Md. Surg. Soc., Phi Beta Kappa, Alpha Omega Alpha, Omicron Delta Kappa, Pi Delta Epsilon, Phi Rho Sigma. Republican. Roman Catholic. Home: 8009 York Rd Baltimore MD 21204-7025 Office: NIH Nat Cancer Inst Surgery Brg Bethesda MD 20892

SINDEN, HARRY, professional hockey team executive; b. Collins Bay, Ont., Can., Sept. 14, 1932; m. Eleanor Sinden; children: Nancy, Carol, Dawn, Julie. Player Hull-Ottawa Eastern Pro League hockey team; player-coach Kingston team, from 1961; coach numerous teams Central League, until 1967; coach Boston Bruins, Nat. Hockey League team, 1966-70, mng. dir., from 1972, now pres., gen. mgr., alt. gov.; TV hockey commentator, 1970-72; coach Team Can., 1973, Stanley Cup team, 1970. Office: Boston Bruins 150 Causeway St Boston MA 02114-1310*

SINDLER, ROBERT BRIAN, state legislator, veterinarian; b. Sumter, S.C., Aug. 1, 1952; s. Allan Jay and Sophie (Payeff) S. BS, Clemson U., 1975; DVM, U. Ga., 1977. Track veterinarian Seminole Harness Raceway, Casselberry, Fla., 1978-80, Seminole Greyhound Park, Casselberry, 1980-84; veterinarian North Orange Animal Hosp., Apopka, Fla., 1977-86, Broadway Animal Hosp., Oviedo, Fla., 1987-88; lectr., univ. veterinarian U. Ctrl. Fla., Orlando, 1985-86; mem. Fla. Ho. of Reps., Tallahassee, 1988—. With USAR, 1987—. Named Child Adv. of Yr., Children's Home Soc., 1991, Orlando, Fla. Juvenile Legislator of Yr. dept. criminal justice U. Ctrl. Fla., Outstanding Fla. Humane Legislator, Humane Soc. U.S., 1992. Mem. AVMA, Fla. Vet. Medicine Assn. (Spl. Svc. award 1991), Apopka C. of C. (past bd. dirs.), Sertoma (past b. dirs.), Rotary (past bd. dirs. Apopka). Avocations: swimming, running, nature study. Home: 409 S Park Ave Apopka FL 32703-5261 Office: Fla Ho of Reps 20 House Ofc Bldg Tallahassee FL 32399

SINDLINGER, VERNE E., bishop. Bishop Lincoln Trails Synod, Indpls. Office: Presbyterian Church USA 1100 W 42nd St Indianapolis IN 46208-3302

SINDONI, ELIO, physics educator; b. Merate, Como, Italy, Nov. 1, 1937; s. Adolfo and Amalia (Tocco) S. Laurea in Physics, U. Milan, 1961, PhD in Nuclear Physics, 1966. Asst. U. Milan, 1961-66, assoc. prof., 1967-90; prof. U. Udine, Italy, 1990-91, prof. gen. physics, 1991—; postdoctoral fellow Princeton (N.J.) U., 1969-70; prof. environ. sci. U. Milan, 1991—; sci. sec. Internat. Sch. Plasma Physics, Piero Caldirola, Milan-Varenna, Italy, 1971-84, pres., dir., 1984—; organizer, chmn. various internat. meetings on relationships between sci., philosophy, theology, art and ethics. Author: Electromagnetismo I and II, 1976, Il Fuoco della Fusione, 1984; editor various courses and workshops and confs.; editor: (book) Third Millennium: Man, His Limits and His Hopes, 1995; contbr. over 60 rsch. papers on plasma physics, thermonuclear fusion. Mem. Italian Phys. Soc., Am. Phys. Soc. Roman Catholic. Avocation: classical music. Home: Via Della Sila 15, 20131 Milan Italy Office: Dept Environ Scis U Milan, Via Emanueli 15, 20126 Milan Italy

SINEATH, TIMOTHY WAYNE, library educator, university dean; b. Jacksonville, Fla., May 21, 1940; s. Holcombe Asbury and Christine Marcel (Cook) S.; m. Patricia Ann Greenwood, June 8, 1962; children: Philip Greenwood, Paul Byron. B.A., Fla. State U., 1962, M.S., 1963; Ph.D. (Higher Edn. Act fellow), U. Ill., 1970. Reference librarian U. Ga., 1963-64, catalog librarian, 1964-66; acad. coordinator continuing edn. in library sci. U. Ill., 1966-68; asst. prof. library sci. Simmons Coll., 1970-74, coordinator doctoral program, 1974-77; prof., dean Coll. Library Sci. and Info. Sci., U. Ky., Lexington, 1977—; cons. to libraries, schs., chs., industry; mem. Lexington (Ky.) Public Library Bd., 1978—. Author profl. reports; contbr. articles on library and info. sci., gen. info. mgmt., organizational and small group behavior to profl. jours. Mem. ALA, Am. Soc. Info. Sci., Assn. for Libr. and Info. Sci. Edn. (pres. 1993). Episcopalian. Home: 3418 Bay Leaf Dr Lexington KY 40502-3804 Office: U Ky MI King Bldg Lexington KY 40508-1557

SINEGAL, JAMES D., variety store wholesale business executive; b. 1936. With Fed-Mart Corp., 1954-77, exec. v.p.; v.p. Builders Enporium, 1977-78; exec. v.p. Price Co., 1978-79; with Sinegal/Chamberlin & Assocs., 1979-83; pres., chief oper. officer Costco Wholesale Corp., 1983—, chief exec. officer, 1988—, bd. dirs. Office: Costco Wholesale Corp 10809 120th Ave NE Kirkland WA 98033-5024*

SINEX, FRANCIS MAROTT, biochemist, educator; b. Indpls., Jan. 11, 1923; s. Francis Herr and Helen Myrtilla (Marott) S.; m. Virginia Hofer, 1948 (dec.); 1 dau., Katherine; m. Joan S. Martin, May 19, 1951; children—Ellen Jane, Margaret Ann. A.B., DePauw U., 1944; M.A., Ind. U., 1946; Ph.D., Harvard, 1950. Exec. officer biochemistry div., med. dept. Brookhaven Nat. Lab., Upton, N.Y., 1952-57; chmn. dept. biochemistry Boston U. Sch. Medicine, 1957-77; co-dir. Gerontology Center, 1974-77, head bio-med. gerontology sect., 1977—. Pres. Eastern Mass. Alzheimer Disease and Related Disorders Soc., 1980-89. Fellow Gerontol. Soc. (pres. 1969-70); mem. Soc. Biol. Chemists. Home: T8 60 Glen Rd Brookline MA 02146 Office: 80 E Concord St Boston MA 02118-2394

SINFELT, JOHN HENRY, chemist; b. Munson, Pa., Feb. 18, 1931; s. Henry Gustave and June Lillian (McDonald) S.; m. Muriel Jean Vadersen, July 14, 1956; 1 son, Klaus Herbert. B.S., Pa. State U., 1951; Ph.D., U. Ill., 1954, D.Sc. (hon.), 1981. Research engr. Exxon Research Engring. Co., Linden, N.J., 1954-57; sr. research engr. Exxon Research Engring. Co., 1957-62, research assoc., 1962-68, sr. research assoc., 1968-72, sci. advisor, 1972-79, sr. sci. advisor, 1979—; vis. prof. chem. engring. U. Minn., 1969; Lacey lectr. Calif. Inst. Tech., 1973; Reilly lectr. U. Notre Dame, 1974; Frontiers in Chemistry lectr. Case-Western Res. U., 1978; Matthew Van Winkle lectr. U. Tex., 1979; Francois Gault lectr. catalysis Coun. Europe Rsch. Group Catalysis, 1980; Mobay lectr. in chemistry U. Pitts., 1980; disting. vis. lectr. in chemistry U. Tex., 1981; Robert A. Welch Found. lectr. Confs. on Chem. Rsch., 1981; Camille and Henry Dreyfus lectr. UCLA, 1982; Edward Clark Lee Meml. lectr. U. Chgo., 1983; disting. vis. lectr. U. Alberta, Can., 1983; Dow disting. lectr. in chemistry Mich. State U., 1984; Arthur D. Little lectr. Northeastern U., 1985; Vollmer W. Fries lectr. Rensselaer Poly. Inst., 1986; disting. lectr. Ctr. Chem. Physics U. Fla., 1988; David M. Mason lectr. Stanford U., 1995. Contbr. articles to sci. jours. Recipient Dickson prize Carnegie-Mellon U., 1977, Internat. prize for new materials Am. Phys. Soc., 1978, Nat. medal of Sci., 1979, Perkin medal in chemistry Soc. Chem. Industry, 1984, Disting. Alumnus award Pa. State U., 1985; named to N.J. Inventors Hall of Fame, 1991. Fellow AIChE (Alpha Chi Sigma award 1971, Profl. Progress award 1975), Am. Acad. Arts and Scis., Am. Inst. Chemists (Chem. Pioneer award 1981, Gold medal 1984); mem. Am. Chem. Soc. (Carothers lectr. Del. sect. 1982, Petroleum Chemistry award 1976 Murphree award 1986), Catalysis Soc. (Emmett award 1973), Am. Philos. Soc., Nat. Acad. Scis., Nat. Acad. Engring. Methodist. Achievements include introduction and development of concept of bimetallic clusters as catalysts; invention of polymetallic cluster catalysts used commercially in petroleum reforming. Office: Exxon Research Engineering Co Clinton Township Route 22 East Annandale NJ 08801

SING, WILLIAM BENDER, lawyer; b. Houston, Oct. 16, 1947; s. William Bender Sr. and Alice Irene (Detmers) S.; m. Doris Anne Spradley, Sept. 1, 1967; children: Erin Elaine, Emily Elizabeth. BS cum laude, U. Houston, 1968, JD magna cum laude, 1971. Bar: Tex. 1971. Assoc. Fulbright & Jaworski, LLP, Houston, 1973-80, ptnr., 1980—. Elder St. Andrew's Presbyn. Ch., Houston; past pres., bd. dirs. St. Andrew's Presbyn. Sch., Houston; past pres. Houston C.C. Place Civic Assn. 1st lt. U.S. Army, 1971-73. Mem. ABA, Tex. Bar Assn., Houston Bar Assn., Phi Delta Phi, Phi Kappa Phi, Order of the Baron's Law Honor Soc., Phi Delta Phi, Phi Kappa Phi, Omicron Delta Epsilon. Presbyterian. Avocation: reading history and literature. Office: Fulbright & Jaworski LLP 1301 McKinney St Houston TX 77010-3095

SINGEL, MARK STEPHEN, state official; b. Johnstown, Pa., Sept. 12, 1953; s. Stephen and Jean Ann (Mertle) S.; m. Jacqueline Lynn Schonek; children: Allyson Jean, Jonathan Albert, Christopher Mark. BA, Pa. State U., 1974, postgrad., 1975; postgrad., George Washington U., 1979. Legis. intern Pa. Ho. of Reps., 1972-73; legis. asst. to U.S. Rep. Helen S. Meyner, 1975; adminstrv. asst. to U.S. Rep. Helen S. Mayner, 1976-79, to U.S. Rep. Peter A. Peyser, 1979; U.S. senator from Pa., 1980-87; lt. gov. State of Pa., 1987—, acting gov., 1993; Chmn. Pa. Energy Office, Pa. Emergency Mgmt. Coun., Pa. Heritage Affairs Commn.; mem. Pa. Econ. Devel. Partnership Bd.; trustee Pa. State U.; mem. Nat. Gov.'s Task Force on Hazardous Materials; mem. adv. bd. U. Pitts.-Johnstown, Indiana U. of Pa.; bd. dirs. Johnstown Flood Mus. Recipient Man of Yr. award Archdiocese of Pitts. Byzantine Rite, 1982, Community Achievement award Johnstown Lodge 214 Order Italian Sons and Daughters Am., 1986, Disting. Svc. award Pa. Industries for Blind and Handicapped, 1988, Humanitarian award Chapel of Four Chaplains, Valley Forge, 1990. Mem. adv. bd. U. Pitts.-Johnstown, Indiana U. of Pa.; bd. dirs. Johnstown Flood Mus. Recipient Man of Yr. award Archdiocese of Pitts. Byzantine Rite, 1982. Mem. Cambria County Young Dems., Travelers Protective Assn., Johnstown Sportsmen's Assn., Greek Catholic Union, Elks, Pi Kappa Phi (alumni bd. dirs.), Phi Kappa Phi, Omicron Delta Kappa. Democrat. Office: Office of Lt Gov 200 Main Capitol Bldg Harrisburg PA 17120-0022

SINGER, ALLEN MORRIS, lawyer; b. Mpls., Dec. 30, 1923; s. William and Ida (Simenstein) S. JD, U. Chgo., 1948; LLM, Harvard U., 1958. Bar: Ill. 1948, Calif. 1949. Sole practice, 1950-55, 59—; v.p., sec., gen. counsel Am. Bldg. Maintenance Industries, San Francisco, 1969-85; assoc. prof. law U. Oreg., 1955-59; lectr. law Stanford, 1960-62; of counsel Cooper, White & Cooper, San Francisco, 1970—. Contbr. articles to profl. jours. Mem. U. Chgo. Nat. Alumni Cabinet, 1978-80. Served as 2d lt., USAAF, 1943-45. Mem. ABA, San Francisco Bar Assn., Calif. Bar Assn., Am. Arbitration Assn. (nat. panel of arbitrators). Home: 1070 Green St Apt 703 San Francisco CA 94133-3677 Office: Cooper White & Cooper 201 California St Fl 17 San Francisco CA 94111-5001

SINGER, ARMAND EDWARDS, foreign language educator; b. Detroit, Nov. 30, 1914; s. Elvin Satori Singer and Fredericka Elizabeth (Edwards) Singer Goetz; m. Mary Rebecca White, Aug. 8, 1940; 1 child, Fredericka Ann Hill. A.B. Amherst Coll., 1935; M.A., Duke U., 1939, Ph.D., 1944; diplôme, Université de Paris, 1939; postgrad., Ind. U., summer 1964. Teaching fellow in sci. Amherst Coll., 1935-36; instr. French and Spanish, part-time Duke, 1938-40; teaching fellow Romance langs. W.Va. U., Morgantown, 1940-41, instr., 1941-47, asst. prof., 1947-55, assoc. prof., 1955-60, prof., 1960-80, prof. emeritus, 1980—; chmn. program for humanities, 1963-72, chmn. dept. integrated studies, 1963, acting chmn. dept. religion and program for humanities, 1973, dir. W.Va. U. ann. colloquium on modern lit., 1976-80, 85-86. Author: A Bibliography of the Don Juan Theme: Versions and Criticism, 1954, The Don Juan Theme, Versions and Criticism: An Annotated Bibliography, 1965, Paul Bourget, 1976, The Don Juan Theme: A Bibliography of Versions, Analogues, Uses, and Adaptations, 1993, The Armand E. Singer Tibet 1809-1975, 1995; co-author: (with J.F. Stasny) Anthology of Readings: Humanities I, 1966, Anthology of Readings: Humanities II, 1967; editor: (with Jürgen E. Schlunk) Martin Walser: International Perspectives, 1987; editor W.Va. U. Philol. Papers, 1948-50, 53-55, editor in chief, 1951-52, 55—; editor, contbr. Essays on the Literature of Mountaineering, 1982; contbr. numerous articles to profl. and philatelic jours. Bd. dirs. Community Concert Assn., Morgantown, 1959-60, Humanities Found. W.Va., 1981-87. Recipient 4th Ann. Humanities award W.Va. Humanities Coun., 1990. Mem. MLA (internat. bibliography com. 1956-59, nat. del. assembly 1975-78), So. Atlantic MLA (exec. com. 1971-74), Am. Assn. Tchrs. Spanish and Portuguese, Am. Philatelic Soc., Nepal and Tibet Philatelic Study Circle, Nepal Philatelic Soc., Collectors Club of N.Y., Phi Beta Kappa. Republican. Home: 248 Grandview Ave Morgantown WV 26505-6925 In an age of deteriorating standards, I want to be counted among those educators who stand against the tide. We ask too little of others, we ask too little of ourselves; others ask too little of us. When we constantly encounter shoddy construction, shoddy merchandise, shoddy performances, shoddy ethics, shoddy education, we may be tempted to forswear our standards. But through our hands pass tomorrow's leaders. As teachers we must help stop this erosion of our national pride. If we fail, make no mistake: it could well destroy us all.

SINGER, ARTHUR LOUIS, JR., foundation executive; b. Scranton, Pa., Feb. 14, 1929; s. Arthur and Isabel S.; m. Joan Cristal, June 26, 1952; children—Arthur, Philip, Charles. A.B., Williams Coll., 1950; M.B.A., U. Mich., 1952. Adminstr. Mass. Inst. Tech., 1955-63; exec. asso. (Carnegie Corp.), N.Y.C., 1963-66; pres. Edn. Devel. Center, Newton, Mass., 1966-68; v.p. Alfred P. Sloan Found., N.Y.C., 1968-94, cons., 1994—. Served to lt. (j.g.) USNR, 1952-55. Home: 23 Owenoke Park Westport CT 06880-6834 Office: 630 5th Ave Ste 2550 New York NY 10111-0001

SINGER, BURTON HERBERT, statistics educator; b. Chgo., June 12, 1938; married; 3 children. B.S., Case Inst. Tech., 1959, M.S., 1961; Ph.D. in Stats., Stanford U., 1967. From asst. to assoc. prof. stats. Columbia U., N.Y.C., 1967-77, prof. math. stats., 1977-85, chmn. dept. math. stats., 1985-89; then chmn. biostats., then chmn. and assoc. dean pub. health dept. epidemiology and pub. health Yale U., New Haven, 1989-91, chmn. epidemiology and pub. health, 1991-93, Ira Vaughan Hiscock prof. epidemiology and pub. health, 1991-94, prof. econs. and stats. dept. epidemiology and pub. health, 1991-94; prof. demography and pub. affairs Princeton (N.J.) U., 1994—; research assoc. statistician Princeton U., 1972-73. Mem. AAAS, Nat. Acad. Scis., Am. Statis. Assn., Psychometric Soc. Office: Princeton Univ Office Population Rsch 21 Prospect Ave Princeton NJ 08544-2091

SINGER, CECILE DORIS, state legislator. BA, Queens Coll. Past rep. Spl. Svcs. for Children, N.Y.C.; past exec. dir. N.Y. State Assembly Social Svcs. and Judiciary Coms., Joint Legis. Com. on Corps., Authorities and Commns.; past pub. rep. Yonkers (N.Y.) Emergency Control Bd.; past coord. Westchester County Assembly Dels.; past chief of staff for dep. minority leader; mem. N.Y. State Assembly, Albany, 1988—, leadership sec. Rep. Conf., mem. assembly children & families com., mem. various other coms.; past rep. Temp. Commn. To Revise Social Svcs. Law; mem. Presdl. Commn. on Privacy Conf., N.Y. State Senate Transp. Conf.; mem. task force on substance abuse Am. Legis. Exch. Coun., task force on econ. devel., on crime victim's rights, on hosp. crisis, on women's issues, com. on mass. transit; sec. Rep. Conf. Nat. Adv. Panel Child Care Action Campaign. Mem. adv. bd. Legal Awareness for Women, Big Bros. and Big Sisters; mem. task force on certiorari Westchester County Sch. Bds. Assn.; sch. and community chmn. Yonkers PTA; bd. dirs. Yonkers Gen. Hosp., Yonkers chpt. United Jewish Appeal. Recipient Jenkins Meml. award, Nat. PTA award. Mem. Mental Health Assn. (bd. dirs., mem. nominating and pub. affairs coms. Westchester County chpt.), Rotary. Home: 117 Cliffside Dr Yonkers NY 10710-3144 Office: NY State Assembly Lob Rm 720 Albany NY 12248

SINGER, CRAIG, broker, consultant, investor; b. N.Y.C., Aug. 13, 1947; s. Albert and Dorothy (Blackman) S.; m. Ellen Rappaport, Aug. 31, 1969; children: Chad Adam, Cara Danielle. BS, Cornell U., 1969; JD, Columbia U., 1972. Bar: N.Y. 1973. Exec. Continental Wingate Co., Inc., N.Y.C., 1972-74; exec. v.p. Integrated Resources, Inc., N.Y.C., 1974-87; chmn. bd. Integrated Resources Housing Corp., Integrated Funding, Inc., Resources Funding Corp., AIM Capital Mgmt. Corp., 1983-87; cons., investor, broker, Bedford, N.Y., 1989—; pres. Westminster Fin. Group, Inc., 1989—. Former dir. Assn. Govt. Assisted Housing, Inc., 1976-84; former mem. exec. com. Coalition for Low and Moderate Income Housing; former mem. edn. adv. bd. Bur. Nat. Affairs Housing and Devel. Reporter. Home and Office: 148 Meeting House Rd RFD 4 Bedford Corners NY 10549

SINGER, DANIEL MORRIS, lawyer; b. Bklyn., Oct. 10, 1930; s. Samuel W. and Fannie G. (Sabloff) S.; m. Maxine Frank, June 15, 1952; children—Amy E., Ellen R., David B., Stephanie F. B.A. with honors, Swarthmore Coll., 1951; LL.B., Yale U., 1954. Bar: N.Y. 1956, U.S. Dist. Ct. D.C. 1957, U.S. Ct. Appeals (D.C. cir.) 1957, U.S. Supreme Ct., 1959. Motions clk. U.S. Ct. Appeals D.C. Cir., 1956-57, law clk. to Judge George T. Washington, 1957-58; assoc. Fried, Frank, Harris, Shriver & Jacobson, Washington, 1958-64, ptnr., 1965-87, counsel, 1987—; arbitrator complex comml. case and constrn. nat. panels; mediator US Dist. Ct., Washington; vol. atty. Lawyers Com. for Civil Rights Under Law, 1965, 66; mem. exec. com. Washington Lawyers Com. for Civil Rights Under Law, 1973—; bd. mgrs. Swarthmore Coll., 1987-91. Bd. dirs., sec.-treas. Nat. Com. Tithing in Investment, 1964-65; dir. sec.-treas. Council for a Livable World, 1962-64; mem. gov. council, exec. com. Am. Jewish Congress, 1986—, v.p. 1988-92; dir. Am. Soc. for the Protection of Nature in Israel, 1986—. With Signal Corps, U.S. Army, 1954-56. Mem. ABA, D.C. Bar. Home: 5410 39th St NW Washington DC 20015-2902 Office: Fried Frank Harris Shriver 1001 Pennsylvania Ave NW Ste 800 Washington DC 20004-2505

SINGER, DAVID MICHAEL, marketing and public relations company executive; b. Bklyn., Feb. 11, 1957; s. Seymour Allen and Ellen Sybil (Pavnick) S.; m. Pamela Rae Silton, July 20, 1986; 1 child, Max Ira Benjamin. BA in History, NYU, 1978; MA in Communications, Syracuse U., 1979; MA in Media, New Sch. Social Research, 1983; JD, Yeshiva U., 1981. Cons. pub. rels. Burson-Marsteller, N.Y.C., 1979-81, The Haas Group, N.Y.C. 1981-84; Braff & Co., N.Y.C., 1987-89; pub., editor-in-chief Lodestone Pub., N.Y.C., 1984-87; chief oper. officer Pentagon Ltd., N.Y.C., 1989-91; v.p. pub. rels. Braff & Co., N.Y.C., 1991-92; v.p. G.S. Schwartz & Co., N.Y.C., 1993—; lectr. evening div. NYU, 1982—; dir. media rels. Braff & Co. Contbr. articles and poems to profl. and consumer jours. and mags. Pres. Jewish Cultural Found., N.Y.C., 1976. Named Mem. of Yr., N.Y. State Kiwanis, 1976, Outstanding Young Man of Am., Jaycees, 1977; recipient Cert. Recognition Am. Film Inst., 1982, ANDY Design award Advt. Club N.Y., 1983, Proclamation Bklyn. Borough Pres., 1987. Mem. Alpha Epsilon Pi (Bro. of Yr. 1976). Avocations: baseball, politics, ping-pong, films, theater.

SINGER, DAVID VINCENT, bottling company executive; b. Northumberland, Pa., June 18, 1955; s. Harold William and Dolores Elizabeth (Galonian) S.; m. Barbara Brown, Feb. 19, 1983; children: Brian, Andrew. BS, Pa. State U., 1977, MBA, 1979. Mgmt. trainee Mellon Bank, Pitts., 1979-81, corp. fin./lending officer, 1981-86; v.p. treas. Coca-Cola Bottling Co. Consol., Charlotte, N.C., 1986-87; v.p., chief fin. officer Coca-Cola Bottling Co. Consol., Charlotte, 1987—. Avocation: golf. Home:

10221 Balmoral Cir Charlotte NC 28210-7836 Office: Coca-Cola Bottling Co 1900 Rexford Rd Charlotte NC 28211-3440

SINGER, DONALD IVAN, architect; b. Trenton, N.J., Feb. 20, 1938; s. Harold William and Beatrice (Lavine) S.; m. Elaine Ruth Segall, Aug. 23, 1959; children: Lauren Elizabeth, Susan Meredith. BArch, U. Fla., 1960; MS in Architecture, Columbia U., 1961. Registered architect, Fla. Draftsman Charles Reed, Jr. Architect, Hollywood, Fla., 1961-62; pvt. practice architecture Ft. Lauderdale, 1964—; mem. design adv. bd. Formica Corp., N.Y.C., 1977-82, design critique com. Dade County Aviation Authority, Miami, Fla., 1987-89. Prin. works include office bldg. R.J. Pavlik Corp. Hdqrs., 1980 (honor award Fla. Assn. AIA 1981), City Pk. Urban Pla. and Garage, Ft. Lauderdale, Fla., 1982 (honor award Fla. Assn. AIA 1983), office bldg. Fire Prevention Bur., 1987 (honor award Fla. Assn. AIA 1987), prototype sch. Forest Glen Middle Sch., 1989 (Fla. Concrete Assn. award 1990). Pres. Downtown Coun., Ft. Lauderdale, 1980-81; trustee Mus. Art, Ft. Lauderdale, 1980-85; vice chmn. Riverwalk Com., Ft. Lauderdale, 1989-91; chmn. Art-in-Pub. Places Com., Broward County, Fla., 1990-91; chmn. Design Broward, 1994-95. With USAF, 1961-62. Recipient Morretti award Cultural Affairs Coun. of Broward County, 1983, Disting. Alumni award Sch. Architecture, U. Fla., 1991. Fellow AIA; mem. Fla. Assn. AIA (honor award for design 1984, chmn. conf. com. 1986-87, chmn. design awards com. 1988-89). Republican. Jewish. Avocation: photography. Office: 13 W Las Olas Blvd Fort Lauderdale FL 33301-1823

SINGER, ELEANOR, sociologist, editor; b. Vienna, Austria, Mar. 4, 1930; came to U.S., 1938; d. Alfons and Anna (Troedl) Schwarzbart; m. Alan Gerard Singer, Sept. 8, 1949; children: Emily Ann, Lawrence Alexander. BA, Queens Coll., 1951; PhD, Columbia U., 1966. Asst. editor Am. Scholar, Williamsburg, Va., 1951-52; editor Tchrs. Coll. Press, N.Y.C., 1952-56, Dryden-Holt, N.Y.C., 1956-57; rsch. assoc., sr. rsch. assoc., sr. rsch. scholar Columbia U., N.Y.C., 1966-94; rsch. scientist Inst. for Social Rsch. U. Mich., Ann Arbor, 1994—; editor Pub. Opinion Quar., N.Y.C., 1975-86. Author: (with Carol Weiss) The Reporting of Social Science in the Mass Media, 1988, (with Phyllis Endreny) Reporting On Risk, 1993; editor: (with Herbert H. Hyman) Readings in Reference Group Theory and Research, 1968, (with Stanley Presser) Survey Research Methods: A Reader, 1989; contbr. articles to profl. jours. Mem. Am. Assn. Pub. Opinion Research (pres. N.Y.C. chpt. 1983-84, pres. 1987-88), Am. Sociol. Assn., Am. Statis. Assn. Office: U Mich Inst Social Rsch Box 1248 Survey Rsch Ctr Ann Arbor MI 48106

SINGER, EMEL, staffing industry executive; b. Gaziantep, Turkey, Apr. 7, 1944; came to U.S., 1960; d. Mehmet Resit and Nesrin (Kescioglu) Tuzun; m. James Michael Singer, Apr. 28, 1968 (dec. 1987); children: Justin Michael, Jodi Michelle. BBA, Bradley U., 1968. Adminstrv. asst. U. Ky. Med. Ctr., Lexington, 1968; exec. sec. Hoffman Products/Cortron Industries, Chgo., 1968-70; co-founder, adminstr. Banner Personnel Svc., Inc., Chgo., 1970-87, chmn., CEO, 1988—; founder Banner Technical Staffing, 1995—, Clayton Singer Assocs., 1995—; guest speaker Chgo. Entrepenurship Program, U. Ill., Chgo., 1993, 94, 95. Parents bd. Bradley U., Peoria, Ill., 1989-90, assoc. trustee, 1992—; alumni master, 1993, Bradley coun., 1993—. Listed in features Chgo. Bus. as a Top Woman-Owned Firm, 1989, 90, 91; finalist Entrpreneur of the Year award Ernst & Young, Inc. magazine, Merrill Lynch, 1993, 94; named to Entrepreneurship Hall of Fame, 1993. Mem. Nat. Assn. Pers. Svcs., Nat. Assn. Temp. Svcs., Ill. Assn. Pers. Svcs., Ill. Assn. Temporary Svcs. Avocations: skiing, scuba diving, traveling, gardening. Home: 165 Maple Hill Rd Glencoe IL 60022-1252 Office: Banner Personnel Svc Inc 122 S Michigan Ave Chicago IL 60603

SINGER, FRANK J., insurance company executive, lawyer; b. N.Y.C., Mar. 12, 1944; s. Frank James and Margaretta (Barnes) S.; m. Christine Heins, Feb. 14, 1987; children: Frank, Blake, Cole, Deborah, Victoria. BS, Calif. Western U., 1983, MBA, 1987; JD, La Salle U., 1994. Cert. ins. counselor. Sales mgr. Liberty Mut. Ins. Co., Boston, 1963-74; v.p. Sentry Ins., Stevens Point, Wis., 1974-87; pres., CFO Comml. Acceptance Ins. Co., Sacramento, 1987—; chmn., CFO, Artisan Contractors Ins. Am., Sacramento, 1989—. With U.S. Army, 1962-65. Mem. Mensa. Republican. Office: Comml Acceptance Ins Co 2150 Professional Dr Ste 170 Roseville CA 95661-3732

SINGER, FREDERICK RAPHAEL, medical researcher, educator; b. St. Louis, June 27, 1939; s. Meyer and Lee (Minkle) S.; m. Sandra Joy Barnes, Aug. 16, 1964; children: Stefanie, Jeffrey. Student UCLA, 1956-59; BS, U. Calif.-Berkeley, 1960; MD, U. Calif.-San Francisco, 1963. Diplomate Am. Bd. Internal Medicine, Am. Bd. Endocrinology and Metabolism. Intern UCLA Affiliated Hosp., 1963-64; resident VA Hosp., Los Angeles, 1964-65, 68-69; instr. in medicine Harvard U., Boston, 1971-72; asst. prof. medicine UCLA, 1972-73; asst. prof. medicine U. So. Calif., L.A., 1973-74, assoc. prof., 1974-78, prof., 1978-89, prof. orthopaedic surgery, 1980-89; dir. Bone Ctr. Cedars-Sinai Med. Ctr., L.A., 1989-92; prof. medicine, UCLA, 1989-92, clin. prof. medicine, 1993—; dir. Osteoporosis/Metabolic Bone Disease program St. Johns Hosp. and Health Ctr., Santa Monica, 1992—; dir. Skeletal Biology Lab, John Wayne Cancer Inst., Santa Monica, 1992—; mem. endocrine and metabolic drug adv. com. FDA, USPHS, Bethesda, Md., 1983-87. Author: Paget's Disease of Bone, 1977. Contbr. numerous articles, revs. to profl. jours. Vice chmn. community adv. com. Univ. High Sch., L.A., 1984. Served as capt. USAF, 1965-67. Calif. State scholar, 1956-60; clin. investigator VA, 1971-73. Mem. Endocrine Soc., Am. Soc. Clin. Investigation, Am. Soc. Bone and Mineral Research (chmn. pub. affairs 1981-86, coun. 1987, pres.-elect 1989, pres. 1990), Paget's Disease Found. (chmn. bd. dirs. 1990—). Office: John Wayne Cancer Inst 2200 Santa Monica Blvd Santa Monica CA 90404

SINGER, GARY JAMES, lawyer; b. L.A., Oct. 8, 1952; s. Stanley Merle and Ernestine Alice (Brandstattir) S.; m. Melanie Carol Rabin, Mar. 19, 1978; children: Brian, Kimberly, Andrew. BA, U. Calif., Irvine, 1974; JD, Loyola U., 1977. Bar: Calif. 1977, U.S. Dist. Ct. (fed. dist.) 1978. Assoc. O'Melveny & Myers, Newport Beach, Calif., 1977-84; ptnr. O'Melveny & Myers, 1985—; bd. dirs. Irvine Theatre. Avocations: golf, skiing, reading. Office: O'Melveny & Myers 610 Newport Center Dr Newport Beach CA 92660-6419

SINGER, GERALD MICHAEL, lawyer, educator, author, arbitrator and mediator; b. Mpls., Sept. 9, 1920; s. Charles and Rachael Caroline (Feldman) S.; m. Lillian Kaplan, July 10, 1944; children: Barbara Ellen, Alan Mark. JD, Loyola U., L.A., 1968. Bar: Calif. 1969, U.S. Dist. Ct. Calif. (so dist.) 1969, U.S. Ct. Appeals (9th cir.) 1969, U.S. Supreme Ct. 1972. Pres. Bigg of Calif., Inc., 1948-69; pvt. practice, Encino, Calif., 1969—; adj. prof. law Loyola U., 1975-85, 92; judge pro tem Calif. Superior Ct., 1973—; arbitrator, 1976—; judge pro tem Calif. Mcpl. Ct., 1973—; arbitrator, mediator, 1988—; sr. panel mem. AAA Comml. Arbitrators, L.A., Internat. Arbitration World Ct., The Hague; lectr. to various law schs., bar assns. and legal groups, 1976—. Author: How To Go Directly Into Solo Law Practice (Without Missing a Meal), 1976, rev. edit. as How To Go Directly Into Your Own Computerized Solo Law Practice Without Missing a Meal (Or a Byte), 1986, updated, 1989, rev. edit. as How To Go Directly Into, and Manage, Your Own Solo Law Practice (Without Missing a Meal), 1994, 100 page supplement, 1994. Mem. Com. To Elect Ricard Nixon, Com. to Reelect Richard Nixon, Com. to Elect and Reelect Ronald Reagan, L.A. Staff sgt. Signal Corps, U.S. Army and USAAF, 1942-46. Mem. Am. Arbitration Assn. (arbitrator 1973—). Republican. Avocations: golf, sailing, horseback riding, photography, videography. Office: 16000 Ventura Blvd 5th fl Encino CA 91436-2730

SINGER, HENRY A., behavioral scientist, institute director; b. Mt. Vernon, N.Y., Apr. 13, 1919; s. A.D. and Evelyn (Zierler) S.; m. Rosina Scimonelli, Jan. 7, 1944 (dec. Jan. 1991); children: Victoria, David Anthony. BS, Columbia U., 1942; MA, NYU, 1947, PhD (Rockefeller fellow 1947-48), 1950, PhD, 1973. Instr. Human Rels. Ctr. NYU, 1948-50; assoc. prof. SUNY, Fredonia, 1950-51; adviser U.S. Mission to Philippines, 1951-54; cons. Conn. Edn. Assn., 1954-56; dir. edn. Hilton Hotel Corp., 1956-58; cons. Conn. Assn. Mental Health, 1958-59; dir. edn. Remington Rand div. Sperry Rand, 1959-62; exec. dir. Soc. Advancement Mgmt., 1963-66; higher edn. officer CUNY, 1966-68; exec. dir. Human Resources Inst. Inc., Westport, Conn., 1969—; with Diebold Inst. Pub. Policy Studies, N.Y.C., 1981-87; exec. asst. Am. Nobel Com., N.Y.C., Conn., 1947-50, vice chmn.,

1961-66, exec. officer, 1986-92, hon. chair, 1992—; vis. prof. Cornell U., 1949-83, U. Philippines, 1952-53, NYU, 1960-62, CUNY, 1962-63, Columbia U., 1963-64, Western Conn. U., 1964-70, U. Tehran, 1975, 77, Empire State Coll., SUNY, 1981; vis. prin. lectr. Hong Kong Poly., 1976-78, U. Hong Kong, 1992; sr. dir. Experience Compression Lab., Barnum Internat., 1960-93. Editor: Connecticut Teacher, 1954-56, Connecticut Mental Health News, 1958-59, Advanced Management, 1959-66; Contbr. articles to U.S. and internat. publs. Vis. expert AID mission, Spain, 1962, Internat. Human Resources, Tehran, Iran, 1965, 75, 77; assoc. dir. engring. mgmt. workshops Columbia U., 1963-66; vis. lectr. Asian Inst. for Mgmt., 1977; bd. dirs. Conn. Assn. Mental Health, 1960-62, Mohonk Home for Boys, Westport, Conn., 1981—, NYU Alumni Coun., 1990—; bd. dirs. Fairchild 1st Bank, 1994—. Recipient award Council Internat. Progress in Mgmt., 1963; Rockefeller fellow, 1948-49. Fellow Am. Soc. Applied Anthropology, Hong Kong Psych. Soc., Internat. Acad. Counseling and Psychotherapy; Mem. APA (life). Clubs: Overseas Press (gov.), Columbia U., Princeton (N.Y.C.); Fgn. Corres. (Hong Kong). Home: 1617 Bayhouse Ct 219 Sarasota FL 34231-6788 Office: One Morningside Dr N Westport CT 06880-5051 *Perhaps life teaches us that relating successfully to others is the one sure road to survival in an increasingly crowded environment. One measurement of this successful human relationship is the degree to which one human being is able to inconvenience himself for another.*

SINGER, IRVING, philosopher; b. N.Y.C., Dec. 24, 1925; s. Isidore and Nettie (Stromer) S.; m. Josephine Fisk, June 10, 1949; children—Anne, Margaret, Emily, Benjamin. AB summa cum laude, Harvard U., 1948, MA, 1949, PhD, 1952. Instr. philosophy Cornell U., 1953-56; asst. prof. U. Mich., 1956-59; vis. lectr. Johns Hopkins U., 1957-58; mem. faculty M.I.T., 1958—, prof. philosophy, 1969—. Author: Santayana's Aesthetics, 1957, The Nature of Love: Plato to Luther, 1966, rev. edit., 1984, The Goals of Human Sexuality, 1973, Mozart and Beethoven, 1977, The Nature of Love: Courtly and Romantic, 1984, The Nature of Love: The Modern World, 1987, Meaning in Life: The Creation of Value, 1992, The Pursuit of Love, 1994. Served with AUS, 1944-46. Fellow Guggenheim Found., 1965, Rockefeller Found., 1970, Bollingen Found., 1966; grantee Am. Council Learned Socs., 1966; Fulbright fellow, 1955. Mem. Am. Philos. Assn., Am. Soc. Aesthetics. Office: MIT Rm 20E210A Cambridge MA 02139

SINGER, ISADORE MANUEL, mathematician, educator; b. Detroit, May 3, 1924; married; 5 children. BS, U. Mich., 1944; MS, U. Chgo., 1948, PhD in math., 1950; ScD (hon.), Tulane U., 1981; LLD (hon.), U. Mich., 1989, U. Ill., Chgo. Moore instr. math. MIT, Cambridge, 1950-52, prof. math., 1956-70, Norbert Wiener prof., 1970-79, John D. MacArthur prof. math. (1st holder), 1983—, Inst. prof., 1987—; asst. prof. UCLA, 1952-54; vis. prof. math U. Calif., Berkeley, 1977-79, prof., 1979-83, Miller prof. math., 1982-83, prof. math., 1977-83; vis. asst. prof. math. Columbia U., N.Y.C., 1954-55; mem. Inst. Advanced Study, 1955-56; past steering com. Ctr. for Non-Linear Scis., Los Alamos Nat. Labs; adj. bd. Inst. Theoretical Physics, U. Calif., Santa Barbara; bd. dirs. Santa Fe Inst.; mem. various organizing coms. and editor proc. for confs. in field. Former editor profl. jours. Alfred P. Sloan fellow, 1959-62; Guggenheim fellow, 1968-69, 75-76; recipient Nat. Medal of Sci., 1983. Mem. NAS (past councillor, former mem. com. math. and phys. sics., other coms.), Am. Philos. Soc., Am. Acad. Arts and Scis. Am. Math. Soc. (v.p. 1970-72, past exec. com., Bocher Meml. prize 1969, Pub. Svc. award 1993), Am. Phys. Soc., Internat. Congress Mathematicians (program com. 1986, Wigner prize 1989). Office: MIT Dept Math Rm 2 174 Cambridge MA 02139

SINGER, JOEL DAVID, political science educator; b. Bklyn., Dec. 7, 1925; children: Kathryn Louise, Eleanor Anne. BA, Duke U., 1946; LLD (hon.), Northwestern U., 1983; PhD, NYU, 1956. Instr. NYU, 1954-55, Vassar Coll., 1955-57; vis. fellow social relations Harvard U., 1957-58; vis. asst. prof. U. Mich., Ann Arbor, 1958-60; sr. scientist Mental Health Research Inst. U. Mich., 1960-82, assoc. prof., 1964-65, prof. polit. sci., 1965—, coordinator World Politics Program, 1969-75, 81-90; vis. prof. U. Oslo and Inst. Social Research, 1963-64, 90, Carnegie Endowment Internat. Peace and Grd. Inst. Internat. Studies, Geneva, 1967-68, Zuma and U. Mannheim (W. Ger.), 1976, Grad. Inst. Internat. Studies, Geneva, 1983-84; cons. in field. Author: Financing International Organization: The United Nations Budget Process, 1961, Deterrence, Arms Control and Disarmament: Toward a Synthesis in National Security Policy, 1962, rev. 1984, (with Melvin Small) The Wages of War, 1816-1965: A Statistical Handbook, 1972, (with Susan Jones) Beyond Conjecture in International Politics: Abstracts of Data Based Research, 1972, (with Dorothy La Barr) The Study of International Politics: A Guide to Sources for the Student, Teacher and Researcher, 1976, Correlates of War I and II, 1979, 80, (with Melvin Small) Resort to Arms: International and Civil War, 1816-1980, 1982, Models, Methods, and Progress: A Peace Research Odyssey, 1990, (with Paul Diehl) Measuring the Correlates of War; monographs; contbr. articles to profl. jours.; mem. editorial bd. ABC: Polit. Sci. and Govt., 1968-84, Polit. Sci. Reviewer, 1971—, Conflict Mgmt. and Peace Sci., 1978—, Etudes Polemologiques, 1978—, Internat. Studies Quar., 1989—, Jour. Conflict Resolution, 1989—, Internat. Interactions, 1989—. With USNR, 1943-66. Ford fellow, 1956; Ford grantee, 1957-58; Phoenix Meml. Fund grantee, 1959-, 1981-82; Fulbright scholar, 1963-64; Carnegie Corp. research grantee, 1963-67; NSF grantee, 1967-76, 1986-89, 1992-94; Guggenheim grantee, 1978-79. Mem. Am. Polit. Sci. Assn. (Helen Dwight Reid award com. 1967, chmn. Woodrow Wilson award com., chmn. nominating com. 1970), Internt. Polit. Sci. Assn. (chmn. conflict and peace research com. 1974—), World Assn. Internat. Relations, Internat. Soc. Polit. Psychology, Internat. Soc. Research on Aggression, Social Sci. History Assn., Peace Sci. Soc., Internat. Peace Research Assn. (pres. 1972-73), Consortium on Peace Research, Edn. and Devel., AAAS, Fedn. Am. Scientists (nat. coun. 1991—), Union Concerned Scientists, Arms Control Assn., Internat. Studies Assn. (pres. 1985-86), Com. Nat. Security, Am. Com. on East-West Accord, SANE, World Federalist Assn. Office: U Mich Dept Polit Sci Ann Arbor MI 48109 *As a researcher, teacher, consultant and activist, my goal has been to bring rigorous scientific methods to bear on the causes of war question, and to encourage the integration of ethical concern and hard evidence.*

SINGER, KURT DEUTSCH, news commentator, author, publisher; b. Vienna, Austria, Aug. 10, 1911; came to U.S., 1940, naturalized, 1951; s. Ignaz Deutsch and Irene (Singer) S.; m. Hilda Tradelius, Dec. 23, 1932 (div. 1954); children: Marian Alice Birgit, Kenneth Walt; m. Jane Sherrod, Apr. 9, 1955 (dec. Jan. 1985); m. Katherine Han, Apr. 8, 1989. Student, U. Zürich, Switzerland, 1930, Labor Coll., Stockholm, Sweden, 1936; Ph.D., Div. Coll. Metaphysics, Indpls., 1951. Escaped to Sweden, 1934; founder Ossietzky Com. (successful in release Ossietzky from concentration camp); corr. Swedish mag. Folket i Bild, 1935-40; founder Niemöller Com.; pub. biography Göring in Eng. (confiscated in Sweden), 1940; co-founder pro-Allied newspaper Trots Allt, 1939; corr. Swedish newspapers in, U.S., 1940; editor News Background, 1942; lectr. U. Minn., U. Kans., U. Wis., 1945-49; radio commentator WKAT, 1950; corr. N.Am. Newspaper Alliance, N.Y.C., 1953—; pres. Singer Media Corp., 1987—; dir. Oceanic Press Service, San Clemente, Calif. Author, editor: underground weekly Mitteilungsblätter, Berlin, Germany, 1933; author: The Coming War, 1934, (biog.) Carl von Ossietzky, 1936 (Nobel Peace prize); Germany's Secret Service in Central America, 1943, Spies and Saboteurs in Argentina, 1943, Duel for the Northland, 1943, White Book of the Church of Norway, 1944, Spies and Traitors of World War II, 1945, Who are the Communists in America, 1948, 3000 Years of Espionage, 1951, World's Greatest Women Spies, 1952, Kippie the Cow; juvenile, 1952, Gentlemen Spies, 1953, The Man in the Trojan Horse, 1954, World's Best Spy Stories, 1954, Charles Laughton Story; adapted TV, motion pictures, 1954, Spy Stories and Asia, 1955, More Spy Stories, 1955, My Greatest Crime Story, 1956, My Most Famous Case, 1957, The Danny Kaye Saga; My Strangest Case, 1958, Spy Omnibus, 1959, Spies for Democracy, 1960, Crime Omnibus Spies Who Changed History, 1961, Hemmingway-Life and Death of a Giant, 1961, True Adventures in Crime, Dr. Albert Schweitzer, Medical Missionary, 1962, Lyndon Baines Johnson-Man of Reason, 1964, Ho-i-man; juveniles, 1965; Kurt Singer's Ghost Omnibus, 1965; juvenile Kurt Singer's Horror Omnibus; The World's Greatest Stories of the Occult, The Unearthly, 1965, Mata Hari-Goddess of Sin, 1965, Lyndon Johnson-From Kennedy to Vietnam, 1966, Weird Tales Anthology, 1966, I Can't Sleep at Night, 1966, Weird Tales of Supernatural, 1967, Tales of Terror, 1967, Famous Short Stories, 1967, Folktales of the South Pacific, 1967, Tales of The Uncanny, 1968, Gothic Reader, 1968, Bloch and Bradbury, 1969, Folktales of Mexico, 1969, Tales of the

Unknown, 1970, The House in the Valley, 1970, Hablan Los Artistas, 1970, Tales of the Macabre, 1971, Three Thousand Years of Espionage, 1971, El Mundo de Hoy, 1971, Cuentos Fantasticos del Mas, 1971, Aldous Huxley, El Camino al Infierno, 1971, Ghouls and Ghosts, 1972, The Unearthly, 1972, The Gothic Reader, 1972, Satanic Omnibus, 1973, The Plague of the Living Dead, 1973, Gothic Horror Omnibus, 1974, Dictionary of Household Hints and Help, 1974, Supernatural, 1974, They are Possessed, 1976, True Adventures into the Unknown, 1980, I Spied-And Survived, 1980, Great Adventures in Crime, 1982, The Oblong Box, 1982, Shriek, 1984, First Target Book of Horror, 1984, 2d, 1984, 3d, 1985, 4th, 1985, Solve A Crime, 1994, The Ultimate Quiz Book, 1994, The Complete Guide to Career Advancement, 1994, The Sex Quiz Book, 1994, The Marriage Quiz Book, The Psychology Quiz Book, The Teenage Quiz Book, Success Secrets, 1995; editor: UN Calendar, 1959-58; contbr. articles to newspapers, popular mags., U.S., fgn. countries, all his books and papers in Boston U. Library-Spl. Collections. Mem. UN Speakers Research Com., UN Children's Emergency Fund, Menninger Found. Mem. Nat. Geog. Soc., Smithsonian Assos., Internat. Platform Assn. (v.p.), United Sch. Assemblies (pres.). Address: Singer Media Corp Seaview Business Pk 1030 Calle Cordillera # 106 San Clemente CA 92673-6234 *In the sunset years of my life, I feel stronger than ever that the most important contribution one makes in a lifetime is to plant as many seeds as possible with many people, and perhaps many countries. Who knows where the seeds of ideas survive and expand?.*

SINGER, MARCUS GEORGE, philosopher, educator; b. N.Y.C., Jan. 4, 1926; s. David Emanuel and Esther (Kobre) S.; m. Blanche Ladenson, Aug. 10, 1947; children: Karen Beth, Debra Ann. A.B., U. Ill., 1948; Ph.D. (Susan Linn Sage fellow), Cornell U., 1952. Asst. in philosophy Cornell U., Ithaca, N.Y., 1948-49; instr. philosophy Cornell U., 1951-52; instr. philosophy U. Wis.-Madison, 1952-55, asst. prof., 1955-59, assoc. prof., 1959-63, prof. philosophy, 1963-92, prof. emeritus, 1992—, chmn. dept. philosophy, 1963-68; chmn. philosophy dept. U. Wis. Center System, 1964-66; dir. pub. lectr. series Royal Inst. Philosophy, London, 1984-85; vis. fellow Birkbeck Coll., U. London, 1962-63; research assoc. U. Calif.-Berkeley, 1969; vis. Cowling prof. philosophy Carleton Coll., Northfield, Minn., 1972; vis. prof. humanities U. Fla., Gainesville, 1975; vis. fellow U. Warwick, 1977, 84-85; vis. Francis M. Bernardin disting. prof. humanities U. Mo., Kansas City, 1979; hon. research fellow Birkbeck Coll., U. London, 1984-85; acad. visitor London Sch. Econs., U. London, 1984-85. Author: Generalization in Ethics, 2d edit., 1971, Verallgemeinerung in der Ethic, 1975; editor: Morals and Values, 1977, American Philosophy, 1986; contbr. Essays in Moral Philosophy, 1958, Ency. of Philosophy, 1967, Law and Philosophy, 1970, Skepticism and Moral Principles, 1973, Morals and Values, 1977, Acad. Am. Ency., 1982, 1984, 1989, World Book Ency., 1984, 86, Gewirth's Ethical Rationalism, 1984, Morality and Universality, 1985, American Philosophy, 1986, New Directions in Ethics, 1986, The Handbook of Western Philosophy, 1988, Applying Philosophy, 1988, Moral Phiosophy: Historical and Contemporary Essays, 1989, Key Themes in Philosophy, 1990, Essays on Henry Sidgwick, 1992, Ency. of Ethics, 1992, A History of Western Ethics, 1992, Ethics, 1993; co-editor: Introductory Readings in Philosophy, 2d edit., 1974, Reason and the Common Good, 1963, Belief, Knowledge and Truth, 1970, Legislative Intent and Other Essays on Law, Politics and Morality, 1993. Served with USAAF, 1944-45. Am. Philos. Assn. Western Div. fellow, 1956-57; Summer Research grant Social Sci. Research Council, 1958; Guggenheim fellow, 1962-63; Inst. for Research in Humanities fellow U. Wis., 1984. Mem. Am. Philos. Assn. (v.p. Western divsn. 1984-85, pres. Ctrl. divsn. 1985-86, bd. officers 1991-94), Royal Inst. Philosophy, AAUP, Aristotelian Soc., Mind Assn., Wis. Acad. Scis., Arts and Letters, Sidgwick Soc. (coun.), Phi Beta Kappa, Phi Kappa Phi. Home: 5021 Regent St Madison WI 53705-4745

SINGER, MARCUS JOSEPH, biologist, educator; b. Pitts., Aug. 28, 1914; s. Benjamin and Rachel (Gershenson) S.; m. Leah Horelick, June 8, 1938; children: Robert H., Jon Fredric. BS, U. Pitts., 1938; MA, Harvard U., 1940, PhD, 1942. Mem. faculty Harvard Med. Sch., 1942-51, asst. prof. anatomy, until 1951; vis. prof. anatomy L.I. Coll. Medicine, 1950; asso. prof., then prof. zoology and child devel. Cornell U., 1951-61; vis. fellow Dutch Brain Inst., Amsterdam; formerly H.W. Payne prof. anatomy, dir. dept. Case Western Res. U. Sch. Medicine, Cleve., now emer. prof.; asso. dir. Devel. Biology Center Case Western Res. U. Sch. Medicine, from 1961; vis. prof. anatomy Hebrew U., Jerusalem, 1974; Zyskind hon. vis. prof. faculty health scis. Ben Gurion U. Negev, Beersheba, Israel, 1975-76; vis. prof. Gunma U., Japan, 1977; mem. cell biology study sect. NIH, 1971-74, neurology study sect., from 1976. Author: (with P. Yakovlev) Human Brain in Sagittal Section, 1954, Dog Brain in Section, 1962; editor: Jour. Morphology, 1965-70, asso. editor, 1970-72, Jour. Exptl. Zoology, 1963-68, 70-71, editorial bd., 1970-74; contbr. articles on nervous system, histochemistry regeneration, cytology to profl. publs. Guggenheim fellow Rome, 1967; von Humboldt fellow W. Ger., 1980-81. Fellow Am. Acad. Arts and Scis., Ohio Acad. Sci., AAAS; mem. Am. Neurol. Assn. (asso.), Am. Assn. Anatomists, Soc. Zoologists, Internat. Brain Research Orgn., Assn. Research Nervous and Mental Diseases, Soc. Devel. and Growth, Biol. Stain Commn., Sigma Xi. Office: Case Western Reserve U Dept Anatomy Cleveland OH 44106

SINGER, MARKUS MORTON, retired trade association executive; b. N.Y.C., Dec. 20, 1917; s. Isadore and Nettie (Stromer) S.; m. Phyllis Berger, June 26, 1945; children—Fredric L., Robert B. B.C.S., NYU, 1939; postgrad., George Washington U., 1951-55. With Nat. Food Brokers Assn., Washington, 1946—, v.p., 1961-65, exec. v.p., 1965-71, pres., 1972-83, pres. emeritus, 1983—, acting pres., chief exec. officer, 1987-88; lifetime hon. trustee Nat. Food Brokers Assn. Edn. and Tng. Found. Served with AUS, 1942-45. Recipient Pres.'s award as Man of Yr. Can. Food Brokers Assn., 1976. Mem. European Food Brokers Assn. (hon. life), Frozen Food Industry Disting. Order of Zerocrats. Jewish.

SINGER, MAXINE FRANK, biochemist; b. N.Y.C., Feb. 15, 1931; d. Hyman S. and Henrietta (Perlowitz) Frank; m. Daniel Morris Singer, June 15, 1952; children: Amy Elizabeth, Ellen Ruth, David Byrd, Stephanie Frank. AB, Swarthmore Coll., 1952, DSc (hon.), 1978; PhD, Yale U., 1957; DSc (hon.), Wesleyan U., 1977, Swarthmore Coll., 1978, U.Md.-Baltimore County, 1985, Cedar Crest Coll., 1986, CUNY, 1988, Brandeis U., 1988, Radcliffe Coll., 1990, Williams Coll., 1990, Franklin and Marshall Coll., 1991, George Washington U., 1991, NYU, 1992, Lehigh U., 1992, Dartmouth Coll., 1993, Yale U., 1994, Harvard U., 1994. USPHS postdoctoral fellow NIH, Bethesda, Md., 1956-58; rsch. chemist biochemistry NIH, 1958-74; head sect. on nucleic acid enzymology Nat. Cancer Inst., 1974-79; chief Lab. of Biochemistry, Nat. Cancer Inst., 1979-87, rsch. chemist, 1987-88; pres. Carnegie Inst. Washington, 1988—; Regents vis. lectr. U. Calif., Berkeley, 1981; bd. dirs. Johnson & Johnson; mem. sci. coun. Internat. Genetics and Biophysics, Naples, Italy, 1982-86; Chulabhorn Rsch. Inst. (adv. bd. 1990—). Mem. editorial bd. Jour. Biol. Chemistry, 1968-74, Sci. mag., 1972-82; chmn. editorial bd. Procs. of NAS, 1985-88; author (with Paul Berg) 2 books on molecular biology; contbr. articles to scholarly jours. Trustee Wesleyan U., Middletown, Conn., 1972-75, Yale Corp., New Haven, 1975-90; bd. govs. Weizmann Inst. Sci., Rehovot, Israel, 1978—; bd. dirs. Whitehead Inst., 1985-94; chmn. Smithsonian Coun., 1992-93. Recipient award for achievement in biol. scis. Washington Acad. Scis., 1969, award for research in biol. scis. Yale Sci. and Engring. Assn., 1974, Superior Service Honor award HEW, 1975, Dirs. award NIH, 1977, Disting. Service medal HHS, 1983, Presdl. Disting. Exec. Rank award, 1987, U.S. Disting. Exec. Rank award, 1987, Mory's Cup Bd. Govs. Mory's Assn., 1991, Wilbur Lucius Cross Medal of Honor Yale Grad. Sch. Assn., 1991, Nat. Medal Sci. NSF, 1992. Fellow Am. Acad. Arts and Scis.; mem. NAS (coun. 1982-85, coun. Sci. Engring and Pub. Policy 1989-91), AAAS (Sci. Freedom and Responsibility award 1982), Am. Soc. Biol. Chemists, Am. Soc. Microbiologists, Am. Chem. Soc., Am. Philos. Soc., Inst. Medicine of NAS, Pontifical Acad. of Scis, Human Genome Org, N.Y. Acad. Scis. Home: 5410 39th St NW Washington DC 20015-2902 Office: Carnegie Inst Washington 1530 P St NW Washington DC 20005-1933

SINGER, NORMAN H., lawyer; b. N.Y.C., Apr. 14, 1945. AB, St. Lawrence U., 1967; JD, Washington & Lee U., 1970. Bar: Va. 1971, D.C. 1974. Ptnr. Keck, Mahin & Cate, Washington; teaching asst. Sch. Law Washington & Lee U., 1969-70. Mem. ABA, Va. Bar Assn., D.C. Bar, Va. State Bar, Bar Assn. D.C., Va. Trial Lawyers Assn. Office: Keck Mahin & Cate 1201 New York Ave NW PH Washington DC 20005-3919

SINGER, NORMAN SOL, food products executive, inventor; b. Phila., Dec. 10, 1937; s. Herman and Thelma (Scheinberg) S.; m. Anne Goldstein, Aug. 23, 1959; children: Amy Debra, Judith Ellen. BS, Rutgers U., 1961. Sr. lab. technician Bur. Biological Rsch., New Brunswick, N.J., 1960-61; food scientist Thomas J. Lipton, Inc., Englewood Cliffs, N.J., 1961-68; rsch. dir. McCain Foods, Florenceville, Can., 1968-70; sr. scientist John Labatt Ltd., London, Ontario, Can., 1970-84; fellow/dir. exploration The NutraSweet Co., Deerfield, Ill., 1984-94; pres. Ideas Workshop Cons., Inc., Highland Park, Ill., 1994—; co-founder, CEO Sous Chef Culinary Supply Inc., Highland Park, Ill., 1994—. Patentee in field. Recipient Outstanding Am. Inventor award Intellectual Property Owners Found., Washington, 1989. Mem. Inst. Food Technology, Product Devel. and Mgmt. Assn., Chgo. Horticultural Soc., Sigma Xi. Avocations: gourmet cooking, carving bone and antler, collecting amerind carvings, bicycling. Home: 40 Ridge Rd Highland Park IL 60035-4337 Office: Sous Chef Culinary Supply Highland Park IL 60035

SINGER, PAUL MEYER, lawyer; b. Pitts., May 20, 1943; s. Sidney Morris and Doris (Lyttle) S.; m. Laurie Stern, 1989. BS in Bus., U. Minn., 1965; JD, U. Pitts., 1968; LLM, Harvard U., 1970. Law clk. to presiding justice Pa. Supreme Ct., Pitts., 1970-71; atty. Am. Express Credit Corp. N.Y.C., 1971-73; ptnr. Reed, Smith, Shaw & McClay, Pitts., 1973—. Fellow Am. Coll. Bankruptcy; mem. Harvard-Yale-Princeton Club, Duquesne Club. Office: Reed Smith Shaw & McClay 435 6th Ave Pittsburgh PA 15219-1809

SINGER, ROBERT NORMAN, motor behavior educator; b. Bklyn., Sept. 27, 1936; s. Abraham and Ann (Norman) S.; children: Richard, Bonni Jill. BS, Bklyn. Coll., 1961; MS, Pa. State U., 1962; PhD, Ohio State U., 1964. Instr. phys. edn. Ohio State U., Columbus, 1963-64, asst. prof., 1964-65; asst. prof. Ill. State U., Normal, 1965-67, dir. motor learning lab., 1965-69, assoc. prof., 1968-69, asst. dean Coll. Applied Sci. and Tech., 1967-69; asso. prof., dir. motor learning lab. Mich. State U., East Lansing, 1969-70; prof. Fla. State U., Tallahassee, 1970-87, dir. motor learning lab., 1970-72, dir. div. human performance, 1972-75, dir. Motor Behavior Ctr., 1975-87; chair dept. of exercise and sport scis. U. Fla., Gainesville, 1987—; lectr. in N.Am., S.Am., Africa, Australia, Asia and Europe; cons. in field. Author: Motor Learning and Human Performance, 1968, rev. edit., 1975, 80, Coaching, Athletics, and Psychology, 1972, Physical Education, 1972, Teaching Physical Education, 1974, rev. edit., 1980, Laboratory and Field Experiments in Motor Learning, 1975, Myths and Truths in Sports Psychology, 1975, The Learning of Motor Skills, 1982, Sustaining Motivation in Sport, 1984, Peak Performance, 1986; editor: Readings in Motor Learning, 1972, The Psychomotor Domain, 1972, Foundations of Physical Education, 1976, Completed Research in Health, Phys. Edn. and Recreation, 1968-74, Handbook of Research on Sport Psychology, 1993; mem. editorial bd.: Research Quar., 1968-81, Jour. Motor Behavior, 1968-81, Jour. Sport and Exercise Psychology, 1979-92, The Sport Psychologist, 1986—, The Internat. Jour. Sport Psychology, 1977-88, Jour. Applied Sport Psychology, 1987—; reviewer numerous jours.; contbr. articles to numerous anthologies and profl. jours. Served with U.S. Army, 1955-58. Recipient Disting. Alumnus award Bklyn. Coll., 1989. Mem. AAHPERD, APA, Am. Psychol. Assn. (pres.-elect divsn. of exercise and sport psychology 1993-94), Am. Acad. Kinesiology and Phys. Edn. (pres.-elect 1993-94), Internat. Soc. Sport Psychology (pres. 1985-89, 89-93), Am. Ednl. Rsch. Assn., N.Am. Soc. Sport Psychology and Phys. Activity. Home: 6305 NW 56th Ln Gainesville FL 32606-3116 Office: U Fla 302 Florida Gym Gainesville FL 32611 *I have always enjoyed my activities and have looked forward to new challenges and horizons. Intrinsic motivational values have guided my involvement in various endeavors, and the outcomes have been extremely rewarding.*

SINGER, SAMUEL L(OEWENBERG), journalist; b. Phila., May 2, 1911; s. Benjamin and Hattie May (Loewenberg) S.; m. Betty Janet Levi, June 12, 1939; children—Ruth Babette, Samuel Lawrence, Robert Benjamin. B.S. in Journalism, Temple U., 1934. Mem. staff Phila. Inquirer, 1934-81, music editor, 1955-81, emeritus, 1981—; public service editor, 1973-81; tchr. undergrad. journalism course Temple U., 1946—, tchr. music criticism, 1965-70, adj. prof. journalism, 1973—; tchr. theatre and music reviewing Main Line Sch. Night, 1994—. Condr. radio program This Week's Music, 1961-72; author: Reviewing the Performing Arts, 1973. Organist Congregation Temple Judea, 1931-41, Phila. Ethical Soc., 1942-56, Main Line Reform Temple, 1951-55, Beth Israel, Phila., 1956-65, Coatesville, Pa., 1966-88, Zion Evang. Luth. Ch., 1956-82, St. Matthew's Evang. Luth. Ch., 1972-82, IHS Episcopal Ch., Drexel Hill, Pa, 1984—. Served with USNR, 1943-45. Named Outstanding 1934 Journalism Alumnus, Temple U., 1988. Mem. Am. Guild Organists (editor Phila. chpt. publ. Crescendo 1971-76), Newspaper Guild, Phila. Press Assn., Mus. Fund Soc. Phila., Music Critics Assn. Phila. Mus. Art, Phila. Orch. Assn., Sigma Delta Chi (life). Home: 1431 Greywall Ln Wynnewood PA 19096-3811 *Never do anything you can't tell your children.*

SINGER, SANFORD ROBERT, diversified energy company executive; b. Murfreesboro, Tenn., Aug. 25, 1930; s. Isadore M. and Bertye (Katz) S.; m. Ella Rita Raab; children: Halley Lynne, Michael Elliot. BA, U. Tenn., 1952, MS, 1955; PhD in Econs, Ohio State U., 1960. With Fed. Res. Bank Dallas, 1960-63; economist R & D ENSERCH Corp. (formerly Lone Star Gas Co.), Dallas, 1963-67, v.p. planning and info. data systems, 1967-68, sr. v.p., chief fin. officer, 1968—. Contbr. articles to profl. jours. 1st lt. U.S. Army, 1952-54, Korea. Mem. Am. Gas Assn., Nat. Assn. Bus. Economists, Fin. Execs. Inst., Dallas Petroleum Club. Republican. Office: Enserch Corp 300 S St Paul St Dallas TX 75201-5598

SINGER, SARAH BETH, poet; b. N.Y.C., July 4, 1915; d. Samuel and Rose (Dunetz) White; m. Leon Eugene Singer, Nov. 23, 1938; children: Jack, Rachel. B.A., NYU, 1934; postgrad., New Sch. Social Research, 1961-63. Tchr. creative writing Hillside Hosp., Queens, N.Y., 1964-75, Samuel Field YMHA, Queens, 1980-82. Author: Magic Casements, 1957, After the Beginning, 1975, Of Love and Shoes, 1987, The Gathering, 1992; contbr. poetry to anthologies, poetry mags. and quars. including American Women Poets, 1976, Yearbook of American Poetry, 1981, The Best of 1980, 1981, Filtered Images, 1992, The Croton Rev., The Lyric, Bitterroot, Judaism, Encore, The Jewish Frontier, Yankee, Hartford Courant, Poet Lore, N.Y. Times, Christian Sci. Monitor, Voices Internat., The Round Table, Orphic Lute, Brussels Sprout, Poetry and Medicine Column Jour. AMA, The Shakespeare Newsletter Midstream, The Penwoman; cons. editor Poet Lore, 1975-81. Recipient Stephen Vincent Benet award Poet Lore, 1968, 71, Dellbrook award Shenandoah Valley Acad. Lit. and Dellbrook-Shenandoah Coll. Writers' Conf., 1978, 79, C.W. Post poetry award, 1979-80, award for best poem Lyric quar., 1981, biennial award for achievement in poetry Seattle br. Nat. League Am. Penwomen, 1988; award for traditional poetry Wash. Poets Assn., 1995, cert. of merit Muse mag., 1990, Editor's Choice award for haiku Brussels Sprout, 1992, poem chosen for Metro Bus. Poetry Project Seattle, 1992, poem Upon My Demise transl. into Russian, recorded, 1st prize Marj McAlister award Voice Internat., 1993, hon. mehtion Lily Peter Meml. award, 1993. Mem. PEN, Nat. League Am. Penwomen (poetry chmn. L.I. br. 1957-87, publicity chmn. 1990, sec. Seattle br. 1990, pres. 1992—, v.p. 1994—, publicity chmn. for State of Wash. 1992—), Marion Doyle Meml. award 1976, 1st prize nat. poetry contest 1976, Drama award 1977, Poetry award 1977, 1st prize for modern rhymed poetry 1978, Lectr. award 1980, Sonnet award Alexandria br. 1980, 81, Catherine Cushman Leach award 1982; poetry award Phoenix br. 1983, Pasadena br. 1984, Alexandria br. 1985, 1st prize award Portland br. 1990, structured verse award Spokane br. 1992, Della Crowder Miller Meml. Petrarchan Sonnet award 1994, 2d prize Catherine Cushman Leach Poetry award 1994, Honorable Mention Anita Marie Boggs Meml. award 1994, Owl award Seattle br. 1994), Poetry Soc. Am. (v.p. 1974-78, exec. dir. L.I. 1979-83, James Joyce award 1972, 1977, Consuelo Ford award 1973, Gustav Davidson award 1974, 1st prize award 1975, Celia Wagner award 1976), Poets and Writers, Annual award for Achievement in Poetry Seattle Branch Nat. League Am. Penwomen, 1994. Address: 2360 43rd Ave E Apt 415 Seattle WA 98112-2703 *As a poet, I have sought never to compromise my standards as to what constitutes poetry, despite fads that come and go. My goal has been to achieve whatever perfection I can in my work, and to preserve enough humility to realize that the best is never good enough.*

SINGER, S(IEGFRIED) FRED, geophysicist, educator; b. Vienna, Austria, Sept. 27, 1924; came to U.S., 1940, naturalized, 1944; s. Joseph B. and Anne (Kelman) S.; m. Candace Carolyn Crandall, 1990. B.E.E., Ohio State U., 1943, D.Sc. (hon.), 1970; A.M., Princeton, 1944, Ph.D. in Physics, 1948. Instr. physics Princeton, 1943-44; physicist, applied physics lab. Johns Hopkins, 1946-50; sci. liaison officer Office Naval Research, Am. embassy, London, 1950-53; asso. prof. physics U. Md., College Park, 1953-59; prof. U. Md., 1959-62; dir. Nat. Weather Satellite Center, Dept. Commerce, 1962-64; dean Sch. Environ. and Planetary Scis., U. Miami, 1964-67; dep. asst. sec. for water quality and research Dept. Interior, Washington, 1967-70; dep. asst. adminstr. EPA, Washington, 1970-71; prof. environ. scis. U. Va., Charlottesville, 1971-87; chief scientist U.S. Dept. Transp., Washington, 1987-89; Disting. rsch. prof. Inst. for Space Sci. and Tech., Gainesville, Fla., 1989—; pres. Sci. and Environ. Policy Project, 1990—; vis. research prof. Jet Propulsion Lab., Calif. Inst. Tech., 1961-62; Fed. Exec. fellow Brookings Instn., 1971; vis. Sid Richardson prof. LBJ Sch., U. Tex., 1978; sr. fellow Heritage Found., 1982-83; vis. eminent scholar George Mason U., 1984-86; head sci. eval. group, astronautics and space exploration com. Ho. of Reps., 1958; mem. research adv. bd. Center for Strategic and Internat. Studies, Georgetown U.; cons. U.S Treasury, GAO, Office Tech. Assessment, U.S. Congress.; Mem. bd. Nat. Com. on Am. Fgn. Policy; mem. White House Panel on U.S.-Brazil Sci. and Tech. Exchange, 1987; guest scholar Nat. Air & Space Mus. Smithsonian Instn., 1991, Woodrow Wilson Internat. Ctr. for Scholars, 1991, Hoover Instn., 1992; bd. dirs. AMREP Corp., Patent Enforcement Fund, Inc., Excelco Energy Inc. Author: Geophysical Research with Artificial Earth Satellites, 1956, Manned Laboratories in Space, 1970, Global Effects of Environmental Pollution, 1970, Is There an Optimum Level of Population, 1971, The Changing Global Environment, 1975, Arid Zone Development: Potentialities and Problems, 1977, The Economic Effects of Demographic Changes, 1977, Energy, 1979, Price of World Oil, 1983, Free Market Energy, 1984, Global Climate Change, 1990, Origins of The Universe, 1990, The Ocean in Human Affairs, 1990, The Greenhouse Debate Continued, 1992; sci. adv. com. Dept State 1981; vice chmn. Nat. Adv. Com. Oceans and Atmosphere, 1981-86; contbr. articles on space, energy, environment and population problems to profl. jours. Served with USNR, 1944-46. Recipient Presdl. commendation, 1958, gold medal for exceptional service Dept. Commerce, 1965; named Outstanding Young Man U.S. Jr. C. of C., 1959. Fellow Am. Geophys. Union, Am. Phys. Soc., AAAS, AIAA; mem. AAAS (com. coun. affairs 1970), Internat. Acad. Astronautics, Pan Am. Med. Assn. (pres. sect on environ. health scis. 1973—), Cosmos Club (Washington), Colonnade Club (Charlottesville). Office: 4084 University Dr Ste 101 Fairfax VA 22030-6812

SINGER, SUZANNE FRIED, editor; b. N.Y.C., July 9, 1935; d. Maurice Aaron and Augusta G. (Ginsberg) Fried; m. Max Singer, Feb. 12, 1959; children: Saul, Alexander, Daniel, Benjamin. BA with honors, Swarthmore Coll., 1956; MA, Columbia U., 1958. Program asst. NSF, Washington, 1958-60; assoc. editor Bibl. Archaeology Rev., Washington, 1979-84, mng. editor, 1984—; mng. editor Bibl. Rev., Washington, 1985-94, exec. editor, 1994—; mng. editor Moment, Washington, 1990—. Mem. Am. Schs. Oriental Rsch., Soc. Bibl. Lit. Jewish. Office: Bibl Archaeology Soc 4710 41st St NW Washington DC 20016

SINGER, THOMAS ERIC, industrial company executive; b. Vienna, Austria, Mar. 6, 1926; came to U.S. 1938, naturalized, 1944; s. Henry and Berthe (dePokroi) S.; m. Ellen Colt, Dec. 20, 1952; children: Dominique, Mary F., Carlyle, Henry, Ellen. BA, George Washington U., 1950; MA, Harvard coll., 1952. Fgn. affairs officer State Dept., 1952-55; export mgr. Polaroid Corp., Cambridge, Mass., 1955-58; with Gillette Co., 1958-79, exec. v.p., 1971-79; sr. v.p. Ingalls Assocs., Boston, 1979-81; chmn. Pontara Ltd., 1981-86; pres. Sontek Industries, 1983-84; prin. Thomas Singer and Daus., Boston, 1986—; bd. dirs. Galaxy Cheese Co. Trustee Faulkner Hosp., Boston; corporator Babson Coll., Wellesley, Mass., Childrens Mus., Boston; mem. Mayor's Com. for Cultural Affairs. With U.S. Army, 1944-46. Named hon. consul of Peru in Boston, 1969. Mem. Algonquin Club, Harvard Club (N.Y.C.), Essex County Club (Manchester, Mass.). Home: PO Box 362 Ipswich MA 01938-0362 Office: Thomas Singer and Daus 180 Beacon St Boston MA 02116-1455

SINGER, THOMAS KENYON, international business consultant, farmer; b. Wilson, N.Y., Jan. 30, 1932; s. Harold Thomas and Grace (Kenyon) S.; m. Jacqueline Germain Moulin, June 8, 1957; children: Marc Andre, Viviane George Singer Scott, Claire Anne, Michelle Moulin Singer Ross, Gail Kenyon. BS in Econs., U. Pa., 1954. Dir. mktg. Europe Kaiser Aluminum & Chem. Corp., London, 1965-67; v.p. Kaiser LeNickel subs., Oakland, Calif., 1967-73, div. mgr., 1973-75; v.p. govt. relations Kaiser Aluminum & Chem. Corp., Washington, 1975-81; corp. v.p. Kaiser Aluminum & Chem. Corp., Oakland, Calif., 1977-86; pres. Kaiser Internat. Corp., Oakland, Calif., 1982-86, also dir.; dir., pres. IBA, Inc. Served to capt. USAF, 1955-57, Casablanca, Morocco. Mem. French-Am. C. of C. (trustee). Republican. Episcopalian. Clubs: Army and Navy (Washington). Home: 4706 Foxhall Crescents NW Washington DC 20007

SINGER-MAGDOFF, LAURA JOAN SILVER (MRS. SAMUEL MAGDOFF), psychotherapist; b. N.Y.C., Mar. 21, 1917; d. Max David and Minnie (Stabsky) Silver; m. Edward I. Plotkin, 1938 (dec. 1945); 1 child, JoAnn Melanie; m. Arthur I. Singer, 1948 (div. 1962); m. Samuel Magdoff, Dec. 23, 1963. Student, NYU, 1934-38; A.M., U. Minn., 1938-39; BS, MA, Columbia U., 1946, EdD, 1961. Diplomate Am. Bd. Sexology; cert. sex educator, therapist Am. Assn. Sex Educators, Counselors and Therapists. Nursery and elem. sch. tchr.; dir. Bronxville, N.Y., 1943-45; tchr. Cherry Lawn Sch., Darien, Conn., 1943-44, Columbia Grammar Sch., 1951-53, N.Y. Children's Colony, 1953-54; psychotherapist, marital, family counselor Community Guidance Service, N.Y.C., 1958—; pvt. practice, 1958—; founder, pres. Save A Marriage, Inc., 1974—; pres. Interpersonal Devel. Inst., Inc., 1983, co-producer Gleam Prodns., 1989; adj. prof. Tchrs. Coll., Columbia U. 1961-74; vis. faculty New Sch. for Social Research; faculty Am. Assn. for Psychoanalysis and Psychotherapy; psychotherapist TV series Living Together; past mem. exec. bd. Sex Info. and Edn. Council of U.S., Community Sex Info.; adviser bd. trustees Nat. Accreditation Assn. for Psychoanalysis, Inc.; supr. dept. psychology CUNY, 1991-92. Co-author: (with Barbara L. Stern) Stages the Crises that Shape Your Marriage, 1980; (with JoAnn Magdoff) Sexual Relations and Therapeutic Practice; author: (with others) Human Sexuality, 1988, Family Therapy Collection: Aspen, 1989; cons. editor Jour. Sex and Marital Therapy; former mem. adv. bd. Jour. Marriage and Family Counselors; former mem. editorial bd. Jour. Divorce; co-producer (documentary film) Door of Hope, 1991. Fellow Am. Inst. Psychotherapy and Psychoanalysis, Am. Assn. Marriage and Family Therapists (past pres., supr.), Am. Orthopsychiat. Assn., Soc. Sci. Study Sex, Am. Acad. Clin. Sexologists (clin. fellow); mem. World Fedn. Mental Health, N.Y. Soc. Clin. Psychologists (past editor Newsletter, mem. exec. bd.), Am. Family Therapy Assn. (charter), Am. Psychol. Assn., Am. Soc. Psychologists in Pvt. Practice, Assn. Applied Psychoanalysis, Nat. Council Family Relations. Address: 1 Lincoln Plz New York NY 10023-7129

SINGERMAN, MARTIN, newspaper publishing executive. Pub. N.Y. Post, N.Y.C. Office: NY Post 210 South St New York NY 10002*

SINGH, AMARJIT, engineering executive, scientist, management consultant; b. Ramdas, India, Nov. 19, 1924; s. Jagdish and Ishar (Kaur) S.; m. Bimla Jaspal, May 10, 1950 (dec. Nov. 1952); m. Surinder Kaur, Nov. 21, 1953; children: Harinder Jit, Narinder Jit, Arvind Jit. BS with honors, Punjab U., India, 1944, MSc with honors, 1945, DSc (hon.), 1975; M in Engring. Scis., Harvard U., 1947, PhD, 1949. Lectr. radio physics U. Delhi, India, 1949-53; sci. officer Nat. Phys. Lab., New Delhi, 1953-57; asst. dir. Cen. Electronics Engring. Rsch. Inst., Pilani, Raj, India, 1957-59, in charge, 1959-62, dir., 1963-84; rsch. engr. U. Mich., Ann Arbor, 1962-63, Bell Telephone Labs., Murray Hill, N.J., 1963; nat. project coord. UN Devel. Program, Pilani, 1984-87; vis. scientist U. Md., College Park, 1987—; mem. electronics com. Govt. of India, 1963-66, Univ. Grants Commn., 1974-77, Sci. and Engring. Rsch. Coun., 1978-82, governing body Coun. Sci. and Indsl. Rsch., 1972-74, 78-80. Co-author, editor: Microwave Integrated Circuits, 1976; contbr. articles to profl. pubs. Mem. Mcpl. Bd., Pilani, 1963-83. Recipient Indsl. Rsch. award Fedn. Indian C. of C. and Industry, New Delhi, 1979, Padma Bhushan award Pres. of India, 1985. Life fellow IEEE (listed in Century of Honors 1985). Sikh. Avocations: photography, music. Office: U Md 1202 Inst For Plasma Rsch # F College Park MD 20742

SINGH, JASWANT, environmental company executive; b. Gurne Kalan, Punjab, India, Aug. 12, 1937; came to U.S. 1963; s. Chanan and Ripudaman (Khara) S.; m. Mary Kathryn Todd, Feb. 5, 1939; children: David Paul, Monica Maria. PhD, Punjab U., 1963. Diplomate Am. Acad. Indsl. Hygiene. Rsch. assoc. U. So. Calif., L.A., 1963-65; rsch. fellow NRC of Can., Ottawa, 1965-68; dir. rsch. Pollution Dynamics Corp., Rochester, N.Y., 1968-70; tech. dir. Galson Tech. Svcs., Syracuse, N.Y., 1970-77; tech. dir., sr. v.p. Clayton Environ. Cons., Novi, Mich., 1977-89, Cypress, Calif., 1989—; bd. dirs. Am. Bd. Indsl. Hygiene, 1987—; leader Citizen Ambassador Program del. to China, U.S. Indsl. Hygiene, 1989. Author: Standard Handbook of Plant Engineering, 1983; contbr. articles to profl. jours. Mem. Am. Chem. Soc., Am. Indsl. Hygiene Assn., Brit. Occupational Hygiene Soc., Air. Pollution Control Assn., Applied Indsl. Hygiene Assn. (editor jour. 1985—). Avocations: sailing, traveling. Office: Clayton Environ Cons 22345 Roethel Dr Novi MI 48375-4710

SINGH, JYOTI SHANKAR, political organization director; b. Pathalgaon, India, Apr. 15, 1935; came to U.S., 1972; s. Brijnath Kumar and Tirthmani (Singh) S.; m. Maria Luz Molares, 1962; children: Anil, Rajeev, Ajit. BA, Banaras U., India, 1952, MA, 1954, LLB, 1955; MA, NYU, 1979; D (hon.), Inst. Internacional de Integracion, Bolivia, 1980. Assoc. sec. coordinating secretariat Leiden, The Netherlands, 1960-61, sec. gen. coordinating secretariat, 1961-64; programme cons. Internat. Youth Centre, New Delhi, 1965-66; sec. gen. World Assembly of Youth, Brussels, 1966-72; liaison officer Fund for Population Activities UN, N.Y.C., 1972-73, asst. exec. sec. World Population Yr., 1973-74, dep. chief info. and pub. affairs, 1975-80, chief info. and external rels., 1980-85, dir. info. and external rels., 1986-90; dir. tech. and evaluation div. UN Population Fund, N.Y.C., 1990-95; dep. exec. dir. tech. svcs. UN Population Fund, 1995—; hon. prof. Cen. Am. U., Managua, Nicaragua, 1975; exec. coord. UN Internat. Conf. on Population, 1982-84; exec. coord. Internat. Conf. on Population and Devel., 1992-94. Author: A New International Economic Order, 1977; editor: World Population Policies, 1979; editor-in-chief Populi, 1980-90. Mem. Soc. for Internat. Devel. Home: 10 Waterside Plz Apt 26D New York NY 10010-2606 Office: UN Population Fund 220 E 42nd St New York NY 10017-5806

SINGH, KRISHNA PAL, mechanical engineer; b. Patna, India, May 1, 1947; s. Balmiki Singh and Ram Rati Devi; m. Martha J. Trimble, May 18, 1974; children: Amy, Kris. BSME, BIT Sindri, India, 1967; MSME, U. Pa., 1969, PhD, 1972. Registered profl. engr., Pa., Mich. Prin. engr. Joseph Oat Corp., Camden, N.J., 1971-74, chief engr., 1974-79, v.p. engring., 1979-86; pres., CEO Holtec Internat., Cherry Hill, N.J., 1986—. Co-author: Mechanical Design of Heat Exchangers and Pressure Vessel Components, 1984; contbr. to profl. publs. Fellow ASME; mem. AICE, AM. Nuclear Soc., Thermal Exchangers Mfg. Assn. (vibration com.). Achievements include patents for heat exchanger for withstanding cycle changes in temperature and radioactive fuel cell storage rack. Office: Holtec Internat 2060 Fairfax Ave Cherry Hill NJ 08003-1612*

SINGH, MANMOHAN, orthopedic surgeon, educator; b. Patiala, Punjab, India, Oct. 5, 1940; came to U.S., 1969; s. Ajmer and Kartar (Kaur) S.; m. Manjit Anand, Jan. 1, 1974; children: Kirpal, Gurmeet. MB, BS, Govt. Med. Coll., Patiala, 1964; MSurgery, Panjab U., Chandigarh, India, 1968. Diplomate Am. Bd. Orthopaedic Surgery. Rsch. fellow Inst. Internat. Edn., Chgo., 1969-74; resident in orthopedic surgery Michael Reese Hosp. and Med. Ctr., Chgo., 1974-78, mem. attending staff, dir. orthopedic rsch., 1979—; fellow in orthopedic oncology Mayo Clinic and Mayo Found., Rochester, Minn., 1978-79; asst. prof. U. Ill., Chgo., 1983—; mem. vis. faculty Mayo Grad. Sch., Rochester, 1969. Developer x-ray method (Singh Index) and bone density method (Radius Index) for diagnosis of osteoporosis. Fulbright travel grantee, 1968. Fellow Am. Acad. Orthopaedic Surgeons, Am. Orthopedic Foot and Ankle Soc.; mem. Orthopaedic Rsch. Soc., Am. Soc. for Bone and Mineral Rsch. Democrat. Sikh. Avocations: stamp collecting, photography, tennis. Office: Michael Reese Hosp/Med Ctr 2929 S Ellis Ave Chicago IL 60616

SINGH, RAJENDRA, mechanical engineering educator; b. Dhampur, India, Feb. 13, 1950; came to U.S., 1973; s. Raghubir and Ishwar (Kali) S.; m. Veena Ghungesh, June 24, 1979; children: Rohit, Arun. BS with honors, Birla Inst., 1971; MS, U. Roorkee, India, 1971; PhD, Purdue U., 1975. Grad. instr. Purdue U., West Layfayette, Ind., 1973-75; sr. engr. Carrier Corp., Syracuse, N.Y., 1975-79; asst. prof. Ohio State U., Columbus, 1979-83, assoc. prof., 1983-87, prof., 1987—; adj. lectr. Syracuse (N.Y.) U., 1977-79; bd. dirs. Nat. Conf. Fluid Power, Milw.; gen. chmn. Nat. Noise Conf., Columbus, 1985; vis. prof. U. Calif., Berkeley, 1987-88; cons., lectr. in field. Contbr. articles to profl. jours. Recipient Gold medal U. Roorkee, 1973, R. H. Kohr Rsch. award Purdue U., 1975, Excellence in Teaching award Inst. Noise Control Engring., 1989, George Westinghouse award Am. Soc. Engring. Edn., 1993. Fellow ASME, Acoustical Soc. Am.; mem. Soc. for Exptl. Mechanics, Inst. Noise Control Engring., Am. Soc. Engring. Edn. (George Westinghouse award 1993). Achievements include patent for rolling door; development of new analytical and experimental techniques in machine dynamics, acoustics, vibration and fluid control. Home: 4772 Belfield Ct Dublin OH 43017 Office: Ohio State U 206 W 18th Ave Columbus OH 43210-1107

SINGHAL, AVINASH CHANDRA, engineering administrator, educator; b. Aligarh, India, Nov. 4, 1941; s. Shiam Sunder and Pushpa Lata (Jindal) S.; m. Uma Rani Sharma; Sept. 5, 1967; children: Ritu Chanchal, Anita, Neil Raj. BSc, Agra U., Kanpur, India, 1957; BSc in Engring., St. Andrews U., Dundee, Scotland, 1959, BSC in Engring. with honors, 1960; MS, MIT, 1961, CE, 1962, ScD, 1964. Registered profl. engr., N.Y., Que., Ariz. Rsch. engr. Kaman Aircraft, Burlington, Mass., 1964-65; prof. Laval U., Quebec, Can., 1965-69; asst. program mgr. TRW, Redondo Beach, Calif., 1969-71; mgr. GE, Phila., 1971-72; mgr. tech. svcs. Engrs. India Ltd., New Delhi, 1972-74; project engr. Weidlinger Assocs., N.Y.C., 1974-77; prof. Ariz. State U., Tempe, 1977—; dir. Cen. Bldg. Rsch. Inst., Govt. of India, 1992-93; dir. Earthquake Rsch. Lab., Tempe, 1978-89; grad. coord. structural engring. Ariz. State U., Tempe, 1991-92, 95-96; cons. McDonnell Aircraft Corp., St. Louis, 1977-78, Sperry Corp., 1978-80, McDonnell Douglas Helicopter Co., 1990-91, Ariz. Nuc. Power Plant, 1991-92; reviewer of proposals NSF, Washington, 1980-91; rev. of proposals CSIR, India, 1990-93; U.S. del. U.S./ China Workshop on Arch Dams, Beijing, 1987, Can. del. Shell Structures, USSR, 1964; session chmn. Fifth Internat. Conf. on Soil Dynamics and Earthquake Engring., Karlsruhe, Fed. Republic of Germany, 1991; rsch. prof. Nat. Cen. U. Taiwan, Republic of China, 1990; vis. prof. U. Melbourne, Australia, 1983-84, U. Auckland, New Zealand, 1983-84; nodal dir. wood substitute rsch. program, India, 1992-93; chmn. mgmt. coun. ctr. bldg. Rsch. Inst. Roorkee. Mem. editorial bd. Soil Dynamics and Earthquake Engring., 1991—; contbr. Nuclear Waste Storage, 1986, (proceeding publ.) Earthquake Behavior of Buried Pipelines, 1989, Wood Substitute: A National Priority, 1992, System Flexibility and Reflected Pressures, 1993, Simulation of Blast Pressures on Flexible Panels, 1994; editor: Seismic Performance of Pipelines & Storage Tanks, 1985, Recent Advances in Lifeline Earthquake Engineering, 1987, Seismic Ground Motions Response, Repair and Instrumentation of Pipes and Bridges, 1992; contbr. articles to Jour. Performance of Constructed Facilities, Am. Soc. of Civil Engrs., Jour. Computers and Structures, Jour. ASME, Jour. Aerospace Engring. ASCE; reviewer, bd. editors Jour. Earthquake Engring. and Structural Dynamics, Structural Engring. Papers Jour. ASCE. Chm. bd. dirs. India Assn. Greater Phoenix, 1985-86; pres. India Assn. Greater Boston, 1964-65; v.p.; treas. Dobson Ranch Homeowners Assn., Mesa, Ariz., 1988-91; founding mem. Asian Am. Assn. Ariz., Phoenix, 1987-89; founding mem. pres. Asian Am. Faculty Assn., Ariz. State U., Tempe, 1986-88; mem. sci. adv. com. 5th Internat. Conf. on Soil Dynamics, Germany, 1991; cons. UN Devel. Program, New Delhi, 1991-92. McLintock fellow MIT, 1960, Carnegie fellow MIT, 1960-63, fellow Royal Astron. Soc., London, 1961-64, rsch. fellow Kobe U., Japan, 1990; Denninson scholar Instn. Civil Engrs., London, 1959; Henry Adams Rsch. medal Structural Engrs., London, 1972; grantee Can. Def. Rsch. Bd., 1966-69, NSF, 1978-82, Engring. Found, 1978-79, U.S. Army Corps Engrs., 1984-86, U.S. Dept. Interior, 1986-88, Office Naval Rsch., 1994; recipient 1st prize bridge bldg. Instn. Strucral Engrs., Merit award Inst. Engrs., India. Fellow ASCE, N.Y. Acad. Scis., Sigma Xi, Tau Beta Pi, Chi Epsilon. Achievements include research in forensic engineering, blast effects on structures, in lifeline engineering, earthquake strengthening of deteriorated arch dams, buildings, bridges, building materials, wood substitution and non-linear structural dynamics. Home: 2631 S El Marino Mesa

AZ 85202-7302 Office: Ariz State U Dept Civil Engring 5306 Tempe AZ 85287-5306

SINGHAL, KISHORE, engineering administrator; b. Allahabad, India, Dec. 28, 1944; came to U.S., 1966; s. Jagdish Chandra and Pushpa Lata (Mital) S.; m. Kumud Agrawal, Aug. 17, 1973; children: Monica, Nina. B Tech. with honors, Indian Inst. Tech., Kharagpur, 1966; MS, Columbia U., 1967, ScD in Engring., 1970. Postdoctoral fellow U. Waterloo, Ont., Can., 1970-71, lectr., 1972, assoc. prof., 1973-77, assoc. prof., 1977-83, prof., 1983-88, adj. prof., 1988—, assoc. chmn. grad. studies in systems design, 1977-83; cons., then vis. mem. staff AT&T Bell Labs., Murray Hill, N.J., 1984-85; supr. AT&T Bell Labs., Allentown, Pa., 1985—; cons. Bell No., Ottawa, Ont., 1972-82. Author: Computer Aided Circuit Design, 1983 (transl. into Russian, Chinese and Pharsi), 2d edit., 1993; editor: Analog Circuit Design, 1987. Higgins fellow Columbia U., 1966, Boese fellow, 1967. Fellow IEEE. Avocations: reading, hiking. Office: AT&T Bell Labs 1247 S Cedar Crest Blvd Allentown PA 18103-6209

SINGHVI, SURENDRA SINGH, finance and strategy consultant; b. Jodhpur, Rajasthan, India, Jan. 16, 1942; came to U.S., 1962, naturalized 1986; s. Rang Raj and Ugam Kanwar (Surana) S.; m. Sushila Bhandari, July 7, 1965; children: Seema, Sandeep. B in Commerce, Rajasthan U., 1961; MBA, Atlanta U., 1963; PhD, Columbia U., 1967. Cert. mgmt. acct., CPA. Asst. prof. fin. Miami U., Oxford, Ohio, 1967-69, assoc. prof., 1969-70; fin. mgr. ARMCO Inc., Middletown, Ohio, 1970-79, asst. treas., 1979-83, gen. fin. mgr., 1983-86; v.p. and treas. Edison Bros. Stores, Inc., St. Louis, 1986-90; pres. Singhvi & Assocs., Spring Valley, Ohio, 1990—; adj. prof. fin. Miami U., 1970—; bd. dirs. Columbia Indsl. Sales Corp. Author: Planning for Capital Investment, 1980; co-editor: Frontiers of Financial Management, 4th edit., 1984; contbr. over 90 articles to profl. jours., U.S., Can., Europe, India. Treas. local PTO, 1981, local Boy Scouts Am., 1982, N. Am. Fedn. Indian Orgns., 1984-86; pres. Jain Ctr. of Greater St. Louis, 1986-90; dir. Fedn. Jain Assn. N. Am., 1986—; v.p. fin. Middletown Symphony, Inc., 1984-86. Recipient Chancellor's Gold medal Rajasthan U. Mem. Planning Forum, Inst. Mgmt. Accts. (Bayer Silver medal 1978), Fin. Mgmt. Assn., Nat. Assn. Corp. Treas., Fin. Execs. Inst., Assn. Indian in Am. (life), Rotary (dir. internat. program Middletown chpt. 1973-86), India Club (pres. Dayton chpt. 1980). Avocations: swimming, bridge, ping pong, photography, writing. Home: 439 Ridge Line Ct Spring Valley OH 45370 Office: Singhvi and Assocs 439 Ridge Line Ct Spring Valley OH 45370

SINGLE, RICHARD WAYNE, SR., lawyer; b. Balt., June 17, 1938; s. William and Lillian (Griffin) S.; m. Emily K. Kaffl, Nov. 4, 1962; children: Richard W. Jr., Stacey Lyn. AB, U. Md., 1959, JD, 1961. Bar: Md. 1961, U.S. Dist. Ct. Md. 1961, U.S. Supreme Ct. 1978. Staff atty. Legal Aid Bur. Balt., 1962-64; house counsel Gen. Automatic Prodns. Corp., Balt., 1964-67; resident counsel Nat. Industries, Inc., Odenton, Md., 1967-69; asst. counsel McCormick & Co., Inc., Hunt Valley, Md., 1969-72, asst. sec., asst. counsel, 1972-75, asst. sec., assoc. gen. counsel, 1975-82, div. gen. counsel, v.p., 1983-86, gen counsel, v.p., sec., 1986—, also bd. dirs.; bd. dirs. McCormick Can. Inc., London, Ont., Can., McCormick de Mexico, Mexico City, Helix Health System, Balt. Trustee Franklin Sq. Hosp., Balt., 1986—. Mem. ABA, Md. Bar Assn. Republican. Avocation: boating. Office: McCormick & Co Inc PO Box 6000 18 Loveton Cir Sparks MD 21152-6000

SINGLEHURST, DONA GEISENHEYNER, horse farm owner; b. Tacoma, June 19, 1928; d. Herbert Russell and Rose Evelyn (Rubish) Geisenheyner; m. Thomas G. Singlehurst, May 16, 1959 (dec.); 1 child, Suanna Singlehurst. BA in Psychology, Whitman Coll., 1950. With pub. rels. and advt. staff Lane Wells, L.A., 1950-52; staff mem. in charge new bus. Bishop Trust Co., Honolulu, 1953-58; mgr. Town & Country Stables, Honolulu, 1958-62; co-owner, v.p. pub. rels. Carol & Mary, Ltd., Honolulu, 1964-84; owner Stanhope Farms, Waialua, Hawaii, 1969—; internat. dressage judge, sport horse breeding judge Am. Horse Shows Assn.; sr. judge Can. Dressage Fedn. Chmn. ways and means com. The Outdoor Cir., Hawaii, 1958-64, life mem.; pres. emeritus Morris Animal Found., Englewood, Colo., 1988—, pres., 1984-88; bd. dirs. pres. Delta Soc., 1994—; mem. Jr. League of Honolulu. Recipient Best Friends award Honolulu Vt. Soc., 1986, Spl. Recognition award Am. Animal Hosp. Assn., 1988, Recognition award Am. Vet. Med. Assn., 1992. Mem. NAFE, Hawaii Horse Show Assn. (Harry Hutaff award 1985, past pres., bd. dirs.), Hawaii Combined Tng. Assn. (past pres. bd. dirs.), Calif. Dressage Soc., U.S. Dressage Fedn., U.S. Equestrian Team (area chmn. 1981-85), Hawaiian Humane Soc. (life), U.S. Pony Clubs (dist. commr. 1970-75, nat. examiner 1970-75), Pacific Club, Outrigger Canoe Club. Republican. Episcopalian. Avocations: music, travel. Home and Office: Stanhope Farms Waialua HI 96791

SINGLETARY, MICHAEL, retired professional football player; b. Houston, Oct. 9, 1958; m. Kim Singletary; children: Kristin, Matthew. BA in Mgmt., Baylor U., 1981. Middle linebacker Chgo. Bears, 1981-93. Named Defensive MVP, season 1985; named to Pro Bowl team, 1983-91, Sporting News All-Pro team, 1984-89, 91, Sporting News Coll. All-Am. team, 1980. mem. NFL Super Bowl Championship Team, 1985. Office: Chgo Bears Halas Hall 250 Washington Rd Lake Forest IL 60045-2499*

SINGLETARY, MICHAEL WILLIS, journalism, educator; b. Washington, July 14, 1938; s. Willis Raymond and Bernice Anna (Long) S.; m. Juanita Carole Lark, Apr. 13, 1963; 1 child, Angela Lark. BA, U.S.C., 1969, MA, 1970; PhD, So. Ill. U., 1973. News reporter West Columbia (S.C.) Jour., 1963-64, Sta. WBTW-TV, Florence, S.C., 1964-69; instr. journalism Va. Commonwealth U., Richmond, 1972-74; from asst. to assoc. prof. journalism Shippenburg (Pa.) State Coll., 1974-81; assoc. dean to grad. sch. U. Tenn., Knoxville, 1994—. Author: Communication Theory and Research Applications, 1988, Mass. Communication Research: Contemporary Methods and Applications, 1994; contbr. articles to profl. jours. With USAF, 1956-60. Mem. Assn. Edn. Journalism and Mass Comm., Soc. Profl. Journalists, Broadcast Edn. Assn., Internat. Comm. Assn. Avocations: guitar, five-string banjo, basketball, fiddle. Home: 309 Lawton Blvd Knoxville TN 37922 Office: U Tenn Sch Journalism Knoxville TN 37996

SINGLETARY, OTIS ARNOLD, JR., university president emeritus; b. Gulfport, Miss., Oct. 31, 1921; s. Otis Arnold and May Charlotte (Walker) S.; m. Gloria Walton, June 6, 1944; children: Bonnie, Scot, Kendall Ann. B.A., Millsaps Coll., 1947; M.A., La State U., 1949, Ph.D., 1954. Mem. faculty U. Tex., Austin, 1954-61, prof. history, 1960-61, assoc. dean Sch. Arts and Scis., 1956-59, asst. to pres., 1960-61; chancellor U. N.C. Greensboro, 1961-66; v.p. Am. Council on Edn., Washington, 1966-68; on leave as dir. Job Corps, OEO, Washington, 1964-65; exec. vice chancellor acad. affairs U. Tex. System, 1968-69; pres. U. Ky., Lexington, 1969-87, prof. emeritus, 1987—; bd. dirs. Howell Corp. Author: Negro Militia and the Reconstruction, 1957, The Mexican War, 1960; editor: American Universities and Colleges, 1968. Regional chmn. Woodrow Wilson Nat. Fellowship Found., 1959-61; chmn. N.C. Rhodes Scholarship Com., 1964-66; chmn. Ky. Rhodes Scholarship Com., 1970-71, 73-74, 77, 83-84, 84-86; mem. So. Regional Edn. Bd., 1969—; chmn. dept. Army history adv. com., 1972-80; bd. visitors Air U., Maxwell AFB, 1973-76. Served with USNR, 1943-46, 51-54. Recipient Scarborough Teaching Excellence award U. Tex., 1958, Students Assn. Teaching Excellence award, 1958, 59; Carnegie Corp. grantee, 1961. Mem. Am. Hist. Assn., So. Hist. Assn., Am. Mil. Inst. (Moncado Book Fund award 1954), Am. Assn. Higher Edn. (dir. 1969—), Phi Beta Kappa (senator 1977-94, v.p. 1985-88, pres. 1988-91), Phi Alpha Theta, Omicron Delta Kappa, Pi Kappa Alpha. Democrat. Methodist. Office: U of Ky 104 King Library N Lexington KY 40506

SINGLETERRY, GARY LEE, investment banker; b. Seattle, May 10, 1948; s. Richard W. and Anita J. (Fowler) S.; m. Mary Beth Burfeind, Nov. 29, 1969; children: Douglas, Laura. AB, Harvard U., 1970; MBA, Stanford U., 1974. Assoc. Morgan Stanley & Co., N.Y.C., 1974-79, Wm Sword & Co., Princeton, N.J., 1979-80; v.p. Thomson, McKinnon & Co., N.Y.C., 1981-82; mng. dir. Dean Witter Reynolds, N.Y.C., 1983-85, Prudential-Bache Securities, N.Y.C., 1985-91; pres. Singleterry & Co., Parsippany, N.J., 1991—. Mem. FNMA Nat. Adv. Coun., 1991. Republican. Office: Singleterry & Co 4 Campus Dr Parsippany NJ 07054

SINGLETON, ALMA NICKELL, law librarian; b. Conway, S.C., Apr. 22, 1947; d. George Dewey and Alma (Nickell) S.; m. Roger Holcombe, May 1,

1976; children: Melanie R. Holcombe, Samuel R., Devon J., John S. BA, U. S.C., 1972, MLS, 1975, JD, 1979. Reference libr. Nova Law Ctr., Ft. Lauderdale, Fla., 1981-84; assoc. law libr. U. Pitts., 1984-92, interim dir. Law Libr., 1992-94; dir. law libr., assoc. prof. law U. Okla., Norman, 1994—. Mem. ABA, Am. Assn. Law Librs., S.C. Bar. Office: U Okla Law Libr 300 Timberdell Rd Norman OK 73019

SINGLETON, DONALD EDWARD, journalist; b. Morristown, N.J., Nov. 8, 1936; s. Edward Leslie and Charlotte (Angerbauer) S.; m. Maureen Ann McNiff, Aug. 8, 1959 (div. 1977); children: Nancy Ann, Mark Aram, Jill Susan. Student, Fairleigh Dickinson U., 1955-58. Reporter Dover (N.J.) Advance, 1959-61, Morristown Daily Record, 1961-63, Newark Eve. News, 1963-64; feature reporter-writer N.Y. Daily News, 1964—. Organizer Com. to Save Church Sq. Park, Hoboken, N.J.; vice chmn. Hoboken Environment Com.; mem. due process com. ACLU., Mem. bd. edn., City of Hoboken, 1974-77. Recipient Pub. Service award N.Y. Council Civic Affairs, 1967; President's Distinguished Service award N.Y.C. Council, 1969; Newspaper award merit Women's Press Club N.Y.C., 1970, 79; citation VFW, 1970; Heywood Broun Meml. award Am. Newspaper Guild, 1970; Silver medal for pub. service journalism N.Y. chpt. Pub. Relations Soc. Am., 1970; certificate merit Am. Bar Assn., 1971; Page One award Newspaper Guild N.Y., 1970; Feature award Newspaper Reporters Assn. N.Y., 1972; Consistent Excellence award Uniformed Firefighters Assn., 1991. Mem. Am. Newspaper Guild. Club: Press (N.Y.C.). Home: 366 Ogden Ave Jersey City NJ 07307-1115 Office: 220 E 42d St New York NY 10017 *In reporting, I try very hard to avoid gathering facts in such a way as to fulfill a preconception. I also attempt to force myself to review constantly my opinions about my subjects, and to keep my mind as open as possible. In writing, I try to ask myself the following questions regularly: "Is this what I really believe? Or am I simply writing this way because I believe that this is what some other person or group would like me to write?" Unless I can answer the first question in the affirmative, and the second in the negative, I am not satisfied with a particular story.*

SINGLETON, FRANCIS SETH, dean; b. Phila., July 13, 1940; s. William Francis and Anna A. (Setian) S.; m. Margaret Neff, June 14, 1962 (div. 1983); children: William, Andrew; m. Charlotte T. Kennedy, Jan. 15, 1988. AB, Harvard U., 1962; MA, Yale U., 1963, PhD, 1968. Budget examiner Bur. of Budget, Washington, 1964-65; dean Pearson Coll. Yale U., New Haven, 1966-69; lectr. U. Dares Salaam, Tanzania, 1969-70; asst. prof. U. Alta., Edmonton, Can., 1970-71; from assoc. prof. to prof., chair politics and govt. Ripon (Wis.) Coll., 1972-83; rsch. assoc. Russian Ctr. Harvard U., Cambridge, Mass., 1983-84; dean arts and scis. Pacific U., Forest Grove, Oreg., 1984-91; prof. govt., 1991—; academic dean Espiritu Santo U., Guayaquil, Ecuador, 1994—; ampart lectr. U.S.I.A., Africa, 1983, 90; bd. dirs. Oreg. Internat. Coun., Salem, 1986—; lectr. Ural U., Russia, 1991; cons. Russia Fedn. Govt., 1992. Author: Africa in Perspective, 1968; contbr. articles to profl. pubs., chpts. to books. Bd. dirs. Com. Fgn. Rels., Portland, 1989—; mem. adv. com. Light Rail Tri-Met, Portland, Oreg., 1989—; Grantee Rockefeller Found., 1969-70, Nat. Coun. Soviet and E. Europe Rsch., 1983-84. Avocations: sailing, outdoor activities. Home: 3421 NW Thurman St Portland OR 97210-1228 Office: Pacific U 2043 College Way Forest Grove OR 97116-1756

SINGLETON, HARRY MICHAEL, lawyer; b. Meadville, Pa., Apr. 10, 1949; s. Getdins T. and Rose Ann (Fucci) S.; children: Harry M. Jr., Leah Rose DiFucci. B.A., Johns Hopkins U., 1971; J.D., Yale U., 1974. Bar: D.C. 1975, U.S. Dist. Ct. D.C. 1975, U.S. C. Appeals (D.C. cir.) 1975, U.S. Ct. Mil. Appeals 1975, Pa. 1976. Assoc. Houston & Gardner, Washington, 1974-75, Covington & Burling, Washington, 1976-77; atty. FTC, Washington, 1975-76; dep. minority counsel Com. on D.C./U.S. Ho. of Reps., Washington, 1977-79, minority chief counsel, staff dir., 1979-81; dep. asst. sec. U.S. Dept. Commerce, Washington, 1981-82; asst. sec. U.S. Dept. Edn. Washington, 1982-86; pres. Harry M. Singleton & Assocs., Washington, 1986-91; pvt. practice law Washington, 1991—; legis. cons. Am. Enterprise Inst., Washington, 1975. Pres. bd. trustees Barney Neighborhood House, Washington, 1978-80; corp. bd. dirs. Children's Hosp. Nat. Med. Ctr., Washington, 1984-88; mem. D.C. Rep. State Com., 1991—, Rep. Nat. Com., 1992—, R.N.C. exec. coun., 1993-95. Mem. Rep. Nat. Lawyers Assn. (bd. dirs. D.C. chpt. 1990-91), Coun. of 100 Black Reps. (bd. dirs. 1991-92), D.C. Black Rep. Coun. (chmn. 1992-93), Rep. Nat. African-Am. Coun. (nat. chmn. 1993—), D.C. Rep. Nat. African-Am. Coun. (chmn. 1993—), Rep. Nat. Hispanic Assembly Washington, Lions. Republican. Presbyterian. Office: 2300 M St NW Ste 800 Washington DC 20037-1434

SINGLETON, HENRY EARL, industrialist; b. Haslet, Tex., Nov. 27, 1916; s. John Bartholomew and Victoria (Flores) S.; m. Caroline A. Wood, Nov. 30, 1942; children: Christina, John, William, James, Diana. S.B., S.M., Mass. Inst. Tech., 1940, Sc.D., 1950. V.p. Litton Industries, Inc., Beverly Hills, Calif., 1954-60; CEO Teledyne Inc., Los Angeles, 1960-86; chmn. Teledyne Inc., 1960-91, Singleton Group, Beverly Hills, Calif., 1988—; chmn. exec. com. Teledyne, Inc., L.A., 1991—. Home: RR 3 Box 32 Santa Fe NM 87505-9802 Office: 335 N Maple Dr Ste 177 Beverly Hills CA 90210-3858

SINGLETON, JAMES KEITH, federal judge; b. Oakland, Calif., Jan. 27, 1939; s. James K. and Irene Elisabeth (Lilly) S.; m. Sandra Claire Hoskins, Oct. 15, 1966; children: Matthew David, Michael Keith. Student, U. Santa Clara, 1957-58; AB in Polit. Sci., U. Calif., Berkeley, 1961, LLB, 1964. Bar: Calif. 1965, Alaska, 1965. Assoc. Delaney Wiles Moore and Hayes, Anchorage, 1963, 65-68, Law Offices Roger Cremo, Anchorage, 1968-70; judge Alaska Superior Ct., Anchorage, 1970-80, Alaska Ct. Appeals, Anchorage, 1980-90, U.S. Dist. Ct. for Alaska, Anchorage, 1990—; chmn. Alaska Local Boundary Commn., Anchorage, 1966-69. Chmn. 3d Dist. Rep. Com., Anchorage, 1969-70. Mem. ABA, Alaska Bar Assn., Phi Delta Phi, Tau Kappa Epsilon. Office: US Dist Ct 222 W 7th Ave No 41 Anchorage AK 99513-7524

SINGLETON, JOHN, director, screenwriter; b. L.A., Jan. 6, 1968; s. Danny Singleton and Sheila Ward. BA, U. So. Calif., 1990. Writer, dir. Boyz N the Hood, 1991 (Acad. award nominee Best Dir. and Best Screenplay 1992); writer, dir., prodr. Poetic Justice, 1993, Higher Learning, 1995; dir., prodr., screenwriter Michael Jackson's Remember the Time video, 1992. First African-American and youngest person to be nominated for an Academy Award for Best Director. Office: Creative Artists Agy 9830 Wilshire Blvd Beverly Hills CA 90212-1825 also: New Deal Prodns 10202 Washington Blvd Culver City CA 90232-3119

SINGLETON, JOHN KNOX, hospital administrator; b. Atlanta, July 9, 1948; married. BA, U. N.C., 1970; MA, Duke U., 1973. Adminstrv. asst. U. Hosp., Cleve., 1970-71; sr. adminstrv. asst. Guy's Hosp., London, 1973-75; asst. dir. Milton S. Hershey Med. Ctr., Hershey, Pa., 1975-76, assoc. dir., 1976-78, dir., 1978-83; exec. v.p. Fairfax Hosp., Falls Church, Va., 1983-85; pres. Inova Health Systems, Inc., Springfield, Va., 1985—. Office: Inova Health System 8003 Forbes Pl # 310 Springfield VA 22151-2215

SINGLETON, JOHN VIRGIL, JR., retired federal judge, lawyer; b. Kaufman, Tex., Mar. 20, 1918; s. John Virgil Sr. and Jennie (Shelton) S.; m. Jane Guilford Tully, Apr. 18, 1953 (dec. Apr. 1991); m. Sylvia Gregg, May 13, 1991. BA, U. Tex., LLB, 1942. Bar: Tex. 1942. Assoc., gen. counsel Houston Harris County Ship Channel Navigation Dist. Fulbright, Crooker, Freeman & Bates, 1944-56; ptnr. Bates, Bright & Singleton, 1954-56, Bell & Singleton, 1957-61, Barrow, Bland, Rehmet & Singleton, 1962-66; judge U.S. Dist. Ct. (so. dist.) Tex., 1966-92, chief judge, 1979-88, sr. judge, 1988-92; pres. Houston Jr. Bar Assn., 1952-53; co-chmn. 5th cir. dist. judges div. Jud. Conf., 1969, chmn., 1970, rep. from 5th cir. Jud. Conf. U.S., 1980-83, also chmn. legis. com.; mem. Fifth Cir. Jud. Coun., 1984—; bd. dirs. First Nat. Bank, Houston, 1964-66. Mem. Tex. Depository Bd., 1963-66; co-chmn. Harris County Lyndon B. Johnson for Pres. Com., 1964-66; del.-at-large Dem. Nat. Conv., 1956, 60, 64; regional coord. 7-state area Dem. Nat. Com., Lyndon B. Johnson-Hubert Humphrey Campaign for Pres., 1964; mem. exec. com., Tex. Dem. Com., 1962-65, chmn. fin. com. 1964-66; former bd. dirs. Houston Speech and Hearing Ctr.; trustee Houston Legal Found., Retina Rsch. Found.; mem. chancellor's coun. U. Tex.; mem. exec. com. Lombardi Awards Trophy; mem. Tex. Longhorn Edn. Found.; sponsor Found. for Tex. Excellence. Lt. comdr. USNR, 1942-46. Named to Waxahachie High Sch. Hall of Fame. Mem. ABA (liaison rep. to spl. com. evaluation disciplinary

enforcement, litigation sect. ad hoc com. on tng. for spl. masters, jury comprehension com.), Fed. Judges Assn. (bd. dirs. 1974—, mem. exec. com.), Houston Bar Assn. (v.p. 1956-57, editor Houston Lawyer 1954-55, chmn. unauthorized practice law com. 1961-62), Tex. Bar Found. (charter mem. fellows), Tex. Bar Assn. (dist. dir.), State Bar Tex. (adminstrn. justice com. chmn. unauthorized practice of law com., 1961-62, chmn. grievance com. 22d dist. 1965-66, bd. dirs. 1966, fed. jud. liaison to state bd. dirs. 1984-85, pres. state bar task force Thurgood Marshall Sch. Law, 1986—, charter mem. fellows Tex. Bar Found.), U. Tex. Ex-Students Assn. (life mem., pres. Houston chpt. 1961-62, mem. exec. com., chmn. scholarship com., at large mem. 1969-80), Cowboys (foreman, straw boss), Am. Judicature Soc., Delta Tau Delta (pres. 1940-41), Phi Alpha Delta, Lakeside Country Club (Houston, past sec , bd. dirs.), Rotary. Episcopalian. Office: 314 N Post Oak Ln Houston TX 77024

SINGLETON, LARRY WILLIAM, financial officer; b. Miami, Fla., Aug. 7, 1950; s. Ollice Monroe and Shirley (Surles) S.; m. Gloria Leonard, Aug. 19, 1972; children: Adam B., Tyler M. BS, Fla. State U., 1972; MBA, U. North Fla., 1982. CPA. Tax mgr. Peat, Marwick & Mitchell, Jacksonville, Fla., 1972-79; with The Charter Co., Jacksonville, 1979—, exec. v.p., chief fin. officer, 1987—. Mem. Fla. Inst. CPA's, Am. Inst. CPA's. Democrat. Methodist. Club: Seminole. Avocation: racquetball. Home: 9085 Bay Cove Ln Jacksonville FL 32257-4913 Office: The Charter Co PO Box 17707 Jacksonville FL 32245-7707

SINGLETON, MARVIN AYERS, otolaryngologist, senator; b. Baytown, Tex., Oct. 7, 1939; s. Henry Marvin and Mary Ruth (Mitchell) S.; B.A., U. of the South, 1962; M.D., U. Tenn., 1966. Intern, City of Memphis Hosps., 1966-67; resident in surgery Highland Alameda City Hosp., Oakland, Calif., 1967-68, resident in otolaryngology U. Tenn. Hosp., Memphis, 1968-71; Am. Acad. Otolaryngology and Ophthalmology fellow in otolaryngic pathology Armed Forces Inst. Pathology, Washington, 1971; fellow in otologic surgery U. Colo. at Gallup (N.Mex.) Indian Med. Center, 1972; practice medicine specializing in otolaryngology and allergies, Joplin, Mo., 1972—; founder, operator Home and Farm Investments, Joplin, 1975—; staff mem. Freeman Hosp., St. John's Hosp., Joplin, Oakhill Hosp.; cons. in otolaryngology Parsons (Kans.) State Hosp. and Tng. Center, Mo. Crippled Children's Service, Santa Fe R.R.; pres. Ozark Mfg. Co., Inc., Joplin. Mem. Internat. Arabian Racing Bd., 1983-88; mem. Mo. State Senate, 1990—, chmn. Senate Rep. Caucus; del. Rep. Nat. Conv., 1988, 92. Served with USNG, 1966-72. Diplomate Am. Bd. Otolaryngology. Fellow A.C.S., Am. Acad. Otolaryngologic Allergy; (past pres.), Am. Assn. Clin. Immunology and Allergy; mem. AMA (Mo. del.), Mo. State, So., Jasper County med. assns., Council of Otolaryngology, Mo. State Allergy Assn., Ear, Nose and Throat Soc. Mo. (past pres.), Joplin C. of C, Masons (32 degree), Sigma Alpha Epsilon, Phi Theta Kappa, Phi Chi. Methodist. Club: Elks. Contbr. articles to profl. jours. Home: Five Mile Ranch, Route 2 Box 138, Seneca, MO 64856 Office: 3401 McIntosh Circle Joplin MO 64804

SINGLETON, PHILIP ARTHUR, corporate executive; b. Detroit, May 2, 1914; m. Eleanor A. DeVilbiss, Aug. 16, 1941; children: Kimberley P., Janet D., John R.M., Tobias T. (dec.). BSME magna cum laude, U. Mich., 1935; cert., Harvard U. Bus. Sch., 1940; LL.B., Yale U., 1941, J.D., 1946. Bar: Conn. 1941, U.S. Supreme Ct 1946; enrolled Inns of Ct., London, Middle Temple, 1952-55; registered profl. engr. With Monsanto Chem. Co. (and assoc. cos.), 1940-55; successively at Merrimac div., Everett, Mass.; asst. to pres. of Monsanto Co., Washington; exec. v.p. Nealco-Monsanto Co., Everett; asst. dir. fgn. dept. Monsanto Co., St. Louis, 1949-50; mng. dir. Monsanto Chems., Ltd., London, Eng., 1956; asst. to pres., sec. exec. com. Monsanto Chems. Co., St. Louis, 1956; dir., mem. exec. com. Forth Chems., Ltd., Scotland; dir. Monsanto Chems., India, Bombay, Monsanto Chem., Australia, Tororo Exploration Syndicate, Uganda, Monsanto Boussois S/A, Paris, Casco A/B, Stockholm, S.I.C.E., Milan, S.I.D.A.C. S/A, Brussels, 1951; exec. v.p. Prophy-lactic Brush Co., Florence, Mass., 1951-56; pres., dir. Prophy-lactic Brush Co., 1957-66; v.p. Vistron Corp.; pres. Pro Brush and Prolon Dinnerware divs., 1957-68; with Warner-Lambert Pharm. Co., Morris Plains, N.J., 1956-63, also sr. v.p. parent firm, 1960-63; with responsibility for indsl. divs. including Md. Glass Corp., Balt., Gulfport Glass Corp., Miss., Nepera Chem. Co., Harriman, N.Y.; chmn. chief exec. officer Singleton Assocs. Internat., Amherst, Mass., 1967-90; chmn. bd. Hoodfoam Industries, Inc., Marblehead, Mass., 1968-72; chmn. bd. dir. Mazzucchelli, Inc., N.Y.C., 1968-71; chmn., chief exec. officer Plastics Industry Adv. Services, Far East Trading and Tech.; pres. Environ. Research Services, High Arctic Tech. Services, 1986-94; ret., Vine div., mem. audit com., div. policy com. Mass. Mut. Life Ins. Co.; dir. Keuffel & Esser Co., Morristown, N.J., Davis Cos. Inc., Denver, Hood Enterprises Inc., Marblehead, Mass., Deerfield Plastics Co., South Deerfield, Mass., Barry Wright Corp., Watertown, Mass., Hardigg Industries Inc., South Deerfield, Mass., Howard Mfg. Co., Littleton, Colo., Amtel. Inc., Koehring Co., Compo Industries Inc., Davis Cos., Denver, Towle Mfg. Co., Courier Corp.; dir., mem. compensation com. and employee benefit com. Hershey Foods Corp., Pa.; chmn., dir., mem. audit com. Werner & Pfleiderer Corp.; mem. Park St. Investment Trust, Boston.; mem. regional appeals bd. War Manpower Commn., 1943-45; employer mem. U.S. delegation ILO, Geneva, Switzerland, 1953-54; pres. Plastics Industry Adv. Services, Amherst, Mass., 1968-83; chmn., chief exec. officer Polar Technology Services-High Arctic and Antarctica. Mem. nat. adv. council Hampshire Coll., Amherst; mem. corp. Northeastern U., Boston., Boston Mus. Sci.; mem. Park St. Ptnrs., 1982—; founding bd. dirs. Plastics Edn. Found. Mem. NAM (dir. 1961-63), Am. Chem. Soc., Soc. Plastics Industry (dir.-at-large 1962-64, v.p. 1965-66, pres. dir. 1967-69), Pilgrims Soc., Soc. Chem. Industry London, U.S. C. of C London (dir. 1953-56), Internat. C of C (overseas investment com., Paris 1953-55), Am. Brush Mfrs. Assn. (dir., pres.), Asso. Industries Mass. (v.p. 1963-65, dir. 1966—), Explorers Club, Union Club (Boston), Royal Thames Yacht Club (London), Cruising Club Am., Edarmoc Club (Detroit), Rotary (Amherst club), Beta Gamma Sigma (hon.), Phi Kappa Psi, Tau Beta Pi (nat. officer, pres. Mich. chpt., editor Council Bull.), Phi Eta Sigma. Republican. Presbyterian. Clubs: Comml., Mchts., Union (Boston); Five Islands Yacht (Maine); Ends of the Earth, Philippics, Royal Cruising, Royal Thames Yacht (London); Intrepids, Travellers Century (Calif.); Beefeaters; Plastics Pioneers (N.Y.); Michigamua, Vulcans (Ann Arbor, Mich.). Home: RD 1 1072 S East St Amherst MA 01002-3075 Office: 1072 S East St Amherst MA 01002-3075

SINGLETON, SAMUEL WINSTON, physician, pharmaceutical company executive; b. Blackpool, Eng., Nov. 17, 1928; came to U.S., 1953, naturalized, 1955; s. Samuel Smith and Jessica Constance M. (Knights) S.; m. Sheila Yolande C. Kershaw, Aug. 23, 1953; 1 child, Diane Jane. M.B., Ch.B., U. Manchester, 1952. Diplomate: Am. Bd. Pediatrics. Intern Chester, Pa., 1953-54; pediatric resident Oakland, Calif., 1956-58; assoc. physician, dir. clin. investigation, med. dir., v.p. Burroughs Wellcome Co., Research Triangle Park, N.C., 1960-89; asst. clin. prof. pediatrics Duke U., Durham, N.C., 1972-90; dir. B.W. Fund. Served with M.C. USNR, 1954-60. Home: 429 Tranquility Rd Moneta VA 24121

SINGLETON, WILLIAM DEAN, newspaper publisher; b. Graham, Tex., Aug. 1, 1951; s. William Hyde and Florence E. (Myrick) S.; m. Adrienne Casale, Dec. 31, 1983; children: William Dean II, Susan Paige, Adam Nicholas. Student, Tyler (Tex.) Jr. Coll., El Centro Coll., Dallas, U. Tex., Arlington. Various positions with The Dallas Morning News, Tyler Morning Telegraph, Wichita Falls Record News, and others, 1966-78; various positions with Albritton Communications Co., 1976-78, pres. newspaper div., 1978-83; pres. Gloucester County Times, Inc., 1983-85; pres. MediaNews Group, Inc., 1985-88, vice chmn., pres., CEO, 1988—; chmn., pres. The Houston Post, 1988—. Mem. Salvation Army, Am. Heart Assn. of Ft. Bend County. Mem. Newspaper Assn. Am. (bd. govs.), So. Newspapers Assn., New Eng. Newspaper Assn., N.J. Press Assn., Tex. Daily Newspaper Assn., Greater Houston Partnership Assn. Baptist. Office: The Houston Post PO Box 4747 4747 South Fwy Houston TX 77004-6063 also: Media News Group Loop Central One 4888 Loop Central Dr Ste 525 Houston TX 77081-2237

SINGLETON-WOOD, ALLAN JAMES, publishing executive; b. Newport, Monmouthshire, Eng., Feb. 13, 1933; emigrated to Can., 1965; s. Charles James and Violet Anne (Bond) S.-W.; m. Joan Davies, June 23, 1956; children: Ceri, Glendon. Student, London U., 1949-51. TV and radio musical dir., 1953-57, TV producer, 1957-61; freelance producer for BBC, 1962-64; indsl. advt. mgr. Western Mail, Cardiff, Wales, 1964; advt. dir. Voice of Brit. Industry Mags., London, 1966; mktg. services exec. The Sun and The People, I.P.C. Newspapers, London, 1966-68; mktg. services mgr. Fin. Post, Toronto, Ont., Can., 1969-71; research mgr. Fin. Post, 1971-76, nat. sales mgr., 1976-77; pub. Fin. Post Mag., 1983-87; v.p. pub. Bedford House Ltd., 1980-83; pub. Small Bus. Mag., 1983-87; v.p. pub. Bedford House Ltd., Toronto, Ont., Can., 1987-88; pub. Small Bus. mag., v.p. CB Media Ltd., Toronto, 1988—; v.p. pub. Can. Bus. and Small Bus. mags., Who's Who in Can. Bus., Who's Who in Can. Fin., 1989—; corp. pub., gen. mgr. Sentry Comm., Willowdale, Ont., 1991-92; group pub. Bus. Publs. divsn. MacLean Hunter Ltd., Toronto, Ont., 1992-93; pres. Can. Productivity divsn. CB Media Ltd., Toronto, 1994—; lectr. at various univs.; cons. in field; pres. Can. Productivity Awards, 1994. Composer: contemporary music including title theme of Swing High, BBC nat. network series, 1953-57. Mem. Anglican Ch. Office: CB Media Ltd, 777 Bay St, Toronto, ON Canada M5W 1A7

SINGLEY, JOHN EDWARD, JR., environmental engineer, consultant; b. Wildwood, N.J., July 31, 1924; s. John Edward Singley and Dorothy Mae (Pfrommer) S.; m. Virginia H. Ragsdale, Mar. 17, 1950; children: Gladys, Ann, Margaret, Patricia. B.S., Ga. Inst. Tech, 1950; M.S., Ga. Inst. Tech., 1952; Ph.D., U. Fla., 1966. Chemist Redstone Arsenal, Huntsville, Ala., 1950-51; dir. tech. services Tenn. Corp., College Park, Ga., 1951-64; lectr. chemistry Ga. State U., Atlanta, 1954-64, assoc. prof., 1964-67; prof. environ. engring. sci. U. Fla., Gainesville, 1967-90, prof. emeritus, 1990—; dir. TREEO Ctr., Gainesville, 1978-86; v.p. James M. Montgomery, Cons. Engrs., Inc., Gainesville, 1984-93, Montgomery Watson Cons. Engrs. Inc., Gainesville, 1993—; sr. v.p. Environ. Scis. Engring. Inc., Gainesville, 1977-84; prin. Water and Air Rsch., Gainesville, 1970-77. Patentee in field of polymers. Mem. Fulton County Rep. Exec. Com., 1962-64; trustee Water for People, 1990-92. With USN, 1943-45. Recipient Donald R. Boyd award Met. Water Agys., 1992. Fellow Am. Inst. Chemists, Inst. Water and Environ. Mgmt.; mem. Am. Water Works Assn. (hon., life, bd. dirs. 1984-87, exec. com. 1985-87, 89-93, v.p. 1989-90, pres.-elect 1990-91, pres. 1991-92, Fuller award 1974, rsch. award 1983, Abel Wolmon award of excellence 1995, Disting. Pub. Svc. award 1995), Fla. Water and Pollution Control Operators Assn. (Flanigan award 1979), Nat. Lime Assn. (Recognition award), Internat. Water Supply Assn., Nat. Assn. Corrosion Engrs., Internat. Ozone Assn. (bd. dirs. 1985-93). Presbyterian. Club: Gainesville, Civitan (pres. 1972, lt. gov. Fla. dist. 1973-76). Home: 1719 NW 23rd Blvd Gainesville FL 32605-3082 Office: Montgomery Watson Cons Engrs Inc 1020 NW 23rd Ave Ste D Gainesville FL 32609

SINGLEY, MARK ELDRIDGE, agricultural engineering educator; b. Delano, Pa., Jan. 25, 1921; s. Maurice and Clara (Rhodes) S.; m. Janet Twichell, Oct. 3, 1942; children: Donald Heath, Frances Marvin, Jeremy Mark, Paul Victor. BS, Pa. State U., 1942; MS, Rutgers U., 1949. Adminstrv. asst. UNRRA, 1946; prof. II biol. and agrl. engring. Rutgers U., New Brunswick, N.J., 1947-87; chmn. dept. Rutgers U., 1961-71; v.p. rsch. and devel. Bedminster Bioconversion Corp., Haddonfield, N.J., 1987—; bd. dirs. Agriplane. Chmn. Hillsborough Twp., Somerset County (N.J.) Planning Bd., 1956-73; pres. Hillsborough Twp. (N.J.) Democratic Club, 1979-80, Agrl. Mus. State of N.J., 1983—, pres. bd. trustee, 1984-89. With USNR, 1942-46. Named Prof. of Yr. Cook Coll., 1985. Fellow AAAS (sect. com. O), Am. Soc. Agrl. Engrs. (chmn. North Atlantic region 1966, bd. dir. 1973-75, Massey-Ferguson medal 1987); mem. Am. Forage and Grassland Council (bd. dir. 1966-69). Home and Office: 335 Amwell Rd Belle Mead NJ 08502-1203

SINHA, RAMESH CHANDRA, plant pathologist; b. Bareilly, India, Feb. 10, 1934; s. Bhawani Prasada and Ram Pyari; m. Indu Bala Sinha; children: Sanjeev, Sangita. BS, Bareilly Coll., 1953; MS, Lucknow (India) U., 1956; PhD, London U., 1960, DSc, 1975. Exptl. officer Rothamster Exptl. Sta., Harpenden, 1959-60; research assoc. U. Ill., Urbana, 1960-65; research scientist Agriculture Can., Ottawa, Ont., Can., 1965—, prin. research sci., 1965—. Contbr. articles in field. Fellow Royal Soc. Can.; mem. Can. Phytopathol. Soc., Indian Phytopathol. Soc. Avocations: badminton, golfing, bridge. Home: 21 Barran St, Nepean, ON Canada K2J 1G3 Office: Plant Rsch Centre, K W Neatby Bldg, Agric Canada, Ottawa, ON Canada K1A 0C6

SINICROPI, ANTHONY VINCENT, industrial relations and human resources educator; b. Olean, N.Y., Mar. 30, 1931; s. Anthony and Christina Maria (LaBella) S.; m. Margaret Frances Michienzi, June 16, 1956; children—Stephen, Christine, Angela, Anthony J., Annette, Joseph. B.A. in Econs. cum laude, St. Bonaventure Coll., 1956; M.I.L.R., Cornell U., 1958; Ph.D., U. Iowa, 1968. Instr. St. Bonaventure Coll., Olean, N.Y., 1958-60; asst. prof. Gannon Coll., Erie, Pa., 1960-63; John F. Murray prof. indsl. relations and human resources U. Iowa, Iowa City, 1963-93, John F. Murray prof. emeritus, 1993—; ombudsperson, 1985-89; labor arbitrator, Washington, 1963—. Co-author: Evidence in Arbitration, 1982, Remedies in Arbitration, 1983, Management Rights in Arbitration, 1986; contbr. numerous articles to profl. jours. Served with USAF, 1951-53. Mem. Indsl. Relations Research Assn., Soc. Profls. in Dispute Resolution (pres. 1979), Nat. Acad. Arbitrators (bd. govs. 1983-91, pres. 1991-92). Avocation: music.

SINICROPI, STEPHEN ANTHONY, radio station executive; b. Olean, N.Y., June 9, 1957; s. Anthony Vincent and Margaret Frances (Michienzi) S.; m. Laura Marie Schwaigert, Jan. 8, 1983. BBA in Indsl. Relations, U. Iowa, 1983. Account exec. Sta. KKRQ-FM, Iowa City, Iowa, 1982-83, sales mgr. Cedar Rapids, 1983-84, gen. sales mgr., 1984-86; gen. mgr. Stas. KKRQ-FM and KXIC-AM, Iowa City, 1987; v.p., gen. mgr. Sta. WLUM-AM-FM, Milw., 1987—. Republican. Roman Catholic. Avocations: cooking, travel, spectator sports, reading, computers. Home: 1601 E Blackthorne Pl Milwaukee WI 53211-1139 Office: Sta KKRQ-KXIC Interstate 80 N Iowa City IA 52240 Office: Sta WLUM-FM 2500 N Mayfair Rd Milwaukee WI 53226-1409

SINISE, GARY, actor, director; b. 1955. co-founder, artistic dir. Steppenwolf Theatre, Chgo. Appeared in (plays) The Indian Wants The Bronx, 1977, Getting Out, 1980 (Joseph Jefferson award), Of Mice And Men, 1980, Loose Ends, 1982, True West, 1983 (also dir., Obie award best dir. 1982-83), Balm in Gilead, 1984, Streamers, 1985, The Caretaker, 1986, Grapes of Wrath, 1990 (Tony award and Drama Desk), (TV films) The Final Days, 1989, My Name is Bill W., 1989, The Stand, 1994 (dir. theatrical films) Miles from Home, 1988, Of Mice and Men, 1991 (also actor); (actor) Jack The Bear, 1991, A Midnight Clear, 1991, Forrest Gump, 1994, The Quick and the Dead, 1995, Apollo 13, 1995; various TV appearances including Crime Story (also dir.), Hunter, True West, Grapes of Wrath; dir. (plays) Frank's Wild Years, Action, The Miss Firecracker Contest, Waiting for the Parade, Tracers, Orphans, Landscape of the Body, 1984, (TV tapes) thirtysomething, 1989, China Beach, 1991. Office: care CAA/Rob Scheidlinger 9830 Wilshire Blvd Beverly Hills CA 90212-1804 Office: Bernstein Fox Attn Martin Licker 1875 Century Park E #1300 Los Angeles CA 90067-2501

SINK, JOHN DAVIS, leadership consultant, scientist; b. Homer City, Pa., Dec. 19, 1934; s. Aaron Tinsman and Louella Bell (Davis) S.; m. Nancy Lee Hile, Nov. 9, 1956 (dec. Aug. 1961); 1 child, Lou Ann. (dec.); m. Claire Kaye Huschka, June 13, 1964 (div. Feb. 1987); children: Kara Joan, Karl John; m. Sharon Ferrando Padden, July 15, 1989; 1 child, Lisa Michelle Padden. BS in Animal/Vet. Sci., Pa. State U., 1956, MS in Biophysics/ Animal Sci., 1960, PhD in Biochemistry/Animal Sci., 1962; EdD in Higher Edn., U. Pitts., 1986. Adminstrv. officer, exec. asst. to sec. agr. State of Pa., Harrisburg, 1962; prof. group leader dept. food, dairy and animal sci. Inst. Policy Rsch. and Evaluation, Pa. State U., University Park, 1962-79; pres. Collegian, Inc., 1971-72; joint planning and evaluation staff officer Sci. and Edn. Adminstrn., U.S. Dept. Agr., Washington, 1979-80; prof., chmn. intercoll. program food sci. and nutrition, interdivisional program agrl. biochemistry and div. animal and vet. scis. W.Va. U., Morgantown, 1980-85; pres., CEO Pa. State U.-Uniontown, 1985-92; pres. Sink, Padden & Assocs. Atlanta, 1992—; dir. S.W. Inst., Uniontown, 1989-92; exec. asst. naval rep. Pa. State W.Va., Charleston, 1981-84; cons. Allied Mills, Inc., Am. Air Lines, Am. Home Foods, Inc., Apollo Analytical Labs.,

Armour Food Co., Atlas Chem. Industries, others. Mem. nat. adv. bd. Am. Security Council, 1981—; mem. nat. adv. council Nat. Commn. Higher Edn. Issues, 1980-82; bd. dirs. W.Va. Cattleman's Assn., 1981-83, W.Va. Poultry Assn., 1980-83, Pembroke Welsh Corgi Club Am., 1980-83, Penn State Stockmen's Club, 1969-71, Greater Uniontown Indsl. Fund, 1986-91, Fayette County Econ. Devel. Council, 1985-93, Westmoreland-Fayette coun. Boy Scouts Am., 1986-91, Westmoreland-Fayette Hist. Soc., 1986-91, Fayette County Soil Conservation Dist., 1990-93, Pa. Youth Found., 1989-93, Fayette County Coop. Extension Bd., 1992-93, Pa. Masonic Found., 1993. Capt. USNR, 1956-86, ret. Decorated Army commendation medal; recipient Nat. Merit Trophy award Nat. Block and Bridle Club, 1956; W.Va. Disting. Achievement medal; Disting. Leadership award Am. Security Council Found., 1983. Pa. Meat Packers Assn. scholar, 1958-62; hon. fellow in biochemistry U. Wis., 1965-65; NSF postdoctoral fellow, 1964-65; Darbaker prize Pa. Acad. Sci., 1967. Fellow AAAS, Am. Inst. Chemists, Inst. Food Technologists; mem. Am. Meat Sci. Assn. (pres. 1974-75), Pa. Air N.G. Armory (trustee 1968-80), Pa. Acad. Sci., U.S. Naval Inst., Naval Res. Assn., Navy League U.S., Res. Officers Assn., Armed Forces Communications and Electronics Assn., Acad. Polit. Sci. (world affairs coun. Pitts. chpt.), Am. Assn. Higher Edn., Am. Assn. Univ. Adminstrs., Am. Chem. Soc., Biophys. Soc., Am. Soc. Animal Sci., Inst. Food Technologists, Soc. Rsch. Adminstrs., Am. Cancer Soc. (bd. dirs. 1988-91), Greater Uniontown C. of C. (bd. dirs. 1989-91), Greater Connellsville C. of C. (pres., bd. dirs. 1989-91), North Fayette C. of C. (bd. dirs. 1986-89), Mon Valley Tri-State Network, Inc. (chmn. bd. dirs. 1989-92), Rotary (sec. State Coll. 1969-71, Paul Harris fellow 1991), Elks, Internat. Assn. of Turtles, Consistory, Shriners, Masons, Alpha Zeta, Omicron Delta Kappa, Gamma Sigma Delta, Sigma Xi, Phi Lambda Upsilon, Gamma Alpha, Phi Tau Sigma, Phi Sigma, Phi Delta Kappa, Pi Sigma Phi. Democrat. Methodist. Author: The Control of Metabolism, 1974, Citizen Extraordinarire, 1993; contbr. numerous articles to profl. publs. Home: 2726 Phillips Dr Marietta GA 30064-4224 Office: PO Box 43264 Atlanta GA 30336-0264

SINKFORD, JEANNE CRAIG, dentist, educator; b. Washington, Jan. 30, 1933; d. Richard E. and Geneva (Jefferson) Craig; m. Stanley M. Sinkford, Dec. 8, 1951; children: Dianne Sylvia, Janet Lynn, Stanley M. III. BS, Howard U., 1953, MS, 1962, DDS, 1958, PhD, 1963; DSc (hon.), Georgetown U., 1978; DSc (Hon.), U. Med. and Dentistry of N.J., 1992. Instr. prosthodontics Sch. Dentistry Howard U., Washington, 1958-60, mem. faculty dentistry, 1964—, rsch. coord., co-chmn. dept. restorative dentistry, assoc. dean, 1968-75, dean, 1975-91, prof. Prosthodontics Grad. Sch., 1977-91; dean emeritus, prof. Sch. Dentistry Howard U.; spl. asst. Am. Assn. Dental Schs., 1991-93, dir. office women and minority affairs, 1993—; instr. rsch. and crown and bridge Northwestern U. Sch. Dentistry, 1963-64; cons. prosthodontics and rsch. VA Hosp., Washington, 1965—; resident Children's Hosp. Nat. Med. Ctr., 1974-75; cons. St. Elizabeth's Hosp.; mem. attending staff Freedman's Hosp., Washington, 1964—; adv. bd. D.C. Gen. Hosp., 1975—; mem. Nat. Adv. Dental Rsch. Coun., Nat. Bd. Dental Examiners; mem. ad hoc adv. panel Tuskegee Syphilis Study for HEW; sponsor D.C. Pub. Health Apprentice Program; mem. adv. coun. to dir. NIH; adv. com. NIH/NIDR/NIA aging Rsch. Coun.; mem. dental devices classification panel FDA; mem. select panel for promotion child health, 1979-80; mem. spl. med. adv. group VA; bd. overseers U Pa. Dental Sch., Boston U. Dental Sch.; bd. advs. U. Pitts. Dental Sch.; mem. anat. rev. bd. for D.C. NRC Gov. Bd.; cons. Food and Drug Adminstrn.; Nat. Adv. Rsch. Coun., 1993—; active Nat. Rsch. Coun. Governing Bd. Mem. editorial rev. bd. Jour. Am. Coll. Dentists, 1988—. Adv. bd. United Negro Coll. Fund, Robert Wood Johnson Health Policy Fellowships; mem. Mayor's Block Grant Adv. Com., 1982; mem. parents' coun. Sidwell Friends, 1983; mem. adv. bd. D.C., mem. Women's Health Task Force, NIH; bd. dirs. Girl Scouts U.S.A., 1993—. Louise C. Ball fellow grad. tng., 1960-63. Fellow Am. Coll. Dentists (sec.-treas. Wash. met. sect.), Internat. Coll. Dentists (award of merit); mem. ADA (chmn. appeal bd. coun. on dental edn. 1975-82), Am. Soc. for Geriatric Dentistry (bd. dirs.), Internat. Assn. Dental Research, Dist. Dental Soc., Am. Inst. Oral Biology, North Portal Civic League, Inst. Grad. Dentists (trustee), So. Conf. Dental Deans (chmn.), Wash. Coun. Adminstrv. Women, Assn. Am. Women Dentists, Am. Pedodontic Soc., Am. Prosthodontic Soc., Fed. Prosthodontic Orgn., Nat. Dental Assn., Inst. Medicine (coun.), Am. Soc. Dentistry for Children, N.Y. Acad. Scis., Smithsonian Assocs., Dean's Coun., Proctor and Gamble, Golden Key Honor Soc., Links Inc., Sigma Xi (pres.), Phi Beta Kappa, Omicron Kappa Upsilon, Psi Chi, Beta Kappa Chi. Address: 1765 Verbena St NW Washington DC 20012-1048

SINNER, GEORGE ALBERT, former state governor, farmer, corporate executive; b. Fargo, N.D., May 29, 1928; s. Albert and Katherine (Wild) S.; m. Elizabeth Jane Baute, Aug. 10, 1951; children: Robert, George, Elizabeth, Martha, Paula, Mary Jo, Jim, Jerry, Joe, Eric. BA in Philosophy, St. Johns U., St. Cloud, Minn., 1950. Farmer Sinner Bros. and Bresnahan, Casselton, N.D., 1952-93; mem. N.D. Senate, 1962-66; mem. N.D. Ho. of Reps., 1982-84, chmn. fin. and tax com., 1983; gov. State of N.D., Bismarck, 1985-93; v.p. pub. & govt. affairs Am. Crystal Sugar Co. Moorhead, Minn., 1990—; U.S. del. Inter-Am. Food and Agr. Conf., 1966; founder, chmn. N.D. Crops Coun., Fargo, 1978-83; chmn. No. Crops Inst. Coun., Fargo, 1980-83; mem. Interstate Oil Compact Commn., 1986-88; chmn. Am. Energy Assurance Coun., 1987-89; presdl. appointee to Adv. Commn. on Govtl. Rels., 1989-92. Candidate for U.S. Congress, 1964; chmn., bd. dirs S.E. Region Mental Health and Retardation Clinic, Fargo, 1964-66; mem. N.D. Bd. Higher Edn., Bismarck, 1966-75, chmn., 1970, Broadcasting Coun., 1968-73; co-founder bd. dirs. Tri-Coll. Univ. Bd., Fargo, N.D., and Moorhead, Minn., 1970-84; del. N.D. Constl. Conv., Bismarck, 1972; mem. Casselton Planning and Zoning Commn., 1982-85. With N.D. N.G., 1950-51. Recipient Rotary Diversified Farming award, 1960, Outstanding Farming award N.D. State U., 1964, L.B. Hartz Profl. Achievement award Moorhead (Minn.) State U., 1980, EPA Nat. Wetlands award, 1992, Nat. Ducks Unltd. Wetlands Conservation award, 1992; named Nat. Water Statesman of Yr., 1992, Doctor of Law, St. John's U., 1992, Doctor of Humanities, N.D. State U., 1993. Mem. Nat. Gov.'s Assn. (chmn. energy and environment, lead gov. out-of-state sales tax collection), Western Govs. Assn. (chmn. 1989-90, lead gov., mem. water pollution com. 1985-93, chmn. 1989-90), N.D. Cattle Feeders' Assn. (farm prodn.), Red River Valley Sugarbeet Growers Assn. (pres. bd. dirs. 1975-79), Greater N.D. Assn. (bd. dirs. 1981), N.D. Farm Bur. (farm prodn.), N.D. Wheat Producers (farm prodn.), N.D. Crop Improvement Assn. (farm prodn.), N.D. Stockmen's Assn. (farm prodn.), Am. Soybean Assn. (farm prodn.), N.D. Barley Coun. (farm prodn.), N.D. Farmers Union (farm prodn.), Am. Legion. Avocations: family, tennis, basketball, hockey, softball, reading. Office: 101 3rd St N Moorhead MN 56560-1952

SINOR, DENIS, Orientalist, educator; b. Kolozsvar, Hungary, Apr. 17, 1916; s. Miklos and Marguerite (Weitzenfeld) S.; m. Eugenia Trinajstic; children: Christophe (dec.). Sophie. BA, U. Budapest, 1938; MA, Cambridge (Eng.) U., 1948; doctorate (hon.), U. Szeged, Hungary, 1971. Attache Centre National de la Recherche Scientifique, Paris, 1939-48; univ. lectr. Altaic studies Cambridge U., 1948-62; prof. Uralic and Altaic studies and history Ind. U., Bloomington, 1962-81, disting. prof. Uralic and Altaic studies and history, 1975-86, disting. prof. emeritus Uralic and Altaic studies and history, 1986—, chmn. dept. Uralic and Altaic studies, 1963-1981, dir. Lang. and Area Ctr., 1963-88, dir. Asian studies program, 1963-87, dir. Asian Studies Rsch. Inst., 1967-79, dir. Rsch. Inst. for Inner Asian Studies, 1979-1981, 85-86; Sec. gen. Permanent Internat. Altaistic Conf., 1960—; rsch. project dir. U.S. Office Edn., 1969-70; sec. Internat. Union Orientalists 1954-61; vis. prof. Institut Nat. des Langues et Civilizations Orientales, Paris, spring 1974; scholar-in-residence Rockefeller Found. Study Ctr., Bellagio, 1975; vice chmn. UNESCO Commn. for History Civilization Cen. Asia, 1981—, mem. consultative com. UNESCO Silk Rd. Project, 1990—; summer seminar dir. NEH, 1988. Author: Orientalism and History, 1954, History of Hungary, 1959, Introduction a l'étude de l'Eurasie Centrale, 1963, Aspects of Altaic Civilization, 1963, Inner Asia, 1968, Inner Asia and its Contacts with Medieval Europe, 1977, Tanulmányok, 1982, Essays in Comparative Altaic Linguistics, 1990; editor, contbr.: Modern Hungary, 1977, Studies in Finno-Ugric Linguistics, 1977, Uralic Languages, 1988, Essays on Uzbek History, Culture and Languages, 1993; also numerous articles.; editor, contbr.: Cambridge History of Early Inner Asia, Handbook of Uralic Studies, Jour. Asian History, Ind. U. Uralic and Altaic Series. Served with Forces Françaises de l'Intérieur, 1943-44; with French Army, 1944-45. NEH grantee, 1981, 87, 88; recipient Jubilee prize U. Budapest, 1938, Barczi Geza Meml. medal, 1981, Gold medal Permanent Internat. Altaistic Conf., 1982, Arminius

Vambery Meml. medal, 1983, The Thomas Hart Benton Mural Medallion, Hungarian Order of Star, 1986; Am. Philos. Soc. Research grantee, 1963; Am. Council Learned Soc. research grantee, 1962; Guggenheim fellow, 1968-69, 1981-82. Fellow Kőrösi Csoma Soc. (hon.); mem. Royal Asiatic Soc. (hon. sec. 1954-64, Denis Sinor medal for Inner Asian Studies named in his honor 1992), Am. Oriental Soc. (pres. Midwest br. 1968-70, nat. pres. 1975-76), Assn. Asian Studies, Am. Hist. Assn., Soc. Asiatique, Tibet Soc. (pres. 1969-74), Mongolia Soc. (pres. 1987-94), Hungarian Acad. Scis. (hon.), Acad. Europaea (fgn.), Deutsche Morgenlandische Gesellschaft, Suomalais-Ugrilaisen Seura (hon. corr.), Soc. Uralo-Altaica (v.p. 1964-94), Internat. Union Oriental and Asian Studies (v.p. 1993—), Cosmos Club (Washington), Explorers Club (N.Y.C.), United Oxford and Cambridge Club (London). Home: 5581 E Lampkins Ridge Rd Bloomington IN 47401-8674 Office: Indiana U Dept Ctrl Eurasian Studies Goodbody Hall Bloomington IN 47405

SINOR, HOWARD EARL, JR., lawyer; b. New Orleans, Sept. 6, 1949; s. Howard E. and Beverly M. (Bourgeois) S.; m. Terran Ann Woodward, June 10, 1972; children: Sally, Vera Sue, Sarah, Sadie. BA with hons., U. New Orleans, 1971; JD cum laude, Harvard U., 1975. Bar: La. 1975, U.S. Supreme Ct. 1983, U.S. Ct. Appeals (5th and 11th cir.), U.S. Dist. Ct. (ea., middle, we.) Dist. La. Assoc. Jones, Walker, Waechter, Poitevent, Carrere & Denegre, New Orleans, 1975-80; sr. ptnr. Jones, Walker, Waechter, Poitevent, Carrere & Denegre, 1980—. Contbg. author: La. Appellate Practice Handbook, 1990, 93; editor: CLE Manual of Recent Developments, 1985, 2d edit., 1986; contbr. articles to profl. jours. Recipient Pres.'s award, La. State Bar Assn., 1987. Fellow La. Bar Found.; mem. ABA, Fed. Bar Assn., New Orleans Bar Assn., La. State Bar Assn. (chmn. antitrust sect. 1987-89). Avocations: golf, hiking, cross-country skiing. Office: Jones Walker Waechter Poitevent Carrere & Denegre 201 Saint Charles Ave New Orleans LA 70170-1000

SINSHEIMER, ROBERT LOUIS, retired university chancellor and educator; b. Washington, Feb. 5, 1920; s. Allen S. and Rose (Davidson) S.; m. Flora Joan Hirsch, Aug. 8, 1943 (div. 1972); children: Lois June (Mrs. Wickstrom), Kathy Jean (Mrs. Vandagriff), Roger Allen; m. Kathleen Mae Reynolds, Sept. 10, 1972 (div. 1980); m. Karen Current, Aug. 1, 1981. S.B., MIT, 1941, M.S., 1942, Ph.D., 1948. Staff mem. radiation lab. MIT, Cambridge, 1942-46; assoc. prof. biophysics, physics dept. Iowa State Coll., Ames, 1949-55; prof. Iowa State Coll., 1955-57; prof. biophysics Calif. Inst. Tech., Pasadena, 1957-77; chmn. div. biology Calif. Inst. Tech., 1968-77; chancellor U. Calif., Santa Cruz, 1977-87, chancellor emeritus, 1987—; prof. U. Calif., Santa Barbara, 1988-90, prof. emeritus, 1990—. Editor: Jour. Molecular Biology, 1959-67, Ann. Rev. Biochemistry, 1966-72. Named Calif. Scientist of Year, 1968; recipient N.W. Beijerinck-Virologie medal Netherlands Acad. Sci., 1969. Fellow Am. Acad. Arts and Scis.; mem. Am. Soc. Biol. Chemists, Biophys. soc. (pres. 1970), AAAS, Nat. Acad. Scis. (mem. council 1970-73, chmn. bd. editors Proc. 1972-80), Inst. Medicine. Achievements include discovery of single-stranded DNA, circular DNA; co-investigator in first in vitro replication of infective DNA. Office: Univ of Calif Dept Biol Sci Santa Barbara CA 93106

SINSHEIMER, WARREN JACK, lawyer; b. N.Y.C., May 22, 1927; s. Jerome William and Elizabeth (Berch) S.; m. Florence Dubin, Mar. 30, 1950; children: Linda Ruth, Ralph David, Alan Jay, Michael Neal. Student, Ind. U., 1943-47; J.D. cum laude, N.Y. Law Sch., 1950; LL.M., NYU, 1957; M.Phil., Columbia U., 1977. Bar: N.Y. bar 1950. Ptnr. Sinsheimer, Sinsheimer & Dubin, N.Y.C., 1950-78, Satterlee & Stephens, N.Y.C., 1978-86, Patterson, Belknap, Webb & Tyler, N.Y.C., 1986-91; counsel Patterson Belknap Webb & Tyler, N.Y.C., 1991—; pres., bd. dirs. Neighborhood Bagel Corp., 1994—; pres. Plessey, Inc., N.Y.C., 1956-70, chmn., CEO, 1970-89; dir. oversees ops. and devel. The Plessey Co., Ltd., Illford, Essex, Eng., 1969-70, dep. chief exec., dir., 1976-89; dir. Plessey, Inc.; pres., chief exec. dir. The Neighborhood Bagel Corp. Chmn. Com. of 68, 1964-67; Mem Westchester County Republican Com., 1956-73; chmn. Nat. Scranton for Pres. Com., 1964; mem. N.Y. State Assembly, 1965-66; Bd. visitors Wassaic State Sch., 1962-64. Served with USNR, 1944-45; with USAF, 1950-52. Mem. ABA, Assn. Bar City N.Y., Am. Digital Radio Soc. (pres. 1994), Am. Friends of Shalom HArtman Inst. (dir. 1991—), Torch and Scroll, Century Club (Purchase, N.Y.), Zeta Beta Tau. Jewish. Home: 22 Murray Hill Rd Scarsdale NY 10583-2828 Office: Patterson Belknap Webb & Tyler 1133 Avenue of the Americas New York NY 10031

SINSKEY, ANTHONY JOHN, microbiology educator; b. Highland, Ill., Apr. 1, 1940; m. ChoKyun Rha, Aug. 26, 1969. BS, U. Ill., 1962; ScD, MIT, 1966. Postdoctoral fellow Harvard U. Sch. Pub. Health, Boston, 1967-68; from asst. prof. to prof. microbiology MIT, Cambridge, Mass., 1968-1988; prof. MIT, Cambridge, 1988—, prof. applied microbiology, 1977-88; dir. Bioinformation Assn., Boston, 1981—; mem. doctoral examination com., Dept. Biology, MIT, 1969—, undergrad. writing requirement coord., 1989—, summer courseBiotechnology: Principles and Processes, 1983—; mem. Com. on Toxic Chems., MIT, 1990-93, chmn. BPEC Annual Symposium, 1987—; mem. adv. bd. Cen. Biotechnology Engring. Northeastern U., 1990—, Nat. Rsch. Coun.'s Associateship Program Review Panel, 1988—, NSF/France Joint Biotechnology Panel, 1987—, NSF Biotechnology Review Panel, 1986—. Author: (with others) Biotechnology of Marine Polysaccharides, 1985, Biotechnology in the Marine Sciences, 1984, Microbiology of Foods and Food Processing, 1972; numerous technical reports, publs. and articles in profl. jours. Recipient Samuel Cate Prescott Internat. Food Technologists Outstanding Young Rsch. award, 1975, Internat. Food Technologists Gerber scholarship award, 1960-62, Disting. Lectureship award Taiwan Nat. Rsch. Coun., 1989. Mem. Am. Acad. Microbiology, Am. Soc. Microbiology, Can. Soc. Microbiology, Inst. Food Technologists, Am. Chem. Soc., Soc. for Indsl. Microbiology. Achievements include research in microbiology, biotechnology, biopolymer engineering, and mammalian cell culture. Home: 285 Commonwealth Ave Boston MA 02115-2001 Office: MIT Dept Biology Rm 68-370 Cambridge MA 02139

SINTON, PETER, newspaper editor, journalist. Bus./fin. editor The San Francisco Chronicle, sr. bus. writer, 1995—. Office: Chronicle Pub Co 901 Mission St San Francisco CA 94103-2988*

SINTZ, EDWARD FRANCIS, librarian; b. New Trenton, Ind., Feb. 6, 1924; s. John and Edith E. (Rudicil) S.; m. Donna Norris, Apr. 12, 1952; children—Ann Kristin, Lesley Elizabeth, Julie Melinda. B.A., U. Kans., 1950; M.A. in L.S, U. Denver, 1954; M.S. in Pub. Adminstrn, U. Mo., 1965. With Kansas City (Mo.) Pub. Library, 1954-66, asst. dir., 1964-66; asso. librarian St. Louis Pub. Library, 1966-68; dir. pub. libraries Miami, Fla., 1968-89, ret.; instr. Washington U., St. Louis, 1966-67; library surveys for Mo. State Library, 1967-68; library bldg. cons., 1965—. Editor: Mo. Library Assn. Quar, 1956-58. Served with USAAF, 1942-45. Mem. ALA, Fla. Library Assn. (pres. 1975-76), Southeastern Library Assn. Club: Kiwanian. Home: 7105 Lakeside Dr Charlotte NC 28215

SINTZOFF, MICHEL, computer scientist, educator; b. Brussels, Aug. 12, 1938; s. Serge and Anna (Emeljanoff) S.; m. Jeanne de Strycker, Dec. 26, 1964; children: André, Marie, Ivan, Catherine, Paul. BS in Math., U. Louvain, Belgium, 1962; Dr.h.c., U. J. Fourier, Grenoble, 1993. Teaching asst. U. Lumumbashi, Zaire, 1962-64; researcher Philips Rsch. Lab., Brussels, 1964-82; prof. U. Louvain, Louvain-la-Neuve, Belgium, 1982—; vis. lectr. U. Brussels, 1971-74, U. Louvain, 1972-82, U. P. and M. Curie, Paris, 1973-75; assoc. prof. U. Edmonton, Can., 1972-73; hon. prof. U. Brussels, 1974—; vis. sr. researcher Ctr. Nat. Rsch. Sci., Nancy, France, 1977-78; mem. numerous editorial bds.; sci. bds. Co-author: Manuel du Langage Algorithmique ALGOL68, 1975, Report on the Algorithmic Language ALGOL68, 1976, Mes Premières Constructions de Programmes, 1977, Raisonner pour Programmer, 1986; founding editor-in-chief Sci. Computer Programming, 1981—; contbr. articles to profl. jours. Recipient Soc. for Worldwide Interbank Fin. Telecommunications award Fonds Nat. de Rsch. Sci., Belgium, 1989, Chevalier des Palmes Académiques (France), 1993; named Officer of the Order of Léopold, 1989. Mem. Academia Europaea. Avocations: reading, movies, music, sports. Home: 7 av du Château, B-1330 Rixensart Belgium Office: U Cath Louvain, Informatique 2 pl Ste Barbe, B-1348 Louvain la Neuve Belgium

SION, MAURICE, mathematics educator; b. Skopje, Yugoslavia, Oct. 17, 1928; came to Can., 1960; s. Max and Sarah (Alalouf) S.; m. Emilie Grace Chisholm, Sept. 15, 1957; children—Crispin, Sarah, Dirk. B.A., NYU, 1947, M.A., 1948; Ph.D., U. Calif.-Berkeley, 1951. Mathematician Nat. Bur. Standards, Washington, 1951-52; instr. U. Calif.-Berkeley, 1952-53; mem. Inst. for Advanced Study, Princeton, N.J., 1955-57, 62; asst. prof. U. Calif.-Berkeley, 1957-60; asst. prof. U. B.C., Vancouver, 1960, assoc. prof., 1961, prof., 1964-89, prof. emeritus, 1989—, head math. dept., 1984-86; dir. Quadra Inst. Math., Vancouver, 1970-89, prof. emeritus, 1989—. Author: Introduction to Methods of Real Analysis, 1969; Theory Semi Group Valued Measures, 1973. Contbr. articles to profl. jours. Served with U.S. Army, 1953-55. Mem. Am. Math. Soc., Can. Math. Soc. (v.p. 1972-74). Office: U BC, Dept Math, Vancouver, BC Canada V6T 1Z2

SIOUI, RICHARD HENRY, chemical engineer; b. Bklyn., Sept. 25, 1937; s. Joseph Fernand and Ellen Annette (Johnson) S.; m. Mary Ann Kapinos, July 21, 1962; children: Kathleen, Thomas, Daniel, Rebecca, Linda, Michelle. BS, Northeastern U., 1964; PhD, U. Mass., 1968. Sr. rsch. engr. Norton Co., Superabrasives div., Worcester, Mass., 1968-71, rsch. supr., 1971-78, tech. mgr., 1978-83, rsch. dir., 1983-87, dir. of tech., 1987—. Com. chmn. Boy Scouts Am. Troop 178, Holden, Mass., 1981-86. With USAF, 1955-59. Mem. AIChE, Am.Indian Sci. and Engring. Sci., Diamond Wheel Mfrs. Inst. (standards, safety and health com.). Achievements include patents relative to the manufacture and composition of abrasive products in which diamond or cubic boron nitride is the abrasive. Home: 22 Streeter Rd Hubbardston MA 01452-1433 Office: Norton Co 1 New Bond St Worcester MA 01606

SIPES, LARRY L., lawyer. AB, U. So. Calif.; JD, NYU. Asst. U.S. atty. Office U.S. Atty., L.A., 1966; dir., counsel Calif. Constn. Revision Commn., 1966-70; dir. Chief Justice's Select Com. on Trial Court Delay State of Calif., 1971-72; dir. western regional office Nat. Ctr. for State Cts., Williamsburg, Va., 1973-86, pres., 1990—; spl. master Marin County Superior Ct., 1986-91; adj. prof. law Hastings Coll. Law U. Calif., 1973-75. Recipient Justice Tom C. Clark award Nat. Conf. Met. Cts. Office: Nat Ctr for State Cts 300 Newport Ave Williamsburg VA 23187

SIPFLE, DAVID ARTHUR, philosophy educator; b. Pekin, Ill., Aug. 29, 1932; s. Karl Edward and Louis Adele (Hinners) S.; m. Mary-Alice Slauson, Sept. 4, 1954; children: Ann Littlefield (dec.), Gail Elizabeth. BA in Math., Philosophy magna cum laude, Carleton Coll., 1953; MA, Yale U., 1955, PhD, 1958. Instr. philosophy Robert Coll., Istanbul, Turkey, 1957-58, Am. Coll. for Girls, Istanbul, 1957-60; asst. prof. Carleton Coll., Northfield, Minn., 1960-67, assoc. prof., 1967-70, chmn. dept., 1968-71, 89-92, prof., 1970-92, William H. Laird prof. philosophy and liberal arts, 1992—; vis. fellow Wolfson Coll., Cambridge U., 1975-76. Translator: (with Mary-Alice Sipfle) Emile Meyerson, The Relativistic Deduction: Epistemiological Implications of the Theory of Relativity, 1985, Explanation in the Sciences, 1991; contbr. articles to profl. jours. NEH Younger Humanist fellow, Nice, France, 1971-72, NSF Sci. Faculty fellow, Cambridge, Eng., 1975-76; Carleton Coll. Faculty Devel. grantee, 1981-83, 86-87. Mem. Am. Philos. Assn., Metaphysical Soc. Am., Philosophy of Sci. Assn., History of Sci. Soc. Avocation: cross country skiing. Office: Carleton Coll One N Coll St Northfield MN 55057

SIPHRON, JOSEPH RIDER, lawyer; b. Cin., Apr. 15, 1933; s. Joseph William and Florence (Rider) S.; m. Mary John Wilson, June 22, 1957; 1 son, John Rider. B.A., Yale U., 1955; postgrad., Oxford U., Eng., 1955-56; LL.B., Yale U., 1959. Bar: N.Y. 1960. Assoc. Milbank, Tweed, Hadley & McCloy, N.Y.C., 1959-67, ptnr., 1968-88; adminstrv. ptnr., 1989-93. Trustee The Buckley Sch., N.Y.C., 1975-80; trustee The Hotchkiss Sch., Lakeville, Conn., 1978-80, Southampton Hosp., N.Y., 1981-84; bd. dirs. Lab. of Ornithology, Cornell U., 1983-89; chmn. N.Y. State birdlife adv. com., 1987-89. Mem. ABA, Nat. Audubon Soc. (dir. 1982-88), Brazilian-Am. C. of C. (dir. 1988-91). Clubs: Union. Home: 50 E 72d St New York NY 10021 Office: Milbank Tweed Hadley & McCloy 1 Chase Manhattan Plz New York NY 10005-1401

SIPIORA, LEONARD PAUL, retired museum director; b. Lawrence, Mass., Sept. 1, 1934; s. Walter and Agnes S.; m. Sandra Joyce Coon, 1962; children—Alexandra, Erika. A.B. cum laude, U. Mich., 1955, M.A., 1956. Dir. museums City of El Paso, Tex., 1967-90; ret.; co-founder, pres. El Paso Arts Council, 1969-71; sec.-treas. El Paso Council Internat. Visitors, 1968-71; trustee El Paso Mus. Art; bd. dirs. Tex. Com. Humanities, Assn. Southwestern Humanities Council; adv. bd. S.W. Arts Found. Bd. dirs. Community Concert Assn. El Paso, El Paso Symphony Orch., El Paso Hist. Soc. Mem. Assn. Mus. Dirs., Mountain Plains Mus. Assn. (pres. 1978-79), Tex. Assn. Museums (pres. 1977-79), Knights of Malta (decorated Grand Cross), Prior of Tex., Kappa Pi. Republican. Lutheran. Home: 1012 Blanchard Ave El Paso TX 79902-2727

SIPPEL, WILLIAM LEROY, lawyer; b. Fond du Lac, Wis. Aug. 14, 1948; s. Alfonse Aloysious and Virginia Laura (Weber) S.; m. Barbara Jean Brost, Aug. 23, 1970; children: Katharine Jean, David William. Ba, U. Wis., JD. Bar: Wis. 1974, U.S. Dist. Ct. (we. dist.) Wis. 1974, Minn. 1981, U.S. Dist. Ct. Minn. 1981, U.S. Ct. Appeals (10th cir.) 1984, U.S. Ct. Appeals (8th cir.) 1985. Research assoc. dept. agrl. econs. U. Wis., Madison, 1974-75; counsel monopolies and comml. law subcom. Ho. Judiciary Com., Washington, 1975-80; spl. asst. to asst. gen. antitrust div. U.S. Dept. of Justice, Washington, 1980-81; from assoc. to ptnr. Doherty, Rumble & Butler, Mpls. and St. Paul, Minn., 1981—. Co-author: The Antitrust Health Care Handbook, 1988. Mem. program com. Minn. World Trade Assn., Mpls., St. Paul, 1985-86, bd. dirs., 1986, Minn. With USAR, 1971-77. Mem. ABA (antitrust sect., vice chmn. ins. industry com. 1990-91), Minn. bar Assn. (co-chmn. antitrust sect. 1986-88, internat. law sect. coun. 1986-89, treas. 1989-90, sec. 1990-91), Minn. Med. Alley Assn. (co-chair internat. bus. com.), Hennepin County Office Internat. Trade (bd. dirs.), Phi Beta Kappa. Roman Catholic. Avocations: computers, reading. Home: 1448 Pinewood Dr Saint Paul MN 55125-2028 Office: Doherty Rumble & Butler PA 2800 Minnesota World Trade Ctr Saint Paul MN 55101

SIPPLE, JOHN HARRISON, physician; b. July 1, 1930. BA, Cornell U., 1952; MD, Cornell Med. Coll., 1955. Diplomate Am. Bd. Internal Medicine, Pulmonary Disease. Intern Upstate Med. Ctr./SUNY, 1955-56, resident, 1956-59; fellow Johns Hopkins Hosp., Balt., 1961-62; clin. prof. medicine SUNY Health Sci. Ctr., Syracuse; attending phys. Crouse Irving Meml. Hosp., 1962—, State Univ. Hosp.; cons. Syracuse VA Med. Ctr., Syracuse State Sch., 1962-78; med. dir. Onondaga C.C. Respiratory Therapy Tech. Cert. Program, 1976-78; cons. physician Comm. on the Handicapped, Jamesville-Dewitt Sch. Dist., 1975-77; cons. Cayuga Health Ctr., 1977-78, Laurentian Med. Group, 1976-77, others. Contbr. articles to profl. jours. and publs. Vol. physician Empire State Games, 1984, 87; mem.-at-large med. bd. Univ. Hosp., 1994-96, others. Fellow Am. Coll. Physicians (program chmn. 1977, mem. coun. of N.Y. state chpt. 1986-93, gov.-elect upstate N.Y. 1988, gov. 1989-93, mem. med. informatics com. 1992-93), Am. Coll. Chest Physicians; mem. Am. Fedn. Clin. Rsch., AMA, Med. Soc. State of N.Y., Onondaga County Med. Soc., Heart Assn. of Upstate N.Y., Trudeau Soc. (mem. chmn. 1971), Am. Thoracic Soc.

SIQUELAND, EINAR, psychology educator; b. Glasgow, Mont., Nov. 15, 1932; s. Harald and Anna Lydia (Kristersen) S.; m. Marian McGrail, Dec. 1960 (div. May, 1970); children: Lynne Ruth, Beth Ann; m. Jillian E.A. Godfree, June 29, 1973. BA, Pacific Luth. U., 1954; MS, U. Wash., 1962, PhD, 1963. Rsch. assoc. pharmacology U. Wash., Seattle, 1958-59; clin. intern psychology VA Mental Hygiene Clinic, Seattle, 1960-61; asst. prof. dept. psychology Brown U., Providence, 1965-69, assoc. prof., 1969-88, prof., 1988—; rsch. scientist dept. Pediatrics Women's and Infants' Hosp. Providence, 1991—. Contbr. articles to profl. jours., chpts. to books. With U.S. Army, 1956-58, Korea. Predoctoral fellow USPHS, 1961-63, postdoctoral fellow, 1963-65. Mem. AAUP, APA, Am. Psychol. Soc., Soc. Rsch. in Child Devel., Sigma Xi. Office: Brown U Dept Psychology PO Box 1853 Providence RI 02912-1853

SIRI, WILLIAM E., physicist; b. Phila., Jan. 2, 1919; s. Emil Mark and Caroline (Schaedel) S.; m. Margaret Jean Brandenburg, Dec. 3, 1949; children: Margaret Lynn, Ann Kathryn. B.Sc., U. Chgo., 1942; postgrad. in physics, U. Calif.-Berkeley, 1947-50. Licensed profl. engr., Calif. Research

---

engr. Baldwin-Lima-Hamilton Corp., 1943; physicist Manhattan Project Lawrence-Berkeley Lab., U. Calif., Berkeley, 1943-45, prin. investigator biophysics and research, 1945-74, mgr. energy analysis program, 1974-81, sr. scientist emeritus, 1981—; cons. energy and environment, 1982—; lectr. U. Calif. Summer Inst., 1962-72; vis. scientist Nat. Cancer Inst., 1970; exec. v.p. Am. Mt. Everest Expdn., Inc.; field leader U. Calif. Peruvian Expdns., 1950-52; leader Calif. Himalayan Expdn., 1954; field leader Internat. Physiol. Expdn. to Antarctica, 1957; dep. leader Am. Mt. Everest Expdn., 1963. Author: Nuclear Radiations and Isotopic Tracers, 1949, papers on energy systems analyses, biophys. research, conservation and mountaineering. Pres. Save San Francisco Bay Assn., 1968-88; bd. dirs. Sierra Club Found., 1964-78; gov. gen. Mountain Medicine Inst., 1988—; vice chmn. The Bay Inst., 1985—; bd. dirs. San Francisco Bay-Delta Preservation Assn., 1987—, treas., 1987—. Lt. (j.g.) USNR, 1950-59. Co-recipient Hubbard medal Nat. Geog. Soc., 1963, Elsa Kent Kane medal Phila. Geog. Soc., 1963, Sol Feinstone Environ. award, 1977, Environ. award East Bay Regional Park Dist., 1984. Mem. Am. Phys. Soc., Biophys. Soc., Am. Assn. Physicists in Medicine, Sigma Xi. Democrat. Lutheran. Clubs: Sierra (dir. 1955-74, pres. 1964-66, William Colby award 1975, John Muir award 1994), American Alpine (v.p.), Explorers (certificate of merit 1964). Home: 1015 Leneve Pl El Cerrito CA 94530-2751 Office: U Calif Lawrence Berkeley Lab 1 Cyclotron Rd Berkeley CA 94720

SIRICA, ALPHONSE EUGENE, pathology educator; b. Waterbury, Conn., Jan. 16, 1944; s. Alphonse Eugene and Elena Virginia (Mascolo) S.; m. Annette Marie Murray, June 9, 1984; children: Gabrielle Theresa, Nicholas Steven. MS, Fordham U., 1968; PhD in Biomed. Sci., U. Conn., 1976. Asst. prof. U. Wis., Madison, 1979-84; assoc. prof. Med. Coll. Va. Commonwealth U., Richmond, 1984-90, prof. of pathology, 1990—, divsn. chair exptl. pathology, 1992—; regular mem. sci. adv. com. on carcinogenesis and nutrition Am. Cancer Soc., Atlanta, 1989-92, metabolic pathology study sect., NIH, Bethesda, 1991-95. Editor; author: The Pathobiology of Neoplasia, 1989, The Role of cell Types in Hepatocarcinogenesis, 1992, Cellular and Molecualr Pathogenesis - A Textbook of Experimental Pathology, 1995; mem. editl. bd. Pathobiology, 1990—, Hepatology, 1991-94; rev. bd. In Vitro Cellular and Devel. Biology, 1987—; contbr. rsch. papers to Am. Jour. Pathology, Cancer Rsch., others. Mem. AAAS, Am. Soc. Cell Biology, Am. Assn. Cancer Rsch. (chmn. Va. state legis. com. 1992-95), Soc. for In Vitro Biology, Am. Clin. Scientist, Am. Soc. Investigative Pathology (chair perogram com. 1994-96), Am. Assn. Study Liver Diseases, N.Y. Acad. Scis., Soc. Exptl. Biology and Medicine, Hans Popper Hepatopathology Soc., Sox. Toxicology. Mem. AAAS, Am. Soc. Cell Biology, Am. Assn. Cancer Rsch. (chmn. Va. state legis. com. 1992-95), Soc. for In Vitro Biology, Assn. Clin. Scientist, Am. Soc. Investigative Pathology (chair program com. 1994-96), Am. Assn. Study Liver Diseases, N.Y. Acad. Scis., Soc. Exptl. Biology and Medicine, Hans Popper Hepatopathology Soc., Soc. Toxicology. Democrat. Roman Catholic. Achievements include development of collagen gel-nylon mesh system for culturing hepatocytes; first establishment and characterization of hyperplastic bile ductular epithelial cells in culture; research in hepato and biliary carcinogenesis, pathobiology of hepatocyte and biliary epithelial cells. Office: Med Coll Va Va Commonwealth U PO Box 980297 Richmond VA 23298-0297

SIRIGNANO, WILLIAM ALFONSO, aerospace and mechanical engineer, educator; b. Bronx, N.Y., Apr. 14, 1938; s. Anthony P. and Lucy (Caruso) S.; m. Lynn Haisfield, Nov. 26, 1977; children: Monica Ann, Jacqueline Hope, Justin Anthony. B.Aero.Engring., Rensselaer Poly. Inst., 1959; Ph.D., Princeton U., 1964. Mem. research staff Guggenheim Labs., aerospace, mech. scis. dept. Princeton U., 1964-67, asst. prof. aerospace and mech. scis., 1967-69, assoc. prof., 1969-73, prof., 1973-79, dept. dir. grad. studies, 1974-78; George Tallman Ladd prof., head dept. mech. engring. Carnegie-Mellon U., 1979-85; dean Sch. Engring., U. Calif.-Irvine, 1985-94; cons. industry and govt., 1966—; lectr. and cons. NATO adv. group on aero. research and devel., 1967, 75, 80; chmn. nat. and internat. tech. confs.; chmn. acad. adv. council Indsl. Research Inst., 1985-88; mem. space sci. applications adv. com. NASA, 1985-90, chmn. combustion sci. microgravity disciplinary working group, 1987-90; chmn. com. on microgravity rsch. space studies bd. NRC. Assoc. editor: Combustion Sci. and Tech, 1969-70; assoc. tech. editor Jour. Heat Transfer, 1985-92; contbr. articles to nat. and internat. profl. jours., also research monographs. United Aircraft research fellow, 1973-74; Disting. Alumni Rsch. award U. Calif. Irvine, 1992. Fellow AIAA (Pendray Aerospace Lit. award 1991, Propellants and Combustion award 1992), ASME (Freeman Scholar award 1992), IDERS (Oppenheim award 1993), AAAS; mem. Combustion Inst. (treas. internat. orgn., chmn. ea. sect.), Soc. Indsl. and Applied Math., Orange County Engring. Coun. (Excellence award 1994), Am. Electronics Assn. (recognition 1994). Office: U Calif Sch Engring S 3202 Engring Gateway Irvine CA 92717

SIRIS, ETHEL SILVERMAN, endocrinologist; b. Clifton, N.J., Aug. 21, 1945; s. Irving A. and Gertrude (Gollop) Silverman; m. Samuel G. Siris, June 2, 1971; children: Benjamin A., Sara A. AB in Biology magna cum laude, Radcliffe Coll. Harvard U., 1963-67; MD, Columbia U. Coll. Physicians and Surgeons, 1967-71. Nat. Bd. of Medical Examiners, Diplomate Am Bd. Internal Medicine, Diplomate Am. Bd. Internal Medicine, Certification in Endocrinology and Metabolism. Intern, asst. resident dept. medicine Presbyn. Hosp., N.Y.C., 1971-74, asst. attending physician, 1977-84, assoc. attending physician, 1984-91, attending physician, 1991—; NIH guest worker Reproduction Rsch. Br. Nat. Inst. Child Health and Human Devel., NIH, 1974-75, NIH rsch. fellow, 1975-76; fellow in Endocrinology Columbia U. Coll. of Physicians & Surgeons and Presbyn. Hosp., N.Y.C., 1976-77; bd. dirs. The Paget Fdn. for Paget's Disease of Bone and related disorders (v.chmn. 1989—); bd. trustees Nat. Osteoporosis Fdn.; editl. bd. Jour. Bone &Mineral Rsch; mem. instl. review bd. Columbia-Presbyn. Med. Ctr.; asst. prof. Dept. Medicine Columbia U., 1977-84; assoc. prof. clin. medicine, 1984-91; prof. clin. medicine Dept. Medicine Columbia U., 1991—; course dir. Physical Diagnosis Dept. Medicine Columbia U., 1985—; assoc. program dir. Irving Ctr. Clin. Rsch. Columbia Presbyn. Med. Ctr., 1990—; mem. Endocrinologic & Metabolic Drugs Advisory Com. FDA, 1992-1995; dir. programs in osteoporosis Ctr. for Women's Health Columbia Presbyn. Med. Ctr., 1993—. Contbr. numerous articles to profl. jours. Upjohn award Columbia U. Coll. of Physicians and Surgeons, 1971, Mary Putnam Jacobi award for Clin. Rsch., 1979, Rsch. award The Paget's Disease Fdn., 1986, 87. Am. Soc. for Bone and Mineral Rsch., Endocrine Soc., Am. Assn. of Clin. Endocrinologists, Phi Beta Kappa, Alpha Omega Alpha. Home: 60 Prescott St Demarest NJ 07627 Office: Dept Medicine Columbia U Coll Physicians & Surgeons 630 W 168th St New York NY 10032

SIRKIN, JOEL H., lawyer; b. Pitts., Jan. 7, 1946; s. Sidney and Marion (Wolkin) S.; m. Karen Sargent, Aug. 7, 1977; children: Alex S., Jacob O. BA magna cum laude, Johns Hopkins U., 1967; JD cum laude, Harvard U., 1972. Bar: Mass. 1972. Prin. Cambridge (Mass.) Pilot Sch., 1970-71; staff atty. Cambridge-Somerville Legal Services, 1972-74; sr. ptnr. Hale & Dorr, Boston, 1974—. Author: Public School Law. Dir. Mass. Children's Lobby, Boston, 1980-84; mem. fin. com. Town of Wayland, Mass., 1993—. Mem. Phi Beta Kappa. Avocations: gardening, tennis, golf. Home: 10 Wildwood Rd Wayland MA 01778-2122 Office: Hale & Dorr 60 State St Boston MA 02109-1816

SIRKIS, ROBERT LANE, retail industry executive; b. Washington, Nov. 5, 1951; s. Joseph A. and Eleanor B. (Block) S.; m. Kendall Kay Whitham, Aug. 30, 1986. BA, Johns Hopkins U., 1973; MBA, Harvard U., 1975. Dir. mktg. Dobbs Houses Inc., Memphis, 1975-79; cons. Arthur D. Little Inc., Cambridge, Mass., 1979-81; v.p. rocky mountain region Pizza Hut Inc., Denver, 1981-83; v.p. ops. services Pizza Hut, Inc., Wichita, Kans., 1983-86; v.p. east cen. region Pizza Hut Inc., Downers Grove, Ill., 1987; sr. v.p., chief exec. officer Florenz, Inc. div. Jerrico, Inc., Lexington, Ky., 1987-88; exec. v.p. ops. Jerrico, Inc., Lexington, Ky., 1988-90; sr. v.p. mktg. Silo, Inc., Phila., 1990-91, exec. v.p. ops., 1991, pres., chief exec. officer, 1991—. Contbr. articles on foodservice industry. Home: 1321 Beverly Dr Overland Park KS 66209-3812 Office: Silo, Inc 6900 Lindbergh Blvd Philadelphia PA 19142-2598

SIROIS, CHARLES, communications executive; b. Chicoutimi, Que., Can., May 22, 1954; m. Thérèse Dallaire; children: Françoise-Charles, Marie-Hélène. B in Fin., U. de Sherbrooke, Sherbrooke, Que., 1978; M in Fin., U.

Laval, Que., 1979. CEO Nat. Mobile Radio Comm. Inc. (now BCE Mobile Comm.), Montreal, 1986-88; chmn., CEO Nat. Pagette, Montreal, 1986-88, BCE Mobile Comm., Montreal, 1988-90, Teleglobe Internat., Inc., Montreal, 1992-94, Telesystem Fin. Corp., Montreal, 1990—, Nat. Telesystem Ltd., Montreal, 1990—; pres., CEO Teleglobe Inc., Montreal, 1992-94, chmn., CEO, 1994—; chmn. Teleglobe Can., Inc., Montreal, 1992—; bd. dirs. Radiomutuel, Inc., Montreal, Hydro-Quebec, Montreal, DMR Group, Inc., Montreal. Co-author: The Medium and the Muse. Active Info. Hwy. Adv. Coun., Ottawa, Ont., Can., 1994—. Mem. Order of Can. Office: Teleglobe Inc, 1000 de la Gauchetière St West, Montreal, PQ Canada H3B 4X5

SIROIS, GERARD, pharmacy educator; b. Andreville, Kamouraska, Que., Can., Dec. 5, 1934; s. Paul-Etienne and Marie-Anna (Caron) S.; children: Nathalie, Stephane. B.Pharm., U. Montreal, 1960; M.S., Purdue U., 1962, Ph.D., 1965. Lic. pharmacist, Que. Asst. prof. pharmacy U. Montreal, 1965-71, assoc. prof., 1971-76, prof., 1976-84, pres. Ethic Com. for Health, 1984—. Grantee Med. Research Council Can., 1974-79; grantee Ministere d'Education du Que., 1972-74. Mem. Am. Pharm. Assn., Assn. Faculties of Pharmacy of Can., Am. Assn. Pharm. Scientists, Can. Soc. Hosp. Pharmacists, Sigma Xi. Roman Catholic. Home: 6352 Matte St, Montreal-Nord, PQ Canada H1G 2E8 Office: U Montreal Faculte Pharmacie, 2900 Blvd Edouard Montpetit, Montreal, PQ Canada H3C 3J7

SIROTKIN, PHILLIP LEONARD, educational administrator; b. Moline, Ill., Aug. 2, 1923; s. Alexander and Molly (Berghaus) S.; m. Cecille Sylvia Gussack, May 1, 1945; children—Steven Marc, Laurie Anne. B.A. (McGregor Found. scholar), Wayne State U., 1945; M.A., U. Chgo., 1947, Ph.D. (Walgreen Found. scholar, Carnegie fellow), 1951. Lectr. U. Chgo., 1949-50; instr. Wellesley Coll., 1950-52, asst. prof. polit. sci., 1953-57; asso. dir. Western Interstate Commn. Higher Edn., Boulder, Colo., 1957-60; exec. asst. to dir. Calif. Dept. Mental Hygiene, Sacramento, 1960-63; asst. dir. NIMH, 1964-66, asso. dir., 1967-71, cons., 1971-73; exec. v.p., acad. v.p State U. N.Y. at Albany, 1971-76; exec. dir. Western Interstate Commn. Higher Edn., Boulder, Colo., 1976-90, sr. adviser, 1990—; sr. adviser Midwestern Legis. Higher Edn. Steering Com., Boulder, Colo., 1990-91; sr. cons. Midwestern Higher Edn. Commn., 1991—; bd. dirs. Boulder County Mental Health Ctr., 1992—; mem. ovesight commn. Hispanic Agenda, Larasa, 1992—; cons. Nebr. Post-Secondary Edn. Commn., 1994; mem. nat. adv. com. Soc. Coll. and Univ. Planning, 1976, adv. panel, rev. state system higher edn. in N.D., 1986, adv. gov's com. on bi-state med. edn. plan for N.D. and S.D., 1988-90, Edn. Commn. States' Nat. Task Force for Minority Achievement in Higher Edn., 1989-91; cons. Bur. Health Manpower Edn., NIH, 1972-74, Nat. Ctr. Health Svcs. Rsch., 1975-85; spl. cons. AID, 1963-64; case writer Resources for the Future, 1954-55; mem. 1st U.S. Mission on Mental Health to USSR, 1967. Author: The Echo Park Dam Controversy and Upper Colorado River Development, 1959. Bd. dirs. Council Social Work Edn., 1959-60. Served to 1st lt. AUS, 1943-46. Recipient Superior Service award HEW, 1967; Wellesley Coll. Faculty Research award, 1956. Home: 299 Green Rock Dr Boulder CO 80302-4745 Office: PO Drawer P Boulder CO 80302

SIROWITZ, LEONARD, advertising agency executive; b. N.Y.C., June 25, 1932; s. Abraham and Sadie (Schoenwetter) S.; m. Myrna Florman, Jan. 22, 1955; children: Laura, Michael. Cert., Pratt Inst., 1953, DFA (hon.), 1983. Art dir. Grey Advt., N.Y.C., 1956-57; advt. designer CBS-TV Network, N.Y.C., 1957-58, NTA TV, N.Y.C., 1958-59; sr. v.p. Doyle, Dane, Bernbach, N.Y.C., 1959-70, creative mgmt. supr., 1959-70; co-chmn., dir. creative dept. Rosenfeld, Sirowitz, Humphrey & Strauss, N.Y.C., 1970—. Head Nat. Campaign for Eugene McCarthy, 1968; vol. Child Find Project for Handicapped Children, 1976; trustee Pratt Inst., 1992. Served with U.S. Army, 1953-55. Recipient over 100 awards and medals from profl. orgns; named to Art Dirs. Hall of Fame, 1985. Mem. Am. Assn. Advt. Agys., Art Dirs. Club N.Y., One Club for Art & Copy (pres. 1982-83). Democrat. Jewish. Office: Rosenfeld Sirowitz & Strauss 111 Fifth Ave New York NY 10003

SIRPIS, ANDREW PAUL, insurance company executive; b. Portland, Maine, May 30, 1944; s. Alexander Fotis and Catherine (Nicholas) S.; m. Helene Victoria Scourby, June 18, 1967; children: Alexander Peter, Matthew Paul. BA, Lafayette Coll., Easton, Pa., 1967; MS, Rensselaer Poly. Inst., 1981. CLU, ChFC. Sales mgmt. trainee Procter & Gamble, Scarsdale, N.Y., 1967-68; ins. salesman Conn. Gen. Life, Washington, 1970-75; dir. pension mktg. Conn. Gen. Life, Hartford, 1975-77, dir. ins. products, 1978-80; dir. tng. CIGNA, Hartford, 1981-82, dir. fin. planning, 1982-84; sales mgr. CIGNA Individual Fin. Svcs., McLean, Va., 1984-91; asst. v.p. CIGNA Individual Fin. Svcs., Vienna, Va., 1992—. Capt. USAR, 1968-70. Mem. Nat. Assn. Life Underwriters, Gen. Agts. and Mgrs. Assn. (dir. greater Washington chpt. 1989-90, sec.-treas. 1991-92, 2d v.p. 1992-93, v.p. 1993-94, pres. 1995-96), Am. Soc. Pension Actuaries, No. Va. Soc. CLU & ChFC (dir. 1987-89), Internat. Assn. Fin. Planners. Greek Orthodox. Avocations: golf, fishing, woodworking. Home: 13801 Foggy Hills Ct Clifton VA 22024 Office: CIGNA Individual Fin Svcs 2070 Chain Bridge Rd Ste 300 Vienna VA 22182

SIRTORI, CARLO, research physicist. Rsch. scientist AT&T Bell Labs, Murray Hill, N.J. Recipient Newcomb Cleveland prize AAAS, 1993-94. Office: AT&T Bell Labs 600 Mountain Ave Murray Hill NJ 07974*

SIS, PETER, illustrator, children's book author, artist, filmmaker; b. Brno, Czech Republic, May 11, 1949; came to U.S., 1982, naturalized, 1988; s. Vladimir and Alena (Petrvalska) S.; m. Terry Ann Lajtha, Oct. 23, 1990; children: Madeleine, Matej. BA, Acad. Fine Arts, Prague, Czech Republic, 1968, MA, 1974. Author, illustrator: Rainbow Rhino, 1987, Waving, 1988, Going Up, 1989, Beach Ball, 1990, Follow the Dream, 1991, An Ocean World, 1992, A Small, Tall Tale from the Far Far North, 1993, Komodo!, 1993, The Three Golden Keys, 1994; illustrator: Fairy Tales of the Brothers Grimm, 2 vols., 1976, 77, Hexe Lakritze and Buchstabenkonig, 1977, Zizkov Romances, 1978, Hexe Lakritze and Rhino Rhinoceros, 1979, Poetry, 1980, Baltic Fairy Tales, 1981, Little Singer, 1982, Bean Boy, 1983, Stories to Solve, 1984, Whipping Boy, 1985 (Newberrey medal 1987), Oaf, 1986, Three Yellow Dogs, 1986, Higgledy Piggledy, 1986, Jed and the Space Bandits, 1987, After Midnight, 1987, City Lights, 1987, Scarebird, 1988, Alphabet Soup, 1988, Halloween, 1989, The Ghost in the Noonday Sun, 1989, The Midnight Horse, 1990, More Stories to Solve, 1991, Rumpelstiltskin, 1993, The Dragons Are Singing Tonight, 1993, Still More Stories to Solve, 1994, The 13th Floor, 1995; filmaker: (TV series) Hexe Lakritze, 1982, (short films), Mimikry, 1975, Island For 6,000 Alarm Clocks, 1977, Heads, 1979 (Golden Bear award Berlin Film Festival 1980), Players, 1981 (Grand Prix Toronto Film Festival 1981), You Gotta Serve Somebody, 1983 (CINE Golden Eagle award 1983), Aesop's Fables, 1984, Twelve Months, 1985; artist one man shows include Gallery Martinska, Gallery Nerudova, Gallery Rubin, Prague, 1977-79, Gallery Klostermauer, St. Gallen, 1975, Gallery Ploem, Delft, 1977, Gallery Vista Nova, Zurich, 1980, Gallery Medici, London, 1981, Sch. Art U. Ohio, Athens, 1990, Pub. Libr., N.Y.C., 1992; group shows include Berlin, 1975, London, 1979, L.A., 1982, Montreal, 1984, Sch. Art U. Oreg., Portland, 1986, Internat. Gallery, San Diego, 1986, Henry Feiwel Gallery, N.Y.C., 1990-91, Stedelijk Mus., Schiedam, Holland, 1992, Santa Monica Heritage Mus., 1992-93. Recipient Best Illustrated Book award N.Y. Times, 1988, 90, 92, 93, 94; gold medal Soc. Illustrators, 1993, silver medal, 1994; Horn Book honor book award Boston Globe, 1993, 94. Home: 252 Lafayette # 5E New York NY 10012 Office: care Greenwillow Books 1350 Ave of Americas New York NY 10019-4701

SIS, RAYMOND FRANCIS, veterinarian, educator; b. Munden, Kans., July 22, 1931; s. Frank J. and Edvie (Shimanek) S.; m. Janice L. Murphy, Aug. 31, 1953; children: Susan, Valerie Mark, Michael, Amy. B.S., Kans. State U., 1953, D.V.M., 1957; M.S., Iowa State U., 1962, Ph.D., 1965. Clinician Blue Cross Animal Hosp., Albuquerque, 1957; asst. prof. small animal surgery Iowa State U., Ames, 1964-66; assoc. prof. anatomy Tex. A&M U., College Station, 1966-68, prof., 1968—; head dept. vet. anatomy, 1968-83. Served with USAF, 1957-61; mem. Res., 1961-91. Mem. Am. Vet. Med. Assn., Tex. Vet. Med. Assn. (dir. 1970-75), Tex. Assn. Lab Animal Sci. (pres. 1973), Am. Assn. Vet Anatomists (sec.-treas. 1973, pres. 1975), World Assn. Vet Anatomists, Am. Assn. Vet. Clinicians, Brazos Valley Vet. Med. Assn. (pres. 1971), Tex. Acad. Vet. Practice (v.p. 1973), Internat. Assn. for Aquatic Animal Medicine (bd. dirs. 1984-86, pres. 1991-92), World

Aquaculture Soc., The Crustacean Soc., Tex. Aquaculture Assn., U.S. Aquaculture Soc., Serra Club (pres. 1985-86), Blue Key, Sigma Xi, Phi Zeta (exec. councilman 1969), Alpha Zeta, Phi Kappa Phi, Phi Sigma, Gamma Sigma Delta, Alpha Gamma Rho (adviser 1962-65, 77-85, pres. 1953, pres. alumni assn. 1976-83). Lodges: K.C. (trustee 1969, pres. 1968), Lions. Home: 2519 Willow Bend Dr Bryan TX 77802-2461 Office: Tex A&M U College Station TX 77843

SISCHY, INGRID BARBARA, magazine editor, art critic; b. Johannesburg, Republic of South Africa, Mar. 2, 1952; came to U.S., 1967; d. Benjamin and Claire S. BS, Sarah Lawrence Coll., 1973; PhD (hon.), Moore Coll. Art, 1987. Assoc. editor Print Collector's Newsletter, N.Y.C., 1974-77; dir. Printed Matter, N.Y.C., 1977-78; curatorial intern Mus. Modern Art, N.Y.C., 1978-79; editor ArtForum Mag., N.Y.C., 1979-88; editor-in-chief Interview, N.Y.C., 1989—. Office: Interview Magazine 575 Broadway 5th Fl New York NY 10012-3230

SISCO, JOSEPH JOHN, management consultant, corporation director, educator, government official; b. Chgo., Oct. 31, 1919; m. Jean Churchill Head, Mar. 26, 1946; children: Carol Bolton, Jane Murdock. Student, Morton Jr. Coll., 1937-39; A.B. magna cum laude, Knox Coll., 1941; M.A., U. Chgo., 1947, Ph.D., 1950. Newspaper reporter, 1936-40; with City News Bur., Chgo., 1937; high sch. tchr., 1941, govt. service, 1950-51; staff Dept. State, 1951-76; successively fgn. affairs officer, specialist internat. orgnl. affairs, officer-in charge Gen. Assembly, Security Council affairs, fgn. service officer, officer-in-charge UN Polit. affairs, 1951-58; dep. dir. Office UN Polit. and Security Affairs, 1958-60, dir., 1960-63; dep. asst. sec. Bur. Internat. Orgn. Affairs, 1963-65, asst. sec. state internat. orgn. affairs, 1965-69; asst. sec. state Near East-South Asia, 1969-74; under sec. state for polit. affairs, 1974-76; pres. Am. U., Washington, 1976-80; chancellor Am. U., 1980-81; ptnr. Sisco Assocs. (mgmt. cons.), Washington, 1981—; bd. dirs. Raytheon Govt. Svcs., Inc., Tenneco InterPublic Group Inc., Braun Govt. Svcs., Inc.; mem. U.S. delegation UN Collective Measures Com., 1952, U.S. delegations to UN Gen. Assembly, 1952-68; U.S. del. Spl. UN Gen. Assembly, session of Mid East, 1967; exec. officer, 1954-57; polit. adviser U.S. delegation Internat. Atomic Energy Agy., 1959; lectr. Fgn. Svc. Inst. Contbr. articles on internat. orgn., fgn. affairs to publs. Served as 1st lt., inf. AUS, 1941-45. Recipient Top Ten Career Service award Civil Service League, 1966, Rockefeller pub. service award, 1971; Silver Helmet Peace award Am. Vets. Com., 1973. Clubs: Cosmos (Washington), Internat. (Washington). Home: 2517 Massachusetts Ave NW Washington DC 20008-2823 Office: 1250 24th St NW Washington DC 20037-1124

SISISKY, NORMAN, congressman, soft drink bottler; b. Balt., June 9, 1927; m. Rhoda Brown, June 12, 1949; children: Mark B., Terry R., Richard L., Stuart J. BS in Bus. Adminstrn., Va. Commonwealth U., 1949; LLD (hon.), Va. State U. Pres., owner Pepsi-Cola Bottling Co. of Petersburg, Inc.; pres., dir. Lee Distbg. Co., Inc., Petersburg, Rhonor Corp., Petersburg; pres. Belfield Land, Inc., Petersburg; mem. Va. Gen. Assembly, Richmond, 1974-82, 98th-104th Congresses from 4th Va. dist., Washington, 1983—; mem. Ho. nat. security com., ranking mem. mil. readiness subcom., subcom. mil. procurement, panel on morale, welfare & recreation, Ho. small bus. com., subcom. procurement, exports & bus. opportunities; dir. Bank of Va., Richmond; vice-chair defense and security com. North Atlantic Assembly. Pres. Appomattox Indls. Devel. Corp.; bd. visitors Va. State U.; commr. Petersburg Hosp. Authority; trustee Va. State Coll. Found.; bd. dirs. Southside Va. Emergency Crew and Community Resource Devel. Bd. Served with USN 1945-46. Recipient Nat. Security Leadership award, Peace Through Stregnth Victory award, Douglas MacArthur award, Watchdog Treasury award, Thomas Jefferson award, 1994 Achievement award Va. Jaycees, Spirit of Enterprise U.S. C. of C., Small Bus. award Nat. Fedn. Ind. Bus. Mem. Nat. Soft Drink Assn. (chmn. bd. 1981-82), Petersburg C. of C. (v.p.). Democrat. Jewish. Club: Moose. Office: US Ho of Reps 2352 Rayburn Washington DC 20515-3604

SISK, DANIEL ARTHUR, lawyer; b. Albuquerque, July 12, 1927; s. Arthur Henry and Myrl (Hope) S.; m. Katharine Banning, Nov. 27, 1954; children: John, Sarah, Thomas. B.A., Stanford U., 1950, J.D., 1954. Bar: N.Mex. 1955, Calif. 1954. Ptnr. firm Modrall, Sperling, Roehl, Harris & Sisk, Albuquerque, 1954-70, 71—; justice N.Mex. Supreme Ct., Santa Fe, 1970; chmn. bd. Sunwest Fin. Svcs., Inc., Albuquerque, 1975-90. Pres. Legal Aid Soc., Albuquerque, 1960-61; trustee Sandia Sch., 1962-72, Albuquerque Acad., 1971-73, A.T. & S.F. Meml. Hosps., Topeka, 1966-82; bd. dirs. N.Mex. Sch. Banking Found., 1981-85. Served with USNR, 1945-46, PTO; to capt. USMCR, 1951-52, Korea. Mem. N.Mex. Bar Assn., Albuquerque Bar Assn. (dir. 1962-63), ABA, State Bar Calif. Presbyn. (elder). Office: Sunwest Bldg 500 4th St NW # 2168 Albuquerque NM 87102-2183

SISK, ROBERT JOSEPH, lawyer; b. Hartford, Conn., Nov. 8, 1928; s. David and Pearl S.; m. Kathryn L. Norton, Mar. 27, 1955 (dec. Mar. 1967); m. Xenia Dahlberg, May 16, 1968 (div. 1993); children: Julie N., Robert J., Jr., Kathryn L. Tucker, Laura A., Philip A., John; m. Sandra L. Clark, June 17, 1995. AB, Dartmouth Coll., 1950; LLB, Yale U., 1956. Bar: N.Y. 1957. Assoc. Hughes Hubbard & Reed, N.Y.C., 1956-63, ptnr., 1964—, chmn., 1994—; bd. dirs. Allied Artists Pictures Corp., 1969-75, Allied Art Industries, 1976-79, Allen-Bradley Co., 1973-85; chmn. planning and program com. 2nd Cir. Jud. Conf. Served to lt. (j.g.) USN, 1950-53; Korea. Fellow Am. Coll. Trial Lawyers; mem. Assn. Bar of City of N.Y., Century Assn. (N.Y.), Yale Club (N.Y.C.), Nisi Prius (N.Y.C.). Democrat. Avocations: sailing; tennis; skiing. Home: 23 Meadow Rd Deer Park Greenwich CT 06830 Office: Hughes Hubbard & Reed 1 Battery Park Plz New York NY 10004-1403

SISKE, ROGER CHARLES, lawyer; b. Starkville, Miss., Mar. 2, 1944; s. Lester L. and Helen (Cagan) S.; m. Regina Markunas, May 31, 1969; children: Kelly, Jennifer, Kimberly. BS in Fin., Ohio State U., 1966; JD magna cum laude, U. Mich., 1969. Bar: Ill. 1969. Assoc. Sonnenschein Nath & Rosenthal, Chgo., 1969-78, ptnr., 1978—, chmn. nat. employee benefits and exec. compensation dept. Past chmn., sec. coun. employee benefits Ill. State Bar Assn. Served to capt. U.S. Army, 1970-71. Decorated Bronze Star. Mem. ABA (past chmn. tax sect. employee benefits com., past chmn. joint com. on employee benefits and exec. compensation and bus. law sect., employee benefits com., past chmn. employee benefits and exec. compensation com.), Chgo. Bar Assn. (past chmn. employee benefits com., mem. exec. council of tax com.), Order of Coif (editor law review). Republican. Office: Sonnenschein Nath Rosenthal 233 S Wacker Dr Ste 8000 Chicago IL 60606-6404

SISKEL, GENE (EUGENE KAL SISKEL), film critic; b. Chgo., Jan. 26, 1946; s. Nathan W. and Ida (Kalis) S.; m. Marlene Iglitzen, 1980; children: Kate Adi, Callie Gray. BA, Yale U., 1967; postgrad., Dept. Def. Info. Sch., 1968; PhD of Letters (hon.), Ill. Coll., 1989. Fellow Coro Found., 1968; film critic Chgo. Tribune, 1969—; CBS This Morning, 1990—, WBBM-TV, Chgo., 1974—. Host. Nightwatch, Sta. WTTW-TV, 1979-80 (Emmy award 1979); co-host (with Roger Ebert) Sneak Previews, Sta. WTTW-TV and PBS Network, 1975-82 (Emmy award 1980), At the Movies, syndicated TV, 1982-86, Siskel & Ebert, syndicated TV, 1986—; author (with Ebert) The Future of the Movies, 1991. Mem. Arts Club Chgo. Office: care Chgo Tribune PO Box 25340 Chicago IL 60625-0340

SISKIN, EDWARD JOSEPH, engineering and construction company executive; b. Bklyn., Apr. 30, 1941; s. Haskell and Sylvia (Steckler) S.; m. Patricia Ann Moore, June 26, 1965 (div. Apr. 1990); children: Candice P. Howard, Cristin Jo; m. Jean Elizabeth Bowen, Dec. 17, 1994. BSEE, U. Pa., 1963; cert., Bettis Reactor Engring. Sch., West Mifflin, Pa., 1965; postgrad., George Washington U., 1963-67. Registered profl. engr., Pa., Mass., N.Y., N.J., Ill., Fla., W.Va., Ind., S.C., Tex., La., Nebr., Calif., Ala. Engr. U.S. AEC, Washington, 1963-67; field office mgr. U.S. AEC, Pitts., 1967-70, Groton, Conn., 1970-77; project mgr. Stone & Webster Engring. Corp., Boston, 1977-78, asst. engring. mgr., 1978-79; engring. mgr. Stone & Webster Engring. Corp., N.Y.C., 1979-83, v.p. & mgr., sr. v.p. & mgr. Stone & Webster Engring. Corp., Cherry Hill, N.J., 1987-88; exec. v.p. Stone & Webster Engring. Corp., Boston, 1985-90; gen. mgr. Superconducting Supercollider Lab., Dallas, 1990-94; pres. Enerjoin Svcs., Inc., 1994—; mem. adv. com. Inst. of Nuclear Power Ops., Atlanta, 1987-90, adv. bd. Ctr. for Chem. Plant Safety, N.Y.C., 1988-90. Bd. dirs. PenJerDel Coun., Phila., 1987-90. Lt.

USN, 1963-69. Sr. mem. IEEE; mem. Am. Nuclear Soc., Am. Philatelic Soc. (State College, Pa.). Jewish. Avocation: stamp collecting. Office: PO Box 17 Haddonfield NJ 08033-0016

SISKIND, ARTHUR, lawyer, director; b. N.Y., Oct. 11, 1938; s. William and Sylvia (Schuman) S.; m. Mary Ann Silverman. Nov. 10, 1962; children: Laura, Julie, Kenneth. BA in Liberal Arts, Cornell U., 1960, LLB with distinction, 1962. Ptnr. Squadron, Ellenoff, Plesent & Lehrer, N.Y., 1970-91; exec. v.p.; group gen. counsel, dir. The News Corp. Ltd., N.Y., 1991—. Capt. U.S. Army, 1963-65. Mem. ABA, City Bar Assn., Cornell Club, Bonnie Briar Country Club. Office: News Am Holdings Inc 1211 Ave of the Americas New York NY 10036

SISKIND, DONALD HENRY, lawyer; b. Providence, Dec. 25, 1937; s. Samuel and Sadie (Wasserman) S.; m. Beth Mohel, July 15, 1962; children: Steven M., Edward M. BS, U. Pa., 1959; LLB, Columbia U., 1962. Bar: Mass. 1962, N.Y. 1963. Assoc. Marshall Bratter Greene Allison & Tucker, N.Y.C., 1962-69, ptnr., 1969-82; ptnr. Rosenman & Colin, N.Y.C., 1982—; bd. dirs. Chgo. Title Ins. Co.; mem. various seminars Practicing Law Inst., 1974—; vis. lectr. Columbia U. Sch. Law, 1993—; mem. adv. bd. Wharton Real Estate Ctr. Mem. adv. bd. Real Estate Fin. Jour.; contbr. articles to profl. jours. Pres. Greenville Community Coun., 1974-76; pres. bd. edn. Union Free Sch. Dist., Scarsdale, N.Y., 1978-81. Mem. ABA, Am. Coll. Real Estate Lawyers (v.p.), Anglo Am. Real Property Inst., N.Y. State Bar Assn., Assn. Bar City of N.Y., Phi Alpha Psi. Home: 876 Park Ave New York NY 10021-1832 Office: Rosenman & Colin 575 Madison Ave New York NY 10022-2511

SISKIND, PAUL M., retired executive; b. 1917. Former dean, prof. law Boston U.; chmn. bd. dirs. UST Corp., Boston. Office: 20 William St Ste 150 Wellesley MA 02181

SISKIND, RALPH WALTER, lawyer; b. Washington, May 29, 1949; m. Linda Paula Friedman. BS, Case Inst. Tech., 1971; MS, U. Pa., 1973; JD, Temple U., 1977. Bar: Pa. 1977, U.S. Dist. Ct. (ea. dist.) Pa. 1977. Engr. Westinghouse Electric Corp., Phila., 1971-74, Standard Pressed Steel, Jenkintown, Pa., 1974, U.S. Mint, Phila., 1975-78; atty. U.S. EPA, Phila., 1978-85; assoc. Blank, Rome, Comisky & McCauley, Phila., 1985-90; ptnr. Wolf, Block, Schorr & Solis-Cohen, Phila., 1990—. Co-author quarterly articles Jour. Environ. Regulation, 1991—; contbr. articles to profl. jours. Office: Wolf Block Schorr 12 Fl Packard Bldg SE Corner 15 & Chestnut Sts Philadelphia PA 19102-2678

SISLER, HARRY HALL, chemist, educator; b. Ironton, Ohio, Mar. 13, 1917; s. Harry C. and Minta A. (Hall) S.; m. Helen E. Shaver, June 29, 1940; children: Elizabeth A., David F., Raymond K., Susan C.; m. Hannelore L. Wass, Apr. 13, 1978. BSc, Ohio State U., 1936; MSc, U. Ill., 1937, PhD, 1939; Doctorate honoris causa, U. Poznan, Poland, 1977. Instr. Chgo. City Colls., 1939-41; from instr. to assoc. prof. chemistry U. Kans., Lawrence, 1941-46; from asst. prof. to prof. chemistry Ohio State U., Columbus, 1946-56; Arthur and Ruth Sloan vis. prof. chemistry Harvard, fall, 1962-63; prof., chmn. dept. chemistry U. Fla., Gainesville, 1956-68; dean Coll. Arts and Scis. U. Fla. 1968-70, exec. v.p., 1970-73, dean grad. sch., 1973-79, Disting. Svc. prof. chemistry, 1979—; indsl. cons. W.R. Grace & Co., Martin Marietta Aerospace, Naval Ordnance Lab., TVA; chemistry adv. panel, also vis. scientists panel NSF, 1959-62; cons. USAF Acad., Battelle Meml. Inst., chmn. interinstl. com. nuclear research, Fla., 1958-64; mem. Fla. Nuclear Devel. Commn. Teaching Sci. and Math., 1958; chemistry adv. panel Oak Ridge Nat. Lab., 1965-69; dir. sponsored rsch. U. Fla., 1976-79. Author: Electronic Structure, Properties, and the Periodic Law, 2d edit, 1973, Starlight-A Book of Poems, 1976, Of Outer and Inner Space—A Book of Poems, 1981, Earth, Air, Fire and Water-A Book of Poems, 1989, (with others) Gen. Chemistry—A Systematic Approach, 2d edit, 1959, Coll. Chemistry—A Systematic Approach, 4th edit, 1980, Essentials of Chemistry, 2d edit, 1959, A Systematic Laboratory Course in Chemistry, 1950, Essentials of Experimental Chemistry, 2d edit, 1959, Semimicro Qualitative Analysis, 1958, rev. edit., 1965, Comprehensive Inorganic Chemistry, Vol. V, 1956, Chemistry in Non-Aqueous Solvents, 1961, The Chloramination Reaction, 1977, Dying-Facing the Facts, 1988, Inorganic Reactions and Methods, Vol. 7, 1988, Encyclopedia of Inorganic Chemistry, Vol. 5, Nitrogen: Inorganic Chemistry, 1994; cons. editor: (with others) Dowden, Hutchinson & Ross, 1971-78; series editor: (with others) Phys. and Inorganic Textbook Series, Reinhold Pub. Corp, 1958-70; contbr. (with others) articles to profl. jours. Decorated Royal Order North Star(Sweden); Named Outstanding Chemist in South, Am. Chem. Soc., 1969, Outstanding Chemist in Southeast, Am. Chem. Soc., 1960, James Flack Norris award Am. Chem. Soc., 1979; recipient Outstanding Centennial Achievement award Ohio State U., 1970. Mem. Am. Chem. Soc. (nat. chmn. div. chem. edn. 1957-58, exec. com. 1957-60, bd. publ. Jour. Chem. Edn. 1956-58), Phi Beta Kappa, Sigma Xi, Phi Delta Kappa, Phi Lambda Upsilon, Phi Kappa Phi, Alpha Chi Sigma. Methodist. Patentee in field. Home: 6014 NW 54th Way Gainesville FL 32653-3265

SISLER, WILLIAM PHILIP, publishing executive; b. Yonkers, N.Y., May 4, 1947; s. William Andrew and Doris Elizabeth (Krasko) S.; m. Elaine Herg, Aug. 23, 1969; 1 child, Jonathan William. BA magna cum laude, Canisius Coll., 1969; PhD, Johns Hopkins U., 1977, M in Adminstrv. Sci., 1983. Asst. then assoc., sr. humanities editor Johns Hopkins U. Press, Balt., 1973-83; exec. editor Oxford U. Press, N.Y.C., 1983-86, v.p., exec. editor humanities and social scis., 1987-90; dir. Harvard U. Press, Cambridge, Mass., 1990—. Johns Hopkins U. fellow, 1969-73. Mem. Century Assn., Harvard Club of N.Y.C. Roman Catholic. Office: Harvard U Press 79 Garden St Cambridge MA 02138-1499

SISLEY, BECKY LYNN, physical education educator; b. Seattle, May 10, 1939; d. Leslie James and Blanche (Howe) S.; m. Jerry Newcomb, 1994. BA, U. Wash. 1961; MSPE, U. N.C., 1964, EdD, 1973. Tchr. Lake Washington High Sch., Kirkland, Wash., 1961-62; instr. U. Wis., Madison, 1963-65, U. Oreg., Eugene, 1965-68; prof. phys. edn. U. Oreg., 1968—, women's athletic dir., 1973-79, head undergrad. studies in phys. edn., 1985-92. Co-author: Softball for Girls, 1971; contbr. articles to profl. jours. Admitted to Hall of Fame, N.W. Women's Sports Found., Seattle, 1981, Honor Award, N.W. Dist. Assn. for Health, Phys. Edn., Recreation and Dance, 1988, State of Oreg. Sports Hall of Fame, 1993; recipient Honor award Nat. Assn. for Girls and Women in Sports, 1995; record holder Age 50-59-Triple Jump, Javelin, High Jump, Age 50-59 Javelin, Age 50-59 Pule Vault. Mem. AAHPERD, Oreg. Alliance Health, Phys. Edn., Recreation and Dance (hon. life mem.), Western Soc. for Phys. Edn. of Coll. Women (exec. bd. 1982-85), Oreg. High Sch. Coaches Assn., Nat. Softball Coaches Acad., N.W. Coll. Women's Sports Assn. (pres. 1977-78), Oreg. Women's Sports Leadership Network (dir. 1987—), Phi Epsilon Kappa, others. Office: University of Oregon Phys Activity & Recreation Svcs Eugene OR 97403

SISLEY, G. WILLIAM, lawyer; b. Morristown, N.J., Feb. 25, 1944; s. George William and Dorothy (Woods) S.; m. Doris Mortenson, Feb. 3, 1979; children: Amanda, Andrew. A.B., Princeton U., 1966; J.D., NYU, 1969. Bar: N.J. 1970, N.Y. 1970, Conn. 1983. Legal sec. Superior Ct. N.J., 1969-70; assoc. Pitney, Hardin & Kipp, Newark, 1970-74; corp. atty., counsel to bus. equipment group SCM Corp., N.Y.C., 1974-78; asst. gen. counsel The Continental Group Inc., Stamford, Conn., 1978-85, corp. sec., 1980-85; ptnr. Davidson, Dawson & Clark, New Canaan, Conn., 1986-89; of counsel Winthrop, Stimson, Putnam & Roberts, Stamford, Conn., 1989-91, ptnr., 1991—. Mem. Am. Soc. Corp. Secs., Corp. Transfer Agt. Assn., Westchester-Fairfield County Corp. Counsel Assn., Assn. of Bar of City of N.Y. Clubs: Princeton (N.Y.C.); Innis Arden Golf (Old Greenwich, Conn.). Home: 26 Keofferam Rd Old Greenwich CT 06870-2127 Office: Wintrop Stimson et al 695 E Main St Stamford CT 06901-2138

SISLEY, NINA MAE, physician, public health officer; b. Jacksonville, Fla., Aug. 19, 1924; d. Leonard Percy and Verna (Martin) S.; m. George W. Fischer, May 16, 1962 (dec. 1990). BA, Tex. State Coll. for Women, 1944; MD, U. Tex., Galveston, 1950; MPH, U. Mich., 1963. Intern City of Detroit Receiving Hosp., 1950-51; resident in gen. practice St. Mary's Infirmary, Galveston, Tex., 1951-52; sch. physician Galveston Ind. Sch. Dist., 1953-56; dir. med. svcs. San Antonio Health Dept., 1960-63, acting dir., 1963-64; resident in pub. health Tex. Dept. Pub. Health, San Antonio, 1963-65; dir. community health svcs. Corpus Christi-Nueces County (Tex.)

Health Dept., 1964-67; dir. Corpus Christi-Nueces County (Tex.) Dept. Pub. Health, 1987—; dir. Tb control region 5 Tex. Dept. Health, Corpus Christi, 1967-73; dir. pub. health region 11 Tex. Dept. Health, Rosenberg, 1978-87; chief chronic illness control City of Houston Health Dept., 1973-78; lectr. Incarnate Ward Coll., San Antonio, 1963-64; adj. prof. U. Tex. Sch. Pub. Health, Houston, 1980—; guest lectr. Corpus Christi State U., 1987—; pvt. practice, Galveston, Stockdale, Hereford, Borger, Tex., 1952-59. Bd. dirs. Coastal Bend chpt. ARC, Corpus Christi, 1990-94, United Way-Coastal Bend, Coastal Bend Coalition on AIDS, 1988—, Coastal Bend chpt. Am. Diabetes Assn., 1990—. Fellow Am. Coll. Preventive Medicine; mem. AMA, Tex. Med. Assn. Nueces County Med. Soc., Am. Assn. Pub. Health Physicians, Tex. Assn. Pub. Health Physicians, Am. Pub. Health Assn., Tex. Pub. Health Assn. Episcopalian. Avocations: fishing, crossword puzzles, raising African violets. Home: 62 Rock Creek Dr Corpus Christi TX 78412 Office: Corpus Christi-Nueces County Dept Health 1702 Horne Rd Corpus Christi TX 78416-1902

SISMAN, ELAINE ROCHELLE, musicology educator; b. N.Y.C., Jan. 20, 1952; d. Irving and Margot (Weintraub) S.; m. Martin Fridson, June 14, 1981; children: Arielle, Daniel. AB, Cornell U., 1972; MFA, Princeton U., 1974, PhD, 1978. Instr. music history U. Mich., Ann Arbor, 1976-79, asst. prof., 1979-82; asst. prof. Columbia U., N.Y.C., 1982-90, assoc. prof., 1990-94, prof., 1995—. Author: Haydn and the Classical Variation, 1993, Mozart's "Jupiter" Symphony, 1993; assoc. editor: 19th Century Music, Beethoven Forum; also articles; contbg. editor Beethoval Forum. Recipient Gt. Tchr. award Columbia U., 1992; fellow NEH, 1981-82; travel grantee Am. Coun. Learned Socs. Mem. Am. Musicological Soc. (pres. Greater N.Y. chpt. 1982-84, bd. dirs. 1992-94, Einstein award 1983), Am. Brahms Soc. (bd. dirs. 1993—), Soc. Fellows in Humanities Columbia U. (chmn. 1992-94). Office: Columbia U Dept Music 703 Dodge New York NY 10027

SISSEL, GEORGE ALLEN, lawyer, manufacturing executive; b. Chgo., July 30, 1936; s. William Worth and Hannah Ruth (Harlan) S.; m. Mary Ruth Rusvold, Oct. 5, 1968; children: Jenifer Ruth, Gregory Allen. B.S. in Elec. Engring., U. Colo., 1958; J.D. cum laude, U. Minn., 1966. Bar: Colo. 1966, Ind. 1973, U.S. Supreme Ct. 1981. Assoc. Sherman & Howard, Denver, 1966-70; with Ball Corp., Muncie, Ind., 1970—; assoc. gen. counsel Ball Corp., 1974-78, gen. counsel, 1978—, corp. sec., 1980—, v.p., 1981-87, sr. v.p., 1987—; acting pres., CEO Ball Corp., Muncie, 1994-95, bd. dirs., 1995—; with First Chgo. Equity Capitol, 1995—. Asso. editor: U. Minn. Law Rev., 1965-66. Served with USN, 1958-63. Mem. MIT Soc. Sr. \$Execs. (bd. govs. 1987-95), Am. Soc. Corp. Secs., ABA, Colo. Bar Assn., Ind. Bar Assn., Order of Coif, Sigma Chi, Sigma Tay, Eta Kappa Nu. Methodist. Lodge: Rotary. Home: 2600 W Berwyn Rd Muncie IN 47304-5115 Office: Ball Corp 345 S High St Muncie IN 47305-2326

SISSOM, LEIGHTON ESTEN, engineering educator, dean, consultant; b. Manchester, Tenn., Aug. 26, 1934; s. Willie Esten and Bertha Sarah (Davis) S.; m. Evelyn Janelle Lee, June 13, 1953; children: Terry Lee, Denny Leighton. B.S., Middle Tenn. State Coll., 1956; B.S. in Mech. Engring., Tenn. Technol. U., 1962; M.S. in Mech. Engring., Ga. Inst. Tech., 1964, Ph.D., 1965. Diplomate Nat. Acad. Forensic Engrs.; registered profl. engr., Tenn. Draftsman Westinghouse Electric Corp., Tullahoma, 1953-57; mech. designer ARO, Inc., Tullahoma, 1957-58; instr. mech. engring. Tenn. Technol. U., Cookeville, 1958-62, chmn. dept. mech. engring., 1965-79, dean engring., 1979-88, dean of engring. emeritus, 1988—; prin. cons. Sissom & Assocs., Cookeville, Tenn., 1962—; bd. dirs. Accreditation Bd. Engring. and Tech., N.Y.C., 1978-86, treas., 1982-86. Author: (with Donald R. Pitts) Elements of Transport Phenomena, 1972, Heat Transfer, 1977, 1,000 Solved Problems in Heat Transfer, 1991; contbr. articles to various publs. Fellow ASME (sr. v.p. 1982-86, gov. 1986-88, Golden medallion), Am. Soc. Engring. Edn. (bd. dirs. 1984-87, pres. 1991-92), Accreditation Bd. Engring. and Tech.; mem. NSPE, Soc. Automotive Engrs., Nat. Engring. Deans Coun. (chmn. 1984-87), Order of the Engr. (chmn. bd. govs. 1994-95), Tau Beta Pi (v.p. 1986-89, councillor 1986-89). . Home and Office: 1151 Shipley Church Rd Cookeville TN 38501-7730

SISSON, EVERETT ARNOLD, industrial developer, business executive; b. Chgo., Oct. 24, 1920; s. Emmett B. and Norma (Merbitz) S.; m. Betty L. DeGrado, Apr. 7, 1984; children: Nancy Lee Sisson Rassbach, Elizabeth Anne Sisson Levy. AB, Valparaiso U., 1942. Sales mgr. Ferrotherm Corp., Cleve., 1946-51, Osborn Mfg. Co., Cleve., 1951-56; dir. sales Patterson Foundry & Machine Co., East Liverpool, Ohio, 1956-58; mgr. sonic energy products Bendix Corp., Davenport, Iowa, 1958-60; pres., chief exec. officer, dir. Lamb Industries, Inc., Toledo, 1960-65, Lehigh Valley Industries, Inc., N.Y.C., 1965-66, Am. Growth Industries, Inc., Chgo., 1966—, Workman Mfg. Co., Chgo., 1966-69, Am. Growth Devel. Corp. (name changed to Am. Growth Group, Inc.), Chgo., 1966-92; CEO The Springs Inc., Spring Green, Wis., 1992—; chmn. bd., chief exec. officer G.F.I. Inc., 1976-87; pres. Peru Properties, Inc., Oak Brook, 1976-87; chmn. AMBRIANCE! Inc., Burr Ridge, Ill., 1988—; bd. dirs. Century Life of Am., Waverly, Iowa, Telco Capital Corp., Hickory Furniture Co., N.C., Acton Corp., Raleigh, N.C., Century Life Ins. Co., Waverly, Iowa, Coronet Ins. Co., Chgo. Pres. coun. Mayfield Heights, Ohio, 1952-57; adviser to bd. trustees Valparaiso (Ind.) U., 1960-69; bd. regents Calif. Luth. Coll., 1968—, fellow, 1969. Capt. USAAF, 1943-46. Mem. Am. Mgmt. Assn., Cleve. Engring. Soc, Pres.'s Assn., Gt. Lakes Yachting Club, Ocean Reef Club, DuPage Club, Desert Highlands Country Club, Scotsdale, Ariz., Tau Kappa Epsilon. Office: The Springs Inc Spring Green WI 53588 also: The Am Growth Group 10040 Happy Valley Rd Scottsdale AZ 85255

SISSON, GEORGE ALLEN, SR., physician, educator; b. Mpls., May 11, 1920; s. Clark R. and Alberta (Chatfield) S.; m. Mary Alice Reed, Mar. 25, 1944; children: Marjorie Ann Sisson Swelsted, George Allen, Kathryn Alberta. A.B., Syracuse U., 1942, M.D., 1945. Intern Syracuse Med. Ctr., 1945-46, Bellevue Hosp. NYU Postgrad. Sch., 1948-49; resident Manhattan Eye, Ear and Throat Hosp., N.Y.C., 1949-51, Am. Cancer Soc. head and neck fellow, 1952-53; practice medicine specializing in head and neck surgery Syracuse, 1953-67, Chgo., 1967; prof., chmn. dept. otolaryngology, head and neck surgery Northwestern U. Med. Sch., 1967-89, prof. and chmn. emeritus, 1989—; prof. otolaryngology, bronchoesophagology Rush Med. Coll., Chgo; sr. attending physian dept. otolaryngology-head and neck surgery Rush-Presbyn.-St. Luke's Med. Ctr., Chgo.; attending physician Holy Family Med. Ctr., Des Plaines, Ill.; chmn., rehab. com. head and neck surgery Northwestern Meml. Hosp., 1967-89; sr. attending physician Cook County Hosp., 1989—; chmn., rehab. com. head and neck surgery Ill. div. Am. Cancer Soc.; adv. com. Nat. Inst. Neurol. Disease, 1975-78. Editorial bd.: Archives of Otolaryngology, Head and Neck Cancer Jour.; contbr. articles to profl. jours. and chpts. to books; producer films illustrating operative techniques for facial plastic and reconstructive surgery. Capt. M.C. U.S. Army, 1946-48. Fellow ACS (gov. 1965, adv. com. 1967-68, cancer comm. 1986—), Am. Acad. Otolaryngology-Head and Neck Surgery (pres. 1983); mem. Am. Laryngeal, Rhinol. and Otol. Soc., Am. Soc. Head and Neck Surgery (pres. 1969-70), Am. Acad. Depts. Otolaryngology (pres. 1978-79), Soc. Univ. Otolaryngologists (pres. 1971-72), Am. Acad. Facial Plastic and Reconstructive Surgery (v.p. 1972, pres. 1978-79), Soc. Head and Neck Surgeons, Am. Laryngol. Soc., Am. Bd. Otolaryngology (pres. 1979-83). Office: 1400 E Golf Rd Des Plaines IL 60016

SISSON, RAY L., dean; b. Pueblo, Colo., Apr. 24, 1934; s. William Franklin and Lillie Mae (Hall) S.; m. Dixie Lee McConnell, Oct. 5, 1952; children: Mark Lynn, Bryan Keith, Tammy Sue Ann. BSEE, U. Colo. 1960; MSEE, Colo. State U., 1966; AA, Pueblo Coll., 1958; EdD, U. No. Colo., 1973. Electronic technician TV Svcs. Co., Pueblo, 1958, Sid's Appliance Ctr., Tucson; from instr. engring. to asst. prof. So. Colo. State Coll., Pueblo, 1960-63, assoc. prof., 1963-76, engring. electronics dept. head, 1968-70; dean Sch. Applied Sci. and Engring. Tech. U. So. Colo., Pueblo, 1973-84, prof., 1976—, interim dean Coll. Engring. and Sci., 1984-85, dean Coll. Applied Sci. and Engring. Tech., 1985—; cons. Escuela Superior Politecnica del Litoral, Ecuador, 1979-82, SUNY, Alfred, Farmingdale, 1982, Moorhead U., 1985, N.Mex. Highlands U., 1985, 90, Kans. State U., Salina, 1994. Bd. dirs. Colo. Transp. Inst., 1994—; dir. So. Colo. Bus. and Tech. Ctr. 1994—. Recipient James H. McGraw award Am. Soc. Engring. Edn., 1990; NSF grantee, 1964, 65, 67, 68, 80-83. Mem. IEEE, ABET (tech. accreditation commn. 1990—, chmn. definition com. 1991, vice chmn. tech. accreditation commn., 1993—), Am. Soc. Engring. Edn. (active, spectrum com.

1989-90, chmn. definition com. 1991, fellow 1993), Engring. Tech. Leadership Inst. (founding mem., bd. dirs. 1983-88, chmn. 1984-85), Profl. Engrs. Colo. (So. chpt., assoc. mem., chair young engrs. 1969, scholarship, edn. com. 1969, chair state scholarship com. 1968), Phi Delta Kappa, Eta Kappa Nu, Tau Alpha Pi. Home: 403 Starlite Dr Pueblo CO 81005-2685 Office: U So Colo 2200 Bonforte Blvd Pueblo CO 81001-4901

SISSON, ROBERT F., photographer, writer, lecturer, educator; b. Glen Ridge, N.J., May 30, 1923; s. Horace R. and Frances A. S.; m. Patricia Matthews, Oct. 15, 1978; 1 son by previous marriage, Robert F.H.; 1 stepson, James A. Matthews. With Nat. Geographic Soc., Washington, 1942-88, chief nat. sci. photographer, 1981-88; free-lance photographer, 1988—; lectr. in field; mem. nature staff Sarastoa Mag., 1989; owner Macro/Nature Workshops, Englewood, Fla. Photographer one-man shows, Nat. Geog. Soc., Washington, 1974, Washington Press Club, 1976, Berkshire (Mass.) Mus., 1976, Brooks Inst., Santa Barbara, Calif., 1980, U. Miami, 1993, Sea Ctr., Santa Barbara, Calif., 1993, Corcoran Gallery of Art's Spl. World Tour, 1988, permanent collections. Mus. Art, N.Y.C. Recipient 1st prize for color photograph White House News Photographers Assn., 1961; recipient Canadian Natural Sci. award, 1967, Louis Schmidt award, 1991. Fellow Biol. Photographers Assn.; mem. Biol. Photog. Assn. (awards for color prints 1967), Nat. Audubon Soc., Nat. Geog. Soc., Nat. Wildlife Fedn., Soc. Photog. Scientists and Engrs., N.Y. Acad. Scis., Sigma Delta Chi. Office: Macro/Nature Photography PO Box 1649 Englewood FL 34295-1649 *The true wonders of the natural world gave me inspiration and a challenge. My cameras and I are privileged to share images of this world with all people.*

SISSON, VIRGINIA BAKER, geology educator; b. Boston, Apr. 8, 1957; d. Thomas Kingsford and Edith Virginia (Arnold) S.; m. William Bronson Maze, Oct. 14, 1989. AB, Bryn Mawr Coll., 1979; MA, Princeton U., 1981, PhD, 1985. Rsch. assoc Princeton (N.J.) U., 1985-86; rsch. assoc. Rice U., Houston, 1986-87, lectr., 1987-92, asst. prof. geology, 1992—; cons. Exxon Prodn. Rsch., Houston, 1988—, U.S. Geol. Survey, Anchorage, 1984—. Contbr. 12 articles to sci. publs. Rsch. grantee, NSF, Houston and Calif., 1988, Houston and Scotland, 1990, Alaska, 1990, Venezuela, 1990, Alaska, 1993. Mem. JOI-Calif., Assn. Women Geologists, Am. Women in Sci., Am. Geophys. Union, Geol. Soc. Am., Mineral. Soc. of Am., Mineral. Assn. Can. Avocations: pilot, cross-country skiing, soccer, recorder playing. Home: 1201 Bering Dr Houston TX 77057-2307 Office: Rice U Dept Geology and Geophys 6100 South Main St Houston TX 77251

SISSONS, JOHN ROGER, educational administrator; b. Monroe, Wis., Aug. 10, 1938; s. John F. and Pearl J. (Eichstadt) S.; m. Patricia M. Wiese, May 21, 1960; children: John A., Theresa M. Sissons, Kirstein. BA, U. Wis., Whitewater, 1971, MA, 1980. Cert. elem. tchr., Wis. Tchr. Postville Sch., Blanchardville, Wis., 1959-62; jr. high sch. tchr. Hollandale (Wis.) Sch., 1962-64; jr. high tchr., prin. DeSoto (Wis.) Sch. Dist., 1964-65; jr. high math. and sci. tchr. Walworth (Wis.) Grade Sch., 1965-68; math. sci. tchr. Reek Elem. Sch., Lake Geneva, Wis., 1968-81; dist. mgr. World Book, Inc., Chgo., 1981-92; goal tchr. Black Hawk Tech. Coll., Janesville, Wis., 1990-92; CEO, adminstr. Kid's Sta., Inc., Walworth, 1990—; computer cons. So. Lakes United Educators, Burlington, Wis., 1983-86. Mem. Am. Legion, K.C. Democrat. Roman Catholic. Avocations: RV camping, nature walks, classic cars. Office: Kid's Sta Inc PO Box 323 507 N Main St Walworth WI 53184-0323

SISTO, ELENA, artist, educator; b. Boston, Jan. 11, 1952; d. Fernando Jr. and Grace Sisto; m. John David Kirkpatrick. BA, Brown U., 1975; grad., N.Y. Studio Sch., 1977; postgrad., Yale U., Norfolk, Conn., 1975, Skowhegan (Maine) Sch., 1976. Gallery artist Vanderwoude Tanabaum, N.Y.C., 1983-89; gallery artist Damon Brandt Gallery, N.Y.C., 1989-91, Germans Van Eck, N.Y.C., 1991—; tchr. Bates Coll., Maine, 1986, Colby Coll., Maine, 1986, SUNY-Purchase, 1988, R.I. Sch. Design, Providence, 1987—, N.Y. Studio Sch., N.Y.C., 1987—, Bard Coll., summer, 1990, Columbia U., N.Y.C. Exhibited in one-man shows at David Beitzel Gallery, 1995; represented in various pub. and pvt. collections. Fellow Skowhegan Sch., 1970, Yale Norfolk, 1975, NEA, 1983, 89-90, Millary Colony, 1987, Handhollow Found., 1995.

SISTO, FERNANDO, mechanical engineering educator; b. La Coruña, Spain, Aug. 2, 1924; s. Fernando Cartelle and Clara (Reiss) S.; m. Grace Jeanette Wexler, June 27, 1946; children: Jane Caroll, Ellen Gail, Todd Frederic. Student, NYU, 1940-43; BS, U.S. Naval Acad., 1946; ScD, MIT, 1952; M Engring. (hon.), Stevens Inst. Tech., 1962. Registered profl. engr., N.J. Commd. ensign USN, 1946, service in the Pacific, ret., 1949; propulsion div. chief Curtiss-Wright Research, Clifton, N.J., 1952-58; prof. mech. engring. Stevens Inst. Tech., Hoboken, N.J., 1959—, chmn. dept., 1966-79, George Meade Bond prof., 1978—, dean of the grad. sch., 1993-94; bd. dirs., trustee Am. Capital Mut. Funds, Houston, 1960—, chmn. bd., 1992—; bd. dirs. Dynalysis of Princeton; cons. UN Devel. Program at Nat. Aero. Lab., Bangalore, India, 1978. Co-author: (textbook) A Modern Course in Aeroelasticity, 1978, 3d edit., 1995. Lt. USN, 1943-49. R.C. DuPont fellow MIT, 1951-52. Fellow ASME; mem. Adirondack Mountain Club. Avocations: skiing, tennis, woodworking, sculling. Office: Stevens Inst Tech Dept Mech Engring Hoboken NJ 07030-5991

SITARZ, ANNELIESE LOTTE, pediatrics educator, physician; b. Medellin, Colombia, Aug. 31, 1928; came to U.S., 1935; d. Hans and Elisabeth (Noll) S. BA cum laude, Bryn Mawr (Pa.) Coll., 1950; MD, Columbia U., 1954. Diplomate Nat. Bd. Med. Examiners, Am. Bd. Pediatrics., Am. Bd. Pediatric Hematology and Oncology. With Columbia U., N.Y.C., 1957—, assoc. prof. clin. pediatrics, 1974-83, prof. clin. pediatrics, 1983—; cons. pediatrics, hematology and oncology Harlem Hosp., N.Y.C., 1967-72, Overlook Hosp., Summit, N.J., 1975—. Contbr. numerous articles to profl. jours. Pres. Mt. Prospect Assn., Summit, 1987—. Fellow Am. Acad. Pediatrics; mem. Am. Assn. Cancer Rsch., Am. Soc. Clin. Oncology, Am. Soc. Hematology, Internat. Soc. Hematology, Harvey Soc. Republican. Episcopalian. Avocations: gardening, sewing, skiing, hiking, stamp collecting. Office: Babies and Children's Hosp 3959 Broadway New York NY 10032-1537

SITEMAN, ALVIN JEROME, banker; b. St. Louis, Mar. 23, 1928; s. Philip L. and Bertha (Newman) S.; m. Ruth Levinsohn, June 22, 1952; children: Estelle, Nancy, Joanne, Suzanne. BS in engring. adminstrn., MIT, 1948. Pres., bd. dirs. Fuel Oil Corp., St. Louis, 1960—, The Siteman Orgn. Inc., St. Louis, 1960—, Site Oil Co. Mo., St. Louis, 1970—; vice chmn. Mark Twain Bancshares Inc., St. Louis, 1979-86, chmn., 1987—; also bd. dirs.; bd. dirs. S.S.& L. Oil & Gas Co., St. Louis, Insituform Mid-Am. Inc., St. Louis. Trustee, commr. St. Louis Art Mus., 1984—; trustee, mem. exec. com. Washington U., 1985-93, Jewish Hosp. St. Louis, 1985—. Republican. Avocations: fishing, hunting, golf, flying. Office: The Siteman Orgn Inc 50 S Bemiston Ave Saint Louis MO 63105-3306

SITES, JAMES PHILIP, lawyer, consul; b. Detroit, Sept. 17, 1948; s. James Neil and Inger Marie (Krogh) S.; m. Barbara Teresa Mazurek, Apr. 9, 1978; children: Philip Erling, Teresa Elizabeth. Student, U. Oslo, Norway, 1968-69; BA, Haverford Coll., 1970; JD, Georgetown U., 1973, ML in Taxation, 1979. Bar: Md. 1973, D.C. 1974, U.S. Supreme Ct. 1978, Mont. 1984, U.S. Tax Ct. 1984, U.S. Dist. Ct. Mont. 1984, U.S. Ct. Appeals (9th cir.) 1988. Law clk. to judge James C Morton, Jr. U.S. Ct. Spl. Appeals Md., Annapolis, 1974-75; law clk. to judge Orman W. Ketcham Superior Ct. D.C., Washington, 1975-76; gen. atty. U.S. Immigration & Naturalization Svc., Washington, 1976-77; trial atty. tax div. U.S. Dept. Justice, Washington, 1977-84; ptnr. Crowley, Haughey, Hanson, Toole & Dietrich, Billings, Mont., 1984—; consul for Govt. of Norway State of Mont., Billings, 1987—; instr. Norwegian Ea. Mont. Coll., 1987-88, Sons of Norway, 1989—. v.p. Scandinavian Studies Found., 1989—; bd. dirs. Billings Com. on Fgn. Rels., 1988—; mem. Mont. Coun. for Internat. Visitors, The Norsemen's Fedn. mem. local exec. bd. World Savior U. Billings, 1993—. U. Oslo scholar, 1969; recipient Peace Rsch. award Haverford Coll., 1970. Mem. Md. State Bar Assn., Mont. State Bar (com. on income and property taxes 1987-91, chair tax and probate sect. 1991-92, chair tax litigation subcom. 1992—), D.C. Bar, Am. Immigration Lawyers Assn., Norwegian-Am. C. of C., Billings Petroleum Club, Hilands Golf Club, Kenwood Golf and Country Club, Billings Stamp Club, Elks, Masons.

Avocations: philately, sports card collecting, hiking, Nordic skiing. Office: Crowley Haughey Hanson Toole & Dietrich Consulate for Norway 490 N 31st St Billings MT 59101-1256

SITKOFF, THEODORE, public management executive; b. Phila., Jan. 25, 1932. BS in Econs., U. Pa., 1953, Masters of Govt. Adminstr., 1955. Acct. Commonwealth of Pa., 1955-59, comptr. dept. pub. welfare, 1959-61, dir. accounts gov.'s office of adminstrn., 1961-64; mem. hdqs. staff Pub. Adminstrn. Svc., McLean, Va., 1964-69, v.p., 1973-77, pres., 1977—, CEO; fin. dir. Fed. Land Devel. Authority Govt. of Malaysia and UN Exec. Corp., 1970-72; founder Ctr. Privatization. Office: Public Administration Service 8301 Greensboro Dr Ste 420 Mc Lean VA 22102

SITRICK, JAMES BAKER, lawyer; b. Davenport, Iowa, Feb. 21, 1935; s. Philip and Miriam (Baker) S.; m. Anne H.M. Helmers, Aug. 21, 1971; children: James Baker Jr., Margaret A., Catherine Baker. BA, U. Wis., 1957; LLM, Yale U., 1960. Bar: N.Y. 1961. Spl. asst. to asst. sec. treasury for internat. taxation U.S. Treasury, Washington, 1965-67; ptnr. Courdert Bros., N.Y.C., 1975—; chmn. exec. com. Coudert Bros., N.Y.C., 1982-93, sr. ptnr., 1993—; mem. mgmt. com. Ctrl. Suiker Maatschappij, The Netherlands, 1984—; lectr. numerous confs. and orgns. Contbr. articles to profl. jours. Mem. Coun. on Fgn. Rels.; mem. bus. com. Mus. Modern Art; chmn. Glyndebourne Opera Assn. Am., Benjamin Franklin Found. for Bibliotuque Nat., Paris, English Chamber Orch. Am.; mem. bd. overseers faculty arts and scis. NYU; trustee French Inst. Alliance-Francais, Folger Shakespeare Libr., Washington; bd. dirs. Coun. for U.S. and Italy; vice chmn. coun. fellows, dir. roundtable Pierpont Morgan Libr. 1st U.S. Army, 1960-61. Frick Collection fellow. Mem. Grolier Club, Century Assn., Knickerbocker Club, Racquet and Tennis Club, Meadow Club (Southampton, N.Y.). Office: Coudert Bros 1114 Avenue Of The Americas New York NY 10036-7701

SITRICK, MICHAEL STEVEN, communications executive; b. Davenport, Iowa, June 8, 1947; s. J. Herman and Marcia B. (Bofman) S.; m. Nancy Elaine Eiseman, July 1, 1969; children: Julie, Sheri, Alison. BS in Bus. Adminstrn. and Journalism, U. Md., 1969. Coordinator press services Western Electric, Chgo., 1969-70; asst. dir. program services City of Chgo., 1970-72; asst. v.p. Selz, Seabolt & Assocs., Chgo., 1972-74; dir. communications and pub. affairs Nat. Can Corp., Chgo., 1974-81; dir. communications Wickes Cos., Inc., San Diego 1981-82; v.p. communications Wickes Cos. Inc., Santa Monica, Calif., 1982-84, sr. v.p. communications, 1984-89; chmn., chief exec. officer Sitrick and Co., L.A. and N.Y.C., 1989—. Office: Sitrick and Co 1875 Century Park E Ste 950 Los Angeles CA 90067-2510

SITTER, JOHN EDWARD, English literature educator; b. Cumberland, Md., Jan. 4, 1944; s. Vivian S. Snider; m. Deborah Ayer, June 19, 1971; children: Zachary, Amelia, Benjamin. AB, Harvard U., 1966; PhD, U. Minn., 1969. asst. prof. English U. Mass., Amherst, 1969-75, assoc. prof. English, 1975-80; prof. English Emory U., Atlanta, 1980-85, Dobbs prof. English, 1985-93, Charles Howard Candler prof., 1993—, chmn. dept. English, 1994—; vis. lectr. U. Kent, Canterbury, Eng., 1974-75. Author: The Poetry of Pope's "Dunciad", 1971, Literary Loneliness, 1982 (Gottschalk prize 1982), Arguments of Augustan Wit, 1991; editor: The Eighteenth Century Poets, 2 Vols., 1990-91; contbr. articles to profl. jours. Nat. Def. Edn. Act fellow U. Minn., 1966-69, Nat. Humanities Ctr fellow, 1978-79. Mem. Am. Assn. Univ. Profs., Modern Language Assn., Am. Soc. 18th Century Studies. Office: Emory U Dept Of English Atlanta GA 30322

SITTON, CLAUDE FOX, newspaper editor; b. Emory, Ga., Dec. 4, 1925; s. Claude B. and Pauline (Fox) S.; m. Eva McLaurin Whetstone, June 5, 1953; children: Lea Sitton, Clinton, Suzanna Sitton Greene, McLaurin. BA, Emory U., 1949, L.H.D., 1984. Reporter Internat. News Service, 1949-50; with U.P., 1950-55; writer-editor U.P., N.Y.C., 1952-55; information officer USIA, 1955-57; mem. staff N.Y. Times, 1957-68, nat. news dir., 1964-68; editorial dir. The News and Observer Pub. Co., Raleigh, N.C., 1968-90; dir. The News and Observer Pub. Co., 1969-90, v.p., 1970-90; editor News and Observer, 1970-90; sr. lectr. Emory U., Atlanta, 1991—; active Pulitzer Prize Bd., 1985-94, chmn., 1992-93; bd. counselors Oxford Coll. Emory U., 1993—. Lay mem. Commn. on Evaluation of Disciplinary Enforcement, Ga. Supreme Ct., 1995. With USNR, 1943-46. Recipient Pulitzer prize for commentary, 1983. Mem. Am. Soc. Newspaper Editors (dir. 1977-83). Home: PO Box 1326 Oxford GA 30267-1326

SIVAM, THANGAVEL PARAMA, aerospace engineer; b. Madukkur, India, June 12, 1944; s. Thangavel Arumugam Chettiar and Sivapackiam Thangavel (Vadivel) Achi; m. Maheswari Uthirapathy, Sept. 14, 1972; children: Uma Devi, Senthil Kumar, Sunthosh Kumar. MS, Indian Inst. Tech., Madras, 1971; PhD, SUNY, Buffalo, 1978. Project engr. Indian Space Rsch. Orgn.; Trivandrum, 1971-74; rsch. asst. SUNY, Buffalo, 1974-78; asst. prof. W.Va. Tech., Montgomery, 1978; sr. structures engr. Gates Learjet Corp., Wichita, Kans., 1978-82; asst. prof. Wichita State U., 1982-87; prin. engr. Boeing Mil. Airplane, Wichita, 1987-89; sr. staff specialist Chrysler Techs. Airborne Systems, Inc., Waco, Tex., 1989—; cons. Precision Composites, Wichita, 1984-86; rsch. assoc., adj. faculty Inst. for Aviation Rsch. at Wichita State U., 1986-89. Contbr. articles to profl. jours. Merit scholar Govt. of India, 1965; grantee NASA, 1982-84, U.S. Army, 1987-90, USAF/Raytheon, 1989—. Mem. AIAA, Soc. Automotive Engrs. (chmn. structures com. 1985—). Achievements include invention of natural fiber/epoxy composites; originated steel wire-reinforced fiberglass/epoxy cylindrical shells. Office: Chrysler Techs Airborne Systems 7500 Maehr Rd MS 1135 Waco TX 76715

SIVASUBRAMANIAN, KOLINJAVADI NAGARAJAN, neonatologist, educator; b. Coimbatore, Madras, India, May 9, 1945; came to U.S., 1971; s. Kolinjavadi Ramaswamy and Sukanthi (Subramanian) Nagarajan; m. Kalyani Hariharier, Feb. 5, 1975; children: Ramya, Rajeev, Ranjan. BSc, Madras U., 1964, MD, 1969. Diplomate Am. Bd. Pediatrics and Neonatal-Perinatal Medicine. Intern in pediatrics Jewish Hosp. and Med. Ctr., Bklyn., 1971-72; resident in pediatrics U. Md. Hosp., Balt., 1972-74; fellow in neonatology Georgetown U. Hosp., Washington, 1974-76, attending neonatologist, 1976—, dir. nurseries, chief neonatology, 1981—, vice chair pediatrics, 1988—, prof. pediatrics and ob-gyn.; mem. bd. dirs., co-founder Coun. of Hindu Temples of U.S.A., 1992—; coord. & co-founder United Hindu Temples of Metropolitan Washington D.C.; 1st v.p. Interfaith Conf., 1995—. Editor: Trace Elements/Mineral Metabolism During Development, 1993; editor pub. SIDS Series, 1985; editor jour. Current Concepts in Neonatology, India, 1990—; internat. editor Indian Jour. Pediatrics, India, 1988—. Bd. trustees, chmn. Sri Siva Vishnu Temple, Lanham, Md., 1981-91; mem. Fetus and New Born Com., Washington, 1988—; bd. dirs. Coun. of Hindu Temples of U.S.A., 1984—, coord.-co-founder United Hindu Temples of Met. Washington, 1992; 1st v.p. Interfaith Conf., Washington, 1994—. Recipient "Preemies" cover article Newsweek, 1988. Fellow Am. Coll. Nutrition, Am. Acad. Pediatrics; mem. AAAS, N.Y. Acad. Sci., Internat. Soc. for Trace Element Rsch. in Humans, Soc. for Bioethics Consultation, Am. Soc. Law, Medicine and Ethics. Hindu. Achievements include research in neonatology, trace elements kinetics, reduction in infant mortality and bioethics. Office: Georgetown U Hosp 3 South Hospital 3800 Reservoir Rd NW Washington DC 20007-2196

SIVCO, DEBORAH L., research physicist. Rsch. scientist AT&T Bell Labs, Murray Hill, N.J. Recipient Newcomb Cleveland prize AAAS, 1993-94. Office: AT&T Bell Labs 600 Mountain Ave Murray Hill NJ 07974*

SIVE, DAVID, lawyer; b. Bklyn., Sept. 22, 1922; s. Abraham Leon and Rebecca (Schwartz) S.; m. Mary Robinson, July 23, 1948; children: Rebecca, Helen, Alfred, Walter, Theodore. A.B., Bklyn. Coll., 1943; LL.B., Columbia U., 1948. Bar: N.Y. 1948, U.S. Supreme Ct. 1964. Partner Sive, Paget & Riesel, and predecessors; N.Y.C., 1957—; adj. lectr. law Columbia Law Sch. and other law schs., 1965—; short term sr. Fulbright scholar, 1974. Author: (with Reed Rowley) Rowley on Partnerships, 1959; contbr. articles to law revs. Dem. candidate for N.Y. State Supreme Ct., 1965; trustee Natural Resources Def. Coun., Inc., 1969-93. Decorated Purple Heart and oak leaf cluster. Mem. Am., N.Y. State (Root/Stimson award for pub. service 1977) bar assns., Assn. of Bar of City of N.Y. (mem. exec. com. 1972-76, chmn. environ. law com. 1971-75), Am. Law Inst., Sierra Club (chmn. Atlantic chpt. 1968-69, nat. dir. 1968-69). Home: Millbrook Rd Margaretville NY 10503 Office: 460 Park Ave New York NY 10022-1906

SIVE, REBECCA ANNE, public affairs company executive; b. N.Y.C., Jan. 29, 1950; d. David and Mary (Robinson) S.; m. Clark Steven Tomashefsky, June 18, 1972. BA, Carleton Coll., 1972; MA in Am. History, U. Ill., Chgo., 1975. Asst. to chmn. of pres.' task force on vocations Carleton Coll., Northfield, Minn., 1972; asst. to acquisitions librarian Am. Hosp. Assn., Chgo., 1973; rsch. asst. Jane Addams Hull House, Chgo., 1974; instr. Loop Coll., Chgo., 1975, Columbia Coll., Chgo., 1975-76; cons. Am. Jewish Com., Chgo., 1975, Ctr. for Urban Affairs, Northwestern U., Evanston, Ill., 1977, Ill. Consultation on Ethnicity in Edn., 1976, MLA, 1977; dir. Ill. Women's History Project, 1975-76; founder, exec. dir. Midwest Women's Ctr., Chgo., 1977-81; exec. dir. Playboy Found., 1981-84; v.p. pub. affairs/pub. rels. Playboy Video Corp., 1985; v.p. pub. affairs Playboy Enterprises, Inc., Chgo., 1985-86; pres. The Sive Group, Inc., Chgo., 1986—; guest speaker various edul. orgns., 1972—; instr. Roosevelt U., Chgo., 1977-78; dir. spl. projects Inst. on Pluralism and Group Identity, Am. Jewish Com., Chgo., 1975-77; cons. Nat. Women's Polit. Caucus, 1978-80; bd. dirs. NOVA Health Systems, Woodlawn Community Devel. Corp.; trainer Midwest Acad.; mem. adv. bd. urban studies program Associated Colls. Midwest; proposal reviewer NEH. Contbr. articles to profl. jours. Commr. Chgo. Park Dist., 1986-88; mem. steering com. Ill. Commn. on Human Rels., 1976; mem. structure com. Nat. Women's Agenda Coalition, 1976-77; del.-at-large Nat. Women's conf., 1977; mem. Ill. Gov.'s Com. on Displaced Homemakers, 1979-81, Ill. Human Rights Com., 1980-87, Ill. coordinating com., Internat Womens Yr.; coord. Ill. Bicentennial Photog. Exhbn., 1977; mem. Ill. Employment and Tng. Coun.; mem. employment com. Ill. Com. on Status of Women; bd. dirs. Nat. Abortion Rights Action League and NARAL Found., Ill. div. ACLU, Midwest Women's Ctr. Recipient award for outstanding community leadership YWCA Met. Chgo., 1979, award for outstanding community leadership Chgo. Jaycees, 1988. Home: 3529 N Marshfield Ave Chicago IL 60657-1224 Office: The Sive Group 359 W Chicago Ave Ste 201 Chicago IL 60610-3025

SIVERD, ROBERT JOSEPH, lawyer; b. Newark, July 27, 1948; s. Clifford David and Elizabeth Ann (Klink) S.; m. Bonita Marie Shulock, Jan. 8, 1972; children: Robert J. Jr., Veronica Leigh. AB in French, Georgetown U., 1970; JD, 1973; postgrad. LaSorbonne, Paris, 1969. Bar: N.Y. 1974, U.S. Dist. Ct. (so. and ea. dists.) N.Y. 1974, U.S. Ct. Appeals (2nd cir.) 1974, U.S. Supreme Ct. 1980, U.S. Dist. Ct. (ea. dist.) Pa. 1984, U.S. Ct. Appeals (3rd cir.) 1984, (6th cir.) 1985, Ohio 1991, Ky. 1992. Assoc. Donovan Leisure Newton & Irvine, N.Y.C., 1973-83; staff v.p., litigation counsel Am. Premier Underwriters, Inc., Greenwich, Conn., 1983-86, v.p. litigation counsel, 1986-87, v.p. assoc. gen. counsel, cin. 1987-92; exec. v.p., gen. counsel and sec. Gen. Cable Corp., 1992-94. Mem. ABA, Cin. Bar Assn., Assn. of Bar of City of N.Y., Ky. Bar Assn. Republican. Office: Gen Cable Corp 4 Tesseneer Dr Newport KY 41076-9753

SIVERSON, RANDOLPH MARTIN, political science educator; b. Los Angeles, July 29, 1940; s. Clifford Martin and Lorene (Sanders) S.; m. Mary Suzanne Strayer, Dec. 31, 1966; children: Andrew, Erica, Courtney. AB, San Francisco State U., 1962, MA, 1965; PhD, Stanford U., 1969. Lectr. polit. sci. Stanford U., Calif., 1967; asst. prof. U. Calif., Riverside, 1967-70; asst. prof. U. Calif., Davis, 1970-75, assoc. prof., 1975-81, prof., 1981—; Fulbright lectr. El Colegio de Mexico, Mexico City, 1974-75; vis. prof. Naval Postgrad. Sch., Monterey, Calif., 1980. Co-author: The Diffusion of War, 1991; editor: (with others) Change in the International System, 1980; editor Internat. Interactions, 1984-91; mem. editorial bd. Am. Polit. Sci. Rev., 1989-91. Mem. Internat. Studies Assn., Am. Polit. Sci. Assn., Western Polit. Sci. Assn. (pres. 1991), Midwest Polit. Sci. Assn. Roman Catholic. Office: U Calif Davis Dept Polit Sci Davis CA 95616

SIVIN, NATHAN, historian, educator; b. May 11, 1931; m. Carole Delmore. BS in Humanities and Sci., MIT, 1958; MA in History of Sci., Harvard U., 1960, PhD in History of Sci., 1966. Prof. Chinese history and history of sci., dept. history and sociology of sci. U. Pa., Phila., 1977—, acting chmn. dept., 1989; vis. lectr., Singapore U., 1962; vis. prof. Rsch. Inst. Humanistic Studies, Kyoto, Japan, 67-68, 71-72, 74, 79-80; vis. scientist Sinologisch Inst., Leiden, The Netherlands, Cambridge U., Eng., People's Republic China; vis. assoc., dir. Needham Rsch. Inst., Cambridge, 1987—; advisor Acad. Traditional Chinese Medicine, Beijing; numerous lectures and colloquia in Europe, Asia, N.Am. Author: (monograph) Chinese Alchemy: Preliminary Studies, 1968, Chinese trans. 1973, Cosmos and Computation in Early Chinese Mathematical Astronomy, 1969, Traditional Medicine in Contemporary China, 1987, Science in Ancient China: Researches and Reflections, 1995, Medicine, Philosophy and Religion in Ancient China: Researches and Reflections, 1995; author with others, editor or co-editor: Chinese Science, 1973, Science and Technology in East Asia, 1977, Astronomy in Contemporary China, 1979, Science and Civilisation in China, Vol.5, 1980, Science and Medicine in Twentieth-Century China, 1989, The Contemporary Atlas of China, 1989; also numerous articles for profl. jours., essays, prefaces to books, book revs.; editor, pub. Chinese Science, 1973-92; mem. editorial bd. U. Pa. Press, 1980-83, numerous jours.; gen. editor: (monograph series) Science, Medicine and Technology in East Asia, 3 Vol. MIT E. Asian Sci. Series, 6 vol.; adv. editor Tech. and Culture, 1973—. Mem. adminstrv. bd. Chinese Cultural and Community Ctr., Phila., 1983-84. Guggenheim fellow, 1971-72; Japan Soc. Promotion of Sci. rsch. fellow, 1979-80; grantee NSF, 1968-70, 79-81, Ford Found., 1970, Nat. Libr. Medicine NIH, 1976, IBM Corp., 1985, Nat. Program Advanced Study and Rsch. China, 1986-87. Contbr. Am. Acad. Arts and Scis.; mem. Assn. for Study of Religion (exec. com. 1982-83, v.p 1993—), Soc. for Studies Chinese Religion (bd. dirs., exec. coun. 1986-89), T'ang Studies Soc. (bd. dirs. 1986—), Internat. Soc. for History East Asian Sci., Tech. and Medicine (pres. 1990-93), Chinese Acad. Scis. (hon. prof. 1989—), Franklin Inn Club (sec., bd. dirs. 1989-90), Acad. Internat. D'histoire des Scis. Home: 8125 Roanoke St Philadelphia PA 19118-3949 Office: U Pa Dept History & Sociology Sciences Philadelphia PA 19104-3325

SIX, FRED N., state supreme court justice; b. Independence, Mo., Apr. 20, 1929. AB, U. Kans., 1951, JD with honors, 1956; LLM in Judicial Process, U. Va., 1990. Bar: Kans. 1956. Asst. atty. gen. State of Kans., 1957-58; pvt. practice Lawrence, Kans., 1958-87; judge Kans. Ct. Appeals, 1987-88; justice Kans. Supreme Ct., 1988—; editor-in-chief U. Kans. Law Review, 1955-56; lectr. on law Washburn U. Sch. Law, 1957-58, U. Kans., 1975-76. Maj. USMC, 1951-53; USMCR, 1957-62. Recipient Disting. Alumnus award U. Kans. Sch. Law, 1994. Fellow Am. Bar Found. (chmn. Kans. chpt. 1983-87); mem. ABA (judicial adminstrn. div.), Internat. Law Assn. (Am. br.), Am. Judges Assn., Am. Judicature Soc., Kans. Bar Assn., Kans. Bar Found., Kans. Law Soc. (pres. 1970-72), Kans. Inn of Ct. (pres. 1993-94), Order of Coif, Phi Delta Phi. Office: Kans Supreme Ct 301 SW 10th Ave Topeka KS 66612

SIZEMORE, CAROLYN LEE, nuclear medicine technologist; b. Indpls., July 22, 1945; d. Alonzo Chester and Elsie Louise Marie (Osterman) Armstrong; m. Jessie S. Sizemore Sr., June 9, 1966; 1 child, Jessie S. Jr. AA in Nuclear Medicine, Prince George's Community Coll, Largo, Md., 1981; BA in Bus. Adminstrn., Trinity Coll., 1988. Registered technologist (nuclear medicine); cert. nuclear medicine technologist, Md.; lic. nuclear med. technologist. Nuclear med. technologist Washington Hosp. Ctr., 1981-88; chief technologist, mem. com. Capitol Hill Hosp., Washington, 1988-91; chief technologist, asst. radiation safety officer Nat. Hosp. Orthopaedics and Rehab., Arlington, Va., 1991—; mem. Am. Registry of Radiologic Technologists Nuclear Medicine Exam. Com., 1990-93. Contbr. articles to profl. jours. mem. com. Medlantic Rsch. Found., Washington, 1989-93; sec. Crestview Area Citizens Assn., 1994—. Mem. Va. Soc. Radiol. Technologists, Potomac Dist. Soc. Radiol. Technologists, Md. Soc. Radiol. Technologists, Md. Soc. Nuclear Medicine Technologists, Soc. Nuclear Medicine (chmn. mem. 1983-85, sec. 1985-87, 88-89, co-editor Isotopics 1991, editor Isotopics 1992—), MEC-SNM nom. com. 1995—, nat. nom. com. 1995—), Nuclear Medicine Adv. Bd. Am. Legion Aux. (exec. com. 1975-76), Internat. Platform Assn. Republican. Lutheran. Avocations: various crafts, reading, aerobics, weight lifting. Home: 6700 Danford Dr Clinton MD 20735-4019

SIZEMORE, HERMAN MASON, JR., newspaper executive; b. Halifax, Va., Apr. 15, 1941; s. Herman Mason and Hazel (Johnson) S.; m. Connie Catterton, June 22, 1963; children: Jill, Jennifer. AB in History, Coll. William and Mary, 1963; postgrad., U. Mo., 1965; MBA, U. Wash., 1985. Reporter Norfolk (Va.) Ledger-Star, summers 1961, 62, 63; copy editor Seattle Times, 1965-70, copy-desk chief, 1970-75, asst. mng. editor, 1975-77, mng. editor, 1977-81, prodn. dir., 1981-83, asst. gen. mgr., 1984, v.p. gen. mgr., 1985, pres., chief operating officer, 1985—; vis. instr. Sch. Comms. U. Wash., 1972-78; bd. dirs. Times Comms. Co., Walla Walla Union-Bull, Inc., Yakima Herald-Republic, Times Community Newspapers, Inc., Northwestern Mut. Life Ins. Co., 1993—, mem. policyowner examining com., 1985, chmn., 1986. Bd. dirs. Ctrl. Puget Sound Campfire Coun., 1985-91, pres. 1989-90; bd. dirs. Ptnrs. in Pub. Edn. 1987-88, United Way of King County, 1994—, Downtown Seattle Assn.; adv. coun. Puget Sound Blood Ctr. and Program; adv. bd. USO-Puget Sound Area. Named Seattle Newsmaker of Tomorrow, 1978. Mem. AP Mng. Editors, Soc. Profl. Journalists, Newspaper Assn. Am., Pacific N.W. Newspaper Assn., Allied Daily Newspapers Washington, Coll. William and Mary Alumni Assn. (bd. dirs.), Greater Seattle C. of C., U. Wash. Exec. MBA Alumni Assn. (pres. 1988, bd. dirs.), Wash. Athletic Club, Rainier Club, Rotary. Methodist. Office: Seattle Times PO Box 70 Seattle WA 98111-0070

SIZEMORE, JAMES MIDDLETON, JR., state commissioner, lawyer; b. Mobile, Ala., May 25, 1942; s. James Middleton S. and Margaret Lee (Davidson) Douglass; m. Stephenie Ann Freeman, Aug. 6, 1966 (div. Oct. 1984); 1 child, Rebecca Lee; m. Brenda Kay Champlin, Nov. 9, 1985; stepchildren: Charlotte Champlin Smith, Alexander Smith V. AB, Samford U., 1963; LLM in Tax, U. Ala., 1966; LLM in Tex, U. Va., 1981. Atty. pvt. practice, Sylacwuga, Ala., 1967-87; commr. Ala. Dept. Revenue, Montgomery, 1987-92; dir. Ala. Devel. Office, Montgomery, 1992—; chmn. NATA/IRS Bankruptcy Com., 1987-89. Mem. Southeast Assn. Tax Adminstrs. (pres. 1989-90). Republican. Presbyterian. Avocation: flying. Office: Ala Devel Office Revenue Dept Gordon Persons Bldg 50 N Ripley St Montgomery AL 36130-0624

SIZEMORE, ROBERT DENNIS, school counselor, educational administrator; b. Indpls., July 30, 1943; s. George R. and Thelma L. (Lagle) S.; m. Leslie Ann, June 14, 1969; children: Christopher J., Kelly Ann. BS in Edn., Ind. U., 1967; MS in Secondary Edn., U. Bridgeport, 1972; cert., Portland State U., 1987. Cert. secondary tchr. and counselor, Oreg. Tchr. Marseilles (Ill.) Jr. High, 1967-69, Greenwich (Conn.) High Sch., 1969-76, Oregon City (Oreg.) High Sch., 1976-77; tchr., counselor, adminstr., asst. prin. curriculum Reynolds High Sch., Portland, Oreg., 1977—; presenter Nat. Coun. Social Studies Conventions; mem. high sch. reform network N.W. Regional Ednl. Lab.; officer COSA-OASSA, 1995—; cons. in field. Mem. ASCD, NEA, AACD, Nat. Assn. Secondary Sch. Prins., Congress Oreg. Sch. Adminstrs. (conv. presenter). Office: 1698 SW Cherry Park Rd Troutdale OR 97060-1481

SIZEMORE, WILLIAM CHRISTIAN, college president; b. South Boston, Va., June 19, 1938; s. Herman Mason and Hazel (Johnson) S.; m. Anne Catherine Mills, June 24, 1961; children: Robert C., Richard M., Edward S. BA, U. Richmond, 1960; BD, Southeastern Bapt. Theol. Sem., Wake Forest, N.C., 1963; MLS, U. N.C., 1964; MLS (advanced), Fla. State U. 1971, PhD, 1993; postgrad., Harvard U., 1989. Library asst. U. N.C., Chapel Hill, 1963-64; assoc. librarian, instr. grad. research Southeastern Bapt. Theol. Sem., 1964-66; librarian, assoc. prof. South Ga. Coll., Douglas, 1966-71, acad. dean, prof., 1971-80, dean coll., prof., 1980-83, acting pres., 1982-83; pres. Alderson-Broaddus Coll., Philippi, W.Va., 1983-94, William Jewell Coll., Liberty, Mo., 1994—; cons. Continental R&D, Shawnee Mission, Kans., 1987-92, So. Assn. Colls. and Schs., Atlanta, 1977, S.A.C.S. Commn. on Higher Edn., Columbia, 1975-76, State Coun. Higher Edn. for Va., Richmond, 1969-70, Software Valley Corp., 1989-94. Contbr. articles to profl. jours. Mem. Barbour County Devel. Authority, Philippi, 1984-94, Barbour County Emergency Food and Shelter Bd., 1985-94, Barbour County Extension Com., 1990-94; mem. exec. coun. Yellow Pine area Boy Scouts Am., Valdosta, 1974-76; pres. Satilla Librarians Ednl. Coun., Douglas, 1969-71; lectr., workshop leader on Bible studies various orgns., 1966—; mem. bd. advisors Swatow Kakwang Profl. Acad., Peoples Republic China; pres. bd. dirs. W.Va. Intercollegiate Athletic Conf., 1985-86, coun. of pres. Nat. Assn. Intercollegiate Athletics; bd. dirs., mem. exec. com. Broaddus Hosp., Philippi, 1983-94; chmn. W.Va. Productive Industry Efforts Found., 1993-94; mem. mktg. com. W.Va. Life Scis. Park Found., 1989-94, Gov.'s Partnership for Progress, 1989-94; mem. adv. panel W.Va. Rural Health Initiative, 1991-94; mem. gov. bd., bd. dirs. W.Va. Alliance of Hosps., 1991-94. Joseph Ruzicka scholar N.C. Library Assn., 1963; recipient Douglas Pilot Club Edn. award, 1981. Mem. ALA, Am. Assn. for Higher Edn., Am. Assn. Univ. Adminstrs., Nat. Coun. Instrnl. Adminstrs., W.Va. Assn. Coll. and Univ. Pres. (exec. com., v.p., pres. 1992), Mountain State Assn. Colls., W.Va. Found. for Ind. Colls. (dir. 1983-84, v.p. 1988-92), Mo. Colls. Fund, Barbour County C. of C. (bd. dirs. 1988-94, v.p. 1988-90, pres. 1990-92, chmn. bd. 1992-94), Liberty Area C. of C. (bd. dirs. 1995—), Kansas City Club, Univ. Club. Democrat. Baptist. Avocations: woodworking, gardening. Home: 510 E Mississippi St Liberty MO 64068 Office: William Jewell Coll Office of Pres 500 College Hill Liberty MO 64068-1896

SIZEMORE, WILLIAM HOWARD, JR., newspaper editor; b. South Boston, Va., Dec. 8, 1948; s. W. Howard and Genevieve T. (Walton) S.; m. Mary K. Lamont, Jan. 29, 1972; children: Justin, Jennifer, Julie. BA in Philosophy, Coll. William and Mary, 1971. Editor The Clarksville (Va.) Times, 1972-75; reporter The Roanoke (Va.) Times, 1975-76, The Times-Herald, Newport News, Va., 1976-81; editor, pub. The York Town Crier, Yorktown, Va., 1981-88; copy editor The Ledger-Star, Norfolk, Va., 1982-89, news editor, 1989-95; writer, editor The Virginian-Pilot, Norfolk, Va., 1995—. Recipient various Excellence in Writing and Layout awards Va. Press Assn., 1972-95. Avocations: tennis, music, bicycling, camping. Home: 107 Azalea Dr Yorktown VA 23690 Office: Virginian-Pilot/Ledger-Star 150 W Brambleton Ave Norfolk VA 23510

SIZER, IRWIN WHITING, biochemistry educator; b. Bridgewater, Mass., Apr. 4, 1910; s. Ralph Waldo Emerson and Annie Jenkins (Scott) S.; m. Helen Whitcomb, June 23, 1935; 1 child, Meredith Ann (Mrs. Twomey). A.B., Brown U., 1931, Sc.D. (hon.), 1971; Ph.D., Rutgers U., 1935. Teaching fellow Rutgers U., 1931-35; dir. oyster pest control investgation for N.J. U.S. Bur. Fisheries, 1935; instr. MIT, Cambridge, 1935-39; asst. prof. MIT, 1939-42, asso. prof. physiology, 1942-56, prof. biochemistry, 1956—, exec. officer biology, 1954-55, acting head biol. dept., 1955-56, head biol. dept., 1956-67, dean Grad. Sch., 1967-75, cons. resource devel., 1975-85; pres. Whitaker Health Sci. Fund, Inc., 1974-84; cons. in resource devel. MIT, 1992-95; bd. dirs. Boston Fed. Savs. Bank, Lexington, Mass.; cons. in biochemistry to pharm. industry Ford Found., 1990-95; dir. Biol. Scis. Curriculum Study. Contbr. sci. papers, enzymology, biochemistry to profl. jours.; mem. adv. bd. Tech. Rev. Trustee, bd. govs. Rutgers U.; trustee Boston Biomed. Research Inst.; corp. mem. Lesley Coll.; trustee Mus. of Sci., Theobold Smith Research Inst. Honored byIrwin Sizer award for acad. innovation, 1975—; named hon. mem. MIT Class of 1924, hon. mem. MIT Alumni Assn. Fellow Am. Acad. Arts and Sci., Am. Inst. Chemists; mem. Am. Physiol. Soc., Am. Soc. Zoologists, Am. Soc. Biol. Chemists, Am. Chem. Soc., Sigma Xi (pres. Mass. Inst. Tech. 1958-59), Phi Beta Kappa (hon. mem.), Delta Omega. Home: 52 Dartmouth Ct Bedford MA 01730

SIZER, PHILLIP SPELMAN, consultant, retired oil field services executive; b. Whittier, Calif., Apr. 11, 1926; s. Frank Milton and Helen Louise (Saylor) S.; m. Evelyn Sue Jones, Aug. 16, 1952; children: Phillip Spelman, Ves Warner. BME, So. Meth. U., 1948. Registered profl. engr., Tex., Okla. With Otis Engring. Corp., Dallas, 1948-91; project engr. Otis Engring. Corp., 1958-62, chief devel. engr., 1962-70, v.p. R & D, 1970-73, v.p engring. and resch. 1973-76, v.p., tech. bd. dirs., 1977-91, bd. dirs., 1975-91; pres. Sizer Engring. Inc., 1992—; bd. dirs. DHV Internat., Inc.; cons. in field; mem. exec. com. Offshore Tech. Conf., 1976-79. Patentee in field. Mem. U. Tex. Mech. Engring. Dept. Vis. Com., 1977-83. Named to Hall of Achievement Coll. Engring., U. Tex., Arlington, 1983. Fellow ASME (chmn. exec. com. petroleum divsn. 1974-75, SPEE-1 chmn. main com. 1981-88, engr. of Yr. award North Tex. sect. 1971, centennial medal 1980, OIL-DROP award petroleum divsn. 1982, Dedicated Svc. award 1985, Silver Patent award 1990); mem. Soc. Petroleum Engrs., S.W. Rsch. Inst. (trustee 1982—), Petroleum Engrs., Club of Dallas, Rotary Internat., Tau Beta Pi, Kappa Mu Epsilon. Home: 14127 Tanglewood Dr Dallas TX 75234-3851

SIZER, THEODORE R., education educator; b. New Haven, June 23, 1932; m. Nancy Faust. BA in English Lit., Yale U., 1953; MAT in Social Studies, Harvard U., 1957, Phd in Edn. and Am. History, 1961; PedD (hon.), Lawrence U., 1969; LittD (hon.), Union Coll., 1972; LLD (hon.), Conn. Coll., 1984; LHD (hon.), Williams Coll., 1984; MA ad eundem, Brown U., 1985; LHD (hon.), Lowell U., 1985, Dartmouth Coll., 1985, Lafayette Coll., 1991; Webster U., 1992, Ind. U., 1993, Mt. Holyoke Coll., 1993, U. Maine, 1993. English and math. tchr. Roxbury Latin Sch., Boston, 1955-56; history and geography tchr. Melbourne (Australia) Grammar Sch., 1958; asst. prof. edn., dir. MA in tchrs. program Harvard U., Cambridge, Mass., 1961-64; dean grad. sch. edn. Harvard U., Cambridge, 1964-72; headmaster, instr. in history Phillips Acad., Andover, Mass., 1972-81; chmn. A Study of High Schs., 1981-84; chmn. edn. dept. Brown U., Providence, 1984-89, Walter H. Annenberg prof. edn., 1993-94; dir. Annenberg Inst. Sch. Reform, 1994—; vis. prof. U. Brisol, U.K., 1971, Brown U., Providence, spring 1983. Author: Secondary Schools at the Turn of the Century, 1964, The Age of the Academies, 1964, Religion and Public Education, 1967, (with Nancy F. Sizer) Moral Education: Five Lectures, 1970, Places for Learning, Places for Joy: Speculations on American School Reform, 1972, Horace's Compromise: The Dilemma of the American High School, 1984, rev. edit., 1985, Horace's School: Redesigning the American High School, 1992. Capt. U.S. Army, 1953-55. Named Guggenheim fellow, 1971; recipient citations Am. Fedn. Tchrs., Nat. Assn. Secondary Sch. Prins., Phillips Exeter Acad., Boston C. of C., Andover C. of C., Lehigh U. Edn. Alumni, 1991, Nat. Assn. Coll. Admissions Counsellors, 1991, Anthony Wayne award Wayne State U., 1981, Gold medal for excellence in undergrad. teaching CASE, 1988, Tchrs. Coll. medal Tchrs. Coll., Columbia U., 1991, Harold W. McGraw prize in edn., 1991, James Bryant Conant award Edn. Commn. States, 1992, Disting. Svc. award Coun. Chief State Sch. Officers, 1992, Coun. Am. Private Edn., 1993, Nat. Award Distinction U. Pa., 1993. Office: Brown Univ Coalition of Essential Schs PO Box 1969 Providence RI 02912-1969

SJOBERG, DONALD, bishop. Formerly bishop Western Can. Synod Lutheran Ch. in Am.-Can.; pres. Evangel. Luth. Ch. in Can., Winnipeg, Man., 1986—, Can. Council of Churches, 1988—. Office: Evang Luth Ch, 1512 St James St, Winnipeg, MB Canada R3H 0L2

SJOERDSMA, ALBERT, research institute executive; b. Lansing, Ill., Aug. 31, 1924; s. Sam and Agnes S.; m. Fern E. MacAllister, Dec. 2, 1950; children—Leslie, Ann, Albert, Britt. Ph.B., U. Chgo., 1944, B.S., 1945, Ph.D., 1948, M.D., 1949. Research asst. U. Chgo., 1947-49, NIH postdoctoral research fellow, 1950; intern U. Mich. Hosp., Ann Arbor, 1949-50; resident physician Michael Reese Hosp., Chgo., 1951; resident in internal medicine USPHS Hosp., Balt., 1951-53; sr. investigator, chief exptl. therapeutics br. Nat. Heart and Lung Inst., Bethesda, Md., 1953-71; v.p. Merrell Internat. Co., Strasbourg, France, 1971-78; v.p. pharm. research and devel. Richardson-Merrell Inc., 1978-81; v.p. pharm. research Merrell Dow Pharms., Cin., 1981-83; pres. Merrell Dow Research Inst., Cin., 1983-89; pres. emeritus Merrell Dow Research Inst., Cin., 1989-94; vis. spl. fellow Gen. Hosp., Malmo, Sweden, 1959-60; spl. lectr. George Washington U., 1959-71; Anton Julius Carlson lectr. U. Chgo., 1984; hon. chmn. 2d World Conf. on Clin. Pharmacology and Therapeutics, Washington, 1983; clin. prof. medicine U. Cin. Med. Ctr., 1986-91. Mem. AAAS (Theobold Smith award med. scis. 1958), Am. Soc. Pharm. and Exptl. Therapeutics (Harry Gold award in clin. pharmacology 1977, Exptl. Therapeutics award 1990), Am. Soc. Clin. Pharmacology and Therapeutics (Oscar B. Hunter Meml. award in therapeutics 1981), Internat. Soc. Hypertension, Coun. High Blood Pressure Rsch., Am. Heart Assn., Am. Fedn. Clin. Rsch., Am. Soc. Clin. Investigation, Am. Soc. Exptl. Biology and Medicine, Asso. Am. Physicians, Am. Coll. Neuropsychopharmacology. Home: 5475 Waring Dr Cincinnati OH 45243-3933 Office: 2110 E Galbraith Rd Cincinnati OH 45215-6300

SJOSTRAND, FRITIOF STIG, biologist, educator; b. Stockholm, Sweden, Nov. 5, 1912; s. Nils Johan and Dagmar (Hansen) S.; m. Marta Bruhn-Fahraeus, Mar. 24, 1941 (dec. June 1954); 1 child, Rutger; m. Ebba Gyllenkrok, Mar. 28, 1955; 1 child, Johan; m. Birgitta Petterson, Jan. 23, 1969; 1 child, Peter. M.D., Karolinska Institutet, Stockholm, 1941, Ph.D., 1945; Ph.D. (hon.), U. Siena, 1974, North-East Hill U., Shillon, India, 1989. Asst. prof. anatomy Karolinska Institutet, 1945-48, assoc. prof., 1949-59, prof. histology, 1960-61; research assoc. MIT, 1947-48; vis. prof. UCLA, 1959, prof. zoology, 1960-82, prof. emeritus molecular biology, 1982—. Author: Über die Eigenfluoreszenz Tierischer Gewebe Mit Besonderer Berücksichtigung der Sägertierniere, 1944, Electron Microscopy of Cells and Tissues, Vol. I, 1967, Deducing Function from Structure, Vols. I and II, 1990; also numerous articles. Decorated North Star Orden Sweden; recipient Jubilee award Swedish Med. Soc., 1959, Anders Retzius gold medal, 1967; Paul Ehrlich-Ludwig Darmstaedter prize, 1971. Fellow Royal Micros. Soc. (hon. London), Am. Acad. Arts and Scis.; mem. Electron Microscopy Soc. Am. (hon., Disting. Scientist award 1992), Japan Electron Microscopy Soc. (hon.), Scandinavian Electron Microscopy Soc. (hon.). Achievements include development technique for high resolution electron microscopy of cells, fluorescence microspectrography; inventor ultramicrotome.

SKADDEN, DONALD HARVEY, professional society executive, accounting educator; b. Danville, Ill., Jan. 26, 1932; s. Harvey Frank and Lois Mary (Shawbridge) S.; m. Barbara Ann Meade, June 16, 1966 (dec.); children: John D., David H.; m. Karin Matson, Mar. 18, 1985. BS, U. Ill., 1948, MS, 1949, PhD, 1955. CPA, Ill. Asst. prof. acctg. U. Ill., Urbana, 1955-58, assoc. prof., 1958-61, prof., 1961-73, assoc. dean Coll. Commerce and Bus. Adminstrn., 1969-71; sr. acct. Haskins & Sells, 1957-58; Arthur Young prof. accounting U. Mich., Ann Arbor, 1973-87, chmn. acctg. faculty, 1976-79, assoc. dean for acad. affairs, 1979-87; v.p. taxation AICPA, 1987-92; exec. dir. Am. Tax Policy Inst., 1992—; dir. Paton Acctg. Ctr., 1976-79; mem. Fin. Acctg. Stds. Adv. Commn., 1980-84, ABA Commn. on Taxpayer Compliance, 1984-88; mem. commrs. adv. group IRS, 1990-91; active Nat. Conf. Lawyers and CPAs, 1993—. Author: Federal Income Tax: Student Workbook, 1965; Co-author: Principles of Federal Income Taxation; Editor: The Illinois CPA, 1964-66; editorial bd.: The Tax Adviser, 1969-74, The Accounting Review, 1973-75. Alderman, City of Urbana, 1961-69, mayor, 1969. With AUS, 1943-46, ETO. Decorated Combat Inf. badge. Mem. Am. Inst. CPA's (exec. com. of fed. tax div. 1979-82, council 1980-83), Ill. Soc. CPA's (bd. dirs. 1966-68, chair in accountancy 1968-73), Am. Acctg. Assn. (pres. 1979-80), Am. Taxation Assn. (pres. 1977-78), Urbana Assn. Commerce and Industry (bd. dirs. 1970-73), Beta Gamma Sigma, Phi Kappa Phi, Beta Alpha Psi. Methodist. Home: 1666 34th St NW Washington DC 20007-2746

SKAER, LAURA ELIZABETH, lawyer; b. Kermit, Tex., Feb. 28, 1948; d. Arthkur Tine and Edathy Lorine (Bixier) S.; children: Brittney, Mackenzie. BS in Bus. Administrn., U. Mo., 1970, JD cum laude, 1974. Bar: Mo., Colo. Assoc., then ptnr. Blackwell, Sanders, Matheny, Weary & Lombardi, Kansas City, Mo., 1974-79; gen. counsel, then COO Skaer Enterprises, Inc., Denver, 1979-93; gen. counsel, bus. cons. Pease Oil & Gas, Co., Denver, 1993—; bd. dir. Eagle Bank, Broomfield, Colo., 1985—; chair minerals, energy and geology policy adv. bd. Colo. Dept. Nat. Resources, Denver, 1992—. Recipient Disting. Svc. award Colo. Oil and Gas Assn., 1990, Faculty Alumni award U. Mo., 1991. Mem. Indep. Petroleum Assn. Mt. States (pres. 1987-93), Colo. Bar Assn., Colo. Women's Bar Assn., Colo. Oil and Gas Assn., Ind. Petroleum Assn. Am. (regional v.p. 1989-91), Denver Petroleum Club (bd. dir.). Avocations: flying, garding, outdoor sports, rock and roll music. Office: Pease Oil & Gas Co 633 17th St #1500 Denver CO 80202

SKAFF, ANDREW JOSEPH, lawyer, public utilities, energy and transportation executive; b. Sioux Falls, S.D., Aug. 30, 1945; s. Andrew Joseph and Alice Maxine (Skaff) S.; m. Lois Carol Phillips, Oct. 4, 1971; children—Amy Phillips, Julie Phillips. B.S. in Bus. Adminstrn, Miami U., Oxford, Ohio, 1967; J.D., U. Toledo, 1970. Bar: Calif. 1971, U.S. Supreme Ct. 1974. Prin., sr. counsel Calif. Public Utilities Commn., 1977; gen. counsel Delta Calif. Industries, Oakland, 1977-82; sec. Delta Calif. Industries, 1978-82; mem. Silver Rosen, Fischer & Stecher, San Francisco, 1982-84; sr. ptnr. Skaff and Anderson, San Francisco, 1984-90; pvt. practice Law Office of Andrew J. Skaff, 1990—; officer Delta Calif. Industries and subs. Contbr. articles to legal jours.; contbg mem. law rev. U. Toledo, 1970. Mem. Calif. Bar Assn., Conf. Calif. Pub. Utiliites Counsel, Calif. Cogenera-

tion Coun., Assn. Transp. Practitioners, San Francisco Bar Assn., Alameda County Bar Assn. Office: Lake Merritt Plz 1999 Harrison St Ste 1300 Oakland CA 94612-3517

SKAFF, JOSEPH JOHN, state agency administrator, retired army officer; b. Charleston, W.Va., June 13, 1930; s. Michael Joseph and Zahia S.; m. Maree A. Fleming, Aug. 4, 1957; children: Joseph M., Lynn M. Johnson, Gregory M., Nancy E. Kochman. B.S., U.S. Mil Acad., 1955; M.S., George Washington U., 1968. Commd. 2d lt. U.S. Army, 1955; commanded 1/27 FA battalion, 1968-69; advanced through grades to maj. gen.; dep. dir. internat. negotiations U.S Army Joint Chiefs of Staff, Washington, 1979-81; mem. staff and faculty U.S. Mil. Acad., 1972-76; also dep. commr. U.S. del. Standing Consultative Commn., Geneva, 1979-81; dep. dir. ops. readiness and moblzn. Hdqrs. Dept. Army, Washington, 1981-83; dep. commdg./chief staff U.S Army in Japan, 1982-84; dep. commdg. gen., commdg. gen. 1st U.S. Army, Fort Devens, Mass., 1985-89; adj. gen., sec. pub. safety Charleston, W.Va., 1989—. Decorated D.S.M., Def. Superior Svc. medal, Legion of Merit, Bronze Star, Air medal, others. Mem. Assn. Grads. U.S. Mil. Acad., Assn. U.S. Army, Arty. Assn., Adj. Gens. Assn. U.S., Nat. Guard Assn. U.S., Officers Christian Fellowship, Fellowship Christian Athletes. Eastern Orthodox.

SKAGGS, DAVID E., congressman; b. Cin., Feb. 22, 1943; s. Charles and Juanita Skaggs; m. Laura Locher, Jan. 3, 1987; 1 child, Matthew; stepchildren: Clare, Will. BA in Philosophy, Wesleyan U., 1964; student law, U. Va., 1964-65; LLB, Yale U., 1967. Bar: N.Y. 1968, Colo. 1971. Assoc. Newcomer & Douglass; Boulder, Colo., 1971-74, 77-78; chief of staff Congressman Tim Wirth, Washington, 1975-77; ptnr. Skaggs, Stone & Sheehy, Boulder, 1978-86; mem. 100th-104th Congresses from 2d Colo. dist., Washington, 1987—; mem. Appropriations com., subcoms. Commerce and Justice, Interior; mem. Colo. Ho. of Reps., Denver, 1980-86, minority leader 1982-85. Former bd. dirs. Rocky Mountain Planned Parenthood, Mental Health Assn. Colo., Boulder County United Way, Boulder Civic Opera. Served to capt. USMC, 1968-71, Vietnam; maj. USMCR, 1971-77. Mem. Colo. Bar Assn., Boulder County Bar Assn., Boulder C. of C. Democrat. Congregationalist. Office: US Ho of Reps 1124 Longworth Bldg Washington DC 20515-0602 also: 9101 Harlan St Ste 130 Westminster CO 80030

SKAGGS, RICHARD WAYNE, agricultural engineering educator; b. Grayson, Ky., Aug. 20, 1942; s. Daniel M. and Gertrude (Adkins) S.; m. Judy Ann Kuhn, Aug. 25, 1962; children: Rebecca Diane Skaggs Ramsey, Steven Glen. BS in Agr. Engring., U. Ky., 1964, MS in Agr. Engring., 1966; PhD, Purdue U., 1970. Registered profl. engr., N.C. Grad. asst. U. Ky., Lexington, 1964-66; grad. instr. in rsch. Purdue U., West Lafaytte, Ind., 1966-70; asst. prof. agrl. engring. N.C. State U., Raleigh, 1970-74, assoc. prof., 1974-79, prof., 1979-84, William Neal Reynolds prof., 1984—, disting. univ. prof., 1991—; cons. on drainage U.S. AID, Egypt, 1989—; cons., lectr. on water mgmt., India, 1992, Malaysia, 1993, New Zealand, 1993. Contbr. over 240 articles on water mgmt. and hydrology to profl. jours. Recipient Outstanding Young Scientist award N.C. State U. chpt. Sigma Xi, 1978; alumni rsch. award N.C. State U. Alumni Assn., 1983, Alumni Disting. Profl. award for grad. teaching, 1991; Superior Svc. award USDA, 1986, 90; named to Drainage Hall of Fame, Ohio State U., 1984, Engring. Hall of Distinction, U. Ky., 1994; named Outstanding Alumnus Agrl. Engr., U. Ky., 1985. Fellow Am. Soc. Agrl. Engrs. (chmn. nat. drainage symposium com. 1976, mem. nominating com. 1979, 95, Hancor Soil and Water Engring. award 1986, bd. dirs. 1992-94, John Deere Gold medal 1993); mem. NAE. Avocations: basketball, golf, reading. Home: 2824 Sandia Dr Raleigh NC 27607 Office: NC State U Dept Biol-Agrl Eng PO Box 7625 Raleigh NC 27695-7625

SKAGGS, RICKY, country musician; m. Sharon White, 1981; 3 children. First profl. job, age 15, playing mandolin with Ralph Stanley group Clinch Mountain Boys; subsequently with Country Gentlemen, J.D. Crowe and New South; then formed own group Boone Creek; joined Emmylou Harris backup group Hot Band, 1977; played with The Whites; joined Grand Ole Opry, 1982; albums include Waitin' for the Sun to Shine, 1981, Highways and Heartaches, Don't Cheat in Our Hometown, Country Boy, 1984, Favorite Country Songs, Live in London, Love's Gonna Get Ya!, Comin' Home To Stay, 1988, Kentucky Thunder, 1989, My Father's Son, 1991, Super Hits, 1993. Recipient Horizon award for best newcomer Country Music Assn., male vocalist of yr. award, 1982, best instrumental group award, 1983, 84, 85, 6 Country Music Assn. awards including Entertainer of Yr. award, 1985, Vocal Event of Yr. award, 1991, Grammy award for best country instrumental, 1984, 85, 86, Grammy award for best country vocal collaboration, 1992, 6 Acad. of Country Music awards, MusicDove award Gospel Music Assn., Playboy Reader's Poll Best Country Instrumental Performance, 1989, Eng.'s Country Music Round Up Most Popualr Internat. Male, 1986-87, Edison award, 1987, 50th Anniversary award USO, 1989, various awards Music City News, Cash Box, Radio and Records; named Christian Country Artist of Yr. Gospel Voice Mag., 1993, Musician of Yr. award Christian Country Music Assn., 1994. Office: 54 Music Sq E Ste 301 Nashville TN 37203-4315

SKAGGS, SANFORD MERLE, lawyer; b. Berkeley, Calif., Oct. 24, 1939; s. Sherman G. and Barbara Jewel (Stinson) S.; m. Sharon Ann Barnes, Sept. 3, 1976; children: Stephen, Paula Ferry, Barbara Gallagher, Darren Peterson. B.A., U. Calif.-Berkeley, 1961, J.D., 1964. Bar: Calif. 1965. Atty. Pacific Gas and Electric Co., San Francisco, 1964-73; gen. counsel Pacific Gas Transmission Co., San Francisco, 1973-75; ptnr. Van Voorhis & Skaggs, Walnut Creek, Calif., 1975-85, McCutchen, Doyle, Brown & Enersen, San Francisco and Walnut Creek, 1985—; mem. Calif. Law Revision Commn., 1990—, chmn., 1993; adv. coun. Lawrence Hall of Sci. U. Calif. at Berkeley, 1988—. Councilman City of Walnut Creek, 1972-78, mayor 1974-75, 76-77; bd. dirs. East Bay Mcpl. Utility Dist., 1978-90, pres., 1982-90; trustee Calif. Symphony, 1992—, Contra Costa County Law Libr., 1978—. Mem. Calif. State Bar Assn., Contra Costa County Bar Assn., Urban Land Inst., Lambda Alpha, Alpha Delta Phi, Phi Delta Phi. Republican. Office: McCutchen Doyle Brown & Enersen PO Box V 1331 N California Blvd Walnut Creek CA 94596

SKAGGS, WAYNE GERARD, financial services company executive; b. Bonneterre, Mo., Dec. 12, 1929; s. Jasper Pinkney and Lattie May (Duren) S.; m. Hana Kaneko, June 1, 1952; children: Robert Kenneth, Melody Jane, Joy Elizabeth. Student, Mo. Inst. Acctg. and Law, 1947-48, U. Mo., Columbia, 1954-55. With Advantage Capital Corp. (formerly Am. Capital Corp.), Houston, 1955—; pres., chief oper. officer Mktg. Group of Cos., Houston, 1976-80; corp. v.p., cons. Mktg. Group of Cos., 1972-90. Served with USAF, 1950-54, Korea. Mem. Nat. Assn. Securities Dealers (nat. vice chmn. 1977, dist. chmn. 1972), Nat. Bus. Conduct (gov., chmn. 1976), Investment Co. Inst. Republican. Presbyterian. Club: Optimists (pres. club 1966, life mem.). Home: PO Box 726 Wimberley TX 78676-0726

SKAHAN, PAUL L(AURENCE), bank executive, lawyer; b. Pittsburg, Kans., Feb. 13, 1925; s. James Thomas and Mary Agnes (Quinn) S.; m. Kermalene Cloa Voss, Dec. 27, 1954; children: Larry, Jeffrey, Scott, Daniel, Shauna, Kelli, Mike. J.D., U. Mo.-Kansas City, 1952. Bar: Mo. 1952. Staff atty. Prudential Ins. Co., Kansas City, Mo., 1952-53; supt. claims State Farm Mut. Ins. Co., Kansas City, 1953-63; assoc. Silks & Silks, Kansas City, 1963-64; trust counsel United Mo. Bank Kansas City, N.A., 1964-89. Trustee Wornall Charitable Found., Kansas City, 1975—. Cpl. U.S. Army, 1943-45, PTO. Mem. Mo. Bar, Kansas City Bar Assn. Republican. Roman Catholic. Home: 5931 Ballentine St Shawnee Mission KS 66203-2921 Office: United Mo Bank Kans City NA 10th St And Grand Ave Kansas City MO 64141

SKALAK, RICHARD, engineering mechanics educator, researcher; b. N.Y.C., Feb. 5, 1923; s. Rudolph and Anna (Tuma) S.; m. Anna Lesta Allison, Jan. 24, 1953; children: Steven Leslie, Thomas Cooper, Martha Jean, Barbara Anne. BS, Columbia U., 1943, CE, 1946, PhD, 1954; MD (hon.), Gothenburg U., Sweden, 1990. Instr. civil engring. Columbia U. N.Y.C., 1948-54, asst. prof., 1954-60, assoc. prof., 1960-64, prof., 1964-77, James Kip Finch prof. engring. mechanics, 1977-88, emeritus, 1988—; dir. Bioengring. Inst., 1978-88; prof. bioengring. U.Calif., San Diego, 1988—; dir. Inst. for Mechs. and Materials, 1992—; Hunter lectr. Clemson U., 1994; mem. panel Gov.'s Conf. on Sci. and Engring., R&D, 1989-90. Contbr. articles to sci.

jours. Bd. dirs. Biotech. Inst., Gothenburg, Sweden, 1978—; mem. adv. bd. Ctr. for Biomed. Engring., N.Y.C., 1994—. Recipient Great Tchr. award Columbia Coll. Soc. of Older Grads., 1972, Merit medal Czechoslovakian Acad. Scis., 1990. Fellow AAAS, ASME (Centennial medal 1980, Melville medal 1990, editor jour. 1984), Am. Acad. Mechanics, Soc. Engring. Sci., Am. Inst. Med. and Biol. Engring. (founding); mem. NAE, Soc. Rheology, Am. Heart Assn., Microcirculatory Soc., Internat. Soc. Biorheology (Poiseuille medal 1989), Biomed. Engring. Soc. (Alza medal 1983), Cardiovascular System Dynamics Soc., Am. Soc. for Engring. Edn., Tau Beta Pi, Sigma Xi. Democrat. Presbyterian. Office: U Calif San Diego Ames Dept Bioengring La Jolla CA 92093-0412

SKALKA, ANNA MARIE, molecular biologist, virologist; b. N.Y.C., July 2, 1938. AB, Adelphi U., 1959; PhD in Microbiology, NYU, 1964. Am. Cancer Soc. fellow molecular biology genetics rsch. unit Carnegie Inst., 1964-66, fellow, 1966-69; asst. mem. dept. cell biology lab. molecular and biochemical genetics Roche Inst. Molecular Biology, 1969-71, assoc. mem., 1971-76, mem., 1976-80, head, 1980—; now dir. Inst. Cancer Rsch., Phila.; vis. prof. dept. molecular biology Albert Einstein Coll. Medicine, 1973—, Rockefeller U., 1975. Mem. AAAS, Am. Soc. Microbiology, Am. Soc. Biol. Chem., Assn. Women Sci., Sigma Xi. Achievements include research in the structure and function of DNA, host and viral functions in the synthesis of viral DNA and RNA, phage DNA as a vehicle for the amplification and study of eukaryotic genes, molecular biology of avian retroviruses. Office: Inst for Cancer Rsch Fox Chase Cancer Ctr 7701 Burholme Ave Philadelphia PA 19111-2497

SKALKA, HAROLD WALTER, ophthalmologist, educator; b. N.Y.C., Aug. 22, 1941; s. Jack and Sylvia Skalka; m. Barbara Jean Herbert, Oct. 2, 1965; children: Jennifer, Gretchen, Kirsten. AB with distinction, Cornell U., 1962; MD, NYU, 1966. Intern Greenwich (Conn.) Hosp., 1966-67; resident in ophthalmology Bellevue Hosp., Univ. Hosp., Manhattan VA Hosp., 1967-70; fellow in retinal physiology and ultrasonography, 1970-71; cons. in ophthalmology St. Jude's Hosp., Montgomery, Ala., 1971-73; asst. prof. ophthalmology U. Ala., Birmingham, 1973-75, assoc. prof., 1975-80, prof., 1980-81, assoc. prof. dept. medicine, 1980—, prof., chmn. combined program in ophthalmology, 1981—; acting chmn. combined program ophthalmology U. Ala., 1974-76; ophthalmologist Lowndes County Bd. Health Community Health Project, 1972. Contbr. articles to Am. Jour. Ophthalmology, Eye, Ear, Nose and Throat Monthly, Annals of Ophthalmology, Ophthalmic Surgery, Jour. Clin. Ultrasound, Jour. Pediatric Ophthalmology and Strabismus, The Lancet, AMA Archives of Ophthalmology, Jour. So. Med. Assn., Acta Ophthalmologica, Metabolic and Pediatric Ophthalmology, Applied Radiology, British Jour. Ophthalmology, Blood, Neuro-Ophthalmology; editorial bd.: Ala. Jour. Med. Sci. Major USAFMC, 1971-73. Mem. AAAS, AMA, ACS, SIDUO, Ala. Sight Conservation Assn., Ala. Conservancy, Ala. Wildlife Fedn., Eye Bank Bd., Am. Acad. Ophthalmology, Am. Inst. Ultrasound in Medicine, Internat. Soc. for Clin. Electrophysiology of Vision, Internat. Soc. on Metabolic Eye Disease, Assn. for Rsch. in Vision and Ophthalmology, AAUP, Am. Intraocular Implant Soc., Am. Assn. Ophthalmology, Pan Am. Assn. Ophthalmology, Ala. Med. Assn., Rsch. to Prevent Blindness, Ala. Acad. Ophthalmology, Ala. Med. Assn., Jefferson County Med. Soc., Contact Lens Assn. Ophthalmologists, Ala. Ultrasound Soc., Royal Soc. Medicine, N.Y. Acad. Scis., Am. Soc. Standardized Ophthalmic Echography (charter exec. bd. mem.), Am. Coll. Nutrition. Office: Eye Found Hosp U Ala 700 18th St S Ste 300 Birmingham AL 35233-1859

SKALKO, RICHARD GALLANT, anatomist, educator; b. Providence, Apr. 10, 1936; s. Francis Charles and Emilie Margaret (Gallant) S.; m. Louise Marie Luchetti (div. 1982); m. Priscilla Ann Brown, 1985; children—Patricia, Margaret, Christine. A.B., Providence Coll., 1957; M.S., St. John's U., 1959; Ph.D., U. Fla., 1963. Instr. anatomy Cornell U. Med. Coll., 1963-66, asst. prof., 1966-67; asst. prof. anatomy La. State U. Med. Ctr., New Orleans, 1967-69, assoc. prof., 1969-70; dir. Embryology Lab., Birth Defects Inst., N.Y. State Health Dept., Albany, 1970-77; assoc. prof. anatomy and toxicology Albany Med. Coll., 1970-76, prof., 1976-77; prof. anatomy and cell biology East Tenn. State U. Coll. Medicine, Johnson City, 1977—, chmn. dept., 1977—; mem. sci. adv. bd. NCTR, FDA, 1976-79; vis. prof. Institut fur Toxikologie und Embyronalpharmakologie, Freie U., Berlin, 1978; mem. human embryology and devel. study sect., NIH, 1990-94. Mem. Am. Assn. Anatomists, Teratology Soc., Soc. Devel. Biology, European Teratology Soc., Soc. Toxicology. Democrat. Roman Catholic. Author: Basic Concepts in Teratology, 1985; editor: Heredity and Society, 1973; Congenital Defects, 1974. Home: 3302 Pine Timbers Dr Johnson City TN 37604-1404 Office: East Tenn State U Coll Medicine Dept Anatomy and Cell Biology Johnson City TN 37614-0582

SKALL, GREGG P., lawyer; b. El Paso, Tex., Mar. 28, 1944; s. Ben Milton and Lottie (Berger) S.; m. Monte Kaye Leake, June 27, 1971; 1 child, Brandon Cornell. BS, Ohio State U., 1966; JD, U. Cin., 1969. Bar: Ohio 1969, D.C. 1971, D.C. Dist. Ct. 1971, U.S. Dist. Ct. (no. dist.) Ohio 1972, D.C. Ct. Appeals 1971. Atty. gen. State of Ohio, Cleve., summer 1967; intern U.S. Dept. Justice, div. Civil Rights, Washington, summer 1968; tax law specialist IRS, Washington, 1969; gen. atty. FCC, Washington, 1970-72; ptnr. Garber, Simon, Haiman, Gutfeld, Wertheimer & Friedman, Cleve., 1972-75; acting gen. counsel Office Telecommunications Policy Exec. Office of the Pres. of the U.S., Washington, 1975-78; chief counsel Nat. Telecommunications and Info. Adminstrn., Washington, 1978-80; ptnr. Blum, Nash & Railsback, Washington, 1980-84, Baker & Hostetler, Washington, 1984—; professorial lectr. telecommunications law and regulatory policy George Washington U., Washington, 1978-80. Co-author: The Broadcaster's Survival Guide: A Handbook of FCC Rules and Regulations for Radio and TV Stations, 1988; contbr. articles to law jours. Mem. Fed. Bar Assn. (chmn. regulated industries com. 1979-81), ABA, Fed. Communications Bar Assn. Lodge: Masons. Office: Pepper & Corazzini 200 Montgomery Bldg 1776 K St NW Washington DC 20006-2304

SKALLA, JOHN LIONELL, insurance agent; b. Marysville, Kans., July 25, 1933; s. Ernest John and Charlotte Violet (Rychel) S.; m. Allene Davison, Aug. 17, 1957; children: Camille, Johnette. BA, U. Nebr., 1957. CLU, ChFC. Agt. Conn. Mut. Life Ins. Co., Lincoln, Nebr., 1957-61; gen. agt. Conn. Mut. Life Ins. Co., Des Moines, 1961-69, Houston, 1969—; bd. dirs., mem. strategy and ops. com. Conn. Mut. Life Ins., Hartford, chmn. adv. com. Conn. Mut. Gen. Agts., 1989; nat. bd. dirs. Gen. Agts. and Mgrs. Conf., Washington; bd. dirs. Univ. of Houston Sch. of Ins. and Fin. Svcs. Contbr. articles to profl. jours. Trustee U. Nebr. Found. Bd., Lincoln; gen. chmn. Vice Lombardi Award Dinner, Houston, 1978; past pres. Whitehall Club, Houston; bd. dirs. Am. Cancer Soc., Houston; trustee Goodwill Industries, Houston; mem. Houston Bus. and Estate Planning Coun., Houston Estate and Fin. Forum. Mem. Nat. Assn. Life Underwriters (Nat. Quality awards 1962-94), Million Dollar Round Table, Am. Soc. CLU and ChFc (Woody Woodson award 1993, Hall of Fame 1993), Tex. Assn. Life Underwriters, Houston Assn. Life Underwriters, Houston Estate and Fin. Forum, Rotary, Houston Bus. & Estate Planning Coun. Republican. Episcopalian. Avocations: travel, reading, writing, speaking. Office: John L Skalla & Assocs 4265 San Felipe 7th Fl Houston TX 77027

SKAMBIS, CHRISTOPHER CHARLES, JR., lawyer; b. Painesville, Ohio, Jan. 21, 1953; s. Christopher Charles and Anne (haritos) S.; m. Susan Elaine Adrianson, Dec. 18, 1976; children: Adrianne Elaine, Christopher Roy. Student, U. Pa., 1970-72; BA, U. Conn., 1972-74; JD, Ohio State U. Coll. Law, Columbus, 1975-78. Bar: Fla. 1978, Fla. Supreme Ct. 1978, U.S. Dist. Ct. (ctrl. dist.), 1979, U.S. Ct. Appeals (5th and 11th cir.) 1981, U.S. Supreme Ct. 1989. Assoc. VandenBerg, Gay & Burke, Orlando, Fla., 1978-81, ptnr., 1982; ptnr. VandenBurg, Gay, Burke, Wilson & Arkin, Orlando, Fla., 1982-85, Foley & Lardner, Orlando, Fla., 1985—; mem. Orange County Bar Assn., Orlando, Fla., 1978, Fla. Bar 9D Grievance Commn., Orlando, Fla., 1989; arbitrator Fla. Bar 9th Cir. Fee Arbitration Commn., Orlando, Fla., 1987; co-chair Federal and State Trial Practice Co., Orlando, Fla., 1992—. Mem. Am. Judicature Soc., ABA. Avocations: amateur ham radio operator, little league, coalition for homeless. Office: Foley & Lardner PO Box 2193 111 N Orange Ave Ste 1800 Orlando FL 32802-2193

SKATES, RONALD LOUIS, computer manufacturing executive; b. Kansas City, Mo., Sept. 25, 1941; s. Raymond and Suzanne (Lispi) S.; m. Mary

Austin; children: Melissa, Elizabeth. AB cum laude, Harvard U., 1963, MBA, 1965. Acct. Price Waterhouse, Boston, audit ptnr., 1976-86; sr. v.p. fin. and adminstrn. Data Gen. Corp., Westboro, Mass., 1986-88, dir., exec. v.p., chief oper. officer, 1988-89; pres., CEO Mass. Gen. Hosp., Boston, 1990—, overseer, 1992—. Overseer Mus. Fine Arts, 1989. Mem. AICPA, Mass. Soc. CPAs. Office: Data Gen Corp 4400 Computer Dr Westborough MA 01580-0001

SKEELS, JACK WILLIAM, economics educator, consultant; b. Wausau, Wis., Nov. 3, 1929; s. Lawrence John and Gertrude (Preuss) S.; m. Joyce Vivian Goldy, Jan. 29, 1956 (div. 1976); children: Jack Allen, Jennifer Joy. BA, U. Wis., 1951, PhD, 1957. Asst. prof. econs. Mich. State U., East Lansing, 1957-59, Wayne State U., Detroit, 1959-63; assoc. prof. econs. No. Ill. U., DeKalb, 1963-65, full prof. econs., 1965—, chmn. econs. dept., 1964-69, 77-82, assoc. provost, 1975-76; pvt. practice econs., DeKalb, 1972—. Contbr. articles to profl. jours. With USN, 1951-53, PTO. Mem. AAUP (state exec. coun.), Am. Econ. Assn., Assn. Comparative Econ. Studies (nat. exec. sec. 1971-73, nat. sec.-treas. 1964-71), Midwest Econ. Assn. (v.p. 1975-76). Avocations: fishing, tennis, jogging, gardening. Home: 608 Russell Rd De Kalb IL 60115-2257 Office: No Ill U Dept Econs De Kalb IL 60115

SKEEN, JOHN KENNETH, sales executive; b. Taft, Calif., Sept. 20, 1941; s. Kenneth Charles and Mildred (Harman) S.; m. Michelle Lee Bailey, May. BA in Econs., Stanford U., 1963, MBA, 1966. Stockbroker J. Barth, San Francisco, 1966-70, Dean Writter, San Francisco, 1970-76; v.p., stockbroker Donaldson Lufkin & Jennette, San Francisco, 1976-79; gen. ptnr., dir. sales Montgomery Securities, San Francisco, 1979—; pres. Mill Valley Soc. Security Analysts, 1976. Contbr. Ed. 2s Chau for Congress, 1984; sponsor John Heinz for Senator. Mem. Inst. Investor Roundtable. Republican. Avocations: skiing, scuba diving. Home: 3983 Happy Valley Rd Lafayette CA 94549-2423 Office: Montgomery Securities 600 Montgomery St San Francisco CA 94111-2702

SKEEN, JOSEPH RICHARD, congressman; b. Roswell, N.Mex., June 30, 1927; s. Thomas Dudley and Ilah (Adamson) S.; m. Mary Helen Jones, Nov. 17, 1945; children: Mary Elisa, Mikell Lee. B.S., Tex. A&M U., 1950. Soil and water engr. Ramah Navajo and Zuni Indians, 1951; rancher Lincoln County, N.Mex., 1952—; mem. N.Mex. Senate, 1960-70, 97th-103rd Congresses from 2nd N.Mex. dist., Washington, D.C., 1981—; mem. appropriations com., subcom. agr., chmn. appropriations com., subcom. def. Chmn. N.Mex. Republican Party, 1963-66. Served with USN, 1945-46; Served with USAFR, 1949-52. Mem. Nat. Woolgrowers Assn., Nat. Cattle Growers Assn., N.Mex. Woolgrowers Assn., N.Mex. Cattle Growers Assn., N.Mex. Farm and Livestock Bur. Republican. Club: Elks. Office: House of Representatives Washington DC 20515

SKEES, WILLIAM LEONARD, JR., lawyer; b. Indpls., Jan. 26, 1947; s. William Leonard and Marian Catherine (Fagan) S.; m. Ila Harrington, Aug. 20, 1967 (div.); children: Kristina Suzanne, Elizabeth Ann; m. Dena Kay Wynalda, July 23, 1983; children: Catherine Fagan, William Leonard III (dec.), Samuel Jackson. BA, Ball State U., 1969; JD, Ind. U., 1971. Bar: Ind. 1971, Ky. 1981. Law clk. U.S. Dist. Ct. (no. dist.), Fort Wayne, Ind., 1971-72; assoc. Ice, Miller Donadio & Ryan, Indpls., 1972-80; ptnr. Brown, Todd & Heyburn, Louisville, 1981—. Contbr. articles to jours. in field. Mem. bd. visitors Ind. U. Sch. Law, 1975-91; bd. dirs., past pres. The Louisville Housing Partnership, 1978—, Stage One, Louisville Children's Theatre, pres., 1990-91; bd. dirs. Ky. Chpt. Nat. SIDS Found. Recipient Disting. Citizen award Mayor of Louisville, 1983, Cert. Merit Bd. Aldermen, Louisville, 1984, Cert. Appreciation Fiscal Ct., Louisville, 1986. Mem. ABA, Ky. Bar Assn., Ind. Bar Assn., Louisville Bar Assn., Jefferson Club. Office: Brown Todd & Heyburn 3200 Providian Center Louisville KY 40202-2873

SKEETE, F. HERBERT, bishop; b. N.Y.C., Mar. 22, 1930; s. Ernest A. and Elma I. (Ramsey) S.; m. Shirley C. Hunte, Oct. 4, 1952; children—Michael H., Mark C. BA, Bklyn. Coll., 1959; MDiv, Drew U., 1962, D in Ministry, 1975; STM, N.Y. Theol. Sem., 1970; DHL(hon.), Philander Smith Coll., 1983, Jewish Theol. Sem. N.Y., 1986; DD, Ea. Bapt. Theol. Sem., 1986. Ordained to ministry United Meth. Ch., 1961; pastor Union United Meth. Ch., South Ozone Park, N.Y.C., 1960-67, N.Y.C. Mission Soc., 1967-68, Salem United Meth. Ch., Harlem, N.Y.C., 1968-80; bishop Phila. area United Meth. Ch., Valley Forge, Pa., 1980-88, Boston area, 1988—. Office: United Methodist Ctr care Beverly Abbotte PO Box 277 Winthrop ME 04364

SKEFF, KELLEY MICHAEL, health facility administrator; b. Center, Colo., 1944. MD, U. Chgo., 1970. Diplomate Am. Bd. Internal Medicine. Intern Harbor Gen. Hosp., Torrance, Calif., 1970-71; resident in internal medicine U. Colo. Med. Ctr., Denver, 1974-75; resident in internal medicine, 1975-76, fellow in internal medicine, 1976; program dir. Stanford U. Recipient Alpha Omega Alpha award Assocs. Am. Med. Coll., 1994. Office: Stanford U Dept Med 300 Pasteur Dr Stanford CA 94305*

SKELLY, THOMAS FRANCIS, manufacturing company executive; b. Boston, Jan. 19, 1934; s. Michael Gerard and Katherine Agnes (Kelly) S.; m. Patricia A. Limerick, Sept. 6, 1958; children—Thomas Francis, John M., Peter G., Matthew M. B.S., Northeastern U., 1956; M.B.A., Babson Coll., 1966. Mgr. Peat, Marwick, Mitchell & Co. (C.P.A.'s), Boston, 1957-67; with Gillette Co., Boston, 1967—; controller Gillette Co., 1973—, v.p., 1979-80, sr. v.p. fin., 1980—; mng. dir. Gillette Overseas Fin. Corp. N.V., Netherlands Antilles; dir. Neworld Bank, Boston. Bd. dirs. nat. coun. Northeastern U., bd. trustees; bd. dirs. Nat. Fgn. Trade Coun. Capt. AUS, 1957-59. Home: 54 Magnolia Dr Westwood MA 02090-3215 Office: Gillette Co Prudential Tower Bldg Boston MA 02199

SKELOS, DEAN G., senator; b. Rockville Center, N.Y.; m. Gail Skelos; 1 child, Adam. BA in History, Washington Coll., 1970; JD, Forham U., 1975. State assemblyman N.Y., 1981-82; senator N.Y. State Senate, 1984; dep. majority leader; chmn. standing com. on aging N.Y. State Senate, 1984-94, Majority Task Force on Aging in 21st Century, 1987-92, co-chmn. legislative task force on demographic rsch. and reapportionment, mem. majority task force on religious desecration and bigotry, mem. legis. commn. on sci. and tech., mem. majority task force on def. spending, chmn. task force on econ. recovery and job devel., mem. numerous coms. Mem. fact-finding mission to Israel Jewish Community Rels. Coun.; former mem. Coun. of Nat. Inst. on Aging. Recipient Torch of Liberty award B'nai B'rith. Mem. Elks, Sons of Italy, Kiwanis, Order of AHEPA. Office: Legislative Office Bldg 609 Albany NY 12247 also: 55 Front St Rockville Centre NY 11570

SKELTON, BYRON GEORGE, federal judge; b. Florence, Tex., Sept. 1, 1905; s. Clarence Edgar and Avis (Bowmer) S.; m. Ruth Alice Thomas, Nov. 28, 1931; children: Sue, Sandra. Student, Baylor U., 1923-24; AB, U. Tex., 1927, MA, 1928, LLB, 1931. Bar: Tex. 1931, Circuit Ct. Appeals 1937, U.S. Supreme Ct. 1946, FCC 1950, Tax Ct. US 1952, U.S. Treasury Dept 1952, ICC 1953. Practice of law Temple, Tex., 1931-66; partner Saulsbury & Skelton, 1934-42, Saulsbury, Skelton, Everton, Bowmer & Courtney, 1944-55, Skelton, Bowmer & Courtney, 1955-66; judge U.S. Ct. Claims, Washington, 1966-77; sr. fed. judge U.S. Ct. Claims, 1977-82, U.S. Ct. Appeals (fed. cir.), Washington, 1982—; county atty., Bell County, Tex., 1934-38; spl. asst. U.S. amb. to Argentina, 1942-45; city atty., Temple, 1945-60; dir. First Nat. Bank of Temple. Dem. nat. committeeman for Tex., 1956-64; del. Dem. Nat. Conv., 1948, 56, 60, 64; del. Tex. Dem. Conv., 1946, 48, 50, 52, 54, 56, 58, 60, 62, 64, vice chmn., 1948, 58; chmn. Dem. Adv. Coun. of Tex., 1955-57; former pres. Temple YMCA; pres. Temple Indsl. Found., 1966. Appointed Ky. Col. and Adm. in Tex. Navy, 1959; recipient Legion of Honor DeMolay, 1980, Temple Outstanding Citizen award, 1984. Mem. ABA, State Bar Tex., Bell-Lampasas amd Mills Counties Bar Assn. (past pres.), Am. Law Inst., Am. Judicature Soc., Temple C. of C. (past pres., dir.), Gen. Soc. Mayflower Descendants (John Howland Mayflower ancestor), Ex-Students' Assn. U. Tex. (past pres., mem. exec. coun.), Phi Beta Kappa Pi Sigma Alpha, Sigma Delta Pi, Delta Theta Phi (hon.). Democrat. Methodist. Clubs: Mason (past worshipful master; Shriner), Kiwanian (past pres.). Home: 1101 Dakota Dr Temple TX 76504-4905 Office: US Ct Appeals 305 Fed Bldg Temple TX 76501

SKELTON, DON RICHARD, consulting actuary, retired insurance company executive; b. Des Moines, Dec. 9, 1931; s. Donald Harold and Wanda Mae (Johnson) S.; m. Barbara Joan Harris (dec. 1962); children: David, Janet; m. Alyce Mae Washington, May 15, 1964 (div. 1979); children: Laura, Lisa, James; m. Patricia Ann Matroni, July 10, 1981. BSBA, Drake U., 1953. Actuarial trainee Monarch Life Ins. Co., Springfield, Mass., 1953-57, mgr. group ins. dept., 1957-58, asst. actuary, 1958-64, group pensions actuary, 1964-67, asst. v.p., group actuary, 1967, v.p. R & D, 1967-83; v.p. Monarch Capital Corp., Springfield, Mass., 1980-91; sr. v.p. Monarch Life Ins. Co., Springfield, 1988-91; v.p. Monarch Fin. Svcs., Inc., 1989-91; pres., chief exec. officer First Variable Life Ins. Co., 1985-87, 91, also bd. dirs., sr. v.p., 1992; cons. actuary Longmeadow, Mass., 1992—. Mem. budget com. Pioneer Valley United Way, Springfield, 1964-69, chmn. 1969-70. Fellow Soc. Actuaries, Life Office Mgmt. Assn.; mem. Coll. Life Underwriters. Republican. Clubs: Hartford (Conn.) Actuaries; Boston Actuaries. Avocations: golf, sailing, physical fitness. Home: 8 Althea Dr Longmeadow MA 01106-1707

SKELTON, DOROTHY GENEVA SIMMONS (MRS. JOHN WILLIAM SKELTON), art educator; b. Woodland, Calif.; d. Jack Elijah and Helen Anna (Siebe) Simmons; BA., U. Calif., 1940, MA, 1943; m. John William Skelton, July 16, 1941. Sr. rsch. analyst War Dept., Gen. Staff, M.I. Div. G-2, Pentagon, Washington, 1944-45; vol. rschr. monuments, fine arts and archives sect. Restitution Br., Office Mil. Govt. for Hesse, Wiesbaden, German, 1947-48; vol. art tchr. German children in Bad Nauheim, Germany, 1947-48; art educator, lectr. Dayton (Ohio) Art Inst., 1955; art educator Lincoln Sch., Dayton, 1956-60; instr. art and art edn. U. Va. Sch. Continuing Edn., Charlottesville, 1962-75; rschr. genealogy, exhibited in group shows, Calif., Colo., Ohio, Washington and Va.; represented in permanent collections Madison Hall, Charlottesville, Madison (Va.) Center. Mem. Nat. League Am. Pen Women, AAUW, Am. Assn. Museums, Coll. Art Assn. Am., Inst. for Study of Art in Edn., Dayton Soc. Painters and Sculptors, Nat. Soc. Arts and Letters (life), Va. Mus. Fine Arts, Cal. Alumni Assn., Air Force Officers Wives Club. Republican. Methodist. Clubs: Army Navy Country, Lake of the Woods (Va.) Golf and Country. Chief collaborator: John Skelton of Georgia, 1969; author: The Squire Simmons Family, 1746-1986, 1986. Address: Lotos Lakes Brightwood VA 22715

SKELTON, DOUGLAS H., architect; b. Cottage Grove, Oreg., Apr. 17, 1939; s. Harry Edward and Mary Jane (Caldwell) S.; m. Bonita L. Baker, June 17, 1961; children: Paul D., Cynthia J., Justin D. Student, Oreg. State U., 1957-59; degree in architecture, U. Oreg., 1963. Registered architect, Oreg. Draftsman Payne & Struble Architecture, Medford, Oreg., 1965-66; intern architect Wayne Struble Architect, Medford, Oreg., 1966-70, assoc., 1973-78; project architect William Seibert Architect, Medford, Oreg., 1970-73; ptnr. Struble & Skelton Architects, Medford, Oreg., 1978-83; owner Douglas Skelton Architect, Medford, Oreg., 1983-89; ptnr. Skelton, Straus & Seibert Architects, Medford, Oreg., 1989—; mem. law rev. com. State Bd. Architects, Oreg., 1991. Design bldg. renovation (911 Mag. award 1991). Chmn. Hist. and Archtl. Rev. Commn., City of Jacksonville, 1992—; bd. dirs. Rogue Valley Christian Ch., 1994. Recipient Outstanding Sch. Bldg. award Am. Sch. and Univ. mag., 1987. Mem. AIA (v.p. So. Oreg. chpt. 1972, pres. 1973), Architects Coun. Oreg. (del., treas. 1989), Medford/Jackson C. of C. (devel. com. 1992—), Rotary (bd. dirs. Jacksonville/Applegate chpt. 1994). Avocations: camping, fishing, boating, bicycling, cross-country skiing. Office: Skelton Straus & Seibert 26 Hawthorne St Medford OR 97504-7114

SKELTON, ISAAC NEWTON, IV (IKE SKELTON), congressman; b. Lexington, Mo., Dec. 20, 1931; s. Isaac Newton and Carolyn (Boone) S.; m. Susan B. Anding, July 22, 1961; children: Ike, Jim, Page. AB, U. Mo., 1953, LLB, 1956. Bar: Mo. 1956. Pvt. practice Lexington; pros. atty. Lafayette County, Mo., 1957-60; spl. asst. atty. gen. State of Mo., 1961-63; mem. Mo. Senate from 28th dist., 1971-76; mem. 95th-104th Congresses from 4th Mo. Dist., 1977—, ranking minority mem. nat. security subcom. on mil. procurement. Active Boy Scouts Am. Mem. Phi Beta Kappa, Sigma Chi. Democrat. Mem. Christian Ch. Clubs: Masons, Shriners, Elks. Home: 1814 Franklin St Lexington MO 64067-1708 Office: US Ho of Reps 2227 Rayburn House Bldg Washington DC 20515*

SKELTON, JOHN EDWARD, computer technology consultant; b. Amarillo, Tex., May 10, 1934; s. Floyd Wayne and Lucille Annabelle (Padduck) S.; m. Katherine Dow, Mar. 22, 1959; children: Laura Ann, Jeanette Kay, Jeffrey Edward. BA, U. Denver, 1956, MA, 1962, PhD, 1971. Mathematician U.S. Naval Ordnance Lab., Corona, Calif., 1956-59; various sales support and mktg. positions Burroughs Corp., Denver, Detroit, Pasadena, Calif., 1959-67; asst. prof. U. Denver, 1967-74; dir. Computer Ctr. U. Minn., Duluth, 1974-85; prof., dir. computing svcs. Oreg. State U., Corvallis, 1985-94; cons. World Bank, China, 1988, Educom Cons. Group, 1985. Author: Introduction to the Basic Language, 1971; co-auhtor: Who Runs the Computer, 1975; also articles. Mem. Assn. for Computing Machinery (pres. Rocky Mountain chpt. 1971, faculty advisor U. Minn. 1980-82, peer rev. team 3 regions 1981-90), Assn. for Spl. Interest Group on Univ. Computing (bd. dirs. 1987-91), Rotary (dist. youth exch. com. 1991—), Sigma Xi (chpt. pres. 1983-84), Phi Kappa Phi (chpt. pres. 1989-90). Episcopalian. Avocations: travel, photography, hiking.

SKELTON, RED (RICHARD SKELTON), comedian, artist; b. Vincennes, Ind., July 18, 1913; s. Joseph and Ida (Mae) S.; m. Edna Marie Stillwell, June 1932 (div. 1940, dec.); m. 2d, Georgia Maureen Davis, Mar. 1945 (dec.); children: Valentina Maureen Alonso, Richard Freeman (dec.); m. 3d, Lothian Toland, Oct., 1973. HHD, Ball State U., 1986. Began acting career at age of 10 yrs.; successively with a tent show, a minstrel show, on a show boat, a clown in Hagenbeck & Wallace Circus, on burlesque in the Midwest, Walkathon contests (as master of ceremonies); appeared at Loew's Montreal Theatre in vaudeville (developed the doughnut dunking pantomime), 1936; made Broadway debut, June 1937; first motion picture appearance in Having a Wonderful Time, 1939; has since appeared in Flight Command, 1940, The People vs. Dr. Kildare, 1941, Dr. Kildare's Wedding Day, 1941, Lady Be Good, 1941, Whistling in the Dark, 1941, Whistling in Dixie, 1942, Maisie Gets Her Man, 1942, Panama Hattie, 1942, Ship Ahoy, 1942, I Dood It, 1943, Whistling in Brooklyn, 1943, DuBarry Was A Lady, 1943, Thousands Cheer, 1943, Bathing Beauty, 1944, Ziedfield Follies, 1946, The Show Off, 1946, Merton of the Movies, 1947, The Fuller Brush Man, 1948, A Southern Yankee, 1948, Neptune's Daughter, 1949, The Yellow Cab Man, 1950, Three Little Words, 1950, Watch the Birdie, 1950, The Fuller Brush Girl, 1950, Dutchess of Idaho, 1950, Excuse My Dust, 1950, Texas Carnival, 1951, Lovely to Look At, 1952, The Clown, 1952, Halfa Hero, 1953, The Great Diamond Robbery, 1953, Susan Slept Here, 1954, Around the World in 80 Days, 1956, Public Pigeon Number One, 1957, Ocean's Eleven, 1960, Those Magnificent Men in Their Flying Machines, 1965, Eighteen Again, 1988; had first own radio program, 1937, Red Skelton's Scrpabook of Satire, 1942; The Red Skelton Show on TV, 1951-71; nightclub performer, also writer and composer for radio, TV, movies; entertained service men World War II and Korea as pvt. in F.A.; artist original oil paintings and hand sketched linens. Bd. dirs. Red Skelton Needy Children's Fund. Recipient AMVETS Silver Helmet Americanism award, 1969, Freedom's Found. award, 1970, Nat. Comdrs. award Am. Legion, 1970; winner 3 Emmy awards, Golden Globe award, 1978, Am. Achievement award SAG, 1987, Am. Comedy Hall of Fame award, 1993. Address: PO Box 390190 Anza CA 92539-0190

SKELTON, ROBERT BEATTIE, language educator; b. Auburn, Mich., Apr. 23, 1913; s. Glen Beattie and Irene (Richardson) S.; m. Mary Carmack, June 2, 1940; children—Susan, Robert Thomas, Rebecca and Melissa (twins). Student, Bay City (Mich.) Jr. Coll., 1934-35; A.B., Eastern Mich. U., 1937; M.A. (univ. scholar 1937-38), U. Mich., 1938, Ph.D. (Horace H. Rackham spl. fellow 1949-50, Am. Council Learned Socs. grantee Linguistics Inst. 1950), 1950; postgrad. (Roosevelt fellow), U. Brazil, 1942-43; postgrad. (Chilean Govt. fellow), U. Chile, 1943; postgrad., U. Salamanca, U. Paris, 1972, U. Perugia, 1979. Mem. faculty Auburn (Ala.) U., 1939-76, prof., 1954-76, research prof. comparative linguistics, 1967-76, head dept. fgn. langs., 1954-67; vis. scholar Linguistics Inst., 1967. Contbr. articles, monographs to profl. jours. Served to lt. USN, 1943-46, to comdr. USNR, ret. 1973. Mem. Nat. Geog. Soc., Modern Lang. Assn., Am. Assn. Tchrs. French, Am. Assn. Tchrs. German, Am. Assn. Tchrs. Spanish and Portuguese, Linguistic Soc. Am., Inst. Internat. Edn. (asso.), Nat. Assn.

Standard Med. Vocabulary, Am. Mus. Natural History (asso.), Acad. Tamil Culture (asso.). Home: 426 Scott St Auburn AL 36830-6010

SKELTON, ROBERT EUGENE, aeronautics and astronautics educator; b. Elberton, Ga., Mar. 21, 1938; s. Sara (Dickerson) Clardy; m. Sarah Moore, June 1, 1960 (div. 1969); children: Leigh, David; m. Judith King Skelton, June 26, 1971; children: Jeff, Buzz. BSEE, Clemson U., 1963; MSEE, U. Ala., 1970; PhD, UCLA, 1976. From asst. to assoc. prof. Sch. Aeronautics & Astronautics Purdue U., West Lafayette, Ind., 1975-82, prof. Sch. Aeronautics & Astronautics, 1982—; dir. Space Systems Control Lab., Inst. Interdisciplinary Engring. Studies, 1991—; appointee Aeronautics and Space Engring. Bd., 1983-88; mem. ad hoc com. NASA-Univs. Rels. in Aero/Space Engring., Nat. Rsch. Coun., 1984-85; mem. univ. senate Purdue U., 1983-86, mem. ednl. com., 1983-86; vice chmn. applications tech. com. Internat. Fedn. of Automatic Control; Russell Severance Springer prof. U. Calif., Berkeley, 1991. Recipient Sr. U.S. Scientist award Alexander von Humboldt Found., 1991; W.F. Poole Alumni scholar Clemson U., 1962-63, Clemson Engring. Found. scholar, 1961-62; fellow Japan Soc. for Promotion of Sci., 1986. Fellow AIAA, IEEE, Tau Beta Pi (chmn. Clemson chpt. 1962-63), Phi Kappa Phi, Phi Eta Sigma, Sigma Gamma Tau, Sigma Xi. Avocations: scuba, tennis. Office: Purdue U Space Systems Control Lab 1282 Grissom Hall West Lafayette IN 47907-1282

SKENE, G(EORGE) NEIL, publisher, lawyer; b. Jackson, Miss., Aug. 29, 1951; s. George Neil and Louise (Pate) S.; m. Madelyn Miller, Aug. 4, 1984; children: Christopher, Jennifer, Katherine. BA, Vanderbilt U., 1973; JD, Mercer U., 1977. Bar: Fla. 1978. Intern Macon (Ga.) Telegraph & News, 1968-70; reporter Tampa (Fla.) Times, 1973-74; reporter St. Petersburg (Fla.) Times, 1977-78, asst. city editor, 1978-80; capital bur. chief St. Petersburg (Fla.) Times, Tallahassee, 1980-84; editor Evening Ind., St. Petersburg, 1984-86; exec. editor Congl. Quar. Inc., Washington, 1986-89, pres., editor, pub., 1990—; bd. dirs. Times Pub. Co., St. Petersburg. Mem. bd. visitors Law Sch., Mercer U., Macon, Ga., 1986-94; trustee Poynter Inst. for Media Studies, St. Petersburg, 1988—; mem. bd. advisers Grad. Sch. Journalism, U. Cal., Berkely, 1991—. Mem. Fla. Bar Assn. Office: Congressional Quarterly Inc 1414 22nd St NW Washington DC 20037

SKERRITT, TOM, actor; b. Detroit, Aug. 25, 1933. Student, Wayne State U. Films: War Hunt, 1962, One Man's Way, 1964, Those Calloways, 1964, M*A*S*H, 1970, Wild Rovers, 1972, Fuzz, 1972, Big Bad Mama, 1974, Thieves Like Us, 1974, The Devil's Rain, 1975, The Turning Point, 1977, Up In Smoke, 1978, Alien, 1979, Ice Castles, 1979, Silence of the North, 1981, A Dangerous Summer, 1981, Savage Harvest, 1981, Fighting Back, 1982, The Dead Zone, 1983, Top Gun, 1986, Space Camp, 1987, The Big Town, 1987, Wisdom, 1987, Opposing Force, 1987, Maid to Order, 1987, Poltergeist III, 1988, Steel Magnolias, 1989, Big Man On Campus, 1990, The Rookie, 1991, Blue Movie Blue, 1991, Poison Ivy, 1991, A River Runs Through It, 1992; TV shows: Ryan's Four, 1983, On The Edge, 1987, Cheers, 1987-88, Picket Fences, 1992— (Emmy award Outstanding Lead Actor in a Drama Series, 1993); TV movies: The Bird Man, The Last Day, Maneaters Are Loose!, Calendar Girl Murders, Miles to Go, True Believer, Parent Trap II, A Touch of Scandal, Poker Alice, Nightmare At Bitter Creek, Moving Target, The Heist, Red King White Knight, The China Lake Murders, Child of the Night, In Sickness and In Health, Getting Up and Going Home. Office: Guttman Assocs 118 S Beverly Dr Beverly Hills CA 90212-3003

SKERRY, PHILIP JOHN, English educator; b. Boston, May 6, 1944; s. Angelina (Creilson) S.; m. Amy Simon, June 15, 1968; children: Jessica Blythe, Ethan Amadeus. BA in English, U. Mass., 1966; MA in English, Case Western Res. U., 1968; PhD, Ind. U. of Pa., 1975. Instr. English Lakeland Community Coll., Mentor, Ohio, 1968-69, prof., 1973—, chmn. dept., 1991-93; assoc. prof. Tarrant County Jr. Coll., Hurst, Tex., 1971-73; project dir. Early English Composition Assessment Program Ohio Bd. Regents, Columbus, 1985-92; participant Dir. Guild Am. summer sem., 1988, 92. Host TV talk show Western Res. Connection, 1980-86; contbg. author: Superman at 50: The Persistence of a Legend, 1987, Beyond the Stars IV, 1993; contbr. articles to profl. jours. Chmn. Jump Rope for your Heart program Am. Heart Assn., Cleve., 1980-83, mem. adv. com., 1984; trustee, pres. Sussex Community Assn., Shaker Heights, Ohio, 1982; mem. adv. com. N.E. Ohio Assn. for Children with Learning Disabilities, 1975-76; bd. dirs. Shaker Heights Youth Ctr., 1991-92. Grantee NEH, 1983, Martha Holden Jennings Found., 1991-92; Humanities scholar Ohio Program for the Humanities, 1983—. Mem. NEA, Nat. Coun. Tchrs. English, Popular Culture Assn. Democrat. Avocations: collecting movies, coffee roasting. Home: 3655 Sutherland Rd Cleveland OH 44122-5134 Office: Lakeland Cmty Coll 7700 Clock Tower Dr Kirtland OH 44094

SKIBITZKE, HERBERT ERNST, JR., hydrologist; b. Benton Harbor, Mich., Mar. 30, 1921; s. Herbert Ernst and Jennie (Richie) S.; m. Eva Hegel, Mar. 22, 1943; 1 child, Herbert William (dec.). Student, Ariz. State U., 1947; Hon. ScD, U. Ariz., 1988. Registered profl. engr. 11 states; registered ground water hydrologist. Mathematician U.S. Geol. Survey, Phoenix, 1948-54, rsch. hydrologist, 1954-76; pres., sr. hydrologist Hydro Data, Inc., Tempe, Ariz., 1976-85; cons. Skibitzke Engrs. & Assocs., Phoenix, 1986-90; pres., sr. hydrologist Hydro Analysis, Inc., Tempe, 1990—; co-founder, instr. Sch. Hydrology, U. Ariz., Tucson, 1960-64; adv. bd. Sch. Hydrology, Tarleton State U., Stephensville, Tex., 1986-90, Am. Inst. Hydrology, Mpls., 1989—. Contbr. articles to profl. jours., chpts. to books. Lt. USN, 1943-46. Fellow ASCE; mem. NSPE, Am. Inst. Hydrology (C.V. Theis award 1991), Assn. Ground Water Scientists and Engrs., Geol. Soc. Washington. Achievements include developed first computer (electric analog) applied to GW studies; patent on electronic flowmeter for U.S. Geological Survey; pioneered development/application of remote sensing techniques to collect information on water resources; methods to analyze contaminant movement in ground water systems. Office: Hydro-Analysis Inc PO Box 27334 Tempe AZ 85285-7334

SKIDD, THOMAS PATRICK, JR., lawyer; b. Norwalk, Conn., July 2, 1936; s. Thomas Patrick and Anne (Sims) S.; m. Judith Chase Roberts, Sept. 10, 1960; children: Suanne C., Sherry E., Thomas Patrick III, Jody E. BA in Econs., Georgetown U., 1958; LLB, Yale U., 1961. Bar: Conn. 1961, U.S. Supreme Ct. 1963. Ptnr. Cummings & Lockwood, Stamford, Conn., 1961—; bd. dirs., mem. exec. com. Comm. Attys. Title Ins. Co., Rocky Hill, Conn. Mem. Conn. Bar Assn. (real estate sect.), Stamford-Norwalk Regional Bar Assn., Roton Point Club (Rowayton, Conn.). Roman Catholic. Avocation: phonograph record collector. Office: Cummings & Lockwood 10 Stamford Forum Stamford CT 06904-0120

SKIDDELL, ELLIOT LEWIS, rabbi; b. Chelsea, Mass., Mar. 3, 1951; s. Jack and Evelyn (Starr) S.; m. Julie F. Goldberg, May 27, 1979; children: Sarit, Elanit. BA, U. Mass., 1974; MA, Temple U., 1979. Ordained rabbi, 1980. Rabbi Temple Beth El, Newark, Del., 1977-80; asst. rabbi Har Zion Temple, Penn Valley, Pa., 1980-82; rabbi Ramat Shalom Synogogue, Plantation, Fla., 1982—; placement dir. Reconstructionist Rabbinical Assn. Wyncote, Pa., 1985—; pres. Jewish Nat. Fund Broward and Palm Beach, 1987-89, North Broward Bd. Rabbis, Ft. Lauderdale, 1986-87, Reconstructionist Rabbinical Assn., 1980-82. Co-editor booklet: Mordecai Kaplan Centennial Resource Booklet, 1981. Bd. dirs. Jewish Fedn. Greater Ft. Lauderdale, 1986-89. Office: 11301 W Broward Blvd Fort Lauderdale FL 33325-2598 *I believe that the most important task facing us today is the creation of community and a sense of belonging to a community. For our own sake and for future generations, the sense of belonging to something larger than ourselves needs to be instilled.*

SKIDMORE, GARY J., marketing executive; b. Lubbock, Tex., Aug. 7, 1954; s. Joe Mack and Virginia Nell (Barnett) S.; m. Millie Pickett Warden, June 5, 1976; children: Kathrine Lindsey, Shelby Kristen. BA in Religious Edn., Lubbock Christian U., 1976; MBA, St. Edward's U., 1981. Sales cons. Sweet Pub. Co., Austin, Tex., 1976-78, mktg. mgr., 1979, v.p. mktg. div., 1980; pres. Select Mktg., Inc., Austin, 1981—. Mem. alumni bd. Lubbock Christian U., 1985-88; bd. dirs. Am Heart Assn., Austin, 1989—. Mem. Bus. and Profl. Advt. Assn. (bd. dirs., pres. 1986-88), Austin C. of C. (bd. dirs. NE coun. 1989—). Republican. Avocation: golf. Home: 12307 Beartrap Ln Austin TX 78729-7302 Office: Select Mktg Inc 9020 II Cap Tex Hwy N # 400 Austin TX 78759

SKIDMORE, HOWARD FRANKLYN, public relations counsel; b. Bklyn., Sept. 24, 1917; s. William F. and Mae (White) S.; m. Zaza Irina O'Hara, Dec. 4, 1943; children: Joel Michael, Susan Irina. Student, Coll. City N.Y., 1938-39. Editorial staff N.Y. Herald Tribune, 1937-42, 45-47; asst. to dir. pub. relations C. & O. Ry., N.Y.C., 1948; exec. asst. to v.p. passenger traffic, pub. relations, also C. & O. Ry., Cleve., 1949-53; dir. pub. relations C. & O. Ry., 1954-59, spl. asst. to chmn. bd., 1954-77, dir. pub. relations and passenger traffic, 1959-63; v.p. C. & O Ry., also B. & O. Ry., 1963-77, Western Md. Ry., 1973-77, Chessie System, Inc., 1974-77; pres. Howard Skidmore Co., Inc., Cleve., 1977-83. Trustee Cleve. Music Sch. Settlement, 1958—. Served with USNR, 1942-45. Mem. Soc. Silurians, R.R. Pub. Relations Assn. (pres. 1958), Pub. Relations Soc. Am., Soc. Profl. Journalists. Clubs: Nat. Press (Washington); Carmel Valley Racquet; Canterbury Golf (Cleve.). Home: 26360 Monte Verde St Carmel CA 93923-9233

SKIDMORE, JAMES ALBERT, JR., management, computer technology and engineering services company executive; b. Newark, June 30, 1932; s. James A. and Frances W. (Barker) S.; m. Peggy Ann Young, July 10, 1954; children: Jacqueline Sue Skidmore, James Albert III. BA, Muhlenberg Coll., 1954. Customer sales rep. N.J. Bell Telephone Co., Newark, 1957-65, then dist. sales mgr., div. mktg. mgr.; asst. to pres. for pub. affairs Pepsi Co., Inc., N.Y.C., 1966-69; asst. to Pres. of U.S., 1968-69; v.p. Handy Assoc., N.Y.C., 1969-70, pres., 1971-72; pres., CEO Sci. Mgmt. Corp., Basking Ridge, N.J., 1972—, chmn. bd. dir. Newark Brush Co., 1974-79; bd. dirs. Franklin State Bank, Somerset, N.J., Franklin Bancorp, United Jersey Banks, United Jersey Bank Franklin State exec. com. UJB Fin., 1989-93, Blue Cross & Blue Shield N.J., Inc., Enterprise Holding Co., Inc.; trustee Blue Cross of N.J., 1983—; dir. Coca Cola, N.Y., 1980-85, Mariner Communications, 1983-85; mem., chmn. mktg. com. Seton Hall Commn., 1987; mem. dean's adv. coun. Rutgers U. Grad. Sch. Mgmt., 1989; trustee Pub. Affairs Rsch. Inst. N.J., 1989; lectr. U. Amsterdam (The Netherlands), 1967, U. Toronto (Ont., Can.), U. Helsinki (Finland), 1967, Tokyo U. Mem. Nat. Council on Crime and Delinquency, 1965-66; mem. Nat. Commn. on Youth Employment, 1966-67; state chmn. N.J. Nat. Found. March of Dimes, 1966-73; mem. exec. bd. Watchung Area council Boy Scouts Am., 1972-77, dir. NE region, 1983-90; mem. Citizen's Adv. Bd. on Youth Opportunity 1969-75; state chmn. United Citizens for Nixon-Agnew, N.J., 1968; bd. govs. Alpha Tau Omega Found., 1967-83; bd. dirs. Muhlenberg Coll., Allentown, Pa., 1980-92, N.E. region Boy Scouts Am., 1983—. Recipient Disting. Citizens award Boy Scouts Am., 1983, Private Sector Initiative award Pres. Reagan, 1985. Trustee Brick Twp. Hosp., Inc., Brick Town, N.J., 1976-80; bd. dirs. Am. Christmas Trains and Trucks, chmn., 1966; pres. Project Concern, San Diego,1966-78. Served to capt. USMC, 1954-57. Decorated Order of St. John (Eng.); recipient Internat. Understanding award, Brussels, 1966, Disting. Service award St. Paul, 1966, Freedom Found. George Washington Medal of Honor award, 1965, Outstanding Achievement in Life award Muhlenberg Coll. Alumni, 1966, Ambassador award U.S Jaycees, 1977, Trinidad and Tobago award Prime Minister of Ireland, 1970 Human Relations award Soc. Advancement of Mgmt., 1982; Statesman award N.J. Jaycees, 1983; Disting. Citizens award Boy Scouts Am., 1983; inducted into U.S. Jaycees Hall of Leadership, 1983. Mem. N.J. State C. of C. (bd. dirs.), Muhlenberg Coll. Alumni Assn., Alpha Tau Omega. Clubs: Sky N.Y.C., Baltusrol Golf, Longboat Key. Guest columnist Rotary Internat. mag., 1966-68, Kiwanis mag., 1966-68, Japan Times on Community Responsibility and Leadership, 1965-67. Home: 641 Ocean Ave Sea Girt NJ 08750-3102 also: 1401 Gulf of Mexico Dr Longboat Key FL 34228 Office: Sci Mgmt Corp 721 Rte 202-206 Bridgewater NJ 08807

SKIDMORE, PAUL HAROLD, insurance broker; b. Golden Lake, Ark., Jan. 28, 1918; s. William Raymond Skidmore and Frances Beatrice Webster; m. Nancy Lee DiFiore, Sept. 21, 1952 (div. Nov. 1983); children: Paul Harold Jr., Kathleen Frances, Jacqueline Lea. Student, Washington U., St. Louis, 1945-46. Owner Arrow Ins. Agy., Chgo., 1949—. Mem. nat. adv. bd. Am. Security Coun., Boston, 1980-88; vol. dep. sheriff Lake County, Ill., 1981—; sustaining mem. Rep. Nat. Com., Washington, 1980—. Sgt. C.E. U.S. Army, 1941-49. Mem. Am. Legion, Experimental Aircraft Assn., Inc. Republican. Baptist. Avocation: photography. Home: 745 Bradley Rd Lake Forest IL 60045-1085 Office: Arrow Ins Agy 700 Milwaukee Ave Ste 109 Vernon Hills IL 60061-1523

SKIDMORE, REX AUSTIN, social work educator; b. Salt Lake City, Dec. 31, 1914; s. Charles H. and Louise (Wangsgaard) S.; m. Knell Spencer, Aug. 31, 1939; children: Lee Spencer, Larry Rex. BA, U. Utah, 1938, MA, 1939; PhD, U. Pa., 1941. Instr. sociology U. Pa., 1940-41, Utah State Agrl. Coll., Logan, 1941-42; spl. agt. FBI, Miami, Fla., San Francisco, San Antonio, 1943-45; dir. bur. student counsel U. Utah, 1947-57, asso. prof., 1947-50, prof., 1950-85, dean Grad. Sch. Social Work, 1956-75. Author: Mormon Recreation: Theory and Practice, 1941, Building Your Marriage, 1951, 3d edit., 1964, Marriage Consulting, 1956, Introduction to Social Work, 1964, 6th edit., 1994, Introduction to Social Work, 1964, 6th edit., 1994, Introduction to Mental Health, 1979, Social Work Adminstration, 1983, 3d edit., 1995; contbr. articles to sociol. jours. Chmn. Western Mental Health Council, Western Interstate Commn. Higher Edn., 1964-65; mem. Nat. Adv. Council Nat. Manpower and Tng. Recipient distinguished service awards Community Service Council, Nat. Assn. Social Work, 1975, distinguished service awards Utah Conf. on Human Services, 1976. Mem. Coun. on Social Work Edn., Phi Kappa Phi, Pi Kappa Alpha, Pi Gamma Mu. Mem. Ch. of Jesus Christ Latter-Day Saints. Home: 1444 S 20th E Salt Lake City UT 84108 *A significant idea for successful living is knowing that: Loving is the central ingredient in human relationships; and the essence of loving is giving, not getting.*

SKIDMORE, THOMAS ELLIOTT, history educator; b. Troy, Ohio, July 22, 1932; s. Ernest Anton and Josephine (Hale) S.; m. Felicity Margaret Hall, Aug. 31, 1957; children—David, James, Robert. B.A., Denison U., 1954, Litt.D., 1975; B.A. (Fulbright fellow), Oxford (Eng.) U., 1956; Ph.D., Harvard U., 1961. Instr. history Harvard U., 1960-61, research fellow in Latin Am. studies, 1961-64, asst. prof. history, 1964-66; asst. prof. dept. history U. Wis. Madison, 1966-67; assoc. prof. U. Wis., 1967-68, prof., 1968-88; dir. Ibero-Am. studies, 1980-85; Carlos Manuel de Cespedes prof. Modern Latin Am. History Brown U., 1988—; vis. prof. Oxford U., 1972; lectr. Fgn. Svc. Inst., State Dept. Social Sci.; dir. Ctr. for Latin Am. Studies, 1989—. Author: Politics in Brazil, 1967, Black Into White: Race and Nationality in Brazilian Thought, 1974, The Politics of Military Rule in Brazil, 1964-85, 88; co-author: Modern Latin America, 2d edit., 1989; co-editor: Encyclopedia of Latin America and the Caribbean, 1985; co-editor: Luso-Brazilian Rev., 1977-87. Research Council fellow, 1966-67; Woodrow Wilson Internat. Center for Scholars fellow, 1971-72; Guggenheim fellow, 1974-75; Fulbright Faculty Research Abroad grantee, 1979. Mem. AAUP, Am. Hist. Assn., Latin Am. Studies Assn. (pres., past mem. exec. coun., Bryce Wood award 1989), Coun. Fgn. Rels., Ctr. for Inter-Am. Rels. Home: 44 Halsey St # 3 Providence RI 02906-1417

SKIGEN, PATRICIA SUE, lawyer; b. Springfield, Mass., June 16, 1942; d. David P. and Gertrude H. (Hirschhaut) S.; m. Irwin J. Sugarman, May 1973 (separated May 1992); 1 child, Alexander David. BA with distinction, Cornell U., 1964; LLB, Yale U., 1968. Bar: N.Y. 1968, U.S. Dist. Ct. (so. dist.) N.Y. 1969. Law clk. Anderson, Mori & Rabinowitz, Tokyo, 1966-67; assoc. Rosenman Colin Kaye Petschek Freund & Emil, N.Y.C., 1968-70; assoc. Willkie Farr & Gallagher, N.Y.C., 1970-75, ptnr., 1977-95; dep. supt., gen. counsel N.Y. State Banking Dept., N.Y.C., 1975-77, 1st dep. supt. banks, 1977; v.p.; co-chair corp. fin. divsn., legal dept. Chase Manhattan Bank, 1995—; adj. prof. Benjamin Cardozo Law Sch. Yeshiva U., 1979. Contbr. articles to profl. jours. Cornell U. Dean's scholar, 1960-64, Regent's scholar, 1960-64, Yale Law Sch. scholar, 1964-68. Mem. ABA (corp. banking and bus. law sect.), Assn. of Bar of City of N.Y. (chmn. com. banking 1991-94, mem. long range planning com. 1994—), Phi Beta Kappa, Phi Kappa Phi. Office: Chase Manhattan Bank One Citicorp Ctr One Chase Manhattan Plz New York NY 10081

SKILES, JAMES JEAN, electrical and computer engineering educator; b. St Louis, Oct. 16, 1929; s. Coy Emerson and Vernetta Beatrice (Maples) S.; m. Deloris Audrey McKenney, Sept. 4, 1948; children: Steven, Randall, Jeffrey. BSEE, Washington U., St. Louis, 1948; MS, U. Mo.-Rolla, 1951; PhD, U. Wis., 1954. Registered profl. engr., Wis. Engr. Union Electric Co. St. Louis, 1948-49; instr. U. Mo.-Rolla, 1949-51; prof. elec. engring. U. Wis.,

Madison, 1954-89, prof. emeritus, 1989—, chmn. Dept. Elec. Engring., 1967-72, dir. Univ. Industry Rsch. program, 1972-75, dir. Energy Rsch. Ctr., 1975-95; cons. in field. Contbr. articles to profl. jours. Mem. Monona Grove Dist. Schs. Bd., Wis., 1961-69; mem. adv. com. Wis. Energy Office, Madison, 1979-80, Wis. Pub. Service Commn., 1980-81. Recipient Wis. Electric Utilities Professorship in Energy Engring. U. Wis., 1975-89; recipient Benjamin Smith Reynolds Teaching award, 1980, Kiekhofer Teaching award, 1955, Acad of Elec. Engring. award U. Mo.-Rolla, 1982. Mem. IEEE (sr.), Am. Soc. Engring. Edn. Home: 8099 Coray Ln Verona WI 53593-9073 Office: Univ of Wisconsin Dept Elec & Computer Engring 1415 Johnson Dr Madison WI 53706-1691

SKILES, PAUL, church administrator. Dir. Communications Division of the Church of the Nazarene, Kansas City, Mo. Office: Church of the Nazarene 6401 The Paseo Kansas City MO 64131

SKILLICORN, JUDY PETTIBONE, gifted/talented education coordinator; b. Cleve., June 16, 1943; d. C. Arthur and Dorothy Laura (Parratt) Pettibone; m. Robert Charles Skillicorn, Aug. 21, 1965; children: Jodie Lynn, Brian Jeffrey, Jennifer Laura. BS in Edn., Ohio State U., 1965; MEd, Cleve. State U., 1988. 6th grade tchr. Windermer Sch., Upper Arlington, Ohio, 1965-68; pvt. tutor, 1968-71; adminstr. Westshore Montessori Sch., Elyria, Lorain & Amherst, Ohio, 1981; ch. educator First Congl. Ch., Elyria, 1982-84, St. Peters United Ch. of Christ, Amherst, Ohio, 1984; tchr. gifted Clearview Local Schs., Lorain, 1985-90; coord. gifted Lorain County Bd. Edn., Elyria, 1990—; planning dir. county-wide sch. creative & performing arts; founder Arts Advocacy of Lorain County, 1994. Author: Young Authors Handbook, 1991, 92, 93, 94, 95. Chairperson tickets Elyria 150th Bicentennial Celebration; pageant dir. Ch. Medieval Feast, Elyria, 1988-91; chmn. diaconate First Congl. Ch., Elyria, 1990-93. Recipient Partnership in Edn. for Young Authors Program Nat. Assn. Coll. Stores, Oberlin, 1993-95, for Writers Conf. Program, Oberlin, 1993-95; Jennings scholar tchr. Martha Holden Jennings Found., 1990-91. Mem. Nat. Assn. Tchrs. English, Writing Tchrs. Network (publ. com. 1991-93), North Ctrl. Consortium for Gifted (treas., v.p. 1991-93), Lorain County Elem. Sch. Adminstrs. (sec.-treas. 1993, v.p. 1993-94, pres. 1994-95), Consortium Ohio Coords. for Gifted, Ohio Assn. Gifted Children, Chautauqua Lit. Soc., Internat. Network for Visual and Performing Arts Schs., Phi Delta Kappa. Avocations: reading including children's literature, travel, attending plays, arts actvities and concerts. Office: Lorain County Office Edn 1885 Lake Ave Elyria OH 44035

SKILLIN, EDWARD SIMEON, magazine publisher; b. N.Y.C., Jan. 23, 1904; s. Edward Simeon and Geraldine Madeleine (Fearons) S.; m. Jane Anne Edwards, Jan. 27, 1945; children: Edward John, Elizabeth Ann Skillin Flanagan, Arthur Paul, Susan Geraldine Skillin Thuvanuti, Mary Jane Skillin Davis. Grad., Phillips Acad., Andover, Mass., 1921; AB, Williams Coll., 1925; MA, Columbia U., 1933; LHD (hon.), St. Benedict's Coll. Atchison, Kans., 1954, Fordham U., 1974; LLD, St. Vincent's Coll., Latrobe, Pa., 1959, St. Francis Xavier U., Antigonish, N.S., Can., 1966, Stonehill Coll., 1979. With ednl. dept. Henry Holt & Co., N.Y.C., 1925-32; mem. staff Commonweal Found., N.Y.C., 1933-38, editor, 1938-67, pub., 1967—. Editor: The Commonweal Reader, 1949. Recipient Centennial citation St. John's U., Collegeville, Minn., 1957, St. Francis de Sales award Cath. Press Assn., 1987, Pax Christi award St. John's U., 1990. Mem. Cath. Commn. on Intellectual and Cultural Affairs, Phi Beta Kappa, Phi Gamma Delta. Office: Commonweal Found 15 Dutch St New York NY 10038-3719 *Grateful for many things: faith, family, the influence of 3 friends, good health, and 60 years with a socially-minded Christian journal of opinion.*

SKILLING, DAVID VAN DIEST, manufacturing executive; b. St. Louis, Sept. 16, 1933; s. David Miller Jr. and Eloise Margaret (van Diest) S.; m. Barbara Jo Chaney, Aug. 4, 1956; children: Kimberly Alice, Mark Chaney. BS, Colo. Coll., 1955; MBA, Pepperdine U., 1977. With TRW Inc., Los Angeles, 1970-83, Cleve., 1983-93, Orange, Calif., 1993—; dir. mktg. energy group TRW, Inc., Los Angeles, 1978-83, v.p. planning and devel., indsl. and energy sector, 1983-86, v.p. corp. planning and devel., 1987-89, exec. v.p., gen. mgr. infosystems and svcs., 1989—; bd. dirs. Lamson & Sessions, Cleve. Bd. dirs. ISI, 1995—; bd. trustees The Colo. Coll., 1994—, Nat. Commn. on Children. Mem. Nat. Assn. Mfrs. (bd. dirs. 1988-93), Assn. for Corp. Growth, Calif. Bus. Roundtable (exec. com. 1994—). Republican. Office: TRW Inc 505 City Pkwy W Orange CA 92608

SKILLING, JOHN BOWER, structural and civil engineer; b. L.A., Oct. 8, 1921; s. Harold C. and Helen M. (Bower) S.; m. Mary Jane Stender, May 1, 1943; children: William, Susan, Ann. B.S., U. Wash., 1947. Design engr. W.H. Witt Co., Seattle, 1947-52; partner successor firm Worthington, Skilling, Helle and Jackson, Seattle, 1959-67, Skilling, Helle, Christiansen, Robertson, Seattle, 1967-82; chmn., CEO successor firm Skilling Ward Rogers Barkshire, Inc., Seattle, 1983-87; chmn. Skilling Ward Magnusson Barkshire, Inc. and successor firm, Seattle, 1987—; mem. Bldg. Research Adv. Bd. Mem. Seattle Found. Fellow ASCE; mem. NAE, Am. Concrete Inst., Internat. Assn. Shell Structures, Structural Engrs. Assn. Wash., AIA (hon.), Am. Inst. Steel Constrn., Wash. Athletic Club, Seattle Tennis Club, Broadmoor Golf Club, Lampda Alpha. Clubs: 101; Dean's, Pres.'s (Univ. Wash.). Home: 539 McGilvra Blvd E Seattle WA 98112-5047 Office: Skilling Ward Magnusson Barkshire Inc 1301 5th Ave Ste 3200 Seattle WA 98101-2699

SKILLING, RAYMOND INWOOD, lawyer; b. Enniskillen, U.K., July 14, 1939; s. Dane and Elizabeth (Burleigh) S.; m. Alice Mae Welsh, Aug. 14, 1982; 1 child by previous marriage, Keith A. F. LLB, Queen's U., Belfast, U.K., 1961; JD, U. Chgo., 1962. Solicitor English Supreme Ct. 1966. Bar: Ill 1974. Assoc. Clifford-Turner (now Clifford Chance), London, 1963-69, ptnr., 1969-76; exec. v.p., chief counsel Aon Corp. (and predecessor cos.), Chgo., 1976—; bd. dirs. Aon Corp. (and predecessor cos.). Commonwealth fellow, U. Chgo., 1961-62, Bigelow teaching fellow U. Chgo. Law Sch., 1962-63; Fulbright scholar U.S. Ednl. Commn., London, 1961-63; recipient McKane medal Queen's U., Belfast, 1961. Mem. ABA, Ill. Bar Assn., Chgo. Bar Assn. The Casino Chgo., Chgo. Club, Econ. Club Chgo., Racquet Club Chgo., The Carlton Club London. Office: Aon Corp 123 N Wacker Dr Chicago IL 60606-1700

SKILLMAN, THOMAS GRANT, endocrinology consultant, former educator; b. Cin., Jan. 7, 1925; s. Harold Grant and Faustina (Jobes) S.; m. Elizabeth Louise McClellan, Sept. 6, 1947; children: Linda, Barbara. B.S., Baldwin-Wallace Coll., 1946; M.D., U. Cin., 1949. Intern Cin. Gen. Hosp., 1949-50, resident, 1952-54; instr. medicine U. Cin., 1952-57; asst. prof. medicine Ohio State U., Columbus, 1957-61; dir. endocrinology and metabolism Coll. Medicine Ohio State U., 1967-74, Ralph Kurtz prof. endocrinology, 1974-81, prof. emeritus, 1981—, cons. to v.p. med. affairs, 1981—; asso. prof. medicine Creighton U., Omaha, 1961-67. Editor: Case Studies in Endocrinology, 1971; Contbr. numerous articles to med. jours. Served with USNR, 1943-45; 1950-52, Korea. Recipient Golden Apple award Student Am. Med. Assn., 1966. Mem. Am. Diabetes Assn., Central Soc. Clin. Investigation, Am. Fedn. for Clin. Research, Alpha Omega Alpha. Club: Ohio State Golf (Columbus). Home: 4179 Stoneroot Dr Hilliard OH 43026-3023 Office: Ohio State U Hosps Meiling Hall # 200G Columbus OH 43210

SKILLMAN, WILLIAM ALFRED, consulting systems engineering executive; b. Lakehurst, N.J., Jan. 22, 1928; s. Wilbur Newton and Greta Alfreda (Ekman) S.; m. Anne Marie Cavender, Sept. 19, 1948; children—Thomas R., Gregory A., Karen L. B.S. in Engring. Physics, Lehigh U., 1952; M.S. in Physics, U. Rochester, 1954. Assoc. engr. Westinghouse Electric Corp., Balt., 1954-56, engr., 1956-58, sr. engr., 1958-61, supervisory engr. 1961-64, advisory engr., 1964-73, sr. adv. engr., 1973-85, cons. engr., 1986-93, cons. electronic systems group, 1993—. Author: Radar Calculations Using the TI-59 Programmable Calculator, 1983; author: (with others) Radar Handbook, 2d edit., 1990. Patentee in field. Served with USN, 1946-48. Fellow IEEE; mem. Phi Beta Kappa. Republican. Methodist. Avocations: photography; canoeing; hiking; programming. Home and Office: 605 Forest View Rd Linthicum Heights MD 21090-2819

SKILLRUD, HAROLD CLAYTON, minister; b. St. Cloud, Minn., June 29, 1928; s. Harold and Amanda Skillrud; m. Lois Dickhart, June 8, 1951; children: David, Janet, John. BA magna cum laude, Gustavus Adolphus Coll., 1950; MDiv magna cum laude, Augustana Theol. Sem., Rock Island,

Ill., 1954; STM, Luth. Sch. Theology, Chgo., 1969; DD (hon.), Augustana Coll., 1978, Newberry Coll., 1988. Ordained to ministry Evang. Luth. Ch. in Am., 1954. Supply pastor Saron Luth. Ch., Big Lake, Minn., 1950-51; mem. staff 1st Luth. Ch., Rock Island, Ill., 1951-52; intern, organizer new mission Faith Luth. Ch., Syosset, N.Y., 1952-53; sr. pastor St. John's Luth. Ch., Bloomington, Ill., 1954-79, Luth. Ch. of the Redeemer, Atlanta, 1979-87; bishop Southeastern Synod Evang. Luth. Ch. in Am., Atlanta, 1987-95, regional rep. bd. pensions, 1995—; del. to various convs. Luth. Ch. in Am., Luth. World Fedn. in Helsinki, 1963, mem. bd. publ., 1976-84, pastor-evangelist Evang. Outreach Emphasis program, 1977-79, mem. exec. bd. Ill. synod, 1977-79, pres. bd. publ., 1980-84, leader stewardship cluster Southeastern synod, 1983, mem. exec. bd. Southeastern synod, 1984-87; mem. exec. coun., Luth. Ch. in Am., 1984-87; mem. task force on new ch. design Commn. on New Luth. Ch., task force on ch. pub. house, 1985; del. constituting conv. Evang. Luth. Ch. in Am., 1987, del. assemblies Evang. Luth. Ch. in Am., 1989, 91, 93, 95; mem. commnn. on clergy confidentiality Luth. Coun. in USA, 1987; co-chair USA Luth.- Roman Cath. Dialogue; mem. Task Force on Theol. Edn. Author: LSTC: Decade of Decision, 1969; mem. editorial bd. Partners mag., 1978-80; contbr. articles and sermons to religious jours. Former bd. dirs. Augustana Theol. Sem.; del. bd. dirs. Augustana Coll., 1969-77, chmn. bd., 1976-77; bd. dirs. Kessler Reformation Collection, Newberry Coll., Luth. World Relief, Augsburg Fortress; chmn. bd. dirs. Luth. Sch. Theology, Chgo., 1962-69; mem. Leadership Atlanta, 1980-81, United Way, Atlanta, 1980-81; mem. Bishop's Commn. on Econ. Justice, 1985-86; pres. bd. dirs. Atlanta Samaritan House, 1986-87. Recipient Alumni award Luth. Sch. Theology, Chgo., 1976, award Leadership Atlanta, 1981. Mem. Luth. Sch. Theology Alumni Assn. (pres. 1975-77), Conf. of Bishops, Kiwanis (pres. Midtown chpt. 1984-85). Avocations: travel, photography. Home: 368 E Wesley Rd NE Atlanta GA 30305-3824 Office: Evang Luth Ch in Am Southeastern Synod 756 W Peachtree St NW Atlanta GA 30308-1138

SKILTON, JOHN SINGLETON, lawyer; b. Washington, Apr. 13, 1944; s. Robert Henry and Margaret (Neisser) S.; m. Carmen Fisher, Jan. 28, 1967; children: Laura Anne, Susan Elizabeth, Robert John. BA, U. Wis., 1966, JD, 1969. Bar: Wis. Supreme Ct. 1969, U.S. Dist. Ct. (ea. and we. dists.) Wis. 1969, U.S. Ct. Appeals (7th cir.) 1969, U.S. Supreme Ct. 1989. Law clk. 7th Cir. Ct. Appeals, Milw., 1969-70; assoc. Foley & Lardner, Milw., 1970-77; ptnr. Foley & Lardner, Madison, Wis., 1977—. Bd. visitors U. Wis. Law Sch., Madison, 1982-90, chmn., 1988-89; chair Wis. Fed. Nominating Commn., 1994; mem. Gov.'s Task Force on Bus. Ct., 1994—. Fellow Am. Bar Found.; Am. Coll. Trial Lawyers; mem. Am. Law Inst., Am. Acad. appellate Lawyers, 7th Cir. Bar Assn. (pres. 1985-86, chmn. 7th cir. adv. com. on rules 1994—), State Bar Wis. (pres. 1995—, Pres.'s award of excellence 1989), Western Dist. Wis. Bar Assn. (pres. 1992-93), Western Dist. Adv. Group (chmn. 1991), James E. Doyle Am. Inn of Ct. (coun. 1992-94), Am. Inns of Ct. Found. (bd. trustees 1995—), U. Wis. Law Alumni Assn. (bd. dirs. 1991—, pres. 1993—). Home: 8 N Prospect Ave Madison WI 53705-3936 Office: Foley & Lardner First Wis Plz PO Box 1497 1 S Pinckney St Madison WI 53703-2808

SKINNER, ALASTAIR, accountant; b. Hamilton, Ont., Can., Apr. 4, 1936; s. Allistair and Isabelle (Drysdale) S.; m. Patricia Skinner; children: Lisa, Iain, James, Graeme. CA, Queens U., Kingston, Ont., Can., 1959; MBA, Harvard U., 1963. Cert. mgmt. cons. Served to maj. Can. Army Res., 1954-71; nat. mng. ptnr. MacGillivray & Co. (name now Doane Raymond), 1977-83; ptnr.-in-charge Toronto (Ont.) Office, Spicer MacGillivray (name now Doane Raymond), 1984-86, 88-91; ptnr. Doane Raymond, Toronto, 1991—. Co-author: profl. manuals. Fellow Inst. Chartered Accts. of Ont. (pres. 1983-84), Soc. Mgmt. Accts. of Can. (bd. dirs.); mem. Inst. Mgmt. Cons. of Ont., Can. Tax Found. (bd. govs.). Club: Albany (Toronto), Devil's Glen Country Club (dir.). Avocations: skiing, bridge. Office: Doane Raymond Ste 1100, Royal Bank Plz Box 55 N Tower, Toronto, ON Canada M5J 2P9

SKINNER, B. FRANKLIN, retired telecommunications executive; b. Covington, Va., Nov. 4, 1931; s. B. Franklin and Charlotte Frances (Walton) s.; m. Ruth Ann Gee, Nov. 25, 1955; children: Ruth Anne, Christian Franklin, Lisa Page (dec.). B.A., U. Richmond, 1952, D.C.S. (hon.), 1985; L.L.D. (hon.), Jacksonville U., 1986; DHL (hon.), Interdenominational Theological Ctr., Atlanta, 1987. Div. traffic mgr. Chesapeake & Potomac Telephone Cos., Richmond, Va., 1964-66, gen. comml. mgr., 1966-70; v.p. ops. Chesapeake & Potomac Telephone Cos., Washington, 1970-73; v.p. gen. mgr. So. Bell Tel. & Tel., Charlotte, N.C., 1973-79; v.p. Fla. So. Bell Tel. & Tel., Miami, 1979-82; exec. v.p. mktg. and external affairs. co. hdqrs. So. Bell Tel. & Tel., Atlanta, 1982, pres., chief exec. officer, 1982-91; chmn., chief exec. officer BellSouth Telecommunications, Atlanta, 1991-92; ret. Bellsouth Telecommunications, Atlanta, 1992, Bell South Telecommunications, Atlanta, 1992; bd. dirs. Nats. Bank Corp., Atlanta, Cen. Atlanta Progress. Chmn. bd. dirs. United Way Metro Atlanta; S.E. region chmn. nat. corp. leadership devel. United Way Am.; mem. adv. bd. Met. Atlanta United Negro Coll. Fund; chmn. nat. adv. bd. Salvation Army, 1988-89; trustee U. Richmond, Va., Davidson Coll., N.C., J. M. Tull Charitable Found., Atlanta; bd. advisors Habitat for Humanity; elder Peachtree Presbn. Ch., Atlanta. With U.S Army, 1952-54. Recipient Top Mgmt. award Sales and Mktg. Execs., 1978, Reubin Askew Awareness award Greater Miami Urban League, 1980, Brotherhood award Nat. Conf. of Christians and Jews, 1992. Mem. Telephone Pioneers Am. (assn. pres. 1986-87), Met. Atlanta C. of C. (chmn. 1992), Capital City Club, Commerce Club (bd. dirs.), Rotary, Omicron Delta Kappa, Sigma Phi Epsilon, Pi Delta Epsilon. Presbyterian. Home: 675 Tuxedo Pl NW Atlanta GA 30342-3616

SKINNER, BRIAN JOHN, geologist, educator; b. Wallaroo, South Australia, Dec. 15, 1928; came to U.S., 1958, naturalized, 1963; s. Joshua Henry and Joyce Barbara Lloyd (Prince) S.; m. Helen Catherine Wild, Oct. 9, 1954; children: Adrienne Wild, Stephanie Wild, Thalassa Wild. B.Sc., U. Adelaide, Australia, 1950; A.M., Harvard U., 1952, Ph.D., 1955. Lectr. U. Adelaide, 1955-58; research geologist U.S. Geol. Survey, 1958-62, chief br. exptl. geochemistry and mineralogy, 1962-66; prof. geology and geophysics, chmn. dept. Yale U., New Haven, 1966-73; Eugene Higgins prof. Yale U., 1972—; Hugh Exton McKinstry Meml. lectr. Harvard U., 1978; Alex L. du Toit lectr. Combined Socs. South Africa, 1979; Cecil H. and Ida Green lectr. U. B.C., 1983; Thayer Lindsley Meml. lectr. U. Econ. Geologists, 1983; Soc. Econ. Geologists Overseas lectr., 1985; Hoffman lectr. Harvard U., 1986, Joubin-James lectr. U. Toronto, 1987; mem. exec. com. div. earth scis. NRC, 1966-69; chmn. com. mineral resources and the environment Nat. Acad. Scis.-NRC, 1973-75; mem. Lunar Sample Analysis Planning Team, 1968-70, Lunar Sci. Rev. Bd., 1971-72, U.S. Nat. Com. for Geochemistry, 1966-67, U.S. Nat. Com. for Geology, 1973-77, 85-93, chmn., 1987-93; chmn. bd. earth scis. NRC, 1987-88, earth scis. and resources, 1989-90, mem. bd. Internat. Geol. Correlation Program, UNESCO-IUGS, 1985-89, 90—, chmn., 1986-89; cons. Office Sci. and Tech. Policy, 1977-80, NSF, 1977-82; dir. Econ. Geology Pub. Co.; Chmn. governing bd. Am. Jour. Sci., 1972—. Author: Earth Resources, 1969, 77, 86, Man and the Ocean, 1973, Physical Geology, 1974, 77, 87, Rocks and Rock Minerals, 1979, The New Iron Age Ahead, 1987, Resources and World Development, 1987, The Dynamic Earth, 1989, 92, 95, The Blue Planet, 1995; editor: Econ. Geology, 1969—, Oxford Univ. Press Monographs in Geological Sciences, 1979—; editl. bd. Am. Scientist, 1974-90, chmn., 1987-90. Trustee Hopkins Grammar Sch., 1978-83. Guggenheim fellow, 1970; recipient Disting. Contbns. award Assn. Earth Sci. Editors, 1979; Silver medal Soc. Econ. Geologists, 1981. Fellow Geol. Soc. Am. (councillor 1976-78, chmn. spl. publs. com. 1980-81, chmn. com. on coms. 1983, pres. 1985); mem. Geochem. Soc. (pres. 1972-73), Conn. Acad. Sci. and Engring. (div. chmn. 1978-80, coun. 1982-87), Am. Econ Geologists (pres. 1995). Home: PO Box 894 Woodbury CT 06798-0894

SKINNER, CHARLES SCOFIELD, technology management service executive, consultant, mechanical engineer; b. Cleve., Feb. 10, 1940; s. Harry Harrison and Margaret Charlotte (Scofield) S.; m. Nancy Lee Cleveland, Sept. 20, 1974; children: Jeffrey Charles, Melinda Lee. MME, Cornell U., 1969; MBA, Case Western Res. U., 1979; BSME, Cornell U., 1963; postgrad., MIT, 1972, Stanford U., 1977, Harvard U., 1982. Registered profl. engr., N.Y., Ohio. Mfg. engr. GM, Detroit, 1963-64; market researcher Exxon Corp., N.Y.C., 1964-65; sr. ptnr. Booz-Allen & Hamilton, Inc., N.Y.C., 1970-85; pres., CEO Strategic Technology Inc., Cleve., 1985—; cons. Booz-Allen & Hamilton, Inc., 1970-85, Strategic Tech., Inc., 1985—; also bd. dirs.; cons. First Pacific Networks, Inc., Sunnyvale, Calif., 1988-89. Author: CIM Implementation Planning Guide, 1988, (with others) The Management

of Productivity, 1986; contbr. numerous articles to profl. jours. Fundraiser Culver (Ind.) Ednl. Found., 1969-92, Cornell U., Ithaca, N.Y., 1975—, Old Trail Sch., Akron, Ohio, 1988—, Univ. Sch., Shaker Hts., Ohio, 1991—. Capt. U.S. Army, 1965-68. Decorated Air medal with 23 oak leaf clusters, Vietnam Campaign medal with device, Aviator medal, Vietnam Service medal, Exxon Corp. grantee, 1968-69. Mem. Soc. Mfg. Engrs. (chmn. mfg. and planning divsn., tech. coun. 1982-83), Culver Legion (life), Cornell Club of N.Y., Mid-Day Club, Cornell Club of N.E. Ohio (treas. 1993), Sigma Chi (treas. 1962-63), SAR, We. Res. Soc., Scabbard and Blade (hon.), Phoebus (hon.), Masons, Shriners, Vietnam Vets. Am., VFW. Avocations: squash, golf, piloting. Office: Strategic Tech Inc 24200 Chagrin Blvd Cleveland OH 44122-5509

SKINNER, CLIFFORD, insurance company executive; b. 1929. BS, Allegheny Coll., 1951; MD, Temple U., 1955. Physician Arthur, Bugbee and Skinner, Denver, 1961-65; chmn. bd. Permanente Med. Group, Inc., Oakland, Calif., 1965—. Office: Permanente Medical Group Inc 1950 Franklin St Oakland CA 94612-5103

SKINNER, DAVID BERNT, surgeon, educator; b. Joliet, Ill., Apr. 28, 1935; s. James Madden and Bertha Elinor (Tapper) S.; m. May Elinor Tischer, Aug. 25, 1956; children: Linda Elinor, Kristin Anne, Carise Berntine, Margaret Leigh. B.A. with high honors, U. Rochester, N.Y., 1958, Sc.D. (hon.), 1980; M.D. cum laude, Yale U., 1959. Diplomate: Am. Bd. Surgery (dir. 1974-80), Am. Bd. Thoracic Surgery. Intern, then resident in surgery Mass. Gen. Hosp., Boston, 1959-65; sr. registrar in thoracic surgery Frenchay Hosp., Bristol, Eng., 1963-64; teaching fellow Harvard U. Med. Sch., 1965; from asst. prof. surgery to prof. Johns Hopkins U. Med. Sch., also surgeon Johns Hopkins Hosp., 1968-72; Dallas B. Phemister prof. surgery, chmn. dept. U. Chgo. Hosps. and Clinics, 1972-87; prof. surgery Cornell U., 1987—; pres., chief exec. officer N.Y. Hosp., 1987—; dir. Omnis Surg. Inc., 1984-85, Churchill Livingston, 1990-93; mem. President's Biomed. Research Panel, 1975-76; past cons. USPHS, Office Surgeon Gen. U.S. Navy. Author: Atlas of Esophageal Surgery, 1991; author: (with others) Gastroesophageal Reflux and Hiatal Hernia, 1972, Management of Esophaeal Diseases, 1988—; editor: Surgical Practice Illustrated, 1988; editor Current Topics in Surg. Research, 1969-71, Jour. Surg. Research, 1972-83; co-editor: Surgical Treatment of Digestive Disease, 1985, Esophageal Disorders, 1985, Reconstructive Surgery of the Gastrointestinal Tract, 1985, Primary Motility Disorders of the Esophagus, 1991; mem. editorial bd.: Jour. Thoracic and Cardiovascular Surgery, Annals of Surgery, Surg. Gastroenterology; contbr. profl. jours., chpts. in books. Elder Fourth Presbyn. Ch., Chgo., 1976-87, clk. of session, 1978-82, 84-87; bd. visitors Cornell U. Med. Coll., 1980-87. Served to maj. M.C. USAF, 1966-68. Decorated Chevalier Nat. Order of Merit (France); John and Mary Markle scholar acad. medicine, 1969-74. Fellow ACS; mem. AMA, Internat. Surg. Group, Am., Western, So. surg. assns., Soc. Univ. Surgeons (pres. 1978-79), Am. Soc. Artificial Internal Organs (pres. 1977), Soc. Surg. Chmn. (pres. 1980-82), Am. Assn. Thoracic Surgery (council 1981-86), Soc. Vascular Surgery, Soc. Thoracic Surgery, Soc. Pelvic Surgeons, Soc. Surgery Alimentary Tract, Société Internationale de Chirurgie, Collegium Internationale Chirurgiae Digestivae, Am. Coll. Chest Physicians, Central Surg. Soc., Internat. Soc. Diseases Esophogus (pres. 1992—), Assn. Acad. Surgery, Halsted Soc., Soc. Clin. Surgery (pres. 1986-88), Phi Beta Kappa, Alpha Omega Alpha. Clubs: Quadrangle (Chgo.); Cosmos (Washington); University (N.Y.C.); River (N.Y.C.). Home: 79 E 79th St New York NY 10021-0202 Office: Soc NY Hosp Office Pres 525 E 68th St New York NY 10021-4873

SKINNER, G(EORGE) WILLIAM, anthropologist, educator; b. Oakland, Calif., Feb. 14, 1925; s. John James and Eunice (Engle) S.; m. Carol Bagger, Mar. 25, 1951 (div. Jan. 1970); children: Geoffrey Crane, James Lauriston, Mark Williamson, Jeremy Burr; m. Susan Mann, Apr. 26, 1980; 1 dau., Alison Jane. Student, Deep Springs (Calif.) Coll., 1942-43; B.A. with distinction in Far Eastern Studies, Cornell U., Ithaca, N.Y., 1947, Ph.D. in Cultural Anthropology, 1954. Field dir. Cornell U. S.E Asia program, also Cornell Research Center, Bangkok, Thailand, 1951-55; rsch. assoc. in Indonesia, 1956-58; assoc. prof., then prof. anthropology Cornell U., Ithaca, N.Y., 1960-65; asst. prof. sociology Columbia, 1958-60; sr. specialist in residence East-West Ctr. Honolulu, 1965-66; prof. anthropology Stanford, 1966-89; Barbara Kimball Browning prof. humanities and scis., 1987-89; prof. anthropology U. Calif., Davis, 1990—; vis. prof. U. Pa., 1977, Duke U., spring, 1978, Keio U. Tokyo, spring, 1985, fall, 1988, U. Calif.-San Diego, fall, 1986; field rsch. China, 1949-50, 77, S.W. Asia, 1950-51, Thailand, 1951-53, 54-55, Java and Borneo, 1956-58, Japan, 1985, 88; mem. joint com. on contemporary China Social Sci. Rsch. Coun.-Am. Acad. Learned Socs., 1961-65, 80-81, internat. com. on Chinese studies, 1963-64, mem. joint com. on Chinese studies, 1981-83; mem. subcom. rsch. Chinese Soc. Social Sci. Rsch. Coun., 1961-70, chmn., 1963-70; dir. program on East Asian Local Systems, 1969-71; dir. Chinese Soc. Bibliography Project, 1964-73; assoc. dir. Cornell China Program, 1961-63; dir. London-Cornell Project Social Rsch., 1962-65; mem. com. on scholarly communication with People's Republic of China, Nat. Acad. Scis., 1966-70, mem. social scis. and humanities panel, 1982-83; mem. adv. com. Ctr. for Chinese Rsch. Materials, Assn. Rsch. Librs., 1967-70; bd. dirs. Nat. Ctr. for Geographic Info. and Analysis, 1989-92; mem. policy and planning com. China in Time and Space, 1993—. Author: Chinese Society in Thailand, 1957, Leadership and Power in the Chinese Community of Thailand, 1958; also articles; Editor: The Social Sciences and Thailand, 1956, Local, Ethnic and National Loyalties in Village Indonesia, 1959, Modern Chinese Society: An Analytical Bibliography, 3 vols, 1973, (with Mark Elvin) The Chinese City Between Two Worlds, 1974, (with A. Thomas Kirsch) Change and Persistence in Thai Society, 1975, The City in Late Imperial China, 1977, The Study of Chinese Society, 1979. Served to ensign USNR, 1943-46. Fellow Center for Advanced Study in Behavioral Scis., 1969-70; Guggenheim fellow, 1969; NIMH spl. fellow, 1970. Mem. NAS, AAAS, Am. Anthrop. Assn., Am. Sociol. Assn., Asian Studies (bd. dirs. 1962-65, chmn. nominating com. 1967-68, pres. 1983-84), Soc. for Cultural Anthropology, Internat. Union for Sci. Study of Population, Social Sci. History Assn., Am. Ethnol. Soc., Population Assn. Am., Siam Soc., Soc. Qing Studies, Soc. Econ. Anthropology, Phi Beta Kappa, Sigma Xi. Office: Dept Anthropology U Calif Davis CA 95616

SKINNER, HARRY BRYANT, orthopaedic surgery educator; b. Cleve., Oct. 13, 1943; s. Harry Bryant and Maryan (Eastlick) S. BS, Alfred U., 1965; MS, PhD, U. Calif., Berkeley, 1970; MD, Med. U. S.C., 1975. Asst. prof. Youngstown (Ohio) State U., 1970-71; postdoctoral research assoc. Clemson (S.C.) U., 1971-72; lectr. Calif. State U., Sacramento, 1977-79; asst./assoc. prof. Tulane U., New Orleans, 1979-82; assoc. prof. orthopaedic surgery U. Calif., San Francisco, 1983-86, prof., 1986-94; prof. mech. engring. U. Calif., Berkeley, 1993—; chair grad. group U. Calif., Berkeley and San Francisco; prof., chmn. dept. orthopedic surgery U. Calif., Irvine, 1994—; adj. asst./assoc. prof. Sch. Engring., Tulane U., New Orleans, 1979-82; dir. rehab. research and devel. VA Med. Ctr., San Francisco, 1983—. Mem. editorial bd. Orthopaedics jour., 1984-88, guest editor, 1985, Jour. Biomed. Materials Research, 1983-; contbr. articles to profl. jours. Grantee NIH, 1978-84, Nat. Inst. Dental Rsch., 1978-84, VA, 1975—; Schleider Found., 1980-82. Am. Fedn. Aging Rsch., 1986-89. Fellow ACS, Am. Acad, Orthopaedic Surgeons; mem. Orthopaedic Rsch. Soc., Soc. for Biomaterials (dir. 1987-89), Am. Orthopaedic Assn., The Hip Soc., Sigma Xi. Office: U Calif Dept Orthopaedic Surge # U-454 San Francisco CA 94143

SKINNER, HELEN CATHERINE WILD, biomineralogist; b. Bklyn., Jan. 25, 1931; d. Edward Herman and Minnie (Bertsch) Wild; m. Brian John Skinner, Oct. 9, 1954; children: Adrienne W.S. Scott, Stephanie Skinner, Thalassa Skinner. BA, Mt. Holyoke Coll., 1952; MA, Radcliffe/Harvard, 1954; PhD, Adelaide (Australia) U., 1959. Mineralogist sect. molecular structure Nat. Inst. Arthritis and Metabolic Diseases, NIH, 1961-65; mem. sect. crystal chemistry Lab. Histology and Pathology Nat. Inst. Dental Rsch., NIH, 1965-66; lectr. dept. geology and geophysics Yale U., 1967-69, rsch. assoc. dept. geology, 1967-72; sr. rsch. assoc. dept. surgery, 1972-75; Alexander Agassiz vis. lectr. dept. biology Harvard U., 1976-77; lectr. dept. biology Yale U., 1977-83; assoc. prof. biochemistry in surgery Yale U., New Haven, 1978-84, lectr. dept. orthopaedic surgery, 1977—; rsch. assoc. in geology and geophysics, 1985—; pres. Conn. Acad. Arts and Scis., 1986-94; mineralogist AEC, summer 1953; master Jonathan Edwards Coll., Yale U., 1977-82; vis. prof. sect. ecology and systematics dept. biology Cornell U., 1980-83; dental adv. com. Yale-New Haven Hosp., 1973-80; mem. faculty adv. com. Yale-New Haven Tchrs. Inst., 1983—; chmn. site visit team Nat.

Inst. Dental Rsch., 1974-75. Author: (with others) Asbestos and other Fibrous Materials: Mineralogy, Crystal Chemistry and Health Effects, 1988; co-editor: Biomineralization Process of Iron and Manganese: Modern and Ancient Environments, 1992; tech. abstractor Geol. Soc. Am., 1961-65; sect. editor Am. Mineralogist, 1978-82; contbr. over 40 articles to profl. jours. Mem. bd. edn. com. Conn. Fund for Environ., 1983-89, mem. sci. adv. com., 1989-92; founder, pres. Investor's Strategy Inst., New Haven, 1983-85; trustee Miss Porter's Sch., Farmington, Conn., mem. edn. com., 1986-88, mem. salaries and benefits com., 1988-91; treas. YWCA, New Haven, 1983-84. Fellow AAAS, Geol. Soc. Am., Mineral. Soc. Am. (fin. counsel 1981-86); mem. Am. Soc. Bone and Mineral Rsch., Am. Assn. Crystal Growth, Am. Assn. Dental Rsch., Internat. Assn. Dental Rsch., Mineral Soc. Can. Home: PO Box 894 Woodbury CT 06798-0894 Office: Yale U Dept Geology Geophysics P O Box 208109 New Haven CT 06520-8109

SKINNER, JAMES LAURISTON, chemist, educator; b. Ithaca, N.Y., Aug. 17, 1953; s. G. William and Carol (Bagger) S.; m. Wendy Moore, May 31, 1986; children: Colin Andrew, Duncan Geoffrey. AB, U. Calif., Santa Cruz, 1975; PhD, Harvard U., 1979. Rsch. assoc. Stanford (Calif.) U., 1980-81; from asst. prof. to prof. chemistry Columbia U., N.Y.C., 1981-90; Hirschfelder prof. chemistry U. Wis., Madison, 1990—; vis. scientist Inst. Theol. Physics U. Calif., Santa Barbara, 1987; vis. prof. physics U. Jos. Fourier, Grenoble, France, 1987. Contbr. articles to profl. jours. Recipient Fresenius award Phi Lambda Upsilon, 1989, Camille and Henry Dreyfus Tchr.-Scholar award, 1984, NSF Presdl. Young Investigator award, 1984, Humboldt Sr. Scientist award, 1993; NSF grad fellow, 1975, NSF postdoctoral fellow, 1980, Alfred P. Sloan Found. fellow, 1984, Guggenheim fellow, 1993. Mem. AAAS, Am. Chem. Soc., Am. Phys. Soc. Achievements include fundamental research in condensed phase theoretical chemistry. Office: U Wis Dept Chemistry Theoretical Chem Inst 1101 University Ave Madison WI 53706-1322

SKINNER, JAMES STANFORD, physiologist, educator; b. Lucedale, Miss., Sept. 22, 1936; married, 1963 (div. 1994); 2 children. BS, U. Ill., 1958, MS, 1960, PhD in Phys. Edn. and Physiology, 1963. Assoc. physiologist sch. medicine George Washington U., 1964, asst. prof. lectr., 1964-65; rsch. assoc. cardiologist sch. medicine U. Wash., Seattle, 1965-66; asst. prof. lab. human performance rsch. Pa. State U., University Park, 1966-70; rsch. assoc. med. clin. U. Freiburg, Germany, 1970-71; assoc. prof. phys. edn., rsch. assoc. inst. cardiology U. Montreal, 1971-77; prof. phys. edn. U. Western Ont., 1977-82, Ariz. State U., Tempe, 1982—; dir. exercise and sport rsch. inst. Ariz. State U., 1983—. Fellow Am. Coll. Sports Medicine (pres. 1979-80, treas. 1994-96, citation 1986), Am. Heart Assn., Am. Acad. Phys. Edn. (sec.-treas. 1990-92); mem. AAHPERD, Internat. Coun. Sport Sci. and Phys. Edn. (v.p. 1994—). Achievements include research in physiology of exercise, especially pertaining to cardiovascular disorders, in exercise, training and genetics.

SKINNER, KNUTE RUMSEY, poet, English educator; b. St. Louis, Apr. 25, 1929; s. George Rumsey and Lidi (Skjoldvig) S.; m. Jeanne Pratt, 1953; divorced 1954; 1 child, Frank; m. Linda Kuhn, Mar. 30, 1961 (div. Sept. 1977); children: Dunstan, Morgan; m. Edna Kiel, Mar. 25, 1978. Student, Culver-Stockton Coll., 1947-49; B.A., U. Ano. Colo., 1951; M.A., Middlebury Coll., 1954; Ph.D., U. Iowa, 1958. Instr. English U. Iowa, Iowa City, 1955-56, 57-58, 60-61; asst. prof. English Okla. Coll. for Women, 1961-62; lectr. creative writing Western Wash. U., Bellingham, 1962-71; asso. prof. English Western Wash. U., 1971-73, prof. English, 1973—; pres. Signpost Press Inc., nonprofit corp., 1983-95. Author: Stranger with a Watch, 1965, A Close Sky Over Killaspuglonane, 1968, 75, In Dinosaur Country, 1969, The Sorcerers: A Laotian Tale, 1972, Hearing of the Hard Times, 1981, The Flame Room, 1983, Selected Poems, 1985, Learning to Spell "Zucchini," 1988, The Bears and Other Poems, 1991, What Trudy Knows and Other Poems, 1994; editor: Bellingham Rev., 1977-83, 93-95; contbr. poetry, short stories to anthologies, textbooks, periodicals. Nat. Endowment for the Arts fellow, 1975. Mem. Am. Conf. Irish Studies, Wash. Poets Assn. Office: Western Washington U HU 323 Bellingham WA 98225-9055

SKINNER, PATRICIA MORAG, state legislator; b. Glasgow, Soctland, Dec. 3, 1932; d. John Stuart and Frances Charlotte (Swann) Robertson; m. Robert A. Skinner, Dec. 28, 1957; children: Robin Ann, Pamela. BA, NYU, 1953. Mdse. trainee Lord & Taylor, N.Y.C., 1955-59; adminstrv. asst. Atlantic Products, N.Y.C., 1954-59; newspaper corr. Salem Observer, N.H., 1964-84; mem. N.H. Ho. of Reps., 1973-94, chmn. labor, human resources and rehab. com., 1975-86, House Edn. Com., 1987, chmn., 1989-94, exec. com. Nat. Conf. State Legislatures, 1987-90; chmn. N.H. Adv. Council Unemployment Compensation. Bd. dirs. chmn. Castle Jr. Coll., 1975, chmn. bd., 1988—; v.p. bd. Swift Water council Girl Scouts U.S., v.p. 1987-92; mem. chmn. coun. N.H. Voc-Tech. Coll., Nashua, 1978-83; trustee Nesmith Library, Windham, N.H., 1982—, chmn. bd. trustees, 1994. Mem. N.H. Fedn. Women's Clubs (parliamentarian, legis chmn. 1984—), N.H. Fedn. Republican Women's Clubs (pres. 1979-82). Christian Scientist. Club: Windham Woman's (pres. 1981-83). Lodge: Order Eastern Star.

SKINNER, PETER GRAEME, publishing executive, lawyer; b. London, Ont., Can., July 27, 1944; came to U.S., 1952; s. George Woodley and Marjorie Grace S. A.B., Princeton U., 1966; J.D., Columbia U., 1970, M.B.A., 1970. Bar: N.Y. 1971. Assoc. Patterson, Belknap, Webb & Tyler, N.Y.C., 1970-77; ptnr. Patterson, Belknap, Webb & Tyler, 1977-85; sr. v.p., gen. counsel, sec. Dow Jones & Co., N.Y.C., 1985-95; pres. Dow Jones TV, N.Y.C., 1995—. Mem. ABA, N.Y. State Bar Assn., Assn. Bar City N.Y. Office: Dow Jones & Co Inc 200 Liberty St New York NY 10281-1003

SKINNER, SAMUEL BALLOU, III, physics educator, researcher; b. Russellville, S.C., Sept. 24, 1936; s. Samuel Ballou Jr. and Mary (Timmons) S.; m. Beverly Corinne Jones, Dec. 21, 1958; children: Teresa Lynn, Curtis Ballou, Mary Angela. BS, Clemson U., 1958; MA in Teaching, U. N.C., 1963, PhD, 1970. Sci. tchr. Franklin (Tenn.) High Sch., 1959-60, Irmo (S.C.) High Sch., 1960-62; asst. prof. physics St. Andrews Presbyn. Coll., Laurinburg, N.C., 1964-67; assoc. prof. physics Columbia (S.C.) Coll., 1970-72; prof. physics S.C. Coastal Carolina U., Conway, S.C., 1972—; dir. acad. affairs U. S.C. Coastal Carolina U., Conway, 1972-74; advisor Gov.'s Nuclear Adv. Coun., Columbia, 1977-80, S.C. Joint Legis. Com. on Energy, Columbia, 1980-85; U.S.A. rep. Internat. Symposium on Nuclear Waste, Vienna, Austria, 1980; researcher in current aerospace problems, nuclear radiation physics and crit. thinking devel.; project counselor Space Life Sci. Tng. Program, Kennedy Space Ctr., 1990. Author: Education and Psychology, 1973, Energy and Society, 1981; contbr. articles to profl. jours. Pres. Horry County Am. Cancer Soc., Conway, 1974-75, Horry County Literacy Coun., 1989-93; mem. Horry County Assessment Appeals Bd., 1981-91. Recipient fellowships NASA (6), 1987-93, Dept. Energy (5), 1972-86, USAF, 1985; grantee Dept. Energy, 1984; physics edn. del. to Vietnam, Citizen Amb. Program, 1993; participant Institut Teknologi MARA Mucia Program, Malaysia, 1993-94. Mem. Am. Assn. Physics Tchrs., Am. Assn. Higher Edn., S.C. Acad. Sci., U. S.C. Coastal Carolina Athletic Club (bd. dirs.), Lions (pres. Conway Club 1977-78). Presbyterian. Avocations: tennis, camping, sports spectator, travel. Home: 126 Citadel Dr Conway SC 29526 Office: Coastal Carolina U Physics Dept Conway SC 29526

SKINNER, SAMUEL KNOX, utilities executive, lawyer; b. Chgo., June 10, 1938; s. Vernon Orlo and Imelda Jane (Curran) S.; m. Mary Jacobs, 1989; children: Thomas, Steven, Jane. B.S., U. Ill., 1960; J.D., DePaul U., 1966. Bar: Ill. 1966. Asst. U.S. atty. No. Dist. Ill., Chgo., 1968-74, 1st asst. U.S. atty., 1974-75, U.S. atty., 1975-77; ptnr. Sidley & Austin, Chgo., 1977-89; chmn. Regional Transp. Authority, Chgo., 1984; U.S. sec. of transp., 1989-91; chief of staff White House, Washington, 1991-92; gen. chmn. Republican Nat. Com., Washington, 1992-93; pres. Commonwealth Edison Co., Chgo. Chmn. Ill. Capitol Devel. Bd., 1977-84. Served as 1st lt. U.S. Army, 1960-61. Mem. ABA, Ill. Bar Assn., Chgo. Bar Assn., Chgo. Club, Shoreacres Club. Republican. Presbyterian. Office: Commonwealth Edison Co 1 1st Nat Plz Chicago IL 60603

SKINNER, STANLEY THAYER, utility company executive, lawyer; b. Fort Smith, Ark., Aug. 18, 1937; s. John Willard and Irma Lee (Peters) S.; m. Margaret Olsen, Aug. 16, 1957; children—Steven Kent, Ronald Kevin. B.A. with honors, San Diego State U., 1960; M.A., U. Calif., Berkeley, 1961, J.D., 1964. Bar: Supreme Ct. Calif. bar 1965, U.S. Circuit

Ct. Appeals for 9th Circuit bar 1965, 10th Circuit bar 1966. Atty. Pacific Gas and Electric Co., San Francisco, 1964-73; sr. counsel Pacific Gas and Electric Co., 1973, treas., 1974-76, v.p. fin., 1976, sr. v.p., 1977, exec. v.p., 1978-86, exec. v.p., chief oper. officer, 1982-85, vice chmn. bd., 1986-91, pres., chief oper. officer, 1991-94; pres., CEO Pacific Gas and Electric Co., San Francisco, 1994—, also chmn. bd. dirs.; chmn. bd. dirs., CEO Pacific Gas and Electric Co., 1995—; bd. dirs. Pacific Gas Transmission Co., Elec. Power Rsch. Inst. Bd. dirs. United Way of Bay Area, campaign chmn., 1992; trustee, former chmn. bd. dirs Golden Gate U.; bd. dirs Bay Area chpt. ARC. Mem. Calif. State Bar Assn., Pacific Coast Elec. Assn. (bd. dirs.), Pacific Coast Gas Assn., Calif. State C. of C. (bd. dirs.), San Francisco C. of C. (bd. dirs.), Bankers Club San Francisco, Moraga Country Club. Republican. Presbyterian. Office: Pacific Gas & Electric Co 77 Beale St San Francisco CA 94111-5330

SKINNER, THOMAS, broadcasting and film executive; b. Poughkeepsie, N.Y., Aug. 17, 1934; s. Clarence F. and Frances D. S.; m. Elizabeth Burroughs, June 22, 1957; children: Kristin Jon, Karin Anne, Erik Lloyd. B.S., SUNY, Fredonia, 1956; M.A., U. Mich., 1957, Ph.D., 1962. Instr. speech U. Mich., 1960; assoc. prof., exec. producer dept. broadcasting San Diego State U., 1961-66; asst. mgr. Sta. WITF-TV, Hershey, Pa., 1966-70; v.p. Sta. WQED-TV, Pitts., 1970-72; exec. v.p., chief oper. officer QED Communications Inc. (WQED-TV, WQED-FM, Pittsburgh mag., WQEX-TV), 1972-93; founder, pres., exec. prodr. Windrush Assocs., 1993—; head of prodn. ETV Properties, Boston, 1993—. Exec. prodr. numerous spls. and series for PBS including Nat. Geog. spls. Planet Earth, The Infinite Voyage, Conserving America. Recipient award as exec. prodr. DuPont Columbia, 1979, Oscar award as dir. Acad. Motion Picture Arts and Scis., 1967, Peabody award as exec. prodr., 1980, 86. Mem. Nat. Acad. TV Arts and Scis. (Emmy award as exec. producer 1979, 83, 84, 86, 87). Episcopalian. Address: Box 446 Suttons Bay MI 49682

SKINNER, WALTER JAY, federal judge; b. Washington, Sept. 12, 1927; s. Frederick Snowden and Mary Waterman (Comstock) S.; m. Sylvia Henderson, Aug. 12, 1950; 4 children. A.B., Harvard, 1948; J.D., 1952. Bar: Mass. 1952, U.S. Dist. Ct. 1954. Assoc. firm Gaston, Snow, Rice & Boyd, Boston, 1952-57; pvt. practice law Scituate, Mass., 1957-63; asst. dist. atty. Plymouth County, 1957-63; town counsel Scituate, 1957-63; asst. atty. gen., chief Criminal Div., Commonwealth of Mass., 1963-65; mem. firm Wardwell, Allen, McLaughlin & Skinner, Boston, 1965-74; judge U.S. Dist. Ct. of Mass., 1974—. Bd. dirs. Douglas A. Thom Clinic, 1966-70. Mem. ABA, Mass. Bar Assn., Boston Bar Assn. Clubs: Longwood Cricket, City; Eight O'Clock (Newton, Mass.). Office: US Dist Ct 1503 Us Courthouse Boston MA 02109

SKINNER, WICKHAM, business administration educator; b. Cin., Feb. 20, 1924; s. Charles Wickham and Ruth (Hargrave) S.; m. Alice Sturges Blackmer, May 18, 1946; children: Polly Gay (Mrs. David Light), Charles Barry. B.Engring., Yale U., 1944; M.B.A., Harvard U., 1948, D.B.A., 1961. Chem. engr. Manhattan project at Los Alamos, 1944-48; with Honeywell Corp., 1948-58, asst. sec., 1957-58; mem. faculty Harvard Grad. Sch. Bus. Adminstrn., 1960-86, prof., 1967-74, James E. Robison prof. bus. adminstrn., 1974-86, asso. dean, 1974-77, dir. div. internat. activities, 1967-70; tchr. Pakistan, France, Vietnam, Australia, Singapore, Turkey, Tunisia, Ital; bd. dirs. Wilevco Corp., Helix Tech. Corp., Somerset Industries, Bath Iron Works. Author: American Industry in Developing Economies, 1968, Manufacturing in Corporate Strategy, 1977, Manufacturing: The Formidable Competitive Weapon, 1985; also articles. Mem. spl. coms. Weston (Mass.) Sch. Com., 1962-64, 64-68; acad. adv. Bunting Inst., Work-in-Am. Inst.; mem. planning com., Wayzata, Minn., 1955-56; pres. Eastern Acad. Mgmt., 1968-69; Candidate for mayor, Wayzata, 1955; bd. dirs. Fla. Philharmonic Orch., 1956-58; bd. dirs. Nat. Resources Council Maine, 1986-93, pres. 1989-92; class agt. Yale Alumni Fund, 1944-69; trustee, treas. Urbana (Ohio) U., 1960-70; trustee Babson Coll., 1981-85, Mass. Audubon Soc., 1983-84; mem. Mfg. Studies Bd. NAS, 1979-84, chmn. 1987-89; bd. dirs. Farnsworth Mus., Rockland, Maine, 1990—, v.p., 1991-94, pres., 1994—. Served with AUS, 1944-46. Recipient McKinsey prize Harvard Bus. Rev., 1986. Fellow Acad. Mgmt.; mem. Ops Mgmt. Assn. (bd. dirs. 1987—). Mem. Swedenborgian Ch. Home: PO Box 282B Saint George ME 04857-9998 Office: Harvard U Bus Sch Soldiers Field Rd Boston MA 02163

SKINNER, WILLIAM POLK, lawyer; b. St. Louis, Apr. 4, 1951; s. Edwin Lemoine Jr. and Grizelda Gilchrist (Polk) S.; m. Karen Kenny, Aug. 2, 1975; children: Suzanne, William. BA, Harvard U., 1972, JD, 1975. Bar: Mo. 1976, D.C. 1976. Assoc. Covington & Burling, Washington, 1976-83, ptnr., 1983—. Home: 5903 Skyline Heights Ct Alexandria VA 22311-1020 Office: Covington & Burling PO Box 7566 1201 Pennsylvania Ave NW Washington DC 20044

SKIPPER, HENRY T., JR., manufacturing company executive; b. 1924. Sales mgr. Great Dane Trailers Inc., Savannah, Ga., 1944-64, from v.p. to exec. v.p. mktg., 1964—. Office: Gt Dane Trailers Inc PO Box 67 Savannah GA 31402-0067

SKIPPER, JAMES EVERETT, librarian; b. Bartow, Fla., Dec. 10, 1920; s. Glenn Blount and Nina (Bigham) S.; m. Florene Wilkins, Aug. 9, 1947 (div.); children: Glenn Michael, Nancy Sue; m. Margaret L. Meigs, June 10, 1961; children—William Meigs, Ann Meigs. A.B., U.N.C., 1943; B.S. in L.S, U. Mich., 1948; M.S. in L.S, 1949, Ph.D., 1960; postgrad. (Carnegie fellow advanced library adminstrn.), Rutgers U., 1958. Asst. librarian Washington and Jefferson Coll., 1949-50; asst. acquisitions librarian, then acquisitions librarian Ohio State U., 1950-55; instr. library sci. U. Mich., 1954; asst. librarian tech. services Mich. State U., 1956-59; dir. libraries U. Conn., Storrs, 1959-63; exec. sec. Assn. Research Libraries, 1963-67; asso. librarian Princeton Library, 1967-68; chief U. Calif. at Berkeley Library, 1968-71; exec. v.p. Kraus-Thomson Orgn., 1971-74; dir. Research Libraries Group, 1974-79; exec. dir. Midwest Regional Library Network, 1980-83. Contbr. articles to profl. jours. Served with AUS, 1943-45, ETO. Mem. ALA, Mich. Library Assn. (pres. coll. sect. 1957-58), New Eng. Library Assn., Conn. Library Assn., Franklin County (Ohio) Library Assn. (pres. 1953-54), Mich. Acad. Arts, Letters and Sci., Conn. Acad. Arts and Scis., Phi Eta Sigma, Beta Phi Mu. Clubs: Cosmos, Yale. Home: 16 Snyder Hill Ct Ithaca NY 14850-6368

SKIPPER, NATHAN RICHARD, JR., lawyer; b. Wilmington, N.C., May 29, 1934; s. Nathan Richard and Mary Dell (Sidbury) S.; m. Barbara Lynn Renton, Sept. 5, 1959 (div. June 1978); children: Nathan Richard III, Valerie Lynne; m. Karen Marie Haughton, Sept. 26, 1987. AB, Duke U., 1956, JD, 1962; AAS, Oakland Community Coll., 1980. Bar: N.Y. 1963, U.S. Dist. Ct. (so. dist.) N.Y. 1964, Mich. 1971, U.S. Dist. Ct. (ea. dist.) Mich. 1979, N.C. 1991. Assoc. Cravath, Swaine & Moore, N.Y.C., 1962-70; counsel financings Ford Motor Co., Dearborn, Mich., 1970-78; gen. counsel, sec. Volkswagen Am., Inc., Troy, Mich., 1978-89, consulting counsel, 1989-91; assoc. Ward and Smith, P.A., New Bern, N.C., 1990-93, ptnr., 1994—. Served to capt. USAF, 1956-59, USAFR, 1962-75. Mem. ABA, SAR, N.C. Bar Assn., Ea. Carolina Yacht Club, Phi Delta Phi. Avocations: photography, boating, tennis. Home: 1108 Country Club Dr New Bern NC 28562-7102

SKIRNICK, ROBERT ANDREW, lawyer; b. Chgo., Apr. 23, 1938; s. Andrew and Stella (Sanders) S.; children: Rebecca, David; m. Maria Ann Castellano, Oct. 4, 1974; 1 child, Gabriella. BA, Roosevelt U., 1961; JD, U. Chgo., 1966. Bar: U.S. Dist. Ct. (no. dist.) Ill. 1966, U.S. Ct. Appeals (7th cir.) 1968, U.S. Supreme Ct. 1970, U.S. Ct. Appeals (5th and 9th cirs.) 1982, N.Y. 1982, U.S. Ct. Appeals (3d cir.) 1983, U.S. Dist. Ct. (ea. dist.) Mich. 1988, (so. dist. and ea. dist.) N.Y. 1989, U.S. Ct. Appeals (2nd cir.) 1990, U.S. Dist. Ct. (no. dist.) Calif. 1992, U.S. Ct. Appeals (11th Cir.) 1992, U.S. Dist. Ct. (so. dist.) Tex. 1992, U.S. Dist. Ct. Ariz. 1993. Atty. office gen. counsel honors program HEW, Washington, 1966-68; ptnr. Fortes, Enger, Epstein & Skirnick, Chgo., 1975-77, Much, Shelist, Freed, Chgo., 1977-79, Wolf, Popper, Ross, Wolf & Jones, N.Y.C., 1979-87, Kaplan, Kilsheimer & Foley, N.Y.C., 1988-89, Wechsler, Skirnick, Harwood, Halebian & Feffer, N.Y.C., 1989—; instr. NYU, 1979-80; com. Nat. Legal Aid and Def. Assn., Chgo., 1968-69; spl. asst. atty. gen. Ill. Atty Gen. Office, Chgo., 1972-73; spl. antitrust counsel State of Conn., 1976-77; mem. adv. bd. Small Bus. Legal Def. Commn., San Francisco, 1982—; lectr. Practicing Law Inst., N.Y.C. 1986-87; spl. master So. Dist. N.Y., 1988-91. Author: (with others) Federal

Subject Matter Jurisdiction of U.S. District Courts, Federal Civil Practice, 1974, Antitrust Class Actions-Twenty Years Under Rule 23, 1986, The State Court Class Action-A Potpourri of Differences in the ABA Forum, Summer 1985; bd. editors Ill. Bar Antitrust Newsletter, 1969-73; topic & articles editor Jour. Forum Com. on Franchising, 1981-86. Atty. Office Gen. Counsel Honors Program, U.S. Dept. HEW, 1966-68; chmn. Ill. Legis. Com. Antitrust Section Ill. Bar., 1970-71; Topic and Articles Editor, Jour. Forum Com. on Franchising, 1981-86; mem., bd. dirs., Nat. Assn. for Pub. Interest Law fellowships, Washington, 1991—. Mem. ABA (co-chair securities law subcom., litigation sect. 1987, com. on futures regulation, forum com. on franchising), ATLA, Fed. Bar Coun. (com. on second cir cts. 1983-86), N.Y. State Bar Assn. (class action com.), N.Y. State Trial Lawyers Assn., Ill. Bar Assn. (chmn. antitrust sect. Ill. legis. com. 1970-71), Nat. Assn. for Pub. Interest Law Fellowships (mem. exec. com., mem. selection com., mem. investment and fin. com., bd. dirs. 1991—, v.p. 1994—), Navy League of U.S. (N.Y. coun., jour. com. 1995—), Plandome Country Club. Office: Wechsler Skirnick Harwood Halebian & Feffer 805 Third Ave 7th Fl New York NY 10022

SKLANSKY, JACK, electrical and computer engineering educator, researcher; b. N.Y.C., Nov. 15, 1928; s. Abraham and Clara S.; m. Gloria Joy Weiss, Dec. 24, 1957; children: David Alan, Mark Steven, Jeffrey Paul. BEE, CCNY, 1950; MSEE, Purdue U., 1952; D in Engring. Sci., Columbia U., 1955. Research engr. RCA Labs., Princeton, N.J., 1955-65; mgr. Nat. Cash Register Co., Dayton, Ohio, 1965-66; prof. elec. and computer engring. U. Calif., Irvine, 1966—; pres. Scanicon Corp., Irvine, 1980-89. Author: (with others) Pattern Classifiers and Trainable Machines, 1981; editor: Pattern Recognition, 1973, (with others) Biomedical Images and Computers, 1982; editor-in-chief: Machine Vision and Applications, 1987. Recipient best paper award Jour. Pattern Recognition, 1977; rsch. grantee NIH, 1971-84, Army Rsch. Office, 1984-91, NSF, 1992—. Fellow IEEE, Internat. Assn. for Pattern Recognition; mem. ACM. Office: U Calif Dept Elec & Computer Engring Irvine CA 92717

SKLAR, ALEXANDER, electric company executive, educator; b. N.Y.C., May 18, 1915; s. David and Bessie (Wolf) S.; student Cooper Union, N.Y.C., 1932-35; M.B.A., Fla. Atlantic U., 1976; m. Hilda Rae Gevarter, Oct. 27, 1940; 1 dau., Carolyn Mae (Mrs. Louis M. Taff). Chief engr. Aerovox Corp., New Bedford, Mass., 1933-39; mgr. mfg., engring. Indsl. Condenser Corp., Chgo., 1939-44; owner Capacitron, Inc., 1944-48; exec. v.p Jefferson Electric Co., Bellwood, Ill., 1948-65; v.p., gen. mgr. electro-mech. div Essex Internat., Detroit, 1965-67; adviser, dir. various corp., 1968—; vis. prof. mgmt. Fla. Atlantic U., Boca Raton, 1971-92; ret. 1993; lectr. profl. mgmt. U. Calif. at Los Angeles, Harvard Grad. Sch. Bus. Adminstrn., U. Ill. Mem. Acad. Internat. Bus., Soc. Automotive Engrs. Address: 4100 Galt Ocean Dr Fort Lauderdale FL 33308-6002

SKLAR, KATHRYN KISH, historian, educator; b. Columbus, Ohio, Dec. 26, 1939; d. William Edward and Elizabeth Sue (Rhodes) Kish; m. Robert A. Sklar, 1958 (div. 1978); children: Leonard Scott, Susan Rebecca Sklar Friedman; m. Thomas L. Dublin, Apr. 30, 1988. B.A. magna cum laude, Radcliffe Coll., 1965; Ph.D., U. Mich. 1969. Asst. prof., lectr. U. Mich. Ann Arbor, 1969-74; assoc. prof. history UCLA, 1974-81, prof., 1981-88, chmn. com. to administer program in women's studies Coll. Letters and Sci., 1974-81; Disting. Prof. history SUNY, Binghamton, 1988—; Pulitzer juror in history, 1976; fellow Newberry Libr. Family and Community History Seminar, 1973; NEH cons. in women's studies U. Utah, 1977-79, Santa Clara U., 1978-80, Roosevelt U., 1980-82; hist. cons. AAUW; active Calif. Coun. for Humanities, 1981-85, N.Y. Coun. for Humanities, 1992—. Author: Catharine Beecher: A Study in American Domesticity, 1973 (Berkshire prize 1974); editor: Catharine Beecher: A Treatise on Domestic Economy, 1977, Harriet Beecher Stowe: Uncle Tom's Cabin, or Life Among the Lowly: The Minister's Wooing, Oldtown Folks, 1981, Notes of Sixty Years: The Autobiography of Florence Kelley, 1849-1926, 1984, (with Thomas Dublin) Women and Power in American History: A Reader (2 vols.), 1991, (with Linda Kerber and Alice Kessler-Harris) U.S. History as Women's History: New Feminist Essays, 1995; co-editor: The Social Survey Movement in Historical Perspective, 1992, Florence Kelley and the Nation's Work: The Rise of Women's Political Culture, 1830-1900, 1995; mem. editl. bd. Jour. Women's History, 1987—, Women's History Rev., 1990—, Jour. Am. History, 1978-81; contbr. chpts. to books. Fellow Woodrow Wilson Found., 1965-67, Danforth Found., 1967-69, Radcliffe Inst., 1973-74, Nat. Humanities Inst., 1975-76, Rockefeller Found. Humanities, 1981-82, Woodrow Wilson Internat. Ctr. for Scholars, 1982, 1992-93, Guggenheim Found., 1984, Ctr. Advanced Study Behavioral and Social Scis., Stanford U., 1987-88, AAUW, 1990-91; Daniels fellow Am. Antiquarian Soc., 1976, NEH fellow Newberry Library, 1982-83; Ford Found. faculty rsch. grantee, 1973-74; grantee NEH, 1976-78, UCLA Coun. for Internat. and Comparative Studies, 1983. Mem. Am. Hist. Assn. Continuing com. on women historians 1980-83, v.p. Pacific Coast br. 1986-87, pres. 1987-88), Orgn. Am. Historians (exec. bd. 1983-86, Merle Curti award com. 1978-79, lectr. 1982—), Am. Studies Assn. (coun. mem.-at-large 1978-80), Berkshire Conf. Women Historians, Am. Antiquarian Soc., Phi Beta Kappa. Avocation: photography. Office: SUNY Dept History Binghamton NY 13902

SKLAR, MORTY E., publisher, editor; b. Sunnyside, N.Y., Nov. 28, 1935; s. Jack and Selma (Ehrlich) S.; m. Shelley Joy Sterling, Aug. 17, 1981 (div. 1983); m. Marcela B. Bruno, June 7, 1993; children: Patricio Bruno, Marcos Bruno. BA in English, U. Iowa, 1972. Founding editor, pub. The Spirit That Moves Us Press, Jackson Heights, N.Y., 1974—. Author: The Night We Stood Up For Our Rights, 1977; editor: The Casting of Bells, 1983 (Jaroslav Seifert, Nobel prize 1984). Founder (with others) Phoenix House, N.Y.C., 1966; active Increase the Peace Vol. Corps., N.Y.C., 1992—. With U.S. Army, 1954-56. Mem. PEN, Acad. Am. Poets, Small Press Ctr. Democrat. Jewish. Avocations: photography, reading. Office: The Spirit That Moves Us Press PO Box 720820 Jackson Heights NY 11372

SKLAR, RICHARD LAWRENCE, political science educator; b. N.Y.C., Mar. 22, 1930; s. Kalman and Sophie (Laub) S.; m. Eva Molineux, July 14, 1962; children: Judith Anne, Katherine Elizabeth. A.B., U. Utah, 1952; M.A., Princeton U., 1957, Ph.D., 1961. Mem. faculty Brandeis U., U. Ibadan, Nigeria, U. Zambia; mem. faculty SUNY-Stony Brook; now prof. emeritus polit. sci. UCLA; mem. fgn. area fellowship program Africa Nat. Com., 1970-73; Simon vis. prof. U. Manchester, Eng., 1975, Fulbright vis. prof. U. Zimbabwe, 1984; Lester Martin fellow Harry S. Truman Rsch. Inst., Hebrew U. Jerusalem, 1979; fellow Africa Inst. of South Africa, 1994—. Author: Nigerian Political Parties: Power in an Emergent African Nation, 1963, Corporate Power in an African State, 1975; co-author: Postimperialism: International Capitalism and Development, 1987, African Politics and Problems in Development, 1991; contbr. articles to profl. jours. Served with U.S. Army, 1952-54. Rockefeller Found. grantee, 1967. Mem. Am. Polit. Sci. Assn., African Studies Assn. (dir. 1976-78, 80-83, v.p. 1980-81, pres. 1981-82), AAUP (pres. Calif. Conf. 1980-81). Home: 1951 Holmby Ave Los Angeles CA 90025-5905

SKLAREN, CARY STEWART, lawyer; b. Bklyn., Sept. 26, 1943; s. Jules Joseph and Florence (Somber) S.; m. Linda Genero, May 25, 1972; children: Robyn Alison, Adam William. BA, NYU, 1964; JD, Fordham U., 1967. Bar: N.Y. 1969, Mich. 1980. Assoc. product liability counsel Bristol-Myers Co., N.Y.C., 1969-79; sr. atty. Ford Mtr. Co., Dearborn, Mich., 1979-81; asst. gen. counsel Am. Mtrs. Corp., Southfield, Mich., 1981-84; ptnr. Herzfeld & Rubin, P.C., N.Y.C., 1984—. Contbr. articles to profl. jours.; author: (with others) Practical Products Liability, 1988, Products Liability, 1989. Capt. U.S. Army, 1967-69. Mem. ABA, Assn. Bar City of N.Y. Home: 851 President St Brooklyn NY 11215 Office: Herzfeld & Rubin PC 40 Wall St New York NY 10005-1303

SKLAREW, ROBERT JAY, biomedical research educator, consultant; b. N.Y.C., Nov. 25, 1941; s. Arthur and Jeanette (Laven) S.; m. Toby Willner, July 15, 1970; children: David Michael, Gary Richard. BA in Zoology, Cornell U., 1963; MS, NYU, 1965, PhD in Biology, 1970. Assoc. rsch. scientist Sch. of Medicine NYU, N.Y.C., 1965-70, rsch. scientist Sch. of Medicine, 1971-73, sr. rsch. scientist Sch. of Medicine, 1973-79; rsch. asst. prof. pathology Sch. of Medicine Goldwater Meml. Hosp., N.Y.C., 1979-87, rsch. assoc. prof. pathology Sch. of Medicine, 1987-88, dir. cytokinetics and imaging lab. NYU Rsch. Svc., 1980-88; prof. cell biology, anatomy and

medicine N.Y. Med. Coll., Valhalla, 1988—; rsch. assoc. dept. pathology Lenox Hill Hosp., N.Y.C., 1981-88; pres., CEO R.J. Sklarew Imaging Assoc., Inc., Larchmont, N.Y., 1990—; chmn. consensus panel for diagnostic cancer imaging Nat. Cancer Inst., 1994. Author: Microscopic Imaging of Steroid Receptors, 1990; sr. author: Cytometry, Jour. Histochem. Cytochem., Cancer, Exptl. Cell Rsch. Mem. Beth Emeth Synagogue, Larchmont, 1974—; group leader Boy Scouts Am., Larchmont, 1978-80. Grantee Am. Cancer Soc., Nat. Cancer Inst./NIH Conc. for Tobacco Rsch., R.J. Reynolds Industries Found., NYU; recipient Shannon award Nat. Cancer Inst., 1991. Mem. AAAS, Cell Kinetics Soc. (sec. 1983-85, 85-87, v.p. 1987-88, pres. 1988-89, chmn. nominations 1991, 93), N.Y. Acad. Sci., Soc. for Analytic Cytology, Soc. for Cell Biology, Tissue Culture Assn., Union Concerned Scientists, Kappa Delta Rho. Democrat. Achievements include development of methodology, algorithms and Receptogram analytic software for application of microscopic imaging in medical research and in pathodiagnosis of cancer, imaging methods for simultaneous densitometry and autoradiographic analysis; research in diagnostic imaging of steroid receptors, oncogenes and DNA ploidy in cancer, proliferative patterns and cell cycle kinetics of human solid tumors. Home: 8 Vine Rd Larchmont NY 10538-1247 Office: NY Med Coll Cancer Rsch Inst 100 Grasslands Rd Elmsford NY 10523-1110

SKLARIN, BURTON S., endocrinologist; b. N.Y.C., Feb. 28, 1932; s. Louis and Molla (Beiser) S.; m. Ann Hirsch, June 29, 1960; children: Laurie, Richard, Peter. A.B., NYU, 1953, M.D., 1957. Diplomate: Am. Bd. Internal Medicine, Am. Bd. Endocrinology and Metabolism. Intern Bellevue Hosp., N.Y.C., 1957-58, resident, 1958-61, asst. vis. clin. physician, 1961—; practice medicine specializing in endocrinology Lawrence, N.Y., 1961—; chief endocrinology St. John's Episcopal Hosp., N.Y., 1961—, pres. med. staff, 1978-80, also chmn. med. exec. com.; asst. prof. clin. medicine NYU, 1961—, asst. in medicine Univ. Hosp., 1961; endocrinologist, staff physician L.I. Jewish Hosp.; cons. Franklin Gen Hosp. Contbr. articles on endocrinology to profl. publs. Vice pres. bd. trustees Woodmere Acad. Fellow ACP, Am. Coll. Endocrinology, N.Y. Acad. Medicine, Soc. Nuclear Medicine; mem. Nassau County Med. Soc., N.Y. Diabetes Assn., Endocrine Soc., Rockaway Med. Soc. (past pres.), Am. Assn. Clin. Endocrinologists. Club: Woodmere (N.Y.). Home and Office: 501 Broadway Lawrence NY 11559

SKLARSKY, CHARLES B., lawyer; b. Chgo., June 13, 1946; s. Morris and Sadie (Brenner) S.; m. Elizabeth Ann Hardzinski, Dec. 28, 1973; children: Jacob Daniel, Katherine Gabrielle, Jessica Leah. AB, Harvard U., 1968; JD, U. Wis., 1973. Bar: Wis. 1973, Ill. 1973, U.S. Dist. Ct. (no. dist.) Ill. 1973, U.S. Ct. Appeals (7th cir.) 1978, U.S. Ct. Appeals (2nd cir.) 1986. Asst. states atty. Cook County, Chgo., 1973-78; asst. U.S. atty. U.S. Dist. Ct. (no. dist.) Ill., Chgo., 1978-86; ptnr. Jenner & Block, Chgo., 1986—. Mem. ABA, Chgo. Bar Assn. Office: Jenner & Block 1 IBM Plz Chicago IL 60611

SKLENAR, HERBERT ANTHONY, industrial products manufacturing company executive; b. Omaha, June 7, 1931; s. Michael Joseph and Alice Madeline (Spicka) S.; m. Eleanor Lydia Vincenz, Sept. 15, 1956; children: Susan A., Patricia I. BSBA summa cum laude, U. Omaha, 1952; MBA, Harvard U., 1954. CPA, W.Va. V.p., comptr. Parkersburg-Aetna Corp., W.Va., 1956-63; v.p., dir. Marmac Corp, Parkersburg, 1963-66; mgr. fin. control Boise-Cascade Corp., Idaho, 1966-67; exec. v.p. fin. and adminstrn., sec. Cudahy Co., Phoenix, 1967-72; chmn. bd. dirs., CEO Vulcan Materials Co., Birmingham, Ala., 1972—; bd. dirs. Amsouth Bancorp., Birmingham, Protective Life Corp., Birmingham, Temple-Inland, Inc., Diboll, Tex. Author: (with others) The Automatic Factory: A Critical Examination, 1955. Trustee So. Rsch. Inst., Leadership Birmingham, Leadership Ala.; chmn. bd. trustees Birmingham-So. Coll. Recipient Alumni Achievement award U. Nebr.-Omaha, 1977, cert. merit W.Va. Soc. CPAs, Elizah Watts Sells award AICPA, 1965, Brotherhood award NCCJ, 1993. Mem. Shoal Creek Club, Birmingham Country Club, The Club, Univ. Club N.Y.C., Chgo. Club, Delta Sigma Pi (Leadership award 1952), Omicron Delta Kappa, Phi Kappa Phi, Phi Eta Sigma. Republican. Presbyterian. Home: 2809 Shook Hill Cir Birmingham AL 35223-2618 Office: Vulcan Materials Co 1 Metroplex Dr Birmingham AL 35209-6805

SKODON, EMIL MARK, diplomat; b. Chgo., Nov. 25, 1953; s. Emil John and Anne (Soltes) S.; m. Dorothea Shaffer, Mar. 6, 1982; children: Catherine Marie, Christine Louise. BA, U. Chgo., 1975, MBA, 1976. Consular officer U.S. Embassy, Bridgetown, Barbados, 1977-79; econ. officer U.S. Embassy, East Berlin, Germany, 1979-81, Office of So. African Affairs, Dept. State, Washington, 1982-84; econ. officer U.S. Embassy, Vienna, Austria, 1984-88, Kuwait City, Kuwait, 1989-91; dep. chief mission U.S. Embassy, Singapore, 1995—; consul gen. U.S. Consulate Gen., Perth, Australia, 1991-94. Mem. Nat. Trust for Hist. Preservation. Avocations: visiting historic sites, good food, spending time with family. Office: US Embassy, 30 Hill St, Singapore 0617, Singapore also: US Embassy Singapore PSC 470 Box DCM FPO AP 96534-0001

SKOG, LAURENCE EDGAR, botanist, plant taxonomist; b. Duluth, Minn., Apr. 9, 1943; s. Edgar Herman and Magnhild Albertine (Collander) S.; m. Judith Ellen Troop, June 22, 1968; 1 son, Jeremy Owen. BA, U. Minn., 1965; MS, U. Conn., 1968; PhD, Cornell U., 1972. Asst. editor Flora N.Am. program Smithsonian Instn., Washington, 1972-73, assoc. curator dept. botany, 1973-86, curator and rsch. sci., 1986—, chmn., 1987-92; bot. cons. Reed Herbarium, Balt., 1973; adj. prof. biology George Mason U., Fairfax, Va.; hort. interchange fellow Royal Bot. Garden, Edinburgh, 1968-69; vis. rsch. fellow Manchester Mus., Eng., 1984; mem. edn. com. Pacific Tropical Bot. Garden, 1983-85, mem. rsch. adv. com. Nat. Tropical Bot. Garden, 1985-92; hon. prof. Open Lab. Inst. Botany Chinese Acad. Scis., Beijing; lectr. in field. Contbr. articles to profl. jours. Fellow Bot. Soc. Edinburgh; mem. Am. Inst. Biol. Sci. (coun. 1990—), Assn. for Tropical Biology (sec.-treas. 1981-85), Bot. Soc. Am., Bot. Soc. Washington (pres. 1977-78), Biol. Soc. Washington, Internat. Orgn. Plant Info. (mem. coun. 1991-93), Internat. Assn. for Plant Taxonomy (coun. 1985—), Assn. Latinoamericana Botanica, Commn. Flora Neotropica (bd. dirs. 1990—, sec. 1993—), Flora of Guianas (adv. bd. 1985—), Am. Soc. Plant Taxonomists, Flora of China (mem. editorial bd. 1990—), Washington Biologists Field Club (bd. mgrs. 1984-85, 1989-92), Sigma Xi, Phi Kappa Phi. Lutheran. Home: 611 Roberts Dr NW Vienna VA 22180-4178 Office: Smithsonian Inst Dept Botany NHB-166 Washington DC 20560-0001

SKOGLUND, ELIZABETH RUTH, marriage, child and family counselor; b. Chgo., June 17, 1937; d. Ragnar Emmanuel and Elizabeth Alvera (Benson) S. BA, UCLA, 1959; MA, Pasadena Coll., 1969. Cert. tchr., Calif.; cert. marriage, family and child counselor, Calif. Tchr. Marlborough Sch., Los Angeles, 1959-61; tchr., counselor Glendale (Calif.) High Sch., 1961-72; pvt. practice family counseling Burbank, Calif., 1972—. Author: over 20 books including It's OK to Be a Woman Again, 1988, Making Bad Times Good, 1991, Safety Zones, 1991, Harold's Dog Horace is Scared of the Dark, 1992, The Welcoming Hearth, 1993, Amma: The Life and Words of Amy Carmichael, 1994. Mem. Calif. Assn. Marriage and Family Therapists, Simon Wiesenthal Ctr. Republican. Avocations: photography, miniatures, cooking.

SKOGLUND, JOHN C., former professional football team executive. Former treas., chmn. bd., bd. dirs. Minn. Vikings Ventures, Inc.; chmn. Minn. Vikings Football Club; chmn. bd., pres. Skoglund Comms., Inc., Duluth, Minn. Office: Minn Vikings 9520 Viking Dr Eden Prairie MN 55344-3825*

SKOGMAN, DALE R., bishop. Bishop No. Great Lakes Synod, Marquette, Mich. Address: Evangelical Lutheran Church 1029 N 3rd St Marquette MI 49855-3509

SKOL, MICHAEL, diplomat; b. Chgo. Oct. 15, 1942; s. Ted and Rebecca (Williams) S.; m. Claudia Serwer, Sept. 29, 1973. BA, Yale U., 1964. U.S. fgn. svc. officer Dept. State, 1965—; polit. officer U.S. Embassy, Buenos Aires, 1966-67, Saigon, Viet Nam, 1968-70; desk officer Dept. State, Washington, 1970-72; comml. attache U.S. Embassy, Santo Domingo, Dominican Republic, 1972-75; econ. comml. officer U.S. Consulate Gen., Naples, Italy, 1975-76; comml. attache U.S. Embassy, Rome, 1976-78; polit. counselor U.S. Embassy, San Jose, Costa Rica, 1978-82; dep. dir. policy planning Inter-Am. Affairs Bur. Dept. State, Washington, 1982-85; dep. chief of mission U.S.

Embassy, Bogota, Colombia, 1985-87; dir. Andean affairs Dept. State, Washington, 1987-88; dep. asst. sec. state for S. Am. U.S. Dept. of State, Washington, 1988-90; amb. U.S. Embassy, Caracas, Venezuela, 1990-93; prin. dep. asst. sec. for Latin Am./Caribbean Dept. State, Washington, 1993—. Mem. Yale Club of Colombia, Yale Club of Venezuela, Yale Club of Washington. Home: 3033 Cleveland Ave NW Washington DC 20008-3532 Office: Dept State Washington DC 20520

SKOLAN-LOGUE, AMANDA NICOLE, lawyer, consultant; b. Los Angeles, Feb. 19, 1954; d. Carl Charles and Estelle (Lubin) Skolan; m. James Edward Logue, Dec. 10, 1983. BS, U. Calif., Los Angeles, 1973; MBA, U. So. Calif., 1976; JD, Southwestern U., Los Angeles, 1982. Bar: Calif. 1982, U.S. Dist. Ct. (cen., no. and ea. dists.) Calif. 1982, N.Y. 1986. Sr. internal cons. Getty Oil Co., Los Angeles, 1976-80; atty. litigation ACLU of So. Calif., Los Angeles, 1982-83; corp. atty. Am. Can Co., Greenwich, Conn., 1983-86; assoc. Shereff, Friedman, Hoffman & Goodman, N.Y.C., 1986-88; region counsel Gen. Electric Capital Corp., Danbury, Conn., 1988—. Mem. ABA, N.Y. State Bar Assn. Republican. Home: 33 Musket Ridge Rd New Fairfield CT 06812-5101 Office: Gen Electric Capital Corp 44 Old Ridgebury Rd Danbury CT 06810-5107

SKOLAS, JOHN ARGYLE, lawyer; b. Westby, Wis., June 18, 1952; s. Argyle Carlyle and Ardys Margaret (Trygestad) S.; m. Joan Larson, Apr. 21, 1979. BA, Luther Coll., 1974; JD, U. Wis., 1977; MBA, Harvard U., 1988. Bar: Wis. 1977, Minn. 1977; CPA, Iowa. Tax specialist Coopers & Lybrand, Mpls., 1977-78; assoc. Johns, Flaherty & Gillette, LaCrosse, Wis., 1979-80; from assoc. to ptnr. Muchin, Muchin, Bendix & Skolas, Manitowoc, Wis., 1980-86; v.p., legal counsel N.Am. THORN EMI Inc., Boston, 1988-91; pres., corp. officer the Ams. THORN EMI Inc., Boston, Wilmington, Del., 1992—. Dir. Planned Parenthood, Manitowoc, 1984-86; deacon Faith Luth. Ch., Valders, Wis., 1984-86, St. Paul Luth. Ch., Arlington, Mass., 1991-92. Mem. Minn. Bar Assn., Wis. Bar Assn. Avocations: running, drawing, reading, travel. Office: Thorn EMI N Am Holdings 2751 Centerville Rd Ste 205 Wilmington DE 19808-1627

SKOLER, LOUIS, architect, educator; b. Utica, N.Y., Apr. 5, 1920; s. Harry and Etta (Mitkoff) S.; m. Celia Rebecca Stern, 1952; children: Elisa Anne, Harry Jay. BArch, Cornell U., 1951. Maj. designer Sargent, Webster, Crenshaw & Folley, Syracuse, N.Y., 1951-59; design critic Cornell U., Ithaca, N.Y., 1956-57; pvt. practice architecture, Syracuse, 1956-69; faculty Sch. Architecture Syracuse (N.Y.) U., 1959-90, prof. emeritus, 1990—; head of Masters in Architecture I Program, 1980-82, head undergrad. program, 1989-90, architecture programs abroad, London, 1977, Scandinavia, 1985, Japan, 1988; ptnr. Architects Partnership, Syracuse, 1969-71; pres. Skoler & Lee Architects, P.C., Syracuse, 1971-89. Named Best in Residential Design, Design-in-Steel, 1968-69. Mem. AIA. Home: 213 Scottholm Ter Syracuse NY 13224-1737

SKOLFIELD, MELISSA T., government official; b. New Orleans, June 25, 1958; m. Frank W. Curtis. BA in Econ. and Behavioral Sci., Rice U., 1980; MA in Pub. Affairs, George Washington U., 1986. Account exec. McDaniel & Tate Pub. Rels., Houston, 1981-84; press sec. Rep. Michael Andrews of Tex., 1985-87; press. sec. Senator Dale Bumpers of Ark., 1987-93; dep. asst. sec. for pub. affairs for policy and strategy Dept. Health and Human Svcs., Washington, 1993—. Press asst. Dem. Nat. Com., Dem. Nat. Conv., 1988, Clinton Pres. Campaign, Dem. Nat. Com., 1992. Mem. Senate Press Secs. Assn. (pres.), Assn. Dem. Press Assts., Pub. Rels. Soc. Am. Office: Dept Health & Human Svcs 200 Indendence Ave SW Washington DC 20201

SKOLNICK, JEROME H., legal educator; b. 1931. B.B.A., CCNY, 1952, M.A., 1953; Ph.D., Yale U., 1957. Research assoc. Yale U., New Haven, 1956-60, asst. prof., 1960-62; asst. prof. U. Calif.-Berkeley Law Sch., 1962-67, prof., 1970—; vis. assoc. prof. NYU, 1966; vis. prof. U. Denver, 1967; assoc. prof. U. Chgo., 1967-69; prof. U. Calif.-San Diego, 1969-70; dir. Ctr. Study of Law and Soc., 1972—; cons. Bd. dirs. Pres.'s Commn. on Causes and Prevention of Violence, 1968-69. Carnegie fellow, 1956-66; Guggenheim fellow, 1980. Mem. Am. Criminol. Assn., ACLU, Am. Soc. Criminology (pres.), Law and Soc. Assn. (trustee). Author: (with D. Bayley) The New Blue Line, 1986, Justice Without Trial, 1966; House of Cards, 1978; (with R.D. Schwartz) Society and the Legal Order, 1970, (with J. Fyfe) Above the Law. Office: U Calif Berkeley Law Sch 225 Boalt Hall Berkeley CA 94720

SKOLNICK, MALCOLM HARRIS, biophysics researcher, educator, patent lawyer, mediator; b. Salt Lake City, Aug. 11, 1935; s. Max Cantor and Charlotte Sylvia (Letman) S.; m. Lois Marlene Ray, Sept. 1, 1959; children: Michael, David, Sara, Jonathan. BS in Physics (with honors), U. Utah, 1956; MS in Physics, Cornell U., 1959, PhD in Theoretical Physics, 1963; JD, U. Houston, 1986. Bar: Tex. 1988, U.S. Patent Office 1990. Staff scientist Elem. Sci. Study, Watertown, Mass., 1962-63; mem. Inst. for Advanced Study, Princeton, N.J., 1963-64; instr. Physics Dept. MIT, Cambridge, Mass., 1964-65; staff scientist dir. Edn. Devel. Ctr., Watertown, 1965-67; assoc. prof. physics Physics Dept. SUNY, Stony Brook, 1967-70; assoc. prof. dir. comm. Health Sci. Ctr. SUNY, Stony Brook, 1968-71; prof. biophysics grad. sch. biomed. sci. U. Tex. Health Scis. Ctr., Houston, 1971-94, prof. biomedical comm., 1971-83, prof. health svcs. rsch., 1988-93, dir. neurophysiology rsch. ctr., 1985-91; dir. office tech. mgmt. U. Tex. Health Sci. Ctr., Houston, 1991—; prof. tech. and health law Sch. Pub. Health; chmn. health care tech. study sect. Nat. Ctr. Health Svcs. Rsch. HHS, 1975-79; editorial assoc. Cts., Health Sci. and Law, Washington, 1989-93. Patentee in field; contbr. numerous articles to profl. jours. With USNR, 1953-61. Recipient Silver Beaver award Boy Scouts Am., 1978; Ford Found scholar, U. Utah, 1952; rsch. grantee Nat. Inst. for Drug Abuse. Mem. ABA, Am. Bd. Forensic Examiners, Soc. Neurosci., Licensing Exec. Soc., Am. Intellectual Property Law Assn., Tex. Tech. Transfer Assn. (bd. dirs.), Houston Intellectual Property Law Assn., Houston Soc. Engring. in Medicine and Biology (bd. dirs.), Am. Soc. Law and Medicine, S.W. Assn. Biotech. Cos. (bd. dirs.), Soc. Accident Reconstrn., Tex. Empowerment Network (bd. dirs., pres. 1995), Assoc. Univ. Tech. Mgrs. Office: Office Tech Mgmt PO Box 20334 Houston TX 77225-0334

SKOLNIK, BARNET DAVID, lawyer; b. N.Y.C., Feb. 8, 1941; s. Jack and Edythe (Savitz) S.; children: Sarah, Deborah, Daniel, Joseph, Benjamin, Rebecca. AB in Am. Govt. cum laude, Harvard U., 1962, LLB, 1965. Bar: D.C. 1966, Md. 1984, Maine 1991. Atty. criminal div. U.S. Dept. Justice, Washington, 1966-68; asst. U.S. atty. for Dist. Md., Balt., 1968-78; chief public corruption unit U.S. Atty.'s Office, Balt., 1973-78; pvt. practice law Washington, 1978-83, 89-91, Balt., 1983-89, Portland, Maine, 1991—; tchr., lectr. on trial practice, white collar criminality, public corruption. Recipient Spl. Achievement award Dept. Justice, 1972, 74, Spl. Commendation for Outstanding Svc., Dept. Justice, 1978, Younger Fed. Lawyer award Fed. Bar Assn., 1974, Atty. Gen.'s Disting. Service award, 1974, Legal award Assn. Fed. Investigators, 1977. Mem. ABA. Office: One Canal Plz PO Box 7320 Portland ME 04112

SKOLNIK, MERRILL I., electrical engineer; b. Balt., Nov. 6, 1927; s. Samuel and Mary (Baker) S.; m. Judith Magid, June 4, 1950; children: Norma Jean, Martin Allen, Julia Anne, Ellen Charlotte. BEng, Johns Hopkins U., 1947, MSEng, 1949, DEng, 1951. Research scientist Johns Hopkins U., Balt., 1947-54; vis. prof. Johns Hopkins U., 1973-74; engring. specialist Sylvania Electric, Boston, 1954; staff mem. MIT Lincoln Lab., Lexington, Mass., 1954-59; research mgr. Electronic Communications, Timonium, Md., 1959-64, Inst. Def. Analyses, Arlington, Va., 1964-65; supr. radar div. Naval Research Lab., Washington, 1965—; mem. bd. visitors Duke U. Engring. Sch., Durham, N.C., 1979-93; disting. vis. sci. Jet Propulsion Lab., 1990-92; mem. Md. Gov.'s Exec. Adv. Com., 1993-95. Author: Introduction to Radar Systems, 1962, 2d edit., 1980, Radar Handbook, 1970, 2d edit., 1990; editor: Radar Applications, 1988. Recipient Heinrich Hertz premium instn. Electronic and Radio Engrs., London, 1964, Disting. Civilian Service award U.S. Navy, 1982; Meritorious Exec. award Sr. Exec. Service, 1986; Disting. Alumnus award Johns Hopkins U., 1979; named to Soc. of Scholars, Johns Hopkins U., 1975. Fellow IEEE (editor Proceedings 1986-89, Harry Diamond award 1983, Centennial medal 1984); mem. Nat. Acad. Engring. Home: 8123 McDonogh Rd Baltimore MD 21208-1005 Office: Naval Research Lab Washington DC 20375

SKOLNIKOFF, EUGENE B., political science educator; b. Phila., Aug. 29, 1928; s. Benjamin H. and Betty (Turoff) S.; m. Winifred S. Weinstein, Sept. 15, 1957; children: David, Matthew, Jessica. B.S., M.I.T., 1950, M.S., 1950, Ph.D., 1965; B.A., Oxford (Eng.) U., 1952, M.A., 1955. Registered profl. engr. Rsch. asst. in elec. engring. Uppsala U., Sweden, 1950; prof. polit. sci. M.I.T., 1965—, chmn. polit. sci. dept., 1970-74; dir. Center for Internat. Studies, 1972-87; vis. rsch. prof. Carnegie Endowment for Internat. Peace, Geneva, 1969-70; vis. fellow Balliol Coll., U. Oxford, 1989; systems analyst Inst. for Def. Analyses, Washington, 1957-58; mem. White House staff Office Spl. Asst. to Pres. for Sci. and Tech., Washington, 1958-63; adj. prof. Fletcher Sch. Law and Diplomacy, Tufts U., Medford, Mass., 1965-72; sr. cons. White House Office of Sci. and Tech. Policy, 1977-81, also vice chmn. adv. com. on sci., tech. and devel.; mem. policy rev. com. on nat. low-level nuclear waste mgmt., 1980-86; cons. Dept. State, Office of Tech. Assessment, AID, OECD, Resources for the Future, Am. Soc. Internat. Law, Ford Found., Inst. Def. Analyses; chmn., pres. Sci. and Public Policy Studies Group, 1967-73; mem. Internat. Council Sci. Policy Studies; Montague Burton vis. prof. U. Edinburgh, 1977. Author: Science, Technology and American Foreign Policy, 1967, International Imperatives of Technology, 1972, The Elusive Transformation: Science, Technology, and the Evolution of International Politics, 1993; co-editor: World Eco-Crisis, 1972, Visions of Apocalypse, End or Rebirth?, 1985; contbr. articles to publs.; chmn. editorial bd. Pub. Sci., 1971-75; mem. editorial bd. Tech. Rev., 1976-78, Social Studies of Sci., 1970-75, Internat. Orgn., 1974-80. Trustee German Marshall Fund, 1979-87, chmn., 1980-86; trustee UN Rsch. Inst. for Social Devel., 1979-85; bd. dirs. Saco Def., 1984-86; mem. Overseas Devel. Coun.; mem. U.S. del. UN Commn. for Social Devel., 1979; mem. State Dept. Adv. Com. on Sci. and Tech., 1987—. Served with U.S. Army Security Agy., 1955-57. Rhodes scholar, 1950-52; Rockefeller Found. fellow, 1963-65; decorated Comdr.'s Cross Fed. Republic Germany, Order of Rising Sun, Golden Rays, Neck Ribbon, Japan. Fellow Am. Acad. Arts and Scis. (councillor 1973-77), AAAS (sec. sect. K 1967-69, mem. com. on sci. and pub. policy 1973-74, com. on sci., engring. and pub. policy 1984-89); mem. UN Assn., Am. Coun. on Germany, Fedn. Am. Scientists, (coun. 1981-85), Coun. Fgn. Rels., Am. Assn. Rhodes Scholars, Soc. for Internat. Devel., Soc. for Social Studies of Sci., Sigma Xi, Tau Beta Pi, Eta Kappa Nu. Patentee hybrid circuits. Home: 3 Chandler St Lexington MA 02173-3601 Office: MIT E51-228 77 Massachusetts Ave Cambridge MA 02139

SKOLOVSKY, ZADEL, concert pianist, educator; b. Vancouver, B.C., Can.; came to U.S., 1923, naturalized, 1929; s. Max and Kate (Jones) S.; m. Alice Maffett Glass, July 29, 1947 (div. 1953). Diploma, Curtis Inst. Music, 1937; studied piano with, Isabelle Vengerova and Leopold Godowsky; conducting with, Fritz Reiner and Pierre Monteux; violin with, Edwin Bachmann. Prof. music Ind. U., 1975-87, prof. emeritus, 1987—; juror NYU Internat. Tchaikovsky Piano Competition, 1978, 3d Latin Am. Teresa Carreno Piano Competition, Caracas, Venezuela, 1978, U. Md. Internat. Piano Competition, 1981, Joanna Hodges Internat. Piano Competition, Palm Desert, Calif., 1983; tchr. master classes; concert tour of U.S., S. Am. and Far East, 1989-90. Debut at Town Hall as winner of the Walter W. Naumburg award, 1939; appearances in recitals in Carnegie Hall, N.Y.C., 1939—, ann. concert tours U.S.A. and Can., 1939—; biennial tours Europe, Israel, S.Am., Far East, also condr. master classes, 1986—; soloist with N.Y. Philharmonic Symphony Orch.; soloist under condrs. Dimitri Mitropoulos, Charles Munch, Leonard Bernstein, Lorin Maazel, Erich Leinsdorf, Jan Kubelik, Paul Kletzki, Arthur Rodzinski, Paul Paray; appeared as a soloist Lewishohn Stadium, N.Y. and Robin Hood Dell, Phila., under condrs. Vladimir Golschmann, Pierre Monteux, Alexander Smallens; soloist with NBC Orch., Nat. Orch. Assn., Phila. Orch., Nat. Orch., Washington, San Francisco Symphony, Israel Philharmonic, Residentie Orch. at The Hague, L'Orchestre Nat. de Belgique, B.B.C. Scottish Orch., orchs. of Luxembourg, Lisbon, Portugal, Hilversum Radio, Holland, Paris, London, Ravinia, Chgo., N.Y.C.; also appeared on TV; first performance Second Piano Concerto by Prokofieff with N.Y. Philharmonic Orch. under Charles Munch, 1948; world premier Concerto No. 4 of Darius Milhaud with Boston Symphony, 1950; 1st extensive European tour, 1953; appeared with Residency Orch. of the Hague, 2d tour, appeared as soloist with Israel Philharmonic Orch. at opening concert World Festival Music, 1954, appeared in Mexico, 1965, European tour, Eng., Holland, Scandinavia, Belgium, 1965-66, 67, recital, Queen Elizabeth Hall, London, Eng., 1971, 73, recitals, B.C., 1975; concert tour of, S. Am., 1978, U.S., Can. and Europe, 1981-82, Can., 1991; 1st concert tour of Far East, 1983; mus. films for TV., recorded for Columbia Masterworks Records, Philips Records; transcontinental Can. tour, 1991, U.S.A., 1991; annual concert tours U.S.A., Can., Europe, 1992-93. Recipient prizes from Nat. Fedn. Music Clubs, 1943, Nat. Music League, 1940, Robin Hood Dell Young Am. Artists award 1939; recipient Walter W. Naumburg award, 1939. Democrat. Jewish. Club: Lotos (N.Y.C.). Avocations: tennis, chess, literature, theater.

SKOM, JOSEPH HARRY, medical educator; b. Aurora, Ill.; m. Edith Rosen Skom, June 27, 1948; children: Harriet Meyer, Roler. Intern Johns Hopkins Hosp., Balt., 1952-53; resident in medicine U. Chgo. Clinics, 1953-55, rsch. fellow in medicine, 1955-56; instr. in medicine U. Chgo., 1956-57; instr., assoc. in medicine Northwestern U., Chgo., 1957-66, asst. prof. medicine, 1966-73, assoc. prof. medicine, 1973-85, prof. clin. medicine, 1985—. Author: (with others) Obstetrics & Gynecology, 1978, Treatment of Juvenilee Diabetics, 1980; contbr. articles to profl. jours. Chmn. Com. on Preservation Adolescents; mem. Joint Commn. on Accreditation of Health Care Orgns., 1989—. With U.S. Army, 1943-46. U. Geneva faculty fellow 1969. Fellow ACP; mem. AMA (chmn. com. drug abuse 1973-85, pres. No. Ill. and Greater Chgo. chpt. 1973-75, exec. com. coun. sci. affairs 1980-90), Am. Diabetes Assn. (past pres. No. Ill. chpt., bd. dirs.), Ill. Med. Soc. (pres. 1976-77). Avocations: biography, history, tennis, golfing, bridge, music. Office: Assocs in Internal Medicine 211 E Chicago Ave Chicago IL 60611

SKOMAL, EDWARD NELSON, aerospace company executive, consultant; b. Kansas City, Mo., Apr. 15, 1926; s. Edward Albert and Ruth (Bangs) S.; m. Elizabeth Birkbeck, Mar. 4, 1951; children: Susan Beth, Catherine Anne, Margaret Elaine; m. Joan Kerner, Apr. 9, 1988. BA, Rice U., Houston, 1947, MA, 1949. Engr., Socony Rsch. Labs., Dallas, 1949-51; asst. sect. head Nat. Bur. Standards, Washington, 1951-56; project engr. Sylvania Research Lab., Palo Alto, Calif., 1956-59; mgr. applications engring., chief applications engr. Motorola Solid State Systems Div., Phoenix, 1959-63; dir. communications dept. Aerospace Corp., El Segundo, Calif., 1963-86, ret., 1986; mem. Presdl. Joint Tech. Adv. Com. on Electromagnetic Compatibility, Washington, 1965-70, 71-75. Author: Man Made Radio Noise, 1978, Automatic Vehicle Location Systems, 1980; Measuring the Radio Frequency Environment, 1985; contbr. articles to profl. jours. Patentee in field of radio systems, solid state devices, radar cross sect. reduction of ballistic reentry vehicles and solid state microwave components. Elder First Presbyterian Ch., Redlands, Calif. Served with USN, 1944-6. Fellow IEEE (life, chmn. tech. adv. com. 1982-86, chmn. tech. com. electromagnetic environments 1976-82, standards com. 1980—, nat. com. standards coordinating com. on definitions 1986—; Richard A. Stoddart award 1980, cert. of Achievement 1971, Paper of Yr. award 1970); mem. IEEE Electromagnetic Soc. (life), Am. Phys. Soc., Internat. Union Radio Scientists, Sigma Xi. Republican. Presbyterian. Home: 1831 Valle Vista Dr Redlands CA 92373-7246

SKOMOROWSKY, PETER P., accounting company executive; b. Leipzig, Germany, Nov. 14, 1932. Home: 25 E 86th St New York NY 10028-0553 Office: care Grant Thornton 605 3rd Ave New York NY 10158-0180

SKONIECZKA, RICHARD GERALD, retired police chief, coroner; b. Erie, Pa., Jan. 16, 1932; s. Alois Frank and Margaret (Kloor) S.; m. Marilyn Ann Hultman, Oct. 13, 1951 (dec. Oct. 1986); children: Cheryl, Sandra, Carrie, Richard Jr.; m. Angela Marie Stanton, Dec. 1987; stepchildren: Michael Stanton, Donald Stanton. Switchman, crane operator Hammermill Paper Co., Erie, 1955-57; patrolman Bur. of Police, Erie, 1957-62, detective sgt., 1962-72, dep. chief patrol, 1972-80, chief of police, 1980-88; now dep. coroner Erie, 1988-93, retired 1993. Office: Bur of Police 815 E 33rd St Erie PA 16504-1766

SKOOG, DONALD PAUL, retired physician, educator; b. Sioux City, Iowa, Sept. 29, 1931; m. Mary Ann Bunn, 1955; children: Robert Eugene, David Alan (dec.), Kristin Marie. BA magna cum laude, Midland Lutheran Coll., Fremont, Nebr., 1953; MD cum laude, U. Nebr., 1958; DSci (hon.), Midland

Luth. Coll., 1993. Diplomate Am. Bd. Pathology. Intern, then resident in pathology Bishop Clarkson Meml. Hosp., Omaha, 1958-62; resident in pathology Parkland Meml. Hosp., Dallas, 1962-63; fellow in pathology U. Tex. Southwestern Med. Sch., Dallas, 1962-63; practice medicine specializing in pathology Omaha, 1963-92; pathologist Bishop Clarkson Meml. Hosp., 1963-88, chmn. dept. pathology, 1978-80, dir. dept., 1986-87, chmn. med. edn. com., 1978-83, sec.-treas. med. staff, 1982-87; prof. pathology and microbiology U. Nebr. Med. Sch., 1977-93, mem. dean's faculty adv. coun., 1977-79, mem. grad. and continuing edn. com., 1980-85, mem. council for affiliated instns., 1981-83, mem. admissions com. 1986-91, sr. cons. pathology and microbiology, 1993—; assoc. med. dir. ARC Blood Svcs., Midwest region, Omaha, 1988, med. dir./dir. 1989-91, dir./prin. officer, 1991-92, mem. computer systems selection com., 1991; med. affairs com. ARC Blood Svcs., Washington, 1991-92; bd. dirs., exec. com. Health Planning Coun. of the Midlands, 1975-77; mem. exec. com., chmn. loan com. Nebr. Med. Edn. Fund, 1983-91, sec., treas., 1984-91. Mem. editorial bd. Lab. Medicine, 1979—; contbr. articles to med. jours. Councilman Luther Meml. Luth. Ch., Omaha, 1966-72, 87-91, vice chmn., 1969-72; trustee Midland Luth. Coll., 1968-87, chmn., 1973-75. Recipient Alumni Achievement award Midland Luth. Coll., 1972, Disting. Svc. award Sch. of Allied Health Program, U. Nebr. Med. Ctr., 1990. Fellow Am. Soc. Clin. Pathologists (hematology profl. self-assessment com. 1972, 75,78, adv. coun. 1972-78, chmn. coun. hematology 1978-81, editor Hematology Check Sample 1983-88, Disting. Svc. award Commn. on Continuing Edn. 1985, mem. bd. censors 1987-89, mem. nat. meeting activities com. 1989-92, chmn. 1990-92, Israel Davidsohn disting. svc. award 1993), Coll. Am. Pathologists (hematology resource com. 1981-86, vice chmn. 1982-85); mem. AMA, Am. Assn. Blood Banks, Nebr. Assn. Pathologists, Nebr. Med. Assn., Met. Omaha Med. Soc. (coun. on grievances and profl. ethics 1983-91), Midland Luth. Coll. Alumni Assn. (pres. 1969-70), Alpha Omega Alpha (pres. U. Nebr. chpt. 1976-77, counsellor 1984-90). Home: 706 S 96th St Omaha NE 68114-4918

SKOOG, FOLKE KARL, botany educator; b. Fjärås, Sweden, July 15, 1908; came to U.S., 1925, naturalized, 1935; s. Karl Gustav and Sigrid (Person) S.; m. Birgit Anna Lisa Bergner, Jan. 31, 1947; 1 dau., Karin. B.S., Calif. Inst. Tech., 1932, Ph.D., 1936; Ph.D. (hon.), U. Lund, Sweden, 1956, D.Sc. (hon.), U. Ill., 1980; D. Agr. Sc. (hon.), U. Pisa, Italy, 1991; D.Agr.Sc. (hon.), Swedish U. Agrl. Scis., Uppsala, 1991. Teaching asst., research fellow biology Calif. Inst. Tech., 1934-36; NRC fellow U. Calif., Berkeley, 1936-37, summer 1938; instr., tutor biology Harvard U., 1937-41, research assoc., 1941; assoc., assoc. prof. biology Johns Hopkins U., 1941-44; chemist Q.M.C.; also tech. rep. U.S. Army ETO, 1944-46; asso. prof. botany U. Wis.-Madison, 1947-49, prof., from 1949, C. Leonard Huskins prof. botany, now emeritus.; vis. physiologist Pineapple Research Inst., U. Hawaii, 1938-39; assoc. physiologist NIH, USPHS, 1943; vis. lectr. Washington U., 1946, Swedish U. Agrl. Scis., Ultuna, 1952; v.p. physiol. sect. Internat. Bot. Congress, Paris, 1954, Edinburgh, 1964, Leningrad, 1975. Editor: Plant Growth Substances, 1951, 80; contbr. articles to profl. jours. Track and field mem. Swedish Olympic Team, 1932. Recipient cert. of merit Bot. Soc. Am., 1956, Nat. Medal of Sci., U.S., 1991, Cosimo Ridolfi medal, 1991, John Ericsson medal, 1992. Mem. NAS, Bot. Soc. Am. (chmn. physiol. sect. 1954-55), Am. Soc. Plant Physiologists (v.p. 1952-53, pres. 1957-58, Stephen Hales award 1954, Reid Barnes life membership award 1970), Soc. Developmental Biology (pres. 1971), Am. Soc. Gen. Physiologists (v.p. 1956-57, pres. 1957-58), Internat. Plant Growth Substances Assn. (hon. life mem., v.p. 1976-79, pres. 1979-82), Am. Soc. Biol. Chemists, Am. Acad. Arts and Scis., Deutsche Akademie der Naturforscher Leopoldina, Swedish Royal Acad. Scis., Tissue Culture Assn. (hon. life mem. 1991, Life Achievement award 1992), Russian Soc. Plant Physiologists (hon.). Achievements include patents in field. Home: 2820 Marshall Ct Madison WI 53705-2270 Office: U Wis Dept Botany Madison WI 53706

SKOOG, GERALD DUANE, science educator; b. Sioux City, Iowa, Feb. 27, 1936; s. Paul and Mary Ann Skoog; m. Elizabeth Ann Lee, Dec. 28, 1962; children: Jeffrey, John, Sarah. B.S., U. Nebr., 1958; M.A., U. No. Iowa, 1963; Ed.D., U. Nebr., 1969. Tchr. various schs., Nebr., Ill., 1958-69; instr. U. Nebr., Lincoln, summer 1969; asst. prof. curriculum and instrn. Tex. Tech U., Lubbock, 1969-72, assoc. prof., coordinator program, 1972-74, assoc. prof., chmn. secondary edn., 1976-80, prof., chmn. secondary edn., 1980-90, prof., chmn. curriculum and instrn., 1990—; pres. faculty senate Tex. Tech U., 1986-87; vis. prof. Western Ill. U., summer 1972; lectr. in field; participant, facilitator numerous workshops; cons. Contbr. numerous articles to profl. jours., also reviewer articles and papers; co-author secondary sch. science textbooks. Bd. dirs. Gloria Dei Luth. Ch., Lubbock, 1971-74, 92-93; bd. dirs. Luth. Coun. Cmty. Action, 1970-71, Good Neighbor Ministry, 1982-84; leader Boy Scouts Am., 1978-79; foster parent Luth. Social Svcs. Tex.; bd. dirs. Triangle Coalition for Sci. and Tech., 1986-95. Recipient Pres.'s Faculty Achievement award Tex. Tech U., 1986. Mem. Nat. Sci. Tchrs. Assn. (life, bd. dirs. 1977-79, pres. 1985-86, various coms., Disting. Svc. to Sci. Edn. award 1994), Nat. Assn. Rsch. Sci. Teaching, Assn. Edn. Tchrs. Sci., Assn. Supervision and Curriculum Devel., Nat. Sci. Suprs. Assn., Sci. Tchrs. Assn. Tex. (hon. mem., past pres.), Nat. Assn. Biology Tchrs., Tex. Assn. Tchr. Edn. (com. 1981-82), Soc. Study Edn., Phi Delta Kappa. Home: 3214 67th St Lubbock TX 79413-6206 Office: Tex Tech U Coll Edn Lubbock TX 79409

SKOOG, RALPH EDWARD, lawyer; b. Topeka, Dec. 17, 1929; s. Ralph O. and Anna C. (Haley) S.; m. Beth Henry, Nov. 19, 1953; children:—Eric S., Peter R., Carl E., Curt A. Edward. BSCE, BS in Geology, Kans. State U., 1952; JD, Washburn U., 1959. Bar: Kans. 1959, U.S. Supreme Ct. 1971; registered profl. engr., Kans. Engr. and geologist Howard, Needles, Tammen & Bergendoff, Topeka, 1954-59; ptnr. Cook, Flatt & Skoog (Cons. Engrs.), Topeka, 1960-63, Dickinson, Crow & Skoog, 1962-71, Crow & Skoog, (Attys.), 1971-74; pvt. practice Ralph E. Skoog, P.A., Topeka, 1975—; Congl. Homes, Inc., 1977—, pres., 1991-93; lectr. Washburn U., 1971-76. Pres. Community Resources Coun., 1972-73; mem. Kans. Ho. of Reps., 1961-65, 67-69; mem. fin. com. Rep. State Com., 1971-72, mem., 1973-74; chmn. 2d Congl. Dist., 1977-78; del. Rep. Nat. Conv., 1976; bd. dirs. Topeka Inst. Urban Affairs, 1964-74. Served to 1st lt. AUS, 1952-54. Mem. ABA, Kans. Bar Assn., Topeka Bar Assn. (pres. 1991-92), Topeka Inn of Ct., NSPE, ASCE, Geol. Soc. Am., Kans. State U. Alumni Assn. (internat. pres. 1967-69), Assn. Trial Lawyers Am., Kans. Trial Lawyers Assn. (pres. 1983-84), Phi Alpha Delta, Sigma Tau, Sigma Alpha Epsilon, Phi Kappa Phi, Sigma Gamma Epsilon. Congregationalist. Home: 235 SW Greenwood Ave Topeka KS 66606-1227 Office: 434 SW Topeka Blvd Topeka KS 66603-3180

SKOOG, WILLIAM ARTHUR, former oncologist; b. Culver City, Calif., Apr. 10, 1925; s. John Lundeen and Allis Rose (Gatz) S.; m. Ann Douglas, Sept. 17, 1949; children: Karen, William Arthur, Janes Douglas, Allison. AA, UCLA, 1944; BA with gr. distinction, Stanford U., 1946, MD, 1949. Intern medicine Stanford Hosp., San Francisco, 1948-49, asst. resident medicine, 1949-50; asst. resident medicine N.Y. Hosp., N.Y.C., 1950-51; sr. resident medicine Wadsworth VA Hosp., Los Angeles, 1951, attending specialist internal medicine, Los Altos, Calif., 1959-61; pvt. practice hematology and oncology Calif. Oncologic and Surg. Med. Group, Inc., Santa Monica, Calif., 1971-72; pvt. practice med. oncology San Bernardino, Calif., 1972-94; assoc. staff Palo Alto-Stanford (Calif.) Hosp. Center, 1959-61, U. Calif. Med. Center, San Francisco, 1959-61, asso. attending physician U. Calif. at Los Angeles Hosp. and Clinics, 1961-78; vis. physician internal medicine Harbor Gen. Hosp., Torrance, Calif., 1962-65, attending physician, 1965-71; cons. chemistry Clin. Lab., UCLA Hosp., 1963-68; affiliate cons. staff St. John's Hosp., Santa Monica, Calif., 1967-71, courtesy staff, 1971-72; courtesy attending med. staff Santa Monica Hosp., 1967-72; staff physician St. Bernardine (Calif.) Hosp., 1972-94, hon. staff, 1994—; staff physician San Bernardino Community Hosp., 1972-90, courtesy staff, 1990-94; chief sect. oncology San Bernardino County Hosp., 1972-76; cons. staff Redlands (Calif.) Community Hosp., 1972-83, courtesy staff, 1983-94; asst. in medicine Cornell Med. Coll., N.Y.C., 1950-51; jr. research physician UCLA Atomic Energy Project, 1954-55; instr. medicine, asst. research physician dept. medicine UCLA Med. Center, 1955-56, asst. prof. medicine, asst. research physician, 1956-59; clin. assoc. hematology VA Center, Los Angeles, 1956-59; co-dir. metabolic research unit UCLA Center for Health Scis., 1955-59, 61-65; co-dir. Health Scis. Clin. Research Center, 1965-68, dir., 1968-72; clin. instr. medicine Stanford, 1959-61; asst. clin. prof. medicine, assoc. research physician U. Calif. Med. Center, San Francisco, 1959-61; lectr. medicine

UCLA Sch. Medicine, 1961-62, assoc. prof. medicine, 1962-73, assoc. clin. prof. medicine, 1973—. Served with USNR, 1943-46, lt. M.C., 1951-53. Fellow ACP; mem. Am., Calif. med. assns., So. Calif. Acad. Clin. Oncology, Western Soc. Clin. Research, Am. Fedn. Clin. Research, Los Angeles Acad. Medicine, San Bernardino County Med. Soc., Am. Soc. Clin. Oncology, Am. Soc. Internal Medicine, Calif. Soc. Internal Medicine, Inland Soc. Internal Medicine, Phi Delta Kappa, Alpha Omega Alpha, Sigma Xi, Alpha Kappa Kappa. Episcopalian (vestryman 1965-70). Club: Redlands Country. Contbr. articles to profl. jours. Home: 1119 Kimberly Pl Redlands CA 92373-6786

SKOPIL, OTTO RICHARD, JR., federal judge; b. Portland, Oreg., June 3, 1919; s. Otto Richard and Freda Martha (Boetticher) S.; m. Janet Rae Lundy, July 27, 1956; children: Otto Richard III, Casey Robert, Shannon Ida, Molly Jo. BA in Econs., Willamette U., 1941, LLB, 1946, LLD (hon.), 1983. Bar: Oreg. 1946, IRS, U.S. Treasury Dept., U.S. Dist. Ct. Oreg., U.S. Ct. Appeals (9th cir.), U.S. Supreme Ct. 1946. Assoc. Skopil & Skopil, 1946-51; ptnr. Williams, Skopil, Miller & Beck (and predecessors), Salem, Oreg., 1951-72; judge U.S. Dist. Ct., Portland, 1972-79; chief judge U.S. Dist. Ct., 1976-79; judge U.S. Ct. Appeals (9th cir.), Portland, 1979—; chmn. com. adminstrn. of fed. magistrate sys. U.S. Jud. Conf., 1980-86; co-founder Oreg. chpt. Am. Leadership forum; chmn. 9th cir. Jud. Coun. magistrates adv. com., 1988-91; chmn. U.S. Jud. Conf. Long Range Planning Com., 1990-95. Hi-Y adviser Salem YMCA, 1951-52; appeal agt. SSS, Marion County (Oreg.) Draft Bd., 1953-66; master of ceremonies 1st Gov.'s Prayer Breakfast for State Oreg., 1959; mem. citizens adv. com., City of Salem, 1970-71; chmn. Gov.'s Com. on Staffing Mental Instns., 1969-70; pres., bd. dirs. Marion County Tb and Health Assn., 1958-61; bd. dirs. Willamette Valley Camp Fire Girls, 1946-56, Internat. Christian Leadership, 1959, Fed. Jud. Ctr., 1979; trustee Willamette U., 1969-71; elder Mt. Park Ch., 1979-81. Served to lt. USNR, 1942-46. Recipient Oreg. Legal Citizen of Yr. award, 1986, Disting. Alumni award Willamette U. Sch. Law, 1988. Mem. ABA, Oreg. Bar Assn. (bd. govs.), Marion County Bar Assn., Am. Judicature Soc., Oreg. Assn. Def. Counsel (dir.), Def. Research Inst., Assn. Ins. Attys. U.S. and Can. (Oreg. rep. 1970), Internat. Soc. Barristers, Prayer Breakfast Movement (fellowship council). Clubs: Salem, Exchange (pres. 1947), Illahe Hills Country (pres., dir. 1964-67). Office: US Ct Appeals 232 Pioneer Courthouse 555 SW Yamhill St Portland OR 97204-1336

SKORCZ, STEPHEN, hospital association executive; b. Chgo., July 17, 1939; s. Arthur Lawrence and Regina Frances (Kowalski) S. BS, U. Ill., Chgo., 1966; MPH, Yale U., 1970. Dir. pharmacy svcs., then adminstrv. asst. Alexian Bros. Hosp., Chgo., 1966-68; adminstrv. resident Montefiore Med. Ctr., Bronx, N.Y., 1970; cons. Alexian Bros. Am., Chgo., 1970-71; v.p. Alexian Bros. Med. Ctr., Elk Grove Village, Ill., 1971-74; coord. planning Ont. Ministry Health, Toronto, Can., 1974-77; exec. dir. Univ. Tchg. Hosp. Assn., Toronto, 1977-80, Hosp. Coun. Met. Toronto, 1977-80; exec. dir., then pres. Capital Area Health Consortium, Newington, Conn., 1980-88; pres. Rochester (N.Y.) Area Health Corp., 1988-92; v.p. Ont. Hosp. Assn. Toronto, 1992—; U.S. coord., mem. exec. com. N.E. Can.-Am. Health Coun., 1984-87, U.S. co-chmn., 1987-88; bd. dirs. Rochester Healthcare Info. Group, Inc., 1988-90, chmn., 1990-92; bd. dirs. Regional Hosp. Svcs., Inc. 1988-90. Mem. corp. various hosps., Conn., N.Y., Ill., 1980-90. Fellow Am. Coll. Healthcare Execs., Can. Coll. Healthcare Execs. (cert. health exec.), Yale U. Hosp. Adminstrn. Alumni Assn. (sec. 1982-86, pres. 1986-88), Assn. Yale Alumni in Pub. Health (treas. 1983-89, rep., chmn. pub. health alumni fund 1988-92). Democrat. Roman Catholic. Avocations: cooking, reading, making dollhouses, gardening. Office: Ontario Hosp Assn, 150 Ferrand Dr, Toronto, ON Canada M3C 1H6

SKORTON, DAVID JAN, university official, physician, educator; b. Milw., Nov. 22, 1949; s. Samuel and Pauline (Millstein) S.; 1 child, Joshua Samuel. BA, Northwestern U., 1970; MD, Northwestern U., Chgo., 1974. Diplomate Nat. Bd. Med. Examiners, Am. Bd. Internal Medicine, Am. Bd. Cardiovascular Disease. Resident UCLA, 1974-77, fellow in cardiology 1977-80, chief resident in medicine, 1978-79, adj. asst. prof., 1978-80; instr. medicine U. Iowa, Iowa City, 1980-81, asst. prof., 1981-84, asst. prof. elec. and computer engring., 1982-84, assoc. prof. medicine and elec. and computer engring., 1984-88, prof., 1988—; acting dir., then dir. div. gen. internal medicine U. Iowa Coll. Medicine, 1985-89, assoc. chmn. for clinical programs, 1989-92, v.p. for rsch., 1992—; dir. echocardiology lab. VA Med. Ctr., Iowa City, 1980-89; mem. internat. and coop. projects study sect. NIH, 1988-92, chmn., 1990-92; lectr. in field numerous sci. sessions, nat. and internat. meetings; manuscript reviewer maj. jours. in field. Editor: Cardiac Imaging and Image Processing, 1986, Cardiac Imaging, 1990; mem. editorial bd. Am. Jour. Cardiac Immaging, Am. Jour. Noninvasive Cardiology, Cardiology, Circulation, 1986-88, Jour. Am. Coll. Cardiology, 1989-93, Echocardiography, Internat. Jour. Cardiac Imaging, Ultrasonic Imaging, Cardiovascular Imaging (Italy), Clin. Cardiology; sect. editor Jour. Am. Soc. Echocardiography; contbr. numerous articles and sci. abstracts to profl. jours., chpts. to books. Regents' scholar UCLA, 1967-68; named Intern-of-Yr., UCLA, 1975; recipient Rsch. Assoc. Career Devel. award U. Iowa City, 1981-84, Rsch. Career Devel. award Nat. Heart Lung & Blood Inst., Iowa City, 1984-89. Fellow ACP (governing coun. Iowa 1983-85), Am. Coll. Cardiology (chmn. computer applications com. 1984-90, gov. Iowa sect. 1987-90, trustee 1991-96), Am. Heart Assn., Am. Physiol. Soc.; mem. AAAS, Am. Soc. Echocardiography (bd. dirs. 1983-86), Am. Inst. Ultrasound in Medicine (bd. govs. 1986-89), Am. Fedn. for Clin. Rsch., Assn. Univ. Cardiologists, Internat. Soc. for Adult Congenital Cardiac Disease, Soc. Magnetic Resonance Imaging, Soc. Magnetic Resonance in Medicine. Jewish. Office: U Iowa VP for Rsch 201 Gilmore Hall Iowa City IA 52242-1320

SKOTAK, ROBERT F., film production company executive; b. Dearborn, Mich.. Visual effects artist Hollywood, Calif., 1976—; co-founder, pres., visual effects dir. 4-Ward Prodns., Inc., L.A., 1989—. Visual effects artist, designer, supr. (films) Battle Beyond the Stars, Escape from New York, To Be or Not To Be, Strange Invaders, Forbidden World (Top Honor in visual effects French Film Festival 1982), Aliens (Am. and Brit. Acad. award 1986), The Abyss, 1989, (with 4-Ward Prodns.) Tremors, Darkman, 1989, Clifford, True Identity, Cast A Deadly Spell, Terminator 2, (Am. and British Acad. award, Saturn award Acad. of Sci. Fiction 1991), Batman Returns (Am. and British Academy award nominations), 1992, Honey, I Blew Up the Baby, 1992, Dracula, 1992, Heart and Souls, 1993, Fatal Instinct, 1993, No Escape, 1994; visual effects artist, designer, supr., co-prodn. designer (films) Galaxy of Terror, Creature (Acad. Sci. Fiction Best Visual Effects nomination 1984); author: Alien Worlds, 1978; universal filmscript series: This Island Earth, 1990; pub. Famastasne Mag., 1975-78. Mem. Writers Guild Am., Acad. Motion Picture Arts & Scis. Office: 4-Ward Prodns Inc 2801 Hyperion Ave Studio 104 Los Angeles CA 90027-7206

SKOTHEIM, ROBERT ALLEN, museum administrator; b. Seattle, Jan. 31, 1933; s. Sivert O. and Marjorie F. (Allen) S.; m. Nadine Vail, June 14, 1953; children—Marjorie, Kris, Julia. BA, U. Wash., 1955, MA, 1958, PhD, 1962; LLD (hon.), Hobart and William Smith Colls., Geneva, N.Y., 1975; LittD (hon.), Whitman Coll., 1988, LHD (hon.), Coll. Idaho, 1988, Occidental Coll., 1989, Ill. Wesleyan U., 1990; DFA (hon.), Willamette U., 1989. Prof. history U. Wash., 1962-63; prof. history Wayne State U., Detroit, 1963-66; prof. UCLA, 1966-67, U. Colo., Boulder, 1967-72; provost, dean faculty Hobart and William Smith Colls., 1972-75; pres. Whitman Coll., Walla Walla, Wash., 1975-88, Huntington Libr., Art Collections & Bot. Gardens, San Marino, Calif., 1988—. Author: American Intellectual Histories and Historians, 1966, Totalitarianism and American Social Thought, 1971; Editor: The Historian and the Climate of Opinion, 1969; co-editor: American Social Thought: Sources and Interpretations, 2 vols, 1972 Guggenheim fellow, 1967-68. Mem. Phi Beta Kappa (hon.). Office: Huntington Library Art Collections & Bot Gardens 1151 Oxford Rd San Marino CA 91108-1299*

SKOV, ARLIE MASON, petroleum engineer, consultant; b. Perry, Okla., Sept. 21, 1928; s. Arnold and Mary (Mason) S.; m. Luella Luticia Sloan, July 31, 1951; children: Gregory Morgan, Jeffrey Markham, Tamara Kay. BS in Petroleum Engring., U. Okla., 1956; postgrad., U. Va., 1966. Engr. Sohio Petroleum Co., Pauls Valley, Okla., 1957-58; staff engr. Sohio Petroleum Co., Oklahoma City, 1958-65, mgr. spl. projects, 1966-75, asst. mgr. engring., 1975-76; mgr. prodn. planning BP Alaska Inc., San Francisco, 1977-80; project advisor Sohio Gas Pipeline Co., San Francisco, 1980-81; mgr. new

tech. devel. Sohio Petroleum Co., San Francisco, 1981-83; dir. prodn. tech. Sohio Petroleum Co. and Standard Oil Prodn., Dallas, 1983-88; sr. cons. BP Exploration, Inc., Houston, 1989-92; owner Arlie M. Skov, Inc. Petroleum Consulting, Houston, 1993—. Recipient Disting. Svc. award Okla. Petroleum Coun. 1973. Mem. AIME (bd. dirs. 1977-79, trustee 1990-92), Soc. Petroleum Engrs. (bd. dirs. 1972-74, exec. com. 1990-92, pres. 1991, Disting. mem.). Avocations: reading, travel.

SKOVE, THOMAS MALCOLM, retired manufacturing company financial executive; b. Cleve., June 27, 1925; s. Thomas Malcolm and Ethel C. (Rush) S.; m. Helen Busing, June 12, 1948; children: Margaret, Thomas, Richard, Marcie, Douglas. B.S., Bucknell U., 1949. Controller, treas. Cleve. Twist Drill Co., 1949-68; treas. Acme-Cleve. Corp., 1968-81, dep. treas., 1981-86, treas., 1986-88. Councilman, City of Aurora, Ohio, 1977-83; chmn. Aurora Meml. Library Trust, 1984-89. Served with USN, 1943-46. Mem. Sugar Mill Country Club (pres. 1993-94). Republican. Home: 209 Bromely Cir New Smyrna Beach FL 32168-2006

SKOWRONSKI, VINCENT PAUL, concert violinist, recording artist, executive producer, producer classical recordings; b. Kenosha, Wis., Jan. 22, 1944. MusB, Northwestern U., 1966, MusM, 1968. V.p. Eberley-Skowronski, Inc., Evanston, Ill., 1973-92; internat. dir. mktg. and pub. rels. Vincent Skowronski: Producer of Classical Recordings, Evanston, 1993—; internat. broker rare instruments Strings & Things, Evanston, 1973-92; owner Vincent Skowronski: Fine Violins, Evanston, 1993—; internat. dir. mktg. and pub. rels. EB-SKO Prodns., Evanston, 1978-92; dir. media comm. E-S Mgmt., Evanston, 1985-92; instr. violin Northwestern U., 1969-71; asst. prof. violin U. Wyo., 1971-72; prt. violin tchr., chamber music coach, lectr., master classes. Solo violinist debut Chgo. Youth Orch., 1959; soloist Chgo. Civic Orch., 1968; solo guest artist Am. Artist Gala, Nat. Puerto Rican TV, 1960; solo guest artist Young Am. Musicians Sta. WKAR-TV Mich. State U., 1966, N.Am. premiere R. Nanes' Rhapsody Pathetique for violin and orch., Chgo. Cultural Ctr., 1994, Beijing, 1994, DePaul U. Ctr., Chgo., 1994, Skowronski in Recital: 20 Years Remembered, Northwestern U., Evanston, Ill., 1994, IV Internat. Tchaikovsky Competition Commemorative Recital-Moscow Remembered: 1970-95, Evanston, Ill., 1995; featured solo artist Artist Showcase, Sta. WGN-TV Chgo., 1966-71; featured soloist Honors Concert-Northwestern U., 1966, guest solo artist A.M. Am., Sta. ABC-TV, 1977—; numerous concerts and recitals in Europe, Cen.Am., Mex. and U.S.; solo guest artist radio appearances include Continental Bank Concerts, Sta. WFMT-FM Chgo., 1983, 85-86, 88, 90, United Airlines Presents, Live!, Sta. WFMT-FM Chgo., Schumann, 1986, Szymanowski, 1987, Bloch, 1988, Saint-Saens, 1989, Grieg, 1991, Excursions in Music: The Artistry of Vincent P. Skowronski, Sta. KQED-FM San Francisco, 1979, Skowronski: Musical Giant, Interlake Profiles, Sta. WFMT-FM Chgo., 1980, Skowronski at 50: A Birthday Celebration Sta. WNIB-FM, Chgo., 1994; guest solo artist, producer, annotator Separate but Equal, 1976, All Brahms, 1977; solo artist, exec. producer, annotator Gentleman Gypsy, 1978, Strauss and Szymanowski, 1979, Franck and Szymanowski, 1982, Skowronski Alone, 1995; producer, annotator Opera Lady I, 1978, Eberley Sings Strauss, 1980, American Girl, 1983, Opera Lady II, 1984; guest performances numerous TV stas. Bd. dirs. Chgo. Youth Orch., 1973-77, v.p., 1974-77; artistic cons. Classical and Protege Symphony Orchs., Chgo., 1994—; adjudicator Ice skating shows and competitions Wilmette (Ill.) Park Dist., 1985-89; guest panelist classical performance-career forum Sch. of Music, Northwestern U., Evanston, 1992, 94; guest cons. career symposium Edwin G. Foreman High Sch., Chgo., 1989; mem. mayor's founding com. Evanston Arts Coun., 1974-75. Recipient Am. Fedn. Musicians award, 1961, Roy Harris award Inter-Am. U., San German, P.R., 1960, McCormick Found. award Chicago Tribune 1965; selected as one of seven violinists chosen to represent U.S. in the IV Internat. Tchaikovsky Competition, Moscow, 1970. Mem. Sigma Nu, Internat. Platform Assn.

SKRAMSTAD, HAROLD KENNETH, museum administrator, consultant; b. Washington, June 3, 1941; s. Harold K. and Sarah (Shroat) S.; m. Susan Chappelear, Dec. 28, 1963; children: Robert, Elizabeth. AB, George Washington U., 1963, PhD, 1971. Asst. dir. Am. studies program Smithsonian Instn., Washington, 1969-71, spl. asst. to dir. Nat. Mus. Am. History, 1971, chief spl. projects Nat. Mus. Am. History, chief exhibit programs Nat. Mus. Am. History, 1971-74; dir. Chgo. Hist. Soc., 1974-80; pres. Henry Ford Mus. and Greenfield Village, Dearborn, Mich., 1981—; mem. mus. mgmt. adv. com. J. Paul Getty Trust, L.A., 1984-90. Chmn. bd. Met. Detroit Conv. and Visitors Bur., 1981—, chmn., mem. exec. com., 1985—; trustee Coll. Art and Design, Detroit, 1981—; mem. Mich. Travel Commn., 1989—. Recipient Charles Frankel prize Nat. Endowment for the Humanities, 1992. Mem. Am. Assn. Mus. (v.p. 1984-88, accreditation commn. 1982, ethics commn. 1992-93), Smithsonian Instn. Nat. Air and Space Mus. (pub. programming adv. com. 1990—), Greater Detroit and Windsor Japan-Am. Soc. (bd. dirs. 1989—), Detroit Club, Cosmos Club (Washington). Home: Stone Mill 20900 Oakwood Blvd Dearborn MI 48124 Office: Henry Ford Mus Greenfield Village PO Box 1970 Dearborn MI 48121-1970

SKRATEK, SYLVIA PAULETTE, mediator, arbitrator, dispute systems designer; b. Detroit, Dec. 23, 1950; d. William Joseph and Helen (Meskauskas) S.; m. John Wayne Gullion, Dec. 21,1984. BS, Wayne State U., 1971; MLS, Western Mich. U., 1976; PhD, U. Mich., 1985. Media specialist Jackson (Mich.) Pub. Schs., 1971-79; contract specialist Jackson County Edn. Assn., 1976-79; field rep. Mich. Edn. Assn., E.Lansing, 1979-81; contract adminstr. Wash. Edn. Assn., Federal Way, 1981-85, regional coord., 1985-88, program adminstr., from 1988; dir. mediation svcs. Conflict Mgmt. Inst., Lake Oswego, Ore., 1986-87; exec. dir. N.W. Ctr. for Conciliation, 1987-88; served in Wash. State Senate, 1990-94; tng. cons. City of Seattle 1986—; trustee Group Health Coop. of Puget Sound, Wash., 1984-87; sole proprietor Skratek & Assocs., 1980—; pres. Resolutions Internat., 1990—. Contbr. articles to legal jours. Mem. Soc. for Profls. in Dispute Resolution, Indsl. Rels. Rsch. Assn. Avocations: jogging, piano, Asian cooking, cross country skiing.

SKREBNESKI, VICTOR, photographer; b. Chgo., Dec. 17, 1929; s. Joseph and Anna (Casper) S. Student, Art Inst. Chgo., 1945, Inst. Design, 1947. Propr. Skrebneski Studio, Chgo., 1956—. Author: Skrebneski, 1969, The Human Form, 1973, Skrebneski Portraits: A Matter of Record, 1978. Exhbns. include Charles Cowles Gallery, N.Y.C., 1992. Bd. dirs. Chgo. Internat. Film Festival. Recipient award Art Directors Soc., 1958-75. Mem. Dirs. Guild Am., Soc. Photographers in Communications. Club: Arts (Chgo.). Address: 1350 N LaSalle St Chicago IL 60610

SKRETNY, WILLIAM MARION, federal judge; b. Buffalo, Mar. 8, 1945; s. William S. and Rita E. (Wyroski) S.; m. Carol Ann Mergenhagen; children: Brian Alexander, Brooke Ann, Nina Clare. AB, Canisius Coll., 1966; JD, Howard U., 1969; LLM, Northwestern U., 1972. Bar: Ill. 1969, U.S. Dist. Ct. (no. dist) Ill. 1969, N.Y. 1971, U.S. Ct. Appeals (7th cir.) 1972, U.S. Dist. Ct. (we. dist.) N.Y. 1973, U.S. Ct. Appeals (2d cir.) 1976, U.S. Supreme Ct. 1980. Asst. U.S. atty. Office of U.S. Atty. No. Dist. Ill., Chgo. 1971-73; asst. U.S. atty. Office of U.S. Atty. We. Dist. N.Y., Buffalo, 1973-81, 1st asst., 1975-81; gen. ptnr. Duke, Holzman, Yaeger & Radlin, Buffalo, 1981-83; 1st dep. dist. atty. Office Dist. Atty Erie County, Buffalo, 1983-88; assoc. Gross, Shuman, Brizdle and Gillfillan, PC, Buffalo, 1988; of counsel Cox, Barrell, Buffalo, 1989-90; judge U.S. Dist. Ct. (we. dist.) N.Y., Buffalo, 1990—; task force atty. tng. Office U.S. Atty Gen., 1978; spl. counsel U.S. Atty Gen.'s Advocacy Inst., 1979; staff atty. Office Spl. Prosecutor, Dept. Justice, Washington, 1980; faculty advisor Nat. Coll. D.A.s, Houston, 1987; lectr. Northwestern U., Chgo., 1980; mem. jud. com. on security, space and facilities Erie and N.Y.State Bar Assns. Contbr. articles to profl. jours. Bd. dirs. Sudden Infant Death Found. We. N.Y., 1979, Cerebral Palsy Foun. We. N.Y., 1985; co-v.p. PTA Harlem Rd. Sch., 1982; chmn. major corps. divsn. Studio Arena Theatre, Buffalo, 1982; chmn. Polish Culture, Canisius Coll. 1985, trustee, 1989; regional chmn. Cath. Charities Appeal, 1986-87. Scholar Howard U., 1966; fellow Ford Found., 1969; named Citizen of Yr. Am Pol Eagle Newspaper, 1977, 90, Disting. Grad. Nat. Cath. Edn. Assn. Dept. Elem. Sch. 1991, Disting. Alumnus Canisius Coll. 1993. Mem. ABA, Fed. Bar Assn., Fed. Judges Assn., Western N.Y. Trial Lawyers Assn., Thomas More Legal Soc. (pres. 1980), Advocates Soc. Western N.Y., Erie County Bar Assn., Chgo. Bar Assn., Canisius Coll. Alumni Assn. (pres. 1989), Di Gamma, Phi Alpha Delta. Republican. Roman Catholic. Office: US District Court 65 Court St Rm 507 Buffalo NY 14202-3406

SKROMME, LAWRENCE H., consulting agricultural engineer; b. Roland, Iowa, Aug. 26, 1913; s. Austin G. and Ingeborg B. (Holmedal) S.; m. Margaret Elizabeth Gleason, June 24, 1939; children: Cherlyn Sue Granrose, Inga Jean Hill, Karen Ann Sequino. B.S. with honors, Iowa State U., Ames, 1937. Registered profl. engr., Pa. Design and test engr. Goodyear Tire and Rubber Co., Akron, Ohio, 1937-41; project engr., asst. chief engr. Harry Ferguson Inc., Detroit, 1941-51; chief engr. Sperry New Holland div. Sperry Corp., New Holland, Pa., 1951-61, v.p. engring., 1961-78; cons. agrl. engr. Lancaster, Pa., 1978—; mem. adv. bd. U.S. Congress Com. on Sci. and Tech., 1989—; cons. AID, World Bank, others, 1978-85, Saudi Arabia, 1985-86. Patentee; contbr. articles to profl. jours. Rsch. adv. com. U.S. Dept. Agr., Washington, 1964-68; gov.'s com. agr. and land preservation Gov. of Pa., 1965-69; bd. dirs. awards com. Engrs. Joint Coun., N.Y.C., 1967-75; dir., v.p., pres. Farm and Home Found. Lancaster County, 1968—; Lancaster County Agrl. Land Preservation Bd., 1978—, sec.-treas. 1989—. Mem. Am. Soc. Agrl. Engrs. (gold medal 1974, v.p. 1952-55, pres. 1959-60, fellow 1965—), NAE (peer and membership com. 1978—), Nat. Soc. Profl. Engrs., Internat. Assn. Agrl. Engrs. (v.p. 1974-79, pres. farm machine div.), Am. Soc. Engring. Edn., Phi Kappa Phi, Alpha Zeta, Tau Beta Pi. Republican. Methodist. Avocations: collecting old tools and antiques.

SKROWACZEWSKI, STANISLAW, conductor, composer; b. Lwow, Poland, Oct. 3, 1923; came to U.S., 1960; s. Pawel and Zofia (Karszniewicz) S.; m. Krystyna Jarosz, Sept. 6, 1956; children: Anna, Paul, Nicholas. Diploma faculty philosophy, U. Lwow, 1945; diploma faculties composition and conducting, Acad. Music Lwow, 1945, Conservatory at Krakow, Poland, 1946; L.H.D., Hamline U., 1963, Macalester Coll., 1972; L.H.D. hon. doctorate, U. Minn. Guest condr. in Europe, S.A., U.S., 1947—; Composer, 1931—; pianist, 1928—, violinist, 1934—, condr., 1939—; permanent condr. music dir. Wroclaw (Poland) Philharmonic, 1946-47, Katowice (Poland) Nat. Philharmonic, 1949-54, Krakow Philharmonic, 1955-56, Warsaw Nat. Philharmonic Orch., 1957-59, Minnesota Orch., 1960-79; prin. condr., mus. adviser Halle Orch., Manchester, Eng., 1984-91; musical advisor St. Paul Chamber Orchestra, 1986-87; first symphony and overture for orch. written at age 8, played by Lwow Philharm. Orch., 1931. Composer: 4 symphonies Prelude and Fugue for Orchestra (conducted first performance Paris), 1948, Overture, 1947 (2d prize Szymanowski Concours, Warsaw 1947); Cantiques des Cantiques, 1951, String Quartet, 1953 (2d Prize Internat. Concours Composers, Belgium 1953), Suite Symphonique, 1954 (first prize, gold medal Composers Competition Moscow 1957), Music at Night, 1954, Ricercari Notturni, 1978 (3d prize Kennedy Center Friedheim Competition, Washington), Concerti for Clarinet and Orch., 1980, Violin Concerto, 1985, Concerto for Orch., 1985, Fanfare for Orch., 1987, Sextett for Oboe, Violin, Viola, Orchestra, 1980, String Trio for Violin, Viola, 1990, Triple Concerto for Violin, Clarinet, Piano, Orchestra, 1992, Fantasie per Tre (Flute, Oboe, Cello), 1993, Chamber Concerto, 1993; also music for theatre, motion pictures, songs and piano sonatas, English horn concerto; rec. by Mercury, Columbia, RCA Victor, Vox, EMI, Angel. Recipient nat. prize for artistic activity Poland, 1953; First prize Santa Cecilia Internat. Concours for Condrs., Rome, 1956. Mem. Union Polish Composers, Internat. Soc. Modern Music, Nat. Assn. Am. Composers-Condrs., Am. Music Center. Office: Orch Hall 1111 Nicollet Mall Minneapolis MN 55403-2406

SKUBE, MICHAEL, journalist, critic; b. Springfield, Ill.; 1 child, Noah. Degree in polit. sci., La. State U. Former tchr. math and sci. La.; formerly with U.S. Customs Svc., Miami, Fla.; book reviewer Miami Herald, from 1974; Raleigh (N.C.) bur. chief Winston-Salem (N.C.) Jour., 1978-82; editorial writer The News and Observer, Raleigh, 1982-86, became book editor, 1986; now book editor Atlanta Jour. and Constn. Recipient Pulitzer Prize for criticism, 1989, Disting. Writing award for commentary and column writing Am. Soc. Newspaper Editors, 1989, 1st Pl. award for columns N.C. Press Assn. Office: Atlanta Jour and Constn 72 Marietta St Atlanta GA 30303*

SKULINA, THOMAS RAYMOND, lawyer; b. Cleve., Sept. 14, 1933; s. John J. and Mary B. (Vesely) S. AB, John Carroll U., 1955; JD, Case Western Res. U., 1959, LLM, 1962. Bar: Ohio 1959, U.S. Supreme Ct. 1964, ICC 1965. Ptnr. Skulina & Stringer, Cleve., 1967-72, Riemer Oberdank & Skulina, Cleve., 1978-81, Skulina, Fillo, Walters & Negrelli, 1981-86, Skulina & McKeon, Cleve., 1986-90, Skulina & Hill, Cleve., 1990—; atty. Penn Cen. Transp. Co., Cleve., 1960-65, asst. gen. atty., 1965-78, trial counsel, 1965-76; with Consol. Rail Corp., 1976-78; bd. dirs. High Temperature Systems, Inc., Active Chem. Systems, Inc.; tchr. comml. law Practicing Law Inst., N.Y.C., 1970; practicing arbitrator Am. Arbitration Assn., Fed. Mediation and Conciliation Svc., 1990—; arbitrator Mcpl. Securities Rulemaking Bd., 1994—. Contbr. articles to legal jours. Income tax and fed. fund coord. City of Warrensville Heights, Ohio, 1970-77; spl. counsel City of North Olmstead, Ohio, 1971-75, spl. counsel to Ohio Atty. Gen., 1983-93, Cleve. Charter Rev. Commn., 1988; pres. Civil Svc. Commn., Cleve., 1977-86, referee, 1986—; fact-finder State Employees Rels. Bd., Ohio, 1986—. With U.S. Army, 1959. Mem. ABA (R.R. and motor carrier com. 1988—, jr. chmn. 1989—), Soc. Profls. in Dispute Resolution, Cleve. Bar Assn. (grievance com. 1987-93, chmn. 1989-90, trustee 1993—), Ohio Bar Assn. (bd. govs. litigation sect. 1986—, negligence law com. 1989—, ethics and profl. responsibility com. 1990—), Fed. Bar Assn., Ohio Trial Lawyers Assn., Am. Arbitration Assn. (labor panel 1988—), Nat. Assn. R.R. Trial Counsel, Internat. Assn. Law and Sci., Pub. Sector Labor Rels. Assn., Indsl. Rels. Rsch. Assn. Democrat. Roman Catholic. Home: 3162 W 165th St Cleveland OH 44111-1016 Office: Skulina & Hill 24803 Detroit Rd Cleveland OH 44145-2512

SKULLY, RICHARD PATRICK, airline consultant; b. Rochester, N.Y., Jan. 2, 1921; s. Thomas John and Marie Elizabeth (Fardette) S.; m. Mary Jane Woodley, Nov. 6, 1943; children: Michael Thomas, David Woodley. Student, SUNY-Geneseo, 1939-41. Flight insp. FAA, N.Y.C., 1947-62; dir. flight standards FAA, Washington, 1974-78; sr. v.p. ops. Air Fla. Miami, 1978-84; sr. v.p. ops. and maintenance Arrow Air, Miami, 1984-87; cons. on aviation, 1987—. Served to col. USAF, 1942-65. Decorated Air medal with cluster, D.F.C., Breast Order Yun Hui, Chinese Nat. Govt.; recipient award for meritorious achievement Dept. Transp., 1977. Home: 115 N River Dr W Jupiter FL 33458-3764

SKUPINSKI, BOGDAN KAZIMIERZ, artist; b. Poland, July 16, 1942; came to U.S., 1971, naturalized, 1976; s. Kazimierz Stanislaw and Irena Lucja (Kanar) S. BA, Acad. Fine Arts, Krakow, Poland, 1969, MA, 1971; cert., Ecole Nationale Superieure de Beaux Arts, Paris, 1971. Pres. Bogdan & Assoc., N.Y.C. Graphic artist: painting Proclamation, 1968, Escape, 1968, Return, 1969, Good Journey, (permanent collection N.J. State Mus., 1971, The Stable, (permanent collection Library of Congress), 1971, Nouvel Ordre, 1970 (annual prize Ministry of Cultural Affairs of France), Gare du Nord, 1970 (award Commn. Fine Arts. Paris), anti-war themes, 1969-76; life and work of John F. Kennedy and Albert Michelson, 1969-76. Recipient Grand Prix, Nat. Salon Young Artists, 1968, People's Choice award 2d Nat. Graphic Rev., Karkow, 1969, ann. Batoczek and Babrowski award Polish Ministry Art and Culture, 1970, 1st prize for prints and drawings Nat. Conn. Acad. Exhbn., Hartford, 1971, medal Internat. Exhbn. Graphic Art, Frechen, Fed. Republic Germany, 1976, Presdl. Medal of Merit, 1990; fellow Ecole Nat. Superieure Beaux Arts. Fellow Pratt Inst.; mem. NAD (Cannon prize for graphics 1971), Kosciuszko Found., Rep. Presdl. Task Force. Roman Catholic. Home: Cathedral Sta PO Box 849 215 W 104th St New York NY 10025-9998

SKUPSKY, STANLEY, laser scientist. Prof., dir. lab. for laser energetics U. Rochester, N.Y. Recipient award for Excellence in Plasma Physics Rsch. Am. Physical Soc., 1993. Office: Lab for Laser Energetics U Rochester Rochester NY 14627*

SKURLA, LAURUS See LAURUS

SKUTT, THOMAS JAMES, insurance company executive; b. Omaha, Nov. 1, 1930; s. Vestor Joseph and Angela (Anderson) S.; m. Jeanne Cecille Plunkett, Sept. 3, 1955; children: Mary Elizabeth Sutton, Kimberly Ann Davis, Thomas V.J. BA, Yale U., 1952; LLB, Creighton U., 1957; postgrad., Harvard U., 1979. Ptnr. Spire, Morrow & Skutt, Omaha, 1961-69; with Mut. of Omaha, 1969—, exec. v.p., sec., 1980-81, vice chmn. bd. dirs., 1981-84, 1st vice chmn. bd. dirs., chief exec. officer, 1984-86, chmn. bd. dirs., chief exec. officer, 1986—, chmn. bd. dirs., chief exec. officer United of Omaha subs., 1986—; bd. dirs. United of Omaha, Nat. Omaha Ins. Co., Companion Life Ins. Co., FirsTier Fin., Inc., United World Life Ins. Co. Past pres., selected Citizen of Yr., Mid-Am. Coun. Boy Scouts Am., 1987, 89, 93.mem. exec. bd. 1980—; mem. consultation com. SAC, Omaha, 1984; bd. dirs. Omaha Zool. Soc., 1978—, pres., 1987-88, past. bd. dirs.; gen. chmn. campaign United Way of Midlands, 1979-80, bd. dirs., 1981—; bd. dirs. Creighton U., Omaha, 1983—. Mem. Greater Omaha C. of C. (bd. dirs. 1979—, chmn. 1983, past chmn.), Mpls. Club, Yale Club N.Y.C., Knights of Ak-Sar-Ben (bd. govs. 1985, King XCVI 1992). Republican. Roman Catholic. Avocations: golf, tennis. Home: 400 N 62d St Omaha NE 68132 Office: Mut Omaha Ins Co Mut Omaha Plz Omaha NE 68175

SKVORECKY, JOSEF VACLAV, English educator, novelist; b. Nachod, Czechoslovakia, Sept. 27, 1924; arrived Can., 1969; s. Josef Karel and Anna (Kurazova) S.; m. Zdenka Josefa Salivarova, Mar. 30, 1958. Ph.D., Charles U., Czechoslovakia, 1951; LHD (hon.), SUNY, 1986; postgrad., Masaryk U., 1991, U. Calgary, 1992, U. Toronto, 1992. Vis. lectr. U. Toronto, Ont., Can., 1969-70; writer-in-residence U. Toronto, 1970-71, assoc. prof., 1971-75, prof. English, 1975-90; prof. emeritus, 1990—; lectr. on lit. topics Voice of Am., 1973—; adv. to Pres. Vaclav Havel, 1990. Editor: Sixty Eight Publ. Corp., Toronto, 1972—; author: The End of the Nylon Age, 1967, Republic of Whores, 1969, The Miracle Game, 1972, The End of Lieutenant Boruvka, 1975, The Swell Season, 1975, The Bass Saxophone, 1979, The Cowards, 1980, The Return of Lieutenant Boruvka, 1980, The Engineer of Human Souls, 1984, Miss Silver's Past, 1985, Dvorak in Love, 1986, The Bride from Texas, 1992; short story collections: The Menorah, 1964, The Life of High society, 1965, The Mournful Demeanor of Lieutenant Boruvka, 1966, A Babylonian Story, 1967, The Bitter World, 1969, Sins for Father Knox, 1973, Oh, My Papa! 1972; plays: The New Men and Women CBC Radio 1977, God in Your House, 1980 (1st prize Multicultural Theatre Festival Hamilton 1980); films: The Tank Battalion, 1991, The Swell Season, 1994; essays: Reading Detecive Stories, 1965, They-Which Is We, 1968, All the Bright Young Men and Women, 1972, Working Overtime, 1979, Talkin' Moscow Blues, 1989. Decorated Order of the White Lion; apptd. mem. Order of Can., 1992; Recipient Neustadt Internat. prize for lit., U. Okla., 1980, Gov. Gen. Can.'s award, 1985, lit. prize Echoing Green Found., 1990; Guggenheim fellow, 1980. Fellow Royal Soc. Can.; mem. Can. Writers' Union, Authors' League Am., Crime Writers Can., Mystery Writers Am., The Internat. PEN Club, Can. br. Czechoslovak Nat. Assn. Can. (mem. Presidium), Coun. Free Czechoslovakia (mem. Presidium), Order of Can. Progressive Conservative. Roman Catholic. Avocation: swing music. Home: 487 Sackville St, Toronto, ON Canada M4X 1T6

SKWAR, DONALD R., newspaper editor. Exec. sports editor Boston Globe. Office: Boston Globe 135 Morrissey Blvd Boston MA 02107*

SKWIERSKY, PAUL, accountant; b. N.Y.C., Aug. 14, 1925; s. Abraham and Dora (Rainer) S.; m. Gloria Evelyn Lederman, Dec. 27, 1947; children: Janet S., Denise C. Skwiersky Cohen. BS, NYU, 1948. CPA, N.Y., N.J. Mng. ptnr. Benjamin Nadel & Co., N.Y.C., 1942-87, Skwiersky, Alpert & Bressler, N.Y.C., 1987—; bd. dirs. Philip & Janice Levin Found., North Plainfield, N.J., Darcy Found., Inc., N.Y.C., 1980-87, Levin Mgmt. Corp., North Plainfield, Allstate Constrn. Corp., North Plainfield; panelist, arbitrator Am. Arbitration Assn., N.Y.C. Dir. Birchwood Park Civic Assn., Syosset, N.Y., 1962. Sgt. U.S. Army, 1943-46. Mem. Fiber Producers Credit Assn., Textile Distbrs. Assn., Inc., N.Y. Credit & Fin. Mgmt. Assn., N.Y. State Soc. CPAs, Masons (master 1977-79), Fountains of Palm Beach Country Club. Avocations: reading, travel, golf. Office: Skwiersky Alpert Bressler 462 7th Ave New York NY 10018

SKY, ALISON, artist, designer; b. N.Y.C.. BFA, Adelphi U., 1967; student, Art Students League, 1967-69, Columbia U. Co-founder, v.p. Sculpture in the Environ./SITE, 1969-91; co-founder, prin. SITE Projects, N.Y.C., 1970-91; adj. faculty mem. Parsons Sch. Design, N.Y.C., 1994, Cooper Union, N.Y.C., 1995; vis. artist Purchase Coll., SUNY, 1994-95; artist in residence Urban Glass, 1994-95; lectr. in field. Exhbns. include The Venice Biennale, 1975, The Pompidou Ctr. and Louvre, Paris, 1975, The Mus. Modern Art, N.Y.C., 1979, 84, Ronald Feldman Fine Arts, N.Y.C., 1980, 83, The Wadsworth Atheneum, Hartford, Conn., 1980, The Va. Mus. Fine Arts, Richmond, Va., 1980, Neuer Berliner Kunstverein, 1982, Castello Sforzesco, Sala Viscontea, 1983, Victoria and Albert Mus., London, 1984, Nat. Mus. Modern Art, Tokyo, 1985-86, The Triennale di Milano, Tialy, 1985, Whitney Mus. Am. Art, N.Y.C., 1985-86, Grey Art Gallery, N.Y.C., 1987-88, Documenta 8, Kassel, Germany, 1987; permanent collections include, Smithsonian Instns., Washington, Mus. Modern Art, N.Y.C., Avery Libr., Columbia U., N.Y.C., Formica Corp., N.J.; projects include Williwear Ltd., N.Y.C. and London, 1982-89, The Mus. Borough of Bklyn., N.Y.C., 1985, Laurie Mallet House Memories, N.Y.C., 1986, Hwy 86, Vancouver, Can., 1986, Pershing Sq., L.A., 1986, MTV Sets, N.Y.C., 1988, SWATCH, N.Y.C. and Zurich, Switzerland, 1990, Rockplex, Music Complex, Universal City, Calif., 1989, Peace Garden, Washington, 1989, NASA Exhibit, Sevilla, Spain, 1990, N.Y.C. Pub. Libr., 1990, Franz Mayer, Munich, 1991, BEST Products, 1979-84, SITE Studio, 1984; author: (series of books) Onsite, 1971-76, Unbuilt America, 1976; pub. numerous books on art, 1971-76. Artery Arts finalist, Boston, 1994-95, RTA Arts-in-Transit finalist, Cleve., 1994, Pub. Art Commn. finalist, Cleve., 1994; Design fellow NEA, 1984, 90, Pollock-Krasner Found. fellow, 1991, Fulbright Indo-Am. fellow, 1992. Fellow Am. Acad. Rome. Studio: 60 Greene St New York NY 10012-4301

SKYLSTAD, WILLIAM S., bishop; b. Omak, Wash., Mar. 2, 1934; s. Stephen Martin and Reneldes Elizzbeth (Danzl) S. Student, Pontifical Coll. Josephinum, Worthington, Ohio; M.Ed., Gonzaga U. Ordained priest Roman Catholic Ch., 1960; asst. pastor Pullman, Wash., 1960-62; tchr. Mater Cleri Sem., 1961-68, rector, 1968-74; pastor Assumption Parish, Spokane, 1974-76; chancellor Diocese of Spokane, 1976-77; ordained bishop, 1977; bishop of Yakima, Wash., 1977-90, Spokane, Wash., 1990—. Office: Diocese of Spokane PO Box 1453 1023 W Riverside Ave Spokane WA 99201-1103 Home: 1025 W Cleveland Ave Spokane WA 99205-3320*

SKYLV, GRETHE KROGH, rheumatologist, anthropologist; b. Copenhagen, Denmark, May 31, 1938; d. Aage Krogh and Herdis Fischer (Lindeskov) Christoffersen; m. Axel Skylv, Jan. 12, 1962 (div. Feb. 1994); children: Lise, Kirsten, Mikael; m. Klaus Bruhn Jensen, Oct. 15, 1994. MD, U. Copenhagen, 1967, MA in Anthropology, 1990. Resident various hosps., Copenhagen, 1967-79; pvt. practice Hillerod, Denmark, 1979-84; dept. head Rehab. Ctr. for Torture Victims, Copenhagen, 1985-92; cons. Danish Red Cross, 1993—; rsch. scholar on cross-cultural interpersonal comm. Faculty of Humanities, U. Copenhagen, 1994—; cons. Orgn. for Manual Therapy, Denmark, 1985—, Internat. Rehab. Medicine Assn., 1991—; bd. dirs. Network for Interdisciplinary Qualitative Rsch., Denmark, 1989—. Guest editor: Danish Soc. for Anthropology Soc. Jour., 1988-89; contbr. articles to profl. jours. Recipient Honorary award Cranio-Facial Pain Ctr. 1990. Fellow European Assn. Social Anthropologists, Danish Med. Assn., Danish Assn. for Manual Medicine, Danish Manual Therapy Orgn., Danish Assn. for Rheumatology, Danish Assn. Internat Medicine, Danish Soc. for Social Anthropology. Avocation: black belt in jujitsu. Home: Mosesvinget 54, DK-2400 Copenhagen Denmark

SLAATTE, HOWARD ALEXANDER, minister, philosophy educator; b. Evanston, Ill., Oct. 18, 1919; s. Iver T. and Esther (Larsen) S.; m. Mildred Gegenheimer, June 20, 1951; children: Elaine Slaatte Tran, Mark, Paul. A.A., Kendall Coll., 1940; B.A. cum laude, U. N.D. 1942; B.D. cum laude, Drew U., 1945, Ph.D., 1956; Drew fellow, Mansfield Coll., Oxford (Eng.) U., 1949-50. Ordained to ministry Meth. Ch. as elder, 1943. Pastor Detroit Conf. United Meth. Ch., 1950-65; assoc. prof. systematic theology Temple U., 1956-60; vis. prof.; prof. philosophy and religion McMurry Coll., 1960-65; prof. dept. philosophy Marshall U., Huntington, W.Va., 1965-89, prof. emeritus, 1989—; chmn. dept., 1966-81, mem. grad. council, 1970-73, mem. research bd., 1974-76 mem. acad. standards and policy com., 1975-77; research grantee, 1976, 77; mem. bd. Campus Christian Center, 1973-75; prof. ethics St. Leo (Fla.) Coll., 1993; lectr. Traverse City (Mich.) State Hosp., 1966-71, Am. Ontoanalytical Assn. internat. conf., Acapulco, Mex., 1970, World Congress Logotherapy, San Diego, 1980, other orgns.; mem. W.Va. Conf., United Meth. Ch., 1965-85. Baritone soloist. Author: Time

and Its End, 1962, Fire in the Brand, 1963, The Pertinence of the Paradox, 1968, The Paradox of Existentialist Theology, 1971, Modern Science and The Human Condition, 1974, The Arminian Arm of Theology, 1977, The Dogma of Immaculate Perception, 1979, Discovering Your Real Self, 1980, The Seven Ecumenical Councils, 1980, The Creativity of Consciousness, 1983, Contemporary Philosophies of Religion, 1986, Time, Existence and Destiny, 1988, Critical Survey of Ethics, 1988; co-author: The Philosophy of Martin Heidegger, 1983, Religious Issues in Contemporary Philosophy, 1988; contbr.: Analecta Frankliana, 1981; gen. editor: (series) Contemporary Existentialism; contbr. to theol. and philos. jours. Mem. W.Va. Conf. United Meth. Ch., 1966—; bd. dirs. Inst. for Advanced Philos. Research, 1979-90; chmn. bd. dirs. Salvation Army of Huntington, W. Va. Recipient Outstanding Educators of Am. award, 1975, Profl. Excellence award Faculty Merit Fedn., State of W.Va., 1986; named to Honorable Order of Ky. Colonels, W.Va. Ambassador of Good Will; named Internat. Man of Yr., 1993; NSF fellow, 1965, Benedum Found. rsch. grantee, 1970, NSF rsch.-grantee, 1965, 71. Mem. W.Va. Philos. Assn. (pres., 1966-67, 83-84), Am. Philos. Assn., AAUP, Am. Acad. Religion. Home: 14123 Oak Knoll St Brooksville FL 34609-3157 *Most knowledge is relative, a balanced existential position with empirical implications, except for the divine Absolute encountered by faith in existence. The revealed principles opened up thereby, especially the ultimacy of sacrifical love (Agape) give basis and motivation for vital morality and a healthy culture. True freedom springs from commitment to these principles.*

SLABON, ROLAND MICHAEL, writer; b. Breslau, Germany, Oct. 31, 1941; came to U.S., 1950, naturalized, 1964; s. Hans Josef and Else Adelheid (Stadtlander) S.; m. Susan Mary Boudo, Dec. 24, 1978; children: Stephanie Helene, Alena Michelle, Michael Patrick. BA, Cornell U., 1964; law student, Boston Coll., 1964-65. Editor, pub. Vintage BMW Bull., Exeter, N.H., 1973—; treas. Vintage BMW Motorcycle Owners, Ltd., Exeter 1985—, pres., 1986—; contbg. editor On the Level, BMW Riders Assn. Melbourne Beach, Fla., 1984—; author Classic Motorbooks, Osceola, Wis. 1990—. Author: Illustrated BMW Buyers Guide, 1990, BMW Motorräder, 1992, BMW Restoration Guide, 1990; contbr. articles to mags. Lt. USN, 1966-69. Mem. Owl's Head (Maine) Mus. of Transp. (life), Vintage Sports Car Club Am., Antique Motorcycle Club Am., BMW Veteranen Club Deutschland, Tau Kappa Epsilon. Republican. Congregationalist. Avocations: history, restoration of vintage autos and motorcycles, journalism. Office: Vintage BMW Motorcycle Owners Ltd PO Box 67 Exeter NH 03833-0067

SLACK, EDWARD DORSEY, III, financial systems professional, consultant; b. Fairmont, W.Va., June 2, 1942; s. Edward Dorsey Jr. and Margaret Elaine (Higgs) S.; m. Donna Jean Carter, Oct. 19, 1944; children: Ted, Robyn. BS in Indsl. Engring., W.Va. U., 1965, postgrad., 1965-66. Registered profl. engr., W.Va. Assoc. systems and procedures analyst Westinghouse Atomic Power divs., Pitts., 1966-69; systems and procedures analyst Westinghouse Nuclear Energy Systems, Pitts., 1969-72, sr. systems analyst, 1972-75, mgr. payroll and fin. systems, 1975-77; mgr. standard ledger conversion Westinghouse Energy Systems, Pitts., 1977, mgr. fin. systems and control, 1978-90, mgr. fin. systems and standard ledger, 1990-91, mgr. payroll, cost and fin. systems control, 1991-94; data processing analyst Braddock (Pa.) Med. Ctr., 1995—; developer computer programs; designer fin. systems computer modules. Developer computer programs; designer computer modules. Mem. NSPE, W.Va. Soc. Profl. Engrs. Avocations: walking, jogging, basketball, spectator sports, sports cards. Home: 179 Autumn Dr Trafford PA 15085-1448 Office: Braddock Med Ctr 400 Holand Ave Braddock PA 15064

SLACK, JERALD DAVID, adjutant general of Wisconsin, civil engineer; b. Peoria, Ill., Feb. 14, 1936; s. Clarence E. and Lois M. (Pearson) S.; m. Sherill Ann Cordts, Mar. 26, 1959; children: Ann, Sara Slack Lenz, John Cordts. BS in Civil Engring., Bradley U., 1959. Profl. engr., Wis. Commd. 2d lt. USAF, 1961, advanced through grades to maj. gen., 1990, vice wing comdr. 128th Tactical Fighter Wing, 1983-85, dir. ops. Wis. Air Nat. Guard, 1985-87, chief of staff Wis. Air Nat. Guard, 1987-89; adj. gen. Wis. Dept. Mil. Affairs, Madison, 1989—; chief engr. Wis. Dept. Natural Resources, Madison, 1973-86; adminstr. Div. Facilities Mgmt., Madison, 1986-89. Decorated Legion of Merit, Meritorious Svc. medal. Mem. Nat. Guard Assn. U.S. Adj. Gen. Assn., Wis. Nat. Guard Assn. Unitarian. Avocation: flying jet fighters. Office: Mil Affairs Dept PO Box 8111 3020 Wright St Madison WI 53708-8111

SLACK, JOHN MARK, III, lawyer; b. Charleston, W.Va., Sept. 15, 1942; s. John Mark and Frances (Reid) S.; m. Barbara Henderson, Sept. 21, 1963; children—John Mark IV, Jeanne Reid. B.A., U. N.C.-Chapel Hill, 1965; J.D., U. Tenn.-Knoxville, 1969. Bar: W.Va. 1969, U.S. Dist. Ct. (so. and no. dists.) W.Va. 1970, U.S. Ct. Appeals (4th cir.) 1970, U.S Supreme Ct. 1974. Assoc., Jackson Kelly Holt & O'Farrell, Charleston, 1969-76, ptnr., 1976—. Democrat. Lodges: Masons, Shriners, Jesters. Office: Jackson & Kelly 1600 Laidley Twr PO Box 553 Charleston WV 25322

SLACK, LEWIS, organization administrator; b. Phila., Apr. 15, 1924; s. Lewis and Martha (Fitzgerald) S.; m. Sarah Hunt Wyman, Dec. 29, 1948; children—Elizabeth Wyman, Susan Towne, Christopher Morgan. S.B. Harvard U., 1944; Ph.D., Washington U., St. Louis, 1950. Physicist U.S Naval Research Lab., 1950-54; assoc. prof. physics George Washington U., Washington, 1954-57; prof. physics George Washington U., 1957-62, acting head physics dept., 1957-60; asst. exec. sec. div. phys. scis. Nat. Acad. Scis.-NRC, Washington, 1962-67; sec. com. nuclear sci. NRC, 1962-67, mem. commn. human resources, 1974-78; dir. ednl. programs Am. Inst. Physics, N.Y.C., 1967-87; cons. Gen. Atomics div. Gen. Dynamics Corp., La Jolla, Calif., summers, 1959, 60; chmn. phys. scis. Am. exhibit Internat. Conf. Peaceful Uses Atomic Energy, Geneva, Switzerland, 1958; mem. Sci. Manpower Commn., 1968-87, pres., 1974-75, treas., 1976; mem. U.S nat. com. Internat. Union for Pure and Applied Physics, 1972-78, sec., 1974-78; Mem. adv. com. Physics Today, 1963-67, chmn., 1967. Mem. Bruce Mus., Greenwich, Conn. (collections com., adn. com., exhbns. com., 1983-90). With USNR, 1943-46. Fellow Washington Acad. Scis., AAAS (mem. council 1971-72, 76-78); mem. Am. Phys. Soc., Am. Assn. Physics Tchrs. Episcopalian. Research beta ray and gamma ray spectroscopy. Home: 2104 Tadley Dr Chapel Hill NC 27514

SLADE, BERNARD, playwright; b. St. Catharines, Ont., Can., May 2, 1930; s. Frederick and Bessie (Walbourne) Newbound; m. Jill Florence Hancock, July 25, 1953; children: Laurel, Christopher. Ed., Carnarvon Grammar Sch. Eng. Actor: Garden Center Theatre, Vineland, Ont., Crest Theatre, Toronto, Ont., CBC-TV, Citadel Theatre, Edmonton, Alta., screenwriter for Can. Broadcasting Corp., CBS, ABC, NBC, 1957—; writer/creator (TV series) Love on a Rooftop, The Partridge Family, The Flying Nun; (plays) A Very Close Family, 1962, Same Time Next Year (drama Desk award 1975, Tony award nomination, 1975), Tribute, 1978, Romantic Comedy, 1979, Special Occasions, 1981, Fatal Attraction, 1984, Return Engagements, 1986, Sweet William, 1987, An Act of the Imagination, 1987, I Remember You, 1991, You Say Tomatoes, 1993, Everytime I See You, 1994, Same Time, Another Year, 1994; (screenplays) Same Time Next Year, 1977, Tribute, 1978, Romantic Comedy, 1979. Recipient Acad. award nomination Motion Picture Arts and Scis., 1978. Mem. Dramatists Guild Am., Writers Guild Am., Acad. Motion Picture Arts and Scis., (Acad. award nomination, 1978), Soc. Authors and Artists (France). Avocation: tennis. Office: care Jack Hutto Agy 405 W 23rd St New York NY 10011 *I am a prisoner of a childhood dream: to write for the theatre. The fulfillment of that dream has lived up to all my expectations. I believe the theatre should be a celebration of the human condition and that the artist's job is to remind us of all that is good about ourselves. I feel privileged to be given a platform for my particular vision of life, and, whether my plays succeed or fail, I am always grateful for the use of the hall.*

SLADE, BERNARD NEWTON, electronics company executive; b. Sioux City, Iowa, Dec. 21, 1923; s. William Charles and Katherine Gertrude Slotsky; m. Margot Friedlein, Aug. 18, 1946; children: Steven P., Eric J. BSEE, U. Wis., 1948; MS, Stevens Inst. Tech., 1954. Devel. engr. tube div. RCA, Harrison, N.J., 1948-55; devel. engr. RCA Labs., Princeton, N.J., 1955-56; mgr. tech. program IBM, Poughkeepsie, N.Y., 1956-60; mgr. product dev. IBM, Hopewell Junction, N.Y., 1960-64; mgr. mfg. tech. IBM World Trade Corp., Armonk, N.Y., 1964-65; corp. dir. of mfg. tech. IBM Corp., Armonk,

1965-84; sr. cons. Arthur D. Little, Inc., Cambridge, Mass., 1984-86, Gemini Cons., Morristown, N.J., 1986-93; sr. v.p., pres. ea. and European ops. Yieldup Internat. Corp., 1993—. Co-author: Winning the Productivity Race, 1985; author: Compressing the Product Development Cycle, 1992; contbr. numerous articles to tech. jours.; patentee in field. 2d lt. AUS, 1943-46. Mem. IEEE (sr.), Sigma Xi. Home: 12 Merry Hill Rd Poughkeepsie NY 12603-3214 Office: Yieldup Internat Corp 2672 Bayshore Pky Mountain View CA 94043

SLADE, GERALD JACK, publishing company executive; b. Utica, N.Y., May 24, 1919; s. John H. and Sada (Jacobson) S.; m. Dorothy Casler, Oct. 24, 1942; children—John, Carolyn, David. B.A. summa cum laude, Colgate U., 1941; M.B.A., Harvard, 1943. Chmn. bd., pres., chief exec. officer Western Pub. Co., Racine, Wis.; dir. Mattel, Inc., Wells-Gardner Electronics Corp., 1st Nat. Bank of Racine, Joseph Schlitz Brewing Co.; Past pres. Nat. Assn. Electronic Organ Mfrs. Mem. Phi Beta Kappa, Kappa Delta Rho. Home: 3352 SE Fairway W Stuart FL 34997-6030

SLADE, JOHN DANTON, lobbyist, radio talk show host; b. Balt., Apr. 5, 1939; s. Eldon and Marie (Smith) S.; m. Dale Iris Walden, Mar. 14, 1964 (dec. Dec. 1965); 1 child, Kenyatta Conrad; m. Deborah Faye Douglas, Dec. 11, 1987. BA in Sociology, Morgan State U., 1964; MA in Sociology, CUNY, 1966. Mgmt. trainee IBM, N.Y.C., 1966-69; producer, dir. WBAL-TV, Balt., 1969-71, WGBH-TV, Boston, 1971-73, KPIX-TV, San Francisco, 1973-75; announcer KEST Radio, San Francisco, 1975-76; gen. mgr. Channel 8 Access TV, San Francisco, 1975-79; owner Swansbriar Plantation, Cumberland, Va., 1979-85; asst. prof. military sci., dept. chmn. Howard U., Bowie State U., Georgetown U., Washington, 1985-88; acting chief Nat. Guard Bur., Washington, 1988-92; exec. dir. Assn. Reserve Minority Svc. Members, Inc., Washington, 1992—; talk show host WOL Radio, Washington; bd. dirs. Meridian Distributors, St. Thomas, V.I.; guest lectr. Stanford (Calif.) U., Northeastern U., Boston, Morgan State Coll., Balt., Merritt Coll., Oakland, Calif., U. Mass., Amherst; mem. spl. com. San Francisco Chronicle; mem. Balt. Community Rels. Commn.; mem. N.G. Drug Reduction Bd., 1990-91. Author: Last Testament of an American, 1993, Flight of an Angel, 1993, The Founding and Ascendancy of Iota Phi Theta, 1994; Man-Made (Guide to Single Mothers Raising Black Boys Alone), 1994; film producer Breaking the Chains of Bondage, 1972. Lt. col. U.S. Army, 1985-92. Recipient Roy Wilkens Renown Svc. award, 1991, Award of Honor, NAACP, Balt., Community Svc. award Les Hommes Civic and Social Club, Hampton, Va., 1991. Mem. Iota Phi Theta (founding mem., bus. mgr. 1963-64). Republican. Office: ARMS 1401 Madison St NW Washington DC 20011-6805

SLADE, LLEWELLYN EUGENE, lawyer, engineer; b. Carroll, Iowa, May 1, 1911; s. Llewellyn and Mary (Veach) S.; m. Jane England Dickinson, June 8, 1945 (dec. Dec. 1992); 1 child, Yvonne Slade Tidd. BS in Elec. Engring., Iowa State U., 1938, M.S., 1942; J.D., Drake U., 1951. Registered profl. engr., Iowa. With Iowa Power & Light Co., Des Moines, 1940-68; exec. v.p. ops., dir. Iowa Power & Light Co., 1964-68; cons. Nebr. Public Power Dist. nuclear project; pvt. practice as exec. counsellor, atty., profl. engr., 1968—; fed. ct. bankruptcy trustee, Solid Waste Com. City of Des Moines; past mgmt. adv. and dir. Wright Tree Service Cos.; mem. panel arbitrators U.S. Fed. Mediation and Conciliation Service, Iowa Pub. Employees Relations Bd. Former chmn., trustee Des Moines Metro Transit Authority. Mem. Fed. Am., Iowa, Polk County bar assns., Iowa Engring. Soc. (Anson Marston award for outstanding svc. 1957, Outstanding Svc. award 1987), Nat. Soc. Profl. Engrs., Engrs. Club Des Moines, Atomic Indsl. Forum, Greater Des Moines C. of C., Iowa Arboretum (bd. dirs.), Des Moines Club, Men's Garden Club of Am., Masons (32 deg.), Shriners, Rotary. Lutheran. Home: 5833 Pleasant Dr Des Moines IA 50312-1211

SLADE, LYNN H., lawyer; b. Santa Fe, N.Mex., Jan. 29, 1948; m. Deborah Slade (div.); 1 child, Jessica; m. Susan Zimmerman; 1 child, Benjamin. BA in Econs., U. N.Mex., 1973, JD, 1976. Bar: N.Mex. 1976, U.S. Dist. Ct. N.Mex. 1976, U.S. Ct. Appeals (10th cir.) 1978, U.S. Ct. Appeals (D.C. cir.) 1984, U.S. Supreme Ct. 1984. Dir. Modrall, Sperling, Roehl, Harris & Sisk, PA, Albuquerque, 1976—; adj. prof. U. N.Mex. Sch. Law, Albuquerque, 1990. Author: Coal Surface Mining on Indian Lands, 1989, Structuring and Financing Natural Resource and Energy Development on Indian Lands, 1993; co-author: Accomodating Historic and Cultural Resources and Indian Religious Freedom on Federal Public Lands, A Practical Primer, 1992; editor New Mexico Law Rev., 1975-76. Fellow N.Mex. Bar Found.; mem. ABA (chair com. on Native Am. natural resources 1991—), N.Mex. State Bar (bd. dirs. sect. of natural resources 1983-87, bd. dirs. Indian law sect. 1987-90). Office: Modrall Sperling Roehl Harris & Sisk PA 500 4th St NW Ste 1000 Albuquerque NM 87102

SLADE, REJANE DE OLIVEIRA, Portuguese language educator; b. Santo Antônio do Monte, Minas Gerais, Brazil, Sept. 2, 1938; came to U.S., 1985; d. Alvaro and Erundina Batista (Castro) De Oliveira; m. John Anderson Slade, Jan. 22, 1988. Cert. in elem. edn., Our Lady of Oliveira Coll., Minas Gerais, 1957; degree in sch. adminstrn., Inst. Edn., Belo Horizonte, Minas Gerais, 1967; B in Edn., Philosophy U. Belo Horizonte, 1972; studies in art and art history, Fed. U., Belo Horizonte, 1974, 82-84. Cert. tchr., sch. supr., sch. dir., sch. insp. Tchr. history and Portuguese Our Lady of Fatima Sch., Santo Antônio do Monte, 1960-65; elem. sch. tchr. Minas Gerais State Govt., Santo Antônio do Monte, 1959-61, sch. dir., 1961-65; program supr. Minas Gerais State Govt., Belo Horizonte, 1968-70, tchr. adminstrn. and psychology, 1972-73; insp. schs., 1970-84; instr. Portuguese SUNY/Med. Sch. Columbia U., N.Y.C., 1989-91, NYU, 1992—, New Sch. for Social Rsch., N.Y.C., 1993—; gen. pmr. Braminas, Bklyn., 1989—. Author: Português Básico Para Estrangeiros, 1993; one woman art exhbns. include Varig Airlines, N.Y.C., 1990, Ministry of Comm., Brasilia, Brazil, 1981; group shows in Brazil, U.S., France, Israel. Mem. Am. Assn. Tchrs. Spanish and Portuguese, Nat. Assn. Women Artists, Art Students League, Brazilian-Am. C. of C. Roman Catholic. Avocations: gardening, travel, crafts. Office: Braminas 175 Luquer St Brooklyn NY 11231

SLADE, ROY, artist, college president, museum director; b. Cardiff, U.K., July 14, 1933; came to U.S., 1967, naturalized, 1975; s. David Trevor and Millicent (Stone) S. N.D.D., Cardiff Coll. Art, 1954; A.T.D., U. Wales, 1954; D of Arts, Art Inst. So. Calif., 1994. Tchr. art and crafts Heolgam High Sch., Wales, 1956-60; lectr. art Clarendon Coll., Nottingham, Eng., 1960-64; sr. lectr. fine art Leeds Coll. Art, Eng., 1964-67; prof. painting Corcoran Sch. Art, Washington, 1967-68, assoc. dean, 1969-70, dean, 1970-77; dir. Corcoran Gallery of Art, Washington, 1972-77; pres., dir. Cranbrook Acad. Art, Bloomfield Hills, Mich., 1977-94; sr. lectr. Leeds Coll. Art, Eng. 1968-69; vis. Boston Mus. Fine Arts, 1970. Exhibited one-man shows Howard Roberts Gallery, Cardiff, Wales, 1958, New Art Ctr., London, 1960, U. Birmingham, 1964, 69, Herbert Art Gallery and Mus., Coventry, 1964, Va. State Art League, 1967, Mus. of Arts and Crafts, Columbus, Ga., 1968, Jefferson Place Gallery, Washington, 1968, 70, 72, 73, Park Sq. Gallery, Leeds, 1969, St. Mary's Coll., Md., 1971, Guelph U., Ont., Can., 1971, Hood Coll., 1974, Pyramid Gallery, Washington, 1976, Robert Kidd Gallery, 1981, 92, Herman Miller, Inc., Mich., 1985; group shows in U.K., Washington, Can.; represented in permanent collections Arts Council Gt. Brit., Contemporary Art Soc., Nuffield Found., Ministry of Works, Eng. Brit. Embassy, Washington, Brit. Overseas Airways Corp., U. Birmingham, Wakefield City Art Gallery, Clarendon Coll., Cadbury Bros., Ltd., Eng., Lord Ogmore, Local Edn. Authorities. Mem. D.C. Commn. on Arts.; bd. dirs. Artists for Environment Found., Nat. Assn. Schs. Art; chmn. Nat. Council Art Adminstrs., 1981. Served with Brit. Army, 1954-56. Decorated knight 1st class Order of White Rose (Finland), Royal Order of Polar Star (Sweden); recipient award Welsh Soc., Phila., 1974, Gov.'s Arts Orgn. award, 1988; Fulbright scholar, 1967-68. Mem. Nat. Soc. Lit. and Arts, Detroit chpt. AIA (hon.). Home: Box 48 Harsens Island MI 48028

SLADE, THOMAS BOG, III, lawyer, investment banker; b. Balt., June 22, 1931; s. Thomas Bog Jr. and Blanche Evangeline (Hall) S.; m. Sanya Johanna Bowen, July 25, 1959 (div. 1976); children: Sunya Kirsten, DeWitt Bowen, Vivian Watson; m. Mary Stewart Bolton, Apr. 3, 1976. BA, U. Va., 1953, LLB, 1954. Bar: Fla. 1956, U.S. Supreme Ct. 1966. Assoc. Patterson, Freeman, Richardson & Watson, Jacksonville, Fla., 1956-61; ptnr. Freeman, Richardson, Watson, Slade, McCarthy & Kelly, Jacksonville, 1961-80; pvt. practice Jacksonville, 1980-81; ptnr. Foley & Lardner, Jacksonville, 1981-92;

sr. v.p. Gardnyr Michael Capital, Inc., Jacksonville, 1992—. Served to 1st lt., U.S. Army, 1954-56. Mem. Fla. Bar (bd. govs. 1966-69, pres. young lawyers sect. 1967-68), Nat. Assn. Bond Lawyers, Jacksonville Bar Assn. Club at World Trade Ctr. (N.Y.C.), Fla Yacht Club, Univ. Club of Jacksonville. Office: Gardnyr Michael Capital Inc 5568 La Moya Ave Ste 14 Jacksonville FL 32210-5784

SLADEK, CELIA DAVIS, neuroscientist, educator; b. Denver, Mar. 25, 1944; d. Charles Willard Davis and Mildred (Bozarth) Davis TeSelle; m. John R. Sladek, May 23, 1970; children: Jonathan A., Stefan Z., Jessica A. BA, Hastings Coll., 1966; MS, Northwestern U., 1969, PhD, 1971. Asst. prof. physiology U. Ill. Sch. Medicine, Chgo., 1970-73; asst. prof. biology SUNY, Brockport, 1973-74; research assoc. in neurology U. Rochester (N.Y.) Sch. Medicine, 1974-76, asst. prof. neurology, 1976-80, assoc. prof. neurology and neurobiology, 1980-88, prof. neurology and neurobiology, 1988-91; prof. physiology Chgo. Med. Sch., North Chicago, Ill., 1991—; cons. Am. Heart Assn., Dallas, 1986-89; dir. interdepartmental neurosci. grad. program U. Rochester, 1989-91. Grantee NINDS, 1977-82, 91—, NIDKD, 1977-91, NIHLBI, 1982-88, Nat. Inst. Aging, 1978-81, 90-91, 94—. Mem. Soc. for Neurosci., Endocrine Soc., N.Y. Acad. Sci. Am. Physiol. Soc. Office: Chgo Med Sch Dept Physiology North Chicago IL 60064

SLADEK, LYLE VIRGIL, mathematician, educator; b. Pukwana, S.D., Oct. 13, 1923; s. Charles Frank and Emma Margaret (Swanson) S.; m. Patricia Knotts, Sept. 12, 1948; children: Susan, Ann, Laura, Karen. B.S., S.D. State U., 1948; M.A., U. S.D., 1949, Stanford U., 1963; Ph.D., UCLA, 1970. Tchr. high sch. Mitchell, S.D., 1950-56; asst. prof. math. Black Hills State Coll., S.D., 1957-62; prof. math. Calif. Luth. Univ., Thousand Oaks, 1963-94, prof. emeritus, 1994—; lectr. in field. Contbr. short stories, poems to mags. and newspapers. Pres. congregation Our Savior's Lutheran Ch., Spearfish, S.D., 1961. Served as officer U.S. Army, 1943-46, PTO, ETO. Shell Merit fellow, 1956; NSF fellow, 1956-57, 62-63; recipient Meritorious Achievement award edn. S.D. Mines and Tech., 1957; Fulbright-Hays lectr. Bahamas, 1980-81. Mem. Math. Assn. Am., Blue Key, Pi Kappa Delta, Phi Delta Kappa. Home: 3243 Pioneer St Thousand Oaks CA 91360-2730 *I learned from my parents during the dust bowl years that adversity often can be overcome through patience and determination, and that problems provide challenges that add spice to life. I have sought to return full measure to society for all the opportunities and joys of life that have come my way.*

SLADEK, RONALD JOHN, physics educator; b. Chgo., Sept. 19, 1926; s. James Joseph and Rose (Vachulka) S.; m. Jeanne T. McFadden, Sept. 19, 1953; children—Linda, James, Frances, Stephen, Rosemarie, Edward. Ph.B., U. Chgo., 1947, S.B., 1949, S.M., 1950, Ph.D. (AEC fellow), 1954. Research physicist Westinghouse Research Labs., Pitts., 1953-60, fellow scientist, 1960-61; assoc. prof. physics Purdue U., West Lafayette, Ind., 1961-66, prof., 1966-91, acting head dept. physics, 1969-71, assoc. dean sci., 1974-87; vis. scientist Sci. Center, N.Am. Rockwell Corp., Thousand Oaks, Calif., summer 1967; sabbatical scientist Xerox Research Center, Palo Alto, Calif., 1976-77. Contbr. articles to profl. jours. With USNR, 1945-46. Fellow Am. Phys. Soc. Home: 963 Ridgeview Dr Reno NV 89511-8506

SLAGLE, JACOB WINEBRENNER, JR., food products executive; b. Balt., Jan. 18, 1945; s. Jacob Winebrenner and Anna Dorothea (Vernon-Williams) S.; m. Sharon Carol Muth, Nov. 18, 1973 (div. 1982); children: Alexander, Dylan; m. Nina Kathleen Tou, May 20, 1994. Student, U. Ariz., 1963-65; BA in Sociology, U. Md., 1969; diploma, Broadcasting Inst. Md., balt., 1975. Claims adjuster Govt. Employees Ins. Co., Towson, Md., 1969-71; exec. Slagle & Slagle, Inc., Balt., 1971-81, pres., 1981-92; bd. dirs. H.S.A., Inc., Marietta, Ga., 1992, 93; freelance writer for various nespapers and mags.; monthly columnist Jake About Town, Balt. Chronicle, 1989-93; mem. bd. advisors Broadcasting Inst. Md., 1990-93. Contbg. author: Baltimore: A Living Renaissance, 1981. Bd. dirs. Hist. Balt. Soc., 1979—, v.p., 1989—; bd. dirs. Intervention with Pact, Balt., 1982-89; pres. Hanover House Condominium Assn., Balt., 1983—; arbitrator BBB Greater Md., Balt., 1983-91. Mem. Homebuilders Assn. Md. (bd. dirs. remodelers coun. 1989-93, Remodeling Assn. of Yr. award 1992), Md. Splty. Foods Assn. (bd. dirs. 1994—), Balt. Blues Soc. (bd. dirs. 1992—, sec. 1995—), Rotary (bd. dirs. Balt. 1992-94).

SLAGLE, JAMES ROBERT, computer science educator; b. Bklyn., 1934; married; 5 children. BS summa cum laude, St. John's U., 1955; MS in Math., MIT, 1957, PhD in Math., 1961. Staff mathematician Lincoln Lab. MIT, 1955-63; group leader Lawrence Livermore Radiation Lab. U. Calif., Livermore, 1963-67; chief heuristics lab. divsn. computer rsch. and tech. NIH, Bethesda, Md., 1967-74; chief computer sci. lab. comm. scis. divsn. Naval Rsch. Lab., Washington, 1974-81, spl. asst., 1981-84; Disting. prof. computer sci. U. Minn., Mpls., 1984—; mem. faculty dept. elec. engring. MIT, 1962-63; mem. faculty dept. computer sci. and elec. engring. U. Calif., Berkeley, 1964-67; mem. faculty dept. computer sci. Johns Hopkins U., 1967-74; cons. in field. Author: Artificial Intelligence: The Heuristic Programming Approach, 1971. Contbr. articles to profl. jours. Named one of Ten Outstanding Young Men of Am., U.S. Jaycees, 1969; recipient Outstanding Handicapped Fed. Employee of Yr. award, 1979; Mary P. Oenslager Career Achievement award, Recording for the Blind, 1982. Fellow AAAS, IEEE, Am. Assn. Artificial Intelligence; mem. Computer Soc. of IEEE. Office: U Minn Computer Sci Dept 4-192 EE/Csi Bldg 200 Union St SE Minneapolis MN 55455-0154

SLAGLE, LARRY B., human resources specialist; b. Templeton, Pa., Dec. 17, 1934; s. William Harry and Luella (Armstrong) S. AB, Wabash Coll., 1956; postgrad., Am. U., 1967-71. Dep. admistr. for mgmt. and budget USDA Animal & Plant Health Inspection Svc., Washington, 1978-88, assoc. adminstr., 1988-90; dir. pers. USDA, Washington, 1990-94; pvt. practice human resources and orgnl. cons., 1994—; bd. dirs. Fgn. Aid Through Edn. With U.S. Army, 1957-59, Korea. Named Meritorious Exec. President Reagan, 1985, President Bush, 1991. Avocation: cycling. Home and Office: 208 6th Ave SE Washington DC 20003

SLAIBY, THEODORE GEORGE, aeronautical engineer, consultant; b. Washington, Conn., Apr. 12, 1929; s. George and Afifi (Buzaid) S.; m. Margaret Sullivan, June 29, 1957; children: Peter E., Jeffrey M., Barbara E. BS in Aero. Engring., Rensselaer Poly. Inst., 1950. Engr. tech. and rsch. group Pratt & Whitney Aircraft Engines, East Hartford, Conn., 1950-56, asst. project engr., tech. and rsch. group, 1956-60, devel. engr., advanced engines, 1960-67, mgr. new project devel. programs, 1967-76, dir. design & analytical engring., 1976-81, v.p product integrity, 1981-83, v.p engring., 1983-87, ret., 1987; engring. cons. United Techs. Corp., Hartford, Conn., 1987—; cons. to various engring. cos. Author or co-author numerous tech. papers, 1958-70; patentee in field. Avocations: farming, hunting, fishing, history, language study. Home: 251 Spring St Manchester CT 06040-6640

SLAIN, GEORGE CEDRIC, finance executive; b. Chgo., Oct. 3, 1950; s. Cedric Cletis and Violet (decker) S.; m Susan Diane Childers, Sept. 25, 1976 (div. Dec. 1987). BA in Fin., MBA in Fin., Ind. U., 1973. Asst. v.p. Security Pacific Nat. Bank., Los Angeles, 1973-78; v.p., mng. dir. Security Pacific SW, Inc., Houston, 1978-81; v.p., treas. Pacific Resources, Inc., Honolulu, 1981—. Mem. Fin. Execs. Inst., Nat. Assn. Corp. Treas.'s, Beta Gamma Sigma. Office: Pacific Resources Inc 733 Bishop St Honolulu HI 96813-4020

SLAIN, JOHN JOSEPH, legal educator; b. Jan. 21, 1927. A.B. Providence Coll., 1952; LL.B., NYU, 1955. Bar: N.Y. 1956. Assoc Cravath, Swaine & Moore, 1955-60; v.p., gen. counsel AIM Cos., Inc., 1961-66, dir., 1964-71; assoc. prof. law Ind. U.-Indpls., 1965-70; prof. law Ohio State U., Columbus, 1970-77, NYU, N.Y.C., 1977—. Dir., treas. Indpls. Legal Services Orgn., 1966-71; dir. Ohio Catholic Charities, 1975-77. Republican. Episcopalian. Office: NYU Law Sch 40 Washington Sq S New York NY 10012-1099

SLAKEY, LINDA LOUISE, biochemistry educator; b. Oakland, Calif., Jan. 2, 1939; d. William Henry and Georgia Evelyn (Finnerty) S. BS, Siena Heights Coll., 1962; PhD, U. Mich., 1967; postgrad., U. Wis., 1970-73. Elem. sch. tchr. Saint Edmund's Sch., Oak Park, Ill., 1958-61; tchr. Resur-

rection High Sch., Lansing, Mich., 1962-63; instr. in chemistry St. Dominic's Coll., St. Charles, Ill., 1967-69; rsch. assoc. Argonne (Ill.) Nat. Labr., 1969-70; project assoc. dept. physiol. chemistry U. Wis., Madison, 1970-73; asst. prof. dept. biochemistry U. Mass., Amherst, 1973-79, assoc. prof. dept. biochemistry, 1979-87, prof. biochemistry, 1987—, head dept. biochemistry and molecular biology, 1986-91, dean Coll. Natural Scis. and Math., 1993—; adv. com. arteriosclerosis and hypertension Nat. Heart & Lung and Blood Inst., Washington, 1978-81, mem. rev. com. B, 1981-87; vis. scientist Clin. Rsch. Ctr, Harrow, Eng., 1984-85. Contbr. articles to profl. jours. NSF predoctoral fellow U. Mich., 1963-67, NIH spl. fellow, 1970-73. Fellow Am. Heart Assn. (established investigator 1977-82), Arteriosclerosis Soc. of Am. Heart Assn.; mem. Am. Soc. Cell Biology, Am. Soc. for Biochemistry and Molecular Biology, Sigma Xi, Sigma Delta Epsilon. Office: U Mass Coll Natural Sci & Math 722 Lederle Tower B Amherst MA 01003

SLANE, CHARLES JOSEPH, chain drug store executive; b. Yonkers, N.Y., June 10, 1947; s. Donald Joseph and Helen (Stella) S.; m. Carolyn Croxton, June 5, 1971; children: Carrie Joyce, Charles Jr., Katie Joyce. BA, Rutgers U., 1969; JD, Columbia U., 1972. Bar: N.J. 1972, Pa. 1978. Assoc. counsel Sills, Beck Law Firm, Hackensack, N.J., 1972-74; gen. counsel Prel Corp., Paramus, N.J., 1974-75, Landcom Devel. Inc., Elmont, N.Y., 1975-77; v.p., asst. gen. counsel Rite Aid Corp., Harrisburg, Pa., 1977—. Mem. Am. Bar Assn. Republican. Roman Catholic. Avocations: golf, tennis, basketball. Home: 6135 Westover Dr Mechanicsburg PA 17055-2373 Office: Rite Aid Corp 30 Hunter Ln Camp Hill PA 17011-2404

SLANE, HENRY PINDELL, broadcasting executive; b. Peoria, Ill., Dec. 29, 1920; s. Carl P. and Frances (Pindell) S.; children by previous marriage: John, Elizabeth Jean, Henry Pindell, Barbara. A.B., Yale U., 1943. Became pub. Peoria Newspapers, Inc., Peoria Broadcasting Co.; now pres. Peoria Jour. Star, Inc.; pres. PJS Publs., Inc. (Sew News, Shooting Times and Rotor & Wing, Profitable Crafts Merchandising and Crafts mags.). Served with USNR, 1943-46. Mem. Am. Soc. Newspaper Editors, Chi Psi, Sigma Delta Chi. Clubs: Peoria Country, Creve Coeur (Ill.) Country, Sturgeon Bay (Wis.). Home: 5188 N Prospect Rd Peoria IL 61614-5354 Office: Peoria Jour Star Inc 1 News Plz Peoria IL 61643-0001

SLANSKY, JERRY WILLIAM, investment company executive; b. Chgo., Mar. 8, 1947; s. Elmer Edward and Florence Anna (Kosobud) S.; m. Marlene Jean Cannella, Jan. 29, 1950; children: Brett Matthew, Blake Adam. BA, Elmhurst Coll., 1969; MA, No. Ill. U., 1971. Mktg. rep. Bantam Book Co., Chgo., 1972-73, Charles Levy Circulating Co., Chgo., 1973-76; account exec. Merrill Lynch, Chgo., 1976-77; account exec. Oppenheimer & Co., Inc., Chgo., 1977—, asst. v.p., 1978, v.p., 1979, sr. v.p., 1981, mng. dir., 1986, ptnr., 1986—. Bd. dirs. Lake Geneva (Wis.) Beach Assn., 1987—, Glen Ellyn Youth Ctr., Glenbard West H.S. Mem. Nat. Assn. Securities Dealers (arbitrator 1988—), N.Y. Stock Exch., Chgo. Bd. Options, Am. Arbitration Assn, Omaha C. of C. Presbyterian. Avocations: swimming, water skiing, golf. Office: Oppenheimer & Co Inc 311 S Wacker Dr Chicago IL 60606-4614

SLAPPEY, STERLING GREENE, writer, journalist, researcher; b. Ft. Valley, Ga., June 18, 1917; s. Jenkins Sterling and Elma Louise (Greene) S.; m. Margaret Byne Sellers, Jan. 13, 1945; children—Margaret, Charles. Student, Ala. Poly. Inst. (now Auburn U.), 1937, 38, U. Ga., Atlanta, 1938-39. Reporter Atlanta Georgian & Sunday Am., 1938-39, Atlanta Constn., 1940, 41, 45, 46, AP, Atlanta, London, Moscow, 1947-59; specialist in racial affairs U.S. News & World Report, 1960-62; Central European bur. chief Los Angeles Times, based in Bonn, West Germany, 1963-66; sr. editor Nation's Bus., Washington, 1966-78; dir. Future of Bus. Program; dir. public affairs Georgetown U. Center for Strategic and Internat. Studies, Washington, 1978-84, supr. spl. events, 1984-88; columnist Washingtonian Mag., 1971-74; free-lance writer various publs.; sec. Iberian Imports Inc., Alexandria, 1969-78; pres. Alexandria Bath and Linen Co., 1978-84. Author: novel Exodus of the Damned, 1968, Pioneers of American Business, 1973, Future of Business, 1980. Served with AUS, 1941-45. Mem. Overseas Writers, Landmarks Soc., White House Corrs. Assn., State Dept. Corrs. Assn., Friends Kennedy Center, Assn. for Preservation Va. Antiquities, Smithsonian Assos., Alexandria Assembly, Nat. Trust Historic Preservation, Am. Acad. Polit. Sci., Acad. Social and Polit. Sci., Phi Delta Theta, Internat. Club (Washington). Home: 2525 Peachtree Rd Apt 4 Atlanta GA 30305

SLASH (SAUL HUDSON), guitarist; b. Stoke-on-Trent, Eng., July 23, 1965; s. Anthony and Ola Hudson; m. Renée Suran, Oct. 10, 1992. Guitarist Guns n' Roses, 1985—. Albums: (with Guns N' Roses) Live Like a Suicide, 1986, Appetite for Destruction, 1987, GN'R Lies, 1988, Use Your Illusion I, 1991, Use Your Illusion II, 1991, The Spaghetti Incident?, 1993, (with Slash's Snakepit) It's Five O'Clock Somewhere, 1995; worked as guitarist with Iggy Pop, Bob Dylan, Michael Jackson, Lenny Kravitz. Office: care Geffen Records 9130 W Sunset Blvd West Hollywood CA 90069-3110*

SLATE, FLOYD OWEN, chemist, materials scientist, civil engineer, educator, researcher; b. Carroll County, Ind., July 26, 1920; s. Ora George and Gladys Marie (Miller) S.; m. Margaret Mary Magley, Oct. 14, 1939; children: Sally Lee Slate McEnteer, Sandra Kay Slate Miller, Rex Owen. B.S., Purdue U., 1941, M.S., 1942, Ph.D., 1944. Chemist Manhattan Project, N.Y.C., Oak Ridge and Decatur, Ill., 1944-46; asst. prof. civil engring. Purdue U., Lafayette, Ind., 1946-49; v.p., dir. Geotechnics & Resources Inc., White Plains, N.Y., 1959-63; prof. engring. materials Cornell U., Ithaca, N.Y., 1949-87; prof. emeritus, 1987; internat. lectr.; cons. concrete, low-cost housing. Author books, research papers on concrete, low-cost housing, soil stabilization, 1944—. Recipient Excellence in Teaching award Cornell U., 1976, sr. fellow East-West Center, 1976, NSF research grantee, 1960-86. Fellow Am. Concrete Inst. (hon., Wason Research medal 1957, 65, 74, 86, Anderson award 1983), Am. Inst. Chemists; mem. ASCE, ASTM, Am. Chem. Soc. Research on internal structure of concrete vs. properties, chemistry applied to engring. problems, and low-cost housing for developing countries. Home: 255 The Esplanade N Apt 306 Venice FL 34285-1518 Office: Hollister Hall Cornell U Ithaca NY 14853 *Think positively and be optimistic. Be considerate of others, try to help others, and enjoy life.*

SLATE, JOE HUTSON, psychologist, educator; b. Hartselle, Ala., Sept. 21, 1930; s. Murphy Edmund and Marie (Hutson) S.; m. Rachel Holladay, July 1, 1950; children: Marc Allan, John David, James Daryl. B.S., Athens Coll., 1960; M.A., U. Ala., 1965, Ph.D., 1970. Mem. faculty Athens (Ala.) State Coll., 1965-92, prof. psychology, 1974-92, chmn. behavioral scis., 1974-92; pvt. practice psychology Athens, 1970-92, Hartselle, 1992—; v.p. Slate Security Systems, Hartselle, Ala., 1984—. Author: Psychic Phenomena, 1988, Self-Empowerment, 1991, Psychic Empowerment, 1995. Named hon. prof. Montevallo U., 1973, prof. emeritus Athens State, Coll., 1992. Mem. APA, Am. Soc. Clin. Hypnosis, Inst. Parapsychol. Rsch. (founder), Coun. for Nat. Register Health Svc. Providers in Psychology, NEA, Ala. Edn. Assn., Delta Tau Delta, Phi Delta Kappa, Kappa Delta Pi. Home and Office: 1807 Hwy 31 NW Hartselle AL 35640

SLATE, JOHN BUTLER, biomedical engineer; b. Schenectady, N.Y., Sept. 27, 1953; s. Herbert Butler and Violet (Perugi) S. BSEE, U. Wis., 1975, MEE, 1977, PhDEE, 1980. Spl. fellow of cardiovascular surgery U. Ala., Birmingham, 1980-81, dept. biomed. research engr., 1981-82; microbiology fellow, 1981-82; sr. research engr. IMED Corp., San Diego, 1982-83, sr. research scientist, 1983-86; sci. dir. Pacesetter Infusion Ltd. (dba MiniMed Technologies), Sylmar, Calif., 1986-87; v.p. tech. MiniMed Technologies, Sylmar, Calif., 1987-91; v.p. R & D Siemens Infusion Systems, Sylmar, Calif., 1991-93; v.p. tech. devel. Via Med., San Diego, 1993-94; pres. Slate Engring., San Diego, 1994—. Mem. IEEE (IEE Ayrton award), Biomed. Engring. Soc., Sigma Xi. Office: Slate Engring 3914 Kendall St San Diego CA 92109

SLATE, MARTIN IRA, pension benefit executive. Grad. Harvard U., 1967; JD, Yale U., 1970; LLM in Taxation, Georgetown U., 1988. Dir. field svcs. EEOC, 1980-81; dir. ERISA program IRS, 1986-92; exec. dir. Pension Benefit Guaranty Corp., 1993—; adj. prof. in taxation Georgetown Law Ctr., 1988-92. Contbr. articles to profl. publs. Mem. Phi Beta Kappa. Office: Pension Benefit Guar Corp 1200 K St NW Washington DC 20005

SLATE, WILLIAM KENNETH, II, international dispute resolution association executive; b. Winston-Salem, N.C., Jan. 17, 1943; s. William Kenneth Slate and Elsie (Corrine) Runge; m. Sheryl Ruth Barker, Nov. 25, 1979; 1 child, Eliza Hayes. BA, Wake Forest U., 1965; JD, U. Richmond, 1968; postgrad., Oxford U., 1974, Harvard U., 1984; MBA, U. Pa., 1990. Bar: Va. 1968, U.S. Ct. Appeals (4th cir.) 1972, U.S. Ct. Appeals (3d cir.) 1984, U.S. Supreme Ct. 1975. Atty. FBI, U.S. Justice Dept., Washington, 1968-70; adminstr. The Hustings Ct., Richmond, 1972-; U.S. Ct. Appeals (4th cir.), Richmond, 1972-84; cir. exec. 3d Jud. Cir. U.S., Phila., 1984-87; CEO Va. State Bar, 1987-88; dir. Congressionally Chartered Fed. Cts. Study Com., 1988-90; cons. Supreme Ct. of U.S., 1991-92; founder, pres. Justice Rsch. Inst., Phila. and Washington, 1993-94; pres. Am. Arbitration Assn., 1994—; founder Nat. Conf. Appellate Ct. Adminstrs., Washington, 1973; founder, bd. dirs. Council for Ct. Excellence, Washington, 1982-87; mem. Chief Justice Task Force on Fed. Rule Making, Washington, 1979; mem. governing bd. Va. State Bar, 1980-84. Contbr. articles and book revs. to profl. jours. Founder Richmond, Va. Audubon Soc., 1972; pres. Region XII Episcopal Diocese of Va., Richmond, 1975-78; mem. adv. bd. Wake Forest U., Winston-Salem, Chowan Coll., Murfreesboro, N.C., Inst. for Ct. Mgmt. Mem. ABA, Richmond Bar Assn. (mem. exec. com. 1992-94), Am. Judicature Soc. (exec. com. 1984-87, treas. 1986-87, v.p. 1988-90), Va. State Bar for Young Lawyers (pres. 1975-76). Avocations: birding, opera music, reading. Home: 750 S 2nd St Philadelphia PA 19147-3427 Office: Am Arbitration Assn 140 W 51st St New York NY 10020-1203

SLATER, CHRISTIAN, actor; b. N.Y.C., Aug. 18, 1969; s. Michael Hawkins and Mary Jo Slater. Appearances include (theatre) The Music Man, 1980, Between Daylight and Boonville, 1980, Copperfield, 1981, Macbeth, 1982, Merlin, 1983, Landscape of the Body, 1984, Dry Land, 1986, (TV movies) Living Proof: The Hank Williams Jr. Story, 1983, Desperate for Love, 1989, (films) The Legend of Billy Jean, 1985, The Name of the Rose, 1986, Tucker: The Man and His Dream, 1988, Gleaming the Cube, 1989, Heathers, 1989, Beyond the Stars, 1989, The Wizard, 1989, Tales from the Darkside: The Movie, 1989, Young Guns II, 1990, Pump Up the Volume, 1990, Robin Hood: Prince of Thieves, 1991, Mobsters, 1991, Star Trek VI: The Undiscovered Country, 1991, Kuffs, 1992, Ferngully...The Last Rainforest (voice), 1992, Where the Day Takes You, 1992, Untamed Heart, 1993, True Romance, 1993, Jimmy Hollywood, 1994, Interview with the Vampire, 1994, Murder in the First, 1995. Office: Creative Artists Agy care Rich Kurtzman 9830 Wilshire Blvd Beverly Hills CA 90212*

SLATER, DONALD J., restaurant executive; b. 1948. BS in Hotel and Restaurant Mgmt., Fla. State U., 1975. With Steak & Ale Restaurant Corp., Dallas, 1976—, regional mgr. S.W. region, 1983-84, v.p., gen. mgr. divsn. Bennigan's, 1984-85, sr. v.p., gen. mgr. divsn. Bennigan's, 1985-87, pres. 1987-89, pres., CEO, 1989—. Office: Steak & Ale Restaurant Corp 12404 Park Central Dr Dallas TX 75251

SLATER, DORIS ERNESTINE WILKE, business executive; b. Oakes, N.D.; d. Arthur Waldemar and Anna Mary (Dill) Wilke; m. Lawrence Bert Slater, June 4, 1930 (dec. 1960). Grad. high sch. Sec. to circulation mgr. Mpls. Daily Star, 1928-30; promotion activities Lions Internat. in U.S., Can., Cuba, 1930-48; exec. sec. parade and spl. events com. Inaugural Com., 1948-49; exec. sec. Nat. Capital Sesquicentennial Commn., 1949-50, Capitol Hill Assos., Inc., 1951, Pres.'s Cup Regatta, 1951; adminstrv. asst. Nat. Assn. Food Chains, 1951-60; v.p., sec.-treas. John A. Logan Assos., Inc., Washington, 1960—; v.p., sec.-treas. Logan, Seaman, Slater, Inc., 1962—; mng. dir. Western Hemisphere, Internat. Assn. Chain Stores, 1964—. With pub. relations div. Boston Met. chpt. ARC, 1941-42; mem. Nat. Cherry Blossom Festival Com., 1949—; mem. Inaugural Ball Com., 1953, 57, 65. Methodist. Lion. Home and Office: 2500 Wisconsin Ave NW Washington DC 20007-4505

SLATER, GEORGE RICHARD, retired banker; b. Indpls., Feb. 13, 1924; s. George Greenleaf and Chloe (Shoemaker) S.; m. Mary Catherine Brown; children: George Greenleaf, Kathleen Slater Hamar, John Goodwill, Frederick Richard. BS, Purdue U., 1946, MS, 1957, PhD, 1963. Chief economist Allis-Chalmers Mfg. Co., Milw., 1957-60; v.p. Citizens Nat. Bank of Decatur (Ill.), 1960-64; sr. v.p., group exec. Met. Group, Harris Trust & Savs. Bank, Chgo., 1964-76; pres., chief exec. officer Marine Bank, N.A., Milw., 1976-83; chmn., chief exec. officer Marine Corp. (now Banc One Wis. Corp.), Milw., 1978-89; chmn. Banc One Corp., Columbus, Ohio, 1988-89, ret., 1989; adv. coun. J.L. Kellogg Grad. Sch. Mgmt. Northwestern U.; bd. dirs. Bank One Wis. Corp., Marcus Corp., John's Island Club. 1st lt. F.A. U.S. Army, 1943-46. Episcopalian. Home: John's Island 275 Cocunut Palm Rd Vero Beach FL 32963 *Man has the obligation to his fellow man to strive for productivity, excellence and harmony.*

SLATER, HELEN RACHEL, actress; b. N.Y.C., Dec. 15, 1963; d. Gerald and Alice Joan (Chrin) S. Stage appearances include Responsible Parties, 1985, Almost Romance, 1987; films: Supergirl, 1984, The Legend of Billie Jean, 1985, Ruthless People, 1986, The Secret of My Success, 1987, Sticky Fingers, 1988, Happy Together, 1989, City Slickers, 1991, Lassie, 1994; TV appearances include (series) Capital News, 1990, (movies) Chantilly Lace, 1993, 12:01, 1993. Office: Innovative Artists 1999 Ave of Stars/Ste 2850 Los Angeles CA 90211*

SLATER, JAMES MUNRO, radiation oncologist; b. Salt Lake City, Jan. 7, 1929; s. Donald Munro and Leone Forestine (Fehr) S.; m. JoAnn Strout, Dec. 28, 1948; children: James, Julie, Jan, Jerry, Jon. B.S. in Physics, U. Utah, Utah State U., 1954; M.D., Loma Linda U., 1963. Diplomate: Am. Bd. Radiology. Intern Later Day Saints Hosp., Salt Lake City, 1963-64; resident in radiology Latter Day Saints Hosp., 1964-65; resident in radiotherapy Loma Linda U. Med. Ctr., White Meml. Med. Center, Los Angeles; fellow in radiotherapy Loma Linda U. Med. Ctr., White Meml. Med. Center, 1967-68, U. Tex.-M.D. Anderson Hosp. and Tumor Inst., Houston, 1968-69; mem. faculty Loma Linda (Calif.) U., 1975—, prof. radiology, 1979—, chmn. radiation scis. dept., 1979-89, dir. nuclear medicine, 1970—, dir. radiation oncology, 1975-79, chmn. dept. radiation oncology, 1990—, dir. Cancer Inst., 1993—, exec. v.p. Med. Ctr., 1994—; treas. med. ctr., 1995—; co-dir. cmty. radiology oncology program L.A. County-U. So. Calif. Comprehensive Cancer Ctr., 1978-83; mem. cancer adv. coun. State of Calif., 1980-85; clin. prof. U. So. Calif., 1982—; founding mem. Proton Therapy Coop. Group, 1985—, chmn., 1987-91; cons. charged particle therapy program Lawrence Berkeley Lab., 1986—; cons. R&D monoclonal antobodies Hybrotech Inc., 1985-94; bd. dirs., 1985-94; mem. panel cons. Internat. Atomic Energy Agy. UN, 1994—; cons. Sci. Applications Internat. Corp., 1979—. Bd. dirs. Am. Cancer Soc., San Bernardino/Riverside, 1976—, exec. com., 1976—; pres. Inland Empire chpt., 1981-83. NIH fellow, 1968-69; recipient exhbn. awards European Assn. Radiology, 1975, exhbn. awards Am. Soc. Therapeutic Radiologists, 1978, Pres.'s Com Loma Linda U. Alumnus of Yr. award, 1993, 94. Fellow Am. Coll. Radiology; mem. AMA, ACS (liaison mem. to commn. on cancer 1976-84), Am. Radium Soc., Am. Soc. Clin. Oncology, Am. Soc. Therapeutic Radiologists, Assn. Univ. Radiologists, Calif. Med. Assn., Calif. Radiol. Soc., Gilbert H. Fletcher Soc. (pres. 1981-82), Loma Linda U. Med. Sch. Alumni Assn. Radiol. Soc. N.Am., San Bernardino County Med. Soc., Soc. Chairmen Acad. Radiation Oncology Programs, So. Calif. Radiation Therapy Soc., Alpha Omega Alpha. Home: 1210 W Highland Ave Redlands CA 92373-6659 Office: Loma Linda U Radiation Medicine Loma Linda CA 92350

SLATER, JILL SHERRY, lawyer; b. N.Y.C., Apr. 8, 1943. BA with distinction and honors, Cornell U., 1964; JD cum laude, Harvard U., 1968. Bar: Mass. 1968, Calif. 1971, U.S. Dist. Ct. (cen. dist.) Calif. 1971, U.S. Ct. Appeals (9th cir.) 1974, U.S. Dist. Ct. (so. dist.) Calif. 1977, U.S. Dist. Ct. (ea. dist.) Calif. 1984, U.S. Dist. Ct. (no. dist) Calif. 1985, U.S. Ct. Appeals (Fed. cir.) 1982, U.S. Supreme Ct. 1986. N.Y. 1988. Atty. Boston Redevel. Authority, 1968-70; from assoc. to ptnr. Latham & Watkins, L.A., 1970—; Woodrow Wilson fellow, 1964. Mem. ABA, L.A. County Bar Assn. (exec. litigation sect., fed. cts. com.), A.m. Intellectual Property Law Assn., Assn. Bus. Trial Lawyers, Phi Beta Kappa. Office: Latham & Watkins Ste 1000 885 Third Ave New York NY 10022-4802

SLATER, JOHN BLACKWELL, landscape architect; b. Kansas City, Mo., Mar. 20, 1943; s. Marcus Bedford and Helen (Butler) S.; m. Sue Stallings, June 22, 1968; 1 child, Alice Butler. B in Landscape Architecture, Syracuse

U., 1965; student, SUNY, Syracuse U. Registered landscape architect, Md., N.Y., Va. Landscape architect A.E. Bye Assocs., Cos Cob, Conn., 1969-71, The Rouse Co., Columbia, Md., 1971-74, Slater Assocs., Columbia, 1974—; mem. bd. examiners of landscape architects State of Md., 1991—. Prin. works include design Sully Plantation Hist. Park, Oakland Mills Courtyard, Benjamin Banneker Hist. Park, Port Deposit Hist. Restoration of Streetscape, Columbia Town Ctr. Park, S.I. Mall Expansion. Lt. USN, 1966-69. Fellow Am. Soc. Landscape Architects (trustee 1981-87, v.p. 1987-88, awards md. chpt. 1979, 89, 90), Howard County Assn. Landscape Architects (pres. 1991), Rotary. Avocations: sailing, gardening, photography. Home: 4993 Dalton Dr Columbia MD 21045-1805 Office: Slater Assocs Inc 5560 Sterrett Pl Ste 302 Columbia MD 21044-2616

SLATER, JOHN GREENLEAF, manufacturing company executive; b. Milw., Mar. 25, 1935; s. Thomas McIndoe and Margaret Mary (McAnarney) S.; m. Colleen Mary Conway, July 19, 1958; children: James C., John T., Ann E. BS in Econs, Marquette U., 1958, MA, 1960. With First Wis. Nat. Bank, Milw., 1960-69; with First Wis. Nat. Bank, Madison, 1969-79, exec. v.p., 1973-79; sr. v.p. Fifth Third Bank, Cin., 1979-82; pres., chief exec. officer Slater Carley Group, Inc., Cin., 1982-85; exec. v.p., bd. dirs. E. W. Buschman Co., Cin., 1985-94; pres., CEO Diamond Machine Co., Inc., Cin., 1994—; bd. dirs. Bhat Industries, CinTech Inc. Mem. Madison Adv. Com. Drug Abuse, 1970-71; mem. long-range planning com. Edgewood High Sch., Madison, 1972-75; mem. long-range planning task force OKI Regional Planning Commn., 1980-81; bd. dirs. First Offenders Sch., 1975-79. Mem. Wis. Bus. Economists Assn. (pres. 1973), Nat. Assn. Bus. Economists, Cin. Inst. for Small Enterprise, Fin. Execs. Inst., Nat. Venture Capital Assn., Conveyer Equipment Mfrs. Assn., Cin. New Bus. Devel. Council (chair 1989), Phi Gamma Mu. Roman Catholic. Home: 3748 Fallentree Ln Cincinnati OH 45236-1036 Office: Diamond Machine Co 4440 Carver Woods Dr Cincinnati OH 45242

SLATER, JONATHAN E., director. Dir. Shady Hill Sch., Cambridge, Mass. Office: Shady Hill Sch 178 Coolidge Hl Cambridge MA 02138-5598

SLATER, JOSEPH ELLIOTT, educational institute administrator; b. Salt Lake City, Aug. 17, 1922; m. Annelore Kremser, Dec. 20, 1947; children: Bonnie Karen Hurst, Sandra Marian Slater. BA with honors, U. Calif.-Berkeley, 1943, postgrad., 1943; LLB with honors, Colo. Coll.; PhD (hon.), U. Denver, U. N.H., Kung Hee, Korea. Teaching asst., reader U. Calif.-Berkeley, 1942-43; dep. U. sec. Allied Control Council, Berlin, Germany, 1945-48; UN planning staff Dept. State, Washington, 1949; sec.-gen. Allied High Commn. for Germany, Bonn, 1949-52; exec. sec., U.S. spl. rep. in Europe, U.S. sec. to U.S. del. to NATO and OEEC, Paris, France, 1952-53; chief economist Creole Petroleum Corp. (Standard Oil Co. N.J.), Caracas, Venezuela, 1954-57; mem. and dir. internat. affairs program Ford Found., 1957-68, study dir. spl. com. to establish policies and programs, 1961-62; asst. mng. dir. Devel. Loan Fund, Washington, 1960-61; dep. asst. sec. state for edn. and cultural affairs, 1961-62; pres. Salk Inst., LaJolla, Calif., 1967-72, hon. trustee, pres. emeritus; pres., CEO trustee Aspen Inst. for Humanistic Studies, 1969-86, pres. emeritus, trustee, sr. fellow, 1986—; chmn. John J. McCloy Internat. Ctr., 1986—; pres. Anderson Found., N.Y.C., 1969-72; adv. bd. Volvo Internat.; dir. Volvo N.Am. Sec. Pres.'s Com. on Fgn. Assistance (Draper Com.), 1959; del. Atlantic Conf., 1959; mem. devel. assistance panel Pres.'s Sci. Adv. Com., 1960-61; cons. Dept. State, 1961-68; founder, dir., bd. dirs. Creole Found., 1956-57; trustee Carnegie Hall Corp., 1960-86, Asia Soc., 1971-86, Am. Coun. on Germany, 1971-86; mem. vis.com., dept. philosophy MIT, 1981-83; trustee Acad. for Ednl. Devel., Internat. Council Ednl. Devel., John J. McCloy Fund; bd. dirs. Eisenhower Exchange Fellowships, Internat. Inst. Environ. Devel., Ctr. for Pub. Resources. Served to lt. USNR, 1943-46; mil. govt. planning officer London, Paris, Berlin; trustee Lovelace Med. Found., 1993—. Decorated Order of Merit Fed. Republic Germany). Mem. Inst. Strategic Studies (London), Council Fgn. Relations, Center for Inter-Am. Relations, Am. Acad. Arts & Scis., NAS (mem. pres.'s coll.), Am. Coun. for Jean Monnet Studies (dir.), N.Y. Acad. Scis., Phi Beta Kappa. Clubs: Century Assn. (N.Y.C.), Mid-Atlantic (N.Y.C.). Home: 870 Un Plz New York NY 10017

SLATER, MANNING, broadcasting consultant; b. Springfield, Mass., Aug. 29, 1917; s. Ely and Sarah Deenah (Hurwitz) Slotnick; m. Anita Norman, July 1, 1977; children—Gary Edward, Richard Stuart. B.A., Am. Internat. Coll., 1939. Pres. Community Markets, Springfield, Mass., 1939-46; v.p.; treas. Bridgeport Broadcasting Co., Conn., 1947-58; pres., chmn. bd. Hercules Broadcasting Co., Sacramento and Seattle, 1959—; also Slater Broadcasting Co.; pres. Slater Investment Co. Bd. govs. Mercy Hosp., Sacramento. Named Man of Yr. State of Israel Bonds, 1989. Mem. Nat. Assn. Broadcasters, Radio Advt. Bur., Sacramento C. of C., B'nai B'rith. Democrat. Jewish. Clubs: University, Comstock Club Sacramento. Home: 660 Lake Wilhaggin Dr Sacramento CA 95864-7227 also: 48 635 Sundrop Ct Palm Desert CA 92260 Office: 1337 Howe Ave Ste 110 Sacramento CA 95825-3361

SLATER, MARILEE HEBERT, theatre administrator, producer, director, consultant; b. Laredo, Tex., Feb. 25, 1949; d. Minos Joseph and Eulalie (Fisher) Hebert; m. Stewart E. Slater, Dec. 3, 1972 (div. July 1978). BA, Baylor U., 1970, MA, 1972. Cert. secondary sch. tchr., Tex. Actress, dir., assoc. producer Everyman Players, Ky. and La., 1972-80; community rels. dir. Actors Theatre of Louisville, 1973-74, dir. children's theatre, lunchtime & cabaret theatre, 1974-76, dir., apprentice intern program, 1974-77, new play festivals coord., 1979-81, mgr. internat. touring, 1980—, assoc. dir., 1981—; guest dir. Louisville Children's Theatre, 1978; grants panelist Ky. Arts Coun., La. Arts Coun.; conf. lectr. Ky. Arts Coun., Va. Arts Commn., Southeastern Theatre Conf., S.W. Theatre Conf., So. Arts Fedn. Author: (play) Hey Diddle Diddle!, 1976. Pres. Ky. Citizens for Arts, 1985-86, 90-92; co-chmn. subcom. on arts Edn. Workforce, 1990-93; mem. program com. Leadership Louisville, 1989-94, bd. dirs., 1992—; vice chmn. Focus Louisville, 1994—; vice chair Louisville Downtown Mgmt. Dist., 1995—; mem. Downtown Devel. Implementation Com., Louisville, 1991-93; Louisville Forum adv. coun., 1995—; pres. Park IV Condo Assn., 1989-91, sec. Main St. Assn., 1992—; staging dir., cons. Walnut St. Bapt. Ch., 1980—. Recipient Outstanding Alumna award Baylor U., Waco, Tex., 1986. Democrat. Baptist. Avocations: photography, travel, hiking, music. Office: Actors Theatre Louisville 316 W Main St Louisville KY 40202-4218

SLATER, OLIVER EUGENE, bishop; b. Sibley, La., Sept. 10, 1906; s. Oliver Thornwell and Mattie (Kennon) S.; m. Eva B Richardson, Nov. 25, 1931; children: Susan Slater Edenborough, Stewart Eugene. AB, So. Meth. U., 1930, BD, 1932, LLD (hon.), 1964; DD (hon.), Southwestern Coll., 1951; LHD, Southwestern Coll., Winfield, Kans., 1961; LLD, Baker U., 1962. Ordained to ministry Meth. Ch., 1932. Pastor Rochelle, Tex., 1932-33, Menard, Tex., 1933-36, Ozona, Tex., 1936-42, San Antonio, 1942-44, Houston, 1944-50; pastor Polk St. Ch., Amarillo, Tex., 1950-60; consecrated bishop, 1960; bishop Kans. area Meth. Ch., 1960-64, Kans. area Meth. Ch., San Antonio-N.W. Tex. area, 1964-68, San Antonio area United Meth. Ch., 1968-76; bishop-in-residence Perkins Sch. Theology, So. Meth. U., 1976-80, bishop in residence emeritus, 1980—; Mem. jurisdictional confs. Meth. Ch., 1948, 56, 60, gen. confs., 1956, 60, pres. gen. bd. edn. (now of United Meth. Ch.), 1964-72; mem. commn. on archives and history United Meth. Ch., 1968-76, mem. interboard com. on enlistment for ch. occupations, 1968-72; pres. designate Council Bishops, 1971-72, pres., 1972-73. Author: (autobiography) Oliver's Travels, One Bishop's Journey, 1988. Chmn. Commn. on Archives, 1972-76; Trustee So. Meth. U., 1960-76, vice chmn. trustees, 1973-76; trustee Southwestern U.; mem. Bd. Global Ministries, 1972-76. Recipient Disting. Alumnus award So. Meth. U., 1975. Home: 74249 W Northwest Hwy Dallas TX 75225

SLATER, RICHARD JAMES, engineering company executive; b. Taunton, Eng., May 14, 1946; came to U.S., 1980; s. James and Gladys (Wilford) S.; m. Marie-Christine, Sept. 15, 1948; children: Thomas James, Magali Jeanne. BSc with honors, Aston Coll., 1967. Sr. v.p. Jacobs Engring. Group Inc., Pasadena, Calif., 1980—. Home: 1235 Hillcrest Ave Pasadena CA 91106-4434 Office: Jacobs Engring Group Inc 251 S Lake Ave Pasadena CA 91101-3003

SLATER, RODNEY E., federal administrator; b. Tutwyler, Miss., Feb. 23, 1955; m. Cassandra Wilkins; 1 child. BS, Ea. Mich. U., 1977; JD, U. Ark.,

1980. Asst. atty. gen. State of Ark., 1980-82; spl. asst. for community and minority affairs Gov. of Ark., 1983-85, exec. asst. for econ. and community programs, 1985-87; dir. intergovernmental rels. Ark. State U., 1987-93; adminstr. fed. hwy. adminstrn. Dept. Transp., Washington, 1993—; mem. Ark. State Hwy. and Transp. Commn., 1987-93, chair, 1992-93; dep. campaign mgr., sr. traveling advisor Clinton for Pres. Campaign, 1992; dep. to chair Clinton/Gore Transition Team, 1992-93. Ark. liaison Martin Luther King, Jr. Fed. Holiday Commn., 1993-87; mem. Ark. Sesquicentennial Commn., 1986. Mem. Ark. Bar Assn. (sec.-treas. 1989-93), W. Harold Flowers Law Soc. (pres. 1985-92). Office: Fed Hwy Adminstrn 400 7th St SW Washington DC 20590-0001

SLATER, THOMAS GLASCOCK, JR., lawyer; b. Washington, Mar. 15, 1944; s. Thomas G. and Hylton R. S.; m. Kathryn Holden, June 18, 1966; children: Thomas Glascock, Tacie Holden, Andrew Fletcher. B.A., Va. Mil. Inst., 1966; LL.B., U. Va., 1969. Bar: Va. 1969, U.S. Dist. Ct. (ea. dist.) Va. 1970, U.S. Dist. Ct. (we. dist.) Va. 1979, U.S. Ct. Appeals (4th cir.) 1975, U.S. Ct. Appeals D.C. 1980, U.S. Supreme Ct. 1981. Assoc. Hunton & Williams, Richmond, Va., 1969-76, ptnr., 1976—; lectr. Trustee VMI Found. Fellow ABA, Va. Law Found.; mem. 4th Cir. Jud. Conf., Va. Bar Assn., Va. State Bar Coun., D.C. Bar Assn., Richmond Bar Assn. (pres. 1989-90), Va. Mil. Inst. Alumni Assn. (past pres.). Office: Hunton & Williams Riverfrnt Plaza East Tower 951 E Byrd St Richmond VA 23219-4040

SLATKIN, LEONARD EDWARD, conductor, music director, pianist; b. L.A., Sept. 1, 1944; s. Felix Slatkin and Eleanor Aller; m. Linda Hohenfeld, Mar. 29, 1986. Began violin study, 1947; piano study with, Victor Aller and Selma Cramer, 1955; composition study with, Castelnuovo-Tedesco, 1958; viola study with, Sol Schoenbach, 1959; conducting study with, Felix Slatkin, Amerigo Marino and Ingolf Dahl; student, Ind. U., 1962, L.A. City Coll., 1963, Juilliard Sch.; student (Irving Berlin fellow in musical direction), beginning 1964; student of, Jean Morel and Walter Susskind. founder, music dir. and condr. St. Louis Symphony Youth Orch., beginning 1969; musical adv., 1979-80; mus. dir., condr. St. Louis Symphony Orch., 1979-95; mus. dir. Nat. Symphony Orch., Washington, 1995—; current mgmt. ICM Artist, Ltd., Harold Holt, Ltd., Konzertdirektion/Schmidt. Conducting debut as asst. condr., Youth Symphony of N.Y., Carnegie Hall, 1966; asst. condr., Juilliard Opera Theater and Dance Dept., 1967, St. Louis Symphony Orch., 1968-71, assoc. condr., 1971-74; guest conductor Concertgebouw, Royal Danish Orch., Tivoli, English Chamber Orch., BBC Manchester, London Philharmonic, London Synphony Orch., Philarmonia Orch., Nat. Orch. Paris, Stockholm, Oslo, Goetborg, Scottish Nat. Orch., NHK Tokyo, Israel, Berlin, Vienna State Opera, Lyric Opera Chgo., Stuttgart Opera and throughout the world; debut with Chgo. Symphony Orch., 1974, N.Y. Philharmonic, 1974, Phila. Orch., 1974, European debut with Royal Philharmonic Orch., 1974, debut with USSR orchs., 1976-77, Tokyo debut, 1986, Met. Opera debut, 1991; prin. guest condr. Minn. Orch., beginning 1974; summer artistic dir., 1979-89, music dir., New Orleans Philharmonic Symphony Orch., 1977-78, artistic dir. Great Woods, 1990; artistic adminstr. Blossom, 1991; composer: The Raven, Dialogue for Two Cellos and Orchestra, (string quartets) Extensions 1, 2, 3, 4; numerous recordings for RCA, Angel EMI, Vox. Telarc, Philips, Warner Bros. and others. Recipient 2 Grammy awards for Prokofiev Symphony No. 5 with St. Louis Symphony Orch. Nat. Acad. Rec. Arts and Scis., 1985, Declaration of Honor in Silver Austrian Govt., 1986, 5 Honorary Doctorates. Mem. Nat. Acad. Rec. Arts and Scis. (Chgo. chpt. bd. govs.). Office: St Louis Symphony Orch Powell Symphony Hall 718 N Grand Blvd Saint Louis MO 63103 also: National Symphony Orchestra John F Kennedy Ctr Washington DC 20566*

SLATKIN, MURRAY, paint sundry distribution executive; b. N.Y.C., June 6, 1905; s. Hyman Noah and Rose (Goldman) S.; m. Lillian Selsky, June 19, 1938; children—Joan, Robert. A.B., Johns Hopkins U., 1925; J.D., U. Md., 1929. Bar: Md. With Felmor Corp., Balt., 1925-38, pres., 1938-92; pres. Nat. Paint Distbrs., Des Plaines, Ill., 1966-68; Chmn. bd. dirs. Felmor Corp., Balt., 1992. Hon. v.p. Zionist Orgn. Am., 1980—. Recipient 1st Judge Sobeloff award, 1973. Mem. Screen Actors Guild, Am. Fedn., T.V. & Radio Artists. Democrat. Jewish. Lodge: B'nai B'rith (Man of Yr. award Menorah lodge 1969, hon. pres. 1982—). Office: Felmor Corp 2020 Hollins Ferry Rd Baltimore MD 21230-1694

SLATKIN, NORA, government official; b. Glen Cove, N.Y., May 5, 1955; d. Carl L. and Muriel (Breen) S.; m. Deral Willis, July 4, 1982 stepchildren: Nick, Lisa, Kelly. BA in Internat. Rels., Lehigh U., 1977; MS in Fgn. Svc., Georgetown U., 1979. Def. analyst Congl. Budget Office, Washington, 1977-84; mem. profl. staff House Armed Svcs. Com., Washington, 1984-93; asst. Sec. of Navy for rsch., devel., acquisition Washington, 1994—; spl. asst. to under sec. of def. for acquistion Office Sec. Def., Washington, 1993. Grad. fellow Nat. Security Coun. Dept. State CIA. Mem. Phi Beta Kappa. Avocation: boating. Home: 36 Chesapeake Landing Annapolis MD 21403 Office: Asst Sec Navy Rsch Devel Acquisition 1000 Navy Pentagon Washington DC 20350

SLATOPOLSKY, EDUARDO, nephrologist, educator; b. Buenos Aires, Argentina, Dec. 12, 1934; (parents Am. citizens); married, 1959; 3 children. BS, Nat. Coll. Nicolas Avellaneda, 1952; MD, U. Buenos Aires, 1959. Postdoctoral renal USPHS, renal divsn., Dept. Internal Medicine Washington U. Sch. Medicine, 1963-65, instr. med. nephrology, 1965-67, from asst. prof. to assoc. prof. medicine dept. nephrology, 1967-75; dir. Chromalloy Am. Kidney Ctr., Washington U. Sch. medicine, St. Louis, 1967—, co-dir. renal divsn., 1972—, prof. medicine, nephrology dept., 1975—, Joseph Friedman Prof. renal disease medicine, 1991—; adv. mem. regional med. program, renal program sch. medicine Washington U., 1970-75; chmn. transplantation com. Barne Hosp., 1975—; fellow com. Kidney Found. Ea. Mo. and Metro.-E., 1978; mem. adv. com. artificial kidney-chronic uremia program NIH, 1978-90, rep. Latin-Am. nephrology, 1983-88; mem. study sect. Gen. Med., NIH, 1984-88. Recipient Frederick C. Bartter award 1991. Mem. AAAS, Am. Fedn. Clin. Rsch., Internat. Soc. Nephrology, Am. Soc. Nephrology, Endocrine Soc., Sigma Xi. Achievements include pathogenesis and treatment of secondary hyparathyroidism and bone disease in renal failure; studies conducted at both levels: clinical, on patients maintained on chronic dialysis and on animals with experimentally induced renal feilure; detailed studies of the effects of calcitriol on PTH MRNA and the extra-renal production of calcitriol by macrophages; vitro studies in primary culture of bovine parathyroid cells used to understand the mechanisms that control the secretion of PTH. Office: Washington U Chromalloy Am Kidney Ctr PO Box 8129 Saint Louis MO 63156-8129

SLATTERY, CHARLES WILBUR, biochemistry educator; b. La Junta, Colo., Nov. 18, 1937; s. Robert Ernest Slattery and Virgie Belle (Chamberlain) Tobin; m. Arline Sylvia Reile, June 15, 1958; children: Scott Charles, Coleen Kay. BA, Union Coll., 1959; MS, U. Nebr., 1961, PhD, 1965. Instr. chemistry Union Coll., Lincoln, Nebr., 1961-63; asst. prof., assoc. prof. chemistry Atlantic Union Coll., South Lancaster, Mass., 1963-68; rsch. assoc. biophysics MIT, Cambridge, 1967-70; asst. prof., then prof. biochemistry Loma Linda U., Calif., 1970-80, prof. biochemistry-pediatrics, 1980—, chmn. dept., 1983—; vis. prof. U. So. Calif., L.A., 1978-79. Contbr. articles to profl. jours. NIH grantee, 1979-82, 86-89, Am. Heart Assn. (Calif.) 1981-83, 83-84. Mem. AAAS, Am. Chem. Soc. (biochemistry div.), Am. Dairy Sci. Assn., Am. Heart Assn. Thrombosis Coun., N.Y. Acad. Scis., The Protein Soc., Am. Soc. Biochemistry and Molecular Biology. Internat. Soc. for Rsch. on Human Milk and Lactation, Sigma Xi. Office: Loma Linda U Sch of Medicine Dept of Biochemistry Loma Linda CA 92350

SLATTERY, EDWARD J., bishop; b. Chgo., Aug. 11, 1940. Student, St. Mary of the Lake Sem., Mundelein, Ill., Loyola U. Chgo. Ordained priest Roman Cath. Ch., 1966. Ordained priest Chgo., 1966; v.p. Cath. Ch. Ext. Soc., 1971-76, pres., 1976-94; ordained bishop Diocese of Tulsa, 1994—. Office: Diocese of Tulsa Chancery Office PO Box 2009 Tulsa OK 74101*

SLATTERY, JAMES ARTHUR, electronics company executive; b. Utica, N.Y., Oct. 11, 1942; s. Arthur F. and Helen (Barry) S.; m. Alison Linder, Feb. 27, 1971; children: Stephen, Scott. BS, Syracuse U., 1965. Chem. engr. Sperry-Univac, Utica, 1967-76; chem. engr. Indium Corp. Utica, 1976-81, v.p. New Product Devel., 1981—. Author (patents) Semiconductor Lid, 1986, 87; co-author (patent) Purification of Indium 1989. Mem. Am. Chem.

Soc., IEEE, Am. Electroplater's Soc., Materials Rsch. Soc. Avocations: skiing, gardening, amateur radio. Office: Indium Corp Am 1676 Lincoln Ave Utica NY 13502-5398

SLATTERY, JAMES CHARLES, lawyer, real estate executive; b. Good Intent, Kans., Aug. 4, 1948; s. Charles and Rose S.; m. Linda Smith, May 18, 1974; children: Jason, Michael. BS in Polit. Sci., Washburn U., Topeka, 1970; JD, Washburn U., 1974; student, Netherlands Sch. Internat. Bus. and Econs., 1969-70. Mem. Kans. Ho. of Reps., Topeka, 1973-79, speaker pro tem, 1977-79; acting sec. of revenue State of Kans., Topeka, 1979; pres. Brosius, Slattery & Meyer, Inc., Topeka, 1979-83; mem. 98th-103d Congresses from 2d Dist. Kans., 1983-94; ptnr. Wiley, Rein & Fielding, Washington, 1995—. Former bd. regents Washburn U. 2d lt. U.S Army N.G., 1970-75. Democrat. Roman Catholic. Office: Wiley Rein & Fielding 1776 K St NW Washington DC 20006

SLATTERY, JAMES JOSEPH (JOE SLATTERY), actor; b. Memphis, Feb. 7, 1922; s. James Joseph and Katie May (Carlin) S.; m. Mary Margaret Costello, May 23, 1944 (dec. Aug. 1987); children: James Joseph, John P., Ann, Mary, Nancy; m. Marilyn Daus, Sept. 16, 1989. A.B., Hendrix Coll., Conway, Ark., 1947. pres. Am. Fedn. TV and Radio Artists, 1976-79; dir. Bank No. Ill., Glenview, Ill. Actor. Served with USAAF, 1942-46; to lt. col. USAF (ret.). Recipient Disting. Grad. award Hendrix Coll., 1986. Mem. Screen Actors Guild. Roman Catholic. Address: 5 Court Of Bayview Northbrook IL 60062

SLATTERY, JAMES LEE, lawyer; b. N.Y.C., Apr. 6, 1939; s. John Joseph and Grace (Lee) S.; m. Noel Kingsland Cockcroft, June 4, 1963; children: James Spencer, Jared T. BS, NYU, 1962; JD, Washington & Lee U., 1968. Bar: R.I. 1968, Pa. 1981. Assoc. Tillinghast, Collins & Graham, Providence, 1968-71; assoc. gen. counsel Itek Corp., Lexington, Mass., 1971-75; gen. counsel Lukens Steel Co., Coatsville, Pa., 1975-85; sr. v.p., gen. counsel Paradyne Corp., Largo, Fla., 1985—. Pres. Amherst (N.H.) Reps., 1974; bd. dirs. Chester County (Pa.) Airport Authority, West Chester, 1980-85. Served to lt. USNR, 1962-65. Mem. R.I. Bar Assn., Pa. Bar Assn. Episcopalian. Clubs: Dunedin (Fla.) Boat; Nantucket (Mass.) Yacht. Avocations: tennis, sailing. Office: Paradyne Corp 8550 Ulmerton Rd E Largo FL 34641-3842*

SLATTERY, PAUL FRANCIS, physicist, educator; b. Hartford, Conn., July 21, 1940; s. James Francis and Katherine (Ahearn) S.; m. Jean Frances Breitenbach, Aug. 29, 1964; 1 child, Ryan Lahey. BS in Physics magna cum laude, U. Notre Dame, 1962; MS in Physics, Yale U., 1963, PhD in Physics, 1967. Rsch. assoc., AEC postdoctoral fellow U. Rochester, N.Y., 1967-69, asst. prof., 1969-73, assoc. prof., 1973-78, prof., 1978—, chmn. dept. physics and astronomy, 1986—; vix. prof. Stanford Linear Accelerator Ctr., Stanford U., 1978; sci. spokesman Experiment 706 Fermi Nat. Accelerator Lab., Batavia, Ill., 1981—, guest scientist, 1992—; prin. investigator U.S. DOE, 1976—, spokesman for prin. investigators, 1980-87; regional rep. Fermi Nat. Accelerator Lab.; bd. overseers Univs. Rsch. Assn., Inc., Washington, 1989-95, chmn. phyics com., 1991-95. Contbr. numerous articles on high energy physics to profl. jours. Raycroft Walsh scholar United Aircraft Corp., 1958-62; NASA predoctoral grantee Yale U., 1963-66; Sterling fellow Yale U., 1966, Guggenheim Meml.Found. fellow, 1992-93. Fellow Am. Phys. Soc.; mem. Fermilab Users Orgn. (exec. com. 1976-77). Office: U Rochester Dept Physics & Astronomy Rochester NY 14627

SLAUGH, LYNN H., chemist. With Shell Devel. Co., Houston. Recipient Indsl. Chemistry award Am. Chem. Soc., 1995. Office: Shell Development Comp PO Box 2463 1 Shell Plz 900 Louisiana Houston TX 77252-2463*

SLAUGHTER, ALEXANDER HOKE, lawyer; b. Charlottesville, Va., Nov. 24, 1937; s. Edward Ratliff and Mary (Hoke) S.; m. Virginia Borah, July 18, 1964 (div.); 1 child, David A.; m. Mary Peeples, Mar. 1, 1971. BA, Yale U., 1960; LLB, U. Va., 1963. Democrat. Episcopalian. Home: 1410 Pump House Dr Richmond VA 23221-3915 Office: McGuire Woods Battle & Boothe 1 James Ctr 901 E Cary St Richmond VA 23219-4057

SLAUGHTER, EDWARD RATLIFF, JR., lawyer; b. Raleigh, N.C., Sept. 15, 1931; s. Edward Ratliff and Mary McBee (Hoke) S.; m. Anne Limbosch, July 25, 1957; children: Anne-Marie, Hoke, Bryan. A.B., Princeton U., 1953; postgrad. (Rotary Found. fellow), U. Brussels, 1955-56; LL.B., U. Va., 1959. Bar: Va. 1959, D.C. 1981. Assoc. firm McGuire, Woods & Battle (now McGuire, Woods, Battle & Boothe) and predecessors, Charlottesville, Va., 1959-64; ptnr. McGuire, Woods & Battle and predecessors, 1964-79, head dept. litigation, 1964-79; spl. asst. for litigation to atty. gen. U.S., 1979-81; ptnr. firm Whitman & Ransom, Washington, 1981-84; prin. Slaughter & Redinger, P.C., Charlottesville, 1984—; vis. lectr. trial advocacy U. Va., State Bar, 1992—; counsel Thomas Jefferson Inn of Ct., 1994—. Chmn. Albemarle County (.) Dem. Com., 1969-73; pres. Charlottesville-Albemarle United Way, 1972; commr. accounts Albemarle County, 1986—; trustee Lime Kiln Arts, Inc., 1992—. Served with USNR, 1953-55. Fellow Am. Bar Found., Am. Coll. Trial Lawyers; mem. Am. Bar Assn., D.C. Bar, Charlottesville-Albemarle Bar Assn. (pres. 1976-77), Va. Bar Assn. (pres. 1978), Va. State Bar (bd. govs. internat. practice sect. 1992—), Va. Trial Lawyers Assn., Thomas Jefferson Am. Inn Ct. (counsel 1994—). Club: Boar's Head Sports. Home: 111 Falcon Dr Charlottesville VA 22901-2035 Office: Slaughter & Redinger PC PO Box 2964 250 W Main St Ste 300 Charlottesville VA 22902-2964

SLAUGHTER, FRANK GILL, author, physician; b. Washington, Feb. 25, 1908; s. Stephen Lucius and Sallie Nicholson (Gill) S.; m. Jane Mundy, June 10, 1933; children: Frank G., Randolph M. A.B., Duke U., 1926; M.D. Johns Hopkins U., 1930; L.H.D., Jacksonville U., 1975. Diplomate Am. Bd. Surgery. Intern, asst. resident and resident surgeon Jefferson Hosp., Roanoke, Va., 1930-34; practice medicine specializing in surgery Jacksonville, Fla., 1934-42; ret., 1946; lectr. W. Colston Leigh, Inc., N.Y.C., 1947-49. Author: That None Should Die, 1941, Spencer Brade, M.D, 1942, Air Surgeon, 1942, Battle Surgeon, 1944, A Touch of Glory, 1945, In a Dark Garden, 1946, The New Science of Surgery, 1946, The Golden Isle, 1947, Sangaree, 1948, Medicine for Moderns, 1948, Divine Mistress, 1949, The Stubborn Heart, 1950, Immortal Magyar, 1950, Fort Everglades, 1951, The Road to Bithynia, 1951, East Side General, 1952, The Galileans, 1953, Storm Haven, 1953, The Song of Ruth, Apalachee Gold, 1954, The Healer, Flight from Natchez, 1955, The Scarlet Cord, 1956, The Warrior, 1956, Sword and Scalpel, 1957, The Mapmaker, 1957, Daybreak, 1958, The Thorn of Arimathea, 1958, The Crown and the Cross, 1959, Lorena, 1959, The Land and the Promise, 1960, Pilgrims in Paradise, 1960, Epidemic, 1961, The Curse of Jezebel, 1961, David: Warrior and King, 1962, Tomorrow's Miracle, 1962, Devil's Harvest, 1963, Upon This Rock, 1963, A Savage Place, 1964, The Purple Quest, 1965, Constantine: The Miracle of the Flaming Cross, 1965, Surgeon, U.S.A., 1966, God's Warrior, 1967, Doctor's Wives, 1967, The Sins of Herod, 1968, Surgeon's Choice, 1969, Countdown, 1970, Code Five, 1971, Convention M.D., 1972, Women in White, 1974, Stonewall Brigade, 1975, Plague Ship, 1976, Devil's Gamble, 1977, The Passionate Rebel, 1979, Gospel Fever, 1980, Doctor's Daughters, 1981, Doctors At Risk, 1983, No Greater Love, 1984, Transplant, 1987. Served from maj. to lt. col. M.C., U.S. Army, 1942-46. Fellow ACS. Presbyterian (elder). Home: PO Box 14 Jacksonville FL 32210-0014

SLAUGHTER, JOHN BROOKS, university president; b. Topeka, Mar. 16, 1934; s. Reuben Brooks and Dora (Reeves) S.; m. Ida Bernice Johnson, Aug. 31, 1956; children: John Brooks, Jacqueline Michelle. Student, Washburn U., 1951-53; BSEE, Kans. State U., 1956, DSc (hon.), 1988; MS in Engring., UCLA, 1961; PhD in Engring. Scis. U. Calif., San Diego, 1971; D Engring. (hon.), Rensselaer Poly. Inst. 1981; DSc (hon.), U. So. Calif. 1981, Tuskegee Inst., 1981, U. Md., 1982, U. Notre Dame, 1982, U. Miami, 1983, U. Mass., 1983, Tex. So. U., 1984, U. Toledo, 1985, U. Ill., 1986, SUNY, 1986; LHD (hon.), Bowie State Coll., 1987; DSc (hon.), Morehouse Coll., 1988, Kans. State U., 1988; LLD (hon.), U. Pacific, 1989; DSc (hon.), Pomona Coll., 1989; LHD (hon.), Alfred U., 1991, Calif. Luth. U., 1991, Washburn U., 1992. Registered profl. engr., Wash. Electronics engr. Gen. Dynamics Convair, San Diego, 1956-60; with Naval Electronics Lab. Center, San Diego, 1960-75, div. head, 1965-71, dept. head, 1971-75; dir. applied physics lab. U. Wash., 1975-77; asst. dir. NSF, Washington, 1977-79; dir. NSF, 1980-82; acad. v.p., provost Wash. State U., 1979-80; chancellor U. Md.,

College Park, 1982-88; pres. Occidental Coll., Los Angeles, 1988—; bd. dirs., vice chmn. San Diego Transit Corp., 1968-75; mem. com. on minorities in engring. Nat. Rsch. Coun., 1976-79; mem. Commn. on Pre-Coll. Edn. in Math., Sci. and Tech. Nat. Sci. Bd., 1982-83; bd. dirs. Monsanto Co., ARCO, Avery Dennison Corp., IBM, Northrop Grumman Corp.; chmn. advancement com. Music Ctr. of L.A. County, 1989-93. Editor: Jour. Computers and Elec. Engring, 1972—. Recipient San Diego Urban League, 1962-66, pres., 1964-66; mem. Pres.'s Com. on Nat. Medal Sci., 1979-80; trustee Rensselaer Poly. Inst., 1982; chmn. Pres.'s Com. Nat. Collegiate Athletic Assn., 1986-88; bd. govs. Town Hall of Calif., 1990; bd. dirs. L.A. World Affairs Coun., 1990. Recipient Engring. Disting. Alumnus of Yr. award UCLA, 1978, UCLA medal, 1989, Roger Revelle award U. Calif.-San Diego, 1991, Disting. Svc. award NSF, 1979, Svc. in Engring. award Kans. State U., 1981, Disting. Alumnus of Yr. award U. Calif.-San Diego, 1982; Naval Electronics Lab. Ctr. fellow, 1969-70; elected to Topeka High Sch. Hall of Fame, 1983, Hall of Fame of Am. Soc. Engring. Edn., 1993; named Kansan of Yr. by Kans. Native Sons and Daus., 1994. Fellow IEEE (chmn. com. on minority affairs 1976-80), Am. Acad. Arts and Scis.; mem. NAE, Nat. Collegiate Athletic Assn. (chmn. pres. commn.), Am. Soc. for Engring. Edn. (inducted into Hall of Fame 1993), Phi Beta Kappa (hon.), Tau Beta Phi, Eta Kappa Nu. Office: Occidental Coll 1600 Campus Rd Los Angeles CA 90041-3314

SLAUGHTER, LOUISE MCINTOSH, congresswoman; b. Harlan County, Ky., Aug. 14, 1929; d. Oscar Lewis and Grace (Byers) McIntosh; m. Robert Slaughter, 1956; children: Megan Rae, Amy Louise, Emily Robin. BS, U. Ky., 1951, MS, 1953. Bacteriologist Ky. Dept. Health, Louisville, 1951-52, U. Ky., 1952-53; market researcher Procter & Gamble, Cin., 1953-56; mem. staff Office of the Lt. Gov. N.Y., Albany, 1978-82; state rep. N.Y. Gen. Assembly, Albany, 1983-86; mem. 100th-103rd Congresses from 30th (now 28th) N.Y. dist., Washington, D.C., 1987—; mem. Ho. Govt. Reform and Oversight com., Ho. Budget com. Del. Dem. Nat. Conv., 1972, 76, 80, 88, 92; mem. Monroe County Pure Water Adminstrn. Bd., Nat. Ctr. for Policy Alternatives Adv. Bd., League of Women Voters, Nat. Women's Polit. Caucus. Office: US Ho of Reps Office of House Mems 2421 Rayburn Washington DC 20515-3228

SLAUGHTER-DEFOE, DIANA TRESA, educator; b. Chgo., Oct. 28, 1941; d. John Ison and Gwendolyn Malva (Armstead) S.; m. Michael Defoe. BA, U. Chgo., 1962, MA, 1964, PhD, 1968. Instr. dept. psychiatry Howard U., Washington, 1967-68; rsch. asso., asst. prof. Yale U. Child Study Ctr., New Haven, 1968-70; asst. prof. dept. behavioral scis. and edn. U. Chgo., 1970-77; assoc. prof. edn. and African Am. studies and ctr. for Urban Affairs and Policy Rsch. Northwestern U., Evanston, Ill., 1977-90, prof., 1990—; mem. nat. adv. bd. Fed. Ctr. for Child Abuse & Neglect, 1979-82, coord. Human Devel. and Social Policy Program, 1994—; mem. nat. adv. bd. Learning Rsch. and Devel. Ctr. U. Pitts., Ednl. Rsch. & Devel. Ctr., U. Tex., Austin, Am. Psychological Assn. (ele. mem. 1995—); chmn., dir. public policy program com. Chgo. Black Child Devel. Inst., 1982-84; dir. Ill. Infant Mental Health Com., 1982-83; mem. res. adv. bd. Chgo. Urban League, 1986—. Fellow Am. Psychol. Assn.; mem. Am. Psychol. Assn. (mem. dvsn. ethnic and minority affairs, com. on children, youth & families, Disting. Contbn. to Rsch. in Pub. Policy award 1993), Soc. for Rsch. in Child Devel. (governing coun. 1981-87), Am. Ednl. Rsch. Assn., Assn. Black Psychologists, Nat. Head Start (mem. R & E adv. bd.), Nat. Acad. Scis. (com. on child devel. and publ. policy, 1987-93), Delta Sigma Theta. Contbr. articles to profl. jours. Home: 835 Ridge Ave Evanston IL 60202-1776 Office: 2115 N Campus Dr Evanston IL 60208-0002

SLAVENS, THOMAS PAUL, information and library studies educator; b. Cincinnati, Iowa, Nov. 12, 1928; s. William Blaine and Rhoda (Bowen) S.; m. Cora Pearl Hart, July 9, 1950; 1 son, Mark Thomas. B.A., Phillips U., 1951; M.Div., Union Theol. Sem., 1954; M.A., U. Minn., 1962; Ph.D., U. Mich., 1965. Ordained to ministry Christian Ch., 1953. Pastor First Christian Ch., Sac City, Iowa, 1953-56, Sioux Falls, S.D., 1956-60; librarian Divinity Sch., Drake U., Des Moines, 1960-64; teaching fellow Sch. Info. and Libr. Studies, U. Mich., Ann Arbor, 1964-65, instr., 1965-66, asst. prof., 1966-69, assoc. prof., 1969-77, prof., 1977—; vis. prof. U. Coll. of Wales, 1978, 80, 93; vis. scholar U. Oxford, Eng., 1980; adv. bd. Marcel Dekker Inc., N.Y.C., 1982—; cons. Nutrition Planning Abstracts-UN, N.Y.C., 1977-79. Author-editor: Library Problems in the Humanities, 1981, (with John F. Wilson) Research Guide to Religious Studies, 1982, (with W. Eugene Kleinbaur) Research Guide to History of Western Art, 1982, (with Terrence Tice) Research Guide to Philosophy, 1983, Theological Libraries at Oxford, 1984, (with James Pruett) Research Guide to Musicology, 1985, The Literary Adviser, 1986, A Great Library through Gifts, 1986, The Retrieval of Information, 1989, Number One in the U.S.A.: Records and Wins in Sports, Entertainment, Business, and Science, 1988, 2d edit., 1990, Doors to God, 1990, Sources of Information for Historical Research, 1994, Introduction to Systematic Theology, 1992, Reference Interviews Questions and Materials, 3d edit., 1994. Served with U.S. Army, 1946-48. Recipient Warner Rice Faculty award U. Mich., 1975; H.W. Wilson fellow, 1960; Lilly Endowment fellow Am. Theol. Library Assn., 1963. Mem. ALA (chmn. coms. 1964—), Assn. Libr. and Info. Sci. Edn. (pres. 1972), Beta Phi Mu. Home: 3745 Tremont Ln Ann Arbor MI 48105-3022 Office: U Mich Sch Info and Libr Studies 550 E University Ave Ann Arbor MI 48109-1092

SLAVICH, DENIS MICHAEL, engineering and construction company executive; b. San Francisco, June 1, 1940; s. Francis Luke and Betsy Florence (Carpenter) S.; m. Michele Christine Meyer, June 15, 1963 (div. July 1, 1979) 1 child: Samantha Nicole; m. Debbie Teh-Yan Chao, Nov. 22, 1980; children: David Francis, Destinie Florence. BSEE, U. Calif., Berkeley, 1964; MBA, U. Pitts., 1967; PhD, MIT, 1971. Elec. engr. Douglas Aircraft, Santa Monica, Calif., 1964-65, Hughes Aircraft, Culver City, Calif., 1965-66; prof. Boston U., 1969-71, Stanford U., Palo Alto, Calif., 1984; sr. v.p. Bechtel Group, Inc., San Francisco, 1971-91; v.p. Fluor Daniel, Inc., Irvine, Calif., 1991-95; exec. v.p., CFO Morrison Knudsen Corp., Boise, 1995—. Contbr. articles to profl. jours. Mem. Am. Fin. Assn., Atomic Indsl. Forum Inc., Nat. Assn. Bus. Econs., U. Calif. Engring. Alumni Soc., San Francisco C. of C. (bd. dirs. 1987-89), Olympic Club, Pacific Union, Beta Gamma Sigma. Avocations: golf; hiking. Office: Morrison Knudsen Corp PO Box 73 Boise ID 83729

SLAVIN, ALEXANDRA NADAL, artistic director, educator; b. Port-au-Prince, Haiti, Oct. 26, 1943; came to U.S., 1946; d. Pierre E. and Marie Therese (Clerié) Nadal; m. Eugene Slavin, Dec. 24, 1967; 1 child, Nicholas V. Grad. high sch., Chgo. Dancer Ballet Russe de Monte Carlo, N.Y.C., 1960-61, Chgo. Opera Ballet and N.Y.C. Opera Ballet, 1961-64, Am. Ballet Theatre, N.Y.C., 1965-66, Ballet de Monte Carlo, 1966-67, The Royal Winnipeg (Can.) Ballet, 1967-72; artistic dir. Ballet Austin, Tex., 1972-89; owner, dir. The Slavin Nadal Sch. Ballet, Austin, 1989—. Recipient Achievement in the Arts award Austin chpt. YWCA, 1987. Roman Catholic. Avocation: gardening. Office: Slavin-Nadal Sch Ballet 5521 Burnet Rd Austin TX 78756-1603

SLAVIN, ARLENE, artist; b. N.Y.C., Oct. 26, 1942; d. Louis and Sally (Bryck) Eisenberg; m. Neal Slavin, May 24, 1964 (div. 1979); m. Eric Bregman, Sept. 21, 1980; 1 child, Ethan. BFA, Cooper Union for the Advancement of Sci. and Art, 1964; MFA, Pratt Inst., 1967. One woman exhbns. include Brooke Alexander Gallery, N.Y., 1976, Alexander Milliken Gallery, N.Y.C., 1979, 80, 81, 83, U. Colo., 1981, Pratt Inst., N.Y.C., 1981, Am. Embassy, Belgrad, Yugoslavia, 1984, Hecksher Mus., Huntington, N.Y., 1987, Katherine Rich Perlow Gallery, 1988, Chauncey Gallery, Princeton, N.J., 1990, The Gallery Benjamin N. Cardoza Sch. Law, 1991, Norton Ctr. for Arts, Danville, Ky., 1992, Kavesh Gallery, Ketchum, Idaho, 1993; exhibited in group shows at Bass Mus. Art, Fla., Madison (Wis.) Art Ctr., Santa Barbara (Calif.) Mus., Winnipeg (Can.) Art Gallery, Gensler Assocs., San Francisco, 1986, Eliane Benson Gallery, Bridgehampton, N.Y. 1987, 89, 91, 93, City of N.Y. Parks and Recreation Central Park, N.Y.C. 1989, Benton Gallery, Southampton, N.Y., 1991, Parish Mus., Southampton, 1991, Michele Miller Fine Art, 1991, 92; executed murals N.Y. Aquarium, Bklyn., 1982, Pub. Art Fund, N.Y.C., 1983, Albert Einstein Sch. of Medicine, Bronx, N.Y., 1983, Hudson River Mus., Yonkers, N.Y., 1983, Bellevue Hosp. Ctr., N.Y.C., 1986; represented in permanent collections at Met. Mus. of Art, N.Y.C. Bklyn. Mus., Fogg Art Mus., Cambridge, Mass., Hudson River Mus., Yonkers, N.Y., Hecksler Mus., Huntington, N.Y., Cin.

Art Mus., Readers' Digest, Pleasantville, N.Y., Guild Hall, East Hampton, N.Y., Allen Meml. Art Mus., Oberlin, Ohio, Norton Mus., Palm Beach, Fla., Portland (Oreg.) Mus., Orlando (Fla.) Mus. Art, Neuburger Mus., Purchase, N.Y.; commd. work iron gates Cathedral St. John the Divine, N.Y.C., 1988, 55' steel fence Henry St Settlement, N.Y., 1992, metal work stairway De Soto Sch., N.Y. Sch. Art, 1994-95. Grantee Nat. Endowment for Arts, 1977-78, Threshold Found., 1991. Home and Studio: 119 E 18th St New York NY 10003

SLAVIN, CRAIG STEVEN, management and franchising consultant; b. Tucson, Sept. 7, 1951; s. Sidney and Eileen (Gilbert) S.; m. Carol Lynn Haft, Aug. 30, 1982; children: Carly Blair, Samantha Illyna. Student, U. Ariz., 1969073, U. Balt., 1978. Dir. franchising and sales Evelyn Wood Reading Dynamics, Walnut Creek, Calif., 1974-75; dir. franchising Pasquale Food Co., Birmingham, Ala., 1975-77; exec. v.p. Franchise Concepts, Flossmoor, Ill., 1977-80; pres. Franchise Architects, Chgo., 1980-88; mng. dir. franchise practice Arthur Andersen & Co., Chgo., 1988-91; chmn. Franchise Architects, Riverwoods, Ill., 1991—; founder, bd. dirs. Franchise Broadcast Network, Riverwoods, 1991—. Author: Complete Guide to Self-Employment in Franchising, 1991, Franchising for the Growing Company, 1993, AMACON, The Franchising Handbook; creator of Franchise Success System. Mem. ABA (faculty), Am. Arbitration Assn., Internat. Franchise Assn., Nat. Assn. Info. Suppliers, Water Quality Assn., Inst. Mgmt. Cons., Coun. Franchise Suppliers (adv. bd. dirs.), Nat. Restaurant Assn. Avocations: golf, chess, saltwater fish. Home and Office: The Franchise Architects 3 Metawa Ln Deerfield IL 60015

SLAVIN, NEAL, photographer; b. Bklyn., Aug. 19, 1941; s. Harry and Ida (Pomerantz) S.; 1 child, Olivia Frederica Annika. B.F.A., Cooper Union, 1963. Graphic designer Macmillan Pub. Co., 1965; instr. photographer Cooper Union, Sch. Visual Arts, Queens Coll., Manhattanville Coll.; ptnr. Slavin/Schaffer Films. One-man shows Royal Ont. (Can.) Mus., Toronto, 1976, Light Gallery, N.Y.C., 1976, Center for Creative Photography, Tucson, 1976, Wadsworth Atheneum, Hartford, 1976, Internat. Ctr. Photography, N.Y.C., 1986, Nat. Mus. Photography, Film and TV, Bradford, Eng., 1986; group shows include Galerie Zabriskie, Paris, 1977, Chgo. Center for Contemporary Photography, 1978, Nat. Mus. Photography, Eng., 1984; represented in permanent collections Met. Mus. Art, N.Y.C., Mus. Modern Art, N.Y.C., Mus. of Photography, Rochester, N.Y., Centre National de la Photographie, Paris; retrospective exhbns. Ctr. for Creative Photography, Tucson, Exch. Nat. Bank, Chgo., Palais de Tokyo, Paris; photog. books include Portugal, 1971, When Two or More are Gathered Together, 1976, Britons, 1986. Recipient Augustus Saint Gaudens award Cooper Union Sch. Art and Architecture, 1988; Fulbright grantee, 1968, Nat. Endowment Arts grantee, 1972. Mem. Am. Soc. Mag. Photographers (Corp. Photographer of Yr. 1986), Dirs. Guild of Am. Address: 62 Greene St New York NY 10012 *Nothing in my life has been worth anything unless it has had risk.*

SLAVIN, RAYMOND GRANAM, allergist, immunologist; b. Cleve., June 29, 1930; s. Philip and Dinah (Baskind) S.; m. Alberta Cohrt, June 10, 1953; children: Philip, Stuart, David, Linda. A.B., U. Mich., 1952; M.D., St. Louis U., 1956; M.S., Northwestern U., 1963. Diplomate: Am. Bd. Internal Medicine, Am. Bd. Allergy and Immunology (treas.). Intern U. Mich. Hosp., Ann Arbor, 1956-57; resident St. Louis U. Hosp., 1959-61; fellow in allergy and immunology Northwestern U. Med. Sch., 1961-64; asst. prof. internal medicine and microbiology St. Louis U., 1965-70, assoc., 1970-73, prof., 1973—; dir. div. allergy and immunology, 1965—; mem. NIH study sect., 1985-89; cons. U.S. Army M.C. Contbr. numerous articles to med. publs.; editorial bd.: Jour. Allergy and Clin. Immunology, 1975-81, Tice Practice Medicine, 1973-84, Jour. Club of Allergy, 1978-80. Chmn. bd. Asthma and Allergy Found. Am., 1985-88. With M.C., U.S. Army, 1957-59. Grantee NIH, 1967-70, 84—, Nat. Inst. Occpl. Safety and Health, 1974-80. Fellow ACP, Am. Acad. Allergy and Immunology (exec. bd., historian, pres. 1983-84); mem. Am. Assn. Immunologists, Central Soc. Clin. Research, AAAS. Democrat. Jewish. Home: 631 E Polo Dr Saint Louis MO 63105-2629 Office: 1402 S Grand Blvd Saint Louis MO 63104-1004

SLAVIN, SIMON, social administration educator; b. N.Y.C., Jan. 20, 1916; s. Isadore and Mary (Sushansky) S.; m. Jeannette Rose Littinsky, Jan. 16, 1938; children: Rayna (Mrs. Robert Epstein dec.), Vicky Jane, Johanna. B.S. in Social Sci, CCNY, 1937; M.A., Columbia U., 1938, Ed.D., 1953. Regional supr. United Service Orgn. Jewish Welfare Bd., Chgo., 1945-46; exec. dir. YM-YWHA, Mt. Vernon, N.Y., 1946-53; exec. sec. div. recreation and group work and sect. on services to handicapped Welfare and Health Council of N.Y.C., 1953-54; exec. dir. Ednl. Alliance, N.Y.C., 1954-60; asso. prof. social work Columbia U., 1960-63; prof., Hesib adm. community orgn. area, 1960-66, chmn. advanced programs, 1966-67; Simon Sr. Research fellow U. Manchester, Eng., 1967-68; dean Sch. Social Adminstrn., Temple U., 1968-78, prof., 1978-80, prof., founding dean emeritus 1983—; chmn. regional adv. com. Region III Dept. Pub. Welfare, Phila., 1972-74; instr. Adelphi Coll., 1955-58, N.Y. U., 1956-57, Chgo. U., 1958-59; cons. N.Y.C. Commr. of Drug Addiction Services. Author, co-editor: Leadership in Social Administration, 1980; editor: Social Administration: The Management of Social Services, 1978, Applying Computers in Social Service and Mental Health Agencies, 1983, An Introduction to Human Services Management, 1985, Managing Finances, Personnel and Information in Human Services, 1985; contbr. chpts. to Migration and Social Welfare, 1971, Evaluation of Social Intervention, 1972, A Design for Social Work Practice, 1974, Social Work Futures, 1983, Educating Managers of Nonprofit Organizations, 1988; editor in chief Adminstrn. in Social Work, 1977-92; book series editor Haworth Press, 1990—; also numerous articles to profl. jours. Mem. personnel adv. com. Nat. Urban League, 1964-66. Recipient Assn. for Community Orgn. and Social Adminstrn. Outstanding Life Achievement award, 1993. Home: Kimball Fams 235 Walker St Lenox MA 01240

SLAVIN, SUSAN ANN, secondary educator; b. Green Bay, Wis., Oct. 9, 1942; d. John James and Mary Jane (Christophersen) Wheeler; m. Laurence E. Slavin, Dec. 8, 1962; children: Susan, Karen, Mary, Laurence Jr., Fred Obley, Marc, Edward. Student. BA in English. Ariz. State U., 1968, MA in Polit. Sci./Govt. Cert. prin., ESL tchr. Acting asst. prin. Alhambra High Sch., Phoenix; tchr. computer assisted English composition Alhambra High Sch.; course developer computer assisted English and govt. Rio Salado Jr. Coll. Remedial English; grant writer. Co-author ESL Curriculum Guides; contbr. articles to profl. jours. Recipient 1st place, Nat. Paper Microcomputer Conf. in Edn., 1989. Mem. ASCD, Tchrs. English Speakers Other Langs., Nat. Assn. Secondary Sch. Prins., Ariz. Coaches Assn. (high sch. and coll. track and field ofcl.).

SLAVITT, DAVID WALTON, retired lawyer; b. Chgo., Mar. 15, 1931; s. Isaac and Fay (Goldstein) S.; m. Roberta Chelnek, July 26, 1953; children: Steven, Denise, Howard. B.S., UCLA, 1952, J.D., 1955. Bar: Calif. 1956; C.P.A., Calif. Since practiced in Los Angeles; pres. Slavitt & Borofsky (P.C.), 1969-87; moderator continuing edn. programs. Author articles in field. Served with USNR, 1955. Mem. Am. Assn. Atty.-C.P.A.s (pres. 1964), ABA, State Bar Calif. Calif. Assn. Atty.-C.P.A.s (pres. 1963), Beverly Hills Bar Assn. (vice chmn. continuing edn. of bar 1970, asst. chmn. law practice mgmt. com. 1973).

SLAVITT, EARL BENTON, lawyer; b. Chgo., Sept. 12, 1939; s. Harold Hal and Rose (Hoffman) S.; m. Amy Lerner, July 12, 1987; 1 child, Gabriel Harrel; children from previous marriage: Andrew Miller, Lesley Deborah. BS in Econs., U. Pa., 1961, JD, 1964. Bar: Ill. 1964, U.S. Dist. Ct. (no. dist.) Ill. 1964, U.S. Supreme Ct. 1971. Assoc. Wisch, Crane & Kravets, Chgo., 1964-67; Ressman & Tishler, Chgo., 1967-69; assoc., then ptnr. Levy & Erens, Chgo., 1969-78; ptnr. Tash & Slavitt, Chgo., 1978-81, Katten Muchin & Zavis, Chgo., 1981—. Contbr. articles to profl. jours.; author poems and plays. Vol. Physician of Ill. Masonic Med. Ctr., Chgo., 1987-89, Pro bono Advocates, 1989, Chgo. Ho., 1991 (recipient Outstanding Vol. award), Lawyers for the Creative Arts, Bus. Vols. for the Arts, 1992—; bd. dirs. Playwrights Ctr., Chgo., 1987, Jewish Reconstructionist Congregation, Chgo., 1978, 91, 92, Legal Clinic for the Disabled, 1993—, pres., 1995—, Sarah's Circle, 1994—. Mem. Ill. State Bar Assn. (mem. real estate com. 1976, recipient Pro Bono Cert. Accomplishment 1994), Chgo. Bar Assn. (mem. real estate com. 1976, real estate fin. com. 1982), Chgo. Coun. Lawyers (mem. jud. selection com. 1969), Lawyers in Mensa (bd. govs.

1983). Democrat. Jewish. Office: Katten Muchin & Zavis 525 W Monroe St Ste 1600 Chicago IL 60661-3693

SLAVOFF, HARRIET EMONDS, learning disabilities teacher, consultant; b. Elmer, N.J., Mar. 18, 1931; d. Lewis Arthur and Margaret (Miles) Emonds; m. Eugene Victor Slavoff, Feb. 3, 1951; children: Stephen, Stephanie Slavoff Perry, Eugene Jr. BA, Glassboro Coll., 1969, MA, 1976. Cert.-N.J. Tchr. kindergarten Olivet Sch., Pittsgrove Twp., N.J., 1953; remedial tchr. Upper Pittsgrove Sch., 1964-74; learning disabilities tchr. cons. Salem County Schs., Woodstown, N.J., 1976, Pittsgrove Twp., N.J., 1977-78, Oldmans Twp. Sch., Pedricktown, N.J., 1979-83, Logan Sch., Bridgeport, N.J., 1985; child study team coord. East Greenwich Schs., Mickleton, N.J., 1987-93; supr. student tchrs. Rowan Coll., 1994-94; learning disabilities cons.; ct. clk., Elmer, N.J., 1976, chair Juvenile Conf. Com., 1976-82; adj. prof. Rowan Coll., 1993-95. Pub. History of Elmer, 1893-1993, 1993. Mem. election bd. Dem. com., Elmer; mem. ch. choir; pres. Elmer PTA. Avocations: library work, flowers, crafts, reading. Home: 110 Front St Elmer NJ 08318-2139

SLAY, A. MICHELE, fundraiser; b. Geneva, Ala., May 1, 1967; d. Robert Huey and Annie Mavis (Ausley) S. BS in Pub. Adminstr., Samford U., 1989; M of Pub. Adminstr., U. Ala. 1991. Project asst. Muscular Dystrophy Assn., Birmingham; asst. project dir. Ala. Pub. TV, Birmingham; devel. mgr. Ala. Symphony Orch., Birmingham; campaign assoc. United Way of Ctrl. Ala., Birmingham, 1993—. Mem. Shelby County Econ. Devel. Coun., Inverness, Ala., 1993—; internship Ala. Rep. Party, Birmingham, 1989. Mem. Nat. Soc. of Fund Raising Execs., Am. Soc. of Pub. Adminstrs., North Shelby County C. of C., Gamma Sigma Sigma (nat. pres. 1993-95, nat. sec. 1991-93, dist. dir. 1989-91, Nat. Sister of the Yr. 1989). Republican. Southern Bapist. Avocations: reading, cooking, swimming, traveling, volunteering. Home: 306 Woodmere Ln Birmingham AL 35226 Office: United Way of Ctrl Ala 3600 8th Ave S Birmingham AL 35222

SLAY, KEN, sales executive; b. 1941. Sr. exec. v.p. Ga. Crown Distributing Ctr., Columbus. Office: Georgia Crown Distributing Ctr 7 Crown Cir Columbus GA 31907

SLAYDEN, JAMES BRAGDON, retired department store executive; b. Seattle, Sept. 28, 1924; s. Philip Lee and Ruth Alwin (Bragdon) S.; m. Barbara Marie McBride, May 7, 1955; children: Tracy Anne, James Bragdon. B.A., U. Wash., 1948; M.B.A., U. So. Calif., 1949. Buyer Frederick & Nelson (dept. store), Seattle, 1949-59; div. mdse. mgr. Frederick & Nelson (dept. store), 1959-65; gen. mgr. Bullocks Westwood, Los Angeles, 1965-69; exec. v.p. gen. mdse. mgr. May D&F Co. (dept. store), Denver, 1969-72; pres., chief exec. officer J.W. Robinson dept. store, L.A., 1972-78; exec. v.p. ops. Marshall Field & Co., Chgo., 1978-80; lectr. mktg. U. So. Calif., 1985—. Active United Crusade, United Way, L.A., 1973-78, Chgo. Heart Assn., 1978-79; chmn. Pvt. Industry Coun.; cons. Internat. Exec. Svc. Corps., 1987—. With U.S. Army, 1943-45. Mem. Phi Kappa Psi. Republican. Christian Scientist. Home: 37 Mela Ln Palos Verdes Peninsula CA 90275-5086

SLAYDEN, HOWARD THEO, accounting company executive; b. San Diego, May 6, 1947; s. Elijah Al and Pearl Minnette (Lehrer) S.; m. Susan Marie Drake, Aug. 23, 1970; children: Matthew Drake, Samuel William. BA in Econ., Claremont McKenna U., 1968; JD, U. Calif. at Berkeley, 1971. Bar: Calif., 1972; CPA, Calif., 1972. Tax specialist Coopers & Lybrand, Palo Alto, Calif., 1971-76; ptnr. in charge tax svcs. Coopers & Lybrand, Houston, 1976-82, San Jose/Menlo Pk., Calif., 1982-90; ptnr. in charge fin. adv. svcs. Coopers & Lybrand, San Francisco, 1990—; lectr. taxation Golden Gate U., San Francisco, 1973, San Jose State U., 1987-88. Commr. Am. Youth Soccer Orgn., Menlo Pk., 1987—. Mem. Calif. Soc. CPA's, Calif. State Bar Assn., Tex. Soc. CPA's (chmn. tax curriculum com. 1980-82). Avocations: woodworking, reading, skiing. Office: Coopers & Lybrand 333 Market St San Jose CA 95113

SLAYMAKER, GENE ARTHUR, public relations executive; b. Kenton, Ohio, Sept. 15, 1928; s. Edwin Paul and Anne Elizabeth (Grable) S.; divorced; children: Jill Brook, Scott Wood, Leslie Beth; m. Julie Ann Graff, Feb. 3, 1979; 1 adopted child, Peter Fredric Bannon II; stepchildren: Jennifer Elizabeth Nash, David Frank Nash. B.A. in Radio Journalism, Ohio State U. Announcer, reporter WLWC-TV, Columbus, Ohio, 1951-52; anchor reporter WKBN-AM-FM-TV, Youngstown, Ohio, 1952-56, KYW-TV, Cleve., 1956-60; editor news Sta. WFBM-AM-FM-TV, Indpls., 1960-68; dir. news, sports, pub. affairs WTLC-FM and WTUX-AM, Indpls., 1976-92; community rels. liaison Marion County Pros. Atty. Office, Indpls., 1993; pres., founder Slaymaker and Assocs., Indpls., 1969—. Past bd. dirs. Park-Tudor Father's Assn.; mem. Meridian Kessler Neighborhood Assn., pres., 1968-69. Recipient Disting. Service award (2). Mem. Ind. AP Broadcasters Assn. (awards), UPI (awards), Nat. Fedn. Press Women, Soc. Profl. Journalists (awards Ind. chpt., bd. dirs., chpt. pres. 1991-92, Radio-TV News Dirs. Assn. (region bd. dirs. 1987-91), Indpls. Press Club, Women's Press Club Ind. Democrat. Clubs: Nat. Headliners, Unity. Avocations: writing; painting; singing; gardening; tennis. Home: 5161 W Washington Blvd Indianapolis IN 46205-1071

SLAYMAKER, H. OLAV, geography educator; b. Swansea, Wales, Jan. 31, 1939; came to Can., 1968; s. Arthur J. and Astri H. (Breen) S.; m. Margaret A. Rapson, Apr. 8, 1967; children—Karen M., Paul O., Sarah J., Heidi R. B.A., King's Coll., Cambridge, Eng., 1961; A.M., Harvard U., 1963; Ph.D., Cambridge U., 1968. Asst. lectr. U. Coll. Wales, Aberystwyth, 1964-66; lectr. U. Coll. Wales, 1966-68; asst. prof. geography U.B.C., Vancouver, Can., 1968-70; assoc. prof. U.B.C., 1970-81, prof., 1981—, head dept., 1982—; cons. water quality br. Inland Waters, Vancouver, 1976—. Editor: Mountain Geomorphology, 1972, Field Experiments, 1978, High Mountains, 1981, Extreme Landforming Events, 1983, Geomorphology and Land Management, 1986, Erosion Budgets and Their Hydrologic Basis, 1986. Senate mem. Vancouver Sch. Theology, 1973-75; bd. dirs. Regent Coll., Vancouver, 1975-78, U. B.C., 1984-87. Research grantee Natural Sci. and Engring. Research Council, Ottawa, Ont., Can., 1968—. Mem. Can. Assn. Geographers, Am. Geophys. Union, Internat. Geog. Union (commn. chmn., sec., chmn. Can. Nat. Com. 1984-88). Anglican. Club: Faculty (Vancouver). Avocations: mountain hiking; philately. Home: 7076 Arbutus, Vancouver, BC Canada V6P 5S8 Office: Univ BC Dept Geography, 2329 West Mall, Vancouver, BC Canada V6T 1W5

SLAYMAN, CAROLYN WALCH, geneticist, educator; b. Portland, Maine, Mar. 11, 1937; d. John Weston and Ruth Dyer (Sanborn) Walch; m. Clifford L. Slayman; children—Andrew, Rachel. B.A. with highest honors, Swarthmore Coll., 1958; Ph.D., Rockefeller U., 1963; D.Sc. (hon.), Bowdoin Coll., 1985. Instr., then asst. prof. Case Western Res. U., Cleve., 1967; from asst. prof. to prof. genetics Yale U. Sch. Medicine, New Haven, 1967—, Sterling prof. genetics, 1991—, chmn. dept. genetics, 1984—; chmn. genetic basis of disease rev. commn. NIH, 1981-85, nat. adv. gen. med. scis. coun., 1989-93; bd. dirs. J. Weston Walch Pub., Portland, Maine, The Perkin-Elmer Corp.; mem. sci. rev. bd. Howard Hughes Med. Inst., 1992—. Mem. editorial bd. Jour. Biol. Chemistry, 1989-94; contbr. articles to sci. jours. Trustee Foote Sch., New Haven, Conn., 1983-89, Hopkins Sch., New Haven, 1988-93; bd. overseers Bowdoin Coll., Brunswick, Maine, 1976-88, trustee, 1988—. Recipient Deborah Morton award Westbrook Coll., 1986. Mem. Am. Soc. Biol. Chemists, Genetics Soc. Am., Soc. Gen. Physiologists, Am. Soc. Microbiology, Phi Beta Kappa. Office: Yale U Sch Medicine Dept Genetics 333 Cedar St New Haven CT 06510-3289

SLAYMAN, CLIFFORD LEROY, JR., biophysicist, educator; b. Mt. Vernon, Ohio, July 7, 1936; s. Clifford Leroy and Ethel May (Stantz) S.; m. Carolyn Ruth Walch, Dec. 26, 1959; children: Andrew Lowell, Rachel Whitehouse. AB, Kenyon Coll., 1958; PhD, Rockefeller Inst., 1963; DSc (hon.), Kenyon Coll. 1991. NSF fellow Cambridge (Eng.) U., 1963-64; asst. prof. Western Res. U., Cleve., 1964-67; from asst. prof. to prof. physiology Yale U., New Haven, 1967—; mem panel on pre-doctoral fellowships NSF, Washington, 1969-71; DOE-DOA-NSF panel on Plant Sci. Ctrs., Washington, 1988. Editor: Electrogenic Ion Pumps, 1982; contbr. articles to profl. jours. and revs.; editorial bd. Bio Sci. Jour., 1985-88, Jour. Membrane Biology, 1982—. Mem. Hamden (Conn.) Neighborhood Preservation Com., 1980-82. Grantee NIH, 1964-91, NSF, 1979-82, DOE, 1985—. Mem.

AAAS, Am. Physiol. Soc., Am. Soc. Plant Physiologists, N.Y. Acad. Scis., Soc. Gen. Physiologists, Conn. Acad. Scis. Avocations: antique house restoration, conservation, nature watching. Office: Yale Sch Medicine 333 Cedar St New Haven CT 06510-3289

SLAYTON, GUS, association executive; b. Pocahontas, Ark., Jan. 20, 1937; s. Alvin M. and Eula Inis (Milam) S.; m. Ruth Virginia Furr, May 27, 1961 (dec. Nov. 1989). B.A., U. Md., College Park, 1973. Served as enlisted man U.S. Army, 1957-63, commd. 2d lt., 1963, advanced through grades to lt. col., 1978; various operational and research and devel. assignments, including The Pentagon, 1974-78, ret., 1980; exec. dir. Assn. of Old Crows, Alexandria, Va., 1980-92, AOC Ednl. Found., 1992—. Decorated Legion of Merit (2), Bronze Star (2). Republican. Avocation: real estate investment. Home: 25165 Elk Lick Rd Chantilly VA 22021

SLAYTON, JOHN ARTHUR, electric motor manufacturing executive; b. St. Joseph, Mo., Aug. 12, 1918; s. Ernest Roy and Cora Belle (Hutchison) S.; m. Elizabeth Van Horn Duerr, Aug. 15, 1942; children: Richard, Elizabeth, Jane, James, Robert, Sarah, Mary. B.S., U. Mo., 1940. Salesman Burroughs Co., Chgo., 1940-42; acct. Standard Brands, Green Bay, Wis., 1945-48; exec. v.p. Marathon Electric, Wausau, Wis., 1948-88, pres., vice chmn., 1988—. Pres. C. of C. Found., Wausau, 1981-89, Woodson YMCA Found., 1977—; bd. dirs. Wausau Hosp. Ctr., 1976-82, North Ctrl. Mental Health Found. 1980-85, Wausau Area Vol. Exch., 1983-89, Wausau Health Found., 1975—; pres., bd. dirs. Grant Theatre Found., 1985—; bd. dirs., treas. Lehigh Yawkey Woodson Art Mus., 1985—; trustee, elder 1st Presbyn. Ch., 1960-65. With USN, 1942-44. Recipient Citation of Merit U. Mo., Columbia, 1976,W ausau Disting. Community Service award, 1983, Wis. Gov.'s award, 1986; Paul Harris fellow, 1977. Mem. Wausau Area C. of C. (pres., dir. 1977-81). Republican. Clubs: Wausau Country (pres., dir. 1958-61), Wausau, YMCA (pres., dir. 1961-67). Lodge: Rotary (pres., dir. 1960-63). Home: 1804 Town Line Rd Wausau WI 54403-9119 Office: Marathon Electric 100 W Randolph St Wausau WI 54401-2569

SLAYTON, THOMAS KENNEDY, editor, writer; b. Burlington, Vt., July 29, 1941; s. Ronald Alfred and Dorothy (Kennedy) S.; m. Elizabeth Craig Wilson; 1 child, Ethan Augustus. BA, U. Vt., 1963. Reporter Rutland (Vt.) Herald newspaper, 1964-72; reporter, bur. chief Vt. Press Bur., Montpelier, 1972-79; asst. editor, editor Times-Argus newspaper, Barre, Vt., 1979-85; editor in chief Vt. Life Mag., Montpelier, 1985—; mem. adv. bd. confs. Windham Found., Grafton, Vt., 1986-89; adj. prof. journalism dept. St. Michael's Coll., Winooski, Vt., 1988—. Author: Finding Vermont, 1986, Sabra Field, The Art of Place, 1993; author introduction to book The Vermont Experience, 1987. Bicentennial fellow U. Vt., Burlington, 1988-91. Mem. Vt. Press Assn., Regional Pubs. Assn. (bd. dirs., pres. 1993-94). Mem. Soc. of Friends. Office: Vt Life Mag 61 Elm St Montpelier VT 05602-2713

SLAYTON, WILLIAM LAREW, planning consultant, former government official; b. Topeka, Dec. 2, 1916; s. Clarence Harvey and Mary (Larew) S.; m. Mary Prichard, Aug. 30, 1941; children: Mary Elizabeth Slayton Campbell, Barbara Slayton Shelton. Student, U. Omaha, 1937-39; A.B., U. Chgo., 1940, M.A., 1942; D.H.L. (hon.), Clarkson Coll. Tech., 1965. Polit. sec. Alderman Paul H. Douglas, Chgo., 1940-42; planning analyst Milw. Planning Commn., 1944-45, 46-47; municipal reference librarian Milw., 1947-48; asso. dir. Urban Redevel. Study, Chgo., 1948-50; field rep. div. slum clearance and urban redevel. HHFA, Washington, 1950; dir. redevel. Nat. Assn. Housing and Redevel. Ofcls., Washington, 1950-55; v.p. planning, redevel. Webb & Knapp, Inc., Washington, 1955-60; planning partner I.M. Pei & Partners, N.Y.C., 1956-61; commr. Urban Renewal Adminstrn., HHFA, HUD, Washington, 1961-66; dir. Urban Policy Center, Urban Am., Inc., Washington, 1966; exec. v.p. Urban Am., Inc., 1966-69, 1969; exec. v.p. AIA, Washington, 1969-77, AIA Found., 1970-77; mem. bd. AIA Corp., 1970-77; vice chmn. AIA Research Corp., 1973-77; chmn. urban devel. advisory com. HUD, 1967-68; mem. U.S. del. Econ. Commn. for Europe, 1970; dep. asst. sec. of state for fgn. bldgs., 1978-83; cons. Nat. Assn. Housing and Redevel. Ofcls., 1983-87, Am. Planning Assn., 1987—. Served with USNR, 1945-46. Recipient gold medal Royal Instn. Chartered Surveyors, Great Britain, 1965, Justin Herman award Nat. Assn. Housing and Redevel. Ofcls., 1994. Mem. Potomac Inst. (dir.), AIA (hon.), Am. Planning Assn., Am. Inst. Cert. Planners.

SLEATOR, TYCHO, physics educator. Asst. prof. dept. physics N.Y.U. Recipient Packard Fellowship David & Lucile Packard Found., 1993. Office: New York U Dept Physics 70 Washington Sq S New York NY 10012*

SLEBODNIK, TRESSA ANN, elementary education educator; b. Belle Vernon, Pa., Nov. 11, 1931; d. Michael Ferdinand and Elizabeth (Skruber) Nusser; m. Thomas Patrick Slebodnik, June 6, 1953; children: Thomas, Anita, Eleanor, Edward, Charles, Kathleen, Linda. BS, California (Pa.) State Tchrs. Coll., 1953. Cert. tchr., Pa. Tchr. kindergarten Yough Sch. Dist., West Newton, Pa., 1969-76; tchr. first grade Yough Sch. Dist., Sutersville, Pa., 1976-80, Smithton, Pa., 1980-81; tchr. kindergarten Yough Sch. Dist., Smithton and Ruffsdale, Pa., 1981-82, Ruffsdale, 1982—; devel. Approach to Sci. and Health, Ruffsdale, 1990-95; grade level coord., mentor tchr. and curriculum coun. Pres. St. Edward Bowling League, Herminie; active Altar-Rosary Soc., Herminie. Mem. NEA, Pa. State Edn. Assn., Keyston State Reading Assn., Yough Edn. Assn. (bldg. rep.), Westmoreland County Reading Coun. Democrat. Roman Catholic. Avocations: bowling, cards, reading, bingo, gardening. Home: RD 1 Box 200 Irwin PA 15642 Office: Mendon Elem Sch RD 1 Box 680 Ruffs Dale PA 15679

SLECHTA, ROBERT FRANK, biologist, educator; b. N.Y.C., June 4, 1928; s. Frank C. and Helen (Pospisil) S.; m. Betty S. Youngren, May 16, 1953; 1 son, Marc William. A.B., Clark U., 1949, M.A., 1951; postgrad., Columbia, 1951-52; Ph.D., Boston U., 1955. Research asst. Worcester Found., Shrewsbury, Mass., 1952-53; biologist U.S. Army Med. Nutrition Lab., Denver, 1953-55; instr., research asso. Tufts U., 1955-58; mem. faculty Boston U., 1958—, prof. biology, 1965-91, prof. emeritus, 1991—, assoc. dean Grad. Sch., 1967-78. Author: (with M. Hawthorne and E. Blaustein) Laboratory Manual for General Biology, 1965; also articles and book revs. Mem. Boston Zool. Soc. (dir. 1967-78, trustee 1978-79), Am. Inst. Biol. Scis., AAAS, Microcirculation Soc., Am. Soc. Zoologists, Soc. Study Reprodn., Sigma Xi. Research on limb regeneration in urodeles, starvation in prisoners of war, human factors in aircraft seating, effects on progestational compounds on reprodn. (early work on contraceptive pill), quantitative studies of blood flow in living microscopic vessels in mammals and amphibians. Home: 101 Wilson Rd Bedford MA 01730-1320 Office: Boston U Biology Dept 2 Cummington St Boston MA 02215-2425

SLEDGE, CLEMENT BLOUNT, orthopedic surgeon, educator; b. Ada, Okla., Nov. 1, 1930; s. John B. and Mollie D. (Blount) S.; m. Georgia Kurrus, Apr. 13, 1957; children—Margaret, John, Matthew, Claire. M.D., Yale U., 1955; M.A. (hon.), Harvard U., 1970; ScD (hon.), U. The South, 1987. Diplomate: Am. Bd. Orthopedic Surgery. Intern Barnes Hosp., St. Louis, 1955-56; resident in orthopedic surgery Harvard U., 1960-63; fellow in orthopedic pathology Armed Forces Inst. Pathology, 1963; vis. scientist Strangeways Research Lab., Cambridge (Eng.) U., 1963-66; asst. prof. orthopedic surgery Harvard U., 1963-67, asso. prof., 1967-70, prof., 1970—, chmn. dept., 1970—; chmn. dept. orthopedic surgery Brigham and Women's Hosp. Editor: Textbook of Rheumatology, 1981, 85, 89; contbr. more than 100 articles to sci. jours. Active Arthritis Found.; chmn. Nat. Arthritis Adv. Bd., 1978-80. Served with M.C. USNR, 1956-58. Fellow Med. Found. Boston, 1963-66; Gebbie research fellow, 1968; NIH grantee, 1967—. Mem. Am. Acad. Orthopedic Surgeons (pres. 1985-86), Orthopedic Rsch. Soc. (pres. 1978-80), Am. Rheumatism Assn., Inst. of Medicine, Nat. Acad. Sci., Interurban Orthopedic Club, The Hip Soc. (pres. 1985). Episcopalian. Office: Harvard Medical Sch 25 Shattuck St Boston MA 02115-6195

SLEDGE, JAMES SCOTT, federal judge; b. Gadsden, Ala., July 20, 1947; s. L. Lee and Kathryn (Privott) S.; m. Joan Nichols, Dec. 27, 1969; children: Joanna Scott, Dorothy Privott. BA, Auburn U., 1969; JD, U. Ala., 1974, postgrad., 1999. Bar: Ala. 1974, U.S. Ct. Appeals (5th cir.) 1975, U.S. Ct. Appeals (11th cir.) 1981. Ptnr. Inzer, Suttle, Swann & Stivender, P.A., Gadsden, 1974-91; mcpl. judge, Gadsden, 1975-91; judge U.S. Bankruptcy Ct. No. Dist. Ala., 1991—; instr. U. Ala., Gadsden, 1975-77, Gadsen State

Community Coll., 1989-90. Lay minister, vestryman Holy Comforter Episc. Ch., Gadsden, 1976—; mem. Ala. Coun. on the Arts, 1994—; incorporator Episc. Day Sch., Gadsden, 1976, Kyle Home for Devel. Disadvantaged, Gadsden, 1979; bd. dirs. Salvation Army, 1984-91, Etowah County Health Dept., 1975-91, Episc. Day Sch., 1992—, Gadsden Symphony, 1993—; mem. Ala. Dem. Exec. Com., 1990-91, Etowah County Dem. Exec. Com., 1984-91; county coordinator U.S. Senator Howell Heflin, Etowah County, Ala., 1978, 84, 90; founder Gadsden Cultural Arts Found., 1983, chmn., 1986-91. Capt. U.S. Army, 1969-71, Vietnam. Decorated Bronze Star, Legion of Honor (Vietnam); recipient Governor's award for art Ala. Coun. of the Arts, 1993. Mem. Ala. State Bar (charter mem. bankruptcy sect., vice chmn. 1984, regional liaison bankruptcy bench and bar 1984), Gadsden-Etowah C. of C. (gen. counsel, v.p., bd. dirs. 1986-93), Phi Kappa Phi, Phi Eta Sigma. Lodge: Kiwanis (bd. dirs. 1981-84). Home: 435 Turrentine Ave Gadsden AL 35901-4059

SLEED, JOEL, newspaper editor; b. N.Y.C., Jan. 29, 1929; m. MaryLou Kalwara, Nov. 15, 1983; children: Jodie Parenti, Jill, Jeffrey, Kristin Kalwara, Karen Hepler. Travel editor The Star-Ledger, Newark, N.J.; travel columnist Newhouse News Svc., N.Y.C. Office: Newhouse News Svc 140 E 45th St New York NY 10017 also: Star-Ledger Star-Ledger Plz Newark NJ 07102

SLEICHER, CHARLES ALBERT, chemical engineer; b. Albany, N.Y., Aug. 15, 1924; s. Charles Albert and Beatrice Eugena (Cole) S.; m. Janis Jorgensen, Sept. 5, 1953; children—Jeffrey Mark, Gretchen Gail. B.S., Brown U., 1946; M.S., M.I.T., 1949; Ph.D., U. Mich., 1955. Asst. dir. M.I.T. Sch. Chem. Engring.; Practice Bangor, Maine, 1949-51; research engr. Shell Devel. Co., Emeryville, Calif., 1955-59; assoc. prof. chem. engring. U. Wash., Seattle, 1960-66, prof., 1966-92, prof. emeritus, 1993—, dept. chmn., 1977-89; cons. Westinghouse-Hanford Co.; profl. photographer, 1994—. Contbr. articles on extraction, heat transfer, fluid mechanics, pesticide transport to profl. jours. Served with USN, 1943-47. NSF postdoctoral fellow, 1959-60; SEED grantee, 1973-74; research grantee NSF; research grantee Chevron Research Corp.; research grantee Am. Chem. Soc. Fellow Am. Inst. Chem. Engrs. (program, awards coms.); mem. Am. Chem. Soc., Coun. Chem. Rsch. (governing bd.), AAAS, Sigma Xi. Chem. reactor design patentee. Home: 5002 Harold Pl NE Seattle WA 98105-2809 Office: U Wash Chem Engring Bf # 10 Seattle WA 98195

SLEIGH, SYLVIA, artist, educator; b. Llandudno, North Wales; came to U.S., 1961; d. John Harold and Katherine Amy (Miller) S.; m. Lawrence Alloway, June 28, 1954. Student, Sch. Art, Brighton, Sussex, Eng., 1932-36; diploma, U. London Extra-Mural Dept., 1947. Vis. asst. prof. SUNY-Stony Brook, 1978; instr. New Sch. Social Research, N.Y.C., 1974-77, 78-80; Edith Kreeger Wolf disting. prof. Northwestern U., Evanston, Ill., 1977; vis. artist Baldwin Seminar Oberlin Coll., Ohio, 1982. One person shows include Bennington (Vt.) Coll., 1963, Soho 20 Art Gallery, N.Y.C., 1974, 80, A.I.R. Gallery, N.Y.C., 1974, 76, 78, Ohio State U., Columbus, 1976, Matrix, Wadsworth Atheneum, Hartford, Conn., 1976, G.W. Einstein, Inc., N.Y.C., 1980, 83, 85, Zaks Gallery, Chgo., 1985, 95, Milw. Art Mus., Butler Inst., Youngstown, Ohio, 1990, Stiebel Modern, N.Y.C., 1992; exhibited in group shows Newhouse Gallery, Staten Island, N.Y., Stamford (Conn.) Mus., 1985, Albany (N.Y.) Inst. Art, Cin. Art Mus., New Orleans Mus. Art, Denver Art Mus., Pa. Acad. Fine Arts, 1989, Carlsten Art Gallery, Stevens Point, Wis., 1993. Panelist Creative Artists Pub. Service Program, N.Y.C., 1976. Nat. Endowment for Arts grantee, 1982, Pollock-Krasner Found. grantee, 1985. Home: 330 W 20th St New York NY 10011-3302

SLEIGHT, ARTHUR WILLIAM, chemist; b. Ballston Spa, N.Y., Apr. 1, 1939; s. Hollis Decker and Elizabeth (Smith) S.; m. Betty F. Hilberg, Apr. 19, 1963; children: Jeffrey William, Jeannette Anne, Jason Arthur. Faculty, U. Stockholm, Sweden, 1963-64; with E.I. du Pont de Nemours & Co., Inc., Wilmington, Del., 1965-89, rsch. mgr. solid state/catalytic chemistry, 1981-89; Harris Chair prof. materials sci. Oreg. State U., Corvallis, 1989—; adj. prof. U. Del., 1978-89. Mem. Presdl. Commn. Superconductivity, 1989. Recipient Phila. chpt. Am. Inst. Chemists award, 1988. Mem. Am. Chem. Soc. (award Del. sect. 1978). Editor Materials Rsch. Bull., 1994—; editorial bd. Inorganic Chemistry Rev., 1979—, Jour. Catalysis, 1986—, Applied Catalysis, 1987—, Solid State Scis., 1987—, Chemistry of Materials, 1988—, Materials Chemistry and Physics, 1988—, Jour. of Solid State Chemistry, 1988—; patentee in field; contbr. articles to profl. jours. Home: PO Box 907 Philomath OR 97370-0578 Office: Oreg State U Dept Chemistry Gilbert 153 Corvallis OR 97331-4003

SLEMON, GORDON RICHARD, electrical engineering educator; b. Bowmanville, Ont., Can., Aug. 15, 1924; s. Milton Everitt and Selena (Johns) S.; m. Margaret Jean Matheson, July 9, 1949; children: Sally, Stephen, Mark, Jane. B.A.Sc., U. Toronto, 1946, M.A.Sc., 1948; D.I.C., Imperial Coll. Sci., London (Eng.) U., 1951, Ph.D., 1952; D of Engring. (hon.), Meml. U. Nfld., 1994. Asst. prof. elec. engring. N.S. Tech. Coll., Can., 1953-55; assoc. prof. U. Toronto, Ont., Can., 1955-63, prof., 1964-90, chmn. dept. elec. engring., 1966-76, dean of faculty of applied sci. and engring., 1979-86, prof. emeritus, 1990—; Colombo plan adviser, India, 1963-64; pres. Elec. Engring. Consociates, 1976-79; bd. dirs. Inverpower Controls Ltd. Author: (with J.M. Ham) Scientific Basis of Electrical Engineering, Magnetoelectric Devices, (with A. Straughen) Electric Machinery; (with S.B. Dewan, A. Straughen) Power Semiconductor Drives, Electric Machines and Drives; contbr. articles to profl. jours. Chmn. bd. Innovations Found., 1980—, Microelectronics Devel. Ctr., 1983-88. Recipient excellence in teaching award Western Electric, 1965, Can. Centennial medal, 1967, Ross medal, 1978, 83, Gold medal Jugoslav Union of Nikola Tesla Socs., Engring. Alumni medal, Educator of Yr. award Can. Engrs., 1992, Hall of Distinction award U. Toronto, 1992. Fellow Can. Acad. Engring., Engring. Inst. Can., Instn. Elec. Engrs. (officer of Order of Can. 1995), IEEE (Centennial medal 1984, Nikola Tesla award); mem. Am. Soc. Engring. Edn., others. Patentee in field. Home: 40 Chatfield Dr, Don Mills, ON Canada Office: U Toronto, Faculty Applied Sci and Engring, Toronto, ON Canada

SLEPIAN, DAVID, mathematician, communications engineer; b. Pitts., June 30, 1923; s. Joseph and Rose Grace (Myerson) S.; m. Janice Dorothea Berek, Apr. 18, 1950; children: Steven Louis, Don Joseph, Anne Maria. Student, U. Mich., 1941-43; MA, Harvard U., 1947, PhD, 1949; postdoctoral studies, Cambridge U., Eng., 1949, Sorbonne, Paris, 1950. With AT&T Bell Labs., Murray Hill, N.J., 1950-82, head math. studies dept., 1970-82; prof. elec. engring. U. Hawaii, Honolulu, 1970-81; McKay prof. elec. engring. U. Calif., Berkeley, 1957-58, Regents lectr., 1977. Editor, author: Development of Information Theory, 1973; contbr. articles to profl. jours.; patentee in field. Served with U.S. Army, 1943-46, ETO. Von Neumann lectr. Soc. for Indsl. and Applied Math., 1982; Parker fellow in physics Harvard U., 1949-50. Fellow IEEE (editor Procs. 1969-70, Alexander Graham Bell award 1981), AAAS, Inst. Math. Stats.; mem. NAS, NAE, Am. Acad. Arts and Scis. Avocations: music, travel, languages. Home: 212 Summit Ave Summit NJ 07901-2966

SLEPIAN, PAUL, mathematician, educator; b. Boston, Mar. 26, 1923; s. Philip and Ida (Goldstein) S.; children—Laura, Jean. S.B., Mass. Inst. Tech., 1950; Ph.D., Brown U., 1956. Mathematician Hughes Aircraft Co., 1956-60; assoc. prof. math. U. Ariz., 1960-62; assoc. prof. Rensselaer Poly. Inst., Troy, N.Y., 1962-65; prof. math. Rensselaer Poly. Inst., 1965-69; prof., chmn. dept. math. Bucknell U., Lewisburg, Pa., 1969-70; prof. math. Howard U., Washington, 1970—; summer vis. staff mem. Los Alamos Sci. Lab., 1976, 78, 79. Mem. Am. Math. Soc., Soc. Indsl. and Applied Math., Math. Assn. Am. Home: 1331 W 40th St Baltimore MD 21211-1728

SLESNICK, WILLIAM ELLIS, mathematician, educator; b. Oklahoma City, Feb. 24, 1925; s. Isaac Ralph and Adele (Miller) S. B.S., U.S. Naval Acad., 1945; B.A., U. Okla., 1948; B.A. (Rhodes scholar), Oxford (Eng.) U., 1950, M.A., 1954; A.M.; Harvard, 1952; A.M. (hon.), Dartmouth, 1972. Math. master St. Paul's Sch., Concord, N.H., 1952-62; vis. instr. Dartmouth Coll., 1958-59, mem. faculty, 1062-94, prof. math., 1971-94; prof. emeritus, 1994—; asst. dir. ednl. uses Kiewit Computation Center, 1966-69; mem. N.H. Rhodes Scholar Selection Com.; mem. advanced placement exam. com. math. Coll. Entrance Exam. Bd., 1967-71; mem. Nat. Humanities Faculty, 1972—. Co-author: 12 math. textbooks including (with R.H. Crowell) Calculus With Analytic Geometry, 1968. Active Boy Scouts Am., 1937—,

attache world bur., 1955, 67, coun. exec. bd., 1964—, dist. chmn., 1974-76; mem. nat. com. Order of Arrow, 1965—, mem. internat. com., 1974-93; mem. Nat. Jewish Com. Scouting, 1973—, internat. ambassador, 1993—; mem. assembly of overseers Mary Hitchcock Meml. Hosp., Hanover; trustee Lawrence L. Lee Mus., Hanover-Norwich Youth Fund, New Hampton (N.H.) Sch., 1975-81; mem. selection com. Okla. Found. for Excellence, 1986-91. With USN, 1942-47. Recipient Vigil Honor, 1948, Nat. Disting. Svc. award Order of Arrow, 1967, Silver Beaver award Boy Scouts Am., 1967, Silver Antelope award, 1972, Disting. Svc. award Daniel Webster Coll., 1994, Wendell C. Badger award Dartmouth Coll., 1978, Disting. Eagle Scout award, 1979, Shofar award, 1979, Silver Buffalo award, 1990, Presidential medal Dartmouth Coll., 1991. Mem. Nat. Council Tchrs. Math., Math. Assn. Am., Assn. Tchrs. Math. in New Eng., Assn. Am. Rhodes Scholars, Phi Beta Kappa (chpt. pres. 1974-77), Phi Eta Sigma, Pi Mu Epsilon, Alpha Phi Omega. Home: 306 Kendal at Hanover 80 Lyme Rd Hanover NH 03755-1218

SLETTEBAK, ARNE, astronomer, educator; b. Free City of Danzig, Aug. 8, 1925; came to U.S., 1927, naturalized, 1932; s. Nicolai and Valerie (Janczak) S.; m. Constance Pixler, Aug. 28, 1949; children: Marcia Diane, John Andrew. B.S. in Physics, U. Chgo., 1945, Ph.D. in Astronomy, 1949. Mem. faculty Ohio State U., Columbus, 1949—, prof. astronomy, 1959—, chmn. dept. astronomy, 1962-78; dir. Perkins Obs., Delaware, Ohio, 1959-78, mem. steering com. Earth Sci. Curriculum Project, 1965-68; mem. NRC Commn. on Astronomy adv. to Office Naval Research, 1963-65, chmn., 1965-66; mem. adv. panel for astronomy NSF, 1968-71; Fulbright lectr., vis. prof. U. Vienna, 1974-75, 81, 91; vis. prof. U. Louis Pasteur, Strasbourg, 1991; mem. nat. screening com. grad. study grants Fulbright Com., 1987-89. Fulbright rsch. fellow Hamburg, Fed. Republic Germany, 1955-56, Japan Soc. for Promotion Sci. fellow, 1988. Mem. Assn. Univs. for Research Astronomy (dir. 1961-79, chmn. sci. com. 1970-73), Am. Astron. Soc. (coun. 1964-67), Internat. Astron. Union (v.p. commn. 45, 1976-79, pres. 1979-82, chmn. working group on Be stars, 1982-85), Sigma Xi. Home: 601 Seabury Dr Worthington OH 43085-3557 Office: Ohio State U Dept Astronomy Columbus OH 43210

SLETTEN, JOHN ROBERT, construction company executive; b. Gt. Falls, Mont., Sept. 19, 1932; s. John and Hedvig Marie (Finstad) S.; m. Patricia Gail Thomas, Dec. 16, 1962; children: Leighanne, Kristen Gail, Erik John. BS in Archtl. Engring., Mont. State U., 1956. Estimator Sletten Constrn. Co., Gt. Falls, 1956-63; v.p., area mgr. Sletten Constrn. Co., Las Vegas, Nev., 1963-65; pres., chief exec. officer Sletten Constrn. Co., Gt. Falls, 1969—; bd. dirs. 1st Banks, Gt. Falls, Blue Cross-Blue Shield, Helena, Mont. Chmn. Gt. Falls Mil. Affairs Com., 1985; pres. President's Cir., Mont. State U., Bozeman, 1986; trustee Mont. Hist. Soc., Helena, 1987. with USMC, 1950-52. Mem. Mont. Contractors Assn. (bd. dirs. 1969-75, pres. 1974), Mont. C. of C. (chmn. 1984), Pachyderm Club, Rotary (bd. dirs. Gt. Falls), Elks. Republican. Lutheran. Avocations: skiing, fishing, hunting. Office: Sletten Inc 1000 25th St N PO Box 2467 Great Falls MT 59403-2467

SLEWITZKE, CONNIE LEE, retired army officer; b. Mosinee, Wis., Apr. 15, 1931; d. Leo Thomas and Amelia Marie (Hoffman) S. BSN, U. Md., Balt., 1971; MA in Counseling and Guidance, St. Mary's U., San Antonio, 1976. Commd. 1st lt. U.S. Army, 1957, advanced through grades to brig. gen., 1987; ret., 1987; chief dept. nursing Letterman Army Med. Ctr. U.S. Army, San Francisco, 1978-80; asst. chief nurse Army Nurse Corps U.S. Army, Washington, 1980-83; chief brigadier gen. U.S. Army, 1983-87; mem. Va. Adv. Com. on Women Vets. Contbr. articles to profl. jours. Decorated D.S.M., Legion of Merit, Bronze Star medal. Mem. ANA, Va. Nurses Assn., Alumni Assn. U.S. Army War Coll., Assn. U.S. Army, Women in Mil. Svc. for Am. Found. (v.p.), Sigma Theta Tau. Avocations: photography; travel; music.

SLICHTER, CHARLES PENCE, physicist, educator; b. Ithaca, N.Y., Jan. 21, 1924; s. Sumner Huber and Ada (Pence) S.; m. Gertrude Thayer Almy, Aug. 23, 1952 (div. Sept. 1977); children: Sumner Pence, William Almy, Jacob Huber, Ann Thayer; m. Anne FitzGerald, June 7, 1980; children—Daniel Huber, David Pence. AB, Harvard U., 1946, MA, 1947, PhD, 1949. Research asst. Underwater Explosives Research Lab., Woods Hole, Mass., 1944-46; mem. faculty U. Ill., Urbana, 1949—, prof. physics, 1955—, prof. Ctr. for Advanced Study, 1968—, prof. chemistry, 1986—; Morris Loeb lectr. Harvard U., 1961; dir. Polaroid Co.; mem. Pres.'s Sci. Adv. Com., 1964-69, Com. on Nat. Medal Sci., 1969-74, Nat. Sci. Bd., 1975-84, Pres.'s Com. Sci. and Tech., 1976. Author: Principles of Magnetic Resonance, 1963, 3d edit., 1989; Contbr. articles to profl. jours. Former trustee, mem. corp. Woods Hole Oceanographic Instn. Recipient Langmuir award Am. Phys. Soc., 1969; Alfred P. Sloan fellow, 1955-61. Mem. Nat. Acad. Scis. (Comstock prize 1993), Am. Acad. Arts and Scis., Am. Philos. Soc., Internat. Soc. Magnetic Resonance (pres. 1987-90, Triennie prize 1986), Harvard Corp. Home: 61 Chestnut Ct Champaign IL 61821-7121

SLICK, GRACE WING, singer; b. Chgo., Oct. 30, 1939; d. Ivan W. and Virginia (Barnett) Wing; m. Gerald Robert Slick, Aug. 26, 1961 (div. 1970); 1 dau., China; m. Skip Johnson, Nov. 29, 1976. Student, Finch Coll., 1957-58, U. Miami, Fla., 1958-59. Singer with, Great Society, 1965-66, Jefferson Airplane, 1966-72, Jefferson Starship, 1974—; solo albums include: Manhole, 1974, The Best of the Great Society, Dreams, 1980, Welcome to the Wrecking Ball, 1981, Software, 1984; albums with Jefferson Starship include: Surrealistic Pillow, 1967, Earth, 1978, Modern Times, 1980, Winds of Change, 1982, Blows against the Empire, 1988, DragonFly, 1988, Freedom at Point Zero, 1979, Nuclear Furniture, Red Octopus, 1975, Jefferson Airplane, 1989, Gold, 1991, Jefferson Airplane Loves You, 1992, Jefferson Starship at their Best, 1993; albums with Starship included Knee Deep in the Hoopla, 1985, No Protection, 1987, Love Among The Cannibals, 1989, Greatest Hits (Ten Years and Change), 1991. Office: care Starship 1319 Broadway Sausalito CA 94965*

SLIEPCEVICH, CEDOMIR M., engineering educator; b. Anaconda, Mont., Oct. 4, 1920; s. Maksim and Jovanka (Lubibratich) S.; m. Cleo L. Whorton, Oct. 21, 1955. BS, U. Mich., 1941, MS, 1942, PhD, 1948. Assoc. prof. dept. chem. and metall. engring. U. Mich., 1946-55; prof., chmn. Sch. Chem. Engring.; also assoc. dean Coll. Engring., U. Okla., 1955-62, George Lynn Cross Rsch. prof., 1963-91, Robert W. Hughes Centennial prof. engring., 1989-91, prof. emeritus, 1991—; pres. Univ. Engrs., Inc., 1965-78, Univ. Technologists, Inc., 1977—; cons. chem. engr. Author numerous tech. papers. Recipient Curtis W. McGraw Research award, 1958; Ipatieff award, 1959; George Westinghouse award, 1964; Sesquicentennial award U. Mich., 1967; Okla. Outstanding Scientist award, 1975; Disting. Service citation U. Okla., 1975; William H. Walker award, 1978; Gas Industry Research award 1986; named Okla. Profl. Engr. of Yr., 1973, Nat. Profl. Engr. of Year, 1974; inducted into Okla. Hall Fame, 1974. Fellow Am. Inst. Chem. Engrs.; mem. Nat. Acad. Engrs., U. Okla. Coll. Engring. Disting. Grads. Soc. (1st hon. mem.). Home: RR 1 Box 41-B1 Washington OK 73093

SLIFKA, ALFRED A., oil corporation executive; b. Boston, June 3, 1932; s. Abraham and Sonya S.; m. Gilda Koritz; children: Adam, Jennifer, Eric. Grad. high sch., Boston, 1949. Pres., dir., co-owner Global Petroleum Corp., Waltham, Mass., CEO; bd. dirs. New England Fuel Inst., 1974—, Better Home Heat Coun., Petroleum Inst. Rsch. Found., N.Y.C.; past bd. dirs. U.S. Trust Co., Boston. Contbr. articles to profl. jours. vice chmn. Hebrew Rehab. Ctr., Boston; trustee Combined Jewish Philanthropies, Boston; bd. dirs. Griffith Consumers Co., Cheverly, Md. With U.S. Army. Mem. N.Y. Merc. Exch., Pine Brook Country Club (past gov. 1985-89). Avocations: jogging, golf, tennis. Office: Global Petroleum Corp 800 South St Waltham MA 02154*

SLIFKIN, LAWRENCE MYER, physics educator; b. Bluefield, W.Va., Sept. 29, 1925; s. Isaac L. and Eva (Baden) S.; m. Miriam Kresses, July 4, 1948; children: Anne, Rebecca, Merle, Naomi. BA, NYU, 1947; PhD, Princeton U., 1950. Rsch. assoc., asst. prof. U. Ill., Urbana, 1950-54; asst prof. U. Minn., Mpls., 1954-55; asst. prof., then prof. physics U.N.C., Chapel Hill, 1955-91, Bowman Gray prof., 1979-82, Alumni Disting. prof., 1983-91, prof. emeritus, 1991—; liaison sci. U.S. Office Naval Rsch., London, 1969-70; collaborateur étranger, CEN-Saclay, France, 1975-76. Editor: (with J. H. Crawford): Point Defects in Solids, vol. I, 1972, vol. II,

1975; contbr. more than 125 articles to profl. jours. and books. With U.S. Army, 1944-46, PTO. Fellow Am. Phys. Soc. (exec. com. div. condensed matter physics 1978-80, Jesse Beams award rsch. excellence S.E. Sect. 1977), Soc. Photographic Scientists and Engrs.; mem. Am. Assn. Physics Tchrs. Democrat. Jewish. Avocations: music, travel, reading, swimming, grandfathering. Home: 313 Burlage Cir Chapel Hill NC 27514-2703 Office: U NC-Chapel Hill Cb 3255 Phillips Hall Chapel Hill NC 27599

SLINGER, MICHAEL JEFFERY, law library director; b. Pitts., Apr. 12, 1956; s. Maurice and Mary Helen (Kengerski) S.; m. Cheryl Blaney, Apr. 19, 1980; children: Rebecca, Sarah. BA, U. Pitts., 1978; M Librianship, U.S.C., 1979; JD, Duquesne U., 1984. Reference libr. Duquesne U. Sch. Law, Pitts., 1983-84; rsch. libr. U. Notre Dame (Ind.) Sch. Law, 1984-85, head rsch. svcs., 1985-86, assoc. dir. pub. svcs., 1986-90; law libr. dir., assoc. prof. law Suffolk U. Sch. Law, Boston, 1990-93, law libr. dir., prof. law, 1994—. Contbr. articles to profl. jours., chpt. to book. Mem. ABA, ALA, Am. Assn. Law Librs., Am. Assn. Law Schs. (creative bd. sect. on law librs. 1993—), New Eng. Law Libr. Consortium (treas. 1992—), Ohio Regional Assn. Law Librs. (v.p. 1987-88, pres. 1988-89, Pres. award 1989). Avocations: reading, sports, family. Office: Suffolk U Law Sch Libr 41 Temple St Boston MA 02114

SLIVE, SEYMOUR, museum director, fine arts educator; b. Chgo., Sept. 15, 1920; s. Daniel and Sonia (Rapoport) S.; m. Zoya Gregorevna Sandomirsky, June 29, 1946; children: Katherine, Alexander, Sarah. A.B., U. Chgo., 1943, Ph.D., 1952; M.A. (hon.), Harvard U., 1958, Oxford (Eng.) U., 1972. Instr. fine arts Oberlin (Ohio) Coll., 1950-51; chmn. art dept. Pomona (Calif.) Coll., 1952-54; mem. faculty Harvard U., Cambridge, Mass., 1954—, prof. fine arts, 1961—, Gleason prof. fine arts, 1973-91, Gleason prof. fine arts emeritus, 1991—, chmn. dept. fine arts, 1968-71, dir. Fogg Art Mus., 1975-82; Elizabeth and John Moors Cabot dir. emeritus Harvard art museums, 1982; exchange prof. Leningrad (USSR) U., 1961; Ryerson lectr. Yale U., 1962; Slade prof. Oxford (Eng.) U., 1972-73. Author: Rembrandt and His Critics, 1630-1730, 1953, The Rembrandt Bible, 1959, Catalogue of the Paintings of Frans Hals, 1962, Drawings of Rembrandt, 1965, (with Jakob Rosenberg and E.H. ter Kuile) Dutch Art and Architecture 1600-1800, 2d edit., 1978, Rembrandt's Drawings, 1965, Frans Hals, 3 vols., 1970-74, Jacob van Ruisdael, 1981, Frans Hals, 1989. Trustee Solomon R. Guggenheim Found., 1978—; Norton Simon Mus., 1989-91; bd. dirs. Burlington mag. Found.—. Lt. (j.g.) USNR, 1943-46, PTO. Decorated officer Order Orange Nassau Netherlands, 1962; Fulbright fellow Netherlands, 1951-52; Guggenheim fellow, 1956-57, 78-79; Fulbright research scholar Utrecht (Netherlands) U., 1959-60. Fellow Am. Acad. Arts and Scis.; hon. mem. Karel van Mander Soc.; mem. Coll. Art Assn. (dir. 1958-62, 65-69), Renaissance Soc., Dutch Soc. Scis. (fgn. mem.). Office: Harvard U Sackler Art Museum Cambridge MA 02138

SLIWA, STEVEN MARK, engineering executive, academic administrator. BS in Engring., Princeton (N.J.) U., 1977; MEng, George Washington U., 1978; Phd in Engring., Stanford U., 1983, M in Bus. Mgmt., 1989. Program mgr. controls and human factors div. NASA, Washington; dep. div. chief guidance and control div. NASA/Langley Rsch. Ctr., Hampton, Va.; v.p. product devel. Integrated Systems, Inc., Santa Clara, Calif., 1989—; pres. Embry-Riddle Aero. U., Dayton Beach, Fla., 1991—; chmn. nat. flying qualities strategic planning and flight systems planning coms. Nat. Aerospace Plane Tech. Maturation Plan; owner Sliwa Enterprises, Inc.; tchr. grad. level engring. in automatic controls for flight vehicles George Washington U., 1987, 88. NASA fellow. Fellow AIAA (chmn. guidance, navigation and control tech. com., past adv. bd. Jour. of Guidance). Office: Embry-Riddle Aero U Office of President 600 S Clyde Morris Blvd Daytona Beach FL 32114-3966*

SLOAN, ALLAN HERBERT, journalist; b. Bklyn., Nov. 27, 1944; s. Samuel and Doris (Shanblott) S.; m. Nancy Nolan, June 29, 1969; children: Sharon R., Susan M., Dena A. BA, Bklyn. Coll., 1966; MS, Columbia U., 1967. Reporter Charlotte (N.C.) Observer, 1968-72, Detroit Free Press, 1972-79; assoc. staff writer Forbes Mag., N.Y.C., 1979-81; writer Money Mag., N.Y.C., 1982-84; sr. editor Forbes Mag., N.Y.C., 1984-88; columnist N.Y. Newsday, N.Y.C., 1989-95; Wall St. editor Newsweek Mag., N.Y.C., 1995—. Author: Three Plus One Equals Billions: The Bendix-Martin Marietta War, 1982. Recipient Loeb award for fin. journalism Loeb Found., 1974, 84, 91, 93, Hancock award for fin. journalism Hancock Found., 1992. Jewish. Office: Newsweek 257 W 57th St New York NY 10019

SLOAN, DAVID EDWARD, retired corporate executive; b. Winnipeg, Man., Can., Mar. 29, 1922; s. David and Annie Maud (Gorvin) S.; m. Kathleen Lowry Craig, Dec. 26, 1947; children: Pamela Jane, John David, Kathleen Anne. B.Commerce, U. Man., 1942. With Monarch Life Assurance Co., Winnipeg, 1946-47; with Can. Pacific Ltd., 1947-88, treas., 1969-88; pres. and chief exec. officer Can. Pacific Securities Ltd., 1985-88; bd. dirs. Citadel Gen. Assurance Co., Citadel Capital Corp., Winterthur Can. Fin. Corp., Norma Products of Can. Ltd., Kent Gen. Ins. Corp., Gen. Ins. Corp. New Brunswick; mem. adv. com. Can. Pension Plan, Can. Govt., 1967-76, chmn., 1974-76. Lt. Royal Can. Army Service Corps, 1942-45. Mem. Fin. Exec. Inst. Can. (past pres. Montreal chpt.), Toronto Soc. Fin. Analysts, Soc. Internat. Treas. (internat. chmn. 1985-86, mem. coun. advisors 1978-87), Assn. Investment Mgmt. and Rsch., U. Man. Alumni Assn., The Toronto Hunt, Royal Montreal Golf Club. Mem. United Ch. Can. Home: 316 Rosemary Rd, Toronto, ON Canada M5P 3E3

SLOAN, DAVID W., lawyer; b. Rahway, N.J., June 23, 1941. AB, Princeton U., 1963; MS, Stanford U., 1965; JD, Harvard U., 1970. Ptnr. Jones, Day, Reavis & Pogue, Cleve.; adj. prof. law Case Western Reserve U., 1975. Office: Jones Day Reavis & Pogue North Point 901 Lakeside Ave Cleveland OH 44114

SLOAN, FRANK ALLEN, economics educator; b. Greensboro, N.C., Aug. 15, 1942; s. Harry Benjamin and Edith (Vortrefflich) S.; m. Paula Jane Rackoff, June 22, 1969; children: Elyse Valerie, Richard Matthew. A.B., Oberlin Coll., 1964; Ph.D., Harvard U., 1969. Research economist Rand Corp., Santa Monica, Calif., 1968-71; asst. prof. econs. U. Fla., Gainesville, 1971-73, assoc. prof. 1973-76; prof. econs. Vanderbilt U., Nashville, 1976-84; Centennial prof. econics. Vanderbilt U., 1984—, chmn. dept., 1986-89; dir. Health Policy Ctr. Vanderbilt U. Inst. Pub. Policy Studies, 1976—; mem. Inst. Medicine, Washington, 1982—; dist. medicine coun. 1990—; mem. Nat. Coun. Health Care Tech., Washington, 1979-81, Nat. Allergy and Infectious Disease Council, Washington, 1971-74; cons. adv. coun. Social Security, Washington, 1983. Co-author: Private Physicians and Public Programs, 1978, Hospital Labor Markets, 1980, Insurance, Regulation and Hospital Costs, 1980, Uncompensated Hospital Care: Rights and Responsibilities, 1986, Insuring Medical Malpractice, 1991. Mem. Am. Econ. Assn., So. Econ. Assn., Western Econ. Assn. Home: 109 Millbrae Ln Chapel Hill NC 27514-1477 Office: Vanderbilt U Health Policy Ctr Box 1503 Sta B Nashville TN 37217

SLOAN, FRANK KEENAN, lawyer, writer; b. Johnson City, Tenn., Oct. 11, 1921; s. Z. Frank and Maria Pearl (Witten) S.; m. Helen Rhett Yobs, Feb. 23, 1946 (dec. 1978); children: Richard O., Lewis W., Christine McC., Frank Keenan; m. Alice E. Hamburger, June 22, 1979; children: Carl Francis, Alline Elizabeth. B.A., U.S.C., 1943, LL.B., J.D., 1948. Bar: S.C. 1948. With firm Cooper & Gary, Columbia, S.C., 1948-62; dep. asst. sec. Dept. Def., Washington, 1962-65; S.E. regional dir. OEO, Atlanta, 1965-67; sole practice law Columbia, 1967-77, 87—; chief dep. atty. gen. State of S.C., Columbia, 1977-87; from instr. to assoc. prof. law U. S.C., 1954-62; syndicated news columnist, Columbia, 1989-94. Author: (with J.F. Flanagan) S.C. Rules of Civil Procedure; contbr. articles to legal jours. Exec. dir., sec. S.C. Dem. Party, 1960-62, county atty., county exec., Richland County, S.C. 1970-72. Served with USN, 1943-46, 51-52; capt. Res. (ret.). Mem. Mil. Order of World Wars, Phi Beta Kappa. Democrat. Lutheran. Clubs: Rotary (Columbia), Forest Lake (Columbia). Home: 3320 Devereaux Rd Columbia SC 29205-1919

SLOAN, HUGH WALTER, JR., automotive industry executive; b. Princeton, N.J., Nov. 1, 1940; s. Hugh Walter and Elizabeth (Johnson) S.; m. Deborah Louise Murray, Feb. 20, 1971; children: Melissa, Peter, Jennifer, William. A.B. in History with honors, Princeton U., 1963. Staff asst. to

Pres. U.S., White House, Washington, 1969-71; treas. Pres. Nixon's Re-election Campaign, Washington, 1971; spl. asst. to pres. Budd Co., Troy, Mich., 1973-74, exec. asst. internat., 1974-77, mgr. corp. mktg., 1977-79; pres., gen. mgr. Budd Can. Inc., Kitchener, Ont., 1979-85; pres. automotive The Woodbridge Group, Troy, Mich., 1985—; bd. dirs. Woodbridge Foam Corp., Cartex Corp., Mfrs. Life Ins. Co., Schneider Corp. Trustee Princeton U.; bd. dirs. The Cmty. House, Jr. Achievement of Can. Lt. USNR, 1963-65. Recipient Outstanding Bus. Leader award Wilfrid Laurier U., 1987. Mem. World Pres. Orgn., Automotive Parts Mfrs. Assn. (past chmn.), Automotive Market Rsch. Coun. (past pres.), Bloomfield Hills (Mich.) Country Club. Republican. Office: Woodbridge Group 2500 Meijer Dr Troy MI 48084-7146

SLOAN, JEANETTE PASIN, artist; b. Chgo., Mar. 18, 1946; d. Antonio and Anna (Baggio) Pasin; children: Eugene Blakely, Anna Jeanette. BFA, Marymount Coll., Tarrytown, N.Y., 1967; MFA, U. Chgo., 1969. Exhibited one-woman shows, G.W. Einstein Gallery, N.Y.C., (5 shows) 1977-85. Landfall Press Gallery, Chgo. and N.Y.C., 1978, 87, Frumkin & Struve Gallery, Chgo., 1981, Roger Ransay Gallery, Chgo., 1987, 89, 92, Adams-Middleton Gallery, Dallas, 1987, Tatischeff Gallery, Santa Monica, Calif., 1989, Steven Scott Gallery, Balt., 1989, Butters Gallery, Portland, Oreg., 1989, 91, 94, Tatischeff Gallery, N.Y.C., 1995, Elliot Smith Gallery, St. Louis, 1994, Peltz Gallery, Milw., 1994, 95; represented in permanent collections Art Mus. Chgo., Cleve. Mus. art, Ill. State Mus., Indpls. Mus. Art, Canton (Ohio) Art Inst., Ball State Mus., Mpls., Inst. Art, Fogg Mus. of Harvard U., Yale U. Art Gallery, Snite Mus. of U. Notre Dame, Met. Mus. Art, N.Y.C., Herbert F. Johnson Mus. of Cornell U., Ithaca, N.Y.; exhibited in various group shows. Fellow, Ill. Arts Coun., 1986; recipient Watson F. Blair prize Art Inst. Chgo., 1981. Studio: 535 Keystone Ave River Forest IL 60305-1611

SLOAN, JERRY (GERALD EUGENE SLOAN), professional basketball coach; b. Mar. 28, 1942; m. Bobbye; 3 children: Kathy, Brian, Holly. Student, Evansville Coll., Evansville, Ind. Professional basketball player, Baltimore, 1965-66, Chicago Bulls, NBA, 1966-76; head coach Chicago Bulls, 1979-82; scout Utah Jazz, NBA, Salt Lake City, 1983-84, asst. coach, 1984-88, head coach, 1988—; player 2 NBA All-Star games; named to NBA All-Defensive First Team, 1969, 72, 74, 75. Office: care Utah Jazz Delta Ctr 301 West South Temple Salt Lake City UT 84101-1105*

SLOAN, L. LAWRENCE, publishing executive; b. N.Y.C., 1947. Grad., UCLA. Chmn. Price Stern Sloan, Inc., West Hollywood, Calif.; pres. Sloan Co. also: 11150 W Olympic Blvd Los Angeles CA 90064-1817

SLOAN, RICHARD, artist; b. Chgo., Dec. 11, 1935; s. Samuel Theodore and Lelia (Beach) S.; m. Arlene Florence Miller, Aug. 11, 1962 (dec. June 1994). Attended, Am. Acad. Art, 1951-53. Advt. illustrator; staff artist Lincoln Park Zoo, Chgo.; master wildlife artist Leigh Yawkey Woodson Art Mus., 1994. Exhbns. include Explorer's Hall Nat. Geographic Soc., Brit. Mus. Natural History, Royal Scottish Acad., Carnegie Mus., Calif. Acad. Scis., Boston Mus. Sci., Am. Mus. Natural History, Nat. Collection Fine Art Smithsonian Inst., Washington, 1979, Leigh Yawkey Woodson Art Mus. (13 exhbns., 1979—), Beijing Mus. Natural History, 1987; Roger Tory Peterson Inst. Natural History nat. mus. tour, 1993, James Ford Bell Mus. Nat. History, U. Minn., 1994; spl. guest artist 1st Vancouver Internat. Wildlife Art Show, 1994; permanent collections Smithsonian Inst., Leigh Yawkey Woodson Art Mus., Ill. State Mus.; pvt. collections throughout world; contbr. Nat. Wildlife Stamp Program, World Wildlife Fund, international stamps; paintings featured Nat. and Internat. Wildlife Mag., U.S. Art, Wildlife Art News, Ariz. Wildlife Mag., numerous others; artist, illustrator Encyc. Brit., 1963, (book) Raptors of Arizona, 1994. Recipient Award of Excellence Cin. Mus. Nat. History, 1984, Award of Merit Anchorage Audubon Soc., 1985. Mem. Soc. Animal Artists (award of excellence 1990). Home: 3322 Swaan Ln Sarasota FL 34235

SLOAN, STANLEY, management consultant; b. Phila., Jan. 7, 1943; s. Jack and Betty Sloan; m. Sarah Meszar, May 25, 1980; children: Rebecca, Susan. AB, Temple U., 1964; MS, Kans. State U., 1966; PhD, U. Wis.-Madison, 1969. Assoc. The Hay Group, Dallas, 1969-71, prin., Atlanta, 1974-78, sr. cons., 1978-94; dir. human resources Pizza Hut, Inc., Wichita, Kans., 1972-74; mng. prin. Sloan Mgmt. Cons., Atlanta, 1995—. Contbr. articles to profl. jours. Officer various cmty. bds., Atlanta, 1979—. Mem. Indsl. Rels. Rsch. Assn., Inst. Mgmt. Cons. (Met. Atlanta chpt., past pres., v.p., chmn. bd. dirs.). Avocation: jogging. Home: 2340 Haverstraw Ct Atlanta GA 30338-6602

SLOAN, STEPHEN STEHLY, investment banker; b. Rochester, Minn., July 17, 1948; s. Wyman Platt and Jeanne (Stehly) S.; m. Mollie Magill, Sept. 12, 1971; 1 child, Spencer Magill. B.A. in English, U. Ga. Various positions White, Weld & Co., Atlanta, 1971-74; various positions Jared, Mulcay & Co., Atlanta, 1974-75; sr. v.p. E.F. Hutton and Co., Inc., N.Y.C., 1975—. Clubs: Apawamis, Manursing Island (Rye, N.Y.). Avocations: golf; tennis. Home: Julian St Rye NY 10580 Office: E F Hutton & Co Inc 1 Battery Park New York NY 10004-1412

SLOANE, BEVERLY LEBOV, writer, consultant; b. N.Y.C., May 26, 1936; d. Benjamin S. and Anne (Weinberg) LeBov; m. Robert Malcolm Sloane, Sept. 27, 1959; 1 child, Alison Lori Sloane Gaylin. AB, Vassar Coll., 1958; MA, Claremont Grad. Sch., 1975, doctoral study, 1975-76; cert. in exec. mgmt., UCLA Grad. Sch. Mgmt., 1982, grad. exec. program., 1982; grad. profl. pub. course, Stanford U., 1994; grad. intensive bioethics course Kennedy Inst. Ethics, Georgetown U., 1987, advanced bioethics course 1988; grad. sem. in Health Care Ethics, U. Wash. Sch. Medicine, Seattle, summer 1988, 89, 90, 94; grad. Summer Bioethics Inst. Loyola Marymount U., summer, 1990; grad. Annual Summer Inst. on Teaching or Writing, Columbia Tchrs. Coll., summer 1990; grad. Annual Summer Inst. on Advanced Teaching of Writing, summer, 1993, Annual Inst. Pub. Health and Human Rights, Harvard U. Sch. Pub. Health, 1994, Annual Exec. Mgmt. Inst. in Health Care, U. So. Calif., 1995; cert. in ethics corps tng. program, Josephson Inst. of Ethics, 1991; ethics fellow Loma Linda U. Med. Ctr., 1989; cert. clin. intensive biomedical ethics, Loma Linda U. Med. Ctr., 1989. Circulation librarian Harvard Med. Library, Boston, 1958-59; social worker Conn. State Welfare, New Haven, 1960-61; tchr. English, Hebrew Day Sch., New Haven, 1961-64; instr. creative writing and English lit. Monmouth Coll., West Long Branch, N.J., 1967-69; freelance writer, Arcadia, Calif., 1970—; v.p. council grad. students, Claremont Grad. sch., 1971-72, adj. dir. Writing Ctr. Speaker Series Claremont Grad. Sch., 1993—; mem. adv. council sch. and profl. writing Dept. English, Calif. State U., Long Beach, 1980-82; mem. adv. bd. Calif. Health Rev., 1982-83; mem. Foothill Health Dist. Adv. Council L.A. County Dept. Health Svcs., 1987-93, pres., 1989-91, immediate past pres., 1991-92. Ann. Key Mem. award, 1990. Author: From Vassar to Kitchen, 1967, A Guide to Health Facilities: Personnel and Management, 1971, 2nd edit. 1977, 3d edit., 1992. Mem. pub. relations bd. Monmouth County Mental Health Assn., 1968-69; chmn. creative writing group Calif. Tech. Woman's Club, 1975-79; mem. ethics com., human subjects protection com. Jewish Home for the Aging, Reseda, Calif., 1994—, Santa Teresita Hosp., 1994—; mem. task force edn. and cultural activities, City of Duarte, 1987-88; mem. strategic planning task force com., campaign com. for pre-eminence Claremont Grad. Sch., 1986-87, mem. alumni coun., 1993—, bd. dirs., steering com. alumni assn., 1993—, mem. alumni coun., mem. steering com. annual alumni day 1994—, bd. govs. governing com. alumni assn., 1994—, mem. alumni awards com., 1994—, mem. alumni events com., 1994—, mem. vol. devel. com., 1994—; Vassar Coll. Class rep. to Alumnae Assn. Fall Coun. Meeting, 1989, class corr. Vassar Coll. Quarterly Alumnae Mag., 1993—; co-chmn. Vassar Christmas Showcase New Haven Vassar Club, 1965-66, rep. to Vassar Coll. Alumnae Assn. Fall Coun. Meeting, 1965-66; co-chmn. Vassar Club So. Calif. Annual Book Fair, 1970-71; chmn. creative writing group Yale U. Newcomers, 1965-66, dir. creative writing group Yale U. Women's Orgn., 1966-67; grad. AMA Ann. Health Reporting Conf., 1992, 93; mem. exec. program network UCLA Grad. Sch. Mgmt., 1987—; trustee Ctr. for Improvement of Child Caring, 1981-83; mem. League Crippled Children, 1982—; bd. dirs., 1988-91, treas. for gen. meetings, 1990-91, chair hostesses com., 1988-89, pub. rels. com., 1990-91; bd. dirs. L.A. Commn. on Assaults Against Women, 1983-84; v.p. Temple Beth David, 1983-86; mem. cmty. rels. com. Jewish Fedn. Council Greater Los Angeles, 1985-87; del. Task Force on Minorities in Newspaper

Bus., 1987-89; cmty. rep. County Health Ctrs. Network Tobacco Control Program, 1991. Recipient cert. of appreciation City of Duarte, 1988, County of L.A., 1988; Coro Found. fellow, 1979; named Calif. Communicator of Achievement, Woman of Yr. Calif. Press Women, 1992. Fellow Am. Med. Writers Assn. (pres. Pacific Southwest chpt. 1987-89, Pacific S.W. del. to nat. bd. 1980-87, 89-91, chmn. various conv. coms., chmn. nat. book awards trade category 1982-83, chmn. Nat. Conv. Networking Luncheon 1983, 84, chmn. freelance and pub. relations coms. Nat. Midyr. Conf. 1983-84, workshop leader ann. conf. 1984-87, 90, 91, 92, nat. chmn. freelance sect. 1984-85, gen. chmn. 1985, Asilomar Western Regional Conf., gen. chmn. 1985, workshop leader 1985, program co-chmn. 1987, speaker 1985, 88-89, program co-chmn. 1989, nat. exec. bd. dirs. 1985-86, nat. administr. sects. 1985-86, pres.-elect Pacific S.W. chpt. 1985-87, pres. 1987-89, immediate past pres. 1989-91, bd. dirs., 1991-93, moderator gen. session nat. conf. 1987, chair gen. session nat. conf.. 1986-87, chair Walter C. Alvarez Meml. Found. award 1986-87, Appreciation award for outstanding leadership 1989, named to Workshop Leaders Honor Roll 1991); mem. Women in Comm. (dir. 1980-82, 89-90, v.p. cmty. affairs 1981-82, N.E. area rep. 1980-81, chmn. awards banquet 1982, sem. leader, speaker ann. nat. profl. conf., 1985, program adv. com. L.A. chpt. 1987, v.p. activities 1989-90, chmn. Los Angeles chpt. 1st ann. Agnes Underwood Freedom of Info. Awards Banquet 1982, recognition award 1983, nominating com. 1982, 83, com. Women of the Press Awards luncheon 1988, Women in Comm. awards luncheon 1988), Am. Assn. for Higher Edn., AAUW (legis. chmn. Arcadia br. 1976-77, books and plays chmn. Arcadia br. 1973-74, creative writing chmn. 1969-70, 1st v.p. program dir. 1975-76, networking chmn. 1981-82, chmn. task force promoting individual liberties 1987-88, named Woman of Yr., Woman of Achievement award 1986, cert. of appreciation 1987), Coll. English Assn., Am. Pub. Health Assn., Am. Soc. Law, Medicine and Ethics, Calif. Press Women (v.p. programs L.A. chpt. 1982-85, pres. 1985-87, state pres. 1987-89, past immediate past state pres. 1989-91, chmn. state speakers bur. 1989—, del nat. bd. 1989—, moderator ann. spring conv., 1990, 92, chmn. nominating com. 1990-91, Calif. lit. dir. 1990-92, dir. state lit. com. 1990-92, dir. family literacy day Calif., 1990, Cert. of Appreciation, 1991, named Calif. Communicator of Achievement 1992), AAUP, Internat. Comm. Assn., N.Y. Acad. Scis., Ind. Writers So. Calif. (bd. dirs. 1989-90, dir. Specialized Groups 1989-90, dir. at large 1989-90, bd. dirs. corp. 1988-89, dir. Speech Writing Group, 1991-92), Hastings Ctr., AAAS, Nat. Fedn. Press Women, (bd. dirs. 1987-93, nat. co-chmn. task force recruitment of minorities 1987-89, del. 1987-89, nat. dir. of speakers bur. 1989-93, editor of speakers bur. directory 1991, cert. of appreciation, 1991, 93, Plenary of Past Pres. state 1989—, workshop leader-speaker ann. nat. conf. 1990, chair state women of achievement com. 1986-87, editor Speakers Bur. Addendum Directory, 1992, editor Speakers Bur. Directory 1991, 92, named 1st runner up Nat. Communicator of Achievement 1992), AAUW (chpt. Woman of Achievement award 1986, chmn. task force promoting individual liberties 1987-88, speaker 1987, Cert. of Appreciation 1987, Woman of Achievement-Woman of Yr. 1986), Internat. Assn. Bus. Communicators, Soc. for Tech. Comm. (workshop leader, 1985, 86), Kennedy Inst. Ethics, Soc. Health and Human Values, Assoc. Writing Programs, Authors Guild. Clubs: Women's City (Pasadena), Claremont Colls. Faculty House, Pasadena Athletic, Town Hall of Calif. (vice chair cmty. affairs sect. 1982-87, speaker 1986, faculty-instr. Exec. Breakfast Inst. 1985-86, mem. study sect. council 1986-88). Lodge: Rotary (chair Duarte Rotary mag. 1988-89, mem. dist. friendship exch. com. 1988-89, mem. internat. svc. com. 1989-90, info. svc. com. 1989-90) Home and Office: 1301 N Santa Anita Ave Arcadia CA 91006-2419

SLOANE, CARL STUART, business educator, management consultant; b. N.Y.C., Feb. 9, 1937; s. George and Dorothy (Cohen) S.; m. Toby Tattlebaum, Dec. 27, 1958; children: Lisa Beth, Amy Rachel, Todd Cowan. BA, Harvard U., 1958, MBA, 1960. Asst. to pres. Revlon, Inc., N.Y.C., 1960-62; mgmt. cons. Harbridge House, Inc., Boston, 1962-69 ; exec. v.p.; treas. Temple, Barker & Sloane, Inc., Lexington, Mass., 1970-78, pres., CEO, 1978-90, chmn., CEO, 1990-91; prof. bus. adminstrn. Harvard Grad. Sch. Bus. Adminstrn., 1991—; mem. policyholders' examining com. N.W. Mut. Life Ins. Co.; mem. bus. adv. com. Transp. Ctr., Northwestern U., 1984-91; mem. adv. com. Ctr. for Sci. and Internat. Affairs, Kennedy Sch. Govt., Harvard U., 1984—; bd. dirs. Am. Pres. Co.'s Ltd., Oakland, Calif., 1983-90, Moore McCormack Resources Inc. Stamford, Conn., 1976-88, Leaseway Transp., Inc., 1993—, Ionics, Inc., 1995—. Bd. dirs. Harvard-Radcliffe Hillel, Cambridge, Mass., 1987—, chmn., 1994—; bd. dir., trustee Beth Israel Hosp., Boston, 1993—; nat. fund chmn. Harvard U. Bus. Sch., 1987-89, also vis. com. Mem. Assn. Mgmt. Cons. Firms (chmn. 1984-86), Harvard U. Bus. Sch. Alumni Assn. (v.p. 1989, pres. 1989-91), Boston Yacht Club (Marblehead). Home: Sargent Rd Marblehead MA 01945-3744 Office: Harvard Bus Sch Soldiers Field Boston MA 02163

SLOANE, MARSHALL M., banker; b. Somerville, Mass., 1926; s. Jacob and Rose (Jacobson) S.; m. Barbara Gluck, Mar. 7, 1954; children—Barry Richard, Jonathan Gary, Linda Ruth. Chmn. bd., CEO, founder Century Bank and Trust Co., Somerville, Mass., 1969—; chmn. bd., pres. Century Bancorp Inc., Somerville, 1972—, Sloane Furniture Co., 1952-68. Chmn. bd. visitors Boston U.; bd. trustees Boston U.; exec. bd. Boy Scouts Am., trustee Nat. Mus. Boy Scouts Am.; bd. dirs. R.C. Archdiocese of Boston, Catholic Found. of the Archdiocese of Boston, Cath. Charitable Bur. of Boston; mem. Small Bus. Adv. Council (appointed by Pres. Lyndon B. Johnson); active Corp. Mass. Gen. Hosp., Corp. Perkins Sch. for Blind. Served with USN. Recipient Good Scout award Greater Boston Council Boy Scouts Am., 1983, Shofar award Nat. Jewish Relationships Council Boy Scouts Am., 1984, Mortimer Schiff award Jewish Relationships Com. Boy Scouts Am., Commendation from Nat. Baptist Relationships Boy Scouts Am., 1985, Silver Beaver award Boy Scouts Am., 1979, Silver Antelope award, 1983, Silver Buffalo award, 1988, Allah-O-Akbar award Nat. Islamic Com. on Scouting, 1985, Theo. Storer award for svc. to Boston community, 1986, Israeli Peace medal, 1987, St. George medal Nat. Cath. Community, BSA, 1990, Bus. and Profl. award Religious Heritage, 1991, Sword of Hope award Am. Cancer Soc., 1992; named Baden Powell inductee World scout Found. Boy Scouts Am., 1989; decorated Knight of St. Gregory The Great by Pope John Paul II, 1994. Mem. Mass. Bankers Assn., Exec. Club, Algonquin Club, Pinebrook Club, Masons. Jewish. Office: Century Bancorp Inc 400 Mystic Ave Medford MA 02155

SLOANE, NEIL JAMES ALEXANDER, mathematician, researcher; b. Beaumaris, Wales, Oct. 10, 1939; came to U.S., 1961; s. Charles Ronald and Jessie (Robinson) S.; m. Susanna Stevens Cuyler, Mar. 8, 1980. BA with honors, U. Melbourne, Australia, 1959, BEE, 1960; MS, Cornell U., 1964, PhD, 1967. Asst. prof. Cornell U., Ithaca, N.Y., 1967-69; mem. tech. staff ATT Bell Labs., Murray Hill, N.J., 1969—. Author: Handbook of Integer Sequences, 1973; co-author: (with F.J. MacWilliams) Theory of Error-Correcting Codes, 1977, (with J.H. Conway) Sphere-Packings, Lattices and Groups, 1988, 2d edit., 1993, (with A.D. Wyner) Claude Elwood Shannon: Collected Papers, 1993, (with S. Plouffe) Encyclopedia of Integer Sequences, 1995. Fellow IEEE (editor in chief Trans. Info. Theory jour. 1978-80); mem. Math. Assn. Am. (Chauvenet prize 1979, Earle Raymond Hedrick lectr. 1984), Am. Math. Soc. Avocation: rock climbing. Office: AT&T Bell Labs 600 Mountain Ave Rm 2C-376 Murray Hill NJ 07974

SLOANE, ROBERT MALCOLM, hospital administrator; b. Boston, Feb. 11, 1933; s. Alvin and Florence (Goldberg) S.; m. Beverly LeBov, Sept. 27, 1959; 1 dau., Alison. A.B., Brown U., 1954; M.S., Columbia U., 1958. Adminstrv. resident Mt. Auburn Hosp., Cambridge, Mass., 1957-58; med. adminstrt. AT&T, N.Y.C., 1959-60; asst. dir. Yale New Haven Hosp., 1961-67; assoc. adminstr. Monmouth Med. Center, Long Branch, N.J., 1967-69; adminstrt. City of Hope Nat. Med. Center, Duarte, Calif., 1969-80; pres. Los Angeles Orthopedic Hosp., Los Angeles Orthopedic Found., 1980-86; pres., CEO Anaheim (Calif.) Meml. Hosp., 1986-94; pres. Vol. Hosp. Am. West, Inc., Anaheim, 1995—; mem. faculty Columbia U. Sch. Medicine, 1958-59, Yale U. Sch. Medicine, 1963-67, Quinnipiac Coll., 1963-67, Pasadena City Coll., 1972-73, Calif. Inst. Tech., 1973-85, U. So. Calif., 1976-79, clin. prof. 1987—, UCLA, 1985-87; chmn. bd. Health Data Net, 1971-73; bd. dirs. Intervalley Health Plan; pres. Anaheim (Calif.) Meml. Hosp., 1986-94, Anaheim Meml. Devel. Found. 1986-94. Author: (with B. L. Sloane) A Guide to Health Facilities: Personnel and Management, 1971, 3d edit., 1992; mem. editorial and adv. bd. Health Devices, 1972-90; contbr. articles to hosp. jours. Bd. dirs. Health Systems Agy. Los Angeles County, 1977-78; bd. dirs. Calif. Hosp. Polit. Action Com., 1979-87, vice chmn., 1980-83, chmn., 1983-85. Served to lt. (j.g.) USNR, 1954-56. Fellow Am. Coll. Hosp.

Adminstrs. (regent 1989-93, nominations com., 1994—); mem. Am. Hosp. Assn., Hosp. Council So. Calif. (bd. dirs., sec. 1982, treas. 1983, chmn. elect 1984, chmn. 1985, past chmn. 1986, 89), Calif. Hosp. Assn. (bd. dirs., exec. com. 1984-86, 89), Vol. Hosps. Am. (bd. dirs. west region 1986—, vice-chmn. 1990-93, chmn 1993-94, pres. 1995—), Anaheim C. of C. (bd. dirs. 1994). Home: 1301 N Santa Anita Ave Arcadia CA 91006-2419 Office: 12555 W Jefferson Blvd Ste 325 Los Angeles CA 90066

SLOANE, THOMAS CHARLES, lawyer; b. Wilkes-Barre, Pa., Oct. 27, 1922; s. Charles Benedict and Marie Agnes (McHugh) S.; m. Virginia Louise French, June 28, 1952; children: Thomas Henry, Sarah Jane. BA, Pa. State U., 1947; LLB, Columbia U., 1951. Bar: N.Y. 1951. Practice law N.Y.C. 1951-63; dep. gen. counsel Fed. Res. Bank of N.Y., N.Y.C., 1963-76, sr. v.p., sr. advisor, 1976-83; chmn. on Fiscal Agy., 1973-76, Joint Task Force for Planning, 1978-81; mem. Com. on Internat. Monetary Law, 1942-46. Served to 1st lt. USAAF. Democrat. Home: 1278 Clays Tr Oldsmar FL 34677

SLOANE, THOMAS O., speech educator; b. West Frankfort, Ill., July 12, 1929; s. Thomas Orville and Blanche (Morris) S.; m. Barbara Lee Lewis, Nov. 1, 1952; children—Elizabeth Alison, David Lewis, Emily. B.A., So. Ill. U., 1951, M.A., 1952; Ph.D., Northwestern U., 1960. Instr. English, Washington and Lee U., 1958-60; asst. prof. speech U. Ill., 1960-65, assoc. prof., 1965-70, assoc. head dept., 1967-68, asst. dean liberal arts and scis., 1966-67; prof. rhetoric, chmn. rhetoric dept. U. Calif., Berkeley, 1970-92, pres.'s chair 1987-90; dir. Nat. Endowment Humanities Summer Seminar for Coll. Tchrs., 1979. Editor: The Oral Study of Literature, 1966, The Passions of the Minde in Generall (Thomas Wright), 1971, (with Raymond B. Waddington) The Rhetoric of Renaissance Poetry, 1974, (with Joanna H. Maclay) Interpretation, 1972; Donne, Milton and the End of Humanist Rhetoric, 1985; contbr. articles to profl. jours. Served to lt. USNR, 1952-55. Faculty research fellow, 1964; U. Ill. instructional devel. awardee, 1965; Henry H. Huntington Library research awardee, 1967; U. Calif. humanities research fellow, 1974; Guggenheim fellow, 1981-82. Mem. MLA, Renaissance Soc. Am., Speech Communications Assn. Office: U Calif Berkeley CA 94720

SLOCOMB, PAUL D., lawyer; b. Seattle, July 9, 1945. BS, U. Wash., 1967; JD, Harvard U., 1972. Bar: Ill. 1972. Ptnr. Baker & McKenzie, Chgo. Office: Baker & McKenzie 1 Prudential Plz 130 E Randolph Dr Chicago IL 60601

SLOCOMBE, DOUGLAS, cinematographer; b. London, Eng., Feb. 10, 1913. Cinematographer: (films) (with Wilkie Cooper) The Big Blockade, 1942, (with Ernest Palmer) For Those in Peril, 1944, The Girl on the Canal, 1947, The Loves of Joanna Godden, 1947, Another Shore, 1948, (with Jack Parker) The Captive Heart, 1948, It Always Rains on Sunday, 1949, Kind Hearts and Coronets, 1949, Saraband, 1949, Cage of Gold, 1950, Dance Hall, 1950, (with J. Saeholme) Hue and Cry, 1950, A Run for Your Money, 1950, The Lavender Hill Mob, 1951, Crash of Silence, 1952, His Excellency, 1952, The Man in the White Suit, 1952, The Titfield Thunderbolt, 1953, Lease of Life, 1954, The Love Lottery, 1954, The Light Touch, 1955, Decision Against Time, 1957, Panic in the Parlour, 1957, The Smallest Show on Earth, 1957, All at Sea, 1958, Davy, 1958, Tread Softly Stranger, 1959, The Boy Who Stole a Million, 1960, Circus of Horrors, 1960, The Mark, 1961, Scream of Fear, 1961, Freud, 1962, The L-Shaped Room, 1962, Wonderful to Be Young!, 1962, Guns at Batasi, 1964, The Servant, 1964 (British Academy award best cinematography 1964), The Third Secret, 1964, A High Wind in Jamaica, 1965, The Blue Max, 1965, Promise Her Anything, 1966, Fathom, 1967, The Fearless Vampire Killer; or, Pardon Me but Your Teeth Are in My Neck, 1967, Robbery, 1967, Boom!, 1968, The Lion in Winter, 1968, The Italian Job, 1969, The Buttercup Chain, 1971, Murphy's War, 1971, The Music Lovers, 1971, Travels with My Aunt, 1972 (Academy award nomination best cinematography 1972), Jesus Christ, Superstar, 1973, The Destructors, 1974, The Great Gatsby, 1974 (British Academy award best cinematography 1974), Hedda, 1975, The Maids, 1975, Rollerball, 1975, That Lucky Touch, 1975, The Bawdy Adventures of Tom Jones, 1976, Nasty Habits, 1976, The Sailor Who Fell from Grace with the Sea, 1976, Julia, 1977 (Academy award nomination best cinematography 1977, British Academy award best cinematography 1977), Close Encounters of the Third Kind, 1977, Caravans, 1978, Lost and Found, 1979, The Lady Vanishes, 1980, Nijinsky, 1980, (with Paul Beeson) Raiders of the Lost Ark, 1981 (Academy award nomination best cinematography 1981), Never Say Never Again, 1983, The Pirates of Penzance, 1983, Indiana Jones and the Temple of Doom, 1984, Water, 1985, Lady Jane, 1986, (with Beeson and Robert Stevens) Indiana Jones and the Last Crusade, 1989, (TV movie) The Corn Is Green, 1979; dir. photography: (films) Dead of the Night, 1945, Ludwig II, 1954, Heaven and Earth, 1956; photographer: (TV movie) Love Among the Ruins, 1975, (documentary) Lights Out in Europe. Address: 24 Hereford Sq, London SW7, England Office: London Mgt, 235/241 Regent St, London WR1 7AG, England*

SLOCUM, DONALD WARREN, chemist; m. Laurel Hopper, 1990; children from previous marriage: Warren, Matthew. BS in Chemistry, BA in English, U. Rochester; PhD in Chemistry, NYU, 1963. Postdoctoral rsch. assoc. Duke U., Durham, N.C., 1963-64; asst. prof. chemistry Carnegie Inst. Tech., Pitts., 1964-65; from asst. to assoc. prof. chemistry So. Ill. U., Carbondale, 1965-72; prof. So. Ill. U., 1972-81, adj. prof., 1981-84; program dir. chem. dynamics sect., chemistry div. NSF, Washington, 1984-85; program leader div. ednl. programs, sr. scientist chem. tech. div. Argonne (Ill.) Nat. Lab., 1985-90; head dept. chemistry Western Ky. U., Bowling Green, 1990-95, prof. chemistry, 1995—; sr. scientist Gulf Rsch. and Devel. Co., Pitts., 1980-82; vis. prof. U. Ill., 1970, U. Bristol, Eng., 1973, U. Cin., 1976; vis. fellow U. Bristol, 1972; vis. lectr. Carnegie-Mellon U. and U. Pitts., 1983-84; organized symposia on organometallic chemistry and catalysis; cons. in field; mem. bd. dirs. Ctrl. States Univs. Inc., 1986-88, Arts at Argonne, 1988-90; mem. bd. XVth Internat. Com. on Organometallic Chemistry, Warsaw, 1992; mem. NSF/EPSCoR subcom. Ky., 1993-94. Co-editor: Advances in Chemistry Series of Am. Chem. Soc., Vol. 230, 1992, Methane and Alkane Activation (Plenum), 1995; contbr. over 60 articles to profl. jours., chpts. to books. Mem. AAAS, Am. Chem. Soc. (sec. gen. elect catalysis and surface sci. secretariat 1992, sec. gen. 1993, rep. to catalysis and surface sci. secretariat, 1993—, co-chmn. symposium, San Diego 1994—), Chem. Soc. Gt. Britain, Catalysis Soc., Phi Lambda Upsilon, Sigma Xi. Avocations: skiing, music, literature, sports. Office: Western Ky U Dept Chemistry Bowling Green KY 42101

SLOCUM, ELIZABETH, newspaper editor; b. Boston, Mar. 21, 1947; d. William and Elizabeth (Dowell) Dulligan; m. James Jackson Slocum, Nov. 21, 1969. B.S. in Journalism, M.A., U., Columbia, 1969. Reporter So. Illinoisan, Carbondale, 1969; reporter, copy editor North Shore Pub. Co., Milw., 1970-72; reporter, copy editor Milw. Jour., 1972-77, asst. mag. editor, 1972-79, mag. editor, 1979-86, Features/Lifestyle editor, 1986-92, Features editor, 1993, asst. mng. editor Features, 1994—; editor-in-residence So. Ill. U., Carbondale, 1980, U. Wis, Eau Claire, Wis., 1982, U. So. Fla., Jacksonville, 1983; bd. dirs. Nat. Editorial Bd. for Sunday Mags., N.Y.C., 1983-86. Mem. TEMPO, Milw., 1983—. Recipient best mag. story award Milw. Press Club, 1978, Penney-Mo. award for best Lifestyle sect., 1991. Mem. Milw. Press Club (pres. 1979), Sigma Delta Chi (treas. Milw. chpt. 1977). Avocations: skiing, hiking. Office: Milw Jour/Features PO Box 661 Milwaukee WI 53201-0661*

SLOCUM, GEORGE SIGMAN, energy company executive; b. East Orange, N.J., Sept. 9, 1940. B.A., Cornell U., 1962, M.B.A., 1967. Mgmt. trainee Richardson-Merrell, Inc., 1962; v.p. Citibank N.A., 1967-78; v.p. fin. Transco Energy Co., Houston, 1978-80, sr. v.p., 1980-81, exec. v.p., CFO, dir., 1981-84, pres., COO, dir., 1984-87, pres., CEO, dir., 1987-92. Bd. dirs. Houston Hospice, Soc. for Performing Arts, Houston; trustee Boy Scouts Am., Cornell U.; mem. alumni adv. coun. Cornell U. Grad. Sch. Mgmt. Served with U.S. Army, 1963-65. Mem. Am. Gas Assn., Nat. Petroleum Coun. Avocation: tennis. Home: 10776 Bridlewood St Houston TX 77024-5413 Office: Cayuga Lake Farm 3533 R and 90 Aurora NY 13026

SLOCUM, R.C., university athletic coach. Asst. football coach Tex. A&M U. Aggies, 1972-80, 82-89, U. So. Calif., 1981; head football coach Tex. A&M U. Aggies, 1989—. Office: Texas A&M Univ College Station TX 77843-1228*

SLOGOFF, STEPHEN, anesthesiologist, educator; b. Phila., PA, July 7, 1942; s. Israel and Lillian (Rittenberg) S.; m. Barbara Anita Gershman, June 2, 1963; children: Michele, Deborah. AB in Biology, Franklin and Marshall Coll., 1964; MD, Jefferson Med. Coll., 1967. Diplomate Am. Bd. Med. Examiners, Am. Bd. Anesthesiology (jr. assoc. examiner 1977-80, sr. assoc. examiner 1980-81, bd. dirs. 1981-93, pres. 1989-90, joint coun. on in-tng. exams, vice chmn. 1983-86, chmn. 1986-92). Intern Harrisburg (Pa.) Hosp., 1967-68; resident in anesthesiology Jefferson Med. Coll. Hosp., 1968-71; chief anesthesia sect. U.S. Army, Brooke Army Med. Ctr., Fort Sam Houston, Tex., 1971-74; staff anesthesiologist Baylor Coll. Medicne, Houston, 1974-75; attending cardiovascular anesthesiologist U. Tex. Health Sci. Ctr., Houston, 1974-93, clin. asst. prof., 1977-81, clin. assoc. prof., 1981-85, clin. prof., 1985-93; prof., chmn. dept. anesthesiology Loyola U., Chgo., 1993—; chmn. rsch com., co-dir. rsch. labs Tex. Heart Inst., Houston, 1990-93. Contbr. articles to profl. jours. Mem. Am. Soc. Anesthesiologists, Alpha Omega Alpha. Avocations: tennis,jogging. Office: Loyola U Med Ctr Dept Anesthesia 2160 S First Ave Maywood IL 60153

SLOMANSON, LLOYD HOWARD, architect, musician; b. N.Y.C., July 31, 1928; s. Albert Jerome and Dorothea (Jacobson) S.; m. Joan Barbara Kanel; children: Peter, Eric. BArch, Syracuse U., 1949. Registered architect, 18 states including N.Y. and N.J.; NCARB; registered profl. planner, N.J.; registered interior designer, Tex. Archtl. draftsman Rich & Conn Architects, Bklyn., 1949-50; project architect Fordyce & Hamby/ Raymond Loewy, N.Y.C., 1951-53; project architect, assoc. ptnr. Serge P. Petroff, Architect, N.Y.C., 1953-58; project dir. Robert W. Hegardt, Architect, N.Y.C., 1959-60; project architect, ptnr. Fordyce & Hamby Assocs., N.Y.C., 1960-67; ptnr. Fordyce, Hamby & Kennerly, N.Y.C., 1967-69, Hamby, Kennerly & Slomanson, N.Y.C., 1969-72, Kennerly, Slomanson & Smith, N.Y.C., 1972-81; mng. ptnr. Slomanson, Smith & Barresi, N.Y.C., 1981—; arbitrator Am. Arbitration Assn., N.Y.C. Author articles. Served with U.S. Army, 1950-51. Recipient 1st prize for design S.I. C. of C., 1967, 84. Mem. AIA, N.Y. Soc. Architects (Store of Yr. award 1985, Design award 1993), N.Y. State Assn. Architects, Bldg. Ofcls. Conf. Am., Univ. Club, The Players. Avocations: playing music with a big band, photography. Office: Slomanson Smith & Barresi 65 Bleecker St New York NY 10012

SLONAKER, NORMAN DALE, lawyer; b. Havre, Mont., Sept. 16, 1940; s. Frederick and Agnes (Monson) S.; m. Helen Bogumil, Aug. 29, 1964. BS, U. Wash., Seattle, 1962; LLM, Harvard U., 1965. Bar: N.Y. 1966. Assoc. Brown & Wood, N.Y.C., 1965-72, ptnr., 1973—. Office: Brown & Wood 1 World Trade Ctr New York NY 10048-0202

SLONE, ADOLPH, liquor manufacturing executive; b. 1922. BS, Carnegie Inst., 1947. With Schenley Industries Inc., N.Y.C., 1947, now pres., also bd. dirs. Office: Schenley Industries Inc 888 7th Ave New York NY 10106-0001

SLONE, R. WAYNE, utility company executive; b. 1935. Pres., chief exec. officer, chmn. bd. CILCO (Ctrl. Ill. Light Co.), Peoria, Ill. Office: CILCO 300 Liberty St Peoria IL 61602-1404*

SLONECKER, CHARLES EDWARD, anatomist, medical educator, author; b. Gig Harbor, Wash., Nov. 30, 1938; s. William Mead and Helen Spencer (Henderson) S.; m. Jan Hunter, June 24, 1961; children—David Charles, Derron Scott, John Patrick. Student, Olympic Coll., 1957-58; student in Sci., U. Wash., 1958-60, DDS, 1965, PhD in Biol. Structure, 1967. Sci. asst. in pathology U. Bern, Switzerland, 1967-68; asst. prof. U. B.C., Vancouver, Canada, 1968-71, assoc. prof., 1971-76, prof., 1976, head of anatomy, 1981-92, dir. ceremonies and univ. rels., 1989—. Advisor Community Unit YMCA, Vancouver, 1981-92; group com. chmn. Boy Scouts Can., 1976-82. Served with U.S. Army, 1956-61. Recipient Award of Merit Am. Acad. Dental Medicine, 1965; recipient Award of Merit Wash. State Dental Assn., 1965, Dennis P. Duskin Meml. award U. Wash., 1965, Master Tchr. award, Cert. of Merit U. B.C., 1975-76. Fellow Am. Coll. Dentists; mem. Am. Assn. Anatomists (Centennial Gold medal 1987, program sec. 1982-90, v.p. 1991-93, pres. 1994), Can. Assn. U. Tchrs., Sigma Xi (pres. U. B.C. 1981-82, 88-89), Omicron Kappa Upsilon (chpt. sec.), U. B.C. Faculty Club. Anglican. Home: 6007 Dunbar St, Vancouver, BC Canada V6N 1W8 Office: Univ BC, 6251 Cecil Green Park Rd, Vancouver, BC Canada V6T 1W5

SLONIM, ARNOLD ROBERT, biochemist, physiologist; b. Springfield, Mass., Feb. 15, 1926; s. Sam and Esther (Kantor) S.; married, 1951; 3 children; m. 1984. BS, Tufts Coll., 1947; AM, Boston U., 1948; PhD, Johns Hopkins U., 1953. Rsch. asst. nutrition Sterling-Winthrop Rsch. Inst., Rensselaer, N.Y., 1948-49; rsch. asst. pharmacology George Washington U. Med. Sch., Washington, 1949-50; rsch. asst., jr. instr. biology Johns Hopkins U., Balt., 1950-53; rsch. assoc. chemotherapy Children's Cancer Rsch. Found. Harvard U., Boston, 1953-54; head chem. lab. Lynn (Mass.) Hosp., 1955-56; various positions including chief applied ecology, supervisory rsch. biologist, physiologist & biochemist, phys. sci. administr., biotech. mgr. Aerospace Med. Rsch. Lab., Wright-Patterson AFB, Ohio, 1956-86; cons., pres. ARSLO Assocs., Columbus, Ohio, 1987—; lectr. Mass. Sch. Physiotherapy, Boston, 1955-56, Antioch U., 1984-85; mem. internat. bioastronautics com. Internat. Astronautical Fedn., 1966—; mem. environ. carcinogens program Internat. Agy. for Rsch. on Cancer/WHO, Paris, 1981—. Mem. com. on biol. handbooks Fedn. Am. Socs. for Exptl. Biology, 1966-71; mem. editorial bd. Aerospace Medicine, 1967-71; contbr. articles to profl. jours. Served with USN, 1944-46. Mem. Aerospace Med. Assn., Am. Soc. Biochemistry and Molecular Biology, Am. Physiol. Soc., N.Y. Acad. Sci., Internat. Acad. Aviation and Space Medicine, Sigma Xi, Masons, Scottish Rite, Shriners. Office: 630 Cranfield Pl Columbus OH 43213-3407

SLONIMSKY, NICOLAS, conductor, composer; b. St. Petersburg, USSR, Apr. 27, 1894; came to U.S., 1923, naturalized, 1931; s. Leonid and Faina (Vengerova) S.; m. Dorothy Adlow, July 30, 1931; 1 dau., Electra. Ed., Conservatory of Music, St. Petersburg; D.F.A. (hon.), Northwestern U., 1980. Condr. Pierian Sodality, Harvard, 1928-30; instr. Eastman Sch. Music, Rochester, N.Y., 1923-25, Boston Conservatory Music, 1925-45; instr. Slavic langs. and lits. Harvard U., 1946-47; vis. prof. Colo. Coll., summer 1940, 47-49; lectr. music Simmons Coll., 1947-49, Peabody Conservatory, 1956-57, U. Calif. at Los Angeles, 1964-67; guest condr., Paris, Berlin, Budapest, Havana, San Francisco, Los Angeles, Hollywood, 1931-33, S.A., 1941-42. Concert tours as pianist, Europe, 1921-22, U.S., 1923—, S.Am., 1941-42; wrote for ballet, orch., piano, voice.; author: Music since 1900, 5th edit., 1994, Music of Latin America, 4th edit., 1972, Lexicon of Musical Invective, 1953, Perfect Pitch: A Life Story, 1988, Lectionary of Music, 1989; editor: Internat. Cyclo. of Music and Musicians, 4th-8th edits., 1946-58, Baker's Biog. Dictionary of Musicians, 5th edit., 1958, 6th edit., 1978, 7th edit., 1984, 8th edit., 1991, Concise Baker's Biographical Dictionary of Musicians, 1988, 93; mem. Am. music editorial bd.: Ency. Brit., 1958—; contbr. arc. am. music surveys to Ency. Brit. Year Books, 1950-68. Mem. (hon.) Am. Acad. Inst. Arts and Letters. Home: 2630 Midvale Ave Los Angeles CA 90064-4214

SLOOK, GEORGE FRANCIS, finance company executive; b. Phila., Aug. 14, 1946; s. Herbert F. and Eleanor L. (Barth) S.; m. Nancy Kathleen Krupsha, Sept. 23, 1972; children—Sally Ann, George Michael. BSBA, Villanova U., 1968; MBA in Fin., Widener U., 1982. Corp. auditor Sears, Roebuck & Co., Chgo., 1971-72; acct. Sears, Roebuck & Co., N.Y.C., 1972-73; mechanization coord. Sears, Roebuck & Co., Chgo., 1973-75, corp. acct., 1975-77; asst. treas. Sears Roebuck Acceptance Corp., Wilmington, Del., 1977-80, v.p., comptr., from 1980, now sr. v.p. fin., also bd. dirs. Rep. precinct capt., Hoffman Estates, Ill., 1976; treas. Longview Farms Civic Assn., Wilmington, 1979-81; bd. dirs. Jr. Achievement, Delaware, 1985—; treas. 1986—. Served with U.S. Army, 1968-70. Mem. Fin. Execs. Inst. (dir. Phila. chpt. 1985, pres. Del. chpt. 1986), Nat. Assn. Accts. Roman Catholic. Office: Sears Roebuck Acceptance Corp 3711 Kennett Pike Wilmington DE 19807-2102

SLORP, JOHN S., academic administrator; b. Hartford, Conn., Dec. 5, 1936. Student, Ocean Coll., Calif., 1956, Taft Coll., Calif., 1961; BFA Painting, Calif. Coll. Arts and Crafts, 1963, MFA Painting, 1965. Grad. tchr. U. N.D., Grand Forks, 1966; in house designer Nat. Canner's Assn., Berkeley, Calif., 1965; mem. faculty Md. Inst. Coll. Art, Balt., 1965-82; chair Found. Studies Md. Inst. Coll. Art, 1972-78; mem. faculty Emma Lake

program U. Sask., Can., 1967-68, 70; selection, planning group for Polish Posters Smithsonian Instn., Mad. Inst. Coll. Art, Warsaw, Poland, 1977; planner, initiator visual arts facility, curriculum Balt. High Sch. Arts, 1979-81; adjudicator Arts Recognition and Talent Search, Princeton, N.J., 1980-82; mem. Commn. Accredation Nat. Assn. Schs. Art and Design, 1985-88; pres. Memphis Coll. Art, 1982-90, Mpls. Coll Art and Design, 1990—; com. Advanced Placement Studio Art Ednl. Testing Svc., Princeton, N.J., 1975-82; chair Assn. Memphis Area Colls. and Univs., 1986-88. Prodr. film A Romance of Calligraphy; calligrapher various brochures, manuscripts, album covers, children's books. Mem. Hotel aciv. com. City of Memphis and Shelby County Convention Hotel, 1982; adv. bd. Memphis Design Ctr.; bd. trustees Opera Memphis, 1985—, ART Today Memphis Brooks Mus., 1988—. Avocations: painting, calligraphy, computer graphics. Office: Mpls Coll Art Design Office of President 2501 Stevens Ave Minneapolis MN 55404

SLOSBERG, MIKE, advertising executive; b. Phila., Aug. 29, 1934; s. Sam M. and Florence (Frank) S.; m. Joan Shidler, Aug. 29, 1957 (div. 1984); children: Sydney Ellen, Robert Morton; m. Janet Cohn, June 10, 1987. BSBA, U. Denver, 1960. Copy writer Young & Rubicam, Inc., N.Y.C., 1960-65, v.p. creative supr., 1965-69, sr. v.p., assoc. creative dir., 1971-78; v.p. creative dir. Young & Rubicam, Inc. Los Angeles, 1969-71; pres. Wunderman, Rocotta & Kline, N.Y.C., 1978-83; exec. v.p., exec. creative dir. Marsteller, Inc., N.Y.C., 1983-84; exec. v.p., exec. creative dir. Bozell Jacobs, Kenyon & Eckhardt, N.Y.C., 1984-86, pres. direct mktg. div., 1986-87; exec. creative dir. Bronner Slosberg Humprey, Boston, 1987—. Author: The August Strangers, 1978. Mem. Direct Mktg. Assn., Boston Advt. Club, New Eng. Direct Mktg. Assn., The One Club, Direct Mktg. Idea Exchange, Friars Club, N.Y. Athletic Club. Avocations: writing novels, skiing. Office: Bronner Slosberg Humprey 695 Atlantic Ave Boston MA 02111-2623

SLOSHBERG, LEAH PHYFER, museum director; b. New Albany, Miss., Feb. 21, 1937; d. Sisco Knox and Mary Rachel (Sandlin) Phyfer; m. Willard Sloshberg, Dec. 8, 1961; 1 son, Simeon. B.F.A., Miss. State Coll., 1959; M.A. (Woodrow Wilson fellow), Tulane U., 1961. Arts curator N.J. State Mus., Trenton, 1968-69, asst. dir., 1969-71, dir., 1971—. Home: PO Box 190 Stockton NJ 08559-0190 Office: NJ State Mus 205 W State St PO Box 530CN Trenton NJ 08625

SLOTIN, RONALD DAVID, state legislator; b. Atlanta, Jan. 24, 1963; s. Theodore Herbert and Peggy Ann (Schaffer) S. BBA, U. Ga., 1985. Mem. Ga. State Senate, Atlanta, rules com., mem. health and human svcs. com. Office: 304 Legislative Office Bui Atlanta GA 30334

SLOTKIN, RICHARD SIDNEY, American studies educator, writer; b. Bklyn., Nov. 8, 1942; s. Herman and Roselyn B. (Seplowitz) S.; m. Iris F. Shupack, June 23, 1963; 1 child, Joel Elliot. B.A., Bklyn. Coll., 1963; Ph.D., Brown U., 1967; M.A. (hon.), Wesleyan U., Middletown, Conn., 1976. Mem. faculty Wesleyan U., 1966—, prof. English, 1976—, Olin prof., 1982—, chmn. dept. Am. studies, 1976—. Author: Regeneration Through Violence: The Mythology of the American Frontier, 1600-1860, 1973 (Albert Beveridge award Am. Hist. Assn.), (with J.K. Folsom) So Dreadfull a Judgement: Puritan Responses to King Philip's War, 1675-1677, 1978, The Crater: A Novel of the Civil War, 1980, The Fatal Environment: The Myth of the Frontier in the Age of Industrialization, 1800-1890, The Return of Henry Starr, 1988, Gunfighter Nation: The Myth of the Frontier in Twentieth Century America, 1992 (National Book award nominee, 1993); and articles. Fellow Center Humanities; fellow Wesleyan U., 1969-70, 74-75, 80—; fellow NEH, 1973-74, Rockefeller Found., 1976-77; recipient Don D. Walker prize AQ; lit. award Little Big Horn Assocs., 1986. Fellow Soc. Am. Historians; mem. Am. Film Inst., Am. Studies Assn., Am. Hist. Assn., Orgn. Am. Historians, MLA, Western History Assn., AAUP, Authors' Guild, PEN, Western Writers Am. Jewish. Office: Wesleyan Univ English Dept Middletown CT 06459

SLOTNICK, MORTIMER H., artist; b. N.Y.C., Nov. 7, 1920; s. Max S. and Sarah B. S.; m. Phyllis June Gluckin, July 26, 1953; children: Debra Jan, Mark Stuart. B.S.S., CCNY, 1942; M.A., Tchrs. Coll., Columbia U., 1942. Tchr. visual arts, public schs. New Rochelle, N.Y., 1946-64; supr. arts and humanities City Sch. Dist., 1964-72; prin. Davis Elem. Sch., 1972-84; adj. prof. art CCNY, 1964-72; prof. art Coll. New Rochelle, N.Y., 1972-78; adj. prof. edn. Pace U., 1988-93. One-man show Ada Ahrtz Galleries, N.Y.C., 1959, Westport (Conn.) Art Gallery, 1988, New Rochelle Coun. on the Arts, 1989; exhibited in group shows Nat. Acad. N.Y., World Trade Center, N.Y.C., Lever House, N.Y.C., Am. Artists Profl. League, Nat. Arts Club, Salmagundi Club; represented in permanent collections Nat. Mus. Am. Art, Smithsonian Instn., New Britain Mus. Am. Art, Johnson Mus. Art Cornell U., Nat. Archives., Washington, Truman Home, Independence, Mo., F.D.R. Mus., Hyde Park, N.Y., also pvt. and corp. collections. Mem. City Art Commn. New Rochelle, 1977-80. Served with AUS, 1942-46, ETO, PTO. Mem. N.Y. Artists Equity Assn., Allied Artists Am., Am. Artists Profl. League, Coll. Art Assn., Nat. Assn. Humanities Edn., Art. Pub., Am. Artists Group, Bernard Picture Co., McLeery-Cumming Co., Donald Art. Co., Scafa-Tornabene Art Publ. Club: Masons. Home: 43 Amherst Dr New Rochelle NY 10804-1814 *An artist must respect the totality of his art. His work must express his integrity, his honesty and his wish to communicate with the viewer. It must strive toward the sublime. Anything less is unworthy of being called art.*

SLOTT, PHIL, advertising agency executive; b. N.Y.C., Aug. 28, 1942. B.A., Dickinson Coll., Carlisle, Pa., 1964. With Batten, Barton, Durstine & Osborn Inc., N.Y.C.; chmn., chief exec. officer BBDO Ltd., London, exec. v.p., dir.; chmn., chief creative officer Tracy-Locke, Dallas, Tex., 1988—. Served with USAR. Recipient Clio award, One Show award, Art Dirs. Club award, Cannes Film Festival award, Gold Key award.

SLOVIN, BRUCE, diversified holding company executive; b. N.Y.C., 1935. BA, Cornell U., 1957; JD, Harvard U. Law Sch., 1960. Pvt. practice N.Y.C., 1960-64; with Kane Miller Corp., 1964-74, Hanson Industries, Inc., 1974-80; with MacAndrews & Forbes Group, Inc., N.Y.C., 1980—, now pres., dir.; pres., dir. MacAndrews & Forbes Holdings, Inc. (parent), Wilmington, Del.; pres., chief operating officer, dir. Revlon Group, Inc. (subs.), N.Y.C.; chmn. exec. com. Revlon, Inc. (subs.), N.Y.C.; dir. Oak Hill Sportswear Corp., Gulf Resources & Chem. Corp., Moore Med. Corp., Four Star Internat. Inc. Office: Revlon Group 555 SW 12th Ave Pompano Beach FL 33069-3531 also: Revlon Group Inc 35 E 62nd St New York NY 10021-8016 Office: MacAndrews & Forbes 36 E 63rd St New York NY 10021-8005*

SLOVITER, DOLORES KORMAN, federal judge; b. Phila., Sept. 5, 1932; d. David and Tillie Korman; m. Henry A. Sloviter, Apr. 3, 1969; 1 dau. Vikki Amanda. AB in Econs. with distinction, Temple U., 1953, LHD (hon.), 1986; LLB magna cum laude, U. Pa., 1956; LLD (hon.), The Dickinson Sch. Law, 1984, U. Richmond, 1992; LL.D. (hon.), Widener U., 1994. Bar: Pa. 1957. Assoc., then ptnr. Dilworth, Paxson, Kalish, Kohn & Levy, Phila., 1956-69; mem. firm Harold E. Kohn (P.A.), Phila., 1969-72; assoc. prof., then prof. law Temple U. Law Sch., Phila., 1972-79; judge U.S. Ct. Appeals (3d cir.) Phila., 1979—, chief judge, 1991—; mem. hearing panel Disciplinary Bd. Supreme Ct. Pa., 1978-79. Mem. S.E. region Pa. Gov.'s Conf. on Aging, 1976-79, Com. of 70, 1976-79; trustee Jewish Publ. Soc. Am., 1983-89; Jud. Conf. U.S. com. Bicentennial Constitution, 1987-90, com. on Rules of Practice and Procedure, 1990-93. Recipient Juliette Low medal Girl Scouts Greater Phila., Inc., 1990, Honor award Girls High Alumnae Assns., 1991, Jud. award Pa. Bar Assn., 1994; Disting. Fulbright scholar, Chile, 1990. Mem. ABA, FBA, Fed. Judges Assn., Am. Law Inst., Nat. Assn. Women Judges, Am. Judicature Scc. (bd. dirs.), mem. bd. overseers U. Pa. Law Sch., Phila. Bar Assn. (gov. 1976-78), Order of Coif (pres. U. Pa. chpt. 1975-77), Phi Beta Kappa. Office: US Ct Appeals 18614 US Courthouse 601 Market St Philadelphia PA 19106-1510

SLOVITER, HENRY ALLAN, medical educator; b. Phila., June 16, 1914; s. Samuel and Rose (Seltzer) S.; m. Dolores Korman, Apr. 3, 1969. A.B., Temple U., 1935, A.M., 1936; Ph.D., U. Pa., 1942, M.D., 1949. Chemist, U.S. Naval Base, Phila., 1936-45; intern Hosp. U. Pa., 1949-50; research fellow U. Pa. Sch. Medicine, 1945-49, asst. prof., 1952-56, asso. prof., 1956-68, prof., 1968—; vis. scientist biochemistry dept. Tokyo U.; U.S. project officer USPHS Fogarty Internat. Center program Inst. for Biology, Belgrade, Yugoslavia, 1971, 74; vis. prof. Academia Sinica, China, 1983; rsch. scientist Tokyo Met. Inst. Med. Rsch., 1984; vis. lectr. King Edward Meml. Hosp., Bombay, 1990. Contbr. articles profl. jours. Am. Cancer Soc. fellow Nat. Int. Med. Rsch., London, 1950-52; Coll. de France endocrinology inst. rsch. fellow Paris, 1952; sr. internat. fellow USPHS Fogarty Internat. Ctr., St. Mary's Hosp. Med. Sch., London, 1978; recipient glycerine rsch. award, 1954; exch. scholar Tokyo U., 1963, USSR, 1965, 71, India, 1967; recipient alumni award Temple U., 1992. Fellow AAAS; mem. Internat. Soc. Neurochemistry, Am. Soc. Biol. Chemists, Internat. Soc. Blood Transfusion, Am. Physiol. Soc., Belgian Soc. for Anesthesia and Reanimation (hon.), Hungarian Soc. Hematology and Blood Transfusion. Home: 310 S Front St Philadelphia PA 19106-4310 Office: U Pa Sch Medicine Philadelphia PA 19104

SLOVUT, GORDON, reporter. Health and science reporter The Mpls. Star Tribune, Minn. Office: Mpls. Star Tribune 425 Portland Ave S Minneapolis MN 55488

SLOYAN, GERARD STEPHEN, religious studies educator, priest; b. N.Y.C., Dec. 13, 1919; s. Jerome James and Marie (Kelley) S. A.B., Seton Hall U., 1940; S.T.L., Cath. U. Am., 1944, Ph.D., 1948; DLitt (hum.), 1984; DHum, St. Ambrose U., 1995. Ordained priest Roman Cath. Ch., 1944. Asst. pastor in Trenton, Maple Shade, N.J., 1947-50; mem. faculty Cath. U. Am., Washington, 1950-67, chmn. dept. religion, 1957-67; prof. N.T. studies Temple U., Phila., 1967-90, chmn. dept. religion, 1970-74, 84-86; vis. prof. Cath. U. Am., Washington, 1992—, Iowa State U., 1995. English editor: N.T., The New American Bible, 1970; author: Jesus on Trial: Development of the Passion Narratives, 1973, Commentary on the New Lectionary, 1975, Is Christ the End of the Law?, 1978, Jesus in Focus, 1983, 2nd edit., 1993, The Jesus Tradition, 1986, John: "Interpretation" Commentary, 1988, Jesus, Redeemer and Divine Word, 1989, What Are They Saying About John?, 1991, 1, 2, and 3 John, 1995, The Crucifixion of Jesus, History, Myth, Faith, 1995. Recipient Pro Ecclesia et Pontifice medal, 1970, Johannes Quasten medal Cath U. Am., 1985, Michael Mathis award Notre Dame Ctr. Pastoral Liturgy, 1994. Mem. AAUP, Cath. Bibl. Assn., Soc. Bibl. Lit., Cath. Theol. Soc. Am. (John Courtney Murray ward 1981, pres. 1993-94), Coll. Theology Soc. (pres. 1964-66), Liturg. Conf. (pres. 1962-64, v.p 1970-71, 75-88, chmn. bd. dirs. 1980-88), N.Am. Acad. Liturgy (Berakah award 1986). Democrat.

SLOYAN, PATRICK JOSEPH, journalist; b. Stamford, Conn., Jan. 11, 1937; s. James Joseph and Annamae (O'Brien) S.; m. Phyllis Hampton, Nov. 19, 1960; children: Nora, Amy, Patrick, John. BS, U. Md., 1963. Reporter Albany (N.Y.) Times-Union, 1957-58, Balt. News Post, 1958-60, United Press Internat., Washington, 1960-69, Hearst News Svc., Washington, 1969-74; reporter Newsday, Washington, 1974-81, bur. chief, 1986-88, sr. corr., 1988—; bur. chief Newsday, London, 1981-86; chmn. Fund for Investigative Journalism, Washington, 1987—. With U.S. Army, 1955-57. Recipient Best Writing award Am. Soc. Newspaper Editors, 1982, War Reporting award George Polk Awards, 1992, Pulitzer Prize for internat. reporting, 1992. Roman Catholic. Avocations: swimming, tennis, gardening. Home: RR 1 Box 76 Paeonian Springs VA 22129-9701 Office: Newsday 1001 Pennsylvania Ave NW Washington DC 20004-2505

SLOYAN, SISTER STEPHANIE, mathematics educator; b. N.Y.C., Apr. 18, 1918; d. Jerome James and Marie Virginia (Kelley) S. BA, Georgian Ct. Coll., 1945; MA in Math., Cath. U. Am., 1950, PhD, 1952. Asst. prof. math. Georgian Ct. Coll., Lakewood, N.J., 1952-56, assoc. prof., 1956-59, prof., 1959—, coll. pres., 1968-74; lectr. Grad. Sch. Arts and Scis., Cath. U. Am., Washington, 1960-82. Mem. Math. Assn. Am. (bd. govs. 1988-91), Am. Math. Soc., Sigma Xi. Democrat. Roman Catholic. Office: Georgian Ct Coll Dept Math Lakewood NJ 08701

SLUDIKOFF, STANLEY ROBERT, publisher, writer; b. Bronx, N.Y., July 17, 1935; s. Harry and Lillie (Elberger) S.; m. Ann Paula Blumberg, June 30, 1972; children: Lisa Beth, Jaime Dawn, Bonnie Joy. B.Arch., Pratt Inst., 1957; grad. student, U. So. Calif., 1960-62. Lic. architect, real estate broker. Project planner Robert E. Alexander, F.A.I.A. & Assos., Los Angeles, 1965-66, Daniel, Mann, Johnson & Mendenhall (City and Regional Planning Cons.), Los Angeles, 1967-70; pres., publisher Gambling Times Inc., also Two Worlds Mgmt., Inc., Los Angeles, 1971—; v.p. Prima Quality Farms, Inc., P.R.; chmn. Creative Games, Inc., 1992—; pres. Las Vegas TV Weekley, also Postal West, Las Vegas, 1975-79; founder Stanley Roberts Sch. Winning Blackjack, 1976; instr. city and regional planning program U. So. Calif., 1960-63. Author: (under pen name Stanley Roberts) Winning Blackjack, 1971, How to Win at Weekend Blackjack, 1973, Gambling Times Guide to Blackjack, 1983; author: The Beginner's Guide to Winning Blackjack, 1983, According to Gambling Times: The Rules of Casino Games, 1983, The Casino Gourmet, 6 vols., 1984, Casinos of the Caribbean, 1984; also monthly column, 1977—; inventor Daily Digit lottery game; patentee in field. Mem. Destination 90 Forum, Citizens Planning Group, San Fernando Valley, Calif., 1966-67, Rebuild L.A. land use com., 1992—. Served to lt. col. U.S. Army, now Res. ret. Recipient commendation from mayor Los Angeles for work on model cities funding, 1968. Mem. AIA, Am. Planning Assn., Am. Inst. Cert. Planners, Internat. Casino Assn. (sec. 1980—), Res. Officers Assn. (life), Mensa (life). Home: 17147 Vintage St Northridge CA 91325-1653 Office: 16140-B Valerio St Van Nuys CA 91406-2912 *The challenge of being alive lies in the development of one's maximum potential. To do less is to fly in the face of the gifts of creation, to shorten the aspect of one's life and to deny the fullness of existence. "The weakness of the flesh" prevents anyone's full development from reaching fruition but the personal and societal loss lies in giving up too soon, before we have fully tested our limits.*

SLUSHER, KIMBERLY GOODE, researcher; b. Benham, Ky., Oct. 4, 1960; d. Herschel James and Nevelyn Faye (Hayes) Goode; m. Joe Allan Slusher, May 1, 1985; 1 child, Tarah Rene. BS in Agr., Ea. Ky. U., 1982; MS in Agr., U. Tenn., 1989. Rsch. asst. U. Tenn., Knoxville, 1983-89; info. analyst Oak Ridge (Tenn.) Nat. Lab., 1989—, tchr., cons. sci. honors program, 1993. Author: Teratogens: Chemicals Which Cause Birth Defects, 1993. Methodist. Avocations: gardening, piano. Office: Biomed & Environ Info Analysis Sect 1060 Commerce Park Oak Ridge TN 37831-6480

SLUSSER, WILLIAM PETER, investment banker; b. Oakland, Calif., June 20, 1929; s. Eugene and Thelma (Donovan) S.; m. Joanne Eleanor Briggs, June 20, 1953; children: Kathleen E., Martin E., Wendelin M., Caroline E., Sarah A. BA cum laude, Stanford U., 1951; MBA, Harvard U., 1953. Mgr. spl. situations dept. Dean Witter & Co., N.Y.C., 1955-60; partner, sr. v.p. in charge corp. fin. dept., 1960-75, also dir.; mem. exec. com. Shields & Co.; co-mgr. investment banking div., sr. v.p. Paine Webber, Inc., 1975-80; mng. dir., head merger and aquisitions dept. Paine Webber, Inc., N.Y.C., 1980-88; pres. Slusser Assocs., Inc., N.Y.C., 1988—; underwriter or fin. cons. Square D. Co., Times Mirror Co., Ashland Oil, Inc., Ga. Pacific, TRW, Inc., Avon Products, TransAm. Realty Investors, Atex, Inc. subs. Eastman Kodak Co., Perini Corp., Downey Savs. & Loan, Booth Newspapers, Inc., Holly Hill Lumber Co., Stanhome, Inc., Santee Portland Cement Co., Grow Group, Crown Cork & Seal Co., Dr. Pepper Co. of So. Calif., Cap Gemini Sogeti, Ltd., London, De La Rue, P.L.C., London, VNU Inc., Haarlem, Netherlands, Bertlesmann Pub. Co., Fed. Republic Germany, ADT Ltd., London, Bank of Guam, Houghton Mifflin Co., Orion Research, Inc., Pacific Holding Co., also vice chmn., 1969-73; bd. dirs. Ampex Corp., ADT Ltd.; founder original Stockholder Assoc. Mortgage Cos. Lectr. to profl. assns. Mem. Ends of the Earth; bd. fin. advisors Columbia U. Bus. Sch., Calif. Senate Commn. on Local Govt. Investments. Served to 1st lt. USAF, 1953-55. Mem. Investment Assn. N.Y., Soc. Calif. Pioneers, Alpha Delta Phi (exec. council 1956-62, treas. 1961). Clubs: Knickerbocker, Downtown, Stanford Assocs., Harvard (N.Y.C.); Lawrence Beach, Stanford of N.Y. Author numerous articles; contbr.; Handbook of Mergers, Acquisitions and Buyouts, The Mergers & Acquisitions Handbook. Home: 901 Lexington Ave New York NY 10021-5952 also: Slusser Ranch Windsor CA X5492 Office: Slusser Assocs Inc 1 Citicorp Ctr 153 E 53rd St Fl 5100 New York NY 10022-4611

SLUTSKY, KENNETH JOEL, lawyer; b. N.Y.C., Sept. 18, 1953; s. Clement and June (Gross) S.; m. Nancy Ellen Goldfarb, Jan. 15, 1978; children: Rachel, Jason, Jenna. BA, Columbia U., 1975; JD, Harvard U., 1978. Bar: N.J. 1978, U.S. Dist. Ct. N.J. 1978. Assoc. Lowenstein, Sandler, Brochin,

Kohl, Fisher & Boylan, Roseland, N.J., 1978-83; mem. firm Lowenstein, Sandler, Kohl, Fisher & Boylan, P.A., Roseland, N.J., 1984—. Mem. met. N.J. chpt. Am. Jewish Com., Millburn, Jewish Family Svc. Metrowest N.J., Florham Park. Mem. ABA, N.J. Bar Assn. Home: 2 Hampton Ct N Caldwell NJ 07006-4701 Office: Lowenstein Sandler Kohl Fisher & Boylan PA 65 Livingston Ave Roseland NJ 07068-1725

SLUTSKY, LORIE ANN, foundation executive; b. N.Y.C., Jan. 5, 1953; d. Edward and Adele (Moskowitz) S. BA, Colgate U., 1975; MA in Urban Policy and Analysis, New Sch. for Social Rsch., N.Y.C., 1977. Program officer N.Y. Community Trust, N.Y.C., 1977-83, v.p., 1983-87, exec. v.p., 1987-89, pres., chief exec. officer, 1990—; mem., formerly chmn. bd. trustees Coun. on Founds., Inc., Washington, 1986-95. Trustee Colgate U., Hamilton, N.Y., 1989—; vice chmn., bd. dirs. Found. Ctr., Inc., N.Y.C., United Way, N.Y.C. Office: NY Community Trust 2 Park Ave New York NY 10016

SLY, RIDGE MICHAEL, physician, educator; b. Seattle, Nov. 3, 1933; s. Ridge Joseph and Eva Jean (Ruddell) S.; m. Ann Turner Jennings, June 12, 1957; children—Teresa Ann, Cynthia Marie. A.B., Kenyon Coll., 1956; M.D., Washington U., St. Louis, 1960. Diplomate Am. Bd. Pediatrics, Am. Sub-Bd. Pediatric Allergy, Am. Bd. Allergy and Immunology. Intern, resident in pediatrics St. Louis Children's Hosp, 1960-62; chief resident in pediatrics U. Ky. Med. Ctr., Lexington, 1962-63; fellow in allergy and immunology UCLA Med. Ctr., 1965-67; asst. prof., assoc. prof., prof. pediatrics La. State U. Med. Ctr., New Orleans, 1967-78; dir. allergy and immunology Children's Nat. Med. Ctr., Washington, 1978—; prof. pediatrics George Washington U., Washington, 1978—. Author: Textbook of Pediatric Allergy, 1985; mem. editl. bd. Annals of Allergy, Asthma, & Immunology, 1982—, Jour. Asthma, 1982-93, Clin. Revs. in Allergy, 1982—, Pediat. Asthma, Allergy, & Immunology, 1987—; assoc. editor Annals of Allergy, Asthma, & Immunology, 1989-90, editor, 1990—; contbr. articles to profl. jours. Served to capt. USAF, 1963-65. Recipient La. plaque Am. Lung Assn. of La., 1978. Fellow Am. Acad. Allergy, Asthma & Immunology (chmn. com. on drugs 1981-87), Am. Acad. Pediats. (sect. on allergy com. 1972-75), Am. Coll. Allergy, Asthma, and Immunology (Disting. Fellow award 1993); mem. Am. Thoracic Soc., Assn. for Care of Asthma (pres. 1980-81, dir. postgrad. courses 1980—, Pershkin Meml. award 1983), Am. Med. Writer's Assn., Coun. Biology Editors, Phi Beta Kappa. Republican. Baptist. Avocations: music (organ, piano). Office: Children's Nat Med Ctr 111 Michigan Ave NW Washington DC 20010-2970

SLYE, LEONARD FRANKLIN See ROGERS, ROY

SMAGORINSKY, JOSEPH, meteorologist; b. N.Y.C., Jan. 29, 1924; s. Nathan and Dinah (Azaroff) S.; m. Margaret Knoepfel, May 29, 1948; children: Anne, Peter, Teresa, Julia, Frederick. BS, NYU, 1947, MS, 1948, PhD, 1953; ScD (hon.), U. Munich, 1972. Research asst., instr. meteorology N.Y. U., 1946-48; with U.S. Weather Bur., 1948-50, 53-65, chief gen. circulation research sect., 1955-63; meteorologist Inst. Advanced Study, Princeton, N.J., 1950-53; acting dir. Inst. Atmospheric Scis. Environ. Scis. Services Adminstrn., Washington, 1965-66; dir. Geophys. Fluid Dynamics Lab. Environ. Scis. Services Adminstrn.-NOAA, Washington and Princeton, 1964-83; cons., 1983—; vice chmn. U.S. Com. Global Atmospheric Research Program, Nat. Acad. Sci., 1967-73, 80-87, officer, 1974-77, mem. climate bd., 1978-87, chmn. com. on internat. climate programs, 1979, bd. internat. orgns. and programs, 1979-83, chmn. climate research com., 1981-87; chmn. joint organizing com. Global Atmospheric Research Program, Internat. Council Sci. Unions/World Meteorol. Orgn., 1976-80, officer, 1967-80; chmn. Joint Sci. Com. World Climate Research Program, 1980-81; chmn. climate coordinating forum Internat. Council Sci. Unions, 1980-84; vis. lectr. with rank of prof. Princeton U., 1968-83, vis. sr. fellow, 1983—; Sigmx Xi nat. lectr., 1983-85; Brittingham vis. prof. U. Wis., 1986. Contbr. to profl. publns. 1st lt. USAAF, 1943-46. Decorated Air medal; recipient Gold medal Dept. Commerce, 1966, award for sci. research and achievement Environ. Sci. Services Adminstrn., 1970, U.S. Presdl. award, 1980, Buys Ballot Gold medal Royal Netherlands Acad. Arts and Scis., 1973, IMO prize and Gold medal World Meteorol. Orgn., 1974. Fellow AAAS, Am. Meteorol. Soc. (hon. mem., councilor 1974-77, assoc. editor jour. 1965-74, Meisinger award 1967, Wexler Meml. lectr. 1969, Carl-Gustaf Rossby Research Gold medal 1972, Cleveland Abbe award for disting. service to atmospheric sci. 1980, pres. 1986, Charles Franklin Brooks award 1991); mem. Royal Meteorol. Soc. (hon., Symons Meml. lectr. 1963, Symons Meml. gold medal 1981). Home: 21 Duffield Pl Princeton NJ 08540-2605

SMALDONE, EDWARD MICHAEL, composer; b. Wantagh, N.Y., Nov. 19, 1956; m. Karen Ajamian, Aug. 5, 1979; children: Laura, Gregory, Julia. BA in Music, Queens Coll., 1978, MA in Music, 1980; PhD in Music, CUNY, 1986. Lectr. SUNY, Purchase, 1986-90; adj. asst. prof. Hofstra U., Hempstead, N.Y., 1988-90; vis. assoc. prof. New Sch. for Social Rsch., N.Y.C., 1988; adminstrv. dir. Speculum Musicae, N.Y.C. 1988-89; artistic dir. Sounds for the Left Bank, Rego Park, N.Y., 1985-92; asst. prof. Copland Sch. of Music, CUNY, Flushing, 1990—; composer in residence N.Y.C. Pub. Schs., 1994, 95; Carlisle Project Choreographer and Composer Collaboration Commn., 1994. Composer: Two String Quartets, 1980, 86, Dialogue for orch., 1987, Double Duo (flute, clarinet, violin, cello), 1987, Transformational Etudes (solo piano), 1990, Rhapsody for piano and orch., 1992, Suite for violin and piano, 1993. Recipient Standard award ASCAP, 1986—, Creative Incentive award CUNY Rsch. Found., 1992, 95; residency fellow Yaddo Corp., 1986, 87, Composer's fellow Charles Ives Ctr. for Am. Music, 1990, residency fellow MacDowell Colony, 1994, Goddard Lieberson fellow Am. Acad. Arts and Letters, 1993; prize winner Percussive Arts Soc., 1994. Home: 228 Manhasset Ave Manhasset NY 11030-2220 Office: Copland Sch of Music Queens College Flushing NY 11030

SMALE, JOHN GRAY, diversified industry executive; b. Listowel, Ont., Can., Aug. 1, 1927; s. Peter John and Vera Gladys (Gray) S.; m. Phyllis Anne Weaver, Sept. 2, 1950; children: John Gray, Catherine Anne, Lisa Beth, Peter McKee. BS, Miami U., Oxford, Ohio, 1949, LLD (hon.), 1979; LLD (hon.), Kenyon Coll., Gambier, Ohio, 1974; DSc (hon.), DePauw U., 1983; DCL (hon.), St. Augustine's Coll., 1985; LLD (hon.), Xavier U., 1986. With Vick Chem. Co., 1949-50, Bio-Rsch., Inc., N.Y.C., 1950-52; pres. Procter & Gamble Co., 1974-86, chief exec., 1981-90, chmn. bd., 1986-90, dir.; chmn General Motors Corp., Detroit, 1992—, also bd. dirs.; bd. dirs. Gen. Motors Corp., J.P. Morgan & Co., Procter & Gamble. Co. Bd. govs. Nature Conservancy; emeritus trustee Kenyon Coll. With USNR, 1945-46. Mem. Bus. Coun. (exec. com.). Country Club, Queen City Club, Cin. Country Club. Office: GM PO Box 599 Cincinnati OH 45201-0599

SMALES, FRED BENSON, corporate executive; b. Keokuk, Iowa, Oct. 7, 1914; s. Fred B. and Mary Alice (Warwick) S.; m. Constance Brennan, Dec. 11, 1965; children: Fred Benson III, Catherine (Mrs. Jonathan Christensen); children by previous marriage: Patricia (Mrs. Murray Pilkington), Nancy (Mrs. Bruce Clark). Student public schs., Los Angeles. With Champion Internat., Inc., 1933-68, successively San Francisco mgr., 1938-44, Los Angeles, Western div. mgr., 1944-55, v.p. Western sales div., 1955-65, v.p., regional dir., 1965-68; pres. Lewers & Cooke, Inc. div. Champion Internat., Inc., Honolulu, 1966-68; chmn. Securities of Am., Inc., 1968-70; chmn., dir. Hawaiian Cement Co., 1970-84; pres. Transpacific Cons., 1984-94, Plywood Hawaii, 1995—. Trustee Hawaii-Pacific Univ., Hawaii Maritime Ctr.; dir. Hawaiian Ednl. Coun., Unitek Environ. Recipient Disting. Citizen award Nat. Govs. Assn., 1986. Mem. C. of C Hawaii (past chmn.), So. Calif. Yachting Assn. (sr. staff commodore), Balboa Yacht Club (Newport Beach, Calif., sr. staff commodore), Transpacific Yacht (bd. dirs.), Waikiki Yacht (staff commodore), Pacific Club (past pres.), Royal Hawaiian Ocean Racing (vice commodore), Sequoia Yacht Club (Redwood City, Calif., sr. staff commodore). Home and Office: 46-422 Hulupala Pl Kaneohe HI 96744

SMALKIN, FREDERIC N., federal judge. BA, Johns Hopkins U., 1968; JD, U. Maryland, 1971. Atty. office of judge advocate gen. Dept. Army, 1972-74, asst. to gen. counsel, 1974-76; pvt. practice Monkton, Md., 1976; magistrate U.S. Dist. Ct. Md., Balt., 1976-86, judge, 1986—; lectr. comml. law U. Md., Balt., 1978—, SMH bar rev., Balt., 1985-86, 93—, BRI/Modern Bar Rev. Course, Inc., Balt., 1980-81; panel speaker on Utilization of Magistrates at the 1985 fourth cir, Judicial Conf. Capt. U.S. Army, 1968-76, lt.

col. CAP (USAF Auxiliary). Mem. Fed. Bar Assn., Order of Coif, Phi Beta Kappa. Office: US Dist Ct 101 W Lombard St Baltimore MD 21201-2626

SMALL, ALDEN THOMAS, federal judge; b. Columbia, S.C., Oct. 4, 1943; s. Alden Killin and Shirley Edna (Eldridge) S.; m. Judy Jo Worley, June 25, 1966; children—Benjamin, Jane. Duke U., 1965; JD, Wake Forest U., 1969. Bar: N.C. 1969. Asst. v.p. First Union Corp., Greensboro, N.C., 1969-72; assoc. dir., gen. counsel Community Enterprise Devel. Corp. Alaska, Anchorage, 1972-73, v.p., assoc. gen. counsel, First Union Corp., Raleigh, N.C., 1973-82; judge U.S Bankruptcy Ct. (ea. dist.) N.C., 1982—, chief judge, 1992—; bd. govs. Nat. Conf. of Bankruptcy Judges, 1987-90; adj. prof. law Campbell U. Sch. Law, 1980-82; bd. dirs. Am. Bankruptcy Inst.; chmn. Nat. Conf. Bankruptcy Judges Ednl. Endowment, 1993-94; mem. long range planning com. U.S. Judicial Conf.; mem. faculty Nat. Comml. Lending Sch., 1981-82; cons. Nat. Coalition for Bankruptcy Reform, 1981-82. Contributing editor Norton Bankruptcy Law and Practice. Mem. ABA, Am. Bankers Assn. (bankruptcy task force 1980-82), N.C. Bankers Assn. (bank counsel com. 1980-82), N.C. Bar Assn. (bankruptcy council), Kappa Sigma, Phi Alpha Delta. Republican. Office: US Bankruptcy Ct PO Box 2747 Raleigh NC 27602-2747

SMALL, ARNOLD MCCOLLUM, psychologist, educator; b. Springfield, Mo., Sept. 16, 1929; s. Arnold Milroy and Grace Aida (McCollum) S.; m. Greta Faye Crawford, Mar. 22, 1951 (div. 1981); children: Janet, Lawrence, Rebecca, Tara, Brian; m. Gerri Kahn, Jan. 3, 1989. BA with distinction, San Diego State U., 1951; MS, U. Wis., 1953, PhD, 1954. Rsch. assoc. human factor div. USN Elec. Lab., San Diego, 1948-51; staff mem. elec. rsch. lab. MIT, Cambridge, 1951; rsch. asst. dept. psychology U. Wis., Madison, 1951-54; asst. prof. dept. psychology Lehigh U., Bethlehem, Pa., 1954-58; from asst. prof. to prof. various depts. U. Iowa, Iowa City, 1958—, chair dept. speech and hearing, 1984, 93—, dir. div. phys. edn., 1986-89; vis. scholar hearing and speech sci. Stanford U., Palo Alto, Calif., 1976-77; dept. psychology U. Sydney, 1989; cons. RCA, Princeton, N.J., 1960-65, Cen. Inst. for Deaf, St. Louis, 1975-85, VA Med. Ctr., Iowa City, 1970—; prin investigator NSF, Bethlehem, 1956, Iowa City, 1960, 64, 78. Author: Elements of Hearing Science, 1978; contbr. chpts. to books and articles to profl. jours. V.p. Iowa City Community Sch. Bd., 1965-70; pres. Lake Macbride Assn., Iowa City, 1975-77; active Johnson County Regional Planning Com., Iowa City, 1970-74, Land Use Tech. Com., Iowa City, 1972-74, Coralville Lake Assn., Iowa City, 1990—. Recipient Nat. Rsch. Svc. award NIH, 1954, 77, Alumnus of Yr. award Coll. Health and Human Svcs., San Diego State U., 1993. Fellow Acoustical Soc. Am. (editor 1969-77), Am. Speech and Hearing Assn. (editor 1984-89), AAAS; mem. Psychonomics Soc., Midwest Psychol. Assn., Sigma Xi (pres. Iowa chpt. 1972-73). Achievements include research in auditory perception, most significantly in pitch perception, frequency selectivity and attention. Avocations: sailboat racing, running, handball, gardening, sports cars. Office: U Iowa 127C Shc Iowa City IA 52242

SMALL, ELAINE LUCHAK, banker; b. Medicine Hat, Alta., Can., Mar. 31, 1953; d. George and Elizabeth (Szilaggi) Luchak; m. W. Thomas Small Jr. BA in Philosophy, Princeton U., 1975; postgrad., Mich. Inst. Fin., 1981. Securities trader Bankers Trust, N.Y.C., 1975-84; v.p. fin. dept. and corp. coverage group First Boston Corp., N.Y.C., 1984—. Mem. Jr. com. Nat. Down Syndrome Soc., 1985-86, N.Y.C. Opera, 1986-89, 3rd St Music Settlement, N.Y.C., 1989. Home: 1175 Park Ave # 13C New York NY 10128-1211 Office: J P Morgan Securies Inc 60 Wall St New York NY 10260

SMALL, ELISABETH CHAN, psychiatrist, educator; b. Beijing, July 11, 1934; came to U.S., 1937; d. Stanley Hong and Lily Luella (Lum) Chan; m. Donald M. Small, July 8, 1957 (div. 1980); children Geoffrey Brooks, Philip Willard Stanley; m. H. Sidney Robinson, Jan. 12, 1991. Student, Immaculate Heart Coll., Los Angeles, 1951-52; BA in Polit. Sci., UCLA, 1955, MD, 1960. Intern Newton-Wellesley Hosp., Mass., 1960-61; asst. dir. for venereal diseases Mass. Dept. Pub. Health, 1961-63; resident in psychiatry Boston State Hosp., Mattapan, Mass., 1965-66; resident in psychiatry Tufts New Eng. Med. Ctr. Hosps., 1966-69, psychiat. cons. dept. gynecology, 1973-75; asst. clin. prof. psychiatry Sch. Medicine Tufts U., 1973-75, assoc. clin. prof., 1975-82, asst. clin. prof. ob-gyn, 1977-80, assoc. clin. prof. ob-gyn, 1980-82; assoc. prof. psychiatry, ob-gyn U. Nev. Sch. Med., Reno, 1982-85; practice psychiatry specializing in psychological effects of bodily changes on women, 1969—; clin. prof. psychiatry U. Nev. Sch. Medicine, Reno, 1985-86, prof. psychiatry, 1986-95, clin. assoc. prof. ob-gyn, 1985-88, emeritus prof. psychiatry and behavioral scis., 1995—; mem. staff Tufts New Eng. Med. Ctr. Hosps., 1977-82, St. Margaret's Hosps., Boston, 1977-82, Washoe Med. Ctr., Reno, Sparks (Nev.) Family Hosp., Truckee Meadows Hosp., Reno, St. Mary's Hosp., Reno; chief psychiatry svc. Reno VA Med. Ctr., 1989-94; lectr. various univs., 1961—; cons. in psychiatry; mem. psychiatry adv. panel Hosp. Satellite Network; mem. office external peer rev. NIMH, HEW; psychiat. cons. to Boston Redevelopment Authority on Relocation of Chinese Families of South Cove Area, 1968-70; mem. New Eng. Med. Ctr. Hosps. Cancer Ctr. Com. 1979-80, Pain Control Com., 1981-82, Tufts Univ. Sch. Medicine Reproductive System Curriculum Com., 1975-82. Mem. editorial bd. Psychiat. Update Am. (Psychiat. Assn. ann. rev.), 1983-85; reviewer Psychosomatics and Hosp. Community Psychiatry, New Eng. Jour. of Medicine, Am. Jour. of Psychiatry Psychosomatic Medicine; contbr. articles to profl. jours. Immaculate Heart Coll. scholar, 1951-52; Mira Hershey scholar UCLA, 1955; fellow Radcliffe Inst., 1967-70. Mem. AMA, Am. Psychiat. Assn. (rep. to sect. com. AAAS, chmn. ad hoc com. Asian-Am. Psychiatrists 1975, task force 1975-77, task force cost effectiveness in consultation 1984—, caucus chmn. 1981-82, sci. program com. 1982-88, courses subcom. chmn. sci. program com. 1986-88), Nev. Psychiat. Assn., Assn. for Acad. Psychiatry (fellowship com. 1982), Washoe County Med. Assn., Nev. Med. Soc., Am. Coll. Psychiatrists (scientific program com. 1989-96), Ea. Profl. Ski Instrs. Assn. Avocations: snow skiing, culinary arts. Home: 602 Alley Oop Reno NV 89509 Office: 475 Hill St Reno NV 89501

SMALL, ERWIN, veterinarian, educator; b. Boston, Nov. 28, 1924. Cert., Vt. State Sch. Agr., 1943; BS, U. Ill., 1955, DVM, 1957, MS, 1965. Diplomate: Am. Coll. Vet. Internal Medicine, Am. Coll. Vet. Dermatology. Intern Angell Meml. Animal Hosp., Boston, 1957-58; with U. Ill. Coll. Vet. Medicine, Urbana, 1958-92; prof. vet. clin. medicine U. Ill. Coll. Vet. Medicine, 1968-92, assoc. dean alumni and public affairs, chief of medicine, 1970-84, asst. dept. chmn., 1989-92; prof. emeritus, assoc. dean alumni and pub. affairs U. Ill. Coll. Vet. Medicine, Urbana, 1992—. Contbr. articles to profl. jours. Served with USMC, 1944-46, 50-51, PTO. Recipient Nat. Gamma award Ohio State U., 1971, Ill. State VMA Svc. award, 1973, Nat. Zeta award Auburn U., 1974, Bustad Companion Animal Veterinarian award, 1993, Disting. Svc. award U. Ill. Alumni Assn., 1995; named Outstanding Tchr., Nordens Labs., 1967, Outstanding Educator, 1973, Outstanding Faculty Mem., Dad's Assn. U. Ill., 1990, Veterinarian of Yr., Mass. Soc. for Prevention Cruelty to Animals, 1993. Fellow Am. Coll. Vet. Pharmacology and Therapeutics; mem. Am. Vet. Med. Assn. (chmn. coun. edn. 1981-82, chmn. program com. 1983-87, Pres.'s award 1992), Am. Animal Hosp. Assn. (award 1983, Midwest Region Svc. award 1989), Am. Coll. Vet. Dermatology (pres.), Internat. Vet. Symposia (pres.), Am. Assn. Vet. Clinics (pres., Faculty Achievement award 1992), Ill. Vet. Med. Polit. Action Com. (past chmn.), Am. Legion VFW, Moose, Omega Tau Sigma (pres. 1971-79), Phi Zeta, Gamma Sigma Delta. Republican. Jewish. Home: 58 E Daniel St A-4 Champaign IL 61820-5921 Office: Vet Med Adminstrn U Ill Coll Vet Medicine Urbana IL 61801

SMALL, GEORGE LEROY, geographer, educator; b. Malden, Mass., Mar. 27, 1924; s. George Arthur and Alice Mildred (Weston) S.; m. Geraldine H. Koepke, July 4, 1970; 1 dau., Elizabeth Mary. B.A., Brown U., 1950; M.I.A., Columbia U., 1952, Ph.D., 1968. French tchr. pvt. schs. Ariz., 1955-62; instr. geography Hunter Coll., 1964-68; assoc. prof. geography Coll. S.I., CUNY, 1968—; cons. problems of whaling to environ. groups. Author: The Blue Whale, 1971. Served with U.S. Army, 1942-46. Recipient Nat. Book award, 1972; Rotary Found. fellow, 1952-53. Mem. Assn. Am. Geographers. Office: CUNY Coll Staten Is New York NY 10301

SMALL, HAMISH, chemist; b. Newtown Crommelin, North Ireland, Oct. 5, 1929; s. Johnston and Jean (Wilson) S.; m. Beryl Maureen Burley, Mar. 27, 1954; children: Deborah Jane, Claire Leslie. BS, Queens U., Belfast, Northern Ireland, 1949, MS, 1953. Chemist U.S. Atomic Energy Authority,

Harwell, England, 1949-55; rsch. scientist Dow Chem. Co., Midland, Mich., 1955-83; chemist ind. rsch. and consulting, 1983—. Author: Ion Chromatography, 1990; patentee in field; contbr. 30 articles to profl. jours. Recipient Albert F. Sperry award Instrument Soc. Am., 1978, A.O. Beckman award, 1983, Herbert H. Dow Gold Medal Dow Chem. Co., 1983, Stephen Dal Nogare award, 1984, Am. Chem. Soc. award in Chromatography, 1991. Mem. Am. Chem. Soc. Avocations: painting, sketching, music, walking. Home: 4176 Oxford Dr Leland MI 49654-9701

SMALL, HENRY GILBERT, information scientist, researcher; b. Chgo., June 17, 1941. B.A. in Chemistry, U. Ill., 1963; M.A. in Chemistry, U. Wis.-Madison, 1966, Ph.D. in Chemistry and History of Sci., 1971. Research assoc. Am. Inst. Physics., N.Y.C., 1969-70, acting dir. ctr. for History of Physics, 1971-72; dir. grant research Inst. for Sci. Info., Phila. 1972-80, dir. corporate research, 1980—; sr. fellow hist. sci. U. Pa., Phila., 1974-79; mem. sci. and arts com. Franklin Inst., 1985—. Editor: Physics Citation Index: 1920-29, 1980. Mem. editorial bd.: Sciento-metrics, 1979—. Contbr. articles to profl. jours. Recipient Derek Price medal, 1987. Fellow AAAS; mem. Am. Soc. Info. Sci. (Best Paper award 1987), Soc. Social Study of Sci. (council 1979-81, editor newsletter 1977-81), History of Sci. Soc. Home: 105 Rolling Rd Bala Cynwyd PA 19004-2614 Office: Inst Sci Info 3501 Market St Philadelphia PA 19104-3389

SMALL, JEFFREY, lawyer, law educator; b. N.Y.C., Oct. 11, 1941; s. I Maxwell and Norma Small; children: Lara, David. AB, Cornell U., 1963; JD, NYU, 1966. Bar: N.Y. 1967. Assoc. in law U. Calif., N.Y.C., 1968; assoc. adj. prof. law NYU, N.Y.C., 1978—; assoc. Davis, Polk & Wardwell, N.Y.C., 1968-76, ptnr., 1976—. Fulbright scholar, Madrid, 1967. Office: Davis Polk & Wardwell 450 Lexington Ave New York NY 10017-3911

SMALL, JONATHAN ANDREW, lawyer; b. N.Y.C., Dec. 26, 1942; s. Milton and Teresa Markell (Joseph) S.; m. Cornelia Mendenhall, June 8, 1969; children: Anne, Katherine. BA, Brown U., 1964; student, U. Paris, 1962-63; LLB, Harvard U., 1967; MA, Fletcher Sch. of Law and Diplomacy, 1968; LLM, NYU, 1974. Bar: N.Y. 1967. VISTA vol. Washington and Cambridge, Mass., 1968; law clk. to judge U.S. Ct. Appeals (2d cir.), 1968-69; assoc. Debevoise & Plimpton, N.Y.C., 1969-75, ptnr., 1976—; cons. Spl. Task Force on N.Y. State Taxation, 1976. Trustee Brearley Sch., 1985—; bd. dirs. Nonprofit Coordinating Com. of N.Y., 1985—, Muscular Dystrophy Assn., 1986-88. Mem. ABA, N.Y. State Bar Assn. (chmn. tax sect. com. exempt orgns. 1980-82, co-chmn., 1995), Assn. Bar City N.Y., Nonprofit Forum, Phi Beta Kappa. Home: 60 E End Ave New York NY 10028-7907 Office: Debevoise & Plimpton 875 3rd Ave New York NY 10022-6225

SMALL, JOYCE GRAHAM, psychiatrist, educator; b. Edmonton, Alberta, Can., June 12, 1931; came to U.S., 1956; d. John Earl and Rachel C. (Redmond) Graham; m. Iver Francis Small, May 26, 1954; children: Michael, Jeffrey. BA, U. Saskatchewan, Can., 1951; MD, U. Manitoba, Can., 1956; MS, U. Mich., 1959. Diplomat Am. Bd. Psychiatry and Neurology, Am. Bd. Electroencephalography. Instr. in psychiatry Neuropsychiat. Inst. U. Mich., Ann Arbor, 1959-60; instr. in psychiatry med. sch. U. Oreg., Portland, 1960-61, asst. prof. in psychiatry med. sch., 1961-62; asst. prof. in psychiatry sch. of medicine Washington U., St. Louis, 1962-65; assoc. prof. in psychiatry sch. of medicine Ind. U., Indpls., 1965-69, prof. psychiatry sch. of medicine, 1969—; mem. initial rev. council NIMH, Washington, 1972-76, 79-82, 87-91; assoc. mem. Inst. Psychiat. Rsch., Indpls., 1974—. Editorial bd.: Quar. Jour. of Convulsive Therayp, 1984, Clin. Electroencephalography, 1990, and more than 150 publs. in field; contbr. articles to profl. jours. Rsch. grantee NIMH, Portland, Oreg., 1961-62, St. Louis, 1962-64, Indpls., 1967—, Epilepsy Found., Dreyfus Found., Indpls., 1965; recipient Merit award NIMH, Indpls., 1990. Fellow Am. Psychiat. Assn., Am. Electroencephalographic Soc. (councillor 1972-75, 1982); mem. Soc. Biol. Psychiatry, Cen. Assn. Electroencephalographers (sec., treas. 1967-68, pres. 1970, councillor 1971-72), Sigma Xi. Office: Larue D Carter Meml Hosp 1315 W 10th St Indianapolis IN 46202-2885

SMALL, KENNETH ALAN, economics educator; b. Sodus, N.Y., Feb. 9, 1945; s. Cyril Galloway and Gertrude Estelle (Andrews) S.; m. Adair Bowman, June 8, 1968; 1 child, Gretchen Lenore. BA, BS, U. Rochester, 1968; MA, U. Calif., Berkeley, 1972, PhD, 1976. Asst. prof. Princeton (N.J.) U., 1976-83; rsch. assoc. Brookings Inst., Washington, 1978-79; assoc. prof. U. Calif., Irvine, 1983-86, prof. econs., 1986—, assoc. dean social sci., 1986-92, chmn. econs., 1992-95; vis. prof. Harvard U., Cambridge, Mass., 1991-92; cons. N.Y. State Legislature, Albany, 1982-83, Rand Corp., Santa Monica, Calif., 1985-86, ECO N.W., Eugene, Oreg., 1987—, World Bank, Washington, 1990—, Port Authority of N.Y. and N.J., 1994; mem. adv. coun. South Coast Air Quality Mgmt. Dist., El Monte, Calif., 1989-92; mem. study com. on urban transp. congestion pricing NRC, 1992-94. Co-author: Futures for a Declining City, 1981, Urban Decline, 1982, Road Work, 1989; Author: Urban Transportation Economics, 1992; co-editor: Urban Studies Glasgow, Scotland, 1992—, Kluwer Acad. Publs. book series, Dordrecht, The Netherlands, 1993—; assoc. editor Regional Sci. and Urban Econs., Amsterdam, The Netherlands, 1987—; editorial bd. Jour. Urban Econs., San Diego, 1989—, Transportation, Dordrecht, 1993—; contbr. articles, book revs. to profl. jours. Grantee NSF, 1977-87, Inst. Transp. Studies U. Calif., 1984-89, Haynes Found., L.A., 1987-88, U.S. and Calif. Depts. Transp., 1988—. Mem. Am. Econ. Assn., Econometric Soc., Transp. Rsch. Bd., Royal Econ. Soc., Regional Sci. Assn., Am. Real Estate and Urban Econs. Assn. Office: Univ Calif Dept Econs Irvine CA 92717

SMALL, LAWRENCE FARNSWORTH, history educator; b. Bangor, Maine, Dec. 30, 1925; s. Irving Wheelock and Geneva May (Turner) S.; m. Elfie Joan Ames, Aug. 9, 1947; children: Kathleen Ann, Linda Jean, Lawrence Farnsworth, Daniel Irving (dec.). BD, Bangor Theol. Sem., 1948; BA, U. Maine, 1948, MA, 1951; PhD, Harvard U., 1955, LHD (hon.), 1991. Ordained to ministry Congregational Ch., 1950; minister Paramus (N.J.) Congl. Ch., 1955-59; assoc. prof. history Rocky Mountain Coll., Billings, Mont., 1959-61; prof. Rocky Mountain Coll., 1975-90, dean of coll., 1961-65, acting pres., 1965-66, pres., 1966-75; chmn. Mont. commn. Higher Edn. Facilities Act, 1965-75; exec. dir. Mont. Assn. Chs., 1984-90. Author: Montana Passage, A Century of Politics on the Yellowstone, Journey with the Law, The Life of Judge William J. Jameson; editor: Religion in Montana, Pathways to the Present, vols. I and II. Pres. Yellowstone County Council Chs., 1968-70; trustee Mont. Conf., United Ch. of Christ, 1970-73; chmn. bd. dirs. Western Independent Colls. Found.; bd. dirs. Community Concert Assn., Yellowstone County Mental Health Assn., Billings Citizens for Community Devel., Billings United Fund; trustee Billings Deaconess Hosp.; chmn. bd. dirs. Inst. for Peace Studies, Mont. Mem. Phi Beta Kappa, Phi Kappa Phi. Club: Kiwanis (pres. Billings, lt. gov.). Home: 7320 Sumatra Pl # 4 Billings MT 59106-2526 *One does not have to be great to embrace great ideas, but having done so, one's life will be changed for the better.*

SMALL, LAWRENCE M., financial organization executive; b. 1941. BS, Brown U., 1963; JD (hon.), Morehouse Coll. Vice chmn. bd., chmn. exec. com., dir. Citicorp, N.Y.C., 1964-91; pres., COO Fed. Nat. Mortgage Assn., 1991—; bd. dirs. Chubb Corp., Marriott Internat. Trustee emeritus Brown U.; trustee Moorehouse Coll., Atlanta, 1973—, N.Y.U. Med. Ctr.; bd. dirs. Spanish Repertory Theatre; mem. U.S. Holocaust Meml. Coun. Office: Fed Nat Mortgage Assn 3900 Wisconsin Ave NW Washington DC 20016-2892

SMALL, MARSHALL LEE, lawyer; b. Kansas City, Mo., Sept. 8, 1927; s. Phillip and Lillian (Mendelsohn) S.; m. Mary Rogell, June 27, 1954; children: Daniel, Elizabeth. BA, Stanford U., 1949, J.D., 1951. Bar: Mo. 1951, Calif. 1955, N.Y. 1990. Law clk. to Justice William O. Douglas U.S. Supreme Ct., Washington, 1951-52; assoc. Morrison & Foerster, San Francisco, 1954-60, ptnr., 1961-92, sr. of counsel, 1993—; reporter corp. governance project Am. Law Inst., 1982-92. 1st lt. U.S. Army, 1952-54. Mem. ABA (com. corp. laws 1975-82), Phi Beta Kappa, Order of Coif. Office: Morrison & Foerster 345 California St San Francisco CA 94104

SMALL, MELVIN, history educator; b. N.Y.C., Mar. 14, 1939; s. Herman Z. and Ann (Ashkinazy) S.; m. Sarajane Miller, Oct. 23, 1958; children: Michael, Mark. BA, Dartmouth Coll., 1960; MA, U. Mich., 1961, PhD, 1965. Asst. prof. history Wayne State U., Detroit, 1965-68, assoc. prof., 1968-76, prof., 1976—, chmn. dept. history, 1979-86; vis. prof. U. Mich., Ann Arbor, 1968, Marygrove Coll., Detroit, 1971, Aarhus (Denmark) U.,

1972-74, 83, Windsor (Ont., Can.) U., 1977-78. Author: Was War Necessary, 1980, Johnson, Nixon and the Doves, 1988, Covering Dissent, 1994, Democracy and Diplomacy, 1995; co-author: Wages of War, 1972, Resort to Arms, 1982; editor: Public Opinion and Historians, 1970; co-editor: International War, 1986, Appeasing Fascism, 1991, Give Peace a Chance, 1992; mem. editl. bd. Internat. Interactions, 1987-91, Peace and Change, 1989—; restaurant critic Detroit Metro Times, 1982-95; history book reviewer Detroit Free Press, 1988—. Recipient Disting. Faculty award Mich. Assn. Governing Bds., 1993; Am. Coun. Learned Socs. fellow, 1969; Stanford Ctr. for Advanced Study fellow, 1969-70; grantee Am. Coun. Learned Socs., 1983, Johnson Libr., 1982, 88, Can. Govt., 1987. Mem. Coun. on Peace Rsch. in History (nat. coun. 1986-90, pres. 1990-92), Am. Hist. Assn., Atlantic Coun. (acad. assoc.), Orgn. Am. Historians, Soc. for Historians of Am. Fgn. Rels. (Warren Kuehl prize 1989). Home: 1815 Northwood Blvd Royal Oak MI 48073-3919 Office: Wayne State U Dept History 3119 Fab Detroit MI 48202

SMALL, MELVIN D., physician, educator; b. Somerville, Mass., May 22, 1925; s. Sidney J. and Ida (Gelbsman) S.; m. Judith Nogee, Dec. 23, 1962; children: Michael Dorian, Michele. AB, U. Wis.; MD, Duke U. Sch. Medicine, 1959; studied under Dr. Gregory Pincus, Worcester Found. Exptl. Biol. and Medicine, 1950-53; studied under Prof. Brian Abel-Smith, London Sch. Econs., 1986-90. Lic. physician, Fla., Md., D.C., Va. Intern Georgetown U. Med. Ctr., Washington, 1959-60, resident, 1960-61; chief gastrointestinal rsch. Georgetown U. Med. Ctr., 1961-64, instr. medicine, 1961-66, asst. prof. medicine, 1966-67, asst. clin. prof. medicine, 1967-81, 93—; chief gastroenterology sect. Georgetown divsn. D.C. Gen. Hosp., 1964-68; cons. Children's Hosp., Washington, 1962-66; active staff Fairfax (Va) Hosp., 1961-73, Commonwealth Drs. Hosp., Fairfax, 1969-74, Arlington (Va.) Hosp., 1961-85, Circle Terr. Hosp., Alexandria, 1965-85, Mt. Vernon Hosp., Alexandria, 1976-85; hon. staff mem. Alexandria Hosp., 1985-89, 92—; attending physician D.C. Gen. Hosp., 1961-68, Georgetown U. Hosp., 1961-81, 93—, Mt. Sinai Hosp., Miami Beach, Fla., 1992—; chief animal experimentation Cancer rsch. under Dr. Sidney Farber Children's Med. Ctr., Boston, 1948-50; rsch. asst. Boston U. Sch. Medicine, 1956-57; chmn. dept. medicine Alexandria Hosp., 1964-85; founder, chmn., No. Va. Consortium for Continuing Med. Edn., 1974-86, chmn. emeritus, 1986; lectr. in field. Contbr. articles to profl. jours. Trustee Jefferson Meml. Hosp., 1965-74, mem. founding group, 1965, chmn. pharmacy com., 1965-76, co-chmn. tissue com., 1965-74. With U.S. Army, 1942-45. Rsch. fellow under Dr. Noman Zamcheck Mallory Inst. Pathology, Boston, 1953-59, Gastroenterology rsch. under Dr. Franz Ingelfinger AEC, 1951-53. Mem. AMA, Am. Coll. Gastroenterology, ACP, Am. Gastroent. Assn., Am. Inst. Nutrition, Am. Physiol. Soc., Am. Soc. Gastrointestinal Endoscopy, D.C. Med. Soc., Med. Soc. Va. (chmn. commn. on continuing med. edn. 1978-81), Alexandria Med. Soc. (v.p. 1979-80), Royal Soc. Medicine.

SMALL, MICHAEL, composer; b. 1939. Scores include (films) Out of It, 1969, Puzzle of a Downfall Child, 1970, Jenny, 1970, The Revoltionary, 1970, The Sporting Club, 1971, Klute, 1971, Child's Play, 1972, Dealing: Or the Berkeley-to-Boston Forty-Brick Lost-Bag Blues, 1972, Love and Pain and the Whole Damned Thing, 1973, The Parallax View, 1974, The Drowning Pool, 1975, The Stepford Wives, 1975, Night Moves, 1975, Marathon Man, 1976, Audrey Rose, 1977, Girlfriends, 1978, The Driver, 1978, Comes a Horseman, 1978, Going in Style, 1979, Those Lips, Those Eyes, 1980, The Postman Always Rings Twice, 1981, Continental Divide, 1981, Rollover, 1981, The Star Chamber, 1983, Kidco, 1984, Firstborn, 1984, Target, 1985, Dream Lover, 1986, Brighton Beach Memoirs, 1986, Black Widow, 1987, Orphans, 1987, Jaws the Revenge, 1987, 1969, 1988, See You in the Morning, 1989, Mountains of the Moon, 1990, Mobsters, 1991, Consenting Adults, 1992, Wagons East!, 1994, (documentaries) Pumping Iron, 1977, American Dream, 1989, (TV movies) The Boy Who Drank Too Much, 1980, The Lathe of Heaven, 1980, Chiefs, 1983, Nobody's Child, 1986, Queen, 1993. Office: Marks and Vangelos Mgt 19301 Ventura Blvd Ste 206 Tarzana CA 91356*

SMALL, PARKER ADAMS, JR., pediatrician, educator; b. Cin., July 5, 1932; s. Parker Adams and Grace (McMichael) S.; m. Natalie Settimelli, Aug. 26, 1956; children: Parker Adams, Peter McMichael, Carla Edmea. Student, Tufts U., 1950-53; MD, U. Cin., 1957. Med. intern Pa. Hosp., Phila., 1957-58; research assoc. Nat. Heart Inst. NIH, Washington, 1958-60; research fellow St. Mary's Hosp., London, Eng., 1960-61; sr. surgeon NIMH, Washington, 1961-66; prof. immunology and med. microbiology U. Fla., 1966—, chmn. dept., 1966-75, prof. pediatrics, 1979—; dir. Ctr. for Coop. Learning for Health Sci. U. Fla., 1988—; vis. prof. U. Lausanne, Switzerland, 1972, U. Lagos, Nigeria, 1982, Al Hada Hosp., Saudi Arabia, 1983; vis. scholar Assn. Am. Med. Colls., Washington, 1973; assoc. life scis. panel Nat. Acad. Scis., 1981-88, co-chmn., 1982-83; bd. dirs. biol. scis. curriculum study Biol. Sci. Curriculum Study, 1984-90, exec. bd., 1987-90; mem. edn. adv. com. Nat. Fund Med. Edn., 1984-87; mem. study com. Nat. Bd. Med. Examiners, 1983-85, mem. nat. vaccine adv. com., 1987-91, chmn. subcom. on new vaccines, 1987-91; cons. in field. Creator patent oriented problem solving system/POPS, for teaching immunology and coop. learning to med. students and Team Packs for teaching K-12 & college students health edn. and coop. learning; editor: The Secretory Immunologic System, 1971; mem. editorial bd. Infection and Immunity, 1974-76, Jour. Med. Edn., 1978-80; cons. editor Microbios, Cytobios; contbr. articles to profl. jours. Sec., treas. Oakmont, Md., 1965-66, mayor, 1965-66; chmn. Citizens for Pub. Schs. Gainesville, Fla., 1969-70. With USPHS, 1958-60, 61-66. Named Tchr. of Yr., U. Fla. Coll. Medicine, 1978-79, Disting. Lectr., AMA, 1986; recipient Presdl. medallion U. Fla., 1987, Nat. Basic Sci. Disting. Tchg. award, Alpha Omega Alpha, 1993; Jacob Ehrenzeller award, 1995; NIH Spl. fellow, 1960-61, rsch. grantee, 1966—, U. Fla. Tchr./Scholar and commencement spkr., 1987; invited lectr. Assn. Am. Med. Colls., 1992. Mem. AAAS, Am. Assn. Immunologists (edn. com. 1983-86), Physicians for Social Responsibility, Fla. Med. Assn., Phi Beta Kappa, Sigma Xi, Theta Delta Chi. Home: 3454 NW 12th Ave Gainesville FL 32605-4811 Office: U Fla Coll Med PO Box 100266 Gainesville FL 32610

SMALL, RALPH MILTON, publisher, clergyman; b. Richland Center, Wis., Oct. 26, 1917; s. John Marion and Jessie Angeline (Rowe) S.; m. Patricia Courson Small, June 11, 1977; children—Gregory, Randall. B.A. cum laude, Cin. Bible Sem., 1939, postgrad, 1939-41; postgrad, U. Cin., 1941, Clarion State Tchrs. Coll., 1941, Lincoln Christian Coll., 1947; D.D., Pacific Christian Coll., 1971. Ordained to ministry Ch. of Christ, 1939. Minister Antioch Ch. of Christ, Hoopeston, Ill., 1939-63; Bible Sch. cons. Standard Publ. Co., Cin., 1963; weekly columnist The Lookout, 1964-69, dir. dept. ch. growth, 1964-70; editor Seek, 1970, exec. editor, 1970, v.p., publisher, 1971-86; sr. adults min. Clovernook Christian Ch., Cin., 1992—; cons. Standard Pub. Co. Moderator: The Living Word, WDAN-TV, 1954-59. Trustee Milligan Coll., chmn., 1990-91; nat. chmn. Milligan Coll. Capital Funds Campaign, 1989-91; dir. Nat. Christian Edn. Conv., 1965-86; bd. dirs. Fellowship, Inc., Muscular Dystrophy, Danville, Ill.; sec. bd. advisers Directory of Ministry, Christian Chs./Chs. of Christ, 1973-83; sec. bd. dirs. Christian Ch. Found. for the Handicapped, Knoxville, Tenn., 1981—; Chaplain AUS, 1945. Mem. Delta Aleph Tau. Home: 207 W Sequoya Trl Greensburg IN 47240-8302

SMALL, RICHARD DAVID, research scientist; b. Syracuse, N.Y., Jan. 6, 1945; s. Sydney Morton Small and Gertrude (Burman) Goldberg; m. Tsipora Meirson, Dec. 11, 1977; children: Eileen Lara, Carrie Ayala, Sharon Yael. BS, Rutgers U., 1967, MS, 1968, MPhil., 1969, PhD, 1971. Instr. Rutgers U., New Brunswick, N.J., 1971-78; sr. lectr. Technion, Haifa, Israel, 1971-78; rsch. scientist, dir. for thermal scis. Pacific-Sierra Rsch. Corp., L.A., 1979-94; pres. Eastwind Rsch. Corp., Westlake Village, Ca, 1994—; vis. asst. prof. U. Calif., L.A., 1977-79; vis. scholar U. Calif., 1979-81, San Francisco State U., 1994—; lectr. various univs. and confs.; adv. com. City Savs. and Loan Assn., 1985; mem. adv. and rev. coms. NAS, other sci. orgns. Contbr. more than 100 tech. articles; reviewer profl. jours., confs. and symposia. With Israeli Army, 1977. Recipient Rothschild Fund. prize, 1974; NDEA fellow, 1967-70; N.J. Soc. Profl. Engrs. scholar, 1967. Mem. AAAS, AIAA, Sigma Xi. Jewish. Developed model for environmental impact of Kuwait oil fires; research on smoke production from global nuclear exchanges was focal point in nuclear winter debate. Office: Eastwind Rsch Corp 1465 Eastwind Cir Westlake Village CA 91361

SMALL, RICHARD F., mechanical engineer, consultant; b. Buffalo, July 2, 1936; s. Frank and Rose (Cohn) S.; m. Marilyn A. Schroeder, Jan. 14, 1984; children: Scott, Mark, James. AS in Mech. Engring. Tech., SUNY, Buffalo, 1957; BSME, Tri-State U., 1968; MBA, UCLA, 1973, JD, 1974. Registered profl. engr., Calif., Ill., Fla., Eng., Italy. Engring. mgr. Worthington Corp., Buffalo, 1959-68; div. mgr. Pulsation Controls Corp., Santa Paula, Calif., 1968-70; project mgr. Pioneer Svc. & Engring. Corp., Chgo., 1970-72; mgr. internat. projects Bechtel Power Corp., Norwalk, Calif., 1972-74; v.p. VTN Corp., Irvine, 1974-76, STD Rsch. Corp., Arcadia, Calif., 1977-78; dir. U.S. Dept. Energy, Oakland, Calif., 1976-77; sr. ptnr. Western Pacific Assocs., Costa Mesa, Calif., 1978-88; dir. architecture and engring. Orange County Gen. Svcs. Agy., Santa Ana, Calif., 1988-89; sr. ptnr. Rimar Assocs., Mission Viejo, Calif., 1989—; prin. cons. Arco, Mobil, Shell, Texaco, Unocal; sr. cons. Airesearch Mfg. Co., Torrance, Calif., 1980-85; contract cons. Rockwell Space Standards, Downey, Calif., 1980-81. Author: Energy Alternatives, 1976; contbr. numerous articles on energy to profl. jours.; patentee equipment for energy conversion. Counselor, advisor Phoenix House Found., Santa Ana, 1982. Sgt. U.S. Army, 1951-54, Korea, mem. Res. ret. Mem. Nat. Soc. Profl. Engrs., ASME, Am. Nuclear Soc., Am. Mgmt. Assn., Orange County Mfmt. Forum. Avocations: collecting art, photography, enology. Home: 26534 Montiel Mission Viejo CA 92691-5932 Office: Rimar Assocs Mission Viejo CA 92691

SMALL, ROBERT E., architect, architecture educator; b. N.Y.C., Mar. 10, 1927; s. James J. and Elsie K. (Kohrs) S.; m. Charity V. Williams, Aug. 21, 1955; children—Thomas, Catherine, John. B.S. in Archtl. Engring., Kans. State U., 1952; M.Arch., U. Oreg., 1955. Registered architect, Wash., Kans. Prin. Robert E. Small and Assocs., Architects, Seattle, 1968—; chmn. dept. architecture U. Wash., Seattle, 1982—; Cons. to various agencies on design for elderly and disabled including U.S. Nat. Bur. Standards, Wash. State, Alaska State, Seattle Housing Authority, 1974—. Author: Site Planning for Housing, 1976; Designing Accessable Environments, 1976. Served with USN, 1944-46, PTO. Recipient numerous research grants HUD, Nat. Bur. Standards, others. Mem. AIA, Assoc. Coll. schs. of Architects. Home: 13110 70th Ln NE Kirkland WA 98034-1603 Office: U Wash Coll Architecture and Urban Planning Dept Architecture Seattle WA 98105

SMALL, S(AUL) MOUCHLY, psychiatrist, educator; b. N.Y.C., Oct. 11, 1913; s. Joseph and Esther (Mouchly) S.; m. Sophie Scholl, June 13, 1937; children: Susan Steinhart, Laurie Block, Jonathan, Cynthia McDonald. BS, CCNY, 1933; MD cum laude, Cornell U., 1937. Diplomate Am. Bd. Psychiatry and Neurology. Instr. psychiatry Cornell Med. Coll., N.Y.C., 1940-43; lectr. psychiatry Columbia U., N.Y.C., 1948-51; adj. and assoc. attending psychiatrist Mt. Sinai Hosp., N.Y.C., 1946-51; prof., chmn. dept. psychiatry SUNY, Buffalo, 1951-78; prof. emeritus dept. psychiatry SUNY, 1978—; dir. psychiatry Meyer Meml. Hosp., Buffalo, 1951-78; attending psychiatrist Erie County Med. Ctr., Buffalo, 1951—, Buffalo Gen. Hosp., 1963—; chief psychiatric cons. VA Hosp., Buffalo, 1952—; neuropsychiat. cons. Surgeon Gen. U.S. Army, Washington, 1947-70; cons. U.S. DOD, Washington, 1966—; mem. N.Y. State Bd. Profl. Med. Conduct, Albany, 1985—; emeritus dir. Am. Bd. Psychiatry and Neurology, 1986—. Coauthor textbook: Handbook of Psychiatry, 1943; contbr. articles to profl. jours., chpts. to books. Acting dir. Erie County Mental Health Bd., Buffalo, then mem. bd. dirs.; pres. Muscular Dystrophy Assn., N.Y.C., 1980-89, bd. dirs., chmn. exec. com., 1989—, pres. emeritus, 1989—. Fellow Am. Psychiat. Assn. (Disting. Svc. citation 1978, Psychiatrist of Yr. award 1975), Am. Coll. Psychiatrists (Bowis gold medal 1975), Am. Coll. Psychoanalysts, Am. Assn. Social Psychiatry; mem. AMA, N.Y. Acad. Medicine. Avocations: photography, swimming. Home: 75 Oakbrook Dr # G Buffalo NY 14221-2560 Office: Erie County Med Ctr K-Annex Bldg 462 Grider St Buffalo NY 14215-3021

SMALL, WILLIAM ANDREW, mathematics educator; b. Cobleskill, N.Y., Oct. 16, 1914; s. James Arner and Lois (Patterson) S.; children: Lois (Mrs. Paul Gindling). James (dec.). B.S., U.S. Naval Acad., 1936; A.B., U. Rochester, 1950, M.A., 1952, Ph.D., 1958. Commd. ensign U.S. Navy, 1936, advanced through grades to lt. comdr., 1944; comdt. cadets, instr. DeVeaux Sch., Niagara Falls, N.Y., 1945-48; instr. U. Rochester, 1951-55; Alfred (N.Y.) U., 1955-56; asst. prof. math. Grinnell (Iowa) Coll., 1956-58, assoc. prof., chmn. dept., 1958-60; prof. math. Tenn. Tech. U., 1960-62, State Univ. Coll., Geneseo, N.Y., 1962-63; chmn. dept. math. State Univ. Coll., 1962-78; prof. emeritus, disting. service prof. SUNY, 1985—; Fulbright-Hays lectr. math. Aleppo U., Syrian Arab Republic, 1964-65. Contbr. articles to profl. jours. Mem. Math. Assn. Am., U.S. Naval Inst., Mil. Order World Wars, Ret. Officers Assn., Seneca Army Depot Officers Club, Am. Legion, Rotary (pres. Geneseo club 1990-91), Phi Beta Kappa. Episcopalian. Home: 28 Court St PO Box 367 Geneseo NY 14454-0367

SMALL, WILLIAM EDWIN, JR., association executive; b. Jackson, Mich., Jan. 18, 1937; s. William Edwin and Lena Louisa (Hunt) S.; m. Ruth Ann Toombs, Mar. 28, 1959; children: Suzanne Marie, William Edwin III, Bryan Anthony. AS, Jackson C.C., 1959; BS in Geology, Mich. State U., 1961, MA in Journalism, 1964. Reporter Sci. Svc., Washington, 1961-62; writer sci. U. Chgo., 1963-64; sci. info. officer Pa. State U., State College, 1964-66; corr. McGraw-Hill, Washington, 1966-69; staff com. pub. works U.S. Senate, 1969; founding editor Biomed. News, 1969-71; dir. pub. info. Nat. Bur. Standards, Washington, 1972-76; editor Am. Pharmacy Jour., 1979-82; dir. media and info. svcs. AMA, Washington, 1982-86; exec. dir. Nat. Found. Infectious Disease, Washington, 1986-91, Assn. Biotech. Cos., 1991-93; CEO Bioconfs. Internat., Bethesda, Md., 1993—; owner recreation resort Small Country Va., Louisa, 1976—. Author: Third Pollution, 1971. With Security Agy., AUS, 1955-59. Recipient Superior Accomplishment award U.S. Dept. Commerce, 1974. Fellow AAAS; life mem. Nat. Assn. Sci. Writers. Home: PO Box 343 Louisa VA 23093-0343 Office: BioConferences Internat 4405 E-W Hwy Bethesda MD 20814

SMALLEY, CHRISTOPHER JOSEPH, pharmaceutical company professional; b. Phila., June 26, 1953; s. Charles Wilfred and Verna May (Coulter) S.; m. Maria Visniskie, Aug. 9, 1974; children: Christa Maria, Mark Charles, Lora Loray. BS, Phila. Coll. Pharmacy and Sci., 1976; MBA, Temple U., 1982; PhD, LaSalle U., 1991. Mfg. pharmacist supr. McNeil Labs., Fort Washington, Pa., 1976-77; mfg. pharmacist group supr. McNeil Consumer Products Co., 1978-79; mfg. pharmacist mgr., 1980-85; tech. svcs. mgr. Janssen Pharmaceutica, 1985-88, plant mgr., 1988-94; quality assurance dir. Sterling Winthrop Pharm. Rsch., Collegeville, Pa., 1994—. Mem. Rep. Nat. Com., 1979—. With the USNR Med. Corps., 1986—. Mem. Am. Pharm. Assn., Assn. Mil. Surgeons of U.S., Am. Assn. Pharm. Scientists, Internat. Soc. Pharm. Engrs., Aerospace Med. Assn., Am. Acad. Med. Adminstrs., Naval Res. Assn., Assn. Med. Svc. Corps Officers, Pa. Pharm. Assn., Inst. Environ. Scis., Eastern Assn. GMP Trainers, Parenteral Drug Assn. (chmn. tng. com.), Pharm. Mfrs. Assn. (prodn. section), Phila. Pharm. Forum, USn Inst., Am. Numismatic Assn., NRA, Kappa Psi. Presbyterian. Home: 421 Drayton Rd Oreland PA 19075-2010 Office: Sterling Winthrop Pharm Rsch Divsn 1250 S Collegeville Rd Collegeville PA 19426-0900

SMALLEY, DAVID VINCENT, lawyer; b. N.Y.C., Mar. 27, 1935; s. Vincent R. and Ethel A. (Sullivan) S.; m. Patricia Doyle Tolles, Nov. 28, 1964; children—Brian W., Gregory T. B.A., Hamilton Coll., LL.B. Bar: N.Y. 1960. Assoc. Debevoise & Plimpton, N.Y.C., 1959-67, ptnr., 1968—. Mem. ABA, Assn. of Bar of City of N.Y. Home: 14 E 90th St New York NY 10128-0671 Office: Debevoise & Plimpton 875 3rd Ave New York NY 10022-6225

SMALLEY, EUGENE BYRON, plant pathology educator, forest pathologist, mycologist; b. L.A., July 11, 1926; s. Guy Byron and Lena Ernestina S.; m. Gladys Louise Doerksen, Feb. 5, 1954 (div. 1974); children: Daniel B., Lisa L., Sara C., Anthony B., Andrew J.; m. Joan Alice Potter, June 4, 1978. BS, UCLA, 1949; MS, U. Calif., Berkeley, 1953, PhD, 1957. Rsch. asst. plant pathology U. Calif., Berkeley, 1953-57; asst. prof. plant pathology U. Wis., Madison, 1957-64, assoc. prof., chmn. dept., 1964-69, prof., 1969-94, prof. emeritus, 1994—, acting chair dept. plant pathology, 1988-89; mem. exec. com. Ctr. Environ. Toxicology, 1967—; rsch. advisor Elm Rsch. Inst., Harrisville, N.H., 1974—; Pitney Bowes Elms Across Europe, 1979—; U.S. advisor EEC Dutch Elm Disease Program, 1979; lectr. Gordon Rsch. Conf., 1967, 86. Contbr. articles to profl. jours.; patentee in field. Mem. com. NRC, 1982-83. With USN, 1944-46. Recipient numerous rsch. grants. Mem. AAAS, Am.

Phytopath. Soc., Wis. Arborists Assn. (hon.), Mycological Soc. Am., Sigma Xi, Gamma Sigma Delta. Democrat. Episcopalian. Home: 2831 Pleasant View Hts Cottage Grove WI 53527-9517 Office: U Wis Dept Plant Pathology 1630 Linden Dr Madison WI 53706-1598

SMALLEY, KENNETH LEE, oil company executive; b. Custer City, Okla., Feb. 18, 1930; s. Richard Emory and Leila Floy (Ferguson) S.; m. Janet Marie Glasgow, Sept. 5, 1953; children—Susan Jill Smalley Arbour, Mary Kathleen, Lee Anne. B.S. in Engring., U. Okla., 1954. Pres. chems. Phillips Petroleum Europe-Africa, Brussels, 1972-77; mgr. splty. chems. Phillips Chem. Co., Bartlesville, Okla., 1977-79, v.p. petrochems., 1979-81; v.p. minerals Phillips Petroleum Co., Denver and Dallas, 1980-85; sr. v.p. Phillips Petroleum Co., Bartlesville, 1985—; bd. dirs. First Bancshares Inc., First Nat. Bak Bartlesville. Pres. bd. dirs. Internat. Sch., Brussels, 1974-76; bd. dirs. St. Joseph Hosp., Denver, 1982. Decorated Order of Leopold (Belgium). Mem. Natural Gas Processors Assn. (exec. com. 1985), Natural Gas Supply Assn. (exec. com. 1985), Western Regional Conf. (issues com. 1984), U. Okla. Alumni Assn. (bd. dirs. 1977-80). Club: Hillcrest Country (Bartlesville). Avocations: golf; walking. Home: Denver Pl Bartlesville OK 74003 Office: Phillips Petroleum Co 17 Phillips Bldg Bartlesville OK 74004

SMALLEY, RICHARD ERRETT, chemistry and physics educator, researcher; b. Akron, Ohio, June 6, 1943; s. Frank Dudley and Virgnia (Rhodes) S.; m. Judith Grace Sampieri, May 4, 1968 (div. July 1979); 1 child, Chad; m. Mary Lynn Chapieski, July 10, 1980 (div. Nov. 1994). BS in Chemistry, U. Mich., 1965; MA in Chemistry, Princeton U., 1971, PhD in Chemistry, 1973; Doctor Honoris causa, Univ. Liege, Belgium, 1991; DSc (hon.), U. Chgo. Assoc. The James Franck Inst., Chgo., 1973-76; asst. prof. William Marsh Rice U., Houston, 1976-80, prof., 1981-82, Gene & Norman Hackerman prof. chemistry, 1982—; prof. Dept. Physics Rice U., Houston, 1990—; chmn. Rice Quantum Inst., Houston, 1986—. Contbr. numerous articles to profl. jours. Recipient Grand award Popular Sci. mag., 1991, Robert A. Welch Award in Chemistry, Robert A. Welch Found., 1992, J.S. Kilby award North Dallas C. of C., 1992, E.O. Lawrence award U.S. Dept. Energy, 1992, Auburn-G.M. Kosolapoff award, 1992, John Scott awawrd City of Phila., 1993, Hewlett-Packard Europhysics prize European Phys. Soc., 1994; Harold W. Dodds fellow Princeton U., 1973. Fellow Am. Phys. Soc. (divsn. chem. physics, Irving Langmuir prize 1991, Internat. New Materials prize 1992, Nichols medal 1993); mem. AAAS, NAS, Am. Chem. Soc. (divsn. phys. chemistry, William H. Nichols medal 1993, S.W. regional award 1992, Harrison Howe award Rochester sect. 1994, Madison Marshall award North Ala. sect. 1995), Materials Rsch. Soc., Am. Acad. Arts and Scis., Sigma Xi. Office: Rice U Dept Chemistry Mail stop 100 PO Box 1892 Houston TX 77251-1892

SMALLEY, ROBERT MANNING, government official; b. Los Angeles, Nov. 14, 1925; s. William Denny and Helen (McConnell) S.; m. Lois Louisa Williamson, Nov. 28, 1948 (div.) m. Rosemary Sumner, Jan. 4, 1957; children—Leslie Estelle, David Christian. Student, UCLA, 1946-48. Radio news editor Mut. Radio Broadcasting System, Los Angeles, 1950-55; mgr. Agrl. Info. Inc., Sacramento, Calif., 1957-59; with Whitaker & Baxter, San Francisco, 1956-57, 59-61; sec. Mayor, San Francisco, 1961-63; asst. dir. pub. relations Republican Nat. Com., 1964; press sec. Republican vice presl. candidate William E. Miller, 1964; dir. pub. relations Republican Nat. Com., 1965; v.p. Whitaker & Baxter, San Francisco, 1966-68; asst. press sec. Republican vice presl. candidate Spiro Agnew, 1968; spl. asst. Sec. Commerce, Washington, 1969-72; adminstrv. asst. U.S. Senator Robert P. Griffin, Washington, 1972-73; dir. corp. affairs Potomac Electric Power Co., Washington, 1973-75; U.S. rep. devel. assistance com. O.E.C.D., Paris, France, 1975-77; spl. asst. U.S. Senator Robert P. Griffin, Washington, 1977-78; asst. to campaign mgr. Reagan for Pres. Com., Washington, 1979; sr. advisor mgmt. communications IBM, 1979-82; dep. asst. sec. of state pub. affairs Dept. of State, Washington, 1982-87; U.S. amb. to Kingdom of Lesotho, 1987-89; lectr. in pub. policy The Kendig Group, Columbia Artists Mgmt., Inc., N.Y.C., 1990—. Served with USN, 1944-46, PTO. Episcopalian. Office: PO Box 823 Arlington VA 22216

SMALLEY, WILLIAM EDWARD, bishop; b. New Brunswick, N.J., Apr. 8, 1940; s. August Harold and Emma May (Gleason) S.; m. Carole A. Kuhns, Sept. 12, 1964; children: Michelle Lynn, Jennifer Ann. BA in Sociology, Lehigh U., 1962; MDiv, Episcopal Theol. Sch., 1965; MeD, Temple U., 1970; D of Ministry, Wesley Theol. Sem., 1987. Ordained to ministry Episcopal Ch., 1965, bishop, 1989. Vicar St. Peter's Episcopal Ch., Plymouth, Pa., 1965-67, St. Martin-in-the-Fields Ch., Nuangola, Pa., 1965-67; rector All Saints' Episcopal Ch., Lehighton, Pa., 1967-75; fed. program adminstr. Lehighton Area Schs., 1970-72; rector Episcopal Ministry of Unity, Palmerton, Pa., 1975-80; bishop Episcopal Diocese Kans., Topeka, 1989—. Pres. Gaithersburg (Md.) Pastoral Counseling Inc., 1986-89; bd. dirs. Washington Pastoral Counseling, 1988-89; chmn. Turner House Inc., Kansas City, Kans., 1989—; Episcopal Social Svcs., Wichita, Kans., 1989—; bd. dirs. Christ Ch. Hosp., Topeka, 1989—, St. Francis Acad. Atchison, Kans., 1989—; v.p. Province VII, The Episcopal Ch.; pres. Province VII House of Bishops; mem. Ch. Devel. Bd.; chair Presiding Bishop's Coun. Advice; mem. joint nominating com. for Presiding Bishop. Mem. Omicron Delta Kappa. Democrat. Avocations: gardening, swimming, cross-stitching, reading. Address: Bethany Pl Topeka KS 66612

SMALLMAN, BEVERLEY N., biology educator; b. Port Perry, Ont., Can., Dec. 11, 1913; s. Richard Benjamin and Ethel May (Doubt) S.; m. Hazel Mayne, Dec. 11, 1937 (dec. 1962); 1 child, Sylvia Gail; m. Florence Hazel Cook, July 27, 1965. B.A., Queens U., Kingston, Ont., 1936; M.Sc., Western U. Ont., Can., 1938; Ph.D., U. Edinburgh, Scotland, 1941; LL.D.(hon.), Trent U., Ont., 1982. Mem. staff Stored Grain Insect Investigations Bd. of Grain Commrs., Winnipeg, 1941-45; officer-in-charge Stored Products Lab., Agrl. Can., Winnipeg, 1945-50; head entomol. sect. rsch. inst. Agrl. Can., London, 1950-57; chief entomol., rsch. dir. entomology, plant pathology Agrl. Can., Ottawa, 1957-63; prof., head dept. biology Queens U., Kingston, Ont., Can., 1963-73, prof. biology, 1973-78, prof. emeritus biology, 1979—; vis. scientist Nat. Inst. Med. Rsch., London, Eng., 1954-56, CSIRO Labs., Brisbane, Australia, 1970-71, 76; apiary insp. Province of Ont., 1981-91; cons., lectr. in field. Prin. author: Agricultural Science in Canada, 1970, Queen's Biology, 1992; co-author: Good Bye Bugs, 1983. Contbr. articles to profl. jours. Fellow Royal Soc. Can.; mem. Entomol. Soc. Can., Zool. Soc. Can., Entomol. Soc. Man. (founding pres. 1945), Entomol. Soc. Ont. Avocations: Mini-farming; beekeeping; writing popular science reviews. Home: RR 2, Yarker, ON Canada K0K 3N0

SMALLWOOD, FRANKLIN, political science educator; b. Ridgewood, N.J., June 24, 1927; s. J. William and Carolyn (Linkroum) S.; m. Ann Logie, Sept. 8, 1951; children: Susan, Sandra, David, Donald. A.B., Dartmouth Coll., 1951, A.M. (hon.), 1968; M.P.A., Harvard U., 1953, Ph.D., 1958. With AEC, 1953-57; asst. to pres. Dartmouth Coll., 1957-59, mem. faculty, 1959-92, prof. govt., 1967-92, Nelson A. Rockefeller prof. govt. emeritus, 1992—; U. Vt., Burlington, 1989—, chmn. city planning and urban studies program Dartmouth Coll., 1965-72, chmn. social sci. div., 1968-72, assoc. dean faculty, 1968-72, acting dean, 1972, v.p. student affairs, 1975-77, chmn. policy studies program, 1977-83, dir. Nelson A. Rockefeller Center for Social Scis., 1983-86; chmn. Vt. Gov.'s Commn. Intergovtl. Relations, 1985-86, Vt. Legis Apportionment Bd., 1990—; fenceviewer Norwich, Vt., 1976-90. Author: Metro Toronto: A Decade Later, 1963, Greater London: The Politics of Metropolitan Reform, 1965, Free and Independent, 1976, The Politics of Policy Implementation, 1980, The Other Candidates, 1983. Mem. Vt. Senate, 1973-75; trustee Vt. State Colls., 1967-73, chmn., 1973. Served with AUS, 1944-46. Recipient Superior Achievement award AEC, 1957, Dartmouth Presdl. Leadership medal, 1991; fellow Inst. Pub. Adminstrn., 1960; Dartmouth Coll. Faculty fellow, 1962-63; Nuffield Coll. (Oxford U.), vis. fellow, 1981, 86-87. Mem. Am. Soc. Pub. Adminstrn., Phi Beta Kappa. Office: 38 Northshore Dr Burlington VT 05401-1259

SMALLY, DONALD JAY, consulting engineering executive; b. Cleve., 1922; s. Daniel James and Alice (Rohrheimer) S.; m. Ruth Janet Glasser, July 8, 1944; children: Alan John, Leonard Arthur. B.M.E., U. Cin., 1949. Prodn. engr. N. Ransonhoff, Inc., Cin., 1949-50; chief engr. Mosby Engring. Assocs., Sarasota, Fla., 1952-55; prin. Smally, Wellford & Nalven, Inc., Sarasota, 1956-91; mem. tech. adv. com. Manatee Community Coll.,

Sarasota, 1965-90; mem. adv. com. Vocat.-Tech. High Sch., Sarasota, 1968-80. Vice pres. Sarasota YMCA, 1968-71; v.p. Sarasota Opera Assn., 1975-88, pres., 1988-89; chmn. Sarasota Vol. Talent Pool, 1973-76; sec.-treas. Civitan Found., 1965-79; bd. dirs. Suncoast Heart Assn., 1976; mem. Fla. Coordinating Coun. for Vocat. and Adult Edn., 1984—, chmn., 1986-88; chmn. Sarasota Hist. Preservation Bd., 1988-91; pres. Sarasota County Rd. Improvement Task Force, 1990—; mem. Sarasota County Pub. Sch. Found., 1990—, chmn., 1990-91; v.p. Hist. Soc. Sarasota, 1990-91, Children's Haven and Adult Ctr. Bd., 1983—, pres., 1991-94; pres. John Ringling Ctr. Found., 1991—; mem. Plymouth Harbor Bd., 1994—. Served with AUS, 1942-45. Recipient Good Citizenship award SAR, 1975, Disting. Alumni award U. Cin. Engring. Coll., 1985, Outstanding Svc. award Myakna Chpt. Fla. Engring. Soc., 1993; named Citizen of Yr. Sarasota Civitan Club, 1975, Engr. of Yr. Sarasota-Manatee Engrs. Soc., 1976. Fellow Am. Cons. Engrs. Council (treas. 1980-82), Fla. Engring. Soc. (pres. Sarasota-Manatee chpt. 1956-58); mem. Sarasota County of C. (past dir., v.p. 1983), Cons. Engrs. Council Fla. (pres. 1968), Fla. Soc. Profl. Land Surveyors (chpt. pres. 1973), Am. Water Works Resources Assn. (pres. Fla. Soc. 1981), Sarasota-Manatee Engring. Soc.

SMARDON, RICHARD CLAY, landscape architecture and environmental studies educator; b. Burlington, Vt., May 13, 1948; s. Philip Albert and Louise Gertrude (Peters) S.; m. Anne Marie Graveline, Aug. 19, 1973; children: Regina Elizabeth, Andrea May. BS cum laude, U. Mass., 1970, MLA, 1973; PhD in Environ. Planning, U. Calif., Berkeley, 1982. Environ. planner, landscape architect Wallace, Floyd, Ellenzweig, Inc., Cambridge, Mass., 1972-73; assoc. planner Exec. Office Environ. Affairs, State of Mass., Boston, 1973-75; environ. impact assessment specialist USDA extension svc. Oreg. State U., Corvallis, 1975-76; landscape architect USDA Pacific S.W. Forest and Range Expt. Sta., Berkeley, 1977; rsch. landscape architect U. Calif., Berkeley, 1977-79; prof. landscape architecture, sr. rsch. assoc. SUNY Coll. Environ. Sci. and Forestry, Syracuse, 1979-86, prof. environ. studies, 1987—; dir. Inst. for Environ. Policy and Planning, 1987—; co-dir. Gt. Lakes Rsch. Consortium, Syracuse, 1986—; guest lectr. numerous univs.; adj. asst. prof. U. Mass. Amherst, 1974-75; Sea Grant trainee Inst. for Urban and Regional Devel., Berkeley, 1976; condr.; presenter numerous seminars and workshops; cons. to numerous orgns.; mem. com. on environ. design and landscape Transp. Rsch. Bd.-NAS, 1985; mem. tech. adv. bd. Wetlands Rsch., Inc., Chgo., 1985; mem. adv. bd. Wetlands Fund, N.Y., 1985; v.p. Integrated Site Inc., Syracuse. Co-editor: Out National Landscape, 1979, spl. issue Coastal Zone Mgmt. Jour., 1982, The Future of Wetlands, 1983, Foundations for Visual Project Analysis, 1986, The Legal Landscape, 1993; mem. edit. bd. Northeastern Environ. Sci. Jour., 1981, Landscape and Urban Planning, 1991; contbr. over 100 articles to profl. jours. Bd. dirs. Sackets Harbor Area Hist. Preservation Found., Watertown, N.Y., 1984—; pres. Save the County, Inc., Fayetteville, N.Y., 1986-88; appointed to Great Lakes (N.Y.) Adv. Commn., chmn., 1993. Recipient Beatrice Farrand award U. Calif., 1979, Am. Soc. Landscape Architects award, 1972, Pub. Svc. award in edn., 1990, Progressive Architecture mag. award 1992, Pres.'s Pub. Svc. award 1994. Mem. AAAS, Am. Land Resource Assn. (charter), Internat. Assn. for Impact Assessment, Coastal Soc., Alpha Zeta (life), Sigma Lambda Alpha. Avocations: folk guitar, hiking, skiing, travel. Office: SUNY Inst Environ Policy Planning Syracuse NY 13210 Office: Integrated Site Inc 886 E Brighton Ave Syracuse NY 13205

SMART, ALLEN RICH, II, lawyer; b. Chgo., July 3, 1934; s. Jackson W. Smart and Dorothy (Byrnes) Bowles. Student, Deerfield Acad., 1949-52; AB magna cum laude, Princeton U., 1956; LLB, Harvard U., 1961. Bar: Ill. 1961. Assoc. Bell Boyd & Lloyd, Chgo., 1961-69, ptnr., 1970-91, of counsel 1992—. Bd. dirs. Rec. for Blind, Inc., Chgo., 1984—, vice-chmn., 1987-90; co-chmn. zoning com. Old Town Triangle Assn., Chgo., 1987—; bd. dirs. Lawrence Hall Sch. for Boys, 1965-70, Old Masters Soc., Art Inst., 1987—; governing mem. Orchestral Assn. Lt. USNR, 1956-58. Mem. ABA, Ill. Bar Assn., Chgo. Bar Assn., Infant Welfare Soc. Chgo. (bd. dirs. 1971—, pres. 1982-86), Friends of the Parks Chgo. (bd. dirs. 1986—), Renaissance Soc. Chgo. (bd. dirs. 1988—), University (bd. dirs. 1986-89), Arts, Legal, Law, Economic clubs of Chgo. Home: 1732 N North Park Ave Chicago IL 60614-5710 Office: Bell Boyd & Lloyd 3200 Three First Nat Pl Chicago IL 60602

SMART, CHARLES RICH, retired surgeon; b. Ogden, Utah, Nov. 7, 1926; s. Junius Hatch and Avon (Rich) S.; m. Dorothea Jean Cannon Sharp, Dec. 23, 1952; children—Thomas, Edward, Christopher, Angela, Cynthia, David. B.S. with honors, U. Utah, 1945; M.D. with honors, Temple U., 1955. Intern Los Angeles County Hosp., 1955-56; resident Hosp. U. Pa., Phila., 1956-61; asst. prof. surgery in residence UCLA, 1963-66; assoc. prof. surgery Coll. Medicine, U. Utah, 1966-69, cancer coordinator, 1967-69, clin. assoc. prof. surgery, 1969-75, clin. prof. surgery, 1975-85; mem. staff, chief of surgery Latter-day Saints Hosp., 1974-84; chmn. SEER Group Nat. Cancer Inst., 1976-78, chief community oncology and rehab. br., 1985-86, chief early detection br., 1987-92; ret., 1992; dir. Rocky Mountain Coop. Tumor Registry, 1969-85; bd. dirs. Am. Cancer Soc., 1976-79. Contbr. research articles to med. jours. Fellow ACS; mem. Utah Med. Assn., AMA, Pan-Pacific Surg. Soc., Bay Surg. Soc., Los Angeles Surg. Soc., Salt Lake Surg. Soc., Internat. Soc. Chemotherapists, Am. Assn. Cancer Edn., Am. Soc. Clin. Oncology, Soc. Head and Neck Surgeons, Am. Soc. Surg. Oncologists, Alpha Omega Alpha. Republican. Mormon. Home: 1262 Chandler Dr Salt Lake City UT 84103-4240

SMART, CLAUDE HARLAN, JR., lawyer; b. Tacoma, Mar. 25, 1927; s. Claude Harlan Sr. and Alma (Brown) S.; m. Barbara Olive Powell, Aug. 18, 1962; children: Suzanne, Joan, Stephen. Student, San Jose (Calif.) State Coll., 1947-48; AB, U. Calif., Berkeley, 1950, LLB, 1953. Bar: Calif. 1954. Assoc. Law Office of Wm. McCarthy Thornton, Exeter, Calif., 1954-55, Miller, Kroloff & Brown, Stockton, Calif., 1955-61; ptnr. Kroloff, Brown, Belcher & Smart, Stockton, 1961-75, Kroloff, Belcher, Smart, Perry & Christopherson, Stockton, 1975—. Chancellor Episcopal Diocese San Joaquin County; bd. dirs. Salvation Army, Stockton; with U.S. Army Infantry, 1945-46. Mem. ABA, Am. Bd. Trial Advs. (nat. exec. com., 1982-84, pres. Sacramento chpt., 1984), Internat. Assn. Def. Counsel, Def. Rsch. Inst. (regional v.p., 1984-86, v.p. 1990—, bd. dirs. 1987-90), State Bar Calif. (Calif. State Bar Jud. Coun., Joint Commn. on Discovery, 1984-86), Northern Calif. Assn. Def. Counsel (past pres., 1979). Office: Internat Jour Sociology Law, 24-28 Oval Rd, London NW1 7DX, England

SMART, JACKSON WYMAN, JR., business executive; b. Chgo., Aug. 27, 1930; s. Jackson Wyman and Dorothy (Byrnes) S.; m. Suzanne Tobey, July 6, 1957; 1 son, Jackson W. III. B.B.A., U. Mich., 1952; M.B.A., Harvard, 1954. With First Nat. Bank, Chgo., 1956-64; exec. v.p. comml. banking Bank of Commonwealth, Detroit, 1964-69; pres., dir. MSP Industries Corp. (subsidiary W.R. Grace & Co. 1972), Center Line, Mich., 1969-71; pres., CEO, 1971-75; chmn., pres., treas., dir. The Delos Internat. Group, Inc. (subs. Automatic Data Processing Inc. 1976), Princeton, N.J., 1975-77; chmn., pres., CEO, dir. Central Nat. Bank (merged with Exch. Nat. Bank, Chgo. 1982), Chgo., 1977-82; chmn. fin. com. Exch. Internat. Corp., Chgo., 1982-83; chmn. exec. com. Thomas Industries, Inc., Louisville, Ky., 1983-87; chmn., CEO, dir. MSP Communications, Inc., Chgo., 1988—; bd. dirs. Fed. Express Corp., Memphis, chmn. fin. com., 1976-78, N.Am. Pvt. Equity Fund, Chgo., Goldman Sachs Funds Group, N.Y.C.; chmn. Banctec (formerly Terminal Data Corp.), Moorpark, Calif., 1992-94, 1st Commonwealth Inc. Chgo. Bd. dirs. Evanston (Ill.) Hosp., Hadley Sch. Blind, Winnetka, Ill., chmn. 1987-89. Mem. Chief Execs. Orgn. Clubs: Birmingham (Mich.) Athletic; Commercial, Economic, University, Hundred of Cook County, Chicago (Chgo.); Indian Hill (Winnetka); Ocean of Fla. (Ocean Ridge, Fla.); Country of Fla. (Golf, Fla.); Coral Beach and Tennis (Bermuda). Office: 1 Northfield Plz Northfield IL 60093-1251

SMART, JACOB EDWARD, management consultant; b. Ridgeland, S.C., May 31, 1909; s. William Edward and Alma (Nettles) S.; m. Elizabeth Gohmert, Feb. 20, 1932 (div. 1946); children—Jean Elizabeth, Jacklyn Cabell, William Edward. Rosemary. Student, Marion Mil. Inst., 1926-27; B.S., U.S. Mil. Acad., 1931; student, Nat. War Coll., 1949-50. Commd. lt. USAF, 1931, advanced through grades to gen.; 1963; served various posts U.S. and Europe, 1931-55; asst. vice chief of staff USAF, Washington, 1955-59; comdr. (12th Air Force), Waco, Texas, 1959-60; vice comdr. tactical air command Langley AFB, 1960-61; comdr. 5th Air Force and U.S. Forces in

Japan, Japan, 1961-63, Cinc. Pacific Air Forces, 1963-64; dep. comdr. in chief (Hdqrs. U.S. European Command), 1964-66; ret., 1966; spl. asst. to adminstr. NASA, 1966-67, asst. adminstr. for policy, 1967-68; asst. adminstr. for Dept. Def. and inter-agy. affairs, 1968-73; v.p. Earth Satellite Corp., Washington, 1973-75; cons., 1975—. Decorated D.S.C., D.S.M. with 4 oak leaf clusters, Legion of Merit, D.F.C., Air medal with 3 oak leaf clusters, Purple Heart, Commendation Ribbon; hon. comdr. Order Brit. Empire; Order of Service Merit 1st class Korea; Medal of Cloud and Banner with Grand Cordon China; comdr. Legion of Honor France; Order of Sacred Treasures Japan). Mem. Assn. Grads. U.S. Mil. Acad., Air Force Assn. Home: PO Box Y Ridgeland SC 29936-0925

SMART, L(OUIS) EDWIN, JR., lawyer, business executive; b. Columbus, Ohio, Nov. 17, 1923; s. Louis Edwin and Esther (Guthery) S.; m. Virginia Alice Knouff, Mar. 1, 1944 (div. 1958); children: Cynthia Stephanie, Douglas Edwin; m. Jeanie A. Milone, Aug. 29, 1964; 1 child, Dana Gregory. AB magna cum laude, Harvard U., 1947, JD magna cum laude, 1949. Bar: N.Y. 1950. Assoc. firm Hughes, Hubbard & Ewing, N.Y.C., 1949-56; ptnr. firm Hughes Hubbard & Reed, N.Y.C., 1957-64, counsel, 1965—; pres. Bendix Internat.; dir. Bendix Corp. (and fgn. subs.), 1964-67; sr. v.p. external affairs Trans World Airlines, Inc., 1967-71; sr. v.p. corp. affairs, 1971-75, vice chmn., 1976, chmn. bd., chief exec. officer, 1977-78, chmn. bd., 1979-85; chmn. bd., chief exec. officer Transworld Corp. (name now Flagstar Cos., Inc.), 1978-87, chmn. exec. com., 1987-89, also bd. dirs.; chmn. bd. Hilton Internat. Co., 1978-86; of counsel Hughes Hubbard & Reed, N.Y.C., 1989—; bd. dirs. Continental Corp., Sonat Inc., Flagstar Cos., Inc., Flagstar Corp. Editor Harvard Law Rev., 1947-48. Lt. USNR, 1943-46. Mem. ABA, N.Y. County Lawyers Assn., Harvard Club, Marco Polo Club, Phi Beta Kappa, Sigma Alpha Epsilon. Office: Hughes Hubbard & Reed 1 Battery Park Plz New York NY 10004-1412

SMART, MARRIOTT WIECKHOFF, research librarian consultant, information manager; b. Memphis, Aug. 26, 1935; d. Gerhard Emil and Beatrice (Flanegan) Wieckhoff; m. John A. Smart, May 9, 1959; children: Denise, Holly. B.S. in Geology, U. Tex.-Austin, 1957; M.L.S., U. Pitts., 1976. Geophysicist Mobil Corp., New Orleans, 1957-59; geologist Hanson Oil Co., Roswell, N.Mex., 1959-62; info. specialist Gulf Corp., Pitts., 1977-79, library mgr., Denver, 1979-84, library cons. team, Pitts., 1984; supr. Library-Info. Ctr., Amoco Minerals Co., Englewood, Colo., 1984; dir. Library-Info. Ctr., Cyprus Minerals Co., 1985-92; cons. ask marriott, Littleton, Colo., 1992—. Choir mem. Grace Presbyn. Ch., Littleton, 1979—. Mem. Spl. Libraries Assn. (bull. bus. mgr. 1982, treas. petroleum and energy divsn. 1984-86, chmn. petroleum and energy divsn. 1987-88, pres. Rocky Mountain chpt. 1991-92), Women in Mining, Alpha Chi Omega. Home: 3337 E Easter Pl Littleton CO 80122-1910

SMART, PAUL M., utility company executive, lawyer; b. Middleport, Ohio, Jan. 6, 1929. A.B. summa cum laude, Capital U., 1952; J.D. summa cum laude, Ohio State U., 1953. Bar: Ohio 1953. Ptnr. Fuller & Henry, Toledo, 1959-84; v.p. Toledo Edison Co., 1974-78, sr. v.p., gen. counsel corp. devel., 1984-85, pres., chief oper. officer, 1985-88, vice-chmn., 1988—, also dir.; past exec. v.p. Centerior Energy Corp., Cleve., vice chmn., 1989—. Fellow Ohio State Bar Found.; mem. Am. Bar Found., Order of Coif, Phi Delta Phi. Office: Toledo Edison Co 300 Madison Ave Toledo OH 43652-1000

SMART, STEPHEN BRUCE, JR., business and government executive; b. N.Y.C., Feb. 7, 1923; s. Stephen Bruce and Beatrice (Cobb) S.; m. Edith Minturn Merrill, Sept. 10, 1949; children: Edith Minturn Smart Moore, William Candler, Charlotte Merrill Smart Rogan, Priscilla Smart Schwarzenbach. Student, Milton Acad.; A.B. cum laude, Harvard U., 1945; S.M., MIT, 1947. Sales engr. Permutit Co., N.Y., 1947-51; various sales, gen. mgmt. positions Continental Group, Inc. (formerly Continental Can Co.), N.Y.C., 1953-85, v.p. Central metal div., 1962-65, v.p. marketing and corporate planning, 1965-67, v.p. assn. gen. mgr. paper operations, 1967-69, group v.p. paper operations, 1969-71, exec. v.p. paper operations, 1971-73, vice chmn. bd., 1973-75, pres., 1975-85, chmn., chief exec. officer, 1981-85; undersec. for internat. trade Dept. Commerce, Washington, 1985-88; cons. Dept. State, Washington, 1988-89; sr. fellow World Resources Inst., Washington, 1988-95; bd. dirs. Chevron Corp., World Resources Inst., Inform Inc. Editor: Beyond Compliance: A New Industry View of the Environment, 1992. Vestryman, sr. warden Trinity Ch., Upperville, Va. 1st lt. AUS, 1943-46; C.E., 1951-53. Mem. Coun. Fgn. Rels., The Bus. Coun., Sigma Xi. Clubs: Pequot Yacht, Tennis (Middlebury, Va.). Home and Office: 20561 Trappe Rd Upperville VA 22176-9708

SMARTSCHAN, GLENN FRED, educational administrator; b. Allentown, Pa., Dec. 11, 1946; s. Fred Gotfred and Joyce Isabel (Hensinger) S.; m. Linda Susan Bastinelli, Mar. 18, 1972; children: Erin Joy, Lauren Nicole. BS in Edn., Kutztown State Coll., 1968; MS in Edn., Temple U., 1972; EdD in Ednl. Adminstrn., Lehigh U., 1979. Cert. tchr. history and comprehensive social studies, secondary prin.; supt., Pa. Tchr. 8th grade social studies South Mountain Jr. High Sch., Allentown Sch. Dist., 1968-76, adminstrv. asst. to prin. Raub Jr. High Sch., 1976-78, prin., 1978-80, dist. dir. curriculum, 1980-84, asst. to supt. for curriculum and community services, 1984-86; supt. of schs. Brandywine Heights Area Sch. Dist., Topton, Pa., 1986-90; supt. of sch. Mt. Lebanon Sch. Dist., Pitts., 1990—; adj. prof. Cedar Crest Coll., 1986-88; chief exec. officer Ednl. Dynamics Cons., Assoc. Cambridge Group, 1993; assoc. The Cambridge Group, 1993—; speaker, cons. on alternative edn.; scope and sequence devel., criterion referenced testing; strategic planning bd. dirs. Alternative House Inc., Bethlehem, Pa., 1976-81, chairperson program com., 1977-78, v.p., 1979, pres., 1980; mem. adv. com. Lehigh County (Pa.) Hist. Mus., 1980-86; bd. dirs. Girls' Club Allentown, 1983-86, v.p., 1985. Mem. Assn. Supervision and Curriculum Devel., Pa. Assn. Supervision and Curriculum Devel. (exec. com., registrar eastern regional meeting, v.p. Eastern region, pres. Eastern region 1988), Am. Assn. Sch. Adminstrs., Pa. Assn. Sch. Adminstrs., Pa. Sch. Bds. Assn., Alumni Coun. Lehigh U. (pres. 1986), Phi Delta Kappa, Fleetwood Club, Rotary (charter mem. Allentown club, exec. com. 1985), Dormont-Mt. Lebanon Club. Roman Catholic. Home: One Spalding Circle Pittsburgh PA 15228 Office: Mt Lebanon Sch Dist 7 Horsman Dr Pittsburgh PA 15228-1107

SMATHERS, FRANK, JR., banker, horticulturist; b. Atlantic City, July 17, 1909; s. Frank and Lura (Jones) S.; m. Mary Belle Wall, Mar. 27, 1935; children: Lowry, Pamela Smathers MacCorquodale, Ann Smathers Prescott, Lura Smathers Bergh. Student, U. N.C., 1928-30; LLB, U. Miami, 1933; student, Grad. Sch. Banking, Rutgers U., 1939-42. Bar: Fla. 1933. Asst. state atty. State of Fla., 1934-35; asst. trust officer Miami Beach (Fla.) 1st Nat. Bank, 1936-39, v.p., trust officer, dir., 1936-56, asst. pres., trust officer, 1956-57, pres., 1957-67, chmn., 1966-74; chmn. United Nat. Bank, Miami, 1964-74; chmn. Coral Gables 1st Nat. Bank, 1966-74, United Bancshares, 1966-73, Security Exch. Bank, West Palm Beach, Fla., 1970-73; vice chmn. United Nat. Bank, Dadeland, 1968-74; chmn. United Nat. Bank, Westland, Fla., 1972-74; pres., chief exec. officer United 1st Fla. Banks, Inc., 1973-74; chmn., chief exec. officer Flagship Banks Inc., 1974-75. Pres. Fedn. Econ. Concern, Dade County, Fla.; vice chmn. Assn. Governing Bds. Colls. and Univs.; trustee U. Miami, Rutgers U., Grad. Sch. Banking, St. Francis Hosp., Miami Beach., Fairchild Tropical Garden; bd. dirs. Fla. Coun. 100. With U.S. Army, 1928, 42-43; with Office Price Adminstrn., Washington, 1944-45. Mem. Iron Arrow Hon. Soc., SAR, Metropolitan Club (Washington), Indian Creek Country Club, Coral Reef Yacht Club, Yale Club (N.Y.C.), Royal and Ancient Golf Club, Pine Valley Golf Club, Delta Kappa Epsilon. Methodist. Home: 11511 SW 57th Ave Miami FL 33156-5002

SMATHERS, JAMES BURTON, medical physicist, educator; b. Prairie du Chien, Wis., Aug. 26, 1935; s. James Levi and Irma Marie (Stindt) S.; m. Sylvia Lee Rath, Apr. 20, 1957; children—Kristine Kay, Kathryn Ann, James Scott, Ernest Kent. B.Nuclear Enging., N.C. State Coll., 1957, M.S., 1959; Ph.D., U. Md., 1967. Diplomate Am. Bd. Radiology, Am. Bd. Med. Physics, Am. Bd. Medical Physics; cert. in radiation oncology physics registered profl. engr., D.C., Tex., Calif. Research engr. Atomics Internat., Canoga Park, Calif. 1959, Walter Reed Army Inst. Research, Washington, 1961-67; prof. nuclear engring. Tex. A and M. U., College Station, 1967-80; prof., head bioengring. Tex. A. and M. U., 1976-80; prof., head med. physics, dept. radiation oncology UCLA, 1980—; cons. U.S. Army, Dept. Energy, also pvt.; industry. Served with U.S. Army, 1959-61. Recipient Excellence in Teaching award Gen. Dynamics, 1971; Excellence in Research award Tex. A. and M. U. Former Students Assn., 1976. Mem. Am. Nuclear Soc., Health Physics Soc.; Am. Assn. Physcists in Medicine, Am. Soc. Engring. Edn. (Outstanding Tchr. award in nuclear engring. div. 1972), Radiation Research Soc., Nat. Soc. Profl. Engrs., Calif. Soc. Profl. Engrs., Sigma Xi, Sigma Pi Sigma, Phi Kappa Phi. Home: 18229 Minnehaha St Northridge CA 91326-3427 Office: UCLA Dept Radiation Oncology B265 200 UCLA Med Plz Los Angeles CA 90095

SMEAL, ELEANOR CUTRI, organization executive; b. Ashtabula, Ohio, July 30, 1939; d. Peter Anthony and Josephine E. (Agresti) Cutri; m. Charles R. Smeal, Apr. 27, 1963; children: Tod, Lori. BA, Duke U., 1961, LLD (hon.), 1991; MA, U. Fla., 1963. Mem. bd. Upper St. Clair (Pa.) chpt. LWV, 1968-72, sec.-treas. Allegheny County Council, 1971-72; mem. NOW, 1971—; convenor, 1st pres. S. Hills (Pa.) chpt. NOW, 1971-73, 1st pres., state coordinator, 1972-75; nat. bd. dirs. NOW, 1973-75, chairwoman bd., 1975-77, pres., 1977-82, 85-87, mem. bd. Legal Def. and Edn. Fund, 1975—, chairwoman ERA Strike Force, 1977—; pres. Fund for Feminist Majority, Arlington, Va., 1987—; mem. 1st nominating com., founding conf. Nat. Women's Polit. Caucus, 1971; bd. dirs. Allegheny County Women's Polit. Caucus, 1971-72; co-founder, bd. dirs. S. Hills NOW Day Nursery Sch. 1972—; mem. Nat. Commn., Observance of Internat. Women's Year, 1977; mem. exec. com. Leadership Conf. on Civil Rights, 1979—; mem. Nat. Adv. Com. on Women, 1978. Named One of 25 Most Influential Women in U.S. World Almanac, 1978. Office: Fund For The Feminist Majority 1600 Wilson Blvd Ste 704 Arlington VA 22209-2513*

SMEAL, PAUL LESTER, retired horticulture educator; b. Clearfield, Pa., June 11, 1932; s. Walter Vernon and Agatha (Cowder) S.; m. Gladys Matilda Smeal, July 17, 1954; children: Lester Alan, Gwen Hope, Tracy Gay. BS, Pa. State U., 1954; MS, U. Md., 1958, PhD, 1961. Asst. prof. horticulture Va. Poly. Inst. and State U., Blacksburg, 1960-61, assoc. prof., 1961-67, prof., 1967-92, prof. emeritus, 1993—; pres. faculty senate Va. Poly. Inst. and State U., 1984-86. Advisor Alpha Zeta, 1984-86. Recipient Quill and Trowel Comm. award Garden Writers Assn. Am., 1986, 87, Disting. Svc. award Nat. Assn. Country Agrl. Agts., 1987, L.C. Chadwick Teaching award Am. Assn. Nurserymen, 1988, Nursery Ext. award Am. Assn. Nurserymen, 1990. Fellow Am. Soc. Hort. Sci. (mem. pub. affairs com. 1979-82, chmn. ad hoc com 1984-86, pres. so. region 1978-79, sec.-treas. 1989—, others, Carl S. Bittner Extension award 1984, Henry M. Covington Extension award 1991); mem. Internat. Plant Propagator's Soc. (chmn. rsch. com. ea. region 1987-90, bd. dirs. 1991, 2d v.p. 1991, v.p. 1992, pres. 1993), Va. Nurserymen's Assn. (hon.). Republican. Lutheran. Home: 1107 Kentwood Dr Blacksburg VA 24060-5656

SMEDINGHOFF, THOMAS J., lawyer; b. Chgo., July 15, 1951; s. John A. and Dorothy M.; m. Mary Beth Smedinghoff. B.A in Math., Knox Coll., 1973; J.D., U. Mich., 1978. Bar: Ill. 1978, U.S. Dist. Ct. (no. dist.) Ill. 1978. Assoc. McBride, Baker & Coles and predecessor McBride & Baker, Chgo., 1978-84, ptnr., 1985—. adj. prof. computer law John Marshall Law Sch., Chgo. Author: Legal Guide to Developing, Protecting and Marketing Software, 1986, The Software Publisher's Association Legal Guide to Multimedia, 1994. Mem. ABA (vice chair Elec. Data Interchange and info. tech. divsn., sect. sci. and tech. 1992—), Chgo. Bar Assn. (chmn. computer law com. 1984-85), Ill. State Bar Assn., Computer Law Assn., Editorial Adv. Panel (John Marshall Jour. of Computer & Information Law). Office: McBride Baker & Coles Northwestern Atrium Ctr 500 W Madison St Fl 40 Chicago IL 60661-2598

SMEDLEY, BERNARD RONALD (BERNIE SMEDLEY), communications executive; b. McDonald, Pa., July 29, 1936; s. Leonard and Violet (Veydt) S.; m. Lois Lorraine Starr, Aug. 15, 1959; children: Chreyl Smedley Glombicki, Denise, Susan Smedley Furnis. BA in Engring., Washington and Jefferson Coll., 1961; BEE, Carnegie-Mellon U., 1962. Program mgr. Goodyear Aerospace Corp., Akron, Ohio, 1962-69; engring. mgr. Xerox Data Systems, Rockville, Md., 1969-76; data communications mgr. Motorola Inc., Schaumburg, Ill., 1979-80, sr. prodn. mgr., 1980-81, group prodn. mgr., cellular, 1981-83; div. dir. Motorola Inc., Arlington Heights, Ill., 1983-84, div. v.p., dir., 1984-85, div. v.p., gen. mgr., 1985-88, group sr. v.p., gen. mgr., 1988—. Contbr. articles to profl. jours. With U.S. Army, 1954-56. Mem. Nat. Communications Forum, Am. Mgmt. Assn. Republican. Lutheran. Office: Motorola Inc 1475 W Shure Dr Arlington Heights IL 60004-7811

SMEDLEY, LAWRENCE THOMAS, organization executive; b. Lorain, Ohio, Sept. 2, 1929; s. Robert E. and Gerda Sofia (Johnson) S.; m. Carmen Nancy Suarez, June 29, 1962; children: Lorraine, Robert, Lawrence, Richard. BA, Bowling Green State U., 1952; MA, U. Mich., 1957; PhD, Am. U., 1972. Analyst Social Security dept. AFL-CIO, Washington, 1962-65, asst. dir. dept., 1965-73, assoc. dir. dept. occupation safety-health-social security, 1973-88; exec. dir. Nat. Coun. Sr. Citizens, Inc., Washington, 1988—; former mem. numerous presdl. task forces and coms. on older Ams. and disabled; mem. planning and adv. coms. White House Conf. on Aging, 1971, 81; former mem. adv. coun. on employee welfare and pension plans Dept. Labor, also former mem. spl. task force examining policies relating to asset reversions from over-funded pension plans. Co-chmn. Leadership Coun. Aging Orgns., Washington, 1988—; sec. Citizens for Tax Justice, Washington, 1988—; treas. Save Our Security Coalition, Washington, 1990—; mem. exec. bd. Com. for Nat. Health Ins., Washington, 1989—; mem. policy conv. White House Conf. on Aging, 1995. With M.I., U.S. Army, 1952-55, Korea. Recipient Disting. Svc. award Commn. on Accreditation of Facilities of Rehab., 1975, Dedicated Svc. award White House Conf. on Handicapped, 1977, award of honor Industry-Labor Coun., 1981, Outstanding Svc. award Pres.'s Com. on Employment of Handicapped, 1987. Democrat. Lutheran. Home: 1616 Winding Waye Ln Silver Spring MD 20902-1456 Office: Nat Council of Senior Citizens 1331 F St NW Washington DC 20004-1107

SMEDS, EDWARD WILLIAM, food company executive; b. Chgo., Feb. 15, 1936; s. Sigvard A. and Ida S.; m. Alice J. Lawler, Jan. 26, 1957; children—Ellen R., Brad W. BS, Carthage Coll., 1957; MS, U. Ill., 1959; grad. advanced mgmt. program, Harvard U., 1977. With Borg Warner Corp., 1958-61; with Kraft Foods div. Kraft Inc., 1961-75, v.p. dir. personnel, ops. group, 1976-78, v.p. human resources, 1978-79, sr. v.p. human resources, 1979-80, sr. v.p. fin. and adminstrn., 1980-84; pres. Kraft Asia Pacific, 1984-88; chmn. Kraft Foods Ltd., Australia, 1984-88; pres. Kraft Ltd. Can., 1988-89; sr. v.p. ops. and logistics Kraft Gen. Foods, Glenview, Ill., 1990-93; pres. customer svc. and ops. Kraft Gen. Foods, Northfield, Ill., 1993—. Trustee Carthage Coll., Cornerstone Found. Mem. Global Bus. Mgmt. Coun., Econ. Club of Chgo., Chgo. Coun. on Fgn. Rels., Sunset Ridge Country Club, Club at Pelican Bay. Home: 10 Regentwood Rd Northfield IL 60093-2728 also: 6814 Pelican Bay Blvd Naples FL 33963-8218 Office: Kraft Gen Foods 3 Lakes Dr Northfield IL 60093

SMEE, JOHN, church administrator. Dir. Missionary Ministries of the Church of the Namzarene, Kansas City, Mo. Office: Church of the Nazarene 6401 The Paseo Kansas City MO 64131

SMEETON, THOMAS ROONEY, congressional staff director; b. Evanston, Ill., Sept. 26, 1934; s. Cecil Brooks, Jr. and Florence Mary (Rooney).; m. Susan Diane Tollefson, Feb. 23, 1963; children: Sean, Timothy, Shannon, Brendan, Colin. BS in History, Marquette U., 1958; postgrad., U. Notre Dame, 1958-59; grad., Armed Forces Staff Coll., 1972. Intellience officer U.S. CIA, Langley, Va., 1962-73; v.p., gen. mgr. Nowicki Fla. Devel. Corp., Ft. Lauderdale, 1973-75; cons. spl. projects com. on fgn. affairs U.S. House Reps., Washington, 1975-86, minority counsel permanent select com. on intelligence, 1986-92, minority staff dir. Iran/Contra com., 1987-88, exec. dir. Rep. policy com., 1993-94; adminstr., chief investigator House Judiciary Com., Washington, D.C. 1995—. Contbg. author: (with Hyde) For Every Idle Silence, 1985. With U.S. Army, 1959-62. Recipient Agy. Seal medallion CIA, 1993. Mem. Notre Dame Club Washington (vice chmn. 1982-84), Am. Legion. Republican. Roman Catholic. Avocation: golf. Home: 9414 Wallingford Dr Burke VA 22015 Office: House Judiciary Com Rayburn Office Bldg Rm 2138 Washington DC 20515-6415

SMEGAL, THOMAS FRANK, JR., lawyer; b. Eveleth, Minn., June 15, 1935; s. Thomas Frank and Genevieve (Andreachi) S.; m. Susan Jane

Stanton, May 28, 1966; children: Thomas Frank, Elizabeth Jane. BS in Chem. Engring., Mich. Technol. U., 1957; JD, George Washington U., 1961. Bar: Va. 1961, D.C. 1961, Calif. 1964, U.S. Supreme Ct. 1976. Patent examiner U.S. Patent Office, Washington, 1957-61; staff patent atty. Shell Devel. Co., San Francisco, 1962-65; patent atty. Townsend and Townsend, San Francisco, 1965-71, mng. ptnr., 1974-89; sr. ptnr. Graham and James, San Francisco, 1992—; mem. U.S. del. to Paris Conv. for Protection of Indsl. Property. Pres. bd. dirs. Legal Aid Soc. San Francisco, 1982-84, Youth Law Ctr., 1973-84; bd. dirs. Nat. Ctr. for Youth Law, 1978-84, San Francisco Lawyers Com. for Urban Affairs, 1972—, Legal Svcs. for Children, 1980-88; presdl. nom., Legal Svcs. Corp., 1984-90, 93—. Capt. Chem. Corps, U.S. Army, 1961-62. Recipient St. Thomas More award, 1982. Mem. Ct. of Appeals for Federal Ct. (adv. com. 1992—), ABA (chmn. PTC sect. 1990-91, ho. of dels. 1988—, mem. standing com. Legal Aid and Indigent Defendants, 1991-94, chair sect. officer conf., 1992-94, mem. bd. govs., 1994—), Nat. Coun. Intellectual Property Law Assn. (chmn. 1989), Nat. Inventors Hall Fame (pres. 1988), Calif. Bar Assn. (v.p. bd. govs. 1985-87), Am. Patent Law Assn. (pres. 1986), Internat. Assn. Intellectual Property Lawyers (v.p.), Bar Assn. San Francisco (pres. 1978), Patent Law Assn. San Francisco (pres. 1974). Republican. Roman Catholic. Clubs: World Trade, Olympic, Golden Gate Breakfast (San Francisco); Claremont (Berkeley). Contbr. articles to publs. in field. Office: Graham & James 1 Maritime Plz Ste 300 Alco Bldg San Francisco CA 94111

SMELKINSON, ROBERT N., wholesale distribution executive. Pres. Smelkinson Bros. Corp., Jessup, Md. Office: Smelkinson Bros Corp PO Box 215 Jessup MD 20794-0215 also: 8000 Dorsey Run Rd Box 10089 Jessup MD 20794*

SMELLEY, JOYCE MARIE, special education supervisor; b. New Iberia, La., Oct. 17, 1937; d. Monroe Carroll and Ethel Marie (Williams) Simpson; m. John T. Williamson, Feb. 1967 (div. 1972); 1 child, Tamara Marie; m. Roy David Smelley Sr., Sept. 25, 1990; children: Rebecca Marie, Roy David Jr. BS, East Tex. Bapt. Coll., 1960; cert. in spl. edn., U. Denver, 1969; MEd, La. State U., Shreveport, 1981; cert., Northwestern Coll., Natchitoches, La., 1982. Cert. tchr., La., Tex., Colo. Elem. tchr. Pine Tree Ind. Sch. Dist., Longview, Tex., 1960-67, Paris Elem. Sch., Aurora, Colo., 1967-69, Mound Elem. Sch., Burleson, Tex., 1972-73; tchr. Stanley (La.) High Sch., 1973-75, tchr. spl. edn., 1978-79; tchr. Town and Country Sch., Mansfield, La., 1975-78; tchr. spl. edn. Second Ward Sch., Gloster, La., 1979-80; assessment tchr. DeSoto Parish Evaluation Team, Mansfield, La., 1980-87, coord. pupil appraisal, 1987-88; supr. spl. edn. DeSoto Parish Sch. System, Mansfield, 1988—. Mem. Coun. Exceptional Children, La. Edn. Assn., La. Assn. Sch. Execs., La. Assn. Spl. Edn. Adminstrs., Pilots Club (pres. Mansfield 1992—), Order Ea. Star (organist 1992, worthy matron 1995). Baptist. Home: 134 Hope St Mansfield LA 71052-2906 Office: DeSoto Parish Schs PO Box 975 Mansfield LA 71052-0975

SMELSER, NEIL JOSEPH, sociologist; b. Kahoka, Mo., July 22, 1930; s. Joseph Nelson and Susie Marie (Hess) S.; m. Helen Thelma Margolis, June 10, 1954 (div. 1965); children: Eric Jonathan, Tina Rachel; m. Sharin Fateley, Dec. 20, 1967; children: Joseph Neil, Sarah Joanne. B.A., Harvard U., 1952, Ph.D., 1958; B.A., Magdalen Coll., Oxford U., Eng., 1954; M.A., Magdalen Coll., Oxford U., 1959; grad., San Francisco Psychoanalytic Inst., 1971. Mem. faculty U. Calif., Berkeley, 1958-94, prof. sociology, 1962—, asst. chancellor ednl. devel., 1966-68, assoc. dir., 1969-73, 80-89, Univ. prof. sociology, 1972-94; prof. emeritus, 1994—; dir. edn. abroad program for U. Calif., Berkeley, 1977-79, spl. advisor Office of Pres., 1993-94, dir. Ctr. for Advanced Study in Behavioral Scis., 1994—; bd. dirs. Found. Fund for Rsch. in Psychiatry, 1967-70, Social Sci. Rsch. Coun., 1968-71, chmn., 1971-73; trustee Ctr. for Advanced Study in Behavioral Scis., 1980-86, 87-93, chmn., 1984-86, Russell Sage Found., 1990—; mem. subcom. humanism Am. Bd. Internal Medicine, 1981-85, 89-90; mem. com. econ. growth Social Sci. Rsch. Coun., 1961-65; chmn. sociology panel Behavioral and Social Scis. survey NAS and Social Sci. Rsch. Coun., 1967-69; mem. com. on basic rsch. in behavioral and social scis. NRC, 1980-89, chmn., 1984-86, co-chmn., 1986-89. Author: (with T. Parsons) Economy and Society, 1956, Social Change in the Industrial Revolution, 1959, Theory of Collective Behavior, 1962, The Sociology of Economic Life, 1963, 2d edit., 1975, Essays in Sociological Explanation, 1968, Sociological Theory: A Contemporary View, 1971, Comparative Methods in the Social Sciences, 1976, (with Robin Content) The Changing Academic Market, 1980, Sociology, 1981, 2d edit., 1984, 3d edit. 1987, 4th edit. 1991, 5th edit., 1995, Social Paralysis and Social Change, 1991, Effective Committee Service, 1993, Sociology, 1994; editor: (with W.T. Smelser) Personality and Social Systems, 1963, 2d edit., 1971, (with S.M. Lipset) Social Structure and Mobility in Economic Development, 1966, Sociology, 1967, 2d edit., 1973, (with James Davis) Sociology: A Survey Report, 1969, Karl Marx on Society and Social Change, 1973, (with Gabriel Almond) Public Higher Education in California, 1974, (with Erik Erikson) Themes of Work and Love in Adulthood, 1980, (with Jeffrey Alexander et al) The Micro-Macro Link, 1987, Handbook of Sociology, 1988, (with Hans Haferkamp) Social Change and Modernity, 1992, (with Richard Munch) Theory of Culture, 1992, (with Richard Swedberg) The Handbook of Economic Sociology, 1994; editor Am. Sociol. Rev., 1962-65, 89-90; adv. editor Am. Jour. Sociology, 1960-62. Rhodes scholar, 1952-54; jr. fellow Soc. Fellows, Harvard U., 1955-58; fellow Russell Sage Found., 1989-90. Mem. Am. Sociol. Assn. (coun. 1962-65, 67-70, exec. com. 1963-65), Pacific Sociol. Assn., Internat. Sociol. Assn. (exec. com. 1986-94, v.p 1990-94), Am. Acad. Arts and Scis. (hon.), Am. Philos. Soc. (hon.), Nat. Acad. of Scis. (hon.). Home: 890 Robb Rd Palo Alto CA 94306

SMELT, RONALD, retired aircraft company executive; b. Houghtonle Spring, Durham, Eng., Dec. 4, 1913; came to U.S., 1948, naturalized, 1955; s. Henry Wilson and Florence (Bradburn) S.; m. Marie Anita Collings, Nov. 2, 1940 (dec. May 1964); 1 son, David; m. Jean Stuart, Jan. 15, 1965. B.A., King's Coll., Cambridge (Eng.) U., 1935, M.A., 1939, Ph.D. Stanford, 1961. With Royal Aircraft Establishment, 1935-48, chief high speed flight, 1940-45, chief guided weapons dept., 1945-48; dep. chief aeroballistic research dept. USN Ordnance Lab., 1948-50; chief gas dynamics facility ARO, Inc., Tullahoma, Tenn., 1950-57; dir. research and devel. Lockheed Aircraft Corp. (missile systems div.) Sunnyvale, Calif., 1958-59; mgr. Lockheed Aircraft Corp. (Discoverer Satellite system), 1959-60, chief scientist, 1960-62, v.p., gen. mgr. space programs div., 1962-63, v.p., chief scientist, 1963-78; Guggenheim lectr. Internat. Congress Aero. Sci., 1978; Mem. com. on space vehicle aerodynamics NASA, 1965-66, chmn. research adv. com. on space vehicles, 1966-73, chmn. research and tech. adv. council, 1973-77; chmn. tech. adv. bd. Dept. Transp., 1970-74; mem. engring. adv. com. Stanford U., 1988-89; adv. com. NASA-Stanford Ctr. for Turbulence Rsch. Fellow Cambridge Philos. Soc., Royal Aero. Soc. (London), Am. Astronautical Soc., AIAA (hon.); dir.-at-large 1966-68, pres. 1969, 70); mem. Nat. Acad. Engring.,. Home: 7250 Driver Valley Rd Oakland OR 97462

SMERCINA, CHARLES JOSEPH, mayor, accountant; b. Cleve., Sept. 18, 1932; s. Edward Steven and Barbara Rose (Vincik) S.; m. Dorothy Rita Pazdernik, May 9, 1953; children: Cynthia Bomeli Smercina, David. ABA in Acctg., Fenn Coll.; ABA in Mgmt., BBA in Acctg., Cleve. State U.; postgrad., Kent State U., Case Western Res. U., Youngstown (Ohio) State U. CPA, Ohio. Chmn. CSC, Solon, 1956-66; councilman City of Solon, Ohio, 1966-68, vice mayor, 1966-67, income tax administr., 1968-73, mayor, 1974-75, 78-87; cons. taxation, mcpl. fin. various Ohio communities, 1970—; lectr. polit. sci., corp. fin. Case Western Res. U. Mem. Am. Soc. Pub. Adminstrs., Mayors Assn. Ohio, Cuyahoga County Mayors and City Mgrs. Assn., Mcpl. Fin. Officers Am., Nat. League of Cities, Nat. Soc. Pub. Accts., Ohio Assn. Pub. Safety Dirs., Ohio Assn. Tax Adminstrs (past pres.), Ohio Mcpl. League, Water Pollution Control Fedn., Solon C. of C., VFW, Council on Human Relations, Ohio Nature Conservancy, Nat. Arbor Day Found. Democrat. Roman Catholic. Lodges: Rotary, K.C. Home: 5075 Brainard Rd Cleveland OH 44139-1101

SMERDON, ERNEST THOMAS, academic administrator; b. Ritchey, Mo., Jan. 19, 1930; s. John Erle and Ada (Davidson) S.; m. Joanne Duck, June 9, 1951; children: Thomas, Katherine, Gary. BS in Engring., U. Mo., 1951, MS in Engring., 1956, PhD in Engring. 1959. Registered profl. engr., Ariz. Chmn. Dept. agrl. engring. U. Fla., Gainesville, 1968-74, asst. dean for rsch., 1974-76; vice chancellor for acad. affairs U. Tex. System, Austin, 1976-82; dir. Ctr. for Rsch. in Water Resources U. Tex., 1982-88; dean Coll.

Engring. and Mines U. Ariz., Tucson, 1988-92; vice provost, dean Engring U. Ariz., 1992—; mem. bd. sci. and tech. for internat. devel. NRC. Washington, 1990-94. Editor: Managing Water Related Conflicts: The Engineer's Role, 1989. Mem. Ariz. Gov.'s Sci. and Tech. Coun., Tucson, 1989—; bd. dirs. Greater Tucson Econ. Coun., Tucson, 1990-95. Recipient Disting. Svc. in Engring. award U. Mo., 1982. Fellow AAAS, ASCE (hon. mem., Outstanding Svc. award irrigation and drainage divsn. 1988, Royce Tipton award 1989), NAE (peer com. 1986-90, acad. adv. bd. 1989-95, tech. policy options co. 1990-91), Am. Soc. Agrl. Engrs., Am. Water Resources Assn. (Icko Iben award 1989), Am. Soc. Engring. Edn. (chmn., bd. dirs. engring. dean's coun.), Am. Geophys. Union, Univ. Coun. on Water Resources, Ariz. Soc. Profl. Engrs. (Engr. of Yr. award 1990), Sigma Xi, Phi Kappa Phi, Tau Beta Pi, Pi Mu Epsilon. Avocations: hiking, golf, scuba diving, painting. Office: University of Arizona Engineering Experiment Sta Tucson AZ 85721

SMERNOFF, RICHARD LOUIS, oil company executive; b. N.Y.C., July 26, 1941; s. George Stephen and Anna Theresa (Dutoit) S.; m. Agnes Elizabeth Neubauer, Sept. 27, 1969; children—Richard Louis Jr., Christopher Max. B.B.A., CCNY, 1966. CPA, N.Y. Asst. to controller F. Levy Levy & Co., N.Y.C., 1967-70; audit supr. Coopers & Lybrand, N.Y.C., 1970-74; dir. fin. controls Internat. Paper Co., N.Y.C., 1974-78; sr. v.p. Amerada Hess Corp., Woodbridge, N.J., 1978-91; pres. Am. Ultramar, Tarrytown, N.Y., 1991-92; fin. officer Datascope Corp., Montvale, N.J., 1992-94; fin. dir. Lasmo Plc, London, 1994—. Mem. AICPA. Republican. Roman Catholic. Avocations: golf, fishing. Home: 3 Trevor Sq Knightsbridge, London SW7 1DT, England Office: 100 Liverpool St, London EC2M 2BB, England

SMETANKA, MARY JANE, reporter. Education and learning reporter Minn. Star Tribune, Mpls. Office: Mpls. Star Tribune 425 Portland Ave Minneapolis MN 55488

SMETHERAM, HERBERT EDWIN, business executive; b. Seattle, Sept. 9, 1934; s. Francis Edwin and Grace Elizabeth (Warner) S.; m. Beverly Joan Heckert, Sept. 7, 1963; children: Alice, Helen, Charles. BA, U. Wash., 1956; diploma, Naval Intelligence Sch., 1962; MA, U. Md., 1971; diploma in Swedish, U.S. Fgn. Svc. Inst., 1978; MBA, Rollins Coll., 1991. Ensign USN, 1956, advanced through grades to capt., 1976; comdr. USS Lind (DD-703), 1971-73; attache to Sweden USN, Stockholm, 1978-81; comdr. Naval Adminstrn. Command, Orlando, Fla., 1981-84; ret. USN, 1984; strategic planner electronics, info. and missiles group Martin Marietta Corp., Orlando, 1985-93; exec. dir. Naval Tng. Ctr. Re-Use Com., Orlando, 1993—; mem. U.S. Senator Hawkins Naval Acad. Nominating Com., Orlando, 1982-86, Orlando Naval Tng. Ctr. Retention Com., 1991-93, Fla. Gov.'s Def. Reinvestment Task Force, 1992-93; mem. USO Coun. Ctrl. Fla., Orlando, 1981-93, pres., 1991-93. Mem. steering com. U.S. Congressman McCollum for Re-election. Decorated Royal Order of North Star (Sweden). Mem. AIAA, SAR, Electronics Industry Assn. (requirements com. 1985-93), Nat. Assn. Indsl. Developers, Ret. Officers Assn., Navy League, Army Navy Country Club, Orlando Tennis Ctr., Royal Tennis Club Stockholm, Fla. Tennis Assn., Delta Kappa Epsilon. Republican. Episcopalian. Avocation: tennis. Home: 3985 Lake Mira Dr Orlando FL 32817-1643

SMETHURST, E(DWARD) WILLIAM, JR., brokerage house executive; b. Newark, Apr. 15, 1930; s. Edward William and Helen Lea (Wiener) S.; m. Ludlow Bixby, June 30, 1953; children: James, Andrew, Katherine. AB, Amherst Coll., 1952; MBA, Harvard U., 1958. Credit analyst Chase Manhattan Bank, N.Y.C., 1958-60; mgr. securities Irwin Mgmt. Co., Columbus, Ind., 1961-64; ptnr. Wertheim & Co., N.Y.C., 1965-79; sr. v.p. Cyrus J. Lawrence Inc., N.Y.C., 1980-87; mng. dir. Wertheim Schroder & Co. Inc., N.Y.C., 1988—; chmn., chief investment officer Wertheim Schroder Investment Svcs., Inc., 1990—; chmn. Ctr. Redevel. Corp., South Hadley, Mass., 1988—. Trustee Mount Holyoke Coll., South Hadley, Mass., 1982—. Lt. USN, 1952-55. Episcopalian. Home: 861 Bingham Rd Ridgewood NJ 07450-2111 Office: Wertheim Schroder & Co Inc 787 7th Ave New York NY 10019-6018

SMETHURST, ROBERT GUY, lawyer; b. Calgary, Alta., Can., May 28, 1929; s. Herbert Guy and Muriel (Wilson) S.; m. Carol Ann Higgins; children from previous marriage: Linda Anne, David Guy. Student, U. B.C. 1946-47; LL.B., U. Man., 1952. Bar: Man. 1953, created Queen's counsel 1968. Practice in Winnipeg, 1954-87; partner firm D'Arcy and Deacon (formerly D'Arcy, Irving, Haig & Smethurst), 1965-87; exec. dir. B.C. br. Can. Bar Assn., 1987—; commr. Uniform Law Conf., 1964-86, pres., 1978-79; counsel Man. Pub. Utility Bd., 1968-69; Mem. Man. Law Reform Com., 1971-80; pres. Victorian Order Nurses Can., 1976-79. Mem. Can. Bar Assn. (pres. Man. br. 1971-73), Man. Bar Assn. (pres. 1969-70), Can. Bar Ins. Assn. (pres. 1983-85), Phi Delta Theta. Office: 845 Cambie St 10th flr, Vancouver, BC Canada V6B 5T3

SMIALOWSKA, SUSAN, engineering educator; b. Lwow, Poland, Aug. 23, 1925; d. Piotr Szklarski and Michalina Szklarska; m. Michal Smialowski, May 30, 1952 (dec. 1990). MSc, PhD, Silesian Tech. U., Gliwice, Poland, 1948. Rsch. fellow Metall. Inst., Gliwice, Poland, 1948-60; head corrosion and electrochemistry divsn. Polish Acad. Scis., Warsaw, Poland, 1952-82; prof. Ohio State U., Columbus, 1982—. Author: Corrosion Inhibitors, 1978, Pitting Corrosion of Metals, 1986; mem. editl. bd. Jour. Corrosion Sci.; contbr. articles to profl. jours. Mem. Nat. Assn. Corrosion Engrs. Office: Ohio State U 2041 N College Rd Columbus OH 43210-1124

SMIDDY, JOSEPH CHARLES, retired college chancellor; b. Jellico, Tenn., June 20, 1920; s. Joseph F. and Sara Nan (Tye) S.; m. Reba Graham, Sept. 6, 1985; children—Joseph F., Elizabeth Lee. BA, Lincoln Meml. U., 1948, LHD, 1970; MA, Peabody Coll., 1952; LLD, U. Richmond, 1975; LHD, Coll. William and Mary, 1986; DAm, Cumberland Coll., 1993. Tchr. Jonesville High Sch., 1948-51, prin., 1951-52; sec.-treas. Powell Valley Oil Co., Big Stone Gap, Va., 1952-53; prof. biology Clinch Valley Coll., U. Va., Wise, 1953-56; dean Clinch Valley Coll., U. Va., 1956-57, dir., 1957-68, chancellor, 1968-85, chancellor emeritus, 1985—; mem. Charter Day Award Emory and Henry Coll., 1980, Commonwealth Day awrd James Madison U., 1985. Folk music performer, collector and composer. Trustee Bapt. Sem. at Richmond, Va. Served with AUS, 1942-45, PTO. Named Outstanding Citizen of Wise County, 1970. Mem. Baptist Gen. Assn. Va. (pres. 1974—). Clubs: Masons, Shriners, Kiwanis. Home: Ridgefield Acres Wise VA 24293 Office: PO Box 3160 Wise VA 24293-3160

SMILEY, D. E., petroleum company executive. JD, La. State U., 1955. Former ptnr. Sartain, McCollister & Smiley, Baton Rouge, La.; with law dept. Exxon Corp., New Orleans, 1961-66, mgr. Washington office, 1966-78, v.p. Washington office, 1978—. Office: Exxon Corp Washington Office 2001 Pennsylvania Ave NW # 300 Washington DC 20006-1850

SMILEY, E. THOMAS, tree pathologist. BS, U. Wis., 1978; MS, Colo. State U., 1979; PhD, Mich. State U., 1985. With Yoder Bros. Fla., Fort Myers, 1979-80; tech. adv. advisor ACRT Environ. Svcs., Kent, Ohio, 1985-88; rsch. scientist Bartlett Tree Rsch. Lab., Charlotte, N.C., 1986—. Contbr. articles to Jour. of Arboriculture. Mem. ISA, ANSI, Am. Forestry Assn. Office: Bartlett Tree Rsch Lab 13768 Hamilton Rd Charlotte NC 28278-8200

SMILEY, FREDERICK MELVIN, education educator, consultant; b. Yuba City, Calif., Apr. 13, 1943; s. Lester Boomer and Claire Leone (DeChesne) S. AA, Yuba Coll., 1963; BA, Chico State U., 1966; MA in Edn., Chapman Coll., 1973, MA in English, 1978, MA in Spl. Edn., 1982; PhD, U. Santa Barbara, 1982; EdD, Okla. State U., 1992. Tchr., coach, v.p. McDermitt (Nev.) High Sch., 1978-80; resource specialist Eagle Mt. (Calif.) High Sch., 1980-81; instr. spl. edn. Mary Stone Sch., San Mateo, Calif., 1981-86; dept. leader Quaezar Corp., Bridgeport, Conn., 1986-87; cons., researcher Multifunctional Resource Ctr., Stillwater and Norman, Okla., 1988-91; asst. prof. edn. Cameron U., Lawton, Okla., 1991—. Conducts research to profl. jours.; contbg. editor Think!, The Writing Teacher. Mary Aaron scholar Mary Aaron Trust, Marysville, Calif., Blue Key scholar Chico State U. Mem. TESOL, Coun. for Exceptional Children, AAUP, Am. Assn. for Teaching and Curriculum, ASCD, Okla. Assn. Tchr. Educators, Soc. Educators and Scholars, Kappa Delta Pi, Phi Delta Kappa. Democrat. Lutheran. Avocations: reading, writing, racing, tennis, golf. Office: Cameron U 2800 W Gore Blvd Lawton OK 73505

SMILEY, JANE GRAVES, author, educator; b. L.A., Sept. 26, 1949; d. James La Verne and Frances Nuelle (Graves) S.; m. John Whiston, Sept. 4, 1970 (div.); m. William Silag, May 1, 1978 (div.); children: Phoebe Silag, Lucy Silag; m. Stephen Mark Mortensen, July 25, 1987; 1 child, Axel James Mortensen. BA, Vassar Coll., 1971; MFA, U. Iowa, 1976, MA, 1978, PhD, 1978. Asst. prof. Iowa State U., Ames, 1981-84, assoc. prof., 1984-89, prof., 1989-90, Disting. prof., 1992—; vis. asst. prof. U. Iowa, Iowa City, 1981, 87. Author: (fiction) Barn Blind, 1980, At Paradise Gate, 1981 (Friends of American Writers prize 1981), Duplicate Keys, 1984, The Age of Grief, 1987 (Nat. Book Critics Cirle award nomination 1987), The Greenlanders, 1988, Ordinary Love and Goodwill, 1989, A Thousand Acres, 1991 (Pulitzer Prize for fiction 1992, Nat. Book Critics Cirle award 1992, Midland Authors award 1992, Amb. award 1992, Heartland prize 1992), Moo: A Novel, 1995; (non-fiction) Catskill Crafts: Artisans of the Catskill Mountains, 1987. Grantee Fulbright U.S. Govt., Iceland, 1976-77, NEA, 1978, 87; recipient O. Henry award, 1982, 85, 88. Mem. Author's Guild, Screenwriters Guild. Avocations: cooking, swimming, playing piano, quilting. Office: Iowa State U Dept English 201 Ross Ames IA 50011-1401*

SMILEY, LOGAN HENRY, journalist, public concern consulant; b. Atlanta, Feb. 1, 1926; s. Logan Smiley and Gladys (McCullum) Butcher. BA in Cinema, U. So. Calif., 1950; MS in Journalism, U. Calif., L.A., 1953. Pub. rels. dir. L.A. Open Golf Tournament, 1953-54; producer, dir., co-founder Bishop's Co., Westwood, Calif., 1953-55; producer ABC-TV, Hollywood, Calif., 1957-58; asst. producer Marlon Brando Prodns., Paramount Pictures, Hollywood, Calif., 1957-58, Paris, 1959-60; cons. L.A. C. of C., 1953-56, United Artists Corp., L.A., 1958-60, Russell Birdwell, Pub. Rels., N.Y.C. and London, 1960-64; pres. Pub. Concern Films, Ft. Lauderdale, Fla., 1990—. Nat. Comm. Assocs., Miami, also Jalapa, Mex., 1948—. Writer, columnist San Antonio Light, 1948-50; editor Art Direction Mag., 1968-70, Group Travel Mag., 1970-71; editor, assoc. pub. CLIO Mag., 1968-74, Musical Am. Mag., 1964-66; editor, designer New Spirit Mag. of Social Svc., 1978-80. Mem. Fla. press corps Jimmy Carter for Pres., Atlanta, 1976; chmn. So. Fla. Jerry Brown for Pres., Miami, 1992. With USNR, 1943-45. Recipient Barnett Peace prize Southwestern U., 1944, scholarship S.W. State Tchrs. Coll., 1943, 1st place award Tex. Secondary Sch. System, 1943. Democrat. Avocations: art and book collector, journal/diary writing. Home: 18301 NE 11th Ave Miami FL 33179 Office: Nat Comms Assn PO Box 600495 Miami FL 33164-0220

SMILEY, MARILYNN JEAN, musicologist; b. Columbia City, Ind., June 5, 1932; d. Orla Raymond and Mary Jane (Bailey) S. BS (State scholar), Ball State U., 1954; MusM, Northwestern U., 1958; cert., Ecoles d'Art Americaines, Fontainebleau, France, 1959; Ph.D. (Grad. scholar, Delta Kampa Gamma scholar), U. Ill., 1970. Public sch. music tchr. Logansport, Ind., 1954-61; faculty music dept. SUNY-Oswego, 1961—, Disting. Teaching prof., 1974—, chmn. dept., 1976-81; presenter papers at confs. Contbr. articles to profl. jours. Bd. dirs. Oswego Opera Theatre, 1978—, Oswego Orch. Soc., 1978—, Penfield Libr. assocs., 1985—. SUNY Research Found. fellow, summers 1971, 72, 74. Mem. AAUW (br. coun. rep. dist. III, N.Y. State div. 1986-88, br. coun. coord. N.Y. State div. 1988-90, pres. Oswego br. 1984-86, N.Y. divsn. area interest rep. cultural interests 1990-92, grantee 1984, N.Y. divsn. diversity coord. 1993—), NEH (rsch. grantee 1990-91), Am. Musicological Soc. (chmn. N.Y. chpt. 1975-77, chpt. rep. to AMS Coun. 1993—), Medieval Acad. Am., Music Library Assn., Coll. Music Soc., Renaissance Soc. Am., Sonneck Soc. Am., Oswego County Hist. Soc., Heritage Found. of Oswego, Delta Kappa Gamma, Phi Delta Kappa, Delta Phi Alpha, Pi Kappa Lambda, Sigma Alpha Iota, Sigma Tau Delta, Kappa Delta Pi. Methodist. Office: SUNY Dept Music Oswego NY 13126

SMILEY, RICHARD WAYNE, research center administrator, researcher; b. Paso Robles, Calif., Aug. 17, 1943; s. Cecil Wallace and Elenore Louise (Hamm) S.; m. Marilyn Luis Wenning, June 24, 1967; 1 child, Shawn Elizabeth. BSc in Soil Sci., Calif. State Poly. U., San Luis Obispo, 1965; MSc in Soils, Wash. State U., 1969, PhD in Plant Pathology, 1972. Asst. soil scientist Agrl. Rsch. Svc., USDA, Pullman, Wash., 1966-69; rsch. asst. dept. plant pathology Wash. State U., Pullman, Wash., 1966-69; soil microbiologist Commonwealth Sci. and Indsl. Rsch. Orgn., Adelaide, Australia, 1972-73; rsch. assoc. dept. plant pathology Cornell U., Ithaca, N.Y., 1973-74, asst. prof., 1975-80, assoc. prof., 1980-85; supt. Columbia Basin Agr. Rsch. Ctr., prof. Oreg. State U., Pendleton, 1985—; vis. scientist Plant Rsch. Inst., Victoria Dept. Agr., Melbourne, Australia, 1982-83. Author: Compendium of Turfgrass Diseases, 1983, 2d edit., 1992; contbr. more than 200 articles to profl. jours.; author slide set illustrating diseases of turfgrasses. Postdoctoral fellow NATO, 1972. Fellow Am. Phytopath. Soc. (sr. editor APS Press 1984-87, editor-in-chief 1987-91); mem. Am. Soc. Agronomy, Internat. Turfgrass Soc., Am. Sod Producers Assn. (hon. life), Coun. Agrl. Sci. and Tech., Rotary (pres. Pendleton chpt. 1991-92, Paul Harris fellow 1993). Achievements include discovery of the etiology of a serious disease of turfgrasses, which led to a redefinition of studies and disease processes in turfgrasses. Office: Oreg State U Columbia Basin Agr Rsch Ctr PO Box 370 Pendleton OR 97801-0370

SMILEY, ROBERT HERSCHEL, university dean; b. Scottsbluff, Nebr., Mar. 17, 1943; s. Eldridge Herschel and Lucile Agnes (Kolterman) S., m. Sandra P. Mason (div. 1975); children: Peter, Michael, Robin; m. JoAnn Charlene Cannon, June 3, 1978; 1 child, Matthew. BS, UCLA, 1966, MS, 1969; PhD, Stanford U., 1973. Sr. aerospace engr. Martin Marietta Co., Littleton, Colo., 1966-67; mem. tech. staff, engr. Hughes Aircraft Co., Culver City, Calif., 1967-69; prof. econs. and policy, assoc. dean Grad. Sch. Mgmt. Cornell U., Ithaca, N.Y., 1973-89; dean, prof. mgmt. Grad. Sch. Mgmt. U. Calif., Davis, 1989—; econ. cons. IBM, GM, Amex, SBA, Air Transport Assn., others; mem. rsch. adv. bd. NFIB, 1988—, policy adv. com. Ctr. for Coops, Davis, 1989—, adv. bd. Tech. Devel. Ctr., Davis, 1990—. Editor Sinergie, 1984—, Small Bus. Econs., 1988—; mem. editorial bd. Comstock's Mag., 1989—; contbr. articles to econs. and mgmt. jours. Bd. dirs. Sacramento Valley Forum, 1990—, Japan-Am. Conf., Sacramento, 1991—; chair sponsors com. Access '91, Sacramento, 1991; bd. govs. Capitol Club. SBA grantee, DOE grantee. Mem. Am. Econs. Assn., European Assn. for Rsch., Western Econs. Assn., Beta Gamma Sigma, Capitol Club. Avocations: skiing, tennis, swimming, playing piano. Office: U Calif-Davis Dept Grad Sch Mgmt Davis CA 95616-8609

SMILEY, ROBERT WILLIAM, industrial engineer; b. Phila., Oct. 18, 1919; s. Albert James and Laura Emma (Hoiler) S.; children from previous marriage: Robert, James, Lauralee, Mary; m. Gloria Morais, Jun. 30, 1990; stepchildren: Deborah, Sheila, Vicki, James, Sonja, Michelle. Certificate in Indsl. Engring, Gen. Motors Inst., 1942; student, U. Rochester, 1948; student mgmt. program for execs., U. Pitts. Grad. Sch. Bus., 1968; student, San Jose State Coll., 1969; BSBA, Coll. Notre Dame, Belmont, Calif., 1972, MBA, 1974. Registered profl. engr.: Calif. With A.S. Hamilton (cons. engrs.), Rochester, N.Y., 1946-48; commd. lt. comdr. USN, 1952, advanced through grades to comdr., 1960; engaged in tech. contract mgmt. (Poseidon/ Polaris and Terrier Missile Programs), 1952-64; officer in charge (Polaris Missile Facility Pacific), Bremerton, Wash., 1964-66; resigned, 1966; mgr. product assurance Missile Systems div. Lockheed Missiles and Space Co., Sunnyvale, Calif., 1966-72; mgr. materiel Missile Systems div. Lockheed Missiles and Space Co., 1972-77; mgr. product assurance McDonnell Douglas Astronautics, 1977-78; dir. product assurance Aerojet Tactical Systems, Sacramento, 1978-83; dir. quality assurance Aerojet Solid Propulsion Co., Sacramento, 1984-92, Tahoe Surg. Instruments, Inc., 1992—; frequent guest lectr. at colls. on quality control and reliability; chmn. Polaris/ Minuteman/Pershing Missile Nondestruct Test Com., 1958-64; quality control cons. Dragon Missile Program, U.S. Army, 1971. Contbr. articles to sci. jours., chpt. to Reliability Handbook, 1966, Reliability Engineering and Management, 1988. Served with USNR, 1942-46, 51-52; now capt. ret. Recipient letters of Commendation for work on Polaris/Poseidon Sec. of Navy, 1960, certificate of Honor Soc. for Nondestructive Testing, 1966. Fellow Am. Soc. Quality Control (chmn. San Francisco sect. 1969-70, exec. bd. 1966—, chmn. reliability divsn. 1971, 81, nat. v.p 1984-85; mem. SCORE (chmn. Sacramento chpt. 1993—), Aircraft Industries Assn. (chmn. quality assurance com.), Navy League, AAAS, Am. Mgmt. Assn. Home and Office: 9144 Green Ravine Ln Fair Oaks CA 95628-4110 *A man can*

consider himself successful only if he leaves the world better than he found it partly through his efforts.

SMILEY, ROBERT WILLIAM, JR., investment banker; b. Lansing, Mich., Nov. 17, 1943; s. Robert William Sr. and Rebecca Lee (Flint) S. AB in Econs., Stanford U., 1970; postgrad., San Fernando Valley Coll. Law, 1973-75; MBA in Corp. Fin., City U. Los Angeles, 1979; LLB, LaSalle U., 1982. Bar: Calif. 1984. Sr. v.p. mktg. Actuarial Systems Inc., San Jose, Calif., 1972-73; founder, chmn. Benefit Systems Inc., Los Angeles, and SE Nev., 1973-84, Brentwood Square Savs. and Loan, Los Angeles, 1982-84; chmn., CEO The Benefit Capital Cos. Inc., Los Angeles, 1984—; lectr. U. Calif. Extension, Los Angeles and Berkeley, 1977—; instr. Am. Coll. Life Underwriters. Editor, contbg. author: Employee Stock Ownership Plans: Business Planning, Implementation, Law and Taxation, 1989—; contbg. author: The Handbook of Employee Benefits, 1984, 3d edit., 1992; contbr. articles to profl. jours. Mem. nat. adv. coun., trustee Reason Found., Santa Monica, Calif., 1983-91; bd. dirs. Nat. Ctr. for Employee Ownership, Oakland, Calif. With USN, 1961-64, Vietnam. Recipient Spl. Achievement award Pres.' Commn. on Pension Policy, 1984. Fellow Life Mgmt. Inst.; mem. Employee Stock Ownership Plan Assn. (founder, pres., bd. dirs., lifetime dir.), Assn. for Corp. Growth, Western and SW Pension Confs., Nat. Assn. Bus. Economists, ABA, Calif. Bar Assn. Office: The Benefit Capital Cos Inc PO Box 542 Logandale NV 89021

SMILEY, TERAH LEROY, geosciences educator; b. Oak Hill, Kans., Aug. 21, 1914; s. Terah Edward and Frances Angelina (Huls) S.; m. Marie Lemley, July, 1935; 1 child, Terrie Lucille Scheele; m. Winifred Whiting Lindsay, June 10, 1947; children: John, Maureen, Kathlyn; 1 stepchild, Margaret Ann Perry (dec.). Student, U. Kans., 1934-36; M.A., U. Ariz., 1949. With U.S. Nat. Park Service, 1939-41, U.S. Immigration Service, 1941-42; research Lab. of Tree-Ring, U. Ariz., Tucson, 1946-60; dir. Lab. of Tree-Ring, U. Ariz., 1958-60, dir. geochronology labs., 1957-67, head dept. geochronology, 1967-70, prof. geosciences, 1970-83; Gen. chmn. Internat. Conf. on Forest Tree Growth, Tucson, 1960; vice chmn. U.S. Com. on Internat. Assn. for Quaternary Research, Nat. Acad. Sci., 1961-66; gen. chmn. First Internat. Conf. on Palynology, Tucson, 1962; mem. U.S. Com. on Internat. Hydrological Decade, Nat. Acad. Sci., 1964-66; gen. chmn. Internat. Conf. on Arid Lands, Tucson, 1969. Editor: (with James H. Zumberge) Polar Deserts and Modern Man, 1974, The Geological Story of the World's Deserts, 1982; (with Nations, Péwé and Schafer) Landscapes of Arizona, the Geological Story, 1984; contbr. articles to profl. jours. Research fellow Clare Coll., Cambridge, U., 1970; vis. prof. Kvartärgeologiska Institutionen, Uppsala (Sweden) U., 1970-71; hon. v.p. 2d Internat. Conf. on Palynology, Utretch, 1966. Fellow AAAS, Geol. Soc. Am., Ariz. Acad. Sci.; mem. Am. Meteorol. Soc., Tree-Ring Soc., Ariz. Geol. Soc. (past pres.), Ariz. Archeol. Soc. (past pres.), Sigma Xi. Home: 2732 N Gill Ave Tucson AZ 85719-3220

SMILLIE, THOMSON JOHN, opera producer; b. Glasgow, Scotland, Sept. 29, 1942; s. John Baird and Mary (Thomson) S.; m. Anne Ivy Pringle, July 14, 1965; children: Jane, Jonathan, Julia, David. MA, Glasgow U., 1963. Dir. pub. rels. Scottish Opera, 1966-78; artistic dir. Wexford Festival, Ireland, 1973-78; gen. mgr. Opera Co., Boston, 1978-80; gen. dir. Ky. Opera, Louisville, 1981—. Contbr. articles to various pubs. Avocations: reading, collecting antiques. Home: 4701 Kitty Hawk Way Louisville KY 40207

SMILOW, MICHAEL A., mortgage company executive. Dep. dir. U.S. Dept. Housing & Urban Devel., 1978-80; exec. v.p. Mortgage Guaranty Ins. Corp., 1980-84; pres. MGIC Mortgage Mktg. Corp.; exec. v.p. mortgage ops. Fed. Nat. Mortgage Assn., Washington, 1984—. Office: Fed Nat Mortgage Assn 3900 Wisconsin Ave NW Washington DC 20016-2892

SMINK, MARY JANE, graphic communications technology educator; b. Charlotte, N.C., Feb. 19, 1939; d. Arthur Elmore and Louise (Belue) Moore; m. George Thomas Smink Jr.; children: George Thomas III, Karl Frederich. BS, Winthrop Coll., 1959; MA in Indsl. Arts, Appalachian State U., 1970; EdD in Indsl. Arts, N.C. State U., 1983. Cert. technology edn., N.C. Tchr. Columbia (S.C.) City Schs., 1959-61, Mars City/Adams Twp. Schs., Mars, Pa., 1961-63; tchr. Cleveland County Schs., Shelby, N.C., 1964-65, dir. audio visual, 1966-67; coord. adult edn. Wilkes C.C., Wilkesboro, N.C., 1967-70; dir. career exploration Wilkes County Schs., Wilkesboro, N.C., 1970-71; tchr. Wake County Schs., Raleigh, N.C., 1971-79; cons. N.C. Dept. Pub. Instrn., Raleigh, N.C., 1980-90; asst. prof. N.C. A&T State U., Greensboro, 1990—; contbr. articles to profl. jours. Organist Milner Meml. Presbyn. Ch., Raleigh, 1971—; leader Boy Scouts Am., Raleigh, 1973-78. Edn. Profl. Devel. Act fellow, 1980; recipient William Warner Rsch. award Epsilon Pi Tau, 1983, Epsilon Pi Tau Laureate citation N.C. State U., 1987, Award of Distinction, Tech. Student Assn., Inc., 1988, Hall of Fame citation Ednl. Exhibitors Assn. and SHIP, 1995; named State Supr. of Yr., Internat. Tech. Edn. Assn. Coun. of Suprs., 1986. Mem. S.E. Tech. Edn. Assn., N.C. Tech. Edn. Assn. (pres.-elect 1994-95), Internat. Tech. Edn Assn. (Disting. Tech. Educator award 1991, Meritorious Svc. award 1992, pres. bd. 1988), Tech. Student Assn., Inc. (bd. dirs., pres. bd. 1986-87), Nat. Assn. Indsl. Tech. (jour. rev. bd. 1993—), Phi Delta Kappa (capital area chpt.), Phi Kappa Phi. Avocation: model railroading. Home: 5907 S Sharon Dr Raleigh NC 27603-4665 Office: NC A&T State Univ Sch of Technology Greensboro NC 27411

SMIRNI, ALLAN DESMOND, lawyer; b. N.Y.C., Aug. 27, 1939; s. Donald W. and Ruby M. (King) S.; 1 child, Amie Joy. BA, CUNY, 1960; JD, U. Calif., Berkeley, 1971. Bar: Calif. 1972, U.S. Dist. Ct. (no. dist.) Calif. 1972, U.S. Ct. Appeals (9th cir.) 1972. Assoc. Brobeck, Phleger & Harrison, San Francisco, 1971-74; asst. gen. counsel Envirotech Corp., Menlo Park, Calif., 1975-81; chief counsel sec. Televideo Systems, Inc., Sunnyvale, Calif., 1982-86; v.p., gen. counsel sec. Memorex Corp., Santa Clara, Calif., 1987-89; v.p., gen. counsel Pyramid Tech. Corp., San Jose, Calif., 1989—. Adv. bd. dirs. Social Advocates for Youth, Cupertino, Calif., 1985—. Capt. USAF, 1961-67. Mem. Am. Corp. Counsel Assn., Am. Soc. Corp. Secs., Charles Houston Bar Assn. Roman Catholic. Avocations: reading, walking, movies, theatre. Home: 1363 Lennox Way Sunnyvale CA 94087-3129 Office: Pyramid Tech Corp 3860 N 1st St San Jose CA 95134-1702

SMIRNOFF, BEAR, recreational facility executive. Pres. Big Bear Internat Cruise Lines Inc, Miami, Fla. Office: Big Bear Internat Cruise Lines Inc 306 Miami Sun Miami FL 33280*

SMISKO, NICHOLAS RICHARD, bishop, educator; b. Perth Amboy, N.J., Feb. 23, 1936; s. Andrew and Anna (Totin) S. BTh, Christ the Saviour Sem., 1959; BA, U. Youngstown, 1961; Lic. in Theology, Halki (Greece) Sch. Theology, 1965. Ordained priest Carpatho-Russian Orthodox Greek Cath. Ch., 1959. Pastorate Sts. Peter and Paul Ch., Windber, Pa., 1959-62; prefect of discipline Christ the Saviour Sem., Johnstown, Pa., 1963-65; pastor Sts. Peter and Paul Ch., Homer City, Pa., 1965-71, St. Michael's Ch., Clymer, Pa., 1971-72; pastorate St. Nicholas Ch., N.Y.C., 1972-77; abbot Monastery of the Annunciation, Tuxedo Park, N.Y., 1978-83; bishop of Amissos Carpatho-Russian Orthodox Diocese, 1983—; mem. del. Ecumenical Patriarchate World Coun. Chs. 6th Gen. Assembly, Vancouver, B.C.; mem. standing conf. Canonical Orthodox Bishops in Ams.; active Orthodox-Cath. Consultation of Hierarchs. Mem. Halki Alumni Assn. Am., Christ the Saviour Sem. Alumni Assn., Am. Soc. Constantinople. Home and Office: 312 Garfield St Johnstown PA 15906

SMISKO, RICHARD G. See NICHOLAS

SMIT, HANS, law educator, academic administrator, lawyer; b. Amsterdam, Netherlands, Aug. 13, 1927; came to U.S. 1952; s. Eylard Albertus and Trijntje (de Jong) S.; m. Beverly M. Gershgol, Aug. 1, 1954; children: Robert Hugh, Marion Tina. LLB with highest honors, U. Amsterdam, 1946, JD with highest honors, 1949; AM, Columbia U., 1953, LLB with highest honors, 1958; D. (hon.), U. Paris I, 1991. Bar: Supreme Ct. Netherlands 1946, N.Y. 1974. Ptnr. Bodenhausen, Blackstone, Rueb, Bloemsma & Smit, The Hague, 1952-58; assoc. Sullivan & Cromwell, N.Y.C., 1958-60; mem. faculty law Columbia U., N.Y.C., 1960—, assoc. prof., 1960-62, prof.,

1962—, Stanley H. Fuld prof. law, 1978—; dir. Parker Sch. Fgn. and Comparative Law, 1978—; vis. prof. U. Paris, Sorbonne-Pantheon, 1975-76, 89-90, 92-94; dir. Project on Internat. Proc., Columbia U.; reporter U.S. Com. on Internat. Rules Jud. Procedure, 1960-67; bd. dirs. Project on European Legal Inst., 1968, Leyden-Amsterdam-Columbia Summer Program in Am. Law; cons. internat. comml. transactions, internat. litig.; arbitrator ICC and AAA. Author: International Co-operation in Litigation, 1963, (with others) Elements of Civil Procedure, 5th edit., 1985, International Law, 3d edit., 1993, (with Pechota) World Arbitration Reporter, 1986, (with Herzog) The Law of the European Economic Community, 1978, editor-in-chief Am. Rev. of Internat. Arbitration. Mem. All-Dutch Waterpolo team 1946-48, All-Am. Waterpolo team, AAU, 1954. Knight Order of Netherlands Lion, 1987. Mem. ABA, Internat. Bar Assn., Am. Fgn. Law Assn., Assn. of Bar of City of N.Y., Am. Soc. Internat. Law, German-Am. Lawyers' Assn., Internat. Assn. Jurists of U.S.A.-Italy, Internat. Acad. Comparative Law, Royal Dutch Soc. Arts and Scis. (assoc.). Home: 351 Riverside Dr New York NY 10025-2739 Office: Columbia U Sch Law 435 W 116th St New York NY 10027-7201

SMITH, A. ROBERT, editor, author; b. York, Pa., Feb. 13, 1925; s. Arthur R. and Inez (Dunnick) S.; m. Yvonne Franklin, 1945 (div. 1965); 1 child, Dana C.; m. Elizabeth McDowell Morgan, 1967 (div. 1988); children: Philip S. Morgan IV, Edward A.M. Morgan, Elizabeth A. Weatherly; m. Jane Dreifus, 1993. BS, Juniata Coll., 1950; postgrad., George Washington U., 1950. Reporter Huntingdon (Pa.) Daily News, 1947, Evening Star, Washington, 1950; Washington corr. Eugene (Oreg.) Register-Guard, 1951-78, Portland Oregonian, 1952-72, King Broadcasting, 1976-78; assoc. editor Virginian-Pilot, Norfolk, 1978-83; editor Venture Inward, Assn. Rsch. and Enlightenment mag., Virginia Beach, Va., 1984—. Author: The Tiger in the Senate, 1962, Hugh Lynn Cayce: About My Father's Business, 1988; co-author: (with Eric Sevareid and Fred J. Maroon) Washington: Magnificent Capital, 1965, (with James V. Giles) An American Rape, 1975. With USNR, 1943-46, PTO. Office: ARE 67th And Atlantic Ave Virginia Beach VA 23451

SMITH, AARON, health researcher, clinical psychologist; b. Boston, Nov. 3, 1930; s. Harry and Anne (Gilgoff) S.; m. Sept. 7, 1952 (div.); children—Naomi E., Jeffrey O., David G., Andrew H.; m. D. Sharon Casey, Jan. 7, 1972. A.B. Brown U., 1952; Ph.D., U. Ill., 1958. Co-dir., Northeast Psychol. Clinic, Phila., 1959-75; dir. research Haverford State Hosp., Pa., 1962-73, asst. hosp. dir., 1973-75; assoc. rsch. prof. U. Nev., Reno, 1975—; dir. rsch VA Med. Ctr., Reno, 1975—; exec. dir. Sierra Biomedical Rsch. Corp., 1999—; chmn. Nev. Legislature Mental Health Task Force, Carson City, 1978; sci. adviser Gov.'s Com. on Radiation Effects, Carson City, 1979-82. Co-author: Anti-depressant Drug Studies 1956-66, 1969; Medications and Emotional Illness, 1976; co-editor: Goal Attainment Scaling: Application, Theory, and Measurement, 1994; contbr. chpts. to books and articles to profl. jours. Grantee Squibb Inst. Med. Research, 1965-69, NIMH, 1965-69, Smith Kline & French Labs., 1968-69, VA Health Services Research, 1976-93. Mem. Am. Psychol. Assn., Western Psychol. Assn., Gerontol. Soc. Am., Assn. Health Svcs. Rsch. Home: 12790 Roseview Ln Reno NV 89511-8671 Office: VA Med Ctr 1000 Locust St Reno NV 89520-0102

SMITH, ADA L., state legislator; b. Amherst County, Va., Apr. 18, 1945; d. Thomas and Lillian Smith. Grad., CUNY. Dep. clk. N.Y.C.; state senator N.Y. Legislature, Albany, 1988—; mem. various coms. N.Y. Legislature, ranking corp. commn. and authorities, 1994, minority whip; mem. Senate Dem. Task Force Women's Issues, Senate Dem. Task Force Financing Affordable Housing, Senate Dem. Task Force Child Care 2000, Sen. Dem. Task Force Affirmative Action and Econ. Devel., Senate Dem. Task Force Primary Health Care, Senate Minority Puerto Rican and Hispanic Task Force; chair Senate Minority Task Force on Privatization of Kennedy and Laguardia Airports. Bd. visitors Bklyn. Ctr. for the Mentally Retarded and the Developmentally Disabled, 1981, 85; trustee, life dir. Coll. Fund Baruch Coll.; mem. Community I Bd. (chair social svcs. com.); chair. N.Y. Community Scvs. Coalition, Bklyn. Coalition Area Policy Bds.; treas. Bklyn. Pla. Med. Ctr., Friends Lindsay Park Anti-Crime Com.; bd. mgrs. Ea. Dist. YMCA; officer Williamsburg Tenants Assn.; mem. Community Action Bd.; exec. mem. Ctr. for Community Orgns.; mem. adv. bd. Woodhull Hosp.; mem. Area Policy Bd. 4; past pres. Williamsburg/Greenpoint Coalition Community Orgns.; past chair Area Policy Bd. 1; past bd. dirs., pres. Lindsay Park Housing Corp. Recipient Roberto Clemente Community Svc. award, Women of the Yr. award YMCA, Pulaski Community Svc. award, Outstanding Alumni award Baruch Coll., Pres.'s medal, Williamsburg/ Greenpoint COCO Community Svc. award, others. Mem. African Am. Clergy and Elected Ofcls., Inc. (treas.), N.Y. State Black and Puerto Rican Legis. Caucus (vice-chair), Baruch Coll. Alumni Assn. (pres., Disting. Svc. award, Outstanding Achievement award). Home: 67 Manhattan Ave Brooklyn NY 11206-3156 Office: NY State Senate Rm 304 Legis Office Bldg Albany NY 12247 Office: Queens Dist Office 130-08 Rockaway Blvd South Ozone Park NY 11420 also: Bklyn Dist Office 545 Broadway 4th fl Brooklyn NY 11206

SMITH, ADAM See GOODMAN, GEORGE JEROME WALDO

SMITH, ADRIAN DEVAUN, architect; b. Chgo., Aug. 19, 1944; s. Alfred D. and Hazel (Davis) S.; m. Nancy L. Smith, Aug. 17, 1968; children: Katherine, Jason. Student, Tex. A&M U., 1962-66; B.Arch., U. Ill., Chgo., 1969. Registered architect Ill., Ohio, N.J., N.Y., Mass., Iowa, Md., Conn., D.C., Fla., Ind., Mo., R.I., Tex. Design ptnr. Skidmore, Owings & Merrill, Chgo., 1967—, prtnr., 1980—, CEO, 1994—; vis. faculty Sch. Architecture, U. Ill., Chgo., 1984; chmn. Senator Richard A. Newhouse Bldg. Competition Jury, 1982, U. Ill. Sch. Archtl. Alumni Assn., AIA Jury on Inst. Honors; chmn. Skidmore Owings Merrill Found.; mem. Chgo. Ctrl. Area; recipient U. Ill. Alumni Achievement award. cons. and lectr. in field. Designer numerous projects including Jin Mao Tower (World's Tallest Mixed-Use Project), Shanghai, China, Banco de Occidente, Guatemala City (CCAIA Interior Architecture award 1981, NAIA Honor award 1982), Three 1st Nat. Bank Chgo. (CCAIA Lighting Soc. award 1984), United Gulf Bank, Manama, Bahrain (Progressive Architecture award 1984, CCAIA Disting. Bldg. award 1988, NAIA Honor award 1988, CCAIA Disting. Detail Honor Bldg. award 1988, 222 N. LaSalle, Chgo. (Disting Bldg. award CCAIA 1988), Art Inst. Chgo. 2d Fl. Galleries (CCAIA Disting. Bldg. award 1987), Rowes Wharf, Boston (Build Am. award 1988, Build Mass. award 1989, ULI award 1989, PCI Profl. Design award 1989, CCAIA Hon. award 1990, Nat. AIA Honor award 1994), AT&T Corp. Ctr., Chgo. (recipient Gold Metal Ill. Ind. Masonry award), NBC Tower (Chgo. Sun Times Bldg. of Yr. award 1989, CCAIA Disting. Bldg. award 1990, PCI Design award 1989), 75 State St., Boston (Archtl. Woodwork Inst. award 1989, Nat. Comml. Builder's Coun. Merit award 1990, Bldg. Stone Inst. Tucker Archtl. award 1990), Arthur Anderson Training Ctr. (Masonry award 1988), St. Charles, Ill., USG Hdqs. Chgo., Heller Internat. Tower, Chgo., designer numerous other fgn. projects including: Monterey Cultural Ctr., Mex., 1978; hdqrs. Banco de Occidente, Guatemala City, 1978 (AIA Nat. Honor award, Bus. Interior Design award Guatemala 1981, CCAIA Interior Architecture award 1982, NAIA Honor award), Canary Wharf Fin. Ctr., London, Eng., 1988, 10 Ludgate (CCAIA 1994 Honor award), 100 Ludgate, London, 1992, Aramco Hdqs. Dahrain Saudi Arabia, Sanghai China, 1994; contbr. articles to profl jours.; subject numerous publs. in architecture. Mem. com. Task Force for New City Plan, Chgo., Light Up Chgo., Cen. Area Task Force, Chgo.; chmn. Senator Richard A. Newhouse Bldg. Competition Jury, 1982, Progressive Architecture Design Jury, 1985. Fellow AIA (mem. Young Architects Award Design Jury, 1987, Mich. Jury 1988, Disting. Bldg. award 1990), Royal Inst. Brit. Architects, Archtl. Registration Coun. U.K., Nat. Coun. Archtl. Registration Bds., Architecture Soc. of Art Inst. Chgo., Chgo. Arch. Found. (bd. dirs.), Chgo. Archtl. Club, Urban Land Inst. (bd. dirs.), University Club, Arts Club. Home: 1100 W Summerfield Dr Lake Forest IL 60045-1545 Office: Skidmore Owings & Merrill 224 S Michigan Ave Ste 1000 Chicago IL 60604

SMITH, AL FREDERICK, professional football player; b. Los Angeles, Calif., Nov. 26, 1964. Student, Calif. State Polytech., Pomona; BS in Sociology, Utah State, 1987. Linebacker Houston Oilers, 1987—. Played in Pro Bowl, 1991-92. Office: Houston Oilers 6910 Fannin St Fl 3 Houston TX 77030-3875*

SMITH, ALAN HARVEY, former editor; b. Wilkes-Barre, Pa., May 4, 1920; s. Harold Daniel and Florence (Sugden) S.; m. Ruth Zimmerman, Nov. 3, 1944; 1 child, Jill Clerihew Smith. BA, Bucknell U., 1941; MA, Columbia U., 1951; postgrad., Harvard U., 1948-49. Tchr. Lewisburg (Pa.) High Sch. 1941-42; instr. English Rensselaer Poly. Inst., Troy, N.Y., 1946-48; asst. editor Americana Ann., Grolier, Inc., N.Y.C., 1950-53; sr. asst. editor Americana Ann., Grolier, Inc., 1953-58; assoc. editor Americana Annual, Grolier, Inc., 1958-59, Ency. Americana, N.Y.C., 1959-65; exec. editor Ency. Americana, N.Y.C., then Danbury, Conn., 1965-81, editor-in-chief, 1981-85. With USNR, 1942-45. Democrat. Presbyterian. Home: 6 Hemlock Park Dr Groton MA 01450-1450

SMITH, ALAN JAY, computer science educator, consultant; b. N.Y.C., Apr. 10, 1947; s. Harry and Elsie (Mark) S. SB, MIT, 1971; MS, Stanford (Calif.) U., 1973, PhD in Computer Sci., 1974. From asst. prof. to full prof. U. Calif., Berkeley, 1974—; assoc. editor ACM Trans. on Computers Systems, 1982-93; vice-chmn. elec. engring. & computer sci. dept. U. Calif., Berkeley, 1982-84; nat. lectr. ACM, 1985-86; mem. editorial bd. Jour. Microprocessors and Microsystems, 1988—; subject area editor Jour. Parallel and Distbn. Computing, 1989—; mem. IFIP working group 7.3. Fellow IEEE (disting. visitor 1986-87); mem. Assn. for Computing Machinery (chmn. spl. interest group on computer architecture 1991-93, chmn. spl. interest group on ops. systems 1983-87, bd. dirs. spl. interest group on performance evaluation 1985-89, bd. dirs. spl. interest group on computer architecture 1993—), Computer Measurement Group. Office: U Calif Dept of Computer Sci Berkeley CA 94720

SMITH, ALAN W., JR., management consultant; b. Pensacola, Fla., Nov. 16, 1943; s. Alan W. and Eleanor C. (Handy) S.; m. Mary Kate, June 12, 1965 (div. May 1978); children: Alison, Andrew; m. Patricia A. Waterfield, May 26, 1979; children: Amy, Cary. AB, Harvard U., 1965. Personnel rep. John Hancock, Boston, 1966-68; cons. Cole & Assocs. Inc., Boston, 1968-72; exec. v.p. Cole Surveys Inc., Boston, 1972-79; v.p. The Wyatt Co., San Francisco, 1979—. Contbr. articles to profl. jours. Mem. Am. Compensation Assn., Western Pension Conf. Avocations: music, photography. Office: The Wyatt Co 601 13th St NW Washington DC 20005-3807

SMITH, ALBERT ALOYSIUS, JR., electrical engineer, consultant; b. Yonkers, N.Y., Dec. 2, 1935; s. Albert Aloysius and Jean Mary (Misiewicz) S.; B.S.E.E., Milw. Sch. Engring., 1961; M.S.E.E., N.Y.U., 1964; m. Rosemarie Torricelli, Apr. 4, 1964 (dec. 1982); children—Denise, Matthew. Staff engr. Adler/Westrex, New Rochelle, N.Y., 1961-64; adv. engr. IBM, Kingston, N.Y., 1964-78, sr. engr., Poughkeepsie, N.Y., 1978-85, Kingston, N.Y., 1985-91; cons., 1991—. Com. chmn. Woodstock Boy Scout Troup 34, 1978-79; com. chmn. Woodstock Cub Pack 34, 1976-78. Served with USN, 1953-56. Recipient Outstanding Alumnus award Milw. Sch. Engring., 1981. Invention Achievement awards IBM, 1979, 90, Div. award, 1981. Fellow IEEE (tech. com. on electromagnetic environments, assoc. editor Trans. on EMC); mem. Am. Nat. Standards Com. Roman Catholic. Author: Coupling of External Electromagnetic Fields to Transmission Lines, 1977; Measuring the Radio Frequency Environment, 1985. Home: 11 Streamside Ter Woodstock NY 12498-1521

SMITH, ALBERT CHARLES, biologist, educator; b. Springfield, Mass., Apr. 5, 1906; s. Henry Joseph and Jeanette Rose (Machol) S.; m. Nina Grönstrand, June 15, 1935; children: Katherine (Mrs. L. J. Campbell), Michael Alexis; m. Emma van Ginneken, Aug. 1, 1966. AB, Columbia U., 1926, PhD, 1933. Asst. curator N.Y. Bot. Garden, 1928-31, asso. curator, 1931-40; curator herbarium Arnold Arboretum of Harvard U., 1940-48; curator div. phanerogams U.S. Nat. Mus., Smithsonian Instn., 1948-56; program dir. systematic biology NSF, 1956-58; dir. Mus. of Natural History, Smithsonian Instn., 1958-62, asst. sec., 1962-63; prof. botany, dir. research U. Hawaii, Honolulu, 1963-65; Gerrit Parmile Wilder prof. botany U. Hawaii, 1965-70, prof. emeritus, 1970—; Ray Ethan Torrey prof. botany U. Mass., Amherst, 1970-76; prof. emeritus U. Mass., 1976—; editorial cons. Nat. Tropical Bot. Garden, Hawaii, 1977-91; bot. expdns., Colombia, Peru, Brazil, Brit. Guiana, Fiji, West Indies, 1926-69; del. Internat. Bot. Congresses, Amsterdam, 1935, Stockholm, 1950; v.p. systematic sect., Montreal, 1959, Internat. Zool. Congress, London, 1958; pres. Am. Soc. Plant Taxonomists, 1955, Bot. Soc. Washington, 1962, Biol. Soc. Washington, 1962-64, Hawaiian Bot. Soc., 1967. Author: Flora Vitiensis Nova: a New Flora of Fiji, Vol. I, 1979, Vol. II, 1981, Vol. III, 1985, Vol. IV, 1991, Vol. V, 1991; also tech. articles; Editor: Brittonia, 1935-40, Jour. Arnold Arboretum, 1941-48, Sargentia, 1942-48, Allertonia, 1977-88; editorial com.: International Code Botanical Nomenclature, 1954-64. Bishop Mus. fellow Yale U., 1933-34, Guggenheim fellow, 1946-47; recipient Robert Allerton award for Excellence in Tropical Botany, 1979, Asa Gray award Am. Soc. Plant Taxonomists, 1992, Charles Reed Bishop medal, 1995. Fellow Am. Acad. Arts and Scis.; mem. NAS, Bot. Soc. Am. (Merit award 1970), Assn. Tropical Biology (pres. 1967-68), Internat. Assn. Plant Taxonomy (v.p. 1959-64), Fiji Soc. (hon.), Washington Biologists' Field Club (pres. 1962-64). Home: 2474 Aha Aina Pl Honolulu HI 96821

SMITH, ALEXANDER FORBES, III, engineering consulting firm executive; b. Reading, Pa., Feb. 7, 1929; s. Alexander Forbes and Ethyl Mohn (Wahl) S.; m. Mary Louise Taylor, Dec. 29, 1970; children: Sandra, Robin, Douglas, Steven. BSME, Lehigh U., 1950, MSME, 1951. Marine engr. U.S. Naval Boiler & Turbine Lab., Phila., 1951-54; mech. engr. Gilbert Assocs., Inc., Reading, Pa., 1955-62, asst. to chief engr., 1962-68, project mgr., 1963-68, v.p. ops., 1968-70, v.p., gen. mgr., 1970-73, exec. v.p., 1973-77, group v.p., COO, 1977-78, pres., CEO, 1979-94, chmn. bd., 1986—, also bd. dirs., 1970—; chmn. Gilbert/Commonwealth, Inc., 1984—, United Energy Svcs. Corp., 1984—, GAI-Tronics Corp., 1980—, Resource Cons. Inc., 1988—, Green Hills Mgmt. Co., 1986—; bd. dirs Stratton Growth Fund, Inc., Stratton Monthly Dividend Shares, Inc.; bd. dirs. Reading Hosp. & Med. Ctr. Patentee in field. Chmn. adv. bd. Berks Campus Pa. State Univ., 1979-80; chmn. Berks County Bd. Assistance, 1966-67; trustee YMCA, 1979-86. Mem. NSPE, ASME, NAM (past bd. dirs.), Pa. Soc. Profl. Engrs., C. of C. (past bd. dirs.), Mfrs. Assn. Berks County (bd. dirs.), 1988—), Pa. Bus. Roundtable, Tau Beta Pi, Omicron Delta Kappa, Pi Tau Sigma, Delta Tau Delta. Republican. Episcopalian. Home: Cricket Springs PO Box 182 Geigertown PA 19523-0182 Office: Gilbert Assocs Inc PO Box 1498 Reading PA 19603-1498*

SMITH, ALEXANDER GOUDY, physics and astronomy educator; b. Clarksburg, W.Va., Aug. 12, 1919; s. Edgell Ohr and Helen (Reitz) S.; m. Mary Elizabeth Ellsworth, Apr. 19, 1942; children: Alexander G. III, Sally Jean. B.S., Mass. Inst. Tech., 1941; Ph.D., Duke U., 1949. Physicist Mass. Inst. Tech., Radiation Lab., Cambridge, 1943-46; research asst. Duke U., Durham, 1946-48; asst. prof. to prof. physics U. Fla., Gainesville, 1948-61; asst. dean grad. sch. U. Fla., 1961-69, acting dean grad. sch., 1971-73, chmn. dept. astronomy, 1962-71, prof. physics and astronomy, 1956—, Disting. prof., 1981—; dir. U. Fla. Radio Obs., 1956-85, Rosemary Hill Obs., 1989—. Author: (with others) Microwave Magnetrons, 1958, (with T.D. Carr) Radio Exploration of the Planetary System, 1964 (also Swedish, Spanish and Polish edits), Radio Exploration of the Sun, 1966; also numerous articles in field. Fellow AAAS, Optical Soc. Am., Am. Phys. Soc., Royal Micros. Soc.; mem. Am. Astron. Soc. (editor Photo-Bull. 1975-87), Astron. Soc. Pacific, Internat. Astron. Union, Internat. Sci. Radio Union, Fla. Acad. Scis. (treas. 1957-62, pres. 1963-64, medal 1965), Assn. Univs. for Rsch. in Astronomy (dir., cons.), S.E. Univs. Rsch. Assn. (trustee 1981-91), Soc. Photog. Scientists and Engrs., Sigma Xi (nat. lectr. 1968, past pres. Fla. chpt.), Athenaeum Club (past pres.), Db Racquet Club, Gainesville Country Club, Sigma Xi (nat. lectr. 1968, past pres. Fla. chpt.), Phi Kappa Phi, Sigma Pi Sigma. Republican. Christian Scientist. Home: 1417 NW 17th St Gainesville FL 32605-4014 Office: U Fla Dept Astronomy 211 Space Scis Bldg Gainesville FL 32611

SMITH, ALEXANDER JOHN COURT, insurance executive; b. Glasgow, Scotland, Apr. 13, 1934; s. John Court and Mary Walker (Anderson) S.; m. Margaret Gillespie, Oct. 15, 1968. Student, Scottish schs. Actuarial trainee Scottish Mut. Ins. Co, Glasgow, 1957; asst. actuary Zurich Life Ins. Co. Toronto, Can., 1958-61; from actuary to exec. v.p. William M. Mercer Ltd., Toronto, 1961-74; pres. William M. Mercer, Inc. Toronto, 1974-82; sr. v.p., dir. Marsh & McLennan, Inc., N.Y.C., 1974-78; group v.p. cons. and fin. svcs. group Marsh & McLennan Cos., N.Y.C., 1982-84, pres. of group, 1984-

85, pres., 1984-85, vice chmn., 1984-86, pres., 1986-92, chmn., CEO, 1992—; pres. MMC Cons. & Fin. Svcs. Group, 1984-85. Trustee The Putnam Funds, 1986—, Cen. Park Conservancy, 1988—, Carnegie Hall Soc., 1992—. Fellow Faculty Actuaries Edinburgh, Can. Inst. Actuaries, Conf. Cons. Actuaries; mem. Soc. Actuaries (assoc.), Am. Acad. Actuaries, Internat. Congress Actuaries, Internat. Assn. Cons. Actuaries, Racquet and Tennis Club, Royal Can. Yacht Club, Apawamis Club, Caledonian Club, Blind Brook Club Inc. Home: 630 Park Ave New York NY 10021-6544 Office: Marsh & McLennan Cos Inc 1166 Ave of the Americas New York NY 10036-2708

SMITH, ALEXANDER WYLY, JR., lawyer; b. Atlanta, June 9, 1923; s. Alexander Wyly and Laura (Payne) S.; m. Betty Rawson Haverty, Aug. 31, 1946; children—Elizabeth Smith Crew, Clarence Haverty, Laura Smith Brown, James Haverty, Edward Kendrick, Anthony Marion, William Rawson. Grad., Marist Sch., 1941; student, Holy Cross Coll., 1941-42; B.B.A., U. Ga., 1947, LL.B. cum laude, 1949. Bar: Ga. 1948. Practiced in Atlanta, 1948—; partner firm Smith, Gambrell & Russell and predecessor, 1949-94; ret., 1994; dir. Haverty Furniture Co., Inc. Bd. dirs. Our Lady of Perpetual Help Free Cancer Home; bd. dirs., planning and devel. coun. Cath. Archdiocese Atlanta, Marist Sch., Atlanta, John and Mary Franklin Found. Served with USAAF, 1943-46. Mem. Ga. Bar Assn., Atlanta Bar Assn., Ctrl. Atlanta Progress (pres. 1966, dir. 1966-94), Phi Delta Phi, Chi Phi, Piedmont Driving Club Atlanta, Peachtree Golf Club Atlanta (pres. 1989-91). Clubs: Piedmont Driving (Atlanta), Peachtree Golf (Atlanta) (pres. 1989-91). Home: 158 W Wesley Rd NW Atlanta GA 30305-3523 Office: 300 Promenade II 1230 Peachtree St NE Atlanta GA 30309

SMITH, ALFRED GOUD, anthropologist, educator; b. The Hague, Netherlands, Aug. 20, 1921; s. William G. and Joan (Wraslouski) S.; m. Britta Helen Bonazzi, May 30, 1946. A.B. (Simon Mandlebaum scholar, Am. Council Learned Socs. fellow in Oriental Langs.), U. Mich., 1943; postgrad., Princeton U., Yale U., 1943; M.A., U. Wis., 1947, Ph.D., 1956. Far East analyst OSS and Dept. State, Washington, 1944-46; asst., instr. philosophy and anthropology U. Wis., 1946-50; supr. linguistics, Pacific area specialist Trust Ter. Pacific Islands and Dept. Interior, Micronesia and Washington, 1950-53; asst. prof. anthropology Antioch Coll., Yellow Springs, Ohio, 1953-56; asst. prof., asso. prof. anthropology Emory U., Atlanta, 1956-62; asso. prof., prof. anthropology, community service and pub. affairs. U. Oreg., Eugene, 1962-73; dir. Center for Communication Research, U. Tex., Austin, 1973-78; prof. anthropology Ctr. Communication Research Sch. Communication, U. Tex., 1973—. Consle. Ga. Dept. Pub. Health, 1956-60, Peace Corps, 1965-69, Job Corps, 1968-70, USIA, 1972-79, 82; U.S. State Dept. specialist, Mex., 1978; cons. on problems of communication and anthropology to state and fed. agys., industry, museums, instns. of higher learning; staff mem. AID Communication Seminars, 1966-81; lectr. in field, Eng., Mex. and Can. Author: Communication and Culture, 1966, Cognitive Styles in Law Schools, 1979; mem. editorial bd. Communication and Info. Scis., Info. and Behavior, Progress in Communication Scis.; contbr. articles to profl. jours., revs., chpts. in books. Served to 1st lt. AUS, 1942-45. Fellow Am. Anthrop. Assn., AAAS; mem. Internat. Communication Assn. (pres. 1973-74, dir.), Sigma Xi, Alpha Kappa Delta, Phi Kappa Phi. Club: Town and Gown. Home: 1801 Lavaca St Austin TX 78701-1304 Office: U Tex Coll Communication Austin TX 78712

SMITH, ALLIE MAITLAND, university dean; b. Lumberton, N.C., June 9, 1934; s. Allie McCoy and Emma Hattie (Wright) S.; m. Sarah Louise Whitlock, June 16, 1957; children: Sara Leianne, Hollis Duval, Meredith Lorren. BME with honors, N.C. State U., Raleigh, 1956, MS, 1961, PhD, 1966. Assoc. engr. Martin Co., Balt., 1956-57; devel. engr. Western Electric Co., 1957-60; mem. tech. staff Bell Tel. Labs., Burlington, N.C., 1960-62; instr., then asst. prof. extension N.C. State U., 1958-62; rsch. project engr. Rsch. Triangle Inst., Durham, N.C., 1962-66; rsch. supr. Sverdrup/ARO, Inc., Arnold Air Force Sta., Tenn., 1966-79; adj. prof. U. Tenn., Tullahoma, 1967-79; prof. mech. engring., dean Sch. Engring. U. Miss., 1979—; bd. dirs., mem. scholarship bd. Miss. Mineral Resources Inst.; exec. chmn. 14th conf. Southeastern Conf. on Theoretical and Applied Mechanics, mem. exec. com. 13th through 16th confs.; mem. ops. com. and policy com., 1990-94, session chair, 1994; mem. organizing com., internat. sci. adv. bd., plenary session presiding officer Internat. Conf. on Hydrosci. and Engring., 1993, 95. Author: Fundamentals of Silicon Integrated Device Technology, Vol I: Oxidation, Diffusion and Epitaxy, 1967, also articles, revs.; editor: Radiative Transfer and Thermal Control, 1976, Thermophysics of Spacecraft and Outer Planet Entry Probes, 1977, Fundamentals and Applications of Radiation Heat Transfer, 1987, Developments in Theoretical and Applied Mechanics, Vol. XIV, 1988, Radiation Heat Transfer: Fundamentals and Applications, 1990, Fundamentals of Radiation Heat Transfer, 1991, Radiative Heat Transfer: Theory and Applicatons, 1993. Fellow ASME, AIAA (asso. thermophysics tech. com. 1975-77, chmn. terrestrial energy sustems tech. com. 1979-81, chmn. confs. 1975, 79, assoc. editor jour. 1975-77, 86—, mem. nat. publ. com. 1979-83, Nat. Thermophysics award 1978, Hermann Oberth award 1984-85, Space Shuttle Flag Challenger plaque 1984, supernumerary dir. Ala.-Miss. sect. 1994—); mem. AAUP, NSPE (pres. N.E. Miss. chpt. 1990-91), Am. Soc. Engring. Edn. (host Nat. Engring. Deans' Inst. 1991), N.Y. Acad. Scis., Rotary, Sigma Xi, Phi Kappa Phi, Tau Beta Pi, Pi Tau Sigma, Upsilon Pi Epsilon, Sigma Pi (scholar 1955), Order of the Engr. Club: Rotary. Achievements include discovery of anomalous refraction maxima phenomenon. Home: PO Box 1857 University MS 38677-1857 Office: U Miss 101 Carrier Hall University MS 38677

SMITH, ANDREW J., chemicals executive; b. 1941. Grad., Concordia Coll., 1963. With E.I. Du Pont de Nemours & Co., Gregory, Tex., 1965-76, Consolidated Thermoplastics, Dallas, 1976-84; with Rexene Corp., Dallas, 1984-91, CEO, 1992—; with Itex Enterprises Inc., Dallas, 1991-92. Office: Rexene Corp 5005 Lyndon B Johnson Fwy Dallas TX 75244-6119*

SMITH, ANDREW VAUGHN, telephone company executive; b. Roseburg, Oreg., July 17, 1924; s. Andrew Britt and Ella Mae (Vaughn) S.; m. Dorothy LaVonne Crabtree, Apr. 25, 1943; children: Janet L., James A. B.S in Elec. Engring. Oreg. State U., 1950. Registered profl. engr., Oreg. With Pacific N.W. Bell Tel. Co., 1951-88; asst. v.p. ops. Pacific N.W. Bell Tel. Co., Seattle, 1965, v.p. ops., 1970-78; v.p., gen. mgr. Pacific N.W. Bell Tel. Co., Portland, Oreg., 1965-70; pres. Pacific N.W. Bell Tel. Co., Seattle, 1978-88; pres. ops. U.S. West Communications, 1988-89; exec. v.p. U.S. West Inc., 1989; pres. Telephone Pioneers of Am., 1989-90; ret. U.S. West Inc., 1989; bd. dirs. Univar Corp., Seattle, Cascade Natural Gas, Seattle, Airborne Freight Corp., Seattle Prime Source, Pennsouken, N.J. Hon. trustee Oreg. State U. Found., U. Wash. Grad. Sch. Bus., 1985, chmn. bd. trustees, 1984-85; gen. chmn. United Way of King County, 1980-81; mem. Wash. State Investment Com., Olympia, 1989-92; mem. bd. trustees U. Wash., 1989—. With USNR, 1943-46. Mem. Seattle C. of C. (chmn. 1985-86). Mem. Wash. Athletic Club, Seattle Yacht Club, Rainier Club, Overlake Golf and Country Club, Multnomah Club (Portland), Columbia Tower Club (Seattle), Desert Island Country Club (Palm Desert, Calif.), The Palm Springs (Calif.) Club. Episcopalian. Office: 1600 Bell Plz Rm 1802 Seattle WA 98191

SMITH, ANN C., nursing educator; b. Weehawken, N.J., Aug. 11, 1937; d. John Aloysius Smith and Ruth Dorothea-Louise Wiese. Diploma, Bellevue Schs. of Nursing, N.Y.C., 1959; BS, MA, NYU, 1966, 68; MA, New Sch. for Social Rsch., N.Y.C., 1982; MSN, CUNY, 1988. Gerontol. nurse practitioner, N.Y. Prof. Bronx (N.Y.) Community College/CUNY. Capt. USAR Nurse Corp. 1959-63. Mem. ANA, N.Y. State Nurses Assn., Am. Nurses Found., Am. Acad. Nurse Practitioners, N.Y. State Coalition of Nurse Practitioners, Sigma Theta Tau.

SMITH, ANNA DEAVERE, actress, playwright; b. Baltimore, Sept. 18, 1950; d. Deavere Young and Anna (Young) S. BA, Beaver Coll., Pennsylvania, 1971; MFA, Am. Conservatory Theatre, 1976. Ann O'Day Maples prof. arts and drama Stanford U. Playwright, performer one-woman shows: On the Road: A Search for American Character, 1983, Aye, Aye, Aye, I'm Integrated, 1984, Piano, 1991 (Drama-Logue award), Fires in the Mirror, 1992 (Obie award 1992, Drama Desk award 1992, Pulitzer Prize nomination for drama 1993), Twilight: Los Angeles 1992 (Obie award, 2 Tony award nominations, Drama Critics Cir. Special citation, Outer Critics Cir. award Drama Desk award, Audelco award), 1993; creator with Judith Jamison, performer Hymn, 1993; other appearances include (stage) Horatio, 1974,

Alma, the Ghost of Spring Street, 1976, Mother Courage, 1980, Tartuffe, 1983; (television) All My Children, 1983; (film) Soup for One, 1982, Dave, 1993, Philadelphia, 1993. Named one of Women of the Yr., Glamour Mag., 1993; fellow Bunting Inst. Radcliffe Coll. Office: Tantleff Office 375 Greenwich St New York NY 10013 also: Stanford Univ Dept of Drama Memorial Hall Stanford CA 94305

SMITH, ANNA NICOLE, model; b. Mexia, Tex.; 1 child, Daniel; m. J. Howard Marshall II, Jun. 27, 1994. Model for Guess? jeans. Appeared in films Naked Gun 33 1/3: The Final Insult, 1994, The Hudsucker Proxy, 1994; cover model Playboy, 1992 (Playmate of the Yr. 1994). Office: Elite Model Mgmt Corp 111 E 22nd St 2d Fl New York NY 10010

SMITH, ANNE BOWMAN, academic administrator, editor; b. Craigsville, Va., Dec. 17, 1934; d. Joseph Benjamin and Louise Frances (Smith) Bowman; m. William Jerry Smith, June 29, 1957; children: Stacey Anne, Joan Elizabeth. Student, Madison Coll., 1951-54, Old Dominion U., 1979-82; BA, Cath. U. Am. Reporter The Richmond (Va.) Times-Dispatch, 1955-56, The Miami (Fla.) Herald, 1965-68, 70-72, The Virginian-Pilot, Norfolk, 1968-70, 72-78; Portsmouth-Chesapeake city editor The Virginian-Pilot, 1978, govt. editor, 1978-80, asst. met. editor, 1980-82; dir. pub. info. Cath. U. Am., Washington, 1982-84, exec. dir. pub. affairs, 1984—; editor in chief Cath. U. Am. mag., 1989—; lectr. journalism, pub. rels. Cath. U. Am., Washington, 1988-92. Editor: Century Ended, Century Begun, 1990. Bd. dirs. Summer Opera Theatre Co., Washington, 1990—. Recipient numerous awards including Va. Press Assn., Va. Press Women, Nat. Fedn. Press Women, Cath. Press Assn. Mem. Soc. Profl. Journalists, Cath. Press Assn., Coun. Advancement and Support of Edn., Assn. Am. Univs., Coll. News Assn. Office: Cath U Am Washington DC 20064

SMITH, APOLLO MILTON OLIN, retired aerodynamics engineer; b. Columbia Mo., July 2, 1911; s. Orsino Cecil and Blanche Alice (Whitaker) S.; m. Elisabeth Caroline Krost, Dec. 5, 1943; children: Tove Anne, Gerard Nicholas, Kathleen Roberta. BS in Mech. Engring., Calif. Inst. Tech., 1936, MS, 1937, MS in Aero. Engring., 1938; DSc (hon.), U. Colo., 1975. Asst. chief aerodynamicist Douglas Aircraft Co., El Segundo, Calif., 1938-42, 1944-48, supr. design rsch., 1948-54; supr. aerodynamic rsch. McDonnell Douglas Corp., Long Beach, Calif., 1954-69; chief engr. Aerojet Engring. Corp., Pasadena, Calif., 1942-44; chief aerodynamics engr. rsch. McDonnell Douglas Corp., Long Beach, 1969-75; adj. prof. UCLA, 1975-80; cons. aerodyn. engr., San Marino, Calif., 1975-86. Author: (with others) Analysis of Turbulent Boundary Layers, 1974, contbr. over 65 tech. papers. Recipient Robert H. Goddard award Am. Rocket Soc., 1954, Engring. Achievement award Douglas Aircraft Co., 1958, Casey Baldwin award Can. Aeros. and Space Inst., 1971, Fluids Engring. award ASME, 1985. Fellow AIAA (hon.); Wright Bros. lectr. 1974); mem. NAE. Home: 2245 Ashbourne Dr San Marino CA 91108-2304

SMITH, ARTHUR, radio and television producer, composer; b. Clinton, S.C., Apr. 1, 1921; s. Clayton Seymour and Viola (Fields) S.; m. Dorothy Byars, Apr. 12, 1941; children: Arthur Reginald, Constance (Mrs. Wiley Brown), Robert Clayton. Grad. high sch. Rec. artist RCA Victor, 1936-38; band leader, composer Sta. WSPA, Spartanburg, S.C., 1938-41, Sta. WBT, Charlotte, N.C., 1941-43; band leader, composer, producer CBS Radio, WBT, WBTV, Charlotte, 1945-70; producer WSOC-TV Cox Broadcasting Co., Charlotte, 1970—; dir. Hardware Mut. Ins. Co., Am. Bank & Trust Co., Meat Centers; pres. Clay Music Corp., Charlotte, 1960-76; owner Arthur Smith Studios, Charlotte, 1961—; v.p. CMH Records, L.A.; founder Arthur Smith King Mackerel Tournament, Myrtle Beach, S.C., 1976, Arthur Smith Kingfish, Dolphin, Wahoo Tournament of the Palm Beaches (Fla.), 1983. Prin.: The Arthur Smith Show, 1971-76; composer: numerous compositions, including Guitar Boogie, 1946; also rec. artist: more than 100 albums for MGM, DOT, Monument and Starday, numerous compositions, including Dueling Banjos, 1973 (BMI Song of Year 1973); composer: (with Clay Smith) sound track of film Death Driver, 1975, Dark Sunday, 1976; musical score for Living Legend and Lady Grey-Superstar, 1979; co-host with Clay Smith of syndicated radio show "The Arthur Smith Sportsman Journal." Bd. dirs. Charlotte Sch. of Arts, Am. Heart Assn., Marine Sci. Council; trustee, dir. Gardner Webb Coll.; trustee Boys Homes N.C.; founder, chmn. Arthur Smith Bluefish Tournament of N.Y. Served with USN, 1943-45. Named Bapt. Layman of Yr. Southeastern Sem. Louisville, 1969; named to N.C. Broadcasters Hall of Fame, 1990; recipient Religion Emphasis award Am. Legion, 1971, S.C. Tourism award State of S.C., 1979, Cine Golden Eagle award for film The Hawk and John McNeely, 1980, Lung Assn. award, 1993. Mem. Am. Fedn. Musicians (dir. local 342, pres. local 342 1943-76), AFTRA, Salt Water Anglers Tournament Soc. (founder, chmn. bd.), U.S. Sportsfishing Assn. (chmn. 1985). Democrat. Clubs: Masons, Shriners, Kiwanis, Charlotte City, Red Fez. Home: 7224 Sardis Rd Charlotte NC 28270-6062 Office: Arthur Smith Studios 100 Smithfield Dr Charlotte NC 28270-6543 *To me, success is not a destination - it's a journey. Integrity is not a business principle - it's a matter of right or wrong. Whatever I shall achieve in this world I owe to complete trust in, and commitment to God through Christ, a loving and understanding wife and family and loyal associates.*

SMITH, ARTHUR B(EVERLY), JR., lawyer; b. Abilene, Tex., Sept. 11, 1944; s. Arthur B. and Florence B. (Baker) S.; m. Marya Argetsanger, Dec. 30, 1968; children: Arthur C., Sarah R. B.S., Cornell U., 1966; J.D., U. Chgo., 1969. Bar: Ill. 1969, N.Y. 1976. Assoc. Vedder, Price, Kaufman & Kammholz, Chgo., 1969-74; asst. prof. labor law N.Y. State Sch. Indsl. and Labor Rls., Cornell U., 1975-77; ptnr. Vedder, Price, Kaufman & Kammholz, Chgo., 1977-86; founding mem. Murphy, Smith & Polk, Chgo., 1986—; guest. lectr. Northwestern U. Grad. Sch. Mgmt., 1979, Sch. Law, spring 1980; mem. hearing bd. Ill. Atty. Registration and Disciplinary Commn. Recipient award for highest degree of dedication and excellence in teaching N.Y. State Sch. Indsl. and Labor Relations, Cornell U., 1977. Mem. ABA (co-chmn. com. on devel. law under Nat. Labor Relations Act, Sect. Labor Rels. Law 1976-77), N.Y. State Bar Assn., Phi Eta Sigma, Phi Kappa Phi. Presbyterian. Clubs: Chgo. Athletic Assn., Monroe (Chgo.). Author: Employment Discrimination Law Cases and Materials, 4th edit., 1994; Construction Labor Relations, 1984, supplement, 1993; co-editor-in-chief: 1976 Annual Supplement to Morris, The Developing Labor Law, 1977; asst. editor: The Developing Labor Law, 3d edit., 1992; contbr. articles to profl. jours. Office: Murphy Smith & Polk 2 First National Plz Fl 25 Chicago IL 60603

SMITH, ARTHUR JOHN STEWART, physicist, educator; b. Victoria, B.C., Can., June 28, 1938; s. James Stewart and Lillian May (Geernaert) S.; m. Norma Ruth Askeland, May 20, 1966; children: Peter James, Ian Alexander. B.A., U. B.C., 1959, M.Sc., 1961; Ph.D., Princeton U., 1966. Postdoctoral fellow Deutsches Electronen-Synchrotron, Hamburg, W. Germany, 1966-67; mem. faculty dept. physics Princeton U., 1967—, prof., 1978—, Class of 1909 prof., 1992—, assoc. chmn. dept., 1979-83, chmn. dept. physics, 1990—; vis. scientist Brookhaven Nat. Lab., 1967—, Fermilab, 1974—, Superconducting Supercollider Lab., 1990—. Assoc. editor Phys. Rev. Letters, 1986-89; contbr. articles to profl. jours. Fellow Am. Phys. Soc. (vice-chmn. div. of particles and fields 1990, chmn. div. of particles and fields 1991). Achievements include research on experimental high-energy particle physics; kaon decays and quark structure of hadrons. Home: 4 Ober Rd Princeton NJ 08540-4918 Office: PO Box 708 Princeton NJ 08544-0708

SMITH, ARTHUR KITTREDGE, JR., university official, political science educator; b. Derry, N.H., Aug. 15, 1937; s. Arthur Kittredge and Rena Belle (Roberts) S.; m. June Mary Dahar, Nov. 29, 1959; children: Arthur, Valerie, Meredith. B.S., U.S. Naval Acad., 1959; M.A., U. N.H., 1966; Ph.D., Cornell U., 1970. Vis. prof. El Colegio de Mexico, Mexico City, 1968-69; asst. prof. polit. sci. SUNY-Binghamton, 1970-74, assoc. prof., 1974-84, prof., 1984-88, provost for grad. studies and research, 1976-83, v.p. for administrn., 1982-88; prof. govt. and internat. studies U. S.C., Columbia, 1988-91, exec. v.p. for acad. affairs, provost, 1988-90, 91, interim pres., 1990-91; pres., prof. polit. sci. U. Utah, Salt Lake City, 1991—. Author: (with Claude E. Welch, Jr.) Military Role and Rule: Perspectives on Civil-Military Relations, 1975; contbr. articles to profl. jours. Active Am. Stores Co., First Security Corp. Served with USN, 1959-63. Lehman fellow, 1966-69, NDEA fellow, 1969-70. Mem. Am. Polit. Sci. Assn., L.Am. Studies Assn., Inter-Univ. Sem. on Armed Forces and Soc., Am. Coun. on Edn., World Affairs

Coun. (pres. Binghamton chpt. 1976-76), Phi Beta Kappa, Pi Sigma Alpha, Omicron Delta Kappa, Phi Delta Kappa, Beta Gamma Sigma, Phi Kappa Phi. Home: 1480 Military Way Salt Lake City UT 84103-4455 Office: U Utah Office of the Pres 203 Park Building Bldg Salt Lake City UT 84112-1201

SMITH, BAKER ARMSTRONG, management executive, lawyer; b. Brunswick, Ga., Oct. 3, 1947; s. William Armstrong and Priscilla (Baker) S.; m. Deborah Elizabeth Ellis, Nov. 13, 1982; children: Ellis Armstrong, Elizabeth Anne, Everett Baker, Emery Manning. BS, U.S. Naval Acad., 1969; MBA, Northeastern U., 1975; JD cum laude, Suffolk U., 1977; LLM in Labor, Georgetown U., 1981. Bar: Ga. 1977, D.C. 1978, U.S. Supreme Ct. 1980; cert. turnaround profl., 1994. Commd. ensign U.S. Navy, 1969, advanced through grades to lt., 1974; exec. dir., founder The Center on Nat. Labor Policy, Inc., North Springfield, Va., 1977-81; asst. to sec. dir. labor relations U.S. Dept. HUD, Washington, 1981-83; exec. v.p. U.S. Bus. and Indsl. Council, Nashville, 1983-84; pres. Am. Quality Builders, Inc., Nashville, 1984-86; v.p. Hopeman Bros., Inc., Waynesboro, Va., 1986-88; ptnr. Morris, Anderson, Atlanta, 1988—; sec., founder U.S. Constitutional Rights Legal Def. Fund, Inc., Atlanta, 1983—; trustee Leadership Inst., Springfield, Va., 1978—; dir. Turnaround Mgmt. Assn., 1994—, Assn. Cert. Turnaround Profls., 1994—; mem. Council for Nat. Policy, Washington, 1981—, Civil Rights Reviewing Authority U.S. Dept. Edn., Washington, 1984-88; transition team leader Office of the Pres.-Elect of the U.S., NLRB, Occupational Safety and Health Review Commn., Fed. Mediation and Conciliation Service, Nat. Mediation Bd., Fed. Labor Relations Authority, Washington, 1980-81; instr. law, faculty sec. No. Va. Law Sch., Alexandria, Va., 1980-83; instr. law D.C. Law Sch., Washington, 1978-80. Contbg. author: Mandate for Leadership, 1981; contbr. articles to profl. jours. Served to lt. USN, 1969-74. Mem. St. George's House, Windsor Castle (assoc.), ABA (Nat. Law Day chmn. 1976-77, Silver Key award 1977), Phila. Acad. U.S. Supreme Ct. Hist. Soc., Federalist Soc., Joseph Story Soc., Beta Gamma Sigma, Phi Delta Phi (pres. 1989-91). Republican. Presbyterian. Club: Capitol Hill (Washington), Jefferson (Roanoke). Home: 3360 E Terrell Branch Ct Marietta GA 30067-5164

SMITH, BARBARA, camping administrator; b. Fox Point, Wis., Apr. 17, 1952; d. Robert Wayne and Katherine Mary (Neuzerling) S. BS, U. Wis., 1975; EdM, SUNY, Amherst, 1978. Cert. N.Y. State Swim Official. Camp dir. Patriot's Trail Girl Scout Council, Boston, 1976-77; field and camp dir. Sparand Spindle Girl Scout Council, Middleton, Mass., 1978-79; adult edn. dir. Niagara County Council of Girl Scouts, Inc., Niagara Falls, N.Y., 1979-80; camping services dir. Girl Scout Council of Buffalo and Erie County, Inc., Buffalo, 1980—. Mem. Am. Camping Assn. (planner 1985—), N.Y. State Outdoor Edn. Assn., Assn. Girl Scout Exec. Staff, Girl Scouts of U.S.A., ARC (lifeguard instr. 1969—, trainer 1980—). Mem. Society of Friends Ch. Avocations: downhill skiing, whitewater canoeing, running, swimming, horseback riding, camping, photography, writing. Office: Girl Scout Coun Buffalo/Erie 70 Jewett Pky Buffalo NY 14214-2391

SMITH, BARBARA ANNE, healthcare management company consultant; b. N.Y.C., Oct. 10, 1941; d. John Allen and Lelia Maria (De Silva) Santoro; m. Joseph Newton Smith, Feb. 5, 1961 (div. Sept. 1984); children: J. Michael, Robert Lawrence. Student, Oceanside/Carlsbad Coll. Real estate agt. Routh Robbins, Inc., Washington, 1973-75; gen. mgr. Mall Shops, Inc., Kansas City, Kans., 1975-80; regional mgr. FAO Schwarz, N.Y.C., 1980-84; clin. adminstr. North Denver Med. Ctr., Thornton, Colo., 1984-88; adminstrv. dir. Country Side Ambulatory Surgery Ctr., Leesburg, Va., 1989-91; pres. SCS Healthcare Mgmt. Inc., Washington, 1991—; bd. dirs. Franz Carl Weber Internat., Geneva, 1982-84. Pres. Am. Women Chie, 1968; v.p. Oak Park Assn., Kansas City, 1977-78, pres., 1978-79; vol. Visitor Info. and Assn. Reception Ctr. program Smithsonian Instn., Washington. Mem. NAFE, Network Colo., Profl. Bus. Women Assn., Med. Group Mgmt. Assn., Federated Ambulatory Surgery Assn.

SMITH, BARBARA BARNARD, music educator; b. Ventura, Calif., June 10, 1920; d. Fred W. and Grace (Hobson) S. BA., Pomona Coll., 1942; Mus.M., U. Rochester, 1943, performer's cert., 1944. Mem. faculty piano and theory Eastman Sch. Music, U. Rochester, 1943-49; mem. faculty U. Hawaii, Honolulu, 1949—; assoc. prof. music U. Hawaii, 1953-62, prof., 1962-82, prof. emeritus, 1982—; sr. fellow East-West Center, 1973; lectr., recitals in Hawaiian and Asian music, U.S., Europe and Asia, 1956—; field researcher Asia, 1956, 60, 66, 71, 80, Micronesia, 1963, 70, 87, 88, 90, 91, Solomon Islands, 1976. Author publs. on ethnomusicology. Mem. Internat. Soc. Music Edn., Internat. Musicol. Soc., Am. Musicol. Soc., Soc. Ethnomusicology, Internat. Coun. for Traditional Music, Asia Soc., Am. Mus. Instrument Soc., Coll. Music Soc., Soc. for Asian Music, Music Educators Nat. Conf., Pacific Sci. Assn., Assn. for Chinese Music Rsch., Phi Beta Kappa, Mu Phi Epsilon. Home: 581 Kamoku St Apt 2004 Honolulu HI 96826-5210

SMITH, BARBARA JEAN, lawyer; b. Washington, Jan. 9, 1947; d. Harry Wallace and Jean (Fraser) S.; m. Philip R. Chall, July 13, 1991; children: Brian C.S. Brown, Craig F.S. Brown, Amy E. Chall, Carrie A. Chall. BA, Old Dominion Coll., 1968; MBA, Pepperdine U., 1974; JD, Case Western Res. U., 1977. Bar: Ohio 1977. Assoc. Squire, Sanders & Dempsey, Cleve., 1977-88, ptnr., 1988-93; shareholder McDonald, Hopkins, Burke & Haber Co., L.P.A., Cleve., 1993—. Bd. editors Health Law Jour. of Ohio, 1989-95; contbr. articles to health jours. and periodicals. Trustee Urban Community Sch., Cleve., 1984-86. Mem. Ohio Women's Bar Assn. (pres. 1994-95), Cleve. Bar Assn. (trustee 1992-95, chair health law sect. 1991-92, Appreciation award 1989, 91), Nat. Health Lawyers Assn., Am. Acad. Hosp. Attys., Ohio State Bar Assn. (health law com. 1991—), Soc. Ohio Hosp. Attys. Democrat. Mem. United Ch. of Christ. Avocations: reading, hiking. Home: 220 Grey Fox Run Chagrin Falls OH 44022 Office: McDonald Hopkins Burke Haber Co 2100 Bank One Ctr 1600 Superior Ave E Cleveland OH 44114

SMITH, BARBARA JEANNE, librarian; b. Jersey Shore, Pa., Apr. 14, 1939; d. Moyer Emmerson and Mary Kathryn (Ebner) S. BS in Edn. (Biology), Pa. State U., 1961, DEd in Higher Edn., 1981; MS in Edn. (English), SUNY, Oswego, N.Y., 1967; MLS U. Pitts., 1970. Reference libr. Pa. State U. Librs., University Park, 1970-75, commonwealth campus coord., 1975-82, asst. dean librs., head commonwealth campus librs. divsn., 1982-89; dir. Smithsonian Instn. Librs., Washington, 1989—; gen. sci. tchr. Binghamton (N.Y.) City Schs., 1961-62; English tchr. North Syracuse (N.Y.) Ctrl. Schs., 1970-75; mem. Interlibrary Loan Compensation Adv. Com., Adv. Com. for Continuing Edn., State Task Force Continuing Edn. for Libr. Personnel, 1970-89, Space Com. for Adminstrv. Svc. Ctr., Coun. of Info. and Edn. Dirs., Smithsonian Instn. Rsch. Info. Svc. (chair 1993-95), Planning Adv. Group, 1989—; chair Internet Implementation Com., Smithsonian Instn. Librs. User Adv. Com., 1989—. Contbr. articles to profl. jours.; speaker in field. UCLA Grad. Sch. of Libr. and Info. Sci. Sr. fellow, 1982. mem. ALA (elected to coun., 1987-91, site visitor com. on accreditation, 1989-93), Dist. Columbia Libr. Assn., Cosmos Club, Washington, Centre County (Pa.) Hist. Soc. (life), Am. Assn. U. Women, 1970—, U. Pitts. Alumni Assn. (bd. dirs. 1991-94), Beta Phi Mu Libr. (hon.). Office: Smithsonian Instn Librs NHB 22 MRC 154 10th & Constitution Ave NW Washington DC 20560

SMITH, BARBARA MARTIN, art educator; b. St. Louis, Feb. 3, 1945; d. Charles Landon and Mary Louise (Nolker) Martin; m. Timothy Van Gorder Smith, Nov. 27, 1976; children: Brian Eliot, Marjorie Van Gorder. BA, Lawrence U., 1967; MFA, So. Ill. U., 1975. Cert. tchr., Mo. Art instr. Horton Watkins High Sch., Ladue, Mo., 1968-76; leader Experiment in Internat. Living, Brattleboro, Vt., 1974; art tchr. Michigan City (Ind.) Ctr. for the Arts, 1979-80, Cleve. Mus. of Art, 1981-83; art instr. Villa Duchesne, St. Louis, 1986—; edn. dir. Dunes Art Found., Michigan City, 1979; co-chmn. Internat. Wives Group, Cleve. Coun. on World Affairs, 1982-84; bd. dirs. Webster Groves (Mo.) Sch. Found., 1992. Exhibited in shows at Art Inst. of Chgo., 1979, So. Ill. U. Alumnae Exhibit, 1982, Focus Fiber, Cleve. Mus. of Art, 1982, Nova, Wearable Art, Kuban Gallery, Cleve., 1983, Drawings & Prints, St. Louis Artist's Guild, 1988. Recipient Grad. Fellowship Ann. Grad. award So. Ill. U., 1975; named Artist in Residence/Artist in Schs. Ind. Arts Commn./NEA, 1978-79; named to Honors Seminar for Advancement of Art Edn., R.I. Sch. of Design, 1988, Mem. Art Edn. Delegation to Japan, 1992. Mem. Nat. Art Edn. Assn., Internat. Soc. for Edn.

through Art, St. Louis Art Mus., St. Louis Artist Guild. Home: 135 Jefferson Rd Webster Groves MO 63119 Office: Villa Duchesne Oak Hill Sch 801 Spoede Rd Des Peres MO 63131

SMITH, BARNARD ELLIOT, management educator; b. Mpls., May 6, 1926; s. Sheldon Strong and Jessie (Gould) S.; m. Betty Lou Strohschein, Aug. 28, 1949; children: Carolyn Louise, Eileen Elizabeth. B.S. in Mech. Engring. with distinction, U. Minn., 1949, M.S., 1950; Ph.D., Stanford U., 1961; M.A. (hon.), Dartmouth Coll., 1971. Asst. prof. mech. engring. U. N.D., 1950-51; mfg. specialist A.O. Smith Co., Milw., 1951-54; asst. prof. indsl. engring. Oreg. State Coll., 1954-58, Stanford U., 1958-61; asso. prof. mgmt. Sloan Sch. Mgmt., MIT, 1961-68; prof. mgmt. Indian Inst. Mgmt., Calcutta, 1965-68; prof. engring. Thayer Sch. Engring. Dartmouth Coll., 1968-71; dean Stuart Sch. Mgmt. and Finance, Ill. Inst. Tech., 1971-75, prof. mgmt., 1975-80; David M. French disting. prof. mgmt. U. Mich., Flint, 1980-89, emeritus, 1989; pres. Vineyards of the Acad., 1989, The Acad. of Wine of Oreg. Inc., 1993—; cons. in field. Served with USNR, 1944-46. Mem. Phi Tau Sigma, Beta Gamma Sigma. Home: 18200 Highway 238 Grants Pass OR 97527-8631

SMITH, BARRY DAVID, obstetrician-gynecologist, educator; b. Suffern, N.Y., July 3, 1938; s. Alexander N. and Beatrice (Morris) S.; m. Maryann Blair, Oct. 11, 1963; children: Gillian, Adam. AB, Dartmouth Coll., 1959; MD, Cornell U., 1962. Diplomate Am. Bd. Ob-Gyn. Resident in ob-gyn N.Y. Hosp. Cornell U. Med. Ctr., N.Y.C., 1963-67, chief resident, instr., 1967-68; staff obstetrician/gynecologist Mary Hitchcock Meml. Hosp., Hanover, N.H., 1970—; asst. prof. Dartmouth Coll., Hanover, 1970-78, assoc. prof., 1979—; chief sect. ob-gyn Mary Hitchcock Clinic, 1977—, bd. govs. 1975-85, bd. dirs. 1980-86; chief sect. ob-gyn Dartmouth Med. Ctr., 1977—, chmn. dept. ob-gyn, 1992—. Treas., pres. Norwich (Vt.) Recreation and Conservation Council, 1975-77. Served to comdr. USNR. Fellow Am. Coll. Ob-Gyn (v.p. N.H. sect. 1991-94, pres. 1994—), Am. Fertility Soc., Am. Soc. Colposcopy. Avocations: skiing, tennis, sailing. Office: Dartmouth Hitchcock Clinic 1 Medical Center Dr Lebanon NH 03756-0002

SMITH, BERNALD STEPHEN, retired airline pilot, aviation consultant; b. Long Beach, Calif., Dec. 24, 1926; s. Donald Albert and Bernice Merrill (Stephens) S.; m. Marilyn Mae Spence, July 22, 1949; children: Lorraine Ann Smith Foute, Evelyn Donice Smith DeRoos, Mark Stephen, Diane April (dec.). Student, U. Calif., Berkeley, 1944-45, 50-51. Cert. airline transport pilot, flight engr., FAA. Capt. Transocean Air Lines, Oakland (Calif.) and Tokyo, 1951-53, Hartford, Conn., 1954-55; 1st officer United Air Lines, Seattle, 1955, San Francisco, 1956-68; tng. capt. United Air Lines, Denver and San Francisco, 1961-68; capt. United Air Lines, San Francisco, 1968-86, 2d officer, 1986-93, ret., 1993; founder, v.p. AviaAm., Palo Alto, Calif., 1970-72, AviaInternat., Palo Alto, 1972-74; cons. Caproni Vizzola, Milan, 1972-84; prin., cons. Internat. Aviation Cons. and Investments, Fremont, Calif., 1985—; instr. aviation Ohlone Coll., Fremont, 1976; founder Pacific Soaring Coun.; founder, trustee AirSailing, Inc., 1970—, Soaring Safety Found., 1985—. Author/editor: American Soaring Handbook, 1975, 80; contbr. articles to profl. jours. Trustee Nat. Soaring Mus., 1975—, pres. 1975-78; mem. RTCA, SSA del., 1992—. Comdr. USNR, 1944-75. Mem. AIAA (pub. bd. 1977-94), Soaring Soc. Am. (pres. 1969-70, chmn. pub. bd. 1971-84, chmn. ins. com. 1975-93, bd. dirs. 1963—, Warren Eaton Meml. Trophy 1977, Exceptional Svc. award 1970, 75, 82, 88, 91, named to Hall of Fame 1984), Soc. Automotive Engring., Nat. Aero. Assn., Exptl. Aircraft Assn., Aircraft Owners and Pilots Assn., Airline Pilots Assn., Seaplane Pilots Assn., Orgn. Scientifique et Technique Internat. du Vol a Voile (bd. dirs., U.S. del. 1981—), Fedn. Aeronautique Internat. (Paul Tissandier Diplome 1992, Lilienthal medal 1993, Highest Soaring award, U.S. del. 1991—), Commn. de Vol A Voile (U.S. del. 1970-71, 78, 85—, v.p. 1988—), U. Calif. Alumni Assn. (life). Democrat. Methodist. Office: Internat Aviation Cons Investments PO Box 3075 Fremont CA 94539-0307

SMITH, BERT KRUGER, mental health services professional, consultant; b. Wichita Falls, Tex., Nov. 18, 1915; d. Sam and Fania (Feldman) Kruger; m. Sidney Stewart Smith, Jan. 19, 1936; children: Sheldon Stuart, Jared Burt (dec.), Randy Smith Huke. BJ, U. Mo., 1936; MA, U. Tex., 1949; DHL (hon.), U. Mo., 1985. Soc. and entertainment editor Wichita Falls Post, 1936-37; freelance writer Juneau, Alaska, 1937; assoc. pub. Coleman Daily Dem. Voice, 1950-51; assoc. editor Jr. Coll. Jour., Austin, Tex., 1952-55; spl. cons., exec. Hogg Found. for Mental Health, Austin, 1952—; chmn. bd. Austin Groups for the Elderly, 1989—. Author: No Language But A Cry, 1964, Your Non-Learning Child, 1968, A Teaspoon of Honey, 1970, Insights for Uptights, 1970, Aging in America, 1973, The Pursuit of Dignity, 1977, Looking Forward, 1983; contbr. numerous articles to profl. jours. Bert Kruger Smith professorship St. Social Work U. Tex., 1982; recipient Disting. Svc. award City of Austin, 1988, Cert. of Appreciation, Tex. Dept. Human Svcs., 1989, Ann Bert Smith award Sr.'s Respite Svc., 1989, S.W. Found. Founders' Spirit award, 1990, Tex. Leadership award Ann. Tex. Joint Conf. on Aging, 1992, Tex. Leadership award Tex. Dept. on Aging, 1992; named to Tex. Women's Hall of Fame, 1988. Mem. Women in Comm. (Lifetime Achievement award 1994), Am. Fedn. for Aging Rsch., Adult Svc. Coun. (bd. dirs. 1970—), Family Eldercare (bd. dirs. 1979—), Authors Guild, Nat. Assn. Sci. Writers, Hadassah, B'nai B'rith Women, Delta Kappa Gamma (hon.). Jewish. Avocations: walking, reading. Home: 5818 Westslope Dr Austin TX 78731-3633 Office: Hogg Found Mental Health PO Box 7998 Austin TX 78713-7998 also: U Tex Austin Austin TX 78713

SMITH, BETTY EDMISTON, university dean, nurse; b. Clay, La., Sept. 27, 1929; d. Purvis Alvin and Marjorie Mae (Youngblood) Edmiston; widow; children: Frances, Martha. BSN, Northwestern State U., Natchitoches, La., 1964; MS in Nursing, Emory U., 1967; PhD, U. So. Miss., 1976. RN, La. Mem. nursing support staff pub. and pvt. hosps., Ruston, La., 1950-64; head nurse Lincoln Gen. Hosp., Ruston, 1964-66; asst. prof. nursing NE La. U., Monroe, 1967-73, assoc. prof., 1973-80, prof., 1980-83, dir. nursing, 1974-83; dean Sch. Nursing, Grambling (La.) State U., 1983—; mem. adv. bd. La. Coun. Adminstrn. in Nursing Edn., 1980—; mem. subcom. Joint La. Legis. Com. on Edn., 1983—. Contbr. articles to profl. publs. Pres. Bethel Christian Sch. PTA, Ruston, 1984; speaker to civic orgns., 1985, 86; fund raiser Leukemia Found., Grambling, 1990; vol. Am. Cancer Soc.; Sunday sch. tchr. Bapt. Ch., Ruston. Grantee USPHS, 1988-91, U.S. Dept. Edn., 1989-90. Mem. ANA, La. Nurses Assn., La. Tchrs. Assn., Monroe Dist. Nurses Assn., Emory U. Alumni Assn., U. So. Miss. Alumni Assn., Grambling State U. Found. Club, Kappa Delta Phi. Office: Gramblin State U Sch Nursing 1 Cole St Grambling LA 71245

SMITH, BETTY FAYE, textile chemist; b. Magnolia, Ark., June 29, 1930; d. Carl Excel and Nannie (Nall) S. B.S., U. Ark., 1951; M.S., U. Tenn., 1957; Ph.D., U. Minn., 1960, 65. Home agt. Ark. Agrl. Extension Service, 1951-56; mem. faculty Cornell U., 1965-70, assoc. prof. textiles, 1965-70, chmn. dept., 1968-69; prof. textiles, chmn. dept. U. Md., 1970-91, prof. textiles, 1991-92; prof. materials engring., 1992—. Author papers in field. Fellow Textile Inst.; mem. Fiber Soc., Am. Chem. Soc., Am. Assn. Textile Chemists and Colorists, Soc. Dyers and Colourists, AAUP, Sigma Xi, Omicron Nu, Phi Upsilon Omicron, Iota Sigma Pi. Democrat. Methodist. Home: 9216 St Andrews Pl College Park MD 20740-3937 Office: Univ Md Dept Matls & Nuclear Engring Rm 2100 Marie Mount College Park MD 20742

SMITH, BILLIE M., retired aircraft company executive; b. Littlefield, Tex., Sept. 4, 1933; s. James W. and Gracie Inez (Ratliff) S.; m. Faye Brewer, May 5, 1985. BS in Math. and Chemistry, Tex. A&I U., 1953. Project engr. Phillips Petroleum Co., McGregor, Tex., 1953-54, 55-58; project mgr., minuteman Thiokol Chem. Corp., Brigham City, Utah, 1958-60; program dir. Titan III United Tech. Corp., Sunnyvale, Calif., 1960-66; mgr. advanced launch systems LTV Aerospace and Def. Co., Mich., 1966-67, chief engr. systems integration, 1967-68, dep. program dir. Lance, 1968-69, v.p. Lance, 1970-72, v.p., gen. mgr., 1972-77; sr. v.p. advanced programs LTV Aerospace and Def. Co., Dallas, 1977-78; sr. v.p. Multiple Launch Rocket System program, 1978-83, sr. v.p., gen. mgr. MLRS div., 1983-85, exec. v.p., gen. missiles and advanced programs div., 1985-89, pres. aircraft products group, 1985-89, ret., 1989. Vice chmn. Dallas County U.S. Savs. Bond Campaign, Dallas, 1986-87, Tarrant County U.S. Savs. Bond Campaign, Ft. Worth, 1987. Served as sgt. U.S. Army, 1954-55. Recipient Outstanding Achievement award Missiles and Rockets Mag., 1965. Mem. Am. Def. Preparedness

Assn., Assn. U.S. Army, AIAA, U.S. Field Artillery Assn., Navy League (life), Alphi Chi. Avocations: fishing, boating.

SMITH, BRADLEY YOULE, lawyer; b. N.Y.C., Feb. 11, 1948; s. Bradley and Christine (Brown) S.; m. Anne Barre, Dec. 31, 1986; children: Bradley McLaren, Andrew Robert, Lauren Barre, Timothy James. BA in History cum laude, Yale U., 1970; JD, NYU, 1974. Bar: N.Y. 1975, U.S. Dist. Ct. (so. dist.) N.Y. 1975, U.S. Ct. Appeals (2d cir.) 1975. With Davis Polk & Wardwell, N.Y.C., 1974—, ptnr., 1980—. Trustee Royal Coll. Surgeons Found., Inc. Mem. ABA (chmn. subcom. secured trans. 1983-87, moderator and panelist com. banking law and uniform comml. code), Am. Law Inst. (drafting com. uniform comml. code article 9, 1993—), N.Y. State Bar Assn. (banking law com.). Office: Davis Polk & Wardwell 450 Lexington Ave New York NY 10017-3911

SMITH, BRIAN J., diversified chemical executive; b. N.Y.C., Apr. 14, 1944; s. John W. and Helen T. (Fitzsimmons) S.; m. Janet Vanden Heuvel, Sept. 1, 1979. BS in Acctg., U. Scranton, 1965; postgrad., Ga. State U., 1972-73. CPA, N.Y.C. Auditor, sr. acct. Price Waterhouse, N.Y.C., 1965-71; audit mgr. Price Waterhouse, Atlanta, 1971-74; asst. controller W.R. Grace & Co., N.Y.C., 1974-79, v.p., controller, 1981-86; v.p., chief fin. officer agrl. chems. group W.R. Grace & Co., Memphis, 1979-81, 1979-81; sr. v.p., dep. group exec. W.R. Grace & Co., N.Y.C., 1986-87; sr. v.p., group exec. officer, corp. adminstrv. officer W.R. Grace & Co., 1987-89, exec. v.p., chief fin. officer, 1989—. Bd. dirs. Grand Case Beach Club, St. Martin, W.I., 1985-88, Fifth Ave. Condominium, N.Y.C., 1985—. Served to 1st lt. U.S. Army, 1966-69. Mem. Fin. Exec. Inst., Am. Inst. CPA's. Club: Sky. Office: W R Grace & Co 1114 Avenue Of The Americas New York NY 10036-7701

SMITH, BRIAN RAY DOUGLAS, rail transportation executive, lawyer; b. Victoria, B.C., July 7, 1934; s. Douglas Edgar and E. Eleanor (Parfitt) S.; m. Barbara; children: Claire E, Christopher C. BA, U. B.C., 1956, LLB, 1960; MA, Queen's U., 1960. Min. edn. B.C., 1979-82, min. energy, mines, and petroleum resources, 1982-83, atty. gen., 1983-88; chmn. Can. Nat. Rlwy., 1989—; bd. dirs. Internat. Comml. Arbitration Ctr., Vancouver, B.C., Ballet B.C., Tennis Can.; mem. Vancouver Bd. of Trade. Mayor Oak Bay, B.C., 1974-79; bd. dirs. Ballet B.C., Tennis Can., Vancouver Bd. Trade. Mem. Union Club, Victoria U. of C., Vancouver Lawn and Tennis Club, Victoria Golf Club. Office: Canadian Nat Railway Co, PO Box 8100, Montreal, PQ Canada H3C 3N4

SMITH, BRIAN WILLIAM, lawyer, former government official; b. N.Y.C., Feb. 3, 1947; s. William Francis and Dorothy Edwina (Vogel) S.; m. Donna Jean Holverson, Apr. 24, 1976; children: Mark Holverson, Lauren Elizabeth. BA, St. John's U., N.Y.C., 1968, JD, 1971; MS, Columbia U., 1981. Bar: N.Y. 1972, D.C. 1975, U.S. Dist. Ct. (ea. and so. dists.) N.Y. 1975, U.S. Supreme Ct. 1976, U.S. Dist. Ct. D.C. 1986. Atty. Am. Express Co., N.Y.C., 1970-73, CIT Fin. Corp., N.Y.C., 1973-74; assoc. counsel, mng. atty. Interbank Card Assn. (named changed to Master Card Internat., Inc.), N.Y.C., 1974-75; sr. v.p., corp. sec., gen. counsel, 1975-82; chief counsel Compt. of Currency, Washington, 1982-84; ptnr. Stroock & Stroock & Lavan, Washington, 1984-92, mng. ptnr., 1986-92; ptnr. Mayer, Brown & Platt, Washington and N.Y.C., 1992—. Capt., USAR, 1970-78. Mem. ABA, N.Y. State Bar Assn., D.C. Bar Assn., Assn. Bar City N.Y., Fed. Bar Assn., N.Y. Athletic Club, Met. Club N.Y. Home: 35 W Lenox St Chevy Chase MD 20815-4208 Office: Mayer Brown & Platt 2000 Pennsylvania Ave NW Washington DC 20006-1812

SMITH, BRICE REYNOLDS, JR., engineering company executive; b. St. Louis; s. Brice Reynolds and Frances Matilda (Cook) S.; m. Jane Medart; children: Brice Reynolds III, Victoria D. Smith Trauscht, Hollis M. Smith Norman, Karen C. Smith Branom, Todd E. BCE, U. Mo., Columbia, 1951; MCE, MIT, 1952; Cert. advanced mgmt. program, Harvard U., Hawaii, 1961. Registered profl. engr., D.C., Fla., Kans., Md., Mass., Mich., Mo., N.D., Ohio, Oreg., Tenn., Va., N.C., N.Y. Resident engr. Sverdrup & Parcel, St. Louis, 1954-59, asst. to v.p. fgn. ops., 1959-64, treas., 1964-69, v.p., treas., 1970-75; exec. v.p. Sverdrup Corp., St. Louis, 1976-81, pres., 1982-86, 1986-94, CEO, 1986-94; also chmn. bd. dirs. Sverdrup Corp.; dir. Boatmen's Trust Co., St. Louis; bd. dirs. Convention Plaza Redevel. Corp., St. Louis. Bd. dirs. Civic Progress, Inc., Greater St. Louis campaign United Way; bd. dirs. Arts and Edn. Coun. Greater St. Louis, St. Louis Area coun. Boy Scouts Am., Hawthorn Found., Mo., Mo. Hist. Soc., Constrn. Industry Pres. Forum. 1st lt. USAF, 1952-54. Recipient Mo. Honor award for Disting. Service to Engring., U. Mo., 1979; Levee Stone award, Downtown St. Louis, Inc., 1982. Fellow Am. Cons. Engrs. Coun.; mem. ASCE, NSPE, Mo. Soc. Profl. Engrs., Cons. Engrs. Coun. Mo. (past pres.), The Moles, Newcomen Soc. U.S., Bellerive Country Club, Log Cabin Club, St. Louis Club. Office: Sverdrup Corp 13723 Riverport Dr Maryland Heights MO 63043-4848

SMITH, BRUCE, professional football player; b. Norfolk, Va., June 18, 1963. Student, Va. Tech. U. With Buffalo Bills, 1985—; player Super Bowl XXV, 1990, XXVI, 1991, XXVII, 1992, XXVIII, 1993. Recipient Outland trophy, 1984; named to Pro-Bowl, 1987-90, 92, 93, Sporting News All-Pro team, 1987-88, 90. Office: Buffalo Bills 1 Bills Drive Orchard Park NY 14127-2296*

SMITH, BRUCE DAVID, archaeologist; b. Iowa City, Iowa, Mar. 24, 1946; s. Goldwin Albert and Emily C. (Bateman) S.; m. Martha Mary Johnson, Sept. 22, 1973; children: David Vernon, Jonathan Oliver. B.A., U. Mich., 1968, M.A., 1971, Ph.D., 1973. Mem. faculty Loyola U., Chgo., 1973-74, U. Ga., Athens, 1974-77; curator N.Am. archaeology Nat. Mus. Natural History, Smithsonian Instn., Washington, 1977—, sr. scientist, dir. archaeobiology program, 1991—, spl. asst. to dir., 1983, asst. dir., 1986; mem. anthropology rev. panel NSF, 1982-83. Author: Mississippian Patterns of Animal Exploitation, 1975, Prehistoric Patterns of Human Behavior, 1978, Mississippian Settlement Patterns, 1978, Mississippian Emergence, 1990, Rivers of Change, 1992, Emergence of Agriculture, 1994. Horace H. Rackham prize fellow, 1971-73; recipient Smithsonian Instn. Regents Pub. fellowship, 1987. Mem. Soc. Am. Archaeology (sec. 1985-89, pres. 1993-95), Southeastern Archaeol. Conf. (pres. 1982-84). Home: 2202 White Oaks Dr Alexandria VA 22306-2551 Office: Smithsonian Instn Nat Mus Natural History Dept Anthropology Washington DC 20560

SMITH, BRUCE L., secondary education educator; b. Springfield, Mo., Nov. 29, 1966; s. Owen L. and Carol V. (Quigg) S. BA, Northwestern U., 1989; MEd, U. Mo., 1991. Cert. social studies, English tchr. Counselor Ctr. Talent Devel., Evanston, Ill., 1987-88; customer svc. Sears & Roebuck, Columbia, Mo., 1989-90; circulation clk. Daniel Boone Regional Libr., Columbia, Mo., 1990-93; tutor pvt. practice, Columbia, Mo., 1990-94; substitute tchr. Columbia Pub. Schs., 1990-93; tchr. world and European history Hickman H.S., 1993—; rsch. cons. Mo. Dept. Elem. and Secondary Edn., Jefferson City, Mo., 1990-91. Intern, vol. Mo. Div. Family Svcs., Sedalia, 1988; tutor Nat. Coll. Edn., Chgo., 1987-89; mem. Northshore Barbershop Chorus, Evanston, 1986-89. Named Eagle Scout, 1984. Mem. Nat. Coun. Tchrs. English, Nat. Coun. Social Studies, Mo. Coun. Social Studies, Phi Beta Kappa, Alpha Lambda Delta. Avocations: reading, music, sports, drama, writing. Home: 1708-A Oxford Columbia MO 65203

SMITH, BRUCE R., English language educator; b. Jackson, Miss., Mar. 21, 1946. Student, U. Birmingham, England, 1966-67; BA magna cum laude in English with honors, Tulane U., 1968; MA, U. Rochester, 1971, PhD with distinction, 1973. From asst. prof. to assoc. prof. English Georgetown U., Washington, 1972-87, prof., 1987—; faculty Bread Loaf Sch. Eng. Middlebury Coll., 1994, 95. Author: Ancient Scripts and Modern Experience on the English Stage 1500-1700, 1988, Homosexual Desire in Shakespeare's England: A Cultural Poetics, 1991, Roasting the Swan of Avon: Shakespeare's Redoubtable Enemies and Dubious Friends, 1994; mem. editl. bd. Shakespeare Quarterly, 1985—; contbr. chpts. to books, articles to profl. jours. Summer Acad. Rsch. grantee Georgetown U., 1976, 84, 87, 89, 91, 92, Intercultural Curriculum Devel. grantee, 1982, grantee Ageroft Assn., 1990; jr. fellow Folger Inst., 1979, 85, fellow, 1990, Am. Coun. Learned Socs., 1979-80, NEH fellow Folger Shakespeare Libr., 1987-88, fellow Va. Found. Humanities, 1989. Mem. Shakespeare Assn. Am. (pres. 1994-95). Office: Georgetown U Dept English Washington DC 20057

SMITH, BYRON OWEN, lawyer; b. Mitchell, S.D., July 28, 1916; s. Frank B. and Elizabeth (Klosterman) S.; m. Jean Knox Harris, Dec. 20, 1938; children: Sheryl S. (Mrs. Kenneth P. King), Laird W., Ryland R., Ford R. A.B., Stanford, 1937, J.D., 1940. Bar: Calif. 1940. Assoc. Stephens, Jones, Inch & LaFever, Los Angeles, 1940-41; ptnr. Stephens, Jones, LaFever & Smith, Los Angeles, 1945-77, Adams, Duque & Hazeltine, Los Angeles, 1977—. Served to comdr. USNR, 1942-45, 51. Fellow Am. Coll. Trust and Estate Counsel; mem. Calif. State Club Assn. (dir., pres. 1974), So. Calif. Golf Assn. (dir. 1966-71), Annandale Golf Club (dir. 1963-66, pres. 1966), Eldorado Country Club (sec., dir. 1970-72), Calif. Club, Phi Delta Phi, Alpha Delta Phi. Home: 1 S Orange Grove Blvd Pasadena CA 91105-1782 Office: Adams Duque & Hazeltine 777 S Figueroa St Los Angeles CA 90017-2513

SMITH, C. KENNETH, corporate executive; b. Brackenridge, Pa., Feb. 1, 1918; s. Clarence H. and Mary (Ferguson) S.; m. AnnaBell Amlin. Degree in bus., U. Pitts., 1942. Mng. ptnr. Ernst & Young, CPAs, Columbus, Ohio, 1964-78; fin. dir., mem. mayor's cabinet City of Columbus, 1983; mng. dir. Fairoaks Internat., 1978—; profl. outside dir. various corps.; guest lectr. Ohio State U. Mem. exec. com. Nat. Football Found. and Hall Fame, Columbus Sports Arena Task Force; co-founder, past chmn. Greater Columbus Arts Coun.; advisor Columbus Found.; bd. govs. Westerville Fund, chmn., 1984-87; mem. Forward Columbus Com.; bd. dirs. Devel. Com. Greater Columbus, Quality Edn. Com., Columbus Zool Park, Columbus Jr. Achievement, Nat. Jr. Achievement; mem. Otterbein Coll. Theatre Adv. Bd.; trustee Columbus Symphony Orch., gen. chmn. symphony grand ball, 1975; trustee Franklin U., 1970—, chmn. bd.; adv. bd. Kenyon Rev., Kenyon Coll.; co-founder, trustee Columbus Leadership Program. Named One of 10 Top Men in Columbus, Columbus Citizen Jour., 1971; named in Columbus Dispatch Blue Chip Profile, 1977; named to Hon. Order Ky. Cols. Mem. AICPA, Am. Acad. Arts and Scis., Am. Mgmt. Assn. (pres.'s coun.), Am. Acctg. Assn., Columbus Area C. of C. (chmn. bd. 1968-70, Man of Yr. award 1979), Ohio C. of C. (dir. 1974), Columbus Soc. Fin. Analysts, Nat. Assn. Corp. Dirs., Columbus Assn. Performing Arts (pres., chmn. bd. 1970-72, chmn. profl. theatre com.), Columbus Gallery Fine Art, Columbus Civic Ballet, Nat. Audubon Soc., Am. Forestry Assn., Am. Tree Farm System, Nature Conservancy, Ohio Hist. Soc., The Ohio State U. Alumni Assn. Conglist. Clubs: Mason (32 deg., Shriner), Rotarian (dir. 1976—, pres. 1978-79), Columbus (dir. 1968-74), Columbus Country, Royal Commonwealth (London), Torch (pres. 1979-80), Athletic (Columbus); Zanesfield Rod and Gun, Maennerchor, U. Pitts. Alumni Assn., Ohio State U. Alumni Assn. (life); Faculty (Ohio State U.), Presidents (Ohio State U.); Press of Ohio, Ohio Commodore. Home and Office: Fairoaks Farm Westerville OH 43081-9580

SMITH, C. LEMOYNE, publishing company executive; b. Atkins, Ark., Sept. 15, 1934; s. Cecil Garland and Salena Bell (Wilson) S.; m. Selma Jean Tucker, May 23, 1964; 1 child, Jennifer Lee. B.S., Ark. Tech. U., 1956; M.Ed., U. Ark., 1958. Tchr. pub. schs., Little Rock, 1956-58; instr. bus. adminstrn. Ark. Tech. U., Russellville, 1958-60; sales rep. South-Western Pub. Co., Cin., 1960-67, editorial staff, 1967-82, pres., chief exec. officer, 1982-90, chmn., 1990-91, ret., 1991. Bd. dirs. Cin. Council on World Affairs, 1983—. Mem. Am. Vocat. Assn., Nat. Bus. Edn. Assn., Delta Pi Epsilon. Republican. Methodist. Avocations: bridge; travel. Office: South-Western Pub Co 5101 Madison Rd Cincinnati OH 45227-1427

SMITH, CALLIE W., health facility administrator; b. 1931. Bachelors degree, East Tex. State U., 1951; Masters degree, Tex. A&I U., 1963. With Harlendale Ind. Sch. Dist., San Antonio, Lowghview (Tex.) Ind. Sch. Dist., Tex. State Tchrs. Assn., Austin, 1974-79; with Bapt. Meml. Hosp. Sys., San Antonio, 1979—, now pres., CEO. Office: Bapt Meml Hosp System 111 Dallas St San Antonio TX 78205-1201*

SMITH, CARL BERNARD, education educator, writer; b. Dayton, Ohio, Feb. 29, 1932; s. Carl R. and Elizabeth Ann (Lefeld) S.; m. Virginia Lee Cope, Aug. 30, 1958; children—Madonna, Anthony, Regina, Marla. B.A., U. Dayton, 1954; M.A., Miami U., Oxford, Ohio, 1961; Ph.D., Case Western Res. U., 1967. Tchr., Cathedral Latin High Sch., Cleve., 1954-57; customer corr. E.F. MacDonald Co., Dayton, 1958-59; tchr. Kettering (Ohio) High Sch., 1959-61; editor Reardon Baer Pub. Co., Cleve., 1961-62; tchr./researcher Case Western Res. U., Cleve., 1962-65, Cleve. Pub. Schs., 1966-67; asst. prof. edn. Ind. U., Bloomington, 1967-69, assoc. prof., 1970-72, prof., 1973—; dir. ERIC Ctr., 1988—, Family Literacy Ctr., 1990—. Pres. Bd. Edn., St. Charles Sch., Bloomington, 1976-80. Recipient Sch. Bell award NEA, 1967. Mem. Internat. Reading Assn., Nat. Council Tchrs. of English, Assn. Supervision and Curriculum Devel., Am. Ednl. Research Assn., Phi Delta Kappa. Republican. Roman Catholic. Author: Reading Instruction through Diagnostic Teaching, (Pi Lambda Theta Best Book in Edn. award, 1972; Getting People To Read, 1978; sr. author: Series r, 1983, New View, 1993; Teaching Reading and Writing Together, 1984, Connect! Getting Your Kids to Talk to You, 1994, World History A Resource Book, 1995. Home: 401 Serena Ln Bloomington IN 47401-9226 Office: Sch Edn Ind U ERIC Clearinghouse Smith Rsch Ctr Bloomington IN 47405

SMITH, CARL RICHARD, association executive, former air force officer; b. New Holland, Pa., Dec. 20, 1933; s. Lemmon Lloyd and Martha Marie (Grabill) S.; m. Mariana Roth, June 15, 1956; children: Timothy Carl, Jeffry Francis, Desi Marie. B.S. in Econs., Franklin and Marshall Coll., Lancaster, Pa., 1955; M.S. in Bus. Adminstrn., George Washington U., 1966. Commd. 2d lt. U.S. Air Force, 1955, advanced through grades to lt. gen.; 1986; served in Vietnam and Belgium; assigned Hdqrs. USAF, Washington, 1966-70, 76-78, 86-91; mil. assist. to sec. def., 1978-83; assigned comdr. Lackland AFB, Tex., 1983-86; asst. vice chief of staff Hdqrs. USAF, 1986-91, ret., 1991; exec. v.p. Armed Forces Benefit Assn., Alexandria, Va., 1991—. Decorated Def. D.S.M. with oak leaf cluster, Air Force D.S.M., Legion of Merit with oak leaf cluster, D.F.C., Bronze Star, Meritorious Service medal, Air medal with 2 oak leaf clusters, Air Force Commendation medal. Mem. Air Force Assn., Lambda Chi Alpha. Methodist. Home: 2345 S Queen St Arlington VA 22202-1550 Office: Armed Forces Benefit Assn 909 N Washington St Alexandria VA 22314-1555

SMITH, CARLTON MYLES, military officer; b. Sacramento, Sept. 21, 1920; s. Carl Walter and Minnie Clamina (Friberg) S.; m. Phyllis Lee Routzahn, Nov. 2, 1947; children: Fredrick Benjamin Brown, Brian Webb Smith, Randal Lee Smith, Dennis Stuart Smith. BA, U. Calif., Berkeley, 1946. Joined USAF, 1942, advanced through ranks to lt. col.; various intelligence assignments to chief Advanced Intelligence Courses Br./Def. Intelligency Agy., retired, 1972. Co-author: Stonyford Pedigree, 1988; compiler Genealogist's Historiograph, 1986, (computer program) Genealogist's Historiograph, 1988. Decorated Air medal, WWII, Bronze Star, Meritorious Svc. medal. Mem. Calif. State Geneal. Alliance (pres. 1985-87), Nat. Geneal. Soc. (merit award 1985), 303rd Bomb Group Assn. (mem. chmn. 1991-95). Avocations: geneal. and hist. rsch., travel, writing. Home: 12700-54 Red Maple Cir Sonora CA 95370-5269

SMITH, CAROL G., health facility administrator; b. Lorton, Va., Mar. 27, 1944; d. Michael A. and Judith (Bundick) Gardner; m. Robert Edward Smith, Aug. 24, 1963. Diploma, Riverside Sch. Profl. Nursing, 1965; BA, Christopher Newport Coll., 1972; MS, George Washington U., 1975. RN, Va.; cert. nursing adminstr.; cert. nurse exec. Student pers. dir. Riverside Sch. Profl. Nursing, Newport News, Va., 1972-76; employee rels. mgr. Riverside Regional Med. Ctr., Newport News, 1976-82, dir. nursing, 1982-86, asst. v.p. for nursing, 1986-91; project dir. case mgmt. Riverside Health System, Newport News, 1991-93, dir. sr. svcs. and case mgmt., 1993-95; dir. managed care Peninsula Health Care, Newport News, 1995—. Mem. Am. Orgn. Nurse Execs., Va. Orgn. Nurse Execs., Tidewater Orgn. Nurse Execs. (pres. 1989), Sigma Theta Tau. Office: Riverside Health System 610 Thimble Shoals Blvd Ste 201 Newport News VA 23606-4504

SMITH, CECE, venture capitalist; b. Washington, Nov. 16, 1944; d. Linn Charles and Grace Inez (Walker) S.; m. John Ford Lacy, Apr. 22, 1978. B.B.A., U. Mich., 1966; M.L.A., So. Meth. U., 1974. C.P.A., Tex. Staff accountant Arthur Young & Co. (C.P.A.s), Boston, 1966-68; staff accountant, then asst. to controller Wyly Corp., Dallas, 1969-72; controller, treas. sub. Univ. Computing Co., Dallas, 1972-74; controller Steak and Ale Restaurants Am., Inc., Dallas, 1974-76; v.p. fin. Steak and Ale Restaurants Am., Inc., 1976-80, exec. v.p.; 1980-81; exec. v.p. Pearle Health Services, Inc., 1981-84, pres. Primacare div., 1984-86; gen. ptnr. Phillips-Smith Specialty Retail Group, 1986—; pres. Le Sportsac Dallas, Inc., 1981-87; bd. dirs. Henry Silverman Jewelers, Inc., Cheers, Inc., Lil Things, Inc., Hot Topic, Inc.; chmn. Fed. Res. Bank of Dallas 1994—. Former co-chmn. pres.'s rsch. coun. U. Tex. S.W. Med. Ctr. Dallas; mem. vis. com. U. Mich. Grad. Sch. Bus.; former exec. bd. So. Meth. U. Cox Sch. Bus.; former v.p., bd. dirs. Jr. Achievement Dallas, past pres. Charter 100; past treas. Dallas Assembly; former bd. dirs. Taco Villa, Inc., BizMart, Inc., A Pea in the Pod, Inc. Mem. Tex. Soc. CPAs (former dir.). Home: 6412 Williams Pky Dallas TX 75205-1717 Office: 5080 Spectrum Dr Ste 700 W Dallas TX 75248-4658

SMITH, CHARLES CONARD, refractory company executive; b. Mexico, Mo., Feb. 10, 1936; s. Charles Adelbert and Waldine (Barnes) S.; m. Constance Nagel, Oct. 6, 1962; children: Stewart Ashley, Graham Prior. BS in Ceramic Engring., Iowa State U., 1958; MBA, Stanford U., 1962. Process engr. Kaiser Refractory divsn. Kaiser Aluminum, Moss Landing, Calif., 1962-65; materials mgr. Kaiser Refractory divsn. Kaiser Aluminum, Mexico, Mo., 1965-67; divsn. planning Kaiser Refractory divsn. Kaiser Aluminum, Oakland, Calif., 1967-69; v.p., gen. mgr. Kaiser Refractories Argentina, Buenos Aires, 1969-74; with divsn. planning Kaiser Refractories divsn. Kaiser Aluminum, Oakland, 1974-77, mktg. mgr.; 1977-80, gen. mgr. mfg., 1980-82, v.p., gen. mgr. refractories divsn., 1982-85; chmn., pres., CEO Nat. Refractories and Mineral Corp., Livermore, Calif., 1985—. Patentee in refractory field. Lt. USNR, 1958-60. Mem. Refractories Inst. (past chmn., exec. com.). Republican. Avocations: fishing, biking, kite flying, photography, music. Home: 63 Lincoln Ave Piedmont CA 94611

SMITH, CHARLES HADDON, geoscientist, consultant; b. Dartmouth, N.S., Can., Sept. 3, 1926; s. Albion Benson and Dora Pauline (McGill) S.; m. Mary Gertrude Saint, Sept. 5, 1949; children: Charles Douglas, Richard David, Alan Michael, Timothy McGill. B.Sc. and Diploma in Engring, Dalhousie U., Can., 1946, M.Sc. in Geology, 1948; M.S., Yale U., 1951, Ph.D. in Econ. Geology, 1952. Instr. Dalhousie U., Halifax, N.S., 1946-48; geologist Cerro de Pasco Copper Corp., Morococha, Peru, 1949, Geol. Survey of Can., Ottawa, Ont., 1952-64; chief petrological scis. div. Geol. Survey of Can., 1964-67, chief crustal geology div., 1967-68; sci. adviser Sci. Council Can., Ottawa, 1968-70; dir. planning Dept. Energy Mines and Resources, Ottawa, 1970-71; asst. dep. minister sci. and tech. Dept. Energy Mines and Resources, 1971-75, sr. asst. dep. minister, 1975-81; pres. Charles H. Smith Cons., 1982-94; mem. adv. coun. Dept. geology and geophysics Princeton U., 1967-76; sci. advisor Can. Commn. for UNESCO, 1983-89; exec. dir. Can. Nat. Com./World Energy Conf., 1983-90; bd. govs. Can. Inst. Radiation Safety, 1983-86; hon. mem. Energy Coun. Can., 1991—; coord. 150th anniversary Geol. Survey Can., 1990-93. Mem. editl. bd. Am. Jour. Sci., 1967-72, Mineralium Deposita, 1968-83, Jour. Petrology, 1966-70, Econ. Geology, 1966-70; contbr. articles to profl. jours. Fellow Royal Soc. Can. (fgn. sec. 1986-90), Mineral. Soc. Am., Soc. Econ. Geologists (v.p. N.Am. 1968-70); mem. Can. Inst. Mining and Metallurgy (life mem., v.p. 1982-84), Assn. Profl. Engrs. Ont., Geol. Assn. Can., Can. Geosci. Coun. (pres. 1984), Rotary.

SMITH, CHARLES HENRY, JR., industrial executive; b. Cleve., July 28, 1920; s. Charles H. and Florence (Reno) S.; m. Rhea Day, Sept. 18, 1943 (dec. Jan. 1990); children: Charles Henry, Deborah Rhea Smith Potantus, Hudson Day; m. Florence M. Johnson, Mar. 9, 1991. B.S., Mass. Inst. Tech., 1942. Pres., dir. Steel Improvement & Forge Co. (name changed to Sifco Industries, Inc.), Cleve., 1943-70; chmn., chief exec. officer Steel Improvement & Forge Co. (name changed to Sifco Industries, Inc.), 1970-83, chmn., 1970—; pres. Can. Steel Improvement, Etobicoke, Ont., 1951-54; chmn. bd. Sifco Custom Machining Inc., Mpls., Sifco Selective Plating Inc., Cleve., Sifco Bearing Inc., Avon, Ohio, 1970-88; chmn., consultative coun. Sifco do Brazil, Sao Paulo, 1959-81; chmn. Sifco Turbine Component Svcs., Tampa, Fla.; dir. Sifco Turbine Components Ltd., Cork, Ireland; adv. com. bd. dirs. New Eng. Mut. Life Ins. Co., 1973-77; dir. Bharat Forge Co. Ltd., Poona, India, Aikoh Sifco Co. Ltd., Tokyo, 1970-83, Industrias Kaiser Argentina, 1958-63; mem. Com. on Manpower Resources for Nat. Security, 1953-54; U.S. employer del. Internat. Labor Conf., Geneva, 1956, 75-92, Buenos Aires, 1961; mem. adv. coun. U.S.-Japanese reln. U.S. State Dept., 1970-75; dir., mem. com. experts study relationship between multinat. corps. and social policy ILO, mem. governing body, 1975-78; dir. U.S.-USSR Econ. and Trade Coun., 1975; chmn. U.S. sect. Brazil-U.S. Bus. Coun., 1976-77. Trustee Cleve. YMCA; chmn. bd. mgrs. Addison br., chmn. internat. adv. com. Center Internat. Mgmt. Studies, chmn., 1982-88; bd. dirs. YMCA of the U.S.A., 1983-88, chmn. internat. com.; vice chmn. No. Ohio Rep. Fin. Com.; chmn. No. Ohio Rep. Small Bus. Com., 1956, Partners of Alliance for Ohio, 1969-72; trustee Defiance Coll., 1958-74, St. Alexis Hosp., 1960-70, Booth Meml. Hosp., 1964-74, Judson Park; trustee Ednl. Research Council Am., 1976-86, chmn., 1978-86; trustee bd. trustees Forging Industry Edn. and Research Found., 1961-65; bd. dirs. Nat. Endowment for Democracy, 1983-91; adv. bd. Salvation Army. Named One of Ten Outstanding Young Men Am., 1955. Mem. Forging Industry Assn. (dir. 1954-55, pres. 1956-58), Young Pres.'s Orgn. (chmn. Cleve. chpt. 1956-57), U.S.C. of C. (chmn. internat. bus. com. 1967-81, v.p. 1970-73, treas. 1973-74, chmn. bd. 1974-75, chmn. exec. com. 1975-76), The Ocean Club Fla. (Ocean Ridge), Union Club (Cleve.), Shaker Heights Country Club (dir.), Pine Lake Trout Club, Burning Tree Club (Bethesda, Md.), Va. Hot Springs Golf and Tennis Club, Pepper Pike Club, La Mirador (Mt. Pelerin, Switzerland), Delray Dunes Golf and Tennis Club (Boynton Beach, Fla.). Home: 4565 S Lake Dr Boynton Beach FL 33436 also: 3885-1 Lander Rd Chagrin Falls OH 44022-1368 also: North Ridge Hot Springs VA 24445

SMITH, CHARLES ISAAC, geology educator; b. Hearne, Tex., Feb. 9, 1931; s. Walter Lee and Nellie Lucille (Clearwater) S.; m. Anita Lou Howell, Aug. 22, 1961; children: Lanita Maylene, James Emmett, Timothy Stephen, Sheila Nell. B.S., Baylor U., 1952; M.A., La. State U., 1955; Ph.D., U. Mich., 1966. Geologist Shell Devel. Co., Houston, 1955-60, 62-65; prof. geology U. Mich., Ann Arbor, 1965-77, chmn. dept., 1970-77; prof. geology U. Tex., Arlington, 1977-93, prof. emeritus, 1994—, chmn. dept., 1977-89, cons. geologist, 1993—. Author research papers. Mem. Geol. Soc. Am., Am. Assn. Petroleum Geologists, Am. Inst. Profl. Geologists (cert.). Home: 207 Fletcher Dr Del Rio TX 78840-3044 Office: Univ Tex Dept Geology Arlington TX 76019

SMITH, CHARLES KENT, family medicine physician; b. Des Moines, June 30, 1938; s. Herman Joseph and Elizabeth (Opinham) S.; m. Patricia Hughes Moore, Sept. 1977; children: Laurence, Eleanor, Andrew, Matthew. BA, Northwestern U., 1960, MD, 1963, MS, 1964. Diplomat Am. Bd. Internal Medicine, Am. Bd. Family Practice. Rotating intern U. Mich. Hosp., Ann Arbor, 1963-64, asst. resident medicine, 1967-68; sr. rsch. fellow in medicine (endocrinology) U. Wash. Hosp., Seattle, 1968-70, resident dept. psychiatry, 1970-72, attending staff, 1972-85; instr. dept. internal medicine U. Wash., 1970-71, from instr., asst. prof. to assoc. prof. dept. family medicine, 1971-81, prof., 1981-85, acting chmn. dept., 1976, vice chmn. dept., 1977-85, affiliate Diabetes Rsch. Ctr., 1980-85; prof., chmn. dept. family and community medicine Ea. Va. Med. Sch., Norfolk, 1985-88, mem. dean's coun. chmn. and allied coms., mem. minority affairs coms., 1985-88; prof., chmn. dept. family medicine Case Western Res. U., Cleve., 1988—; Dorothy Jones Weatherhead prof. dept. family medicine Case Western Rev. U., Cleve., 1992—; mem. com. on med. edn., med. coun. and allied coms. U. Hosps. Cleve., 1988—, chmn. com. med. edn., 1992—; dir. family medicine dept.; gen. practice, locum tenens, Wrangell, Alaska, May.-June, 1970; attending staff Children's Orthopedic Hosp., Seattle, 1972-85, Med. Ctr. Hosps., Norfolk, 1985-88, Children's Hosp. of King's Daughters, Norfolk, 1986-88; cons. family mediation panel Family Ct., Superior Ct. King County, Wash., 1976-80; co-presenter 6th Internat. Workshop/Seminar Life Planning Ctr., Practice and Edn. Primary Care Medicine, Jichi Med. Sch., Japan, 1983; vis. prof. Hunan Med. Sch., Changsha, Peoples Republic China, 1984; grant reviewer HHS, Health Resources Adminstrn., Bur. Health Professions, others. Author numerous abstracts, proc., book revs., articles in profl. jours.; reviewer Jour. Family Practice, 1977-90, book jour. AMA, 1977—. Capt. USAF, 1963-65. Royal Soc. Medicine U.K. travelling fellow, 1974; grantee prin. investigator Spl. Project Family Medicine, 78-61, U. Wash. 1981-86, Ea. Va. Med. Sch., 1986-89, 87-90, 88-91, Case Western U., 1988-94. Fellow ACP, Am. Acad. Family Physicians (mem. chpts. in Wash. Va., Ohio, others; mem. Soc. Tchrs. Family Medicine (constn. and by-laws com. 1982-84), Assn. Depts. Family Medicine (treas. 1988—), N.Am. Primary

SMITH, CHARLES OLIVER, engineer; b. Clinton, Mass., May 28, 1920; s. Oliver E. and Flora (Small) S.; m. Mary J. Boyle, Feb. 9, 1946; children: Mary J., Charles M., John P., Susan M., Peter G., Robert A., Katherine M. BS in Mech. Engring., Worcester Poly. Inst., 1941; SM, MIT, 1947, ScD in Metallurgy, 1951. Instr. mech. engring. Worcester Poly. Inst., 1941-43; instr., then asst. prof. Mass. Inst. Tech., 1946-51; research engr. Alcoa Research Lab., 1951-55, Oak Ridge Nat. Lab, 1955-65; prof. engring. U. Detroit, 1965-76, U. Nebr., 1976-81, Rose-Hulman Inst. Tech., 1981-86. Author: Product Liability: Are You Vulnerable?, Nuclear Reactor Materials, Science of Engineering Materials, Introduction to Reliability in Design; also numerous papers on materials, design, product liability, engring. edn. Served with USNR, 1943-46. Recipient St. George award Boy Scouts Am. Fellow ASME (Triodyne Safety award 1992, Machine Design award, 1993), Am. Soc. Engring. Edn. (Fred Merryfield award 1981); mem. AIME, Am. Soc. Metals, Sigma Xi, Tau Beta Pi, Pi Tau Sigma, Phi Kappa Theta. Home: 1920 College Ave Terre Haute IN 47803-4035

SMITH, CHARLES PAUL, newspaper publisher; b. Hartford, Conn., Nov. 1, 1926; s. Thomas S. and Kathryn (Klingler) S.; m. Carolyn Calkins, Feb. 12, 1966; children: Charles, Timothy. BS, U.S. Naval Acad., 1947. Commd. ensign USN, 1947, advanced through grades to lt., line officer, 1947-58, resigned; mgr. Container Corp. Am., Phila., 1958-66, Chattanooga, 1966-68; pub. Daily Intelligencer, Doylestown, Pa., 1968—. Roman Catholic. Office: Calkins Newspapers Inc 333 N Broad St Doylestown PA 18901-3407

SMITH, CHARLES RAYMOND, JR., lawyer; b. Wilkes-Barre, Pa., Apr. 4, 1948; s. Charles Raymond and Dorothy (Huminik) S.; m. Laura Anne Vassamillet, June 16, 1984; children: Emilie Rose, Madeleine Anne. BS magna cum laude, Syracuse U., 1970; JD cum laude, U. Pitts., 1974. Bar: Pa. 1974. Acct. Arthur Andersen & Co., Pitts., 1970-71; atty. Kirkpatrick & Lockhart, Pitts., 1974—. Chmn. bd. dirs. Greater Pitts. Conv. and Visitors Bur., 1988-90. Mem. ABA, Pitts. Tax Club, Shannopin Country Club, Edgeworth Club, Duquesne Club, Order of Coif. Avocations: golf, travel. Home: 130 Woodland Rd Sewickley PA 15143-1125 Office: Kirkpatrick & Lockhart 1500 Oliver Building Bldg Pittsburgh PA 15222-2312

SMITH, CHARLES THOMAS, retired dentist, educator; b. San Diego, Mar. 22, 1914; s. Sydney Alexander and Lydia Ellen (Hoff) S.; m. Ruth Anita Anderson, May 20, 1935 (dec. Jan. 1979); children: Charlyn Ruth, Charles Thomas; m. Mary Lou Sessums, July 21, 1979. A.B., Pacific Union Coll., 1935; D.D.S., Coll. Phys. and Surg., 1940; LL.H., Loma Linda U. Sch. of Dentistry, 1971. Tchr. Glendale Union Acad., 1935-36; pvt. practice dentistry San Diego, 1940-53; dean-elect Sch. Dentistry, Loma Linda U., 1959-60, dean, 1960-71, dean emeritus, 1971; prof. emeritus Loma Linda U., 1973—; program coordinator div. Physicians and Health Profession Edn., NIH, 1971-73; prof. dept. community dentistry U. Tex. at San Antonio, 1973-83, acting dean student affairs Dental Sch., 1975-76, assoc. dean for acad. affairs, 1976-77, acting chmn. dept. community dentistry, 1977-83; Cons. dental facilities rev. com. USPHS, 1964-69; mem. grants and allocations com. Am. Found. for Dental Health, 1973-80. Dir. Paradise Valley Sanitarium and Hosp., 1947-59, San Diego Union Acad., 1947-53; founder San Diego Children's Dental Health Center; exhibit chmn. Pacific Coast Dental Conf., 1957; pres. Am. Cancer Soc., 1950; trustee Loma Linda U., 1976-90. Served as maj. AUS Dental Corps, 1953-55. Fellow Am. Coll. Dentists (vice chmn. So. Calif. chpt. 1967-68, chmn. 1968-69), Internat. Coll. Dentists; mem. So. Calif. Dental Assn. (chmn. council on dental edn. 1963-68, treas. 1967-71), San Diego County Dental Soc. (pres. 1949), Am. Acad. Dental Practice Adminstrn., Western Dental Deans Assn. (chmn. 1960-67), Western Deans and Dental Examiners (v.p. 1969—, pres. 1970), Am. Assn. Dental Schs. (mem. exec. com., v.p. council deans 1971), Acad. Dentistry Internat. (v.p. 1985-89, treas. 1985-89, chmn. awards com. 1989-90, assoc. chmn., 1986—), Nat. Assn. Seventh Day Adventists, Am. Acad. Periodontology, Acad. Dentistry Internationale, Delta Sigma Delta, Tau Kappa Omega, Omicron Kappa Upsilon. Home: 34-895 Surrey Way Thousand Palms CA 92276

SMITH, CHARLES WILLIAM, social sciences educator, sociologist; b. Providence; s. Joseph and Clara (Loitman) S.; m. Rita Cope, Sept. 3, 1963; children: Abigail Cope, Jonathan Cope. AB, Wesleyan U., 1960; MA, Brandeis U., 1966, PhD in Sociology, 1966. Instr. sociology Simmons Coll., Boston, 1964-65; from lectr. to assoc. prof. Queens Coll., Flushing, N.Y., 1965-71, from assoc. to prof. sociology, 1979—; grad. faculty Grad. Ctr. CUNY, 1986—; vis. scholar Nuffield Coll., Oxford, Eng., 1979-80, Wesleyan U., Middletown, Conn., 1987-88; chair dept. sociology Queens Coll., Flushing, 1988-91, acting dean of faculty social sci., 1991-92, dean faculty social sci., 1992—; cons. auctions, 1986—. Author: The Mind of the Market: A Study of Stock Market Philosophies, Their Uses and Implications, 1981, Critique of Sociological Reasoning: An Essay in Philosophic Sociology, 1982, Auctions: The Social Construction of Values, 1989; editor Jour. for Theory of Social Behavior, 1983—. Bd. dirs., pres. Cmty. Action Program of White Plains, N.Y., 1974-79; bd. trustees, v.p. Temple Israel Ctr. of White Plains, 1975-94; class agt., alumni activities Wesleyan U., Middletown, Conn., 1960—. Recipient FIPSE award Dept. Edn., 1993-96, Ford Found. Diversity grant, 1990-93. Office: Queens Coll CUNY 65-30 Kissena Blvd Flushing NY 11367

SMITH, CHARLES WILSON, JR., university dean; b. Ft. Lauderdale, Fla., Apr. 15, 1949; m. Constance Killen; children: Thaddeus, Cameron, Amber, Logan, Jordan, Rachael. MD, U. N.C., 1974, BS, 1979. Diplomate Am. Bd. Family Practice (bd. dirs., com. mem., treas., pres. 1991-92). Resident in psychiatry U. N.C. Meml. Hosp., 1974-75, resident in family practice, 1975-78; pvt. practice, Muscatine, Ia., 1978-79; asst. prof. Wright State U., 1979-83, assoc. prof., 1983-86; chief of family medicine sch. of primary med. care U. Ala., Huntsville, 1986-87, assoc. dean clin. affairs, 1986-87, acting dean, 1986; assoc. dean U. Ala. Sch. of Medicine, Huntsville, 1986-89; exec. assoc. dean for clin. affairs U. Ark. for Med. Scis., Little Rock, 1989—, prof. family and community medicine, 1989—, exec. dir. faculty practice plan, 1991—; dir. family practice residency program Miami Valley Hosp., Dayton, Ohio, 1979-86. Co-author: Family Practice Desk Reference, 2nd edit.; editor Primary Care Currents, 1985—; dep. editor Am. Family Physician, 1987—; contbr. numerous articles to profl. jours. Bd. dirs. Nicholas J. Pisacano Found., 1990—. Mem. AMA, Am. Acad. Family Physicians (editor mag.), Ark. Acad. Family Physicians, Ark. Med. Assn., Pulaski County Med. Soc. Home: 4 Chelsea Rd Little Rock AR 72212-3723 Office: U Ark for Med Scis 4301 W Markham St Slot 719 Little Rock AR 72205

SMITH, CHARLES Z., state supreme court justice; b. Lakeland, Fla., Feb. 23, 1927; s. John R. and Eva (Love) S.; m. Eleanor Jane Martinez, Aug. 20, 1955; children: Carlos M., Michael O., Stephen P., Felica L. BS, Temple U., 1952, JD, U. Wash., 1955. Bar: Wash. 1955. Law clk. Wash. Supreme Ct., Olympia, 1955-56; dep. pros. atty., asst. chief criminal div. King County, Seattle, 1956-60; ptnr. Bianchi, Smith & Tobin, Seattle, 1960-61; spl. asst. to atty. gen. criminal div. U.S. Dept. Justice, Washington, 1961-64; judge criminal dept. Seattle Mcpl. Ct., 1965-66; judge Superior Ct. King County, 1966-73; former assoc. dean, prof. law U. Wash., 1973; now justice Wash. Supreme Ct., Olympia. Mem. adv. bd. NAACP, Seattle Urban League, Wash. State Literacy Coun., Boys Club, Wash. Citizens for Migrant Affairs, Medina Children's Svc., Children's Home Soc. Wash., Seattle Better Bus. Bur., Seattle Foundation, Seattle Symphony Orch., Seattle Opera Assn., Community Svc. Ctr. for Deaf and Hard of Hearing, Seattle U., Seattle Sexual Assault Ctr., Seattle Psychoanalytic Inst., The Little Sch., Linfield Coll., Japanese Am. Citizens League, Kawabe Meml. Hous, Puget Consound Counseling Ctr., Am. Cancer Soc., Hutchinson Cancer Rsch. Ctr., Robert Chinn Found.; pres. Am. Bapt. Chs. U.S.A., 1976-77. Lt. col. reserve. USMCR. Mem. ABA, Am. Judicature Soc., Washington Bar Assn., Seattle-King County Bar Assn., Order of Coif., Phi Alpha Delta, Alpha Phi Alpha. Office: Wash Supreme Ct Temple of Justice (AV-11) PO Box 40929 Olympia WA 98504

SMITH, CHARLOTTE REED, retired music educator; b. Eubank, Ky., Sept. 15, 1921; d. Joseph Lumpkin and Cornelia Elizabeth (Spenser) Reed;

m. Walter Lindsay Smith, Aug. 24, 1949; children—Walter Lindsay IV, Elizabeth Reed. B.A. in Music, Tift Coll., 1941; M.A. in Mus. Theory, Eastman Sch. of Music, 1946; postgrad. Juilliard Sch., 1949. Asst. prof. theory Okla. Bapt. U., 1944-45, Washburn U., 1946-48; prof. music Furman U., Greenville, S.C., 1948-92; chmn. dept. music, 1987-92. Editor: Seven Penitential Psalms with Two Laudate Psalms, 1983; author: Manual of Sixteenth-Century Contrapuntal Style, 1989. Mem. Internat. Musicological Soc., Am. Musicological Soc., Soc. for Music Theory, AAUP (sec.-treas. Furman chpt. 1984-85), Nat. Fedn. Music Clubs, Pi Kappa Lambda. Republican. Baptist.

SMITH, CHESTER LEO, lawyer; b. Kansas City, Mo., Jan. 23, 1922; s. Chester Leo and Alameda Mariposa (West) S.; m. Ann Smith; 1 dau., Blithe. BA, U. Chgo., 1942; JD, Harvard U., 1948. Bar: Ill. 1949, Calif. 1951. Asst. to v.p. Cuneo Press, Chgo., 1948-49; individual practice Los Angeles, 1951-87, ret., 1987. Author: Midway 4 June, 1942, 1962, (plays) My Empress Eva Darling, The Last Execution, Images of Che, Cross-Examination at Auschwitz; editor: (Wu Han): The Dismissal of Hai Jui, 1968; contbr. stories to, Collier's, Am. Legion mag. Served to 1st lt. Air Corps, USMCR, 1942-45, Okinawa, Borneo. Decorated Air medal (3). Mem. State Bar Calif. Address: PO Box 49590 Los Angeles CA 90049-0590

SMITH, CHESTERFIELD HARVEY, lawyer; b. Arcadia, Fla., July 28, 1917; s. Cook Hall and Grace (Gilbert) S.; m. Vivian Lee Parker, Jan. 29, 1944 (dec. Feb. 1987); children: Rhoda Smith Kibler, Chesterfield Harvey Jr.; m. Jacqueline Pearce Allee, July 25, 1987. J.D., U. Fla., 1948, hon. degrees: LL.D., 1972; LL.D., John B. Stetson U., 1972, Suffolk U., 1973, Norwich U., 1973, Akron U., 1973, Western State U. Coll. Law, 1977; H.H.D., St. Leo Coll., 1974; D.C.L., Jacksonville U., 1975; LLD, St. Thomas U., 1987. Bar: Fla. 1948. Assoc. Treadwell & Treadwell, Arcadia, 1948-50, Holland, Bevis & McRae, Bartow, Fla., 1950-51; ptnr. Holland & Knight, Lakeland, Ft. Lauderdale, Miami, Orlando, Tallahassee, Tampa, Jacksonville, Washington; city commr., Bartow, 1955, city atty., 1956-59; bd. dirs. Citrus & Chem. Bank of Bartow, Greenwich Air Svcs., Inc., The Wackenhut Corp.; trustee, chmn. The Emerald Funds, Gen. Devel. Corp.; chmn. Fla. Constl. Revision Commn., 1965-67; chmn. Fla. Gov.'s Citizens for Jud. Reform, 1972; mem. Fla. Gov.'s Commn. for Govt. by the People, 1991—; Decade to Discover Fla. com., 1991—, Fla. Coun. of 100, 1970-74, Fed. Jud. Nominating Commn. Fla., 1975-77; bd. dirs. Lawyers Com. for Civil Rights Under Law, 1975—, So. Legal Counsel, Inc., 1977; mem. Coun. for Pub. Interest Law, 1975-78; hon. co-chmn. Nat. Resource Ctr. for Consumers of Legal Svcs., 1975-85; bd. advisers Ctr. for Govtl. Responsibility, 1974—; mem. legal adv. com. Southeastern Legal Found., 1976-78; trustee Inst. for Ct. Mgmt., 1970-72, Legis. 50, The Ctr. for Legis. Improvement, 1970-78, mem. exec. com., 1976-78; mem. nat. adv. com. Nat. Inst. for Citizen Edn. in Law, chmn., 1982-86; trustee Collins Ctr. for Pub. Policy, 1989—. Mem. coun. advisers U. Fla.; assoc. trustee U. Pa. Law Sch., bd. overseers, 1978-86; mem. bd. visitors U. Miami Sch. Law, 1982—, McGeorge Sch. Law, 1987—; vice-chmn. nat. adv. coun. ACLU, 1983—; mem. adv. bd. LWV Fla., 1984—; trustee Nat. Found. for Advancement in Arts, 1984—, chmn., 1988-90; trustee Fla. Network of Youth and Family Svcs., 1988—; bd. dirs. Shriver Peace Worker Prog., 1986—, The Internat. League for Human Rights, 1984, Fla. FFA Found., 1988—. Maj. U.S. Army, 1940-45, ETO. Recipient Disting. Service award John B. Stetson U., 1965, Significant Alumni award U. Fla., 1966, Disting. Floridian award Fla. C. of C., 1969, medal of Merit Bartow Rotary Club, 1975, Outstanding Citizen award Bartow Lions Club, 1975, Nelson Poynter award ACLU, 1983, Learned Hand award The Am. Jewish Com., 1984; named Fla. Patriot Bicentennial Commn. Fla., 1975; named to Bartow Hall of Fame, 1978. Fellow Internat. Acad. Trial Lawyers, Am. Coll. Trial Lawyers, Am. Bar Found.; mem. ABA (ho. of dels. 1966—, state del. 1968-70, bd. govs. 1969-70, 72-75, pres. 1973-74, ABA Medal award 1981), Fla. Bar Assn. (bd. govs. 1958-65, chmn. continuing legal edn. 1961-62, pres. 1964-65, ctr. com. 1962-64), 10th Jud. Circuit Bar Assn. (pres. 1956-57), Nat. Conf. Bar Pres.'s (exec. com. 1965-70, v.p. 1967-68, pres. 1968-69), Am. Law Inst., Inst. Jud. Adminstrn., Nat. Legal Aid and Defender Assn. (chmn. membership for state and local bar assns. 1969-71, dir. 1971—, Arthur von Briesen award 1974), Am. Judicature Soc. (dir. 1965-72, exec. com. 1969-72, Herbert Lincoln Harley award 1973), U. Fla. Law Center Assn. (trustee 1963), Fla. C. of C. Found. Inc. (trustee 1985—), Fla. Supreme Ct. Hist. Soc. (pres. 1987-89, trustee, 1986—), U.S. Supreme Ct. Hist. Soc. (trustee)—, Fla. Blue Key, Order of Coif, Phi Beta Kappa, Alpha Tau Omega, Phi Delta Phi, Phi Kappa Phi. Democrat. Methodist. Office: Holland & Knight PO Box 015441 1200 Brickell Ave Miami FL 33131-3209 also: Holland & Knight 2100 Pennsylvania Ave NW # 400 Washington DC 20037-3202

SMITH, CHRISTOPHER CASE, newspaper editor; b. Honolulu, July 22, 1934; s. Dudley Wall and Elizabeth McLean (Case) S.; m. Marjorie Anne Nurse, June 21, 1959; children: Suzanne Elizabeth, Patricia Louise (dec.), Sandra Kathleen. AB, Princeton U., 1956; MA, Stanford U., 1959. Adminstrv. asst. Calif. Assn. Ins. Agts., Berkeley, 1960-62; fin. writer The San Diego Union, 1962-68; asst. editor Bus. Week, Los Angeles, 1968-71; fin. writer The Honolulu Advertiser, 1971—. Bd. dirs. Friends of the Cancer Rsch. Ctr. Hawaii, 1984—. Served to lt. j.g., USNR, 1956-58. Recipient first prize media awards for econ. understanding Dartmouth Amos Tuck Sch., 1978. Mem. Am. Soc. Profl. Journalists. Avocation: trombone. Office: The Honolulu Advertiser 605 Kapiolani Blvd Honolulu HI 96813-5195

SMITH, CHRISTOPHER HENRY, congressman; b. Rahway, N.J., Mar. 4, 1953; s. Bernard Henry and Katherine Joan (Hall) S.; m. Marie Hahn, July 2, 1977; children: Melissa, Christopher, Michael Jonathan, Elyse. Student, Worcester Coll., Eng., 1973-74; B.A. in Bus. Adminstrn., Trenton State Coll., 1975. Exec. dir. N.J. Right to Life Com., 1976-77; dir. instl. sales Leisure Unltd. Inc., Woodbridge, N.J., 1978-80; mem. 97th-104th Congresses from 4th N.J. dist., Washington, D.C., 1981—; chmn. internat. rels. subcom. on internat. ops. and human rights 97th-104th Congresses from 4th N.J. dist., mem. vets. affairs com., chmn. Helsinki com.; U.S. rep. to UN internat. conf. immunizing world's children. Active human rights movements Romania, China, USSR, Vietnam. Named Legislator of Yr. VFW, Legislator of Yr. Internat. Assn. Chiropractors, Legislator of Yr. KC, 1989; recipient Leader for Peace award Peace Corps. Mem. Nat. Fedn. Ind. Bus. Republican. Roman Catholic. Office: 2370 Rayburn Ho Office Bldg Washington DC 20515*

SMITH, CLAIR S., JR., oil industry executive. With Lion Oil, El Dorado, Ark., 1954-70; CEO P & O Falco, Bossier City, La., 1970-84; with Enron Oil, Houston, 1984-87; pres. C.S. SmithEnterprises, Shreveport, La., 1982—; chmn. bd. S & D Falco, Inc., Shreveport, La., 1989—. Office: S & D Falco Inc 950 Wells Island Rd Shreveport LA 71107*

SMITH, CLAIR SCOTT, III, petroleum company executive; b. 1963. Pres., CEO Enron Oil Corp., Midland, Tex., 1984-90, S & D Falco Inc., Shreveport, La., 1990—. Office: S & D Falco Inc 950 Wells Island Rd Shreveport LA 71107*

SMITH, CLAIRE LAREMONT, language educator; b. Panama City, Panama, Dec. 30, 1939; came to U.S., 1965; d. Sebastian Hamlet and Ambrozine Beatriz (Simon) Laremont; m. Stephen E. Greaves, Nov. 29, 1961 (div. 1968); children: Liza N. Greaves Smith, Katia T. Laremont Smith; m. James Elliott Smith, Dec. 20, 1969; 1 child, Raquel J. Student, U. Panama, Panama City, 1959-62; BA, SUNY, Fredonia, 1968, MS, 1970; postgrad., SUNY, Buffalo, 1983-93. Cert. tchr. secondary social studies, elem. bilingual edn., secondary Spanish and ESL, N.Y. Bilingual stenographer, bookkeeper, cashier Foto Internat., Panama City, 1960-65; tchr. secondary social studies and Spanish Forestville (N.Y.) Cen. Schs., 1968-69; grad. asst. dept. history SUNY, Fredonia, 1969-70; substitute tchr. Am. Overseas Schs. of Army Dependants, Camp Livorno, Italy, 1970-71; tchr. early childhood bilingual Dunkirk (N.Y.) Migrant Daycare Ctr., 1972-73; tchr., home instr. Head Start program Durkirk Schs., 1973-74; tchr. adult basic edn. N.Y. State Migrant Workers Opportunities, Dunkirk, 1977-80; tchr. social studies, bilingual, Spanish and ESL Dunkirk Mid. Sch., 1973—; adj. instr. ESL SUNY, Fredonia, 1992, 93; mem. affirmative action com. on cultural ethnic rels. SUNY, Fredonia, 1989-92, 93; mem. com. on discipline Dunkirk Sch. Dist., 1991-93, compact learning com., 1993-94, 94—, Youth Empowerment System, wellness com.; mem. sch. improvement team Dunkirk Med. Sch., 1991-92; presenter profl. confs., U.S., Mex.; gues speaker Hispanic Heritage

Week Celebration, N.Y. State Migrant Daycare, Fredonia, 1991. V.p. Dunkirk chpt. NAACP, 1975; bd. dirs. North County Counseling Svc., Dunkirk, 1992-93, People's Action Coalition, Dunkirk, 1992-94, v.p., 1993-94, 94—; chairperson cultural awareness task force Dunkirk Community Challenge; bd. dirs. Chautauqua County Connections, 1993-94; harborfest com. City of Dunkirk, 1992-92, 93-94. Mem. AAUW, N.Y. State Assn. Bilingual Educators, Tchrs. of English to Speakers of Other Langs., Nat. Assn. Bilingual Edn., Dunkirk Tchrs. Assn. (bilingual scholarship fund, annual dinner awards program, 1979-92, active voter registration drive 1992) N.Y. State United Tchrs., SUNY Buffalo Grad. Student Assn. (senator 1990-92, co-pres. dept. learning and instrn. 1991-92), Phi Delta Kappa (SUNY Buffalo chpt.). Democrat. Roman Catholic. Avocations: jogging, reading, travel. Home: 2138 King Rd Forestville NY 14062 Office: Dunkirk Schs 201 Lake Shore Dr E Dunkirk NY 14048

SMITH, CLARENCE O'FARRELL, publishing company executive; b. Bronx, N.Y., Mar. 31, 1933; s. Clarence and Millicent (Fry) S.; m. Elaine Goss, June 22, 1963; children: Clarence, Craig. Attended, Baruch Sch. Bus., 1960-61. Spl. rep. Prudential Ins. Co. Am., N.Y.C., 1963-69; registered rep. Investors Planning Corp., N.Y.C., 1966-69; pres., founder Essence Comms. Inc., N.Y.C., 1969—. Mem. African American Task Force Media-Advt. Partnership for Drug-Free Am. With U.S. Army, 1957-59. Named Communicator of Yr., Nat. Assn. Market Developers, 1990, Entrepreneur of Yr., Ernst & Young, 1994; recipient Meritorious Svc. award UNCF, 1990, Annual Achievement award Black Enterprise Mag., 1980, Prin's. award Henry Highland Garnet Sch. Success, 1988-89, Black Achievement award Equitable Assurance Soc. U.S., 1985. Mem. African Am. Mktg. and Media Assn. (chmn. 1991), Cosmetic, Toiletry & Fragrance Assn. (bd. dirs.), Am. Mgmt. Assn., Advt. Coun. (dir.-at-large, chmn. ethnic perspectives com.), TransAfrica Forum (trustee 1993—). Office: Essence Comms 1500 Broadway New York NY 10036-4015

SMITH, CLIFFORD LEE, clergyman; b. Barberton, Ohio, Feb. 27, 1945; s. Howard Donald and Alpha Louisa (McCaman) S.; m. Paulette Joan Wall, Sept. 28, 1963; 1 child, Christina Marie. BA, Ky. Christian Coll., Grayson, 1972, BTh, 1973, MMin, 1987. Ordained to ministry Ch. of Christ, 1972. Minister Allentown Ch. of Christ, Wheelersburg, Ohio, 1969-71, Bradford Ch. of Christ, Pomery, Ohio, 1971-75, First Christian Ch., Havre de Grace, Md., 1976-87; pres. Eastern Christian Coll., Bel Air, Md., 1988-92, trustee, 1977-88; clergyman The Christian Ch., Arnold, Md., 1992—; pres. Ea. Christian Coll., Bel Air, Md., 1988-92; v.p. Eastern Christian Conv., N.E. U.S., 1990; 1st v.p. Mid-Atlantic Christian Ch. Evangelism, 1980-85. Republican. Avocations: fishing, hunting, reading. Home and Office: PO Box 9683 Arnold MD 21012-2139

SMITH, CLIFFORD VAUGHN, JR., academic administrator; b. Washington, Nov. 29, 1931; s. Clifford Vaughn and Jean (Murray) S.; m. Nina Marie Smith, Aug. 22, 1953; children: Sharon, Debra, Patricia. BSCE, State U. Iowa, 1954; MS Engring., Johns Hopkins U., 1960, PhD, 1966; PhD (hon.), Tuskegee U., 1991. V.p. Oreg. State U., Corvallis, 1978-81, spl. asst. to chancellor, dir. Council Adv. Sci. and Engring. Edn., 1983-85, dir. Radiation Ctr., 1985-86; exec. engr. Bechtel Nat. Inc., Oak Ridge, Tenn., 1981-83; chancellor U. Wis., Milw., 1986-90; pres. GE Found., Fairfield, Conn., 1990—; bd. dirs. Astronautics Corp. Am., Milw.; cons. NSF, Washington, 1985—, Envirodyne Engrs., St. Louis, 1985—; mem. radiation adv. com. to sci. adv. bd. U.S. EPA, Washington, 1984—; adv. com. nuclear waste U.S. Nuclear Regulatory Commn., 1988-90; EHR adv. com. NSF, 1991—; steering com. human resources devel. for tech. industry simulation UNESCO, 1992—; mem. Nat. Bd. Fund for Improvement Postsecondary Edn., U.S. Dept. Edn., 1993—. Bd. dirs. Milw. County Research Park, 1987—, Greater Milw. Com., 1987—; Columbia Hosp. Health System Inc., Milw., 1987—; at-large-gov. Am. Heart Assn., Milw., 1987—; trustee Inst. Internat. Edn., 1992—; bd. assocs. Gallaudet Univ., 1993—. Recipient Gold medal for exceptional service EPA, 1973; named Eminent Engr., Tau Beta Pi, 1979; hon. faculty mem. Blue Key Nat. Honor Fraternity, 1980. Mem. ASCE, NSPE, Am. Soc. Engring. Edn., Am. Nuclear Soc., Phi Kappa Phi. Roman Catholic. Club: Univ. (Milw.). Avocations: reading historical novels, travel. Home: 12 Valley View Rd Newtown CT 06470-1922 Office: GE Found 3135 Easton Tpke Fairfield CT 06431-0002

SMITH, CLODUS RAY, academic administrator; b. Blanchard, Okla., May 15, 1928; s. William Thomas and Rachel (Hale) S.; m. Pauline R. Chaat; children: Martha Lynn, William Paul, Paula Diane. Assoc. degree, Cameron State Coll., 1948; BS in Agrl. Edn., Okla. A & M Coll., 1950; MS in Vocat. Edn., Okla. State U., 1955; EdD in Vocat. Edn., Cornell U., 1960. Grad. asst. Cornell U., 1957-59; asst. prof. U. Md., 1959-62, assoc. prof., 1962-63, dir. Summer Sch., 1963-72, adminstrv. dean, 1972-73, asst. to pres. Cleve. State U., 1973-74, v.p. for univ. rels., 1974-83; pres. Rio Grande Coll. and Rio Grande Community Coll., Ohio, 1983-86, Lake Erie Coll., Painesville, Ohio, 1986-92, Okla. Ind. Coll. Found., Oklahoma City, 1993—, Okla. Assn. Ind. Colls. and Univs., 1993—; cons. NEA, Naval Weapons Lab. Dehlgren, Va.; researcher Personal and Profl. Satisfactions; contract investigator Nat. Endowment for Humanities; dir. Human Resources and Community Devel., Prince George's County, Md. Author: Planning and Paying for College, 1958, Rural Recreation for Profit, 1971, A Strategy for University Relations, 1975, State Relations for the 1980 Decade, 1982. Amb. Natural Resources, Ohio, 1984, chmn. dept.; founder N.Am. Assn. of Summer Schs., 1979. Recipient Rsch. award Nat. Project in Agrl. Communications, 1959, Edn. award Prince George's C. of C., 1971. Mem. Am. Assn. U. Adminstrs., Am. Assn. for Higher Edn., Nat. Soc. for Study Edn., Coun. for Support and Advancement Edn., Am. Alumni Coun., Al Koran Hunter's Club, Shriners. Methodist. Avocations: hunting, fishing. Home: 600 NW 4th St Unit 220 Oklahoma City OK 73102 Office: Okla Ind Coll Found 114 E Sheridan Ste 101 Oklahoma City OK 73104

SMITH, CLYDE CURRY, historian, educator; b. Hamilton, Ohio, Dec. 16, 1929; s. Charles Clyde and Mabel Ethel Ola (Curry) S.; m. Ellen Marie Gormsen, June 13, 1953; children: Harald Clyde, Karen Margaret Evans. BA in Physics cum laude and MS, Miami U., Oxford, Ohio, 1951; BDiv, U. Chgo., 1954, MA, 1961, PhD, 1968. Ordained to ministry Christian Ch. (Disciples of Christ), 1954. Exec. asst. to dean Disciples Div. House, Chgo., 1956-57; lectr. in O.T., Univ. Coll. U. Chgo., 1957; asst. prof. St. John's Coll. U. Manitoba, Winnipeg, Can., 1958-63; instr. Brandeis U. Waltham, Mass., 1963-65; prof. ancient history and religious studies U. Wis., River Falls, 1965-90, prof. emeritus, 1990—; vis. prof. religious studies Culver-Stockton Coll., Canton, Mo., 1990, U. Newcastle-upon-Tyne, Eng., 1992-94; vis. lectr. div., Edge Hill Coll. of Edn., Ormskirk, Eng., 1970-71; postdoctoral fellow Johns Hopkins U., Balt., 1977; NEH fellow-in-residence U. Calif., Santa Barbara, 1978-79; vis. rsch. fellow, lectr. religious studies U. Aberdeen, Scotland, 1980, 85-86. Contbr. articles to profl. publs. Mem. Pierce County Hist. Assn., River Falls, 1965—; Wis. Dems., 1965—, Dem. Nat. Com., 1983—; charter mem. Sci. Mus. of Minn., St. Paul, 1973—. Recipient Gov.'s Spl. award State of Wis., 1990, several grants. Mem. Assn. Ancient Historians, Can. Soc. Ch. History (founder, treas. 1960-63), N.Am. Patristic Soc., Can. Soc. for Mesopotamian Studies, Soc. for Promotion Roman Studies of London, Hellenic Soc. London, Brit. Sch. Archaeology in Iraq, Brit. Inst. Archaeology in Ankara, Oriental Inst. U. Chgo., Phi Beta Kappa. Democrat. Avocations: outerspace, battleships, dinosaurs. Home: 939 W Maple St River Falls WI 54022-2055 *We can begin thought with the assumption that there is a world which knows neither origin nor end but which includes us; we can conclude with the affirmations that there was a "when" whatever is was not, and that whatever is will with time cease to be. Our concern then can be to enhance value and empower others, especially those who follow.*

SMITH, CLYDE R., counselor educator; b. Donaldson, Ark., June 15, 1933; s. Clyde Raymond Smith and Annie Pearl (Burnett) Cypert; m. Jannis Lowery, July 31, 1952; 1 child, Renee Lowery. BS, Ark. State U., 1957; MEd, U. Mo., 1958; EdD, U. Tenn., Knoxville, 1969. Employment placement counselor Mo. Bur. for the Blind, Kansas City, Mo., 1958-60; counselor Presbyn. Guidance Ctr., Rhodes U., Memphis, 1960-67; assoc. prof. Brandeis U., Peoria, Ill., 1969—; vocat. cons. Social Security Adminstrn. Bur. Hearings and Appeals, Memphis, 1963-69, Peoria, 1969-78. Contbr. articles to profl. jours. Bd. dirs. Peoria Hts. Sch. Dist. 325, 1974-76, Children's Home Assn. Ill., Peoria, 1978-80. Recipient Jefferson award Am. Inst. for Pub. Svc., 1978, Tom Connor award C. of C., Peoria, 1978, Others

award Salvation Army, 1984. Mem. Am. Counseling Assn. (life), Nat. Career Devel. Assn., Peoria Lions (life; pres. 1975-76, bd. dirs. 1978-81, 85-91, dep. dist. gov. 1982-83, zone chmn. 1983-84). Republican. Presbyterian. Avocations: reading, music, hiking, collecting old movies. Home: 1511 W Callender Ave Peoria IL 61606-1615 Office: Bradley U 306 Westlake Hall Peoria IL 61625

SMITH, CORLIES MORGAN, publishing executive; b. Phila., Mar. 31, 1929; s. Charles Ross and Mary Howard (Stewart) S.; m. Sheila de Peyster Carey, June 17, 1950; children: Mark, Nicholas, Peter, Baylies, Timothy. BA, Yale U., 1951. Assoc. editor J.B. Lippincott Co., Phila., 1955-62; sr. editor The Viking Press, N.Y.C., 1962-83; editorial dir. Ticknor & Fields, N.Y.C., 1984-89; editor in chief Harcourt Brace & Co., N.Y.C., 1990-94, editorial con., 1995—. Home and Office: 1435 Lexington Ave New York NY 10128-1625

SMITH, CRAIG RICHARDS, manufacturing executive; b. Los Angeles, June 2, 1940; s. Max Boley and Dorcas (Richards) S.; m. Diann Kuhni, June 2, 1960; children: Bradley, Sharee, Tracy, Cindy, Kristen, Michelle. BS in Physics, Brigham Young U., 1962, MBA, 1965. V.p. ops. WER Indsl. div. Emerson Electric, Grand Island, N.Y., 1972-76; v.p., gen. mgr. Carborundum Bonded Abrasives Div., Buffalo, 1976-70; v.p., div. mgr. Raymark Corp., Trumbull, Conn., 1980-85, now bd. dirs.; pres., chief exec. officer Raytech Corp., Shelton, 1985—, also bd. dirs. Republican. Mormon. Avocations: running, golf, tennis, basketball. Office: Raytech Corp 1 Corporate Dr Ste 512 Shelton CT 06484-6211

SMITH, CULLEN, lawyer; b. Waco, Tex., May 31, 1925; s. Curtis Cullen and Elizabeth (Brient) S.; m. Laura Risher Dossett, Mar. 6, 1948; children: Sallie Chesnutt Smith Wright, Andrea Risher Smith Gilbert, Elizabeth Brient Smith. Student, Emory U., 1943-44, Duke U., 1944; B.B.A. Baylor U., 1948, J.D., 1950. Bar: Tex. 1950. Ptnr. firm McIlheran & Smith, Weslaco, Tex., 1950-53, Naman, Howell, Smith & Lee (P.C.), Waco, 1953—; lectr. law Baylor U. Sch. Law, 1964-72. Contbr. articles to legal publs. Mem. standing com. Episcopal Diocese of Tex., 1960-63, 74-75; trustee Episcopal Theol. Sem. of S.W., 1962-67; mem. Waco City Coun., 1983-86; chmn. bd. Vanguard Sch., 1975; bd. dirs. G.H. Pape Found., 1993-94; bd. dirs., vice chmn. Tex. Ctr. for Legal Ethics and Professionalism, 1994—. 1st lt. USMCR, 1943-46. Named One of 5 Outstanding Young Texans Tex. Jr. C. of C., 1957, Baylor Lawyer of Yr., 1980. Fellow Am. Bar Found., Tex. Bar Found. (chmn. bd. 1973-74), fellow Coll. of Law Practice Mgmt.; mem. ABA (chmn. standing com. econs. law practice 1965-69, chmn. spl. com. on law book pub. practices 1970-72, chmn. gen. practice sect. 1973-74, mem. ho. of dels. 1974-81), Am. Law Firm Assn. (chmn. 1989-90), Waco-McLennan County Bar Assn. (pres. 1956-57), Mont. Bar Assn. (hon.), State Bar Tex. (pres. jr. bar 1957-58, chmn. profl. econs. com. 1959-61, chmn. spl. com. on revision Tex. Canons Ethics 1969-71, dir. 1971-74, pres. 1978-79), Baylor U. Law Alumni Assn. (pres. 1962-63), Order of Coif, Delta Sigma Phi, Phi Delta Phi. Clubs: Ridgewood Country (pres. 1965), Hedonia (pres. 1957). Lodge: Rotary. Avocation: photography. Home: Oak Grove Farm 447 Meandering Way China Spring TX 76633 Office: Naman Howell Smith & Lee PC Tex Ctr PO Box 1470 Waco TX 76703-1470

SMITH, CURTIS JOHNSTON, government executive; b. Honolulu, Jan. 7, 1947; s. Robert Johnston and Sara Adelaide (Marshall) S.; m. Susan Helen Manell, June 17, 1967; 1 dau., Morgan Lynn. BA, Calif. Luth. Coll., Thousand Oaks, 1969; MA, Ohio State U., 1972, PhD, 1975. Legis. asst. Office of Pers. Mgmt., Washington, 1977-80, spl. asst. to assoc. dir. for compensation, 1980-82, dep. asst. dir. for pay and benefits policy, 1982-84, sr. examiner office mgmt. and budget, 1984-85, policy advisor to dir., 1985-86, assoc. dir. for career entry and employee devel., 1986-89, assoc. dir. ret., ins., 1989-94; dir. Fed. Exec. Inst., Charlottesville, Va., 1994—; mem. Nat. Accountancy Pub. Adminstrs. panel on pub. svc. Assn. Va. Health Policy Ctr. Mem. Am. Soc. Pub. Adminstrn., Internat. Personnel Mgmt. Assn., Trout Unlimited (No. Va.). Avocations: fishing, golf, bicycling. Office: Fed Exec Inst Office Pers Mgmt 1301 Emmet St Charlottesville VA 22903

SMITH, DALLAS R., federal official; b. Bolton, N.C., Oct. 1, 1942; s. John William and Bonnie Arlene (Jacobs) S.; m. Shirley Ann Turner, Apr. 10, 1966; 2 children. BS, N.C. Agrl. and Tech. U., 1965; postgrad., U. Md., 1968-69. Agrl. ext. agent N.C. ext. svc. tobacco and peanuts divsn. agrl. stabilization and conservation svc. Dept. Agr., 1965-68, cotton mktg. specialist, 1969-75, chief peanut br., 1976-77, dep. dir., 1977-85, dir., 1985-93; dep. under sec. internat. affairs and commodity programs office of sec. Dept. Agr., Washington, 1993—. Active Patuxent River 4-H Ctr. Sgt. U.S. Army, res. Nat. 4-H fellow. Presbyterian. Avocations: woodworking, tennis. Office: Dept of Agrl Internat Affairs & Commodity Pgm 14th & Independence Ave SW Washington DC 20250-0002

SMITH, DAN F., oil company executive. With Atlantic Richfield Co, Los Angeles, CA, 1967-88; CFO, former v.p., dir. Lyondell Petrochemical Co. Office: Lyondell Petrochemical Co 1221 Mckinney St Houston TX 77010-2003

SMITH, DANIEL CLIFFORD, lawyer; b. Cin., Aug. 9, 1936; s. Clifford John and Vivian Aileen (Stone) S.; m. Carroll Cunningham; children—Edward, Andrew, Scott. B.S., Ariz. State U., 1960; postgrad. George Washington U., 1961-62; J.D., Am. U., 1965. Bar: D.C. 1965, U.S. Ct. Appeals (D.C. cir.) 1966, U.S. Ct. Appeals (Fed. cir.), U.S. Dist. Ct. D.C. 1966, Va. 1967, U.S. Supreme Ct. 1969, U.S. Ct. Appeals (4th cir., 5th cir., 7th cir., 9th cir., 11th cir.), U.S. Ct. Claims, U.S. Ct. Customs and Patent Appeals, U.S. Tax Ct. Assoc. Alpern & Feissner, Washington, 1963-66; atty. FTC, Washington, 1966-70; ptnr. Arent, Fox, Kintner, Plotkin & Kahn, Washington, 1970-93, Canfield & Smith, Washington, 1993—. Pres., dir. Country Pl. Citizens Assn., Inc., 1974-77; bd. dirs. Sea Watch Condominium, Ocean City, Md., 1978—, treas., 1982-86, pres. 1986—; active Supreme Ct. Hist. Soc., Friends Nat. Zoo, Smithsonian Inst. Assocs., Ariz. State Soc. Served with USMC. Mem. D.C. Bar Assn. (dir. 1974-76, chmn. consumer protection com. 1972-74, chmn. D.C. affairs sect. 1976-75), Va. State Bar Assn., ABA (antitrust law sect, FTC com.), Fed. Bar Assn., Assn. Trial Lawyers Am., Direct Selling Assn. (lawyers council), Ariz. State U. Alumni Assn., Delta Theta Phi. Clubs: Rotary (pres. 1987-88), Optimist (pres. 1972-73), Country Glen, Internat. Town and Country (dir. 1969-73), Masons. Contbr. articles to legal jours. Office: Canfield & Smith Fed Bar Bldg 1815 H St NW Ste 1001 Washington DC 20006-3604

SMITH, DANIEL R., bank holding company executive; b. 1934. With First of Am. Bank-Mich., 1955-82, sr. v.p., 1971-77, pres., then pres., chief exec. officer, 1977-82; with First of Am. Bank Corp., Kalamazoo, 1982—, pres., 1982-85, chmn. bd., chief exec. officer, 1985—, also bd. dirs. Capt. USAR, 1955-64. Office: First of Am Bank Corp 211 S Rose St Kalamazoo MI 49007

SMITH, DARRELL WAYNE, metallurgical engineering educator, consultant; b. Long Beach, Calif., July 31, 1937; s. Joseph Sidney and Bethel Irene (Monroe) S.; m. Marilyn Margaret Meese, Dec. 20, 1958 (dec. 1992); children: Mark Kevin, Barbara Dean, Paul Edwin. BS MetE, Mich. Technol. U., 1959; MS in Metallurgy, Case Western Res. U., 1965, PhD, 1969. Process metallurgist Babcock & Wilcox, Beaver Falls, Pa., 1959-62; project engr. GE, Cleve., 1962-68, rsch. metallurgist, 1968-70; prof. metall. engring. Mich. Technol. U., Houghton, 1970—; pres. SCS Assocs. Inc., Houghton, 1984—; bd. dirs. Peninsula Copper Industries, Hubbell, Mich., 1983—; metall. engring. cons. various corps. and nat. labs. Contbr. article to profl. jours. Mem. ASM Internat. (bd. dirs. 1995—), Am. Powder Metall. Inst. (bd. dirs. 1992—). Republican. Avocations: flying, sport fishing, piano playing. Home: Half Moon Beach RR 2 Box 462 Chassell MI 49916 Office: Mich Technol U Dept Metall Engring Houghton MI 49931

SMITH, DARWIN EATNA, lawyer, retired manufacturing executive; b. Garrett, Ind., Apr. 16, 1926; s. K. Bryant and Hazel (Sherman) S.; m. Lois Claire Archbold, Aug. 19, 1950; children: Steven, Pamela, Valerie, Blair. BS in Bus. with distinction, Ind. U., 1950; LLB cum laude, Harvard U., 1955. Bar: Ill. 1955. Assoc. atty. Sidley, Austin, Burgess & Smith, Chgo., 1955-58; with Kimberly-Clark Corp., Neenah, Wis., 1958-91, gen. atty., 1960-91, v.p.,

1962-67, v.p. fin. and law, 1967-70, pres., 1970-91, chmn., CEO, 1971-91, ret., 1991. Served with AUS, 1944-46.

SMITH, DATUS CLIFFORD, JR., former foundation executive, publisher; b. Jackson, Mich., May 3, 1907; s. Datus Clifford and Marion (Houston) S.; m. Dorothy Hunt, Aug. 29, 1931 (dec. 1973); children: Sandra, Karen. B.S., Princeton U., 1929, M.A. (hon.), 1958. Grad. mgr. student employment Princeton U., 1929-30; editor Princeton Alumni Weekly, 1931-40; editor Princeton U. Press, 1941-53, dir. sec., 1942-53; assoc. prof. Princeton U., 1943-47, prof., 1947-53; chmn. Franklin Book Programs, 1975-79; v.p. JDR 3d Fund, 1967-73; asso. John D. Rockefeller 3d, 1967-73; coordinator Japan philanthropy project Council on Founds., 1974-75; cons. Asia Soc., Nat. Endowment for Humanities, Hazen Found., Am. Council Learned Socs., Assn. Am. Pubs., Indo-U.S. Subcom. Edn. and Culture; past chmn. Found. Internat. Group; Bowker lectr. N.Y. Pub. Library, 1958; adv. council Ctr. for Book, Library of Congress; past pres. Assn. Am. Univ. Presses; dir. Am. Book Pub. Council; Past chmn. editorial com. Pub. Opinion Quar.; vis. com. Harvard Press; Nat. Book Com.; trustee Center Applied Linguistics, Japan Center Internat. Exchange, Mason Early Edn. Found.; hon. life trustee Asia Soc., 1983—; trustee JDR 3d Fund, Haskins Labs.; pres. U.S. Bd. on Books for Young People, 1981-84. Author: Land and People of Indonesia, 1961, 83, Guide to Book Publishing, 1966, 68, 94, Economics of Book Publishing in Developing Countries, 1976; contbr. to Fgn. Affairs, Atlantic Monthly, Scholarly Pub., Internat. Ency. Book Pub., Ency. Asian History; project dir., Publishers Weekly; mng. editor Meadow Lark. Trustee, pres. U.S. Com. for UNICEF, 1977-79, vice chmn., 1979-81; past mem. U.S. nat. commn. UNESCO; sec. Meadow Lakes Forum; mem. Dem. County com., Mercer County. Decorated Order of Homayoun Iran; recipient Disting. Svc. award Assn. Am. Univ. Presses, 1975, Princeton in Asia award 1989, Helenka Pantaleoni award UNICEF, 1989, Asalaksen Internat. Publ. award, 1991; named to Pub. Hall of Fame, 1985. Mem. PEN, Am. Ctr. Clubs: Princeton, Rockefeller Center, Dutch Treat (N.Y.C.). Home: 708 Meadow Lks Hightstown NJ 08520 Office: US Com for UNICEF 331 E 38th St New York NY 10016-2772

SMITH, DAVID A., real estate developer; b. 1944. BA, Oreg. State U., 1968, MBA, 1969. With So. Pacific Corp., San Francisco, 1969-84, Santa Fe Pacific Corp., Schaumburg, Ill., 1984-89; with Catellus Devel. Corp., San Francisco, 1989—, now sr. v.p. Office: Catellus Development Corp 201 Mission St # 30 San Francisco CA 94105-1831*

SMITH, DAVID BRUCE, lawyer; b. Moline, Ill., May 9, 1948; s. Neal Schriever and Barbara Jean (Harris) S.; m. Yvonne Bess Smith, May 27, 1972; children: Neal, Stephanie. BSME, U. Iowa, 1970; JD, U. Tex., 1973. Bar: Tex. 1973, Wis. 1975. Patent examiner U.S. Patent and Trademark Office, Washington, 1973-74; atty. Nilles & Kirby S.C., Milw., 1974-76, Globe-Union, Inc., Milw., 1976-77, Michael Best & Friedrich, Milw., 1978—. Pres. Milw. County coun. Boy Scouts Am., Milw., 1994-95. Mem. ABA, State Bar Wis., Wis. Intellectual Property Law Assn., Ozarkee Country Club, Milw. Club. Office: Michael Best & Friedrich 100 E Wisconsin Ave Milwaukee WI 53202-4107

SMITH, DAVID BROOKMAN, federal judge; b. 1951. BA, Franklin and Marshall Coll., 1973; JD, Dickinson Sch. Law, 1976. Pvt. practice Jubelirer, Carothers, Krier, Halpern & Smith, Altoona, Pa., 1976-84; judge Ct. Common Pleas of Blair County, Pa., 1984-88, U.S. Dist. Ct. (w. dist.) Pa., 1988—; asst. dist. atty. Blair County, part-time, 1981-83, dist. atty., part-time, 1983-84; instr. Pa. State U., Altoona campus, 1977-87, St. Francis Coll., 1986—. Trustee St. Francis Coll. Mem. Pa. Bar Assn., Am. Judicature Soc., Pa. Soc., Amen Corner, Blair County Game, Fish and Forestry Assn., Masons, Pi Gamma Mu. Office: US Courthouse 7th And Grant St Rm 936 Pittsburgh PA 15219

SMITH, DAVID C., dean; b. LaPorte, Ind., June 10, 1932; m. Betty Irene Rule; children: Pauline, Earl. BA, No. Iowa U., 1954, MA, 1958; PhD, Northwestern U., 1966. Cert. sch. adminstrn., psychology, ednl. psychology. Tchr., prin. Cresco (Iowa) Pub. Schs., 1954-56; prin. Decorah (Iowa) Community Sch. Dist., 1957-58, dir. elem. edn., 1958-60; tchr. child growth Luther Coll., Decorah, 1960 summer; assoc. prof. Coll. Edn. Mich. State U., East Lansing, 1966-70; assoc. dean Coll. Edn. No. Ill. U., DeKalb, 1970-72; area coord. Coll. Edn. U. Ark., Fayetteville, 1972-76; dean sch. edn. U. Mont., Missoula, 1976-78; dean Coll. Edn. U. Fla., Gainesville, 1978—; cons. Assn. Am. Schs., Sao Paulo, Brazil, 1984, Am. Community Sch., Aman, Jordan, 1987, Colegio Maya, Guatemala City, Guatemala, 1988; chmn. Edn. Standards Commn. State of Fla., 1980-88. Editor: Essential Knowledge for Beginning Educators, 1983; assoc. editor Jour. of Tchr. Edn., 1990; contbr. articles to profl. jours. Mem. Gov.'s Profl. Tchr. Task Force, State of Fla., 1985, Comprehensive System of Personnel Devel. Oversight Com., State of Fla., 1986; resolution of commendation Fla. Cabinet for Leadership and Svc., State of Fla., 1988. Recipient Alumni Achievement award U. No. Iowa, Cedar Falls, 1984, Resolution of Commendation award Fla. Cabinet for Leadership and Svc., State of Fla., 1988, Recognition award Fla. Coun. of Economic Edn., 1989. Mem. Assn. for Advancement of Internat. Edn. (bd. dirs. 1979—), Fla. Assn. of Colls. for Tchr. Edn. (pres. 1981, 92), Am. Assn of Colls. for Tchr. Edn. (pres. 1984, 78—), Nat. Assn. of Sec. Sch. Prins. (adv. bd. dirs., com. sch.-coll. rels. 1983-86), Am. Coun. on Edn. (bd. dirs. 1985), Nat. Coun. for Accreditation of Tchr. Edn. (bd. examiners 1988-91), So. Regional Consortium of Colls. of Edn. (pres.-elect 1990, pres. 1991, adv. coun. state reps., 1993, Edward C. Pomeroy Outstanding Contbn. to Edn. award 1992, Edn. Standards Commn. 1993—), Profl. Archers Assn. Home: 8612 SW 1st Pl Gainesville FL 32607-1486 Office: U Fla Coll of Edn 140 Norman Hall Gainesville FL 32611

SMITH, DAVID CALLAWAY, retired accounting firm executive; b. Dallas, Aug. 28, 1941; s. Stanley W. and Julia M. (Callaway) S.; m. Marijane Dekema, May 5, 1961; children: Stephanie, Scott. BBA, Western Mich. U., 1964. Profl. staff, mgr. Peat Marwick Mitchell & Co., Chgo., 1964-71, ptnr., 1971-78; ptnr. in charge tax dept. Peat Marwick Mitchell & Co., Houston, 1978-87; vice-chmn. tax dept. KPMG Peat Marwick, N.Y.C., 1987-93; ret., 1993. Bd. govs. Citizen Scholarship Found. Am. Mem. AICPA, N.Y. State Soc. CPA's, Econ. Club of N.Y. Republican. Presbyterian. Avocations: reading, golf, swimming, amateur radio.

SMITH, DAVID CLARK, research scientist; b. Owensboro, Ky., Feb. 8, 1937; s. Robert Emmitt and Mary Margaret (Flaherty) S.; m. Kathleen Sue Kohne, June 27, 1964; children—Christine, Jennifer, Paula. B.S.M.E., U. Dayton, 1959; M.S., Northwestern U., 1961, Ph.D., 1966; postgrad. 1964. Research scientist United Technologies Research Ctr., East Hartford, Conn., 1965-67, sr. research scientist, 1967-68, prin. scientist, 1968-80, mgr. exptl. optics, 1980-82, mgr. optical physics, 1982-91, cons. DCS Assoc., 1992—, Conn. Tech. Assocs., 1992—. Author: (with G. Bekefi) Principles of Laser Plasmas, 1976. Contbr. articles to profl. jours. Patentee in field. Chmn. Youth and Family Resource Ctr. Commn., 1979-84; bd. dirs. Glastonbury A Better Chance, Conn., 1970-78; mem. Glastonbury Energy Com., 1979-83; tutor YMCA Read to Success Literacy; vol. Habitat for Humanity. Named Man of Yr., Friends of Glastonbury Youth, 1984; recipient Outstanding Service award, 1985, Glastonbury, Conn., United Technologies Outstanding Service award., 1987. Mem. IEEE, Am. Phys. Soc., AAAS, Sigma Xi. Democrat. Roman Catholic. Avocations: tennis; sailing. Home: 44 Candlelight Dr Glastonbury CT 06033-2537 Office: DCS Assoc PO Box 157 East Glastonbury CT 06025

SMITH, DAVID EDMUND, geophysicist; b. Brentford, Eng., Nov. 3, 1934; came to U.S., 1968; s. Alfred Edmund and Violet (Hicks) S.; m. Veronica Mary Sparnon, July 1, 1961; children: Keri Elizabeth, Alistair David, Jeremy Edmund, Meredith Louise. B.Sc. in Math, U. Durham (Eng.), 1958; M.Sc. in Math, U. London, 1962, Ph.D. in Satellite Geodesy, 1966. Sci. officer Radio and Space Research Sta., Slough, Eng., 1958-68; sr. scientist Wolf Research and Devel. Corp., Riverdale, Md., 1968-69; staff scientist NASA Goddard Space Flight Ctr., Greenbelt, Md., 1969-71, head geodynamics br., 1971-87, assoc. chief Lab. for Terrestrial Physics, 1987-90, chief Lab. for Terrestrial Physics, 1990—, prin. investigator Mars Observer Project; scientist Crustal Dynamics Project NASA Goddard Space Flight Center, Greenbelt, Md., 1980—; mem. commn. on satellite geodesy Internat. Union Geodesy and Geophysics; mem. study groups on fundamental constants, atmospheric circulation and excitation of the earth's rotation, reference systems for geodesy Internat. Assn. Geodesy; mem. working group on earth rotation Internat. Astron. Union, also com. on space research, tech. panel on dynamics of artificial satellites and space probes, com. for coordination of space tech. for geodynamics. Contbr. numerous articles to profl. publs. Recipient Exceptional Sci. Achievement medal NASA, 1974, John C. Lindsay Meml. award Goddard Space Flight Ctr., 1978; Am. Geophys. Union fellow, 1985. Fellow Am. Geophys. Union (pres. geodesy sect. 1988), Royal Astron. Soc. Home: 8000 Lions Crest Way Laytonsville MD 20879-5637 Office: Goddard Space Flight Ctr Lab for Terrestrial Physics Code 920 Greenbelt MD 20771*

SMITH, DAVID ELVIN, physician; b. Bakersfield, Calif., Feb. 7, 1939; s. Elvin W. and Dorothy (McGinnis) S.; m. Millicent Buxton; children: Julia, Suzanne, Christopher Buxton-Smith, Sabree Hill. Intern San Francisco Gen. Hosp., 1965; fellow pharmacology and toxicology U. Calif., San Francisco, 1965-67, assoc. clin. prof. occupational medicine, clin. toxicology, 1967—, dir. psychopharmacology study group, 1966-70; practice medicine specializing in toxicology and addiction San Francisco, 1965—; physician Presbyn. Alcoholic Clinic, 1965-67, Contra Cost Alcoholic Clinic, 1965-67; dir. alcohol and drug abuse screening unit San Francisco Gen. Hosp., 2967-68; co-dir. Calif drug abuse info. project U. Calif Med. Ctr., 1967-72; founder, med. dir. Haight-Ashbury Free Med. Clinic, San Francisco, 1967—; research dir. Merritt Peralta Chem. Dependency Hosp., Oakland, Calif., 1984—; chmn. Nat. Drug Abuse Conf., 1977; mem. Calif. Gov's. Commn. on Narcotics and Drug Abuse, 1977—; nat. health adviser to former U.S. Pres. Jimmy Carter; mem. Pres. Clinton's Health Care Task Force on Addiction and Nat. Health Reform, 1993; dir. Benzodiazepine Research and Tng. Project, Substance Abuse and Sexual Concerns Project, PCP Research and Tng. Project; cons. numerous fed. drug abuse agys. Author: Love Needs Care, 1970, The New Social Drug: Cultural, Medical and Legal Perspectives on Marijuana, 1971, The Free Clinic: Community Approaches to Health Care and Drug Abuse, 1971, Treating the Cocaine Abuser, 1985, The Benzodiazepines: Current Standard Medical Practice, 1986, Physicians' Guide to Drug Abuse, 1987; co-author: It's So Good, Don't Even Try it Once: Heroin in Perspective, 1972, Uppers and Downers, 1973, Drugs in the Classroom, 1973, Barbiturate Use and Abuse, 1977, A Multicultural View of Drug Abuse, 1978, Amphetamine Use, Misuse and Abuse, 1979, PCP: Problems and Prevention, 1981, Sexological Aspects of Substance Use and Abuse, Treatment of the Cocaine Abuser, 1985, The Haight Ashbury Free Medical Clinic: Still Free After all these Years, Drug Free: Alternatives to Drug Abuse, 1987, Treatment of Opiate Dependence, Designer Drugs, 1988, Treatment of Cocaine Dependence, 1988, Treatment of Opiate Dependence, 1988, The New Drugs, 1989, Crack and Ice in the era of Smokeable Drugs, 1992, others; also drug edn. films; founder, editor Jour. Psychedelic Drugs (now Jour. Psychoactive Drugs), 1967—; contbr. over 100 articles to profl. jours. Pres. Youth Projects, Inc.; founder, chmn. bd., pres. Nat. Free Clin. Council, 1968-72. Recipient Rsch. award Borden Found., 1964, AMA Rsch. award, 1966, Cmty. Svc. award U. Calif San Francisco, 1974, Calif. State Drug Abuse Treatment award, 1984, Vernelle Fox Drug Abuse Treatment award, 1985, UCLA Sidney Cohen Addiction Medicine award, 1989, medal of honor U. Calif. San Diego Med. Ctr., 1995. Mem. AMA (alt. del.), Calif. Med. Assn. (alt. del.), Am. Pub. Health Assn., Calif. Soc. on Addiction Medicine (pres., bd. dirs.), Phi Beta Kappa, Sigma Xi. Methodist. Home: 289 Frederick St San Francisco CA 94117-4051 Office: 409 Clayton St San Francisco CA 94117-1911

SMITH, DAVID ENGLISH, physician, educator; b. San Francisco, June 9, 1920; s. David English and Myrtle (Goodin) S.; m. Margaret Elizabeth Bronson, June 9, 1948; children: Ann English Smith Elbert, David Bronson, Mary Margaret. A.B., Central Coll. Mo., 1941; M.D. cum laude, Washington U. St. Louis, 1944. Intern, resident pathology Barnes Hosp., St. Louis, 1944-46; instr. pathology Washington U. Med. Sch., 1948-51, asst. prof., 1951-54, asst. head dept., 1953-54, assoc. prof., 1954-55; prof. pathology U. Va. Sch. Medicine, 1955-73, chmn. dept., 1958-73; dir. div. U. Va. Sch. Medicine (Cancer Studies), 1972-73; prof. pathology Northwestern U. Sch. Medicine, 1974-75, U. Pa. Sch. Medicine, 1976-80; prof. pathology Tulane U. Sch. Medicine, 1980-85, assoc. dean, 1980-85; prof. pathology U. Tex. Med. Br., 1986—; assoc. dir. Am. Bd. Med. Spltys., 1974-75; v.p.; sec., dir. undergrad. evaluation Nat. Bd. Med. Examiners, 1975-80; trustee Am. Bd. Pathology, 1966-73, v.p., 1973; mem. Nat. Bd. Med. Examiners, chmn. pathology test com., 1966-72; chmn. test com. Ednl. Commn. for Fgn. Med. Grads., 1979-91. Editor: Survey of Pathology in Medicine and Surgery, 1966-70; contbr. articles to profl. publs. Pres. Va. div. Am. Cancer Soc., 1967-69. Served from 1st lt. to capt. M.C. AUS, 1946-48. Mem. Va. Soc. Pathology (pres. 1960), Am. Assn. Pathologists, Internat. Acad. Pathology (council 1956-59, pres. 1964-65), Am. Soc. Clin. Pathologists (co-dir. self assessment program 1970-75), AMA, Am. Assn. Neuropathologists, AAAS, Sigma Xi, Alpha Omega Alpha, Phi Beta Pi, Alpha Epsilon Delta. Home: 59 Colony Park Cir Galveston TX 77551-1737

SMITH, DAVID EUGENE, business administration educator; b. Boise, Idaho, Dec. 14, 1941; s. Roy Arthur and Anna Margaret (Fries) S.; m. Patricia Stroy, Aug. 4, 1973; 1 child, Zachary Adam. BA in Applied Stats., San Francisco State Coll., 1964, MS in Mgmt. Sci., 1966; MBA, PhD in Bus. Adminstrn., U. Santa Clara, 1969. Asst. to dir. mgmt ctr. Grad. Sch. Bus., U. Santa Clara, Calif., 1966-69, lectr. mktg., 1968; asst. prof. bus. adminstrn. Mktg./Quantitative Studies Dept., San Jose State U., Calif., 1969-71, assoc. prof. bus. adminstrn., 1971-76, prof. bus. adminstrn., 1976—, chmn. dept., 1986-89. Author: Quantitative Business Analysis, 1977, Internat. Edit., 1979, 1982; contbr. articles to profl. jours. Mem. Inst. Mgmt. Sci., Ops. Research Soc. Am., Decision Scis. Inst., Phi Kappa Phi, Beta Gamma Sigma. Republican. Avocations: tennis, fishing, skiing. Home: 22448 Tim Tam Ct Los Gatos CA 95030-8521 Office: San Jose State U Mktg/MIS/Decision Scis One Washington Sq San Jose CA 95192

SMITH, DAVID GILBERT, political science educator; b. Norman, Okla., Oct. 10, 1926; s. Gilbert Harmer and Virginia (Haizlip) S.; m. Carlota Shipman (div. 1967); m. 2d, Eleanor Cowan; children: Alison Claire, Joel Anthony; stepchildren: Laura Gergen, Stan Gergen. BA, U. Okla., 1948, MA, 1950; PhD, Johns Hopkins U., 1953. Instr. polit. sci. Swarthmore (Pa.) Coll., 1953-55, asst. prof. polit. sci., 1957, prof., 1967—, Centennial prof., 1977-87, Richter prof. polit. sci., 1987-92, chmn., 1970-87, prof. emeritus, 1992—; asst. prof. polit. sci. Stanford U., Palo Alto, Calif., 1956-57; cons. HEW, NAS, NRC, Ford Found. Author: (with J. Roland Pennock) Political Science: An Introduction, 1965, The Convention and the Constitution, 1965, 2d edit., 1987, Paying for Medicare, 1992; also articles. Chmn. ACLU, Delaware County, Pa., 1965-70, Health and Welfare Coun., Delaware County, 1970-73; v.p. Delaware Valley HMO, Concordville, Pa., 1978-81; pres. Media (Pa.) Child Guidance, 1980-82; bd. dirs. Friends Life Care at Home, 1990—. Sgt. U.S. Army, 1945-46. Mem. Am. Soc. for Polit. and Legal Philosophy, Phi Beta Kappa. Democrat. Methodist. Home: 448 S Jackson St Media PA 19063

SMITH, DAVID JEDDIE, American literature educator; b. Portsmouth, Va., Dec. 19, 1942; s. Ralph Gerald and Catherine Mary (Cornwell) S.; m. Deloras Mae Weaver, Mar. 31, 1966; children: David Jeddie, Lael Cornwell, Mary Catherine. BA, U. Va., 1965; MA, So. Ill. U., 1969; PhD, Ohio U., 1976. Staff creative writing Bennington (Vt.) Coll. summer prog., 1980-87; instr. English We. Mich. U., Kalamazoo, 1973-74; asst. prof. English Cottey Coll., Nevada, Mo., 1974-75; assoc. prof. English U. Utah, Salt Lake City, 1976-80; vis. prof. English SUNY, Binghamton, 1980-81; assoc. prof. English U. Fla., Gainesville, 1981-82; prof. Am. it. U. Commonwealth U., Richmond, 1982-89; prof. Am. Lit. La. State U., 1990—; lectr. in field; cons. in field. Author: Local Assays, 1985, The Roundhouse Voices: Selected and New Poems, 1985, The Morrow Anthology of Younger American Poets, 1985, Gray Soldiers, 1984, Southern Delights, 1984, In the House of the Judge, 1983, The Pure Clear Word: Essays on the Poetry of James Wright, 1982, Onliness, 1981, Homage to Edgar Allan Poe, 1981, Cuba Night, 1990, Night Pleasures: New and Selected Poems, 1992, Farers: Poems, 1995, and others; contbr. articles to profl. jours.; editor New Virginia Rev., 1987, The Morrow Anthology of Younger American Poets, 1985, The Back Door: A Poetry Mag., Southern Rev., 1990. Recipient Va. Prize in Poetry, 1988, Prairie Schooner poetry prize, 1980, Portland Rev. poetry prize, 1979, Sou'wester poetry prize, 1973, others; Guggenheim fellow, 1981, Lyndhurst fellow, 1987, 88, 89, others. Mem. MLA, Poetry Soc. Am., Poetry Soc. Va., PEN, Nat. Book Critics Cir., Assoc. Writing Progs., Writers in Va. (bd.

dirs.), So. Modern Lang. Assn., Modern Lang. Assn., Acad. Am. Poets. Office: La State U So Rev 43 Allen Hall Baton Rouge LA 70803

SMITH, DAVID JOHN, physicist, educator; b. Melbourne, Australia, Oct. 10, 1948; arrived in U.S., 1984; s. Arthur and Agnes Frances S.; m. Gwenneth Paula Bland, Sept. 18, 1971 (div. 1992); children: Heather F., Marion J. BSc with honors, U. Melbourne, Australia, 1970, PhD, 1978, DSc, 1988. Post-doctoral asst. Cavendish Lab. U. Cambridge, Eng., 1976-78, sr. rsch. assoc., 1979-84; assoc. prof. Ariz. State U., Tempe, 1984-87, prof., 1987—; dir. Cambridge U. High Resolutin Electron Microscope, 1979-84, NSF Ctr. for High Resolution Electron Microscopy, Tempe, 1991—. Author 7 chpts. in books; editor 10 conf. procs.; contbr. over 200 articles to profl. jours. Recipient Faculty Achievement award Burlington Resources Found., 1990. Fellow Inst. Physics (U.K., Charles Vernon Boys prize 1985); mem. Royal Micros. Soc. (U.K.), Am. Phys. Soc., Material Rsch. Soc., Microscopy Soc. Am. Office: Ariz State U Ctr Solid State Sci Tempe AZ 85287

SMITH, DAVID JOHN, JR., plastic surgeon; b. Indpls., Feb. 20, 1947; s. David John and Carolyn (Culp) S.; m. Nancy Loonsten, June 7, 1975; children: Matthew, Peter, Hadley. BA, Wesleyan U., 1969; MD, Ind. U., 1973. Diplomate Am. Bd. Plastic Surgery. Resident Emory U.-Grady Hosp., Atlanta, 1973-78; resident Ind. U. Med. Ctr., Indpls., 1978-80; Christine Kleinert fellow in hand surgery, 1979; asst. prof. surgery Ind. U. Sch. Medicine, 1980-84; assoc. prof. surgery Wayne State U. Sch. Medicine, 1984-87; assoc. prof. plastic surgery, surgery sect. head U. Mich. Med. Ctr., Ann Arbor, 1987-92, prof. surgery sect. head, 1992—; cons. Mich. Peer Rev. Orgn., 1988—; vice-chmn. Residency Rev. Com. for Plastic Surgery, 1994. Mem. editl. bd. Jour. of Surg. Rsch., 1989—, Annals of Plastic Surgery, 1992—, assoc. editor, 1994, Yearbook of Hand Surgery, 1989—; guest reviewer Surgery, 1988—, Plastic and Reconstructive Surgery, 1988—; contbr. numerous articles to profl. jours. Recipient numerous grants. Fellow ACS (many coms.), Soc. of Univ. Surgeons, Am. Assn. Plastic Surgeons, Am. Surg. Assn., Am. Bd. Plastic Surgeons, Assn. for Acad. Surgery, Western Surg. Assn., Cen. Surg. Assn., Am. Soc. for Surgery of the Hand, Am. Soc. of Plastic and Reconstructive Surgeons, Plastic Surgery Ednl. Found. (bd. dirs. 1988—, treas. 1994, v.p., other coms.), Plastic Surgery Rsch. Coun., Am. Burn Assn., Am. Burn Life Support Nat. Faculty, Am. Assn. for Hand Surgeons (pres. 1994). Home: 769 Heatherway St Ann Arbor MI 48104-2731 Office: U Mich Med Ctr 2130 Taubman Health Ctr 1500 E Medical Center Dr Ann Arbor MI 48109-0999

SMITH, DAVID KING, newspaper publishing executive; b. L.A., Oct. 12, 1963; s. Michael David and Dorothy Margaret (Mason) S.; m. Kirstin Andrea Gustafson, June 20, 1991; 1 child, Zachary David Smith. BA, UCLA, 1987. Salesperson, advt. exec. Calif. Newspaper Svc., 1989-91; leadership cons. Phi Gamma Delta Internat. Fraternity, Lexington, Ky. 1987-89. Republican. Episcopalian. Avocations: fishing, tennis, motivational tapes, reading, child-rearing. Office: Daily Journal Co PO Box 54026 915 E 1st St Los Angeles CA 90012-4050

SMITH, DAVID LEE, newspaper editor; b. Shelby, Ohio, Apr. 4, 1939; s. Ferris Francis and Rita Ann (Metzger) S.; m. Betty Stewart Walker, Sept. 10, 1960; children: Stacie Lynn, Stefanie Linn, David Lee, II (dec.). Student, Pontifical Coll. Josephinum, Worthington, Ohio, 1953-56, Ohio State U., Mansfield, 1961. Sports writer Mansfield News-Jour., 1960-61; sports editor Ashland (Ohio) Times-Gazette, 1961-63, Miami (Fla.) News, 1963-67, Ft. Lauderdale (Fla.) News, 1967-70, Boston Globe, 1970-78, Washington Star, 1978-81; dep. mng. editor, exec. sports editor Dallas Morning News, 1981—; condr. seminars. Bd. dirs. Doak Walker Nat. Running Back Award, The Dallas Athletic Club, GTE-SMU Athletic Forum. Served with USMC, 1957-60. Mem. AP Sports Editors Assn. (1st pres. 1974-75), Baseball Writers Assn. (Red Smith award for major contbns. to sports journalism 1990), Football Writers Assn., Golf Writers Assn., Dallas Athletic Club (pres.). Roman Catholic. Home: 5723 Berkshire Ln Dallas TX 75209-2401 Office: Dallas Morning News Communications Center Dallas TX 75265

SMITH, DAVID MARTYN, forestry educator; b. Bryan, Tex., Mar. 10, 1921; s. John Blackmer and Doris (Clark) S.; m. Catherine Van Aken, June 16, 1951; children: Ellen, Nancy. B.S., U. R.I., 1941; postgrad., NYU, 1942; M.F., Yale U., 1946, Ph.D., 1950; D.Sc. (hon.), Bates Coll., 1986, U. R.I., 1993. Instr. Sch. Forestry and Environ. Studies, Yale U., 1946-47, 48-51, asst. prof., 1951-57, asst. dean, 1953-58, assoc. prof., 1957-63; prof. Yale U., 1963-90, Morris K. Jesup prof. silviculture, 1967-90, Morris K. Jesup prof. emeritus, 1990—; cons. Baskahegan Co.; vis. prof. U. Munich, Germany, 1981; silviculture cons. Pres.'s Adv. Panel on Timber and Environ., 1972-73; mem. Conn. Forestry Practices Bd., 1991—; pres., bd. dirs. Connwood Foresters, Inc. Author: Practice of Silviculture, 1962, 86. Capt. Weather Svc., USAAF, 1942-45. Fellow Soc. Am. Foresters (Disting. Svc. New Eng. sect. award 1969, 93); mem. Am. Forestry Assn. (Disting. Svc. award 1990), Nat. Acad. Forest Scis. Mex. (corr.), Ecol. Soc. Am., Conn. Forest and Park Assn. (dir.), Sigma Xi, Phi Kappa Phi. Mem. United Ch. of Christ. Home: 55 Woodlawn St Hamden CT 06517-1338 Office: 360 Prospect St New Haven CT 06511-2104

SMITH, DAVID RYAN, museum director; b. Ft. Worth, Apr. 23, 1952; s. David Earnest and Helen Virginia (Armstrong) S.; m. Peggy Lou Bennett, Mar. 9, 1974; children: Jennifer Renee, Kenneth Ryan. BS in Am. Studies, Harding U., 1974; MA in History, U. Tex., 1979. Dir. Star of the Republic Mus., Washington, Tex., 1977-87, Panhandle-Plains Hist. Mus., Canyon, Tex., 1987-91; exec. dir. Tex. Energy Mus., Beaumont, Tex., 1992—; field reviewer Inst. Mus. Svcs., Wash., 1985—. Chmn. Tex. Antiquities Com., 1990-92; mem. Summerlee Commn. on Tex. History, 1989-92. Bd. dirs. Edison Pla. Mus., Beaumont; mem. community adv. coun., Mobil refinery chmn. Beaumont History Conf. Named Outstanding Alumnus Harding U., 1987. Mem. Am. Assn. Mus. (surveyor mus. assessment program), Tex. State Hist. Assn., Tex. Assn. Mus. (coun. 1979-81, 84-86), Cen. Tex. Mus. Assn. (chmn. 1979-81, 84-86), S.E. Tex. Mus. Assn. (treas. 1995—), Rotary. Mem. Ch. of Christ. Avocations: backpacking, canoeing, tennis, running. Home: 9265 Meadowbend Dr Beaumont TX 77706 Office: Tex Energy Mus 600 Main St Beaumont TX 77701

SMITH, DAVID SHIVERICK, lawyer, former ambassador; b. Omaha, Jan. 25, 1918; s. Floyd Monroe and Anna (Shiverick) S.; m. June Noble, Dec. 8, 1945 (div. 1968); children:Noble, David Shiverick, Jeremy T., Bradford D.; m. Mary Edson, Feb. 14, 1972. Degre Superieur, Sorbonne, Paris, 1938; B.A. magna cum laude, Dartmouth Coll., 1939; J.D., Columbia U., 1942. Bar: N.Y. 1942, Conn. 1950, D.C. 1954. Assoc. Breed, Abbott & Morgan, N.Y.C., 1946-48; legal dept. ABC, N.Y.C., 1948-50; partner Chapman, Bryson, Walsh & O'Connell, N.Y.C. and Washington, 1950-54; spl. asst. to undersec. Dept. State, Washington, 1954; asst. sec. Air Force, 1954-59; dir. internat. fellows program Columbia U., 1959-75, coordinator internat. studies, 1960-75, asso. dean sch. internat. affairs, 1960-74; cons. AEC, 1959-60; partner Baker & McKenzie (and predecessor), N.Y.C. and Washington, 1960-75, Martin & Smith (and predecessors), Washington, 1975-76, 77-88; ambassador to Sweden, 1976-77; dir. United Svcs. Life Ins. Corp., Internat. Bank, USLICO Corp., Liberian Svcs., Inc.; mem. Coun. Fgn. Rels.; dir. Fgn. Policy Assn.; mem. adv. coun. Sch. Advanced Intenat. Studies, Johns Hopkins U., 1962—; pres., dir. Ctr. for Inter-Am. Rels., N.Y.C., 1969-74. Adv. and contbg. editor: Jour. Internat. Affairs, 1960-74; editor: The Next Asia, 1969, Prospects for Latin America, 1970, Concerns in World Affairs, 1973, From War to Peace, 1974. Chmn. bd. George Olmsted Found., 1977—; active in past various charitable orgns. Lt. USNR, 1942-54; PTO; col. USAFR, 1955-75. Decorated Purple Heart. Mem. ABA, Am. Soc. Internat. Law, Am. Fgn. Law Assn., N.Y. State Bar Assn., Conn. Bar Assn., Fed. Bar Assn. (v.p. for N.Y., N.J. and Conn.), Pilgrims of U.S, France-Am. Soc., English Speaking Union, Asia Soc., Coun. on Foreign Rels., Hudson Inst., Washington Inst. Fgn. Affairs, Coun. Fgn. Rels., Coun. Am. Ambs. (bd. dirs., sec.), Soc. Mayflower Descs., Brook Club (N.Y.C.), Met. Club (Washington), Chevy Chase Club, Bathing Corp. of Southampton (N.Y.), Meadow Club (Southampton), Bath and Tennis Club, Everglades Club (Palm Beach), The Crocodiles, Old Guard Soc. Palm Beach Golfers, Phi Beta Kappa. Home: 525 S Flagler Dr Apt 20-c West Palm Beach FL 33401-5925

SMITH, DAVID THORNTON, lawyer, educator; b. Pawtucket, R.I., Dec. 11, 1935; s. Herbert Jeffers and Harriet Amelia (Thornton) S.; m. Sandra

June Gustavson, Dec. 20, 1958; children—David T., Douglas A., Daniel H. B.A., Yale U., 1957; J.D. cum laude, Boston U., 1960. Bar: Mass. 1961, U.S. Supreme Ct. 1964. Instr. law Ind. U., Bloomington, 1960-62; asst. prof. law Duquesne U., Pitts., 1962-63, Case Western Res. U., Cleve., 1963-65; asso. prof. Case Western Res. U., 1965-68; asso. prof. law U. Fla., Gainesville, 1968-69; prof. U. Fla., 1969—; lectr. Fla. Bankers Assn., Fla. Trust Sch., 1973—. Author: (with M. Sussman and J. Cates) The Family and Inheritance, 1970, Florida Probate Code Manual, 1975. Mem. Am. Bar Assn., Mass. Bar Assn., Am. Law Inst., Am. Judicature Soc., AAUP (past pres. U. Fla. chpt.), Fla. Blue Key, Selden Soc., Omicron Delta Kappa, Phi Alpha Delta. Lutheran. Home: 6405 NW 18th Ave Gainesville FL 32605-3209 Office: Univ Fla Coll Of Law Gainesville FL 32611

SMITH, DAVID TODD, publishing company executive; b. Stamford, Conn., Nov. 19, 1953; arrived in Can., 1956; m. Margaret Beryl Starke, Dec. 30, 1978; children: Erik Joseph, Maximilian Peter Starke. BBA in Fin. and Econs., Wilfrid Laurier U., Waterloo, Ont., Can., 1976; MBA in Fin., McMaster U., Hamilton, Ont., 1978. Cert. gen. acct., Ont. Fin. analyst Economical Mut. Ins. Co., Kitchener, Ont., 1976-78; portfolio mgr. Mcht. Trust Co., Toronto, Ont., 1978-80; treasury officer Harlequin Enterprises Ltd., Toronto, 1980-82, asst. treas., 1982-89; treas. Torstar Corp., Toronto, 1989—. Office: Torstar Corp, 1 Yonge St, Toronto, ON Canada M5E 1P9

SMITH, DAVID WALDO EDWARD, pathology educator, physician; b. Fargo, N.D., Apr. 3, 1934; s. Waldo Edward and Martha (Althaus) S.; m. Diane Leigh Walker, June 18, 1960. BA, Swarthmore Coll., 1956; MD, Yale U., 1960. Intern, asst. resident, research fellow pathology Yale U. Med. Sch., 1960-62; research assoc. lab. molecular biology Nat. Inst. Arthritis and Metabolic Diseases, 1962-64, investigator lab. exptl. pathology, 1964-67; assoc. prof. pathology and microbiology Ind. U. Med. Sch., 1967-69; prof. pathology Northwestern U. Med. Sch., 1969—, dir. Ctr. on Aging, 1988—; Guest investigator Internat. Lab. Genetics and Biophysics, Naples, Italy, 1969; mem. ad hoc biochemistry study sect. NIH, 1974-75, mem. pathobiol. chemistry study sect., 1975-79, cons., 1982; sabbatical leave NIH, 1986-87; chmn. NIH Conf. on Gender and Longevity: Why Do Women Live Longer Than Men?, 1987. Author: Human Longevity, 1993, also research papers, chpts. in books.; editorial bd. Yale Jour. Biology and Medicine, 1957-60. Sr. surgeon USPHS, 1958-67. Recipient Career Devel. award NIH, 1968-69. Mem. AAAS, Am. Soc.for Investigative Pathology, Am. Assn. for Biochem. and Molecular Biology, Gerontol. Soc. Am., Sigma Xi, Alpha Omega Alpha. Home: Apt 33AN 1212 N Lake Shore Dr Chicago IL 60610 Office: Northwestern U Med Sch Dept Pathology 303 E Chicago Ave Chicago IL 60611-3008

SMITH, DAVID WAYNE, psychologist; b. Ind., Apr. 16, 1927; s. Lowell Wayne and Ruth Elizabeth (Westphal) S.; m. Marcene B. Leever, Oct. 20, 1948; children: David Wayne, Laurreen Lea. B.S., Purdue U., 1949; M.S., Ind. U., 1953, Ph.D., 1955. Prof. rehab., dir. Rehab. Center; asso. dean, later asst. v.p. acad. affairs Ariz. Health Scis. Center, U. Ariz., Tucson, 1975-80; research prof. rehab., adj. prof. medicine, cons. in research S.W. Arthritis Center, Coll. Medicine, 1980-87; prof. rehab. and rheumatology, dept. medicine U. Ariz., 1987—, also dir. disability assessment program; pres. allied health professions sect. Nat. Arthritis Found.; nat. vice chmn. bd. dirs. Nat. Arthritis Found., nat. vice chmn. bd. dirs.; mem. NIH Nat. Arthritis Adv. Bd., 1977-84; also chmn. subcom. community programs and rehab.; mem. staff Ariz. Legislature Health Welfare, 1972-73; Mem. Gov.'s Council Dept. Econ. Security, 1978-85; pres., bd. dirs. Tucson Assn. for Blind, 1974-86; chmn. Gov.'s Council on Blind and Visually Impaired, 1987—; active Gov.'s Coun. on Arthritis and Musculoskeletal Disease, 1987—. Author: Worksamples; contbr. chpts. to books and articles to profl. jours. Recipient Gov.'s awards for leadership in rehab., 1966, 69, 72, 73; awards for sci. and vol. services Nat. Arthritis Found., 1973, 75; 1st nat. Addie Thomas award Nat. Arthritis Found., 1983, Benson award, 1989, Govt. Affairs award, 1989; Arthritis Found. fellow, 1983. Mem. Am. Psychol. Assn. (div. 17 counseling psychology), Assn. Schs. Allied Health Professions, Nat. Rehab. Assn., Ariz. Psychol. Assn. Home: 5765 N Camino Real Tucson AZ 85718-4213 Office: U Ariz Ariz Health Scis Ctr Tucson AZ 85724

SMITH, DEAN, communications advisor, arbitrator; b. N.Y.C., Aug. 10, 1925; s. Franklin Grant and Anna Lucille (Kranebell) S.; m. Andree Marie Praileur, Aug. 9, 1947; children—David F., Christopher P. Student, NYU, 1945-46, Columbia U., 1946-47, N.Y. Sch. Printing, 1946-47. Editor ShowBill Mag., N.Y.C., 1946-47; news editor Boulder City (Nev.) Daily News, 1947-49; owner, pub., editor Tucson Sun-News, N.Y.C., 1949-51; dir. radio and TV news Sta. WBEN/WBEN-TV, Buffalo, 1951-53; dir. pub. svc. and promotion Indpls. Times, Buffalo, 1953-56; v.p., gen. mgr Kendall Assocs., Inc., N.Y.C., 1956-60; dir. Office Pubis. and Info. Washington, D.C., 1961-70, dir. publs. div., 1970; asst. dir. Nat. Tech. Info. Svc., Springfield, Va., 1971-81, dir. office of market devel., 1982-83; assoc. dir. NTIS, Springfield, Va., 1984-85, self-employed communications advisor, 1986—. Chmn. for fed. mail list policy Vice Pres.'s Com. on Right of Privacy; chmn. presdl. domestic policy rev. work group on fed. acquisition of fgn. tech., 1979; bd. dirs. Commerce Fed. Credit Union. Served with AUS, 1943-45. Decorated Silver Star with oak leaf cluster, Bronze Star, Purple Heart with oak leaf cluster; recipient award Ariz. Newspaper Assn., 1950, Ind. Photo Journalism award, 1954. Mem. Am. Arbitration Assn. (panelist), Soc. Mayflower Descendants, Sons of Revolution (treas.), Flagon and Trencher, Soc. for the Descendants of the Colonial Clergy. Democrat. Home and Office: 2325 49th St NW Washington DC 20007-1002

SMITH, DEAN EDWARDS, university basketball coach; b. Emporia, Kans., Feb. 28, 1931; s. Alfred Dillon and Vesta Marie (Edwards) S.; m. Linnea Weblemoe, May 21, 1976; children: Sharon, Sandy, Scott, Kristen, Kelly. B.S. in Math. and Phys. Edn., U. Kans., 1953. Asst. basketball coach U.S. Air Force Acad., 1955-58; asst. basketball coach U. N.C. 1958-61, head basketball coach, 1961—; mem. U.S. and Canadian Basketball Rules Com., 1967-73; U.S. basketball coach Olympics, Montreal, Que., Can. 1976; lectr. basketball clinics, Germany, Italy. Served with USAF, 1954-58. Named Coach of Year Atlantic Coast Conf., 1967, 1968, 1971, 1976, 1977, 79, Nat. Basketball Coach of Year, 1977, Nat. Coach of Yr. U.S. Basketball Writers, 1979, Naismith Basketball Hall of Fame, 1982. Mem. Nat. Assn. Basketball Coaches (Nat. Basketball Coach of Year 1976, dir. 1972—, pres. 1981-82), Fellowship Christian Athletes (dir. 1966-70). Baptist. Office: U NC Office Basketball Coach PO Box 2126 Chapel Hill NC 27515-2126

SMITH, DENNIS (EDWARD), publisher, author; b. N.Y.C., Sept. 9, 1940; s. John and Mary (Hogan) S.; m. Patricia Ann Kearney, Aug. 24, 1963 (div. May 1988); children: Brendan, Dennis, Sean, Deirdre and Aislinn (twins). BA, NYU, 1970, MA, 1972. Adj. asst. prof. Coll. New Rochelle, 1973-74; fireman City of N.Y., 1963-80; founder, pub., editor in chief Firehouse Mag., N.Y.C., 1976-89. Author: Report from Engine Co. 82, 1972, Final Fire, 1975, Firehouse, 1977, Dennis Smith's History of American Firefighting, 1978, Glitter and Ash, 1980, The Aran Islands—A Personal Journey, 1980, Steely Blue, 1985, Firefighters, Their lives in Their Own Words, 1988, The Little Fire Engine That Saved the City, 1990. Mem. bd. advisors Boys and Girls Clubs Am., N.Y.C., N.Y.C. Cultural Affairs; bd. dirs. The New York Fire Safety Found.; bd. dirs., chmn. Kips Bay Boys and Girls Club, N.Y.C., N.Y. Acad. Art; bd. dirs., pres. Found. for Health and Safety Am. Firefighters; bd. dirs. Ireland House at NYU. With USAF, 1957-60. Recipient Christopher award for non-fiction, 1973. Mem. Union League Club. Democrat. Roman Catholic. Home and Office: 50 Hidden Cove Ct Southampton NY 11968

SMITH, DEREK ARMAND, publishing company executive; b. Hamilton, Ont., Can., Sept. 2, 1953; came to U.S., 1981; s. Alastair A.G. and Jessie Mead (Maben) S.; m. Rebecca Oldfield, Oct. 10, 1981; 1 child, Alastair Maben Oldfield. BCom., U. Toronto, 1976. Chartered acct.; CPA, Mass. Staff acct. Office of Auditor Gen., Ottawa, 1976-78; chartered acct. Peat Marwick Thorne, Ottawa, 1978-79; v.p. fin. Adminstrn. Can. Dry Bottling Ltd., Kingston, Ont., 1979-81; supervising sr. Peat Marwick, Boston, 1981-82; mgr. corp. reporting Warren, Gorham & Lamont, Inc., Boston, 1984-85; asst. contr. Warren, Gorham & Lamont, Inc., N.Y.C., 1982-84, sr. v.p., CFO, 1988-90; sr. v.p., CFO Penguin Books USA Inc., N.Y.C., 1990—; pres. Trinity Coll. Sch. Fund, Darien, Conn., 1992; gov. Trinity Coll. Sch., Port Hope, Ont., 1992. Trustee John Hart Hunter Ednl. Found., N.Y.C., 1992. Mem. Assn. of Chartered Accts. in the U.S. Ltd. (treas. 1990-93, dir. 1989-

94, hon. dir. 1994—), Kappa Alpha Soc. (mem. exec. coun., v.p. 1991-93, pres. 1993—). Episcopalian. Avocations: skiing, sailing, tennis, paddle tennis, golf. Office: Penguin Books USA Inc 375 Hudson St New York NY 10014-3658

SMITH, DERRIN RAY, information systems company executive; b. Columbus, Ohio, Feb. 19, 1955; s. Ray Stanley Smith and Clara (Diddle) Craver; m. Catherine Marie Massey, Aug. 18, 1979; children: Shannon Cathleen, Allison Collette, Micayla Colleen, Nicole Catherine. BS, Regis U., 1981; MBA, U. Phoenix, 1984; PhD, U. Denver, 1991. Test lab. mgr. Ball Aerospace Systems, Ball Corp., Boulder, 1975-84; sr. systems engr. Martin Marietta Info. Systems, Denver, 1984-87; tech. cons. MITRE Fed. R & D Ctr., Colorado Springs, 1988-92; pres. DRS Scis., Inc., Denver, 1992—; nat. program mgr. cable/telephone/full svc. network Time-Warner Entertainment, 1995—; tech. cons. U.S. Space Command--RAPIER, Colorado Springs, 1989-91, Unisys Corp., Greenwood Village, Colo., 1992; adj. prof. CIS dept. Univ. Coll., U. Denver, 1992; secretariat Corp. Planner's Roundtable, St. Louis, 1982-84; speaker in field. Author: Evolving the Mountain; Defense Acquisition Management of Strategic Command and Control System Procurements, 1991; contbr. articles to profl. jours. Res. police officer Federal Heights (Colo.) Police Dept., 1979-82. With USMC, 1978-84. Recipient Outstanding Achievement award Rocky Mountain News, 1981, Reservist of Yr. award Navy League U.S., 1981. Mem. Assn. Former Intelligence Officers (pres. Rocky Mountain chpt.). Roman Catholic. Avocations: martial arts, skiing, sailing, creative writing, mountaineering. Home: 3746 E Easter Cir S Littleton CO 80122 Office: DRS Scis Inc Arco Tower Ste 2900 707 17th St Denver CO 80202

SMITH, DIANA MARIE, business educator; b. Des Moines, Oct. 25, 1940; d. Nathan Henry and Helen (Hall) Kitchen; m. Robert Nelson Smith, Jan. 26, 1971; 1 child, Stephen. BA, Drake U., 1968, MA, 1971. Cert. tchr., Iowa; authorized tng. instr. WordPerfect. Stenographer Polk County Welfare Dept., Des Moines, 1960-67; typist Polk County Auditor, Des Moines, 1968, Gen. Life Assurance Co., Des Moines, 1976-79; computer oper. IRS, Des Moines, 1988; lead specialist II Norwest Bank, Des Moines, 1978—; sec. Shive-Hattery Engrs., Des Moines, 1976-90; adult edn. instr. Des Moines Ind. Dist., 1969—; tchr. bus., computers Des Moines Pub. Schs., 1968—; ind. computer cons.; instr.-authorized tng. assoc. program for Word Perfect, 1994; Mary Kay beauty cons., 1993—. Chair meml. com. Burns United Meth. Ch., Des Moines, 1988. Sunday sch. tchr., 1961-83, 92—; sec. adminstrv. bd. Mem. NEA, Nat. Bus. Edn. Assn., Iowa Bus. Edn. Assn., Des Moines Bus. Edn. Assn., Iowa State Edn. Assn., Des Moines Edn. Assn. Democrat. Avocations: reading, computers. Office: Cen Campus 1800 Grand Ave Des Moines IA 50309

SMITH, DOLORES MAXINE PLUNK, dancer, educator; b. Webster City, Iowa, Dec. 22, 1926; d. Herschel Swanson and Kathryn (Wilke) Hassig; m. Del O. Furrey, Aug. 26, 1945 (div. Feb. 1960); children: Bob H. Furrey, Jon B. Furrey, Kathryn E. Furrey; m. Dewey Pechota, 1962 (div. 1963); m. Leon Plunk, 1965 (div. 1966); m. Harold Burdick, 1974 (div. 1977); m. Floyd E. Smith, July 13, 1985. BS in Edn., Black Hills Tchrs. Coll., 1962; MA, Tex. Woman's U., 1964, PhD, 1974. Owner, operator pvt. dance studios, S.D., 1953-62; tchr. rural schs. Rosebud Reservation, S.D., 1945-49; tchr. Mellette County Pub. Schs., White River, S.D., 1958-60, St. Francis Indian Day Sch., 1960-61, Converse County (Wyo.) High Sch., 1961-62; grad. asst. Tex. Woman's U., Denton, 1962-64, 71; asst. prof. dance Sam Houston U., Huntsville, Tex., 1964-65; prof. Ctrl. Mo. State U., Warrensburg, 1965—; judge dance contest Kansas City Dance Theatre Co., 1987, 88, World Dance Assn., 1988, Mo. State Fair, 1989; judge Miss Am. Co-ed Pageants, 1991-93; dir. Dance Partisans Assn., Ctrl. Mo. State U., 1982—; dir., tchr. cmty. dance program, 1988—; dir. show dance team, 1991—; dance coord. Internat. Coun. Health, Phys. Edn., Recreation, Sport and Dance, 1994—; presenter Japanese Asia Dance Events, Malaysia, 1994, Dance Edn. Conf., Mich. State U., 1994. Contbr. articles to profl. jours. Bd. dirs. Kansas City Dance Theatre Co., 1987—. Mem. Dance Masters Am. (sec. 1985-87, chmn. Mr. and Miss Dance Contest 1985, scholarships com. 1988-90), AAHPERD (honors award cen. dist. chpt., cen. dist. presentor 1991-92, dance chair, coll. chair, dance performance chair 1989-90, v.p. dance 1991-93), Mo. Assn. Health, Phys. Edn., Recreation and Dance (pres. 1972, svc. award), Nat. Dance Assn. (v.p. dance edn. 1991-93, chmn. Heritage luncheon 1968, 78, 87, Heritage award com. 1988-89, mem. ad hoc spl. svcs. com. 1989—, pub. Spotlight 1989-90), Mid-Am. Dance Network (on-site coord. choreographers/dancers workshop 1992, bd. dirs., sec. 1992—), Mo. Art Coun. Basic Arts Edn. (basic arts edn. task force higher edn.), Dance and Child Internat. (display chair, presider 1991), Asian Pacific Conf. Arts Edn. (presenter 1989—), Assn. Supervision and Curriculum Devel., Internat. Congress Health, Phys. Edn. and Recreation Presenters (congress dels. representing dance, presenter 1991, 93), Internat. Phys. Edn. and Sports for Girls and Women, Phys. Edn. and Recreation, Mo. Alliance for Arts Edn. Republican. Avocations: raising and showing Belgium and Shire draft horses, stained glass, cake decorating. Home: 130 SW 400th Rd Warrensburg MO 64093-8109 Office: Ctrl Mo State U Dept Physical Education Warrensburg MO 64093

SMITH, DONALD ARTHUR, mechanical engineer, researcher; b. Hartford, Conn., Apr. 9, 1945; s. Winfred Arthur and Marguerite Elisabeth (Johnson) S.; m. Marianne Carol Taverna, June 17, 1967; 1 child, Adam James. BS in Mech. Engring., U. Hartford, 1968. Rsch. engr. Combustion Engring. Inc., Windsor, Conn., 1968-71; supr. fluid rsch. Combustion Engring. Inc., Windsor, 1971-77, mgr. combustion rsch., 1977-84; dir. R&D Hartford Steam Boiler Inspection & Ins. Co., 1984—; co. rep. Indsl. Rsch. Inst., Washington, 1989—; chmn. Am. Flame Rsch. Com. 1983—. Tech. editor: HSB Locomotive, 1990-91. Haddam (Conn.) Planning and Zoning Commn., 1991-95; pres. Sherwood Camp Assn., Haddam, 1971-81. Named Engr. Yr. ASME (Hartford sect.), 1989. Mem. U. Hartford Alumni Bd., Lions. Republican. Roman Catholic. Achievements include patents in spray atomizers, burners, ignitors and flame scanning systems for indsl. application. Established Combustion Engring.'s fluid mechanics and combustion rsch. facilities, Hartford Steam Boiler's corp. R&D program. Home: PO Box 95-42 Smith Hill Rd Haddam CT 06438 Office: Hartford Steam Boiler One State St Hartford CT 06102

SMITH, DONALD EUGENE, banker; b. Terre Haute, Ind., Nov. 4, 1926; s. Henry P. and Ruth I. (Bius) S.; m. Mary F. Ryan, June 25, 1947; children: Virginia Lee, Sarah Jane. Student, Ind. U., 1945-47, Ind. State U., 1947-48. Pres. Deep Vein Coal Co., Terre Haute, Ind., 1947—; with R.J. Oil Co., Inc. 1948—; pres. Princeton Mining Co., Terre Haute, 1947—, Terre Haute Oil Corp., 1947—; ceo Terre Haute First Nat. Bank First Fin. Corp., 1969—; pres. Deep Vein Coal Co., R.J. Oil Co., Princeton Mining Co., Terre Haute Oil Co.; bd. dirs. So. Ind. Gas and Electric Co. Trustee Ind. State U.; bd. mgrs. Rose-Hulman Inst. Tech., 1978—; pres. Alliance for Growth and Progress, 1987—; treas. Terre Huate Econ. Devel. Commn., 1981—; mem. Ind. Econ. Devel. Coun. Mem. Terre Haute C. of C. (bd. dirs. 1982—). Club: Country of Terre Haute. Lodge: Elks. Home: 94 Allendale Terre Haute IN 47802-4751 Office: Terre Haute First Nat Bank One First Financial Pla Terre Haute IN 47807

SMITH, DONALD EUGENE, financial analyst; b. Norfolk, Nebr., July 25, 1953; s. Albert Lee and Blanche Anna (Koski) S.; m. Nancy Lynn Moeller, May 26, 1979; children: Stephanie Dawn, Brittany Lea. BSBA, U. Nebr., 1980, MBA, 1981. Pvt. practice fin. analysis and planning Lincoln, Nebr., 1981—; fin. feasability analyst Nebr. Dept. Health, Lincoln, 1984—. With USN, 1971-75, Vietnam, USNR, Desert Storm/Shield, 1990-91. Republican. Methodist. Avocation: waterskiing. Home: 6249 Briar Rosa Dr Lincoln NE 68516-2732

SMITH, DONALD EUGENE, healthcare facility management administrator owner; b. Mishawaka, Ind., Oct. 15, 1936; s. Ernest Hartmann and Lucile Emma (Krumanaker) S.; m. Nancy Mae Jaffke, Sept. 2, 1961; children: Adam, Reid, Lynn. AB, Wabash Coll., 1959; MBA, U. Chgo., 1963. Adminstrv. resident Ind. U. Med. Ctr., 1960-61; assoc. dir. Ind. U. Hosps., 1966-72; pres. Henderson & Smith Corp., Indpls., 1978—; lectr. in health adminstrn. Ind. U., 1965-66, adj. asst. prof. in health adminstrn., 1966-78; ptnr. Covington (Ind.) Manor Health Care Ctr., Carmel (Ind.) Care Ctr., Countryside Manor, Anderson, Ind., Dearborn Enterprises, Lawrenceburg, Ind., Manor House at Riverview, Noblesville, Ind., Rawlins House, Pen-

dleton, Ind., Manor House of Carmel, Ind., Northridge, Crawfordsville, Ind., Power Purchasing, Inc., Greenwood, Ind.; chmn. Ind. State Bd. Registration and Edn. Health Facility Adminstrs., 1969-82. Bd. dirs. Ind. U. Med. Ctr. Fed. Credit Union, 1965-68, Ind. Blue Cross, 1966-71; med. ctr. chmn. United Fund Drive, 1962-65; sec. Carmel (Ind.) Classic, 1979, v.p., 1981, pres., 1982-83; bd. trustees Wabash Coll., 1985—, mem. exec. com., 1986—, chmn. capital campaign drive, 1987-91, mem. long range planning com., 1985; active Hamilton County Rep. Fin. Com., 1990—. Fellow ACHS; mem. Am. Health Care Assn., Ind. Health Care Assn., Wabash Coll. Alumni Assn., U. Chgo. Hosp. Adminstrn. Alumni Assn., Woodland Country Club, Skyline Club. Office: Henderson & Smith Corp 10333 N Meridian St Ste 250 Indianapolis IN 46290-1081

SMITH, DONALD EUGENE, political science educator; b. Phoenixville, Pa., Sept. 1, 1927; s. George John and Anna Rhoda (Loux) S.; m. Violet Ramanjulu, July 1, 1950. B.A., Eastern Baptist Theol. Sem., Pa., 1951; B.D., Eastern Baptist Theol. Sem., 1953; M.A., U. Pa., 1953, Ph.D., 1956. Instr. U. Pa., Phila., 1955-56; from asst. prof. to assoc. prof. U. R.I., Kingston, 1956-64; from assoc. prof. to prof. U. Pa., Phila., 1964—. Author: India As a Secular State, 1961; Religion and Politics in Burma, 1965; Religion and Political Development, 1971; co-editor: Anti-Americanism in the Third World, 1985. Chmn., Main Line Housing Improvement Corp., Wayne, Pa., 1968-80. Fulbright fellow, New Delhi, 1954, 60; grantee, Carnegie Corp., 1961-63, Social Sci. Research Council, 1968, East-West Ctr., 1970-71. Mem. Asia Soc. (chmn. Sri Lanka council 1975-83), Am. Polit. Sci. Assn., Assn. Asian Studies. Home: 740 Red Oak Ter Wayne PA 19087-2340 Office: U Pa Dept Polit Sci 36th and Walnut Sts Philadelphia PA 19104

SMITH, DONALD N., Restaurant chain executive. With McDonald Corp., Oak Brook, Ill., 1966-77, Burger KingCorp., Miami, 1977-80, Pepsico, Inc., N.Y.C., 1980-83, Diversifoods, Inc., Itasca, Ill., 1983-84, Perkins Family Restaurants, Memphis, Tenn., 1985—; now chmn., CEO Perkins Mgmt. Co., Inc., Memphis, Tenn. Office: Perkins Family Res 6075 Poplar Ave Ste 800 Memphis TN 38119-4717*

SMITH, DONALD NICKERSON, food service executive; b. Can., Sept. 12, 1940; came to U.S., 1946, naturalized, 1956; s. Fred Raymond and Hazel (Nickerson) S.; m. Beverley Thorell, Dec. 1961 (div.); children: Jeffrey, Stacy, Darby; m. Angela Dangerfield, Mar. 8, 1984. BA, U. Mont., 1962; D in Bus. Adminstrn. (hon.), Upper Iowa U., 1980. Sr. exec. v.p. sr. ops. officer McDonald's Corp., Oak Brook, Ill., 1964-77; pres., chief exec. officer Burger King Corp., Miami, 1977-80; sr. v.p., pres. food svc. div. PepsiCo, Inc., Purchase, N.Y., 1980-83; pres., chief exec. officer Chart House, Inc. (name changed to Diversifoods, Inc.), Itasca, Ill., 1983-85; chmn., pres., chief exec. officer Tenn. Restaurant Co., Itasca, 1985—; chmn., pres., CEO Friendly Holding Corp., Wilbraham, Mass. With USMCR, 1957-65. Named Adman of the Yr., Advt. Age mag., 1979.

SMITH, DONALD W., association executive; b. Johnstown, Pa., July 13, 1932; s. Thomas E. and Bertha E. (Alwine) S. BA, U. Pitts., 1955; MA, St. Francis Coll., Loretto, Pa., 1973. Indsl. analyst Bethlehem Steel Corp., Johnstown, Pa., 1959-84; exec. dir. Am. Topical Assn., Johnstown, 1984—. Pub. more than 20 philatelic books. With U.S. Army, 1955-59. Named Disting. Topical Philatelist, Am. Topical Assn., 1976. Office: American Topical Assn PO Box 630 Johnstown PA 15907

SMITH, DONALD WILLIAM, airport manager; b. Hydro, Okla., Dec. 13, 1933; s. Thomas Sylvester and Ruth Lavena (Hearn) S.; m. Mildred June Winter, Oct. 12, 1956; children—Lynn, Larry, Curtis. B.B.A., U. Tex, El Paso. Asst. mgr. ops. El Paso Internat. Airport, Tex., 1962-67; gen. mgr. Airport Investors Inc., Hayward, Calif., 1967-70; airport mgr. King County Internat. Airport, Seattle, 1970—. Served to capt. U.S. Army, 1956-58. Accredited Airport Exec., Am. Assn. Airport Execs., 1966; recipient Pres.'s award Internat. N.W. Aviation Council, 1981. Mem. Am. Assn. Airport Execs. (bd. dirs. 1979-83), Internat. N.W. Aviation Council (bd. dirs. 1975-89, pres. 1990-91). Avocations: Flying; golf; fishing. Office: Boeing Field King County Intl PO Box 80245 7233 Perimeter Rd Seattle WA 98108

SMITH, DONN L., university dean; b. Denver, Nov. 1, 1915; s. Arthur M. and Elizabeth (Setzer) S.; m. Ruth E. Perrin, Apr. 3, 1937; children: Eileen Smith Burg, Darlene Louise Smith Osterholt. A.B., U. Denver, 1939, M.S. (Upjohn scholar 1941) 1941; Ph.D., U. Colo., 1948, M.D. 1958. Asst. prof. physiology U. Denver, 1948-50; asso. prof. physiology U. Colo. Sch. Medicine, 1950-60, asso. dean, 1960-63; prof. physiology, dean Sch. Medicine, U. Louisville, 1963-70; dir. (Med. Center) dean Coll. Medicine, U. South Fla., Tampa, 1970-76; prof. comprehensive medicine and pharmacology Coll. Medicine, U. South Fla., 1976—; interim v.p., dean U. So. Fla., 1986-88; prof., dean emeritus Coll. Medicine, U. So. Fla., 1988—; Med. adv. Ky. SSS. Author: (with Philip Ellis) Handbook of Ocular Therapeutics and Pharmacology, 4th edit, 1973; also numerous articles. Served with Inf. AUS, 1942-46. Fellow Am. Coll. Clin. Pharmacology; mem. AMA (council on drugs 1965-72), Fla. Med. Assn., AAAS, Soc. Exptl. Biology and Medicine, Am. Soc. Pharmacology and Exptl. Therapeutics (AMA rep to U.S. Adopted Names Coun.), Alpha Omega Alpha. Home: 5212 E 127th Ave Tampa FL 33617-1436

SMITH, DORIS CORINNE KEMP, retired nurse; b. Bogalusa, La., Nov. 22, 1919; d. Milton Jones and Maude Maria (Fortenberry) Kemp; m. Joseph William Smith, Oct. 13, 1940 (dec.). BS in Nursing, U. Colo., 1957, MS in Nursing Adminstrn., 1958. RN, Colo. Head nurse Chgo. Bridge & Iron Co., Morgan City, La., 1941-45, Shannon Hosp., San Angelo, Tex., 1945-50; dir. nursing Yoakum County Hosp., Denver City, Tex., 1951-52; hosp. supr. Med. Arts Hosp., Odessa, Tex., 1952-55; dir. insvc. edn. St. Anthony Hosp., Denver, 1961-66; coord. Sch. Vocat. Nursing, Kiamichi Area Vocat.-Tech. Nursing Sch., Wilburton, Okla., 1969-77; supr. non-ambulatory unit Lubbock (Tex.) State Sch., 1978-85, ret., 1985; mem. steering com. Western Interstate Commn. on Higher Edn. for Nurses, Denver, 1963-65; mem. curriculum and materials com. Okla. Bd. Vocat.-Tech. Edn., Stillwater, 1971-76; mem. Invitational Conf. To Plan Nursing for Future, Oklahoma City, 1976-77; mem. survey team to appraise Sch. of Vocat.-Tech. Edn. Schs. for Okla. Dept. Vocat.-Tech. Edn., 1975-76. Author, editor: Survey of Functions Expected of the General Duty Nurse, State of Colorado, 1958; co-editor: Curriculum Guides; contbr. numerous articles to profl. jours. Recipient citation of merit Okla. State U., 1976; named Woman of Yr. Sunrise chpt. Am. Bus. Women's Assn. 1994-95. Mem. AAAS, ANA, AAUW (life), Nat. League for Nursing, Tex. League for Nursing, Tex. Nurses Assn., Dist. 18 Nurses Assn., Tex. Employees Assn. (v.p. 1984-85), U. Colo. Alumni Assn., Am. Bus. Women's Club (pres. Lubbock chpt. 1986-87, rec. sec. 1989-90), Bus. and Profl. Women's Assn. (sec. 1992—), Pi Lambda Theta (sec. local chpt. 1957-58). Republican. Avocations: gardening, swimming, walking, travel, fishing. Home: 2103 55th St Lubbock TX 79412-2612

SMITH, DORIS VICTORIA, educational agency administrator; b. N.Y.C., July 5, 1937; d. Albin and Victoria (Anderson) Olson; m. Howard R. Smith, Aug. 21, 1960; children: Kurt, Steven, Andrea. BS in Edn., Wagner Coll., 1959; MA in Edn., Kean Coll., 1963, cert., 1980; EdD, Fairleigh Dickinson U., 1984, Nova Southeastern U. Cert. adminstr., tchr. elem. edn., N.J. Thorough and efficient coord. East Hanover (N.J.) Twp. Sch. Dist., 1977-79; ednl. specialist N.J. State Dept. Edn., Morristown, 1979—, ednl. planner, 1982-87, ednl. mgr., 1987—; pres. N.E. Coalition Ednl. Leaders, Inc.; founding mem. Morris County Curriculum Network. Author: Affirmative Action—Rules and Regulations, 1982, Supervising Early Childhood Programs, 1984. Past pres. bd. trustees Florham Park Libr.; founding mem. Morris Area Tech. Alliance; founding mem., pres. Calvary Nursery Sch.; bd. of trust office N.J. Coun. Edn.; pres. bd. trustees Madison/Chatham Adult Sch.; trustee Morris County Children's Svcs. Recipient Disting. Svc. award N.E. Coalition Ednl. Leaders, 1991, Disting. Svc. award Morris County Prins. and Suprs. Assn.; tchr. insvc. grantee. Mem. N.J. Coun. Edn., N.J. Schoolmasters Assn., Phi Delta Kappa.

SMITH, DOROTHY JEAN, principal; b. McAlester, Okla., May 3, 1942; d. Erby Roy and Hildred Mae (Smith) Webb; m. Leslie Robert Smith, Sept. 14, 1963; children: Leah Lynette, John Robert. BS in Edn., Southeastern Okla. State U., 1972, M in Early Childhood Edn., 1978. Cert. elem. tchr. and prin., Okla. Tchr. Will Rogers Elem. Sch., McAlester, Okla., 1973-89; prin. elem. Washington Sch., McAlester, Okla., 1989—. Mem. exec. coun.

young children Kiamichi Vo-Tech., McAlester, Okla., 1989—; mem. adv. coun. parents as teachers McAlester Pub. Schs., 1990—. Mem. NAESP, Okla. Assn. Children Under Six, Coop. Coun. for Okla. Sch. Adminstrn., So. Assn. Children Under Six, Women in Edn. Adminstrn., Delta Kappa Gamma, Kappa Kappa Iota. Baptist. Avocations: bicycling, hiking, reading, painting, weight training. Home: 1801 Mockingbird Ln McAlester OK 74501 Office: Washington Sch 700 S 6th St McAlester OK 74501

SMITH, DOUGLAS V., manufacturing executive, heavy; b. 1943. BS Mech. Engring., Clemson U.; MS Mech. Engring., U. Ky.; MBA, Harvard Bus. Sch. Pres., CEO, dir. Lufkin (Tex.)Industries, Inc., 1993—. Office: Lufkin Industries Inc 601 S Raguet St Lufkin TX 75904-3951*

SMITH, DUDLEY RENWICK, insurance company executive; b. N.Y.C., June 10, 1937; s. Crosby Tuttle and Vernon (Siems) S.; m. Juliana Buros, Nov. 17, 1962; children: Clayton Tuttle, Bradley Renwick, Gregory Dudley. AB, Dartmouth Coll., 1960. V.p. Fed. Ins. Co., Warren, N.J.; sr. v.p. Chubb & Son Inc., Warren, 1961—; trustee Chubb Found. Home: 55 Montadale Cir Princeton NJ 08540-7619 Office: Chubb & Son Inc 15 Mountain Blvd Warren NJ 07060

SMITH, DWIGHT MORRELL, chemistry educator; b. Hudson, N.Y., Oct. 10, 1931; s. Elliott Monroe and Edith Helen (Hall) S.; m. Alice Beverly Bond, Aug. 27, 1955 (dec. 1990); children—Karen Elizabeth, Susan Allison, Jonathan Aaron; m. Elfi Nelson, Dec. 28, 1991. B.A., Central Coll., Pella, Iowa, 1953; Ph.D., Pa. State U., 1957; ScD (hon.), Cen. Coll., 1986; LittD (hon.), U. Denver, 1990. Postdoctoral fellow, instr. Calif. Inst. Tech., 1957-59; sr. chemist Texaco Rsch. Ctr., Beacon, N.Y., 1959-61; asst. prof. chemistry Wesleyan U., Middletown, Conn., 1961-66; assoc. prof. Hope Coll., Holland, Mich., 1966-69, prof., 1969-72; prof. chemistry U. Denver, 1972—, chmn. dept., 1972-83, vice chancellor for acad. affairs, 1983-84, chancellor, 1984-89; pres. Hawaii Loa Coll., Kaneohe, 1990-92; mem. adv. bd. Solar Energy Rsch. Inst., 1989-91; mem. vis. com. Zettlemoyer Ctr. for Surface Studies Lehigh U., 1990—. Editor Revs. on Petroleum Chemistry, 1975-78; contbr. articles to profl. jours.; patentee selective hydrogenation. Chmn. Chs. United for Social Action, Holland, 1968-69; mem. adv. com. Holland Sch. Bd., 1969-70; bd. commrs. Colo. Adv. Tech. Inst., 1984-88, Univ. Senate, United Meth. Ch., Nashville, 1987-88, 91-93; mem. adv. bd. United Way, Inst. Internat. Edn., Japan Am. Soc. Colo., Denver Winter Games Olympics Com.; mem. ch. bds. or consistories Ref. Ch. Am., N.Y., Conn., Mich., United Meth. Ch., Colo. DuPont fellow, 1956-57, NSF fellow Scripps Inst., 1971-72; recipient grants Research Corp., Petroleum Research Fund, NSF, Solar Energy Research Inst. Mem. Am. Chem. Soc. (chmn. Colo. 1976, sec. western Mich. 1970-71, award indsl. sect. 1986), Catalysis Soc., Soc. Applied Spectroscopy, Mile High Club, Pinehurst Country Club, Sigma Xi. Home: 1931 W Sanibel Ct Littleton CO 80120 Office: U Denver Denver CO 80208

SMITH, DWIGHT RAYMOND, ecology and wildlife educator, writer; b. Sanders, Idaho, July 28, 1921; s. Andrew Leonard and Effie Elizabeth (Simons) S.; m. Carol Elizabeth Breclaw (dec. 1983); children Alan Dwight (dec.), Sharon Lee Smith Dequine, Gary Robert, Mark Jonathan (dec.). BS in Forestry, U. Idaho, 1949, MS in Wildlife Mgmt., 1951; PhD in Ecology, Utah State U., 1971. Rsch. biologist Idaho Fish and Game Dept., Salmon, 1950-52, area game mgr., 1953-56; range scientist U.S. Forest Svc., Ft. Collins, Colo., 1957-61, wildlife rsch. biologist, 1962-65; asst. prof. Colo. State U., Ft. Collins, 1965-70, assoc. prof., 1971-75, prof., 1975-83, prof. emeritus, 1983—; nature photographer Alan Landsburg Prodns., Hollywood, Calif., 1971; energy cons. CF&I Steel, Pueblo, Colo., 1981. Author: Above Timberline: A Wildlife Biologist's Rocky Mountain Journal, 1981; writer/photographer (film) Research in the Rockies: A Scientist Explores the Alpine, 1973; contbr. articles to profl. jours. Served to 2d lt. inf. U.S. Army, 1942-45, PTO, ETO. Decorated Bronze Star. Rsch. grantee, Wildlife U.S. Fish and Wildlife Svc., 1949-50, Wildlife Mgmt. Inst., 1950, Nat. Wildlife Fedn., 1954-55. Fellow Explorers Club; mem. Toastmasters (ednl. v.p. local chpt. 1960-62, pres. 1963), Xi Sigma Pi, Sigma Xi, Gamma Sigma Delta, Phi Kappa Phi. Democrat. Roman Catholic. Avocations: photography, piloting, bicycling, skiing, square dancing. Home: 1916 Harmony Dr Fort Collins CO 80525-3442

SMITH, EDGAR BENTON, physician; b. Houston, June 2, 1932; s. Burt Benton and Lela Elizabeth (Grant) S.; m. Francis Elaine Newton, Aug. 1, 1953; children—Sheri Elaine Smith Dinehart, Robin Marie Smith Fredrickson. Student, Rice U., 1950-53; BA, U. Houston, 1956; MD, Baylor U., 1957; diploma clin. medicine of the tropics, U. London, 1967. Intern Walter Reed Gen. Hosp., Washington, 1957-58; resident Brooke Gen. Hosp., Ft. Sam Houston, Tex., 1960-63; asst. prof. dermatology U. Miami Sch. Medicine, 1967-68, Baylor Coll. Medicine, Houston, 1968-71; asso. prof. medicine (dermatology) U. N.Mex. Sch. Medicine, Albuquerque, 1971-75; prof. U. N.Mex. Sch. Medicine, 1975-78; prof., chmn. dept. dermatology U. Tex. Med. Br., Galveston, 1978—. Contbr. articles in field to profl. jours. Served with U.S. Army, 1956-66. Recipient Khatali award U. N.Mex. Sch. Medicine, 1976; Fulbright scholar London Sch. Hygiene and Tropical Medicine, 1966-67; Alfred Stengel travelling scholar ACP, 1967. Mem. AMA, Am. Acad. Dermatology (bd. dirs. 1978-82, pres.-elect 1988, pres. 1989, Sulzberger internat. lectr. 1992), Assn. Profs. Dermatology (sec.-treas. 1979-82), Am. Dermatol. Assn., Am. Fedn. Clin. Rsch., Southwestern Dermatol. Soc. (sec. 1974-77, pres. 1978), South Ctrl. Dermatol. Congress (sec.-gen. 1973-76, pres. 1976-81), Tex. Dermatol. Soc. (trustee 1986), So. Med. Assn. (chmn. dermatology sect. 1988), Galveston Arty. Club, Yacht Club, Baker Street Irregulars, Alpha Omega Alpha. Democrat. Methodist. Home: 3017 Ave O Galveston TX 77550 Office: U Tex Med Br Dept Dermatology Galveston TX 77555-0783

SMITH, EDGAR EUGENE, biochemist, university administrator; b. Hollandale, Miss., Aug. 6, 1934; s. Sam and Augusta Lillie (McCoy) S.; m. Inez Oree Wiley, May 27, 1955; children—E. Donald, Anthony R., Stephen S., Gregory S. B.S., Tougaloo Coll., 1955; M.S., Purdue U., 1957, Ph.D., 1960. Rsch. fellow in surgery (biochemistry) Harvard Med. Sch., Boston, 1959-61; rsch. assoc. Harvard Med. Sch., 1961-68; assoc. in surg. rsch. Beth Israel Hosp., Boston, 1959-68; asst. prof. surgery (chemistry) Boston U. Sch. Medicine, 1968-70, assoc. prof. biochemistry, 1970-74; assoc. prof. biochemistry U. Mass. Med. Sch., Worcester, 1974-80, prof. emeritus biochemistry and molecular biology, 1991—; assoc. dean acad. affairs U. Mass. Med. Sch., 1974-77, provost, 1975-83; asst. dean minority affairs, prin. investigator Bur. Health Manpower Spl. Project grant Boston U. Sch. Medicine, 1972-74; v.p. acad. affairs U. Mass. System, 1983-91; v.p. Nellie Mae, 1990-93; acting pres. Tougaloo Coll., 1995—; mem. governing bd. Robert Wood Johnson Health Policy Fellowship Program, Inst. Medicine, NAS, 1978-85. Contbr. writings to sci. publs. Chmn. bd. overseers Sch. Medicine Morehouse Coll.; trustee Tougaloo Coll., Metco Scholarship Fund, Lexington, Mass.; bd. dirs. Dimock Community Health Center, Boston, New Urban League of Greater Boston, So. Edn. Found., 1976-79; chmn. Boston Com. for Nat. Med. Fellowships, Inc. Recipient research career devel. award Nat. Cancer Inst., 1969-74, award for outstanding achievement in biochemistry Nat. Consortium for Black Profl. Devel., 1976, human relations award Mass. Teachers Assn., 1977, health award NAACP, 1977; Robert Wood Johnson Health Policy fellow Inst. Medicine, Nat. Acad. Scis., 1977-78; named Alumnus of Yr. Tougaloo Coll., 1969, Disting. Alumnus Nat. Assn. for Equal Opportunities in Higher Edn., 1979, 92, Old Master Purdue U., 1978. Fellow Am. Inst. Chemists; mem. Am. Soc. Biol. Chemists, Am. Chem. Soc. (div. biol. chemists), AAAS, N.Y. Acad. Scis., Am. Assn. for Cancer Research, Boston Cancer Research Assn., Am. Polit. Sci. Assn., Am. Soc. Biol. Chemists (com. on minorities 1980-83), Josiah Macy, Jr. Found. Scholarship Com. Marine Biol. Lab., Woods Hole, Mass., Sigma Xi, Phi Lambda Upsilon, Alpha Phi Alpha. Home: 81 Hill St Lexington MA 02173-6532

SMITH, EDWARD HERBERT, radiologist, educator; b. N.Y.C., Feb. 18, 1936; s. Nathan Leon and Rebecca Ada (Brodsky) S.; m. Anne Chantler Oliphant, June 27, 1971; children: Peter Chantler, Jeffrey Martin. A.B., Columbia Coll., 1956; M.D., SUNY, 1960. Intern U. Calif. Hosp., San Francisco, 1960-61; resident in internal medicine Montefiore Hosp., N.Y.C., 1961-62; resident in radiology Kings County Hosp., Ctr. Bklyn., 1964-67, radiologist, 1967-69; instr. SUNY-Bklyn., 1967-69; radiologist Children's Hosp. Med. Ctr., Boston, 1969-70, Peter Bent Brigham Hosp., Boston, 1969-

80; dir. div. radiology Charles A. Dana Cancer Research Ctr., Boston, 1974-80; instr. Harvard Med. Sch., Boston, 1969-70, asst. prof., 1970-75, assoc. prof., 1975-80, lectr. radiology, 1980—; radiologist U. Mass. Med. Ctr., Worcester, 1980—, prof., chmn. dept. radiology, 1980—; prof. U. Mass. Med. Sch., Worcester, 1980—; prof. dept. surgery in urology U. Mass. Med. Sch., 1983—; vis. radiologist Rambam Govt. Hosp., Haifa, Israel, 1972; vis. prof. dept. ultrasound U. Copenhagen, Herlev, Denmark, 1977-78, Shanghai Med. Ctr., Peoples Republic China, 1987; cons. Tng. Program in Diagnostic Ultrasound for Physicians and Technologists, Va., 1974-75; reviewer profl. jours. Author: (with others) Abdominal Ultrasound: Static and Dynamic Scanning, 1980; contbr. articles to profl. jours. Fogarty sr. internat. fellow John E. Fogarty Internat. Ctr. for Advanced Study in Health Scis., NIH, Copenhagen, 1977-78. Fellow Am. Coll. Radiology; mem. Am. Univ. Radiologists, Am. Inst. Ultrasound in Medicine, Am. Roentgen Ray Soc., Radiol. Soc. N.Am., Soc. Radiologists in Ultrasound (charter mem.), New Eng. Soc. Ultrasound in Medicine (charter mem., pres. 1978-79), New Eng. Roentgen Ray Soc. (pres. 1989-90), Mass. Radiologic Soc. (exec. coun.). Office: U Mass Med Ctr Dept Radiology 55 Lake Ave N Worcester MA 01655-0002

SMITH, EDWARD K., economist, consultant; b. Buffalo, Apr. 12, 1922; s. Clifford Kershaw and Helen (Baro) S.; m. Mary Alice Pendergast, Dec. 20, 1948; children: Benjamin, Christopher, Loretta Christopher, Katherine Smith Fuscoe, Alice Ryan, Margarita Treuth, James, Daniel. B.A., Hobart Coll., 1946; M.A., U. Buffalo, 1950, Harvard U., 1955; Ph.D., Harvard U., 1960. From asst. to assoc. prof. econs. Boston Coll., 1956-64; dep. asst. sec. U.S. Dept. Commerce, Washington, 1965-68; prof., chmn. dept. econs. Colo. State U., Ft. Collins, 1968-70; v.p. Nat. Bur. Econ. Research, N.Y.C., 1970-77; sr. econ. cons. Brimmer & Co. Inc., Washington, 1977-83; dir. Internat. Banking Ctr., Fla. Internat. U., Miami, 1982, Bur. Ind. Econs., U.S. Dept. Commerce, Washington, 1983; assoc. dir. Bur. Econ. Analysis, 1984-88; cons. economist, 1988—; vis. prof. econs. U. Colo., 1965, Yale U., New Haven, 1971, Fla. Internat. U., Miami, 1982. Author: The Economic State of New England, 1954. Fiscal advisor Lt. Gov. Mass., Boston, 1955; mem. Pres.'s Task Force on Environ., 1966, Pres.'s Task Force on Housing, 1968, Gov. Carey's Task Force on Unemployment, N.Y.C., 1974; trustee St. Mary's Coll., Newburgh, N.Y., 1972-77. Served with U.S. Army, 1943-46. Mem. Am. Econs. Assn., Nat. Assn. Bus. Economists, So. Regional Sci. Assn., Nat. Economists Club (v.p. 1984, bd. dirs. 1985-86). Democrat. Episcopalian.

SMITH, EDWARD PAUL, JR., lawyer; b. Westbury, N.Y., Jan. 13, 1939; s. Edward Paul Sr. and Margaret (Eisenhauer) S.; m. Mary Elizabeth Neagle, Mar. 29, 1980; children: Nora, Edward, Brian, Thomas, Brendan. BA, Coll. of the Holy Cross, 1960; LLB, Columbia U., 1963. Bar: N.Y. 1964, Fla. 1966. Assoc. Chadbourne & Parke, N.Y.C., 1964-75, prin., 1975—; corp. sec. Am. Bur. Metal Statis., N.Y.C., 1978—. Author: Regulation of Employee Benefit Plans, Under Erisa, 1990. Capt. USAF, 1964-67. Mem. N.Y. State Bar Assn., Fla. Bar Assn. Roman Catholic. Home: 36 Avon Rd Bronxville NY 10708-1614 Office: Chadbourne & Parke 30 Rockefeller Plz New York NY 10112

SMITH, EDWARD REAUGH, retired lawyer, cemetery and funeral home consultant; b. Flora, Ill., Sept. 23, 1932; m. Jo Anne Myers, Sept. 10, 1954; children: Mark and Michael (twins), Jillian. BS, Midwestern U., 1953; LLB, So. Meth. U., 1957. Bar: Tex. 1957, U.S. Dist. Ct. (so. dist.) Tex. 1957, U.S. Dist. Ct. (no. dist.) Tex. 1961, U.S. Tax Ct. 1961, U.S. Ct. Appeals (5th cir.) 1971, U.S. Ct. Claims 1971, U.S. Supreme Ct. 1982; CPA, Tex. Atty. Vinson, Elkins, Weems & Searls, Houston, 1957-59, Nelson, McCleskey & Harringer, Lubbock, Tex., 1959-61; pvt. practice Lubbock, 1961-62; ptnr. Smith, Baker, Field & Clifford Inc. (formerly Smith & Baker Inc.), Lubbock, 1962-84; CPA Tex., 1955-92; chmn., CEO Resthaven Funeral Home and Cemetery, Lubbock, 1979-93; cons. Svc. Corp. Internat., Lubbock, 1993—; bd. dirs. Briercroft Savs. Assn., 1962-84, Tex. Cemetery Assn., 1986-87, 90-91; pres., bd. chmn. Resthaven Funeral Home, 1965-69, Resthaven of Lubbock, Inc., 1979-93, Lakeview Meml. Gardens, 1978-86; lectr. profl. meetings on taxes and estate planning; bd. visitors So. Meth. U. Law Sch., 1968-71; chmn. estate planning seminar for women Tex. Tech. Found., 1971; pres. South Plains Trust and Estate Coun., 1963-64, others. Contbr. articles to profl. jours. Mem. Lubbock Planning and Zoning Commn., 1964-65, chmn., 1966, budget div. United Fund.; co-chmn. profl. div. United Way, 1981; tchr., bd. dirs. First Meth. Ch., Lubbock, 1963-88; pres. Haynes Elem. Sch. PTA, 1968-69; past mem. pres.'s adv. bd. Lubbock Christian Coll.; bd. dirs. Tex. Tech U. Found., 1968-89, sec., 1969-76, vice-chmn., 1976-78, chmn., 1978-81, chmn. fund raising com. 1979-81; bd. dirs. Tex. Tech U. Med. Sch. Found., 1970-78, vice-chmn., 1972-73, chmn., 1973-74; mem. pres.'s coun. Tex. Tech U., 1979—; speaker ann. banquet Flora Acad. Found., Flora High Sch., 1991. Mem. Am. Anthroposophical Soc., Tex. Cemeteries Assn. (hon. life), Alpha Chi. Avocations: mountain trails, research, writing.

SMITH, EDWARD SAMUEL, federal judge; b. Birmingham, Ala., Mar. 27, 1919; s. Joseph Daniel and Sarah Jane (Tatum) S.; m. Innes Adams Comer, May 5, 1942; children: Edward Samuel, Innes Smith Cameron Richards. Student, Ala. Poly. Inst., 1936-38; B.A., U. Va., 1941, J.D., 1947. Bar: Va. 1947, D.C. 1948, Md. 1953. Assoc., then ptnr. firm Blair, Korner, Doyle & Appel, Washington, 1947-54; ptnr. firm Blair, Korner, Doyle & Worth, 1954-61; gen. counsel Nat. Cath. Edn. Assn., 1958-61; chief trial sect., tax div. Dept. Justice, 1961, asst. for civil trials, dep. asst. atty. gen., 1961-63; ptnr. firm, head tax dept. Piper & Marbury, Balt., 1963-78; mng. ptnr. Piper & Marbury, 1971-74; assoc. judge U.S. Ct. Claims, Washington, 1978-82; judge U.S. Ct. Appeals (Fed. Cir.), Washington, 1982—; sr. circuit judge, 1989—; liaison atty. gen. to Lawyers Com. Civil Rights Under Law, 1963; adj. faculty Cumberland Sch. Law, Samford U., 1992—. Bd. dirs. Roland Park Civic League, Inc., Balt., 1977-78; pres., St. Andrew's Soc. Washington, 1956-58. Served to lt. USNR, 1941-46; to comdr. USNR, Ret. 1968. Mem. ABA (chmn. com. on tax litigation 1977-78), Fed. Bar Assn., Md. State Bar Assn. (chmn. sect. of taxation 1971-72), D.C. Bar Assn., Va. State Bar, Met. Club, Chevy Chase Club, Lawyers Club of Washington, Summit Club (Birmingham), Lambda Chi Alpha. Democrat. Episcopalian. Office: Hugo Black US Courthouse 1729 5th Ave N Birmingham AL 35203-2052 also: US Ct Appeals Fed Crct Nat Cts Bldg 717 Madison Pl NW Washington DC 20439-0002 *The second most important rule of life is that we should never become disillusioned with the Golden Rule when others do not follow it.*

SMITH, EDWIN ERIC, lawyer; b. Louisville, Sept. 29, 1946; s. Lester Henry and Nancy Joy (Heyman) S.; m. Katharine Case Thomson, Aug. 16, 1969; children: Benjamin Clark, George Lewis, Andrew Laurence. BA, Yale U., 1968; JD, Harvard Law Sch., 1974. Bar: Mass. 1974, U.S. Dist. Ct. Mass. 1974. Assoc. Bingham, Dana & Gould, Boston, 1974-81, ptnr., 1981—; lectr. in field; Mass. commr. on uniform state laws; mem. uniform comml. code articles 5 and 9 drafting com. Lt. USNR, 1969-74. Recipient Achievement Medal USN, 1971. Mem. ABA (chmn. uniform comml. code com. bus. sect.), Am. Law Inst. (Uniform Comml. Code article 9 study com.), Am. Coll. Comml. Fin. Lawyers (bd. regents), Assn. Comml. Fin. Attys. Home: 4 Chiltern Rd Weston MA 02193-2714 Office: Bingham Dana & Gould 150 Federal St Boston MA 02110-1726

SMITH, EDWIN IDE, medical educator; b. Norfolk, Va., May 13, 1924; s. Charles Carroll and Lila (Ide) S.; m. Matilda Janet Snelling, Mar. 31, 1951; children: Sarah Pinckney Smith Crotty, Susan Ide Smith Thurmond, Charles Carroll III. Student, Harvard Coll., 1942-44, Georgetown U., 1944-46; MD, Johns Hopkins U., 1948. Diplomate Am. Bd. Surgery. Intern Johns Hopkins Hosp., Balt., 1948-49; Halsted fellow in surgery Johns Hopkins Sch. Medicine, Balt., 1949-50; resident Boston Children's Hosp., 1950, 52-53, 55-56, Vanderbilt U. Hosp., Nashville, 1953-55; pvt. practice pediatric surgery Norfolk, Va., 1956-63; assoc. prof. surgery U. Mo. Coll. Medicine, Kansas City, 1963-68, U. Okla. Coll. Medicine, Oklahoma City, 1968-71; prof. surgery U. Okla. Coll. Medicine, 1971-89; prof. surgery U. Tex. S.W. Med. Ctr., Dallas, 1989-94, emeritus prof., 1994—; surgeon-in-chief Children's Mercy Hosp., Kansas City, Kans., 1963-68; chief pediatric surgery Children's Hosp. Oklahoma City, 1968-87, U. Tex. S.W. Med. Ctr., Dallas, 1989-92. Contbr. articles to profl. jours., chpts. to books. Mem. hosp. care commn. Am. Acad. Pediatrics, 1973-79; mem. select com. med. tech. Okla. Health Planning Commn., 1981-85; trustee Ctrl. Okla. Ambulance Trust, Oklahoma City, 1976-80. Mem. Am. Burn Assn., ACS, Am. Pediatric Surgery Assn.,

Am. Surg. Assn., Soc. Surg. Oncology, So. Surg. Assn. Republican. Episcopalian. Avocations: tennis, travel. Office: U Tex SW Med Ctr 5323 Harry Hines Blvd Dallas TX 75235-9031

SMITH, EDWIN O., real estate executive, state legislator; b. Brattleboro, Vt., Sept. 12, 1945; s. Orson G. and Eleanor (Stearns) S.; m. Sharron Holmes, Aug. 21, 1969; children: Dwight H., Jason E. Grad., Northampton (Mass.) Jr. Coll., 1968. With Peerless Ins. Co., Keene, N.H., 1968-70; ind. agt. Colton Ins. Agy., Hinsdale, N.H., 1970-88; real estate broker River Valley Realty Inc., Hinsdale, 1987—; mem. N.H. Ho. of Reps., Concord, 1992—. Asst. majority whip N.H. Ho. of Reps.; trustee, vice chmn. Rescue Inc., Brattleboro, Vt., 1981—; mem. Hinsdale Budget Com., 1971-86, also chmn. Mem. Aircraft Owners and Pilots Assn., Masons, Elks, Lions (pres. dir.). Republican. Home: PO Box 26 1761 Brattleboro Rd Hinsdale NH 03451 Office: River Valley Realty Inc 16 Main St Hinsdale NH 03451

SMITH, ELAINE DIANA, foreign service officer; b. Glencoe, Ill., Sept. 15, 1924; d. John Raymond and Elsie (Gelbard) S. BA, Grinnell Coll., 1946; MA, Johns Hopkins U., 1947; PhD, Am. U., 1959. Commd. fgn. service officer U.S. Dept. State, 1947; assigned to Brussels, 1947-50, Tehran, Iran, 1951-53, Wellington, N.Z., 1954-56; assigned to Dept. State, Washington, 1956-60, Ankara, Turkey, 1960-69, Istanbul, Turkey, 1969-72; assigned to Dept. Commerce Exchange, 1972-73; dep. examiner Fgn. Service Bd. Examiners, 1974-75; Turkish desk officer (Dept. State), Washington, 1975-78; consul gen., Izmir, Turkey, 1978—. Author: Origins of the Kemalist Movement, 1919-1923, 1959. Recipient Alumni award Grinnell Coll. 1957. Mem. U.S. Fgn. Svc. Assn., Phi Beta Kappa. Home: The Plaza 800 25th St NW Apt 306 Washington DC 20037

SMITH, ELDRED GEE, church leader; b. Lehi, Utah, Jan. 9, 1907; s. Hyrum Gibbs and Martha E. (Gee) S.; m. Jeanne A. Ness, Aug. 17, 1932 (dec. June 1977); children: Miriam Smith Skeen, Eldred Gary, Audrey Gay Smith Vance, Gordon Raynor, Sylvia Dawn Smith Isom; m. Hortense H. Child, May 18, 1978; stepchildren: Carol Jane Child Burdette (dec.), Thomas Robert Child. Employed with sales div. Bennett Glass & Paint Co., Salt Lake City, 6 years; mech. design engr. Remington Arms Co., 2 years; design engr., prodn. equipment design Tenn. Eastman Corp., Oak Ridge, Tenn., 3 years; now presiding patriarch Ch. Jesus Christ of Latter-day Saints. Home: 2942 Devonshire Cir Salt Lake City UT 84108-2526 Office: 47 E South Temple Salt Lake City UT 84150-1005

SMITH, ELDRED REID, library educator; b. Payette, Idaho, June 30, 1931; s. Lawrence E. and Jennie (Reid) S.; m. Judith Ausubel, June 25, 1953; children: Steven, Janet. B.A., U. Calif.-Berkeley, 1956, M.A., 1962; M.L.S., U. So. Calif., 1957. Aquisition reference librarian Long Beach State Coll. Library, 1957-59; reference librarian San Francisco State Coll. Library, 1959-60; bibliographer U. Calif.-Berkeley Library, 1960-65, head search div. acquisition dept., 1966-69, head loan dept., 1969-70, asso. univ. librarian, 1970-72, acting univ. librarian, 1971-72; dir. libraries, also prof. SUNY, Buffalo, 1973-76; univ. librarian U. Minn., 1976-87, prof., 1976—; lectr. Sch. Library Sci., U. Wash., 1972; bd. dirs. Center for Research Libraries, 1975-77. Author: The Librarian, The Scholar, and the Future of the Research Library, 1990; contbr. articles to libr. jours. Council on Library Resources fellow, 1970. Mem. ALA, Assn. Research Libraries (dir. 1979-85, pres. 1983-84), Assn. Coll. and Research Libraries (pres. 1977-78, dir. 1976-79, com. on academic status 1969-74, chmn. univ. libraries sect. 1974-75). Home: 576 Montcalm Pl Saint Paul MN 55116-1730 Office: Univ Minn 149 Nicholson Hall 216 Pillsbury Dr SE Minneapolis MN 55455-0138

SMITH, ELEANOR JANE, academic administrator; b. Circleville, Ohio, Jan. 10, 1933; d. John Allen and Eleanor Jane (Dade) Lewis; m. James L. Banner, Aug. 10, 1957 (div. 1972); 1 child, Teresa M. Banner Watters; m. Paul M. Smith Jr. BS, Capital U., 1955; PhD, The Union Inst., Cin., 1972. Tchr. Columbus (Ohio) Pub. Schs., 1956-64, Worthington (Ohio) Pub. Schs., 1964-72; from faculty to administrator U. Cin., 1972-88; dean Smith Coll., Northampton, Mass., 1988-90; v.p. acad. affairs, provost William Paterson Coll., Wayne, N.J., 1990-94; chancellor U. Wis.-Parkside, Kenosha, 1994—; dir. Afrikan Am. Inst., Cin., 1977-84; adv. bd. Edwina Bookwalter Gantz Undergrad. Studies Ctr., Cin. Spl. Arts Night Com., Northampton, 1988-89. Named career woman of achievement YWCA, Cin., 1983. Mem. Nat. Assn. Women in Higher Edn., Am. Assn. for Higher Edn., Leadership Am. (bd. dirs., treas. 1993-95), Nat. Assn. Black Women Historians (founder, co-dir. 1979-82. Avocations: music, travel, reading. Home: 40 Harborview Dr Racine WI 53403 Office: U Wis Parkside 900 Wood Rd Kenosha WI 53141

SMITH, ELISE FIBER, international non-profit development agency administrator; b. Detroit, June 14, 1932; d. Guy and Mildred Geneva (Johnson) Fiber; m. James Frederick Smith, Aug. 11, 1956 (div. 1983); children: Gregory Douglas, Guy Charles. BA, U. Mich., 1954; postgrad., U. Strasbourg, France, 1954-55; MA, Case Western Res. U., 1956. Tchr. U.S. Binat. Ctr., Caracas, Venezuela, 1964-66; instr. English Am. U., 1966-68; prof. lang. faculty Catholic U., Lima, Peru, 1968-70; coord. English lang. and culture program, lang. faculty El Rosario U., Bogota, Colombia, 1971-73; lang. specialist, mem. faculty Am. U., English Lang. Inst., 1975-78; exec. dir. OEF Internat. (name formerly Overseas Edn. Fund), Washington, 1978-89, bd. dirs.; dir. Leadership Program, Winrock Internat. Inst. for Agrl. Devel., 1989—; v.p, bd. dirs. Pvt. Agys. Collaborating Together, N.Y.C., 1983-89; trustee Internat. Devel. Conf., Washington, 1983—, mem. exec. com., 1985-90; mem. hon. com. for Global Crossroads Nat. Assembly, Global Perspectives in Inc. (PACT), N.Y.C., 1984, D.C., 1984-92, mem. gen. assembly, 1992; mem. nat. com. Focus on Hunger '84, L.A.; sec. bd. dirs. U.S. Binat. Sch., Bogota, Colombia, 1971-73; ofcl. observer UN Conf. on Status of Women, 1980; mem. mental health adv. com. Dept. State, 1974-76; U.S. del. planning seminar integration women in devel. OAS, 1978; ofcl. observer UN Conf. on Status of Women, Nairobi, Kenya, 1985; participant Women, Law and Devel. Forum; bd. dirs. Interaction (Am. Council for Vol. Internat. Action), 1985-88, mem. exec. com., co-chair commn. advancement women, 1994; bd. dirs. Sudan-Am. Found.; mem. adv. bd. Global Links Devel. Edn., Washington, 1985-86; adv. coun. Global Fund for Women, 1988-93. Coeditor: Toward Internationalism: Readings in Cross-cultural Communication, 1979, 2d edit. 1986. Bd. dirs. Internat. Ctr. Rsch. on Women, 1992—; mem. adv. com. on vol. fgn. aid U.S. AID, 1994—. Rotary Internat. fellow Strasbourg, France, 1954-55; grantee Dept. State, 1975. Mem. Soc. Internat. Devel., Assn. Women in Devel., Soc. Intercultural Edn. Tng. and Rsch., Coalition Women in Internat. Devel. (co-founder 1979, chair 1993—), Pvt. Agys. in Internat. Devel. (co-chmn. 1980-82, pres. 1982-85), Nat. Assn. Fgn. Student Affairs (grantee 1975), U. Mich. Alumni Assn., Women's Fgn. Policy Group. Unitarian. Home: Apt 304 4701 Connecticut Ave NW Washington DC 20008-5617 Office: Winrock Inst Ste 600 1611 N Kent St Arlington VA 22209-2111

SMITH, ELIZABETH PATIENCE, oil industry executive, lawyer; b. N.Y.C., June 21, 1949; d. Harry Martin and Frances (Blauvelt) S.; m. Kwan-Lan Mao, Apr. 1, 1989. BA cum laude, Bucknell U., 1971; JD, Georgetown U., 1976. Atty. Texaco Inc., White Plains, N.Y., 1976-84, dir. investor rels., 1984-89, v.p. corp. communications div., investor rels., 1989-92, v.p. investor rels. and shareholder svcs., 1992—. Mem. bd. trustees Marymount Coll., Tarrytown, N.Y.; bd. dirs. Westchester Edn. Coalition, Texaco Found. Mem. Petroleum Investor Rels. Assn., Nat. Investor Rels. Inst., Investor Rels. Assn., N.Y. Bar Assn. Office: Texaco Inc 2000 Westchester Ave White Plains NY 10650-0001

SMITH, ELMER W., federal government administrator; b. Trenton, N.J., June 10, 1928; s. Elmer Watson and Violet Mae (Thatcher) S.; m. Caroline Jo Elliott Crea, June 23, 1956; children: Caroline Elinore, Elliott Pearson, David Grant, Eric Graham. BA, Drew U., 1951; MPA, Syracuse U., 1952. Budget analyst Dept. HEW, Washington, 1956-64; exec. officer Welfare Adminstrn., Washington, 1964-67; dep. regional commr. Social and Rehab. Svc., Charlottesville, Va., 1968-70; regional commr. Social and Rehab. Svc., N.Y.C., 1970-76; assoc. commr. for policy and planning Social Security Adminstrn., Balt., 1976-79; dir. office of eligibility policy Health Care Financing Adminstrn., Balt. 1979-90, sr. program advisor Medicaid Bur., 1990-93, dir. Medicaid Spec. program initiatives staff, 1993—; pres., bd. dirs. Wm. H. Masson & Co., Balt., 1992—. Vestry mem. Christ the King Ch., Woodlawn, Md., 1977-88. Mem. Am. Soc. for Pub. Adminstrn. Episcopalian. Avocations: coin collecting, gardening, hiking. Office: Health Care

Fin Adminstrn Medicaid Bur Rm 400 EHR 6325 Security Blvd Baltimore MD 21207

SMITH, ELSKE VAN PANHUYS, retired university administrator; b. Monte Carlo, Monaco, Nov. 9, 1929; came to U.S., 1943; d. Johan Abraham AE and Vera (Craven) van Panhuys; m. Henry J. Smith, Sept. 10, 1950 (dec. June 1983); children: Ralph A., Kenneth A. BA, Radcliffe U., 1950, MS, 1951, PhD, 1956. Rsch. assoc. Sacramento Peak Observatory, Sunspot, N.Mex., 1955-62; rsch. fellow Joint Inst. for Lab. Astrophysics, Boulder, Colo., 1962-63; assoc. to prof. U. Md., College Park, 1963-80, asst. provost, 1973-78, asst. vice chancellor, 1978-80; dean, coll. humanities and scis. Va. Commonwealth U., Richmond, 1980-92, interim dir. environ. studies, 1992-95; ret., 1995; cons. NASA, Greenbelt, Md., 1964-76, reviewer, Washington, 1970's, NSF, Washington, 1970's, 86; vis. com. Assn. of Univ.'s for Rsch. in Astronomy, Tucson, 1975-78. Author: (with others) Solar Flares, 1963, Introductory Astronomy and Astrophysics, 1973, 3d edit., 1992; also numerous articles. Mem. various environ. orgns. Rsch. grantee Rsch. Corp., 1956-57, NSF, 1966-69, 90, NIH, 1981-90, NASA, 1974-78; program grantee Va. Found. for Humanities, 1985, NEH, 1987, Assn. Am. Colls., 1987. Fellow AAAS; mem. Am. Astron. Soc. (counselor 1977-80, vis. prof. 1975-78), Internat. Astron. Union (chief U.S. del. 1979, U.S. Nat. com.), Coun. Colls. of Arts and Scis. (bd. dirs. 1989), Phi Beta Kappa. Democrat. Avocations: hiking, travel, environmental issues. Home: PO Box 756 Lee MA 01238

SMITH, ELVIE LAWRENCE, corporate director; b. Eatonia, Sask., Can., Jan. 8, 1926; s. Harry Burton and Laura Mae (Fullerton) S.; m. Jacqueline Moy Colleary, Dec. 15, 1956; children: Ronald, Paul, David, Marguerite. BS with great distinction, U. Sask., 1947; MSME, Purdue U., 1949; LLD (hon.), Concordia U., 1983; D in Engring., Carleton U., 1984, Purdue U., 1987. Exptl. engr. Nat. Research Council, Ottawa, Ont., Can., 1949-56; with Pratt & Whitney Can. Inc., 1957—, exec. v.p. ops., 1978-80, pres., CEO, 1980-84, chmn., 1984-94, dir., 1970—. Decorated Order of Can., 1992; recipient Sawyer award ASME, 1986, Gold Medal Polish People's Republic, 1985, Aerospace Leadership award SAE, 1994; named to Can. Aviation Hall of Fame, 1993. Fellow Can. Aeronautics and Space Inst. (McCurty award 1976, C.D. Howe award 1983); mem. Aerospace Industries Assn. Can. (life, chmn. 1982-83), Gatineau Gliding Club. Home: St-Lambert, PQ Canada Office: Pratt & Whitney Can Inc, 1000 Marie Victorin, Longueuil, PQ Canada J4G 1A1

SMITH, ELVIN T., communications executive; b. Aztec, N.M., June 30, 1930; s. Orville V. and E. Avisa (Townsend) S.; m. Elaine C. Andersen, May 21, 1959; children: Eric T., Ellen C. BA, Ft. Lewis Coll., 1956. Sales exec. Sta. KOAT-TV, Albuquerque, 1962-75, sales mgr., 1975—; owner W.A. Group, Albuquerque, 1980-88. Photo dir. TV program Sandia Tram, 1970. Dir. Crime Stoppers, Albuquerque, 1988. Avocations: flying, fishing, travel. Office: Sta KOAT-TV 3801 Carlisle Blvd NE Albuquerque NM 87107-4501

SMITH, ELWIN EARL, mining and oil company executive; b. Ellicottville, N.Y., Sept. 30, 1922; s. Henry B. and Beatrice M. (Spellman) S.; m. Mary Ellen Kirchmaier, Nov. 4, 1944; children: Peter E., Michael E., Timothy E. Student, U. Ala., 1941-43, NYU, 1954, Internat. Program, Harvard Bus. Sch., 1962. Sales engr. Cities Service Oil Co., N.Y.C., 1949-55; gen. sales mgr. Climax Molybdenum Co., N.Y.C., 1955-64; exec. v.p., dir. Lithium Corp. Am., Gastonia, N.C., 1964-69; pres., chief exec. officer Lithium Corp. Am., 1969-77; v.p., dir. Gulf Resources & Chem. Co., Houston, 1970-77; pres., dir. Asia Lithium Corp., Osaka, Japan, 1970-77; pres. Amax Iron Ore, Greenwich, Conn., 1977-80; group v.p. group exec. for indsl. minerals and resources group Amax Iron Ore, 1978-80; exec. v.p. Amax Inc., Greenwich, 1981-82, sr. exec. v.p., 1982-85; prin. Elwin Smith Internat. Sales Engrs., Darien, Conn., 1986—; dir. Essex Chem. Corp., 1983-88, Freeport Mac Mo Ran Copper Co., 1988—, Am. Metal & Coal Co., Greenwich, Ct., Ethanol Corp., Sydney, Australia; chmn. Seven Seas Cinema, Stamford, Conn., 1985—. Served to 1st lt. U.S. Army Paratroopers, 1943-48. Decorated Combat Inf. badge, Bronze Star, sr. parachute badge. Mem. AIME, Am. Soc., Mining and Petroleum Club of Sydney (Australia), Copper Club N.Y., Weeburn Country Club, Masons. Republican. Home and Office: 7 Tokeneke Trl Darien CT 06820-6126

SMITH, EMIL L., biochemist, consultant; b. N.Y.C., July 5, 1911; s. Abraham and Esther (Lubart) S.; m. Esther Press, Mar. 29, 1934; children—Joseph Bernard, Jeffrey Bernard. B.S., Columbia U., 1931, Ph.D. 1936. Instr. biophysics Columbia U., N.Y.C., 1936-38; John Simon Guggenheim fellow Cambridge U., Eng., 1938-39, Yale U., New Haven, 1939-40; fellow Rockefeller Inst., N.Y.C., 1940-42; biophysicist, biochemist E. R. Squibb & Sons, New Brunswick, N.J., 1942-46; assoc. prof. to prof. biochemistry U. Utah, Salt Lake City, 1946-63; prof. biol. chemistry Sch. Medicine UCLA, 1963-79, prof. emeritus, 1979—; cons. NIH, Am. Cancer Soc., Office Naval Research. Author: (with others) Principles of Biochemistry, 7th edit., 1983; also numerous articles. Recipient Stein-Moore award Protein Soc., 1987. Mem. NAS, Am. Acad. Arts and Scis., Am. Philos. Soc., Am. Soc. Biol. Chemists, Am. Chem. Soc., Protein Soc., Acad. Scis. USSR (fgn.). Office: UCLA Sch Medicine Los Angeles CA 90095-1737

SMITH, EMMITT J., III, professional football player; b. Pensacola, Fla., May 15, 1969; s. Emmitt Jr. and Mary Smith. Student, U. Fla. With Dallas Cowboys, 1990—; player Pro-Bowl, 1990-92, NFC Championship game, 1992, 93, Super Bowl XXVII, 1992, Super Bowl XXVIII, 1993; owner Emmitt Inc. Recipient MVP award for season, 1993, MVP award for Super Bowl, 1993; named Running Back, Sporting News Coll. All-Am. team, 1989, Offensive Rookie of Yr., 1990, Running Back, Sporting News NFL All-Pro team, 1992, 93, NFL Player of Yr., Sporting News, 1993; named to Pro-Bowl, 1993. Led NFL in rushing, 1991, 92, 93; Led NFL running backs in scoring, 1992. Office: Dallas Cowboys One Cowboys Pkwy Irving TX 75063*

SMITH, EPHRAIM PHILIP, university dean, educator; b. Fall River, Mass., Sept. 19, 1942; s. Jacob Max and Bertha (Horvitz) S.; m. Linda Sue Katz, Sept. 3, 1967; children—Benjamin, Rachel, Leah. B.S., Providence Coll., 1964; M.S., U. Mass., 1965; Ph.D., U. Ill., 1968. Chmn. dept. acctg. U. R.I., Kingston, 1972-73; dean Sch. Bus. Shippensburg State Coll., Pa., 1973-75; dean Coll. Bus. Adminstrn. Cleve. State U., 1975-90; dean Sch. Bus. Adminstrn. and Econ. Calif. State U., Fullerton, 1990—. Co-author: Principles of Supervision: First and Second Level Management, 1984, Federal Taxation-Advanced Topics, 1995, Federal Taxation-Basic Principles, 1995, Federal Taxation Comprehensive Topics, 1995; contbr. articles to profl. jours. Mem. Am. Acctg. Assn., Am. Taxation Assn., Am. Inst. for Decision Scis., Fin. Execs. Inst., Beta Gamma Sigma, Beta Alpha Psi. Office: Calif State U Sch Bus Adminstrn and Econ 800 N State College Blvd Fullerton CA 92631-3547

SMITH, ERIC, wholesale distribution executive; b. 1953. Graduate, Ball State U., 1976. With ADIAppliances, Indpls., 1975-96; with Major Video Concepts, Inc., Indpls., 1984—, now v.p. Office: Major Video Concepts Inc 7998 Georgetown Rd Indianapolis IN 46268*

SMITH, ERIC ALAN, meteorology educator; b. West Palm Beach, Fla., July 16, 1951; s. Karl V. and Margaret (Foltz) S.; m. Karen Sue Greiner, Jan. 1, 1984 (dec. Nov. 1985); 1 child, Debra; m. Ann Rose Nelson, Feb. 20, 1993. BS, U. Wis., 1966; MS, Colo. State U., 1980, PhD, 1984. Project specialist U. Wis., Madison, 1966-68, project specialist Space Sci. & Engring. Ctr., 1969-75; rsch. assoc. in atmospheric sci. Colo. State U., Ft. Collins, 1975-79, assoc. rsch. scientist, 1979-80, 81-84; asst. prof. King Abdul-Aziz U., Jeddah, Saudi Arabia, 1981; assoc. prof. meteorology dept. Fla. State U., Tallahassee, 1985-89, prof., 1990—; cons. in field. Contbr. articles to profl. jours., chpts. to books. Pres. Madison (Wis.) Measure for Measure, 1967-69, Madison Area Peace Action Coun., 1972-74. Grantee NASA, 1986—, NSF, 1979—, Fla. Tech. R&D Authority, 1989. Fellow Am. Meteorol. Soc.; mem. Am. Geophys. Union, Sigma Xi, Chi Epsilon Pi. Avocations: canoeing, white water rafting, old furniture refinishing. Home: 312 Millbranch Rd Tallahassee FL 32312-1506 Office: Fla State U Dept Meteorology Tallahassee FL 32306

SMITH, ERNEST E., lawyer, educator; b. Gonzales, Tex., Sept. 8, 1936; s. Ernest Edgar and Sue (Harris) S.; m. Paula Virginia Young; children—Brian, Carter. B.A., So. Methodist U., 1958; LL.B., Harvard U., 1962. Asst. prof. law U. Tex., Austin, 1963-65, assoc. prof., 1965-68, prof., 1968—, dean, 1974-79; of counsel Hughes & Luce, Attys., Dallas, 1983—. Co-author: Cases and Materials on Oil and Gas, 1972, Probate and Decendents Estates, 1971, Oil and Gas Law, 1985, Texas Oil & Gas Law, 1989; bd. editors Oil and Gas Reporter, Dallas, 1982—; contbr. articles to profl. jours. Treas. St. Andrew's Episcopal Sch., Austin, 1981-83; trustee Rocky Mountain Law Found., 1986—, Ea. Mineral Law Found., 1988—. Mem. Federacion Interamericana de Abogados, State Bar Tex. (sec., treas., chmn. oil and gas law sect. 1982—). Methodist. Avocation: Spanish language. Home: 1400 Winsted Ln Austin TX 78703-3852 Office: U Tex Sch Law 727 E 26th St Austin TX 78705-3224

SMITH, ERNEST KETCHAM, electrical engineer; b. Peking, China, May 31, 1922; (parents Am. citizens); s. Ernest Ketcham and Grace (Goodrich) S.; m. Mary Louise Standish, June 23, 1950; children: Priscilla Varland, Nancy Smith, Cynthia Jackson. BA in Physics, Swarthmore Coll., 1944; MSEE, Cornell U., 1951, Ph.D., 1956. Chief plans and allocations engr. Mut. Broadcasting System, 1946-49; with Nat. Bur. Standards, 1951-65; chief ionosphere research sect. Nat. Bur. Standards, Boulder, Colo., 1957-60; div. chief Nat. Bur. Standards, 1960-65; dir. aeronomy lab. Environ. Sci. Services Adminstrn., Boulder, 1965-67; dir. Inst. Telecommunication Scis., 1968, dir. univ. relations, 1968-70; assoc. dir. Inst. Telecommunications Scis. Office of Telecommunications, Boulder, 1970-72, cons., 1972-76; mem. tech. staff Jet Propulsion Lab. Calif. Inst. Tech., Pasadena, 1976-87; adj. prof. dept. Elec. and Computer Engring. U. Colo., Boulder, 1987—; vis. fellow Coop. Inst. Rsch. on Environ. Scis., 1968; assoc. Harvard U. Coll. Obs., 1965-75; adj. prof. U. Colo., 1969-78, 87—; internat. vice-chmn. study group 6, Internat. Radio Consultative Com., 1958-70, chmn. U.S. study group, 1970-76; mem. U.S. commn. Internat. Sci. Radio Union, mem.-at-large U.S. nat. com., 1985-88; pres. U. Colo. chpt. Sigma Xi, 1994—; convenor Boulder Gatekeepers to the Future, 1990—. Author: Worldwide Occurrence of Sporadic E, 1957; (with S. Matsushita) Ionospheric Sporadic E, 1962. Contbr. numerous articles to profl. jours. Editor: Electromagnetic Probing of the Upper Atmosphere, 1969; assoc. editor for propagation IEEE Antennas and Propagation Mag., 1989—. Mem. 1st Congl. Ch., moderator elect, 1995. Recipient Diploma d'honneur, Internat. Radio Consultative Com., Internat. Telecommunications Union, 1978. Fellow IEEE (fellow com. 1993, 94, 95), AAAS; mem. Am. Geophys. Union, Electromagnetics Acad., Svc. Club, Kiwanis, Univ. Club, Athenaeum (Pasadena), Boulder Country Club. Home: 5159 Idylwild Trl Boulder CO 80301-3667 Office: U Colo Dept Elec and Computer Engring Campus Box 425 Boulder CO 80309

SMITH, EUGENE WILSON, retired university president and educator; b. Forrest City, Ark., June 10, 1930; s. Milton Saumel and Frank Leslie (Wilson) S.; m. Rebecca Ann Slaughter, May 27, 1956; children: Lucinda Anne, Bradley Eugene. B.A., Ark. State U., 1952; M.Ed., U. Miss., 1955, Ed.D., 1958. Mem. faculty Ark. State U., State University, 1958-92, prof. emeritus, 1971-92, v.p. adminstrn., 1968-71, dean Grad. Sch., 1971-84, interim pres., 1980, sr. v.p., 1980-84, pres., 1984-92, 94-95; pres. emeritus Ark. State U., State University, 1992—, interim pres., 1994-95; pres. Jonesboro Indsl. Devel. Corp., 1983-94; mem. exec. com. Conf. So. Grad. Schs., 1973-74, Ark. State Coun. on Econ. Edn., 1987-90; mem. So. Athletic Conf., 1987-89; dir. Mercantile Bank of Jonesboro, Union Planteus Bank of Northeast Ark. Alderman, City of Jonesboro, 1982-84. Served to 1st lt. AUS, 1952-54, Korea. W.K. Kellogg Found. rsch. fellow, 1954-58. Mem. Ark. Adv. Council Elem. and Secondary Edn., Jonesboro C. of C. (dir. 1967-69, 80-85, v.p. 1981-82, pres. 1982-83), Phi Kappa Phi, Phi Delta Kappa, Kappa Delta Pi. Club: Rotary (pres. 1974-75). Home: 407 Lynne Ct Jonesboro AR 72401-5161

SMITH, EVERETT G., chemicals executive; b. 1909. Grad., Dartmouth Coll., 1930. With Edgar Ricker & Co., 1930-38; treas. Albert Trostel & Sons Co., Milw., 1938-46, v.p., 1946-51, exec. v.p., 1951-62, pres., treas., 1962—, also chmn. bd. dirs., treas.; pres. Everett Smith Investment Co. Ltd. of Del., Inc., Milw.; v.p. Maysteel Corp., Menomonee Falls, Wis. Office: Albert Trostel & Sons Co 10201 W Lincoln Ave Milwaukee WI 53227-2136*

SMITH, F. ALAN, automobile manufacturing company executive; b. 1931. BBA, Dartmouth Coll., 1952, MBA, 1953. Jr. statistician and analyst Gen. Motors Corp., 1957-63, staff asst. Office of Chmn., 1963-65, section dir. treasurer's staff, 1965-68, dir. fin. analysis, 1968-70, asst. treas., 1970-73, gen. asst. treas., then corp. treas., 1973-75, corp. v.p. fin. staff, 1975-81, pres., gen. mgr. Gen. Motors Can. Ltd., 1978-81, exec. v.p. fin., 1981—, also bd. dirs. Served with USN, 1953-56. Office: GM 3044 W Grand Blvd Detroit MI 48202-3091

SMITH, FERN M., judge; b. San Francisco, Nov. 7, 1933. AA, Foothill Coll., 1970; BA, Stanford U., 1972, JD, 1975. Bar: Calif. 1975. m. F. Robert Burrows; children: Susan Morgan, Julie. Assoc. firm Bronson, Bronson & McKinnon, San Francisco, 1975-81, ptnr., 1982-86; judge San Francisco County Superior Ct., 1986-88, U.S. Dist. Ct. for Northern Dist. Calif., 1988—; mem. U.S. Jud. Conf., Adv. Com. Rules of Evidence, 1993—; mem. hiring, mgmt. and pers. coms.; active recruiting various law schs. Contbr. articles to legal publ. Apptd. by Chief Justice Malcolm Lucas to the Calif. Jud. Coun.'s Adv. Task Force on Gender Bias in the Cts., 1987-89; bd. visitors Law Sch. Stanford U. Mem. ABA, Queen's Bench, Nat. Assn. Women Judges, Calif. Women Lawyers, Women's Forum West/Internat. Women's Forum, Bar Assn. of San Francisco, Fed. Judges Assn., 9th Cir. Dist. Judges Assn., Am. Judicature Soc., Calif. State Fed. Judicial Coun., Phi Beta Kappa.

SMITH, FLOYD LESLIE, insurance company executive; b. Silver Creek, N.Y., Nov. 12, 1931; s. Harry Lee and Fanny Diem (Arnold) S.; m. Jane Kathryn Efters, Feb. 18, 1956; children: Keith Arnold, Bruce Erik. A.B., Oberlin Coll., (Ohio), 1953; M.B.A., NYU, 1962. Investment trainee Mut. of N.Y., N.Y.C., 1953-64 dir. investments, 1964-66; asst. v.p. securities investment Mut. of N.Y., N.Y.C., 1966-69; 2d v.p. securities investment Mut. of N.Y., N.Y.C., 1969-74, v.p. securities investment, 1974-78, sr. v.p., 1978-81, chief investment officer, 1981-83, exec. v.p., chief investment officer, 1983-89; vice chmn., chief investment officer Mut. of N.Y., 1989-91; trustee The Mut. Life Ins. Co. of N.Y., 1988-91; dir. MONY Series Fund, 1983—; trustee MONY Real Empire Fidelity Investments Life Ins. Co., 1994—; trustee MONY Real Estate Investors, N.Y.C., 1981-90; bd. dirs., chmn. exec. com. Ins. Systems Am., Atlanta, 1974-82. Trustee Friends Sem., N.Y.C., 1975-84, Village of Saltaire, 1984-87; dir. St. Maarten Condo. Assn., Naples, Fla., 1993—; mem. Saltaire (N.Y.) Zoning Bd. Appeals, 1982-84. With Signal Corps, U.S. Army, 1954-56. Mem. Ft. Worth Boat Club, Edgewater Club.

SMITH, FLOYD RODENBACK, utilities executive; b. San Francisco, June 25, 1913; s. Floyd M. and Elizabeth (Rodenback) S.; m. Marion LaFrae Blythe, Oct. 5, 1935; children: Marion Katherine Smith Crain, Virginia Helene. Student, Long Beach (Calif.) Jr. Coll., 1931-33; B.S., N.Mex. State U., 1935; postgrad., Harvard Bus. School, 1962. Registered profl. engr., Tex. With Gulf States Utilities Co., Beaumont, Tex., 1935-78; dir. Gulf States Utilities Co., 1965-78, v.p. Baton Rouge div., 1965-67, v.p. div. ops., 1967-69, exec. v.p., 1969, pres., 1970-73, prin. exec. officer, 1970-78, chmn. bd., prin. exec. officer, 1973-78; pres. S.W. Atomic Energy Assocs., 1971-77; mgmt. cons., 1978-85. Bd. dirs., past chmn. Beaumont chpt. ARC; bd. dirs. Central City Devel. Corp., 1971-81, YMCA, 1980-83; trustee United Appeals, pres., 1975; pres. Tex. Atomic Energy Research Found., 1976-78. Named Disting. Alumnus Engring. Sch., N.Mex. State U., 1977. Mem. Tex. Atomic Energy Rsch. Found. (bd. dirs. 1976-78, pres. 1976-78), Southeastern Elec. Exch. (pres. 1975-76, bd. dirs. 1970-78), Tex. Rsch. League (bd. dirs. 1970-78), Assn. Electric Cos. of Tex. (chmn. 1978-79), Utility Shareholders Assn. of Tex. (chmn. 1986-93), Beaumont C. of C. (bd. dirs. 1970-76). Presbyterian (deacon). Clubs: Beaumont Country, Beaumont (dir. 1974-76). Home: Tower Club 21 Cheska Hole Beaumont TX 77706-2750

SMITH, FRANK EDWARD, publisher, editor; b. Easton, Pa., Oct. 1, 1912; s. Frank Edward and Ella (Heavener) S.; m. Arlene K. Mumbower, Sept. 9, 1937; 1 child, Nancy Joan. m. Lena June Popenciu, Sept. 16, 1950; m. Margaret Zimmer, Oct. 21, 1989. BS, East Stroudsburg (Pa.) U., 1934; MA, NYU, 1946; D Hypnotherapy (hon.), Brodheadsville U., 1981; grad., Pasco

County Sheriff's Office Citizens Police Acad., 1991. Cert. hypnologist; cert. hypnotherapist. Tchr., coach pub. schs. Easton, 1934-36; supervising prin., 1936-38; dir. employee activities Riegel Paper Co., Milford, N.J., 1938-43; nat. field rep. ARC, 1943-44; recreation dir. Gen. Electric Co., Erie, Pa., 1947-50; adminstrv. asst. C. J. La Roche Advt. Agy., N.Y.C., 1950-52; promotion mgr. McFadden Publs., N.Y.C., 1952-54; mgr. Buttenheim Pub. Co., Cleve., 1954-62; pub. School Product News; editor Changing Sch. Market Indsl. Pub. Co., Cleve., 1962-77; editorial cons., staff columnist Peter Li Inc., Dayton, Ohio, 1977-79; staff columnist 18 mags. Sieber Pub., New Port Richey, Fla., 1979—; chmn. Frank E. Smith Inc., 1978-79; mem. faculty Black Hills Mgmt. Seminar, 1983. Chief co-author: It Doesn't Pay to Work Too Hard; Monthly columnist: Ednl. Dealer, Money Making Magic Mag., Service Business Mag., 1980-81; contbr. articles to profl. jours. Bd. dirs. Beacon Woods (Fla.) Civic Assn., 1979-85, 1987-88, publicity chmn. 1979-85; warrant officer U.S. Mcht. Marines, 1945-46; mem. exec. com. Rep. Party, 1991. Recipient Spl. award Nat. Sch. Supply and Equipment Assn., 1971, Black Hills Gang plaque, 1976, Spl. Pres.'s award, 1976, Alumni award East Stroudsburg State U., 1979, cert. of appreciation Assn. Sch. Bus. Ofcls., 1975-76, Disting. Svc. award Pasco County, 1992. Mem. Nat. Sch. Supply Assn. (hon. life mem.; dir., exec. com. 1973-74, com. long range planning 1975-79), Internat. Assn. Counselors and Therapists, Nat. Audio Visual Assn. (cert. media specialist; faculty U. Ind. Inst. 1970-79, Spl. award 1973, 77, profl. devel. bd. 1974-80, public relations com. 1976-79, Inst. cert. 1970-75, com. chmn. continuing edn. com., disting. service award 1981), Edn. Industries (dir., sec.-treas. 1974—), Assn. Ednl. Communications and Tech. (exhibitors com. 1971—), Edn. Mgmt. Council (chmn. 1976), Internat. Communications Industries Assn. (communications tech. specialist), Fla. Free-lance Writers Assn., Phi Delta Kappa, Kappa Delta Pi. Clubs: High Twelve Internat, Masons. Home: 12846 Ironwood Cir Bayonet Point FL 34667-2351

SMITH, FRANK FORSYTHE, JR., lawyer; b. Crystal City, Tex., June 2, 1942; s. Frank F. and Allyne Y. (Allen) S.; m. Martha S. Stroud, Aug. 7, 1965; children: Martha Lee, Amanda L. BA, U. Tex., 1964, JD, 1968; MA, U. Mich., 1965. Bar: Tex. 1968. Assoc., ptnr. Vinson & Eklins, Houston, 1968—. Contbr. articles to profl. jours. Mem. Am. Land Title Assn. Lender's Coun., State Bar of Tex., Am. Coll. Real Estate Lawyers. Office: Vinson & Elkins 3536 First City Tower 1001 Fannin Houston TX 77002-6760

SMITH, FRANKLIN SUMNER, JR., retired insurance executive; b. Athens, Ga., Jan. 11, 1924; s. Franklin Sumner and Florence (Davis) S.; m. Eleanor Deanne Milligan, Feb. 22, 1947 (dec. Dec. 1982); children: Franklin Sumner III, Katharine Ruth; m. Jane Martin, Apr. 6, 1986. Student, Davidson Coll., 1940-41, Furman U., 1941-42. V.p., sec. Frank S. Smith Co., Inc., Columbia, S.C., 1946-60; resident mgr. Dick & Merle-Smith, N.Y.C., 1961-66; with Colonial Life & Accident Ins. Co., Columbia, 1966-93, vice chmn. bd., 1987-92, pres., CEO, 1992-93; vice chmn. bd. Colonial Cos., Inc., Columbia, 1989-92, pres., CEO, 1992-93, bd. dirs., 1989-94. Mem. Richland County Coun., Columbia, 1965-70, chmn. 1967-69; chmn. bd. trustees Richland Meml. Hosp., 1971-80, 93—; mem. United Way of Midlands, S.C., gen. campaign chmn., 1977, pres., 1979; pres. Greater Columbia C. of C., 1974-75, S.C. C. of C., 1987-88, U. S.C. Ednl. Found., 1992—. Recipient Vol. of Yr. award United Way of S.C., 1977, Humanitarian of Yr. award United Way of Midlands, 1989, Amb. of Yr. award Greater Columbia C. of C., 1991, Humanitarian award Richland Meml. Hosp. Found., 1993, Outstanding Philanthropist award Assn. Fundraising Execs. (Ctrl. S.C. chpt.), 1994. Mem. Assn. of S.C. Life Ins. Cos. (pres. 1973, 82), S.C. Mcpl. Assn. (pres. 1964-65), Assn. of U.S Army (pres. Palmetto chpt. 1978-82, Civilian of Yr. award 1983), Pine Tree Hunt Club (pres. 1954-56), The Palmetto Club (pres. 1976-89, chmn. 1990—). Presbyterian. Home: 4720 Wrenwood Ln Columbia SC 29206-4650

SMITH, FRED WESLEY, communications company executive; b. Arkoma, Okla., Jan. 1, 1934; s. Erma (Howard) Wells; m. Mary Blanche Moore, May 1961; children: Fred W. Jr., Jonathan Paul, Deborah Lee. Student, Ark. Poly. Tech. Coll. Classified advt. salesman S.W. Times Record, Ft. Smith, Ark., 1951-53; classified advt. mgr. Southwest Times Record, Ft. Smith Ark., 1953-55, nat. advt mgr. 1956-59, advt. mgr., 1959-60, asst. gen. mgr., 1960-61; gen. mgr. Las Vegas Rev. Jour., 1961-66; v.p. western newspaper div. Donrey Media Group, Las Vegas, 1966-73, exec. v.p. 1973-87, pres., 1987—; bd. dirs. First Interstate Bank of Nev., Reno. Former bd. dirs. United Fund, Clark County Boys Club, Las Vegas; mem. exec. bd. Boy Scouts Am., Las Vegas; former mem., chmn. adv. bd. Salvation Army, Las Vegas; bd. trustees U. Nev. Las Vegas Found., U. of the Ozarks; nat. adv. bd. First Comml. nank, Little Rock. Mem. Sigma Delta Chi. Avocations: boating, golfing, skiing. Office: Donrey Media Group 601 N Hollywood Blvd Las Vegas NV 89110-4105 also: Las Vegas Review-Journal PO Box 70 1111 W Bonanza Rd Las Vegas NV 89106-3545

SMITH, FREDA M., minister; b. Pocatello, Idaho, Nov. 22, 1935; s. Alfred Avery and Mary V. (Clark) S. BA in Psychology, Calif. State U., Sacramento, 1974, MA in Psychology, 1989; D of Ministry (hon.), Samaritan Theol. Inst., 1990. Ordained to ministry Universal Fellowship Met. Cmty. Chs., 1973. Pastor Cathedral of Promise, Met. Cmty. Chs., Sacramento, 1972—; instr. Samaritan Theol. Inst., L.A., 1974—; dir. evangelism Universal Fellowship Met. Cmty. Chs., worldwide, 1993—, vice-moderator, bd. elders, 1973-93. Author: Dear Dora/Dangerous Derek, 1970; author video series Homosexuality and the Bible, 1993; author audio series Manna for the Journey, 1988. Chair Sacramento LGB Town Coun., 1992-93; co-chair Calif. Com. for Law Reform, 1971-74. Recipient Eleanor Roosevelt Club award, 1975, Woman in History award for courage Sacramento History Ctr., 1991. Mem. Phi Kappa Phi. Avocations: photography, chess, gold panning, 4 wheeling, reading. Home: 6209 Governor Ln Sacramento CA 95828 Office: River City Met Cmty Chs PO Box 245125 Sacramento CA 95824

SMITH, FREDDYE L(EE), financial planner; b. Oklahoma City, Oct. 16, 1938; d. Frederick Douglass and Leeoshia M. (Harris) Moon; divorced; children: Karyn Smith Cole, Stanford Brandon. BA, Fisk U., 1959; MA, U. Chgo., 1964. CFP, 1984. Tchr. of French Chgo. Bd. Edn., 1961-69, guidance counselor, 1969-80; fin. planner Waddell & Reed, Chgo., 1980—. Contbr. articles to profl. jours. Dir. Community Mental Health Coun., Chgo., 1982—, Chgo. State U. Found. Bd., 1990—. Recipient Black Rose award League of Black Women, Chgo., 1985; named Outstanding Bus. Woman, Parkway Community House, Chgo., 1988. Mem. Internat. Assn. Fin. Planning, Internat. Bd. Stds. and Practices for CFP, Chatham Avalon Pk. Coun., Alpha Kappa Alpha, Iota Phi Lambda. Mem. Trinity United Ch. Christ. Avocations: interior design, photography. Office: Waddell & Reed 1525 E 53d Ste 803 Chicago IL 60615

SMITH, FREDERICK COE, manufacturing executive; b. Ridgewood, N.J., June 3, 1916; s. Frederick Coe and Mary (Steffee) S.; m. Ruth Pfeiffer, Oct. 5, 1940; children: Frederick Coe, Geoffrey, Roger, William, Bart. B.S., Cornell U., 1938; M.B.A., Harvard U., 1940. With Armstrong Cork Co., Lancaster, Pa., 1940-41; with Huffy Corp., Dayton, Ohio, 1946-86; pres., chief exec. officer Huffy Corp., 1961-72, chmn., chief exec. officer, 1972-76, chmn., 1976-78, chmn. exec. com., 1979-86. Chmn. Sinclair C.C. Found.; past chmn. nat. bd. dirs. Planned Parenthood Fedn., Internat. Planned Parenthood Fedn.; past chmn. Dayton Found.; trustee emeritus Alan Gutmacher Inst., Ohio United Way; chmn. employment and tng. com. Gov.'s Human Investment Coun. Lt. col. USAAF, 1941-46. Decorated Legion of Merit.

SMITH, FREDERICK ROBERT, JR., social studies educator; b. Lynn, Mass., Sept. 19, 1929; s. Frederick Robert and Margaret Theresa (Donovan) S. m. Mary Patricia Barry, Aug. 28, 1954; children: Brian Patrick, Barry Frederick, Brendan Edmund. A.B., Duke U., 1951; M.Ed., Boston U., 1954; Ph.D., U. Mich., 1960. Tchr. social studies public Jackson, Mich., 1954-58; instr. Eastern Mich. U., 1959, U. Mich., 1959-60; mem. faculty Sch. Edn., Ind. U., Bloomington, 1960-94; prof. Sch. Edn., Ind. U., 1969-94, chmn. social studies edn., 1965-69, chmn. secondary edn. dept., 1969-72, chmn. dept. curriculum and instrn., 1983-84, assoc. dean adminstrn. and devel., 1975-78, dir. external rels., 1991-94; dir. devel. Bloomington campus and annual giving Ind. U. Found., 1991-1994; prof. emeritus retired, 1994; vis. prof. U. Wis., summer 1967, U. Hawaii, summer 1972. Co-author: New

Strategies and Curriculum in Social Studies, 1969, Secondary Schools in a Changing Society, 1976; co-editor 2 books. USAF, 1951-53. Recipient Booklist award Phi Lambda Theta, 1965, 69. Mem. Ind. Coun. Social Studies (pres. 1968-69), Phi Delta Kappa, Kappa Sigma, Phi Kappa Phi. Roman Catholic. Home: 2306 E Edgehill Ct Bloomington IN 47401-6839 Office: Indiana Univ Sch of Edu Rm 3032 Bloomington IN 47405

SMITH, FREDERICK WALLACE, transportation company executive; b. Marks, Miss., Aug. 11, 1944; s. Frederick Smith; m. Diane Avis. Grad., Yale U., 1966. Cert. comml. pilot. Owner Ark Aviation, 1969-71; founder, pres. Fed Express Corp., Memphis, 1971—, chmn. bd., pres, CEO, 1975—. Served with USMC, 1966-70. Office: Fed Express Corp 2005 Corporate Ave PO Box 727 Memphis TN 38116*

SMITH, FREDRICA EMRICH, rheumatologist, internist; b. Princeton, N.J., Apr. 28, 1945; d. Raymond Jay and Carolyn Sarah (Schleicher) Emrich; m. Paul David Smith, June 10, 1967. AB, Bryn Mawr Coll., 1967; MD, Duke U., 1971. Intern, resident U.N.Mex. Affiliated Hsops., 1971-73; fellow U. Va. Hosp., Charlottesville, 1974-75; pvt. practice, Los Alamos, N.Mex., 1975—; chmn. credentials com. Los Alamos Med. Ctr., 1983—, chief staff, 1990; bd. dirs. N.Mex. Physicians Mut. Liability Ins. Co., Albuquerque. Contbr. articles to med. jours. Mem. bass sect. Los Alamos Symphony, 1975—; mem. Los Alamos County Parks and Recreation Bd., 1984-88, 92—, Los Alamos County Med. Indigent Health Care Task Force, 1989—; mem. ops. subcom. Aquatic Ctr., Los Alamos County, 1988—. Fellow ACP, Am. Coll. Rheumatology; mem. N.Mex. Med. Soc., N.Mex. Soc. Internal Medicine (councillor), Friends of Bandelier. Democrat. Avocations: swimming, music, reading, hiking. Office: Los Alamos Med Ctr 3917 West Rd Los Alamos NM 87544

SMITH, G. E. KIDDER, architect, author; b. Birmingham, Ala., Oct. 1, 1913; s. F. Hopkinson and Annie (Kidder) S.; m. Dorothea Fales Wilder, Aug. 22, 1942; children: G.E. Kidder, Hopkinson Kidder. A.B., Princeton U., 1935, M.F.A., 1938; student, Ecole Americaine, Fontainbleau, France, 1935. Registered architect, N.Y., Ala., N.C. Architect Princeton Expdn. to, Antioch, Syria, 1938; designer, site planner, camoufleur with Caribbean Architect-Engr. on Army bases, Caribbean, 1940-42; own archtl. practice, 1946—; lectr. numerous European archtl. socs., also many Am. univs. and museums; archtl. critic Yale U., 1948-49; vis. prof. MIT, 1955-56; guest arch. Archtl. Inst. Japan, 1988. Author: (with P.L. Goodwin) Brazil Builds, 1943, Switzerland Builds, 1950, Italy Builds, 1955, Sweden Builds, 1950, rev. edit., 1957, The New Architecture of Europe, 1961, The New Churches of Europe, 1963, A Pictorial History of Architecture in America, 1976, The Architecture of the United States, 3 vols, 1981, The Beacon Guide to New England Churches, 1989, Looking at Architecture, 1990, Source Book of American Architecture, 1995; also contbr. articles to encys.; exhibits, Stockholm Builds, 1940, Brazil Builds, 1943; installed: Power in the Pacific, USN, 1945 (all at Museum Modern Art, N.Y.C.); New Churches of Germany, Goethe House, N.Y.C., and Am. Fedn. Arts, 1957-58, Masterpieces of European Posters (donated), Va. State Mus., Richmond, 1958; Work of Alvar Aalto, Smithsonian Instn., 1965-82, Am.'s Archtl. Heritage for, Smithsonian Instn., 1976, Smithsonian, 1976, photographs in collection, Mus. Modern Art, Met. Mus., N.Y.C. Served to lt. USNR, 1942-46. Recipient Butler prize Princeton, 1938; fellow Am. Scandinavian Found., 1939-40; Guggenheim Found. fellow, 1946-47; President's fellow Brown U., 1949-50; research Fulbright fellow Italy, 1950-51; research Fulbright fellow India, 1965-66; Samuel H. Kress grantee India, 1967; Brunner scholar, 1959-60; Graham Found. for Advanced Study in Arts-Nat. Endowment on Arts joint fellowship, 1967-69; Nat. Endowment Arts fellow, 1974-75; Ford Found. grantee, 1970-71, 75-76; decorated Order So. Cross Brazil; Premio ENIT gold medal Italy; recipient gold medal (archtl. photography) AIA, 1964; E.M. Conover award, 1965; subject of public TV spl., 1976. Fellow AIA, Internat. Inst. Arts and Letters (life; Switzerland); mem. Soc. Archtl. Historians, Assn. Collegiate Schs. of Architecture, Municipal Art Soc. N.Y.C., Coll. Art Assn. Episcopalian. Clubs: Century Assn. (N.Y.C.); Cooperstown Country. Address: 163 E 81st St New York NY 10028

SMITH, G. ELAINE, religious organization executive. Pres. ABC Bd. of Nat. Ministries, Valley Forge, Pa. Office: ABC Board of National Ministries PO Box 851 Valley Forge PA 19482

SMITH, G. SCOTT, insurance company executive; b. 1951. Graduate, Stephen F. Austin State U., 1974. With Peat, Marwick, Mitchell & Co., Dallas, 1975-78; pres. Nat. Health Ins. Co., Grand Prairie, Tex., 1978—. Office: Nat Health Ins Co 1901 N Highway 360 Grand Prairie TX 75050*

SMITH, GARDNER WATKINS, physician; b. Boston, July 2, 1931; s. George Van Siclen and Olive (Watkins) S.; m. Susan Elizabeth Whiteford, Sept. 6, 1958; children—Elizabeth Whiteford, Rebecca Tremain, George Van Siclen II. Grad., Phillips Acad., 1949; M.D., Harvard, 1956; A.B., Princeton, 1969. Diplomate: Am. Bd. Surgery, Am. Bd. Thoracic Surgery. Intern Johns Hopkins Hosp., Balt., 1956-57; asst. resident Johns Hopkins Hosp., 1958-59, fellow, 1957-58, asst. in surgery, 1957-59, prof. surgery, 1970—, surgeon, 1970—, dep. dir. dept. surgery, 1978-85; asst. resident U. Va., Charlottesville, 1959-61, resident, 1961-62, asst. in surgery, 1959-63, cardiovascular resident, 1962-63, instr., 1963-65, asst. prof., 1965-68, assoc. prof., 1968-70, surgeon, 1963-70; chief surgery Balt. City Hosp., 1970-79, vis. surgeon, 1979-85; chmn. sect. surg. scis. Johns Hopkins Bayview Med. Ctr., 1985—; cons. Greater Balt. Med. Ctr., 1970-91, Loch Haven VA Hosp., Balt., 1971-92, Walter Reed Army Med. Ctr., 1976-90, Nat. Naval Med. Ctr., 1984-90. Contbr. articles to med. jours. Mem. Soc. U. Surgeons, Am., So. surg. assns., A.C.S., Am. Gastroenterol. Assn., Assn. for Acad. Surgery, Balt. City Med. Soc., Halsted Soc., Med. and Chirurgical Faculty of Md., Soc. Surgery Alimentary Tract, Soc. Vascular Surgery, Internat. Cardiovascular Soc., So. Soc. Clin. Surgeons, Southeastern Surg Congress, So. Assn. Vascular Surgery, Va. Surg. Assn., Cum Laude Soc., Alpha Omega Alpha, Nu Sigma Nu. Home: 1503 Old Orchard Ln Baltimore MD 21204-3654 Office: Johns Hopkins Bayview Med Ctr 4940 Eastern Ave Baltimore MD 21224-2780

SMITH, GENE R., engineering company executive; b. 1933. Exec. v.p. Nooter Eriksen Sys., St. Louis. Office: Nooter Eriksen Systems 1400 S 3rd St Saint Louis MO 63104*

SMITH, GEOFFREY ADAMS, special purpose mobile unit manufacturing executive; b. Bay Shore, N.Y., Mar. 17, 1947; s. Ian Morrison and Dorothy Brumbach (Adams) S.; m. Linda Ann Lehmann, July 15, 1972; 1 child, Chad William. BS in Managerial Sci., Lehigh U., 1969. Supr. Roadway Express, South Kearny, N.Y., 1969-72; v.p. mktg. Med. Coaches, Inc., Oneonta, N.Y., 1972-76, pres., chief exec. officer, 1976—, chmn. bd., 1976—; adv. dir. Astoria Fed. Savs. and Loan, 1976—, Preferred Mut. Ins., New Berlin, N.Y., 1979—; bd. dirs. and v.p. Wilderness Properties Ltd., Oneonta, 1986—; bd. dirs. Moex, Inc., Jefferson, Oreg. Bd. dirs. N.Y. State Dist. Export Council, 1982—; bd. dirs., v.p. Thomas A. Dooley Found., 1984—; trustee A.O. Fox Meml. Hosp. Found., 1984—; adv. com. Oneonta Ctr. for Econ. and Community Devel.; advocacy com. Nat. Soccer Hall Fame; coun. mem. citizens bd. Hartwick Coll.; bd. dirs. Future of Oneonta Found., Otsego Orthops. Sports Medicine Found. Served with Army N.G., 1969-76. Mem. Greater Oneonta C. of C. (pres., bd. dirs. 1976-82), Am. Legion, Oneonta Country Club (bd. dirs.), Rotary (pres., bd. dirs. Oneonta club 1975-82), Elks. Republican. Methodist. Avocations: racquetball, softball, photography, travelling, golf. Home: Hcr # 862 West Oneonta NY 13861 Office: Medical Coaches Inc PO Box 129 Hemlock Rd Oneonta NY 13820

SMITH, GEOFFREY R.W., lawyer; b. San Francisco, May 26, 1945. AB with honors, Stanford U., 1967, JD, 1970. Bar: Calif. 1971, D.C. 1971. Assoc. gen. counsel Pharm. Mfgs. Assn., 1979-87; ptnr. McDermott, Will & Emery, Washington. Mem. bd. editors Food, Drug and Cosmetic Law Jour., 1987-90. Mem. ABA (mem. bus. law sect. 1970-88, mem. antitrust sect. 1970—, mem. torts and ins. sects. 1978—, mem. adminstrv. law sect. 1975—, mem. food and drug com. 1972—, mem. ad hoc tort reform com. 1988, chmn. subcom. punitive damages 1991, mem. health reform com.), Am. Tort Reform Assn. (chmn. 1987-88, bd. dirs. 1987—), Regulatory Affairs Soc. Office: McDermott Will & Emery 1850 K St NW Washington DC 20006-2213

SMITH, GEORGE CURTIS, lawyer, judge; b. Columbus, Ohio, Aug. 8, 1935; s. George B. and Dorothy R. S.; m. Barbara Jean Wood, July 10, 1963; children: Curtis, Geoffrey, Elizabeth Ann. BA, Ohio State U., 1957, JD, 1959. Bar: Ohio 1959, U.S. Dist. Ct. (so. dist.) Ohio 1987. Asst. city atty. City of Columbus, 1959-62; exec. asst. to Mayor of Columbus, 1962-63; asst. atty. gen. State of Ohio, 1964; chief counsel to pros. atty. Franklin County, Ohio, 1965-70, pros. atty., 1971-80; judge Franklin County Mcpl. C., Columbus, 1980-85; judge Franklin County Common Pleas Ct., 1985-87; mem. Ohio Supreme Ct. Coun. on Victims Rights, 1988-94; judge in residence Law Sch. U. Cin., 1993; faculty Ohio Jud. Coll., Litigation Practice Inst.; chmn. 1994; lectr. Fed. Bench-Bar Conf., 1995, ABA Anti-Trust Sec., 1995; pres. Young Rep. Club, 1963; exec. com. Franklin County Rep. Party, 1971-80; Elder Presbyn. Ch. Recipient Superior Jud. Service award Supreme Ct. Ohio; Resolution of Honor, Columbus Bldg. and Constrn. Trades Coun. Mem. Ohio Pros. Attys. Assn. (pres., Ohio Prosecutor of Yr, Award of Honor, Leadership award), Columbus Bar Assn., Assn. Trial Lawyers Am., Columbus Bar Found., Fed. Bar Assn., Ohio Mcpl. Judges Assn. (v.p. 1983), Columbus Athletic Club (pres., dir.), Lawyers Club of Columbus (pres. 1975), Masons (33d degree). Presbyterian. Office: 85 Marconi Blvd Columbus OH 43215-2823

SMITH, GEORGE DRURY, publisher, editor, collagist, writer; b. Dayton, Ohio, Mar. 10, 1927; s. Martin Jefferson and Viola (Haas) S.; m. Anne Liard Jennings, Apr. 1967 (div. 1975). A.B. cum laude, Marietta Coll., 1953; Diplome de Phonetique, U. Grenoble, 1950; student, U. Madrid, 1950-51, Heidelberg U., 1951-52, U. Minn., 1953-55, U. Calif.-Berkeley, 1965, UCLA, 1968. Assoc. pub., chief fin. officer Argonaut newspaper, 1972—; dir. Lambda Point Cons. and Pentacle Group, 1984—. Editor: Beyond Baroque, 1968-80; NewLetters, 1969-75; (book series) New Books, 1976-78. Mem. Mcpl. Arts Adv. Bd., Los Angeles, 1980-82; chmn. Save Westminster Auditorium Com., Venice, 1977-80; advisor Venice Cultural Ctr. Com., 1981-83. Served with U.S. Army, 1944-47. Grantee Nat. Endowment for Arts, 1973-80; grantee Calif. Arts Council, 1977-80, Cpl. Arts Commn., 1977-80, Coordinating Council Lit. Mags., 1974-80. Mem. Rosicrucians. Democrat. Office: The Argonaut PO Box 9995 Marina Del Rey CA 90295 *I believe that if we have faith we can live without fear; that the universe is benevolent if we can love unconditionally; that we can live righteously and prosper if we are honest and seek divine guidance; and that our mission is to enjoy life and strive for beauty.*

SMITH, GEORGE E., chemical company executive. Pres., chief exec. officer Alco Industries Inc., Valley Forge, Pa. Office: Alco Industries Inc PO Box 937 Rt 363 Betzwood Brg Valley Forge PA 19482-0937

SMITH, GEORGE FOSTER, retired aerospace company executive; b. Franklin, Ind., May 9, 1922; s. John Earl and Ruth (Foster) S.; m. Jean Arthur Farnsworth, June 3, 1950; children—David Foster, Craig Farnsworth, Sharon Windsor. BS in Physics, Calif. Inst. Tech., 1944, M.S., 1948, Ph.D. magna cum laude (Standard Oil fellow 1949-50), 1952. Founding staff mem. Engring. Research Assocs., St. Paul, 1944-48; teaching fellow, resident assoc. Calif. Inst. Tech., 1948-52; mem. staff Hughes Research Labs., Malibu, Calif., 1952-87; asso. dir. Hughes Research Labs., 1962-69, dir., 1969-87; v.p. Hughes Aircraft Co., 1965-81, sr. v.p., 1981-87, mem. policy bd., 1966-87; adj. asso. prof. elec. engring. U. So. Calif., 1959-62; cons. Army Sci. Adv. Panel, 1975-78. Contbr. numerous articles to profl. jours. Adv. local Explorer post Boy Scouts Am., 1965-70; bd. mgrs. Westchester YMCA, 1974—, chmn., 1979-81; chmn. trustees Pacific Presbyn. Ch., Los Angeles, 1959-62. Served to lt. (j.g.) USNR, 1944-46. Recipient Disting. Alumnus award Calif. Inst. Tech., 1991. Fellow IEEE (pres. Sorenson fellows 1972-73, Frederick Philips award 1988), Am. Phys. Soc.; mem. AAAS, Caltech Assocs. (bd. dirs. 1990—, pres. 1993-94), Sierra Club, Sigma Xi (chpt. pres. 1957-58), Tau Beta Pi. Achievements include 6 patents in field; directed leading industrial research in electronics, lasers, and electrooptics; conducted first laser range finder experiments. Office: Hughes Aircraft Co Rsch Labs 3011 Malibu Canyon Rd Malibu CA 90265-4737

SMITH, GEORGE LEONARD, JR., industrial engineering educator; b. State College, Pa., Sept. 6, 1935; s. George Leonard and Frieda Regina (Droege) S.; m. Patricia Gallagher, Dec. 29, 1962; children: Stephanie Ann, Seana Maureen. BS in Indsl. Engring., Pa. State U., 1957; MS in Indsl. Engring., Lehigh U., 1958, MS in Psychology, 1967; PhD in Indsl. Engring., Okla. State U., 1969. Registered profl. engr., Pa. Asst. prof. Ohio State U., Columbus, 1968-72, assoc. prof., 1972-77, prof. indsl. engring., 1977—, chmn. dept. indsl. and systems engring., 1982-94, assoc. dean for acad. affairs, 1991-93; arbitrator Fed. Mediation and Conciliation Service, 1970—; vis. Disting. Prof. New U. of Lisbon, Portugal, 1990—. Editor: Human Factors, 1980-83; author: Work Measurement: A Systems Approach, 1978. Pub. mem. Ohio Power Siting Commn., 1970-75. Recipient Disting. Teaching award Coll. Engring., Ohio State U., 1982. Fellow Human Factors Soc., Inst. Indsl. Engrs. (div. dir. 1979-81, v.p. edn. rsch. 1988-91, Spl. citation ergonomics divsn.), World Acad. of Productivity Sci.; mem. Am. Soc. Engring. Edn. Democrat. Roman Catholic. Home: 858 Katherines Ridge Ln Columbus OH 43235-3462 Office: 1971 Neil Ave Columbus OH 43210-1210

SMITH, GEORGE LESTER, lawyer; b. Ft. Meade, Md., July 14, 1951; s. Dale Ellison and Jane (Sheppard) S.; m. Patricia P. Smith, July 25, 1981; 1 child, Bradford D. BA, Claremont McKenna Coll., 1973; JD, U. Calif., Davis, 1976; LLM, U. Fla., 1987. Bar: Wash. 1980, Calif. 1976; CPA, Calif. Wash. Acct. Touche Ross & Co., San Francisco, 1976-78; assoc. Graham & Dunn, Seattle, 1982-87; ptnr. Foster Pepper & Shefelman, Seattle, 1987—. Capt. JAGC, U.S. Army, 1978-82. Office: Foster Pepper & Shefelman 777 108th Ave NE Ste 1500 Bellevue WA 98004-5120

SMITH, GEORGE PATRICK, II, lawyer, educator; b. Wabash, Ind., Sept. 1, 1939; s. George Patrick and Marie Louise (Barrett) S. B.S., Ind. U., 1961, J.D., 1964; certificate, Hague Acad. Internat. Law, 1965; LL.M., Columbia U., 1975. Bar: Ind. 1964, U.S. Supreme Ct. 1968. Kannert teaching fellow Ind. U. Sch. Law, 1964-65; instr. law U. Mich. Sch. Law, 1965-66; practiced in Ind. and Washington, 1965—; legal adviser Fgn. Claims Settlement Commn., Dept. State, Washington, 1966; asst. prof., asst. dean State U. N.Y. at Buffalo Law Sch., 1967-69; vis. asst. prof. law George Washington U. Nat. Law Center, summer 1968; assoc. prof. law U. Ark., 1969-71; spl. counsel EPA, Washington, 1971-74; adj. prof. law Cath. U. Law Sch., Washington, 1973-74, prof., 1977—; adj. prof. law Georgetown U. Law Ctr., 1971-75; assoc. prof. law U. Pitts. Sch. Law, 1975-78; Commonwealth fellow in law, sci. and medicine Yale U., New Haven, 1976-77; vis. prof. law U. Conn., 1977; disting. vis. scholar Kennedy Bioethics Inst., Georgetown U., 1977-81; vis. scholar Cambridge (Eng.) U., summer 1975, spring 1978-79, Hoover Inst. on War, Revolution and Peace Stanford (Calif.) U., summer 1983, Inst. Soc., Ethics and Life Scis., Hastings Ctr., N.Y., 1981, Lilly Rare Books Libr., Ind. U., July 1981, The Kinsey Inst. for Rsch. in Sex, Gender and Reproduction, U. Ind., July 1981, Am. Bar Found., Chgo., 1986, 87, Vatican Libr., Rome, July, 1989; Rockefeller Found. resdl. scholar, Bellagio, Italy, 1980; lectr. Sch. Medicine, Uniformed Svcs. U. Health Scis., Bethesda, Md., 1979-87; cons. environ. legislation Govt. of Greece, 1977; spl. counsel to Gov. Ark. for environ. affairs, 1970-71; cons. Ark. Planning Commn., 1970-71; mem. Ark. Waterway Commn., 1970-71; pres. com. on Environ. Control, 1970-71; mem. com. on hwy. rsch. NRC, NAS, 1971-81; life mem. Ind. U. Found.; univ. fellow Columbia U. Law Sch., 1974-75; fellow Max Planck Inst., Heidelberg, Fed. Republic of Germany, summer 1983; mem. Pres. Reagan's Pvt. Sector Survey on Cost Control, 1982; vis. fellow Clare Hall Cambridge U., 1983-84, summer 87, law, sci. and medicine Hughes Hall, Cambridge (Eng.) U., 1989, also vis. mem. law faculty, Apr.-Aug., 1989; Fulbright vis. prof. U. New South Wales, Syndey, Australia, 1984, vis. prof., vis. fellow Ctr. for Law and Tech., 1987; vis. fellow Inst. Advanced Study, Ind. U., 1985; vis. prof. law U. Notre Dame, 1986; vis. scholar Am. Bar Found., Chgo., 1986, 87; sr. vis. fellow U. Singapore, 1987; vis. fellow McGill U. Ctr. for Medicine, Ethics and Law, Montreal, 1988, Ctr. for Biomed. Ethics U. Va. Health Scis. Ctr., Charlottesville, 1990, Ctr. for Bioethics Monash U., Melbourne, Australia, 1990, Working Ctr. Studies in German and Internat. Med. Malpractice Law Free U. Berlin, 1992; vis. rsch. fellow Ctr. for Advanced Study of Ethics Georgetown U., Washington, 1990-91; rsch. fellow Divinity Sch. Yale U., New Haven, 1991; assoc. Med. Inst. for Law Faculty, Cleve. Clinic Ctr. Creative Thinking in Medicine Cleve. State U., 1991; vis. prof. rsch. U. Auckland Law Faculty, 1991, U.

Sydney Law Faculty, 1991, U. Victoria Law Faculty, B.C., Can., 1992, Trinity Coll., 1992, Dublin U., Ireland, 1992, Wolfson Coll. Cambridge U., 1992, Ind. U. Sch. Public and Environ. Affairs, 1992, Queensland U. Faculty Law, Australia, 1993; vis. scholar Ctr. Biomed. Ethics U. Minn. Med. Sch., Mpls., 1991, Ctr. for Socio-Legal Studies Oxford U., July 1992, Princeton (N.J.) Theol. Sem., 1993, Ctr. Med. Ethics Pritzker Sch. Medicine U. Chgo., 1993; vis. fellow Ctr. for Internat. Malpractice Law Free U. Berlin, Jan. 1992, King's Coll. Ctr. for Med. Law and Ethics U. London, June 1992; vis. sr. fellow Ctr. for Study Aging and Human Devel. Duke U. Med. Ctr., 1994; vis. prof. Rsch. U. Otiago, 1994; faculty of law, vis. fellow U. Bioethics Rsch. Ctr., Dunedin, New Zealand, 1994; vis. scholar Poynter Ctr. for Study of Ethics Am. Instns., Ind. U., Bloomington, 1994, law, medicine and ethics Schs. Medicine and Pub. Health Boston U., 1995. Author: Genetics, Ethics and the Law, 1981, Restricting the Concept of Free Seas, 1980, Legal, Ethical and Social Issues of the Brave New World, 1980, Medical-Legal Aspects of Cryonics, 1983, The New Biology, 1989, Final Choices: Autonomy in Health Care Decisions, 1989, Bioethics and the Law, 1993, Legal and Healthcare Ethics for the Elderly, 1995; contbr. articles to profl. jours. U. Ark. del. Pacem In Maribus Conf., Malta, 1970. Recipient Disting. Alumni award Ind. U. Bd. Trustees, 1985, citation for Path-Breaking Work; establishment of George P. Smith II Disting. Research Professorship Ind. U., Bloomington, 1986. Mem. Nat. Cathedral Assn. Washington, Am. Bar Assn. (rep. UN Conf. on Human Environment, Stockholm 1972, rep. Law of Sea Conf., UN, N.Y.C. 1976, Switzerland 1979), Ind. Bar Assn., Am. Friends of Cambridge U., Am. Law Inst., Order of St. John Hospitaller, Alpha Kappa Psi, Phi Alpha Delta, Sigma Alpha Epsilon, Order of Omega, Order of St. John Hospitaller. Republican. Club: Cosmos (Washington). Office: Catholic Univ 2500 Q St NW Ste 521 Washington DC 20007-4364 *Think big, work hard and, above all, have a dream: these are the simple guideposts for a fulfilling life.*

SMITH, GEORGE S., JR., communications financial executive; b. Newark, Dec. 8, 1948; m. Pamela Smith. BS in Acctg., Hiram Scott Coll., Scott's Bluff, Nebr., 1971. Cash mgr. Diamondhead Corp., N.Y.C., 1971-75, Texasgulf Inc., N.Y.C., 1975-77; dir. fin. svcs. Viacom Internat. Inc., N.Y.C., 1977-79, dir. fin. planning, 1979-81, controller radio div., 1981-83, v.p. fin. and adminstrn. broadcast group, 1983-85, v.p., controller, 1985-87, sr. v.p., chief fin. officer Viacom Inc., 1987—. Mem. Broadcast Fin. Mgmt. Assn., Fin. Execs. Inst. Office: Viacom Inc 1515 Broadway New York NY 10036-5702

SMITH, GEORGE THORNEWELL, retired state supreme court justice; b. Camilla, Ga., Oct. 15, 1916; s. George C. and Rosa (Gray) S.; m. Eloise Taylor, Sept. 1, 1943. Grad., Abraham Baldwin Agrl. Coll., 1940; LLB, U. Ga., 1948. Bar: Ga. 1947. Assoc. Cain & Smith, Cairo, Ga., 1947-71; city atty. Cairo, 1949-58; atty. Grady County, 1950-59; solicitor Cairo City Ct., 1951-59; mem. Ga. Ho. of Reps., 1959-67, speaker of the house, 1963-67; lt. gov. State of Ga., 1967-71; city atty. East Point, Ga., 1973-76; judge Ga. Ct. Appeals, 1976-81; justice Ga. Supreme Ct., Atlanta, 1981-91, presiding justice, 1990-91; of counsel Barnes, Browning Tanksley and Casurella, Marietta, Ga., 1992—; past mem. exec. com. Nat. Conf. Appellate Judges; vice chmn. Nat. Conf. Lt. Govs. Trustee Nat. Arthritis Found. Lt. comdr. USN, 1940-45. Only person in the state's history to serve in an elective capacity in all 3 brs. of govt. Mem. ABA, State Bar Ga., Cobb County Bar Assn., Lawyers Club Atlanta, Am. Legion, VFW, Moose, Kiwanis. Avocations: hunting, bowling, golf. Office: Barnes Browning Tanksley and Casurella 166 Anderson St Ste 225 Marietta GA 30060-1984

SMITH, GEORGE WOLFRAM, physicist, educator; b. Des Plaines, Ill., Sept. 19, 1932; s. Murray Sawyer and Alice Lucile (Wolfram) S.; m. Mary Lee Sackett, Sept. 7, 1956; children—Dean, Grant. B.A., Knox Coll., 1954; M.A., Rice U., 1956, Ph.D., 1958. Welch Found. fellow Rice U., 1958-59; sr. rsch. physicist GM, Warren, Mich., 1959-76; dept. rsch. scientist GM, 1976-81, sr. staff rsch. scientist, 1981-87, prin. rsch. scientist, 1987—; lectr. physics and astronomy Cranbrook Inst. Sci., Bloomfield Hills, Mich., 1963-87; tchr. Lawrence Inst. Tech., 1963-65; vice chmn. Gordon Rsch. Conf. on Orientational Disorder in Crystals, 1976, chmn., 1978; co-chmn. internat. symposium on particulate carbon, 1980; mem. rev. com. Liquid Crystal Inst., Kent (Ohio) State U., 1984-85; mem. sci. adv. com. Cranbrook Inst. Sci., 1989—; mem. adv. com. Conf. on Electrorheological Fluids, 1991, 93. Coeditor: Particulate Carbon: Formation During Combustion, 1981; editl. cons. Ency. Applied Physics, 1988—; contbr. Handbook of Chemistry and Physics; contbr. articles to sci. and tech. jours.; patentee on temperature measuring device, liquid crystal device tech., dielectric heating, graphite fiber growth, polymer-dispersed liquid crystals. Mem. Mich. Regtl. Civil War Roundtable, 1965—, pres., 1971-72. Recipient Knox Coll. Achievement award 1977, John M. Campbell Research award, 1980, Charles L. McCuen Achievement award, Gen. Motors, 1985. Fellow Am. Phys. Soc. (com. on applications of physics 1988-91, chmn. 1991, chmn. com. on tutorials 1991, mem. Pake Prize Com. 1993-94); mem. Soc. Info. Display (program com. 1990-93), Phi Beta Kappa, Sigma Xi (chpt. pres. 1980-81), Phi Delta Theta, Alpha Delta. Home: 1882 Melbourne St Birmingham MI 48009-1163 Office: GM Rsch and Devel Ctr Dept Physics Warren MI 48090-9055

SMITH, GERALD FRANCIS, rendering company executive; b. Winchester, Va., Mar. 9, 1961; s. Gerald Francis Sr. and Dolores Ann (Snyder) S.; m. Kaye Anita DeHaven, Dec. 28, 1985. BS in Acctg., Wake Forest U., 1983. CPA, Va. Staff acct. Price Waterhouse, Winston Salem, N.C., 1983-85; corp. sec. Valley Proteins, Inc., Winchester, Va., 1985-87. Committeeman, Eagle Scout Boy Scouts of Am., Winchester; mem. Circle K Wake Forest U., Winston Salem, 1979-83. Mem. Am. Inst. CPAs, Va. Soc. CPAs. Republican. Roman Catholic. Avocations: aviation, golf.

SMITH, GERARD PETER, neuroscientist; b. Phila., Mar. 24, 1935; s. Stanley Alward and Agnes Marie (McLarney) S.; m. Barbara McInnis, May 12, 1962; children: Christopher, Mark, Hilary, Maura. BS, St. Joseph's U., Phila., 1956; MD, U. Pa., 1960. Intern, resident N.Y. Hosp., 1960-62; asst. prof. physiology U. Pa. Sch. Medicine, Phila., 1964-68; from asst. to assoc. prof. Cornell U., N.Y.C., 1968—, prof. psychiatry (behavioral neurosci.), 1973—; vis. prof. MIT, 1973-74, Rockefeller U., 1979-80; adj. prof., 1982-86; cons. NIH; Curt Richter lectr. Johns Hopkins U., 1976; Leon lectr. U. Pa., 1990, Sellar lectr. U. Pa., 1993; Rushton lectr. Fla. State U., 1992, Merck, Sharpe, and Dohm prof. neurosci. U. Flinder, Australia, 1992; dir. Eating Disorders Inst., N.Y. Hosp.-Cornell Med. Ctr., 1984-88. Recipient Rsch. Scientist USPHS, 1982; NIH grantee. Mem. AAAS, Am. Physiol. Soc., Soc. Neurosci., Ea. Psychol. Assn., Am. Assn. Rsch. Nervous and Mental Disease, Endocrine Soc., Soc. Biol. Psychiatry, Soc. for Study Ingestive Behavior (pres.), Internat. Behavioral Neurosci. (pres.), Alpha Omega Alpha, Alpha Sigma Nu. Office: EW Bourne Behavioral Rsch Lab NY Hosp Cornell Med Ctr 21 Bloomingdale Rd White Plains NY 10605-1504

SMITH, GLEE SIDNEY, JR., lawyer; b. Rozel, Kans., Apr. 29, 1921; s. Glee S. and Bernice M. (Augustine) S.; m. Geraldine B. Buhler, Dec. 14, 1943; children: Glee S., Stephen B., Susan K. AB, U. Kans., 1943, JD, 1947. Bar: Kans. 1947, U.S. Dist. Ct. 1951, U.S. Supreme Ct. 1973, U.S. Ct. Mil. Appeals 1988. Ptnr. Smith, Burnett & Larson, Larned, Kans., 1947—; of counsel Barber, Emerson et. al., Lawrence, Kans., 1992—. Kans. state senator, 1957-73, pres. Senate, 1965-73; mem. Kans. Bd. Regents, 1975-83, pres., 1976; bd. govs. Kans. U. Law Soc., 1967—; mem. Kans. Jud. Coun., 1963-65; county atty. Pawnee County, 1949-53; Kans. commr. Nat. Conf. Commn. on Uniform State Laws, 1981—. Bd. dirs. Nat. Legal Svcs. Corp., 1975-79. Served to 1st lt. U.S. Army, 1943-45. Recipient Disting. Svc. award, U. Kans. Law Sch., 1976; Disting. Svc. citation U. Kans., 1984. Fellow Am. Coll. Probate Counsel, Am. Bar Found.; mem. ABA (bd. of govs. 1987-90, chmn. ops. com. 1989-90, exec. com. 1989-90, chmn. task force on solo and small firm practitioner 1991-92, chmn. com. on solo and small firm practitioners 1992-94, chmn. task force on applying fed. legis. to congress), Kans. Bar Assn. (del. to ABA ho. of dels. 1982-92, bd. govs. 1982-92, leadership award 1973, medal of Distinction 1993), Southwest Kans. Bar Assn., Am. Judicature Soc. Republican. Presbyterian. Clubs: Kiwanis, Masons. Home: 115 E 9th St Apt 5 Larned KS 67550-2647 Home: 4313 Quail Pointe Rd Lawrence KS 66047

SMITH, GLEN B., consumer products company executive. Grad., Pa. State Tchrs. Coll. With K Mart Corp., 1953—; asst. mgr. Kresge store K Mart Corp., Ohio, 1956-57; asst. sales dept. K Mart Corp., Detroit, 1957-59; sr.

asst. Kresge store K Mart Corp., Pa., 1959-60; mgr. Kresge stores K Mart Corp., N.J., Pa., Conn., 1960-68; dist. mgr. ea. region K Mart Corp., 1968-70, 72-75, co-mgr. Pa. store, 1970-72, regional merchandise mgr. ea. region, 1975-79, buyer toys, then v.p., pres. Kmart fashions, 1979-91, now exec. v.p. merchandising, 1991—. With U.S. Army, 1951-53. Office: K Mart Corp 3100 W Big Beaver Rd Troy MI 48084-3004 Office: 7373 Westside Ave N North Bergen NJ 07047

SMITH, GLENDA IRENE, elementary school educator; b. St. Paul, May 4, 1940; d. Otis Alvin and Bella Gladys (Elven) Anderson; m. Herbert Smith, Dec. 22, 1962; 1 child, Melanie Marjorie. BA, N.W. Nazarene Coll., 1962. Cert. elem. tchr., Calif. Tchr. Spring Lake Park Dist. Schs., Mpls., 1962-63, 64-65, Parma (Idaho) Sch. Dist., 1965-66, Nampa (Idaho) City Schs., 1966-69; tchr. Modesto (Calif.) City Schs., 1969-70, 71-78, tchr., mentor, 1985—; tchr., vice prin. Turlock (Calif.) Christian Schs., 1978-82. Author: Stories, Songs, Puppets, 1972. Mem. Nat. Tchr. Assn., Calif. Tchr. Assn., Modesto Tchr. Assn. Democrat. Episcopalian. Avocations: catering, reading, music, travel. Home: 110 Hayes Turlock CA 95380-1106 Office: Robertson Rd Sch 1821 Robertson Rd Modesto CA 95351

SMITH, GLENN STANLEY, electrical engineering educator; b. Salem, Mass., June 1, 1945; s. Stanley Ernest and Florence Estelle (Chaney) S.; m. Linda Lee Holmquist, Aug. 4, 1968; children: Geoffrey Douglas, Eleanor Leigh. BS, Tufts U., 1967; MS, Harvard U., 1968, PhD, 1972. Postdoctoral rsch. fellow Harvard U., Cambridge, Mass., 1972-75; rsch. assoc., lectr. Northeastern U., Boston, 1973-75; asst. prof. elec. engring. Ga. Inst. Tech., Atlanta, 1975-79, assoc. prof., 1979-84, prof., 1984-89, Regents' prof., 1989—. Co-author: Antennas in Matter, 1981; assoc. editor Radio Sci., 1983-87. Fellow IEEE (editorial bd. IEEE Press 1988-91); mem. Internat. Union Radio Sci. Home: 2518 Hazelwood Dr NE Atlanta GA 30345-2145 Office: Sch Elec Engring Ga Inst Tech Atlanta GA 30332

SMITH, G(ODFREY) T(AYLOR), retired college president; b. Newton, Miss., Nov. 12, 1935; s. Taylor and Edna Young (Blanton) S.; m. Martha Joan Eaton, Sept. 1, 1956; children: Paul Brian, Sherry Lynn. BA, Coll. of Wooster, 1956; MPA with distinction, Cornell U., 1960; LLD (hon.), Bethany Coll., 1979. Asso. dir. devel. Cornell U., 1960-62; dir. devel. Coll. Wooster, 1962-66, v.p., 1966-77; pres. Chapman U., Orange, Calif., 1977-88, pres. emeritus, 1988—; lectr. in field. Contbr. numerous articles on coll. mgmt. to profl. publs. Bd. dirs. Wayne County (Ohio) Indsl. Devel. Corp., 1966-72, World Affairs Coun. Orange Coun., Calif., 1978-89, Orange County chpt. NCCJ, 1979-86, Orange County coun. Boy Scouts Am., 1980-85, Coun. Ind. Colls., 1985-87; bd. dirs. div. higher edn. Christian Ch. (Disciples of Christ), 1980-86, chmn., 1984-86; bd. dirs., mem. exec. com. Assn. Ind. Colls. So. Calif., 1979-86, pres., 1981-82; mem. exec. com. Assn. Ind. Colls. and Univs., 1980-88, treas., 1982-87. Recipient Steuben Apple award for Tchg. Excellence, Coun. for Advancement and Support of Edn., 1984, Disting. Alumnus award Coll. of Wooster, 1991, Faith and Reason award Christian Ch. (Disciples of Christ), 1993; Smith Hall dedicated at Chapman U., 1988; Alfred P. Sloan fellow Cornell U., 1960. Presbyterian. Home: 2200 Lupine Dr Ashland OR 97520-3642 If we treat people as they are, they will stay as they are. But if we treat them for what they might be and might become, they will become those better selves.

SMITH, GOFF, industrial equipment manufacturing executive; b. Jackson, Tenn., Oct. 7, 1916; s. Fred Thomas and Mabel (Goff) S.; m. Nancy Dall, Nov. 28, 1942 (dec. 1972); children: Goff Thomas, Susan Knight; m. Harriet Schneider Oliver, June 23, 1973. BSE, U. Mich., 1938, MBA, 1939; MS, MIT, 1953. Trainee Bucyrus Erie, South Milwaukee, Wis., 1939-40; mem. sales staff Amsted Industries, Chgo. and N.Y.C., 1946-55; subsidiary pres. Amsted Industries, Chgo., 1955-60, v.p., 1960-69, pres., 1969-74, pres., CEO, dir., 1974-80, chmn., 1980-82. Pres. Village of Winnetka, Ill., 1967-69; pres., bd. dirs. United Way Chgo., 1976-85; bd. dirs. Rehab. Inst., Chgo., Chgo. Theol. Sem., Presbyn. Home, Evanston, Ill.; trustee Sigma Chi Found. Maj. U.S. Army, 1940-46. Sloan Fellow MIT, 1952-53. Republican. Avocations: hunting, fishing, golf.

SMITH, GORDON E., religious organization executive. Exec. dir. ABC Ministers & Miss. Benefit Bd., Valley Forge, Pa. Office: ABC Ministers & Miss Benefit Bd PO Box 851 Valley Forge PA 19482

SMITH, GORDON H., civil engineer; b. N.Y.C., Mar. 17, 1936; s. Henry and Theodora (Augenstern) S.; m. Norma Kaplan, Feb. 28, 1960; children: Randy Smith Aberg, Robin Smith Kolstad. BS in Engring., Yale U., 1957. Registered profl. engr., Mich., N.Y. V.p., chief engr. Albro Metal Products Corp., N.Y.C., 1957-69, pres., 1969-75; pres. Gordon H. Smith Corp., N.Y.C., 1975—. Contbr. articles to Archtl. Record, Progressive Arch., ASTM, Chgo. High Rise Com. Mem. NSPE, ASTM, ASCE, AIA (Inst. Honors 1994), Nat. Assn. Archtl. Metal Mfrs. (v.p., prs., bd. dirs.), Archtl. Aluminum Mfrs. Assn. (v.p., bd. dirs.), Nat. Assn. Miscellaneous, Ornamental and Archtl. Metal Mfrs. (bd. dirs.), Constrn. Specifications Inst. Office: Gordon H Smith Corp 200 Madison Ave New York NY 10016-3903

SMITH, GORDON HOWELL, lawyer; b. Syracuse, N.Y., Oct. 26, 1915; s. Lewis P. and Maud (Mixer) S.; m. Eunice Hale, June 28,1947; children: Lewis Peter, Susan S. Rizk, Catherine S. Maxson, Maud S. Daudon. BA, Princeton U., 1932-36; LL.B., Yale U., 1939. Bar: N.Y. 1939, Ill. 1946. Asso. Lord, Day & Lord, N.Y.C., 1939-41, Gardner, Carton & Douglas, Chgo., 1946-51; partner Mackenzie, Smith & Michell, Syracuse, 1951-53; partner Gardner, Carton & Douglas, 1954-57, 60-85, of counsel, 1986—; sec., dir. Smith-Corona, Inc., 1951-54, v.p., Syracuse, 1957-60. Bd. dirs. Rehab. Inst. Chgo., chmn., 1974-78, 83-86; bd. dirs. United Way Met. Chgo., 1962-85. Served to lt. comdr. USNR, 1941-46. Mem. Am. Soc. Corporate Secs., Am., Ill., Chgo. bar assns. Clubs: Comml., Law, Econ., Legal, Chgo., Old Elm (Chgo.). Home: 1302 N Green Bay Rd Lake Forest IL 60045-1108 Office: 321 N Clark St Ste 3400 Chicago IL 60610-4717

SMITH, GORDON PAUL, management consulting company executive; b. Salem, Mass., Dec. 25, 1916; s. Gordon and May (Vaughan) S.; m. Daphne Miller, Nov. 23, 1943 (div. 1968); m. Ramona Chamberlain, Sept. 27, 1969; children: Randall B., Roderick F. B.S. in Econs. U. Mass., 1947; M.S. in Govt. Mgmt, U. Denver (Sloan fellow), 1948; postgrad. in polit. sci., NYU, 1948-50; DHL (hon.), Monterey Inst., 1994. Economist Tax Found., Inc., N.Y.C., 1948-50; with Booz, Allen & Hamilton, 1951-70; partner Booz, Allen & Hamilton, San Francisco, 1959-62, v.p., 1962-67, mng. pntr. Western U.S., 1968-70; partner Harrod, Williams and Smith (real estate devel.), San Francisco, 1962-69; state dir. fin. State of Calif., 1967-68; pres. Gordon Paul Smith & Co., Mgmt. Cons., 1968—; pres., chief exec. officer Golconda Corp., 1972-74, chmn. bd., 1974-85; pres. Cermetek Corp., 1978-80; bd. dirs. exec. com. First Calif. Co., 1970-72, Gronman Corp., 1976-85; bd. dirs. Madison Venture Capital Corp.; adviser task force def. procurement and contracting Hoover Commn., 1954-55; spl. asst. to pres. Republic Aviation Corp., 1954-55; cons. Hawaii, 1960-61, Alaska, 1963; cons. Wash. Hwy. Adminstrn., 1964, also 10 states and fed. agys., 1951-70, Am. Baseball League and Calif. Angels, 1960-62; bd. dirs. Monterey Coll. Law; chmn. Ft. Ord Econ. Devel. Adv. Group, 1991; chmn. Coalition on Rsch. and Edn., 1993—; bd. dirs. Monterey Bay Futures Project; over 750 TV, radio and speaking appearances on econs., mgmt. and public issues. Author articles on govt., econs. and edn. Mem. 24 bds. and commns. State of Calif., 1967-72; mem. Calif. Select Com. on Master Plan for Edn., 1971-73; mem. alumni council U. Mass., 1950-54, bd. dirs. alumni assn., 1964-70; bd. dirs. Alumni Assn. Mt. Hermon Prep. Sch., 1963; bd. dirs. Stanford Med. Ctr., 1960-62, pres., chmn., 1962-66; chmn. West Coast Cancer Found., 1976-87, Coalition Rsch. and Edn., 1993—; trustee, chmn. Monterey Inst. Internat. Studies, 1978-92; trustee Northfield Mt. Hermon Sch., 1983-93, Robert Louis Stevenson Sch., 1993—; mem. devel. council Community Hosp. of Monterey Peninsula, 1985—; bd. dirs. Friends of the Performing Arts, 1985—; bd. dirs. Monterey County Symphony Orch., 1991—, Monterey Bay Futures Project, 1992—. Served to 1st lt., cav. AUS, 1943-46, ETO. Recipient spl. commendation Hoover Commn., 1955; Alumni of Year award U. Mass., 1963; Trustee of Yr. award Monterey-Peninsula, 1991, Monterey-Peninsula Outstanding Citizen of Yr. award, 1992; Laura Bride Powers Heritage award, 1991; U.S. Congl. award, 1992; Calif. Senate and Assembly Outstanding Citizen award, 1992; Wisdom award of honor Wisdom Soc., 1992; permanent Gordon Paul Smith Disting. Chair for Internat. Study established at Monterey Inst. Internat. Studies; Gordon Paul Smith Scholarship Fund

named in his honor Northfield Mt. Hermon Sch.; named to Honorable Order of Ky. Colonels. Mem. Monterey History and Art Assn. (bd. dirs. 1987-92, pres. 1985-87, chmn. 1987-92, hon. lifetime dir. 1992—), The Stanton Ctr. Heritage Ctr. (chmn. 1987-92, chmn. emeritus 1992—), Salvation Army (bd. dirs.) Monterey Peninsula Mus. Art, Carmel Valley (Calif.) Country Club, Monterey Peninsula Country Club, Old Capital Club. Home: 253 Del Mesa Carmel CA 93923 *If the quest for personal success is only for an accumulation of prestige. power or wealth, then personal failure will be assured. Genuine personal success can surely be found, however, through a significant and lasting contribution toward helping the progress of others. This is the true mark of leadership.*

SMITH, GORDON RAY, utilities executive; b. San Francisco, Feb. 26, 1948; s. Margaret C. Orlando; m. Elizabeth Anne Rulfo, Sept. 26, 1981; children: Adam R., Alexandra R. BS in Fin., U. Calif., Berkeley, 1970; MBA in Fin., U. San Francisco, 1974. Fin. analyst Pacific Gas & Electric Co., San Francisco, 1970-76, sr. fin. analyst, 1976-78, dir. project financing, 1978-80, asst. treas., 1980-82, treas., 1982-83, v.p. fin., treas., 1983-87, v.p. fin. and rates, 1987—. Mem. Mayor's Fiscal Adv. Com., San Francisco, 1986, Investment Rev. Com., San Francisco Found., 1986. Mem. Fin. Officers No. Calif., Pacific Coast Electric Assn., Pacific Coast Gas Assn., Bankers Club San Francisco, Moraga Country Club. Office: Pacific Gas & Electric Co 444 Market St Ste 1900 San Francisco CA 94111-5330

SMITH, GORDON ROSS, retired English language educator; b. Monmouth County, N.J., May 23, 1917; s. Mortimer Dickerson and Elizabeth Clara (Ross) S.; m. Jane Pakenham, Aug. 29, 1948; children: Gordon Ross, Corinna Pakenham Posner. B.S., Columbia U., 1948, M.A., 1949; Ph.D., Pa. State U., 1956. Instr. English, Waynesburg (Pa.) Coll., 1949-50; instr. English, Pa. State U., 1950-56, asst. prof., 1956-59, assoc. prof., 1959-63, prof., 1963-66; Folger Shakespeare Library fellow, 1958; Fulbright lectr. Royal U. Malta, 1962-63; prof. English, Temple U., Phila., 1966-84, prof. emeritus, 1984—. Author: A Classified Shakespeare Bibliography, 1936-58, 1963, Essays on Shakespeare, 1965; cons. editor: Jour. History of Ideas; editorial bd.: Film Forum Rev, Columbia U., 1948-49; contbr. articles to scholarly jours. Democratic party committeeman, State College, Pa., 1952-56. Served with AUS, 1943-46. Mem. Shakespeare Assn. Am., Pa. Hist. Soc., Huguenot Hist. Soc., Du Bois Assn. (pres. 1983-84 v.p. 1980-83, 85-89), Geneal. Soc. Pa., Pilgrim Soc., Internat. Shakespeare Assn. Home: 35 Red Oak Rd Oreland PA 19075-2111

SMITH, GRANT WARREN, II, university administrator, physical sciences educator; b. Kansas City, Mo., Jan. 21, 1941; m. Constance M. Krambeer, 1962; 1 child, Grant Warren III. BA, Grinnell Coll., 1962; PhD, Cornell U., 1966, postgrad., 1967. Asst. prof. chemistry Cornell U., Ithaca, N.Y., 1966-68, vis. prof. Am. Council on Edn. fellow, 1973-74; assoc. prof. U. Alaska, Fairbanks, 1968-77, prof., 1977-78, head dept. chemistry and chem. engring., 1968-73, acting head dept. gen. sci., 1972-73; pres. univ. assembly U. Alaska System, 1976-77; prof. phys. scis., dean Sch. Scis. and Techs. U. Houston, Clear Lake, 1979-84; prof. chemistry Southeastern La. U., Hammond, 1984—, v.p. for acad. affairs, 1984-86, pres., 1986—. Bd. dirs. Houston Area Research Ctr., 1982-83; violinist, pres. exec. bd. Clear Lake Symphony, 1980-84. NIH fellow, 1963-66, DuPont fellow, 1967. Fellow Royal Soc. Chemistry (London, chartered chemist), Explorers Club; mem. Am. Assn. Higher Edn., Am. Assn. Univ. Adminstrs. (bd. dirs. 1982-85, 86-88, v.p. 1988-90), AAAS, Am. Chem. Soc., Internat. Assn. Univ. Pres., Soc. Econ. Botany, Am. Soc. Pharmacognosy, Ethnopharmacology Soc., Soc. of Ethnobiology, Nat. Speleological Soc., Am. Spelean History Assn., Arctic Inst. N.Am., Hammond C. of C. (bd. dirs. 1988-90), Rotary, Sigma Xi, Phi Kappa Phi, Beta Gamma Sigma, Phi Eta Sigma. Office: Southeastern La U # 784 Hammond LA 70402

SMITH, GREGORY ALLAN, lawyer; b. Washington, Dec. 9, 1945; s. Allan F. and Alene M. (Mulikin) S.; m. Barbara M., Jan. 28, 1967; children: Michelle Anne Risch-Smith, Pamela Cheryl Smith. BA, Princeton U., 1968; JD, U. Wis., 1971. Bar: Wis. 1971. Calif. 1972. Assoc. Pillsbury, Madison & Sutro, San Francisco, 1971-78, ptnr., 1979-89; ptnr. Heller, Ehrman, White & McAuliffe, San Francisco, 1990—. Mem. ABA (tax sect.), Western Pension and Benefits Conf., Calif. State Bar (tax sect., employee benefits com.). Democrat. Avocations: golf, music, bridge. Office: Heller Ehrman White & McAuliffe 333 Bush St San Francisco CA 94104

SMITH, GREGORY ALLGIRE, academic director; b. Washington, Mar. 31, 1951; s. Donald Eugene and Mary Elizabeth (Reichert) S.; m. Susan Elizabeth Watts, Oct. 31, 1980; 1 child, David Joseph Smith-Watts. BA, The Johns Hopkins U., 1972; MA, Williams Coll., Williamstown, Mass., 1974. Adminstrv. asst. Washington Project for the Arts, 1975; intern Walker Art Ctr., Mpls., 1975-76; asst. devel. officer The Sci. Mus. of Minn., St. Paul, 1977; asst. dir. Akron (Ohio) Art Inst., 1977-80; asst. to dir. Toledo Mus. Art, 1980-82, asst. dir. adminstrn., 1982-86; exec. v.p. Internat. Exhbns. Found., Washington, 1986-87; dir. The Telfair Mus. Art, Savannah, Ga., 1987-94, Art Acad. of Cin., 1994—. Mem. Am. Assn. Mus. (surveyor mus. assessment program 1988—), Assn. Art Mus. Adminstrs. (founder 1984-85), Ohio Found. on the Arts (v.p. 1981-83, trustee 1981-84), Coll. Art Assn., Univ. Club, Rotary. Avocations: collecting arts & crafts movement objects, repairing old houses, landscape design. Home: 2533 Erie Ave Cincinnati OH 45208 Office: Art Acad of Cin 1125 St Gregory St Cincinnati OH 45202

SMITH, GREGORY DALE, lawyer; b. Knoxville, Feb. 1, 1963; s. James C. and Essie Pearl (Norman) S.; m. Cynthia Luckett, Oct. 15, 1988; 1 child, Leora. BS, Middle Tenn. State U., 1985; JD, Cumberland Law Sch., 1988. Bar: Tenn., U.S. Supreme Ct., U.S. Ct. Appeals (fed. crct.), U.S. Ct. Mil. Appeals, U.S. Dist. Ct. (mid., ea. and we. dists.) Tenn., Army Ct. of Mil. Rev., U.S. Ct. Vet. Appeals. Mcpl. magistrate City of Birmingham, Ala., 1987-88; assoc. Marks, Marks & Shell, Clarksville, Tenn., 1988-89; juvenile referee Montgomery County Juvenile Ct., Clarksville, Tenn., 1992—; assoc. Richardson & Richardson, Clarksville, Tenn., 1989-93; pvt. practice Clarksville, 1993—; adj. prof. Austin Peay State U., Clarksville, 1989—; lectr. in field. Author: The TACDL Guide to Defending Juvenile Cases in Tennessee, 1993; contbr. articles to profl. jours.; contbg. author/editor: Richardson & Richardson Collection Procedures, 1990. Bd. dirs. United Way of Clarksville and Montgomery County, 1992—; Treehouse Daycare Ctr., 1991—; sec., 1992, v.p., 1993, pres. 1994; active Leadership Clarksville; Sun. sch. tchr. Madison St. United Meth. Ch., Clarksville, 1988—. Named Internat. Man of the Yr. Internat. Biog. Ctr., Cambridge, Eng., 1992. Mem. ABA (juvenile justice com. nat. chmn. 1990-92, nat. vice chmn. litigation 1992-93), Tenn. Assn. Criminal Def. Lawyers (chmn. juvenile justice com. 1991—), Montgomery County Young Lawyers (pres. 1991—), Tenn. Young Lawyers Conf. (bd. dirs. 1992—). Democrat. Office: Law Offices Gregory D Smith 1 Public Sq Ste 321 Clarksville TN 37040-3463

SMITH, GREGORY WHITE, writer; b. Ithaca, N.Y., Oct. 4, 1951; s. William R. and Kathryn (Smith) S. BA, Colby Coll., 1973; JD, Harvard U., 1977, MEd, 1980. Bar: Mass., 1980. Fellow Thomas J. Watson, 1973-74; pres. Woodward/White, Inc.; overseer Colby Coll.; mem. bd. trustees Columbus Acad. Author: (with Steven Naifeh) Moving Up in Style, 1980, Gene Davis, 1981. How to Make Love to a Woman, 1982, What Every Client Needs to Know About Using a Lawyer, 1982, The Bargain Hunter's Guide to Art Collecting, 1982, Why Can't Men Open Up?: Overcoming Men's Fear of Intimacy, 1984, The Mormon Murders: A True Story of Greed, Forgery, Deceit, and Death, 1988, Jackson Pollock: An American Saga, 1989 (Nat. Book award nomination for nonfiction 1990, Pulitzer Prize for biography 1991), Final Justice: The True Story of the Richest Man Ever Tried for Murder, 1993, A Stranger in the Family: A True Story of Murder, Madness, and Unconditional Love, 1995; editor: (with Naifeh) The Best Lawyers in America, The Best Doctors in America. Office: 129 First Ave SW Aiken SC 29801*

SMITH, GROVER CLEVELAND, English language educator; b. Atlanta, Sept. 6, 1923; s. Grover C. and Lillian Julia (McDaniel) S.; m. Phyllis Jean Snyder, June 19, 1948 (div. 1965); children: Alice Elizabeth, Charles Grover; m. Dulcie Barbara Soper, Dec. 29, 1965; children: Stephen Kenneth, Julia Margaret. BA with honors, Columbia U., 1944, MA, 1945, PhD (Alexander M. Proudfit fellow), 1950. Instr. English Rutgers U., 1946-48, Yale U., 1948-52; instr. English Duke U., 1952-55, asst. prof., 1955-61, asso. prof., 1961-66, prof., 1966-93; prof. emeritus, 1993—; mem. summer faculty

CUNY, 1946, 47, 48, Columbia U., 1963, 64, NYU, 1963, Wake Forest U., 1966, vis. lectr., 1963, 64. Author: T.S. Eliot's Poetry and Plays: A Study in Sources and Meaning, 1956 (Poetry Chapbook award), Archibald MacLeish, 1971, Ford Madox Ford, 1972, The Waste Land, 1983, T.S. Eliot and the Use of Memory, 1996; editor: Josiah Royce's Seminar, 1913-1914: As Recorded in the Notebooks of Harry T. Costello, 1963, Letters of Aldous Huxley, 1969. Served with U.S. Army, 1943. Guggenheim fellow, 1958; Am. Philos. Soc. grantee, 1965; Am. Learned Socs. grantee, 1965; Nat. Endowment Humanities grantee, 1979; fellow, 1980. Mem. T.S. Eliot Soc. (bd. dirs. 1986-94, v.p. 1986-88, editor News and Notes, 1987-88, 90-91, pres. 1989-91), Am. Lit. Assn. (rep. to coun. of Am. Author Socs. 1990-91), Nat. Assn. Scholars. Office: Duke U Dept English PO Box 90015 Durham NC 27708-0015

SMITH, GUY LINCOLN, IV, strategic communications company executive; b. New Orleans, Mar. 16, 1949; s. Guy Lincoln III and Laura Louise (Orr) S.; m. Marjorie Russell, June 19, 1971; children: Abigail, Guy Lincoln V, Laura. Student, Bowling Green State U., 1967-68, U. Tenn., 1968-70, Am. U., 1971, U.S. Dept. Agrl. Grad. Sch., Washington, 1971. Reporter, asst. city editor The Knoxville Jour., 1967-70; dir. info. Appalachian Regional Commn., Washington, 1970-72; dir. info., press sec. to mayor City of Knoxville, 1972-76; mgr. corp. affairs Miller Brewing Co., Milw., 1976-79; v.p. corp. affairs The Seven-Up Co., St. Louis, 1979-84, Philip Morris U.S.A., N.Y.C., 1984-88; v.p. corp. affairs Philip Morris Cos. Inc., N.Y.C., 1989-91, pub., 1989-91; COO Hill and Knowlton, Inc., N.Y.C., 1991-93; chmn. Smith Worldwide, Inc., N.Y.C., 1993—; mem. pvt. sect. com. on pub. rels. USIA. Bd. dirs. Laumeier Internat. Sculpture Park, St. Louis, 1979—; Jackie Robinson Found., N.Y.C., 1983—; Barrier Island Trust, Tallahassee, Fla., 1991— (chmn.), AmeriCares, Inc. Recipient Excellence in News Writing award William Randolph Hearst Found., 1969, Achievement award Puerto Rican Family Inst., 1988; named confrere Sovereign Military Order of St. John of Jerusalem, of Rhodes, and of Malta, 1986, Outstanding Pub. Rels.-Pub. Affairs Exec. of Yr. Gallagher Report, 1988. Mem. Nat. Press Club, Kappa Alpha. Roman Catholic. Office: 171 Madison Ave New York NY 10016

SMITH, GUY W., health care executive; b. Alton, Ill., May 31, 1940; s. Guy and Claudine (Young) S.; m. Nancy Smith; children: Guy W., Lynn, Teresa, Michael. Cert. restaurant mgmt., INT Industries, Pasadena, Calif., 1964; nursing home adminstrn. tng., Milw. Area Tech. Coll.-Unicare Health Program, 1969; continuing edn., Marquette U., Milw., 1980-83. Owner, mgr. Internat. House of Pancakes Restaurant, Milw., 1964-67; nursing home adminstr. Unicare Health, Milw., 1967-69, adminstr., 1969-72, v.p., 1972-80, exec. v.p., 1980-83; pres. United Health, Milw., 1983—; bd. dirs. Universal Savs. Bank; mem. adv. bd. IN-Speech, Phila., 1982-84. Fund Raiser Hunger Task Force, Milw., 1986; mem. boy's club Am. Boosters, Milw., 1967-86, Ranch Bd., Milw., 1982-86; bd. dirs. Art Reach, 1987. Mem. Assn. Healthcare Adminstrs. (mem. multiple facility commn. 1983-86), Am. Mgmt. Assn. Republican. Roman Catholic. Club: Milw. Athletic. Avocations: horses, sports, reading. Home: 1407668 NW Lilly Rd Menomonee Falls WI 53051 Office: United Health Inc PO Box 13122 Milwaukee WI 53213-0122

SMITH, HAL W., restaurant management company executive; b. 1946; married. Ed., Okla. U., Central State U. Asst. mgr. Across the Street Restaurant, 1965-68; owner, mgr. Tilly's Pancake House, 1968-70; mgr. Cross Timbers Restaurant, 1970-73; with S&A Restaurant Corp., Dallas, 1973—; pres., chief operating officer S&A Restaurant Corp., 1980-83, chmn., chief exec. officer, 1983-84; pres., chief operating officer Chili's Restaurant Corp., 1984-86; chmn., pres., chief exec. and operating officer Chi-Chi's Inc., Louisville, 1986—. Office: Chi-Chi's Inc Box 32338 10200 Linn Station Rd Louisville KY 40223

SMITH, HALE, data processing services executive. Grad., Colo. Coll., 1972; Harvard Bus, Sch. CPA. V.p., fin. 1st Data Technol, Inc., Medford, Wash. Mem. Am. Inst. of Cert. Pub. Acct. Office: 1st Data Technol Inc 1 Cabot Rd Medford MA 02155*

SMITH, HALLETT DARIUS, retired English literature educator; b. Chattanooga, Aug. 15, 1907; s. Charles Wilson and Elizabeth Russell (Atkinson) S.; m. Mary Elizabeth Earl, Dec. 30, 1931; children—Diana Russell Smith Gordon, Hallett Earl. A.B., U. Colo., 1928, L.H.D., 1968; Ph.D., Yale U., 1934. Instr. English Williams Coll., Williamstown, Mass., 1931-36, asst. prof., 1937-40, assoc. prof., 1940-45, prof., 1946-49; prof. Calif. Inst. Tech., Pasadena, 1949-75, chmn. div. humanities, 1949-70; Guggenheim fellow, 1947-48; vis. prof. Columbia U., summer 1949; sr. research asso. Huntington Library, 1970—; Henry W. and Albert A. Berg prof. Eng. lit. N.Y. U., spring 1977; vis. prof. U. B.C., Spring 1980; Mem. Commn. English. Author: The Golden Hind, 1942, The Critical Reader, 1949, Elizabethan Poetry, 1951, Renaissance England, 1956, Twentieth Century Interpretations of The Tempest, 1970, Shakespeare's Romances, 1972, The Tension of the Lyre: Poetry in Shakespeare's Sonnets, 1981; contbr. articles to ednl. jours. Trustee Am. Univs. Field Staff, Poly. Sch.; mem. adv. com. Guggenheim Found. Recipient Poetry Chapbook prize Poetry Soc. Am., 1952; Phi Beta Kappa vis. scholar, 1959-60. Fellow Am. Acad. Arts and Scis.; mem. Modern Lang. Assn. Am., Phi Beta Kappa (senator at large). Home: Bradbur Oaks Rm # 200 1763 Royal Oaks Dr Duarte CA 91010-1986

SMITH, HAMILTON OTHANEL, molecular biologist, educator; b. N.Y.C., N.Y., Aug. 23, 1931; s. Bunnie Othanel and Tommie Harkey S.; m. Elizabeth Anne Bolton, May 25, 1957; children: Joel, Barry, Dirk, Bryan, Kirsten. Student, U. Ill., 1948-50; A.B. in Math, U. Calif., Berkeley, 1952; M.D., Johns Hopkins U., 1956. Intern Barnes Hosp. St. Louis, 1956-57; resident in medicine Henry Ford Hosp. Detroit, 1959-62; USPHS fellow dept. human genetics U. Mich., Ann Arbor, 1962-64; rsch. assoc. U. Mich., 1964-67; asst. prof. molecular biology and genetics Sch. Medicine Johns Hopkins U., Balt., 1967-69; assoc. prof. Johns Hopkins U., 1969-73, prof., 1973—; assoc. Inst. für Molekularbiologie der U. Zurich, Switzerland, 1975-76; assoc. Rsch. Inst. Molecular Pathology, Vienna, 1990-91. Contbr. articles to profl. jours. Served to lt. M.C. USNR, 1957-59. Recipient Nobel Prize in medicine, 1978; Guggenheim fellow, 1975-76. Mem. Am. Soc. Microbiology, AAAS, Am. Soc. Biol. Chemists, Nat. Acad. Sci. Office: Johns Hopkins U Sch Med Dept Molecular Biology Genetics 725 N Wolfe St Baltimore MD 21205-2105

SMITH, HARMON LEE, JR., clergyman, moral theology educator; b. Ellisville, Miss., Aug. 23, 1930; s. Harmon Lee Sr. and Mary (O'Donnell) S.; children: Pamela Lee, Amy Joanna, Harmon Lee III. AB, Millsaps Coll., 1952; BD, Duke U., 1955, PhD, 1962. Ordain to priest Episcopal Ch., 1972. Asst. dean Duke U. Divinity Sch., Durham, N.C., 1959-65, asst. prof. Christian ethics, 1962-68, assoc. prof. moral theology, 1968-73, prof. moral theology, 1973—, prof. community and family medicine, 1974—; cons. med. ethics; vis. prof. U. N.C., 1964, 70, 72, U. Edinburgh, Scotland, 1969, U. Windsor, Ont., 1974. Author books med. ethics; sr. editor: Social Science and Medicine, 1973-89; Contbr.: articles on Christian ethics to various publs. Lilly Found. fellow, 1960; Gurney Harris Kearns Found. fellow, 1961; Nat. Humanities Ctr. fellow, 1982-83. Mem. Am. Assn. Theol. Schs., Am. Soc. Christian Ethics, Am. Acad. Religion, Soc. for Religion in Higher Edn., Soc. Health and Human Values. Home: 3510 Randolph Rd Durham NC 27705-5347 Office: Duke U The Divinity Sch Durham NC 27706

SMITH, HAROLD B., manufacturing executive; b. Chgo., Apr. 7, 1933; s. Harold Byron and Pauline (Hart) S. Grad., Choate Sch., 1951; B.S., Princeton U., 1955; M.B.A., Northwestern U., 1957. With Ill. Tool Works, Inc., Chgo., 1954—; exec. v.p. Ill. Tool Works, Inc., 1968-72, pres., 1972-81, vice chmn., 1981, chmn. exec. com., 1982—; also bd. dirs.; bd. dirs. W.W. Grainger, Inc., No. Trust Corp.; trustee Northwestern Mut. Life Ins. Co. Mem. Rep. Nat. Com., 1976—; chmn. Ill. Rep. Com., 1993—; del. Rep. Nat. Conv., 1964, 76, 88, 92; bd. dirs. Adler Planetarium, Boys and Girls Clubs Am., Northwestern U. Rush-Presbyn.-St. Luke's Med. Ctr., Newberry Libr. Mem. Mfrs. Alliance Productivity and Innovation (bd. dirs.). Clubs: Chicago, Commercial, Commonwealth, Economic, Northwestern, Princeton (Chgo.). Office: Ill Tool Works Inc 3600 W Lake Ave Glenview IL 60025-1215

SMITH, HAROLD CHARLES, private pension fund executive; b. N.Y.C., Jan. 11, 1934; s. Harold Elmore and Hedwig Agnes (Gronke) S. BA cum laude with honors, Ursinus Coll., 1955, DD (hon.), 1993; MBA, NYU, 1958; M in Div., Union Theol. Sem., N.Y.C., 1958. DD Ursinus Coll., 1993. CFA; ordained minister United Ch. of Christ, 1959. Vice pres. YMCA Retirement Fund, Inc., N.Y.C., 1958-69, portfolio mgr., 1960—, assoc. sec., 1969-77, v.p., 1977-80, exec. v.p., 1980-82, pres. elect, 1982-83, pres., 1983—; pastor 1st E&R Ch., Bridgeport, Conn., 1958-88, Unity Hill United Ch. of Christ, 1988—; assoc. prof. bus. and fin. L.I. U. 1969-71; trustee Bank Mart, Bridgeport, Conn., 1983-91; bd. dirs. Y Mut. Ins. Co., trsee. 1988—, United Ch. Residencies, 1962-65. Trustee YWCA Greater Bridgeport, 1975-79, Pension Funds United Ch. of Christ, 1968—, Springfield Coll. (Mass.), 1983—; bd. dirs. YMCA Greater N.Y., 1983—, Bridgeport Area Found., 1989—, Ursinus Coll., Pa., 1994—, Coun. of Chs. of Greater Bridgeport. Mem. N.Y. Soc. Security Analysts, Am. Econs. Assn., Fin. Analysts Fedn., World and Trade Club, Mcht's Club, Masons, Marco Polo Club, Order Eastern Star. Author: Getting it All Together for Retirement, 1977. Office: YMCA Retirement 225 Broadway New York NY 10007-3000*

SMITH, HARRY DELANO, educational administrator; b. Florence, Ala., June 10, 1954; s. Cornelius Everett and Nadine (Olive) S.; m. Wanda Joy Skipworth, Nov. 23, 1978; children: Benjamin Delano, Rebekah Joy. BS, U. North Ala., 1975, MA, 1977, EdS, 1983; EdD, U. Ala., Tuscaloosa, 1989. Cert. class AA supr.-prin., Ala. Exec. dir. Christian Student Ctr., Florence, 1980-83; head dept. math Mars Hill Bible Sch., Florence, 1983-87; tchr. math. and physics Muscle Shoals (Ala.) High Sch., 1975-80, asst. prin., 1987-88, prin., 1989—; farmer, Killen, Ala., 1974-80; tchr. summer sch. Sheffield (Ala.) High Sch., 1977-78; dir. scholars program Muscle Shoals Schs., 1987-88; asst. prin. Avalon Mid. Sch., Muscle Shoals, 1987-88, prin., 1988-89; math. cons. Cartersville (Ga.) City Schs., 1991-92; curriculum cons. Eufaula (Ala.) High Sch., 1991-92; co-chmn. Ala. Learner Outcomes Com., Montgomery, 1991-92; dist. judge All-State Acad. Team, Athens, Ala., 1991-92; coach Ala. Mathcounts team NSPE, Birmingham, 1985. Dir. music and edn. Shoals Ch. of Christ, 1992. Named Outstanding Young Educator, No. Dist. Ala. Jaycees, 1987; Beeson fellow Samford U., 1987. Mem. ASCD, Nat. Assn. Secondary Sch. Prins., Am. Assn. Sch. Adminstrs., Ala. Coun. Sch. Adminstrs. and Suprs., Ala. Assn. Secondary Sch. Prins., Kappa Delta Pi, Phi Kappa Phi. Avocations: travel, stamp collecting, reading, bowling. Home: 1403 Brookford Pl Muscle Shoals AL 35661-2670 Office: Muscle Shoals High Sch 100 E Trojan Dr Muscle Shoals AL 35661-3173

SMITH, HARRY LEE, laboratory technician, chemist; b. Panama City, Fla., Oct. 19, 1936; s. Sanders and Pearl Jane (Williams) S. AA, Gulf Coast Coll., 1968; BS, U. Fla., Gainesville, 1971. Chemist, lab technician St. Joe Paper Co., Port Saint Joe, Fla., 1955—; supt. St. Joe Stevedoring Co., Fla., 1985—; pres. St. Joe Papermakers Fed. Credit Union, Fla., 1968—; pres. Local 1713, St. Joe, Fla., 1992—. E3 U.S. Army, 1959-65. Mem. Mason, Scottish Rite. Home: PO Box 394 Port Saint Joe FL 32456 Office: St Joe Papermakers Credit Union PO Box 236 Port Saint Joe FL 32456-0236

SMITH, HARVEY ALVIN, mathematics educator, consultant; b. Easton, Pa., Jan. 30, 1932; s. William Augustus and Ruth Carolyn (Krauth) S.; m. Ruth Wismer Kolb, Aug. 27, 1955; children: Deirdre Lynn, Kirsten Nadine, Brinton Averill. B.S., Lehigh U., 1952; M.S., U. Pa., 1955, A.M., 1958, Ph.D., 1964. Asst. prof. math Drexel U., 1960-65; mem. tech. staff Inst. Def. Analyses, Arlington, Va., 1965-66; assoc. prof. math Oakland U., 1966-68; ops. research scientist Exec. Office of Pres., Washington, 1968-70; prof. math. Oakland U., 1970-77; prof. Ariz. State U., Tempe, 1977—; cons. Inst. Def. Analyses, 1967-69, Exec. Office Pres., 1967-73, U.S. Arms Control and Disarmament Agy., 1973-79, Los Alamos Nat. Lab. Author: Mathematical Foundation of Systems Analysis, 1969. NSF fellow, 1964-65; recipient Meritorious Service award Exec. Office of Pres., 1970. Mem. Soc. Indsl. and Applied Math., Am. Math. Soc., AAAS, Sigma Xi. Home: 18 E Concorda Dr Tempe AZ 85282-3517 Office: Ariz State U Dept Math Tempe AZ 85287

SMITH, HEDRICK LAURENCE, journalist, television comentator, author, lecturer; b. Kilmacolm, Scotland, July 9, 1933; s. Sterling L. and Phebe (Hedrick) S.; m. Ann Bickford, June 29, 1957 (div. Dec. 1985); children: Laurel Ann, Jennifer Laurence, Sterling Scott, Lesley Roberts; m. Susan Zox, Mar. 7, 1987. Grad., Choate Sch., 1951; BA, Williams Coll., 1955, LittD (hon.), 1975; postgrad. (Fulbright scholar), Balliol Coll., Oxford, Eng., 1955-56; LittD (hon.), Wittenburg U., 1989, N.H. Coll., 1991; LHD (hon.), Columbia Coll., 1992; LittD (hon.), Amherst Coll., 1992; LHD (hon.), U. S.C., 1992. With U.P.I., Memphis, Nashville, Atlanta, 1959-62; with N.Y. Times, 1962-88, Washington and S.E., 1962-63; with Vietnam, 1963-64; Middle East corr. N.Y. Times, Cairo, U.A.R., 1964-66; diplomatic news corr. N.Y. Times, Washington, 1962-64, 66-71; Moscow Bur. chief N.Y. Times, 1971-74, dep. nat. editor, 1975-76, Washington Bur. chief, 1976-79, chief Washington corr., 1980-85; Washington correspondent N.Y. Times mag., 1987-88; vis. journalist Am. Enterprise Inst., 1985-87; fellow Fgn. Policy Inst., Johns Hopkins U. Sch. Advanced Internat. Studies, 1989—; panelist Washington Week in Rev.., PBS. Author: The Russians, 1975 (Overseas Press Club award 1976), The Power Game: How Washington Works, 1988, The New Russians, 1990 (Overseas Press Club citation 1991), Rethinking America, 1995; co-author: The Pentagon Papers, 1972, Reagan the Man, the President, 1981, Beyond Reagan: The Politics of Upheaval, 1986, Seven Days That Shook the World, 1991; TV documentaries Star Wars, 1985, Moscow Jews, 1986, Space Bridge, Chernobyl: Three Mile Island, 1987, 4-part Power Game series, PBS, 1989, Countdown to White House: The Bush Transition, 1989, 4-part series Inside Gorbachev's USSR, 1990 (George Polk award, Gold Baton award Columbia-Du Pont), Guns, Tanks and Gorbachev, 1991, Soviets, 1991 (George Peabody award), 4-part series PBS, Challenge to America, 1994. Mem. Pulitzer prize team N.Y. Times, pub. svc. Pentagon Papers Series, 1972; trustee Williams Coll. 1982—. With USAF, 1956-59. Recipient Pulitzer prize for internat. reporting from Soviet Union and Ea. Europe, 1974; Nieman fellow Harvard U., 1969-70. Mem. Gridiron Club, Phi Beta Kappa.

SMITH, HENRY CHARLES, III, symphony orchestra conductor; b. Phila., Jan. 31, 1931; s. Henry Charles Jr. and Gertrude Ruth (Downs) S.; m. Mary Jane Dressner, Sept. 3, 1955; children—Katherine Anne, Pamela Jane, Henry Charles IV. BA, U. Pa., 1952; artist diploma, Curtis Inst. Music, Phila., 1955. Solo trombonist Phila. Orch., 1955-67; condr. Rochester (Minn.) Symphony Orch., 1967-68; assoc. prof. music Ind. U., Bloomington, 1968-71; resident condr., ednl. dir. Minn. Orch., Mpls., 1971-88; prof. music U. Tex., Austin, 1988-89, Frank C. Erwin Centennial Prof. of Opera, 1988-89; music dir. S.D. Symphony, Sioux Falls, 1989—; prof. Ariz. State U., Tempe, 1989-93, prof. emeritus, 1993—; vis. prof. U. Tex., Austin, 1987-88; founding mem. Phila. Brass Ensemble, 1956—. Composer 5 books of solos for trombone including Solos for the Trombone Player, 1963, Hear Us As We Pray, 1963, First Solos for the Trombone Player, 1972, Easy Duets for Winds, 1972; editor 14 books 20th century symphonies lit. Served to 1st lt. AUS, 1952-54. Recipient 3 Grammy nominations, 1967, 76, 1 Grammy award for best chamber music rec. with Phila. Brass Ensemble, 1969. Mem. Internat. Trombone Assn. (dir.), Am. Symphony Orch. League, Music Educators Nat. Conf., Am. Guild Organists, Am. Fedn. Musicians, Tubist Universal Brotherhood Assn., Acacia Fraternity. Republican. Congregationalist. Home: 8032 Pennsylvania Rd Bloomington MN 55438

SMITH, HENRY CLAY, retired psychology educator; b. Catonsville, Md., May 9, 1913; s. Harry C. and Lovell (Figgins) S.; m. Nancy Woollcott, Aug. 27, 1938; children—David Barton, Woollcott Keston, Barbara Sunderland. A.B. magna cum laude, St. John's Coll., Annapolis, Md., 1934; Ph.D., Johns Hopkins U., 1939. Instr. psychology U. Vt., Burlington, 1940-43; dir. tng. and research Western Electric Co., Balt., 1943-45; assoc. prof. Knox Coll., Galesburg, Ill., 1945-46; asso. prof. psychology, chmn. dept. Hamilton Coll., Clinton, N.Y., 1946-49; prof. psychology Mich. State U., East Lansing, from 1949; ret., 1983; Fulbright research fellow, Italy, 1955-56; cons. professor Waseda U., Tokyo, 1960. Author: Sensitivity Training, 2d edit, 1973, Personality Development, 2d edit, 1974; co-author: Social Perception, 1968, Psychology of Industrial Behavior, 3d edit, 1972, Ten Keys to Understanding People, 1987. Fellow APA; mem. Phi Beta Kappa. Home: PO Box 3086 West Tisbury MA 02575-0086

SMITH, HERALD ALVIN, JR., transportation executive; b. Beaconsfield, Iowa, Dec. 23, 1922; s. Herald Alvin and Iva Viola (Briggeman) S.; m. Miriam Gayle Armstrong, Oct. 5, 1946; children: Sharon Konchar, John, Susan Johnson, Jim. Student, U. Iowa, 1942-43, Coe Coll., Cedar Rapids, Iowa, 1944-45. Pres., chmn. bd. CRST, Inc., Cedar Rapids, 1955-77, chmn. bd., chief exec. officer, 1977-83; chmn. bd. CRST Internat., Inc., Cedar Rapids, 1983—; chmn. bd., pres. Crest Microfilm, Inc., Cedar Rapids, 1980—. Mem. Gov.'s Blue Ribbon Task Force on Transp., Iowa, 1982; trustee Regional Transit Authority, Cedar Rapids, 1967-78; campaign mgr. United Way, 1973-74; bd. dirs. CMC Colls. Associated, 1979, Cornell Coll., Mt. Vernon, Iowa, 1979-87, Four Oaks Treatment Ctr., 1986—. Mem. Am. Trucking Assn., Inc. (interstate carriers conf. 1st v.p. 1980-81, pres. 1981-82, chmn. 1982-83), Iowa Motor Truck Assn. (pres., chmn. bd. 1978-79, exec. bd. 1979—). Avocations: tennis, sailing, running a resort. Home: PO Box 73 Ellison Bay WI 54210-0073 Office: CRST Internat Inc 3930 16th Ave SW Cedar Rapids IA 52404-2332

SMITH, HERRICK HAYNER, landscape architect, educator, consultant; b. Troy, N.Y., Oct. 26, 1930; s. Herrick Alfred and Gladys Jenette (Hayner) S.; m. Mary Hazel Phillips, June 8, 1957; children—Marthanne Phillips-Smith, Herrick Alfred, Jane Elizabeth. B.S., Cornell U., 1958, M.S., 1959; M.L.A., U. Ga., 1961. Registered landscape architect, Fla. Asst. prof. Okla. State U., Stillwater, 1961-63, Kans. State U., Manhattan, 1963-66; prof. landscape architecture U. Fla., Gainesville, 1966—, chmn. dept., 1966—; mem. Fla. Bd. Landscape Architects, Tallahassee, 1972-80, chmn. bd. 1976-80, ednl. advisor to bd., 1980-90; cons. in landscape architecture Gainesville 1966—; pres. Coun. Landscape Archtl. Registration Bds., 1983; vis. prof. U. Francesco Marroquin, Guatemala, 1989. Contbr. articles and book revs. to profl. publs. and jours.; works include several pub. gardens, urban spaces in Fla. Mem. Gainesville City Plan Bd., 1972-75; chmn. land planning com. Fla. Defenders of Environ., Gainesville, 1980-82; bd. dirs. Fla. Inst. Phosphate Rsch., 1980-83. With USAF, 1951-54. Fellow Am. Soc. Landscape Architects (edn. award 1982, writing award 1983, chmn. ann. meeting Fla. chpt. 1983, U.S. del. to Internat. Fedn. Landscape Architects 1989-90, dir. dept. studies abroad in Italy 1985). Republican. Methodist. Avocations: camping; travel; old houses and cars. Office: U of Fla Coll of Architecture Dept Landscape Architecture Gainesville FL 32611

SMITH, HILARY CRANWELL BOWEN, investment banker; b. Balt., Nov. 1, 1937; s. Henry Bowen and Clayton (Cranwell) S.; m. Janet Simmons, June 9, 1962. BA, Colgate U., 1960; MBA, U. Va., 1967. V.p. Goldman, Sachs & Co., N.Y.C., 1969-74, E. F. Hutton & Co., N.Y.C., 1974-77; sr. v.p. Blyth Eastman Dillon, N.Y.C., 1977-79; mng. dir. Salomon Bros., N.Y.C., 1979-90, Dillon, Read & Co., Inc., N.Y.C., 1990—. Trustee Greenwich (Conn.) Acad. Lt. USN, 1960-63. Mem. Univ. Club, Hillsboro Club (bd. dirs.). Home: 334 Lake Ave Greenwich CT 06830 Office: Dillon Read & Co Inc 535 Madison Ave 15th Fl New York NY 10022

SMITH, HOKE LAFOLLETTE, university president; b. Galesburg, Ill., May 7, 1931; s. Claude Hoke and Bernice (LaFollette) S.; m. Barbara E. Walvoord, June 30, 1979; children by previous marriage: Kevin, Kerry, Amy, Glen. B.A. (Harold fellow), Knox Coll., 1953; M.A., U. Va., 1954; Ph.D. (fellow 1958), Emory U., 1958; hon. degree, Sung Kyun Kwan U., Korea, 1993, Knox Coll., 1995. Asst. prof. polit. sci. Hiram Coll., Ohio, 1958-64; assoc. prof. polit. sci. Hiram Coll., 1964-67; asst. to pres., prof. polit. sci. Drake U., Des Moines, Iowa, Md., 1967-70; interim governing com. Drake U., 1971-72, v.p. acad. adminstrn., 1970-79; pres. Towson (Md.) State U., 1979—; mem. univ. adv. council Life Ins. Council Am., 1969-71. Chmn. exec. com. Coun. Econ. Edn., Md., Towson, 1979—; bd. dirs. Balt. Coun. on Fgn. Rels.; chmn. Very Spl. Arts of Md. With U.S. Army, 1954-56. Recipient Eileen Tosney award Am. Assn. Univ. Administs., 1991; Congl. fellow Am. Polit. Sci. Assn., 1964-65. Mem. Am. Assn. State Colls. and Univs. (bd. dirs. 1984-88, bd. dirs. found., 1985-87, chmn. elect. 1985-86, chmn. 1986-87), Am. Coun. Edn. (bd. dirs., coun. com. 1988-94, chmn. elect 1991-92, chmn. 1992-93, past chmn. 1993-94), Am. Assn. Higher Edn., Soc. for Coll. and Univ. Planning (bd. dirs. 1986-88), Balt. C. of C. (adv. coun.), Phi Beta Kappa, Phi Kappa Phi, Omicron Delta Kappa, Delta Sigma Rho, Gamma Gamma, Pi Sigma Alpha. Office: Towson State U Office Pres Baltimore MD 21204

SMITH, HOWARD, film editor. Editor: (films) Live a Little, Steal a Lot, 1975, Mackintosh & T.J., 1975, Tex, 1982, Twilight Zone-The Movie ("Terror at 20,000 Feet"), 1983, (with David Garfield and Suzanne Petit) Sylvester, 1985, (with David Bretherton) Baby-Scared of the Lost Legend, 1985, At Close Range, 1986, Near Dark, 1987, (with Sonya Sones Tramer) River's Edge, 1987, The Abyss, 1989, Big Man on Campus, 1989, (with Joel Goodman and Conrad Buff) After Dark, My Sweet, 1990, Point Break, 1991, Glengarry Glen Ross, 1992, The Saint of Fort Washington, 1993, Two Bits, 1994, (TV movies) Flying Blind, 1990. Office: care Lawrence Mirisch The Mirisch Agency 10100 Santa Monica Blvd Ste 700 Los Angeles CA 90067*

SMITH, HOWARD E., manufacturing executive, light; b. 1934. Sr. v.p. Sealright Co., Inc., Shawnee Mission, Kas., 1990—. Office: Sealright Packaging Co 7101 College Blvd Shawnee Mission KS 66210-1823*

SMITH, HOWARD MCQUEEN, librarian; b. Charlotte, N.C., July 25, 1919; s. Daniel Holt and Pearl Elizabeth (Truitt) S.; m. Elaine Betty Wiefel, June 27, 1949; children: Leslie, Steven Holt. B.A., U. Va., 1941; A.B. in L.S. U. Mich., 1946. M. Pub. Adminstrn., 1947. Reference asst. Enoch Pratt Free Library, Balt., 1947-49; coordinator library activities Richmond (Va.) Area Univ. Center, 1949-50; exec. asst. to dir. Enoch Pratt Free Library, 1950-53, head films dept., 1953-55; personnel officer Free Library Phila. 1955-59; city librarian Richmond Pub. Library, 1959-84. Served to lt. (s.g.) USNR, 1942-46. Mem. ALA.

SMITH, HOWARD ROSS, economics educator, academic administrator, researcher, consultant; b. Des Moines, July 6, 1917; s. John Truman and Miriam Sylvia (Ross) S.; m. Gwendolyn Thomas Collins, Feb. 20, 1943; children—David, Janet, Richard. A.B., Simpson Coll., 1938; M.A., La. State U., 1940, Ph.D., 1945. Instr. La. State U., Baton Rouge, 1940-43; economist War Prodn. Bd., Washington, 1943-46; assoc. prof. U. Ga., Athens, 1946-49, prof., 1949—, dept. head, 1963-76. Author: Economic History of U.S., 1955, Government and Business, 1958, Democracy and Public Interest, 1960, The Capitalist Imperative, 1975, Management, 1980. Rockefeller Found. fellow, 1948-49; recipient Ford Found. award, Egypt, 1961-63; Fulbright award, Columbia, 1973. Mem. Acad. Mgmt. Democrat. Presbyterian. Home: 382 Westview Dr Athens GA 30606-4636 Office: Univ Ga Athens GA 30602

SMITH, HOWARD RUSSELL, manufacturing company executive; b. Clark County, Ohio, Aug. 15, 1914; s. Lewis Hoskins and Eula (Elder) S.; m. Jeanne Rogers, June 27, 1942; children: Stewart Russell, Douglas Howard, Jeanne Ellen Smith James. A.B., Pomona Coll., 1936. Security analyst Kidder, Peabody & Co., N.Y.C., 1936-37; economist ILO, Geneva, 1937-40; asst. to pres. Blue Diamond Corp., Los Angeles, 1940-46; pres., dir. Avery Dennison Corp., Pasadena, Calif., 1946-75, chmn. bd., 1975-84, chmn. exec. com., 1984—; chmn. bd. Kinsmith Fin. Corp., San Marino, Calif., 1979—. Bd. dirs., past pres., chmn. Los Angeles Philharm. Assn.; chmn. emeritus, bd. trustees Pomona Coll., Claremont, Calif.; past chmn. bd. Children's Hosp. Los Angeles, Community TV of So. Calif. (Sta. KCET), Los Angeles. With USNR 1943-46. Home: 1458 Hillcrest Ave Pasadena CA 91106-4503 Office: Avery Dennison Corp 150 N Orange Grove Blvd Pasadena CA 91103

SMITH, HOWARD WESLEY, engineering educator; b. N.Y.C., Nov. 24, 1929. BS, Wichita State U., 1951, MS, 1958; PhD, Okla. State U., Stillwater, 1968. Registered profl. engr., Kans. Stress engr. Boeing Co. Wichita, Kans., 1950-68; staff engr. Boeing Co., Seattle, 1969-70; assoc. prof. engring. U. Kans., Lawrence, 1970-74, assoc. dean, 1974-76, prof., 1977—. Author: Aerospace Structural Design, 1980, Aerospace Structural Loads, 1981, Head Injury Research, 1983, Aerospace Materials and Process, 1984, Matrix Methods for Structural Analysis, 1984, Aerospace Structures Supportability, 1990, Aircraft Crashworthiness, 1990, Geriatrics of Commercial Airframes, 1990; patentee osteoclast for whole bone testing, 1984 and longbone goniometer, 1985; editor: Aerospace Design Engineers Guide, 1983. Rockety supt. 4-H Club, Lawrence, Kans., 1978-85. Assoc. fellow AIAA; mem. Am. Soc. Engring. Edn. Home: 1612 Crescent Rd Lawrence KS 66044-3123 Office: U Kans Dept Engring 2004 Learned Hall Lawrence KS 66045-2221

SMITH, IAN CORMACK PALMER, biophysicist; b. Winnipeg, Man., Can., Sept. 23, 1939; s. Cormack and Grace Mary S.; m. Eva Gunilla Landvik, Mar. 27, 1965; children: Brittmarie, Cormack, Duncan, Roderick. BS, U. Man., 1961, MS, 1962; PhD, Cambridge U., England, 1965; Filosophie Doktor (hon.), U. Stockholm, 1986; DSc (hon.), U. Winnipeg, 1990. Fellow Stanford U., 1965-66; mem. rsch. staff Bell Tel. Labs., Murray Hill, N.J., 1966-67; rsch. officer divsn. biol. scis. NRC, Ottawa, 1967-87, dir. gen., 1987-91; dir.-gen. Inst. Biodiagnostics, Winnipeg, 1992—; adj. prof. chemistry and biochemistry Carleton U., 1973-90, U. Ottawa, 1976-92; adj. prof. chemistry, physics and anatomy U. Man., 1992—; adj. prof. biophysics U. Ill., Chgo., 1974-80; allied scientist Ottawa Civic Hosp., 1985-92, Ottawa Gen. Hosp., 1989-92, Ont. Cancer Found., 1989-92, St. Boniface Hosp., 1992—, Health Scis. Ctr., 1993—, Econ. Tech. Innovation Coun., Man., 1994—. Contbr. chps. to books, articles in field to profl. jours. Recipient Barringer award Can. Spectroscopy Soc., 1979, Harzberg award, 1986, Organon Teknika award Can. Soc. Clin. Chemists, 1981, Sr. Scientist award Sigma Xi, 1995. Fellow Chem. Inst. Can. (Merck award 1978, Labatt award 1984), Royal Soc. Can., Soc. Magnetic Resonance Medicine (exec. com. 1989-94); mem. Internat. Coun. Sci. Unions (gen. com. 1993—), Am. Chem. Soc., Biophys. Soc., Can. Biochem. Soc. (Ayerst award 1978), Biophys. Soc. Can., Internat. Union Pure and Applied Biophysics (coun. 1993—), U. Man. Alumni Assn. (bd. dirs. 1993—). Office: Inst Biodiagnostics, Winnipeg, MB Canada R3B 1Y6

SMITH, ILEENE ANDREA, book editor; b. N.Y.C., Jan. 21, 1953; d. Norman and Jeanne (Jaffe) S.; m. Howard A. Sobel, June 3, 1979; children: Nathaniel Jacob, Rebecca Julia. BA, Brandeis U., Waltham, Mass., 1975; MA, Columbia U., 1978. Editorial asst. Atheneum Publishers, N.Y.C., 1979-82; sr. editor Summit Books, N.Y.C., 1982-91, lit. editor, 1991-92; editl. cons. The Elie Wiesel Found. for Humanity, 1993—; cons. editor Paris Review, N.Y., 1987—. Author introductory scripts for Met. Opera Telecasts, 1987—. Jerusalem fellow, 1987; recipient Tony Godwin Meml. award, 1982, PEN/Roger Klein award for editl. excellence, 1988, Contbg. to Prodn. of Aida cent. NATAS, 1990.

SMITH, IVAN HURON, architect; b. Danville, Ind., Jan. 25, 1907; s. Calvin Wesley and Irma (Huron) S.; m. Sara Butler, Aug. 18, 1972; 1 child by previous marriage, Norma Smith Benton. Student, Ga. Inst. Tech., 1926; B.Arch., U. Fla., 1929. With Ivan H. Smith (architect), 1936-41; partner Reynolds, Smith & Hills (architects and engrs.), Jacksonville, Fla., 1941-70; chmn. bd. emeritus Reynolds, Smith & Hills (Architects, Engrs., Planners, Inc.), Jacksonville, Tampa, Orlando, Merritt Island and Ft. Lauderdale, Fla., 1971-77; sec. Jacksonville Bldg. Code Adv. Bd., 1951-68; mem. Duval County Govt. Study Commn., 1966-67; chmn. Jacksonville Constrn. Trades Qualification Bd., 1971. Important works include City Hall, Jacksonville, Duval County Ct. House, Jacksonville, Baptist Hosp, Jacksonville, Engring. Bldg, Nuclear Sci. Bldg, Fla. Field Stadium at, U. Fla.; dormitories Council Bldg, Jacksonville U.; fed. bldgs., Jacksonville, Gainesville, Fla., So. Bell Telephone bldgs; Internat. Airport, Tampa, Fla.; (with Edward Durell Stone) Fla. State Capitol Center. Mem. council Jacksonville U., 1958-76; pres. Jacksonville Humane Soc., 1956-59; bd. dirs. Jacksonville-Duval Safety Council. Served with USNR, 1943-45. Recipient U. Fla. Disting. Alumnus award, 1981, Jacksonville U. Order of the Dolphin, 1985; Paul Harris fellow, 1980. Fellow AIA (Outstanding Service award Fla. region 1965, chpt. pres. 1942, 56); mem. Fla. Assn. Architects (dir. 1957, Gold medal 1981), Jacksonville C. of C. (dir. 1957-59), Beta Theta Pi, Phi Kappa Phi, Sigma Tau. Clubs: Gargoyle (U. Fla.); River (Jacksonville), Univ. (Jacksonville), San Jose Country (Jacksonville), Epping Forest Yacht (Jacksonville), Rotary (Jacksonville, Paul Harris fellow 1980). Home: 6000 San Jose Blvd # 201 Jacksonville FL 32217-2352 Office: 4651 Salisbury Rd Jacksonville FL 32256-6107

SMITH, J. BRIAN, advertising executive, public affairs consultant, campaign management firm executive; b. Boston, Jan. 25, 1950; s. Leonard Francis and Rose Geraldine (McDonald) S.; m. Catherine Healy, Dec. 9, 1978; children: Maris, Daniel, Brian, Michael. BA, Loyola Coll., 1971. Chief writer domestic affairs Rep. Nat. Com., Washington, 1971-72; press sec.to John J. Rhodes of Ariz. U.S. Ho. Minority Leader, Washington, 1973-76; pres. Smith & Harroff, Inc., Washington, 1976. Contbr. numerous articles to profl. jours., popular mags; scriptwriter documentary films; polit. commentator for many TV, radio programs. Bd. dirs. Alexandria (Va.) Country Day Sch., 1989—. Mem. Am. Assn. Polit. Cons. Roman Catholic. Office: Smith & Harroff Inc 11 Canal Center Plz Ste 104 Alexandria VA 22314-5504

SMITH, J. E. GENE, electric power industry executive. V. chmn. Ala. Electric Coop., Andalusia, Ala. Office: Alabama Electric Coop Hwy 29 Andalusia AL 36420*

SMITH, J. KELLUM, JR., foundation executive, lawyer; b. N.Y.C., June 18, 1927; s. James Kellum and Elizabeth Barter (Walker) S.; m. Sarah Tod Lohmann, July 22, 1950 (div. 1993); children: Alison Andrews, Timothy Kellum, Jennifer Harlow, Christopher Lohmann; m. Angela Marina Brown, Feb. 3, 1995. Grad., Phillips Exeter Acad., 1945; A.B. magna cum laude, Amherst Coll., 1950; LL.B., Harvard, 1953. Bar: N.Y. 1955. Assoc. Lord, Day & Lord, N.Y.C., 1953-59; asst. sec. John Simon Guggenheim Meml. Found., 1960-62; mem. staff Rockefeller Found., 1962-74, asst. sec., 1963-64, sec., 1964-74; v.p., sec. Andrew W. Mellon Found., N.Y.C., 1974-89, sr. fellow, 1989-92; sr. advisor, 1992—. Trustee Nat. Sculpture Soc., 1955-71, Nat. Ins. Archtl. Edn., 1961-69, St. Bernard's Sch., N.Y.C., 1968-78, Found. for Child Devel., 1968-74; trustee Brearley Sch., N.Y.C., 1964-80, pres., 1973-78; trustee Am. Acad. in Rome, 1964-95, treas., 1965-66, 22 d v.p., 1968-72, 84-88, sec., 1973-84, 89-95. With USAAF, 1945-46. Mem. Phi Beta Kappa. Club: Century Association (N.Y.C.). Home: 550 Number 37 Rd Saranac NY 12981 Office: Mellon Found 140 E 62nd St New York NY 10021-8142

SMITH, J. ROY, education educator; b. Washington, Ga., Sept. 13, 1936; s. James Roy and Nellie Irene (Mansfield) S. BA, Mercer U., 1956; postgrad., Brown U., 1957; cert., Oxford U., Eng., 1963. Tchr. City of Cranston, R.I., 1957-59; with Charleston County, Charleston, S.C., 1962-64, 76-79; tchr. Fulton County, Fairburn, Ga., 1965-76, Berkeley County, Moncks Corner, S.C., 1979-94. Lt. (j.g.) USN, 1959-62. Charleston Area Writing Project fellow; recipient English Speaking Union scholarship Oxford U., 1963; Newspaper Fund of the Wall Street Jour. fellow. Mem. SAR (sec./treas. S.C. Soc. 1977-78), Soc. Second War with Great Britain, Sons and Daus. of Pilgrims (gov. Ga. br. 1976, hon. gov. 1976—), S.C. Hist. Soc., Ga. Hist. Soc., Kappa Phi Kappa (registered tour guide, lectr.). Home and Office: 110 Coming St Charleston SC 29403-6103

SMITH, J. STEVEN, electric power industry executive. MBA, Ind. U., 1977. Asst. dir. Ind. Statewide Assn. Rural Electric Coops., 1974-77; with Hoosier Energy Rural Electric Coop., Bloomington, Ind., 1977—, sr. v.p., 1991, now pres., CEO. Office: Hoosier Energy Rural Elec Coop 7398 N State Rd 37 Bloomington IN 47404*

SMITH, J. W., dean. Exec. dean N.D. State U., Bottineau. Office: ND State U Bottineau Office Exec Dean Bottineau ND 58318

SMITH, JACK, food service executive. Prtn. Smith Realty, Grundy, Va., 1955—; chmn. K-VA-T Food Stores, Grundy, Va. Office: K-VA-T Food Stores 329 N Main St Grundy VA 24614

SMITH, JACK CARL, foreign trade consultant; b. Cleve., Sept. 11, 1928; s. John Carl and Florence Agnes (O'Rourke) S.; m. Nannette June Boyd, Dec. 1, 1962; 1 dau., Colleen Wentworth. Student, Baldwin Wallace Coll., 1948-51, postgrad., 1958; B.A., Ohio U., 1954. Rep. Flying Tiger Line Inc., Los Angeles, 1958-61; prin. Pub. Rep. bus., Cleve., 1961-64; pub. Penton Pub., Cleve., 1964-90; sr. fellow Am. Fgn. Policy Coun., Washington, 1990—; dir. Central Cleve. Corp. Nat. Distbn. Terminals; graduated Air Tng. Command Intelligence Officer Sch., served from 1958-62 AFR. Trump Presdl. task force, Rep. Senatorial Inner Circle, Coun. of Logistics Mgmt., U.S. Bus. and Indsl. Coun. With USAF, 1954-58. Mem. Am. Mgmt. Assn., Material Handling Inst., Am. Trucking Assn., Nat. Council Phys. Distbn. Mgmt., Family Motor Coach Assn., Recreation Vehicle Industry Assn., Am. Bus.

Press, Mag. Pubs. Assn., Sci. Research Soc., Internat. Platform Assn., Sigma Xi, Sigma Chi. Club: Wings (N.Y.C.). Home: 457 Devonshire Ct Bay Village OH 44140-3009 Office: Am Fgn Policy Coun 621 Pennsylvania Ave SE Washington DC 20003 *Do your best and God will forgive you the rest.*

SMITH, JACK CLIFFORD, journalist, author; b. Long Beach, Calif., Aug. 27, 1916; s. Charles Franklin and Anna Mary (Hughes) S.; m. Denise Bresson, June 17, 1939; children: Curtis Bresson, Douglas Franklin. Student, Bakersfield (Calif.) Coll., 1937-38. Reporter Bakersfield Californian, 1937-38, Honolulu Advertiser, 1941-42, UPI, Sacramento, 1943, Los Angeles Daily News, 1946-49, Los Angeles Herald-Express, 1950-52; reporter Los Angeles Times, 1953-58, columnist, 1958—. Author: Three Coins in the Birdbath, 1965, Smith on Wry, 1970, God and Mr. Gomez, 1974, The Big Orange, 1976, Spend All Your Kisses, Mr. Smith, 1978, Jack Smith's L.A, 1980, How to Win a Pullet Surprise, 1982, Cats, Dogs and Other Strangers at My Door, 1984, Alive in La La Land, 1989. Served with USMC, 1944-45. Club: Sunset. Home: 4251 Camino Real Los Angeles CA 90065-3960 Office: Times Mirror Sq Los Angeles CA 90053

SMITH, JACK PRESCOTT, journalist; b. Paris, Apr. 25, 1945; s. Howard Kingsbury and Benedicte (Traberg) S.; divorced; 1 child, Alexander Kingsbury. BA in History, Carnegie-Mellon U., 1971, Oxford (Eng.) U., 1974. Writer-producer Sta. WIIC-TV News, Pitts., 1969-70; producer-reporter Sta. WLS-TV News, Chgo., 1974-76; fgn. corr. ABC-TV News, Paris, 1976-80; corr. ABC-TV News, Washington, 1980—. Served with inf. U.S. Army, 1964-67. Decorated Purple Heart, Army Commendation medal; recipient citation for best mag. reporting in fgn. affairs Overseas Press Club, 1967. Office: ABC News 1717 Desales St NW Washington DC 20036-4407

SMITH, JACKIE, former professional football player. Student, Northwestern Louisiana State U. With St. Louis Cardinals, 1963-77, Dallas Cowboys, 1978. NFL Hall of Fame, 1994. Retired as the leading receiver among tightends. Office: care Pro Football Hall of Fame 2121 George Halas Dr NW Canton OH 44708-2630*

SMITH, JAMES A., lawyer; b. Akron, Ohio, June 11, 1930; s. Barton H. and Myrna S. (Young) S.; m. Melda I. Perry, Jan. 17, 1959; children: Hugh, Sarah Louise. AB, Western Res. U., 1952; postgrad., Columbia U., 1954-56, LLB, 1961; postgrad., Yale U., 1956-58. Bar: Ohio 1961, U.S. Dist. Ct. (no. dist.) Ohio 1963, U.S. Ct. Appeals (6th cir.) 1973, U.S. Supreme Ct. 1974, U.S. Ct. Appeals (11th cir.) 1983, U.S. Ct. Appeals (D.C. cir.) 1984. Assoc. Squire, Sanders and Dempsey, Cleve., 1961-70, ptnr., 1970-91, counsel, 1991—; mem. spl. adv. com. Nat. Conf. Commrs. on Uniform State Laws, 1972-74. Trustee Chagrin Falls Community Park, 1968-78, Greater Cleve. Neighborhood Ctrs. Assn., 1973-78, Legal Aid Soc. Cleve., 1977-80, Cleve. Inst. Music, 1994—; mem. Charter Rev. Commn., Chagrin Falls, 1966. Lt. (j.g.) USNR, 1952-54. Fellow Am. Coll. Trial Lawyers; mem. ABA, Ohio Bar Assn., Cleve. Bar Assn. (trustee 1988-92), U.S. Ct. Appeals for 6th Cir. Jud. Conf. (life), Ohio Ct. Appeals for 8th Jud. Dist. Conf. (life), Am. Inns of Ct. (master of bench), Ct. of Nisi Prius (dk. 1975-76, judge 1994-95), Phi Beta Kappa, Omicron Delta Kappa, Delta Sigma Rho. Democrat. Office: Squire Sanders & Dempsey 4900 Soc Ctr 127 Public Sq Cleveland OH 44114-1304

SMITH, JAMES BROWN, JR., secondary school educator; b. Greenville, N.C., Apr. 6, 1943; s. James Brown Sr. and Clara Lucille (Avery) S.; m. Donna Drake, Aug. 12, 1967; children: Caryn Frances, James Brown III, Sarah Elizabeth. BS, East Carolina U., 1966; MEd, Va. State U., 1976. Cert. tchr., postgrad. prof., Va. Tchr. Great Bridge Jr. High Sch., Chesapeake, Va., 1966-68, Queen's Lake Sch., York County, Va., 1968-76, Bruton High Sch., York County, 1976—; cons. Acad. Tech, Hampton, Va., 1992-93; tchr. intern Va. Peninsula C. of C., Hampton, 1992. Mem. York County Edn. Assn., Va. Edn. Assn., NEA, Va. Vocat. Assn., Am. Vocat. Assn., Kiwanis (bd. dirs. 1984-92). Methodist. Avocations: photography, gardening, auto repair, fishing. Home: 135 John Pott Dr Williamsburg VA 23188-6328 Office: Bruton High Sch 185 Rochambeau Dr Williamsburg VA 23188-2198

SMITH, JAMES C., telecommunications industry executive. V.p. The Ohio Bell Tele. Co., Cleve., 1992—. Office: The Ohio Bell Tel Co 45 Erieview Plz Cleveland OH 44114*

SMITH, JAMES CLOUDIS, secretary of state, former state attorney general; b. Jacksonville, Fla., May 25, 1940; s. John Albert and Elizabeth F. (West) S.; m. Carole Ann Clark, Dec. 29, 1962; children: Kathryn Elizabeth, Robert Scott, James Clark. BA, Fla. State U., 1962; JD, Stetson U., 1967, LLD (hon.), 1987. Bar: Fla. 1967. Exec. asst. to Fla. Sec. of State, Tallahassee, 1969-71; exec. asst. to lt. gov. Fla., 1971; dep. to Sec. of Commerce State of Fla., Tallahassee, 1971, sr. staff asst. to Gov., 1971-72, atty. gen., 1979-87, chief of staff Office of Gov., 1987, sec. of state of Fla., 1987—; chmn. Gov.'s Adv. Com. on Corrections; mem. Article V Rev. Commn., Fla. Coun. on Criminal Justice, Sentencing Guidelines Study Commn., Commn. on Bail Bond Reform, Fla. Law Revision Commn. Mem. bd. overseers Stetson Coll. Law; trustee Univ. Found., Fla. State U.; mem. adv. bd. Nat. Fedn. Parents for Drug-Free Youth. Served to capt. U.S. Army, 1962-64. Named Conservationist of Yr. Fla. Audubon Soc.; recipient Disting. Alumnus award Stetson U., award for effectiveness in drug enforcement Dept. Justice. Mem. ABA (criminal law com.), Fla. Bar Assn., Tallahassee Bar Assn., Am. Judicature Soc. Republican. Methodist. Office: Office Sec of State The Capitol PL-02 Tallahassee FL 32399-1250

SMITH, JAMES COPELAND, controller; b. Gastonia, N.C., Dec. 29, 1945; s. John Barr and Mary Erixna (White) S.; m. Jane Giles, June 20, 1970; children: James C. Jr., Christopher Matthew. AA, Gaston Coll., Gastonia, 1966; BS in Acctg., U. N.C., Charlotte, 1968. CPA. Mem. audit staff Peat Marwick Mitchell & Co., Charlotte, N.C., 1968-74, audit supr., 1974-76, audit mgr., 1976-79; v.p., contr. J.A. Jones Constrn. Co., Charlotte, 1986, 1991—; v.p., contr. Jones Group Inc., Charlotte, 1986-91. Mem. U. N.C.-Charlotte Bd. Govs., 1977-1980. Recipient Legion of Honor award, Order of DeMolay, Gastonia, 1970. Mem. AICPA, N.C. Assn. CPAs, Gaston Area CPAs, Constrn. Fin. Mgmt. Assn. (Charlotte area chpt.), Gaston Country Club, Masons. Democrat. Methodist. Avocation: music. Home: 2354 Erika Ln Gastonia NC 28056-8800 Office: J A Jones Inc J A Jones Dr Charlotte NC 28287

SMITH, JAMES EDWARD, newspaper company executive; b. N.Y.C., June 26, 1945; s. James Edward and Loretta Anne (Johnston) S.; m. Beverly Lynn Jermyn, Feb. 23, 1980; children: Allison Bridget, Cori Patricia. BA, State U. N.Y., 1969; MA, Cornell U., 1973, PhD, 1976. Asst. prof. Sociology, U. Miami, Coral Gables, Fla., 1973-80; research mgr. News & Sun-Sentinel Co., Ft. Lauderdale, Fla., 1980—; v.p. mktg., v.p./dir. mktg. and promotion Ft. Lauderdale Sun Sentinel, 1991—; bd. dirs. Newspaper Research Council Des Moines. Contbr. articles to profl. jours. Mem. Syndicated Research Task Force, N.Y.C., 1987—, Future Advt. Task Force on Mktg. Data, N.Y.C., 1986-87; pres. Econ. Forum Broward, 1982-85; research chmn. Broward Tourist Devel. Council, 1984—; research cons. Discovery Ctr., Ft. Lauderdale, 1988. Recipient Gavel award Am. Bar Assn. 1981. Mem. Leadership Broward (Best Group 1986), Leadership Broward Alumni. Home: 9321 NW 10th Ct Fort Lauderdale FL 33322-4929 Office: News & Sun-Sentinel Co 200 E Las Olas Blvd Fort Lauderdale FL 33301-2293*

SMITH, JAMES EDWARD, petroleum engineer, consultant; b. Phoenix, Aug. 11, 1935; s. Edward Tracy and Willie (Neel) S.; widowed, June, 1992; children: Paula, James David. Student, Arlington State Coll., 1955-57; BS in Petroleum Engring., Tex. A&M U., 1958. Registered profl. engr., Tex. Field engr. RRC, Abilene, Tex., 1958-60, asst. dist. dir., 1960-61, dist. dir., 1962-67; dist. dir. RRC, Kilgore, Tex., 1967-74; field ops. dir. RRC, Austin, Tex., 1974-76; v.p. Petro-Mgmt., Inc., Tyler, Tex., 1976-78; pres. Smith and Harman Engring. Co., Tyler, 1978-81, James E. Smith and Assocs., Inc., Tyler, 1981—; past chmn. East Tex. Chpt. Joint Engrs. Banquet, East Tex. Symposium on Hydrogen Sulfide Opers.; instr. Petro-Mgmt., Inc.; advisor, cons. in field, guest speaker in field; developer, conductor safety tng. seminars Tex. Pub. Safety Personnel. Contbr. articles to profl. jours.; pub. papers in field. Congregation Chmn. Our Saviour Luth. Ch., Kilgore, 1972;

former scout master Boy Scouts Am.; active adv. com. Tex. Railroad Commn., 1984. Recipient Cert. Appreciation award West Ctrl. Tex. Mple. Water Dist., Desk and Derrick Club, Nat. Profl. Engrs. Hall of Fame, Lubbock Area Firemen Conf.; named Hon. Citizen of Kilgore. Mem. Nat. Soc. Profl. Engrs., Am. Assn. Drilling Engrs., Soc. Profl. Engrs., N.Y. Acad. Scis. Achievements include development of Texas Railroad Commission Rule 36 for Hydrogen Sulfide Public Safety, H2S Safety Plan, H2S System on H2S operation for drilling, completion and production; research in development of the Cotton Valley Geopressure Zone in Panola County, Texas using air/N2 drilling and openhole completion techniques, texas regulations for sour gas operations, regulations of offshore and onshore disposal, pollution control practices in East Texas, application of engineering concepts to the solution of pollution problems, application of steam for crude oil recovery. Office: James E Smith and Assocs Inc 1324 S Beckham Ave Ste 147 Tyler TX 75701-3321

SMITH, J(AMES) E(VERETT) KEITH, psychologist, educator; b. Royal, Iowa, Apr. 30, 1928; s. James H. and Naomi Dorothy (James) S.; m. Greta Standish, Sept. 10, 1949. B.S. in Math, Iowa State U., 1949; A.M. in Psychology, U. Mich., 1952, Ph.D., 1954. Staff psychologist Mass. Inst. Tech., Lincoln Lab., Cambridge, Mass., 1954-64; research psychologist Mental Health Research Inst., Ann Arbor, Mich., 1964-67; prof. psychology U. Mich., Ann Arbor, 1964—; prof. statistics U. Mich., 1977—, chmn. dept. psychology, 1971-76; lectr. Brandeis U., 1960. Cons. editor Psychol. Bull., 1967-70; editor Jour. Math. Psychology, 1971-74. Mem. Commn. on Human Factors, NRC, 1980-82. hon. Research fellow Univ. Coll., London, 1972; mem. rev. panels NSF, 1972-74, Nat. Inst. Gen. Med. Sci., 1967-71; vis. scholar Beijing U., 1985; chmn. spl. study sect. NIH, 1985. Fellow Am. Psychol. Assn.; mem. Am. Statis. Assn., Psychometric Soc., Inst. Math. Statis., Sigma Xi, Phi Kappa Phi, Pi Mu Epsilon, Delta Upsilon. Home: 1160 Heatherway St Ann Arbor MI 48104-2838

SMITH, JAMES F., oil industry executive; b. 1932; married. Student, St. Louis U.; grad., U. Tulsa, 1956. Various positions in oil industry, 1951-72; with Tesoco Petroleum Corp., Houston, 1972-86; pres., chief ops. officer Crown Cen. Petroleum Corp., Balt., 1986—. Office: Crown Cen Petroleum Corp 1 N Charles St Ste 1168 Baltimore MD 21201-3719 Office: 425 Mcmurrey Dr Tyler TX 75702-6326

SMITH, JAMES FINLEY, economist, educator; b. Dallas, Nov. 4, 1938; s. Emerson Russell and Achsah Elizabeth (Foster) S.; m. Susan Schreiber, Aug. 18, 1962; children: Carter Emerson, Jamie, Curtis Noel, Marshall Edward. B.A., So. Meth. U., 1961, M.A., 1964, Ph.D., 1971. Math. analyst Sears, Roebuck & Co., Oak Brook, Ill., 1965-68; adminstrv. asst. to v.p. and treas. Sears, Roebuck & Co., Chgo., 1968-69, dir. econometric rsch., 1969-75; sr. economist Bd. Govs. FRS, Washington, 1975-77; dir. credit rsch. Sears, Roebuck & Co., Chgo., 1977-80; chief economist Union Carbide Corp., Danbury, Conn., 1980-85; dir. regional svcs. and U.S. cons. Wharton Econometric Forecasting Assocs., Phila., 1986; dir., chief economist Bur. Bus. Rsch. U. Tex., Austin, 1987-88; prof. fin. U. N.C., Chapel Hill, 1988—; mem. econ. adv. bd. U.S. Dept. Commerce, 1977-80, 83—; cons. Pres.'s Coun. of Econ. Advisers, Washington, 1978-83; pres. Nat. Bus. Econ. Issues Coun., N.Y.C., 1981-83; dir. Nat. Bur. Econ. Rsch., Cambridge, Mass., 1992—; mem. bd. advisors Thurston Arthritis Rsch. Ctr., Chapel Hill, N.C., 1994—. Author: (annual) UNC Business Forecast, 1988—, (with others) Economic Growth and Investment in Higher Education, 1987, The Chemical Industry in America, 1988, The New Texas Economy, 1988, (with Elsie Echeverri-Carroll) The Economic Impact of Travel on Texas Counties: 1986, 1988; contbr. articles to profl. jours. Served to lt. U.S. Army, 1961-62. NDEA fellow, 1962-65. Fellow Nat. Assn. Bus. Economists (v.p. 1988-89, pres. 1989-90, dir. 1989-90, 84-92); mem. Nat. Economists Club (bd. govs. 1984-87), Am. Econ. Assn., Economists Group Switzerland, Fin. Mgmt. Assn., Soc. Bus. Economists U.K. Mem. United Ch. of Christ. Home: 104 Hotelling Ct Chapel Hill NC 27514-3254 Office: U NC Kenan-Flagler Bus Sch Dept Fin Carroll Hall Campus Box 3490 Chapel Hill NC 27599-3490

SMITH, JAMES FOREST, JR., retired banker; b. Knoxville, Tenn., Dec. 11, 1929; s. James Forest and Alice (Madden) S.; m. Meta Johnson Kenan, Feb. 4, 1956; children: Dean Madden, Thomas Kenan, Janet Smith Lucas, Marguerite Smith Hogan. BS, U. Tenn., 1951; postgrad., Rutgers U., 1965-67. Various positions to sr. v.p. Valley Fidelity Bank & Trust Co., Knoxville, 1953-71; v.p., then exec. v.p. East Tenn. Packing Co., Knoxville, 1971-75; sr. v.p. Park Nat. Bank (merged with 1st Am. Corp.), Knoxville, 1975-77, pres., 1977, chief exec. officer, chmn., 1975-78, vice chmn. 1st Am. Bank, Knoxville, 1983-89; vice chmn. 1st Am. Corp., Knoxville, 1989-90, chmn., pres., CEO, 1990-91, chmn., 1991-94, also bd. dirs.; bd. dirs. Plasti-Line, Inc., Knoxville, Pilot Corp., Knoxville. Named Disting. Bus. Exec., U. Tenn. Coll. Bus. chpt. Beta Gamma Sigma, 1982. Mem. Cherokee Country Club, Belle Meade Country Club. Office: 1st American Center Nashville TN 37237

SMITH, JAMES FRANCIS, utilities executive; b. Saugus, Mass., May 15, 1936; s. James Gregory and Marion Irene (Huckins) S.; m. Margaret Ellen Frame, Nov. 30, 1963; children: Ellen Hawley Anne, James Gregory. AB, Bentley Coll., 1956. Security analyst Boston Safe Deposit & Trust Co., 1956-58; public acct. Robert C. O'Connell (CPA), Boston, 1958-60; controller Precision Microwave Co., Saugus, 1960-65; fin. v.p., dir. Bay State Gas Co., Exeter & Hampton Electric Co., Concord Electric Co., Fitchburg Gas & Electric Light Co., Boston, 1965-75; with Orange and Rockland Utilities, Inc., Pearl River, N.Y., 1965—; v.p. Orange and Rockland Utilities, Inc., Pearl River, 1969-75, exec. v.p., chief fin. officer, 1975-78, vice chmn. bd., 1978, chmn., 1979—; also dir.; bd. dirs. N.Y. State Coun. on Fiscal and Econ. Priorities. Mem. energy com. Coalition of N.E. Govs.; bd. dirs. Bus. Coun. N.Y. State, Inc., 1988, Commerce and Industry Assn. of N.J.; mem. N.Y. State Energy R & D Authority, 1988; mem. gov.'s Mario Cuomo's Commn. on the Adirondacks in the 21st Century, Trust for Pub. Land Adv. Coun. With AUS, 1958-61. Mem. Am. Gas Assn., Edison Electric Inst. (bd. dirs.), Commerce and Industry Assn. N.J. (bd. dirs.), Tuxedo Club, Met. Club. Home: Club House Rd Tuxedo Park NY 10987 Office: Orange & Rockland Utilities Inc Blue Hill Plz Pearl River NY 10965

SMITH, JAMES FREDERICK, securities executive; b. N.Y.C., Jan. 6, 1944; s. James Arthur and Agnes Rose (Kollenz) S.; m. Joan Ann Kelly, June 18, 1966; children: James Patrick, John Michael. BBA in Accountancy Practice, Pace U., 1970. CPA, N.Y.; registered fin. & operational prin., registered rep. Mgmt. trainee Chase Manhattan Bank, N.Y.C., 1965-67; internal auditor MW Kellogg & Co., N.Y.C., 1967-69; sr. acct. Price Waterhouse, N.Y.C., 1969-72; asst. treas. and contr. Henderson Bros. Inc., N.Y.C., 1972-80; pvt. practice Clearwater, Fla., 1980-82; sr. audit mgr. Price Waterhouse, N.Y.C., 1982-84; v.p. & contr. Integrated Resources, N.Y.C., 1984-86; pres., CFO, Freeman Securities, Jersey City, 1986—. With USN, 1961-65. Mem. AICPA, Internat. Soc. CEBS (charter mem.), N.Y. State Soc. CPA, Securities Industry Assn., Nat. Securities Assn., Wall St. Tax Assn. Avocation: carpentry. Home: 3 Greenfield Ter Congers NY 10920-2606 Office: Freeman Securities 30 Montgomery St Jersey City NJ 10732

SMITH, JAMES GILBERT, electrical engineer; b. Benton, Ill., May 1, 1930; s. Jesse and Ruby Frances S.; m. Barbara Ann Smothers, July 29, 1955; 1 child, Julie. BS in Elec. Engring. U. Mo., Rolla, 1957, M.S., 1959, Ph.D., 1967. Instr., then asst. prof. U. Mo., Rolla, 1958-66; mem. faculty So. Ill. U., Carbondale, 1966-93, prof. elec. engring., 1972-93, chmn. dept. elec. scis. and systems engring., 1971-80, prof. emeritus, 1993—. Served with AUS, 1951-53, Korea. Decorated Bronze Star. Faculty fellow NSF, 1961. Mem. Rotary (Paul Harris fellow 1988). Office: So Ill U Coll Engring Carbondale IL 62901

SMITH, JAMES HAMILTON, paper, packaging, construction material and chemicals company executive; b. Montreal, Que., Can., July 14, 1931; s. Alexander L. and Margaret (Binning) S.; m. Lois Margaret Tanner, Oct. 2, 1954; children: Sandra, Terri, Scott. B.Comm., McGill U., 1953. Chartered acct. With Price Waterhouse & Co., Montreal, Que., Can., 1953-66; asst., then controller Domtar Inc., Montreal, 1966-71; exec. v.p. Domtar Pulp & Paper Products, Montreal, 1971-74; pres. Domtar Packaging, Toronto, Ont., Can., 1979; v.p. fin. Domtar, Inc., Montreal, 1974-78; exec. v.p. Domtar Inc., Montreal, 1978; pres. Domtar, Inc., Montreal, 1981, pres., chief exec. officer, 1982, chmn. bd., pres., chief exec. officer, 1989—; also bd. dirs.; dir.

Domtar Inc., Mut. Life of Can., Inc. Mem. Bus. Council on Nat. Issues, Ottawa, 1982, adv. com. Internat. Trade, Coun. Montreal Bd. of Trade, 1989-90; bd. govs. Concordia U.; bd. mgmt. Montreal Gen. Hosp. Rsch. Inst. Mem. Bus. Council on Nat. Issues, Inst. of Chartered Accts. of Ont., Order of Chartered Accts. of Quebec. Clubs: St. James of Montreal, Royal Montreal Golf, Mount Royal, Forest and Stream. Avocations: golf, skiing, baseball, swimming. Office: Domtar Inc, 395 de Maisonneuve W Blvd, Montreal, PQ Canada H3A 1L6

SMITH, JAMES JOHN, physiologist; b. St. Paul, Jan. 28, 1914; s. James W. and Catherine (Welsch) S.; m. Mariellen Schumacher, Mar. 17, 1945 (dec.); children: Philip W., Lucy G. Shaker, Paul R., Gregory K. M.D., St. Louis U., 1937; Ph.D., Northwestern U., 1946. Intern St. Paul-Ramsey Med. Ctr., 1937-38; fellow in pathology Cook County Hosp., Chgo., 1938-39; Koesler research fellow in physiology Northwestern U., Chgo., 1939-41; dean Stritch Sch. Med., Loyola U., 1946-50, assoc. prof. physiology, 1946-50; chief adm. div., dept. medicine and surgery VA, 1950-52; prof., dir. dept. physiology Med. Coll. Wis., Milw., 1952-79; prof. physiology and medicine Med. Coll. Wis., 1979—; dir. human performance lab. and dep. dir. Cardiopulmonary Rehab. Ctr. VA Med. Ctr., Milw., 1978—; assoc. clin. prof. George Washington U. 1950-52 Fulbright research prof. U. Heidelberg, Physiology Inst., Germany, 1959-60; medico-legal cons. on retirement policy for high stress professions. Author textbooks on circulatory physiology, numerous articles in field. Decorated Legion of Merit; recipient Disting. Service award Med. Coll. Wis., 1982. Mem. Soc. Exptl. Biology, Am. Physiol. Soc., Am. Gerontol. Assn., Sigma Xi. Roman Catholic. Researcher in aviation medicine, U.S. Air Force, 1941-46. Home: 11050 W Maple Ln Milwaukee WI 53225-4428 Office: 8701 W Watertown Plank Rd Milwaukee WI 53226-4801

SMITH, JAMES LAWRENCE, research physicist; b. Detroit, Sept. 3, 1943; s. William Leo and Marjorie Marie (Underwood) S.; m. Carol Ann Adam, Mar. 27, 1965; children: David Adam, William Leo. BS, Wayne State U., 1965; PhD, Brown U., 1974. Mem. staff Los Alamos (N.Mex.) Nat. Lab., 1973-82, fellow, 1982-86, dir. ctr. materials sci., 1986-87, fellow, 1987—; chief scientist Superconductivity Tech. Ctr., 1988-95; editor Philos. Mag. B., 1995—. Co-editor Philos. Mag., 1990-95; editor Philos. Mag. B, 1995—; contbr. articles to profl. jours. Recipient E.O. Lawrence award, 1986, Disting. Alumni award Wayne State U., 1993. Fellow Am. Phys. Soc. (internat. prize for new materials 1990); mem. AAAS, Materials Rsch. Soc., Minerals Metals Materials Soc., Am. Crystallographic Assn. Achievements include patents for design of magnetic fields. Office: Los Alamos Nat Lab Superconductivity Tech Ctr Mail Stop K763 Los Alamos NM 87545

SMITH, JAMES LOUIS, III, lawyer; b. Fort Worth, Tex., Mar. 21, 1943; s. James Louis Jr. and Ellen Vickers (Smedley) S.; m. Jane Benton, Mar. 25, 1965 (div. Oct. 1982); children: Rebecca, Sarah; m. Sandra Howell, Dec. 29, 1984; stepchildren: Kristen, Mason. BA cum laude with distinction, Dartmouth Coll., 1965; JD, Duke U., 1968. Bar: Ga. Assoc. Sutherland, Asbill & Brennan, Atlanta, 1968-74, ptnr., 1974-82; shareholder Trotter Smith & Jacobs, Atlanta, 1983-92; ptnr. Troutman Sanders, Atlanta, 1992—. Contbr. articles profl. jours.; mng. editor Duke Law Jour. Chmn. legal divsn. United Way, 1989, fundraiser mem. allocation com. homeless and hungry, 1991, 92; co-chmn. pledge fulfillment com. YES! Atlanta Coun. 1991-92; mem. adv. com. Atlanta Vols. Lawyers Found.; mem. Assn. Corp. Growth, Northwest Presbyn. Ch. Mem. ABA (fed. securities law com. 1933 act registration statements subcom., ptnrships and unincorp. bus. orgns. com. bus. law sect.), State Bar Ga. (chmn. corp. and banking law sect., chmn. gen. ptnrship and limited ptnrship law revision coms. corp. sect. 1982-91, chmn. subcom. Ga. bus. corp. code rev. com. 1987-89, exec. com. corp. and banking law sect. 1982-91, lectr. 2d, 6th, 7th, 9th, 10th, 12th annual corp. and banking law inst. 1983, 87, 88, 90, 91, 93), Atlanta Bar (lectr. 5th, 10th ann. corp. bus. seminar 1983, 88, advanced securities seminar 1989, 94), Practicing Law Inst. (lectr. securities filings 1994), Order of Coif. Presbyterian. Avocations: canoeing, hiking, tennis, jogging, travel. Office: Troutman Sanders 600 Peachtree St NE Atlanta GA 30308-2216

SMITH, JAMES MORTON, museum administrator, historian; b. Bernie, Mo., May 28, 1919; BEd. So. Ill. U., 1941; MA, U. Okla., 1946; PhD, Cornell U., 1951; DHL (hon.). Widener U., 1984; m. Kathryn Hegler, Jan. 5, 1945; children: Melissa Jane, James Morton. Editor, Inst. Early Am. History and Culture, Williamsburg, Va., 1955-66; prof. history Cornell U., Ithaca, N.Y., 1966-70, U. Del., Newark, 1976-90; dir. State Hist. Soc. Wis., Madison, 1970-76, Henry Francis DuPont Winterthur (Del.) Mus., 1976-84. Lt. USCGR, 1943-45. Mem. Am. Assn. Art Mus. Dirs., Am. Assn. Museums, Am. Hist. Assn., Orgn. Am. Historians, Am. Assn. State and Local History, Soc. Historians of Early Am. Republic. Author: Freedom's Fetters, 1956, Liberty and Justice, 1958, Seventeenth-Century America, 1959, George Washington: A Profile, 1969, The Constitution, 1971, Politics and Society in American History, 1973, The Republic of Letters, 1995. Home: 120 Sharpless Dr Elkton MD 21921-2073

SMITH, JAMES OSCAR (JIMMY SMITH), jazz organist; b. Norristown, Pa., Dec. 8, 1928; s. James and Grace Elizabeth (Weldon) S.; m. Edna Joy Goins, Mar. 31, 1957; children: James Oscar, Jia Charlene. Student, Ornstein Sch. Music, Phila., 1946-49. Jazz organist, 1951—; owner, dir. Edmy Music Pub. Co., 1962—, Trieste Builders Co., 1962—, Jay Cee Corp. 1962—; appeared at Antibes (France) Jazz Festival, 1962, Complain-de-Tour Jazz Festival, Belgium, 1963. composer, performer background music film Where the Spies Are, 1965; composer music film La Metamorphose de Clopertes, 1965; performed with Art Blakey, Stanley Turrentine, Jackie McLean, Hank Mobley, others; composer numerous organ pieces; compiler organ books; numerous recordings including The Sermon, A Walk on the Wild Side, Got My Mojo Working, Slaughter On Tenth Avenue, Bluesette, House Party, 1985, Plays the Blues, 1988, Midnight Special, 1989, Best Of, 1991, Fourmost, 1991, Sum Serious Blues, 1993. Recipient downbeat Mag's. Reader and Critics award, 1962, 63, 64; also downbeat Mag's. Reader's Poll, 1989. Mem. Broadcast Music Inc., AFTRA, NAACP, Nat. Acad. Recording Arts and Scis. Lodge: Masons. Office: care Abby Hoffer 22312 E 48th St New York NY 10017-1538 Office: care CEMA 1750 Vine St Los Angeles CA 90028-5247*

SMITH, JAMES PATRICK, economist; b. Bklyn., Aug. 3, 1943; s. James P. and Winefred (Harrison) S.; m. Sandra Berry, Oct. 25, 1983; children: Gillian Claire, Lauren Teresa. B.S., Fordham U., 1965; Ph.D., U. Chgo., 1972. Research assoc. Nat. Bur. Econ. Research, N.Y.C., 1972-74; sr. economist Rand Corp., Santa Monica, Calif., 1974—, dir. of research labor and population, 1977—. bd. mem. Occupational Safety and Health Standards State Calif. Editor: Female Labor Supply, 1980; bd. editors Am. Econ. Rev., 1980-83; author articles in field. Recipient Merit award NIH. Mem. NIA (steering com., health and retirement survey), Nat. Adv. Bd. Poverty Inst. Mem. Am. Econ. Assn., Phi Beta Kappa. Office: RAND PO Box 2138 Santa Monica CA 90407-2138

SMITH, JAMES R., diversified financial services company executive; b. 1945. Grad., U. Minn., 1971. V.p., corp. actuary, CFO Western States Life Ins. Co., Fargo, N.D., 1972-88; v.p. Mut. Group Inc., Brookfield, Wis., 1988—; active in subs. Mut. Group Inc. Fellow Soc. Actuaries. Office: Mutual Group Inc 401 N Executive Dr Brookfield WI 53005-6012*

SMITH, JAMES ROLAND, state legislator; b. Aiken, S.C., Feb. 26, 1933; s. Walter Daniel and Maebell Smith; m. Peggy Cato, Mar. 3, 1953; children: Garry R., Todd D., Caroline M. Student, Oral Roberts Univ., U. S.C., So. Meth. U.; DDiv, Universal Bible Inst., 1975. Rural postal carrier U.S. Postal Svc., Warrenville, S.C., 1969-88; min. Aiken, S.C., 1965—; legislator S.C. Ho. of Reps., Columbia, 1989—. Dir. Beech Island (S.C.) Rural Water Dist., 1973-83; bd. dirs. Aiken County Bd. dirs. 1983-88. Mem. Am. Legion (post 153), Midland Valley C. of C., Midland Valley Lions Club, Graniteville (S.C.) Exch. Club, Beech Island Agriculture Club, Jackson Agriculture Club. Republican. Avocation: family. Home: PO Drawer D Langley SC 29834 Office: SC Ho of Reps 416 Beatty Rd Bldg B Columbia SC 29210-4620

SMITH, JAMES T., electronics company executive. Chmn., pres., chief exec. officer, dir. Magnavox Govt. and Indsl. Electronics Co., Ft. Wayne, Ind.

SMITH, JAMES THOMAS, food products executive; b. Pitts., Sept. 8, 1947; s. James Thomas and Evelyn (Sassano) S.; m. Lynn Johnson, Aug. 14, 1971; children: James Thomas III, Jennifer Lynn. BA in Chemistry, Cornell U., 1969, MBA, 1971. Various positions Procter & Gamble, Cin., 1971-88; mgr. mktg. Procter & Gamble, Egham, Eng., 1988-89; gen. mgr. Procter & Gamble, Madrid, 1989-90, Kroneberg, Germany, 1990-91; pres. Gerber Products Co., Fremont, Mich., 1991-93.

SMITH, JAMES TODD See LL COOL J

SMITH, JANE FARWELL, civic worker; b. Chgo.; d. John Charles and Jessie Greene (Delaware) Farwell; m. Wakelee R. Smith, Feb. 7, 1929; children—Diana Jane Smith Gauss, Carol Louise Smith, Anderson. Student, U. Chgo., 1925-28. Pres. Infant Soc. Chgo., Beverly Hills (Ill.) Center, 1949; chmn. Am. heritage com. DAR, Ill., 1963-65; Am. heritage com. nat. vice chmn. DAR, 1965-68, Insignia chmn., Ill., 1966, Ill. treas., 1966-68, mem. nat. Americanism and manual for citizenship com., 1968, Ill. regent, 1969-71; mem. U.S.A. Bicentennial Commn., DAR, 1971-74; nat. corr. sec. gen. DAR, 1971-74, 1st. v.p. gen., 1974-75, pres. gen., 1975-77, hon. life pres. gen., 1977-81, mem. long range planning commn., 1988-93; trustee U.S. Capitol Hist. Soc., 1976-82; pres. 4th Div. Ex-Regents Club, 1981-82. Mem. Kate Duncan Sch. Bd., Grant, Ala., 1975-86, Tamassee Sch. Bd., Tamassee, S.C., 1975-77. Recipient Gold medal of appreciation Ill. chpt. S.A.R., 1970, resolution of congratulation Senate of 80th Assembly of State of Ill., 1977. Mem. Nat. Gavel Soc. (life), DAR (pres. exec. club 1983-85, pres. nat. officers' club 1986-88), DAR Museum (life), Daus. Colonial Wars, Nat. Soc. New Eng. Women, Alden Kindred Am., Colonial Dames Am., Daus. Am. Colonists, Daus. Founders and Patriots, Nat. Soc. Women Desc. Ancient and Hon. Arty. Co., Am. Nat. Soc. Old Plymouth Colony Descs., Soc. Mayflower Descs., Colonial Daus. 17th Century, Hereditary Order of First Families of Mass., Colonial Wars Nat. Soc., New. Eng. Women. Episcopalian. Home: 851 W Heather Ln River Hills WI 53217

SMITH, JANET ERLENE, advertising executive; b. Athens, Ga., Apr. 7, 1956; d. Phyletus Robert and Elsie Erlene (Hendricks) S. BS, Ga. Southern U., 1978. Staff asst. White House Press Office, Washington, 1978-81; exec. asst. Gansat, Washington, 1981; sales rep. USA Today, Washington, 1981-85, dir. nat. sales, 1987-90, v.p. nat. sales, 1990-91, v.p. advt., 1991—. Office: USA Today 1000 Wilson Arlington VA 22229

SMITH, JANET MARIE, professional sports team executive; b. Jackson, Miss., Dec. 13, 1957; d. Thomas Henry and Nellie Brown (Smith) S. BArch, Miss. State U., 1981; MA in Urban Planning, CCNY, 1984. Draftsman Thomas H. Smith and Assocs. Architects, Jackson, 1979; mktg. coord. The Eggers Group, P.C. Architects and Planners, N.Y.C., 1980; program assoc. Ptnrs. for Livable Places, Washington, 1980-82; coord. asst. Lance Jay Brown, Architect and Urban Planner, N.Y.C., 1983-84; coord. architecture and design Battery Park City Authority, N.Y.C., 1982-84; pres., chief exec. officer Pershing Sq. Mgmt. Assn., L.A., 1985-89; v.p. stadium planning and devel. Balt. Orioles Oriole Park at Camden Yard, 1989-94; v.p. sports facilities Turner Properties, Atlanta, 1994—; dir. planning and devel. Atlanta, Braves, 1994—; bd. dirs. Assn. Collegiate Schs. Architecture, Washington, 1979-82, Assn. Student Chpts. AIA, Washington, 1979-82. Guest editor: Urban Design Internat., 1985; assoc. editor: Crit, 1979-82; contbr. articles to profl. jours. Named Disting. Grad., Nat. Assn. State Univs. and Land Grant Colls., 1988, One of Outstanding Young Women of Am., 1982; recipient Spirit of Miss. award, Sta. WLBT, Jackson, 1987. Mem. AIA (assoc.), Urban Land Inst. Democrat. Episcopalian. Office: Turner Properties Inc 1 CNN Center Ste 275 Atlanta GA 30303

SMITH, JEAN CHANDLER, former museum official; b. Phila., Apr. 13, 1918; d. Chandler White and Philena Pennell (Cheetham) S. AB, Bryn Mawr Coll., 1939; MS, Yale U., 1953; MLS, Cath. U. Am., 1973. Reference librarian D.C. Pub. Library, 1939-43; translator C.Z., 1943-44; librarian Nat. Air Sta., Kaneohe Bay, Oahu, Hawaii, 1944-46; reference librarian, also research assoc. biology Yale U., 1947-58; acting chief acquisitions NIH Library, Bethesda, Md., 1959-63; chief reader services U.S. Dept Interior, Washington, 1964-65; with Smithsonian Instn. Libraries, Washington, 1965-81; asst. dir. instn. services Smithsonian Instn. Libraries, 1972-79, acting dir., 1977-79; ret., 1981; research assoc. Smithsonian Instn., 1981-94; Mem. friends of library com. Bryn Mawr Coll. Compiler: Georges Cuvier, An Annotated Bibliography of his Published Works, 1993. Mem. Conn. Acad. Arts and Scis., Soc. History of Natural History, Bibliog. Soc. Am., History of Sci. Soc.

SMITH, JEAN KENNEDY, ambassador; b. Brookline, Mass., Feb. 20, 1928; d. Joseph P. and Rose Kennedy; m. Stephen E. Smith (dec.); 4 children. BA, Manhattanville Coll. Founder, dir., chair Very Spl. Arts, 1974—; amb. to Ireland Dublin, 1993—. Author: (with George Plimpton) Chronicles of Courage, 1993; contbr. articles on the disabled to profl. jours. Trustee Joseph P. Kennedy, Jr. Found., 1964—, John F. Kennedy Ctr. Performing Arts. Recipient Sec.'s award Dept. Vets. Affairs, Vol. of Yr. award People-to-People Com. Handicapped, Margaret Mead Humanitarian award Coun. Cerebral Palsy Auxs., Jefferson award Am. Inst. Pub. Svc., Spirit of Achievement award Yeshiva U., Humanitarian award Capital Children's Mus. Address: Am Embassy, 42 Elgin Rd, Ballsbridge Dublin Ireland

SMITH, JEAN WEBB (MRS. WILLIAM FRENCH SMITH), civic worker; b. L.A.; d. James Ellwood and Violet (Hughes) Webb; B.A. summa cum laude, Stanford U., 1940; m. George William Vaughan, Mar. 14, 1942 (dec. Sept. 1963); children: George William, Merry; m. William French Smith, Nov. 6, 1964. Mem. Nat. Vol. Service Adv. Coun. (ACTION) 1973-76; vice chmn., 1974-76; dir. Beneficial Standard Corp., 1976-85. bd. dirs. Community TV So. Calif., 1979-93; mem. Calif. Arts Commn., 1971-74, vice chmn., 1973-74; bd. dirs. The Founders, Music Center, L.A., 1971-74; bd. dirs. costume coun. L.A. County Mus. Art, 1971-73; bd. dirs. United Way, Inc., 1973-80, Rosebud Good Samaritan, 1973-80, L.A. chpt. NCCJ, 1977-80, Nat. Symphony Orch., 1980-85, L.A. World Affairs Coun., 1990, L.A. chpt. ARC, 1994—; bd. fellows Claremont Univ. Ctr. and Grad. Sch., 1987—; bd. dirs. Hosp. Good Samaritan, 1973-80; mem. exec. com., 1975-80; mem. nat. bd. dirs. Boys' Clubs Am., 1977-80; mem. adv. bd. Salvation Army, 1979—; bd. overseers The Hoover Instn. on War, Revolution and Peace; mem. President's Commn. on White House Fellowships, 1980-90, Nat. Coun. on the Humanities, 1987-90; bd. govs. Calif. Community Found., 1990—; bd. regents Children's Hosp. L.A., 1993—. Named Woman of Yr. for community service L.A. Times, 1958; recipient Citizens of Yr. award Boys Clubs Greater L.A., 1982, Life Achievement award Boy Scouts Am., L.A. coun., 1985. Mem. Jr. League of L.A. (pres. 1954-55), Assn. Jr. Leagues of Am. (dir. Region XII, 1956-58, pres. 1958-60), Phi Beta Kappa, Kappa Kappa Gamma. Home: 11718 Wetherby Ln Los Angeles CA 90077

SMITH, J(EFFERSON) VERNE, state senator, business executive; b. Greer, S.C., Jan. 15, 1925; s. Jefferson Verne and Lillian (Farley) S.; m. Jean Myers, Nov. 27, 1947; children: Jefferson Verne III, Carole Jean Olmert. Student, Presbyn. Coll., Clinton, S.C., 1942-43; LHD (hon.), Med. U. S.C., 1990. Pres. The Tire Exch.; senator State of S.C., Columbia; chmn. senate labor, commerce & industry com., legis. study com. on alcohol & drug abuse; vice chmn. med. affairs com., health care planning and oversight com.; vice chmn. fin. com., rules com. gen. com., others; bd. dirs. So. Nat. S.C. Greer. Chmn. bd. commrs. Comm. on Pub. Works, Greer, 1969-72; mem. steering com. S.C. Dem. Party; past chmn. Greenville County Dem. Party; bd. govs. Shriners Hosp. for Crippled Children; bd. commrs. Cedar Springs Inst. for Deaf and Blind; bd. dirs. Peace Ctr. for the Performing Arts, 1989. Named Legislator of Yr. S.C. Autism Soc., 1987-88, S.C. Health Care Assn. 1990, S.C. Hosp. Assn., 1991, Outstanding Senator of Yr. S.C. Sch. Bd. Assn., 1992; recipient plaque for svc. to North Greenville County Travelers Rest City Coun., 1992; J. Verne Smith award named in his honor S.C. Assn. Residental Care Homes, 1989; recipient Meritorious medal S.C. Mil. Dept., 1992; Verne Smith Week declared City of Greer, 1992; Verne Smith Libr. & Tech. Resource Ctr. named in his honor Greenville Tech. Coll., 1992. Mem. Masons, Scottish Rite, Shriners, Kappa Alpha. Democrat. Presbyterian. Avocations: reading, walking. Office: SC Senate Box 142 Columbia SC 29202

SMITH, JEFFREY E., historian, educator; b. Columbus, Ohio, July 5, 1956; s. George Edward and Anna Marie (Fisher) S.; m. Kristine Runberg, Aug. 15, 1987; 1 child, Lucy Kathryn. BA, Mount Union Coll., Alliance, Ohio, 1978; MFA, Syracuse U., 1981; PhD, U. Akron, 1991. Dir. Summit County Hist. Soc., Akron, Ohio, 1981-90; exec. dir. St. Louis Merc. Libr., St. Louis, 1990-94; instr. Washington U., St. Louis, 1992—; pres. Janus Applied History Group, St. Louis, 1994—; adj. prof. U. Akron, 1984-86. Contbr. articles to profl. jours. mem. Am. Assn. for State and Local History (Award of Merit 1987), Ohio Assn. Hist. Socs. and Mus. (various award 1984-90), Orgn. Am. Historians, Ohio Mus. Assn. (sec., trustee), Hower House Mus. (bd. dirs.). Office: Janus Applied History Group 3920 Cleveland Ave 6th FL Saint Louis MO 63110

SMITH, JEFFREY E., pharmaceutical executive; b. 1947. BS, Fairleigh Dickinson U., 1968. CPA. With Coopers & Lybrand, CPAs, 1972-82; treas., contr. LCP Chemicals and Plastics, Inc., 1983-84; v.p. finance, CFO A.L. Labs., Inc., Ft. Lee, N.J., 1984-91, exec. v.p., CFO, 1991—. Office: A L Labs Inc 1 Executive Dr Fort Lee NJ 07024-3303*

SMITH, JEFFREY GREENWOOD, industry executive, retired army officer; b. Ft. Sam Houston, Tex., Oct. 14, 1921; s. Henry Joseph Moody and Gladys Adrienne (Haile) S.; m. Dorothy Jane Holland, June 2, 1948; children: Meredith B. Exnicios, Jennifer H. Meyer, Jeffrey Greenwood, Tracy E. McDonald, Melissa A. Deutsch, Ashley A. Pollock. B.S. in Civil Engring, Va. Mil. Inst., 1943; M.S. in Mech. Engring, Johns Hopkins U., 1949; M.A. in Internat. Affairs, George Washington U., 1964. Commd. 2d lt. U.S. Army, 1944, advanced through grades to lt. gen., 1975; service in CBI, Korea, Germany and Vietnam; comdr. 2d Inf. Div., Korea, 1971-73; dep. chief staff ops. Hdqrs. Army Forces Command, Ft. McPherson, Ga., 1973-74; chief staff Hdqrs. Army Forces Command, 1974-75; comdr. 1st U.S. Army, Ft. Meade, Md., 1975-79; ret., 1979; dir. govt. rels. Ethyl Corp., Washington, 1980—, v.p. govt. rels., 1992—; ret., 1994. Decorated D.S.M., Silver Star, Legion of Merit with 3 oak leaf clusters, D.F.C., Bronze Star with V device and 2 oak leaf clusters, Air medal with 12 oak leaf clusters, Army Commendation medal with oak leaf cluster, Purple Heart with oak leaf cluster, Combat Inf. badge (2); breast Order Yun Hui Republic China; Order Security Merit Korea; Gallantry Cross with silver and gold stars (Vietnam) Army Distinguished Service Order. Mem. Assn. U.S. Army, Mil. Order Carabao, Kappa Alpha. Clubs: Army and Navy. Home: 3000 Sevor Ln Alexandria VA 22309-2221

SMITH, JEFFREY L. (THE FRUGAL GOURMET), cook, writer; b. Seattle, Jan. 22, 1939; s. Emely S.; m. Patricia M. Dailey, 1964; children: Jason, Channing. BA, U. Puget Sound, 1962, DHL (hon.), 1987; MDiv, Drew U., 1965, DDiv (hon.), 1993. Ordained to ministry United Meth. Ch., 1965. Served Meth. chs. Hartsdale, N.Y., rural, Wash.; chaplain, asst. prof. religion U. Puget Sound, Tacoma, Wash., 1966-72; founder The Chaplain's Pantry, Tacoma, 1972-83; host Seattle Today TV program The Frugal Gourmet (formerly Cooking Fish Creatively), 1973-77; host PBS program The Frugal Gourmet, 1983—. Author: The Frugal Gourmet, 1984, The Frugal Gourmet Cooks with Wine, 1986, The Frugal Gourmet Cooks American, 1987, The Frugal Gourmet Cooks Three Ancient Cuisines: China, Greece and Rome, 1989, The Frugal Gourmet on Our Immigrant Ancestors: Recipes You Should Have Gotten From Your Grandmother, 1990, The Frugal Gourmet's Culinary Handbook, 1991, The Frugal Gourmet Celebrates Christmas, 1991, The Frugal Gourmet Whole Family Cookbook, 1992, The Frugal Gourmet Cooks Italian: Recipes from the New and Old World Simplified for the American Kitchen, 1993. Recipient Daytime Emmy nominations (5), Best of the West Edn. TV award Western Ednl. Network, 1986. Office: The Frugal Gourmet Inc 88 Virginia St Unit 2 Seattle WA 98101-1047

SMITH, JEFFREY MICHAEL, lawyer; b. Mpls., July 9, 1947; s. Philip and Gertrude E. (Miller) S.; 1 son, Brandon Michael. BA summa cum laude, U. Minn., 1970; student U. Malaya, 1967-68; JD magna cum laude, U. Minn., 1973. Bar: Ga. 1973. Assoc. Powell, Goldstein, Frazier & Murphy, 1973-76; ptnr. Rogers & Hardin, 1976-79; ptnr. Bondurant, Stephenson & Smith, 1979-85, Arnall, Golden & Gregory, 1985-92, Katz, Smith & Cohen, 1992—; vis. lectr. Duke U., 1976-77, 79-80, 89—; adj. prof. Emory U., 1976-79, 81-82; lectr. Vanderbilt U., 1977-82. Co-author: Preventing Legal Malpractice, 1995, Legal Malpractice, 1995. Bd. visitors U. Minn. Law Sch., 1976-82. Mem. ABA (vice chmn. com. profl. officers and dirs. liability com., 1979-83, chmn. 1983-84, vice chmn. com. profl. liability 1980-82, mem. standing com. lawyer's profl. liability 1981-85, chmn. 1985-87, standing com. lawyer competency 1993—), State Bar of Ga. (chmn. profl. liability and ins. com. 1978-89, trustee Inst. of Continuing Legal Edn. in Ga. 1979-80), Order of Coif, Phi Beta Kappa. Home: 145 15th St NE Apt 811 Atlanta GA 30309-3559 Office: Katz Smith & Cohen Ivy Place 2d Fl 3423 Piedmont Rd NE Atlanta GA 30305-1751

SMITH, JEFFREY P., supermarket chain executive; b. 1950. Student, Utah State U., 1968-70. With Smith's Food and Drug Ctrs., Salt Lake City, 1970—, pres., COO, 1984-88, chmn., CEO, 1988—, also bd. dirs. Office: Smith's Food & Drug Ctrs Inc 1550 S Redwood Rd Salt Lake City UT 84104-5105*

SMITH, JEFFRY ALAN, health administrator, physician, consultant; b. L.A., Dec. 8, 1943; s. Stanley W. and Marjorie E. S.; m. Jo Anne Hague. BA in Philosophy, UCLA, 1967, MPH, 1972; BA in Biology, Calif. State U., Northridge, 1971; MD, UACJ, 1977. Diplomate Am. Bd. Family Practice. Resident in family practice WAH, Takoma Park, Md., NIH, Bethesda, Md., Walter Reed Army Hosp., Washington, Children's Hosp. Nat. Med. Ctr., Washington 1977-80; occupational physician Nev. Test Site, U.S. Dept. Energy, Las Vegas, 1981-82; dir. occupational medicine and environ. health Pacific Missile Test Ctr., Point Mugu, Calif., 1982-84; dist. health officer State Hawaii Dept. Health, Kauai, 1984-86; asst. dir. health County of Riverside (Calif.) Dept. Health, 1986-87; regional med. dir. Calif. Forensic Med. Group, Salines, 1987-94; med. dir. Cmty. Human Svcs., Monterey, Calif., 1987-94, Colstrip (Mont.) Med. Ctr., 1994—. Fellow Am. Acad. Family Physicians; mem. AMA, Am. Occupational Medicine Assn., Flying Physicians, Am. Pub. Health Assn. Avocations: pvt. pilot. Home: PO Box 1538 Forsyth MT 59327

SMITH, JEROME HAZEN, pathologist; b. Omaha, Oct. 9, 1936; s. Hazen Dow and Helen Kellogg (Hewitt) S.; m. Marilyn Kay Stauber, 1961; children: Nathaniel, Kathryn Hewitt, Andrew Kellogg. B.S. in Medicine, U. Nebr., 1960, M.D., 1963, M.S. in Anatomy, 1962; M.Sc. Hygiene in Tropical Pub. Health, Harvard U., 1969. Diplomate: Am. Bd. Pathology. Rotating intern Mpls.-Hennepin County Gen. Hosp., 1963-64; from jr. asst. resident in pathology to chief resident in clin. pathology Peter Bent Brigham Hosp., Boston, 1964-72; assoc. pathologist, 1973; from tech. fellow in pathology to instr. Harvard U. Med. Sch., Boston, 1964-73; pathologist, head dept. Inst. Med. Evangelique, Kimpese, Congo, 1968; chief autopsy svcs. Inst.Tropical Medicine, Hosp. Mama Yemo, Fomeco, Kinshasa, Zaire, 1973-74; med. dir. anatomic pathology Inst. Tropical Medicine, Hosp. Mama Yemo, Fomeco, Kinshasa, Zaire, 1974; asst. prof. anatomic pathology U. Ariz. Med. Sch., Tucson; dir. anatomic pathology and microbiology Tucson VA Hosp., 1975-76; mem. faculty U. Tex. Med. Br., Galveston, 1976-84, 90—; prof. pathology, 1979-84, 90—, dir. autopsy service, 1977-84, dir. clin. parasitology lab., 1977-81, 90-94, dir. pathology edn., 1993—; prof. grad. sch., 1980-84, 90—, adj. prof. pathology, 1989-90; cons. Shriners Burn Inst., Galveston, 1980-84, 90-91; prof pathology and lab. medicine Tex. A&M U. Coll. Medicine, College Station, 1984-88. Contbr. numerous articles to med. jours. Comdr. M.C. USNR, 1969-71. Recipient Avalon tuition award, 1961; NSF fellow, 1959; Poynter fellow, 1960; USPHS trainee, 1961, 68-69. Mem. NRA (life), Am. Soc. Clin. Pathologists, U.S.-Can. Acad. Pathologists, Am. Soc. Parasitologists, N.Y. Acad. Scis., Tex. Med. Assn., Tex. Soc. Pathologists, Tex. Soc. Infectious Diseases, Galveston County Med. Soc., Am. Soc. Tropical Medicine and Hygiene, Houston Soc. Clin. Pathologists (Harlan Spjat awardee 1995), Houston Safari Club (bd. dirs. 1994—), Sigma Xi. Republican. Home: 2706 Wilmington Dickinson TX 77539 Office: U Tex Med Br Dept Pathology Galveston TX 77550

SMITH, JERRY EDWIN, federal judge; b. Del Rio, Tex., Nov. 7, 1946; s. Lemuel Edwin and Ruth Irene (Henderson) S.; m. Mary Jane Blackburn, June 4, 1977; children: Clark, Ruth Ann. BA, Yale U., 1969, JD, 1972.

Bar: Tex. 1972. Law clk. to judge U.S. Dist. Ct. (no. dist.) Tex., Lubbock, 1972-73; assoc. then ptnr. Fulbright & Jaworski, Houston, 1973-84; city atty. City of Houston, 1984-88; cir. judge U.S. Ct. Appeals (5th cir.), Houston, 1988—. Chmn. Harris County Rep. Party, Houston, 1977-78; committeeman State Rep. Exec. Com., Tex., 1976-88. Mem. State Bar Tex., Houston Bar Assn. Methodist. Home: PO Box 130608 Houston TX 77219-0608 Office: US Ct Appeals 12621 US Courthouse 515 Rusk St Houston TX 77002-2698

SMITH, JESSE GRAHAM, JR., dermatologist, educator; b. Winston-Salem, N.C., Nov. 22, 1928; s. Jesse Graham and Pauline Field (Griffith) S.; m. Dorothy Jean Butler, Dec. 28, 1950; children: Jesse Graham, Cynthia Lynn, Grant Butler. B.S., Duke U., 1962, M.D., 1951. Diplomate: Am. Bd. Dermatology (dir. 1974-83, pres. 1980-81). Intern VA Hosp., Chamblee, Ga., 1951-52; resident in dermatology Duke U., 1954-56, assoc. prof. dermatology, 1960-62, prof., 1962-67; resident U. Miami, 1956-57, asst. prof., 1957-60; prof. dermatology Med. Coll. Ga., 1967-91, chmn. dept. dermatology, 1967-91, acting chmn. dept. pathology, 1973-75, acting v.p. devel., 1984-85; chief staff Talmadge Meml. Hosp., Augusta, Ga., 1970-72; prof. dermatology, chief div. of dermatology U. South Ala., Mobile, 1991—; mem. advisory council Nat. Inst. Arthritis, 1975-79. Editorial bd. Archives of Dermatology, 1963-72, Jour. Investigative Dermatology, 1966-67, Jour. AMA, 1974-80; editorial bd. So. Med. Jour., 1976—, assoc. editor, 1991-92, editor, 1992—; editor Jour. Am. Acad. Dermatology, 1978-88; contbr. chpts. to books, articles to profl. jours. Served with USPHS, 1952-54. Recipient Disting. Alumnus award Duke U. 1981. Fellow A.C.P., Royal Soc. Medicine; mem. Am. Dermatol. Assn. (sec. 1976-81, pres. 1981-82), Soc. Investigative Dermatology (dir. 1964-69, pres. 1979-80), Am. Acad. Dermatology (dir. 1971-74, 78-88, pres.-elect 1988-89, pres. 1989-90), Southeast Dermatol. Assn. (sec. 1970-71, pres. 1975-76), Ga. Soc. Dermatology (pres. 1979-80), So. Med. Assn. (chmn. sect. dermatology 1973-74), AMA (chmn. sect. dermatology 1981-84), Assn. Profs. Dermatology (dir. 1976-77, 80-82, pres. 1984-86), Med. Rsch. Found. Ga. (bd. dir. 1967-91, pres. 1974-75), Can. Dermatol. Assn. (hon.), other hon. assns., Alpha Omega Alpha. Home: 4272 Bitand Spur # 4 Mobile AL 36608 Office: USAMC 3401 Medical Park Dr Ste 103 Mobile AL 36693-3318

SMITH, JIM, advertising executive; b. Liverpool, Eng., May 1, 1953; s. Jim and Lillian (McKay) S.; children: Gerry, Sally, Kitty. BA in English and English Lit., Oxford (Eng.) U., 1974. Sales exec. Thomson Regional Newspapers, London, 1975-76; account handler Young & Rubicam, London, 1976-84; mktg. dir. Ky. Fried Chicken, Eng., 1984-85; head client services WCRS, London, 1985-86, dep. mng. dir., 1986-87; exec. v.p. Della Femina, McNamee WCRS Inc., N.Y.C., 1987—. Mem. London Inst. Dirs., London Mktg. Soc. Home: 248 W 88th St New York NY 10024-2362 Office: Della Femina McNamee WCRS Inc 350 Hudson St New York NY 10014-4504

SMITH, JO ANNE, writer, retired educator; b. Mpls., Mar. 18, 1930; d. Robert Bradburn and Virginia Mae S. BA, U. Minn., 1951, MA, 1957. Wire and sports editor Rhinelander (Wis.) Daily News, 1951-52; staff corr., night mgr. UPI, Mpls., 1952-56; interim instr. U. N.C., Chapel Hill, 1957-58; instr. U. Fla., Gainesville, 1959-65; asst. prof. journalism, communications U. Fla., 1965-68, assoc. prof., 1968-76, prof., 1976-88, disting. lectr., 1977. Author: JM409 Casebook and Study Guide, 1976, Mass Communications Law Casebook, 1979, 3d edit., 1985. Active, Friends of Libr., Alachua County Humane Soc. Recipient outstanding Prof. award Fla. Blue Key, 1976; Danforth assoc., 1976-85. Mem. Women in Communications, Assn. Edn. in Journalism, Phi Beta Kappa, Kappa Tau Alpha. Democrat. Unitarian. Home: 208 NW 21st Ter Gainesville FL 32603-1732

SMITH, JOAN PETERSEN, nursing administrator, educator; b. Aurora, Nebr., Apr. 4, 1943; d. Ardean Leroy and Leone Eleanor (Ketterer) Petersen; m. Tyrone Wilson Smith, Aug. 15, 1979; 1 child, Steven. BSN, Boston U., 1967; MPA, Roosevelt U., 1977. Dir. ambulatory nursing Michael Reese Hosp., Chgo., 1977-80; v.p. patient care svcs. Marin Gen. Hosp., Greenbrae, Calif., 1980-84, Alta Bates Hosp., Berkeley, Calif., 1984-86; assoc. dir. hosp. and clinics, dir. nursing Santa Clara Valley Med. Ctr., San Jose, Calif., 1986—; asst. clin. prof. U. Calif. Sch. Nursing, San Francisco, 1985—. Recipient Tribute to Women in Industry award YWCA Santa Clara Valley, 1995; mgmt. fellow Nat. Assn. Pub. Hosps., 1991. Mem. Am. Orgn. Nurse Execs., Calif. Orgn. Nurse Execs., Sigma Theta Tau. Home: 1944 Melvin Rd Oakland CA 94602-2027 Office: Santa Clara Valley Med Ctr 751 S Bascom Ave San Jose CA 95128-2604

SMITH, JODY BRANT, philosophy and humanities educator; b. Macon, Ga., May 7, 1943; s. Jody Bass and Gladys Irene (Patterson) S.; m. Deborah Faye Everett, Aug. 20, 1971 (div. 1978); children: Heather Deborah, Jody Brant II; m. Germana D. Teixeira, Nov. 10, 1981 (div. 1990). AB, Mercer U., 1965; MA, U. Miami, 1966, postgrad., 1970. Asst. prof. philosophy and humanities Pensacola Jr. Coll., 1970-81, assoc. prof., 1981—; pres. Pyrrho Press, Inc., Gulf Breeze, Fla., 1974-77; pres. Image of Guadalupe Research Project, Inc., 1979-82; invited reader Indian Philos. Congress, New Delhi, 1975. Bd. dirs. Pensacola Right to Life, Inc., 1973-76, Fla. State Right to Life Com., Inc., 1974-75; provider written testimony U.S. Ho. of Reps. and U.S. Senate coms., 1975, 76, 83. Recipient NEH Seminar award, 1987; Fla. Endowment for Humanities grantee, 1974; Nat. Endowment for Humanities summer fellow, 1987. Fellow Am. Soc. Psychical Rsch.; mem. Cath. Philos. Assn., Phys. Rsch. Found., Beta Beta Beta. Co-author: The Tilma—An Infrared Study, 1981; author: Guadalupan Studies, 1982; The Image of Guadalupe, 1983; The Guadalupe Madonna, 1983, rev. edit., 1985, The Guadalupe Mystery, 1994; participant (TV series) Unsolved Mysteries, 1993, 94, 95; contbr. articles to profl. jours. Home: 1503 E Lakeview Ave Pensacola FL 32503-5375 Office: 1000 College Blvd Pensacola FL 32504-8998

SMITH, JOE, recording industry executive. Pres. Capital EMI Music Inc., L.A. Office: Capitol EMI Music Inc 1750 Vine St Los Angeles CA 90028*

SMITH, JOE DORSEY, JR., newspaper executive; b. Selma, La., Apr. 6, 1922; s. Joe Dorsey and Louise (Lindsay) S.; m. Margaret Jane Wilson, Nov. 20, 1943; 1 child, Lawrence Dorsey. B.A., La. Coll. Pineville, 1939-43. Gen. mgr. Alexandria Daily Town Talk, La., 1958—; pub. Alexandria Daily Town Talk, 1965—; pres. McCormick & Co., Inc., 1968—, chmn., 1990. Served with USAF, 1942-45. Mem. Newspaper Assn. Am. Democrat. Episcopalian. Clubs: Alexandria Golf and Country, Boston, New Orleans. Home: 2734 Georges Ln Alexandria LA 71301-4721 Office: Alexandria Daily Town Talk PO Box 7558 1201 3rd St Alexandria LA 71301-8200

SMITH, JOE MAUK, chemical engineer, educator; b. Sterling, Colo., Feb. 14, 1916; s. Harold Rockwell and Mary Calista (Mauk) S.; m. Essie Johnstone McCutcheon, Dec. 23, 1943; children—Rebecca K., Marsha Mauk. B.S., Calif. Inst. Tech., 1937; Ph.D., Mass. Inst. Tech., 1943. Chem. engr. Texas Co., Standard Oil Co. of Calif., 1937-41; instr. chem. engring. Mass. Inst. Tech., 1943; asst. prof. chem. engring., Md., 1945; prof. chem. engring. Purdue U., 1945-56; dean Coll. Tech., U. N.H., 1956-57; prof. chem. engring. Northwestern U., 1957-59, Walter P. Murphy prof. chem. engring., 1959-61; prof. engring. U. Calif., 1961—, chmn. dept. chem. engring., 1964-72; hon. prof. chem. engring. U. Buenos Aires, Argentina, 1964—; Fulbright lectr., Eng., Italy, Spain, 1965, Argentina, 1963, 65, Ecuador, 1970, Brazil 1990; Mudaliar Meml. lectr. U. Madras, India, 1967; UNESCO cons., Venezuela, 1972-82; spl. vis. professorship Yokohama Nat. U., Japan, 1991. Author: Introduction to Chemical Engineering Thermodynamics, 1949, 4th edit, 1986, Chemical Engineering Kinetics, 1956, 3d edit., 1981. Guggenheim research award for study in Holland; also Fulbright award, 1953-54. Mem. Am. Chem. Soc., Am. Inst. Chem. Engrs. (Walker award 1960, Wilhelm award 1977, Lewis award 1984), Nat. Acad. Engring., Sigma Xi, Tau Beta Pi. *

SMITH, JOEY SPAULS, mental health nurse, biofeedback therapist, bodyworker, hypnotist; b. Washington, Oct. 9, 1944; d. Walter Jr. and Marian (Och) Spauls; children: Kelly, Sean. BSN, Med. Coll. Va., 1966; MA in Edn., U. Nebr., Lincoln, 1975. RNC, ANA; cert. psychiat. and mental health nurse; cert. massage practitioner , cert. hypnotist, cert. biofeedback therapist. Staff nurse Booth Meml. Hosp., Omaha, 1969-71; asst. house supr. Nebr. Meth. Hosp., Omaha, 1971-72; head nurse, clin. instr. U. Calif., Davis, 1976-78; staff nurse Atascadero State Hosp., Calif. Dept. Mental Health, 1978-79; nurse instr. psychiat. technician Atascadero State

Hosp., 1979-84, insvc. tng. coord., 1984-86; nursing coord. chem. dependency recovery program French Hosp. Med. Ctr., San Luis Obispo, Calif., 1986-87; nurse instr., health svcs. staff devel. coord. Calif. Men's Colony, Dept. Corrections, San Luis Obispo, 1987-92; pvt. practice San Luis Obispo, Calif., 1990—; relief house supr. San Luis Obispo County Gen. Hosp., 1982-88, regional program assoc. statewide nursing program Consortium Calif. State U., 1986-88; clin. instr. nursing div. Cuesta Coll., 1988—. 1st lt. U.S. Army Nurse Corps., 1965-67. Mem. Assn. Applied Psychophysiology and Biofeedback, Am. Holistic Nurses Assn., Consol. Assn. Nurses in Substance Abuse (cert. chem. dependency nurse), Biofeedback Cert. Inst. Am. (cert. biofeedback therapist, cert. stress mgr., stress mgmt. edn.), Alpha Sigma Chi, Phi Delta Gamma. Home: 1321 Cavalier Ln San Luis Obispo CA 93405-4905 Office: PO Box 4823 San Luis Obispo CA 93403-4823

SMITH, JOHN ANTHONY, lawyer; b. Poughkeepsie, N.Y., Sept. 10, 1942; s. John Charles and Eunice C. (Hatfield) S.; m. Carol A. Bechtel; children: Jessica R., Michael Anthony. B.S., Cornell U., 1964, J.D., 1971. Bar: U.S. Dist. Ct. Alaska 1971, Alaska 1971, U.S. Supreme Ct. 1978, U.S. Ct. Appeals (9th cir.) 1971. Assoc. firm Kay, Miller, Libbey, Kelly, Christie & Fuld, 1971, ptnr., 1972-73; ptnr. Gruenberg, Willard & Smith, 1973-74; sole practice, Anchorage, Alaska, 1974-77; ptnr. Smith & Taylor, 1978; ptnr. Smith, Taylor & Gruening, Anchorage, 1979, sr. partner, 1979-84; sr. ptnr. Smith, Robinson & Gruening, 1984-85; sr. ptnr. Smith, Robinson, Gruening & Brecht, 1985-86, Smith, Gruening, Brecht, Evans & Spietzfadden, 1986; commr. of Commerce and Econ. Devel., State of Alaska, 1986-88; ptnr. Davis, Wright & Tremaine, 1989-92; of coun. Bliss & Riordan, 1993-94; chmn. State Bond Com., State of Alaska, 1987-88; chmn. Alaska Housing Fin. Corp., 1987-88, Alaska Indsl. Devel. and Export Authority, 1987-88; chmn. Alaska Mcpl. Bond Bank, 1988-91; chmn. Alaska Ctr. for Internat. Bus., 1987-92, dir. 1992—; adj. prof. U. Alaska Sch. Criminal Justice; mem. exec. com. House-Senate Dem. Council, nominee U.S. Senate, 1992, U.S. House, 1994; pres. Alaska Inst. Research and Pub. Service; coordinator U. Alaska Paralegal Program; chmn. Bush Justice Com.; chmn. Gov.'s Bodily Injury Reparation Commn., 1979-80. Bd. dirs. Alaska Bus. Monthly; mem. Internat. Relations com. Nat. Olympic Com., 1986-93; mem. exec. com. Anchorage Organizing Com. for the Winter Olympics. Columnist Anchorage Times; contbg. editor Alaska Jour. Commerce. Bd. dirs., counsel Anchorage Olympic Devel. Com.; dir. Glacier Creek Acad. Served to lt. (j.g.), USN, 1964-67. Mem. Alaska Bar Assn. (chmn. specialization com.), ABA, Am. Judicature Soc., Am. Trial Lawyers Assn. Anchorage C. of C. Democrat. Quaker. Address: 6861 Lovitt Cir Anchorage AK 99516

SMITH, JOHN BREWSTER, dean library sciences, director; b. Bryan, Tex., June 26, 1937; s. Elmer Gillam and Sara Roland (Lull) S.; m. Ida Hawa, Dec. 28, 1963; children: Susan Helen, Rona Esther. B.A., Tex. A & M U., 1960; M.S., Columbia U., 1963, cert. advanced librarianship, 1984, DLS, 1991. Asst. law librarian Columbia U. N.Y.C., 1963-66; asst. library dir. for pub. services Tex. A & M U., College Station, 1966-69, dir. libraries, 1969-74; dir. libraries, dean library scis. SUNY, Stony Brook, 1974—. Named Librarian of Year Tex. Library Assn., 1972. Mem. ALA, N.Y. Libr. Assn., State U. N.Y. Libr. Assn., L.I. Archives Conf. Home: 121 Gnarled Hollow Rd East Setauket NY 11733-1959 Office: SUNY Stony Brook Librs F Melville Jr Meml Libr Stony Brook NY 11794

SMITH, JOHN BURNSIDE, transportation company executive; b. Indpls., 1931; m. Barbara J.; children: John S., Lynn B., Nancy L. Grad., U. Ind., 1957, postgrad. Sch. Bus. Adminstrn., 1958; LL.D. (hon.), Butler U., 1984. Pres., chmn., chief exec. officer, dir. Mayflower Group, Indpls.; dir. Citizens Gas & Coke Utility, Ind. Nat. Corp. Bd. govs. James Whitcomb Riley Assocs.; bd. dirs. Wholesale Club. Mem. Ind. State C. of C. (bd. dirs.). Office: Mayflower Group Inc 9998 N Michigan Rd Carmel IN 46032

SMITH, JOHN EDWIN, philosophy educator; b. Bklyn., May 27, 1921; s. Joseph Robert and Florence Grace (Dunn) S.; m. Marilyn Blanche Schulhof, Aug. 25, 1951; children: Robin Dunn, Diana Edwards. AB, Columbia U., 1942, PhD, 1948; BD, Union Theol. Sem., N.Y.C., 1945; MA, Yale U., 1959; LL.D., U. Notre Dame, 1964. Instr. religion and philosophy Vassar Coll., 1945-46; instr., then asst. prof. Barnard Coll., 1946-52; mem. faculty Yale U., 1952—, prof. philosophy, 1959—, chmn. dept., 1961—, Clark prof. philosophy, 1972-91, Clark prof. philosophy emeritus, 1991—; vis. prof. Union Theol. Sem., 1959, U. Mich., 1958; guest prof. U. Heidelberg, Germany, 1955-56; Fagothey chair of philosophy U. Santa Clara, 1984, vis. prof. Boston Coll., 1992; Dudleian lectr. Harvard, 1960; lectr. Am. Week, U. Munich, Germany, 1961; Suarez lectr. Fordham U., 1963; pub. lectr. King's College, Univ. London, 1965; Aquinas lectr. Marquette U., 1967; Warfield lectr. Princeton Theol. Sem., 1970; Fulbright lectr. Kyoto U., Japan, 1971; Sprunt lectr. Union Theol. Sem., va., 1973; Mead-Swing lectr. Oberlin Coll. 1975; H. Richard Niebuhr lectr. Elmhurst Coll., Ill., 1977; Merrick lectr. Ohio Wesleyan U., 1977; Roy Wood Sellars lectr. Bucknell U., 1978; O'Hara lectr. U. Notre Dame, 1984; Hooker disting. vis. prof. Mc Master U., 1985; mem. adv. com. Nat. Humanities Inst., New Haven, 1974, dir., 1977—. Author: Royce's Social Infinite, 1950, Value Convictions and Higher Education, 1958, Reason and God, 1961, The Spirit of American Philosophy, 1963, The Philosophy of Religion, 1965, Religion and Empiricism, 1967, Experience and God, 1968, Themes in American Philosophy, 1970, Contemporary American Philosophy, 1970, The Analogy of Experience, 1973, Purpose and Thought: The Meaning of Pragmatism, 1978, America's Philosophical Vision, 1992, Jonathan Edwards, Puritan, Preacher, Philosopher, 1992, Quasi-Religions: Humanism, Marxism, Nationalism, 1994; translator: (R. Kroner): Kant's Weltanschauung, 1956; editor: (Jonathan Edwards): Religious Affections, Vol. 2, 1959; gen. editor, Yale edit.: Works of Jonathan Edwards; Editorial bd.: Monist, 1962—, Jour. Religious Studies, Philosophy East and West, Jour. Chinese Philosophy, The Personalist Forum, Jour. Faith and Philosophy, Jour. Speculative Philosophy. Named Hon. Alumnus, Harvard Div. sch., 1960; recipient Herbert W. Schneider award Soc. for Advancement of Am. Philosophy, 1990; Am. Coun. Learned Socs. fellow, 1964-65. Mem. Culinary Inst. Am. (dir. New Haven affiliate), Am. Philos. Assn. (v.p. 1980, pres. 1981), Am. Theol. Soc. (pres. 1967-68), Metaphys. Soc. Am. (pres. 1970-71), Hegel Soc. Am. (pres. 1971), Charles S. Peirce Soc. (pres. 1992). Home: 300 Ridgewood Ave Hamden CT 06517-1428 Office: PO Box 201562 New Haven CT 06520-1562

SMITH, JOHN F., computer company executive; b. 1935. BSEE, Northeastern U., 1961. Engr. Digital Equipment Corp., Maynard, Mass., 1958—, supr. prodn., 1962, mgr. productivity, 1966, mgr. group mfg., 1972, v.p. systems mfg., 1976, v.p. mfg. engring., 1977, sr. v.p. mfg., 1986, COO; interim sr. v.p. ops. Digital Europe, 1986—. With USMC, 1954-56. Office: Digital Equipment Corp 111 Powder Mill Rd Maynard MA 01754-1482*

SMITH, JOHN FRANCIS, materials science educator; b. Kansas City, Kans., May 9, 1923; s. Peter Francis and Johanna Teresa (Spandle) S.; m. Evelyn Ann Ross, Sept. 1, 1947; children—Mark Francis, Letitia Ann Smith Harder. BA with distinction, U. Mo.-Kansas City, 1948; PhD, Iowa State U., 1953. Grad. asst. Iowa State U., Ames, 1948-53; faculty and research scientist Iowa State U., Ames, 1953-88; dept. chmn., div. chief Ames Lab. Iowa State U., Ames, 1966-70; cons. Tex. Instruments, Inc., Dallas and Attleboro, Mass., 1958-63, Argonne Nat. Lab., Ill., 1964-70, Iowa Hwy. Commn., Ames, Los Alamos Nat. Lab., N.Mex., 1984-88, bur. standards Nat. Inst. Standards and Tech., Gaithersburg, Md., 1988-91, Sandia Nat. Lab., Albuquerque, N.M., 1991-92, ASM Internat., Cleve., 1992—. Patentee ultrasonic determination of texture in metal sheet and plate, lead-free soldier; author: Phase Diagrams of Binary Vanadium Alloys; Hellcats Over the Philippine Deep; co-author: Thorium: Preparation and Properties, 1975; editor: Calculation of Phase Diagrams and Thermochemistry of Alloy Phases, 1978; editor Jour. Phase Equilibria; contbr. articles to profl. publs. Mem., former coordr. Ames-Boone Squad Civile Air PAtrol, Ames, 1970—. Served with USN, 1942-46, PTO; to comdr. USNR, 1946-64. Recipient Disting. Service award Civil Air Patrol, Maxwell AFB, Ala., 1979; Faculty Citation Iowa State Alumni Assn., Ames, 1977. Fellow Am. Inst. Chemists, ASM (chmn. Des Moines chpt. 1966); mem. AIME, Materials Research Soc., Alpha Sigma Mu (trustee 1984-86). Roman Catholic. Clubs: Silent Knights, Inc. (trustee 1980—), Exptl. Aircraft Assn. Avocation: flying. Home: RR 5 Box 343 Ames IA 50010-9520 Office: Iowa State U Ames Lab 122 Metallurgy Ames IA 50010

SMITH, JOHN FRANCIS, JR., automobile company executive; b. Worcester, Mass., Apr. 6, 1938; s. John Francis and Eleanor C. (Sullivan) S.; children: Brian, Kevin; m. Lydia G. Sigrist, Aug. 27, 1988; 1 stepchild, Nicola. B.B.A., U. Mass., 1960; M.B.A., Boston U., 1965. active U.S.-Japan Bus. Coun.; co-chmn. Joint Industry Supplier Govt. Action Coun. Fisher Body div. mgr. Gen. Motors Corp., Framingham, Mass., 1961-73; asst. treas Gen. Motors Corp., N.Y.C., 1973-80; comptroller Gen. Motors Corp., Detroit, 1980-81, dir. worldwide product planning, 1981-84; pres., gen. mgr. Gen. Motors Can., Oshawa, Ont., Can., 1984-85; exec. v.p. Gen. Motors Europe, Glattbrugg, Switzerland, 1986-88, pres., 1987-88; exec. v.p. internat. ops. Gen. Motors Corp., Detroit, 1988-90; vice chmn. internat. ops. Gen. Motors Corp., 1990, bd. dirs., mem. fin. com., 1990-92, pres., COO, 1992—; CEO, pres., 1992—; chmn. fin. com. GM, pres.'s coun. N.Am. ops. strategy bd.; bd. dirs. EDS, GMHE; co-chmn. Bd. Econ. Alliance for Mich.; mem. Bus. Roundtable Policy Com., internat. campaign com. Boston U.; mem. U.S.-Japan Bus. Coun.; Am. Soc. Corp. Execs.; co-chmn. Joint Industry Supplier Govt. Action Coun. Mem. chancellors adv. commn., U. Mass., Polish-Am. Enterprise Fund. Mem. Am. Soc. Corp. Execs., (Am. Auto Mfrs. Assn. (bd. dirs.), Econ. Club Detroit (bd. dirs.), Beta Gamma Sigma (dirs.' table). Roman Catholic. Office: GM 3044 W Grand Blvd Detroit MI 48202-3091

SMITH, JOHN FRANCIS, III, lawyer; b. White Plains, N.Y., Sept. 24, 1941; s. John Francis and Mary Dake (Mairs) S.; m. Susan Brown; children: John, Stephen, Peter. AB, Princeton U., 1963; LLB, Yale U., 1970. Bar: Pa. 1970, U.S. Supreme Ct. 1985. Assoc. Dilworth, Paxson, Kalish & Kauffman, Phila., 1970-75, ptnr., 1975-86, sr. ptnr., 1986-91; sr. litigation ptnr. Reed Smith Shaw & McClay, Phila., 1991—, mem. exec. com., 1993—. Mem. exec. com. Employment Discrimination Referral Project, 1971-74; pres. Society Hill Civic Assn., 1975-76, Phila. Chamber Ensemble, 1977-80; bd. govs. Pa. Economy League, 1983—; chair Health Care Task Force, 1993—; bd. dirs. World Affairs Council Phila., 1983-87, chmn. program com., 1986-87; Burn Found., 1987—; moderator Main Line Unitarian Ch., 1986-89. Served to lt. (j.g.) USNR, 1963-67; Vietnam. Mem. ABA, Phila. Bar Assn., Yale Law Sch. Alumni Assn. (exec. com. 1982-88, sec. 1987-88). Club: Princeton (Phila.). Office: Reed Smith Shaw & McClay 2500 One Liberty Pl Philadelphia PA 19103

SMITH, JOHN GELSTON, lawyer; b. Chgo., Aug. 10, 1923; s. Fred G. and Ferne (Keiser) S.; m. JoAnn Stanton, Aug. 17, 1944; children: Carey S., JoAnne G. B.S., U. Notre Dame, 1949, LL.B., 1950. Bar: Ill. 1950. Assoc. Lord, Bissell & Brook, Chgo., 1950-54, 57, ptnr., 1958-90, of counsel, 1990—; asst. atty. gen. State of Ill., Springfield, 1954-56; bd. dirs. Lloyd's of London Press, Inc.; lectr. ins. law Northwestern U., Evanston, 1952, 56-57; chmn. 1st Non-Profit Ins. Co., 1991-93. Chmn. Gov.'s Transition Task Force, Ill. Dept. Ins., Springfield, 1969; chmn. Gov.'s Adv. Bd. Ill. Dept. Ins., 1969-73; atty.-in-fact Underwriters at Lloyd's, London, 1974-88; adv. com. William J. Campbell Library of U.S. Cts., Chgo., 1963-87; trustee Lake Bluff (Ill.) Village Bd., 1965-69. Served to 1st lt. USAAF, 1942-45. Mem. ABA, Chgo. Bar Assn., Ill. Bar Assn. Clubs: Union League, Knollwood Country. Home: 382 Ravine Park Dr Lake Forest IL 60045-1341 Office: Lord Bissell & Brook 115 S La Salle St Chicago IL 60603-3801

SMITH, JOHN J. (JACK SMITH), advertising agency executive. Formerly exec. v.p. for creative svcs. Leo Burnett Co. Inc., Chgo., now vice-chmn., corp. dir. creative svcs. Office: Leo Burnett Co Inc 17 Bougainvillea Ave Key West FL 33040-6226

SMITH, JOHN J., manufacturing company executive; b. Woodland, Mich., Dec. 9, 1911; s. Owen Benjamin and Ethyl (Katherman) S.; m. Elinor S. Lamoreaux, Dec. 10, 1938. Student, Argubright Coll., 1929-31; D Bus. Adminstrn. (hon.), Hillsdale Coll., 1992. C.P.A. 1940. Sr. partner Smith & Skutt (C.P.A.s), 1942-50; dir. Sparton Corp., now chmn., also CEO, bd. dirs.; chmn. (Sparton Can. Ltd.), London, Ont.; dir. Lake Odessa Machine Products, Inc., Mich., Kent Products, Inc., Grand Haven. Mem. Chief Execs. Forum, Mich. Assn. C.P.A.s, am. Inst. C.P.A.s. Club: Detroit Athletic (Detroit). Home: 1839 S Walmont Rd Jackson MI 49203-5267 Office: Sparton Corp 2400 E Ganson St Jackson MI 49202-3772*

SMITH, JOHN JAMES, JR., environmental engineering laboratory executive; b. Franklin, N.J., Dec. 6, 1936; s. John James Smith and Estelle Mary (Gurka) Cook; m. Sondra Lanphear, Dec. 19, 1956; 1 child, James H. BS in Chemistry, U. Fla., 1967. Dir. consulting svcs., v.p. Black, Crowe & Eidsness, Gainesville, Fla., 1968-77; divsn. mgr., v.p. water & wastewater CH2M Hill, Gainesville, 1977-78, regional mgr., sr. v.p., 1978-90; dist. mgr., sr. v.p. CH2M Hill Environ. Engring. Lab., Gainesville, 1990-93; pres. Quality Analytical Labs. subs. CH2M Hill Ltd., Gainesville, 1994—. Author conf. proc.; contbr. articles to profl. jours. Bd. dirs. Fla. Arts Celebration, Coun. on Econ. Outreach. With USAF. Mem. Am. Chem. Soc., Am. Water Works Assn. (nat. chmn. water quality monitoring com., trustee Fla. sect. 1979-82, chmn. Fla. sect. 1985-86, George Warren Fuller award 1988), Fla. Inst. Cons. Engrs., Fla. Chem. Industry Coun., N.E. Fla. Regional Fla. Engring. Ednl. Delivery System Coun., U. Fla. Engring. Adv. Coun., Internat. Assn. Water Pollution Rsch., Water Pollution Control Fedn., Rotary, Sigma Xi. Achievements include development, design and research in numerous water and wastewater systems and facilities. Office: Quality Analytical Labs Inc 2772 NW 43rd St S Ste C Gainesville FL 32606

SMITH, JOHN JOSEPH, lawyer; b. Pitts., Nov. 14, 1911; s. John J. and Alta Ethel (McGrady) S.; m. Ruth Lee Snavely, July 11, 1942; children: John Joseph Jr., Robert William. AB, Birmingham So. Coll., 1931; AM, U. Va., 1932, postgrad. in Econs., 1932-34; JD, U. Ala., 1937. Bar: Ala. 1937, U.S Dist. Ct. (no. dist.) Ala. 1940, U.S. Supreme Ct. 1945, U.S. Ct. Appeals (5th cir.) 1950. Assoc. Murphy, Hanna & Woodall, Birmingham, Ala., 1937; asst. prof. U. Va., Charlottesville, 1937-39; office solicitor U.S. Dept. Labor, Washington, 1939-42; enforcement atty. Office of Price Adminstrn., Atlanta, 1942-43; legal counsel Bechtel-McCone Corp., Birmingham, 1943-46; pvt. practice Birmingham, 1946—. Author: Selected Principles of the Law of Contracts, Sales and Negotiable Instruments, 1938. Founder, commr. Homewood (Ala.) Joy Open Baseball League, 1958-72, dir., 1972-90; gov's staff Ala., 1963-71; chmn. Homewood Citizens Action Com. Against Annexation; life mem. Ala. Sheriffs' Boys and Girls Ranches Builders Club. Recipient Youth Service award Pop Warner Conf., Phila., 1961, Clifford Crow Meml. Community Service award, Shades Valley Civitan Club, Homewood, 1981; received key to City of Homewood, 1982, 88. Mem. ABA, Ala. Bar Assn., Birmingham Bar Assn. (ethics com., unlawful practice of law com., fee arbitration com., econs. of law com., acct.'s liaison com., meml. com.), Order of Coif (founder Farrah Order of Jurisprudence, pres. 1937, alumni organizer U. Ala. Sch. Law chpt., pres. 1969-73, life historian). Methodist. Clubs: The Club (Homewood); City Salesmen's (Birmingham) (Man of Yr. award 1986). Lodges: Masons (life mem. master 1956-57, chmn. legal adv. com. for grand lodge), KT, Shriners, Royal Order Scotland, Scottish Rite (So. jurisdiction). Home: 1506 Primrose Pl Birmingham AL 35209-5426 Office: Smith & Smith Marathon Bldg 618 38th St S Birmingham AL 35222-2414

SMITH, JOHN JOSEPH, III, textile company executive, educator; b. Fall River, Mass., Feb. 11, 1913; s. John J. and Mabel E. (Reid) S.; m. Mary C. Moson, Aug. 8, 1936; children—Nancy S. (Mrs. John Lee Lesher, Jr.), Robert J. B.S in Chem. Engring., Tufts U., 1935. With Johnson & Johnson subsidiary Chicopee Mfg. Corp., New Brunswick, N.J., 1935—; pres. Chicopee Mfg. Corp., 1959—, chmn., 1971-74; with Chicopee Mills, Inc., N.Y.C., 1959—; pres. Chicopee Mills, Inc., 1960—, chmn., 1971-75; dir. Johnson & Johnson, New Brunswick, 1961-74, mem. exec. com., 1966-74; chmn. Chicopee Cuyk Holland, David Woodierburn Scotland; prof. Fla. Atlantic U., Boca Raton, adj. prof., 1976-82. Mem. Am. Assn. Tech. Colorists and Chemists, Am. Chem. Soc., Gulf Stream Golf Club, The Little Club, Delray Beach (Fla.) Club, The Misguamicut Club, Watch Hill (R.I.) Yacht Club. Home: 1225 S Ocean Blvd Delray Beach FL 33483-6534

SMITH, JOHN LEE, JR., minister, former association administrator; b. Fairfax, Ala., Dec. 11, 1920; s. John Lee and Mae Celia (Smith) S.; m. Vivian Herrington, Aug. 15, 1942; children—Vicky Smith Davis, Joan Smith Wimberly, Jennifer Lee Smith Ruscilli. A.B., Birmingham So. Coll., 1947; student, New Orleans Bapt. Theol. Sem., 1950-51, 53; D.D., Ohio Christian Coll., 1967, Birmingham Bapt. Bible Coll., 1979; postgrad., Auburn U., 1956,

Baylor U., 1972-73; LL.D., Nat. Christian U., 1974. Owner Smith's Grocery Co., Montgomery, Ala., 1945-47; ordained minister Bapt. Ch., 1947; pastor Dolomite Bapt. Ch., Birmingham, Ala., 1947-50, Elim Bapt. Ch., Brewton, Ala., 1950-51; pastor 1st Bapt. Ch., Tallapoosa, Ga., 1951-52, Villa Rica, Ga., 1952-54, Fairfax, Ala., 1954-57; pastor West End Bapt. Ch., Birmingham, 1957-59, 88-94, Dalraida Bapt. Ch., Montgomery, 1959-66, 83-86, 1st Bapt. Ch., Demopolis, Ala., 1966-69; assoc. exec. dir. Ala. Council Alcohol Problems, Birmingham, 1969-70, exec. dir., 1970-78; exec. dir. Am. Council Alcohol Problems, Washington, 1972-74, sec., 1974-79, v.p., 1979-87; pastor Benton (Ala.) Bapt. Ch., 1987-88, Vinesville (Ala.) Bapt. Ch., 1994—; tchr., dir. Bessemer Bapt. Inst., 1978-83; exec. dir. missions Bessemer Bapt. Assn., 1978-83; tchr. Mercer U. extension, Carrollton, Ga., 1953-54; tchr. Extension div. Samford U., Fairfax, Ala., 1955-57, South Ala. area dir., 1986-87; mem. bd. ministerial edn. Bapt. Ch., 1958-59, Christian Life Commn., 1959-60; pres. Bessemer Ministers Alliance, 1979-81. Contbr. profl. jours. Chmn. Marengo County Cancer Soc., 1967-68, Good News Ala., Jefferson County, 1977-79, Gov.'s Commn. on Pornography, 1970-78, Nat. Temperance and Prohibition Council, 1973-80, Nat. Coordinating Council on Drug Edn., 1972-78, Alcohol Drug Problems Assn. Am., 1972-78; exec. dir. Temperance Edn., Inc., Washington, 1972-74; trustee Internat. Reform Fedn., 1973-74; adv. bd. JCCEO, 1975-82; bd. dirs. Bessemer Rescue Mission, 1978-83, 89-94, Bessemer YMCA, 1978-83; mem. adv. bd. Bessemer Salvation Army, 1978-83. Served to capt. USAAF, 1942-45, ETO. Mem. C. of C., Trident, Phi Kappa Phi. Club: Mason. Home: PO Box 535 Helena AL 35080-0535

SMITH, JOHN LEWIS, III, lawyer; b. Washington, Aug. 8, 1941. BA, Princeton U., 1963; JD, Georgetown U., 1967. Bar: D.C. 1968. Mng. ptnr. Baker & Hostetler, Washington. mem. D.C. Bar. Office: Baker & Hostetler 1050 Connecticut Ave NW Ste 11 Washington DC 20036-5303

SMITH, JOHN M., trucking executive; b. 1948. Degree in econs., Cornell Coll., 1971; MBA, Cornell U., 1974. With CRST Internat. Inc., Cedar Rapids, Iowa, 1971-72, 74—, pres., CEO. Office: CRST Internat Inc 3960 16th Ave SW Cedar Rapids IA 52404-2332*

SMITH, JOHN M., bishop; b. Orange, N.J., June 23, 1935. Ed., Immaculate Conception Sem., Darlington, N.J., South Orange, N.J., Cath. U., Washington. Ordained priest Roman Cath. Ch., 1961. Titular bishop Tre Tavern, aux. bishop Newark Roman Cath. Ch., 1988-91; bishop of Pensacola-Tallahassee Roman Cath. Ch., Fla., 1991—. Office: Diocese of Pensacola-Tallahassee 11 N B St Pensacola FL 32501*

SMITH, J(OHN) MALCOLM, political science educator; b. Vancouver, B.C., Can., Jan. 24, 1921; (parents Am. citizens); s. George John and Henrietta E. (Smith) S.; m. Connie Grace Shaw, June 2, 1943; children: Sheila C., Nancy L., Patricia L. BA, U. Wash., 1946; MA, Stanford U., 1948, PhD, 1951. Asst. prof. polit. sci. U. Calif., Riverside, 1945-57; instr. polit. sci. Stanford (Calif.) U., 1947-50; instr. pub. law and govt. Columbia U., N.Y.C., 1950-52; organizer World Affairs Coun., L.A., 1952-54; prof. polit. sci. Calif. State U., Hayward, 1965—; cons. Office of Sec. USAF, Washington, 1957-58, Commn. on Civil Rights, Washington, 1958-59; spl. asst. minority whip U.S. Senate, Washington, 1959-61; vis. prof. U. S.D., 1961-62, Ariz. State U., 1962-63; Merrill prof. Utah State U., 1976; mem. Ctr. for Study of Presidency. Co-author: Powers of the President During Crisis, 1961, President and National Security, 1972; contbr. articles to profl. jours. Grantee Ford Found., 1955-56, John S. Sheppard, 1951-52. Mem. Acad. Polit. Sci., The Supreme Ct. Hist. Soc. Home: 2289 East Ave Hayward CA 94541-5631 Office: Calif State U Dept Polit Sci Hayward CA 94542

SMITH, JOHN MATTHEW, insurance company executive; b. Bklyn., Mar. 21, 1936; s. John Bernard and Mary (Lukas) S.; m. Kathryn Ellen Hurley, May 30, 1959; children—Mary Ellen, Kathryn Ann Jacques, Sarah Jane. B.A., Bklyn. Coll., 1959. With Met. Life Ins. Co., N.Y.C., 1959-68; with Guardian Life Ins. Co., N.Y.C., 1968—, v. v.p., 1983-94, exec. v.p., 1995—; adj. prof. Coll. Ins., N.Y.C., 1975—; pres. Guardian Investor Svcs. Corp., N.Y.C., 1977—, Baillie Gifford Internat. Fund, N.Y.C., 1990—; exec. v.p. Guardian Ins. & Annuity Co., N.Y.C., 1981—. Served with U.S. Army, 1956-58. Mem. Nat. Assn. Securities Dealers (registered prin.). Democrat. Roman Catholic. Avocations: woodworking; electronics. Office: Guardian Life Ins Co 201 Park Ave S New York NY 10003-1605

SMITH, JOHN MCNEILL, JR., lawyer; b. Rowland, N.C., Apr. 9, 1918; s. John McNeill and Roberta (Andrew) S.; m. Louise Jordan; children: Louise Smith Nichols, Anne Smith Cole, John McNeill III, Eleanor. AB, U. N.C., 1938; LLB, Columbia U., 1941. Bar: N.C. 1941, N.Y. 1942. Assoc. Root Clark Buckner & Ballantine, N.Y.C., 1941, Smith Wharton & Jordan, Greensboro, N.C., 1945-48; ptnr. Smith Wharton Sapp & Moore and successor firm: Smith Helms Mulliss & Moore, Greensboro, 1948—; vis. prof. U. N.C. Law Sch., Chapel Hill, 1964-65; faculty Nat. Inst. Trial Advocacy. Author, editor: Equal Protection of the Laws in North Carolina, 1963; contbr. articles to jours in field. Mem. N.C. Ho. of Reps., 1970, N.C. Senate, 1971-78; bd. dirs. Alt. Energy Corp. N.C., 1980-88, N.C. Ctr. for Pub. Policy Rsch., 1980-92; chmn. N.C. State Bd. Ethics, 1980-84; pres. N.C. Vol. Lawyers for the Arts, 1984-89. Served to lt. comdr. USNR, 1941-48. Recipient award NCCJ, 1990; named one of 100 Most Influential Lawyers, Nat. Bar Jour., 1985, 88, 91. Mem. ABA (chmn. individual rights and responsibilities 1972, ho. of dels. 1974, chmn. commn. on mentally disabled 1979, Ctrl. and Ea. European law initiate liaison to Rep. Estonia 1992-93), Internat. Bar Assn., N.C. Bar Assn. (Liberty Bell award 1990, chair constitutional rights and responsibilities 1994—), Greensboro Bar Assn., N.C. Acad. Trial Lawyers, N.C. Assn. Def. Attys., Am. Bus. Club (pres. 1968-70). Avocations: concert band, photography, bicycling, tennis. Home: 2501 W Market St Greensboro NC 27403-1519 Office: Smith Helms Mulliss & Moore PO Box 21927 300 N Greene St Ste 1400 Greensboro NC 27401-2167

SMITH, JOHN R., electronics executive. BBA, Memphis State U., 1970; attended, U. Wash., 1970-72. With Fluke Corp., Everett, Wash., 1972—, v.p. and controller, 1981, v.p., treas., 1987—; v.p., treas. Fluke Internat. Corp., 1992—. Office: John Fluke Mfg Co Inc 6920 Seaway Blvd Everett WA 98203-5829*

SMITH, JOHN R., agricultural products executive; b. 1942. Grad., U. Notre Dame, 1965. With Trans World Airlines, St. Louis, 1964-68, Am. Flyers Airlines, Ft. Lauderdale, Fla., 1971-76, Sea World of Fla., Orlando, 1976-80; pvt. practice in spl. events promotions St. Louis, 1980-89; with Vigoro Industries Inc., Fairview Heights, Ill., 1990—, now v.p. Office: Vigoro Industries Inc 2017 W Hwy 50 Fairview Heights IL 62208*

SMITH, JOHN ROBERT, physicist; b. Salt Lake City, Oct. 1, 1940; married; 2 children. BS, Toledo U., 1962; PhD in Physics, Ohio State U., 1968. Aerospace engr. surface physics Lewis Rsch. Ctr. NASA, 1965-68; sr. rsch. physicist, head surface and interface physics group Gen. Motors, Warren, Mich., 1972-80, sr. staff scientist, head solid state physics group, 1980-86, prin. rsch. scientist rsch. lab., 1986—; adj. prof. dept. physics U. Mich., 1983—. Air Force Office Sci. Rsch., Nat. Rsch. Coun. fellow U. Calif. 1970-72. Fellow Am. Phys. Soc. (David Adler Lectureship award in field of materials sci. 1991); mem. Am. Vacuum Soc., Sigma Xi. Achievements include research in the theory of solid surfaces, electronic properties, magnetic properties and chemisorption, adhesion, metal contact electronic structure, defects and universal features of bonding in solids. Office: General Motors Research Lab Physics Dept 30500 Mound Rd Warren MI 48092-2031

SMITH, JOHN STUART, lawyer; b. Rochester, N.Y., Sept. 4, 1943; s. Cecil Y. and Helen M. (Van Patten) S.; m. Nancy Schauman, Aug. 28, 1965; children—Kristan, Debra Barton. A.B. magna cum laude, Harvard U., 1965; LL.B. cum laude, 1968. Bar: N.Y. 1968, D.C. 1968, U.S. dist. ct. (we. dist.) N.Y. 1969, U.S. dist. ct. (so. dist.) N.Y. 1973, U.S. dist. ct. (ea. dist.) N.Y. 1977, U.S. dist. ct. (no. dist.) Tex. 1980, U.S. Ct. Apls. (5th cir.) 1971, (2d cir.) 1972, (9th cir.) 1980, U.S. Sup. Ct. 1978. Assoc. Nixon, Hargrave, Devans & Doyle, Rochester, N.Y., 1968-74, mem., 1975—. Bd. dirs. Rochester Chamber Orch., 1970-75, Geva Theater, 1988. Mem. ABA, N.Y.

State Bar Assn. (past chmn. criminal procedure subcom. antitrust sect.), Monroe County Bar Assn. Office: PO Box 1051 1 Clinton Sq Rochester NY 14603 also: 1 Thomas Circle Washington DC 20005 also: # 702 1026 16th ST NW Washington DC 20036

SMITH, JOHN WEBSTER, retired naval officer, company executive; b. Atlanta, Del., May 3, 1921; s. Frank Louis and Dorothy (Andrew) S.; m. Patricia Catherine Metzner, Jan. 9, 1943 (div. 1958); 1 child, Edward Marc; m. Beverly Brabner, Aug. 21, 1958 (div. July 1983); 1 child, David Andrew; m. Sandra Seefeld, Jan. 5, 1985. BA, Washington Coll., Chestertown, Md., 1942; MS, George Washington U., 1973. Served to rear admiral USN, 1942-73, served in ETO, Korea, Vietnam, Pacific, other locations, 1942-73, ret., 1973; supt., prof. Tex. Maritime Coll./Tex. A&M U., Galveston, 1973-78; v.p. Sealcraft Ops., Inc., Galveston, 1978-83; dir. tng. Tidewater Marine Svcs. Assn., New Orleans, 1983-84; pres. various cos. Houston, 1984-86; mng. dir. Grand Hotel, Houston, 1986-87; exec. asst. to CEO Taylor Energy Co., New Orleans, 1988—; cons. Soc. Marine Cons., New Orleans, 1986-88; bd. dirs. Met. Safety Coun., New Orleans, 1989—; mem. Sec. of State's Archives Commn., La.; chmn. Galveston County Pvt. Industry Coun., 1980-82; chmn. bd. dirs. Gulf Coast Coun. Fgn. Affairs, Galveston, 1979-82; asst. in devel. of world's 1st nuclear radiation course after Bikini Atom Bomb test at Navy Dept. Contbr. articles, papers to profl. publs. Decorated 2 Legion of Merit medals, Bronze Star medal. Mem. Navy League of U.S. (bd. dirs. New Orleans coun.), Coun. Am. Master Mariners, La. Sheriffs Assn., Ret. Officers Assn., Pelican Club Galveston, Rotary (pres. Galveston chpt. 1983), Lambda Chi Alpha. Republican. Methodist. Avocations: reading, maps and charts, travel. Home: 113 Rue Holiday Slidell LA 70461 Office: Patrick F Taylor Found Taylor Energy Co Ste 500 234 Loyola Ave New Orleans LA 70112

SMITH, JOHN WILLIS, banker; b. Paden, Miss., Sept. 4, 1935; s. Clovis Allen and Zelma (McClung) S.; m. Delores Crane, May 17, 1956; children: Roger Willis, Terisa Lynn. BA, M in Profl. Accountancy, Miss. State U., 1961. CPA, Miss. Gen. banking Bank of Belmont, Miss., 1955-57; tax acct. Humble Oil & Refining Co., Houston, 1961-65; controller Am. Seating Co., Booneville, Miss., 1965-71; auditor Peoples Bank & Trust Co., Tupelo, Miss., 1971-73, adminstrv. v.p., 1973-76, exec. v.p., asst. to pres., 1976-77, also bd. dirs.; exec. v.p., mgr. Peoples Bank & Trust Co., Booneville, 1977-81; exec. v.p., COO, 1981-93; pres., CEO The Peoples Bank & Trust, Tupelo, 1993—. Mem. fin. com. North Miss. Health Svcs., Tupelo, 1984—, mem. exec. com., 1985—, chmn. bd., 1994—; treas. Yocona Area coun. Boy Scouts Am., 1979-87; chmn. bd. trustees Miss. Sch. Banking, 1989-92, chmn. bus. divsn. Cmty. Devel. Found., 1990-91, 1st vice chmn., 1992-93, chmn., 1993-94, also mem. task force, exec. com. nominating com., others; ex-officio bd. dirs. Tenn. Comml. Credit Sch. With U.S. Army, 1957-59. Mem. AICPA, Miss. Soc. CPA's, Miss. Bankers Assn. (exec. com. 1987-90), Rotary (pres. Tupelo 1987). Baptist. Office: Peoples Bank & Trust Co PO Box 709 Tupelo MS 38802-0709

SMITH, JOHN WILSON, III, newspaper editor, columnist, statistician; b. Pottsville, Pa., June 2, 1935; s. John Wilson II and Hannah (Morris) S.; m. Jean Ann Longenecker, Nov. 21, 1973; children: Jeffrey W., Jennifer L., Jodi A. BA in History Mgmt. magna cum laude, Franklin & Marshall Coll., 1957; MA in Journalism, Syracuse U., 1959. Sports writer Reading (Pa.) Eagle, 1958-81, sports editor, 1981-82; news editor, columnist Reading Eagle/Times, 1983-87, religion editor, columnist, 1988—; copy chief Reading Eagle, 1987—; statistician Ea. Pa. Football Conf., Hazleton, 1981—, Dist. 11, Allentown, Pa., 1984—; moderator Reading Bapt. Assn., 1966-68. Pres. Western Berks Jr. Baseball League, West Lawn, Pa., 1993—; sports ofcl. Pa. Interscholastic Athletic Assn., Mechanicsburg, 1955-95. Named to Pa. Am. Legion Sports Hall of Fame, 1964-72, St. Clair, Pa. Oldtimers Sports Hall of Fame, 1993. Mem. Religion Newswriters Assn., Phi Beta Kappa, Sigma Delta Chi. Am. Bapt. Avocation: youth baseball administrator and coach. Home: 1121 Whitfield Blvd West Lawn PA 19609 Office: Reading Eagle Times PO Box 582 Reading PA 19603

SMITH, JOSEF RILEY, internist; b. Council Bluffs, Iowa, Oct. 1, 1926; s. George William Smith and Margaret (Wood) Hill; divorced; children: Sarah L. Kratz, David L., Mary E. Loeb, John R., Ruthann P. Sherrier, Mark A.; m. Susan Frances Irwin, Feb. 9, 1973; 1 child, Christopher I. Student, Tulane U., 1944-46; BM, Northwestern U., 1950, MD, 1951; MSEE, Marquette U., 1964. Diplomate Am. Bd. Internal Medicine. Instr. internal medicine U. Miss. Med. Sch., Jackson, 1956-59; asst. prof. Marquette U. Med. Sch., Milw., 1959-63; from assoc. prof. to full prof. U. Mich. Med. Sch., Ann Arbor, 1963-72; physician Youngstown (Ohio) Hosp., 1972-79, Group Health Med. Assn., Tucson, 1979-84, Assocs. in Internal Medicine, Tucson, 1985-87; pvt. practice Tucson, 1987—. Co-author: Clinical Cardiopulmonary Physiology, 1960, Textbook of Pulmonary Disease, 1965, 2d rev. edit., 1974; contbr. articles to profl. jours. Controller Mahoning County TB Clinic, Youngstown, 1973-79. Served to lt. USNR, 1952-54. Fellow ACP, Sigma Xi; mem. Ariz. Med. Assn., Pima County Med. Assn., Am. Thoracic Soc., Ariz. Thoracic Soc., Bioengring. Med. Soc. (founder). Avocations: photography, computer programming. Office: 2224 N Craycroft Rd Ste 109 Tucson AZ 85712-2802

SMITH, JOSEPH BENJAMIN, communications company executive; b. Chelsea, Mass., Jan. 26, 1928; s. Philip and Lillian Esther (Schlafman) S.; m. Dione Greenstone, Aug. 25, 1957; children: Jeffrey Duke, Julie. B.A., Yale University., 1950. Radio broadcaster in Va., Pa. and Mass., 1950-61; with Warner Bros. Records, Burbank, Calif., 1961-75; pres. Warner Bros. Records, 1971-75; chmn. bd. Elektra/Asylum Records, 1975-83; pres., chief exec. officer Home Sports Entertainment div. Warner Amex Cable, 1983-84; pres. Unison Prodns., Inc., 1984-93, CEO, chmn., 1993—; pres., chief exec. officer Capitol-EMI Music Inc., 1987-93; dir. Capitol-EMI Music, Inc., GM Records, WEA Distbg. Co.; Pres. community relations for rec. industry, 1968—; pres., bd. dirs. Nat. Acad. Recording Arts and Scis., 1986-87; dir. Westwood One Productions, Rock and Roll Hall of Fame. Mem. Pres.'s Council on Phys. Fitness and Sports, 1977—; founder Los Angeles Music Center, Mus. Contemporary Art; mem. pres.'s adv. com. for music Yale U.; trustee Calif. Sch. of Arts; bd. govs. Cedar-Sinai Hosp.; trustee Calif. Inst. of the Arts; bd. dirs. T.J. Martell Found.; trustee Basketball Hall of Fame; bd. dirs. Magic Johnson Found. Served with AUS, 1945-47. Recipient Industry Exec. of Yr. award Nat. Assn. Record Merchandisers, 1975; Promotion Exec. of Yr. award Bill Gavin Report, 1963, 64, 65; named Man of Yr. Anti-Defamation League, 1973; Man of Yr. Record Industry Promotion Assn., 1969; Exec. of Yr. Radio Broadcasters, 1976, Humanitarian of Yr. City of Hope, 1988. Mem. Nat. Acad. Rec. Arts and Scis. (pres. 1986), Country Music Assn. (v.p.), Record Industry Assn. Am. (dir.). Clubs: Variety (dir.), Hillcrest Country, Malibu Riding and Tennis. Office: Capitol-EMI Music Inc 1750 Vine St Los Angeles CA 90028

SMITH, JOSEPH NEWTON, III, retired architect, educator; b. Jacksonville, Fla., July 4, 1925; s. Joseph Newton, Jr. and Oneal (Kemp) S.; m. Gloria Bevis, Aug. 24, 1946; 1 child, Gordon Kemp. BS., Ga. Inst. Tech., 1948, B.Arch., 1949. Designer and/or architect archtl. firms in Miami, Fla., 1949-56; propr. Joseph N. Smith, Architect, Miami, 1956-63; partner firm Smith, Polychrone and Wolfcale, Atlanta, 1966-69; gen. cons. architecture, 1969—; mem. faculty Sch. Architecture, Ga. Inst. Tech., 1963-82, prof. architecture, asst. to dean, 1971-77, asst. dean, 1977-82; v.p. interior design Thompson, Ventulett, Steinback and Assocs., Architects and Interior Designers, Atlanta, 1982-88; ptnr. TVS & Assocs. One-man shows: Archtl. Book Show Atlanta, 1987, Connell Gallery, Atlanta, 1992. Served to lt. (j.g.) USNR, 1943-46. Recipient Birch Burdette Long Meml. award Archtl. League N.Y., 1956; award merit S. Atlantic region AIA for Key Biscayne (Fla.) Presbyn. Ch., 1964, for Friendship Center, low income housing Atlanta, 1970; named Honored Artist of Year, Young Women of Arts, 1974. Fellow AIA. Presbyterian. Home: 2466 Ridgewood Rd NW Atlanta GA 30318-1316

SMITH, JOSEPH PHELAN, film company executive; b. N.Y.C.; s. John William and Margaret Mary (Phelan) S.; m. Madelyn Eleanor Davis, Jan. 17, 1942; children: Kevin, Karen, Margaret, Lisa. BS, Colvala U. Former salesman Van Alstyne Noel & Co., N.Y.C.; former salesman RKO Radio Pictures, Inc., Boston, Omaha, div. mgr., Los Angeles, Portland, Oreg., San Francisco, 1938-47; former exec. v.p. Lippert Prodns., Hollywood, Calif.; former v.p., gen. mgr. sales Telepictures, N.Y.C.; founding pres. Cinema Vue

Corp.; now pres. Pathe News Inc., N.Y.C., Pathe Pictures Inc., N.Y.C. Served with U.S. Army. Mem. Motion Picture Pioneers, Am. Film Inst., Elks. Republican. Office: Pathe News Inc 270 Madison Ave 5th FL New York NY 10016

SMITH, JOSEPH SETON, electronics company executive, consultant; b. N.Y.C., July 16, 1925; s. William Thomas and Loretto Agnes (Gorman) S.; m. Marion Susan McManus, June 14, 1952; children: Marion R., Loretto A., Joseph S., John J., Eleanor M., William T., Vincent C., Regina M. BSEE, Iowa State U., 1946; MEE, NYU, 1950, DSc, 1955. Rsch. assoc. prof. NYU, N.Y.C., 1947-55; asst. chief engr. Burroughs Corp., Bklyn., 1955-59; div. mgr. Sperry Rand Corp., Gt. Neck, N.Y., 1959-66; v.p. Litton Industries, Beverly Hills, Calif., 1966-72; sr. v.p. Figgie Internat. Corp., Cleve., 1972-79; pres. J.S. Smith Corp., Cleve., 1979-87; exec. dir. Ctr. for Venture Devel., Cleve., 1983-87; v.p., gen. mgr. CSD Telephonics Corp., Farmingdale, N.Y., 1987-93; v.p. Technology Telephonics Corp., 1993—; bd. dirs. Waterlox Corp., Cleve.; trustee Enterprise Devel. Inc. subs. Case Western Res. U., Cleve.; cons. on creation and growth tech. cos. Contbr. articles on radar, systems integration, instrumentation, and entrepreneurship to profl. jours. Organizer, keynote speaker Cleve. Entrepreneurship Confs., 1984, 85; music dir. Ch. St. Gregory the Great, Cleve. Lt. (j.g.) USN, 1943-46. Fellow IEEE (chmn. N.Y. sect. 1957-58); mem. Hermit Club (Cleve.), Mayfield Country Club (Cleve.), Sigma Xi, Eta Kappa Nu, Pi Mu Epsilon. Home: 4912 Countryside Rd Lyndhurst OH 44124-2515 Office: Telephonics Corp Command Systems Div 815 Broadhollow Rd Farmingdale NY 11735-3904

SMITH, JOYCE CAMILLE, elementary education educator; b. Houston, Nov. 28, 1940; d. Jack William and Aline Doris (Hays) Langerhans; m. Harold Wayne Smith, Dec. 30, 1961; children: Kenneth, DeWayne. BFA, U. Tex., 1962; MEd, Xavier U., 1977. Cert. secondary educator, elem. educator, adminstr. Elem. educator Houston Ind. Schs., 1965-67; tchr. 5th grade N.W. Local Schs., Cin., 1967-89, tchr. 6th grade, 1989—; drama dir. N.W. Local Schs., Cin., 1980-82, Winton Woods City Schs., Cin., 1982-83, sch. bd. adv. coun., 1977-79; entrepreneur Weddings Unlimited, Inc. Author: (with others) Zoo Educational Curriculum. Charter pres. Ohio Jaycee Women, 1970s, nat. v.p., 1973-74. Recipient Golden Apple Achiever award, 1993; named one of Outstanding Young Women of Am., 1970s. Mem. NEA (congrl. contact team, 1990—), ASCD, N.W. Assn. Educators (v.p., pres. 1988-90), Ohio Edn. Assn., Phi Delta Kappa. Methodist. Avocations: photography, gardening, theatre. Home: 11355 Kenshire Dr Forest Park OH 45240-2351 Office: Northwest Local Schools 3240 Banning Rd Cincinnati OH 45239-5207

SMITH, JUDY SERIALE, social services administrator, state legislator; b. Lafayette, La., Mar. 10, 1953; d. Joseph and Vernice (Bellard) S.; m. Sylvester Lee Smith, Jr., Dec. 10, 1974; children: Sylvester Lee Smith III, Joseph Seriale Smith. BA in Social Work, Grambling (La.) State U., 1974. Social svc. coord. Case de Vida, Lake Charles, La., 1976-78; behavioral sci. instr. Family Doctor's Clinic, Lake Charles, 1978-79; caseworker FEMA, Camden, Ark., 1979; community svc. coord. Community Action Authority, Camden, 1980-84; exec. dir. People Are Concerned, Inc., Camden, 1984—; mem. Ark. House of Reps., Little Rock; regional coord. Ark. for Drug Free Youth, Little Rock, 1989—. Trustee Ark. Mus. of Sci. and History, Little Rock, 1991—; mem. Workmen's Comp. Rev. Team, Little Rock, 1993—, Ark. Juvenile Justice Coalition, Little Rock, 1991—; mem. com. on pub. health welfare and labor Ark. Ho. of Reps., 1991—, mgmt. com.; mem. Aging. and Legis. Affairs, Ark., 1991—; Interim Commn. on Children and Youth, Ark., 1991—; vice chair Joint Com. on Children and Youth. Named to Top Ten Legislators Ark., Dem. Gazette, 1993, Ark. Top 15 Women in Leadership, Ark. Bus. Weekly, 1993, Top 100 Women in Ark.; recipient Legislator award Ark. Counselor's Assn., 1992, Cmty. Svc. award Ark. State Press, 1992. Mem. Warren L. Strickland Found., Alpha Kappa Alpha. Democrat. Baptist. Avocations: reading, C-Span watcher, listening to music. Home: 620 Terminal Rd Camden AR 71701-4467 Office: People Are Concerned Inc 351 Washington Ste 221 Camden AR 71701

SMITH, JULIA LADD, medical oncologist, hospice physician; b. Rochester, N.Y., July 26, 1951; d. John Herbert and Isabel (Walcott) Ladd; m. Stephen Slade Smith; 1 child. BA, Smith Coll., 1973; MD, N.Y. Med. Coll., 1976. Diplomate Am. Bd. Internal Medicine, Am. Bd. Med. Oncology. Intern in medicine N.Y. Med. Coll., N.Y.C., 1976-77; resident in medicine Rochester Gen. Hosp., 1977-79; internist Genesee Valley Group Health, Rochester, 1979-80; oncology fellow U. Rochester, 1980-82, asst. prof. oncology in medicine sch. medicine & dentistry, 1986—; oncologist Med. Ctr. Clinic, Ltd., Pitts., 1982-83; oncologist, internist Rutgers Community Health Plan, New Brunswick, N.J., 1983-86; med. dir. Genesse Region Home Care Assn./Hospice, Rochester, 1988—. Bd. dirs. Am. Cancer Soc., Monroe County, 1988-92. Rsch. grantee Nat. Cancer Inst., 1993—. Mem. ACP, Am. Soc. Clin. Oncology, Acad. Hospice Physicians. Unitarian-Universalist. Avocations: sailing, reading, movies, bridge. Address: PO Box 704 601 Elmwood Ave Rochester NY 14642

SMITH, JULIAN CLEVELAND, JR., chemical engineering educator; b. Westmount, Que., Can., Mar. 10, 1919; s. Julian Cleveland and Bertha (Alexander) S.; m. Joan Elsen, June 1, 1946; children: Robert Elsen, Diane Louise Smith Brook, Brian Richard. B.Chemistry, Cornell U., 1941, Chem. Engr., 1942. Chem. engr. E. I. duPont de Nemours and Co., Inc., 1942-46; mem. faculty Cornell U., 1946—, prof. chem. engring., 1953-86, prof. emeritus, 1986—, dir. continuing engring. edn., 1965-71; assoc. dir. Cornell U. (Sch. Chem. Engring.), 1973-75, dir., 1975-83; vis. lectr. U. Edinburgh, 1971-72; cons. to govt. and industry, 1947—; UNESCO cons. Universidad de Oriente, Venezuela, 1975. Author: (with W. L. McCabe and P. Harriott) Unit Operations of Chemical Engineering, 1956, 5th edit., 1993, also articles; sect. editor: Perry's Chemical Engineers Handbook, 1963. Fellow Am. Inst. Chem. Engrs.; mem. Am. Chem. Soc., Sigma Xi, Tau Beta Pi, Phi Kappa Phi, Alpha Delta Phi. Clubs: Ithaca Country, Statler (Ithaca). Home: 711 The Pky Ithaca NY 14850

SMITH, JULIAN PAYNE, gynecological oncologist, educator; b. Portsmouth, Ohio, Mar. 23, 1930; s. Emory Farl and Lola Blanche (Payne) S.; m. Eleanore G. Stankunas, June 5, 1954; children: Susan Sharon, Charles Douglas, Geraldine Gigi, David James. Student, U. Mich., 1947-48; BA, Ohio Wesleyan U., 1951; MD, Columbia U., 1955. Diplomate Am. Bd. Ob-Gyn. Intern Univ. Hosps., Cleve., 1955-56; resident in ob/gyn Cornell N.Y. Hosp., 1956-57; resident in ob-gyn Columbia Presbyn. Med. Ctr., N.Y.C., 1957-59; fellow in gynecology-oncology U. Tex., Houston, 1963-66; pvt. practice Portsmouth, 1961-63; prof. U. Tex. System Cancer Center, M.D. Anderson Hosp. and Tumor Inst., Houston, 1973-77; prof. ob-gyn, dir. gynecologic oncology Wayne State U. Med. Sch., Detroit, 1977-83; pvt. practice medicine specializing in gynecologic oncology Southfield, Mich., 1983-86; prof. of ob-gyn Loyola U., Chgo., 1986-88; prof., dir. gynecology oncology Loyola U. Med. Ctr., Maywood, Ill., 1986-88; prof. ob-gyn, dir. gynecologic oncology U. Md. Sch. Medicine, Balt., 1988—. Editor: (with Gravlee) Endometrium, 1977, A Review of the World Literature, 1977, (with Delgado) Management of Complications in Gynecologic Oncology, 1982, (with Hafez) Carcinoma of the Cervix, 1982; contbr. articles to profl. jours. Bd. dirs. Am. Cancer Soc., Wayne County, Mich., 1980-81. Capt. M.C., USAR, 1959-61. Mem. AMA, Am. Coll. Ob-Gyn., Am. Radium Soc., Am. Assn. Ob.-Gyn., Felix Rutledge Soc. (pres. 1968-70), Am. Gynecol. Soc., Am. Gynecol. and Obstet. Soc., Soc. Gonecol. Oncologists (pres. 1984-85), Soc. Pelvic Surgeons (pres. 1994-95), Mid. Atlantic Gynecol. Oncology Soc. (pres. 1991-92), Meth. Ch. Soc. Md. Republican. Methodist. Home: 22 Treadwell Ct Lutherville Timonium MD 21093-3764 Office: U Md Sch Medicine Dept Ob-Gyn 22 S Greene St Baltimore MD 21201-1544

SMITH, JUNE BURLINGAME, English educator; b. Barrington, N.J., June 1, 1935; d. Leslie Grant and Esther (Bellini) Burlingame; m. Gregory Lloyd Smith, July 6, 1963; children: Gilia Cobb Burlingame Smith, Cyrus Comstock. BA, Reed Coll., 1956; MS, Ind. U., 1959; MA, Calif. State U., Dominquez Hills, 1986. Sec. to dean Reed Coll., 1956-57; residence hall supr. Ind. U., 1957-59; buyer Macy's Calif., 1959-63; residence hall supr. U. Wash., 1963, interviewer Tchr. Placement Bur., 1964; music tchr. Chinook Jr. High Sch., Bellevue, Wash., 1964-68; pvt. practice music tchr., 1971-83; gifted grant coord. South Shores/CSUDH Magnet Sch., 1981; tchr. cons. L.A. Unified Sch. Dist., 1981-82; instr. English L.A. Community Colls.,

Harbor Coll., Wilmington, Calif., 1989—; sexual harrasment officer Harbor Coll., Wilmington, Calif., 1991-92. Chair Sex Equity Commn., L.A. Unified Sch. Dist., 1988-91; bd. dirs. Harbor Inter Faith Shelter, 1994—. Mem. AAUW (pres. San Pedro, Calif. br. 1989-90, mem. task force Initiative for Equity in Edn. 1991—), Am. Acad. Poets, Phi Kappa Phi. Democrat. Home: 3915 S Carolina St San Pedro CA 90731-7115 Office: LA Community Coll Harbor 1111 Figueroa Pl Wilmington CA 90744-2311

SMITH, JUNE ELLEN, secondary and special education educator; b. Wilmington, Del., Aug. 20, 1942; d. Samuel Medford and Audrey Iona (Yunt) S. AA, Wesley Coll., 1962; BS, Del. State Coll., 1973, MEd, 1988. Cert. spl. edn., phys. edn., health edn., drivers edn. tchr., Del. Child care counselor State of Del., Wilmington, 1970-73; phys. edn. tchr. Cath. Diocese, Elkton, Md., 1973-75, Wilmington, Del., 1973-75; occupational/recreational therapist St. Francis Hosp., Wilmington, Del., 1975-78; spl. edn. tchr. Christina Sch. Dist., Newark, Del., 1978—; head coach Girls High Sch. Athletics, Newark, Del., 1980-91; tutor Learning Ctr., Newark, 1991. Coord. Community Watch-Collins Park, New Castle, Del., 1977, 78; bd. dirs. Girls Little League Softball, New Castle, 1972-81. Mem. NEA, Del. Edn. Assn., Coun. for Exceptional Children (presenter state conf. 1990), Learning Disabilities Assn. Am. (presenter internat. conf. 1990), Dupont Country Club, Lions (treas. Capital Trail club 1990-94, pres. 1995—), McDonald's LPGA Championship, TSA Vol. Network Internat. vol. corps. of LPGA Tournament Sponsors Assn. Methodist. Avocations: boating, fishing, camping, tennis, golf. Home: 1127 Elderon Dr Wilmington DE 19808

SMITH, JUSTINE TOWNSEND, recreational association executive; b. Evanston, Ill., June 28, 1936; d. William West and Justine Wilhelmina (Laituri) Townsend; m. Edward Charles Smith, Oct. 15, 1955 (div. 1983); 1 child, Leigh Ann. Student, Evanston Bus. Coll., 1954. Cert. assn. exec., 1989. Chief proofreader Melville series dept. English, 1965-70, asst. editor Library of Living Philosophers, Northwestern U., 1959-64; owner J.J. Creations, Buffalo Grove, Ill., 1972-79; ice skating profl. Northbrook Sports Complex, Ill., 1974, Watts Ice Rink, Glencoe, Ill., 1975; exec. dir. Ice Skating Inst. Am., Wilmette, Ill., 1981—; v.p. Women in Mgmt., Downers Grove, Ill., 1986. vice pres. Shelter Inc., Arlington Heights, Ill., 1980; trustee Ice Skating Inst. Am. Edn. Found., 1988—; mem. adv. coun. Wheeling High Sch., 1993—. Mem. Am. Soc. Assn. Execs. (cert.), Nat. Council Youth Sports (pres. 1987-89). Officer: Ice Skating Inst Am 355 W Dundee Rd Buffalo Grove IL 60089-3500

SMITH, KARL, mortgage company executive; b. 1935. With HUD, Harrisburg, Pa., 1961-68; dir. dept. cmty. affairs Bur. Housing and Devel. of Commonwealth of Pa., 1968-80; dep. dir. Pa. Housing Fin. Agy., 1980-81, 83-87, exec. dir., 1982, 87—. Office: Pa Housing Fin Agy PO Box 8029 Harrisburg PA 17105•

SMITH, KATHLEEN TENER, bank executive; b. Pitts., Oct. 19, 1943; d. Edward Harrison Jr. and Barbara Elizabeth (McCormick) Tener; m. Roger Davis Smith, May 30, 1970 (dec.); children: Silas Wheelock, Jocelyn Tener, Luke Ewing Taft. BA summa cum laude, Vassar Coll., 1965; MA in Econs., Harvard U., 1968. Research assoc. Harvard U. Grad. Sch. Bus., Cambridge, Mass., 1967-69; assoc. economist Chase Manhattan Bank, N.Y.C., 1969-70, asst. treas., 1971, 2d v.p., 1972, v.p., 1973—; sec. asset liability mgmt. com., 1985-90, treas. Global Bank, 1990, divsn. exec. structured investment products, 1990-92, global mktg. and comms. exec. Global Risk Mgmt. Sect., 1993-94; global mktg. and comms. product devel. exec. Chase Global Markets Sect., 1994—. Trustee Vassar Coll., Poughkeepsie, N.Y., 1979-91, mem. exec. com. 1987-91; mem. subcom. on edn. Chase Manhattan Found., N.Y.C., 1985-90. NSF fellow, 1965-67. Mem. Am. Fin. Assn., Am. Econ. Assn., Yale Club (N.Y.C.), Fin. Mktg. Assn., Phi Beta Kappa. Republican. Episcopalian. Home: 454 Rt 32 N New Paltz NY 12561 Office: Chase Manhattan Bank 1 Chase Manhattan Plz New York NY 10081-0001

SMITH, KATHY ANN, educator, state senator; b. Muncie, Ind., Apr. 10, 1944; d. John Francis and H. Emily (Walter) Wallace; m. George Frederick Smith, June 22, 1979; 1 child, Alison Marie Smith. BS in Edn., Ind. U., 1966; postgrad., Ball State U., 1973. Cert. secondary lang. arts tchr., Ind. English tchr. New Albany (Ind.) Floyd Co. Sch. Corp., 1966—; adj. faculty Ind. U. S.E., New Albany, 1977-84. Ind. State senator Ind. Gen. Assembly, Indpls., 1986—; del. Dem. Nat. Conv., N.Y., 1976-80, San Francisco, 1984, Atlanta, 1988, Ind. Dem. State Conv., Indpls., 1980, 82, 84, 86, 88, 90; mem., del. Dem. Nat. Platform Com., Washington, 1984. Mem. New Albany Floyd County Edn. Assn. (legis. chair 1977-86, exec. com 1979-86), Ind. State Tchrs. Assn. (chair polit. action com. 1978-81, 83-86), NEA (NEA polit. action com. 1978-81, 83-84), Nat. Coun. Tchrs. of English, Pi Lambda Theta (hon., pres. 1986-88), Psi Iota Xi. Democrat. Avocations: reading, aerobics, skiing, writing. Home: 1214 Beechwood Ave New Albany IN 47150-2521 Office: Ind State Senate State Capital Indianapolis IN 46204

SMITH, KEITH, protective services official. Now fire chief City of Indpls. Office: Fire Dept 555 N New Jersey Indianapolis IN 46204

SMITH, KEITH A., artist; b. Tipton, Ind., May 20, 1938; s. Vern and Edna (Andrews) S. B.A., Sch. Art Inst. Chgo., 1967; M.S. in Photography, Ill. Inst. Tech., 1968. Instr. photography UCLA, 1970, Art Inst. Chgo., 1971-75; coordinator printmaking Visual Studies Workshop, Rochester, N.Y., 1975—. Author: When I Was Two, 1977; (coll. textbook) Structure of the Visual Book, 1984; one-man exhbns. include, Gallerie Civica D'Arte Moderne, Turin, Italy, 1973, Mus. Modern Art, N.Y.C., 1975, Lichtroppen, Agen, W.Ger., 1976, Stuart Wilber Inc., Chgo., 1979, Detroit Inst. Arts, 1980, Phila. Coll. Art, 1980; group exhbns. include Mus. Modern Art, 1975, Santa Barbara Mus. Art, 1979, Art Inst. Chgo., 1979; represented in permanent collections, Mus. Modern Art, N.Y.C., Nat. Gallery Can., Gallerie Civica Moderne Art, Torino, Italy, George Eastman House, Rochester, N.Y., Houghton Rare Books Library, Harvard U. Guggenheim fellow, 1972, 80; Nat. Endowment Arts grantee, 1978. Home: 22 Cayuga St Rochester NY 14620-2153 Office: care New Eng Sch Art & Design 28 Newbury St Boston MA 02116-3276

SMITH, KENNETH ALAN, chemical engineer, educator; b. Winthrop, Mass., Nov. 28, 1936; s. James Edward and Alice Gertrude (Walters) S.; m. Ambia Marie Olsson, Oct. 14, 1961; children: Kirsten Heather, Edward Eric, Andrew Ian Beaumont, Thurston Garrett. S.B., MIT, 1958, S.M., 1959, Sc.D., 1962; postgrad., Cambridge (Eng.) U., 1964-65. Asst. prof. chem. engring. MIT, 1961-67, assoc. prof., 1967-71, prof., 1971—, Edwin R. Gilliland prof. chem. engring., 1989—, acting head dept., 1976-77, assoc. provost, 1980-81, assoc. provost. v.p. rsch., 1981-91, dir. Whitaker Coll. Health Sci. and Tech., 1989-91; cons. chem. and oil cos. NSF fellow, 1964-65; Overseas fellow, Churchill Coll., (Eng.) 1993. Mem. Am. Chem. Engrs., Nat. Acad. Engring., Am. Chem. Soc., AAAS, Sigma Xi, Phi Lambda Upsilon, Tau Beta Pi. Episcopalian. Home: 32 School St Manchester MA 01944-1336 Office: MIT Bldg 66-540 Cambridge MA 02139

SMITH, KENNETH BLOSE, former financial executive; b. Monmouth, Ill., Jan. 29, 1926; s. Elmer Edwin and Florence (Logan) S.; m. Julia M. Stupp, June 17, 1950; children: Donald E., Paul C., Marilyn D. B.S., U. Iowa, 1947. Internal auditor Deere & Co, Moline, Ill., 1947-52; treas. John Deere Chem. Co., Pryor, Okla., 1952-65; fin. mgr. Deere & Co., Moline, Ill., 1965-71, asst. treas., 1971-81, treas., 1981-85. Republican. Lutheran.

SMITH, KENNETH BRYANT, seminary administrator; b. Montclair, N.J., Feb. 19, 1931; m. Gladys Moran; children: Kenneth Bryant Jr., Kourtney Beth, Kristen Bernard. BA, Va. Union U., 1953; postgrad., Drew U., 1953-54; BD, Bethany Theol. Sem., 1960; DD (hon.), Elmhurst Coll. 1971, Shaw U., 1987; D Ps (hon.), Nat. Lewis U. 1981; LittD (hon.), Chgo. State U. 1990; STD, Olivet Coll., 1992. Ordained to ministry United Ch. of Christ, 1960. Assoc. min. Park Manor Congl. Ch., Chgo., 1957-61; min. Trinity United Ch. of Christ, Chgo., 1961-66; min. urban affairs The Community Renewal Soc., 1966-68; sr. min. Ch. of Good Shepherd, Chgo., 1968-84; pres. Chgo. Theol. Sem., U. Chgo., 1984—. Mem. Met. Chgo. YMCA, 1986—, Community Renewal Soc., 1966-68. Office: Chgo Theol Sem 5757 S University Ave Chicago IL 60637-1507

SMITH, KENNETH CARLESS, electrical engineering educator; b. Toronto, Ont., Can., May 8, 1932; s. Reginald Thomas and Viola Evelyn (Carless) S.; children—K. David, Kevin A. B.A.Sc., U. Toronto, 1954, M.A.Sc. in Elec. Engring., 1956, Ph.D. in Physics, 1960. Transmission engr. Can. Nat. Telegraphs, Toronto, 1954-55; rsch. engr. U. Toronto at U. Ill., Urbana, 1956-58; asst. prof. elec. engring. U. Ill., Urbana, 1961-64, assoc. prof., 1964-65; asst. prof. elec. engring. U. Toronto, 1960-61, assoc. prof. elec. engring. and computer sci., 1965-70, prof., 1970-81, prof. depts. elec. engring., computer sci., library and info. sci., mech. engring., 1981—, chmn. dept. elec. engring., 1976-81; adv. prof. Shanghai Inst. Rwy. Tech., People's Republic China, 1989—; pres. Elec. Engring. Consociates Ltd., Toronto, 1974-76; dir. several small firms, U.S. and Can.; mem. Ont. Task Force on Microelectronic Tech., 1980-81; vis. prof. Hong Kong U. Science and Tech., Clearwater Bay, Hong Kong, 1993. Author: (with A.S. Sedra) Microelectronic Circuits, 1982, 2d edit., 1987, Spanish edit., 1985, 3d edit., 1991, Hebrew edit., 1990, Korean edit. 1989, Greek edit., 1994, Lab. Explorations, 1991, Trial and Success, 1992; contbr. articles to profl. jours., chpts. to books; patentee in field. Fellow IEEE, Circuits and Systems Soc. (chmn. confs. procedures and planning, publs. coun.), Can. Soc. for Profl. Engrs. (bd. dirs. 1984—, pres. 1988-91), Internat. Solid State Circuit Conf. (exec. com., awards chmn. 1975—). Liberal. Mem. Anglican Ch. Home: 56 Torbrick Rd, Toronto, ON Canada M4J 4Z5 Office: U Toronto Dept Elec and Computer Engring, 10 King's Coll. Rd, Toronto, ON Canada M5S 1A4

SMITH, K(ERMIT) WAYNE, computer company executive; b. Newton, N.C., Sept. 15, 1938; s. Harold Robert and Hazel K. (Smith) S.; m. Audrey M. Kennedy, Dec. 19, 1958; 1 son, Stuart W. B.A., Wake Forest U., 1960; M.A. (Danforth fellow, Woodrow Wilson fellow), Princeton U., 1962, Ph.D., 1964; postgrad., U. So. Calif., 1965; LLD (hon.), Ohio U., 1992. Instr. Princeton U., 1963; asst. prof. econs. and polit. sci. U.S. Mil. Acad., 1963-66; spl. asst. to asst. sec. def. for systems analysis Washington, 1966-69; program mgr. def. studies RAND Corp., Santa Monica, Calif., 1969-70; dir. program analysis Nat. Security Council, Washington, 1970-72; group v.p. planning Dart Industries, Los Angeles, 1972-73; group pres. resort devel. group Dart Industries, 1973-76; exec. v.p. Washington Group, Inc., 1976-77; mng. partner Coopers & Lybrand, Washington, 1977-80; group mng. partner Coopers & Lybrand, 1980-83; chmn., chief exec. officer World Book, Inc., 1983-86; prof. Wake Forest U., 1986-88; pres., chief exec. officer OCLC Online Computer Libr. Ctr., Inc., Dublin, Ohio, 1989—, also bd. dirs.; sr. cons. Dept. Def., Dept. State, NSC, NASA, Dept. Energy, OMB, GAO; bd. dirs. Excelco Corp., Nat. City Bank, Columbus, Info. Dimensions, Inc. Author: How Much is Enough? Shaping the Defense Program, 1961-69, 1971; contbr. articles to profl. jours. Vis. com. Brookings Instn., Washington, 1971-79; bd. visitors Wake Forest U., 1974-78, 82-90, chmn. bd. visitors, 1976-78, trustee, 1991—; bd. visitors Def. Sys. Mgmt. Coll., 1982-85, Lenoir Rhyne Coll., 1988-94, Mershon Ctr. Ohio State U., 1990-92, Columbus Assn. for Performing Arts, 1992—, U. Pitts. Sch. Libr. and Info. Sci., 1992—; bd. visitors Bowman Gray Bapt. Hosp. Med. Ctr., 1992—, chmn., 1993—. Mem. ALA, Coun. Fgn. Rels., Internat. Inst. Strategic Studies, Inst. Internat. Edn., Coun. Higher Edn., Am. Assn. for Higher Edn., Am. Soc. for Info. Sci., Washington Golf and Country Club, Diego Club, Lakes Golf and Country Club, Catawba County Country Club, Capital Club, Phi Beta Kappa, Omicron Delta Kappa, Kappa Sigma. Methodist. Home: 8530 Preston Mill Ct Dublin OH 43017-9648 Office: Online Computer Libr Ctr Inc 6565 Frantz Rd Dublin OH 43017-5308

SMITH, KERRY CLARK, lawyer; b. Phoenix, July 12, 1935; s. Clark and Fay (Jackson) S.; m. Michael Waterman, 1958; children: Kevin, Ian. AB, Stanford U., 1957, JD, 1962. Bar: Calif. 1963, U.S. Supreme Ct. 1980. Assoc. Chickering & Gregory, San Francisco, 1962-70, ptnr., 1970-81; ptnr. Petit & Martin, San Francisco, 1981-95, Hovis, Smith, Larson, Stewart, Lipscomb & Cross, San Francisco, 1995—. Mem. editorial bd. Stanford Law Rev., 1961-62. Lt. USN, 1957-60. Mem. ABA (bus. law sect.), banking and savs. and loan coms.), Calif. Bar Assn. (bus. law sect.), San Francisco Bar Assn., Orinda County Club, La Quinta Golf Club, San Francisco Univ. Club. Office: Hovis Smith Larson et al 21st Fl 100 Pine St San Francisco CA 94111

SMITH, KIM LEE, educator; b. Boise City, Okla., Oct. 25, 1941; d. Sidney Earl and Lois Mae (Miller) Ferguson; m. Worley John Smith, Dec. 21, 1962 (div. 1984); children: Colleen Lee Feese, Colette Marie Trammell, Karl Tracy Smith. BA, West Tex. State U., Canyon, 1972; MA, West Tex. State U., 1974; PhD, Tex. Tech U., Lubbock, 1988. Prof. Spanish and English Panhandle State U., Goodwell, Okla., 1974—. Exxon Edn. Found. grantee, 1982. Mem. Am. Assn. Tchrs. Spanish and Portuguese, Okla. Edn. Assn. (chpt. pres. 1989—), MLA. Democrat. Avocations: sailing, playing classical and flamenco guitar, photography, writing, reading. Home: 411 Faculty Row Goodwell OK 73939 Office: Panhandle State U Aggie Ave Goodwell OK 73939-9751

SMITH, LAMAR SEELIGSON, congressman; b. San Antonio, Nov. 19, 1947; s. Campbell and Eloise Keith (Seeligson) S.; m. Elizabeth Schaefer, Mar. 20, 1992; children: Nell Selligson, Tobin Wells. BA, Yale U., 1969; JD, So. Meth. U., 1975. Mgmt. intern SBA, Washington, 1969-70; bus. writer The Christian Sci. Monitor, Boston, 1970-72; assoc. Maebius & Duncan, Inc., San Antonio, 1975-76; chmn. Rep. Party of Bexar County, San Antonio, 1978-81; state rep. Dist. 57-F, San Antonio, 1981-82; county commr. Precinct 3 Bexar County, 1982-85; mem. 100th-104th Congresses from 21st Tex. dist., 1987—; mem. budget com., jud. com., subcom. crime and criminal justice; ptnr. Lamar Seeligson Ranch, Fremont, Tex., 1975—. Christian Scientist. Office: US Ho of Reps 2443 Rayburn Washington DC 20515*

SMITH, LANE, illustrator, author; b. Tulsa, Aug. 25, 1959; s. Lewis Gene and Mildred Annette (Enlow) S. BFA, Art Ctr. Coll. Design, Pasadena, Calif., 1983. Freelance editl. illustrator, N.Y.C., 1983-94, book illustrator, author, 1987—; film conceptual artist Disney Studios, San Francisco, 1994. Author, illustrator: (children's books) The Big Pets, 1991, The Happy Hocky Family, 1993; illustrator: The True Story of the Three Little Pigs, 1989; dir., writer, prodr. film Water Ride, 1994. Recipient award for One of 10 Best Illustrated Books, N.Y. Times, 1987, 93, Golden Apple award Bienalle of Illustration, Bratislava, 1992, Caldecott honor ALA, 1993. Avocations: filmmaking, animation. Office: 37 W 20th St Ste 1004 New York NY 10011

SMITH, LANE JEFFREY, automotive journalist, technical consultant; b. Honolulu, May 17, 1954; s. Gerald Hague and JoEllen (Lane) S.; m. Susan Elizabeth Gumm, May 24, 1980; children: Amber Elizabeth, Graham Hague. BS in Journalism, Iowa State U., 1978. Feature editor Car Craft mag. Peterson Pub., L.A., 1979—, tech. editor, sr. editor, editor Hot Rod Mag., 1987-92, exec. editor, 1993—; speaker in field. Avocations: military history, aviation, building and racing high performance automobiles. Home: 18320 Citronia Northridge CA 91325 Office: Hot Rod Mag 6420 Wilshire Blvd Los Angeles CA 90048-5515

SMITH, LANTY L(LOYD), lawyer, business executive; b. Sherrodsville, Ohio, Dec. 11, 1942; s. Lloyd H. and Ellen Ruth (Newell) S.; m. Margaret Hays Chandler, June 11, 1966; children: Abigail Lamoreaux, Margaret Ellen, Amanda Prescott. BS with honors in Math., Wittenberg U., Springfield, Ohio, 1964; LLB with honors, Duke U., 1967. Bar: Ohio 1967. Assoc. Jones, Day, Cockley & Reavis, Cleve., 1967-68, 69-73; ptnr. Jones, Day, Reavis & Pogue, Cleve., 1974-77; exec. v.p., sr. gen. counsel Burlington Industries, Inc., Greensboro, N.C., 1977-86, pres., 1986-88; chmn., chief exec. officer Precision Fabrics Group Inc., Greensboro, 1988—; chmn. The Greenwood Group, Inc., Raleigh, N.C., 1992—; chmn. bd. visitors Duke U. Sch. Law; vice chmn., bd. visitors N.C. Agrl. and Tech. State U.; bd. dirs. mem. exec. com. 1st Union Corp., Masland Corp. So. Optical Co., Wikoff Color. Bd. govs. Ctr. for Creative Leadership, N.C. Inst. Polit. Leadership; chmn. Cone Hosp.; pres. Found. Greater Greensboro; mem. Greensboro Devel. Corp. Mem. ABA, N.C. Inst. Medicine, N.C. Textile Found., Greensboro Rotary. Episcopalian. Home: 1401 Westridge Rd Greensboro NC 27410-2912 Office: 301 N Elm St 6th Fl Greensboro NC 27401

SMITH, LARRY GLENN, retired state judge; b. Montgomery, Ala., Aug. 6, 1924; s. Alonzo Nathan and Louise (Norman) S.; m. Mary Emmalyn Murphree, Feb. 28, 1948; children: Cynthia Lynn Smith Ramirez, Larry Glenn Jr., Celia Dell Smith Rudolph. Student, U. Ala., Tuscaloosa, 1942-

43, 46-48; LLB, U. Fla., 1949. Bar: Fla. 1949. Pvt. practice, Panama City, Fla., 1949-53; assoc. Mathis & Mathis, Panama City, 1953-57; asst. state's atty. Office State's Atty. for 14th Cir., Panama City, 1953-57; rsch. asst. Fla. Supreme Ct., Tallahassee, 1958-60; ptnr. Baker, Baker & Smith, Orlando, Fla., 1960-64, Isler, Welch, Smith, Higby & Brown, Panama City, 1964-72; judge cir. ct. Fla. 14th Jud. Cir., Panama City, 1973-79; judge Fla. 1st Dist. Ct. Appeal, Tallahassee, 1979-94; ret., 1994; chief judge Fla. 1st Dist. Ct. Appeal, Tallahassee, 1987-89; ret., 1994; sr. judge State of Fla.; Mem. Fla. Bd. Bar Examiners, Tallahassee, 1967-72, Fla. Ct. Edn. Coun., Tallahassee, 1979-81, 86-91, Fla. Bench and Bar Commn., Tallahassee, 1990-91; pres. Fla. Conf. of Dist. Ct. Appeals Judges, Tallahassee, 1986-87. Mem. Panama City Airport Authority, 1952-55; past pres. Bay County Libr. Assn., Panama City. Lt. (j.g.) USNR, 1943-45. Mem. ABA, Fla. Bar, Tallahassee Bar Assn., Am. Judicature Soc. Avocations: hiking, biking, skiing, photography, reading. Home: 4115 W 17th St Panama City FL 32401

SMITH, LARRY VAN, lawyer; b. Dallas, Aug. 22, 1947; s. Chester Cleo and Ann (Simmel) S.; m. Andrea Vaughan, Nov. 13, 1976; children—Elizabeth, Jordan. B.A., So. Methodist U., 1969, J.D., 1973. Bar: Tex. 1973. Ptnr., Locke, Purnell, Rain, Harrell (and predecessor firms), Dallas, 1973—. Served with USNG, 1969-75. Protestant. Home: 4701 Kelsey Rd Dallas TX 75229-6507 Office: Locke Purnell Rain Harrell 2200 Ross Ave Ste 2200 Dallas TX 75201-6766

SMITH, LAUREN ASHLEY, lawyer, journalist, clergyman, physicist; b. Clinton, Iowa, Nov. 30, 1924; s. William Thomas Roy and Ethel (Cook) S.; m. Barbara Ann Mills, Aug. 22, 1947; children: Christopher A., Laura Nan Smith Pringle, William Thomas Roy II. BS, U. Minn., 1946, JD, 1949; postgrad., U. Chgo., 1943-49; MDiv, McCormick Theol. Sem., 1950; postgrad., U. Iowa, 1992. Bar: Colo. 1957, Iowa 1959, Ill. 1963, Minn. 1983, U.S. Supreme Ct. 1967; ordained to ministry Presbyn. Ch., 1950. Pastor Presbyn. Ch., Fredonia, Kans., 1950-52, Lamar, Colo., 1952-57; pastor Congl. Ch., Clinton, 1975-80; editor The Comml., Pine Bluff, Ark., 1957-58; pvt. practice Clinton, 1959—; internat. conferee Stanley Found., Warrenton, Va., 1963-72; legal observer USSR, 1978; co-sponsor All India Renewable Energy Conf., Bangalore, 1981; law sch. conferee U. Minn., China, 1983. Author: (jurisprudence treatise) Forma Dat Esse Rei, 1975, (monograph) First Strike Option, 1983; co-author: India On to New Horizons, 1989; columnist Crow Call, 1968—; co-editor Press and News of India, 1978-82; pub. Crow Call; pseudonym Christopher Crow, 1981—; editor Asian Econ. Community Jour.; contbr. articles to religious publs. Minister-at-large Presbyn. Ch. U.S.A., Iowa, 1987—, mem. nat. New Spiritual Formation Network; bd. dirs. Iowa divsn. UN Assn. U.S.A., Iowa City, 1970-85. Mem. Iowa Bar Assn., Ill. Bar Assn., St. Andrews Soc., Clinton County Bar Assn. (pres. 1968, Best in Iowa citation), Clinton Ministerial Assn., Samaritan Health Systems Chaplain Corps., Quaker Internat. Yokefellow, Nat. Network for New Spiritual Formation Presbyn. Ch. USA.

SMITH, LAVERNE BYRD, educational association administrator; b. Richmond, Va., Dec. 14, 1927; d. Charles Edward and Lena (Dickens) Byrd; m. Lewis Jr. Smith Nov. 25, 1948. BA, Va. Union U., 1948; MS, Va. State U., 1964; PhD, U. Md., 1985. Cert. elem. and secondary tchr., Va. Tchr. Richmond (Va.) Pub. Schs., 1948-64; asst. prof. Va. State Coll., Ettrick, Va., 1964-67; asst. prof. edn., dir. Reading Ctr. Va. Union U., Richmond, 1967-74; state supr. reading and lang. devel. Va. Dept. Edn., Richmond, 1974-90, ret., 1990; acad. skills coord. Va. Union U., Richmond, 1991-93; free lance writer, 1994—; bd. dirs. J. Sgt. Reynolds C.C. Contbr. articles, poems, stories. to profl. jours. Historian First bapt. Ch. So. Richmond, 1991-93. Recipient Gov. award for 42 years of Svc. to Public Edn. in Va., 1990, Outstanding Educators of Am., 1974, Outstanding Woman in Comm. Richmond, Va. 1995. Mem. ASCD, NAACP, Am. Ednl. Rsch. Assn., Richmond Area Reading Assn. (past pres.), Va. Reading Assn. (past pres.-elect, Literacy award), Internat. Reading Assn., Nat. Polit. Caucus of Black Women, Bapt. Hist. Soc., Continental Soc., Inc., Alpha Kappa Alpha, Phi Delta Kappa (past chpt. pres.).

SMITH, LAWRENCE BEALL, artist; b. Washington, Oct. 2, 1909; s. Gerald Karr and Leah (Beall) S.; m. Winn Revere, June 20, 1935; children: Dustin Beall, Leslie Winn, Lochlin Revere. PhB, U. Chgo., 1931; attended, Art Inst. Chgo.; studied with Ernest Thurn, Gloucester, Charles Hopkinson, Boston, Harold Zimmerman, Boston. art instr. Walker Sch. Art, Boston, 1932-36; artist war correspondent WWII. Solo exhbns. include Grace Horn Gallery, Boston, 1940, Assn. Am. Artists, N.Y.C., 1948, 60, Katonah Mus. Gallery, N.Y., 1955-69, 82, Vose Gallery, Boston, 1962, Narden Gallery, Cross River, N.Y., 1989; exhbns. include Whitney Mus., N.Y.C., 1940, 58, Art Inst. Chgo., 1945, Boston Mus., 1945, Nat. Acad. Design, N.Y.C., 1972, Carnegie Inst. Art, 1972, Wichita Mus., 1981, 87; represented in collections Fogg Mus., Cambridge, Mass., John Herron Art Inst., Indpls., Wichita Art Mus., Andover (Mass.) Mus., Chrysler Mus., Norfolk, Va., Sheridan Swope Art Gallery, Terre Haute, Ind., Mus. City of N.Y., Libr. Cong., Washington, Worcester Found., Shrewsbury, Conn., Met. Mus., N.Y.C., Harvard U., U. Chgo., Colby Coll., MIT, U. Ariz., U. Mo., Brandeis U., West Point, Am. Tobacco Co., Upjohn, Abbott Labs., Lever Bros., Standard Oil; portrait painter univs., corps.; represented in pvt. collections; book illustrator: Tom Jones, Washington Square, Age of Innocence, Anderson's Fairy Tales, Robin Hood, Garland of Fairy Tales; sculpture exhbns. include Katonah Gallery, Maine Coast Galleries, Wichita Mus., Nat. Acad. Design; represented in sculpture collections Worcester Found., Wichita Mus., Round Hill Community Ch., pvt. collections; pvt., mus. collections graphics, lithography, monotype. Recipient Am. Inst. Graphic Arts award, Art Dirs. Club award, Ellen Speyer Sculpture prize Nat. Acad. Design, Purchase prize drawing Norfolk Mus. Office: Rte 121 Cross River NY 10518

SMITH, LAWRENCE J., bishop. Pres., regionary bishop The Liberal Cath. Ch.-Province of the U.S.A., Evergreen Park, Ill. Office: Liberal Cath Ch 9740 S Avers Ave Evergreen Park IL 60642-2946

SMITH, LAWRENCE LEIGHTON, conductor; b. Portland, Oreg., Apr. 8, 1936; s. Lawrence Keller and Bonita Evelyn (Wood) S.; children by previous marriage: Kevin, Laura, Gregory; stepchildren: Kristine, John. B.S. cum laude, Portland State Coll., 1956; grad. magna cum laude, Mannes Coll. Music, N.Y.C., 1959; Ph D (Hon.), Ind. U., 1992; D (hon.), U. Louisville Ind. State U. Mem. faculty Mannes Coll. Music, 1959-62; prof. piano Boston U., 1963-64; asst. condr. Met. Opera, 1964-67; mem. faculty Curtis Inst., Phila., 1968-69, Calif. Inst. Arts, 1970-72, U. Tex., 1962-63; prin. guest condr. Phoenix Symphony, 1970-73; music dir., condr. Austin (Tex.) Symphony, 1971-72, Oreg. Symphony, Portland, 1973-80; pres., music dir. San Antonio Symphony, 1980-85; music dir., condr. Louisville Orch., 1983-95, condr. laureate, 1995—; faculty mem. Yale U., 1994—; guest condr. N.Y. Philharm., L.A. Philharm., Tulsa Philharm., Winnipeg (Man., Can.) Orch. Minn. Orch., Cin. Symphony, St. Louis Symphony, Moscow Philharm., Tokyo Philharm. Recipient 1st prize Met. Internat. Condrs. competition, 1964, Ditson Condrs. award Columbia U., 1988. Mem. Am. Fedn. Musicians, Mensa. Buddhist.

SMITH, LAWRENCE R., lawyer; b. Oak Park, Ill., Jan. 27, 1948. AB cum laude, Coll. of Holy Cross, 1970; JD, U. Mich., 1973. Bar: Ill. 1973. Ptnr. Querrey & Harrow Ltd., Chgo.; panel Am. Arbitration Assn. Mem. ABA, Ill. State Bar Assn., Chgo. Bar Assn., Ill. Assn. Def. Trial Counsel (pres. 1988-89), Def. Rsch. Inst. Address: 180 N Stetson Ave Ste 3500 Chicago IL 60601-6710

SMITH, LEE ARTHUR, professional baseball player; b. Jamestown, La., Dec. 4, 1957. Student, Northwestern State U., La. Pitcher Chgo. Cubs, 1975-87, Boston Red Sox, 1987-90, St. Louis Cardinals, 1990-93, N.Y. Yankees, 1993-94; with Balt. Orioles, 1994, Calif. Angels, 1994—. Named Nat. League Fireman of Yr., Sporting News, 1991, 94; holder maj. league record for most consecutive errorless games by pitcher, Nat. League single-season record for most saves; Nat. League Saves Leader, 1983, 91-92; mem. Nat. League All-Star team, 1983, 87, 91-94; named Nat League Co-Fireman of Yr., Sporting News, 1983, 92. Office: Calif Angels 2000 Gene Autry Way Anaheim CA 92806*

SMITH, LEE CLARK, apparel company executive; b. Plainfield, N.J., Apr. 13, 1942; s. Harold Irving and Dorothy Taylor (Clark) S.; m. Perry Lea Donovan, Nov. 5, 1966. B.S., Pa. State U., 1964. Mktg. mgmt. trainee Levi

Strauss & Co., San Francisco, 1966-72; gen. mgr. Levi Strauss & Co., Thailand, 1972-73, Portugal, 1973-74; mktg. dir. no. Europe div. Levi Strauss & Co., 1974-76, pres., 1976-78, pres. Asia Pacific div., 1978-80, pres. diversified apparel products div., 1980-81, v.p., 1984-85; sr. v.p. Levi Strauss & Co., San Francisco, 1985—. Served to lt. U.S. Army, 1964-66. Avocation: all water sports. Home: 117 Hacienda Dr Belvedere Tiburon CA 94920-1103 Office: Levi Strauss Internat 1155 Battery St San Francisco CA 94111-1230

SMITH, LEE ELTON, surgery educator, retired military officer; b. Ventura, Calif., July 19, 1937; s. Raymond Elroy and Edith Irene (Jordan) S.; m. Carole Sue Smith; children: Justine Diane, Alexander Loren. BA, U. Calif., Berkeley, 1959; MD, U. Calif., San Francisco, 1962. Diplomate Am. Bd. Surgery, Am. Bd. Colon and Rectal Surgery (pres. 1992-93). Commd. ens. USN, 1960, advanced through grades to capt., 1977; intern U. Utah, Salt Lake City, 1962-63; resident USN, San Diego, Calif., 1966-70; staff surgeon USN, Bremerton, Wash., 1970-72; resident colorectal surgery U. Minn., Mpls., 1972-73; dir. colorectal surgery Nat. Naval Med. Ctr. USN, Bethesda, Md., 1973-82; ret. USN, 1983, Seattle, 1982; prof. surgery George Washington U., Washington, 1983—; pres. Am. Bd. Colon and Rectal Surgery, 1993-94. Editor: Practical Guide to Anorectal Physiology, 1990, 2d edit., 1995; assoc. editor Diseases of the Colon & Rectum, 1984—, Perspectives in Colon and Rectal Surgery, 1989—. Mem. ACS (pres. Met. Washington chpt. 1993-94), Soc. Am. Gastrointestinal Endoscopic Surgeons (pres. 1989-90), Am. Cancer Soc. (v.p. D.C. chpt. 1985—). Home: 1200 N Nash # 518 Arlington VA 22209 Office: George Washington U 2150 Pennsylvania Ave NW Washington DC 20037-2396

SMITH, LEE HERMAN, business executive; b. Ector, Tex., Jan. 7, 1935; s. Lee Herman and Willie Mae (Morrison) S.; m. Eva Landers, Feb. 18, 1960; 1 dau., Diette. B.S. in Math., Tex. A&M U., 1957, Ph.D. in Stats., 1964; M.S. in Engring. Adminstrn., So. Methodist U., 1961. Various engring. positions, 1957-65; asst. prof. Sch. Bus., U. Tex., Arlington, 1965-66, assoc. dean, assoc. prof., 1967-68; exec. planning adviser N.Am. Aviation Co., Los Angeles, summer 1966; prof., chmn. dept. quantitative mgmt. sci. U. Houston, 1969-71; dean faculties, prof. mgmt. sci. U. Tex., Dallas, 1971-72, v.p. acad. affairs, prof. mgmt. sci., 1972-74; pres. S.W. Tex. State U., San Marcos, 1974-81, TRAVELHOST, Inc., 1981-87, 89-93; chief exec. officer Neuro Systems Inc., 1984-85; pres. J & P Petroleum Products, Inc., 1986-87, Standard Life Ins. Co. of Miss., Jackson, 1987-89, Intercontinental Life Ins. Co. of N.J., 1987-89; exec. search cons. Sandhurst Assocs., 1993-94; pres. Voyager Expanded Learning Inc., 1995—; cons. in field; mem. sci. adv. com. Callier Hearing and Speech Center, Dallas; mem. Am. Assn. State Colls. and Univs. trip to People's Republic of China, 1975, Republic of China, 1976; chmn. bd. Central Tex. Higher Edn. Authority, 1977-78; mem. Gov.'s Higher Edn. Mgmt. Effectiveness Council, 1980-81. Author books, articles, revs. in field. Tex. A & M Coll. Opportunity scholar, 1953-57; Iowa State U. Research Found. fellow, 1961; Gen. Electric Co. fellow, 1962; Ling-Temco-Vought fellow, 1963-64; U. Tex. travel grantee, 1967. Mem. Am. Statis. Assn. (pres. N.Tex. chpt. 1967-68), Ops. Research Soc. Am., Inst. Mgmt. Scis. (program chmn. meetings), Am. Inst. Decision Scis. (v.p. planning and devel. 1970-71, council 1971-72), S. Tex. C. of C., Delta Sigma Pi, Phi Kappa Phi. Home: 2300 Grayson Dr Apt 212 Grapevine TX 76051-7001

SMITH, LEE L., hotel executive; b. Long Beach, Calif., Oct. 15, 1936; s. Lowell Llake and Violet Margaret (Chrissman) S.; m. Sharon M.C. Lanahan, (div. 1977). AA, Long Beach City Coll., 1958; BA in Music, Chapman Coll., 1965; postgrad., Calif. State U., Long Beach, 1966-67, U. Calif., Santa Barbara, 1974. Cert. tchr. Calif.; lic. ins. agt., Calif. Owner, mgr. Lee's Land Cattle Ranch, Cuyama Valley, Calif., 1960—; chr. Cuyama Valley Schs., New Cuyama, Calif., 1967-79; owner, mgr. Cuyama Buckhorn Restaurant & Motel, New Cuyama, 1979-83; owner Allstate Ins. Agy., Desert Hot Springs, 1983-91; owner S & S Printing 1990—, Lee's Land Bed & Breakfast, 1992—. Violinist Bakersfield (Calif.) Symphony, 1967—, Brook String Quartet, Palm Springs, Calif., 1984-91; dir. Planning Commn., Desert Hot Springs, 1985-87; chmn. Environ. Rev., Desert Hot Springs, 1986-88; mem. Redevel. Com., Desert Hot Springs, 1983-88; mem. exec. bd. growth and devel. Boys and Girls Club; bd. dirs. Food Now Program, 1988-91. Mem. Am. Fedn. Musicians, Desert Hot Springs C. of C. (Bus. Person Yr. 1987), Breakfast Rotary (pres. 1987-88), Taft Rotary, Elks. Republican. Avocations: hiking, flying. Home: St Rte 1 Box 185B Maricopa CA 93252 Office: S & S Printing 623 Center St Taft CA 93268

SMITH, LEIGHTON WARREN, JR., naval officer; b. Mobile, Ala., Aug. 20, 1939; s. Leighton W. Sr. and Sara Wallace (Griffith) S.; m. Dorothy Dunn McDowell, June 23, 1962; children: Leighton W. III, Susan Page, Dorothy McDowell. BS, U.S. Naval Acad., 1962; postgrad., Air Command and Staff Coll., Montgomery, Ala., 1973-74; MS in Psychology, Troy State U., 1974. Commd. ensign USN, 1962, advanced through grades to vice adm., 1991; comdr. Attack Squadron 86 USN, Cecil Field, Fla., 1974-76; comdr. Light Attack Wing One USN, Cecil Field, 1980-81; comdr. Carrier Air Wing 15 USN, San Diego, 1976-78; head comdr. assignments Naval Mil. Pers. Command USN, Arlington, Va., 1978-80; comdg. officer USS Kalamazoo (AOR6) USN, Norfolk, Va., 1982-83; asst. chief staff readiness, Naval Air Force, U.S. Atlantic Fleet USN, Norfolk, Va., 1983-84, comdg. officer USS America, 1984-85; strategic studies group Naval War Coll. USN, Newport, R.I., 1985-86; dir. tactical readiness div. OPNAV Chief of NavalOps. USN, Washington, 1986-88; comdr. Carrier Group 6 USN, Mayport, Fla., 1988-89; dir. ops. U.S. European Command J-3 USN, Stuttgart, Fed. Republic Germany, 1989-91; dep. chief of naval ops. for plans, policy and ops. USN, 1991—. Decorated D.S.M. Legion of Merit with two gold stars, DFC with one gold star, Meritorious Service medal with one gold star, 29 Air medals. Mem. Meninac (Jacksonville, Fla.), Rotary. Episcopalian. Avocations: golf, squash, racquet ball, fishing. Office: The Pentagon Navy Department Washington DC 20350-2000

SMITH, LEO GILBERT, hospital administrator; b. Oroville, Calif., July 29, 1929; s. Leo Paul and Laura Mae (Hoffschulte) S.; m. Marcia Elise Ernest, Jan. 26, 1952; children: Matthew Paul, Mara Lee, Bridget Mari, Leo Ernest. B.S.C., U. Santa Clara, 1951; M.P.H., U. Calif., 1958. Adminstrv. resident San Diego County Gen. Hosp., 1958-59; asst. hosp. adminstr. Santa Clara Valley Med. Center, 1959-67, adminstr., 1967-76, dir. planning, 1976-77; health care cons., 1977-80; adminstr. Puget Sound Hosp., 1980-82; mgr. Tacoma Family Medicine dept Multicare Med. Ctr., Tacoma, Wash., 1982-86, dir. clinic services, 1986-91; clinic mgr. Providence Factoria Family Healthcare div. Providence Med. Ctr., Seattle, 1992; ret. Bd. dirs. Children's Home Soc. of Calif., chmn. dist. bd., 1969-70; chmn. br. bd. Children's Home Soc. of Wash., 1985. Served in mil. 1952-54. Mem. Cen. Coast Hosp. Conf. (pres. 1970), Hosp. Coun. No. Calif. (dir. 1970-73), Am. Coll. Hosp. Adminstrs., Med. Group Mgrs. Assn., Tacoma Sunrise Rotary (pres. 1982-83, Dist. 5020 Youth Exch. officer 1991—). Home: 7122 Turquoise Dr SW Tacoma WA 98498-6431

SMITH, LEON POLK, artist; b. Chikasha, Okla., May 20, 1906. B.A., East Cen. State U., 1934; M.A., Columbia U., 1938. Lectr. Brandeis U., 1968; resident artist U. Calif.-Davis, 1972; lectr. SUNY-Old Westbury, 1978, Yale U., 1983, East Cen. U., Ada, Okla., 1986. One-man shows include San Francisco Mus. and Rose Mus. retrospective, 1968, Musée National d'Art Modern, Georges Pompidou (Beaubourg), Paris, Washburn Gallery, N.Y.C., 1981, 82, Nat. Galerie, Berlin, 1983, Burnett Miller Gallery, L.A., 1985, Hoffmann Galerie, Friedberg, Fed. Republic Germany, 1987, Venice Biennale, 1987, Cleve. Mus. Art, Inyedian Art Gallery, Lausanne, Switzerland, Schlégl Gallery, Zurich; group shows include Haus der Kunst, Munich, 1982, Nat. Gallery, Washington, 1984, Nat. Mus., Berlin, 1984, U. Okla. Mus. Art, 1989; maj. retrospective exhbns.: Wilhelm-Hack-Mus., Ludwigshafen, Fed. Republic Germany, 1988, Grenoble Mus., France, 1989, Bklyn. Mus., 1995; represented in permanent collections Guggenheim Mus., N.Y.C., Met. Mus. Art, N.Y.C., Mus. Modern Art, N.Y.C., Birmingham Mus. Art, Whitney Mus. Art, N.Y.C., Hirshhorn Mus., Nat. Gallery, Berlin, Peter Ludwig, Vienna, Austria, Nürnberg Kunsthalle, Germany, Wilhelm Hack Mus., Ludwigshafen-an Rhein, Germany, Wiesbaden Mus., Germany, Nurnberg Mus. Art, Germany, Grenoble Mus., France, Wiesbaden Mus., Germany, Bklyn. Mus., 1993. Solomon R. Guggenheim fellow, 1943; recipient Hassum Speicher Fund Purchase Exhbn. award Am. Acad. and Inst. Arts and Letters, 1979, Disting. Alumnus award East Ctrl. U., 1986;

grantee Nat. Coun. Arts, 1967, Tamarind, 1968, Longview grantee, 1958. Office: 31 Union Sq W Studio 14E New York NY 10003

SMITH, LEONARD BINGLEY, musician; b. Poughkeepsie, N.Y., Sept. 5, 1915; s. Frank Roderick and Ethel (Schubert) S.; m. Helen Gladys Rowe, Apr. 20, 1940 (dec. 1993); 1 dau., Sandra Victoria. Student, N.Y. Mil. Acad., 1930-33, Ernest Williams Sch. Music, 1933-36, NYU, 1936-37, Curtis Inst. Music, 1943-45; H.H.D., Detroit Inst. Tech., 1965. Pres. Accompaniments Unltd., Inc., 1952—. Cornet soloist, Ernest Williams Band, 1933-36, The Goldman Band, summers 1936-42; 1st trumpet, Barrere Little Symphony, 1935-37, Detroit Symphony Orch., 1937-42, Ford Sunday Evening Hour, 1937-42; condr., The Leonard Smith Concert Band, 1945—; Detroit Concert Band, 1945—, U. Detroit Bands, 1949-50, Moslem AAONMS Band, 1945-57, Scandinavian Symphony Orch. of Detroit, 1959-61, guest condr., Indpls. Symphony Orch., 1967; guest condr., soloist, clinician numerous concerts, U.S., Can.; mus. dir. John Philip Sousa documentary for BBC, 1970; Sousa Am. Bicentennial Recorded Collection; record series Gems concert band, Blossom Festival Band; condr. Blossom Festival Concert Band, 1972—; The Indomitable Teddy Roosevelt; producer: Our Am. Heritage in Music, 1970; pres., Bandland, Inc., 1951-61; Author: Treasury of Scales; over 350 pub. compositions; mem. bd. advisors Instrumentalist mag. Chmn. music com. Mich. Civil War Centennial Commn., 1961-64; gov. bd. Mac Award. With USNR, 1942-45. Recipient spl. medal Mich. Polish Legion Am. Vets., Distinguished Service medal Kappa Kappa Psi; Mich. Minuteman Gov.'s award, 1973; Freedom Found. award, 1975; Gen. William Booth award, 1976, Embassy Mich. Tourism award, 1979; named Alumnus of Distinction N.Y. Mil. Acad., 1976. Mem. ASCAP, Philippine Bandsmen's Assn. (hon.), Am. Fedn. Musicians, Internat. Platform Assn., Assn. Concert Bands (pres. 1982-83). Clubs: Masons (33 deg.), Shriners, K.T., Jesters. Office: care Detroit Concert Band Inc 7443 E Butherus # 100 Scottsdale AZ 85260

SMITH, LEONARD KELLEY, former plastic and reconstructive surgeon, consultant; b. Springfield, Mass., Apr. 18, 1918; s. Earle Leonard and Margaret Lillian (Kelley) S.; m. Marjorie Louise Hill, May 22, 1946 (div. 1979); children: Geoffrey, Lawrence, Linda, Brian, Jennifer; m. Susanne Mary Shadley, Apr. 14, 1979. AB, Amherst Coll., 1941; MD, U. Rochester, 1944. Cert. surgery, plastic and reconstructive surgery. Intern Lakeside Hosp., Cleve., Ohio; resident surgery Strong Meml. Hosp., Rochester, 1949-51; res. surgeon Roswell Park Meml. Inst., Buffalo, 1951-52; plastic surgeon Mary Hitchcock Meml. Hosp., Hanover, 1951-53, Hartford, Conn., 1955-89; pvt. practice Hartford, 1955-90; chief plastic surgery Newington (Conn.) Children's Hosp., 1976-89; med. cons. Aetna Ins. Co., Hartford, 1989—; mem. residency review com. for plastic surgery, 1972-78; guest examiner Am. Bd. Plastic Surgery. Lt. comdr. USN, 1945-46, 54-55. Mem. Am. Soc. Plastic and Reconstructive Surgeons, Am. Coll. Surgeons, N.E. Soc. Plastic Surgery (pres. 1968-69), Hartford Club, Hartford Rotary Club. Republican. Congregationalist. Avocations: painting, gardening, skiing, tennis. Home: 75 Stagecoach Rd Avon CT 06001

SMITH, LEROY, JR., bank executive; b. Athens, Ga., June 26, 1951; s. Leroy and Vallie Christine (Barnes) S.; m. Gloria Jane Johnson, June 20, 1981; 1 child, Jonathan Leroy. BA in Polit. Sci., Morris Brown Coll., 1973; JD, John Marshall Law Sch., 1976. Ops. C&S Nat. Bank, Atlanta, 1972-76, factoring credit, collector, 1976-77, factoring credit trainee, 1977-79, factoring credit mgr., 1979-80, asst. factoring officer to asst. v.p., 1980-86, v.p., div. mgr., 1986—; treas. Textile Yarn nat. Assn. Credit Mgrs., Atlanta, 1985—. Head personnel policy bd. St. Phillip Day Care Ctr., Decatur, Ga., 1981-85; dir. Trinity Ensemble, Athens, 1977—;. Recipient Humanitarian award Social Action Com., Athens, 1984, Human Relations award Human Relations Com., Athens, 1985. Mem. Atlanta Urban Bankers Assn., Am. Inst. Banking, Nat. Assn. Credit Mgmt., Morris Brown Coll. Alumni (v.p. 1973—, named oustanding alumni), Nu Beta Epsilon. Democrat. Methodist. Avocations: music, tennis, volleyball. Office: Citizens & So Comml Corp 2059 Northlake Pky Tucker GA 30084-5399

SMITH, LEROY HARRINGTON, JR., mechanical engineer, aerodynamics consultant; b. Balt., Nov. 3, 1928; s. Leroy Harrington and Edna (Marsh) S.; m. Barbara Ann Williams, July 7, 1951; children: Glenn Harrington, Bruce Lyttleton, Cynthia Ann. BS in Engring., Johns Hopkins U., 1949, MS, 1951, Dr. Engring., 1954. Compressor aerodynamacist Gen. Electric Co. Cin., 1954-61, mgr. turbomachinery devel., 1961-68, mgr. compressor & fan design tech., 1968-75, mgr. turbomachinery aerodynamics tech., 1975-92; cons. technologist Turbomachinery Aerodynamics Gen. Electric Co., 1992—. Contbr. articles to ASME Trans.; holder 12 patents. Recipient Perry T. Egbert Jr. awards, 1969, 83, Charles P. Steinmetz award, 1987 Gen. Electric Co. Fellow ASME (Gas Turbine award 1981, 87, R. Tom Sawyer award 1987, Aircraft Engine Tech. award 1992); mem. NAE, Ohio River Launch Club. Office: GE Aircraft Eng Mail Drop A411 1 Neumann Way Cincinnati OH 45215-1915

SMITH, LESLIE E., physical chemist; b. N.Y.C., Jan. 6, 1941. BSc, Case Inst. Tech., 1962; PhD in Chemistry, Cath. U. Am., 1970. Phys. chemist polymers divsn. Nat. Bur. Stds., 1964-66, 69-74, chief polymer stability and stds., 1974-82; chief polymers divsn. Nat. Inst. Stds. & Tech., 1982—. Editor Polymer Commun., 1984—. Mem. AAAS, Am. Chem. Soc. Office: Nat Inst of Stds and Tech Polymers Divsn Bldg 224 Rm A309 Gaithersburg MD 20899

SMITH, LESLIE ROPER, hospital administrator; b. Stockton, Calif., June 20, 1928; s. Austin J. and Helen (Roper) S.; m. Edith Sue Fincher, June 22, 1952; children: Melinda Sue, Leslie Erin, Timothy Brian. A.B., U. Pacific, 1951; M.S. in Pub. Adminstrn, U. So. Calif., 1956. Adminstrv. asst. Ranchos Los Amigos Hosp., Downey, Calif., 1953-57; asst. administr. Harbor Gen. Hosp., Torrance, Calif., 1957-65; administr. Harbor Gen. Hosp., 1966-71; acting regional dir. Los Angeles County Coastal Health Services Region, 1973; pres. San Pedro Peninsula Hosp., San Pedro, Cal., 1974-86; exec. dir. Los Angeles County/U. So. Calif. Med. Center, 1971-73; adminstr. Long Beach (Calif.) Hosp., 1965-66; assoc. clin. prof. community medicine and pub. health, also emergency medicine U. So. Calif., 1968-78; instr. U. So. Calif. (Sch. Pub. Adminstrn.), 1968; preceptor hosp. adminstrn. UCLA Sch. Pub. Health, 1964—; chief exec. officer French Hosp. Med. Ctr. and Health Plan, 1986-87; dir. health care services McCormack & Farrow, 1987—; lectr. in field, 1963—; cons. emergency health services HEW, 1970-73; chmn. com. diaster preparedness Hosp. Council So. Calif., 1966-72, sec., 1971—, pres., 1973; mem. Calif. Assembly Com. on Emergency Med. Services, 1970, Calif. Emergency Med. Adv. Com., 1972-75, Los Angeles County Commn. on Emergency Med. Services, 1975-83, Los Angeles Health Planning and Devel. Agy. Commn., 1980-83; bd. dirs. Blue Cross of So. Calif.; mem. hosp. relations com. Blue Cross of Calif.; mem. adv. com. on emergency health services Calif. Dept. Health, 1974-75; bd. dirs., mem. exec. com. Truck Ins. Exchange of Farmers Ins. Group, 1977-82; bd. dirs. Hosp. Council of So. Calif., 1966-76, 81-86, Health Resources Inst., 1985-86; chmn. Preferred Health Network, 1983-86. Mem. goals com., Torrance, 1968—; pres. Silver Spur Little League, Palos Verdes, 1969-70. Served with AUS, 1946-48. Recipient Silver Knight and Gold Knight award Nat. Mgmt. Assn., 1970, 85, Walker Fellowship award, 1976. Fellow Am. Coll. Health Care Execs. (life); mem. Am. Nat. mgmt. assns., Am. Hosp. Assn. (chmn. com. on community emergency health services 1973), Calif. Hosp. Assn. (chmn. com. emergency services 1965-70, trustee 1973-76, bd. dirs. Calif. Ins. Service Group 1980-82), County Suprs. Assn. Calif. (mem. subcom. on emergency care 1970). Presbyn. (elder, trustee). Home: 27 Marseille Laguna Beach CA 92677-5400

SMITH, LESTER MARTIN, broadcasting executive; b. N.Y.C., Oct. 20, 1919; s. Alexander and Sadie S.; m. Bernice Reitz, Sept. 28, 1962; 1 child, Alexander. B.S. in Bus. Adminstrn, NYU, 1940. Chief exec. officer Alexander Broadcasting Co., radio stas. in, 1954—; gen. partner 700 Investment Co.; past dir. Seattle C. of C.; past chmn. dir. Radio Advt. Bur. Served to maj. U.S. Army, 1942-46. Decorated Bronze Star. Mem. Nat. Assn. Broadcasters (past dir.), Oreg. Assn. Broadcasters (past pres.), Broadcast Pioneers. Clubs: Rotary (Seattle), Rainer (Seattle), Wash. Athletic (Seattle). Address: 700 112th NE Bellevue WA 98004

SMITH, LEVIE DAVID, JR., real estate appraiser, consultant; b. Lakeland, Fla., Oct. 19, 1924; s. Levie David and Grace (Ross) S.; m. Annie

Laurie Hogan, Aug. 29, 1948; children: Nancy, L. David, Judy. BS, Fla. So. Coll., 1947. Salesman Smith & Smith, Realtors, Lakeland, 1947-50; staff appraiser Smith & Son, Appraisers, Lakeland, 1952-72; pres. Levie D. Smith & Assoc., Inc., Lakeland, 1973—; chmn. bd. dirs. First Fed. of Fla., Lakeland, acting pres., 1992-95; pres. Fla. Assn. Realtors, Orlando, 1970; chmn. Fla. Real Estate Commn., Orlando, 1979. Past trustee Polk Theatre, Inc., pres. 1989, chmn. adv. bd., 1994-95; mem. adv. bd. Imperial Symphony Orch., 1993—; mem. exec. bd. Gulf Ridge Boy Scouts Am., 1984. chmn. 1995—; mem. real estate adv. bd. U. Fla. Lt. USN, 1943-46, 50-52. Recipient Silver Beaver award Gulf Ridge Coun., Boy Scouts Am., 1984. Mem. Am. Inst. Real Estate Appraisers (govt. coun. 1976-83, v.p. 1982-83, SE Meritorious award 1987), Lakeland Rotary Club (pres. 1976-77, Paul Harris fellow, 4 way test award). Presbyterian. Avocations: gardening, camping, fishing. Home: 515 Laurel Ln Lakeland FL 33813-1650 Office: Levie D Smith & Assocs Inc 101 Doris Dr Lakeland FL 33813-1004

SMITH, LEWIS DENNIS, academic administrator; b. Muncie, Ind., Jan. 18, 1938; s. Thurman Lewis and Dorothy Ann (Dennis) S.; m. Suzanne F. Metcalfe; children: Lauren Kay, Raymond Bradley. AB, Ind. U., 1959, PhD, 1963. Asst. biologist Argonne (Ill.) Nat. Lab., 1964-67, assoc. biologist, 1967-69; assoc. prof. Purdue U., West Lafayette, Ind., 1969-73; prof. biology Purdue U., West Lafayette, 1973-87, assoc. head dept. biol. scis., 1979-80, head dept., 1980-87; prof. dept. devel. and cell. U. Calif., Irvine, 1987-94, dean Sch. Biol. Scis., 1987-90, exec. vice chancellor, 1990-94; pres. U. of Nebr., 1994—; instr. embryology Woods Hole (Mass.) Marine Biology Lab., summers 1972, 73, 74, 88, 89; mem. Space Sci. Bd., Washington, 1986-91; chmn. Space Biology and Medicine, Space Sci. Bd., 1986-91; mem. cell biology study sect. NIH, Bethesda, Md., 1971-75; chmn., 1977-79, bd. sci. counselors Nat. Inst. Child Health and Human Devel., 1990-95, chmn. 1992-95; mem. space biology peer rev. bd. AIBS, 1980-85. Guggenheim fellow, 1987. Mem. Am. Soc. Biochemistry and Molecular Biology, AAAS, Internat. Soc. for Devel. Biology, Soc. for Devel. Biology, Am. Soc. Cell Biology. Home: 5930 Norman Rd Lincoln NE 68512 Office: Varner Hall 3835 Holdrege Lincoln NE 68583-0745

SMITH, LEWIS MOTTER, JR., advertising and direct marketing executive; b. Kansas City, Mo., Nov. 4, 1932; s. Lewis Motter and Virginia (Smith) S.; m. Alice Allen, June 28, 1975; children: Katherine Allen, Patience Allen. Student, Kenyon Coll., 1951-53, Columbia U., 1956-58. Copywriter mail order div. Grolier Soc., Inc., N.Y.C., 1957-59; free lance copywriter Santa Fe, N.M., 1960-61; v.p. creative services Grolier Enterprises Inc., N.Y.C., 1962-67; v.p., creative planning dir. Wunderman, Ricotta & Kline, Inc., N.Y.C., 1968-72; exec. v.p., creative dir., 1972-79; exec. v.p. Young & Rubicam Direct Mktg. Group, 1980; sr. v.p., dir. mktg. Book-of-the-Month Club, Inc., 1980-84, dir., 1981-84; exec. v.p., creative dir. SSC&B: Vos Direct Inc., N.Y.C., 1985-87; pres., dir. creative services Lintas: Direct Inc. (formerly SSC&B: Vos Direct Inc.), N.Y.C., 1987-89; pres. Lew Smith & Assocs., Inc., 1989—. Bd. dirs. Young Concert Artists, Inc., N.Y.C., 1966-67, Harlem Sch. Arts, 1967-68. Served with U.S. Army, 1953-56. Mem. Delta Phi. Episcopalian. Home and Office: 45 Knollwood Rd Rhinebeck NY 12572

SMITH, LEY S., pharmaceutical company executive; b. 1934. BA, U. Western Ont., Can., 1958. With Upjohn Co., Kalamazoo, Mich., 1958—, now pres. & COO. Office: Upjohn Inter Am Corp 7000 Portage Rd Kalamazoo MI 49001

SMITH, LINDA A., congresswoman, former state legislator; d. Vern Smith; children: Sheri, Robi. Office mgr.; former mem. Wash. State Ho. of Reps.; mem. Wash. State Senate; congresswoman, Wash. 3rd Dist. U.S. House Reps., Washington, D.C., 1995—. Republican. Home: 10009 NW Ridgecrest Ave Vancouver WA 98685-5159 Office: Senate House Legislative Bldg Olympia WA 98504*

SMITH, LIZ (MARY ELIZABETH SMITH), newspaper columnist, broadcast journalist; b. Ft. Worth, Feb. 2, 1923; d. Sloan and Sarah Elizabeth (McCall) S. B.J., U. Tex., 1948. Editor Dell Publns., N.Y.C., 1950-53; assoc. producer CBS Radio, 1953-55, NBC-TV, 1955-59; assoc. on Cholly Knickerbocker newspaper column, N.Y.C., 1959-64; film critic Cosmpolitan mag., 1966; columnist Chgo. Tribune-N.Y. Daily News Syndicate (now Tribune Media Services), 1976-91, New York Newsday, L.A. Times Syndicate, 1991—; Family Circle mag., 1993—; TV commentator WNBC-TV, N.Y.C., 1978-91; commentator Fox-TV, N.Y.C., 1991—; freelance mag. writer, also staff writer Sports Illus. mag.; commentator Gossip Show E! Entertainment, 1993—. Author: The Mother Book, 1978. Office: N Y Newsday 2 Park Ave New York NY 10016 *A career in Journalism? Any career at all? I say learn to type. Read a lot. Keep on keeping on. Work is its own reward and success is loving your work. And remember, never give up. After the Middle Ages comes the Renaissance.*

SMITH, LLOYD, musician; b. Cleve. Dec. 1, 1941; s. Thomas George Russell and Anita May (Speer) S.; m. Rheta R. Naylor, Mar. 30, 1967 (div. Nov., 1994); 1 child, Peter Eldon. Mus.B., Curtis Inst. Music, 1965. Tchr. Settlement Music Sch., 1970-72, 92—. Cellist Pitts. Symphony, 1965-67, Phila. Orch., 1967—; asst. prin. cello, 1988—; soloist Indpls. Symphony, 1958, 68, Garden State Philharmonic, 1964, Lansdowne Symphony, 1965, West Jersey Chamber Orch., 1991, Haverford-Bryn Mawr Symphony, 1992; mem. Huntingdon Trio, 1974-93, Wister quartet, 1988—. Alumni rep. Curtis Inst. Music Bd. Trustees, chmn. Parents' Com., 1989-90; bd. dirs. Phila. Youth Orch., 1987-91, Community Out Reach Partnership, 1988-90. Mem. Am. Soc. Ancient Instruments (asst. artistic dir. 1975-77, music dir. 1977-80), Curtis Inst. Music Nat. Alumni Assn. (treas., bd. dirs. 1989-90), 1807 and Friends (bd. dirs. 1994—). Home: 5639 E Wister St Philadelphia PA 19144-1522 Office: 5639 E Wister St Philadelphia PA 19144-1522

SMITH, LLOYD HILTON, independent oil and gas producer; b. Pitts., July 9, 1905; s. Roland Hilton and Jane (Lloyd) S.; m. Jane Clay Gravely, Sept. 7, 1931; children: Camilla; m. Elizabeth Keith Wiess, May 25, 1940; children: Sandra Keith, Sharon Lloyd, Sydney Carothers. Ph.B., Yale U., 1929. Statistician Biggs, Mohrman & Co., N.Y.C., 1932; mgr. New York office Laird & Co., 1933-34; v.p. Argus Research Corp., 1934-35; chmn., dir. Paraffine Oil Corp., 1949-81; past dir. 1st City Nat. Bank Houston, Nat. Rev., Curtis-Wright Corp., Info. Storage Systems, Falcon Seaboard, Inc. Mem. Houston Mus. Sci.; trustee Pine Manor Coll., 1963-74; past dir. DeBakey Med. Found. Lt. comdr. USNR, 1942-45. Republican. Clubs: Bayou, Ramada (Houston); Everglades, Bath and Tennis (Palm Beach); Racquet and Tennis (N.Y.C.), Brook (N.Y.C.), River (N.Y.C.); Nat. Golf Links of America, Southampton, Meadow. Home: 101 El Vedado Way Palm Beach FL 33480

SMITH, LLOYD MUIR, chemist, educator; b. Calgary, Can., Feb. 20, 1917; came to U.S., 1950; s. John Huntly and Lillian Sarah (Muir) S.; m. Edythe Clarissa Dodds, June 26, 1948; children: Michael Bruce, Douglas Lloyd. BS, U. Alberta, Edmonton, Can., 1943, MS, 1949; PhD, U. Calif., Davis, 1953. Instr., lectr. Dairy Industry U. Alberta, Edmonton, 1946-49; grad. asst. Dairy Industry U. Calif., Davis, 1950-52; asst. prof. U. Alta., Edmonton, Canada, 1952-54; asst. prof., then prof. Food Sci. and Tech. dept. U. Calif., Davis, 1954-87; prof. emeritus, 1987—; cons. edible oils, fats and dairy processing orgns. Served to lt. Can. Army, 1943-46. Fulbright fellow, New Zealand, 1961-62, Brazil, 1986; Nat. Research Council, 1950-52. Mem. Am. Oil Chemists' Soc. (award of merit 1983), Am. Dairy Sci. Assn., Inst. Food Technologists. Republican. Presbyterian. Avocations: travel, bridge, biking. Home: 715 Oeste Dr Davis CA 95616-3532 Office: U Calif Dept Food Sci and Tech Davis CA 95616

SMITH, LOIS ANN, real estate executive; b. Chgo. Jan. 1, 1941; d. Alburn M. and Ruth A. (Beaver) Beaudoin; m. Dickson K. Smith, Mar. 24, 1962 (div. May 1982); children: Michelle D., Jeffrey D. BA, U. Utah, 1962; MBA, Marquette U., 1972. Asst. mgr. prodn. Northwestern Mut. Life Ins. Co., Milw., 1979-83, asst. mgr., asset mgr., 1983-88; assoc. dir., asset mgmt. Asset Mgmt., 1988-89; dir. asset mgmt. Northwestern Mut. Life Ins. Co., Milw., 1990-95, dir. real estate equities, 1995—. Cons. Girl Scouts Am., Milw., 1986, YWCA, Milw., 1986, bd. dirs. YWCA, 1981-87; bd. dirs. Wis. Rep. Orgn., 1985-87. Mem. Internat. Council Shopping Ctrs., Profl. Dimensions, Beta Gamma Sigma. Unitarian. Home: 21N W 25090 Cir E

Pewaukee WI 53072 Office: Northwestern Mut Life Ins Co 720 E Wisconsin Ave Milwaukee WI 53202-4703

SMITH, LOIS ARLENE, actress, writer; b. Topeka, Nov. 3, 1930; d. William Oren and Carrie D. (Gottshalk) Humbert; m. Wesley Dale Smith, Nov. 5, 1948 (div. 1973); 1 child, Moon Elizabeth. Student, U. Wash., studied with Lee Strasberg, Actor's Studio, N.Y.C., 1955—. guest dir. Juilliard Sch., 1987; Clarence Ross fellow Am. Theater Wing at Eugene O'Neill Theater Ctr., 1983; mem. adv. panel program fund Pub. Broadcasting Service, 1981-82; hon. founder Harold Clurman Theatre Artists Fund, Ctr. for Arts, SUNY-Purchase, 1981. Author: play All There Is, 1982; debut in Time Out for Ginger, 1952; actress Broadway and off-Broadway prodns., 1952—; stage appearances include Theater of the Living Arts, Mark Taper Forum, Long Wharf Theater and Steppenwolf Theater Co.; appears on network and pub. TV programs; stage appearances include, The Young and the Beautiful, 1955, The Glass Menagerie, 1956, Blues for Mr. Charlie, 1964, Orpheus Descending, 1957, Miss Julie, 1966, Uncle Vanya, 1965, 69, The Iceman Cometh, 1973, Harry Outside, 1975, Hillbilly Women, 1979, 81, the Vienna Notes, 1985, The Stick Wife, April Snow, 1987, The Grapes of Wrath, 1988-89, 90, Measure for Measure, Beside Herself, 1989, Escape from Happiness, 1993; films include East of Eden, 1955, Five Easy Pieces, 1970, Next Stop Greenwich Village, 1975, Resurrection, 1980, Green Card, 1990, Fried Green Tomatoes, 1991, Falling Down, 1993. Named Best Supporting Actress for Five Easy Pieces, Nat. Soc. Film Critics, 1971; named to Filmdom's Famous Fives for East of Eden, Film Daily mag., 1955. Mem. SAG, AFTRA, Actors Equity Assn., Dramatists Guild, Actors Studio, Ensemble Studio Theater, Steppenwolf Theatre Co. Ensemble.

SMITH, LONNIE MAX, diversified industries executive; b. Twin Falls, Idaho, July 28, 1944; s. Lonnie E. and Christie (Stuart) S.; m. Cheryl Diane Smith, June 10, 1968; children: Kristen, Maryam, Rebecca, Michael, Catherine. BSEE, Utah State U., 1967; MBA, Harvard U., 1974. Engr., mgr. field services, mgr. tech. services to asst. to v.p. plans and control IBM Corp., San Francisco, Palo Alto, Calif., and White Plains, N.Y., 1967-74; mgr., corp. strategy, then cons. Boston Cons. Group, 1974-76; exec. v.p. Am. Tourister, Inc., Warren, R.I., 1978-81; sr. v.p. corp. planning Hillenbrand Industries, Inc., Batesville, Ind., 1977-78, sr. exec. v.p., 1982—, also bd. dirs.; pres., chmn. bd. Hillenbrand Internat. Sales Corp.; v.p., bd. dirs. Forecorp, Inc., Batesville; bd. dirs. Hillenbrand Investment Adv. Corp., Batesville Casket Co., Batesville Internat. Corp., Hill-Rom Co., The Forethought Group, Inc., Hilico Life Inst. Co., all in Batesville; bd. dirs. Medeco Security Locks, Inc., Salem, Va., Support Systems Internat., Inc., Charleston, S.C., Lozier Corp., Omaha. Served to 1st lt. U.S. Army, 1969-72. Republican. Mormon. Avocation: tennis. Office: Hillenbrand Industries Inc 700 State Rte 46 E Batesville IN 47006-8835

SMITH, LOREN ALLAN, federal judge; b. Chgo., Ill., Dec. 22, 1944; m. Catherine Yore; children: Loren Jr., Adam. BA in Polit. Sci., Northwestern U., 1966, JD, 1969. Bar: Ill. 1970, U.S. Ct. Mil. Appeals 1973, U.S. Ct. Appeals (D.C. cir.) 1974, U.S. Supreme Ct. 1974, U.S. Ct. Claims, 1985, U.S. Ct. Appeals (fed. cir.) 1986. Gen. counsel, sec.-treas. Kimberly-Churchill, Inc., 1970-71, Dental Inst. U.S., 1970-71; gen. counsel, corp. dir. Robert Suggs, Inc., 1971-73; cons. Sidley & Austin, Chgo., 1972-73; gen. atty. FCC, 1973; asst. to spl. counsel to the pres. White House, Washington, 1973-74; spl. asst. U.S. atty. D.C., 1974-75; counsel Reagan for Pres. campaigns, 1975-77, 79-80; assoc. prof. Del. Law Sch., 1976-80; dep. dir. Office Exec. Br. Mgmt. Presdl. Transition, 1980-81; chmn. Adminstrv. Conf. U.S., 1981-85; appointed judge U.S. Claims Ct., 1985, designated chief judge, 1985—; adj. prof. Internat. Law Sch., 1973-74, Georgetown U. Law Ctr., 1992—, Am. U. Sch. Law, 1993—; past mem. Pres.' Cabinet Coun. on Legal Policy, Pres.' Cabinet Coun. on Mgmt. and Adminstrn.; chmn. Coun. Ind. Regulatory Agys. Contbr. articles to profl. jours. Recipient Presdl. medal Cath. U. Am. Law Sch., 1993. Mem. WETA (mem. cmty. adv. coun., sr. conf. fellow, adminstr. conf. U.S. 1985—), Nat. Lawyers Club (hon.), Ct. Fed. Claims Bar Assn., B'nai B'rith, Univ. Club (Washington) (hon.). Republican. Jewish. Office: US Ct of Fed Claims 717 Madison Pl NW Washington DC 20005-1011

SMITH, LORNA WATSON, accountant, environmental health administrator; b. St. Croix, V.I., Sept. 15, 1935; d. James St. Clair and Evadnie (Thomas) Watson; m. Randolph Bratsen Smith; children: Sherilyn, Stephanie, Shelton, Sharleen, E. Smith. AA in Bus. Mgmt., Coll. V.I., St. Thomas, 1972, BA in adminstrn., 1977. Clk.-typist III V.I. Dept. Labor, St. Croix, 1960-61; account clk. III V.I. Dept. Health, St. Croix, 1961; account clk. III V.I. Dept. Health, St. Thomas, 1962-72, adminstrv. officer environ. office, 1977-78; acct. III environ. health, 1978; adminstr. environ. health V.I. Dept. Health, St. Thomas, 1978-84, asst. dir. environ. health, 1987-91, dir. environ. health, 1991-94; ret. V.I. Dept. Health, 1994. Mem. steering com. All Saints Episcopal Sch., St. Thomas, 1987—; mem. Friends of Bethlehem House (Homeless), St. Thomas, 1989, Danny's Children, St. Jude Hosp for Rsch., Memphis, 1979. Morris F. DeCastro fellow Bd. Edn., V.I., 1977. Mem. AAUW, NAFE, Assn. Govt. Accts., Nat. Environ. Health Assn., Eta Phi Beta (Alpha Chi chpt.). Roman Catholic. Home: PO Box 533 Charlotte Amalie VI 00804-0533 Office: VI Dept Health Old Hospital Complex Saint Thomas VI 00802

SMITH, LOUISE ZANDBERG, English studies educator, writer; b. Grand Rapids, Mich., May 24, 1942; d. Louis G. and Loraine T. (Lehnen) Zandberg; m. George W. Smith Jr., Aug. 21, 1965; children: Allison Hart, George W. III. BA in English magna cum laude, U. Mich., 1964; MA in Comparative Lit., U. Calif., Berkeley, 1966; PhD in English, U. Va., 1974. English instr. St. Paul's Coll., Lawrenceville, Va., 1966-68; rhetoric instr. Boston U., 1972-74; asst. prof. English U. Mass., Boston, 1974-89, assoc. prof. English, 1989—, dir. tutoring program, 1977-94, campus rep. Mellon Humanities fellowships, 1982-93, dir. freshman English, 1982-89, faculty rep. commn. on role and status of part-time faculty, 1985-86, faculty rep. univ. task force on orientation and retention, 1986-87, supr., mentor grad. tchg. asst. program, 1987—; gen. edn. coun. U. Mass., Boston, Boston State Coll., Boston Pub. Schs., Simmons Coll., Brandeis U., 1981-83; writing program and writing-across-the-curriculum cons. Mary Washington Coll., Fredericksburg, Va., 1986, U. So. Maine, Portland, 1987, Houghton (N.Y.) Coll., 1987, Boston Area C.C. Consortium, 1987-89, Roger Williams Coll., Bristol, R.I., 1987, Middlebury (Vt.) Coll., 1988, Boston U., 1988, Merrimack Coll., North Andover, Mass., 1988, Syracuse (N.Y.) U., 1992; reviewer Houghton Mifflin, Harper-Collins Pub., St. Martin's Press, Blair Press, Ohio State U. Press, others; presenter papers in field. Author: (with others) Keats's Narrative Poetry, 1980, Only Connect: Reading and Writing at the College Level, 1986, Introductory College Literature Courses, 1991, Approaches to Teaching Keats's Poetry, 1991; rev. editor Coll. English, 1985-92, editor, 1992—; bibliographer Nat. Bibliography Project, 1985, 86; contbr. articles to profl. jours. Recipient scholarship U. Mich., 1960-64, Outstanding Achievement in Scholarship, Tchg., and Svc., U. Mass., 1985-86; Woodrow Wilson fellow, U. Calif., 1964-65; NEH fellow, 1975, Woodrow Wilson Found. fellow, 1980-81, Coll. Assessment Program Evaluation fellow, 1986. Mem. MLA, N.E. MLA, Nat. Coun. Tchrs. English, Conf. on Coll. Composition and Commn. (exec. com. 1988-91), Coun. of Writing Program Adminstrn., Nat. Writing Ctrs. Assn., N.E. Writing Ctr. Assn., Coun. of Editors Learned Jours. Office: U Mass Dept English 100 Morrissey Blvd Boston MA 02043

SMITH, LOWELL, dancer; b. Memphis. Mem. Dance Theatre of Harlem, 1977—, prin. dancer, also acting sch. dir.; instr. Memphis Acad. of Ballet, N.Y. Drama Sch. Performances include Swan Lake (Act II), The Four Temperaments, Scheherazade, Holberg Suite, Serenade, Footprints Dress for Red, Equus, Troy Game, Fall River Legen, A Song for Dead Warriors; TV appearances include PBS's Dance in America showing of Streetcar Named Desire, NBC's airing of Giselle; performed at the White House State Dinner, 1981. Office: Dance Theatre of Harlem 466 West 152nd St New York NY 10031*

SMITH, LUCIUS SKINNER, III, educational foundation administrator; b. Boulder, Colo., July 11, 1919; s. Lucius Skinner jr. and Georgie Elizabeth (Hoxie) S.; m. Josephine Lamb Butler, 1942 (div. 1963); children: Lucius S. IV (dec.), Suzy Smith Hunt, Alexander Gavin Butler, Alan Bret, Anthony Butler Mason; m. Emilie Jensen, 1964 (div. 1974); m. Maria Katalin Feher,

Sept. 27, 1974. BA in Modern European History, U. Calif., Berkeley, 1941. Cons., lobbyist Am. Bar Ctr. and Keogh Act for the Self-Employed, 1955-60; journalist Hearst Corp., Boston, 1970-75; pub. rels. and exec. search Washington and St. Louis, 1976-86; cons. Am. Freedom Train for Am.'s Bicentennial, 1975; adj. gen. Nat. Assn. Atomic Vets., Independence, Mo., 1985-90; pres. Atomic Libr. and Tech. Found., Washington, 1988—. Supported enactment of Radiation-Exposed Vets. Compensation Act, 1988. Naval aviator USMC, 1941-45, PTO, Lt. col. ret. USMC Res. Decorated DFC, Bronze star, Air medal with gold star, Presl. unit citation. Office: 218 N Washington DuQuoin IL 62832

SMITH, LYNN HOWARD, manufacturing company executive; b. Ft. Wayne, Ind., Mar. 9, 1936; s. Lester Earl and Catherine Lois (McCurdy) S.; student Ind.-Purdue U. Extension, Ft. Wayne, 1956-57; grad. Internat. Harvester Tech. Sch., 1961; m. Jean Marie Bauman, Sept. 2, 1955; children—Julie, Linnett, Jeffery, Lisa. Methods engr. Jervis Corp., Grandville, Mich., 1964-67; project engr. Twigg Industries, Martinsville, Ind., 1967-70; project engr. Tri Industries, Terre Haute, Ind., 1970-74; tool and mfg. engr. Berko Electric Mfg. Co., Peru, Ind., 1974-77, fabrication supt., 1977-78, mgr. mfg. engring., 1978-79, plant supr., 1979; chief project engr. Tube Processing Corp., Indpls., 1979-85; plant mgr. Tube Forming and Mfg. Corp., Lebanon, Ind., 1985-91; engring. mgr. Dexter Component Repair; cons. Groteness Machine Works, Chgo. Pres. Harlan (Ind.) Days Assn., 1962; adv. Jr. Achievement, Terre Haute, Ind., 1972-73. Named Jr. Achievement Adv. of Yr., Terre Haute Jr. Achievement, 1973. Methodist. Clubs: Berko Mgmt., Masons (Harlan lodge master 1964), Shriners. Developed proprietary spot welding process and equipment, 1966, proprietary high temperature brazing process, 1970-74; developer, editor Berko Electric Mfg. Procedures Man. 1975-79; sr. design engr. hydraulic control system for A340 Airbus Thrust Reversers, 1989-91. Home: 17 Barksdale Dr Dayton OH 45431 Office: Ferco Tech Corp 291 Conover Dr Franklin OH 45005-1944

SMITH, MACON STROTHER, architect; b. Raleigh, N.C., Feb. 24, 1919; s. Junious Walters and Mary Macon (Strother) S.; m. Jeanette Marjorie Williams, Feb. 14, 1944; children: Stephen Williams, Patricia Macon Smith Hoover. BS in Archtl. Engring. with honors, N.C. State U., 1941; BS in Aero. Engring. with honors, U.S. Naval Sch. Engring., NYU, 1941. Registered architect, N.C. Part-time draftsman F. Carter Williams, Architects, Raleigh, 1940-41, project architect, 1946-55, ptnr., 1955-80, v.p., 1980—; draftsman Cooper & Shumaker, Architects, Raleigh, 1945-46; part-time instr. Sch. Design N.C. State U., Raleigh, 1957-58, junior student work; mem. Gov.'s Low Cost Housing Com., Raleigh, 1966-67; chmn. Gov.'s City and County Subcom. Low Cost Housing, 1967-68. Co-designer addition class rm. bldg. project displayed in Nat. Gold Medal Exhbn. Bldg. Arts, Archtl. League N.Y., 1957 (citation South Atlantic AIA). V.p. Raleigh Lions Club, 1965. Lt. comdr. USNR, 1941-45. Recipient 2d prize weathermaker home competition for S. and S.W. U.S.A Carrier Corp., 1953, 2d award Ch. Architecture Guild, 1956. Fellow AIA (dir. South Atlantic regional bd. 1964-71, mem. fellow selection com. 1973-75, chmn. 1975); mem. N.C. chpt. AIA (treas., v.p., pres., dir. 1962-67, mem. com. to establish archtl. sch. at U. N.C. Charlotte 1966-69, adv. com. new sch. 1970-73, Merit award ch. design 1958), N.C. Archtl. Found. (sec.-treas., v.p., pres. 1963-71), Carolina Country Club. Presbyterian. Avocations: tennis, golf. Home: 3721 Lassiter Mill Rd Raleigh NC 27609-7042 Office: 606 Wade Ave Raleigh NC 27605-1237

SMITH, DAME MAGGIE, actress; b. Ilford, Eng., Dec. 28, 1934; d. Nathaniel and Margaret (Hutton) S.; m. Robert Stephens, 1967 (div. 1974); m. Beverley Cross, 1974. Grad., Oxford High Sch. Girls; D.Litt. (hon.), St. Andrews, 1971; DLitt (hon.), Oxford U., 1994. dir. United British Artists, 1982—. Stage and film actress, 1952—; stage appearances include: New Faces, debut N.Y.C., 1956, Share My Lettuce, 1957, The Stepmother, 1958, Rhinoceros, 1960, Strip The Willow, 1960, The Rehearsal, 1961, The Private Ear and The Public Eye, 1962, Mary, Mary, 1961; appearances at Old Vic, 1959-60, Nat. Theatre, London, 1963—; productions at Nat. Theatre include Private Lives, 1972, Othello, Hay Fever, Master Builder, Hedda Gabbler, Much Ado About Nothing, Miss Julie, Black Comedy, Stratford Festival, Ont., Can., 1976, 77, 78, 80, Antony and Cleopatra, Macbeth, Three Sisters, Richard III, Night and Day, London and N.Y.C., 1979-80, Virginia, London, 1981, Way of the World, Chichester Festival, London, 1984-85, Interpreters, London, 1985-86, Lettice and Lovage, 1988, also in N.Y., 1990, The Importance of Being Earnest, 1993, Three Tall Women, 1994; films include Othello, 1966, The Honey Pot, 1967, Oh What a Lovely War, 1968, Hot Millions, 1968, The Prime of Miss Jean Brodie, 1968 (Acad. award for best actress), Love and Pain and The Whole Damn Thing, 1971, Travels With My Aunt, 1972, Murder by Death, 1976, Death on the Nile, 1977, California Suite, 1978 (Acad. award for best supporting actress), Quartet, 1978, Clash of the Titans, 1981, Evil under the Sun, 1981, The Missionary, 1982, A Private Function, 1984 (best actress award Brit. Acad. of Film & TV Arts, 1985), Lily in Love, 1985, A Room With a View, 1985, The Lonely Passion of Judith Hearn, 1987 (Brit. Acad. of Film & TV Arts award, 1989), Paris By Night, 1988, Hook, 1991, Sister Act, 1992, The Secret Garden, 1993; TV films include Memento Mori, 1992, Suddenly Last Summer, 1993 (Lead Actress-Miniseries Emmy nominee, 1993); BBC-TV appearance Bed Among the Lentils, 1988. Recipient Best Actress award Eve. Std., 1962, 70, 82, 85, 94, Best Film Actress award Soc. Film and TV Arts U.K., 1968, Film Critics Guild, 1968, Taomina Gold award, 1985, Antoinette Perry award (Tony), 1990, Shakespeare prize, 1991; decorated Dame Brit. Empire, 1989; named Actress of Yr., Variety Club, 1963, 72, Brit. Acad. Best Screen Actress, 1985; Brit. Film Inst. fellow, 1992, Theater Hall of Fame, 1994. Office: Write on Cue, 15 New Row 3d Fl, London WC2N 4LA, England

SMITH, M(AHLON) BREWSTER, psychologist, educator; b. Syracuse, N.Y., June 26, 1919; s. Mahlon Ellwood and Blanche Alice (Hinman) S.; m. Jean Dresden Schwartz, June 1943 (div. 1945); m. Deborah Anderson, June, 1947; children: Joshua H., T. Daniel, Rebecca M., J. Torquil. Student, Reed Coll., Portland, Oreg., 1935- 38; A.B. Stanford U., 1939, A.M., 1940; Ph.D., Harvard U., 1947. Rantoul scholar Harvard U., 1940-41; jr. analyst Office Coordinator of Information, U.S. Govt., 1941; Social Sci. Research Council fellow Harvard U., 1946-47; asst. prof. social psychology Harvard U. (Dept. Social Relations), 1947-49; prof. psychology, chmn. dept. Vassar Coll., 1949-52; staff Social Sci. Research Council, 1952-56; prof. psychology NYU, 1956-59; prof. psychology U. Calif. at Berkeley, 1959-68, dir. Inst. Human Devel., 1965-68; prof., chmn. dept. psychology U. Chgo., 1968-70; prof. psychology U. Calif. at Santa Cruz, 1970-88, prof. emeritus, 1988—, vice chancellor social scis., 1970-75; fellow Center Advanced Studies Behavioral Scis., 1964-65; Vice pres. Joint Commn. Mental Illness and Health, 1955-61. Author: Social Psychology and Human Values, 1969, Humanizing Social Psychology, 1974, Values, Self and Society, 1991; co-author: The American Soldier, 1949, Opinions and Personality, 1956; editor: Jour. Social Issues, 1951-55, Jour. Abnormal Soc. Psychology, 1956-61; contbr. articles to profl. jours. Served from pvt. to maj. Adj. Gen. Div. AUS, 1942-46; research officer Information and Edn. div. War Dept., 1943-46; research asso. soc. com. on soldier attitudes Social Sci. Research Council 1946. Decorated Bronze Star medal.; NIMH fellow, 1964-65, NEH fellow, 1975-76; Belding scholar Found. for Child Devel., 1982-83; Gold medal award lifetime contbn. to psychology in pub. interest Am. Psychol. Found., 1992. Fellow AAAS, Am. Psychol. Assn. (pres. 1978, Disting. Contbn. to Pub. Interest award 1988, Henry A. Murray award in personality psychology 1993), mem. Soc. Psychol. Study Social Issues (pres. 1959, Kurt Lewin Meml. award 1986), Western Psychol. Assn. (pres. 1986), Psychologists for Social Responsibility (pres. 1987-90), Internat. Soc. Polit. Psychol. (Harold Lasswell award 1993), Internat. Soc. Applied Psychology (divsn. Polit. Psychology, pres. 1994—), Sigma Xi, Phi Beta Kappa. Democrat. Club: Cosmos (Washington). Home: 316 Escalona Dr Santa Cruz CA 95060-2607

SMITH, MALBERT, III, computer technology executive, psychologist; b. Fayetteville, N.C., Mar. 21, 1953; s. Malbert Jr. and Virginia (Little) S.; m. Alisa Edwards, May 15, 1978; children: Virginia Alise, Elizabeth Edwards, Malbert IV. BA magna cum laude, Duke U., 1975; MEd in Edn. Psychology, U. N.C., 1976, PhD in Edn. Psychology, 1978-79 psychologist, N.C. Tchg. fellow Sch. Edn., U. N.C., Chapel Hill, 1978-79; tech. mgr. social sys. rsch. divsn. Applied Mgmt. Sci., Silver Spring, Md., 1979-81; sr. rschr. NTS Rsch. Corp., Durham, N.C., 1981-82; pres., CEO co-founder Durham Computer Svcs., Inc., Morrisville, N.C., 1982—; prin. investigator Small Bus. Innovative Rsch. Grant Program of NIMH, also tech. reviewer, 1985-88; chmn. Metametrics, Durham, 1985—. Contbr. ar-

ticles to profl. jours. Bd. dirs. YMCA of Durham, 1985-87, Duke Children's Classic, Child Guidance Clinic, 1988-89, N.C. Blind, Deaf Assn.; deacon Grey Stone Bapt. Ch.. Mem. Am. Ednl. Rsch. Assn., Nat. Coun. Measurement in Edn., N.C. Assn. Rsch. in Edn., Raleigh C. of C., Durham C. of C., Young Pres. Orgn., Durham Rotary. Democrat. Avocations: tennis, racquetball. Home: 4215 Cobscook Dr Durham NC 27707 Office: ComputerLand 1100 Perimeter Park West Ste 112 Morrisville NC 27560-9117

SMITH, MALCOLM BARRY ESTES, philosophy educator, lawyer; b. Houston, Oct. 24, 1939; s. Fairleigh Estes and Norna Barry (McNab) S.; m. Patricia Sweetser; children: Malcolm, Eric. BA, Va. Mil. Inst., 1961; PhD, Cornell U., 1969; JD, U. Calif., Berkeley, 1984. BarL Mass. 1985, U.S. Supreme Ct. 1992. Instr. philosophy Smith Coll., Northampton, Mass., 1967-69, asst. prof. philosophy, 1969-74, assoc. prof., 1974-79, prof., 1979—. Served to capt. USAR, 1964-66. Mem. ABA, Mass. Bar Assn., Am. Philos. Assn. Home: 9 Park St Northampton MA 01060-1236 Office: Smith Coll Dept Philosophy PO Box 839 Northampton MA 01061-0839

SMITH, MALCOLM BERNARD, investment company executive; b. Lynn, Mass., May 27, 1923; s. Philip and Ida (Zenis) S.; m. Betty Booth, June 20, 1948; children: Eric, Daniel. B.A. summa cum laude, Dartmouth Coll., 1944; M.A. in Econs., Harvard U., 1948. Sec. Gen. Am. Investors Co., N.Y.C., 1956-57, treas., 1957-59, v.p., 1958-61, pres., 1961-89, vice chmn., 1989—, also bd. dirs. Chmn. fin. com. N.Y. Found., 1973-82, treas., 1979-82, trustee, 1973-89, 91—, chmn., 1982-85; chmn. New Sch. for Social Rsch., N.Y.C., 1985—, trustee, 1982—, treas., 1982-84, chmn. ednl. policy com., 1984-85, chmn. exec. com., 1985—; trustee John Simon Guggenheim Meml. Found., 1982—, chmn. fin. com., 1985—, Human Rights Watch, 1993—; mng. trustee Permanent Fund of MLA, 1987—; mem. investment com. Fedn. Jewish Philanthropies, N.Y., 1975—, Phi Beta Kappa Found., 1987—; bd. dirs. Learning Smith Inc., 1993-94. With U.S. Army, 1943-46. Mem. Investment Co. Inst. (bd. govs. 1987—), Assn. Publicly Traded Investment Funds (bd. dirs. 1970-87, chmn. 1977-79), AAAS (chmn. investment and fin. com. 1975—), Coun. on Fgn. Rels., N.Y. Soc. Security Analysts, Phi Beta Kappa Assocs. (adv. com. 1984-93, bd. dirs 1993—), Phi Beta Kappa. Club: Harvard (bd. mgrs. 1984-86), Century Assn. (N.Y.C.). Home: PO Box 358 Pound Ridge NY 10576-0358 Office: Gen Am Investors Co Inc 450 Lexington Ave New York NY 10017

SMITH, MALCOLM NORMAN, manufacturing company executive; b. Milw., Feb. 25, 1921; s. Samuel H. and Dorothea (Werner) S.; m. Muriel J. Foreman, Feb. 14, 1943; 1 dau., Louise K. BS in Econs, U. Pa., 1942. With Ekco Products Co., Chgo., 1946-50, 56-63; v.p. Ekco Products Co., 1956-63; dir. Platers & Stampers Ltd. (Brit. div. Ekco), London, 1950-56; pres., chief exec. officer, dir. Argus, Inc., Chgo., 1963-68; pres. Malcolm N. Smith & Co., Chgo., 1968-70; adminstrv. v.p., cashier Am. Nat. Bank and Trust Co., Chgo., 1970-75; pres. Macromatic div. Macromatic Inc., 1975-88; pres. Macromatic Divsn. of Milw. Electronics Corp., Chgo., 1988-93, Newmac, Inc., 1994—; profl. lectr. U. Chgo. Grad Sch. Bus., 1968-82; bd. dirs. Acorn Internat. Fund. Bd. dirs. The Acorn Fund. 1st lt. USMCR, 1942-46. Decorated Silver Star. Mem. Friends of Franklin, Inc. (pres. 1992—), Lake Shore Country Club, Econ. Club, The Casino Club, Royal Tennis St. Club, Hampton Ct. Palace. Home: 309 Maple Ave Highland Park IL 60035-2056

SMITH, MALCOLM SOMMERVILLE, bass; b. Rockville Centre, N.Y., June 22, 1933; s. Carlton Newell and Margaret (Sommerville) S.; m. Margaret Yauger, Oct. 4, 1975. B.Music Edn., Oberlin Coll., 1957, B.Mus., 1960; M.A. in Ednl. Adminstrn, Columbia Tchrs. Coll., 1958; student, Ind. U. Sch. Music, 1960-62. Dir. choral music, Ramapo Regional High Sch., Wyckoff, N.J., 1958-60; basso, Lyric Opera, Chgo., 1961, 63; bass soloist Russian tour, Robert Shaw Choral, 1962; leading bass, N.Y.C. Opera, 1965-70, Deutsche Oper Am Rhein, Dusseldorf, Germany, 1971—; Vienna State Opera, 1973-74, 86 Met. Opera, Japan Tour, spring 1975, Met. Opera, N.Y.C., 1975-77, Paris Opera, 1978, Barcelona Opera, 1978, Sao Paulo, Brazil, 1978, Mexico City, 1979, 80, Berlin Opera, 1979, 80, Montreal Symphony, 1979, 80, 81, 82, Hamburg Opera, 1981, Köln Opera, 1980, Stuttgart Opera, 1980, Frankfurt Opera, 1980, Rome Opera, 1980, Trieste (Italy) Opera, 1981, Berlin Staatsoper, 1982, 85, Lyric Opera Phila, 1982, Los Angeles Philharm. at Hollywood Bowl, 1984, Mannheim Opera, Fed. Republic Germany, 1986, Turin Opera, Italy, 1986, 88, Bordeaux, France, 1987, Dresden Opera, German Dem. Republic, 1987, Hannover Opera, Fed. Republic Germany, 1987, Staats Oper Berlin Japan Tour, 1987, Polish TV, 1989, Oslo Opera, 1987, Paris Radio, 1988-89, Orange Festival France, 1988, Penderecki Festival, Krakow, Poland, 1988; maj. soloist Schleswig Holstein Festival, Fed. Republic Germany, 1989, Krakow Philharmonic, Poland, 1988, Maggio Musicale, Florence, Italy,1988, Boston Symphony, Minn., Cin., Houston, Utah, Seattle, Chgo., Phila., Balt. Symphony, 1993, Mexico Nat. Symphony, 1993, Nat. symphonies, also, Cin. Summer Opera, Central City (Colo.) Summer Opera, Festival of two Worlds, Spoleto, Italy., Saratoga Festival, 1985, debut, La Scala, Milan, Italy, 1982, Salzburg Festival, 1986, Athens Festival, 1987, Bordeaux (France) Opera, 1987, Ft. Worth Opera, 1988, Orange Festival, France, 1988, Staatsoper Munich, 1990, Bastille Opera, Paris, 1991, Heidelberg Summer festival, 1991, 92, Brussels Opera, 1992, 93, 94, Opera Nice, France, 1992, Opera Montpelier, France, 1992, Cin. Opera, 1994, Düsseldorf Opera, 1994, tour Japan, 1994; recorded War and Peace, 1986, Penderecki Requiem, 1990. Served with AUS, 1954-56. Congregationalist. Office: care Thea Dispeker Artists Rep 59 E 54th St New York NY 10022-4211 Hard work and a sense of humor.

SMITH, MARGARET PHYLLIS, editor, consultant; b. Plymouth, Pa., Aug. 24, 1925; d. Harold Dewitt and Mae Elmira (Bittenbender) S. AB magna cum laude, Bucknell U., 1946, AM, 1947; postgrad., U. Pa., summer 1951-54. Instr. English Bucknell U., Lewisburg, Pa., 1947-52, asst. prof., 1952-55; personnel asst. RCA Labs., Princeton, N.J., 1955-58, staff writer pub. affairs dept., 1958-76, adminstr. communications, 1976-87; editor spl. projects David Sarnoff Rsch. Ctr. (formerly RCA Labs.), Princeton, 1987-92, contbg. editor, 1992—; mng. editor Vision mag. David Sarnoff Rsch. Ctr., 1987—, editor UPDATE newsletter, 1969—. Editor: 1942-67 Twenty-five Years at RCA Laboratories, 1968. Mem. corp. communications com. United Way, Princeton, 1976-88. Mem. AAUW, N.J. Press Women (publicity dir. 1985-86), Internat. Assn. Bus. Communicators. Episcopalian. Office: David Sarnoff Rsch Ctr 201 Washington Rd Princeton NJ 08540-6449

SMITH, MARIE EDMONDS, real estate agent, property manager; b. Quapaw, Okla., Oct. 5, 1927; d. Thomas Joseph and Maud Ethel (Douglas) Edmonds; m. Robert Lee Smith, Aug. 14, 1966 (dec. 1983). Grad. vocat. nurse, Hoag Hosp., Costa Mesa, Calif., 1953; BA, So. Calif. Coll., 1955; MS, U. Alaska, 1963. Lic. vocat. nurse, Calif.; cert. sci. tchr., Alaska. Nurse Calif. Dept. Nurses, Costa Mesa, 1952-60; tchr. Alaska Dept. Edn., Aniak and Anchorage, 1955-60; tchr. sci. Garden Grove (Calif.) Sch. Dist., 1960-87; property mgr. Huntington Beach, Calif., 1970—; agent Sterling Realtors, Huntington Beach, 1988—. Author: Ocean Biology, 1969. Bd. dirs., tchr. Harbor Christian Fellowship, Costa Mesa, 1966-83; com. chmn. Garden Grove Unified Sch. Dist. PTA, 1977. NSF grantee, 1960-62. Mem. AAUW, So. Calif. Coll. Alumnae Assn. Republican. Avocations: skin diving, travel. Home: 83ll Reilly Dr Huntington Beach CA 92646 Office: L8l53 Brookhurst St Fountain Valley CA 92708

SMITH, MARION PAFFORD, avionics company executive; b. Waycross, Ga., Dec. 12, 1925; s. Rossa Elbert and Lillian Solee (Pafford) S.; m. Esther Pat Davis, Nov. 23, 1952; children: Bryan P., Danton D., Patricia Anne. Student, Okla. State U., 1944, Yale U., 1945; BS in EE, La. State U., 1949; postgrad., U. So. Fla., 1966-70. Engr. Bell Telephone Co., Baton Rouge, 1949-51; mgr. engring. Vitro Labs., Silver Spring, Md., 1952-57; design engring. mgr. deptl. design and control. flight hand contrs. Space Shuttle and Space Sta. Honeywell Avionics Div., Clearwater, Fla., 1957—; vice chmn., bd. dirs. First Union Largo, Fla.; cons. U.S. Army Mgmt. Engring. Tng. Agy., 1975-79; U.S. del. Internat. Elec. Tech. Commn., 1965-85, chmn. chief U.S. tech. adviser com. on reliability and maintainability, 1975-85, v.p., exec. com. U.S. nat. com., 1975-84; U.S. del. NATO Quality Conf., 1973; mem. White House Summit Conf. on Inflation, 1975; del. White House Conf. on Handicapped, 1977; mem. nat. adv. coun. on devel. disabilities HEW, 1974-78, Fla. Adv. Coun. on Devel. Disabilities, 1974-78, Fla. Gov.'s Commn. on Advocacy for Devel. Disabled, 1983—; mem. devel. coun. Morton Plant Hosp., Clearwater, 1971-74. 1st lt. Signal Corps, AUS,

1944-45, 51-52. Served to 1st lt. Signal Corps AUS, 1944-45, 51-52. Recipient McDonald award Fla. Rehab. Assn. 1968; Bilgore award Citizen of Year Clearwater, Fla., 1969; Outstanding Service award Am. Soc. Quality Control, 1968-69; United Comml. Travelers award Most Outstanding Service Retarded Fla., 1970; named Engr. of Year Fla. W. Coast, 1970; Service to Mankind award Sertoma Clubs, 1977. Fellow IEEE (dir., Nat. Reliability award 1979); mem. Assn. Retarded Citizens USA (pres. 1973-75, nat. govt. affairs chmn. 1975-83), Am. Assn. Mental Deficiency, Nat. Symposium Reliability Quality Control (gen. chmn.), Sigma Chi. Presbyterian elder. Club: Kiwanis (Marion P. Smith award established in his honor). Home: 1884 Oakdale Ln N Clearwater FL 34624-6441 Office: 13350 US Hwy 19 Clearwater FL 34624-7226 True turning points in life are sometimes difficult to recognize, but for those who have become parents of a handicapped child, particularly a mentally retarded child, then that turning point is easy to recognize. After the difficult period of adjustment, one becomes aware of a realization that all persons have human dignity and worth and can make a contribution to humanity and to society.

SMITH, MARJORIE AILEEN MATTHEWS, museum director; b. Richmond, Va., Aug. 19, 1918; d. Harry Anderson and Adelia Charlotte (Howland) Matthews; m. Robert Woodrow Smith, July 23, 1945 (dec. Mar. 1992). Pilot lic., Taneytown (Md.) Aviation Svc., 1944, cert. ground sch. instr., 1945. Founder, editor, pub. Spinning Wheel, Taneytown, 1945-63; v.p. Antiques Publs., Inc., Taneytown, 1960-68; pres. Prism Inc., Taneytown, 1968-78; mus. dir. Trapshooting Hall of Fame, Vandalia, Ohio, 1976—, sec., 1993—. Co-author: Handbook of Tomorrow's Antiques, 1954; contbr. articles to profl. publs. Sec. Balt. area coun. Girl Scouts USA, 1950. Named to All-Am. Trapshooting team Sports Afield mag., 1960, 61. Mem. Nat. League Am. Pen Women, Amateur Trapshooting Assn. (life), Am. Contract Bridge League, Internat. Assn. Sports Mus. and Halls of Fame (bd. dirs. 1993-94). Lutheran. Avocations: duplicate bridge, trapshooting, antiques collecting. Office: Trapshooting Hall of Fame 601 W National Rd Vandalia OH 45377

SMITH, MARK HALLARD, architect; b. Detroit, June 28, 1955; s. John Hallard and Barbara Ruth (Hinkle) S.; m. Janee Lynne Batey, July 18, 1981; children: Elizabeth Anne, Jacquelyne Ruth. BS, Ga. Inst. Tech., 1977, MArch, 1979. Registered architect, Fla.; cert. Nat. Coun. Archtl. Registration Bds. Draftsman Kirkland/Ogram Architects, Atlanta, 1979-80; project mgr. Bailey Vrooman Allegret, Atlanta, 1980-81, Rabun Hatch and Dendy, Atlanta, 1981; project architect C. Randolph Wedding & Assocs., St. Petersburg, Fla., 1981-83, Stearman Architects, St. Petersburg, 1983-90, Carl Abbott Arch. FAIA PA, Sarasota, Fla., 1990-94; prin. Smith Architects, Sarasota, 1994—; panelist Ringling Mus. Art, Sarasota, 1991. Asst. editor Centerline, 1990. Chmn. Sarasota Design Conf., 1993-94; mem. steering com. John Ringling Ctr. Found., Sarasota, 1995; pres. Men's Club, St. Michael The Archangel Ch., 1993—. Mem. AIA (archtl. juror Palm Beach chpt. 1993, pres. Fla. Gulf Coast chpt. 1994-95, Fla. award of excellence 1993, Fla. bd. dirs. 1995—, Fla. Pres. award 1994), Nat. Trust for Hist. Preservation, Tiger Bay Club. Republican. Roman Catholic. Avocation: tennis. Home: 5562 Cape Aqua Dr Sarasota FL 34242 Office: Smith Architects Sarasota FL 34242

SMITH, MARK LEE, architect; b. L.A., Nov. 16, 1957; s. Selma (Moidel) Smith. BA in History of Architecture, UCLA, 1978, MA in Architecture, 1980. Registered architect Calif., Nev., Oreg., Wash., Tenn., Colo. Designer, drafter John B. Ferguson and Assocs., L.A., 1976-83, architect, 1983; pvt. practice architecture L.A., 1984—; mem. Los Angeles County Archtl. Evaluation Bd., 1990—. Contbr. articles to profl. jours. Bd. govs. UCLA John Wooden Ctr., 1978-80. Regents scholar, U. Calif., Berkeley, UCLA, 1975-78; UCLA Grad. Sch. Architecture Rsch. fellow, 1979-80. Mem. AIA (treas. San Fernando Valley chpt. 1986, bd. dirs. 1986—, v.p. 1987, pres. 1988, Design award 1988, 89, 90, 91, chmn. Design awards 1994, bd. dirs. Calif. coun. 1989-94, v.p. 1991-94, chmn. continuing edn. 1991-93, chmn. 1992 conf.), Phi Beta Kappa. Office: 18340 Ventura Blvd Ste 225 Tarzana CA 91356-4234

SMITH, MARKWICK KERN, JR., management consultant; b. N.Y.C., Feb. 14, 1928; s. Markwick Kern and Elizabeth (Morning) S.; m. Martia Reed, Mar. 2, 1951; children—Karen, Rebecca, Mark David, Jennifer. B.S., Mass. Inst. Tech., 1951, Ph.D., 1954; M.F.A., Vt. Coll., 1988. Vice pres., then exec. v.p. Geophys. Service Inc., Dallas, 1962-67, pres., 1967-69; v.p. Tex. Instruments, Dallas, 1967-73; mgmt. cons., author Norwich, Vt., 1973—. Served with USNR, 1946-48. Mem. NAE. Congregationalist. Address: PO Box 189 Main St Norwich VT 05055

SMITH, MARSCHALL IMBODEN, lawyer; b. San Antonio, Oct. 3, 1944; s. Lowell B. and Jacqueline I. Smith; m. Elizabeth Braswell (div. 1973); m. Ann McNamara, June 3, 1976; children: Catherine, Elizabeth, Margaret, Austin, Lillian. AB, Princeton U., 1966; LLB, U. Va., 1973; MBA, U. Chgo., 1987. Bar: N.Y. 1974, Ill. 1981. Assoc. Debevoise & Plimpton, N.Y.C., 1973-75; Paul Weiss, Rifkind Wharton & Garrison, N.Y.C., 1975-81; atty. Baxter Travenol Labs., Deerfield, Ill., 1980-82; pres. Medcom Inc. subs. Baxter Internat. Inc., Deerfield, 1982-83, corp. counsel, 1983-85, asst. gen. counsel, 1985-87, assoc. gen. counsel, 1987—. Maj. USMC, 1966-73; Vietnam. Home: 2 S Maywood Rd Lake Forest IL 60045-3265 Office: Baxter Healthcare Corp 1 Baxter Pky Deerfield IL 60015-4625

SMITH, MARSHALL SAVIDGE, government official, academic dean, educator; b. East Orange, N.J., Sept. 16, 1937; s. Marshall Parsons and Ann Eileen (Zulauf) S.; m. Carol Goodspeed, June 25, 1960 (div. Aug. 1962); m. Louise Nixon Claiborn, Aug. 1964; children: Adam, Jennifer, Matthew, Megan. AB, Harvard U., 1960, EdM, 1963, EdD, 1970. Computer analyst and programmer Raytheon Corp., Andover, Mass., 1959-62; instr., assoc. prof. Harvard U., Cambridge, Mass., 1966-76; asst., assoc. dir. Nat. Inst. Edn., Washington, 1973-76; asst. commr. edn. HEW, Washington, 1976-79, chief of staff to U.S. Dept. Edn. sec., 1980; prof. U. Wis., Madison 1980-86; prof., dean Sch. Edn. Stanford (Calif.) U., 1986-93; under-sec. edn. U.S. Dept. Edn., 1993—; task force, chmn. Clinton Presl. Transition Team, 1992-93; chmn. PEW Forum on Ednl. Reform; chmn. bd. internat. com. studies in edn. NAS, 1992-93. Author: The General Inquirer, 1967, Inequality, 1972; contbr. several articles to profl. jours, chpts. to books. Pres. Madison West Hockey Assn., 1982-84. Mem. Am. Ednl. Rsch. Assn. (chmn. orgn. instl. affiliates 1985-86), Cleve. Conf., Nat. Acad. Edn. Cosmos Club. Democrat. Avocation: environmental issues, coaching youth soccer. Home: 900 N Stafford St Apt 1817 Arlington VA 22203-1848 Office: US Dept Edn Under Sec Edn 600 Independance Ave SW Washington DC 20202-0001 also: Stanford U Stanford CA 94305

SMITH, MARTIN BERNHARD, journalist; b. San Francisco, Apr. 20, 1930; s. John Edgar and Anna Sophie (Thorsen) S.; m. Joan Lovat Muller, Apr. 25, 1953; children: Catherine Joan, Karen Anne. AB, U. Calif., Berkeley, 1952, M Journalism, 1968. Reporter, city editor Modesto (Calif.) Bee, 1952-57; reporter, mng. editor Sacramento Bee, 1964-75; polit. editor, columnist McClatchy Newspapers, Sacramento, 1975-92; ret., 1992. Episcopalian.

SMITH, MARTIN CRUZ, author; b. Reading, Pa., Nov. 3, 1942; s. John and Louisa (Lopez) S.; m. Emily Stanton Arnold, June 15, 1968; children: Ellen, Luisa, Samuel. BA, U. Pa., 1964. Author: Gorky Park, 1981, Stallion Gate, 1986, Polar Star, 1989, Red Square, 1992.

SMITH, MARTIN HENRY, pediatrician; b. Gainesville, Ga., Nov. 3, 1921; s. Charles E. and Mamie Mae (Emmett) S.; m. Mary Gillis, Feb. 25, 1950; children: Susan, Margaret, Mary. MD, Emory U., 1945. Diplomate Am. Bd. Pediatrics. Intern City Hosp. System, Winston-Salem, N.C., 1945-46; fellow in infectious diseases Grady Meml. Hosp., Atlanta, 1948-49; resident Henrietta Egleston Hosp., Atlanta, 1949-50, Children's Hosp., Washington, 1950-51; practice medicine, specializing in pediatrics Gainesville, Ga.; ret., 1988; clin. asst. prof. Emory U. Hosp., Atlanta; chief of staff Hall County Hosp., Gainesville, 1965-66; mem. Nat. Vaccine Adv. Commn., 1990—, chmn., 1991. Contbr. articles to profl. jours. Chmn. Nat. Vaccine Adv. Com., 1991—. Capt. M.C. U.S. Army, 1946-48. Fellow Am. Acad. Pediatrics (chpt. chmn. 1966-69, dist. chmn. 1977-83, pres.-elect 1984-85, pres. 1985-86); mem. Hall County Med. Soc. (pres. 1960), Ga. Pediatric Soc. (pres.

1965-66), Med. Assn. Ga., AMA, Alpha Omega Alpha. Episcopalian. Clubs: Chattahoochee Country (Gainesville); Piedmont Driving (Atlanta).

SMITH, MARY ALICE See ALICE, MARY

SMITH, MARY ANNE, lawyer; b. Chgo., Sept. 10, 1944. BA in Math., Mundelein Coll., 1966; MS in Math., Ill. Inst. Tech., 1973, JD with honors, 1977. Bar: Ill. 1977. Math. tchr. various high sch. and community coll. levels, 1967-78; staff counsel Ill. Inst. Tech., Chgo., 1977-81, univ. counsel, 1981—. Contbr. articles to profl. jours. Vol. atty., bd. dirs. Chgo. Vol. Legal Svcs. Mem. ABA (labor and employment law sect.), Chgo. Bar Assn. (labor and employment law com.), Nat. Assn. Coll. and Univ. Attys. (bd. dirs.). Home: 5435 S East View Park Chicago IL 60615-5915 Office: Ill Inst Tech 10 W 33rd St Rm 224 Chicago IL 60616-3793

SMITH, MARY LOU, librarian; b. Huntington, Ind., Mar. 8, 1927; d. Harry Martin and Birtha (Fox) Bowers; m. Donald Eugene Smith, Oct. 2, 1948; children: Larry Wayne, Samuel Lee, Lynn Ellen Smith Worch, Michael Ray. BS in Edn., Huntington Coll., 1971; MS in Edn., Ball State U., 1973, MLS, 1973. Cert. tchr.; cert. libr.; cert. audio visual. Profl. musician Ft. Wayne (Ind.) Civic Symphony, 1942-45, Philharmonic Orch., Ft. Wayne, 1945-57, Civic Symphony, Chgo., 1947-49; owner M.L. Smith Reed Co., Huntington, Ind., 1950-65; libr., audio-visual specialist Huntington Sch. Systems, 1971-75; libr. Huntington Coll., 1975-77, Warsaw (Ind.) High Sch., 1978-85, Pub. Libr., Port Isabel, Tex., 1994—; area coord. Am. Inst. Fgn. Study, Huntington, 1978-85. Head ladies dept. YMCA, Huntington, 1966-70; bd. dirs., sec.-treas. Outdoor Resorts, Port Isabel, 1986-92; swimming instr. ARC, 1966-69; mem. Rosary Sodality, Huntington. Mem. AAUW, Ind. Sch. Libr. Assn. (sec. 1973-75), Ind. Sch. Libr. Assn., Ind. Ret. Tchrs. Assn., Altrusa Internat. (editor Warsaw chpt. 1983-86), Sigma Phi Gamma. Roman Catholic. Avocations: golf, bowling, bridge. Home: 950 S Garcia St Unit 53 Port Isabel TX 78578-4010 Home phone: 901 Evergreen Ave Huntington IN 46750 Office: Port Isabel Libr 213 N Yturria St Port Isabel TX 78578-4602

SMITH, MARY LOUISE, politics and public affairs consultant; b. Eddyville, Iowa, Oct. 6, 1914; d. Frank and Louise Anna (Jager) Epperson; BA, U. Iowa, 1935; LHD (hon.), Drake U., 1980; LLD (hon.), Grinnell Coll., 1984; m. Elmer Milton Smith, Oct. 7, 1934; children: Robert C., Margaret L., James E. Mem. Eagle Grove (Iowa) Bd. Edn., 1955-60; Republican precinct committeewoman, Eagle Grove, 1960-62, vice-chairwoman, Wright County, Iowa, 1962-63; mem. Rep. Nat. Com., 1964-84, mem. exec. com., 1969-84, mem. conv. reforms com., 1966, vice-chairwoman Steiger com. on conv. reform, 1973, co-chmn. nat. com., 1974, chmn. Com., 1974-77; vice-chairwoman U.S. Common. on Civil Rights, 1982-83; vice-chairwoman Midwest region Rep. Conf., 1969-71; del. Rep. Nat. Conv., 1968, 72, 76, 80, 84, alt. del., 1964, hon officer, 1988, 92, organized and called to order, 1976; vice-chairwoman Iowa Presdl. campaign, 1964; nat. co-chmn. Physicians Com. for Presdl. Campaign, 1972; co-chairwoman Iowa Com. to Reelect the Pres., 1972; mem. Nat. Commn. on Observance Internat. Women's Year, 1975-77, del. Internat. Women's Yr. Conf., Houston, 1977; vis. fellow Woodrow Wilson Fellowship Found., 1979. Mem. U.S. del. to Extraordinary Session of UNESCO Gen. Conf., Paris, 1973; mem. U.S. del. 15th session population commn. UN Econ. and Social Council, Geneva, 1969; mem. Pres.'s Commn. for Observance of 25th Anniversary of UN, 1970-71; mem. Iowa Commn. for Blind, 1961-63, chairwoman, 1963; mem. Iowa Gov.'s Commn. on Aging, 1962; trustee Robert A. Taft Inst. Govt., 1974-84, Herbert Hoover Presdl. Libr. Assn., Inc., 1979-91. Pres. Eagle Grove Cmty. Chest; bd. dirs. Mental Health Center North Iowa, 1962-63, YWCA of Greater Des Moines, 1983-87, Orchard Place Resdl. Facility for Emotionally Disturbed Children, 1983-88, Learning Channel, cable TV, 1984-87, Iowa Peace Inst., 1985-90, Planned Parenthood of Greater Iowa, 1986-92, U. Iowa Found., 1987—; trustee Drake U., 1990—; bd. dirs. U.S. Inst. Peace, 1990—, Chrysalis Womens Found., 1994—; bd. dirs., nat. co-chair Rep. Mainstream Com.; bd. dirs. Alliance for Arts and Understanding, 1993—; mem. adv. coun. U. Iowa Hawkeye Fund Women's Program, 1982-87, co-founder Iowa Women's Archives, 1991; chairperson UN Day for Iowa, 1987; polit. communication ctr. conf. U. Okla., 1987; disting. vis. exec. Coll. Bus. Asminstrn. U. Iowa, 1988; co-chmn. select com. on drug abuse City of Des Moines, 1989-90; mem. Des Moines Human Rights Commn., 1995—. Named hon. col., mil. staff Gov. Iowa, 1973; Iowa Women's Hall of Fame, 1977; recipient Disting. Alumni award U. Iowa, 1984, Hancher Medallion award, 1991; Cristine Wilson medal for equality and justice Iowa Commn. on Status of Women, 1984, Elinor Robson award Coun. for Internat. Understanding, 1992, Pres. award Midwest Archives Conf., 1994; Mary Louise Smith award named in her honor YWCA, 1988. Mem. Women's Aux. AMA, UN Assn., Nat. Conf. Christians and Jews, Nat. Women's Polit. Caucus (adv. bd. 1978—), PEO, Kappa Alpha Theta. Address: 654 59th St Des Moines IA 50312 *The concept of "giving back" to the community in return for the benefits you have received establishes a sound basis for public service. I also believe that a woman who has achieved any degree of success in any field has an obligation to help other women in their efforts to succeed.*

SMITH, MAURICE EDWARD, lawyer, business consultant; b. Denver, Mar. 30, 1919; s. Edward Daniel and Junie Ardella (Fox) S.; m. Gloria Tanner, June 17, 1944; children: Christine, Kathryn, Carol (dec.), Daniel. Student, Brigham Young U., 1938-40; B.S. in Commerce, U. Denver, 1942; LL.B., Stanford U., 1948. Mem. staff Ralph B. Mayo & Co., Denver, 1949-50; v.p. bar, gen. counsel Husky Oil Co., Cody, Wyo., 1950-61; exec. v.p. Cen. Nat. Ins. Group, Omaha, 1961-65; treas., legal counsel Sunnen Products Co., St. Louis, 1965-69; v.p., treas. Global Marine, Inc., Los Angeles, 1969-78; pvt. bus. cons., 1978—. Mem. Cody City Council, 1955-57. Served with USNR, 1942-45. Mem. Calif. Bar Assn. Mem. Ch. Jesus Christ of Latter-day Saints. Home: 2755 N 175 E Provo UT 84604-5938

SMITH, MERLIN GALE, engineering executive, researcher; b. Germantown, Ky., May 12, 1928; s. Allen Edward and Gladys Myrtle (Kaiser) S.; m. Elinore Klein, Dec. 23, 1955; children: Laurence Robin, Derek Randall, April Rena. B.E.E., U. Cin., 1950; M.E.E., Columbia U., 1957. With IBM, N.Y.C. and Yorktown Heights, N.Y., 1952-92; engring. mgr. large scale integration IBM, Yorktown Heights, 1964-70; research staff mem. IBM, 1970-92; pvt. practice cons., 1992—; bd. govs. Computer Soc., 1970-80, 87-88, sec., 1972-73, v.p., 1975-76, 87-88, pres. 1977-78; bd. dirs. Nat. Computer Conf., 1973-77, chmn., 1975, cond. chmn., 1978. Contbr. articles to profl. jours. Served with Signal Corps AUS, 1951-52. Fellow IEEE (mem. tech. activities bd. 1977-78, 83-84, bd. dirs. 1983-86, exec. v.p. 1985, v.p. tech. activities 1986); mem. Am. Fedn. Info. Processing Socs. (dir. 1977-79, exec. com. 1978-79). Patentee in field. Home and Office: Farnham Point Rd PO Box 215 East Boothbay ME 04544-0215

SMITH, MERRITT ROE, history educator; b. Waverly, N.Y., Nov. 14, 1940; s. Wilson Niles and Mary Eleanor (Fitzgerald) S.; m. Bronwyn M. Mellquist, Aug. 24, 1974. A.B., Georgetown U., 1963; M.A., Pa. State U., 1965, Ph.D., 1971. Asst. prof. history Ohio State U., Columbus, 1970-74, assoc. prof., 1974-78; vis. prof. history and sociology of sci. U. Pa., Phila., 1976; Leverett and William Cutten prof. history of tech., program in sci., tech. and soc. M.I.T., Cambridge, 1978—; Metcalfe prof. engring. and the liberal arts, 1992-9, dir. progam in sci., tech. and soc., 1992—. Author: Harpers Ferry Armory and the New Technology, 1977, Military Enterprise and Technological Change, 1985, Science, Technology and the Military, 2 vols., 1988, Does Technology Drive History?, 1994; mem. editorial bd. Tech. and Culture, 1973-91, Bus. History Rev., 1978-85, MIT Press, 1986-91. Mem. Mass. Hist. Soc.; trustee Hagley Mus. and Libr., Mus. Am. Textile History, Charles Babbage Inst.; bd. advisors MIT Mus. Recipient Cert. of Commendation Am. Assn. State and Local History, 1978; Disting. Teaching award Ohio State U., 1978; grantee Ohio State U., 1972, Am. Philos. Soc., 1974, Harvard Bus. Sch., 1974-75, Eleutherian Mills-Hagley Found., 1978-79; Guggenheim fellow, 1983-84; Regents fellow Smithsonian Instn., 1984-85. Mem. AAAS, Am. Acad. Arts and Scis., Soc. History Tech. (mem. exec. council, Dexter Prize com., Da Vinci medal com., mus. com., v.p., pres. 1989-91), Orgn. Am. Historians (Frederick Jackson Turner award 1977), Bus. History Conf., Am. Antiquarian Soc., Newcomen Soc. N. Am., Soc. Indsl. Archeology, History Sci. Soc. (Pfizer award 1978), Phi Kappa Phi, Phi Alpha Theta. Home: 17 Longfellow Rd Newton MA 02162-1505 Office: MIT Rm E51-110 Cambridge MA 02139

SMITH, MICHAEL, biochemistry educator; b. Blackpool, Eng., Apr. 26, 1932. BSc, U. Manchester, Eng., 1953, PhD, 1956. Fellow B.C. Rsch. Coun., 1956-60; rsch. assoc. inst. Enzyme Rsch., U. Wis., 1960-61; head chem. sect. Vancouver Lab. Fisheries Rsch. Bd. Can., 1961-66; med. rsch. assoc. Med. Rsch. Coun. Can., 1966-71, career investigator, 1971—; assoc. prof. biochem. U. B.C., Vancouver, 1966-70, prof., 1970—, u. prof., 1993—, Univ. prof., 1993—; Peter Wall disting. prof. biotech., 1994—. Named to Order of B.C., 1994, Champion of Order of Can., 1995; recipient Gairdner Found. Internat. award, 1986, Nobel Prize in Chemistry, Nobel Found., 1993. Fellow Chem. Inst. Can., Royal Soc. (London), Royal Soc. Can. Royal Soc. Chemistry; mem. Sigma Xi. Achievements include rsch. in nucleic acid and nucleotide chemistry and biochemistry using in-vitro mutagenesis gene expression. Home: 303-2466 W 3d Ave, Vancouver, BC Canada V6K 1L8 Office: U BC Biotech Lab, 6174 University Blvd, Vancouver, BC Canada V6T 1Z3

SMITH, MICHAEL A., aerospace engineer, engineering executive; b. 1943; m. Mary, three sons, one daughter. BSc, MSc aerospace engineering, U. Notre Dame, MSc aerospace engineering. V.p., gen. manager G.E. Aircraft Electronics Div., G.E. Astro-Space Division, East Windsor, N.J., 1991—. Office: Astro-Space PO Box 800 Princeton NJ 08543-0800

SMITH, MICHAEL ALEXIS, petroleum geologist; b. Boston, Nov. 8, 1944; s. Albert Charles and Nina (Gronstrand) S.; m. Nancy Laura Wilson, Dec. 19, 1971; 1 child, Christine Lara. B.S., U. Mich., 1966; M.S., U. Kans., 1969; Ph.D., U. Tex., 1975. Marine geologist U.S. Geol. Survey, Washington, 1966-68, petroleum geologist, 1975-81, geochemist, 1976-81; rsch. geochemist Getty Oil Co., Houston, 1981-83, supr. basin evaluation and structural geology, 1983-84; rsch. assoc. Texaco Inc., Houston, 1984-92; chief geologist Geo-Strat, Inc., Houston, 1992—; adj. prof. geology Emory U., Atlanta, 1988-89; geophysicist Minerals Mgmt. Svc., New Orleans, 1994—. Contbr. articles to profl. jours. and books. Fellow Geol. Soc. Am.; mem. Am. Assn. Petroleum Geologists, Am. Geophys. Union, Houston Geol. Soc., Am. Assn. of Stratigraphic Palynologists, Rocky Mountain Assn. Geologists, Soc. Organic Petrology (founding mem.). Avocations: music; running. Research interest: geol. and depositional facies controls on petroleum occurrence; regional source-rock geochemistry and organic petrology; biostratigraphy, paleogeography, and paleoecology. Home: 1123 Shillington Dr Katy TX 77450-4204 Office: Geo-Strat Inc 1718 Triway Ln Houston TX 77043-3346

SMITH, MICHAEL E., legal educator, lawyer; b. 1935. B.A., Haverford Coll., 1956; M.A., Harvard U., 1963; J.D., U. Mich., 1964. Bar: Calif. 1968. Law clk. to judge U.S. Ct. Appeals (2d cir.), 1964-65; law clk. to Chief Justice Earl Warren, U.S. Supreme Ct. 1965-66; acting prof. U. Calif.-Berkeley, 1967-72, prof., 1972—; chief staff counsel U.S. Ct. Appeals (D.C. cir.), 1976-77. Mem. Order of Coif. Office: U Calif Law Sch 225 Boalt Hall Berkeley CA 94720

SMITH, MICHAEL HOWARD, ecologist; b. San Pedro, Calif., Aug. 30, 1938; s. William Smith and Frances Harriet (Ryder) Roe; m. Irma Beatrice Summers, Apr. 9, 1958; children: Michael William, Karen Marie. BA, San Diego State U., 1960, MA, 1962; PhD, U. Fla., 1966. Asst. prof. U. Ga., Athens, 1966-71, assoc. prof., 1971-77, prof. ecology, 1977—; dir. Savannah River Ecology Lab., Aiken, S.C., 1973—; vis. assoc. prof. U. Tex., Austin, 1970-71; hon. lectr. U. London, 1977-78; rsch. assoc. U. Calif.-Berkeley, 1987; rev. panel NSF, 1974-77; adv. group Clemson (S.C.) U., 1983—. Editor: Mineral Cycling in Southeastern Ecosystems, 1975, Mammalian Population Genetics, 1981; contbr. chpt. to Population Genetics of the White-Tailed Deer, 1984, Genetic Variability and Antler Development, 1990, Population Genetics of the Sika Deer, 1990. Mem. Am. Soc. Mammalogists (life, bd. dirs. 1978-81, 86-89, Merriam award 1985), Evolution Soc., Ecol. Soc. Am., Sigma Xi (life). Home: 1129 Parsons Ln Aiken SC 29803-5323 Office: Savannah River Ecology Lab Drawer E Aiken SC 29801

SMITH, MICHAEL JAMES, industrial engineering educator; b. Madison, Wis., May 12, 1945; s. James William and Ruth Gladys (Murphy) S.; m. Patricia Ann Bentley, June 22, 1968; children: Megan Colleen, Melissa Maureen. BA, U. Wis., 1968, MA, 1970, PhD, 1973. Rsch. analyst Wis. Dept. Industry Labor, Madison, 1971-74; rsch. psychologist Nat. Inst. for Occupational Safety and Health, USPHS, Cin., 1974-84; prof. U. Wis., Madison, 1984—; owner, prin. M.J. Smith Assocs. Inc., Madison, 1991—. Contbr. articles to profl. jours. Mem. APA, Inst. Indsl. Engrs. (sr.), Human Factors Soc., Assn. Computer Machinery, Am. Soc. Testing and Measurement. Avocation: tennis. Home: 6719 Shamrock Glen Cir Middleton WI 53562 Office: U Wis Dept Indsl Engring Human Factors Rsch Lab 1513 University Ave Madison WI 53706-1572

SMITH, MICHAEL JOSEPH, composer, pianist, lecturer; b. Tiline, Ky., Aug. 13, 1938; s. Marvin Gilford and Bobbie Bell (Vinson) S.; m. Kerstin Alli-Maria Andersson, May 1973; children: Tanja Michaelsdotter, Kassandra Michaelsdotter. Student, New Eng. Conservatory Music, Juilliard Sch. Pres., bd. dirs World Music (U.S.A.), Inc., Atlanta, 1993—; composer-in-residence, Ga., 1980, 88-90; lectr., performer Agnes Scott Coll., Atlanta, Bowdoin Coll. Maine, Ctrl. Conservatory Music, Beijing and Xian, China; rschr. IBM Corp. Scandinavia and Roland Synthesizer Corp., from 1986;. Performed 1st European concert tour, 1970; on concert tours of jazz ensembles in Western Europe and U.S., from 1972; composer 10 major ballet works, scores for major films and TV projects, 500 works for various ensembles; commns. include Moscow Philharm., Tbilisi Chamber Orch., various European ensebles, ballet cos.; performances include Bolshoi Theatre, Moscow, Leningrad U., Royal Swedish Opera, Stockholm, Lincoln Ctr., N.Y.C., Carnegie Hall, N.Y.C., Philharm. Hall, Berlin; numerous recs., from 1970. With USN, 1955-59. Mem. Swedish Composers Soc., Internat. Soc. Contemporary Music. Home and Office: PO Box 81107 Conyers GA 30208

SMITH, MICHAEL L., transportation executive. BA, De Pauw U., 1970. Chmn. bd., CEO Mayflower Contract Svcs., Shawnee Mission, Kas., 1991—. Office: Mayflower Contract Svcs 5360 College Blvd Shawnee Mission KS 66211*

SMITH, MICHAEL L., transportation company executive; b. 1948. BA, DePauw U., 1970. V.p. Coll. Mktg. & Rsch. Corp., 1968-70; with Arthur Andersen & Co., 1970-75; div. contr. Mayflower Group, Carmel, Ind., 1975-77, group v.p., warehouse div., 1977, then exec. v.p., now pres., chief oper. officer, 1989—; also bd. dirs.; with Mayflower Transit Co. subs. Mayflower Group, Carmel, 1975—, then sr. v.p., chmn., CEO, 1989—; also bd. dirs. Office: Mayflower Group Inc 9998 N Michigan Rd Carmel IN 46032-9640

SMITH, MICHAEL PETER, social science educator, researcher; b. Dunkirk, N.Y., Aug. 2, 1942; s. Peter Joseph and Rosalie Barbara (Lipka) S.; m. Patricia Anne Lendway, Aug. 21, 1965. BA magna cum laude, St. Michael's Coll., 1964; MA in Polit. Sci., U. Mass., 1966, PhD in Polit. Sci. 1971. Instr., asst. prof. dept. govt. Dartmouth Coll., Hanover, N.H., 1968-71; asst. prof. polit. sci. Boston U., 1971-74; assoc. prof., prof. dept. polit. sci. Tulane U., New Orleans, 1974-86; prof. community studies U. Calif., Davis, 1986—, chmn. dept. applied behavioral scis., 1986-91; vis. prof. pub. policy U. Calif., Berkeley, 1981, city planning U. N.C., Chapel Hill, 1982, city planning U. Calif., Berkeley, 1985; vis. scholar in govt. U. Essex, Eng., 1979; vis. scholar polit. and social sci. U. Cambridge, Eng. 1982; vis. scholar Inst. Urban and Regional Devel., U. Calif., Berkeley, 1990. Author: The City & Social Theory, 1979, City, State and Market, 1988; co-author: Restructuring the City, 1983, California's Changing Faces, 1993; editor: Cities in Transformation, 1984, Breaking Chains, 1991, After Modernism, 1992, Comparative Urban & Community Research, 1986—; co-editor: The Capitalist City, 1987—, The Bubbling Cauldron, 1995; mem. editorial bd. U. Press Am., 1978—. Mem. Internat. Polit. Sci. Assn., Am. Polit. Sci. Assn., Internat. Sociol. Assn. Research Coms. on Urban & Regional Devel. and Comparative Community Research. Office: U Calif Dept Of Applied Sci Davis CA 95616

SMITH, MICHAEL TOWNSEND, author, editor, stage director; b. Kansas City, Mo., Oct. 5, 1935; s. Lewis Motter and Dorothy (Pew) S.; children: Julian Bach, Alfred St. John. Student, Yale U., 1953-55. Theatre critic Village Voice, N.Y.C., 1959-68, 1971-74, assoc. editor, 1962-65; curator, judge Obie awards for theatre, 1962-68, 1971-74; playwright mem.

SMITH, MICHELE, lawyer; b. Ogden, Utah, Feb. 12, 1955; d. Max S. and Grace B. (Gerstman) Smith; m. Philip A. Turner, Aug. 25, 1985. BA, SUNY, Buffalo, 1976; JD, U. Chgo., 1979. Law clk. U.S. Ct. Appeals (7th cir.), Chgo., 1979-81; asst. atty. no. dist. U.S. Atty's Office, Chgo., 1981-89; sr. counsel Navistar Internat. Transportation Corp., Chgo., 1989—. Mem. Am. Corp. Counsel Assn., Phi Beta Kappa. Office: Navistar Internat Transp Corp 455 CityFront Plz Dr Chicago IL 60611

SMITH, MILTON RAY, computer company executive, lawyer; b. Idaho, 1935. AA, Long Beach (Calif.) City Coll., 1958; BS, Portland State U., 1962; MS, Oreg. State U., 1969; JD, Lewis & Clark Coll., 1970. Bar: Oreg. 1970, U.S. Dist. Ct. Oreg. 1970, U.S. Ct. Appeals (9th cir.) 1971, U.S. Supreme Ct. 1973. Tech. writer Northrop Corp., Hawthorne, Calif., 1957-58; engring. writer Tektronix Inc., Beaverton, Oreg., 1958-60, design engr., 1960-63, project engr., 1963-65, program mgr., 1966-70; asst. engring. mgr. Eldorado Electronics, Concord, Calif., 1965-66; ptnr. Acker, Underwood & Smith, Portland, Oreg., 1970-86; chmn., chief exec. officer Floating Point Systems Inc., Beaverton, 1986-88, pres., chief exec. officer, 1991-92, also vice chmn. bd. dirs.; chief exec. officer Thrustmaster Inc., Tigard, Oreg., 1992-94; pres., CEO Zeelan Tech., Inc., Beaverton, Oreg., 1994—; CEO Test Sys. Strategies, Inc., Beaverton, Oreg., 1992-93; bd. dirs. ThrustMaster, Inc., Beaverton, Analogy, Inc., Beaverton, Zeelan Tech., Inc., Beaverton. Bd. dirs. Oreg. Bus. Council, Portland, 1986-88; mem. bd. visitors Northwestern Sch. Law, Portland, 1986—. With USN, 1953-56. Mem. Am. Electronics Assn. (exec. com. Oreg. chpt. 1987-93, vice chmn. 1994—), Oreg. State Bar, Founders Club of Portland. Republican. Office: Thrustmaster Inc 10150 SW Nimbus Ave Portland OR 97223-4306

SMITH, MONCRIEFF HYNSON, psychology educator; b. St. Louis, Sept. 21, 1917; s. Moncrieff Hynson and Nell Drane (Galbraith) S.; m. Malvene Parker Grimshaw, Sept. 12, 1941 (div. Oct. 1959); children: Mason, Virginia, Parker; m. Mary Mildred Devine, June 12, 1960; children: MacKenzie, Laurie. AB, U. Mo., 1940, MA, 1941; postgrad., U. Iowa, 1941-42; PhD, Stanford U., 1947. Instr. Harvard U., Cambridge, Mass., 1947-49; from asst. prof. to prof. U. Wash., Seattle, 1949-88, prof. emeritus, 1988—, chair jt. PhD program in physiology and psychology, 1960-85; cons. USAF, Sacramento, 1949, San Antonio, 1950, Rsch. Lab. Electronics, MIT, Cambridge, 1951-53. Capt. U.S. Army, 1942-46. Fellow Am. Psychol. Assn. Avocations: photography, bridge. Home: 6003 50th Ave NE Seattle WA 98115-7703 Office: Univ Wash Dept Psychology Dept Psychology NI-25 Seattle WA 98195

SMITH, MORTON EDWARD, ophthalmology educator, dean; b. Balt., Oct. 17, 1934. BS, U. Md., 1956, MD, 1960. Bd. cert. Ophthalmology Bd.; lic. physician Mo., Md. Rotating intern Denver Gen. Hosp., 1960-61; resident, nat. inst. of neurol. diseases and blindness fellow in opthalmology Washington U. Sch. Medicine-Barnes Hosp., 1961-63; NIH spl. fellow in ophthalmic pathology Armed Forces Inst. of Pathology, Washington, 1964; chief resident, instr. ophthalmology Washington U. Sch. Medicine, St. Louis, 1965-66, instr. ophthalmology, 1966-67, asst. prof. ophthalmology and pathology, 1967-69, assoc. prof. ophthalmology and pathology, 1969-75, prof. ophthalmology and pathology, 1975—, asst. dean, 1978-91; assoc. dean Washington U. Sch. Medicine, 1991—; vis. scholar Eye Inst., Columbia Presbyn. Med. Ctr., N.Y.C., 1966; prof./lectr. Montefiore Hosp., Pitts., 1969, U. Ark., 1970, 77, 80, 82, 84, 86, 88, U. Fla., 1972, 81, U. Tex. and Lackland AFB, San Antonio, 1973, U. Colo., 1974, 82, U. Mo., 1974, 79, 80, 88, So. Ill. U., Springfield, 1974, U. Md., 1975, Montreal (Can.) Gen. Hosp., 1975, U. Wis., 1976, 87, 93, U. Pitts., 1977, 83, 87, U. Iowa, 1977, 87, Cleve. Clinic, 1978, Colo. Ophthalmol. Soc., 1978, Brooke Army Hosp., San Antonio, 1979, Wills Eye Hosp., Phila., 1980, USPHS Hosp., San Francisco, 1981, U. Calif., Davis, 1981, Sinai Hosp., Balt., 1985, 89, 94, U. Calif., San Diego, 1985, Tufts U., Boston, 1985, Cornell U., Ithaca, N.Y., 1988, U. Wash., Seattle, 1990, Brown U., Providence, 1990, Vanderbilt U., Nashville, 1991, Duke U., Durham, N.C., 1992; Chandler lectr. Harvard U., 1988; The Lois A. Young-Thomas Meml. lectr. U. Md., 1991; Braley lectr. U. Iowa, 1993; Havener Meml. lectr. Ohio State, 1994. Editor pathology sect.: Perspectives in Ophthalmology, 1977; mem. editl. bd. Ophthalmic Plastic & Reconstructive Surgery, 1986-90; contbr. articles to profl. jours. With USAR M.C., 1958-66. Scholar U. Md., 1958, 59. Fellow Am. Acad. Ophthalmology (ophthalmic pathology com. 1977-83, chmn. ophthalmic com. 1979-83, Honor award for svc. 1981, Sr. Honor award 1992); mem. AMA, Am. Bd. Ophthalmology (diplomate, bd. dirs. 1992—), Assn. for Rsch. in Vision and Ophthalmology (chmn. sect. pathology ann. meeting 1971), Am. Assn. Ophthalmic Pathologists (pres. 1977-80), Assn. Am. Med. Colls. (group med. edn. 1985—), Mo. Med. Assn., Mo. Ophthalmol. Soc., Verhoeff Soc., Theobald Soc., St. Louis Med. Soc., St. Louis Ophthalmol. Soc., Soc. Med. Coll. Dirs. for Continuing Med. Edn., Alpha Omega Alpha (sec.-treas. Wash. U. chpt. 1993—). Office: Washington U Sch Medicine Campus Box 8096 660 S Euclid Ave Saint Louis MO 63110-1093

SMITH, MORTON HOWISON, religious organization administrator, educator; b. Roanoke, Va., Dec. 11, 1923; s. James Brookes and Margaret Morton (Howison) S.; m. Lois Virginia Knopf, July 7, 1925; children: Samuel Warfield, Susanne Rochet Margaret. BA, U. Mich., 1947; BD, Columbia Theol. Sem., 1953; ThM, ThD, Free U., Amsterdam, The Netherlands, 1962. Ordained to ministry Presbyn. Ch., 1954. Pastor Springfield-Roller Presbyn. Chs., Carroll County, Md., 1954; prof. bible Belhaven Coll., Jackson, Miss., 1954-63; guest lectr. Westminster Theol. Sem., Phila., 1963-64; prof. Reformed Theol. Sem., Jackson, 1964-73; stated clk. gen. assembly Presbyn. Ch. in Am., Decatur, Ga., 1973-88; prof. systematic theology, dean faculty Greenville Presbyn. Theol. Sem., 1987—; advisor to bd. dirs. Greenville (S.C.) Presbyn. Theol. Sem., 1986—; mem. bd. dirs. Presbyn. Jour., Asheville, N.C., 1965-87; lectr. on theology Republic of So. Africa , June-July, 1988, Riga, Latvia, 1992, Budapest, Hungary, 1994, Prague, Czech Republic, 1994, 95, Trinidad and Tobago, 1995, on mission, Republic of Korea, June-July, 1989. Author: Studies in Southern Presbyterian Theology, 1962, 2d edit. 1987, How Is the Gold Become Dim, 1973, (pamphlet) Reformed Evangelism, 1970, Testimony, 1986, Commentary on the Book of Church Order, 1990, Harmony of the Westminster Confession and Catechisms, 1990, Systematic Theology, 1994; contbr. articles to Reformed Theology in Am., 1985. Trustee Covenant Coll., Lookout Mountain, Tenn., 1982-90. 1st lt. USAAF, 1942-45. Fulbright fellow Free U., 1958. Mem. N.Am. Presbyn. and Reformed Coun. of Chs. (sec. 1977-92). Avocations: flying, traveling, genealogy. Office: Greenville Presbyn Theol Sem PO Box 9279 Greenville SC 29604-9279

SMITH, MURRAY LIVINGSTONE, advertising executive; b. London, Nov. 21, 1937; came to U.S., 1967; s. Thomas Phillip Livingstone and Agnes Breckenridge (Murray) S.; m. Francoise Henriette Frapport, Jan. 12, 1960 (div. 1968); 1 child, Alexander Livingstone, Gertrude-Mercer Livingstone. BSC with honors in Econs., U. London, 1959, MSC in Econs., 1961. Account exec. Colman, Prentis & Varley, London, 1961-62; mgr. Colman, Prentis & Varley, Athens, Greece, 1962-66; dept. M.D. Colman, Prentis & Varley, Paris, 1966-67; v.p. account supr. Kenyon & Eckhardt, N.Y.C., 1967-72; sr. v.p. Latin Am. Kenyon & Eckhardt, N.Y.C., Sao Paulo, Brazil, 1972-78; exec. v.p. internat. Kenyon & Eckhardt, N.Y.C., 1978-86; pres. internat. Bozell, Jacobs, Kenyon & Eckhardt, N.Y.C., 1986—. Mem. Internat. Advt. Assn. (product service com.), Assn. Am. Advt. Agys. (internat com. mem., 1979-82, 86—). Clubs: Aston Martin Owners, Vintage Sports Car, Bugatti Owners, Ferrari Owners. Avocations: motor sports, archaeology, ornithology, literature. Home: SC 1225 Park Ave New York NY 10128 Office: Bozell Jacobs Kenyon & Eckhardt 40 W 23rd St New York NY 10010-5200

SMITH, MURRAY THOMAS, transportation company executive; b. Hudson, Oct. 8, 1939; s. Rex D. and Frances M. Smith; m. Diane R. Cramer, Dec. 4, 1959 (div. June 1994); children: Lisa B., Thomas M., Amy R.; m. Donna Thomas Kjonaas, Jan. 1995. V.p. Overland Express Inc., Indpls., 1978-82; v.p. ops. R.T.C. Transp. Inc., Forest Pk., Ga., 1982-83; with Midwest Coast Transport L.P., Sioux Falls, S.D., 1983—; sr. v.p., 1983-84; pres. Midwest Coast Transport L.P., Sioux Falls, S.D., 1984-89, prin., pres., chief exec. officer, 1989—, also bd. dirs.; bd. dirs. Interstate Carrier Conf., Nat. Penslake Logistics Assn. 1991—, United Way, Sioux Falls, 1991—. Office: Midwest Coast Transport LP 1600 Benson Rd Sioux Falls SD 57104-0822

SMITH, MYRON GEORGE, former government official, consultant; b. Terrebonne, Minn., June 9, 1920; s. Adrian G. and Marie E. (Crompe) S.; m. Louise J. Hennessey, May 22, 1944 (div. 1973); children: Michael, Thomas, John, Patricia, Dennis; m. Nguyen Anh My, Aug. 30, 1975; children: Yvette, Bryan. BS in Agrl. Econs. and Soil Sci., U. Minn., 1946. Soil scientist USDA, 1946-50, agrl. ext. advisor, 1950-58; owner No. Ill. Agrl. Svc., 1958-62; with U.S. AID, Dept. State, 1962-84; agrl. sales advisor U.S. AID, Dept. State, India, 1962-66; asst. dir. crop prodn. Vietnam U.S. AID, Dept. State, 1966-70, chief agrl. divsn. Indonesia, 1970-73; assoc. dir. U.S. AID, Dept. State, Vietnam, 1974-75; chief agrl. divsn. Mali U.S. AID, Dept. State, 1976-81, chief agrl. project mgr. West Africa, 1981-84; agrl. cons. U.S. AID, Dept. State, Zaire, 1990-92, Indonesia, 1993-94; assoc. prof. U. Ark., 1985. 1st lt. USAAF, 1941-45. Decorated Purple Heart, Air medal with 6 oak leaf clusters, D.F.C.; recipient Agr. medal 2d class, Vietnam, 1969, Agr. medal 1st class, Vietnam, 1970, Labor medal 1st class, Vietnam, 1970, Economy medal 2d class, Vietnam, 1970. Mem. Am. Fgn. Service Assn. Office: USAID Box 4 APO AP 96520-8135

SMITH, MYRON JOHN, JR., librarian, author; b. Toledo, May 3, 1944; s. Myron John and Marion Oliva (Herbert) S.; 1 son, Myron John III. Student, Coll. Steubenville, 1962; AB, Ashland Coll., 1966; MLS, Western Mich. U., 1967; MA, Shippensburg U., 1969; postgrad., U. Wis., Purdue U.; LittD, Cardinal Newman Coll., 1982. Rsch. librarian G.W. Blunt White Libr., Mystic Seaport, Conn., 1967-68; asst. librarian Western Md. Coll., Westminster, 1969-72; libr. dir. Huntington (Ind.) Pub. Libr., 1972-76; prof. history and libr. sci., dir. librs. Benedum Libr. Salem-Teikyo U.; dir., then assoc. dir. aviation program Salem (W.Va.) Coll., 1976-90; prof. history and libr. sci., libr. dir. Tusculum Coll., Greeneville, Tenn., 1990—; mem. Am. Com. on History 2d World War, Assn. for Bibliography of History. Author: American Naval Bibliography Series, 1972-74, Huntington Centennial Handbook, 1973, The Sophisticated Lady: The Battleship Indiana in World War II, 1973, World War II at Sea: A Bibliography of Sources in English, 1976, (with Robert Webber) Sea Fiction Guide, 1976, The Cloak and Dagger Bibliography, 1976, World War I in the Air, 1977, Air War Chronology 1939-45, 1977, Air War Bibliography Series, 1977—, The Mountain State Battleship: USS West Virginia, 1979, Air War Southeast Asia, 1979, The Soviet Navy, 1941-1978, 1979, The Secret Wars Series, 1980-81, The Soviet Air and Strategic Rocket Forces, 1941-1980, 1981, The Soviet Army, 1941-1980, 1981, Equestrian Studies: The Salem College Guide, 1981, The Cloak and Dagger Fiction Guide: An Annotated Guide to Spy Thrillers, 1981, (with Terry White) 3d edit., 1994, The Mountaineer Battlewagon: USS West Virginia, 1982, The Keystone Battlewagon: USS Pennsylvania, 1983, The Golden State Battlewagon: USS California, 1983, Watergate: A Bibliography, 1983 World War II: Mediterranean and European Theaters, 1984, The United States Navy and Coast Guard, 1946-1983: A Bibliography of English Language Works and 16mm Films, 1984, U.S. Television Network News: A Guide to Sources in English, 1984, Battleships and Battlecruisers, 1884-1984: A Bibliography and Chronology, 1985, Baseball: A Comprehensive Bibliography, 1986, 99th Infantry Division Bibliography, 1986, The Airline Bibliography: The Salem College Guide to Sources on Commercial Aviation, Vol. I, The United States, 1986, Vol. II, Airliners and Foreign Carriers, 1987, Passenger Airliners of the United States, 1926-86: A Pictorial Guide, 1987, rev. edit. through 1991, 1991, 3d rev. edit. through 1995, 1995, Brooklyn/Los Angeles Dodgers: A Bibliography, 1987, American Warplane Bibliography, 1989, Volunteer Battlewagon: The U.S.S. Tennessee (BB-43), 1989; editor: Sports Teams and Players Bibliography Series, 1987, Battle and Leaders Bibliography Series, 1988, 100 Years of Opportunity: A Pictorial History of Salem College, 1888-1988, 1988, Pro Football Bio-Bibliography, 1920-1988, 1989, Pearl Harbor, December 7, 1941: An Annotated Bibliography, 1991, Battles of the Coral Sea and Midway, 1942: A Bibliography, 1991, World War II at Sea, 1974-1989: A Bibliography, 1990, Professional Football: The Official Pro Football Hall of Fame Bibliography, 1993, Baseball: A Comprehensive Bibliography-1st Supplement: 1985-1991, 93, The College Football Bibliography, 1994, Glimpses of Tusculum College: A Pictorial History, 1794-1994, 1994; contbr. articles to various jours. Recipient Nelson Ross award Profl. Football Rsch. Assn., 1993; 1st Am. recipient Richard Franck Gold medal Bibliothek für Zeitgeschichte, Stuttgart, Fed. Rep. Germany, 1981. Mem. ALA, U.S. Naval Inst., U.S. Mil. Inst., U.S. Air Force Found., Assn. Bibliog. of History (pres. 1981-82), Beta Phi Mu, Phi Alpha Theta. Club: Optimist. Office: Tusculum Coll PO Box 5087 Greeneville TN 37743-0001

SMITH, NANCY HOHENDORF, sales and marketing executive; b. Detroit, Jan. 30, 1943; d. Donald Gerald and Lucille Marie (Kopp) Hohendorf; m. Richard Harold Smith, Aug. 21, 1978 (div. Jan. 1984). BA, U. Detroit, 1965; MA, Wayne State U., 1969. Customer rep. Xerox Corp., Detroit, 1965-67; mktg. rep. Univ. Microfilms Inc. Xerox Corp., Ann Arbor, Mich., 1967-73, mktg. coord., 1973-74, mgr. dir. mktg., 1975-76; mgr. mktg. Xerox Corp., Can., 1976-77; major account mktg. exec. Xerox Corp., Hartford, Conn., 1978-79, New Haven, Conn., 1979-80; account exec. State of N.Y. Xerox Corp., N.Y.C., 1981; N.Y. region mgr. customer support Xerox Corp., Greenwich, Conn., 1982, N.Y. region sales ops. mgr., 1983; State of Ohio account exec. Xerox Corp., Columbus, 1983; new bus. sales mgr. Xerox Corp., Dayton, Ohio, 1983, major accounts sales mgr., 1984; info. systems sales and support mgr., quality specialist Xerox Corp., Detroit, 1985-87, new product launch mgr., ops. quality mgr., 1988, dist. mktg. mgr., 1989-91, major accounts sales mgr., 1992—. Named to Outstanding Young Women of Am., 1968, Outstanding Bus. Woman, Dayton C. of C., 1984, Women's Inner Circle of Achievement, 1990. Mem. NAFE, Am. Mgmt. Assn., Women's Econ. Club Detroit, Detroit Inst. Arts Founders' Soc., Greater Detroit C. of C. Republican. Roman Catholic. Avocations: interior decorating, reading, music, art. Home: 23308 Reynard Dr Southfield MI 48034-6924 Office: Xerox Corp Galleria Officentre Bldg 300 Southfield MI 48034

SMITH, NANCY LYNNE, journalist, real estate agent, public relations consultant; b. San Antonio, July 31, 1947; d. Tillman Louis and Enid Maxine (Woolverton) Brown; m. Allan Roy Jones, Nov. 28, 1969 (div. 1975); 1 dau., Christina Elizabeth Woolverton Jones. BA, So. Meth. U., 1968; postgrad. So. Meth. U., 1969-70, Vanderbilt U., 1964, Ecole Nouvelle de la Suisse Romande, Lausanne, Switzerland, 1962. Tchr. spl. edn. Hot Springs Sch. Dist. (Ark.), 1970-72; reporter, soc. editor Dallas Morning News, 1974-82; soc./celebrity columnist Dallas Times Herald, 1982—; owner, pub. High Soc. Fax; realtor, Ebby Halliday Realtors; stringer Washington Post, 1978; contbg. editor Ultra mag., Houston, 1981-82, Tex. Woman mag., Dallas, 1979-80, Profl. Woman mag., Dallas, 1979-80; mem. bd. advisors Ultra Mag., 1985—; owner Nancy Smith Pub. Rels. Appeared on TV series Jocelyn's Weekend, Sta. KDFI-TV, 1985. Bd. dirs. TACA arts support organ., Dallas, 1980—, asst. chmn. custom auction, 1978-83; judge Miss Tex. USA Contest, 1984; bd. dirs. Am. Parkinson Disease Assn. (Dallas chpt.), mem. adv. bd. Cattle Baron's Ball Com., Dallas Symphony

Debutante presentations; hon. mem. Dallas Opera Women's Bd., Northwood Inst. Women's Bd., Dallas Symphony League; mem. Friends of Winston Churchill Meml. and Library, Dallas Theatre Ctr. Women's Guild, Childrens' Med. Ctr. Auxiliary; hon. mem. Crystal Charity Ball Com.; mem. Community Council Greater Dallas Community Awareness Goals Com. Impact '88, 1985—; co-chmn. Multiple Sclerosis San Simeon Gala, 1988; celebrity co-chmn. Greer Garson Gala of Hope 1990-91; gala chmn. Greer Garson Gala of Hope for Am. Parkinson's Disease Assn., 1991-93; chmn. gala benefit Northwood U., 1994; co-chmn. star studded stomp Mar. Dimes, 1994; mem. Femmes du Monde com. Dallas Coun. World Affairs. Mem. Soc. Profl. Journalists (v.p. communications 1978-79), Nat. Press Club, Dallas Press Club, DAR, Daus. of Republic of Tex. (registrar 1972), Dallas So. Memorial Assn., Dallas County Heritage Soc., Dallas Mus. Art League, Dallas Opera Guild. Club: Argyle (sec. 1983-84), The 500 (Dallas), Energy. Home: 6324D Bandera Ave Dallas TX 75225-3614 Office: 8333 Douglas Ste 100 Dallas TX 75225

SMITH, NATHAN MCKAY, library and information sciences educator; b. Wendell, Idaho, Apr. 22, 1935; s. M. Blair and Vaunda H. (Hawkes) S.; m. Joyce A. Carman, July 5, 1953; children: Nathan M., Jeffrey M., Pamela J., Russell A., Kristen E. BS in Secondary Edn., Eastern Oreg. Coll., 1961; MS in Gen. Sci., Oreg. State U., 1965; MLS, Brigham Young U., 1969, PhD in Zoology, 1972. Tchr. sci. Dalles Jr. High Sch., The Dalles, Oreg., 1961-64; asst. sci. librarian Brigham Young U., Provo, Utah, 1968, life sci. librarian, 1970-73; prof. Sch. Library and Info. Sci., Brigham Young U., Provo, Utah, 1973-82, dir., 1982-93, life sci. libr., 1993—; cons. Weber County Library, Ogden, Utah, 1980—; back issues sec. Herpetologists League, 1976-81. Served to sgt. USAF, 1953-57. Yr. scholar NSF Acad., 1964; fellow NDEA Title IV, 1969; recipient research award Assn. Library and Info. Sci. Edn., 1983. Mem. ALA (councilor legis. council), Assn. Library Info. Sci. Edn., Mountain Plains Library Assn., Utah Library Assn. (exec. bd., pres.), N. Am. Soc. Adlerian Psychology, Phi Kappa Phi, Sigma Xi, Beta Phi Mu. Mem. LDS Ch. Home: 1606 Locust Ln Provo UT 84604-2806 Office: Brigham Young U Bean Mus Provo UT 84602

SMITH, NEIL, professional football player; b. New Orleans, Apr. 10, 1966. Student, U. Nebr. Defensive end Kansas City Chiefs, 1988—. Played in Pro Bowl, 1991-93; named defensive lineman The Sporting News All-America team, 1987. Office: Kansas City Chiefs 1 Arrowhead Dr Kansas City MO 64129*

SMITH, NICK, congressman, farmer; b. Addison, Mich., Nov. 5, 1934; s. LeGrand John and Blanche (Nichols) S.; m. Bonnalyn Belle Atwood, Jan. 1, 1960; children: Julianna, Bradley, Elizabeth, Stacia. BA, Mich. State U., 1957; MS, U. Del., 1959. Radio & TV farm editor Sta. WDEL, Wilmington, Del., 1957-59; radio editor Sta. KSWD, Wichita Falls, Tex., 1959-60; capt. intelligence USAF, Tex., 1959-61; mem. twp. bd. Somerset Twp., Addison, 1962-68; asst. dep. adminstr. USDA, Washington, 1972-74; state rep. Mich. Ho. of Reps., Lansing, 1978-82; state senator Mich. State Senate, Lansing, 1982-92; mem. 103rd-104th Congresses from 7th Mich. dist., 1993—; chmn. Senate Agrl. Com., 1982-92, Senate Corrections Appropriation Com., 1984-90, Senate Mil. Affairs Com., 1984-90, Senate Fin. Com., 1990-92; mem. agriculturecom., budget com. Leader's Task Force on Economy, 1993—. Del. Am. Assembly on World Population & Hunger, Washington, 1973; nat. del. on U.S.-Soviet Cooperation and Trade, 1991; former trustee Somerset Congl. Ch. Capt. USAF, 1959-61. Fellow Kellogg Found., 1965; named Hon. FFA State Star Farmer, 1987, SCF Conservator of Yr. Hillsdale County, 1988. Mem. Mich. Farm Bur. (bd. dirs.), Jackson C. of C., Mich. State U. Alumni Club, Masons. Republican. Office: US House of Reps 1530 Longworth Hob Washington DC 20515-2207*

SMITH, NOEL WILSON, psychology educator; b. Marion, Ind., Nov. 2, 1933; s. Anthony and Mary Louise (Wilson) S.; m. Marilyn C. Coleman, June 17, 1954; children: Thor and Lance (twins). AB, Ind. U., 1955, PhD, 1962; MA, U. Colo., 1958. Asst. prof. psychology Wis. State U., Platteville, 1962-63; asst. prof. psychology SUNY, Plattsburgh, 1963-66, assoc. prof., 1966-71, prof., 1971—. Author: Greek and Interbehavioral Psychology, 1990, rev. edit., 1993, An Analysis of Ice Age Art: Its Psychology and Belief, 1992; co-author: The Science of Psychology: Interbehavioral Survey, 1975; sr. editor: Reassessment in Psychology, 1983; editor: Interbehavioral Psychology newsletter, 1970-77; contbr. articles to profl. jours. Fellow APA; mem. AAUP (pres. SUNY coun. 1980-82), Am. Psychol. Soc., Cheiron Internat. Soc. History of Behavior Sci., Sigma Xi. Home: 7 W Court St Plattsburgh NY 12901 Office: SUNY Dept Psychology Beaumont Hall Plattsburgh NY 12901

SMITH, NORMA JANE, elementary education educator; b. N.Y.C., Aug. 19, 1933; d. Raymond and Thelma (Kavares) Schneider; m. Thomas Edward Smith; children: Robyn, Sharon, Ilene. BA, CUNY, 1955. Cert. tchr. N.Y. Tchr. grade 1 Plainedge (N.Y.) Pub. Schs., 1956-59; tchr., reading specialist Half Hollow Hills Schs., Dix Hills, N.Y., 1969-70, tchr. grade 4, 1970—, tng. and supervision of student tchrs., 1972-93, drama dir., 1982—, social studies coord., 1982, 83, sci. coord., 1988, 89; instr. in-svc. tchr. edn. courses, Half Hollow Hills, 1989, 90, 91; advisor Math Olympiads, Chestnut Hill, 1994—. Author: The Queen's Mirrors, 1973, Pot Pourri, 1984, Spelling Pizazz, 1992, A Fish Named Willie Blue, 1992. Mem. San Remo (N.Y.) Civic Assn. Recipient award for 20 yrs. of dedicated svc. to children of Chestnut Hill, Chestnut Hill PTA, 1990. Mem. Half Hollow Hills Tchrs. Assn. (rep. 1974-79). Avocations: writing, piano, art, theater arts. Home: 17 Acacia Rd Kings Park NY 11754

SMITH, NORMAN CLARK, fund raising consultant; b. Hartford, Conn., Jan. 2, 1917; s. Raymond W. and Elinor (Smith) S. A.B., Middlebury Coll., 1939; postgrad., Hartford Coll. Law, Trinity Coll. Tchr. Loomis Schs., 1945-50, adminstr., tchr., 1952-53, asst. bus. mgr., 1953-55, bus. mgr., 1955-58, controller, 1958-63; treas. Vassar Coll., 1963-64; v.p. devel., planning Emory U., Atlanta, 1964-76; v.p. univ. devel. U. Del., 1976-79. Bd. dirs., past chmn. bd. Nat. Soc. Fund Raising Execs.; past trustee Loomis Inst.; Watkinson Sch.; past chmn. Ga. Conservancy; past pres. Mashantucket Land Trust of Southeastern Conn.; trustee emeritus, past pres. Conn. River Mus., Essex; mem. Conn. State Coun. on Environ. Quality; mem. citizens adv. coun. Project Oceanology; trustee Conn. Antiquarian and Landmarks Soc.; mem. Naval War Coll. Found; former mem. Nat. Exec. Svc. Corps. Capt. USNR, 1941-45, 50-52. Decorated Navy Cross. Mem. Chi Psi, Omicron Delta Kappa. Club: Rotary. Home and Office: 161 Pequot Ave Mystic CT 06355-1728

SMITH, NORMAN CUTLER, geologist, business executive, educator; b. Paterson, N.J., Mar. 18, 1915; s. Archibald Nicholas and Ruth (Cutler) S.; m. Dorothy Phyllis Barnes, June 12, 1942; children—Roxanne Lorraine, Lee Cutler. Student, Pennington Prep. Sch., 1930-33, Drew U., 1933-34; AB in Geology and Biology cum laude, Washington and Lee U., 1937; postgrad., Harvard U., 1940-42, U. Okla., 1947. Field geologist Standard Oil Co. Venezuela, 1938-40; teaching fellow Harvard Grad. Sch. Geology, 1941-42; geologist Humble Oil & Refining Co., 1946-49; cons. geologist and photogeol. specialist, 1949-62; exec. dir. Am. Petroleum Geologists, 1963-72; pres. Resource Devel. Internat., Inc., 1973-88; with U. N.C., Asheville; dir. Oil Mining Energy Group, Sr. Acad. for Intergenerational Learning, 1988-93, Oil Mining Corp., v.p. 1993—; founder, 1st pres. Coun. Sci. Socs., Dallas-Ft. Worth area, 1958, chmn. bd., 1960; mem. standing com. Nat. Com. on Geology, 1962-72. Author articles, chpts. in books in field. Bd. dirs. Tulsa Sci. Found., 1967; trustee Tulsa Sci. Center, 1967-72. Served to lt. (s.g.) USNR, 1942-46, PTO. Fellow Geol. Soc. Am., A.A.A.S.; mem. Am. Assn. Execs., Tulsa Soc. Assn. Execs. (pres. 1958, hon.), Dallas Geol. Soc. (pres. 1958-59, exec. com. 1956-60, hon. mem.), Am. Assn. Petroleum Geologists, Soc. Petroleum Engrs., Soc. Exploration Geophysicists, Council Engring. and Sci. Soc. Secs. Home: 105 Windward Dr Asheville NC 28803-9555 Office: U NC-Asheville Rhoades Hall Rm 116 One University Heights Asheville NC 28804

SMITH, NORMAN E., metal products executive; b. 1935. With Vincent Brass & Aluminum Co., Inc., Mpls., 1963-84; with Rio Algom, Mpls., 1984—, now v.p. Office: Rio Algom Inc 700 24th Ave SE Minneapolis MN 55414*

SMITH, NORMAN OBED, physical chemist, educator; b. Winnipeg, Man., Can., Jan. 23, 1914; came to U.S., 1950, naturalized, 1958; s. Ernest and Ruth (Kilpatrick) S.; m. Anna Marie O'Connor, July 1, 1944; children: Richard Obed, Graham Michael, Stephen Housley. B.Sc., U. Man., 1935, M.Sc., 1936; Ph.D., NYU, 1939. Teaching fellow NYU, 1936-39; mem. faculty dept. chemistry U. Man., Winnipeg, 1939-50; asst. prof. U. Man., 1946-49, assoc. prof., 1949-50; assoc. prof. Fordham U., N.Y.C., 1950-65; prof. chemistry Fordham U., 1965-84, prof. emeritus, 1984—, chmn. dept., 1974-78; sr. phys. chemist Arthur D. Little, Inc., Cambridge, Mass., 1957; indsl. cons. Author: (with others) The Phase Rule and Its Applications, 1951, Chemical Thermodynamics, A Problems Approach, 1967, Elementary Statistical Thermodynamics, A Problems Approach, 1982; contbr. to: Ency. Brit., 1974. Fellow Chem. Inst. Can.; mem. Am. Chem. Soc., Asso. Can. Coll. Organists, Am. Guild Organists (dir. chpt. 1964-66, 79-82, 91-92), Sigma Xi, Phi Lambda Upsilon. Home: 59 Monrovia Blvd Tuckahoe NY 10707-1023 Office: Fordham U Dept Chemistry New York NY 10458-5198

SMITH, NORMAN RAYMOND, college president; b. Toronto, Ont., Can., Oct. 24, 1946; s. William Raymond and Jeanne (Malin) S.; m. Susan Robinson, Dec. 26, 1981; 1 child, Caroline Robinson. BS, Drexel U., 1969, MBA, 1971; EdD, Harvard U., 1984. Assoc. dean students Drexel U., Phila., 1971-73; dean of students, professor Phila. Coll. Textiles and Sci., 1973-78; asst. dean Harvard Grad. Sch. Edn., Cambridge, Mass., 1978-80, John F. Kennedy Sch. Govt., Harvard U., Cambridge, 1980-84; exec. v.p. Moore Coll. Art, Phila., 1984-87; pres. Wagner Coll., S.I., N.Y., 1988—; dir. Dime Bancorp; assoc. Harvard U. Philosophy of Edn. Rsch. Ctr., Cambridge, 1987—. Author: How to Make The Right Decisions About College, 1993. Chair mayor's cabinet transition search City of Boston, 1983-84; trustee N.Y. Coun. of Ind. Colls. and Univs., 1994—. Lt. U.S. Army, 1969-73. Recipient U. medal Drexel U., 1993, Pres.'s medal NYU, 1994. Mem. Ind. Coll. Fund N.Y. (sec.-treas.), Harvard Club of N.Y.C., Richmond County Country Club. Home: 79 Howard Ave Staten Island NY 10301-4404 Office: Wagner College Office of Pres Staten Island NY 10301

SMITH, NORMAN T., lawyer; b. Akron, Ohio, Nov. 23, 1935; s. Norman and Margaret (Stall) S.; m. Marilyn Deanna Richards, Oct. 1, 1960; children: Brian T., Valerie E., Gregory D. BS, Ohio State U., 1957; MBA, Case Western Res. U., 1959; JD, U. Mich., 1963. Bar: Ohio 1963. Ptnr. Porter, Wright, Morris & Arthur (and predecessor firms), Columbus, Ohio, 1963—; past. exec. dir. Ohio Title Ins. Rating Bur., Columbus, 1972-89; instr. Capital U. Legal Assistant Program, Columbus, 1985—. Sr. warden St. Marks Episcopal Ch., Upper Arlington, Ohio, 1970-73, 85; pres. 412 Sycamore, Inc., Cin., 1983—; mem. bd. edn. Upper Arlington, 1980-83, Bd Zoning Adjustment, Columbus, 1977-85. Recipient Merit award Ohio Legal Ctr. Inst. Fellow Ohio State Bar Found., Columbus Bar Found.; mem. ABA, Ohio State Bar Assn. (coun. dels. 1985—, chmn. real property bd. govs. 1980-82), Am. Coll. Real Estate Lawyers, Ohio Land Title Assn. (pres. 1976), Columbus Bar Assn., Nat. Conf. Bar Examiners (real property drafting com. of multistate bar exam 1988-95), Columbus Athletic Club, Leatherlips Yacht Club (gov. 1970-71). Republican. Episcopalian. Office: Porter Wright Morris & Arthur 41 S High St Columbus OH 43215-6101

SMITH, NUMA LAMAR, JR., lawyer; b. Rock Hill, S.C., Nov. 22, 1915; s. Numa Lamar and Grace (Hanes) S.; m. Mary Catherine Gray, Mar. 24, 1941; children: Patricia Gray, Elizabeth Hanes, Lamar Douglas. A.B., Furman U., 1938; LL.B. with distinction, Duke U., 1941. Bar: N.Y. 1942, D.C. 1946. Assoc. firm White & Case, N.Y.C., 1941-42, Miller & Chevalier, Washington, 1946-49; partner Miller & Chevalier, 1949-83, counsel, 1983—; bd. visitors, 1973-83; sr. fellow Duke U. Law Sch., 1979-80. Author: editor Duke Law Jour., 1940-41. Served with U.S. Army, 1942-46; with Judge Adv. Gen. Corps 1944-46. Recipient Gen. Excellence award Furman U., 1938. Fellow Am. Bar Found.; mem. ABA, D.C. Bar Assn., Am. Law Inst., Duke Law Alumni Assn. (pres. 1967-69), Order of Coif, Met. Club (Washington), Burning Tree Club (Bethesda, Md.), Washington Golf Club (Arlington, Va.), Sigma Alpha Epsilon. Baptist. Home: 3841 N Tazewell St Arlington VA 22207-9999

SMITH, ORIN ROBERT, chemical company executive; b. Newark, Aug. 13, 1935; s. Sydney R. and Gladys Emmett (DeGroff) S.; m. Stephanie M. Bennett-Smith; children: Lindsay, Robin; 1 stepchild, Brendan. BA in Econometrics, Brown U., 1957; MBA in Mgmt., Seton Hall U., 1964; PhD in Econs. (hon.), Centenary Coll., 1991; LLD (hon.), Monmouth Coll., 1994. Various sales and mktg. mgmt. positions Allied Chem. Corp., Morristown, N.J., 1959-69; dir. sales and mktg. Richardson-Merrell Co., Phillipsburg, N.J., 1969-72; with M&T Chems., Greenwich, Conn., 1972-77, pres., 1975-77; with Engelhard Minerals & Chems. Corp., Menlo Park, Edison, N.J., 1977-81, corp. sr. v.p., 1978-81, pres. div. minerals and chems., 1978-81, also bd. dirs., 1979-81, pres., dir. various U.S. subs., 1979-81; exec. v.p. pres. div. minerals and chems. Engelhard Corp., Menlo Park, Edison, N.J., 1981-84, also bd. dirs.; pres., CEO, Engelhard Corp., Iselin, N.J., 1984-95, chmn., CEO, 1995—, also bd. dirs., $D; bd. dirs. Summit Trust Co., The Summit Bancorp, Vulcan Materials Co., La. Land and Exploration Co., Perkin-Elmer Corp., Ingersoll-Rand Corp., Minorco, Engelhard Corp. Trustee Mfrs. Alliance, Inst. for Tech. Advancement, N.J. Corp. for Advanced Tech., Welkind Rehab. Hosp.; bd. overseers N.J. Inst. Tech.; trustee-at-large Plimoth Plantation; 1st vice chmn. bd. trustees Centenary Coll.; past dir. Newark Mus.; past chmn. Ind. Coll. Fund N.J.; past dir.-at-large U. Maine Pulp and Paper Found. Lt. (j.g.) USN, 1957-59. Mem. NAM (bd. dirs.), Chem. Mfrs. Assn. (past bd. dirs.), Am. Mgmt. Assn. (gen. mgmt. coun.), N.J. C. of C. (trustee, bd. dirs.), Econ. Club N.Y.C., Union League Club (N.Y.), Roxiticus Golf Club (Mendham, N.J.), Duxbury Yacht Club, New Bedford Yacht Club, N.Y. Yacth Club. Office: Engelhard Corp 101 Wood Ave Iselin NJ 08830-0770

SMITH, ORVILLE AUVERNE, physiology educator; b. Nogales, Ariz., June 16, 1927; s. Orville Auverne and Bess (Gill) S.; m. Clara Jean Smith; children—Nanette, Marcella. B.A. in Psychology, U. Ariz., 1949; M.A., Mich. State U., 1950, Ph.D., 1953. Instr. psychology Mich. State U., East Lansing, 1953-54; fellow U. Pa., Phila., 1954-56; trainee dept. physiology and biophysics U. Wash., Seattle, 1956-58, instr. physiology and biophysics, 1958-59, asst. prof., 1959-61, 62-63; asst. dir. Regional Primate Research Ctr., 1962-69, assoc. prof., 1963-67, prof., 1967—; assoc. dir. Regional Primate Research Center, 1969-71, dir. 1971-88. Contbr. articles to profl. jours. Mem. Am. Physiol. Soc., Am. Soc. Primatologists (pres. 1977-79), Internat. Congress Physiol. Scis., Am. Assn. Anatomists, AAAS, Pavlovian Soc. N.Am. (pres. 1977-78), Internat. Primatological Soc., AAUP, Neurosci. Soc. Home: 7521 30th Ave NE Seattle WA 98115-4719 Office: U Wash Regional Primate Research Ctr SJ-50 Seattle WA 98195

SMITH, OZZIE (OSBORNE EARL SMITH), professional baseball player; b. Mobile, Ala., Dec. 26, 1954; m. Denise Jackson, Nov. 1, 1980; children: Osborne Earl Jr., Dustin Cameron. Grad., Calif. State Poly. U., San Luis Obispo. Shortstop San Diego Padres Baseball Club, Nat. League, 1977-82, St. Louis Cardinals Baseball Club, Nat. League, 1982—. Player Nat. League All-Star Team, 1982-92, 94, All-Star Team Sporting News, 1982, 84-87, World Series Championship Team, 1982; recipient Most Valuable Player award Nat. League Championship Series, 1985, Gold Glove award, 1980-92, Silver Slugger award, 1987. Avocations: jazz, word puzzles, backgammon. Office: St Louis Cardinals Busch Meml Stadium 250 Stadium Plz Saint Louis MO 63102-1722*

SMITH, PATRICIA GRACE, government official; b. Tuskegee, Ala., Nov. 10, 1947; d. Douglas and Wilhelmina (Griffin) Jones; m. J. Clay Smith, Jr., June 25, 1983; children—Eugene Douglas, Stager Clay, Michelle L., Michael L. B.A. in English, Tuskegee Inst., 1968; postgrad. Auburn U., 1969-71, Harvard U., 1974, George Washington U., 1983; cert. in exec. service 1987; exec. mgmt. tng. devel. assignments Dept. Def., 1986, U.S. Senate Commerce Com., 1987. Instr. Tuskegee Institute, Ala., 1969-71; program mgr. Curber Assocs., Washington, 1971-73; dir. placement Nat. Assn. Broadcasters, Washington, 1973-74, dir. pub. affairs, 1974-77; assoc. producer Group W Broadcasting, Balt., 1977, producer, 1977-78; dir. affiliate relations and programming Sheridan Broadcasting Network, Crystal City, Va., 1978-80; dep. dir. policy, assoc. mng. dir. pub. info. and reference svcs., FCC, Washington, 1992-94, acting assoc. mng. dir., pub. info. and reference svcs., 1994; dep. dir. Office Pub. Affairs, 1994—; assoc. mng. dir. office of coml. space transp., Office of the Sec., U.S. Dept. Transp., 1994—. vice chmn. Nat. Conf.

Black Lawyers Task Force on Communications, Washington, 1975-87. Mem. D.C. Donor Project, Nat. Kidney Found., Washington, 1984—; trustee, mem. exec. com., nominating com., youth adv. com. Nat. Urban League, 1976-81; mem. communications com. Cancer Coordinating Council, 1977-84; mem. Braintrust Subcom. on Children's Programming, Congl. Black Caucus, 1976—; mem. adv. bd. Black Arts Celebration, 1978-83; mem. NAACP; mem. journalism and communications adv. council Auburn U., 1976-78; mem. Washington Urban League, 1985—; bd. dirs. Black Film Rev., 1989-91; mem D.C. Commn. on Human Rights, 1986-88, chmn. 1988-91; mem. adv. coun. Nat. Insts. Health, 1992—; mem. bd. advisors The Salvation Army, 1993—. Named Outstanding Young Woman of Yr., Washington, 1975, 78; recipient Sustained Superior Performance award FCC, Washington, 1982-94. Mem. Women in Communications, Inc. (mem. nat. adv. com.), Lambda Iota Tau. Club: Broadcasters (bd. dirs. 1976-77). Democrat. Baptist. Avocations: writing, swimming. Home: 4010 16th St NW Washington DC 20011-7002 Office: DOT/OCST 400 7th St Rm 5415 Washington DC 20590

SMITH, PATRICIA K., reading educator; b. East Stroudsburg, Pa., Mar. 8, 1934; d. Joseph George and Mabel Lorraine (Repsher) Kuchinski; m. Edwin Raymond Smith, Aug. 18, 1956; children: Timothy E., Steven M.. Marianne F. BS in Edn., East Stroudsburg U., 1955; MA, W.va. U., 1969, EdD, 1975. Elem. tchr. Pleasantdale Elem. Sch., West Orange, N.J., 1955-56, Tuscarora Sch. Dist., Mercersburg, Pa., 1956-59; reading specialist Robert F. Kennedy Ctr., Morgantown, W.va., 1970-72; asst. prof. W.va. U., Morgantown, 1975-79, assoc. prof. reading and lang. arts, 1979-86, prof., 1986—, senate faculty sec., 1992—; mem. rev. bd. Prentice-Hall, Inc., Englewood Cliffs, N.J., 1979-91; vis. prof. Beijing U. and Beijing Coal Mining Inst., 1991,92; cons. Chpt. 1, Monongalia Pub. Schs., Morgantown, W.va., 1983-84. Co-author: Keeping Yourself Out of Federal Court, 1980, 2d revision, 1986; mem. editorial bd. Reading Improvement, Chula Vista, Calif., 1983—. Postdoctoral teaching fellow Lilly Endowment, Inc., 1975-76; recipient Outstanding Tchr. award Coll. Human Resources and Edn., Morgantown, W.va., 1978. Mem. W.va. State Reading Council (pres. 1979-80), Human Resources and Edn. Alumni Assn. (pres. 1979-80, exec. dir. 1981-85), Kappa Delta Pi, Phi Delta Kappa. Democrat. Roman Catholic. Avocations: traveling, reading. Home: 1456 Dogwood Ave Morgantown WV 26505-2310 Office: WVa U 607 Allen Hall Morgantown WV 26506-6122

SMITH, PAUL EDMUND, JR., philosophy and religion educator; b. Northampton, Mass., Feb. 6, 1927; s. Paul Edmund and Mary Jane (Murphy) S.; A. U. Mass., 1948; postgrad. Harvard U., 1948-49; M.A., Boston U., 1957; B.D., Columbia Theol. Sem., 1957, M.Div., 1971; postgrad. U. N.C., 1967-68. Instr. Latin and French, Chester (Vt.) High Sch., 1949-53, Loris (S.C.) High Sch., 1953-54; lectr. history U. Ga., Albany, 1957-59; instr. Latin, Rocky Mount (Va.) High Sch., 1959-61; minister Henderson Presbyn. Ch., Albany, 1957-59, Rocky Mount (Va.) Presbyn. Ch., 1959-64; asst. prof. religion Ferrum (Va.) Coll., 1961-68; vis. lectr. history John Tyler C.C., Chester, Va., 1968-69; instr. philosophy and religion Richard Bland Coll., Petersburg, Va., 1968-71, asst. prof., 1971-76, asso. prof., 1976—, chmn. dept., 1971—. Mem. Am. Hist. Assn., Presbytery of the Peaks. Democrat. Presbyterian. Office: Richard Bland Coll Commerce Hall Petersburg VA 23805

SMITH, PAUL FREDERICK, plant physiologist, consultant; b. Copeland, Kans., Dec. 17, 1916; s. Frederick Eugene and Susie Irene (Wikoff) S.; m. Marjorie Haselwood, July 6, 1940; children: Gary Lynn, Carol Jeanne. BS, U. Okla., 1938, MS, 1940; PhD, U. Calif., 1944. Asst. plant physiologist USDA, Salinas, Calif., 1943-45, Orlando, Fla., 1946-50; assoc. physiologist USDA, 1950-55, plant physiologist, 1956-61, prin. physiologist, 1962-71, head physiologist, 1971-75, hort. cons., 1975—. Contbr. chpts. to books and articles to profl. publs. With USN, 1945-46. Fellow Am. Soc. Hort. Sci.; mem. Fla. Hort. Soc. (hon. life, Presdl. Gold medal 1970). Achievements include research in streamlining fertilization practices on citrus thereby avoiding deficiencies and excesses. Home and Office: 2695 Ashville St Orlando FL 32818-9018

SMITH, PAUL J., museum administrator; b. Buffalo; student Art Inst. Buffalo, Sch. Am. Craftsmen, Rochester, N.Y.; DFA (hon.) New Sch. Social Research, 1987. Staff mem. Am. Craft Coun., N.Y.C., 1957—, dir. Am. Craft Mus., 1963-87, dir. emeritus, 1987—; juror numerous exhibitions; lectr. and cons. in field of contemporary crafts and design. Trustee Louis Comfort Tiffany Found.; trustee emeritus Haystack Mountain Sch. Crafts, Deer Isle, Maine; Renwick Gallery Nat. Mus. Am. Art; adv. bd. Atlantic Ctr. for Arts, Inc.; internat. council Pilchuck Sch., Seattle. Office: PO Box 6735 Yorkville Station New York NY 10128

SMITH, PAUL JAMES, manufacturing company executive; b. Trumbull, Tex., July 16, 1932; s. Earl J. and Bessie K. (Pierce) S.; m. Barbara A. McConnell, Aug. 9, 1954; children: Marc, Cynthia. BSEE, U. Tex., 1959; postgrad. So. Meth. U., 1959-60. Mgr. mil. computer bus., consumer calculator bus., div. gen. mgr. digital systems Tex. Instruments, Dallas, 1959-75; dir. comml. electronics Martin Marietta Corp., Orlando, Fla., 1975-79; v.p., gen. mgr. semiconductor digital products div. Harris Corp., Melbourne, Fla., 1979-83; group v.p. line printer, then exec. v.p Dataproducts Corp., Woodland Hills, Calif., 1983-88; sr. v.p. Data Products div. Xidex/Anacomp Corp., Santa Clara, Calif., 1988—. Served with USN, 1953-55. Mem. IEEE, Machinery and Allied Products Inst., Mensa, Tau Beta Pi, Eta Kappa Nu.

SMITH, PAUL LESTER, photography company executive; b. Columbus, Ohio, Oct. 7, 1935; s. Lester Wikel and Opal Mary (Spain) S.; m. Susan Virginia Wilson, June 14, 1958; children—Jennifer Louise, Paul Brian. B.A., Ohio Wesleyan U., 1957; M.B.A., Northwestern U., 1958. Various positions Eastman Kodak Co., Rochester, N.Y., 1958-82, v.p., 1982-83, sr. v.p. fin., 1983-93; ret., 1993. Bd. dirs. Rochester Gen. Hosp., Rochester Area Hosp. Corp.; trustee Internat. Mus. Photography at George Eastman House, Rochester. Mem. Fin. Execs. Inst. Republican. Episcopalian. Club: Country (Rochester). Avocations: golf; fishing; skiing. Home: 77 Babcock Dr Rochester NY 14610-3304

SMITH, PAUL LETTON, JR., geophysicist; b. Columbia, Mo., Dec. 16, 1932; s. Paul Letton and Helen Marie (Doersam) S.; m. Mary Barbara Noel; children: Patrick, Melody, Timothy, Christopher, Anne. BS in Physics, Carnegie Inst. Tech., 1955, MSEE, 1957, PhD in Elec. Engring., 1960. From instr. to asst. prof. Carnegie Inst. Tech., Pitts., 1955-63; sr. engr. Midwest Rsch. Inst., Kansas City, Mo., 1963-66; from rsch. engr. to sr. scientist and group head Inst. Atmospheric Scis., S.D. Sch. Mines and Tech., Rapid City, 1966-81; vis. prof. McGill U., Montreal, Que., Can., 1969-70; chief scientist Air Weather Svc. USAF, Scott AFB, Ill., 1974-75; dir. Inst. Atmospheric Scis., S.D. Sch. Mines and Tech., Rapid City, 1981—; lectr. Tech. Svc. Corp., Silver Spring, Md., 1972—; dir. S.D. Space Grant Consortium, Rapid City, 1991—. Contbr. over 40 articles to profl. jours. Fellow Am. Meteorol. Soc. (Editor's award 1992); mem. IEEE (sr.), Weather Modification Assn. (Thunderbird award 1995), Sigma Xi. Home: 2107 9th St Rapid City SD 57701 Office: SD Sch Mines & Tech 501 E Saint Joseph St Rapid City SD 57701

SMITH, PAUL THOMAS, financial services company executive; b. Garden City, N.Y., May 17, 1938; s. Joe Joseph and Martha Duncan (Perine) S.; m. Carole A. Dlugolenski, Sept. 1, 1962; children—Laura Jane, Paul Thomas, Elizabeth Ann, Kathryn Celinda. B.B.A., U. Notre Dame, 1960; M.B.A., Harvard U., 1964. C.P.A., N.Y. chartered fin. analyst. In charge accountant Deloitte & Touche, N.Y.C., 1964-67; from investment analyst to 2d v.p. N.Y. Life Ins. Co., N.Y.C., 1967-78, v.p. investments, 1978-83, v.p., chief equity investment officer, 1983-88, sr. v.p. corp. planning and devel., 1988-91, sr. v.p. venture capital, chief equity investment officer, 1991—. Served to lt. USN, 1960-62. Mem. Inst. Chartered Fin. Analysts, N.Y. Soc. Security Analysts. Club: Cherry Valley. Office: 51 Madison Ave New York NY 10010-1603

SMITH, PAUL TRAYLOR, mayor, former business executive, former army officer; b. Burkesville, Ky., June 22, 1923; s. Samuel Joseph and Bonnie (Ferguson) S.; m. Elizabeth C. Nolte, July 2, 1942; m. Phyllis Jean Corbin, Oct. 11, 1975; children: Gregory L., Douglas B., Paula J. Smith Richardson. Mary K. B.A., U. Md., 1960, M.B.A., 1962. Enlisted in U.S. Army, 1940, advanced through grades to maj. gen., 1975; service in Japan, Ger., Korea,

Vietnam; adj. gen. Continental Army Command, 1968-70, comdg. gen. U.S. Army Computer Systems Command, 1973-75; adj. gen. U.S. Army, 1975-77; exec. v.p. Taylorcraft Devel. Corp., Inc., Burkesville, Ky., 1977-82; mayor City of Burkesville, Burkesville, Ky., 1982. Bd. dirs. Lake Cumberland Area Devel. Dist. Inc., Lake Cumberland Housing Agy., Inc.; bd. dirs., mem. exec. com., legis. policy com. Ky. League of Cities, also trustee investemnt pool bd., 1st v.p.; chmn. Lake Area Inspection Svc. Inc.; chmn. bd. dirs. Lake Cumberland Area Devel. Dist., Revolving Loan Fund Com., Lake Cumberland Housing Agy., Burkesville Manor Inc., trustee Ky. Mcpl. Risk Mgmt. Agy. Decorated D.S.M., Legion of Merit with 2 oak leaf clusters, Bronze Star. Mem. Assn. U.S. Army, Ret. Officers Assn. Address: PO Box 607 Burkesville KY 42717-0607

SMITH, PAUL VERGON, JR., corporate executive, retired oil company executive; b. Lima, Ohio, Apr. 25, 1921; s. Paul Vergon and Aleta Rose (Bowers) S.; m. Alta Fern Chipps, Mar. 2, 1945; children: Douglas, Marsha, Jeffrey, Alison. AB, Miami U., Oxford, Ohio, 1942; MS, U. Ill., 1943, PhD, 1945. With Exxon Research & Engring. Co., 1946-66, 72-86, mgr. pub. affairs, 1972-80, mgr. ednl. and profl. soc. relations, Florham Park, N.J., 1981-86; asst. dir. chem. research Esso Petroleum Co., Abingdon, Eng., 1966-67; dir. chem. research Esso Research S.A., Brussels, 1967-71; mem. adv. bd. Cache, Inc., Austin, Tex., 1979-86; pres. APS Assocs., Westfield, N.J., 1986-90; bd. dirs., treas. Jets, Inc., Alexandria, Va.; dir. CENTCOM, Ltd.; mem. exec. bd. N.J. Bus./Industry/Sci. Edn. Consortium. Patentee in field; contbr. numerous articles to profl. jours., chpts. to books. Bd. dirs. United Way of Union County, N.J., 1980-86; chmn. research adv. council Miami U. 1980-84. Recipient Pres.'s award Am. Assn. Petroleum Geologists, 1955; Spl. award N.J. Sci. Tchrs. Assn., 1985. Mem. AAAS, Am. Chem. Soc. (dir. 1978-86, chmn. bd. 1984-86; Belden award 1984), Am. Soc. Engring. Edn. (dir. 1980-86, v.p 1980-86), Country Club Naples, Phi Beta Kappa, Sigma Xi, Omicron Delta Kappa, Phi Eta Sigma, Alpha Chi Sigma, Pi Mu Epsilon, Sigma Pi Sigma, Phi Lambda Upsilon. Republican. Methodist.

SMITH, PAYTON, lawyer; b. Ft. Worth, Oct. 21, 1932; s. Paxton and Thelma (Aldrige) S.; m. Patricia J. Linden, Dec. 28, 1963; children: Kevin, Shelley, Elizabeth. BA, So. Meth. U., 1954; JD, U. Chgo., 1957. Bar: Wash. 1957, U.S. Ct. Appeals (9th cir.) 1958, U.S. Supreme Ct. 1965. Practice in Seattle, 1957—; atty. Safeco Ins., 1957-58; assoc. Smith and Smith, 1958-60, McBride and Hanify, 1961-63; chief asst. U.S. atty. U.S. Atty.'s Office, Seattle, 1961-63; ptnr. Howe, Davis, Riese & Jones, 1963-69, Davis, Wright, Todd, Riese & Jones, 1969-85, Davis, Wright & Tremaine, Seattle, 1986—; chmn. litigation dept. Davis, Wright & Jones, 1975—; counsel to speaker Wash. State Ho. of Reps., Olympia, 1959, 61. Contbr. articles to profl. jours. and handbooks. Pres. Wash. State Young Dems., 1960; bd. dirs. Seattle-King County YMCA, 1975-79; pres. Alki Found., Seattle, 1982; gen. counsel Seattle-King County C.C., 1981-83, Wash. State-China Rels. Counsel, 1980-81, 89—; found. assoc. Pacific Sci. Ctr., Seattle, 1986-91. Fellow Am. Coll. Trial Lawyers; mem. Wash. State Bar Assn. (chmn. antitrust sect. 1980-82, spl. investigator 1985-89), Wash. Bar Assn., Seattle Tennis club, Rainier Club (Seattle). Home: 5535 NE 55th St Seattle WA 98105-2824 Office: Davis Wright & Tremaine 1501 4th Ave Seattle WA 98101-1662

SMITH, PETER, chemist, educator, consultant; b. Sale, Cheshire, Eng., Sept. 7, 1924; came to U.S., 1951; s. Peter and Winifred Emma (Jenkins) S.; m. Hilary Joan Hewitt Roe, 1951; children: Helen Andrews Winifred, Eric Peter, Richard Harry, Gillian Carol. B.A. Queens' Coll., Cambridge U. 1946, M.A., 1949, Ph.D., 1953. Jr. sci. officer Royal Aircraft Establishment, Farnborough, Hampshire, Eng., 1943-46; demonstrator chemistry dept. Leeds U., Yorkshire, England, 1950-51; postdoctoral research fellow in chemistry Harvard U., Cambridge, Mass., 1951-54; asst. prof. chemistry Purdue U., West Lafayette, Ind., 1954-59; asst. prof. chemistry Duke U., Durham, N.C., 1959-61, assoc. prof., 1961-70, prof. chemistry, 1970—. Contbg. author: chem. research jours. Fulbright post-doctoral scholar Fulbright Commn., Harvard U., 1951-53. Mem. Am. Chem. Soc., Royal Soc. Chemistry, Am. Phys. Soc., Sigma Xi, Phi Lambda Upsilon, Alpha Chi Sigma. Home: 2711 Circle Dr Durham NC 27705-5726 Office: Dept Chemistry Paul M Gross Chem Lab PO Box 90346 Durham NC 27708-0346

SMITH, PETER BENNETT, banker; b. N.Y.C., Sept. 24, 1934; s. Richard Joyce and Sheila (Alexander) S.; B.A., Yale U., 1956; m. Elizabeth Weinberg, May 10, 1980; children—Marjorie, Alison, Peter, Michael, Madeleine, Hannah, Elizabeth. With J.P. Morgan & Co., 1958-59; with Morgan Guaranty Trust Co., N.Y.C., 1959—, sr. v.p. mgmt., 1976-79, exec. v.p., 1979-86; chmn. credit policy com., 1986—; mng. dir. Banco Frances del Rio de la Plata, Buenos Aires, Argentina, 1968-72, Bank Mees & Hope, Amsterdam, Netherlands, 1972-75; pres. Bank Morgan LaBouchere N.V., Amsterdam, 1976; trustee Canterbury Sch., Sharon Conn Hosp.; bd. dirs. Dravo Corp., 1984-90, N.Y.C. Ballet, 1985-92; trustee Marine Corps Command and Staff Coll. Found. Served to capt. USMCR, 1956-58. Mem. Coun. on Fgn. Rels., Bankers' Roundtable Roman Catholic. Clubs: Economic, Yale (N.Y.C.); Rolling Rock, Sharon Country, Kittansett, Mill Reef. Office: J P Morgan & Co Trust Co 60 Wall St New York NY 10260

SMITH, PETER DOUGLAS, dean; b. Lowestoft, England, Aug. 13, 1933; s. William and Gladys Ethel (Lakey) S.; m. E. Gwenda Jones, Nov. 14, 1964 (div.); 1 child, W. Morgan Smith. BA, U. Birmingham, England, 1954; MLitt, U. Durham, England, 1964; MA (hon.), Dartmouth Coll., 1980. Asst. to registrar McMaster U., Hamilton, Can., 1956-58, asst/assoc. dir. extension, 1958-65; asst. to chancellor U. Calif., Santa Cruz, 1965-67, asst. vice chancellor, 1967-69; dir. Hopkins Ctr. Dartmouth Coll., Hanover, N.H., 1969-81, historian of the Dickey Presidency 1982-87; dean Sch. of the Arts Columbia U., N.Y., 1987—; trustee Vt. Coun. on the Arts, 1983-86, pres. 1985-86. Mem. Century Club. Avocations: acting, letter writing, listening to music. Home: 15 Claremont Ave New York NY 10027 Office: Sch of the Arts Columbia U New York NY 10027

SMITH, PETER GARTHWAITE, energy consultant; b. July 22, 1923; s. Karl Garthwaite and Fannie (Jones) S.; m. Anne Allerton Ward, Dec. 23, 1950; children—Allerton G., Thomas G., Amy G., Abigail G. A.B., Princeton U., 1948; L.L.B. Yale U., 1951. Assoc. Hughes, Hubbard & Reed, N.Y.C., 1951-55; corp. sec. So. Natural Gas Co., Birmingham, Ala., 1963-71; gen. counsel So. Natural Gas Co., Birmingham, 1966-73; exec. v.p. Sonat, Inc., Birmingham, 1973-82, vice chmn., 1984-94, cons., 1984—. Bd. dirs. First Ala. Bank, Birmingham, 1978-92. Chmn. bd. dirs. Ala. Sch. Fine Arts, Birmingham, 1982-88; pres. Met. Devel. Bd., Birmingham, 1982-86; bd. dirs. Episcopal Ch. Found., N.Y.C., 1980-91, Birmingham Turf Club, Inc., 1985-87, Children Can Soar Inc., 1987-89; trustee Ala. Symphony Assn., Birmingham, 1981-85. Served with USAAF, 1943-46. Mem. ABA, Am. Gas Assn. (bd. dirs. 76-80, 82-84), Interstate Natural Gas Assn. (bd. dirs. 1976-84, chmn. bd. dirs. 1983-84), Mid-Continent Oil Gas Assn. (bd. dirs. 1977-84), So. Gas Assn. (bd. dirs. 1977-77), Mountain Brook Club, Downtown Club, Princeton Club, Nassau Club. Avocations: tennis; fly fishing. Home: 2605 Caldwell Mill Ln Birmingham AL 35243-1713 Office: New South Fed Savs Bldg 215 2d Ave N Birmingham AL 35203

SMITH, PETER HOPKINSON, political scientist, consultant, author; b. Bklyn., Jan. 17, 1940; s. Joseph Hopkinson and Mary Edna (Sullivan) S.; children: Jonathan Yeardley, Peter Hopkinson Jr. BA, Harvard U., 1961; MA, PhD, Columbia U., 1966. Assst. prof. Dartmouth Coll., Hanover, N.H., 1966-68; from asst. prof. to prof. U. Wis., Madison, 1968-80; prof. MIT, Cambridge, 1980-86; Simón Bolívar prof. Latin Am. studies U. Calif., San Diego, 1987—; cons. Ford Found., N.Y.C., 1984—; vis. mem. Inst. for Advanced Study, Princeton, N.J., 1972-73. Author: Politics and Beef in Argentina: Patterns of Conflict and Change, 1969, Argentina and the Failure of Democracy: Conflict among Political Elites, 1904-55, 1974, Labyrinths of Power: Political Recruitment in Twentieth-Century Mexico, 1979, Mexico: The Quest for a U.S. Policy, 1980, Mexico: Neighbor in Transition, 1984; co-author: Modern Latin America, 1984, 89, 92, editor: Statistics, Epistemology, and History, 1984, Drug Policy in the Americas, 1992, The Challenge of Legration: Europe and the Americans, 1993; co-editor: New Approaches to Latin Am. History, 1974, The Family in Latin America, 1978; contbr. articles to profl. jours. Guggenheim fellow, 1975-76; disting. Fulbright lectr. Mexico, 1984. Mem. Latin Am. Studies Assn. (pres. 1981), Am. Polit. Sci. Assn., Am. Hist. Assn., Coun. for Internat. Exch. Scholars, Coun. on Fgn.

Rels. Office: U Calif San Diego Ctr. for Iberian & Latin Am Studies 9500 Gilman Dr La Jolla CA 92093-0510

SMITH, PETER JOHN, geographer, educator; b. Rakaia, New Zealand, Sept. 18, 1931; s. Sidney Charles and Ethel May (Pettit) S.; m. Sheana Mary Lee, May 30, 1959; children: Katrina, Hugh. BA, U. New Zealand, 1953, MA, 1954; diploma of town and regional planning (Central Mortgage and Housing Corp. planning fellow), U. Toronto, 1959; Ph.D., U. Edinburgh, Scotland, 1964. Tchr. schs. New Zealand and Gt. Britain, 1951-55; research planner Calgary City Planning Dept., 1956-59; mem. faculty dept. geography U. Alta., Edmonton, Can., 1959-94, prof., 1969-94, chmn. dept., 1967-75, prof. emeritus, 1994—; Planning cons., 1958—. Author: Population and Production: An Introduction to Some Problems in Economic Geography, rev. edit, 1971, The Edmonton-Calgary Corridor, 1978; editor: The Prairie Provinces, 1972, Edmonton: The Emerging Metropolitan Pattern, 1978, Environment and Economy: Essays on the Human Geography of Alberta, 1984, A World of Real Places: Essays in Honor of William C. Wonders, 1990. Recipient certificate of distinction Town Planning Inst. Can., 1959; Social Scis. and Humanities Research Council grantee, 1977, 84; Leave fellow Can. Council, 1970. Mem. Canadian Assn. Geographers (newsletter editor 1969-77, councillor 1966-70, v.p. 1972-73, pres. 1973-74, editor Can. Geographer 1978-84, award for svc. to the profession), Canadian Inst. Planners, Am. Assn. Geographers, Internat. Planning Hist. Soc. (councillor 1993—), Am. Soc. City and Regional Planning History. Home: 64 Marlboro Rd, Edmonton, AB Canada T6J 2C6

SMITH, PETER LANSDOWN, art director. Art dir.: (films) Chapter Two, 1979, Seems Like Old Times, 1980, The Last Married Couple in America, 1980, Paternity, 1981, Night Shift, 1982, Fandango, 1985, Jagged Edge, 1985, Big Trouble, 1986, Star Trek IV: The Voyage Home, 1986, Nadine, 1987, Blind Date, 1987, Tequila Sunrise, 1988, Fat Man and Little Boy, 1989, Groundhog Day, 1993; prodn. designer: (films) Going Berserk, 1983, The New Kids, 1985. Office: care Art Directors Guild 11365 Ventura Blvd #315 Studio City CA 91604*

SMITH, PETER WALKER, finance executive; b. Syracuse, N.Y., May 19, 1923; s. Stanley Sherwood and Elizabeth Wilkins (Young) S.; m. Lucile Elizabeth Edson, June 22, 1946; children: Andrew E., Laurie (Mrs. Samuel J. Falzone), Pamela C. (Mrs. Denison W. Schweppe, Jr.), Stanley E. B.Chem. Engring., Rensselaer Poly. Inst., 1947; M.B.A., Harvard U., 1948; LL.B. Cleve. Marshall Law Sch., 1955. Bar: Ohio 1955; Registered profl. engr., Ohio. Div. controller Raytheon Co., Lexington, Mass., 1958-66; v.p. finance, indsl. systems and equipment group Litton Industries Inc., Stamford, Conn., 1966-70; v.p. finance, treas. Copeland Corp., Sidney, Ohio, 1970-74; v.p. fin., treas., dir. Instrumentation Lab. Inc., Lexington, Mass., 1974-78; chief fin. officer, treas. Ionics, Inc., Watertown, Mass., 1978-80; v.p. fin., treas. Data Printer Corp., Malden, Mass., 1980-84, Orion Research Inc., Boston, 1984-87; pvt. practice cons. Concord, Mass., 1987—. Mem. fin. adv. bd. Northeastern U., Boston. Lt. AUS, 1943-46, 50-52. Mem. Fin. Execs. Inst., Am. Prodn. and Inventory Control Soc. (founding), Rensselaer Soc. Engrs., Sigma Xi, Tau Beta Pi. Home and Office: 155 Monument St Concord MA 01742-1808

SMITH, PETER WILLIAM EBBLEWHITE, electrical engineering educator, scientist; b. London, Nov. 3, 1937; m. Jacqueline Marie Mankiewicz, June 18, 1967; children: Christal, Dawn N. BSc, McGill U., Montreal, Que., Can., 1958, MSc, 1961, PhD, 1964. Mem of staff Can. Marconi Co., Mont., 1958-59; mem. tech. staff Bell Labs., Holmdel, N.J., 1963-83; dist. mgr. Bellcore, Red Bank, N.J., 1984-87, div. mgr., 1989-92; prof. elec. and computer engring. U. Toronto, 1992—; exec. dir. Ont. Laser and Lightwave Rsch. Ctr., 1992—. Editor-in-chief IEEE Press Progress in Lasers and Electro-Optics Series, 1987-91; editor: Optics Letters, 1989—; contbr. over 140 articles to profl. jours. Board dirs. Monmouth Arts Found., Red Bank, 1965-82. Recipient Sr. Scientist award NATO, 1979. Fellow IEEE (Quantum Electronics award 1986), Optical Soc. Am.; mem. IEEE Lasers and Electro-Optics Soc. (pres. 1984), Am. Phys. Soc., Can. Assn. Physicists. Achievements include first demonstration of waveguide gas laser, non-linear optical interface; development of hybrid bistable optical devices; 32 patents in field. Office: U Toronto, Dept Elec & Computer Engrin, Toronto, ON Canada M5S 1A4

SMITH, PETER WILSON, symphony administrator; b. Utica, N.Y., Mar. 15, 1938; s. Stanley W. and Frances (Brown) S.; m. Kay Gardner, 1960 (div. 1972); children: Juliana, Jennifer; m. Lynn Perrott, 1976. B.Mus., U. Mich., 1965. Asst. mgr. Indpls. Symphony, 1966-67; asst. mgr. St. Louis Symphony, 1967-68; exec. dir. Norfolk Symphony, Va., 1968-72; ops. mgr. Buffalo Philharmonic, 1972-74; ops. administr. Carnegie Hall Corp., N.Y.C., 1974-76; mng. dir. Fort Wayne Philharmonic, Ind., 1976-85; exec. dir. Grand Rapids Symphony, Mich., 1985—. Served to airman 1st class USAF, 1961-64. Mem. Met. Orch. Mgrs. Assn. (pres. 1979-81), Regional Orch. Mgr.'s Assn. (v.p. 1987-89), Am. Symphony Orch. League (bd. dirs. 1989-91), Mgrs. Am. Orch. (vice-chmn. 1989-91). Office: Grand Rapids Symphony Orch 220 Lyon St NW Ste 415 Grand Rapids MI 49503-2273

SMITH, PHILIP DANIEL, academic administrator, education educator; b. Dayton, Ohio, Dec. 25, 1933; s. Hubert Edgar and Edith (Parker) S.; m. Marilyn Brown, Nov. 25, 1953; children: Carolyn Smith Valentine, Norman Daniel, Stanley Nathan. BS cum laude, Bob Jones U., 1953, MEd, Miami U., Oxford, Ohio, 1956; EdD, Pa. State U., 1964. Dean coll. arts and sci. Bob Jones U., Greenville, S.C., 1961-65, registrar, 1965-81, prof. edn., 1956—, provost, 1981—. cons. for books Beginnings for Christian Schools, English Skills for Christian Schools. Pres. Bob Jones U. Alumni Assn., Greenville, 1970-71; mem. coll. parallel adv. com. Tri-County Tech. Coll., Pendleton, S.C., 1973-86. Mem. Assn. Ednl. Communications and Tech. (life mem.) membership coordinator for profl. assns 1969-72, vice chair nat. membership com. 1972-73, chair nat. membership com. 1973-75, council del. S.C. chpt. 1972-73, audiovisual instrn. editorial adv. com. 1974-75, del. to Lake Okoboji ednl. media leadership conf. 1972, 74), Assn. Ednl. Communications and Tech. of S.C. (bd. dirs. 1970-75, pres. 1972-73, award for outstanding contbns. and service 1971), Am. Assn. Collegiate Registrars and Admissions Officers, Phi Delta Kappa. Republican. Baptist. Office: Bob Jones U Greenville SC 29614

SMITH, PHILIP EDWARD LAKE, anthropology educator; b. Fortune, Nfld., Can., Aug. 12, 1927; s. George Frederick and Alice Maggie (Lake) S.; m. Fumiko Ikawa, 1959; 1 son, Douglas Philip Edward. B.A., Acadia U., 1948; M.A., Harvard U., 1957, Ph.D., 1962; postgrad., Universite de Bordeaux, 1958-59; D. Litt. (hon.), Meml. U. Nfld., 1976. Lectr. anthropology U. Toronto, Ont., Can., 1961-63; asst. prof. U. Toronto, 1963-65, asso. prof., 1965-66; asso. prof. archaeology Universite de Montreal, 1966-69, prof., 1969—; v.p. Ednl. Found. for Anthropology and the Public, 1981-84. Author: Le Solutreen en France, 1966, Food Production and Its Consequences, 1976, Japanese edit., 1986, Palaeolithic Archaeology in Iran, 1986; co-editor: The Hilly Flanks and Beyond, 1983; fgn. corr. L'Anthropologie (Paris); contbr. articles to profl. jours.; mem. internat. adv. com. Anthropologie et Societies (Que.). Can. Council Research grantee, 1969, 71, 74, 77; Leave grantee, 1970; research grantee, 1983; NRC research grantee, 1967; Soc. Sci. and Humanities Research Council Can. leave grantee, 1981; exchange research visitor to China, 1984. Fellow Royal Soc. Can., Am. Anthrop. Assn.; mem. Internat. Union Prehistoric and Protohistoric Scis. (permanent coun.), Current Anthropology (assoc.), Can. Soc. for Archaeology Abriad (past pres.), Internat. Union Anthrop. and Ethnol. Scis. (interim chmn. Can. to permanent coun. 1979-84, dep. chmn. 1981-84), Can. Inst. Baghdad. Archaeol. expdn. dir., Egypt, 1962-63, Iran, 1965, 67, 69, 71, 74, 77; other field work in Mex., U.S.A., France, Iraq, French W. Indies, India, 1954-82. Home: 3955 Ramezay Ave, Montreal, PQ Canada H3Y 3K3 Office: Univ de Montreal, Dept Anthropologie, Montreal, PQ Canada H3C 3J7

SMITH, PHILIP JONES, lawyer; b. York, Pa., May 14, 1941; s. Clark S. and Margaret Ann (Jones) S.; m. Ann F. Johnson, Apr. 21, 1973; 1 child, James M. BA cum laude, Williams Coll., 1963; LLB, U. Va., 1966. Bar: Mass. 1967. Assoc. Ropes & Gray, Boston, 1967-76, ptnr., 1976—; lectr. Boston U. Sch. of Law, Boston, 1985—. Contbr. chpts. to books, articles to profl. jours. Bd. dirs., past pres. Greater Boston Youth Symphony Orch., Boston, 1978—; bd. dirs., v.p. The Keewaydin Found., Salisbury, Vt.,

1980—; bd. dirs., past treas. Project STEP, Boston, 1987—; overseer, chair facilites com. New Eng. Conservatory, Boston, 1989-95. Fulbright scholar U. Madrid, 1966-67. Mem. ABA, Eastern Yacht Club (sec. 1977-83), N.Y. Yacht Club, Essex Country Club, Order of Coif. Home: 35 Harbor Ave Marblehead MA 01945-3719 Office: Ropes & Gray One Internat Pl Boston MA 02110-2624

SMITH, PHILIP MEEK, science policy consultant, writer; b. Springfield, Ohio, May 18, 1932; s. Clarenc Mitchell S. and Lois Ellen (Meek) Dudley. B.S., Ohio State U., 1954, M.A., 1955; DSc (hon.), N.C. State U. 1986. Mem. staff U.S. Nat. Com. for Internat. Geophys. Yr., Nat. Acad. Scis., 1957-58; program dir. NSF, 1958-63, dir. ops. U.S. Antarctic Research program, 1964-69, dep. head div. polar programs, 1970-73; chief gen. sci. br. Office Mgmt. and Budget Exec. Office of Pres., 1973-74; exec. sec. Pres.'s Com. Nat. Medal of Sci., 1974-76; assoc. dir. Office Sci. and Tech. Policy, Exec. Office of Pres., 1976-81; spl. asst. to chmn. Nat. Sci. Bd., 1981; exec. officer NRC-Nat. Acad. Scis., Washington, 1981-94; corp. mem. Woods Hole Oceanographic Instn., 1983-89; pres. Cave Research Found., Yellow Springs, Ohio, 1957-63; chmn. tech. panels Fed. Coordinating Council Sci. and Engring. and Tech., 1976-80; ptnr. McGeary and Smith, Washington, 1995—; mem. adv. consulting bd. Geophysical Inst., U. Ala., 1994—; bd. dirs. Aurora Flight Scis. Corp., 1995—. Author: (with others) Defrosting Antarctic Secrets, 1962; The Frozen Future, a Prophetic Report from Antarctica, 1973; contbr. numerous articles to profl. jours. Bd. dirs. Washington Project for Arts, 1983-84, Washington Sculptors Group, 1983-84. 1st lt. U.S. Army, 1955-57. Decorated Commendation medal and Antarctic Service medal U.S. Navy, 1957; recipient Meritorious Service medal NSF, 1972. Mem. AAAS, Antarctican Soc., Cosmos Club (Washington), Am. Alpine Club (N.Y.C.), Coun. Excellence Govt. (prin.). Office: McGeary and Smith 464 M St SW Washington DC 20024-2609

SMITH, PHILIP S., oil and gas company executive; b. 1936. BS, Miss. State Univ., 1957. Ptnr. Arthur Andersen & Co., 1957-58, 60-80; sr. v.p. adminstrn. dept., pres. Mitchell Energy & Devel. Corp., 1980—. 1st lt. U.S. Army, 1958-60. Office: Mitchell Energy & Devel Corp PO Box 4000 The Woodlands TX 77387

SMITH, PHILIP WALTER, savings and loan association executive, real estate consultant; b. Cumberland, Md., Aug. 21, 1945; s. Charles David and Beatrice Estella (Lewis) S.; m. Evelyn Kay Baker, Aug. 7, 1965; 1 child, Valerie Leigh. AA, Strayer Coll., 1965; BS in Applied Econs., U. San Francisco, 1984; AS in Real Estate, Mt. San Antonio Coll., 1987; postgrad., Calif. Poly. Inst., 1991—. Lic. real estate broker. Supr. bookkeeping Montgomery Ward & Co., Wheaton, Md., 1967; controller, mgr. credit Nat. Jet., Inc., LaVale, Md., 1968; treas. Maine Raceways, Inc. (Ogden Corp.), Scarborough, 1969-72; gen. mgr. R/C Ventures, Scarborough, 1972-77; fin. cons. Scarborough, Walnut, Calif., 1977-83; major loan officer Huntington Savs. and Loan, Huntington Beach, Calif., 1985-90; fin. cons. Diamond Bar, Calif., 1990-91; sr. v.p., chief lending officer Universal Savs. Bank, Orange, Calif., 1991-92; asset mgr. Long Beach Bank, f.s.b., Orange, 1992—; dir., CFO McBo Corp., 1993—; speaker Internat. Coun. Shopping Ctrs., N.Y.C., 1973-75; tchr. real estate Mt. San Antonio Coll., Walnut, 1989—, Inst. Fin. Edn., L.A., 1991—; real estate broker Calif. Dept. Real Estate, Sacramento, 1987. Co-inventor method to convert sewerage sludge to gas and organic fertilizer. Founder Secondary Info. Network Group, 1985; mem. cable adv. bd. City of Walnut, 1986-91, mem. fin. com., 1987, mem. econ. devel. com., 1989; mem. real estate adv. com. Mt. San Antonio Coll., Walnut, 1991—. Strayer Coll. scholar, 1963. Mem. Calif. League Savs. Instns. (panelist/moderator 1986-92, secondary market com., real estate com., exec. lending com.), Calif. Real Estate Educators Assn., Real Estate Edn. Assn. Avocations: reading, coin collecting, golf. Office: Long Beach Bank 1100 Town and Country Rd Orange CA 92668

SMITH, PHILIP WAYNE, writer, communications company executive; b. Fayetteville, Tenn., Sept. 2, 1945; s. Clyde Wilson and Chastain (Finch) S.; m. Susan Jones, June 22, 1968; 1 child, Alan Wayne. Student, U. So. Miss., 1963-64, Athens Coll., 1964-65, 69-70. Reporter The Huntsville (Ala.) Times, 1964-66, The Elk Valley Times, Fayetteville, 1969-70; edn. reporter The Huntsville Times, 1970-71; Washington corr. The Huntsville Times, Washington, 1971-76; White House corr. Newhouse News Svc., Washington, 1977-80, Pentagon corr., 1981-84; writer Huntsville, 1984—; pres. P.S. Comms., Huntsville, 1994—; pub. rels. cons. Teledyne Brown Engring., Huntsville, 1984—; safety film producer VECO, Inc., Prudhoe Bay, Alaska, 1991. Co-author: Protecting the President, 1985 (Literary Guild Alternate Selection 1986); screenwriter Our Land Too, 1987, Chems. in War, 1989, Security: Everyone's Job, 1990, Face to Face Prospecting, 1992, Investigating Child Abuse, 1992, Lead Generation, 1993, Telephone Prospecting, 1993, Delayed Enlistment Program Management, 1993, Recruiter Sales Presentation, 1994, Duties and Responsibilities of Recruiting Station Commanders, 1994, Training Future Leaders, 1994, Rehabilitative Training Instructor Program, 1994. Sgt. USMC, 1966-69, Vietnam. Decorated Navy Achievement medal with combat V; named for Reporting Without Deadline, Ala. Press Assn., 1972, News Feature Writing, Ala. AP, 1975. Mem. Tenn. Screenwriting Assn., VFW. Democrat. Episcopalian. Avocations: tennis, swimming. Home and Office: 8007 Hickory Hill Ln SE Huntsville AL 35802-3252

SMITH, PHILLIP CARL, marine and ship pilot, rancher; b. Wewahitchka, Fla., Aug. 12, 1941; s. Ottis Benjamin and Bessie (Kemp) S.; m. Belle Melancon, Feb. 28, 1966; children: Debra Kay, Phillip Carl Jr. Diploma, Wewahitchka High Sch., 1959. Commd. radar observer, unltd. 1st class pilot lic. for Sabine Waterway and tributaries, Tex. From deckhand to capt. Sabine Towing Co., Groves, Tex., 1959-64; ship pilot, ptnr./owner Sabine Pilots, Groves, Tex., 1965—; rancher Tex., 1979—; rancher, owner Red S Ranch, Kirbyville, Tex., 1979—; cons. in field, 1965—; expert witness maritime ct. cases, Beaumont, Tex. Elder LDS Ch., Port Arthur, Tex., 1973—. With U.S. Army, 1962-67. Mem. Masons (32 degree). Avocations: ranching, boating, RV travel, conservation, nature lover. Home: 324 Farm Dr Bridge City TX 77611-2723

SMITH, PHILLIP HARTLEY, steel company executive; b. Sydney, Australia, Jan. 26, 1927; came to U.S., 1950, naturalized, 1960; s. Norman Edward and Elizabeth (Williams) S.; m. Martha Frances Dittrich, June 4, 1955; children: Elizabeth, Thomas, Johanna, Alice, Margaret, Sarah. B.Engring. with 1st class honors in Mining and Metallurgy, U. Sydney, 1950; Metall. Engr., MIT, 1952; diploma indsl. rels., U. Chgo., 1958; LLD, Grove City Coll., 1975. Successively trainee, metallurgist, foreman Indiana Harbor, Ind., Inland Steel Co., 1952-55; successively trainee, metallurgist, dir. purchasing and planning La Salle Steel Co., Hammond, Ind., 1956-64; with Copperweld Corp., Pitts., 1964-77; pres. Copperweld Corp., 1964-77, chmn., 1973-77; pres., chief exec. officer Bekaert Steel Wire Corp., Pitts., 1978-82; mng. ptnr. Hartley Smith & Ptnrs., 1982-84; chmn. Smith, Yuill & Co. Inc., 1984—; bd. dirs. Mitech Labs. Inc., Salem Coll.; adj. prof. bus. Grove City Coll.; vis. dean sr. exec. program Dalian U. Tech., Peoples Republic of China. Patentee in field; editor: Mechanical Working of Steel, 1961; author: Essays in Management, A Guide to Young Managers on the Way Up. Trustee Berea (Ky.) Coll., Wheeling Jesuit U., 1978-85, Gove City Coll.; chmn. Inroads Inc.; chair Sydney U. Found. Cadet officer Australian Mcht. Marine, 1942-43, Royal Australian Fleet Aux., 1943. Recipient Nat. Steelmaking award, 1955, Outstanding Chief Exec. Officer in Steel Industry award Fin. World, 1975; Nuffield scholar, 1949; Fulbright fellow, 1950. Mem. Univ. Club of Chgo., Duquesne Club of Pitts., Fox Chapel Golf Club, Rolling Rock Club (Ligonier, Pa.), Sigma Xi. Home: 102 Haverford Rd Pittsburgh PA 15238-1620

SMITH, PHILLIPS GUY, banker; b. Orange, N.J., Sept. 15, 1946; s. Phillips Upham and Helen Ottilie (Voderberg) S.; m. Ann Dixon Schickhaus, Dec. 29, 1973; children: Guy Dixon, William Schickhaus, Louisa Upham. B in engring., Stevens Inst. Tech., Hoboken, N.J.; MBA, U. Pitts., 1975. Comml. banking rep. The Bank of N.Y., N.Y.C., 1976-78, asst. treas., 1978-79, asst. v.p., 1979-80, v.p., 1980-85, sr. v.p., 1985-93; mng. dir. N.Am. Internat. Strategy Svcs., Inc., N.Y.C., 1993—. Vestryman Ch. of The Heavenly Rest, N.Y.C., 1983-88, treas., 1985-87; trustee Tabor Acad., Marion, Mass., 1987—, treas., 1991—. Lt. USN, 1970-74, Vietnam. Mem.

Racquet and Tennis Club, Down Town Assn., Rockaway Hunting Club, Nantucket Yacht Club. Episcopalian. Home: 9 E 94th St New York NY 10128 Office: Internat Strategy Svcs Inc 2 Wall St New York NY 10005

SMITH, PIERCE REILAND, stock brokerage, investment banking executive; b. Bangor, Maine, Oct. 5, 1943; s. Warren Reiland and Pamela Pierce (Morse) S.; m. Carol Kirsten Hynning, May 28, 1968. BS, Yale U., 1966; MBA, Stanford U., 1972. V.p. Comml. Credit Co., Balt., 1973-80, Mellon Bank, Pitts., 1980-82; sr. v.p., treas. Norwest Corp., Mpls., 1982-87; exec. v.p., treas. PaineWebber Inc., N.Y.C., 1987—. Lt. USCG, 1966-70. Avocations: boating, collecting art. Office: PaineWebber Inc 1285 Ave Of The Americas New York NY 10019-6028

SMITH, R. EVAN, lawyer; b. N.Y.C., Nov. 12, 1941; s. Clay Rice and Elizabeth (Edwards) S.; m. Linda Muller, Aug. 8, 1964; children: Rowland E., Victor H. BA, Swarthmore Coll., 1963; LLB, Columbia U., 1966. Bar: N.Y. 1967, U.S. Dist. Ct. (so. dist.) N.Y. 1967. Assoc. Breed, Abbott & Morgan, N.Y.C., 1966-72, ptnr., 1972-87; then ptnr. Olwine, Connelly, Chase, O'Donnell & Weyher, N.Y.C.; now ptnr. Winston & Strawn, N.Y.C. Mem. Irvington (N.Y.) bd. edn., 1980-86; trustee Abbott House, Irvington, 1987—; mem. Abbott Sch. bd. edn., 1989-93. Office: Winston & Strawn 175 Water St New York NY 10038

SMITH, R. GENE, health facility administrator; b. 1935. V. chmn. Vencor Inc., Louisville, 1995—. Office: Vencor Inc Brown Williamson Twr Ste 700 Louisville KY 40202*

SMITH, R. GORDON, lawyer; b. Roanoke, Va., May 28, 1938. BA with highest honors, U. Va., 1960; LLB magna cum laude, Harvard Law Sch., 1964. Bar: Va. 1964. Law clk. to judge U.S. Ct. Appeals (5th cir.), 1964-65; ptnr. McGuire, Woods, Battle & Boothe, Richmond, Va.; exec., legislation editor Harvard Law Rev., 1963-64. Fellow Am. Bar Found.; mem. Va. Bar Assn. (pres. 1987-88), Am. Law Inst., Phi Beta Kappa, Omicron Delta Kappa. Office: McGuire Woods 1 James River Plz Richmond VA 23219-3229

SMITH, R. JEFFERY, grain company executive; b. 1950. BA, Boston Coll., 1972; MBA, Cornell U., 1974. Various trading and mgmt. positions Continental Grain, N.Y.C., 1974-87; v.p. trading Ctrl. Soya Co., Ferruzzi Group, Ft. Wayne, Ind., 1987—; pres., COO Ferruzzi Trading USA, Inc., N.Y.C., 1990—. Office: Ferruzzi Trading USA Inc 1114 Ave of the Americas New York NY 10036

SMITH, RALPH ALEXANDER, cultural and educational policy educator; b. Ellwood City, Pa., June 12, 1929; s. J.V. and B. V. S.; m. Christiana M. Kolbe, Nov. 16, 1955. A.B., Columbia Coll., 1954; M.A., Teachers Coll. Columbia U., 1959, Ed.D., 1962. Faculty, art history and arts edn. Kent (Ohio) State U., 1959-61, Wis. State U., Oshkosh, 1961-63, SUNY, New Paltz, 1963-67; faculty edn. and art edn. U. Ill., Urbana-Champaign, 1967—; also prof. cultural and edni. policy & aesthetic edn. U. Ill.; first Italo DeFrancesca Meml. lectr. Kutztown State U., 1974, Leon Jackman Meml. lectr., Perth, Australia, 1985, Dean's lectr. Coll. Fine Arts and Comm., Brigham Young U., 1985, Dunbar lectr. Millsaps Coll., 1993; disting. vis. prof. Ohio State U., 1987; sr. scholar Coll. Edn. U. Ill., 1991. Author: (with Albert William Levi) Art Education: A Critical Necessity, 1991; founder, editor Jour. Aesthetic Edn., 1966—; editor: Aesthetics and Criticism in Art Education, 1966, Aesthetic Concepts and Education, 1970, Aesthetics and Problems of Education, 1971, Regaining Educational Leadership, 1975, Cultural Literacy and Arts Education, 1991; co-editor: Research in the Arts and Aesthetic Education: A Directory of Investigators and Their Fields of Inquiry, 1978, Excellence in Art Education: Ideas and Initiatives, 1987; editor: Discipline-Based Art Education, 1989, The Sense of Art: A Study in Aesthetic Education, 1989, (with Alan Simpson) Aesthetics and Arts Education, 1991, (with Bennett Reimer) The Arts, Education and Aesthetic Knowing, 1992, (with Ronald Berman) Public Policy and the Aesthetic Interest, 1992, General Knowledge and Arts Education, 1994, Excellence II: The Continuing Question Art Education, 1995. Bd. govs. Inst. Study of Art in Edn.; trustee Nat. Ctr. Study of Art in Edn. With Med. Svc., U.S Army, 1954-57. Recipient spl. merit recognition Coll. Edn., U. Ill., 1975, Disting. lectr. Studies in Art Edn. award, 1991. Fellow Nat. Art Edn. Assn. (Disting., Manuel Barkan Meml. award 1973); mem. Coun. Policy Studies in Art Edn. (first exec. sec. 1978-82), Ill. Art Edn. Assn. (Disting.). Home: 2909 Heathwood Ct Champaign IL 61821-7659 Office: U Ill 361 Education 1310 S 6th St Champaign IL 61820-6925

SMITH, RALPH EARL, virologist; b. Yuma, Colo., May 10, 1940; s. Robert C. and Esther C. (Schwarz) S.; m. Sheila L. Kondy, Aug. 29, 1961 (div. 1986); 1 child, Andrea Denise; m. Janet M. Keller, 1988. BS, Colo. State U., 1961; PhD, U. Colo., 1968. Registered microbiologist Am. Soc. Clin. Pathologists. Postdoctoral fellow Duke U. Med. Ctr., Durham, N.C., 1968-70, asst. prof., 1970-74, assoc. prof., 1974-80, prof. virology, 1980-82; prof., head dept. microbiology Colo. State U., Ft. Collins, 1983-88, prof. microbiology, assoc. v.p. rsch., 1989—; interim v.p. rsch., 1990-91, prof. microbiology, assoc. v.p. rsch., 1991—; cons. Bellco Glass Co., Vineland, N.J., 1976-80, Proctor & Gamble Co., Cin., 1985-86, Schering Plough Corp., Bloomfield, N.J., 1987-89. Contbr. articles to profl. jours.; patentee in field. Bd. dirs. Colo. Ctr. for Environ. Mgmt., v.p. for rsch.; mem. pollution prevention adv. bd. Colo. Dept. Pub. Health and Environment; mem. Rocky Mountain U. Consortium on Environ. Restoration, Environ. Inst. Rocky Mountain; asst. scoutmaster Boy Scouts Am., Durham, 1972-82, com. mem., Ft. Collins, 1986-91; mem. adminstrv. bd. 1st United Meth. Ch., Ft. Collins. Eleanor Roosevelt fellow Internat. Union Against Cancer 1978-79. Mem. AAAS, Am. Soc. Microbiology, N.Y. Acad. Scis., Am. Soc. Virology, Am. Assn. Immunologists, Am. Assn. Avian Pathologists, Am. Assn. Cancer Rsch., Gamma Sigma Delta. Democrat. Methodist. Avocations: photography, hiking. Home: 2406 Creekwood Dr Fort Collins CO 80525-2034 Office: Colo State U VP Rsch Fort Collins CO 80523

SMITH, RALPH LEE, author, musician; b. Phila., Nov. 6, 1927; s. Hugh Harold and Barbara (Schatkin) S.; m. Betty H. Smith, Sept. 1954 (div. Jan. 1963); children: David Bruce, Robert Hugh; m. Mary Louise Hollowell, 1971 (div. 1977); m. Shizuko Maruyama, 1977; 1 child, Lisa Koyuki. BA, Swarthmore Coll., 1951; MEd, U. Va., 1987. Editor Nat. Better Business Bur., N.Y.C., 1954-58; free-lance writer, 1958-73; assoc. prof. Sch. Communications Howard U., 1973-76; telecommunications exec. and cons., 1976-86. Publs. editor Nat. Assn. Home Bldrs. Rsch. Ctr.; folk musician on Appalachian dulcimer; recs. include Dulcimer: Old Time and Traditional Music, 1973, Tunes of the Blue Ridge and Great Smoky Mountains, 1983; author: The Health Hucksters, 1960, At Your Own Risk, 1969, The Wired Nation, 1970, The Story of the Dulcimer, 1986, Smart House: The Coming Revolution in Housing, 1987. Recipient Russell L. Cecil Disting. Med. Writing award Arthritis Found., 1963; AMA Jour. award, 1965, Nat. Mag. award Columbia U. Grad. Sch. Journalism, 1971, Bus. and Fin. Journalism award Columbia U., 1972; Nelson Poynter fellow in journalism and comms. Yale U., 1972. Home: 1662 Chimney House Rd Reston VA 22090-4302 Office: 400 Prince Georges Blvd Upper Marlboro MD 20772-8731

SMITH, RALPH WESLEY, JR., federal judge; b. Ghent, N.Y., July 16, 1936; s. Ralph Wesley and Kathleen S. (Callahan) S.; m. Nancy Ann Fetzer, Dec. 30, 1961 (div. 1981); children: Mark Owen, Tara Denise, Todd Kendall; m. Barbara Anne Milian, Nov. 8, 1982; stepchildren: Kim Highter, Jeffrey Highter, Eric Highter. Student, Sorbonne U., Paris, 1954-55; BA, Yale U., 1956; LLB, Albany Law Sch., 1966. Bar: N.Y. 1966, U.S. Dist. Ct. (no. dist.) N.Y. 1966. Assoc. Hinman, Straub Law Firm, Albany, N.Y., 1966-69; chief asst. dist. atty. Albany County, N.Y., 1969-73, dist. atty., 1974; regional dir. state nursing home investigation Nat. Atty. Gen., Albany, 1975-77; dir. State Organized Crime Task Force, 1978-82; U.S. magistrate judge U.S. Dist. Ct. (no. dist.) N.Y., Albany, 1982—; judge moot ct. Albany Law Sch., 1983—; lectr. N.Y. State Bar Assn., 1985—. Capt. USNR, 1957-82. Mem. Federal Magistrates Assn., Columbia County Bar Assn., Columbia County Magistrates Assn. Republican. Roman Catholic. Avocations: fishing, bicycling, skiing, sailing, camping. Home: 2375 Route 66 Chatham NY 12037-9717 Office: US Dist Ct 445 Broadway Rm 314 Albany NY 12207-2925

SMITH, RANDY P., metal products executive; b. 1949. MBA, U. Toledo, 1972. CFO, v.p. Automatic Switch Co., Florham Park, N.J., 1993—. Office: Automatic Switch Co 50-60 Hanover Rd Florham Park NJ 07932*

SMITH, RAY E., church officer; b. Mar. 29, 1932; m. Helen N. Smith; children: Danene, Stephen. Grad. Open Bible Coll., 1953; postgrad., Ea. Mont. U. Lic. Open Bible Standard Chs., 1953, ordained, 1955. Pioneer pastor Open Bible Standard Chs., Billings, Mont., 1953-59; pastor Open Bible Standard Chs., Rapid City, S.D., 1959-67; supt. S.D. dist. Open Bible Standard Chs., 1959-63, supt. Mountain Plains region, 1963-67, pres., 1967-76, 79—, mem. nat. bd. dirs., 1959—; pastor Lighthouse Temple, Eugene, Oreg., 1976-79. Bd. adminstrs. Pentecostal Fellowship N.Am., 1967—; 1st vice chmn. Pentecostal Fellowship of N.Am.; founding dir. Citizens for Better TV, 1975, Coun. for Nat. Righteousness, 1975. Mem. Nat. Assn. Evangelicals (mem. bd. adminstrn. 1967—). Office: Open Bible Standard Chs Inc 2020 Bell Ave Des Moines IA 50315-1096

SMITH, RAYMOND, dancer; b. Edinburgh, Scotland. Grad., Nat. Ballet Sch. Corps de ballet Nat. Ballet Can., 1975-78, 2d soloist, 1978-80, prin. dancer, 1980—; guest artist, Scottish Ballet, Edinburgh, 1983; prin. dancer London Festival Ballet. Appeared in Mad Shadows, 1977, The Sleeping Beauty, 1978, 80-81, Swan Lake, 1978, 83, The Nutcracker, 1978, Les Sylphide, 1978, 80, 81-82, Romeo and Juliet, 1978, La Fille Mal Gardee, 1980-81, Etudes, 1980-81, Song of a Wayfarer, 1980-81, Giselle, 1981-82, Napoli, 1981-82, Don Quixote, 1982, Liebestod, 1982, Sphinx, 1983, Here We Come, 1983, Sylvia, 1983, Onegin, 1984; choreographer roles in Newcomers, 1980, All Night Wonder, 1981, Portrait of Love and Death, 1982, Components, 1984; created roles in works by Patsalas, Kudelka, McFall, Tetley, Forsythe, Alleyne, and Bennathan. Office: National Ballet of Canada, 157 King St E, Toronto, ON Canada M5C 1G9*

SMITH, RAYMOND LEIGH, plastic surgeon; b. Norristown, Pa., Sept. 27, 1940; s. Walter Joseph and Pauline C. (Wolfskill) S.; m. Coralynn Elder, Jan. 8, 1966; children—Susabeth, Elizabeth, Christine. B.S., Ursinus Coll., 1962; M.D., Temple U., 1966. Diplomate Nat. Bd. Med. Examiners, Am. Bd. Plastic Surgery. Active staff Reading Hosp., Pa., 1976—, chief sect. of plastic surgery, 1994—, St. Joseph Hosp., Reading, 1976—, Community Gen. Hosp., Reading, 1976—. Mem. Republican Majority Found., Washington Legal Found. Mem. Am. Soc. Plastic and Reconstructive Surgery, Robert H. Ivy Soc., A.C.S., Am. Assn. Hand Surgery, AMA, Northeastern Soc. Plastic Surgeons. Lutheran. Office: 926 Penn Ave Wyomissing PA 19610

SMITH, RAYMOND LLOYD, former university president, consultant; b. Vanceboro, Maine, Jan. 25, 1917; s. Ivan and Genevieve (Gatcomb) S.; m. Beatrice Bennett, Dec. 4, 1943; children: Bennett Charles, Martin Lloyd. B.S. cum laude, U. Alaska, 1943; M.S. in Metall. Engring. U. Pa., 1951, Ph.D. in Metall. Engring, 1953; D.Sc. (hon.), Western Mich. U.; LL.D., No. Mich. U.; D.Eng. (hon.), Mich. Technol. U.; S.D. Sch. Mines and Tech. Instr. math. U. Alaska, 1946-47, asst. prof. metallurgy, 1948-49; rsch. assoc. dept. metallurgy U. Pa., 1949-53; sr. rsch. metallurgist Franklin Inst. Labs., Phila., 1953; sect. chief metallurgy Franklin Inst. Labs., 1954-56, assoc. dir., 1957, tech. dir., 1958-59; prof., head metall. dept. Mich. Technol. U., Houghton, 1959-64, coord. rsch., 1960-64, pres., 1965-79; pres. Am. Soc. Metals, 1979-80, Houghton (Mich.) Daily Mining Gazette, 1979-81, R. L. Smith, Inc.; Am. Soc. Metals/The Metallurgical Soc. joint disting. lectr. in materials, 1983; mem. indsl. adv. bd. mining engring. dept. Mich. Tech. U.; chairman U.; mining engring. U.; Contbr. numerous articles to bd. dirs. Lake Superior & Ishpeming R.R. Contbr. numerous articles to metall. sci. jours.; patentee in field. Bd. dirs. Community Water Co., Green Valley. With AUS, 1943-46. Recipient Distinguished Alumnus award U. Alaska, Clair M. Donovan award Mich. Tech. U., D. Robert Yarnall award U. Pa. Engring. Sch.; Outstanding Service award Air Force ROTC; Rotary Paul Harris fellow. Fellow Metall. Soc., AIME (Henry Krumb meml. lectr. 1981), Am. Soc. for Metals (hon.); mem. Internat. Exec. Svc. Corps., Scabbard and Blade, Blue Key, Tau Beta Pi, Alpha Sigma Mu (hon. lectr. 1982), Alpha Phi Omega, Phi Kappa Phi, Theta Tau. Home: PO Box 726 Green Valley AZ 85622-0726

SMITH, RAYMOND THOMAS, anthropology educator; b. Oldham, Lancashire, Eng., Jan. 12, 1925; s. Harry and Margaret (Mulchrone) S.; m. Flora Alexandrina Tong, June 30, 1954; children: Fenela, Colin, Anthony. B.A., Cambridge (Eng.) U., 1950, M.A., 1951, Ph.D., 1954. Sociol. research officer govt. Brit. Guiana, 1951-54; research fellow U. W.I., 1954-59; prof. sociology U. Ghana, 1959-62; sr. lectr. sociology, prof. anthropology U. West Indies, 1962-66; prof. anthropology U. Chgo., 1966—, chmn. dept. anthropology, 1975-81, 84-85, 94-95; vis. prof. U. Calif. - Berkeley, 1957-58, McGill U., Montreal, 1964-65; mem. com. on child devel. research and public policy NRC, 1977-80; dir. Caribbean Consortium Grad. Sch., 1985-86. Author: The Negro Family in British Guiana, 1956, British Guiana, 1962, 2d edit., 1980, Kinship and Class In The West Indies, 1988, The Matrifocal Family, 1995; co-author: Class Differences in American Kinship, 1978; editor: Kinship Ideology and Practice in Latin America, 1984; contbr. articles to profl. jours. Co-investigator urban family life project U. Chgo., 1986-90. Served with RAF, 1943-48. Guggenheim fellow, 1983-84. Fellow Am. Anthrop. Assn.; mem. Assn. Social Anthropologists. Office: U Chgo 1126 E 59th St Chicago IL 60637-1539

SMITH, RAYMOND VICTOR, paper products manufacturing executive; b. Vancouver, B.C., Can., Apr. 28, 1926; s. Stanley Victor and Kathryn Stewart (Hunter) S.; m. Marilyn Joyce Meldrum, Oct. 17, 1947; children—Vicki, Kathi, Stan. Student, U. B.C., Banff Sch. Advanced Mgmt.; student Advanced Mgmt. Program, Harvard U. Trumpeter Dal Richards Band, 1942; ptnr. Warren McCuish Mens' Clothiers, 1947; sales rep. Vancouver Paper Box, 1949-54; with Home Oil Distbrs., 1954-57; domestic rep. kraft paper and board sales MacMillan Bloedel Ltd., 1957-67; asst. mgr. Kraft Paper & Board Sales, 1961-65; newsprint rep. Powell River-Alberni Sales Corp., Pasadena, Calif., 1965-67; mgr. Powell River-Alberni Sales Corp., Pasadena, 1967-68; mgr. supply control and sales adminstrn. MacMillan Bloedel Ltd., Vancouver, 1968-70, gen. mgr., 1970-71, v.p. mktg. paper and pulp, 1971-73, v.p., gen. mgr. newsprint, 1973-77, group v.p. pulp and paper, 1977-79, v.p. pulp and paper, 1979-80, chief oper. officer, 1980-83, pres., 1980-90, chief exec. officer, 1983-90, chmn. bd., 1991—; bd. dirs. Can. Imperial Bank of Commerce. Served with Can. Army, 1944. Clubs: Capilano Golf and Country, Vancouver. Avocations: music, golf. Office: MacMillan Bloedel Ltd, 925 W Georgia St, Vancouver, BC Canada V6C 3L2

SMITH, RAYMOND W., telecommunications company executive; b. Pittsburgh, PA, 1937. B.S., Carnegie-Mellon U., 1959; M.B.A., U. Pitts., 1967. Dir. budget planning and analysis comptroller dept. AT&T, 1976-77; with Bell of Pa., Phila., 1959-75, 77-85, div. ops. mgr. Western area, 1971-74; asst. v.p. pub. relations Bell of Pa. and Diamond State Telephone, Phila., 1974-75; v.p., gen. mgr. Eastern region Bell of Pa. and Diamond State Tel., Phila., 1977-81, v.p.-regulatory, 1981-83, pres., chief exec. officer, 1983-85; vice chmn., chief fin. officer, dir. parent co. Bell Atlantic Corp., Phila., 1985-88; pres., chief oper. officer Bell Atlantic Corp., 1988; chmn., chief exec. officer Bell Atlantic Corp., Phila., 1989—; bd. dirs. USAir Group, Core States Fin. Corp.; mem. Bus. Roundtable, 1990—; mem. nat. adv. bd. Pvt. Sector Coun., 1990—; mem. James Madison nat. coun. Libr. of Congress, 1990—. Pub. playwright. Vice chmn. Phila. blood donor campaign ARC; mem. bd. advisors Arden Theatre Co., 1991—. With Signal Corps, U.S. Army, 1959-60. Office: Bell Atlantic Corp 1717 Arch St Philadelphia PA 19103-2713*

SMITH, REBECCA BEACH, federal judge; b. 1949. BA, Coll. William and Mary, 1971; postgrad., U. Va., 1971-73; JD, Coll. William and Mary, 1979. Assoc. Wilcox & Savage, 1980-85; U.S. magistrate Ea. Dist. Va., 1985-89; dist. judge U.S. Dist. Ct. (ea. dist.) Va., Norfolk, 1989—; exec. editor Law Review, 1978-79. Active Chrysler Mus. Norfolk; Jean Outland Chrysler Libr. Assocs., Va. Opera Assn., Friends of the Zoo, Friends of Norfolk Pub. Libr., Ch. of the Good Shepherd. John Marshall Soc. fellow; recipient Acad. Achievement and Leadership award St. George Tucker Soc.; named one of Outstanding Women of Am. 1979. Mem. ABA, Va. State Bar Assn., Fed. Bar Assn. Supreme Ct. Hist. Soc., Fourth Cir. Judicial Conf. The Harbor Club, Order of Coif, Phi Beta Kappa. Office: US Dist Ct US Courthouse 600 Granby St Rm 358 Norfolk VA 23510-1915

SMITH, REBECCA MCCULLOCH, human relations educator; b. Greensboro, N.C., Feb. 29, 1928; d. David Martin and Virginia Pearl (Woodburn)

McCulloch; m. George Clarence Smith Jr., Mar. 30, 1945; 1 child, John Randolph. BS, Woman's Coll., U. N.C., 1947, MS, 1952; PhD, U. N.C., Greensboro, 1967; postgrad., Harvard U., 1989. Tchr. pub. schs., N.C. and S.C., 1947-57; instr. U. N.C., Greensboro, 1958-66, asst. to prof. emeritus human devel. and family studies, 1967-91, adj. prof. emeritus, 1991-94, dir. grad. program, 1975-82; adj. prof. ednl. cons. depts. edn. N.C., S.C., Ind., Ont., Man.; vis. prof. N.W. La. State U., 1965, 67, U. Wash., 1970, Hood Coll., 1976, 86. Named Outstanding Alumna Sch. Home Econs., 1976; recipient Sperry award for service to families N.C. Family Life Coun., 1979. Mem. Nat. Coun. Family Rels. (exec. com. 1974-76, treas. 1987-89, Osborne award 1973), U. N.C. at Greensboro Alumni Assn. (chair membership recruitment com. 1994—). Author: Teaching About Family Relationships, 1975, Klemer's Marriage and Family Relationships, 2d edit., 1975, Resources for Teaching About Family Life Education, 1976, Family Matters: Concepts in Marriage and Personal Relationships, 1982; co-author: History of the School of Human Environmental Sciences: 1892-1992, 1992, assoc. editor Family Relations (Jour. Applied Family and Child Studies), 1980-90; ednl. cons. Current Life Studies, 1977-84. Home: 1212 Ritters Lake Rd Greensboro NC 27406 Office: U NC Dept Human Devel Sch Human Environ Scis Greensboro NC 27412

SMITH, REGINALD BRIAN FURNESS, anesthesiologist, educator; b. Warrington, Eng., Feb. 7, 1931; s. Reginald and Betty (Bell) S.; m. Margarete Groppe, July 18, 1963; children—Corinne, Malcolm. M.B., B.S., U. London, 1955; D.T.M. and H., Liverpool Sch. Tropical Medicine, 1959. Intern Poole Gen. Hosp., Dorset, Eng., 1955-56, Wilson Meml. Hosp., Johnson City, N.Y., 1962-63; resident in anesthesiology Med. Coll. Va., Richmond, 1963-64; resident in anesthesiology U. Pitts., 1964-65, clin. instr., 1965-66; asst. prof., 1969-71, assoc. clin. prof., 1971-74, prof., 1974-78, acting chmn. dept. anesthesiology, 1977-78; prof., chmn. dept. U. Tex. Health Sci. Center, San Antonio, 1978—; anesthesiologist in chief hosps. U. Tex. Health Sci. Ctr., 1978—, med. dir. hyperbaric medicine unit Univ. Hosp., 1993—; dir. anesthesiology Eye and Ear Hosp., Pitts., 1971-76; Univ. Hosp.; anesthesiologist in chief Presbyn. Univ. Hosp., Pitts., 1976-78. Contbg. editor: Internat. Ophthalmology Clinics, 1973, Internat. Anesthesiology Clinics, 1983; contbr. articles to profl. jours. Served to capt. Brit. Army, 1957-59. Fellow ACP, Am. Coll. Anesthesiologists, Am. Coll. Chest Physicians; mem. AMA, Internat. Anesthesia Rsch. Soc., Am. Soc. Anesthesiologists (pres. Western Pa. 1974-75), Tex. Soc. Anesthesiologists, San Antonio Soc. Anesthesiologists (pres. 1990), Tex. Med. Assn., Bexar County Med. Soc. Home: 213 Canada Verde St San Antonio TX 78232-1104 Office: 7703 Floyd Curl Dr San Antonio TX 78284-6200

SMITH, REX WILLIAM, journalist; b. Danville, Ill., Oct. 19, 1952; s. Ralph William and Lillian Grace (Hart) S.; m. Marion Roach, July 15, 1989. BA cum laude, Trinity U., San Antonio, 1974; MS with highest honors, Columbia U., N.Y.C., 1980. Mng. editor Rensselaer (Ind.) Republican newspaper, 1974-75; legis. asst. U.S. Rep. Floyd J. Fithian, Washington, 1975-79; reporter, spl. writer Newsday, L.I., N.Y., 1980-87, chief Albany (N.Y.) bur., 1987-91; editor The Record, Troy, N.Y., 1991-95; mng. editor Times Union, Albany, N.Y., 1995—. Contbr. numerous articles to newspapers and mags. Recipient Community Svc. award Rensselaer C. of C., 1975, Media award World Hunger Fund, 1983, Disting. Svc. medal Soc. Profl. Journalists, 1987, Editorial award Common Cause, 1992, award for disting. community svc. N.Y. State Pubs. Assn., 1994; Rotary fellow, 1979, Pulitzer Travel fellow Columbia U., 1982. Presbyterian. Home: Fox Hollow Lodge Dill Brook Rd Petersburgh NY 12138 Office: Times Union Box 15000 Albany NY 12212

SMITH, RICHARD ALAN, publishing and speciality retailing executive; b. Boston, 1924; married. BS, Harvard U., 1946; LLD (hon.), Boston Coll., 1988. With Smith Mgmt. Co., 1947-61; chmn. bd., CEO, Gen. Cinema Corp. (name changed to Harcourt Gen., Inc. 1993), Chestnut Hill, Mass., 1961-91, Neiman Marcus Group, Chestnut Hill, Mass., 1987—; chmn. Harcourt Gen., Inc., Chestnut Hill, 1991—; chmn., CEO, pres. GC Cos., Inc., Chestnut Hill, 1993—; bd. dirs. Liberty Mut. Ins. Co., 1st Nat. Bank of Boston Corp. Office: Harcourt Gen Inc 27 Boylston St Chestnut Hill MA 02167-1719

SMITH, RICHARD ALLEN, retired manufacturing company executive; b. Caro, Mich., June 19, 1939; s. Mark Roy and Doris Smith; m. Barbara A. Smith; children: Nicole A. Smith Braun, Eric A. BSME, GMI Engring. and Mgmt. Inst., Flint, Mich., 1962; MBA, Mich. State U., 1978. With Chevrolet div. Gen. Motors Corp., Bay City, Mich., 1958-70; various positions to dir. ops. steering and suspension group TRW, 1970-81; v.p., gen. mgr., later owner Rochester (Mich.) Gear, Inc., 1981-85; pres., COO, dir. Newcor Inc., Bloomfield Hills, Mich., 1986-95, CEO, 1990-95; retired, 1995, dir. coating specialties, 1995—; bd. dirs. Newcor, Inc., Bloomfield Hills; trustee GMI, 1991—, chmn. devel./capital campaign planning com., exec., com., fin. and audit com. Recipient CEO of Yr. Bronze medal Fin. World, 1992. Office: Newcor Inc 1825 S Woodward Ave Ste 240 Bloomfield Hills MI 48302-0574

SMITH, RICHARD ANTHONY, investment banker; b. St. Louis, July 17, 1939; s. Jack and Ruth Smith; children: Richard Adam, Jonathan. Student, Yale U., 1961. With Salomon Bros., N.Y.C., 1969-75, Morgan Stanley & Co., N.Y.C., 1975-92; mng. dir. Morgan Stanley, N.Y.C., 1983, mem. mgmt. com., 1988-92; bd. dirs. Chateau D'Eau. Bd. dirs. Rabbi Marc H. Tanenbaum Found. Mem. Bd. Am. Jewish World Svc., Shelter Island Yacht Club.

SMITH, RICHARD BOWEN, retired national park superintendent; b. Grandville, Mich., Mar. 8, 1938; s. William Jr. and Mary Elizabeth (Bowen) S.; m. Katherine Theresa Short, Sept. 21, 1980. BA in History, Albion Coll., 1960; MA in English, Mich. State U., 1967. Tchr. Grand Rapids (Mich.) Jr. High Sch., 1960-66; vol. Peace Corps, Asuncion, Paraguay, 1968-70; ranger Nat. Park Service, Yosemite, Calif., 1971-76; ranger, instr. Nat. Park Service, Grand Canyon, Ariz., 1976-78; ranger, legis. specialist Nat. Park Service, Washington, 1978-80; asst. supt. Nat. Park Service, Everglades, Fla., 1980-83; assoc. regional dir. ops. Nat. Park Service, Phila., 1984-86; supt. Nat. Park Service, Carlsbad Caverns, N.Mex., 1986-88; assoc. regional dir. ops. Nat. Park Service, Santa Fe, 1988-89, assoc. regional dir. resources mgmt., 1990-94; cons. on protected area mgmt. in L.Am., 1994—; temporary supt. Yellowstone Nat. Park, 1994—. Recipient Meritorious Svc. award Dept. of Interior, 1992. Home: 2 Roadrunner Trl Placitas NM 87043-9424

SMITH, RICHARD CARLISLE, history educator; b. Marietta, Okla., May 13, 1930; s. Richard C. and Sue V. (Brigham) S.; m. Eddie-Lee Embry, June 1, 1954; children: Mark R., Bruce A., Scott D., Brian D. B.A., Austin Coll., 1951; B.D., Louisville Presbyn. Sem., 1954; M.A., U. Ky., 1957; Ph.D., U. Ill., 1961. Ordained to ministry Presbyterian Ch., 1954; minister Presbyn. Ch., Troy, Ky., 1954-57, Bement, Ill., 1958-60; asst. prof. history Wis. State U., Superior, 1961-62, Tex. Christian U., Ft. Worth, 1962-65; asst. prof. classics U. Alta., Edmonton, 1965-68; assoc. prof. U. Alta., 1969-77, prof., 1977—, dept. chmn., 1975-82; dir. U. Alta. (Alta. Sch. of Rome), summer 1974-78; minister Presbyn. Ch. in Can., Edmonton, 1971—. Mem. Am. Rsch. Ctr. in Egypt, Hellenic Soc., Archaeol. Inst. Am. Home: 3323 108th St, Edmonton, AB Canada T6J 3C9 Office: U Alta Dept Classics, Edmonton, AB Canada

SMITH, RICHARD D., insurance holding company executive; b. 1928; married. BA, Fordham Coll., 1948; JD, Fordham U., 1952. With Chubb Corp. (formerly Chubb and Son Inc.), Warren, N.J., 1952—, former exec. v.p., now pres. Office: Chubb Corp PO Box 1615 15 Mountain View Rd Warren NJ 07061

SMITH, RICHARD D., supermarkets and drug stores executive; b. 1954. With Smiths Food & Drugs Ctrs. Inc., 1971—; formerly exec. v.p., pres., chief exec. oper. officer. Office: Smith's Mgmt Corp 1550 S Redwood Rd Salt Lake City UT 84104-5105

SMITH, RICHARD EMERSON (DICK SMITH), make-up artist; b. Larchmont, N.Y., June 26, 1922; s. Richard Roy and Coral (Brown) S.; m. Jocelyn De Rosa, Jan. 10, 1949; children: Douglas Todd, David Emerson. BA, Yale U., 1944. Pioneer dir. first TV make-up dept. NBC-TV,

N.Y.C., 1945-59; make-up dir. David Susskind Prodns., N.Y.C., 1959-61; freelance make-up artist, cons., 1961—; cons. lectr. Yoyogi Animation Sch., Tokyo, 1992—. Credits include Requiem for a Heavyweight, 1962, The World of Henry Orient, 1963, Mark Twain, Tonight!, 1967 (Emmy award 1967), Midnight Cowboy, 1968, Little Big Man, 1969, The Godfather, 1971, The Exorcist, 1973, The Godfather, Part II, 1974, The Sunshine Boys, 1975, Taxi Driver, 1975, Altered States, 1979, Scanners, 1980, Ghost Story, 1981, The Hunger, 1982, Amadeus, 1983 (U.S. Acad. award 1984, Brit. Acad. award 1985), Starman, 1984, Poltergeist III, 1987, Everybody's All-American, 1988, Sweet Home (Japanese film), 1988, Dad, 1989, Death Becomes Her, 1991, Forever Young, 1992; author: The Advanced Professional Make-Up Techniques. Home and Office: 5313 Siesta Ct Sarasota FL 34242-1706

SMITH, RICHARD ERNEST, retired insurance company executive; b. Adrian, Mich., Oct. 29, 1935; s. Albert Forrest and Thelma (Brock) S.; m. Joanne Piplow, Oct. 11, 1955; children: Kathryn, Albert, Sharon, Richard, Heidi. Student, Spring Arbor Coll., 1955. CLU. Mgr. White Hardware, Adrian, 1950-59; dist. mgr. Met. Life, Adrian and Lafayette, Ind., 1959-75; dir. regional Ohio Nat. Life, Cin., 1975-78; agy. v.p. Provident Life, Bismarck, N.D., 1978-86, pres., 1986-90; bd. dirs. Provident Life Ins. Co. Commr. City of Adrian, 1966-71; trustee Medctr. One, Bismarck, 1986—, Bismarck State Coll. Found., 1987-91; bd. dirs. Macinac Straits Hosp., St. Ignace, Mich., 1995—, Bismarck Devel. Assn., 1987-91, Greater Adrian Devel. Assn., 1966-70. Republican. Club: Apple Creek Country (Bismarck). Lodge: Elks. Avocation: travel. Home: N 5072 Epoufette Bay Rd Naubinway MI 49762-9722 Office: Provident Life Ins Co 316 N 5th St Bismarck ND 58501-4078

SMITH, RICHARD GRANT, retired telecommunications executive, electrical engineer; b. Flint, Mich., Jan. 19, 1937; s. Grand Ladd and Pauline Lorain (Lott) S.; m. Carol Ann Treanor, Apr. 18, 1965; children: Scott, Holly, Melinda. BSEE, Stanford U., 1958, MSEE, 1959, PhDEE, 1963. Mem. tech. staff Bell Labs., Murray Hill, N.J., 1963-68, supr., 1968-82, dept. head, 1982-87; dir. AT&T Bell Labs., Breinigsville, 1987-93; ret., 1993; ind. cons., 1993—; chmn. CLEOS, 1980. Contbr. chpts. in books. Vice chmn. Bernards Twp. Parks and Recreation, 1976-78. Fellow IEEE (Centennial award 1984), OSA; mem. Phi Beta Kappa, Tau Beta Pi, Theta Delta Chi.

SMITH, RICHARD HOWARD, banker; b. Tulare, Calif., Aug. 27, 1927; s. Howard Charles and Sue Elizabeth (Cheyne) S.; B.A., Principia Coll., 1958; LL.B., LaSalle U., 1975; postgrad. Sch. Banking U. Wash., 1970-72; m. Patricia Ann Howery, Mar. 12, 1950; children—Jeffrey Howard, Holly Lee, Gregory Scott, Deborah Elaine. Prin., Aurora Elementary Sch., Tulare, 1951-53; prin. Desert Sun Sch., Idyllwild, Calif., 1953-55; trust administr. trainee Bank of Am., San Diego, 1955-58, asst. trust officer, Ventura, Redlands, Riverside and L.A., 1958-65; asst. trust officer Security Pacific Bank, Fresno, Calif., 1965-68; trust officer, 1968-72, v.p., mgr., 1972-88, Pasadena, 1988—; instr. San Bernardino Valley Coll., 1962—, Fresno City Coll., 1977—. With USN, 1945-46. Mem. Pasadena Bar Assn. Home: 400 S Mentor Ave Apt 306 Pasadena CA 91106-3342 Office: Bank of Am Office Trust Adminstrn Ctr 234 E Colorado Blvd Pasadena CA 91101-2206

SMITH, RICHARD JOSEPH, history educator; b. Sacramento, Oct. 30, 1944; s. Joseph Benjamin and Margaret Elaine (Stoddard) S.; m. Alice Ellen Weisenberger, July 1, 1967; 1 child, Tyler Stoddard. BA, U. Calif., Davis, 1966, MA, 1968, PhD, 1972. Lectr. Chinese U. Hong Kong, 1972-73, U. Calif., 1972-73; asst. prof. history Rice U., Houston, 1973-78, assoc. prof., 1978-83, prof., 1983—, Minnie Stevens Piper prof., 1987, Sarofim Disting. Teaching prof., 1993—; adj. prof. U. Tex., Austin, 1983—; cons. FBI, CIA, Washington, 1985—, NEH, Washington, 1983—, various mus., Houston, Boston, N.Y.C., 1987—. Author: Mercenaries and Mandarins, 1978, Traditional Chinese Culture, 1978, China's Cultural Heritage, 1983, 2d edit., 1994, Fortune-Tellers and Philosophers, 1991, Robert Hart and China's Early Modernization, 1991, Chinese Almanacs, 1993, Cosmology, Ontology and Human Efficacy, 1993, H.B. Morse: Customs Commissioner and Historian of China, 1995. adj. docent Houston Mus. Fine Arts, 1986—; guest curator Children's Mus., Houston, 1987-89, 91—; pres. Tex. Found. for China Studies, Houston, 1988-93. Mem. Assn. for Asian Studies (pres. S.W. conf. 1990-91), Asia Soc. (bd. dirs. Houston Ctr. 1976—), Nat. Com. on U.S.-China Rels., Tex. China Coun., Assn. for Asian Studies, Houston-Taipei Soc. (bd. dirs. 1990—), Phi Kappa Phi. Democrat. Avocations: sports, travel, music. Home: 2403 Goldsmith St Houston TX 77030-1813 Office: Rice U Dept History MS-42 6100 South Main St Houston TX 77005-1892

SMITH, RICHARD MELVYN, government official; b. Lebanon, Tenn., May 2, 1940; s. Roy D. and V. Ruth (Draper) S.; m. Patti Hawkins, Feb. 29, 1964; 1 child, Douglas. B.S.E.E., Tenn. Technol. U., 1963. Asst. Engr.-incharge FCC, Phila., 1972, Balt., 1971-72; chief investigations br. FCC, Washington, 1974-77, asst. chief enforcement div., 1977-80, dep. chief Field Ops. Bur., 1981-94, chief Office Engring. and Tech., 1994—. Recipient sr. exec. service award FCC, 1983, 84, 85, 86, 87, 88. Avocations: instrument-rated pvt. pilot. Office: FCC 2000 M St NW Ste 480 Washington DC 20554

SMITH, RICHARD MILLS, editor in chief, magazine executive; b. Detroit, Jan. 12, 1946; s. William Steele Smith and Janet (Mills) Morrison; m. Lee Ann Vanderstoep (div.); children: Scott William, Anna Mills; m. Soon-Young Yoon, Oct. 20, 1978; 1 child, Song-Mee. BA summa cum laude, Albion Coll., 1968; postgrad., Columbia U., 1968-69, MS, 1970; LLD (hon.), Albion Coll., 1993. Reporter Associated Press, 1966, 1969; assoc. editor foreign dept. Newsweek, N.Y., 1970-73, gen. editor nat. affairs dept., 1973-74; editor Asian region, bur. chief Hong Kong Newsweek, Asia, Hong Kong, 1974-77; mng. editor Newsweek Internat., N.Y., 1977-81; editor Newsweek, N.Y.C., 1982, exec. editor, 1983, editor in chief, 1984-91, editor in chief, pres., 1991—. Trustee Albion Coll.; bd. dirs. Hewitt Nat. Design Mus., Smithsonian Institution. Recipient Disting. Alumni award Albion Coll., 1974. Mem. Am. Soc. Mag. Editors (mem. exec. com. 1985-88), Mag. Pubs. Assn. (bd. dirs.), Coun. on Fgn. Rels., Century Assn., Phi Beta Kappa. Office: Newsweek Inc 251 W 57th St New York NY 10019

SMITH, RICHARD MULDROW, lawyer; b. Jefferson City, Mo., Sept. 2, 1939; s. Elmer Clyde and Mary (Muldrow) S.; children—Stephen, Michael. J.D., U. Ark., 1963; postgrad. U: Ill., 1963-64. Bar: Ark. 1963, D.C. 1980, U.S. Ct. Appeals (D.C. cir.) 1980, U.S. Supreme Ct. 1980. Asst. counsel U. N.C., Chapel Hill, 1964-67, assoc. prof., 1967-73, prof. 1973-79; spl. counsel FPC, Washington, 1976-77; mem. White House Energy Policy Staff, Washington, 1978-79; dir., Office of Policy Coordination, Dept. of Energy, Washington, 1978-79; ptnr. Mayer, Brown & Platt, Washington, 1979-91; pres. Little Creek Marina Inc., Norfolk, Va., 1992—. Author (with others) North Carolina Uniform Commercial Code Forms Annotated, 2 vols., 1967. Mem. ABA (pub. utility law sect., council mem. 1985-88, chmn. gas com. 1988-89, chmn. publ. com. 1989-91). Home: 4800 Pleasure House Ct Virginia Bch VA 23455-2258 Office: 4801 Pretty Lake Ave Norfolk VA 23518-2005

SMITH, RICHARD THOMAS, electrical engineer; b. Allentown, Pa., June 15, 1925; s. Raymond Willard and Mary (Rau) S.; m. Naomi Elsie Anthony, May 26, 1956; children: Cynthia Louise, Carol Ann. B.S. with high honors, Lehigh U., 1946, M.S., 1947; Ph.D., Ill. Inst. Tech., 1955. Registered profl. engr., Mass., Okla., Tex., Gt. Britain. Instr., Lehigh U., Bethlehem, Pa., 1947-50; analytical and design engr. Gen. Electric Co., Schenectady, 1952-58; asso. prof. U. Tex., Austin, 1958-61; George Westinghouse prof. elec. engring. Va. Poly. Inst., Blacksburg, 1961-62; project dir. Tracor, Inc., Austin, 1962-64; sr. engr., asst. dir., dir., v.p. Southwest Research Inst., San Antonio, 1964-66; Okla. Gas and Electric prof. elec. engring. U. Okla., Norman, 1966-68; prof. elec. machinery Rensselaer Poly. Inst., Troy, N.Y., 1968-70; NSF fellow U. Colo., 1970; Alcoa&UMR Disting. prof. elec. engring. U. Mo., Rolla, 1970-73; inst. engr., dir. Nondestructive Testing Info. Analysis Center, Southwest Research Inst., San Antonio, 1973-83; cons., 1983—; adj. prof. U. Tex., 1974-83, prof., 1983-87; cons., reviewer numerous cos. Author: Analysis of Electrical Machines, 1982. Recipient Excellence Fund U. Tex., 1959, DuPont Meml. prize Lehigh U., 1946. Fellow AIAA (assoc.), Instn. Elec. Engrs. (Eng.); mem. Am. Soc. Engring. Edn., I.E.E.E. (1st paper prize 1960, 63, sr.). N.Y. Acad. Scis., I.E.E.E. (numerous coms.), Internat. Electrotech. Commn. (adv. group 1971-74), Sigma Xi, Tau Beta Pi, Pi Mu Epsilon, Phi Eta Sigma, Eta Kappa Nu, Phi Kappa Phi. Office: 402 Yosemite Dr San Antonio TX 78232-1251

SMITH, RICHEY, chemical company executive; b. Akron, Ohio, Nov. 11, 1933; s. Thomas William and Martha (Richey) S.; m. Sandra Cosgrave Roe, Nov. 25, 1961; children: Mason Roe, Parker Richey. BS, U. Va., 1956. Asst. to pres. Sun Products Corp., Barberton, Ohio, 1960-64, v.p., 1964-67, gen. mgr., dir., 1967-69; chmn., CEO Sun Products Corp., 1969-76; prin. A.T. Kearney Co., Cleve., 1977-87; chmn., CEO Richey Industries, Inc., Medina, Ohio, 1987—; dir. Jaite Packaging, Inc. Mem. exec. com. Great Trail coun. Boy Scouts Am., 1973-75; chmn. capital funds dr. Summit County Planned Parenthood, 1970-71; trustee Old Trail Sch., Barberton Citizens Hosp., Medina County Arts Coun.; treas. Friends of Metro Park; vestryman St. Paul's Episcopal Ch.; corp. bd. Cleve. Mus. of Art. Mem. Navy League (pres. Akron coun. 1972-73), Young Pres. Orgn., Portage Country Club (bd. dirs.), Mayflower Club, Ponte Vedra Club (Fla.), Farmington Club (Charlottesville, Va.), Rotary (trustee Akron club 1974-75), Chi Psi. Home: 721 Delaware Ave Akron OH 44303-1303 Office: PO Box 928 910 Lake Rd Medina OH 44256-2453

SMITH, RITA SUE, administrator; b. Winter Haven, Fla., Apr. 19, 1954; d. Vernon Harris and Sarah Olive (Williams) S. AA, Polk C.C., 1974; BS in Psychology, Mich. State U., 1976. Childcare worker Wallace Village for Children, Broomfield, Colo., 1980-81; counselor, program supr. Alternatives to Family Violence, Commerce City, Colo., 1981-84; counselor Ending Violence Effectivly, Denver, 1984-86; dir. Women in Crisis, Arcada, Colo., 1986-88; freelance television and film prodn. Ctrl. Fla., 1989-92; dir. Nat. Coalition Against Domestic Violence, Denver, 1992—. Co-author: (manual) Family Violence: The LEgal Response, 1987. Vol. Peace River Spouse Abuse Shelter, Lakeland, Fla., 1989-91, Refuge House, Tallahassee, 1991-92, Adams County (Colo.) Rape Task Force, 1982. Democrat. Avocations: reading, biking, racquetball. Office: Nat Coalition Against Domestic Violence PO Box 18749 Denver CO 80218

SMITH, ROBERT BOULWARE, III, vascular surgeon, educator; b. Atlanta, June 15, 1933; s. Robert Boulware Jr. Smith and Mary Eva (Black) Fanning; m. Florence Chance Limehouse, Aug. 22, 1953; children: Victoria Joanne Smith Harkins, Robert Boulware IV, Brian Scott. MD, Emory U., 1957. Diplomate Am. Bd. Surgery, Am. Bd. Vascular Surgery. Intern in surgery Columbia Presbyn. Hosp., N.Y.C., 1957-58, resident in surgery, 1960-65; asst. prof. surgery Emory U. Sch. Medicine, Atlanta, 1966-69, assoc. prof., 1969-77, prof., 1977—, head gen. vascular surgery, 1984—; chief surg. svc. VA Med. Ctr., Atlanta, 1969-88; assoc. med. dir. Emory U. Hosp., 1993—. Contbr. numerous articles, book chpts. to profl. publs.; co-editor: Trauma to the Thorax and Abdomen, 1969, Medical Management of the Surgical Patient, 1982, 3d edit., 1995. Capt. M.C., U.S. Army, 1958-60. Mem. ACS, Am. Surg. Assn., So. Assn. Vascular Surgery (sec. 1986-91, pres. 1992-93), Soc. Vascular Surgery, Assn. VA Surgeons (pres. 1983-84, Disting. Svc. award 1988), Ga. Surg. Soc. (pres. 1992-93), Atlanta Vascular Soc. (pres. 1986-88), Phi Beta Kappa, Alpha Omega Alpha. Republican. United Methodist. Avocation: music, travel. Home: 2701 Coldwater Canyon Dr Tucker GA 30084-2358 Office: The Emory Clinic 1365 Clifton Rd NE Atlanta GA 30307-1013

SMITH, ROBERT BRUCE, former security consultant, retired army officer; b. De Quincy, La., Apr. 22, 1920; s. Malcolm Monard and Jewell (Perkins) S.; m. Gladys Opal Borel, Feb. 22, 1941; children: Susan, Richard, Bruce. B.J., La. State U., 1941; grad, Command and Gen. Staff Coll., 1951-52, Army War Coll., 1958-59. Commd. 2d lt. U.S. Army, 1941, advanced through grades to maj. gen., 1969; plans and ops. officer 83d Div. Arty., Europe, 1943-45; personnel officer Philippine-Ryukyus Command, Manila, 1947-49; prof. mil. sci. and tactics ROTC, Lanier High Sch., Macon, Ga., 1949-51; chief res. officers sect., procurement br. Dept. Army, 1952-55; chief troop info. Office Chief Info., Dept. Army, 1962-63, dep. chief info., 1968-69; comdg. officer 8th F.A. Bn., 25th Inf. Div., Hawaii, 1955-56; G-1 25th Inf. Div. and U.S. Army Hawaii, Hawaii, 1956-58; mem. staff, faculty Command and Gen. Staff Coll., Fort Leavenworth, Kans., 1959-62; chief Alt. Nat. Mil. Command Center, Fort Ritchie, Md., 1963-64; dep. dir. ops. Office Joint Chiefs of Staff, 1964-65; asst. div. comdr. 7th Inf. Div., Korea, 1965-66; dep. comdt. Army War Coll., Carlisle, Pa., 1966-68; dep. comdg. gen. Ryukyus Islands, 1969-72, 6th U.S. Army, Presidio of San Francisco, 1972-73; ret. active duty, 1973; reporter, news editor Lake Charles (La.), 1946-47; region adminstrv. mgr. Burns Security Service, Oakland, Calif. 1974-76; ptnr. constrn. co. Napa, Calif., 1976-77, Burns Security Service, 1978-81; now ret.; dir. 1st Am. Title Co., Napa, Calif., 1988-92. Trustee Queen of Valley Hosp. Found., 1987-89; mem. Nat. coun. Boy Scouts Am., 1969-70; pres. Silverado Property Owners Assn., inc., 1990-92. Decorated D.S.M. with oak leaf cluster, Legion of Merit with 2 oak leaf clusters, Bronze Star with oak leaf cluster. Club: Silverado Country (Napa, Calif.). Home: 350 St Andrews Dr Napa CA 94558-1544

SMITH, ROBERT BRUCE, college administrator; b. Phila., July 8, 1937; s. Graeme Conlee and Margaret Edith (Moote) S.; m. Eileen Adele Peznick, Aug. 21, 1959; children—Monica, Sara, Douglas. B.S., Wheaton (Ill.) Coll., 1958; Ph.D., U. Calif. at Berkeley, 1962. Asst. prof. chemistry U. Nev., Las Vegas, 1961-66; asso. prof., chmn. dept. U. Nev., 1966-68; prof., dean U. Nev. (Coll. Sci., Engring. and Math.), 1968-81; v.p. acad. affairs Weber State U., Ogden, Utah, 1981-93, provost, 1993—; mem. Nev. Bd. Examiners Basic Scis., 1970-75, Nev. Bd. Pharmacy, 1972-77; mem. Commn. on Colls., Northwest Assn. Schs. and Colls., 1993-97, mem. Commn. on Colls. 1989-94; dir. Am. State Colls. and Univs. Acad. Leadership Inst., 1986-93. NSF fellow, 1959-61. Mem. AAAS, Am. Assn. Higher Edn., Sigma Xi, Phi Kappa Phi. Home: 2732 Polk Ave Ogden UT 84403-0431 Office: Weber State Univ Ogden UT 84408-1004

SMITH, ROBERT BURNS, newspaper magazine executive; b. Columbus, Ohio, Feb. 24, 1929; s. Edwin Clyde and Blanche (Burns) S.; m. Marjorie Ann Otten. BS, Ohio State U., 1949. Reporter, then asst. news editor Ohio State Jour., Columbus, 1948-59; with Columbus Dispatch, 1959—, mng. editor, 1968-80; editor-in-chief Living Single mag., 1980-86, Ohio mag., 1980-89; editor Columbus Dispatch, 1989—; v.p. Dispatch Features, Columbus, 1968—, Dispatch Charities, Columbus, 1990—; bd. dirs. Dispatch Printing Co.; v.p. Ohio Mag. Inc., 1990-95, pres., 1995—. Sec.-treas. James Faulkner Meml. Fund, Columbus, 1967—; trustee Ohio Hist. Soc., 1986—, pres., 1988—; trustee Dawes Arboretum, 1988—; Hayes Presdl. Ctr., 1995—; active Ohio Privacy Bd., 1977-81. Mem. Blue Pencil Ohio (v.p. 1969, pres. 1970), AP Ohio (v.p. 1974, pres. 1975), Mag. Pub. Assn., Am. Soc. Mag. Editors, Am. Soc. Newspaper Editors, Regional Pubs. Assn. (bd. dirs. 1986-89), York Temple Country Club, Masons, Rotary, Sigma Delta Chi, Delta Tau Delta. Presbyterian. Home: 1456 Sandalwood Pl Columbus OH 43229-4445 Office: The Columbus Dispatch 34 S 3rd St Columbus OH 43215-4241

SMITH, ROBERT CLINTON, senator; b. Trenton, N.J., Mar. 30, 1941; s. Donald and Margaret (Eldridge) S.; m. Mary Jo Hutchinson, July 2, 1966; children: Jennifer L., Robert Clinton, Jason H. A.A., Trenton Jr. Coll., 1963; B.A., Lafayette Coll., 1965; postgrad., Long Beach State U., 1968-69. Tchr., realtor Wolfeboro, N.H., 1975-85; chmn. Gov. Wentworth Dist. Sch. Bd., 1978-84; mem. 99th-101st Congresses from 1st N.H. dist., 1985-90; mem. U.S. Senate, 1990—; mem. armed svcs., environ. and pub. works, econ. task force, govt. affairs, ethic com. With USN, 1965-67, Vietnam; with USNR, 1965-67, 67-69. Decorated campaign medal (Republic of Vietnam). Mem. VFW, Am. Legion, NRA, Theta Xi. Republican. Roman Catholic. Office: US Senate 332 Dirksen Senate Ofc Washington DC 20510

SMITH, ROBERT DRAKE, railroad executive; b. Ft. Worth, Oct. 26, 1944; s. Kermit Rudebeck and Lynne Grace (Harris) S. BA with honors, U. Puget Sound, 1966; MBA, U. Pa., 1968. Planning analyst C. & N.W. Ry. Co., Chgo., 1968; supr. program planning C. & N.W. Ry. Co., 1969, mgr. program planning 1970-73; corp. sec. Chgo. & North Western Transp. Co., 1973-82, v.p., corp. sec. 1982-84, sr. v.p. corp. communications, sec., 1985-86; sr. v.p. investor relations CNW Corp., Chgo., 1986-89; chmn. Aberdeen Ptnrs., Inc., 1990—. Mem. governing bd. Chgo. Symphony Orch.; vol. Juvenile Ct. Cook County, 1970-78. Mem. Am. Soc. Corp. Secs., Assn. Am. R.R.s, Nat. Investor Rels. Inst., N.Y. Soc. Security Analysts, Chgo. Coun. Fgn. Rels., Wharton Sch. Alumni Assn., Assn. for Investment Mgmt. and Rsch., N.Y. Athletic Club, Cliff Dwellers Club, Penn Club (N.Y.C.), Alpha Kappa Psi. Home: 1212 N Lake Shore Dr Apt 26bn Chicago IL 60610-2388 Office: Aberdeen Pntr Inc 500 N Michigan Ave Ste 1920 Chicago IL 60611-3703

SMITH, ROBERT EARL, space scientist; b. Indpls., Sept. 13, 1923; s. Harold Bennett and Bernice (McCaslin) S.; m. Elizabeth Lee Usak, Jan. 3, 1947 (dec. 1984); children: Stephanie Lee, Robert Michael, Cynthia Ann, Kelly Andrew; m. Lyla Lee Lewellen, July 1, 1988. B.S., Fla. State U., 1959, M.S., 1960; M.S., U. Mich., 1969, Ph.D., 1974. Enlisted U.S. Army Air Force, 1943-44; advanced through grades to maj. U.S. Air Force, 1955; airway traffic controller Berlin, Germany, 1945; staff weather reconnaissance officer 9th Air Force, 1956; ret., 1963; project scientist Atmospheric Cloud Physics Lab.; dep. chief atmospheric scis. div. NASA/Marshall Space Flight Ctr., Ala., 1963-86; sr. scientific cons. Univs. Space Rsch. Assn., Huntsville, Ala., 1986-87; sr. computer cons. Computer Scis. Corp., Huntsville, 1987-89; chief space sci. and applications div. FWG Assocs., Inc., Huntsville, 1989-92; NASA program mgr. Physitron, Inc., Huntsville, 1992—. Mem. AIAA, Am. Meterol. Soc., Pi Mu Epsilon, Sigma Phi Epsilon. Home: 125 Westbury Dr SW Huntsville AL 35802-1619 Office: 3304 Westmill Dr SW Huntsville AL 35805-6132

SMITH, ROBERT EVERETT, lawyer; b. N.Y.C., Mar. 15, 1936; s. Arthur L. and Augusta (Cohen) S.; m. Emily Lucille Lehman, July 17, 1960; children: Amy, Karen, Victoria. BA, Dartmouth Coll., 1957; LLB, Harvard U., 1960. Bar: N.Y. 1960, U.S. Dist. Ct. (so. dist.) N.Y. 1962, U.S. Ct. Appeals (2d cir.) 1963, U.S. Supreme Ct. 1967, U.S. Dist. Ct. (ea. dist.) N.Y. 1969, U.S. Ct. Appeals (3d cir.) 1982, U.S. Ct. Appeals (9th cir.) 1988. Assoc. Paul, Weiss, Rifkind, Wharton & Garrison, N.Y.C., 1960-65; from assoc. to ptnr. Baar, Bennett & Fullen, N.Y.C., 1965-74; ptnr. Guggenheimer & Untermyer, N.Y.C., 1974-85, Rosenman & Colin, N.Y.C., 1985—. With U.S. Army, 1961-64. Mem. ABA, N.Y. State Bar Assn., Assn. of Bar of City of N.Y., Fed. Bar Coun., N.Y. County Lawyers Assn., Am. Arbitration Assn. (nat. panel arbitrators), The Am. Law Inst. Office: Rosenman & Colin 575 Madison Ave New York NY 10022-2511

SMITH, ROBERT F., banker; b. Staten Island, N.Y., Oct. 11, 1932; s. Norman Stanley and Lida (Martin) S.; m. Miriam D. Smith; children—Brenda M., Robert F. BA, Bentley Coll., Boston, 1953; D Letters, St. Anselm Coll., 1986. Various positions GE, 1953-77; staff exec. Gen. Electric Co., 1977-81; sr. v.p., treas. Am. Express Co., 1981; vice chmn., dir. Am. Express Bank Ltd. (formerly Am. Express Internat. Banking Corp.), N.Y.C., from 1981, vice chmn., co-chief operating officer, mem. Office of Chief Exec. Officer and Mgmt. Com., 1982-83, pres., chief operating officer, 1983-85, chmn. bd., chief exec. officer, 1985-89.

SMITH, ROBERT FREEMAN, history educator; b. Little Rock, May 13, 1930; s. Robert Freeman and Emma Martha Gottlieb (Buerkle) S.; m. Alberta Vester, Feb. 1, 1950 (dec. 1985); children: Robin Ann, Robert Freeman III; m. Charlotte Ann Coleman, Sept. 9, 1985. BA, U. Ark., 1951, MA, 1952; PhD, U. Wis., Madison, 1958. Instr. U. Ark., Fayetteville, 1953; asst. prof. Tex. Luth. Coll., Seguin, 1958-62; assoc. prof. U. R.I., Kingston, 1962-66, U. Conn., Storrs, 1966-69; prof. history U. Toledo, 1969-86, disting. univ. prof., 1986—; vis. prof. U. Wis., Madison, 1966-67. Author: The United States and Cuba: Business and Diplomacy 1917-1960, 1961 (Tex. Writers' Roundup award 1961), What Happened in Cuba: A Documentary History of U.S.-Cuban Relations, 1963, The United States and Revolutionary Nationalism in Mexico, 1916-1932, 1973 (Ohio Acad. History award 1973), The Era of Caribbean Intervention, 1890-1930, 1981, The Era of Good Neighbors, Cold Warriors, and Hairshirts, 1930-82, 1983, The Caribbean World and the United States: Mixing Rum & Coca-Cola, 1994; contbr. to numerous publs. Lt. col. 43rd Mil. Police Bn., Ohio Mil. Res. 1st lt. U.S. Army, 1953-55. Knapp fellow in history U. Wis., 1957; Tom L. Evans rsch. fellow Harry S. Truman Libr., Independence, Mo., 1976-77, Mexican Ministry Fgn. Rels. fellow, 1991-92. Mem. Soc. Historians of Am. Fgn. Rels., Soc. Mil. History, U.S. Naval Inst., Ohio Acad. History, So. Hist. Assn., Orgn. Am. Historians, Assn. U.S. Army, State Guard Assn. of U.S., Am. Legion, Masons, Scottish Rite, Shriners, Phi Beta Kappa, Phi Alpha Theta. Episcopalian. Avocation: photography. Home: 4110 Dunkirk Rd Toledo OH 43606-2217 Office: U Toledo Dept History Toledo OH 43606

SMITH, ROBERT G., lawyer, assemblyman, educator; b. Scranton, Pa., Mar. 25, 1947; s. Philip and Ruth (Delmar) S.; m. Ellen Theresa Foster, 1968; children: Karen Elizabeth, Lisa. BA in History, U. Scranton, 1969, MS in Chemistry, 1970; MS in Environ. Sci., Rutgers U., 1973; JD, Seton Hall U., 1981. Bar: N.J. 1981. Sci. tchr. Lourdesmont High Sch., Clark Summit, Pa., 1968-70; environ. health sci. curriculum coordinator Middlesex County Coll., Edison, N.J., 1972-73, adminstrv. asst. to dean sci., 1974-77, instr., 1970-74, asst. prof., 1974-76, assoc. prof., 1976-79, prof. chemistry and environmental sci., 1979-86; law clk. N.J. Dept. Environ. Protection, Trenton, 1980; pvt. practice law, Piscataway, N.J., 1981—; ptnr. Smith and Schechter; zoning bd. atty. City of New Brunswick, N.J., 1993—. Mayor of Piscataway Twp., 1981-86; N.J. assemblyman N.J. 17th Legis. Dist., 1986—, mem. appropriations com. and environ. quality com., assembly select com. on ocean pollution, 1988, assembly energy and hazardous waste com. policy and rules, 1994; parliamentarian Assembly Dem. caucus, 1988-90, chmn. task force on environment, 1987; chmn. Piscataway Dem. Orgn., 1981-90; counsel N.J. State Dem. Platform Com., 1987, 89; chmn. Middlesex County Dem. Orgn., 1991-92; elected Assembly Dem. Dep. Minority Leader, 1993—; councilman-at-large Piscataway Twp., 1977-80, pres. council, 1979, v.p.; 1978; mem. Middlesex County Transp. Coordinating Com., 1980-86; chmn. Piscataway Environ. Commn., 1971-75; mem. Piscataway Planning Bd., 1981-86, sec., 1975, chmn., 1976; bd. dirs. N.J. Conf. Mayors, 1984-86; mem. tech. adv. com. air pollution Middlesex County Planning Bd., 1973-74; mem. Greenbrook Basin com. Area 208 Mgmt. Planning Program, 1975-76; mem. commr.'s adv. com. N.J. Dept. Environ. Protection, 1972-86; mem. Joyce Kilmer dist. Thomas A. Edison council Boy Scouts Am., 1983-86. Recipient Disting. Citizen award Piscataway Jewish Congregation B'nai Shalom, 1982; named Legis. of Yr. Eden Inst., 1990, Environ Legislator of Yr., N.J. Environ. Fedn.; U. Scranton Presdl. scholar, 1965-69. Mem. Middlesex County Bar Assn. Roman Catholic. Contbg. author Jour. of Air Pollution Control Assn., 1976; contbg. author; Environmental Health Science, 1975; co-editor: New Jersey State Wastewater Treatment Operations Manual, 1979. Office: 216 Stelton Rd Rm 250 Piscataway NJ 08854-3284 also: 44 Stelton Rd Piscataway NJ 08854

SMITH, ROBERT HOUSTON, archeologist, religious studies educator; b. McAlester, Okla., Feb. 13, 1931; s. Vaughn Hubert and Bobbie Louise (Nelson) S.; m. Geraldine Warshaw, Jan. 26, 1969; 1 child, Vanessa Eleanor. BA, U. Tulsa, 1952; BD, Yale U., 1955, PhD, 1960. Instr. Coll. Wooster, Ohio, 1960-62, asst. prof., 1962-65, assoc. prof., 1965-70, prof., 1970-72, Fox prof. religious studies, 1979-93, chmn. dept., 1981-93, chmn. archaeology program, 1979-93; Grosvenor lectr. Nat. Geographic Soc., Washington, 1985; dir. Coll. Wooster Archeol. Expdn. to Pella, Jordan, 1966-85; cons. on devel. bus. and profl. codes of ethics. Author: Excavations at Khirbet Kufin, 1962, Pella of the Decapolis, vol. 1, 1973, vol. 2, 1989, Patches of Godlight: The Pattern of Thought of C.S. Lewis, 1986, The Passmores in America: A Quaker Family Through Six Generations, 1992; co-author: Pella in Jordan 1, 1982, Pella in Jordan 2, 1992; lectr. Digging Up the Past, NBC-TV Edn. Exchange series, 1968; contbr. articles to profl. jours. Trustee Am. Ctr. Oriental Research, Amman, Jordan, 1979-85. NEH grantee, 1979-81, Nat. Geographic Soc. grantee, 1979-85; Yale U. fellow Am. Sch. Oriental Research, 1958-59. Mem. Am. Schs. Oriental Research, Soc. Profl. Archaeologists, Soc. Biblical Lit., Archaeological Inst. Am. Democrat. Presbyterian. Avocation: landscape painting. Home: 2900-5 Tice Creek Dr Walnut Creek CA 94595

SMITH, ROBERT HUGH, engineering construction company executive; b. Wichita, Kans., Dec. 29, 1936; s. Richard Lyon and E. Eileen (O'Neal) S.; m. Melinda Louise Fitch, Sept. 26, 1959 (div. Dec. 1969); children: Robert Blake, Thomas Hugh; m. Margaret Ann Moseley, Dec. 11, 1971; 1 child, Steven Richard. BS, Kans. State U., 1959; MS, U. Kansas, 1964, PhD, 1970. Sr. process engr. FMC Corp., Lawrence, Kans., 1959-64; rsch. engr. Phillips Petroleum Co., Bartlesville, Okla., 1964-66; group leader Standard Oil of Ohio, Warrenville Heights, Ohio, 1966-67; sr. rsch. advisor, group leader Atlantic Richfield, Plano, Tex., 1970-80; regional mgr., sr. mgr., sales mgr. Fluor Daniel, Houston and Marlton, N.J., 1980-90; sr. gen. mgr. Badger Design & Construction, Tampa, Fla., 1990-93; exec. v.p., COO The Pritchard Corp., Overland Park, Kans., 1993—. Patentee in the field; contbr. to profl. jours. Adv. bd. dept. chem. engring U. Kans., Lawrence, 1993—. Mem. AIChE (chmn., vice chmn., sec. 1962—, Engr. of Yr. award

Dallas 1980), Phi Lambda Upsilon, Sigma Xi. Avocations: tennis, sailing, skiing, reading. Office: Pritchard Corp 10590 Grandview St Shawnee Mission KS 66210

SMITH, ROBERT HUGHES, JR. (BOB SMITH), municipal official; m. Viveca Holder; children: Alison, Audrey, Bobby. BS, Baylor U., 1976; D Dentistry, U. Texas, 1979. Assoc. prof. dentistry U. Texas Dental, 1989-90; mayor City of Garland, Tex., 1992-94; mem. Garland City Coun., 1989-92, Turnpike com., Dallas Regional Mobility Coalition, City Plan Commn., 1985-89; chmn. Plan Commn., 1989. Coach Garland Soccer League, 1989-91; bd. dirs. Garland YMCA (Top Fundraiser 1992). Recipient Outstanding Svc. award Garland NAACP, 1992; named Garland Sch. Dist. Employer of Yr., 1982. Baptist. Office: Office of the Mayor PO Box 469002 Garland TX 75046-9002 also: 200 N 5th St Garland TX 75046

SMITH, ROBERT JAMES, immunopharmacologist; b. Bklyn., May 30, 1944; s. James and Carmela (Denza) S.; m. Florence Christine Varrone, Aug. 8, 1970; 1 son, James Michael. B.S., St. John's U., 1966; M.S., U. Md., 1970, Ph.D., 1971. NIH research postdoctoral fellow Tulane Med. Sch., New Orleans, 1972-74; research scientist Schering Corp., Bloomfield, N.J., 1974-78; research scientist Upjohn Co., Kalamazoo, 1978-83, sr. research scientist, 1983-88, sr. scientist, 1988—; lectr. in field. Sect. editor sci. jour.; contbr. articles to profl. jours. Sci. fair judge St. Monica's Sch., Kalamazoo, 1981-85. NSF fellow, 1969; Chesapeake Bay Research fellow, 1971; U. Md. Grad. Sch. dissertation fellow, 1970-71; USPHS fellow, 1972-74. Mem. Am. Soc. Pharmacology and Exptl. Therapeutics, Am. Assn. Immunologists, Am. Rheumatism Assn., Am. Soc. Hematology, Am. Soc. Cell Biology, Soc. Exptl. Biology and Medicine, Reticuloendothelial Soc., AAAS, Inflammation Rsch. Assn., N.Y. Acad. Sci., Sigma Xi, Phi Sigma. Office: Upjohn Co 301 Henrietta St Kalamazoo MI 48001-4940 *As a scientist one is trained to employ the scientific method in a logical and analytical fashion, and to respect the fact that the key to success is often found in the ability to ask the right question. Nonetheless, one should strive to be humbled by and thankful for success, rather than making the unfortunate mistake of perceiving that we are larger in life than our accomplishments.*

SMITH, ROBERT JOHN, anthropology educator; b. Essex, Mo., June 27, 1927; s. Will Dan and Fern (Jones) S.; m. Kazuko Sasaki, Aug. 22, 1955. B.A. summa cum laude, U. Minn., 1949; M.A., Cornell U., 1951, Ph.D., 1953. Engaged in cultural anthrop. field research N.S., Can., 1950, Japan, 1951-52, 55, 57-58, Brazil, 1966-67; mem. faculty Cornell U., 1953—, prof. anthropology, 1963-74, Goldwin Smith prof. anthropology, 1974—, chmn. dept. Asian studies, 1961-66, chmn. dept. antropology, 1967-71, 76-82; vis. prof. anthropology U. Ariz., 1971, U. Hawaii, 1978, Nat. Mus. Ethnology, Osaka, Japan, 1982. Author: (with Cornell) Two Japanese Villages, 1956, (with Cornell, Saito and Maeyama) Japanese and Their Descendants in Brazil, 1967; editor: (with Beardsley) Japanese Culture: Its Development and Characteristics, 1962, Social Organization and the Applications of Anthropology, 1974, Ancestor Worship in Contemporary Japan, 1974, Kurusu: The Price of Progress in a Japanese Village, 1951-75, 1978, (with Wiswell) Women of Suye Mura, 1982, Japanese Society: Tradition, Self and the Social Order, 1983, (with K. Smith) Diary of a Japanese Innkeeper's Daughter, 1984. Served with AUS, 1944-46. Tng. grantee Social Sci. Rsch. Coun., Japan, 1951-52; recipient Individual Exch. award to Japan Inst. Internat. Edn., 1957-58; Fulbright lectr. Tokyo Met. U., 1962-63; NSF rsch. grantee, 1965-67; Japan Found. grantee, 1979; awarded Order of the Rising Sun, Govt. of Japan, 1993. Fellow Am. Anthrop. Assn., Assn. for Asian Studies (v.p. 1987-88, pres. 1988-89), Soc. Applied Anthropology (editor jour. Human Orgn. 1961-66). Home: 107 Northview Rd Ithaca NY 14850-6039 Office: Dept Anthropology Cornell U Ithaca NY 14853

SMITH, ROBERT JOHN, health facility administrator; b. Vancouver, B.C., Can., Oct. 23, 1944; s. Robert Sanford and Gladys (McHardy) S.; m. Agnes Patricia Kelly, Dec. 31, 1970; children: Andrea Lynn, Kelly Anne, Jocelyn Marie. B in Comm., U. B.C., Can., 1968, MBA, 1971. Exec. dir. The Arthritis Soc., Vancouver, B.C., Can., 1978-80; dep. dir. The Cancer Control Agy., Vancouver, B.C., Can., 1980-88; pres., CEO Lions Gate Hosp., North Vancouver, B.C., 1988—; bd. dirs. B.C. Health Svcs. Ltd., Vancouver, 1991-94, Western Interprovincial Network, Vancouver, 1993-94. Fellow Can. Coll. Health Svc. Exec., Can. Hosp. Assn. (past chair 1994). Avocations: softball, skiing, hiking. Home: 3220 Del Rio Dr, North Vancouver, BC Canada V7A 4C2 Office: Lions Gate Hosp, 231 East 15th St, North Vancouver, BC Canada V7L 2L7

SMITH, ROBERT KIMMEL, author; b. Bklyn., July 31, 1930; s. Theodore and Sally (Kimmel) S.; m. Claire Medney, Sept. 4, 1954; children: Heidi Medney, Roger Kimmel. Student, CUNY Bklyn. Coll., 1947-48. Copywriter Doyle, Dane, Bernbach Advt., N.Y.C., 1957-61; copy chief Grey Advt., N.Y.C., 1961-63; group head, creative dir. West, Weir, Bartel Advt., N.Y.C., 1964-67; co-owner, creative dir. Boyce, Smith & Toback Advt., N.Y.C., 1967-69; author, playwright Bklyn., 1970—. Author: (novels) Ransom, 1971, Sadie Shapiro's Knitting Book, 1973, Sadie Shapiro in Miami, 1977, Sadie Shapiro, Matchmaker, 1980, Jane's House, 1982; (juveniles) Chocolate Fever, 1972, Jelly Belly, 1981, The War With Grandpa, 1984, Mostly Michael, 1987, Bobby Baseball, 1989, The Squeaky Wheel, 1990; (plays) A Little Singing, A Little Dancing, 1971, A Little Dancing, 1974. Bd. dirs. Prospect Pk. South Assn., Bklyn., 1976-86, pres., 1984-86. With U.S. Army, 1951-53. Recipient Best Book award ALA, 1983, Nene prize Hawaii Libr. Assn., 1984, Children's Book award S.C. Libr., 1984, 86, Tenn. Libr. Assn., 1988, Ga. Libr. Assn., 1989, Ala. Libr. Assn., 1989, Dorothy Canfield Fisher award Vt. Libr. Assn., 1986, Mark Twain award Mo. Libr. Assn., 1987, Golden Sower award Nebr. Libr. Assn., 1987, William Allen White Young Reader's Choice award Kans. Libr. Assn., 1987, Pacific N.W. Libr. Assn., 1987, Young Readers' medal Calif. Libr. Assn., 1990, Knickerbocker award N.Y. State Libr. Assn., 1995. Mem. Authors Guild, Writers Guild, Soc. Children's Book Writers, Eugene O'Neill Theater. Avocations: gardening, reading, cooking, tennis. Address: care Harold Ober Assocs 425 Madison Ave New York NY 10017

SMITH, ROBERT L., principal. Prin. Thomson (Ga.) High Sch. Recipient Blue Ribbon award U.S. Dept. Edn., 1990-91. Office: Thomson High Sch PO Box 1077 Thomson GA 30824

SMITH, ROBERT LEE, photographic company executive; b. Parsons, Kans., July 7, 1939; s. George Robert and Ella Elizabeth (Headley) S.; m. Sally Ann Ossian, Sept. 3, 1961; children—Stephen Robert, Kent Alan. B.S. in Bus. Adminstrn., U. Kans., 1961; M.S. in Mgmt., MIT, 1978. With Eastman Kodak Co., Rochester, N.Y., corp. v.p., gen. mgr. Latin Am. region, 1980-86; corp. v.p., gen. mgr. photofinishing systems div. Eastman Kodak Co., Rochester, 1986-89; corp. v.p., gen. mgr. Asia Pacific region Eastman Kodak Co., Tokyo, 1989—; adminstrv. mgr. Kodak Argentina SAIC, Buenos Aires, 1968-70, Kodak Brasileira Ltda, Sao Paulo, 1971-77; gen. mgr. Kodak Mexicana SAdeCV, Mexico City, 1978-80. Trustee Council of Am., 1985. Mem. Am. C. of C. (bd. govs. Japan), Kans. U. Alumni Assn., Sloan Fellows Soc., Rochester Area C. of C., Beta Gamma Sigma. Home: 343 State St # 160NJ Rochester NY 14650-0001 Office: Eastman Kodak Co, Asia Pacific Region, Tokyo Japan

SMITH, ROBERT LEE, retired civil engineering educator; b. Schaller, Iowa, Oct. 31, 1923; s. Lester Martens and Edith (Bright) S.; m. A. Lucille Johnson, Sept. 6, 1947; children: Barbara Lucille, Milton (dec.), Deborah Lee. B.S., U. Iowa, 1947, M.S., 1948. Research asst. Iowa Inst. Hydraulic Research, Iowa City, 1947-48; asst. prof. applied mechanics U. Kans., Lawrence, 1948-52, Parker prof. water resources, 1962-66, prof., chmn. dept. civil engring., 1967-72, Deane E. Ackers prof. engring., 1972-88; prof. dir. Iowa Natural Resources Council, Des Moines, 1952-55; exec. sec., chief engr. Kans. Water Resources Bd., Topeka, 1955-62; spl. asst. Office Sci. and Tech., The White House, 1966-67; design engr. and hydraulic engr. to numerous firms; water resources cons. Black & Veatch Cons. Engrs., Kansas City, Mo., 1968—; chmn. com. on water resources rsch. Fed. Coun. for Sci. and Tech.; cons. in field. Contbr. articles to profl. jours. Mem. U.S. Geol. Survey Adv. Com. Water Data for Pub. Use, 1966-89; chmn. commn. on flood ins. research NRC, 1979-82, mem. water sci. and tech. bd., 1982-86, mem. commn. on engring. and tech. systems, 1988-90; trustee Ctr. for Research, Inc., Lawrence, 1981-84. Served with AUS, 1943-46, PTO. Recipient Key Meml. award Kans. Engring. Soc., 1966, Outstanding Engr. award Kans.

Engring. Soc., 1967, U.S. Geol. Survey Centennial Plaque, 1980, Ray Linsley award Am. Inst. Hydrology, 1990; U. Kans. Miller Prof. Service award 1985, Disting. Alumni Achievement award U. Iowa, 1990, Disting. Engring. Svc. award U. Kans., 1993. Fellow ASCE (past pres. Kans. sect., Julian Hinds award 1988), AAAS; mem. Nat. Acad. Engring. (elected 1975), NSPE, Kans. Engring. Soc., Am. Water Works Assn., Am. Geophys. Union, Am. Soc. Engring. Edn., Am. Inst. Hydrology (Ray K. Linsley award 1991), Pres.'s Club U. Iowa, Chancellors Club U. Kansas, Masons, Sigma Xi, Delta Chi, Theta Tau, Tau Beta Pi, Chi Epsilon. Republican. Congregationalist. Home: 4001 Vintage Ct Lawrence KS 66047-3400

SMITH, ROBERT LEE, agriculturalist; b. Ottawa, Ill., Apr. 2, 1921; s. Charles Emanuel and Helen Beatrice (Cray) S.; m. Lillian Pearl Francisco, 1947 (div. 1969); children: Charles, Jerome (dec.), Rodger, Lawrence, Eileen, Arlene. PhD in Humane Sci. (hon.), Cleo U., 1990. Elder, tchr. Meth. Ch., El Paso, Ill., 1955-67; dir. rsch. Ill. Farmers Union, Springfield, 1963-68; radio officer, pilot search and rescue unit Civil Air Patrol, Woodford County, 1964-69; lectr. U. Ill., Champaign, 1989-90. Contbr. articles to profl. jours. Dir. Ill. Youth Corps. No. Ill., 1965-68; Dem. candidate for state rep. Capt. USAF, 1944-46; with USAFR, 1955-68. Mem. Mensa (life, pres. cen. Ill. chpt. 1980-85, editor 1981-84), Moose. Avocations: writing, bridge, dancing, hiking, reading. Home: 1120 Northwood Dr N Champaign IL 61821-2116

SMITH, ROBERT LEO, ecologist, wildlife biologist; b. Brookville, Pa., Mar. 23, 1925; s. Leo F. and Josephine Elizabeth (Ferguson) S.; m. Alice Elizabeth Casey, Nov. 15, 1952; children: Robert Leo, Thomas Michael, Pauline Ann, Maureen Elizabeth. B.S., Pa. State U., 1949, MS, 1954; PhD, Cornell U., 1956. Asst. prof. biology SUNY, Plattsburgh, 1956-58; prof. wildlife ecology W.Va. U., Morgantown, 1958—; cons. in ecology to pubs. and govt. Author: Ecology and Field Biology, 5th edit, 1995, The Ecology of Man: An Ecosystem Approach, 1976, 2d edit., Russian transl., 1982, Elements of Ecology and Field Biology, 1977, Elements of Ecology, 1985, 3d edit., 1992; contbr. to: Ency. Brit. and World Book Ency., also profl. jours. and books; adv. bd., contbr.: Funk and Wagnalls Ency. Served with U.S. Army, 1950-52. Mem. Ecol. Soc. Am., Am. Ornithologists Union, Wildlife Soc., Am. Soc. Mammalogists, Am. Soc. Naturalists, Am. Inst. Biol. Scis., Outdoor Writers Assn. Am., Wilson Ornithol. Soc., Cooper Ornithol. Soc., Sigma Xi. Republican. Roman Catholic. Home: RR 7 Box 660 Morgantown WV 26505 Office: Div Forestry WVa U Morgantown WV 26506 *Success, by whatever standard it may be measured, comes only strong motivation, hard work, persistence, a competitive spirit, self-discipline, a willingness to keep current, and an adversion to stagnation. Above all, don't take yourself too seriously.*

SMITH, ROBERT LONDON, commissioner, retired air force officer, political scientist, educator; b. Alexandria, La., Oct. 13, 1919; s. Daniel Charleston and Lillie (Roberts) S.; m. Jewel Busch, Feb. 5, 1949; children: Jewel Diane, Robert London, Karl Busch. B.A., Coll. St. Joseph, 1954; M.A., U. Okla., 1955; Ph.D., Am. U., 1964. Commd. 2d lt. USAAF, 1941; advanced through grades to lt. col. USAF, 1961; various assignments in aircraft engring., command and logistics, 1941-60; rsch. logistics Hdqs. Office Aerospace Rsch., 1960-63; project sci., adminstr. postdoctoral rsch. program, asst. dir. NAS, Hdqs. Office Sci. Rsch., 1963-65; ret., 1965; assoc. prof. polit. sci., head dept. eve. classes and corr. study U. Alaska, College, 1966-68, dean Coll. Bus., Econs. and Govt., 1968-70, prof., head dept. polit. sci., 1966-84, prof. emeritus, 1984—; commr. Alaska Dept. Health and Social Services, 1983—; mem. govt. panels and planning groups; dir. Arctic 1st Fed. Savs. & Loan Assn.; corporator Mt. McKinley Mut. Savs. Bank. Author: (with others) Squadron Adminstration, 1951; also publs. on nat. security and nat. def.; Contbr. to: (with others) The United Nations Peace University, 1965. Committeeman Western region Boy Scouts Am., 1968-73; mem. exec. bd. Midnight Sun council, 1973-74, committeeman-at-large nat. council, 1968—; mem. Alaska Gov.'s Employment Commn.; pres. United Service Orgn. Council, Fairbanks, Alaska; mem. active corps execs. SBA. Recipient Silver Beaver award Boy Scouts Am.; named Outstanding Prof. U. Alaska, 1975. Mem. Nat. Acad. Econs. and Polit. Sci., AAAS, Air Force Hist. Found., Nat. Inst. Social and Behavioral Scis., Nat. Inst. U.S. in World Affairs, Am. Polit. Sci. Assn., Assn. U.S. Army (bd. dirs. Polar Bear chpt.), Alaska C. of C. (en. com.), Pi Gamma Mu, Pi Sigma Alpha. Roman Catholic. Club: Rotary. Home: Smithhaven 100 Goldizen Ave Fairbanks AK 99709-3634 also: Smithport 9994 Salcha Dr North Pole AK 99705 also: Smithawaii Nani Kai Hale Apt 607 73 N Kihei Rd Kihei Maui HI 96753 also: Costa Vida Unit #920-921, KM 4,456 Carr, Postal 186 PTO, Vallarta Jalisco, Mexico

SMITH, ROBERT LOUIS, construction company executive; b. Parkersburg, W.Va., Apr. 19, 1922; s. Everett Clerc and Janet (Morrison) S.; m. June Irene Odbert, Oct. 25, 1948; children: Peter Clerc, Morrison James, Edna Louise. B.S. in Civil Engring., Lehigh U., 1944. Design engr. Chrysler Corp., 1944-46; engr. Harrison Constrn. Co., Charleston, W.Va., 1946-47; sr. engr. Creole Petroleum Co., Las Piedras, Venezuela, 1947-55; v.p. Rea Constrn. Co., Charlotte, N.C., 1955-64; exec. v.p. Warren Bros. Co., Cambridge, Mass., 1964-68; pres. Warren Bros. Co., 1968-79; also dir.; sr. v.p. Ashland Oil, Inc., Ky., 1974-79; pres. Robert L. Smith & Assocs., Lexington, 1979—; pres., dir. Tree Farm Devel. Corp., Cambridge, 1979—; dir. Panastalto (S.A.), Wilder Constrn. Co., Inc., J.H. Shears Sons, Inc. Fellow ASCE; mem. Nat. Asphalt Pavement Assn. (dir.), Phi Beta Kappa, Tau Beta Pi, Sigma Chi. Republican. Unitarian. Home and Office: 140 Worthen Rd Lexington MA 02173-7020

SMITH, ROBERT MASON, university dean; b. Fort Sill, Okla., May 5, 1945; s. Arnold Mason and Lillyan (Scott) S.; m. Ramona Lynne Stukey, June 15, 1968; children: David, Angela. BA, Wichita State U., 1967; MA, Ohio U., 1968; PhD, Temple U., 1976. Debate coach Princeton U. (N.J.), 1971-73, Wichita (Kans.) State U., 1973-87, assoc. dean Coll. Liberal Arts and Scis., 1977-87; dean sch. arts and scis. U. Tenn., Martin, 1987—, spl. asst. U.S. Dept. HHS, Washington, 1980-81; cons. in field; chmn. corp. communication bd. Ea. Airlines, Miami, Fla., 1984-86. Contbr. articles to profl. jours. Mem. State Behavorial Sci. Regulatory Bd., Topeka, 1985-87; trustee Leadership Kans., Topeka, 1986-87; founder, bd. dirs. WestStar Regional Tenn. Leadership Program, 1989—. Recipient Excellence in Teaching award Coun. for Advancement and Support of Edn., 1984, 95; HHS fellow, 1980. Mem. Kans. Speech Communication Assn. (Outstanding Coll. Speech Tchr. award 1977, pres. 1978), Assn. for Communication Adminstrn. (pres. 1988), Tenn. Coun. Colls. Arts & Scis. (pres. 1989-90), Kans. Assn. Commerce and Industry (Kans. Leadership award, 1982), Tenn. Speech Comm. Assn. (pres. 1993-94), Phi Kappa Phi, Phi Eta Sigma, Beta Theta Pi, Phi Theta Kappa, Rotary. Baptist. Home: 168 Weldon Dr Martin TN 38237-1322 Office: U Tenn Sch Arts & Scis Martin TN 38238

SMITH, ROBERT MCNEIL, university dean; b. Balt., Jan. 14, 1932; s. Walter H. and Clara (Goodwin) S.; m. Bette A. Smith, June 15, 1961; children: David, Andrew, Michele, Denise, Jonathan, Kristen. B.S., U. Md., 1957; M.Ed., U. Ill., 1958, Ed.D., 1962. Assoc. prof., research assoc. cleft palate research center Sch. Dentistry, U. Pitts., 1963-66; assoc. prof. U. Del., 1966-67; prof. spl. edn. Pa. State U., 1967-78, asst. provost, 1974-78; dean Coll. Edn., Va. Poly. Inst. and State U., Blacksburg, 1978-92; cons. in field. Author books, monographs, articles in field, also chpts. in books. Served with AUS, 1953-55. Fellow Am. Council Edn., 1973, U.S. Office Edn., 1961; resident fellow U. Md., 1958. Fellow Am. Assn. Mental Deficiency; mem. Coun. Exceptional Children, Am. Cleft Palate Assn., AAAS, Nat. Assn. Accts., Am. Coll. Sports Medicine, Phi Delta Kappa, Kappa Delta Pi, Iota Lambda Sigma Psi. Home: 3336 Mcever Rd Blacksburg VA 24060-8710 Office: Va Tech 300 War Memorial Hall Blacksburg VA 24061

SMITH, ROBERT MICHAEL, lawyer; b. Boston, Nov. 4, 1940; s. Sydney and Minnie (Appel) S.; m. Catherine Kersey, Apr. 14, 1981 (dec. 1983). AB cum laude, Harvard Coll., 1962; Diploma, Centro de Estudos de Espanol, Barcelona, 1963; MA in Internat. Affairs, Columbia U., 1964, MS in Journalism with high honors, 1965; JD, Yale U., 1975. Bar: Calif., N.Y., D.C., U.S. Supreme Ct. Intern in econ. devel. UN, Geneva, 1964; corres. Time Mag. N.Y.C., 1965-66, The N.Y. Times, Washington, 1968-72, 75-76; atty. Heller, Ehrman, White & McAuliffe, San Francisco, 1976-78; spl. asst. Office of Atty. Gen. of U.S., Washington, 1979-80; dir. Office Pub. Affairs U.S. Dept. Justice, Washington, 1979-80; mem. U.S. delegation Internat. Ct. of Justice, The Hague, 1980; asst. U.S. atty. No. Dist. Calif., San Francisco,

1981-82; counsel, sr. counsel to sr. litigation counsel Bank of Am. NT & SA, San Francisco, 1982-86; pvt. practice law San Francisco, 1988—; lectr. FBI Acad., Quantico, Va., 1980, Internat. Bankers Assn. Calif., 1994, Cmty. Bankers No. Calif., 1994, 95; judge Golden Medallion Broadcast Media awards State Bar of Calif., 1985; judge pro tem Mcpl. Ct. City and County of San Francisco, 1989—. Bd. editors Yale Law Jour., 1974-75; editor Litigation, jour. ABA litigation sect., 1978-81; mem. editl. adv. bd. Bancroft-Whitney, 1991-94; contbr. articles to profl. jours. Bd. dirs. Neighborhood Legal Assistance Found., San Francisco, 1985-87, Nob Hill Assn., San Francisco, 1985-93; bd. dirs., fin. com. St. Francis Found. San Francisco, 1993-94. 1st lt. inf., USAR, 1965-71. Recipient UPI Award for Newswriting, 1958; Harvard Coll. scholar, 1958-62, Fulbright scholar, 1962-63; Columbia U. Internat. fellow, 1964-65. Mem. ABA (corp. counsel com. 1986—, alternative dispute resolution sect. 1994—), Assn. Atty. Mediators (v.p. No. Calif. chpt. 1995), State Bar of Calif. (pub. affairs com. 1982-85, litigation sect. 1990—), Bar Assn. of San Francisco (bench-bar media com. 1985—, alternative dispute resolution com. 1994—), Assn. Bus. Trial Lawyers No. Calif., Assn. of Former U.S. Attys. No. Dist. Calif., Am. Arbitration Assn. (mem. comml. arbitration panel, No. Calif. adv. coun., mediator Am. Arbitration Ctr. for Mediation), Profl. Atty. Mediators, Cmty. Bds. of San Francisco (conciliator), German-Am. C. of C. West U.S., Harvard Club of San Francisco (bd. dirs. 1986-94, pres. 1992-94), Yale Club of San Francisco (bd. dirs. 1989-94), Soc. Profls. in Dispute Resolution (assoc. mem.), Columbia U. Alumni Club of No. Calif. (exec. com. 1978-92). Democrat.

SMITH, ROBERT MOORS, anesthesiologist; b. Winchester, Mass., Dec. 10, 1912; s. Francis E. and Elsie C. (Davis) S.; m. Margaret Louise Nash, Aug. 7, 1937; children: Jonathan E., Marcia A., Karen E. A.B., Dartmouth Coll., 1934; M.D., Harvard U., 1938. Diplomate: Am. Bd. Anesthesiology. Rotating intern Faulkner Hosp., Jamaica Plain, Mass., 1938-39; asst. in pathology Faulkner Hosp., 1939; intern in surgery Boston City Hosp., 1939-41; gen. practice medicine Cohasset, Mass., 1941-42; anesthesiologist Children's Hosp. Med. Center, Boston, 1946-81; dir. anesthesiology Children's Hosp. Med. Center, 1946-80, pres. staff, 1966-68; assoc. anesthesiologist Peter Bent Brigham Hosp., Boston, 1958-61; assoc. anesthesiologist Boston Lying-In Hosp., 1964-70; instr. anesthesia Harvard Med. Sch., Boston, 1948-63; assoc. in anesthesia Harvard Med. Sch., 1955, asst. clin. prof. anesthesia, 1963-66, assoc. clin. prof., 1966-81, clin. prof. anesthesia, 1976-81, clin. prof. emeritus, 1981—; chief anesthesiology Kennedy Meml. Children's Hosp., 1981-88; anesthesiologist Framingham Children's Hosp., 1988-94. Bd. dirs. Minuteman council Boy Scouts Am. Served to maj. U.S. Army, 1941-46. Recipient Disting. Svc. award Am. Soc. Anesthesiologists, 1988. Fellow Am. Coll. Anesthesiologists (gov. 1952-58); mem. AMA, Mass. Med. Soc., New Eng. Soc. Anesthesiologists (pres. 1966), Mass. Soc. Anesthesiologists (pres. 1955, dir. 1965-68), New Eng. Pediatric Soc., Assn. Univ. Anesthesiologists, Am. Acad. Pediatrics (clin. com. pediatric anesthesiology 1963-64, 76-77), Royal Acad. Surgeons (Ireland) (hon.), Pan Am. Med. Soc. Home: 4 Leslie Rd Winchester MA 01890-3123

SMITH, ROBERT NATHANIEL, broadcasting executive, lawyer; b. Detroit, July 13, 1944; s. Melvyn Maxwell Smith and Sara Evelyn Stein; m. Anne Fuchs, Sept. 11, 1971; children: Jennifer, Michael. BA, U. Mich., 1967, JD, 1970. Bar: Mich. 1971, D.C. 1971. Lawyer FCC, Washington, 1971-74; youth dir. Dem. Nat. Com., Washington, 1974-77; nat. coord. GOTV dr. Dem. nat. Com., Washington, 1976; mem. staff White House, Washington, 1977; asst. dir. Community Svcs. Adminstrn., Washington, 1977-79; pvt. practice Birmingham, Mich., 1980-83; v.p. Heritage Broadcasting Co., Birmingham, 1983-85; pres. Smith Broadcasting Group, Inc., Santa Barbara, Calif., 1985—; chmn. bd. dirs. Smith Broadcasting of Santa Barbara, Evergreen Broadcasting Co., Johnstown, Pa., Smith TV of N.Y., Elmira, N.Y., Smith TV Group, L.P., St. Petersburg, Fla. Bd. overseers Hebrew Union Coll., L.A. Mem. Birmingham Athletic Club. Home: 221 E Constance Ave Santa Barbara CA 93105-3517 Office: Smith Broadcasting Group Inc 127 El Paseo Santa Barbara CA 93101-2229

SMITH, ROBERT NELSON, former government official, anesthesiologist; b. Toledo, Apr. 2, 1920; s. Robert Frederick and Amy Laura (Nelson) S.; children: Sandralyn, Sharon, Robert Nelson, Marilyn Anne, Marcia, Elizabeth. Student, U. Mich., 1938-39; BS, U.S. Mil. Acad., 1943; MS, MIT, 1945; MD, U. Nebr., 1952. Diplomate Am. Bd. Anesthesiologists. Commd. capt. USAAF, 1943, resigned, 1948; intern Toledo Hosp., Ohio, 1952-53; resident Toledo Hosp., 1954-57; anesthesiologist KFC Med. Corp., Toledo, 1954-76; asst. sec. def. for health affairs Washington, 1976-78; bd. dirs. Ohio Med. Indemnity Corp., Columbus., 1968-78; mem. anesthetic and life support drugs adv. com. FDA, Dept. HHS, 1986-90; mem. disability adv. coun. SSA, Dept. HHS, 1986-89. Chmn. State Health Planning Council, 1974-76; mem. Statewide Health Coordinating Council, until 1976. Recipient Sec. Def. medal for outstanding pub. service, 1977. Mem. AMA (Ho. of Dels. Resolution of Commendation), Ohio Med. Assn. (pres. 1970, commendation 1977), Am. Soc. Anesthesiology, Inverness Club, Rotary. Club: Inverness (Toledo). Home: 3424 Gallatin Rd Toledo OH 43606-2442

SMITH, ROBERT PEASE, retired physiatrist; b. Burlington, Va., Apr. 26, 1917; s. Leon Pease and Julia (Pease) S.; m. Caroline Wheelock, July 5, 1947; children: Robert Pease Jr., Cynthia W., Julia Smith Wilson, Sarah Smith Neagle, Alexander Wheelock. AB, Princeton U., 1939; MD, Harvard U., Boston, 1943; postgrad., Harvard U., 1947. Diplomate Am. Bd. Phys. Medicine and Rehab. Intern Mass. Gen. Hosp., Boston 1943-44; asst. resident in pathology New Eng. Deaconess Hosp., Boston, 1943; resident in medicine Mary Fletcher Hosp., Burlington; rsch. fellow Harvard U., Cambridge, Mass., 1955; dir. Vermont Rehab. Clinic, 1956-66; dir. rehab. Gaylord Hosp., Wallingford, 1969-72; cons. Norwalk Hosp.; asst. prof. Yale U. Sch. Medicine, 1972-80, N.Y. Med. Coll., 1972-83; staff mem. Jewish Meml. Hosp., K., Children's Hosp., Louisville Gen. Hosp., Meth. Evangelical Hosp., VA Hosp, Norton Meml. Infirmary; asst., assoc. prof. Coll. Medicine U. Louisville. Contbr. articles to med. jours. Capt. M.C., AUS, 1944-46, ETO. Decorated Bronze Star Combat Med. Badge. Fellow ACP, Am. Acad. Phys. Medicine, Am. Congress Rehab. Medicine; mem. Am. Acad. Phys. Med. and Rehab., Am. Congress Med. Rehab. (past pres. ea. sect.), Am. Soc. for Clin. Evoked Potentials, Chittenden County Med. Soc. (life). Congregationalist. Home: RR 2 Box 2506 Charlotte VT 05745

SMITH, ROBERT POWELL, foundation executive, former ambassador; b. Joplin, Mo., Mar. 5, 1929; s. Powell Augusta and Estella (Farris) S.; m. Alice Irene Rountree, Aug. 22, 1953; children: Michael Bryan, Steven Powell, Karen Louise, David Robert. B.A., Tex. Christian U., 1954, M.A., 1955. Fgn. svc. officer Dept. State, 1955-81; press officer Washington, 1955; vice-consul Lahore, West Pakistan, 1956-58; 2d sec. Beirut, Lebanon, 1959-61; consul and prin. officer Enugu, Nigeria, 1962-65; officer-in-charge Ghanaian Affairs, 1966; officer-in-charge Nigerian Affairs, dep. dir. Office West African Affairs, 1967-69; dep. chief of mission, counselor of embassy Pretoria, South Africa, 1970-74; ambassador to Malta, 1974-76, Ghana, 1976-79, Liberia, 1979-81. Pres. Africa Wildlife Leadership Found., 1981-85. Served with USMCR, 1946-49, 50-52. Decorated Air medal.; recipient Meritorious Honor award State Dept., 1967. Mem. Am. Fgn. Service Assn. Baptist.

SMITH, ROBERT RUTHERFORD, university dean, communication educator; b. Buffalo, Nov. 18, 1933; s. Thomas Newlands and Mary Jane (Rutherford) S.; m. Suzanne Louise Stines, June 7, 1958; children: Eric Anthony, Gwendolyn Anne. B.A. cum laude, U. Buffalo, 1955; M.A., Ohio State U., 1956, Ph.D., 1963. Prof. communication, chmn. div. broadcasting and film Sch. Pub. Communication, Boston U., 1961-78; prof., dean Sch. Communication and Theater Temple U., Phila., 1978—; cons. Nat. Endowment for Arts, others. Author: poems Participations, 1972; criticism Beyond the Wasteland, 1980; editorTV Quar., 1971, Feedback, 1973-76; contbr. articles to profl. jours. Mem. communication com. Mass. Council Chs., 1971-76. Served with AUS, 1959-61. Mem. Broadcast Edn. Assn. (pres. 1984-85), Speech Communication Assn., Broadcase Pioneers (pres. Phila. 1985-86), Soc. Profl. Journalists (pres. 1983-85), Appalachian Mountain Club (Boston), Delmont Club (pres. 1992-94). Home: 1215 Church Rd Oreland PA 19075-2255 Office: Temple U Sch Communication And Philadelphia PA 19122

SMITH, ROBERT SAMUEL, banker, former agricultural finance educator; b. Laconia, N.H., June 16, 1920; s. Samuel W. and Winnifred (Page) S.; m.

Mary Morgan, June 20, 1942; children: Patricia, Peggy, Morgan Scott, Sharon, Starlee. BS, Cornell U., 1942, MS, 1950, PhD, 1952. County agrl. agt. Livingston County, Mt. Morris, N.Y., 1942-44, Lewis County, Lowville, N.Y., 1944, Belknap County, Laconia, 1947-49; assoc. prof. edn. Cornell U. Ithaca, N.Y., 1952-54, assoc. prof. farm mgmt., 1954-58, prof. agrl. fin., 1958-77, W.T. Myers prof. agrl. fin., 1977-81; chmn. Tompkins County Trust Co., Ithaca, 1978-92, chmn. emeritus, 1992—; trustee Mut. of N.Y./MONY Fin. Svcs., N.Y.C., 1981-93, emeritus, 1993—; bd. dirs. Growth and Income, Clifton, N.J., Challenge Industries, Ithaca, N.Y.; advisor Ministry of Agr., Israel, 1960-61, Agrl. Devel. Bank of Iran, 1968. Contbr. numerous articles to profl. jours. Elder First Presbyn. Ch., Ithaca, 1970; bd. dirs. Am. Agriculturist Found., Ithaca, 1980, East Lawn Cemetery Assn., Ithaca, 1987, Hospicare Found., Ithaca. 1st lt. U.S. Army, 1944-47, ETO. Recipient Tax Edn. award IRS, Buffalo, 1973, Disting. Svc. citation N.Y. State Agrl. Soc., 1982. Mem. Country Club of Ithaca, City Club Ithaca, Phi Kappa Phi, Epsilon Sigma Phi. Republican. Avocations: golf, bridge. Home: 60 Wedgewood Dr Ithaca NY 14850-1063 Office: Tompkins County Trust Co The Commons Ithaca NY 14850

SMITH, ROBERT SELLERS, lawyer; b. Samson, Ala., July 31, 1931; s. Abb Jackson and Rose (Sellers) S.; m. June Claire West, Feb. 2, 1963; children-Robert Sellers, David West, Rosemary True, Adam Douglas. BS, U. Va., 1953, LLB, 1958, LLM, 1990. Bar: Ala. 1959. Asst. counsel spl. com. to investigate campaign expenditures U.S. Ho. of Reps., 1960; counsel U.S. Senate Labor and Pub. Welfare Com., 1961-63; ptnr. firm Smith, Huckaby & Graves (P.A.), Huntsville, 1963-85, Bradley, Arant, Rose & White, Huntsville, 1985—; instr. econs., Am. econ. history U. Ala., 1963-64; Mem. industry adv. com., select com. small bus. U.S. Senate. Author: West's Tax Law Dictionary and 11 other books; mem. bd. editors U.S. Tax Lawyer, 1994—. Pres. Madison County (Ala.) Legal Aid Soc., 1971-75; pres. North Ala. Estate Planning Council, 1974. Served with U.S. Navy, 1953-57. Mem. ABA, Internat. Bar Assn., Ala. Bar Assn., Huntsville-Madison County Bar Assn. (pres. 1988). Episcopalian. Home: 6004 Macon Ct SE Huntsville AL 35802-1932 Office: Bradley Arant Rose & White 200 Clinton Ave W Ste 900 Huntsville AL 35801-4918

SMITH, ROBERT VICTOR, university administrator; b. Glendale, N.Y., Feb. 16, 1942; s. Robert Arthur and Marie Marlene (Florence) S. BS in Pharm. Sci., St. John's U., Jamaica, N.Y., 1963; MS in Pharm. Chemistry, U. Mich., 1964, PhD in Pharm. Chemistry, 1968. Asst. prof., then assoc. prof. U. Iowa, Iowa City, 1968-74; assoc. prof., asst. dir. U. Tex., Austin, 1974-77, area coordinator basic pharmaceutics, 1975-76, assoc. dir. Drug Dynamics Inst., 1977-78, dir. Drug Dynamics Inst., Coll. Pharmacy, 1979-85, James E. Bauerle Centennial prof. Coll. Pharmacy, 1983-85; prof., dean Coll. Pharmacy Wash. State U., Pullman, 1985-86, vice provost for research, dean Grad. Sch., 1987—; cons. E. R. Squibb, New Brunswick, N.J., 1979-82, Upjohn Co., Kalamazoo, Mich., 1982-85; external examiner U. Malaysia, Penang, 1981-82; mem. sci. adv. bd. Biodecision Labs., Pitts., 1985-86; Wash. Biotech. Found., 1989-90; mem. noms. com. Coun. Grad. Schs., Washington, 1990-91; accreditation evaluator Northwest Assn. Schs. and Colls., Seattle, 1991—; mem. exec. com. grad. deans African-Am. Inst., N.Y., 1992— Author: Textbook of Biopharmaceutical Analysis, 1981, Graduate Research: A Guide for Students in the Sciences, 1990, Development and Management of University Research Groups, 1986. Bd. dirs. Wash. Tech. Ctr., 1990-92. Grantee NIH, 1974-83; fellow Acad. Pharm. Scis., 1981, Am. Assn. Pharm. Scientists, 1987; recipient Disting. Alumnus award Coll. Pharmacy U. Mich., 1990, Outstanding Svc. award Wash. State U., Grad. and Profl. Student Assn., 1993. Mem. Am. Assn. Colls. Pharmacy (chmn. research and grad. affairs com. 1983-84), U.S. Pharmacopeia (revision com. 1985-90), Acad. Pharm. Scis. (chmn., vice chmn. 1983-85, 90, Presdl. citation 1993), Wash. Rsch. Found. (bd. dirs. 1989—). Unitarian. Home: SE 570 Quar Ridge Dr Pullman WA 99163 Office: Grad Sch Wash State U Pullman WA 99164

SMITH, ROBERT WALTER, food company executive; b. Chgo., Nov. 11, 1937; s. Ernest Gilmer and Anna (Mayo) S.; m. Audrey Mavis Segar, Apr. 20, 1962; children: Melissa Ann, Kathleen Diane, Michael Robert. BS, U. Ariz., 1963. Mgmt. trainee Fleming Cos. Inc., Houston, 1963-64, mgr. store planning, 1964-65; mgr. store planning Fleming Cos. Inc., Austin, 1965-66, Phila., 1966-72; dir. site selection Fleming Cos. Inc., Topeka, 1972-75, dir. store devel., 1975-83; v.p. store devel. Fleming Cos. Inc., Oklahoma City, 1983—, sr. v.p. store devel., 1993—. Mem. Internat. Council Shopping Ctrs., Nat. Assn. Corp. Real Estate Execs. Republican. Lutheran. Office: Fleming Cos Inc Box 26647 6301 Waterford Blvd Oklahoma City OK 73126

SMITH, ROBERT WESTON See WOLFMAN JACK

SMITH, ROBERT WILLIAM, former insurance company executive, lawyer; b. Catskill, N.Y., Apr. 2, 1923; s. Victor and Leda Leone (Cline) S.; m. Inez R. Iuzzolino, Jan. 31, 1976; children: Jeffrey, Timothy, Kathy. BS cum laude, Syracuse U., 1948; JD cum laude, Seton Hall U. Coll. of Law, 1987. Bar: N.J. 1987; accredited pers. exec.; CLU. With Prudential Ins. Co. Am., Newark, 1948-84; sr. v.p. Prudential Ins. Co. Am., 1973-84; mem. adv. council on mgmt. and personnel research (Conf. Bd.), 1975-83, chmn., 1977-78; now ret.; chmn. LOMA Personnel Council, 1971-72; bus. adminstr., City of Newark, 1970. Trustee Coll. of Ins., 1974-83; trustee State Theater of N.J., 1983-92, chmn., 1984-87; cons. Nat. Exec. Svc. Corps, 1988—. Served to 1st lt. USAAF, 1942-45. Decorated Air medal with 5 oak leaf clusters. Mem. Beta Gamma Sigma, Kappa Psi, Sigma Phi Epsilon. Home: 41 Woodbine Rd Florham Park NJ 07932-2647

SMITH, ROBERTA HAWKINS, plant physiologist; b. Tulare, Calif., May 3, 1945; d. William Brevard and Freda Lois (Kessler) Hawkins; m. James Willie Smith Jr., Sept. 17, 1968; children: James Willie III, Cristine Lois. BS, U. Calif., Riverside, 1967, MS, 1968, PhD, 1970. Postdoctoral fellow dept. plant sci. Tex. A&M U., College Station, 1972-73, asst. prof. dept. plant sci., 1974-79, assoc. prof. dept. plant sci., 1979-85, prof. dept. soil and crop sci., 1985—; asst. prof. Sam Huston State U., Huntsville, Tex., 1973-74. Editorial bd. Biotech. Advances, 1986—, Plant Physiology, 1984—. Mem. Crop Sci. Soc. Am. (chmn. C-7 divsn. 1990-91), Internat. Crops Rsch. Inst. Semi-Arid Tropics (bd. govs. 1989-95), Faculty of Plant Physiology (chmn. 1987-89), Tissue Culture Assn. (chmn. plant divsn. 1983-86, pres. 1994—). Republican. Methodist. Avocations: English and Western horseback riding, gardening, reading. Home: RR 1 Box 701 Hearne TX 77859-9734 Office: Tex A&M Univ Dept Soil And Sci College Station TX 77843

SMITH, ROBIN DOYLE, judge; b. Oklahoma City, Jan. 23, 1957; s. Travis Ray and Juanita Mae (Stephens) S.; m. Donna Jean Bartlett, Sept. 29, 1984. BS, Okla. State U., 1979; JD, Tex. Tech. U., 1981. Bar: Tex. 1982. Asst. city atty. City of Midland, Tex., 1982-83, presiding judge 1984—; sole practice Midland 1983-84; bd. dirs. Tex. Mcpl. Cts. Assn., 2d v.p. 1989-90, pres.-elect, 1990-91, pres., 1991—; bd. dirs. Tex. Mcpl. Cts. Tng. Ctr., Austin. Contbg. author Tex. Mcpl. Court Procedures Manual, 1988, Tex. Mcpl. Ct. Tng. Ctr. Newsletter, 1987; pub. Tex. Mcpl. Ct. Justice Ct. News, 1987—. Grad. Leadership Midland, 1987. Mem. ABA (del. to conf. of spl. ct. judges 1988, 89, 90, 91, exec. com. 1990—), State Bar Tex. (chmn. mcpl. judges sect. 1988-89, state bar coll. 1986—), Midland County Young Lawyers. Republican. Avocations: water sports, scuba diving, outdoor activities. Home: PO Box 585 Midland TX 79702-0585 Office: City of Midland Tex PO Box 1152 Midland TX 79702-1152

SMITH, RODGER FIELD, financial executive; b. Milw., Jan. 23, 1941; s. Millard Beale and Alice Catherine (Field) S.; m. Sarah Godfrey, June 19, 1964; children: Rodger F. Jr., Scott G., Reid W. BSChemE, U. Wis., 1964, MBA in Fin. with distinction, 1965. V.p. Allis Chalmers, Milw., 1966-76; ptnr. Greenwich (Conn.) Assocs., 1987—; trustee Harbor Funds, Toledo 1989—; bd. dirs. Arlington Capital, London, 1972-76. Author articles on investing pension funds. Fund raiser United Way, Milw., 1966-76. Mem. U. Wis. Alumni Assn. (nat. bd. dirs. 1994—), Wee Burn Country Club, Bascom Hill Soc., Tau Beta Pi (chmn. trust adv. com. 1986—), Beta Gamma Sigma. Avocations: travel, golf, tennis, coin collecting. Office: Greenwich Assocs Office Park Eight Greenwich CT 06830

SMITH, RODNEY, electronics executive; b. 1941. BSEE, Southampton Coll. Advanced Tech., Eng. Various positions to v.p., gen. mgr. Fairchild Semiconductor Corp., Mountain View, Calif., 1969-83; chmn., pres., CEO

Altera Corp., San Jose, Calif., 1983—. Office: Altera Corp 2610 Orchard Pky San Jose CA 95134-2020*

SMITH, ROGER BONHAM, automotive manufacturing executive; b. Columbus, Ohio, July 12, 1925; s. Emmet Quimby and Bess (Obetz) S.; m. Barbara Ann Rasch, June 7, 1954; children: Roger Bonham, Jennifer Anne, Victoria Belle, Drew Johnston. Student, U. Mich., 1942-44, B.B.A., 1947, M.B.A., 1949. With GM, Detroit, 1949-90; treas. GM, 1970-71, v.p. charge fin. staff, 1971-73, v.p., group exec. in charge of non-automotive and def. group, 1973-74, exec. v.p., 1974-80, vice chmn. fin. com., 1975-81, chmn., chief exec. officer, 1981-90, bd. dir., ret., 1990; bd. dirs. GM Corp., Citicorp, Johnson & Johnson, Pepsico, Internat. Paper. Mem. Bus. Coun. Clubs: Detroit, Detroit Athletic, Orchard Lake (Mich.) Country, Bloomfield Hills Country; Links (N.Y.C.). Office: GM Corp 31 E Judson St Pontiac MI 48342-2206

SMITH, ROGER DEAN, pathologist; b. N.Y.C., Oct. 6, 1932; s. Joseph Leslie and Matilda (Feigelson) S.; m. Margaret Helen Smith, Apr. 24, 1957; children—Wade Russell, Craig Andrew, Douglas Dean, Roger Len. A.B., Cornell U., 1954; M.D., N.Y. Med. Coll., 1958. Diplomate Am. Bd. Pathology, Nat. Bd. Med. Examiners (flex test com. 1982-94, chmn. 1983-90, U.S. med. licensing exam. step 3 devel. com. 1992-94, med. licensing exam. step 3 com. 1994—). Asst. prof. dept. pathology U. Ill. Coll. Medicine, Chgo., 1966; cons. renal pathology Presbyn. St. Lukes Hosp., W. Side VA Hosp., Chgo., 1969; asso. prof. dept. pathology U. Ill. Coll. Medicine, Chgo., 1970; dir. ind. study program, asst. dean U. Ill. Coll. Medicine (Coll. Medicine), 1971-72; Mary M. Emery prof., dir. dept. pathology U. Cin., 1972-90; dir. lab. services U. Cin. Hosp.; mem. test coms. Nat. Bd. Med. Examiners, 1976-93. Contbr. research papers to profl. jours. Capt. M.C. U.S. Army, 1959-61. Recipient Hoektoen award Chgo. Pathology Soc.; USPHS pathology research fellow, 1962-66; Am. Cancer Soc. grantee, 1965-68; NIH grantee, 1968-72, 75-79. Mem. Am. Assn. Pathologists (chmn. 1972, pres. 1985-88), Coll. Am. Pathologists (chmn. edn. com. and manpower task force 1983-90), Internat. Acad. Pathology, Am. Assn. Clin. Pathologists, Armed Forces Inst. Pathology (sci. adv. bd. 1989-94). Home: 1319 Dillon Ave Cincinnati OH 45208-4208 Office: U Cin Coll Medicine Dept Pathology Cincinnati OH 45267

SMITH, ROGER WINSTON, political theorist, educator; b. Birmingham, Ala., July 9, 1936; s. Buford Houston and Sarah Louise (Trucks) S.; m. Martha Christin Daniels, Jan. 16, 1960; children—Louisa, David. A.B. magna cum laude, Harvard U., 1958, postgrad. in law, 1958-59; M.A. in Polit. Sci., U. Calif.-Berkeley, 1963, Ph.D. in Polit. Sci., 1971. Teaching assoc. U. Calif.-Berkeley, 1965-66; asst. prof. govt. Coll. William and Mary, Williamsburg, Va., 1967-72, assoc. prof., 1972-80, prof, 1980—; sr. lectr. politics Glasgow U., Scotland, 1977-78; lectr. N.E.H., 1988; cons. Nelson-Hall Pubs., Chgo.; mem. council Inst. Internat. Conf. on the Holocaust and Genocide, Jerusalem; film cons. Aremnian Heritage Project. Co-author, editor: Guilt: Man and Society, 1971; co-author: Genocide and the Modern Age, 1986, Genocide, vol. 2, 1991, Bearing Witness to the Holocaust, 1939-89; contbg. editor Internet on the Holocaust and Genocide; contbr. articles to profl. jours. Served to 1st lt. U.S. Army, 1960-62, Japan. Fellow NSF, 1966, College of William and Mary, 1977. Mem. Am. Polit. Sci. Assn., Amnesty Internat., Cultural Survival. Democrat. Baptist. Avocations: gardening; walking. Home: 102 Lake Dr Williamsburg VA 23185-3113 Office: Coll William and Mary Dept Govt Williamsburg VA 23185

SMITH, ROGERS MOOD, political science educator; b. Spartanburg, S.C., Sept. 20, 1953; s. Henry Dale and Betty (Mood) S. B.A. in Polit. Sci., Mich. State U., 1974; M.A., Harvard U., 1978, Ph.D, 1980. Asst. prof. polit. sci. Yale U., New Haven, 1980-85, assoc. prof., 1985—. Author: Liberalism and American Constitutional Law, 1985; Citizenship Without Consent, 1985. Contbr. articles to profl. jours. Recipient Disting. Undergrad. Teaching award Yale U., 1984; Charles Sumner prize Harvard U., 1981. Mem. Am. Polit. Sci. Assn., New Eng. Polit. Sci. Assn. (Pres.'s award 1982). Avocation: baseball. Office: Yale U Dept Politcal Science 124 Prospect New Haven CT 06520

SMITH, RONALD EMORY, telecommunications executive; b. Shelburne, N.S., Can., May 26, 1950; s. Edgar Earle and Ida Mae (Porter) S.; children: Stephen, Sarah, Susan. BBA, Acadia U., Wolfville, N.S., 1971. Chartered acct., N.S. Staff acct., mgr. Clarkson Gordon (now Ernst & Young), Halifax, N.S., 1971-78, Toronto, Ont., Can., 1978-80; prin., ptnr. Woods Gordon (now Ernst & Young), Toronto, 1980-87; v.p. fin. and bus. svcs. Maritime Tel. & Tel., Halifax, 1987—; bd. dirs. The Island Telephone Co. Ltd., Charlottetown, P.E.I., Can., MT&T Leasing Inc., Halifax, MT&T Mobile Inc., Halifax. Dir. Coun. for Can. Unity, 1994—; bd. govs. Acadia U., 1994—; chmn. Atlantic Provinces Econ. Coun., Halifax, 1989—, Grace Maternity Hosp. Bd. Trustees, 1989—, vice chmn.; pres. CAn. Assn. for Cmty. Living, 1989-93, chmn. Min.'s Task Force on Physician Policy Devel., N.S., 1991-93; mem. coun. fin. execs. Conf. Bd. Mem. Fin. Execs. Inst., Can. Inst. Chartered Accts., Inst. Chartered Accts. N.S., Ashburn Golf Club. Roman Catholic. Avocations: golf, hiking, travel. Office: Maritime Tel & Tel Co Ltd, 1505 Barrington St PO Box 880, Halifax, NS Canada B3J 2W3

SMITH, RONALD LEE, academic administrator, public policy educator; b. Indpls., June 10, 1937; s. Emerson Wellman and Dorothy Elizabeth (Schaefer) S.; m. Betty Joan Bobbitt, Aug. 22, 1959; children: Byron Thomas (dec.), Evan Ronald, Deanna Marie, Kathleen Elizabeth. B.M.E., Gen. Motors Inst., 1960; M.S., Purdue U., 1962, Ph.D., 1967. Asst. prof. humanities Gen. Motors Inst., 1963-67, asso. prof., 1967-68; prof., chmn. dept. communication and organization behavior, 1968-73; prof. mgmt., dean Coll. Bus. Adminstrn. U. Nebr., Lincoln, 1973-77; prof., dean Sch. Bus. Adminstrn., Georgetown U., 1977-86; exec. dir. Lincoln Inst. of Land Policy, Cambridge, Mass., 1986-92, pres., 1992—; bd. dirs. Minnegasco, 1976-93, 1st Greatwest Corp., 1975-78, Land Reform Tng. Inst., Taiwan, 1992—; chair adv. bd. Land Tenure Ctr., U. Wis., Madison, 1993—. Mem. editorial bd., cons. editor: Jour. Communication, 1973-81; Contbr. chpts. to books. Mem. Council Communication Socs. (pres. 1978-80), Am. Psychol. Assn., Acad. Mgmt., Internat. Communication Assn., Beta Gamma Sigma, Delta Sigma Pi, Theta Xi (pres. 1978-80). Mem. United Ch. of Christ. Home: 169 George St Medford MA 02155-5438 Office: Lincoln Inst Land Policy 113 Brattle St Cambridge MA 02138-3400

SMITH, RONALD LYNN, health system executive; b. Algona, Iowa, Sept. 22, 1940; s. Russell Malcom and Helen Lucille (Gridley) S.; m. Jacqueline Sue Yarger, Dec. 23, 1962 (div. Aug. 1981); children: Sheri Rene, Gregory Mark, Brenton Alan; m. Sylvia Jo Gregan, Dec. 31, 1982; 1 child, Russell Lynn. B.S., Iowa State U., 1962; postgrad., U. S.D., 1963; M.A., U. Iowa, 1965. With Harris Hosp.-Methodist, Ft. Worth, 1967-82, assoc. exec. dir., 1974-76, exec. dir. 1977-82; pres. Harris Meth. Health System, Ft. Worth, 1982—; trustee Am. Healthcare Systems, Nat. Com. for Quality Health Care, 1991; mem. adv. coun. Hill-Rom Co., 1991; mem. healthcare exec. adv. coun. IBM, 1991. Trustee Tarrant County United, 1987—; campaign chmn., 1992, chmn. bd., 1993, chmn. area-wide svcs., self-sufficiency task force. Fellow Am. Coll. Hosp. Execs.; mem. Tex. Hosp. Assn. (trustee 1983-87, chmn. 1986-87), Dallas-Ft. Worth Hosp. Coun. (pres. 1981), Ft. Worth C. of C. (bd. dirs. 1992), Rotary. Methodist.

SMITH, ROWLAND JAMES, educational administrator; b. Johannesburg, S. Africa, Aug. 19, 1938; s. John James and Gladys Spencer (Coldrey) S.; m. Catherine Anne Lane, Sept. 22, 1962; children: Russell Claude, Belinda Claire. B.A., U. Natal, 1959, Ph.D., 1967; M.A., Oxford U., Eng., 1967. Lectr. English U. Witwatersrand, Johannesburg, S. Africa, 1963-67; asst. prof. Dalhousie U., Halifax, N.S., Can., 1967-70, assoc. prof. English, 1970-77, prof., 1977-88, McCulloch prof., 1988-94, chmn. English dept., 1977-83, 85-86, dir. Centre for African Studies, 1976-77, asst. dean arts and sci., 1972-74, dean arts and social scis., 1988-93, provost Coll. Arts and Scis., 1988-89, 90-91, 92-93; vis. prof., rsch. assoc. Multidisciplinary Ctr. Can. Studies, U. Rouen, 1994; prof. Wilfrid Laurier U., Waterloo, Ontario, 1994—, v.p. acad., 1994—. Author: Lyric and Polemic: The Literary Personality of Roy Campbell, 1972; editor: Exile and Tradition: Studies in African and Caribbean Literature, 1976, Critical Essays on Nadine Gordimer, 1990. bd. govs. Halifax Grammar Sch., 1972-74; bd. govs. Neptune Theatre Found., 1977-78; mem. selection com. IODE Meml. Scholarships for N.S., 1969-71, Rhodes Scholarships N.S., 1972-74; mem. edn. com.

Victoria Gen. Hosp., 1986-90; dir. publicity and promotion N.S. Rugby Football Union, 1987-89; chair liaison com. edn. dept. N.S. U., 1990-93; mem. book prize jury, Can. Fedn. for Humanities, 1990, regional judge (Can. and the Caribbean) Commonwealth Writers Prize, 1991. Recipient Transvaal Rhodes scholar, 1960; vis. fellow Dalhousie U., 1965-66; Can. Council leave fellow, 1974-75, research grantee, 1977; grantee Social Scis. and Humanities Research Council of Can., 1978, internat. grantee, 1985. Mem. Assn. Can. Univ. Tchrs. English (sec.-treas. 1968-70, profl. concern com. 1979-81), Can. Assn. for Commonwealth Lit. and Lang. Studies (exec. mem. 1989-92), Can. Assn. Chmn. English (v.p. 1981-82, prs. 1982-83, exec. mem.-at-large 1985-86), Can. Fedn. Humanities (aid to scholarly publs. com. 1979-85, bd. dirs. 1992-94), MLA (div. chmn. 1984). Office: Wilfrid Laurier U, Office of VP Acad, Waterloo, ON Canada N2L 3C5

SMITH, ROY FORGE, art director, production designer. Art dir.: (films) Far from the Madding Crowd, 1967, The Assassination Bureau, 1969, The Amazing Mr. Blunden, 1972, Yesterday, 1980, The Last Chase, 1981, Mrs. Soffel, 1984; prodn. designer: (films) Monty Python and the Holy Grail, 1974, The House By the Lake, 1976, Jabberwocky, 1977, The Hound of the Baskervilles, 1979, Running, 1979, Funeral Home, 1981, Melanie, 1983, Curtains, 1983, The Believers, 1987, Burnin' Love, 1987, The Kiss, 1988, Bill & Ted's Excellent Adventure, 1989, Teenage Mutant Ninja Turtles, 1990, Teenage Mutant Ninja Turtles II: The Secret of the Ooze, 1991, Warlock, 1991, Teenage Mutant Ninja Turtles III, 1993, Robin Hood: Men in Tights, 1993, The Page Master, 1994, (TV movies) Clown White, 1980, A Deadly Business, 1986, Haunted By Her Past, 1987, The Lost Capone, 1990, (TV series) SCTV, 1983. Office: Sandra Marsh Mgt 9150 Wilshire Blvd Ste 220 Beverly Hills CA 90210*

SMITH, ROY PHILIP, federal judge; b. S.I., N.Y., Dec. 29, 1933; s. Philip Aloysius and Virginia (Collins) S.; m. Elizabeth Helen Wink, Jan. 23, 1965; children: Matthew P., Jean E. BA, St. Joseph's Coll., Yonkers, N.Y., 1956; JD, Fordham U., 1965. Bar: N.Y. Asst. reg. counsel FAA, N.Y.C., 1966-79; adminstrv. law judge U.S. Dept. Labor, Washington, 1979-83; adminstrv. appeals judge Benefits Rev. Bd., Washington, 1983—, chmn., chief adminstrv. appeals judge, 1988-90; adj. prof. aviation law Dowling Coll., Oakdale, N.Y., 1972-79; adj. prof. transp. law Adelphi U., Garden City, N.Y., 1975-79; vis. prof. Georgetown U. Law Sch., 1989—. With U.S. Army, 1957-59. Mem. Assn. of Bar of City of N.Y. (sec.-treas. aeronautics com. 1978-79), Fed. Adminstrv. Law Judges Conf. (treas. 1983-84, mem. exec. com. 1982-83), Internat. Platform Assn., Friendly Sons of St. Patrick, Edgemoor Club. Avocation: tennis. Home: 6700 Pawtucket Rd Bethesda MD 20817-4836 Office: Benefits Rev Bd 800 K St NW Washington DC 20001-3742

SMITH, RUSSELL JACK, former intelligence official; b. Jackson, Mich., July 4, 1913; s. Lee C. and Georgia L. (Weed) S.; m. Rosemary Thomson, Sept. 5, 1938; children: Stephen M., Scott T., Christopher G. AB, Miami U., Oxford, Ohio, 1937; PhD, Cornell U., 1941. Asst. instr. English Cornell U., 1937-41; instr. English Williams Coll., 1941-45; with OSS, 1945; asst. prof. English Wells Coll., 1946-47; with CIA, 1947-74, mem. bd. nat. estimates, 1957-62, dir. current intelligence, 1962-66, dep. dir. for intelligence, 1966-71; spl. asst. U.S. Embassy, New Delhi, 1971-74; rsch. cons., 1975—; assigned Nat. War Coll., 1951-52, U.S. rep. Brit. Joint Intelligence Com., Far East, Singapore, 1954-56. Author: John Dryden, A Study in Controversy, 1941, The Unknown CIA: My Three Decades with the Agency, 1989, (novels) The Secret War, 1986, The Singapore Chance, 1991, Lodestone, 1993, Whirligig, 1994. Recipient Nat. Civil Svc. League award, 1971, Disting. Intelligence medal CIA, 1974. Mem. Phi Beta Kappa, Phi Delta Theta, Omicron Delta Kappa. Home: 1138 Bellview Rd Mc Lean VA 22102-1104

SMITH, RUSSELL L., film critic; b. Dallas, Nov. 11, 1956. BJ, U. Tex., Arlington, 1983. Pop music critic Dallas Morning News, 1984-89, film critic, 1989—. Recipient First Pl. award criticism Tex. AP Mng. Editors, 1989, awards of merit Gay and Lesbian Assn. Against Defamation, Dallas, 1992, Tex. Lesbian and Gay Journalists Assn., Austin, 1993. Office: Dallas Morning News 508 Young St Dallas TX 75202-4808

SMITH, RUTH LILLIAN SCHLUCHTER, librarian; b. Detroit, Oct. 18, 1917; d. Clayton John and Gertrude Katherine (Kastler) Schluchter; m. Thomas Guilford Smith, Sept. 28, 1946; 1 son, Pemberton, III. AB, Wayne State U., Detroit, 1939; AB in Libr. Sci., U. Mich., Ann Arbor, 1942. Libr. Detroit Pub. Libr., 1942-43; rsch. asst. Moore Sch. Elec. Engring. U. Pa., Phila., 1946-47; libr. Bethesda (Md.) Meth. Ch. Libr., 1955-61; reference libr., chief reader svcs. Inst. Def. Analyses, Arlington, Va., 1961-65, chief unclassified libr. sect., 1965-67, head libr., 1967-75, mgr. tech. info. svcs., 1975-81; dir. office customer svcs. Nat. Tech. Info. Svc., 1981-88, cons., 1988—; leader ch. libr. workshops Nat. Tech. Info. Service, 1960—; speaker profl. meetings; founder, chmn. Com. Info. Hang-ups, 1969-86; mem. Depository Libr. Coun. to Pub. Printer, 1975-78, Def. Tech. Info. Ctr. Resource Sharing Adv. Group, 1980-82; chmn. edn. working group Fed. Libr. and Info. Ctr. Com., 1984-88, cons., 1988—. Author: Publicity for a Church Library, 1966, Workshop Planning, 1972, (with Claudia Hannaford) Promotion Planning, 1975, Getting the Books off the Shelves, 1975, rev. edit., 1985, 2nd rev. edit., 1991, Cataloging Made Easy, 1978, rev. edit., 1986, Setting up a Library: How to Begin or Begin Again, 1979, rev. edit., 1987, 2nd rev. edit., 1994, Running a Library, 1982; contbr. articles to library and religious jours. Author: Publicity for a Church Library, 1966, Workshop Plannign, 1972, (with Claudia Hannaford) Promotion Planning, 1975, Getting the Books off the Shelves, 1975, rev. edit. 1985, rev. edit. 1991, Cataloging Books, Step By Step, 1977, Cataloging Made Easy, 1978, rev. edit. 1986, Setting up a Library; How to Begin of Begin Again, 1979, rev. edit. 1987, 1994, Running a Library, 1982; contbr. articles to library and religious jours. Mem. ALA, Am. Soc. Info. Sci., and Synagogue Library Assn. (founding mem., life mem., pres. 1967-68), Fedn. Info. Users (v.p. interactive affairs 1973-75), Spl. Libraries Assn. (chmn. aerospace div. 1975-76, chmn. library mgmt. div. 1978-79, chmn. div. cabinet 1980-81, John Cotton Dana award 1979, SLA Fellow award 1987, Hall of Fame award 1988). Republican. Methodist. Home: 5304 Glenwood Rd Bethesda MD 20814-1406

SMITH, SALLYE WRYE, librarian; b. Birmingham, Ala., Nov. 11, 1923; d. William Florin and Margaret (Howard) Wrye; m. Stuart Werner Smith, Sept. 20, 1947 (dec. June 1981); children: Carol Ann, Susan Patricia, Michael Christopher, Julie Lynn, Lori Kathleen. BA, U. Ala., 1945; MA, U. Denver, 1969. Psychometrician U.S. Army, Deshon Gen. Hosp., Butler, Pa., 1945-46, U.S. Vet. Adminstrn. Vocat. Guidance, U. Ala., Tuscaloosa, 1946; clin. psychologist U.S. Army, Walter Reed Gen. Hosp., Washington, 1946-47, U.S. Army, Fitzsimons Gen. Hosp., Denver, 1948, U.S. Vets. Adminstrn., Ft. Logan, Colo., 1948-50; head sci.-engring. libr. U. Denver, Colo., 1969-72; instr., reference libr. Penrose Libr., U. Denver, 1972-80, asst. prof., reference libr., 1980-90, interim dir., 1990-92; vis. prof. U. Denver Grad. Sch. Libr. Info. Mgmt., 1975-77, 83; info. broker Colo. Rschrs., Denver, 1979—; cons., presenter The Indsl. Info. Workshop Inst. de Investigaciones Tecnologicas, Bogota, Colombia, 1979, LIPI-DRI-PDIN workshop on R&D mgmt., Jakarta, Indonesia, 1982; mem. BRS User Adv. Bd., Latham, N.Y., 1983-86. Recipient Cert. of Recognition, Sigma Xi, U. Denver chpt., 1983. Mem. ALA, Spl. Libr. Assn., Colo. Libr. Assn., Phi Beta Kappa, Beta Phi Mu.

SMITH, SAM K., engineering company executive; b. 1932. With Tex. Instruments, Dallas, 1960-83, Computer Thought Corp., Plano, Tex., 1983-88; pres., CEO Merit Tech., Inc., Plano, 1984—; chmn. bd. dirs. Landmark Graphics Corp., Houston. Office: Landmark Graphics Corp 15150 Memorial Dr Houston TX 77079-4304*

SMITH, SAM P., columnist, author; b. Bklyn., Jan. 24, 1948; s. Leon and Betty (Britzker) S.; m. Kathleen Ellen Rood, Jan. 24, 1976; 1 child, Connor. BBA in Acctg., Pace U., N.Y.C., 1970; MA in Journalism, Ball State

U., Muncie, Ind., 1974. Acct. Arthur Young & Co., N.Y.C., 1970-72; reporter Ft. Wayne (Ind.) News Sentinal, Ft. Wayne, 1973-76, States News Svc., Washington, 1976-79; writer/reporter Chgo. Tribune, 1979-90, columnist, 1991—. Author: The Jordan Rules, 1991; contbr. articles to mags. including Inside Sports, Sport, Basketball Digest. With USAR, 1970-76. Recipient Journalism award AP, UPI. Office: Chicago Tribune 435 N Michigan Ave Chicago IL 60611-4001

SMITH, SAMUEL BOYD, history educator; b. Adams, Tenn., Oct. 23, 1929; s. Carl S. and Annie (Tolleson) S.; m. Martha Sue Fitzsimmons, Dec. 23, 1956; children—David Fitzsimmons, Mark Tolleson, Stephen Boyd. Student, Milligan Coll., 1947-48, U. Tenn., 1948-49, Syracuse U., 1951-52; B.S., Peabody Coll., 1956; M.A., Vanderbilt U., 1960, Ph.D., 1962. Asst. prof. history U. South Fla., 1961-64; state librarian and archivist, chmn. Tenn. Hist. Commn., 1964-69; lectr. history Peabody Coll., 1965-66; assoc. prof. history U. Tenn., 1969-71, prof., editor Andrew Jackson Presdl. Papers, 1972-79; prof. Tenn. State U., Nashville, 1979—. Co-author: This is Tennessee, 1973; Editor and compiler: Tennessee History: A Bibliography, 1974; co-editor: The Papers of Andrew Jackson, vol. I, 1980. Served with USAF, 1951-54. Mem. Orgn. Am. Historians, Am. Hist. Assn., Tenn. Hist. Assn., Shakespeare Club, Academy Found. Democrat. Methodist. Home: 1135 Sewanee Rd Nashville TN 37220-1017 Office: Tenn State U Downtown Nashville TN 37203

SMITH, SAMUEL DAVID, artist, educator; b. Thorndale, Tex., Feb. 11, 1918; s. Otto Frank and Jeanette (Joyce) S.; m. Elizabeth Marie Smith; children: Cezanne, Rembrandt, Michelangelo. Ed. pub. schs. Prof. art U. N.Mex., 1956-84, prof. art emeritus, 1984—. Illustrator: Roots in Adobe, 1967, Cowboy's Christmas Tree, 1956; also: Coronet mag; one man exhbns. include Corcoran Gallery Art, Washington, 1949, Santa Fe Mus. Art, 1947, Roswell (N.Mex.) Mus. Fine Art, 1953, 64, Goodwell (Okla.) Hist. Mus., 1964, Panhandle Plains Mus., Canyon City, Tex., 1964, Biltomore Galleries, Los Angeles, 1946, First Nat. Bank, Los Alamos, 1968, group exhbns. include, Baker Galleries, Lubbock, Tex., 1964-73, Met. Mus., N.Y.C., 1944, Blue Door Gallery, Taos, N.Mex., 1946-53, Galeria del Sol, Albuquerque, 1968-73, Brandywine Galleries, 1972-73, Watercolor Workshop, Teluride, Colo., 1964; one-man show includes Retrospective Exhbn. U. of N.Mex., Albuquerque, 1986. Served as combat artist AUS, 1942-45. Hon. life mem. N.Mex. Art League. Mem. Artist Equity Assn. (pres. N.Mex. chpt. 1957-58, 66-67, 70-71). Club: Elk. Gallery: PO Box 2006 Telluride CO 81435-2006

SMITH, SAMUEL HOWARD, university vice president, plant pathologist; b. Salinas, Calif., Feb. 4, 1940; s. Adrian Reed and Elsa (Jacop) S.; m. Patricia Ann Walter, July 8, 1960; children: Samuel Howard, Linda Marie. BS in Plant Pathology, U. Calif., Berkeley, 1961, PhD, 1964; D (hon.), Nihon U., Tokyo, 1989. NATO fellow Glasshouse Crops Research Inst., Sussex, Eng., 1964-65; asst. prof. plant pathology U. Calif., Berkeley, 1965-69; assoc. prof. Pa. State U., Arendtsville, 1969-71; assoc. prof. Pa. State U., University Park, 1971-74, prof., 1974-85, head dept. plant pathology, 1976-81, dean Coll. agr. Pa. Agrl. Expt. Sta. and Coop. Extension Service, 1981-85; pres. Wash. State U., 1985—; bd. dirs. Assoc. Western Univs., 1993—; adv. com. Wash. Sch. Employees Credit Union, 1993—; exec. adv. com. Tri-Cities Commercialization Partnership, 1993—; mem. adv. com. Battelle Pacific N.W. Lab., 1993—; chair Pacific-10 Conf. CEOs, 1993-94; bd. dirs. All-Nations Alliance for Minority Participation; mem. pres.' commn. NCAA, 1994—, divsn. I chair, 1995—. Bd. dirs. Forward Wash., 1986—, China Rels. Coun.; mem. Wash. Coun. Internat. Trade, Western Interstate Commn. Higher Edn., Am. Coun. on Edn.; bd. dirs. Assoc. Western Univs., 1993—; chair divsn. I NCAA Pres. Commn., 1995—; mem. NCAA Pres. Commn., 1994—. Mem. AAAS, Am. Phytopath. Soc., Nat. Assn. State Univs. and Land-Grant Colls. (bd. dirs. 1994—), chair commn. info. tech. 1994—), Gamma Sigma Delta, Alpha Zeta, Epsilon Sigma Phi, Sigma Xi, Omicron Delta Kappa, Golden Key, Phi Kappa Alpha (hon.). Home: 755 NE Campus St Pullman WA 99163-4223 Office: Wash State U French Adminstrn Bldg Pullman WA 99164-1048

SMITH, SAMUEL JOSEPH, soil scientist; b. Montgomery, Ala., July 19, 1939; s. Samuel Alexander and Lucy (Poje) S. BS, Auburn U., 1961; PhD, Iowa State U., 1967. Soil scientist USDA Agrl. Rsch. Svc., Beltsville, Md., 1969-71; soil scientist USDA Agrl. Rsch. Svc., Durant, Okla., 1971-78, soil scientist, rsch. leader, 1978-94; collaborator Soil Sci., 1994—. Contbr. over 120 articles to rsch. publs. in soil and water sci. Roman Catholic. Office: USDA Agrl Rsch Svc PO Box 1430 Durant OK 74702-1430

SMITH, SAMUEL STUART, lawyer; b. Harrisburg, Pa., Nov. 18, 1936; s. Joseph and Fannie (Latt) S.; m. Susan Ruth Egert, Dec. 10, 1960; children: Jeffrey Alan, Gary Michael, Lauren Paige. BBA, U. Miami, 1958, JD, 1960. Bar: Fla. 1960, U.S. Dist. Ct. (so. dist.) Fla. 1960, U.S. Supreme Ct. 1960. Ptnr. Smith & Mandler, P.A., Miami Beach, Fla., 1960-87, Ruden, Barnett, McClosky, Smith, Schuster & Russell, Miami, Fla., 1987—. Bd. dirs. WPBT-TV, Miami, Jewish Family Svc., Miami, Guardianship Program Dade County, Comprehensive Personal Care Inc. Capt. U.S. Army, 1960-61. Fellow Am. Bar Found., Am. Coll. Trust and Estate Counsel, Fla. Bar Found. (pres. 1989-90); mem. ABA (chmn. law econs. sect. 1979-80, gov. 1985-87, sec.-elect 1992-93, sec. 1993—), Miami Beach Bar Assn. (pres. 1972-73), Fla. Bar Assn. (pres. 1989-90), Dean's Nat. Adv. Coun. (chair 1992-93). Democrat. Avocations: tennis. Office: Ruden Barnett McClosky Smith Schuster & Russell 701 Brickell Ave Ste 1900 Miami FL 33131-2822

SMITH, SANDRA LYNN, lawyer; b. Shreveport, La., June 10, 1960; d. Donald Wayne and Alyce Jacquelyn (Wood) S. BA, U. Ark., 1982; JD, Wash. U., 1985. Bar: Ark. 1985, U.S. Dist. Ct. (ea. and we. dists.) Ark. 1985, U.S. Ct. Appeals (8th cir.) 1985, U.S. Supreme Ct. 1991. Assoc. Mitchell Law Office, Little Rock, 1985-86; asst. gen. counsel Arkla Gas Co., Little Rock, 1986—. Pres., bd. dirs. Family Svc. Agy., 1991—; 1st vice-chair Ark. Fedn. Young Reps., 1988-90; vol. United Cerebral Palsy. Mem. ABA (exec. com. young lawyers' div. pub. uitilites com. 1989—), corp. counsel com. 1990—), Ark. Bar Assn., Pulaski County Bar Assn., MENSA, Little Rock Jr. C. orf C., Phi Beta Kappa. Methodist. Avocations: golf, tennis, music, antique collecting. Home: 2 Golden Oak Cv Little Rock AR 72212-2132 Office: Arkla Gas Co 400 E Capitol Ave Little Rock AR 72202-2465

SMITH, SCOTT CLYBOURN, communications company executive; b. Evanston, Ill., Sept. 13, 1950; s. E. Sawyer and Jerolanne (Jones) S.; m. Martha Reilly, June 22, 1974; children—Carolyn Baldwin, Thomas Clybourn. B.A., Yale U., 1973; M.Mgmt., Northwestern U., 1976. Comml. banking officer No. Trust Co., Chgo., 1973-77; fin. planning mgr. Tribune Co., Chgo., 1977-79, asst. treas., 1979-81, treas., 1981-82, v.p., treas., 1982-84, v.p. fin. 1984-89, sr. v.p., chief fin. officer, 1989-91, sr. v.p. for devel., 1991-93; pres., CEO, pub. Sun Sentinel Co., Ft. Lauderdale, Fla., 1993—. Bd. dirs. United Way of Broward County, Broward Workshop, Broward C.C. Found., Boys and Girls Club of Broward, Mus. of Discovery and Sci., Econ. Coun. Palm Beach. Episcopalian. Clubs: Glen View (Golf, Ill.), Lauderdale Yacht Club, Fort Lauderdale Country Club. Office: Sun Sentinel 200 E Las Olas Blvd Fort Lauderdale FL 33301

SMITH, SELMA MOIDEL, lawyer, composer; b. Warren, Ohio, Apr. 3, 1919; d. Louis and Mary (Oyer) Moidel; 1 child, Mark Lee. Student U. Calif., 1936-39, U. So. Calif., 1939-41; JD, Pacific Coast U., 1942. Bar: Calif. 1943, U.S. Dist. Ct. 1943, U.S. Supreme Ct. 1958. Gen. practice law; mem. firm Moidel, Moidel, Moidel & Smith. Field dir. civilian adv. com. WAC, 1943; mem. nat. bd. Med. Coll. Pa. (formerly Woman's Med. Coll. Pa.), 1953—, exec. bd., 1970-86, pres., 1980-82, chmn. past pres. com., 1990-92. Decorated La Order del Merito Juan Pablo Duarte (Dominican Republic). Mem. ABA, State Bar Calif. (servicemen's legal com., Disting. Svc. award 1993), L.A. Bar Assn. (psychopathic ct. com., Outstanding Svc. award 1993), L.A. Lawyers Club (pub. defenders com.), Nat. Assn. Women Lawyers (chmn. com. unauthorized practice of law, social commn. UN, regional dir. western states, Hawaii 1949-57, mem. jud. adminstrn. com. 1960, nat. chmn. world peace through law com. 1966-67), League of Ams. (dir.), Inter-Am. Bar Assn., So. Calif. Women Lawyers (pres. 1947, 48), Women Lawyers Assn. L.A. (chmn. Law Day com. 1966, subject of oral hist. project, 1986), State Bar Conf. com., Coun. Bar Assns. L.A. County (charter sec. 1950), Calif. Bus. Women's Coun. (dir. 1951), L.A. Bus. Women's Coun. (pres. 1952), Calif. Pres.'s Coun. (1st v.p.), Nat. Assn. Composers U.S.A. (dir. 1974-79, ann. luncheon chmn. 1975), Nat. Fedn.

Music Clubs (nat. vice chmn. for Western region, 1973-78), Calif. Fedn. Music Clubs (state chmn. Am. Music 1971-75, state conv. chmn. 1972), Docents of L.A. Philharm. (v.p. 1973-83, chmn. Latin Am. community rels. 1972-75, press and pub. rels. 1972-75, cons. coord. 1973-75), Assn. Learning in Retirement Orgns. in West (pres. 1993-94, exec. com. 1994-95, disting. svc. award 1995), Euterpe Opera Club (v.p. 1974-75, chmn. auditions 1972, chmn. awards 1973-75), ASCAP, Iota Tau Tau (dean L.A., supreme treas.), Plato Soc. of UCLA (Toga editor, 1990-93, sec. 1991-92, chmn. colloquium com. 1992-93, discussion leader UCLA Constitution Bicentennial Project, 1985-87, moderator UCLA extension lecture series 1990, Exceptional Leadership award 1994). Composer: Espressivo-Four Piano Pieces (orchestral premiere 1987, performance Nat. Mus. Women in the Arts 1989). Home: 5272 Lindley Ave Encino CA 91316-3518

SMITH, SEYMOUR MASLIN, financial advisor, investment banker; b. Hartford, Conn., Sept. 19, 1941; s. Seymour Ewing and Margaret Ruth (Maslin) S.; m. Anita P. Streeter, Nov. 12, 1966. A.B., Hamilton Coll., 1963; M.B.A., Columbia U., 1970. With Conn. Bank and Trust Co., Hartford, 1970-85, sr. v.p., 1976-80, exec. v.p., treas., 1980-85; pres. Am. Cruise Lines Inc., 1986-89; exec. v.p., chief fin. officer New Eng. Savs. Bank, New London, 1989-93; fin. advisor, investment banker pvt. practice, Essex, Conn., 1993-94; v.p., CFO Patient Edn. Media, Inc. (an affiliate of Time Life, Inc.), 1995—. Trustee Conn. Public Expenditure Council, Conn. State U., 1973-83. Served to lt. USN, 1963-68, Vietnam. Republican. Episcopalian.

SMITH, SHARMAN BRIDGES, state librarian; b. Lambert, Miss., Sept. 2, 1951; d. Gilbert Asa and Vivian Pearl (Murphree) Bridges; m. Gary Walter Smith, Oct. 3, 1975; children: Heather Elisabeth, Millicent Helen. BS, Miss. U. for Women, Columbus, 1972; MLS, George Peabody Coll., Nashville, 1975. Head libr. Clinton (Miss.) Pub. Libr., 1972-74; asst. dir. Lincoln-Lawrence-Franklin Regional Libr., Brookhaven, Miss., 1975-77, dir., 1977-78; info. svcs. mgr. Miss. Libr. Commn., Jackson, 1978-87, asst. dir. libr. ops., 1987-89, dir. libr. svcs. div., 1989-92; state librarian State Libr. of Iowa, Des Moines, 1992—; pres. bd. trustees Bibliog. Ctr. for Rsch., Denver, 1994—. Office: State Libr Iowa E 12th St Grand Des Moines IA 50319

SMITH, SHARON PATRICIA, university dean; b. Jersey City, Nov. 6, 1948; d. Vincent C. and Dorothy (Linehan) S. AB, Rutgers U., 1970, MA, 1972, PhD, 1974. Rsch. assoc. Princeton (N.J.) U., 1974-76, vis. sr. rsch. economist, 1988-90; economist Fed. Res. Bank, N.Y.C., 1976-81, sr. economist, 1981-82; dist. mgr. AT&T, N.Y.C. and Piscataway, N.J., 1982-90; prof. mgmt. systems, dean Coll. of Bus. Adminstrn. Fordham U., Bronx, 1990—; vis. assoc. prof. N.Y. State Sch. Indsl. and Labor Rels., Ithaca, N.Y., 1981; adj. assoc. Drew U., Madison, N.J., 1984. Author: Equal Pay in the Public Sector: Fact or Fantasy, 1977, (with Albert Rees) Faculty Retirement in the Arts and Sciences, 1991; contbr. articles to profl. jours. NDEA fellow, 1970-73. Mem. Am. Econ. Assn., N.J. Human Resource Planners Assn., Indsl. Rels. Rsch. Assn., Am. Assn. for Higher Edn., Princeton Club N.Y. Democrat. Roman Catholic. Home: 45 Wellington Ave Short Hills NJ 07078-3307 Office: Fordham U Coll of Bus Adminstrn 101 Thebaud Hall Bronx NY 10458

SMITH, SHARRON WILLIAMS, chemistry educator; b. Ashland, Ky., Apr. 3, 1941; d. James Archie and May (Waggoner) Williams; m. William Owen Smith, Jr., Aug. 16, 1964; children: Leslie Dyan, Kevin Andrew. BA, Transylvania U., 1963; PhD, U. Ky., 1975. Chemist, Procter & Gamble, Cin., 1963-64; tchr. sci. Lexington pub. schs., Ky., 1964-67; chemist NIH, Bethesda, Md., 1974-75; asst. prof. chemistry Hood Coll., Frederick, Md., 1975-81, assoc. prof., 1981-87, prof. 1987—, chair dept. chemistry, physics and astronomy, 1982-86, acting dean grad. sch. 1989-91, Whitaker prof. Chemistry, 1993—. NDEA fellow, 1967-70, Dissertation Yr. fellow U. Ky., Lexington, 1970-71; grantee Hood Coll., 1983, 85, 91, Beneficial-Hodson faculty fellow Hood Coll., 1984, 92; grantee NSF, 1986. Mem. AAAS, Am. Chem. Soc., Middle Atlantic Assn. Liberal Arts Chemistry Tchrs. (pres. 1984-85). Democrat. Office: Hood Coll Dept Chemistry Frederick MD 21701

SMITH, SHERWOOD DRAUGHON, retired hospital administrator; b. Durham, N.C., Feb. 12, 1925; s. Cody Hood and Eula (Draughon) S.; m. Patricia Ann Collins, Jan. 27, 1952; children—David Cody, Kenneth Heber, Sherwood Allan, Steven Collins, Sarah Amy. B.A., Duke, 1950, M.S., 1952. Asst. adminstr. Hubbard Hosp., Nashville, 1952-54; adminstr. Hubbard Hosp., 1954-56; exec. dir. Lakeland (Fla.) Gen. Hosp., 1956-88, ret., 1988. Bd. dirs., exec. com. Suncoast Health Council; bd. dirs. Blue Cross Fla.; past pres., bd. dirs. Southeastern Hosp. Conf., del., 1968-80; pres. Central Fla. Hosp. Council, 1961-62; mem. Fla. Health Planning Council, 1971—; Mem. Adv. Com. Employment, Lakeland; mem. Polk County Planning Council, 1970—; bishop Ch. of Jesus Christ of Latter-day Saints. Served with AUS, 1942-46. Fellow Am. Coll. Hosps. Adminstrs. (regent dist. III 1970-73); mem. Fla. Hosp. Assn. (pres. 1966, bd. dirs.), Am. Hosp. Assn. (Fla. del. 1967-73, trustee 1974-80, chmn. regional adv. bd.). Club: Rotarian. Home: 1515 Leighton Ave Lakeland FL 33803-2518

SMITH, SHERWOOD HUBBARD, JR., utilities executive; b. Jacksonville, Fla., Sept. 1, 1934; s. Sherwood Hubbard and Catherine Gertrude (Milliken) S.; m. Eva Hackney Hargrave, July 20, 1957; children: Marlin Hamilton, Cameron Hargrave, Eva Hackney. AB, U. N.C., 1956, JD, 1960; D civil laws, St. Augustine's Coll., 1988; LDD, Campbell U., 1990; HHD, Francis Marion Coll., 1992. Bar: N.C. 1960. Assoc. Lassiter, Moore & Van Allen, Charlotte, 1960-62; ptnr. Joyner & Howison, Raleigh, 1963-65; assoc. gen. counsel Carolina Power & Light Co., Raleigh, 1965-70, sr. v.p., gen. counsel, 1971-74, exec. v.p., 1974-76, pres., 1976-92, chmn. bd., 1980—; also pres. & CEO Carolina Power & Light Co., Raleigh, NC; bd. dirs. Global TransPark Found., Inc., Hackney Bros., Inc. No. Telecom Ltd., Northwestern Mut. Life Ins. Co., Springs Industries, Wachovia Corp.; dir. Nuclear Energy Inst., Edison Electric Inst., 1994—; chmn. Am. Nuclear Energy Coun., 1980-83, Edison Electric Inst. 1985-83, Southeastern Elec. Reliability Coun., 1988-90, Nuclear Power Oversight Com., 1990-94, U.S. Coun. for Energy Awareness, 1993-94. Mem. N.C. Coun. Mgmt. and Devel.; trustee Z Smith Reynolds Found., 1991—, Nat. Humanities Ctr.; bd. dirs. N.C. Citizens for Bus. and Industry, chmn. 1985-86; bd. dirs. Rsch. Triangle Found. of N.C.; mem. com. U.S. World Energy Conf.; bd. dirs. Microelectronics Ctr. of N.C., 1980—; mem. Pres.'s Coun. for Internat. Youth Exch., Kenan Inst. Pvt. Enterprise; trustee Com. Econ. Devel.; mem. Bus. Coun., 1991—, Bus. Roundtable; former bd. trustees, chmn. Rex Hosp. Recipient Nat. Humanitarian award Am. Lung Assn., 1993, Outstanding Leadership award in Mgmt. scis. Am. Soc. Mech. Engrs., 1983, A.E. Finley Disting. Svc. award Greater Raleigh C. of C., 1985. Mem. Elec. Power Rsch. Inst. (bd. dirs. 1984-89), Greater Raleigh C. of C. (pres. 1979), Am. Nuclear Soc., U.S. C. of C. (energy com.), Assn. Edison Illuminating Cos. (pres. 1990-91), Phi Beta Kappa. Home: 408 Drummond Dr Raleigh NC 27609-7006 Office: Carolina Power & Light Co PO Box 1551 411 Fayetteville Street Mall Raleigh NC 27602-1551

SMITH, SHIRLEY, artist; b. Wichita, Kans., Apr. 17, 1929; d. Harold Marvin and Blanche Carrie (Alexander) S. BFA, Kans. State U., 1951; postgrad., Provincetown (Mass.) Workshop, 1962-66. One woman exhbns. 55 Mercer St. Gallery, N.Y.C., 1973, Wichita Art Mus, 1978, Stamford Mus. and Nature Ctr., Conn., 1987, Aaron Gallery, Washington, 1987, 88, Joan Hodgell Gallery, Sarasota, Fla., 1987; group exhbns. include Chrysler Mus., Provincetown, The Va. Mus., Richmond, 1970, Whitney Mus. Am. Art, 1971, Colo. Springs Fine Art Ctr., 1972, Everson Mus., Syracuse, N.Y., 1976-80, Nat. Acad. Design, N.Y.C., 1986, One Penn Pla., N.Y.C., 1987, 88, Am. Acad., Inst. Arts and Letters, N.Y.C., 1990, 91; permanent collections Whitney Mus. Am. Art, N.Y.C., U. Calif. Art Mus., Berkeley, Phoenix Art Mus., The Aldrich Mus. Contemporary Art, Ridgefield, Conn., Ulrich Mus., Wichita, Everson Mus., Syracuse, South County Bank collection, St. Louis, Prudential Life Ins., Newark, N.J., King Features Syndicate, N.Y.C., Chase Manhattan Bank Collection, N.Y.C., Senator Nancy Kassabaum Russel Senate Bldg., Washington. Recipient Grumbacher Cash award for mixed media New Eng. Exhibition, Silvermine, Conn., 1967, Acad. Inst. award Am. Acad. Arts and Letters, N.Y.C., 1991. Mem. Artist Equity. Democrat. Presbyterian. Avocation: bike riding. Home: 141 Wooster St New York NY 10012-3163

SMITH, SIBLEY JUDSON, JR., historic site administrator; b. Alexandria, La., June 26, 1955; s. Sibley Judson and Eunice Lee (Raulins) S.; m. Alice Laurie Casey, Nov. 28, 1980; children: Jacob Lee, Casey Rose. Student, N.E. La. U., 1973-76; BA in History magna cum laude, Christopher Newport Coll., 1985; MA in Am. Studies, Coll. of William and Mary, 1992. Mus. interpreter Colonial Williamsburg (Va.) Found., 1979-87; coord. of interpretation Historic Hudson Valley, Inc., Tarrytown, N.Y., 1987-88; historic site mgr. Philipse Manor Hall State Historic Site, Yonkers, N.Y., 1988-91; exec. dir. Allaire (N.J.) Village, Inc., 1991—. Mem. Alpha Chi, Alpha Psi Omega. Avocations: gardening, theater, movies, mus. Office: Hist Allaire Village PO Box 220 Farmingdale NJ 07727-0220

SMITH, SIDNEY OSLIN, JR., lawyer; b. Gainesville, Ga., Dec. 30, 1923; s. Sidney Oslin and Isabelle Price (Charters) S.; m. Patricia Irwin Horkan, Aug. 4, 1944; children—Charters Smith Wilson, Ellen Smith Andersen, Sidney Oslin III. A.B. cum laude, Harvard Coll., 1947; LL.B. summa cum laude, U. Ga., 1949. Bar: Ga. 1948. Ptnr. Telford, Wayne & Smith, Gainesville, Ga., 1949-62; asst. solicitor Superior Cts., Northeastern Jud. Cir. Ga., 1951-61, judge, 1962-65; judge U.S. Dist. Ct. (no. dist.) Ga., 1965-68, chief judge, 1968-74; ptnr. Alston, Miller & Gaines, Atlanta, 1974-82, Alston & Bird, Atlanta, 1982—. Chmn. Gainesville Bd. Edn., 1959-62; trustee Brenau Coll., Gainesville, 1974—, chmn., 1976-84; mem. state bd. regents Univ. System of Ga., 1980-87, chmn., 1984-85. Served to capt. U.S. Army, 1943-46, ETO. Fellow ABA, Am. Coll. Trial Lawyers; mem. Am. Law Inst., Am. Judicature Soc., Commerce Club, Chattahoochee Club, Phi Beta Kappa, Phi Kappa Phi, Phi Delta Phi, Phi Delta Theta. Democrat. Episcopalian. Home: 2541 Club Dr NW Gainesville GA 30506-1769 Office: Alston & Bird 1 Atlantic Ctr 1201 W Peachtree St Atlanta GA 30309-3424

SMITH, SIDNEY RUFUS, JR., linguist, educator; b. Greensboro, N.C., Sept. 18, 1931; s. Sidney Rufus and Page (Johnston) S.; m. Vera Pautzsch, Apr. 19, 1969 (div. 1975); children: Stephanie Alice, Eric Brian. B.A., Duke U., 1953; Ph.D., U. N.C., 1965. Asst. prof. U. Conn., Storrs, 1965-66; asst. prof. U. N.C., Chapel Hill, 1966-71, assoc. prof., 1971-79, prof., 1979—, chmn. Germanic langs., 1979-89, 94—, chmn. linguistics, 1981-84. Author numerous articles for profl. publs. Local troop leader Girl Scouts U.S.A. Served to sgt. AUS, 1953-56. Recipient Northeast Conf. Teaching Langs. Stephen Freeman award, 1969. Mem. Linguistic Soc. Am., MLA, Soc. Advancement Scandinavian Study, Am. Assn. Tchrs. German, S. Atlantic MLA, Internat. Brotherhood Magicians. Democrat. Office: U NC Dept Germanic Langs Chapel Hill NC 27599

SMITH, SINJIN, volleyball player. Profl. volleyball tour player. Mem. Assn. Volleyball Profls. Office: c/o Assn Volleyball Profls 15260 Ventura Blvd Ste 2250 Sherman Oaks CA 91003*

SMITH, SPENCER BAILEY, engineering and business educator; b. Ottawa, Ont., Can., Jan. 31, 1927; s. Sidney B. and Etta (Bailey) S.; m. Mildred E. Spidell, Dec. 31, 1954. B.Eng., McGill U., 1949; M.S., Columbia U., 1950, Eng.Sc.D., 1958. Adminstrv. engr. Mergenthaler Linotype Co., N.Y.C., 1953-58; ops. research mgr. Raytheon Co., Newton, Mass., 1958-61; ops research mgr. Montgomery Ward & Co., Chgo., 1961-66; assoc. prof., then prof. Ill. Inst. Tech., 1966—, chmn. dept. indsl. and systems engring., 1971-77, dir. Stuart Sch. Office of Research, 1977-82; tchr. TV courses Nat. Tech. U. Author: Computer-Based Production and Inventory Control, 1989; contbr. articles to profl. jours.; patentee on order quantity calculator, 1964. Vol. cons. on sch. redistricting Elem. Sch. Dist., Evanston, Ill., 1972-74. Research grantee Harris Trust and Savs. Bank, 1968-70, Ill. Law Enforcement Commn., 1972-74, U.S. Army C.E., 1981, Am. Prodn. and Inventory Control Soc., 1980. Mem. Ops. Rsch. Soc. Am., Inst. Mgmt. Sci., Inst. Indsl. Engrs., Am. Statis. Assn., ASME, Am. Prodn. and Inventory Control Soc., Soc. Mfg. Engrs. Presbyterian. Club: University (Chgo.). Home: 2530 Lawndale Ave Evanston IL 60201-1158 Office: Ill Inst Tech 565 W Adams Chicago IL 60661

SMITH, STAN VLADIMIR, economist, financial service company executive; b. Rhinelander, Wis., Nov. 16, 1946; s. Valy Zdenek and Sylvia S.; children: Cara, David. BS in Ops. Research, Cornell U., 1968; MBA, U. Chgo., 1972, postgrad., 1973. Lectr. U. Chgo., 1973; economist bd. govs. Fed. Res. System, Washington, 1973-74; staff economist First Nat. Bank of Chgo., 1974; assoc. December Group, 1974-77; founding pres. Seaquest Internat., Chgo., 1977-85; mgr., ptnr. Ibbotson Assocs., Chgo., 1981-85; pres. Corp. Fin. Group, Ltd., Chgo., 1981-85; expert econ. witness in field; adj. prof. Coll. Law DePaul U., Chgo. Author: Economic/Hedonic Damages, 1990; founding editor Stocks, Bonds, Bills and Inflation yearbook, 1983; bd. editors Jour. Forensic Economics, 1991—; also contbr. articles in field. Fellow Allied Chem., 1967, John McMullen Trust, 1969; grantee Ford Found., 1972, U.S. Fed. Res., 1973. Mem. Am. Econ. Assn., Am. Fin. Assn., Nat. Assn. Forensic Econs., Nat. Acad. Econ. Arbitrators (founder 1989—), Am. Arbitration Assn. (arbitrator), Nat. Futures Assn. (arbitrator), Am. Bd. Forensic Examiners, Alpha delta Phi. Office: Corp Fin Group 1165 N Clark St Ste 650 Chicago IL 60610-2845

SMITH, STANFORD SIDNEY, state treasurer; b. Denver, Oct. 20, 1923; s. Frank Jay and Lelah (Beamer) S.; m. Harriet Holdrege, Feb. 7, 1947; children: Monta Smith Ramirez, Franklin Stanley. Student, Calif. Inst. Tech., 1941-42, Stanford U., 1942-43; BS, U.S. Naval Acad., 1946. Pres. Vebar Livestock Co., Thermopolis, Wyo., 1961-89; mem. Wyo. Senate, 1974-76; pres. Wyo. Wool GrowersAssn., 1976-78; mem. Wyo. Ho. of Reps., Cheyenne, 1978-82; treas. State Wyo., Cheyenne, 1983—; dir. Coun. of State Govts., 1990-92; v.p. Wyo. Wool Growers, dir., 1976-82. Country commr. Hot Springs County, Wyo, 1966-74. Lt. USN, 1943-54. Decorated Bronze Star. Mem. Nat. Assn. State Treas. (pres. 1990-91). Republican. Methodist. Office: State of Wyoming State Capital Cheyenne WY 82002

SMITH, STANLEY O'NEIL, SR., retired military officer; b. Lawsonville, N.C., Aug. 1, 1941; s. Curvie Leonard and Mildred Ruth (Gunter) S.; m. Linda Lou Morton, Mar. 24, 1962; children: Candace Lea, Stanley O'Neil Jr. BSBA, Va. Poly. and State U., 1963; MA in Indsl. Mgmt., Cen. Mich. U., 1974; grad., Air Command and Staff Coll., Maxwell AFB, Ala., 1975, War Coll., Washington, 1980. Commd. 2d lt. USAF, 1963, advanced through grades to brig. gen., 1987; ops. officer 524 bomb squadron 379 Bomb Wing, Wurtsmith AFB, Mich., 1973-74; ops. officer air staff Hdqrs. USAF Pentagon, Washington, 1975-77, exec. officer to dir. plans, 1977-79; comdr. 37 bomb squadron 28 Bomb Wing, Ellsworth AFB, S.D., 1980-81; cinc sac sgt. asst. B-1B matters Hdqrs. Strategic Air Command, Offutt AFB, Nebr., 1981-82; comdr. 42 bomb wing Strategic Air Command, Loring AFB, Maine, 1983-85; dep. dir. for ops. and tng. HQUSAF, 1985-86, dep. dir. force devel., 1986, dep. dir. plans and policy, 1986-87; commdr. 45 Air Div. Strategic Air Command, Pease AFB, N.H., 1987-89; chief of staff Def. Mapping Agy., Washington, 1989-91. Decorated DFC (3), Air medal (16), Legion of Merit (2), Def. Superior Svc. medal. Mem. Air Force Assn., Order of Daedalians. Methodist. Avocation: golf. Home: 3504 Lela Ct Raleigh NC 27606-4487

SMITH, STANLEY ROGER, retired professional tennis player; b. Pasadena, Calif., Dec. 14, 1946; s. Charles Kenneth and Rhoda (Widmer) S.; m. Marjory Logan Gengler, Nov. 23, 1974; children: Ramsey Gengler, Trevor Austin, Logan Widmer, Austin Church. B.A., U. So. Calif., 1969; L.H.D., Greenville Coll., 1974, Winthrop Coll., N.C. Profl. tennis player, 1968—; mem. U.S. Davis Cup Team, 1968-79, 81; adviser Pres.'s Council on Phys. Fitness, 1971-75; chmn. Stan Smith Design, Inc.; dir. coaching USTA; cons. Sea Pines Plantations, 1971—, Adidas, Landersheim, France, 1971—, Fischer G.m.b.H., Austria, 1980-86, Prince Adv. Staff, 1986—; bd. dirs. Hilton Head Br. Citizens & So. Nat. Bank S.C. Writer: nationally syndicated newspaper column Stan Smith's Tennis Tips, 1971—; Author: Inside Tennis, 1974, Stan Smith's Six Tennis Basics, 1974, The Executive Tennis Diary 1975, 1974, Stan Smith's Guide to Better Tennis, 1975, (with Bob Lutz) Modern Doubles, 1975, It's More Than Just a Game, 1977; also video with Arthur Ashe, Vic Braden: Tennis Our Way. Bd. dirs. Greater Los Angeles Big Bros. Am., 1966-71; hon. tennis chmn. Duke's Children's Classic, 1982—; hon. chmn. Am. Festival Fitness and Sport, 1987. Served with AUS, 1970-72. Decorated D.S.M.; named Martini and Rossi Player of Year, 1971, 72; holder 26 U.S. singles and doubles titles, including, U.S. Open singles, 1971, U.S. Open doubles, 1968, 74, 78, 80; ranked number one in U.S. doubles, 1968, 69, 1970, 71, 72, 74; number one in U.S. singles, 1969,

71, 72, 73; winner Wimbledon singles title, 1972, 6 World championship tennis titles in 1973, including; World Championship of Tennis Finals in singles, also; Rothman's World Doubles title; ranked world's number one tennis player, 1972, 73; Lebair Sportsmanship Trophy, 1969; Johnston Sportsmanship Trophy, 1968; champion 35 & Over Cir. Singles and Doubles Championships, 1982, 84, 86; named to U.S. Collegiate Hall of Fame, 1984, to Carolina Tennis Hall of Fame, 1986, to Internat. Hall of Fame, 1987. Mem. Assn. Tennis Profls. (dir. 1972-79, 81-83), Men's Internat. Profl. Tennis Council, Athletes in Action, Beta Theta Pi. Republican. Presbyterian. Clubs: Sea Pines Plantation, Los Angeles Tennis, All England, West Side Tennis, No. Century XXI, Balboa Bay. Office: 1101 Wilson Blvd Ste 1800 Arlington VA 22209-2248 *God has given me certain talents. I feel a great opportunity and responsibility to develop and use these talents to their fullest on and off the tennis courts. I see great potential in our country and especially in our youth today, and I hope to provide some leadership and direction that this youth will need to develop their potential constructively. God has given me a great life so far and I plan to rely on His guidance to take me the rest of the way.*

SMITH, STANTON KINNIE, JR., utility executive, lawyer; b. Rockford, Ill., Feb. 14, 1931; s. Stanton Kinnie and Elizabeth (Brown) S.; m. Mary Beth Sanders, July 11, 1953; children: Stanton E., Kathryn A., Dana. BA, Yale U., 1953; JD, U. Wis., 1956. Bar: Ill. 1956, Mich. 1976. Ptnr. Sidley & Austin, Chgo., 1964-84; vice-chmn., gen. counsel Am. Natural Resources Co., Detroit, 1984-87; sr. v.p. Costal Corp., Houston, 1985-87, also dir.; vice chmn., gen. counsel CMS Energy Corp., 1987-88, pres. 1988-92, vice chmn., 1992—, also bd. dirs.; bd. dirs. Clarcor Corp., Mich. Nat. Corp. Trustee Founders Soc., Detroit Inst. Arts, Rockford Coll., Devel. Bd. Yale U., Mich. Opera Theater; bd. advisors U. Wis. Law Sch., Mich. State U., Pub. Utility Inst. Office: CMS Energy Corp 330 Town Center Dr Dearborn MI 48126-2711

SMITH, STANTON THOMAS, insurance company executive; b. Portland, Maine, Aug. 2, 1925; s. Cheever Stanton and Doris Faye (Campbell) S.; m. Betty Ann Brown, June 9, 1950; children: Stephen Neil, Gary Stanton, Rae Ellen. BA in Econs., Bates Coll., 1950. Adjuster super claims Liberty Mut. Ins. Co., Boston, 1950-60, methods analyst, 1960-68, methods mgr., 1968-72, asst. v.p. stats., 1972-80, v.p. data processing, 1980—. Served with U.S. Merchant Marine, 1945-46. Mem. Assn. for System Mgmt. (pres. Mayflower chpt. 1968-69). Office: Liberty Mut Ins Co 225 Borthwick Ave Portsmouth NH 03801-4152

SMITH, STEPHANIE MARIE, lawyer; b. Manhattan, Kans., May 15, 1955; d. William C. and Joyce A. (Davis) S. BS in Fgn. Studies, Georgetown U., 1977; JD, U. Mich., 1980. Bar: Colo. 1980, U.S. Dist. Ct. Colo. 1980, U.S. Ct. Appeals (10th cir.) 1980, (9th cir.) 1995, Ariz. 1985, Nev. 1985, U.S. Dist. Ct. Nev. 1985. Assoc. Fishman & Geman, Denver, 1980-81, Hart & Trinen, Denver, 1982-85; ptnr. Jolley, Urga, Wirth & Woodbury, Las Vegas, Nev., 1985—; lawyer rep. 9th Cir. Jud. Conf., 1994—, chmn. Nev. delegation, 1995. Mem. ABA, Nev. Bar Assn., Am. Bankruptcy Inst., So. Nev. Bankruptcy Lawyers' Assn. Office: Jolley Urga Wirth & Woodbury 300 S 4th St Ste 800 Las Vegas NV 89101-6018

SMITH, STEPHEN ALEXANDER, retail and wholesale food distribution company executive; b. Toronto, Ont., Can., Mar. 1, 1957; s. Alexander and Norma Eileen (McEwan) S.; m. Mary E. Cavasin, June 14, 1980; children: Lauren, Carolyn. B Commerce, U. Toronto, 1979. Chartered acctg., Ont. Acct. Price Waterhouse, Toronto, 1979-84, mgr., 1984-85; mgr. systems and internal control Loblaw Cos. Ltd., Toronto, 1985-86, asst. contr., 1986-87, contr., 1987—, v.p., 1989—, sr. v.p., 1994—. Office: Loblaw Cos Ltd, 22 St Clair Ave E Ste 1500, Toronto, ON Canada M4T 2S8

SMITH, STEPHEN GRANT, journalist; b. N.Y.C., Mar. 6, 1949; s. John J. and Nora O.S.; m. Sarah Rowbotham Bedell, May 22, 1982; children: R. Kirk Bedell, Elisabeth DeCou Bedell, David Branson Smith. Student, Deerfield Acad.; BA, U. Pa., 1971. City Hall reporter Daily Hampshire Gazette, Northampton, Mass., 1971-73; spl. assignment reporter Albany Times-Union, 1973-74; dep. regional editor Phila. Inquirer, 1974-76; asst. met. editor Boston Globe, 1976-78; sr. editor Horizon Mag., 1978; staff writer Time Mag., 1978-80, sr. editor, 1980-82, Nation editor, 1982-85, acting asst. mng. editor, 1985-86; exec. editor Newsweek Mag., 1986-91; Washington news editor Knight-Ridder newspapers, 1991-94; editor Civilization Mag., 1994—. Trustee Mid-Atlantic U. Pa. Mem. Am. Soc. Mag. Editors, Coun. on Fgn. Rels., World Affairs Coun. Washington, Nat. Press Club (Washington), Fourth Estate Golf Soc.; clubs: Brook, Century (N.Y.C.), Metropolitan (Washington). Home (summer): Box 183 Little Compton RI 02837 Office: Civilization Magazine 666 Pennsylvania Ave SE Washington DC 20003

SMITH, STEPHEN KENDALL, lawyer; b. Burlington, Vt., May 31, 1941; s. Lester Hurlin and Elizabeth Helen (Mitchell) S.; m. Margaret Anne Weir, Sept. 2, 1967; children: Andrew Kendall, Edward Anthony, Charles Franklin, Charlotte Catherine. AB with distinction, Ind. U., 1964; BA, Oxford U., 1966, MA, 1971; JD, Columbia U., 1972. Bar: Ind. 1972, U.S. Dist. Ct. (so. dist.) Ind. 1972, U.S. Dist. Ct. (no. dist.) Ind. 1978, U.S. Ct. Appeals (7th cir.) 1972. Assoc. Barnes, Hickam, Pantzer & Boyd and predecessors, Indpls., 1972-79, ptnr., 1980-81; ptnr. Barnes & Thornburg and predecessors, Indpls., 1981—, co-chair litigatin mgmt. and econs. com., 1991-94, co-chair equality in the law com., 1994—. Contbr. articles to legal jours. Sec. Indpls. Com. on Fgn. Rels., 1978-87, chmn., 1987—. Capt. U.S. Army, 1966-69. Rhodes scholar, 1964. Mem. ABA (litigation sect., jury instrn. project 1983—), Fed. Bar Assn., Ind. Bar Assn., Indpls. Bar Assn., 7th Cir. Bar Assn., SAR (chancellor Ind. Soc. 1985—). Democrat. Presbyterian. Home: 4414 N Meridian St Indianapolis IN 46208-3534 Office: Barnes & Thornburg 11 S Meridian St Ste 1313 Indianapolis IN 46204

SMITH, STEVE, retail executive; b. 1951. Pres. Kwik Shop, Inc., Hutchinson, Kas., 1974—. Office: Kwik Shop Inc 734 E 4th Ave Hutchinson KS 67501-2274*

SMITH, STEVEN ALBERT, philosophy educator; b. What Cheer, Iowa, May 12, 1939; s. Irving James and Mary (Emmons) S.; m. Daryl Goldgraben, Aug. 2, 1970 (div. Mar. 1987); 1 child, David Irving; m. Patricia Adkisson, Aug. 11, 1991. BA, Earlham Coll., 1961; MA, Harvard U., 1963, PhD, 1972. Instr. Claremont (Calif.) McKenna Coll., 1968-72, asst. prof., 1972-75, assoc. prof., 1975-90, full prof. philosophy, 1990—. Author: Satisfaction of Interest and the Concept of Morality, 1974; editor: Ways of Wisdom, 1983, Everyday Zen, 1989; contbr. articles to profl. jours. Elected bd. mem. Mt. Baldy (Calif.) I&W Assn., 1973-75. Grantee Nat. Endowment for Humanities, 1972. Mem. Am. Philos. Assn., Am. Assn. Philosophy Tchrs., N.Am. Soc. Social Philosophy. Democrat. Quaker. Home: 914 Redding Way Apt C Upland CA 91786-3837 Office: Claremont McKenna Coll 890 Columbia Ave Claremont CA 91711-3901

SMITH, STEVEN DELANO, professional basketball player; b. Highland Park, Mich., Mar. 31, 1969. Student, Mich. State U. Guard Miami Heat, 1991-94; with Atlanta Hawks, 1994—. Named Sporting News All-Am. First Team, 1990, 91, NBA All-Rookie Team, 1992, Dream Team II, 1994. Office: Atlanta Hawks South Tower One CNN Ctr Ste 405 Atlanta GA 30303*

SMITH, STEVEN JAMES, insurance company executive; b. Ft Wayne, Ind., Jan. 25, 1945; s. Richard Hibbins and Helen Lucile (Coplen) S.; m. Carol Morreale, Feb. 19, 1972; children: Lucas, Tyler. AB, U. Mich., 1967; MBA, Harvard U., 1970. C.L.U. Asst. v.p. Lincoln Nat. Life Co., Ft. Wayne, Ind., 1970-75; v.p. Mut. Benefit Life Co., Kansas City, Mo., 1975-82; sr. v.p. Continental Ins. Co., N.Y.C., 1982-85; exec. v.p. Continental Ins. Co., N.Y.C., 1985—; bd. dirs. Ins. Info. Inst., 1990—; trustee Internat. Ctr. Photography, 1992—. Mem. Chatham Sch. Bd., 1988—, v.p., 1989-91, pres. 1991-93; bd. dirs. Inroads Inc., 1987-90, Inroads No. N.J., Newark, 1983-90; pres. Learning Exch., Kansas City, Mo., 1980-82, Inroads/Kansas City, 1980-82; v.p. Pub. TV Nineteen Inc., Kansas City, 1979-81. Branstrom-scholar; McAndless scholar. Mem. Am. Soc. CLUs. Home: 21 Aubrey St Summit NJ 07901 Office: Continental Corp 180 Maiden Ln New York NY 10038-4925

SMITH, STEVEN RAY, law educator; b. Spirit Lake, Iowa, July 8, 1946; s. Byrnard L. and Dorothy V. (Fischbeck) S.; m. Lera Baker, June 15, 1975. BA, Buena Vista Coll., 1968; JD, U. Iowa, 1971, MA, 1971. Bar: Iowa 1971, Ky. 1987, Ohio 1992. From asst. to assoc. dean Sch. Law U. Louisville, 1974-81, acting dean, 1974-75, 76, prof. law, 1971-88, assoc. in medicine Med. Sch., 1983-88; dep. dir./ Assoc. dean Am. Law Schs., 1987-88; dean, prof. law Cleve. State U., 1988—. Author: Law, Behavior and Mental Health: Policy and Practice, 1987; contbr. chpts. to books, articles to profl. jours. Trustee U. Louisville, 1980-82, SCRIBES, 1993—; chmn. faculty adv. com. Ky. Council Higher Edn., 1981-82; pres. Ky. Congress of Senate Faculty Leaders, 1982-84; bd. trustees Am. Bd. Profl. Psychology, 1994—. Recipient Grawemeger award Innovative Teaching. Fellow Ohio State Bar Found.; mem. ABA (standards rev. com. 1991—, govt. rels. com. 1993—, joint commn. ABA/Assn. Am. Law Schs. financing of legal edn. 1993—), Am. Econs. Assn., Assn. Am. Law Schs. (chmn. libraries com., dep. dir. 1987-88, mem. accreditation com. 1993—, chair accreditation com. 1994—), Ohio State Bar Assn. (coun. of dels. 1992—), Order of Coif, City Club of Cleve. (pres. 1994—). Office: Cleve State U Cleveland-Marshall Coll Law 1801 Euclid Ave Cleveland OH 44115-2223

SMITH, STEVEN SIDNEY, molecular biologist; b. Idaho Falls, Idaho, Feb. 11, 1946; s. Sidney Ervin and Hermie Phyllis (Robertson) S.; m. Nancy Louise Turner, Dec. 20, 1974. BS, U. Idaho, 1968; PhD, UCLA, 1974. Asst. research scientist Beckman Research Inst. City of Hope Nat. Med. Ctr., Duarte, Calif., 1982-84, staff Cancer Ctr., 1983—, asst. research scientist depts. Thoracic Surgery and Molecular Biology, 1985-87, assoc. research scientist, 1987—, dir. dept. cell and tumor biology, 1990—; cons. Molecular Biosystems Inc., San Diego, 1981-84, Am. Inst. Biol. Scis., Washington, 1994. Contbr. articles to profl. jours. Grantee NIH, 1983-93, Coun. for Tobacco Rsch. 1983-92, March of Dimes, 1988-91, Smokeless Tobacco Rsch. Coun., 1992—, Office of Naval Rsch., 1994—; Swiss Nat. Sci. Found. fellow U. Bern, 1974-77, Scripps Clinic and Rsch. Found., La. Jolla, Calif., 1978-82, NIH fellow Scripps Clinic, 1979-81. Mem. Am. Soc. Cell Biology, Am. Assn. Cancer Rsch., Am. Crystallographic Assn., Am. Chem. Soc., Am. Weightlifting Assn., Phi Beta Kappa. Avocation: backpacking. Office: City of Hope Nat Med Ctr 1500 Duarte Rd Duarte CA 91010-3012

SMITH, STEVEN WARREN, public relations executive; b. L.A., Mar. 21, 1949. AA in Journalism, Santa Monica Coll., 1970; BA in Journalism, Calif. State U., 1972. Acct. supr. Harshe, Rotman & Druck, 1974-77; acct. supr. Rogers & Cowan, 1977, sr. v.p., ptnr., 1977-80; v.p., group supr. Daniel Edelman, 1981; v.p. CTA, 1981-82; exec. v.p. Carl Terzian Assocs., 1982-83; pres. The Stoorza/Smith Co., 1983-86, Smith Mktg. Comms., 1986-89; pres., CEO Rowland Co./West, 1989-92; chmn. Smith/Fischer & Ptnrs.,Inc., 1992—. Office: Smith/Fischer & Ptnr Inc 4640 Admiralty Way #800 Marina Del Rey CA 90292

SMITH, STUART A., lawyer; b. N.Y.C., Mar. 16, 1941; s. Sydney S. and Gertrude (Blinder) S.; m. Helaine Levi, Mar. 14, 1982. AB, Columbia Coll., N.Y.C., 1961; LLB, Harvard U., 1964. Bar: N.Y. 1964, U.S. Tax Ct. 1965, U.S. Supreme Ct. 1967, D.C. 1970. Law clk. to chief judge U.S. Tax Ct., Washington, 1964-66; atty. U.S. Dept. Justice Tax Div., Washington, 1966-70; pvt. practice Washington, 1970-73; tax asst. to solicitor gen. U.S. Dept. Justice, Washington, 1973-83; pvt. practice N.Y.C., 1983-91; ptnr. Piper & Marbury, N.Y.C., 1991—. Author: How You Can Get the Most from the New Tax Law, 1982; contbr. articles to law revs. Mem. ABA (chmn. tax sect. subcom.), Assn. of Bar of City of N.Y. (fed. taxation com.), Am. Law Inst. (tax adv. group), Merchants Club (N.Y.C., bd. govs.), Univ. Club (N.Y.C., Washington), Harvard Club (N.Y.C.), RAC Club (London). Office: Piper & Marbury 31 W 52nd St New York NY 10019-6118

SMITH, STUART LYON, psychiatrist, corporate executive; b. Montreal, Que., Can., May 7, 1938; s. Moe Samuel and Nettie (Krainer) S.; m. Patricia Ann Springate, Jan. 2, 1964; children: Tanya, Craig. B.Sc., McGill U., 1958, M.D.C.M., 1962, Dip. Psych., 1967; LLD (hon.), Mt. Allison U., 1992. Intern. Montreal Gen. Hosp., 1962-63, resident in psychiatry, 1963-67; from asst. prof. to assoc. prof. medicine McMaster U., Hamilton, Ont., Can., 1967-75; mem. Ont. Legislature, 1975-82, also leader Ont. Liberal Party, 1976-82, and leader of the opposition, 1977-82; chmn. Sci. Council of Can., Ottawa, 1982-87; pres. RockCliffe Research and Tech., Inc., 1987—, Philip Utilities Mgmt. Corp., Toronto, Ont., 1994—; sr. v.p. Philip Environment Inc., Toronto, 1994—; bd. dirs. Can. Trade Group Inc.; chmn. Ensyn Techs., Inc., 1990—; vice prof. psychiatry McMaster U., 1982-93; adj. prof. psyhiatry U. Ottawa, 1986-94; chair com. of inquiry on Can. U. Edn., 1990-91; chmn., bd. trustees Ottawa Gen. Hosp., 1991-94; mem. bd. govs. U. Ottawa, 1989-94. Bd. govs. U. Ottawa, 1989-94. Decorated knight Nat. Order of Merit, France, 1988; McLaughlin travelling fellow, 1964-65. Fellow Royal Coll. Physicians and Surgeons of Can. Jewish.

SMITH, STUART SEABORNE, writer, government official, union official; b. N.Y.C., Jan. 27, 1930; s. Purcell Leonard and Elizabeth (Wright) S.; m. Birte Moeller Jacobsen, Apr. 27, 1956 (div. 1972); children: Stuart Seaborne, Bjarne Moeller; m. Editha Maria Fuchs, Jan. 3, 1973; children: Cornelia Gerda, Melanie Carla. Grad., Lawrenceville (N.J.) Sch., 1948; student, Princeton U., 1948-51, U. Heidelberg, Germany, 1953-54, U. Madrid, Spain, 1954-55, U. Copenhagen, Denmark, 1955-56. Reporter Balt. Sun, 1957-65, fgn. corr. chief Bonn (Germany) bur., 1965-69, corr. Washington Bur., 1969-70; with ABA, 1970-71, Dept. Justice, Washington, 1971—; exec. dir. Capitol Employees Organizing Group, 1979—; pub. Balt. Banner, 1965. Served with AUS, 1951-53. Recipient Spl. award for meritorious svc. Washington-Balt. Newspaper Guild, 1965, meritorious award Dept. Justice, 1985, 87, Sustained Superior Performance award Dept. Justice, 1992, 93. Mem. Am. Fedn. State, County and Mcpl. Employees (pres. coun. 26 1977-80, 87-95, chief steward Local 2830 1975-80, 81-82, pres. 1982—), Meritorious Svc. award Local 2830, 1980). Home: 10522 Tyler Ter Potomac MD 20854-4059 Office: Office of Justice Programs Washington DC 20531 *I believe in honor and democracy and social justice. I further believe that for the most part we are the ignorant slaves of political and philosophical superstitions, but in the end the truth shall set us free.*

SMITH, SUE FRANCES, newspaper editor; b. Lockhart, Tex., July 4, 1940; d. Monroe John Baylor and Myrtle (Krause) Mueck; m. Michael Vogtel Smith, Apr. 20, 1963 (div. July 1977); 1 child, Jordan Meredith. B. Journalism, U. Tex., 1962. Feature writer, photographer Corpus Christi Caller Times, 1962-64; feature writer, editor Chgo. Tribune, 1964-76; features editor Dallas Times Herald, 1976-82; asst. mng. editor for features Denver Post, 1983-84, assoc. editor, 1984-91; asst. mng. editor in charge of Sunday paper Dallas Morning News, 1991-94, asst. mng. editor Lifestyles, 1994—; active Coun. Pres., 1993. Mem. Am. Assn. Sunday and Feature Editors (pres. 1993), Newspaper Features Coun. (bd. dirs.), Delta Gamma. Home: 6060 Jereme Trl Dallas TX 75252-5130 Office: 508 Young St Dallas TX 75202-4808

SMITH, TAD RANDOLPH, lawyer; b. El Paso, Tex., July 20, 1928; s. Eugene Rufus and Dorothy (Derrick) S.; m. JoAnn Wilson, Aug. 24, 1949; children: Laura Bonsch, Derrick, Cameron Ann Compton. BBA, U. Tex. 1952, LLB, 1951. Bar: Tex. 1951; assoc. firm Kemp, Smith, Duncan & Hammond, P.C., El Paso, 1951, ptnr., 1952-81, CEO, 1975—, shareholder, 1981—; bd. dirs. El Paso Indsl. Devel. Corp. Active United Way of El Paso; chmn. El Paso County Reps., 1958-61, Tex. Rep. State Exec. Com., 1961-62; alt. del. Rep. Nat. Conv., 1952, 62, del., 1964; dir. El Paso Electric Co., 1961-90, State Nat. Bank of El Paso, 1969-90, Petro, Inc., 1987—, The Leavell Co., 1970—; trustee Robert E. and Evelyn McKee Found. 1970-90, Property Trust of America, 1971-91; mem. devel. bd. U. Tex. El Paso, 1973-81, v.p., 1975, chmn. 1976; dinner treas. Nat. Jewish Hosp. and Research Ctr., 1977, chmn. 1978, presenter of honoree, 1985; bd. dirs. Southwestern Children's Home, El Paso, 1959-78, Nat. Conf. Christians and Jews, 1965-76, chmn. 1968-69, adv. dir. 1976—; trustee Hervey Found., 1990—, Lydia Patterson Inst., 1994—. Named Outstanding Young Man El Paso, El Paso Jaycees, 1961; recipient Humanitarian award El Paso chpt. NCCJ, 1983. Fellow Tex. Bar Found.; mem. ABA, Tex. Bar Assn., El Paso Bar Assn. (pres. 1971-72), El Paso C. of C. (dir. 1979-82), Sigma Chi. Republican. Methodist. Home: 1202 Thunderbird Dr El Paso TX 79912-2028 Office: Kemp Smith Duncan & Hammond 2000 State Nat Plz 221 N Kansas St El Paso TX 79901-1443

SMITH, TAYLOR, professional football team executive; b. Atlanta, GA, May 3, 1953; m. Louise; children: Ryan, Brooks, Rebecca. BBA, U. Ga., 1976. With Atlanta Falcons, Ga., former mem. front office staff, former corp. sec., former exec. v.p.; now pres. Atlanta Falcons, Atlanta, GA. Bd. dirs. Gwinnett Found.; active Falcons Youth Found. Mem. Rotary. Office: Atlanta Falcons Atlanta Falcons Complex 2745 Burnette Rd Suwanee GA 30174-2198*

SMITH, TED JAY, III, mass communications educator; b. Dobbs Ferry, N.Y., Sept. 14, 1945; s. Ted Jay Jr. and Marie Glencora (Hershey) S.; m. Rosemary Tibbe, June 12, 1971. Student, U. Pitts., 1963-64; Student, U. So. Miss., 1968-69; BA with high honors, Mich. State U., 1971, MA, 1972, PhD, 1978. Commd. 2nd lt. USAF, 1971, advanced through grades to 1st lt., 1973, from electronics technician to electronics instr., 1965-70; airman edn. & commissioning program student USAF, E. Lansing, Mich., 1970-71; info officer USAF, 1971-74, resigned, 1974; grad. teaching/rsch. asst. Mich. State U., E. Lansing, 1974-77; asst. prof. SUNY, Albany, 1977-79; lectr. I Warrnambool Inst. Advanced Edn., Warrnambool, Australia, 1979-82; asst. prof. U. Va., Charlottesville, 1982-87, dir. grad. studies, 1984-87; assoc. prof. Va. Commonwealth U., Richmond, 1987—, dir. grad. studies, 1990-94; Bradley resident scholar Heritage Found., Washington, 1992-93; pres. Applied Analytics, Inc., Richmond, Va., 1986—; sr. analyst Rowan & Blewitt, Inc., Washington, 1986—; co-founder, sr. rsch. fellow Centre for Communication Rsch., Warrnambool, 1982—; mem. nat. adv. bd. Communication Rsch. Corp., Washington, 1986—, nat. adv. coun. The Media Inst., Washington, 1987—; faculty adviser FBI Nat. Acad., Quantico, Va., 1983-87; bd. dirs. Nat. Assn. Scholars, 1990—; mem. Main St. Commn., Rockford Inst., 1992—; mem. educators adv. bd. Inst. for Pub. Rels. Rsch. & Edn., 1992—; co-founder Statis. Assessment Svc., 1993. Author: The Vanishing Economy, 1988, Moscow Meets Main Street, 1988; editor: Propaganda: A Pluralistic Perspective, 1989, Communication in Australia, 1983; co-editor: Communication and Government, 1986; co-editor human communication book series SUNY Press, Albany, 1987—; contbr. articles to profl. jours. Mem. The Nature Conservancy, Albany, 1977-79, Charlottesville, 1982—, Accuracy in Media, Washington, 1982—; contbg. mem. Va. Mus. Fine Arts, Richmond, 1987—. Grantee FBI, U. Va., Warrnambool Inst., Bradley Found., Raldolph Found., Scaife Found. Mem. Am. Assn. for Pub. Opinion Rsch., Assn. for Edn. in Journalism and Mass Communication, Australian Communication Assn. (founding), Internat. Communication Assn., Nat. Assn. Scholars (bd. dirs. 1990—), Pub. Rels. Soc. Am., U. Profs. for Acad. Order, Va. Assn. Scholars (founding bd. dirs., pres. 1990—), So. Speech Communication Assn., Speech Communication Assn., Va. Speech Communication Assn. (chair theory divsn. 1986-91, 1st v.p. 1991-94), Phi Kappa Phi, Kappa Tau Alpha. Republican. Anglican Catholic. Avocations: nature study, fine arts and crafts, classical music. Home: 4010 Sherbrook Rd Richmond VA 23235-1643 Office: Va Commonwealth U Sch Mass Communications 901 W Main St Richmond VA 23284-2034

SMITH, TEFFT W., lawyer; b. Evanston, Ill., Nov. 18, 1946. BA, Brown U., 1968; JD, U. Chgo., 1971. Bar: Ill. 1971. Ptnr. Kirkland & Ellis, Chgo. Mem. ABA (litigation sect., antitrust law sect.). Office: Kirkland & Ellis 200 E Randolph Dr Chicago IL 60601-6401

SMITH, TERENCE FITZGERALD, television news correspondent; b. Bryn Mawr, Pa., Nov. 18, 1938; s. Walter W. and Catherine M. (Cody) S.; m. Phyllis Ann Charnley, June 20, 1964 (div. 1987); children: Elizabeth Reed, Christopher Wellesly. B.A., U. Notre Dame, 1960. Reporter Stamford (Conn.) Adv., 1960-62, N.Y. (N.Y.C.) Herald Tribune, 1963-65; with N.Y. Times, N.Y.C., 1965-85; fgn. corr. N.Y. Times, Israel, Thailand; Vietnam bur. chief N.Y. Times, 1969-70; diplomatic corr. N.Y. Times, Washington, 1970-72; chief corr. N.Y. Times, Israel, 1972-76; dep. fgn. editor N.Y. Times, 1976-77, chief White House corr., 1978-81, sr. corr. Washington bur., 1981, editor Washington Talk page, 1981-85; Washington corr. CBS Morning News, 1985-86; White House corr. CBS News, Washington, 1986-88; Washington corr. CBS News, 1989-90; sr. corr. CBS Sunday Morning, 1991—; lectr. freelance writer. Mem. Overseas Writers Assn., Washington. Office: CBS News 2020 M St NW Washington DC 20036-3368

SMITH, TERRY, metal products executive; b. 1954. BS in Acctg., U. Akron, 1976. V.p., CFO Barmet Aluminum Corp., Akron, 1980—, Castech Aluminum Group, Akron. Office: Barmet Aluminum Corp 753 W Waterloo Rd Akron OH 44314 also: Castech Aluminum Group 753 W Waterloo Rd Akron OH 44314*

SMITH, THELMA TINA HARRIETTE, gallery owner, artist; b. Folkston, Ga., May 5, 1938; d. Harry Charles and Malinda Estelle (Kennison) Causey; m. Billy Wayne Smith, July 23, 1955; children: Sherry Yvonne, Susan Marie, Dennis Wayne, Chris Michael. Student, U. Tex., Arlington, 1968-70; studies with various art instrs. Gen. office worker Superior Ins. Corp., Dallas, 1956-57, Zanes-Ewalt Warehouse, Dallas, 1957-67; bookkeeper Atlas Match Co., Arlington, 1967-68; sr. acct. Automated Refrigerated Air Conditioner Mfg. Corp., Arlington, 1968-70; acct. Conn. Gen. Life Ins. Corp., Dallas, 1972-74; freelance artist Denton, Tex., 1974—; gallery owner, custom framer Tina Smith Studio-Gallery, Mabank, Tex., 1983—. Painting in pub. and pvt. collections in numerous states including N.Y., Fla., La. and N.D.; editor Cedar Creek Art Soc. Yearbook, 1983—. Treas. Cedar Creek Art Soc., 1987-88, 89—; mem. com. to establish state endorsed Arts Coun. for Cedar Creek Lake Area, Gun Barrel City, Tex. Recipient numerous watercolor and pastel awards Henderson County Art League, Cedar Creek Art Soc., Cmty. Svc. award Mayor Wilson Tippit, Gun Barrel City, Tex., 1986. Mem. Southwestern Watercolor Soc. (Dallas), Pastel Soc. of the S.W. (Dallas), Cedar Creek Art Soc. (Gun Barrel City) (v.p. 1983-86, treas.), Profl. Picture Framers Assn. Baptist. Avocations: water activities, gardening. Office: Tina Smith Studio-Gallery 139 W Main St Gun Barrel City TX 75147

SMITH, THEODORE GOODWIN, chemical engineering educator; b. Balt., Aug. 12, 1934; s. Walter Huber and Clara Lee (Goodwin) S.; m. Carol Ann Smith, June 26, 1965; children: Michael R., Heather R. B in Engring. Sci., Johns Hopkins U., 1956, M in Engring. Sci., 1958; DSc, Washington U., St. Louis, 1960. Registered profl. engr., Md. Research engr. E.I. DuPont Co., Wilmington, Del., 1960-63; prof. U. Md., College Pk., 1963—; pres. ENSCI Inc., College Pk., 1972—. Mem. Am. Inst. Chem. Engrs. Office: U Md Dept Chem Engring Dept Chem Nuclear Engr College Park MD 20472

SMITH, THEODORE W., construction executive; b. 1927. Pres. Dinwiddie Constrn. Co., San Francisco, 1947—. Office: Dinwiddie Constrn Co Crocker Ctr W Tower 275 Battery St Ste 300 San Francisco CA 94104-2806*

SMITH, THOMAS CLAIR, manufacturing company executive; b. Indiana, Pa., Mar. 14, 1925; s. William Bryan and Edna Louise (Thomas) S.; m. Marilyn Louise Globisch, May 29, 1948; children: Claudia Lynn Smith Holtry, Craig Randall. BSME, Pa. State U., 1946; A, Alexander Hamilton Bus. Inst., 1949. Registered profl. engr., Pa. Structural test engr. Chance Vought Aircraft Co., Bridgeport, Conn., 1946-48; test engr. Fed. Mogul Bearings Co., Lancaster, Pa., 1949-51; fuse engr. to mgr. materials Hamilton Watch Co. (name now Hamilton Tech.), Lancaster, Pa., 1952-70; plant mgr. Woodstream Corp., Lititz, Pa., 1970-79, v.p. mktg., 1980—; faculty, coach Lacrosse Franklin and Marshall Coll., Lancaster, 1950-53. Pub. Smith, Bryan, Allison & Morris Geneal. Chart, 1989; author and pub. of 1600 person geneal. chart in Libr. of Congress, 1989; patentee electric watch, 1957, swivel snap, 1975; author Penna Law 110 and Pa. Law 22 of 1994/saving ancestral cemetaries. Pres., bd. dirs. Lancaster County Mental Health Assn., 1952-60, Lancaster County Community Svc. Ctr., 1968-78, Am. Cancer Soc., 1968—; bd. dirs. Hearing Conservation Assn., Lancaster, 1955-60, ARC, Lancaster, 1967—, United Way Lancaster, 1968-72, Ephrata (Pa.) Area Rehab. Ctr., 1986—; mem. All-Am. Lacrosse Team, 1945, Heritage Ctr. Lancaster, 1980—; Ind. County Hist. Soc., 1984—, Greene County Hist. Soc., Waynesburg, Pa., 1985—, Selective Svc. Bd., 1992—; trustee Lancaster Hist. Soc., 1992—, mem. 1983—. With USMC, 1951. Recipient Outstanding Svc. award Mental Health Assn., Lancaster, 1961, Edward D. Eshelman award as Humanitarian of Yr., Am. Cancer Soc., Lancaster, 1991; named Boss of Yr. Am. Bus. Womens Assn., 1978, Man of Yr. Am. Cancer Soc., 1984, Tennis Family of Yr., Pa., N.J., Del., 1970. Mem. Order of Crwon of Charlemagne in U.S.A. (life), Pa. State U. Alumni Club (life), Pa. Sons Revolution (bd. dirs. 1985—, sec. 1990—), Phi Delta Theta (pres. Pa.

SMITH, TOM EUGENE, retail food company executive; b. Salisbury, N.C., May 2, 1942; s. Ralph Eugene and Cora Belle (Ervin) S.; m. Martha Hatley; children: Leigh Ann, Nancy Thompson. AB in Bus. Adminstrn., Catawba Coll., 1964, LLD (hon.), 1986. With Del Monte Sales Co., 1964-67; account mgr. Del Monte Sales Co., Hickory, N.C., 1967-68; sales supr. Del Monte Sales Co., Charlotte, N.C., 1969-70; buyer Food Lion Stores, Inc., Salisbury, 1970-74, v.p. distbn., 1974-77, exec. v.p., 1977-81, pres., 1981—, chief exec. officer, 1986—, also bd. dirs.; chmn. bd., 1990—; chief exec. officer Food Lion Inc., Salisbury, 1986—; bd. dirs. N.C. Nat. Bank (chmn. bd. Salisbury chpt.), N.C. Food Dealers (pres. 1988). Trustee Catawba Coll., 1986—; bd. dirs. United Way, Salisbury, 1975-77. Recipient Martin Luther King Humanitarian award 1987, bronze and silver Chief Exec. Officer of Yr. awards Fin. World Mag., 1988. Mem. Nat. Assn. Retail Grocers, Sales Execs. Club (bd. dirs. 1974-79, pres. 1980), N.C. Food Dealers Assn. (bd. dirs. 1981—, 3d v.p. 1985, 2d v.p. 1986—), Am. Legion, C. of C. (bd. dirs. 1975-77). Republican. Lutheran. Club: Salisbury Country. Lodge: Rotary (bd. dirs. 1975-76). Avocations: traveling. Office: Food Lion Inc PO Box 1330 2110 Executive Dr Salisbury NC 28147-9047*

SMITH, THOMAS EUGENE, investment company executive, financial consultant; b. Brown's Summit, N.C., Aug. 23, 1930; s. Howard Cleveland and Annie May (Warren) S.; m. Joan Cretcher Hopkins, Sept. 22, 1948; 1 dau., Vicki Joan. Student, George Washington U., 1948-50, Am. U., 1950-55 (intermittently). Pres., dir. T. Eugene Smith, Inc. investment co. and real estate and fin. cons. co., Falls Church, Va., 1950—; pres. The Potomac Corp., Falls Church, Va., 1960-74; pres., dir. Nat. Bank of Fairfax, Va., 1975-81, dir.; exec. v.p First & Mchts. Nat. Bank, Richmond, Va., 1981-83; chmn., dir. Decisions and Designs, Inc., McLean, Va., 1983-86; ptnr. Braddock-Ravensworth Ltd. Partnership, 1964—; sec., dir. Port Royal, Inc., 1965—; ptnr. Lee Graham Shopping Ctr., 1969—; chmn., pres., dir. Am. Mobile Home Towns, Inc., holding co., 1969-85; dir., pres. Topsail, Inc., 1983-89; ptnr. Potomac Greens Assn., 1986—; bd. dirs. Growth Fund of Washington, Am. Funds Tax Exempt Series I, Washington Mut. Investors, M.G. Thalheimer Realty Advisors, Inc.; chmn., bd. dirs. River Capital Corp., Alexandria, Va., 1986-89, J. Webb, Inc., 1986—; acting dir. mem. mgmt. com. Alexandria 20/20, 1989-91, acting dir. 1988-89; pres., dir. Pender Marina Holdings, Inc., 1988—, Pender Land Holdings, Inc., 1990—; mem. CSX Realty Adv. Bd., 1992—. Bd. dirs. Wolftrap Found., Washington, 1974-84; trustee Sta. WETA-TV, 1978-86; mem. Nat. Capital Planning Commn., Washington, 1980-83, vice chmn., 1981-83; mem. Va. Hwys. and Transp. Commn., Richmond, 1982-86; trustee Ch. Schs., Diocese of Va., 1983-88; mem. Va. Gov.'s Coun. Econ. Advisors, 1985-94, Met. Washington Airports Authority, 1986-94; chmn. Fairfax County Transp. Commn. for the Future, 1988-89; dir. Air and Space Heritage Coun., 1987-90. Mem. Nat. Assn. Small Bus. Investment Cos. (treas. and bd. dirs. 1962-66), Commonwealth Club (Richmond), Met. Club (Washington). Democrat. Episcopalian. Home: 666 Tintagel Ln Mc Lean VA 22101-1835

SMITH, THOMAS HUNTER, ophthalmologist, ophthalmic plastic and orbital surgeon; b. Silver Creek, Miss., Aug. 10, 1939; s. Hunter and Wincil (Barr) S.; m. Michele Ann Campbell, Feb. 27, 1982; 1 child, Thomas Hunter IV. BA, U. So. Miss., 1961; MD, Tulane U., 1967; BA in Latin Am. Studies, Tex. Christian U., 1987. Diplomate Am. Bd. Ophthalmology. Intern Charity Hosp., New Orleans, 1967-68; resident in ophthalmology Tulane U., New Orleans, 1968-71; dir., sec. bd. dirs. Ophthalmology Assocs., Ft. Worth, 1971—; clin. prof. Tex. Tech. U. Med. Sch., Lubbock, 1979—; bd. examiners Am. Bd. Ophthalmology, 1983-90; guest lectr., invited speaker numerous schs., confs., symposia throughout N.Am., Ctrl. Am., South Am., Europe and India; hon. mem. ophthalmology dept. Santa Casa de São Paulo Med. Sch. Contbr. articles to profl. jours. Bd. dirs. Planned Parenthood Assn. Tarrant County; cons. ophthalmologist Hellen Keller Internat.; deacon South Hills Christian Ch. Recipient Tex. Chpt. award Am. Assn. Workers for the Blind, 1978, Recognition award Lions Club Sight & Tissue Found., Cen. Am., 1977-79; named to Alumni Hall of Fame U. So. Miss., 1989. Fellow ACS, Am. Acad. Ophthalmology, Am. Acad. Facial Plastic and Reconstructive Surgery; mem. Tex. Med. Assn. (socio-econs.), Pan-Am. Assn. Ophthalmology (adminstr. 1988-93, bd. dirs. 1993—), Internat. Cos. Cryosurgery, Royal Soc. Medicine (affiliate), Tex. Soc. Ophthalmology and Otolaryngology, Peruvian Ophthalmol. Soc. (hon. mem.), Santa Casa De São Paulo (hon. assoc.), Tex. Ophthalmol. Assn. (past mem. exec. coun., treas.), Tex. Med. Assn., Tarrant County Med. Soc., Byron Smith Eh Fellows Assn., Tarrant County Ophthalmology Soc., (past pres.) Tarrant County Multiple Sclerosis Soc. (past pres.), Tarrant County Assn. for Blind, Tulane Med. Alumni Assn. (bd. dirs.), S.Am. Explorers Club, Colonial Country Club, Petroleum Club Ft. Worth, Omicron Delta Kappa, Sigma Xi. Mem. Disciples of Christ. Avocations: hunting, fishing, flying, world travel. Office: Ophthalmology Assocs 1201 Summit Ave Fort Worth TX 76102

SMITH, THOMAS KENT, radiologist; b. Bowling Green, Ohio, Aug. 21, 1934; s. Robert O. and Roslyn Smith; m. Jaleh Saidi, Feb. 1, 1974; children: Jeffrey, Todd, Mark, Blake, Tyler. BS with high honors, U. Cin., 1957; MD, Case Western Res. U., 1961. Intern Nat. Naval Med. Ctr., Bethesda, Md., 1961-62; resident in radiology VA Med. Ctr., Long Beach, Calif., 1965-69; dir. radiology Harriman Jones Med. Group, Long Beach, 1969-88; fellow in MRI/CT U. Calif., San Francisco, 1988-89; dir. MRI Orange County MRI, Fountain Valley, Calif., 1989-90; chmn. dept. diagnostic imaging Kaiser Permanente Med. Ctr., Honolulu, 1990—; fellow in radiologic pathology Armed Forces Inst. of Pathology, Washington, 1968; mem. adv. bd. Hawaii Permanente Med. Group, Honolulu, 1990-94; bd. dirs. Harriman Jones Med. Group, Harriman Jones Assocs.; assoc. clin. prof. radiology U. Hawaii, Honolulu, 1990-94; asst. clin. prof. U. Calif. Irvine, 1970-88; clin. instr. U. Calif. San Francisco, 1988-89, asst. clin. prof., 1989-94. Lt. USN, 1961-65. Mem. Hawaii Radiol. Soc. (pres. 1990-94), Radiol. Soc. N.Am., Am. Coll. Radiology, Soc. Magnetic Resonance, Margulis Soc., Calif. Radiol. Soc., Alpha Omega Alpha. Avocations: fishing, travel, photography. Home: 46-434 Haiku Plantations Dr Kaneohe HI 96744 Office: Kaiser Permanente Med Ctr 3280 Moanalua Rd Honolulu HI 96819

SMITH, THOMAS SHORE, lawyer; b. Rock Springs, Wyo., Dec. 7, 1924; s. Thomas and Anne E. (McTee) S.; m. Jacqueline Emily Krueger, May 25, 1952; children: Carolyn Jane, Karl Thomas, David Shore. BSBA, U. Wyo., 1950, JD, 1959. Bar: U.S. Dist. Ct. Wyo. 1960, U.S. Ct. Appeals (10th cir.) 1960, U.S. Tax Ct. 1969, U.S. Supreme Ct. 1971. Of counsel Smith, Stanfield & Scott, LLC, Laramie, Wyo., 1963—; atty. City of Laramie, 1963-86; instr. mcpl. law U. Wyo., 1987, mem. dean's adv. com. Law Sch.; dir. budget and fin. Govt. of Am. Samoa, 1954-56. Bd. dirs. Bur. Land Mgmt., Rawlins, Wyo., 1984-89, chmn. bd. dirs., 1989; pres. Ivinson Hosp. Found., 1994-95; v.p.u Wyo. Found., 1991—. Francis Warren scholar, 1958. Mem. Wyo. Bar Assn. (pres. 1984-85), Albany County Bar Assn., Western States Bar Conf. (pres. 1985-86), Elks. Republican. Episcopalian. Avocations: golf, tennis. Office: Smith Stanfield & Scott LLC PO Box 971 515 E Ivinson Ave Laramie WY 82070-3157

SMITH, THOMAS WINSTON, cotton marketing executive; b. Crosbyton, Tex., Mar. 16, 1935; s. Lance L. and Willie Mae (Little) S.; m. Patricia Mae Zachary, Dec. 13, 1958; children—Janna Olean, Thomas Mark. B.S., Tex. A&M U., 1957; P.M.D., Harvard U., 1964. Various positions Calcot Ltd., Bakersfield, Calif., 1957-77, exec. v.p., pres., 1977—; v.p. Amcot, Inc., Amcot Internat., Inc., Bakersfield, 1977—, also bd. dirs.; v.p. Nat. Cotton Coun., Memphis; bd. mgrs. N.Y. Cotton Exchange, N.Y.C. Bd. dir. Greater Bakersfield Meml. Hosp.; mem. pres.'s adv. commn. Calif. State Coll., Bakersfield. Mem. Rotary.

SMITH, THOMAS WOODWARD, cardiologist, educator; b. Akron, Ohio, Mar. 29, 1936; s. Luther David and Beatrice Pearl (Woodward) S.; m. Sherley Louise Goodwin, Sept. 13, 1958; children: Julia Goodwin, Geoffrey Woodward, Allison Lloyd. A.B., Harvard U., 1958, M.D., 1965. Diplomate: Am. Bd. Internal Medicine, Am. Bd. Cardiovascular Diseases. Intern in medicine Mass. Gen. Hosp., Boston, 1965-66, asst. resident in medicine, 1966-67, clin. and research fellow in cardiology, 1967-69, Nat. Heart and Lung Inst. spl. fellow, 1969-71, asst. in medicine, 1969-72, assoc. program dir. myocardial infarction research unit, 1972-74, asst. physician, 1972-77, cons. in medicine, 1977—; asst. prof. medicine Harvard U. Med. Sch., 1971-73, assoc. prof., 1973-79, prof., 1979—; physician Peter Bent Brigham Hosp. (now Brigham and Women's Hosp.), Boston, chief cardiovascular div.; cons. in cardiology Children's Hosp. Med. Ctr. and Sidney Farber Cancer Inst. (now Dana-Farber Cancer Inst.); prof. medicine MIT div. Health Scis. and Tech.; Hall vis. prof., Sydney, Australia, 1977; Sir Henry Hallett Dale vis. prof. Johns Hopkins U. Med. Sch., 1979; Nahum lectr. Yale U. Sch. Medicine, 1979. Reviewer med. jours.; contbr. articles to profl. publs. Mem. Am. Heart Assn. (council clin. cardiology, council basic sci., council on circulation, established investigator 1971-76 Rosenthal award), Am. Fedn. Clin. Research, Paul Dudley White Soc., AAAS, Am. Soc. Pharmacology and Exptl. Therapeutics, Am. Soc. Clin. Investigation, Am. Coll. Cardiology, ACP, Assn. Univ. Cardiologists, Am. Physiol. Soc., Assn. Am. Physicians, Soc. Gen. Physiologists, Alpha Omega Alpha. Home: 128 Wellesley St Weston MA 02193-1555 Office: Brigham and Women's Hosp 75 Francis St Boston MA 02115-6195

SMITH, TURNER TALIAFERRO, JR., lawyer; b. Washington, Dec. 16, 1940; s. Turner Taliaferro and Lois (Fisk) S.; m. Christine H. Perdue; children: Turner T., III, John Webb Tyler. BA magna cum laude, Princeton U., 1962; LLB cum laude, Harvard U., 1968. Bar: Va. 1968, D.C. 1977. Ptnr. Hunton & Williams, Richmond, Va., 1975—; tchr. environ. law Washington and Lee U., 1978, Coll. William and Mary, 1979, 80. Mem. ABA (chmn. standing com. environ. law 1983, 84, 85, chmn. corp., banking and bus. law sect.'s com. on environ. controls 1973-80), Va. Bar Assn., Richmond Bar Assn., Internat. Bar Assn. Home: Av Général de Gaulle 42, 1050 Brussels Belgium Office: Hunton & Williams, Ave Louise 106, 1050 Brussels Belgium

SMITH, V. KERRY, economics educator; b. Jersey City, Mar. 11, 1945; s. Vincent C. and Dorothy E. (Linehan) S.; m. Pauline Anne Taylor, May 10, 1969; children: Timothy, Shelley. AB, Rutgers U., 1966, PhD, 1970. Asst. prof., then assoc. prof. Bowling Green State U., Ohio, 1969-72; assoc. prof. Resources for Future, Washington, 1971-73; assoc. prof. SUNY, Binghamton, 1973-75, prof., 1975-78; sr. fellow Resources for Future, Washington, 1976-79; prof. U. N.C., Chapel Hill, 1979-83; Centennial prof. Vanderbilt U., Nashville, 1983-87; Univ. Disting. prof. N.C. State U., 1987-94; Arts and Scis. prof. environ. econs. Duke U., 1994—; adviser energy div. Oak Ridge Nat. Lab., 1978-80, U. N.C. Inst. Environ. Studies, 1980-83; mem. panel NSF, 1981-83, sci. adv. bd. EPA. Author: Monte Carlo Methods, 1973, Technical Change, Relative Prices and Environmental Resource Evaluation, 1974, The Costs of Congestion: An Econometric Analysis of Wilderness Recreation, 1976, Structure and Properties of a Wilderness Travel Simulator: An Application to the Spanish Peaks Area, 1976, The Economic Consequences of Air Pollution, 1976, Scarcity and Growth Reconsidered, 1979, (with others) Explorations in Natural Resource Economics, 1982, (with W.H. Desvousges) Measuring Water Quality Benefits, 1986, (with others) Environmental Resources and Applied Welfare Economics, 1988, (with R.J. Kopp) Valuing Natural Assets: The Economics of Natural Resource Damage Assessment, Resources for the Future, 1993; editor Advances in Applied Micro Econs. series; contbr. numerous articles to profl. jours. Guggenheim fellow, 1976; grantee Resources for Future, 1970, 73, 74, 86, Fed. Energy Adminstrn. 1975, N.Y. Sea Grant Inst., 1975, Ford Found., 1976, NSF, 1977, 79, 83, Electric Power Rsch. Inst., 1978, Nat. Oceanic and Atmospheric Adminstrn., 1980, Sloan Found., 1981, 86, EPA, 1983-88, N.C. Sea Grant Program, 1987-93. Russell Sage Found., 1989-91; recipient Frederick V. Waugh medal Am. Agrl. Econ. Assn., 1992. Mem. Am. Econ. Assn., Am. Statis. Assn., Econometric Soc., So. Econ. Assn. (exec. com. 1981-83, 1st v.p. 1987, pres. elect 1988, pres. 1989), Assn. Environ. and Resource Economists (bd. dirs. 1975-79, v.p. 1979-80, chmn. 1982-83, pres. 1985-86, Disting. Svc. award 1989).

SMITH, VERNON G., education educator, state representative; b. Gary, Ind., Apr. 11, 1944. BS, Ind. U., 1966, MS, 1969, EdD, 1978; postgrad. Ind.U.-Purdue U., 1986-90. Tchr. Gary Pub. Schs. Systems, 1966-71, resource tchr., 1971-72; asst. prin. Ivanhoe Sch., Gary, 1972-78; prin. Nobel Sch., Gary, 1978-85, Williams Sch., Gary, 1985-92; part-time counselor edn. div. Ind. U. N.W., Gary, 1967-69, adj. lectr. 1987-92, asst. prof., 1992—; mem. Ind. Ho. of Reps., Indpls., 1990—; columnist Gary Crusader, 1969-71; speaker Devel. Tng. Inst., 1986—. Author: (with D. McClam) Building Bridges Instead of Walls—History of I.U. Dons, Inc., 1979; also articles. Mem. Gary City Coun., 1972-90; precinct committeeman Gary Dem. Com., 1972-92; founder, chmn. Gary City-Wide Festival Com.; bd. dirs. N.W. Ind. Urban League; founder, pres. I.U. Dons, Inc.; past pres. Gary Community Mental Health Bd.; v.p. Gary Common Coun., 1982, 85-87, pres., 1976, 83-84, 88; past mem. bd. dirs. Little League World Series; founder, past sponsor Youth Ensuring Solidarity, Young Citizens' League. Recipient citation in edn. Gary NAACP, 1970, Good Govt. award Gary Jaycees, 1977, Outstanding Svc. award Gary Young Dems., 1979, Businessman of Yr. award Gary Downtown Mchts., 1979, Bd. Dirs. Svcs. award Gary Community Health Ctr., 1982, Educator Par Excellence award Williams Sch., 1987, appreciation award Ind. Assn. Chief Police, 1992, Meth. Hosp., 1992, Bros. Keeper appreciation award, 1992, svc. award Ind. Assn. Elem. and Mid. Sch. Prins., 1992; numerous others. Mem. NAACP (life), Ind. Assn. Sch. Prins., No. Ind. Assn. Black School Educators (founder), Ind. U. N.W. Alumni Assn. (life, Disting. Educator award 1992), Phi Delta Kappa, Omega Psi Phi (life, Omega Man of Yr. award 1974, Citizen of Yr. award 10th dist. 1989, appreciation award Omicron Rho chpt. 1991). Baptist. Home: PO Box M622 Gary IN 46401-0622 Office: Ind U NW 3400 Broadway Hawthorn # 336 Gary IN 46408

SMITH, VERNON LOMAX, economist, researcher; b. Wichita, Kans., Jan. 1, 1927; s. Vernon Chessman and Lula Belle (Lomax) S.; m. Joyce Harkleroad, June 6, 1950 (div. Aug. 1975); m. Carol Breckner, Jan. 1, 1980. BSEE, Calif. Inst. Tech., 1949; MA in Econs., U. Kans., 1952; PhD in Econs., Harvard U., 1955; D of Mgmt. (hon.), Purdue U., 1990. Asst. prof. econs. Purdue U., West Lafayette, Ind., 1955-58, assoc. prof., 1958-61, prof., 1961-65, Krannert prof., 1965-67; prof. Brown U., Providence, 1967-68, U. Mass., Amherst, 1968-75; prof. U. Ariz., Tucson, 1975—; Regents' prof.; Contbr. articles to profl. jours. Fellow Ctr. for Advanced Study in Behavioral Scis., Stanford, Calif., 1972-73; Sherman Fairchild Disting. Scholar Calif. Inst. Tech., Pasadena, 1973-74; adj. scholar CATO Inst., Washington, 1983—. Fellow AAAS, Am. Acad. Arts and Scis., Econometric Soc., Am. Econ. Assn. (Disting. fellow); mem. Pvt. Enterprise Edn. Assn. (Adam Smith award). Home: 2122 E Camino El Ganado Tucson AZ 85718-4108 Office: Univ Ariz Dept Economics Tucson AZ 85718

SMITH, VERONICA LATTA, real estate corporation officer; b. Wyandotte, Mich., Jan. 13, 1925; d. Jan August and Helena (Hulak) Latta; m. Stewart Gene Smith, Apr. 12, 1952; children: Stewart Gregory, Patrick Allen, Paul Donald, Alison Veronica, Alisa Margaret Lyons, Glenn Laurence. BA in Sociology, U. Mich., 1948, postgrad., 1948. Tchr. Coral Gables (Fla.) Pub. System, 1949-50; COO Latta Ins. Agy, Wyandotte, 1950-62; treas. L & S Devel. Co. Grosse Ile, Mich., 1963-84; v.p. Regency Devel., Riverview, Mich., 1984—. Active U. Mich. Bd. Regents, 1985-93, regent emeritus, 1993—; mem. pres. Martha Cook Bd. Govs., U. Mich., 1972-78, 76-78; del. Rep. County Conv., Wayne County, Mich., 1988—, Rep. State Conv., Grand Rapids, Mich., 1985, 87, 89, 91, 92, 94, Detroit, 1986, 88, 90, 92; mem. pres. adv. com. Campaign for Mich., 1992—, mem. campaign steering coun. Mem. Mich. Lawyers Aux. (treas. 1975, chmn. 1976, 77, 78, 79), Nat. Assn. Ins. Women (cert.), Faculty Women's Club U. Mich. (hon.), Radrick Farms Golf Club (Ann Arbor), Pres.'s Club U. Mich., Investment Club (pres. 1976, sec. 1974-75, treas. 1975-76), Alpha Kappa Delta. Home: 22225 Balmoral Dr Grosse Ile MI 48138

SMITH, VICTOR EARLE, economist, educator; b. Lansing, Mich., Apr. 9, 1914; s. Earle Baker and Isabelle (Emery) S.; m. E. Margaret French, Nov. 29, 1940; children—David, Michael. A.B., Mich. State Coll., 1935, M.A., 1936; Ph.D., Northwestern U., 1940. Instr. econs. Northwestern U., Evanston, Ill., 1940-42; asst. prof. econs. Yale, 1942-44, Wellesley (Mass.) Coll., 1944-47, Brown U., Providence, R.I., 1947-48; assoc. prof. econs. Mich. State U., East Lansing, 1948-53; prof. econs. Mich. State U., 1953-84, prof. foods nutrition, 1963, chmn. dept. econs., 1974-76, prof. emeritus, 1984—; vis.

prof. econs. U. Mich., Ann Arbor, 1963; cons., U.S. Aid Tunisia, 1974, Sierra Leone, 1985, Rwanda, 1986-87. Author: Electronic Computation of Human Diets, 1964, Efficient Resource Use for Tropical Nutrition: Nigeria, 1975; Contbr. articles in field to profl. jours. research grantee Inst. Internat. Agr., 1970; research grantee AID, 1978-81; research grantee study Nigerian rural devel. Midwest Univs. Consortium Internat. Activities, East Lansing, 1966-68; Fund Advancement Edn. faculty fellow, 1954-55; Ford Found. research fellow, 1958-59; NSF research grantee, 1965-67; Rockefeller Found. research grantee, 1968-70. Mem. Am. Econ. Assn., Midwest Econ. Assn., Mich. Acad. Arts Sci., AAUP. Home: 4378 Keller Rd Holt MI 48842-1214 Office: Mich State U Econs Dept 5 Old Botany East Lansing MI 48824-1301

SMITH, VINCENT DACOSTA, artist; b. Bklyn., Dec. 12, 1929; s. Beresford Leopold and Louise S.; m. Cynthia I. Linton, July 15, 1972. Student, Art Students League, N.Y.C., 1953, Bklyn. Mus. Sch., 1955-56; B. Profl. Services, Empire State Coll., 1980. Instr. painting and graphics Whitney Mus. Art, N.Y.C., 1967-76; instr. painting Ceda Project, 1978-80; artist in residence Smithsonian Conf. Center, Elkridge, Md., 1967, Cite des Arts Internat., Paris, 1978; participant 2d World Black and African Festival Arts and Culture, Lagos, Nigeria, 1977; commns. include Impressions: Our World Portfolio of Prints, 1974, mural at Boys and Girls High Sch., Bklyn., 1976, mural for Tremont/Crotona Social Svc. Ctr. Human Resources Adminstrn. and CETA Project, N.Y.C., 1980, mural for Oberia D. Dempsey Multi-Svc. Ctr. for Cen. Harlem, Dept. Cultural Affairs, N.Y.C., 1988, 2 murals for 116 St. Sta., N.Y.C. Met. Transit Authority; film tapes and videos include Bernie Casey: Black Dimensions in Contemporary Am. Art, Carnation Co., Los Angeles, 1971, Tee Collins, Barbara Cobb: The First Water, Theatre Eleven, 1977, Robert Fassbinder: The Creative Pulse of Afro-Am. Culture, WTVG, N.J., 1978, Bearden Plays Bearden, Third World Cinema, 1980, Works on Paper, Storefront Mus./Paul Robeson Theatre, Jamaica, N.Y., 1981; host bi-weekly program, discussions with 45 activists WBAI-FM Radio. Illustrator: Folklore Stories from Africa, 1974; exhbns. include Hall of Springs Mus., Saratoga, N.Y., 1970, Contemporary Black Am. Artists, Whitney Mus. Am. Art, N.Y.C., 1971, Two Generations, Newark Mus., 1971, Mus. of Sci. and Industry, Chgo., 1975, Bronx Mus. Art, 1977, Bklyn. Mus., 1979; one-man exhbns. include Lacarda Gallery, N.Y.C., 1967, 68, 70, 73, 75, 77, Paa Ya Paa Gallery, Nairobi, Kenya, 1973, Chemchemi Creative Arts Center, Arusha, Tanzania, 1973, Kibo Art Gallery, Mt. Kilimanjaro, Tanzania, 1973, Portland (Maine) Art Mus., 1974, Reading (Pa.) Public Mus., 1974, Erie (Pa.) Art Center, 1977, Gallery 7, Detroit, 1977; represented in permanent collections, Mus. Modern Art, N.Y.C., Newark Mus., Bklyn. Mus., U. Va. Art Mus.; also subject of TV film; host Vincent Smith Dialogues with Contemporary Artists, Radio Sta. WPAI-FM, 1986-88. Served with U.S. Army, 1948-49. Recipient Thomas B. Clark prize N.A.D., 1974; Winslow and Newton prize Nat. Soc. Painters in Casein and Acrylic, 1978; John Hay Whitney fellow, 1959; Nat. Endowment Arts grantee, 1973; Nat. Inst. Arts and Letters grantee, 1968; Cultural Council Found. grantee, 1971. Mem. Nat. Conf. Artists. Home: 264 E Broadway New York NY 10002 *I have tried to develop three things which I feel are necessary to achieving some success in one's chosen field: a philosophy in which one keeps physically fit, mentally aware and consistent in one's work. Through a belief in the importance of the work one can constantly strive to grow and reach new heights.*

SMITH, VINCENT MILTON, lawyer; b. Barbourville, Ky., Nov. 21, 1940; s. Virgil Milton and Louis (McGalliard) S.; 1 child, Jessica Todd. BA, Harvard U., 1962; LLB, Yale U., 1965. Bar: N.Y. 1966. Assoc. Breed, Abbott & Morgan, N.Y.C., 1965-70; assoc. Debevoise & Plimpton, N.Y.C., 1970-75, ptnr., 1975—; mem. adv. bd. Chgo. Title Ins. Co., N.Y.C., 1979—. Trustee Chatham Players, N.J., 1967-77, 87-91, Summit Friends Meeting, Chatham, 1973—. N.J. Shakespeare Festival, Madison, 1975-80, Playwrights Theatre N.J., 1989-91. Mem. ABA, N.Y. State Bar Assn., Assn. of Bar of City of N.Y., Am. Land Title Assn., Urban Land Inst. Home: Soc. of Friends. Clubs: Harvard, N.Y. Athletic. Office: Debevoise & Plimpton 875 3rd Ave New York NY 10022-6225

SMITH, VIRGIL CLARK, state legislator; b. Detroit, July 4, 1947; s. Virgil Columbus and Eliza (Boyer) S.; m. Evelyn Owens (div.); children: Virgil Kai, Adam Smith; m. Elizabeth Ann Little. BA in polit. sci., Mich. State U., 1969; JD, Wayne State U., 1972. Legal advisor various community groups, Detroit, 1972-73; supervising atty. Wayne County Legal Svcs., Detroit, 1973-74; sr. asst.corp. counsel law dept. City of Detroit, 1974-75; mem. Mich. State Ho. Reps., 1976-88, Mich. State Senate, 1988—; mem. Appropriations Comm. Mem. Nat. Caucus Black State Legislators, Nat. Caucus of State Legislators, Mich. Legis. Black Caucus (2d chair 1991-92). Democrat. Avocations: golf, swimming, bowling, skiing. Office: State Senate PO Box 30036 Lansing MI 48909-7536 Address: 19316 Norwood Detroit MI 48234

SMITH, VIRGINIA DODD (MRS. HAVEN SMITH), congresswoman; b. Randolph, Iowa, June 30, 1911; d. Clifton Clark and Erville (Reeves) Dodd; m. Haven N. Smith, Aug. 27, 1931. A.B., U. Nebr., 1936; hon. degree, Nebr. U., 1987, Chadron State Coll., 1988. Nat. pres. Am. Country Life Assn., 1951-54; nat. chmn. Am. Farm Bur. Women, 1954-74; dir. Am. Farm Bur. Fedn., 1954-74, Country Women's Council; world dep. pres. Asso. Country Women of World, 1962-68; mem. Dept. Agr. Nat. Home Econs. Research Adv. Com., 1960-65; bd. dirs. Norwest Bank Cmty. Bd., Property Owners and Residents Bd., Sun Health Corp. Bd., Recreation Ctrs. Sun City West, sec., mem. gov. bd. Mem. Crusade for Freedom European inspection tour, 1958; del. Republican Nat. Conv., 1956, 72; bd. govs. Agrl. Hall of Fame, 1959—; mem. Nat. Livestock and Meat Bd., 1955-58, Nat. Commn. Community Health Services, 1963-66; adv. mem. Nebr. Sch. Bds. Assns., 1949; mem. Nebr. Territorial Centennial Commn., 1953, Gov.'s Commn. Status of Women, 1964-66; chmn. Presdl. Task Force on Rural Devel., 1969-70; mem. appropriations com., ranking minority mem. agrl. appropriations subcom., appropriations subcom. on energy and water devel. 94th-101st Congresses from 3d dist. Nebr.; v.p Farm Film Found., 1964-74, Good Will ambassador to Switzerland, 1950. Apptd. adm. Nebr. Navy; bd. dirs. Shepherd of the Hills Meth. Ch. Recipient award of Merit, DAR, 1956; Disting. Service award U. Nebr., 1956, 60; award for best pub. address on freedom Freedom Found., 1966; Eyes on Nebr. award Nebr. Optometric Assn., 1970; Internat. Service award Midwest Conf. World Affairs, 1970; Woman of Achievement award Nebr. Bus. and Profl. Women, 1971; selected as 1 of 6 U.S. women Govt. France for 3 week goodwill mission to France, 1969; Outstanding 4H Alumni award Iowa State U., 1973, 74; Watchdog of Treasury award, 1976, 78, 80, 82, 83, 84, 86, 88; Guardian of Small Bus. award, 1976, 78, 80, 82, 84, 86, 88; Nebr. Ak-Sar-Ben award, 1983, Agrl. Achievement, Nebr. U., 1987; named Favorite Community Leader, Sun City West, 1994. Mem. AAUW, Delta Kappa Gamma (state hon. mem.), Beta Sigma Phi (internat. hon. mem.), Chi Omega, PEO (past pres.), Eastern Star. Methodist. Club: Business and Professional Women. Address: 13828 Terra Vista Dr Sun City West AZ 85375 *As a fifteen-year-old high school valedictorian, I wrote these words in my valedictory message, "There is no excellence without great labor." Almost half a century later, I continue to live by this philosophy.*

SMITH, VIVIAN LOUISE, substance abuse prevention professional, social worker; b. Tampa, Fla., Oct. 4, 1931; d. Oliver and Janie (Peterson) Clark; m. Julius S. Smith Sr., Oct. 4, 1952 (div.); children: Julius L. Jr., Michael E. BA, Ohio State U., 1951; MSW, Cath. U. Am., 1960. Lic. and cert. social worker. Social worker, supr. social svcs. dept. St. Elizabeths Hosp., Washington, 1960-69, dir. cmty. liaison and pub. edn. Area D Cmty. Mental Health Ctr., 1969-73, acting dep. dir., 1973, dep. dir., 1973-74, acting dir., 1974-78, dir., 1978-87; cmty. coord. mental health sys, reorganization office Dept. Human Svcs., Washington, 1984-87; dep. dir. office substance abuse prevention/office administr., alcohol, drug abuse and mental health administrn. PHS, Rockville, Md., 1987-92, acting dir., 1992-94; dep. dir. Ctr. Substance Abuse Prevention, Substance Abuse and Mental Health Svcs. Administrn., Washington, 1992—; lectr. nursing St. Elizabeths Hosp., 1963-66, Cath. U. Sch. Nursing, 1964-66; with The Washington Sch. Psychiatry, 1972-75, Met. Mental Health Skills Ctr., 1973-74; chairperson D.C. Bd. Social Work, 1987-94. Bd. dirs. Frederick Douglas Meml. and Hist. Assn., 1973—; also trustee, treas., pres. Frederick Douglas Housing Corp., Washington, 1975-82; active Mt. Moriah Bapt. Ch., Washington, also past asst. supt. Sunday sch., deptl. supt. and tchr., deptl. supt. and tchr. Vacation Bible sch., chair various coms. and programs. With USAF, 1951-53. Recipient Appreciation cert. City of Washington, 1973, Greater Southeast Ctr. for Aging, 1982, Mental Health award Delta Sigma Theta, 1976,

Kiwanis Club, 1977, Outstanding Svc. award Washington Area D Coun. on Alcoholism and Drug Abuse, 1977, Frederick Douglas Meml. and Hist. Assn., 1981, Cmty. Svc. award East of River Health Assn., 1980, Good Neighbor award Congress Heights Civic Assn., 1981, Dedicated Svc. award Vols. in Edn., 1981, Disting. Svc. award Nat. Coun. Cmty. Mental Health Ctrs., 1982, Vol. award DHHS, 1982, Outstanding and Dedicated Svc. award Frederick Douglas Housing Corp., 1982, Meritorious Contbn. award Middletown Jaycees, 1988, LeBaron D. Brazier Cmty. Svc. award D.C. Bd. Social Work, 1990. Mem. NASW, Am. Coll. Mental Health Adminstrn. (treas. membership com., chair ann. meeting, pres.-elect, pres. 1994), Am. Cancer Soc. (bd. dirs. D.C. divsn. 1977-83, asst. sec. 1979-82, sec. 1982-83, S.E. unit, pres., chairperson income devel. and crusade, Outstanding Leadership award 1981, Disting. Svc. to Cause of Cancer award 1982, Charles E. Qualls award 1985, Edward F. Bartlet award 1986, Appreciation award 1990), Nat. Conf. Social Workers, Med. Soc. St. Elizabeths. Home: 3523 Carpenter St SW Washington DC 20020 Office: Ctr for Substance Abuse Prevention 5600 Fishers Ln Rockville MD 20857-0001

SMITH, VME (VERNA MAE EDOM SMITH), sociology educator, free-lance writer, photographer; b. Marshfield, Wis., June 19, 1929; d. Clifton Cedric and Vilia Clarissa (Patefield) Edom; children: Teri Freas, Anthony Thomas. AB in Sociology, U. Mo., 1951; MA in Sociology, George Washington, 1965; PhD in Human Devel., U. Md., 1981. Tchr. Alcohol Safety Action Program Fairfax County, Va., 1973-75; instr. sociology No. Va. C.C., Manassas, 1975-77, asst. prof., 1977-81, assoc. prof., 1981-84, prof., 1984-94, prof. emerita, 1995; coord. coop. edn. No. Va. Community Coll., Manassas, 1983-89; Chancellor's Commonwealth prof. Manassas, 1991-93; freelance writer, editor and photographer, 1965—; co-dir. Clifton C. Edom Truth With a Camera (photography seminars); asst. producer history of photography program Sta. WETA-TV, Washington, 1965; rsch. and prodn. asst., photographer, publs. editor No. Va. Edl. TV, Sta. WNVT, 1970-71; cons. migrant div. Md. Dept. Edn., Balt., summer 1977; researcher, photographer Roundabout presch. high sch. series on Am. Values Sta. WNVT, 1970-71. Author, photographer: Middleburg and Nearby, 1986; co-author: Small Town America, 1993; contbr. photography to various works including Visual Impact in Print (Hurley and McDougall), 1971, Looking Forward to a Career in Education (Moses), 1976, Child Growth and Development (Terry, Sorrentino and Flatter), 1979, Photojournalism (Edom), 1976, 80, Migrant Child Welfare, 1977, (Cavenaugh), Caring for Children, 1973 (5 publs. by L.B. Murphy), Dept. Health, Edn. and Welfare, Nat. Geog., 1961, Head Start Newsletter, 1973-74. Mem. ednl. adv. com. Head Start, Warrenton, Va. Recipient Emmy Ohio State Children's Programming award; Fulbright-Hays Rsch. grantee, 1993. Mem. Va. Assn. Coop. Edn. (com. mem.). Democrat. Office: No Va Community Coll 6901 Sudley Rd Manassas VA 22110-2399

SMITH, W. P., JR., food products executive. Chmn. Gold Kist, Inc. Office: Gold Kist Inc 244 Perimeter Center Pkwy NE Atlanta GA 30346-2302*

SMITH, W. STUART, hospital administrator; b. Binghamton, N.Y., May 3, 1943; married. B, Washington & Lee U., 1965; M, Mich. State U., 1967, Va. Commonwealth U., 1974. Adminstrv. resident MUSC Med. Ctr., Charleston, 1973-74, asst. dir., 1974-79, assoc. dir., 1979-83, dir. optical svcs., 1983-87, dir. mktg., 1987-92, exec. dir., 1993—. Mem. S.C. Hosp. Assn. (bd. dirs.). Home: 8 Smith St Charleston SC 29401 Office: MUSC Med Ctr Med U SC 171 Ashley Ave Charleston SC 29425

SMITH, WALLACE A., radio company executive; b. Nov. 29, 1934. BA, Waynesburg Coll., 1957; ThM., Pitts. Theol. Sem., 1960; MA, U. So. Calif., L.A., 1969, PhD, 1972. Gen. mgr. Sta. KUSC-FM, L.A., 1972-87; v.p., gen. mgr. Sta. WNYC-AM/FM, N.Y.C., 1987-88; pres. USC Radio, U. So. Calif., L.A., 1988—; gen. mgr. Sta. KUSC-FM, U. So. Calif., L.A., 1988—; chair interim internat. working group Corp. for Pub. Broadcasting, 1987—; founding mem., bd. dirs. Am. Pub. Radio, 1983—; mem. radio adv. com. Calif. Pub. Broadcasting Commns.; participant CPB Radio Task Force, Profile of a Pub. Radio Sta., 1980. Mem. Assn. Calif. Pub. Radio Stations (sec. 1975-76, pres. 1976-77). Office: Sta KUSC 3716 S Hope St Los Angeles CA 90007-4344

SMITH, WALLACE BUNNELL, physician, church official; b. Independence, Mo., July 29, 1929; s. William Wallace and Rosamond (Bunnell) S.; m. Anne M. McCullough, June 26, 1956; children—Carolyn, Julia, Laura. A.A., Graceland Coll., Lamoni, Iowa, 1948; B.A., U. Kans., 1950, M.D., 1954. Diplomate: Am. Bd. Ophthalmology. Intern Charity Hosp. of La., 1955; resident in medicine U. Kans. Med. Center, 1958, resident in ophthalmology, 1959-62; pvt. practice medicine specializing in ophthalmology, 1962-76; ordained to ministry Reorganized Ch. of Jesus Christ of Latter Day Saints, 1945; asso. pastor Walnut Park Congregation, Independence, Mo., 1966-70, Pleasant Heights Congregation, Independence, 1975-76; president-designate Reorganized Ch. of Jesus Christ of Latter Day Saints, 1976-78, pres., 1978—; clin. assoc. U. Kans. Med. Center, 1962-76; dir. Pacific Land Devel. Assn. Bd. dirs. Mo. State Hist. Soc., Am. Lung Assn. West Mo., Independence Cmty. Found. Lt. M.C., USNR, 1955-58. Fellow ACS, Am. Acad. Ophthalamology; mem. AMA, Jackson County Med. Soc., Independence C. of C., Rotary, Phi Beta Pi. Home: 337 E Partridge St Independence MO 64055-1452 Office: Auditorium PO Box 1059 Independence MO 64051-0559

SMITH, WALTER DOUGLAS, retired college president; b. Harriman, Tenn., Nov. 17, 1918; s. Walter Blaine and Jeanetta Mae (Scarborough) S.; m. Rhondda Verle Miller, Apr. 5, 1947; children: Ian Douglas Miller, Walter Henry. B.A., Lincoln Meml. U., Harrogate, Tenn., 1943; M.A., U. Mich., 1947, Ph.D., 1950. Faculty psychology Fla. State U., 1950-59; dean coll. prof. psychology Winthrop Coll., Rock Hill, S.C., 1959-66; v.p. acad. affairs, dean of faculty Winthrop Coll., 1966-68; pres. Salisbury (Md.) State Coll., 1968-70, Francis Marion Coll., Florence, S.C., 1970-83. Served with USNR, 1943-46. Mem. Am. Psychol. Assn. Presbyterian. Home: 609 S Graham St Florence SC 29501-5142

SMITH, WALTER S., JR., federal judge; b. Marlin, Tex., Oct. 26, 1940; s. Walter S. and Mary Elizabeth Smith; children—Debra Elizabeth, Susan Kay. BA, Baylor U., 1964, JD, 1966. Bar: Tex. Assoc. Dunnam & Dunnam, Waco, Tex., 1966-69; ptnr. Wallace & Smith, Waco, 1969-78, Haley & Fulbright, Waco, 1978-80; judge Tex. Dist. Ct., 1980-83; U.S. magistrate U.S. Dist. Ct. (we. dist.) Tex., 1983-84; judge U.S. Dist. Ct. (we. dist.) Tex., Waco, 1984—. Named Outstanding Young Lawyer of Yr., Waco-McLennan County Bar Assn., 1976. Office: US Dist Ct PO Box 1908 Waco TX 76703-1908

SMITH, WALTER SAGE, environmental engineer, consultant; b. Hammond, Ind., Nov. 12, 1938; s. Reading Barlow and Lois Cora (Riddle) S.; m. Doris Jean Bryson, Oct. 23, 1961 (div. Sept. 1976); children: Cami Stryker Davis, Adam Smith, Kelly A. Stryker, Alex Smith; m. Jacqueline P. Stryker, June 4, 1977. BSChemE, Bucknell U., 1961. Registered profl. engr., N.C., N.J. Engr. Pub. Health Svc. Commn. Corp., Cin., 1961-72; co-owner, pres. Entropy Environmentalists, Inc., Research Triangle Park, N.C., 1972-92, pres., cons., 1974-76; owner, pres. Walter Smith & Assocs., Inc., Cary, N.C., 1993—; v.p. Nutech Corp., Raleigh, N.C., 1974-76, Housing Corp. of the South, Raleigh, 1977-78, Umstead Devel. Corp., Raleigh, 1977-80. Editor (newsletter) Stack Sampling News, Entropy Quarterly. Vice pres. Black Horse Run Homeowners Assn., Raleigh, 1984. Fellow Air and Waste Mgmt. Assn.; mem. Am. Acad. Environ. Engrs. (diplomate 1985), Carolinas Air Pollution Control Assn., Source Evaluation Soc. (founder 1984). Episcopalian. Avocations: swimming, sailing, reading. Home: 6225 Splitrock Trl Apex NC 27502-9778 Office: Walter Smith & Assocs Inc P O Box 117 Cary NC 27511-0117

SMITH, WALTER TILFORD, shipbuilding company executive; b. Norfolk, Va., Oct. 9, 1907; s. Walter Edmond and Laura Alice (Griffin) S.; m. Elizabeth Harriet Parrish, Aug. 20, 1933; 1 son, Walter Tilford. B.S. in Civil Engring, N.C. State Coll.; 1929; grad. Advanced Mgmt. Program, Harvard, 1955; grad., Coll. Indsl. Armed Forces, 1952. With Newport News Shipbldg. & Dry Dock Co., Va., 1929—; asst. to pres. Newport News Shipbldg. & Dry Dock Co., 1962-63, v.p. charge prodn., 1963-64, exec. v.p., 1964-66, sr. v.p., 1966-69, sr. v.p. and asst. to pres., 1969—; dir. Central Nat. Bank, Richmond, Va.; Vice pres., dir., mem. exec. finance com.

Shipbuilders Council Am. Trustee Patrick Henry Hosp., Newport News, Peninsula United Fund, City of Newport News Pensions and Retirement Fund; vice chmn. Newport News chpt. A.R.C.; bd. dirs. Riverside Convalescent Ctrs., Riverside Retirement Svc., Tilden and Virginia Davis Support Found., Newport News. Mem. Soc. Naval Architects and Marine Engrs., Am. Soc. Naval Engrs., Navy League U.S., Nat. Def. Transp. Assn. (v.p.), NAM (nat. def. com.), N.C. State Coll. Alumni Assn. (bd. dirs.), Newcomen Soc., Engineer's Club N.Y.C., Scabbard and Blade, Theta Tau, Phi Kappa Phi. Episcopalian. Clubs: Lion (bd. dirs., past v.p.), Propeller U.S. (past pres. Newport News, past nat. v.p.), James River Country (dir., past pres.), Newport News. Home: 129 James River Dr Newport News VA 23601-3603 Office: Newport News Shipbldg & Dry Dock Co Newport News VA 23607

SMITH, WALTON NAPIER, lawyer; b. Macon, Ga., Feb. 26, 1942; s. Robert Monroe and Marion Rose (Napier) S.; m. Susan Rush Baum, Oct. 10, 1970; children—Rush Hendley, Berkeley Bosman. A.B. cum laude, Dartmouth Coll., 1964; J.D., Harvard U., 1967. Bar: Ga. 1966, D.C. 1972, Ill. 1978, U.S. Supreme Ct. 1971. Counsel, Nat. R.R. Passenger Corp., Washington, 1971-75; assoc. Lord, Bissell & Brook, Washington and Chgo., 1975-79, ptnr., Chgo. and Atlanta, 1980—. Served to capt. JAGC, U.S. Army, 1964-71. Decorated Bronze Star, Army Commendation medal. Mem. ABA, Ill. Bar Assn., State Bar Ga., Nat. Assn. R.R. Trial Counsel. Democrat. Episcopalian. Clubs: Union League (Chgo.); Commerce Club. Office: Lord Bissell & Brook 1201 W Peachtree St NW Atlanta GA 30309-3400

SMITH, WARD, manufacturing company executive, lawyer; b. Buffalo, Sept. 13, 1930; s. Andrew Leslie and Georgia (Ward) S.; m. Gretchen Keller Diefendorf, Oct. 29, 1960; children: Jennifer Smith Collison, Meredith Smith Weil, Jonathan Andrew, Sarah Katherine. Student, Georgetown U., 1948-49; AB, Harvard, 1952; JD, U. Buffalo, 1955. Bar: N.Y. 1955, Mass. 1962, Ohio 1977. Assoc. Lawler & Rockwood, N.Y.C., 1959-62; sec., gen. counsel Whitin Machine Works, Whitinsville, Mass., 1962-66; sec. White Consol. Industries, Inc., Cleve., 1966-69, v.p., 1967-69, sr. v.p., 1969-72, exec. v.p., 1972-76, pres., chief adminstrv. officer, 1976-84, pres., chief operating officer, 1984-86, pres., chief exec. officer, 1985-86, chmn., 1986; pres. NACCO Industries, Inc., Cleve., 1986-89, chief exec. officer, 1986-91, chmn. bd., 1987-94; trustee various mut. funds administered by Mass. Fin. Svcs. Co., Boston; bd. dirs. Sundstrand Corp., Rockford, Ill. Pres., trustee The Musical Arts Assn.; op. The Cleve. Orch., Case Western Res. U., Cleve., others. Served to lt. USNR, 1955-59. Mem. ABA, N.Y. State Bar Assn., Cleve. Skating Club, Pepper Pike Club, The Country Club (Cleve.), Tavern Club, Union Club (Cleve.). Office: NACCO Industries Inc 5875 Landerbrook Dr Mayfield Heights OH 44124-4017

SMITH, WARREN JAMES, optical scientist, consultant, lecturer; b. Rochester, N.Y., Aug. 17, 1922; s. Warren Abrams and Jessica Madelyn (Forshay) S.; m. Mary Helen Geddes, May 18, 1944; children: David Whitney, Barbara Jamie. BS, U. Rochester, 1944; postgrad., U. Calif., Santa Barbara, 1960. Physicist Clinton Engr. Works, Tenn. Eastman Co., Oak Ridge, 1944-46; chief optical engr. Simpson Optical Mfg. Co., Chgo., 1946-59; mgr. optical sect. Raytheon Corp., Santa Barbara, 1959-62; v.p. R & D, Infrared Industries, Santa Barbara, 1962-87; chief scientist Kaiser Electro-Optics, Inc., Carlsbad, Calif., 1987—; lectr. U. Wis., Madison, 1972—, U. Rochester, 1988—, Genesee Computer Ctr., Rochester, 1982-93, Sinclair Optics, 1994—; cons. in field; expert witness. Author: Modern Optical Engineering, 1966, 2d edit., 1990, Modern Lens Design, 1992; editor McGraw-Hill series Optical and Electro-Optical Engineering; also articles. Fellow Optical Soc. Am. (pres. 1980, organizer, chmn. tech. confs.), Soc. Photo-Optical Instrumentation Engrs. (life), Internat. Soc. Optical Engring. (pres. 1983, organizer, chmn. tech. confs., Gold medal 1985, Dirs. award 1992), Sigma Chi. Avocations: tennis, sailing. Home: 1165 Countrywood Ln Vista CA 92083-5334 Office: Kaiser Electro-Optics Inc 2752 Loker Ave W Carlsbad CA 92008-6603

SMITH, WARREN L., electrical engineer, physicist; b. Wayne, Nebr., July 6, 1924; s. James M. and Mattie M. (Meng) S.; m. Frances M. Dowd, June 18, 1948; children: Marjory, Catherine, James, Gerald, Janine. BSEE, U. Wis., 1944. Rsch. asst. U. Wis., Madison, 1947-51; mem. tech. staff Bell Telephone Labs., Murray Hill, N.J., 1954-87; ret., 1987; tech. cons. to Tech. Com. 49 of IEC, 1973-91. Contbr. 17 publs. to confs. and symposium proceedings; contbr. 3 chpts. to books. Lt. USN, 1942-46, 51-54. Fellow IEEE; mem. AAAS, Electronic Industries Assn. (quartz devices sect.). Achievements include research on quartz crystals. Home: 3046 Meadowbrook Cir N Allentown PA 18103-5422

SMITH, WAYMAN FLYNN, III, brewery executive, lawyer; b. St. Louis, June 18, 1940; s. Wayman Flynn and Edythe (Meaux) S.; 1 child, Kymberly Ann. Student, Washington U., St. Louis, 1957-59; B.S., Monmouth Coll., West Long Branch, N.J., 1962; J.D., Howard U., 1965. Bar: Mo. 1966, U.S Dist. Ct. (ea. dist.) Mo. 1966. Dir. conciliation Mo. Commn. on Human Rights, Jefferson City, 1966-69; judge City of St. Louis, 1971-75; mem. Wilson, Smith, McCullin, St. Louis, 1969-80; v.p. corp. affairs Anheuser-Busch Cos., St. Louis, 1980—; dir. Anheuser-Busch, Inc., St. Louis. Mem. bd. alderman City of St. Louis, 1975-87. Named Disting. Alumni, Howard U., 1983, Monmouth Coll., 1983. Mem. ABA, Nat. Bar Assn., Mound City Bar Assn., Bar Assn. Met. St. Louis. Democrat. Episcopalian. Office: Anheuser-Busch Cos 1 Busch Pl Saint Louis MO 63118-1852

SMITH, WAYNE CALVIN, chemical engineer; b. Beaver, Okla., Mar. 19, 1935; s. Dean C. and Loraine S.; m. Suellyn Joyce Canon, Aug. 18, 1984. BS, Okla. U., 1958, MSChemE, 1964; PhDChemE, Colo. U., 1974. Registered profl. engr., Tex., Okla., Colo.; cert. emergency response specialist. Process engr. Shell Oil Co., Deer Park, Tex., 1958-59; sr. devel. engr. Chemstrand Co. div. Monsento, Pensacola, Fla., 1965-66; project leader Phillips Petroleum Co., Bartlesville, Okla., 1967-69; acting chief process control EPA Nat. Enforcement Investigations Ctr., Denver, 1971-78; firm wide mgr. pollution control Dames & Moore, Golden, Colo., 1978-81; regional mgr. Hittman Assocs., Englewood, Colo., 1981-82; pres. Encon Environs Control Svcs., Golden, Colo., 1982-83; chief hazardous waste mgmt. Woodword-Clyde Cons., Englewood, 1983-84; exec. cons. Kellogg Corp., Littleton, Colo., 1984-86; program mgr. Radian Corp., Austin, Tex., 1986-93; prin. engr., office mgr. Tetra Tech, Inc., Oklahoma City, 1993—. Contbr. over 30 articles to profl. jours. Capt. USMC, 1959-62. Scholar Magnolia Petroleum Co., 1956-58; fellow Phillips Petroleum Co., 1962-64, Marathon Oil Co., 1964-67, Gulf Oil Co., 1969-71. Mem. AICE, Am. Arbitration Assn., Water Pollution Control Fedn., Soc. Plastics Engrs., The Greens Country Club, Sigma Xi. Baptist. Avocations: golf, woodworking. Office: Tetra Tech Inc 806 West Curtis Dr Ste I Midwest City OK 73110-2835

SMITH, WAYNE THOMAS, healthcare company executive; b. 1946. BS, Auburn Univ, 1968, MS, 1969; M in hosp. adminstrn., Trinity U.; postgrad., King's Fund Coll. Hosp. Adminstrn. With Trinity Univ, 1971-73; with Humana Inc, Louisville, 1973—, v.p. ctrl. hosp. region, 1978-80, sr. v.p., 1980-85, exec. v.p., 1985-86, pres., COO group health divsn., 1986—, also bd. dirs.; exec. v.p. Human Health Care Ops., Louisville, 1991—; exec. v.p. health plan ops., bd. dirs. Humana Health Plan, Inc., Louisville; pres. Humana Health Ins. Nev., Inc., Humana Health Plan Fla., Inc., Humana Health Plan Ohio, Inc., Humana Health Chgo. Ins. Co., Humana Kansas City, Inc.; pres., COO Humana Health Plan Tex., Prime Health Mgmt. Svcs.; pres., bd. dirs. HMPK, Inc. Bd. dirs. Gov.'s Scholars Program, Ky., Actors Theatre of Louisville, Ky. Ctr. for the Arts, The Louisville Orchestra; bd. overseers U. Louisville; mem. exec. com. Greater Louisville Fund for the Arts; past chair bd. dirs. Louisville Collegiate Sch. With U.S. Army, 1969-73, capt., 1973. Mem. Group Health Assn. Am. (bd. dirs.), Health Ins. Assn. Am. (bd. dirs.). Office: Humana Inc 500 W Main St Ste 1438 Louisville KY 40202-2941

SMITH, WENDELL MURRAY, graphic arts control and equipment manufacturing executive; b. Bklyn., May 15, 1935; s. J. Henry and Roberta (Foard) S.; m. Margaret McGregor, Aug. 24, 1957; children: Karen, Wendy, Kimberley, Kathryn, Jennifer. AB, Dartmouth Coll., 1957, MS in Engring., 1958. Devel. engr. Sikorsky Aircraft Co., Stratford, Conn., 1958-60; sales engr., mgr. Barnes Engring. Corp., Stamford, Conn., 1960-65; v.p. mktg.

Baldwin-Gegenheimer Corp., Stamford, 1966-70, pres. chief exec. officer, 1971-79; pres. Polestar Corp., Stamford, 1980—; pres. chmn. bd., chief exec. officer Baldwin Tech. Co., Inc., Rowayton, Conn., 1984—; bd. dirs. Am. Maize Corp., Stamford, Conn., Goble Ticket and Label Co., Bowne & Co. Recipient John L. Kronenberg Industry Leadership award, 1991. Mem. Rsch. and Engring. Coun. (pres.), Graphic Comms. Assn. (bd. dirs., vice chmn.), Soderstrom Soc. of Nat. Assn. Printers and Lithographers, Stamford Ctr. for the Arts (bd. dirs.), Stamford Yacht Club, N.Y. Yacht Club, Royal Bermuda Yacht Club, Mid-Ocean Club. Republican. Methodist. Home: 10 Manor House, Smith's FL07 Bermuda Office: Baldwin Tech Co Inc 65 Rowayton Ave Norwalk CT 06853-1600

SMITH, WHITNEY BOUSMAN, music and drama critic; b. Cin., May 31, 1956; s. Lawrance Spencer and Ruby Virginia (Bousman) S. BA in Journalism, Ind. U., 1978. Reporter South Bend (Ind.) Tribune, 1977, The Repository, Canton, Ohio, 1978-82; reporter Comml. Appeal, Memphis, 1982—, on spl. assignment in Italy, 1992. Compiler guide to papers of early 20th century Memphis drama critic Hugh Higbee Huhn, 1988. Trombonist Germantown (Tenn.) Symphony Orch., 1987-88. Recipient Community Svc. award League Women Voters, 1980. Office: Comml Appeal 495 Union Ave Memphis TN 38103

SMITH, WILBURN JACKSON, JR., retired bank executive; b. Charlotte, N.C., June 13, 1921; s. Wilburn Jackson and Banna (Oswalt) S.; B.S. in Acctg., U. N.C., 1943; postgrad. in comml. banking Rutgers U. Sch. Banking, 1953, postgrad. in investment banking, 1956; m. Terry Mosteller, Jan. 4, 1944; children: Kenneth M., M. Scott (dec.), Wilburn Jackson III, Curtis Todd. With First Union Nat. Bank, Charlotte, 1946-74, exec. v.p., 1960-67, 1st exec. v.p., 1967-74; pres., mng. trustee Cameron-Brown Investment Group, Raleigh, N.C., 1974-78; chmn. loan policy com. N.C. Nat. Bank, Charlotte, 1979-88; bd. dirs. Charter Bancshares, Inc., Houston, Burroughs & Chapin Co. Inc., Myrtle Beach, S.C.; cons. in field. Served with USN, 1943-46. Recipient Citizenship award Charlotte Civitan, 1972. Mem. Robert Morris Assocs. Baptist. Club: Myers Park Country (Charlotte).

SMITH, WILFRED IRVIN, former Canadian government official; b. Port La Tour, Can., May 20, 1919; s. Claude Albert and Deborah (Inglis) S.; m. Joan Eileen Capstick, Nov. 27, 1946; children: Gordon, Heather, Gail. B.A., Acadia U., Wolfville, N.S., Can., 1943, M.A., 1946, D.C.L., 1975; Ph.D., U. Minn., 1968. Lectr. U. Minn., 1948, U. Sask., 1948-50, Carleton U., 1955-60; mem. staff Pub. Archives Can., 1950-84, dir. hist. br., 1964-65, asst., then acting dominion archivist, 1965-70, dominion archivist, 1970-84; mem. Canadian Nat. Library Adv. Bd., Canadian Permanent Com. Geog. Names, Historic Sites and Monuments Bd. Can, Indian Hist. Manuscripts Commn.; former mem. internat. adv. com. documentation, libraries and archives UNESCO. Author: Code Word Canloan, 1992; contbr. articles to profl. jours. Served to maj. Canadian and Brit. armies, 1943-45. Decorated officer Order Can.; recipient Can. decoration, 1958, Centennial medal, 1967, Jubilee medal, 1978, Royal Soc. Can. medal, 1980, Outstanding Achievement award Can. Govt., 1983. Fellow Soc. Am. Archivists (past pres.); hon. life mem. Internat. Council Archives (sec. gen.), Canadian Hist. Assn. (past editor hist. booklets), Assn. Canadian Archivists, Order St. John; mem. Soc. Archivists, Am. Antiquarian Assn., Canadian Heraldry Soc. (hon. v.p.), United Empire Loyalists Assn. (hon. v.p.), Guards Assn., Friends of Can. War Mus. Home: 201-71 Somerset St W, Ottawa, ON Canada K2P 2G2

SMITH, WILL, actor, rapper; b. Phila.; m. Sheree Smith; 1 child, Willard Smith III. Albums (as The Fresh Prince with DJ Jazzy Jeff): And in this Corner..., 1989, Homebase, 1991, Rock the House, 1991 reissue, He's the DJ, I'm the Rapper, 1988; TV series: The Fresh Prince of Bel-Air, 1990–; Movies: Where the Day Takes You, 1992, Made in America, 1993, Six Degrees of Separation, 1993, Bad Boys, 1995. Office: CAA 9830 Wilshire Blvd Beverly Hills CA 90212*

SMITH, WILLIAM BURTON, chemist, educator; b. Muncie, Ind., Dec. 13, 1927; s. Merrill Mark and Felice Hoy (Richardson) S.; m. Marian Louise Roseborough, Aug. 9, 1954; children: Mark W., Frederick D., Mary F. BA, Kalamazoo Coll., 1949; PhD, Brown U., 1954. Research asso. Fla. State U., 1953-54, U. Chgo., 1954-55; asst. prof., then asso. prof. Ohio U., 1955-61; R.A. Welch vis. prof. chemistry Tex. Christian U., 1960-61, prof. chemistry, chmn. dept., 1961-81; Research participant Oak Ridge Inst. Nuclear Studies, 1956—. Author: A Modern Introduction to Organic Chemistry, 1961, Molecular Orbital Methods in Organic Chemistry, 1974; also rsch. articles. Recipient Chancellor's award, 1989. Fellow Royal Soc. of Chemistry; mem. Am. Chem. Soc. (Doherty award 1990), Sigma Xi. Home: 3604 Wedghill Way Fort Worth TX 76133-2156

SMITH, WILLIAM CHARLES, lawyer; b. Batavia, N.Y., June 9, 1930; s. William F. and Verna B. (Busmire) S.; m. Lucia P. Pierce, July 10, 1954; children: William Charles, Leonard P., Victoria J. B.A., U. Buffalo, 1952; LL.B., Harvard U., 1955. Bar: Maine 1955, U.S. Dist. Ct. Maine 1956, U.S. Tex. Ct. 1960, U.S. Supreme Ct. 1960, D.C. 1962, U.S. Ct. Appeals (1st cir.) 1977, U.S. Ct. Claims 1985, Fla. 1995. Assoc. Portland, Maine, 1955-57; ptnr. Hutchinson, Pierce, Atwood & Allen, Portland, 1957-59; counsel Office Tax Legis. Counsel, U.S. Treasury Dept., Washington, 1959-61; ptnr. Pierce, Atwood, Scribner, Allen, Smith and Lancaster, Portland, 1961—; exec. com. Fed. Tax Inst., New Eng. Vice chmn. budget com. United Community Services, 1966-68, chmn., 1968-70, nat. budget and consultation com., 1969-71; bd. dirs. Portland Goodwill, Inc., 1967-69, United Way, Inc., 1968-74, 75-80, Portland Widow's Wood Soc., 1962—; trustee Portland Regional Opportunity Program, 1967-68, Freyburg Acad., 1976—, Found. Blood Research, 1979-85. Mem. ABA, Maine Bar Assn., Cumberland County Bar Assn., Am. Law Inst., Am. Coll. Trust and Estate Counsel, Am. Coll. Tax Counsel. Republican. Unitarian. Clubs: Portland Country, Mid-Ocean (Bermuda); Naples Country (Maine); Meadows Country (Fla.). Home: 392 Spring St Portland ME 04102-3642 Office: Pierce Atwood Scribner Allen Smith & Lancaster One Monument Sq Portland ME 04101-1110

SMITH, WILLIAM DEE, naval officer; b. Denver, Feb. 9, 1933; s. Thomas Jerry and Frieda Lena (Heisler) S.; m. Sabra Harriman, Dec. 17, 1956; children: Frederick William, Evangeline. BA in Engring., U.S. Naval Acad., 1955. Commd. ensign U.S. Navy, 1955, advanced through grades to adm., 1991; served on Atlantic-based destroyers, 1955-58, various Atlantic and Pacific submarines, 1958-68; mem. submarine staff (Strategic Target and Plans Office), Pearl Harbor, Hawaii, 1968-70; comdg. officer Henry L. Stimson strategic missile submarine New London, Conn., Charleston, S.C. 1970-74; mem. Pacific Nuclear Propulsion Exam. Bd. Pearl Harbor, 1974-76; mgr. nuclear power program Chief Naval Personnel Washington, 1976-78; comdr. Submarine Group 8 Naples, Italy, 1983-85; navy budget officer, staff chief naval ops., 1985-87, dep. chief naval ops. for program planning, 1987-91; U.S. rep. mil. com. NATO, 1991—. Active Boy Scouts Am. Decorated D.S.M. with one gold star, Legion of Merit with 3 gold stars, Meritorious Svc. medal with gold star. Mem. Naval Inst., Armed Forces Communications and Electronic Assn. (dir.). Republican. Office: OPNAV US Navy Washington DC 20350-2000

SMITH, WILLIAM HENRY PRESTON, writer, editor, former corporate executive; b. Pleasanton, Tex., Sept. 8, 1924; s. Sidney Newton and Willie Gertrude (Cloyd) S.; m. Frances Dixon, July 1, 1950; children: Juliet, Dixon, David. B.J., U. Tex., 1949. Reporter Dallas Morning News, 1949-52; advt. asst. Dallas Power & Light Co., 1952-55; dir. pub. relations Greater Boston C. of C., 1955-58; with New Eng. Telephone and Telegraph Co., Boston, 1958-86, asst. v.p., 1966-75, corp. sec., 1975-83, dir. pub. relations, 1983-86; free-lance writer Dover, Mass., 1986—. Editor: Bus. Ethics Resource Newsletter. Bd. dirs., v.p. Mass. Soc. for Prevention Cruelty to Children; bd. dirs. Urban Dynamics Adv. Com.; mem. support policies com. United Way Mass. Served with paratroops U.S. Army, 1943-46. Decorated Purple Heart. Mem. Am. Soc. Corp. Secs., Friars, Sigma Delta Chi, Delta Kappa Epsilon. Republican. Clubs: Dedham Country and Polo, Down Town. Home and Office: 10 Turtle Ln Dover MA 02030-2053

SMITH, WILLIAM HULSE, forestry and environmental studies educator; b. Trenton, N.J., May 9, 1939; s. Philip Andrews and Marion (Hulse) S.; m. Judith Chapin Pease, July 6, 1963 (div. 1982); children—Scott William, Philip Chapin; m. Deborah Banks Coit, June 17, 1983; 1 child, Tyler Banks. B.S., Rutgers U., 1961, Ph.D., 1965; M.F., Yale U., 1963. Asst. prof. forestry Rutgers U., 1965-66; asst. prof. Yale U., 1966-72, assoc. prof., 1972-75, prof., 1975—, dean, 1981-83, Clifton R. Musser prof. forest biology, 1985—. Author: Tree Pathology, 1970, Air Pollution and Forest Ecosystems, 1981, 2d edit., 1990. Mem. Conn. Siting Council, 1985. NSF grantee, U.S. Dept. Agr. Forest Service grantee. Mem. Soc. Am. Foresters, Am. Phytopath. Soc., Ecol. Soc. Am. Home: 1 Northwinds Dr Ivoryton CT 06442-1261 Office: Sch Forestry and Environ Studies Yale U 370 Prospect St New Haven CT 06511-2104

SMITH, WILLIAM HUSTON, communication company executive; b. Berwyn, Ill., June 13, 1925; s. Lewis Alway and Dorothy Genevieve (Harter) S.; m. Patricia Ann Morell, Sept. 02, 1950; children: Scott Douglas, Wendy Allison, Kendall Allen. BS in Bus., U. of Colo., Boulder, 1949. Sales rep. Lakeside Lab., Gary, Ind., 1951-59; pres. Allied Film and Video, Detroit, 1960–. Pres. Farmington Community Ctr., Farmington Hills, Mich., 1972. Fellow Soc. Motion Pictures and TV Engrs. (presdl. citation) (gov. 1974-76), mem. Assn. Film and Video Labs, pres 1975-78. Republican. Protestant. Avocation: skiing. Office: Allied Film and Video 7375 Woodward Ave Detroit MI 48202-3121

SMITH, WILLIAM J., lawyer; b. Pitts., Jan. 9, 1941. BSBA, Duquesne U., 1967, JD, 1971. Bar: Pa. 1971. Ptnr. Reed Smith Shaw & McClay, Pitts. Office: Reed Smith Shaw & McClay James H Reed Bldg Mellon Sq 435 6th Ave Pittsburgh PA 15219-1886

SMITH, WILLIAM JAY, author; b. Winnfield, La., Apr. 22, 1918; s. Jay and Georgia (Campster) S.; m. Barbara Howes, Oct. 1, 1947 (div. June 1965); children: David Emerson, Gregory Jay; m. Sonja Haussmann, Sept. 3, 1966. Student, Institut de Touraine, Tours, France, 1938; B.A., Washington U., St. Louis, 1939, M.A., 1941; postgrad., Columbia U., 1946-47; postgrad. Rhodes scholar, Oxford U., 1947-48; postgrad., U. Florence, Italy, 1948-50; Litt.D., New Eng. Coll., 1973. Asst. in French Washington U., 1939-41; instr. English and French Columbia U., 1946-47; lectr. English Williams Coll., 1951, poet in residence, lectr. English, 1959-64, 66-67; Ford Found. fellow Arena Stage, Washington, 1964-65; writer in residence Hollins Coll., 1965-66, prof. English, 1967, 70-80, prof. emeritus, 1980; cons. poetry Libr. of Congress, Washington, 1968-70, hon. cons. in Am. letters, 1970-76; vis. prof., acting chmn., writing divsn. Sch. Arts, Columbia U., 1973, 74-75; mem. staff Salzburg (Austria) Seminar, 1975; mem. jury Nat. Book award, 1962, 70, 75, Neustadt Internat. prize for lit., 1978, Com. of Pegasus Prize for Lit., 1979—; poet in residence Cathedral St. John the Divine, N.Y., 1985-88. Author: Poems, 1947, Celebration at Dark, 1950, Laughing Time, 1955, Poems, 1947-57, Boy Blue's Book of Beasts, 1957, Puptents and Pebbles: A Nonsense ABC, 1959, Typewriter Town, 1960, The Spectra Hoax, 1961, What Did I See, 1962, Ho for a Hat, 1964, (with Louise Bogan) The Golden Journey; Poems for Young People, 1965, The Tin Can and Other Poems, 1966, Poems from France, 1967, If I Had a Boat, 1967, Mr. Smith and Other Nonsense, 1968, New and Selected Poems, 1970, The Streaks of the Tulip, selected criticism, 1972, Poems from Italy, 1973, Venice in the Fog, 1975, The Telephone, 1977, Laughing Time, 1980, The Traveler's Tree, New and Selected Poems, 1980, Army Brat, a Memoir, 1980, A Green Place: Modern Poems, 1982, Plain Talk: Epigrams, Epitaphs, Satires, Nonsense, Occasional Concrete and Quotidian Poems, 1988, Ho for a Hat (rev.), 1989, Collected Poems 1939-1989, 1990, Laughing Time: Collected Nonsense, 1990, Birds and Beasts, 1990, Big and LIttle, 1992 (with Carol Ra) Behind the King's Kitchen: A Roster of Rhyming Riddles, 1992; translator: (with Emanuel Brasil) Brazilian Poetry 1950-80, 1984, (with Ingvar Schousboe) The Pact: My Friendship with Isak Dinesen by Thorkild Bjernvig, 1983, (with J.S. Holmes) Dutch Interior: Post-War Poetry of the Netherlands and Flanders, 1984, Scirocco by Romualdo Romano, 1951; Poems of a Multimillionaire by Valery Larbaud, 1955, Selected Writings of Jules Laforgue, 1956, Children of the Forest by Elsa Beskow, 1969, Two Plays by Charles Bertin: Christopher Columbus and Don Juan, 1970, The Pirate Book by Lennart Hellsing, 1972, (with Leif Sjöberg) Agadir by Artur Lundkvist, 1979, Moral Tales of Jules Laforgue, 1985, Collected Translations: Italian, French, Spanish, Portuguese, 1985, (with Dana Gioia) Poems from Italy, 1985, (with Leif Sjöberg) Wild Bouquet: Nature Poems by Harry Martinson, 1985, (with Sonja Haussmann Smith) The Madman and the Medusa by Tchicaya U Tam'Si, 1989, Songs of Childhood by Federico Garcia Lorca, 1994; editor: Herrick, 1962, Light Verse and Satires by Witter Bynner, 1978, (with F.D. Reeve) An Arrow in the Wall: Selected Poetry and Prose by Andrei Voznesensky, 1986 (one of 16 Best Books of 1986, N.Y. Times), Life Sentence: Selected Poems of Nina Cassian, 1990. Mem. Vt. Ho. of Reps., 1960-62. Served to lt. USNR, 1941-45. Recipient Alumni citation Washington U., 1963; prize Poetry mag., 1945, 64; Henry Bellamann Major award, 1970; Russell Loines award Nat. Inst. Arts and Letters, 1972; Gold medal Labor Hungary, 1978; Golden Rose award New Eng. Poetry Club, 1979, médaille de vermeil French Acad., 1991, Pro Cultura Hungarica medal, Hungary, 1993; Nat. Endowment for Arts fellow, 1972, 95; NEH fellow, 1975, 89; Ingram Merrill fellow, 1982; Camargo Found. fellow, 1986. Mem. Am. Acad. Arts and Letters (v.p. for literature 1986-89), Am. Assn. Rhodes Scholars, Acad. Am. Poets, Authors Guild (council), P.E.N. Club: Century. Home: 63 Luther Shaw Rd Cummington MA 01026-9787 also: 52-56 rue d'Alleray, 75015 Paris France Office: care Harriet Wasserman 137 E 36th St # 19D New York NY 10016-3527

SMITH, WILLIAM K., real estate developer; b. 1944. BA, U. Redlands, 1966; JD, UCLA, 1969. With Mission Viejo (Calif.) Co., 1969—, officer, 1974—, now v.p./sec., gen. counsel. Office: Mission Viejo Co 26137 La Paz Rd Mission Viejo CA 92691*

SMITH, WILLIAM LEO, meteorologist, researcher, educator; b. Detroit, May 13, 1942; s. Rolland Francis and Ruth Mary (Gerhardstein) S.; m. Marcia Jean Simmerer, Aug. 11, 1962; children: William Jr., Jeanne, Steven, Julie, Joanna, Jonathon, Sarah, Kiara. BS, St. Louis U., 1963; MS, U. Wis., 1964, PhD, 1966. Chief br. radiation NOAA/Nat. Environ. Satellite Data Info. U.S. Dept. Commerce, Washington, 1966-73, dir. Atmospheric and Oceanic Scis. devel. lab., 1973-84; dir. Cooperative Inst. for Meterol. Satellite Studies U. Wis., Madison, 1984—; sec./v.p. Internat. Radiation Commn., 1989—. Author: (with others) Handbook of Applied Meteorology, 1983; contbr. over 100 articles to profl. jours. Fellow Am. Meteorol. Soc. Roman Catholic. Achievements include development of first algorithms for operational processing of satellite sounding data, of high special resolution interferometer sounder, of infrared temperature profile radiometer, of earth radiation budget radiometer, and of high resolution infrared radiation sounder. Office: U Wis 1225 W Dayton St Madison WI 53706-1695

SMITH, WILLIAM LEWIS, hotel executive; b. Cleve., Nov. 7, 1925; s. Floyd Holland and Florence (Goebelbecker) S.; m. Dorothy Losch, Aug. 2, 1945; children: Diane, William, Bradley, Tracey. Student, John Carroll U., Kent State U., Darden Sch., U. Va. Cert. hotel adminstr., cert. engring. ops. exec. With Halle Bros. Co., Cleve., 1946-58; with Hilton Hotel Corp., various locations, 1958-89, Statler Hilton, Cleve., 1958-61, Hilton Inn, Tarrytown, N.Y., 1961-63, N.Y. Hilton, N.Y.C., 1963-68, Conrad Hilton Hotel, Chgo., 1968-78, Fontainebleau Hilton, Miami Beach, Fla., 1978-80, Washington Hilton, 1980-84, Chgo. Hilton and Towers, 1984-89; asst. sec. Hilton Hotels Corp., 1971-89; with Bus. Cons. Internat., Barrington, Ill., 1989—; vis. lectr. U. Wis.-Stout, 1974, U. Notre Dame, 1975, 76, U. Houston, 1980, Cornell U., Ithaca, N.Y., 1987; bd. dirs. LaSalle Nat. Bank, 1985—. Bd. dirs. Mich. Blvd. Assn., 1968-78, Good Shepherd Manor, Momence, Ill., 1973-89, Maur Hill Prep. Sch., Atchison, Kans., 1973-79, Met. Fair and Expn. Authority Chgo., 1975-78, Chgo. Conv. and Vis. Bur., Chgo. Conv. and Tourism Bur., 1975-78, 84-89, Miami Beach Visitor and Conv. Authority, 1978-80, Burnham Park Planning Bd., 1984-86; mem. Nat. 4-H Service Com., 1969-76, mem. adv. com., 1977-78; mem. adv. bd. Mercy Hosp. and Med. Ctr., Chgo., 1973-78, 84—, Echols Internat. Hotel Schs., Inc., 1984-89; mem. D.C. Bldg. Code Adv. Com., 1981-84, Near South Task Force Chgo. Cen. Area Com., 1984-89; mem. exec. com. Washington Conv. and Visitors Assn., 1981-84; mem. hotel/motel mgmt. adv. bd. Howard U., 1983-84; mem. bus. adv. council Coll. Bus. Adminstrn., U. Ill., Chgo., 1984-86; mem. steering com. South Side Planning Bd., 1984-89. Served with USNR, 1943-45. Recipient Partner-in-4-H award, 1971; Good Scout award Boy Scouts Am. 1974; Ignatian award, 1975. Mem. Am. Hotel and Motel Assn. (life, exec. engr. com. 1983-89), Washington Hotel Assn. (bd. dirs.

1980-84), Ill. Restaurant Assn. (bd. dirs. 1984-89, chmn. 1989), Hotel-Motel Assn. Ill. (bd. dirs. 1986-89, life). Address: 16 Champlain Rd Barrington IL 60010

SMITH, WILLIAM RANDOLPH (RANDY SMITH), health care management association executive; b. Spartanburg, S.C., July 23, 1948; s. Jesse Edward and Helen (Knox) S.; m. Donna Marie HAwthorne, July 18, 1970; children: Kirstin Leigh, Andrea Marie. BA, Furman U., 1970; MHA, Duke U., 1972. Exec. dir. Riverside Hosp., Wilmington, Del., 1974-79; assoc. exec. dir. Brookwood Med. Ctr., Brimingham, Ala., 1979-81, exec. dir., 1983-85; v.p. ops. Am. Med. Internat., Atlanta, 1981-89; interim chief fin. officer Am. Med. Internat., Beverly Hills, Calif., 1989-90; Chief adminstrv. officer Am. Med. Internat., Dallas, 1990, exec. v.p. ops., 1990-94; exec. v.p. Tewet Health Corp., 1994—; bd. dirs. EPIC Healthcare Group, Dallas, 1989-92. Bd. dirs. Ala. Symphony Assn., Birmingham, 1985, State of Ala. Ballet, Birmingham, 1983-85. Lt. U.S. Army, 1972-74. Mem. Fedn. Am. Health Systems (bd. dirs. 1989—, pres. 1993, chmn. 1994). Episcopalian. Avocations: skiing, tennis, automobiles. Office: Am Med Holdings Inc 14001 Dallas Pkwy Ste 200 Dallas TX 75240

SMITH, WILLIAM RANDOLPH, lawyer; b. Houston, July 30, 1928; s. Angie Frank and Bess Patience (Crutchfield) S.; m. Margaret Ann Pickett, Nov. 25, 1950; children: Sherren Bess (dec.), William Randolph Jr., Margaret Moody, David Christian. B.A., So. Meth. U., 1948; LL.B., U. Tex., 1951. Assoc. Vinson & Elkins, Houston, 1951-64, ptnr., 1965-91; dir. Weatherford Internat., Houston, 1979—; several pvt. corps. Bd. dirs. Meth. Hosp. System, Houston, 1970—; trustee M.D. Anderson Hosp., 1975-92, So. Meth. U., Dallas, 1975-88, Briarwood Sch./Brookwood Community, Houston, 1970—. 1st lt. USAF, 1952-53. Mem. Houston Country Club, Ramada Club (sec. 1978—). Home: 58 E Broad Oaks Dr Houston TX 77056-1202 Office: Vinson & Elkins 3314 First City Tower 1001 Fannin St Houston TX 77002-6760

SMITH, WILLIAM RAY, retired biophysicist, engineer; b. Lyman, Okla., June 26, 1925; s. Harry Wait and Daisy Belle (Hull) S. BA, Bethany Nazarene Coll., 1948; MA, Wichita State U., 1950; postgrad. U. Kans., 1950-51; PhD, UCLA, 1967. Engr., Beech Aircraft Corp., Wichita, Kans., 1951-53; sr. group engr. McDonnell Aircraft Corp., St. Louis, 1953-60; sr. engr. Lockheed Aircraft Corp., Burbank, Calif., 1961-63; sr. engr. scientist McDonnell Douglas Corp., Long Beach, Calif., 1966-71; mem. tech. staff Rockwell Internat., L.A., 1973-86, CDI Corp.-West, Costa Mesa, Calif., 1986-88, McDonnell Douglas Aircraft Corp., Long Beach, 1988-93; ret., 1993. tchr. math. Pasadena Coll. (now Point Loma Coll., San Diego), 1960-62, Glendale Coll., Calif., 1972; asst. prof. math. Mt. St. Mary's Coll., L.A., 1972-73. Recipient Recognition certificate NASA, 1982. Mem. UCLA Chancellor's Assocs., Internat. Visitors Coun. L.A., Town Hall Calif., Yosemite Assocs., Santa Monica Yacht Club, L.A. World Affairs Coun., Sigma Xi, Pi Mu Epsilon. Republican. Presbyterian. Avocations: sailing, photography, teaching Sunday sch. first grade. Home: 2405 Roscomare Rd Los Angeles CA 90077-1839

SMITH, WILLIAM YOUNG, consultant, former air force officer; b. Hot Springs, Ark., Aug. 13, 1925; s. Ray Sammons and Elisabeth Randolph (Young) S.; m. Maria Helene Petschke, May 30, 1957; children: Raymond P., Mark P., Derek P. Student, Washington and Lee U., 1943-44; BS, U.S. Mil. Acad., 1948; MPA, Harvard U., 1954, PhD, 1961; grad., Nat. War Coll., 1965. Commd. 2d lt. USAF, 1948, advanced through grades to gen., 1979; jet fighter pilot Korea, 1951-52; assoc. prof. social scis. U.S. Mil. Acad., 1954-58; mem. staff Pres.' Commn. to Study Mil. Assistance Program, 1959; mem. war plans staff USAF Hdqrs., 1960; staff asst. to Gen. Maxwell Taylor, mil. rep. to Pres. J.F. Kennedy White Ho., 1961-62; mem. staff NSC and staff asst. to chmn. Joint Chiefs of Staff, 1962-64; dep. chief, policy and negotiations, chief war plans Hdqrs. USAF, Europe, 1965-67; comdr. 603d Air Base Wing, Sembach AFB, Fed. Republic Germany, 1967-68; mil. asst. to sec. Air Force, 1968-71; vice comdr., then comdr. Oklahoma City Air Materiel Command, 1971-73; dir. doctrine, concepts and objectives Hdqrs. USAF, 1973-74; dir. policy plans and nat. security affairs Office Asst. Sec. Def. for Internat. Security Affairs, 1974-75; asst. to chmn. Joint Chiefs of Staff, 1975-79; chief of staff SHAPE, Belgium, 1979-81; dep. comdr. in chief U.S. European Command, Stuttgart, Fed. Republic Germany, 1981-83; ret. USAF, 1983; fellow Woodrow Wilson Internat. Ctr. for Scholars, Smithsonian Inst, Washington, 1983-84; pres. Inst. for Def. Analyses, Alexandria, Va., 1985-91, pres. emeritus, 1991—, also trustee; treas., chmn. fin. com., Atlantic Coun.; mem. exec. com., bd. dirs. Nat. Security Archive. Life fellow Met. Mus. Art. Decorated DSM with oak leaf cluster, Air Force DSM with oak leaf cluster, Silver Star, Legion of Merit with oak leaf cluster, DFC, Air medal with 3 oak leaf clusters, Joint Svc. Commendation medal, Purple Heart, Armed Forces Cross in Gold (Fed. Republic Germany), Ordre Nationale de Merite (France), DOD medal for disting. pub. svc. Mem. Nat. Acad. Pub. Adminstrn., Nat. War Coll. Alumni Assn. (pres. 1985-87), West Point Soc. of D.C. (pres. 1987-89), Coun. Fgn. Rels., Cosmos Club. Office: Inst Def Analyses 1801 N Beauregard St Alexandria VA 22311-1733

SMITH, WILLIS ALLEN, retired consultant, former food company executive; b. Balt., Oct. 26, 1919; s. Willis Alfred and Grace Lee (Roberts) S.; m. Joann Cobb, Aug. 29, 1970. Student, Johns Hopkins U., 1937-41, 46-48, Coll. William and Mary, Norfolk, Va., 1941-42. C.P.A., Md., Ohio, N.Y. Clk. Gas & Electric Co., Balt., 1936-41; acct. F. W. Lafrentz & Co., Balt., 1946-51; mgr. F.W. Lafrentz & Co., Salisbury, Md., 1952-53; partner F.W. Lafrentz & Co., Cleve., 1953-62, Main Lafrentz & Co., N.Y.C., 1963-74; comptroller CPC Internat. Inc., Englewood Cliffs, N.J., 1974-81, v.p., 1981-84; mem. bd. Internat. Acctg. Standards Com., 1979-82; lectr. Third Commodity Conf., Chgo., 1973, Internat. Acctg. Conf., N.Y.C., 1977, 10th Corp. Acctg. and Fin. Reporting Inst., Washington, 1979, Audit Mgmt. Conf., N.Y.C., 1982, Auditing and Acctg. Symposium, N.J., 1987. Contbr.: Accountants Handbook, 6th edit. 1981; articles to profl. jours. Served with USNR, 1941-45, PTO. Mem. AICPA (v.p. 1982-83), N.Y. State Soc. CPAs (v.p. 1977-78, Outstanding Svc. award 1983), Fin. Execs. Inst., Inst. Mgmt. Accts., Am. Acctg. Assn., Ridgewood Country Club (N.J.), The Club Pelican Bay, Club at Edgewater, Shriners. Home: Apt 407 792 Willowbrook Dr Naples FL 33963-8536

SMITH, WINTHROP HIRAM, JR., financial services executive; b. N.Y.C., Aug. 5, 1949; s. Winthrop Hiram Sr. and Vivian Gordon (Brown) S.; m. Margaret Dunn, Aug. 7, 1971. BA, Amherst Coll., 1971; MBA, U. Pa., 1974. Investment banker Merrill Lynch, Pierce, Fenner & Smith, N.Y.C., 1974-77, mgr. fin. analysis, 1977-78, mgr. compensation and benefits, 1978-80, dir. human resources, 1980-82; dir. strategic devel. and mktg. Merrill Lynch Capital Markets, N.Y.C., 1982-84, dir. emerging investor svcs., 1984-85; sr. v.p., regional dir. Merrill Lynch, Pierce, Fenner & Smith, 1985-90, nat. sales dir., 1990-92; exec. v.p., chmn. Merrill Lynch Internat., 1992—. Bd. dirs. Cancer Rsch. Inst., N.Y.C. Ballet; trustee Deerfield Acad.; advisor Outward Bound. Mem. Coun. on Fgn. Rels., Fgn. Policy Assn. (bd. dirs.), Greewich Country Club, Blind Brook Club, F Street Club, The Links. Republican. Episcopalian. Avocations: running, golf, riding, bicycling, skiing. Office: Merrill Lynch Pierce Fenner Smith World Financial Ctr 250 Vesey St New York NY 10281-1325

SMITH, ZACHARY ALDEN, political science and public administration educator; b. Stanford, Calif., Aug. 8, 1953; s. Alden Wallace and Lelia (Anderson) S.; m. Lisa Friel, May 20, 1983. BA, Calif. State U. Fullerton, 1975; MA, U. Calif., Santa Barbara, 1979, PhD, 1984. Adj. lectr. polit. sci. U. Calif. Santa Barbara, 1981-82; asst. prof. dir. Ctr. for Island and Ocean Resources Mgmt. U. Hawaii, Hilo, 1982-87, assoc. prof. 1987-89; assoc. prof. No. Ariz. U., Flagstaff, 1989-93, prof., 1993—. Author: Groundwater and the Future of the Southwest, 1984, Groundwater Policy in the Southwest, 1985, Groundwater in the West, 1989, The Environmental Policy Paradox, 1992, 2d edit., 1995, Hawaii State and Local Government, 1992, Politics and Public Policy in Arizona, 1993, 2d edit., 1995, Environmental Politics and Policy in the West, 1993. Active campaign for various state propositions, 1970, 74, 76; elected to Orange County (Calif.) Dem. Cen. Com., 1976-78. Research grantee U. Calif., Los Alamos (N.Mex.) Sci. Lab., Water Resources Ctr., Davis., Calif. Mem. Am. Water Resources Assn., Am. Polit. Sci. Assn., Southwestern Social Sci. Assn., Western Polit. Sci. Assn., Am. Soc. Pub. Adminstrn., Western Social Sci. Assn. Office: No Ariz U Dept Polit Sci Box 15036 Flagstaff AZ 86011

SMITH, ZACHARY TAYLOR, II, retired tobacco company executive; b. Mt. Airy, N.C., June 15, 1923; s. Eugene Gray and Leonita (Yates) S. AB in Econs., U. N.C., 1947; LLD (hon.), Wake Forest U., 1989. With R.J. Reynolds Tobacco Co., 1947-85, treas., dir., 1970-85. Trustee, past pres. Z. Smith Reynolds Found.; trustee Wake Forest U.; bd. dirs. Mary Reynolds Babcock Found., Med. Found. N.C., Arts and Scis. Found., U. N.C.; mem. nat. devel. coun. U. N.C.; past bd. dirs. Leadership Winston-Salem; past mem. adv. council The Carolina Challenge; past chmn. bd. visitors U. N.C. Chapel Hill; past mem. Reynolds Scholarship Com., past mem. bd. visitors Wake Forest U.; mem. adv. council to hosp., past mem. bd. visitors inst. policy studies and pub. affairs Duke U.; past bd. dirs. N.C. Sch. Arts Found., Devotion Found., N.C. Outward Bound Sch., Small Bus. Devel. Com., Winston-Salem Symphony, Citizens Planning Council; past trustee Forsyth Hosp. Authority; past pres., dir. Child Guidance Clinic Forsyth County, YMCA, Red Shield Boy's Clubs; past pres. Z. Smith Reynolds Found., Mary Reynolds Babcock Found.; past chmn. indsl. div. Arts Council fund drive; past v.p., dir. Arts Council; past v.p., dir. Amos Cottage; past bd. visitors Meredith Coll.; past trustee St. Augustine Coll.; past. bd. dirs. alumni assn. U. N.C.; vice chmn., dir. Friends of U. N.C.-Greensboro Library; co-founder Club Med. Sch. U. N.C., Chapel Hill. Served to lt. USNR, 1943-46. Mem. Old Town Club, Rotary. Democrat. Episcopalian. Home: 2548 Forest Dr Winston Salem NC 27104

SMITHBURG, WILLIAM DEAN, food manufacturing company executive; b. Chgo., July 9, 1938; s. Pearl L. and Margaret L. (Savage) S.; children: Susan, Thomas. BS, DePaul U., 1960; MBA, Northwestern U., 1962. With Leo Burnett Co., Chgo., 1961-63, McCann-Erickson, Inc., Chgo., 1963-66; various positions Quaker Oats Co., Chgo., 1966-71, gen. mgr. cereals and mixes divsn., 1971-75, pres. food divsn., 1975-76, exec. v.p. U.S. grocery products, 1976-79, pres., 1979-83, chief exec. officer, 1979—, chmn., 1983—, also bd. dirs. Served with USAR, 1959-60. Roman Catholic. Office: Quaker Oats Co 321 N Clark St Chicago IL 60610-4714*

SMITHEE, JOHN TRUE, lawyer, state legislator; b. Amarillo, Tex., Sept. 7, 1951; s. John J. and Mildred B. (True) S.; m. Becky Collins, Aug. 18, 1979; children: Jennifer, Rebecca, John True. BBA, West Tex. State U., Canyon, 1973; JD, Tex. Tech U., 1976. Bar: Tex. 1976, U.S. Supreme Ct., 1983. Atty. Templeton, Smithee, Hayes & Fields, Amarillo, Tex., 1976—; mem. Tex. Ho. of Reps., Austin, 1985—, chmn. ins. com., 1993—. Mem. State Bar Tex., Amarillo Bar Assn. Republican. Home: 2808 S Parker Amarillo TX 79109 Office: Templeton Smithee Hayes & Fields 600 S Tyler # 12075 Amarillo TX 79101

SMITHER, HOWARD ELBERT, musicologist; b. Pittsburg, Kans., Nov. 15, 1925; s. Elbert S. and Ethel (Schwab) S.; m. Doris J. Arvin (div. 1976); children: Thomas A., Ann. L.; m. Ann M. Woodward. AB magna cum laude, spl. honors in music, Hamline U., 1950; MA in musicology, Cornell U., 1952; postgrad., U. Munich, 1953-54; PhD in musicology, Cornell U., 1960. Instr. Oberlin Coll. and Conservatory of Music, Oberlin, Ohio, 1955-57, asst. prof., 1957-60; asst. prof. U. Kans., Lawrence, 1960-63; assoc. prof. Tulane U., New Orleans, 1963-68; assoc. prof. U. N.C., Chapel Hill, 1968-71, prof., 1971-79, dir. grad. studies in music, 1977-79, 83-84, 86-88, James Gordon Hanes prof. humanities in music, 1979-92, James Gordon Hanes prof. emeritus humanities in music, 1992—; John Bird prof. of music U. Wales, Cardiff, 1993-95; Lectr., chmn. panels regional, nat. and internat. meetings, confs., symposiums, 1964-90. Author: A History of the Oratorio, Vol. 1, The Oratorio in the Baroque Era: Italy, Vienna, Paris, 1977 (transl. Italian), Vol. 2, The Oratorio in the Baroque Era: Protestant Germany and England, 1977 (Deems Taylor award ASCAP 1978), The Oratorio in the Classical Era, 1987; editor The Italian Oratorio 1650-1800, Vols. 1-3, 6, 8, 11, 12, 13, 16, 18, 19, 20, 24, 25, 27, 1986-87; editor, translator poems in Alfred Einstein's The Italian Madrigal, 1971; author publs. in periodicals, dictionaries, encys., congress reports, record-jacket notes, abstracts, revs.; music rev. editor Notes, 1967-69; mem. editorial bd. Detroit Monographs in Musicology, 1971-87; chmn. editorial bd. Early Musical Masterworks: Editions and Commentaries, 1978-83; mem. editorial bd. Videodisc Music Series, NEH, 1982-86; editor Oratorios of the Italian Baroque, 1983—. Fellow Cornell U., 1953-54, NEH, Italy, 1972-73, England, 1979-80, Guggenheim, 1984-85; Fulbright sr. rsch. grant in Italy, 1965-66, sr. Fulbright lectr. Moscow State Conservatory, 1990. Mem. Am. Mus. Soc. (S.E. chpat. 1969-71, mem. coun. 1969-71, 75-77, bd. dirs. 1977-79, pres. 1980-82, del. to Am. Coun. Learned Socs., 1984-88), Internat. Congress Strasbourg, 1982), Music Libr. Assn. (bd. dirs. 1968-70), Sonneck Soc. Avocations: hiking, photography.

SMITH-MILLER, HENRY HOUCK, architect; b. N.Y.C., Feb. 9, 1942; s. Theodore Roosevelt and Mary Elizabeth (Houck) S.-M. BA, Princeton U., 1964; BArch, Yale U., 1964-65; MArch, U. Pa., 1966. Registered architect, N.Y., Pa., Md., N.C., Calif. Archtl. designer Michael Graves & Peter Eisenman Architects, Princeton, N.J., 1964; architect Richard Meier & Ptnrs., Architect, N.Y.C., 1970-77; ptnr. Rubin & Smith-Miller, Architects, N.Y.C., 1977-81, Smith-Miller & Hawkinson, Architects, N.Y.C., 1981—; vis. critic architecture U. Va. Sch. Architecture, Charlottesville, 1978-79, Columbia U. Sch. Architecture, N.Y.C., 1981, 84, Harvard U. Grad. Sch. Architecture, Cambridge, Mass., 1987; Thomas Jefferson prof. architecture U. Va. Sch. Architecture, 1989—. Trustee Creative Time, N.Y.C., 1986—. Recipient Architecture Record awards; Fulbright scholar, 1967-69. Mem. AIA (Design awards N.Y. chpt. 1986, 87, 89, 91, 92, 94), Contemporary Coun. Mus. Modern Art. Democrat. Home and Office: Smith-Miller & Hawkinson Architects 305 Canal St New York NY 10013-2569

SMITH-PIERCE, PATRICIA A., speech professional; b. Washington, May 24, 1939; d. Harold Milton and Mary Louise (Reimbold) Anderson; m. Wayne D. Pierce, Mar. 25, 1978. BA, Ohio State U., 1961; MA, U. Utah, 1970; PhD, Wash. State U., 1977. Stewardess Am. Airlines, Chgo., 1962-63; selling supr. The Emporium, San Francisco, 1963-65; buyer Cain-Sloan Co., Nashville, 1967-68; speech coach William Rainey Harper Coll., Palatine, Ill., 1970-76, prof., 1970—, chmn. speech dept., 1985—, dir. corp. svcs., 1990-91; cons. Inst. Mgmt. Devel., Palatine, 1983—; bd. dirs. Ill. Women's Agenda, 1981-87, v.p., 1982-83, pres., 1983-85; bd. dirs. Women in Charge, Chgo., 1987-90; cons. various corp. and govtl. agys.; mem. com. Ill. Commn. on Status of Women, 1983-85; trainer Mex. Am. Legal Def. and Edn. Fund, Leadership Program Chgo., 1986—. Mem. Ill. Minority and Female Bus. Enterprise Coun., 1984-94. Mem. AAUW (1st v.p. state orgn. 1985-87, bd. dirs. 1981-87, nat. trainer 1987—), Human Resources Mgmt. Assn. Chgo., Zonta Internat. Avocations: reading, golf. Office: William Rainey Harper Coll 1200 W Algonquin Rd Palatine IL 60067-7398

SMITHSON, LOWELL LEE, lawyer; b. Kansas City, Mo., Apr. 29, 1930; s. Spurgeon Lee and Lena Louise (Ruddy) S.; m. Rosemary Carol Leitz, Jan. 30, 1960 (div. Sept. 1985); m. Phyllis Galley Westover, June 8, 1986; children: Carol Maria Louise, Katherine Frances Lee. AB in Polit. Sci., U. Mo., 1952, JD, 1954. Bar: Mo. 1954, U.S. Dist. Ct. (we. dist.) Mo. 1955, U.S. Supreme Ct. 1986. Ptnr. Smithson & Smithson, Kansas City, 1965-59; assoc. Spencer, Fane, Britt & Browne, Kansas City, 1959-64, ptnr., 1964—; adj. prof. law U. Mo., Kansas City, 1982. Pres. Kansas City Mental Health Assn., 1963-65; mem. bd. pres. All Souls Unitarian Ch. Kansas City, 1965-67; chmn. com. select dean for law sch. U. Mo., 1983. 1st lt. U.S. Army, 1954-56, Korea. Mem. Kansas City Bar Assn., Lawyers Assn. Kansas City, Assn. Trial Lawyers Am., Western Mo. Def. Lawyers Assn., Fed. Energy Bar Assn., Phi Beta Kappa, Phi Delta Phi. Democrat. Unitarian Ch. Avocations: skiing, reading, tennis, swimming, canoeing. Home: 1215 W 65th St Kansas City MO 64113-1803 Office: Spencer Fane Britt & Browne 1000 Walnut 1400 Commerce Bank Bldg Kansas City MO 64106

SMITHSON, LUTHER HARRIS, diversified electronics research company executive; b. Birmingham, Ala., July 20, 1932; s. Luther Harris and Mamee (Champenois) S.; m. Marilyn Anderson, Mar. 24, 1956; children: Kistrina Marie, Paul John. BS in Chemistry, U. Wash., 1957; MS in Phys. Chemistry, UCLA, 1960. Chemist Calif. Research Co., Richmond, 1960-66; lab. mgr. Varian Corp., Palo Alto, Calif., 1966-70; dir. mktg. Smith Kline INst., Palo Alto, 1970-73; dir. biotech. SRI Internat., Menlo Park, Calif., 1973—. Contbr. articles to profl. jours.; patentee in field. Served as cpl. U.S. Army, 1952-55. Avocations: pottery, reading, writing. Home: 2261 Greer Rd Palo Alto CA 94303-3129 Office: Plant Cell Rsch Inst Inc 1114 Avenue Of The Americas New York NY 10036-7701

SMITS, EDWARD JOHN, museum consultant; b. Freeport, N.Y., Dec. 11, 1933; s. Karl M. and Jennie (Spring) S.; m. Ruth K. Hall; children: E. John, Robert K., Theodore R. BA, Hofstra U., 1955; MA, NYU, 1959. Curator Nassau County Hist. Mus., East Meadow, N.Y., 1956-70; dir. mus. svcs. Div. Mus. Svcs. Nassau County, Syosset, N.Y., 1971-92; Nassau County historian, 1985—. Author: Long Island Landmarks, 1970, Creation of Nassau County, 1959, Nassau, Suburbia U.S.A., 1974. Trustee Friends for L.I.'s Heritage, Nassau County Hist. Soc.; trustee, past pres. Levittown Libr. Bd. 1st lt. U.S. Army, 1955-56. Fulbright grantee, 1965; recipient Nassau County Disting. Svc. award County of Nassau, 1970, Alumni Disting. Svc. award Hofstra U., 1970, H. Sherwood Historic Preservation on L.I. award Soc. for the Preservatioin of L.I. Antiquities, 1975. Mem. Am. Assn. Mus., Assn. Nassau County Hist. Orgns. Avocations: book collecting, antique toys, golf. Home: 14 Wavy Ln Wantagh NY 11793-1202

SMITS, HELEN LIDA, public adminstrator, physician, educator; b. Long Beach, Calif., Dec. 3, 1936; d. Theodore Richard Smits and Anna Mary Wells; m. Roger LeCompte, Aug. 28, 1976; 1 child, Theodore. BA with honors, Swarthmore Coll., 1958; MA, Yale U., 1961, MD cum laude, 1967. Intern, asst. resident Hosp. U. Pa., 1967-68; fellow Beth Israel Hosp., Boston, 1969-70; chief resident Hosp. U. Pa., 1970-71; chief med. clinic U. Pa., 1971-75; assoc. adminstr. for patient care svcs. U. Pa. Hosp., 1975-77; v.p. med. affairs Community Health Plan Georgetown U., Washington, 1977; dir. health standards and quality bur. Health Care Financing Adminstrn., HHS, Washington, 1977-80; sr. rsch. assoc. The Urban Inst., Washington, 1980-81; assoc. prof. Yale U. Med. Sch., New Haven, 1981-85; assoc. v.p. for health affairs U. Conn. Health Ctr., Farmington, 1985-87; prof. community medicine U. Conn. Sch. Medicine, Farmington, 1985-93; hosp. dir. John Dempsey Hosp., Farmington, 1987-93; dep. administr. Health Care Financing Adminstrn., Washington, 1993—; commr. Joint Com. on Accreditation Hosps., Chgo., 1989-93, chair, 1991-92. Contbr. numerous articles to profl. jours. Bd. dirs. The Ivoryton Playhouse Fedn., Inc., 1990-92, The Connecticut River Mus., 1990-93, Hartford Stage, 1990-93; mem. Dem. Town Com., Essex, Conn., 1982-89. Recipient Superior Svc. award HHS, Washington, 1982; Royal Soc. Medicine Found. fellow, London, 1973; Fulbright scholar, 1959-60. Mem. ACP (master, regent 1984-90), Phi Beta Kappa, Alpha Omega Alpha. Episcopalian. Avocations: sailing, cooking, gardening. Home: 81 Main St Ivoryton CT 06442-1032 Office: Health Care Fin Adminstrn 200 Independence Ave SW Washington DC 20201

SMITS, JIMMY, actor; b. N.Y.C., July 9, 1955; two children. Master's degree, Cornell Univ., 1982. Appearances include Off-Broadway prodns., tours with regional theatres; (TV series) Miami Vice, 1984, L.A. Law, 1986-91 (Outstanding Actor in Dramatics Series Emmy award 1990), NYPD Blue, 1994—; (TV movies) Rockabye, 1986, The Highwayman, 1986, Glitz, 1988, The Broken Cord, 1992, Stephen King's The Tommyknockers, 1993; (films) Running Scared, 1986, The Believers, 1987, Old Gringo, 1989, Vital Signs, 1990, Switch, 1991, Gross Misconduct, 1993, My Family, 1995. Avocations: football, basketball, softball, reading. Office: care Marilyn Sherman 1516 S Beverly Dr Apt 304 Los Angeles CA 90035-3059*

SMITTLE, NELSON DEAN, electronics executive; b. Peebles, Ohio, Sept. 19, 1934; s. Nelson John and Alma Katherine (Green) S.; m. Claire Wiggins, May 5, 1973. BS, BFA, U. Cin., 1962, MA, 1971. Commd. 2d lt. U.S. Army, 1962; staff officer U.S. Army Photo Agy. Pentagon, Washington, 1966; detachment comdr. tactical communications Republic South Vietnam, 1967-68; comdr. 2007th communications squadron Rickenbacker AFB, Ohio, 1972; dir. ops. fixed communications Air Combat Command Langley AFB, Va., 1982; dir. info. systems AWACS Saudi Arabia, 1984-85; dep. chief of staff standard systems Air Material Command Wright-Patterson AFB, Ohio, 1985; comdr. engring. installation divsn. Tinker AFB, Okla., 1988; commn. transferred to USAF, 1970, commd. col., 1988; ret. USAF, Cin., 1991; pres. Falcon Techs., Cin., 1991—; tchr. Princeton City Sch. Dist., Cin., 1992-94; cons. Air War Coll., Air Univ., Maxwell AFB, Ala., 1987—, Defense Systems Mgmt. Coll., Ft. Belvior, Va., 1988—. Author: (book) Army Visual Presentation, 1966 (medal 1966). Mem. Batavia (Ohio) City Coun., 1972; pres. Ohio Buckeye Wing Assn., Columbus, 1973; mem. Air Force Policy Coun., Washington, 1978; congl. campaign mgr., 1993. Decorated Commendation medal; recipient Meritorious Svc. medal Dept. Def., 1986, 91. Mem. Air Force Assn., Res. Officers Assn., DAV, Cin. Art Club (bd. dirs.), Artists of Ohio, Internat. Platform Assn. Avocations: freelance writer, exhibiting artist, woodworking, science fiction. Home and Office: Falcon Techs 159 Francisridge Dr Cincinnati OH 45238

SMIY, PAUL R., manufacturing executive, heavy; b. 1923. With Elliott Co., Jeannette, Pa., pres., CEO, 1986-91, chmn., 1991—; also CEO New Elliott Corp., Jeannette, Pa.; asst. chmn. bd. Jeannette (Pa.) Healthcare Corp. Chmn. bd. Jeannette (Pa.) Dist. Meml. Hosp. Office: Elliott Co 901 N 4th St Jeannette PA 15644-3332*

SMOAK, DAVID S., food company executive; b. Augusta, Ga., Oct. 16, 1947; s. Samuel F. and Constance W. Smoak; m. Charity A. Townsend. BBA, U. Ga., 1968; MPA, Ga. State U., 1969. CPA. Staff acct. Price Waterhouse, Atlanta, 1969-71; sr. acct. Harris Kerr Forster & Co., Atlanta, 1971-73; contr. Rhodes Inc., Atlanta, 1973-76; v.p. Export Import Bank U.S., Washington, 1977-78; exec. dir. White House Conf. on Small Bus., Washington, 1978-79; bus. liaison officer Dept. Commerce, Washington, 1979-81; v.p. Technics, San Jose, Calif., 1981-83; sr. v.p. Doskocil Cos. Inc., Hutchinson, Kans., 1984—; pres., chief exec. officer Wilson Foods Corp., Oklahoma City, 1988—. Mem. Alliance Capital Access, Washington, 1988—; coord. United Way, Oklahoma City, 1989; bd. dirs. Reno County chpt. ARC, Hutchinson, 1987—. Mem. AICPA, Ga. Soc. CPAs (mem. various coms.), D.C. Soc. CPAs (mem. various coms.), Hutchinson C. of C. (bd. dirs. 1981—), Prairie Dunes C. of C. (Hutchinson), Oak Tree Golf and Country Club (Oklahoma City). Home: 301 W 20th Ave Hutchinson KS 67502-2851 Office: Wilson Foods Corp 4545 N Lincoln Blvd Oklahoma City OK 73105-3413

SMOCK, RAYMOND WILLIAM, historian, government official; b. Jeffersonville, Ind., Feb. 8, 1941; s. Richard and Lottie (Paciorek) S.; m. Phyllis Lee Chadwick, Feb. 12, 1961. B.A., Roosevelt U., Chgo., 1966; Ph.D., U. Md., College Park, 1974. Rsch. asst. Md. Constl. Conv., Annapolis, 1967-68; lectr. in history U. Md., College Park, 1968-72; co-editor The Booker T. Washington Papers, 14 vols., 1972-83; pres. Instructional Resources Corp., Lanham, Md., 1976-83; pres. Rsch. Materials Corp., College Park, 1982-83, dir., 1982-85; historian, dir. Office for Bicentennial, U.S. Ho. of Reps., Washington, 1983-89, Office of Historian, U.S. Ho. of Reps., Washington, 1989-95; mem. bd. editorial advisers Md. Historian, College Park, 1971—. Author: A Talent for Detail: The Photographs of Miss Frances Benjamin Johnston 1889-1910, 1974; co-editor: A Guide to Manuscripts in the Presidential Libraries, 1985; editor:Booker T. Washington in Perspective: The Essays of Louis R. Harlan, 1988. Ford Found. fellow, 1970; recipient Philip M. Hamer award Soc. Am. Archivists, 1979. Mem. Nat. Coun. Pub. History, Assn. for Documentary Editing (pres. 1983-84), Orgn. Am. Historians, So. Hist. Assn., Soc. History in Fed. Govt. Avocations: photography; astronomy.

SMOKE, RICHARD, political scientist, political psychologist; b. Huntington, Pa., Oct. 21, 1944; s. Kenneth Ludwig and Lillian Duerer (Harbaugh) S. B.A., Harvard Coll., 1965; Ph.D., MIT, 1972. Asst. dean, lectr. Kennedy Sch. Govt. Harvard U., Cambridge, Mass., 1971-73; postdoctoral fellow Inst. Personality Assessment and Research U. Calif.-Berkeley, 1973-74; fellow Ctr. Advanced Study Behavioral Scis., Palo Alto, Calif., 1974-75, 94-95; rsch. assoc., prof. Wright Inst., Berkeley, 1975-81; interim dean Wright Inst., 1981-82; exec. dir., co-founder Peace and Common Security, San Francisco, 1982-84; prof. polit. sci., rsch. dir. Ctr. for Fgn. Policy Devel. Brown U., Providence, 1984—. Author: National Security and the Nuclear Dilemma, 1984, 3d edit., 1992, War: Controlling Escalation, 1977; co-author: (with Alexander L. George) Deterrence in American Foreign Policy: Theory and Practice, 1974 (winner Bancroft prize 1974); (with Willis Harman) Paths to Peace, 1987; editor: (with Andrei Kortunov) Mutual Security, 1991; assoc. editor Polit. Psychology, 1978-81. Mem. Internat. Soc. Polit. Psychology (governing council 1980-82), Am. Polit. Sci. Assn. (Helen Dwight Reid award), Am. Psychol. Assn. Office: Brown U Ctr for Fgn Policy Devel PO Box 1948 Providence RI 02912-0001

Also: Ctr Advanced Study Behavioral Scis 202 Junipero Serra Blvd Stanford CA 94305

SMOLANSKY, OLES M., humanities educator; b. Ukraine, USSR, May 2, 1930; came to U.S. 1950; s. Mykola S. and Irene (Plinto) S.; m. Bettie Moretz, Dec. 29, 1966; children: Alexandra, Nicholas. BA, NYU, 1953; MA, Columbia U., 1955, PhD, 1959. Instr. UCLA, 1960-62; asst. prof. Lehigh U., Bethlehem, Pa., 1963-66, assoc. prof., 1966-70, prof., 1970-85, univ. prof., 1985—. Author: The Soviet Union and the Arab East Under Khrushchev, 1974, The USSR and Iraq: The Soviet Quest for Influence, 1991; co-editor: Russia and America: From Rivalry to Reconciliation, 1993; contbr. articles to profl. jours. Recipient joint fellowship, Rockefeller Found. and Ford Found., N.Y.C., 1962-63, sr. research joint fellowship, Research Inst. on Communist Affairs and Middle East Inst., Columbia U., N.Y.C., 1972-73, research fellowship, Ford Found., N.Y.C., 1980-81. Mem. Internat. Studies Assn., Am. Assn. for Advancement of Slavic Studies (Marshall Shulman award 1992), Middle East Studies Assn., Mid. East Inst. Democrat. Greek-Orthodox. Avocations: music, sports. Home: 3665 Walt Whitman Ln Bethlehem PA 18017-1553 Office: Lehigh U Dept Internat Rels Bethlehem PA 18015

SMOLAR, EDWARD NELSON, physician, consultant; b. Bklyn., Sept. 26, 1943; s. Harry and Diane (Orans) S.; m. Sharon Elaine Wechsler, June 24, 1973; children: Todd Devon, Gregory Fielding. BS in Biol. Scis. with honors, Union Coll., 1964; MD, Albert Einstein Coll. of Medicine, 1968; MBA with honors, Nova U., 1985, MS, 1990. Diplomate Am. Bd. Internal Medicine, Am. Bd. Endocrinology and Metabolism, Am. Bd. Geriatric Medicine, Nat. Bd. Med. Examiners; CLU, ChFC, CFP. Asst. instr. of medicine SUNY, Bklyn., 1973-75; clin. instr. of medicine N.Y. Med. Coll., 1974-79; physician pvt. practice, N.Y., 1975-80; asst. prof. of clin. medicine N.Y. Med. Coll., 1979-80; pvt. practice, N.Y.C., 1975-80; pvt. practice, pvt. practice, Pompano Beach, 1980-84, Ft. Lauderdale, Fla., 1984—; clin. asst. prof. medicine U. Miami, Fla., 1982-89; adj. faculty Friedt Sch. Bus., Nova U., Ft. Lauderdale, Fla., 1987-88; cons. Profl. Fin. Cons. Palm Beach, Inc., Boca Raton, Fla., 1988—. Contbr. articles to med. jours. Pres. Am. Diabetes Assn., 1980-81, bd. dirs., 1987—; mem. adv. bd. Hospice, Inc., 1985—. Surgeon USPHS, 1968-71, inactive res., 1971—. Fellow ACP, Am. Coll. Angiology, Am. Coll. Endocrinology, N.Y. Acad. Medicine (life), Royal Soc. Health, Royal Soc. Medicine, Am. Acad. Polit. and Social Sci.; mem. Endocrine Soc., Am. Acad. Polit. Sci. (life), Assn. Mil. Surgeons U.S. (life), Am. Soc. CLUs and ChFCs. Republican. Jewish. Avocations: antique collecting, gourmet food, jazz music, history and nostalgia, hiking. Office: 5601 North Dixie Hwy Fort Lauderdale FL 33334

SMOLENSKY, EUGENE, economics educator; b. Bklyn., Mar. 4, 1932; s. Abraham and Jennie (Miller) S.; m. Natalie Joan Rabinowitz, Aug. 16, 1952; children: Paul, Beth. B.A., Bklyn. Coll., 1952; M.A., Am. U., 1956; Ph.D., U. Pa., 1961. Prof. econs. U. Wis., Madison, 1968-88, chmn. dept., 1978-80, 86-88; dir. Inst. for Research on Poverty, U. Wis., 1980-83; dean Grad. Sch. Pub. Policy U. Calif., Berkeley, 1988—. Author: Public Expenditures, Taxation and the Distribution of Income: The U.S., 1950, 61, 70, 77. Mem. Nat. Acad. Pub. Adminstrn., 1994; mem. com. on child devel. rsch. and pub. policy NAS, Washington, 1982-87, mem. com. on status of women in labor market, 1985-87. With USN, 1952-56. Mem. Am. Econs. Assn. Democrat. Jewish. Avocation: collecting old master etchings and lithographs. Home: 669 Woodmont Ave Berkeley CA 94708-1233 Office: U Calif Dept Pub Policy 2607 Hearst Ave Berkeley CA 94709-1005

SMOLEV, TERENCE ELLIOT, lawyer, educator; b. Bklyn., Oct. 5, 1944; s. Lawrence and Shirley (Lebowitz) S.; m. Sherry Gale Rosen, Nov. 24, 1968 (div.); children: Cindy, Scott. BBA, Hofstra U., 1966; JD, American U., 1969; LLM, NYU, 1974. Bar: N.Y. 1970. Acct. Peat Marwick & Mitchell, N.Y.C., 1969-70; dir. deferred giving Hofstra U., Hempstead, N.Y., 1971-74; editor Panel Publishers, Greenvale, N.Y., 1970-71; ptnr. Naidich & Smolev, P.C., Bellmore, N.Y., 1972-92; mem. bd. trustees Hofstra U., 1992—; adj. prof. Hofstra U., Hempstead, N.Y., 1971—; dist. counsel North Merrick (N.Y.) UFSD, 1975—; bd. dirs. Hofstra U. Club, Hempstead, 1981—. Author of book chpt. Mem. Nassau County, N.Y. Dem. Com., 1972-80, mem. judicial screening com., 1992—; mem. IRS Small Bus. Adv. Com., Washington D.C., 1975-77. Recipient George M. Estabrook award Hofstra U., 1991, Alumni Achievement award Hofstra U., 1993; named Senator of Yr., Hofstra U., 1985. Mem. ABA, N.Y. State Bar Assn., Nassau County Bar Assn., N.Y. State Assn. Sch. Attys. (pres. 1984), Hofstra U. Alumni Senate (pres. 1987-89). Avocations: photography, golf. Office: 120 Mineola Blvd Ste 500 Mineola NY 11501-4077

SMOLIN, RONALD PHILIP, publisher; b. Phila., Aug. 12, 1941; s. Harry and Frances (Gordon) S. B.A., Pa. State U., 1963. Staff writer Prudential Ins. Co., Newark, 1964-65; pub. info. officer Newark War on Poverty program, 1965-66; dir. publs. N.Y.C. Human Resources Adminstrn., 1966-75; chmn. Beekman Pubs., Inc., N.Y.C., 1973-77; pres. Internat. Ideas Inc., N.Y.C., 1977-85, Am. Investor Info. Services Inc., 1983-89, Trans-Atlantic Publs. Inc., 1985—, Coronet Books Inc., 1986—; pres. Premium PET Kitchen Inc., 1992—. Address: Coronet Books Inc 311 Bainbridge St Philadelphia PA 19147

SMOLINSKI, EDWARD ALBERT, holding company executive, lawyer, accountant, deacon; b. N.Y.C., Jan. 6, 1928; s. Albert John and Adele (Weber) S.; m. Joan E. Winslow, Nov. 12, 1955; children: Albert, Edward, Linda, Donna. B.S. in Acctg., L.I. U., 1948; M.B.A., NYU, 1950, J.D., 1956. Bar: N.Y. 1957; C.P.A.; N.Y.; ordained deacon Roman Cath. Ch., 1977. Acct. various cert. pub. acctg. firms N.Y.C., 1948-53; acctg. supr. Curtiss Wright Co., Woodridge, N.J., 1953-60; mem. treasury staff Sperry-Rand Corp., Great Neck, N.Y., 1960-62; corp. controller Fairchild Camera and Instrument Co., Syosset, N.Y., 1962-69; v.p., treas., chief fin. officer Grow Group, Inc., N.Y.C., 1969-89; asst. treas./sec. United Indsl. Corp., N.Y.C., 1989—; adj. asst. prof. Hunter Coll., 1989. Bd. dirs. Long Island U.-Bus. Game, N.Y.C., 1977-83, NYU Mgmt. Decision Lab., 1983-88; deacon Diocese of Bklyn., Roman Cath. Ch., 1977—. Mem. AICPA (com. on nat. def. 1963), N.Y. Bar, Fin. Execs. Inst. Roman Catholic. Lodge: Elks. Home: 70-19 June St Forest Hills NY 11375 Office: United Indsl Corp 18 E 48th St New York NY 10017-1014

SMOLLA, RODNEY ALAN, lawyer, educator; b. Pueblo, Colo., Mar. 13, 1953; s. Richard Paul and Harriet (Waskowiak) S.; m. Linda A. Malone, Apr. 13, 1979. BA, Yale U., 1975; JD, Duke U., 1978. Bar: Ill. 1979, U.S. Supreme Ct. 1987. Law clk. to presiding judge U.S. Ct. Appeals, Jackson, Miss., 1978-79; assoc. Mayer, Brown & Pratt, Chgo., 1979-80; asst. prof. De Paul U. Sch. Law, Chgo., 1980-81, U. Ill. Coll. Law, 1981-83; prof. U. Ark. Sch. Law, 1983-87; vis. prof. U. Denver Coll. Law, 1987-88; Arthur B. Hanson prof. constl. law Coll. of William and Mary, Williamsburg, Va., 1988—; dir. Inst. Bill of Rights Law, 1988—. Author: Suing the Press: Libel, The Media & Power, 1986 (cert. of merit ABA 1987), Law of Defamation, 1986, Jerry Falwell v. Larry Flynt: The First Amendment on Trial, 1988, (with Banks and Braveman) Constitutional Law: Structure and Rights in Our Federal System, 1991, Free Speech in an Open Society, 1992 (William O. Douglas award 1993), Smolla and Nimmer on Freedom of Speech, 1994, Federal Civil Rights Acts, 1994. Fellow, cons. Annenberg Washington Program in Communications, 1987—; project dir. Annenberg Libel Reform Task Force, 1988-89; reporter Bill of Rights Adv. Com. to the Commn. on the Bicentennial of U.S. Constitution, 1989—. Recipient Disting. Prof. of Yr. award U. Ark., 1986. Mem. ABA, Ill. Bar Assn., AAUP (mem. litigation com. 1988—). Home: 119 Richneck Rd Williamsburg VA 23185-3245 Office: William and Mary Sch Law Inst Bill Of Law Williamsburg VA 23187

SMOLTZ, JOHN ANDREW, professional baseball player; b. Warren, Mich., May 15, 1967. With Detroit Tigers, 1985-87; pitcher Atlanta Braves, 1987—; player Nat. League All-Star Game, 1989, 92, 93. Leader in strikeouts in Nat. League, 1992. Office: Atlanta Braves PO Box 4064 Atlanta GA 30302*

SMOLUCHOWSKI, ROMAN, physicist, emeritus educator; b. Zakopane, Austria, Aug. 31, 1910; came to U.S., 1935, naturalized, 1946; s. Marian and Sophia (Baraniecka) S.; m. Louise Catherine Riggs, Feb. 3, 1951; children: Peter, Irene. MA, U. Warsaw, 1933; PhD, U. Groningen, Holland, 1935. Mem. Inst. Advanced Study, Princeton, 1935-36, instr., research asso.

physics dept., 1939-41;; research assoc., head physics sect. Inst. Metals, Warsaw, 1936-39; research physicist Gen. Electric Research Labs., Schenectady, 1941-46; assoc. prof.; staff Metals Research Lab., Carnegie Inst. Tech., 1946-50; prof. physics and metall. engring., 1950-56, prof. physics, 1956-60; prof. solid state scis., head solid state and materials Princeton U., 1960-78; prof. astronomy and physics U. Tex., Austin, 1978–; vis. prof. Internat. Solid State Physics, Mol, Belgium, 1963, Facultédes Sciences, Paris, 1965-66; lectr. Sch. Planetary Physics, Super-Besse, France, 1972; Fulbright prof. U. Sorbonne-Paris, 1955-56; lectr. Internat. Sch. Solid State Physics, Varenna, Italy, 1957, U. Liège, Belgium, 1956, Faculté des Scis., Paris, 1965-66; vis. prof. NRC of Brazil, 1958-59, Tech. U. Munich, 1974; mem. solid state panel Research and Devel. Bd., Dept. Def., 1949, sec. panel, 1950-61; mem. tech. adv. bd. Aircraft Nuclear Propulsion, 1950; chmn com. on magnetism Office Naval Research, 1952-56; chmn. com. on solids NRC, 1950-61, chmn. solid state scis. panel, 1961-67, chmn. div. phys. scis., 1969-75; mem. space sci. bd. Nat. Acad. Scis., 1969-75, mem. physics survey, 1963-66, 1969-72; adv. com. metallurgy Oak Ridge Nat. Lab., 1960-62, mem. com. on planetary and lunar exploration, 1980-84. Author: (with Mayer and Weyl) Phase Transformations in Nearly Perfect Crystals, 1952, (with others) Molecular Science and Molecular Engineering, 1959, The Solar System—Sun, Planets and Life, 1983; editor: (with N. Kurti) Monograph Series on Solid State, 1957, (with J. W. Wilkins and E. Burstein) Comments in Condensed Matter Physics, (with M. Glazer) Phase Transitions; (with others) Ices in the Solar System, The Galaxy and the Solar System, Radiation Effects and Defects in Solids; editor-in-chief: Crystal Lattice Defects and Amorphous Materials; assoc. editor: Fundamentals of Cosmic Physics; contbr. articles to profl. jours. Chmn. bd. trustees Simon's Rock Coll., 1971-72. Guggenheim Meml. fellow, 1974; fellow Churchill Coll. Cambridge U., Eng., 1974. Fellow Am. Phys. Soc. (chmn. div. solid state physics 1944-46), Am. Acad. Arts and Scis.; mem. AAAS, Internat. Astron. Union, Finnish Acad. Scis. and Letters, Am. Astron. Soc., Mex. Acad. Engring., Brazilian Acad. Scis., Sigma Xi, Alpha Sigma Mu, Pi Mu Epsilon. Home: 1401 Ethridge Ave Austin TX 78703-2539 Office: U Tex Dept Physics and Astronomy Austin TX 78712

SMOOK, MALCOLM ANDREW, chemist, chemical company executive; b. Seattle, Aug. 22, 1924; s. Joseph Murray and Bonnie (Hanson) S.; m. Mary Louise Nominee, Dec. 19, 1945; children—Frances Lynn, Valerie Dale. B.S., U. Calif., Berkeley, 1945; Ph.D. in Organic Chemistry, Ohio State U., 1949. With E. I. duPont de Nemours & Co., Wilmington, Del., 1949–; research supr. E. I. duPont de Nemours & Co., 1952-53, div. head, 1953-57, asst. lab. dir., 1957-60, lab. dir., 1960-63, asst. research dir., 1963-75, gen. lab. dir., 1975-80, mgr. patents and regulatory affairs, 1980-84; cons. Malcolm A. Smook, Inc.,; 1985–; mem. adv. com. NASA, 1971-76. Contbr. articles to profl. jours. Served to lt. (j.g.) USN, 1943-46. Socony Vacuum fellow, 1948-49. Mem. Am. Chem. Soc., Sigma Xi. Patentee in field (6). Home and Office: 59 Rockford Rd Wilmington DE 19806-1003

SMOOT, E. PHILIP, chemicals executive; b. 1939. Graduate, Long Beach State Coll., 1959. With Lee Smith & Co., Santa Rosa, Calif., 1964-66; v.p. Bell Industries, Inc., Santa Rosa, Calif., 1966-73; with Cirtel, Inc., Irvine, Calif., 1973-74, Electro-Etched Circuits, L.A., 1974-77, Gulton Piezo Co., L.A., 1977-70, Oak Industries, Inc., San Diego, 1979-81; with Park Electrochemical Corp., New Hyde Park, N.Y., 1981–, now exec. v.p.; bd. dirs. New Eng. Laminates Co., Inc., Walden, N.Y. With USAF, 1959-64. Office: Park Electrochem Corp 5 Dakota Dr New Hyde Park NY 11042-1109*

SMOOT, GEORGE FITZGERALD, III, astrophysicist; b. Yukon, Fla., Feb. 20, 1945. BS in math., BS in physics, MIT, 1966, Ph.D. in physics, 1970. Rsch. physicist MIT, 1970; rsch. physicist Univ. Calif., Berkeley, Calif., 1971–; Lawrence Berkeley Lab., 1974–; team leader, differential microwave radiometer experiment, COBE (Cosmic Background Explorer) satellite. Author: (with Keay Davidson) Wrinkles in Time, 1993. Recipient Space/Missiles Laurels award Aviation Week & Space Technology, 1992. Mem. Internat. Astron. Union, Am. Phys. Soc., Am. Astron. Soc., Sigma Xi. Home: 10 Panoramic Way Berkeley CA 94704*

SMOOT, HAZEL LAMPKIN, retired piano teacher, poet; b. Kamiah, Idaho, Oct. 17, 1916; d. Albert Chuning and Cora Benson (Buckland) Weaver; m. Daniel Joseph Smoot, Feb. 18, 1939 (div. 1960); children: Daniel Jerome, David Reed. AA, Sacramento City Coll., 1937; student, Linfield Coll., 1938. Contbr. poetry to anthologies published by World of Poetry, also to Vantage Press and The Golden Treasury of Great Poems, Great American Poetry Anthology. Scholar Linfield Coll; recipient Golden Poetry awards World of Poetry, 1987, 88, 89. Avocations: poetry, walking, reading, music, singing.

SMOOT, LEON DOUGLAS, research director, former university dean, chemical engineering educator; b. Provo, Utah, July 26, 1934; s. Douglas Parley and Jennie (Hallam) S.; m. Marian Bird, Sept. 7, 1953; children: Analee, LaCinda, Michelle, Melinda Lee. BS, Brigham Young U., 1956, B in Engring. Sci., 1957; MS, U. Wash., 1958, PhD, 1960. Registered profl. engr., Utah. Engr. Boeing Corp., Seattle, 1956; teaching and research asst. Brigham Young U., 1954-57; engr. Phillips Petroleum Corp., Arco, Idaho, 1957; engr., cons. Hercules Powder Co., Bacchus, Utah, 1961-63; asst. prof. Brigham Young U., 1960-63; engr. Lockheed Propulsion, Redlands, Calif., 1963-67; vis. asst. prof. Calif. Inst. Tech., 1966-67; asso. prof. to prof. Brigham Young U., 1967–, chmn. dept. chem. engring., 1970-77, dean Coll. Engring. and Tech., 1977-94, dean emeritus, 1994–; dir. Advanced Combustion Engring. Rsch. Ctr., 1986–; expert witness on combustion and explosions; dir. Advanced Combustion Engring. Research Ctr. (NSF), 1986–; cons. Hercules, Thiokol, Lockheed, Teledyne, Allied Research Corp., Raytheon, Redd and Redd, Billings Energy, Ford, Bacon & Davis, Jaycor, Intel Com Radiation Tech., Phys. Dynamics, Nat. Soc. Propellants and Explosives, France, DFVLR, West Germany, Martin Marietta, Honeywell, Phillips Petroleum Co., Exxon, Nat. Bur. Standards, Eyring Research Inst., Systems, Sci. and Software., Los Alamos Nat. Lab., others. Author 5 books on coal combustion; contbr. over 200 articles and tech. jours. Mem. adv. coun. U.S. Office of Tech. Assessment. Mem. AIChE, Am. Soc. Engring. Edn., Combustion Inst., Rsch. Soc. Am., Sigma Xi, Tau Beta Pi, Phi Lambda Epsilon. Republican. Mem. LDS Ch. Home: 1811 N 1550 Provo UT 84604-5709 Office: Brigham Young U Advanced Combustion Engring Rsch Ctr 45 Crabtree Tech Bldg Provo UT 84602

SMOOT, OLIVER REED, JR., lawyer, trade association executive; b. San Antonio, Aug. 24, 1940; s. Oliver Reed and Angie Frances (Watters) S.; m. Sandra Lee Curry, July 25, 1964; children: Stephen Reed, Sheryl Anne. BS, MIT, 1962; JD, Georgetown U., 1966. Bar: D.C. 1966. Va. 1967. Computer systems mgr. Inst. for Def. Analyses, Arlington, Va., 1962-69; program mgr., v.p., then exec. v.p. and treas. Computer and Bus. Equipment Mfrs. Assn., Washington, 1969–. Author: (with others) Computers and the Law, 3d edit., 1981; chpt. editor: Toward a Law of Global Communications Networks, 1986. Bd. dirs. Am. Nat. Standards Inst. Mem. ABA (chmn. sci. and tech. sect. 1989-90), Computer Law Assn. (pres. 1990-91), Assn. for Computing Machinery. Methodist. Avocations: alpine skiing, gardening. Office: Computer & Bus Equip Mfrs Assn 1250 I St Ste 200 Washington DC 20005

SMOOT, WENDELL MCMEANS, JR., investment counselor; b. Salt Lake City, Jan. 15, 1921; s. Wendell M. and Rebecca (Clawson) S.; m. Barbara Davis, June 24, 1942; children: Wendell M. III, Margaret, David, John, Mary. B.A., U. Utah, 1942. Gen. ptnr. J.A. Hogle & Co., Salt Lake City, 1945-63, Goodbody & Co., N.Y.C., 1963-70; chmn. Smoot, Miller, Cheney & Co., Salt Lake City, 1971–. Pres. Great Salt Lake council Boy Scouts Am., 1968-70; chmn. Utah State Pioneer Meml. Theatre, 1978-79; pres. Mormon Tabernacle Choir. Served to capt. U.S. Army, 1942-45; ETO. Mem. Fin. Analysts Soc. Republican. Mem. Ch. of Jesus Christ of Latter Day Saints. Club: The Country. Lodge: Rotary.

SMOTHERS, DICK, actor, singer; b. Nov. 20, 1939; s. Thomas B. and Ruth Smothers; children: Susan, Dick, Steven, Sara, Remick. Student, San Jose State Coll. Night club appearances at Harrah's, Lake Tahoe, Riviera, Las Vegas; former co-star half hour situation comedy TV series Smothers Bros. Show, 1965-66; TV show Smothers Brothers Comedy Hour, 1967-69, 70; co-star weekly variety hour The Smothers Bros. Show, NBC-TV, 1975;

---

appeared on Broadway in I Love My Wife, 1978; appeared in TV movie Terror at Alcatraz, 1982; starred in Smothers Brothers Special, 1988.

SMOTHERS, TOM, actor, singer; b. Feb. 2, 1937; s. Thomas B. and Ruth Smothers; children: Tom, Bo; m. Marcy Carriker, Sept. 9, 1990. Student, San Jose State Coll. owner winery, Kenwood, Calif. Nightclub appearances at Harrah's, Lake Tahoe, Riviera, Las Vegas; co-star half hour TV situation comedy Smothers Brothers Show, 1965-66, Smothers Brothers Comedy Hour, CBS-TV, 1967-69; weekly variety hour the Smothers Brothers Show, NBC-TV, 1975; starred in films The Silver Bears; starred on Broadway in I Love My Wife, 1978-79; appeared in TV movie Terror at Alcatraz, 1982; starred in Smothers Brothers Special, 1988. Office: Knave Prodns 8489 W 3rd St Los Angeles CA 90048

SMOTHERS, WILLIAM EDGAR, JR., geophysical exploration company executive; b. Shawnee, Okla., July 9, 1928; s. William Edgar and Lena Rivers (Randolph) S.; m. Marilyn Myrtle Cales, Sept. 6, 1952; children: Bill, Susan. BS in accounting, Okla. State U., 1950. Staff acct. Amoco Prodn. Co., Tulsa, 1953-56; chief internal auditor Seismography Svc. Corp., Tulsa, 1956-63, mgr. tax and auditing, 1964-77, v.p., treas., 1978–. Vice chmn. Tulsa United Way Drive, 1976, chmn., 1977. Capt. U.S. Army, 1951-53. Mem. Am. Mgmt. Assn., Tax Execs. Inst., Nat. Assn. Accts., Systems Mgmt. Assn., Petroleum Club, Tulsa Country Club. Democrat. Presbyterian. Home: 9103 E 38th Pl Tulsa OK 74145-3437 Office: Seismograph Svc Corp PO Box 1590 Tulsa OK 74102

SMOTRICH, DAVID ISADORE, architect; b. Norwich, Conn., Oct. 6, 1933; s. Max Z. and Ida (Babinsky) S.; m. Bernice D. Strachman, Mar. 25, 1956; children—Ross Lawrence, Maura Faye, Hannah. AB, Harvard U., 1955, MArch, 1960. Mem. master planning team Town of Arad, State of Israel, 1961-62; assoc. Platt Assocs. (architects), N.Y.C., 1963-65; gen. partner Smotrich & Platt (architects), N.Y.C., 1965-74, Smotrich Platt & Buttrick, 1975-76, Smotrich & Platt, 1976-85, David Smotrich & Ptnrs., 1985–; Cons. to Jerusalem Master Plan Office, Israel Ministry of Housing, 1967. Mem. planning bd. Town of New Castle, N.Y., 1974-81; mem. exec. bd. Road Rev. League, Bedford, N.Y., 1966-70. Served with AUS, 1955-57. Recipient Bard award, 1969, 85; Archtl. Record award, 1971, 73, 74, 75, 78; Design award HUD, 1980. Mem. AIA (Nat. Honor award 1969, N.Y. State Honor awards 1984, 94, Cmty. Design awards 1991, 93, AIA Coll. of Fellows 1993), Assn. Engrs. and Archs. in Israel, Phi Beta Kappa, Harvard Club (N.Y.C.). Home: 7 Mayberry Close Chappaqua NY 10514-1113 Office: David Smotrich & Partners 227 E 45th St New York NY 10017-3306

SMOUSE, H(ERVEY) RUSSELL, lawyer; b. Oakland, Md., Aug. 13, 1932; s. Hervey Reed and Vernie (Rush) S.; m. Creta M. Staley, June 15, 1955; children: Kristin Anne, Randall Forsyth, Gregory Russell. AB, Princeton U., 1955; LLB, U. Md., 1958. Bar: Md. 1958, U.S. Tax Ct. 1979, U.S. Ct. Appeals (4th cir.) 1960, U.S. Supreme Ct. 1974. Atty., Atty. Gen.'s Honors Program, Dept. Justice, Washington, 1958-60, asst. U.S. atty. Dist. Md., 1960-62; assoc. Pierson and Pierson, Balt., 1962-64; atty. B.&O. R.R., Balt., 1964-66; mem. Pierson and Pierson, 1966-69; mem. Clapp, Somerville, Black & Honemann, Balt., 1969-74; Law Offices H. Russell Smouse, 1974-81; mem. Melnicove, Kaufman, Weiner & Smouse, P.A., Balt., 1981-89, Whiteford, Taylor & Preston, Balt., 1989-93, chair, litigation dept., 1989-93; head gen. litigation Law Offices Peter G. Angelos, 1993—; v.p. Legal Aid Bur. Balt. City, 1972-73; bd. dirs. Md. Legal Svcs. Corp., 1987—. Fellow Am. Coll. Trial Lawyers; mem. ABA, Md. State Bar Assn. (gov. 1981-83), Bar Assn. Balt. City (chmn. grievance com. 1969-70, chmn. judiciary com. and nominating com. 1980, mem. exec. com. 1969-70, 80, chmn. exec. com. lawyers' com. for ind. judiciary 1989—), Nat. Assn. R.R. Trial Counsel (exec. com., v.p. 1986-92). Republican. Presbyterian. Office: 210 W Pennsylvania Ave Ste 515 Baltimore MD 21204-5325

SMUCK, HAROLD VERNON, retired minister, religious organization administrator; b. Huntington, Ind., Oct. 12, 1920; s. Vaughn M. and Elsie J. (Whiteman) S.; m. Evelyn May Sutton, Aug. 27, 1944; children: Norman, Amelia, Vernon. BRE, Ind. Wesleyan U., 1943; BD, Christian Theol. Sem., 1946; MA, Earlham Coll., 1950. Ordained to ministry Friends United Meeting, 1940. Missionary, pastor, youth sec. Friends United Meeting, 1957-66; sec. World Ministries Commn. Friends United Meeting, Richmond, Ind., 1966-81, Ministry Team leader W. Richmond, 1982-86; clk. Friends World Com. (sect. of the Ams.), Phila., 1982-89, Friends United Meeting, 1993—. Author: I Do Not Climb This Mountain Alone, 1986, Friends in East Africa, 1987; contbr. articles to jours. in field. Home: PO Box 1661 Richmond IN 47375-1661

SMUCKER, BARBARA CLAASSEN, former librarian, writer; b. Newton, Kans., Sept. 1, 1915; dual citizen U.S. and Can.; d. Cornelius Walter and Addie (Lander) Claassen; m. Donovan Ebersole Smucker, Jan. 21, 1939; children: Timothy, Thomas, Rebecca. BS, Kans. State U., 1936; postgrad., Rosary Coll., 1963-65; LittD (hon.), U. Waterloo, 1986; DHL (hon.), Bluffton Coll., 1989. English tchr. Harper (Kans.) High Sch., 1937-38; reporter Evening Kansan Republican, Newton, 1939-41; tchr. Ferry Hall Sch., Lake Forest, Ill., 1960-63; children's librarian Kitchener (Ont.) Public Library, 1969-77; reference librarian, head librarian Renison Coll., U. Waterloo, Ont., 1977-82, sr. fellow Renison Coll., 1982—; writer Am. Educator Ency., Lake Bluff, Ill., 1960-63; convocation speaker U. Waterloo, Ont., 1986. Author: Henry's Red Sea, 1955, Cherokee Run, 1957, Wigwam in the City, Susan, 1970, Underground to Canada, 1977, Les Chemins Secrets de la Liberte, 1978, Runaway to Freedom, 1977, June Lilly, 1981, Folge dem Nordstern, 1979, Under Jorden Til Canada, 1977, Days of Terror, 1980, Amish Adventure, 1983, Huida al Canada, 1983, Nubes Negras, 1984, Dagen Van Angst, 1985, White Mist, 1985, Jacob's Little Giant, 1987 (selected as gift to Prince Harry by govt. Ont.), Incredible Jumbo, 1990 (I.O.D.E. award 1991), Race To Freedom, 1994; (oratorio, libretto) The Abiding Place, 1984, Garth and the Mermaid, 1992; (interpretation) Oxford Companion to Canadian Literature, 1985, Michelle Landsberg's Guide to Children's Books, 1986; illustrator (autobiography) Something About the Author, 1991. Recipient prizes Can. Council, 1980, Ruth Schwartz Found., 1980, Distng. Service award Kans. State U., 1980, Brotherhood award NCCJ, 1980; $2000 Vicki Metcalf prize for outstanding contbn. to Can. children's lit. Can. Authors Assn., 1988, Kitchener award, 1990. Mem. AAUW, Canadian Assn. Univ. Women, Canadian Soc. Children's Authors, Illustrators and Performers, Children's Reading Round Table, Chgo. Home: 20 Pinebrook Dr Bluffton OH 45817-1145

SMUCKLER, RALPH HERBERT, university dean, political science educator; b. Milw., Apr. 10, 1926; s. Robert H. and Celia (Berland) S.; m. Lillian Zemelburg, July 6, 1946; children: Gary, Sandra, Harold. BA, U. Wis., 1948, MA, 1949, PhD, 1952. Mem. faculty Mich. State U., East Lansing, 1951-93, prof. polit. sci., 1963-93, dean internat. studies and programs, 1968-90, asst. to pres., 1987-91, emeritus prof., dean, 1993—; chief advisor tech. assistance team in Saigon, Mich. State U., 1955-56, 58-59; v.p. Edn. and World Affairs, N.Y.C., 1963-64; rep. Ford Found., Pakistan, 1967-69; dir. U.S. Internat. Sci. and Tech. Coop. Planning Office, Washington, 1978-79; mem. rsch. adv. com. AID, 1972-82, chmn., 1973-82, dep. asst. adminstr., 1991-92. Author: (with Leroy Ferguson) Politics in the Press, 1953, (with George Belknap) Leadership and Participation in Urban Political Affairs, 1956, (with R. Berg) New Challenges New Opportunities: U.S. Cooperation for International Growth and Development in the 1990s, 1988; contbr. articles to profl. jours. Bd. dirs. Midwest Univs. Consortium Internat. Activities, 1965-67, 69-90; trustee Inst. Internat. Edn., 1974-91; mem. adv. com. Kellogg Found. Nat. Fellowship Program, 1980-84; mem. bd. sci. and tech. for internat. devel. Nat. Acad. Sci., 1982-88, chmn., 1984-88; v.p. Mich. UN Assn., 1972-76; State of Mich. UN Day, 1960. With Inf. AUS, 1944-46. Recipient Disting. Citizen award Steuben Jr. High Sch., Milw., 1965, John Gilbert Winant Humanitarian award Marine City, Mich., 1976; Phi Beta Delta internat. scholar, Outstanding Faculty award, 1990. Mem. Am. Polit. Sci. Assn., Soc. Internat. Devel., Internat. Studies Assn., Assn. Internat. Edn. Adminstrs. (pres. 1986-87), Nat. Assn. State Univs. and Land-Grant Colls. (chmn. internat. acad. affairs com. 1986-90), Nat. Assn. Fgn. Student Affairs (governing bd. 1986, M. Houlihan award 1990), Mich. State Univ. Club, Phi Kappa Phi (named Disting. Mem. 1990). Jewish. Home: 4201 Cathedral Ave NW Apt 814W Washington DC 20016-4965

SMUIN, MICHAEL, choreographer, director, dancer; b. Missoula, Mont., Oct. 13, 1938; m. Paula Tracy; 1 child, Shane. Studied with Christensen Bros.; studied, San Francisco Ballet Sch.; DFA, U. Mont., 1984. Dancer U. Utah Ballet, Salt Lake City, 1955-57; dancer, choreographer, dir. San Francisco Ballet, 1957-62, 73-85; dancer Am. Ballet Theatre, N.Y. State Theatre, N.Y.C., 1967; prin. dancer, choreographer Am. Ballet Theatre, 1969-73; resident choreographer Am. Ballet Theatre, N.Y.C., 1992—; founder, dir. Smuin Ballets/SF, 1994—; worked as free-lance dancer with wife Paula Tracy, ind. choreographer; co-chmn. dance adv. panel Nat. Endowment for the Arts, Washington; mem. U.S. dance study team, People's Republic of China, 1983. Dir., musical stager, choreographer: (with Donald McKayle) Sophisticated Ladies, 1981 (Tony award nomination best direction of musical 1981, Outer Critics Circle award 1981); dir., choreographer: Chaplin, 1983, Shogun, 1990; choreographer: Anything Goes, 1987 (Tony award best choreography 1988, Drama Desk award best choreography 1988), Pulcinella Variations, Private Lives, 1991; staged dance works for Leslie Caron, Mikhail Baryshnikov, Rudolf Nureyev with Am. Ballet Theatre/Paris Opera Ballet, 1986; prodr. for San Francisco Ballet: Cinderella, Romeo and Juliet, The Tempest, A Song for Dead Warriors; dir.: Faustus in Hell, Peter and the Wolf; choreographer: (films) Rumble Fish, 1983, The Cotton Club, 1984, Fletch Lives, 1989, Bram Stoker's Dracula, 1992, So I Married an Axe Murderer, 1993, Angie, 1994, The Fantasticks, 1995; tech. adviser: (film) The Golden Child, 1986; choreographer: (TV) The Tempest, 1981 (Emmy award nomination outstanding achievement in choreography, 1981), A Song for Dead Warriors, 1984 (Emmy award outstanding achievement in choreography 1984), Cinderella, 1985, Romeo and Juliet; dir.: (TV spls.) Jinx, 1985, Voice/Dance: Bobby McFerrin and the Tandy Beal Dance Company, 1987; choreographer: (TV episode) Corridos! Tales of Passion and Revolution, 1987; creator: (TV show) The Omo, 1987; dir., choreographer: (TV spl.) Linda Ronstadt's Canciones de Mi Padre, 1989, Aid and Comfort. Recipient Dance Magazine award, 1983. Office: Smuin Ballets/SF 1314 34th Ave San Francisco CA 94122*

SMULDERS, ANTHONY PETER, biology educator; b. Oss, North Brabant, The Netherlands, July 6, 1942; came to U.S., 1963; s. Arnoldus A.P. and Maria A.A. (Horsten) S. T.C. in Edn. and Psychology, St. Stanislaus T.T.C., Tilburg, The Netherlands, 1962; BS in Biology summa cum laude, Loyola U., Los Angeles, 1966; PhD in Physiology with distinction, UCLA, 1970. Joined Bros. of Our Lady Mother of Mercy, Roman Cath. Ch., 1959. Tchr. Loon op Zand (The Netherlands) elem. schs., 1962-63, Santa Clara High Sch., Oxnard, Calif., 1965-67; research physiologist UCLA, 1970—; prof. biology Loyola Marymount U., Los Angeles, 1970—, assoc. dean sci., 1972-94, dir. health professions info. program, 1995—; mem. L.A. County Narcotics and Dangerous Drugs Commn., 1973—, Calif. State Adv. Bd. on Drug Programs, 1982-92. Contbr. articles to profl. jours. Mem. AAUP, AAAS, The Biophys. Soc., Nat. Assn. Advisors for Health Professions (pres. 1978-84), Western Assn. Advisors for Health Professions, Sigma Xi, Sigma Pi Sigma. Democrat. Lodge: KC. Avocations: stamps, photography, travel, refereeing soccer. Office: Loyola Marymount U 7101 W 80th St Los Angeles CA 90045-2699

SMULL, SCOTT, electronics executive. CFO Comstream Corp., San Diego. Office: Comstream Corp 10180 Barnes Canyon Rd San Diego CA 92121*

SMULLEN, JAMES DENNIS, lawyer; b. Palestine, Tex., Dec. 12, 1916; s. James Dennis and Augusta May (Stafford) S.; m. Margaret Eleanor Scrivner, Aug. 7, 1948 (dec. Jan. 1977); 1 child, James Dennis; m. Claire Nell Mattox, Feb. 18, 1979. J.D., U. Tex., 1939. Bar: Tex. 1937, U.S. Ct. Appeals (5th cir.) 1942, U.S. Supreme Ct. 1943, U.S. Dist. Ct. Hawaii 1944, U.S. Dist. Ct. (we. and ea. dists.) Tex. 1942, U.S. Dist. Ct. (so. dist.) Tex. 1955. Asst. atty. gen. State of Tex., Austin, 1939-43, 45-48; spl. asst. and counsel U.S. Navy, Honolulu, 1943-45; ptnr. Butler & Binion, Houston, 1948-87; ret., 1987; Mem. ICC, 1953—. Mem. ABA, State Bar Tex., Travis County Bar Assn., Hays County Bar Assn., Houston Bar Assn., Houston Club, Masons, Shriners. Episcopalian. Home: PO Box 2206 Wimberley TX 78676-7106 Office: Butler & Binion 1600 First Interstate Plz Houston TX 77002

SMULYAN, JEFFREY, radio station executive, owner pro baseball team; children: Cari, Bradley. AB in History and Telecommunications, U. So. Calif., 1969, JD, 1972. Prin., owner, chmn. Seattle Mariners; chmn. bd. Emmis Broadcasting Corp., Indpls. Recipient Tree of Life award Jewish Nat. Fund; named Entrepreneur of Yr. Indpls. Bus. Jour., 1986. Mem. ABA, Ind. Bar Assn., Fed. Bar Assn., Communications Bar Assn. Office: Seattle Mariners PO Box 4100 Seattle WA 98104-0100 also: Emmis Broadcasting Corp. 200 S Capitol Ave Indianapolis IN 46225-1059

SMULYAN, LISA, educator; b. Syracuse, N.Y., Dec. 5, 1954; d. Harold and Ruth (Finkelstein) S.; m. Michael Steven Langton Markowicz, June 13, 1982; children: Benjamin Markowicz Smulyan , Amanda Smulyan Markowicz. BA, Swarthmore (Pa.) Coll., 1976; MAT, Brown U., 1977; EdD, Harvard U., 1984. Tchr. Brookline (Mass.) Pub. Schs., 1977-80, 84; lectr. U. N.H., Durham, 1983; adj. faculty Lesley Coll., Cambridge, Mass., 1983; lectr. Lincoln-Sudbury (Mass.) Pub. Schs., 1984-85; asst. prof. Program in Edn., Swarthmore Coll., 1985-90, acting dir., 1988—, assoc. prof., 1990—; cons. HM Study Skills Program, Cambridge, 1982-89; dir. Adventures in Math and Sci., Swarthmore, 1986-88. Co-author: Adolescent Portraits, 1992, Collaborative Action Research, 1989; editor HM Study Skills Program, 1982-83; contbr. articles to profl. jours. Bd. dirs. ABC Swarthmore, 1988-91. Recipient Fulbright fellowship U. Warwick, Eng., 1989, Joel Dean grant Swarthmore Coll., 1987, 89, Faculty Rsch. grant, 1986—, Brown U. fellowship, 1976. Mem. AAUW, Am. Ednl. Rsch. Assn., Consortium for Excellence in Tchr. Edn., Educators for Social Responsibility, Phi Delta Kappa, Phi Beta Kappa.

SMURFIT, MICHAEL WILLIAM JOSEPH, manufacturing company executive; b. 1936. With Jefferson Smurfit Group PLC, Dublin, Ireland, 1961—, pres., from 1966, now chmn., chief exec. officer; pres. Jefferson Smurfit Corp., Alton, Ill., 1979-82, now chief exec. officer, chmn. bd., 1982—. Office: Jefferson Smurfit Corp 8182 Maryland Ave Saint Louis MO 63105-3786*

SMUTNY, JOAN FRANKLIN, academic director, educator; b. Chgo.; d. Eugene and Mabel (Lind) Franklin; m. Herbert Paul Smutny; 1 child, Cheryl Anne. BS, Northwestern U., MA. Tchr., New Trier High Sch., Winnetka, Ill.; mem. faculty, founder, dir. Nat. High Sch. Inst., Northwestern U. Sch. Edn., Chgo.; mem. faculty, founder dir. high sch. workshop in critical thinking and edn., chmn. dept. communications Nat. Coll. Edn., Evanston, Ill., exec. dir. high sch. workshops, 1970-75, founder, dir. Woman Power Through Edn. Seminar, 1976-94, dir. Right to Read seminar in critical reading, 1973-74, seminar gifted high sch. students, 1973, dir. of Gifted Programs for 6, 7 and 8th graders pub. schs., Evanston, 1978-79, 1st-8th graders, Glenview (both Ill.) 1979—; dir. gifted programs Nat.-Louis U., Evanston, 1980-82, dir. Center for Gifted, 1982—; dir. Bright and Talented and Project 1986—, North Shore Country Day Sch., Winnetka, 1982—; dir. Job Creation Project, 1980-82; dir. New Dimensions for Women, 1973, dir. Thinking for Action in Career Edn. project, 1974-77, dir. Individualized Career Edn. Program, 1976-79, dir. TACE, dir. Humanities Program for Verbally Precocious Youth, 1978-79; co-dir., instr. seminars in critical thinking Ill. Family Svc., 1972-75. Writer ednl. filmstrips in Lang. arts and Lit. Soc. for Visual Edn., 1970-74; mem. speakers bur. Counc. Fgn. Rels., 1968-69 ; mem. adv. com. edn. professions devel. act U.S. Office Edn., 1969—; mem. state team for gifted, Ill. Office Edn., Office of Gifted, Springfield, Ill., 1977; writer, cons. Radiant Ednl. Corp., 1969-71 ; cons. ALA, 1969-71 , cons., workshop leader and speaker in area of gifted edn., 1971—; coord. of career edn. Nat. Coll. Edn., 1976-78, dir. Project 1987—, dir. Summer Wonders, 1986—, Creative Children's Acad., bd. dirs., Worlds of Wisdom and Wonder, 1978—; dir. Future Tchrs. Am. Seminar in Coll. and Career, 1970-72; cons. for research and devel. Ill. Dept. Vocat. Edn., 1973—; cons. in career edn. U.S. Office Edn., 1976—; evaluation cons. DAVTE, IOE, Springfield, Ill., 1977, mem. Leadership Tng. Inst. for Gifted, U.S. Office Edn., 1973-74; dir. workshops for high sch. students; cons., speaker in field; dir. Gifted Young Writer's and Young Writer's confs., 1978, 79; dir. Project '92 The White House Conf. on Children and Youth; mem. adv. bd. Educating Able Learners, 1991—; chmn. bd. dirs. Barbereux Sch., Evanston, 1992—; asst. editor and mem. adv. coun. Understanding Our

Gifted, 1994—. Mem. AAUP, Nat. Assn. for Gifted Child (nat. membership chmn. 1991—, co-chmn. schs. and programs, co-editor newsletter early childhood divsn.), Nat. Soc. Arts and Letters (nat. bd., 1st and 3d v.p. Evanston chpt., dir. 1983-92, pres. Evanston chpt. 1990-92), Mortar Bd., Outstanding Educators of Am. 1974, Pi Lambda Theta, Phi Delta Kappa (v.p. Evanston chpt., rsch. chmn. 1990-92). Author: (with others) Job Creation: Creative Materials, Activities and Strategies for the classroom, 1982, A Thoughtful Overview of Gifted Education, 1990, Your Gifted Child - How to Recognize and Develop the Special Talents in Your Child from Birth to Age Seven, 1989, paperback, 1991, Education of the Gifted: Programs and Perspectives, 1990; editor, contbr. Maturity in Teaching; writer ednl. filmstrips The Brother's Grimm, How the West Was Won, Mutiny on the Bounty, Dr. Zhivago, Space Odessey 2001, Christmas Around the World; editor Jour. for Gifted, Ill., 1984—, Ill. Coun. Gifted Jour., 1985-93; contbg. editor Roeper Review, 1994—; editor IAGC Jour. for Gifted, 1994—, Potential and Promise: A Collection of Readings on the Gifted Young Child, 1995; contbg. editor numerous books in field; contbr. articles to profl. jours. including Chgo. Parent Mag. Reviewer of Programs for Gifted and Talented, U.S. Office of Edn., 1976-78. Home: 633 Forest Ave Wilmette IL 60091-1713

SMYNTEK, JOHN EUGENE, JR., newspaper editor; b. Buffalo, Aug. 24, 1950; s. John Eugene Sr. and Leona (Kluczynski) S.; m. Barbara Murphy, 1972 (div. Mar. 1982); m. Rebecca Anne Van Dine, 1982 (div. July 1988). BA, U. Detroit, 1972. Asst. instr. Mich. State U., East Lansing, 1981; features editor Free Press, 1985-92; dir. online svcs. and dir. libr. Free Press Plus, Detroit, 1992—; vis. fellow in journalism Duke U., 1988; profl. student publs. advisor U. Detroit Mercy, 1992-94. Recipient Fine Arts Reporting award Detroit Press Club, 1985. Roman Catholic. Office: Detroit Free Press 321 W Lafayette Blvd Detroit MI 48226

SMYSER, ADAM ALBERT, newspaper editor; b. York, Pa., Dec. 18, 1920; s. Adam Milton and Miriam (Stein) S.; m. Elizabeth Harrison Avery, Dec. 25, 1943 (dec. 1983); children: Heidi, Avery; m. Doris H. Prather, Apr. 24, 1984. B.A., Pa. State U., 1941. Rewrite man Pitts. Press, 1941-42; with Honolulu Star-Bull., 1946—, city editor, 1953-60, mng. editor, 1960-65, editor, 1966-75, editor editorial page, 1975-83, contbg. editor, 1983—; mem. Pulitzer Journalism Awards Jury, 1970. Author: Hawaii's Future in the Pacific: Disaster, Backwater or Future State?, 1988, Hawaii as an East-West Bridge, 1990; past freelance writer McGraw-Hill mags. Chmn. temp. commn. on statewide environ. planning, 1973; bd. dirs. Corp. for Community TV; chmn. steering com. Gov.'s Congress on Hawaii's Internat. Role, 1988; mem. community adv. bd. Tokai U. Pacific Ctr.; Lt. USNR, 1942-46, PTO. Recipient Disting. Alumnus award Pa. State U., 1976, Hawaii's Outstanding Journalist award, 1989, Award for Disting. Contbn. to Hawaii Journalism Honolulu Cmty.-Medic Coun., 1994, award for promotion of U.S.-Asia/Pacific rels. Pacific and Asian Affairs Coun., 1994. Mem. Hawaii Econ. Assn., Honolulu Social Sci. Assn., Honolulu Acad. Arts, Am. Soc. Newspaper Editors, Japan-Am. Soc. Hawaii, Honolulu Cmty.-Media Coun., Honolulu Press Club (named to Hall of Fame 1987), Honolulu Rotary. Home: 1052 Iiwi St Honolulu HI 96816-5111 Office: Honolulu Star-Bull 605 Kapiolani Blvd Honolulu HI 96813-5129

SMYTH, ANNE, elementary school educator; b. Oceanside, N.Y., Sept. 28, 1943; d. David Anthony and Filomena Mary (Pascale) Caruso; m. Denis Charles Smyth, Apr. 6, 1968; children: Michael David, Carolyn Anne. BS in Edn. and Social Studies, Cabrini Coll., 1965; MS in Spl. Edn., Adelphi U., 1980. Cert. tchr., (life), N.Y. Tchr. Belmnot Elem. Sch., North Babylon, N.Y., 1965-68, Forrest Sherman Elem. Sch., Naples, Italy, 1968-71, Centre Ave. Elem. Sch., E. Rockaway, N.Y., 1971—; supr. Great Books Club, E. Rockaway, 1988—; mem. Ctr. Ave Teacher Adv. Com., E. Rockaway, 1988—. Pub. rels. agt. (vol.) Boy Scouts Am., Troop 163, Rockville Ctr., N.Y., 1988—. Mem. Am. Fedn. Tchrs. Roman Catholic. Avocations: reading, skiing, aerobic dancing, hiking, family activities. Home: 92 Muirfield Rd Rockville Centre NY 11570

SMYTH, BERNARD JOHN, retired newspaper editor; b. Renovo, Pa., Nov. 16, 1915; s. John Bernard and Alice C. (Russell) S.; m. Eva Mae Stone, Dec. 31, 1936; children: Constance, Joe, Pamela, Lisa. Grad., Dickinson Jr. Coll., 1935. Machinist helper Pa. R.R. Renovo Shops, 1936-39; mgr. Smyth Bros., Renovo, 1939-45; editor, pub., owner Renovo Daily Record, 1946-53; owner, editor, pub. Del. State News, Dover, 1953-70; chmn. bd. Independent Newspapers Inc., 1970-85; pres. Valley News League, Tempe, Ariz., 1971-85. Served with AUS, 1944-45. Mem. Soc. Profl. Journalists, Ariz. Newspaper Assn., Sigma Delta Chi. Home: 4200 N Miller Rd Apt 422 Scottsdale AZ 85251-3631

SMYTH, CRAIG HUGH, fine arts educator; b. N.Y.C., July 28, 1915; s. George Hugh and Lucy Salome (Humeston) S.; m. Barbara Linforth, June 24, 1941; children: Alexandra, Edward Linforth (Ned). BA, Princeton U., 1938, MFA, 1941, PhD, 1956; MA (hon.), Harvard U., 1975. Rsch. asst. Nat. Gallery Art, Washington, 1941-42; officer-in-charge, dir. Cen. Art Collecting Point, Munich, 1945-46; lectr. Frick Collection, N.Y.C., 1946-50; asst. prof. Inst. Fine Arts NYU, 1950-53, assoc. prof. Inst. Fine Arts, 1953-57, prof. Inst. Fine Arts, 1957-73, acting dir. Inst. Fine Arts, acting head dept. fine arts Grad. Sch. Arts and Scis., 1951-53, dir. inst., head dept. fine arts Grad. Sch., 1953-73; prof. fine arts Harvard U., 1973-85, prof. emeritus, 1985—; Samuel Kress prof. Ctr. for Advanced Study in Visual Arts Nat. Gallery Art, Washington, 1987-88; dir. Villa I Tatti Harvard U. Ctr. Italian Renaissance Studies, Florence, 1973-85; art historian in residence Am. Acad. in Rome, 1959-60; mem. U.S. Nat. Com. History Art, 1955-85; alt. U.S. mem. Comité Internat. d'Histoire de l'Art, 1970-83, U.S. mem., 1983-85; consultative chmn. adv. com. J. Paul Getty Ctr. History of Art and Humanities, 1982—; mem. architect selection com. J. Paul Getty Trust, 1983-84; mem. organizing com., keynote speaker 400th Anniversary of Uffizi Gallery, 1981-82; vis. scholar Inst. Advanced Study, Princeton, N.J., 1971, mem., 1978, visitor, 1983, 85-86; vis. scholar Bibliotheca Hertziana, Max Planck Soc., Rome, 1972, 73; mem. vis. com. dept. art and archaeology Princeton U., 1956-73, 85-89; mem. adv. com. Villa I Tatti, 1985—; trustee Hyde Collection, Glens Falls, N.Y., 1985-87, The Burlington mag., 1987—; mem. commn. Ednl. & Cultural Exch. between Italy and U.S., 1979-83. Author: Mannerism and Maniera, 1963, rev. edit. with introduction by E. Cropper, 1992, Bronzino as Draughtsman, 1971, Michelangelo Architetto (with H.M. Millon), 1988, English edit., 1988, Repatriation of Art for the Collecting Point in Munich After World War II, 1988; editor: Michelangelo Drawings (Nat. Gallery of Art), 1992; editor, contbr. (with Peter M. Lukehart) The Early Years of Art History in The United States, 1994; contbr. (with H.M. Millon) articles on Michelangelo and St. Peter's to profl. jours. Hon. trustee Met. Mus. Art, N.Y.C., 1968—; trustee Inst. Fine Arts, NYU, 1973—; mem. mayor's com. Piazza Della Signoria, Florence, 1975-78. Lt. USNR, 1942-46. Decorated Chevalier Legion of Honor France, U.S. Army Commendation medal; sr. Fulbright Rsch. fellow, 1949-50. Mem. Am. Acad. Arts and Scis., Am. Philos. Soc., Coll. Art Assn. Am. (bd. dirs. 1953-57, sec. 1956), Accademia Fiorentina delle Arti del Disegno (academician, assoc.), Harvard Club, Club N.Y.C., Century Assn. (N.Y.C.). Address: PO Box 39 Cresskill NJ 07626-0039

SMYTH, DAVID JOHN, economist; b. Twickenham, Eng., Apr. 19, 1936; came to U.S., 1967; s. John Richard and Ena Caryle (Stuart) S.; m. Jane Mair, July 19, 1969; children: Seamus John, Alexander David. B.Econs., U. Queensland, Australia, 1957, M.Econs., 1960; Ph.D., U. Birmingham, Eng., 1968. Lectr. econs. U. Queensland, 1957-60; univ. research scholar London Sch. Econs., 1960-63; lectr. econs., then sr. lectr. math. econs. U. Birmingham, 1963-67; prof. SUNY, Buffalo, 1967-70; prof. econs. Claremont (Calif.) Grad. Sch., 1971-76, chmn. dept., 1973-76; prof. econs. Wayne State U., Detroit, 1976-86, chmn. dept., 1976-85; LSU Found. Disting. prof. econs. La. State U., Baton Rouge, 1987—; mem. internat. adv. bd. Jour. Econ. Surveys, 1989—; mem. adv. bd. N.Am. Econ. and Fin. Assn., 1989—; mem. interdisciplinary adv. bd. Policy Studies Orgn., 1991—; visitor Ctr. for Econ. Rsch., Tilburg U., The Netherlands, 1993. Author: The Demand for Farm Machinery, 1970, Forecasting the United Kingdom Economy, 1973, Size, Growth, Profits and Executive Compensation in the Large Corporation, 1975; editor: Jour. Macroeconomics, 1977—; contbr. articles to profl. jours. Recipient award Bd. Govs. Wayne State U., 1980; Erskine fellow U. Canterbury, New Zealand, summer 1990. Mem. Am. Econ. Assn., Econometric Soc., Royal Econ. Soc., So. Econ. Assn., Am. Fin. Assn., Western Econ. Assn., Am. Agrl. Econ. Assn., AAUP (chpt. pres. 1975-76),

Acad. of Scholars of Wayne State U. Home: 12812 Woodshire Pl Baton Rouge LA 70816-2547 Office: La State U Dept Econs 2107 CEBA Baton Rouge LA 70803

SMYTH, DONALD MORGAN, chemical educator, researcher; b. Bangor, Maine, Mar. 20, 1930; s. John Robert and Selma (Eubanks) S.; m. Elisabeth Luce, Aug. 1, 1951; children: Carolyn, Joanne. BS in Chemistry, U. Maine, 1951; PhD in Inorganic Chemistry, MIT, 1954. Sr. chemist Sprague Electric Co., North Adams, Mass., 1954-58, sect. head, 1958-61, dept. head, 1961-71; assoc. prof. Lehigh U., Bethlehem, Pa., 1971-73, prof., 1973—, dir. Materials Rsch. Ctr., 1971-92, Paul B. Reinhold prof. materials sci., engring. and chemistry, 1988—; mem. various coms. Lehigh U., 1971—; mem. materials rsch. adv. com. NSF, 1984-88, chmn., 1985-86, co-chair ad-hoc com. to brief dir. 1986; mem. coun. materials sci. Dept. Energy, 1986-90; presenter in field. Contbr. articles to profl. jours. Recipient Libsch Rsch. award Lehigh U., 1990, Buessem award Dielectrics Rsch. Ctr., Pa. State U., 1991; grantee in field. Fellow Am. Inst. Chemists, Am. Ceramic Soc. (mem. com. edn. electronics divsn. 1974-78, chmn. Lehigh Valley sect. 1978-79, counselor 1982—, assoc. editor jour. 1988-92, Best Paper award 1987, Kraner award Lehigh Valley sect. 1990); mem. Am. Chem. Soc., Materials Rsch. Soc., Electrochem. Soc. (mem. various coms., sec. dielectrics and insulation divsn. 1967-69, vice chmn. 1969-70, chmn. 1970-71, Rsch. award Battery div. 1960). Achievements include patents (with others) for Solid-State Battery Cell with Complex Organic Electrolyte Material, Capacitor with Dielectric Film Having Phosphorous-Containing Component Therein, Solid Barrier Electrolyte Incorporating Additive, others; research in defect chemistry and electrical properties of complex oxides. Home: 3429 Mountainview Cir Bethlehem PA 18017-1807 Office: Lehigh U Materials Rsch Ctr 5 E Packer Ave Bethlehem PA 18015-3102

SMYTH, GEORGE, electronics company executive, researcher. With Northern Telecom Ltd., Can.; now pres. BNR Inc., Research Triangle Park, N.C., 1987—. Office: BNR Inc 35 Davis Rd Research Triangle Park NC 27709*

SMYTH, GLEN MILLER, management consultant; b. Abingdon, Va., July 26, 1929; s. Glen Miller and Kathleen (Dunn) S.; m. Cynthia Olson, Aug. 25, 1954 (div. 1967); children: Catherine Ellen, Glen Miller, III, Cynthia Allison; m. Lilian Castel Edgar, Oct. 31, 1968; children: Stephanie Castel, Kimberley Forsyth, Lindsay Dunn. BA, Yale U., 1951; MS in Psychology, Rutgers U., 1958. Mktg. rep. Wheeling Stamping Co., N.Y.C., 1953-56; personnel dir. Celanese Internat., N.Y.C., 1958-71; mgr. orgn. and Manpower Internat. and Can. group Gen. Electric Co., N.Y.C., 1971-73; sr. v.p. human resources Northwest Bancorp., Mpls., 1973-82; sr. v.p. Calif. Fed. Savs., L.A., 1983-85; v.p. Career Transition Group, L.A., 1985-87; pres. Fuchs, Cuthrell & Co., Inc., L.A., 1987-93, Fuchs & Co., L.A., 1993-94; pres., CEO Smyth, Fuchs & Co., Inc., L.A., 1995—; leader seminars. Co-author: International Career Pathing, 1971; Contbr. articles to profl. jours. Served with AUS, 1951-53. Mem. Am. Psychol. Assn., Nat. Fgn. Trade Coun. (founder, past chmn. human resources, orgn. com. 1966—), Human Resources Planning Soc., Employment Mgmt. Assn., Jonathan Club, Yale Club of N.Y., North Ranch Country Club, Phi Gamma Delta. Home: 1860 Mesa Ridge Ave Thousand Oaks CA 91362-5251

SMYTH, JOEL DOUGLAS, newspaper executive; b. Renovo, Pa., Nov. 8, 1941; s. Bernard Dinan and Eva Mae (Stone) S.; m. Madonna Robertson, Nov. 29, 1959; children: Deborah Sue, Susan Kelly, Michael Robertson, Patricia Ann, Rebecca Lee, Jennifer Neilia. Student, Lycoming Coll., 1959. Reporter Del. State News, Dover, 1960-62, news editor, 1962-65, mng. editor, 1965-70, editor, pres., 1970-78; editor Del. Sunday News, 1964-65; pres. Ind. Newspapers, Inc., Dover, 1970-89, chmn., CEO, 1989—. Founding pres. Valley Citizen's League, 1987-90. Recipient writing awards. Mem. AP Mng. Editors Assn. (dir.), Am. Soc. Newspaper Editors, Young Pres.'s Orgn., Sigma Delta Chi. Winter home: 33811 N 70th Way Scottsdale AZ 85262 Summer home: 260 Forest Highlands Flagstaff AZ 86001-8422

SMYTH, JOHN MCDONNELL, III, merchant, lawyer; b. Chgo., Apr. 1, 1915; s. John McDonnell II and Ethel (Walsh) S.; m. Judith Fox, Jan. 14, 1941; children: India Smith, Jack, Malinda Wagner, Andrew. AB, Princeton U., 1937; JD, Northwestern U., 1940. Bar: Ill. Atty. Eugene P. Kealy law firm, Chgo., 1940-42; officer John M. Smyth Co., Chgo., 1945—. Lt. USN, 1942-45, ETO, PTO. Republican. Roman Catholic. Avocations: astronomy, golf, gardening.

SMYTH, JOSEPH PATRICK, retired naval officer, physician; b. Norwalk, Conn., Mar. 2, 1933; s. Patrick and Helen (Heffernan) S.; m. Ursula Marie (Kirwin) Dec. 28, 1960; children: Donna, Jennifer, Joseph. BA, Fairfield U., 1960; MD, Creighton U., 1964. Diplomate Am. Bd. Med. Examiners. Commd. ensign USN, 1963, advanced through grades to rear adm., 1988; intern Phila. Naval Hosp., 1964-65, internal medicine resident, 1965-68, staff physician, 1968-69; internist, chief of medicine U.S. Naval Hosp., DaNang, Vietnam, 1969-70, Guantanamo Bay, Cuba, FL, 1970-76; chief of medicine, exec. officer U.S. Naval Hosp., Yokosuka, Japan, 1976-80; exec. officer U.S. Naval Hosp., Oakland, Calif., 1980-82, comdg. officer, 1984-86; comdg. officer U.S. Naval Hosp., Okinawa, Japan, 1982-84, Naval Med. Command European Region, London, 1986-90; dep. dir. for med. readiness The Joint Staff, Pentagon, Washington, 1990-92; retired US Navy, 1992; med. dir. Volusia County (Fla.) Dept. of Corrections, 1994—; instr. medicine Jefferson Med. Coll., 1966-69; preceptor USN Physician Asst. Program, Orlando, 1971-76; inst. mgmt. course Navy Med. Dept., Washington, 1986; Joint Staff coord. for entire mil. med. build-up for Operation Desert Shield/Storm, Saudi Arabia, 1990-91. Physician Orange County, Fla. Alcohol Ctr., Orlando, 1974-76. Decorated Def. Superior Svc. medal, Legion of Merit, Meritorious Svc. medals with 2 oak leaf clusters, Navy Commendation medal. Mem. AMA, Assn. Mil. Surgeons of U.S., Am. Acad. Med. Administrs. (Levandowski award 1991), Fla. Med. Assn., Am. Acad. Physician Execs., Orange County Med. Soc. Republican. Roman Catholic. Home: 400 Sweetwater Blvd S Longwood FL 32779

SMYTH, JOSEPH PHILIP, travel industry executive; b. N.Y.C., Aug. 16, 1939; s. Joseph P. and Virginia S. (Gibbs) S.; m. Janet Hughes; 1 child, Philip. BA, Hamilton U., 1961; MBA, Harvard U., 1967; student, Naval Intelligence Sch., 1961-62. Dir. planning N.E. Airlines, Boston, 1967-70; acct. supr. Wells, Rich, Greene, N.Y.C., 1970-72; sr. v.p. mktg. Inter-Continental, N.Y.C., 1972-86, Hilton Hotels, Beverly Hills, Calif., 1986-88; head of ops. Cunard, N.Y.C., 1988-94; sr. v.p. fleet ops. Holland Am., Seattle, 1994; chmn Gibbs Bros., Huntsville, Tx., 1995—. Lt. USN, 1961-65, ETO. Mem. Internat. Coun. Cruise Lines, Univ. Club, Harvard Club. Avocation: running. Home: 1088 Park Ave New York NY 10128 Office: Gibbs Bros Box 711 Huntsville TX 77342

SMYTH, JOSEPH VINCENT, manufacturing company executive; b. Belfast, Ireland, July 18, 1919; s. Joseph Leo and Margaret M. (Murray) S.; m. Marie E. Cripe, Mar. 22, 1941; children: Kevin W., Brian J., Ellen M., Vincent P. B.S. cum laude, U. Notre Dame, 1941. With Arnolt Corp., Warsaw, Ind., 1946-63; exec. v.p., gen. mgr. Arnolt Corp., until 1963; pres., gen. mgr. Hills-McCanna Co., Carpentersville, Ill., 1963-72; pres. Lunkenheimer Co., Cin., 1972-79; v.p. Condec Flow Control Group, Chgo., 1979-82; cons., 1982—. Club: Pinecrest Golf and Country (N.C.). Lodge: K.C. Home: 740 Saint Andrews Ln Apt 34 Crystal Lake IL 60014-7043

SMYTH, PAUL BURTON, lawyer; b. Phila., Aug. 15, 1949; s. Benjamin Burton and Florence Elizabeth (Tomlinson) S.; m. Denise Elaine Freeland, May 31, 1975. BA, Trinity Coll, Hartford, Conn., 1971; JD, Boston Coll. 1974. Bar: Conn. 1974, D.C. 1975, U.S. Dist. Ct. D.C., 1980, U.S. Supreme Ct., 1985. With Dept. Interior, 1974—, atty. Office of Hearings and Appeals, Arlington, Va., 1974-76, atty. Office of Solicitor, Washington, 1976-82, asst. solicitor for land use and realty, Washington, 1982-87; deputy assoc. solicitor for energy and resources, Washington, 1987-93, acting dir. Office of Hearings and Appeals, Arlington, 1993-94, dep. assoc. solicitor for energy and resources, 1994—. Contbr. articles to legal publs. Mem. ABA (coun. 1991-94, budget officer 1994—, sect. natural resources, energy and environ. law). Office: Office of Solicitor Dept Interior 18th and C Streets NW Washington DC 20240

SMYTH, PETER HAYES, radio executive; b. Apr. 25, 1952; s. Arthur and Irene (McNamara) S.; m. Catherine Comerford Smyth, Aug. 8, 1976; children: Nancy, Colin, Kathleen. BA, Holy Cross Coll., Worcester, Mass., 1975; postgrad., Fordham U., 1975-76. Retail sales man Sta. WROR Radio, Boston, 1975-76, gen. sales mgr., 1976-83; gen. sales mgr. Sta. WOR Radio, N.Y.C., 1983-86; v.p., gen. mgr. Sta. WMEX-AM/WMJX-FM/WBCS-FM, Boston, 1986—; cons. Greater Media Cable, North Oxford, Mass., 1988-89. Bd. dirs. Holy Cross Coll., Worcester, Univ. Club, Boston, United Way of Mass., 1993, 94. Mem. New England Broadcast Assn. (bd. dirs. 1987, v.p., pres. 1992—). Republican. Roman Catholic. Avocations: golfing, swimming, skiing. Office: WMEX-AM/WMJX-FM/WBCS-FM 330 Stuart St Boston MA 02116-5229

SMYTH, REGINALD (REGGIE SMYTHE), cartoonist; b. Hartlepool, Eng., Oct. 7, 1917; s. Richard Oliver and Florence (Ritson) S.; m. Vera Toyne, Aug. 13, 1949. Student, Galleys Field Sch., 1922-31. With Brit. Civil Service, 1945-54; cartoonist, 1955—. Creator: Andy Capp daily comic strip, 1956. Served with Brit. Army, 1936-45. Recipient Best Brit. Cartoon award, 1961-65; Premio Cartoon award Lucca, 1969; Best Cartoonist award Genoa, 1973; Best Strip Cartoonist award Am. Cartoonists Soc., 1974. Mem. Nat. Cartoonists Soc. Mem. Ch. of Eng. Address: Whitegates 96 Caledonian Rd, Hartlepool England

SMYTH, RICHARD HENRY, foreign service officer; b. Oakland, Calif., June 12, 1951; s. Ronald Henry and Alyce Miriam (Swensson) S.; m. Janice Eileen Sullivan, Mar. 10, 1979; children: Caitlin, Alison. BA, U. Wash., 1973; grad. cert., U. Ala., Tuscaloosa, 1977. Cmty. planner Tuscaloosa, 1975-78; 3d sec. U.S. Embassy, Kabul, Afghanistan, 1979-80; 2d sec. U.S. Embassy, New Delhi, India, 1980-81, Jakarta, Indonesia, 1985-87; 1st sec. U.S. Embassy, Copenhagen, 1987-90; 2d sec. Belgian Embassy, Baghdad, Iraq, 1981-84; with U.S. Dept. of State, Washington, 1990-92; consul gen. U.S. Consulate, Peshawar, Pakistan, 1992—. Vol. U.S. Peace Corps, Kabul, Afghanistan, 1973-75. Mem. Assn. Am. Geographers, Am. Fgn. Svc. Assn. Avocations: Oriental studies, angling. Home and Office: 11 Hosp Rd, Peshawar Cantt NWFP Pakistan Office: AMCOMS Pesh 8 APO AE 09812-2217

SMYTHE, SHEILA MARY, academic dean; b. N.Y.C., Nov. 1, 1932; d. Patrick John and Mary Catherine (Gonley) S. Student, Creighton U., 1952; BA, Manhattanville Coll., 1952; MS, Columbia U., N.Y.C., 1956; LHD (hon.), Manhattanville Coll., 1974. From rsch. assoc. to asst. dir. of rsch. and planning Blue Cross Assn., Chgo., 1957-63; exec. assoc. to pres. Empire Blue Cross & Blue Shield, N.Y.C., 1963-72, v.p., 1972-74, sr. v.p., 1974-78, exec. v.p., 1978-82, pres., chief oper. officer, 1982-85; health fin. and mgmt. cons. N.Y.C. and Washington, 1986-87; chief health policy advisor GAO, Washington, 1987—; dean grad. sch. health scis. N.Y. Med. Coll., N.Y.C., 1990—; adj. asst. prof. Grad. Sch. Pub. Health, Columbia U., 1980-86; bd. dirs. Mut. of Am., product & mktg. com. 1991-93, nominating com., 1992-94, audit com., 1993—, strategic planning com., 1994—; bd. dirs. Nat. Health Coun., Inc., mem. fin. com., 1987-94; bd. dirs. Hudson Valley Health Sys. Agy., sec., 1993-94, 1st v.p., 1994-95, pres., 1995—; active N.Y. State Hosp. and Rev. Planning Coun., 1994—. Chmn. of bd. Manhattanville Coll., Purchase, N.Y. 1994—, trustee affairs, acad. affairs, exec coms.; bd. dirs. Cath. Charities-U.S.A., 1989—, mem. exec. pers. coms.; bd. dirs. March of Dimes Birth Defects Found., 1989—, vice chair, mem. fin. com., chair pub affairs com., dir. Greater N.Y. March of Dimes, 1985-89. Recipient Elizabeth Cutter Morrow award YWCA, N.Y., 1977, Disting. Alumni award Manhattanville Coll., 1981, Excellence in Leadership award Greater N.Y. March of Dimes, 1989. Mem. Nat. Arts Club N.Y.C. Roman Catholic. Office: NY Med Coll Grad Sch Health Scis Valhalla NY 10595

SMYTHE, WILLIAM RODMAN, physicist, educator; b. Los Angeles, Jan. 6, 1930; s. William Ralph and Helen (Keith) S.; m. Carol Richardson, Nov. 27, 1954 (dec. Dec. 1987); children: Stephanie, Deborah, William Richardson, Reed Terry; m. Judith Brean Travers, Jan. 1, 1989. B.S., Calif. Inst. Tech., 1951, M.S., 1952, Ph.D., 1957. Engr. Gen. Electric Microwave Lab., Palo Alto, Calif., 1956-57; asst. prof. U. Colo., 1958-63, assoc. prof., 1963-67, prof., 1967—, chmn. nuclear physics lab., 1967-69, 81-83, 90-92. Group leader Rocky Mountain Rescue Group, 1967-68. Mem. Am. Phys. Soc. Club: Colorado Mountain (Boulder). Achievements include inventing negative ion cyclotron, fractional turn cyclotron. Home: 2106 Knollwood Dr Boulder CO 80302-4706

SMYTHE-HAITH, MABEL MURPHY, consultant on African economic development, speaker, writer; b. Montgomery, Ala., Apr. 3, 1918; m. Hugh H. Smythe, June 22, 1939 (dec. 1977); 1 child, Karen Pamela; m. Robert Haith, Jr., Oct. 18, 1985. Student, Spelman Coll., 1933-36, LLD (hon.) 1980; BA, Mt. Holyoke Coll., 1937, LHD (hon.), 1977; MA, Northwestern U., 1940; PhD, U. Wis., 1942, LLD (hon.), 1991; LHD (hon.), U. Mass., 1979. Asst. prof. Lincoln U., Mo., 1942-45; prof. Tenn. A. and I. U., 1945-46, Bklyn. Coll., 1946-47; vis. prof. Shiga U., Japan, 1951-53; dep. dir. rsch. for sch. segregation cases NAACP Legal Def. and Edn. Fund, 1953; tchr., prin. New Lincoln High Sch., N.Y.C., 1954-69; with Phelps-Stokes Fund, 1970-77, dir. research and publs., 1970-72, v.p., 1972-77; U.S. amb. to United Republic of Cameroon, Yaounde, 1977-80; U.S. amb. to Equatorial Guinea, 1979-80; dep. asst. sec. for African affairs Dept. State, 1980-81; Melville J. Herskovits prof. African studies Northwestern U., Evanston, Ill., 1981-83, disting. prof., 1983-85, prof. emeritus, 1985—; co-dir. internat. internship program, 1983-85; co-dir. African seminar Nat. Assn. Equal Opportunity in Higher Edn., 1985; mem. Adv. Com. on Ednl. Exchange U.S. Dept. State, 1961-62, Adv. Commn. on Internat. Ednl. and Cultural Affairs, 1962-65; mem. Dept. State adv. coun. on African Affairs, 1962-65; U.S. del. 13th gen. conf. UNESCO, 1964; trustee Conn. Coll., 1964-65, 69-77, Mt. Holyoke Coll., 1971-76, vice chmn., 1975-76, trustee fellow, 1988—; Spelman Coll., 1980-89, life trustee, 1991—, Hampshire Coll., 1971-77, 85-88, vice chair, 1975-76; mem. U.S. Nat. Com. for UNESCO, 1965-70, Nat. Adv. rev. Bd., 1974-77; co-dir. African seminar for pres. black colls., 1971; bd. dirs. Nat. Corp. for Housing Partnerships, 1972-77; scholar-in-residence U.S. Commn. on Civil Rights, 1973-74; U.S. del. Internat. Conf. for Assistance to Refugees in Africa, 1981, So. African Devel. Coordination Conf. II, 1980; guest scholar Woodrow Wilson Internat. Ctr. for Scholars, Smithsonian Instn., Washington, 1982; mem. Aspen Inst. Humanistic Studies Exec. Seminar, 1983; mem. study mission to Japan with Assn. Black Am. Ambassadors, 1984, 85; mem. com. on policy for racial justice Joint Ctr. for Polit. and Econ. Studies, 1983-92; co-leader: Md. Consortium to Togo, Sierra Leone, Senegal, Liberia and Cameroon from 1970; co-dir. Mission to Malawi Women's Commn. on Refugee Women and Children, Malawi, 1989; adv. commn. Howard Univ. Patricia Roberts Harris Public Affairs Program, 1989—; adv. bd. Lincoln Univ. (Pa.) Ctr. for Public Policy and Diplomacy, 1991—; bd. dirs. Ralph Bunche Inst. on UN, CUNY, 1986-94; co-chair African-Am. Inst. Del. to observe presdl. elections, Madagascar, Feb., 1993. Author introduction: A Slaver's Log Book or 20 Years Residence in Africa, 1976; co-author: The New Nigerian Elite, 3d edit, 1971, Intensive English Conversation, Vol. I, 1953, Vol. II, 1954; editor: The Black American Reference Book, 1976; co-editor: Curriculum for Understanding, 1965; contbr. chpts. to coop. books, articles to profl. jours. Bd. dirs. Refugee Policy Group, 1983-89, adv. coun., 1989—; cons. African Devel. Found., 1986—; mem. Friends Inst. for Democracy in South Africa (formerly Inst. for a Democratic Alternative in South Africa), 1990—. Decorated grand officer Order of Valor (Cameroon); Grand Dama D'Inore, Order of Royal Crown of Crete (Malta); recipient Top Hat award Pitts. Courier, 1979, Mary McLeod Bethune award, 1981, Decade of Service award Phelps-Stokes Fund, 1982, Ella T. Grasso award Mt. Holyoke Coll., 1982, Northwestern U. Alumna of Year award, 1983, Disting. Service award Nat. Coalition of 100 Black Women, 1984, Disting. Service award USIA, 1986, Am. Bicentennial Presdl. Inaugural award, 1989, Black History Makers award Associated Black Charities, 1990. Mem. Coun. Fgn. Rels., Nat. Coun. Negro Women U.S., Coun. Am. Ambassadors, Assn. Black Am. Ambassadors (exec. com.). Hugh H. and Mabel M. Smythe Internat. Service citatiod annually by InterFuture, Inc. Address: Watergate South Ste 317 700 New Hampshire Ave NW Washington DC 20037-2406 *Living in challenging times brings, along with its problems, opportunities for discovering new and better solutions to our difficulties, for making creative contributions to a world which so sorely needs positive input, for learning to enjoy the beauty and hope which are within our grasp.*

SNADER, JACK ROSS, publishing company executive; b. Athens, Ohio, Feb. 25, 1938; s. Daniel Webster and Mae Estella (Miller) S.; m. Sharon Perschnick, Apr. 4, 1959; children: Susan Mae, Brian Ross. BS, U. Ill., 1959. Cert. mgmt. cons. With mktg. Richardson-Merrell, Cin., 1959-65, Xerox Corp., N.Y.C., 1965-67, Sieber & McIntyre, Chgo., 1967-69; pres. Systema Corp., Northbrook, Ill., 1969—; bd. dirs. 1st Fed. Bank, Waukegan, Ill. Author Systematic Selling, 1987, The Sales Relationship, 1981. Mem. Nat. Soc. Performance and Instruction, Am. Soc. Tng. Devel., Am. Mktg. Assn., Am. Mgmt. Assn. Office: Systema Corporation 60 Revere Dr Ste 600 Northbrook IL 60052

SNAPE, WILLIAM JOHN, JR., physician; b. Camden, N.J., Aug. 24, 1943; s. William John and Barbara (Fleischman) S.; m. Margaret Fry, Mar. 7, 1982; children: William John III, Rebecca Jane. BA, Princeton U., 1965; MD, Jefferson Med. Coll., 1969. Intern Bronx (N.Y.) Municipal Hosp., 1969-70, resident, 1970-71; fellow in gerontology U. Pa., 1973-75; asst. to assoc. prof. U. Pa., Phila., 1975-82; prof. UCLA, 1982—. Lt. comdr. USNR, 1971-73. Fellow ACP, Am. Coll. Gastroenterology. Office: 2650 Elm Ave Ste 201 Long Beach CA 90806

SNAPP, ELIZABETH, librarian, educator; b. Lubbock, Tex., Mar. 31, 1937; d. William James and Louise (Lanham) Mitchell; BA magna cum laude, North Tex. State U., Denton, 1968, MLS, 1969, MA, 1977; m. Harry Franklin Snapp, June 1, 1956. Asst. to archivist Archive of New Orleans Jazz, Tulane U., 1960-63; catalog librarian Tex. Woman's U., Denton, 1969-71, head acquisitions dept., 1971-74, coordinator readers services, 1974-77, asst. to dean Grad. Sch., 1977-79, instr. library sci., 1977-88, acting Univ. libr., 1979-82, dir. librs., 1982—; chair-elect Tex. Coun. State U. Librs., 1988-90, chmn., 1990-92; mem. adv. com. on library formula Coordinating Bd. Tex. Coll. and Univ. System, 1981-92; del. OCLC Nat. Users Council, 1985-87, mem. by-laws com., 1985-86, com. on less-than-full-services networks, 1986-87; trustee AMIGOS Bibliographic Coun., Inc., 1994—; project dir. NEH consultancy grant on devel. core curriculum for women's studies, 1981-82; chmn. Blue Ribbon com. 1986 Gov.'s Commn. for women to select 150 outstanding women in Tex. history; project dir. math./sci. anthology project Tex. Found. Women's Resources. Co-sponsor Irish Lecture Series, Denton, 1968, 70, 73, 78. Sec. Denton County Dem. Caucus, 1970. Recipient Ann. Pioneer award Tex. Women's U., 1986. Mem. AAUP, ALA (standards com. 1983-85), Tex. Libr. Assn. (program com. 1978, Dist. VII chmn. 1985-86, archives and oral history com. 1990-92, co-chair program com. Tex. Libr. Assn. Ann. Conf. 1994, mem. Tall Texan selection com. 1995), Tex. Hist. Commn. (judge for Farenbach History prize 1990-93), Women's Collecting Group (chmn. ad hoc com. 1984-86), AAUW (legis. br. chmn. 1973-74, br. v.p. 1975-76, br. pres. 1979-80, state historian 1986-88), AAUW Ednl. Found. (rsch. and awards panel 1990-94), So. Conf. Brit. Studies, Tex. Assn. Coll. Tchrs. (pres. Tex. Woman's U. chpt. 1976-77), Alliance Higher Edn. (chair coun. libr. dirs. 1993-95), Woman's Shakespeare Club (pres. 1967-69), Beta Phi Mu (pres. chpt. 1976-78; sec. nat. adv. assembly 1978-79, pres. 1979-80, nat. 1981-83), Alpha Chi, Alpha Lambda Sigma (pres. 1970-71), Pi Delta Phi. Methodist. Club: Soroptimist Internat. (Denton) (pres. 1986-88). Asst. editor Tex. Academe, 1973-76; contbg. book reviewer Library Resources and Tech. Services, 1973—. Contbr. articles to profl. jours. Home: 1904 N Lake Trl Denton TX 76201-0602 Office: TWU Sta PO Box 24093 Denton TX 76204-2093 *The idealistic dreams of youth can be translated into making a difference in the work place and in your personal life if you develop a big picture that includes the ideas of individuals of diversity and if you give life your full attention, enthusiasm, and courage and give a few your steadfast friendship.*

SNAPP, HARRY FRANKLIN, historian; b. Bryan, Tex., Oct. 15, 1930; s. H.F. and Ethel (Manning) S.; B.A., Baylor U., 1952, M.A., 1953; Ph.D., Tulane U., 1963; m. Elizabeth Mitchell, June 1, 1956. Instr., U. Coll. Tulane U., 1960-62; asst. prof. history Wofford Coll., 1963-64; asst. prof. history U. North Tex. (formerly North Tex. State U.), Denton, 1964-69, assoc. prof., 1969-94; dir. Tex. Rsch. Ctr. for Biog. Study of Women, Denton, 1995—. Editor Brit. Studies Mercury, 1970—, Tex. Academy, 1973-76; coeditor: Read All About Her! Texas Women's History: A Working Bibliography, 1995; author: (with others) West Texas Historical Association Year Book, 1994; contbr. articles to profl. jours. Mem. Friends of Winchester Cathedral, Am. Com. for Irish Studies; mem. adv. com. on acad. freedom and tenure policy, coordinating bd. Tex. Coll. and Univ. System. Recipient North Tex. State U. Faculty Research award, 1966, 67. Mem. AAUP (pres. North Tex. chpt. 1968-69, pres. Southwestern regional conf. 1971-72, pres. Tex. conf. 1974-76, nat. council 1976-86), So. Conf. Brit. Studies (sec.-treas.), Am. Hist. Assn., So. Hist. Assn., Hist. Assn. (London), Library Research Round Table, Library History Round Table, Northamptonshire Record Soc., Butler Soc. (Ireland), Econ. History Soc., Ch. Hist. Soc., Tulane U. Alumni Assn., Alpha Chi, Lambda Chi Alpha. Episcopalian. Home: 1904 N Lake Trl Denton TX 76201-0602 Office: Tex Rsch Ctr for Biog Study of Women Tex Woman's U PO Box 24053 Denton TX 76204-2053

SNAPP, MANCO, chemicals executive; b. 1943. Mgmt. various divsns. Internat. Paper Co., Inc., Purchase, N.Y., 1964-85; with Arizona Chem. Co., Panama City, Fla., 1985—, now pres.; bd. dirs. First Fed. Savings Bank, Panama City, Fla. With USAF, 1964-71. Office: Arizona Chemical Co 1001 E Highway 98 Panama City FL 32401*

SNAPP, ROY BAKER, lawyer; b. Strang, Okla., May 9, 1916; s. Harry Moore and Verda Mildred (Austin) S.; m. Dorothy Faye Loftis, Jan. 27, 1942; children: Deborah, Bryan Austin, Martha Lynn, Barbara, James. Lawyer. B.S. in Pub. Adminstrn, U. Mo., 1936; LL.B., Georgetown U., 1941, LL.M., 1942. With U.S. State Dept., 1941; spl. advisor comdg. gen. (Manhattan (Atomic Bomb) Project), 1946; dir. internat. affairs U.S. AEC, 1947, sec., 1948-54, asst. to chmn., 1954-55, sr. staff mem. nat. security coun., 1953-55; v.p. atomic div. (Am. Machine & Foundry), 1957; v.p. Am. Machine & Foundry Co., Washington office, 1961; bd. dirs. Electro-Nucleonics, Inc.; ptnr. Bechhoefer, Snapp and Trippe, 1966. Commd. ensign USNR 1942; assigned secretariat of U.S. Joint Chiefs of Staff and Combined (U.S.-Brit), Chiefs of Staff; naval mem. 1945; Intelligence Staff of Joint Chiefs Staff and Combined Chiefs Staff promoted to lt. comdr. 1945. Recipient D.S.M. AEC, 1955. Mem. SVC, Nat. Assn. Mgrs. (chmn. atomic energy com. 1963-64, dir. 1964-65), Phi Gamma Mu, Delta Theta Phi. Baptist. Clubs: Univ. (Washington), Columbia Country (Washington). Home: 11446 Savannah Dr Fredericksburg VA 22407-9108

SNAPPER, ERNST, mathematics educator; b. The Netherlands, Dec. 2, 1913; came to U.S., 1938, naturalized, 1942; s. Isidore and Henrietta (Van Buuren) S.; m. Ethel Lillian Klein, June 1941; children—John William, James Robert. MA, Princeton U., 1939, PhD, 1941; MA (hon.), Dartmouth Coll., 1964. Instr. Princeton, 1941-45, vis. assoc. prof., 1949-50, vis. prof., 1954-55; asst. prof. U. So. Calif., 1945-48, asso. prof., 1948-53, prof., 1953-55; NSF post-doctoral fellow Harvard, 1953-54; Andrew Jackson Buckingham prof. math. Miami U., Oxford, Ohio, 1955-58; prof. math. Ind. U., 1958-63; prof. math. Dartmouth, 1963—; Benjamin Pierce Cheney prof. math., 1971—. Mem. Am. Math. Soc., Math. Assn. Am. (pres. Ind. sect. 1962-63, Carl B. Allendoerfer award 1980), Assn. Princeton Grad. Alumni (governing bd.), Soc. for Preservation Bridges of Konigsburg, Phi Beta Kappa (hon.), Pi Mu Epsilon (hon.). Home: PO Box 67 Norwich VT 05055-0067

SNAVELY, WILLIAM PENNINGTON, economics educator; b. Charlottesville, Va., Jan. 25, 1920; s. Tipton Ray and Nell (Aldred) S.; m. Alice Watts Pritchett, June 4, 1942; children: Nell Lee, William Pennington, Elizabeth Tipton. Student, Hampden-Sydney Coll., 1936-37; BA with honors, U. Va., 1940, MA, 1941, PhD, 1950; postgrad. (Bennett Wood Green fellow), Harvard U., 1946-47. Mem. faculty U. Conn., 1947-73, prof. econs., 1961-73, chmn. dept., 1966-72, economist econ. edn. workshop summers 1954, 55, 56; prof. econs. George Mason U., 1973-84, chmn. dept., 1973-81; acting dean CAS, summer 1981, 85-86, assoc. dean, 1982-85; prof. econs. Liberty U., 1986-93; cons. Ford Found., Jordan Devel. Bd., Amman, 1961-62, Ministry of Planning, Beirut, Lebanon, 1964-65, Saudi Arabian Cen. Planning Orgn., Riyadh, 1964-65, Am. U. Beirut, 1969-70, Bahrain Ministry Fin. and Nat. Economy, 1974, 75, 76, UN, Jordan Nat. Planning Coun., Amman, 1972; mem. Danforth Workshop, summer 1966; mem. adv.

com. Willimantic Trust Co., Conn., 1968-73; v.p. Contemporary Econs. & Bus. Assn., 1988—. Author: (with W.H. Carter) Intermediate Economic Analysis, 1961, Theory of Economic Systems, 1969, (with M.T. Sadik) Bahrain, Qatar and the United Arab Emirates, 1972; contbr. articles to jours.; articles Ency. Americana. Bd. regents Liberty U. Capt. AUS, 1942-46. Fellow Fund Advancement Edn. Harvard, 1951-52; faculty-bus. exchange fellow Chase Nat. Bank, N.Y.C., summer 1952; fellow Merrill Center Econs., summer 1957; Fulbright research fellow Rome, 1958-59. Mem. Am. Econ. Assn., So. Econ. Assn., Am. Christian Economists, Assn. Comparative Econs., Va. Assn. Economists (pres. 1979-80), Phi Beta Kappa, Phi Kappa Phi. Home: 1551 Dairy Rd Charlottesville VA 22903-1303

SNEAD, DAVID L., superintendent; b. Detroit, Oct. 15, 1943; s. Herman Jr. and Edythe (Burrell) S.; m. Joan Walton, Mar. 11, 1978; children: Deborah, David, Brandon. BS, Tuskegee Inst., 1968; MA, U. Mich., 1970, PhD, 1984. Cert. tchr., Mich. Supr. health, tchr. phys. edn. Central High Sch., Detroit; prin. Cass Tech. High Sch. Detroit Bd. Edn., Detroit; prin. Cass Tech High Sch, Detroit; asst. supt. for parent and adult edn. Detroit Bd. Edn. Contbr. articles to profl. jours. With AUS, 1964-66. Mem. U. Mich. Accreditation Adv. Com., Oreg. Sch. Adminstrs. and Suprs., Contract Negotiating Team. Office: 5057 Woodward Ave Detroit MI 48202-4049

SNEAD, ELEANOR LEROY MARKS, secondary school educator; b. Florence, S.C., Oct. 21, 1943; d. Franklin Leroy and Hazel Eleanor (Wallace) Marks; m. Samuel Everette Snead, Aug. 14, 1965; children: Robin Lynne, Ashley Eleanor. BA, Meredith Coll., 1965; MA, U. N.C., Greensboro, 1985. Cert. secondary bus. and marketing tchr., N.C. Tchr. Selma (N.C.) High Sch., 1965, Laurinburg (N.C.) High Sch. (now Scotland High Sch.), 1965-76, 84—, Hoke County High Sch., Raeford, N.C., 1980-84; curriculum writer N.C. Dept. Pub. Instrn., Raleigh, 1985, 90; presenter workshops Mktg. edn. divsn. Vocat. Edn., N.C. Dept. Pub. Instrn. Named Scotland County Outstanding Young Educator. Mem. NEA, N.C. Assn. Educators, Mktg. Educator's Assn. (treas. 1991—), Solid Gold Tchr. 1989, Gold Link Tchr. 1990, Outstanding Mem. of N.C. 1994), Am. Vocat. Assn., N.C. Vocat. Assn., Scotland County Area C. of C., Delta Kappa Gamma (treas. Delta Omicron chpt.), Delta Pi Epsilon. Methodist. Avocations: flower and shrub gardening, needlework, sewing. Office: Scotland High Sch 1000 W Church St Laurinburg NC 28352

SNEAD, GEORGE MURRELL, JR., army officer, scientist, consultant; b. San Diego, Nov. 6, 1922; s. George Murrell and Helen (Olsen) S.; m. Kathleen Hill Dawson, Apr. 26, 1947; children: George Murrell III, James M., William M., John P., Edward W. B.S., Va. Mil. Inst., 1943; M.S., U. Ill., 1948; Ph.D., U. Va., 1953. Commd. 2d lt. U.S. Army, 1943, advanced through grades to brig. gen., 1969; with Central Germany campaign 805th Signal Co., Europe, 1945-46; Aleutian sector comdr. Alaska Communication System, 1949-50; sta. at Electronic Warfare Center Ft. Monmouth, N.J. and Ft. Huachuca, Ariz., 1953-56; student U.S. Army Command and Gen. Staff Coll., 1956-57; signal adviser MAAG Vietnam, 1957-58; signal officer Dept. Army, 1958-60; acting dir. research ballistic missile def. Advanced Research Projects Agy., 1960; with U.S. Army Satellite Communications Agy. Ft. Monmouth, 1960-63; student Nat. War Coll., 1963-64, div. signal officer 24th Inf. Div., 1964-65, comdg. officer 7th Signal Group, 1965; dir. Communication /ADP Lab. Ft. Monmouth, 1966-68; exec. asst. chief of staff Communications Electronics, Dept. Army, 1968; dir. army research Dept. Army Washington, 1968-71; dep. comdr. Army Strategic Communications Command, 1971-73; prin. scientist Gen. Research Corp. McLean, Va., 1973-82; pres. Nat. Sci. Ctr. Found., Burke, Va., 1982-84; chmn. bd. Am. Fed. Savs. & Loan Assn., Lynchburg, Va., 1985-86; sci./bus. cons., 1986—. Active local Boy Scouts Am., 1958-68; bd. dirs. Central Youth Summer Activities, Ft. Monmouth, 1960-63, Arthritis Found., Washington, 1981-84, Lynchburg Symphony, 1990—; pres. Acad. Music Theatre, Lynchburg, 1985—; elder Presbyn. Ch., 1986—. Decorated D.S.M., Legion of Merit with oak leaf cluster, Bronze Star, Air medal, Army Commendation medal with 4 oak leaf clusters. Mem. Assn. U.S. Army, Armed Forces Communications and Electronics Assn. (sec. Washington chpt. 1968-69), Sigma Xi, Kappa Alpha. Home: 957 Rothowood Rd Lynchburg VA 24503-1113 Office: PO Box 3306 Lynchburg VA 24503-0306

SNEAD, JAMES ARRINGTON, architect; b. Richmond, Va., June 24, 1950; s. John Elwood and Anna Ruth (Reiche) S. BA, U. N.C., 1972; MArch, Va. Tech. U., 1978. Designer Hord Coplan & Macht, Balt., 1978-80; assoc. CS&D Architects, Balt., 1980-84; v.p. pres. Ziger Hoopes & Snead, Balt., 1984-93; pres. Ziger/Snead Architects, Balt., 1994—. Trustee Gilman Sch., Balt., 1990—; mem. adv. bd. Md. Inst. Sch. Continuing Studies, Balt., 1991—. Mem. AIA. Democrat. Presbyterian. Avocations: golf, travel, sailing. Office: Ziger/Snead Architects 1006 Morton St Baltimore MD 21201

SNEAD, RICHARD THOMAS, retail company executive; b. Washington, Apr. 19, 1951; s. Walter Thomas and Ruth Claire (Reeves) S.; m. Marilyn Wolke; children: Richard Adam, Eric Thomas. BS in Engring., U. Tenn., 1973. Project mgr. First Fla. Bldg. Corp., Miami, 1974-78; constrn. mgr. Burger King Corp., San Francisco, 1978-79; nat. constrn. dir. Miami, 1979-81; dir. devel. Boston, 1981-84; regional v.p. Detroit, 1984-86; sr. v.p. devel. Miami, 1986-87, exec. v.p. devel. eastern div. mgr. (including responsibility for black minority affairs), 1987-88; pres. Burger King Internat. Div., 1988-89; mng. dir. Burger King U.K., 1989-92, Lenscrafters div. of U.S. Shoe, U.K., 1992-93; sr. v.p. Lenscrafters U.S.A., 1993-94, pres. Sight & Save divsn., sr. v.p. internat. divsn., 1994—. Republican. Avocations: running, golf, snow skiing, boating. Office: 8650 Governor's Hill Dr Cincinnati OH 45242-9580

SNEAD, SAMUEL JACKSON, former professional golfer; b. Hot Springs, Va., May 27, 1912; m. Audrey; children: Samuel Jackson, Terrance. Profl. golfer, from 1935. Author: How To Hit a Golf Ball, 1940, How To Play Golf, 1946, (with Al Stump) Education of a Golfer, 1962, The Driver, 1974, Golf Begins at Forty, 1978. Served with USNR, 1942-45. Recipient Vardon trophy Profl. Golfers' Assn., 1938, 49, 50, 55, Player of Year award, 1949, elected to Hall of Fame, 1953. Winner Profl. Golfers' Assn. Championship, 1942, 49, 51, Brit. Open, 1946, Masters Golf Tournament, 1949, 52, 54, Legends of Golf Championship, 1982. Office: care PGA of Am PO Box 12458 West Palm Beach FL 33410-9600*

SNEDAKER, CATHERINE RAUPAGH (KIT SNEDAKER), editor; b. Fargo, N.D., Apr. 2; d. Paul and Charity (Primmer) Raupagh; B.A., Duke U.; m. William Brooks; children—Eleanor, Peter William; m. 2d, Weldon Snedaker. Pub. relations exec. United Seamen's Service, 1950-57; promotion mgr. sta. WINR-TV and WNBF-TV, Binghamton, N.Y., 1957-60; TV editor, feature writer Binghamton Sun, 1960-68; mem. staff Los Angeles Herald Examiner, 1968—, food editor 1978—, restaurant critic, 1978-80, food and travel editor, 1980-86; editor The Food Package; columnist Copley News Svc. Author: The Great Convertibles; contbr. numerous articles on food and travel to nat. mags. and newspapers; guest editor Mademoiselle mag., 1942. Recipient 3 awards Los Angeles Press Club, VISTA award, 1979. Mem. Soc. Am. Travel Writers, Travel Journalist's Guild, Internat. PEN U.S.A. Ctr. West. Democrat. Home: 140 San Vicente Blvd Apt A Santa Monica CA 90402-1533

SNEDDEN, JAMES DOUGLAS, health service management consultant; b. Toronto, Ont., Can., Mar. 4, 1925; s. David Morrison and Sarah Hayton (Monteith) S.; m. Elizabeth Ann McCauley, Dec. 20, 1953. B.Comm., U. Toronto, 1948; C.A., Inst. Chartered Accts. Ont., 1951. With Hosp. for Sick Children, Toronto, 1953-58, asst. dir., 1961-67, adminstr., 1967-70, chief exec. officer, 1970-86; nat. dir. health and social service cons. Peat, Marwick & Ptnrs., 1986-87; pres. J. Douglas Snedden and Assocs., 1987—; bd. dirs. Mallinckrodt Can., Cyberfluor Can. Hon. dir. Woodgreen Community Centre, Toronto 1963-65, v.p., 1965-67, pres., 1967-69, hon. mem. bd. dirs., 1973—; past bd. dirs. Hosp. Coun. Met. Toronto; mem. Bd. Trade Met. Toronto, 1965—; bd. dirs. United Way Met. Toronto, 1986-89; bd. dirs. Wedgewood at Bonita Bay, Bonita Springs, 1990-94, pres., 1992-94. Served with RCAF, 1943-45. Decorated Can. Centennial medal. Fellow Can. Coll. Health Service Execs. (founding mem. 1970, bd.dir. 1972-83, treas., 1978-79, sec., 1979-80, chmn. elect., 1980-81, chmn. 1981-82, past chmn., 1982-83), Inst. Chartered Accts. Ont., Acad. of Medicine, Toronto; mem. Am. Coll. Healthcare Execs., Am. Mgmt. Assn. Presbyterian. Clubs: University, Bd. of

Trade. Office: #1005, 1 Aberfoyle Crescent, Etobicoke, ON Canada M8X 2X8

SNEDEKER, JOHN HAGGNER, university president; b. Plainfield, N.J., May 30, 1925; s. Alfred H. and Anna Marie (Ward) S.; m. Noreen I. Davey, Dec. 30, 1950; children—John D., Philip A., Patrick W. B.S. cum laude, N.Y. U., 1951, M.A., 1951; Ed.D., Ind. U., 1959. Dir. lab. human devel. U. Mont., 1952-56; cons. psychologist research Purdue U., 1955; asso. prof., dir. bur. research Ball State U., 1956-61; instr. higher edn., research asso. Ind. U., 1958; prof., chmn. div. edn. Western Wash. State U., Bellingham, 1961-62; pres. Western N.Mex. U., Silver City, 1962—; mem. exec. bd. Internat. Coun. Spl. Edn. 1952-56; Rocky Mountain regional rep. APA, 1953-56; mem. Gov. Wash. Com. Licensing Tchr. Edn., 1961, Wash. State Legislature Rsch. Tech. Com. 1961. Author or co-author rating scales, attitude and opinion measurement devices; contbr. jours. Bd. dirs. Nat. Sci. Fair; trustee N.Mex. Health Found. Served with AUS, 1943-48. Fellow AAAS; mem. Midwest Psychol. Assn., Inter-Am. Soc. Psychology, Am. Ednl. Research Assn., Holland Soc. N.Y. Address: 2117 Pinon St Silver City NM 88061

SNEDEKER, ROBERT D., air transportation executive; b. 1943; married. AB, Princeton U.; MBA, Harvard U., 1966. Fin. analyst Time, Inc., N.Y., 1966-68; prin. Lorenzo Carney & Co., Inc., 1968-72; sr. v.p. Tex. Internat. Airlines, 1972—; sec., treas. Jet Capital Corp.; sr. v.p., treas. Tex. Air Corp., Houston. Office: Tex Air Corp 333 Clay St Ste 4040 Houston TX 77002 also: Continental Airline Holdings Inc 2929 Allen Pkwy Ste 210 Houston TX 77019

SNEED, ALBERTA NEAL, retired elementary education educator; b. Tipton County, Tenn., Jan. 13, 1926; d. Robert and Mary Lou (Wilks) Neal; m. Sollie Jr. Sneed, Jan. 26, 1968; 1 child, Hortense Yolanda Johnson Jeans. BS, Lane Coll., 1949; MEd, Memphis State U., 1975, postgrad., 1982. Cert. elem. and secondary tchr., Tenn., supr. and adminstr. Tchr. Ouachita Parish Sch. Bd., Monroe, La.; tchr. Covington (Tenn.) City Bd. Edn., ret.; cons. Tipton County Bd. Edn., Covington. Mem. ASCD, NEA, Tenn. Assn. Supervision and Curriculum Devel., Tenn. Edn. Assn, TCEA, WTEA, Delta Sigma Theta.

SNEED, ELLOUISE BRUCE, nursing educator; b. Monroe, La., June 21, 1945; d. Wesley Newton Bruce and Oza Celeste Parker; m. Gary Arnold, Aug. 10, 1978. RN, Mather Sch. Nursing, New Orleans, 1966; BS in Nursing, William Carey Coll., Hattiesburg, Miss., 1975; MS in Nursing, Med. Coll. Ga., Augusta, 1978; EdD, U. So. Miss., Hattiesburg, 1981. Cert. CPR instr. Instr. community-psychiat. nursing Charity Hosp. Sch. Nursing, New Orleans, 1975-77; family nurse cons. Drs. R. Gregory and G. Keller, Mandeville, La., 1978-83; assoc. prof. Sch. Nursing William Carey Coll., New Orleans, 1980-88; employee well health and health fair cons. St. Tammany Parish Hosp., Covington, La., 1987-88; prof., Holder Coughlin Sanders chair nursing La. Coll., Pineville, 1988—; ednl. program cons., 1984-85; speaker-presenter for profl. orgns. and instns. throughout La. Contbg. author: Crisis Intervention Theory and Practice: A Clinical Handbook, 1980, Mosby's 1988, 92 Secured Assess Test: A Practice Test Exam for RN Licensure, 1988, 92. Bd. dirs. Am. Cancer Soc. of Rapides Parish. Named a Great One Hundred Nurse, New Orleans Dist. Nurses Assn., 1987. Mem. ANA (cert. community nursing), ARC, Nat. League Nursing, La. Assn. Mental Health, La. Coun. Adminstrs. Nursing Edn., La. State Nurses Assn., Alexandria Dist. Nurses Assn., Sigma Theta Tau. Home: 4703 Warwick Way Alexandria LA 71303-2610

SNEED, GAIL, mortgage company executive. Exec. v.p. Master Fin. Inc., Orange, Calif., 1993—. Office: Master Fin Inc 333 S Anita Dr 150 Orange CA 92668*

SNEED, JAMES H., lawyer; b. Bartlesville, Okla., Nov. 27, 1947; s. James H. and Genevieve (Harris) S.; m. Maree Sneed, Dec. 27, 1969. BA, U. Okla., 1969, JD, 1972. Bar: D.C. 1974, Ill. 1982, U.S. Dist. Ct. (no. dist.) Ill., U.S. Dist. Ct. D.C., U.S. Ct. Appeals (9th, 10th, 11th and D.C. cirs.). Trial atty. FTC, Washington, 1972-74, gen. counsel, dir. bur. consumer protection, asst. dir. bur. competition, 1977-82; assoc. Hogan & Hartson, Washington, 1974-77; ptnr. McDermott, Will & Emery, Chgo., 1982-86, Washington, 1986—. Mem. ABA (chmn. competition sub., FTC com., antitrust sect.), Order of Coif. Office: McDermott Will & Emery 1850 K St NW Ste 500 Washington DC 20006-2296

SNEED, JOANNE LAWSON, elementary school educator, author; b. Barren County, Ky., Ky., Aug. 16, 1940; d. Bobby Lee and Mary Clorine (Jones) Lawson; m. Thomas Nelson Sneed, June 9, 1965 (dec. May, 1986); 1 child, Thomas Nelson II. AA, Freed Hardeman U., 1960; BS, Western Ky. U., 1962, MA, 1967. Cert. elem. tchr., Ky. Sec. to dean Freed-Hardeman U., Henderson, Tenn., 1960-61; tchr. Nebo (Ky.) Jr. High Sch., 1962-64, Waddill Elem. Sch., Madisonville, Ky., 1964-68, Hall St. Elem. Sch., Madisonville, 1968-74, Pride Elem. Sch., Madisonville, 1978—. Author: Buford The Big-Eared Mouse, 1978, Buford Tales, 1986, Buford and the New Car, 1987, Buford Listens, 1992. Outreach trainer Widowed Perons Svc., Madisonville, 1988-90. Named Outstanding Young Educator, Madisonville Jaycees, 1969. Mem. NEA, Ky. Edn. Assn., Hopkins County Edn. Assn. Democrat. Mem. Ch. of Christ. Avocations: sewing, painting, travel, writing, walking. Home: 107 Ayr Pkwy Madisonville KY 42431 Office: Pride Elem Sch 861 Pride Ave Madisonville KY 42431

SNEED, JOSEPH DONALD, philosophy educator, author; b. Durant, Okla., Sept. 23, 1938; s. Dabney Whitfield and Sallybelle (Atkinson) S. B.S., Rice U., 1960; M.S., U Ill., 1962; Ph.D., Stanford U., 1964. Prof. Stanford U., Palo Alto, Calif., 1966-73; policy analyst SRI Internat., Menlo Park, Calif., 1973-74; prof. U. Munich, 1974-75, U. Eindhoven, Holland, 1976-77, SUNY, Albany, 1977-79; prof. philosophy Colo. Sch. Mines, Golden, 1980—. Author: The Logical Structure of Mathematical Physics, 1971, (with W. Balzer and C. Moulines) An Architectonic for Science, 1987; editor: (with S. Waldhorn) Restructuring the Federal System, 1974. Mem. Am. Philos. Assn. Office: Colo Sch Mines Golden CO 80401

SNEED, JOSEPH TYREE, III, federal judge; b. Calvert, Tex., July 21, 1920; s. Harold Marvin and Cara (Weber) S.; m. Madelon Juergens, Mar. 15, 1944; children—Clara Hall, Cara Carleton, Joseph Tyree IV. B.B.A., Southwestern U., 1941; LL.B., U. Tex., Austin, 1947; asst. prof. law U. Tex., 1947-51, asso. prof., 1951-54, prof., 1954-57, asst. dean, 1949-50; counsel Graves, Dougherty & Greenhill, Austin, 1954-56; prof. law Cornell U., 1957-62, Stanford Law Sch., 1962-71; dean Duke Law Sch., 1971-73; dep. atty. gen. U.S. justice dept., 1973; judge U.S. Ct. Appeals (9th cir.), San Francisco, 1973—, now sr. judge; Cons. estate and gift tax project Am. Law Inst., 1960-69. Author: The Configurations of Gross Income, 1967; Contbr. articles to profl. jours. Served with USAAF, 1942-46. Mem. ABA, State Bar Tex., Am. Law Inst., Order of Coif. Office: US Ct Appeals P O Box 193939 San Francisco CA 94119-3939*

SNEED, MICHAEL (MICHELE), columnist; b. Mandan, N.D., Nov. 16, 1943; d. Richard Edward and June Marie (Ritchey) S.; m. William J. Griffin, Sept. 16, 1978; 1 child, Patrick. BS, Wayne State U., 1965. Tchr. Barrington High Sch., Ill., 1965-66; legis. asst. Congressman Ray Clevenger, 1966-67; reporter City News Bur., Chgo., 1967-69; reporter Chgo. Tribune, 1969-86, columnist, 1981-86; pres. sec. Mayor Jane Byrne, Chgo., 1979; gossip columnist Chgo. Sun-Times, 1986—. Co-editor Chgo. Journalism Rev., 1971-72. Vice pres. No. Mich. U. chpt. Young Democrats, 1962. Roman Catholic. Club: Women's Athletic. Avocation: gardening. Office: Chgo Sun-Times Inc 401 N Wabash Ave Rm 110 Chicago IL 60611-3532

SNEED, RONALD ERNEST, engineering educator emeritus; b. Oxford, N.C., Nov. 23, 1936; s. Henry Ernest and Jewel Leigh (Hughes) S.; m. Shelba Jean Walters, June 8, 1958; children: Kathy Geneva Grosvenor, Jennie Leigh Berrier. BS in Agrl. Engring., N.C. State U., 1959, PhD in Biol. and Agrl. Engring., 1971. Registered profl. engr., N.C.; cert. irrigation designer. Sales trainee John Deere Co., 1959-60; ext. specialist N.C. State U., 1960-62, ext. instr., 1962-69, 70, ext. asst. prof., 1971-75, ext. assoc. prof., 1971-80, prof., 1980-92, prof. emeritus, 1993—; project engr. Agri-Waste Tech., Inc., 1993—; cons. Lexington (N.C.) Swine Breeders, 1973, 1st Colony

Farms, Creswell, N.C., 1977-78, Greek Tobacco Co., Uruguay, 1973-84, Internat. Potato Ctr., Lima, Peru, 1981-85, Philip Morris Tobacco Co., Richmond, Va., 1992, Agri-Waste Tech., Inc., Raleigh, 1993-94, Stowe's Nursery, Inc., Belmont, N.C., 1993-94, Floyd Harrell Farms, Inc., Conetoe, N.C., 1994, Gilliam & Mason, Inc., Harrellsville, N.C., 1994, Connestee Falls Property Owners Assn., Inc., Brevard, N.C. 1994. Active Civitan, Raleigh, 1994. With U.S. Army, 1960. Recipient Outstanding Paper award So. region Am. Soc. Horticultural Sci., 1986, 91; Ronald E. Sneed Irrigation Soc., Inc. scholarship established in his honor, 1991. Fellow Am. Soc. Agrl. Engrs. (ednl. aids competition blue ribbon 1963, 64, 68, 78, 79, 85, 89, 91, 92, Gunlogson Countryside Engring. award 1992, Outstanding Paper award 1984), The Irrigation Assn. (life-tech. mem., Man of Yr. award 1981), N.C. Irrigation Soc., Inc. (Outstanding Contbn. to Irrigation award 1973, former tech. advisor), Soil and Water Conservation Soc., N.C. Land Improvement Contractors Assn. (former tech. advisor), Carolinas Irrigation Assn. (hon.), Res. Officers Assn. (life),. Democrat. Baptist. Office: 3405 Malibu Dr Raleigh NC 27607

SNEIDER, MARTIN KARL, retail company executive; b. N.Y.C., Sept. 23, 1942; s. Sidney Louis and Adeline (Speckter) S.; m. Jill Allyn Frank, June 19, 1966; children: Mark, Julie. BA, Washington St. Louis, 1964; MA in Journalism, U. Mo., 1966; MBA, Harvard U., 1968. Adminstrv. asst. Edison Bros. Stores, St. Louis, 1968-71, v.p. fin. Jeans West div., 1971-74, pres. Jeans West div., 1974-81; chmn. Edison Bros. Apparel Stores, St. Louis, from 1981; pres. Edison Bros. Stores, Inc., St. Louis, 1987—, also bd. dirs. Vice chmn. budget panel Jewish Fedn., St. Louis, 1980—; mem. devel. Bd/ Children's Hosp. St. Louis, 1985—. Served with USAR, 1967-73. Clubs: Harvard (N.Y.C.); Mo. Athletic, Alliance Française, Harvard (St. Louis). Avocations: French lit. and culture, baseball. Office: Edison Bros Stores Inc 501 N Broadway Saint Louis MO 63102-2196

SNELL, BRUCE M., JR., state supreme court justice; b. Ida Grove, Iowa, Aug. 18, 1929; s. Bruce M. and Donna (Potter) S.; m. Anne Snell, Feb. 4, 1956; children: Rebecca, Brad. AB, Grinnell Coll., 1951; JD, U. Iowa, 1956. Bar: Iowa 1956, N.Y. 1958. Law clk. to presiding judge U.S. Dist. Ct. (no. dist.) Iowa, 1956-57; asst. atty. gen., 1961-65; judge Iowa Ct. Appeals, 1976-87; justice Iowa Supreme Ct., 1987—. Comments editor Iowa Law Rev. Mem. ABA, Iowa State Bar Assn., Am. Judicature Soc., Order of Coif. Methodist. Home: PO Box 192 Ida Grove IA 51445-0192 Office: Iowa Supreme Ct St Capitol Bldg Des Moines IA 50319

SNELL, ESMOND EMERSON, biochemist; b. Salt Lake City, Sept. 22, 1914; s. Heber Cyrus and Hedwig Emma (Ludwig) S.; m. Mary Caroline Terrill, Mar. 15, 1941; children: Esmond Emerson (dec.), Richard T., Allan G., Margaret Ann. B.A., Brigham Young U., 1935; M.A., U. Wis., 1936, Ph.D., 1938, D.Sc. (hon.), 1982. Rsch. assoc. chemistry U. Tex., 1939-41, asst. prof. chemistry, 1941-43, assoc. prof., 1943-45, prof. chemistry, 1951-56; assoc. prof. biochemistry U. Wis., 1945-47, prof., 1947-53, on leave 1951-53; prof. biochemistry U. Calif., 1956-76, chmn. dept., 1956-62; prof. microbiology and chemistry U. Tex., Austin, 1976-90, Ashbel Smith prof., 1981-90, prof. emeritus, 1990—, chmn. dept. microbiology, 1976-80; Guggenheim Meml. Found. fellow U. Cambridge, 1954-55, Max-Planck Institut für Zellchemie, München, 1962-63, U. Wash., Seattle, Rockefeller U., N.Y.C., Hebrew U., Jerusalem, 1969; Walker-Ames prof. biochemistry U. Wash., Seattle, spring 1953. Author numerous research articles in sci. jours.; Editor: Volume III Biochemical Preparations, 1963-64, Chemical and Biological Aspects of Pyridoxal Catalysis, 1963, Pyridoxal Catalysis, Enzymes and Model Systems, 1968; Mem. editorial bd. Jour. Am. Chem. Soc, 1948-58, Jour. Biol. Chemistry, 1949-59, Biochemistry, 1961-70, Biochem. and Biophys. Research Communication, 1970-85, Biofactors, 1988-91; editor: Ann. Rev. Biochemistry, 1969-83. Recipient U.S. Sr. Scientist award Alexander von Humboldt Found., 1977. Fellow AAAS, Am. Inst. Nutrition (Meade-Johnson B-Complex award 1946, Osborne-Mendel award 1951); mem. Nat. Acad. Scis., Am. Acad. Arts and Scis., Japanese Biochem. Soc. (hon.), Am. Chem. Soc. (chmn. div. biol. chemistry 1954, Kenneth A. Spencer award 1974, Nebr. Lectureship award 1983), Am. Soc. Biol. Chemists (pres. 1961-62, William Rose award 1985), Soc. Am. Bacteriologists (Eli Lilly award in bacteriology and immunology 1945), Am. Acad. Microbiology. Home: 5001 Greystone Dr Austin TX 78731-1118

SNELL, GEORGE DAVIS, geneticist; b. Bradford, MA, Dec. 19, 1903; s. Cullen Bryant and Katharine (Davis) S.; m. Rhoda Carson, July 28, 1937; children: Thomas Carleton, Roy Carson, Peter Garland. B.S., Dartmouth Coll., 1926; M.S., Harvard U., 1928, Sc.D., 1930; M.D. (hon.), Charles U., Prague, 1967; LL.D. (hon.), Colby Coll., 1982; Sc.D. (hon.), Dartmouth Coll., 1974, Gustavus Adolphus Coll., 1981, U. Maine, 1981, Bates Coll., 1982, Ohio State U., 1984. Instr. zoology Dartmouth Coll., 1929-30, Brown U., 1930-31; asst. prof. Washington U., St. Louis, 1933-34; rsch. assoc. Jackson Lab., 1935-73, sci. adminstr., 1949-50, sr. staff scientist, 1957-73, sr. staff scientist emeritus, 1973—. Author: Search for a Rational Ethic, 1988, (with others) Histocompatibility, 1976; also sci. papers in field; editor: The Biology of the Laboratory Mouse, 1941. Recipient Bertner Found. award in field cancer research, 1962; Griffin award Animal Care Panel, 1962; career award Nat. Cancer Inst., 1964-68; Gregor Mendel medal Czechoslovak Acad. Scis., 1967; Internat. award Gairdner Found., 1976; Wolf Found. prize in medicine, 1978; award Nat. Inst. Arthritis and Infectious Disease-Nat. Cancer Inst., 1978; Nobel prize in medicine (with Dausset and Benacerraf), 1980; NRC fellow U. Tex., 1931-33; NIH health research grantee for study genetics and immunology of tissue transplantation, 1950-73 (allergy and immunology study sect. 1958-62); Guggenheim fellow, 1953-54. Mem. Nat. Acad. Scis., Transplantation Soc., Am. Acad. Arts and Sci., French Acad. Scis. (fgn. asso.), Am. Philos. Soc., Brit. Transplantation Soc. (hon.), Phi Beta Kappa.

SNELL, JACK EASTLAKE, federal agency administrator; b. Evanston, Ill., Nov. 29, 1935; s. Clarence Eastlake and Ruth (Meloy) S.; m. Elizabeth Kercher, Oct. 15, 1966; children: Jeffrey Eastlake, Julie Elizabeth. B.S.E. with honors in Aero. Engring. Princeton U., 1957; M.S. in Indsl. Engring. Northwestern U., 1965, Ph.D. in Civil Engring. (Walter P. Murphy scholar, Transp. Center fellow), 1966; grad., Fed. Exec. Inst., 1979. Aircraft maintenance engr. Pan Am. World Airways, N.Y.C., 1960; asst. prof. transp. engring., and dir. Transp. and Urban Systems Lab., Princeton U., 1966-71; chief bldg. service systems sect. Nat. Bur. Standards, Washington, 1971-73; asst. chief bldg. environ. div. Nat. Bur. Standards, 1973-74; chief Office Energy Conservation, 1974-76; dir. Office Energy Programs, 1976-81; dir. Ctr. Fire Research Nat. Engring. Lab., 1981-91, deputy dir. bldg. and fire rsch. lab., 1991—; mem. various fed. interagy. energy task forces, 1973-79; steering com. Intersoc. Energy Conversion Engring. Conf.; mem. Nat. Gov.'s Sci. Adv. Council, 1976—; chmn. U.S-Japan Panel on Fire Research and Safety. Contbr. articles to profl. jours. Served to 1st lt. USAR, 1953-60. Recipient Silver medal Dept. Commerce, 1975, Gold medal Dept. Commerce, 1987. Fellow ASME (chmn. advanced energy systems divsn. 1981), Nat. Fire Protection Assn. (bd. dirs., chmn. toxicity adv. com.). Presbyterian. Office: Natl Inst Standards & Technology Gaithersburg MD 20899

SNELL, JAMES LAURIE, mathematician, educator; b. Wheaton, Ill., Jan. 15, 1925; s. Roy Judson and Lucille (Ziegler) S.; m. Joan Perry, Dec. 30, 1952; children: John, Mary Paige. BA, U. Ill., 1947, MA, 1948, PhD, 1951. Instr. math. Princeton U., 1951-54; mem. faculty Dartmouth Coll., Hanover, N.H., 1954—; prof. math., 1962—; exch. prof. U. Paris, 1965. Author: (with J.G. Kemeny and G.L. Thompson) Introduction to Finite Mathematics, 1959, (with J.G. Kemeny) Finite Markov Chains, 1960, (with J.G. Kemeny and A.W. Knapp) Denumerable Markov Chains, 1966; Introduction to Probability, 1988. With USNR, 1944-46. Mem. Am. Math. Soc., Math. Soc. Am. Home: 34 E Wheelock St Hanover NH 03755-1514 Office: Dartmouth Coll Dept of Math Hanover NH 03755

SNELL, JOHN RAYMOND, civil engineer; b. Soochow, China, Dec. 9, 1912; (parents Am. citizens); s. John A. and Grace (Birkett) S.; m. Florence Moffett, Dec. 8, 1939; children: Dorothea Snell Fenska, Karen Snell Dailey, Martha E. Snell Rood, John Raymond, David Moffett. BE, Vanderbilt U., 1934; MS, U. Ill., 1936; DSc, Harvard U., 1939. Registered profl. engr. Mass., Mich., Ohio, Ill., Ind., La. Wis., N.Y., Tex. Fla. Idaho, Oreg., Ont., Can.; cert. san. engr.; diplomate Am. Acad. Environ. Engrs. Instr. civil engring. Hangchow U., 1934-35; with Water Supply Fed. Pub. Works Dept., Venezuela, 1939-40; design engr. Metcalf & Eddy, also Fay Spofford and

Thorndyke, Stone & Webster, Boston, 1941-42; san. engr., head water and sewage sect. 1st Svc. Command, Boston, 1946; assigned UNRA restoration water, sewage, solid wastes 5 China San. Engring. Services Inc., 1945-46; project engr. Burns & Kenerson, Boston, 1947; pres., chief engr. Engring. Svcs. Inc., Boston, 1948-51; lectr. MIT, 1949-51; prof., head dept. civil and san. engring. Mich. State U., 1951-55; owner John R. Snell & Assocs., 1956-60; sr. prin. Mich. Assocs., cons. engrs., 1956-60; pres. John R. Snell Engrs. Inc., 1960-75; pres. Snell Environ. Group, 1975-80, hon. chmn. bd., spl. cons., 1980-88; joint venturer Snell-Republic Assocs. Ltd., Lahore, West Pakistan, 1961-80; with Assoc. Architects & Engrs., Dacca, Bangladesh, 1965-80; pres. Caribbean Devel. Corp. and subs. Gen. Shrimp Ltd., Belize, 1984-92; sr. adj. scientist Mich. Biotech. Inst., 1990—; 1994 guest of China-Suzhou Hosp. 110 Aniv.; solid waste cons. Xiaogan Recycling Treatment Utilization of Organics, Peoples Republic of China, 1995; founder Trans Mich. Waterway Inc., S.W. Waterway (Ont.) Ltd., N.Y.; spl. cons. on ast high rate compost plant to Govt. of Japan, 1955-56; cons. in Orient, WHO, 1956; chmn. bd. Bootstrap Internat. Inc., 1972; expert witness on over 50 ct. cases. Author 12 sects. Environment Engineering Handbook; co-author: Municipal Solid Waste Disposal; contbr. articles to profl. jours.; patentee in composting field. Maj. USPHS, 1945-47. Recipient Prescott Eddy award, 1944. Mem. Nat., Mich. (life) socs. profl. engrs., Am. Water Works Assn., Hwy. Rsch. Bd., ASTM, ASCE, Am. Pub. Works Assn., Water Pollution Control Fedn. (life), Mich. Engring. Soc. (life), Cons. Engrs. Coun. (past dir.), Cons. Engrs. Assn. Mich. (past pres.), Inter-Am. Assn. San. Engrs., World Aquaculture Soc., Composters Inc. (pres. Worldwide Techs. Inc. East Lansing 1980—), Rotary, Tau Beta Pi, Chi Epsilon. Home and Office: 918 Rosewood Ave East Lansing MI 48823-3127

SNELL, NED COLWELL, financial planner; b. Cowley, Wyo., May 16, 1944; s. Jay Hatton and Freda Hope (Colwell) S.; m. Barbara Anne Frandsen, Apr. 24, 1969; children: Taylor Anthony, Trevor Cameron. BA, U. Utah, 1969; CLU, Am. Coll., 1983, ChFC, 1985. English tchr. Granite Sch. Dist., Salt Lake City, 1969-71; ins. agt. Prudential Ins. Co., Salt Lake City, 1971-76; pres. Snell Fin. Corp., Salt Lake City, 1976—. Bd. dirs. Utah chpt. Arthritis Found., Salt Lake City, 1980-82, pres. 1982-83; missionary Mormon Ch. 1963-66; chmn. voting dist. 2604 Rep. Nominating Convs., 1986, 90. Mem. NALU (Nat. Sales Achievement award 1971-89, Nat. Quality award), Am. Soc. CLU and ChFC (bd. dirs. Utah chpt. 1990-93, treas. 1993-94, v.p. 1994—, Golden Key Soc. Devel. award 1990), Million Dollar Round Table (knight 1988-94), Salt Lake Assn. Life Underwriters (bd. dirs. 1974-76, 80-82). Republican. Avocations: creative writing, fly tying, fishing, basketball, tennis. Home: 1101 S 2000 E Salt Lake City UT 84108-1971 Office: 1800 S West Temple Ste 416 Salt Lake City UT 84115-1874

SNELL, PATRICIA POLDERVAART, librarian, consultant; b. Santa Fe, Apr. 11, 1943; d. Arie and Edna Beryl (Kerchmar) Poldervaart; m. Charles Eliot Snell, June 7, 1966. BA in Edn., U. N.M., 1965; MSLS, U. So. Calif., 1966. Asst. edn. libr. U. So. Calif., L.A., 1966-68; med. libr. Bedford (Mass.) VA Hosp., 1968-69; asst. law libr. U. Miami, Coral Gables, Fla., 1970-71; acquistions libr. U. N.Mex. Law Sch. Libr., Albuquerque, 1971-72; order libr. Los Angeles County Law Libr., 1972-76, cataloger, 1976-90; libr. Parks Coll., Albuquerque, 1990-92; records technician Technadyne Engring. Cons. to Sandia Nat. Labs., 1992-93; instr. libr. sci. program Coll. Edn. U. N.Mex., Albuquerque, 1991—; libr. Tireman Learning Materials Ctr., 1993—. Ch. libr.: Beverly Hills Presbyn. Ch., 1974-90, ch. choir libr., 1976-90. Southwestern Library Assn. scholar 1965. Mem. ALA, N.Mex. Libr. Assn., Pi Lambda Theta. Avocations: travel, reading, gospel singing. Office: U N Mex Coll Edn EM/LS Program Tireman Libr Albuquerque NM 87131

SNELL, RICHARD, holding company executive; b. Phoenix, Nov. 26, 1930; s. Frank L. and Elizabeth (Berlin) S.; m. Alice Cosette Wiley, Aug. 1, 1954. BA, Stanford U., 1952, JD, 1954. Bar: Ariz. Ptnr. firm Snell & Wilmer, Phoenix, 1956-81; pres., chmn., chief exec. officer Ramada Inc., Phoenix, 1981-89; chmn., chief exec. officer Aztar Corp., 1989-90, chmn., bd. dirs., 1990-92; chmn., chief exec. officer, pres. Pinnacle West Capital Corp., Phoenix, 1990—, bd. dirs.; bd. dirs. Bank One Ariz. Corp., Bank One Ariz. NA, Aztar Corp.; bd. dirs., chmn. Ariz. Pub. Svc. Co. Trustee Am. Grad. Sch. Internat. Mgmt., Phoenix; past pres. YMCA Met. Phoenix and Valley of Sun. With U.S. Army, 1954-56. Mem. ABA, Ariz. Bar Assn., Paradise Valley Country Club, Phoenix Country Club. Republican. Lutheran. Office: Pinnacle West Capital Corp 400 East Van Buren St Phoenix AZ 85004-2132 also: Arizona Public Service Co PO Box 53999 # 9960 Phoenix AZ 85072-3999

SNELL, RICHARD SAXON, anatomist; b. Richmond, Surrey, Eng., May 3, 1925; came to U.S. 1963; s. Claude Saxon and Daisy Lilian S.; m. Maureen Cashin, June 4, 1949; children: Georgina Sara, Nicola Ann, Melanie Jane, Richard Robin, Charles Edward. M.B., B.S., Kings Coll., U. London, 1949, Ph.D., 1955, M.D., 1961. House surgeon Sir Cecil P.G. Wakeley, Kings Coll. Hosp. and Belgrave Hosp. for Children, London, 1948-49; lectr. anatomy Kings Coll., U. London, 1949-59, U. Durham, Eng., 1959-63; asst. prof. anatomy and medicine Yale U., 1963-65, assoc. prof., 1965-67, vis. prof. anatomy, 1969; prof., chmn. dept. anatomy N.J. Coll. Medicine and Dentistry, Jersey City, 1967-69; vis. prof. anatomy Harvard U., 1970, 71, 80, 86; prof. anatomy Coll. Medicine, U. Ariz., Tucson, 1970; prof., chmn. dept. anatomy George Washington U. Med. Ctr., Washington, 1972-88, prof. emeritus, 1988—. Author: Clinical Embryology for Medical Students, 1972, 3d edit., 1983, Clinical Anatomy for Medical Students, 1973, 5th edit., 1995, Atlas of Normal Radiographic Anatomy, 1976, Atlas of Clinical Anatomy, 1978, Gross Anatomy Dissector, 1978, Clinical Neuroanatomy for Medical Students, 1980, 3d edit., 1992, Student's Aid to Gross Anatomy, 1986, Clinical Anatomy for Anesthesiologists, 1988, Clinical Anatomy of the Eye, 1989, Gross Anatomy: A Review With Questions and Explanations, 1990, Neuroanatomy: A Review with Questions and Explanations, 1992, Clinical Anatomy for Emergency Medicine, 1993; contbr. articles to med. jours. Med. Research Council grantee, 1959; NIH grantee, 1963-65. Mem. Anat. Soc. Gt. Britain, Am. Soc. Anatomists, Alpha Omega Alpha. Home: 518 Boston Post Rd Madison CT 06443

SNELL, THADDEUS STEVENS, III, lawyer, retired building materials manufacturing company executive; b. Ida Grove, Iowa, Feb. 23, 1919; s. Thaddeus Stevens and Catharine (Noble) S.; m. Mary Ward, Nov., 1951 (div. 1965); children: William, Kathleen, Pamela, Debra, Robert; m. Gloria Cramer Brent, July, 1966 (dec. 1981); m. Eleanor Larson Hawes, Nov. 24, 1982. BS, Northwestern U., 1941, postgrad. Law Sch., 1941-42; postgrad. U.S. Naval Acad. Postgrad. Sch., 1944-45; LLB, Yale U., 1947. Bar: Ill. 1948, Iowa 1948. Assoc. Keck, Mahin & Cate and predecessors, Chgo., 1947-58, ptnr., 1959-71; v.p., corp. counsel U.S Gypsum Co., Chgo., 1971-82, v.p., gen. counsel, 1982-84; v.p., gen. counsel USG Corp., 1984-85; pvt. practice, Northbrook, Ill., 1986-93. Deacon Glenview (Ill.) Community Ch., 1958-61; pres. Kenilworth (Ill.) Citizens Adv. Comn., 1973-74. Served to lt. USNR, 1942-46. Mem. ABA, Ill. Bar Assn., Iowa Bar Assn., Chgo. Bar Assn., Legal Club Chgo.,. Clubs: University (Chgo.), Sunset Ridge Country (Chgo, Ill.), Quail Ridge Country (Boynton Beach, Fla.). Lodge: Masons. Home: 3537 Royal Tern Ln Boynton Beach FL 33436-5427

SNELLING, BARBARA, state official; b. Fall River, Mass., Mar. 22, 1928; d. Frank Taylor and Hazel (Russell) Weil; m. Richard Arkwright Snelling (five-term Gov. Vt.), June 14, 1947 (wid. Aug. 1991); children: Jacqueline, Mark, Diane, Andrew. AB magna cum laude, Radcliffe Coll., 1950; D of Pub. Svc. (hon.), Norwich U., 1981. V.p. U. Vt., 1974-82; pres. Snelling and Kolb, Inc., 1982—; lieut. gov. State of Vt., 1993—; bd. dirs., chmn. Chittenden Bank Corp. Trustee Radcliffe Coll., 1990—; bd. dirs. Vt. Community Found., 1986—, Shelburne Mus., 1988—; mem. Vt. Ednl. Partnerships, 1992—; v.p. for devel. and external affairs U. Vt., 1974-82; mem. Vt. State Bd. Edn., 1971-77; trustee Champlain Coll., 1971-74; mem. Vt. Alcohol and Drug Rehab. Commn., 1970-73, Shelburne Sch. Bd. 1958-73, chmn. 1965-73; mem. Vt. Ednl. Adv. Coun., 1968-71, Vt. Tchr. Edn. Adv. Com., 1968-70, Bd. of Sch. Dirs., Champlain Valley Union High Sch., 1962-69, chmn. 1962-68, others. Recipient Fanny G. Shaw award for Disting. Community Svc., Burlington Community Coun., 1972, Laymen's award Vt. Edn. Assn., 1965. Office: Lieut Gov State House Montpelier VT 05609-0101

SNELLING, GEORGE ARTHUR, banker; b. St. Petersburg, Fla., June 27, 1929; s. William Henry and Eula Hall S.; m. Carolyn Shiver, Mar. 3, 1963;

children—George, John S. B.S.B.A., U. Fla., 1951. Partner Smoak, Davis, Nixon & Snelling, C.P.A.s, Jacksonville, Fla., 1956-66; v.p. planning Barnett Banks of Fla., Jacksonville, 1966-76; exec. v.p. 1st Bancshares of Fla., Boca Raton, 1976-78; exec. v.p. Fla. Nat. Banks of Fla., Jacksonville, 1978-80; exec. v.p. corp. devel., chief fin. officer Sun Banks of Fla., Orlando, 1981-85; exec. v.p. corp. devel. SunTrust Banks, Inc., Atlanta, 1986-90; pres. Unicoy, Inc., Atlanta, 1991—. Trustee Fla. So. U. Served with USAF, 1951-55. Mem. AICPA. Democrat. Methodist. Home: 2682 Varner Dr NE Atlanta GA 30345-1559 Office: Unicoy Inc 2682 Varner Dr NE Atlanta GA 30345-1559

SNELLING, ROBERT ORREN, SR., franchising and employment executive; b. Phila., Aug. 16, 1932; s. Louis Raymond and Gwendolyn Anne (Preble) S.; m. Joan E.; 1951 (dec. 1970); children—Robert, Krista; m. Anne Morris, June 30, 1979; children—Rick Spragins, Leigh Crews, Linda Paulk. Student, Pa. State U., 1951-52; Dr. Lit. (hon.), Albright Coll., 1968. Profl. employment counsellor, Snelling & Snelling, Phila., 1952-53, gen. mgr., 1954-67, pres., 1962-68, chmn. bd., 1969—; speaker, lectr. in field. Author: The Opportunity Explosion, 1969, Jobs-What They Are-Where They Are-What They Pay, 1985, rev. edit., 1992, The Right Job, 1987, rev. edit., 1992; contbr. articles to profl. jours. Mem. long-range planning Sarasota 2000, 1976; mem. pvt. sector employment svcs. com. Dept. Labor, 1982; mem. Com. on Skilled Employment Brokering Svcs., 1984; mem. White Ho. Com. on Small Bus., 1986; mem. adv. com to U.S. Sec. William Brock, 1986; mem. Gov.'s Select Com. on Workforce 2000, 1988-89, chmn. govtl. regulations and benefits subcom., 1989. With U.S. Army, 1953-54. Recipient Golden Plate award, 1964; W.O. Blanchet award Pa. Assn. Personnel Service, 1976; Outstanding Citizen award Assn. Personnel N.Y., 1977; award for excellence Am. Acad. Achievement, 1964; Harold B. Nelson award, 1985. Mem. Internat. Franchise Assn., Nat. Assn. Personnel Cons., Nat. Assn. Temp. Svcs., U.S. C. of C. Republican. Baptist. Avocations: reading, photography.

SNELSON, KENNETH DUANE, sculptor; b. Pendleton, Oreg., June 29, 1927; s. John Tavner and Mildred F. (Unger) S.; m. Katherine Eve Kaufmann, May 2, 1972; 1 child, Andrea Nicole. Numerous. Student, U. Oreg., 1946-47, Black Mountain Coll., 1948-49, Chgo. Inst. Design, 1950-51, Academie Montmartre, Paris, 1951-52; D of Arts and Humane Letters (honoris causa), Rensselaer Poly. Inst., 1985. Subject of articles in art publs.; one-man shows U.S. and Germany, Holland, including Portrait of an Atom, Balt., 1979-80, De Cordova and Dana Mus. and Park, Lincoln, Mass., 1984, Zabriskie Gallery, 1984, Yoh Art Gallery, Osaka, Japan, 1991, Contemporary Sculpture Ctr., Tokyo, 1995, Maxwell Davidson Gallery, N.Y.C., 1994; major retrospective, Hirshhorn Mus. and Sculpture Garden of Smithsonian Instn., 1981, Albright-Knox Art Gallery, Buffalo, 1981, N.Y. Acad. Scis., 1989; group shows include Mus. Modern Art, N.Y.C., 1967, Whitney Mus., N.Y.C., 1966, 69, 70, Albright Knox Gallery, 1968, Prospect '68, Dusseldorf, Germany, 1968, Salon International de Galeries Pilotes, Lausanne, Switzerland, 1970, Sammlun Etzold, Kolnischer Kunstverein, Cologne, Germany, 1970, Expo '70, Osaka, Japan, 1970, Fondation Maeght, St. Paul de Vence, France, 1970, Art Inst. Chgo., 1972; represented in permanent collections including, Mus. Modern Art, Whitney Mus. Am. Art, cities of Hannover and Hamburg, Germany, Rijksmuseum Kroller Muller, Otterlo, Holland, Rijksmuseum, Amsterdam, Holland, Japan Iron, Steel Fedn., Osaka, City of Balt., Hirshhorn Mus., Milw. Art Center, City of Buffalo, Mus. Modern Art, Shiga, Japan; author: Full Circle: Panoramas of Paris, Venice, Rome, Siena and Kyoto, 1990. Served with USNR, 1945-46. DAAD fellow Berlin Kunstlerprogram, 1976; recipient AIA Artist's medal, 1981, Art award Am. Inst. Arts and Letters, 1987, Prix Ars Electronica Siemens AG for Computer Graphics, Linz, Austria, 1989. Mem. Am. Acad. Arts and Letters. Patentee discontinuous compression structures, model for atomic forms. *My art is concerned with nature in its most fundamental aspect, the patterns of physical forces in space.*

SNELSON, PAMELA, health facility administrator; b. Adak, Alaska, May 10, 1951; d. Buford C. and Virginia Ellen (Paul) Hartwick; m. Walter Graves Snelson II, Sept. 2, 1983; children: Bobbie Jean, Michael Robert. Diploma in practical nursing, Amarillo Coll., 1979, ADN, 1982. Staff nurse High Plains Bapt. Hosp., Amarillo, Tex.; utilization rev. coord. St. Anthony's Hosp., Amarillo, dir. urology, asst. v.p. nursing; v.p. nursing, staff operating rm. nurse Panhandle Surg. Hosp., asst. adminstr. nursing. Mem. Am. Orgn. Nurse Execs., Nat. League Nursing, ANA. Office: St Anthony's Hosp 200 NW Sevent Amarillo TX 79107

SNETSINGER, DAVID CLARENCE, retired animal feed company executive; b. Barrington, Ill., Apr. 22, 1930; s. Clarence J. and Helen (Mills) S.; m. Phoebe Burnett; children: Penny, Tom, Carol, Susan. BS, U. Ill., 1952, MS, 1957, PhD, 1959. Registered profl. animal scientist. Asst. prof. U. Minn., 1959-62, assoc. prof., 1962-67; poultry area mgr. Purina Mills Inc., St Louis, 1967-69, dir. poultry group, 1970-87, v.p. rsch., 1987-91; ret., 1991. Patentee in field of poultry feeding programs and equipment; author 116 sci. and popular trade articles on poultry nutrition. 1st lt. U.S. Army, 1952-54. Fellow Poultry Sci. Assn. (pres. 1988-89); mem. World's Poultry Sci. (v.p. 1989-92), Fedn. Food Animal Scis. (sec.-treas. 1989-92), Animal Sci. Assn., Am. Inst. Nutrition, Dairy Sci. Assn., Internat. Brotherhood Magicians (pres. 1982-83, 93-94), Soc. Am. Magicians (v.p. St. Louis chpt. 1980-81), Sigma Xi.

SNETZER, MICHAEL ALAN, multi-industry executive; b. Denver, May 26, 1940; s. Robert Ellis and Kathryn (Wake) S.; m. Peggy Ann Sparks, Jan., 1964 (div. 1973); children: Michael Ellis, Gregory Alan; m. Deborah Kay Gee, Mar. 15, 1975; 1 child, Robert Adam. BS, U. Ark., 1963; MBA, So. Meth. U., 1969. Indsl. engr. Collins Radio Co., Dallas, 1966-69; v.p. fin. UCCEL Corp., Dallas, 1969-77; v.p. fin. Contran Corp., Dallas, 1977-84, exec. v.p., 1984—; pres. Valhi, Inc., Dallas, 1980—; chmn., CEO Medite Corp., 1985—; with Valcor, Inc., 1993—; bd. dirs. NL Industries, Inc., Houston, Baroid Corp., Houston, Amalgamated Sugar Co., Ogden, Utah; chmn., dir. Medite Corp. wholly owned subs. Valhi Inc. Served to capt. Spl. Forces, U.S. Army, 1963-66, Vietnam. Recipient Bronze star. Mem. Univ. Club, Bent Tree Country Club. Republican. Methodist. Home: 18722 Campbell Rd Dallas TX 75252-5123 Office: Valhi Inc 3 Lincoln Ctr 5430 Lyndon B Johnson Fwy Dallas TX 75240-2601 also: Medite Corp 1901 N Pacific Hwy Medford OR 97501-1663

SNIBBE, RICHARD W., architect; b. Balt., Oct. 31, 1916; s. George W. and Mildred (Robinson) S.; m. Miriam Bergman, Jan. 3, 1942 (dec.); children: John Robinson, Paul Clor; m. Patricia Lois Miscall, Sept. 8, 1962. B.A., St. Johns Coll., 1939; postgrad., Harvard Grad. Sch. Design, 1939-41. Registered profl. archit.; lic. architect N.Y. Assoc. Edward D. Stone (architect), N.Y.C., 1951-56; partner Ballard, Todd & Snibbe, N.Y.C., 1957-61; individual practice architecture N.Y.C., 1962; partner Myller, Snibbe, Tafel, N.Y.C., 1962-67, Snibbe, Tafel, Lindholm, 1967-73, Wilson & Snibbe (architects, planners, engrs.), N.Y.C., from 1970; formed Snibbes Inc. (producers archtl. films), 1981; instr. Cooper Union, N.Y.C., 1949; vis. critic Columbia, N.Y.C., 1956, Pratt Inst., N.Y.C., 1962; founder Archtl. Film Library, 1982. Author: Small Commercial Buildings, 1956, Selected Works and Essays, 1983; important works include U.S. embassy, New Delhi, India (as assoc.), 1955, Tennis Pavilion, Princeton, 1960 (AIA honor award 1962), grad. dormitories Princeton U., 1961, comprehensive campus plan and bldgs. State U. Coll, Geneseo, N.Y., 1962-72, Handloser Project, Future Town, 1973, entry to Paris Opera Competition 1983; pub. L'Arca, 1990; exhibited in Mus. Modern Art, N.Y.C., Transformations in Modern Architecture, 1979; producer: (film) Maison La Roche-Jeanneret by Le Corbusier, 1983, (TV film) Great Modern Architecture of the Last 25 Years, 1994. Chmn. aesthetics com., bd. dirs. Gramercy Neighborhood Assn. Inc. Brunner scholar N.Y. chpt. AIA, 1957. Fellow AIA (chmn. nat. com. on aesthetics 1963, mem. emeritus 1990—); mem. Nat. Com. on Aesthetics (founder, chmn. 1963, mem. emeritus 1990—), Harvard Grad. Sch. Design Assn., Am. Arbitration Assn., Players Club. Patentee for suspended structure, Landspan. Address: 139 E 18th St New York NY 10003

SNIDER, EDWARD MALCOLM, professional hockey club executive; b. Washington, Jan. 6, 1933; s. Sol C. and Lillian (Bonas) S.; m. Martha McGeary, March 4, 1984; children: Craig Alan, Jay Thomas, Lindy Lou, Tina Suzanne, Sarena Lynn, Samuel Everett. B.S., U. Md., 1955. CPA, Md. Maj. stockholder, exec. v.p. Edge Ltd., Washington, 1957-63; v.p. Phila. Eagles Football Club, 1964-67; owner Phila. Flyers Hockey Club, 1967—;

chmn. bd. Spectrum Arena, Phila., 1967—; bd. govs. NHL, 1967—; established spectator, sports, entertainment and comm. firm adv. bd. Sol C. Snider Entrepreneurial Ctr. U Pa.; bd. overseers Wharton Sch. U. Pa.; bd. dirs. Inst. for Cancer and Blood Diseases Hahnemann U., Simon Weisenthal Ctr.; bd. trustees Inst. for Objectivist Studies. Office: Phila Flyers Pattison Pl Philadelphia PA 19148

SNIDER, ELIOT L., lumber company executive; b. Cambridge, Mass., Apr. 10, 1921; s. Harry and Lena (Korelitz) S.; m. Ruth Freund, 1945; children: Andrew, Paul, Nancy. BA, Harvard U., 1941, MBA, 1943. Pres. Mass. Lumber Co., Cambridge, 1953—; chmn., dir. George McQuesten Co., Inc., Eastern Terminals, Inc.; dir. Masco Corp., Kravis Ctr.; dir. corps. Chmn. Beth Israel Hosp., Boston, 1982-86, trustee 1976—; overseer Mus. Fine Arts; mem. Mass. Gen. Hosp. Corp., dean's coun. Harvard U. Sch. Pub. Health. Pres. Snider Charitable Trust. Served to lt. USN, 1943-45. Mem. Chief Execs. Orgn., World Bus. Coun. Republican. Clubs: Longwood, Harvard, N.Y. Yacht, Rotary. Office: Mass Lumber Co 929 Massachusetts Ave Cambridge MA 02139-3143

SNIDER, ERIC ROSS, music critic; b. Cleve., Apr. 21, 1954; s. Donald ross and Erma Marie (Ceschini) S.; m. Barbara Ann Gartner, June 12, 1982; children: Karin Alison, Daniel Ryan. BA, SUNY, Cortland, 1976. Critic Jazziz Mag., Gainesville, Fla., 1982-88; editor, writer Music Mag., St. Petersburg, Fla., 1980-87; pop music critic St. Petersburg Times, 1987—. Recipient Gen. Excellence in Criticism award Fla. Press Club, 1987, 89. Avocations: basketball, softball, general sports. Office: St Petersburg Times 490 1st Ave S Saint Petersburg FL 33701-4204

SNIDER, GORDON LLOYD, physician; b. Toronto, Ont., Can., Apr. 11, 1922; came to U.S., 1946, naturalized, 1956; s. Isadore Leonard and Rebecca (Freeman) S.; m. Ruth Charlotte Tobias, May 18, 1945; children: Barry Bernard, Martin David, Rebecca Eve. MD, U. Toronto, 1944. Intern Toronto Gen. Hosp., 1944-45; resident in medicine Bronx Hosp., 1946-47; resident in pathology Mass. Meml. Hosps., Boston, 1947-48; fellow in medicine Lahey Clinic, Boston, 1948-49; fellow in pulmonary medicine Trudeau San., Trudeau, N.Y., 1949-50; asst. chest dept. Michael Reese Hosp., Chgo., 1950-61; attending physician Winfield (Ill.) Hosp., 1950-61; cons. physician, dir. pulmonary function lab. Mcpl. Tb San., Chgo., 1954-68; chief div. thoracic medicine Mt. Sinai Hosp., Chgo., 1961-66; acting chmn. depts. medicine Chgo. Med. Sch. and Mt. Sinai Hosp., 1965-66; chief pulmonary disease sect. Wood VA Hosp.; attending physician Milwaukee County Gen. Hosp., Wood, Wis., 1966-68; asst. prof. Chgo. Med. Sch., 1958-61, assoc. prof., 1961-64, prof., 1964-66; prof. Marquette U. Sch. Medicine, 1966-68; prof. medicine, head pulmonary medicine sect. Boston U. Sch. Medicine, 1968-87; chief pulmonary medicine sect., Boston VA Med Ctr., 1968-88, chief med. svc., 1986—; pulmonary sect. mem. Evans Dept. Clin. Rsch., Univ. Hosp., Boston, 1968—; Maurice B. Strauss prof. medicine, Boston U. and Tufts U. Schs. Medicine, 1986-93, Boston U. Sch. Medicine, 1993—; Presdl. lectr. Soc. European Pulmonologists, 4th Ann. Congress, Stressa-Milan, Italy, 1986, Blankenhorn lectr. Cin. Soc. Ind. Medicine, 1989; Parker B. Francis lectr. 6th Thomas L. Petty Aspen Lung Conf., 1991; vis. prof. U. Cin. Sch. Medicine, 1989; Frank T. Fulton vis. physician-in-chief pro tempore R.I. Hosp. and Brown U., Providence, 1988; med. adv. bd. Puritan-Bennett Corp.; chmn. sci. adv. com. Norman B. Salvesen Emphysema Trust, U. Edinburgh, 1981-93; Irving Kass lectr. U. Nebr., 1992. Served to capt. M.C. Royal Can. Army, 1945-46. Co-recipient Alton Ochsner award minimizing smoking and health, 1990; NIH grantee, 1962-91; Francis S. North travel fellow, 1978; 6th Robert K. Match Disting. scholar L.I. Jewish Hosp., 1991. Fellow Am. Coll. Chest Physicians (Simon Rodbard lectr. 1985), ACP; mem. Am. Fedn. Clin. Research, Am. Thoracic Soc. (pres. 1986, Amberson lectr. 1992), Central Soc. Clin. Research, Sigma Xi, Alpha Omega Alpha. Jewish. Home: 24 Holly Rd Newton MA 02168-1449 Office: VA Med Center 150 S Huntington Ave Jamaica Plain MA 02130-4820

SNIDER, HARLAN TANNER, former manufacturing company executive; b. Owensboro, Ky., July 20, 1926; s. George William and Lydia (Tanner) S.; m. Helen Boswell, Mar. 7, 1953; children—William Jeffrey, Katherine Snider. B.A., Transylvania U., 1949. Territory salesman Sunray DX Corp., Owensboro, 1950-57; dist. sales mgr. Sunray DX Corp., Ind. 1958-63; div. mgr. Sunray DX Corp., Iowa, 1963-65; dir. mktg. services Sunray DX Corp., Tulsa, 1955-67; pres. Red Bar Chems., Tulsa, 1967-69; dir. petrochems. Sun Oil Co., Phila., 1969-71; v.p. mktg. Sun Oil Co., 1973-75; pres. Sunmark Industries, Phila., 1975-79; sr. v.p., external affairs Sun Co., Inc., Radnor, Pa., 1980-84; sr. v.p. planning publ. affairs Sun Co., 1984-88; ret., 1988. Served with USAF, 1944-46. Mem. Am. Petroleum Industry, 25 Yr. Club Petroleum Industry. Republican. Presbyterian. Clubs: Capitol Hill (Washington), Union League (Phila.); Aronimink Golf (Newtown Square, Pa.), Mariner Sands Golf Club (Stuart, Fla.). Home (winter): 7013 SE Pacific Dr Stuart FL 34997-8606

SNIDER, HAROLD WAYNE, risk and insurance educator; b. Puyallup, Wash., Apr. 16, 1923; s. P. Marion and Grace Stevenson (Short) S.; m. Isobel Milne Dice, Jan. 20, 1961. BA, U. Wash., 1946, MA, 1950; PhD, U. Pa., 1955. Instr. bus. U. Wash., 1952-54; assoc. prof. Ill. Wesleyan U., 1954-57; asst. prof. U. Pa., 1957-64; prof. risk mgmt. and ins. Temple U., Phila., 1964-91, prof. emeritus, 1991—; dir. Planned Protection Ins. Co. Author: Life Insurance Investment in Commercial Real Estate, 1956, Risk Management, 1963, (with Denenberg and others) Risk and Insurance, 1964, The Automobile Accident Problem: Saskatchewan Approach, 1973, Employee Benefit Administration, 1981; contbg. author: The Job of Risk Management, 1962. Bd. dirs. Planned Parenthood Fedn., Am., 1980-83. Served with AUS, 1943-46. S.S. Huebner Found. fellow, 1950-52. Mem. Risk and Ins. Mgmt. Soc., Am. Mgmt. Assn., Am. Risk and Ins. Soc., Phi Beta Kappa, Beta Gamma Sigma. Home: Unit 2A The Meadows 501 N Bethlehem Pike Apt 2A Ambler PA 19002-2516 Office: Sch Bus Adminstrn Temple U Philadelphia PA 19122

SNIDER, JAMES RHODES, radiologist; b. Pawnee, Okla., May 16, 1931; s. John Henry and Gladys Opal (Rhodes) S.; B.S., U. Okla., 1953, M.D., 1956; m. Lynadell Vivion, Dec. 27, 1954; children—Jon, Jan. Intern, Edward Meyer Meml. Hosp., Buffalo, 1956-57; resident radiology U. Okla. Med. Center, 1959-62; radiologist Holt-Krock Clinic and Sparks Regional Med. Center, Ft. Smith, Ark., 1962—; dir. Fairfield Community Land Co., Little Rock, 1968-87, Fairfield Communities, Inc., 1968-87. Mem. Ark. Bd. Pub. Welfare, 1969-71. Bd. dirs. U. Okla. Assn., 1967-70, U. Okla. Alumni Devel. Fund, 1970-74; bd. visitors U. Okla. Served to lt. comdr. USNR, 1957-62. Mem. Am. Coll. Radiology, Radiol. Soc. N.Am., Am. Roentgen Ray Soc., AMA, Phi Beta Kappa, Beta Theta Pi, Alpha Epsilon Delta. Assoc. editor Computerized Tomography, 1976-88. Home: 5814 S Cliff Dr Fort Smith AR 72903-3845 Office: 1500 Dodson Ave Fort Smith AR 72901-5193

SNIDER, JEROME GUY, lawyer; b. Lakewood, N.J., Mar. 14, 1950; s. Theodore Charles and Minnie Snider; m. Naomi S. Herman, Sept. 20, 1981; 1 child, Benjamin Herman. A.B, Rutgers U., 1972; JD, U. Pa., 1975. Bar: N.Y. 1976, U.S. Dist. Ct. (so. and ea. dists.) N.Y. 1976, U.S. Dist. Ct. (no. dist.) Calif. 1979, U.S. Supreme Ct. 1980, U.S. Dist. Ct. D.C. 1983, U.S. Ct. Appeals (6th cir.) 1984, U.S. Ct. Appeals (D.C. cir.) 1986. Law clk. to chief judge U.S. Dist. Ct. (so. dist.) N.Y., N.Y.C, 1975-77; assoc. Davis Polk & Wardwell, N.Y.C., 1977-82, ptnr., Washington, 1983—. Mem. ABA, Fed. Bar Assn. Jewish. Home: 4821 43rd St NW Washington DC 20016-4064 Office: Davis Polk & Wardwell 1575 I St NW Washington DC 20005-1196 also: Davis Polk & Wardwell 450 Lexington Ave New York NY 10017-3911

SNIDER, JOHN JOSEPH, lawyer; b. Seminole, Okla., July 25, 1928; s. George Nathan and Katherine (Harris) S.; m. Harriet Jean Edmonds, June 14, 1952; children—John Joseph, Dorothy Susan (Mrs. Mark E. Blohm), William Arnold. A.B., U. Okla., 1950, LL.B., 1955. Bar: Okla. bar 1955. Since practiced in Oklahoma City; atty. Fellers, Snider, Blankenship, Bailey & Tippens, 1964-93, counsel to, 1993—; mem. Okla. adv. council Nat. Legal Services Corp., 1976-77. Pres. Okla. Soc. to Prevent Blindness, 1965-71; bd. dirs. Hosp. Hospitality House, Okla., 1978-86; bd. dirs. Nat. Soc. Prevention Blindness, 1971-75; vice chmn. Oklahoma City Crime Prevention Council, 1976-77. Served to 1st lt. USAF, 1950-53. Fellow Am. Bar Found. (Okla. chmn. 1986-88); mem. Oklahoma City C. of C., ABA, Okla. Bar Assn., Okla. County Bar Assn., Am. Judicature Soc., Phi Delta Phi, Phi Kappa Psi.

Methodist. Home: 2018 Redbud Pl Edmond OK 73013-7733 Office: First Nat Bldg Oklahoma City OK 73102

SNIDER, L. BRITT, government executive; b. Rocky Mount, N.C., Jan. 12, 1945; s. Arnold Holmes and Kate Mills (Suiter) S.; m. Virginia Lansford, Aug. 24, 1974; 1 child, Britt Arnold. BA, Davidson (N.C.) Coll., 1966; JD, U. Va., 1969. Counsel judiciary subcom. on constl. rights U.S. Senate, Washington, 1971-75, counsel select com. on intelligence, 1975-76; ptnr. Ketner & Snider, Salisbury, N.C., 1976-77; counsel govt. ops. subcom. on govt. info. U.S. Ho. Reps., Washington, 1977; asst. dep. undersec. counter-intelligence and security Dept. Def., Washington, 1977-87; minority counsel U.S. Senate Intelligence Com., Washington, 1987-89, gen. counsel, 1989-95, staff dir. commn. on roles and capabilities of U.S. Intelligence Cmty., 1995—; staff dir. Commn. to Rev. Security Practices and Procedures Dept. Def., Washington, 1985. Served to capt. U.S. Army, 1969-71, Vietnam. Mem. Va. Bar Assn., D.C. Bar Assn. Democrat. Episcopalian. Avocations: tennis, jogging, reading.

SNIDER, LAWRENCE K., lawyer; b. Detroit, Dec. 28, 1938; s. Ben and Ida (Hertz) S.; m. Maxine Bobman, Aug. 12, 1962; children: Stephanie, Suzanne. BA, U. Mich., 1960, JD, 1963. Bar: Mich. 1964, Ill. 1991. Ptnr. Jaffe, Snider, Raitt & Heuer, Detroit, 1968-91, Mayer, Brown & Platt, Chgo., 1991—; mem. Nat. Bankruptcy Conf., Am. Coll. Bankruptcy, 1991—. Contbr. articles to profl. jours. Mem. Mich. Coun. for the Arts, 1990-91. Avocations: photography, collections. Office: Mayer Brown & Platt 190 S La Salle St Chicago IL 60603-3410

SNIDER, ROBERT F., chemistry educator, researcher; b. Calgary, Alta., Can., Nov. 22, 1931; s. Edward C. and Agnes S. (Klaeson) S.; children: Wendy A., Timothy J., Terry E., Geoffrey Y, Eric A. M. Burrough. B.S., U. Alta., 1953; Ph.D., U. Wis. 1958. Postdoctoral fellow Nat. Research Council Can., Ottawa, 1958; instr. II U. B.C., Vancouver, 1958-60, asst. prof., 1960-65, assoc. prof., 1965-69, prof., 1969—; vis. research prof. U. Leiden, Netherlands, 1973-74. Recipient gov. gen. gold medal U. Alta., 1953; U. Wis. WARF unassigned fellow, 1953-55; Izaac Walton Killam Meml. fellowship, 1985-86. Fellow Chem. Inst. Can., Royal Soc. Can.; mem. Am. Phys. Soc., Can. Assn. Physicists. Home: 3952 W 29th St, Vancouver, BC Canada V6S 1T9 Office: U BC, 2036 Main Mall, Vancouver, BC Canada V6T 1Z1

SNIDER, ROBERT LARRY, management consultant; b. Muskogee, Okla., Aug. 10, 1932; s. George Robert and Kathryn (Smiser) S.; m. Gerlene Rose Tipton, Nov. 26, 1953; children: Melody Kathryn Porter, Rebecca Lee. B.S. in Indsl. Engring., U. Houston, 1955, postgrad., 1956; postgrad., Pomona Coll., 1960. Cert. mgmt. cons. Instr. U. Houston Coll. Engring., 1955-56; sr. indsl. engr. Sheffield Steel Corp., Houston, 1955-59, Kaiser Steel Co., Fontana, Calif., 1959-60; cons. Arthur Young & Co., Los Angeles, 1960-61; mgmt. analyst Iranian Oil Exploration & Producing Co., Masjidi-Suliman, Iran, 1961-62; cons., 1962-65; v.p. operating methods div. Booz, Allen & Hamilton, Inc., Dallas, 1965-67; v.p., mng. officer internat. prodn. and inventory control div. Booz, Allen & Hamilton, Inc., 1967-69; prin., gen. cons. practice Peat Marwick Mitchell, CPAs, Houston, 1969-71; exec. v.p. mfg. Sterling Electronics Corp., Houston, 1971-72, pres., chief operating officer, 1972-77; pres., chief exec. officer Rapoca Energy Corp., Cin., 1977-79; mng. partner, cons. Coopers & Lybrand, Southwest, Houston, 1979-81; mng. dir. Southwest region Korn Ferry Internat., Houston, 1981-86; ptnr.-in-charge Houston Mgmt. Cons. Practice, 1986-91; ptnr. cons. Southwest Enterprise Coopers & Lybrand, Houston, 1991-92; ptnr. S.W. Mfg. Consulting Process Improvement Group Coopers & Lybrand, Houston, Pakistan/Mid. Asia, 1992-93; internat. cons. ptnr. Coopers & Lybrand, Houston, 1993—. Past mem. bd. dirs., exec. com. Houston Jr. Achievement; pastchmn. bd. mem. found. bd.and adminstrv. bd. Chapel Wood Meth. Ch.; ret. exec. com., bd. dirs. Houston Grand Opera. Served with C.E. AUS, 1956. Recipient Outstandng Mil. Engr. award Soc. Mil Engrs., 1955; named Disting. Alumni, Cullen Coll. Engring., U. Houston, 1991. Mem. Soc. Mining Engrs., U. Houston Alumni Assn. (past bd. dirs., exec. com., past pres., chmn.), Houston Club, Houstonian Club, Houston City Club, Phi Theta Kappa, Phi Kappa Phi. Home: 11643 Greenbay St Houston TX 77024-6430 Office: Coopers & Lybrand 1100 Louisiana St Ste 4000 Houston TX 77002-5218

SNIDER, TIM, mining executive. Pres. Phelps Dodge Morenci Inc., Morenci, Ariz. Office: Phelps Dodge Morenci Inc 4521 US Hwy 191 Morenci AZ 85540*

SNIFFEN, MICHAEL JOSEPH, hospital administrator; b. Ossining, N.Y., June 16, 1949; s. John Francis and Mary Agnes (Madden) S.; m. Anne Marie Gillick; children: Kevin, Kristina. BS, Fordham U., 1971; MBA in Hosp. Adminstrn., Baruch Coll., 1977. Dir. of fin. planning Westchester div. N.Y. Hosp., White Plains, N.Y., 1971-74; assoc. dir. N.Y. Hosp., N.Y.C., 1974-80, sr. assoc. dir., assoc. dean Cornell Med. Ctr., 1980-87; pres., chief exec. officer Overlook Hosp., Summit, N.J., 1987—; exec. dir. Cornell Health Policy Program, N.Y.C., 1984-87; adminstr. program Commonwealth Fund, N.Y.C., 1978-81; adv. bd. Robert Wood Johnson Found.-Teaching Nursing Home Program, Princeton, N.J., 1980-86. Vol. March of Dimes, Tarrytown, N.Y., 1984-88; bd. dirs. St. Columbans Sch., Peekskill, N.Y., 1981-84; mem. various Father's Clubs, Westchester County, N.Y., 1976-91. Mem. Am. Coll. Healthcare Execs., Hosp. Fin. Mgmt. Assn. (advanced mem.), Echo Lake Country Club (Westfield, N.J.), Beacon Hill Country Club, Baltusrol Country Club (Springfield, N.J.), Rotary. Roman Catholic. Avocations: golf, college basketball. Home: 49 Drum Hill Rd Summit NJ 07901-3141 Office: Overlook Hosp 99 Beauvoir Ave Summit NJ 07902

SNIFFIN, JOHN HARRISON, retail executive; b. N.Y.C., Feb. 25, 1942; s. Harrison Webb and Elizabeth (Wood) S.; m. Beverly Ann Bailey, Sept. 24, 1966; children: Christine, John, Ned, Ellen. BBA, Ga. State U., 1967, MBA, 1969. Internal audit mgr. Sears, Roebuck and Co., Atlanta, 1961-69; asst. controller Heilig-Meyers Co., Richmond, Va., 1969-72, asst. treas., 1972-84, treas., 1984-86, v.p., treas., sec., 1986, v.p. mdse., 1986-89, sr. v.p. merchandising, 1989-92; sr. v.p. govt. rels., 1992—. Mem. retail exec. adv. com. Ctr. for Retailing, James Madison U. Mem. Fin. Execs. Inst., So. Home Furnishings Assn. (exec. com., v.p.), Va. Retail Mchts. Assn. (bd. dirs.), N.C. Retail Mchts. Assn. (bd. dirs.), Ky. Retail Fedn. (bd. dirs.), Pa. Retailers Assn. (bd. dirs.). Republican. Roman Catholic. Avocations: music, golf. Office: Heilig-Meyers Co 2235 Staples Mill Rd Richmond VA 23230-2946

SNIPES, WESLEY, actor. Grad., SUNY, Purchase, 1980. Appeared in Broadway plays Boys of Winter, Execution of Justice, Death and King's Horsemen; films include Streets of Gold, 1986, Vietnam War Story (ACE award for best actor 1989), Mo'Better Blues, 1990, Major League, 1989, New Jack City, 1991, Jungle Fever, 1991, The Waterdance, 1992, White Can't Jump, 1992, Passenger 57, 1992, Rising Sun, 1993, Demolition Man, 1993, Boiling Point, 1993, Sugar Hill, 1994, Drop Zone, 1994, To Wong Foo, Thanks for Everything, Julie Newmar, 1995, The Money Train, 1995. *

SNITOW, CHARLES, lawyer; b. N.Y.C., Feb. 7, 1907; m. Virginia Levitt, Nov. 2, 1935; children: Ann Barr, Alan Mark. AB, Cornell U., 1928, JD, 1930. Ptnr. Pomerance & Snitow, N.Y.C., 1931—; pres. Nat. Hardward Show Inc., N.Y.C., 1945-70, World Hobby Exposition, Chgo., Phila., 1948-53, Charles Snitow Orgn., N.Y.C., 1950-79, Internat. Auto Show, N.Y.C. 1952-80, Nat. Fancy Food Conf. Show, N.Y.C., 1955-70, U.S. World Trade Fair Inc., N.Y.C., San Francisco, 1957-66, Internat. Photography & Travel Show Inc., N.Y.C., 1960-72, Consumer Electronics Show, N.Y.C., 1967-71, Snitow Show Consultants, Inc., N.Y.C., 1975—; cons. Soviet Expn. Sci. and Tech., N.Y.C., 1959, N.C. Internat. Fair, Charlotte, 1959, Brit. Expn., N.Y.C., 1960, Cahners Expn. Group divsn. Reed Exhbn. Cos., N.Y.C., 1970-87, Brazil Expo, N.Y., Chgo., L.A., Dallas, Atlanta, Miami, Fla., 1981, Greater N.Y. Internat. Auto Show, 1982—, East/Cen. Europe Auto Expo, N.Y., 1994. Contbr. articles to Cornell Law Quar. Bd. dirs. Bill of Rights Found., N.Y.C., 1980; mem. Met. Opera Chorus, Schola Cantorum, Collegiate Chorale. Recipient cert. of honor March of Dimes, Gold Key-Medal of Honor, City of N.Y., 1960-62, Gran Prix Am., France, 1965, Garcia Moreno medal Equador, 1966; named knight, Order of Merit, Republic of Italy, 1963; named to Order Hon. Ky. Cols., La. Cols. Mem. Nat. Assn. Expn. Mgrs. (hon., Kings Glove award for excellence 1991), Latin Am. C. of

C., Cornell Club, Savage Club, Phi Beta Kappa, Alpha Kappa Delta. Avocation: singing. Home: 81 Walworth Ave Scarsdale NY 10583-1140 Office: Snitow Show Cons Inc 4 Sniffen Ct New York NY 10016-3505

SNITZER, ELIAS, physicist; b. Lynn, Mass., Feb. 27, 1925; s. Isaac and Jenny (Sussman) S.; m. Shirley Ann Wood, Nov. 22, 1950; children: Sandra, Barbara, Peter, Helen, Louis. B.S.E.E., Tufts U., 1946; M.S. in Physics, U. Chgo., 1950, Ph.D., 1953. Research physicist Honeywell Corp., Phila., 1954-56; assoc. prof. Lowell Technol. Inst., Mass., 1956-58; dir. research Am. Optical Co., Southbridge, Mass., 1959-76; mgr. applied physics United Technologies Research, East Hartford, Conn., 1977-84; mgr. fiber optics Polaroid, Cambridge, Mass., 1984-88; prof. Rutgers U., 1989—. Contbr. articles to profl. jours. Inventor glass laser. Served with USN, 1943-46. Fellow Optical Soc. Am., Ceramic Soc.; mem. NAE, IEEE (George Morey award 1971, Quantum Electronics award 1979, Charles Townes award 1991, John Tyndall award 1994), Am. Phys. Soc. Democrat. Jewish. Home: 8 Smoke Tree Close Piscataway NJ 08854-5109 Office: Rutgers U Fiber Optics Materials Rsch Program PO Box 909 Piscataway NJ 08855-0909

SNODDON, LARRY ERLE, public relations executive; b. Grosse Pointe, Mich., June 10, 1945; s. Firman and Evelyn Marie (McDonnell) S.; m. Kathleen McGreevy, Mar. 2, 1985; children: Elizabeth, Sarah, Emily. B.A., U. Mich.; M.A., U. Wis.-Madison. Corp. pub. relations rep. Gen. Motors Corp., Detroit, 1968-70; corp. pub. relations mgr. Am. Express Co., N.Y.C., 1970-72; pres. for Ams. Burson-Marsteller, N.Y.C., 1972-87; pres. for Europe Burson-Marsteller, London, 1987-91; pres., CEO Burson-Marsteller, N.Y.C., 1992-95; vice chmn. Young & Rubicam, Inc., N.Y.C., 1995—; bd. dirs. Young & Rubicam, Inc. Bd. dirs. Am. II Syndicate for 1987 Am.'s Cup, U.S.-China Arts Exchange; mem. coun. Bus. in the Community, London. Fellow Royal Soc. London, Prince of Wales Bus. Leaders Forum; mem. Univ. Club, N.Y. Yacht Club, Greenwich Country Club, Riverside Yacht Club, Royal Automobile Club. Avocation: sailing.

SNODDY, JAMES ERNEST, education educator; b. Perrysville, Ind., Oct. 6, 1932; s. James Elmer and Edna May (Hayworth) S.; m. Alice Joanne Crowder, Aug. 15, 1954; children—Ryan Anthony, Elise Suzanne. B.S., Ind. State U., 1954; M.Ed., U. Ill., 1961, Ed.D., 1967. Tchr. Danville (Ill.) Public Schs., 1954-57, prin., 1961-64; instr. U. Ill., Champaign, 1965-67; prof. edn. Mich. State U., East Lansing, 1967-72; chmn. dept. elem. and spl. edn. Mich. State U., 1972-78, prof. edn., 1978—; dir. Program CORK, 1978-82. Served with U.S. Army, 1955-57. Mem. Am. Assn. for Adult and Continuing Edn., Commn. of Profs. of Adult and Continuing Edn. Methodist. Home: 2194 Lagoon Dr Okemos MI 48864-2711 Office: Mich State U 419 Erickson Hall East Lansing MI 48824-1034

SNODGRASS, W. D., writer, educator; b. Wilkinsburg, Pa., Jan. 5, 1926; s. Bruce DeWitt and Jesse Helen (Murchie) S.; m. Lila Jean Hank, June 6, 1946 (div. 1953); 1 child, Cynthia Jean; m. Janice Marie Ferguson Wilson, Mar. 19, 1954 (div. Aug. 1966); children—Kathy Ann Wilson (stepdau.), Russell Bruce; m. Camille Rykowski, Sept. 13, 1967 (div. 1977); m. Kathleen Brown, June 20, 1985. Student, Geneva Coll., 1943-44, 46-47; B.A., State U. Iowa, 1949, M.A., 1951, M.F.A., 1953; hon. doctorate, Allegheny Coll., 1991. Faculty English dept. Cornell U., Ithaca, N.Y., 1955-57; faculty English dept. U. Rochester, N.Y., 1957-58; prof. English Wayne State U., Detroit, until 1968; prof. English and speech Syracuse U., N.Y., 1968-76; Disting. prof. of creative writing and contemp. poetry U. Del., Newark, 1979-94, retired, 1994; faculty Morehead Writers' Conf., Ky., summer 1955, Antioch Writers' Conf., Yellow Springs, Ohio, summer 1958, 59; disting. vis. prof. Old Dominion U., Norfolk, Va.; instr. Narrative Poetry Workshop SUNY, Binghamton, 1977, Cranbrook Writers' Conf., Birmingham, Mich., 1981. Author: (poems) Heart's Needle (Pulitzer prize 1960), 1959, After Experience, 1968, Remains (under pseudonym S.S. Gardons) 1970, The Fuhrer Bunker, 1977, If Birds Build With Your Hair, 1979, The Boy Made of Meat, 1982, Magda Goebbels (poems from The Fuhrer Bunker, 1983), Heinrich Himmler (poems from The Fuhrer Bunker) 1983, D.D. Byrde Calling Jennie Wrenne, 1984, A Colored Poem, 1986, The House the Poet Built, 1986, 1987, Selected Poems, 1957-87, W.D.'s Midnight Carnival: Poems by W.D. Snodgrass and Paintings by DeLoss McGraw, 1988, The Death of Cock Robin: Poems by W.D. Snodgrass and Paintings by DeLoss McGraw, 1989, Autumn Variations, 1990; translator: (with Lore Segal) Gallows' Songs of Christian Morgenstern, Six Troubadour Songs, 1977, Traditional Hungarian Songs, 1978, Six Minnesinger Songs, 1983, The Four Seasons (translations of Vivaldi's Sonnets) 1984, (essays) In Radical Pursuit, 1975, Star and Other Poems, 1990, Five Romanian Ballads, 1991, Snow Songs, 1992, Each in His Season, 1993, The Fuhrer Bunker: The Complete Cycle, 1995; contbr. essays, poems, translations to lit. mags. Recipient Ingram-Merrill award, 1958, Longview lit. award, 1959, spl. citation Poetry Soc. Am., 1960, Pulitzer prize for poetry, 1960, Guinness Poetry award, 1961, Miles Modern Poetry award, 1966; Hudson Rev. fellow in poetry, 1958-59; fellow Guggenheim Found., 1972-73, Acad. Am. Poets, 1973, Bi-Centennial Medal William and Mary Coll., 1976, Centennial Medal Govt. Romania, 1977; Ingram-Merrill fellow 1979; sabbatical grantee Nat. Council on Arts, 1966-67, Ctr. for Advanced Study U. Del. grantee, 1983-84. Mem. Nat. Inst. Arts and Letters (grantee 1960), Poetry Soc. Am., PEN, Dramatists Guild. Home: RD Box 51 Erieville NY 13061-9801

SNORTLAND, HOWARD JEROME, educational financial consultant; b. Sharon, N.D., June 22, 1912; s. Thomas and Aline (Vig) S.; m. Anna Adeline Anderson, Sept. 1, 1940; children—Jan Signe, Kristi Jo, Howard Jay. B.A., U. N.D., 1937, M.S., 1958. Cashier N.D. Workmen's Compensation Bur., 1937-42, N.D. State Treas.'s Office, 1945-48; with N.D. Dept. Pub. Instrn., Bismarck, 1948-81; supt. pub. instrn. N.D. Dept. Pub. Instrn., 1977-81; ednl. fin. cons., 1981—; pres. State Econ. Council, 1978; nat. pres. Com. Ednl. Data Systems, 1965-67. Chmn. Burleigh ARC, 1963-67, bd. dirs., 1946—, vice chmn., 1964—; bd. dirs. Burleigh County Tb Assn., 1950—; stated clk. United Presbyterian Ch., 1942—; pres. N.D. United Christian Campus Fellowship, 1964-67, N.D. Westminster Found., 1963-70; mem. N.D. Synod Council, 1970—; chmn. United Way Fund, 1983. Served with USAAF, 1942-45. Recipient Summit Conf. award for outstanding pub. service, 1976. Mem. NEA, N.D. Edn. Assn., N.D. Sch. Bus. Ofcls., N.D. Assn. Adminstrs., Nat. Assn. Adminstrs., N.D. Assn. Ret. Employees (pres. 1987—), Am. Assn. Ret. Persons (vice chmn. N.D. legis. com. 1992-94, chmn. 1994—), Kiwanis, Phi Beta Kappa, Phi Delta Kappa.

SNOW, CUBBEDGE, JR., lawyer; b. Macon, Ga., May 20, 1929. AB, Emory U., 1951; JD magna cum laude, Mercer U., 1952. Bar: Ga. 1952. Ptnr. Martin, Snow, Grant, Napier, Macon. Col. JAGC, USAFR, 1952-89. Fellow Am. Coll. Trial Lawyers, Am. Bar Found. (state chmn. 1988-92), Fedn. Ins. and Corp. Counsel, Ga. Def. Lawyers Assn., Am. Prepaid Legal Svcs. Inst. (bd. dirs. 1983-89); mem. ABA (ho. of dels. 1984—, chmn. prepaid legal svcs. com. 1986-88, bd. govs. 1993-96), Macon Bar Assn. (pres. 1967), State Bar Ga. (pres. 1974-75), Am. Judicature Soc. (bd. dirs. 1978-82, Herbert Harley award 1986), Phi Beta Kappa, Phi Alpha Delta, Omicron Delta Kappa. Office: Martin Snow 240 3rd St PO Box 1606 Macon GA 31202

SNOW, DAVID FORREST, judge; b. Boston, Mar. 15, 1932; s. Albert Grindle and Hope (Farrington) S.; m. Rosemary Allsman, Oct. 7, 1957 (div. Jan. 1982); children: Nicholas David, Sarah Alison, Catherine Ann; m. Joyce Neiditz, Mar. 15, 1985. BA, Dartmouth Coll., 1954; JD, Harvard U. 1960. Ptnr. Jones, Day, Reavis & Pogue, Cleve., 1960-88; asst. prof. law U. Iowa, Iowa City, 1967-68; bankruptcy judge U.S. Dist. Ct., Cleve., 1988—. Mem. ABA, Cleve. Bar Assn. Home: 2330 Ardleigh Dr Cleveland OH 44106-3128 Office: US District Court 424 US Courthouse 201 Superior Ave NE Cleveland OH 44114

SNOW, ELIZABETH JEAN, poet, inventor, farmer, small business owner; b. Northampton, Mass., Mar. 1, 1943; d. Dwight Clary and Jean Kennedy (Johnston) S. Student, Northampton Comml. Coll., 1961-62, U. Mass. Tufts Sch. Mus. Fine Arts. Typist, sec., editor, transcriptionist, proofreading svcs., cons. various agys. including Kelly Svcs. Inc., Olsten Svcs. Inc., Boston, 1965-88; proctor Harvard U., Cambridge, Mass., 1987-91; owner, dir. E.J. Snow dba Revisions Lit. Svcs. & Farm Holding, Williamsburg, 1992—. Author: (poetry) The Grand Collection of Poems, 11 Poem Series, A Collection of Poems; artist, working in oils. Drake Internat. Title of Champions, 1987. Address: PO Box 353 Williamsburg MA 01096

SNOW, GEORGE ABRAHAM, physicist; b. N.Y.C., Aug. 24, 1926; s. Joseph and Anna (Snow) Ginsberg; m. Lila Alpert, June 20, 1948; children: Zachary, Andrew, Sara Ellen. B.S., CCNY, 1945; M.A., Princeton U., 1947, Ph.D., 1949. Jr. physicist Brookhaven Nat. Lab., Upton, N.Y., 1948-51; assoc. physicist Brookhaven Nat. Lab., 1951-55; physicist Naval Research Lab., Washington, 1955-58; vis. prof. dept. physics and astronomy U. Md., College Park, 1957-58, assoc. prof., 1958-61, prof., 1961-92, prof. emeritus, sr. rsch. scientist, 1992—; mem. Inst. for Advanced Study, Princeton, 1952-53; vis. lectr. U. Wis., Madison, 1955-56; vis. prof. U. Rome, 1965-66, U. Paris (France), Oxford, 1972-73, Tohoku U., Sendai, Japan, 1979; vis. scientist CERN, 1980, U. Bologna, 1986; mem. high energy physics adv. panel AEC, 1970-72; mem. high energy physics vis. com. Argonne Nat. Lab., 1969-71, Princeton-Pa. Accelerator, 1969-70, Lawrence Radiation Lab., Berkeley, Calif., 1980-83; mem. high energy physics adv. com. Brookhaven Nat. Lab., 1967-69; cons. to physics editor Prentice Hall, Inc., 1971-76. Trustee URA, 1973-78, vice chmn., 1974, chmn. sci. com., 1975-77. Recipient Disting. Scholar-Tchr. award U. Md., 1988-89; NSF sr. postdoctoral fellow, 1961-62, John S. Guggenheim sr. fellow, Fulbright scholar, 1965-66; cited by Washington Acad. Scis., 1963. Fellow AAAS, Am. Phys. Soc. (mem. exec. coun. div. particles and fields 1968-70, vice chmn. div. particles and fields 1975, chmn. 1976, editor Phys. Rev. D 1981-83); mem. Fedn. Am. Scientists, European Phys. Soc., Phi Beta Kappa. Home: 4816 Essex Ave Bethesda MD 20815-5548 Office: U Md Dept Physics College Park MD 20742

SNOW, JAMES BYRON, JR., physician, research administrator; b. Oklahoma City, Mar. 12, 1932; s. James B. and Charlotte Louise (Andersen) S.; m. Sallie Lee Ricker, July 16, 1954; children: James B., John Andrew, Sallie Lee Louise. B.S., U. Okla., 1953; M.D. cum laude, Harvard U., 1956; M.A. (hon.), U. Pa., 1973. Diplomate: Am. Bd. Otolaryngology (dir. 1972-90). Intern Johns Hopkins Hosp., Balt., 1956-57; resident Mass. Eye and Ear Infirmary, Boston, 1957-60; prof., head dept. otorhinolaryngology Sch. Medicine U. Okla., Oklahoma City, 1962-72; prof., chmn. dept. otorhinolaryngology and human communication U. Pa. at Phila., 1972-90; dir. Nat. Inst. on Deafness and Other Communication Disorders, Bethesda, Md., 1990—; mem. nat. adv. coun. neurol. and communicative disorders and stroke NIH, 1972-76, 82-86; chmn. Nat. Com. Rsch. Neurol. and Communicative Disorders, 1979-80; sr. exec. svc. presdl. meritorious exec. rank, 1994. Editor: Am. Jour. Otolaryngology, 1979-83; Contbr. articles to sci. and profl. jours. Served with M.C. AUS, 1960-62. Recipient Regents award for superior teaching U. Okla., 1970, Golden award Internat. Fedn. Otorhinolaryngological Socs., 1989, Disting. Achievement award Deafness Rsch. Found., 1993, Presdl. Exec. Rank award, 1994; named to Soc. of Scholars Johns Hopkins U., 1991. Fellow Japan Broncho-Esophagological Soc. (hon.), Am. Laryngol. Assn. (hon., editor 1983-89, pres. 1990-91); mem. ACS (regent 1982-90), AMA (coun. on sci. affairs 1975-86), Soc. Univ. Otolaryngologists (pres. 1975), Am. Acad. Otolaryngology-Head and Neck Surgery, Assn. Acad. Depts. Otolaryngology (pres. 1981-82), Am. Laryngol., Rhinol., and Otol. Soc., Am. Otol. Soc., Am. Broncho-esophagol. Assn. (editor trans. 1973-77, pres. 1979), Collegium Otorhinolaryngologicum, Phi Beta Kappa, Alpha Omega Alpha. Home: 119 Discoll Way Gaithersburg MD 20878 Office: Nat Inst Deafness & Other Comm Disorders Bldg 31 9000 Rockville Pike Bethesda MD 20892

SNOW, JOEL ALAN, research director; b. Brockton, Mass., Apr. 1, 1937; s. George H. and Mary W. (Sproul) S.; m. Laetitia Harrer, June 29, 1957 (div. 1983); children: Jonathan, Nicholas; m. Barbara Kashian, 1992. BS in Physics, U. N.C., 1958; MA in Physics, Wash. U., St. Louis, 1963, PhD in Physics, 1967. Program dir. for theoretical physics NSF, Washington, 1968-70, head office of interdisciplinary rsch., 1970-71, dep. asst. dir. for sci. and tech., rsch. applications, 1971-74, dir. office of planning and resources, 1974-76, dir. div. of policy rsch. and analysis, 1976; sr. policy analyst, office of sci. and tech. policy Exec. Office of the Pres., Washington, 1976-77; assoc. dir. for rsch. policy U.S. Dept. Energy, Washington, 1977-81, dir. sci. and tech. affairs, 1981-88; assoc. v.p. for rsch. and Argonne U. Chgo., 1988-92; dir. Inst. for Phys. Rsch. and Tech. Iowa State U., Ames, 1993—; rsch. assoc. dept. physics U. Ill., Urbana, 1967-68; instr. physics and electronics, U.S. Navy Nuclear Power Sch., New London, Conn., 1958-61; organizer Pres. Conf. on Superconductivity, 1987, NSF program rsch. applied to nat. needs. Contbr. over 120 articles to mags. and profl. jours. Lt. (j.g.) USN, 1958-61. Fellowship Ctr. for Advanced Study, U. Ill., 1967-68, NSF, 1963-65, 1967-68; recipient Meritorious Svc. Award NSF, 1972, Meritorious Award William A. Jump Found., 1973, Arthur S. Fleming Award Downtown Jaycees, 1974. Fellow AAAS; mem. Am. Chem. Soc., Am. Phys. Soc., Am. Nuc. Soc., World Future Soc., Sigma Xi. Achievements include pioneering development of federal programs in solar and geothermal energy and energy conservation. Office: IPRT/Iowa State U 109 Office Lab Bldg Ames IA 50011

SNOW, JOHN WILLIAM, railroad executive; b. Toledo, Aug. 2, 1939; s. William Dean and Catharine (Howard) S.; m. Fredrica Wheeler, June 11, 1964 (div. 1973); children: Bradley, Ian; m. Carolyn Kalk, Aug. 31, 1973; 1 child, Christopher. B.A., U. Toledo, 1962; Ph.D., U. Va., 1965; LL.B., George Washington U., 1967. Asst. prof. econs. U. Md., College Park, 1965-67; assoc. Wheeler & Wheeler, Washington, 1967-72; asst. gen. counsel Dept. Transp., Washington, 1972-73, dep. asst. sec. for policy, plans and internat. affairs, 1973-74, asst. sec. for govtl. affairs, 1974-75, dep. under sec., 1975-76; administr. Nat. Hwy. Traffic Safety Adminstrn., Washington, 1976-77; v.p. govt. affairs Chessie System Inc., Washington, 1977-80; sr. v.p. corp. services CSX Corp., Richmond, Va., 1980-84, exec. v.p., 1984-85; pres., chief exec. officer Chessie System R.R.s, Balt., 1985-86, CSX Rail Transport, Jacksonville, Fla., 1986-87, CSX Transp., Jacksonville, Va., 1987-88; pres., chief operating officer CSX Corp., Richmond, Va., 1988-89, pres., chief exec. officer, 1989-91, chmn., pres., chief exec. officer, 1991—, also bd. dirs.; adj. prof. law George Washington U., 1972-75; vis. fellow Am. Enterprises Inst., Washington, spring 1977; bd. dirs. NationsBank Corp., Bassett Furniture Industries Inc., USX Corp., Textron Inc. Bd. trustees Johns Hopkins U., chmn. The Bus. Roundtable. Mem. Va. State Bar. Episcopalian. Clubs: Chevy Chase, Metropolitan (Washington); Commonwealth, Country of Va. (Richmond).

SNOW, KARL NELSON, JR., public management educator, university administrator, former state senator; b. St. George, Utah, July 1, 1930; s. Karl Nelson and Wanda (McGregor) S.; m. Donna Jean Dahn, Jan. 29, 1960; children: Karl Nelson, III, Melissa, Daniel D., Jeanmarie, Elisabeth, Howard H. B.S., Brigham Young U., Provo, Utah, 1956; M.A. (State of Minn. Adminstrv. fellow 1956-57), U. Minn., 1958; M.P.A. (univ. fellow 1959-61), U. So. Calif., 1965, D.P.A., 1972. Budget examiner Minn. Dept. Adminstrn., 1956-59; staff asst., instr. Sch. Pub. Adminstrn. U. So. Calif. 1959-62; mem. faculty Brigham Young U., Provo, Utah, 1962—, dir. Inst. Govt., 1969-79, prof. public mgmt., 1979—, asst. exec. v.p., 1987-91; state legis. fiscal analyst, 1966-70; mem. Utah Senate from 16th Dist., 1972-85, majority leader, 1981-85; cons. in field; mem. Utah State House Fellowship Commn., 1973-79; chmn. Utah Constl. Revision Commn., 1977-89; bd. dirs. Legis. Leaders Found., 1981-85; chmn. bd. trustees Utah Tech. Fin. Corp., 1983-94; pres., trustee Utah Tech. Equity Found., 1994—. Bd. editors Public Adminstrn. Rev, 1969-70, State and Local Govt. Rev, 1977-83; contbr. articles to profl. jours. Missionary Mormon Ch., 1950-52, mem. stake high council, 1975-85, bishop, 1985-90; mem. Warren Burger Prison Task Force, 1983-87; bd. dirs. Utah Innovation Found., 1984-88. Mem. Am. Soc. Pub. Adminstrn. (chpt. pres. 1968-69), dir. nat. council (1969-72), Sons Utah Pioneers. Home: 1847 Oak Ln Provo UT 84604-2140 Office: Brigham Young U 768 Tnrb Provo UT 84602-1133

SNOW, LURANA S., judge; b. Brooklyn, N.Y., May 10, 1951; d. Lawrence James and Elizabeth Catherine (Luckso) Schling. AB magna cum laude, Radcliffe Coll., 1972; JD, Harvard Law Sch., 1975. Bar: Mass. 1975, Fla. 1977, D.C. 1980. Law clk. to Judge Joe Eaton U.S. Dist. Ct., Miami, 1975-77; asst. fed. public defender Miami, 1977-79; asst. U.S. atty. U.S. Dept. of Justice, Ft. Lauderdale, 1980-86; pvt. practice, 1984; magistrate judge U.S. Dist. Ct. (do. dist.) Fla., Ft. Lauderdale, 1986—. Recipient Spl. Achievement award Drug Enforcement Adminstrn., 1981, 84, 86, U.S. Secret Svc., 1984, U.S. Customs, 1984, Bureau of Alcohol, Tobacco and Firearms, 1984, South Fla. Vice Presidential Task Force, 1984. Mem. Fla. Bar Assn., Mass. Bar Assn., D.C. Bar Assn., Fed. Bar Assn. Avocations: scuba, skiing, travel, reading, photography. Office: US Courthouse 299 E Broward Blvd Rm 204 Fort Lauderdale FL 33301-1944

SNOW, MARINA SEXTON, reference librarian, playwright; b. Boston, Apr. 9, 1937; d. Charles Ernest Snow and Katherine Alice Townsend; m. Richard DeVere Horton, Aug. 30, 1958 (div. 1968); children: Heather Kertchem, James Horton; m. Charles A. Washburn, Jan. 7, 1978 (div. 1979). BA, U. Iowa, 1958; MA in Speech Pathology, N.Mex. State U., 1967; MA in Librarianship, San Jose State U., 1976; MA in Theatre Arts, Calif. State U., Sacramento, 1979. Cert. clin. competence Am. Speech and Hearing Assn. Tchr. ESL Inst. Colombo-Americano, Cali, Colombia, 1958-59; tchr. Las Cruces (N.Mex.) Pub. Schs., 1964-66; speech therapist Sutter County Schs., Yuba City, Calif., 1967-72; reference libr. Calif. State U. Libr., Sacramento, 1976—. Contbr. articles to profl. jours.; author 2 plays: Apricot Coffee, Alkali Flat. Pres. Alkali Flat Neighborhood Assn., Sacramento, 1987—; mem. Sacramento Old City Assn., 1979—. Mem. Calif. Acad. and Rsch. Librs., Calif. State U. Librs., Theatre Libr. Assn., Music Libr. Assn. Avocations: theatre arts, historic preservation, gardening. Office: Calif State U Libr 2000 Jed Smith Dr Sacramento CA 95819-2640

SNOW, ROBERT ANTHONY, journalist; b. Berea, Ky., June 1, 1955; s. James Allen and Betty Jo (Threlkeld) S.; m. Jill Ellen Walker, Sept. 26, 1987; 1 child, Kendall Elizabeth. BA, Davidson Coll., 1977; postgrad. in Philosophy and Econs., U. Chgo., 1978-79. Editorial writer The Greensboro (N.C.) Record, 1979-81, The Virginian Pilot, Norfolk, 1981-82; editorial page writer The Daily Press, Newport News, Va., 1982-84; dep. editorial page editor The Detroit News, 1984-87, columnist, 1993—; editorial page editor The Washington Times, 1987-91; dep. asst. to pres. comm., dir. speech-writing The White House, Washington, 1991-92, dep. asst. for media affairs to Pres., 1992-93; columnist USA Today, Arlington, Va., 1993—; syndicated columnist Creators Syndicate, 1993—; commentator Nat. Pub. Radio, 1993—; substitute host The Rush Limbaugh Radio Program, 1994—; polit. analyst Good Morning America, 1995. Appearances include Good Morning Am., Crossfire, Inside Politics, Reliable, Sources, Late Edition, The Fox Morning News, Politically Incorrect, The McLaughlin Group, Equal Time, 1993—. Active Leadership Washington. Mem. Coun. Fgn. Rels., Nat. Conf. Edtl. Writers. Avocations: sports, music, traveling, writing. Office: Gannett News Svc 1000 Wilson Blvd Arlington VA 22229

SNOW, THEODORE PECK, astrophysics educator; b. Seattle, Jan. 30, 1947; s. Theodore P. and Louise (Wertz) S.; s. Constance M. Snow, Aug. 23, 1969; children: McGregor A., Tyler M., Reilly A. BA, Yale U., 1969; MS, U. Wash., 1970, PhD, 1973. Mem. rsch. staff Princeton (N.J.) U., 1973-77; prof. U. Colo., Boulder, 1977—, dir. Ctr. for Astrophysics and Space Astronomy, 1986—. Author: (textbook) The Dynamic Universe, 1983, 4th edit., 1991, Essentials of the Dynamic Universe 4th edit., 1993 (textbook excellence award Text and Academic Authors Assn. 1994), Physics, 1986; contbr. over 200 articles to profl. jours. Fellow Royal Astron. Soc.; mem. Am. Astron. Soc., Astron. Soc. Pacific, Sigma Xi. Achievements include discovery, through observations in ultraviolet visible, and infrared wavelengths, of several important processes involving interstellar gas and dust, and their roles in star formation and late stages of stellar evolution. Office: U Colo Ctr Astrophysics Space Astronomy Campus Box 389 Boulder CO 80309

SNOW, TOWER CHARLES, JR., lawyer; b. Boston, Oct. 28, 1947; s. Tower Charles and Margaret (Harper) S.; m. Belinda L. Snow. AB cum laude English, Dartmouth Coll., 1969; JD, U. Calif., Berkeley, 1973. Bar: Calif. 1973, U.S. Dist. Ct. (no. dist.) Calif. 1973, U.S. Ct. Appeals (9th cir.) 1973, U.S. Supreme Ct. 1976, U.S. Dist. Ct. (ea. dist.) Calif. 1979, U.S. Ct. Appeals (fed. cir.) 1980, U.S. Ct. Claims 1980, U.S. Ct. Appeals (2d cir.) 1987, N.Y. 1988, U.S. Dist. Ct. (ea. and so. dist.) N.Y. 1988, U.S. Dist. Ct. (cen. dist.) Calif. 1989. Ptnr., chmn. litigation dept. Orrick, Herrington & Sutcliffe, San Francisco, 1973-89; ptnr., chmn. securities litigation group Shearman & Sterling, San Francisco, 1989-94; ptnr. Brobeck, Phleger & Harrison, San Francisco, 1995—; arbitrator Nat. Assn. Securities Dealers, Am. Stock Exch., N.Y. Stock Exch., Pacific Coast Stock Exch., Superior Ct. City and County San Francisco, Am. Arbitration Assn.; lectr. in field. Author numerous law handbooks and articles to prof. jours. Mem. San Francisco Museum Soc., San Francisco Symphony, San Francisco Ballet. Mem. ABA (chmn. subcom. pub. offering litigation 1984-88, co-chair task force on securities arbitration 1988-89, vice chair securities litigaiton com. 1986-88), Continuing Edn. Bar (bus. law inst. planning com. 1986), San Francisco Bar Assn. (pres. securities litigation sect. 1995), Securities Industry Assn., Nat. Inst. Trial Advocacy. Democrat. Avocations: internat. travel, skiing, running, scuba diving, photography. Home: 177 Ridge Dr Napa Valley CA 94558 Office: Brobeck Phleger & Harrison Spear St Tower One Market St San Francisco CA 94105

SNOWBARGER, VINCENT KEITH, lawyer, state representative; b. Kankakee, Ill., Sept. 16, 1949; s. Willis Edward and Wahnona Ruth (Horger) S.; m. Carolyn Ruth McMahon, Mar. 25, 1972; children: Jeffrey Edward, Matthew David. BA in History, So. Nazarene U., 1971; MA in Polit. Sci., U. Ill., 1974; JD, U. Kans., 1977. Bar: Kans. 1977, U.S. Dist. Ct. Kans. 1977. Mo. 1987. Instr. Mid-Am. Nazarene Coll., Olathe, Kans., 1973-76; ptnr. Haskin, Hinkle, Slater & Snowbarger, Olathe, 1977-84, Dietrich, Davis, Dicus et al, Olathe, 1984-88, Armstrong, Teasdale, Schafly & Davis, Overland Park, Kans., 1989-92; Holbrook, Heaven & Fay, P.C., Merriam, Kans., 1992-94; ptnr. Snowbarger & Veatch LLP, Olathe, Kans., 1994—. Mem. Kans. Legislature, Topeka, 1985—; majority leader Ho. of Reps., 1993—; mem. Olathe Planning Commn., 1982-84, Leadership Olalthe; bd. dirs. Johnson County Cert. Devel. Corp.; divsn. chmn. United Way, Olathe, 1985-88, chmn. citizen rev. com., 1991—. Mem. Kans. Bar Assn., Kans. Assn. Hosp. Attys., Johnson County Bar Assn., Olathe Area C. of C. (bd. dirs. 1984). Republican. Nazarene. Avocation: politics. Home: 1451 E Orleans Dr Olathe KS 66062-5728 Office: PO Box 10121 110 S Cherry Ste 103 Olathe KS 66051-1421

SNOWDEN, FRANK MARTIN, JR., classics educator; b. York County, Va., July 17, 1911; s. Frank Martin and Alice (Phillips) S.; m. Elaine Hill, June 8, 1935; children: Jane Alice, Frank Martin III. Grad., Boston Latin Sch., 1928; AB, Harvard U., 1932, AM, 1933, PhD, 1944; postgrad., Am. Acad. in Rome, summer 1938; Fulbright research scholar, Italy, 1949-50; LLD (hon.), Bard Coll., 1957; DLitt (hon.), Union Coll., 1979; LHD (hon.), Georgetown U., 1985, Howard U., 1985; LHD, U. Md., 1993. Instr. classics Va. State Coll., 1933-36, Spelman Coll., 1936-40; instr. classics Howard U., 1942-44, chmn. dept., 1942-77, asso. prof., 1944-45, prof., 1945-90, prof. emeritus, 1991—; dir. Howard U. (Summer Sch.), 1942-54, Howard U. (Evening Sch. and Adult Edn.), 1942-48; chmn. Howard U. (Humanities Program), 1950-51; dean Howard U. (Coll. Liberal Arts), 1956-68; specialist lectr. Internat. Information Adminstrn., Dept. State, French West Africa, Gold Coast, Nigeria, Libya, Italy, Greece, Austria, 1953; cultural attaché Am. Embassy, Rome, Italy, 1954-56; vis. lectr. Fgn. Service Inst., 1956-62, 66-68; U.S. specialist in India, lectr., Bombay, New Delhi, Lucknow, Calcutta, Madras areas, 1957, lectr. as U.S. specialist, Brazil, summer 1960, studied higher edn., Soviet Union, 1958; participant internat. seminar University Today, Dubrovnik, Yugoslavia, 1958; mem. U.S. del. UNESCO, Paris, 1958, 60, U.S. nat. commn. for, 1958-61; mem. Nat. Humanities Faculty, 1969-70, mem. bd., 1970-73; ann. lectr. Archaeol. Inst. Am., 1970-71, 74-76; vis. scholar U. Center Va., 1971-72; mem. com. Internat. Exchange Persons, 1970-73; mem. jury to select fellows in classics Am. Acad. Rome, 1971-73; mem. com. Folger Fellowship Program, 1972-75; Am. Council Learned Socs. rep. Council on Internat. Exchange of Scholars, 1973-77; mem. D.C. com. on Fulbright scholarships, 1951-54, 68-74; fellow Woodrow Wilson Internat. Center for Scholars, 1977; scholar-in-residence Rockefeller Found., Bellagio, Italy, fall 1977; adj. prof. classics Georgetown U., 1991-92, Blegen vis. disting. rsch prof. Vassar Coll., 1992-93. Author: Blacks in Antiquity: Ethiopians in the Greco-Roman Experience, 1970; co-author: The Image of the Black in Western Art I: From the Pharaohs to the Fall of the Roman Empire (also pub. in French), 1976, Before Color Prejudice: The Ancient View of Blacks, 1983; Contbr. articles to classical and ednl. jours. Mem. D.C. Mayor's Commn. Arts and Humanities, 1972-74; vis. com. bd. overseers dept. classics Harvard Coll., 1977-83. Decorated Medaglia d'Oro for outstanding work in Italian culture and edn. Italy, 1958; Am. Council Learned Socs. fellow, 1962-63; NEH grantee, summer 1970. Mem. Am. Conf. Acad. Deans (sec., editor 1962-63, 1963-64), Am. Council on Edn., Vergilian Soc. Am. (trustee 1956-60), Am. Philol. Assn. (Charles J. Goodwin award of merit 1973, bd. dirs. 1976-79, 2d v.p. 1983-84), Archeol. Inst. Am. (pres. Washington soc. 1971), Classical Soc. Am. Acad. in Rome, Washington Classical Soc. (v.p. 1949-50, pres. 1974-75),

Washington Fedn. Chs. (v.p. 1951-53). Clubs: Cosmos, Harvard. Home: 4200 Massachusetts Ave NW Washington DC 20016-4744

SNOWDEN, LAWRENCE FONTAINE, retired aircraft company executive, retired marine corps general officer; b. Charlottesville, Va., Apr. 14, 1921; s. Lawrence Fontaine Snoddy and Beatrice M. (Huffman) S.; m. Martha Roselyn Ham, Nov. 17, 1942; children: John Stephen, Brian Fontaine. Student, Stetson U., 1938-39; BS, U. Va., 1942; MA, Northwestern U., 1950; advanced mgmt. program, Harvard U., 1968; grad., Indsl. Coll. Armed Forces, 1967. Commd. 2d lt. USMC, 1942, advanced through grades to lt. gen., 1975; comdr. 7th Marine Regt., Vietnam, 1966; ops. officer III Marine Amphibious Force, Vietnam, 1966-67; asst. dir. personnel Hdqrs. Marine Corps, Washington, 1968-69; dir. systems support group Hdqrs. Marine Corps, 1969-70; dir. Marine Corps Devel. Ctr., Quantico, Va., 1970-72; chief of staff U.S. Forces, Japan, 1972-75; U.S. chmn. UN Bd., Japan, 1973-75; chief of staff Hdqrs. U.S. Marine Corps, 1977-79; ret., 1979; v.p. Far East Internat. Service Co. Hughes Aircraft Co., 1979-86; group v.p. Internat. Ground Systems Group Hughes Aircraft Co., Fullerton, Calif., 1986-88; pres. Snowden Internat. Assocs., Tallahassee, Fla., 1988—. Recipient Disting. Eagle Scout award, Silver Beaver award Boy Scouts Am.; decorated Legion of Merit (5), Army Commendation medal, Navy Commendation medal, D.S.M. (2), Purple Heart (2), Cross of Gallantry (3) Vietnam, Second Order of Sacred Treasure Japan. Mem. Marine Corps League, U.S. Navy League, Am. C. of C. in Japan, Am.-Japan Soc., Marine Corps Assn., Sigma Nu. Clubs: Tokyo, Killearn Country.

SNOWE, OLYMPIA J., senator; b. Augusta, Maine, Feb. 21, 1947; d. George John and Georgia G. Bouchles; m. John McKernan. BA, U. Maine, 1969; LLD (hon.), U. Maine, Machias, 1982, Husson Coll., 1981, Bowdoin Coll., 1985. Businesswoman; mem. Maine Ho. of Reps., 1973-76, Maine Senate, 1976-78; mem. 96th-103d Congresses from 2d Maine Dist., 1979-94; mem. budget com., mem. commerce sci. and transp. com., chmn. fgn. rel.subcom. on internat. ops. US Sen. from Maine; co-chair Congl. Caucus for Women's Issues; dep. Republican whip, U.S. senator from Maine, 1995—; corporator Mechanics Savs. Bank. Republican. Greek Orthodox. Club: Philopotchos Soc. Office: US Senate 176 Russell Senate Bldg Washington DC 20510-1902*

SNOWISS, ALVIN L., lawyer; b. Lock Haven, Pa., June 16, 1930; s. Benjamin and Lillian (Kalin) S.; m. Jean Yarnell, Mar. 16, 1973. BA, U. Pa., Phila., 1952, JD, 1955. Bar: Pa. 1956, U.S. Dist. Ct. (mid. dist.) Pa. 1958, U.S. Supreme Ct. 1972. Pvt. practice Lock Haven, 1955-61; ptnr. Lugg & Snowiss, Lock Haven, 1961-74, Lugg, Snowiss, Steinberg & Faulkner, Lock Haven, 1974-86, Snowiss, Steinberg, Faulkner & Rae, Lock Haven, 1987—; solicitor Clinton County, Lock Haven, 1964-72; dir. Mellon Bank, ctrl. region, State College, Pa. Chmn. bd. Lock Haven Hosp. Found., 1986-92; pres. Lock Haven Hosp., 1982-86; bd. govs. Clinton County Cmty. Found., Lock Haven, 1970-95; chmn. adv. bd. Palmer Mus. Art, State Coll; mem. Bucknell U. Ctr. Gallery, Lewisburg, Pa.; mem. nat. devel. coun. Pa. State U., State College, 1990-95; v.p. bd. trustees Ross Libr., Lock Haven, 1963-86; mem. exec. com. Pa. Rep. Com., Harrisburg, 1974-80; state committeeman Clinton County Rep. Com., Lock Haven, 1967-80. Fellow Am. Coll. Trust and Estate Coun., Pa. Bar Found. (founding bd. dirs. 1984-95), Am. Bar Found.; mem. Pa. Bar Assn. (zone del. 1976-82, zone gov. 1983-86, treas. 1987-90), Clinton County Bar Assn. (pres. 1975-76), Kiwanis (pres. Lock Haveen 1966-67). Republican. Avocations: art history, golf, historical research. Home: 414 W Main St Lock Haven PA 17745 Office: 333 N Vesper St Lock Haven PA 17745-1362

SNYDER, ALAN CARHART, insurance company executive; b. N.Y.C., May 25, 1946; s. John I. and Elfrida (Bendix) S.; m. Mary Burgoyne, Feb. 9, 1974. BS, BA, Georgetown U., 1968; MBA, Harvard U., 1973. Cons. Reynolds Securities, N.Y.C., 1972-73; exec. v.p. Dean Witter Reynolds, N.Y.C., 1975-85; sole proprietor Shinnecock Ptnrs., N.Y.C., 1985-89, mng. ptnr., 1989—; pres., chief oper. officer, bd. dirs. First Exec. Corp., L.A., 1990-91; chief oper. officer Exec. Life Ins. Co., L.A., 1991-93; CEO Aurora Nat. Life Assurance Co., LA, 1993-94; cons. Aurora Nat. Life Assurance Co., L.A., 1994—; mng. ptnr. Shinnecock Group, L.A., 1994—. Baker scholar Harvard Bus. Sch., 1973.

SNYDER, ALLEGRA FULLER, dance educator; b. Chgo., Aug. 28, 1927; d. R. Buckminster and Anne (Hewlett) Fuller; m. Robert Snyder, June 30, 1951 (div. Apr. 1975, remarried Sept. 1980); children: Alexandra, Jaime. BA in Dance, Bennington Coll., 1951; MA in Dance, UCLA, 1967. Asst. to curator, dance archives Mus. Modern Art, N.Y.C., 1945-47; dancer Ballet Soc. of N.Y.C. Ballet Co., 1945-47; mem. office and prodn. staff Internat. Film Found., N.Y.C., 1950-52; editor, dance films Film News mag., N.Y.C., 1966-72; lectr. dance and film adv., dept. dance UCLA, 1967-73, chmn. dept. dance, 1970-80, 90-91, acting chair, spring 1985, chair of faculty Sch. of the Arts, 1989-91, prof. dance and dance ethnology, 1973-91, prof. emeritus, 1991—; vis. lectr. Calif. Inst. of Arts, Valencia, 1972; co-dir. dance and TV workshop Am. Dance Fest., Conn. Coll., New London, 1973; dir. NEH summer seminar for coll. tchrs. Asian Performing Arts, 1978, 81; coord. Ethnic Arts Intercoll. Interdisciplinary program, 1974-83, acting chmn., 1986; vis. prof. performance studies NYU, 1982-83; hon. vis. prof. U. Surrey, Guildford, Eng., 1983-84; bd. dirs. Buckminster Fuller Inst.; cons. Thyodia Found., Salt Lake City, 1973-74; mem. dance adv. panel Nat. Endowment Arts, 1968-72, Calif. Arts Commn., 1974-91; mem. adv. screening com. Council Internat. Exchange of Scholars, 1979-82; mem. various panels NEH, 1979-85; mem. adv. bd. Los Angeles Dance Alliance, 1978-84; core cons. for Dancing Sta. WNET-TV, 1988—. Dir. film Baroque Dance 1625-1725, in 1977; co-dir. film Gods of Bali, 1952; dir. and wrote film Bayanihan, 1962 (named Best Folkloric Documentary at Bilboa Film Festival, winner Golden Eagle award); asst. dir. and asst. editor film The Bennington Story, 1952; created films Gestures of Sand, 1968, Reflections on Choreography, 1973, When the Fire Dances Between Two Poles, 1982; created film, video loop and text Celebration: A World of Art and Ritual, 1982-83; supr. post-prodn. film Erick Hawkins, 1964, in 1973. Also contbr. articles to profl. jours. and mags. Adv. com. Pacific Asia Mus., 1980-84, Festival of the Mask, Craft and Folk Art Mus., 1979-84; adv. panel Los Angeles Dance Currents II, Mus. Ctr. Dance Assn., 1974-75; bd. dirs. Council Grove Sch. III, Compton, Calif., 1976-81; apptd. mem. Adv. Dance Com., Pasadena (Calif.) Art Mus., 1970-71, Los Angeles Festival of Performing Arts com., Studio Watts, 1970; mem. Technology and Cultural Transformation com., UNESCO, 1977. Fulbright research fellow, 1983-84; grantee Nat. Endowment Arts, 1981, Nat. Endowment Humanities, 1977, 79, 81, UCLA, 1968, 77, 80, 82, 85; recipient Amer. Dance Guild Award for Outstanding Achievement in Dance, 1992. Mem. Am. Dance Therapy Assn., Congress on Research in Dance (bd. dirs. 1970-76, chairperson 1975-77, nat. conf. chair 1972), Council Dance Adminstrs., Am. Dance Guild (chairperson com. awards 1972, Honoree of Yr. 1992), Soc. for Ethnomusicology, Am. Anthropol. Assn., Am. Folklore Soc., Soc. Anthropology of Visual Communication, Soc. Humanistic Anthropology, Calif. Dance Educators Assn. (conf. chair 1972), Los Angeles Area Dance Alliance (adv. bd. 1978-84, selection com. Dance Kaleidoscope project 1979-81), Fulbright Alumni Assn. Home: 15313 Whitfield Ave Pacific Palisades CA 90272-2548 Office: UCLA Dept Dance 124 Dance Bldg Los Angeles CA 90024*

SNYDER, ALLEN ROGER, lawyer; b. Washington, Jan. 26, 1946; s. Henry and Sylvia (Oxenbury) S.; m. Susan Port, Aug. 10, 1969; children: Joanna, Carolyn. BA with distinction, George Washington U., 1967; JD magna cum laude, Harvard U., 1971. Bar: D.C. 1973, U.S. Dist. Ct. D.C., Md., U.S. Ct. Appeals (D.C., 4th, 5th, 6th, 8th, 11th cirs.), U.S. Supreme Ct. Temp. assoc. Williams, Connolly & Califano, Washington, 1971; law clk. to assoc. justice J. Harlan U.S. Supreme Ct., 1971, law clk. to assoc. justice W. Rehnquist, 1972; assoc. Hogan & Hartson, Washington, 1972-78, ptnr., 1979—; mem., then chmn. D.C. Cir. Commn. on Admissions and Grievances, 1984-90, D.C.C.t. Appeals Bd. Profl. Responsibility, 1978-84; mem. D.C. Jud. Conf., then mem. D.C. Cir. Adv. Com. on Procedures, 1986-92; mem. com. on pro se litigation U.S. Dist. Ct. Bd. dirs. Jewish Found. Group Homes, Rockville, Md., 1982-86. Served with USAR, 1968-74. Fellow Am. Acad. of Appellate Lawyers; mem. D.C. Bar Unified (chmn. steering com. div. cts., lawyers and adminstrn. justice 1974-77, long range planning com. 1976-78, bd. govs. 1977-78), Washington Coun. Lawyers (bd. dirs. 1976-91), Am. Psychiat. Assn. (exec. sec. com. jud. action 1974-77). Office: Hogan & Hartson 555 13th St NW Washington DC 20004-1109

SNYDER, ARTHUR, publishing company executive; b. Valley Stream, N.Y., Feb. 6, 1925; s. Arthur and Kathryn (Staubitzer) S.; m. Betty Lain Harper, July 8, 1950; children—Susan, Arthur, Betsy, Jack, Heidi, Bonnie. B. Metall. Engring., Cornell U., Ithaca, N.Y., 1950, M.B.A., 1952. Mfg. engr. Norton Co., Worcester, Mass., 1952-56; chief accountant Norton Co., 1956-58, asst. controller, 1958-59, mgr. data processing, 1959-61, controller, 1961-65; exec. v.p. A.M. Best Co., Oldwick, N.J., 1965-67; pres. A.M. Best Co., 1968—, chmn., 1971—. Author: Principles of Inventory Control and Managing Capital Expenditures. 1st lt. 95th Inf. div. AUS, 1942-45. Decorated Bronze Star with oak leaf cluster, Purple Heart. Mem. Fin. Execs. Inst., Cornell Soc. Engrs. Presbyterian. Clubs: Roxiticus Golf (Mendham, N.J.); Baltusrol Golf (Springfield, N.J.); U.S. Srs. Golf Assn.; Mendham Valley Gun (Green Village, N.J.). Home: Lloyd Rd Bernardsville NJ 07924-1710 Office: AM Best Company Inc Ambest Rd Oldwick NJ 08858

SNYDER, CAROLYN ANN, university dean, librarian; b. Elgin, Nebr., Nov. 5, 1942; d. Ralph and Florence Wagner; m. Barry Snyder, Apr. 24, 1969. Student, Nebr. Wesleyan U., 1960-61; BS cum laude, Kearney State Coll., 1964; MS in Librarianship, U. Denver, 1965. Asst. libr. sci. and tech. U. Nebr., Lincoln, 1965-67, asst. pub. svc. libr., 1967-68, 70-73; pers. libr. Ind. U. Librs., Bloomington, 1973-76, acting dean of univ. librs., 1980, 88-89, assoc. dean for pub. svcs., 1977-88, 89-91, interim devel. officer, 1989-91; adminstrv. army libr. Spl. Svcs. Agy., Europe, 1968-70; dean libr. affairs So. Ill. U., Carbondale, 1991—; team leader Midwest Univs. Consortium for Internat. Activities-World Bank IX project to develop libr. system and implement automation U. Indonesia, Jakarta, 1984-86; libr. devel. cons. Inst. Tech. MARA/Midwest Univs. Consortium for Internat. Activities Program in Malaysia, 1985. Contbr. chpt. to book and articles to profl. jours. Mem. Humane Assn. Jackson County, 1991—, Carbondale Pub. Libr. Friends, 1991—. Recipient Cooperative Rsch. grant Coun. on Libr. Resources, Washington, 1984. Mem. ALA (councilor 1985-89, Bogle Internat. Travel award 1988, H.W. Wilson Libr. Staff Devel. grantee 1981), Libr. Adminstrn./Mgmt. Assn. (pres. 1981-82), Com. on Instnl. Cooperation/ Resource Sharing (chair 1987-91), Coun. Dirs. State Univ. Librs. in Ill. (chair 1992-93), Ill. Assn. Coll. and Rsch. Librs. (chair Ill. Bd. Higher Edn. liaison com. 1993-94), Ill. Network (bd. dirs.), Ind. Libr. Assn. (chair coll./univ. divsn. 1982-83), U.S. Grant Assn. (bd. dirs. 1992—), Netlllinois (bd. dirs. 1994—), Ill. Libr. Computer System Orgn. (policy coun. 1992—), nat. Assn. State Univs. and Land-Grante Colls. (commn. on infor. tech. and its distance learning bd. 1994—). Avocations: antiques, theater, movies. Office: So Ill U Morris Libr Carbondale IL 62901-6632

SNYDER, CAROLYN SWICK (CARRIE SNYDER), special education educator, vocational program administrator; b. Rapid City, S.D., May 15, 1949; d. Calvin A. and Eula B. (Sharp) Swick; m. Robert R. Snyder, Aug. 15, 1969; children: Sara, Shawn. Student, Sioux Falls Coll., 1967-68; BS in Edn., Augustana Coll., 1971, postgrad.; MS in Counseling and Pers. Svcs., Drake U., 1987, postgrad.; postgrad., U. Calif., Ctrl. Bapt. Theol. Seminary, Kans. State U., Iowa State U., U. No. Colo. Cert. spl. edn. tchr., ednl. cons., secondary sch. counselor, work experience coord., tchr. to mentally disabled, Iowa. Lead tchr. spl. edn. Kans. City (Kans.) Pub. Schs., 1971-73; tchr. spl. edn. Meade (Kans.) Pub. Schs., 1975-79; tchr. spl. edn., coord. work experience Arrowhead Area Ednl. Agy., Ft. Dodge, Iowa, 1980-82; coord. spl. edn. work experience Des Moines Ind. Pub. Schs., 1982—; developer, coord. Neighbors Youth Monitoring Program, Des Moines; facilitator HIV/AIDS spl. edn. curriculum, social skills curriculum Des Moines Pub. Schs.; mem. 11 county multi-agy. transition adv. com., 1992. Co-treas. Ankeny (Iowa) High Sch. Boosters; min. counseling Westover Bapt. Ch.; active leadership tng. program Mid-Am. Bapt. Chs. Recipient Utilization award Outstanding Pub. Educator Nat. Assn. Industry Edn., 1992. Mem. NEA, Iowa State Edn. Assn., Des Moines Edn. Assn., Nat. Coun. Exceptional Children, Iowa Coun. Exceptional Children, Iowa Counseling Assn. Office: Des Moines Pub Schs 1800 Grand Ave Des Moines IA 50309-3310

SNYDER, CHARLES AUBREY, lawyer; b. Bastrop, La., June 19, 1941; s. David and Shirley Blossom (Haas) S.; m. Sharon Rae Veta, Aug. 29, 1963; children: David Veta, Shelby Haas, Claire Frances. B.B.A., Tulane U., 1963; J.D., La. State U., 1966. Bar: La. 1966. Assoc. firm. Milling, Benson, Woodward, Hillyer, Pierson & Miller, and predecessors, New Orleans, 1966-69, ptnr., 1969-; bd. dirs. Delta Petroleum Co., La. Motel and Investment Corp. Trustee Kathyn O'Brien Found., 1970; bd. dirs. New Orleans Speech and Hearing Ctr., pres., 1978-80; bd. dirs. City Pk. Commn., 1991—, pres., 1995; fellow La. Coll. Securities Counsel. Mem. ABA, La. Bar Assn. (chmn. sect. on corp. and bus. law 1982-83), New Orleans Bar Assn., La. Law Inst. (coms. on mineral code and revision of partnership law and community property law), Beta Gamma Sigma. Clubs: Metairie Country, Internat. House, Plimsoll. Home: 1659 Burbank Dr New Orleans LA 70122-2711 Office: Milling Benson Woodward Hillyer Pierson & Mill 909 Poydras St Ste 2300 New Orleans LA 70112-1017

SNYDER, CHARLES ROYCE, sociologist, educator; b. Haverford, Pa., Dec. 28, 1924; s. Edward D. and Edith (Royce) S.; m. Patricia Hanson, June 30, 1951; children—Stephen Hoyt, Christiana Marie, Constance Patricia, Daniel Edward. BA, Yale U., 1945, M.A., 1949, Ph.D., 1954. Mem. staff Ctr. Alcohol Studies Yale U., 1950-60, asst. prof. sociology, 1956-60; prof. sociology So. Ill. U., Carbondale, 1960-85; chmn. dept. So. Ill. U., 1964-75, 81-85, prof. emeritus, 1985-; vis. prof. human genetics Sackler Sch. Medicine, Tel Aviv U., 1980; cons. behavioral scis. tng. com. Nat. Inst. Gen. Med. Scis., NIH, 1962-64; mem. planning com., chmn. program 28th Internat. Congress Alcohol and Alcoholism, 1964. Author: Alcohol and the Jews, 1958; editor: (with D.J. Pittman) Society, Culture and Drinking Patterns, 1962; editorial bd. Quar. Jour. Studies on Alcohol, 1957-83; assoc. editor Sociol. Quar., 1960-63. Mem. theol. commn. United Ch. of Christ, 1964-71; bd. dirs. Ill. Stewardship Alliance, 1990—. Served with USNR, World War II. Fellow Am. Sociol. Assn.; mem. Soc. Study Social Problems (v.p. 1963-64, rep. to council Am. Sociol. Assn. 1964-66), Midwest Sociol. Soc. (bd. dirs. 1970-71), AAUP. Home: 705 S Taylor Dr Carbondale IL 62901-2217

SNYDER, CLAIR ALLISON, banker; b. Reading, Pa., June 12, 1921; s. Augustus M. and Estella G. (Bright) S.; m. Jean Doris George, June 27, 1948; children: Joan Marie Snyder Ferguson, Jerry George. Student, W.Va. U., 1943-44, U. Mich. 1944-45. With Meridian Bancorp, Inc. and Meridian Bank, Reading, 1938-43, 46-88; exec. v.p., gen. banking Meridian Bancorp, Inc. and Meridian Bank, 1973-78, exec. v.p., chmn. credit policy com., 1978-86; pvt. practice fin. cons. Snyder Svcs. Co., Reading, 1987—; sr. cons. Marston Group, Inc., Harrisburg, Pa.; bd. dirs. Magnus Corp t/a Progressive Info. Techs., York, Pa., Terre Hill (Pa.) Concrete Corp., Am. Beton Systems, Terre Hill; asst. sec. Bi-Products, Inc., Fairview, Va. Bd. dirs. Pa. divsn. Am. Cancer Soc., 1965-87, chmn. bd. dirs., 1975-77; bd. dirs. Berks County (Pa.) unit Am. Cancer Soc., 1955—, pres., bd. dirs., 1964-66; chmn. Hope Lodge Com.; chmn. Property Mgmt. Com. With U.S. Army, 1943-46. Recipient Luther Halsey Gulick award Camp Fire Girls, 1966; div. Bronze medal Am. Cancer Soc., also Sword of Hope award. Mem. Internat. Soc. for Philosophic Inquiry, Am. Bankers Assn. (cert.), Pa. Bankers Assn. (past chmn. 1972-73), Robert Morris Assocs. (pres. 1972-73), Am. Legion (post comdr. 1948-49), Greater Hampstead C. of C. (bd. dirs., treas.), Old Point Golf and Country Club, Moselem Springs Golf Club, Belvedere Plantation Golf and Country Club. Republican. Mem. United Chs. of Christ. Home: FLying Hills 92 Medinah Dr Reading PA 19607-3313 also: 616 Sawgrass Rd Olde Point Hampstead NC 28443 *My life has been dedicated to personal achievement, but always with the knowledge that mankind's progress can only occur if each of us is willing to commit some of our efforts and resources to the future.*

SNYDER, C(LAUDE) ROBERT, insurance company executive; b. York, Pa., Feb. 27, 1937; s. Ellis R. Snyder and Margaret V. (Myers) Clemenson; m. Leona Elene Jensen, Jan. 30, 1960; children: Craig R., Laurie E. BS, UCLA, 1960; MBA, U. So. Calif., 1962. Regional v.p. Allstate Ins., Northbrook, Ill., 1962-84; pres., chief exec. officer Ahmanson Ins. Cos., Lakewood, Calif., 1984-86; chmn., chief exec. officer Northwestern Nat. Ins. Group, Brookfield, Wis., 1986—; chmn. bd. dirs. N.N. Ins. Co., 1987—, Northwestern Nat. Casualty Co., Brookfield, Northwestern Nat. Holding Co., Inc., Pacific Nat. Ins. Co., Tustin, Calif., Pacific Automobile Inst. Co., Tustin ;

bd. dirs. BancOne Wis. Corp. Active Greater Milw. Com., 1986—, Med. Coll. Wis. Coun., Milw, 1986-89; adv. coun. Sch. Bus. Adminstrn., U. Wis., Milw., 1986—. With USNR, 1954-62. Republican. Home: 4601 Hewitts Point Rd Oconomowoc WI 53066-3316 Office: Northwestern Nat Ins Group 18650 W Corporate Dr Brookfield WI 53045-6344

SNYDER, DANIEL JAMES, military career officer; b. Clarkson, N.Y., Dec. 31, 1954; s. James Orman and Marilyn Malita (Ophardt) S.; m. Carrie Sue Grimes, May 11, 1985; children: Robert James, Ryan Benjamin. BS, So. Ill. U., 1977; MA, Webster U., 1978. Enlisted USN, 1975, commd. ensign, 1979, advanced through grades to comdr.; hosp. corpsman Naval Hosp. USN, Great Lakes, Ill., 1976-79; comptroller Naval Hosp. USN, Okinawa, Japan, 1979-81; dir. adminstrn. Naval Hosp. USN, Annapolis, Md., 1981-85; head med. planning, chief naval ops. USN, Washington, 1985-88; dir. adminstrn. Naval Hosp. USN, Rota, Spain, 1988-91; head med. planning., chief naval ops. USN, Washington, 1991—. Decorated Meritorious Svc. medal, Navy Commendation medal, numerous Navy Achievement medals. Fellow Am. Coll. Healthcare Execs. (Regent 1993—). Republican. Lutheran. Avocations: sailing, running. Home: 5627 Ridge View Dr Alexandria VA 22310-1465 Office: Chief Naval Ops 2000 Navy Pentagon Washington DC 20350-1002

SNYDER, DAVID L, film production designer; b. Buffalo, Sept. 22, 1944; s. Albert R. and Louise M. (Passero) S.; m. Terry Finn, Aug. 1, 1990; children: David Michael, Amy Lynne. Grad. high sch., Niagara Falls, N.Y. Ind. film prodn. designer Hollywood, Calif.; pres. Snyder Bros. Prodns., Inc., Hollywood; guest speaker Tokyo Internat. Film Festival, 1985. Art dir.: (films) In God We Trust, 1980, The Idolmaker, 1980, Blade Runner, 1982 (Academy award nomination best art direction 1982), Brainstorm, 1983, Racing With the Moon, 1984, The Woman In Red, 1984, My Science Project, 1985, (TV movies) Sins of the Past, 1984; prodn. designer: (films) Strange Brew, 1983, Pee-Wee's Big Adventure, 1985, Armed and Dangerous, 1986, Back to School, 1986, Summer School, 1987, Moving, 1988, She's Out of Control, 1989, Bill & Ted's Bogus Journey, 1991, Class Act, 1992, Super Mario Brothers, 1993, Demolition Man, 1993; assoc. prodr.: (film) Cold Dog Soup, 1990; scenic designer: (TV programs) CNN/Showbiz Today, 1989. Mem. Soc. Motion Picture and TV Art Dirs., Acad. Motion Picture Arts and Scis., Nat. Acad. TV Arts and Scis. Democrat. Avocation: researching history of the film industry in America. Office: Innovative Artists 1999 Ave of the Stars Ste 2850 Los Angeles CA 90067

SNYDER, DAVID MARKEL, marketing executive; b. York, Pa., Aug. 19, 1939; s. Ellis Snyder and Peggy (Myers) Clemensen; m. Linnea Mae Haberland, Aug. 17, 1968; children: David, Greg. BS in Econs., UCLA, 1962. With Hughes Aircraft Co., 1962—, asst. mgr. Hughes Washington D.C., 1969-72, mgr. Boston Dist. Office, 1972-77, assoc. program mgr. Ground System Group, Fullerton, Calif., 1977-80, dir. Hughes Internat. Europe and Middle East, L.A., 1980-85, staff v.p. Hughes Internat. Ops., L.A., 1985-86, v.p., 1986-90, sr. v.p. Hughes Mktg. & Internat., 1987-90; pres. Hughes Aircraft Internat. Svc. Co., Hughes Aircraft Systems Internat., 1980—; also bd. dirs. Internat. scholar Am. Field Svc., 1956. Mem. Assn. U.S. Army, Armed Forces Communications and Electronics Assn., Marine Corps Aviation Assn., Am. Def. Preparedness Assn., Bel-Air Country Club (club champion 1984-86). Republican. Lutheran. Avocations: golf, classical music. Office: Hughes Aircraft Co PO Box 45066 7200 Hughes Terr Los Angeles CA 90045-0066

SNYDER, DAVID RICHARD, lawyer; b. Kalamazoo, Mich., Oct. 9, 1949; s. Richard E. and Margaret L. (Vanderplough) S.; m. Phyllis Alford, Aug. 14, 1971; children: Jason Richard, Carrie Lynn. BA with high honors, Mich. State U., 1971; JD with distinction, Cornell U., 1974. Bar: Calif. 1974. Assoc. Jenkins & Perry, San Diego, 1974-77, ptnr., 1978-83; ptnr. Aylward, Kintz & Stiska, San Diego, 1983-86, Luce, Forward, Hamilton & Scripps, San Diego, 1986-93, Pillsbury Madison & Sutro, San Diego, 1993—; v.p., dir. San Diego Venture Group, 1989-91; adj. prof. Calif. Western Sch. Law, San Diego, 1982-84; lectr. Calif. Continuing Edn. of Bar, 1983—. Co-author: Drafting Legal Instruments, 1982; editor Cornell Law Rev., 1973-74. Bd. dirs. Boys Club Chula Vista, Calif., 1979-83; pres. Corpus Christi Parish Coun., Bonita, Calif., 1988-90; mem. Children's Hosp. Found., San Diego, 1988—, chmn., 1990-92. Mem. ABA (fed. securities law com. 1987—), State Bar Calif., San Diego County Bar Assn., Am. Electronics Assn. (bd. dirs., mem. exec. com. San Diego chpt. 1991-93), Order of Coif, Phi Beta Kappa. Republican. Roman Catholic. Office: Pillsbury Madison & Sutro 101 W Broadway Ste 1800 San Diego CA 92101-8298

SNYDER, DON, retail automotive executive; b. 1939. With Bob Moore Leasing Co., Oklahoma City, 1967-70; gen. mgr. Bob Moore Cadillac, Oklahoma City, 1970-79; pres. Don Davis Auto Group Inc., Arlington, Tex., 1979—, Don Davis Nissan Inc., Arlington, 1979—; with Don Davis Auto Inc., Arlington, 1994—, now v.p.-contr. Office: Don Davis Auto Inc 1661 Wet N Wild Way Arlington TX 76011*

SNYDER, DONALD EDWARD, corporate executive; b. Rochester, N.Y., Nov. 10, 1928; s. Benjamin Orman and Arlien Henrietta (Wing) S.; m. Dorothy Edna Stanke, Oct. 16, 1954; children—Donald Edward, Anne Arlien Snyder Marone, Barbara Lynn Snyder Mitchell, Richard John Snyder. A.B., Cornell U., 1950, J.D., 1952; postgrad., Ind. U., 1962. Bar: N.Y. 1953. Pvt. practice law, 1953-56; with Eastman Savs. and Loan Assn., 1956-68, pres., 1970-75, chmn. bd., 1979-88; asst. to treas. Eastman Kodak Co., Rochester, 1968-70; gen. credit mgr. Eastman Kodak Co., 1975-77, with Comptroller's div., 1977-78, asst. treas., 1978-79, treas., 1979-88; chmn. Eastman Kodak Credit Corp., 1985-88; chief exec. officer, chmn. bd., pres. Corp. Officers and Dirs. Assurance Ltd., Hamilton, Bermuda, 1990-93. Bd. dirs. Greater Rochester chpt. Epilepsy Found. Am., 1979-85, Allendale Mut. Ins. Co., 1983-92; bd. dirs. Luth. Ch.-Mo. Synod, 1983—, vice chmn. bd., chmn. fin. com., mem., chmn. audit com., 1989—; bd. dirs., mem. exec. com. ACE Ltd., 1985-90, EXEL Ltd., 1985-90, CODA Ltd., 1986-93; mem. investment rev. com. United Way of Greater Rochester, 1979—; trustee Seneca Zool. Soc., 1983-90. With USNR, 1946-48. Mem. N.Y. State Bar Assn., Monroe County Bar Assn., Rochester C. of C. (trustee 1980-86), Cornell Club (Rochester), Phi Kappa Tau (nat. fin. advisor, mem. nat. coun. 1988—, treas., mem. exec. com. Phi Kappa Tau Found. 1991—). Home and Office: 48 Church Hill Rd Henrietta NY 14467-9711

SNYDER, FRANK R., building materials manufacturing executive; b. 1939. Grad., Lehigh U., 1962, MBA, 1970. With Bethlehem (Pa.) Steel Corp., 1962-67, Lehigh Portland Cement Co. (Inc.), Allentown, Pa.; v.p., contr., treas. Heidelberg Cement Inc., Allentown. Office: Heidelberg Cement Inc 7660 Imperial Way Allentown PA 18195*

SNYDER, FRANKLIN FARISON, hydrologic engineering consultant; b. Holgate, Ohio, Nov. 11, 1910; s. Samuel Lewis and Nettie May (Farison) S.; m. Mary Elizabeth Bruton, Oct. 1, 1938; children: Marilyn Kay Snyder Lutz, Carol Lamb Snyder Garnett, Gregory Lewis. Student, U. Toledo, 1928-30; B.C.E., Ohio State U., 1932, C.E., 1942; postgrad., Dept. Agr. Grad. Sch., 1940-42, 62. Registered profl. engr., Ohio. Hydraulic engr. U.S. Geol. Survey, Washington, 1934-35; hydraulic engr. TVA, Knoxville, 1936-37, Pa. Dept. Forests and Waters, Harrisburg, 1938-39, U.S. Weather Bur., Pitts. and Washington, 1940-42, Office Chief Engrs., Washington, 1942-66; ptnr. Nunn, Snyder & Assocs., Fairfax, Va., 1972-78; hydrologic engring. cons., McLean, Va., Can., Mex., Sudan, Greece, Bangladesh, Pakistan, Colombia, Jamaica, 1954-90; mem. Internat. St. Lawrence River Bd. Control, 1961-74, U.S. Nat. Com. for Internat. Hydrological Decade, 1964-67. Contbr. articles to profl. publs. Supr. Citizens Assn. Security Patrol, Chesterbrook Woods, McLean, 1978-94. Recipient exceptional civilian service award War Dept., 1946, Outstanding Civil Engring. Alumnus award Ohio State U. Civil Engring. Alumni Assn., 1989, Disting. Alumnus award Ohio State U., 1990; named to Gallery of Disting. Civilian Employees, C.E., 1983. Fellow ASCE (Croes medal); mem. Am. Geophys. Union, Am. Meteorol. Soc., Nat. Acad. Engring., Sigma Xi, Tau Beta Pi Republican. Presbyterian. Clubs: Cosmos (Washington); Officers (Fort Myer, Va.); Washington Golf and Country (Arlington, Va.). Avocations: genealogy; golf; travel. Address: 1516 Laburnum St Mc Lean VA 22101-2527

SNYDER, GARY SHERMAN, poet; b. San Francisco, May 8, 1930; s. Harold Alton and Lois (Wilkie) S.; m. Masa Uehara, Aug. 6, 1967 (div.);

children: Kai, Gen; m. Carole Koda, Apr. 28, 1991. B.A., Reed Coll., 1951; postgrad., Ind. U., 1951-52, U. Calif.-Berkeley, 1953-56. Gen. Lookout Mount Baker Forest, 1952-53; research in Japan, 1956-57, 59-64; lectr. U. Calif., Berkeley, 1964-65; prof. U. Calif., Davis, 1985—. Author: poems Riprap, 1959, Myths and Texts, 1960, Six Sections from Mountains and Rivers Without End, 1965, The Back Country, 1968, Regarding Wave, 1970, Turtle Island, 1974, Axe Handles, 1983, Left Out in the Rain, 1986, No Nature, 1992; prose Earth House Hold, 1969, The Old Ways, 1977, He Who Hunted Birds in His Father's Village, 1979, The Real Work, 1980, Passage Through India, 1984, The Practice of the Wild, 1990, A Place in Space, 1995. Bollingen fellow, 1966-67, Guggenheim fellow, 1968-69; recipient Pulitzer prize for poetry, 1975. Mem. Am. Acad. Arts and Letters, Am. Acad. Arts and Scis. *My work as artist and citizen has been driven by the insight that all is connected and interdependent—nature, societies, rocks, stars. If I seem to set myself "against the times" it is in the name of a larger process; of clarity and of sanity.*

SNYDER, GEORGE EDWARD, lawyer; b. Battle Creek, Mich., Feb. 7, 1934; s. Leon R. and Edith (Dullabahn) S.; m. Mary Jane Belt, July 27, 1957 (div. Sept. 23, 1982); children: Sara Lynn, Elizabeth Jane; m. Claudia Gage Brooks, Feb. 25, 1984. B.S., Mich. State U., 1957; J.D., U. Mich., 1960. Bar: Mich. 1961, U.S. Dist. Ct. (we. and ea. dists.) Mich. 1961. With Gen. Electric Co., 1957-58; asso. firm Miller, Johnson, Snell & Commisky, Grand Rapids, 1960-62, Goodenough & Buesser, Detroit, 1962-66; partner firm Buesser, Buesser, Snyder & Blank, Detroit and Bloomfield Hills, 1966-85, Meyer, Kirk, Snyder & Safford, Bloomfield Hills, 1985—; dir. Bill Knapps Mich., Inc. Chmn. E. Mich. Environ. Action Council, 1974-78; pub. mem. inland lakes and streams rev. com. Mich. Dept. Natural Resources, 1975-76. Served as 2d lt. AUS, 1957. Fellow Am. Acad. Matrimonial Lawyers (pres. Mich. chpt. 1991-92—), Am. Bar Found., Internat. Acad. Matrimonial Lawyers, Mich. Bar Found.; mem. State Bar Mich. (chmn. family law com. 1968-72, mem. rep. assembly 1972-78, chmn. rules and calendar com. 1977-78, mem. family law sect. council.1973-76, environ. law sect. council 1980-85, prepaid legal services com. 1973-82, com. on judicial selection 1974, com. on specialization 1976-82), ABA, Detroit Bar Assn. (chmn. family law com. 1966-68), Oakland County Bar Assn., Am. Judicature Soc., Am. Arbitration Assn. (panel arbitrators), Delta Upsilon (chmn. trustees, alumni chpt. dep. 1965-70), Tau Beta Pi, Pi Tau Sigma, Phi Eta Sigma. Episcopalian. Clubs: Detroit Athletic, Thomas M. Cooley, Birmingham (Mich.) Athletic. Home: 32965 Outland Trl Bingham Farms MI 48025-2555 Office: Meyer Kirk Snyder & Safford 100 W Long Lake Rd Ste 100 Bloomfield Hills MI 48304-2773

SNYDER, GEORGE RICHARD, laboratory director; b. Grand Junction, Colo., July 26, 1929; s. Frank Alexander and Rose Cecile (Krankota) S.; m. Lorraine Elizabeth Brewer; children—Derrick, Gigi, Heather, Hans, Royce, Sterling. B.S. in Fisheries, Colo. State U., 1958, M.S., 1960, Ph.D., U. Ida., 1979. Hatchery helper Colo. Fish & Game Commn., Estes Park, 1949; fish technologist Wyo. Fish and Game Dept., Pinedale, 1957; fishery research biologist Colo. Fish and Game Dept., Ft. Collins, Colo., 1958-60; program leader Fish Passage Research, Seattle, 1968-78; asst. dir. C.E. Div., Seattle, 1961-68; dir. Auke Bay Lab., Juneau, 1980—. Commr., King County Water Dist. 104, Woodinville, Wash., 1968-77. Served with USN, 1950-54. Mem. Am. Inst. Fisheries Research Biologists, Am. Fisheries Soc., Wash. Assn. Water Dists. (pres. 1977). Home: 9454 Herbert Pl Juneau AK 99802-0001 Office: Nat Marine Fisheries Svc Alaska Fisheries Sci Ctr Auke Bay Lab 11305 Glacier Hwy Auke Bay AK 99821-8626

SNYDER, GILES D. H., lawyer; b. Charleston, W.Va., May 28, 1931; s. Harry L. and Cora Ella (Houston) S.; m. Dale S. Davis, May 23, 1975; children—Jesse D. H., Benjamin D. H.; children by previous marriage—Anne H., Giles G., Matthew D. A.B., W.va.U., 1952, LL.B., 1954. Bar: W.Va. Ohio 19, D.C. 19, U.S. Ct. Appeals 19, U.S. Supreme Ct. Asst. atty. gen. State of W.Va., Charleston, 1956-60; atty. Columbia Gas System, N.Y.C., 1960-68; asst. sec. Columbus Group of Columbia System, Ohio, 1968-73; asst. sec. Columbia Gas Transmission Corp., Charleston, W.Va., 1973-83, sec., gen. counsel, 1983-94; spl. counsel Bowles Rice McDavid Graff and Love, Charleston, 1994—. Mem. ABA, W.Va. Bar Assn., Ohio State Bar Assn., Fed. Energy Bar Assn., Order of Coif, Phi Beta Kappa. Democrat. Episcopalian. Home: 1661 Woodvale Dr Charleston WV 25314-2547 Office: Bowles Rice McDavid PO Box 1386 Commerce Sq Charleston WV 25325-1386

SNYDER, HARRY COOPER, state senator; b. July 10, 1928. Student, Wilmington Coll., Ohio U. State senator State of Ohio, Columbus, 1979—. Former exec. com. mem. Ohio Sch. Bds. Assn.; mem. governing bd. Ohio High Speed Rail Authority, Jobs for Ohio Graduates. Recipient Outstanding Legis. Svc. award Citizens United for Responsible Edn., Ohio Ret. Tchrs. Assn., Ohio Coalition for Edn. of Handicapped Children, Ohio Assn. Civil Trial Attys., Guardian of Small Bus. award Nat. Fedn. Ind. Bus., Outstanding Contbr. to Edn. in Ohio award Ohio Confedn. Tchr. Edn. Orgn., Disting. Govtl. Svc. award Ohio Coun. Pvt. Colls. and Schs., Legis. of Yr. Ohio Sch. and Transit Assn. Mem. Am. Legis. Exch. Coun. (edn. com., Outstanding State Legis.-Jefferson award), Nat. Conf. State Legislatures (state/fed. assembly, edn. and job tng. com., assembly of legislature, edn. com.), Ohio Bd. Regents (ad hoc), Rotary Club (pres.), Clinton County Family Y (founder), Clinton County Bd. Edn., Great Oaks Task Force. Republican. Methodist. Avocations: reading, gardening. Home: 6508 Spring Hill Dr Hillsboro OH 45133-9209

SNYDER, HENRY LEONARD, history educator, bibliographer; b. Hayward, Calif., Nov. 3, 1929; s. Henry Runyon and Mary (Rosenberg) S.; m. Janette Marie Hannus, July 21, 1961; children: Michael Jean, Christopher Henry, David Lyle. BA, U. Calif., Berkeley, 1951, MA, 1960, PhD, 1963. Sr. buyer Dohrmann Comml. Co., San Francisco, 1951-59; instr. to prof. U. Kans., Lawrence, 1963-78; assoc. dean to dean research adminstrn. U. Kans., 1967-78; prof. history, dean arts and scis. La. State U., Baton Rouge, 1979-86; prof. history U. Calif., Riverside, 1986—; dir. Ctr. for Bibliog. Studies, 1989—; dean humanities and social scis. U. Calif., Riverside, 1986; vis. lectr. Bedford Coll., U. London, 1965-66; Fulbright lectr., research scholar U. Hamburg, Fed. Republic Germany, 1974; dir. English Short Title Catalogue for N.Am., 1978—. Editor: The Marlborough Godolphin Correspondence, 1975; co-editor: The Scottish Heritage, 1981. Pres. Baton Rouge Opera, 1981-83, Riverside Opera, 1987-90; pres. United Way, Lawrence, 1977; bd. dirs. Arts and Humanities Coun., Baton Rouge, 1981-85; Sigmund, Martin, Heller Traveling fellow U. Calif.-Berkeley, 1962-63. Am. Council Learned Soc. sr. fellow, 1969-70. Fellow Royal Hist. Soc. Gt. Brit., Bibliog. Soc. London; mem. Am. Soc. 18th Century Studies (pres. 1980-81), Conf. Brit. Studies (exec. com. 1978-83), Am. Hist. Assn. Republican. Congregationalist. Home: 220 Trinity Ave Kensington CA 94708 Office: U Calif- Riverside Ctr for Bibliog Studies Riverside CA 92521-0154

SNYDER, IRVIN STANLEY, microbiologist, educator; b. Nanticoke, Pa., May 29, 1931; s. Irvin William and Wanda Dolores S.; m. Marlene Ann Smetana, Sept. 3, 1955; children—Mary Ellen, Carole Jeanne, Irvin John. B.S., Wilkes Coll., 1953; M.A., U. Kans., 1958, Ph.D. 1960. Instr. microbiology U. Iowa Med. Sch., 1960-61, asst. prof., 1961-67, assoc. prof., 1967-72, prof., 1972-73; research prof. Bryn Mawr (Pa.) Coll., 1966; prof., chmn. dept. microbiology W.Va. U. Med. Center, Morgantown, 1973-91, prof., 1991—. Author: (with J.M. Slack) Bacteria and Human Disease, 1978; contbr.: (with R. Finch) chpts. to Modern Pharmacology; author several slide-tape teaching programs; contbr. articles to profl. jours. Served with AUS, 1953-55. Recipient Silver medal Kaw Valley Heart Assn., 1960, teaching awards U. Iowa, teaching awards W.Va. U., Alumni Faculty Appreciation award W.Va. U. Fellow Am. Acad. Microbiology; mem. Am. Soc. Microbiology, Am. Bd. Microbiology, Soc. Exptl. Biology and Medicine, Am. Inst. Biol. Scis., Sigma Xi, Phi Delta Kappa, Omicron Kappa Upsilon. Office: W Va U/Dept Microbiol & Imm Robert C Byrd Health Scis PO Box 9177 Morgantown WV 26506-9177

SNYDER, JACK RALPH, lawyer; b. Gary, Ind., June 24, 1940; s. Jack T. and Margaret (Considine) S.; m. Barbara C. Goins, June 23, 1962 (div. Sept. 1985); children: John, Hilary, Alison, Alfred; m. Mary L. Brzezinski Forster, Oct. 1981. AB, Brown U., 1962; LLB, U. Mich., 1964. Bar: Ind. 1965, U.S. Dist. Ct. (so. dist.) 1965, U.S. Ct. Appeals (7th cir.) 1965, (D.C. cir.) 1980. Assoc. ICE Miller Donadio & Ryan, Indpls., 1965-71, ptnr., 1972—, mng.

ptnr., 1990-93; bd. dirs. Indpls. Motor Speedway Corp. Gen. counsel AAU of U.S., Inc., Indpls., 1978—; counsel Midwestern Collegiate Conf.; trustee Marian Coll.; v.p. Ind. Sports Corp., 1989—. Recipient Louis A. Dawson Outstanding Vol. award Tabernacle Presbyn. Ch., 1980; Monsignor Albert Basalt Outstanding Vol. award, Indpls. Cath. Youth Orgn., 1982. Fellow Ind. Bar Assn.; mem. ABA, Indpls. Bar Found. (bd. dirs.), Skyline Club (Indpls.), Ind. Conv. and Visitors Assn. (bd. dirs.), Phi Delta Phi, Delta Kappa Epsilon. Avocations: running, photography, sports, travel. Office: Ice Miller Donadio & Ryan 1 American Sq Indianapolis IN 46282-0001

SNYDER, JAMES R., wholesale distribution executive, textiles executive; b. 1948. Sec., treas. Shelter Components Indiana, Elkhart, Ind. Office: Shelter Components Indiana 27217 County Rd 6 Elkhart IN 46514*

SNYDER, JEAN MACLEAN, lawyer; b. Chgo., Jan. 26, 1942; d. Norman Fitzroy and Jessie (Burns) Maclean; m. Joel Martin Snyder, Sept. 4, 1964; children: Jacob Samuel, Noah Scot. BA, U. Chgo., 1963, JD, 1979. Bar: Ill. 1979, U.S. Dist. Ct. (no. dist.) Ill. 1979, U.S. Ct. Appeals (7th cir.) 1981. Ptnr. D'Ancona & Pflaum, Chgo., 1979-92; prin. Law Office of Jean Maclean Snyder, Chgo., 1993—. Contbr. articles to profl. publs. Mem. ABA (mem. coun. litigation sect. 1989-92, editor-in-chief Litigation mag. 1987-88, co-chair First Amendment and Media Litigation com. litigation sect. 1992—). Office: Law Office Jean M Snyder 3 First Nat Plaza 70 W Madison St Ste 3600 Chicago IL 60602

SNYDER, JEANNE ANNE, interior designer, educator; b. Detroit, July 23, 1945; d. Paul G. and Mary T. Thoen; m. James C. Snyder, July 13, 1968; children: Jamie Moore, Jennifer Thoen. BS in Design, U. Mich., 1967. Interior designer Skidmore Owings, Chgo., 1967-68; Interior Design Svc., U. Mich., Ann Arbor, 1968-72, Associated Space Design, Atlanta, 1972-76, Kahler, Slater, Fitzhugh Scott, Milw., 1976-80; interior designer Hobbs & Black, Ann Arbor, 1984-91, dir. interior design, 1991—; asst. prof. interior design U. Mich., Ann Arbor, 1980-90. Prin. works include Waukesha Meml. Hosp., 1979, Hobbs & Black Corp. Ctr., 1986, Peachwood Nursing Faculty, 1988, Olds Plaza, 1990, Lansing Ctr., 1994. Mem. Inst. Bus. Designers (affiliate). Roman Catholic. Home: 2963 Warren Rd Ann Arbor MI 48105-9717

SNYDER, JOHN C., oil and gas industry executive; b. 1942. BA in Petroleum Engring., U. Okla., 1964; MBA, Harvard U., 1968. Petroleum engr. Humble Oil & Refining, Houston, 1964-68; with Devtek Inc., Ft. Worth, 1968-69; founder Can.-Am. Resource Fund Inc., Ft. Worth, 1969-71; exec. v.p. May Petroleum Inc., Dallas, 1971-73; ind. oil operator Midland, Tex., 1974-77; founder Tucker-Snyder Exploration Co. (name now Snyder Oil Co.), Ft. Worth, 1977—, now chmn. bd. dirs. Office: Snyder Oil Co 777 Main St Ste 2500 Fort Worth TX 76102*

SNYDER, JOHN JOSEPH, bishop; b. N.Y.C., Oct. 25, 1925; s. John Joseph and Katherine Marie (Walsh) S. Ordained priest Roman Cath. Ch., 1951, consecrated bishop, 1973. Assoc. pastor St. Mel's Parish, Flushing, N.Y., 1951-57; sec. to bishops Diocese Bklyn., 1957-72; titular bishop Forlimopoli, vicar gen., aux. bishop Diocese Bklyn., 1972-79; bishop Diocese of St. Augustine, Fla., 1979—. Office: Chancery Office 11625 Old St Augustine Rd Jacksonville FL 32241*

SNYDER, KENNETH F., lawyer; b. Cleve., Ohio, Sept. 10, 1941. BA, Western Reserve U., 1963; JD, U. Mich., 1966; LLM Taxation, NYU, 1967. Bar: Ohio 1966. Ptnr. Baker & Hostetler, Cleve. Office: Baker & Hostetler 3200 Nat City Ctr 1900 E 9th St Cleveland OH 44114-3303

SNYDER, LEE H., lawyer; b. Oct. 9, 1931. BS, Albright Coll., 1955; JD, U. Mich., 1958. Bar: Pa. 1958. Fla. 1978. Ptnr. Morgan, Lewis & Bockius, Phila. Office: Morgan Lewis & Bockius 2000 One Logan Sq Philadelphia PA 19103

SNYDER, LESLIE, newspaper editor. Education educator Dallas Morning News, Tex. Office: The Dallas Morning News Communications Ctr PO Box 655237 Dallas TX 75266-5237*

SNYDER, LEWIS EMIL, astrophysicist; b. Ft. Wayne, Ind., Nov. 26, 1939; s. Herman Lewis and Bernice (McKee) S.; m. Doris Jean Selma Lautner, June 16, 1962; children: Herman Emil, Catherine Jean. BS, Ind. State U., 1961; MA, So. Ill. U., 1964; PhD, Mich. State U., 1967. Research assoc. Nat. Radio Astronomy Obs., Charlottesville, Va., 1967-69; prof. astronomy dept. U. Va., Charlottesville, 1969-73, 74-75; vis. fellow joint Inst. for Lab. Astrophysics, U. Colo., Boulder, 1973-74; prof. astronomy dept. U. Ill., Urbana, 1975—. Co-editor: Molecules in the Galactic Environment, 1973; contbr. articles to sci. jours. NASA-Am. Soc. Engring. Edn. summer fellow, 1972, 73; Alexander von Humboldt Found. sr. U.S. scientist award, 1983-84. Mem. AAAS, Astron. Soc. Pacific, Am. Phys. Soc., Am. Astron. Soc., Internat. Astron. Union, Union Radio Scientifique Internationale, Sigma Xi. Lutheran. Office: U Ill 1002 W Green St Urbana IL 61801-3547

SNYDER, MARGARET ELIZABETH, assemblywoman, paralegal; b. Elizabethtown, Tenn., Feb. 25, 1940; d. William Clarence Peters and Emma Grace (Elliott) Murphy; m. Melvin Wesley Snyder, Aug. 16, 1968; children: Jonathan L., Jennifer L., David E. Paraplegal cert., Humphreys Coll., 1992. Sec. U.S., Philippines, Germany; assemblywoman State of Calif. Assembly, Sacramento, 1992—. Vol. Family Svc., Philippines, 1962-64, ARC, Germany, 1970-72; bd. dirs., Modesto, Calif., 1981-84; mem. Dem. Ctrl. Com. 1977-86, Stanislaus County Grand Jury, 1978-79; bd. edn. Modesto City Schs., 1985-92; bd. dirs. The Haven, Modesto, 1990-92; mem. Internat. Friendship Com., Modesto, 1988-92. Named Vol. of Yr. Family Svc., Philippines, 1963, ARC, Germany, 1971, Woman of Yr. Stanislaus County Commn. for Women, Modesto, 1992, Woman of Distinction, Soroptomist Internat., Modesto, 1992. Avocations: camping, reading, travel. Office: 1101 Standiford Ave Ste B5 Modesto CA 95350-0981

SNYDER, MARIAN H., nursing educator and administrator; b. Webster, S.D., June 10, 1942; d. Harry C. and Helen L. (Potter) Walker; 1 child, Susan Marin. BSN, U. Conn., 1964; MS in Nursing, U. Ky., 1977; PhD, Marquette U., 1987. Staff nurse USAF, San Antonio, 1965-67; instr. Norton-Children's Hosp., Louisville, 1967-77; faculty Columbia Coll., Milw., 1977-81; dean, chief exec. officer Carroll-Columbia Coll. Nursing, Milw., 1981—. 1st lt. Nurses Corps, USAF. Mem. ANA, NLN, Sigma Theta Tau. Office: Columbia College 2121 E Newport Ave Milwaukee WI 53211-2952

SNYDER, MARION GENE, lawyer, former congressman; b. Louisville, Jan. 26, 1928; s. M. G. and Lois (Berg) S.; 1 son, Mark; m. Patricia C. Robertson, Apr. 10, 1973; 3 step-children. LLB cum laude, Jefferson Sch. Law, Louisville, 1950; JD, U. Louisville, 1969. Bar: Ky. bar 1950, D.C. bar 1970. Practiced law Louisville, 1950-76; ret., farmer, 1957-80; city atty. Jeffersontown, 1953-57; magistrate 1st dist. Jefferson County, 1957-61; real estate broker, 1949—; mem. 88th Congress from 3d Ky. Dist., 1963-65; mem. 90th-99th congresses from 4th Ky. Dist., 1967-87, ret., 1987; sole practice, 1987-91; v.p. Ky. Magistrates and Commrs., 1958. Vice pres. Jeffersontown Civic Center, 1953-54; pres. Lincoln Republican Club Ky., 1960-61, 1st Magisterial Dist. Rep. Club, 1955-57. Mem. Ky. Bar Assn., Ky. Farm Bur., Ky. Real Estate Brokers, Lions, Optimists (prs. Jeffersontown club 1957-58), Jesters, Shriners, Masons. Home (winter): 383 Juli Fe Dr Naples FL 33942-1123

SNYDER, MARVIN, neuropsychologist; b. Bklyn., Oct. 14, 1940; s. Samuel and Sarah (Seidman) S.; m. Arlyne S. Naphtali, June 23, 1963; 1 dau., Sian Leslie. BA (N.Y. State Regents scholar 1958-62, Meml. award psychology 1962), Bklyn. Coll., 1962; PhD (NDEA fellow 1962-65, USPHS fellow 1965-66, trainee 1966-67), Duke U., 1967. Research psychologist NIMH, 1967-71; Nat. Eye Inst., 1971-72; program dir., neuroscis. Nat. Inst. Drug Abuse, 1974-79, dir. research, 1979-90, dir. Office of Sci. Policy, Edn. and Legislation, 1990-94; acting dep. dir. Nat. Inst. on Drug Abuse, 1992-93; pres. Snyder Assocs., 1995—; mem. sr. exec. svc. USPHS exec. com. AIDS, 1983-85, chmn. task force on psychol., psychiat. and addictive aspects of AIDS, 1984-85; mem. DDHS Orphan Products Bd., 1982-88; mem. The White House Task Force on Drug Abuse Health Issues; co-chmn. Interagy. Com. on Smoking and Health for New Therapies for Pain and Discomfort;

exec. sec. Interagy. Com. on Pain and Analgesia, chmn. subcom. on edn. and tng., 1985—; cons. to WHO on drug abuse policy issues, 1985-87; testifier on drug abuse sci. and policy issues to U.S. Congress; mem. FCCSET Com. on Brain and Behavior, 1990-91, Devel. Guidelines for Protection Human Subjects in Drug Abuse Studies, 1991. Author papers on comparative neurology. Recipient Michael Morrison award for excellence in sci. adminstrn. Com. on Problems of Drug Dependence, 1988, Presdl. Meritorious Rank award 1990. Office: Nat Inst Drug Abuse Rm 10A-55 5600 Fishers Ln Rockville MD 20857-0001

SNYDER, MIKE, newspaper editor. Day city editor Houston Chronicle. Office: Houston Chronicle Pub Co 801 Texas St Houston TX 77002-2906*

SNYDER, NATHAN, entrepreneur; b. Hartford, Conn., Oct. 7, 1934; s. Saul and Betsy (Wand) S.; m. Geraldine Wolff, Dec. 27, 1964; children: Hannah Abigail, Alexander Lowell Wolff. AB, Harvard U., 1956; LLB, Columbia U., 1963; postgrad. in bus., NYU, 1967-68. Bar: N.Y. 1963. Assoc. Paul, Weiss, Rifkind, Wharton & Garrison, N.Y.C., 1963-66; v.p., sec. Randolph Computer Corp., Greenwich, Conn., 1966-69, exec. v.p., gen. counsel, bd. dirs., 1969-73; exec. v.p., chief operating officer BanCal Tri-State Corp. (holding co. Bank of Calif.), San Francisco, 1974-76; v.p. acquisitions CBS Inc., N.Y.C., 1976-87; pres. VS & A Communications Ptnrs., N.Y.C., 1987-89, The Snyder Co., New Canaan, Conn., 1989—; lectr. of mgmt. Golden Gate U., San Francisco, 1974-76, Annenberg Sch. Comms., Phila., 1982-87; bd. dirs. Sogen Funds, N.Y.C. Editor: Columbia Law Rev., 1962-63. Vol. legal services Office Econ. Opportunity, 1963. Served to lt. USNR, 1956-60. Harlan Fiske Stone scholar, 1964-65. Mem. ABA, Columbia Law Sch. Alumni Assn. (bd. dirs. 1979), Harvard Club (N.Y.C.), Harvard Club (v.p. Fairfield County). Office: The Snyder Co 163 Parish Rd New Canaan CT 06840-4427

SNYDER, PATRICIA DI BENEDETTO, theater director and administrator. BA in English and Speech Edn., SUNY, Albany, 1967; MA in Theater Arts, Syracuse U., 1967; PhD in Arts and Humanities, NYU, 1991. Tchr. English, speech and drama West Genesee Sr. High Sch., Camillus, N.Y., 1962-64; tchr. English and drama, chair humanities teaching team Chestnut Hill Mid. Sch., Liverpool, N.Y., 1964-66; grad. asst. Syracuse (N.Y.) U., 1966-67; instr. dept. theatre SUNY, Albany, 1967-74, spl. asst. to chancellor, adj. assoc. prof. dept. theatre, 1974-75, founder, producing dir. Empire State Youth Theatre Inst., 1975-92; exec. dir. Gov. Nelson A. Rockefeller Empire State Plz. Performing Arts Ctr. Corp., 1982-89; producing dir., CEO N.Y. State Theatre Inst. Corp., 1992—; cons. Spanish and Portuguese Mins., Madrid and Lisbon, 1968, U.S. Office Edn. 1979, Spanish Min. Culture, 1982, Time Warner, Inc., 1991; mem. edn. bd. Saratoga Performing Arts Ctr., 1973; apptd. arts and humanities planning com. N.Y. State Edn. Dept., 1975; mem. arts task force on arts in edn. NEH, 1977; apptd. N.Y. State Edn. Commr.'s Adv. Coun., 1978; panelist U.S. Children's Lit. Assn., 1978; del. UNESCO Conf., Sibenek, Yugoslavia, 1979; lectr. Syracuse U., 1988; mem. acad. coun. Richard Porter Leach Fund for Arts, 1989; adj. prof. theatre Russell Sage Coll., 1992.; lectr. and presenter in field. Prodr. (stage prodns.) The Wizard of Oz, 1977, Lancashire Lad, 1980, Sleeping Beauty, 1981, 83, 90, Handy Dandy, 1985, Rag Dolly, 1986, Aladdin, 1987, Hizzoner!, 1988, 89, Beauty and the Beast, 1991, Slow Dance on the Killing Ground, 1993; contbr. articles to profl. jours. Guest fellow Hungarian Theatre Inst., 1970, USSR Min. Culture, 1970, 84; recipient Mayor's medal City of Milan, Italy, 1977, Spl. Recognition award John F. Kennedy Ctr. for Performing Arts, 1978, 81, Recognition award NATAS, 1986, Albany League Arts award, 1986, Spl. Recognition award N.Y. State Theatre Edn Assn., 1993. Mem. Am. Theatre Assn. (commn. on theatre devel. 1976, Spl. Recognition citation 1973, 74, Jennie Heiden award 1985), Children's Theatre Assn. Am. (Zeta Phi Eta award 1972), League Am. Theatres and Prodrs., Soc. State Dirs. and Choreographers, Assn. Internat. du Theatre pour l'Enfants et al Jeunesse (del. 1968, 70, 74, 78, 79 congresses, exec. com. 1969, fundraiser 1972 conf., editor ofcl. report 1973, chair U.S. ctr. 1977), N.Y. League Profl. Theatre Women, U. Albany Alumni Assn. (Disting. Alumni award 1987), Cosmopolitan Club, Phi Delta Kappa. Home: 722 N Broadway Saratoga Springs NY 12866-1621 Office: NY State Theatre Inst PO Box 28 Troy NY 12181-0028

SNYDER, PETER LARSEN, public relations executive; b. Phila., Apr. 28, 1952; s. Philip Lerch and Adrienne Louise (Larsen) S.; m. Karen Suzanne Stachiw, June 1, 1973; children: P. Evan, Erik D. BS, Cornell U., 1975. Account exec. Gibbs & Soell Pub. Rels., N.Y.C., 1975-78; account assoc. Ruder & Finn Pub. Rels., N.Y.C., 1978-80; exec. v.p., mng. ptnr. Dorf & Stanton Communications, St. Louis, 1980—, COO, 1992—, pres., 1995—. Cons. Harbor Festival '78, N.Y.C. St. Louis Pub. Sch. Partnership program, 1985-87, St. Louis area ARC, 1987-88, Muscular Dystrophy Assn. St. Louis, 1988; bd. dirs., capital chmn. Rohan-Woods Sch., Warson Woods, Mo., 1986-88; bd. dirs. Kirkwood/Webster YMCA, Webster Groves, Mo., 1984-87, The New Theater, St. Louis, 1994—, Riverway Sch., 1994—, Downtown St. Louis, 1995—, Emmanuel Ch. Found., 1989-92; co-founder, asst. scoutmaster Troop 39, Boy Scouts Am.; chmn. Downtown Parks Bus. Dist., 1990—; co-chair security com. Downtown St. Louis Inc., 1991—; comms. com. Diocese Mo. Episcopal Ch., 1993—; trustee world affairs coun. St. Louis, 1993; v.p., 1994—; commr. downtown pks. taxing dist., 1994—. Mem. Nat. Agri-Mktg. Assn. (named Best of 1983), Cornell Club St. Louis (bd. dirs. 1988—), Media Club, The Newcomen Soc. Episcopalian. Avocations: sailing, scuba diving, skiing. Office: Dorf & Stanton Communications 1221 Locust St Ste 555 Saint Louis MO 63103-2364

SNYDER, RALPH SHELDON, lawyer; b. Harrisburg, Pa., May 15, 1922; s. Louis Sidney and Ann Margaret (Shulman) S.; m. Janet Gushner, Aug. 29, 1948; 1 child, Randy. BA, Pa. State U., 1942; JD, Dickinson Sch. Law, 1948. Bar: Pa. 1949, U.S. Dist. Ct. (ea. dist.) Pa., U.S. Ct. Appeals (3d cir.), U.S. Ct. Appeals (10th cir.), U.S. Supreme Ct. Dep. atty. gen. Commonwealth of Pa., Harrisburg, 1944-92; ptnr. Schnader, Harrison, Segal & Lewis, Phila., 1963—; lectr. law master's program Temple U., Phila., 1977, Villanova U., Phila., 1981-83—; lectr. Pa. Bar Inst., Harrisburg, 1979—. Trustee Fedn. of Jewish Agys., Phila., v.p. 1985-88, 94—, chmn. project renewal campaign, 1984-93; bd. dirs. Jewish Cmty. Ctrs., Phila., 1985—; vice chmn. Fedn. Com. on Jewish Edn., 1971-73; bd. govs. Dropsie U., Phila., 1975-80; pres. Har Zion Temple, Penn Valley, Pa., 1980-82; v.p. Phila. Geriatric Ctr., 1985-89; pres., cabinet Jewish Theol. Sem. Am., Phila., 1984-88. Served to sgt. USAAF, 1942-46. Mem. ABA, Pa. Tax Commn., Pa. Bar Assn. (past chmn. tax law sect., ho. of dels.), Pa. Bar Inst. (pres. 1992-93), Pa. Bar Found. (treas 1984—), Phila. Bar Assn. (past chmn. state and local tax law), Green Valley Country Club, The Locust Club, Phila. Club. Republican. Avocations: golfing; acting; singing. Office: Schnader Harrison Segal & Lewis 1600 Market St Ste 3600 Philadelphia PA 19103-7236

SNYDER, RICHARD ALLEN, manufacturing executive, accountant, treasurer; b. St Paul, Minn., Jan. 9, 1940; s. Elmer F. and Margaret M. (Watzl) S.; m. Elizabeth A. Komor, Oct. 19, 1963; 1 child, Roxane L. BBA in Acctg., U. Minn., 1964. CPA, N.Y., Minn. Former ptnr. Deloitte, Haskins & Sells, N.Y.C., 1975-79; staff acct., audit mgr. Deloitte, Haskins & Sells, Mpls. and N.Y.C., 1964-74; chief auditor Dayton Hudson Corp., Mpls., 1979-81; chief fin. officer, treas., v.p. Tennant Co., 1981—. Staff sgt. U.S. Army N.G., USAF, 1963-69. Mem. AICPA, Minn. CPA Soc. (Harold Utley award 1966), Fin. Execs. Inst., Nat. Assn. Investor Rels. Home: 315 Mt Curve Blvd Saint Paul MN 55105-1215 Office: Tennant Co PO Box 1452 Minneapolis MN 55440-1452

SNYDER, RICHARD ELLIOTT, publishing company executive; b. N.Y.C., Apr. 6, 1933; s. Jack and Molly (Rothman) S.; children: Jacqueline, Matthew, Elliott; m. Laura Yorke, Jan.17, 1992. B.A., Tufts U., 1955. Asst. mktg. dir. Doubleday & Co., N.Y.C., 1958-60, sales mgr., 1960-64; dir. sales Simon & Schuster, N.Y.C., 1964-66, dir. mktg., 1967-68, pub., exec. v.p., 1969-75, pres., 1975—, chief exec. officer, 1979, chief exec. officer, chmn. bd., 1981-94; cons. N.Y.C., 1995—; bd. dirs. Reliance Group Holdings, Franklin Electric Pubs., Inc. Contbr. articles to profl. jours. Chmn. N.Y. area coun. PEN, 1988; co-chmn. benefit com., 1992, chmn. pubs. com. for 48th Internat. PEN Congress; founding mem. Nat. Book Found., Nat. Book Awards, Inc.; mem. bus. coun. N.Y. Zool. Soc., Coun. on Foreign Rels., Soc. Fellows, libr. com. Am. Mus. Natural History; mem. bd. overseers Univ. Librs., Tufts U.; vice chmn. benefit Literacy Vols., N.Y.C., 1991.

Mem. Assn. Am. Pubs. (bd. dirs. 1976-79, 82-85), Econ. Club of N.Y.C. Office: 350 Park Ave 10th flr New York NY 10022

SNYDER, RICHARD G., transportation services executive; b. 1932. BS, Rutgers U. Various mgmt. and exec. positions Kearfott divsn. Gen. Precision, Little Falls, N.J., 1954-79, v.p. bus. devel.; v.p. internat. bus. devel. aerospace sys. group Singer Co., 1979-80; v.p. missile and space programs Kearfott divsn. Gen. Precision, 1980-84; pres. link tactical simulation divsn. CAE Industries Ltd., Silver Spring, Md., 1984-90; pres., CEO Reflectone Inc., Tampa, Fla., 1990—. Office: Reflectone Inc 4908 Tampa West Blvd Tampa FL 33634*

SNYDER, RICHARD JOSEPH, lawyer; b. Boston, June 18, 1939; s. Harris H. and Ruth (Galner) S.; m. Joyce Marshall Aug. 19, 1962 (div.); children: Robert M., Lauren E., John K.; m. Susana Gohiman, Apr. 11, 1982; stepchildren: Joanna Maixner, Adriana Maixner. BSBA with honors, Babson Coll., 1960, LLD, 1994; JD with honors, Boston U., 1963; LLM, Georgetown U., 1966; LLD (hon.), Babson Coll., 1994. Bar: Mass. 1963, U.S. Claims Ct., 1964, U.S. Tx Ct. 1966, U.S. Dist. Ct., 1967, U.S. Ct. Appeals (1st Cir.) 1968, U.S. Supreme Ct. 1968, Vt. 1988. Sr. trial atty. Dept. Justice, Washington, 1963-66; assoc. Epstein & Salloway, Boston, 1966-67, Cohn, Reimer & Pollack (now Reimer & Braunstein), Boston, 1967-69; assoc. then ptnr. Widett & Widett (now Widett, Slater & Goldman), Boston, 1969-76; ptnr. Goldstein & Manello, Boston, 1976-88, chmn., 1988—; lectr. law Babson Coll., Wellesley, Mass., 1967-76. Contbr. Boston U. Law Rev., 1962; contbg. editor Direct Sales Mag., 1976-78. Bd. dirs. Sundy Sch., Inc., 1974-85, pres., 1976-85; trustee Babson Coll., Wellesley, Mass., 1977-89, exec. com., 1979-89, chmn. bd., 1984-89, chmn. Corp., 1989—; mem. bus. and profl. leadership com. Boston Symphony Orch., 1989-91; hon. chmn. Presidents at Pops, 1980, ann. fund com., 1992; bd. dirs. Babson Recreation Ctr., 1987—, chmn. bd. dirs., 1987-89; bd. dirs. Mass. Corp. for Ednl. Telecom., 1985—, vice chmn. bd. dirs., 1986-88, chmn., 1989—; mem. corp. New Eng. Deaconess Hosp, 1992—. Fellow Mass. Bar Found.; mem. ABA, Mass. Bar Assn., Vt. Bar Assn., Boston Bar Assn., Am. Bus. Law Assn. (chmn. real property com. 1976-77, pres. North Atlantic region 1976-77), Nat. Assn. Coll. and Univ. Attys., Mass. Conveyancers Assn., New Eng. Land Title Assn., Babson Coll. Alumni Assn. (pres. 1977-79), Minuteman Yacht Club, Algonquin Club, Downtown Club, Greater Boston C. of C. (chmn. econ. devel. com.). Avocation: sailing. Home: 40 Pearl Rd Nahant MA 01908-1162 Office: Goldstein & Manello 265 Franklin St Fl 20 Boston MA 02110-3192

SNYDER, RICHARD LEE, consumer products company executive; b. Carlisle, Pa., June 24, 1940; s. Paul Bear and Mary (Fishburn) S.; m. Roberta Fitzgerald, Nov. 15, 1970 (div. July 1991). B.S. magna cum laude, Pa. State U., 1961. C.P.A., N.Y. With Coopers & Lybrand, N.Y.C., 1961-64; chief fin. officer Bell Equipment Corp., N.Y.C., 1964-71; treas. Wheelabrator-Frye, N.Y.C., 1971-73, v.p. fin. internat., 1973-75; v.p. fin. and adminstrn. Philip Morris USA, N.Y.C., 1975-79; corp. contr. Philip Morris, Inc., N.Y.C., 1979-81; sr. v.p. adminstrn. Philip Morris Internat., 1981-83, exec. v.p., 1983-87, 90-91; sr. v.p. human resources and adminstrn. Philip Morris Cos., N.Y.C., 1987-90; owner Snyder Quality Llamas. Treas. Sutton Area Comty. Assn., 1976-79; bd. dirs. Nat. Multiple Sclerosis Soc., 1981—, chmn. 1994—; bd. dirs. N.Y. Urban League, 1988-90. With U.S. Army, 1962. Recipient Alumni Achievement award Pa. State U., 1980. Mem. AICPA, Philippine Am. C. of C. (pres. 1986-87). Office: PO Box 927 Milford PA 18337

SNYDER, RICHARD WESLEY, manufacturing executive; b. Kansas City, Mo., Apr. 12, 1938; s. Leonard Lewis and Agnes Emma (Grittinger) S.; m. Roberta Marie Lloyd Nov. 28, 1959; children: Richard Wesley Jr., Robert Lloyd, Stacey Marie. BS in Fin., U. Inc., 1960; MBA in Fin. and Internat. Mktg., U. Detroit, 1964. Fin. trainee Lincoln Mercury Div. Ford Motor Co., Dearborn, Mich., 1960-63, dealer devel. supr. internat. mktg. div., 1963-65; mgr. internat. mktg. Fleetguard div. Cummins Engine Co., Columbus, Ind., 1965-66; dir. sales, v.p. mktg. Frigiking div. Cummins Engine Co., Dallas, 1966-71, pres. Frigiking div., 1971-73; pres., chief exec. officer Gen. Computer Systems, Dallas, 1973-76; v.p., gen. mgr. indsl. battery div. Gould, Inc., Chgo., 1977-79; pres. climate control div. Singer Inc., Carteret, N.J., 1979-82; chmn., chief exec. officer Snyder Gen. Corp., Dallas, 1982—. Mem. Am. Bus. Conf., Air Conditioning Refrigeration Inst. (chmn. 1987—), Gas Appliance Mfrs. Assn. (bd. dirs. 1987—). Avocations: bridge, golf, tennis, reading. Office: Snyder Gen Corp 3232 McKinney Ave Dallas TX 75204-2480

SNYDER, ROBERT C., metals company executive; b. 1933; married. BS in Industrial Engring., Pitts. Tech. Inst., 1956. Gen. mgr. Colson Caster Co., 1971-75; pres. Bishop Tube Co., 1975-77, Leland Tube Co., 1977-79; v.p., chief oper. officer, exec. v.p., now pres. Quanex Corp., Houston, 1979—; also bd. dirs. Quanex Corp.; pres. Viking Metallurgical. With U.S. Army, 1950-52. Office: Quanex Corp 1900 West Loop S Houston TX 77027

SNYDER, ROBERT MARTIN, agriculture consultant, retired government official; b. Lahmansville, W.Va., Sept. 6, 1912; s. Noah W. and Maggie M. (Varner) S.; m. Gail M. Hiser, Nov. 25, 1937; children: Rebecca J. Snyder Peters, Margaret A. Snyder Bensenhaver, Shirley L. Snyder Williams, Robert Martin Jr. B.S. in Agr, W.Va. U., 1937. Engaged in farming, 1929-90; agrl. extension agt. Nicholas County, W.Va., 1937-41; adminstrn. commodity loans crop ins. and program performance AAA, Morgantown, W.Va., 1941-42; adminstrn. grain and oilseed program E central region, AAA USDA, 1942-47, asst. coordinator, CCC, 1950-52; chief agriculturist U.S. mission to Karachi, Pakistan FOA, 1952-54; dir. U.S. Mission and counselor U.S. Embassy Afghanistan, Kabul, 1954-59; rep. ICA to. Brit. East Africa, Kenya, Uganda, Tanganyika, Zanzibar, 1959-60; food and agr. officer West African countries of Ivory Coast, Upper Volta, Niger, Dahomey, 1961-62; acting dir. U.S. AID Mission, Ivory Coast, 1961-63; agr. adviser, area office rep. AID mission to, Rhodesia and Nyasaland, 1964; attache, AID affairs officer Malawi, Africa, 1964-68; cons. World Bank, IBRD, 1967; detail officer fgn. direct investments Dept. Commerce, 1968; AID affairs officers Washington, 1968-69; food and agr. officer U.S. AID, Amman, Jordan, 1969-70; planning adviser Ministry Natural Resources, Nigeria, 1970-72; cons., 1972—; Mem. del. Gen. Mem. Agreements Tariffs and Trade Conf., Torquay, Eng., 1951; mem. Mus. Commn., Library Commn. Served to lt. USNR, 1944-46, PTO. Recipient nat. 4-H alumni award Nat. 4-H Congress, Chgo., 1982, Disting. Alumnus award W.Va. Coll. Agriculture and Forestry, 1987; named to W.Va. Agrl. and Forestry Hall of Fame, 1991. Mem. Fgn. Service Assn., Am. Legion, W.Va. U. Alumni Assn., Am. Acad. Polit. and Social Sci., Soc. Internat. Devel., Internat. Platform Assn., U.S. Nat. Trust for Historic Preservation, Nature Conservancy, Commn. on Aging, Alpha Zeta. Clubs: Masons, Kiwanis, Explorers. Home: Noah Snyder Farm HC 84 Box 32 Lahmansville WV 26731-9702 *I feel that any success which I have achieved in life is in direct relationship to my interest in others and my ability to contribute to a better world situation in which each person can develop and achieve a better life for himself or herself and family.*

SNYDER, SAM A., oil company executive, lawyer; b. Helen, W.Va., Sept. 11, 1930; s. Russell Brown and Bess Kate (Swim) S.; m. Dorothy Martha Berry, Oct. 26, 1973. Student, Concord Coll., Athens, W.Va., 1947-50; LL.B., So. Meth. U., 1953. Bar: Tex. 1953, Calif. 1962. Landman Union Oil Co., Midland, Tex., 1955-60; atty. Union Oil Co., 1961-69, asst. counsel, 1969-73, asst. gen. counsel, 1973-85; v.p., gen. counsel Union Oil Co., L.A., 1985—. Served with U.S. Army, 1953-55. Mem. ABA, Los Angeles County Bar Assn., Am. Soc. Internat. Law, Fgn. Law Assn., Soc. Mining Law Antiquarians. Republican. Clubs: Petroleum, Jonathan (Los Angeles). Avocations: collecting books, home computers; reading. Home: 3740 Greenhill Rd Pasadena CA 91107-2230 Office: Unocal Corp 1201 W 5th St Los Angeles CA 90051 also: 4635 Southwest Fwy Houston TX 77027-7104

SNYDER, SCOTT WILLIAM, geology educator; b. Canton, Ohio, Apr. 8, 1946; s. Russell William and Merrie Elizabeth (Landis) S.; m. Lorna Jean Richmond, Sept. 3, 1966; 1 child, Kimberly Ann. BA in Geology, Coll. of Wooster, 1968; MS in Geology, Tulane U., 1970, PhD in Paleontology, 1974. Lic. geologist, N.C. Asst. prof. East Carolina U. Greenville, N.C., 1972-76, assoc. prof., 1976-83, prof., 1983—, chmn. geology dept., 1988—; acting assoc. dean Coll. Arts and Scis., 1990-91; scientist aboard R/V Glomar Challenger (sponsored by NSF), 1981, R/V Joides Resolution, 1993; mem.

adv. com. N.C. State Geol. Map, Raleigh, 1983-85. Assoc. editor Jour. Foraminiferal Rsch., 1986-94, editor, 1995—, Spl. Pub. #25 Cushman Found., 1988; contbr. articles to profl. jours. Mem. Nat. Wildlife Fedn., 1988—; bd. dirs. Cushman Found., 1991—. Grantee NOAA, 1982, 84, 91, 93, NSF, 1982, 86, Petroleum Rsch. Fund, Am. Chem. Soc., 1988. Fellow Cushman Found. for Foraminiferal Rsch.; mem. Geol. Soc. Am., Paleontol. Soc., Paleontol. Rsch. Inst., Am. Geophys. Union, N.Am. Micropaleontol. Soc., Nat. Assn. Geology Tchrs., Sigma Xi. Democrat. Avocations: jogging, woodworking. Office: East Carolina U Dept Geology Greenville NC 27858

SNYDER, SOLOMON HALBERT, psychiatrist, pharmacologist; b. Washington, Dec. 26, 1938; s. Samuel Simon and Patricia (Yakerson) S.; m. Elaine Borko, June 10, 1962; children: Judith Rhea, Deborah Lynn. M.D. cum laude, Georgetown U., 1962, D.Sc. (hon.), 1986; D.Sc. (hon.), Northwestern U., 1981; PhD (hon.), Ben Gurion U., 1990. Intern Kaiser Found. Hosp., San Francisco, 1962-63; research asso. NIMH, Bethesda, Md., 1963-65; resident psychiatry Johns Hopkins Hosp., Balt., 1965-68; asso. prof. psychiatry and pharmacology Johns Hopkins Med. Sch., 1968-70, prof., 1970-77, disting. Service prof. psychiatry and pharmacology, 1977-80, disting. Service prof. neurosci., psychiatry and pharmacology, 1980—, dir. dept. neurosci., 1980—; NIH lectr., 1979. Author: Uses of Marijuana, 1971, Madness and the Brain, 1973, Opiate Receptor Mechanisms, 1975, The Troubled Mind, 1976, Biologic Aspects of Mental Disorder, 1980, Drugs and the Brain, 1986, Brainstorming, 1989; editor Perspectives in Neuropharmacology, 1971, Frontiers in Catecholamine Research, 1973, Handbook of Psychopharmacology, 1974; contbr. articles to profl. jours. Served with USPHS, 1963-65. Recipient Outstanding Scientist award Md. Acad. Scis., 1969; John Jacob Abel award Am. Pharmacology Soc., 1970; A.E. Bennett award Soc. Biol. Psychiatry, 1970; Gaddum award Brit. Pharm. Soc., 1974; F.O. Schmitt award in neuroscis. MIT, 1974; Nicholas Giarman lecture award Yale U., 1975; Rennebohm award U. Wis., 1976; Salmon award, 1977; Stanley Dean award Am. Coll. Psychiatrists, 1978; Harvey Lecture award, 1978; Lasker award, 1978; Wolf prize, 1983; Dickson prize, 1983; Sci. Achievement award AMA, 1985; Ciba-Geigy-Drew award, 1985; Strecker prize, 1986; Edward Sachar Meml. award Columbia U., 1986; Paul K. Smith Meml. lecture award George Washington U., 1986; Sense of Smell award Fragrance Research Found., 1987; Julius Axelrod lecture award CUNY, 1988; John Flynn Meml. lecture award Yale U., 1988; V. Erspamer lecture award Georgetown U., 1990; J. Allyn Taylor prize, 1990; Pasarow Found. award, 1991; Bower award Achievement Sci. Franklin Inst., 1991; Chauncey Leake lecture award, 1992; William Veatch lectr. award Harvard Med. Sch., 1992; Joseph Priestley prize Dickinson Coll., 1992; Konrad Bloch lectr. award Harvard U., 1992; Basic Neurochem. lectr. award Am. Soc. Neurochem., 1993; Nanine Duke lectr. award Duke U., 1993; Salvador Luria lectr. award MIT, 1993; Rudin lectr. award Columbia U., 1995, Christian Herter lectr. award NYU, 1995, Maclean lectr. award Baylor Med. Coll., 1995. Fellow Am. Coll. Neuropsychopharmacology (Daniel Efron award 1974), Am. Psychiat. Assn. (Hofheimer award 1972, Disting. Svc. award 1989), Am. Acad. Arts and Scis., Am. Philosophical Soc.; mem. Nat. Acad. Scis., Soc. for Neuroscis. (pres. 1979-80), Am. Soc. Biol. Chemists, Am. Pharmacology Soc., Inst. Medicine. Home: 3801 Canterbury Rd Apt 1001 Baltimore MD 21218-2315 Office: Johns Hopkins U Med Sch Dept Neurosciences 725 N Wolfe St Baltimore MD 21205-2105

SNYDER, STEPHEN EDWARD, lawyer; b. Albuquerque, Sept. 14, 1942; s. John Royden and Elaine Stella (Draper) S.; m. Judith Anne Swall, Oct. 27, 1967; children: Sara, Katherine. BBA, U. N.Mex., 1965, MBA, 1967; JD, U. Tex., 1972. Bar: Colo. 1973, N.Mex. 1984. Ptnr. Holme Roberts & Owen, Denver, 1973—. Author: Commercial Bankruptcy Litigation, 1989. Trustee Mile High Transplant Bank, Denver, 1991. Lt. (j.g.) USN, 1967-70. Office: Holme Roberts & Owen 1700 Lincoln St Ste 4100 Denver CO 80203-4541

SNYDER, SUSAN BROOKE, retired English literature educator; b. Yonkers, N.Y., July 12, 1934; d. John Warren and Virginia Grace (Hartung) S. BA, Hunter Coll., CUNY, 1955; MA, Columbia U., 1958, PhD, 1963. Lectr. Queens Coll., CUNY, N.Y.C., 1961-63; instr. Swarthmore Coll., Pa., 1963-66, asst. prof. English lit., 1966-70, assoc. prof., 1970-75, prof., 1975-93, Eugene M. Lang research prof., 1982-86, Gil and Frank Mustin prof., 1990-93; ret.; prof. emeritus Swarthmore Coll., 1993—; rschr. Folger Shakespeare Libr. Author: The Comic Matrix of Shakespeare's Tragedies, 1979; editor: Divine Weeks and Works of Guillaume de Saluste, Sieur du Bartas, 1979, Othello: Critical Essays, 1988, All's Well that Ends Well, 1993; mem. editl. bd. Shakespeare Quar., 1972—. Folger Library sr. fellow, 1972-73; Nat. Endowment for Humanities fellow, 1967-68; Guggenheim Found. fellow, 1980-81; Huntington Library summer grantee, 1966, 71; Folger Library grantee, 1969; Nat. Endowment for Humanities grantee, 1970; Nat. Endowment for Humanities summer grantee, 1976. Mem. Renaissance Soc. Am. (coun. 1979-81), Shakespeare Assn. Am. (trustee 1980-83).

SNYDER, WILLARD BREIDENTHAL, lawyer; b. Kansas City, Kans., Dec. 18, 1940; s. N.E. and Ruth (Breidenthal) S.; m. Lieselotte Dieringer, Nov. 10, 1970 (dec. Nov. 1975); 1 child, Rolf. BA, U. Kans., 1962, JD, 1965; postgrad., Hague Acad. Internat. Law, The Netherlands, 1965-66, U. Dijon, France, 1966; grad. Command and Gen. Staff Coll., Ft. Leavenworth, Kans., 1977. Bar: Kans. 1965, Mo. 1986, U.S. Tax Ct. 1977, U.S. Ct. Mil. Appeals 1981, U.S. Dist. Ct. Kans. 1965, U.S. Supreme Ct. 1977. Atty. Kansas City, 1970-80, 85—; trust officer, corp. trust officer Security Nat. Bank., Kansas City, 1980-83, corp. sec., 1983-85; pres. Real Estate Corp. Inc., Shawnee Mission, 1984—; dir., mem. trust and investment com. Blue Ridge Bank; German Consul (H) for Kans., Western Mo., 1972—. Mem. Platte Woods (Mo.) City Coun., 1983-84; mem. exec. bd. dirs. regional coun. Boy Scouts Am.; bd. govs. Liberty Meml. Assn.; bd. dirs., v.p., treas. McJannett Found., Talloires, France; pres. Breidenthal-Snyder Found.; bd. dirs., mem. exec. com. CORO Found. Col. Kans. Army N.G., ret.; col. USAR. Decorated Bundesverdienst Kreuz, 1982, BVK 1KL (Germany), 1992, Bundeswehr Kreuz (silver), 1987, Ge. Abn., meritorious svc. medal, Army commendation medal; named to Hon. Order Ky. Cols., 1988; recipient Golden Honour badge German Vet. and Rsch. Orgn., Bavaria, 1988, Mil. Order of WW award, OCS Hall of Fame, 1994. Mem. Mo. Bar Assn., Kansas City Bar Assn., Kansas City Hosp. Attys., Kansas City Bd. Trade, Mil. Order of World Wars (chpt. comdr. 1983-84, regional comdr. 1987-91, Patrick Henry award), Nat. Eagle Scout Assn. Avocations: scuba, hunting, Notgeld collections, cartridge collection. Office: 8014 State Line Rd Ste 203 Leawood KS 66208

SNYDER, WILLIAM BURTON, insurance executive; b. Clarksburg, W.Va., July 9, 1929; s. William Burton and Mary Catherine (Cornwell) S.; m. Georgie Gaye, Oct. 27, 1951; children: William Burton, Melissa Ann. B.B.A. in Acctg. cum laude, Tex. Tech. U., 1955. With Travelers Ins. Co., 1955-77, v.p., 1970-77; with Govt. Employees Ins. Co., Washington, 1977-93; chmn., pres., CEO GEICO Corp., 1985-93; chmn. and mem. bd. So. Heritage Ins. Co./Merastar Ins. Co. 1991—; chmn., pres., CEO So. Heritage Holdings, Inc., Merastar Corp., Washington, 1993—. Chmn. econ. adv. coun. Montgomery County; bd. dirs. Capital Area coun. Boy Scouts Am. Capt. USAF, 1950-53. Decorated Air medal. Mem. Nat. Assn. Ind. Insurers (bd. dirs., chmn. 1989-90), Kenwood Country Club (Bethesda, Md.). Republican. Baptist.

SNYDER, WILLIAM D., photojournalist; b. Henderson, KY, July 1, 1959; s. Charles Gordon and Mary Odette (Galloway) S.; m. Amy Barbara Lewy, Sept. 1, 1985; children: Cameron Reid Gray, Scott Ethan. BS with highest honors, Rochester Inst. Tech., 1981. Photographer/intern Henderson Gleaner, 1974-76; photographer Evansville (Ind.) Press, 1977-79; photo intern Ariz. Rep.; Phoenix, 1980; photographer Miami News, Fla., 1981-83, Dallas Morning News, 1983—. Recipient Pro Football Photographer of Yr. award Pro Football Hall of Fame, 1986, Picture of Yr. award -1st pl. newspaper sports action U. Mo., 1986, 1st pl. news pictorial, 1986, Pulitzer prize for explanatory journalism, 1989, Pulitzer Prize for feature photography, 1991, Robert F. Kennedy journalism citation, 1991, Pulitzer Prize for spot news photography, 1993. Mem. Nat. Press Photographers Assn. Democrat. Episcopalian. Avocations: cinema, music. Office: Dallas Morning News Communications Ctr Dallas TX 75265*

SNYDER, WILLIAM E., lawyer; b. Evanston, Ill., Nov. 3, 1944. BS, Northwestern U., 1966, JD cum laude, 1969. Bar: Ill. 1969. Law clk. to Hon. Julius J. Hoffman, 1969-71; mem. Michael, Best & Friedrich, Chgo. Articles editor Northwestern U. Law Rev., 1968-69. Named Nat. Coll. Debate champion, 1966. Mem. ABA, Am. Arbitration Assn. Comml. Panel of Arbitrators, Nat. Assn. Securities Dealers (mem. nat. panel arbitrators), Ill. State Bar Assn., Chgo. Bar Assn. Office: Michael Best & Friedrich 135 S La Salle St Ste 1610 Chicago IL 60603

SNYDER, WILLIAM HARRY, financial advisor; b. Newport, Pa., May 11, 1934; s. William Harry and Mary (Barner) S.; m. Irvil Kear, June, 1956 (div. 1961); 1 child, Geoffrey W.; m. Sandra Elizabeth Wolff, June 25, 1966; 1 child, Tara Elizabeth. BS in Indsl. Engring., Lehigh U., 1956; MS in Applied Stats., Rutgers U., 1961. Cert. fin. planner. Research engr. Johns-Manville Corp., Manville, N.J., 1956-61; indsl. engr., mgr. services and quality control Johns-Manville Corp., Nashua, N.H., 1961-69; mgr. phys. distbn. Johns-Manville Corp., N.Y.C., 1969-72; mgr. div. and corp. planning. Johns-Manville Corp., Denver, 1972-82; dir. corp. devel. Manville Corp. (formerly Johns-Manville Corp.), Denver, 1982-85; prin. Snyder Fin. Services, Littleton, Colo., 1985—; bd. dirs. Manville Employees Fed. Credit Union, Denver, 1985-88; rep. Fin. Network Investment Corp., 1988—; sec., founding mem. Manville Retirees Assn., 1992—; assoc. Fin. Network Adv. Corp., 1993—. Patentee process for making chalkboard; author: (with others) Standard Handbook of Plant Engineering, 1983. Vol. AARP Tax Coun. Program for the Elderly, 1987—. Served as 2d lt. U.S. Army, 1957-58. Mem. Colo. Soc. of Cert. Fin. Planners, Inst. of Cert. Fin. Planners, Pi Kappa Alpha (pres. 1954-55), Tau Beta Pi, Alpha Pi Mu. Republican. Methodist. Lodge: Mason. Avocations: backpacking, skiing, sailing, cycling. Home and Office: Snyder Fin Svcs 1952 W Ridge Rd Littleton CO 80120-3139

SNYDER, WILLIAM PENN, III, manufacturing company executive; b. Pitts., Mar. 11, 1918; s. William Penn and Marie Elise (Whitney) S.; m. Jean Evans Rose, Sept. 30, 1939; children: Marie Elise, J. Brandon. Student, U. Pitts. With The Wilpen Group Inc., now pres.; dir. H.J. Heinz Co., all Pitts., Whitney Nat. Bank, New Orleans. Bd. dirs. Pa. Economy League; chmn. bd. Allegheny Health, Edn. and Rsch. Found., Pitts.; v.p. bd. mgrs. Allegheny Cemetery; trustee Carnegie-Mellon U., Pitts., Carnegie Inst., Carnegie Hero Fund Commn., Western Res. Hist. Soc. Served as lt. (s.g.) USNR, 1942-45. Republican. Episcopalian. Clubs: Duquesne (Pitts.); Rolling Rock (Ligonier, Pa.); Allegheny Country (Sewickley, Pa.); Gulf Stream Golf (Delray Beach, Fla.). Home: Blackburn Rd Sewickley PA 15143-1416

SNYDER, WILLIAM RUSSELL, oil company executive; b. Laytonsville, Md., Mar. 11, 1926; s. Russell L. and Mary C. (Allnutt) S.; m. Ann Lewis, Sept. 10, 1949; children: —Kathryn E., Elaine M. B.S., U. Md., 1951. With Crown Central Petroleum Corp., Balt., 1951—; dir. employee relations Crown Central Petroleum Corp., 1967-71, sec., dir. employee and pub. relations, 1971-74, sec., mgr. corporate adminstrn., 1974-76, v.p. adminstrn., sec., 1977-91, sr. v.p. adminstrn., 1991—; past chmn. Md. Bd. Higher Edn. Served with USAAF, 1944-46. Mem. Am. Soc. Corporate Secs., Am. Petroleum Inst., Toastmasters (lt. gov. 1967-68). Republican. Methodist. Club: Hunt Valley Golf. Home: 2426 Hartfell Rd Lutherville Timonium MD 21093-2555 Office: 1 N Charles St Baltimore MD 21201-3709

SNYDERMAN, REUVEN KENNETH, plastic surgeon, educator; b. Phila., July 6, 1922; s. Harry S. and Anna (Koss) S.; m. Patricia Dawn Kennedy, June 29, 1955 (div. 1969); children: Peri Lynne, Lisa Mari, Scott R.; m. Adrienne E. Nordenschild, Dec. 6, 1970 (dec); m. Catherine Weisel Birkhahn, Jan. 16, 1993. AB, U. Pa., 1943, MD, 1946. Intern U.S. Naval Hosp., Phila. 1946-47; resident in gen. surgery Montefiore Hosp., NYU Med. Center, N.Y.C., 1949-51; resident in plastic and reconstructive surgery Columbia-Presbyn. Med. Center, N.Y.C., 1951-53; resident Meml. Sloan-Kettering Hosp., N.Y.C., 1953; pvt. practice medicine specializing in plastic, reconstructive surgery N.Y.C., 1954-73, Princeton, N.J., 1973-92; mem. staff plastic and reconstructive surgery, head of tissue transplantation sect. Sloan-Kettering Inst. Cancer Research, N.Y.C., 1955-73; attending surgeon Princeton Hosp.; assoc. prof. surgery Med. Sch. Cornell U.; chief div. plastic and reconstructive surgery Robert Wood Johnson Univ. Hosp.; prof. emeritus div. plastic surgery U. Medicine and Dentistry of N.J.; chief div. Comprehensive Breast Svcs. Robert Wood Johnson Med. Sch., to 1991, prof. emeritus, 1992—; chmn. Plastic Surgery Research Council; cons. Nathan Littauer Hosp., Gloversville, N.Y.; spl. cons. Auerbach Corp., Phila. Author: New Parts for People, 1969, Symposium on Neoplastic and Reconstructive Problems of the Female Breast, 1973, The Breast, 1978; contbr. numerous articles to med. jours. With USNR, 1943-45; lt. (j.g.) USMC, 1947-49. Recipient Honor award N.Y. chpt. Hadassah, 1980. Fellow ACS; mem. AMA, N.Y. Regional Soc. Plastic and Reconstructive Surgery (historian), Am. Soc. Plastic and Reconstructive Surgery, N.J. Med. Soc., Mercer County Med. Soc., Webster Soc. (sec.-treas.), Am. Assn. Plastic Surgeons, N.Y. Cancer Soc. Home: 20 Constitution Hl W Princeton NJ 08540-6748 Office: U Medicine and Dentistry NJ Robert Wood Johnson Med Sch 1 Robert Wood Johnson Pl CN 19 New Brunswick NJ 08903-0019

SOAMES, SCOTT, philosophy educator; b. Temple, Tex., Aug. 11, 1945; s. Willard R. and Helen Ruth (Piper) S.; divorced, 1992; children: Gregory, Brian. BA in Philosophy with great distinction, Stanford U., 1968; PhD in Philosophy, MIT, 1976. Instr. linguistics MIT, Cambridge, 1974-75, mem. vis. com. dept. linguistics and philosophy, 1985—; asst. prof. philosophy Yale U., New Haven, 1976-80; asst. prof. philosophy Princeton (N.J.) U., 1980-85, assoc. prof., 1985-89, prof., 1989—; dir. grad. studies philosophy dept., 1990—; vis. assoc. prof. philosophy U. Wash., Seattle, 1986, summers 1987-88, vis. prof., summer 1989; cons. editor Bradford Books, 1982—; lectr. in field. Author: (with Perlmutter) Syntactic Argumentation and the Structure of English, 1979; editor: (with Salmon) Propositions and Attitudes, 1988; mem. editorial bd. Studies in Linguistics and Philosophy, 1984-89; topic editor Oxford Internat. Ency. Linguistics, 1987-89; cons. editor Jour. Symbolic Logic, 1986—; assoc. editor Linguistics and Philosophy, 1982-89, 93—; also numerous articles. Danforth Grad. fellow, 1971-76, Woodrow Wilson Grad. fellow, 1971, John Simon Guggenheim Mem. Found. fellow, 1989-90, NEH Rsch. fellow, 1978-79; Class of 1936 Bicentennial preceptorship Princeton Univ, 1982-85. Mem. Am. Philosophical Assn. (ea. divsn. adv. com. to the program com., 1993—), Phi Beta Kappa. Home: 345 Harrison St Princeton NJ 08544 Office: Princeton U Dept Philosophy 1879 Hall Princeton NJ 08542

SOBEL, ALAN, electrical engineer, physicist; b. N.Y.C., Feb. 23, 1928; s. Edward P. and Rose (Naftalison) S.; m. Marjorie Loebel, June 15, 1952; children: Leslie Ann, Edward Robert. BSEE, Columbia U., 1947, MSEE, 1949; PhD in Physics, Poly. Inst. Bklyn., 1964. Lic. Profl. Engr., N.Y. and Ill. Asst. chief engr. The Electronic Workshop, N.Y.C., 1950-51; head, functional engr. Fairchild Controls Corp., 1951-56; project engr. Skiatron Electronics and TV Corp., 1956-57; sr. rsch. engr. Zenith Radio Corp., Glenview, Ill., 1964-78; v.p. Lucitron inc., Northbrook, Ill., 1978-87, pres., 1987; pvt. practice cons. Evanston, Ill., 1988—; asst., instr. Poly. Inst. Bklyn.,1957-64; mem. program coms. SID Internat. Symposium, Internat. Display Rsch. Conf., 1970—. Inventor: 14 patents on various display and electron devices; author 50 papers on electronics, physics, electronic displays, etc.; editor Jour. Soc. Info. DIsplay, 1991—; contbg. editor Info. Display; assoc. editor: IEEE Trans. on Electron Devices, N.Y., 1970-77. Mem. Democratic Party of Evanston and Ward Orgn., various neighborhood orgns. NSF fellow, 1959, 60. Fellow Soc. Info. Display; mem. IEEE (sr., life), Am. Phys. Soc., SPIE, Sigma Xi. Democrat. Home and Office: 633 Michigan Ave Evanston IL 60202-2552

SOBEL, ARNOLD I., mining executive; b. 1917. With Material Svc. Corp., Chgo., 1948—, now vice chmn. bd. dirs.; also bd. dirs. for other subs. and parent co. Office: Material Svc Corp 222 N La Salle St Chicago IL 60601-1003*

SOBEL, BURTON ELIAS, physician, educator; b. N.Y.C., Oct. 21, 1937; s. Lawrence J. and Ruth (Schoen) S.; m. Susan Konheim, June 19, 1958; children: Jonathan, Elizabeth. A.B., Cornell U., 1958; M.D. magna cum laude, Harvard U., 1962. Intern Peter Bent Brigham Hosp., Boston, 1962-63; resident Peter Bent Brigham Hosp., 1963-64, 66-67; clin. asso. cardiology br. NIH, Bethesda, Md., 1964-66, 67-68; asst. prof. medicine U. Calif. at San Diego, La Jolla, 1968-71; asso. prof. medicine, dir. myocardial infarction research unit, dir. coronary care, 1971-73; asso. prof. medicine Barnes Hosp.-Washington U., St. Louis, 1973-75; prof. Barnes Hosp.-Washington U., 1975—, dir. cardiovascular div., 1973—; program dir. specialied ctr. rsch. in ischemic heart disease, 1975-89, program dir. specialized ctr. rsch. in coronary and vascular diseases, 1990-94, program dir. principles in cardiovascular rsch., 1975-94; chmn., prof. medicine U. Vt., Burlington, 1994—; physician-in-chief Med. Ctr. Hosp. Vt., Burlington, 1994—; program dir. Collaborative Clin. Trial Therapy to Protect Ischemic Myocardium, Washington U., 1977; chmn. cardio renal drugs U.S Pharmacopeial Conv., 1990—. Assoc. med. editor The Heart Bull, 1971-72; editor Clin. Cardiology, 1971-74; mem. circulation bd., 1971—; editor Circulation, 1983-88; mem. editorial bd. Circulation Research, 1974—, Annals of Internal Medicine, 1976—, Am. Jour. Cardiology, 1976—, Cardiology Digest, 1976-77, Jour. Continuing Edn. in Cardiology, 1978—, Cardiology in the Elderly, 1991—; mem. editorial bd., assoc. editor Jour. Clin. Investigation, 1977—; assoc. editor, Am. Jour. Physiology: Heart and Circulatory Physiology, 1978—; Churchill Livingstone editorial advisory bd. Internat. Seminars in Cardiovascular Medicine, 1978—, Cardiology in Review, 1992—; mem. editorial bd. Current Med. Lit., Current Opinion in Cardiology, editor, 1989—, Internat. Jour. Cardiology, Fibrinolysis, 1986, assoc. editor, 1990—; cons. editor Circulation, 1988—; editor Coronary Artery Disease, 1989—, Can. Jour. Cardiology, 1995—. Served to lt. comdr. USPHS, 1964-68. Recipient Career Rsch. Devel. award USPHS, 1972, internat. recognition award Heart Rsch. Found., 1981, Disting. Achievement award Am. Heart Assn. Sci. Couns., 1984, award Robert J. and Claire Posatow Found., 1988, award Va. Heart Ctr., 1991, Drake award Maine Heart Assn., 1992. Fellow ACP; mem. Royal Soc. Medicine, Am. Fedn. Clin. Rsch. (counsilor), Am. Heart Assn. (James B. Herrick award 1992), Am. Coll. Cardiology (Disting. Scientist award 1987), Assn. Univ. Cardiologists, Am. Soc. Clin. Investigation (councilor), Assn. Am. Physicians, Am. Physiol. Soc., Cardiac Muscle Soc., Western Soc. Clin. Rsch., Internat. Soc. Fibrinolysis and Thrombolysis (councilor), Assn. Profs. Cardiology (pres.-elect 1992), Internat. Soc. Applied Cardiovascular Biology, Alpha Omega Alpha. Home: 2 Lost Cove Rd Colchester VT 05446-1840 Office: Fletcher Allen-MCHV Campus Fletcher 311 Burlington VT 05401

SOBEL, HOWARD BERNARD, osteopath; b. N.Y.C., May 15, 1929; s. Martin and Ella (Sternberg) S.; m. Ann Louise Silverbush, June 16, 1957 (dec. May 1978); children—Nancy Sobel Schumer, Janet Sobel Medow, Robert; m. Irene S. Miller, June 8, 1980; stepchildren—Avner Saferstein, Daniel Saferstein, Naomi Saferstein. A.B., Syracuse U., 1951; D.O., Kansas City Coll. Osteopathy and Surgery, 1955. Intern Zieger Osteo. Hosp., Detroit, 1955-56; gen. practice osteo. medicine Redford Twp., Mich., 1956-74, Livonia, Mich., 1974—; chief of staff Botsford Gen. Hosp., Farmington, Mich., 1978; mem. faculty Mich. State U. Coll. Osteo. Medicine, 1969—; clin. assoc. prof. family practice, 1973—; mem. exec. and med. adv. coms. United Health Orgn. Mich.; mem. Venereal Disease Action Com., Mich.; apptd. to asst. impaired osteo. physicians Mich., 1983. Mem. Am. Osteo. Assn. (ho. of dels. 1981—), Mich. Assn. Osteo. Physicians and Surgeons (ho. of dels.), Am. Coll. Osteo. Rheumatologists, Coll. Am. Osteo. Gen. Practitioners, Osteo. Gen. Practice Mich., Wayne County Osteo. Assn. (pres.). Jewish. Home: 6222 Northfield Dr West Bloomfield MI 48322-2431 Office: 28275 5 Mile Rd Livonia MI 48154-3944

SOBEL, SHEPARD MICHAEL, artistic director; b. N.Y.C., Mar. 28, 1947; s. Daniel and Pearl (Schwartz) S.; m. Rhonda Plotkin, Aug. 4, 1968 (div. 1972); 1 child, Sabrina; m. Joanne Camp, Oct. 24, 1983. BA, Hobart Coll., 1968; MA, U. Fla., 1974. Tchr. Canandaigua (N.Y.) Acad., 1968-70, South Fla. State Hosp., Hollywood, 1970-71, Annandale (Va.) High Sch., 1974-78; freelance actor, dir. Washington, 1974-79, N.Y.C., 1979-84; artistic dir. Pearl Theatre Co., N.Y.C., 1982—. Jewish. Office: Pearl Theatre Co 80 St Mark's Pl New York NY 10003

SOBELLE, RICHARD E., lawyer; b. Cleve., Mar. 18, 1935. BA, Stanford U., 1956, JD, 1960; LLM, U. So. Calif., 1967. Bar: Calif. 1961, U.S. Supreme Ct. 1969. Of counsel Baker & Hosteller, L.A. Mem. ABA (mem. corp., banking and bus. law sect. 1969—), State Bar Calif. (del. to conf. state bar dels. 1965-77, mem. exec. com. bus. law sect. 1977-78), L.A. County Bar Assn. (mem. exec. coun., jr. barristers 1965-68, mem. exec. com. bus. and corps. sect. 1973-75). Office: Baker & Hostetler 600 Wilshire Blvd Los Angeles CA 90017-3212

SOBEY, DAVID FRANK, food company executive; b. Stellarton, N.S., Can., Mar. 22, 1931; s. Frank Hoyse and Irene (MacDonald) S.; m. Faye B. Naugle, June 2, 1953; children: Paul David, Janis Irene Hames. D of Commerce (hon.), St. Mary's U., 1991. With Sobeys Inc., Stellarton, 1949—, store mgr., dir. merchandising and advt., v.p., exec. v.p., pres., dep. chmn., chief exec. officer, dir., 1981-85, chmn., dir., 1985—; bd. dirs. Empire Co. Ltd., Sobey Leased Properties Ltd., Atlantic Shopping Ctrs. Ltd., Sobeys Land Holdings Ltd., Clover Group, Ea. Sign Print Ltd., Lumsden Bros. Ltd., Dominion Textile Inc., Evangeline Fin. Svcs. Corp., T.R.A. Foods Ltd., Hannaford Bros. Co., CHC Helicopter Corp.; chmn. The Sobey Found., Frank H. Sobey Fund for Excellence in Bus. Studies. Bd. dirs. Retail Coun. Can., Internat. Assn. Chain Stores, C.I.E.S., Food Mktg. Inst., Tim Horton Children's Found., The Sobey Art Found., Boy Scouts Can., Atlantic Salmon Fedn.; bd. govs. St. Mary's U., chmn. fin. campaign; mem. Halifax Bd. Trade. Clubs: Royal N.S. Yacht Squadron; Halifax; City (New Glasgow), Abercrombie Country. Office: Sobeys Inc, 115 King St, Stellarton, NS Canada B0K 1S0

SOBEY, DONALD CREIGHTON RAE, real estate developer; b. New Glasgow, N.S., Can.; s. Frank Hoyse and Irene (MacDonald) S.; m. Elizabeth H. Purvis; children: Robert George Creighton, Irene Elizabeth, Kent Richard. B of Commerce, Queen's U.; LLD (hon.), Dalhousie U., 1989. Pres. Halifax Devels. Ltd., 1972—, vice chmn., 1989—; pres. Empire Cos. Ltd., 1969; chmn. Empire Co. Ltd., 1985—; also bd. dirs.; bd. dirs. Sobey Leased Properties Ltd., Paribas Participations Limitee PPL, Tuckahoe Fin. Corp., Empire Automotive Ltd., Atlantic Shopping Centres Ltd., Crombie Ins. Ltd., U.K., Jannock Ltd., Lawton's Drug Stores Ltd., Tibbetts Paints Ltd., Toronto-Dominion Bank, Wajax Ltd., Sobeys Inc., Maritime Telegraph and Telephone Co. Ltd.; v.p. Foord Constrn. Ltd., Empire Theatres Ltd. Gov. Olympic Trust Can.; patron 1986 World Congress on Edn. and Tech.; bd. govs. Dalhousie U.; mem. Task Force Future of Port of Halifax; mem. Conf. Bd. Can.; found. chmn. Camp Hill Med. Ctr.; mem. Club de Rels. d'Affaires Can.-France; chmn. Friends of the Nova Scotia Mus. Industry Soc.; co-chair fin. com. Gov. Gen.'s Can. Study Conf. Mem. Internat. Assn. for Students Econs. and Commerce, Lloyd's of London (underwriting). Avocations: skiing, tennis, music, art, travel. Office: Empire Co Ltd, 115 King St, Stellarton, NS Canada B0K 1S0

SOBEY, EDWIN J. C., museum director, oceanographer, consultant; b. Phila., Apr. 7, 1948; s. Edwin J. and Helen (Chapin) S.; m. Barbara Lee, May 9, 1970; children: Ted Woodall, Andrew Chapin. BS, U. Richmond (Va.), 1969; MS, Oreg. State U., 1974, PhD, 1977. Rsch. scientist Sci. Applications, Inc., Boulder, Colo., 1977-79, div. mgr., 1979-81; exec. dir. Sci. Mus., West Palm Beach, Fla., 1981-88, Mus. Sci. and History, Jacksonville, Fla., 1988, Nat. Invention Ctr., Akron, Ohio, 1989-92, Fresno (Calif.) Met. Mus., 1993-95. Alumni v.p. Leadership Palm Beach County; expdn. leader Expdn. Tng. Inst., S.E. Alaska, 1980; mem. U.S. Antarctic Research Program, 1974. Author: Complete Circuit Training Guide, 1980; Strength Training Book, 1981; (with others) Aerobic Weight Training Book, 1982, Increasing Your Audience, 1989, Inventing Stuff, 1995; mem. editorial adv. bd. Invent Mag. 1989-92. Founder, bd. dirs. Visually Impaired Sports Program, Boulder, 1978-81; fitness instr. YMCA Boulder, 1977-81; convener 1st Nat. Conf. Sports for the Blind, 1979; bd. dirs. Leadership Palm Beach; vice chmn. County Com. on Artificial Reefs; treas. Leadership Akron; Alumni Assn., 1990-91, class pres. Leadership Akron; v.p. Ohio Mus. Assn., 1991-92, pres., 1992-93; co-host Blow the Roof Off Ednl TV show, 1992; bd. dirs. Fla. Mus. Assn., 1988-89; mem. adv. bd. Marine Sci. Inst., 1990—. Lt. USN, 1970-73. Fellow Explorers Club; mem. Marine Tech. Soc. (sect. chmn. 1982-84), Coral Reef Soc. (chpt. pres. 1982-87), Nat. Inventive Thinking Assn. (bd. dirs. 1989—). Home: 8806 N 5th St Fresno CA 93720

SOBIESKI, JAROSLAW, aerospace engineer; b. Wilno, Poland, Mar. 11, 1934; came to U.S., 1966; naturalized, 1971.; s. Stanislaw and Sabina

Sobieszczanski; m. Wanda Dlugosz, Dec. 31, 1958; children: Margaret Ann, Ian Patrick. BS aeros., Tech. U. Warsaw, 1955, MS aeros., 1957, DEng. 1964. Cons. Polish Aircraft Industries, Warsaw, Poland, 1957-64; asst. and adj. prof. Tech. U. Warsaw, Warsaw, Poland, 1955-64; rsch. assoc. Tech. U. Norway, Trondheim, 1964-66; assoc. prof. St. Louis U., 1966-71; aerospace engr. NASA Langley Rsch. Ctr., Hampton, Va., 1971-89, head rsch. office, 1979-93, chief scientist, 1993-94, multidisciplinary rsch. coord., 1994—; mem. faculty George Washington U., 1972-92, U. Va., 1982—; pres. and cons. engr. Tech. Analysis Optimization, Inc. Hampton, Va., 1983—. Contbr. articles to profl. jours. Fellow AIAA (tech. com.). Home: 518 Elizabeth Lake Dr Hampton VA 23669-1724 Office: NASA Langley Rsch Ctr Hampton VA 23681-0001

SOBIN, JULIAN MELVIN, international consultant; b. Boston, July 14, 1920; s. Irving Maxwell and Selma Helen (Brodie) S.; m. Leila Feinburg, May 3, 1942; children: Patricia, Jonathan. A.B., Harvard U., 1941; LL.D. (hon.), William Penn Coll., 1979. Trainee to chmn. Sobin Chems. Inc., Boston, 1946-75; sr. v.p. Internat. Minerals & Chem. Corp., 1975-77, dir. internat. bus. devel., 1976-77, exec. cons., 1977-78; exec. v.p. IMC Chem. Group, 1975-76; chmn. trustees Internat. Mktg. Inst., Cambridge, Mass., 1975-84; v.p. Assoc. Metals & Minerals Corp., 1978-82; dir. Comml. Solvents Corp.; exec. cons. China trade Laporte Industries U.K. and U.S.A.; lectr. in field; corporator South Boston Savs. Bank; advisor, cons. to Spl. Rep. of Pres. for Trade Negotiations, Kennedy Round of Tariff Reductions, 1962-63; mem. Pres.'s Adv. Com. Nat. Trade Policy, 1968-69; mem. adv. com. on East/West trade Dept. Commerce, 1976—; internat. trade cons. Internat. Exec. Svc. Corps to San Miguel Corp., Manila, 1984-85; mem. exec. com. Mass. Gov.'s Fgn. Bus. Coun., 1977—; cons. dir. NYBO Internat. Inc., 1987—; sr. advisor C.P. Group, Bangkokk, 1992—, Harcros Chemicals, London, 1992—. Author: (audio album) The China Trader; co-author: Ency. of China Today, The China Guide, 12th edit., 1992; mem. adv. bd. Partisan Review; contbr. numerous articles to profl. jours. Gen. chmn. New Eng. Trade Week, 1959; trustee Nat. Jewish Hosp. and Research Center, Denver, Emerson Coll.; bd. advisors Stonehill Coll., 1975-78; mem. overseers com. to visit dept. fine arts Harvard U., 1968-74; mem. Boston Com. on Fgn. Relations; bd. dirs. Nat. Council U.S.-China Trade, 1976-77; bd. dirs., mem. exec. com. Internat. Trade Ctr. New Eng. Inc.; trustee Lesley Coll., Boston U., Am. Grad. Sch. Internat. Mgmt. (Thunderbird); mem. overseers com. to visit Ctr. Internat. Affairs Harvard U., 1981—. Served to maj. F.A. AUS, 1941-46, CBI. Decorated Legion of Merit; recipient Annual Honor medal Nat. Jewish Hosp. and Research Ctr., 1975; fellow Harvard U. Ctr. for Internat. Affairs, 1987-88; hon. royal consul of Nepal in Boston, 1993—. Mem. Mfg. Chemists Assn., Chemists Club of N.Y., Hong Kong-Am. C. of C., Fgn. Correspondents Club Hong Kong, Internat. Mgmt. Devel. Inst. (corp. strategic planning coun.), Soc. Am. Chem. Industry, Am. Radio Relay League, Harvard Club (Boston, N.Y.C.), Univ. Club (Boston). First Am. businessman invited to Peking, China, spring 1972. Home: 790 Boylston St Boston MA 02199-7928

SOBKOWICZ, HANNA MARIA, neurology researcher; b. Warsaw, Poland, Jan. 1, 1931; came to U.S., 1963; d. Stanislaw and Jadwiga (Ignaczak) S.; m. Jerzy E. Rose, Mar. 12, 1972. B.A., Girls State Lyceum, Gilwice, Poland, 1949; M.D. Med. Acad., Warsaw, 1954, PhD., 1962. Intern. 1st Internal Med. Clinic Med. Acad., Warsaw, 1954-55; resident 1st Internal Med. Clinic, Med. Acad., Warsaw, 1955-59; resident Neurol. Clinic, Med. Acad., 1959, jr. asst., 1959-61, sr. asst., 1961-63; research fellow neurology Mt. Sinai Hosp., N.Y.C., 1963-65; Nat. Multiple Sclerosis Soc. fellow Columbia U., N.Y.C., 1965-66; asst. prof. neurology U. Wis. Madison, 1966-72, assoc. prof., 1972-79, prof., 1979—. Contbr. articles to profl. jours. NIH research grantee, 1968—. Mem. Internat. Brain Rsch. Orgn., Assn. Rsch. in Otolaryngology, Soc. Neurosci., Internat. Soc. Devel. Neurosci. (editorial bd. 1984—), Electron Microscopy Soc. Am. Home: 4169 Cherokee Dr Madison WI 53711-3068 Office: U Wis Dept Neurology 1300 University Ave Madison WI 53706

SOBLE, DAVID S., steel company executive; b. Chgo., July 3, 1943; s. Morris and Eleanor (Leishin) S.; m. Marica Greenstein, Aug. 5, 1966 (div. 1981); children: Michael, Jeffrey; m. Lee Ann Hoffman, Dec. 27, 1985; 1 child, Peggy Hoffman. BS in Econs., U. Pa., 1965. With sales dept. Lesso Steel Corp., Chgo., 1965-69, gen. mgr., 1969-71; v.p. sales Interstate Steel Co., Des Plaines, Ill., 1971-73, exec. v.p., 1973-75, pres., 1975—; pres. Metron Steel Corp., Chgo., 1990—; chmn. govt. affairs Steel Service Ctr. Inst., Cleve., 1985-90. Mem. Industry Sector Adv. com. Office: Interstate Steel Co 401 E Touhy Ave Des Plaines IL 60018-2631 also: Metron Steel Corp 12900 S Metron Dr Chicago IL 60633

SOBLE, JAMES BARRY, lawyer; b. Chgo., Apr. 14, 1942; s. Julius R. Soble and Bernyce (Morris) Rossuck; children—Debra, Jeffrey, Tony, Leslie; m. Ann S. Valenstein, June 29, 1980. B.A., Grinnell Coll., 1963; J.D., Northwestern U., 1966. Bar: Ill. 1966, Fla. 1974. Assoc. Deutsch & Peskin, Chgo., 1966-68; ptnr. Siegel & Soble, 1969-71 Peskin & Soble, 1972-73; exec. v.p., corp. counsel Millstream Corp., Sunrise, Fla., 1973-79; pvt. practice, Ft. Lauderdale, Fla., 1979-81; ptnr., shareholder Jacobs, Robbins, Gaynor, Hampp, Burns, Cole & Shasteen, P.A., St. Petersburg, Fla., 1981-83; ptnr. Taub & Williams, Tampa, Fla., 1984-88; ptnr. Honigman Miller Schwartz and Cohn, 1988—; lectr. Law Forum, Inc., 1982-84. Pres., bd. dirs. Gulf Coast Jewish Family Services of Pinellas County, 1984—; bd. dirs. Better Bus. Bur. West Florida, Inc.; pres. Jewish Fedn. Pinellas County, 1989-91. Mem. ABA, Ill. Bar Assn., Hillsborough County Bar Assn. Jewish. Home: 2996 Sandpiper Pl Clearwater FL 34622-3058 Office: Honigman Miller Scharwtz & Cohn 2700 Landmark Ctr 401 E Jackson St Tampa FL 33602

SOBOL, HAROLD, consultant, retired dean, manufacturing executive; b. Bklyn., June 21, 1930; s. Stanley and Minnie S.; m. Marion Gross, Dec. 29, 1957; children—Diane, Neil, Jessica, Martin. B.S.E.E., CUNY, 1952; M.S.E.E., U. Mich., 1956, Ph.D., 1960. Research asst. Willow Run Labs. U. Mich., 1952-55, research assoc., 1956-59; staff mem. IBM Research, Yorktown Heights, N.Y., 1960-62; with RCA Labs., Princeton, N.J., 1962-73; staff engr. RCA Labs., 1970-72, head communication tech., 1972-73; sr. mem. tech. staff Collins Radio Rockwell-Internat., Dallas, 1973-74; dir. product devel. Collins Transmission Systems div., 1974-85; dir. engring. Rockwell Telecommunications, 1985-86, v.p. engring., 1986-88, ret., 1988; prof. elec. engring., assoc. dean U. Tex., Arlington, 1988-93. Author: Advances in Microwaves Volume 8, 1974; contbr. in field. Cubmaster Tex.-Okla. council Boy Scouts Am., Dallas, 1978-80. Sperry fellow, 1955-56. Fellow IEEE (pres. microwave theory and techniques soc. 1979); mem. Am. Phys. Soc., Nat. Mgmt. Assn., Sigma Xi, Tau Beta Pi, Eta Kappa Nu. Office: U Tex PO Box 19019 Arlington TX 76019

SOBOL, JUDITH ELLEN, museum director, art historian; b. Washington, June 1, 1946. BA, UCLA, 1968; MA, George Washington U., 1970, Mus. Mgmt. Inst., 1992. Asst. to curator, lectr. fine arts Georgetown U., Washington, 1970-72; asst. chmn. edn. div., supr. interpretive svc. Mpls. Inst. Arts, 1973-77; chmn. div. edn. Balt. Mus. Art, 1977-78; exec. dir. Don't Tear It Down, Washington, 1978-81; asst. prof. art history Westbrook Coll., Portland, Maine, 1981-91; dir. Joan Whitney Payson Gallery Art, 1981-91; dir. Grand Rapids (Mich.) Art Mus., 1991—; reviewer Inst. Mus. Svcs., Washington, 1983, 94; mus. panelist Maine Arts Commn., Augusta, 1986-88. Producer cable TV series on Payson Gallery exhibits, 1985-91; author various mus. catalogues; contbr. articles to profl. jours. Trustee Greater Portland Landmarks, 1983-88, Kendall Coll. Art and Design, 1992—. Payson Found. fellow, 1968. Mem. Am. Assn. Mus., Internat. Coun. on Mus., ArtTable. Home: 411 College SE Grand Rapids MI 49301 Office: Grand Rapids Art Mus 155 Division N Grand Rapids MI 49503-2693

SOBOL, LAWRENCE RAYMOND, lawyer; b. Kansas City, Mo., May 8, 1950; s. Haskell and Mary (Press) S.; m. Maureen Patricia O'Connell, May 29, 1976; children: David, Kevin. BBA, U. Tex., 1972; JD, U. Mo., 1975. Bar: Mo. 1975, U.S. Dist. Ct. (ea. dist.) Mo. 1975. Gen. counsel, gen. ptnr. Edward D. Jones & Co., Maryland Heights, Mo., 1975—; allied mem. N.Y.C. Stock Exchange, 1977—; sec. Lake Communications Corp., Conroe, Tex., 1984-86. LHC Inc., EDJ Holding Co. Inc.; sec., bd. dirs. Cornerstone Mortgage Inc., St. Louis, 1986; v.p., bd. dirs. Tempus Corp., St. Louis, 1984—. Omar Robinson Meml. scholar U. Mo., 1974-75. Mem. ABA (securities law com. 1982—), Met. St. Louis Bar Assn. (securities law sect.),

Nat. Assn. Securities Dealers (dist. bus. com., registered prin. officer, nat. arbitration com. 1991—), Securities Industry Assn. (fed. rebulation securities com. 1987-88), Forest Hills Country Club, Phi Eta Sigma. Republican. Jewish. Avocations: tennis, golf. Office: Edward D Jones & Co 201 Progress Pky Maryland Heights MO 63043

SOBOL, THOMAS, state education commissioner; b. Jan. 11, 1932; m. Harriet Sobol; three children. BA in English, Harvard U., 1953, grad., 1954; PhD, Columbia U., 1969. Head dept. English pub. sch. system Bedford, N.Y., 1961-65; dir. instrn., 1965-69; asst. supt. instrn. pub. sch. system Great Neck, N.Y., 1969-71; supt. sch. systems Scarsdale, N.Y., 1971-87; commr. N.Y. State edn. Albany, 1987—. Office: Edn Dept Edn Bldg Washington Ave Albany NY 12234 also: U State of NY Regents Coll Degrees 1450 Western Ave Albany NY 12203-3539

SOBOLEWSKI, JOHN STEPHEN, computer information scientist, director computer services, consultant; b. Krakow, Poland, July 14, 1939; came to U.S., 1966; s. Jan Zygmund and Stefania (Zwolinska) S.; m. Helen Skipper, Dec. 17, 1965 (div. July 1969); m. Carole Straith, Apr. 6, 1974; children: Anne-Marie, Elisa, Martin. BE, U. Adelaide, Adelaide, South Australia, 1962, ME, 1966; PhD in Computer Sci., Wash. State U., 1971. Sci. officer Weapons Research Establishment, Salisbury, South Australia, 1964-66; asst. prof. computer sci. Wash. State U., Pullman, 1966-73; dir. research, assoc. prof. U. Wash., Seattle, 1973-80, dir. computer svcs., 1980-88; assoc. v.p. computing U. N.Mex., Albuquerque, 1988—; cons. govt. and industry, Seattle, 1973—; mem. bd. trustees Fisher Found., Seattle, 1984—. Author: Computers for the Dental Office, 1986; contbr. articles to profl. jours. Served as engr. with Royal Australian Army, 1957-60. Australian govt. scholar, 1961-64. Elec. Res. Bd. scholar CSIRO, Melbourne, Australia, 1961-64. Mem. IEEE, Computer Soc. Roman Catholic. Avocation: mineral collecting. Home: 8501 Northridge Ave NE Albuquerque NM 87111-2107 Office: U NMex CIRT 2701 Campus Ave NE Albuquerque NM 87131

SOBOTTKA, STANLEY E., physics educator; b. Plum City, Wis., Dec. 20, 1930. BS, U. Wis., 1955; MS, Stanford U., 1957, PhD, 1960. Mem. tech. staff plasma physics group Boeing Sci. Rsch. Labs., Seattle, 1959-60; mem. tech. staff Watkins-Johnson Co., Palo Alto, Calif., 1960-64; assoc. prof. physics U. Va., Charlottesville, 1964-71, prof., 1971—; users' adv. com. Space Radiation Effects Lab., 1966-70; vis. staff mem. Los Alamos Meson Physics Facility, 1968-74, mem. tech. adv. panel, 1971-73, chmn. EPICS working group, 1971-73, bd. dirs. users' group, 1973-74; vis. physicist Brookhaven Nat. Lab., 1978. Patentee bifilar helical multiwire proportional chambers; contbr. articles, abstracts to profl. jours. Predoctoral fellow NSF, 1955-56; grantee Oak Ridge Assoc. Univs. Faculty Rsch. Participation, 1977. Mem. Sigma Xi, Phi Beta Kappa, Phi Eta Sigma. Research includes X-ray diffraction, imaging X-ray detector development, experimental nuclear physics. Office: U Va Dept Physics Mccormick Rd Charlottesville VA 22904

SOCHEN, JUNE, history educator; b. Chgo., Nov. 26, 1937; d. Sam and Ruth (Finkelstein) S. B.A., U. Chgo., 1958; M.A., Northwestern U., 1960, Ph.D., 1967. Project editor Chgo. Superior and Talented Student Project, 1959-60; high sch. tchr. English and history North Shore Country Day Sch. Winnetka, Ill., 1961-64; instr. history Northeastern Ill. U., 1964-67, asst. prof., 1967-69, assoc. prof., 1969-72, prof., 1972—. Author: The New Woman, 1971, Movers and Shakers, 1973, Herstory: A Woman's View of American History, 1975, 2d edit., 1981, Consecrate Every Day: The Public Lives of Jewish American Women, 1981, Enduring Values: Women in Popular Culture, 1987, Cafeteria America: New Identities in Contemporary Life, 1988, Mae West: She Who Laughs Lasts, 1992; editor: Women's Comic Visions, 1991; contbr. articles to profl. jours. Nat. Endowment for Humanities grantee, 1971-72. Mem. Am. Studies Assn. Office: Northeastern Ill U 5500 N Saint Louis Ave Chicago IL 60625-4625

SOCIE, DARRELL FREDERICK, mechanical engineering educator; b. Toledo, Oct. 28, 1948; s. Frederick James and Emerence (Lupinski) S.; m. Pamela Sue Doll, 1977; children: Benjamin, Bethany, Michael. BS in Metall. Engring., U. Cin., 1971, MS, 1973; PhD, U. Ill., 1977. Registered prof. engr., Ill., Ohio. Research asst. dept. theoretical and applied mechanics U. Ill., Urbana, 1971-74, vis. asst. prof. dept. theoretical and applied mechanics, 1977-78; asst. prof. Dept. Mech. and Indsl. Engring. U. Ill., Urbana, 1978-81, assoc. prof., 1981-85, prof., 1986—; panelist Coopers & Lybrand Trendsetter Barometer, 1993—; cons. Structural Dynamics, 1974-80, Owens-Corning Fiberglass, 1974-82; pres. SOMAT Corp., 1982—. Recipient Ralph R. Teetor award Soc. Automotive Engrs., 1980, Comdr.'s award for disting. pub. svc. U.S. Army, 1990, Disting. Alumni award U. Cin., 1991. Mem. ASTM (Fatigue Achievement award 1992), Am. Soc. Metals, Sigma Xi, Alpha Sigma Mu. Office: U Ill 144 Mech Engring Bldg 1206 W Green St Urbana IL 61801-2906

SOCKWELL, OLIVER R., JR., financial services company executive; b. Washington, July 27, 1943; s. Oliver R. and Janette Muriel (Nealy) S.; m. Harriet Evelyne Riley, July 28, 1973; children—Kristine Evelyne, Brian Oliver, Jason Wendell. B.S., Howard U., 1965; M.B.A., Columbia U., 1972. Investment banker Smith, Barney & Co., N.Y.C., 1972-74; v.p. mktg. Sallie Mae (Student Loan Mktg. Assn.), Washington, 1974-83; sr. v.p. ops., 1983-84, exec. v.p. fin., adminstn. and planning, 1984-87; pres., chief exec. officer Coll. Constrn. Loan Ins. Assn. (Connie Lee), Washington, 1987—; bd. dirs. Connie Lee Ins. Co., Washington; bd. dirs. D.C. Govt. Retirement Bd., Washington, 1981-83. Trustee Wilberforce U., Ohio, 1983-87; bd. dirs. Washington Project for the Arts, 1985-88, Washington Urban League, 1986-90, Washington Theatre Awards Soc., 1990-94, Capitol City Found., 1989—, Columbia U. Sch. Bus., 1993—, Ford's Theatre, 1995—. Home: 1685 Myrtle St NW Washington DC 20012-1129 Office: Connie Lee 2445 M St NW Washington DC 20037-1435

SOCOL, HOWARD, department store executive. Chmn. Burdine's, Miami, Fla. Office: Burdines 7 W 7th St Cincinnati OH 45202-2424

SOCOL, JERRY M., retail executive; b. 1942. Grad., Ind. U. With Federated Dept. Stores, Cin., 1963-64, Marshall Field, Louisville, 1964-84, The Limited, Columbus, Rich's Dept. Stores, Cin.; pres. Filene's, Boston, chmn., CEO, pres., CEO; pres. J. Baker Inc., Canton, Mass., 1988-90, CEO, 1990—; CEO WGS Corp.; pres., CEO Morse Shoe Inc., JBI Inc.; bd. dirs. Casual Male Inc. Office: J Baker Inc 555 Turnpike St Canton MA 02021-2724*

SOCOLOFSKY, JON EDWARD, banker; b. Chgo., Mar. 27, 1946; s. E. E. and Jane C. (Ward) S.; married; 1 child, Brian Edward. BA, DePauw U., 1968; MBA, Ind. U., 1970. Auditor No. Trust Co., Chgo., 1970-79, v.p., 1979-86, sr. v.p., 1986—. Pres. Cass Sch. Dist. # 63, Darien, Ill., 1987-93. Mem. Internat. Ops. Assn., Internat. Soc. Securities Adminstrs. Republican. Congregationalist. Avocations: water skiing, volleyball, motorcycles. Office: The Northern Trust Co 50 S La Salle St Chicago IL 60603-1003

SOCOLOW, ARTHUR ABRAHAM, geologist; b. Bronx, N.Y., Mar. 23, 1921; s. Samuel and Yetta (Solomon) S.; m. Edith S. Blumenthal, Apr. 10, 1949; children: Carl, Roy. Jeff. BS, Rutgers U., 1942; MA, Columbia U., 1947, PhD, 1955. Photogrammetrist, U.S. Geol. Survey, 1942, 46; with Eagle Picher de Mexico, 1947; instr. geology So. Methodist U., 1948-50; dir. geology field camp Colo., 1948-50; asst. prof. Boston U., 1950-55; geologist Def. Minerals Exploration Authority, Alaska, 1952; assoc. prof. U. Mass., 1955-57; econ. geologist Pa. Geol. Survey, 1957-61, dir., state geologist, 1961-86; cons. geologist Pa. Geol. Survey, Gloucester, Mass., 1986—; prof. environ. geology Salem (Mass.) State Coll., 1993-95; dir. New Eng. Govs. Conf. Project on Aggregate Resources New Eng. 1990-95; cons. geologist Gloucester; mem. Outer Continental Shelf Policy Com., 1974-88, Pa. rep., 1978-88; lectr. mineral conservation Pa. State U., 1959-75; mem. conf. earth sci. source materials NSF, 1959; chmn. ann. field conf. Pa. Geologists, 1961-86; past mem. U.S. Nat. Com. on Tunnelling Tech.; mem. com. on N.Y. State low level waste program Nat. Acad. Sci.; mem. gov.'s adv. com. Nat. Coun. on Environ. Quality; past chmn. Pa. Water Resources Coordinating Com.; geol. advisor Boston Mus. Sci., 1955-57. Former editor Pa. Geol. Bull.; mem. editorial bd. Northeastern Geol. Jour.; contbr. over 100 publs. and papers on environ. and econ. geology to profl. jours. Served with

USAAF, 1942-46. Fellow Geol. Soc. Am. (sec.-treas. N.E. sect., past nat. councilor), Mineral. Soc. Am., AAAS (past pres. geography—geology sect.); mem. AAUP, Soc. Econ. Geologists, Phila. Geol. Soc. (past pres.), Am. Geol. Inst. (com. on manpower), Nat. Assn. Geology Tchrs. (past regional pres., Ralph Digman award for contbns. to geologic edn.1980), Pa. Acad. Sci., Am. Meteoritical Soc., Am. Assn. State Geologists (past pres., editor, compiler State Geological Surveys-A History 1988), Am. Geophys. Union, Am. Commn. Stratigraphic Nomenclature (past chmn.), Harrisburg Geol. Soc., Interstate Oil Compact Commn. (research com., environ. com.), Gloucester Conservation Commn., Fgn. Policy Assn. (past chpt. pres.), Sigma Xi. Club: Internat. Torch (past pres. chpt.). Home and Office: 26 Salt Island Rd Gloucester MA 01930-1945 *I have great respect for the individualism of man in the midst of a society and a world where there is an unavoidable interrelationship and interdependence of man upon man, and of man upon his environment. While we strive to maintain our individualism, we must share our common resources and our common aspirations. This is the challenge that makes our lives worth living.*

SOCOLOW, ROBERT HARRY, engineering educator, scientist; b. N.Y.C., Dec. 27, 1937; s. A. Walter and Edith (Gutman) S.; m. Elizabeth Anne Sussman, June 10, 1962 (div. Apr. 27, 1982); children: David, Seth; m. Jane Ries Pitt, May 25, 1986; stepchildren—Jennifer, Eric. B.A., Harvard U., 1959, M.A., 1961, Ph.D., 1964. Asst. prof. physics Yale U., New Haven, 1966-71; assoc. prof. mech. and aerospace engring. Princeton U. (N.J.), 1971-77, prof. mech. and aerospace engring., 1977—; mem. Inst. Advanced Study, Princeton, 1971; dir. Center for Energy and Environmental Studies, Princeton, 1978—. Author: (with John Harte) Patient Earth, 1971, (with K. Ford, G. Rochlin, M. Ross) Efficient Use of Energy, 1975, (with H.A. Feiveson, F.W. Sinden) Boundaries of Analysis: An Inquiry into the Tocks Island Dam Controversy, 1976, Saving Energy in the Home: Princeton's Experiments at Twin Rivers, 1979, (with C. Andrews, F. Berkhout, V. Thomas) Industrial Ecology and Global Change, 1994; editor Ann. Rev. of Energy and Environment, 1992—. Chmn. bd. Am. Coun. for Energy Efficient Econ., 1989-93; bd. dirs. Nat. Audubon Soc., 1992—. John Simon Guggenheim fellow, 1976-77; German Marshall Fund fellow, 1976-77; NSF Postdoctoral fellow, 1964-66; NSF Predoctoral fellow, 1960-64. Fellow AAAS, Am. Phys. Soc. Jewish. Home: 34 Westcott Rd Princeton NJ 08540-3060 Office: Princeton U H102 Engineering Quad Princeton NJ 08544

SODAL, INGVAR EDMUND, electrical engineer, scientist; b. Hemne, Norway, Feb. 12, 1934; came to U.S., 1962; s. Ingebrigt L. and Johanna (A.) Sodal; m. Sally Rollins; 1 child, Silje M. Degree in elec. engring., Trondheim Tech. Coll., Norway, 1959; BSEE, U. Colo., 1964. Engr. Fjeldseth Engring., Trondheim, 1959-61; rsch. engr. U. Norway, Trondheim, 1961-62; rsch. engr. U. Colo. Med. Ctr., Denver, 1964-66, rsch. assoc., 1966-75, instr., 1975-79; vis. rsch. assoc. dept. engring. U. Colo., Boulder, 1974-75, lectr., 1975-76; asst. prof., div. head. Ohio State U., Columbus, 1979-82, mem. grad. faculty, 1982; pres., chief exec. officer Masstron, Inc., Boulder, Colo., 1983-87; chief scientist Paradygm, Boulder, 1987-89; pres. Pacemark, Inc., Boulder, 1989-90, Med. Physics Colo., Inc., 1991—. Contbr. articles to profl. jours., chpts. to books; holder 6 patents in field. Instr. and/or program coord. in Scandinavian folklore and folk dancing for numerous groups and instns. throughout U.S., Can. and Norway, 1959—. Grantee NIH and various pvt. orgns. Mem. Assn. for Advancement Med. Instrumentation, Instrument Soc. Am., Soc. for Technology in Anesthesia, Biomed. Engring. Soc., Sons of Norway. Office: 1550 Moss Rock Pl Boulder CO 80304-1543

SODD, VINCENT JOSEPH, nuclear medicine researcher, educator; b. Toledo, Ohio, Nov. 20, 1934; s. Abraham and Sarah (Hamway) S.; m. Dorothy P. Langenderfer, Oct. 20, 1956; children: Vincent Joseph, Anthony Newman, Joseph William, Anne Marie. B.S., Xavier U., Cin., 1956, M.S., 1958; Ph.D., U. Pitts., 1964. Dep. chief nuclear medicine lab. FDA, Cin., 1974-77, acting chief, 1971-72, dir., 1974-84; assoc. prof. radiology U. Cin., 1974-77; prof. U. Cinn., 1977—; mem. radiation safety com. U. Con., 1975-86, mem. radioactive drug research com., 1979-86, mem. com. on human research, 1982-86. Author: Radiopharmaceuticals and Radiopharmaceuticals II, 1975,79, Radiation Safety in Nuclear Medicine-A Practical Guide, 1981; contbr. more than 150 articles to profl. jours.; patentee in field. Served to capt. USPHS, 1957-84. Recipient Dorst Chemistry Key Xavier U., 1956; recipient Silver award Ohio State Med. Assn., 1968. Mem. Soc. Nuclear Medicine (pres. Southeastern chpt. 1979-80, mem. council 1981—, trustee 1980-81, bd. govs. Instrumentation Council 1982—), Internat. Commn. Radiol. Protection. Roman Catholic. Office: U Cin Coll Applied Sci ML 103 Cincinnati OH 45267

SODEMAN, WILLIAM ANTHONY, SR., cardiologist; b. Charleroi, Pa., June 13, 1906; s. William Joseph Carl and Anna (Dietz) S.; m. Lucile Marie Kadle, Sept. 23, 1989; children: William Anthony, Thomas Michael. BS, U. Mich., 1928, MD, 1931; ScD, Villanova U., 1959; LHD, Thomas Jefferson U., 1967. Diplomate Am. Bd. Internat. Medicine, Am. Bd. Preventive Medicine. Intern St. Vincent's Hosp., Toledo, 1931-32; instr. medicine Tulane U. Sch. Medicine, New Orleans, 1932-40, 1940-41, prof., head dept. preventive medicine, 1941-46, prof., chmn. dept. tropical medicine, 1946-53; prof., chmn. dept. internal Medicine U. Mo., Columbia, 1953-57; Magee prof., chmn. dept. internal Medicine Jefferson Med. Coll., Phila., 1957-58, dean, prof. medicine, 1958-67; sci. dir. Life Ins. Med. Rsch. Fund, Rosemont, Pa., 1967-70; exec. dir. Commn. on Fgn. Med. Grads., Phila., 1970-73; clin. prof. medicine Med. Coll. Ohio, Toledo, 1974-86; Kellogg scholar Navajo Health Authority, Ariz., 1974-77; cons. U.S. Bur. Hearings and Appeals, Dept. Health; cons. cardiology Sch. Dist. Phila., 1959-63; cons. med. USPHS Hosp. Leprosarium, Carville, La., 1939-53; cons. ICA, State Dept. for Med. Sch. in Ghana, 1961. Author: Patholic Physiology, 1953; contbr. articles on internal medicine to profl. jours. Recipient Disting. Alumni award Med. Ctr. Alumni, U. Mich., Ann Arbor, 1968, Strittmatter award Phila. County Med. Soc., 1975, Disting. Svc. award AMA, 1979. Fellow Am. Coll. Cardiology (pres. 1970-71, disting. fellow 1973); mem. ACP (pres. 1972-73, pres. emeritus 1985), Cosmos Club (Washington). Republican. Lutheran. Home: 4141 Bayshore Blvd Apt 203 Tampa FL 33611-1803

SODEN, PAUL ANTHONY, lawyer; b. N.Y.C., Feb. 3, 1944; s. Leo J. and Mildred E. (Callahan) S.; m. Irene M. Davis, Aug. 3, 1968; children—Christina M., Paul A. A.B., Fordham U., 1965, J.D., 1968. Bar: N.Y. 1968. Assoc. Cahill, Gordon & Reindel, N.Y.C., 1968-74; corp. counsel Technicon Corp., Tarrytown, N.Y., 1974-76, asst. gen. counsel, asst. sec., 1976-78, sr. v.p., gen. counsel, sec., 1978-87; v.p., dir. internat. law Sterling Winthrop Inc., 1987-88; v.p., gen. counsel, sec. Sterling Drug Inc., 1988-95; sr. v.p., gen. counsel The Reader's Digest Assn., Inc., 1995—. Mem. Am. Bar Assn., N.Y. State Bar Assn. Club: Scarsdale (N.Y.) Golf. Office: Reader's Digest Rd Pleasantville NY 10570-7000

SODEN, RICHARD ALLAN, lawyer; b. Bklyn., Feb. 16, 1945; s. Hamilton David and Clara Elaine (Seale) S.; m. Marcia LaMonte Mitchell, June 7, 1969; children: Matthew Hamilton, Mark Mitchell. A.B., Hamilton Coll., 1967; JD, Boston U., 1970. Bar: Mass. 1970. Law clk. to judge U.S. Ct. Appeals (6th cir.), 1970-71; assoc. firm Goodwin, Procter & Hoar, Boston, 1971-79, ptnr., 1979—; instr. Law Sch. Boston Coll., Chestnut Hill, Mass., 1973-74. Mem. South End Project Area Com.; past pres., bd. dirs. United South End Settlements; mem. adv. council Suffolk U. Sch. Mgmt.; vice chmn., bd. dirs. Boston Mcpl. Rsch. Bur.; bd. dirs. Greater Boston council Boy Scouts Am.; chmn., trustee Judge Baker Guidance Ctr.; bd. govs. New England Aquarium; trustee Boston U. Harvard Med. Ctr.; bd. visitors Boston U. Goldman Sch. Grad. Dentistry; mem. of corp., past mem. exec. com. Children's Mus.; mem. bd. overseers WGBH; mem. Mass. Minority Bus. Devel. Commn.; mem. Adv. Task Force on Securities Regulation; mem. Adv. Com. on Legal Edn.; past chmn. Lawyers Com. for Civil Rights Under Law. Mem. ABA, Nat. Bar Assn., Mass. Bar Assn. (past vice chmn. bus. law coun., 1990-91), Boston Bar Assn. (pres.), Mass. Black Lawyers Assn. (pres. 1980-81). Home: 42 Gray St Boston MA 02116-6210 Office: Goodwin Procter & Hoar Exchange Pl Boston MA 02109

SODEN, RUTH M., geriatrics nurse, educator; b. Tipton, Iowa, Nov. 29, 1940; d. Tony and Clarissa Arlene (Beall) Koreman; m. James D. Soden; children: Shannon, Scott, Suzan, Staci. AA, Highline Community Coll., Midway, Wash. Cert. in intravenous therapy. Charge nurse Wildwood

Health Care Ctr., Puyallup, Wash.; admissions coord. Forestglen Nursing Ctr., Seattle, staff devel. dir.; charge nurse Green River Terrace Nursing Ctr., Auburn, Wash.; unit coord. Tacoma Luth. Home; mem. Clover Park Tech. Coll., Tacoma. Mem. Nat. Gerontol. Nursing Assn. (practical nurse program adv. com.), Wash. State Nurses Assn., Assn. for Practitioners in Infection Control, Nat. Coun. on Family Rels., Phi Theta Kappa. Home: 25650 29th Ave S Kent WA 98032-5532

SÖDERBERG, BO SIGFRID, marketing executive; b. Avesta, Sweden, Mar. 22, 1939; came to U.S., 1979; s. John Sigfrid and Elisabet A. (Bjorkvall) S.; m. Kerstin Linnea Nordling; children: Monica, Mikael, Bogge, Margareta. BS in Engring., TGO, Orebro, Sweden, 1960; MBA, Fla. Inst. Tech., 1985. Mng. dir. Scandinavian Computer Systems, Stockholm, 1967-69; pres. Bror Andersson AB (BRA), Stockholm, 1969-78; exec. dir. Cap Gemini Sogeti, Paris, 1978-80, Cap Gemini Inc., Washington, 1980-82; pres. DMA Marketing Inc., Palm Bay, Fla., 1982-86; pres. Prisma Am. Inc., Vero Beach, Fla., 1986-87, also bd. dirs.; pres. Scandinavian USA Bus. Ctr., Inc., Clearwater, Fla., 1988-92, DMA Mktg. Inc., Clearwater, 1993—; seminar instr. Swedish Computer Soc., Stockholm, 1970-78; instr., lectr. Swedish Soc. for Info. Processing, Stockholm, 1972-78; lectr. Fla. Outdoor Advt. Assn., Orlando, Fla., 1986-87. Served as specialist Sweden Air Force, 1960-61. Home: 12000 4th St N Saint Petersburg FL 33716

SODERBERG, DAVID LAWRENCE, chemist; b. Evergreen Park, Ill., Jan. 28, 1944; s. Arthur Lawrence and Jean Van Norden (Freeman) S. AB in Chemistry, Ripon (Wis.) Coll., 1969. Rsch. asst. Ripon Coll., 1968-69, Pomona Coll., Claremont, Calif., 1969-70; chemist animal and plant health inspection svc. USDA, N.Y.C., 1972-73; chemist food safety and quality svc. USDA, Athens, Ga., 1974-83; supervisory chemist food safety and inspection svc. USDA, St. Louis, 1983-87; chemist, program devel. and tech. mgmt. USDA, Washington, 1987—. Contbr. articles to profl. jours. With U.S. Army, 1965-67, Vietnam. Recipient awards USDA, 1976, 87, cert. of merit, 1980. Mem. AAAS, ASTM, Am. Chem. Soc., Assn. Official Analytical Chemists (gen. referee meat and poultry products). Office: USDA FSIS DTMB 300 12th St SW Rm 524 Washington DC 20250-0001

SODERBERG, NANCY, federal agency administrator; b. San Turce, P.R., Mar. 13, 1958; d. Lars Olof and Nancy (MacGilvrey) S. BA French, Econs., Vanderbilt U., 1980; MS Fgn. Svc., Georgetown U., 1984. Budget and reports analyst Bank of New England, Boston, 1980-82; rsch. asst. Brookings Inst., Washington, 1982-83; summer intern UN Devel. Program, Brazzaville, Congo, 1983; rsch. assn. Agy. Internat. Devel., Washington, 1983; del. selection asst. Mondale-Ferraro Com., Washington, 1983, fgn. policy advisor, 1984; dep. issues dir. fgn. policy Dukakis for Pres. Com., Boston, 1988; fgn. policy advisor Senator Edward M. Kennedy, Washington, 1985-88, 89-92; fgn. policy dir. Clinton/ Gore Campaign, Little Rock, 1992; dep. asst. dir. transition nat. security Clinton/ Gore Transition, Little Rock, 1992-93; spl. asst. to Pres. for nat. security affairs, staff dir. Nat. Security Coun., Washington, 1993—; mem. Coun. Fgn. Rels. Office: National Security Council The White House 1600 Pennsylvania Ave NW Washington DC 20500-0001

SODERBERGH, PETER ANDREW, education educator; b. Bklyn., Nov. 14, 1928; s. Sven Eric and Mary Margaret (McGowan) S.; m. Kathryn L. Tillson; children: Susan, Mary, Peter, Katherine, Steven, Charles. BA, Amherst Coll., 1950; MA in Teaching, Harvard U., 1959; Ph.D., U. Tex., 1966. Tchr. public schs. Andover, Mass., 1959-60; prin. Andover Jr. High Sch., 1960-61; instr. English Phillips Andover Acad., summers 1959-61; lectr. in edn. Emory U., Atlanta, 1961-63; asst. prof. edn. U. Tex., Austin, 1966-67; prof. edn. U. Pitts., 1967-73; assoc. dean Sch. Edn., U. Va., Charlottesville, 1973-76; dean Coll. Edn., La. State U., Baton Rouge, 1976-81. Contbr. articles to profl. jours. Served with USMC, 1950-58, Korea. Decorated Purple Heart; Markoe scholar, 1958-59. Mem. Soc. for Cinema Studies, Phi Delta Kappa, Omicron Delta Kappa, Phi Kappa Phi, Alpha Delta Phi. Democrat. Office: Coll Edn La State U Baton Rouge LA 70803

SODERBERGH, STEVEN ANDREW, filmmaker; b. Atlanta, Jan. 14, 1963; s. Peter Andrew and Mary Ann (Bernard) S.; m. Elizabeth Jeanne Brantley, Dec. 1, 1989 (div. Oct. 1994). Writer, dir., editor: (film) sex, lies, and videotape, 1989 (Palme d'Or award Cannes Film Festival 1989), King of the Hill, 1993; dir., editor: (film) Kafka, 1991; exec. prodr.: (film) Suture, 1994; dir.: (film) The Underneath, 1995. Mem. AMPAS, Dirs. Guild Am. Democrat. Office: PO Box 2000 Orange VA 22960

SODERLIND, STERLING EUGENE, newspaper industry consultant; b. Rapelje, Mont., Sept. 6, 1926; s. William John and Florence (Longbotham) S.; m. Helen Boyce, Apr. 9, 1955; children: Steven (dec.), Sarah, Lori. B.A., U. Mont., 1950; B.A. Rhodes Scholar, Oxford U., Eng., 1950-52. Reporter Mpls. Tribune, 1952-55; reporter Wall St. Jour., Chgo. 1955-56; Southeastern bur. chief Wall St. Jour., Jacksonville, Fla., 1956-57; mem. page one editing staff Wall St. Jour., N.Y.C., 1957-65, asst. mng. editor, 1966-70, mng. editor, 1970; econs. editor Dow Jones & Co., Inc., N.Y.C., 1970-77, asst. to pres., 1975-77, v.p., 1977-91; newspaper industry cons., 1992—. Served with USNR, 1944-46. Congregationalist. Home: 58 Wellington Ave Short Hills NJ 07078-3308

SODERQUIST, LARRY DEAN, lawyer, educator, consultant; b. Ypsilanti, Mich., July 20, 1944; s. Hugo E. and Emma A. (Johanson) S.; m. Ann Mangelsdorf, June 15, 1968; children: Hans, Lars. BS, Ea. Mich. U., 1966; JD, Harvard U., 1969. Bar: N.Y. 1971, Tenn. 1981. Assoc. Milbank, Tweed, Hadley & McCloy, N.Y.C., 1971-76; assoc. prof. law U. Notre Dame, South Bend, Ind., 1976-80, prof. 1980-81; vis. prof. law Vanderbilt U. Law Sch., Nashville, 1980-81, prof. 1981—; dir. corp. and securities law inst. 1993—; of counsel Tuke, Yopp & Sweeney; spl. master U.S. Dist. Ct. (no. dist.) Ohio, 1977. Capt. U.S. Army 1969-71. Decorated Army Commendation medal. Mem. ABA, Am. Law Inst. Presbyterian. Author: Corporations, 1979, 3d edit., 1991, Understanding Corporation Law, 1990, Understanding the Securities Laws, 3d edit., 1993, Securities Regulation, 3d edit., 1994, Law of Federal Estate and Gift Taxation: Code Commentary, 1978, Analysis, 1980; contbr. numerous articles to legal jours. Home: 421 Sunnyside Dr Nashville TN 37205-3413 Office: Vanderbilt U Sch Law 21st Ave S Nashville TN 37240

SODINI, PETER J., food service executive. With Fazio's div. of Fisher Foods Inc., 1976-78, Boys Markets Inc., L.A., 1978-1990, Buttrey Food & Drug Co., Great Falls, Mo., 1990-91; pres., ceo Purity Supreme, North Billerica, Mass., 1991—. Office: Purity Supreme 101 Billerica Ave North Billerica MA 01862

SODOLSKI, JOHN, retired association administrator; b. Menasha, Wis., Apr. 11, 1931; s. L.V. and L.W. (Pinkowski) S.; m. C.J. Eppard. BS, U. Wis., 1953. Vice pres. Electronic Industries Assn., Washington, 1961-83; pres. U.S. Telephone Assn., Washington, 1983-93; ret., 1993. Served to 1st lt. USMC, 1955.

SOECHTIG, JACQUELINE ELIZABETH, telecommunications executive; b. Manhasset, N.Y., Aug. 12, 1949; d. Alvin Hermann and Regina Mary (Murphy) Venzke; m. James Decatur Miller, June 28, 1976 (div. Oct. 1982); M. Clifford Jon Soechtig, Oct. 19, 1983. B.A. cum laude, Coll. of New Rochelle (N.Y.), 1974; M.A. summa cum laude, U. So. Calif., 1978. Computer operator IBM, White Plains, N.Y., 1970-72, ops. job scheduler, 1972-74, various spl. assignments, 1974-75, mktg. rep., Bethesda, Md., 1975-76, Charleston, W. Va., 1979-81, adv. regional mktg. rep. Dallas, 1981-82; dist. mgr. Am. Speedy Printing Co., Dallas, 1982-83, nat. sales devel. mgr., Detroit, 1984; regional mgr. major and nat. accounts MCI Telecommunications, Southfield, Mich., 1984-85, dir. nat. accounts 1985-86, v.p. nat. accounts 1987-88, v.p. mktg. and customer svc., 1988-89, v.p. consumer segment, 1989-90; v.p. integrated telecommunications solutions Sprint United, Atlanta, 1990-92; pres., chief exec. officer Precision Systems, 1992—; interviewer, Sergio Segre, Bolonga, Italy, 1977, Radio Free Europe, Brussels, 1978, World Health Program, Rome, 1978, ITT, Brussels, 1977, Franz Josef Strauss, 1978. Recipient Golden Circle Achievement award IBM, 1980, Quar. Recognition award, 1980, 81; named New Bus. Pacesetter, 1980, 81. Republican. Club: German Am. Women's (v.p. Stuttgart, W.Ger. 1977-78). Office: Precision Sys 11800 30th Ct No Saint Petersburg FL 33716

SOEDERSTROM, ELISABETH ANNA, opera singer; b. Stockholm, May 7, 1927; d. Emanuel Albert and Anna (Palasova) S.; student Opera Sch., Stockholm, also pupil of Andrejewa Skilondz; m. Sverker Olow, Mar. 29, 1950; children: Malcolm, Peter, Jens. Appearances include Stockholm Opera, 1950, Salzburg Festival, 1955, Glvndebourne Opera, 1957, 59, 61, 63, 64, Met. Opera, 1959, 60, 62, 63, 83, 86-87; sang three leading roles in Rosencavalier within one year, 1959; toured USSR, 1966; others roles include Fiordiligi in Cosi Fan Tutte, Susanna and Countess in Figaro, Countess in Capriccio; radio, TV and concert appearances in U.S. and Europe; artistic leader Drottingholm Ct. Theatre; author: I Min Tonart, 1978, Sjung ut, Elisabeth!, 1986. Decorated Order of Vasa (Sweden); Stelle Della Solidarieta Dell'Italia; King Olav's reward (Norway); comdr. Most Disting. Order Brit. Empire, CBE; comdr. des Arts et des Lettres; named Singer of the Court (Sweden); recipient prize for best acting Royal Swedish Acad., 1965, Literis et Artibus award, 1969. Mem. Royal Acad. Music Gt. Britain (hon.). Office: Drottningholms Theatre Mus, Box 27050, S-10251 Stockholm Sweden also: care Columbia Artists Mgmt 165 W 57th St New York NY 10019

SOENS, LAWRENCE D., bishop; b. Iowa City, Aug. 26, 1926. Student, Loras Coll., Dubuque, Iowa, St. Ambrose Coll., Davenport, Iowa, Kenrick Sem., St. Louis, U. Iowa. Ordained priest Roman Catholic Ch., 1950, consecrated bishop, 1983. Bishop of Sioux City Iowa, 1983—. Office: Chancery Office PO Box 3379 1821 Jackson St Sioux City IA 51105-1055*

SOERGEL, KONRAD HERMANN, physician; b. Coburg, Germany, July 27, 1929; came to U.S., 1954, naturalized, 1962; s. Konrad Daniel and Erna Henrietta (Schilling) S.; m. Rosina Klara Rudin, June 24, 1955; children: Elizabeth Ann, Karen Theresa, Marilyn Virginia, Kenneth Thomas. M.D., U. Erlangen, Germany, 1954, Dr. med., 1958. Intern Bergen Pines County Hosp., Paramus, N.J., 1954-55; resident in pathology West Pa. Hosp., Pitts., 1955-56; resident in medicine Mass. Meml. Hosp., Boston, 1957-58; fellow in gastroenterology Boston U. Med. Sch., 1958-60, instr., 1960-61; mem. faculty Med. Coll. Wis., Milw., 1961—, prof. medicine, 1969—, prof. physiology, 1993—; chief sect. gastroenterology Med. Coll. Wis., 1961-93, dir. fellowship program, dept. medicine, 1993—; chmn. gastroenterology and clin. nutrition study sect. NIH, 1979-80. Contbr. articles to profl. jours., chpts. to books. Recipient Research Career Devel. award USPHS, 1963-72; Alexander von Humboldt Found. sr. fellow, 1973-74. Mem. Am. Gastroenterol. Assn., Am. Soc. Clin. Investigation, Am. Assn. Physicians, German Soc. for Digestive and Metabolic Disorders (hon.), Ger. Soc. Internal Medicine (hon.). Home: 14245 Hillside Rd Elm Grove WI 53122-1677 Office: Med Coll Wis 9200 W Wisconsin Ave Milwaukee WI 53226-3522

SOETEBER, ELLEN, journalist, newspaper editor; b. East St. Louis, Ill., June 14, 1950; d. Lyle Potter and Norma Elizabeth (Osborn) S.; m. Richard M. Martins, Mar. 16, 1974. BJ, Northwestern U., 1972. Edn. writer, copy editor Chgo. Today, 1972-74; reporter Chgo. Tribune, 1974-76, asst. met. editor, 1976-84, assoc. met. editor, 1984-86, TV and media editor, 1986, met. editor, 1987-89, assoc. mng. editor for met. news, 1989-91, dep. editor editorial page, 1991-94; mng. editor Ft. Lauderdale (Fla.) Sun-Sentinel, 1994—; fellow journalism U. Mich., Ann Arbor, 1986-87. Office: The Sun-Sentinel 200 E Las Olas Blvd Fort Lauderdale FL 33301

SOFAER, ABRAHAM DAVID, lawyer, legal advisor, federal judge, legal educator; b. Bombay, India, May 6, 1938; came to U.S., 1948, naturalized, 1959; m. Marian Bea Scheuer, Oct. 23, 1977; children: Daniel E., Michael J., Helen R., Joseph S., Aaron R., Raphael J. BA in History magna cum laude, Yeshiva Coll., 1962; LLB cum laude, NYU, 1965. Bar: N.Y. 1965. Law clk. to Hon. J. Skelly Wright, U.S. Ct. Appeals, Washington, 1965-66; to Hon. William J. Brennan, Jr., U.S. Supreme Ct., Washington, 1966-67; asst. U.S. atty. So. Dist. N.Y., N.Y.C., 1967-69; prof. law Columbia U., N.Y.C., 1969-79; judge U.S. Dist. Ct. for So. Dist. N.Y., 1979-85; legal advisor Dept. State, Washington, 1985-90; ptnr. Hughes Hubbard & Reed, Washington, 1991-94; George P. Shultz disting. scholar, sr. fellow Hoover Instn., Stanford U., 1994—; hearing officer N.Y. Dept. Environ. Conservation, 1975-76. Author: War, Foreign Affairs and Constitutional Power: The Origins, 1976; contbr. articles to legal, polit., fgn. jours.; editor-in-chief: NYU Law Rev, 1964-65. Served with USAF, 1956-59. Root-Tilden scholar NYU, 1965. Mem. Fed. Bar Assn., Am. Bar Assn., N.Y. Bar Assn., Am. Law Inst. Jewish. Office: The Hoover Instn Stanford U Stanford CA 94305-6010

SOFRANKO, JOEL E., pension fund administrator. Audit supr. Coopers & Lybrand, Columbus, Ohio, 1978-82; gen. manager Muirfield Ltd., Columbus, Ohio, 1982-87; cfo Health Power Management Corp., Columbus, Ohio, 1987-89, School Employees Retirement System, Columbus, Ohio, 1989—. Office: School Empl Retrmnt Sys 45 N 4th St Columbus OH 43215

SOFRO, BARNEY, retail executive; b. 1942. BS, San Jose State Coll., 1964. With House of Fabrics Inc., 1964—, exec. v.p., sec., 1978-81, pres., COO, 1981-85, also bd. dirs., co-chmn. bd. dirs., now chmn. bd. dirs. Office: House of Fabrics Inc 13400 Riverside Dr Van Nuys CA 91423-2511*

SOFTNESS, DONALD GABRIEL, marketing and manufacturing executive; b. Bklyn.; s. Burt H. and Ida (Kaiser) S.; m. Sydell Meyerson; children: Michael, Anita May, Beth. A.B., NYU, 1949, M.B.A., 1959; J.H.D., St. John's U., 1979. Chmn. Softness Group, Inc., N.Y.C., 1960-79; pres. Softness Enterprise, N.Y.C., 1979—, SecureVue, Inc., N.Y.C., 1984—; v.p., maj. prin. Radio Stas. WVNJ-AM-FM, Newark and N.Y.C.; mem. faculty Advt. Week seminars Advt. Age; prodr., sponsor Bklyn. Rollathon (skating marathon); pub. affairs cons. St. John's U., N.Y.C. Co-author: Cardiologists' Guide to Health and Fitness Through Exercise, 1979; contbr. articles to bus. and trade jours. Patentee in field. Served with USN. Mem. Public Relations Soc. Am., Internat. Radio TV Soc., Am. Coll. Sports Medicine. Club: N.Y. Yacht. Home and Office: 28 Trues Dr West Islip NY 11795-5147 Office: SecureVue Inc 251 E 51st St New York NY 10022-6534

SOFTNESS, JOHN, public relations executive; b. Bklyn., Nov. 7, 1930; s. Burt H. and Ida (Kaiser) S.; m. Leona Ruth Golden; children: Barney, David, Daniel. B.A., U. Miami, 1955. Reporter Miami Herald, 1953; reporter Sta. WTVJ, Miami, Fla., 1954; asso. pub. relations dir. aviation dept. Shell Oil Co., N.Y.C., 1958-60; pres., chief exec. officer The Softness Group, Inc., N.Y.C., 1960-91, chmn., 1992—; spl. counselor to Bklyn. Borough pres., 1966-76; adj. prof. communications arts St. John's U., 1981—; counselor communications com. N.Y. Heart Assn. Served to capt. USAF, 1955-58. Mem. Pub. Rels. Soc. Am., Pride and Alarm (chmn.), Counselors' Acad. Home: 245 E 54th St Apt 14F New York NY 10022-4719 Office: The Softness Group Inc 381 Park Ave S New York NY 10016-8806

SOGARD, JEFFREY W., lawyer; b. L.A., Feb. 27, 1945; s. John Maurice and Helen (Collins) S. BA, U. Colo., 1968, JD, 1971. Bar: Mont. 1971, Colo. 1971, Minn. 1981. Ptnr. James Firm, Great Forks, Mont., 1972-77, Dorsey & Whitney, Missoula, Mont., 1978—; counsel Mont. Power Co., Butte, 1977-78; dep. county atty. Cascade County, Great Falls, Mont., 1975-76. 1st lt. U.S. Army, 1971-72. Avocations: athletics, gardening, reading. Home: 498 Skidoo Ln Polson MT 59860-9608 Office: Dorsey & Whitney 127 E Front St Ste 310 Missoula MT 59802-4448

SOGG, WILTON SHERMAN, lawyer; b. Cleve., May 28, 1935; s. Paul P. and Julia (Cahn) S.; m. Saralee Frances Krow, Aug. 12, 1962 (div. July 1975); 1 child, Stephanie; m. Linda Rockar Lehman, Dec. 22, 1979 (div. Dec. 1990). A.B., Dartmouth Coll., 1956; J.D., Harvard U., 1959; Fulbright fellow, U. London, 1959-60. Bar: Ohio 1960, D.C. 1970, Fla. 1970, U.S. Supreme Ct., N.Y. 1985, U.S. Tax Ct. Assoc. Gottfried, Ginsberg, Guren & Merritt, 1960-63, ptnr., 1963-70; ptnr. Guren, Merritt, Feibel, Sogg & Cohen, Cleve., 1970-84; of counsel Hahn, Loeser, Freedheim, Dean and Wellman, Cleve., 1984-85; ptnr. Hahn Loeser & Parks, Cleve., 1986—; trustee, pres. Cleve. Jewish News; adj. prof. Cleve. State Law Sch., 1960—; lectr. Harvard U. Law Sch., 1978-80. Author (with Howard M. Rossen); new and rev. vols. of Smith's Review Legal Gems series, 1969—; editor: Harvard Law Rev.; contbr. articles to profl. jours. Trustee Jewish Community Fedn. of Cleve., 1966-72; bd. overseers Cleveland Marshall Coll. Law, Cleve. State U., 1969—; dir. project for improving delivery of legal svcs. Case We. Res. U. Law Sch., 1991—; mem. U.S. and State of Ohio Holocaust Commns. Recipient Katie Meml. award Jewish Community Fedn., Cleve., 1970; named one of 10 outstanding young men Cleve. Jaycees, 1967, 68. Mem. ABA,

Ohio Bar Assn., Cleve. Bar Assn., Cuyahoga County Bar Assn., Fla. Bar Assn., D.C. Bar Assn., N.Y. State Bar Assn., German Philatelic Soc., Oakwood Club, Union Club, Chagrin Valley Hunt, Phi Beta Kappa. Home: 22176 Parnell Rd Cleveland OH 44122-2727 Office: Hahn Loeser & Parks 3300 BP America Bldg 200 Public Sq Cleveland OH 44114-2303

SOGNEFEST, PETER WILLIAM, manufacturing company executive; b. Melrose Park, Ill., Feb. 4, 1941; s. Peter and Alvera S.; children from previous marriage: Scott, Brian, Jennifer; m. Donna Stilwell, May 7, 1994. BSEE, U. Ill., 1964, MSEE, 1967. Elec. engr. Magnavox Corp., Urbana, Ill., 1964-67; sr. fellow, mgr. research, United Techs. fellow Mellon Inst., Pitts., 1967-71; gen. mgr. for semicondr. ops. United Techs., Pitts., 1971-77; v.p. indsl. electronics unit Motorola Inc., Schaumburg, Ill., 1977-84; chmn., CEO, bd. dirs. Digital Appliance Controls, Inc., Elgin, Ill., 1984-91; pres., CEO IRT Corp., San Diego, 1991-94, also bd. dirs.; pres. CEO LH Rsch., Inc., Costa Mesa, Calif., 1994—; bd. dirs. Two-Six Inc. Patentee in field. Trustee Humana Hosp., Hoffman Estates, Ill., 1989-92; pres. bd. deacons Presbyn. Ch., 1981-82, elder, 1988—. Mem. IEEE, U. Ill. Elec. Engring. Alumni Assn. (pres. 1986-87, Disting. Alumnus award 1989), Coves Property Owners Assn. (pres. 1982), Chancellor's Assocs. (U. Calif. San Diego), Barrington Hills Country Club, Pacific Golf and Country Club. Republican. Office: LH Rsch Inc 345 Baker St Costa Mesa CA 92626-4518

SOHMER, BERNARD, mathematics educator, administrator; b. N.Y.C., July 16, 1929; s. Sol and Florence (Schonfeld) S.; m. Margot Rosette, July 27, 1952; children—Emily, Olivia. B.A., N.Y. U., 1949, M.S., 1951, Ph.D., 1958. Lectr. CCNY, 1952-57, faculty, 1958—, prof. math., 1969—, dean students, 1969-72, v.p. student affairs, 1972-75, chmn. faculty senate, 1977-79, 85-91, ombudsman, 1991—, chmn. liberal arts and sci. faculty council, 1979-85, pres. Hillel, 1988—; asst. prof. N.Y. U., 1957-58; trustee PSC-CUNY Welfare Fund, 1982—. Sec. Univ. Faculty Senate, 1992-94, vice chair, 1994—. Mem. AAAS, AAUP (pres. CCNY chpt. 1966-67, sec. 1977-78), Am. Math. Soc., Math. Assn. Am. (pres.-elect N.Y. Met. sect. 1989-90, pres. 1992-93, past pres. 1993-94), Profl. Staff Congress (pres. CCNY chpt. 1993—). Home: 3345 92nd St Jackson Heights NY 11372 Office: CCNY 139th and Convent Ave New York NY 10031

SOHN, HONG YONG, chemical and metallurgical engineering educator, consultant; b. Kaesung, Kyunggi-Do, Korea, Aug. 21, 1941; arrived U.S., 1966; s. Chong Ku and Soon Deuk (Woo) S.; m. Victoria Bee Tuan Ngo, Jan. 8, 1972; children: Berkeley Jihoon, Edward Jihyun. BS in Chem. Engring., Seoul (Korea) Nat. U., 1962; MS in Chem. Engring., U. N.B., Can., 1966; PhD in Chem. Engring., U. Calif., Berkeley, 1970. Engr., Cheil Sugar Co., Busan, Korea, 1962-64; research assoc. SUNY-Buffalo, 1971-73; research engr. DuPont Co., Wilmington, Del., 1973-74; prof. metall. engring., adj. prof. chem. engring. U. Utah, Salt Lake City, 1974—; cons. Lawrence Livermore Nat. Lab., 1976—, Kennecott Co., Salt Lake City, 1976—, Cabot Corp., 1984—, DuPont Co., 1987—, Utah Power and Light Co., 1987—. Co-author: Gas-Solid Reactions, 1976; co-editor: Rate Processes of Extractive Metallurgy, 1979, Extractive Metallurgy of Refractory Metals, 1980, Advances in Sulfide Smelting, 2 vols., 1983; Recycle and Secondary Recovery of Metals, 1985, Gas-solid Reactions in Pyrometallurgy, 1986, Flash Rection Processes, 1988, Metallurgical Processes for the Year 2000 and Beyond, 1988, Metallurgical Processes for the Early Twenty-First Century, 2 vols., 1994; patentee process for treating sulfide-bearing ores; contbr. numerous articles to sci., tech. jours. Camille and Henry Dreyfus Found. Tchr. Scholar awardee, 1977; Fulbright Disting. lectr., 1983; Japan Soc. for the Promotion of Sci. fellow, 1990. Mem. The Minerals, Metals and Materials Soc. (past dir., Extractive Metallurgy Lectr. award, 1990, Champion H. Mathewson Gold Medal award, 1993, Extractive metallurgical sci. award 1990, 94), Am. Inst. Chem. Engrs., Korean Inst. Chem. Engrs. Office: U Utah 412 Browning Bldg Salt Lake City UT 84112 *Fortunate are those who earn a living by doing what they would rather be doing even if they do not have to do it to earn a living. Material wealth accumulated by doing what one does not enjoy doing is not worth the effort.*

SOHN, JEANNE, librarian; b. Milton, Pa.; d. Robert Wilson and Juliette Lightner (Hedenberg) Gift; m. Steven Neil Sohn, Nov. 23, 1962. BA, Temple U., 1966; MSLS, Drexel U., 1971. Lit. bibliographer Temple U. Phila., 1971-75, chief of collection devel., 1975-81; assoc. dean for collection devel. U. N.Mex., Albuquerque, 1981-86, assoc. dean for libr. svcs., 1986-89; dir. libr. svcs. Cen. Conn. State U., New Britain, 1989—; cons. New Eng. Assn. Schs. and Colls., Winchester, Mass., 1991—. Mem. editorial bd. Collection Mgmt., 1984—; contbr. articles to profl. jours. Mem. Gov.'s Blue Ribbon Commn. on the Future of Libraries, 1994—. Mem. ALA, New Eng. Libr. Assn., Conn. Libr. Assn., Assn. Coll. and Rsch. Librs., Beta Phi Mu. Home: 1820 Boulevard West Hartford CT 06107-2815 Office: Elihu Burritt Libr Cen Conn State U New Britain CT 06050

SOHN, LOUIS BRUNO, lawyer, educator; b. Lwów, Poland, Mar. 1, 1914; came to U.S., 1939, naturalized, 1943; s. Joseph and Fryderyka (Hescheles) S.; m. Elizabeth Mayo. LLM, Diplomatic ScM, John Casimir U., 1935; LLM, Harvard U., 1940, SJD, 1958; LLD (hon.), Free U. Brussels (Flemish sect.), 1990. Asst. to Judge M. O. Hudson, 1941-48; John Harvey Gregory teaching fellow Harvard Law Sch., 1946-47, lectr. law, 1947-51, asst. prof. law, 1951-53, John Harvey Gregory lectr. in world orgn., 1951-81, prof. law, 1953-61, Bemis prof. internat. law, 1961-81; Woodruff prof. internat. law U. Ga., 1981-91; vis. congl. prof. George Washington U., 1991-92; disting. rsch. prof. and dir. rsch. and studies Internat. Rule of Law Inst., 1992—; vis. Congl. prof. George Washington U., 1991-92; Disting. fellow Jennings Randolph Program, U.S. Inst. Peace, 1991-92; cons. U.S. ACDA, 1960-70, Office Internat. Security Affairs, Dept. Def., 1963-70; asst. to del. Permanent Ct. Internat. Justice, San Francisco Conf. UN, 1945; exec. sec. legal subcom. on atomic energy Carnegie Endowment for Internat. Peace, 1946; asst. reporter on progressive devel. internat. law Am. and Canadian bar assns., 1947-48; cons. UN secretariat, 1948, 69, legal officer, 1950-51; counselor internat. law Dept. State, 1970-71; U.S. del. to UN Law of Sea Conf., 1974-82; U.S. del. head Athens Conf. on Settlement Internat. Disputes, 1984. Author: Cases on World Law, 1950, Cases on United Nations Law, 1956, 2d edit., 1967, (with G. Clark) World Peace Through World Law, 1958, 3d edit., 1966, Basic Documents of African Regional Organizations, 4 vols, 1971-72, (with T. Buergenthal) International Protection of Human Rights, 1973, (with K. Gustafson) The Law of the Sea, 1984, International Organization and Integration: student edit. 1986; also articles on legal subjects; editor devel. internat. law: Am. Bar Assn. Jour, 1947-50; editorial bd.: Am. Jour. Internat. Law, 1958—. Recipient World Peace Hero award World Federalists of Can., 1974, Grenville Clark award, 1984, William A. Owens award for creative rsch. in social and behavioral scis. U. Ga., 1985, Harry Leroy Jones award Washington Fgn. Law Soc., 1993. Mem. ABA (hon., co-rapporteur joint working group with Can. Bar Assn. on peaceful settlement of disputes 1976—, vice chmn. internat. law and practice sect. 1983-91, chmn. 1992-), Am. Jour. J. Theberge award 1992), Am. Soc. Internat. Law (mem. exec. coun. 1954-57, v.p. 1965-66, hon. v.p. 1980-87, 90—, pres. 1988-90), World Parliament Assn. (legal advisor 1954-64), Internat. Law Assn. (v.p. Am. br.), Am. Law Inst. (assoc. reporter Fgn. Rels. Law 1978-87), Inst. Internat. Law, Fedn. Am. Scientists (vice chmn. 1963, mem. coun. 1964-65, 68-69), Commn. Study Orgn. Peace (chmn. 1986—). Home: 801 15th St S Apt 1504 Arlington VA 22202-5023 Office: George Washington U Nat Law Ctr 720 20th St NW Washington DC 20052

SOIKA, HELMUT EMIL, retirement plan administrator; b. N.Y.C., May 22, 1941; s. Hubert E. and Berta Antonia (Metzger) S. BS, Fordham U., 1963, JD, 1968. Asst. trust officer Nat. Bank of N.Am., N.Y.C., 1968-71; trust officer Bank of N.Y., Westchester, 1971-72; atty. O'Neill, DiManno & Kelly, N.Y.C., 1972-76; atty. & div. mgr. Mut. of Am., N.Y.C., 1976-82; v.p., mgr. retirement plans Prudential-Bache Securities, N.Y.C., 1982-86; sr. v.p., dir. retirement plans Gruntal & Co. Inc., N.Y.C., 1986—. Office: Gruntal & Co Inc 14 Wall St New York NY 10005-2101

SOILEAU, MARION JOSEPH, engineering and physics educator; b. Simmesport, La., June 27, 1944; s. Marion and Mary Ann (Rabalais) S.; m. Cheryl A. Meche; children: Bruce, Aimee. BS in Astronomy/Physics, La. State U., 1967; MS in Physics/Optics, U. Utah, 1968; PhD in Quantum Electronics, U. So. Calif., 1979. Prof. Elec. Engring., Physics. Various positions in field to physicist Naval Weapons Ctr., China Lake, Calif., 1973-80; assoc. prof. physics North Tex. State U., 1980-84, prof. physics, 1984-87;

prof. elec. engring. and physics, dir. Ctr. Rsch. and Edn. in Optics and Lasers, U. Ctrl. Fla., Orlando, 1987—. Contbr. over 100 sci. papers on nonlinear optics; contbr. articles to profl. jours. Trustee Orlando Sci. Ctr., 1991—. Capt. USAF, 1967-72. Co-recipient North Tex. State U. Pres.'s award, 1983. Fellow Optical Soc. Am., Soc. Photo-Optical and Instrumentation Engrs. (bd. govs. 1990-92), SPIE-The Internat. Optical Engring. Soc. (bd. govs. 1990-92, 94—); mem. IEEE (sr.), AAAS, Laser Inst. Am., KC and others. Democrat. Roman Catholic. Avocation: fishing. Home: 100 Tuskawilla Rd Winter Springs FL 32708 Office: U Cen Fla PO Box 162700 Orlando FL 32816-2700

SOIN, RAJESH K., business executive; b. New Delhi, India, July 27, 1947; came to U.S., 1969; m. Indu Soin; children: Vishal, Amol. BSME, Delhi U.; MSIE, Bradley U.; postgrad., Harvard U., U. Pa. Indsl. engr. Firestone Tire & Rubber Co., 1971-78; corp. system mgr. Williams Internat., Walled Lake, Mich., 1978-84; pres., CEO Modern Techs. Corp., Dayton, Ohio, 1984—; pres. JMD Devel. Corp., Dayton, Emerald Constrn. Corp., Dayton; pres. Asian Indian Am. Bus. Group, Dayton. Bd. dirs. Dayton Coun. on World Affairs, Needy Children's Found., Dayton; trustee Ohio/India Project, Dayton Art Inst.; mem. bd. advisors Wright State U. Coll. Bus. and Adminstrn., Dayton. Mem. Dayton Area C. of C. (bd. dirs.), Dayton Rotary Club. Avocation: golf. Home: 2624 Lantz Rd Beavercreek OH 45434-6627 Office: Modern Techs Corp 4032 Linden Ave Dayton OH 45432-3035

SOJKA, GARY ALLAN, biologist, educator, university official; b. Cedar Rapids, Iowa, July 15, 1940; s. Marvin F. and Ruth Ann (Waddington) Sojka Green; m. Sandra Kay Smith, Aug. 5, 1962; children: Lisa Kay, Dirk Allan. B.S., Coe Coll., 1962; M.S., Purdue U., 1965, Ph.D., 1967. Research assoc. Ind. U., Bloomington, 1967-69, asst. prof., 1969-73, assoc. prof., 1973-79, prof., 1979-84, assoc. chmn. biology, 1977-79, chmn. biology, 1979-81, dean arts and scis., 1981-84; pres. Bucknell U., Lewisburg, Pa., 1984-95; prof. biology, 1995—; mem. higher edn. commn. Mid. States Assn. Colls. and Schs., 1992; chmn. tax policy subcom. Nat. Assn. Ind. Colls. and Univs., 1991-93; mem. study group internat. edn. Am. Coun. Edn., 1992—. Chmn. bd. dirs. Stone Belt Coun. Ret. Citizens, Bloomington, 1977-78; mem. nominating com. Ind. Assn. Ret. Citizens, Indpls., 1979; mem. So. Ind. Health Sys. Agy., Bedford; bd. dirs. Geisinger Med. Found., Danville, Pa. Inst. European Studies; trustee St. Mary-of-the-Woods Coll., Ind., 1988-94; chmn. Pa. Commn. Ind. Colls. and Univs., 1989-90; dir. Suncom Industries, Northcumberland, Pa., 1991-93; mem. Pres.'s Commn. NCAA, 1993-95. Recipient Ind. U. Sr. Class Tchg. award, 1975, Frederick B. Lieber award, 1977, Coe Coll. Alumni award of merit, 1982, Gary A. Sojka award Bucknell U., 1992, Cmty. Leadership award Susquahanna Valley Boy Scouts, 1994; named to Coe Coll. Athletic Hall of Fame, 1988. Mem. Am. Assn. Microbiology, Am. Acad. Microbiology, Am. Soc. Biol. Chemists, Soc. Gen. Microbiology, Nat. Assn. Independent Colls. and Univs. (subcom. chmn. 1991-93), Am. Coun. Edn. (mem. study group on internat. edn. 1992—), Sigma Xi, Sigma Nu, Omicron Delta Kappa. Baptist. Home: 441 Creek Rd Middleburg PA 17842-9003 Office: Bucknell U Dept Biology Lewisburg PA 17842

SOKAL, ROBERT REUVEN, biology educator, author; b. Vienna, Austria, Jan. 13, 1926; came to U.S., 1947, naturalized 1958; s. Siegfried and Klara (Rattner) S.; m. Julie Chen-Chu Yang, Aug. 12, 1948; children: David Jonathan, Hannah Judith. BS in Biology, St. John's U., Shanghai, Republic of China, 1947; PhD in Zoology, U. Chgo., 1952; DSc (hon.), U. Crete (Greece), 1990. From instr. to prof. U. Kans., Lawrence, 1951-69; prof., then leading prof., Disting. prof. SUNY, Stony Brook, 1969—; dept. chmn., 1980-83, vice provost for rsch. and grad. studies, 1981-82, disting. prof. emeritus, 1995; Fulbright vis. prof. Hebrew/Tel Aviv U., Israel, 1963-64, U. Vienna, Austria, 1977, 78, 84; vis. prof. Inst. Adv. Studies, Oeiras, Portugal, 1971-80; vis. disting. prof. U. Mich., 1975-76; vis. prof. Coll. de France, Paris, 1989. Author: Principles of Numerical Taxonomy, 1963, Biometry, 1969, 3d rev. edit., 1994, Statistical Tables, 1969, 3rd rev. edit. 1994, Introduction to Biostatistics, 1973, 2d rev. edit., 1987, Numerical Taxonomy, 1973; editor Am. Naturalist Jour., 1969-84. Career investigator NIH, 1964-69; sr. fellow NSF, 1959-60, NATO fellow, 1974, Guggenheim fellow, 1975-76, 84; Ctr. Advanced Study in Behavioral Sci. fellow, 1992-93. Fellow AAAS, Am. Acad. Arts and Scis.; mem. Soc. Study Evolution (pres. 1977), Am. Soc. Naturalists (pres. 1984), The Classification Soc. (Pres. 1969-71), Internat. Fedn. Classification Socs. (pres. 1988-89), Nat. Acad. Scis., Linnean Soc. London (fgn.), Soc. Systematic Zoology (hon.), Natural History Mus. (Paris, corr. mem.), B'nai Brith (pres. 1966). Democrat. Jewish.

SOKEL, WALTER H., German language and literature educator; b. Vienna, Austria, Dec. 17, 1917; married. AB, Rutgers U., 1941, MA, 1944; PhD in German, Columbia U., 1953. Instr. German, Ohio State U., 1946-47, Temple U., 1947-53; from instr. to assoc. prof. German and humanities Columbia U., N.Y.C., 1953-64; prof. Stanford U., 1964-73; Commonwealth prof. German and English. lit. Ctr. Advanced Studies, U. Va., 1973—; Am. Council Learned Socs. grant-in-aid, 1962; exchange prof. U. Hamburg, 1965; NEH sr. fellow, 1971-72; vis. prof. Harvard U., 1978-79. Author: The Writer in Extremis, 1959, Franz Kafka: Tragik und Ironie, 1964, Franz Kafka, 1966; editor: An Anthology of German Expressionist Drama, 1963; contbr. articles to profl. jours. and books in field. Alex von Humboldt research prize, Fed. Republic Germany, 1982. Mem. Internat. Brecht Soc. (v.p. 1974—), MLA, Am. Assn. Tchrs. German, Am. Comparative Lit. Assn. Office: Department of German Cocke Hall University of Virginia Charlottesville VA 22903

SOKLER, BRUCE DOUGLAS, lawyer; b. Newark, May 2, 1949; s. Lester and Aline Irma (Lasner) S.; m. Barbara Adele Cunningham, June 1, 1974; children: Sean, Brendan. AB, Princeton U., 1971; JD, Georgetown U., 1974. Bar: D.C. 1975, Mass. 1984, U.S. Dist. Ct. D.C., U.S. Dist. Ct. Mass., U.S. Ct. Appeals (D.C. cir.), U.S. Ct. Appeals (2d cir.), U.S. Ct. Appeals (8th cir.), U.S. Supreme Ct. Law clk. to judge U.S. Ct. Appeals (D.C. cir.), Washington, 1974-75; assoc. Covington & Burling, Washington, 1975-82; ptnr. Mintz, Levin, Lohn, Ferris, Glovsky & Popeo P.C., Washington, 1982—. Editor-in-chief Georgetown Law Jour., 1973-74. Mem. ABA, Fed. Communications Bar Assn. Home: 217 N Liberty St Arlington VA 22203-1050 Office: Mintz Levin Lohn Ferris Glovsky & Popeo PC 701 Pennsylvania Ave NW Washington DC 20004-2608

SOKMENSUER, ADIL, physician, educator; b. Izmir, Turkey, Jan. 24, 1928; came to U.S., 1956; s. Cevat and Rukiye (Sun) S.; m. Ulku Sakizlioglu, June 22, 1956; children: G. Hakan, Cem Yanki, Kent Halit. BA with honors, Inönü Lisesi, Izmir, 1945; MD, U. Istanbul, Turkey, 1951; student, U. Pa., 1970-71. Intern Loretto Hosp., Chgo., 1956-57; resident Phila. Gen. Hosp., 1957-59; staff physician Cen. Fla. Tb Hosp., Orlando, Fla., 1959; mem. staff A.G. Holley State Hosp., Lantana, Fla., 1959—, dir. clin. svcs., 1963-66, med. dir., supt., 1966-73, cons., 1973-75; pvt. practice internal medicine West Palm Beach, Fla., 1973-89; med. dir. Palm Beach County Home & Gen. Care Facility; cons. chest svc. VA Hosp., Miami (Fla.), 1969-76; clin. instr. Sch. Medicine, U. Miami, 1969-71, asst. prof., 1971-80, assoc. prof. chest medicine, 1980-84; med. dir., cons. internist Palm Beach County GCF, 1973—. With Turkish Army, 1951-52. Mem. Am. Coll. Chest Physicians, Fla. Med. Assn., Palm Beach County Med. Soc., S.E. Fla. Chest Physicians Soc., Am. Thoracic Soc., Fla. Thoracic Soc. (pres. 1972-73). Gerontology Soc. Rsch. in chemotherapy of Tb and Atypical Tb. Home: 320 Dunbar Rd Palm Beach FL 33480-3763 Office: Palm Beach County Home & Gen Care Facility 1200 45th St West Palm Beach FL 33407-2398

SOKOL, DENNIS ALLEN, hospital administrator; b. Chgo., May 3, 1945; s. Stanley John and Mildred Veronica (Krenslake) S.; m. Gwen Noble, Dec. 19, 1971 (div.); children: Anne, Ellen; m. Jolene K. Buehrer, Jan. 28, 1989. BS in Bus., No. Ill. U., 1968; MBA, U. Nebr., Omaha, 1974; M of Hosp. Adminstrn., U. Minn., 1976. Radio personality various stas., Ill., Iowa and Nebr., 1968-72; pub. relations officer Children's Meml. Hosp., Omaha, 1972-73, Meth. Hosp., Omaha, 1973-74; v.p. adminstrn. Golden Valley (Minn.) Health Ctr., 1976-82; pres. Sacred Heart Health Svcs., Yankton, SD, 1982—; instr. health care mgmt. Mt. Marty Coll., 1986-87, U. Minn., 1986-88. Pres. Valley Health Svcs., Inc., 1984—, Health Mgmt. Svcs., 1987—. Fellow Am. Coll. Health Care Execs. (regent 1991—); mem. S.D. Hosp. Assn. (trustee 1990—), Missouri Valley Health Network (v.p. 1986—), Yankton Area C. of C. (pres. 1989-90), Rotary. Republican.

Roman Catholic. Office: Sacred Heart Hosp 501 Summit St Yankton SD 57078-3899

SOKOL, JOHN L., transportation executive. With Penn Turnpike Commn., Highspire, Pa., 1987—, exec. dir. Office: Penn Turnpike Commn Harrisburg East Int Highspire PA 17034*

SOKOL, MARC JEFFREY, arts administrator; b. Phila., Apr. 18, 1961; s. Arnold and Phyllis (Goldman) S. BA in Architecture and Art History, U. Pa., 1984; MFA in Arts Adminstrn., Columbia U., 1992. Instr. Am. architecture and art history Rio de Janeiro, 1984-85; exec. dir. Paris Edits., Cherry Hill, N.J., 1985-87, L'Imagerie Gallery, L.A., 1987-88; pvt. art dealer, Phila., 1988-89; exec. program dir. Sculpture in Environ., Inc. (SITE), N.Y.C., 1990-94; program officer for arts and humanities Ventures in Edn. Inc., N.Y.C., 1994—; mem. edn. adv. com. High Sch. Art and Design, N.Y.C. Contbr. articles to profl. publs. Co-founding mem. night without light com. Visual AIDS N.Y.C.; mem. bus. coalition steering com. Walks of Life. Grantee Van Nostrand Reinhold Co., N.Y. Times Co. Found., Nat. Endowment for Arts, Dreyfus Corp. N.Y. State Coun. on the Arts, Ark. Arts Coun., Recipient of the Am. Inst. of Arch. N.Y. State, 1993 Pres. Citation. Mem. AIA (learning by design com. N.Y.C. chpt.). Avocations: travel, scuba diving, architectural walking tours. Office: Ventures in Edn 245 Fifht Ave Ste 802 New York NY 10016

SOKOL, ROBERT JAMES, obstetrician, gynecologist, educator; b. Rochester, N.Y., Nov. 18, 1941; s. Eli and Mildred (Levine) S.; m. Roberta Sue Kahn, July 26, 1964; children: Melissa Anne, Eric Russell, Andrew Ian. BA with highest distinction in Philosophy, U. Rochester, 1963, MD with honors, 1966. Diplomate Am. Bd. Ob-Gyn (assoc. examiner 1984-86), Sub-Bd. Maternal-Fetal Medicine. Intern Barnes Hosp., Washington U., St. Louis, 1966-67, resident in ob-gyn., 1967-70, asst. in ob-gyn., 1966-70, rsch. asst., 1967-68, instr. clin. ob-gyn., 1970; Buswell fellow in maternal fetal medicine Strong Meml. Hosp.-U. Rochester, 1972-73; fellow in maternal-fetal medicine Cleve. Met. Gen. Hosp.-Case Western Res. U., Cleve., 1974-75, assoc. obstetrician and gynecologist, 1973-83, asst. prof. ob-gyn., 1973-77; asst. program dir. Perinatal Clin. Rsch. Ctr., 1973-78, co-program dir., 1978-82, program dir., 1982-83, acting dir. obstetrics, 1974-75, co-dir., 1977-83, assoc. prof., 1977-81, prof., 1981-83, assoc. dir. dept. ob-gyn., 1981-83; prof. ob-gyn. Wayne State U., Detroit, 1983—, chmn. dept. ob-gyn., 1983-89, mem. grad. faculty dept. physiology, 1984—, interim dean Med. Sch., 1988-89, dean, 1989—, pres. Fund for Med. Rsch. and Edn., 1988—; chief ob-gyn. Hutzel Hosp. Detroit, 1983-89; dir. C.S. Mott Ctr. for Human Growth and Devel., 1983-89; interim chmn. med. bd. Detroit Med. Ctr., 1988-89, chmn. med. bd., 1989—, sr. v.p. med. affairs, 1992—, trustee, 1990—; past pres. med. staff Cuyahoga County Hosps.; mem. profl. adv. bd. Educated Childbirth Inc., 1976-80; sr. Ob cons. Symposia Medicus; cons. Nat. Inst. Child Health and Human Devel., Nat. Inst. Alcohol Abuse and Alcoholism, Ctr. for Disease Control, NIH, Health Resources and Services Adminstrn., Nat. Clearinghouse for Alcohol Info., Am. Psychol. Assn.; mem. alcohol psychosocial research rev. com. Nat. Inst. Alcohol Abuse and Alcoholism, 1982-86; mem. ob/gyn adv. panel U.S. Pharmacopeial Conv., 1985-90. Mem. internat. editorial bd. Israel Jour. Obstetrics and Gynecology; reviewer med. jours.; mem. editorial bd. Jour. Perinatal Medicine; editor-in-chief Interactions: Programs in Clinical Decision-Making, 1987-90; researcher computer applications in perinatal medicine, alcohol-related birth defects, perinatal risk and neurobehavioral devel.; contbr. articles to profl. jours. Mem. Pres.'s leadership council U. Rochester, 1976-80; mem. exec. com. bd. trustees Oakland Health Edn. Program, 1987—; mem. voluntary alumni admissions com. U. Rochester, 1986—. Served to maj. M.C. USAF, 1970-72. Mem. AMA, NAS (Inst. of Medicine), ACOG (chmn. steering com. drug and alcohol abuse contract 1986-87), Am. Med. Informatics Assn., Soc. Gynecologic Investigation, Perinatal Rsch. Soc., Assn. Profs. Gyn.-Ob, Royal Soc. Medicine, Mich. Med. Soc., Wayne County Med. Soc., Detroit Acad. Medicine, Cen. Assn. Obstetricians-Gynecologists, Rsch. Soc. Alcoholism, Soc. Perinatal Obstetricians (v.p., pres.-elect 1987-88, pres. 1988-89, achievement award 1995), Liaison Com. for Ob-Gyn. (vice-chmn. 1990-92, chmn. 1992—), Am. Gynecol. and Obstetrical Soc., Neurobehavioral Teratology Soc., APHA, Am. Med. Soc. on Alcoholism and Other Drug Dependencies, Soc. for Neuroscis. (Mich. chpt.), Internat. Soc. Computers in Obstetrics, Neonatology, Gynecology (v.p. 1987-89, pres. 1989-92, immediate past pres. 1992—), World Assn. Perinatal Medicine, Soc. Physicians Reproductive Choice and Health, Am. Assn. Med. Colls. (coun. of deans), Detroit Physiol. Soc. (hon.), Polish Gynecologists World Club, Phi Beta Kappa, Sigma Xi, Alpha Omega Alpha. Republican. Jewish. Home: 5200 Rector Ct Bloomfield Hills MI 48302-2654 Office: Wayne State U Sch Medicine 540 E Canfield St Detroit MI 48201-1928 *The drive for academic accomplishment was instilled early in childhood in a home environment which placed value on a multiplicity of interests in science and the arts-my parents taught me what to do. In retrospect, exposure to strong role models-professors of philosophy, pathology, psychiatry and obstetrics-gynecology-takes on increased importance-these individuals showed me how to do it. My family continues to support me in seeking and meeting new challenges. The opportunity to develop and transmit new knowledge sustains a high level of activity. I enjoy what I do.*

SOKOL, SAUL, insurance agency executive; b. Columbus, Ohio, Mar. 27, 1920; s. Nathan and Rose (Klyst) S.; m. Phyllis Davis, Jan. 15, 1950; children: Jay Bradford, Samara Sokol Fields. Student, Ohio State U., 1939-40. CLU, CPCU. Propr. Sokol Ins. Agy., Columbus, 1946—; bd. dirs. Ohio Indemnity Co., Columbus, Bancinsurance Corp., Columbus. Author: Your Insurance Adviser, 1977; writer ins. articles The Columbus Dispatch. Mem. adv. bd. Salvation Army, Columbus, 1972—; trustee Alzheimer's Assn., Columbus, 1987-94, Wexner Heritage Village, Columbus, 1991—; trustee Syntaxis Youth Homes, Columbus, 1973. S/Sgt. Signal Corps, U.S. Army, 1942-46, ETO. Recipient Vol. Svcs. award Salvation Army, 1990. Mem. Am. Soc. CLU (Hall of Fame award 1992), Am. Soc. CPCU (pres. Columbus chpt. 1984-85), Columbus Life Underwriters Assn. (disting. hon.; pres. 1976-77), Ind. Ins. Agts. Assn., Profl. Ins. Agts. Assn., Press Club of Ohio, Univ. Club (Columbus), B'nai B'rith (pres. 1953-54). Home: 360 S Roosevelt Ave Columbus OH 43209 Office: Sokol Ins Agy 3242 E Main St Columbus OH 43213-3807

SOKOLOF, PHIL, industrialist, consumer advocate; b. Omaha, Dec. 14, 1922; s. Louis and Rose (Jacobson) S.; m. Ruth Rosinsky, June 1, 1947 (dec. Feb. 1982); children: Steven, Karen Sokolof Javitch. Grad. high sch., Omaha, 1939. Founder and chief exec. officer Phillips Mfg. Co., Omaha, 1955-92; founder, pres. Nat. Heart Savers Assn., Omaha, 1985—. Author: Bridge Philosophy, 1971; contbg. editor N.Y. Times, 1991; featured in Time mag., Mar. 1990, in Journal of American Medicine, Dec. 1990 as catalyst of American public's cholesterol consciousness; contbg. ed. Sunday New York Times, 1991. Designated by Congress hon. co-sponsor 1990 Nutrition Labeling and Edn. Act. Conducted "Poisoning of America" nat. media campaigns against major food processors for high cholesterol, high fat content in foods, 1988-1993 (citation FDA, 1993); activist in lowering fat content Nat. Sch. Lunch Program; Pioneered mass cholesterol testing, Grand Island, Nebr., 1985; tested cholesterol levels 200,000 people in 16 cities 1985-87; Created and won congressional approval designating March as Nat. Know Your Cholesterol Month, 1987; "Cholesterol Kills" public service announcements featured on 650 television stations, 1987—; nat. spokesperson to create pub. awareness of danger of cholesterol and saturated fats in food products which promote heart disease; conducted public edn. quiz regarding food labels, 1994; campaigned against milk industry ads, 1995. Named Person of Week, ABC News, Mar. 15, 1991; recipient Food & Drug Admin. Commr's. Spl. Achievement citation, C. Everett Koop Health Advocate award FDA, Nat. Hosp. Assn., 1994. Mem. Am. Contract Bridge League (life master), King Solomon's Cir. philanthropy,1990 (charter). Office: Nat Heart Savers Assn 9140 W Dodge Rd Omaha NE 68114-3317

SOKOLOFF, LOUIS, physiologist, neurochemist; b. Phila., Oct. 14, 1921; married; 2 children. BA, U. Pa., 1943, MD, 1946. Intern Phila. Gen. Hosp., 1946-47; rsch. fellow in physiology U. Pa. Grad. Sch. Medicine, 1949-51, instr., then assoc., 1951-56; assoc. chief, then chief sect. cerebral metabolism NIMH, Bethesda, Md., 1953-68; chief lab. cerebral metabolism NIMH, 1968—. Chief editor Jour. Neurochemistry, 1974-78. Served to capt. M.C. U.S. Army, 1947-49. Recipient F.O. Schmitt medal in neurosci., 1980, Albert Lasker clin. med. research award, 1981, Karl Spencer Lashley award

Am. Philos. Soc., 1987, Disting. Grad. award U. Pa., 1987, Nat. Acad. Scis. award in Neurosci., 1988, Georg Charles de Hevesy Nuclear Medicine Pioneer award Soc. Nuclear Medicine, 1988, Mihara Cerebrovascular Disorder Rsch. Promotion award, 1988. Mem. Am. Physiol. Soc., Assn. Rsch. Nervous and Mental Diseases, Am. Biophys. Soc., Am. Acad. Neurology, Am. Neurol. Assn., Am. Soc. Biol. Chemists, Am. Soc. Neurochemistry, U.S. Nat. Acad. Scis. Achievements include development of methods for measurement of cerebral blood flow and metabolism in animals and man. Office: NIMH Rm 1a-05 Bethesda MD 20892

SOKOLOV, RICHARD SAUL, lawyer; b. Phila., Dec. 7, 1949; M. Susan Saltzman, Aug. 13, 1972; children: Lisa, Anne, Kate. BA, Pa. State U., 1971; JD, Georgetown U., 1974. Bar: Md. 1974. Assoc. Weinberg & Green, Balt., 1974-80, ptnr., 1980-82; v.p.; gen counsel Edward J. DeBartolo Corp., Youngstown, Ohio, 1982-86, sr. v.p. devel., gen. counsel, 1986-94; pres., CEO, bd. dirs. DeBartolo Realty Corp., Youngstown, 1994—; bd. dirs. Ralphs Supermarkets, Inc., Compton, Calif. Bd. dirs. Heritage Manor, 1995—; investment com. Youngstown Fedn. Jewish Agencies, 1992—. Mem. ABA, Urban Land Inst. (assoc.), Internat. Coun. Shopping Ctrs. (trustee 1992—, exec. com. 1993—). Office: DeBartolo Realty Corp PO Box 3287 7620 Market St Youngstown OH 44512-6078

SOKOLOW, MAURICE, physician, educator; b. N.Y.C., May 19, 1911; s. Alexander and Anna (Spiegelman) S.; m. Ethel Schwabacher, June 30, 1941 (dec. 1970); children: Gail Anne, Jane Carol (dec.), Anne May. A.B. cum laude, U. Calif., Berkeley, 1932; M.D., U. Calif., San Francisco, 1936. Intern San Francisco Gen. Hosp., 1935-36; resident U. Calif., San Francisco, 1936-37, research fellow, 1939-40; resident New Eng. Med. Ctr., Boston, 1937-38; research fellow Michael Reese Hosp., Chgo., 1938-39; gen. practice medicine San Francisco, 1946-62; mem. faculty cardiovascular div. Sch. Medicine, U. Calif., San Francisco, 1946—, assoc. prof. medicine, 1952-58, prof. 1958-78, prof. emeritus, 1978—, chief electrocardiograph dept., chief hypertension clinic, 1946-78, chief cardiovascular div., 1954-73; program and founding dir. cardiology tng. grant USPHS, San Francisco, 1960-73; sr. mem. Cardiovascular Rsch. Inst., 1957—; cons. in field. Author: Clinical Cardiology; Contbr. articles to med. jours., texts.; mem. editorial bd.: Jour. Cardiovascular Medicine, 1975—, Western Jour. Medicine, 1946-68. Bd. dirs. Fromm Inst Life Long Learning, U. San Francisco. Served to lt. comdr. M.C. USN, 1942-46. Nat. Heart Inst. grantee, 1950-78; named U Calif. San Francisco Alumnus of Yr., 1986. Fellow Am. Coll. Cardiology (hon.); mem. Am. Fedn. Clin. Research (v.p. 1948-49), Assn. Univ. Cardiologists, Am. Soc. Clin. Investigation, Brit. Cardiac Soc. (corr.), Am. Heart Assn., San Francisco Heart Assn. (pres. 1950-51). Club: Menlo Circus. Home: 3452 Jackson St San Francisco CA 94118-2021 Office: U Calif San Francisco CA 94143

SOKOLSKY, ROBERT LAWRENCE, journalist, entertainment writer; b. Boston, May 18, 1928; s. Henry and Lillian (Gorodetzky) S.; m. Sally-Ann Moss, Aug. 11, 1955; 1 son, Andrew E. A.B., Syracuse (N.Y.) U., 1950. Reporter Springfield (Mass.) Union, 1950; asst. dir. pub. info. ARC, Syracuse, 1952-54; entertainment editor Syracuse Herald-Jour., 1954-61, Buffalo Courier Express, 1961-72, Phila. Bull., 1972-82; entertainment writer Riverside (Calif.) Press-Enterprise, 1983—; syndicated TV columnist Ottaway News Svc., 1988—; radio show host; freelance writer; guest lectr. Contbr. articles to profl. jours. Bd. dirs. Brush Hollow Civic Assn., Evesham Twp., N.J. Served with U.S. Army, 1950-52. Recipient Sigma Delta Chi award for feature writing, 1950, award for entertainment coverage Twin Counties Press Club, 1984, 87. Mem. Am. Newspaper Guild (Page One award for opinion writing), Syracuse Press Club, Greater Buffalo Press Assn., TV Critics Assn., Soc. Profl. Journalists (Excellence in Journalism award 1989, 93), Pen and Pencil Club of Phila., Variety Club. Republican. Jewish. Home: 3080 Saratoga St Riverside CA 92503-5435 Office: Riverside Press-Enterprise 3512 14th St Riverside CA 92501-3814

SOLA, JURE, electronics executive. BSEE, San Jose State U., 1972. Various mgmt. positions Lika Corp., Stockton, Calif., 1972-80; with Sanmina Corp. and predecessor, 1980—, now pres. Office: Sanmina Corp 2121 Otoole Ave San Jose CA 95131-1336*

SOLAITA, TULAFONO FULI, senator; b. Aug. 18, 1918; s. Leopeni Solaita and Soia (Solaita) Levu; children: Milovale, Tulafono, Taualai, Tolia, Peni, Charmaine. Commd. ensign USMC, 1941, advanced 2700 grades to sgt. Min. Meth. ch. Democrat. Office: PO Box 485 Pago Pago AS 96799

SOLANA MORALES, FERNANDO, diplomat, financier, educator; b. Mexico City, Feb. 8, 1931; s. Fernando and Concepcion (Morales) S. Grad. in polit. sci., Nat. U. Mex., 1964. Dir. Mañana weekly mag., 1957-66; prof. polit. sci., pub. adminstrn. and fin. Nat. U. Mex., 1962-77, vice chancellor, 1966-70; fin. dir. Conasupo, 1970-76; pres. bd., 1976-77; minister of commerce, 1976-77, of edn., 1977-82; pres., chief exec. officer Banco Nacional de Méx., 1982-88; minister fgn. rels., Mexico City, 1988-94; min. education, Mexico City, 1994—; pres. bd. dirs. Inst. Mexicano Comercio Exterior, Banco Nat. Comercio Exterior, 1976-77; mem. com. public adminstrn. Secretariat Presidency, 1964-70; cons. to govt. and industry. Author: editor: History of Public Education in Mexico, 1981, Tan Lejos Como Llegue la Educación, 1982, Theory of Public Administration, 1984; others; essays, articles in field. Chmn. bd. El Colegio de Mex., Inst. Nacional de Antropología e Historia, 1977-82. Mem. Mexican Nat. Inst. Pub. Adminstrn. Found. Javier Barros Sierra, Consejo Consultivo Inst. Estudios Políticos, Econs. y Sociales del Partido Revolucionario Instl., Am. Polit. Sci. Assn., Am. Soc. Public Adminstrn., Asociación Mexicana de Bancos (pres. 1987-88). Office: Secretariat Public Education, Ave República de Argentina 28, 06029 Mexico City Mexico

SOLANO, CARL ANTHONY, lawyer; b. Pittston, Pa., Mar. 26, 1951; s. Nick D. and Catherine A. (Occhiato) S; m. Nancy M. Solano, 1989; 1 child, Melanie A. BS magna cum laude, U. Scranton, 1973; JD cum laude, Vilanova U., 1976. Bar: Pa. 1976, U.S. Dist. Ct. (ea. dist.) Pa. 1978, U.S. Ct. Appeals (3rd cir.) 1980, U.S. Ct. Appeals (5th cir.) 1981, U.S. Supreme Ct. 1982, U.S. Ct. Appeals (9th cir.) 1986, U.S. Dist. Ct. (mid. dist.) Pa. 1988, U.S. Ct. Appeals (6th cir.) 1988, U.S. Ct. Appeals (Fed. cir.) 1989. Law clerk Hon. Alfred L. Luongo U.S. Dist. Ct., Ea. Dist. Pa., Phila., 1976-78; assoc. Schnader, Harrison, Segal & Lewis, Phila., 1978-84, ptnr., 1985—. Mem. ABA, Am. Law Inst., Pa. Bar Assn. (statutory law com. 1980—), Phila. Bar Assn., St. Thomas More Soc., Justinian Soc., Order of Coif, Pi Gamma Mu. Roman Catholic. Home: 5 Barrister Ct Haverford PA 19041-1137 Office: Schnader Harrison Segal & Lewis 1600 Market St Ste 3600 Philadelphia PA 19103-7236

SOLAR, RICHARD LEON, banker; b. Boston, Aug. 15, 1939; s. Hervey L. and Mildred (Beckerman) S.; m. Stephanie Bennett; children: Andrew, Lisa. BA, Harvard U., 1961; MBA, Columbia U., 1963. Asst. v.p. Bankers Trust Co., N.Y.C., 1963-71; treas. Val D'Or Inds., N.Y.C., 1971-74, Diamondhead Corp., Mountainside, N.J., 1974-75, mng. dir., 1984—; sr. v.p. Bankers Trust Co., N.Y.C., 1975-84 ; chmn., dir. Bankers Trust Comml. Corp., 1983-90. Mem. Nat. Comml. Fin. Assn. (chmn., dir.). Club: Wyantenuck Country (Great Barrington, Mass.). Office: Bankers Trust Co 14 Wall St New York NY 10006

SOLARI, LARRY THOMAS, manufacturing company executive; b. Stockton, Calif., July 30, 1942; s. John Fredrich and Elizabeth (Rubino) S.; m. Patricia Harlan, Feb. 5, 1966 (div. May 1978); m. Deirdre Duff, Apr. 9, 1980; children: Chris, Ryan, Erin, Brad. BS, San Jose State U., 1965, MBA, 1966. Mfg. trainee Owens Corning Fiberglas, Santa Clara, Calif., 1966-67; salesman Owens Corning Fiberglas, San Francisco, 1967-69; product mgr. Owens Corning Fiberglas, Toledo, 1970-73, mktg. mgr., 1974-78, gen. mgr., v.p., 1979-84, operating v.p., 1985-88, assoc. products group, 1989—; mem. adv. bd. U. Toledo, 1983—, CAE Ltd., 1984-87, bd. dirs. Vitro Fibras, Mex.; pres. bd. dirs. Thermal Insulation Mfrs. Assn. Chmn. bd. dirs. Jr. Achievement, Toledo, 1987—, pres. 1986. Served with U.S. Army, 1966-72. Named Outstanding Young Man in Am., 1971. Republican. Roman Catholic. Home: 105 Secor Woods Ln Perrysburg OH 43551-2749 Office: Owens Corning Fiberglas Corp Fiberglas Tower Toledo OH 43659

SOLARI, R. C., heavy construction company executive; b. 1925; married. With Granite Construction Co., 1946—; formerly pres.; now pres., chief exec. officer, dir. Granite Construction Co., Watsonville, Calif. Office: Granite Constrn Co PO Box 50085 Watsonville CA 95077-5085

SOLARZ, STEPHEN JOSHUA, congressman; b. N.Y.C., Sept. 12, 1940; s. Sanford and Ruth (Fertig) S.; m. Nina Koldin, Feb. 5, 1967; children: Randy, Lisa. B.A., Brandeis U., 1962; M.A., Columbia U., 1967. Mem. N.Y. State Assembly from 45th Dist., 1968-74; mem. 94th through 102nd Congresses from 13th Dist. N.Y., 1975—; Fgn. Affairs Com.; chmn. Fgn. affairs subcom. on Asian and Pacific affairs; mem. Merchant Marine and Fisheries Com., Joint Econ. Com., Permanent Select Com. on Intelligence; Congl. del. UN Gen. Assembly, 1983; past faculty Bklyn. Coll., City U. N.Y. Past nat. affairs editor: Newsfront; past assoc. editor: Greater Philadelphia. Mem. Governing Council Am. Jewish Congress; trustee Brandeis U. Democrat. Office: US Ho of Reps 1536 Longworth House Office Bl Washington DC 20515*

SOLBERG, ELIZABETH TRANSOU, public relations executive; b. Dallas, Aug. 10, 1939; d. Ross W. and Josephine V. (Perkins) Transou; m. Frederick M. Solberg, Jr., Mar. 8, 1969; 1 son, Frederick W. BJ, U. Mo., 1961. Reporter, Kansas City (Mo.) Star, 1963-70, asst. city editor, 1970-73; reporter spl. events, documentaries Sta. WDAF-TV, Kansas City, Mo., 1973-74; prof. dept. journalism Park Coll., Kansas City, Mo., 1975-76, advisor, 1976-79; mng. ptnr. Fleishman-Hillard, Inc., Kansas City, Mo., from 1979, now exec. v.p., sr. ptnr., gen. mgr. Kansas City br. Mem. Kansas City Commn. Planned Indsl. Expansion Authority, 1974-91; mem. long-range planning com. Heart of Am. council Boy Scouts Am., 1980-82, bd. dirs., 1986-89; mem. Clay County (Mo.) Devel. Commn., 1979-88; bd. govs. Citizens Assn., 1975—; mem. exec. com. bd. Kansas City Area Devel. Coun.; trustee Pembroke Hill Sch., U. Kansas City. Recipient award for contbn. to mental health Mo. Psychiat. Assn., 1973. Mem. Pub. Relations Soc. Am. (nat. honors and awards com., co-chmn. Silver Anvil com. 1983, Silver Anvil award 1979-82, chair nat. membership com. 1989-91), Counselor's Acad. (exec. com.), Mo. C. of C. Pub. Relations Council, Greater Kans. City C. of C. (vice chair 1994), Pi Beta Phi. Clubs: Jr. League, Kansas City, Carriage, Central Exchange. Office: Fleishman Hillard Inc 2405 Grand Blvd Ste 700 Kansas City MO 64108-2519

SOLBERG, JAMES JOSEPH, industrial engineering educator; b. Toledo, May 27, 1942; s. Archie Norman and Margaret Jean (Olsen) S.; m. Elizabeth Alice Snow, May 28, 1966; children: Kirsten Kari, Margaret Elizabeth. BA, Harvard U., 1964; MA, U. Mich., 1967, MS, 1967, PhD, 1969. Asst. prof. U. Toledo, 1969-71; assoc. prof. Purdue U., West Lafayette, Ind., 1971-81, prof., 1981—; dir. engring rsch. ctr., 1986—. Author: Operations Research, 1976 (Book of the Yr. 1977); contbr. over 100 articles to profl. jours. Mem. NAE, Inst. Indsl. Engrs. (Disting. Rsch. award 1982), Soc. Mfg. Engrs., AAAS. Achievements include invention of CAN-Q which is a method for predicting performance of manufacturing systems used by hundreds of companies. Office: Purdue U Sch Industrial Engineering West Lafayette IN 47907-1287*

SOLBERG, LOREN ALBIN, state legislator, secondary education educator; b. Blackduck, Minn., Nov. 3, 1941; s. Albin Andy and Mabel Ethel (Bergen) S.; m. Joan Maxine Olsen, Aug. 9, 1969; children: Sean, John, Previn, Kjirstin. BS, Bemidji (Minn.) State U., 1965, MS, 1974; MPA, Harvard U., 1990. Tchr. math. Ind. Sch. Dist. 316, Coleraine, Minn., 1965—; mem. Minn. Ho. of Reps., St. Paul, 1983—; instr. math. Itasca C.C., Grand Rapids, Minn., 1981-83; instr. computer sci. Harvard U., Cambridge, Mass., 1988. Mayor City of Bovey, Minn., 1970-82. Democrat. Lutheran. Home: PO Box 61 Bovey MN 55709-0061 Office: Minn Ho of Reps State Office Bldg Saint Paul MN 55155

SOLBERG, MYRON, food scientist, educator; b. Boston, June 11, 1931; s. Alexander and Ruth (Graff) S.; m. Rona Mae Bernstein, Aug. 26, 1956; children: Sara Lynn, Julie Sue, Laurence Michael. BS in Food Tech, U. Mass., 1952; PhD, MIT, 1960. Commd. 2d lt. USAF, 1952, advanced through grades to lt. col., 1971, ret.; cons. to food industry, 1956-60, 64—; mem. rsch. staff food tech. MIT, 1954-60; quality control mgr. Colonial Provision Co., Inc., Boston, 1960-64; sci. editor Meat Processing mag., Chgo., 1968-69; mem. faculty Rutgers U., 1964—, prof. food sci., 1970—, dir. Ctr. for Advanced Food Tech., 1984—; UN expert on food product quality control, 1973-74; vis. prof. Technion, Israel Inst. Tech., Haifa, 1973-74. Co-editor Jour. Food Safety, 1977-88; contbr. articles to profl. jours. Pres. Highland Park (N.J.) Bd. Health, 1971-72. Recipient numerous research grants. Fellow AAAS, Am. Chem. Soc., Inst. Food Technologists (pres. N.Y. sect. 1971-72, Food Scientist of Yr. N.Y. sect. award 1981, Nicholas Appert award 1990); mem. Am. Soc. Microbiology, Am. Soc. Quality Control, Am. Meat Sci. Assn., N.Y. Acad. Scis., N.J. Acad. Sci. Home: 415 Grant Ave Highland Park NJ 08904-2705 Office: Rutgers U Nabisco Advanced Food New Brunswick NJ 08903

SOLBERG, NELLIE FLORENCE COAD, artist; b. Sault Ste. Marie, Mich.; d. Sanford and Mary (McDonald) Coad; m. Ingvald Solberg, Aug. 24, 1930; children: Jeanine Elaine Solberg Unruh, Walter Eugene, Kay Louise Solberg Link. BA, Minot State U., 1930; MA, N.D. State U., 1963; postgrad. Wash. State U., 1960, U. Wyo., 1964, St. Cloud Coll., 1971. Tchr. Bismarck Elem. Schs., N.D., 1954-63, art dir. high sch., 1963-72; instr. art Bismarck Jr. Coll., 1964-67; cons. Bismarck Art Assn. Galleries, 1973-79, State Capitol Galleries, 1973-78; dir. arts festivals including Statewide Religious Arts Festival, Bismarck, 1969-85, State Treas.'s Gallery, 1977, N.D. State Capitol, Bismarck, 1973-78; co-dir. Indian Art Show, Nat. Congress Am. Indians, Bismarck, 1963. Artist: (print) Prairie Rose for N.D. centennial, 1989; onewoman shows include Minot State Coll., 1963, Dickinson State Coll., 1964, Jamestown Coll., 1964, U. N.D., Valley City State Coll., Bismarck Jr. Coll., 1963, 65, 68, 69, N.D. State U., 1970, 74, Linha Gallery, Minot N.D., 1972, 74-77, Bank of N.D., 1972-74, 76-77, Elan Gallery, 1982; exhibited in group shows at Gov. John Davis Mansion, 1960, Concordia Coll., Moorhead, Minn., 1965, N.D. Capitol, 1968, 69, Internat. Peace Gardens, 1969, Gov. William Guy Mansion, 1971, Gov. George Sinner Mansion, 1991. Mem. Indian Culture Found., 1964—; Civic Music Assn., 1942-89; works included in numerous pvt. collections U.S., Can., Europe; religious arts com. Conf. Chs., 1973; bd. dirs. Citizens for Arts, 1978-81; mem. The Statue of Liberty/Ellis Island Found., 1984-89. Recipient numerous awards including Gov.'s award for arts, 1977, Gov. Allen Olson award, 1982, Gov.'s award Bismarck Art Show, 1982, Dakota Northwestern Bank award, 1983, Dr. Shari Orser Purchase award Religious Arts Festival, 1984, William Murray award Religious Arts Festival, 1984, Mandan Art Assn. award, 1986, 18th ann. 3d prize weaving Festival of Arts, 1987, Dr. Cy Rinkel watercolor purchase award, 1987, Heritage Centennial Art award Heritage Arts, Inc., 1988; named N.D. Woman Artist of Yr., 1974, Heritage Centennial award, 1989; the New Visual Arts Gallery named the Children's Gallery in name of Nellie Solberg; Mem. Bismarck Arts and Galleries Assn. (membership com., mem. Gallery 522, mem. Visual Arts Ctr.), Bismarck Art Assn. (charter, Honor award 1960, pres. 1963-64, 71-72), Jamestown Art Assn., Linha Gallery (Minot), Nat. League Am. Pen Women (pres. N.D. 1964-66, pres. Medora br. 1972-74, treas. 1975-86), Mpls. Soc. Fine Arts, P.E.O. (pres. chpts. 1967-69), Bismarck Vets., Meml. Library (life), Soc. Preservation Gov.'s Mansion (charter, bd. dirs.), Women in the Arts Nat. Mus. (charter), Zonta, Order of Ea. Star, Sigma Sigma Sigma. Republican. Home: 925 N 6th St Bismarck ND 58501-3922

SOLBERG, NORMAN ROBERT, lawyer; b. Toledo, Aug. 28, 1939; s. Archie Norman and Margaret Jane (Olsen) S.; BA, Columbia Coll., 1961; LLB, Columbia U., 1964; postgrad. Parker Sch. Fgn. and Comparative Law, 1969; m. Susan Radcliffe Riley, Oct. 7, 1961; children: Eric Norman, Anne Olsen. Bar: N.Y. 1964, Mass. 1973, Mo. 1978, Ill. 1984. Japan 1992. Assoc. firm Wickes, Riddell, Bloomer, Jacobi & McGuire (now Morgan, Lewis & Bockius), N.Y.C., 1964-69; sr. atty. The Gillette Co., Boston, 1969-75; asst. internat. counsel Monsanto Co., St. Louis, 1975-79; sr. staff counsel Household Internat. Inc., Prospect Heights, Ill., 1979-87; v.p. gen. counsel Alberto-Culver Co., Melrose Park, Ill., 1987-89; pvt. practice, 1989—. Mem. ABA (chmn. law dept. mgmt., corps. and profl. matters, com. on corp. counsel 1983-93, chmn. Asia-Pacific law, internat. bus. law com. 1992-93, sect. bus. law), Ill. Bar Assn., Chgo. Bar Assn. Republican. Lutheran.

Home: 803 Bluff St Glencoe IL 60022-1506 Office: Maison D'Or Michino Ste 901, 2-31 Kanzakicho Chuo-ku, Osaka 540, Japan

SOLBERG, RONALD LOUIS, investment manager, international economist; b. Madison, Wis., May 15, 1953; s. Carl Louis and Gladys Irene Evelyn (Oen) S.; m. Anna Maria Teresa Gorgol, May 16, 1983 (div. Aug. 1992). BA in Econs. with honors, U. Wis., 1975; MA, U. Calif., Berkeley, 1977, PhD, 1984. Country risk analyst Wells Fargo Bank, San Francisco, 1978-79; asst. v.p., economist Wells Fargo Ltd., London, 1979-81; cons. RAND Corp., Santa Monica, Calif., 1982-84; acting instr. econs. U. Calif., Berkeley, 1983; 1st v.p., portfolio risk policy mgr. Security Pacific Corp., L.A., 1984-92; internat. fin. cons., 1992-94; v.p., fixed-income credit rschr. Pacific Investment Mgmt. Co., 1994—; adj. asst. prof. U. So. Calif., L.A., 1985-92. Author: (monograph with G. Grossman) The Soviet Union's Hard-Currency Balance of Payments and Creditworthiness in 1985, 1983; (book) Sovereign Rescheduling: Risk and Portfolio Management, 1988, Country Risk Analysis, 1992; contbr. articles to profl. jours. Research fellow Inst. Internat. Studies, Berkeley, 1982-84. Mem. Am. Econ. Assn., Asia Soc., Nat. Assn. for Bus. Economists, Soc. for Internat. Devel. Avocations: fly fishing, cross-country skiing, squash, billiards. Home: 765 Avacado Ave Corona Del Mar CA 92625 Office: PO Box 9000 840 Newport Center Dr Newport Beach CA 92658-9030

SOLBERG, WINTON UDELL, history educator; b. Aberdeen, S.D., Jan. 11, 1922; s. Ole Alexander and Bertha Georgia (Tschappat) S.; m. Ruth Constance Walton, Nov. 8, 1952; children: Gail Elizabeth, Andrew Walton, Kristin Ruth. A.B. magna cum laude, U. S.D., 1943, LHD (hon.), 1987; student, Biarritz (France) Am. U., 1946; A.M., Harvard, 1947, Ph.D., 1954. Instr., then asst. prof. social scis. U.S. Mil. Acad., 1951-54; instr., then asst. prof. history Yale U., 1954-58; fellow Pierson Coll., 1955-58, Morse fellow, 1958; James Wallace prof. history Macalester Coll., 1958-62; vis. prof. U. Ill., 1961-62, assoc. prof. history, 1962, prof., 1967—, chmn. dept. history, 1970-72; research fellow Ctr. Study History of Liberty in Am., Harvard U., 1962-63; summer research scholar Henry E. Huntington Library, San Marino, Calif., 1959; dir. Coe Found. Am. Studies Inst., summers 1960-62; lectr., cons. Army War Coll., 1959-62; lectr. U.S. Command and Gen. Staff Sch., 1963-64; Fulbright lectr. Johns Hopkins U. Bologna, 1967-68, Moscow (USSR) State U., 1978, U. Calcutta India, 1993; vis. prof. Konan U., Kobe, Japan, 1981; USIA Lectr., Korea and Malaysia, 1985, Korea, 1992. Author: The Federal Convention and the Formation of the Union of the American States, 1958, The Constitutional Convention and the Formation of the Union, 1990, The University of Illinois, 1867-1894, 1968, Redeem the Time: The Puritan Sabbath in Early America, 1977, History of American Thought and Culture, 1983, Cotton Mather, The Christian Philosopher, 1994; also articles. Mem. Ill. Humanities Council, 1973-75; sec. Council on Study of Religion, 1981-85. Served to maj. inf. AUS, 1943-46, 51-54; lt. col. U.S. Army Res. Recipient Faculty Achievement award Burlington No. Found., 1986, Disting. Teaching award U. Ill. Coll. Liberal Arts and Scis., 1988; NEH sr. fellow, 1974-75; NSF research grantee, 1981-82. Mem. Am. Hist. Assn., So. Hist. Assn., Orgn. Am. Historians, Am. Studies Assn. (pres. Mid-Am. 1985-86), Am. Soc. Ch. History (pres. 1985-86), AAUP (chpt. pres. 1965-66, mem. council 1969-72, 1st v.p. 1974-76), Phi Beta Kappa. Episcopalian. Home: 8 Lake Park Rd Champaign IL 61821-7101 Office: U Ill Dept History Urbana IL 61801

SOLBRIG, INGEBORG HILDEGARD, German literature educator, author; b. Weissenfels, Germany, July 31, 1923; came to U.S., 1961, naturalized, 1966; d. Reinhold J. and Hildegard M.A. (Ferchland) S. Grad. in chemistry, U. Halle, Germany, 1948; BA summa cum laude, San Francisco State U., 1964; postgrad., U. Calif., Berkeley, 1964-65; MA, Stanford U., 1966, PhD in Humanities and German, 1969; PhD, U. R.I. Grad. Asst. prof. U. R.I., 1969-70, U. Tenn., Chattanooga, 1970-72, U. Ky., Lexington, 1972-75; assoc. prof. German U. Iowa, 1975-81, prof., 1981-93, prof. emerita, 1993—. Author: Hammer-Purgstall und Goethe, 1973; editor and translator (bilingual edit.) Rilke Heute, Beziehungen und Wirkungen, 1975, Reinhard Goering: Seeschlacht/Seabattle, 1977, Orient-Rezeption, 1995; contbr. numerous articles, rev. and translations to profl. jours., chpts. to books. Mem. Iowa Gov.'s Com. on 300th Anniversary German-Am. Rels. 1683-1983, 1983. Recipient Hammer-Purgstall Gold medal Austria, 1974; named Ky. col., 1975; fellow Austrian Ministry Edn., 1968-69, Stanford U., 1965-66, 68-69; Old Gold fellow U. Iowa, 1977; Am. Coun. Learned Socs. grantee; German Acad. Exch. Svc. grantee, 1980; sr. faculty rsch. fellow in the humanities, 1983; NEH grantee, 1985; May Brodbeck fellow in the humanities, 1989; numerous summer faculty rsch. grants. Mem. MLA (life), Internat. Verein fur Germanische Sprach und Lit. Wiss., Goethe Gesellschaft, Deutsche Schiller Gesellschaft, Am. Soc. for 18th Century Studies, Can. Soc. for 18th Century Studies, Goethe Soc. N.Am., Inc. (founding mem.), Internat. Herder Soc. Prin. Rsch. Interest: contract of eastern and western cultures. Prin. rsch. interest: contact of eastern and western cultures, 17th century to present. Avocation: English and Western styles horseback riding. Home: 30 Rolens Dr A3 Kingston RI 02881 The circumstances of my life took me to many places and cultures. Despite the discord and problems plaguing many parts of this planet, let us not forget that it's the home of the human family, our home.

SOLBRIG, OTTO THOMAS, population biologist, educator; b. Buenos Aires, Argentina, Dec. 21, 1930; came to U.S. 1956; s. Hans Joachim and Rose Mabel (Mugglewroth) S.; m. Dorothy Jane Crosswhite, June 21, 1969; children: Hans Joseph, Heide Frances. PhD, U. Calif., Berkeley, 1959; MA (hon.), Harvard U., 1969. Rsch. asst. U. La Plata, Argentina, 1951-54; teaching asst. U. Calif., Berkeley, 1956-59; prof. U. Mich., Ann Arbor, 1965-69; curator Harvard U., Cambridge, Mass., 1959-66, prof., 1969—; vis. rschr. Carnegie Inst., Stanford, Calif., 1975-76; vis. prof. U. Los Andes, Merida, Venezuela, 1983-84; cons. UNESCO, Paris, 1990-91. Author, editor 17 books; contbr. over 200 articles to profl. jours. Recipient Cooley prize AAPT, 1961, Congl. medal U.S. Congress, 1966, Wildenow medal Berlin Bot. Garden, 1970; Guggenheim fellow, 1974; Silver medal U. Complutense of Madrid; named Academician, Am. Acad. Arts and Scis., 1977. Mem. Internat. Union Biol. Scis. (pres. 1983-92), Soc. Study Evolution (pres., sec. 1976-79), Sigma Xi (sec.-trea.). Office: Harvard Univ 22 Divinity Ave Cambridge MA 02138

SOLDATOS, PAUL W., holding company executive; b. 1950. BA, U. Wis.; MBA, U. Pa. With Chase Manhattan Bank, N.Y.C., 1974-81, Mfrs. Hanover Bank, N.Y.C., 1981-88, Investcorp Internat. Inc., 1988—; with Saks Holding Inc., N.Y.C., now pres. Office: Saks Holdings Inc 280 Park Ave Fl 37W New York NY 10017-1216

SOLDNER, PAUL EDMUND, artist, ceramist, educator; b. Summerfield, Ill.; s. Grover and Beulah (Geiger) S.; m. Virginia I. Geiger, June 15, 1947; 1 child, Stephanie. BA, Bluffton Coll., 1946; MA, U. Colo., 1954; MFA, L.A. County Art Inst., 1956; DFA (hon.), Westminster Coll., 1992. Tchr. art Medina (Ohio) County Schs., 1946-47; supr. art, asst. county supr. Wayne County Schs., Wooster, Ohio, 1951-54; tchr. adult edn. Wooster Coll., 1952-54; vis. asst. prof. ceramics Scripps Coll., 1957-66, prof., 1970-91, prof. emeritus, 1991—; prof. Claremont (Calif.) Grad. Sch., 1957-66, prof., 1970-92; prof. U. Colo., Boulder, 1966-67, U. Iowa, Iowa City, 1967-68; pres. Soldner Pottery Equipment, Inc., Aspen, Colo., 1956-77; mem. steering com. Internat. Sch. Ceramics, Rome, 1965-77; advisor Vols. for Internat. Assistance, Balt., 1966-75; craftsman, trustee Am. Craft Coun., N.Y.C., 1970-74, trustee emeritus, 1976-77; dir. U.S. sect. World Craft Coun., 1970-74; dir. Anderson Ranch Ctr. for Hand Art Sch., 1974-76; speaker 6th Internat. Ceramics Symposium Syracuse, 1989; participant Internat. Russian Artists Exchange Program, Riga, Latvia, 1989; cons. in field. Author: Kilns and Their Construction, 1965, Raku, 1964, Paul Soldner, A Retrospective View, 1991; contbr. articles to profl. jours.; subject of 5 films; 156 one-man shows including Cantini Mus. Modern Art, Marseille, France, 1981, Thomas Segal Gallery, Boston, 1982, Elements Gallery, N.Y., 1983, Louis Newman Gallery, L.A., 1985, Susan Cummins Gallery, Mill Valley, Calif., 1989, Great Am. Gallery, Atlanta, 1986, Patricia Moore Gallery, Aspen Colo., 1987, Coleg Prifysgol Cymru, Aberystwyth, Wales, 1987, Joan Hodgell Gallery, Sarasota, Fla., 1988, Esther Saks Gallery, Chgo., 1986, 88, El Camino Gallery Art, Toraance, Calif., 1987, San Antonio Art Ctr., San Angelo, Tex., 1988, traveling exhibit, 12 U.S. mus., 1992—; 335 group shows including Nelson-Atkins Mus., Kansas City, Mo., 1983, Los Angeles Mcpl. Art Gallery, 1984, 27th Ceramic Nat. Exhibition, Everson Mus. Art, Syracuse, N.Y.,

1986, Victoria & Albert Mus., London, 1986, Chicago Internat. New Art Forms Exposition, 1986, Hanover Gallery, Syracuse, N.Y., 1987, L.A. County Mus. of Art, 1987, Crain/Wolov Gallery, Tulsa, 1987, Contem Crafts Gallery, Portland, Oreg., 1988, Oakland (Calif.) Art Mus., 1988, Munson Gallery, Santa Fe, 1988, Japanese Influence on Am. Ceramics, Everson Mus., Syracuse, N.Y., 1989, traveling retrospective, 1991-93; hon. vis. artist Shigaraki Ceramic Cultural Park, Japan, 1994; works in permanent collections, Nat. Mus. Modern Art, Kyoto, Japan, Victoria and Albert Mus., London, Smithsonian Instn., Washington, Los Angeles County Mus. Art, Oakland Art Mus., Everson Mus. Art, Syracuse Australian Nat. Gallery, Taipei Fine Arts Mus.; curator Mirror Images Exhibit, Craft Alliance Gallery, St. Louis, 1989. Served with U.S. Army, 1941-46. Decorated Purple Heart; grantee NEA, 1991, Louis Comfort Tiffany Found., 1966, 72, Nat. Endowment for Arts, 1976, Colo. Gov.'s award for the Arts & Humanities, 1975; voted one of Top Twelve Potters World-Wide, Ceramics Monthly mag., 1981; Scripps Coll. Faculty Recognition award, 1985; named Hon. Mem. Coun., Nat. Coun. on Edn. for Ceramic Arts, 1989. Fellow Colleaquim of Craftsmen of the U.S.; mem. Internat. Acad. Ceramics, Nat. Coun. on Edn. for Ceramic Arts. Originator Am. Raku philosophy and techniques in ceramics. Home: PO Box 90 Aspen CO 81612-0090 also: 743 W Baseline Rd Claremont CA 91711

SOLDO, BETH JEAN, demography educator, researcher; b. Binghamton, N.Y., Sept. 30, 1948; d. Frank E. and Ruth E. (Dayton) S.; m. T. Peter Bridge, Sept. 20, 1975. BA, Fordham U., 1970; MA, Duke U., 1973, PhD, 1977. Asst. dir. Ctr. Demographic Studies Duke U., Durham, N.C., 1974-77; sr. rsch. scholar Ctr. Population Rsch. Georgetown U., Washington, 1977-86, sr. rsch. fellow Kennedy Inst. Ethics, 1978—, assoc. prof. demography, 1985-92, prof., 1992—, dept. chair, 1986-95; cons. White House Conf. on Aging, Washington, 1984-86, U. Mich. Health and Retirement Survey, Survey Asset and Health Dynamics of Oldest-Old; mem. com. on population NRC/NAS. Co-author: (with R.J. Struyk) Improving the Elderly's Housing: A Key to Preserving the Nation's Housing Stock and Neighborhoods, 1980; contbr. articles to profl. jours. and chpts. in books. Grantee Atlantic Richfield Found., 1984, Commonwealth Fund, 1984-85, Retirement Rsch. Found., 1986-88, competitive grantee Nat. Inst. on Aging, 1986—. Fellow Gerontol. Soc. Am.; mem. Am. Sociol. Assn., Population Assn. Am. (bd. dirs. 1990-92). Office: Georgetown U Dept Demography 233 Poulton Washington DC 20057

SOLE, MICHAEL JOSEPH, cardiologist; b. Timmins, Ont., Can., Mar. 5, 1940; s. Fred and Lillian Sole; m. Susan Karen Samuels, May 26, 1964; children: David Frederick, Leslie Meredith. BSc, U. Toronto, Ont., Can., 1962, MD, 1966. Cert. Coll. Physicians and Surgeons Ont.; diplomate Am. Bd. Internal Medicine. Rotating intern, jr. asst. resident, sr. asst. resident in internal medicine Toronto Gen. Hosp., 1966-69; cardiology fellow cardiovascular rsch. inst. U. Calif., San Francisco, 1969-71; cardiology fellow Peter Bent Brigham Hosp., Boston, 1971-73; jr. assoc. medicine, 1973-74; rsch. assoc. MIT, Cambridge, 1973-74; instr. medicine Harvard Med. Sch., 1973-74; from asst. to assoc. prof. medicine U. Toronto, 1974-83, prof. medicine and physiology, 1983, mem. staff inst. med. sci., 1978—, dir. cardiology rsch., 1987-89, dir. centre cardiovascular rsch., 1989—; staff cardiologist Toronto Hosp., 1974-89, dir. non-invasive cardiology, 1974-79, dir. cardiology rsch., 1979-89, dir. divsn. cardiology, 1989—, dir. cardiovascular program, 1992-93, dir. cardiac centre, 1993—; vis. prof. Harvard U., 1975, NIH, Bethesda, Md., 1981, U. B.C., 1982, 91, 92, Capital Med. Sch. and Beijing Hosp., 1985, U. Tokyo, 1992, others; mem. Can. Govt. Task Force Diagnostic Ultrasound, 1976-78; vice-chmn. econs. com. dept. medicine Toronto Gen. Hosp., 1977, chmn., 1978, 79, chmn. emeritus, 1980, mem. various coms., 1981—, chmn. cardiology rsch. com., 1988-89, mem. exec. com. Centre Cardiovascular Rsch., 1988—, chmn. sci. com., 1989—, mem. exec. com. cardiovascular rsch. lab., 1992—, chmn. rsch. com., 1992—; Pfizer vis. fellow Clin. Rsch. Inst., Montreal, 1988; mem. sr. adv. com. Toronto Western Hosp., 1989-90; Katz vis. prof. U. Chgo., 1989; mem. provincial working group cardiovascular svcs. Ministry of Health, 1990-91, mem. ctrl. east region cardiovascular patient care mgmt. group, 1990-91; mem. trial devel. com. diabetes atherosclerosis intervention study WHO and Fournier Pharms., 1991-93, mem. trial exec. com., 1993—; mem. Joint Med. Rsch. Coun. Can./Pharm. Mfrs. Assn. Can. Adv. Com. Sci., 1993; mem. organizing coms. various sci. meetings; presenter in field. Mem. editorial bd. Can. Jour. Cardiology, 1988-94, Index and Revs. Congestive Heart Failure, 1988-90, Hypertension Can., 1988-90, European Jour. Pharmacology, 1992—; Cardioscience, 1993, Jour. Heart Failure, 1994—; mem. internat. editorial bd. Cardiology Digest, 1992—; reviewer Can. Jour. Cardiology, New Eng. Jour. Medicine, European Jour. Pharmacology, others; contbr. chpts. to books and articles to profl. jours.; patentee Bis Adducts of Tertiary Alcohols and Disocyanates. Grantee Heart & Stroke Found. Ont., 1969—, Med. Rsch. Coun. Can., 1982-92; Ivan Smith Rsch. fellow U. Toronto, 1964, Hunter fellow Ont. Heart Found., 1973; Walter Watkins scholar U. Toronto, 1962. Fellow Am. Coll. Cardiology (abstract reviewer 1989, 91), Royal Coll. Physicians and Surgeons; mem. Am. Soc. Clin. Investigation, Assn. Am. Physicians, Am. Heart Assn. (fellow couns. clin. cardiology, hypertension, circulation and basic sci., mem. exec., basic sci. coun. 1986-89, mem. Katz prize selection com. 1988-90), Can. Soc. Clin. Investigation,rr Soc. (mem. young investigators award panel 1982-84, mem. student presentation award com. 1988-90, mem. nat. task force cardiovascular sci. 1992-93, Ann. Rsch. award 1975, Rsch. Achievement award 1993), Heart and Stroke Found. Can. (mem. sci. rev. bd. 1976-79, vice-chmn. 1980-83, chmn. hypertension and cardiovascular pharmacology panel 1982-83, chmn. molecular biology, biochemistry, pathology panel 1989-90), Can. Med. Assn. (mem. coun. 1982-87), Am. Fedn. Clin. Rsch., Ont. Med. Assn. (alt. del. Toronto Gen. Hosp. bd. 1988-90), Heart and Stroke Found. Ont. (mem. med. rsch. com. 1978-81, bd. dirs. 1986-92, mem. fin. com. 1986-90, mem. corp. rels. com. 1990-92, mem. rsch. policy com. 1991-93, Disting. Rsch. prof. 1989-96, Murray Robertson Meml. lectr. 1989), Internat. Soc. Heart Rsch. (exec. mem. sect. 1979-88), Banting Rsch. Found. (hon. sec.-treas. 1979-81), Gairdner Found. (mem. rev. panel 1979-94), Alpha Omega Alpha. Office: Toronto Hosp Eaton North 13-208, 200 Elizabeth St, Toronto, ON Canada M5G 2C4

SOLECKI, R. STEFAN, anthropologist, educator; b. Bklyn., Oct. 15, 1917; s. Kazimierz John and Mary (Tarnawski) S.; m. Rose Muriel Lilien, June 24, 1955; children—John Irwin, William Duncan. B.Sc., City Coll. N.Y., 1941; M.A., Columbia, 1950, Ph.D. in Anthropology, 1958. Archaeologist Smithsonian Instn., 1948-54; archaeol. asst. anthropology Columbia U., N.Y.C., 1954-55, mem. faculty, 1959-88, prof. anthropology, 1965-88, prof. emeritus, 1988—, chmn. dept., 1975-78; adj. prof. dept. anthropology Tex. A&M Univ., College Station, 1989—; archaeol. expdn. to Iraq, 1950-51, 53, 56-57 (field dir.), 60, 78; assoc. curator old world U.S. Nat. Mus., 1957-59; archaeol. expdns. to Alaska, 1949, 61, Sudanese Nubia, 1961; Turkey and Syria, 1988, 89; archaeol. expdns. to Iran, 1968, Lebanon, 1969-73, France, 1975, Eastern, Midwestern and Western U.S.; collaborator in archaeology Smithsonian Instn., 1953; cons. UNESCO, 1959. Served with AUS, 1943-45. Fulbright scholar, Iraq, 1952-53; William Bayard Cutting travelling fellow Columbia, 1956-57; Fulbright-Hays faculty research awardee Syria, 1980-81; Fulbright fellow, Iraq, 1988-89. Fellow Am. Anthrop. Assn., Arctic Inst. Am., N.Y. Acad. Scis. (chmn. anthropology sect. 1977-79); mem. N.Y. Archaeol. Assn. (pres. 1960-62), N.Y. Oriental Club (pres. 1965), Profl. Archeologists of N.Y.C. (pres. 1980-81), Soc. Archaeology, Am. Schs. Oriental Research (assoc. trustee 1969-71), Prehistoric Soc., Deutsches Archaeologisches Inst., Soc. Préhistorique Français, Archaeol. Inst. Am. (exec. com. 1968-70), Assn. Field Archaeology Press 1972-74). Home: 500 Crescent Dr Bryan TX 77801-3713 Office: Tex A&M Univ Dept Anthropology College Station TX 77843

SOLEMAN, WILLIAM T., industrial services executive; b. 1942. Degree in Engring., So. Meth. U., 1965; MBA, Harvard U., 1967. With Austin Indsl. Inc., 1967—; now chmn. bd. dirs. Office: Austin Industrial Inc 1495 W Cardinal Dr Beaumont TX 77705-6412*

SOLENDER, ROBERT LAWRENCE, financial and real estate corporation officer; b. Rochester, N.Y., Sept. 1, 1923; s. Samuel S. and Catherine (Goldsmith) S.; m. Ellen Van Raalte Karelsen, Nov. 25, 1948; children: Elizabeth, Jefferson, Katherine. BA, Oberlin Coll., 1943. Asst. to pres. Craven & Hedrick, Inc., N.Y.C., 1946-49; with Dallas Times Herald, 1949-75, v.p., advt. dir., 1964-69, v.p. gen. mgr., 1969-75; prin. Robert L. Solender & Assocs., Dallas, 1975—; mng. ptnr. The Devonshire Co., Dallas, 1978—; interim chmn., CEO, AccuBanc Mortgage Corp., 1992. Pres. Dallas Child Guidance Clinic, 1956, Dallas Assn. Mental Health, 1958, Hope Cottage Children's Bur., 1973—; bd. dirs. Dallas Theatre Center, Child Care Assn. Met. Dallas; trustee Southwestern Med. Found.; mem. adv. council Communities Found. of Tex.; assoc. Dallas Mus. Art; bd. dirs., mem. exec. com. Dallas County United Way, 1973. Served to lt. USNR, 1944-46, PTO. Mem. Dallas C. of C., Park City Club, Masons. Home: 9131 Devonshire Dr Dallas TX 75209-2411 Office: 5600 W Lovers Ln Ste 300 Dallas TX 75209-4319

SOLENDER, SANFORD, social worker; b. Pleasantville, N.Y., Aug. 23, 1914; s. Samuel and Catharine (Goldsmith) S.; m. Ethel Klonick, June 19, 1935; children: Stephen, Peter, Ellen, Susan. BS, NYU, 1935; MS, Columbia U., 1937. Dir. activities Neighborhood House, Bklyn., 1935-36; asst. headworker Bronx House, N.Y., 1936-39; headworker Madison House, N.Y.C., 1939-42; exec. dir. Coun. Ednl. Alliance, Cleve., 1942-48; dir. bur. pers. and tng., also dir. Jewish community ctr. div. Nat. Jewish Welfare Bd., N.Y.C., 1948-60, exec. v.p. bd., 1960-70; exec. v.p. Fedn. Jewish Philanthropies N.Y., 1970-81, exec. cons., 1982—; exec. v.p. United Jewish Appeal Fedn. Campaign, 1975-81; past pres. Nat. Conf. Jewish Communal Svc.; past chmn. planning com. Internat. Conf. Jewish Communal Svc.; chmn. Task Force on N.Y.C. Crisis, 1976-81. Contbr. articles to profl. jours., chpts. in books. Mem. Mt. Vernon Bd. Edn., 1953-58, pres., 1957-58, chmn. sec. HEW's ad hoc. com. to study fed. govt. social welfare programs, 1961; adv. coun. pub. welfare HEW, 1963-65; mem. Gov. Hugh Carey's Task Force on Human Svcs., N.Y. State, 1975; bd. dirs. Lavanburg Corner House, Herman Muehlstein Found.; adv. bd. Brandeis U., Hornstein Program in Jewish Communal Svc.; mem. Md. East Watch, Am.'s Watch coms. bds., Nat. Found. for Jewish Culture, 1985—, Jewish Mus., 1982—, Nat. Jewish Ctr. for Learning and Leadership, 1984—. Named Most Disting. Citizen of Mt. Vernon, 1960; recipient Joseph E. Kappel award Nat. Conf. Jewish Communal Svc., 1968, Florence G. Heller award Nat. Jewish Welfare Bd., 1972. Mem. Nat. Assn. Jewish Ctr. Workers (past pres.), Nat. Conf. Social Welfare (past pres.). Home: 1935 Gulf of Mexico Dr Seaplace G7-107 Longboat Key FL 34228 Office: 130 E 59th St New York NY 10022-1302

SOLENDER, STEPHEN DAVID, philanthropic organization executive; b. N.Y.C., Feb. 25, 1938; s. Sanford L. and Ethel (Klonick) S.; m. Elsa Adelman, June 5, 1960; children: Michael, Daniel. BA, Columbia U., 1960, MS, 1962. Dir. community ctrs., community orgn. and fundraising Am. Jewish Joint Distbn. Com., Geneva, 1969-75, dir. svcs. Muslim and Arab countries, 1969-75; dir. social planning and budgeting Assoc. Jewish Charities and Welfare Fund, Balt., 1975-79, pres., 1979-86; exec. v.p. United Jewish Appeal-Fedn. Jewish Philanthropies N.Y. Inc., N.Y.C., 1986—; mem. profl. adv. com. Brandeis U. Hornstein Ctr., Boston, 1982—; mem. health policy forum United Hosp. Fund, N.Y.C., 1987—; mem. presdl. coun., founding chmn. Human Svcs. Coun. N.Y.C., 1990-93; pres. World Coun. Jewish Communal Svc., 1994—; co-chair Human Svcs. Action Group. Bd. dirs. Jill Fox Meml. Fund, Balt., 1979-86, JCC Assn. N.A., 1984-92; bd. govs. Wurzweiler Sch. Social Work, N.Y.C., 1987—; mem. City of N.Y. Man. Boro Com., United Negro Coll. Fund, 1991—; pres. Internat. Conf. of Jewish Communal Svc., 1994—; mem. nat. adv. bd. Balt. Inst. for Jewish Communal Svc., 1995—. Office: UJA-Fedn NY 130 E 59th St New York NY 10022-1302

SOLER, ARTHUR R., food products executive; b. Sliema, Malta, Feb. 12, 1944; arrived in Can., 1964; s. John and Helen (Parlato) S.; m. E. Elizabeth Baker, Aug. 8, 1970; children: Jonathon, Justine, Juliane. Degree in bus. adminstrn. with honours, Ryerson Polytech. Inst., Toronto, Ont., Can., 1967. Fin. planning supr., internal audit mgr. Proctor & Gamble, Toronto, 1964-70; fin. planning mgr. Warner Lambert, Toronto, 1970-73, product mgr., 1973-75; new product devel. mgr. Warner Lambert, London, 1975-76, Brussels, 1976-77; group product mgr. Warner Lambert, Toronto, 1977-80, mktg. dir., 1980-84, v.p. sales and mktg., 1984-90; pres. Neilson Cadbury Ltd., Toronto, 1990—. Mem. Confectionery Mfrs. Can. (bd. dirs. 1989—). Roman Catholic. Avocations: chess, skiing, tennis. Office: Neilson Cadbury Ltd, 277 Gladstone Ave, Toronto, ON Canada M6J 3L9

SOLERI, PAOLO, architect, urban planner; b. Turin, Italy, June 21, 1919; came to U.S., 1947; m. Corolyn Woods, 1949 (dec. 1982); children: Kristine, Daniela. D.Arch., Turin Poly., 1946; hon. doctorates, Dickinson Coll., Moore Coll. Art, Ariz. State U. Fellowship with Frank Lloyd Wright, Taliesin West, Ariz., 1947-49; pvt. practice Turin and So., Italy, 1950-55; founder Cosanti Found., Scottsdale, Ariz. Major works include Dome House, Cave Creek, Ariz., 1949, Earth House, Scottsdale, Ariz., 1956, Mesa City project, 1958-61, Outdoor Theatre, Inst. Am. Indian Arts, Santa Fe, 1966, Arcosanti (community for 5,000 people), nr. Cordes Junction, Ariz., 1970—, Minds for History Inst., 1986, Via Deliziosa (NEA grantee), 1987; exhbns., Mus. Modern Art, N.Y.C., 1961, Brandeis U., Waltham, Mass., 1964, Corcoran Gallery, Washington, 1970, Space for Peace, 1985, also on tour, Xerox Center, Rochester, N.Y., 1976, Space for Peace Exhbn. at NAD and Pacific Design Ctr., San Diego, 1989; collection Howe Architecture Library, Ariz. State U., Tempe; author 7 books. Recipient Craftsmanship medal AIA, 1963, Silver medal Academie d'Architecture in Paris, 1984, Gold medal World Biennale of Architecture, Sofia, Bulgaria, Utopis award Univ. di Bologna, 1989; Graham Found. fellow, 1962; Guggenheim Found. grantee, 1964-67. Address: Cosanti Found 6433 Doubletree Rd Scottsdale AZ 85253

SOLES, ADA LEIGH, former state legislator, government advisor; b. Jacksonville, Fla., May 19, 1937; d. Albert Thomas and Dorothy (Winter) Wall; B.A., Fla. State U., 1959; m. James Ralph Soles, 1959; children—Nancy Beth, Catherine. Mem. New Castle County Library Adv. Bd., 1975-80, chmn., 1975-77; chmn. Del. State Library Adv. Bd., 1975-78; mem. Del. State Ho. Reps., 1980-92; sr. advisor Gov. of Del., 1993-94. Adminstrv. asst. U. Del. Commn. on Status of Women, 1976-77; acad. advisor U. Del. Coll. Arts and Scis., 1977-92. Mem. LWV (state pres. 1978-80), Phi Beta Kappa, Phi Kappa Phi, Mortar Bd., Alpha Chi Omega. Episcopalian.

SOLES, WILLIAM ROGER, insurance company executive; b. Whiteville, N.C., Sept. 16, 1920; s. John William and Margaret (Watts) S.; m. Majelle Marrene Morris, Sept. 22, 1956 (dec. 1993); children: William Roger, Majelle Janette. B.S. in Commerce, U. N.C., 1947, postgrad., 1956; LLD, Campbell U., 1981. With Jefferson Standard Life Ins. Co., Greensboro, N.C., 1947—, v.p., mgr. securities dept., 1962-64, asst. to pres., 1964-66, exec. v.p., mgr. securities dept., 1966, pres., also dir., 1967-86; chmn., pres., chief exec. officer Jefferson-Pilot Life Ins. Co.; retired, 1993; chmn., pres., chief exec. officer Jefferson-Pilot Corp., retired, 1993. Trustee, past chmn. High Point U.; past chmn. Wesley Long Community Hosp.; trustee, past chmn. Ind. Coll. Fund N.C.; past pres. Bus. Found. of N.C.; bd. dirs. N.C. Ins. Edn. Found. Served with USAAF, 1941-45. Mem. N.C. Citizens for Bus. and Industry (past chmn.), Am. Council Life Ins. (past chmn., dir.), Beta Gamma Sigma. Club: Greensboro Country. Home: 604 Kimberly Dr Greensboro NC 27408-4914 Office: Jefferson-Pilot Corp PO Box 21008 Greensboro NC 27420-1008

SOLET, MAXWELL DAVID, lawyer; b. Washington, May 15, 1948; s. Leo and Pearl (Rose) S.; m. Joanne Marie Tolksdorf, Sept. 27, 1970; children: David Marc, Paul Jacob. AB, Harvard U., 1970, JD, 1974. Bar: Mass. 1974, U.S. Tax Ct. 1976, U.S. Ct. Claims 1976, U.S. Supreme Ct. 1976. Assoc. Gaston Snow & Ely Bartlett, Boston, 1974-79, Mintz, Levin, Cohn, Ferris, Glovsky & Popeo, P.C., Boston, 1979-82; ptnr. Mintz, Levin, Cohn, Ferris, Glovsky & Popeo P.C., 1982—. Mem. Boston Bar Assn. (chmn. tax sect. 1987-89), Nat. Assn. Bond Lawyers (steering com. bond atty.'s workshop 1992-95), Mass. Bar Assn., ABA. Home: 15 Berkeley St Cambridge

MA 02138-3409 Office: Mintz Levin Cohn Ferris Glovsky & Popeo PC One Financial Ctr Boston MA 02111

SOLGANIK, MARVIN, real estate executive; b. Chgo., Nov. 7, 1930; s. Harry and Dora (Fastoff) S.; m. Judith Rosenberg, Sept. 11, 1960; children: Randall, Janet, Robert. B.B.A., Western Res. U., 1952. Real estate broker Cleve., 1950-65, Herbert Laronge Inc., Cleve., 1965-68; sr. v.p. real estate Revco D.S., Inc., Twinsburgh, Ohio, 1968—, corp. dir., 1974—; guest lectr. Cleve. State U., Case Western Res. U., Cuyahoga Community Coll., Ohio No. U., Cleve. Real Estate Bd. Vol. jewish Welfare Fund, Shaker heights, Ohio; chmn. capital and budget coms. Jewish Fedn.; chmn. Agnon Sch. Bldg. Com.; bd. dirs. Bellfair-J.C.B.-Home for Emotionally Disturbed Children. Recipient Appreciation award Am. Soc. Real Estate Appraisers, Akron-Cleve. chpt., 1971. Mem. Nat. Assn. Corp. Real Estate Officers, Internat. Council Shopping Ctrs. Office: D S Revco 1925 Enterprise Pky Twinsburg OH 44087-2207

SOLHEIM, JAMES EDWARD, church executive, journalist; b. Thief River Falls, Minn., May 16, 1939; s. Edward and Verna (Sagmoen) S. BA, St. Olaf Coll., 1961; MDiv, Luther Sem., 1968; MS in Journalism, Columbia U., 1975. Admissions counselor St. Olaf Coll., 1962-67; editor Am. Luth. Ch., Mpls., 1968-74; dir. communications St. Peter's Ch., N.Y.C., 1975-77; editor A.D. mag., N.Y.C., 1977-83, Luth. Ch. in Am., Phila., 1983-88; dir. communications Episcopal Diocese Mass., Boston, 1988-89; news dir. Episcopal Ch. in U.S.A., N.Y.C., 1989—. Bush Found. fellow, 1974. Mem. Assn. Ch. Press (v.p. 1987-89, Merit award 1969-89, Writing fellow 1969), Religious Pub. Rels. Coun. (v.p.), St. Olaf Alumni Assn. (pres.), Sigma Delta Chi. Democrat. Lutheran. Avocation: photography. Home: 168 W 100th St New York NY 10025-5145 Office: Episcopal Ch in USA 815 2nd Ave New York NY 10017-4503

SOLHEIM, WILHELM GERHARD, II, anthropologist, educator; b. Champaign, Ill., Nov. 19, 1924; s. Wilhelm Gerhard and Ragnhild Risty S.; m. Ludy Montenegro, Sept. 10, 1973; children: Gary, Kristina, Valerie, Lisa, Mei Li, Siri, Edwin. Student, U. Wis., 1943, U. Chgo., 1943-44; BS, U. Wyo., 1947; MA, U. Calif., 1949; PhD, U. Ariz., 1959. Mus. preparator Mus. Anthropology, U. Calif., Berkeley, 1947-49; research assoc. Mus. Archaeology and Ethnology, U. Philippines, 1950-54; lectr. U. East, Manila, 1950-52; provincial public affairs officer USIA, Manila, 1953-54; asst. prof. anthropology Fla. State U., Talahassee, 1960-61; mem. faculty dept. anthropology U. Hawaii, Honolulu, 1961—; prof. U. Hawaii, 1967-91, prof. emeritus, 1992—; asso. archaeologist Social Sci. Research Inst., 1963-67, archaeologist, 1967-70, editor, 1976-87; vis. prof. Inst. Advanced Studies, U. Malaya, Kuala Lumpur, Malaysia, 1979-80; v.p. R&D Transpacific Assocs., Guam, 1992; rsch. in Sarawak, The Philippines, 1983, Ea. Indonesia, 1990; dir. Ctr. for S.E. Asian Studies, U. Hawaii, 1986-89; bd. dirs. Austro-Tai Studies Inst., Guam, 1992—. Author: The Archaeology of Central Philippines, 1964, (with Avelino M. Legaspi and Jaime S. Neri) Archaeological Survey in Southeastern Mindanao, 1979; editor Asian Perspectives, 1957-91, Asian and Pacific Archaeology Series, 1967-91; contbr. articles to profl. jours. Trustee Hawaii Found. for History and Humanities, 1964-74, 1st v.p., 1972, 2d v.p., 1974; bd. dirs. Balik Bahay, Inc., Honolulu, 1976-93, pres., 1977-93; mem. Hawaii Com. Humanities, 1978-79. With USAF, 1943-46. Fulbright grantee, 1958-59, 83, 90; NSF grantee, 1963-66, 69-72; NEH fellow, 1967-68; Ford Found. grantee, 1972, 75-76; Vis. Scholar Exchange Program fellow Com. on Scholarly Communication with Peoples Republic of China, 1986. Fellow Philippine Assn. Advancement Sci. (founding); mem. Siam Soc., Société des Etudes Indochinoises, Royal Asiatic Soc. (Malaysian br.), Burma Research Soc., Assam Sci. Soc., Indian Archaeol. soc., Far-Eastern Prehistory Assn. (pres. 1971-76), Indo-Pacific Prehistory Assn. (pres. 1976-80), Sigma Xi, Phi Kappa Phi, Phi Delta Theta. Office: U Hawaii Dept Anthropology 2424 Maile Way Honolulu HI 96822-2223

SOLIDUM, JAMES, finance and insurance counselor; b. Honolulu, Mar. 12, 1925; s. Narciso and Sergia (Yabo) S.; student U. Hawaii, 1949-50; m. Vickie Mayo, Aug. 14, 1954; children: Arlin James, Nathan Francis, Tobi John, Kamomi Teresa. BA, U. Oreg., 1953. Promotional salesman Tongg Pub. Co., 1953-54; editor Fil-Am. Tribune, 1954-55; master planning technician Fed. Civil Service, 1955-57; publs. editor Hawaii Sugar Planters Assn., 1957; field agt. Grand Pacific Life Ins. Co., 1957-59, home office asst., 1959-60, supr., 1960-62, asst. v.p., 1962-64; propr. J. Solidum & Assos., Honolulu, 1964—; pres. Fin. Devel. Inst., 1967—; gen. ptnr. R.Z. Limited Partnership, 1981—; v.p. Grand Pacific Life Ins. Co., 1983-90; bd. dirs. Hawaii Econ. Devel. Corp., 1982-89. Mem. adv. com. Honolulu dist. SBA, 1971-77; bd. advisors Philippine Consulate of Hawaii, 1959. Pres., Keolu Elementary P.T.A., 1960-62; mem. satisfaction com. Hawaii Visitors Bur., 1963-66; chmn. budget and rev. panel IV, Aloha United Fund, 1966-72, bd. dirs., 1971-77, 82-88, chmn. bd., 1984; mem. mgmt. svcs. com., 1977, mem. cen. com., 1977-82, chmn. budget and allocations com., 1982-84, ; chmn. Kamehameha Dist. fin. com. Aloha coun. Boy Scouts Am., 1966; vice chmn. Businessmen's Cancer Crusade, 1965; chmn. Operation Bayanihan, Hawaii Immigration Task Force, 1970; participant Oahu Housing Workshop, State of Hawaii, Hawaii chpt. HUD, 1970; mem. task force on housing and transp. Alternative Econ. Futures for Hawaii, 1973; chmn. Bicentennial Filipiniana, 1976; chmn. SBA Bicentennial Com., 1976; campaign chmn. State Rep. Rudolph Pacarro, 1964-68; mem. exec. com. Campaign for Reelection U.S. Senator Hiram L. Fong, 1970, Gov. William Quinn for U.S. Senate, 1970; Rep. candidate for Hawaii Ho. of Reps., 1972; mem. Rep. Citizens Task Force on Housing, 1973; trustee St. Louis Alumni Found., 1970—; Kuakini Med. Ctr., 1984-86, Palama Settlement, 1975-82, v.p., 1976, treas., 1980-82; bd. mgrs. Windward YMCA, 1964-67; bd. advisers St. Louis High Sch., 1963-64; bd. govs. Goodwill Industries; bd. dirs. Children's Ctr., Inc., 1975-77, Hawaii Multi-Cultural Arts Ctr., 1977-81, treas., 1979; fin. fin. chmn. St. Stephen's Parish Coun., 1974—; bd. dirs. St. Louis Fine Arts Ctr., 1985-88. With U.S. Army, 1945-47. C.L.U. Recipient Man of Year award Filipino C. of C., 1965; cert. of merit Aloha United Fund, 1971; Wisdom mag. honor award, 1974; Outstanding Alumnus honor medal St. Louis High Sch., 1976. Mem. Hawaii State C. of C. (bd. dirs. 1964-67, chmn. legis. com. 1966-67, v.p. 1970, chmn. election judges 1971, mem. ad hoc com. bus.-youth rels. 1970), Filipino C. of C. (past pres., com. chmn.), Am. Soc. CLUs, Honolulu Assn. Life Underwriters (bd. dirs. 1963-66, del. nat. conv. 1967, chmn. life underwriters tng. coun. 1962-67), Hawaii Estate Planning Council, Hawaii Plantation Indsl. Editors Assn. (sec.-treas. 1957), St. Louis Alumni Assn. (bd. dirs. 1964—, chmn. fin. 1969-75, pres. 1976, treas. 1977—), Phi Kappa Sigma. Republican. Roman Catholic. Home: 2622 Waolani Ave Honolulu HI 96817-1362 Office: 225 Queen St Apt 12-a Honolulu HI 96813-4600

SOLIMAN, ANWAR S., restaurant company executive. Chmn. Gilbert/ Robinson, Inc., Kansas City, Mo. Office: Am Restaurant Gp 450 Newport Center Dr Newport Beach CA 92660-7610

SOLINGER, DAVID MORRIS, lawyer; b. N.Y.C., Feb. 17, 1906; s. Morris David and Birdie (Bloch) S.; m. Hope Alva Gimbel, Sept. 16, 1937 (div. Apr. 1978); children: Faith Solinger Sommerfield, Lynn Solinger Stern; m. Betty Ann Besch, Jan. 23, 1979. Student, Oxford U., Eng. 1925; BA, Cornell U., 1926; JD, Columbia U, 1929. Bar: N.Y. 1929. Ptnr. Solinger and Gordon, N.Y.C., 1952-82; ptnr. Solinger, Grosz & Goldwasser, N.Y.C., 1982-87, spl. counsel, 1987-92; former lectr. Practicing Law Inst. Co-author: 1953 Copyright Problems Analyzed; editor, co-author Television Agreements; contbr. articles to various publs. Trustee Am. Fedn. Arts, 1953-92; hon. pres., trustee Whitney Mus. Am. Art, pres., 1966-74, 1974-77; emeritus mem. Cornell U. Coun.; chmn. adv. coun. Herbert F. Johnson Mus. Art, 1973-88, former chmn. com. on collections. Mem. ABA, Assn. of Bar of City of N.Y., N.Y. State Bar Assn., N.Y. County Bar Assn., Fed. Communications Bar Assn., Century Assn., Century Country Club (Purchase, N.Y.), Delray (Fla.) Dunes Club. Home and Office: 33 E 70th St New York NY 10021-4946

SOLIS, HILDA LUCIA, educational administrator, state legislator; b. Los Angeles, Oct. 20, 1957; d. Raul and Juana (Sequiera) S.; m. Sam H. Sayyad, June 26, 1982. BA in Polit. Sci., Calif. State Poly. U., 179; MA in Pub. Adminstrn., U. So. Calif., 1981. Interpreter Immigration and Naturalization Service, Los Angeles, 1977-79; editor in chief Office Hispanic Affairs, The White House, Washington, 1980-81; mgmt. analyst Office Mgmt. and Budget, Washington, 1981-82; field rep. Office Assemblyman Art Torres, L.A., 1982; dir. Calif. Student Opportunity and Access, Whittier, 1982—;

rep. 57th assembly dist. Calif. State Assembly, Sacramento, 1992—; cons. South Coast Consortium, L.A., 1986—; mem. South Coast Ednl. Opportunity Pers. Consortium. Bd. dirs. Calif. Commn. on Status of Women, 1993—; corr. pres. Friendly El Monte (Calif.) Dem. Club, 1986—; mem. credentials com. Calif. Dem. Com., 1987-88; trustee Rio Hondo C.C., 1985—. Recipient Meritorious Svc. award Dept. Def., 1981, Young Careerist award El Monte Bus. and Profl. Women, 1987; fellow Nat. Edn. Inst., Kellogg Found., 1984-85. Mem. Western Assn. Ednl. Opportunity Pers. (sec. bd. dirs. 1986—), Comision Feminil de Los Angeles (bd. dirs. 1983-84, edn. chmn.), Women of Moose. Roman Catholic. Home: 11724 E Roseglen St El Monte CA 91732-1446 Office: Calif Student Opportunity and Access 9401 Painter Ave Whittier CA 90605-2729

SOLIS, JIM, state legislator, lawyer; b. Weslaco, Tex., July 7, 1963; s. Santiago Sr. and Maria (Cobarrubias) S.; m. Erendira Tamez, Dec. 26, 1992. BBA, U. Tex.-Pan Am., Edinburg, 1985; JD cum laude, Thurgood Marshall Sch. Law, Houston, 1989. Ptnr. Law Office of Bello & Solis, Houston, 1989-90; assoc. Law Office of Albert Villegas, Brownsville, Tex., 1990-94; mem. Tex. Ho. of Reps., 1993—; pvt. practice law Harlingen, Tex., 1994—; mem. Tex. Pro Bono Legal Project, Brownsville, 1991—. Recipient Cert. of Appreciation, Tex. Assn. Pub. Employees, 1993, Meritorious awrd Tex. Assn. Chicanos in Higher Edn., 1993, others. Mem. State Bar Tex., Cameron County Bar Assn., Nat. Bar Assn., Mexican-Am. Bar Assn., Mexican-Am. Dems. of Tex. (cert. of honor 1993), Dem. Party Club, Tex. Young Dems., AFL-CIO, Phi Kappa Theta. Roman Catholic. Avocations: tennis, golf, hunting, fishing, music (playing the drums). Address: 910 W Buchanan St Harlingen TX 78550-6611 Office: 1318 E Tyler St Ste A Harlingen TX 78550-7142

SOLIS, JORGE ANTONIO, federal judge; b. 1951. BA, McMurray Coll., 1973; JD, U. Tex., 1976. Clk. Indsl. Accident Bd., 1975-76; asst. criminal dist. atty. U.S. Attys. Office, 1976-81; with Moore & Holloway, 1981-82; criminal dist. atty. U.S. Attys. Office, 1983-87, spl. prosecutor narcotics task force, 1988; judge 350th Dist. Ct., Abilene, Tex., 1991—; fed. judge U.S. Dist. Ct. (no. dist.) Tex., 1991—. Bd. dirs. HRC Drug Abuse Treatment Ctr., Abilene, Tex., 1979—, pres. bd. dirs., 1982-83, Meals on Wheels, 1984—, Abilene (Tex.) Girls Home, 1985—; active Gov. Task Force on Drug Abuse, 1987—. Mem. State Bar Tex., Abilene Bar Assn. (past bd. dirs.), Abilene Young Lawyers Assn. (sec.-treas. 1977-78), Tex. Dist. and County Attys. Assn. Office: US Dist Ct 1100 Commerce St # 13B23 Dallas TX 75242

SOLIZ, JOSEPH GUY, lawyer; b. Corpus Christi, Tex., June 25, 1954; s. Oscar and Ola Mae (Trammell) S.; m. Juanita Solis, June 3, 1978; children: Lauren Michelle, Michael. BA with highest honors, S.W. Tex. State U., 1976; JD, Harvard U., 1979. Bar: Tex. 1979, U.S. Dist. Ct. (no. dist.) Tex. 1980, U.S. Ct. Appeals (5th cir.) 1980, U.S. Dist. Ct. (so. dist.) 1987. Atty. Gulf Oil Corp., Houston, 1979-81; assoc. Chamberlain, Hrdlicka, White, Johnson & Williams, Houston, 1981-85, ptnr., 1985-91; of counsel Brill, Sinex & Stephenson, 1991-92, Sinex & Stephenson, 1993—; v.p., gen. counsel, Golden Engring., Inc., 1992-93; pres. ECO Solutions, Inc., Houston, 1993—; adj. prof. South Tex. Coll. of Law, 1990-91. dir. Costal Water Authority, 1994—. Bd. dirs. Wilde-West Recreation Club, Inc., 1988-89, Harris County Pvt. Industry Coun., 1989-93, Big Bros., Big Sisters of Houston, 1989-95, treas., 1992-93, Coastal Water Authority, 1994—, High-Tech Carpets, Inc., 1993—; mem. exec. com. Harris County Dem. Party, 1988-92, 94—; dir. Houston Hispanic Forum, 1989-95, treas. 1992-95. Mem. ABA (natural resources sect.), Tex. Bar Assn., Hispanic Bar Assn. (dir. 1988-89, sec. 1989-90, treas. 1990-93), Houston Bar Assn., Houston Young Lawyers Assn. (Outstanding Com. Leader 1986-87, 87-88, 88-89, dir. 1988-89), Tex. Bd. Legal Specialization (cert. in oil, gas and mineral law), Jobs for Progress of Tex. Gulf Coast Inc. (dir. 1990-95, vice chmn. 1991-92, chmn. 1992-95), Houston Hispanic C. of C. (dir. 1989-90), Delta Tau Kappa, Alpha Chi, Pi Gamma Mu. Democrat. Roman Catholic. Home: 9406 Beverly Hill St Houston TX 77063-3908 Office: 9800 Richmond Ste 320 Houston TX 77042-4100

SÖLL, DIETER, biochemistry educator; b. Stuttgart, Germany, Apr. 19, 1935. PhD in Chemistry, Stuttgart U., 1962. Asst. prof. U. Wis., Madison, 1965-67; assoc. prof. Yale U., New Haven, Conn., 1967-76, prof., 1976—. Recipient Humboldt Press award Humboldt Found., 1988; fellow Guggenheim Found., 1973, 89, AAAS, 1990. Office: Yale Univ Dept Molecular Biophysics & Biochemistry 266 Whitney Ave New Haven CT 06520-8114

SOLL, LARRY, pharmaceutical executive; b. South Bend, Ind., Apr. 26, 1942; s. Manuel and Helenjean (Weiss) S.; m. Jean Newman (dec. 1971); m. Nancy Canavan Maron; children: William, Joel, Jonathan. AB, Princeton U., 1964; PhD, Stanford U., 1971. Vis. asst. prof. MIT, Cambridge, Mass., 1973-74; asst. prof. U. Colo., Boulder, 1974-82; pres. Synergen, Inc., Boulder, 1981-89, chief exec. officer, 1984-89, chmn., 1987—. Chmn. Colo. Advanced Tech. Inst., Denver, 1986-87. Office: Synergen Inc 1885 33rd St Boulder CO 80301-2546

SOLLENBERGER, HOWARD EDWIN, retired government official; b. N. Manchester, Ind., Apr. 28, 1917; s. Oliver Clark and Hazel (Coppock) S.; m. Agnes Hafner, Dec. 31, 1944; children—David Olaf, Roger Hafner (dec.), Zoe Karin. B.A., Manchester Coll., 1941, LL.D. (hon.), 1963. Relief adminstr. Brethern Services Com., also Am. Friends Service Com., N. China, 1938-40; engaged in civilian pub. service, 1941-44; orientation officer UNRRA, 1945-46; liaison officer UNRRA, Shanghai, China, 1946-47; with Fng. Service Inst., State Dept., 1947—; dir. Chinese lang. and area sch. Fng. Service Inst., State Dept., Peiping, China, 1947-50; asso. prof. Chinese Studies Fng. Service Inst., State Dept., Washington, 1950, 55; dean Fng. Service Inst., State Dept. (Sch. Lang. and Area Studies), 1956-65; acting dir. Fng. Service Inst., State Dept. (Inst.), 1965-66, 69-71, asso. dir., 1966-69, dir., 1971-76; cons. internat. edn., 1976—; mem. adv. com. lang. and area programs NDEA, 1962-64; adv. com. Center Applied Linguistics, 1959-62; adviser Georgetown U. Sch. Langs. and Linguistics, 1964-84; Unitarian-Universalist rep. Interfaith Action for Econ. Justice, 1977-88. Author: Read Chinese Script, 1949, Chinese Newspaper Syllabus, 1949, Documentary Chinese, 1949. Pres. McLean (Va.) PTA, 1960; v.p. Fairfax Unitarian Ch., 1961-62, 66-67; pres. Fairfax Meml. Soc., 1969-74; bd. dirs. No. Va. Meml. Soc., 1989—. Recipient Superior Honor award Dept. State, 1964, John Jacob Rogers award, Dept. State, 1976, Svc. citation Brethren Health and Welfare Assn. Mem. MLA, Linguistics Soc. Am., Assn. Asian Studies, Tau Kappa Alpha. Home: 1287 Berry Pl Mc Lean VA 22102-1503

SOLLENDER, JOEL DAVID, management consultant, financial executive; b. N.Y.C., Nov. 11, 1926; s. Samuel and Flora (Blumenthal) S.; m. Dorothy Leaf, Aug. 6, 1958; children: Jeffrey D., Jonathan L. B.S., N.Y. U., 1946. C.P.A., N.Y. Staff auditor Ernst & Young, N.Y.C., 1946-50; with United Mchts. & Mfrs., Inc., N.Y.C., 1950-86; corp. contr. United Mchts. & Mfrs., Inc., 1977—, sr. v.p., 1980—, chief acctg. officer, 1976—; also bd. dirs., officer various subs., mem. mgmt. com. parent co., 1986-88; assoc. dir. N.Y. Hist. Soc., N.Y.C.; mem. adv. coun. to Office of Charities Registration Dept. State, N.Y. State, 1986-89; v.p. fin. Piedmont Industries, N.Y.C., 1987-89; exec. v.p., CFO Earthworm Inc., 1992; fin. mgmt. cons., 1992—. Served with U.S. Army, World War II. Decorated Combat Infantry Badge, Purple Heart with cluster, Prisoner of War medal. Mem. AICPA, N.Y. State Soc. CPAs (chief fin. officer com.), Am. Inst. Corp. Controllers. Clubs: Bailiwick (Greenwich, Conn.); Greenhaven Yacht (Rye).

SOLLMAN, GEORGE HENRY, telecommunications company executive; b. Michigan City, Ind., Nov. 2, 1941; s. Henry Charles and Margaret Elisabeth (Gockel) S.; m. Maureen Tosh, July 12, 1968; children: Jennifer, Erich. Spl. student, MIT, 1965-66; BSEE, Northwestern U., 1964; MSEE, Northeastern U., 1967. Engring. dir. Honeywell Info. systems, Waltham, Mass., 1964-73; product line mgr. Control Data, Hawthorne, Calif., 1973-76; v.p., gen. mgr. Shugart/Xerox, Sunnyvale, Calif., 1976-84; spl. ptnr. Sand Hill Venture Group, Menlo Park, Calif., 1984; pres., chief exec. officer Centigram Corp., San Jose, Calif., 1985—; chmn., nat. bd. dirs. Am. Elec. Assn.; chmn. Silicon Valley Coun.; presidential nomination Semiconductor Tech. Coun.; co-chmn. Alexis d'Toqueville Soc.; mem. Adv. Coun. Joint Venture Silicon Valley. Patentee in field. Co-chmn. United Way of Santa Clara County. Mem. steering com. George Lucas Ednl. Found., Marin County. Home: 242 Polhemus Ave Atherton CA 94027-5439 Office: Centigram Corp 91 E Tasman Dr San Jose CA 95134-1618

SOLLORS, WERNER, English language, literature and American studies educator. Dr. phil., Freie Universität, Berlin, 1975. Wissenschaftlicher asst. and assistenzprofessor John F. Kennedy Inst. Freie Universität, Berlin; from asst. to assoc. prof. English and Comparative Lit. Columbia U.; Henry B. and Anne M. Cabot Prof. English Lit., current prof. Afro-Am. studies Harvard U., Cambridge, Mass. Author: Amiri Baraka/LeRoi Jones: The Quest for a Populist Modernism, 1978, Beyond Ethnicity: Consent and Descent in American Culture, 1986; contbr.: Das amerikanische Drama der Gegenwart, 1976, The Harvard Encyclopedia of American Ethnic Groups, 1980, Reconstructing American Literary History, 1986, Columbia Literary History of the United States, 1988, Critical Terms for Literary Study, 1990, Looking Inward, Looking Outward: From the 1920s through the 1940s, 1990, Nationale und kulturelle Identität: Studien zur Entwicklung des kollektiven Bewusstseins in der Neuzeit, 1991, Immigrants in Two Democracies: French and American Experience, 1992, Intersecting Boundaries: The Theatre of Adrienne Kennedy, 1992, Ilrazzismo e le sue storie, 1992, Swedes in America: Intercultiral and Interethnic Perspectives on Contemporary Research, 1993, Multiculatism and the Canon of American Culture, 1993, Configurations de l'ethnicité aux États-Unis, 1993, History & memory in African-American Culture, 1994; editor: A Bibliographic Guide to Afro-American Studies, 1972, A Bibliographic Guide to Afro-American Studies Supplement I, 1974; co-editor: Bibliographie amerikanistischer Veröffentichungen in der DDR bis 1968, 1976, Varieties of Black Experience at Harvard, 1986, The Invention of Ethnicity, 1989, The Life Stories of Undistinguished Americans As Told by Themselves, 1990, The Return of Thematic Criticism, 1993, Cane, 1993, Blacks at Harvard: A Documentary History of African-American Experience at Harvard and Radcliffe, 1993; contbr. articles to profl. jours. John Simon Guggenheim Meml. fellow, Andrew W. Mellon faculty fellow Harvard U. Office: Harvard U 11 Prescott St Cambridge MA 02138

SOLLOWAY, C. ROBERT, forest products company executive; b. Vancouver, B.C., Can., May 19, 1935; s. Harold Eugene and Elva Merle (McAllister) S.; m. Ila Noreen Kelly. B in Commerce, U. B.C., 1959, LLB, 1960. Bar: Can., 1961. Asst. to exec v.p., asst. to pres. West Coast Transmission Co. Ltd., Vancouver, 1962-68; corp. counsel, asst. sec. Weldwood of Can. Ltd., Vancouver, 1968-73, gen. counsel, sec., 1973-75, v.p., gen. counsel, sec., 1975—. Mem. Law Soc. B.C., Can. Bar Assn., Vancouver Bar Assn. Anglican. Clubs: Vancouver; Vancouver Lawn Tennis and Badminton. Office: Weldwood of Can Ltd, 1055 W Hastings PO Box 2179, Vancouver, BC Canada V6B 3V8

SOLMAN, JOSEPH, artist; b. Vitebsk, Russia, Jan. 25, 1909; came to U.S. 1912; s. Nathan and Rose (Peskin) S.; m. Ruth Romanofsky, Nov. 19, 1908; children: Paul, Ronni. Nat. Acad. of Design, 1927-30. Nat. Academician 1967. Easel painter WPA, N.Y.C., 1935-41; pvt. art instr. N.Y.C., 1951-66; art instr. CUNY, N.Y.C., 1967-75; artist N.Y.C., 1935—. Exhibitions: Retrospective at Phillips Mem. Mus., Washington, 1949, Retrospective at Wichita (Kansas) Mus. of Art, 1984; author: books, Joseph Solman, Crown Publishers, 1966, Monotypoes of Joseph Solman, Da Capo Press, 1977; artist: several paintings. Recipient of several awards for paintings and portraits including the Nat. Inst. of Arts & Letters, 1961, and 8 prizes from the Nat. Acad. of Design Annuals, 1967-89. Mem. Nat. Acad. of Design (treas. 1979-85), Fedn. of Modern Painters & Sculptors (exec. bd. 1968-89); fellow (life) Art Student League. Home: 156 2nd Ave New York NY 10003-5716

SOLMSSEN, PETER, university president; b. Berlin, Nov. 1, 1931. A.B., Harvard U., 1952; J.D., U. Pa., 1959. Atty. Ballard, Spahr, Andrews & Ingersoll, Phila., 1959-60; with U.S. Fgn. Service, 1961; vice consul Singapore, 1962-63; asst. to under sec. of state, 1963-65; 2d sec. Rio de Janeiro, 1965-67; Cultural attache U.S. Dept. State, Sao Paulo, Brazil, 1967-70; adviser on arts Washington, 1974-80, dep. ambassador at large for cultural affairs, 1981-83; pres. Phila. Coll. Art, 1983-87, U. of the Arts, Phila., 1987—. One-man photography exhbns. include: Mus. Art, Sao Paulo. Author and illustrator. Clubs: Philadelphia; Century Assn. Office: Univ Arts Office of Pres Broad And Pine St Philadelphia PA 19104

SOLNIT, ALBERT JAY, commissioner, physician, educator; b. Los Angeles, Aug. 26, 1919; s. Benjamin and Bertha (Pavin) S.; m. Martha Benedict, 1949; children—David, Ruth, Benjamin, Aaron. B.A. in Med. Scis., U. Calif., 1940, M.A. in Anatomy, 1942, M.D., 1943; M.A. (hon.), Yale U., 1964. Rotating intern Ll. Coll. Hosp., 1944, asst. resident in pediatrics, 1944-45; resident in pediatrics and communicable diseases U. Calif. div. San Francisco Hosp., 1947-48; asst. resident dept. psychiatry and mental hygiene Yale U., 1948-49, sr. resident, 1949-50, fellow in child psychiatry, 1950-52, instr. pediatrics and psychiatry, 1952-53, asst. prof., 1953-60, assoc. prof., 1960-64, prof., 1964-70, Sterling prof., 1970—, dir. Child Study Ctr., 1966-83; commr. dept. of mental health State of Conn., Hartford, 1991—; tng. and supervising analyst Western New Eng. Inst. Psychoanalysis, 1962—; N.Y. Psychoanalytic Inst., 1962—; cons. Childrens Bur., HEW; mem. adv. coun. Erikson Inst. for early Childhood Edn. 1966—; nat. adviser Children, publ. of Children's Bur., 1965—; mem. com. on publs. Yale U. Press, 1971—; adv. bd. Action for Children's TV, Newtonville, Mass., 1973—; mem. div. med. scis. Assembly Life Scis., NRC 1974—; cons. div. mental health svc. program NIMH, 1974—; Sigmund Freud Meml. prof. U. Coll. London, 1983-84; Sigmund Freud prof., dir. Freud Ctr. Psychoanalytic Studies Hebrew U., Jerusalem, 1985-87. Author: (with M.J.E. Senn) Problems in Child Behavior and Develpment, 1968), (with A. Freud, J. Goldstein) Beyond the Best Interests of the Child, 19732, (with Goldstein) Divorce and Your Child, 1983, (with R. Lord, B. Nordhaus) When Home Is No Haven, 1992; The Many Meanings of Play, 1993; editor: (with S. Provence) Modern Perspectives in Child Development, 1963; mng. editor Psychoanalytic Study of the Child, 1971—; mem. editorial bd. Israel Annals Psychiatry and Related Disciplines, 1969—. WHO prof. psychiatry and human devel. U. Negev, Beer-Sheva, Israel, 1973-74. With USAAF, 1945-47. Recipient Disting. Svc. award Am. Psychiatric Assn. 1992. Mem. AAAS, Inst. Medicine of NAS, Am. Orthopsychiatric Assn. (editorial bd. jour. 1974-82), Am. Psychoanalytic Assn. (past pres., editorial bd. jour. 1972-74), Am. Acad. Child and Adolescent Psychiatry (past pres., editorial bd. jour. 1975, Simon Wile Award, 1991), Internat. Pediatric Soc., Am. Assn. Child Psychoanalysis (past pres.), Am. Acad. Pediatrics (editorial bd. jour. 1968-76, task force pediatric edn.), Internat. Psychoanalytic Assn., Internat. Assn. Child and Adolescent Psychiatry (pres. 1974-78, hon. pres. 1990—), N.Y. Psychoanalytic Soc., Am. Soc. Profs. Child Psychiatry. Home: 107 Cottage St New Haven CT 06511-2465 Office: 333 Cedar St New Haven CT 06510-3206 also: 90 Washington St Hartford CT 06106-4418

SOLO, ALAN JERE, medicinal chemistry educator, consultant; b. Phila., Nov. 7, 1933; s. David H. and Marion J. (Gottschall) S.; m. Elma Mardirosian, Oct. 5, 1963; children: David Matthew, Julia Ann. SB, MIT, 1955; MA, Columbia U., 1956, PhD, 1959. Rsch. assoc. Rockefeller U., N.Y.C. 1958-62; asst. prof. med. chemistry SUNY, Buffalo, 1962-65, assoc. prof., 1965-70, dir. grad. studies med. chemistry, 1967-69, chmn. med. chemistry, 1969—, prof., chmn., 1970—; cons. Westwood Pharms. Inc., Buffalo, 1971-92. Predoctoral fellow NSF, 1955-56, NIH, 1957-58. Mem. Am. Chem. Soc., N.Y. Acad. Scis., Sigma Xi. Achievements include synthesis and structure-activity correlation of steroid hormone analogs and of calcium channel antagonists of the Dihydropyridine type. Office: SUNY Sch Pharmacy 439 Cooke Hall Buffalo NY 14260

SOLO, ROBERT ALEXANDER, economist, educator; b. Phila., Aug. 2, 1916; s. Louis C. and Rebecca (Muchnick) S.; m. Roselyn Starr; 1 dau., Tova Maria. B.S., Harvard U., 1938; M.A., Am. U., 1941; Ph.D., Cornell U., 1953. Economist fed. and war agys., 1939-41; author, script chief Sta. WCAU-TV, Phila., 1949-50; mem. faculty Rutgers U., New Brunswick, N.J., 1953-55, McGill U., Montreal, Que., Can., 1955-56, CCNY, 1956-58; sr. research economist Princeton U., 1965-66; prof. dept. econs. Mich. State U. East Lansing, 1966-87, prof. emeritus, 1987—; dir. Inst. Internat. Bus. and Devel. Studies, 1966-68; mem. faculty Johns Hopkins U., Balt., summer 1953, U. Mich., Ann Arbor, summer 1957; lectr. L'Ecole Practique des Hautes Etudes, Sorbonne, Paris, 1964-65; research Institut Recherch Economique and Planification, dir. U. Grenoble, France, 1972-73; prof. associe U. Paris IV, Dauphine, 1971, 73; cons. NASA, 1965-67, OECD, 1963-64, Commonwealth of P.R., 1959-61; project chmn. Study on Info. Tech. Nat. Conf. Bd., 1969-72; project dir. Nat. Planning Assn., Washington, 1961-63; U.S. del. Yugoslavian Conf. on Transfer of Tech., Belgrade, 1974; mem. Alan T. Waterman award Com., 1976-77. Author: Economics and the

Public Interest, 1955, Synthetic Rubber: A Case Study in Technological Development under Public Direction, 1959 (reprinted as Across the High Technology Threshold 1980), Economic Organizations and Social Systems, 1967, (with Everett Rogers) Inducing Technological Change for Economic Growth and Development, 1973, The Political Authority and the Market System, 1974, Organizing Science for Technology Transfer in Economic Development, 1975, The Positive State, 1981, (with Charles Anderson) Value Judgement and Income Distribution, 1981, Opportunity Knocks: American Economic Policy after Gorbachev, 1991, The Philosophy of Science and Economics, 1991, also other books in field; contbr. chpts. to books, articles to profl. jours. Fulbright fellow, 1972-73. Mem. Council European Studies (steering com., exec. com., chmn. research com. 1974-77). Home: 4609 Chippewa Dr Okemos MI 48864-2009

SOLOFF, LOUIS ALEXANDER, physician, educator; b. Paris, Oct. 4, 1904; came to U.S., 1905, naturalized, 1930; s. Abraham and Rebecca (Wagenfeld) S.; m. Mathilde Robin, 1933 (dec.); 1 child, Joann Soloff Green. B.A, U. Pa., 1926; M.D., U. Chgo., 1930. Dir. pathology St. Joseph's and St. Vincent's hosps., Phila., 1933-45; dir. pathology Eagleville Sanitorium, Norristown, Pa., 1933-45; with Temple U. and Hosp., Phila., 1930—; chief div. cardiology Temple U. and Hosp., 1956-70, prof. medicine, 1966—; Blanche P. Levy disting. svc. prof., Florence P. Bernheimer prof. cardiology emeritus, 1970—; now chief cardiology emeritus Temple U. Hosp.; chief div. cardiology Episcopal Hosp., 1950-56. Mem. A.C.P., AMA, Am. Heart Assn., Am. Fedn. Clin. Research, Pa. Med. Soc., Am. Heart Assn., Council on Clin. Cardiology, AAUP, Assn. Univ. Cardiologists, Sigma Xi, Alpha Omega Alpha. Research, publs. on cardiovascular disease. Home: 1901 Walnut St Philadelphia PA 19103-4605 Office: Temple U Health Scis Center Philadelphia PA 19140

SOLOMON, ALAN, physician, medical oncologist and clinical investigator; b. N.Y.C., May 16, 1933; s. Joseph and Rita (Schwartz) S.; m. Frances N. Jacobs, June 14, 1959 (div. Jan. 1972); children: David A., Joseph A.; m. Doris A Creekmore Waters, Nov. 27, 1977. BS, Bucknell U., 1953; BS in Medicine, Duke U., 1956, MD, 1957. Diplomate Nat. Bd. Med. Examiners, Am. Bd. Internal Medicine. Intern Mt. Sinai Hosp., N.Y.C., 1957-58; asst. resident medicine Montefiore Hosp., N.Y.C., 1958-59, Mt. Sinai Hosp., N.Y.C., 1959-60; clin. assoc. Nat. Cancer Inst., NIH, Bethesda, Maryland, 1960-62; chief resident medicine Mt. Sinai Hosp., N.Y.C., 1962-63; guest investigator, asst. physician Rockefeller U., N.Y.C., 1963-65; assoc. rsch. prof. U. Tenn., Meml. Rsch. Ctr. Hosp., Knoxville, Tenn., 1966-69, rsch. and clin. prof., 1970-80, prof. medicine, 1981—; Am. Cancer Soc. clin. rsch. prof. U. Tenn. Med. Ctr., Knoxville, Tenn., 1992—; chmn. Clinical Cancer Project Review Com. Nat. Cancer Inst./NIH, Bethesda, 1978-83, mem. Bd. Scientific Counselors Divsn. Cancer Biology, 1993—; head Human Immunology Cancer Program, U. Tenn. Med. Ctr. Knoxville, 1990—. Contbr. to over 140 profl jours. Bd. trustees Knoxville Mus. Art, Tenn., 1982—. Sr. Surgeon USPHS 1960-62, (inactive) 1962-63. Named Special Fellow NIH/ Rockefeller Inst., N.Y.C., 1963-65, Laszlo Meml. Lecturer Montefiore Hosp., N.Y.C., 1984; recipient Rsch. Career Devel. award NIH/U. Tenn. Med. Ctr., 1968-72. Fellow Am. Coll. Physicians; mem. Am. Assn. Cancer Rsch., Am. Soc. Hematology, Am. Assn. Immunologist, Am. Soc. Clin. Investigators, Am. Soc. Clin. Oncology. Jewish. Avocations: gardening, hiking, sculpture. Office: U Tenn Med Ctr 1924 Alcoa Hwy Knoxville TN 37920

SOLOMON, ARTHUR CHARLES, pharmacist; b. Gary, Ind., May 30, 1947; s. Laurence A. and Dorothy B. (Klippel) S.; m. Janet Evelyn Irak, Aug. 23, 1969; children: Thomas, Michael, Mark, Jill. BS in Pharmacy, Purdue U., 1970, MS in Clin. Pharmacy, 1972; PharmD. Registered pharmacist; cert. nuclear pharmacist. Clin. prof. pharmacy U. Tex., Austin, 1972-75; v.p. Nuclear Pharmacy, Inc., Atlanta, 1975-83; exec. v.p., managed care officer Diagnostek, Inc., Albuquerque, 1983—; pres. Health Care Svcs., Inc., 1990—; adj. prof. U. N.Mex., 1992—. Contbr. articles to profl. jours. Mem. Am. Pharm. Assn., Am. Soc. Hosp. Pharmacy, Nat. Assn. Retail Druggists, Nat. Coun. Prescription Drug Programs, Am. Managed Care Pharmacy Assn. (pres., dir.), Am. Soc. Cons. Pharmacists, Rho Chi, Pi Kappa Phi. Republican. Roman Catholic. Avocations: golf, fishing, gardening, tennis. Home: 1504 Catron Ave SE Albuquerque NM 87123-4218 Office: Diagnostek Inc 4500 Alexander Blvd NE Albuquerque NM 87107-6805

SOLOMON, ARTHUR KASKEL, biophysics educator; b. Pitts., Nov. 26, 1912; (married); 2 children. A.B., Princeton U., 1934; M.A., Harvard U., 1935, Ph.D in Phys. Chemistry, 1937; Ph.D. in Physics, Cambridge U., Eng., 1947, Sc.D, 1964. Research assoc. in physics and chemistry Harvard, 1939-41; officer Brit. Ministry Supply, 1941-43; mem. staff Radiation Lab., Mass. Inst. Tech., 1945; asst. prof. phys. chemistry Med. Sch., Harvard, 1946-57, asso. prof. biophysics, 1957-68, prof., 1968-82, prof. emeritus, 1982—; assoc. in biophysics Peter Bent Brigham Hosp., Boston, 1950-72; dir. Read's Inc., Balt., 1946-77; pres. Read's Inc., 1961-77; Mem. U.S. Nat. Com. for Pure and Applied Biophysics, 1965-72, U.S. Nat. Com. for Biology, 1966-71; mem. U.S. Nat. Com. for UNESCO, 1969-74, mem. U.S. del. to gen. assembly, Nairobi, 1976; mem. vis. com. biology dept. Brookhaven Nat. Lab., 1961-65; mem. NRC com. on radiology, 1957-59, com. on growth, 1954-57; sec. Gen. Internat. Union for Pure and Applied Biophysics, 1961-72; mem. NIH radiation study sect., 1960-63, biophys. sci. tng. com., 1963-68, chmn., 1966-68; mem. U.S. del. Gen. Assembly of UNESCO, Paris, 1978; mem. adv. panel on sci., tech. and society UNESCO, 1981-84; mem. bd. internat. orgns. and programs Nat. Acad. Scis., 1977-83, mem. bd. internat. Council Sci. Unions, 1966-72; U.S. del. 17th, 18th Gen. Assemblies of Internat. Council Sci. Unions, Athens, 1978, Amsterdam, 1980; chmn. disting. fellowship com. Internat. Council Sci. Unions-UNESCO, 1980-85; chmn. Harvard com. on higher degrees in biophysics, 1959-80; chmn. Harvard Med. Sch. Oral History Com.; chmn. Harvard Council on the Arts, 1973-76. Mem. editorial bds.: Quarterly Revs. of Biophysics, 1972-74, Journal Gen. Physiology, 1958—. Trustee Inst. Contemporary Art, Boston, 1946-76, pres., 1965-71; bd. overseers Boston Mus. Fine Arts, 1978-84; mem. collectors com. Nat. Gallery Art, Washington, 1985-88. Decorated Order Andres Bello Venezuela). Fellow AAAS, Am. Acad. Arts and Scis.; mem. Am. Chem. Soc., Am. Physiol. Soc., Biophysics Soc., Soc. Gen. Physiology. Clubs: Cosmos (Washington); St. Botolph (Boston); Harvard (N.Y.C. and Boston). Home: 27 Craigie St Cambridge MA 02138-3457 Office: Harvard Med Sch Biophysics Lab 221 Longwood Ave Boston MA 02115-5817

SOLOMON, BARRY JASON, healthcare administrator, consultant; b. Boston, May 16, 1934; s. Samuel and Ethel (Fleishman) S.; m. C. Priscilla Fugate, June 29, 1958; children: R. Stephen, Jon, Julie Ellen. BS in Biology and Chemistry, Tufts U., 1955; MBA in Health Care Adminstrn., Xavier U., Cin., 1960; MPH in Health Care Adminstrn., U. N.C., 1989. Chief med. record adminstr. USPHS Hosp., Lexington, Ky., 1956-59; asst. dir. Union Meml. Hosp., Balt., 1960-61; asst. adminstr. James Lawrence Kernan Hosp., Balt., 1961-67; asst. to dean, lectr. health edn. and med. care sects. Yale U. Sch. Medicine, New Haven, 1967-70; dir. health svcs., clin. asst. prof. pharmacy adminstrn. U. R.I., Kingston, 1970-76; assoc. dir. for adminstrn. USPHS Hosp., Norfolk, Va., 1976-81; dir., COO, sr. fellow in social medicine Montefiore Hosp., Bronx, N.Y., 1981-84; assoc. v.p. for med. affairs, mem. exec. coun. of Med. Sch. U. South Fla., Tampa, 1984-89; assoc. prof., acting com. dept. comprehensive medicine U. So. Fla., Tampa, 1984-89, assoc. prof. Coll. Pub. Health, 1984-89; cons. in health adminstrn., Columbia, Md., 1989-93; v.p. for acad. affairs North Broward Hosp. Dist., Ft. Lauderdale, Fla., 1993—; mem. instnl. rev. bd. Nova Southeastern U. Coll. Osteo. Medicine; bd. dirs. Vis. Nurse Corp., 1987-90; bd. dirs., mem. exec. and nominating coms. Vis. Nurse Assn. Tampa Bay, 1987-90; mem. planning com. of bd. trustees Hillsborough County Hosp. Authority, 1986-88; mem. profl. affairs com. of bd. trustees H. Lee Moffitt Cancer Ctr. and Rsch. Inst., 1986-88; mem. affiliation com. S.W. Fla. Blood Bank, 1988-89; instr. hosp. adminstrn. Xavier U., 1960; course asst., instr. Am. Med. Record Assn., 1962-72; instr. Howard U. Coll. Continuing Edn., Washington, 1993; cons. St. Elizabeth Hosp., Covington, Ky., 1959, City Hosp. Ctr. at Elmhurst, 1965, Hall-Brooke Hosp., Westport, Conn., 1968-69, Conn. Mental Health Ctr., New Haven, 1969-70, South County Hosp., Wakefield, R.I., 1970-76, Centurion Hosp., Tampa, 1989, Primary Care Svcs., Tampa, 1991, Holland & Knight, Tampa, 1991, NCC Internat., Colchester, Eng., 1991, F.W. Assocs., Tampa, 1989-92, Decking Design, Norfolk, 1986-93, SMSinc., Columbia, 1993-93, Internat. Flooring & Protective Coatings, Inc., Norfolk, 1993—; sr. cons. Meisel Assocs., Inc., N.Y.C., 1983—. Contbr.

articles to profl. jours. Trustee Montefiore-Mosholu Cmty. Ctr., 1981-84; mem. Nat. Com. on Religion and Health, 1982-84; mem., vice chmn. Chariho Sch. Bd., Richmond, R.I., 1974-76; mem. Broward Econ. Devel. Coun., Inc. Lt. USPHS, 1956-59, capt., 1976-81. Recipient citation Suncoast chpt. Am. Heart Assn., 1988. Fellow Am. Coll. Healthcare Execs.; mem. APHA. Avocation: tennis. Home: 2864 Via Venezia Deerfield Beach FL 33442 Office: North Broward Hosp Dist 300 SE 17th St Fort Lauderdale FL 33316

SOLOMON, DAN EUGENE, bishop; b. Matador, Tex., Dec. 15, 1936; s. Henry Monroe and Mabel Amy (Jenkins) S.; m. Joy Causseaux, May 30, 1957; children: Stuart, Paul, Julie Beth. BA summa cum laude, McMurry Coll., 1958; M Div with honors, Perkins Sch. Theology, 1961; D Ministry, United Theol. Sem., Dayton, 1973; DD (hon.), Oklahoma City U., 1989. Assoc. pastor First Meth. Ch., Plainview, Tex., 1961-62; sr. pastor St. Stephen United Meth. Ch., Amarillo, Tex., 1962-69, St. John's United Meth. Ch., Corpus Christi, Tex., 1969-76; supt. Kerrville (Tex.) Dist., 1976-77; sr. pastor Travis Park United Meth. Ch., San Antonio, 1977-83, First United Meth. Ch., Corpus Christi, 1983-88; bishop Okla. area, Okla. Ann. Conf., Okla. Indian Missionary Conf. United Meth. Ch., Oklahoma City, 1988—; mem. Gen. Conf. and Jurisdictional Conf., Gen. Bd. Ch. and Soc., Gen. Bd. Status and Role of Women. Author/creator simulation game Cabinet; contbr. articles to profl. pubs. Trustee Oklahoma City U.; bd. dirs. Suicide Prevention Group, Crimestoppers. Recipient Homiletics award Perkins Sch. Theology. Avocation: golf. Office: United Meth Ch 2420 N Blackwelder Ave Oklahoma City OK 73106-1410

SOLOMON, DAVID, investment banker. Pres. Mortgage Acquisition Corp., Boston. Office: Mortgage Acquisition Corp 800 Boylston St Fl 19 Boston MA 02199*

SOLOMON, DAVID EUGENE, engineering company executive; b. Milton, Pa., June 22, 1931; s. Oren Benjamin and Bernardine Claire Solomon; m. Joyce Marie Hoffman, June 24, 1950; children: Timothy, Melissa, Daniel. AB, Susquehanna U., 1958; MS, Bucknell U., 1960; MBA, Ea. Mich. U., 1974. Sr. engr. Westinghouse Electric Corp., Balt., 1959-65; rsch. engr. U. Mich., 1965-67; chief engr. Electro-Optics divsn. Bendix Corp., 1967-72; v.p. ops. KMS Fusion, Inc., Ann Arbor, Mich., 1972-85; pres., CEO Solohill Engring. Inc., 1985—; bd. dirs. Ann Arbor Engring. Inc., SoloHill Labs. Inc. With USN, 1950-55. Fellow IEEE. Patentee in field. Office: 1919 Green Rd Ann Arbor MI 48105-2554

SOLOMON, DAVID HARRIS, physician, educator; b. Cambridge, Mass., Mar. 7, 1923; s. Frank and Rose (Roud) S.; m. Ronda L. Markson, June 23, 1946; children: Patti Jean (Mrs. Richard E. Sinaiko), Nancy Ellen (Mrs. Marvin Evans). A.B., Brown U., 1944; M.D., Harvard U., 1946. Intern Peter Bent Brigham Hosp., Boston, 1946-47, resident, 1947-48, 50-51; fellow endocrinology New Eng. Center Hosp., Boston, 1951-52; faculty UCLA Sch. Medicine, 1952—, prof. medicine, 1966—, vice chmn. dept. medicine, 1968-71, chmn. dept., 1971-81, assoc. dir. geriatrics, 1982-89; dir. UCLA Ctr. on Aging, 1991—; prof. emeritus UCLA, 1993—; chief med. svc. Harbor Gen. Hosp., Torrance, Calif., 1966-71; cons. Wadsworth VA Hosp., L.A., 1952—, Sepulveda VA Hosp., 1971—; cons. metabolism tng. com. USPHS, 1960-64, endocrinology study sect., 1970-73. Editor: Jour. Am. Geriatric Soc., 1988-93; contbr. numerous articles to profl. jours. Recipient Mayo Soley award, 1986. Master ACP; mem. Assn. Am. Physicians, Am. Soc. Clin. Investigation, Western Soc. Clin. Research (councillor 1963-65), Endocrine Soc. (Robert H. Williams award 1989), Am. Thyroid Assn. (pres. 1973-74, Disting. Service award 1986), Inst. Medicine Nat. Acad. Scis., AAAS, Assn. Profs. Medicine (pres. 1980-81), Western Assn. Physicians (councillor 1972-75, pres. 1983-84), Am. Fedn. Aging Rsch. (Irving S. Wright award), Am. Geriatrics Soc. (bd. dirs. 1985-93, Milo Leavitt award 1992, Disting. Svc. award 1993), Phi Beta Kappa, Sigma Xi, Alpha Omega Alpha. Home: 863 Woodacres Rd Santa Monica CA 90402-2107 Office: UCLA Sch Medicine Dept Medicine Los Angeles CA 90024

SOLOMON, EDWARD DAVID, chain store executive; b. Paterson, N.J., Mar. 3, 1931; s. Charles and Lee (Bernstein) S.; m. Regina Ellen Purcell, Mar. 18, 1972; 1 son, David; children by previous marriage—Jerry, Susan. B.S., Wharton Sch. Fin., U. Pa., 1952. Buyer Miles Shoes div. Melville Corp., N.Y.C., 1956-59; buyer, mdse. mgr., exec. v.p., then pres. Gallenkamp Stores Co. div. Scoa Industries Inc., Los Angeles, 1959-69; pres. Karl's Shoe Stores Ltd. div. HRT Industries, Inc., Los Angeles, 1969-74; pres., chief operating officer HRT Industries, Inc., Los Angeles and N.Y.C., 1974-76; pres., chief exec. officer HRT Industries, Inc., 1977—, chmn., 1978-84; pres., chief exec. officer Edward D. Solomon & Co., 1984-89; chief exec. officer Shoe-Town, Inc., Totowa, N.J., 1989—. Trustee City of Hope. Served with USNR, 1953-56. Named Man of Yr., professions and fin. group City of Hope, 1973, Man of Yr. Jack Martin Fund, Mt. Sinai Hosp., N.Y.C., 1977; recipient Community Service award Brandeis U., 1979; T. Kenyon Holly humanitarian award of footwear industry, 1981. Mem. Volume Footwear Retailers Am. (bd. dirs. 1967—, pres. 1961-81), Nat. Retail Mchts. Assn. (bd. dirs. 1981-84), Mass Retailers Inst. (dir. 1977-80). Office: Felsway Corp 994 Riverview Dr Totowa NJ 07512

SOLOMON, EDWARD IRA, chemistry educator, researcher; b. N.Y.C., Oct. 20, 1946; s. Mordecai L. and Sally S. Solomon; m. Darlene Joy Spira, Sept. 15, 1984; children: Mitchell Landau, Paige Elana. BS, Rensselaer Poly. Inst., 1968; PhD, Princeton U. 1972. Rsch. assoc. Princeton (N.J.) U., 1972-73; postdoctoral fellow H.C. Ørsted Inst., Copenhagen, 1973-74, Calif. Inst. Tech., Pasadena, 1974-75; asst. prof. MIT, Cambridge, Mass., 1975-79, assoc. prof., 1979-81, prof., 1981-82; prof. Stanford (Calif.) U., 1982-91, prof. Humanities and Sci., 1991—; cons. prof., World Bank lectr. Xiamen U., People's Republic of China, 1984; O.K. Rice lectr. U. N.C., 1984, Reilly lectr. Notre Dame, 1985; 1st Glen Seaborg lectr. U. Calif., 1990; Frontiers in Chem. Rsch. lectr. Tex. A&M, 1990; ACS lectr., Argentina, 1992; invited prof. Tokyo Inst. Tech., 1992; Xerox lectr. U. Alta., 1993; lectr. NSC Republic of China, 1993; Leermakers lectr. Wesleyan U., 1994; Amoco lectr. Ind. U., 1995. Assoc. editor Inorganic Chemistry, 1985—; edit. adv. bd. Chem. Revs., 1990—, Jour. Inorganic Biochemistry, Chemtracts, Chemistry and Biology; contbr. 215 rsch. articles to Jour. ACS, Inorganic Chemistry, Procs. of the NAS, Phys. Rev. Mem. panels NIH, NSF, Washington; mem. vis. coms. Exxon, U. Calif., Santa Cruz. Recipient Ramsen award Md. ACS and Johns Hopkins U., 1994, NIH Merit award, 1995. Fellow AAAS, Japan Soc. for Promotion of Sci.; mem. ACS, Am. Phys. Soc., Sigma Xi. Achievements include research in structure/function correlations in copper cluster proteins, in electronic structure of the blue copper active site, in spectroscopic definition of the active site in the Cu/ZnO methanol synthesis catalyst, in new spectroscopic probes of non-heme iron enzymes, in excited state potential energy surfaces of inorganic complexes and their contribution to reactivity, on new methods of inorganic spectroscopy; covalency in transition metal complexes. Office: Stanford U Dept Chemistry Roth Way Stanford CA 94305

SOLOMON, EZRA, economist, educator; b. Rangoon, Burma, Mar. 20, 1920; came to U.S., 1947, naturalized, 1951; s. Ezra and Emily (Rose) S.; m. Janet Lorraine Cameron, May 7, 1949; children—Catherine Shan, Janet Ming, Lorna Cameron. A.B. (hons.), U. Rangoon, 1940; Ph.D., U. Chgo., 1950. Instr. U. Chgo., 1948-51, asst. prof. fin., 1951-55, assoc. prof., 1955-57, prof., 1957-61; Dean Witter prof. fin. Stanford U., 1961-71, 73-90; dir. Internat. Ctr. Mgmt. Edn.; mem. Coun. Econ. Advisers, 1971-73; bd. dirs. Ency. Brit. Benham Capital Funds. Author: The Theory of Financial Management, 1963, Money and Banking, 5th edit, 1968, The Management of Corporate Capital, 1959, Metropolitan Chicago: An Economic Analysis, 1958, The Anxious Economy, 1975, An Introduction to Financial Management, 2d edit, 1980, Beyond the Turning Point, 1981; editor: International Patterns of Inflation—A Study in Contrasts, 1984, Jour. Bus, 1953-57; bd. editors Jour. of Finance, 1965-66, Jour. Bus. Finance, 1969-73, Jour. Quantitative and Financial Analysis, 1969-71. Served as lt., Burma div. Royal Naval Vol. Res., 1942-47. Mem. Am. Econ. Assn., Am. Finance Assn. Home: 775 Santa Ynez St Stanford CA 94305-8478 Office: Stanford Univ Grad School Of Busines Stanford CA 94305

SOLOMON, GEORGE FREEMAN, academic psychiatrist; b. Freeport, N.Y., Nov. 25, 1931; s. Joseph C. and Ruth (Freeman) S.; children: Joshua Ben, Jared Freeman. A.B., Stanford U., 1952, M.D., 1955. Intern, Barnes

Hosp., St. Louis, 1955-56; resident in psychiatry Langley Porter Neuropsychiat. Inst., U. Calif. Med. Sch., San Francisco, 1956-59; asst. to asso. prof. psychiatry Stanford U. Med. Sch., 1962-73; dir. med. edn. Fresno County (Calif.) Dept. Health, 1973-83; clin. prof. UCLA Med. Sch., 1974-78; clin. prof. psychiatry U. Calif. Med. Sch., San Francisco, 1976-79, prof., 1980-84, vice-chmn. dept., 1978-83; adj. prof. U. Calif., San Francisco, 1984-90; prof. psychiatry and biobehavioral sci. UCLA, 1984-95, prof. emeritus, 1995—; chief chem. dependency treatment ctr. VA Med. Ctr., Sepulveda, Calif., 1984-89; chief psychoneuroimmunology, 1989-94; chief psychiatry Valley Med. Center, Fresno, 1974-83. Co-author: The Psychology of Strength, 1975; contbr. over 150 papers and articles on psychoneuroimmunology, violence, Vietnam and other topics to profl. jours. and various publs. Capt. USAR, 1959-61. Fellow Internat. Coll. Psychosomatic Medicine, Am. Psychiat. Assn., Acad. of Behavioral Med. Research., Royal Coll. Psychiatrists. Home: 19054 Pacific Coast Hwy Malibu CA 90265-5406 Office: UCLA Sch Med Dean's Office N Cousins Prog Psychoneuro 12-138CHS Los Angeles CA 90024-1722

SOLOMON, GEORGE M., newspaper editor; b. N.Y.C., July 19, 1940; s. Sidney and Fannie (Seidel) S.; m. Hazel Stephanie Bakst, July 23, 1967; children—Aaron, Mark, Gregory. B.S. in Journalism, U. Fla., 1963. Sports editor Sun-Sentinel, Fort Lauderdale, Fla., 1965-70; reporter, columnist Washington Daily News, 1970-72; reporter sports Washington Post, 1972-74, asst. sports editor, 1974-75, asst. mng. editor sports, 1975—. Author: Team Nobody Wanted: the Washington Redskins, 1973. Democrat. Jewish. Avocations: running; tennis. Office: Washington Post 1150 15th St NW Washington DC 20071-0002

SOLOMON, GERALD BROOKS HUNT, congressman; b. Okeechobee, Fla., Aug. 14, 1930; s. Seymour and Rlee Eugenia (Hunt) S.; m. Freda Frances Parker, Feb. 5, 1955; children: Susan, Daniel, Robert, Linda, Jeffrey. Student, Siena Coll., Albany, N.Y., 1948-49, St. Lawrence U., Canton, N.Y., 1953-54. Town supr., chief exec. Queensbury, N.Y., 1967-72; legislator Warren County, N.Y., 1968-73; mem. N.Y. State Assembly, 1972-78, 96th-97th Congresses from 29th N.Y. dist., 1979-83; 98th-104th Congresses from 24th (now 22d) N.Y. dist. 98th-103rd Congresses from 24th (now 22nd) N.Y. dist., Washington, D.C., 1983—; chmn. Rules com., mem. joint com. orgn. congress; ambassador del. UN, 1985; house com. mem. Vets. Affairs Com., 1979-89, Pub. Wks. Com., 1979-83, Fgn. Affairs Com., 1983-89, 2d ranking rep. 1989—, 1st ranking rep. 1991—; founding ptnr. Assoc. of Glens Falls (N.Y.) Inc. ins. and stockbrokerage firm, 1964—. Chmn. Warren County Social Service Com., 1968-72; active Eastern Adirondack Heart Assn., Adirondack Muscular Dystrophy Assn.; mem. Queensbury Cen. Vol. Fire Co., from 1967; bd. dirs. Adirondack Park Assn., Glens Falls Area Youth Ctr.; coun. Boy Scouts of Am.; mem. house rules com. U.S. Congress, 1989—, Task Force, Prisoner and Missing in S.E. Asia; former mem. Ho. Fgn. Affairs Com.; former sr. ranking rep. Vets. Affairs Com.; amb. UN N.Y., 1985, also congl. advisor to UN sesstion on disarmament; former congl. del. North Atlantic Assembly, vice chmn., active, 1982—; chmn. polit. fgn. affairs com. Assembly. With USMC, 1951-58, Korean War. Mem. Queensbury C. of C. (pres. 1972), Queensbury Jaycees (pres. 1964-65). Presbyterian. Lodges: Masons, Shriners, K.T, Elks, Kiwanis (bd. dir. Queensbury club 1965-69), Grange. Office: US Ho of Reps 2206 Rayburn House Office Bldg Washington DC 20515-3222

SOLOMON, HENRY, university dean; b. Bronx, N.Y., Nov. 28, 1926; s. Max and Tillie (Gilerowitz) S.; m. Jacqueline Mona Cohen, May 31, 1953; 1 son, Michael Robert. B.A., Bklyn. Coll., 1949; M.A., NYU, 1950, Ph.D., 1960. Research assoc., then sr. staff investigator and dep. prin. investigator logistics research project George Washington U., 1950-66, prof. econs., chmn. dept., 1962-74, 91—; dean George Washington U. (Grad. Sch. Arts and Scis.), 1974-90; dep. assist. administr. econs., acting asst. adminstr. planning, research and analysis SBA, 1966-67; cons. in field. Assoc. editor: Naval Research Logistics Quar, 1957-90 . Served with U.S. Army, 1945-46. Recipient Founder's Day award N.Y. U., 1960. Mem. Am. Econ. Assn., Am. Statis. Assn. Home: 6311 Stratford Rd Chevy Chase MD 20815-5355 Office: 801 22nd St NW Washington DC 20052

SOLOMON, HOWARD, pharmaceutical company executive; b. N.Y.C., Aug. 12, 1927; s. David and Faye (Gussow) S.; m. Carolyn Ruth Bower, Dec. 17, 1961; children: Andrew Wallace, David Frederick. BSS, CCNY, 1949; LLB, Yale U., 1952. Bar: N.Y. 1952. Atty. Moses & Singer, N.Y.C., 1952-55; atty. Kay Scholer, Fierman Hays & Handler, N.Y.C., 1956-60; pres. Hildred Mgmt. Corp., N.Y.C., 1967-83; dir. Forest Labs., Inc., N.Y.C., 1964—; pres., chief exec. officer Forest Labs., Inc., 1977—; dir. Pharmax Ltd., Bexley, Kent., U.K., 1979—; mem. bd. govs., exec. com. Am. Stock Exch. Mem. Turtle Bay Music Sch., 1975-79; bd. dirs. Met. Opera, N.Y.C. Ballet. Mem. N.Y. State Bar Assn., Am. Bus. Conf. (bd. govs.), Yale Club, Harmonie Club of N.Y. Office: Forest Labs Inc 909 3d Ave New York NY 10022

SOLOMON, IRVIN D., history educator, author; b. Alexandria, La., July 20, 1946; s. Mary Katherine (Rohaly) Solomon Beer. BS in Edn., Edinboro U. of Pa., 1971, MA in History, 1973; PhD in History, U. Akron, 1983. Teaching fellow, teaching asst. U. Akron, 1973-78; tchr. Fairfax County Sch. Dist., Falls Church, Va., 1978-83; instr. Afro-Am. history Prince George's C.C., Largo, Md., 1979-83; grad. instr. human relations George Mason U., Fairfax, Va., 1980-82; prof. history and African-Am. studies Edison C.C., Ft. Myers, Fla., 1988-94; asst. prof. History U. South Fla., Ft. Myers Fla., 1994—; adj. prof. history and African-Am. studies U. Cen. Fla., 1983-88, U. South Fla., Ft. Myers 1990-94; instr. evening sch. Columbia Coll., Orlando, 1983-88; cons. in human rels., Washington, 1978-83. Author: Make It Happen: A Comprehensive Guide and Directory for Americans Wishing to Teach Overseas, 1985, Feminism and Black Activism in Contemporary America: An Ideological Assessment, 1989; editor: Readings in American History: Key Social Issues, 1994; contbr. articles to profl. jours. and newspapers. Co-sponsor Black History Month, Ft. Myers, 1988-90, Women's History Month, Ft. Myers, 1990. Recipient citations for excellence in writing Orlando Sentinel, 1985, 86, 87; Univ. fellow, 1977-78. Mem. Phi Alpha Theta, Phi Delta Kappa. Avocation: travel. Office: U South Fla at Ft Myers Coll Arts and Scis 8111 College Pkwy Fort Myers FL 33919-5163

SOLOMON, JACK AVRUM, lawyer, automotive distributor, art dealer; b. Omaha, Oct. 25, 1928; s. John A. and Matilda (Bienstok) S.; m. Josephine J. Kleiman, June 1948 (div. Mar. 1971); children: Debra, Alisa, Michael, Rena; m. Carolyn Summers, Dec. 1973. B.S., U. Nebr., 1950, LL.B. cum laude, 1952; LL.M. (Cook fellow), U. Mich., 1953. Bar: Nebr. 1950, Ill. 1951. Practice law Chgo., 1950—; with firm Stiefel, Greenberg, Burns, Baldridge & Solomon, 1953-66, ptnr., 1958-66; ptnr. Solomon, Rosenfeld, Elliot & Stiefel, and predecessor, 1966—; sr. ptnr., 1966—; dir. Amco Industries, Inc., Chgo., 1968—, chmn. bd., 1968-69; sec., gen. counsel, 1969—; sec., dir. Mogen David Wine Corp., Chgo., 1964-71; chmn. bd., dir. Arts and Leisure Corp., 1969-76; pres., chmn. bd., dir. Circle Fine Art Corp., 1968—. Mem. Ill. Nebr. bar assns.; mem. Fine Art Pubs. Assn. (pres. 1982—); Mem. Order of Coif. Jewish (pres. temple 1959-61). Club: Nat. Arts (N.Y.C.). Home: 950 N Michigan Ave Chicago IL 60611-4503 Office: 303 E Wacker Dr Ste 830 Chicago IL 60601-5212

SOLOMON, JOEL MARTIN, retired professional society administrator; b. Malden, Mass., Dec. 25, 1932; m. Carol Natalie Levine, June 5, 1960 (div. 1983); children: Elaina Raquel, April Monique, Elissa Danielle; m. Eileen Mary Murphy, Feb. 24, 1984. BS, Boston Coll., 1953; SM, Johns Hopkins U., 1957; PhD, U. Wis., 1963. Dir. immunohematology Biologics Standards div. NIH, Bethesda, Md., 1957-60; rsch. fellow ARC, L.A., 1963-64; dir. lab. tng. ARC, Washington, 1964-67; blood bank dir. Bklyn.-Cumberland Med. Ctr., 1967-70; blood products mktg. dir. E. R. Squibb & Sons, Princeton, N.Y., 1970-73; dep. dir., dir. Blood & Blood Products div. FDA, Bethesda, 1974-81; various positions NIH, Bethesda, 1981-88; exec. dir. Am. Assn. Blood Banks, Bethesda, 1991-94. Capt. USPHS, 1957-91. Home: 15714 Cherry Blossom Ln North Potomac MD 20878-4905 1. Do not agonize over attitudes or policies beyond your control. 2. Be a good listener especially to your wife and secretary. 3. Practice a life style that credits others at the expense of ego.

SOLOMON, JOHN DAVIS, aviation executive; b. Kingfisher, Okla., Oct. 22, 1936; s. Edward Dempsey and Mary Blanche (Smith) S.; m. Mildred

Oraline Brammer, July 16, 1968 (div. Mar. 1984); children: Jennifer Leigh, Jason Lewis; m. Sheila Mary McLeod, Nov. 23, 1985. BA, Okla. State U., 1958. Asst. mgr. airport City of Oklahoma City Dept. Aviation, 1963-66, City of Tulsa Airport Authority, 1966-70; dir. aviation City of Oklahoma City., 1970-77, Clark County Dept. Aviation, Las Vegas, Nev., 1977-86; dir. environ. planning Landrum & Brown, Aviation Planners, Cin., 1986-88; dep. dir. aviation City of Houston Airport System, 1988-90; dir. aviation City of Kansas City, Mo., 1990—. Editor Airport Mgmt. Jour., 1975; contbr. articles to aviation jours. Mem. Am. Assn. Airport Execs. (bd. dirs., ex-officio, accredited 1965, pres. 1979, Pres.'s award 1975, Disting. Svc. award 1991), Airports Coun. Internat. (bd. dirs. 1985-86), Kappa Sigma. Avocations: art, music, collecting military miniatures. Office: Dept Aviation Ste 265 250 Richards Rd Kansas City MO 64116

SOLOMON, JOSEPH, lawyer; b. N.Y.C., Mar. 11, 1904; s. Abraham and Rebecca (Rubin) S.; m. Rita Schwartz, Aug. 31, 1929; children: Alan, Diane Solomon Kempler. LL.B., N.Y. Law Sch., 1927, LL.D. with honors, 1976; L.H.D. (hon.), Bar-Ilan U. 1986. Bar: N.Y. 1928. With Leventritt, Cook, Nathan & Lehman, N.Y.C., 1919-22; asst. to mng. clk. Leventritt, Cook, Nathan & Lehman, 1922-28, mem. legal staff, 1928-45; partner firm Lehman, Rohrlich & Solomon (and predecessor firms), 1945-63, sr. partner, 1963-79; sr. ptnr. firm Pincus, Ohrenstein, Bizar, De Alessandro and Solomon, 1980-83; counsel Ohrenstein & Brown, 1983-87, Milman, Stone, Poltarak, Finell & Solomon, N.Y.C., 1987-90; Gallet, Dreyer & Berkey, N.Y.C., 1990—; mem. com. on character and fitness of applicants for admission to bar appellate div. 1st Jud. Dept., 1977—. Author: Jewish Rights in a Jewish Land, 1987; bd. editors N.Y. Law Jour. Mem. Dr. Alfred Meyer Found. Mt. Sinai Hosp., 1951—; trustee Milton Helpern Libr. Legal Medicine Award, 1980; hon. trustee N.Y. Law Sch., 1985; bd. visitors Columbia U. Sch. Law, 1993—. Decorated cavaliere dell' Ordine al Merito (Italy); recipient Horatio Alger Nat. award, 1978, Disting. Alumnus award N.Y. Law Sch., 1986; Joseph Solomon chair in wills, trusts and estates award in his honor Columbia U. Sch. Law, 1974, Joseph Solomon Fund for arts law internship, Joseph Solomon Presdl. Scholars and Fellows Fund; Joseph Solomon chair in law N.Y. Law Sch., 1975, Rita and Joseph Solomon prof. wills, trusts and estates, 1983, Joseph Solomon Pub. Svc. Scholarship and Endowment Fund N.Y. Law Sch., 1990; Joseph Solomon chair in medicine Mt. Sinai Sch. Medicine, 1976. Mem. ABA, New York County Lawyers Assn. (bd. dirs. 1974-78, certification of appreciation), New York County Lawyers Assn. Found., Assn. Bar City N.Y., Lawyers Club (bd. govs. 1975-79), Am. Soc. Italian Legions of Merit, Phi Delta Phi (hon.). Home: 1025 Fifth Ave New York NY 10028-0134 Office: 845 3d Ave New York NY 10022 Mindful of my debt to various institutions and individuals in my formative years, I have constantly sought to make repayment in some small measure by my acts for the betterment of society in general and people in particular.

SOLOMON, MARTIN M., state senator; b. Jan. 24, 1950; BA magna cum laude, SUNY, Albany; LLB, N.Y. Law Sch. admitted to N.Y. bar, 1976; sole practice, Bklyn.; mem. N.Y. State Senate, 1991—; mem. exec. com. Nat. Conf. Ins. Legislators, ranking mem. sen. ins. com., mem. health, bank, judiciary coms. Mem. Oddfellows, KP. Office: NY State Senate State Capitol Albany NY 12224

SOLOMON, MAYNARD ELLIOTT, music historian, former recording company executive; b. N.Y.C., Jan. 5, 1930; s. Benjamin and Dora (Levine) S.; m. Eva Georgiana Tevan, Jan. 22, 1951; children: Mark Jonathan, Nina Stephanie, Maury David. BA, Bklyn. Coll., 1950; postgrad., Columbia U., 1950-51. Co-founder, co-owner Vanguard Rec. Soc., Inc., N.Y.C., 1950-86; faculty grad. div. CUNY, 1979-81; vis. prof. SUNY Stony Brook, 1988, Columbia U., N.Y.C., 1990, Harvard U., Cambridge, Mass., 1992, Yale U., New Haven, 1994-95. Author: Marxism and Art, 1973, Beethoven, 1977 (translated into German, French, Spanish, Portuguese, Japanese, Italian, Bulgarian), Myth, Creativity and Psychoanalysis, 1978, Beethoven's Tagebuch, 1982, Beethoven's Tagebuch, German translation, 1990, Italian translation, 1992, Beethoven Essays, 1988; Mozart: A Life, 1995; assoc. editor: Am. Imago; mem. editorial bd. Beethovenmaia edit Beethoven's Letters; editor: Memories of Beethoven, 1992; contbr. articles to profl. jours. Recipient Deems Taylor award ASCAP, 1978, 89. Mem. PEN, Am. Musicol. Soc. (bd. dirs. 1984-86, Otto Kinkeldey award 1989), Authors Guild, N.Y. Inst. for Humanities, Phi Beta Kappa. Home: 1 W 72nd St New York NY 10023

SOLOMON, PAUL ROBERT, neuropsychologist, educator; b. Bklyn., Aug. 27, 1948; s. Maynard and Norma Harris (Ruben) S.; m. Suellen Zablow, Aug. 16, 1970; children: Todd, Jessica. BA in Psychology, SUNY, New Paltz, 1970, MA in Psychology, 1972; PhD in Psychology, U. Mass., 1972. lic. Psychologist, Mass. Prof. psychology and neuroscience Williams Coll, Williamstown, Mass., 1976—; neuroscience program chmn., 1990—; dir. memory disorders clinic S.W. Vt. Med. Ctr., Bennington, 1990—; bd. dirs. No. Berkshire Mental Health Assn., North Adams, Mass. Author: Scientific Writings, 1985, Memory, 1989, Psychology 4th edit., 1993; contbr. articles to profl. jours. Bd. dirs. W. Mass. Alzheimers Assn., 1992—. Recipient Distinguished Teaching award U. Mass., Amherst, 1975; Rsch. grantee EPA, NIH, NSF, 1978—; Rsch. fellowships NIH, 1979, NSF, 1980. Fellow APA, AAAS, Am. Psychol. Soc.; mem. Soc. for Neuroscience. Home: 130 Forest Rd Williamstown MA 01267-2029 Office: Williams Coll Dept Psychology Williamstown MA 01262

SOLOMON, PETER R., physicist, physical chemist, engineering executive; b. N.Y.C., Feb. 19, 1939; married 1990, 3 children. BS, City Coll. N.Y., 1960; MA, Columbia U., 1963, PhD in physics, 1965. Rsch. asst. physics Watson Lab. IBM Corp., 1963-65; exp. physicist United Yechnol Rsch. Ctr., 1965-68, prin. sci., 1968-71, asst. to dir. rsch. progs., technol 1971-73, prin. physicist, 1973-80; pres. Advanced Fuel Rsch. Inc., Hartford, Conn., 1980—. Mem. Am. Phys. Soc., Am. Chem. Soc. (henry H. Storch award, 1991), Combustion Inst. Low temp. physics. electrical instabilities in semiconductors, coal sci., superconductivity, instabilities in solids. Office: Advanced Fuel Rsch Inc PO Box 18343 Hartford CT 06118-0343*

SOLOMON, PHILIP MYRON, astronomer, atmospheric scientist; b. N.Y.C., Mar. 19, 1939; s. Nathan and Betty (Safer) S.; m. Sheila Movit; 1 child, Nina Beth. BS in Physics, U. Wis., 1959, MS in Astronomy, 1961, PhD, 1964. Postdoctoral fellow Princeton U., 1964-66; rsch. assoc., lectr. Columbia U., N.Y.C., 1966-71; assoc. prof. Sch. Physics and Atronomy U. Minn., 1971-73; prof. astronomy dept. earth and space scis. SUNY, Stony Brook, 1974—; vis. scientist Inst. Astronomy, Cambridge (Eng.) U., 1967-69, 72, sr. vis. scientist, 1981-82; mem. in Sch. Natural Scis., Inst. for Advanced Study, Princeton, N.J., 1973-74, 86; overseas fellow Churchill Coll., Cambridge, U., 1981-82; vis. prof. Ecole Norman Superieure, Paris, 1989, Max Plauck Inst. for Radioastronomie, Bonn, 1989, Inst. d'Astrophysique, Paris, 1993. Editor: Giant Molecular Clouds in the Galaxy, 1980; contbr. numerous articles to profl. jours. Recipient Sr. Humboldt award Alexander von Humboldt Found., 1989. Mem. Am. Astron. Soc., Internat. Astron. Union. Home: 440 Riverside Dr New York NY 10027 Office: SUNY Stony Book Astronomy Program Dept Earth and Scis Stony Brook NY 11794

SOLOMON, PHYLLIS LINDA, social work educator, researcher; b. Hartford, Conn., Dec. 6, 1945; d. Louis Calvin and Annabell Lee (Nitzberg) S. BA in Sociology, Russell Sage Coll., 1968; MA in Sociology, Case Western Res. U., 1970, PhD in Social Welfare, 1978. Lic. social worker, Pa. Rsch. assoc. Inst. Urban Studies Cleve. State U., 1970-71; program evaluator Cleve. State Hosp., 1971-74; project dir. Ohio Mental Health and Mental Retardation Rsch. Ctr., Cleve., 1974-75; rsch. assoc. Psychiat. Rsch. Found. of Cleve., 1975; project dir. Ohio Mental Health and Mental Retardation Rsch. Ctr., 1977-78; rsch. assoc. dirs. rsch. and mental health planning Fedn. for Community Planning, 1978-88; prof. dept. mental health scis. dir. sect. mental health svcs. and systems research Hahnemann U., Phila., 1988-94; prof. Sch. Social Work U. Pa., Phila., 1994—; secondary appointment Prof. Social Work in Psychiatry U. Pa. Sch. Medicine. Author: (with others) Community Services to Discharged Psychiatric Patients, 1984; co-editor: New Developments in Psychiatric Rehabilitation, 1990, Psychiatric Rehabilitation in Practice, 1993; editorial bd. Community Mental Health Jour., 1988—; contbr. articles to profl. jours. Trustee Cleve. Rape Crisis Ctr., 1981-84, CIT Mental Health Svcs., Cleve., 1985-88; mem. citizen's adv. bd. Sagamore Hills (Ohio) Children's Psychiat. Hosp., 1984-88. Named Evaluator of the Yr., Ohio Program Evaluators Group, 1987;

recipient Ann. award Cuyahoga County Community Mental Health Bd., 1988. Mem. Internat. Assn. Psychosocial Rehab. Svcs. Jewish. Home: 220 E Mermaid Ln Apt 186 Philadelphia PA 19118-3215 Office: U Pa Sch Social Work 3701 Locust Walk Philadelphia PA 19104

SOLOMON, RANDALL L., lawyer; b. Dayton, Ohio, June 8, 1948. BA summa cum laude, Wright State U., 1970; JD, Case Western Res. U., 1973. Bar: Ohio 1973, U.S. Dist. Ct. (no. dist.) Ohio 1973, U.S. Ct. Appeals (6th cir.) 1973, U.S. Ct. Appeals (fed. cir.) 1988. Ptnr. Baker & Hostetler, Cleve.; speaker in field. Fellow Am. Coll. Trial Lawyers; mem. ABA (mem. litigation, tort and ins. practice sects., mem. toxic and hazardous substances and environ. law coms.), Ohio State Bar Assn., Cleve. Bar Assn. (chair litigation sect. 1991-92), Nat. Inst. Trial Advocacy (mem. nat. session 1978), Def. Rsch. Inst. (mem. industrywide litigation com.), Master of Bench, Am. Inn of Ct. Office: Baker & Hostetler 3200 Nat City Ctr 1900 E 9th St Cleveland OH 44114-3303

SOLOMON, RICHARD HARVEY, political scientist; b. Phila., June 19, 1937; s. Bertram Harvey and Ellen (Harris) S.; m. Anne G. Keatley, Dec. 16, 1991. Part-time student, Harvard U., 1959-63, Yale U., 1961, 63-64; SB, MIT, 1960, PhD, 1966. Tech. photographer, lab. worker Photon, Inc., Cambridge, Mass., 1957; researcher Polaroid Corp., 1959-61; research assoc. Ctr. for Chinese Studies U. Mich., Ann Arbor, Mich., 1966-76, from asst prof. to prof. polit. sci., 1966-71; staff mem. NSC, Washington, 1971-76; head. polit. sci dept. The Rand Corp., Santa Monica, Calif., 1976-86, program dir. Internat. Security Policy Research, 1977-83; mem. Pres.' Commn. on Fgn. Lang. and Internat. Studies Washington, 1978-80, mem. Chief of Naval Ops. exec. panel, 1983—; dir. policy planning staff Dept. of State, Washington, 1986-89, asst. sec. of state for East Asian and Pacific affairs, 1989-92; U.S. ambassador to Philippines, 1992-93; pres. U.S. Inst. of Peace, Washington, 1993—. Author: Mao's Revolution and the Chinese Political Culture, 1971, Chinese Political Negotiating Behavior, 1986; contbr. articles to profl. jours. Office: US Inst of Peace Ste 700 1550 M St NW Washington DC 20005-1708

SOLOMON, RICHARD LESTER, retired psychology educator; b. Boston, Oct. 2, 1918; s. Frank and Rose (Roud) S.; children by previous marriage—Janet Ellen, Elizabeth Grace. AB, Brown U., 1940, MSc, 1942, PhD, 1947, ScD (hon.), 1990. Instr. psychology Brown U., 1946; asst. prof. Harvard U., Cambridge, Mass., 1947-50, assoc. prof., 1950-57, prof. social psychology, 1957-60; prof. psychology U. Pa., Phila., 1960-74, James M. Skinner Univ. prof. sci., 1975-85, prof. emeritus, 1985—; staff OSRD, 1942-45. Mem. AAAS, NAS, Am. Psychol. Assn., Ea. Psychol. Assn. (pres.), Psychonomic Soc. (chmn. governing bd.), Am. Acad. Arts and Scis., Soc. Exptl. Psychologists, Phi Beta Kappa, Sigma Xi. Address: 72 Pollard St Conway NH 03818-6155

SOLOMON, ROBERT, economist; b. N.Y.C., May 2, 1921; s. Sol and Betty (Brownstone) S.; m. Fern Rice, Sept. 11, 1946; children: Carol Ann, Barbara Betty, Anne Eleanor. B.A., U. Mich., 1942; M.A., Harvard U., 1947, Ph.D., 1952. With Fed. Res. Bd., 1947-76, assoc. adviser research div., 1963-65, adviser research div., 1965, adviser to bd. govs., 1965-76; dir. div. internat. fin., 1966-72; sr. fellow Brookings Instn., Washington, 1976-80; guest scholar Brookings Instn., 1980—; pres. RS Assos., pub. Internat. Econ. Letter, 1981—; vice chmn. deps. of com. of 20 IMF, 1972-74; adj. prof. Am. U., 1962-67; sr. staff economist Council Econ. Advisers, 1963-64. Author: The International Monetary System, 1945-81, 1982, Partners in Prosperity, 1991, The Transformation of the World Economy, 1980-93, 1994; contbr. articles to profl. jours. Served to 1st lt. USAAF, 1942-45. Decorated D.F.C., Air medal, officier Legion of Honor France; recipient Rockefeller Pub. Service award, 1971. Mem. Am. Econ. Assn., Council on Fgn. Relations. Club: Cosmos (Washington). Home: 8502 W Howell Rd Bethesda MD 20817-6827 Office: Brookings Inst 1775 Massachusetts Ave NW Washington DC 20036-2188

SOLOMON, ROBERT CHARLES, philosopher, educator; b. Detroit, Sept. 14, 1942; s. Charles M. and Vita (Petrosky) S. BA, U. Pa., 1963; MA, U. Mich., 1965, PhD, 1967. Teaching fellow U. Mich., Ann Arbor, 1965-66; lectr. Princeton (N.J.) U., 1966-67, 67-68; asst. prof. U. Pitts., 1969-71, CUNY, 1971-72; assoc. prof. philosophy U. Tex., Austin, 1972-77, prof., 1977—, Quincy Lee Centennial prof., 1986—; vis. prof. U. Pa., UCLA, U. Auckland, N.Z., La Trobe U, Melbourne, Australia, U. B.C.; chmn. Phi Beta Kappa Emerson Award Com.; cons. in field. Author: From Rationalism to Existentialism, 1972, The Passions, 1976, Introducing Philosophy: Problems and Perspectives, 1977, History and Human Nature: A Philosophical Review of European History and Culture, 1750-1850, 1979, Love: Emotion, Myth and Metaphor, 1981, In the Spirit of Hegel, 1983, (with C. Calhoun) What is an Emotion?, 1984, It's Good Business, 1985, (with Kristine Hanson) Above the Bottom Line, 1983, From Hegel to Existentialism, 1987, Continental Philosophy After 1750, 1988, About Love, 1988, A Passion for Justice, 1990, Ethics: A Briefer Introduction, 1991, Ethics and Excellence, 1992, Entertaining Ideas, 1992, (with J. Solomon) Up the University, 1993 (with Kathleen Higgins) A Short History of Philosophy, 1995; editor: Phenomenology and Existentialism, 1972, Nietzsche, 1973, Existentialism, 1974; editor: (with Kathleen Higgins) Reading Nietzsche, 1988, (with Kathleen Higgins) From Africa to Zen, 1993; editor: (with Mark A. Murphy) What is Justice, 1990; contbr. articles to profl. jours. Recipient Outstanding Tchr. award Standard Oil Co., 1973, Pres.' Teaching Excellence award, 1985. Mem. Am. Philos. Assn., N.Am. Nietzsche Soc. (exec. bd.), Internat. Soc. Research on Emotions (bd. dirs.), Soc. for Bus. Ethics.

SOLOMON, ROBERT DOUGLAS, pathology educator; b. Delavan, Wis., Aug. 28, 1917; s. Lewis Jacob and Sara (Ludgin) S.; m. Helen Fisher, Apr. 4, 1943; children: Susan, Wendy, James, William. Student, MIT, 1934-36; BS in Biochemistry, U. Chgo., 1938; MD, Johns Hopkins U., 1942. Intern John's Hopkins Hosp., 1942-43; resident in pathology Michael Reese Hosp., 1947-49; lectr. U. Ill., Chgo., 1947-50; fellow NIH pathology U. Ill., 1949-50; asst. prof. U. Md., Balt., 1955-60; assoc. prof. U. So Calif., L.A., 1960-70; chief of staff City of Hope Nat. Med. Ctr., 1966-67; prof. U. Mo., Kansas City, 1977-78, SUNY, Syracuse, 1978-88; chief of staff The Hosp., Sidney, N.Y., 1985-86; adj. prof. U. N.C. Wilmington 1988—; cons. VA Hosp., Balt., 1955-60, Med. Svc. Lab., Wilmington, 1989—. Co-author: Progress in Gerontological Research, 1967; contbr. papers to profl. jours. V.p. Rotary, Duarte, Calif., 1967; v.p. and pres. Freedom for an Informed Electorate. Capt. Med. Corps, AUS, 1943-46, PTO. Grantee NIH, Fleischmann Found., Am. Heart Assn., Nat. Cancer Inst., 1958-70. Fellow ACP (pres. Md. chpt.); mem. Coll. Am. Pathologists (past pres. Md. chpt.), Am. Soc. Clin. Pathologists, Assn. Clin. Scientists, Am. Chem. Soc., Royal Soc. Medicine (London). Avocations: cruising, astronomy, mathematics, fishing, stamps. Home: 113 S Belvedere Dr Hampstead NC 28443-9212

SOLOMON, SAMUEL, biochemistry educator, administrator; b. Brest Litovsk, Poland, Dec. 5, 1925; s. Nathan and Rachel (Greenberg) S.; m. Sheila R. Horn, Aug. 11, 1953 (div. 1974); children—David Horn, Peter Horn, Jonathan Simon; m. Augusta M. Vineberg, July 12, 1974. B.S. with honors, McGill U., 1947, M.S., 1951, Ph.D. in Biochemistry, 1953. Research asst. Columbia, 1953-55, asso. in biochemistry, 1958-59, asst. prof., 1959-60; asso. prof. biochemistry and exptl. medicine McGill U., 1960-66, prof., 1967-95; prof. emeritus, 1995—; prof. ob-gyn. McGill U., 1976-95; dir. endocrine lab. Royal Victoria Hosp., Montreal, Que., 1965-95; dir. research inst., 1982-85; mem. endocrinology and metabolism grants com. Med. Rsch. Coun. Can., 1967-71, regional dir. for Que., 1993-95; vis. prof. endocrinology U. Vt., 1964; cons. in field; Joseph Price orator, 1982, Am. OB-GYN Soc.; mem. steering com. Pharm. Mfg. Assn. Med. Rsch. Coun. Can. Partnership, 1993—; Med. Rsch. Coun. Can. dir. for McGill U., 1993-95. Co-editor: Chemical and Biological Aspects of Steroid Conjugation, 1970; Editorial bd.: Endocrinology, 1962; asso. editor: Can. Jour. Biochemistry, 1967-71, Jour. Med. Primatology, 1971; Contbr. articles profl. jours. Mem. bd. govs. McGill U., 1975-78; mem. steering com. European Study Group on Steroid Hormones, 1974—; chmn. steering com., 1983-95, chmn. program com., 1990-91; mem. Dublin Commn. of Inquiry Drugs in Athletes, 1988-90. Recipient McLaughlin medal Royal Soc. Can., 1989. Fellow Chem. Inst. Can., Am. Ob-Gyn. Soc. (hon.), Perinatal Rsch. Soc. Am. (pres. 1976), Soc. Gynecol. Investigation (program chmn. 1980), Endocrine Soc. (publ. com. 1986-89). Home: 239 Kensington Ave 804, Montreal, PQ Canada H3Z 2H1

Office: Royal Victoria Hosp Dept Endocrinology, 687 Pine Ave W, Montreal, PQ Canada H3A 1A1

SOLOMON, SEAN CARL, geophysicist, lab director; b. L.A., Oct. 24, 1945. BS geophysics, Calif. Inst. Tech., 1966; PhD geophysics, MIT, 1971. From asst. prof. to prof. geophysics Mass. Inst. Tech., Cambridge, 1972-92; dir. dept. terrestrial magnetism Carnegie Instn., Washington, 1992—; vis. sci. Lunar Sci. Inst., 1975, Jet Propulsion Lab., 1982-83; physicist Lawrence Livermore Lab., 1978; guest investigator Woods Hole Oceanographic Inst., 1979-92; vis. faculty Inst. Geophysics and Planetary physics, dept. Earth and Space Scis. U. Calif. L.A., 1982-83; Roland and Jane Blumberg vis. prof. planetary scis. U. Tex. Austin, 1988; vis. assoc. divsn. geol. and planetary scis. Calif. Inst. tech., 1990-91; mem. NASA, various groups, teams, coms., 1974-95, Earthquake Hazards reduction progam Peer Review panel U.S. Geol. Survey, 1975, 85; lunar and planetary sci. coun. Univs. Space Rsch. Assn., 1978-80, 91-93; working group Inter-Union Commn. Lithosphere, 1981-83; tech. review panel, geophysics review panel Dept. Defense, 1981-86; chmn. steering com. Space Sci. Working group Assn. Am. Univs., 1984-91; review panels NSF, 1986, 88; chmn. standing com. global seismic network Inc. Rsch. Instns. Seismology, 1987-90; participant numerous oceanographic expeditions, 1967-88. Assoc. editor Proceedings of the Lunar and Planetary Sci. Conf., 1976, 78, Jour. Geophys. Rsch., 1976-78, Physics Earth and Planetary Interiors, 1977, Eos Transactions of Am. Geophys. Union, 1979-81, Geophys. Rsch. Letters, 1986-88; editor Tectonophysics, 1981; edit. bd. Physics and Chemistry of Earth, 1981-85; edit. com. Ann. Review Earth and Planetary Scis., 1993—; contbr. over 150 articles to profl. jours. Grad. fellow NSF, 1966-68, postdoctoral fellow, 1971-72; Fannie and John Hertz Found. fellow, 1968-71; Alfred P. Sloan rsch. fellow, 1977-81; John Simon Guggenheim meml. fellow, 1982-83. Fellow Am. Geophys. Union (pres. elect and pres., 1994—, pres. planetology sect. 1984-88, chmn. geophys. monograph bd. 1983-84, numerous coms.); mem. AAAS, Seismological Soc. Am., Geol. Soc. Am., Am. Astron. Soc. (div. planetary scis.), Tau Beta Pi. Office: Carnegie Instn Dept Terrestrial Magnetism 5241 Broad Branch Rd NW Washington DC 20015-1305

SOLOMON, SOLOMON SIDNEY, endocrinologist, pharmacologist, scientist; b. N.Y.C., Dec. 2, 1936; s. Nathan and Irene (Oransky) S.; m. Linda M. Shaw, June 17, 1962 (div. 1980); children: Joan Geller, Rebecca Karen. AB in Chemistry, Harvard U., 1958; MD, U. Rochester, 1962. Intern in internal medicine New Eng. Med. Ctr., Tufts U., Boston, 1963; resident in internal medicine Boston City Hosp., 1964, 65; fellow in endocrinology and metabolism U. Wash. Sch. Medicine, Seattle, 1965-67; teaching fellow Tufts U. and Boston City Hosp., Boston, 1964-65; asst. prof., assoc. prof. then prof. medicine U. Tenn. Sch. Medicine, Memphis, 1969—, assoc. dean for rsch., 1983—, prof. pharmacology, 1986—; chief endocrinology and metabolism VA Med. Ctr., Memphis, 1971—; cons. in field; mem. merit rev. bd. VA Rsch. Svc., Washington, 1978-81. Coeditor: The Lab in Clinical Diagnosis, 1981; contbr. numerous articles and abstracts to profl. jours. Capt. MC, USAF, 1967-69. Harvard Coll. scholar, 1954-58; Whipple scholar, 1959-62; VA and NIH grantee, 1965—. recipient career and devel. award VA Ctrl. Office Rsch. Svc., 1969-71, 1st place for excellence in clin. rsch. Memphis Area Health Industry Couns., 1994. Mem. Am. Diabetes Assn. (pres. Tenn. chpt. 1975-76, rsch. com., chmn. metabolism sect. 1982), So. Soc. Clin. Investigation (chmn. metabolism sect. 1975, 88, nominating com. 1989), Endocrine Soc., Am. Fedn. for Clin. Rsch. (counselor south sect. 1976-79), Am. Soc. Clin. Investigation, Cen. Soc. for Clin. Rsch., Am. Soc. Pharm. and Exptl. Therapy. Jewish. Avocations: antique furniture, history, music, tennis, running. Home: 5196 Longmeadow Dr Memphis TN 38134-4316 Office: VA Med Ctr 1030 Jefferson Ave Memphis TN 38104-2127 At the risk of being mundane, my philosophy in life has always been to get involved...my motto is "I came to play, not to watch."

SOLOMON, STEPHEN MICHAEL, chemical engineer, company executive; b. Bklyn., Oct. 12, 1942; s. Joseph W. Solomon and Friedel (Levi) Sommer; m. Sherry J. Rothstein, June 10, 1967 (div. 1980); m. Kathleen Margaret Murphy, Dec. 21, 1980; children: Sean, Joseph. BChemE, Cornell U., 1965, MChemE, 1966. With Lummus Crest Inc., Bloomfield, N.J., 1965-84, 88—, process design engr., 1965-71, process design mgr., 1971-79, v.p. tech., 1979-84, exec. v.p., 1988-89, pres., 1989—; pres. Combustion Engring. Simcon, Inc., Bloomfield, 1984-88, chmn., 1988-89. Mem. Am. Inst. Chem. Engring. Office: ABB Lummus Crest Inc 1515 Broad St Bloomfield NJ 07003-3002*

SOLOMON, SYD, artist; b. Uniontown, Pa., July 12, 1917; s. Jack E. and Edith (Bennett) S.; m. Ann F. Cohen, Dec. 29, 1941; children—Michele R., Michael. Student, Chgo. Art Inst., 1934, Ecole des Beaux Arts, Paris, 1945. Instr. Art Inst. Pitts., 1947; dir. painting classes Ringling Mus. Art, Sarasota, 1948-50; dir. Sarasota (Fla.) Sch. Art, 1950, 55; mem. of guiding faculty Famous Artists Schs., Inc., Westport, Conn., 1954-70; prof. of art New Coll., Sarasota, 1964-65; vis. instr. painting U. Ill., 1968; vis. instr. Robertson Ctr. Arts and Scis., Binghamton, N.Y., 1969, Tampa Bay (Fla.) Art Ctr., 1972, U. Calif., 1976, Boca Raton (Fla.) Ctr. Art, 1977. Exhbns. include Met. Mus., 1952, Delgado Mus., New Orleans, 1951-57, Butler Mus., Youngstown, 1954-56, Carnegie Inst., 1956, Dallas Mus., 1954, Houston Mus., 1955, Balt. Mus., 1952, High Mus., Atlanta, 1956, Free State Israel Mus., Jerusalem, 1956, Williams Proctor Inst., Utica, N.Y., 1956, Nat. Acad. Art, 1951-56, Birmingham Mus., 1952-62, Saidenberg Gallery, N.Y., 1959-70, Ringling Mus. Art, 1975, N.Y. Cultural Ctr., 1975, Tampa (Fla.) Bay Art Ctr., 1975, Benson Gallery, N.Y., 1975, Adley Gallery, 1978-79, Mus. Fine Arts, St. Petersburg, Fla., Genesis Gallery, N.Y.C., 1981, Art and Culture Ctr., Hollywood, Fla., Nardin Gallery, N.Y.C., 1982, Carone Gallery, Ft. Lauderdale, Phoenix Gallery, Washington, 1983, Boca Raton Mus. Arts, John & Mable Ringling Mus. Art, 1990-91, Polk Mus. Art, Lakeland, Fla., 1992, Butler Inst. Am. Art, Youngstown, Ohio, 1992, Philharm. Ctr. Arts, Naples, Fla., 1993; group exhbn. Painting in the South, 1564-1980, 1984-85; represented in permanent collections including Phila. Mus. Art, Rose Mus., Brandeis U., La. State Mus., Baton Rouge, Guggenheim Mus., Whitney Mus. Am. Art, Wadsworth Athenaeum, Ringling Mus., Birmingham Mus., High Mus., Florida So. Coll., Clearwater (Fla.) Art Mus., Miss. Art Assn., Jackson, Fla., Fedn. Art Miami, Mus. Fine Arts, St. Petersburg, Miami Dade Collection, Fla., Balt. Mus., Weatherspoon Gallery, U. N.C., Corcoran Gallery Art, Washington, Herbert F. Johnson Mus. Art, Cornell U., Lowe Gallery Mus., Miami, Fla., Cin. Mus. Art, Walter P. Chrysler, Jr. Collections, Dewitt Mus., Joseph Hirschhorn Collection, Delgado Mus., Adelphi U. Mus., Tel Aviv Mus., Norton Mus., Ft. Lauderdale Mus., Polk Pub. Mus., Guild Hall, E. Hampton, N.Y., Mus. of South, Memphis, Tampa Bay Art Ctr.; camouflage designer: Engrs. Bd, Washington, 1942. Recipient Hallmark Internat. award, 1952, Purchases prize Fla. Internat., 1952, Lowe Gallery Ann. award, 1953, Southeaster ann. award, 1953, High Mus. award, 1956, Casein Soc. medal of honor, 1957, Audobon Soc. medal of honor, 1957, 1st Purchase watercolor award Butler Mus. Art, 1957, 58, 1st Purchase prize Sarasota Art Assn., Childe Hassam purchase award Hassam and Speicher Fund, 1979, Fla. prize award N.Y. Times, 1987. Mem. Nat. Soc. Lit. and Arts, Artists Equity, Allied Arts Coun. Address: 9210 Blind Pass Rd Sarasota FL 34242-2908 also: Harmon Meek Gallery 386 Broad Ave S Naples FL 33940-7079

SOLOMON, VITA PETROSKY, artist; b. Phila., Dec. 16, 1916; d. Harry and Rose (Bobrow) Petrosky; m. Charles M. Solomon, Apr. 8, 1941; children: Robert Charles, Henry Andrew, Jon David. Diploma, Moore Inst. Art, 1937; B.F.A., Tyler Sch. Fine Arts, Temple U., 1958, B.S. in Edn, 1958, M.F.A., 1960. tchr. art and art history Cheltenham High Sch.; tchr. art and English Elkins Park Jr. High Sch. Exhibited in group shows at United Soc. Artists, London, Pa. Acad. Fine Art, Phila. Art Mus., Detroit Inst. Art, Butler Inst. Art, Silvermine Guild, Conn., N.A.D., Am. Water Color Soc., Audubon Soc., Royal Acad. Arts, London, Paris Salon, Woodmere Art Gallery, Phila. Art Alliance, Royal Inst. London, Nat. Arts Club, N.Y., Met. Mus. Art , others; represented in permanent collections Nat. Portrait Gallery, Phila. Mus. Art, Fed. Res. Bank, Temple U., U. Pa., Phila. City Hall, Free Library Phila., Phila. Psychiat. Inst., Cheltenham Twp. Adminstrn. Bldg., others, including portraits on commn.; one-artist shows include Phila. Art Alliance, 1953, 54, 58, Red Door Gallery, 1959, 60, 61, Newman Gallery, 1964, Moore Coll. Art, 1974, Suzanne Gross Gallery 1979 . J.F. Lewis traveling fellow Europe, by Moore Inst., 1937; recipient Gross Meml. award Silvermine Guild, 1958, Chandler prize Allied Artists Am., 1960, Nat. Arts Club award, 1974, prizes Moore Inst., 1957, 60, 61, purchase prize Temple U., 1959 (2), 1960, painting prize, 1966, Burdine

meml. prize Woodmere Gallery, 1964, painting prize Wharton Art Ctr., 1964, Lowell Painting prize C.L. Wolfe Club, Nat. Arts Club, 1966, Painting prize Silver medal Paris Salon, 1966, award Phila. Watercolor Club, 1973, Benedictine Art award, 1972, Blumenthal prize Cheltenham Art Center, 1973, Jane Peterson medal Audubon Artists, 1975, Eugenia Atwood purchase prize Phila. Print Club, 1975, Eyre medal Phila. Watercolor Club, 1977, Best Figure Painting prize Woodmere Gallery, 1977, Best in Show award Moore Coll. Art, 1980, award of excellence Ariz. Aqueous VII, 1992, 2nd prize Phila. Plastic Show, 1993, Best in Show award Tubac Ctr. Arts, Ariz., 1995. Mem. Am. Watercolor Soc., Cheltenham Twp. Art Centre (award for best profl. painting 1980, 83, 85), Am. Watercolor Soc., Artists Equity, Phila. Water Color Club (Pennell Meml. prize 1987, 88), Allied Artists Am., Am. Color Print Soc. (prize 1987), Western Fedn. Watercolor Socs. (award of excellence 1991), So. Ariz. Watercolor Guild (Excellence award U. Ariz. 1991, Signature mem. 1992, Past Pres.'s award 1994), So. Ariz. Tubac Ctr. Arts (award of excellence 1991, hon. mention 1993), Phila. Sketch Club (Best in Show award ann. pastel show, hon. mention 1990, 3d prize ann. print show 1993). Home: 200 Locust St Apt 24G Philadelphia PA 19106-3920 also: 6298 N Campbell Ave Tucson AZ 85718-3150

SOLOMON, ZACHARY LEON, apparel manufacturing company executive; b. N.Y.C., July 22, 1934; s. Nathan and Rose Solomon; children: Lisa, Michael, Andrew, Romy; m. Susan Phillips. BA, Bklyn. Coll., 1957; MBA, NYU, 1962. Div. mdse. mgr. Abraham & Strauss, Bklyn., 1957-72; v.p., gen. mdse. mgr. Apparel Buying Svcs., Secaucus, N.Y., 1972-73; sr. v.p., gen. mdse. mgr. May Co., L.A., 1974-75, exec. v.p., 1980-82; exec. v.p. The Emporium, San Francisco, 1975-77, pres., 1978-80; exec. v.p. Manhattan Industries, N.Y.C., pres., CEO Perry Ellis, 1983-87; pres. Ellen Tracy Co., N.Y.C., 1987-90; pres., chief exec. officer Associated Merchandising Corp., N.Y.C., 1991—. Trustee Bklyn. Coll. Jewish. Office: Associated Merchandising 1440 Broadway New York NY 10018-2301

SOLOMONS, GUS, JR. (GUSTAVE MARTINEZ), choreographer, dancer, writer; b. Boston; s. Gustave Martinez and Olivia Mae. Student, Boston Conservatory of Music, 1956-59; BArch, MIT, 1961; postgrad., Martha Graham Sch., N.Y.C., 1961-66. Dance soloist Martha Graham Co., N.Y.C., 1964-65, Donald McKayle Co., 1961-64, Merce Cunningham Co., N.Y.C., 1965-68; artistic dir. The Solomons Dance Co., N.Y.C., 1972—; dean, artistic dir. Calif. Inst. of the Arts, Valencia, 1976-78; vis. artist-in-residence U. Calif., Santa Cruz, Calif. State U., Long Beach, others; dance panelist Nat. Endowment Arts; various other other state art couns., 1983—; assoc. prof. dance numerous colls., univs., including UCLA, Un. Nev.-Las Vegas, Tex. Christian U., York, Simon Fraser, NYU; mem. faculty Tisch Sch. of Arts, 1994—; USIA cons. to Nat. Dance Co., Tanzania, East Africa, 1988, Argentina, 1994. Appearances maj. TV networks, Sta. WGBH-TV, Boston; choreographr for various univs. and dance cos.; writer dance criticism for Village Voice, Dance Mag., others. Recipient numerous grants Nat. Endowment for Arts, 1983—, N.Y. State Coun. on the Arts, 1972—; fellow Nat. Endowment for Arts, 1978-80. Studio: 889 Broadway New York NY 10003-1212 *The content of a good dance is the truth about its maker. Performing it is a confession to the audience. The dancer places himself in the position of ultimate vulnerability each time he performs; it is at once cleansing, fulfilling, and courageous.*

SOLOMONS, MARK ELLIOTT, lawyer; b. Buffalo, Mar. 4, 1946; s. Alvin and Trude (Salant) S.; m. Jill E. Kent, Aug. 20, 1978. BA, U. Rochester, 1967; JD, U. Pa., 1970; LLM, George Washington U., 1973. Bar: N.Y. 1971, D.C. 1981. Staff atty. U.S. Dept. Labor, Washington, 1970-73, counsel coal miners benefits, 1973-77, legis. counsel, 1977-80; prin. Kilcullen Wilson & Kilcullen, Washington, 1980-86; ptnr. Arter and Hadden, Washington, 1986—, mem. exec. com. 1989—; guest lectr. law and history SUNY-Stony Brook, 1970-76, U. Mich., 1977-78, Hobart Coll., 1972-76; prin. Coun. for Excellence in Govt., 1991—. Contr. articles to profl. jours. Vice chair Appellate Advocacy Com., 1994—. Mem. ABA (chair workers compensation and employers liability com. 1987-88, sr. vice chair 1988-94), Fed. Bar Assn. (chair regulatory com. 1988—), D.C. Bar Assn., N.Y. Bar Assn., Am. Inn of Ct. (master 1991). Republican. Office: Arter & Hadden 1801 K St NW Washington DC 20006-1301

SOLOMONSON, CHARLES D., corporate executive; b. 1930; m. Sarah B. Auer, 1952; children: Katherine M., Charles W. B.S., Columbia U., 1954; M.B.A., Harvard U., 1956. With Denver Union Stock Yard Co., 1956-60; sec., asst. treas. G. D. Searle & Co., 1960-68; with Jos. Schlitz Brewing Co., 1968-69, treas., 1969-73; v.p. fin. Fairmont Food Co., Omaha, 1969-73, pres., 1973-74, dir., 1972-75; v.p. fin. treas. Hobart Corp., Troy, Ohio, 1975-77, v.p. fin. and Adminstrn., dir., 1977-79; sr. v.p., chief fin. officer Holiday Corp., Memphis, 1979, dir., 1980-88, exec. v.p., chief fin. and adminstrv. officer, 1981-87; ret. Trustee Nebr. Meth. Hosp., 1973-75, Miami Valley Hosp., Dayton, Ohio, 1977-79, Sta. WKNO-TV-FM, Memphis, 1983-88, Dixon Gallery and Gardens, 1985-88. Episcopalian. Home: 1030 N State St Apt 42H Chicago IL 60610-2837

SOLOTOROVSKY, JULIAN, lawyer; b. Plainfield, N.J., Oct. 12, 1951; s. Morris and Mary Louise (Whitty) S.; m. Stacee Levy, Sept. 13, 1980; children: Alec, Scott, Laura. BA, U. Va., 1973; JD, John Marshall Law Sch., Chgo., 1978. Bar: Ill. 1978, U.S. Dist. Ct. (no. dist.) Ill. 1978, U.S. Ct. Appeals (7th cir.) 1978. Asst. U.S. atty., dep. chief spel. prosecutions U.S. Dept. Justice, Chgo., 1978-87; mem. Kelley Drye & Warren, Chgo., 1987—; mem. 7th Cir. Jury Instrn. Com., Chgo., 1979-82. Avocations: running, gardening, carpentry. Office: Kelley Drye & Warren 303 W Madison St Chicago IL 60606-3309

SOLOV, ZACHARY, choreographer, ballet artist; b. Phila., Feb. 15, 1923; s. Carl Nathan and Sima (Silnutzer) S. Student, Littlefield Ballet Sch., 1937-40, U. of the Dance, 1947. Appeared with, Am. Jubilee, N.Y. World's Fair, 1940, tour with, Littlefield Ballet, 1941, Am. Ballet, S.A., 1941; with, Dance Players, summer quarters, New Hope, Pa., 1942, The Lady Comes Across, N.Y. City, 1942, Ballet Theatre, London, 1946; choreographer ballet master, Met. Opera, N.Y. City. Served as staff sgt. A.A.C., 1943-46. Recipient Capezio Dance award, 1952. Office: 200 W 58th St New York NY 10019-1401

SOLOVY, JEROLD SHERWIN, lawyer; b. Chgo., Apr. 10, 1930; s. David and Ida (Wilensky) S.; m. Kathleen Hart; children: Stephen, Jonathan. B.A., U. Mich., 1952; LL.B. Harvard U., 1955. Bar: Ill. 1955. Assoc. Jenner & Block, Chgo., 1955-63, ptnr., 1963—, chmn., 1991—. Active Cook County Jud. Adv. Council, Chgo., 1975-77, 82-89, chmn., 1989-91. Fellow Am. Coll. Trial Lawyers; mem. ABA, Chgo. Bar Assn., Ill. State Bar. Assn. Clubs: Standard; Lake Shore Country (Chgo.). Office: Jenner & Block Bldg 4400 1 E Ibm Plz Ste 4400 Chicago IL 60611-3605

SOLOW, HERBERT FRANKLIN, film producer, writer; b. N.Y.C., Dec. 14, 1930; s. Morris David and Frances Louise (Burnbrum) S.; m. Maxine Debra Turner, Aug. 6, 1954 (div. 1974); children: Jody, Bonnie, Jamie; m. Yvonne Fern, 1995. AB, Dartmouth Coll., 1953. Agt. William Morris Agy., N.Y.C., 1954-58; dir., exec. NBC, N.Y.C., 1958-59, Los Angeles, 1958-60, CBS, Los Angeles, 1961-63; v.p. Desilu Studios, Los Angeles, 1964-69; v.p. prodn. Paramount TV, Los Angeles, 1969; v.p. worldwide prodn. Metro-Goldwyn-Mayer, Los Angeles, 1969-73; pres. Solow Prodn. Co., Los Angeles, 1976-79; v.p. Sherwood Prodns., Los Angeles, 1980-83; ind. producer, writer Los Angeles, 1984—. Mem. Writers Guild Am., Dirs. Guild Am., Acad. Motion Picture Arts and Scis., Acad. TV Arts and Scis.

SOLOW, ROBERT MERTON, economist, educator; b. Brooklyn, N.Y., Aug. 23, 1924; s. Milton Henry and Hannah Gertrude (Sarney) S.; m. Barbara Lewis, Aug. 19, 1945; children: John Lewis, Andrew Robert, Katherine. BA, Harvard U., 1947, MA, 1949, PhD, 1951, DLitt (hon.), 1992; LLD (hon.), U. Chgo., 1967, Brown U., 1972, U. Warwick, 1976, Tulane U., 1983, Dartmouth Coll., 1990, DLitt (hon.), Williams Coll., 1974, Lehigh U., 1977, Wesleyan U., 1982, Boston Coll., 1986, Harvard U., 1992, Colgate U., 1990; DSc (hon.), U. Paris, 1971, U. Geneva, 1982, Bryant Coll., 1988; D of Social Sci. (hon.), Yale U., 1976, U. Mass., Boston, 1989; D Social Sci. (hon.), U. Helsinki, 1990, SUNY, Albany, 1991, U. Glasgow, 1992, Rutgers U., 1994; D honoris causa, U. Chile, 1992; Conservatoire Nat. des Arts et Metiers, Conservatoire Nat. des Arts et Métiers, Paris, 1994. Mem. faculty MIT, 1949-95, prof. econs., 1958-95, inst. prof., 1973-95, prof.

emeritus, 1995—; sr. economist Coun. Econ. Advisers, 1961-62, cons., 1962-68; cons. RAND Corp., 1952-64; Marshall lectr., fellow commonoter Peterhouse, Cambridge (Eng.) U., 1963-64; Eastman vis. prof. Oxford U., 1968-69; overseas fellow Churchhill Coll., Cambridge; sr. fellow Soc. Fellows, Harvard U., 1975-89; bd. dirs. Boston Fed. Res. Bank, 1975-80, chmn., 1979-80; active President's Commn. on Income Maintenance, 1968-70, President's Com. on Tech., Automation and Econ. Progress, 1964-65, Carnegie Commn. Sci., Tech. and Govts., 1988-93, Nat. Sci. Bd., 1994—. Author: Linear Programming and Economic Analysis, 1958, Capital Theory and the Rate of Return, 1963, The Sources of Unemployment in the United States, 1964, Growth Theory, 1970, Price Expectations and the Behavior of the Price Level, 1970, (with M. Dertouzos, R. Lester) Made in America, 1989, The Labor Market as a Social Institution, 1990. Bd. dirs., mem. exec. com. Nat. Bur. Econ. Rsch.; trustee Inst. for Advanced Study, Princeton U., 1972-78, Woods Hole Oceanographic Inst., 1988—, Alfred P. Sloan Found., 1992—, Resources for the Future, 1994—, Urban Inst., 1994—. With AUS, 1942-45. Recipient David A. Wells prize Harvard U., 1951, Seidman award in polit. economy, 1983, Nobel prize in Econs., 1987; fellow Ctr. Advanced Study Behavioral Scis., 1957-58, trustee, 1982—, chmn., 1987-95. Fellow Am. Acad. Arts and Scis., Brit Acad. (corr.); mem. AAAS (v.p. 1970), Am. Philos. Soc., Nat. Acad. Scis. (council 1977-80), Acad. dei Lincei, Am. Econ. Soc. (exec. com. 1964-66, John Bates Clark medal 1961, v.p. 1968, pres. 1979), Econometric Soc. (pres. 1964, mem. exec. com.). Home: 528 Lewis Wharf Boston MA 02110-3906 Office: MIT Dept Econs Cambridge MA 02139

SOLOWAY, ALBERT HERMAN, medicinal chemist; b. Worcester, Mass., May 29, 1925; s. Bernard and Mollie (Raphaelson) S.; m. Barbara Berkowicz, Nov. 29, 1953; children: Madeleine Rae, Paul Daniel, Renee Ellen. Student, U.S. Naval Acad., 1945-46; BS, Worcester Poly. Inst., 1948; PhD, U. Rochester, 1951. Postdoctoral fellow Nat. Cancer Inst. at Sloan-Kettering Inst., N.Y.C., 1951-53; research chemist Eastman Kodak Co., Rochester, N.Y., 1953-56; asst. chemist Mass. Gen. Hosp., Boston, 1956-61, asso. chemist, 1961-73; asso. prof. med. chemistry Northeastern U., Boston, 1966-68, prof. medicinal chemistry, chmn. dept., 1968-71, prof. medicinal chemistry and chemistry, chmn. dept. medicinal chemistry and pharmacology, 1971-74; dean Coll. Pharmacy and Allied Health Professions, 1975-77; dean Coll. Pharmacy Ohio State U., Columbus, 1977-88, prof. medicinal chemistry, 1977—. Author research medicinal chemistry. Served with USNR, 1944-45. Fellow AAAS, Acad. Pharm. Soc.; mem. Am. Chem. Soc., Am. Assn. Coll. Pharmacy, Am. Assn. Cancer Research, Am. Assn. Pharm. Sci., Am. Nuclear Soc. Jewish (trustee temple 1969-77, v.p., 1970-73). Office: Ohio State U 500 W 12th Ave Columbus OH 43210-1214

SOLTI, SIR GEORG, conductor; b. Budapest, Hungary, Oct. 21, 1912; naturalized Brit. citizen, 1972; s. Mor Stern and Theres (Rosenbaum) S.; m. Hedi Oechsli, Oct. 29, 1946; m. Anne Valerie Pitts, Nov. 11, 1967; 2 daus. Ed., Budapest Music High Sch.; MusD (hon.), Leeds U., 1971, Oxford U., 1972, DePaul U., Yale U., 1974, Harvard U., 1979, Furman U., 1983, Sussex U., 1983, London U., 1986, Rochester U., 1987, Bologna (Italy) U., 1988, Roosevelt U., Chgo., 1990. Music dir. Chgo. Symphony Orch., 1969-91, music dir. laureate, 1991—. Mus. asst. Budapest Opera House, 1930-39, pianist, Switzerland, 1939-45; gen. music dir. Munich (Germany) State Opera, 1946-52, Frankfurt (Germany) City Opera, 1952-60; mus. dir. Royal Opera House Covent Garden, London, 1961-71, Orchestre de Paris, 1972-75; prin. condr. and artistic dir. London Philharm., 1979-83; condr. emeritus London Philharm., 1983-90, music dir. laureate Royal Opera House Covent Garden, London, 1992—; pianist Concours Internat., Geneva, 1942; guest condr. various orchs. including N.Y. Philharm., Vienna Philharm., Berlin Philharm., London Symphony, Bayerischer Rundfunk, Norddeutscher Rundfunk, Salzburg, Edinburgh, Glyndebourne, Ravinia and Bayreuth Festivals, Vienna State, Met. Opera; condr. concert tours with Chgo. Symphony to Europe, 1971, 74, 78, 81, 85, 89, 90, Chgo. Symphony to Japan, 1977, 86, 90, Chgo. Symphony to Australia, 1988; artistic dir. Salzburg Easter Festival and Whitsun Concerts, 1992-93; prin. guest condr. Paris Opera Bicentennial Tour, 1976, rec. artist for London Records. Recipient 31 Grammys, Gold medal Royal Philharm. Soc., Gt. Britain, 1992, honored by John F. Kennedy Ctr. for Performing Arts, Washington, for lifetime achievement in music. Office: Royal Coll. Music (London). Office: care Chgo Symphony Orch 220 S Michigan Ave Chicago IL 60604-2508*

SOLTMAN, NEIL M., lawyer; b. Phila., July 20, 1949. BA magna cum laude, Temple U., 1971; JD, Cath. U. Am., 1975. Bar: Calif. 1975. Ptnr. Mayer, Brown & Platt, L.A. Editor articles, book reviews Cath. U. Am. Law Review, 1974-75. Mem. ABA (litigation sect.). Office: Mayer Brown & Platt 350 S Grand Ave Los Angeles CA 90071-1503

SOLTYS, JOHN JOSEPH, JR., lawyer; b. Portsmouth, Va., Feb. 4, 1942; s. John J. Sr. and Antoinette N. Soltys; children: John J. III, Amy Elaine. BS, USCG Acad., 1963; JD, Willamette U., 1970. Bar: Wash. 1970, U.S. Dist. Ct. (we. and ea. dists.) Wash. 1970. From assoc. to sr. ptnr. Karr, Tuttle, Seattle, 1970-89; sr. ptnr. Cozen & O'Connor, Seattle, 1989—. Lt. (j.g.) USCG, 1963-67. Mem. Wash. Def. Trial Lawyers (pres. 1986-87), Fedn. Ins. & Corp. Counsel. Avocations: fishing, hunting, soccer, gardening. Office: Cozen & O'Connor 1201 3rd Ave Ste 5200 Seattle WA 98101-3033

SOLTYSINSKI, STANISLAW J., law educator; b. 1939. A, Mickiewicz U., Poland, 1965; postgrad., London Sch. of Econ., Oxford, 1966-67; LLM, Columbia U, 1973. Prof. U. Pa., 1975-76, 1978—; prof., dean Mickiewicz U., 1981-84. Home: Przeswit 5, Poznan 60-655, Poland Office: Soltysinski Kawecki and Szajkowski, Konstruktorska 1A, Warsaw 02-673, Poland

SOLURSH, LIONEL PAUL, psychiatrist; b. Toronto, Jan. 14, 1936; came to U.S., 1986, naturalized, 1994; s. Coleman Bernard and Zelma Dorothy (Singer) S.; m. Marcia Persin (div.); children: Fern, Susan, Marc; m. Diane Sue Mullenax; children: Lia, Janine. MD, U. Toronto, 1959; Diploma in Psychiatry, U. Toronto, Can., 1962; CRCPC, Royal Coll. Physicians, 1964, FRCPC, 1965. Diplomate Am. Bd. Sexology; bd. cert. sex educator and clin. supr. Asst. prof. U. Toronto, 1965-73; staff psychiatrist Toronto Western Hosp., 1966-80, assoc. head psychiatry, 1973-79; outpatient psychiatrist Toronto East Gen. and Orthopaedic Hosp., 1980-86; assoc. professor psychiatry U. Toronto, 1974-86; cons. psychiatrist Augusta (Ga.) Correctional Med. Inst., 1990—; med. dir. Spl. In-Patient Unit/Post-traumatic Stress Disord., 1986—, med. dir. Ga. Augusta, 1986—; asst. chief svc. psychiatry, 1991—; prof. psychiatry and health behavior Med. Coll. of Ga., Augusta, 1986—; assoc. fellow Am. Coll. Sexology, 1995—; cons. Ga. Regional Hosp., Augusta; speaker in field. Author: (audiotape) Human Sexuality, 1967, 71, (videotape) Art, Symbolism & Mental Health, 1991; contbr. book revs. and more than 148 papers to profl. jours. and chpts. to books. Named R.S. McLaughlin Traveling fellow, 1966, Outstanding Young Canadian, 1974, Minister of Health Gold medalist U. Toronto, 1962. Fellow Am. Orthopsychiat. Assn., Am. Psychiat. Assn., Acad. Clin. Sexologists (assoc.); mem. AMA, Am. Acad. Psychiatrists in Alcoholism and Addictions, Can. Psychiat. Assn., Internat. Soc. for Traumatic Stress Studies, Am. Assn. Sex Educators, Counselors and Therapists. Jewish. Avocations: photography, scuba diving, travel, performing arts, cyberspace touring. Office: VA Med Ctr 1 Freedom Way Augusta GA 30904

SOLVELL, STEFAN, pharmaceutical executive; b. 1954. With Astra USA Inc., 1981—, now treas. Office: Astra USA Inc 50 Otis St Westborough MA 01581*

SOLZHENITSYN, ALEKSANDR ISAYEVICH, author; b. Kislovodsk, Russia, Dec. 11, 1918; imprisoned under Joseph Stalin for critical comments, 1945-53; exiled to Soviet Cen. Asia, 1953; freed from exile, 1956; expelled from USSR, 1974; now living in U.S.; m. Natalya Reshetovskaya, 1940 (div.), remarried, 1956 (div.); m. Natalia Svetlova, 1973; children: Yermoli, Ignat, Stepan. Corr. student in philology, Moscow Inst. History, Philosophy and Lit., 1939-41; degree in math. and physics, U. Rostov, 1941; Litt.D., Harvard U., 1978. Author: Odin den' Ivana Denisovicha, 1962 (pub. as One Day in the Life of Ivan Denisovich, 1963), Dlia pol'zy dela, 1963 (pub. as For the Good of the Cause, 1964), Sluchai na stantsii Krechetovka/Matrenin dvor, 1963 (pub. as We Never Make Mistakes, 1963), Etudy i krokhotnye rasskazy, 1964 (pub. as Stories and Prose Poems, 1971, as Prose Poems, 1971, as Matryona's House and Other Stories, 1975), V kruge pervom, 1968 (pub. as The First Circle, 1968; Prix du Meilleur Livre Etranger France 1969), Rakovyi korpus, 1968 (pub. as Cancer Ward, 1968; Prix du Meilleur Livre Etranger France 1969). Le Droits de l'écrivain, 1969, Sobranie sochinenii (6 vols.), 1969-70, Six Etudes, 1971, Avgust chetyrnadtsatogo, 1971 (pub. as August 1914, 1972), Nobelevskaia lektsiia po literature, 1972 (pub. as Nobel Lecture, 1972, as One Word of Truth, 1972), Arkhipelag Gulag (3 vols.), 1973-76 (pub. as The Gulag Archipelago, 1974-78), Prusskie nochi: poema napisannaia v lagere v 1950, 1974 (pub. as Prussian Nights, 1977), Iz-pod glyb, 1974 (pub. as From Under the Rubble, 1975), Mir i nasilie, 1974, Pis'mo vozhdiam Sovetskogo soiuza, 1974 (pub. as Letter to the Soviet Leaders, 1974), A Pictorial Autobiography, 1974, Solzhenitsyn, the Voice of Freedom, 1975, Bodalsia telenok s dubom, 1975 (pub. as The Oak and the Calf, 1980), Lenin v Tsiurikhe, 1975 (pub. as Lenin in Zurich, 1976), Detente: Prospects for democracy and Dictatorship, 1975, America, We Beg You to Interfere, 1975, Amerikanskie rechi, 1975, Warning to the Western World, 1976, A World Split Apart, 1978, Alexander Solzhenitsyn Speaks to the West, 1978, Sobranie sochinenii, 1978, The Mortal Danger, 1980, East and West, 1980, Issledovaniia noveishei russkoi istorii, 1980, Publitsistika: stat'i i rechi, 1981, Krasnoe koleso: povestvovan'e v otmerennykh srokakh Uzel I: Avgust chetyrnadtsatogo, 1983 (pub. as The Red Wheel: A Narrative in Discrete Periods of Time, 1989), Krasnoe koleso: povestvovan'e v otmerennykh srokakh Uzel II: Oktiabr'shestnadtsatogo, 1984, Krasnoe koleso: povestvovan'e v otmerennykh srokakh Uzel III: Mart semnadtsatogo, 1986, Rasskazy, 1990, Kak nam obustroit' Rossiiu, 1990, Krasnoe koleso: povestvovan'e v otmerennykh srokakh Uzel IV: Aprel'semnadtsatogo, 1991, Rebuilding Russia: Toward Some Formulations, 1991, Les Invisibles, 1992, Nashi pliuralisty: otryvok iz vtorogo toma 'Ocherkov literaturnoi zhizni', 1992, The Russian Question Toward the End of the Twentieth Century, 1995; (plays) Olen' i shalashovka, 1968 (pub. The Love-Girl and the Innocent, 1969), Svecha na vetru, 1968 (pub. Candle in the Wind, 1973), Pir podebitelei, 1981 (pub. as Victory Celebrations, 1983), Plenniki, 1981 (pub. as Prisoners, 1983), P'esy i kinostsenarii, 1981; editor: Russkii slovar' iazykovogo rasshireniia, 1990. Arty. officer Russian Army, World War II. Recipient Lenin prize nomination, 1964, Nobel prize for lit., 1970, Freedoms Found. award Stanford U., 1976, Templeton Found. prize, 1983. Mem. Am. Acad. Arts and Scis., Hoover Inst. War, Revolution and Peace (hon.). •

SOMA, ROSE SMERALDI, broadcaster, writer, women's rights activist, television and radio producer; b. Bronx, N.Y., Feb. 17, 1940) d. Albert and Jeanette (DiCostanzo) Smeraldi; attended NYC public schs. until 1955; m. Fraser Soma, Sept. 13, 1967; children: Michael, Carl, Paul, Steven, Nancy, Errol. Producer, interviewer, reporter WALK radio, L.I., N.Y., 1976—; producer weekly feminist radio program, 1976—; lectr., condr. workshops on women's rights; media public relations cons. feminist issues for radio and TV, 1978. Author: (survey questionnaire) Women Speak Out, 1990. Chmn. reprodn./abortion rights task force Suffolk (N.Y.) chpt. NOW, 1975—; chmn. media task force, 1975—; producer/host Women Speak Out and People Speak Out, Brookhaven Cable TV, Port Jefferson Sta., N.Y., 1979—; Women Speak Out, Sta. WYFA, Medford, N.Y., 1979—; Suffolk Cablevision, 1979—, Sta. WBLI-FM, 1980—; media coordinator, personal mgr. entertainment acts, 1981—; bd. dirs. Planned Parenthood of East Suffolk, 1977—; coordinator L.I. chpt. Nat. Coalition to Defend the Bill of Rights, 1978—; coordinator public relations and media for L.I. chpt. Internat. Women's Yr. Meeting for N.Y. State, 1977; exec. dir., co-founder Americans United to Save Legal Abortion, 1977—; founder Women Speak Out Internat., 1978; adv. bd. Women's Health Alliance L.I., 1978; chmn. abortion rights task force N.Y. State orgn. NOW, 1978; coordinator L.I. Coalition for Reproductive Rights; asso. Women's Inst. for Freedom of Press, 1976—. Mem. Am. Women in Radio and TV, Nat. Fedn. Press Women. Author: Women Speak Out About Abortion, 1978, Women Speak Out About Abortion: Update '92; contbr. numerous articles to profl. jours.; author monthly column for NOW newsletter, 1974—; editorial asst. and AdViews mag.; editorial asst. AdViews mag.; video editor, features editor Good Times mag. Home: PO Box 208 Selden NY 11784-0208 Office: UACC Brookhaven Cable TV Industrial Rd Port Jefferson Station NY 11776 also: Sta WBLI 106 FM Long Island NY 11763 also: AdViews Mag PO Box 268 Greenville NY 12083-0268

SOMASUNDARAN, PONISSERIL, surface and colloid engineering, applied science educator; b. Pazhookara, Kerala, India, June 28, 1939; came to U.S., 1961; s. Kumara Moolayil and Lakshmikutty (Amma) Pillai; m. Usha N., May 25, 1966; 1 child, Tamara. BS, Kerala U., Trivandrum, India, 1958; BE, Indian Inst. Sci., Bangalore, 1961; MS, U. Calif., Berkeley, 1962, PhD, 1964. Rsch. engr. U. Calif., 1964; research engr. Internat. Minerals & Chem. Corp., Skokie, Ill., 1965-67; rsch. chemist R.J. Reynolds Industries, Inc., Winston-Salem, N.C., 1967-70; assoc. prof. Columbia U., N.Y.C., 1970-78, prof. mineral engring., 1978-83, La Von Duddleson Krumb prof., 1983—; chmn. Henry Krumb Sch. Chem. Engring., Materials Sci. and Mining Engring., Columbia U., 1988—, dir. Langmuir Ctr. for Colloids and Interfaces, 1987—; cons. numerous agys., cos. including NIH, 1974, B.F. Goodrich, 1974, NSF, 1974, Alcan, 1981, UNESCO, 1982, Sohio, 1984-85, IBM, 1984, Am. Cyanamd, 1988-89, Duracell, 1988-89, DuPont, 1989, Canmet, 1990-93, Unilever, 1991—, Engelhard, 1991—, UoP, 1991-92, Alcoa, 1991-92; mem. panel NRC; chmn. numerous internat. symposia and NSF workshops; mem. adv. panel Bur. Mines Generic Ctr., 1983-91; keynote and plenary lectr. internat. meetings; hon. prof. Cen. South U. Tech., China; Brahm Prakash chair in metallurgy and material sci. Indian Inst. Sci., Bangalore, 1990; hon. rsch. advisor Beijing Gen. Rsch. Inst., 1991—. Editor books, including Fine Particles Processing, 1980 (Publ. Bd. award 1980); editor-in-chief Colloids and Surfaces, 1980—; Henry Krumb lectr. AIME, 1988; contbr. numerous articles to profl. publs., patentee in field. Pres. Keralasamajam of Greater N.Y., N.Y.C., 1974-75; bd. dirs. Fedn. Indian Assocs., N.Y.C., 1974—, Vols. in Service to Edn. in India, Hartford, Conn., 1974—. Recipient Disting. Achievement in Engring. award, AINA, 1980, Antoine M. Gaudin award Soc. Mining Engrs.-AIME, 1983, Achievements in Applied Sci. award 2d World Malayalam Conf., 1985, Robert H. Richards award, AIME, 1986, Arthur F. Taggart award Soc. Mining Engrs.-AIME, 1987, honor award Assn. Indian in Am., 1988, VHP award of Excellence, Ellis Island medal of Honor, 1990, Commendations citation State of N.J. Senate, 1991; named Mill Man of Distinction, Soc. Mining Engrs.-AIME, 1983, Disting. Alumnus award Indian Inst. Sci., Bangalore, 1989, Outstanding Contbns. and Achievement award Cultural Festival India, 1991, Recognition award SIAA, 1992, Asian-Am. Heritage award Asian Am. Higher Edn. Coun., 1994. Fellow Instn. Mining and Metallurgy (U.K.); mem. AICE, NAE, Soc. Mining Engrs. (bd. dirs. 1982-85, Disting. Mem. award, also others), Engring. Found. (mem. bd. 1994—, chmn. conf. com. 1985-88, bd. exec. com. 1985-88, bd. dirs. 1991—, Frank Aplan award 1992), Am. Chem. Soc., N.Y. Acad. Scis., Internat. Assn. Colloid and Surface Scientists (councillor 1989—), Indian Material Rsch. Soc. (hon.), Sigma Xi. Office: Columbia U 911 SW Mudd Bldg New York NY 10027

SOMERS, ANNE RAMSAY, medical educator; b. Memphis, Sept. 9, 1913; d. Henry Ashton and Amanda Vick (Woolfolk) Ramsey; m. Herman Miles Somers, Aug. 31, 1946; children: Sara Ramsay, Margaret Ramsay. BA, Vassar Coll., 1935; postgrad., U. N.C., 1939-40; DSc (hon.), Med. Coll. Wis. 1975. Ednl. dir. Ladies Garment Workers Union, 1937-42; labor economist U.S. Dept. Labor, 1943-46; rsch. assoc. Haverford Coll., 1957-63; rsch. assoc. indsl. rels. sect. Princeton U., 1964-84; prof. U. Medicine and Dentistry of N.J.-R. Wood Johnson Med. Sch. (formerly Rutgers Med. Sch.), 1971-84, adj. prof., 1984—; adj. prof. geriatric medicine U. Pa. Sch. Medicine, 1990—; mem. Nat. Bd. Med. Examiners, 1983-86; cons. in health econs., health edn., geriatrics, gerontology, related areas. Author: Hospital Regulation: The Dilemma of Public Policy, 1969, Health Care in Transition: Directions for the Future, 1971, (with H.M. Somers) Workmen's Compensation: The Prevention, Rehabilitation and Financing of Occupational Disability, 1954, Medicare and the Hospitals, 1967, Doctors, Patients and Health Insurance, 1961, Health and Health Care: Policies in Perspective, 1977, (with N.L. Spears) The Continuing Care Retirement Community: A Significant Option for Long Care?, 1992; editor: (with D.R. Fabian) The Geriatric Imperative: An Introduction to Gerontology and Clinical Geriatrics, 1981. Mem. bd. visitors. Duke U. Med. Ctr., 1972-77, U. Tex. Health Scis. Ctr., Houston, 1980-86. Recipient Elizur Wright award Am. Risk and Ins. Assn., 1962; named to Health Care Hall of Fame, 1993. Fellow Am. Coll. Hosp. Adminstrs. (hon.), Coll. Physicians Phila. (hon.); mem. Inst. Medicine of Nat. Acad. Scis., Am. Pub. Health Assn., Soc. Tchrs. Family Medicine (hon.). Home: Pennswood Vlg # G-205 Newtown PA 18940

SOMERS, GEORGE FREDRICK, biology educator; b. Garland, Utah, July 9, 1914; s. George Fredrick and Elizbuth (Sorenson) S.; m. Beulah Rich Morgan, June 24, 1939; children: Ralph M., Steven J., Gary F. B.S., Utah State U., 1935; B.A., Oxford U., 1938, B.Sc., 1939; Ph.D., Cornell U., 1942. Faculty Cornell U., 1941-51, asso. prof. biochemistry, 1949-51; plant physiologist U.S. Dept. Agr., 1944-51; faculty U. Del., Newark, 1951—; assoc. dir. Del. Agrl. Expt. Sta., 1951-59; assoc. dean Coll. Agr., 1954-59; chmn. dept. biol. scis. U. Del., 1959-71, H. Fletcher Brown prof. biology, 1962-81, emeritus prof., 1981—; vis. prof. U. Philippines, 1958-59. Author: (with J.B. Sumner) Chemistry and Methods of Enzymes, 3d edit, 1953, Laboratory Experiments in Biological Chemistry, 2d edit, 1949; also articles; Editor: biochem. sect. Chem. Abstracts, 1968-75. Union Pacific scholar, 1930; Rhodes scholar, 1936; Henry Strong Denison fellow, 1939. H.C. fellow AAAS; mem. Am. Assn. Plant Physiology, Bot. Soc. Am., Sigma Xi, Phi Kappa Phi. Research on influence of environ. factors on vitamin C content of vegetables; viscoelasticity in plant tissues as related to cell wall properties; chem. properties of algal cell walls; salt-tolerant plants as food crops. Home: 22 Minquil Dr Newark DE 19713-1312

SOMERS, HANS PETER, lawyer; b. Berlin, Germany, Nov. 11, 1922; came to U.S., 1938; s. Fritz A. and Karoline E. (Neuert) S.; m. Claudia C. Schuette, May 3, 1947; children: Daniel E., Stephen A., Deborah J., Conrad S. B.A., Cornell Coll., 1946; M.A., U. Iowa, 1948; LL.B. magna cum laude, Harvard U., 1951. Bar: Mass. 1951, Pa. 1957. Assoc. Hill & Barlow, Boston, 1951-56; assoc. Morgan, Lewis & Bockius, Phila., 1956-60, ptnr., 1960-88, counsel, 1988—; lectr. law Northeastern U., Boston, 1951-53, Boston U. Law Sch., 1953-55; lectr. Villanova U. Law Sch., Phila., 1959-63; research assoc. Am. Law Inst., Cambridge, Mass., 1955-56. Editor: Harvard Law Rev., 1949-51; contbr. articles to legal jours. Served to 2d lt. AUS, 1943-46, ETO. Mem. ABA (chmn. com. tax sect. 1967-69, real property, probate and trust law 1974-77), Nat. Conf. Lawyers and Corp. Fiduciaries (chmn. 1978-81), Am. Coll. Probate Counsel (mem. editorial bd. dirs. 1976-77), Internat. Acad. of Estate and Trust Law (exec. council 1974-78, 81—). Clubs: Radnor Hunt (Malvern, Pa.) (bd. govs.); Union League (Phila.). Home: 8024 Goshen Rd Newtown Square PA 19073-1122 Office: Morgan Lewis & Bockius 2000 One Logan Sq Philadelphia PA 19103

SOMERS, HAROLD MILTON, economist, educator; b. Toronto, Ont., Can., Sept. 30, 1915; came to U.S., 1937, naturalized, 1947; s. Joseph and Elizabeth (Behr) S.; m. Claire Rosen, June 12, 1939; children: Joan, Margery, Warren. B.Com., U. Toronto, 1937; Ph.D., U. Calif., 1942; student, U. Chgo., 1940; LL.B., U. Buffalo, 1956. Teaching asst. in econs. U. Calif., 1937-39; research asst. govt. fin. U. Chgo., 1940; fellow Social Sci. Research Council, 1940-41; mem. research staff Brookings Instn., summer 1941; teaching fellow in econs. U. Mich., 1941-42, instr. in econs., summer 1942; asst. prof. econs. U. Buffalo, 1942-45, assoc. prof., 1945-46, prof., 1946-61, dean. sch. bus. adminstrn., 1947-61; lectr. U. Buffalo Sch. Law, 1957-59; prof. econs. UCLA, 1961-86, prof. emeritus, 1986—, chmn. dept. econs. 1961-66, dean div. social scis., 1967-70; vis. prof. econs. U. Calif. at Berkeley, summer 1947, Columbia, summer 1954, U. B.C., summer 1953; vis. prof. law Yale Law Sch., 1968; econ. affairs officer in fiscal div. UN, summer 1950, cons., 1950-53; cons. to research div. O.P.A., 1943; arbitrator Fed. Conciliation and Mediation Service, 1950-86, Am. Arbitration Assn., 1955-86, N.Y. State Bd. Mediation, 1952-61, Los Angeles County Employee Relations Commn. Arbitration, 1970-73; cons. U.S. Office Edn., Bur. Higher Edn., 1965-69; mem. Personnel Security bd. AEC, 1957-59; cons. N.Y. State Legis. Com. on Constn., 1957- 58; economist N.Y. State Dept. Commerce, summer 1944, cons., 1944-45; tech. adviser to mayor's full employment com., City of Buffalo, 1945-46, cons. to budget div., 1946-47; chmn. exec. com., fin. subcom. Capital Expenditures Com., 1956-57; chmn. N.Y. State Minimum Wage Bd. for Restaurant Industry, 1956-58; mem seminar adv. com. Fed. Res. Bank, N.Y., 1952; editorial cons. Blakiston Co., Phila., 1947-52; cons. Employment and Youth Opportunities Agy., Los Angeles, 1966, Calif. Adv. Commn. on Tax Reform, 1968. Author: American Policies of Postwar Readjustment (monograph), 1944, Public Finance and National Income, 1949; co-author: Industrial Conflict, 1939, Growth of the American Economy, 1944, rev. edit., 1951, Readings in Business Cycle Theory, 1944, Readings in the Theory of Income Distribution, 1946, Taxation and Business Concentration, 1952, Corporate Tax Problems, 1952, Taxation of Corporate Income in California, 1964, Taxation of Property in California, 1964, Public Finance and Welfare, 1966, A Search for City Revenue, 1968; author monographs The Sales Tax, 1964, Capital Gains, Death and Gift Taxation, 1965; editor: Estate Taxes and Business Management, 1957; editor Western Econ. Jour., 1966-69; editorial bd.: Am. Econ. Rev., 1952-54; contbr.: articles to Ency. Brit. and econ. and law jours. Mem. Am., N.Y. State bar assnss., Am. Econ. Assn. (nominating com. 1969, 70), Econometric Soc. (session chmn. 1947, 51, program chmn. 1949), Am. Fin. Assn. (dir. pub. fin. 1969-71), Nat. Tax Assn. (mem. sales tax com. 1975-77, fed. taxation and fin. com. 1981-84), Phi Beta Kappa, Alpha Kappa Psi, Beta Gamma Sigma. Home: 152 N Kenter Ave Los Angeles CA 90049-2730 Office: Dept Econs U Calif Los Angeles CA 90024

SOMERS, JOHN ARTHUR, insurance company executive; b. Cin., Feb. 24, 1944; s. Arthur Edward and Margaret Mary (Netschke) S.; m. Ann-Christin Ahlander, Dec. 28, 1968; children—Monica Ann, Christina Elizabeth, Mark Edward. B.S. in Econs., Villanova U., 1966; postgrad., Sch. Law, U. Conn., 1966-67; M.B.A. in Fin., U. Conn., 1972. Asst. town mgr. Town of Newington, Conn., 1970-72; v.p. Prudential Ins. Co. Am., Newark, 1972-81; sr. v.p. Tchrs. Ins. & Annuity Assn., N.Y.C., 1981—; bd. dirs., vice chmn. Nat. Realty Com.; bd. dirs. Cmty. Preservation Corp., Emigrant Bank; chmn., adv. bd. N.Y.U. Real Estate Inst. Mem. Urban Land Inst., Nat. Assn. Indsl. and Office Parks, Mortgage Bankers Assn. Am., Internat. Council Shopping Ctrs., N.Y. Real Estate Bd. Roman Catholic. Office: Tchrs Ins & Annuity Assn Am 730 3rd Ave New York NY 10017-3206

SOMERS, LOUIS ROBERT, retired food company executive; b. Pontiac, Mich., Aug. 8, 1926; s. Jay G. and Maggie (Gee) S.; m. Rynda Horinga, July 28, 1950; children: Linda, Laurie. B.S., Mich. State U., 1950. With Kellogg Co., Battle Creek, Mich., 1955-88; controller Kellogg Internat., 1967-70, 72-75; fin. dir. Kellogg Gt. Brit. Ltd., 1970-72; v.p. fin., treas. Kellogg Co., 1975-85, sr. v.p. fin., 1985-88; bd. dirs. Purity Foods, Inc. Trustee Alma Coll., 1982—; bd. dirs. Mich. State U. Devel. Fund, 1983-88; bd. govs. ARC, 1985-92, chmn. audit com.

SOMERSET, HAROLD RICHARD, sugar company executive; b. Woodbury, Conn., Sept. 25, 1935; s. Harold Kitchener and Margaret Mary (Roche) S.; m. Marjory Deborah Ghiselin, June 22, 1957 (dec. Jan. 1984); children: Timothy Craig, Paul Alexander; m. Jean MacAlpine DesMarais, Jan. 2, 1985; stepchildren: Cheryl Lyn DesMarais, James Fenelon DesMarais. B.S. U.S. Naval Acad., 1957; B.C.E., Rensselaer Poly. Inst., Troy, N.Y., 1959; LL.B., Harvard U., 1967. Bar: Mass. 1967, Hawaii 1973. Commd. ensign U.S. Navy, 1957, advanced through grades to lt., 1961; service in U.S. and Hawaii; resigned, 1964; with firm Goodwin, Procter & Hoar, Boston, 1967-72; corp. counsel Alexander & Baldwin, Inc., Honolulu, 1972-74, v.p., gen. counsel, 1974-78, group v.p.-sugar, 1978-79, exec. v.p.-agr., 1979-84; with Calif. & Hawaiian Sugar Co., San Francisco, 1984-93, exec. v.p., chief operating officer, 1984-88, pres., chief exec. officer, 1988-93, bus. cons., 1994—; bd. dirs. World Sugar Rsch. Orgn., Longs Drug Stores Corp., Brown and Caldwell, PLM Internat., Inc., Calif. and Hawaiian Sugar Co. Trustee San Francisco Nat. Maritime Mus., Carquinez Strait Preservation Trust (mgmt. com., pres.). Mem. Sugar Assn. (bd. dirs., fin. com.), St. Mary's Coll. Sch. Edn. (chmn. adv. coun.). Home: 19 Donald Dr Orinda CA 94563-3646 Office: Calif & Hawaiian Sugar Co 830 Loring Ave Crockett CA 94525-1171

SOMERSON, ROSANNE, artist; b. Phila., June 21, 1954; d. Herbert M. and Ileana V. (Reiver) S.; m. Alphonse Mattia, Nov. 9, 1947; 1 child, Isabel Giani. BFA, R.I. Sch. Design, 1976. Mem. staff Fine Woodworking mag., 1976-81; furniture designer and builder, 1978—; mem. faculty Grad. Furniture Design Program R.I. Sch. Design, Providence, 1985—, head Grad. Furniture Design Program, 1992—; instr. Boston Archtl. Ctr., 1981; teaching fellow continuing edn. sculpture and design in wood Harvard U., 1977-79; lectr. in field. Exhibited works at Brockton (Mass.) Art Mus., 1981, 84, 86, Workbench Gallery, N.Y.C., 1982, 83, Hudson River Mus., 1983, Pitts. Ctr. for the Arts, 1984-85, Susan Carr Gallery, Houston, 1985, Esther Saks Gallery, Chgo., 1985, Soc. Arts and Crafts, Boston, 1986, 89, Mus. Art/R.I.

Sch. Dseign, 1987, Sothebys, N.Y.C., 1987, Am. Craft Mus., N.Y.C., 1986-88, Mus. Fine Arts, Boston, 1989, Oakland (Calif.) Mus., 1990, Musee Des Arts Decoratifs, Paris, Oslo Mus. Applied Art, Slovak Nat. Gallery, Peter Joseph Gallery, N.Y., 1991-95, Pritain and Eames Gallery, N.Y., 1984-94, others. Address: 771 Division Rd Westport MA 02790

SOMERSTEIN, AURORA ABRERA, educator; b. Manila, Feb. 17, 1943; d. Bernardo Paez and Rosalia (Sityar) Abrera; m. Jules Leon Somerstein, Dec. 10, 1967; children: Joseph, Sandra, Marc. BA in English, U. Philippines, Manila, 1964; MA in English Edn., NYU, 1978, MA in Elem. Edn., 1987; postgrad., U. Pitts., Oxford (Eng.) U., 1964-66, 86. Cert. tchr., N.Y. Instr. U. Pitts., 1965-66, U. of the East, Manila, 1968-69; tchr. Am. Internat. Sch., Manila, 1966, Domenec High Sch., Pitts., 1967-68; substitute tchr. Lakeland and Peekskill Sch. Dist., N.Y., 1975-77; exec. dir. Internat. Pre-Sch. Ctr., Inc., N.Y.C., 1977—; instr. Bd. Coop. Ednl. Svcs., N.Y.C., 1989-93; exec. sec. Ctr. Ednl. TV, Manila, 1964; sec. NYU, 1973-74, UN, N.Y.C., 1975; producer, interviewer Continental Cablevision, N.Y.C., 1984—; child devel. adviser Westchester County, N.Y.C., 1989—; cons. Hudson Valley Export-Import, Inc., N.Y.C., 1988-92. Vol. Philippine Band of Mercy, Manila, 1963-93. Mem. Nat. Child Care Assn., Nat. Assn. Edn. Young Children, Nat. Coun. Tchrs. English, N.Y. Child Care Assn., Assn. Childhood Edn. Internat., Child Care Coun. Westchester, Manitoga, Peek-skill/Cortlandt C. of C. (bd. dirs. 1989-92). Democrat. Avocations: reading, photography, music, travel, piano. Office: Internat Pre-Sch Ctr Inc PO Box 187 Buchanan NY 10511-0187

SOMERVILLE, CAROLYN JOHNSON, principal; b. Parkersburg, W.Va., Mar. 11, 1942; d. George Hughes and Nellie Maude (Cather) Johnson; m. Ron D. Somerville, Aug. 22, 1965 (div. 1981); children: Jennifer Nicole Somerville Moon, Ron Dean. BS, Asbury Coll., 1963; MEd, Ohio U., 1966. Cert. elem. prin., Okla. Tchr. jr. high Prince George County Schs., Md., 1963-64; grad. asst. Ohio U., Athens, 1964-65; social worker W.Va. Dept. of Welfare, Huntington, 1965-67; counselor jr. high Wood County Schs., Parkersburg, W.Va., 1972-78, tchr. jr. high, 1979-81; substitute tchr. Yukon (Okla.) Schs., 1982-83; asst. prin. elem. Western Heights Schs., Oklahoma City, 1983-85, Skyview Elem. Sch., 1985—; presenter workshops; cons. in field. Mem. adv. bd. Planned Parenthood, Parkersburg, W.Va., 1974-77; counselor, speaker Gov. Com. on Crime and Delinquency, Parkersburg, 1974-77; tchr. Sunday sch. Trinity Bapt. Ch., Yukon, 1982-83; sponsor Alateen, 1988-93. Mem. ASCD, Okla. Assn. Elem. Sch. Prins. (com.), Coop. Coun. Okla. Sch. Adminstrn., Yukon Curriculum Coun. Avocations: reading, writing, sewing, boating. Home: 113 W Vail Yukon OK 73099 Office: Skyview Elem Sch 2800 Mustang Rd Yukon OK 73099

SOMERVILLE, DAPHINE HOLMES, elementary educator; b. Clinton, N.C., Jan. 19, 1940; d. George Henry and Mamie Estelle (Streeter) Holmes; m. Kalford Burton Somerville, Dec. 26, 1970 (div. Sept. 1992); 1 child, Daria Lynn. AA, Blackburn Coll., 1959, BA, 1961; MS in Edn., Hofstra U., 1967; postgrad., Columbia U., 1971. Permanent teaching cert. common br. subjects grades 1-8. Tchr. East Islip (N.Y.) Sch. Dist., 1961—; mem., instr. Outcome Based/Mastery Learning/Excellence in Learning Com., East Islip, 1984-89; mentor East Islip Sch. Dist., 1987-88, mem. sch. improvement team, 1989-91, staff devel. com., 1992—. Co-author: (booklet) Baptist Training Union Study Guide, 1976; founder, co-author: (tutoring program) Adopt-A-School Child/Family, 1990. Mem. Bay Shore (N.Y.) Civic Assn. and Bay Shore Pub. Schs. Task Force for the Advancement of Equality of Ednl. Opportunity, 1967-69; sec. Islip Town NAACP, Bay Shore, 1965-90; mem. First Bapt. Ch., Bay Shore, 1951—, trustee, 1972-90; dir. Bapt. Tng. Union, 1974-81. Recipient Community Svc. award Town Bd.-Town of Islip, Suffolk County, 1982, Br. Recognition award Islip Town NAACP, 1987, Disting. Svc. award L.I. Region NAACP, 1993. Mem. Nat. Coun. Negro Women (life, ednl. involvement award 1993), East Islip Tchrs. Assn. (past bldg. rep.), N.Y. State United Tchrs. Democrat. Avocations: theater, tennis, reading, working with children, traveling. Home: 130 Carman Rd Dix Hills NY 11746-5648 Office: J F Kennedy Elem Sch Woodland Dr East Islip NY 11730

SOMERVILLE, MARGARET ANNE GANLEY, law educator; b. Adelaide, Australia, Apr. 13, 1942; d. George Patrick and Gertrude Honora (Rowe) Ganley; divorced. A.u.A. (pharm.), U. Adelaide, 1963; LLB (hon. I), U. Sydney, 1973; D.C.L., McGill U., 1978; LLD(hon.), U. Windsor, Ont., 1992; LLD (hon.), Macquarie, NSW, 1993. Registered pharmacist; Bar: Supreme Ct. New South Wales 1975, Quebec 1982. New South Wales; Pharmacist NSW, Australia; atty. Mallesons, Sydney, Australia, 1974-75; cons. Law Reform Com. Can., 1976-85; asst. prof. faculty of law Inst. of Comparative Law, 1978, assoc. prof. faculty of law, 1979, prof. faculty of law, 1984—; prof., faculty law, faculty medicine McGill U., 1984—; founding dir. McGill Ctr. Medicine Ethics & Law, 1986—; Gale prof. law McGill U., 1989—; vis. prof. Sydney U., 1984, 86, 90, Ctr. for Human Bioethics, Monash U., 1985-86; cons. to numerous orgns. Editl. bd. Bioethics, 1986—, Kennedy Inst. Ethics Jour., 1990—, Health and Human Rights, 1993—, Ecosystem Health and Medicine, 1993—; Adv. editor Social Sci. and Medicine, 1988—; reviewer Cmty. Health Studies, Jour. Clin. Epidemiology, Can. Jour. Family Law, Jour. Pharmacy Practice, Jour. AIDS, New Eng. Jour. Medicine, Can. Jour. Law and Soc., Dalhousie Law Jour., Am. Jour. Law, Medicine and Ethics, others; contbr. articles to profl. jours. Clin. ethics com. Royal Victoria Hosp., 1980—; prin. investigator Nat. Health R&D Program, 1986-89; assoc. mem. McGill AIDS Ctr., 1990—, Nat. Adv. Com. on AIDS in Can., 1986-92; chmn. Nat. Rsch. Coun. Can., Ethics Com., 1991. Australian Commonwealth scholar, McGill U., 1975; recipient U. Sydney medal, 1976, Joseph Dainow prize McGill U., 1976, Disting. Svc. award Am. Soc. Law & Medicine, 1985; named to Order of Australia. Fellow Royal Soc. Can.; mem. Am. Soc. Pharm. Law, Inst. Soc., Ethics & Life Sci., Hastings Ctr., Am. Soc. Law & Medicine, Assn. des Prof. de Droit du Que., Can. Bar Assn., Can. Pharm. Assn., World Assn. Med. Law, Can. Law Tchrs. Assn., Soc. Health & Human Values, Internat. Acad. Com. Law. Office: McGill Ctr Medicine Ethics & Law, 3690 Peel St, Montreal, PQ Canada H3A 1W9

SOMERVILLE, MASON HAROLD, mechanical engineering educator, university dean; b. Worcester, Mass., Dec. 21, 1941; s. Harold Mervin and Eleanor Ruth (Archibald) S.; children: Mark, Matthew, Meredith, Michael, Michelle. B.S.M.E., Worcester Polytech. Inst., 1964; M.S.M.E., Northeastern U., 1966; Ph.D. in Mech. Engring., Pa. State U., 1971. Profl. engr., N.D., Ark., Tex. Grad. teaching asst Northeastern U., Boston, 1964-66; engr. Norton Co., Worcester, Mass., 1965; instr. mech. engring. dept. Pa. State U., State College, 1966-71; sr. engr. Bettis Atomic Power Lab., West Mifflin, Pa., 1971-73; prof., dir. Engring. Expt. Sta., U. N.D., Grand Forks, 1973-80; prof., head mech. engring dept. U. Ark., Fayetteville, 1980-84; prof., dean engring Tex. Tech U., Lubbock, TX, 1984-94; dean engring. No. Ariz. U., Flagstaff, 1994—; cons. Natural Gas Pipeline, Chgo., 1974-79, Archtl. Alliance, Mpls., 1978-80; bd. dirs. Mid-Am. Solar Energy Corp., Mpls., 1978-80, Ctr. for Advanced Engring and Rsch., TTU/HSC Rsch. Found.; chmn. bd. dirs. N.D. Energy Assn., 1979-80; energy advisor State of N.D., 1978-80; mem. ABET/EAC Commn., 1987-92; speaker to pub. service groups. Author: Coal Gasification Environmental Impact, Analysis of U.S. Weather, 1980; numerous tech. papers. Mem. Lubbock Bd. City Devel., 1985-87. Recipient Ralph R. Teetor award Soc. Automotive Engrs., 1974, Haliburton award; rsch. grantee. Mem. ASME, ASHRAE, Soc. Automotive Engrs., Am. Soc. Elec. Engrs., Am. Soc. Engring. Edn., Lubbock C. of C., Sigma Xi, Pi Tau Sigma. Religion: Episcopalian. Home: 1466 W University Hts Dr N Flagstaff AZ 86001 Office: Northern Arizona Univ Coll of Engring/Tech PO Box 15600 Flagstaff AZ 86011

SOMERVILLE, RICHARD CHAPIN JAMES, atmospheric scientist, educator; b. Washington, May 30, 1941. BS in Meteorology, Pa. State U., 1961; PhD in Meteorology, NYU, 1966. Postdoctoral fellow Nat. Ctr. Atmospheric Rsch., Boulder, Colo., 1966-67; rsch. assoc. geophysical fluid dynamics lab. NOAA, Princeton, N.J., 1967-69; rsch. scientist Courant Inst. Math. Scis., N.Y.C., 1969-71; meteorologist Goddard inst. space studies NASA, N.Y.C., 1971-74; adj. prof. Columbia U., NYU, 1971-74; head numerical weather prediction sect. Nat. Ctr. Atmospheric Rsch., Boulder, 1974-79; prof. meteorology, dir. climate rsch. divsn. Scripps Inst. Oceanography, U. Calif.-San Diego, La Jolla, 1979—; mem. adv. bd. Aspen Global Change Inst.; mem. adv. com. geoscis. NSF; mem. panel climate and global change Nat. Oceanic & Atmospheric Adminstrn.; mem. bd. trustees

Column 1

Univ. Corp. Atmospheric Rsch., mem.'s rep. Scripps Instn. Oceanography, U. Calif., San Diego. Mem. editl. bd. The Sea. Fellow AAAS, Am. Meteorol. Soc. (councilor); mem. Am. Geophys. Union, Oceanography Soc. Office: U Calif San Diego Scripps Instn Oceanography 9500 Gilman Dr La Jolla CA 92093-0224

SOMERVILLE, ROBERT EUGENE, historian; b. New Kensington, Pa.; s. Andrew Eugene and Gladys (Hodel) S.; m. Beatrice Terrien, Dec. 22, 1987. BA, Case Western Res. U., 1964; MA, Yale U., 1965, PhD, 1968. Asst. prof. history Columbia U., N.Y.C., 1969-75, prof. religion and history, 1976—; assoc. prof. religion U. Pa., Phila., 1975-76. Author: Councils of Urban II, 1972, Pope Alexander III and the Council of Tours, 1977, Scotia Pontificia, 1982, Papacy, Councils and Canon Law in The 11th-12th Centuries, 1990. NEH fellow, 1979-80, Guggenheim fellow, 1974-75, 87-88. Fellow AAAS, Commr. Commission Internationale de Diplomatique (corr. fellow), Monumenta Germaniae Historica (corr. mem.); mem. Am. Soc. Ch. History, Medieval Acad. (councillor 1985-88). Office: Columbia U 615 Kent Hall New York NY 10027

SOMERVILLE, ROMAINE STEC, arts administrator; b. Scranton, Pa., May 24, 1930; d. Michael John and Julia (Skwier) Stec; m. Frank P.L. Somerville, Sept. 29, 1962; 1 child, Julia Hooper. B.A., Marymount Coll., 1951; M.A., Columbia U., 1953; postgrad., Yale U., 1958-60. Instr. art history Marywood Coll., 1954-58; curator art Everhart Mus., Scranton, 1954-58; curator decorative arts Balt. Mus. Art, 1960-63; exec. dir. Commn. for Hist. and Archtl. Preservation, Balt., 1966-72; chief curator, asst. dir. Md. Hist. Soc., Balt., 1972-78, dir., 1978-84; field cons. Nat. Endowment for Arts, Washington, 1984-86; exec. dir. The Preservation Soc., Balt., 1993—; mem. faculty Goucher Ctr. Ednl. Resources, Johns Hopkins U. Evening Sch., 1978-80; regional advisor Am. Friends of Attingham. contbg. author, editor: exhibit catalogues Md. Hist. Soc., 1975-90. Bd. dirs. Balt. Heritage, Inc., 1975—, Corpus Christi Hist. Trust, Balt., 1976—, Hampton Hist. Site, Towson, Md., 1989—; mem. adv. bd. Soc. Colonial Dames Am. Md., 1984-88, Gov.'s House, Annapolis, 1978-86; guest curator Roman Cath. Ch. bicentennial exhibit Archdiocese of Balt., 1986-91; cons. Mother Seton House, Balt., 1980-89; pres. Balt. Coalition of Hist. Neighborhoods, 1992—; mem. gov.'s adv. com. Save Outdoor Sculpture, 1992-95. Mem. Victorian Soc. Am., Md. Hist. Soc. (gallery com. 1988—), Preservation Md., Balt. Found. for Architecture, Nat. Trust for Hist. Preservation. Office: 201 W Monument St Baltimore MD 21201-4601

SOMERVILLE, THEODORE ELKIN, lawyer; b. N.Y.C., May 12, 1940; s. Gilbert and Eileen Sarah (Elkin) S. A.B., Brown U., 1961; LL.B., Yale U., 1964; grad. Advanced Mgmt. Program, Harvard U., 1976. Bar: N.Y. 1966. Asso. firm Donovan Leisure Newton & Irvine, N.Y.C., 1964-73; v.p., gen. counsel Alleghany Corp., N.Y.C., 1973—. Mem. Am. Bar Assn., Assn. Bar City N.Y. Republican. Episcopalian. Clubs: Yale (N.Y.C.). Home: 870 Un Plz New York NY 10017 Office: Alleghany Corp 33rd Fl Park Ave Pla New York NY 10055

SOMERVILLE, WALTER RALEIGH, JR., government official; b. Macon, N.C., Feb. 17, 1930; s. Walter Raleigh and Bettie Lou (Hunt) S.; student Morgan State Coll., 1957-60; BA in Bus. Adminstrn., U. Md., 1970; diploma program sr. mgrs. in govt. John F. Kennedy Sch. Govt. Harvard U., 1992; m. Jean Renwick (Nava), Sept. 12, 1975; 1 child, Thomasine A. Walker Adams; 1 stepchild, Pamela Nava-Whitter. Personnel staffing specialist FAA, Washington, 1962-65; personnel mgmt. specialist OEO, 1965-67; personnel mgmt. specialist Office Sec. Transp., 1967-70; chief civilian equal opportunity div. U.S. Coast Guard, Transp. Dept., 1970-83, dir. civil rights 1983—, trainee Fed. Exec. Devel. Program, 1975-76. Chmn. fin. com. Christ United Meth. Ch., Washington, 1976-85, chmn. adminstrv. coun., 1985-86; mem. human relations com. bd. Dept. Def., 1983-85; mem. Dept. of Def. Equal Opportunity Coun.; chmn. placement and counseling com. for industry cluster Paul Quinn Coll. With USAF, 1951-60. Recipient Outstanding Performance award, 1981, 82, 83, Proclamation award City Coun. of New Orleans, 1987, Key to City of Franklin, Ky., 1992, Sr. Exec. Svc. Cash Perf. award, 1993. Mem. Am. Mgmt. Assn., NAACP (golden heritage life mem., Roy Wilkins Meritorious Svc. award, 1987, Benjamin L. Hooks Disting. Svc. award 1993), Sr. Execs. Assn., Washington Urban League (life), U. Md. Alumni Assn. (century club), Nat. Urban League (charter mem. Pres.'s Club, mem. black exec. exch. program, vis. prof. historically black colls. and univs.). Home: 1228 4th St SW Washington DC 20024-2302 Office: 2100 2nd St SW Washington DC 20593-0002

SOMIT, ALBERT, political educator; b. Chgo., Oct. 25, 1919; s. Samuel and Mary (Rosenblum) S.; m. Leyla D. Shapiro, Aug. 31, 1947; children: Scott H., Jed L. A.B., U. Chgo., 1941, Ph.D., 1947. Prof. polit. philosophy N.Y. U., 1945-65; chmn. dept. polit. sci. State U. N.Y. at Buffalo, 1966-69, exec. v.p., 1970-80, acting pres. SUNY, Buffalo, 1976-77; pres. So. Ill. U., Carbondale, 1980-87, disting. service prof., 1987—; fellow Netherlands Inst. Advanced Study, 1978-79; Nimitz prof. polit. philosophy U.S. Naval War Coll., 1961-62. Author: (with Joseph Tanenhaus) The Development of American Political Science: From Burgess to Behavioralism, 1967, expanded edit., 1982, (with Tanenhaus) American Political Science A Profile of A Discipline, 1964, Political Science and the Study of the Future, 1974, Biology and Politics: Recent Explorations, 1976, (with others) The Literature of Biopolitics 1963-1977, 1978, 1980, 1983, 1986, Biopolitics and Mainstream Political Science A Master Bibliography, 1990, (with Wildenmann) Hierarchy and Democracy, 1991, (with Peterson) The Dynamics of Evolution, 1992, (with Wildenmann) The Victorious Incumbent: A Threat to Democracy?, 1994, (with Peterson) The Political Behavior of Older Americans, 1994. Served with AUS, 1950-52. Office: So Ill U Lesar Law Bldg Carbondale IL 62901

SOMJEN, GEORGE GUSTAV, physiologist; b. Budapest, Hungary, May 2, 1929; came to U.S., 1962; s. Laszlo and Margit (Ranschburg) S.; m. Eva Herman, 1952 (dec. 1974); children: Monika, Maria, Georgette, Evelyn; m. Amalia Deutsch, 1976. Grad., U. Amsterdam Med. Faculty, 1956; M.D., U. N.Z., 1962. Research asst. Pharmaco-therapeutic Lab., U. Amsterdam, 1953-56; lectr., sr. lectr. dept. physiology U. Otago, Dunedin, N.Z., 1956-62; prof. physiology Duke U., Durham, N.C., 1963—; cons. Nat. Inst. Environ. Health Scis., 1971-75. Author: Sensory Coding in the Mammalian Nervous System, 1972, Neurophysiology: The Essentials, 1983; editor: Neurophysiology Studied in Man, 1972, Mechanisms of Cerebral Hypoxia and Stroke, 1988. Recipient research grants NIH, 1964—. Mem. Am. Physiol. Soc., Soc. Neurosci., Internat. Union Physiol. Sci. (mem. com. edn. 1986-93, chmn. 1993—), Internat. Physiol. Soc. (mem. com. edn.), Am. Epilepsy Soc. Office: Duke U Dept Cell Biology Div Physiology PO Box 3709 Durham NC 27710

SOMLYO, ANDREW PAUL, physiology, biophysics and cardiology educator; b. Budapest, Hungary, Feb. 25, 1930; s. Anton and Clara Maria (Kiss) S.; m. Avril V. Russell, May 25, 1961; 1 child, Andrew Paul. BS, U. Ill., 1954, MS, 1956, MD, 1956; MS, Drexel Inst. Tech., Phila., 1963; MA (hon.), U. Pa., Phila., 1981. Asst. physician Columbia-Presbyn. Med. Ctr., N.Y.C., 1960-61; rsch. assoc. Presbyn. Hosp., Phila., 1961-67; asst. prof. pathology U. Pa., Phila., 1964-67, assoc. prof., 1967-71, prof., 1971-88, prof. physiology and pathology, 1973-88, dir. Pa. Muscle Inst., 1973-88; Charles Slaughter prof. molecular physiology-biol. physics U. Va., Charlottesville, 1988—, chmn. dept., 1988—, prof. cardiology, 1988—; cons. NIH. Author: (with others) Vascular Neuroeffector Systems, 1971, The Handbook of Physiology, Vascular Smooth Muscle, 1981, Microprobe Analysis of Biological Systems, 1981, Recent Advances in Light and Optical Imaging in Biology and Medicine, 1986; editor: Jour. Muscle Research and Cell Motility; contbr. numerous articles to jour. Biol. Chemistry, Jour. Physiology, Am. Heart Jour., Jour. Pediatrics, Jour. Cell Biology, Cell Calcium, others; mem. editorial bd. Blood Vessels, Am. Jour. Physiology, 1979-83, Magnesium: Experimental and Clinical Rsch., Jour. Structural Biology. Mem. AAAS, Soc. Gen. Physiologists, Am. Physiol. Soc., Biophys. Soc., Electron Microscopy Soc., Micrebeam Analysis Soc., Am. Soc. for Cell Biology, Hungarian Physiol. Soc. (hon.), Microscopy Soc. Am. (Disting. Scientist award for biol. scis. 1994), Alpha Omega Alpha Med. Soc. (CIBA-GEIGY award for Hypertension Rsch.). Office: U Va Sch Medicine Dept Molec Physiol & Biol Phyics 449 Jordan Hall Charlottesville VA 22908

Column 2

SOMMA, BEVERLY KATHLEEN, medical and marriage educator; b. Bayonne, N.J., June 13, 1938; d. Leroy and Isabelle (Lysaght) Latourette; m. Louis Anthony Somma, Nov. 24, 1973; children: Francis, Keith. AS, Ocean County Coll., 1973; BA, Georgian Ct., 1977; MAT, Monmouth Coll., 1978; postgrad., U. Pa., 1980-85, 88-89. Nurse's aide Community Meml. Hosp., Toms River, N.J., 1971-72; with marriage coun. dept. psychiatry U. Pa. Sch. Medicine, Phila., 1993—; with Helene Fuld Med. Ctr. Edn., 1993—; ednl. cons. Ctr. for Cognitive Edn., Yardley, Pa., 1990—, tng. program Archdiocese Phila., Penn Found., Inc., 1993; lectr. Marriage Coun. of Phila. dept. psychiatry, sch. medicine U. Pa., 1993—; with Helene Fuld Med. Ctr. Edn., 1993—. Voter svc. chmn. LWV, Toms River, N.J., 1971-72; contact rep. Pro Life Coalition, Phila.; vol. nursing tutor Ocean County Coll., Toms River, 1972; vol. tchr.'s aide St. Michael the Archangel, Levittown, Pa., 1987-88; vol. VITA; counselor Bucks County Coun. Alcoholism and Drug Dependence, Inc., 1984-93; active World Affairs Coun. Phila. All Am. scholar; recipient U.S. Achievement Acad. Nat. award. Mem. Nat. Soc. for Fund Raising Execs., Alumni Assn. Georgian Ct. Coll., Ocean County Coll., Bucks County C.C., Sigma Tau Delta. Republican. Methodist. Avocations: cooking, tennis, golf, jogging, ice-skating. Home: 1506 Kathy Dr Yardley PA 19067-1717

SOMMER, ALFRED, public health professional, ophthalmologist, epidemiologist; b. N.Y.C., Oct. 2, 1942; s. Joseph and Natalie Sommer; m. Jill Abramson, Sept. 1, 1963; children: Charles Andrew, Marni Jane. BS summa cum laude, Union Coll., 1963; MD, Harvard U., 1967; MHS in Epidemiology, Johns Hopkins U., 1973. Diplomate Am. Bd. Ophthalmology, Nat. Bd. Med. Examiners. Teaching fellow in medicine Harvard U. Med. Sch., Boston, 1968-69; assoc. in medicine Emory U., Atlanta, 1969-70; dir. Nutritional Blindness Prevention Rsch. Program, Bandung, Indonesia, 1976-79; vis. fellow Inst. Ophthalmology U. London, Eng., 1979-80; founding dir., Dana Ctr. for Preventive Ophthalmology Johns Hopkins Med. Insts., Balt., 1980-90; assoc. prof. Johns Hopkins U., Balt., 1981-85, prof. ophthalmology, epidemiology and internat. health, 1985—; dean Johns Hopkins Sch. Hygiene and Pub. Health, 1990—; vis. prof. ophthalmology U. Padjadjaran, Indonesia, 1976-79; cons., advisor Helen Keller Internat., N.Y.C., 1973—; cons., chmn. com. NIH, Bethesda, Md., 1981—; bd. dirs. Internat. Agy. for the Prevention of Blindness, Geneva, Switzerland, 1978—; cons., com. mem. Nat. Acad. Scis., Washington, 1989; chmn. program adv. group on blindness prevention WHO, Geneva, 1989-90, com. mem., 1978-90, expert com., 1990—; chmn. steering com. Internat. Vitamin A Cons. Group, Washington, 1975—; pres. Internat. Fedn. of Tissue Banks; chmn. sci. adv. bd. Edna McConnell Clark Found.; mem. adv. com. Internat. Coun. Ophthalmology. Author: Epidemiology and Statistics for the Ophthalmologist, 1980, Nutritional Blindness: Xerophthalmia and Keratomalacia, 1982, Vitamin A Deficiency: Health, Survival and Vision, 1995, Detection and Control of Vitamin A Deficiency and Xerophthalmia, 1978, 82, 94; chmn. bd. overseers Am. Jour. Epidems, 1990—. Charles A. Dana Found. award for Pioneering Achievements in Health, 1988, Disting. Svc. award for Contbn. to Vision Care APHA, 1988, E.V. McCollum Internat. Lectureship in Nutrition Am. Inst. Nutrition, 1988, Second Annual Am. Coll. Advancement in Medicine Achievement award in Preventive Medicine, 1990, Disting. Contbn. to World Ophthalmology award Internat. Fedn. Ophthalmol. Socs., 1990, Smadel award Infectious Diseases Soc. Am., 1990. Mem. Inst. Medicine of NAS (Food and Nutrition bd.), Am. Acad. Opthalmology (chmn. pub. health com. 1982-88, chmn. Quality of Care/Clin. Guidelines 1986-90, Hon. award 1986), Nat. Soc. to Prevent Blindness (bd. dirs. 1989) Internat. Assn. to Prevent Blindness (bd. dirs. 1978—). Achievements include first to detail and publish epidemiologic approach to disaster assessment; demonstration that nutritional indices predict subsequent mortality in free-living children, surveillance and containment is effective intervention strategy for controlling and eradicating small pox, vitamin A deficiency increases childhood mortality, vitamin A supplementation decreases childhood mortality, nerve fiber layers are valuable diagnostic and prognostic sign of early glaucoma; routine preventive services cost-effective in eye disease; clinical guideline development and importance of outcome assessment; research in epidemiologic and public health approaches to ophthalmology and blindness prevention. Office: Johns Hopkins Sch Hygiene and Pub Health 615 N Wolfe St Rm 1041 Baltimore MD 21205-2103

SOMMER, ALPHONSE ADAM, JR., lawyer; b. Portsmouth, Ohio, Apr. 7, 1924; s. A.A. and Adelaide (Orlett) S.; m. Storrow Cassin, June 13, 1951; children: Susan, Edward, Nancy. A.B., U. Notre Dame, 1948; LL.B., Harvard U., 1950; LL.D., Cleve. State U., 1976. Bar: Ohio 1951, D.C. 1976. Assoc. Calfee, Halter, Calfee, Griswold & Sommer, Cleve., 1950-60; ptnr. Calfee, Halter, Calfee, Griswold & Sommer, 1960-73; commr. SEC, 1973-76; ptnr. Morgan, Lewis & Bockius, Washington, 1979-94, counsel, 1994—; chmn. pub. oversight bd., AICPA. Contbr. articles to profl. jours. Chmn. pub. oversight bd. AICPA. Served with AUS, 1943-46. Mem. Nat. Assn. Securities Dealers (vice chmn.). Home: 7105 Heathwood Ct Bethesda MD 20817-2915 Office: Morgan Lewis & Bockius 1800 M St NW Ste 925 Washington DC 20036-5802

SOMMER, HOWARD ELLSWORTH, textile executive; b. Kansas City, Mo., May 1, 1918; s. Frederick H. and Edna O. (Olsen) S.; m. Sarah Scott McElevey, June 20, 1942; children: Scott E., Paul F. BA magna cum laude, Dartmouth Coll., 1940; MBA, Harvard U., 1942. With Wolf & Co. CPAs, Chgo., 1946-76, chmn. mng. group, 1960-76; dir. Jockey Internat., Kenosha, Wis., 1959—, sr. v.p., chmn. audit com., 1979-89. Author: Procedural Routine for a Business Audit, 1947; also articles. Counsellor, Chgo. chpt. Boy Scouts Am. Lt. col. AUS, 1942-46. Decorated Bronze Star; Croix de Guerre with palms; Medaille de la Reconnaissance (France). Mem. ASME, Assn. Cons. Mgmt. Engrs. (cert. of Award 1956, v.p. 1970-72), Inst. Mgmt. Cons. (cert. mgmt. cons., past dir.), Univ. Club (pres., dir. Chgo. chpt. 1959-61), Indian Hill Club, Harvard Bus. Sch. Club (dir. Chgo. chpt. 1958-59), North Shore Cotillion Club, Dartmouth Club, Halter Wildlife Club, Masons (32 deg.), Shriners, Phi Beta Kappa, Chi Phi. Episcopalian (vestryman, warden).

SOMMER, JEFF, journalist. BA in History with distinction, Cornell U., 1974; MS in Journalism, Columbia U., 1977; MS in Regional Studies-East Asia, Harvard U., 1978. Local reporter The Albany (N.Y.) Knickerbocker News, 1977-79, The Record, Bergen County, N.J., 1979-81, Newsday, N.Y.C., 1981-82; Asia bur. chief Newsday, Beijing, 1983-86; chief corr. Soviet & East European affairs Newsday, Moscow, 1986-89; fgn. editor Newsday, N.Y.C., 1989—. Recipient Hal Boyle award Overseas Press Club, 1985; edited Pulitzer prize-winning coverage in internat. news, 1992, 93. Office: Newsday 235 Pinelawn Rd Melville NY 11747

SOMMER, ROBERT GEORGE, public relations executive; b. N.Y.C., Feb. 6, 1959; s. Ernest Lorge and Donna Anne (Lapin) S.; m. Marjorie Ann Glaser, Oct. 20, 1985; children: Alexander David, William Ernest. MA, Rutgers U., 1984. Policy analyst EPA, Washington, 1984-85; profl. staff, speechwriter energy and commerce com. U.S. Ho. of Reps., Washington, 1985-87; exec. v.p. MWW/Strategic Communications, River Edge, N.J., 1987—. Commr. Environ. Commn. Village of Ridgewood, N.J., 1989—; chmn. Ridgewood Dem. Com., 1989-93; trustee Cmty. Resource Coun., 1990—, Gov. Elect Environ. Task Force, Trenton, N.J., Dem. Nat. Com., Washington, 1992—; del. nat. conv., 1992; commr. N.J. Pub. Broadcasting Authority; vice chair N.J. Network, Newark, 1992-94; mem. N.J. Network Found., 1994—. Mem. Pub. Rels. Soc. Am., Nat. Assn. Profl. Environ. Communicators, N.J. Assn. Environ. Commnrs, Trenton, adv. bd. 1990—. Jewish. Home: 211 Sunset Ave Ridgewood NJ 07450-1424 Office: MWW/Strategic Communications 70 Grand Ave River Edge NJ 07661-1935

SOMMERER, JOHN, accountant; b. Mt. Holly, N.J., Oct. 30, 1947; s. John Price and Barbara Elizabeth (Davis) S.; m. Diane Catherine Kuszaj, Aug. 5, 1967; children: James Peter, John Joseph, Paul Andrew, Matthew Thomas. BS, U. Hartford, 1969; MBA, U. Toronto, 1972; postgrad., Columbia U., 1972-74. CPA, Fla., N.J., N.Y. Sr. cons. Deloitte and Touche, N.Y.C., 1974-78; dir. mgmt. info. systems Pantry Pride Enterprises, Ft. Lauderdale, Fla., 1978-82; mng. ptnr. John Sommerer and Co., P.A., Coral Springs, Fla., 1982—; mayor City of Coral Springs, 1994—. Treas. Coral Springs Cmty. Chest, 1988-94. Mem. Coral Springs Kiwanis (bd. dirs. 1990, 92), Coral Springs C. of C. (pres. 1987, treas. 1986, bd. dirs. 1986-88).

Column 3

Roman Catholic. Home: 9501 NW 44th Pl Coral Springs FL 33065 Office: John Sommerer and Co PA 1881 University Dr Coral Springs FL 33071

SOMMERFELD, NICHOLAS ULRICH, lawyer; b. Frankfurt, Fed. Republic Germany, Sept. 3, 1926; came to U.S., 1933; s. Martin and Helene (Schott) S.; m. Charlotte Ann Abrams, Sept. 11, 1954; children: Gretchen, Amy Fiore. AB, Princeton U., 1948; JD, Harvard U., 1952. Assoc. Gaston Snow & Ely Bartlett, Boston, 1954-61, ptnr., 1961-91; of counsel Hutchins Wheeler & Dittmar, Boston, 1991—. Trustee Perkins Sch. for the Blind, Watertown, Mass., 1982—, Boston Bar Found., 1994—. Lt. USN, 1952-54. Fellow Am. Coll. Trust Estate Counsel; mem. Boston Bar Assn. (chmn. probate com. 1986-87, chmn. steering coun., lawyers com. for civil rights 1980-84, mem. coun. 1993—), Boston Bar Found. (trustee 1994—). Office: Hutchins Wheeler & Dittmar 101 Federal St Boston MA 02110-1800

SOMMERFELD, RAYNARD MATTHIAS, accounting educator; b. Sibley, Iowa, Aug. 10, 1933; s. Ernest Robert and Lillian Emma (Matthias) S.; m. Barbara Ann Spear, June 9, 1956; children: Andrea Joan, Kristin Elaine. B.S.C., U. Iowa, 1956, M.A., 1957, Ph.D., 1963. Asst. prof. Grad. Sch. Bus., U. Tex., Austin, 1963-66; asso. prof. Grad. Sch. Bus., U. Tex., 1966-68, prof., 1968-72, Arthur Young prof., 1972-76; partner Arthur Young & Co., C.P.A.s, 1976-78; John A. White prof. accounting U. Tex., Austin, 1978-83, Glenn Welsch prof., 1983-84, James Bayless/Rauscher Pierce Refsnes prof., 1984-93, prof. emeritus, 1993—; mem. Acctg. Edn. Change Com., 1989-92, CPA exam. rev. bd., 1992-95/. Author: Tax Reform and the Alliance for Progress, 1966, (with H. Anderson and H. Brock) An Introduction to Taxation, 1969, rev. edits., 1972, 76-91, (with G.F. Streuling) Tax Research Techniques, 1976, rev. edits., 1981, 89, The Dow Jones-Irwin Guide to Tax Planning, 1974, rev. edits., 1978, 81, Federal Taxes and Management Decisions, 1974 rev. edits., 1978, 81, 83, 85, 87, 89, (with S. Jones), 91, 93, 94, (with H. Anderson, H. Brock, J. Everett) HBJ Federal Tax Course 1984, 1985, 86, Essentials of Taxation, 1990, A Review of Essentials of Taxation, 1990. Served with USAF, 1957-60. Erskine fellow U. Canterbury, New Zealand, 1995. Mem. AICPA, Am. Taxation Assn. (pres. 1975-76, Outstanding Tax Educator award 1993), Tex. Soc. CPAs (bd. dirs. 1969-72, pres. Austin chpt. 1967-68), Am. Acctg. Assn. (pres. 1986-87, Outstanding Acctg. Educator award 1994, Disting. Internat. Vis. Lectr. 1994-95). Lutheran. Home: 5100 Ranch Rd 620 N Austin TX 78732-1810 Office: U Tex CBA 4M 202 Austin TX 78712

SOMMERFELDT, JOHN ROBERT, historian; b. Detroit, Feb. 4, 1933; s. Melvin John and Virginia Zita (Gruenheck) S.; m. Patricia Natalie Levinske, Aug. 25, 1956; children: Ann, James, John, Elizabeth. AB, U. Mich., 1954, AM, 1956, PhD, 1960. Instr. history Stanford U., 1958-59; from instr. to prof. Western Mich. U., 1959-78; prof. history U. Dallas, 1978—, chmn. dept. history, 1984-87, univ. pres., 1978-80; dir. Medieval Inst., Western Mich. U., 1961-76; exec. dir. Inst. Cistercian Studies, 1973-78; dir. Center Contemplative Studies, 1976-78; pres. Cistercian Publs., 1973-79, chmn. bd., 1976-79. Author: The Spiritual Teachings of Bernard of Clairvaux, 1991; editor: Studies in Medieval Culture, 12 vols., 1964-78, Studies in Medieval Cistercian History, II, 1977, Cistercian Ideals and Reality, 1978, Simplicity and Ordinariness, 1980, The Chimaera of His Age: Studies in Bernard of Clairvaux, 1980, Abba: Guides to Wholeness and Holiness, East and West, 1981, Erudition at God's Service, 1987, Bernardus Magister, 1992, Studiosorum Speculum, 1993. Fulbright scholar, 1954-55; Univ. fellow U. Mich., 1960. Mem. Mediaeval Acad. Am., Am. Hist. Assn., Am. Catholic Hist. Assn., Am. Soc. Ch. History, Phi Beta Kappa, Phi Eta Sigma, Phi Kappa Phi. Republican. Roman Catholic. Home: 2809 Warren Cir Irving TX 75062-8938 Office: U Dallas Dept History Irving TX 75062-4799

SOMMERFELT, SOREN CHRISTIAN, foreign affairs, international trade consultant, former Norwegian diplomat, lawyer; b. Oslo, May 9, 1916; s. Soren Christian and Sigrid (Nicolaysen) S.; m. Frances Bull, June 27, 1947; 1 child, Cathrine. LLD, Oslo U., 1940. Joined Norwegian Fgn. Svc., 1941; pvt. sec. to fgn. minister, UN sec. gen. Trygve Lie, 1941-44; assigned to UN Secretariat, 1946, Div. Refugees' and Displaced Persons, 1st sec. Norwegian Embassy, Copenhagen, 1948-50; counselor Norwegian del. to NATO, 1950-52; dep. head. assoc. dept. Norwegian Ministry Fgn. Affairs, 1953-56, head, 1956-60; amb., head Norwegian del. to European Free Trade Assn., Gen. Agreement on Tariffs and Trade (GATT), and UN European Office, 1960-68; chmn. GATT Contracting Parties, 1968; amb. to Fed. Republic Germany, 1968-73, U.S.A., 1973-79, Italy, 1979-81; head Norwegian del. negotiating entry into European Communities, 1970-72; counsel Arent, Fox, Kintner, Plotkin & Kahn, Washington, 1982-84; ptnr. cons. firm Washington Resources, Inc., 1984-91; sr. ptnr. Sommerfelt Assocs., Washington, 1992—; bd. dirs. Nordic Enterprises, Inc., Internat. Mgmt. and Devel. Inst., Washington. Decorated comdr. Order St. Olav, Norway, grand cross Order of Merit, Fed. Republic Germany, grand cross Order of Merit, Italy, comdr. with star Order of North Star, Sweden, comdr. Order of Leopold II, Belgium, knight Order of Falcon, Iceland, knight Order of Dannebrog, Denmark. Mem. Metropolitan Club (Washington), Chevy Chase Club (Md.), Norske Selskab Club (Oslo). Home: 2700 Calvert St NW Washington DC 20008-2621 Office: Sommerfelt Assocs 1250 24th St NW Washington DC 20037-1124

SOMMERLAD, ROBERT EDWARD, environmental research engineer; b. Jersey City, Aug. 27, 1937; s. Herman Francis and Helen Rita (Joyce) S.; m. Margaret Doreen Breen, Sept. 9, 1961; children: Sharon K., Michael E., Ellen J. BSME, N.J. Inst. Tech., 1960, MSME, 1963, postgrad., 1965. Devel. engr., rsch. assoc. Foster Wheeler Energy Corp., Livingston, N.J., 1960-71, head air pollution control sect., 1971-74; v.p. contract ops. Foster Wheeler Devel. Corp., Livingston, 1974-84; pres. Envirespone Inc., Livingston, 1985-86; dir. bus. devel. Energy and Environ. Rsch. Corp., Edison, N.J., 1987-88; cons., 1988-89; dir. environ. bus. devel. Midwest Rsch. Inst., Falls Church, Va., 1989-90; mgr. combustion tech. Rsch.-Cottrell Cos., 1990-92, cons., 1992-93; mktg. dir. PSI Powerserve, Andover, Mass., 1993-94, cons., 1994—; mem. coal combustion and applications working group U.S. Dept. Energy U. San Diego, 1981-84. Patentee in field. V.p. Cranford (N.J.) Cmty. Pools Parents Assn., 1975-77, 86-87, pres., 1977-79, 84-86, 87-89; chmn. N.J. Swimming and Diving Conf., Cranford, 1986-89. Recipient Outstanding Achievement award Westfield YMCA, 1975. Fellow ASME (mem. rsch. com. indsl. and mcpl. waste 1971—, vice chmn. 1972-74, sec. 1987-91, mem. environ. affairs com. 1982—, mem. dioxin com. 1985—, mem. bd. performance test codes 1986—, chmn. boiler-caloriemeter com. 1986-89, numerous com. and conf. chairmanships); mem. Air and Waste Mgmt. Assn. (vice chmn. 1994—, sec. 1991-94, mem. AE-1 com. on particulate and associated acid gasses), Watchung Amateur Ski Club (mem. exec. bd. 1986-87) (Mountainside, N.J.). Roman Catholic. Club: Watchung Amateur Ski (exec. bd. 1986-87) (Mountainside, N.J.). Home: 31 Tulip St Cranford NJ 07016-1726

SOMMERS, GORDON L., religious organization administrator. Pres. Moravian Ch. in Am., Bethlehem, Pa. Office: Moravian Ch in Am PO Box 1245 1021 Center St Bethlehem PA 18016-1245

SOMMERS, LAWRENCE MELVIN, geographer, educator; b. Clinton, Wis., Apr. 17, 1919; s. Emil L. and Inga (Anderson) S.; m. Marjorie Smith, Apr. 26, 1948; 1 dau., Laurie Kay. B.S., U. Wis., 1942, Ph.M., 1946; Ph.D., Northwestern U., 1950. Prof. geography Mich. State. U., East Lansing, 1949—, successively instr., asst. prof. dept. geography, assoc. prof., 1949-55, prof., 1955-89, prof. emeritus, asst. provost emeritus, 1989—; chmn. dept. geography Mich. State U., East Lansing, 1955-79, mem. Environ. Quality Ctr., 1979-81, asst. provost, 1987-89; Mem. adv. com. geography Office Naval Research and NRC, 1958-61; Fellow Am. Scandinavian Found. Co-author: Outside Readings in Geography, 1955, Introduction to Geography-Selected Readings, 1987, Cultural Geography-Selected Readings, 1967, Energy and the Adaptation of Human Settlements, 1980, Economic Geography-Selected Readings, 1970, World Regional Geography, 1976; author: Michigan: A Geography, 1984; also articles on Norwegian, European, Michigan, marginal areas and economic geography; editor: Atlas of Michigan, 1977, Fish in Lake Michigan, 1981, Land Use: A Spatial Approach, 1981. Served with adj. gen. dept. AUS, 1942-45. Office Naval Research grant for rsch. in Denmark, 1953, Travel grant to Europe, 1960, 82, 86, Social Sci. Rsch. Coun. and Am. Scandinavian Found. grantee for rsch. in Norway, 1948. Mem. AAAS, Am. Geog. Soc., Assn. Am. Geographers (exec. coun. 1967-70, chmn. cons. svc. 1970-77, chmn. pub. com. 1968-70),

Mich. State U. Acad. Coun. and Grad. Coun. (chmn. steering com. 1982-84); Am. Scandinavian Found., Scandinavian Studies Assn., Explorers Club, Phi Kappa Phi (pres. Mich. State U. chpt. 1980-82, regional v.p. North Ctrl. region 1986-89, nat. pres. elect 1989-92, com. 1992—, nat. pres. 1992—), Sigma Xi (pres. Mich. state U. chpt. 1959-60), Phi Delta Beta. Home: 4292 Tacoma Blvd Okemos MI 48864-2734 Office: Mich State U East Lansing MI 48824

SOMMERS, MAXINE MARIE BRIDGET, writer, educator, publisher; b. Crystal Falls, Mich., May 7, 1932; d. Francis Ernest and Irene Catherine (Raher) Munns; m. Clemens Struve, June 10, 1952 (div. 1975); children: Stephen, Jospeh; m. Norval Isom Sommers (dec. 1989). Student, Milw. Downer Coll. for Women, 1948-49, U. Tex. Med. Br., Galveston, 1949-50, St. Mary's Hosp., 1950-51. Owner, operator Pound Sterling Publ., 1982—; Pound Sterling Media Svc., 1983—. Author: A Texan on the Road Again to the Far East, 1992; author 28 books and mini-books on cuisine, and travel, also children's books. Pres. Corpus Christi Symphony Guild, 1967-69, Tex. Assn. Symphony Orchestras, 1969; bd. dirs. Corpus Christi Symphony Soc., 1975—, South Tex. Health Syss. Agy., 1982-85; bd. dirs., pvt. svc. trainer Tex. divsn. Am. Cancer Soc., 1974-94; pres. Tex. Coastal Bend Mental Health Assn., 1976-78. Recipient cert. of award Byliners Tex. Wide Writers, 1992, Bus. Assoc. Night award Am. Bus. Women's Assn., 1992, cert. merit Corpus Christi Symphony Guild, 1969, cert. recognition Tex. Women's Assn. Symphony Orchestras, 1969, various awards Am. Cancer Soc. Mem. Byliners, Austin Writer's League. Avocations: gardening, cooking, traveling. Home: 4270 Ocean Dr Corpus Christi TX 78411-1283

SOMMERS, ROBERT THOMAS, editor, publisher, author; b. Balt., Aug. 6, 1926; s. Thomas Michael and Pearl Florence (Glendenning) S.; m. Helen Louise Ray, Oct. 19, 1952; children—Thomas Michael II, Patricia Ray. B.S., U. Md., College Park, 1950. Reporter Evening Sun, Balt., 1950-62; reporter Evening Star, Washington, 1962-66; editor U.S. Golf Assn. Jour., N.Y.C., 1966-72, Far Hills, N.J., 1972-92. Author: The Oxford Book of Golf Anecdotes, 1995, The U.S. Open: Golf's Ultimate Challenge, 1987, Bobby Jones in Chapman's Library of Golf, 1992; co-author: Great Shots, 1989; contbr. articles to profl. jours. Served with U.S. Coast Guard, 1944-46, PTO. Mem. Golf Writers Assn. Am., Assn. Golf Writers Gt. Britain, Authors Guild, Plainfield (N.J.) Country Club, Ballybunion Golf Club (Ireland), Kingston Heath Golf Club (Australia), Royal and Ancient Golf Club of St. Andrews (Scotland), The Reserve Golf and Tennis Club (Fla.). Republican. Episcopalian. Avocations: reading, golf, music. Home and Office: 8083 Spendthrift Ln Port Saint Lucie FL 34986-3122

SOMMERS, WILLIAM PAUL, management consultant; b. Detroit, July 22, 1933; s. William August and Mary Elizabeth (Baietto) S.; m. Josephine A. Sommers; children: William F., Clare M., John C. Hughes, Joanna M. Weems, Russell L. Hughes. B.S.E. (scholar), U. Mich., 1955, M.S.E., 1956, Ph.D. (Riggs fellow, Texaco fellow, Univ. fellow), 1961. Research asso. U. Mich. Inst. Sci. and Tech., Ann Arbor, 1958-61; chief chem. propulsion space and missile systems Martin Marietta Corp., Balt., 1956-58, 61-63; v.p. Booz, Allen & Hamilton, Inc., Bethesda, Md., 1963-70; pres. Tech. Mgmt. Group Booz, Allen & Hamilton, Inc., 1973-79, sr. v.p. 1979-82; exec. v.p. Iameter, Inc., San Mateo, Calif., 1992-94; pres., CEO SRI Internat., Menlo Park, Calif., 1994—; bd. dirs. Kemper Fin. Svcs., Rohr Inc., Therapeutic Discovery Corp., Litton Industries, Inc. Contbr. articles to profl. jours., also chpt. in book. Pres. Washington chpt. U. Mich. Alumni Club, 1970-71; v.p. Wildwood Manor Citizens Assn., 1968-70; chief Adventure Guide Program, YMCA, 1971-72; dir. Manor Montessori Sch., 1966-68; bd. visitors Coll. Engring., U. Calif.-Davis. Mem. U. Mich. Coll. Engring. Nat. Adv. Bd., Conf. Bd. Internat. Coun. on Innovation and Tech., Criminal Justice Legal Found. (bd. dirs.), Sigma Xi, Tau Beta Pi, Pi Tau Sigma. Republican. Roman Catholic. Clubs: Columbia Country (Bethesda), Willow Bend Country Club (Mashpee, Mass.), San Francisco Tennis, Bankers (San Francisco). Home: 2181 Parkside Ave Hillsborough CA 94010-6452 Office: SRI Internat 333 Ravenswood Ave Menlo Park CA 94025-3493

SOMMERVILLE, MARY ROBINSON, library director; b. Fairfield, Ala., Aug. 16, 1941; d. E. Bryce Robinson, Jr. and Margaret Allen m. Ormond Somerville, July 10, 1964 (d. 1976). BA in English with honors in Writing, U. N.C., 1963; MA in English, U. Colo., 1965; MLS, U. Okla., 1971. Youth svcs. adminstr. Lincoln City (Nebr.) Librs., 1973-78; youth svcs. mgr. Louisville (Ky.) Free Pub. Libr., 1978-88, proj. dir. automation, 1985-86, grans adminstr., 1986-87, mgr. employee rels., 1987-88; youth svcs. adminstr. Broward County Libr., Ft. Lauderdale, Fla., 1988-90; youth svcs. adminstr. Miami-Dade Pub. Libr., 1990-91, asst. dir. branches and spl. svcs., 1991-93, interim dir., 1993-94, dir., 1994—. Named Outstanding Alumnus Sch. Libr. and Info. Studies U. Okla., 1995. Mem. ALA (speaker, lectr. 16 states, pres. Assn. for Libr. Svc. to Children 1987-88, mem. 5 person delegation to former Soviet Union 1989, cons. U.S. Dept. Edn. 1988, chair ALA nominating com. 1992, planning and budget assembly 1992 (elected), coun. 1992 (elected), mem. exec. bd. 1993-95, pres. elect ALA 1995—, initiator projects which won H.W. Wilson Staff Devel. award and 4 John Cotton Dana awards), Phi Beta Kappa. Home: 800 West Ave # 735 Miami Beach FL 33139 Office: Miami Dade Pub Libr System 101 W Flagler St Miami FL 33130-1523

SOMMESE, ANDREW JOHN, mathematics educator; b. N.Y.C., May 3, 1948; s. Joseph Anthony and Frances (Lia) S.; m. Rebecca Rooze DeBoer, June 7, 1971; children: Rachel, Ruth. BA in Math., Fordham U., 1969; PhD in Math., Princeton U., 1973. Gibbs instr. Yale U., New Haven, 1973-75; asst. prof. Cornell U., Ithaca, N.Y., 1975-79; assoc. prof. U. Notre Dame, Ind., 1979-83, prof. of math., 1983—, chair dept. math., 1988-92, Vincent J. Duncan and Annamarie Micus Duncan chair math., 1994—; mem. Inst. for Advanced Study, Princeton, N.J., 1975-76; guest prof. U. Bonn, Germany, 1978-79; guest rschr. Max Planck Inst. for Math., Bonn, 1992-93; cons. GM Rsch., Warren, Mich., 1986—. Editor: Manuscripta Mathematica jour., 1986-93; contbr. articles to profl. publs. Recipient Rsch. award for Sr. U.S. Scientists Alexander Von Humboldt found., 1993; A.P. Sloan Found. rsch. fellow, 1979. Mem. Am. Math. Soc., Soc. for Indsl. and Applied Math., Phi Beta Kappa. Office: U Notre Dame Dept Math Notre Dame IN 46556

SOMNOLET, MICHEL PIERRE, cosmetics company financial executive; b. Chateaurenault, France, Feb. 6, 1940; came to U.S., 1969; s. Raoul Guillaume and Marthe Somnolet; B in Law, Paris Law Sch., 1963; MBA, Hautes Etudes Commerciales, Paris, 1964; m. Ghislaine Elizabeth Tenaille; children: Marc, Karine, Eric, Juliette. With L'Oreal, France, 1964-69; exec. v.p., COO Cosmair, Inc., U.S. Exclusive licensee of L'Oreal, also dir. Chevalier de la Legion d'Honneur, Chevalier de l'Ordre Nat. du Merite. Col. French army, 1964—. Mem. French C. of C. in N.Y., French Res. Officers in U.S.A. (sec. 1978, pres. 1990), Paris-Am. Club, Yacht Club de St. Briac, Mashomack, Millbrook Country Club. Home: 500 E 77th St New York NY 10162-0025 Office: Cosmair Inc 575 5th Ave New York NY 10017-2422

SOMORJAI, GABOR ARPAD, chemist, educator; b. Budapest, Hungary, May 4, 1935; came to U.S., 1957, naturalized, 1962; s. Charles and Livia (Ormos) S.; m. Judith Kaldor, Sept. 2, 1957; children: Nicole, John. BS, U. Tech. Scis., Budapest, 1956; PhD, U. Calif., Berkeley, 1960; D (hon.), Tech. U. Budapest, 1989, U. Paris, 1990, Free Univ Brussels, Belgium, 1992. Mem. research staff IBM, Yorktown Heights, N.Y., 1960-64; dir. Surface Sci. and Catalysis Program Lawrence Berkeley Lab., Calif., 1964—; mem. faculty dept. chemistry U. Calif.-Berkeley, 1964—, assoc. prof., 1967-72, prof., 1972—, Miller prof., 1978; Unilever prof. dept. chemistry U. Bristol, Eng., 1972; vis. fellow Emmanuel Coll., Cambridge, Eng., 1989; Baker lectr. Cornell U., Ithaca, N.Y., 1977; mem. editorial bds. Progress in Solid State Chemistry, 1973—, Jour. Solid State Chemistry, 1976-92, Nouveau Jour. de Chemie, 1977—, Colloid and Interface Sci., 1979—, Catalysis Revs., 1981, Jour. Phys. Chemistry, 1981-91, Langmuir, 1985—, Jour. Applied Catalysis, Molecular Physics, 1992—. Author: Principles of Surface Chemistry, 1972, Chemistry in Two Dimensions, 1981, Introduction to Surface Chemistry and Catalysis, 1994; editor-in-chief Catalysis Letters, 1988—; contbr. articles to profl. jours. Recipient Emmett award Am. Catalysis Soc., 1977, Kokes award Johns Hopkins U., 1976, Albert award Precious Metal Inst., 1986, Sr. Disting. Scientist award Alexander von Humboldt Found., 1989, E.W. Mueller award U. Wis.; Guggenheim fellow, 1969. Fellow AAAS, Am. Phys. Soc.; mem. NAS, Am. Acad. Arts and Scis., Am. Chem. Soc. (chmn. colloid and surface chemistry 1981, Surface and Colloid Chemistry award 1981, Peter Debye award 1989, Arthur W. Adamson award 1994), Catalysis

Soc. N.Am., Hungarian Acad. Scis. (hon. 1990). Office: U Calif Dept Chemistry D 58 Hildebrand Hall Berkeley CA 94720 Home: 665 San Luis Rd Berkeley CA 94707-1725

SOMPOLSKI, TIMOTHY ANDREW, benefits compensation executive; b. Chgo., June 27, 1952; s. Andrew and Sophie (Wharchol) S.; m. Christine Francisco, Oct. 8, 1976; children: Stephen, Nicole. BS, Ill. Inst. Tech., 1974. Mgr. employee rels. Chgo. Bd. Option Exch., 1978-80; cons. compensation & benefits Northwest Industries, Chgo., 1980-81; dir. compensation McGraw Edison Co., Rolling Meadows, Ill., 1981-84; v.p. compensation & benefits Kraft Gen. Foods, Glenview, Ill., 1984-90; v.p. compensation & benefits Philip Morris Cos. Inc., N.Y.C., 1990-94, v.p. corp. human resources, 1994—. Avocations: antique cars, golf, international travel. Office: Philip Morris Cos 120 Park Ave New York NY 10017-5523

SOMROCK, JOHN DOUGLAS, electronic marketing and manufacturing executive; b. Ely, Minn., Aug. 10, 1942; s. John William and Margaret Ann (Seliga) S.; m. Barbara Ann Rien, Oct. 21, 1978; children: Jason, Jeffrey, Lindsay. BSChemE, U. Minn., 1968. Engr. Minnegasco, Inc., Mpls., 1968-75, sr. engr. spl. projects, 1975-77, mgr. gas control, 1977-80, dir. supplemental energy supply, 1980-81, gen. mgr. Minn. alcohol producers, 1981-82, mgr. spl. projects, 1982, v.p. mktg. and sales, 1982-83, sr. v.p. ops. div., 1983-85, pres., chief operating officer, 1985-87; v.p. Diversified Energies, Inc., Mpls., 1983-85, sr. v.p.; 1985-90; pres., chief exec. officer E.F. Johnson Co., Eden Praire, Minn., 1987—; chief exec. officer EnScan, Inc., Eden Praire, 1987—; bd. dirs. Minnegasco, Inc., Mpls. Bd. dirs. Viking Coun. Boy Scouts of Am., Mpls., 1986; bd. trustees Dunwoody Indsl. Inst., 1986; bd. dirs. Downtown Council of Mpls., 1987, E.F. Johnson Co., 1987—, EnScan, Inc. 1987—; chmn. bus. expansion com. Greater Mpls. C. of C., 1987. Mem. Am. Gas Assn. (chmn. mktg. sect. 1985-86, bd. dirs. 1986-87), Midwest Gas Assn. (bd. dirs. 1987). Republican. Roman Catholic. Clubs: Mpls., Mpls. Athletic, Interlachen Country (Mpls.). Avocation: golf. Office: EF Johnson Co PO Box 59089 Minneapolis MN 55459-0089

SONDAG, MICHAEL ROBERT, association executive; b. Red Bud, Ill., Aug. 2, 1952; s. Gene Michael Sondag and Mabel Mary (Friedrich) Offermann; m. Lisa Elaine Bortner, July 3, 1987. BS in Animal Sci., Western Ill. U., 1974. Dist. mgr. Ralston Purina Co., St. Louis, 1974-83; exec. v.p. Ill. Pork Producers Assn., Springfield, 1983—. Recipient Keyman award Peoria (Ill.) Jaycees, 1983. Mem. Ill. Soc. Assn. Execs. (bd. dirs. 1987—, sec.-treas. 1989—, pres. 1991—), Western Ill. U. Alumni Coun., KC, Delta Tau Delta (pres. 1974). Home: 2536 Cherry Rd Springfield IL 62704-3132 Office: Ill Pork Producers Assn 6411 S 6th Street Rd Springfield IL 62707-8642

SONDE, THEODORE IRWIN, lawyer; b. N.Y.C., Jan. 7, 1940; s. Martin and Anne (Greenbaum) S.; m. Susan Kolisch, Sept. 10, 1964; children—Andrea Martine, David Ian. B.A., CCNY, 1961; LL.B., NYU, 1964; LL.M., Georgetown U., 1967. Bar: N.Y. 1964, D.C. 1978, U.S. Supreme Ct. With SEC, Washington, 1964-80, asst. gen. counsel, office of Gen. Counsel, 1970-74, assoc. dir. div. of enforcement, 1974-80; dir. Office of Enforcement, Fed. Energy Regulatory Commn., 1980-81; mem. Cole, Corette & Abrutyn, Washington, 1982—; adj. prof. Georgetown U. Law Sch. 1977—, George Washington U. Nat. Law Ctr., 1976-82. Contbr. articles to legal jours. Office: Dechert Price & Rhoads 1500 K St NW Washington DC 20005

SONDERBY, PETER R., lawyer; b. Chgo., Apr. 24, 1941. BA, U. Ill., 1964, JD, 1967. Bar: Ill. 1967. Assoc., then ptnr. Chadwell & Kayser Ltd., Chgo., 1967-88; ptnr. Keck, Mahin & Cate, Chgo., 1988-94; sole practice Chgo., 1994—; mem. arbitration panels Nat. Assn. Securities Dealers, Nat. Futures Assn., Am. Arbitration Assn. Asst. editor U. Ill. Law Forum, 1966-67. Mem. ABA, Chgo. Bar Assn., Ill. State Bar Assn., Law Club Chgo., Securities Industry Assn., Order of Coif. Office: 19 S Dearborn St Chicago IL 60603-2301

SONDERBY, SUSAN PIERSON, federal bankruptcy judge; b. Chgo., May 15, 1947; d. George W. and Shirley L. (Eckstrom) Pierson; m. James A. De Witt, June 14, 1975 (dec. 1978); m. Peter R. Sonderby, Apr. 7, 1990. AA, Joliet (Ill.) Jr. Coll., 1967; BA, U. Ill., 1969; JD, John Marshall Law Sch., 1973. Bar: Ill. 1973, U.S. Dist. Ct. (cen. and so. dists.) Ill. 1978, U.S. Dist. Ct. (no. dist.) Ill. 1984, U.S. Ct. Appeals (7th Cir.) 1984. Assoc. O'Brien, Garrison, Berard, Kusta and De Witt, Joliet, 1973-75, ptnr., 1975-77; asst. atty. gen. consumer protection div., litigation sect. Office of the Atty. Gen., Chgo., 1977-78; asst. atty. gen., chief consumer protection div. Office of the Atty. Gen., Springfield, Ill., 1978-83; U.S. trustee for no. dist. Ill. Chgo., 1983-86; judge U.S. Bankruptcy Ct. (no. dist.) Ill., Chgo., 1986—; adj. faculty De Paul U. Coll. Law, Chgo., 1986; spl. asst. atty. gen., 1972-78; past mem. U.S. Trustee adv. com., consumer adv. coun. Fed. Res. Bd.; past sec. of State Fraudulent I.D. com., Dept. of Ins. Task Force on Improper Claims Practices. Mem. Fourth Presbyn. Ch., Art Inst. Chgo.; past mem. Westminster Presbyn. Ch., Chgo. Coun. of Fgn. Rels.; past bd. dirs. Land of Lincoln Coun. Girl Scouts U.S.; past mem. individual guarantors com. Goodman Theatre, Chgo.; past chmn. clubs and orgns. Sangamon County United Way Capital campaign; past bd. dirs., chmn. house rules com. and legal subcom. Lake Point Tower; past mem. Family Svc. Ctr., Aid to Retarded Citizens, Henson Robinson Zoo. Master Abraham Lincoln Marovitz Inn of Ct.; fellow Am. Coll. Bankruptcy; mem. Nat. Conf. Bankruptcy Judges (legis. outreach com.), Am. Bankruptcy Inst., Comml. Law League Am. (exec. coun. bankruptcy and insolvency sect., bankruptcy com.), past vice chmn. U.S. Trustee Rev. com., edn. com.), John Marshall Law Sch. Alumni Assn. (bd. dirs., 2d v.p., 1st v.p., chmn. Luncheon Series, chmn. Disting. Svc. Awards com., exec. Long-range Planning com., others), Law Club of Chgo., Legal Club of Chgo. (hon.). Avocations: travel, flying, interior decorating. Office: US Bankruptcy Ct 219 S Dearborn St Ste 638 Chicago IL 60604-1704

SONDEREGGER, THEO BROWN, psychology educator; b. Birmingham, Ala., May 31, 1925; s. Ernest T. and Vera M. (Sillox) B.; children: Richard Paul, Diane Carol, Douglas Robert. BS, Fla. State U., 1946; MA in Chemistry, U. Nebr., 1948, MA in Exptl. Psychology, 1960; PhD in Clin. Psychology, U. Nebr., 1965. Lic. psychologist, Calif; clin. lic., cert. Nebr. Asst. prof. U. Nebr. Med. Ctr., Omaha, 1965-71, Nebr. Wesleyan U., Lincoln, 1965-68; asst. prof. U. Nebr., Lincoln, 1968-71, assoc. prof., 1971-76, prof., 1976-95; ret., 1995; vol. assoc. prof. U. Nebr. Med. Ctr., 1972-77, courtesy prof. med. psychology, 1977-95; ret. 1995. Editor Nebr. Symposium on Motivation, 1974, 84, 91, Problems of Perinatal Drug Dependence: Research and Clinical Implications, 1986, Neurobehavioral Toxicology and Teratology vol. 8, 1989-88, Problems of Perinatal Drug Dependence, 1979, 82, 84, Feminist Therapy Interchange, 1988-89, 91, Perinatal Substance Abuse: Research and Clinical Implications, 1992, Agendas for Aging, 1994. Mem. grant rev. coms. Nat. Inst. Drug Abuse, 1983-84, 85, 91-94. Tribute to Women award Lincoln YMCA, 1985, named Outstanding Rsch. Scientist Nebr. Chpt. Sigma Xi, 1991, Outstanding Contbr. to Status of Women, U N-L Chancellors Commn. on Status of Women, 1994. Fellow AAAS, Am. Psychol. Assn., Am. Psychol. Soc.; mem. Midwestern Psychol. Assn., Internat. Soc. Devel. Psychobiology, Internat. Soc. Psychoneuroendocrinolty, Nebr. Psychol. Assn. (pres. 1972—), Soc. Neurosci., Advanced Feminist Therapy Inst., Region V Adv. Coun. on Drugs, Fetal Alcohol Adv. Coun., Phi Beta Kappa (sec. Nebr. chpt. 1974), Sigma Xi (pres. 1986). Club: Altrusa YWCA. Avocations: painting, photography. Office: U Nebr 229 Burnett Hall Lincoln NE 68588

SONDHEIM, STEPHEN JOSHUA, composer, lyricist; b. N.Y.C., Mar. 22, 1930; s. Herbert and Janet (Fox) S. B.A., Williams Coll. 1950. vis. prof. contemporary theater Oxford U. England, 1990. Composer incidental music Girls of Summer, 1956, Invitation to a March, 1961, Twigs, 1971; lyrics West Side Story, 1957, Gypsy, 1959, Do I Hear A Waltz?, 1965; music and lyrics A Funny Thing Happened on the Way to The Forum, 1962, Anyone Can Whistle, 1964, Evening Primrose, 1966, Company, 1970 (Tony award 1971), Follies, 1971 (Tony award 1972), A Little Night Music, 1973 (Tony award 1973), The Frogs, 1974, Pacific Overtures, 1976, Sweeney Todd, 1979 (Tony award 1979), Merrily We Roll Along, 1981, Sunday in the Park with George, 1984 (Pulitzer prize 1985), Into the Woods, 1987 (Tony award 1988), Assassins, 1991, Passion, 1994 (Tony award 1994); additional lyrics Candide, 1973; anthologies Side by Side by Sondheim, 1976, Marry Me a Little, 1981, You're Gonna Love Tomorrow, 1983, Putting It Together,

1993; film scores Stavisky, 1974, Reds, 1981; composer songs for film Dick Tracy, 1990 (Acad. award); co-author film The Last of Sheila, 1973. Recipient Creative Arts medal Brandeis U., 1982, Grammy award, 1970, 73, 75, 79, 84, 88, Kennedy Ctr. Honor for Lifetime Achievement, 1993. Mem. Am. Acad. and Inst. Arts and Letters. *

SONDHEIMER, JUDITH M., pediatrician, educator; b. Englewood, N.J., Apr. 20, 1944; d. John W. and Harriet H. (Barlow) McConnell; m. Henry M. Sondheimer, June 30, 1969; 2 children. BA, Swarthmore Coll., 1966; MD, Columbia U., 1970. Diplomate Am. Bd. Pediatrics, Am. Bd. Pediatric Gastroenterology. Asst. prof. pediatrics SUNY, Syracuse, 1976-85; assoc. prof. pediatrics U. Colo., Denver, 1985-89, prof. pediatrics, 1989—; chief GI/Nutrition, Children's Hosp., Denver, 1985—. Fellow Am. Acad. Pediatrics; mem. Am. Gastroenterol. Soc., N.Am. Soc. Pediatric Gastroenterology and Nutrition. Office: Childrens Hosp-GI/Nutrition 1056 E 19th Ave Denver CO 80218

SONE, TOSHIO, acoustical engineering educator; b. Furukawa, Japan, May 14, 1935; s. Kikichi and Michio (Haga) S.; m. Noriko Tanaka, Sept. 5, 1964; children: Yasutomo, Atsushi, Susumu. B of Engring., Tohoku U., Sendai, Japan, 1958, M of Engring., 1960, DEng, 1963. Rsch. assoc. engring. faculty Tohoku U., 1963-64, assoc. prof. elec. engring., 1964-79, prof., 1979-81, prof. elec. communications engring., 1981—, dir. computer ctr., 1994—; vice chmn. Western Pacific Commn. on Acoustics, Sendai, 1994—; gen. chmn. INTER-NOISE 94, Yokohama, 1994. Author: Electroacoustic Engineering, 1963, Practice in Electromagnetics, 1973, Foundations of Acoustics, 1990, Life and Sound, 1991. Active Sendai Mcpl. Coun. Environ. Pollution Control, 1978—, Miyagi Prefectural Coun. Environ. Pollution Control, Sendai, Japan, 1982—, Iwate Prefectural Coun. Environ. Pollution Control, Morioka, Japan, 1982—. Rsch. grantee Kajima Sci. Promotion Found., Tokyo, 1984, Sound Tech. Promotion Found., Tokyo, 1987, Hoso-Bunka Found., Tokyo, 1991, Telecomm. Advancement Found., Tokyo, 1994. Fellow Acoustical Soc. Am.; mem. Inst. Electronics, Info. and Comm. Engrs. Japan, Acoustical Soc. Japan (bd. dirs. 1989—, v.p. 1991-93, pres. 1993-95, Sato prize 1992, 94), Inst. Noise Control Engring. Japan (bd. dirs. 1980—, v.p. 1990-92), Inst. Noise Control Engring. U.S.A. (corr.), Japan Soc. Mech. Engrs., Japan Audiological Soc. Avocation: calligraphy. Home: 4-9-5 Midorigaoka, Taihaku-ku, Sendai 982, Japan Office: Tohoku U Rsch Inst Elec Com, 2-1-1 Katahira, Aoba-ku, Sendai 980-77, Japan

SONEA, SORIN I., microbiologist; b. Cluj, Romania, Mar. 14, 1920; arrived in Can., 1950; m. Rodica Vlad, Feb. 2, 1946; children: Ioana, Peter, Michael, Alexander. M.D., Faculty of Medicine, Bucharest, Romania, 1944; Diploma of Hygiene, Faculty of Medicine, Paris, 1949; Doctorate (honoris causa), U. Que., 1988. Cert. specialist in med. microbiology. Asst. prof. microbiology U. Montreal, Que., Can., 1950-55, assoc. prof., 1955-60, prof., 1960-93, prof. emeritus, 1993—, head dept., 1964-79. Author: Introduction a la Nouvelle Bacteriologie, 1980, A New Bacteriology, 1983, Le strutture biologiche Batteri, 1993 contbr. numerous articles to profl. jours. Recipient award Can. Soc. Microbiologists, Montreal, 1978. Fellow Acad. of Sci., Royal Soc. Can., Royal Coll. Physicians and Surgeons of Can.; mem. Corp. Profls. of Medicine of Que. Home: 4282 Badgley St, Montreal, PQ Canada H4P 1N8 Office: Univ Montreal Microbiology Dept, C P 6128, Montreal, PQ Canada

SONENBERG, JACK, artist; b. Toronto, Ont., Can., Dec. 28, 1925; s. Solomon and Leah (Saltzman) S.; m. Phoebe Helman, June 7, 1949; 1 dau., Maya. Student, N.Y. U., 1949; B.F.A., Washington U., 1951. Mem. faculty dept. art Queens Coll., 1970-72, Bklyn. Coll., 1972, Bklyn. Coll. (Sch. of Visual Arts), 1962-73; mem. faculty Pratt Inst., Bklyn., 1968—; chmn. painting and drawing dept. Pratt Inst. Bklyn., 1973—. One-man shows, Byron Gallery, N.Y.C., 1965, 68, Hampton Inst., 1968, U. No. Iowa, 1969, Grand Rapids (Mich.) Art Mus., 1968, Flint Inst. Arts, 1972, Fischbach Gallery, N.Y.C., 1973, 55 Mercer Gallery, N.Y.C., 1980, group shows include, Whitney Mus., 1967, 73, Mus. Modern Art, 1974, Art Inst. Chgo., 1975, Pratt Inst., Bklyn., 1980, Rutgers U., N.J., 1980, Nat. Gallery, Washington, 1980, Moscow Artists Union, 1989; group shows include Painting Self-Evident, Piccolo Spolete, 1992; represented in permanent collections, Guggenheim Mus., Whitney Mus., U. Met. Mus., Bradley U., Nat. Gallery Can., W.Va. U. Ford Found. grantee, 1966; Guggenheim Found. grantee, 1973, N.Y. State CAPS, 1973-76, Nat. Endowment Arts grantee (sculpture), 1984-85, N.Y. Found. for the Arts grantee (painting) 1989. Office: Pratt Inst Sch Art and Design Brooklyn NY 11205

SONENBERG, MARTIN, biochemistry educator, physician; b. N.Y.C., Dec. 1, 1920; s. Berl and Nellie (Gordon) S.; m. Dellie Madeleine Ellis, Jan. 17, 1956; children: Santha, Andrea. B.A., U. Pa., 1941; M.D., NYU, 1944, PhD in Chemistry, 1952. Mem. Sloan-Kettering Cancer Center, N.Y.C., 1950; faculty Cornell U., 1950—, prof. biochemistry, 1967—; prof. medicine, 1972—. Mem. editorial bd.: Endocrinology, 1967-75; contbr. articles to profl. jours. Mem. biomed. adv. com. Population Coun., 1960; mem. adv. com. Am. Cancer Soc., 1971; chmn. endocrinology study sect. NIH, mem. adv. com. divsn. rsch. grants, 1989-91. Recipient Van Meter award Am. Thyroid Assn., 1952; Am. Cancer Soc. scholar, 1952-55; Guggenheim fellow, 1957-58; recipient Sloan award for cancer research, 1968. Fellow Am. Thyroid Assn., Am. Soc. Clin. Investigation, Am. Soc. Biol. Chemists, Endocrine Soc. Research on role of pituitary gland in normal and abnormal growth. Office: 1275 York Ave New York NY 10021-6007

SONENSHEIN, NATHAN, marine consulting company executive, retired naval officer; b. Lodi, N.J., Aug. 2, 1915; s. H. W. and Sarah S.; m. Ila Nina Maria Baker, May 11, 1941; children: Carol Dale Manashil, William Baker. B.S., U.S. Naval Acad., 1938; M.S., MIT, 1946; grad. Advanced Mgmt. Program, Harvard U., 1964. Commd. ensign U.S. Navy, 1938, advanced through grades to rear adm., 1965; various assignments U.S. and Japan, 1938-49; dir. navy facilities div. Bur. Ships, 1949-51; engring. officer U.S.S. Philippine Sea, 1951-53; planning and estimating supt. N.Y. Naval Shipyard, 1953-56; head hull design br. Bur. Ships, 1956-60; fleet and force maintenance officer on staffs comdr.-in-chief and comdr. service force U.S. Pacific Fleet, 1960-62; dir. ship design div. Bur. Ships, 1962-64, asst. chief for design, shipbldg. and fleet maintenance, 1965; project mgr. Fast Deployment Logistics Ship Project, 1965-66; dep. chief naval material for logistic support, 1967-69; comdr. Naval Ship Systems Command, 1969-72; pres. NMC Shipbldg. Council, 1972-73; dir. for energy Dept. Def., 1973-74, ret., 1974; asst. to pres. Global Marine Devel., Inc., Newport Beach, Calif., 1974-84; pres. Sonenshein and Assocs., marine cons. co., Moraga, Calif., 1985—; mem. nat. adv. com. Oceans and Atmosphere, 1984-86. Decorated Legion of Merit with 2 Gold stars. Mem. Am. Soc. Naval Architects and Marine Engrs. (v.p., Am. Soc. Naval Engrs. (past pres., H.E. Saunders medal 1982), Sigma Xi. Home and Office: 1884 Joseph Dr Moraga CA 94556-2711

SONETT, CHARLES PHILIP, physicist; b. Pitts., Jan. 15, 1924; s. Erwin and Helen (Dorner) S.; m. Virginia Hooten, June 20, 1948; children: Eric Erwin, Maria Lisa. BA in Physics, U. Calif., Berkeley, 1949; MS, U. Calif. 1951; PhD in Nuclear Physics, UCLA, 1954. Assoc. physics UCLA, 1953-54; range head devel. group Ramo Wooldridge Corp., 1954-57; mem. sr. staff, head space physics sect., project scientist Pioneer 1, 2, 5, Explorer 6 Space Tech., 1957-60; chief scis. lunar and planetary programs NASA Hdqrs., 1960-62, chief space sci. div., 1962-70; dep. dir. astronautics NASA/Ames Rsch. Ctr., 1970-73; prin. investigator Pioneer 5, 6, 7, 8, 9; Explorer 6, 33, 35; Apollo 12, 15; chief planetary scis., head dept., dir. lunar and planetary lab. U. Ariz., Tucson, 1973-77, prof. planetary scis., 1977-92, regents prof. planetary scis., 1990—, prof. emeritus, 1992—; lectr. engring. UCLA, 1955-58; cons. NASA Hdqrs., Jet Propulsion Lab., Rockwell Internat. Editor Cosmic Electrodynamics, 1970-72; co-editor Astrophysics and Space Sci., 1973-80, mem. editorial bd., 1980—; co-editor The Moon and the Planets, 1973—; mem. editorial com. Ann. Rev. Earth and Planet Scis., 1973-76. With U.S. Army, 1943-46. Decorated Purple Heart; recipient Exceptional Sci. Achievement medal NASA, 1969, 72, Space Sci. award AIAA, 1969; Guggenheim fellow, 1968-69, Carnegie fellow U. Edinburgh, 1985; grantee NASA, 1959—, NSF, 1978, 83-86. Fellow Am. Geophys. Union; mem. AAAS, Internat. Astron. Union, Univ. Space Rsch. Assn. (trustee 1977-83). Home: 5745 N Camino Real Tucson AZ 85718-4213 Office: Univ Ariz Dept Planetary Scis Lunar and Planetary Lab Tucson AZ 85721

SONFIELD, ROBERT LEON, JR., lawyer; b. Houston, Oct. 28, 1931; s. Robert Leon and Dorothy Harriett (Huber) S.; 1 dau., Sheree. B.A., U. Houston, 1956, LL.B., J.D., 1959; Ph.D. (hon.), U. Eastern Fla., 1962; LL.D. (hon.), London Inst. Applied Research, 1973; certificate fed. taxation, NYU, 1973; certificate securities regulation, Harvard U., 1983. Bar: Tex. 1959, U.S. Supreme Ct. 1959, U.S. Dist. Ct. Tex. 1960, U.S. Ct. Appeals 1960, U.S. Ct. Claims 1974. Mng. dir. Sonfield & Sonfield, Houston, 1959—; Mem. nat. adv. council Nat. Fedn. Ind. Bus. Author: Corporate Financing by Sale of Securities to the Public, 1969, Mergers and Acquisitions, 1970, Student Rights, 1971, The Limited Partnership as a Vehicle for Real Estate Investment, 1971, Integration of Partnership Offerings, 1974. Recipient John Garwood award, 1957, Frio-Finnegan Outstanding Alumnus award, 1970-71, citation for outstanding contbn. to legal profession, 1971. Mem. Am. Tax Lawyers Assn. (pres.), Lawyers Soc. Houson, Am. Judicature Soc., ABA, Tex. Bar Assn. (dist. com. on admission to state bar, chmn. clients security fund com.), Houston Bar Assn. (com. chmn. council, tax sect.), Tex. Equal Access to Justice Found., Houston Bar Found., Real Estate Securities and Syndication Inst., Huguenot Soc. of London, Order Stars and Bars, SAR, Sons Confederate Vets., Mil. Order World Wars, Mil. and Hospitaller Order St. Lazarus of Jerusalem, Knightly Assn. St. George the Martyr, Smithsonian Assocs., Houston Heritage Soc., Houston Mus. Fine Arts, Newcomen Soc. N.Am., Phi Delta Phi, Delta Sigma Phi. Clubs: Metropolitan (N.Y.C.); Argyle (San Antonio); Houston, Houstonian. Office: Sonfield & Sonfield 770 S Post Oak Ln Houston TX 77056-1911

SONG, MOON KI, biomedical research scientist; b. Taejon, Korea, May 24, 1931; s. Yong Kuk and Kuy Nam (Min) S.; m. Jong Soon Lee, Feb. 26, 1966; children: Julie Mijin, Albert Moonjin. BA, U. Hawaii, 1964, MS, 1966, PhD, 1972. Rsch. asst. U. Hawaii, Honolulu, 1962-65, jr. researcher, 1965-69; asst. rsch. prof. UCLA Sch. Medicine, 1980-87, assoc. rsch. prof., 1987-93, rsch. prof., 1993—; rsch. chemist Dept. Vet. Affairs Med. Ctr., Sepulveda, Calif., 1974-83, chief rsch. lab., 1983—; postdoctoral fellow Ind. U., Indpls., 1974; manuscript reviewer 10 sci. jours., 1980—; ad hoc rsch. application reviewer NIH, Dept. Vets. Affairs Rsch. Svcs., Am. Diabetic Assn., USDA Rsch. Svcs., 1980—. Contbr. numerous articles to profl. jours.; patentee in field. Mem. of Two com. Northridge (Calif.) United Meth. Ch., 1988—. Cancer rsch. grantee Ind. U. Cancer Rsch. Inst., 1974; DVA Med. Rsch. Svc. grantee, 1982—. Fellow Am. Coll. Nutrition; mem. Am. Inst. of Nutrition, Am. Soc. Clin. Nutrition. Democrat. Home: 10922 Yolanda Ave Northridge CA 91326-2724 Office: Dept Vets Affairs Wilshire & Sawtelle Blvds Los Angeles CA 90073

SONG, XIAOTONG, physicist, educator; b. Taizhou, Jiangsu, People's Republic of China, Oct. 18, 1934; came to U.S., 1989; s. Hoshu Song and Jingying Wang; m. Chuchu Zhu, 1966; 1 child, Jianyang. BS in Physics, Fudan U., Shanghai, China, 1955, PhD in Physics, 1963. Rsch fellow Dept Def., China, 1955-58; asst. prof. Hangzhou U., China, 1958-63; lectr., 1963-66, 77-83, assoc. prof., 1983-86, prof., 1986—; rsch. cons. dept. physics Inst. Nuclear and Particle Physics, U. Va., Charlottesville, 1989-90, rsch. prof., cons., 1990—; adv. com. for professorship exam., Zhejiang, China; dir. theory divsn. dept. physics Hangzhou U., China, 1984-89; referee Phys. Rev., High Energy Physics and Nuclear Physics, Nat. Natural Sci. Found., China; vis. scientist Tech. U. Munich, 1986, 88-89; CERN, Switzerland, 1986-87, Inst. Nat. Fisica Nuclear Turin Sect., Italy, 1986-88, Internat. Ctr. Theoretical Physics, Italy, 1986-88, Los Alamos Nat. Lab., 1987, Utah State U., 1987, Kans. State U., 1989, Brookhaven Nat. Lab. Contbr. articles to profl. jours. Recipient Prize of Natural Sci., Com. Sci. and Tech., Zhejiang Province, China, 1983, 84; grantee Nat. Natural Sci. Found., 1984-87. Mem. AAAS, Internat. Ctr. Theoretical Physics (sr. assoc.), Am. Phys. Soc., Chinese High Energy Physics Soc., Chinese Phys. Soc., N.Y. Acad. Sci., Sigma Xi. Achievements include research in theoretical nuclear and particle physics. Office: U Va Physics Dept Mccormick Rd Charlottesville VA 22901

SONGSTER, JOHN HUGH, legal administrator; b. Springfield, Pa., Mar. 20, 1934; s. James Thomas and Sarah Boyce (McMichael) S. BA, LaSalle Coll., Phila., 1956. Commd. ensign USN, 1956, advanced through grades to comdr., 1971, ret., 1976; asst. treas. Bradford Trust Co. N.Y.C., 1976-80; staff acct. Harcourt Brace Jovanovich, N.Y.C., 1980-83, Software Design Assocs., N.Y.C., 1983-87; legal adminstr. Gold Farrell & Marks, N.Y.C., 1988—. Mem. Assn. Legal Adminstrs. Republican. Roman Catholic. Avocations: reading biographies and memoirs, opera. Office: Gold Farrell & Marks 41 Madison Ave New York NY 10010-2202

SONI, KUSUM KAPILA, mathematics educator; b. Punjab, India, Nov. 14, 1930; came to U.S., 1959; d. Piare Lal and Sushila Devi (Bajaj) Kapila; m. Raj Pal Soni, Apr. 5, 1958; children: Poonam, Sushma. BA with honors, Punjab U., 1949, MA in Math., 1951; PhD, Oreg. State U., 1964. Lectr. Govt. Colls., Punjab, 1952-59; tchr. asst. Oreg. State U. Corvallis, 1959-64; asst. prof. math. U. Tenn., Knoxville, 1966-74, assoc. prof. math., 1970-83, prof. math., 1983—; vis. asst. prof. Oreg. State U., 1966-67; vis. rsch. dept. applied math. Ctr. for Math. and Computer Sci., Amsterdam, 1987, Indian Inst. Sci., Bangalore, India, 1987; vis. mem. U. Dundee (Scotland), 1982; summer mem. Inst. for Advanced Study, Princeton, N.J., 1979; speaker Internat. Symposium, Winnipeg, Can., 1989. Contbr. approximately 40 rsch. articles to profl. jours. Recipient Women of Achievement Rsch. award, U. Tenn., 1983, rsch. and travel grants, 1969, 70, 80, 89. Mem. Am. Math. Soc., Math. Assn. of Am., Sigma Xi. Achievements include research in asymptotic behavior of a class of integral transforms involving slowly varying functions and non absolutely integrable kernels; in development of polynomials associated with uniform asymptotic expansions of integrals with coalescing singularities. Office: Univ Tenn Dept Math Knoxville TN 37996-1300

SONIN, AIN A., mechanical engineering educator, consultant; b. Tallinn, Estonia, Dec. 24, 1937; came to U.S., 1965; s. Elmar and Ina (Herman) S.; m. Epp Jurima, July 24, 1971; children: Juhan, Aldo. BA Sc., U. Toronto, Ont., Can., 1960, MA Sc., 1961, PhD, 1965. Rsch. fellow, teaching asst. U. Toronto, 1960-65; asst. prof. MIT, Cambridge, 1965-68, assoc. prof., 1968-74, prof. mech. engring., 1974—; sr. scientist Thermo Electron Corp., Waltham, Mass., 1981-82; cons. in field. Contbr. over 60 articles to profl. jours. in fluid and thermal sciences. Mem. ASME, AAAS, Am. Phys. Soc., Am. Nuclear Soc. Achievements include 3 patents in field. Office: MIT Rm 3-256 Cambridge MA 02139

SONJU, NORM ARNOLD, professional sports team manager, executive; b. Chgo., Sept. 30, 1938; s. Marinius Anton and Anna (Nesse) S.; m. Carole Lynne Thiesen, June 10, 1967; children: Lynne, Scott, David. B.A., Grinnell Coll., 1960; M.B.A., U. Chgo., 1967. Vice pres., gen. mgr. Service-Master Contract Services, Downers Grove, Ill., 1967-77; pres., gen. mgr. Buffalo Braves, N.Y., 1977-78; v.p. Dallas Mavericks, 1979-87, gen. mgr., 1979—, chief operating officer, 1987—; dir., founder Camp of Woods Basketball Clinic, Speculator, N.Y., 1963—; dir. Correct Craft Boat Co., Orlando, Fla. Bd. dirs. Gospel Vols., Speculator, 1976—; trustee Taylor U., Upland, Ind., 1981—; mem. Dallas Assembly, 1983—. Mem. Nat. Basketball Assn. bd. govs. 1977—, chmn. mktg. com. 1982—). Republican. Clubs: Cress Creek Country (Naperville, Ill.); Brookhaven Country (Dallas). Office: Dallas Mavericks Reunion Arena 777 Sports Pl Dallas TX 75207-4499*

SONKA, STEVEN T., agricultural economics educator, consultant; b. Cedar Rapids, Iowa, July 4, 1948; s. Jerome and Marcella (Pickert) S.; m. Karilyn Mae Stephen, June 5, 1970; children: Tracy, Melissa, Julie, Teresa. BS in Agrl. Bus., Iowa State U., 1970, PhD in Econs., 1974. Resident assoc./staff economist Iowa State U. 1971-75; asst. prof. U. Ill., Urbana, 1975-79, assoc. prof., 1979-83, prof. agr. econ., 1983—; ptnr. Agrl. Edn. and Cons., Champaign, Ill., 1983—; adj. prof. Sci. Ill. State Water Survey, Champaign, 1981—; vis. faculty in resident Arthur Andersen & Co., summer 1982; resident assoc. Ctr. for Advanced Study, Champaign, fall 1986; vis. prof. Inst. Agrl. Bus., Santa Clara, Calif., 1986-87; cons. Orgn. Econ. Coop. and Devel., Paris, 1989, cons. office tech. assessment U.S. Congress, Washington, 1989-90. Author: (books) American Farm Size, 1975, Hail Suppression, 1977, Computers in Farming, 1983. Task force mem. U.S. Senate, Washington, 1982-83. Recipient Van Nostrand Reinhold/A V I Press Teacher awd., Nat. Assn. of Colleges and Teachers of Agriculture, 1992. Mem. Am. Agrl. Econ.

SONKOWSKY, ROBERT PAUL, classicist, educator, actor; b. Appleton, Wis., Sept. 16, 1931; s. Paul and Loretta Stella (Nooyen) S.; m. Barbara Lou Zierke, June 8, 1956; children—Paul Victor, Steven Robert, Michael Edward. B.A., Lawrence Coll., 1954; postgrad., U. Rome, 1956-57; Ph.D., U. N.C., 1958. Instr., asst. prof. U. Tex., 1958-61; fellow Inst. Research in Humanities, U. Wis., 1961-62; asso. prof. U. Mo., 1962-63, U. Minn., Mpls., 1963-64; chmn. dept. classics U. Minn., 1964-78, prof., 1964—; disting. Marbrook vis. prof. Macalester Coll., 1987-88; actor Attic Theatre, Appleton, Wis., 1950-54, Wilderness Rd. Theater Co., Berea, Ky., The Confederacy Co., Virginia Beach, Va., summers, 1955-58, Pillsbury House and Lyric Theaters, Mpls., 1991, Looking Glass Theater, St. Paul, 1993, Theater on the Park, Mpls., 1995. Author books; contbr. articles to profl. jours.; also recitations and recordings of classical Latin lit. in restored pronunciation; lit. recs., ednl. feature and indsl. films, TV commls. Lay reader Episc. Cathedral Ch. of St. Mark; lector Gregorian Singers, 1980-89; mem. St. Paul Sch. Com., 1971-76. Mem. AFTRA, Am. Philol. Assn., Soc. for Oral Reading of Greek and Latin Lit., Classical Assn. Mid West and South Internat. Soc. Chronobiology (nomenclature com.), Fulbright Assn. (pres. Minn. chpt. 1991-92), Phi Beta Kappa (pres. U. Minn. chpt. 1973-74, nat. senator 1976-82, pres. Minn. 1991-95, books reviewer for Key Reporter). Office: U Minn Classical & Near Ea Studies 330 Folwell Hall 9 Pleasant St SE Minneapolis MN 55455-0194

SONNABEND, ROGER PHILIP, hotel company executive; b. Boston, Sept. 17, 1925; s. Abraham M. and Esther (Lewitt) S.; m. Elsa Golub, July 17, 1949 (div.); children: Andrea, Stephanie, Jacqueline, Alan; m. Joan Snider, Feb. 18, 1971; stepchildren: Heidi Norton, Andrea Stoneman. B.A., MIT, 1946; M.B.A., Harvard U., 1949; LL.D. (hon.), U. N.H., 1969. Chief exec. officer Sonesta Internat. Hotel Corp., Boston, 1954—, chmn., 1970—. Contbr. chpts. to books and articles to profl. jours. Mem. exec. com. Nat. Alliance of Businessmen, 1968-69; bd. dirs. Bus. Execs. for Nat. Security, Inc., Washington, 1983-86; exec. com. Northeast NCCJ, 1957, regional cochmn., nat. v.p., 1960-68; trustee Inst. Contemporary Art. Mem. World Bus. Coun., Chief Execs. Orgn., Harvard Club (Boston). Home: 170 Rushton Ln Tavernier FL 33070-3015 Office: Sonesta Internat Hotels Corp 200 Clarendon St Boston MA 02116-5021

SONNEBORN, HENRY, III, former chemical company executive, business consultant; b. Balt., Mar. 11, 1918; s. Henry, Jr. and Lillian B. (Hamburger) S.; m. Clara Louise Lauer, Nov. 12, 1942; 1 child, Peter. A.B., Johns Hopkins U., 1938, Ph.D., 1941; doctorate (hon.), Hebrew U., Jerusalem, 1976. V.p., bd. dirs. Sonneborn Chem. and Refining, N.Y.C., 1950-60; bus. cons., Larchmont, N.Y.; bus. cons. Contbr. articles to profl. jours. Mem. PMI-Strang Clinic, 1969-72; trustee Hosp. for Joint Diseases, 1961—, chmn. bd., 1985-88; pres. Am. Friends Hebrew U., 1974-77; trustee Johns Hopkins U., 1978—. Served to lt. USNR, 1942-46. Jewish. Home: 110 N Chatsworth Ave Larchmont NY 10538-1638 Office: 2 Madison Ave Larchmont NY 10538-1961

SONNECKEN, EDWIN HERBERT, management consultant; b. New Haven, July 22, 1916; s. Ewald and Pauline (Halfmann) S.; m. Elizabeth Gregory, June 3, 1939; children: William H., Richard G., Paul D. B.S., Northwestern U., 1938; M.B.A., 1940. With Montgomery Ward & Co., Chgo., 1940-42; price adminstr. OPA, Chgo., 1943; mgr. sales B.F. Goodrich Co., Akron, Ohio, 1943-53; dir. planning Ford Motor Co., Dearborn, Mich., 1953-57; pres. Market Planning Corp., N.Y.C., 1957-61; from dir. corp. planning and research to v.p. corp. bus. planning Goodyear Tire & Rubber Co., 1961-80; chmn. Mktg. Sci. Inst., Cambridge, Mass., 1980-84; also trustee, chmn. research policy com. Mktg. Sci. Inst.; mgmt. cons., Akron, 1985—; Pres. Akron (Ohio) chpt. Am. Mktg. Assn., 1950, v.p. Detroit chpt., 1955, nat. v.p., dir., 1957, nat. pres., 1964-65, mem. global mktg. coun., 1986—. Pres. YMCA, Akron, 1978; chmn. trustees First Congl. Ch., Akron, 1985, chmn. endowment trust, 1987—. Served with AUS, 1945-46. Mem. Am. Statis. Assn., Am. Assn. Pub. Opinion Research, Nat. Assn. Bus. Economists, Am. Mktg. Assn., Internat. Mktg. Fedn. (pres.), European Soc. for Opinion and Market Research, Beta Gamma Sigma, Portage Country (Akron). Avocation: golf. Home: 736 Hampton Ridge Dr Akron OH 44313-5024

SONNEDECKER, GLENN ALLEN, historian of pharmacy; b. Creston, Ohio, Dec. 11, 1917; s. Ira Elmer and Letia (Linter) S.; m. Cleo Bell, Apr. 3, 1943; 1 child, Stuart Bruce. BS, Ohio State U., 1942; MS, U Wis., 1950, PhD, 1952; Dr. Sci. honoris causa, Ohio State U., 1964, Phila. Coll. Pharmacy and Sci., 1989; PharmD honoris causa, Mass. Coll. Pharmacy, 1974. Lic. pharmacist. Mem. editorial staff Sci. Service, Washington, 1942-43; editor Jour. Am. Pharm. Assn. (practical pharmacy edit.), Washington, 1943-48; asst. prof. U. Wis., 1952-56, asso. prof., 1956-60, prof., 1960-81, Edward Kremers prof., 1981-86; sec. Am. Inst. History of Pharmacy, 1949-57, dir., 1957-73, 81-85, hon. dir. life, chmn. bd., 1988-89; editor-in-chief RPh, 1978-80; sec., bd. dirs. Friends of Hist. Pharmacy, 1945-49; chmn. Joint Com. on Pharmacy Coll. Librs., 1960-61; U.S. del. Internat. Pharm. Fedn., 1953, 55, 62; U.S. rep. to Mid. East Pharm. Congress, Beirut, 1956; sec. sect. history of pharmacy and biochemistry Pan-Am. Congress Pharmacy and Biochemistry, 1957. Co-author books; contbr. to pharm. and hist. publs. Recipient Edward Kremers award (for writings), 1964, Nat. award Rho Chi, 1967, Schelenz plaquette Internat. Soc. for History of Pharmacy, 1971, Remington honor medal Am. Pharm. Assn., 1972, Urdang medal, 1976, Folch Andreu prize, Spain, 1985, Profile award Am. Found. Pharm. Edn., 1994; Am. Found. fellow, 1948-52, Guggenheim fellow, 1955, Fulbright Rsch. scholar, Germany, 1955-56. Mem. Am. Pharm. Assn. (life mem.; sec. sect. history of pharmacy 1949-50, vice chmn. 1950-51, chmn. 1951-52, rsch. assoc. 1964-65, chmn. joint task force with Acad. Pharm Scis. 1985, hon. chmn. bd. trustees 1985), Internat. Acad. History Pharmacy (1st v.p. 1970-81, pres. 1983-91, hon. pres. 1991—), Am. Assn. History of Medicine (exec. coun. 1966-69), Internat. Gesellschaft fur Geschichte der Pharmazie (exec. bd. 1965-89), hon. mem. socs. for history of pharmacy of Italy, Benelux, pan-Arab, Spain; mem. Sigma Xi, Rho Chi (mem. nat. exec. coun. 1957-59), Phi Delta Chi. Unitarian. Home: 2030 Chadbourne Ave Madison WI 53705-4047 Office: Univ Wis Pharmacy Bldg Madison WI 53706

SONNEMAN, EVE, artist; b. Chgo., 1946; d. Eric O. and Edith S. BFA, U. Ill., 1967; MFA, U. N.Mex., 1969. One-woman shows include Castelli Gallery, N.Y.C., 1976, 78, 80, 82, 84-86, Tex. Gallery, Houston, 1976, 78, 80, 82, 85, Galerie Farideh Cadot, Paris, 1978, 80, 83, François Lambert Gallery, Milan, Italy, 1980, 87, Mpls. Inst. Arts, 1980, La Nouveau Musée, Lyon, France, 1980, Musée de Toulon (France), 1983, Centre Georges Pompidou, Paris, 1984, Circus Gallery, L.A., 1989, Jones Troyer Fitzpatrick, Washington, 1989, Zabriskie Gallery, N.Y., 1990, Gloria Luria Gallery, Miami, 1990, Grand Central Terminal, N.Y.C., 1991, Charles Cowles Gallery, 1992; author: America's Cottage Gardens, 1990, Where Birds Live, 1992; photographs subject of book Real Time, 1976. Grantee Nat. Endowment Arts, 1971, 78, Polaroid Corp., 1978; Cartier fellowship, France, 1989. Address: 684 Ave of Americas New York NY 10010

SONNEMANN, HARRY, electrical engineer, consultant; b. Munich, Germany, Sept. 3, 1924; came to U.S., 1938, naturalized, 1944; s. Leopold and Emmy (Markus) S.; m. Shirley E. Battles, Nov. 25, 1949; children: Carol Jean, Joyce Elaine, Patricia Ann. B.S., Poly. Inst. Bklyn., 1954. Research electronance-phalography, 1944-47; asst. to dir. electronics dept. AEC contract, Columbia U., 1947-50; supr. electronics shop Columbia Hudson Labs., 1951-53, head electronics dept., 1954-59; asst. dir. Project Artemis, 1959-64, Project Artemis (Hudson labs.), 1961-64; asst. dir. field operating. Advanced Research Projects Agy., Nuclear Test Detection Office, 1964-67; acting dep. dir. Nuclear Test Detection Office, 1967-68; spl. asst. in electronics to asst. sec. navy for research and devel. Navy Dept., 1968-76; asst. to chief engr. NASA, 1977-78, dep. chief engr., 1978-84, asst. chief engr., 1984-86, cons., 1986—; pres. SBC Assocs. Inc., McLean, Va., 1988—; chmn. Dept. Def. Tactical Satellite Exec. Steering Group, 1968-69, chmn. Dept. Def. nav. satellite exec. steering group, 1969-70, 72-73. Treas. Art League. No. Va., 1967-68; pres. Rotonda Condominium Unit Owners Assn., 1982-84. Clubs: Washington Figure Skating

SONNENBERG, BEN, playwright, poet, editor; b. N.Y.C., Dec. 30, 1936; s. Benjamin and Hilda (Caplan) S.; m. Dorothy Gallagher, Mar. 10, 1981; children by previous marriages: Susanna, Emma, Saidee. Literary advisor Oxford (Eng.) Playhouse, 1963-65; lit. mgr. Repertory Theatre of Lincoln Ctr., N.Y.C. 1971-72; lectr. drama ctr. Juilliard Sch., N.Y.C., 1977-78; editor Grand Street, N.Y.C., 1981-90; pub. Grand Street Books, N.Y.C., 1990—. Author: Poems of Anna Comnena and More Poems, 1990, Lost Property, Memoirs and Confessions of a Bad Boy, 1991; editor: Grand Street Reader, 1986, Performance and Reality: Essays from Grand Street, The Courtship of Rita Hayworth, Mole Wedding; contbr. articles to The Nation, London mag., Yale Rev., Raritan, Harper's/Queen (Eng.). Fellow Royal Soc. of Lit.; mem. PEN. Office: Grand Street Pubs Inc 50 Riverside Dr New York NY 10024

SONNENBERG, HARDY, data processing company research and development executive, engineer; b. Schoensee, Fed. Republic Germany, Apr. 12, 1939; s. Gustav and Wanda (Neumann) S.; m. Doris Linda Adam, June 20, 1964; children: Kevin, Denise. BS, U. Alta., 1962; MS, Stanford U., 1964, PhD, 1967. Registered profl. engr., Ont. Advanced devel. engr. GTE Sylvania, Mountain View, Calif., 1966-68, engring. specialist, 1968-70, sect. mgr., 1970-73; dir. rsch. Optical Diodes Inc., Palo Alto, Calif., 1973-74; mem. rsch. staff Xerox Rsch. Centre Can., Mississauga, Ont., 1975-78, area mgr., 1978-80, lab. mgr., 1980-86, mgr. rsch. ops., 1986-87, mgr. tech. and engring. systems, 1987-94, v.p. rsch. and tech., 1994—; chmn. indsl. adv. coun. McMaster U., Hamilton, Ont., 1987-93, active, 1987—. Contbr. articles to profl. jours. Patentee in field. Chmn. bd. dirs. local ch., Hamilton, Ont., 1983-85, 89-93; pres. Sheridan Park Assn., Mississauga, 1988-89; chmn. Conf. Bd. Can. Rsch. Mgrs. Forum, 1991-93. Recipient cert. of recognition for invention NASA, 1973, 74, Achievement award Xerox Corp., 1981, Charles E. Ives Engring. award, 1983. Mem. IEEE, Am. Phys. Soc., Assn. Profl. Engrs. Ont., Soc. for Imaging Sci. and Tech., Soc. Photographic Scientists and Engrs., Sigma Xi. Avocations: outdoor activities, singing, church participation. Home: 900 Hwy 97 Box 126, Freelton, ON Canada L0R 1K0 Office: Xerox Graphic Systems, 2660 Speakman Dr, 3000 Westchester Ave, Purchase, NY Canada L5K 2L1

SONNENFELD, BARRY, cinematographer, film director. Cinematographer: (films) Blood Simple, 1984, Compromising Positions, 1985, Three O'Clock High, 1987, Raising Arizona, 1987, Throw Momma from the Train, 1987, Big, 1988, When Harry Met Sally..., 1989, Miller's Crossing, 1990, Misery, 1990, (TV movies) Out of Step, 1984 (Emmy award best cinematography 1984); dir.: (films) The Addams Family, 1991, Addams Family Values, 1993; dir.- co-prodr.: For Love or Money, 1993. Office: Gersh Agency 232 North Canon Dr Beverly Hills CA 90210 also: United Talent Agency 9560 Wilshire Blvd Beverly Hills CA 90212*

SONNENFELD, JEFFREY ALAN, management educator; b. Phila., Apr. 1, 1954; s. Burton David and Rochelle (Galant) S. AB, Harvard Coll., 1976; MBA, Harvard U., 1978, D in Bus. Adminstrn., 1980. Merchant retail clothing The Heir & Gentry Shop, Hatboro, Pa., 1968-72; pres. Harvard Radio Broadcasting, Cambridge, Mass., 1974-76; intern in mgmt. Scott Paper, IBM, Phila., Armonk, N.Y., 1976-78; advisor, tutor Harvard Coll., Cambridge, 1976-80; rsch. asst. Harvard U. Cambridge, 1977-80, asst. prof., 1980-84; assoc. prof. Harvard Bus. Sch., Cambridge, 1984-89; prof. Emory U., Atlanta, 1989—; dir. Ctr. for Leadership and Career Studies, 1989—; bd. dirs. Eastgate Pub., N.Y.C., Kloster Cruises Ltd., Miami. Author: Corporate Views of the Public Interest, 1980, Managing Career Systems, 1984, The Hero's Farewell: What Happens When CEOs Retire, 1988 (best seller 1989); mem. bd. editors Acad. Mgmt. Jour., Acad. Mgmt. Exec., Orgnl. Dynamics, Jour. Occupational Behavior; contbr. articles to profl. jours. Advisor, dir. Am. Assn. Ret. Persons, Washington, 1992; mem. Anti-Defamation League, Washington, 1992, Am. Jewish Com., N.Y.C., 1992. Recipient AT&T-Hawthorne award for social sci., 1980, Standout New Mgmt. Book award Bus. Week, 1988. Mem. Acad. Mgmt. (dir., trustee, Outstanding Rsch. in Social Issues award 1981, 84), Kiwanis, Havard Alumni Assn., Harvard Bus. Sch. Club. Democrat. Office: Emory U Sch Bus Ctr for Leadership & Career Studies Atlanta GA 30322

SONNENFELD, MARION, linguist, educator; b. Berlin, Germany, Feb. 13, 1928; d. Kurt and Sibylla (Lemke) S. B.A. with high honors, Swarthmore Coll., 1950; M.A., Yale U., 1951, Ph.D., 1956. Instr., asst. prof. Smith Coll., Northampton, Mass., 1954-62; assoc. prof. Wells Coll., Aurora, N.Y., 1962-67, German chmn., dir. German sch., 1965-67; assoc. prof., prof. SUNY Coll., Fredonia, 1967-77, SUNY disting. teaching prof., 1977-93, emerita, 1993, acting dean arts and humanities, 1980-81; mem. com. on learning assessment Fund for the Improvement of Post Secondary Edn., 1988-90, nat. screening com. for Fulbright grants, 1989-91. English translator of German books and plays. Active Literacy Vols. Am., 1994—. Yale U. Jr. Sterling fellow, 1951-53; NEH postdoctoral fellow Ind. U., 1977; SUNY faculty exchange scholar, 1984—. Mem. MLA, AAUP. Office: SUNY Dept Fgn Langs Lit Fredonia NY 14063

SONNENFELDT, HELMUT, former government official, educator, consultant, author; b. Berlin, Germany, Sept. 13, 1926; came to U.S., 1944, naturalized, 1945; s. Walter H. and Gertrud (Liebenthal) S.; m. Marjorie Hecht, Oct. 4, 1953; children—Babette Sonnenfeldt Lubben, Walter H., Stewart H. A.B., Johns Hopkins, 1950, M.A., 1951. With Dept. State, Washington, 1952-77; formerly dir. Office Rsch. and Analysis for USSR and Eastern Europe, 1965-69; lectr. Sch. Advanced Internat. Studies, Johns Hopkins U., 1958-69, vis. scholar, 1977-78; guest scholar Brookings Instn., Washington, 1978—; sr. mem. Nat. Security Coun., 1969-74; counselor Dept. State, 1974-77. Former gov. UN Assn. of U.S.; dir. Atlantic Coun. of U.S., World Affairs Coun. Washington; trustee Johns Hopkins U. With AUS, 1945-46. Mem. Inst. Strategic Studies (London) (mem. exec. coun.), Coun. on Fgn. Rels. N.Y., Pi Delta Epsilon. Home: 4105 Thornapple St Chevy Chase MD 20815-5129 Office: Brookings Instn 1775 Massachusetts Ave NW Washington DC 20036-2188

SONNENFELDT, RICHARD WOLFGANG, business educator; b. Berlin, July 3, 1923; s. Walter H. and Gertrude (Liebenthal) S.; m. Shirley C. Aronoff, Dec. 23, 1949; m. Barbara A. Hausman, Mar. 8, 1981; children: Ann Elizabeth, Lawrence Alan, Michael William. BS in Elec. Engring. cum laude, Johns Hopkins U., 1949; postgrad., U. Pa., 1953-56. Mgr. engring. and prodn. RCA, 1949-62; gen. mgr. digital systems div. Foxboro Co., 1962-65; chief exec. officer, pres., dir. Digitronics Corp., 1965-70; v.p. RCA Corp., 1970-79; chmn. bd., chief exec. officer Electronic Indsl. Engring. Corp., 1972-75; exec. v.p. ops. NBC, N.Y.C., 1979-82; dean Sch. Mgmt. Poly Inst. N.Y., Bklyn., 1982-84, prof. mgmt., 1984—; chmn. bd. dirs., chief exec. officer NAPP Systems, Inc., 1987-90; lectr. Harvard U. Bus. Sch., Sloan Sch., MIT; cons. in field; bd. dirs. Tektkronix Inc., Foxboro Co., Lee Enterprises, Decision Industries Corp., Compuflight Corp., Biospherics Inc., Deerpark Baking Co., Tridex Corp., Internat. HArvest Group, Communications Satellite Network Corp. Contbr. articles to profl. jours. Fellow IEEE; mem. Am. Coun. Germany, Coun. Fgn. Rels., Tau Beta Pi, Omicron Delta Kappa. Home and Office: 4 Secor Dr Port Washington NY 11050-3418

SONNENSCHEIN, ADAM, lawyer; b. N.Y.C., Oct. 15, 1938; s. Harry D. and Sybil (Reinus) S.; m. Phyllis Cokin, Oct. 25, 1968; children: Andrew, Michael. BA, Amherst Coll., 1960; LLB, Columbia U., 1965. Bar: N.Y. 1965, Mass. 1970. Assoc. Berlack, Israels & Liberman, N.Y.C., 1965-70; ptnr. Sprague Assocs., Boston, 1970-72, Walter & Sonnenschein, Boston, 1972-78, Haussermann, Davison & Shattuck, Boston, 1978-83, Foley, Hoag & Eliot, Boston, 1983—. Mem. ABA, Mass. Bar Assn., Boston Bar Assn., Assn. of Bar of City of N.Y. Office: Foley Hoag & Eliot 1 Post Office Sq Boston MA 02109-2103

SONNENSCHEIN, HUGO FREUND, university president, economics educator; b. N.Y.C., Nov. 14, 1940; s. Leo William and Lillian Silver S.; m. Elizabeth Gunn, Aug. 26, 1962; children: Leah, Amy, Rachel. AB, U. Rochester, 1961; MS, Purdue U., 1963, PhD, 1964; PhD (hon.), Tel Aviv U., 1993; D (honoris causa), U. Autonoma Barcelona, Spain, 1994. Mem. faculty dept. econs. U. Minn., 1964-70, prof., 1968-70; prof. econs. U. Mass.,

Amherst, 1970-73; Northwestern U., 1973-76; prof. econs. Princeton U., 1976-87, Class of 1926 prof., 1987-88; dean and Thomas S. Gates prof. Sch. Arts and Scis. Sch. Arts & Scis., U. Pa., Phila., 1988-91; provost Princeton (N.J.) U., 1991-93; pres., prof. dept. econs. and Coll., U. Chgo. 1993—; vis. prof. U. Andes, Colombia, 1965, Tel-Aviv U., 1972, Hebrew U. 1973, U. Paris, 1978, U. Aix-en-Provence, France, 1978, Stanford U., 1984-85. Editor: Econometrica, 1977-84; asso. editor: Jour. Econ. Theory, 1972-75; bd. editors: Jour. Math. Econs, 1974—, SIAM Jour, 1976-80; Contbr. articles to profl. jours. Trustee U. Rochester, 1992, U. Chgo., 1993—. Social Sci. Research Council fellow, 1967-68; NSF fellow, 1970—; Ford Found. fellow, 1970-71; Guggenheim Found. fellow, 1976-77. Fellow Am. Acad. Arts and Scis., Econometric Soc. (pres. 1988-89); mem. NAS.

SONNENSCHEIN, RALPH ROBERT, physiologist; b. Chgo., Aug. 14, 1923; s. Robert and Flora (Kieferstein) S.; m. Patricia W. Niddrie, June 21, 1952; children—David, Lisa, Ann. Student, Swarthmore Coll., 1940-42, U. Chgo., 1942-43; B.S., Northwestern U., 1943, B.M., 1946, M.S., 1946, M.D., 1947; Ph.D., U. Ill., 1950. Research asst. in physiology Northwestern U. Med. Sch., 1944-46; intern Michael Reese Hosp., Chgo., 1946-47; successively research fellow clin. sci., research asst. psychiatry, research asso. psychiatry U. Ill. Med. Sch., Chgo., 1947-51; mem. faculty U. Calif. Med. Sch., Los Angeles, 1951-88, prof. physiology, 1962-88, prof. emeritus, 1988—; liaison scientist Office Naval Research, London, 1971-72. Author papers on pain, innervation of skin, peripheral circulation. Served with AUS, 1943-46. Spl. research fellow USPHS, 1957-58; fellow Swedish Med. Research Council, 1964-65; grantee USAF; grantee Office Naval Research; grantee NIH; grantee NSF. Mem. Am. Physiol. Soc., Microcirculatory Soc., Soc. Exptl. Biology and Medicine, AAAS, Hungarian Physiol. Soc. (hon.). Home: 18212 Kingsport Dr Malibu CA 90265-5636 Office: U Calif Sch Medicine Dept Physiology Los Angeles CA 90095-1751

SONNETT, NEAL RUSSELL, lawyer; b. Bklyn., Nov. 29, 1942; s. Douglas Murray Sonnett and Carol (Brown) Sonnett Rosen; m. Pat D. (Sallee) Voyles, June 10, 1979; 1 son, Gary. B.A., U. Miami, 1964, J.D., 1967. Bar: Fla. 1967, U.S. Dist. Ct. (so. dist.) Fla. 1967, U.S. Ct. Appeals (5th cir.) 1971, U.S. Ct. Appeals (11th cir.) 1981, U.S. Ct. Appeals (9th cir.) 1982, U.S. Supreme Ct. 1971, U.S. Dist. Ct. (ea. dist.) Mich. 1984. Asst. U.S. atty. So. Dist. Fla., 1967-72, chief criminal div., 1971-72; ptnr. Sonnett, Sale & Kuehne, P.A. (and predecessor firms), Miami, Fla., 1972-93; founded Neal R. Sonnett P.A., 1993—; host of TV show To the Point (Fla. regional Emmy award nominee), WCIX-TV, 1980-82; lectr. in immigration law and advanced federal criminal practice U. Miami Sch. Law; lectr. in cross-exam. techniques Fed. Law Enforcement Tng. Ctr., 1983. Fla. Regional bd. dirs. Anti-Defamation League, B'nai B'rith, 1972, 82—, chmn. Met. Dade County Ind. Rev. Panel, 1981-84; chmn. Community Task Force on Jury Selection, 1984; pres. Fraternal Order Police Assocs., 1972; pres. Transition, Inc., 1976; legal counsel Fla. Jaycees, 1971-72. Named Outstanding Fed. Employee South Fla., 1971-72, Outstanding Young Man of Miami, Greater Miami Jaycees, 1970, Five Outstanding Young Men of Fla., Fla. Jaycees, 1971-72, Outstanding Young Law Enforcement Officer, South Miami Jaycees, 1971-72; recipient Outstanding Service award, Jewish War Vets of U.S., Disting. Service award Dade County Pub. Interest Law Bank, 1983. Mem. Inter-Am. Bar Assn., ABA (sects. on criminal justice and adminstrv. law), Nat. Conf. Bar Pres., Met. Bar Leaders Caucus (nat. exec. com. 1983-84), Calif. Attys. for Criminal Justice, Fla. Criminal Def. Attys. Assn. (treas. 1983-84, pres. 1984-85), Dade County Bar Assn. (pres. 1983-84), Fed. Bar Assn. (pres. South Fla. chpt. 1972), Am. Immigration Lawyers Assn. (pres. South Fla. chpt. 1976, nat. bd. govs. 1977), Nat. Assn. Criminal Def. Lawyers (dir. 1977—), Assn. Trial Lawyers Am., Acad. Fla. Trial Lawyers. Democrat. Jewish. Clubs: Footlighter, Optimist, Elks. Office: Neal R. Sonnett PA 1 Biscayne Tower 2 S Biscayne Blvd Ste 2600 Miami FL 33131

SONNINO, CARLO BENVENUTO, electrical manufacturing company executive; b. Torino, Italy, May 12, 1904; came to U.S., 1952, naturalized, 1959; s. Moise and Amelia S.; m. Mathilde Girodat, Jan. 21, 1949; children—Patricia, Frederic, Bruno. Ph.D., U. Milano, Italy, 1927, LL.B., 1928. Dir. research Italian Aluminum Co., Milano, 1928-34; pres. Laesa Cons. Firm, Milano, 1934-43; tech. adviser Boxal, Fribourg, Switzerland, 1944-52, Thompson Brand, Rouen, France, 1972-76; materials engring. mgr. Emerson Electric Co., St. Louis, 1956-72; staff scientist Emerson Electric Co., 1973—; prof. metall. engring. Washington U., St. Louis, 1960-68, U. Mo., Rolla, 1968—; cons. Monsanto Chem. Co., Wagner Co., other maj. firms, U.S., Europe. Decorated knight comdr. Italian Republic. Fellow Am. Soc. Metals, ASTM (hon.), Alpha Sigma Mu. Patentee process for synthetic cryolite; patentee in field of metallurgy, corrosion; mfr. 1st aluminum cans in world, 1940. Home: 7206 Kingsbury Blvd Saint Louis MO 63130-4140 Office: Emerson E and S Div Emerson Electric Co 8100 W Florissant Ave Saint Louis MO 63136-1417 *I have always been guided by the highest ethical standards in professional, business, and civic life, even in the most difficult moments, and by strong dislike for hypocrisy and greed.*

SONNTAG, BERNARD H., agrologist, research executive; b. Goodsoil, Sask., Can., June 27, 1940; s. Henry R. and Annie (Heesing) S.; m. Mary L. Ortman, Aug. 10, 1963; children: Calvin, Galen, Courtney Anne. BSA, Sask. U., Saskatoon, 1962, MSc, 1965; PhD, Purdue U., 1971. Economist Agriculture Can., Saskatoon, 1962-66; cons. D.W. Carr & Assoc., Ottawa, Ont., Can., 1966-68; economist Agriculture Can., Lethbridge, Alta., 1968-79, Saskatoon, 1979-80; dir. rsch. sta. Agriculture Can., Brandon, Man., 1980-86, Swiftcurrent, Sask., 1986-89, Lethbridge, 1989—; pres. Man. Inst. Agrologists, Brandon, 1984. Recipient Leadership award Bell Can., 1993. Mem. Rotary. Roman Catholic. Home: Box 3000, Lethbridge, AB Canada T1J 4B1 Office: Agriculture Canada, Research Station Box 3000, Lethbridge, AB Canada T1J 4B1

SONOGUCHI, KAZUO, automotive company executive. V.p. corp. planning Mazda Motor Mfg. (USA) Inc., 1987-90; group v.p. dep. gen. mgr. Mazda Motor of Am., Inc., 1990—; pres. Mazda Motor of Am., Inc., Irvine, Calif., 1992—. Office: Mazda Motor of America Inc 7755 Irvine Center Dr Irvine CA 92718-2906

SONS, LINDA RUTH, mathematics educator; b. Chicago Heights, Ill., Oct. 31, 1939; d. Robert and Ruth (Diekelman) S. AB in Math., Ind. U. 1961; MS in Math., Cornell U., 1963, PhD in Math., 1966. Teaching asst. Cornell U., Ithaca, N.Y., 1961-63, instr. math., summer 1963, rsch. asst., 1963-65; asst. prof. No. Ill. U. De Kalb, 1965-70, assoc. prof., 1970-78, prof., 1978—; presdl. tchg. prof. No. Ill. U., DeKalb, 1994—; vis. assoc. prof. U. London, 1970-71; dir. undergrad. studies math. dept. No. Ill. U., 1971-77, exec. sec. univ. coun., 1978-79; chair faculty fund No. Ill. U. Found., De Kalb, 1982—. Author: (with others) A Study Guide for Introduction to Mathematics, 1976, Mathematical Thinking in a Quantitative World, 1990; contbr. articles to profl. jours. Mem. campus ministry com. No. Ill. Dist. Luth. Ch./Mo. Synod, Hillside, 1977—; mem. ch. coun. Immanuel Luth. Ch., De Kalb, 1978-85, 87-89; pres. Luth. Women's Missionary League, 1974-87; bd. dirs., treas. De Kalb County Migrant Ministry, 1967-78. NSF Rsch. grantee, 1970-72, 74-75; recipient 1988 Award for Disting. Svc. of Ill. Sect. of the Math Assn. Am., 1991 Award for Excellence in Coll. Teaching of Ill. Coun. Tchrs. Math. Am. (mem. nat. bd. govs. 1989-92, mem. com undergrad. program in math. 1990—, Disting. Svc. to Ill. Sect. award 1988, Disting. Coll. or U. Tchg. of Math. award 1995), Ill. Math. Assn. (v.p. sect., pres.-elect, pres., then past pres. 1982-87, bd. dirs. 1989-92), London Math. Soc., Phi Beta Kappa (pres. No. Ill. Assn. 1981-85), Sigma Xi (past. chpt. pres.). Achievements include research in classical complex analysis—especially value distribution for meromorphic functions with unbounded characteristic in the unit disc. Office: No Ill U Dept Math Scis De Kalb IL 60115

SONS, RAYMOND WILLIAM, journalist; b. Harvey, Ill., Aug. 25, 1926; s. William Henry and Gladys Lydia (Steinko) S.; m. Bettina Dieckmann; children: David, Pamela Sons Clarke, Ronald. B.A., U. Mich., 1950. Reporter, mng. editor Murphysboro (Ill.) Daily Ind. editor. St. Louis Illinoisan newspaper, 1950-52; assoc. news editor Middletown (Ohio) Jour., 1952-53; reporter, asst. city editor, sportswriter, sports editor Chgo. Daily News, 1953-78; sports editor, columnist Chgo. Sun-Times, 1978-92. Served with USAAF, 1945-46. Recipient Best Sports Story in Ill. award U.P.I., 1970, Marshall Field award for outstanding editorial contbn. to Chgo. Daily News, 1972; Best Sports Column award AP Sports Editors, 1979, Best Sports

Column award Ill. AP, 1987. Roman Catholic. Home: 4100 Torrington Ct Fort Collins CO 80525-3419

SONSINI, LARRY W., lawyer; b. Rome, N.Y., Feb. 5, 1941. AB, U. Calif., Berkeley, 1963; LLB, U. Calif., 1966. Bar: Calif. 1966. Ptnr. Wilson, Sonsini, Goodrich & Rosati, Palo Alto; prof. securities regulation Boalt Hall Sch. law U. Calif., Berkeley, 1984—; mem. exec. com. Securities Reg. Mem. ABA (com. on fed. regulation securities, subcom. on registration statements), Am. Law Inst. Office: Wilson Sonsini Goodrich & Rosati 650 Page Mill Rd Palo Alto CA 94304-1050

SONSKY, STEVE, newspaper editor. Features executive editor Miami Herald, Fla. Office: The Miami Herald Pub Co One Herald Plz Miami FL 33132-1693

SONSTELIE, RICHARD ROBERT, utilities executive; b. Ottawa, Ont., Can., Mar. 31, 1945; s. Robert Daniel and Valerie Marjorie (St. Laurent) S.; m. Cynthia Louise Prussing, Sept. 19, 1970; children: Marit K., Jennifer A. BS, U.S. Mil. Acad., 1966; MS in Nuclear Engring., MIT, 1968; MBA, Harvard U., 1974. Commd. 2d lt. U.S. Army, 1966, advanced through grades to capt., served in Vietnam, 1966-72, resigned, 1972; staff mem., project mgr. Los Alamos (N.Mex.) Sci. Labs., 1969-72; with Puget Sound Power and Light Co., Bellevue, Wash., 1974-80, v.p. engring. and ops., 1980-83, sr. v.p. fin., 1983-85, exec. v.p., 1985-87, pres., 1987—, also bd. dirs., chief oper. officer, 1991—, now also chief exec. officer; bd. dirs. 1st Interstate Bank Wash. Active Mcpl. League, Wash. State Job Tng. Coordinating Coun., Olympia, 1984-88; bd. dirs. Jr. Achievement Greater Puget Sound, Seattle, 1985-90, chmn., 1986-87; bd. dirs. Seattle Ctr., 1987—; trustee Bellevue Community Coll., 1985-90, chmn. 1989-90, civilian aide to Sec. of Army, 1987—; Vietnam Vets. Leadership Program; bd. advisers Resource Ctr. for Handicapped; trustee Children's Hosp. Found., 1990—, Naval Undersea Mus. Found. Decorated Bronze Star. Mem. Edison Electric Ins., Seattle C. of C., West Point Soc. Puget Sound. Lodge: Rotary. Avocations: tennis, travel. Home: 5 Brook Bay Rd Mercer Island WA 98040-4621 Office: Puget Sound Power & Light PO Box 97034 M/S 15 Puget Power Bldg Bellevue WA 98009*

SONTAG, FREDERICK EARL, philosophy educator; b. Long Beach, Calif., Oct. 2, 1924; s. M. Burnett and Cornelia (Nicholson) S.; m. Carol Furth, June 10, 1950; children: Grant Furth, Anne Burnett Karch. BA with great distinction, Stanford U., 1949; MA, Yale U., 1951, PhD, 1952; LLD (hon.), Coll. Idaho, 1971. Instr. Yale U., 1951-52; asst. prof. philosophy Pomona Coll., Claremont, Calif., 1952-55, assoc. prof., 1955-60, prof., 1970—, Robert C. Denison prof. philosophy, 1972—, chmn. dept. philosophy, 1960-67, 76-77, 80-84; chmn. coordinating com. in philosophy Claremont Grad. Sch. and Univ. Ctr., 1962-65; vis. prof. Union Theol. Sem., N.Y.C., 1959-60, Collegio di Sant' Anselmo, Rome, 1966-67, U. Copenhagen, fall 1972; theologian-in-residence Am. Ch. in Paris, fall 1973; Fulbright regional vis. prof., India, East Asia, Pacific areas, 1977-78; mem. nat. adv. council Kent Fellowship Program of Danforth Found., 1963-66. Author numerous books, the most recent being: Love Beyond Pain: Mysticism Within Christianity, 1977; Sun Myung Moon and the Unification Church, 1977, also German, Japanese and Korean transl.; (with John K. Roth) God and America's Future, 1977; What Can God Do?, 1979; A Kierkegaard Handbook, 1979; The Elements of Philosophy, 1984, (with John K. Roth) The Questions of Philosophy, 1988, Emotion, 1989, The Return of the Gods, 1989, Willgenstein and the Mystical, 1995, Uncertain Touch, 1995, The Descent of Women, 1995, The Acts of the Trinity. Pres. bd. dirs. Claremont Family Service, 1960-64; trustee The Coro Found., Los Angeles and San Francisco, 1967-71; bd. dirs., chmn. ways and means com. Pilgrim Place, Claremont, 1970-77. Served with AUS, 1943-46. Vis. scholar Ctr. for Study Japanese Religions, Kyoto, Japan, spring 1974; vis. fellow East-West Ctr., Honolulu, summer 1974. Wig Disting. Prof. award, 1970, 76; Fulbright regional vis. prof. India, East Asia, Pacific areas, 1977-78. Mem. Am. Philos. Assn., Metaphys. Soc. Am., Soc. on Religion in Higher Edn. (Kent fellow 1950-52), Am. Acad. Religion, Phi Beta Kappa. Congregationalist. Office: Pomona Coll 333 N College Ave Claremont CA 91711-4408

SONTAG, FREDERICK H., public affairs and research consultant; b. Breslau, Germany, Apr. 29, 1924; came to U.S., 1937, naturalized, 1943; s. Hugo and Lotte (Lab) S.; m. Edith Virginia Sweeney, Feb. 8, 1958. Grad., Phillips Acad., 1942; A.B., Colby Coll., 1946; grad. student, Columbia, 1947-48. Asso. Earl Newsom & Co. (pub. relations counsel), N.Y.C., 1947-48; asst. dir. Citizens Found., Syracuse, N.Y., 1948-50; pub. relations and advt. cons. Merchants Nat. Bank, Syracuse, 1948-51; central N.Y. corr. Business Week, other McGraw-Hill publs., 1950-51; dir. pub. relations Bus. Week mag., 1951-55; manuscript cons. McGraw-Hill Book Co., 1951-60; spl. cons. to U.S. Sec. Labor, 1954-61, congressman Thomas B. Curtis, 1957-69, Civic Service, Inc., St. Louis and Washington, 1957-83; spl. cons. to 1960 Winter Olympics, Sec. HEW, 1969, 72, U.S. Internat. Trade Commn. chmn., 1975-77; assoc. Aman M. Rosenberg Assocs., 1957-60; spl. cons. Monsanto Co., 1962-77; spl. cons. to Edwin J. Putzell, Coburn, Croft & Putzell, St. Louis and Naples, Fla., 1977-83, 1st Caribbean Mainland Capital Co., Inc., N.Y.C., San Juan, P.R., 1962; pub. affairs cons. Office of Sec. HUD, 1981-83, spl. asst. to regional adminstr., 1983-85, regional program liaison officer, 1985-90; spl. cons. bishop Episcopal Diocese of Springfield, Ill., 1947-72; program and planning assoc. to dir. broadcasting Nat. Council Episcopal Ch., 1956-61; exec. dir. com. increased minority staffing U.S. Ho. of Reps., Washington, 1961-69; co-dir. Study of Am. Polit. Parties, Cambridge, Mass., also South Orange, N.J., 1969-73, dir., 1973—; vis. lectr. Colby Coll., Waterville, Maine, 1975; lectr., discussion leader John F. Kennedy Sch. Govt., Inst. Politics, Harvard, Brookings Inst., Washington, Woodrow Wilson Internat. Center Scholars, Washington, Am. Assembly, Arden House, Columbia.; Analyst-commentator Maine Pub. Broadcasting Network, 1973-75, Suburban Cablevision TV3, East Orange, N.J., 1977-79; spl. cons. Pres.'s Com. on Govt. Employment Policy, 1955-60; bd. advisers Husson Coll., Bangor, Maine, 1965-79, trustee, 1979-89; mem. Com. on Party Renewal, 1982—; cons. Bd. Christian Social Concerns, United Meth. Ch., 1965-71; legis. cons. to N.J. State Senator James H. Wallwork, 1968-79, N.J. Assemblyman C. L. Hardwick, 1979-83, N.J. Assemblyman Harry McEnroe, 1983; free-holder-at-large Lincoln Turner, 1979-82, Senator Carmen Orechio, 1984. Co-author: Parties: The Real Opportunity for Effective Citizen Politics, 1972, softcover, 1973; Editorial adv. bd.: Electoral Studies Yearbook; Contbr.: Op-ed page Los Angeles Times, N.Y. Times; nat. corr.: Scroll; contbg. writer, reviewer: Worrall Newspapers, No. N.J. Trustee Pres. James Monroe Found., Fredericksburg, Va., 1992—. Recipient certificates achievement Am. Pub. Relations Assn., 1952, 54, Silver Anvil award, 1953; Spl. Achievement award U.S. Internat. Trade Commn., 1976; HUD award for superior service on fair housing, 1984; Studer award Montclair Coll., 1984; Outstanding Performance awards HUD 1985-88; special recognition award Martin Luther King, Jr. fed. holiday commn., 1989; named Alumnus of Yr., Harvey Sch., Katohah, N.Y., 1983. Mem. Pub. Relations Soc. Am., Am. Polit. Sci. Assn., Am. Assn. Polit Cons. (charter), N.J. Conf. Promotion Better Govt., Phi Delta Theta, Phi Gamma Mu. Anglo-Catholic. Club: Overseas Press (N.Y.C.). Home: Ste 45 764 Scotland Rd South Orange NJ 07079-3023 also: General Delivery Seal Harbor ME 04675-0207

SONTAG, JAMES MITCHELL, cancer researcher; b. Denver, Dec. 8, 1939; s. Samuel Henry and Rose Hazel (Silverman) S.; m. Elizabeth Crockett Tunis; children: Ariella, Eythan. B.S., Lamar State Coll. Tech., Beaumont, Tex., M.S., U. Ill., 1967; Ph.D. (grad. stipend), Weizmann Inst. Sci., Rehovot, Israel 1971; M.P.H., Harvard U., 1982. Damon Runyon Meml. Fund Cancer Research postdoctoral fellow, 1971-72; guest worker Nat. Cancer Inst., NIH, Bethesda, Md., 1972-73; staff fellow Nat. Cancer Inst., NIH, 1973-74, exptl. oncologist, 1973-76, mgr. carcinogen bioassay program, 1973-76, asst. to dir. cancer cause and prevention, 1976-80; exec. sec. Clearinghouse on Environ. Carcinogens, 1976-80, asst. dir. for interagy. affairs Office of Dir., 1980-82, spl. asst. epidemiology and biostatistics program, 1982—. Author, editor in field. Served with AUS, 1956-59. Beaumont LWV scholar, 1963-65. Mem. Beta Beta Beta. Home: 10500 Rockville Pike Apt 610 Rockville MD 20852-3341 Office: Nat Cancer Inst Exec Plaza North Room 543 Bethesda MD 20892

SONTAG, PETER MICHAEL, travel management company executive; b. Vienna, Austria, Apr. 25, 1943; came to U.S., 1960; s. Otto Schiedeck and Maria Katharina (Schmidt) Cigalle; m. Eleanor Ann Alexander, Jan. 24,

1971; children: Alicia Alexandra, Julie Katherine. Diploma in hotel mgmt., Schule fuer Gastgewerbe, Vienna, 1960; BS magna cum laude, West Liberty State Coll., 1969, LLD, 1991; MBA, Columbia U., 1971. Steel worker Weirton (W.Va.) Steel Co., 1965-69; fin. analyst Citicorp, N.Y.C., 1970-71; ops. staff exec. ITT, N.Y.C., 1971-73; asst. v.p. Sun Life Ins. Co. Am., Balt., 1974-75; exec. v.p. Travel Guide, Inc., Balt., 1975-76; pres. Travelwhirl, Inc., Balt., 1976-78; founder Gelco Travel Services, Mpls., 1978-83; chmn., chief exec. officer Sontag, Annis & Assocs., Washington, 1983-86, US Travel Systems, Inc., Washington, 1986—; prin. CORVES Cons., Inc., Rockville, Md., 1983-86; pub. Travel Bus. Mgr., 1983-86; speaker in field, 1983—. With Austrian Air Force, 1963-64. Named one of Twenty Five Most Influential Execs. in Travel Industry Travel Bus. News, 1985, 87, 88, 89; named Delta Sigma Pi scholar. Mem. Alpha Phi Sigma, Delta Mu Delta (charter), Lakewood Country Club. Republican. Avocations: skiing, sailing, photography, collecting antique cars. Office: US Travel Systems Inc 1401 Rockville Pike Ste 300 Rockville MD 20852-1428

SONTAG, SUSAN, writer; b. N.Y.C., Jan. 16, 1933; m. Philip Rieff, 1950 (div. 1958); 1 son, David. BA, U. Chgo., 1951; MA in English, Harvard U., 1954, MA in philosophy, 1955. Instr. English U. Conn., Storrs, 1953-54; editor Commentary, N.Y.C., 1959; lectr. philosophy City Coll., N.Y.C., 1959-60, Sarah Lawrence Coll., Bronxville, 1959-60; instr. dept. religion Columbia U., N.Y.C., 1960-64; writer in residence Rutgers U., 1964-65. Author: (novels) The Benefactor, 1963, Death Kit, 1967, The Volcano Lover: A Romance, 1992; (plays) Alice in Bed: A Play in Eight Scenes, 1993; (stories) I, etcetera, 1978, The Way We Live Now, 1991; (essays) Against Interpretation, 1966 (Mat. Book award nomination 1966), Styles of Radical Will, 1969, Trip to Hanoi, 1969, On Photography, 1977 (Nat. Book Critics Cirle award for criticism 1978), Illness as Metaphor, 1978, Under the Sign of Saturn, 1980, AIDS and Its Metaphors, 1989; (anthology) A Susan Sontag Reader, 1982; screenwriter, dir.: (films) Duet for Cannibals, 1969, Brother Carl, 1971; dir.: (films) Promised Lands, 1974, Unguided Tour, 1983; editor, author of introduction: Antonin Artaud: Selected Writings, 1976, A Roland Barthes Reader, 1982, Danilo Kis's Homo Poeticus: Essays & Interviews, 1995. Guggenheim fellow, 1966, 75, Rockefeller Found. fellow, 1965, 74, MacArthur fellow, 1990-95; recipient George Polk Meml. award, 1966, Ingram Merrill Found. award in lit. in field of Am. Letters, 1976, Creative Arts award Brandeis U., 1976, Malaparte prize, 1992; named Officier de l'Ordre des Arts et des Lettres, France, 1984. Mem. Am. Acad. Arts and Scis. (elected 1993), Am. Acad. Arts and Letters (Arts and Letters award 1976), PEN (pres. Am. Ctr. 1987-89). Office: Wylie Aitken & Stone 250 W 57th St New York NY 10107*

SONTGERATH, MARY, school system administrator. Head dept. Cath. schs. Archdiocese of Seattle. Office: Cath Schs Dept 910 Marion St Seattle WA 98104

SOO, SHAO LEE, mechanical engineer, educator; b. Peking, China, Mar. 1, 1922; came to U.S., 1947, naturalized, 1962; s. Hsi Yi and Yun Chuan (Chin) S.; m. Hermia G. Dan, June 7, 1952; children: Shirley A. Soo Gorman, Lydia M., David D. BS, Nat. Chiaotung U., 1945; MS, Ga. Inst. Tech., 1948; ScD, Harvard U., 1951. Engr. China Nat. Aviation, Calcutta and Shanghai, 1945-47; lectr. Princeton (N.J.) U., 1951-54, asst. prof., 1954-57, assoc. prof. mech. engring., 1957-59; prof. mech. engring. U. Ill., Urbana, 1959-93, prof. emeritus, 1993—; cons. NASA, NIH, ANL, Dept. Energy, EPA, NATO, Nat. Inst. Standards and Tech.; mem. sci. adv. bd. EPA, 1976-78; adv. energy transp. World Bank, 1979; China, UNDP, 1985, 92, NATO AGARD lectr.; Fulbright-Hays Disting. lectr., 1974—; lectr. Chinese Acad. Sci., 1980; guest lectr. China-Japan Conf. Fluidized Beds, 1985, 88, 91, bd. dirs. S.L. Soo Assocs., Ltd., Urbana; vis. prof. Delft Tech. U., The Netherlands, 1993. Author 7 books on thermodynamics, energy conservation and multiphase flow; mem. editorial bd. Internat. Jour. Multiphase Flow, 1972—, Jour. Pipelines, 1980—, Internat. Jour. Sci. and Engring., 1983, Jour. Engr-ing. Chem. and Metallurgy China, 1990—; contbr. numerous articles to profl. jours. Recipient Applied Mechanics Rev. award, 1972, Disting. Lecture award Internat. Pipeline Assn., 1981, Alcoa Found. award, 1985, NASA award for creative devel., 1992. Fellow ASME; mem. ASEE, AICE (particle tech.), Combustion Inst., Fine Particle Soc. (chmn. fluidized beds com.), Chinese Acad. Sci. (hon. prof.), Internat. Freight Pipeline Soc., Sigma Xi, Pi Tau Sigma (hon.), Phi Kappa Phi. Methodist. Patentee in field (6). Home: 2020 Cureton Dr Urbana IL 61801-6226 Office: 1206 W Green St Urbana IL 61801-2906

SOOKNE, HERMAN SOLOMON (HANK SOOKNE), retirement center senior executive; b. Far Rockaway, N.Y., June 30, 1932; s. Harry Martin Sookne and Sarah (Kopolov) Sterenstein; m. Joan Gilman, Apr. 12, 1954 (div. Apr. 9, 1971); children: Charles Michael, David Howard, Susan Frances; m. Polly Henry Johnson, Mar. 1972. Student, Georgetown U., 1949-50; BS in Bus. & Econs., NYU, 1953. Pres., owner Gilson Bldg. Corp., Merrick, N.Y., 1955-68; divsn. mgr. Boise Cascade Bldg. Corp., Freehold, N.J. 1968-70; dir. property mgmt. and engring. Amprop, Inc., Miami, Fla., 1970-73; pres., CEO Bowman Property Investors, Dallas, 1973-79; gen. mgr. Fidinam, Inc., Houston, 1979-82; mktg. cons. Cooper Communities, Inc., Bella Vista, Ark., 1982-88; dir. mktg. and funds devel. Epworth Villa, Oklahoma City, 1988—. Scoutmaster Boy Scouts Am., L.I., N.Y., 1955-60; bd. dirs., pres. Copperchase Condo's Inc., Oklahoma City, 1991—; trustee United Meth. Ch. of the Servant. With U.S. Army, 1953-55, Korea. Mem. Ark. Bd. Realtors, Nat. Soc. for Fund Raising Execs., Soc. for Advancement of Mgmt., Nat. Assn. Home Builders, Nat. Soc. Heat, Refrigeration & Air Conditioning Engrs; bd. trustees Methodist Ch. Republican. Avocations: sailing, tennis, ch. affairs, woodworking, reading. Home: #152 11300 N Pennsylvania Ave Oklahoma City OK 73120 Office: Epworth Villa Life Care Facility 14901 N Pennsylvania Ave Oklahoma City OK 73134-6071

SOOKRAM, ATMA RAM, transportation engineer; b. Mahaica, Guyana, Nov. 21, 1958; came to U.S., 1982; s. Sookram and Ketri (Ramanooj) Gossai; m. Latchmin Singh, Jan. 11, 1982; children: Sarah Parueena Devi. BA with distinction, U. Guyana, 1980; MS, Polytech. U., Bklyn., 1985. Sr. planning asst., geographer UN Devel. Program, Georgetown, Guyana, 1980-84; sr. assoc., transp. engr. Urbitran Assocs., N.Y.C., 1984—; cons. in field; asst. lectr. U. Guyana, Georgetown, 1981-82. Commonwealth scholar, 1982. Mem. Inst. of Transp. Engrs. (assoc.), Am. Planning Assn. (Transp. planning div., transp rsch. bd.). Hindu. Avocations: swimming, tennis. Office: 71 W 23d St New York NY 10010

SOONG, TSU-TEH, engineering science educator; b. Honan, China, Feb. 10, 1934; s. Tung and Yu-Hsieh (Lee) S.; m. Dorothy Yen-Ling Tsai, June 5, 1959; children—Karen, Stephen, Susan. B.S., U. Dayton, 1955; postgrad., U. Ill., 1955-56; M.S., Purdue U., 1958, Ph.D., 1962. Instr. engring. sci. Purdue U., 1958-62; sr. research engr. Jet Propulsion Lab., Pasadena, Calif., 1962-63; asst. prof. engring. U. State U. N.Y. at Buffalo, 1963-66, asso. prof., 1966-68, prof., 1968-89; Samuel P. Capen prof., 1989—; part-time lectr. engring. U. Calif. at Los Angeles, 1962-63; part-time research mathematician Cornell Aero. Lab., Buffalo, 1964-67, prin. research mathematician, 1970-77. NSF Sci. Faculty fellow Tech. U. Delft, Netherlands, 1966-67; Humboldt Sr. Scientist, U. Hanover, Fed. Republic of Germany, 1987-88. Mem. ASCE, NSPE, Earthquake Engring. Rsch. Inst., Sigma Xi, Tau Beta Pi. Research in stochastic processes and structural control in engring. Home: 249 Wellingwood Dr East Amherst NY 14051-1750

SOOS, JAMES E., electronics executive; b. 1936. BSEE, Iowa State U., 1958; MSEE, Rutgers U.; MS in Mgmt. Sci., MIT; PhD in Sys. Sci., Poly. Inst. Bklyn. With Dept. Army, 1958-82; chief plans divsn. Dept. Army, Ft. Monmouth, N.J., 1971-76; nat. comm. expert NATO com. Dept. Army, Brussels, 1976-79; dir. Ctr. Comm. Sys. Dept. Army, Ft. Monmouth, 1979-82; pres. CMC Electronics Inc., 1982-88; with Cin. Electronics Corp., Mason, Ohio, 1988—, now pres., chmn. bd. dirs., CEO. Office: Cincinnati Electronics Corp 7500 Innovation Way Mason OH 45040*

SOPER, JAMES HERBERT, botanist, curator; b. Hamilton, Ont., Can., Apr. 9, 1916; s. Herbert Armitage and Anna Eliza Gertrude (Cooper) S.; m. Jean Elizabeth Morgan, Aug. 17, 1946; children: Nancy Elizabeth, Mary Florence, Daphne Evans, Ian Morgan. B.A., McMaster U., 1938, M.A.,

1939; Ph.D. (Harris fellow, Austin fellow), Harvard U., 1943. Mem. faculty U. Toronto, 1946-67, curator, 1946-67, prof. botany, 1966-67; chief botanist Can. Mus. Nature, Ottawa, Ont., 1967-81, curator emeritus, 1981—, rsch. assoc., 1993—. Author: Mt. Revelstoke National Park Wildflowers, 1976, Shrubs of Ontario, 1982; contbr. articles to profl. jours. Served with RCAF, 1943-45. Recipient Royal Jubilee medal, 1978. Mem. Royal Canadian Inst. (life) (pres. 1962-63), Canadian Bot. Assn. (pres. 1982-83), Ottawa Field Naturalists Club, Fedn. Ont. Naturalists (hon.). Office: Can Mus Nature, PO Box 3443 Sta D, Ottawa, ON Canada K1P 6P4

SOPER, QUENTIN FRANCIS, chemist; b. Buhl, Minn., Dec. 3, 1919; s. Claude E. and Dessie E. (Zern) S.; m. Genevieve Landreth, Oct. 5, 1946; children—John, Julia, Dan, Jean. B.Chem., U. Minn., 1940; Ph.D. in Organic Chemistry, U. Ill., 1943. Sr. organic chemist Eli Lilly & Co., Indpls., 1944-62; research scientist Eli Lilly & Co., 1962-66; head agrl. organic chemistry research Eli Lilly & Co., Greenfield, Ind., 1965-72, sr. agrl. assoc., 1972-76, research adviser, 1976-84; ret., 1984. Co-inventor Penicillin V; inventor herbicides Treflan, Balan, Paarlan, Surflan, Sonalan, Dipan. Recipient Outstanding Achievement award U. Minn., 1977, John Scott award City of Phila., 1980, Pioneer award Am. Inst. Chemists, 1981. Mem. Am. Chem. Soc., Weed Sci. Soc., N.Y. Acad. Scis. Presbyterian. Home: 2120 W 38th St Indianapolis IN 46208-3202

SOPHER, VICKI ELAINE, museum director; b. Streator, Ill., May 22, 1943; d. Donald Bird and Thelma Elsie (Saxton) Watson; m. Terry Ray Sr., Jan. 20, 1962 (div. Aug. 1982); 1 child, Terry Ray Jr. AA, No. Va. Community Coll., 1973; BA, Am. U., 1976; MS, Bank State Coll. Edn., 1986. Adminstrv. asst. Decatur & Wilson House, Washington, 1977-81; asst. dir. Decatur House/Nat. Trust for Hist. Preservation, Washington, 1981-84, dir., 1984—; cons. curator Monmouth Mus., Freehold, N.J., 1978-80; founder, pres. Historic House Mus. Metropolitan Wash. Mem. Am. Assn. Museums, Mid-Atlantic Assn. Museums, Assn. for State and Local History, Victorian Soc. Am. (bd. dirs.). Home: 2621 S 12th St Arlington VA 22204 Office: Decatur Ho Mus 748 Jackson Pl NW Washington DC 20006-4984

SOPINKA, JOHN, Canadian supreme court justice; b. Broderick, Sask., Can., Mar. 19, 1933; s. Metro and Nancy (Kikcio) S.; m. Marie Wilson, 1956; children: Randall, Melanie. BA, U. Toronto, 1955, LLB, 1958; JD (hon.), Ukrainian Free U., Munich. Bar: Nfld. 1973, N.B. 1975, Sask. 1984, Alta. 1987, Y.T. 1987, N.W.T.1987. Assoc. Fasken & Calvin, Barristers and Solicitors, Toronto, 1960-66, ptnr., 1966-77; ptnr., head litigation dept. Stikeman, Elliott, Barristers & Solicitors, Toronto, 1977-88; puisine judge Supreme Ct. of Can., Ottawa, Ont., 1988—; apptd. Queen's Counsel, 1975; lectr. civil procedure Osgoode Hall Law Sch., 1974-82, U. Toronto Law Sch., 1976-84; mem. Commns. of Inquiry into Royal Can. Mounted Police relationship with Dept. Nat. Revenue, into Certain Deaths Hosp. for Sick Children and Related Matters, into Facts of Allegations of Conflict of Interest Concerning Hon. Sinclair M. Stevens; chief counsel Commn. on Aviation Safety; counsel Commn. of Inquiry into Cessation of Ops. Can. Comml. Bank and Northland Bank; mem. Task Force on Equality of Opportuniy in Athletics; former bencher Law Soc. Upper Can., frequent lectr. continuing edn. series. Author: (with Lederman and Bryant) The Law of Evidence in Canada, 1992, The Trial of an Action, 1981, (with Gelowitz) The Conduct of an Appeal, 1993; contbr. articles to profl. jours. Bd. dirs. Hockey Can., 1960—; mem. Bd. Edn. Town of Oakville, 1967-69; co-chmn. Acad. Tribunal U. Toronto, 1975-80; mem. Police Complaints Bd. Met. Toronto; mem. bd. fgn. advisors Ukranian Legal Found. Fellow Am. Coll. Trial Lawyers (jud.); mem. Advocate's Soc. (bd. dirs., chmn. subcom. adminstrn. Ont. cts., lectr.), Can. Bar Assn. (chmn. Ont. subsect. comparative law sect. 1967-68, nat. chmn. of sect. 1970, lectr.), County of York Law Assn., Univ. Club, Blvd. Club, Lawyer's Club. Avocations: squash, skiing, tennis, music. Home: 161 Carleton St, Rockcliffe Pk, Ottawa, ON Canada K1M OG6 Office: Supreme Ct Can, Wellington St, Ottawa, ON Canada K1A 0J1

SOPKIN, GEORGE, cellist, music educator; b. Chgo., Apr. 3, 1914; s. Isador and Esther (Sopkin) S.; m. Thelma Friedman, July 5, 1936; children—Monica, Paula; m. Carol Borchard Durham, Aug. 30, 1956; children—Edwin, Anthony. Student with Daniel Saidenberg, Am. Conservatory Music, 1930-32; with, Emmanuel Feuermann, Chgo., Mus. Coll., 1932-34; D.Mus. (hon.), Northland Coll., 1977. Assoc. prof. music U. Wis., 1940-42, artist-in-residence, 1963-79, prof., 1967-77, Disting. prof., 1977-85; prof. Carnegie Mellon U., 1985—, formed trio concert tour of Europe, 1985; staff ABC, Chgo., 1946-52; artist-in-residence Northwestern U., 1952-55, U. Wisconsin-Milw., Cleve. Inst.; founder New Eng. Piano Quartette, 1980. Mem., Kansas City (Mo.) Philharmonic Orch., 1933-34, Chgo. Symphony Orch., 1934-40, Pro Arte String Quartet, 1940-42, founder, 1946, since mem., Fine Arts Quartet, Chgo., soloist, Kansas City (Mo.) Philharmonic Orch., Chgo. Symphony Orch., Ill. Symphony Orch., Milw. Chamber Orch., Saidenberg Symphonette, frequent TV appearances; artist of film for, Envy. Brit. films, Nat. Ednl. TV films; recording artist for, Mercury, Decca, Concert-disc, Everest, numerous tours, Europe. Bd. dirs. Contemporary Concerts, Inc., Chgo. Served with USAAF, 1943-45. Mem. Lincoln Acad. Address: Newbury Neck Rd Surry ME 04684

SOPKO, MICHAEL D., mining company executive; b. Montreal, Que., Can., Jan. 22, 1939; s. John and Mary Sopko; m. Mary Raatikainen, Dec. 28, 1979; children: David, Stuart, Andrew. B Metall. Engring., McGill U. Mont., Que., 1960, M Metall. Engring., 1961, PhD, 1964. Jr. engr., mgr. Inco Ltd. Ont. Div., Copper Cliff, Ont., 1964-73; mgr. Iron Ore Recovery Plant, Inco, Copper Cliff, Ont., 1973; ops. mgr. Eximbal (Inco), Guatemala, 1973-78; mgr. copper refinery Inco Ltd.-Ont. Div., Copper Cliff, 1978-79, v.p., 1980-84, pres., 1984-80; v.p. human resources Inco Ltd., Toronto, Ont., 1989-91; pres. Inco Ltd., Toronto, 1991-92, chmn., chief exec. officer, 1992—, also bd. dirs.; bd. dirs. Inco Ltd., The Toronto Dominion Bank; bd. dirs. Conf. Bd. Can., 1994—; mem. Toronto Bd. Trade. Mem. Mining Assn. Can. (bd. dirs., 1st vice chmn. 1991-95), Nickel Devel. Inst. (bd. dirs. 1991-95), Credit Valley Golf and Country Club. Office: Inco Ltd, Royal Trust Tower Box 44, Toronto, ON Canada M5K 1N4

SOPPELSA, GEORGE NICHOLAS, artist; b. Youngstown, Ohio, July 16, 1939; s. Joseph and Rose (Gaiarsa) S. BFA, Ohio State U., 1961. One-man shows include Mulvane Art Ctr., Washburn U., Topeka, 1985, John Szoke Gallery, N.Y.C., 1989, Homer Babbidge Libr., U. Conn., Storrs, 1990, Inter Art Galerie Reich, Cologne, Germany, 1994, The Gallery, St. Mary's Coll. of Md., St. Mary's City, 1991; exhibited in group shows at John Szoke Gallery, N.Y.C., 1989, Art at 100 Pearl, Hartford, Conn., 1989, Butler Inst. Am. Art, Youngstown, Ohio, 1990, Hurlbut Gallery, Greenwich, Conn., 1993; represented in permanent collections at Mulvane Art Ctr., Topeka, Conn. Collection, Hartford. Fellow Nat. Endowment for Arts, 1987, Vt. Studio Colony, 1988; grantee Conn. Commn. on Arts, 1991. Office: Brairton & Tubbs Art Agts 135 Central Ave East Hartford CT 06108-3103

SOPRANOS, ORPHEUS JAVARAS, manufacturing company executive; b. Evanston, Ill., Oct. 4, 1935; s. James Javaras and Marigoula (Papalexatou) S.; m. Angeline Buches, Dec. 31, 1959; children—Andrew, Katherine. A.B., U. Chgo., 1957, M.B.A., 1957. Mgmt. trainee Ford Motor Co., Chgo., 1958-59; with Amsted Industries, Chgo., 1959—; dir. bus. research Amsted Industries, 1966-70, treas., 1970-80, v.p., 1980—; pres. Amsted Internat., 1991-93, corp. v.p., 1993—. Served with U.S. Army, 1958, 61-62. Mem. Am. Inst. C.P.A.s, Ill. Soc. C.P.A.s. Clubs: Univ. (Chgo.), Skokie Country, Mid-Am. Office: 205 N Michigan Ave Chicago IL 60601-5914

SORA, SEBASTIAN ANTONY, business machines manufacturing executive, educator; b. N.Y.C., June 29, 1943; s. Joseph Louis and Angelina Maria (Maletta) S.; m. Janet Lee Dietz, Apr. 11, 1970 (dec. July 1972); 1 child, Joseph Walter; m. Mary Frances Elizabeth Boscketti, Oct. 12, 1974; children: Joseph Walter, Sebastian Nicholas, Frances Ann, Jenny Concetta. BS, Bklyn. Coll., 1964; MBA, Iona Coll., 1974, PMC, 1976; DPS, Pace U., 1989. Math. modeller Assoc. Univs. Inc., 1964-66; with U.S. Coast and Geodetic Survey, Washington, 1967-70; mgr. programming IBM, Yorktown, N.Y., 1966-67, 70-75, programmer, modeller, 1970-72; mgr. program system and design IBM, Fishkill, N.Y., 1971-77; analyst on market models IBM, Harrison, N.Y., 1977-81; sr. programmer IBM, Boeblingen, Fed. Republic Germany, 1981-82; mgr. rsch. staff 1st Josephson system IBM, Yorktown, 1982-84; program dir. Systems Rsch. Inst. IBM, N.Y., 1984-87; mgr. edn. program World Trade Corp. IBM, North Tarrytown, N.Y., 1989-90; mgr.

promotional-artificial intelligence systems IBM, White Plains, N.Y., 1990—; assoc. prof. MIS Montclair State Coll., Upper Montclair, N.J., 1992—; pres. Bus. Edn. Systems Tech., 1992—; assoc. prof. info. sci. Pace U., White Plains, N.Y., 1977—; asst. prof. telecommunications Iona Coll., New Rochelle, N.Y., 1986; asst. prof. mgmt. Manhattan Coll., Bronx, N.Y., 1988; cons. AID, Washington, 1989. Editor Jour. Value Based Mgmt., 1987—, Jour. Cross Cultural Mgmt., Jour. of Am. Mgmt., 1994—; contbr. articles to profl. jours.; patentee fluxless solder, also others. Mem. IEEE (technol. leadership com. 1986—, info. policy com. 1986—), Data Processing Mgmt. Assn. Roman Catholic. Home: Christie Ct Somers NY 10589 Office: IBM Mktg & Svcs Hdqrs 1133 Westchester Ave White Plains NY 10604-3599

SORAN, ROBERT L., manufacturing executive; b. 1944. With Beatrice Cos., Inc., 1973-85; pres. Tropicana Products, Inc., 1985-91; pvt. practice cons. Sarasota, Fla., 1991-92; pres. Uniroyal Tech. Corp., Sarasota, 1992—. Office: Uniroyal Tech Corp 2 N Tamiami Trail Ste 900 Sarasota FL 34236

SORBER, CHARLES ARTHUR, academic administrator; b. Kingston, Pa., Sept. 12, 1939; s. Merritt Walter and Marjory (Roachford) S.; m. Linda Ellen Babcock, Feb. 20, 1972; children: Kimberly Ann, Kingsley Charles. BS in Sanitary Engring., Pa. State U., 1961, MS in Sanitary Engring., 1966; PhD, U. Tex., 1971. Sanitary engr. U.S. Army, France and Fed. Republic Germany, 1961-65; chief gen. engring. br. U.S. Army Environ Hygiene Agy., Edgewood Arsenal, Md., 1966-69; comdr. U.S. Army Med. Environ. Research Unit, Edgewood Arsenal, 1971-73; dir. environ. quality div. U.S. Army Med. Bioengring. R&D Lab., Frederick, Md., 1973-75; asst. dean coll. scis. and math. U. Tex., San Antonio, 1976-77, acting dir. div. earth & phys. scis., 1977-80, dir. Ctr. Applied Research & Tech., 1976-80; assoc. dean coll. engring. U. Tex., Austin, 1980-86, L.B. (Preach) Meaders prof., 1985; dean sch. engring. U. Pitts., 1986-93; pres. U. Tex.-Permian Basin, Odessa, 1993—; bd. dirs. Pitts. Applied Rsch. Corp., chmn., 1992-93; bd. dirs. Tex. Commerce Bank-Odessa, Wilkes U. Coun.; cons. various cos. and agys. Author, co-author more than 130 papers, book chpts., reports on land applicationof wastewater and sludges, water and wastewater reuse, water and wastewater disinfection, and higher edn. Recipient Disting. Alumnus award Wilkes Coll., 1987, Disting. Grad. award Coll. of Engring., U. Tex., Austin, 1994, Outstanding Engring. Alumnus award Pa. State U., 1994; John A. Focht teach fellow U. Tex.-Austin, 1982. Fellow ASCE; mem. NSPE, APHA, Am. Acad. Environ. Engrs. (trustee 1994—, president-elect 1991-92, pres. 1992-93), Am. Soc. Engring. Edn., Am. Water Works Assn., Coun. Pub. Univ. Pres. and Chancellors (exec. com. Tex. 1994—), Odessa Country Club, The Club at Mission Dorado, Petroleum Club (Midland). Office: U Tex Permian Basin 4901 E University Odessa TX 79762-0001

SORBO, ALLEN JON, actuary, consultant; b. Blue Earth, Minn., Aug. 7, 1953; m. Karen Lee Anderson, June 5, 1982; children: Matthew Allen, Sunny Lynn. BA, Gustavus Adolphus Coll., 1975; MS, U. Wis., 1976. Cons. Stennes and Assocs., Mpls., 1976-78; cons. Towers Perrin Forster and Crosby, Mpls., 1978-86, prin., 1986-87; prin.-in-charge health care actuarial svcs. Ernst and Whinney, Chgo., 1987-89; prin. Tillinghast, Towers, Perrin, Mpls., 1989-94; prin. and mgr. Towers Perrin Integrated Health Systems Cons., Mpls., 1995—. Mem. Am. Acad. Actuaries, Soc. Actuaries. Republican. Avocations: golf, skiing, fitness. Office: Towers Perrin Integ Health 8300 Norman Center Dr Minneapolis MN 55437-1059

SORBY, DONALD LLOYD, university dean; b. Fremont, Nebr., Aug. 12, 1933; s. Lloyd A. and Orpha M. (Simmons) S.; m. Jacquelyn J. Burchard, Nov. 7, 1959; children: Thomas, Sharon. BS in Pharmacy, U. Nebr., 1955; M.S., U. Wash., 1958, Ph.D., 1960. Dir. pharm. services U. Calif., San Francisco, 1970-72; chmn. dept. pharmacy research Sch. Pharmacy, U. Wash., Seattle, 1972-74; dean Sch. of Pharmacy, U. Mo., Kansas City, 1974-84, Sch. of Pharmacy, U. Pacific, Stockton, Calif., 1984—. Contbr. articles in field to profl. jours. Assoc. fellow Am. Coll. Apothecaries; mem. Am. Pharm. Assn. (Linwood F. Tice award 1995), Am. Assn. Colls. of Pharmacy (pres. 1980-81), Fedn. Internat. Pharmaceutique, Calif. Pharm. Assn., Acad. Pharm. Rsch. and Scis., Calif. Soc. Hosp. Pharmacists, Assn. Pharm. Scis., Sigma Xi, Phi Kappa Phi, Rho Chi. Home: 4362 Yacht Harbor Dr Stockton CA 95204-1126 Office: U Pacific Sch Pharmacy Stockton CA 95211

SOREFF, STEPHEN MAYER, artist; b. N.Y.C., Feb. 2, 1931; s. Joseph and Jeanne (Goldring) S.; m. Almeda Helen Soreff; children: Alexander, Zachary. BA, Bklyn. Coll., 1954; AA, Pratt Inst., Bklyn., 1960. Engring. designer Slocum & Fuller, N.Y.C., 1954-58; indsl. designer George Kress Assocs., Newark, 1958-62, Walter Darwin Teague Assocs., N.Y.C., 1962-68; prof. art U. Wash., Seattle, 1968-70, C.W. Post Ctr. L.I. U., Greenvale, N.Y., 1970—; pvt. practice artist N.Y.C., 1965—. exhibited works include Crystall Art, Mus. Hudson Highlands, 1988, Star Lake, Emporia Coll., 1988, The Infinite Painting, U. Md., 1988, The Artists Tomb, W&J Coll., 198, The Information Shower, 1992, Richard Humphrey Gallery, N.Y.C., 1995; works in collections of Mus. of Modern Art, N.Y.C., Whitney Mus. Recipient award Art Quest, Inc., Los Angeles, 1987, Metro Art, Inc. Scarsdale, N.Y., 1987, N.Y. chpt. Nat. Drawing Assn., 1987. Home: 79 Mercer St New York NY 10012-4430

SOREL, CLAUDETTE MARGUERITE, pianist; b. Paris; d. Michel M. and Elizabeth S. Grad. with top honors, Juilliard Sch. Music, 1947, postgrad., 1948; student of Sigismund Stojowski, Sari Biro, Olga Samaroff Stokowski, Mieczyslaw Horszowski, Rudolf Serkin; ensemble with, Felix Salmond; musicology with, Dr. Robert Tangeman; music history with, Marian Bauer; grad., Curtis Inst. Music, 1953; B.S. cum laude in Math., Columbia U., 1954. music faculty, vis. prof. Kans. U., 1961-62; assoc. prof. music Ohio State U., 1962-64; prof. music, head piano dept. SUNY Fredonia, 1964—, Disting. Univ. prof., 1969—, univ. artist, 1969—; faculty exchange scholar, 1976—; mem. internat. jury Van Cliburn Internat. Piano Competition, Tex., 1966, Que. and Ont. Music Festivals, 1967, 75; chmn. music panel Presdl. Scholars in Arts Program, 1979—; juror numerous nat. and internat. music competitions; cons. Ednl. Testing Service, Princeton. Author: Compendium of Piano Technique, 1970, 2d edit., 1987, Japanese edit., 1987, Mind Your Musical Manners - Off and On Stage, 1972, 3d revised edit., 1995, The 24 Magic Keys 3 vols, 1974, The Three Nocturnes of Rachmaninoff, 1974, 2d edit., 1975, 3d edit. with cassette in compact disc, 1988, Fifteen Smorgasbord Studies for the Piano, 1975, 2d edit., 1995, Arensky Piano Etudes, 1976; spl. editor: Music Insider; painter of oil portraits; contbr. articles to profl. mags.; Compiler: The Modern Music of Today, 1947, Serge Prokofieff - His Life and Works, 1947, The Ornamentations in Mozart's Music, 1948; Debut at, Town Hall, N.Y.C., 1943; since appeared in, leading cities of U.S., performed with, N.Y. Philharmonic, London Philharmonic, Zurich, Boston, San Antonio, Milw., NBC, Phila., New Orleans and Cin. symphony orchs., Youth Orch. of Am., 200 others; appeared at, Aspen, Berkshire, Chautauqua, other festivals, European concert tours, 1956, 57, 58 to, Eng., Sweden, Holland, Germany, Switzerland, France; appeared on various radio, TV programs; made recordings for, R.C.A. Victor Rec. Co. Monitor Records, Musical Heritage.; compact disc MacDowell Piano Concerto #2 with N.Y. Philharmonic Orch., 1993; 2000 solo appearances, U.S. and Europe. Bd. dirs. Olga Samaroff Found.; Jr. com. aux. bd. N.Y. Philharmonic Symphony Orch., N.Y. State Nat. Fedn. Music Clubs; mem. adv. bd. Univ. Library Soc.; pres. Shelton Apartments, Inc. Fulbright fellow, 1951; Ford Found. Concert grantee, 1962; winner Phila. Orch. Youth Auditions, 1950, to appear with orch. under direction of Eugene Ormandy; U.S. Senatorial Bus. Adv. Com. Fulbright scholar, 1951; recipient Harry Rosenberg Meml., Frank Damrosch prizes, 1947, Nat. Fedn. Music Clubs Young Artist award, 1951; citation svc. to Am. music Nat. Fedn. Music Clubs, 1966, citations Nat. Assn. Composers & Condrs., 1967, Mu Phi Epsilon, 1968, Freedom medal U.S. Senatorial Com., 1994; nominated Kyoto Japan Humanitarian award, 1989, 92; Claudette Sorel Scholarship for Women Ctr. in Music created by NYU. Mem. Nat. Music Coun. (dir. 1973—, chmn. performance com.), Nat. Arts Club, Music Critics Assn., Broadcast Music Incorp., Columbia Univ. Club (N.Y.C.), Pi Kappa Lambda, Mu Phi Epsilon (dir. Meml. Found.), nat. chmn. Sterling Staff Concert Series, citation 1968). Home: 333 West End Ave New York NY 10023-8131 *The most difficult achievement in life is to try to reach one's goals while keeping one's highest idealism and integrity. If these aims can*

also be maintained in an atmosphere of freedom and respect for quality in all aspects of life, then the individual is most fortunate.

SOREL, EDWARD, artist; b. N.Y.C., Mar. 26, 1929; s. Morris and Rebecca (Kleinberg) Schwartz; m. Nancy Caldwell, May 29, 1965; children: Jenny, Katherine; children by previous marriage: Madeline, Leo. Diploma, Cooper Union, 1951. Co-founder Pushpin Studio, 1953; free-lance artist, 1956—; syndicated Sorel's News Service, 1969-70, King Features. Author, illustrator: Making the World Safe for Hypocrisy, 1972; exhibited in, Pushpin Studio retrospective at the Louvre, 1970, other European galleries, 1970-71; exhibited one-man show, Graham Galleries, N.Y.C., 1973, 78, Galerie Bartsch & Chariau, Munich, 1986, Retrospective Exhibition Cooper Union, 1987, Susan Conway Galleries, Washington, 1992, Soc. Illustrators Am. Mus. Illustration, N.Y.C., 1993, Davis and Langdale Galleries, N.Y.C., 1994; illustrator: Pablo Paints a Picture, 1961, Gwendolyn the Miracle Hen, 1963 (N.Y. Herald Tribune Book award for illustration 1962), What's Good for a Five-Year-Old, 1969, The Duck in the Gun, 1969, Word People, 1970, Magical Storybook, 1972, Superpen, 1978, The Zillionaire's Daughter, 1990, First Encounters, 1994; contbr. to The Nation, The New Yorker, American Heritage and The Atlantic mags. Recipient awards Soc. Illustrators, Art Dirs. Club N.Y.; Augustus St. Gauden's medal Cooper Union; George Polk award for satiric drawing, 1981; Page One award Newspaper Guild of N.Y. for best editorial cartoon (magazines), 1988, Hamilton King award Soc. Illustrators, 1990.

SORELLE, RUTH DOYLE, medical writer, journalist; b. Port Arthur, Tex., Oct. 9, 1948; d. Richard Thomas and Ruth Elaine (Droddy) D.; m. Paul Charles SoRelle, Apr. 10, 1970; children: Danielle Amanda, Richard Paul. BJ, U. Tex., 1971; MPH, U. Tex., Houston, 1988. Reporter Port Arthur News, summer 1968, 69, Univ. and Info. Svc., Austin, Tex., 1970-71; med. editor U. Tex. MD Anderson Hosp., Houston, 1973-74; editor Resources Devel. Corp., Houston, 1974-76; med. editor Baylor Coll. Medicine, Houston, 1977-78; copy editor Houston Chronicle, Houston, 1978-79; med. writer Houston Chronicle, 1979—; instr. U. Houston, 1986, 87, 89. Leader Presbyn. Youth Fellowship, Houston, 1989. Recipient John P. McGovern award Am. Med. Writers Assn., Community Svc. award Tex. Assoc. Press, 1993, Katie award Dallas Press Club, 1992, 93, Anson Jones award Tex. Med. Assn., 1981, 83, 85, 86, 88, 90, 92, Francis C. Moore award Harris County Med. Assn., 1984-94, Silver Star Tex. award Tex. Hosp. Assn., 1984, 86, 89, 92, Tex. Pub. Health Assn. award, 1981, 89, 90, 91, 94, Houston Area Health Care Coalition's Health Policy Leadership award, 1990, Paul Ellis award Am. Heart Assn., 1988, others. Mem. Press Club of Houston (Writing award 1982, 89, Deadline Coverage award 1984, Investigative Series award 1990, Mag. Feature award). Home: 5814 Warm Springs Rd Houston TX 77035-2428

SOREN, DAVID, archaeology educator, administrator; b. Phila., Oct. 7, 1946; s. Harry Friedman and Erma Elizabeth (Salamon) Soren; m. Noelle Louise Schattyn, Dec. 22, 1967. B.A., Dartmouth Coll., 1968; M.A., Harvard U., 1972, Ph.D., 1973. Cert. Rome Classics Ctr. Curator of coins Fogg Art Mus., Cambridge, Mass., 1972; asst. prof. U. Mo., Columbia, 1972-76, assoc. prof., dept. head, 1976-81; prof. archaeology U. Ariz., Tucson, 1982-83, dept. head, 1984-89; guest curator Am. Mus.. Natural History, N.Y.C., 1983-90, lectr., 1993—; creator/dir. Kourion Excavations, Cyprus, 1982-89, Portugal, 1983-84, Am. Excavations at Lugnano, Italy, 1988-93; pot cons., field dir. Tunisia Excavations, Chgo. Oriental Inst./ Smithsonian Instn., 1973-78; bbd. dirs. humanities program U. Ariz., 1992-94; dir. excavations Chianciano Terme, Italy, 1995; subject of The Learning Channel TV program: series "Archaeology", 1995. Author: (books) Unreal Reality, 1978, Rise and Fall of Fantasy Film, 1980, Carthage, 1990, French edit., 1994; co-author: Kourion: Search for a Lost Roman City, 1988, Corpus des Mosaiques de Tunisie, 1972, 3rd rev. edit., 1986, Carthage: A Mosaic of Ancient Tunisia, 1987; editor: Excavations at Kourion I, 1987; producer: (film) Carthage: A Mirage of Antiquity, 1987; creator and guest curator: (internat. traveling exhbn.) Carthage: A Mosaic of Ancient Tunisia, 1987-92; editor, founder Roscius, 1993—; creative cons. TV miniseries Lost Civilizations, 1994; contbr. articles to profl. jours. Subject of National Geographic spl. Archeological Detectives, 1985; work subject of feature articles in Newsweek, Conoisseur, National Geographic and others; recipient Cine Golden Eagle, 1980, Angenieux Film award Industrial Photography mag., 1980, Outstanding American Under 40 award C. Johns Hopkins-Britain's Royal Inst. Internat. Affairs, 1985; named Outstanding American Under 40 Esquire mag., 1985, hon. Italian citizen Lugnano, Italy, 1989; grantee NEH, 1979, 87, Fulbright, 1983. Mem. Nat. Geog. Soc. (project dir. 1983-84), Am. Sch. Oriental Rsch. (dept. rep. 1981-85), Archaeol. Inst. Tucson (pres. 1983-86), Luso-Am. Commn. (citation 1983-84), Explorer's Club. Office: U Ariz Dept Classics 371 MLB Tucson AZ 85721

SOREN, HOWARD, textiles executive; b. 1931. BBA, CUNY; JD, Bklyn. Law Sch. CPA. With S.D. Leidesdorf & Co., CPA's, 1953-62, Litton Publs. Inc., 1962-70, Liberty Fabrics of N.Y. Inc., 1970-72; CFO, v.p. fin., treas. FAB Industries Inc., 1972—, also active in all subs. Office: FAB Industries Inc 200 Madison Ave New York NY 10016-3901*

SOREN, TABITHA L., television newscaster, writer; b. San Antonio, Aug. 19, 1967; d. John Thomas and Mary Jane (Quinn) Sornberger. BA cum laude in Journalism, NYU, 1989. Intern Cable News Network, N.Y.C., Sta. WNBC TV, N.Y.C.; desk asst. ABC TV, N.Y.C.; news anchor, statehouse correspondent ABC Sta. WVNY-TV, Vt.; news reporter, anchor MTV News Dept., N.Y.C., 1991—; contbg. corr. NBC News, N.Y.C., 1992—; columnist N.Y. Times Syndication Sales Corp., N.Y.C.; cons. editor Elle, N.Y.C. Contbr. articles to various periodicals. Recipient Peabody Journalism award U. Ga., 1993, Leadership award Nat. League Women Voters, 1993. Office: MTV News 1515 Broadway New York NY 10036

SORENSEN, ALLAN CHRESTEN, service company executive; b. Edson, Alta., Can., Apr. 27, 1938; came to U.S., 1962, naturalized, 1965; s. Henry and Vivien A. (Howie) S.; children: Scott, Jody. B.S. in Pharmacy, Drake U., 1961. Salesman Hoffman LaRoche Pharm. Co., Kitchener, Ont., Can., 1961-62; salesman Personnel Pool of Am., Chgo., 1962-63; sales mgr. Personnel Pool of Am., Inc., 1963-67, dir., pres., 1967-89, chief exec. officer, 1978-91; chmn. interim svcs. Personnel Pool of Am., Inc. (name changed to Interim Svcs. Inc. 1992), 1993—; dir. H&R Block. Bd. dirs. Broward Workshop. Mem. Nat. Assn. Temp. Svcs. (past pres., bd. dirs.), Exec. Assn. Ft. Lauderdale, Home Health Svcs. and Staffing Assn. (past chmn., bd. dirs.). Republican. Club: Rotary. Home: 1500 S Ocean Dr Fort Lauderdale FL 33316-3242 Office: Interim Svcs Inc 2050 Spectrum Blvd Fort Lauderdale FL 33309-3008

SORENSEN, ANDREW AARON, provost; b. Pitts., July 20, 1938; s. Albert Aaron and Margaret (Lindquist) S.; m. Donna Ingemie, Aug. 4, 1968; children: Aaron Ashley, Benjamin Samuel. BA, U. Ill. 1959; BDiv, Yale U., 1962, MPh, 1970, PhD, 1971; MPH, U. Mich., 1966. Asst. prof. Cornell U. Ithaca, N.Y., 1971-73; asst. prof. U. Rochester, N.Y., 1973-76, assoc. prof., 1976-83; prof., dean U. Mass., Amherst, 1983-86; prof. Johns Hopkins U., Balt., 1986-90; provost, v.p. acad. affairs U. Fla., Gainesville, 1990—; chmn. adminstrv. bd. Whitmine Marine Biol. Lab., 1990—; chmn. editorial bd. Univ. Press of Fla., 1990—. Author 5 books; contbr. over 100 articles to profl. jours. Exec. dir. Johns Hopkins AIDS Inst., Balt., 1987-90. U.S. Dept. Edn. fellow Lincoln U., 1966-67, NSF fellow Harvard U., 1975-76. Democrat. Presbyterian. Office: U Fla 235 Tigert Hall Gainesville FL 32611

SORENSEN, BURTON ERHARD, investment banker; b. Chgo., Oct. 28, 1929; s. Soren Kirsten and Christine (Petersen) S.; m. Linda Graf, Aug. 28, 1954 (div. 1970); children: Debra, Jack, Peter, Janice; m. France Elizabeth Pepinger, Dec. 28, 1972. Student, Northwestern U., 1949; B.A., Wheaton Coll., 1955. Vice pres. Kidder, Peabody & Co., N.Y.C., 1956-71; v.p. Goldman, Sachs & Co., N.Y.C., 1972-76, ptnr., 1977-84; chief exec. officer, dir. Provident Life and Accident Ins. Co., Chattanooga, Tenn., Servicemaster Industries Inc. Served to cpl. USMC, 1951-53, Korea. Mem. N.Y. Soc. Security Analysts, City Midday Club (N.Y.C.), Morris County Golf Club (Covent, N.J.), Baltusrol Golf Club, Grandfather Golf and Country Club (Linville, N.C.), The Sanctuary Golf Club (Sanibel Island, Fla.). Republican. Office: Lord Securities Corp 2 Wall St New York NY 10005

SØRENSEN, ERIK, international advisor; b. Randers, Denmark, July 19, 1944; s. Christen and Erna Sørensen; m. Brigitte Berg; children: Anne Marie, Thomas, Anne Louise, Anne Mette, Anne Sophie. MS in Chemistry, Tech. U. Denmark, 1968; MBA in Internat. Fin., Cph Sch. Econs., 1971. Sr. economist Novo Industri A/S, Bagsvaerd, Denmark, 1970-71, mgr. econs. and planning, 1972-74, v.p. sales and mktg., 1974-80; pres. bioindsl. group Novo Industri A/S, Denmark, 1989-95; pres. Navigate A/S, Denmark, 1995—. Lt. Danish Army, 1968-70. Office: Navigate A/S, 32 Nordre Stranvej, 3000 Helsingør Denmark

SORENSEN, GILLIAN MARTIN, United Nations official; b. Columbus, Ohio, Mar. 4, 1941; d. John Butlin and Helen (Hickam) Martin; m. Theodore C. Sorensen, June 28, 1969; 1 child, Juliet. BA, Smith Coll., 1963. Commr. N.Y.C. Commn. for UN and Consular Corps, 1978-90; pres. Nat. Conf., 1990-93; undersec gen., spl. advisor for pub. policy UN, N.Y.C., 1993—. Del. Dem. Nat. Conv., 1976, 84, 88. Mem. Coun. on Fgn. Rels., Bus. Coun. for UN (bd. dirs. 1990—), Women's Forum. Avocations: skiing, tennis, jogging. Office: Rm S-3161 UN New York NY 10017

SORENSEN, JACKI FAYE, aerobic dance company executive, choreographer; b. Oakland, Calif., Dec. 10, 1942; d. Roy C. and Juanita F. (Bullon) Mills; m. Neil A. Sorensen, Jan. 3, 1965. BA, U. Calif., 1964. Cert. tchr., Calif. Ptnr., Big Spring Sch. Dance, 1965; tchr. Pasadena Ave. Sch., Sacramento, 1968; founder, pres., choreographer Jacki's Inc., DeLand, Fla., 1990—; cons., lectr. on phys. fitness. Author: Aerobic Dancing, 1979, Jacki Sorensen's Aerobic Lifestyle Book, 1983; choreographer numerous dance exercises for records and videocassettes. Trustee Women's Sports Found. Recipient Diamond Pin award Am. Heart Assn., 1979, Individual Contbn. award Am. Assn. Fitness Dirs. in Bus. and Industry, 1981, Spl. Olympics Contbn. award, 1982, Contbn. to Women's Fitness award Pres.'s Coun. Phys. Fitness and Sports, 1982, Healthy Am. Fitness Leader award U.S. Jaycees, 1984, Lifetime Achievement award Internat. Dance Exercise Assn., 1985, New Horizons award Caldwell (N.J.) Coll., 1985, Legend of Aerobics award City Sports mag., 1985; Pres. Coun. award Calif. Womens' Leadership Conf., 1986, Hall of Fame award Club Industry mag., 1986, IDEA, 1992. Mem. AAHPERD, AFTRA, Am. Coll. Sports Medicine, Nat. Intramural and Recreation Assn. Office: Jacki's Inc PO Box 289 Deland FL 32721-0289

SORENSEN, JOHN FREDERICK, retired minister; b. Cadillac, Mich., Apr. 4, 1923; s. Neil Thomas and Helga S. (Anderson) S.; m. D. Marieta Moore, Mar. 16, 1944; children: Jack, Keith, Robert. BA, Mich. State U., 1957; MDiv, Garrett Theol. Sem., 1962. Ordained to ministry United Meth. Ch. as deacon, 1960, as elder, 1962. Pastor Mulliken (Mich.) United Meth. Ch., 1951-55, Upton Ave. United Meth. Ch., Battle Creek, Mich., 1955-64, Haven United Meth. Ch., Jackson, Mich., 1964-67, Ithaca (Mich.) United Meth. Ch., 1967-72, 1st United Meth. Ch., Lansing, Mich., 1972-78; assoc. pastor Community United Meth. Ch., Holiday, Fla., 1985-93; mem. various coms. for Conf. Dist., United Meth. Ch., 1962-85; summer exch. pastor to Loughton, Eng., 1975. Contbr. columns to newspapers, 1967-72. Founder Free Health Clinic. With USN, 1942-46. Recipient Spl. Tribute Gov. Mich., 1985, Ionia Hospice award, 1986; named Rural Pastor of Yr. United Meth. Ch., Mich., 1955, Amb., Ionia C of C, 1983-85; commd. Ky. Col., 1995. Fellow Designate Acad. Parish Clergy (elin. comm. 1982-84, state sec. 1994-96), West Pasco Ministerial Assn. Shriners (past master 1972), Masons, commd. a Ky. Col. (1995). Home: 4427 Pelorus Dr New Port Richey FL 34652-5810

SORENSEN, JOHN NOBLE, mechanical and nuclear engineer; b. Mpls., Jan. 2, 1934; s. Alfred Noble and Helen Viola (Baker) S.; m. Joan Elizabeth Reiche, Sept. 15, 1954; children: Laura Elizabeth, Nancy Helen, Karen Lynn. BSME, U. N.D., 1955; MSME, U. Pitts., 1958. Cert. engr. Sr. engr. Westinghouse Electric, Pitts., 1955-67; v.p., gen. mgr. NUS Corp., Rockville, Md., 1967-86; v.p., dir. Grove Engring., Inc., Rockville, 1986-93; tech. asst. to commr. U.S. NRC, Washington, 1993—. Mem. ASME, NSPE, Am. Nuclear Soc., Sigma Xi. Home: 629 Crocus Dr Rockville MD 20850 Office: US NRC Washington DC 20555

SORENSEN, LEIF BOGE, physician, educator; b. Odense, Denmark, Mar. 25, 1928; came to U.S., 1955, naturalized, 1963; s. Henry V. and Mary (Nielsen) S.; 1 child, Heidi. BS, Odense Katedralskole, 1946; MD, U. Copenhagen, Denmark, 1953, PhD in Biochemistry, 1960. Intern Copenhagen County Hosp., Hellerup, Denmark, 1954; resident Copenhagen Municipal Hosp., 1955, U. Chgo. Hosp., 1957-60; mem. faculty, scientist U. Chgo. and Franklin McLean Meml. Research Inst., 1956—; prof. medicine U. Chgo., 1970—; attending physician dept. medicine, assoc. chmn. dept. Pritzker Sch. Medicine, U. Chgo., 1976—; cons. FDA, 1972—. Mem. editorial bd.: Jour. Lab. and Clin. Medicine, 1964-70, Arthritis and Rheumatism, 1965-72; Contbr. articles to profl. jours. With M.C. Danish Army, 1951. Fulbright scholar, 1955; Ill. Arthritis Found. grantee, 1970-72; NIH Fogarty Internat. Center sr. fellow, 1980. Mem. AAAS, Am. Rheumatism Soc., Am. Soc. Clin. Investigation, Central Soc. Clin. Research, N.Y. Acad. Scis., Danish Med. Assn., Ill. Acad. Gen. Practice., Am. Geriatrics Soc., Gerontologic Soc. Am., Am. Fedn. Aging Research. Home: 5140 S Hyde Park Blvd Apt 19B Chicago IL 60615-4266

SORENSEN, ROBERT HOLM, diversified technology company executive, retired; b. Racine, Wis., Mar. 14, 1921; s. Viggo Marius and Lydia Marie (Holm) S.; m. Harriet Norma Kruse, Feb. 27, 1944; children: Anitra A., Scott E., Lyle R. B.S.E.E., Northwestern U., 1947; grad. advanced mgmt. program, Harvard U., 1957; DSc (hon.), Grand View Coll., 1991. Sr. engr. Engring. Research Assocs., Inc., St. Paul, 1947-51; ops. mgr. Sperry Rand Corp. (formerly Remington Rand Inc.), Norwalk, Conn., 1952-59; with Perkin-Elmer Corp., 1959-86; v.p. optical group Perkin-Elmer Corp., Norwalk, 1965-67; sr. v.p. Perkin-Elmer Corp., 1966-73, pres., chief operating officer, 1973-77, chief exec. officer, 1977-84, chmn. bd., 1980-85; retired, 1986. With USN, 1943-46. Recipient Award of Merit, Northwestern U., 1987. Mem. Tau Beta Pi, Eta Kappa Nu. Club: Silver Spring Country (Ridgefield, Conn.).

SORENSEN, SHEILA, state senator; b. Chgo., Sept. 20, 1947; d. Martin Thomas Moloney and Elizabeth (Koehr) Paulus; m. Wayne B. Slaughter, May, 1969 (div. 1976); 1 child, Wayne Benjamin III; m. Dean E. Sorensen, Feb. 14, 1977; (stepchildren) Michael, Debbie, Kevin, Dean C. BS, Loretto Heights Coll., Denver, 1965; postgrad. pediatric nurse practicioner, U. Colo., Denver, 1969-70. Pediatric nurse practicioner Pub. Health Dept., Denver, 1970-71, Boise, Idaho, 1971-72; pediatric nurse practicioner Boise (Idaho) Pediatric Group, 1972-74, Pediatric Assocs., Boise, 1974-77; mem. Idaho State Ho. Reps., 1987-92; mem. Idaho Senate, 1992—, chair senate health and welfare com., 1992-94, chair senate majority caucus, vice chair state affairs com. Precinct committeeman Ada County Rep. Cen. Com., Boise, 1982-86, dist. vice-chair, 1985—; polit. chair Idaho Med. Assn. Aux., 1984-87, Ada County Med. Assocs., 1986-87; bd. dirs. Family Practice Residency Program, 1992—, Univ./Comty. Health Sci. Assn., Bishop Kelly Found., 1993—; chair Senate Majority Caucus, 1995, vice-chair state affairs com. Recipient AMA Nathan Davis award for Outstanding State Legislator, 1994. Mem. Nat. Conf. State Legislators, Nat. Orgn. Women Legislators, Am. Legis. Exch. Coun. Roman Catholic.

SORENSEN, STUART L, actuary; b. Omaha, May 9, 1948; s. Carlyle A. and Rachel (Nurse) M.S.; m. Debra A. Mattson, Oct. 4, 1974. BA, U. Nebr., 1970. Cert. actuary. Asst. v.p., actuary United of Omaha, 1970-74; exec. v.p., chief actuary Security Am. Fin. Enterprises, Mpls., 1975—; bd. dirs. Security Life Ins. Co. Am., Securities Am. Fin. Enterprises, Congress Life Ins. Co. Fellow Soc. Actuaries, Life Mgmt. Inst.; mem. Am. Acad. Actuaries, Am. Soc. CLUs, Am. Soc. Chartered Fin. Cons. Club: Twin Cities Actuarial. Home: 5595 Zachary Ln Plymouth MN 55442 Office: Security Am Fin Enterprises 10901 Red Circle Dr Minnetonka MN 55343-9137

SORENSEN, THEODORE CHAIKIN, lawyer, former special counsel to President of U.S.; b. Lincoln, Nebr., May 8, 1928; s. Christian Abraham and Annis (Chaikin) S.; m. Gillian Martin, June 28, 1969; 1 child, Juliet Suzanne; children from previous marriage: Eric Keiren, Stephen Edgar, Philip Jon. B.S. in Law, U. Nebr., 1949, LL.B. 1951, LL.D. (hon.) 1969; LL.D. (hon.), U. Canterbury, 1966, Alfred U., 1969, Temple U., 1969, Fairfield U., 1969. Bar: Nebr. 1951, N.Y. 1966, U.S. Supreme Ct. 1966, D.C. 1971.

Atty. Fed. Security Agy., 1951-52; mem. staff joint com. r.r. retirement U.S. Senate, 1952; asst. to Sen. John F. Kennedy, 1953-61; sec. New Eng. Senators' Conf., 1953-59; spl. counsel to pres. U.S., 1961-64; mem. firm Paul, Weiss, Rifkind, Wharton & Garrison, N.Y.C., 1966—; mem. Pres.'s Adv. Com. Trade Negotiations, 1978; chmn. Gov.'s panel on N.Y. State Export Credit Agy., 1982. Editor: Nebr. Law Rev, 1950-51; author: Decision Making in the White House, 1963, Kennedy, 1965, The Kennedy Legacy, 1969, Watchmen in the Night: Presidential Accountability After Watergate, 1975, A Different Kind of Presidency, 1984, (with Ralf Dahrendorf) A Widening Atlantic? Domestic Change and Foreign Policy, 1986; editor: Let the Word Go Forth: The Speeches, Statements and Writings of John F. Kennedy, 1988. Dem. candidate for U.S. Senate, 1970; chmn. Dem. Nat. Com. task force on polit. action, 1981-82, mem. task force on fgn. policy, 1986; mem. Internat. Trade Roundtable, 1985; dir. Twentieth Century Fund, 1984—, Coun. on Fgn. Rels., 1993—, Nat. Dem. Inst. for Internat. Affairs, 1993—; trustee N.Y. Acad. Medicine, 1991—; advisor Russian-Am. Press and Info. Ctr., 1993—. Named by Jr. C. of C. as one of ten Outstanding Young Men of Year, 1961. Mem. Order of Coif, Phi Beta Kappa. Office: Paul Weiss Rifkind Wharton & Garrison 1285 Ave of the Americas New York NY 10019-6064

SORENSEN, THOMAS CHAIKIN, financial executive; b. Lincoln, Nebr., Mar. 31, 1926; s. Christian and Annis (Chaikin) S.; m. Mary Barstler (div.); children: Ann Christine Sorensen Ketter, Alan Thomas, Jens Christian; m. Pamela A. Berse; children—Matthew Thomas, Adam Lincoln. B.A., U. Nebr., 1947. Radio announcer, 1943-44, newspaper reporter, 1945-46; asst. night editor Nebr. State Jour., 1946-49; dir. news and pub. affairs radio sta. KLMS, Lincoln, 1949-51; instr. U. Nebr. Sch. Journalism, 1948-50; info. officer, press attaché Am. Embassy, Beirut, Lebanon, 1952-56, Baghdad, Iraq, 1956, Cairo, Egypt, 1957-59; program officer for Near East USIA, Washington, 1959-61; dep. dir. for policy USIA, 1961-65; v.p. U. Calif., 1966-68; sr. fellow Adlai Stevenson Inst., 1968-69; v.p. Leasco Corp., 1969-70; ptnr. Sartorius & Co., N.Y.C., 1971-74; sr. v.p., dir. Advest Inc., 1974-80; v.p. Capital Rsch. Internat., 1980-90; cons. Capital Group Inc., 1990—. Author: The Word War, 1968. Named one of 10 Outstanding Young Men in Fed. Service, 1961. Mem. Washington Inst. of Fgn. Affairs, Va. Inst. Polit. Leadership, Phi Beta Kappa, Sigma Delta Chi, Delta Sigma Rho. Home: Matfield 2725 Hunt Country Ln Charlottesville VA 22901

SORENSEN, W. ROBERT, clergy member, church administrator. Exec. dir. Division for Higher Education and Schools, Evangelical Lutheran Churchin America, Chgo. Office: Evangelical Lutheran Church Am 8765 W Higgins Rd Chicago IL 60631-4101

SORENSON, LIANE BETH MCDOWELL, university administrator, state legislator; b. Chgo., Aug. 13, 1947; d. Harold Davidson McDowell and Frances Elanor (Williams) Daisey; m. Boyd Wayne Sorenson, June 30, 1973; children: Nathan, Matthew, Dana. BS in Edn., U. Del., 1969, M in Counseling with honors, 1986. Tchr. Avon Grove Sch. Dist., West Grove, Pa., 1969-70, Alexis I. duPont Sch. Dist., Wilmington, Del., 1970-73, Barrington (Ill.) Sch. Dist., 1973-75; counseling intern Medill Intensive Learning Ctr.- Christina Sch. Dist., Newark, Del., 1985; counselor Family Violence Shelter CHILD, Inc., Wilmington, 1985, 86-87; dir. parent edn. programs, 1987-88; dir. Office Women's Affairs, exec. dir. Commn. on Status of Women U. Del., Newark, 1988—; mem. Del. Legislature, Dover, 1992—; chair Del. Ho. Edn. Com., 1992—; commr. Edn. Commn. State Del.; mem. tng. com. Nat. Conf. State Legislatures; mem. joint sunset com. Del. Legislature. Presenter papers various meetings & confs. Pres. bd. dirs. Nursing Mothers, Inc., 1980-81; trustee Hockessin Montessori Sch., 1982-84, enrollment chair, 1982-83; trustee Hockessin Pub. Libr., 1982-84, pres. bd., 1982-84; bd. dirs. Del. Coalition for Children, 1986-88; bd. dirs. Children's Bur. Del., 1984-87, sec., 1985-87; pres. Jr. League Wilmington, 1986-87; rsch. coun. v.p., 1985-86; bd. dirs. YWCA New Castle County, 1989-91; pres. Del. Women's Agenda, 1986—; vice chair Women's Leadership Ctr., 1992—; mem. Del. Work Family Coalition. Grantee Del. Dept. Svcs. to Children, Youth and Their Families, 1987-88, 1988, State of Del. Gen. Assembly, 1988. Mem. Am. Assn. for Higher Edn. (chair women's caucus 1991-92, program chair women's caucus 1990-91, pre-conf. workshop coord. women's caucus 1990 Ann Conf.). Republican. Methodist. Avocations: camping, hiking. Office: State of Delaware Legislative Hall Dover DE 19901

SORGENTI, HAROLD ANDREW, petroleum and chemical company executive; b. Bklyn., May 28, 1934; s. Louis J. and Lucille (Sisti) S.; m. Ann Rusnack, June 30, 1962; children: Elizabeth, Lucille. B.S.Ch.E., CCNY, 1956; M.S., Ohio State U., 1959. Research engr. Battelle Meml. Inst., Columbus, Ohio, 1956-59; with Atlantic Richfield Co., 1959-91, v.p. research and engring., products div., 1975-76; sr. v.p. chem. devel. Arco Chem. Co. subs. Atlantic Richfield Co., Phila., 1977-79, pres., 1979-87, pres., CEO, 1987-90, vice chmn. bd., 1991; ptnr. Freedom Group Partnership, Phila., 1991-92; chmn. Freedom Chem. Co., 1992—; bd. dirs. Provident Mut. Life Ins. Co., Core States Fin. Corp., Crown Cork & Seal. Bd. dirs. Phila. Orch. Assn., Pa. Acad. Fine Arts. Mem. Am. Chem. Soc., Am. Inst. Chem. Engrs., Soc. Chem. Industry, Ohio State U. Alumni Assn., CCNY Alumni Assn., Union League. Office: Freedom Chem Co 1735 Market St Ste 3500 Philadelphia PA 19103-7501

SORKIN, ALAN LOWELL, economist, educator; b. Decatur, Ill., Nov. 2, 1941; s. Martin and Sally Eileen (Steinberg) S.; m. Sylvia Jean Swardo, Sept. 9, 1967; children: David, Suzanne. BA, Johns Hopkins U., 1963, MA, 1964, PhD, 1966. Rsch. assoc. Brookings Instn., Washington, 1967-69; asst. prof. internat. health and econs. Johns Hopkins U., Balt., 1969-72, assoc. prof. internat. health and econs., 1972-74, adjt. prof. dept. internat. health Sch. Hygiene and Pub. Health, 1986—; prof., chmn. dept. econs., 1974—; also adj. prof. preventive and social medicine Med. Sch., U. Md., 1974—. Author: Education, Unemployment and Economic Growth, 1974, Health Economics: An Introduction, 1975, 2d edit., 1983, 3d edit., 1992. The Urban American Indian, 1978, Economic Aspects of Natural Hazards, 1982, Health Care and the Changing Economic Environment, 1986, Monetary and Fiscal Policy and Business Cycles in The Modern Era, 1988, Public Health and Development, 1988, (with others) Female Labor Force and Development, 1990, Nutrition, Food Policy and Development, 1995, others; contbr. articles to profl. jours. Mem. Am. Econs. Assn., Phi Beta Kappa, Delta Omega. Republican. Lutheran. Home: 1694 Campbell Rd Forest Hill MD 21050-2342 Office: U Md Dept Econ 5401 Wilkens Ave Baltimore MD 21228-5379 *Personal relationships are more important than material possessions. Persons with many friends have a sense of well-being that can never be embodied in materialism.*

SORKIN, LAURENCE TRUMAN, lawyer; b. Bklyn., Oct. 20, 1942; s. Sidney and Lilly (Kowensky) S.; m. Joan Carol Ross, June 25, 1972; children: Andrew Ross, Suzanne Ross. AB summa cum laude, Brown U., 1964; LLB, Yale U., 1967; LLM, London Sch. Econs. and Polit. Sci., 1968. Bar: N.Y. 1968, D.C. 1972, U.S. Supreme Ct. 1973. Law clk. to judge U.S Ct. Appeals (2d cir.), Hartford, Conn., 1968-69; assoc. Cahill Gordon & Reindel, N.Y.C., 1969-75, ptnr., 1975—; vis. lectr. Yale U., 1972, 73; lectr. Practicing Law Inst., 1977—, and various other profl. orgns.; rsch. asst. to Lester and Bindman for book Race and Law in Great Britain, 1972. Contbr. to State Antitrust Law (Lifland), 1984; author (with Lifland, Sorkin and Van Cise): Understanding the Antitrust Laws, 1986. Fulbright scholar, 1967-68. Bd. dirs. The Legal Aid Soc., N.Y.C., 1984-89, N.Y. Lawyers for Pub. Interest, 1990-93. Mem. ABA (antitrust law sect. 1978—), N.Y. State Bar Assn. (mem. antitrust sect. 1978—, chmn. com. on legis. 1978-79, sec. 1979-80, chmn. com. on mergers 1987-89, chmn. Clayton Act com.1989-94, exec. com. 1989-94), Assn. of Bar of City of N.Y. (mem. com. trade regulation 1974-77, com. on electronic funds transfer 1979-80), Phi Beta Kappa. Office: Cahill Gordon & Reindel 80 Pine St New York NY 10005-1701

SORMANI, CHARLES ROBERT, insurance company executive, actuary; b. Nassau County, N.Y., Sept. 13, 1938; s. Hedwig J. Sormani; m. Margot Klara Haegler; children: Barbara Ann, Charles Daniel; m. 2d, Cheryl A. McGlynn, Nov., 1991. BA, Wabash Coll., 1960. Staff asst. Met. Life Ins. Co., 1963-69; with Union Labor Life Ins. Co., Washington, 1969—, sr. v.p., 1982—; pres. Ulico Casualty Co., 1993—. Fellow Soc. Actuaries; mem. Am. Acad. Actuaries, Internat. Actuarial Assn. Lutheran. Office: ULLICO Inc 111 Massachusetts Ave NW Washington DC 20001-1461

SORO, MAR BAWAI, bishop; b. Kirkuk, Iraq, Mar. 3, 1954; s. Andrew Athniel and Souria (Sada) S. MA in Theology, Cath. U. Am., 1994. Ordained priest Holy Apostolic Cath. Assyrian Ch. of the East. Parish priest Assyrian Ch., Toronto, Ont., Can., 1982-85; diocesian bishop Diocese of Western U.S. Assyrian Ch., San Jose, Calif., 1985-95; gen. sec. Assyrian Ch. of East Commn. on Inter-ch. Rels. and Edn. Devel., Seattle, 1995—; mem. Ctrl. Com., W.C.C., Geneva, 1982-91; mem. official dialogue with Roman Cath. Ch., Vatican City, 1984—, with Middle East Coun. Chs., Limassol, Cypress, 1991—. Pub. The Messenger, 1993—. Avocations: reading, computer applications.

SOROKIN, PETER PITIRIMOVICH, physicist; b. Boston, July 10, 1931; s. Pitirim Alexandrovich and Elena Petrovna (Baratynskaya) S.; m. Anita J. Schell, Oct. 1, 1977; children: Elena P., Paul P. A.B., Harvard U., 1952, M.S., 1953, Ph.D., 1958. Staff physicist IBM Watson Rsch. Ctr., Yorktown Heights, N.Y., 1957-68, fellow, 1968—. Contbr. articles in quantum electronics to profl. jours. Recipient Michelson medal Franklin Soc., 1974; R.W. Wood award Optical Soc. Am., 1978; Harvey prize, 1984; IBM fellow, 1968—; APS Schawlow prize, 1991. Mem. Nat. Acad. Sci. (Comstock award 1983), Am. Acad. Sci., N.Y. Acad. Sci. Patentee laser devices. Home: PO Box 225 Millwood NY 10546-0225 Office: IBM T J Watson Rsch Ctr PO Box 218 Yorktown Heights NY 10598-0218*

SOROS, GEORGE, fund management executive; b. Budapest, Hungary, Aug. 12, 1930; came to U.S., 1956; s. Tivadar and Elisabeth (Szucs) S.; m. Annaliese Witschak, Sept. 17, 1960 (div. June 1983); children: Robert, Andrea, Jonathan; m. Susan Weber, June 19, 1983; children: Alexander, Gregory. BS, London Sch. Econs., 1952; LLD (hon.), New Sch. for Social Rsch., 1990; D. Civil Law, U. Oxford, Eng., 1990; LHD (hon.), Yale U., 1991. Arbitrage trader F.M. Mayer, N.Y.C., 1956-59; analyst Wertheim & Co., N.Y.C., 1959-63; v.p. Arnhold and S. Bleichroeder, N.Y.C., 1963-73; pres. Soros Fund Mgmt., N.Y.C., 1973—. Author: The Alchemy of Finance, 1987, 2nd edit., 1994, Opening the Soviet System, 1990, Underwriting Democracy, 1991. Mem. Coun. on Fgn. Rels., N.Y.C., 1988—, Royal Inst. Internat. Affairs, London, 1990—, Bretton Woods Com., Washington, 1989; mem. exec. com. Helsinki Watch, N.Y.C., 1982—; mem. com. Americas Watch, N.Y.C., 1982—; chmn., founding pres. Ctrl. European U., Prague, Budapest, 1991; chmn. Open Soc. Fund, 1981, Open Soc. Inst., 1993, founds. in Albania, Belarus, Bosnia and Herzegovina, Bulgaria, Croatia, Czech Republic, Estonia, Georgia, Hungary, Kazakhstan, Kyrgyestan, Latvia, Lithuania, Macedonia, Moldova, Poland, Romania, Russia, Slovakia, Slovenia, South Africa, Rroma, Ukraine, Yugoslavia. Recipient honor Lawyers Co. for Human Rights, N.Y.C., 1990. Mem. Brooks' London, Queens Club (London), N.Y. Athletic Club, Town Tennis, Meadow Club (Southampton, N.Y.). Avocations: tennis, skiing, chess, backgammon. Office: Soros Fund Mgmt 888 7th Ave Ste 3300 New York NY 10106-0001

SORREL, WILLIAM EDWIN, psychiatrist, educator, psychoanalyst; b. N.Y.C., May 27, 1913; s. Simon and Lee (Lesenger) S.; m. Rita Marcus, July 1, 1950; children: Ellyn Gail, Joy Shelley, Beth Mara. BS, NYU, 1932; MA, Columbia U., 1934, MD, 1939; PhD, NYU, 1963. Diplomate Am. Bd. Med. Psychotherapists (profl. adv. coun. 1992—); qualified psychiatrist, also cert.examiner N.Y. State Dept. Mental Hygiene. Intern Madison (Tenn.) Sanitarium and Hosp., 1939; resident physician Alexian Bros. Hosp., St. Louis, 1940; officer instrn. St. Louis U. Sch. Medicine, 1940-41; asst. psychiatrist Central State Hosp., Nashville, 1941; assoc. psychiatrist Eastern State Hosp., Knoxville, 1942-44; assoc. attending neuropsychiatrist, chief clin. psychiatry Jewish Meml. Hosp., N.Y.C., 1946-59; assoc. attending neuropsychiatrist, chief clin. child psychiatry Lebanon Hosp., Bronx, N.Y., 1947-65; psychiatrist-in-chief Psychiatry Clinic, Yeshiva U., 1950-66, asst. prof. psychiatry, 1952-54, assoc. prof., 1954-58, prof., 1959-62, psychiatrist-in-chief, assoc. dir. Psychol. Center, 1957-67; prof. human behavior Touro Coll., 1974—; attending psychiatrist St. Clare's Hosp., N.Y.C., 1983—; asst. prof. clin. psychiatry Albert Einstein Coll. Medicine, 1986—; psychiat. cons. SSS, 1951, N.Y. State Workmens Compensation Bd., 1951—, Bronx-Lebanon Med. Ctr., 1985—; vis. psychiatrist Fordham Hosp., N.Y.C., 1951; attending neuropsychiatrist, chief mental hygiene svc. Beth-David Hosp., 1950-60; attending neuropsychiatrist Grand Central Hosp., 1958-66, Morrisania Hosp., 1959-72; psychiatrist-in-chief Beth Abraham Hosp., 1954-60; psychiat. cons. L.I. U. Guidance Ctr., 1955-60, Daytop Village, 1970-71; assoc. psychiatrist Seton City Hosp., 1955; guest lectr. U. London, 1947; vis. prof. Jerusalem, Israel Acad. Med., Hosp. Hebrew U., 1960; mem. psychiat. staff Gracie Sq. Hosp., 1960—; chief psychiatry Trafalgar Hosp., 1962-72; vis. prof. psychiatry Tokyo U. Sch. Medicine, 1964; adj. prof. N.Y. Inst. Tech., 1968; vis. lectr. in psychiatry N.Y. U., 1971-73; Am. del. Internat. Conf. Mental Health, London, 1948; mem. Am. Psychiat. Commn. to USSR, Poland and Finland, 1963, Empire State Med., Sci. and Ednl. Found. Author: (booklets) Neurosis in a Child, 1949, A Psychiatric Viewpoint on Child Adoption, 1954, Shock Therapy in Psychiatric Practice, 1957, The Genesis of Neurosis, 1958, The Prejudiced Personality, 1962, The Schizophrenic Process, 1962, The Prognosis of Electroshock Therapy Success, 1963, Psychodynamic Effects of Abortion, 1967, Violence Towards Self, 1971, Basic Concepts of Transference in Psychoanalysis, 1973, A Study in Suicide, 1972, Masochism, 1973, Emotional Factors Involved in Skeletal Deformities, 1977, Cults & Cult Suicide, 1979; assoc. editor: Jour. Pan Am. Med. Assn., 1992—; contbr. articles on the psychoses. Vice pres. Golden Years Found.; N.Y.C. chmn. Com. Med. Standards in Psychiatry, 1952-54. Recipient Sir William Osler Internat. Honor Med. Soc. Gold Key; 3d prize oil paintings N.Y. State Med. Art Exhibit, 1954; NYU Founders Day award, 1963; Presdl. Achievement award, 1984; others. Fellow Am. Psychiat. Assn. (life, pres. Bronx dist. 1960-61, other offices, Gold medal 1974, 94), Am. Assn. Psychoanalytic Physicians (pres. 1971-72, bd. govs. 1972—); mem. AMA, Am. Psychiat. Assn., N.Y. State Soc. Med. Rsch., Am. Med. Writers Assn., N.Y. Med. Soc., N.Y. County Med. Soc., N.Y. Soc. for Clin. Psychiatry, Pan Am. Med. Assn. (various offices including pres. 1989—, assoc. editor jour. 1992—), Assn. for Advancement Psychotherapy, Bronx Soc. Neurology and Psychotherapy (pres. Bronx-N.Y. 1961, Silver medal 1970), Mensa. Home: 23 Meadow Rd Scarsdale NY 10583-7642 Office: 263 W End Ave New York NY 10023-2612 *Very meaningful to me is the matter of professionalism in the practice of my discipline. A helping service to individuals is to add and enhance their contentment of living; especially in a world of turmoil. Medical science has added greatly to the art of my training; and I apply it daily.*

SORRELL, MARTIN STUART, advertising and marketing executive; b. London, Feb. 14, 1945; s. Jack and Sally (Goldberg) S.; m. Sandra Carol Ann Finestone, Apr. 25, 1971; children: Mark, Robert, Jonathan. BA, Cambridge (Eng.) U., 1966, MA, 1970; MBA, Harvard U., 1968. Cons. Glendinning Assoc., Conn., 1968-70; v.p. Mark McCormack Orgn., London, 1970-74; dir. James Gulliver Assoc., London, 1975-77; group fin. dir. Saatchi & Saatchi, London, 1977-86; group chief exec. WPP Group PLC, London, 1986—; non-exec. dir. Storehouse, London, 1994—. Trustee U. Cambridge Found., Princess Royal Trust for Carers; mem. governing body London Bus Sch.; mem. adv. bd. Instituto de Estudios Superiores de la Empresa, Judge Inst. Mgmt. Studies. Avocation: cricket, skiing. Office: WPP Group PLC, 27 Farm St, London W1X 6RD, England

SORRENTINO, GILBERT, English language educator, novelist, poet; b. Bklyn., Apr. 27, 1929; s. August E. and Ann Marie (Davis) S.; m. Victoria Ortiz; children: Jesse, Delia, Christopher. Student, Bklyn. Coll., 1949-51, 54-56. In various positions, 1947-70; including reins. clk. Fidelity and Casualty Co., N.Y.C., 1947-48; freight checker Ace Assembly Agy., N.Y.C., 1954-56; packer Bennett Bros. Inc., N.Y.C., 1956-57; messenger Am. Houses, Inc., N.Y.C., 1948-49; shipping-room supr. Thermo-fax Sales, Inc., Queens, N.Y., 1957-60; editor Grove Press, N.Y.C., 1965-70; tchr. Columbia U., 1966, Aspen Writers Workshop, 1967, Sarah Lawrence Coll., 1972, The New Sch. for Social Rsch., 1976—; NEH chairperson in lit. U. Scranton, 1979; prof. English Stanford (Calif.) U., 1982—; editorial cons. Contemporary Lit., 1989— Author: The Darkness Surrounds Us, 1960, Black and White, 1964, The Sky Changes, 1966, The Perfect Fiction, 1968, Steelwork, 1970, Imaginative Qualities of Actual Things, 1971, Corrosive Sublimate, 1971, Splendide-Hotel, 1973, Flawless Play Restored, 1974, A Dozen Oranges, 1976, White Sail, 1977, Sulpiciae Elegidia/Elegiacs of Sulpica, 1977, The Orangery, 1978, Mulligan Stew, 1979, Aberration of Starlight, 1980, Selected Poems, 1958-80, 81, Crystal Vision, 1981, Blue Pastoral, 1983, Something Said: Essays, 1984, Odd Number, 1985, Rose Theatre, 1987, Misterioso, 1989, Under the Shadow, 1991, Red the Friend, 1995. With U.S.

Army, 1951-53. Recipient Samuel Fels award in fiction Coord. Coun. Lit. Mags., 1974, John Dos Passos prize, 1981, Am. Acad. and Inst. Arts and Letters award in lit., 1985, Lannan Lit. award for fiction, 1992; John Simon Guggenheim Meml. fellow, 1973-74, 87-88; grantee Creative Artists Pub. Svc. Program, 1974-75, Nat. Endowment for Arts, 1974-75, 78-79, 83-84. Mem. PEN Am. Ctr. Office: Stanford U Dept English Stanford CA 94305

SORRENTINO, RALPH JOSEPH, controller; b. Bklyn., June 28, 1952; s. Vincent Sorrentino and Carmela (Visciano) La Rosa; m. Spyroula Konstantopolos, Feb. 14, 1975 (div. Apr. 1979); m. Jean Marie McAuliffe, Sept. 8, 1984. BS in Acctg., Bklyn. Coll., 1979. CPA, N.Y. Controller Lowe Marschalk, N.Y.C. Mem. Am. Inst. CPA's. Avocation: stock and bond markets. Home: 407 Blauvelt Rd Pearl River NY 10965-2845 Office: Lowe Marschalk 1345 Ave Of The Americas New York NY 10105-0099

SORRENTINO, RENATE MARIA, illustrator; b. Mallnitz, Carinthia, Austria, June 21, 1942; came to the U.S., 1962; d. Johann and Theresia (Kritzer) Weinberger; m. Francis J. Sorrentino, Sept. 4, 1988. Grad. gold and silversmith artist, Höhere Technische Lehranstalt, Austria, 1961. Draftswoman Elecon Inc., N.Y.C., 1962-65; jr. designer Automatics Metal Prod. Corp., N.Y.C., 1965-70; designer, art dir. Autosplice, Inc., Woodside, N.Y., 1970-90; freelance artist Jupiter, Fla., 1990—. Patentee Quick Disconnect from Continuous Wire, 1977. Home: 2301 Marina Isle Way # 404 Jupiter FL 33477 Office: Autosplice Inc 10121 Barnes Canyon Rd San Diego CA 92121-2725

SORSBY, JAMES LARRY, home building company executive; b. Houston, May 31, 1955; s. J.B. Jr. and Viola (Lueckemeyer) S.; m. Terry Prince, July 28, 1984; children: Carson Drew, Cameron Brent. BBA, Stephen F. Austin State U., 1977. Loan officer 1st Mortgage Co Tex., Houston, 1977-82; pres. The MortgageBanque, Inc., Houston, 1982-88; sr. v.p., treas. Hovnanian Enterprises, Inc., Red Bank, N.J., 1988—; bd. dirs. Am. S.W. Fin. Corp., Phoenix. Mem. Mortgage Bankers Assn. Am. Methodist. Office: Hovnanian Enterprises Inc 10 Highway 35 Red Bank NJ 07701

SORTER, BRUCE WILBUR, federal program administrator, educator, consultant; b. Willoughby, Ohio, Sept. 1, 1931; s. Wilbur David and Margaret Louise (Palmer) S.; m. Martha Ann Weirich, Sept. 2, 1960 (div. 1967); 1 child, David Robert. BA, U. Md., 1967; MCP, Howard U., 1969; PhD, U. Md., 1972. Cert. community developer. Commd. USAFR, 1967, advanced through grades to lt. col., 1964; sr. planner, cons. Md. Nat. Capital Park and Planning Comm., 1968-71; instr. psychology, sociology Howard and P.G. C.C., Columbia and Largo, Md., 1971-72; cmty. resource devel. dept. Md. Coop. Extension Svc., U. Md., College Park, Md., 1972-92; coord. rural info. ctr. Md. Coop. Ext. Svc., U. Md., College Park, 1989-92; affiliate prof. U. Md., 1985-92, ret., 1995; ext. advisor USDA Internat. Programs, Washington, 1991—; co-author, co-dir. U.S. Dept. Edn. Coun. Effectiveness Tng. Program, 1979-81; author First County Energy Conservation Plan, Prince George's County, 1978-83. Author, co-author 12 books; contbr. articles to profl. publs., chpts. to books. Developer, dir. teamwork tng. programs U.S. Dept. Edn., U.S. Dept. Agriculture, Brazil, Poland, Nat. Grange, 1972-92; cons. Fed. Power Commn. U.S., 1973-75, State Dept. Natural Resources, Md., 1978-79, Dept. Edn., Brazil, 1981-82, Nat. Grange, 1987, Edn. Ext. Svcs., Poland, 1991-92. Urban Planning fellow Howrad U., 1968, Human Devel. fellow U. Md., 1970; recipient Meritorious Svc. award Dept. Def., 1983, Disting. Community Svc. award Md. Community Resource Devel. Assn., 1983, Citation for Outstanding Svc., Ptnrs. of Am., 1983, Excellence in Ednl. Programs award Am. Express, 1984, Project of Yr. award Am. Psychol. Assn., 1976, Award of Yr. Am. Vol. Assn., 1976, Achievement award Nat. Assn. of Counties, 1980. Mem. Internat. Cmty. Devel. Soc. (bd. dirs., Achievement award for outstanding contbn. to cmty. devel. 1985, Disting. Svc. award 1990), Md. Cmty. Resource Devel. Assn. (sec.-treas. 1979, pres. 1980, 88-89). Republican. Methodist. Avocations: volunteer work, tennis, sailing, skiing.

SORTER, GEORGE HANS, accounting and law educator, consultant; b. Vienna, Austria, Dec. 2, 1927; came to U.S., 1938; s. Alfred and Hertha (Kohn) S.; m. Dorienne Lachman, Aug. 18, 1966; children: David, Ivan, Adrienne. Ph.B, U. Chgo., 1953, M.B.A., 1955, Ph.D., 1963. C.P.A., N.Y. Instr. U. Chgo., 1955-58, asst. prof., 1959-63, assoc. prof., 1963-65, prof., 1966-74; Vincent C. Ross prof. acctg., prof. of law NYU, N.Y.C. 1974—; Arthur Young prof. U. Kans., 1969; Coopers & Lybrand prof. Tuck Sch. Dartmouth Coll., 1982; bd. dirs. NYU Credit Union 1982-85; dir. Greater N.Y. Savs. Bank, N.Y.C., 1983—; audit com. City of N.Y., 1985—. Author: Accounting Theory, 1963, Accounting Thoughts of W.W. Werntz, Boundaries of Accounting Universe, 1978, Relevant Financial Statements, 1978, Financial Accounting: An Events and Cash Flow Approach, 1990, The Mix-Max Co., 1990. Mem. Ill. Sch. Bd. Dist. 233, Flossmoor, 1970-74; bd. dirs. Sch. Emotionally Disturbed Children, Chgo., 1960-74, Renaissance Soc., 1956-74, Found. Acctg. Edn., N.Y.C., 1975-79. Erskine fellow U. Canterbury, 1979. Mem. Am. Acctg. Assn. (v.p 1980-81 Outstanding Acctg. Educator), N.Y. State Soc. C.P.A.s (dir. 1980-82), Am. Inst. C.P.A.s, Fin. Acctg. Standard Adv. Com. Home: 37 Washington Sq W New York NY 10011-9181 Office: NYU Tisch Hall 40 W 4th St New York NY 10012-1106

SORTLAND, TRUDITH ANN, educator, speech and language therapist; b. Butte, Mont., Dec. 3, 1940; d. Kenneth Hjalmer Sortland and Sigrid V. (Kotka) Strand. BS, Minot (N.D.) State U., 1965. Tchr. Westby (Mont.) Sch., 1960-61, Glasgow (Mont.) Southside Sch., 1962-65, Glasgow AFB, Mont., 1965-80; tchr., speech and lang. pathologist Mineral County Sch. Dist., Hawthorne, Nev., 1965-68, 78—; kindergarten tchr. Mineral County Sch. Dist., Mina, Nev., 1968-72; elem. tchr. Mineral County Sch. Dist., Mina, 1978-80; speech, language pathologist Mineral County Sch. Dist., Mina, Republic of Korea, 1980—; tchr. Dept. Def., Pusan, Republic of Korea, 1972-73, Illesheim, Fed. Republic Germany, 1973-78; tchr. Mohall (N.D.) Pub. Sch., 1964-65; cons. Mary Kay Cosmetics, tchr. Glasgow Air Force Base, 1965-68. Supt. Sunday sch. Bethany Luth. Ch., Hawthorne, 1987—; sec. Ladies Aid, 1987-68. Mem. NEA, Nev. Edn. Assn., AAUW (past sec., pres.), Pair O Dice Square Dance Club (sec. 1989—), Delta Kappa Gamma. Avocations: square and round dancing, photography. Home: PO Box 816 Hawthorne NV 89415-0816 Office: Mineral County Sch Dist A St Hawthorne NV 89415

SORTOR, HAROLD EDWARD, financial executive; b. Craig, Nebr., Jan. 18, 1925; s. Harold E. and Ruth (Oldham) S.; m. Dorothy M. Johnson, Oct. 9, 1954; 1 child, Georgia Lynn. B.S., U. Ill., 1949, J.D., 1950. Bar: Ill. bar 1950; C.P.A., Ill. Tax supr. Ernst & Ernst, Chgo., 1950-56; mem. firm McDermott, Will & Emery, Chgo., 1956-59; tax mgr. Amphenol-Borg Electronics Corp. (name changed to Amphenol Corp. 1965), Oak Brook, Ill., 1959-62; asst. controller Amphenol-Borg Electronics Corp. (name changed to Amphenol Corp. 1965), 1962-63, treas., 1963-68; treas. Bunker Ramo Corp., 1968, Montgomery Ward & Co., Chgo., 1968-73; sr. v.p. corporate finance CNA Financial Corp., 1973-75; group v.p. finance Pennzoil Co., 1975-85; lectr. Northwestern U., 1954-59. Mem. Sch. Bd. Dist. 25, Cook County, Ill., 1962-67, pres., 1965-67; bd. dirs. United Charities Chgo., 1971-75, Ill. sect. Am. Cancer Soc., 1972-75. Served with AUS, 1943-46. Mem. AICPA. Home: 11 Little Comfort Rd Savannah GA 31411-1446

SORVINO, PAUL, actor; b. N.Y.C., 1939. Attended, Am. Musical and Dramatic Acad. N.Y.C. stage debut in Bajour, 1964; actor in (plays) including The Baker's Wife, Mating Dance, Skyscraper, That Championship Season, King Lear, An American Millionaire, For My Last Number, We'll Get By, Philemon, (films) including The Gambler, 1970, Where's Poppa, 1970, Panic in Needle Park, 1971, Cry Uncle, Made for Each Other, 1971, The Day of the Dolphin, 1973, A Touch of Class, 1973, I Will, I Will ... For Now, 1976, Oh God!, 1977, The Brink's Job, 1978, Shoot It, Black, Shoot It, Blue, Slow Dancing in the Big City, 1978, The Bloodbrothers, 1979, Lost and Found, 1979, Cruising, 1980, Reds, 1981, That Championship Season, 1982, I, The Jury, 1982, Off the Wall, Turk 182, A Fine Mess, 1985, The Stuff, 1986, Vasectomy, 1986, Dick Tracy, 1990, Good Fellas, 1990, The Firm, 1993, (TV miniseries) Seventh Avenue, 1977, (TV films) including Tell Me Where it Hurts, 1974, It Couldn't Happen to a Nicer Guy, 1974, A Dummy, 1979, A Question of Honor, 1982, Chiefs, 1983, My Mother's Secret Life, 1984, With Intent to Kill, 1984, Surviving, 1985, Betrayed by Innocence, 1986, Don't Touch My Daughter, 1991, Perry Mason: The Case of the Wicked Wives, 1993, Parallel Lives, 1994; star (TV series) We'll Get

By, 1975, Bert D'Angelo/Superstar, 1976, The Oldest Rookie, 1987, Law and Order, 1991-92, Star Trek: The Next Generation (guest appearance), 1994; artistic dir. Am. Stage Co., Teaneck, N.J.; dir., star: All the Kings Men; dir. Two for the Seesaw, The Rainmaker, 1986. Office: C/O William Morris Agency 151 El Camino Beverly Hills CA 90212*

SORVOJA, MARKKU, banker, accountant; b. Ylivieska, Finland, Oct. 23, 1955; came to U.S., 1957; s. Martti and Signe Helena (Valli) S. BBA, U. Alaska, 1984. CPA, Alaska. Auditor, acct. KMG-Main Hurdman, Fairbanks, Alaska, 1985-86; loan rev. officer Nat. Bank Alaska, Anchorage, 1986-87, tax analyst, 1987—; bd. dirs., sec. Sorvoja Corp., Fairbanks. Republican. Lutheran. Avocations: bowling, photography, travel. Home: 222 W 13th Ave Anchorage AK 99501-4470 Office: Nat Bank Alaska 301 W Northern Lights Blvd Anchorage AK 99503-2648

SOSA, ERNEST, philosopher, educator; b. Cardenas, Cuba, June 17, 1940; s. Ernesto and Maria (Garriga) S.; m. Sara Mercedes, Dec. 21, 1961; children: E. David, Adrian J. BA, U. Miami, 1961; MA, U. Pitts., 1962, PhD, 1964. Instr. U. Western Ontario, London, Ontario, Can., 1963-64, U. Pitts., 1964; postdoctoral fellow Brown U., Providence, 1964-66; asst. prof. U. Western Ontario, London, Ontario, Canada, 1966-67; asst. prof. to full prof. Brown U., Providence, 1967-74, chmn. of philosophy, 1977-74, full prof., 1974—; Romeo Elton prof., 1981—; vis. prof. U. Miami, 1970, Nat. U. Mexico, 1979, 80, 81, Harvard U., Cambridge, Mass., 1982. Author: Knowledge in Perspective, 1991; gen. editor book series, Cambridge Univ. Pres., 1990—, Blackwell Publishers, 1991—; contbr. numerous articles to profl. jours. Grantee NSF, 1970-72, Exxon Ednl. Found., 1980-82; recipient Sr. fellowship NEH, 1988-89. Mem. Am. Philos. Assn. (sec.-treas. 1974-82, chair internat. coop. com. 1984-89), Am. Coun. Learned Socs./Soviet Acad. Commn., Internat. Fedn. Philos. Soc. (steering com. mem. 188-89, v.p. 1988-93), Institut Internat. de Philosophie (exec. com. 1993—). Avocations: running, travel. Office: Brown U Providence RI 02912

SOSHNIK, JOSEPH, investment banking consultant; b. Omaha, Feb. 14, 1920; s. Ben Nathan and Clara (Lehman) S.; m. Miriam Saks, June 29, 1941; children—David, Allan (dec.), Robert. B.S.C. summa cum laude, Creighton U., 1941; M.S. (Alfred P. Sloan fellow), U. Denver, 1943; student, U. Colo., 1943-44; Ph.D., U. Nebr., 1952, LHD (hon.), 1988. Instr., asst. prof., asso. prof. Creighton U., 1946-57, auditor, budget cons., 1952-57; with U. Nebr., 1957-71, prof. bus. adminstrn., 1966-71, comptroller, 1957-62, vice chancellor, 1962-68, pres. Lincoln campuses and outstate activities, 1968-71; v.p. Kirkpatrick, Pettis, Smith, Polian, Inc., 1971-73, exec. v.p., 1973-90, chmn. exec. com., 1973-85, also bd. dirs.; investment banking cons. Omaha, 1990—. Contbr. articles to profl. jours. Chmn. Nebr. Commn. Higher Edn. Facilities Act, 1964-71; chmn. Omaha Tomorrow, 1981-82; trustee Nebr. Council Econ. Edn., 1969—, chmn., 1974-75, 83; trustee Nebr. Ednl. TV Council Higher Edn., 1969-71, Omaha Indsl. Found., 1979-91, v.p. 1986-91; trustee U. Nebr. Found., 1978—; mem. higher edn. adv. com. Midwest Regional Conf. Council State Govts., 1963-71; mem. Citizens Adv. Com. Omaha Pub. sch., 1954-57; trustee Lincoln Gen. Hosp. and Lincoln Gen. Hosp. Assn., 1962-71, treas., 1963-67; nat. trustee NCCJ, 1978-83, co-chmn. Midlands exec. bd., 1973-80, bd. govs., 1989—; bd. dirs. Lincoln Hosp. and Health Council, 1962-69, sec. treas., 1962-64; bd. dirs. Lincoln Community Chest, 1963-69, Child Guidance Center, 1960-63, Nebraskans for Pub. TV, 1972-76, Jewish Fedn. Omaha, 1975-78, Father Flanagan's Boys Home, 1978-88, Jr. Achievement Omaha, 1981-83, Met. Arts Council Omaha, 1987—, treas., 1989-93, Nebr. Found. for the Humanities, 1993—; mem. Boys Town Nat. Coun. Friends, 1989—; bd. govs. Omaha Boys' Clubs, 1972-76; mem. Lincoln Found., 1968-71; mem. council bus. execs. Creighton U. Coll. Bus. Adminstrn., 1972-77, chmn., 1973-77; mem. pres.'s council Creighton U., 1973—; trustee Temple Israel, 1973-75, 91-93; mem. citizens assembly United Way Midlands, 1975—; bd. visitors Creighton Inst. Bus., Law and Social Research, 1976-78; mem. pres.'s adv. council U. Nebr., 1977-87; mem. Nebr. Com. for Higher Edn., 1978—; treas., mem. exec. com. St. Joseph Health Care Found., 1982-84; chmn. Leadership Omaha, 1986-88. Served with USNR, 1943-46. Recipient Bus. Leadership award Alumni Assn. U. Nebr., Spl. Charter award Nebr. Council Econ. Edn., Disting. Svc. award; John P. Begley award Creighton U., Alumni Achievement citation Creighton U., Alumni Merit award Creighton U. Mem. Nebr. Assn. Commerce and Industry (dir. 1982-88), Am. Council Edn., Nat. Assn. State Univs. and Land-Grant Colls. (senate joint com. bus. officers 1959-66), Nat. Assn. Coll. and Univ. Bus. Officers, Nebr. Securities Industry Assn. (pres. 1986-87), Greater Omaha C. of C. (bd. dirs. 1980-90, dir. emeritus 1991—, v.p. 1986-88, dir. found. 1985—), Innocents Soc., Highland Country Club, Order of Artus, Beta Gamma Sigma, Alpha Sigma Nu, Pi Lambda Phi, Delta Sigma Pi, Delta Sigma Rho. Home: 834 S 112th Plz Omaha NE 68154-3310

SOSNOW, LAWRENCE IRA, health care company executive; b. Newark, Mar. 7, 1935; s. Emanuel and Edith (Grunt) S.; m. Ellen N. Rosenthal, May 30, 1965; children: Peter, Meg. BBA, Upsala Coll., East Orange, N.J., 1957; postgrad., NYU Grad. Sch. Bus., 1958. Pres. Sosnow & Co., Inc., Newark, 1960-66; chmn., pres. Spade & Archer, N.Y.C., 1966-69; chmn. Gilbert Youth Research, N.Y.C., 1968-69; pres. MIND, Inc., N.Y.C., 1969-74; vice chmn. MIND, Inc., 1974-75; chmn. Patient Care Inc., West Orange, N.J., 1975—; dir. Home Health Agy. Assembly of N.J., 1985-88; chmn. I.V. Therapy Products, Inc., 1989-92; mem. N.Y. State Dept. Health Adv. Com. on Licensure, 1985-86, Home Care Assn. N.Y. Legis. Commn., 1992—. Bd. govs. Boy's Athletic League, N.Y.C., 1969-85, United Cerebral Palsy No. N.J., 1983-86, McBurney Sch., 1985-86. Served with AUS, 1957, 61-62. Mem. Nat. Assn. Home Care (dir. 1979-82). Home: 850 Park Ave New York NY 10021-1845 Office: 100 Executive Dr West Orange NJ 07052

SOSSAMAN, JAMES J., state legislator; b. Phoenix, July 17, 1932; s. Jasper H. and Faith Carolyn (Mather) S.; m. Carolyn Sue Peters, Dec. 12, 1953; children—Kimberlee, Stephen, Scott. Student, Ariz. State U., 1950-52. Mem. Ariz. Ho. of Reps., 1969-87, majority whip, 1976-84, speaker, 1985-87, senator, 1987-93. Precinct committeeman, 1959—; mem. Queen Creek Sch. Bd., 1965-80. Lt. USN, 1952-56, Korea. Recipient Outstanding Young Farmer award Flying Farmers, 1966, Legislator of Yr. award Ariz. Students' Assn., 1977, 78, Disting. Citizen award U. Ariz., 1979, hon. state farmer degree Future Farmers Am., 1980. Mem. Am. Legis. Exchange Council, Western Conf. Council State Govts., Maricopa County Farm Bur. (pres.), Ariz. Cotton Growers Bd. (agriculturalist for 1985). Republican. Methodist. Home: 19105 E Ocotillo Rd Queen Creek AZ 85242-4077

SOSTEK, EDWARD LEON, theater educator, director; b. Boston, Oct. 9, 1926; s. David and Augusta Janet (Berman) S.; m. Antoinette Hurwitz, Feb. 11, 1962; children: Brian David, Hilary. B.A., Tufts U., 1951, M.A., 1961; Ph.D., U. Iowa, 1976. Actor, technician Cleve. Playhouse, 1951-55; mem. faculty dept. English Carleton Coll., Northfield, Minn., 1969—; prof. Carleton Coll., 1982—; actor, dir., stage mgr. summer stock theatres, N.Y., Ohio, Md., Mass., Mo. and Pa., 1951-63; dir. New Ulm Heritagefest, Minn., 1976-77, Original Opera, Northfield, 1982; tenure cons. U. Minn.-Morris, 1983, 87, St. Olaf Coll., Northfield, 1984. Served with USN, 1944-46, ETO and PTO. Mem. Assn. Theatre in Higher Edn., Actors Equity Assn. Jewish. Avocations: squash; sailing; racquetball; running. Home: 200 Maple St Northfield MN 55057-2337 Office: Carleton Coll 1 N College St Northfield MN 55057-4001

SOSTILIO, ROBERT FRANCIS, office equipment marketing executive; b. Boston, Nov. 17, 1942; s. Natale J. and Louise (Caruso) S.; m. Gail Marie McGuinness, Apr. 17, 1966. Student, U. Maine 1960-61, Broward Jr. Coll., Ft. Lauderdale, 1967-70, Miami-Dade Jr. Coll., 1979. Product assurance engr. Saxon Copystatics, Miami, Fla., 1970-77; internat. svc. mgr. Saxon Export Corp., Miami, 1977-80; nat. svc. mgr. Cybernet Internat., Warren, N.J., 1980-81; mgr. nat. copier svc. Monroe Systems for Bus., Morris Plains, N.J., 1981-82; nat. OEM mgr. Panasonic Indsl. Co., Secaucus, N.J., 1982-86; assoc. dir. copier rsch. Dataquest, San Jose, Calif., 1987-90; mgr. product program Ricoh Corp., West Caldwell, N.J., 1986-87, dir. copier mktg., 1990-94, dir. strategic planning, 1994—. Editor newsletter Multifunctionality, 1987, Color Copiers, 1989. Block capt. Meadow Ridge Civic Assn., Basking Ridge, N.J., 1985-87; sgt.-at-arms UNICO Nat., San Jose, 1990. With USN, 1964-67. Roman Catholic. Avocations: woodworking, home remodeling, dog training, travel, cooking. Office: Ricoh Corp 5 Dedrick Pl West Caldwell NJ 07006-6304

SOTER, GEORGE NICHOLAS, advertising executive; b. Chgo., May 16, 1924; s. Nicholas A. and Emily (Damascus) S.; m. Effie Hartocollis, Feb. 7, 1949; children: Nicholas, Thomas, Peter. Student, U. Chgo., 1947-51. Writer McCann-Erickson, Chgo., 1951-53; with Needham, Louis & Brorby, Chgo., 1954-62; v.p., creative dir. Needham, Louis & Brorby, N.Y.C., 1958-62; v.p., assoc. creative dir. Lennen & Newell Inc., N.Y.C., 1962-67; v.p., co-dir. creative svcs., mgmt. supr. Kenyon & Eckhardt Inc., N.Y.C., 1968-73; exec. v.p., creative dir. Pampuzac-Soter Assocs. Inc., N.Y.C., 1974-76; sr. writer Marsteller Inc., N.Y.C., 1980-82; v.p.; creative Lord, Geller, Federico, Einstein, Inc., N.Y.C., 1982-87; sr. v.p., creative dir. Great Scott Advt. Co. Inc., N.Y.C., 1987-93; dir. Soter Advt. & Mktg. Consulting Svcs., N.Y.C., 1993—; founder, pres. Greek Island Ltd., N.Y.C., 1963—; dir. Interpub. Product Devel. Workshop, N.Y.C., 1967. With U.S. Army, 1943-47, ETO. Home: 404 Riverside Dr New York NY 10025-1861

SOTH, LAUREN, art history educator; b. Seattle, Nov. 29, 1934; s. Phillip Sullivan and Bernice Augusta (Freiberg) S.; m. Nancy Britton, Sept. 19, 1957; children: Christopher Britton, Andrew Lauren. BA, Yale U., 1956; MA in Fine Arts, NYU, 1962, PhD in Fine Arts, 1970. From instr. to prof. art history Carleton Coll., Northfield, Minn., 1964—. Contbr. articles to profl. jours. and mags. Office: Carleton Coll 1 N College St Northfield MN 55057

SOTIR, THOMAS ALFRED, healthcare executive, retired shipbuilder; b. Marlboro, Mass., July 8, 1936; s. Nisi and Pauline Violet (Theodore) S.; m. Sandra Losano, Oct. 2, 1960; children: Laura Jean, Mark Joseph, Christine Marie. BS in Indsl. Engring., Northeastern U., 1959; MBA, Xavier U., Cin., 1966. Employee rels. generalist GE, Cin., 1959-66, mgr. incoming materials, 1966-67, mgr. adminstrn., 1967-68, mgr. employee rels., Arkansas City, Kans., 1968-71, mgr. grievance negotiations, Lynn, Mass., 1971-77; with Electric Boat div. Gen. Dynamics Corp., Groton, Conn., 1977-91, dir. labor rels., 1977-79, v.p. human resources, 1979-89, dir. total quality mgmt., 1989-91; cons. human resources R.A. Flath Assocs., New London, Conn., 1991-92; v.p. human resources Kennebec Health System, Augusta, Maine, 1992—; mem. faculty U. New Haven Bus. Sch., 1979-91; adv. panel job evaluation State of Conn., 1985-91. Trustee, exec. com. Thames Sci. Ctr., New London, Conn., 1987-89; bd. dirs. United Way, Groton, 1979-87. Capt. USAR, 1959-69. Mem. Shipbuilders Coun. Am. (chmn. indsl. rels. com. Washington chpt. 1987-88), Kennebec Valley C. of C. (bd. dirs.), Rotary. Republican. Roman Catholic. Avocations: hunting, fishing, cooking. Home: 21 Sewall St Augusta ME 04330-5531

SOTIRHOS, MICHAEL, ambassador; b. N.Y.C., Nov. 12, 1928; m. Estelle Manos; 2 children. B.B.A., CCNY, 1950. Ptnr. Ariston Sales Co., Ltd., 1948, founder, chmn., 1958—; chmn. bd. Ariston Interior Designers, Inc., 1973-85; U.S. amb. to Jamaica, 1985-89; U.S. amb. to Greece Athens, 1989-93; bd. dirs. Atlantic Bank of N.Y., Alexander S. Onassis Found.; cons. various internat. shipping & pharm. firms. Former mem. Nat. Vol. Service Adv. Council; former chmn. Internat. Ops. Com., Peace Corps; mem. nat. adv. council SBA, 1976; former chmn. Nat. Republican Heritage Groups Council. Decorated comdr. Order of Distinction (Jamaica); recipient Man of Yr. award Nat. Rep. Heritage Groups Coun.

SOTIRIOS OF TORONTO See ATHANASSOULAS, SOTIRIOS

SOTO, JOCK, dancer; b. Gallup, N.M., 1965. Student, Phoenix Sch. Nallet, Sch. Am. Ballet. Mem. corps de ballet N.Y.C. Ballet, 1981-84, soloist, 1984-85, prin. dancer, 1985—. Appeared in The Magic Flute, 1981, Bagaku, The Nutcracker, Mozartiana, Rubies, Symphony in C, The Four Temperaments, Western Symphony, Stravinsky Violin Concerto, Symphony in Three Movements, Cortege Hongrois, Liebeslieder Walzer, A Midsummer Night's Dream, Brahms/Handel, Glass Pieces, Moves, The Four Seasons, In The Night, Opus 19/The Dreamer, I'm Old Fashioned, Delibes Divertissement, A Schubertiad, Concerto for Two Solo Pianos, Celebration, Allegro Brillante, A Schubert Sonata, X-Ray; N.Y.C. Ballet's Balanchine Celebration, 1993. Office: NYC Ballet NY State Theater Lincoln Ctr Plz New York NY 10023*

SOTO, RAMONA, training specialist; b. East Chicago, Ind., Apr. 14, 1963; d. Robert Rudy and Antonia (Perez) S. Student, Purdue U., 1982-86, U. Ill., Chgo., 1990, DePaul U., 1990—. Salesperson The Gap, Inc., Ind., 1979-84; asst. mgr. The Gap, Inc., Ind. and Ill., 1984-88; tng. mgr. The Gap, Inc., Ill., 1988-90; tng. specialist Montgomery Ward & Co., Ill., 1990-93; temp. worker The Richard Michael Group, Chgo., 1993, Resort Travel Corp, Oakbrook Terrace, Ill., 1993; ind. tng. cons. Chgo., 1994—; tutor tng. mgr. The Cabrini Green Tutoring Program, Chgo., 1991—; Preparing an Attitude for Learning, Leadership and Success, 1992—. Mem. ASTD. Avocations: fitness, reading, tutoring, biking. Home: 3550 N Lake Shore Dr Chicago IL 60657-1916

SOTOMAYOR, SONIA, federal judge; b. N.Y.C., June 25, 1954; d. Juan Luis and Celina (Baez) S.; m. Kevin Edward Noonan, Aug. 14, 1976 (div. 1983). AB, Princeton (N.J.) U., 1976; JD, Yale U., 1979. Bar: N.Y. 1980, U.S. Dist. Ct. (ea. and so. dists.) N.Y. 1984. Asst. dist. atty. Office of Dist. Atty. County of N.Y., N.Y.C., 1979-84; assoc., ptnr. Pavia & Harcourt, N.Y.C., 1984-92; fed. judge U.S. Dist. Ct. (so. dist.) N.Y., N.Y.C., 1992—. Editor Yale U. Law Rev., 1979. Bd. dirs. P.R. Legal Def. and Edn. Fund, N.Y.C., 1980-92, State of N.Y. Mortgage Agy., N.Y.C., 1987-92, N.Y.C. Campaign Fin. Bd., 1988-92; mem. State Adv. Panel on Inter-Group Rels., N.Y.C., 1990-91. Mem. Phi Beta Kappa. Office: US Courthouse Foley Sq New York NY 10007

SOTT, HERBERT, lawyer; b. Detroit, Jan. 26, 1920; s. Harry and E. Helen (Nalven) S.; m. Elaine D. Davidson, Oct. 14, 1987; children by previous marriage; Lesley Sott Geary, Lynne Sott Jackson. A.B., U. Mich., 1940, M.B.A., 1942, J.D. with distinction, 1943. Bar: Mich. 1946. Since practiced in Detroit; ptnr. Friedman, Meyers & Keys, 1951-68; partner Barris, Sott, Denn & Driker, 1968—. Active Founders Soc. Detroit Inst. Arts, Detroit Grand Opera Assn., Detroit Symphony Assn., Detroit Zool. Assn.; bd. dirs. Detroit Symphony Orch., Mich. Heart Assn., Mich. Cancer Found., Jewish Home for Aged, Jewish Family and Children's Service, Jewish Vocat. Service. Served as lt. (j.g.) USNR, 1943-46. Mem. Detroit, Mich., Am. bar assns. Clubs: Detroit, Franklin Hills. Office: Barris Sott Denn & Driker 15th Flr 211 W Fort St Fl 15 Detroit MI 48226-3202

SOTTILE, BENJAMIN JOSEPH, greeting card company executive; b. Bklyn., 1937; s. John and Nicoletta Sottile; m. Ileana Nardone; children: John, Robert. BSEE, U.S. Naval Acad., 1961. With Colgate Palmolive, 1965-68, Vick Chem. co., 1968-69, Warner Lambert, 1969-80, Warner Communications, Inc., 1980-83; sr. v.p. Revlon, Inc., 1983-86; pres., chief operating officer Gibson Greetings, Inc., Cin., 1986, pres. chief exec. officer, 1987, chief exec. officer, pres., chmn. bd., 1989—; also bd. dirs.; bd. dirs. Decker Communications, San Francisco. Bd. govs. USO, Washington, 1989—. Lt. USN, 1961-65. Mem. Nat. Assn. Chain Drug Stores (adv. bd.). Office: Gibson Greetings Inc 2100 Section Rd Cincinnati OH 45237-3510

SOTTILE, JAMES, financier; b. Charleston, S.C, Oct. 19, 1913; s. James and Louise (Mohlman) S.; m. Ethel Hooks, June 16, 1936; children: Linda Sottile Hammond, James (dec.), Suzanne Sottile Guanci, Jeanne Sottile Walsh, John. Pres., dir. Canaveral Indian River Groves, Inc., 1962-70; pres., dir. Indian River Orange Groves, Inc., 1959-68, chmn. bd., 1968-73; pres., dir. Gulfstream Groves, Inc., 1962-65; pres. Lake Byrd Citrus Packing Co.; pres., dir. Valencia Ctr., Inc.; chmn. bd. dirs. Goldfield Corp., Goldfield Consol. Mines Co., S.E. Power Co., St. Cloud Mining Co., Fla. Transport Corp. Trustee U. Miami, 1956-66. Mem. Fla. C. of C. (dir. at large), Country Club Coral Gables, Riviera Country Club, Eau Gallie Yacht Club (Melbourne, Fla.), K.C., Rotary. Home: 2525 Indian Mound Trl Miami FL 33134-5526 Office: Goldfield Corp 100 Rialto Pl Ste 500 Melbourne FL 32901-3082

SOUCY, ROBERT JOSEPH, history educator; b. Topeka, June 25, 1933; s. William Joseph and Bernice Winefred (Riley) S.; m. Barbara Stone, May 10, 1960 (div. 1979); children: Anne Marie, Alissa Bernice; m. Sharon Fairchild, Jan. 2, 1986. AB, Washburn U., 1955; MA, Kans U., 1956; student, U. Dijon, France, 1956-57; PhD, U. Wis., 1963. Instr. Harvard U., Cambridge,

Mass., 1963-64; asst. prof. Kent (Ohio) State U., 1964-66; assoc. prof. Oberlin (Ohio) Coll., 1966-69, prof., 1969—. Author: Fascism in France, 1972, Fascist Intellectual, 1979, French Fascism, 1924-33, 1986, French Fascism, 1933-39, 1995; mem. editl. bd. French Hist. Studies, 1986-88. 1st lt. USAF, 1957-60. Fullbright scholar, 1956-57; grantee NEH, 1969, 88, ACLS, 1969, 89, Am. Philos. Soc., 1969, 73. Mem. Am. Hist. Soc., French Hist. Soc. (mem. editorial bd. 1986-88). Avocations: tennis, squash. Home: 143 E College St Oberlin OH 44074-1774 Office: Oberlin Coll Dept History W College St Oberlin OH 44074

SOUDER, MARK EDWARD, government official; b. Ft. Wayne, Ind., July 18, 1950; s. Edward Getz and Irma (Fahling) S.; B.S., Ind. U., Ft. Wayne, 1972; M.B.A., U. Notre Dame, 1974; m. Diane Kay Zimmer, July 28; children—Brooke Diane, Nathan Elias. Mgmt. trainee Crossroads Furniture Co., Houston, 1974; mktg. mgr. Gabberts Furniture & Studio, Mpls., 1974-76; mktg. mgr., exec. v.p. Souder's Furniture & Studio, Grabill, Ind., 1976-80, pres., 1981-84; econ. devel. liaison for U.S. Rep. Dan Coats, 1983—; U.S. congressman, Ind. 4th Dist., 1995— . Publicity chmn. Grabill County Fair, 1977—; advisor Dan Coats for Congress Com., 1980-81; mem. Ind. Area Devel. Council; mem. bus. alumni adv. com. Ind. U.-Ft. Wayne. Mem. Midwest Home Furnishings Assn. (dir. 1976-84, past treas., exec. v.p.), Ft. Wayne, Grabill chambers commerce, Allen County Hist. Soc., Alumni Assn. Ind. U. at Ft. Wayne (dir., past pres.), Alumni Assn. U. Notre Dame. Republican. Mem. Apostolic Christian Ch. Home: 13733 Ridgeview Ct Grabill IN 46741 Office: US House Reps 1513 Longworth House Office Bldg Washington DC 20515-1404

SOUDER, ROBERT R., personnel director; b. Sellersville, Pa., Mar. 7, 1940; s. Robert and Francis S.; m. Joan A. Swartley, July 14, 1962; children: Jennifer, Amy. AB in English Lit., Colgate U., 1962. Personnel mgr. Acme Markets, Phila., 1962-69; sr. v.p. personnel Rite Aid Corp., Harrisburg, Pa., 1969—. Pres. Ams. for Competitive Enterprise, Harrisburg, 1988; bd. dirs. Family & Children's Services, Harrisburg, 1986-88; active United Way, Harrisburg, 1978-88. Avocations: skiing, reading, gardening. Office: Rite Aid Corp PO Box 3165 Harrisburg PA 17105

SOUDERS, JAMES P., professional association executive; b. Kansas City, Mo., Mar. 17, 1938; s. Harley Hugh and Mabel V. (Duffels) S.; m. Marianne Geier, June 25, 1959 (div. 1984); children: Suzanne Baldwin, Andrew, Matthew, Christopher. BSBA, Rockhurst Coll., 1959. Commd. officer U.S. Marine Corps., 1959-79; asst. exec. dir. Assn. Records, Mgrs., Adminstrs., Prairie Village, Kans., 1979-87; exec. dir. Assn. Records, Mgrs., Adminstrs., Prarie Village, Kans., 1987—. Lt. col. USMC, 1955-79. Republican. Roman Catholic. Avocations: hunting, fishing. Office: Assoc of Records Managers & Adminstrn 4200 Somerset Ste 215 Prairie Village KS 66208

SOUHAM, GÉRARD, communications executive; b. Paris, May 30, 1928; s. Lucien and Mary-Françoise (Husson) S.; m. Eliane Meyrat, June 23, 1951; children: Glenn (dec.), Yan, Philip. Diploma, Am. Community Sch., Paris, 1948; cert., Ecole Commerciale de Paris. Chargé de mission State Dept., Europe, 1950-52; pub. info. officer Allied Air Forces NATO, Fontainebleau, 1953-55; chmn. bd., chief exec. officer J. Walter Thompson, Paris, 1955-75; v.p. J. Walter Thompson, N.Y.C., 1970-75; prin. SC3 Gerard Souham Group Communication Cos., Paris and Lausanne, Switzerland, 1975—, N.Y.C. 1979—; bd. dirs. Am. Overseas Meml., I.T. Fin., Turner Orodns. S.A., chmn., 1994—; mem. I.T. France, 1994; chmn. bd. Turner Prodn. Europe, 1994; bd. dirs. AVON, France. Author: Général Souham Comte de l'Empire, 1964, Impressions sur..., 1970, Souham, 1989, Sur les Champs de Bataille de la Révolution et de l'Empire, 1990. Mem. pvt. sector internat., pub. rels. coms. USIA, 1984; mem. world bd. govs. USO, Washington, 1984, bd. dirs. Paris coun., 1971, chmn. fundraising com., 1989—. Decorated Knight of Legion of Honor (France); Officer Order of Leopold (Belgium), Knight of Belgian Crown. Mem. Internat. Advt. Assn. (v.p. pub. svc., bd. dirs.), Internat. Inst. Strategic Studies London, France, USA (bd. dirs.), Am. Overseas Meml. Assn. (bd. dirs. 1988—). Roman Catholic. Clubs: HM Guards Polo (Windsor, Eng.) (life); Polo de Bagatelle (Paris); N.Y. Athletic; Yacht of Monaco. Avocation: collecting fine bindings. Office: Souham Group Comm 500 Fifth Ave New York NY 10109-0995

SOULE, CHARLES EVERETT, insurance executive; b. Middleboro, Mass., June 7, 1934; s. Albert Foster and Alberta Nancy (Soule) S.; m. Elna Louise Eayrs, Sept. 4, 1955; children: Kimberly, Charles, Jonathan, Peter. BA, Dartmouth Coll., 1956. Underwriter Paul Revere, Worcester, Mass., 1956-68; 2d v.p. Paul Revere, Worcester, 1968-72, v.p., 1972-78, sr. v.p., 1978-84, exec. v.p., 1984-91; pres., CEO Paul Revere Corp., Worcester, Paul Revere Life Ins. Co., Worcester, Paul Revere Protective Life Ins. Co., Worcester, Paul Revere Variable Annuity Ins. Co., Worcester, 1991—; bd. dirs. New Eng. Electric System, Westboro, Mass. Author: Disability Income Insurance-The Unique Risk, 1984, 2d edit., 1989, 3d edit., 1994. Bd. dirs. Worcester Bus. Devel. Corp., 1988—, Worcester Found. for Exptl. Biology, Shrewsbury, Mass., 1992—; chmn. Worcester C. of C., 1987-88. Fellow Life Office Mgmt. Assn. Republican. Avocations: reading, running. Home: 50 Oneil Dr Westboro MA 01581-3008 Office: Paul Revere Corp 18 Chestnut St Worcester MA 01608-1528

SOULE, GARDNER BOSWORTH, writer; b. Paris, Tex., Dec. 16, 1913; s. Edgar Huckabee and Floy DeVore (Perfect) S.; m. Janie Lee McDowell, Sept. 20, 1940 (dec.); m. Mary Muir Downing, Apr. 23, 1994. B.A., Rice Inst., 1933; B.S., Columbia U., 1935, M.S., 1936. With A.P., N.Y.C., 1936-41, Newspaper PM, 1942; mng. editor Better Homes and Gardens, Des Moines, 1946-50. Free-lance writer articles, books, N.Y.C., 1950—; Author: The Maybe Monsters, 1963, Tomorrow's World of Science, 1963, Gemini and Apollo, 1964, The Mystery Monsters, 1965, Trail of the Abominable Snowman, 1966, The Ocean Adventure: Science Explores the Depths of the Sea, 1966, Sea Rescue, 1966, UFO's and IFO's, 1967, Undersea Frontiers, 1968, Under the Sea, 1969, Strange Things Animals Do, 1970, Wide Ocean, 1970, The Greatest Depths, 1970, Surprising Facts, 1971, New Discoveries in Oceanography, 1974, Wide Ocean, Brit. edit, 1974, Remarkable Creatures of the Seas, 1975, Men Who Dared The Sea: The Ocean Adventures of the Ancient Mariners, 1976, German edit., 1978, The Long Trail: How Cowboys and Longhorns Opened The West, 1976, Mystery Monsters of the Deep, 1981, Mystery Creatures of the Jungle, 1982, Antarctica, 1985, Christopher Columbus, 1988; Contbr.: articles to mags. including Boys' Life. Served to lt. USNR, 1943-46. Mem. Authors League, Columbia University Club (N.Y.C.), Sigma Delta Chi, Sigma Nu. Address: 517 W 113th St New York NY 10025-8078

SOULE, GEORGE ALAN, literature educator; b. Fargo, N.D., Mar. 3, 1930; s. George Alan and Ruth Georgia (Knudsen) S.; m. Carolyn Richards, Nov. 24, 1961; 1 child, Katherine. BA, Carleton Coll., 1947; postgrad., Corpus Christi Coll., Cambridge (Eng.) U., 1952-53; MA, Yale U., 1956, PhD, 1960. Instr. English lit. Oberlin (Ohio) Coll., 1958-60; asst. prof. U. Wis., Madison, 1960-62; from asst. prof. to prof. Carleton Coll., Northfield, Minn., 1962-95, prof. emeritus, 1995—; dir. Centennial, 1965-67; chair English dept. Carleton Coll., Northfield, 1980-83; dir. summer writing program Carleton Coll., Northfield, Minn., 1980-86; cons. Ednl. Testing Svc., Princeton, N.J., 1967-84, 94—. Editor (book) Theatre of the Mind, 1974; contbr. articles, revs. to profl. jours. With U.S. Army, 1954-55. Internat. fellow Rotary, 1952-53, Sterling pre-doctoral fellow Yale U., 1957-58. Mem. Johnson Soc. of Lichfield, Boswell Soc. of Auchinleck, Friends of Dove Cottage, The Charles Lamb Soc., Rotary. Episcopalian. Avocations: cooking, traveling, Jeopardy (Champion Sr. Tournament 1990). Home: 313 Nevada St Northfield MN 55057-2346 Office: Carleton Coll 1 N College St Northfield MN 55057-4001

SOULE, SALLIE THOMPSON, retired state official; b. Detroit, May 13, 1928; d. Hayward Stone and Elizabeth Robinson Thompson; A.B., Smith Coll., 1950; M.A., U. Vt., Burlington, 1952; m. Gardner Northup Soule, July 26. 1958; stepchildren: Gardner Northup, Nancy Soule Brown; children: Sarah Goodwin, Trumbull Dickson. Sec. trade sales dept. Macmillan Pub. Co., N.Y.C., 1952-57; tech. writer sales svc. div. Eastman Kodak Co., Rochester, N.Y., 1957-58; feature writer Brighton-Pittsford Post, Pittsford, N.Y., 1958-68; v.p., gen. mgr. F. H. Horsford Nursery, Inc., Charlotte, Vt., 1968-76; prin., pres. Bygone Books, Inc., Burlington, Vt., 1978—; mem. Vt. Ho. of Reps., 1976-80, mem. ways and means com., 1976-80; mem. Vt. Senate, 1980-84, mem. appropriation com., energy and natural resources

com. 1980-84; commr. Vt. Dept. Employment and Tng., Montpelier, 1985-88; chmn. Vt. Employment Security Bd., 1985-88.

SOURAPAS, STEVE JAMES, manufacturing executive; b. Seattle, Mar. 20, 1935; s. James and Angelika (Stavrou) S.; children: Angela, Alicia. Salesman Northwest Bottling Co., Seattle, 1958-61, sales supr., 1961-68, sales mgr., 1968-77, pres., gen. mgr., 1977—. Served with U.S. Army, 1956-57. Mem. Nat. Assn. Can. Dry Franchise Bottlers (pres. 1987—, bd. dirs.), Royal Crown Bottlers Assn. (bd. dirs 1984—), Dr. Pepper Bottlers Assn. (state rep 1983—), Wash. Soft Drink Assn. (pres. 1987—, bd. dirs.), Assn. of Wash. Bus., Com. for Litter Control and Recycling, Seattle C. of C., Tacoma C. of C. Republican. Greek Orthodox. Avocations: antique advertising. Office: Northwest Beverages 8462 S 190th St Kent WA 98031-1200

SOURES, JOHN M., physicist, researcher; b. Galatz, Romania, Jan. 2, 1943; came to U.S., 1954; s. Michael (Petrakis) and Dia (Petrakis) S.; m. Diana Carrousos, June 29, 1969; children: Mandy M., Nicholas J., Eleni C., Alexander J., Sophia A. BS in Physics, U. Rochester, 1965, PhD in Mech. and Aerospace Scis., 1970. Rsch. assoc. Lab. for Laser Energetics, Rochester, N.Y., 1970-72, sr. scientist, 1972—, group leader, 1976-81, div. dir., 1979—, deputy dir., 1983—; cons. Oak Ridge (Tenn.) Nat. Lab., 1970-71, Lawrence Livermore (Calif.) Nat. Lab., 1988-90. Contbr. articles to profl. jours. Treas., v.p. Greek Orthodox Ch. of Annunciation, Rochester, 1990-92. Recipient APS Divsn. of Plasma Physics award for Excellence in Plasma Rsch., 1993; NASA trainee, 1967-69. Fellow Am. Phys. Soc. (conf. chmn. 1986, 94), Optical Soc. Am. (conf. organizer 1984-86, 92-93). Republican. Orthodox. Achievements include co-invention of the laser beam smoothing system and a Nd: glass amplifier system. Home: 146 E Brook Rd Pittsford NY 14534 Office: Lab for Laser Energetics 250 E River Rd Rochester NY 14623

SOURKES, THEODORE LIONEL, biochemistry educator; b. Montreal, Que., Can., Feb. 21, 1919; s. Irving and Fannie (Golt) S.; m. Shena Rosenblatt, Jan. 17, 1943; children: Barbara, Myra. B.Sc., McGill U., 1939, M.Sc. magna cum laude, 1946; Ph.D., Cornell U., 1948; D.U. honoris causa, U. Ottawa, Can., 1990. Asst. prof. pharmacology Georgetown U. Med. Sch., 1948-50; research assoc. dept. enzyme chemistry Merck Inst. Therapeutic Research, Rahway, N.J., 1950-53; sr. research biochemist Allan Meml. Inst., Montreal, 1953-65; dir. lab. neurochemistry Allan Meml. Inst. Psychiatry, 1965—; mem. faculty McGill U., Montreal, 1954—; prof. biochemistry McGill U., 1965—, prof. psychiatry, assoc. dean of medicine for research Faculty Medicine, 1972-75; prof. pharmacology, 1990—, emeritus, 1991; Mem. Que. Med. Research Council, 1971-77; sr. fellow Parkinson's Disease Found., N.Y.C., 1963-66; assoc. mem. McGill Ctr. for Medicine, Ethics and Law, 1991. Author: Biochemistry of Mental Disease, 1962, Nobel Prize Winners in Medicine and Physiology, 1901-1965, 1967. Decorated Officer Order of Canada. Fellow Royal Soc. Can.; mem. Canadian Biochem. Soc., Pharmacol. Soc. Can., Canadian Coll. Neuropsychopharmacology (Heinz Lehmann award 1982, medal 1990), Am. Soc. Biol. Chemists, Am. Soc. Pharmacology and Exptl. Therapeutics, Am. Soc. Neurochemistry, Internat. Soc. Neurochemistry, Internat. Brain Research Orgn., Venezuelan Order Andrés Bello, Sigma Xi. Research and publs. on drugs for treatment high blood pressure; 1st basic research on methyldopa; elucidation of role of dopamine and other monamines in nervous system; first trials of L-dopa in Parkinson's disease, biochemistry of mental depression, pathways of stress in the nervous system, imaging serotonin in brain, history of biochemistry. Home: 3033 Sherbrooke St W #303, Montreal, PQ Canada H3Z 1A3

SOURS, JAMES KINGSLEY, association executive, former college president; b. Corydon, Iowa, Sept. 16, 1925; s. James N. and Virginia (Kantor) S.; m. Alice Hyde, July 11, 1947; children—James W., Mary Jan. David Bryan. Student, Phillips U., 1943; B.A., U. Wichita, 1949; M.P.A. (Administration fellow 1949-51), Harvard, 1951, Ph.D., 1954. Adminstrv. aid City Mgr.'s Office, Wichita, 1947-49; mem. faculty U. Wichita, 1951-65; prof. polit. sci., head dept., 1958-62; dean Fairmount Coll. Arts and Scis., 1962-65; chmn. Fairmount Coll. Arts and Scis. (Center Urban Studies), 1957-63; pres. So. Oreg. State Coll., Ashland, 1969-79; ednl. cons. Dankook U., Seoul, 1979-80, dir. Inst. Asian Studies and Cultures, 1990—; ednl. cons. Korean Ministry Edn., 1979-80; exec. v.p. Am. Coll. Testing Program, Iowa City, 1965-68; vis. prof. polit. sci. U. Istanbul, Turkey, 1968-69; vis. prof. Dankook U., Seoul, Korea, 1976, 79-80; dir. devel. Oreg. Shakespearean Festival Assn., 1980-85; v.p., bd. dirs. Dankook U. Am., 1990—; bd. dirs. Oreg. Partnership for Internat. Edn., Internat. Wildlife Recovery Ctr., Eagle Point, Oreg., Rogue Valley Manor Found.; chmn. bd. dirs. Aletheia Psycho-Phys. Found., 1988—. Author: series Some Observations on the Management of Large Cities, 1957; also numerous articles. V.p. NCAA, 1959-64; founding pres. Urban League Wichita, 1953-56, Wichita City Commn. Human Rels., 1962; trustee Carpenter Found., 1983-87, v.p., 1984-87; chmn. Sedgwick County chpt. ARC, 1964, Jackson County chpt., 1973-75; bd. dirs. So. Oreg. Hist. Soc., 1987-89; mem. Oreg. Am. Revolution Bicentennial Commn., 1972-76; chmn. com. nursing edn. Wesley Med. Ctr., Wichita, 1962-64; chmn. bd. dirs. Aletheia Found., 1988—. Served with USNR, 1943-46. Democrat. Unitarian. Home: 3100 Payne Rd Medford OR 97504-9407

SOUTAR, CHARLES FREDERICK, utilities executive; b. N.Y.C., 1936. BCE, Poly. Inst. Bklyn., 1958, MCE, 1965. Engr. Consol. Edison N.Y., N.Y.C., 1958-75, asst. pres., 1975-77, v.p. ops. services, 1977-80, sr. v.p. constrn. engring. environ. affairs, 1980-85, exec. v.p. com. services, 1985—. Office: Consol Edison Co NY Inc 4 Irving Pl New York NY 10003-3502

SOUTAS-LITTLE, ROBERT WILLIAM, mechanical engineer, educator; b. Oklahoma City, Feb. 25, 1933; s. Harry Glenn and Mary Evelyn (Miller) Little; m. Patricia Soutas, Sept. 3, 1982; children: Deborah, Catherine, Colleen, Jennifer, Karen. B.S. in Mech. Engring, Duke U., 1955; M.S., U. Wis., 1959, Ph.D., 1962. Design engr. Allis Chalmers Mfg. Co., Milw., 1955-57; instr. mech. engring. Marquette U., 1957-59; instr. U. Wis., Madison, 1959-62; asst. prof. U. Wis., 1962-63, Okla. State U., 1963-65; prof. Mich. State U., 1965—, chmn. dept. mech. engring., 1972-77, chmn. dept. biomechanics, 1977-90; dir. biomechanics evaluation lab., 1989—; cons. A. C. Electronics Co., Ford Motor Co., CBS Research Lab., B. F. Goodrich Co.; lectr. AID, India, 1965. Author: Elasticity, 1973; Contbr. articles to profl. jours. Vice pres. Okemos (Mich.) Sch. Bd., 1967-72; mem. Meridian Twp. (Mich.) Charter Commn., 1969-70, Meridian Twp. Zoning Bd. Appeals, 1969-71. NSF grantee, 1964-69, 79; recipient award for excellence in instrn. engring. students Western Electric Co., 1970-71; NIH grantee, 1973-75, 79—. Mem. Soc. Engring. Sci., ASME, Am. Soc. Biomechanics, Internat. Soc. Biomechanics, Sigma Xi, Pi Tau Sigma, Tau Beta Pi. Home: 2402 Hulett Rd Okemos MI 48864-2512 Office: Mich State U Dept Matls Sci Mechani East Lansing MI 48824

SOUTER, DAVID HACKETT, U.S. supreme court justice; b. Melrose, Mass., Sept. 17, 1939; s. Joseph Alexander and Helen Adams (Hackett) S. BA, Harvard U., 1961, LLB, 1966; Rhodes scholar, Oxford U., 1961-63, MA, 1989. Bar: N.H. Assoc. firm Orr & Reno, Concord, 1966-68; asst. atty. gen. N.H., 1968-71, dep. atty. gen., 1971-76, atty. gen., 1976-78; assoc. justice Superior Ct. N.H., 1978-83, N.H. Supreme Ct., 1983-90; judge U.S. Ct. Appeals (1st cir.) N.H., 1990; assoc. justice U.S. Supreme Ct., Washington, 1990—. Trustee Concord Hosp., 1973-85, pres. bd. trustees, 1978-84; bd. overseers Dartmouth Med. Sch., 1981-87. Mem. Am. Bar Assn., N.H. Bar Assn., N.H. Hist. Soc. (v.p. 1980-85, trustee 1976-85), Phi Beta Kappa. Republican. Episcopalian.

SOUTER, ROBERT TAYLOR, retired banker; b. Melrose, Mass., Feb. 17, 1909; s. Walter Wilson and Mary (Taylor) S.; m. Barbara P. Claybourne, Sept. 7, 1935; children—Scott C., Pamela (Mrs. Darroll Hanssen). Student, Harvard, 1934. Treas. Braintree Coop. Bank, Mass., 1937-42; v.p. U.S. Savs. and Loan League, 1942-47; v.p., dir. Coast Fed. Savs. & Loan Assn., Los Angeles, 1947-55; pres., dir. World Savs. and Loan Assn., Oakland, Calif., 1955-86. Republican. Methodist. Home: 4 Windsor Dr Burlingame CA 94010-6359

SOUTH, FRANK EDWIN, physiologist, educator; b. Norfolk, Nebr., Sept. 20, 1924; s. Frank Edwin and Gladys (Brinkman) S.; m. Berna Deane Phyllis

Casebolt, June 23, 1946; children: Frank Edwin, Robert Christopher. A.B., U. Calif., Berkeley, 1949, Ph.D., 1952. Asst. prof. physiology U. P.R. Sch. Medicine, 1953-54, U. Ill. Coll. Medicine, 1954-61; asso. prof. Colo. State U., 1961-62, prof., 1962-65; prof. U. Mo., 1965-76; prof., dir. Sch. Life and Health Scis., U. Del., Newark, 1976-82; prof. emeritus U. Del., Newark, 1989, Sch. Life and Health Scis., U. Del., Newark, 1989—; mem. governing bd., dir. Hibernation Info. Exchange, 1959—. Mem. editorial bd. Cryobiology, 1989; contbr. numerous articles on physiology of hibernation, temperature regulation, renal function, marine mammals, artificial atmospheres, and sleep to profl. jours. Bd. dirs. Del. Lung Assn., 1976-82, Del. Cancer Network, 1977-82; mem. research com. Del. Heart Assn., 1977-82; mem. N.E. regional research com. Am. Heart Assn.; mem. med. adv. bd. A.I. DuPont Inst., Wilmington, Del., 1978-83. Served with AUS, 1943-45. Decorated Purple Heart with oak leaf cluster, Bronze Star with oak leaf cluster, Pres. unit citation, Croix de Guerre (unit); NIH career devel. awardee, 1961-65; recipient European African Mid East campaign medal with bronze spear head and silver star, World War II victory medal, Army of Occupation medal with Germany clasp, combat med. badge. Fellow AAAS, Sigma Xi; mem. Am. Physiol. Soc., Soc. Hist. Preservation. Episcopalian. Clubs: Ranger Battalions Assn. World War II, Marathon Yacht Club.

SOUTH, MARY ANN, pediatrics educator; b. Portales, N.Mex., May 23, 1933; d. John Anderson and Carrie (Schumpert) S.; m. Allard W. Loutherback, Dec. 29, 1983 (dec. June 1985); children: George Louie, Linda Lee Loutherback Putnam. Student, Baylor U., Waco, Tex., 1951-53; BA, Ea. N.Mex. U., 1955; MD, Baylor U., Houston, 1959. Diplomate Am. Bd. Pediatrics. Intern Presbyn.-St. Luke's Hosp., Chgo., 1959-60, resident in pediatrics, 1960-62; fellow in infectious diseases Baylor U., 1962-64; fellow in immunology, instr. in pediatrics U. Minn., Mpls., 1964-66; asst. prof., assoc. prof. Baylor U. Coll. Medicine, 1966-73; assoc. prof. U. Pa., Phila., 1973-77; prof., chmn. dept. pediatrics Tex. Tech U. Health Scis. Ctr., Lubbock, 1977-79, rsch. prof., 1979-83; med. officer Nat. Inst. Neurol.-Communicative Disorders and Stroke, NIH, Bethesda, Md., 1982-85; vis. scientist Gallaudet Coll., Washington, 1984-85; prof. pediatrics Meharry Med. Coll., Nashville, 1986-89, W.K. Kellogg disting. prof., 1989—. Contbr. over 140 articles to med. jours., chpts. to books. Recipient Disting. Alumnus award Ea. N.Mex. U., 1969, rsch. career devel. award NIH, 1968-73. Fellow Infectious Diseases Soc. Am.; mem. Am. Pediatric Soc., Am. Assn. Immunology, Assn. for Gnotobiology, Am. Med. Women's Assn., Pediatric Infectious Diseases Soc., Alpha Omega Alpha. Home: 6666 Brookmont Ter Nashville TN 37205-4658 Office: Meharry Med Coll 1005 DB Todd Blvd Nashville TN 37208

SOUTHALL, IVAN FRANCIS, author; b. Melbourne, Victoria BNA, Australia, June 8, 1921; s. Francis Gordon and Rachel Elizabeth (Voutier) S.; m. Joy Blackburn, Sept. 8, 1945; children—Andrew John, Roberta Joy, Elizabeth Rose, Melissa Frances; m. Susan Helen Westerlund, Nov. 11, 1976. Ed., pub. schs., Victoria. Free-lance writer, 1947—. Author over 60 books in 22 langs., including: Ash Road, 1965 (Book of Yr. 1966), To the Wild Sky, 1967 (Book of Yr. 1968), Bread and Honey, 1970 (Book of Yr. 1971), Josh, 1971 (Carnegie medal 1971), Fly West, 1975 (Book of Yr. 1976), The Long Night Watch, 1983 (Nat. Children's Book award 1986). Found. pres. Knoxbrooke Day Tng. Centre for Intellectually Handicapped, Victoria, 1967-69. Served as flight lt. Royal Australian Air Force, 1942-47, Europe. Decorated D.F.C., RAF; recipient emeritus fellowship award Australia Coun., 1993. Mem. Order Australia. Methodist. Home: PO Box 25, Healesville, 3777 Victoria Australia Office: Farrar Straus & Giroux Inc 19 Union Sq W New York NY 10003-3304

SOUTHAN, ARTHUR, insurance company executive. Pres. Care Am. So. Calif., Chatsworth, Calif., 1988—. Office: Care Am So Calif 20520 Nordhoff St Chatsworth CA 91311*

SOUTHARD, BILL, public relations executive; b. Passaic, N.J., May 8, 1957. BA in Comms. and Journalism, Seton Hall U., 1979. Asst. A/E Ardrey, 1980-81; A/E Ardrey, Inc., 1981-82; mgr. pub. rels. ApolloTechs., 1982; A/E Dorf., 1982-83; sr. A/E Dorf/MJH, 1983-84; A/S D & S, 1984-86; sr. v.p. Dorf & Stanton, 1986-88; exec. v.p. and gen. mgr. Dorf & Stanton Comms., 1988-92; pres. N.Y. Earle Palmer Brown Pub. Rels., 1992. Mem. Am. Agricultural Editors Assn., Nat. Agricultural Mktg. Assn., Pub. Rels. Soc. Am. Office: Earle Palmer Brown 6935 Arlington Rd Bethesda MD 20814-5281*

SOUTHARD, WILLIAM G., lawyer; b. Toledo, Ohio, May 6, 1953; s. James Theodore and Dorothy (Fergusson) S.; m. Martha Donelan, Aug. 14, 1976; children: Abigail, Margaret, Michael. BA, Williams Coll., 1975; JD, Columbia U., 1978. Bar: Ill. 1978, U.S. Dist. Ct. Ill. 1979, Mass. 1981, U.S. Dist. Ct. Mass. 1981, U.S. Ct. Appeals (1st cir.) 1985. Assoc. Schiff Hardin & Waite, Chgo., 1978-81; assoc. Bingham, Dana & Gould, Boston, 1981-85, ptnr., 1985—; dep. chmn. litigation, 1994—. Assoc. editor Columbia Jour. Transnat. Law, 1978; contbr. articles to profl. jours. Mem. ABA, ASTM, Boston Bar Assn. Office: Bingham Dana & Gould 150 Federal St Boston MA 02110-1726

SOUTHARD-RITTER, MARCIA, nursing administrator; b. Cape Girardeau, Mo., Dec. 12, 1942; d. Leebert Melton and Katherine Louise (Goslin) Loyd; m. C. John Ritter, Dec. 20, 1986; children: Robin Hacket, Emilie Clardy, Stephen Southard, Benjamin Ritter, Daniel Southard. Diploma, Jewish Hosp. Sch. Nursing, St. Louis, 1963; BS in Health Care Adminstrn., St. Joseph Coll., North Windham, Maine, 1984; MS in Health Sci. Adminstrn., Cen. Mich. U., 1986. RN, Mo.; cert. nursing adminstr., lic. nursing home adminstr. Head nurse, staff nurse S.E. Mo. Hosp., Cape Girardeau, 1963-69; cardiovascular nurse Internal Medicine Group, Cape Girardeau, 1969-72; staff nurse, head nurse St. Francis Hosp., Cape Girardeau, 1972-76, dir. critical care, 1976-82, dir. patient care adminstrv. svcs., 1982, v.p. patient care, 1982—. Contbr. articles to profl. jours. Mem. NAFE, AACN, ANA, Mo. Nurses Assn., Am. Coll. Health Care Execs., Am. Orgn. Nurse Execs. Office: St Francis Med Ctr 211 St Francis Dr Cape Girardeau MO 63703

SOUTHERLAND, S. DUANE, manufacturing company executive; b. Durham, N.C., Apr. 24, 1949; s. Sydney Duane and Beatrice Marie (Carver) S.; m. Linda F. Lewis, Jan. 5, 1974, 1 child, S. Duane III. BSE, Duke U., 1971, MS in Engring., 1973, MBA, 1974. Ops. analyst Cooper Group Div. Cooper Industries, Apex, N.C., 1974-78; planning analyst Cooper Industries, Houston, 1978-81; dir. fin. Cooper Electronics Div. Cooper Industries, Nashua, N.H., 1981-83; gen. mgr. Conn. ops. Kirsch Div. Cooper Industries, Beacon Falls, Conn., 1983-87; pres. Kirsch Div. Cooper Industries, Sturgis, Mich., 1987—. Republican. Baptist.

SOUTHERN, HUGH, performing arts consultant; b. Newcastle-on-Tyne, Eng., Mar. 20, 1932; came to U.S., 1955; s. Norman and Phyllis Margaret (Hiller) S.; m. Jane Rosemary Llewellyn, Dec. 18, 1954 (div.); children: Hilary, William Norman; m. Kathy Ayers Dwyer, Dec. 10, 1989; 1 child, Jaime Andres. B.A., King's Coll., Cambridge, Eng., 1956. Assoc. account exec. Fuller & Smith & Ross, N.Y.C., 1956-58; treas. Westport Country Playhouse Conn., 1958; adminstrv. mgr. Theatre Guild-Am. Theatre Soc., N.Y.C., 1959-62; asst. dir. Repertory Theatre, Lincoln Ctr., N.Y.C., 1962-65; gen. mgr. Nat. Repertory Theatre, N.Y.C., 1965-67; mgmt. assoc. San Francisco Opera, 1967-68; exec. dir. Theatre Devel. Fund, N.Y.C., 1968-82; dep. chmn. programs Nat. Endowment for Arts, Washington, 1982-89, acting chmn., 1989; gen. mgr. Met. Opera Assn. Inc., N.Y.C., 1989-90; acting dir. performing arts program N.Y. State Council on Arts, N.Y.C., 1974-75, acting exec. dir., 1976; dir. New Dramatists, N.Y.C., 1978-82, Film Forum, N.Y.C., 1978-82; trustee Actor's Fund Am., N.Y.C., 1978-85. Trustee Manhattan Country Sch., N.Y.C., 1970-82, chmn., 1971-74; mem. Mayor's Com. on Cultural Policy, N.Y.C., 1974-75; dir. Vol. Cons. Group, Inc., N.Y.C., 1976-82, 92—. Home: PO Box 68 Montpelier Station VA 22957-0068*

SOUTHERN, ROBERT ALLEN, lawyer; b. Independence, Mo., July 17, 1930; s. James Allen and Josephine (Ragland) S.; m. Cynthia Agnes Drews, May 17, 1952; children: David D., William A., James M., Kathryn A. B.S. in Polit. Sci., Northwestern U., 1952, LL.B., 1954. Bar: Ill. 1955. Assoc. Mayer, Brown & Platt, Chgo., 1954-64, ptnr., 1965—, mng. ptnr., 1978-91; mng. ptnr. Mayer, Brown & Platt, L.A., 1991—. Editor in chief Northwestern U. Law Rev., 1953-54. Trustee, v.p., gen. counsel LaRabida Children's

Hosp. and Rsch. Ctr., Chgo., 1974-89; trustee Kenilworth (Ill.) Union Ch., 1980-88; pres. Joseph Sears Sch. Bd., 1977-79; trustee Rush-Presbyn.-St. Luke's Med. Ctr., 1983-91, life trustee, 1991—; bd. dirs. Boys and Girls Clubs Chgo., 1986-91; governing mem. Orchestral Assn. Chgo., 1988-93. With U.S. Army, 1955-57. Mem. ABA, Chgo. Bar Assn., Law Club Chgo., Legal Club Chgo., Econ. Club Chgo., Order of Coif, Indian Hill Club, Chgo. Club, City Club on Bunker Hill (L.A.). Office: Mayer Brown & Platt 25th Fl 350 S Grand Ave Los Angeles CA 90071-1563

SOUTHERN, RONALD D., diversified corporation executive; b. Calgary, Alta., Can., July 25, 1930; s. Samuel Donald and Alexandra (Cuthill) S.; m. Margaret Visser, July 30, 1954; children: Nancy, Linda. BSc, U. Alta., Edmonton, 1953; LLD (hon.), U. Calgary, 1976, U. Alberta, 1991. Pres., CEO ATCO Ltd., Calgary, 1954-85, dep. chmn., CEO, 1985-91, chmn., pres., CEO, 1985-93; chmn., CEO Atco Ltd. and Can. Utilities Ltd., Calgary, 1994—, ATCO Ltd., Calgary, 1994—, Can. Utilities Ltd., Calgary, 1994—; bd. dirs. Akita Drilling Ltd., Fletcher Challenge Can. Ltd., Can. Airlines Corp., Can. Pacific Ltd., Chrysler Can. Ltd., IMASCO Ltd., LaFarge Corp., Royal Ins. Ltd., Xerox of Can. Inc., Fletcher Challenge Ltd., New Zealand; co-chmn. Spruce Meadows Tournaments. Chmn. Spruce Meadows Mex.-Can. Econ. Round Table, 1994, Spruce Meadows Britain-Alta. Econ. Round Table, 1994. Recipient Holland Trade award Govt. of the Netherlands, 1985, (with wife) Sportsmen of Yr. award Calgary Booster Club, Internat. Disting. Entrepreneur award U. Man. Faculty Mgmt., 1990; inducted into Can. Bus. Hall, 1995; named Businessman of Yr., U. Alta., 1986, to Order of Can., 1986, mem. Brit. Empire, 1986. Mem. Ranchmen's Club. Calgary Golf and Country Club. Home: 67 Massey Pl SW, Calgary, AB Canada T2V 2G7 Office: ATCO Ltd & Can Utilities Ltd, 1600 909-11 Ave SW, Calgary, AB Canada T2R 1N6

SOUTHWARD, GLEN MORRIS, statistician, educator; b. Boise, Idaho, Oct. 8, 1927; s. Glen P. and Emma M. (Martin) S.; m. M. Lorraine Kissack, Oct. 3, 1974; children from previous marriage: Judith Ann, Richard Todd. BS, U. Wash., 1949, MS, 1956, PhD, 1966. Asst. prof. Stats. Wash. State U., Pullman, 1967-71; biometrician Internat. Pacific Halibut Commn., Seattle, 1971-75; assoc. prof. stats. N.Mex. State U. Las Cruces, 1975-80, prof., 1980-93, prof. emeritus, 1993—. Contbr. articles to profl. jours. Fellow Am. Inst. Fishery Research Biologists; mem. Am. Statis. Assn., Biometric Soc. (sec., treas. Western N.Am. region 1984-91), Sigma Xi. Avocations: photography, cooking. Office: NMex State U Dept Exptl Stats PO Box 30003 Las Cruces NM 88003-8003

SOUTHWAY, PETER, bank holding company executive; b. 1935. Pres., COO Valley Nat. Bancorp, Wayne, N.J., 1952—. Office: Valley Nat Bancorp 1445 Valley Rd Wayne NJ 07470 also: 505 Allwood Rd Clifton NJ 07012*

SOUTHWELL, LEONARD J., dairy corporation executive; b. Sioux City, Iowa, Nov. 9, 1924; s. George P. and Nellie (Van Houten) S.; m. Rosemary Kathern Kirsch, June 9, 1951; children: George, Christine, John. BS in Dairy Ind., Iowa State U., 1951. Mgr. Equity Creamery, Pana, Ill., 1951-64; sales mgr. Prairie Farms Dairy, Carlinville, Ill., 1964-72, asst. gen. mgr., 1972-80, chief oper., 1980-88, chief exec. officer, 1988—; bd. dirs. Milk Industry Found. With USN, 1943-46. Mem. Elks, Masons, Shrine, Consistory. Home: 1000 S Hickory St Pana IL 62557-1928 Office: Praire Farms Dairy Inc PO Box 499 Carlinville IL 62626-0499

SOUTHWICK, ARTHUR FREDERICK, legal educator; b. Pitts., Nov. 22, 1924. BA, Coll. of Wooster, 1947; MBA, U. Mich., 1950, JD, 1951. Bar: Ohio 1951. Atty. trust dept. Nat. City Bank, Cleve., 1951-52; faculty law U. Mich., Ann Arbor, 1956-61, assoc. prof., 1961-66, prof. bus. law, health svcs. mgmt. and policy, 1966-90, prof. emeritus, 1990—. Author: The Law of Hospital and Health Care Administration, 1988; contbr. articles to legal publs. and med. jours. Elder 1st Presbyterian Ch., Ann Arbor, 1963—. Mem. Am. Acad. Health Care Attys., Acad. of Legal Studies in Bus., Nat. Health Lawyers Assn., Am. Soc. Law, Medicine and Ethics. Home: 26 Southwick Ct Ann Arbor MI 48105-1410 Office: U Mich Sch Bus Adminstrn Ann Arbor MI 48109

SOUTHWICK, CHARLES HENRY, zoologist, educator; b. Wooster, Ohio, Aug. 28, 1928; s. Arthur F. and Faye (Motz) S.; m. Heather Milne Beck, July 12, 1952; children: Steven, Karen. B.A., Coll. Wooster, 1949; M.S., U Wis., 1951, Ph.D., 1953. NIH fellow, 1951-53; asst. prof. biology Hamilton Coll., 1953-54; NSF fellow Oxford (Eng.) U., 1954-55; faculty Ohio U., 1955-61; assoc. prof. pathobiology Johns Hopkins Sch. Hygiene and Pub. Health, Balt., 1961-68; prof. Johns Hopkins Sch. Hygiene and Pub. Health, 1968-79; assoc. dir. Johns Hopkins Internat. Ctr. for Med. Rsch. and Tng., Calcutta, India, 1964-65; chmn. dept. environ., population and organismic biology U. Colo., Boulder, 1979-82, prof. biology, 1979—, prof. emeritus, 1993—; researcher and author publs. on animal social behavior and population dynamics, influences animal social behavior on demographic characteristic mammal populations, primate ecology and behavior, estuarine ecology and environmental quality; mem. primate adv. com. Nat. Acad. Sci.-NRC, 1963-75, com. primate conservation, 1974-75; mem. Gov.'s Sci. Adv. Com. State of Md., 1975-78; mem. com. on rsch. and exploration Nat. Geog. Soc., 1979—; mem. adv. bd. Caribbean Primate Rsch. Ctr., 1987—, Wis. Primate Rsch. Ctr., 1990—; mem. Integrated Conservation Rsch., 1989—. Editor: Primate Social Behavior, 1963, Animal Aggression, 1970, Nonhuman Primates in Biomedical Research, 1975, Ecology and the Quality of Our Environment, 1976, Global Ecology, 1985; Ecology and Behavior of Food-Enhanced Primate Groups, 1988. Recipient Fulbright Rsch. award India, 1959-60. Fellow AAAS, Acad. Zoology, Animal Behavior Soc.; mem. Am. Soc. Zoologists, Ecol. Soc. Am., Am. Soc. Mammalogists, Am. Soc. Primatology (Disting. Primatologist award 1994), Internat. Primatology Soc., Am. Inst. Biol. Scis. Avocations Soc. Gt. Britain, Internat. Soc. Study Aggression.

SOUTHWICK, HARRY WEBB, surgeon; b. Grand Rapids, Mich., Nov. 21, 1918; s. G. Howard and Jessie (Webb) S.; m. Lorraine Hinsdale, June 27, 1942; children: Harry Webb Jr., Sandra, Charles Howard, Gay. B.S., Harvard U., 1940, M.D., 1943. Intern Presbyn. Hosp., Chgo., 1944-45, resident in surgery, 1945-46; surg. resident U. Ill. Research and Ednl. Hosps., 1948-50; chmn. dept. gen. surgery Rush-Presbyn.-St. Luke's Med. Center, Chgo., 1970-84; pvt. practice surgery Chgo., 1950-84; clin. assoc. prof. surgery U. Ill. Med. Sch., 1957-63, clin. prof., 1963-71; Helen Shedd Keith prof. surgery Rush Med. Coll., 1971-84; bd. dirs. Howard Young Med. Ctr., 1986—, sec., 1987-89, vice-chmn., 1989-90, chmn., 1990—; bd. dirs. Howard Young Health Care, 1989—. Contbr. articles to med. jours. Pres. Chgo. unit Am. Cancer Soc., 1964-66, pres. Ill. div. 1972-73; bd. dirs. Eagle River Meml. Hosp., 1989—. Lt. (j.g.) M.C., USNR, 1946-48. Fellow ACS; mem. Am. Surg. Assn., Pan Am. Surg. Soc., Minn. Surg. Soc. (hon.), Western Surg. Soc., Cen. Surg. Soc., Chgo. Surg. Soc. (pres. 1979-80), Soc. Head and Neck Surgeons (sec.-treas. 1956-63, pres. 1964-65), Soc. Surgery Alimentary Tract, Soc. Surg. Oncology, Plum Lake Golf Club. Home and Office: 8155 N Lost Lake Dr Sayner WI 54560

SOUTHWICK, PAUL, retired public relations executive; b. West Newton, Mass., Mar. 27, 1920; s. Alfred and Pauline (Winkler) S.; m. Susan Barbara Heider, Feb. 24, 1947; children: Thomas Paul, Peter Alfred, Linda Susan. AB in Econs. cum laude, Harvard Coll., 1943. Coor. AP, Concord, N.H., 1947-49; UP UPI, Washington, 1949-57; mem. profl. staff govt. info. subcom. U.S. Ho. Reps., 1957-59; legis. asst., adminstrv. asst. U.S. Senator Long of Hawaii, 1959-62; dep. adminstr. charge accelerated pub. works program Area Redevel. Adminstrn., 1962-63; spl. asst. The White House, 1963-65; spl. asst. for congl. rels. Office of U.S. Sec. Commerce, 1965-67; v.p. Newmyer Assocs., Inc., Washington, 1967-87; ind. cons., 1987-93, ret., 1993. With USNR, 1941-45, PTO. Mem. Nat. Press Club (Washington), Bethesda (Md.) Country Club. Democrat. Presbyterian. Home: 4012 Underwood St Bethesda MD 20815-5028

SOUTHWORTH, LOUIS SWEETLAND, II, lawyer; b. Huntington, W.Va., Sept. 4, 1943; s. Louis Sweetland and Mary (Davis) S.; m. Sharon Johnson, June 13, 1964; children: Laura Elizabeth, Brian Scott. AB, Marshall U., 1965; JD, W.Va. U., 1968; LLM, NYU, 1970. Lawyer Jackson & Kelly, Charleston, W.Va., 1968—; Trustee U. Charleston (1985-; Greater Kanawha Valley Found., Charleston, 1988—; bd. dirs. CAMC Found.,

Charleston. Fellow Am. Coll. Tax Counsel; mem. Edgewood Country Club, Rotary. Democrat. Methodist. Avocations: golf, tennis, skiing, squash. Home: Grosscup And Bridge Rd Charleston WV 25314 Office: Jackson & Kelly 1600 Laidley Tower Charleston WV 25301-2189

SOUTHWORTH, ROD BRAND, computer science educator; b. Binghamton, N.Y., Aug. 24, 1941; s. William Tanner Southworth and Ruth Evelyn (Brabham) Woods; m. Patrice Marie Gapen, Jan. 10, 1978; children: Suzi Lynn, Judi Leigh, Megan Marie, Robin Ashley. BS in Bus., U. Ariz., 1965; MS in Mgmt. Sci. and Info Systems, Colo. State U., 1978. Mktg. rep. IBM, Denver, 1966-69; system analyst Colo. State U., Fort Collins, 1969-73, grad. teaching asst., 1978-79; project mgr. Systems and Computer Tech., Portland, Oreg., 1975-77; instr. in computer info. systems Laramie County C.C., Cheyenne, Wyo., 1979—. Author: (software) PC-DOS/MS-DOS Simplified, 1st edit. 1988, 3rd edit. 1992, DOS Complete and Simplified, 1990, DOS Essentials, 1991, DOS 5 Simplified, 1992, DOS 6.2 Simplified, 1994. Mem. Civil Air Patrol, Cheyenne, 1991. Mem. Data Processing Mgmt. Assn. (mem. assoc. level model curriculum 1984-85), Assn. Computing Machinery (mem. assoc. level computer info. processing model curriculum 1991-92). Avocations: boating, water skiing, fishing, stamp collecting, tennis. Home: PO Box 5457 Cheyenne WY 82003 Office: Laramie County Comm Coll 1400 East College Dr Cheyenne WY 82007

SOUTHWORTH, WILLIAM DIXON, retired education educator; b. Union City, Tenn., Dec. 28, 1918; s. Thomas and Gertrude (Dyer) S.; m. Violet Kuehn, July 22, 1944; children: Geoffrey Scott, Linda Jean. PhB, Marquette U., 1948, MEd, 1950; PhD, NYU, 1961. Tchr., coach La Follette Sch., Milwaukee County, Wis., 1948-51; teaching dist. prin. Grand View Sch., Milwaukee County, 1951-56; supervising dist. prin. Maple Dale Sch., Milwaukee County, 1956-58; bldg. prin. Main St. Sch., Port Washington, N.Y., 1958-65; asst. supt. for elem. edn. Huntington (N.Y.) pub. schs., 1965-67; assoc. prof., acting head dept. adminstrn. and supervision St. John's U., Jamaica, N.Y., 1967, chmn. dept., 1968-73, prof., 1968-84; parliamentarian for 35 internat. nat., regional orgns., expert witness, pub. moderator, and workshop leader. Author: (pamphlet) Care and Nuture of the Doctoral Candidate, 1968, 74, (unpublished books) The Admiral Disappears, 1989, Captain Quimby Scott, U.S.N., The Art of The Meeting--How to Run Successful Meetings, 1994, The Sensual Sailor--Seven Years of Lusty Living, 1994; contbg. editor Condominium Times; contbr. more thatn 200 articles to endl. jours., condominium and parliamentary publs. Served with USN, 1938-44. Lutheran. Home: # 608 7100 Sunshine Skyway Ln S Saint Petersburg FL 33711-4926 In the conflicting demands of self and society, one must strike a balance: retaining the uniqueness of one's individuality while serving the society that nurtured that uniqueness. It is in the balance thus struck that the complete person evolves—self-esteeming, and socially able.

SOUTTER, THOMAS D., retired lawyer; b. N.Y.C., Nov. 1, 1934; s. Thomas G. and Hildreth H. (Callahan) S.; m. Virginia Hovenden; children: Alexander D., C. Anson, Hadley H. BA, U. Va., 1955, LL.B., 1962; postgrad., Advanced Mgmt. Program, Harvard U., 1980. Bar: N.Y. 1962, R.I. 1969. Atty. Breed, Abbott & Morgan, N.Y.C., 1962-68; with Textron Inc., Providence, 1968-95; gen. counsel Textron Inc., 1972-95, v.p., 1973-80, sr. v.p., 1980-85, exec. v.p., gen. counsel, 1985-95; ret., 1995; mem. adv. bd. Internat. and Comparative Law Ctr., 1975—; mem. Assn. Gen. Counsel: bd. dirs. Avco Fin. Svcs., Inc., Paul Revere Corp.; trustee New England Legal Found. Nat. chmn. ann. giving campaign U. Va. Law Sch., 1992-94; former trustee Providence Preservation Soc., Providence Performing Arts Ctr.; mem. U. Va. Arts and Scis. Alumni Coun.; mem. Narragansett coun. Boy Scouts Am. Lt. USNR, 1955-59. Mem. ABA, N.Y. State Bar Assn., R.I. Bar Assn., Internat. Bar Assn. Office: Textron Inc 40 Westminster St Providence RI 02903-2525

SOUVEROFF, VERNON WILLIAM, JR., corporate executive, investor, author; b. L.A., Aug. 12, 1934; s. Vernon William Sr. and Aileen (Young) S.; m. Aileen Patricia Robinson; children—Gail Kathleen, Michael William. B.S. in E.E., Stanford U., 1957; postgrad., Ohio State U., 1958-59. With Litton Industries, Beverly Hills, Calif., 1960-75; with ITT Corp., N.Y.C., 1975-87, corp. v.p., 1983-84, sr. v.p., 1984-87; pres. ITT Gilfillan, 1979-83; group exec. ITT Def. Space Group, 1983-84; dir. ITT Telecom and Electronics N.Am., 1984-86; pres., chief exec. officer ITT Def. Tech. Corp., 1986-87; exec. dir. Nat. Ctr. for Career Change, 1990—; mem. U.S. Def. Policy Adv. Com. on Trade, Washington, 1984-88; bd. advisors, investor Venture Resources, Venture Capital, 1988—; prin. Bus. Acquisitions and Investments, 1988—; bd. dirs. Elanix, Inc. Author books on career changes. Served as officer USAF, 1957-60. Recipient Exec. Salute award Los Angeles C. of C., 1981; Ring of Quality ITT Corp., 1983. Mem. IEEE, Nat. Contracts Mgmt. Assn., Electronics Industries Assn., Am. Def. Preparedness Assn. (former dir.), Nat. Security Indsl. Assn., Air Force Assn., Navy League, Assn. U.S. Army, Rancho Mirage Racquet Club (Calif.). Presbyterian.

SOUW, BERNARD ENG-KIE, physicist, consultant; b. Pekalongan, Java, Indonesia, Jan. 7, 1942; came to U.S., 1984, naturalized citizen, 1990; s. Tjwan-Ling and Pek-Liang (Kwee) S.; m. Martha Tjoei-Lioe Lim, July 17, 1967; children: Victor, Verena. Diploma in Physics, Tech. U. of Clausthal, Zellerfeld, Fed. Republic of Germany, 1972; D in Natural Scis., U. Duesseldorf, Fed. Republic of Germany, 1981. Rsch. assoc. U. Duesseldorf, 1973-84; rsch. scientist Isotope Rsch. Inst., Haan, Fed. Republic of Germany, 1983; univ. asst. Free U. of Berlin, 1984; vis. scientist A. F. Wright Aero. Labs., Dayton, Ohio, 1984-85; rsch. scientist Brookhaven Nat. Lab., Upton, N.Y., 1985—; cons. cvd-diamond, plasma and laser applications; adj. prof. N.J. Inst. Tech., 1993—. Contbr. articles to Jour. Applied Physics, Jour. Quantitative Spectroscopy, Jour. Plasma Physics, Plasma Physics and Controlled Fusion. Mem. Am. Phys. Soc., L.I. Optical Soc. Office: Brookhaven Nat Lab Bldg 820M Upton NY 11973

SOUZA, ANTHONY P., real estate developer, wholesale distribution services executive, finance company executive; b. 1955. BS in Bus. Adminstrn., U. So. Calif., L.A., 1977. With Deloitte, Haskins and Sells CPAs, L.A., 1977-79; with Telacu Industries, 1979—, now pres. Office: Telacu Industries 5400 E Olympic Blvd Los Angeles CA 90022*

SOVA, RITA WOLZ, community health nurse, educator; b. Joliet, Ill., May 4, 1934; d. August and Eva Mae (Kowalczyk) Wolz; m. Edward John Sova, June 22, 1957; children: Laura Lee, Mary Beth. Diploma in Nursing, Little Company of Mary Hosp., 1956; BSN, U. Ill., Chgo., 1973; MS in Nursing, No. Ill. U., 1977, postgrad., 1982—. Staff nurse St. Joseph Hosp., Joliet, 1956-62, nursing instr. 1973-76; staff nurse St. Mary Hosp., DeKalb, Ill., 1962-64, Will County Pub. Health Dept., Joliet, 1964-72; faculty Joliet Jr. Coll. ADNP, 1976-89, chmn., 1989—. Mem. Sierra Club, Audobon Soc. Mem. ANA, AAUW, Nat. League Nursing, Am. Assn. Assoc. Degree Nursing, Delta Kappa Gamma. Avocations: reading, gardening, travel. Office: Joliet Jr Coll 1216 Houbolt Ave Joliet IL 60436

SOVERN, MICHAEL IRA, law educator; b. N.Y.C., Dec. 1, 1931; s. Julius and Lillian (Arnstein) S.; m. Lenore Goodman, Feb. 21, 1952 (div. Apr. 1963); children: Jeffrey Austin, Elizabeth Ann, Douglas Todd; m. Eleanor Leen, Aug. 25, 1963 (div. Feb. 1974); 1 child, Julie Danielle; m. Joan Wit, Mar. 9, 1974 (dec. Sept. 1993). AB summa cum laude, Columbia U., 1953, LLB (James Ordronaux prize), 1955, LLD (hon.), 1980; PhD (hon.), Tel Aviv U., 1982; LLD (hon.), U. So. Calif., 1989. Bar: N.Y. 1956, U.S. Supreme Ct. 1976. Asst. prof., then assoc. prof. law U. Minn. Law Sch., 1955-58; mem. faculty Columbia Law Sch., 1957—, prof. law, 1960—, Chancellor Kent prof., 1977—, dean Law Sch., 1970-79; chmn. exec. com. faculty Columbia U., 1968-69, provost, exec. v.p., 1979-80, univ. pres., 1980-93, pres. emeritus, 1993; chmn. Nat. Adv. Coun. Freedom Forum Media Studies Ctr., 1993—; research dir. Legal Restraints on Racial Discrimination in Employment, Twentieth Century Fund, 1962-66; spl. counsel N.Y. State Joint Legis. Com. Indsl. and Labor Conditions, 1962-63; spl. counsel to gov. N.J., 1974-77; cons. Time mag., 1965-80; dir. Chem. Bank, AT&T, GNY Ins. Group, Orion Pictures Corp., Warner Lambert; mem. N.J. Bd. Mediation Panel of Arbitrators; mem. panel arbitrators Fed. Mediation and Conciliation Service; bd. dirs. Asian Cultural Council, Shubert Orgn., Shubert Found., Sta. WNET-TV, NAACP Legal Def. Fund.; chmn. N.Y.C. Charter Revision Commn., 1982-83; co-chmn. 2d Circuit Commn. on Reduction of

Burdens and Costs in Civil Litigation, 1977-80; chmn. Commn. on Integrity in Govt., 1986; pres. Italian Acad. Advanced Studies in Am., 1991-93; chmn. Japan Soc., 1993—, Am. Acad. Rome, 1993—; chmn. nat. advisory coun. Freedom Forum Media Studies Ctr., 1993—. Author: Legal Restraints on Racial Discrimination in Employment, 1966, Law and Poverty, 1969, Of Boundless Domains, 1990; host Sta. WNET-TV series Leading Questions. Mem. Pulitzer Prize Bd., 1980-93, chmn. pro tem, 1986-87; trustee Kaiser Family Found., Presidential Legal Expense Trust. Commendatore in the Order of Merit of the Republic of Italy, 1991; recipient Alexander Hamilton medal, 1993, Citizens Union Civic Leadership award, 1993. Fellow Am. Acad. Arts and Scis.; mem. ABA, Coun. Fgn. Rels., Assn. Bar City N.Y., Am. Arbitration Assn. (panel arbitrators), Am. Law Inst., Econ. Club, Nat. Acad. Arbitrators. Office: Columbia U Sch Law 435 W 116th St New York NY 10027-7201

SOVEY, L. TERRELL, JR., textile executive, insurance agent; b. Gainesville, Ga., Apr. 1, 1931; s. Louis Terrell and Kathryn (White) S.; m. Anne Michael Smith, June 5, 1952; children: Kathryn, Louis, Myra. BS in Indsl. Engring., Ga. Inst. Tech., 1952. Lic. ins. agent, S.C., N.C., N.Y., Conn., Ga. Mgr. cost control Owens Corning Fiberglass, Toledo, 1955-56, Ashton, R.I., 1956-57, N.Y.C., 1957-59; v.p. fin. planning Milliken & Co., Spartanburg, S.C., 1959-67, gen. mgr., 1967-77; pres. M. Lowenstein Corp., Spartanburg, 1977-80, Mgmt. Adv. Svcs., Inc., Spartanburg, 1980—; chmn. bd., pres. Texfi Industries, Inc., Spartanburg, 1984—; chmn. bd. dirs. Goldtex, Inc., Precision Cutting Service, Inc., Carolina Connection, Inc. inventor synthetic dyeing composition, 1984. Chmn. Spartanburg Day Sch., Spartanburg, 1979; dir. Spartanburg Boys Home, Spartanburg, 1985. Served to lt. USN, 1948-55. Named Eagle Scout Boy Scouts Am., 1945. Mem. Union League. Republican. Presbyterian. Club: Spartanburg Country. Avocations: swimming, golf, model bldg. Home: 990 Arden Way Spartanburg SC 29302-3301 Office: Mgmt Adv Svcs Inc 367 S Pine St Spartanburg SC 29302-2623

SOVEY, WILLIAM PIERRE, manufacturing company executive; b. Helen, Ga., Aug. 26, 1933; s. Louis Terrell and Kathryn Bell (White) S.; m. Kathryne Owen Doyle. Dec. 28, 1958; children: Margaret Elizabeth, John Todd. B.S.I.E., Ga. Inst. Tech., 1955; grad., Advanced Mgmt. Program, Harvard U., 1976. Gen. mgr. automotive div. Atwood Vacuum Machine Co., Rockford, Ill., 1963-68; v.p. internat. A.G. Spalding & Bros., Inc., Chicopee, Mass., 1968-71; pres. Ben Hogan Co. div. AMF Inc., Ft. Worth, 1971-77; corp. v.p., group exec. indsl. products group AMF Inc., Stamford, Conn., 1977-79; pres., chief operating officer, dir. AMF Inc., White Plains, N.Y., 1982-85; pres., chief operating officer Newell Co., Freeport, Ill., 1986-92, vice chmn. CEO, 1993, also bd. dirs. Served with USN, 1955-58. Home: 5349 Winding Creek Dr Rockford IL 61111-5483 Office: Newell Co PO Box 117 Beloit WI 53512-0117

SOVIE, DONALD E., lawyer; b. Tacoma, Wash., Oct. 16, 1944; s. Harold William and Vivian Aileen (Boulet) S.; m. Ellen Anne O'Brien, Sept. 13, 1969; children: Daniele Marie, Krista Anne, Marisa Ellen. BA cum laude, Seattle U., 1966; JD, U. San Francisco, 1969; postgrad., George Washington U., 1975. Bar: Calif. 1970, U.S. Dist. Ct. (no. dist.) Calif. 1970, U.S. Ct. Appeals (9th cir.) 1970, U.S. Supreme Ct. 1973, U.S. Ct. Claims 1977, U.S. Dist. Ct. (ctrl. dist.) Calif. 1984. Commd. 2d lt. U.S. Army, 1966, advanced through grades to maj., 1974; asst. procurement legal advisor U.S. Army, Vietnam, 1969-70, judge advocate-prosecutor, 1970, asst. procurement counsel, 1970-71; judge advocate/claims officer br. legal office U.S. Army, Germany, 1971-74; sr. trial atty., contract appeals divsn. U.S. Army, Washington, 1975-77, labor advisor, office asst. sec. army, 1977-78; resigned U.S. Army, 1978—; staff atty. Ford Motor Co., Palo Alto, Calif., 1978-81; assoc. counsel Ford Motor Co., Newport Beach, Calif., 1981-90; ptnr. Crowell & Moring, Irvine, Calif., 1990—. Bd. dirs. KIND Found. for Children, San Diego, 1987—. Mem. ABA, Fed. Bar Assn., State Bar Calif. Roman Catholic. Avocations: youth soccer, family, jogging. Home: 28022 Camino La Ronda San Juan Capistrano CA 92675-3826 Office: Crowell & Moring 2010 Main St Ste 1200 Irvine CA 92714-7217

SOVIE, MARGARET DOE, nursing administrator, college dean; b. Ogdensburg, N.Y., July 7, 1934; d. William Gordon and Mary Rose (Bruyere) Doe; m. Alfred L. Sovie, May 8, 1954; 1 child, Scot Marc. Student, U. Rochester, 1950-51; diploma in nursing, St. Lawrence State Hosp. Sch. Nursing, Ogdensburg, 1954; postgrad., St. Lawrence U., 1956-60; BS in Nursing summa cum laude, Syracuse U., 1964, MS in Edn., 1968, PhD in Edn., 1972; DSc (hon.), Health Sci. Ctr. SUNY, Syracuse 1989. Staff nurse, clin. instr. St. Lawrence State Hosp., Ogdensburg, 1954-55, instr. nursing, 1955-62; staff nurse Good Shepherd Hosp., Syracuse, 1962; nursing supr. SUNY Upstate Med. Ctr., Syracuse, 1963-65, insvc. instr., 1965-66, actg. dir. and coord. nursing svc., 1966-71, asst. dean Coll. Health Related Professions, 1972-84, assoc. prof. nursing, 1973-76, dir. continuing edn. in nursing, 1974-76, assoc. dean and dir. div. continuing edn. Coll. Health Related Professions, 1974-76; spl. assignment in pres.'s office SUNY Upstate Med. Ctr. and Syracuse U., 1972-73; assoc. dean for nursing U. Rochester, N.Y., 1976-88, assoc. prof. nursing, 1976-85, prof., 1985-88; assoc. dir. for nursing Strong Meml. Hosp., U. Rochester Med. Ctr., 1976-88; chief nursing officer, assoc. exec. dir. Hosp. U. Pa., Phila., 1988-94, assoc. dean for nursing practice, Jane Delano prof. nursing adminstrn. Sch. Nursing, 1988; prof. nursing Sch. Nursing U. Pa., 1988; dir. Hosp. of Univ. of Pa., Phila., 1989—; assoc. dep. exec. dir. Hosp. of U. Pa., Phila., 1994—; sr. fellow Leonard Davis Inst. Health Econs. U. Pa., Phila., 1992—; trustee bd. U. Pa. Health System, Phila., 1993—; nursing coord. and project dir. Cen. N.Y. Regional Med. Program, Syracuse, 1968-71; mem. edn. dept. State Bd. Nursing, Albany, N.Y., 1974-84, chmn., 1981-83, chmn. practice com., 1975-80, mem. joint practice com., 1975-80, chmn. 1980-81; mem. adv. com. to clin. nurse scholars program Robert Wood Johnson found., Princeton, N.J., 1982-88; adj. assoc. prof. Syracuse U. Sch. Nursing, 1973-76; mem. Gov.'s Health Adv. Panel N.Y. State Health Planning Commn., 1976-82, task force on health manpower policy, 1978, informal support networks sect. steering com., 1980; mem. health manpower tng. and utilization task force State N.Y. Commn. on Health Edn.and Illness Prevention, 1979; mem. task force on nursing personnel N.Y. State Health Adv. Coun., 1980; mem. adv. panel on nursing svcs. U.S. Pharm. Conv. Inc., Washington, 1985-90; cons. Nat. Ctr. for Svcs. Rsch. and Health Care Tech. Assessment, Rockville, Md., 1987—; mem. nursing stds. task force Joint Commn. Accreditation Health Care Orgns., 1988-90; mem. various other adv. coms.; lectr. in field. Mem. editorial bd. Health Care Supr., 1982-87, Nursing Econs., 1983—; manuscript rev. panel Nursing Outlook, 1987-91; mem. editorial bd. Seminars for Nurse Mgrs., 1994—; contbr. articles to profl. jours., chpts. to books. Mem. bd. visitors Sch. Nursing U. Md., Balt., 1984-89; mem. bd. mgrs. Strong Meml. Hosp., Rochester, 1983-88; bd. dirs. Monroe County Assn. for Hearing, Rochester, 1979-82, Vis. Nurse Svc., Rochester and Monroe County, 1978, Southeastern Pa. chpt. ARC, 1991—. Ann. Margaret D. Sovie lectureship inaugurated Strong Meml. Hosp. U. Rochester, 1989; spl. nurse rsch. fellow NIH, 1971-72; grantee various orgns.; recipient Dean's Outstanding Alumni award Coll. of Nursing, Syracuse U., 1994. Fellow Am. Acad. Nursing (program com. 1980-81, task force on hosp. nursing 1981-83, chair expert panel on quality health 1994); mem. ANA (nat. rev. com. for expanded role programs 1975-78, site visitor to programs requesting accreditation 1976-78, cabinet on nursing svcs. 1986-90, cert. bd. nursing adminstrn. 1983-86, Ad Hoc com. on advanced practice 1992—); Am. Orgn. Nurse Execs. (stds. task force 1987), N.Y. State Nurses Assn. (med. surg. nursing group, chmn. edn. com. 1974-76, chmn. cmty. planning group for nursing dist. 4 1974-75, coun. on regional planning in nursing 1974-76, dev. 1978, Nursing Svc. Adminstrn. award 1985), Inst. Medicine (com. design strategy for quality rev. and assurance in Medicare 1988-90), Sigma Theta Tau. Pi Lambda Theta. Republican. Roman Catholic. Avocations: golf, cross-country skiing, swimming, dancing. Office: U Pa Hosp 21 Penn Tower 3400 Spruce St Philadelphia PA 19104

SOVIERO, DIANA BARBARA, soprano; b. Jersey City, Mar. 19, 1946; d. Amerigo and Angelina Catani; student Julliard Sch. Music; Hunter Coll. Opera Workshop. Appearances with opera cos. including Tulsa Opera, Houston Grand Opera, San Diego Opera, Ottawa (Ont., Can.) Opera, Zurich Opera, Goldovsky Opera Theatre, Lake George Opera, New Orleans Opera, Hamburg (W.Ger.) Opera, Dallas Opera, Chgo. Opera, Rome Opera, Paris Opera, Nice Opera, Avignon Opera, San Francisco Opera, Montreal (Que., Can.) Opera, Toulouse, France, Caracas, Venezuela, Vienna Opera, Parma Opera, Italy, Munich Opera, W.Ger., Edmonton (Alta., Can.) Opera, Winnipeg (Man., Can.) Opera, Calgary (Alta.) Opera, Madrid Opera, Greater

Miami Opera, Bastille Opera, Montreal Opera, Covent Garden, Florence Opera, Opera Pacific at Costa Mesa; with Met. Opera, 1986—, now leading soprano; instr. master classes The Faculty, sch. for actors, Los Angeles. Recipient Richard Tucker award. Mem. AFTRA, Am. Guild Musical Artists, SAG. Office: care Royal Opera House-Contracts, Convent Gardens, London WC2, England*

SOVIERO, JOSEPH C., chemical company executive; b. 1938. BS, Polytech. Inst. Bklyn., 1960; MS, NYU, 1965. With Union Carbide Corp., Danbury, Conn., 1960—, now chmn. Office: Union Carbide Corp 39 Old Ridgebury Rd Danbury CT 06817

SOVIK, EDWARD ANDERS, architect, consultant; b. Honan, China, June 9, 1918; s. Edward Anderson and Anna (Tenwick) S.; m. Genevieve Elaine Hendrickson, June 29, 1946; children: Rolf, Martin, Peter. BA, St. Olaf Coll., 1939; student, Art Students League N.Y., 1939-40, Luther Theol. Sem., 1940-42; MArch, Yale U., 1949; DFA (hon.), Concordia Coll., 1981. Ret. chmn. SMSQ, Architects and predecessors, Northfield, Minn.; prof. art emeritus St. Olaf Coll., Northfield; lectr. on ch. design at various confs., schs., univs.; participant, planner, del. numerous domestic and fgn. confs. on religion and architecture; mem., officer various profl., religious and pub. bds. and commns. Author: Architecture for Worship; Contbr. numerous articles to mags., anthologies.; works include chs., coll. and univ. bldgs., instns. Served with USMCR, 1942-45; maj. Res. Decorated D.F.C., Purple Heart, Air medal. Fellow AIA; mem. AIA Minn. (pres. 1977, Gold medal 1981), Phi Beta Kappa. Republican. Lutheran. Home: 711 Summit Ave Northfield MN 55057-1568

SOWADA, ALPHONSE AUGUSTUS, bishop; b. Avon, Minn., June 23, 1933; s. Alphonse B. and Monica (Pierskalla) S. Student, Onamia (Minn.) Sem., 1947-53; grad., Crosier House of Studies, Ft. Wayne, Ind., 1959; M.A., Cath. U. Am., 1961. Ordained priest Roman Cath. Ch., 1958; arrived in Irian Jaya to work among Asmat, 1961, selected as mission superior, 1966; ordained bishop Diocese Agats-Asmat, 1969—; mem. exec. com. Indonesian Conf. of Bishops, 1991—. Contbr. to: Nat. Geog. Yearbook, 1968, other publs. Mem. Order of Alhambra, Crosier Order, Kappa Delta Gamma. Office: 3204 E 43d St Minneapolis MN 55406 Office: Kantor Keuskupan Agats, Asmat Agats 99677, Irian Jaya Indonesia

SOWDER, ROBERT ROBERTSON, architect; b. Kansas City, Kans., Dec. 29, 1928; s. James Robert and Agnes (Robertson) S.; m. Joan Goddard, July 26, 1954; 1 dau., Lisa Robertson Lee. B.A., U. Wash., 1953; B.Arch., U. Va., 1958; grad. diploma in Architecture, Ecole Des Beaux Arts, Fontainebleau, France, 1952. Designer Architects Collaborative, Boston, 1958-59, Peirce & Pierce (architects), Boston, 1959-63; asso. Fred. Bassetti & Co. (architects), Seattle, 1963-67; partner Naramore, Bain, Brady & Johanson (architects), Seattle, 1967-81; pres. NBBJ Internat., 1976-81; architect TRA, Seattle, 1981-83; v.p. Daniel, Mann, Johnson & Mendenhall, San Francisco, 1983-93; prin. RRS Consulting, San Francisco, 1993—; archtl. design critic Boston Archtl. Ctr., 1961-62. Important works include Ridgeway III Dormitories, Bellingham, Wash. (Dept. Housing and Urban Devel. Honor award), Seattle Rapid Transit (HUD Excellence award), Safeco Ins. Co. Home Office Complex, Seattle, King County Stadium, Balt. Conv. Ctr., Oreg. Conv. Ctr., San Francisco (Moscone) Conv. Ctr. Expansion, Honolulu Conv. Ctr., Wilmington (Del.) Conv. Ctr. Served with CIC U.S. Army, 1954-56. Recipient Premier Prix D'Architecture Ecole Des Beaux Arts, Fontainebleau, 1951, 52, Prix D'Remondet Fontainebleau, 1952. Mem. AIA, Internat. Assn. Auditorium Mgrs., Scarab, Sigma Chi. Episcopalian. Clubs: Seattle Tennis, Rainier. Home and Office: 2390 Hyde St San Francisco CA 94109-1505

SOWELL, THOMAS, economist; b. Gastonia, N.C., June 30, 1930. A.B., Harvard U., 1958; A.M., Columbia U., 1959; Ph.D., U. Chgo., 1968. Economist Dept. Labor, 1961-62; instr. econs. Douglass Coll., Rutgers U., 1962-63; lectr. econs. Howard U., 1963-64; econ. analyst AT&T, 1964-65; asst. prof. Cornell U., 1965-69; asso. prof. Brandeis U., 1969-70; asso. prof. econs. UCLA, 1970-74, prof., 1974-80; project dir. Urban Inst., Washington, 1972-74; fellow Center Advanced Study Behavioral Scis., Stanford, Calif., 1976-77; sr. fellow Hoover Instn., 1977, 80—; vis. prof. Amherst Coll., 1977. Author: Ethnic America, 1981, A Conflict of Visions, 1987, Inside American Education, 1993, Race and Culture, 1994; contbr. articles to profl. publs. Served with USMC, 1951-53. Mem. Am. Econ. Assn., Nat. Acad. Edn. Office: Hoover Instn Stanford CA 94305

SOWERS, WESLEY HOYT, lawyer, management consultant; b. Whiting, Ind., Aug. 26, 1905; s. Samuel Walter and Bertha E. (Spurrier) S.; m. Gladys Krueger, Jan. 21, 1929; children: Penny (Mrs. David Buxton), Wesley Hoyt. BS, Purdue U., 1926, MS, 1927; JD, DePaul U., 1941; grad., Advanced Mgmt. Program, Harvard, 1960. Bar: Ill. 1940; registered patent atty. and practitioner ICC. Chemist Shell Oil Co., East Chicago, Ind., 1927-29; sales engr. Nat. Lead Co., St. Louis, 1929-31; lab. super. patent atty. Pure Oil Co., Chgo., 1932-42; v.p. Bay Chem. Co., New Orleans, 1942-50, Frontier Chem. Co., Wichita, Kans., 1950-57; pres. Frontier Chem. div. Vulcan Materials Co., 1957-65; exec. v.p., dir. Vulcan Materials Co., Birmingham, 1958-65; mgmt. counsel, 1965—; former bd. dirs. Gt. Lakes Chem. Co., West Lafayette, Ind., Huntsman Chem. Corp., Salt Lake City; health professions vis. com. Wichita State U. Patentee in field. Past chmn. Met. Planning Commn., Wichita and Sedgwick County, 1958; commr. Kans. Econ. Devel. Bd.; chmn. Kansas Com. for Constitutional Revision, Sedgwick County U.S. Savs. Bonds Sales; past chmn. Kans. Radio Free Europe; past mem. adv. com. Kans. Geol. Survey; mem. Kans. Senate, 1970-81; former mem. engring. adv. council Sch. Engring. and Architecture, Kans. State U.; regent, trustee Wichita State U., HCA/Wesley Med. Ctr., Wichita; bd. dirs. Health Systems Agy. of Southeast Kans., Bd. of Health Sedgwick County, Inst. Logopedics, Quivira council Boy Scouts Am., YMCA, Health Systems Agy. S.E. Kans.; past trustee Midwest Research Inst.; mem. adv. bd. Kans. U. Bus. Sch.; vis. com. Coll. Health Profession, Wichita State U.; chmn. Kans. Health Care Providers Malpractice Commn.; mem. Kans. Health Care Costs Commn., Kans. Health Coordinating Council, Wichita/Sedgwick County Bd. Health; mem. gov.'s adv. commn. Kans. Dept. Health and Environment. Mem. AAAS, Kans. C. of C. (past pres., past dir.), Wichita C. of C. (past pres. 1959, past dir., Uncommon Citizen award 1988), Kans. Assn. Commerce and Industry (past pres., dir.), Am. Chem. Soc., AAAS, Smithsonian Assocs., Soc. Chem. Industry, Ill. Bar Assn., Wichita Bar Assn., Phi Delta Theta. Lodge: Rotary. Home and Office: 2414 N Woodlawn Ste 170 Wichita KS 67220

SOWERS, WILLIAM ARMAND, civil engineer; b. Willis, Va., Apr. 23, 1923; s. Harry Cline and Effie Vivian (Slusher) S.; m. Gale Johnson, May 20, 1978; children: Jane Dixon, Jean Marie. Student, Roanoke Coll., 1940-42; BCE, Va. Poly. Inst., 1947, BS in Archtl. Engring., 1948. Registered profl. engr., Va. Assoc. Brown, Wells & Meagher, Roanoke, Va., 1948-50; ptnr. R.L. Brown and Assocs., Roanoke, 1950-53, Sowers, Knowles & Rooks, Roanoke, 1953-59, Sowers, Rooks & Whitescarver, Roanoke, 1959-84, Sowers & Assocs., Roanoke, 1984-94; DJG Sowers, Mann Roanoke, 1994—. Trustee ACEC Health Life Ins., St. Louis, 1975-83; commr. city planning City of Roanoke, 1976-92. Mem. Am. Cons. Engrs. (nat. pres. 1970-72), Cons. Engrs. Coun. Va. (svc. award 1972), Va. Soc. Profl. Engrs. (Svc. to Profession award 1972), Illuminating Engring. Soc., Hunting Hills Country Club, Masons. Office: PO Box 4038 Roanoke VA 24015-0038

SOWLE, DAVID HUGH, physicist; b. Junesboro, Ark., June 21, 1931; s. Ned W. and Mary B. (Ware) S.; m. Barbara Jean Butler, Apr. 23, 1955 (div. Feb. 1988); children: Jeffry Owen, Jennifer Ann, Kathleen Butler; m. Marcia Hope Burtt, Dec. 24, 1988. BS in Physics, Yale U., 1953; PhD in Physics, U. Minn., 1961. Staff scientist Los Alamos (N.Mex.) Nat. Lab., 1953-56; staff mem. Convair, San Diego, 1961-68; chief, theoretical br. Gen. Atomic, San Diego, 1968-70; pres. Mission Rsch., Santa Barbara, Calif., 1970-89; v.p. Mission Rsch., Santa Barbara, 1989—. Mem. AAAS, Am. Phys. Soc., Am. Meteorology Soc. Office: Mission Rsch Corp 735 State St Santa Barbara CA 93101-3329

SOWLE, DONALD EDGAR, management consultant; b. Mt. Pleasant, Mich., May 27, 1915; s. Sidney Edgar and Mary Agnes (West) S.; m. Gretchen Elizabeth MacRae, July 4, 1942; children: Lisa Sowle Cahill, Mary Ann Sowle Messing. B.S., Central Mich. U., 1940; postgrad., Harvard U.,

1942, M.I.T., 1942; M.B.A., U. Chgo., 1950. Sales rep. Armour & Co., Grand Rapids, Mich., 1940-41; command. 2d lt. USAF, advanced through grades to col., 1958; asst. dir. Jet Propulsion Lab., Calif. Inst. Tech., Pasadena, 1965-68; group v.p. Gulf & Western Industries, Los Angeles, 1968-69; dir. studies Congl. Commn. on Govt. Procurement, Washington, 1970-73; pres., chmn. bd. dirs. Don Sowle Assocs., Inc., Arlington, Va., 1973-81; adminstr. Fed. Procurement Policy, Exec. Office of The Pres. of The U.S., Washington, 1981-85; mgmt. cons., 1985—; dir. Procurement Round Table, 1985; mem. adv. bd. Fed. Contracts Report, Bur. Nat. Affairs, 1965-91; nat. regent Inst. Cost Analysis, 1981; instr. Georgetown U., 1961-65; adj. prof. and mem. adv. council procurement mgmt. program Kogod Coll. Am. U., Washington. Mem. adv. coun. Sch. Bus. Marymount U., 1985-94. Recipient Dept. Def. Joint Svc. Commendation medal, 1963, Legion of Merit award Sec. Def., 1964, Pub. Svc. award Los Angeles County, 1969, award Cen. Mich. U., 1968, 92. Fellow Nat. Contract Mgmt. Assn. (cert. profl. contract mgr., bd. advisers, Herbert Roback Meml. award 1990); mem. U.S. C. of C. (procurement com. 1985), Nat. Security Indsl. Assn. (hon. life), Nat. Assn. Uniforms Svcs. (life mem., bd. dirs 1984-88), Ret. Officers Assn. (life), Ronald Regan Alumni Assn., Am. Legion, Capitol Hill Club, Officers Club, NASA Alumni League, Beta Gamma Sigma. Republican. Roman Catholic. Home: 6643 Mclean Dr Mc Lean VA 22101-4402

SOWMAN, HAROLD GENE, ceramic engineer, researcher; b. Murphysboro, Ill., July 21, 1923; s. Harold Thomas and Thelma (Crombar) S.; m. Gladys May Wright, Dec. 8, 1945; children—Letitia Ann, Daniel Patrick. B.S. in Ceramic Engring., U. Ill., 1948, M.S. in Ceramic Engring., 1949, Ph.D. in Ceramic Engring., 1951. Assoc. ceramist Titanium Alloy, Niagara Falls, N.Y., 1951-52; research assoc. Knolls Atomic Power Lab., Gen. Electric Co., Schenectady, 1952-57; various supervisory and mgmt. positions in nuclear materials research and devel. 3M Co., St. Paul, 1957-65; research specialist 3M Co., 1965-67, sr. research specialist, 1967-70, corp. scientist, 1970-87; Friedberg Meml. lectr. Nat. Inst. Ceramic Engrs., 1988. Author articles, govt. reports on research and devel. of ceramic and nuclear materials; patentee in field. Served to 2d lt. AUS, 1943-46. Recipient Hon. Alumni award for disting. service in engring. U. Ill. Coll. Engring., 1983. Fellow Am. Ceramic Soc. (John Jeppson medal 1985, Samuel Geijsbeek award 1989); mem. Nat. Acad. Engring., Acad. of Ceramics, 3M Carlton Soc., Sigma Xi, Tau Beta Pi (chpt. Eminent Engr. award 1983). Home: 855 Towne Cir Stillwater MN 55082-4131

SOX, HAROLD CARLETON, JR., physician, educator; b. Palo Alto, Calif., Aug. 18, 1939; s. Harold Carleton and Mary (Griffiths) S.; m. Carol Helen Hill, Aug. 26, 1962; children: Colin Montgomery, Lara Katherine. BS, Stanford U., 1961; MD cum laude, Harvard U., 1966. Diplomate Am. Bd. Internal Medicine (pretest writing com. 1992-94). Intern and resident Mass. Gen. Hosp., Boston, 1966-68; clin. assoc. Nat. Cancer Inst., Bethesda, Md., 1968-70; instr. Dartmouth Med. Sch., Hanover, N.H., 1970-73; asst. prof. medicine to prof. Stanford U. Sch. Medicine, Calif., 1973-88; Joseph Huber prof., chmn. dept. medicine Dartmouth Med. Sch., 1988—; panel mem. Nat. Bd. Med. Examiners, Physicians Assts. Nat. Certifying Examination, 1973-76, chair com. on priority-setting for health tech. assessment Inst. Medicine, 1990-91, chair U.S. preventive svcs. task force, 1990—, chair com. on HIV and U.S. blood supply, 1994; chair task force to revise internal medicine residency curriculum Federated Coun. Internal Medicine. Author: Medical Decision Making, 1988; editor: Common Diagnostic Tests, 1st edit. 1987, 2d edit. 1990; contbr. numerous articles to med jours., chpts. to books; mem. editorial bd.: Med. Decision Making, 1980-87, Jour. Gen. Internal Medicine, 1985-87, New Eng. Jour. Medicine, 1990—; cons. assoc. editor Am Jour. Medicine, 1988—; assoc. editor Sci. Am. Medicine, 1995—. Fellow ACP (clin. efficacy assessment subcom. 1985-92, bd. regents, 1991—, chmn. ednl. policy com. 1994—); mem. Soc. for Gen. Internal Medicine (coun. 1980-83), Soc. for Med. Decision Making (trustee 1980-83, pres. 1983-84), Am. Fedn. Clin. Rsch., Assn. Am. Physicians, Assn. Profs. Medicine, Inst. Medicine of NAS, Alpha Omega Alpha. Home: Faraway Ln Hanover NH 03755-2312 Office: Darthmouth-Hitchcock Med Ctr Dept Lebanon NH 03756

SOYER, DAVID, cellist, music educator; b. Phila., Feb. 24, 1923; s. Samson and Esther (Faggin) S.; m. Janet Putnam, June 23, 1957; children: Daniel, Jeffrey. Student pub. schs., N.Y.C.; D.F.A. (hon.), U. South Fla., 1976, SUNY, 1983. Prof. cello Curtis Inst. Music, 1967; prof. music U. Md. Cellist with Bach Aria Group, 1948-49, Guilet Quartet, 1949-51, New Music Quartet, 1954-55, Guarneri String Quartet, N.Y.C., 1964—, (Recipient 5 Grammy awards for Guarneri Quartet recs. 1965-74). Served with USNR, 1942-46. Mem. Century Assn. Jewish. Home: 6 W 77th St New York NY 10024-5125 Home: Box 903 RFD 4 West Brattleboro VT 05301 Office: Herbert Barrett Mgmt care H Beall Mgmt 1776 Broadway New York NY 10019

SOYSTER, MARGARET BLAIR, lawyer; b. Washington, Aug. 5, 1951; d. Peter and Eliza (Shumaker) S. AB magna cum laude, Smith Coll., 1973; JD, U. Va., 1976. Bar: N.Y. 1977, U.S. Dist. Ct. (so. and ea. dists.) N.Y. 1977, U.S. Ct. Appeals (2nd cir.) 1979, U.S. Supreme Ct. 1981, U.S. Ct. Appeals (4th cir.) 1982, U.S. ct. Appeals (11th cir.) 1987, U.S. Ct. Appeals (7th cir.) 1991, U.S. Ct. Appeals (3d cir.) 1992. Assoc. Rogers & Wells, N.Y.C., 1976-84, ptnr., 1984—. Mem. ABA, Assn. of Bar of City of N.Y., Nat. Assn. Coll. and Univ. Attys., Phi Beta Kappa. Office: Rogers & Wells 200 Park Ave Ste 5200 New York NY 10166-0005

SOZEN, METE AVNI, civil engineering educator; b. Turkey, May 22, 1930; m. Joan Bates; children: Timothy, Adria, Ayshe. BCE, Roberts Coll., Turkey, 1951; MCE, U. Ill., 1952, PhD in Civil Engring., 1957; hon. doctorate, Bagazici U., Istanbul, Turkey, 1988. Registered structural engr., Ill. Jr. engr. Kaiser Engrs., Oakland, Calif., 1952; structural engr. Hardesty and Hanover, N.Y.C., 1953; research asst. civil engring. U. Ill., Urbana, 1953-55, research assoc., 1955-57, asst. prof. civil engring., 1957-59, assoc. prof., 1959-63, prof., 1963-94; prof. Purdue U., 1994—; cons. problems related to earthquake-resistant constrn. VA, various firms Europe, S.Am., U.S., UNESCO, UN Devel. Programs; cons. criteria for mass housing projects P.R.; adv. com. structural safety VA, rsch. project NSF, Applied Tech. Coun., Los Alamos and Sandia Nat. Labs.; chief investigator various NSF contracts and grants. Contbr. over 125 tech. papers, monographs, procs., reports to profl. jours.; presenter numerous papers to profl. meetings U.S.A, Japan, Italy, India, Turkey, Mexico. Recipient Drucker award U. Ill. 1986, Howard award, 1987, Boase award, 1988. Mem. NAE, ASCE (hon., Rsch. prize 1963, Raymond C. Reese award 1971, 94, Moiseiff award 1972, Howard award 1987, Raymond C. Reese Rsch. award 1994), Am. Concrete Inst. (Kelly award 1975, Bloem award 1985, Lindau award 1993), Am. Arbitration Assn. (nat. panel) Seismological Soc. Am., Swedish Royal Acad. Engring. Office: Purdue Univ Sch of Civil Engring 4149 Civil Engring Bldg West Lafayette IN 47907-1284

SPACE, THEODORE MAXWELL, lawyer; b. Binghamton, N.Y., Apr. 3, 1938; s. Maxwell Evans and Dorothy Marie (Boone) S.; m. Susan Shultz Aug. 18, 1962 (div. Apr. 1979); children: William Schuyler, Susanna; m. Martha Collins, Apr. 6, 1991. AB, Harvard U., 1960; LLB, Yale U., 1966. Bar: Conn., 1966. Assoc. Shipman & Goodwin, Hartford, Conn., 1966-71, ptnr., 1971—; mng. ptnr., 1984-87, adminstv. ptnr., 1988-91. Mem. Bloomfield (Conn.) Bd. Edn., 1973-85, chmn., 1975-85; treas. Citizens Scholarship Found., Bloomfield, 1971-73; bd. dirs., 1973-91; mem. Bloomfield Human Rels. Commn., 1973-75; mem. Bloomfield Town Dem. Com., 1976-83; corporator Hartford Pub. Libr., 1976—; libr. com. Conn. Hist. Soc., 1990—, chair, 1992—; chmn. libr. com., coun. mem. Unitarian Soc. Hartford, 1988-91. Lt. (j.g.) USNR, 1960-63. Mem. ABA, Conn. Bar Assn. (exec. com. adminstrv. law sect. 1980—), Hartford County Bar Assn., Am. Law Inst., Nat. Health Lawyers Assn., Conn. Health Lawyers Assn., Swift's Inn, Hartford Club. Democrat. Unitarian Universalist. Avocations: reading, classical music. Home: 59 Prospect St Bloomfield CT 06002-3038 Office: Shipman & Goodwin One American Row Hartford CT 06103-2833

SPACEK, SISSY (MARY ELIZABETH SPACEK), actress; b. Quitman, Tex., Dec. 25, 1949; d. Edwin S. and Virginia S.; m. Jack Fisk, 1974; children: Schuyler Elizabeth, Virginia Madison. Student, Lee Strasberg Theatrical Inst. Motion picture appearances include Prime Cut, 1972, Ginger in the Morning, 1973, Badlands, 1974, Carrie, 1976 (Acad. award nomination for best actress 1976), Three Women, 1977, Welcome to L.A.,

1977, Heartbeat, 1980, Coal Miner's Daughter, 1980 (Acad. award for best actress 1980), Raggedy Man, 1981, Missing, 1982 (Acad. award nomination for best actress), The River, 1984 (Acad. award nomination for best actress), Marie, 1985, 'Night Mother, 1986, Crimes of the Heart, 1986 (Acad. award nomination for best actress), Violets Are Blue, 1986, JFK, 1991, The Long Walk Home, 1990, Hard Promises, 1992, Trading Mom, 1994; TV movie appearances include The Girls of Huntington House, 1973, The Migrants, 1973, Katherine, 1975, Verna: USO Girl, 1978, A Private Matter, 1992, A Place for Annie, 1994, The Good Old Boys, 1995; guest host TV show Saturday Night Live, 1977; appeared in episode TV show The Waltons. Named Best Actress for Carrie, Nat. Soc. Film Critics, 1976, Best Supporting Actress, N.Y. Film Critics, 1977. Office: care Creative Artists 9830 Wilshire Blvd Beverly Hills CA 90212-1825

SPACEY, KEVIN, actor; b. South Orange, N.J., July 26, 1959. Student, Juilliard Sch., 1979-81. Stage appearances include Henry IV, part I, 1981, Barbarians, 1982, Hurlyburly, 1985, Long Days Journey into Night, 1986, National Anthems, 1988, Lost in Yonkers, 1991 (Tony award for Best Featured Actor, 1991, Drama Desk award, 1991), Playland, 1993; TV appearances include (series) Wiseguy, 1987-88, (films) The Murder of Mary Phagan, 1988, Will You Remember Me, 1990, Fall From Grace, 1990, Darrow, 1991; films include Heartburn, 1986, Working Girl, 1988, Rocket Gibraltar, 1988, Dad, 1989, See No Evil, Hear No Evil, 1989, A Show of Force, 1990, Henry and June, 1990, Glengarry Glen Ross, 1991, Consenting Adults, 1992, The Ref, 1994, Outbreak, 1995, Swimming With Sharks, 1995, The Usual Suspects, 1995. Office: Altman Greenfield & Salvaje 120 W 45th St/36th Fl New York NY 10036*

SPACH, JULE CHRISTIAN, church executive; b. Winston-Salem, N.C., Dec. 21, 1923; s. Jule Christian and Margaret Stockton (Coyner) S.; m. Nancy Clendenin, Sept. 18, 1948; children: Nancy Lynn Lane, Margaret Cunningham, Ann Thomerson, Cecelia Welborn, Robert. Student, Va. Mil. Inst., 1942-43; B.S. in Chem. Engring. Ga. Inst. Tech., 1949; postgrad., Union Theol. Sem., Richmond, Va., 1951-52, Duke U., 1955-56; M.A. in Ednl. Adminstrn, U. N.C. at Greensboro, 1976; L.H.D. (hon.), Stillman Coll., Tuscaloosa, Ala., 1977; Litt.D. (hon.), Belhaven Coll., Jackson, Miss., 1977; LL.D., King Coll., Bristol, Tenn., 1977. Salesman Mengle Corp. subs. Internat. Container Corp., Winston-Salem, 1950-52; prof. scis., athletic dir. Quinze de Novembro Coll., Garanhuns, Pernambuco, Brazil, 1952-55; pres. Quinze de Novembro Coll., 1956-64; edn. dir. Cruzada ABC-Recife, Pernambuco, 1965-70; pres. Cruzada ABC-Recife, 1969-70; exec. sec. Parliamentary Christian Leadership, Brasilia, Fed. Dist., Brazil, 1970-73; exec. dir. Presbyn. Mission in Brazil, Campinas, Sao Paulo, 1973-75; moderator Gen. Assembly of Presbyn. Ch. in U.S., Atlanta, 1976-77; exec. dir. Triad United Meth. Home, Inc., Winston-Salem, 1977—; dir. First Home Fed. Savs. and Loan. Bd. dirs. Instituto Gammon, Presbyn. Ch. U.S., Forsyth County Coun. on Aging Forsyth County Sr. Svcs. Forsyth County, Covenent Fellowship of Presbyns., William Black Lodge, Synod of N.C., Presbyn. Ch. U.S.A.; bd. visitors Lee's McRae Coll., Montreat Anderson Coll.; mem. cabinet United Way, 1987; chmn. Winston-Salem Forsyth County Coun. on Svcs. to Homeless; chmn. bd. dirs. Sr. Svcs., Inc., Winston-Salem. With USAAF, 1943-45, prisoner of war, Poland. Decorated Purple Heart; recipient Jefferson award, 1991. Mem. Sertoma Club (recipient 3 svc. awards). Republican. Clubs: Lions (Brazil); Rotary (Winston Salem). Home: Arbor Acres 1244 Arbor Rd Apt 197 Winston Salem NC 27104-1136 Office: 1240 Arbor Rd Winston Salem NC 27104-1106 The Christian faith teaches us that the greatest of all gifts is love. This gift comes from God, and it is ours through the presence of His spirit dwelling in us. This love gives man peace within and with his fellow man.

SPACH, MADISON STOCKTON, cardiologist; b. Winston-Salem, N.C., Nov. 10, 1926; s. Jule Christian and Margaret (Stockton) S.; m. Cecilia Goodson, June 25, 1949; children: Madison Jr., Joyce, Susan, David. AB, Duke U., 1950, MD, 1954. Diplomate Am. Bd. Pediatrics, Am. Bd. Pediatric Cardiology. Intern and resident dept. pediatrics Duke U., Durham, N.C., 1954-57, resident, 1955-56, fellow cardiology, 1956-57; prof. pediatrics Duke U. Sch. Medicine, Durham, N.C., 1968—, James B. Duke prof. pediatrics, 1977, prof. physiology, 1978-88, chief pediatric cardiology, 1986-91, prof. cell biology, 1988—; pres. Soc. for Pediatric Rsch., 1974; chmn. Sub-Board of Pediatric Cardiology, 1975-77, Nat. Heart, Lung, Blood Inst. Manpower Com., 1982-85. Author 167 published papers on cardiovascular rsch.; mem. editorial bd. Circulation, 1981-91. With USN, 1944-46, PTO. Fellow Am. Coll. Cardiology, Am. Inst. for Med. and Biomed. Engring.; mem. N.Y. Acad. Scis., Internat. Soc. for Heart Rsch. (Am. sect.), Am. Physiol. Soc., Phi Beta Kappa, Alpha Omega Alpha. Democrat. Presbyterian. Office: Duke U Sch Medicine PO Box 3475 Durham NC 27702-3475*

SPACKMAN, DAVID GLENDINNING, lawyer; b. Wilkes Barre, Pa., Aug. 15, 1948; s. John Worth and Ethel Coates (Farley) S.; m. Judy Ellen Selednik, June 29, 1980; children: Jenna Reiss, Britt Farley. BA, Beloit Coll., 1970; JD, Suffolk U., 1976. Bar: Mass. 1977, U.S. Dist. Ct. Mass. 1977. Gen. counsel Dept. Health and Hosps., Boston, 1976-84; assoc. Gaston & Snow, Boston, 1984-97, ptnr., 1988-90; ptnr. Mintz, Levin, Cohn, Ferris, Glovsky & Popeo, P.C, Boston, 1990—. Office: Mintz Levin Cohn Ferris Glovsky & Popeo PC One Financial Ctr Boston MA 02111

SPACKMAN, THOMAS JAMES, radiologist; b. Oak Park, Ill., Apr. 24, 1937; s. Thomas Frederick and Louise Mary (Kaiser) S.; m. Donna S. Stewart, June 25, 1960; children—Kirsten, Thomas James, Victoria. BA, DePauw U., 1959; MD, Western Res. U., 1964; Diploma in Bus. Studies, London Sch. Econs., 1987. Intern, then resident in internal medicine Yale-New Haven Med. Center, 1964-66, resident in diagnostic radiology, 1966-68, fellow clin. research tng. unit, 1968-69; instr., then asst. prof. radiology Yale U. Med. Sch., 1969-74; asso. prof. U. Pa. Med. Sch., 1974-78; prof. radiology U. Conn. Med. Sch., Farmington, 1978—; head dept. U. Conn. Med. Sch., 1978-90; dir. radiology St. Francis Hosp. and Med. Ctr., Hartford, Conn., 1992-93; pres. Elscint, Inc., Hackensack, N.J., 1993—; v.p. Elscint, Ltd., Haifa, Israel, 1993—; mem. Conn. Med. Exam. Bd., 1980-86; bd. dirs. Elscint, Inc. Mem. editorial adv. bd. Diagnostic Imaging, 1989-92; author articles in field, chpts. in books. Fellow Am. Coll. Radiology; mem. AMA, Assn. Univ. Radiologists, Soc. Pediatric Radiology, Radiol. Soc. N.J. Office: Elscint Inc 505 Main St Hackensack NJ 07601-5900

SPACKS, PATRICIA MEYER, English educator; b. San Francisco, Nov. 17, 1929; d. Norman B. and Lillian (Talcott) Meyer; 1 child, Judith Elizabeth Spacks. BA, Rollins Coll., Winter Park, Fla., 1949, DHL, 1976; MA, Yale U., 1950; PhD, U. Calif., Berkeley, 1955. Instr. English Ind. U., Bloomington, 1954-56; instr. humanities U. Fla., Gainesville, 1958-59; from instr. to prof. Wellesley Coll., Mass., 1959-79; prof. English Yale U., New Haven, 1979-89, chmn. dept., 1985-88; Edgar F. Shannon prof. English U. Va., 1989—, chmn. dept., 1991—. Author: The Poetry of Vision, 1967, The Female Imagination, 1975, Imagining a Self, 1976, The Adolescent Idea, 1982, Gossip, 1985, Desire and Truth, 1990, Boredom: The Literary History of a State of Mind, 1995. Fellow Guggenheim Found., 1969-70, NEH, 1974, Am. Council Learned Socs., 1978-79, Nat. Humanities Ctr., 1982-83, 89. Mem. MLA (2d v.p. 1992, 1st v.p. 1993, pres. 1994, mem. adv. com. 1976-80, mem. exec. coun. 1986-89), Am. Acad. Arts and Scis. (mem. bd. trustees 1992—, v.p. 1994—). Home: 1830 Fendall Ave Charlottesville VA 22903-1614 Office: U of Virginia Dept of English Charlottesville VA 22903

SPADA, JAMES, author, publisher; b. S.I., N.Y., Jan. 23, 1950; s. Joseph Vincent and Mary (Ruberto) S. Student, Wagner Coll., 1968-71, Calif. State U., 1979-80. Pres., Spada Pubs, Los Angeles, pub. Barbra Quar., Los Angeles, 1980-83. Mem. Authors Guild, ACLU. Democrat. Author: Barbra: The First Decade-The Films and Career of Barbra Streisand, 1974, The Films of Robert Redford, 1977, The Spada Report, 1979, Streisand-the Woman and the Legend, 1981, Monroe-Her Life in Pictures, 1982, Judy and Liza, 1983, Hepburn: Her Life in Pictures, 1984, The Divine Bette Midler, 1984, Fonda: Her Life in Pictures, 1985, Shirley and Warren, 1985, Grace: The Secret Lives of a Princess, 1987, Peter Lawford: The Man Who Kept the Secrets, 1991, More Than a Woman: An Intimate Biography of Bette Davis, 1993, Streisand: Her Life, 1995; book packager The 1984 Marilyn Monroe Pin-Up Calendar, 1983, The Telephone Book, 1984, Elizabeth Taylor: A Biography in Photographs, 1984, Bette Davis: A Biography in Photographs, 1985, Natalie Wood: A Biography in Photographs, 1986.

SPADAFORA, DAVID CHARLES, university administrator; b. Hamilton, Ohio, June 4, 1951; s. Samuel Charles and Dorothy (Hardy) S.; m. Carolyn Elizabeth Gaugler, Mar. 24, 1973; children: Andrew, Claire. BA, Williams Coll., 1972; PhD, Yale U., 1981. Instr. Simon's Rock Coll., Great Barrington, Mass., 1977-78; lectr. Univ. Conn., West Hartford, 1978-80; research analyst Conn. Gen. Assembly, Hartford, 1980-81; dean of Morse Coll. Yale U., 1982, lectr. in history, 1982—, dean of Calhoun Coll., 1982-85, assoc. dean of grad. sch., 1985—. Contbr. articles to profl. jours. Bd. dirs. Yale Coop, New Haven, 1987—. Recipient award for meritorious svc., Conn. Gen. Assembly, 1981. Mem. Phi Beta Kappa, Mory's. Avocations: golf, tennis.

SPADER, JAMES, actor; b. Mass., Feb. 7, 1960. Student, Phillips Acad., Michael Chekhov Studio. Appeared in pictures Endless Love (debut 1981), The New Kids, 1985, Tuff Turf, 1985, Pretty in Pink, 1986, Mannequin, 1987, Wall Street, 1987, Less Than Zero, 1987, Baby Boom, 1987, Jack's Back, 1988, The Rachel Papers, 1989, sex, lies and videotape (Best actor award Cannes Festival 1989), 1989, Bad Influence, 1990, White Palace, 1990, True Colors, 1991, Storyville, 1992, Bob Roberts, 1992, The Music of Chance, 1993, Dream Lover, 1994, Wolf, 1994, Stargate, 1994; TV movies Cocaine: One Man's Seduction, 1983, A Killer in the Family, 1983, Family Secrets, 1984, Starcrossed, 1985; TV series The Family Tree, 1983. Office: care Tony Howard/ICM 8942 Wilshire Blvd Beverly Hills CA 90211*

SPAEDER, ROGER CAMPBELL, lawyer; b. Cleve., Dec. 20, 1943; s. Ferd N. and Luceil (Campbell) S.; m. Frances DeSales Sutherland, Sept. 7, 1968; children: Michael, Matthew. BS, Bowling Green U., 1965; JD with honors, George Washington U., 1970. Bar: D.C. 1971, U.S. Dist. Ct. D.C. 1971, U.S. Ct. Appeals (D.C. cir.) 1971, U.S. Supreme Ct. 1976, U.S. Ct. Claims 1979, U.S. Dist. Ct. Md. 1984, U.S. Ct. Appeals (2d and 4th cirs.) 1985. Asst. U.S. atty. D.C., Washington, 1971-76; ptnr. Zuckerman, Spaeder, Goldstein, Taylor & Kolker, Washington, 1976—; faculty Atty. Gen. Advocacy Inst., 1974-76, Nat. Inst. Trial Adv., 1978-79; adj. faculty Georgetown U. Law Ctr., 1979-80, Am. U. Ctr. Adminstrn. Justice, 1976-79; lectr. D.C. Bar Continuing Legal Edn. Programs, 1980—. Recipient Spl. Achievement award Dept. Justice, 1971. Mem. ABA (co-chair com. on complex crimes litigation 1989-92, divsn. co-dir. sect. litigation 1992—), Bar Assn. D.C. (lectr. Criminal Practice Inst. 1977-80), D.C. Bar (com. criminal jury instrns. 1972, div. courts, lawyers, adminstrn. of justice, 1976-78; adv. com. continuing legal edn. 1986), Def. Rsch. Inst., Assn. Trial Lawyers Am., Assn. Plaintiffs' Trial Attys., Nat. Assoc. Criminal Def. Lawyers, Omicron Delta Kappa. Contbr. articles to profl. jours. and chpts. to books. Home: 7624 Georgetown Pike Mc Lean VA 22102-1412 Office: Zuckerman Spaeder Goldstein Taylor & Kolker 1201 Connecticut Ave NW 12th Fl Washington DC 20036

SPAEH, WINFRIED HEINRICH, banker; b. Essen, Fed. Republic of Germany, Dec. 23, 1930; came to U.S., 1961; s. Josef and Anna (Belker) S.; m. Waltraut Shab, Aug. 15, 1964; children: Andrea, Olivier. Abitur, Gymnasium Essen-Werden, 1951; postgrad. Columbia U., 1961-62; With Dresdner Bank, Essen and Düsseldorf, 1951-60; with internat. banking div. Morgan Guaranty Trust Co. of N.Y., N.Y.C., 1961-66, v.p. German offices, Frankfurt, 1969, gen. mgr., 1972; exec. mgr. Dresdner Bank AG, Frankfurt/Main., 1975, dep. of mng. dirs., 1979-82, sr. officer, N.Y.C., 1982—; dir. Dresdner (SE Asia) Ltd., Singapore, 1978-80, Aseambankers Malaysia Berhad, Kuala Lumpur, 1977-80, P.T. Asian and Euro-Am. Capital Corp. Ltd., Jakarta, 1977-80; chmn. Conf. State Bank Suprs./Fgn. Bankers Adv. Coun., Washington, 1993—. Mem. Steuben-Schurz Gesellschaft, Nat. Planning Assn. (exec. com.), Am. Inst. Contemporary German Studies (bd. dirs. 1983—), Bankers Assn. Fgn. Trade (chmn. 1982-90, internat. adv. coun. 1982—), Inst. Internat. Bankers (bd. dirs. 1989-92), German-Am. C. of C. (bd. dirs. 1985-93), N.Y. C. of C. (bd. dirs.), N.Y.C. Partnership (bd. dirs., internat. bus. coun.), Muenchener Herren Club, Union Internat. Club (bd. dirs. 1981—) (Frankfurt), Belle Haven Club (Greenwich, Conn.). Home: 25 Turner Dr Greenwich CT 06831-4415 Office: Dresdner Bank AG 75 Wall St New York NY 10005-2833 also: Juergen-Ponto-Platz 1, 60301 Frankfurt Germany

SPAEPEN, FRANS AUGUST, applied physics researcher, educator; b. Mechelen, Belgium, Oct. 29, 1948; came to U.S., 1971; s. Jozef F.M. and Ursula (Roppe) S.; m. Moniek Steemans, Aug. 21, 1973; children: Geertrui M., Elizabet U., Hendrik J.L. Burgerlijk Metaalkundig Ingenieur, U. Leuven, Belgium, 1971; PhD, Harvard U., 1975. IBM postdoctoral fellow Harvard U., Cambridge, Mass., 1975-77; asst. prof. applied physics Harvard U., 1977-81, assoc. prof. 1981-83, Gordon McKay prof. applied physics, 1983—; vis. prof. U. Leuven, 1984; chmn. Gordon Conf. on Phys. Metallurgy, 1988; dir. Harvard Materials Rsch. Lab., 1990—; mem. solid state scis. com. NRC, 1990-93; Sauveur Meml. lectr. Am. Soc. Metals, 1992; Krengel lectr. Technion, Israel, 1994. Co-editor: Solid State Physics; mem. editl. bd. Jour. Applied Physics, Applied Physics Letters, 1990-93, Applied Physics Revs., 1991—, Phys. Rev., 1994—, Jour. Non-Crystalline Solids, 1990-94; contbr. numerous articles to profl. publs., chpts. to books. Fellow Am. Phys. Soc. (chmn. divsn. materials physics 1992); mem. AIME-Tms Metall. Soc., Am. Soc. Metals (lectr.), Materials Rsch. Soc. (councillor 1986-88, 90-92, co-chmn. fall meeting Boston 1990, chmn. program com. 1993—), Koninklijke Vlaamse Ingenieurs Vereniging, Böhmische Physikalische Gesellschaft, Orde van den Prince. Office: Harvard U Div Applied Scis 29 Oxford St Cambridge MA 02138-2901

SPAETH, EDMUND BENJAMIN, JR., lawyer, law educator, former judge; b. Washington, June 10, 1920; s. Edmund B. and Lena (Link) S. AB magna cum laude, Harvard U., 1942, LLB, 1948. Bar: Pa. 1949. Judge Ct. of Common Pleas, Phila., 1964-73; judge Superior Ct of Pa., 1973-86, pres. judge, 1980-86; of counsel Pepper, Hamilton & Scheetz, Phila., 1986—; adj. prof. U. Pa. Law Sch., 1986—, cons. Ctr. on Professionalism, 1993—. Bd. dirs. Pub. Interest Law Ctr. of Phila., 1987—. Fellow Am. Bar Found. (life); mem. ABA, Am. Law Inst. (life), Pa. Bar Assn., Phila. Bar Assn., Am. Judicature soc., Order of Coif, Phi Beta Kappa. Home: Cathedral Village Apt L-206 600 E Cathedral Rd Philadelphia PA 19128-1933 Office: 3000 Two Logan Sq Philadelphia PA 19103

SPAETH, GEORGE LINK, physician, ophthalmology educator; b. Phila., Mar. 3, 1932; s. Edmund Benjamin and Lena Marie (Link) S.; m. Ann Ward, May 17, 1955; children: Kristin Lea Crowley, George Link Jr., Eric Edmund. BA magna cum laude, Yale U., 1954; MD cum laude, Harvard U., 1959; postgrad., U. Mich., 1960, U. Pa., 1971. Diplomate Am. Bd. Ophthalmology. Resident surgeon Wills Eye Hosp., Phila., 1960-63, attending surgeon, 1970—, dir. glaucoma svc., 1968—; clin. fellow NIH, Bethesda, Md., 1963-65; instr. U. Pa., Phila., 1965-68; prvt. practice Phila., 1965-68; prof. ophthalmology Temple U. Med. Sch., Phila. 1968-75, Jefferson Med. Coll., Phila., 1975—; ophthalmologist Chestnut Hill Hosp., Phila., 1975—; mem. Am. Glaucoma Soc., Boston 1983-85; attending surgeon, Graduate Hosp.; cons., Bryn Mawr Hosp. Author: 11 books on ophthalmology and surgery, 1975—; over 240 articles; editor Ophthalmic Surgery jour., 1985; patentee differometer, tonometer tip cover. Pres. Chestnut Hill Community Assn., Phila., 1970-72; trustee, treas. Thomas Harrison Found., 1975—; founder, pres. E.B. Spaeth and The Eye Disease Found., 1978—; Profls. for Nuclear Army Control, 1985-88; interviewer Yale Alumni Schs. Com., Phila., 1965—; Yale Class coun., 1968; curriculum com. Jefferson Medical Coll., 1987-90; institutional review bd. Jefferson Medical Coll., 1990—. Lt. comdr. USPHS, 1963-68. Recipient Sir Stuart Duke Elder Glaucoma award Internat. Glaucoma Soc., 1986, Newberg award Lawyers Alliance for World Security, 1995; NIH grantee, 1968—. Fellow Am. Acad. Ophthalmology (chmn. ethics com. San Francisco 1987—, coun. 1980—, vice chmn. residency rev. com. Chgo. 1982-88, Sr. Honor award 1988), Ind. Assn. Rsch. in Vision and Ophthalmology, Coll. Ophthalmologist, United Kingdom, 1990—, Danish Ophthalmological Soc., 1985—; mem. Coll. Physicians Phila. (sec. 1976-84), Phila. County Med. Soc., Pa. Acad. Ophthalmology (pres. coun.), Physicians for Social Responsibility (pres. Phila. chpt.), ACS (bd. govs.), Phila. Club, Phila. Cricket Club, Franklin Inn Club (Phila.), Moral Values Book Club, Phi Beta Kappa, Alpha Omega Alpha. Democrat. Episcopalian. Avocations: playing piano, sports, photography, gardening, poetry writing. Office: Wills Eye Hosp 900 Walnut St Philadelphia PA 19107

SPAETH, KARL HENRY, chemical company executive, lawyer; b. Phila., Mar. 12, 1929; s. Edmund Benjamin and Lena Marie (Link) S.; m. Ann Dashiell Wieland, Sept. 14, 1963; children—Karl Henry, Edmund Alexander, Christopher Philip. AB, Haverford Coll., 1951; postgrad. Oxford U., 1955; JD, Harvard U., 1958. Bar: Pa. 1959, U.S. Ct. (ea. dist.) Pa. 1959, U.S. Ct. Appeals (3d cir.) 1959. Assoc. MacCoy, Evans & Lewis, Phila., 1959-62; counsel for fgn. ops. Scott Paper Co., Phila., 1962-69; v.p., corp. sec. Quaker Chem. Corp., Conshohocken, Pa., 1969—; bd. dirs. Greater Phila. Internat. Network, 1991-94, Cen. Phila. Devel. Corp., 1991—; bd. dirs., sec.-treas. Edmund B. Spaeth Clin. Rsch. Found., 1982—; chmn. bd. dirs. Pa. Chem. Industry Coun., 1984-86. Chmn. bd. trustees Quaker Chem. Found., 1982—; bd. overseers Univ. Mus., U. Pa., Phila., 1983-89, 90—; bd. dir. Opera Co. Phila., 1988—; vestry Ch. St. James the Less, Phila., 1992—; bd. dirs. Chestnut Hill Acad., Phila., 1976-83, pres., 1979-83; mem. Whitemarsh Twp. Bd. Suprs., Pa., 1969-75, chmn., 1972-74; mem. Com. of Seventy, Phila., 1984—; internat. adv. com. Phila. First Partnership Econ. Devel., 1994—. Comdr. USNR, 1952-55. Mem. Am. Soc. Corp. Secs., Pa. Bar Assn. (chmn. sect. on internat. and comparative law 1980-92), Montgomery Bar Assn., Phila. Com. on Fgn. Rels. (exec. com., sec. 1984-94), Phila. Club, Phila. Athenaeum, Libr. Co. of Phila., Phila. Cricket Club. Republican. Anglican. Oxford Union, Univ. Barge (sec. 1988-94), Mil. Order Fgn. Wars (registrar 1989-91, vice commdr. 1991-93). Home: Harts Ln Miquon Conshohocken PA 19428 Office: Quaker Chem Corp Elm and Lee Sts Conshohocken PA 19428

SPAETH, NICHOLAS JOHN, lawyer, former state attorney general; b. Mahnomen, Minn., Jan. 27, 1950. A.B., Stanford U., 1972, J.D., 1977; B.A., Oxford U., Eng., 1974. Bar: Minn. 1979, U.S. Dist. Ct. (Minn.) 1979, U.S. Ct. Appeals (8th cir.) 1979, N.D. 1980, U.S. Dist. Ct. (N.D.) 1980, U.S. Supreme Ct. 1984. Law clk. U.S. Ct. Appeals (8th cir.), Fargo, N.D., 1977-78; law clk. to Justice Byron White U.S. Supreme Ct., Washington, 1978-79; pvt. practice, 1979-84; atty. gen. State of N.D., Bismarck, 1984-93; ptnr. Dorsey & Whitney, Fargo, 1993—; adj. prof. law U. Minn., 1980-83. Rhodes scholar, 1972-74. Democrat. Roman Catholic. Office: Dorsey & Whitney PO Box 1344 Fargo ND 58107-1344

SPAFFORD, MICHAEL CHARLES, artist; b. Palm Springs, Calif., Nov. 6, 1935. BA, Pomona Coll., 1959; MA, Harvard U., 1960. One man shows include Seattle Art Mus., 1982, 86, Reed Coll., 1984, Whtcom county Mus., 1987, U. Puget Sound, Tacoma, Wash., 1973, Tacoma Art Mus., 1975, 86, Utah Mus. Fine Arts, Salt Lake City, 1975, Francine Seders Gallery, Seattle, 1965—, Bellevue Art Mus., 1991, Cheney-Cowles Mus., Spokane, Wash., 1994; exhibited in group shows at Wilcox Gallery, Swarthmore Coll., Pa., 1977, Seattle Art Mus., 1977, 80, 84, Am. Acad. and Inst. Arts and Letters, N.Y.C., 1980, 83, 89, Kobe, Japan, 1981, Eastern Wash. U., 1982, Henry Art Gallery, 1982, 86, Bellevue Art Mus., 1987, Cheney Cowles Mus., 1988. Recipient Prix de Rome, 1967-69, award Am. Acad. and Inst. Arts and Letters, 1983; Louis Comfort Tiffany Found. grantee, 1965-66. Home: 2418 E Interlaken Blvd Seattle WA 98112-3029

SPAGNARDI, RONALD LEE, publishing executive; b. Jersey City, Apr. 25, 1943; s. Leo and Lillian (Mastandrea) S.; m. Isabel Marie Giliberti, June 18, 1967; 1 child, Lori Ann. Student, Berklee Sch. Music, 1963; BMus, Montclair Coll., 1968. Owner, mgr. Music Scene, Bloomfield, N.J., 1970-77; pres., editor/publisher Modern Drummer Publs., Cedar Grove, N.J., 1977—. Author: Cross-Sticking, 1976, The Great Jazz Drummers, 1992; inventor drum slide rule. Mem. Nat. Drum Assn., Percussive Arts Soc., Am. Music Conf., Mag. Pubs. Assn., Nat. Assn. Music Mchts. Avocations: reading, music, photography, tennis. Office: Modern Drummer Publs 12 Old Bridge Rd Cedar Grove NJ 07009

SPAGNOLO, JOSEPH A., JR., state agency administrator; b. Mar. 16, 1943. BS, Fairleigh Dickinson U., 1965, MAT, 1966; EdD, U. Va., 1971. Tchr. Henrico High Sch., Henrico County, Va., 1966-67; asst. prin. Burford Jr. High Sch., Charlottesville, Va., 1968-69; prin. Providence Jr. High Sch., Chesterfield County, Va., 1968-69; asst. supt. Henrico County Sch., 1971-73; supt. schs. Lynchburg, Va., 1973-90; supt. pub. instrn. Commonwealth of Va., Richmond, 1990-94; superintendent Ill. State Dept. of Edn., Chgo., 1994—; mem. Coun. Early Childhood Edn. and Day Care, 1988-90, New Standards Governing Bd., 1990—; Coun. Chief State Sch. Officers, 1990—, Edn. Commn. of States, 1990—. Bd. dirs. U. Va. Edn. Found., 1990—; me. Gov.'s Commn. Ednl. Opportunities for all Virginians, 1990—. Recipient Lamp of Knowledge award for contbns. pub. edn. Va. Assn. Secondary Sch. Prins., 1993, Outstanding Contbn. to Elem. Edn. Va. Assn. Elem. Sch. Prins., 1993, Leadership award Va. Assn. Supervision and Curriculum Devel., 1992, Brotherhood award NCCJ, 1990, Disting. Alumnus award Sch. Edn. U. Va., 1990. Mem. Assn. Supervision and Curriculum Devel., Am. Assn. Sch. Adminstrs., Va. Assn. Sch. Adminstrs. Home: 2028 Timbers Hill Rd Richmond VA 23235-3982 Office: Va Dept Edn PO Box 6-q Bldg Richmond VA 23219

SPAGNOLO, SAMUEL VINCENT, medical educator; b. Pitts., Sept. 3, 1939; s. Vincent Anthony and Mary Grace (Culotta) S.; m. Lucy Aleta Weyandt, June 20, 1961 (div. Feb. 1993); children: Samuel, Brad, Gregg. BA, Washington & Jefferson, 1961; MD, Temple U., 1965. Diplomate Am. Bd. Internal Medicine, Nat. Bd. Med. Examiners; lic. physician, Fla., Calif., Md., D.C. Intern Washington (Pa.) Hosp., 1965-66; asst. resident Boston City Hosp., 1968-69; sr. resident Vets. Affairs Med. Ctr., Boston, 1969-70, chief resident, 1970-71; pulmonary fellow Mass. Gen. Hosp., 1971-72; asst. prof. medicine George Washington U., Washington, 1972-75, assoc. prof. medicine, 1975-81, prof. medicine, 1981—; instr. medicine Tufts U., Boston, 1970-71; clin. and rsch. fellow Harvard U., Boston, 1971-72; clin. asst. prof. Georgetown U., Washington, 1975-77; chief pulmonary diseases sect. VA Med. Ctr., Washington, 1976-94; dir. divsn. of pulmonary diseases allergy George Washington U., 1977-93; cons., speaker, and lectr. in field. Contbr. numerous articles to profl. jours. Med. officer USPHS, 1966-68. Decorated Cavaliere in the Order of Merit, Republic of Italy, 1983. Fellow ACP (coun. of critical care 1983—), Am. Coll. Chest Physicians (gov. D.C. coun. of govs 1989—); mem. Am. Thoracic Soc., Am. Registry of Pathology(bd. dirs. 1981-95), Nat. Assn. VA Physicians (sec. 1987-89, pres. 1992—), D.C. Thoracic Soc. (exec. com. 1978-85, 89—, adv. com. 1978-84, pres. 1981-83), D.C. Lung Assn. (bd. dirs. 1981-85), Internat. Lung Found., Cum Laude Soc. (hon.). Avocations: reading, swimming, collecting stamps, gardening. Office: George Washington U 2150 Pennsylvania Ave NW Washington DC 20037

SPAHN, GARY JOSEPH, lawyer; b. N.Y.C., July 23, 1949; s. Harry G. and Mary (Hopkins) S.; m. Lois Luttinger, Aug. 9, 1975; children: Gary J. Jr., Lori J. BA, LL.U., 1971, MA, 1976; JD, U. Richmond, 1975. Bar: Va. 1975, U.S. Ct. Appeals (4th cir.) 1975, U.S. Supreme Ct. 1980. Law clk. to Hon. Judge Dortch Warriner U.S. Dist. Ct. (ea. dist.) Va., Richmond, 1975-77; from assoc. to ptnr. Mays & Valentine, Richmond, 1977—, now ptnr., chmn. products liability and ins. sect.; lectr. in field, 1980—; mem. judicial conf. U.S. Ct. Appeals (4th cir.). Co-author: Virginia Law of Products Liability, 1990. Pres. Southhampton Citizens Assn., Richmond, 1982-85; dir. Southhampton Recreation Assn., Richmond. 1983; mem. coun. Southside Montessori Sch., Richmond, 1983-85. With USAF, 1967-73. Mem. ABA (litigation and tort and ins. sects.), Am. Assn. Ins. Attys., Assoc. Def. Trial Attys., Def. Rsch. Inst., Va. Assn. Def. Attys., Va. Mfrs. Assn., Va. Power Boat (commodore). Avocations: boating, basketball, racquetball. Office: Mays & Valentine PO Box 1122 1111 E Main St Richmond VA 23208-1122

SPAHN, MARY ATTEA, retired educator; b. Buffalo, July 16, 1929; d. George H. and Madeline Barbara (Bitar) Attea. A.B., Nazareth Coll., Rochester, N.Y., 1950; Ed.M., SUNY, Buffalo, 1952, Ed.D., 1966. Tchr. Clarence (N.Y.) Cen. Schs., 1951-65; tchr. reading Sweet Home Cen. Schs. Amherst, N.Y., 1965-68; assoc. prof. elem. edn. D'Youville Coll., Buffalo, 1970-75; prof. curriculum and supervision SUNY Coll., Buffalo, 1975-85, prof. emeritus, 1985—; part time tchr. creativity East Aurora Schs., N.Y., 1988; coordinator Sweet Home secondary sch. summer reading program, 1968-70; cons. to Niagara Wheatfield, Clarence Central, Sweet Home schs. Author: Turning Students on Through Creative Writing, 2d edit., 1979; (poetry) Weep Willow Weep, 1974; Fragments, 1979, Busy Bodies, 1975, Flutterbyes, A Collection of Easy Readings, 1985, (with others) Flutterbyes II, 1992; contbr. articles to profl. jours. Vol. Creative Edn. Found., Creative Problem Solving Inst., Ministry of Care, McCaulley House, 1988—; leader

Bishop's Com. 1987. Mem. NEA, Internat. Reading Assn. (pres. 1968 Niagara Frontier council), N.Y. State Reading Assn. (sec. 1970), Am. Ednl. Research Assn., United Univ. Profs., Nat. Council Tchrs. English, East Aurora Writers Guild, Southtown's Quilters Club, Bernina Club, Penwomen, Phi Delta Kappa. Home: 58 Buffalo Rd East Aurora NY 14052-1628 Persistence, determination, sensitivity, sharing, willingness to take risks and give of myself, plus a faith in God...these are the qualities which have helped me on the road to success.

SPAIN, JACK HOLLAND, JR., lawyer; b. Greenville, N.C., Jan. 24, 1939; s. Jack Holland and Lucy Marie (Hardee) S.; m. Mary Elizabeth Rhamstine, May 9, 1964; children: John Hardee, Sidney Holland. AB, U.N.C., 1960; JD, Harvard U., 1963. Bar: Va. 1964, U.S. Dist. Ct. (ea. dist.) Va. 1964. Assoc. Hunton & Williams, Richmond, Va., 1964-71; ptnr. Hunton & Williams, Richmond, 1971—. Bd. dirs. Maymount Found., Richmond, 1975—, pres., 1980-82; mem. bd. elders 2d Presbyn. Ch., Richmond, City Dem. Com., Richmond; spl. counsel Local Govt. Com., Va. Constl. Revision Com. Lt. comdr. USN. Mem. ABA (chmn. taxation com., local govt. sect.), Va. Bar Assn., Richmond Bar Assn., Harvard U. Law Sch. Assn. Va. (pres.), Phi Beta Kappa, Phi Eta Sigma, Phi Alpha Theta. Club: Bull & Bear (Richmond). Avocations: spectator sports, antiques, Chinese art, farming. Office: Hunton & Williams River Front Pla E Twr 951 E Byrd St Richmond VA 23219

SPAIN, JAMES DORRIS, JR., biochemist, educator; b. Washington, Feb. 3, 1929; s. James Dorris and Frances (Pitkin) S.; m. Patricia Mann, Oct. 3, 1952; children: James Williamson, Caryn Ann, Mary Alisa. Student, Tulane U., 1947-48; B.S., Mich. Technol. U., 1951; M.S., Med. Coll. Va., 1953; Ph.D., Stanford, 1956. Research fellow biochemistry U. Tex.-M.D. Anderson Hosp. and Tumor Inst., 1955-56; assoc. prof. dept. chemistry Mich. Technol. U., Houghton, 1956-62; head dept. biol. scis. Mich. Technol. U., 1962-68, prof. biochemistry, 1962-84, prof. emeritus, 1985—; dir. Ctr. for Instrnl. Computing, Ea. Mich. U., Ypsilanti, 1984-85; vis. prof. Clemson U., S.C., 1985-94; cons. Computer Applications in Biology and Chemistry; dir. SUMIT Courseware Devel. Project, 1979-82. Author: Some Computer Programs for Biology, 1970, Biological Simulation Techniques, 1972, Lake Superior Basin Bibliography, 1976, BASIC Computer Models in Biology, 1978, BASIC Microcomputer Models in Biology, 1982, Developing Chemical Skills with Computerized Instruction, 1990, Computer Simulation in Biology: A BASIC Introduction, 1992, CHEMI-SKILL-BILDR Electronic Homework System, 1994; contbr. articles to profl. jours. Chmn. adv. council St. Josephs Hosp. Sch. Nursing, 1967; Trustee, pres. Portage Twp. Sch. Bd., 1968-76; trustee Copper Country Intermediate Sch. Dist., 1975-78. Recipient Faculty Research award Mich. Technol. U., 1965. Mem. Am. Chem. Soc. (past sect. v.p., chmn.), Sigma Xi, Phi Lambda Upsilon. Episcopalian. Clubs: Miscowaubik (past 1971-74, 79-82), Boscobel Country; Lodge: Rotary. Home: 129 Leslie Ln Pendleton SC 29670-9697

SPAIN, JAMES WILLIAM, political scientist, writer, investor; b. Chgo., July 22, 1926; s. Patrick Joseph and Mary Ellen (Forristal) S.; m. Edith Burke James, Feb. 21, 1951; children: Patrick, Sikandra, Stephen, William. M.A., U. Chgo., 1949; Ph.D., Columbia U., 1959. Cons. sec. army, 1949-50; with U.S. Fgn. Service, 1951-53; researcher, lectr. Columbia, 1955-62; mem. policy planning council State Dept., 1963-64; dir. Office Research and Analysis for Near East and South Asia, 1964-66; country dir. for Pakistan and Afghanistan, 1966-69; charge d'affaires Am. embassy, Rawalpindi, 1969; consul gen. Istanbul, Turkey, 1970-72; minister Am. embassy, Ankara, 1972-74; diplomat-in-residence, vis. prof. history and govt. Fla. State U., Tallahassee, 1974-75; amb. to Tanzania Dar es Salaam, 1975-79; amb., dep. permanent rep. UN, N.Y.C., 1979; amb. to Turkey, Ankara, 1980-81; amb. to Sri Lanka, Colombo, 1985-89; fgn. affairs fellow Carnegie Endowment for Internat. Peace and Rand Corp., Washington, 1982-84; chmn. CML Spain Perry Fin. Svcs. Ltd., Colombo; chmn. Lanka Infrastructure Ltd.; bd. dirs. Hawk Mountain Fed. Express, Ltd.; adj. prof. polit. sci. Am. U., Washington, 1965-67. Author: The Way of the Pathans, 1962, The Pathan Borderland, 1963, American Diplomacy in Turkey, 1984, Pathans of the Latter Day, 1995. Pres. bd. trustees Joseph Frazer Meml. Hosp.; bd. dirs. Inst. Technol. Studies, Philharm. Soc., Rainbow Found. With U.S. Army, 1946-47. Fellow Ford Found., 1953-55; recipient Presdl. Exec. award, 1983, Wilbur J. Carr award for Disting. Diplomacy, 1989. Mem. Coun. Fgn. Rels., Washington Inst. Fgn. Affairs, Am. Fgn. Svc. Assn., Assn. Diplomatic Studies and Tng., Cosmos Club. Home: Galle Face Ct II # 42, Colombo 3, Sri Lanka also: Am Embassy Colombo Dept State Washington DC 20520

SPAIN, WILLIAM J., JR., wholesale distribution executive; b. 1927. With Birdsong Corp., Suffolk, Va., treas., 1966—, exec. v.p., 1971—, pres., 1974—. Office: Birdsong Corp 612 Madison Ave Suffolk VA 23434-4023*

SPAINHOUR, TREMAINE HOWARD, lawyer; b. Rural Hall, N.C., Jan. 15, 1924; s. T. Hobart and Martha (Vaughn) S.; m. Nancy Williamson, Dec. 2, 1944; 1 child, Robert H. B.A., Coll. William and Mary, 1954, J.D., 1956. Ptnr. Kaufman, Obernorfer & Spainhour, Norfolk, Va., 1962-77; ptnr. Spainhour & Hall, Norfolk, 1977-80, McGuire, Woods, Battle & Boothe, Norfolk, 1980-88. Served to capt. USAF, 1948-53. Mem. ABA, Va. State Bar, Va. Bar Assn., Am. Coll. Tax Counsel. Methodist. Clubs: Harbor (Norfolk); Cedar Point (Suffolk, Va.). Avocations: golf; fishing. Home: 1406 Buckingham Ave Norfolk VA 23508-1315

SPAINHOWER, JAMES IVAN, retired college president; b. Stanberry, Mo., Aug. 3, 1928; s. Elmer Enoch and Stella Irene (Cox) S.; m. Joanne Steanson, June 10, 1950; children: Janet Dovell, James Jeffrey. BA, Phillips U., Enid, Okla., 1950, LLD (hon.), 1967; BD, Lexington (Ky.) Theol. Sem., 1953; MA in Polit. Sci., U. Mo., Columbia, 1967, PhD, 1971; U. Ark., 1954; diploma, U. Pacific Sch. Religion, Berkeley, Calif., 1958; DPA (hon.), Culver-Stockton Coll., 1973; LL.D. (hon.), Maryville Coll. St. Louis, 1976; Litt.D. (hon.), Kirksville (Mo.) Coll. Osteo. Medicine, 1977; D.H.L. (hon.), Mo. Valley Coll., 1984; LLD (hon.), Eureka Coll., 1989, Lynchburg Coll., 1993. Ordained to ministry Christian Ch. (Disciples of Christ), 1950; pastor chs. in Ark. and Mo., 1953-70; mem. Mo. Ho. of Reps. from, Saline County, 1963-70; pres. Asso. Med. Schs. Mo., Jefferson City, 1970-72; part-time prof. polit. sci. Lincoln U., Jefferson City, 1970-72; treas. State of Mo., 1973-80; pres. Sch. of Ozarks, Point Lookout, Mo., 1981-82, Lindenwood Coll., St. Charles, Mo., 1983-89; pres. divsn. higher edn. Christian Ch. (Disciples of Christ), 1989-93. Author: Pulpit, Pew and Politics, 1979. Chmn. Mo. del. Dem. Nat. Conv., 1976; elected mem. Acad. Squares, 1981; 1st chmn. Mo. Children's Trust Fund, 1984-86. Recipient Mental Health award Mo. Mental Health Assn., 1967, Meritorious Service award St. Louis Globe Dem., 1968, Harry S. Truman award Saline County Young Democrats, 1970, citation of merit Alumni Assn. U. Mo., 1975; named Mo. Lay Educator of Year Mo. chpt. Phi Delta Kappa, 1968. Home and Office: 8067 Old White River Rd Rogers AR 72756

SPAK, LORIN MITCHELL, office products industry executive; b. Chgo., Oct. 9, 1941; s. Maxwell Spak and Mildred Alice (Kasin) Grabiner; m. Susan Ziffrin, June 7, 1964; children: Jessica Z., Shana Z. BS in Commerce and Law, U. Ill., 1963; JD, DePaul U., 1966. Bar: Ill. 1966. With internal ops. dept. Maxwell Press/TOPS Bus. Forms, Chgo., 1965-70, with area sales mgmt. dept., 1970-72; nat. sales mgr. TOPS Bus. Forms, 1972-75, v.p. sales, 1975-83; dir. mktg. TOPS div. Wallace Computer Svcs., Hillside, Ill., 1983-85; v.p., gen. mgr. Visible Computer Supplies subs. Wallace Computer Svcs., St. Charles, Ill., 1985-87; sr. v.p. corp. mktg. parent co. Wallace Computer Svcs., Hillside, 1987-88, sr. v.p., gen. mgr. 8 divs., 1989-90, v.p., gen. mgr. distbn. divsn., 1992, v.p., gen. mgr. Tops divs., 1992-93; exec. v.p. ACCO/Swingline, Wheeling, Ill., 1990, pres., 1991; pres., COO Herbst Lazar Bell, 1994—. Bd. dirs. Village of Tower Lakes, Ill., 1973, chmn. legal com., 1974; fund raising advisor Nat. Com. To Prevent Child Abuse, Chgo. 1984; pres. Bateman Road Homeowners Assn., Barrington Hills, Ill., 1990—; active Max McGraw Wildlife Found., 1993. Mem. Ill. Bar Assn., Nat. Office Products Assn. (chmn. young execs. com. 1980-82), Wholesale Stationers Assn., Barrington Sportsmen's Club (pres. 1982), Lincoln Park Trap and Skeet Club (Chgo., pres. 1970). Home: 374 N Bateman Cir Barrington IL 60010

SPAKE, NED BERNARR, energy company executive; b. Montpelier, Ohio, Sept. 18, 1933; s. Lewis W. and Gertrude E. (Foley) S.; m. Marilyn Rae

Faulk, July 14, 1956; children: Julie Ann Spake Scott, Cynthia Ann Spake Lovern. B. Indsl. Engring., U. Fla., Gainesville, 1957; MBA, Rollins Coll., Winter Park, Fla., 1967. Mgr. Fla. Power Corp., Winter Park, Fla., 1962-72; dir. Fla. Power Corp., St. Petersburg, Fla., 1972-76, asst. v.p., 1976-78, v.p., 1978-83; v.p. Fla. Progress Corp., St. Petersburg, 1983-86; pres., chief exec. officer, dir. Progress Technologies Corp., St. Petersburg, Fla., 1985-89; pres., chief exec. officer, chmn. bd. Advanced Separation Technologies, Inc., St. Petersburg, Fla., 1985-89, Rein Energy Corp., Alachua, Fla., 1989-92; pres., CEO The Nouveau Group Inc., Winter Park, Fla., 1992—, also bd. dirs. Patentee in field. Mem. adv. coun. Engring. Sch. U. Fla., Gainesville, 1978—; bd. dirs. U. Fla. Rsch. Found., Inc., 1986-94; dir. GelTech, Inc., 1986-87. Lutheran. Home: 2711 Summerfield Rd Winter Park FL 32792-5111 Office: The Nouveau Group Inc 2711 Summerfield Rd Winter Park FL 32792-5111

SPALDING, ANDREW FREEMAN, lawyer; b. Toledo, June 24, 1951; s. Dean and Shirley Louise (Maitland) S.; m. Adele Taylor, May 17, 1980; children: Amy Louise, Adam Freeman, Audrey Wade, Abigail Maitland. BA, U. Calif.-Berkeley, 1973; JD, So. Meth. U., 1977. Bar: Tex. 1977, U.S. Dist. Ct. (so., ea., dist.) Tex. 1978, U.S. Ct. Appeals (5th cir.) 1978; bd. cert. Civil Trial Law Tex., Personal Injury Trial Law, Tex.. Bd. Legal Specialization. Assoc Bracewell & Patterson, Houston, 1977-84, ptnr., 1984—. Notes and comments editor Southwestern Law Jour., Dallas, 1976-77. Fellow Tex. Bar Found., Houston Bar Found.; mem. State Bar Tex., Tex. Assn. Def. Counsel, Houston Bar Assn., Def. Rsch. Inst., Knights Momus, Krewe Maximilian. Clubs: Houston. Office: Bracewell & Patterson 2900 S Tower Pennzoil Pla 711 Louisiana St Houston TX 77002-2716

SPALDING, JAMES STUART, retired telecommunications company executive; b. Edinburgh, Scotland, Nov. 23, 1934; arrived in Can., 1957, permanent resident, 1962; Student, Edinburgh U., 1951-52, Glasgow U., 1953. Gen. mgr., dir. United Corps. Ltd., Montreal, Que., Can., 1970-72; pension fund mgr. BCE, Inc., Montreal, 1972-74, sr. asst. treas., 1974-76, treas., 1976-79, v.p. finance, 1979-83, v.p. fin., 1983-84, exec. v.p. fin., 1984-90; ret., 1990; pub. gov. Can. Investor Protection Fund. Mem. Inst. Chartered Accts. Scotland, Order Chartered Accounts Que., Fin. Execs. Inst. Can. (past chmn.). Home: 54 Aberdeen Ave, Westmount, PQ Canada H3Y 3A4

SPALTY, EDWARD ROBERT, lawyer; b. New Haven, Oct. 1, 1946; s. Kermit and Elinor (Phelan) Turgeon; m. Suzy Clune; children: Thomas John, Kathleen Tess. AB, Emory U., 1968; JD, Columbia U., 1973. Bar: Mo. 1975, U.S. Dist. Ct. (we. dist.) Mo. 1975, U.S. Ct. Claims 1977, U.S. Ct. Appeals (8th cir.) 1984, U.S. Supreme Ct. 1994. Assoc. Webster & Sheffield, N.Y.C., 1973-74; mng. atty. Armstrong, Teasdale, Schlafly & Davis, Kansas City, Mo., 1974—. Contbr. articles to profl. jours. Chmn. bd. dirs. Mo. Easter Seals Soc., 1990-92; bd. dirs. Nat. Easter Seal Soc., former chmn. rules, agenda and resolutions com., former chmn. membership and orgnl. structure com. ho. of dels.; founding mem. Heartland Franchise Assn. With U.S. Army, 1968-70. Mem. ABA (litigation sect., franchising forum com.), Mo. Bar Assn. (civil rules and procedures com.), Kansas City Met. Bar Assn. (franchise law com., co-chair 14th and 16th ann. Nat. Franchise Law Inst.), Lawyers Assn. Kansas City, Mo. Orgn. Def. Attys., Def. Rsch. Inst., Am. Judicature Soc., Internat. Rels. Coun. Kansas City, Am. Arbitration Assn. (nat. panel arbitrators staff, arbitrator U.S. Dist. Ct. we dist. Mo. 1986—), Kansas City (Mo.) Club, Columbia Club (v.p.), Sigma Nu, Pi Sigma Alpha, Phi Delta. Home: 13703 NW 73rd St Parkville MO 64152-1120 Office: Armstrong Teasdale Schlafly & Davis 1700 City Ctr Sq 1100 Main St Kansas City MO 64105-2112

SPAN, ROBERT STEVEN, lawyer; b. N.Y.C., June 30, 1947; s. A. Noel and Dorothy (Herbine) S.; m. Crystal Elizabeth Wampler, May 2, 1971; 1 child, Evan Noel. AB, Dartmouth Coll., 1967; JD, Yale U., 1971. Bar: N.H. 1971, Calif. 1976, U.S. Ct. Appeals (9th cir.), 1976, U.S. Dist. Ct. (cen. dist.) Calif., 1976, U.S. Supreme Ct. 1987. Assoc Normandin, Cheney & O'Neill, Laconia, N.H., 1971-73; legis. dir. to U.S. Senator Thomas J. McIntyre Washington, 1973-76; assoc. Paul, Hastings, Janofsky & Walker, L.A., 1976-81, ptnr., 1981—. Pres. Westside Legal Svcs., Santa Monica, Calif., 1983-84. Fellow Am. Bar Found.; mem. ABA, L.A. County Bar Assn. (trustee 1989-91), Santa Monica Bar Assn. (trustee 1985-90, pres. 1988-89), Phi Beta Kappa. Office: Paul Hastings Janofsky & Walker 555 S Flower St Fl 23 Los Angeles CA 90071-2300

SPANBAUER, JAMES, chemicals executive; b. 1939. BS in Math., U. Wis., Oshkosh, 1962, MBA, 1979. EDP-operator Soo Line R.R., Janesville, Wis., 1957-63; sys. traffic mgr. Am. Can Co., Elm Grove, Wis., 1963-70; with Reynolds Consumer Products, Appleton, Wis., 1970—, now v.p. adminstrn. Office: Reynolds Consumer Products 670 N Perkins St Appleton WI 54914*

SPANDER, ART, sportswriter; b. L.A., Aug. 30, 1938; m. Elizabeth Newman, June 17, 1962; children: Debbie, Wendy. BA in Polit. Sci., UCLA, 1960. With UPI, 1960; joined Santa Monica (Calif.) Evening Outlook, 1963-65, San Francisco Chronicle, 1965-79; columnist San Francisco Examiner, 1979—. Author: Golf: The Passion and the Challenge, 1978, The Art Spander Collection, 1989. Recipient AP Sports Editors awards, Profl. Football Writers Am. awards, 1st place awards San Francisco Press Club, 1st Place Golf Writers Assn. Am. awards, Hayward-Newland Lifetime Achievement award Calif. Golf Writers. Office: San Francisco Examiner 110 5th Ave San Francisco CA 94103

SPANDORFER, MERLE SUE, artist, educator, author; b. Balt., Sept. 4, 1934; d. Simon Louis and Bernice P. (Jacobson) S.; m. Lester M. Spandorfer, June 17, 1956; children: Cathy, John. Student, Syracuse U., 1952-54; BS, U. Md., 1956. Faculty Cheltenham (Pa.) Sch. Fine Arts, 1969—; instr. printmaking Tyler Sch. Art Temple U., Phila., 1980-84; faculty Pratt Graphics Ctr., N.Y.C., 1985-86. One woman shows include Richard Feigen Gallery, N.Y.C., 1970, U. Pa., 1974, Phila. Coll. Textiles and Sci., 1977, Ericson Gallery, N.Y.C., 1978, 79, R.I. Sch. Design, 1980, Syracuse U., 1981, Marian Locks Gallery, Phila., 1973, 78, 82, Temple U., 1984, Tyler Sch. Art, 1985, University City Sci. Ctr., 1987, Gov.'s Residence, 1988, Wenniger Graphics Gallery, Provincetown, Mass., 1989, Mangel Gallery, Phila., 1992, Widener U. Art Mus., 1995; group shows Bklyn. Mus. Art, 1973, San Francisco Mus. Art, 1973, Balt. Mus. Art, 1970, 71, 74, Phila. Mus. Art, 1972, 77, Fundacio Joan Miro, Barcelona, Spain, 1977, Del. Mus. Art, Wilmington, 1978, Carlsberg Glyptotek Mus., Copenhagen, 1980, Moore Coll. Art, Phila., 1982, Tyler Sch. Art, 1983, William Penn Meml. Mus., Harrisburg, Pa., 1984 Ariz. State U., 1985, Tiajin Fine Arts Coll., China, 1986, Beaver Coll., Phila., 1988, The Port of History Mus., Phila. 1987, Sichuan Fine Arts Inst., Chong Qing, People's Republic China, 1988, Glynn Vivian Mus., Swansea, Wales, 1989, Phila. Mus. Art, 1990, Fgn. Mus., Riga, Latvia, 1995; represented in permanent collections Mus. Art, N.Y.C., Whitney Mus. Am. Art, N.Y.C., Mus. Modern Art, N.Y.C., The Israel Mus., Balt. Mus. (gov's prize and purchase award 1970), Phila. Mus. Art (purchase award 1977), Toyoh Bijutsu Gakko, Tokyo, Library of Congress, Temple U.; commd. works represented in U. Pa. Inst. Contemporary Art, 1991; co- author: Making Art Safely, 1993. Recipient award Balt. Mus. Art/Md. Inst. Art, 1971, Govs. prize and Purchase award Balt. Mus. Art, 1970, Outstanding Art Educators award Pa. Art Edn. Assn., 1982, Purchase award Berman Mus., 1995; grantee Pa. Coun. Arts, 1989. Mem. Am. Color Print Soc., Pa. Art Edn. Assn. Jewish. Studio: 307 E Gowen Ave Philadelphia PA 19119-1023

SPANEL, HARRIET ROSA ALBERTSEN, state senator; b. Audubon, Iowa, Jan. 15, 1939; m. Leslie E. Spanel, June 3, 1961; 3 children. BS in Math., Iowa State U., 1961. Rep. Wash. State, 1987-93, senator, 1993—. Home: 901 Liberty St Bellingham WA 98225-5632 Office: PO Box 40440 Olympia WA 98504-0440

SPANGLER, ARNOLD EUGENE, investment banker; b. Ft. Dodge, Iowa, Aug. 1, 1948; s. Kermit Charles and Cora (Buroos) S.; m. Penelope Angell, Nov. 8, 1980; children: Christopher Paul, Allison Elizabeth. BS, Iowa State U., 1970, MBA, Harvard U., 1972. Assoc. Hornblower & Weeks-Hemphill, Noyes, N.Y.C., 1972-74; product officer Citibank, N.Y.C., 1974-76; with Lazard Freres & Co., N.Y.C., 1976-89, gen. ptnr., 1983-89; mng. dir. mergers and acquisitions Paine Webber Inc., N.Y.C., 1989-91; sr. advisor Bentley Assocs., L.P., N.Y.C., 1992-93; mng. dir. Mancuso & Co., N.Y.C.,

1993—; bd. dirs. Syncor Internat. Corp., L.A. Home: 1165 Park Ave New York NY 10128-1210

SPANGLER, CLEMMIE DIXON, JR., university president; b. Charlotte, N.C., Apr. 5, 1932; s. Clemmie Dixon and Veva C. (Yelton) S.; m. Meredith Jane Riggs, June 25, 1960; children: Anna Wildy, Abigail Riggs. BS, U. N.C., 1954; MBA, Harvard U., 1956; LHD (hon.), Queens Coll., 1985; LLD (hon.), Davidson Coll., 1986, Furman U., 1993. Pres. C.D. Spangler Constrn. Co., Charlotte, 1958-86, Golden Eagle Industries, Inc., 1968-86; chmn. bd. Bank of N.C., Raleigh, 1973-82; dir. NCNB Corp., 1983-86; chmn. N.C. Bd. Edn., 1982-86; pres. U. N.C. Chapel Hill, 1986—; bd. dirs. BellSouth Corp., Atlanta, Nat. Gypsum Co., Charlotte. Past deacon Myers Park Bapt. Ch., vice-chmn. Charlotte-Mecklenburg Bd. Edn., Charlotte, 1972-76, So. Regional Edn. Bd., 1987—; past trustee Charlotte Nature Mus., Charlotte Symphony Orch., Crozer Theol. Sem.; past chmn. Charlotte adv. bd. Salvation Army; past bd. dirs. YMCA, Equitable Life Assurance Soc., Jefferson-Pilot Corp.; pres. bd. trustees Mint Mus. Art; bd. dirs. Union Theol. Sem., 1985-90, Assocs. Harvard Bus. Sch. With U.S. Army, 1956-58. Recipient Liberty Bell award Mecklenburg County Bar Assn., 1985, Alumni Achievement award Harvard Bus. Sch., 1988. Mem. Assn. Am. Univs., Bus. Higher Edn. Forum, Harvard Club (N.Y.C.), Univ. Club (N.Y.C.), Quail Hollow Country Club (Charlotte). Office: U NC Gen Adminstrn Office of President PO Box 2688 Chapel Hill NC 27515-2688

SPANGLER, DAVID ROBERT, college administrator, engineer; b. Flint, Mich., Aug. 17, 1940; s. John Solomon and Margaret Inger (McKinley) S.; m. Sally Jeanne Henry, Aug. 28, 1965; children: Timothy David, Megan Marie. BS, U.S. Mil. Acad., 1962; MS in Engring., U. Ill., 1966, PhD in Structural Dynamics, 1977. Registered profl. engr. Commd. 2d lt. U.S. Army, 1962, advanced through grades to lt. col., 1979; prof. math. U.S. Mil. Acad. U.S. Army, West Point, N.Y., 1968-71; engr. Korea Support Command U.S. Army, 1972-73; dep. dist. engr. C.E.U.S. Army, Walla Walla, Wash., 1973-74; research coordinator Def. Nuclear Agy. U.S. Army, Washington, 1976-79; bn. comdr. U.S. Army, Hawaii, 1979-81; inspector C.E. U.S. Army, San Francisco, 1981-82; ret. U.S. Army, 1982; prof. engring. St. Martin's Coll., Lacey, Wash., 1982-84, pres., chmn.—; mem. Nat. Com. for Tunnelling Tech., Washington, 1977-79; cons. Thurston County, Olympia, Wash., 1982-84. Contbr. articles to profl. jours. Bd. dirs. Econ. Devel. Coun., Thurston County, 1985-88, Wash. State Capitol Mus., 1988-91. Decorated Bronze Star with 2 oak leaf clusters, Meritorious Service medal, Def. Nuclear Agy. Joint Service medal. Mem. Soc. Mil. Engrs. (v.p. 1980-81, pres. 1973-74), Nat. Assn. Indsl. Colls. and Univs. (bd. dirs. 1992—, treas. 1994), Ind. Colls. Wash. (bd. dirs.), Assn. Benedictine Colls. and Univs. (pres. 1994-95), Rotary, Sigma Xi. Roman Catholic. Avocation: running. Office: St Martin's Coll Office of Pres Lacey WA 98503

SPANGLER, MILLER BRANT, science and technology analyst, planner, consultant; b. Stoyestown, Pa., Sept. 1, 1923; s. Elbert Bruce and Raye Isabel (Brant) S.; m. Claire Labin Kussart, Sept. 20, 1947; children: Daryl Claire, Philip Miller, Coreen Sue. BS with honors, Carnegie-Mellon U., 1950; MA, U. Chgo., 1953, PhD, 1956. Chem. engr. Gulf Rsch. Corp., Harmarville, Pa., 1950-51; assoc. engr. rsch. corp. IBM, Yorktown Heights, N.Y., 1956-60; mgr., market rsch. fed. systems div. IBM, Rockville, Md., 1960-63; program economist U.S. Agy. for Internat. Devel., Turkey, India, 1963-66; dir. ctr. for techno-econ. studies Nat. Planning Assn., Washington, 1966-72; chief, cost benefit analysis br. U.S. Atomic Energy Commn., Washington, 1972-75; spl. asst. policy devel. U.S. Nuclear Regulatory Commn., Washington, 1975-89; pres. Techno-Planning, Inc., Bethesda, Md., 1989-94; freelance writer, 1994—; mem. adv. bd. NSF Sea Grant Program, Washington, 1969, Environ. Profl. Jour., L.A., 1981-88. Author: New Technology and the Supply of Petroleum, 1956, New Technology and Marine Resource Development, 1970, The Role of Research and Development in Water Resources Planning, 1972, U.S. Experience in Environmental Cost-Benefit Analysis, 1980; contbr. numerous articles and papers to profl. jours. Recipient Planning Rsch. award Program Edn. and Rsch. in Planning U. Chgo., 1953. Mem. N.Y. Acad. Scis., Am. Assn. for the Advancement Sci., Nat. Assn. Environ. Profls., Soc. for Risk Analysis, Internat. Assn. for Impact Assessment., Tau Beta Pi. Republican. Methodist. Avocations: oriental gardening, traveling, photography, fishing. Home: 9115 Mcdonald Dr Bethesda MD 20817-1941

SPANGLER, SCOTT MICHAEL, private investor; b. Toledo, Aug. 4, 1938; s. Walter James and Martha Zoe (Hirscher) S.; m. Jean Galt Schmonsees, June 10, 1963; children—Karen Elizabeth, Scott Michael, Andrew Galt. B.M.E., U. Cin., 1961; M.B.A., Harvard U., 1963. Research asso. M.I.T., 1963-65; fin. exec. Cooper Industries, Inc., Mt. Vernon, Ohio, 1965-68; v.p. indsl. group White Motor Corp., Cleve., 1968-70; pres. Spangler and Co., Houston, 1970-73; dir., pres., chief exec. officer AZL Resources, Inc. (and affiliates), Phoenix, 1973-84; pres., chief exec. officer First Phoenix Capital, Inc., Scottsdale, Ariz., 1984-90; assoc. adminstr. AID, Washington, 1990-93; pres. First Phoenix Capital Inc., Phoenix and Washington, 1993—; bd. dirs. First So. Capital Corp., Alamosa Nat. Bank, Cen. Ariz. Bank, New London Oil Inc. Mem. World Pres.' Orgn., Chief Execs. Orgn., Harvard Club, Paradise Valley Country Club, Met. Club. Republican. Presbyterian. Office: 700 New Hampshire Washington DC 20037-2406

SPANIER, GRAHAM BASIL, university president, family sociologist; b. Capetown, South Africa, July 18, 1948; s. Fred and Rosadele (Lurie) S.; m. Sandra Kay Whipple, Sept. 11, 1971; children: Brian Lockwood, Hadley Alison. BS, Iowa State U., 1969, MS, 1971; PhD, Northwestern U., 1973. Assoc. dean, prof. in charge Pa. State U., University Park, 1973-82, pres., 1995—; vice provost, prof. SUNY, Stony Brook, 1982-86; provost, v.p. for acad. affairs Oreg. State U., Corvallis, 1986-91; chancellor U. Nebr., Lincoln, 1991-95. Author 10 books and 100 articles to profl. jours. Chmn. bd. dirs. Christian Children's Fund, Richmond, Va., 1985-94; del. White House Conf. on Families, Washington, 1980; host Pub. Broadcast TV programs, 1973-76; mem. NCAA Pres. Commn., 1995—. Recipient Moran award Am. Home Econ. Assn., 1987; named Outstanding Young Alumnus Iowa State U., 1982; Am. Assn. Marriage and Family Therapy fellow, 1983—, Woodrow Wilson fellow, 1972. Mem. Nat. Coun. on Family Rels. (pres. 1987-88, Outstanding Grad. Student award 1972), Population Assn. Am., Am. Sociol. Assn. (family sect. chmn. 1983-84), Internat. Sociol. Assn., Am. Assn. Higher Edn., Am. Assn. Family and Consumer Scis. Democrat. Avocations: aviation, magic, athletics. Office: Pa State U Office of Pres Old Main University Park PA 16802

SPANN, GEORGE WILLIAM, management consultant; b. Cuthbert, Ga., July 21, 1946; s. Glinn Linwood and Mary Grace (Hiller) S.; B.S. in Physics with honors, Ga. Inst. Tech., 1968, M.S., 1970, M.S. in Indsl. Mgmt., 1973; m. Laura Jeanne Nason, June 10, 1967; children: Tanya Lynne, Stephen William. Engr., Martin Marietta Corp., Orlando, Fla., 1968-70; research scientist Engring. Expt. Sta., Ga. Inst. Tech., 1970-75; v.p., dir. Metrics, Inc., mgmt. and engring. cons., Atlanta, 1973-78, pres., dir., 1978—; v.p., dir. Exec. Data Systems, Inc., 1981—; mem. Ga. Energy Policy Council, Ga. Metrication Council, NASA applications survey group for Landsat followon; mem. com. on practical applications of remote sensing from space Space Applications Bd. Nat. Research Council; market research cons. NOAA, NASA, pvt. cos. Regents scholar, 1964. Mem. Am. Soc. Photogrammetry, Urban and Regional Info. Systems Assn., Atlanta Jaycees, Tau Beta Pi, Phi Kappa Phi, Sigma Pi Sigma. Author papers, reports. Home: 3475 Clubland Dr Marietta GA 30068-2509 Office: 1640 Powers Ferry Rd Bldg 27 Marietta GA 30067

SPANN, WILMA NADENE, principal; b. Austin, Tex., Apr. 24, 1938; d. Frank Jamison and Nadene (Burns) Jamison Plummer; m. James W. Spann II, Aug. 2, 1958; children: James III, Timothy, Terrance, Kemberly, Kelby, Elverta, Peter, Margo. Ba, Marquette U., 1974; MS, U. Wis., 1985. Sec. Spandagle Coop., Milw., 1969-89; tchr. adult basic edn. Milw. area Tech. Coll., Milw., 1975-80; tchr. Milw. Pub. Sch. System, (1975-90, adminstrv. intern, 1990-91; asst. prin. Clara Barton Elem. Sch., Milw., 1992-93; asst. prin. in charge Greenfield Montessori Sch., Milw., 1993-94, 1993-94, prin., 1994—; asst. prin. in charge Cooper Elem. Sch., Milw., 1993; del. Inter Group Coun. Contbr. articles to profl. jours. Vice chair. vacation bible sch. Tabernacle Community Bapt. Ch., Milw., 1977-80, bd. dirs. Christian edn., 1981-90; v.p. women's aux. Wis. Gen. Bapt. State Conv., 1986&; instr. Wis. State Congress Christian Edn., 1982—, asst. dean Wis. Gen. Bapt. State

Congress Christian Edn., 1985; mem. sr. retreat com. Nat. Bapt. Youth Camp. Recipient cert. of Recognition, women's auxiliary Wis. Gen. Bapt. State Conv., 1986, Bd. Edn. Tabernacle Bapt. Ch., 1990. Mem. NAACP, Internat. Assn. Childhood Edn. (sec. 1990-92), Met. Milw. Alliance Black Sch. Educators, Nat. Bapt. Conv. (life, del. intergroup coun., Myra Taylor scholar com.), Marquette U. Alumni Assn., Assn. Childhood Edn. Internat. (sec. 1990-92), Ch. Women United (life), Phi Delta Kappa. Democrat. Avocations: writing, public speaking, traveling, reading. Home: 1906 W Cherry St Milwaukee WI 53205-2046 Office: Greenfield Montessori Sch 1711 S 35th St Milwaukee WI 53215-2004

SPANNINGER, BETH ANNE, lawyer; b. Bucks County, Pa., July 3, 1950; d. Feryl Louis and Nancy Elizabeth (Hendricks) S. AB magna cum laude, Muhlenberg Coll., 1972; MA, MEd, Lehigh U., 1975; JD, Temple U., 1979. Asst. dist. atty. Phila. Dist. Atty.'s Office, 1979-81; assoc. Bolger, Picker, Hankin & Tannenbaum, Phila., 1981-86, ptnr., 1986-88; sr. counsel SmithKline Beecham Corp., Phila., 1988—. Mem. ABA, Pa. Bar Assn., Phila. Bar Assn., Del. Valley Assn. Corp. Counsel, Animal Health Inst. (law com. 1992—), Phi Beta Kappa. Avocations: literature, jogging, theater, piano.

SPANNUTH, JOHN R., athletic association executive; b. Reading, Pa., Oct. 7, 1933; s. John R. and Virginia Spannuth; children: John III, Virginia. BA in Health and Phys. Edn., West Chester U., 1961. Aquatics dir. YMCA, Reading, 1956, Phillips Petroleum Co., Bartlesville, Okla., 1961-68; swimming coach West Chester (Pa.) U., 1959-61; exec. dir. Amarillo (Tex.) Aquatic Club, 1968-69; nat. aquatics adminstr. Nat. AAU, Indpls., 1970-74; exec. dir. Spl. Olypmics Kennedy Found., Washington, 1974-75; nat. swimming coach Country of Bahrain, 1980-83; dir. recreation Saudi Arabian Air Force, Riyadh, 1984-86; Cleve. County Family YMCA, Norman, Okla., 1986-89; pres., CEO U.S. Water Fitness Assn., Boynton Beach, Fla., 1989—; spkr. in field. Recipient C. Carson award Health & Fitness Leaders, Ranson Arthur award U.S. Masters Swimming Assn. Mem. Am. Swimming Coaches Assn. (pres.), U.S. C. of C. Office: US Water Fitness Assn PO Box 3279 Boynton Beach FL 33424-3279

SPANOGLE, ROBERT WILLIAM, marketing and advertising company executive, association administrator; b. Lansing, Mich., Nov. 13, 1942; s. William P. and Mary A. (Lenneman) S.; m. Ruth Ann Long, Jan. 14, 1967; children: John Paul Stephen Donald, Amy Lynn. AA, Lansing C.C., 1969; BA, Mich. State U., 1971; postgrad., U. Pa., 1985. Cons. Nat. League Cities, Washington, 1971-72; cons. Am. Legion, Indpls., 1972-75, dir. membership, 1975-79; exec. dir. Am. Legion, Washington, 1975-81, nat. adjutant, 1981—; chmn. HP Direct, Inc., Indpls., 1985—; chmn. exec. com. HP Direct, Inc., Washington, 1989—; mem. individual investors adv. com. N.Y. Stock Exch., N.Y.C., 1989-92. Bd. govs. USO, Washington, 1986-92; trustee St. Mary of the Woods Coll., Terre Haute, Ind., 1991—; treas. Civil War Battle Flags Commn. State of Ind., Indpls., 1994—; sec. 500 Festival Assocs., Indpls., 1985-91; mem. Vet.'s Day Coun., Indpls., 1989; bd. dirs. Indpls. Athletic Club, Crossroads Coun. Boy Scouts Am., 1985-92. With U.S. Army, 1962-65. Mem. Am. Legion of Mich. (Hon. Comdr. 1985), Kiwanis (exec. com. 1989-92). Roman Catholic. Avocations: golf, hunting, reading. Home: 672 Yosemite Dr Indianapolis IN 46217 Office: Am Legion 700 N Pennsylvania Indianapolis IN 46204

SPANOS, ALEXANDER GUS, professional football team executive; b. Stockton, Calif., Sept. 28, 1923; m. Faye Spanos; children: Dean, Dea Spanos Berberian, Alexis Spanos Ruhl, Michael. LLD (hon.), U. Pacific, 1984. Chmn. bd. dirs. A.G. Spanos Constrn. Inc., Stockton, Calif., 1960—; chmn. bd. dirs. A.G. Spanos Properties Inc., Stockton, Calif., 1960—, A.G. Spanos Mgmt. Inc., Stockton, Calif., 1967—, A.G. Spanos Enterprises Inc., Stockton, Calif., 1971—, A.G. Spanos Devel. Inc., Stockton, Calif., 1973—, A.G. Spanos Realty Inc., Stockton, Calif., 1978—, A.G. Spanos Jet Ctr. Inc., Stockton, Calif., 1980—, A.G.S. Fin. Corp., Stockton, Calif., 1980—; pres., chmn. bd. dirs. San Diego Chargers, 1984—; Chmn. bd. dirs. A.G.S. Spanos Land Co., Stockton, Calif., 1982—. Former trustee Children's Hosp., San Francisco, San Francisco Fine Arts Mus.; trustee Eisenhower Med. Ctr., Rancho Mirage, Calif.; hon. regent U. Pacific, Stockton, 1972-82; gov. USO, , Washington, 1982—. Served with USAF, 1942-46. Recipient Albert Gallatin award Zurich-Am. Ins. Co., 1973, Horatio Alger award Horatio Alger Found., 1982, medal of Honor Statue of Liberty-Ellis Islan Found., 1982. Mem. Am. Hellenic Edul. Progressive Assn., Calif. C. of C. (bd. dirs. 1980-85). Republican. Greek Orthodox. Avocation: golfing. Office: San Diego Jack Murphy Jack Murphy Stadium PO Box 609609 San Diego CA 92160-9609 also: A G Spanos Constrn Co 1341 W Robinhood Dr Stockton CA 95207-5511*

SPANOS, DEAN A., business executive; b. Stockton, Calif., May 26, 1950; s. Alex G. Spanos; m. Susan Spanos; children: Alexander Gus, John Dean. BBA, U. Pacific, 1972. Formerly engaged in apt. constrn. in various capacities; vice chmn. San Diego Chargers, from 1984; now pres. Spanos corp. orgn.; vice chmn. AGS Fin. Corp. Bd. regents U. Pacific. Co-winner Bing Crosby Nat. Pro-Am. Golf Tournament, 1985; winner Bob Hope Chrysler Classic, 1990, 91, AT&T Nat. Pro-Am. Golf Tournament, 1990; recipient Most Valuable Amateur trophy; mem. winning team in Sr.'s Reunion Tournament, Dallas, 1985. Avocation: golf. Office: San Diego Chargers San Diego Jack Murphy Stad PO Box 609609 San Diego CA 92160-9609

SPANOS, POL DIMITRIOS, engineering educator; b. Messini, Peloponnesus, Greece, Feb. 27, 1950; came to U.S., 1973; s. Dimitrios Constandin Spanos and Aicaterine Polychronis Bonaros; m. Olympia Constandin Critikou, Mar. 22, 1976; children: Demetri, Eudokia. Diploma in mech. engring., Nat. Tech. U., Athens, 1973; MS in Civil Engring., Calif. Inst. Tech., 1974, PhD in Applied Mechanics, 1976. Registered profl. engr., Tex., Greece. Rsch. asst. Calif. Inst. Tech., Pasadena, 1973-76, rsch. fellow, 1976-77; from asst. prof. to assoc. prof. U. Tex.-Austin, 1981-84, P.D. Henderson assoc. prof. engring., 1983-84; prof. mech. engring. and civil engring. Rice U., Houston, 1984-88, L.B. Ryon endowed chair in engring., 1988—; cons. on analytical and numerical applications of theory of dynamics and vibrations, worldwide. Author: Random Vibrations, Probabilistic Offshore Mechanics, Probabilistic Methods in Civil Engineering, Random Vibration and Statistical Linearization, Dynamic Analysis of Non-Linear Structures by the Method of Statistical Quadratization, Stochastic Finite Elements: A Spectral Approach, Computational Stochastic Mechanics, Probabilistic Structural Mechanics: Advances in Structural Reliability Methods, Random Vibrations: A Broad Perspective; contbr. to profl. jour. issues devoted to dynamics and vibrations; mem. editorial bd. 8 jours.; editor or co-editor 2 primary jours. on mechanics. Recipient Grand award of sci. N.V. Phillipps Co., Eindhoven, Netherlands, 1969, Presdl. Young Investigator award in earthquake engring. NSF, 1984-89, Cert. merit McDonnell Douglas Astronautics Co., Houston, 1987; scholar Greek Scholarships Instn., 1968-72. Fellow ASME (participant tech. confs. and coms., ASCE, Pi Sigma Gold medal 1982, G.L. Larson Meml. award 1991), ASCE (participant tech. confs. and coms., W.L. Huber Civil Engring. Rsch. prize 1989, Alfred M. Freudenthal medal, 1992, G.R. Brown award for Superior Teaching, Rice U., 1995, Am. Acad. Mechanics; mem. Earthquake Engring. Rsch. Inst., Internat. Assn. for Structural Safety and Reliability, Hellenic Profl. Soc. (sponsor scholarship com.). Office: Dept Mechanical Engring MS 321 Rice University 6100 Main St Houston TX 77005-1892

SPANOVICH, MILAN, civil engineer; b. Steubenville, Ohio, Feb. 19, 1929; s. Stanley and Katherine (Komazec) S.; m. Sylvia J. Tomko, Apr. 16, 1971. B.S. Civil Engring., Carnegie-Mellon U., 1956, M.S. Civil Engring., 1957. Registered profl. engr., Pa., N.Y., Ohio, Va., W.Va., Mich., N.Mex., Ky., Md., Colo., N.J., D.C., N.C., Fla. Instr. Carnegie-Mellon U., 1957-60; charter assoc., v.p. E. D'Appolonia Assocs., 1957-61; mem. civil engring. staff U. N.Mex., 1961-63; founder, sr. prin., chmn. Engring. Mechs., Inc., Pitts., 1963—. Contbr. articles on soil mechs. to tech. jours.; mem. editorial bd. Carnegie-Mellon Mag. Bd. dirs. Carnegie Mellon U. Andrew Carnegie Soc. Recipient Pitts. Young Civil Engr. of Yr. award, 1969. Fellow ASCE (Pitts. Civl Engr. of the Yr. 1987, chmn. numerous coms.), Am. Cons. Engrs. Council (mem. numerous coms.); mem. Cons. Engrs. Council Greater Pitts. (pres. 1972-74), Engring. Soc. Western Pa. (dir. 1972, 77-83), Nat. Soc. Profl. Engrs., Pa. Soc. Profl. Engrs. (pres. Pitts. chpt. 1971, Hornfeck award Pitts. chpt. 1979, state dir. 1976-79, Disting. Service award Pitts. chpt. 1985, Pa.

Engr. of the Yr. 1988, Profl. Devel. award 1989, Outstanding Svc. award Pitts. chpt. 1993), ASTM (chmn. task com. on relative density of granular soils 1959-63), Am. Concrete Inst., Hwy. Research Bd., Internat. Soc. Soil Mechs. and Found. Engring., Pitts. Geol. Soc., Am. Arbitration Assn., Profl. Engrs. in Pvt. Practice (chmn. 1970-71), Pitts. Builders Exchange, Soc. Explosives Engrs., Am. Soc. Hwy. Engrs., Carnegie-Mellon U. Alumni Assn. (mem. planning com.), Chi Epsilon Nat. Civic Engring. Honor Soc. Patentee found. systems. Home: 216 Eton Rd Pittsburgh PA 15205-1733 Office: 4636 Campbells Run Rd Pittsburgh PA 15205-1316

SPAR, EDWARD JOEL, demographer; b. N.Y.C., Jan. 2, 1939; s. Max and Dora (Miller) S.; m. Rosalind Getzoff, June 10, 1962; 1 dau., Zoe; m. 2d Elizabeth A. Harrington, Sept. 10, 1977; children: Melissa, Daniel, Matthew. B.B.A., CCNY, 1961. Statistician Alfred Politz Research, N.Y.C., 1962-65; sr. statistician Computer Users Co., N.Y.C., 1965-68; v.p. Daniel Starch, Mamaroneck, N.Y., 1968-71; pres. Market Statistics, N.Y.C., 1971—; demographic cons. N.Y. Times, 1982—; exec. dir. Coun. Profl. Assns. on Fed. Stats.; dir. Bill Comms., Strategy Rsch., Miami, Fla., Dualabs, Arlington, Va. Mem. Assn. Pub. Data Users, Am. Statis. Assn., Coun. Profl. Assocs. Fed. Statistics, (exec. dir.), Am. Mktg. Assn. Democrat. Jewish. Home: 5400 Bradley Blvd Bethesda MD 20814 Office: 633 3d Ave #1429 Duke St Alexandria VA 22314

SPARANO, VINCENT THOMAS, editor; b. Newark, Apr. 7, 1934; s. Gaetano and Agnes (Martucci) S.; m. Elizabeth Frances Rooney, Nov. 21, 1959; children: Donna Marie, Michael Thomas, Matthew John, Ellen Elizabeth. Student, Newark Coll. Engring., 1952-53; BS, NYU, 1959. Assoc. editor Sports Afield Mag., N.Y.C., 1959-60; editor Outdoor Life Mag., N.Y.C., 1960—; nat. syndicated columnist Gannett News Svc., 1989—. Author: Complete Outdoors Encyclopedia, 1972 (Library Assn. Outstanding Reference Work award 1973), The Outdoor Sportsman's Illustrated Dictionary, 1980, The American Fisherman's Fresh and Salt Water Guide, 1976; editor: Shooting-Why We Miss, 1977, Greatest Hunting Stories Ever Told, 1983, Classic Hunting Tales, 1986, Tales of Woods and Waters, 1989, Hunting Dangerous Game, 1992, Game Birds and Gun Dogs, 1992. editor-in-chief, pub. Northeast Guides to Saltwater Fishing and Boating, Southeast Guides to Saltwater Fishing and Boating. Committeeman Boy Scouts Am., 1970; chmn. Fairfield Fishing Derby, 1971—; trustee Camp Wyanokie Commn., Fairfield, 1976; bd. dirs. Catch and Release Found. Served to cpl. U.S. Army, 1954-56. Mem. Outdoor Writers Assn. Am. (bd. dirs.), Rod and Gun Editors Assn. Met. N.Y. (pres. 1977-78), Nat. Rifle Assn. (cert. firearms instr.), Fairfield Conservation and Sportsman's Assn. (pres. 1983-85), Sigma Delta Chi, Theta Chi. Roman Catholic. Lodges: Elks, K.C. Avocations: hunting; fishing; boating. Home: 17 Henning Dr Fairfield NJ 07044-1744 also: PO Box 821 190 Arnold Blvd, Barnegat Light Long Beach Island NJ 08008 Office: Outdoor Life Mag 2 Park Ave New York NY 10016-5603

SPARBER, GORDON MARK, music journalist; b. Mahoning Twp., Pa., Feb. 23, 1955; s. Max Isaac and Ethel (Lippman) S. MusB, Peabody Conservatory, 1977; MusM, John Hopkins U., 1979, MusD, 1988. Pianist Balt. Symphony Orch., 1983-90; freelance critic various newspapers and mags., 1983—; music critic Balt. News-Am., 1984-86; music columnist Patuxent Pub., Balt. and Washington, 1985-90; classical music reviewer The Washington Post, 1988-90; music and dance critic Winston-Salem (N.C.) Jour., 1990—; bd. dirs. N.C. Dance Alliance; arch. evaluator N.C. Arts coun., 1994; mem. music panel Md. State Arts Coun., 1990; mem. performing arts panel Western State Arts Fedn., 1992. Fellow Mus. Critics Assn. Insts., 1985-91, Am. Dance Festival Dance Critics Inst., 1991, Nat. Arts Journalism Program, 1995; recipient Pub. Svc. award Md. Soc. Profl. Journalists, 1990 winner Balt. Chamber Orch. Concerto Competition, 1984. Office: Winston-Salem Jour PO Box 3159 Winston Salem NC 27102

SPARBERG, ESTHER B., chemist, educator; b. N.Y.C., June 17, 1922; d. Abraham and Sarah (Kurnick) Braun; m. Lester S. Sparberg, Dec. 31, 1944; children—Andrew, Alice. B.S. in Chemistry, U. N.C., 1943; M.A., Columbia U., Tchrs. Coll., 1945, Ed.D., 1958. Chemist Interchem. Corp., 1943; technician Rockefeller Inst. Med. Research, 1943-44; tchr. chemistry Julia Richman High Sch., N.Y.C., 1946-47; mem. faculty Hofstra U., 1959-95, prof. chemistry, 1977-89, prof. emerita, 1989; also dir. NSF projects for tchrs. Sci. Co-author: A Laboratory Manual of Concepts in Chemistry, 1968, Chemical Quantitative Analysis: A New Approach, 1972, Ideas, Investigation and Thought, A General Chemistry Laboratory Manual, 1978; contbr. articles to profl. jours. Sci. manpower fellow Columbia U., 1956-57. Mem. Am. Chem. Soc., Am. Assn. Physics Tchrs., History Sci. Soc., Am. Sci. Tchrs. Assn., Kappa Delta Pi. Democrat. Jewish. Office: Hofstra U Hempstead NY 11550

SPARBERG, MARSHALL STUART, gastroenterologist, educator; b. Chgo., May 20, 1936; s. Max Shane and Mildred Rose (Haffron) S.; m. Eve Enda, Mar. 15, 1987. B.A., Northwestern U., 1957, M.D., 1960. Intern Evanston Hosp., Ill., 1960-61; resident in internal medicine Barnes Hosp., St. Louis, 1961-63; fellow U. Chgo., 1963-65; practice medicine specializing in gastroenterology Chgo., 1967—; asst. prof. medicine Northwestern U., 1967-72, assoc. prof., 1972-80; prof. clin. medicine, 1980—; instr. Washington U., St. Louis, 1961-63, U. Chgo., 1963-65. Author: Ileostomy Care, 1969, Primer of Clinical Diagnosis, 1972, Ulcerative Colitis, 1978, Inflammatory Bowel Disease, 1982; contbr. numerous articles to profl. jours. Pres. Fine Arts Music Found., 1974-76, Crohn's Disease and Colitis Found. of Am.; bd. dirs. Lyric Opera Guild, 1974—, Chamber Music Chgo., 1978-84; founding mem. Chamber Music Soc. North Shore Chgo., 1984—; physician to Chgo. Symphony Orch., 1981—. With USAF, 1965-67. Named Outstanding Tchr. Northwestern U. Med. Sch., 1972. Mem. AMA, ACP, Am. Gastroent. Assn., Am. Coll. Gastroent. (bd. govs.), Chgo. Med. Soc., Chgo. Soc. Internal Medicine, Chgo. Soc. Gastroenterology (pres.), Chgo. Soc. Gastrointestinal Endoscopy (pres.). Democrat. Jewish. Office: 676 St Clair Ste 1525 Chicago IL 60611

SPARER, MALCOLM MARTIN, rabbi; b. N.Y.C.; m. Erna Reichl (dec. Sept. 1990); children: Ruth, Arthur (dec.), Jennifer, Shoshana. AB, M in Hebrew Lit., Yeshiva U.; MA in Sociology, CCNY; cert. in pastoral counseling, Des Moines Coll. Osteopathic Medicine; PhD in Sociology, NYU. Ordained rabbi, 1953. Rabbi Jewish Home for the Aged, San Francisco; exec. dir. Rabbinical Coun. Calif., L.A., 1957-66; chaplain VA; adminstr. Tchr's. Coll. of West Coast, Torah U. (later Yeshiva U.), 1957-66; rabbi Beth El Jacob, Des Moines, 1966-69; rabbi Chevra Thilim, San Francisco, 1969-72, pres. emeritus, 1977—; pres. No. Calif. Bd. Rabbis, 1977—; sr. lectr. San Francisco Cmty. Coll.; liaison for Union of Orthodox Jewish Congregations Am., 1957-66, moderator radio series Lest We Forget, 1962, moderator TV specials on Jewish religon and holiday observances Sta. KNXT, L.A., 1964-65, Des Moines, 1966-69; instr. dept. philosophy Drake U., 1966-69; pres. San Francisco dist. Zionist Orgn. Am., 1969-82, also bd. dirs.; chmn., mem. nat. bd. San Francisco Bay Area Zionist Fedn., 1971-84; co-chmn. Jerusalem Fair, 25th Anniversary of State of Israel, 1973; chmn. Commn. on Soviet Jewry, Jewish Community Rels. Coun., 1974-81; bd. dirs. Jewish Community Fedn., 1982-84; cons. internat. leaders, founder Menorah Inst.; cons. Commn. on Christian-Jewish and Moslem Rels. to European Paliament Nations; cons. various govt. and non-govt. orgns.; writer, frequent lectr. colls., ch. groups on Judaica and world affairs.; pres. No. Calif. Bd. Rabbis; chmn. dept. world affairs/internat. politics Community Coll. San Francisco; chaplain Letterman Army VA Hosp., San Francisco Presidio; co-founder Black and Jewish Clergy; mem. San Francisco Coun. Chs. (bd. dirs. food bank program), United Jewish Appeal (chmn. rabbinic cabinet of western region); invited mem. del. bishops and ch. leaders various denominations conducting meml. svc. at Dachau, Fed. Republic Germany, 1988. Hon. chmn. Mayor's Commn. on Holocaust Meml., San Francisco; mem. Mayor's Task Force for Homeless; co-chmn. Gov.'s Family Task Force, San Francisco. With USN, World War II, Korean War, chaplain USAF. Address: PO Box 15055 San Francisco CA 94115-0055

SPARK, DAME MURIEL SARAH, writer; b. Edinburgh, Scotland, Feb. 1, 1918; d. Bernard and Sarah Elizabeth Maud (Uezzell) Camberg; m. S.O. Spark, (marriage dissolved); 1 son. Student, Heriot Watt Coll., Edinburgh; DLitt (hon.), Strathclyde U., 1971, U. Edinburgh. 1989. Gen. sec. Poetry Soc., 1947-49; founder Forum, 1949; editor Poetry Rev., 1949. Author: (non-fiction) Child of Light: A Reassessment of Mary Wollstonecraft Shelley,

1951 (rev. as Mary Shelley, 1987), Emily Brontë: Her Life and Work, 1953, John Masefield, 1953, The Essence of the Brontës, 1993; (poetry) The Fanfarlo and Other Verse, 1952, Collected Poems I, 1967, Going Up to Sotheby's and Other Poems, 1982, Curriculum Vitae, 1992; (fiction) The Comforters, 1957, Robinson, 1958, The Go-Away Bird and Other Stories, 1958, Memento Mori, 1959, The Ballad of Peckham Rye, 1960, The Bachelors, 1960, Voices at Play, 1961, The Prime of Miss Jean Brodie, 1961, The Girls of Slender Means, 1963, The Mandelbaum Gate, 1965 (James Tait Black Meml. prize 1966, Yorkshire Post Book of Yr. award 1965), Collected Stories I, 1968, The Public Image, 1968, The Very Fine Clock, 1968, The Driver's Seat, 1970, Not to Disturb, 1971, The Hothouse by the East River, 1973, The Abbess of Crewe, 1974, The Takeover, 1976, Territorial Rights, 1979, Loitering with Intent, 1981 (Booker McConnell prize nomination 1981), Bang-Bang You're Dead and Other Stories, 1982, The Only Problem, 1984, The Stories of Muriel Spark, 1985, A Far Cry from Kensington, 1988, Symposium, 1990, The French Window and the Small Telephone, 1993; (play) The Doctors of Philosophy, 1962; (radio plays) The Party Through the Wall, 1957, The Interview, 1958, The Dry River Bed, 1959, The Ballad of Peckham Rye, 1960 (Prix Italia 1962), The Danger Zone, 1961; editor: A Selection of Poems by Emily Brontë, 1952, My Best Mary: The Letters of Mary Shelley, 1953, The Letters of the Brontës: A Selection, 1954, Letters of John Henry Newman, 1957. Decorated Officier de l'Ordre des Arts et des Lettres, France, 1988, Dame of Order Brit. Empire, 1993; recipient Observer short story prize, 1951, Ingersoll prize, 1992. Mem. AAAL (hon. 1978). Address: care David Higham Assocs Ltd, 5-8 Lower John St, London W1R 4HA, England*

SPARKMAN, BRANDON BUSTER, educator, writer, consultant; b. Hartselle, Ala., Aug. 2, 1929; s. George Olen and Mary Louise (Jones) S.; m. Wanda Phillips, Sept. 13, 1952; children—Ricky Brandon, Rita Sharon, Robert Lee. B.S. Florence (Ala.) State U., 1952; M.A., U. Ala., 1958, Ednl. Specialist, 1961; Ed.D., Auburn (Ala.) U., 1970. Tchr., asst. prin. Phllips High Sch., Bear Creek, Ala., 1954-57; prin. Tuscumbia, Ala., 1957-65; asst. supt., 1965-69; ednl. cons. Auburn Center, 1969-70; mem. faculty dept. sch. adminstrn. Auburn U., 1970; asst. supt. for staff personnel devel. Jackson (Miss.) Pub. Schs., 1970-71, supt.; 1971-73; sr. supt. Richland County Sch. Dist. 1, Columbia, S.C., 1973-75; asst. supt. instruction Hartselle (Ala.) City Schs., 1975-80; supt. Guntersville (Ala.) City Schs., 1980-88; adj. prof. Auburn U., 1988—; pres., chief exec. officer The Right Combination Pub. & Ednl. Svcs. Corp., Guntersville (Ala.), 1984-93. Sr. author: Blueprint for a Brighter Child, 1973, STEPS (System for Teacher Evaluation of Pre-reading Skills), 1974; co-author: Preparing Your Preschooler for Reading, 1977, Competency Tests for Basic Reading Skills, 1978, Soaring High with Science, 1985, Soaring High with Social Studies, 1985; author: How Well Does Your Child Read, 1979; editor: The In-Between Years, 1979; creator: CORE (Program Management Through Computer Systems), 1975; editor, contbg. author: The Advantaged, A Preschool Program for the Disadvantaged, 1969, Writing Composition Made Easy, 1991, Expository Writing, 1993; contbr. articles to profl. jours. Bd. dirs. Morgan County chpt. ARC, United Givers Fund, Colbert-Lauderdale Child Study Center, Sheffield-Tuscumbia Credit Union; bd. govs. Jackson Symphony Orch.; adv. bd. Jackson Mental Health Center. Served with AUS, 1952-54. Recipient Human Relations award Jackson. Mem. Am., Ala assns. sch. adminstrs. (past pres.), Ala. Council Sch. Adminstrn. and Supervision (past pres.), Assn. Supervision and Curriculum Devel., Ala. Assn. Supervision and Curriculum Devel. (past pres.), Florence State U. Alumni Assn. (past pres.). Methodist (ch. sch. tchr., supt., vice chmn. ofcl. bd., chmn. commn. edn.) Lodge: Kiwanis. Home and Office: PO Box 961 Guntersville AL 35976-0961

SPARKMAN, CATHRYN, health facility administrator, lawyer; b. 1947. Degree, U. Tex., 1973. Atty., 1976—; with Rocky Mountain Hosp. & Med. Svc., Denver 1993—. Office: Rocky Mountain Hosp & Med Svc 700 Broadway Denver CO 80203*

SPARKMAN, ROBERT SATTERFIELD, retired surgeon, educator; b. Brownwood, Tex., Feb. 18, 1912; s. Ellis Hugh and Ola (Stanley) S.; m. Willie Ford Bassett, Feb. 21, 1942. B.A., Baylor U., 1935, M.D., 1935, LL.D., 1974. Diplomate Am. Bd. Surgery. Intern Cin. Gen. Hosp., 1935-36, resident in surgery, 1938-40; intern Good Samaritan Hosp., Lexington, Ky., 1936-37; resident in pathology Baylor Hosp., Dallas, 1937-38; practice medicine specializing in surgery Dallas, 1946—; chief dept. surgery Baylor U. Med. Center, Dallas, 1969-81; emeritus chief Baylor U. Med. Center, 1982—; mem. staff Parkland Meml. Hosp., Dallas; clin. prof. surgery U. Tex. Southwestern Med. Sch., Dallas, 1963—; chief civilian surg. cons. 5th U.S. Army Area, 1950-73; cons. to surgeon gen. U.S. Army, 1950—. Editor, also prin. author: The Texas Surgical Society—The First Fifty Years, 1965; editor: Essays of a Louisiana Surgeon, 1977, Minutes of the American Surgical Association, 1880-68, 1972, The Southern .Surgical Association; The First 100 Years, 1887-1987, 1989—; mem. editorial bd.: Am. Jour. Surgery; Contbr. articles to profl. jours. Bd. dirs. Friends of Dallas Pub. Libr., 1968—. Served to col. M.C. AUS, 1940-46, PTO. Decorated Bronze Star medal; recipient Disting. Alumnus award Baylor U., 1976, Disting. Alumnus award Coll. Medicine, 1976, Disting. Alumnus award Tex. Beta chpt. Alpha Epsilon Delta, A.C. Greene award Friends of Dallas Pub. Libr., 1993; commd. hon. Ky. col., 1980. Fellow ACS (bd. govs. 1962-70); mem. AMA, Am. Surg. Assn. (2d v.p. 1977-78), So. Surg. Assn. (pres. 1978, hon. mem. 1983), Okla. Surg. Assn. (hon.), Tex. Surg. Soc. (pres. 1965), Dallas Gen. Surgeons Soc. (pres. 1961), Internat. Soc. Surgery, Tex. Med. Assn., Soc. Med. Cons. to Armed Forces, James D. Rives Surg. Soc., Soc. Surgery Alimentary Tract, Internat. Biliary Assn., Philos. Soc. Tex., Alpha Omega Alpha, Parkland Surg. Soc. (hon. mem.), Petroleum Club, Dallas Country Club. Home: 5351 Wenonah Dr Dallas TX 75209-5517

SPARKMAN, STEVEN LEONARD, lawyer; b. Sarasota, Fla., May 30, 1947; s. Simeon Clarence and Ursula (Wahlstrom) S.; m. Terry Jeanne Gibbs, Aug. 23, 1969; children: Joanna Jeanne, Kevin Leonard. BA, Fla. State U., 1969, JD, 1972. Bar: Fla. 1972, U.S. Dist. Ct. (mid. dist.) Fla. 1974, U.S. Ct. Appeals (5th cir.) 1975. Legal rsch. asst. Office Gen. Counsel, Fla. Dept. Revenue, Tallahassee, 1971; legis. intern com. on community affairs Fla. Ho. of Reps., Tallahassee, 1971-72; jud. rsch. aide Fla. 2d Dist. Ct. Appeals, Lakeland, 1972-73; asst. county atty. Hillsborough County, Tampa, Fla., 1973-75; assoc. Carlton, Fields, Ward, Emmanuel, Smith & Cutler, P.A., Tampa, 1975-80, sr. atty.; mem. Fla. State U. Coll. Law Bd. Visitors, 1994—. Sec., bd. dirs. Bapt. Towers Plant City, Inc., 1981-84; deacon 1st Bapt. Ch., Plant City, 1980—. 1st lt. USAFR, 1973. Mem. ABA, Fla. Bar Assn. (exec. coun. local govt. law sect. 1978-79), Hillsborough County Bar Assn., Tampa Kiwanis (bd. dirs. 1980-82, Layman of Yr. 1984, 89). Democrat. Office: Carlton Fields Ward Emmanuel Smith & Cutler PA 777 S Harbour Island Blvd Tampa FL 33602-5729

SPARKS, BERTEL MILAS, lawyer, educator; b. 1918. BS, Ea. Ky. U., 1938; LLB, U. Ky., 1948; LLM, U. Mich., 1949, SJD, 1955. Bar: Ky. 1948. Instr. NYU, 1949-50, asst. prof., 1950-52, assoc. prof., 1952-54, 1954-67; prof. law Duke U., Durham, N.C., 1967-88; prof. law emeritus Duke U., 1988—; cons. subcom. on constrn. rights Com. Judiciary of U.S. Senate, 1966; mem. drafting com. for rev. laws relating to adminstrn. estates N.C. Gen. Statutes Commn., 1967—; mem. drafting com. multi-state bar exam Nat. Conf. Bar Examiners, 1970—. Author: Contracts to Make Wills, 1956, Cases on Trusts and Estates, 1965; former editor-in-chief: Ky. Law Jour.; contbr. articles to profl. jours. Served as spl. agt. CIC U.S. Army, 1941-45. Mem. Order of Coif. Office: Duke U Law School Durham NC 27706

SPARKS, DAVID EMERSON, bank holding company executive; b. L.I., N.Y., May 7, 1944; m. Anne M. McLaughlin; children—Christopher Drew, Deborah Lee. B.A., Furman U., 1966; A.M.P., Harvard U., 1980. C.P.A. Coopers & Lybrand, 1969-73; chief fin. officer Provident Nat., 1973-81; exec. v.p. and chief fin. officer Provident Nat. Corp. Bank, 1981-83; treas. PNC Fin. Corp., 1983—; exec. v.p. Midlantic Corp., Edison, N.J., 1983-89, ret., 1989; vice chmn., CFO Meridian Bancorp, Reading, Pa., 1990—. Mem. Am. Inst. C.P.A.s, Pa. Inst. C.P.A.s, Fin. Execs. Inst. Office: Meridian Bancorp Inc 35 N 6th St Reading PA 19601

SPARKS, DAVID STANLEY, university administrator; b. Phila., Dec. 8, 1922; s. Richard Frederick and Grace Dorothy (Tuttle) S.; m. Phyllis Ann Bate, June 12, 1949; children: Robert F., E. Anne. A.B., Grinnell (Iowa) Coll., 1944; M.A., U. Chgo., 1945, Ph.D., 1951. Instr., asst. prof., asso.

prof. U. Md., College Park, 1947-65; prof. history U. Md., 1965—, assoc. dean grad. studies and research, 1967-70, dean, 1970-77, acting vice chancellor for acad. affairs, 1976-77, acting v.p. grad. studies and research, 1978-79, v.p. grad. studies and research, 1979-87, acting v.p. for acad. affairs, 1982-83, v.p. acad. affairs, grad. studies and research, 1987-88, vice chancellor for acad. affairs, 1988-91, vice chancellor emeritus, 1991; vis. professorial lectr. dept. history Johns Hopkins, 1965. Co-editor, author: American Civilization: A History of the United States, 1960, The Making of American Democracy, Readings and Documents, 2 vols, 1962; Editor: Inside Lincoln's Army: The Diary of General Marsena Rudolph Patrick, 1964. Recipient research awards Am. Philos. Soc., 1958, Social Sci. Research Council, 1957. Mem. Am. So. hist. assns., Orgn. Am. Historians, Am. Assn. U. Profs. (pres. U. Md. chpt.), Nat. Acad. Univ. Research Adminstrs., Phi Kappa Phi. Club: Cosmos (Washington). Home: 10500 Rockville Pike Apt 1309 Rockville MD 20852-3350

SPARKS, HARVEY VISE, JR., physiologist; b. Flint, Mich., June 22, 1938; s. Harvey Vise and Ellen Louise (Paschall) S.; m. Barbara M. Taylor, Jan. 17, 1969; children—Matthew Taylor, Catherine Elliott, Wendy Sue, Harvey Vise. Student, U. Mich., 1956-59, M.D., 1963. Postdoctoral fellow dept. physiology Harvard Med. Sch., Boston and; U. Goteborg, Sweden; instr. U. Mich., 1966-67, asst. prof. physiology, 1967-70, assoc. prof., 1970-74, prof., 1974-78; asst. to dean U. Mich. (Med. Sch.), 1970-71, asst. dean, 1971-72; prof. physiology Mich. State U., East Lansing, 1978—, chmn. dept., 1979-89, vice provost human health programs, 1989-93; Fulbright lectr. U. Zimbabwe, 1986-87; mem. survey team, liaison com. on med. edn. AMA Am. Assn. Med. Colls.; mem. rev. teams NIH. Author: Casebook of Physiology, 1973, Essentials of Cardiovascular Physiology, 1987; contbr. numerous articles to profl. jours.; editor: (with others) Handbook of Physiology, 1979. Recipient Meritorious Service award Mich. Heart Assn., 1962, Borden award for med. student research, 1963, Merit award NIH, 1988; Mich. Heart Assn. student fellow, 1962-63; John and Mary Markle scholar, 1967-72; USPHS postdoctoral fellow, 1963-66; U. Mich. student research fellow, 1960-61; USPHS grantee, 1963—. Fellow Royal Soc. Medicine; mem. AAAS, Am. Physiol. Soc. (pres. 1987-88, editl. bd. Am. Jour. Physiology 1974-88), Microcirculatory Soc., Am. Heart Assn. (coun. on circulation, editl. bd. Circulation Rsch.), Mich. Pub. Health Inst. (bd. dirs. 1989-94), Internat. Union Physiol. Scis. (treas. 1990—), Coun. Internat. Exch. Scholars (Africa area com. 1988-91), Russian Acad. Sci. (fgn.), Victor Vaughn Soc., Alpha Omega Alpha, Phi Kappa Phi, Phi Zeta. Home: 8122 W Lovejoy Rd Perry MI 48872-8904 Office: Mich State U Dept Physiology East Lansing MI 48824

SPARKS, JOHN EDWARD, lawyer; b. Rochester, Ind., July 3, 1930; s. Russell Leo and Pauline Anna (Whittenberger) S.; m. Margaret Joan Snyder, Sept. 4, 1954; children: Thomas Edward, William Russell, Kathryn Chapman. A.B., Ind. U., 1952; LL.B., U. Calif., Berkeley, 1957; postgrad., London Sch. Econs., 1957-58. Bar: Calif. 1958. Assoc. Brobeck, Phleger & Harrison, San Francisco, 1958-66, ptnr., 1967—; adj. prof. law U. San Francisco, 1967-69; pres. Legal Aid Soc. San Francisco, 1978-79, dir., 1971-81; trustee Pacific Legal Found., Sacramento, 1975-80. Editor U. Calif. Law Rev., 1956-57. Served to 1st lt. Q.M.C. U.S. Army, 1952-54, Korea. Recipient Wheeler Oak Meritorious award U. Calif., Berkeley, 1986. Fellow Am. Bar Found.; Am. Coll. Trial Lawyers; mem. State Bar Calif., Bar Assn. San Francisco (bd. dirs. 1974-75), ABA, Am. Judicature Soc., Boalt Hall Alumni Assn. (pres. 1983-84), Bankers Club, Pacific Union Club (San Francisco), World Trade Club. Democrat. Office: Brobeck Phleger & Harrison Spear St Tower 1 Market Pla San Francisco CA 94105

SPARKS, MORGAN, physicist; b. Pagosa Springs, Colo., July 6, 1916; s. Harry Lysinger and Pearl (Morgan) S.; m. Elizabeth MacEvoy, Apr. 30, 1949; children: Margaret Ellen, Patricia Rae, Morgan MacEvoy, Gordon K. B.A., Rice U., 1938, M.A., 1940; Ph.D., U. Ill., 1943. With Bell Telephone Labs., Murray Hill, N.J., 1943-72; exec. dir. semicondr. components Bell Telephone Labs., 1968-69, v.p. tech. info. and personnel, 1969-71, v.p. electronic tech., 1971-72; pres. Sandia Nat. Labs., Albuquerque, 1972-81; dean Anderson Sch. Mgmt., U. N.Mex., Albuquerque, 1981-84. Contbr. articles on transistors, pn junctions and properties of semicondrs. to profl. jours. Rockefeller Found. fellow U. Ill., 1940-43. Fellow Am. Phys. Soc., IEEE (Jack A. Morton award 1977), Am. Inst. Chemists; mem. Am. Chem. Soc., Nat. Acad. Engring., Phi Beta Kappa, Sigma Xi, Phi Lambda Upsilon. Patentee semicondr. electronics. Home: 904 Lamp Post Cir SE Albuquerque NM 87123-4119

SPARKS, ROBERT DEAN, medical administrator, physician; b. Newton, Iowa, May 6, 1932; s. Albert John and Josephine Emma (Kleinendorst) S.; children: Steven, Robert, Ann Louise, John James. BA, U. Iowa, 1955, MD, 1957; D of Humanitarian Service, Creighton U., 1978. Diplomate Am. Bd. Internal Medicine. Intern Charity Hosp. of La., New Orleans, 1957-58, resident in internal medicine, 1958-59; asst. in medicine Charity Hosp. of La., 1958-59; fellow in gen. medicine and gastroenterology Tulane U. Sch. Medicine, 1959-62, instr. medicine, 1959-63, asst. prof., 1963-64, assoc. prof., 1964-68, prof., 1963-64, acting dean, 1964-67, assoc. dean, acting dean, 1967-68, vice dean, 1968-69, dean, 1969-72, chief sect. gastroenterology, 1968-72; chancellor Med. Ctr. U. Nebr., 1972-76, prof. medicine, 1972-76; v.p. U. Nebr. System, 1972-76; health program dir. W.K. Kellogg Found., Battle Creek, Mich., 1976-81, v.p. programming 1981-82, sr. v.p., 1982, pres., chief programming officer, 1982-86, pres., 1982-87, trustee, 1982-87, pres. emeritus, cons., 1988-92; cons. U. Tenn. Health Svc. Ctr. 1988-90, Boston U. Health Policy Inst., 1989-90; bd. dirs., mem. sci. compensation and trust rev. coms. Syntex Corp., Palo Alto, Calif., 1987-91; mem. overseers com. to visit Harvard U. Med. and Dental Schs., 1984-90; mem. vis. com. U. miami Sch. Medicine, 1982-86; assoc. med. dir. for addiction treatment svcs., dir. for edn. and rsch. Battle Creek Adventist Hosp., 1990-91; v.p. product safety and compliance Syntex Corp., Palo Alto, Calif., 1991-93; v.p. Howe-Lewis Internat. Inc., Menlo Park, N.Y., 1993-94, cons., 1994—. Contbr. articles to profl. jours. Bd. dirs. Nat. Coun. on Alcoholism and Drug Dependence, N.Y.C., 1982-93, treas., 1986-88, chmn., 1989-93, past chmn., 1991-92; bd. dirs. Battle Creek Symphony Orch., 1981-88, Lakeview Sch. Dist., Battle Creek, 1979-83, 88-91; trustee Monsour Med. Found., Jeannette, Pa., 1976-90, interim pres., 1989, chmn. bd., pres., 1989-90; mem. Pres. Reagan's Adv. Bd. Pvt. Sector Initiatives, Washington, 1986-89; chmn. bd. dirs. Bard Coll. Health Policy and Practice Inst., 1988—, Consumer Health Info. Rsch. Inst., 1990—, Chelsea-Arbor Treatment Ctr., 1990-91, Calhoun County Bd. Health, 1988-91, chmn., 1989-91; mem., bd. dirs. Mental Health and Addictions Found. of Mich., Battle Creek, 1991-93. Recipient Harvard Dental award Harvard U. Sch. Dental Medicien, 1992. Fellow ACP; mem. AMA, Nat. Acad. Scis. Inst. Medicine (com. study of treatment and rehab. svcs. for alcoholism and alcohol abuse, bd. mental health and behavioral medicine), Coun. Mich. Founds. (trustee 1986-88), Assn. Am. Med. Colls. (disting. svc. mem. award 1975), Phi Eta Sigma, Alpha Omega Alpha. Republican. Presbyterian. Avocations: tennis, bridge, reading, travel. Home: 7 Robert S Dr Menlo Park CA 94025 Office: Howe-Lewis Internat Inc Ste 360 1010 El Camino Real Menlo Park CA 94025

SPARKS, ROBERT EDWARD, chemical engineering educator; b. Marshall, Mo., Sept. 25, 1930; married; 3 children. BS, U. Mo., 1952; D Engring., Johns Hopkins U., 1960. Research engr. Esso Research & Engring. Co., 1960-62, sr. engr., 1962-63; from asst. to prof. chem. engring. Case Western Res. U., 1963-72; Stanley and Lucy Lapata prof. chem. engring. Washington U., St. Louis, 1972—; also dir. biol. transp. lab., chem. engring. dept.; cons. Nat. Inst. Arthritis and Metabolic Disease, 1965-74, Goodyear Tire & Rubber Co., 1966-74. Mem. AAAS, Am. Inst. Chem. Engrs., Am. Soc. Artificial Internal Orgns. Research in med. engring.; design of the artificial kidney, membrane transport, emulsion breaking, velocity profile control, mass transfer and fluid mechanics in chemical reactors, microencapsulation, controlled drug release, inventive reasoning. Office: Washington Univ Chem Engring Urbauer Hall Lindell-Skinner Blvd Saint Louis MO 63130

SPARKS, ROBERT WILLIAM, publishing executive; b. Seattle, Dec. 30, 1925; s. James Donald and Gladys (Simmons) S. Student, U. Wash., 1947-50; M.A., U. Hawaii, 1954, M.A., 1965. Editor, various publs., 1947-64; mng. editor U. Hawaii Press, 1964-66, dir., 1967-87; cons. East-West Ctr., Jour. Hawaiian History, Japanese and Chinese book pubs., 1987-92; mem. adv. bd. to pres. Kamehameha Schs. Served with AUS, 1944-46, PTO.

Recipient McInerny editorship, 1953; Pacific House citation Pacific and Asian Affairs Council, 1974. Mem. Assn. Am. Univ. Presses, Assn. Am. Publishers, Internat. Assn. Scholarly Publishers, Soc. for Scholarly Pub., Hawaiian Hist. Soc., Hawaii Found. History and Humanities, Honolulu Acad. Arts, Bishop Mus. Assn. Home: 3634 Nihipali Pl Honolulu HI 96816-3307

SPARKS, SAM, federal judge; b. 1939. BA, U. Tex., 1961, LLB, 1963. Aide Rep. Homer Thornberry, 1963; law clk. to Hon. Homer Thornberry U.S. Dist. Ct. (we. dist.) Tex., 1963-65; assoc. to ptnr., shareholder Hardie, Grambling, Sims & Galatzan (and successor firms), El Paso, Tex., 1965-91; dist. judge U.S. Dist. Ct. (we. dist.) Tex., 1991—. Fellow Am. Coll. Trial Lawyers, Tex. Bar Found. (life); mem. Am. Bd. Trial Advocates (advocate), State Bar Tex. Office: US Dist Ct #302 903 San Jacinto Blvd Austin TX 78701

SPARKS, SHERMAN PAUL, osteopathic physician; b. Toledo, Jan. 23, 1909; s. Earnest Melvin and Nancy Jane (Keller) S.; m. Helen Mildred Barnes, Aug. 1, 1930 (div. July 1945); 1 child, James Earl; m. Billie June Wester, Feb. 20, 1946 (dec. Apr. 1959); children: Randal Paul, Robert Dale; m. Joyce Marie Sparks, Jan. 23, 1965 (dec.); 1 child, David Paul. BS, U. Ill., 1932, MS, 1938; DO, Kirksville Coll. Osteopathy and Surgery, 1945. Diplomate Am. Bd. Osteo. Medicine. Tchr. high schs., Kincaid, Pesotum, Mt. Olive, Ill., 1930-42; intern Sparks Hosp. and Clinic, Dallas, 1945-46; pvt. practice, Rockwall, Tex., 1946—; team physician Rockwall High Sch., 1946-78; med. examiner Am. Cancer Soc., Rockwall, 1946-76. Coord. CD, Rockwall, 1946-80; chmn. Rockwall Centennial Assn., 1954, Rockwall County Rep. Com., 1964-78; pres. Rockwall PTA, 1961. Recipient Spirit of Tex. award, TV sta., Dallas, 1985; named Hon. State Farmer, Future Farmer's Am., 1980. Mem. Am. Coll. Gen. Practitioners, Tex. Osteo. Med. Assn. (chmn. chmn. 1946-54, numerous offices), Rockwall C. of C. (pres. 1961), SAR (pres. Plano chpt. 1989), Masons, Psi Sigma Alpha, Alpha Phi Omega. Avocations: travel, inventing. Home: 710 W Rusk St Rockwall TX 75087-3625 Office: Rockwall Osteo Clinic 106 N 2D St Rockwall TX 75087

SPARKS, THOMAS E., JR., lawyer; b. Little Rock, Jan. 11, 1942; s. Thomas E. and Marie Christine Lundgren, Sept. 11, 1976; children: Thomas Gunnar, Erik Richard, Andrew Pal. BS, Washington and Lee U., 1963; JD, U. Ark., 1968; LLM, Harvard U., 1970. Bar: Ark. 1968, Calif. 1970. Assoc. Pillsbury Madison & Sutro, San Francisco, 1970-76; ptnr. Pillsbury, Madison & Sutro, San Francisco, 1977-84, Baker & McKenzie, San Francisco, 1984-87, Pillsbury Madison & Sutro, San Francisco, 1987—. 1st lt. U.S. Army, 1965. Mem. ABA, Calif. Bar Assn., Olympic Club (San Francisco). Office: Pillsbury Madison Sutro 235 Montgomery St San Francisco CA 94104-2902

SPARKS, WALTER CHAPPEL, horticulturist, educator; b. New Castle, Colo., Aug. 22, 1918; s. Lester Elroy and Jean Ivene (Murray) S.; m. Barbara Ferne Gardner, May 31, 1942; children: Robert, Richard, Eugene. Student, Western State Coll., 1936-37; BS, Colo. State U., 1941, MS, 1943; postgrad., U. Minn., 1945, Wash. State U., 1949, 56-57; DSc (hon.), U. Idaho, 1984. Instr., head dept. agr. Pueblo Jr. Coll., 1941; grad. asst. Colo. State U., 1941-43, instr. horticulture, 1943-44, asst. prof., 1947; assoc. prof., 1947; assoc. horticulturist U. Idaho, Aberdeen, 1947-57; acting supt. Aberdeen br. Agrl. Expt. Sta., 1951, 57, 65, horticulturist, 1957—, research prof. horticulture, 1968—, prin. liaison coordinator for potato program, 1976—; exchange prof. Research Inst., Kolding, Denmark, 1972-73; adviser and lectr. on potato problems to various fgn. govts.; cons., adv., Israel, 1980, Philippines, 1981, Jamaica, 1988; dir. Postharvest Inst. Perishables, 1980—. Contbr. articles to profl. jours. Recipient 50th Anniversary medal Fed. Land Banks, 1967; Disting. Svc. in Potato Industry award Gov. of Idaho, 1967; named to Hall of Fame Potato Mus. Brussels, 1977, Alumni Svc. award, 1980, Disting. Faculty award Phi Kappa Phi, 1980, Disting. Svc. award rsch. in potato postharvest storage tech., 1987, Cert. of Appreciation Nat. Potato Rsch. Edn. Found., 1986, Agriculture Svc. award N.W. Food Processor Field Reps., 1987; elected Idaho Agrl. Hall of Fame, 1983; Eldred Jenne Rsch. fellow, 1957; named 1 of 100 "People Make the Difference" in Idaho, 1990. Mem. AAAS, Am. Inst. Biol. Scis., Am. Soc. Hort. Sci. (life), European Assn. Potato Research, N.W. Assn. Horticulturists, Entomologists and Plant Pathologists, Idaho Acad. Sci., Nat. Potato Research and Edn. Found. (cert. appraciation seed potato storage tech. 1986), N.W. Food Processors Assn. (Disting. Service award, 1987), N.W. Fieldman's Assn. (Disting. Agrl. Service award, 1987), Potato Assn. Am. (life mem., past pres., dir.), Western Regional Potato Improvement Group (past pres.), C. of C., Scabbard and Blade, Sigma Xi (Outstanding Research Paper award 1974), Gamma Sigma Delta (Outstanding Research Worker award 1977, award of merit 1978), Alpha Zeta, Beta Beta Beta, Epsilon Rho Epsilon. Club: Rotary. Home: 1100 Burnett Dr # 513 Nampa ID 83651 Office: U Idaho Rsch and Extension Ctr Aberdeen ID 83210 *If the food losses occurring from the farmer to the consumer (including storage) could be minimized or completely eliminated, the food supply could be significantly increased without bringing one more acre of land into production, or using one more pound of fertilizer, or using one additional gallon of fuel. Proper handling and storage can accomplish this goal.*

SPARLING, MARY CHRISTINE, foundation executive; b. Collingwood, Ont., Can., July 8, 1928; d. Alexander and Catherine Henrietta (MacDonald) Malcolm; m. Winfield Henry Sparling, June 17, 1950; children: Margaret, John. BA, Queen's U., Kingston, Ont., 1949; BEd (Gold medal 1970), St. Mary's U., Halifax, N.S., 1970; MA in Edn., Dalhousie U., 1978; DFA (hon), Nova Scotia Coll. Art & Design, 1994. Curator edn. N.S. Mus., Halifax, 1968-73; dir. art gallery Mt. St. Vincent U., Halifax, 1973-94; v.p. Neptune Theatre Found., Halifax, 1994—; cons. in field; bd. mem. Pier 21 Soc. Recipient Ohio State award for film script The Artist in Nova Scotia, 1977, Queen's Silver Jubilee medal, 1977, Outstanding Cultural Exec. award N.S. Cultural Fedns., 1991; Warner-Lambert award for disting. arts adminstrn. in Can., 1993. Fellow Can. Mus. Assn. (pres. 1974-76, coun. 1972-78); mem. N.S. Coalition on Arts and Culture. Unitarian. Home: 6030 Jubilee Rd, Halifax, NS Canada B3H 2E4

SPARLING, MARY LEE, biology educator; b. Ft. Wayne, Ind., May 20, 1934; d. George Hewson and Velmah Evelyn (McClain) S.; m. Albert Alcide Barber, Sept. 1, 1956 (div. Jan. 1975); children: Bonnie Lee Barber, Bradley Paul Barber. BS, U. Miami, Coral Gables, Fla., 1955; MA, Duke U., 1958; PhD, UCLA, 1962. Lectr. UCLA, 1962-63; asst. prof. Calif. State U., Northridge, 1966-72, assoc. prof., 1972-76, prof., 1976—. Contbr. articles to profl. jours. NSF grantee Calif. State U., Northridge, 1971-72, 81-83, 89, NIH grantee Calif. State U., Northridge, 1987-89. Mem. AAUP (pres. 1981-82), Am. Soc. Cell Biology, Soc. for Devel. Biology, Am. Soc. Zoologists, Sigma Xi (bd. dirs. Research Triangle, N.C. 1974-91). Avocations: tennis, gardening, backpacking, travel. Home: 8518 White Oak Ave Northridge CA 91325-3940 Office: Calif State U Biology Dept Northridge CA 91330

SPARLING, PETER DAVID, dancer, dance educator; b. Detroit, June 4, 1951; s. Robert Daniel and Emily Louise (Matthews) S. BFA, Juilliard Sch., N.Y.C., 1973. Dancer José Limón Co., N.Y.C., 1971-73; co. instr. London (Eng.) Contemporary Dance Theatre, 1983-84; prin. dancer Martha Graham Dance Co., N.Y.C., 1973-87; asst. prof. dance U. Mich., Ann Arbor, 1984-87, chmn. dance dept., assoc. prof., 1987—; artistic dir. Peter Sparling Presents Solo Flight, N.Y.C., 1977-82, Peter Sparling Dance Co., N.Y.C., 1980-84; co-dir. Ann Arbor Dance Works, 1984—; guest choreographer Victorian Coll. Arts, 1981, 84, Dance Uptown, Am. Ballet Theatre II, Cloud Dance Theatre, Taiwan, Ballet Gulbenkian, Lisbon, Utah Repertory Dance Theatre, Joseph Holmes Dance Theatre, Corning Dances, Fla. State U. Choreographer Divining Rod, 1973, Little Incantations, 1974, Three Farewells, 1977, Suite to Sleep, 1978, A Thief's Progress or The Lantern Night, 1979, Excursions of Chung Kuei, 1978, Nocturnes for Eurydice, 1978, Once in a Blue Moon, 1978, Harald's Round, 1979, Hard Rock, 1979, What She Forgot He Remembered, 1979, Sitting Harlequin, 1979, In Stride, 1979, Elegy, 1979, The Tempest, 1980, Orion, 1980, Landscape with Bridge, 1980, Nocturnes, Modern Life, Bright Bowed River, A Fearful Symmetry, Alibi, Rounding the Square, De Profundis, Rondo, Wings, Witness, The Boy Who Played With Dolls. Louis Horst Meml. scholar Juilliard Sch., 1973; Nat. Endowment for the Arts fellow 1971, 79, 83; grantee U. Mich. 1985-86, 89, Mich. Coun. for the Arts, 1986; recipient Choreographer's award Mich. Dance Assn., 1988, Artist's award Arts Found. Mich., 1989. Office: Univ of Michigan Dept of Dance Dance Bldg Ann Arbor MI 48109*

SPARR, DANIEL BEATTIE, federal judge; b. Denver, June 8, 1931; s. Daniel John and Mary Isabel (Beattie) S.; m. Virginia Sue Long Sparr, June 28, 1952; children: Stephen Glenwood, Douglas Lloyd, Michael Christopher. BSBA, U. Denver, 1952, JD, 1966. Bar: Colo. U.S. Dist. Ct. Assoc. White & Steele, Denver, 1966-70; atty. Mountain States Telephone & Telegraph Co., Denver, 1970-71; ptnr. White & Steele, Denver, 1971-74; atty. Wesley H. Doan, Lakewood, Colo., 1974-75; prin. Law Offices of Daniel B. Sparr, Denver, 1975-77; judge 2d dist. Colo. Dist. Ct., Denver, 1977-90; judge U.S. Dist. Ct. Colo., Denver, 1990—. Mem. Denver Bar Assn. (trustee 1975-78), Denver Paralegal Inst. (bd. advs. 1976-88), William E. Doyle's/Am. Inns of Ct., Am. Bd. Trial Advs., ABA, Colo. Bar Assn. Office: US Dist Ct US Courthouse C-540 1929 Stout St Denver CO 80294-2900

SPARROW, EPHRAIM MAURICE, mechanical engineering scientist, educator; b. Hartford, Conn., May 27, 1928; s. Charles and Frieda (Gottlieb) S.; m. Ruth May Saltman, Nov. 2, 1952; 1 child, Rachel Bernarr. BS, MIT, 1948, MS, 1949; MA, Harvard Coll., 1950, PhD, 1956; Doutor Honoris Causa, U. Brazil, 1967. Heat transfer specialist Raytheon Mfg. Co., 1952-53; rsch. specialist Lewis Rsch. Ctr., NASA, Cleve., 1953-59; prof. mech. engring. U. Minn., 1959—, chmn. fluid dynamics program, 1968-80; program dir. NSF, 1986-87, dir. chem., biochem. and thermal engring. divsn., 1986-88; vis. prof., chief AID mission U. Brazil, 1966-67; adv. prof. Xi'an Jiaotong U., 1984—; cons. in field, 1960—; pres. 1st Brazilian Symposium on Heat Transfer and Fluid Mechanics, 1966; mem. solar energy panel Fed. Coun. on Sci. and Tech., 1972; U.S. sci. committeeman 5th Internat. Heat Transfer Conf., 1973-74. Author: (with R.D. Cess) Radiation Heat Transfer, 1966, 2nd edit., 1978; editor: Handbook of Numerical Heat Transfer; hon. mem. editorial bd. Internat. Jour. Heat Mass Transfer, 1964—, Internat. Comm. in Heat Mass Transfer, 1975—; sr. editor Jour. Heat Transfer, 1972-80; editor Series in Computational and Phys. Processes in Mechanics and Thermal Scis., 1980—; chmn. editorial adv. bd. Numerical Heat Transfer, 1978—; contbr. over 560 tech. articles to profl. jours. Recipient Ralph Coates Roe award Am. Soc. Engring. Edn., 1978, Outstanding Teaching award U. Minn., 1985, Fed. Engr. of Yr. award NSF, 1988, Sr. Rsch. award Am. Soc. Engring. Edn., 1989, Horace T. Morse award for outstanding contbns. to undergraduate teaching, 1993; named George Hawkins Disting. lectr. Purdue U., 1985. Fellow ASME (Meml. award for outstanding contbn. to sci. heat transfer 1982, Max Jakob award for eminent contbn. 1976, Centennial medal 1980, Disting. Svc. award heat transfer div. 1982, Charles Russ Richards Meml. award 1985, Worcester Reed Warner medal 1986, 50th Anniversary award heat transfer div. 1988, Disting. lectr. 1986-91, 93-94); mem. NAE, Biomed. Engring. Soc. (faculty advisor 1994—), Sigma Xi (Monie A. Ferst medal for contbn. to rsch. through edn. 1993), Pi Tau Sigma. Home: 2105 Hoyt Ave W Saint Paul MN 55108-1314 Office: U Minn Minneapolis MN 55455-0111

SPARROW, HERBERT GEORGE, III, lawyer; b. Ft. Bragg, N.C., May 26, 1936; s. Herbert George and Virginia (Monroe) S.; m. Nancy Woodruff, Mar. 4, 1962; children: Amy Winslow, Edward Harrison, Herbert G. IV, Alison Kubler. AB cum laude, Princeton U., 1958; JD, U. Mich., 1961. Bar: Mich. 1961, Calif. 1964, D.C. 1979, U.S. Ct. Claims 1982, U.S. Tax Ct. 1983, U.S. Ct. Mil. Appeals 1962, U.S. Supreme Ct. 1976. Assoc. Dickinson, Wright, Moon, Van Dusen & Freeman, Detroit, 1965-70, ptnr., 1970—; adj. prof. Detroit Coll. Law, 1977—. Author numerous articles environ. law; speaker in field. Bd. dirs. Family Life Edn. Coun., Grosse Pointe, Mich., 1982-88 Capt. JAGC, U.S. Army, 1962-65. Mem. ABA, Mich. Bar Assn. (rep. assembly 1979-85, environ. law sect. coun. 1985-91), Calif. Bar Assn., D.C. Bar Assn., Detroit Bar Assn., Am. Arbitration Assn. (panel arbitrators 1975—), Mich. State Bar Found. (fellow 1989—), Environment Law Inst. (assoc.), Phi Delta Phi (pres. Kent Inn Assn., Ann Arbor 1985—). Office: Dickinson Wright Moon 500 Woodward Ave Ste 4000 Detroit MI 48226-3425

SPARROW, LARRY J., telecommunications executive. With GTE Corp., Thousand Oaks, Calif., 1967—; pres. GTE Northwest Inc., Thousand Oaks, Calif., 1992—; also prin. GTE Calif., Inc., Thousand Oaks, Calif., 1992—. Office: GTE California Inc One GTE Pl Thousand Oaks CA 91362*

SPARROW, SARA S., psychology educator, psychologist. BA summa cum laude, Montclair State Coll., 1958; MA in Speech Pathology, U. Fla., 1962, PhD in Clin. Psychology, Clin. Neuropsychology, 1968; MA (hon.), Yale U., 1986. Speech therapist Orange County Schs., Orlando, Fla., 1958-61, coord. speech and hearing programs, 1962-64; dir. summer speech clinic dept. speech U. Fla., 1965; postdoctoral fellow dept. psychology Yale U., New Haven, Conn., 1968-69, rsch. staff dept. psychology, 1969-70, rsch. assoc. dept. psychology, 1970-72, acting chief psychologist Yale Child Study Ctr., 1972-73, rsch. assoc., lectr. dept. psychology, Child Study Ctr., 1972-74, asst. prof. dept. psychology & Child Study Ctr., 1974-77, chief psychologist Child Study Ctr., 1974—, dir. psychology internship program Child Study Ctr., 1977—, chief psychologist Sch. Medicine, 1977—, lectr. dept. psychology, 1977-89, prof. psychology, 1986—, prof. dept. psychology, 1989—; chmn. quality rev. com. Conn. State Planning Coun. Devel. Disabilities, 1985-86, mem. 1980-86; evaluator programs in field, 1980—; cons. Community Health Care Ctr. Plan, 1973-79, Wyden Press Pubs., 1977-78, Chilton Book Co., 1979, NBC, 1979, UCLA, 1982-89, Dept. Edn. Hawaii, 1986—, Guilford Press, 1988—, Hallmark Found., 1990—, others; mem. adv. bd. Children's Mus., 1984—, Mental Health Film Bd., 1984—, Conn. Assn. Children Learning Disabilities, 1984-89; mem. project rev. com. tng. grants NIMH; co-chair human resources devel. task force Ctr. Health and Human Svcs., 1993; panelist NICHD, Washington, 1987, 88, chmn. 1989—; mem. consensus devel. panel NIH, 1989; presenter papers in field. Contbr. numerous articles to profl. jours. Recipient Disting. Effort award Conn. Psychological Assn., 1984; New Land Found. grantee, 1983-91, NIH grantee, 1983-92. Fellow Am. Psychological Assn.; mem. Internat. Neuropsychology Soc., Am. Assn. Mental Retardation, Orton Soc., Soc. Pediatric Psychology, Am. Acad. Mental Retardation. Office: Yale Univ Yale Station New Haven CT 06520

SPARROW, WILLIAM HOLLIDAY, corporate financial executive; b. Hagerstown, Md., July 8, 1943; s. Martin Herbert and June Rose (Shank) S.; m. Sybil G. Gibney, Oct. 10, 1964; children: Jeffrey Martin, Gregory William, Alexander Paul. BA in Liberal Arts, Johns Hopkins U., 1967. Various fin. positions CSX Corp. and predecessors, Balt. and Cleve., 1967-80; dir. econ. analysis CSX Corp. and predecessors, Balt., 1980-85, asst. v.p. econ. analysis, 1985, v.p., treas., 1985—. Mem. Parents Coun. James Madison U., Harrisonburg, Va., 1988—, chmn. academics subcom. Mem. Soc. Internat. Treas., Nat. Assn. Corp. Treas., Assn. Am. RRs (chmn. arrangements com. 1986), Brandmill Country Club (Midlothian, Va.), Bull and Bear Club. Avocations: reading, golf, tennis, travel. Home: 4007 Poplar Grove Rd Midlothian VA 23112-4736 Office: Grenberier Resort Mgmt Co Inc Rt 60 White Sulphur Springs WV 24986*

SPARROWE, ROLLIN D., wildlife biologist. BS in Wildlife Biology and Mgmt., Humboldt State Coll., 1964; MS, S.D. State U., 1966; PhD, Mich. State U., 1969. Asst. leader Mo. coop. wildlife rsch. unit Wildlife Mgmt. Inst., 1969-75, supr., 1976-79, chief divsn. coop. fish and wildlife rsch. units, 1979-83, chief divsn. wildlife rsch., 1983-84, chief office migratory bird mgmt., 1984-89, dep. asst. dir. refuges and wildlife, 1989-91; pres. Wildlife Mgmt. Inst., Washington, 1991—; leader planning team Coto Donana Nat. Park, Spain; negotiating team U.S. Can. and Mex.; speaker in field. Contbr. articles to profl. jours. Office: Wildlife Mgmt Inst 1101 14th St NW Ste 801 Washington DC 20005

SPARSHOTT, FRANCIS EDWARD, poet, educator; b. Chatham, Eng., May 19, 1926; emigrated to Can., 1950, naturalized, 1970; s. Frank Brownley and Gladwys Winifred (Head) S.; m. Kathleen Elizabeth Vaughan, Feb. 7, 1953; 1 dau. Pumpkin Margaret Elizabeth. B.A., M.A., Corpus Christi Coll., Oxford, Eng., 1950. Lectr. dept. philosophy U. Toronto, Ont., Can., 1950-55, Univ. Prof., 1982-91; asst. prof. Victoria Coll., 1955-62, assoc. prof., 1962-64, prof., 1964-91, dept. chmn., 1965-70; vis. assoc. prof. Northwestern U., Evanston, Ill., 1958-59; vis. prof. U. Ill., Urbana, 1966. Author: An Enquiry into Goodness and Related Concepts, 1958, The Structure of Aesthetics, 1963, A Divided Voice, 1965, The Concept of Criticism, 1967, A Cardboard Garage, 1969, Looking for Philosophy, 1972, The Naming of the Beasts, 1979, The Rainy Hills, 1979, The Theory of the Arts,

1982, The Cave of Trophonius, 1983, The Hanging Gardens of Etobicoke, 1983, Storms and Screens, 1986, Off the Ground, 1988, Sculling to Byzantium, 1989, Taking Life Seriously, 1994, Views from the Zucchini Gazebo, 1994, A Measured Pace, 1995. Served with Brit. Army, 1944-47. Am. Council Learned Socs. fellow, 1961-62; Killam sr. research fellow, 1977-78. Fellow Royal Soc. Can.; mem. Can. Philos. Assn. (pres. 1975-76), League Canadian Poets (pres. 1977-79), Am. Soc. for Aesthetics (pres. 1981-82), Aristotelian Soc., Classical Assn. Can. Home: 50 Crescentwood Rd, Scarborough, ON Canada M1N 1E4

SPATT, ARTHUR DONALD, federal judge; b. 1925. Student, Ohio State U., 1943-44, 46-47; LLB, Bklyn. Law Sch., 1949. Assoc. Davidson & Davidson, N.Y.C., 1949, Lane, Winard, Robinson & Schorr, N.Y.C., 1950, Alfred S. Julien, N.Y.C., 1950-52, Florea & Florea, N.Y.C., 1953; pvt. practice N.Y.C., 1953-67, Spatt & Bauman, N.Y.C., 1967-78; justice 10th judicial cir. N.Y. State Supreme Ct., 1979-82; adminstrv. judge Nassau County, 1982-86; assoc. justice appellate div. Second Judicial Dept., 1986-89; dist. judge U.S. Dist. Ct. (ea. dist.) N.Y., Bklyn., 1989-90, Uniondale, N.Y., 1990—. Active South Nassau Communities Hosp., Jewish War Vets. Mem. ABA, Assn. Supreme Ct. Justices State of N.Y., Bar Assn. Nassau County, Assn. of Bar of City of N.Y., Jewish Lawyers Assn. Nassau County, Bklyn. Law Rev. Assn., Long Beach Lawyers Assn., Bklyn. Law Sch. Alumni Assn., Theodore Roosevelt Am. Inn of Ct., Master of the Bench. Office: US Dist Ct 2 Uniondale Ave Uniondale NY 11553-1258

SPATT, ROBERT EDWARD, lawyer; b. Bklyn., Mar. 26, 1956; s. Milton E. and Blanche S. (Bakstansky) S.; m. Lisa B. Malkin, Aug. 11, 1979; 1 child, Mark Eric. AB, Brown U., 1977; JD magna cum laude, U. Mich., 1980. Bar: N.Y. 1981. Assoc. Simpson Thacher & Bartlett, N.Y.C., 1980-87, ptnr., 1987—. Mem. ABA, N.Y. State Bar Assn., City of N.Y. Bar Assn., Order of Coif, ACLU. Avocations: photography, boating, reading. Home: 286 West Trl Stamford CT 06903-2402 Office: Simpson Thacher & Bartlett 425 Lexington Ave New York NY 10017-3903

SPATTA, CAROLYN DAVIS, education consultant; b. Gauhati, Assam, India, Jan. 20, 1935; d. Alfred Charles and Lola Mildred (Anderson) Davis; m. John Robert Spatta, June 2, 1957 (div. Feb. 1964); children: Robert Alan, Jennifer Lynn Spatta-Harris; m. S. Peter Karlow, July 25, 1981. AB, U. Calif., Berkeley, 1964; MA, U. Mich., 1968, PhD, 1974. Rsch. asst. U. Calif., Berkeley, 1963-65; instr. Schoolcraft Coll., Livonia, Mich., 1968-74; corp. sec. Oberlin (Ohio) Coll., 1974-78; pres. Damavand Coll., Tehran, Iran, 1978-79; cons. pvt. practice, Washington, 1979-80; v.p., adminstr. E. Mich. U., Ypsilanti, Mich., 1980-81; Dir. Inst. grants programs, and adv. svc. Assn. Am. Colls., Washington, 1982-84; v.p., adminstrn. and bus. affairs Calif. State U. Hayward, 1984-92, prof. geography and environ. studies, 1992-94; cons. higher edn., 1995—; vis. lectr. E. Mich. U., Ypsilanti, 1969, 1970; mem. accreditation team Western Assn. Schs. Colls.; Fulbright scholar, Malaysia, 1994. Contbr. articles to profl. jours. Bd. dirs. Wellness, Inc.; mem. Trinity Parish, Menlo Pk., Calif. (pers., bldg. coms.), U. Mich. Alumni Assn., St. John's Episc. Ch. (pastoral care commn.), Chevy Chase, Md., Oberlin Open Space Com., Tenaya Guild, John Muir Hosp., Walnut Creek, Calif. (pres.), steering com. Ann Arbor Citizens for Good Schs.; trustee Pacific Sch. of Religion, 1992—. Recipient fellowship Nat. Defense Foreign Lang., 1966-68; Fulbright scholar, Malaysia, 1994—. Mem. Am. Assn. Higher Edn., Asian Studies on Pacific Coast, Assn. Asian Studies, Assn. Am. Geographers, Assn. Pacific Coast Geographers. Avocations: travel, reading, walking, cooking and entertaining, golf, art, music.

SPAULDING, FRANK HENRY, librarian; b. Danielson, Conn., July 12, 1932; s. Jacob Lindhurst and Frances (Upham) S.; m. Eugenia Jenewicz, May 25, 1963; children—Geoffrey Michael, Jennifer Anne. A.B., Brown U., 1957; M.S.L.S., Case Western Res. U., 1961. Supr. info. ctr. Colgate-Palmolive Co., Piscataway, N.J., 1961-65; group supr. library tech. processes Bell Labs., Holmdel, N.J., 1965-70, head library ops., 1970-84; mgr. library services AT&T Bell Labs., Holmdel, 1985-87, mgr. mktg. library network, 1984-86; library/info. cons., 1987—; pres. Sp. Libraries. Assn. 1986-87; treas. Am. Soc. for Info. Sci., 1983-86; pres. Documentation Abstracts, N.Y.C., 1983-85; dir. Universal Serials and Book Exchange, Washington, 1983-85, Palinet, Phila., 1979-81. Compiler: Managing the Electronic Library, 1983; author: Today's Information Specialist Tomorrow's Knowlege Technician, Knowledge Counselor in 2006, International Informatin: Informational Librarianship; creator: Task Force on the Value of the Informational Professional. Mem. Buten Mus. Wedgewood, Served to lt. USN, 1957-60. Mem. ALA (com. on accreditation 1989-93), Spl. Librs. Assn. (del. to Internat. Fedn. Libr. Assn. and Inst. 1987-89).

SPAULDING, JOHN PIERSON, public relations executive, marine consultant; b. N.Y.C., June 25, 1917; s. Forrest Brisbine and Genevieve Anderson (Pierson) S.; m. Eleanor Rita Bonner, Aug. 18, 1947; children: Anne Spaulding Balzhiser, John F., Mary T. Spaulding Calvert; m. 2d, Donna Alene Abrescia, May 15, 1966. Student Iowa State Coll., 1935-36, Grinnell Coll., 1936-38, U. Chgo., 1938-39. Reporter, Chgo. City News Bur., UPI, 1939-40; editor Cedar Falls (Iowa) Daily Record, 1940-41; picture editor Des Moines Register & Tribune, 1941-42, 47-50; pub. relations dir. Motor Club Iowa, Davenport, 1950-51; commd. 2d. lt. USAF, 1942, advanced through grades to maj., 1947, recalled, 1951, advanced through grades to lt. col.; ret., 1968; v.p. Vacations Hawaii, Honolulu, 1969-70; dir. pub. relations, mgr. pub. relations services Alexander & Baldwin, Inc., Honolulu, 1970-76; mgr. community relations Matson Navigation Co., Honolulu, 1976-81. Pres., Econ. Devel. Assn., Skagit County, Wash., 1983-85, Fidalgo Island Ednl. Youth Found.; mem. Anacortes (Wash.) Sch. Bd., 1982-88; mem. Gov.'s Tourism Devel. Council, 1983-85; mem. adv. com. State Ferry System, 1982—, productivity coun., 1990—; chmn. Everett chpt. S.C.O.R.E., 1984-86, Bellingham chpt., 1991—. Decorated Air medal. Mem. Pub. Relations Soc. Am. (pres. Hawaii chpt. 1974), Hawaii Communicators (pres. 1973), Nat. Def. Transp. Assn. (pres. Aloha chpt. 1980-81, Disting. Service award 1978-79), Air Force Assn., Can. Inst. Internat. Affairs, Anacortes C. of C., Sigma Delta Chi (life). Clubs: Propeller (pres. Port of Honolulu 1979-80), Honolulu Press, Fidelgo Yacht, Hawaii Yacht, Royal Hawaiian 400 Yacht (commdr. 1977-81), Rotary, Elks. Home: 6002 Sands Way Anacortes WA 98221-4015

SPAULDING, ROBERT MARK, lawyer; b. Buffalo, June 2, 1929; s. Mark Spaulding and Alice (Dee) Sparks; m. Mary Jean Tillett, Aug. 22, 1953; children: Joseph, M. Celia, Robert Mark Jr., William, Alyson. BA, St. Bonaventure U., Allegany, N.Y., 1951; JD, Harvard U., 1954. Bar: N.Y. 1954, U.S. Dist. Ct. (we. dist.) N.Y. 1955, U.S. Dist. Ct. (no. dist.) N.Y. 1972, U.S. Ct. Appeals (2d cir.) 1980. Mem. firm Phillips, Lytle, Hitchcock, Blaine & Huber, Buffalo, 1954—; lectr. in field. Author: Commentaries on Commercial Law. Mem. ABA, N.Y. State Bar Assn., Erie County Bar Assn. Office: Phillips Lytle Hitchcock Blaine & Huber 3400 Marine Midland Ctr Buffalo NY 14203-2834

SPAULDING, SUZANNE MARIE, nursing educator; b. Ithaca, N.Y., Mar. 26, 1939; d. Arthur Kenneth and Edna (Hogan) S. BS in Nursing, Nazareth Coll., Rochester, N.Y., 1960; MS in Nursing Edn., Syracuse U., 1971, PhD in Counseling, 1980. Sch. nurse, tchr. Webster (N.Y.) Central Schs., 1961-64, North Syracuse (N.Y.) Central Schs., 1965-69; staff nurse Community Gen. Hosp., Syracuse, 1964-65; health mgr. European tour Concordia Wind Ensemble, Boston, 1970-72; instr. U. R.I. Coll. Nursing, Kingston, 1971-73; grad. asst. dept. guidance counseling Syracuse U., 1973-76; nurse practitioner, medicine Crouse Irving Meml. Hosp., Syracuse, 1978-87, v.p. edn. Sch. Nursing, 1987—; cons. Onadanga Community Coll., Syracuse, 1975-76; speaker in field. Mem. Onondaga County Long-Term Care Profl. Adv. Bd.; chmn. Explorers post in nursing Hiawatha coun. Boy Scouts Am.; cons. N.Y. Edn. Dept. Helene Fuld Health program, 1989. Mem. Nat. League Nursing, N.Y. State Coalition Nurse Practitioners, N.Y. State Nursing Assn., Fedn. Accessible Nursing Edn. and Licensure, Nat. League Nursing Coun. (resolutions com.), N.Y. Hosp. Assn. (nursing shortage task force). Avocations: boating, biking, music. Home: 24 Ball Rd Syracuse NY 13215-1602 Office: Crouse Irving Meml Hosp Sch Nursing 736 Irving Ave Syracuse NY 13210-1690

SPAULDING, VERNON CHARLES, JR., military officer, gastroenterologist; b. L.A., Oct. 12, 1943; s. Vernon Charles Sr. and Muriel (Foley) S.; m. Paula Cady, Aug. 26, 1967; children: Raymond, Rebecca. BS, U. Calif.,

Berkeley, 1965; MD, Howard U., 1969; grad., Command & Gen. Staff Coll., 1987, U.S. Army War Coll., 1990. Diplomate Am. Bd. Internal Medicine. Am. Bd. Gastroenterology, Am. Bd. Med. Mgmt. Commd. 2d lt. U.S. Army, 1968, advanced through grades to brig. gen., 1993; intern Walter Reed Army Med. Ctr., Washington, 1969-70, resident in internal medicine, 1970-73; chief internal medicine Raymond W. Bliss Army Hosp., Ft. Huachuca, Ariz., 1973-75; gastroenterology fellow Letterman Army Med. Ctr., San Francisco, 1975-77; asst. chief gastroenterology svc. Madigan Army Med. Ctr., Washington, 1977-79, chief, 1979-83; chief dept. ambulatory patient care/dep. chief profl. svcs. Landstuhl Army Regional Med. Ctr., West Germany, 1983-85, dep. comdr. clin. svcs., 1985-87; comdr. Kenner Army Cmty. Hosp., Ft. Lee, Va., 1987-89, Martin Army Cmty. Hosp., Ft. Benning, Ga., 1990-93; commdg. gen. Dwight David Eisenhower Army Med. Ctr., Ft. Gordon, Ga., 1993—; S.E. Health Svc. Support Area; cons. gastroenterology 7th Med. Command, Germany, 1983-85; mem. Pres. Clinton's Task Force Health Care Reform, 1993; lectr. in field. Decorated Army Commendation medal, Order of Mil. Med. Merit, Legion of Merit with two oak leaf clusters. Mem. ACP, Am. Soc. Gastrointestinal Endoscopy, Nat. Med. Assn., Am. Coll. Physician Execs., Soc. Med. Cons. to Armed Forces. Office: Dwight D Eisenhower Army Med Ctr Fort Gordon GA 30905-5650

SPEAKER, RAY, Canadian government official; b. Enchant, Alta., Can., Dec. 13, 1935; m. Ingrid Marie Schwab, 1966; children: Kari Rae Anne, Michael Ray Mark. BEd, U. Alta. Tchr., coach; mem. Alta. Legis., 1963—; Minister Without Portfolio, 1967, Minister of Health and Social Devel., 1968, chmn. human resources devel. authority, 1969, house leader of ofcl. opposition, 1982-85, leader of rep. party, 1984; Minister Mcpl. Affairs Alta. Cabinet, 1989—; owner, operator family farm, 1975—. Coach various community sports programs. Lutheran. Office: Legis Blvd Room 127, Edmonton, AB Canada T5K 2B6

SPEAKES, LARRY MELVIN, public relations executive; b. Cleveland, Miss., Sept. 13, 1939; s. Harry Earl and Ethlyn Frances (Fincher) S.; m. Laura Christine Crawford, Nov. 3, 1968; children: Sondra LaNell, Barry Scott, Jeremy Stephen. Student, U. Miss., 1957-61; Litt. D. (hon.), Ind. Central U., 1982. News editor Oxford (Miss.) Eagle, 1961-62; news editor Bolivar Comml., Cleveland, 1962-63; mng. editor Bolivar Comml., 1965-66; dep. dir. Bolivar County Civil Def., 1963-65; gen. mgr. Progress Pubs., Leland, Miss., 1966-68; editor Leland Progress, Hollandale Herald, Bolivar County Democrat, Sunflower County News; press sec. U.S. Senator J.O. Eastland of Miss., 1968-74; staff asst. Exec. Office of Pres., Mar.-May 1974; press asst. to spl. counsel to Pres., May-Aug. 1974; asst. White House press sec., 1974-76, asst. press sec. to Pres., 1976-77; press sec. to Gerald R. Ford, 1977; v.p. Hill & Knowlton, Inc., internat. pub. relations and pub. affairs counsel, Washington, 1977-81; prin. dep. press sec. and asst. to Pres. of U.S., Washington, 1981-87; sr. v.p. Merrill Lynch & Co., Inc., N.Y.C., 1987-88; v.p. comm. No. Telecom Ltd., Washington and Toronto, Ont., Can., 1991-93; sr. v.p. corp. and legis. affairs U.S. Postal Svc., Washington, 1994—; corp. comm. cons., lectr. on press and politics, 1988-91; mem. pub. rels. seminar. Author: Speaking Out: The Reagan Presidency From Inside the White House; contbr. Crisis Repsponse: Inside Stories on Managing Image Under Siege. Recipient Presdl. Citizens medal, 1987, Gen. Excellence award Miss. Press Assn., 1988, Disting. Journalism Alumni award U. Miss., 1981, Hall of Fame, 1985, Silver Em. Miss. Scholastic Press Assn., 1988, Spl. Achievement award Nat. Assn. Govt. Communications, 1983, Silver Anvil award Pub. Rels. Soc. Am., 1988. Mem. Arthur Page Soc. (trustee), Sigma Delta Chi, Kappa Sigma (Man of Yr. 1982), Lambda Sigma, Omicron Delta Kappa. Methodist. Home: 4800 Thiban Ter Annandale VA 22003-4250

SPEAKS, RUBEN LEE, bishop; b. Lake Providence, La., Jan. 8, 1920; s. Benjamin and Jessie Bell (Nichols) S.; m. Janie Angeline Griffin, Aug. 31, 1947; children: Robert Bernard, Joan Cordelia, Faith Elizabeth. A.B., Drake U., 1946; M.Div., Drew Theol. Sem., 1949; S.T.M., Temple U., 1952; postgrad., Div. Sch., Duke U., 1961; D.D., Hood Theol. Sem., 1972. Ordained deacon Christian Ch., 1942; elder A.M.E. Zion Ch., 1947; minister St. Thomas A.M.E. Zion Ch., Somerville, N.J., 1947, Wallace Chapel A.M.E. Zion Ch., Summit, N.J., 1948-50, Varick A.M.E. Zion Ch., Phila., 1950-56, St. Mark A.M.E. Zion Ch., Durham, N.C., 1956-64, 1st A.M.E. Zion Ch., Bklyn., 1964-72; bishop 10th Episcopal Area, Roosevelt, N.Y., 1972-84, 8th Episcopal Area, Wilmington, N.C., 1984-88, 6th Episcopal Area, Salisbury, N.C., 1988—; ch. world service chmn. Overseas Mission Bd., A.M.E. Zion Ch. Author: Higher Catechism for Ministers and Laymen, 1966, The Minister and His Task, 1968, The Church and Black Liberation, 1972, God, In An Age of Scarcity, 1981, Prelude to Pentecost, A Theology of the Holy Spirit, 1985. Bd. dirs. Durham Com. on Negro Affairs, 1958-63, N.Y. Urban League, 1967-72; trustee Lincoln Hosp., Durham, Livingstone Coll., 1972—, U. N.C. Wilmington, 1984-88; chmn. exec. com. NAACP, 1958-63. Recipient Citizens award City of Durham, 1964, Meritorious Service award N.Y. Urban League, 1968, Chancellor's award for meritorious services as trustee U. N.C. at Wilmington, 1988. Mem. Nat. Acad. Sci. and Religion, World Methodist Coun. (exec. com.), Nat. Coun. Chs. U.S.A., World Coun. Chs. Home: PO Box 986 Salisbury NC 28145-0986 Office: 217 W Salisbury Salisbury NC 28144

SPEAR, ALLAN HENRY, state senator, historian, educator; b. Michigan City, Ind., June 24, 1937; s. Irving S. and Esther (Lieber) S. BA, Oberlin Coll., 1958; MA, Yale U., 1960, PhD, 1965. Lectr. history U. Minn., Mpls., 1964-65, asst. prof., 1965-67, assoc. prof., 1967—; mem. Minn. State Senate, St. Paul, 1973—, chmn. jud. com., 1983-93; chmn. crime prevention com., 1993—; pres. Minn. State Senate, 1993—; vis. prof. Carleton Coll., Northfield, Minn., 1970, Stanford U., Palo Alto, Calif., 1970. Author: Black Chicago, 1967. Mem. Orgn. Am. Historians, com. on suggested state legis. coun. of state govts., Nat. Conf. Gay and Lesbian Elected Offcls.; bd. dirs. Family and Children's Svc. of Mpls. Mem. Democratic Farm Labor Party. Avocations: cooking, travel, reading, classical music. Home: 2429 Colfax Ave S Minneapolis MN 55405-2942 Office: Minn State Senate 27 State Capitol Saint Paul MN 55155-1002

SPEAR, ANTHONY J., aerospace engineer. Project mgr. Magellan NASA, Pasadena, Calif. Recipient Laurels award-Space/Missiles, Aviation Week & Space Tech., 1991. Office: NASA-Jet Propulsion Labs 4800 Oak Grove Dr Pasadena CA 91109*

SPEAR, DEBORAH, surgical nurse, administrator; b. Beech Grove, Ind., June 27, 1954; d. Robert and Barbara Jean (McGee) James. Diploma, Mastin Sch. Nursing, Mobile, Ala., 1975. Cert. operating room nurse. Staff nurse Univ. Ala., Birmingham; head nurse Carraway Meth. Hosp., Birmingham. Mem. Assn. Operating Room Nurses.

SPEAR, HARVEY M., lawyer; b. Providence, May 24, 1922; s. Alfred and Esther (Marcus) S.; m. Ruth Abramson, June 27, 1965; children: Jessica Tjernberg, Elizabeth Anne. A.B., Brown U., 1942; LL.B., Harvard, 1948; M.A., George Washington U., 1949, LL.M., 1952, S.J.D., 1955. Bar: Mass. 1948, D.C. 1948, N.Y. 1954, U.S. Supreme Ct. 1954; CPA, Md. Asst. U.S. atty. D.C., 1948; legal asst. to chmn., asst. to vice chmn. SEC, 1948-50; spl. asst. to atty. gen. Dept. Justice, 1951-54; pvt. practice law N.Y.C. and Washington, 1956—; ptnr. Jacobs, Persinger & Parker, N.Y.C., 1991—. Contbr. articles to legal jours. Founding trustee Harlem Prep. Sch., 1967; mem. Met. Opera Assn., 1961—. Served to maj. USMCR, 1942-45. Mem. ABA, Assn. of Bar of City of N.Y. Home: 765 Park Ave New York NY 10021-4254 also: 78 Hither Ln East Hampton NY 11937 Office: 77 Water St Fl 17 New York NY 10005-4401

SPEAR, H(ENRY) DYKE N(EWCOME), JR., lawyer; b. New London, Conn., Feb. 26, 1935; s. Henry D.N. and Helene (Vining) S.; divorced. BA, Trinity Coll., Hartford, Conn., 1958; JD, U. Conn., 1960. Bar: Conn. 1960. Pvt. practice matrimonial law Hartford, 1961—. Mem. Conn. Bar Assn., Hartford County Bar Assn. Republican. Methodist. Office: 10 Trumbull St Hartford CT 06103

SPEAR, LAURINDA HOPE, architect. BFA, Brown U., 1972; MArch, Columbia U., 1975. Registered architect, Fla., N.Y., Colo.; cert. Nat. Coun. Archtl. Registration. Founding prin. Arquitectonica, Coral Gables, Fla.; mem. faculty U. Miami; lectr. in field. Prins. works include Pink Ho., Miami, Fla., 1978, The Palace, Miami, 1982 (Honor award Miami chpt. AIA 1982), Overseas Tower (Honor award Fla. chpt. AIA 1982, Honor award Miami chpt. 1982), The Atlantis, Miami, 1982 (Miami chpt. AIA award 1983), The Sq. at Key Biscayne (Honor award Miami chpt. AIA 1982), The Imperial, Miami, 1983, Casa los Andes (Record Hos. award Archtl. Record 1986), North Dade Justice Ctr., Miami, 1987 (Honor award Miami chpt. AIA 1989), Rio, Atlanta, 1988 (Honor award Miami chpt. AIA 1989), Banco de Credito del Peru, Lima, 1988 (Honor award Miami chpt. AIA 1989), The Ctr. Innovative Tech., Herndon, Va., 1988 (Honor award Va. chpt. AIA 1989, Honor award Miami chpt. 1990, Merit award Fairfax, Va., County Exceptional Design Awards Program 1990), Sawgrass Mills (Merit award Miami chpt. AIA 1990, Honor award Fla. chpt. 1991), Miracle Ctr. (Honor award Miami chpt. AIA 1989), Internat. Swimming Hall of Fame, Ft. Lauderdale, Fla., 1991, Banque de Luxembourg, 1993, Disney All-Star Resorts, Orlando, Fla., 1994, Foster City (Calif.) Libr., 1994, U.S. Embassy, Lima, 1994, USCG Family Housing, Bayamon, P.R., 1994, Altamira Ctr., Caracas, Venezuela, 1994. Mem. beaux arts support group Lowe Art Mus., Miami; bd. dirs. Miami Youth Mus. Recipient Design Awards citation Progressive Architecture, 1975, 80, Rome Prize in Architecture, 1978, Award of Excellence, Atlanta Urban Design Commn., 1989. Fellow AIA. Office: Arquitectonica 426 Jefferson Ave Miami Beach FL 33139

SPEAR, RAYMOND E., school system administrator. Supt. Coventry (R.I.) Pub. Schs. State finalist Nat. Supt. Yr., 1993. Office: Coventry Pub Schs 60 Wood St Coventry RI 02816-5825

SPEAR, RICHARD EDMUND, art history educator; b. Michigan City, Ind., Feb. 3, 1940; s. Irving S. and Esther Marion (Lieber) S.; m. Athena Tacha, June 11, 1965. B.A., U. Chgo., 1961; M.F.A., Princeton U., 1963; Ph.D., 1965. Mem. faculty Oberlin (Ohio) Coll., 1964—, prof. art history, 1975-83, Mildred Jay prof. art history, 1983—; dir. Allen Meml. Art Mus., 1972-83; disting. vis. prof. George Washington U., Washington, 1983-84; trustee Intermuseum Conservation Assn., 1972-83, pres., 1975-77. Author: Caravaggio and His Followers, 1971, 75, Renaissance and Baroque Paintings from the Sciarra and Fiano Collections, 1972, Domenichino, 1982; editor-in-chief Art Bull., 1985-88; contbr. articles to profl. jours. Regional exec. bd. ACLU, 1974-76. Recipient Premio Daria Borghese Gold medal, 1972; Fulbright scholar Italy, 1966-67; Am. Coun. Learned Socs. fellow, 1971-72; NEH fellow, 1980-81, sr. fellow Ctr. Advanced Study in Visual Arts Nat. Gallery Art, 1983-84, Guggenheim fellow, 1987-88; Nat. Humanities Ctr. fellow, 1992-93. Mem. Coll. Art Assn. Am. Democrat. Home: 291 Forest St Oberlin OH 44074-1509 Office: Oberlin Coll Dept Art Oberlin OH 44074

SPEAR, ROBERT CLINTON, environmental health educator, consultant; b. Los Banos, Calif., June 26, 1939; s. Clinton Wentworth Spear and Maytie Izetta (Patten) Gill; m. Patricia Warner, Dec. 15, 1962; children—Andrew Warner, Jennifer Ellen. B.S., U. Calif.-Berkeley, 1961, M.S., 1962; Ph.D., Cambridge U., 1968. Registered profl. engr., Calif. Systems engr. U.S. Naval Weapons Ctr., China Lake, Calif., 1962-65, 68-69; asst. prof. environ. health Sch. Pub. Health, U. Calif.-Berkeley, 1970-76, assoc. prof., 1976-81, prof., 1981—, dir. No. Calif. Occupational Health Ctr., 1980-89, assoc. dean Coll. of Engring. U. Calif.-Berkeley, 1994—. Contbr. articles on engring. aspects of environ. health to profl. jours. Mem. Nat. Adv. Com. on Occupational Safety and Health, U.S. Dept. Labor, 1986-88. NSF grad. fellow Cambridge U., 1965-68, sr. internat. fellow Fogarty Ctr., NIH, Australian Nat. U., 1977-78, research grantee Nat. Inst. Occupational Safety and Health NIH, State of Calif., 1971—. Mem. ASME, AAAS, Am. Indsl. Hygiene Assn., Assn. Univ. Programs in Occupational Health and Safety (pres. 1984-85). Democrat. Avocation: sailing. Home: 1963 Yosemite Rd Berkeley CA 94707-1631 Office: U Calif Sch Pub Health Berkeley CA 94720

SPEAR, THOMAS TURNER, history educator; b. Coral Gables, Fla., Dec. 23, 1940. BA, Williams Coll., 1962; MA, U. Wis., 1970, PhD, 1974; postgrad., Sch. Oriental and African Studies, 1976-77. Sr. lectr. La Trobe U., Melbourne, Australia, 1973-80; Charles R. Keller prof. Williams Coll., Williamstown, Mass., 1981-92; prof. U. Wis., Madison, 1993—; reviewer NEH; mem. editorial bd. Sprche und Geschichte in Afrika. Author: The Kaya Complex: A History of the Mijikenda Peoples of the Kenya Coast to 1900, 1978, Kenya's Past: An Introduction to Historical Method in Africa, 1981, (with Derek Nurse) The Swahili: Reconstructing the History and Language of and African Soc., 800-1500, 1985; editor: (with Richard Waller) Being Maasai: Ethnicity and Identity in East Africa, 1993; contbr. articles to profl. jours. Grantee Guggenheim Fellowship, 1995—, U. Wis., 1995—, Williams Coll., 1984, 87-89, 91-92, NEH, 1984, Am. Coun. Learned Socs., 1982, La Trobe U., 1976-77; recipient A.C. Jordan prize U. Wis., 1972, Fgn. Area fellowship Social Sci. Rsch. Coun./Am. Coun. Learned Socs., 1970-72, Coll. Tchrs. felloship NEH, 1987-88. Mem. Am. Hist. Soc. (contbr. Guide to Hist. Lit.), African Studies Assn., African Studies Assn. Australia (founder, exec. sec. 1978-80), Internat. African Inst. Office: U Wis Dept History 3211 Humanities 455 N Park St Madison WI 53706

SPEARE, ALDEN, JR., sociology educator; b. Hartford, Conn., Dec. 25, 1939; s. Alden and Elizabeth (George) S.; m. Mary Elizabeth Chapmen, May 21, 1966; children—Philip Alden, Laura Elizabeth. B. Engring. Physics, Cornell U., 1963; M.S. in Nuclear Sci., U. Mich., 1964, M.A. in Sociology, 1967, Ph.D. in Sociology, 1969. Field assoc. Population Council, Jakarta, Indonesia, 1974-76; prof. sociology Brown U., Providence, 1969—, chmn. dept. sociology, 1979-84; vis. researcher Bur. Census, Washington, 1984-85. Author: Residential Mobility Migration, 1975, Urbanization and Development: The Rural-Urban Transition in Taiwan, 1988, Regional and Metropolitan Growth and Decline in the U.S., 1988; contbr. articles to profl. jours. also chpts. to books in field. Mem. Population Assn. Am., Internat. Union Sci. Study Population, Am. Sociol. Assn., Am. Statis. Assn. Unitarian. Avocations: sailing; amateur radio. Home: 25 Orchard Pl Providence RI 02906-5419 Office: Brown U Dept Sociology Providence RI 02912

SPEARING, ANTHONY COLIN, English language educator; b. London, Jan. 31, 1936; came to U.S., 1987; s. Frederick and Gertrude (Calnin) S. MA, Cambridge U., Eng., 1960. W.M. Tapp rsch. fellow Gonville-Caius Coll. Cambridge U., 1959-60, asst. lectr. in English, 1960-64, official fellow Queens' Coll., 1960-87, life fellow, 1987—, dir. studies in English, 1967-85, lectr. in English, 1964-85, reader in medieval English lit., 1985-87; vis. prof. English U. Va., Charlottesville, 1979-80, 84, prof. English, 1987-89, Kenan prof. English, 1989—; William Matthews lectr. Birkbeck Coll., London, 1983-84; invited lectr. numerous colls. and univs. in U.K., Europe, Can. and U.S.; Lansdowne vis. fellow U. Victoria, 1993. Author: Criticism and Medieval Poetry, 1964, rev. edit., 1972; (with Maurice Hussey and James Winny) An Introduction to Chaucer, 1965; The Gawain-Poet: A Critical Study, 1970, Chaucer: Troilus and Criseyde, 1976, Medieval Dream-Poetry, 1976, Medieval to Renaissance in English Poetry, 1985, Readings in Medieval Poetry, 1987, The Medieval Poet as Voyeur, 1993; editor: The Pardoner's Prologue and Tale (Chaucer), 1965, rev. edit., 1994, The Knight's Tale (Chaucer), 1966, rev. edit., 1995, The Franklin's Prologue and Tale (Chaucer), 1966, rev. edit., 1994; co-editor: (with J.E. Spearing) Shakespeare: The Tempest, 1971, Poetry of the Age of Chaucer, 1974, The Reeve's Prologue and Tale (Chaucer), 1979; contbr. numerous articles to profl. jours. Mem. Medieval Acad. Am., Internat. Assn. U. Profs. English, New Chaucer Soc. (trustee 1986-90). Office: Univ Va Dept English Bryan Hall Charlottesville VA 22903

SPEARMAN, LEONARD H. O., SR., ambassador; b. Tallahassee, July 8, 1929; married; 3 children. BS, Fla. A&M U., 1947; MA, U. Mich., 1950, PhD, 1960. Prof. psychology So. U., 1960-70; dir. div. student spl. svcs. Office Edn. HEW, Washington, 1970-72, dir. div. student fin. assistance, 1972-75, assoc. commr. for student assistance, 1975-78, acting dep. commr. for higher and continuing edn., 1976-78, assoc. dep. commr. for higher and continuing edn., 1980; pres. Tex. So. U., 1980-86, disting. prof. psychology, 1986-88; amb. to Rwanda Kigali, 1988-90; amb. to Lesotho Maseru, 1990—.

SPEARS, ALEXANDER WHITE, III, tobacco company executive; b. Grindstone, Pa., Sept. 29, 1932; s. Alexander White and Eva Marie (Elliott) S.; m. Shirley Hence; 1 child, Craig Stewart. BS, Allegheny Coll., Meadville, Pa., 1953; PhD, SUNY, 1960. Research asso., then research fellow SUNY, Buffalo, 1956-58; instr. Millard Fillmore Coll., Buffalo, 1958-59; with Lorillard Corp., Greensboro, N.C., 1959—, v.p. R & D, 1971-74, sr. v.p. ops. and rsch., 1975-79, exec. v.p. ops. and rsch., 1979-91, vice chmn., COO, 1991—; also bd. dirs.; asst. prof. Guilford Coll., 1961-65, mem. bd. assocs., 1990, 91, trustee, 1995—; chmn. bd. visitors Greensboro Coll., 1990-94. Patentee in field; past editor: Tobacco Sci. Jour. Chmn. Coun. on Edn., 1974, mem. exec. com., 1987; chmn. model sch. task force Greensboro Bd. Edn. and Greensboro C. of C., 1975; mem. N.C. Humanities Coun., 1978-81, Piedmont Triad Airport Authority, 1993—; bd. dirs. United Way of Greensboro, 1980-85, N.C. Bus. Com. on Edn., 1983-84, Greensboro Devel. Corp., 1985—, pres., 1992-94; chmn. Greensboro Area United Negro Coll. Fund, 1982, Focus on Excellence campaign, 1984-86, Greensboro Pub. Sch. Fund, 1987; capital campaign chmn. Greensboro Area Girl Scouts U.S., 1987; bd. dirs. N.C. A&T U. Found., 1985-93, trustee, 1990—; bd. dirs. Greensboro NCCJ, 1990-92, chmn. ann. dinner, 1991, N.C. Citizens for Bus. and Industry, 1984-88, YMCA, 1989—, chmn., 1993-95; chmn. Hayes-Taylor Capital Campaign, 1990; bd. dirs. Ctr. Indoor Air Rsch., 1988—, chmn., 1991, Coun. for Tobacco Rsch., 1990—; mem. U.S. Tech. Study Group Cigarette Safety Act of 1984, U.S. CPSC Tech. Adv. Group Cigarette Safety Act of 1990; adv. bd. U. N.C, Greensboro, 1988-94; chmn. fundraiser campaign Greensboro Hist. Mus., 1988-89, trustee, 1989—. With AUS, 1953-55. Recipient Disting. Achievement award in tobacco sci. Philip Morris, 1970; named to Bus. Leaders Hall of Fame Jr. Achievement, 1994. Mem. AAAS, Am. Chem. Soc., Soc. Applied Spectroscopy, Am. Mgmt. Assn., N.Y. Acad. Scis., Internat. Coop. Ctr. Sci. Rsch. Relative to Tobacco (sci. com. 1972), Greensboro C. of C. (bd. dirs. 1974-75, 86-87, Nathaniel Greene award 1975, hon. chmn. 1994 Kmart Greater Greensboro Open), Rotary (bd. dirs. Greensboro club 1995—). Presbyterian. Office: Lorillard Tobacco Co 2525 E Market St Greensboro NC 27401-4815 also: One Park Ave New York NY 10016-5895

SPEARS, FRANKLIN SCOTT, retired supreme court justice; b. San Antonio, Aug. 20, 1931; s. Jacob Franklin and Lois Louise (Harkey) S.; m. Rebecca Nell Errington, Dec. 4, 1977; children: Franklin Scott, Carleton Blaise, John Adrian. Student, So. Meth. U., 1948-50; B.B.A., U. Tex., 1954, J.D., 1954. Bar: Tex. bar 1954, U.S. Dist. Ct. bar for Western Dist. Tex 1956, 5th Circuit Ct. bar 1961, U.S. Supreme Ct. bar 1966. Practiced law San Antonio, 1956-68; mem. Tex. Ho. of Reps., 1958-61, Tex. Senate, 1961-67; dist. judge 57th Jud. Dist. Tex., 1968-78; justice Tex. Supreme Ct., 1979-91; ret. Tex. Supreme Ct., San Antonio, 1991; of counsel Branton & Hall, San Antonio, 1991—. Exec. com. Frontier dist. Boy Scouts Am., 1964-68. Served with U.S. Army, 1955-56. Mem. State Bar Tex., San Antonio Bar Assn., Soc. Preservation and Encouragement Barbershop Quartet Singing in Am., SAR, Masons, Shriners. Democrat. Presbyterian.

SPEARS, GREGORY LUTTRELL, journalist; b. N.Y.C., Mar. 14, 1956; s. Robert Rae and Charlotte Lee (Luttrell) S.; m. Laurie Beth Chamlin, June 26, 1983; children: Michael Chamlin, Genevieve Rachel. Diploma, Kent Sch., 1974; MA, U. Rochester, 1979; MS in Journalism with honors, Northwestern U., 1981. Reporter Brandenton (Fla.) Herald, 1981-82; bus. reporter St. Petersburg (Fla.) Times, 1983-85; Washington corr. Knight-Ridder Newspapers, 1985-94; assoc. editor Kiplinger's Personal Fin. Mag., Washington, 1994—. Chmn. Nat. Press Bldg. Bd., 1993. Mem. Nat. Press Club (pres. 1992). Episcopalian. Home: 6508 40th Ave University Park MD 20782 Office: Kiplinger's 1729 H St NW Washington DC 20006

SPEARS, JAE, state legislator; b. Latonia, Ky.; d. James and Sylvia (Fox) Marshall; m. Lawrence E. Spears; children: Katherine Spears Cooper, Marsha Spears-Duncan, Lawrence M., James W. Student, U. Ky. Reporter Cin. Post, Cin. Enquirer newspapers; research Stas. WLW-WSAI, Cin.; tchr. Jiya Gakuen Sch., Japan; lectr. U.S. Mil. installations East Anglia, Eng.; del. State of W.Va., Charleston, 1974-80, former state senator, 1980-1993; mem. adv. bd. W.Va. Women's Commn., Charleston, 1976—; mem. state visitors com. W.Va. Extension and Continuing Edn., Morgantown, 1977-91, W.Va. U. Sch. of Medicine, 1992—. Chmn. advisory bd. Sta. WNPB, 1992—; congressional liaison Am. Pub. TV Stas. and WNPB-TV, 1992—; mem. coun. W.Va. Autism Task Force, Huntington, 1981—; mem. W.Va. exec. bd. Literacy Vols. Am., 1986-90, 94—, pres. 1990-92; mem. Gov.'s State Literacy Coun., 1991—; bd. dirs. Found. Ind. Colls. W.Va., 1986—; mem. regional adv.com. W.Va. Gov.'s Task Force for Children, Youth and Family, 1989; mem. USS W.Va. Commn., 1989; mem. exec. com. W.Va. Employer Support Group for Guard and Res., 1989, mem. steering com., 1990—. Recipient Susan B. Anthony award NOW, 1982, nat. award Mil. Order Purple Heart, 1984, Edn. award Profl. Educators Assn. W.Va., 1986, Ann. award W.Va. Assn. Ret. Sch. Employees, 1985, Meritorious Service award W.Va. State Vets. Commn., 1984, Vets. Employment and Tng. Service award U.S. Dept. Labor, 1984, award W.Va. Vets. Council, 1984; named Admiral in N.C. Navy, Gov. of N.C., 1982, Hon. Brigadier Gen. W.Va. N.G., 1984. Mem. Bus. and Profl. Women (Woman of Yr. award 1978), Nat. League Am. Pen Women (Pen Woman of Yr. 1984), Nat. Order Women Legislators, DAR, VFW (aux.), Am. Legion (aux.), Delta Kappa Gamma, Alpha Xi Delta. Democrat. Home and office: PO Box 2088 Elkins WV 26241-2088

SPEARS, JAMES GRADY, small business owner; b. Port Arthur, Tex., July 20, 1941; s. John Grady and Dorothy Nell (Haney) S. Grad. high sch., Port Arthur. Adminstr. Child Health & Devel. Studies, Oakland, Calif., 1962-69; sales mgr. Sunshine Biscuits Inc., Houston, 1969-75; owner, pres. S.W. Tookie Inc./Tookie's Restaurant, Seabrook, Tex., 1975—. Mem. Greater Houston Convention & Visitors Bur., Clear Lake Convention & Visitors Bur. With USN, 1959-62. Mem. Tex. Restaurant Assn., Houston Restaurant Assn., Seabrook Assn., Old Seabrook Assn. Republican. Roman Catholic. Avocations: collectibles, fine art, antiques, listening to records, self improvement. Home: 16310 Hickory Knoll Dr Houston TX 77059-5311 Office: SW Tookie Inc/Tookie's Restaurant 1202 Bayport Blvd Seabrook TX 77586-3406

SPEARS, KENNETH GEORGE, chemistry educator; b. Erie, Pa., Oct. 23, 1943. BS, Bowling Green State U., 1966; MS, PhD in Phys. Chemistry, U. Chgo., 1970. NIH predoctoral fellow U. Chgo., 1968-70; NRC-NOAA postdoctoral fellow NOAA, Boulder, Colo., 1970-72; prof. dept. chemistry Northwestern U., 1972—, mem. biomedical engring. dept., 1987—. Bd. editors The Rev. Scientific Instruments, 1980-83; contbr. articles to profl.jours. Alfred P. Sloan Found. fellow, 1974-76. Fellow AAAS; mem. Am. Phys. Soc., Am. Chem. Soc., Midwest Bio-Laser Inst. (adv. bd. 1985—). Office: Northwestern U Dept Chemistry Evanston IL 60208-3113

SPEARS, MARIAN CADDY, dietetics and institutional management educator; b. East Liverpool, Ohio, Jan. 12, 1921; d. Frederick Louis and Marie (Jerman) Caddy; m. Sholto M. Spears, May 29, 1959. BS, Case Western Res. U., 1942, MS, 1947; PhD, U. Mo., 1971. Chief dietitian Bellefaire Children's Home, Cleve., 1942-53; head dietitian Drs. Hosp., Cleve., 1953-57; assoc. dir. dietetics Barnes Hosp., St. Louis, 1957-59; asst. prof. U. Ark., Fayetteville, 1959-68; assoc. prof. U. Mo., Columbia, 1971-75; prof., head dept. hotel, restaurant, instn. mgmt. and dietetics Kans. State U., Manhattan, 1975-89; cons. dietitian small hosps. and nursing homes; cons. dietetic edn. Author: Foodservice Organizations Textbook, 3d edit., 1995; contbr. articles to profl. jours. Mem. Am. Dietetic Assn. (Copher award 1989), Am. Sch. Foodsvc. Assn., Food Systems Mgmt. Edn. Coun., Soc. Advancement of Foodsvc. Rsch., Nat. Restaurant Assn., Coun. Hotel, Restaurant, Inst. Mgmt. Edn., Manhattan C. of C., Sigma Xi, Gamma Sigma Delta, Omicron Nu, Phi Kappa Phi. Home: 1522 Williamsburg Dr Manhattan KS 66502-0408 Office: Kans State U 105 Justin Hall Manhattan KS 66506

SPEARS, MONROE KIRK, English educator, author; b. Darlington, S.C., Apr. 28, 1916; s. James Monroe and Lillian (Fair) S.; m. Betty Greene, Sept. 3, 1941; 1 dau., Julia Herndon. A.B., A.M., U. S.C., 1937; Ph.D., Princeton U., 1940; D. Letters (hon.), U. of South, 1983. Instr. English U. Wis., 1940-42; asst. prof., then assoc. prof. English Vanderbilt U., 1946-52; prof. English U. South, 1952-64; Libbie Shearn Moody prof. English Rice U., 1964-86, prof. emeritus, 1986—; vis. prof. U. Wash., summer 1960, U. Mich., summer 1961, Swarthmore Coll., 1961-62; mem. adv. council dept. English Princeton U., 1960-66, Christian Gauss lectr., 1975; dir. NEH Seminars for Coll. Tchrs. Rice U., 1975, 78. Author: The Poetry of W.H. Auden: The Disenchanted Island, 1963, Hart Crane, 1965, Dionysus and the City: Modernism in Twentieth Century Poetry, 1970, Space Against Time in Modern American Poetry, 1972, The Levitator and Other Poems, 1975, American Ambitions: Selected Essays on Literary and Cultural Themes, 1987, Countries of the Mind: Literary Explorations, 1992, One Writer's

Reality, 1995; editor: (with H.B. Wright) The Literary Works of Matthew Prior, 2 vols., 1959, W.H. Auden: A Collection of Critical Essays, 1964, The Narrative Poetry of Shakespeare, 1968, Sewanee Rev., 1952-61, adv. editor, 1961-73. Served to capt. AUS and USAAF, 1942-46, ETO. Am. Philos. Soc. and Carnegie Found. grantee, 1949; Rockefeller fellow, 1956, Guggenheim fellow, 1965-66, 72-73, Brown Found. fellow, U. South, 1988. Fellowship So. Writers, S.C. Acad. Authors. Democrat. Episcopalian. Home: 117 Carruthers Rd Sewanee TN 37375

SPEARS, RICHARD W., oil company executive; b. 1936; married. BA, Georgetown Coll., 1957; LLB, U. Ky., 1961. Atty. Texaco Inc. 1961-64; staff atty. Ashland Oil Inc., Russell, Ky., 1964-75; gen. counsel Ashland Oil Inc., Russell, 1975-76, v.p. law, 1976-79, adminstrv. v.p., 1979-80, sr. v.p. human resources, 1980-81, sr. v.p. group operating officer human resources and law; now sr. v.p. human resources and law Ashland Oil Inc. With USAR, 1954-61. Office: Ashland Oil Inc PO Box 391 Ashland KY 41105-0391

SPEARS, SALLY, lawyer; b. San Antonio, Aug. 29, 1938; d. Adrian Anthony and Elizabeth (Wylie) S.; m. Tor Hultgreen, July 15, 1961 (div. Jan. 1982); children: Dagny Elizabeth, Sara Kirsten, Kara Spears. BA, U. Tex., 1960, LLB, 1965. Bar: Tex. 1961, Ill. 1971. Practice law Stamford, Conn., 1966-67, Chgo., 1970-71, Northbrook, Ill., 1972-73, Toronto, Ont., Can., 1973-81; assoc. firm Cummings & Lockwood, Stamford, 1966-67, Kirkland & Ellis, Chgo., 1970-71; sr. atty. Allstate Ins. Co., Northbrook, Ill., 1971-73; gen. counsel, sec. Reed Paper Ltd., Reed Ltd., Toronto, 1973-78, Denison Mines Ltd., Toronto, 1978-81; pvt. practice law San Antonio, 1981—. Mem. Tex. Bar Assn., San Antonio Bar Assn., Bankruptcy Bar Assn., Bexar County Women's Bar Assn., San Antonio Country Club, The Club at Sonterra. Home: 433 Evans Ave San Antonio TX 78209-3725 Office: Ste 211 4600 Broadway San Antonio TX 78209

SPEAS, CHARLES STUART, personnel director; b. Phila., Jan. 1, 1944; s. Austin LeRoy and Peggy Elaine (Drake) S.; m. Julie Ellen Royce, Apr. 10, 1965; children: Eric S. Speas, Robert Austin Speas. Student, Tri-State Coll., U. Notre Dame, Purdue U. Lic. agt. in life, accident and health ins., Ind. Sr. scheduling coord. Excel Industries, Elkhart, Ind., 1966-73; corp. dir. pers. EFP Corp., Elkhart, 1973—; cons. various Elkhart, Goshen area bus., 1980—. Contbr. articles profl. jours. Participant Soviet/Am. Conf. on Trade and Econ. Cooperation, Kremlin, 1991. With USAF, 1962-66. Mem. Ind. Pers. Assn., Goshen Indsl. Club (recipient cert. of appreciation 1990), Soc. for Human Resources Mgmt., Elkhart C. of C. (task force on healthcare availability/cost). Republican. Avocations: woodworking, fishing, gardening. Home: 23683 River Dr Goshen IN 46526-9000 Office: EFP Corp 223 Middleton Run Rd Elkhart IN 46516-5488

SPEAS, RAYMOND AARON, retired insurance company executive; b. Lynneville, Iowa, Feb. 10, 1925; s. Harold H. and Susie B. Speas; m. Betty Jane Welshhons, Apr. 27, 1945; children: Raymond D., Gaylynn J. BS in Bus. Adminstrn., Drake U., 1951. CLU. With Equitable Life Ins. Co. of Iowa, Des Moines, 1951—, v.p., cont., 1967-76; sr. v.p., adminstrn. Equitable of Iowa Cos., Des Moines, 1976-77, sr. v.p., treas., 1977-82, exec. v.p., treas., 1982-92, also bd. dirs.; bd. dirs. E.I. Sales Inc.; exec. v.p., treas. Equitable Am. Life Ins. Co. Mem. internat. Youth Coun. YMCA, 1966-74, bd. dirs. Des Moines, 1960-63; exec. bd. Iowa Soc. Christian Chs., 1977; past pres., bd. dirs. Des Moines Jr. Achievement. With U.S. Army, 1943-46. Fellow Life Office Mgmt. Assn.; mem. Life Ins. Agy. Mgmt. Assn., Des Moines Golf and County Club. Home: 7108 Franklin Ave Windsor Hts IA 50322-5850 Office: Equitable of Iowa Cos 604 Locust St Des Moines IA 50309-3705 also: Equitable of Iowa Cos 699 Walnut Hub Tower PO Box 9107 Des Moines IA 50306

SPEAS, ROBERT DIXON, aeronautical engineer, aviation company executive; b. Davis County, N.C., Apr. 14, 1916; s. William Paul and Nora Estelle (Dixon) S.; m. Manette Lansing Hollingsworth, Mar. 4, 1944; children: Robert Dixon, Jay Hollingsworth. BS, MIT, 1940; Air Transport Pilot rating, Boeing Sch. Aero., United Air Lines, 1938. Aviation reporter Winston Salem Jour., 1934; sales rep. Trans World Airlines, 1937-38; engr. Am. Airlines, 1940-44, asst. to v.p., 1944-46, dir. maintenance and engring., cargo div., 1946-47, spl. asst. to pres., 1947-50; U.S. rep. A.V. Roe Can., Ltd., 1950-51; pres., chmn. bd. R. Dixon Speas Assocs., Inc. (aviation cons.), 1951-76; chmn., chief exec. officer Speas-Harris Airport Devel., Inc., 1974-76; chmn. bd. pres. Aviation Consulting, Inc., 1976-82, chmn. bd., 1982-84; pres. PRC Aviation, 1984—; mem. aeros. and space engring. bd. Nat. Rsch. Coun., 1980-84. Author: Airplane Performance and Operations, 1945, Pilots' Technical Manual, 1946, Airline Operation, 1949, Technical Aspects of Air Transport Management, 1955, Financial Benefits and Intangible Advantages of Business Aircraft Operations, 1989. Recipient 1st award Ann. Nat. Boeing Thesis Competition, 1937, rsch. award Am. Transport Assn., 1942, William A. Downes Airport Operators Coun. Internat. award, 1992; inductee Ariz. Aviation Hall of Fame, 1995. Fellow AIAA (treas. and coun. 1963-64, chmn. ethics com. 1989-92, AIAA-SAE Williams Littenwool lectr. 1994), Royal Aero. Soc., Soc. Automotive Engrs. (v.p. 1955, coun. 1964-66); mem. ASME, Flight Safety Found. (bd. govs. 1958-71, 79-90, exec. com. 1979-90), Inst. Aero. Scis. (past treas., coun. 1959-62, exec. com. 1962), Coll. Aeronautics (trustee 1967—), Soc. Aircraft Investigators, Manhasset C of C. (pres. 1962), Wings Club (pres. 1968-69, coun. 1966-71, 73-90, 92—, chmn. devel. com. 1989—, Sight lectr. 1992), Skyline Country Club. Home: 4771 E Country Villa Dr Tucson AZ 85718-2640 Office: 6262 N Swan Rd Tucson AZ 85718-3600

SPECHT, ALICE WILSON, library director; b. Caracas, Venezuela, Apr. 3, 1948; (parents Am. citizens); d. Ned and Helen (Lockwood) Wilson; m. Joe W. Specht, Dec. 30, 1972; 1 child, Mary Helen. BA, U. Pacific, 1969; MLS, Emory U., 1970; MBA, Hardin-Simmons U., 1983. Libr. social scis. North Tex. State U., Denton, 1971-73; reference libr. Lubbock (Tex.) City and County Libr., 1974-75; system coord. Big Country Libr. System, Abilene, Tex., 1975-79; assoc. dir. Hardin-Simmons U., Abilene, 1981-88, dir. univ. librs., 1988—. Author bibliog. instrn. aids, 1981-90; editor: The College Man, For Pilots Eyes Only. Recipient Boss of Yr., Am. Bus. Women's Assn., 1994. Mem. ALA, Tex. Libr. Assn. (chair com. 1978-84, sec.-treas. coll. and univ. librs. divsn. 1993-94, legis. com. 1994—), Abilene Libr. Consortium (chair adminstrv. coun. 1990, 93, coord. nat. conf. 1991, 93), Rotary (charter com. 1989-90). Home: 918 Grand Ave Abilene TX 79605-3233 Office: Hardin-Simmons U 2200 Hickory PO Box 16195 Abilene TX 79698-0001

SPECIALE, RICHARD, bank executive; b. N.Y.C., Aug. 16, 1945; s. Santo and Geraldine (Sinicropi) S. B.S.B.A., Georgetown U., 1967; M.B.A., NYU, 1976. Sr. acct. Price Waterhouse & Co., N.Y.C., 1969-74; sr. v.p. J.P. Morgan and Co. Inc., N.Y.C., 1974—; bd. dirs. instnl. owners divsn. Real Estate Bd. N.Y., 1984—, chmn., 1991—, mem. bd. govs. 1988-90, 92—; bd. dirs. Downtown-Lower Manhattan Assn., Inc., N.Y.C., 1985—; mem. adv. bd. Real Estate Inst. NYU, Grand Ctrl. Partnership Inc. Bd. dirs. Children's Arts and Scis. Workshops, N.Y.C., 1978-84; bd. dirs. instnl. owners divsn. Real Estate Bd. N.Y., 1984—, chmn., 1991—, mem. bd. govs. 1988-90, 92—; dir. Realty Found. of N.Y.; trustee Dance Theatre Found., N.Y.C., 1984—, Alvin Ailey Am. Dance Theatre, N.Y.C., 1984—; mem. real estate and constrn. coun. Lincoln Ctr. Mem. AICPA, N.Y. State Soc. CPAs, Industrial Devel. Rsch. Coun. Office: JP Morgan & Co Inc 60 Wall St New York NY 10005-2807

SPECK, MARVIN LUTHER, microbiologist, educator; b. Middletown, Md., Oct. 6, 1913; s. John Luther and Pearl Lighter (Wilhide) S.; m. Jean Moler Critchlow, Sept. 11, 1940; children: Linda Jean, Martha Loraine, Susan Carol. B.S., U. Md., 1935, M.S., 1937; Ph.D., Cornell U., 1940. Instr. microbiology U. Md., 1940-41; asst. chief bacteriologist Nat. Dairy Research Labs., Balt., 1941-47; mem. faculty N.C. State U. at Raleigh, 1947—, prof. food microbiology, 1951-79, William Neal Reynolds prof. food sci., 1957-79, prof. emeritus, 1979—; lectr. Am. Inst. Chem. Engrs., 1978-79; spl. con. USPHS, 1950-62, HEW, 1967-70. Author: (with others) Dairy Microbiology, 1957; editor: Methods for the Microbiological Examination of Foods, 1976, 84; mem. editorial bd. Jour. Dairy Sci., 1953-68. Recipient J.M. Jarrett award N.C. Pub. Health Assn.; Nordica Internat. Research award Am. Cultured Dairy Products Inst., 1981; Nat. Award for Agrl. Excellence Nat. Agri-Mktg. Assn., 1984. Fellow Am. Acad. Microbiology (bd. govs.

1976), Inst. Food Technologists; mem. Am. Soc. Microbiology (vice chmn. 1976-77, chmn. sect. 1977-78), Am. Dairy Sci. Assn. (Borden award dairy mfg. 1959, Pfizer-Lewis award for research on cheese 1967), N.C. Dairy Products Assn. (Distinguished Service award 1976), Inst. Food Technologists (nat. lectr. 1968), AAAS, Sigma Xi, Phi Kappa Phi, Gamma Sigma Delta, Alpha Zeta. Presbyterian (elder). Home: 3204 Churchill Rd Raleigh NC 27607-6806

SPECK, ROBERT CHARLES, geological engineer; b. Bklyn., June 15, 1944; s. Charles Ernest and Helen Gertrude (York) S.; m. Pia Rey Polanco, July 4, 1971; 1 child, Stephen Ruben. BA, Franklin and Marshal Coll., 1968; BS, U. Missouri, Rolla, 1974, MS, 1975, PhD, 1979. Geologist Peace Corps, Dominican Republic, 1968-70; resident geologist Geokinetics, Inc., Dominican Republic, 1970-72; project geologist Hanson-Rodriguez, S.A., Dominican Republic, 1972-73; staff engr. GAI Cons., Inc., Pitts., 1979-84; prof. U. Alaska, Fairbanks, 1984—. Contbr. articles to profl. jours. Mem. Assn. Engring. Geologists (sect. vice chmn. 1985-89), Soc. Mining Engrs., Am. Inst. Profl. Geologists (lic.), Internat. Soc. for Rock Mechanics, Tau Beta Pi, Sigma Gamma Epsilon. Home: 3030 Forrest Dr Fairbanks AK 99709-5741 Office: U Alaska Dept Mining Geol Engri Fairbanks AK 99775

SPECK, SAMUEL WALLACE, JR., academic administrator; b. Canton, Ohio, Jan. 31, 1937; s. Samuel Wallace Sr. and Lois Ione (Schneider) S.; m. Sharon Jane Anderson, Jan. 20, 1962; children: Samuel Wallace III, Derek Charles. BA, Muskingum Coll., 1959; postgrad., U. Zimbabwe, Harare, 1961; MA, Harvard U., 1963, PhD, 1968. Prof. polit. sci. Muskingum Coll., New Concord, Ohio, 1964—, asst. to pres., 1986-87, exec. v.p., 1987, acting pres., 1987-88, pres., 1988—; mem. Ohio Ho. of Reps., 1971-76; state senator from Ohio 20th Dist., 1977-83; assoc. dir. Fed. Emergency Mgmt. Agy., 1983-86; bd. dirs. CAMCO, Cambridge, Ohio, Cambridge (Ohio) Savs. Bank; pres. Eastern Ohio Devel. Alliance, 1990-92; Fund for Improvement of Postsecondary Edn., 1990-92, chmn. 1991. Contbr.: Southern Africa in Perspective, 1972; also numerous articles on African and Am. govt. and pub. policy. Bd. dirs. Ohio Tuition Trust Authority, 1991-93, Internat. Ctr. for Preservation Wild Animals. Recipient Outstanding Legislator award VFW/DAV/Am. Legion, Conservation Achievement award State of Ohio. Mem. Assn. Ind. Colls. and Univs. of Ohio (chmn. 1992-94). Republican. Presbyterian. Home: 57 College Pl New Concord OH 43762 Office: Muskingum Coll Office of Pres New Concord OH 43762

SPECK, WILLIAM T., health facility administrator. Pres., CEO Presbyn. Hosp. in City of N.Y./Columbia-Presbyn. Med. Ctr., N.Y.C. Office: Presbyn Hosp the City NY Columbia-Presbyn Med Ctr New York NY 10032

SPECTER, ARLEN, senator; b. Wichita, Kans., Feb. 12, 1930; s. Harry and Lillie (Shanin) S.; m. Joan L. Levy, June 14, 1953; children: Shanin, Stephen. Student, U. Okla., 1947-48; BA Internat. Rels., U. Pa., 1951; LL.B., Yale U., 1956. Asst. counsel Warren Commn., Washington, 1964; magisterial investigator Commn. of Pa., 1965; asst. dist. atty. City of Phila., 1959-63, dist. atty., 1966-74; prtnr. Dechert Price & Rhoads, Phila., 1956-66, 74-80; U.S. senator from Pa., 1981—; lectr. law Temple U., 1972-75, U. Pa., 1968-72; chmn. Appropriations Subcom. on Labor, Health and Human Svcs., sel. com. in intelligence, judiciary subcom. on terrorism, tech. and gov. info., spec. com. on aging, vet. affaors, sen. rep. policy com. Bd. editors Law Jour.; contbr. articls to profl. jours. Served to 1st U.S. Army, 1951-53. Recipient Youth Svcs. award B'nai B'rith, 1966; recipient Sons of Italy award, 1968, Community Humanitarian award Bapt. Ch., 1969, man of Yr. award, Temple Beth Ami, 1971, N.E. Cath. High Sch. Outstanding Achievement award, 1973. Mem. Phi Beta Kappa. Republican. Jewish. Office: US Senate 530 Senate Hart Bldg Washington DC 20510-3802*

SPECTOR, ABRAHAM, ophthalmic biochemist, educator, laboratory administrator; b. Nyack, N.Y., Jan. 14, 1926; s. Benjamin and Eva (Kaplovitz) S.; m. Joan Gruden, June 25, 1950 (dec. Jan. 1981); children: David Julian, Paul Joseph; m. Marguerite B. Filson, May 27, 1983. AB, Bard Coll., 1947, DS (hon.), 1985; PhD, NYU, 1957; MD (hon.), U. of the Republic, Uruguay, 1981. Rsch. chemist Lederle Lab., Pearl River, N.Y., 1948-52; instr. ophthalmic rsch. Harvard U., Boston, 1958-64, assoc. ophthalmic rsch., 1964-65; lectr. biol. chemistry Northeastern U., Boston, 1959-62; asst. prof. ophthalmic biochemistry Columbia U., N.Y.C., 1965-67, assoc. prof., 1967-73, prof., 1973—, dir. lab. biochemistry and molecular biology, 1973—, dir. rsch., dept. ophthalmology, 1989-90; mem. Vision Research and Tng. Com., Nat. Eye Inst., 1970-71, chmn. cataract workshop, 1973, mem. visual scis. study sect., 1976-80, chmn., 1978-80, bd. sci. advisors, 1982-85, chmn., 1983-85. mem. sci. adv. com. Fight for Sight, Inc., 1980-84; bd. sci. advisors Inst. Biol. Scis. Oakland U., 1982—; vis. prof. ophthalmology U. P.R., 1982—; vis. prof. biochemistry Med. U. Shanghai, 1986—. Assoc. editor Archives of Ophthalmology, 1968-70; sect. editor Experimental Eye Rsch., 1985-92; mem. editorial bd. Investigative Ophthalmology and Visual Sci., 1968-82, 87-92, Experimental Eye Rsch., 1974-85; contbr. numerous articles to profl. jours. Recipient Bausch & Lomb Sci. medal, 1944, Merit award NIH, 1987, Japanese Coop. Cataract Rsch. Group Internat. award, 1987. Sr. Scientific Investigators award Rsch. to Prevent Blindness, 1987, 94, Alcon Rsch. Inst. award, 1994; Guggenheim fellow, 1971-72, Fulbright fellow, 1981. Mem. AAAS, Assn. for Rsch. in Vision and Ophthalmology (pres. 1976, trustee 1970-75, Proctor medal 1983), Am. Soc. Biol. Chemistry, Am. Chem. Soc., Am. Soc. for Cell Biology, Harvey Soc., Marine Biol. Lab., Oxygen Soc. Home: 808 Broadway Apt 612 New York NY 10003 Office: Columbia U Dept Ophthalmology Eye Research Addition 5th Fl 630 W 168th St New York NY 10032-3702

SPECTOR, DAVID M., lawyer; b. Rock Island, Ill., Dec. 20, 1946; s. Louis and Ruth (Vinikour) S.; m. Laraine Fingold, Jan. 15, 1972; children: Rachel, Laurence. BA, Northwestern U., 1968; JD magna cum laude, U. Mich., 1971. Bar: Ill. 1971, U.S. Dist. Ct. (no. dist.) Ill. 1971, U.S. Ct. Appeals (7th cir.) 1977, U.S. Ct. Appeals (4th cir.) 1984, U.S. Dist. Ct. (cen. dist.) Ill. 1984. Clk. Ill. Supreme Ct., Chgo., 1971-72; ptnr., assoc. Isham, Lincoln & Beale, Chgo., 1972-87; ptnr. Mayer, Brown & Platt, Chgo., 1987—; chair ABA Nat. Inst. on Ins. Co. Insolvency, Boston, 1986; co-chair ABA Nat. Inst. on Internat. Reins.: Collections and Insolvency, New York, 1988; chair ABA Nat. Inst. on Life Ins. Co. Insolvency, Chgo., 1993. Editor (book): Law and Practice of Insurance Company Insolvency, 1986, Law and Practice of Life Insurer Insolvency, 1993; co-editor (book) Law and Practice of International Reinsurance Collections and Insolvency, 1988; contbr. articles to profl. jours.; speaker in field. Mem. ABA (chair Nat. Inst. on Life Insurer Insolvency 1993), Chgo. Bar Assn., Legal Club of Chgo. Home: 2100 N Lincoln Park W Chicago IL 60614-4648 Office: Mayer Brown & Platt 190 S La Salle St Chicago IL 60603-3410

SPECTOR, EARL M., lawyer, retail executive; b. Cleve., Apr. 14, 1939; s. Philip and Lillian (Levine) S.; m. Sharon Zelman, Sept. 9, 1963; children: Jeffrey Scott, Todd Michael, Halle Sarah. B.S., Ohio State U., Columbus, 1962, J.D., 1965. Sole practice Ohio, 1965-68, Arby's Restaurants, Ohio, 1968-69; v.p. real estate Am. Snacks, Mass., 1969-71; with legal dept. Ames Dept. Stores, Inc., Conn., 1971-92, v.p., sec., 1977, sr. v.p., 1983, exec. v.p., 1985; ptnr. BCS Co., Youngstown, Ohio, 1992—. Office: BCS Co 15 Colonial Dr Youngstown OH 44505-2164

SPECTOR, ELEANOR RUTH, government executive; b. N.Y.C., Dec. 2, 1943; d. Sidney and Helen (Kirschenbaum) Lebost; m. Mel Alan Spector, Dec. 10, 1966; children: Nancy, Kenneth. BA, Barnard Coll., 1964; postgrad. sch. pub. administrn., George Washington U., 1965-67; postgrad sch. edn., Nazareth Coll., 1974. Indsl. investigator N.Y. State Dept. Labor, White Plains, 1964-65; mgmt. intern Navy Dept., Washington, 1965, contract negotiator 1965-68, contract specialist, 1975-78, contracting officer/br. head, 1978-82, dir. div. cost estimating, 1982-84; dep. asst. sec. def. for procurement Washington, 1984-91; dir. Def. Procurement, Washington, 1991—; advisor Nat. Contract Mgmt. Assn., 1984—. Recipient Def. Meritorious Civilian Svc. medal, 1986, 93, Meritorious Svc. Presdl. award, 1989, 94, Disting. Civilian Svc. Presdl. award, 1990, Def. Disting. Civilian Svc. medal, 1991. Office: Office Under Sec Defense Acquisition & Technology 3060 Def Pentagon Rm 3E144 Washington DC 30301-3060

SPECTOR, GERSHON JERRY, physician, educator, researcher; b. Rovno, Poland, Oct. 20, 1937; came to U.S., 1949; naturalized, 1956; m. Patsy Carol

Tanenbaum, Aug. 28, 1966. BA, Johns Hopkins U., 1960; MD cum laude, U. Md., 1964. Intern Beth Israel Hosp., Boston, 1964-65; resident in surgery Sinai Hosp., Balt., 1965-66; resident in otolaryngology Mass. Eye and Ear Infirmary, Boston, 1966-69, Peter Bent Brigham Hosp., Boston, 1968-69; teaching fellow in otolaryngology Harvard U. Med. Sch., Boston, 1968-69; assoc. physician Ill. Crippled Children's Svc., Carbondale, 1971; mem. faculty Washington U. Med. Sch., St. Louis, 1971—, assoc. prof. otolaryngology, 1974-76, prof., 1976—; chief dept. otolaryngology St. Louis County Hosp., 1971-77; mem. staff Washington U. Med. Ctr., Barnes Hosp.; dir. temporal bone bank, 1971-81; guest examiner Am. Bd. Otolaryngology, 1975-77; rsch. cons. neurosci. group, G.D. Searle Pharm. Corp. Mem. editl. bd. Laryngoscope, 1978, editor-in-chief, 1984-94; contbr. articles to med. jours. With U.S. Army, 1969-71. Hancock surgeon, 1962. Fellow ACS; mem. AAAS, AMA, Am. Acad. Ophthalmology and Otolaryngology (Honor award 1979), St. Louis Med. Soc., St. Louis County Med. Soc., Am. Coun. Otolaryngology, St. Louis Ear, Nose and Throat Club (pres. 1986), So. Med. Assn., Deafness Rsch. Found., Pan. Am. Assn. Otorhinolaryngology and Broncho Esophagology, Am. Soc. Head and Neck Surgery, Soc. Univ. Otolaryngologists, Am. Laryngological, Rhinological and Otological Soc. (Edmund Prince Fowler award 1974), Am. Soc. Cell Biology, Electron Microscopy Soc., N.Y. Acad. Scis., Am. Assn. Anatomists, Am. Acad. Facial Plastic and Reconstructive Surgery, Am. Neuro-Otology Soc., Gesellschaft fur Neurootologie und Aequilibrimoetrie A.V., Barany Soc., Am. Radium Soc., Assn. Acad. Surgery, Am. Fedn. Clin. Oncologic Socs., Am Otological Soc., Acoustical Soc. Am., Soc. for Neurosci., Internat. Skull Base Soc. (founding), Brazilian Skull Base Soc. (hon.), Centurion Club, Alpha Omega Alpha, Psi Chi. Home: 7365 Westmoreland Dr Saint Louis MO 63130-4241 Office: Washington U Med Sch Saint Louis MO 63110

SPECTOR, HAROLD NORMAN, physics educator; b. Chgo., Feb. 26, 1935; s. Bernard C. and Dorothy (Tartak) S.; m. Sarah Daniel, June 11, 1961; 1 dau., Benyamina Rahel. Student, U. Ill., Chgo., 1953-55; S.B., U. Chgo., 1957, S.M., 1958, Ph.D., 1961. Asst. prof. Case Inst. Tech., Cleve., 1962-63; research physicist Ill. Inst. Tech. Research Inst., Chgo., 1963-66; assoc. prof. Ill. Inst. Tech., Chgo., 1966-76, prof. physics, 1976—; vis. prof. Hebrew U. of Jerusalem, 1973-74; cons. GTE, 1983-86. Fellow Shell Oil Co., 1960-61; fellow NSF, 1961-62, GTE Labs., 1983; grantee NSF, 1976-81; grantee ARO, 1984. Fellow Am. Phys. Soc.; mem. Phi Beta Kappa, Sigma Xi. Office: Ill Inst Tech 3301 S Dearborn Chicago IL 60616-2727

SPECTOR, HARVEY M., osteopathic physician; b. Phila., July 10, 1938; s. Philip and Sylvia (Rischall) S.; m. Rochelle Fleishman, June 16, 1963; children: Jill, Larry. DO, Phila. Coll. Osteo. Medicine, 1963. Osteopathic physician Phila., 1964—; preceptor Hershey (Pa.) Med. Sch., 1987—, Phila. Coll. Osteopathic Medicine, 1989—; assoc. prof. medicine Med. Coll. Pa., 1991—. Recipient Humanitarian award, Chapel of Four Chaplains, Phila., 1984. Mem. Am. Osteo. Assn. (del.), Pa. Osteo. Med. Assn. (del.), Am. Acad. Osteo. Gen. Practitioners, Phila. County Osteo Med. Soc., Med. Club Phila., Abington Dolphins Aquatic Club (pres. 1984-86), B'nai B'rith. Jewish. Avocations: golf, swimming. Office: 1220 Cottman Ave Philadelphia PA 19111-3694

SPECTOR, JOSEPH ROBERT, retired diversified manufacturing executive; b. N.Y.C., Apr. 16, 1923; s. Benjamin and Julia (Wagner) S. A.B., Dartmouth Coll., 1946; LL.B., Cornell U., 1952. Bar: N.Y. bar 1952, Fla. bar 1953. Asst. counsel Equitable Life Assurance Soc., N.Y.C., 1956-64; asst. gen. counsel Gen. Precision Co., Tarrytown, N.Y., 1964-68; corp. counsel Singer Co., N.Y.C., 1968-70; v.p., gen. counsel, sec. UMC Industries, Inc., Stamford, Conn., 1970-81, ret., 1981. Trustee Morocco-Am. Cultural Assn. Charitable Trust, No. Dispensar, 1974-90; pres. 20 East 11 Owners Corp. With USNR, 1942-46. Mem. ABA, Am. Soc. Corp. Secs., Fla. Bar Assn., Assn. of Bar of City of N.Y., Yale Club. Home: c/o DAY c/o DAV 236 Loch Rd Columbia SC 29210-4406 also: 1 Blvd Mohammed V, Tangier Morocco

SPECTOR, LOUIS, retired federal judge, lawyer, arbitrator, consultant; b. Niagara Falls, N.Y., Apr. 4, 1918; s. Jacob and Gussie (Yochelson) S.; children: Gale Anne Spector Pasternack, Arthur George, James Aland. Student (N.Y. State scholar), Niagara U., 1936-37; LL.B. with honors, U. Buffalo (later State U. N.Y.), 1940. Bar: N.Y. bar 1940, D.C. bar 1972, U.S. Supreme Ct. bar 1971, U.S. Ct. Claims bar 1968. Asso. firm Saperston, McNaughton & Saperston, Buffalo, 1941-42; asst. chief legal div. U.S. Army C.E., Buffalo Dist., 1942-43; chief sect. claims appeals and litigation U.S. Army C.E. (Great Lakes Div.), Chgo., 1946; chief legal br. and real estate div. U.S. Army C.E. (Great Lakes Div.), Buffalo Dist., 1946-53; exec. dir. Buffalo Port Authority, 1953-54; mem. Bd. Contract Appeals, Washington, 1954-59; chmn. Army panel Armed Services Bd. Contract Appeals, Washington, 1959-62, Unified Armed Services Bd. Contract Appeals, 1962-68; trial judge U.S. Ct. Claims, Washington, 1968-82, judge, 1982-85; cons., arbitrator, mediator Falls Church, Va., 1985—; lectr., speaker, writer public contracts; Congressional appearances, 1953, 66, 69, 77. Contbr. articles to profl. publs. Served with C.E. U.S. Army, 1943-46. Recipient Freshman medal Niagara U., 1936, Sophomore medal, 1937. Fellow Am. Bar Found.; mem. ABA (chmn. sect. pub. contract law 1967-68); Fellow Nat. Contract Mgmt. Assn. (nat. bd. advisers 1967—); mem. ABA (ho. of dels. 1968-70), Fed. Bar Assn. (gen. editor jour. 1960-74, nat. chmn. com. govt. contracts and procurement law 1961-63, Distinguished Service award D.C. chpt. 1974), Lincoln Law Soc. (alumni pres. 1951). Club: Cosmos. Home: 6219 Beachway Dr Falls Church VA 22041-1425 The concept of justice has been a central concern of my life. It is not a unique concern. Daniel Webster described it as "the great interest of man on earth . . . the ligament which holds civilized beings and nations together." And Reinhold Neibuhr reflected that: "Man's capacity for justice makes democracy possible; but man's inclination to injustice makes democracy necessary.".

SPECTOR, MARSHALL, philosophy educator; b. Chgo., Feb. 11, 1936; s. Israel Hayyim Spector and Pauline (Futorian) Axelrood; m. Nan Shipman, Dec. 26, 1959; children: Anthony, Jessica. BS in Physics, Ill. Inst. Tech., 1957; MS in Physics, U. Chgo., 1959; PhD in Philosophy, Johns Hopkins U., 1963. Asst. prof. philosophy Duke U., Durham, N.C., 1963-68; assoc. prof. SUNY, Stony Brook, 1968-74, prof., 1974—. Author: Methodological Foundations of Relativistic Mechanics, 1972, Concepts of Reduction in Physical Science, 1978. NSF grantee. Office: SUNY Stony Brook Dept Philosophy Stony Brook NY 11794

SPECTOR, MARTIN WOLF, lawyer, business executive; b. Phila., 1938. BA, Pa. State U., 1959; JD, U. Pa., 1962. Bar: Pa. 1962. Judge U.S. Dist. Ct., until 1967; asst. gen. counsel ARA Services, Phila., assoc. gen. counsel, 1969-76, v.p., 1976-83, gen. counsel, 1983—; formerly sr. v.p., exec. v.p., 1985—. Served to lt. USN, 1953-56. Office: ARA Svcs Inc 1101 Market St Philadelphia PA 19107-2934

SPECTOR, MELBOURNE LOUIS, management consultant; b. Pueblo, Colo., May 7, 1918; s. Joseph E. and Dora (Bernstein) S.; m. Louise Vincent, Nov. 23, 1948; 1 son, Stephen David. B.A. with honors, U. N.Mex., 1941. Intern U.S. Bur. Indian Affairs, 1941, Nat. Inst. Pub. Affairs, 1941; personnel asst. Office Emergency Mgmt., 1941-42; chief classification div. War Relocation Authority, 1942-43, Hdqrs. USAAF, 1943-45; employment officer UNRRA, 1945-46; pvt. employment, 1946-47; personnel officer Dept. State, 1947-49; dep. dir. personnel ECA, Marshall Plan, 1949-51; dep. dir., acting dir. personnel Econ. Adminstrn., Mut. Security Adminstrn., FOA, 1951-54; asst., dep. dir. Mission to Mexico, ICA, 1954-57, acting dir., 1957-59; chief C. Am., Mex. and Caribbean div. ICA, 1959-61; dir. Office Personnel Mgmt., AID, 1961-62; exec. dir. Bur. Inter-Am. Affairs, Dept. State, 1962-64; commd. fgn. service officer, 1964; counselor for adminstrv. affairs Am. embassy, New Delhi, India, 1964-66; seminarian Sr. Seminar Fgn. Policy, Dept. State, 1966-67; exec. dir. U.S.-Mex. Commn. for Border Devel. and Friendship, 1967-69, Am. Revolution Bicentennial Commn. 1969-71; mem. mgmt., policy and coordination staffs Dept. State, 1971-73; ret., 1973, cons., 1973—; mem. Fgn. Svc. Grievance Bd., 1976-77; exec. dir. Am. Consortium for Internat. Pub. Adminstrn., 1980-84, 93-94, dir. Marshall Plan Oral History Project, 1987—. Mem. Cosmos Club, Am. Soc. Pub. Adminstrn., Pi Kappa Alpha, Phi Kappa Phi. Home: 6414 Bannockburn Dr Bethesda MD 20817-5430

SPECTOR, MICHAEL JOSEPH, agribusiness executive; b. N.Y.C., Feb. 13, 1947; s. Martin Wilson and Dorothy (Miller) S.; BS in Chemistry, Washington and Lee U., 1968; m. Margaret Dickson, Sept. 14, 1977. Research chemist Am. Viscose, Phila., 1968-69; pres. MJS Entertainment Corp., Miami, Fla., 1970-84, also MJS Internat., Inc.; ptnr. Old Town Key West Devel. Ltd. (Fla.), 1977—; pres. MJS Entertainment of Can. Inc., Toronto, Ont., Margo Farms, MJS Prodns., Inc. N.Y.C.; chmn., pres., chief exec. officer Margo Nursery Farms, Inc., Dorado, P.R., 1984—, also bd. dirs.; bd. dirs. Goodwill Industries So. Fla., v.p. fin. 1980. Served with AUS, 1969-70. Recipient Robert E. Lee research grant Washington and Lee U., 1967-68. Mem. Nat. Assn. Record Merchandisers (dir. Nova div., chmn. one-stop distbn. com. 1982-83), Country Music Assn., Dorado Beach, Golf, and Tennis Club. Patentee synthetic stretching process.

SPECTOR, MORTON, wholesale distribution executive; b. 1929. Attended, Cornell U. With D&H Dist. Co., Harrisburg, Pa., 1950—, now CHB, treas. With U.S. Army (2 years). Office: D & H Dist Co 252535 N 7th St Harrisburg PA 17110*

SPECTOR, PHIL, record company executive; b. Bronx, N.Y., Dec. 25, 1940; m. Veronica Bennett, 1968 (div. 1974); children: Gary Phillip and Louis Phillip (twins), Donte Phillip, Nicole and Phillip (twins). Student, UCLA. Producer with Atlantic Records, 1960-61; founder Philles Records, 1962; now pres. Warner-Spector Records, Inc.; also Mother Bertha Music. Mem. mus. group: Teddy Bears, 1958-59; producer records for Gene Pitney, Ike and Tina Turner, Ben E. King, the Beatles, Righteous Bros., Checkmates, Crystals, Ronettes, John Lennon, George Harrison, The Ramones, Yoko Ono, others; producer album A Concert for Bangladesh (Grammy award); composer songs including You've Lost That Lovin' Feelin', others; appeared in films Tami, Easy Rider; prod., TV documentary film A Giant Stands 5 Ft. 7 In.; prod. film That Was Rock. Named to Rock and Roll Hall of Fame, 1989; named Country Music Song of Yr. Songwriter and Pub. for To Know Him Is To Love Him, 1989; recipient lifetime achievement award U. Calif., Berkeley, 1994, Phila. award Phila. Music Alliance, 1994 (includes star on Phila.'s Walk of Fame). Office: Care Warner-Spector Records Inc 686 S Arroyo Pky Pasadena CA 91105-3262

SPECTOR, ROBERT DONALD, language professional, educator; b. N.Y.C., Sept. 21, 1922; s. Morris and Helen (Spiegel) S.; m. Eleanor Helen Luskin, Aug. 19, 1945; children: Stephen Brett, Eric Charles. BA, L.I. U., 1948, DHL, 1994; MA, NYU, 1949; PhD, Columbia U., 1952. Instr. L.I. U., Bklyn., 1948-59; asst. prof. L.I. U., 1959-62, asso. prof., 1962-65, prof. English, 1965—, chmn. senate, 1966-67, 69-70, chmn. dept., 1970-75, dir. humanities and comm. arts, 1975-84, coord. div. of humanities and div. of comms. and performing arts, 1990—, dir. humanities, 1984-90, prof. emeritus, 1993—; editor, cons. Johnson Reprint Corp., 1967-84. Author: English Literary Periodicals, 1966, Tobias George Smollett, 1968, updated edit., 1989, Pär Lagerkvist, 1973, Arthur Murphy, 1979, Tobias Smollett: A Reference Guide, 1980, The English Gothic, 1983, Backgrounds to Restoration and Eighteenth-Century English Literature, 1989, Political Controversy, 1992, Smollett's Women, 1994; editor: Essays on the Eighteenth Century Novel, 1965, Great British Short Novels, 1970, 9 other vols. English and Am. lit., revs. and articles, poetry. Trustee L.I. U., 1969-70; chmn. George Polk Award Com., 1977—. Served with USCGR, 1942-46. Recipient L.I. U. Trustee award for scholarly achievement, 1978, Tristram Walker Metcalfe Alumnus of Year, 1981; Swedish Govt. travel and research grantee, 1966; fellow Huntington Library, 1974; fellow Folger Library, 1975; fellow Newberry Library, 1976. Mem. MLA, Am.-Scandinavian Found. (publs. com. 1962-84), P.E.N. Home: 1761 E 26th St Brooklyn NY 11229-2405

SPECTOR, STANLEY, foreign language educator; b. N.Y.C., June 10, 1924; s. Irving and Sophie (Braun) S.; m. Betty Peishan Yue, Mar. 8, 1963; children—Pat Lee, Stephanie Spector Van Denberg, Lee Paul, Jon Marc. B.S., Coll. City N.Y., 1945; Ph.D., U. Wash., 1953; postgrad., London Sch. Oriental and African Studies, 1950-51. Instr. history CCNY, 1946; instr. Far Eastern history U. Wash., Seattle, 1951-52, asst. prof., 1955; lectr. in history U. Calif., Los Angeles, 1953; lectr. in history, post-certificate class Chung Cheng Chung Hsueh Singapore, 1954; asst. prof. Far Eastern history Washington U., St. Louis, 1955-58, assoc. prof., 1959-64, assoc. prof. Chinese history, 1964-65, prof. emeritus Asian studies, 1965-89, prof. emeritus, 1989—; chmn. dept. Chinese and Japanese studies, 1964-72, dir. East Asian Lang. and AreaCtr., 1964, Office Internat. studies, 1969; vis. prof. Chinese and Japanese history Columbia U., 1962; vis. prof. U. Singapore, summers 1967-69, 71-73, Waseda U. Tokyo, 1966-67, Ikip U., Bandung, Indonesia, summer 1969. Author: Li Hung-chang and the Huai Army, 1964; co-editor: Guide to the Memorials of Seven Leading Officials of the 19th Century China, 1955. Chmn. Seattle chpt. Am. Vets. Com., 1948-49; co-chmn. Citizens for Stevenson, Seattle, 1952; chmn. St. Louis-Nanjing (Peoples Republic China) Sister City Com. Served with USNR, 1942-43. Social Sci. Research Council fellow, 1950-51, 58-59; Ford Found. fellow, 1953-55; Social Sci. Research Council, Toyo Bunko, 1966-67; Fulbright research scholar Japan, People's Republic of China, Hong Kong, Singapore, Malaysia, 1966-67; Fulbright research scholar USSR, 1975-76. Mem. AAUP, Midwest Conf. on Asian Studies (pres. 1967-68), Chinese Lang. Tchrs. Assn. (pres. 1971—), Am. Polit Sci. Assn., Assn. Asian Studies, Am. Hist. Assn., Internat. Studies Assn. Home: 50 Arundel Pl Saint Louis MO 63105-2278 Office: Washington U PO Box 1088 Saint Louis MO 63130

SPEDALE, VINCENT JOHN, manufacturing executive; b. Chgo., Dec. 2, 1929; s. Joseph and Mildred (Satarino) S.; m. Joan Deeny, Apr. 11, 1953; children: Kathleen, Joseph, Barbara, Judith, Robert, Anthony. BSME, Ill. Inst. Tech., 1952; MS in Indsl. Engring., Wayne State U., 1959; postgrad. in mgmt., MIT, 1977. With Chrysler Corp., 1952-70; v.p. mfg. solar gas turbine div. Internat. Harvester Co., San Diego, 1971-73; v.p. mfg. truck div. Internat. Harvester Co., Chgo., 1973-78, v.p., gen. mgr. engine div., 1978-81; pres. machine tool div. ACME Precision Products, Inc., Detroit, 1982-87; v.p. ops. ICM Industries, Inc., Chgo., 1987-91; CEO, K-Whit Inc, air conditioning equipment mfrs., Fishers, Ind., 1993-94; pres. Hwy. Recycling System Corp., Wausau, Wis., Vinco Mgmt. Cons., Wheaton, Ill.; bd. dirs. Spartan Diesel Co., Harbor Beach, Mich.; CEO Forum Group, Inc., Indpls., 1991-92, Union City (Ind.) Body Co., 1992-93. Mem. Soc. Automotive Engrs. Roman Catholic. Home: 1260 Shady Ln Wheaton IL 60187-3722

SPEECE, RICHARD EUGENE, civil engineer, educator; b. Marion, Ohio, Aug. 23, 1933; s. Irvin Ward S. and Desta May (Speece); m. Jean Margaret Edscorn, Nov. 15, 1969; children: Eric Jordan, Lincoln Dana. BCE, Fenn. Coll., 1956; M of Engring., Yale U., 1958; PhD, MIT, 1961. Assoc. prof. civil engring. U. Ill., Urbana, 1961-65; prof. N.Mex. State U., 1965-70, U. Tex., Austin, 1970-74; Betz chair prof. environ. engring. Drexel U., Phila., 1974-88; Centennial prof. Vanderbilt U., Nashville, 1988—; vis. scholar Cambridge (Eng.) U., 1994; cons. to govt., industry. Contbr. articles to profl. jours.; patentee in field. Recipient hon. mention for best paper Trans. Am. Fisheries Soc., 1973. Mem. Assn. Environ. Engring. Profs. (Disting. Faculty award 1970, disting. lectr. 1978, trustee 1981-83, Engring. Sci. award 1982), ASCE (J. James Cross medal 1983), Am. Soc. Microbiologists, Water Environ. Fedn. (Harrison Prescott Eddy medal 1966), U.S. ANC (Founder's award 1991), Internat. Assn. on Water Pollution Rsch. and Control. Office: Vanderbilt U Nashville TN 37203

SPEED, BILLIE CHENEY (MRS. THOMAS S. SPEED), retired editor, journalist; b. Birmingham, Ala., Feb. 21, 1927; d. John J. and Ruby (Petty) Cheney; m. Thomas S. Speed, July 7, 1968; children: Kathy Lovell Windham, Donna Lovell Adams, Melanie Lovell Wright. Grad., W.Ga. Coll. Reporter, sports writer Birmingham News, 1945; sports writer, gen. assignment reporter, ch. editor Atlanta Jour., 1947-53, with promotion dept., 1955-57, religion editor, 1965-89; feature editor Coach and Athlete Mag., 1958, So. Outdoors, 1958. Recipient Sharp Tack award Cumberland dist. Seventh Day Adventists; Spl. Service award Christian Council of Metro Atlanta, 1974, award for outstanding personnal ministry, 1986, personal service award, 1986; Arthur West award for religious feature writing United Meth. Ch., 1977; Alumni Achievement award West Ga. Coll., 1985; Trustee award Protestant Radio & TV Ctr., 1986; Faith & Freedom award Religious Heritage of Am., 1986. Fellow Religious Pub. Relations Council; mem. Nat. Religion Newswriters Assn., Nat. Fedn. Press Women, Theta Sigma Chi. Methodist. Home: 559 Rays Rd Stone Mountain GA 30083-3142

SPEED, JOHN SACKETT, insurance company executive; b. Dubuque, Iowa, Aug. 29, 1927; s. Lloyd Jeter and Marion (Whitbread) S.; m. Anne Carter Stewart, Apr. 28, 1951; children: Virginia Lyons, Lloyd Rogers (Mrs. William C. Ciccariello), Anne Carter (Mrs. John B. Meyers). A.B., Princeton U., 1950; M.B.A., Harvard Bus. Sch., 1955. V.p. Commonwealth Life Ins. Co., Louisville, 1955-72; v.p., sec., treas. Capital Holding Corp., Louisville, 1972-88; cons. Johnson & Higgins of Ky., Inc., Louisville, 1988—; bd. dirs. Brown-Forman Corp., Beaver Dam Coal Co. Bd. dirs. Hist. Homes Fdn., Greater Louisville Fund for Arts, 1989—; chmn. J.B. Speed Art Mus., 1992-94; 1st v.p. Filson Club Hist. Soc.. Served with USN, 1945-46. Republican. Episcopalian. Clubs: Louisville Country (treas. 1963-70), Pendennis, River Valley, Wynn Stay, Little Harbor. Home: 5913 Brittany Valley Rd Louisville KY 40222-5905 also: 760 Sextant Dr Sanibel FL 33957 also: 3320 Forrest Ave Harbor Springs MI 49740 Office: Starks Bldg Ste 370 Louisville KY 40202

SPEED, STAN, research chemist. Rsch. scientist Exxon Chem. Co., Houston. Recipient Coop. Rsch. in Polymer Sci. & Engring. award Am. Chem. Soc., 1995. Office: Exxon Chemical Corp 13501 Katy Freeway Houston TX 77079*

SPEED, TERENCE PAUL, statistician, educator; b. Victor Harbor, Australia, Mar. 14, 1943; came to the U.S., 1987; s. Harold Hector and Jeanette Elisabeth (Hacklin) S.; m. Freda Elizabeth Pollard, Dec. 22, 1964. BS, Melbourne U., Victoria, Australia, 1965; PhD, Monash U., Victoria, 1969. Tutor Monash U., 1965-67, lectr., 1967-69; lectr. U. Sheffield, United Kingdom, 1969-73; prof. U. Western Australia, 1974-82; chief CSIRO Div. Math. and Statistics, Canberra, Australia, 1983-87; prof. U. Calif., Berkeley, 1987—. Home: 1830 Arch St Berkeley CA 94709-1310 Office: U Calif Dept Statistics Berkeley CA 94720

SPEER, DAVID BLAKENEY, industrial executive; b. Sault Ste. Marie, Ont., Apr. 6, 1951; s. Richard Norwood and Mary (Davis) S.; m. Barbara Ann Brugenhemra, June 22, 1974; children: Blake, Sarah. BS in Indsl. Engring., Iowa State U., 1973; MBA, Northwestern U., 1977. Sales engr. Precision Paper, Wheeling, Ind., 1976-78; sales mgr. Precision Paper, Wheeling, 1976-78; regional sales mgr. ITW Buildex, Itasca, Ill., 1978-81; nat. sales mktg. mgr. ITW Buildex, Itasca, 1981-84, v.p., gen. mgr., 1984-92; v.p., gen. mgr. ITW Paslode, Lincolnshire, Ill., 1992—. Mem. Am. Mgmt. Assn., Am. Mktg. Assn., Am. Soc. Indsl. Engrs., Midwest Indsl. Mfg. Assn. Office: ITW Paslode 2 Marriott Dr Lincolnshire IL 60069

SPEER, DAVID JAMES, public relations executive; b. Mpls., Apr. 30, 1927; s. Ray Patterson and Grace Elizabeth (Kane) S.; m. Nancy How Girouard; children: Robert J. Girouard, Mark J. Girouard. B.A. in Polit. Sci., U. Minn., 1950. Sports reporter Mpls. Tribune, 1945-50; night radio editor AP, Mpls., 1950-51; ptnr. Speer's Publicity Service, Mpls., 1950-59; pres. Sullivan & Speer Inc., Mpls., 1959-61; sr. v.p. Padilla, Sarjeant, Sullivan & Speer, Inc., Mpls., 1961-71, pres., sec., 1971-77; pres., chief operating officer Padilla and Speer, Inc., Mpls., 1977-86; Minn. commr. Trade and Econ. Devel., 1987-91; cons. Padilla Speer Beardsley Inc., Mpls., 1991-93; exec. dir. Friends of the Communication Ctr., St. Paul, Minn., 1993—; cons. pub. relations, Mpls., N.Y.C., 1961-86; dir. pub. relations Minn. State Fair, 1961-68, St. Paul Winter Carnival Assn., 1952-68. Past chmn. Minn. Multiple Sclerosis Soc.; bd. dirs. St. Paul Chamber Orch.; consul of Finland in Minn. Served with USN, 1945-46. Mem. Pub. Rels. Soc. Am. (pres. chpt. 1967), U. Minn. Alumni Assn. (pres. 1975-76), Mpls. Club. Home: 23235 St Croix Tr N Scandia MN 55073 Office: Padilla Speer Beardsley Inc 224 W Franklin Ave Minneapolis MN 55404-2331

SPEER, G. WILLIAM, lawyer; b. Greenville, S.C., Dec. 26, 1940; s. George W. and Elizabeth (Mauldin) S.; m. Ann Meacham, Dec. 27, 1961; children: George William, Tyrus O., Susan C., Sandra A., David E. BA, Duke U., 1962, LLB, 1965. Bar: Ga. 1965, U.S. Dist. Ct. Ga. 1965. Assoc. Powell, Goldstein, Frazer & Murphy, Atlanta, 1965-70, ptnr., 1970—; bd. dirs. So. Electronics Distbrs. Inc.; bd. dirs., sec. QMS, Inc., Mobile, Ala. Co-author: Georgia Corporate Forms, 1988. Mem. ABA, Ga. Bar Assn., Atlanta Bar Assn., Ashford Club (Atlanta), Atlanta City Club. Presbyterian. Office: Powell Goldstein Frazer & Murphy 191 Peachtree St NE 16th FL Atlanta GA 30303

SPEER, JACK ATKESON, publisher; b. Wichita, Kans., July 3, 1941; s. Jack Shelley and Shannon Speer; m. Judith Ann Fuller, Aug. 5,1967; children: Martin Fuller, Elizabeth Fuller. BS in Bus. Adminstrn., Kansas. State U., 1966, ML, 1967; postgrad., U. Mo., 1967, U. So. Calif., 1969; IBM Pres.'s Class, Harvard U., 1980. Mem. advt., editorial, mech. staffs Wichita Eagle-Beacon, 1954-64; editorial asst. Emporia (Kans.) Gazette, 1964-65; supr. libr. data processing Kans. State U., Emporia, 1965-67; mgr. data processing ctr. Kans. State U., Manhattan, 1967-69; mgr. systems and programming John Wiley Inc.-Becker & Hayes Inc., Bethesda, Md., 1969-72; dir. libr. info. systems Informatics Inc. Info. Systems Group, Rockville, Md., 1972-77; v.p. ops. Arcata Real Estate Data Inc., Miami, Fla., 1977-79; mgr. electronic info. systems Arcata Pubs. Group, Norwalk, Conn., 1979-83; v.p. mktg./sales, data imaging group The William Byrd Press, Richmond, Va., 1983-84; sr. v.p. ops. NewsBank Inc, New Canaan, Conn., 1984-85; pres., pub. Buckmaster Pub., Mineral, Va., 1986—; mem. faculty Cath. U. Am. Studies, St. Kans. State U. Libr. Sch. Author: Amateur Radio Call Directory, 1982—, Buckmaster's Ann. Stockholder Reports, 1986—, Front-Page-News (CD-ROM), 1989, HamCall (CD-ROM), 1988—; compiler Libraries and Automation: A Bibliography, 1967, The Living Bible Concordance, 1972. Trustee Jefferson-Madison Regional Libr., 1990-91; commr. Louisa County Planning Commn., 1992—; mem. adv. coun. Louisa County High Sch., 1992. Mem. ALA, NRA, Am. Radio Relay League, Nat. Info. Standards Orgn. (CD-ROM com.), D.C. Libr. Assn. (pres.), Sigma Tau Gamma. Office: Buckmaster Pub Route 4 Box 1630 PO Box 10 Mineral VA 23117

SPEER, JAMES, religious organization administrator. Dir. Daniel Springs Encampment, Gary, Tex. Office: Daniel Springs Encampment PO Box 310 Gary TX 75643

SPEER, RICHARD LYLE, judge; b. Norwalk, Ohio, Aug. 14, 1941; s. Lyle L. and Ruth M. (Gredys) S.; m. Anita Gailitis, Nov. 9, 1968; children—Gretchen, Richard, Jr. B.S. in Edn., Ohio U., 1963, J.D., 1966. Bar: Ohio 1966, U.S. Dist. Ct. (so. dist.) Ohio 1967, U.S. Ct. Appeals (6th cir.) 1968, U.S. Dist. Ct. (no. dist.) Ohio 1969, U.S. Supreme Ct. 1970, U.S. Ct. Mil. Appeals 1970, U.S. Ct. Appeals (9th and D.C. cirs.) 1981, U.S. Ct. Appeals (3d, 4th, 7th and 5th cirs.) 1982, U.S. Ct. Appeals (10th and 11th cirs.) 1983. Asst. atty. gen. State of Ohio, Columbus, 1967-69; assoc. Reinheimer & Reinheimer, Port Clinton, Ohio, 1969-70; ptnr. Rosentreter, Zeitzheim & Speer, Oak Harbor, Ohio, 1970-75; judge U.S. Bankruptcy Ct., Toledo, Ohio, 1975—; real estate instr. Terra Tech. Coll., Fremont, Ohio, 1972—. Named instr. of Yr. Ohio Assn. Realtors, 1978. Mem. ABA, Ohio State Bar Assn., Toledo Bar Assn., Ottawa County Bar Assn. Office: US Dist Ct 113 US Courthouse 1716 Spielbusch Ave Toledo OH 43624-1332

SPEER, WILLIAM THOMAS, JR., banker, investor, consultant, rancher; b. Boston, Feb. 17, 1936; s. William Thomas and Marie Dorothy (DeWolfe) S.; m. Glenda Jane Farris, Nov. 15, 1972; children: Jason Farris, Tyson DeWolfe, Courtland Conley, William Thomas III. AA, Marin Jr. Coll., Kentfield, Calif., 1955; BA in Bus., Calif. State U.-Fullerton, 1962; postgrad. U. Calif-San Francisco, 1955-56. Bank examiner Fed. Res. Bank, 1962-67, 68-70; exec. v.p. First Nat. Bank, Cañon City, Colo., 1967-68; v.p., then sr. v.p. Bank of Idaho, Boise, 1970-74; sr. v.p. Bank of N.Mex., Albuquerque, 1975; prin. organizer, founder, pres., CEO, chmn. bd. Am. Bank of Commerce, Boise, 1975-94; exec. cons. First Security Bank, N.A., 1994—; developer Willowgrove Estates, Meridian, Idaho, Rivers Bend Condominiums, McCrall, Idaho, Snake Riverview Ranches, King Hill, Idaho; guest lectr. Boise State U.; cons. in field. Contbr. articles to profl. jours. Bd. dirs. Idaho chpt. Am. Heart Assn., 1983, chmn. bd., 1985; bd. dirs. Boise Philharm., 1984; active Pub. TV Sta., 1981-83. With U.S. Army, 1957-61. Recipient gov.'s appreciation award Idaho-Oreg. Lions Club, 1982. Mem. Am. Bankers Assn., Idaho Bankers Assn. (exec. coun.), Western Ind. Bankers Assn., Idaho Ind. Bankers Assn. (pres. 1986), Robert Morris Assocs., Nat. Assn. Home Builders, U.S. Indsl. Council, Greater Boise C. of C., Nat. Fedn. Ind. Bus., Idaho Water Users Assn., Boise State U. Club, Ducks

Unltd., Pheasants Forever, Hillcrest Country Club, Centurion Club, Bronco Boasters Club, Elks. Home: PO Box 7566 Boise ID 83707

SPEERING, ROBIN, computer specialist, educator; b. Athens, Ga., Apr. 23, 1937; s. Harry and Effie (Adams) S. BS, U. Ga., 1962, MEd, 1970, EdS, 1974; MRE, Southwestern Bapt. Sem., 1964. Cert. tchr., Ga. Ind. audiovisual equipment specialist Athens, 1957-69; asst. mgr. Speering Printing Co., Athens, 1965-67, asst. mgr., computer specialist, 1986—; tchr. Oconee County High Sch., Watkinsville, Ga., 1968-69, Barrow County Schs., Winder, Ga., 1970-73, Comer (Ga.) Elem. Sch., 1974-76, Tadmore Elem. Sch., Hall County, Ga., 1976-77, Richmond County Schs., Augusta, Ga., 1977-85; freelance writer Athens, 1986—. Contbr. articles to newsletters, area newspapers. Organist, tchr. Christian Fellowship Ch., Athens, 1990—. Mem. ASCD, NEA, Ga. Assn. Educators, Printing Industry Assn. Ga., Kappa Delta Pi. Avocations: music, photography, electronics. Home: PO Box 6943 Athens GA 30604 Office: Speering Printing Co 278 Hodgson Dr Athens GA 30606

SPEERS, ROLAND ROOT, II, lawyer; b. Jacksonville, Fla., Oct. 8, 1933; s. Roland Root and Alice (Calkins) S.; m. Florence Briscoe, Dec. 18, 1954; children: Kirsten, Guy, Gina Marie. B.A. cum laude, UCLA, 1955, J.D., 1958. Bar: Calif. 1958, D.C. 1978. Dep. commr. corps. Calif. Dept. Corps., Los Angeles, 1958-59; sec., gen. counsel Suburban Cos., Pomona, Calif., 1959-64, Amcord, Inc., Los Angeles, 1964-67; asst. to pres. Amcord, Inc., 1967, v.p. corp. devel., 1968; v.p., gen. counsel Amcord, Inc., Newport Beach, Calif., 1970; sr. v.p. Amcord, Inc., 1971, exec. v.p., 1972-75, pres., 1975-94; ptnr. Speers, Dana, Teal Balfour & MacDonald, Costa Mesa, Calif., 1977-94; dir. Logicon, Inc., Torrance, Calif. Trustee Pitzer Coll., Pomona, 1975-80; bd. councillors Center Pub. Affairs U. So. Calif., 1978-82; bd. dirs. Newport Harbor Art Mus., 1977-82. Mem. D.C. Bar Assn., State Bar Assn. Calif., UCLA Alumni Assn., UCLA Law Sch. Alumni Assn., Phi Alpha Delta. Clubs: Big Canyon Country (Newport Beach); Center (Costa Mesa). Office: 611 Anton Blvd PO Box 3936 Costa Mesa CA 92628

SPEERT, ARNOLD, college president, chemistry educator; b. Bronx, N.Y., June 19, 1945; s. David Jack and Dorothy Bernice (Feldman) S.; m. Myrna Goldstein, June 11, 1967; children: Alan Michael, Debra Beth. BS, CCNY, 1966; PhD, Princeton U., 1971. Asst. to dean grad. and rsch. program William Paterson Coll., Wayne, N.J., 1970-71, from asst. to assoc. prof. chemistry, 1970-80, prof., 1980—, asst. to v.p. acad. affairs, 1971-78, assoc. dean acad. affairs, 1978-79, v.p. acad. affairs, 1979-85, pres., 1985—; bd. dirs. State Farm Indemnity Co., Better Bus. Bur. Trustee Barnert Hosp., Paterson, 1986—, Jewish Fedn. North Jersey, Wayne, 1986—, YM & YWHA No. N.J., Wayne, 1988—, Respiratory Health Assn., 1990-93; bd. dirs. William Paterson Coll. Found., 1985—. Mem. Am. Assn. State Colls. and Univs. (bd. dirs.), Tri-County C. of C. (bd. dirs.), N.J. State Bd. Examiners. Home: 48 Brandon Ave Wayne NJ 07470-6032 Office: William Paterson Coll 300 Pompton Rd Wayne NJ 07470-2153

SPEES, EMIL RAY, philosophy educator; b. Rosiclare, Ill., July 25, 1935; s. Ray Clifton and Mattie (Clemens) S.; m. Edith Calvert, May 15, 1968; children: Edith Elizabeth, Ray Calvert. BA, So. Ill. U., 1957, MS, 1959; PhD, Claremont (Calif.) Grad. Sch., 1969. Asst. to dean of students Claremont Men's Coll.; rehab. counselor Rancho Los Amigos Hosp., Downey, Calif.; dean of student life So. Ill. U., Carbondale, assoc. prof. philosophy, women's studies, ednl. adminstrn.; rschr. in field and in Buddhism. Author: The Academic Profession, 1982, Higher Education: An Arena of Conflicting Philosophies, 1989; contbr. articles to profl. jours. Mem. Am. Coll. Pers. Assn. (media chmn., chmn. Internat. student devel. commn., comms.), Soc. for Intercultural Edn., Tng., and Rsch. Internat. Home: 3925 Chautauqua Rd Carbondale IL 62901 Office: So Ill U Dept Ednl Admin & Higher Edn Carbondale IL 62901-4606

SPEHR, STEVEN, real estate company executive. Sr. v.p. Coldwell Banker Ira E. Berry, St. Louis. Office: Coldwell Banker Ira E. Berry 530 Maryville Centre Dr Saint Louis MO 63141*

SPEICHER, OPAL, church administrator. Pres. Missionary Women Intern. of the Missionary Church, Fort Wayne, Ind. Office: The Missionary Ch PO Box 9127 3811 Vanguard Dr Fort Wayne IN 46809-3304

SPEICHER, WILLIAM CLAYTON, transportation executive; b. Accident, Md., Apr. 1, 1937; s. Clayton Everett and Leila (Rodgers) S.; m. Louise Coddington, Feb. 4, 1961; children: Michael William, Julie Rebecca. BS in Transp., U. Md., 1961. Lic. comml. pilot. Mgmt. trainee United Airlines, Washington, 1967-68; airport mgr. United Airlines, Balt., 1968-69; various duties United Airlines, Chgo., 1970-76; v.p. Hawaii div. United Airlines, Honolulu, 1976-78; sr. v.p. mktg. United Airlines, Chgo., 1978-81; sr. v.p. East United Airlines, N.Y.C., 1981-87; sr. v.p. Pacific United Airlines, Honolulu, 1988—; bd. dirs. First Ins. Co. of Hawaii; mem. commn. on jud. rev., 1992—; mem. Air Force Civilian Adv. Coun., 1988—; chmn. mktg. com. Hawaii Visitors Bur., Honolulu, 1992-93. Mem. Hawaii Bus. Roundtable, 1992—. Capt. USAF, 1961-66. Mem. Japan-Hawaii Econ. Coun., Nat. Def. Transp. Assn., c. of C. of Hawaii (bd. dirs. 1990—), Waialae Country Club. Republican. Avocations: golf, reading, music. Office: United Air Lines Inc 6600 Kalanianaole Hwy Honolulu HI 96825-1273

SPEIDEL, DAVID HAROLD, geology educator; b. Pottsville, Pa., Aug. 10, 1938; s. Harold O. and Edith M. (Rosser) S.; m. Margaret Helen Liebrecht, Sept. 8, 1962. B.S., Franklin and Marshall Coll., Lancaster, Pa., 1960; Ph.D., Pa. State U., 1964. Research asso. Pa. State U., 1964-66; asst. prof. to prof. dept. geology Queens Coll., CUNY, Flushing, 1966—; chmn. dept. Queens Coll., CUNY, 1980-88, dean faculty sci., 1970-79, chmn. faculty senate, 1992—; maj. projects sect. head, earth scis. NSF, 1988-89; vis. scholar Sr. Specialists div. Congl. Research Service, Washington, 1977-78. Author: (with A.F. Agnew) Natural Geochemistry of Our Environment; editor (with L. Ruedisili and A.F. Agnew) Perspectives on Water: Uses and Abuses; contbr. articles to profl. jours. Mem. AAAS, Geol. Soc. Am., Am. Ceramic Soc., Mineral. Soc. Am., Am. Geophys. Union, Am. Inst. Profl. Geologists, Nat. Hazards Soc., N.Y. Acad. Scis., Soc. Environ. Geochemistry and Health, Sigma Xi. Office: Queens Coll Dept Geology Flushing NY 11367

SPEIDEL, JOHN JOSEPH, physician, foundation officer; b. Iowa City, Iowa, Sept. 17, 1937; s. Thomas Dennis and Edna (Warweg) S.; divorced; 1 child, Sabrina Brett. A.B. cum laude, Harvard U., 1959, M.D., 1963, M.P.H., 1965. Diplomate: Nat. Bd. Med. Examiners, Am. Bd. Preventive Medicine. Intern St. Luke's Hosp., N.Y.C., 1963-64; resident N.Y.C. Dept. Health, 1965-67, dep. dir. maternal and infant care project, 1966-67; chief research div. Office of Population, AID, Dept. State, Washington, 1969-76; assoc. dir. Office of Population, 1977, dep. dir., acting dir. office, 1978-83; v.p. Population Action Internat. (formerly Population Crisis Com.), 1983-87, pres., 1987-95; program officer for population Hewlett Found., 1995—; lectr. population and family planning Georgetown U., 1973-75. Contbr. articles to profl. jours.; Editor: (with others) Female Sterilization, 1971, Hysteroscopic Sterilization, 1974, Intrauterine Devices, 1974, Control of Male Fertility, 1975, Advances in Female Sterilization Technology, 1976, Risks, Benefits and Controversies in Fertility Control, 1978, Reversal of Sterilization, 1978, Pregnancy Termination, 1979, Vaginal Contraception, 1979. Served to maj. U.S. Army, 1967-69. Recipient Meritorious Unit citation Office of Population, 1969-71, Arthur S. Flemming award Washington Downtown Jaycees, 1972. Mem. Am. Pub. Health Assn. (Carl S. Shultz award 1982), Population Assn. Am. Office: William & Flora Hewlett Found 525 Middlefield Rd Ste 200 Menlo Park CA 94025-3495

SPEIER, JOHN LEO, JR., chemist; b. Chgo., Sept. 29, 1918; s. John L. and Mary Jane (Dickman) S.; m. A. Louise Kimmel, Oct. 21, 1944; children—Susan, Genevieve, Dorothy, Margaret, John L. III, Thomas J. B.Sc., St. Benedict's Coll., 1941; M.Sc., U. Fla., 1943; Ph.D., U. Pitts., 1947. Naval Stores research fellow U. Fla., 1941-43; research fellow Mellon Inst., Pitts., 1943; sr. fellow Mellon Inst., 1947-56; mgr. organic research Dow Corning Corp., Midland, Mich., 1956-69; scientist in corp. research Dow Corning Corp., 1969-75, sr. scientist in corp. research, 1975-93; retired, 1994. Contbr. numerous articles to profl. jours., 1950—; holder 100 patents prodn. organosilicon compounds and allied products. Named Indsl.

Research and Devel. Scientist of Yr. Indsl. Research/Devel. mag., 1978. Mem. AAAS, Am. Chem. Soc. (Frederick Stanley Kipping award 1990), Sigma Xi. Office: Dow Corning Corp Dept Research Midland MI 48640

SPEIGEL, I. JOSHUA, neurosurgery educator; b. Ft. William, Ont., Can., Aug. 16, 1915; came to U.S., 1937; s. Jeremiah and Dora (Slobed) S.; m. Rosalynde Speigel, June 25, 1942; children: Virginia, Jonathan, Petra. MD, U. Toronto, 1937. Diplomate Am. Bd. Neurol. Surgery. Rotating intern Mt. Sinai Hosp., Cleve., 1937-38; asst. resident Neuropsychiatry State Hosp., Howard, R.I., 1938-39; asst. resident in neurol. surgery Boston City Hosp., 1939-40; sr. resident St. Luke's Hosp., Chgo., 1940-41; chief resident Cook County Hosp., Chgo., 1941-42; chief resident in neurology and neurol. surgery Neuropsychiat. Inst., Chgo., 1942; clin. prof. emeritus neurol. surgery U. Chgo., 1974-85; sr. neurological surgeon Michael Reese Hosp. and Med. Ctr., Chgo., 1985—; cons. neurol. surgeon Thorek Hosp., South Chgo. Community Hosp., South Shore Hosp., Jackson Park Hosp.; med. advisor U.S. Dept. Health and Human Services; mem. med. adv. council Assn. Brain Tumor Research. Contbr. articles to profl. jours. Served to maj. MC, AUS, 1942-46. Mem. AMA, Internat. Coll. Surgeons (chmn. U.S. div. neurosurg. sect. 1960—, vice regent U.S. div. 1983), Internat. Bd. Surgery (chmn. U.S. div. 1960—), Ill. State Med. Soc., Chgo. Neurol. Soc., Cook County Med. Soc., Chgo. Med. Soc., Assn. Mil. Surgeons of U.S., Am. Assn. Neurol. Surgeons, Am. Bd. Neurol. Surgeons, Neurosurg. Soc. Am. (treas. 1948-55, pres. 1957, Disting. Service award 1976), Congress Neurol. Surgeons, Interurban Neurosurg. Soc., Cen. Neurosurg. Soc. Royal Soc. Medicine, Ill. State Neurosurg. Soc., Soc. Neurovascular Surgery. Democrat. Jewish. Clubs: Explorer's (N.Y.C.); Standard, The Art, Adventurer's (Chgo.). Avocations: hunting, fishing, sculpture, prehistoric paintings and sculpture. Home: 1420 N Lake Shore Dr Chicago IL 60610-1628 Office: Neurol Surgery 55 E Washington St Chicago IL 60602-2103

SPEIGHT, JAMES GLASSFORD, research company executive; b. Murton, Eng., June 24, 1940; came to U.S., 1980; s. George Madison and Elizabeth (Glassford) S.; m. Sheila Elizabeth Stout, Dec. 28, 1963; 1 child, James. BSc in Chemistry with honors, Manchester U., Eng., 1961, PhD in Organic Chemistry, 1965. Research fellow Manchester U., 1965-67; research officer Research Council, Edmonton, Alta., Can., 1967-80; research assoc. Exxon Corp., Linden, N.J., 1980-84; chief sci. officer Western Rsch. Inst., Laramie, Wyo., 1984-89, chief exec. officer, 1990—; adv. com. Grant McEwan Community Coll. Edmonton, 1975-80; chmn. petroleum-natural gas research task force, Alta. Research Council, 1978-79; search com. V.P. for Research and Grad. Studies, U. Wyo., 1985; external mem. promotions com. U. Mosul, Iraq, 1985; thesis examiner, Indian Inst. Techn., Bombay, 1974, U. Mosul, 1976, 77, 78; vis. lect. petroleum sci., U. Mosul, Iraq, 1978; lect. petroleum sci., U. Alberta, Edmonton, Can., 1976-80, U. Calgary, Alta., 1979-80. Editor Fuel Sci. and Tech. Internat., 1983—; refereed numerous jours., manuscripts; contbr. over 150 sci. articles to profl. jours. Fellow Am. Inst. Chemists, Royal Soc. Chemistry (chartered chemist), Chem. Inst. Can. (treas. Edmonton sect. 1971-78, editor newsletter 1975-77); mem. Am. Chem. Soc. (program com. petroleum divsn. 1981-91, 94—, bus. mgr. petroleum divsn. 1982-85), Sigma Xi. Office: Western Rsch Inst 365 N 9th St Laramie WY 82070-3380

SPEIGHT, VELMA RUTH, university administrator; b. Snow Hill, N.C., Nov. 18, 1932; d. John Thomas and Mable Lee (Edwards) S.; m. Howard H. Kennedy, 1953 (div. 1961); 1 child, Chineta. BS, N.C. A&T U., 1953; MEd, U. Md., 1965, PhD, 1976. Cert. counselor, tchr., N.C. Tchr. math., French Kennard High Sch., Centreville, Md., 1954-60; counselor Kennard High Sch., Centreville, 1960-66; coord. guidance dept. Queene Anne's County High Sch., Centreville, 1966-69; adv. specialist in civil rights Md. State Dept. Edn., Balt., 1969-72, supr. guidance, 1972-76, dep. asst. state supt., 1976-82, asst. state supt., 1982-86; dir. EEO recruitment U. Md., College Park, 1972; coord. guidance and counseling U. Md. Ea. Shore, Princess Anne, 1986-87; assoc. prof. counselor edn. East Carolina U., Greenville, 1989; chmn. dept. edn., coord. grad. prog. guidance and counseling U. Md., Eastern Shore, Greenville, 1989-93, chmn. dept. edn., 1990-94; dir. alumni affairs N.C. A&T U., Greensboro, 1993—; adj. prof. Loyola U., Balt., 1976-80, Johns Hopkins U., Balt., 1980; cons., 1987—; speaker numerous seminars. Mem. Nat. Coalition for Chpt. 1 Parents, Washington, 1980-87, Human Rights Commn., Howard County, Md., 1987—; chmn. Gov.'s com. Studying Sentencing Alternatives for Women, Annapolis, Md., 1987; founder, chmn. Mothers to Prevent Dropouts, Centreville. Recipient Early Childhood Edn. award Japanese Govt., 1984, Md. State Tchrs'. Assn. Minority award Black Chs. for Excellence in Edn.; Fulbright Hayes scholar, 1991. Mem. Am. Counseling Assn., Nat. Alliance Black Educators, Assn. for Supervision and Curriculum Devel., Assn. Tchr. Edn., Md. Assn. Coll. Tchr. Edn., Md. Counseling assn., N.C. A&T U. Alumni Assn. (nat. pres. 197983, Excellence award 1983), Tchr. Edn. and Profl. Standards Bd. Democrat. Presbyterian. Club: Community Action (Centreville). Avocations: reading, cooking, sewing, bicycling. Home: 11 Carissa Ct Greensboro NC 27407-6366 Office: NC A&T State U Greensboro NC 27411

SPEIRS, DEREK JAMES, diversified corporation financial executive; b. Montreal, Que., Can., Dec. 21, 1933; s. James B. and Marie C. (Hunt) S.; m. Carol Alice Cumming, Dec. 8, 1967 (div. Feb. 1989); children: Lara Marie, Gregory Ross, Scott Lawrence Gordon. B. Commerce with honors in Econs., McGill U., 1954, M.B.A., 1959. Chartered acct., Can., chartered corp. sec. Devel. dir. fine papers, corp. acctg. dir. Domtar, Inc., Montreal, 1970-72, dir. corp. devel., 1976-78, v.p. fin., corp. devel., 1978-89, sr. v.p. fin. and corp. devel., 1989-91; v.p., sec. fin. Consoltex, Montreal, 1972-76, bus. cons., 1991—; pres. Speirs Cons. Inc. Mem. Can. Inst. Chartered Accts., Fin. Execs. Inst., C.D. Howe Inst., Lac Marois Country Club, St. James Club, Montreal Amateur Athletic Assn. Avocations: travel, skiing. Home: 365 Stanstead Ave, Ville Mont-Royal, Montreal, PQ Canada H3R 1X5 Office: Ste 1100, 2 Pl Alexis Nihon, Montreal, PQ Canada H3Z 3C1

SPEISER, THEODORE WESLEY, astrophysics, planetary and atmospheric sciences educator; b. Del Norte, Colo., Nov. 23, 1934; s. Alfred Theodore and Virginia Melva (Pickens) S.; m. Patricia Jane McCrummen, June 10, 1956; children: Tanya Lee, Kelly Ann, Tertia Ava. BS, Colo. State U., 1956; MS, Calif. Inst. Tech., 1959; PhD, Pa. State U., 1964. Asst. prof. U. Colo., Boulder, 1969-74, assoc. prof., 1974-85, prof. astrophysics, planetary and atmospheric scis., 1985—; cons. NOAA, Boulder, 1970—. Contbr. articles to profl. jours. Served to capt. U.S. Army, 1960-61. Recipient U.S. Sr. Scientist award A.V. Humboldt Found., 1977; Fulbright fellow, 1956. Mem. Am. Geophys. Union (local br. v.p. 1986-87, pres. 1987). Avocations: photography, hiking, cross-country skiing, tennis. Home: 2335 Dartmouth Ave Boulder CO 80303-5209 Office: U Colo Dept of Astrophysics Planetary & Atmospheric Scis C Box 391 Boulder CO 80309

SPEITEL, GERALD EUGENE, consulting environmental engineer; b. Phila., Feb. 4, 1930; s. Edmond Joseph and Lillian M. (Kohlschreiber) S.; m. Rosemarie Noller, Aug. 22, 1953; children: Gerald Eugene, Edmond C. BS, Drexel Evening Coll., 1963; M.S. in Engring. Mgmt, Drexel U., 1967. With Dept. Water, City of Phila., 1948-51, Day & Zimmerman, Phila., 1953-54; with John G. Reutter Assocs., Camden, N.J., 1954-72, v.p., 1970-72; pres. Speitel Assos., Marlton, N.J., 1972-88; dir. Environ. Measurements and Analysis, Hammonton, N.J., 1979-86; sr. v.p. BCM Engrs., Inc., 1986-90; prin. Gerald E. Speitel, Forensic Engr., 1991—. Served with C.E. U.S. Army, 1951-53. Named Honor Man of Yr. Drexel Evening Coll., 1983, 90; recipient Del. Valley Engr. of Yr. award, 1989, Disting. N.J. Civil Engr. award ASCE, 1989, Penjerdel award, 1989, Mary S. Irick Drexel medal, 1991. Fellow ASCE (life, pres. South Jersey br. 1979-80, nat. dir. dist. 1 1981-84, v.p. 1987-89, N.J. Engr. of Yr. 1984), Am. Cons. Engrs. Coun., mem. NSPE (life), N.J. Soc. Profl. Engrs. (Disting. Svc. award 1993), Nat. Acad. Forensic Engrs. (diplomate), Am. Acad. Environ. Engrs. (diplomate), Cons. Engrs. Coun. N.J. (pres. 1967-68, Engring. Excellence award 1979, 80, Grand award 1980), KC, Atlantic City Country Club. Roman Catholic. Home and Office: 921 Third St Ocean City NJ 08226-4019

SPEJEWSKI, EUGENE HENRY, physicist, educator; b. East Chicago, Ind., Sept. 15, 1938; s. Henry Louis and Carrie Jane (Fuss) S.; m. Norma Beverly Seekins, June 8, 1963; children: Maria Suzanne, Beverly Anne, Andrew John, Jeannette Michelle. B.S., U. Notre Dame, 1960; Ph.D., Ind. U., 1966. Research assoc. Ind. U., Bloomington, 1965-67; research assoc. Princeton U., 1967-69, instr., 1969-71; asst. prof. Oberlin Coll., Ohio, 1971-

72; dir. UNISOR, Oak Ridge Assoc. Univs., 1972-85, mgr. SDS program, 1985-86, chmn. spl. projects div., 1986-89; v.p.; dir. tng. and mgmt. systems div. Oak Ridge Inst. for Sci. and Edn., 1989—; vis. prof. physics U. Tenn., Knoxville, 1981-84; mem., chmn. HHIRF Users Exec. Com., Oak Ridge Nat. Lab., 1982-84; referee U.S. Dept. Energy, various profl. jours. Coeditor: Future Directions in Studies of Nuclei Far from Stability, 1980; contbr. articles to profl. jours. Referee U.S. Soccer Fedn.; bd. dirs. Oak Ridge Community Playhouse, 1985-88. Mem. AAAS, Am. Phys. Soc., Am. Mgmt. Assn., Oak Ridge Sertoma Club (sec., treas., pres., chair bd. dirs.), Sigma Xi.

SPELKER, ARNOLD WILLIAM, banker; b. Newark, July 15, 1934; s. William M. and Helen F. (Wilhelm) S.; children: Mark, Scott, Matthew. BS in Acctg., Rutgers U., 1960; MBA, Fairleigh Dickinson U., 1978; postgrad., Harvard U., 1975. CPA, N.J. Sr. acct. KPMG Peat Marwick, N.Y.C., 1960-61; audit supr. Ernst & Young, N.Y.C., 1961-67; dir. op. auditing CBS, Inc., N.Y.C., 1967-70; v.p., asst. controller Chem. Bank, N.Y.C., 1970-81; sr. v.p., chief fin. officer U.S. Credit Suisse, N.Y.C., 1981—; sec., treas. Credit Suisse Investment Corp., Credit Suisse Capital Corp. Mem. parent's adv. coun. Dickinson Coll., 1981-85; mem. pres.'s alumni adv. coun. Fairleigh Dickinson U., 1985-86. Percy H. Johnston scholar Chem. Bank, 1978; recipient Anthony L. Gervino Outstanding Alumni award. Mem. AICPA, N.J. Soc. CPAs, Fin. Execs. Inst. (bd. dirs. 1982-95, pres. N.Y.C. chpt. 1988-89, nat. membership com. 1987-88), Inst. Internat. Bankers (bd. trustees 1986-90), Fairleigh Dickinson U. Alumni Assn. (bd. govs. 1986-90). Avocations: mil. and polit. history, real estate investment, tennis. Home: 6050 Boulevard E West New York NJ 07093-3901 Office: Credit Suisse 165 Broadway New York NY 10006

SPELLACY, WILLIAM NELSON, obstetrician-gynecologist, educator; b. St. Paul, May 10, 1934; s. Jack F. and Elmyra L. (Nelson) S.; m. Lynn Larsen; children: Kathleen Ann, Kimberly Joan, William Nelson. B.A., U. Minn., 1955, B.S., 1956, M.D., 1959. Diplomate: Am. Bd. Ob-Gyn, subsplty. cert. in maternal and fetal medicine. Intern Hennepin County Gen. Hosp., Mpls., 1959-60; resident U. Minn., Mpls., 1960-63; practice medicine specializing in ob-gyn. Mpls., 1963-67, Miami, Fla., 1967-73, Gainesville, Fla., 1973-79, Chgo., 1979-88; prof., head dept. U. Ill. Coll. Medicine, Chgo., 1979-88; prof., chmn. dept. U. So. Fla. Coll. Medicine, Tampa, 1988—; prof. dept. obstetrics and gynecology U. Miami, 1967-73; prof., chmn. dept. U. Fla., 1974-79. Contbr. articles to med. jours. Mem. AMA, Am. Gynecol. Soc., Am. Assn. Obstetricians and Gynecologists, Am. Gynecol. and Obstet. Soc., Soc. Gynecol. Investigation, Am. Coll. Obstetricians and Gynecologists, Endocrine Soc., Am. Fertility Soc., Assn. Profs. Gynecology and Obstetrics, Am. Diabetes Assn., Perinatal Research Soc., South Atlantic Soc. Obstetrics and Gynecology, Central Assn. Obstetrics and Gynecology, Soc. Perinatal Obstetricians, Ill. Med. Soc. Inst. of Medicine. Episcopalian. Club: Rotary. Home: 845 Seddon Cove Way Tampa FL 33602-5704 Office: U South Fla Coll Medicine Dept OBGYN 4 Columbia Dr Ste 514 Tampa FL 33606-3568

SPELLER, BENJAMIN FRANKLIN, JR., librarian, educator; b. Windsor, N.C., Sept. 21, 1940; s. Benjamin Franklin and Mamie (Bond) S. A.B., N.C. Coll., 1962; M.A.T., Ind. U., 1965, Ph.D., 1973. Acquisitions libr. Livingstone Coll., Salisbury, N.C., 1965-67; catalogue libr. Elizabeth City (N.C.) State U., 1967-69; asst. to chancellor, 1969-73, asst. acad. dean, 1973-76; prof. N.C. Cen. U., Durham, 1976—; commr. N.C. Pub. Librarian's Cert. Bd., Raleigh, 1983—; mem. N.C. State Hist. Records Adv. Bd., 1989—. Author: Zero-Based Budgeting, 1979; editor: Microcomputing in Libraries, 1982. Bd. dirs. St. Joseph's Hist. Found., Durham, 1984—, N.C. Ctr. Study of Black History, 1988—, N.C. Perservation Consortium, 1989—; mem. Durham Arts Council, 1978, Friends of Durham County Library, 1979—. Recipient Alumni Disting. Service award Sch. Library and Info. Sci., N.C. Central U., Durham, 1982, Disting. Service award Elizabeth City State U., Elizabeth City, 1971, Louise Maxwell award Ind. U. 1987; Library Sci. scholar N.C. State Library, Raleigh, 1964. Mem. ALA, Assn. for Library and Info. Sci. Edn., Durham County Library Assn. (pres. 1977-78, 82-83), NEA, N.C. Library Assn. (dir. resources and tech. services sect. 1967-69, chmn. library resources com. 1969-71, chmn. resources and tech. services sect. 1983-85, mem. goals and objectives com. 1976-83), Southeastern Library Assn., Phi Delta Kappa, Beta Phi Mu. Democrat. Baptist. Avocations: gardening; historical preservation. Home: 1004 Shepherd St Durham NC 27701-1328 Office: NC Ctrl U Sch Libr & Info Sci 1801 Fayetteville St Durham NC 27707-3198*

SPELLING, AARON, film and television producer, writer; b. Dallas, Apr. 22, 1923; s. David and Pearl (Wall) S.; m. Carole Gene Marer, Nov. 23, 1968; children: Victoria Davey, Randall Gene. Student, Sorbonne, U. Paris, France, 1945-46; B.A., So. Meth. U., 1950. Co-owner with Danny Thomas Thomas-Spelling Prodns., 1969-72; co-pres. Spelling-Goldberg Prodns., 1972-76; pres. Aaron Spelling Prodns., Inc., Los Angeles, 1977-86, chmn., chief exec. officer, 1986—. Writer numerous TV plays and movies; producer over 40 TV programs including Dynasty, The Colbys, Love Boat, Hotel, Beverly Hills 90210, Melrose Place, 1992; also 160 Movies of the Week for ABC, CBS, NBC; producer theatrical films including Mr. Mom, 'night, Mother, Surrender, Cross My Heart, Soapdish. Bd. dirs. Am. Film Inst. Served with USAAF, 1942-45. Decorated Bronze Star medal, Purple Heart with oak leaf cluster; recipient Eugene O'Neill awards, 1947, 48, NAACP Image awards 1970, 71, 73, 75; named Man of Yr., Publicists Guild Am., 1971, Man of Yr. B'nai B'rith, Beverly Hills chpt., 1972, 85, Humanitarian of Yr., 1983, Man of Yr. Scopus Orgn., 1993. Mem. Writers Guild Am. (award 1962), Producers Guild Am., The Caucus of Producers, Writers and Directors, Hollywood Radio and TV Soc., Hollywood TV Acad. Arts and Scis., Acad. Motion Picture Arts and Scis. Democrat. Jewish. Clubs: Friars, Big Brothers of Am. Office: Aaron Spelling Prodns 5700 Wilshire Blvd Ste 575 Los Angeles CA 90036*

SPELLMAN, GEORGE GENESER, SR., internist; b. Woodward, Iowa, Sept. 11, 1920; s. Martin Edward and Corinne (Geneser) S.; m. Mary Carolyn Dwight, Aug. 26, 1942; children: Carolyn Anne Spellman Rambow, George G. Jr., Mary Alice, Elizabeth Spellman-Chrisinger, John Martin Pile-Spellman, Loretta Suzanne Spellman Hoffman. B.S., St. Ambrose Coll., 1940; M.D., State U. Iowa, 1943. Diplomate Am. Bd. Internal Medicine. Intern Providence Hosp., Detroit, 1944; resident in internal medicine State U. Iowa, Iowa City, 1944-46; practice medicine specializing in internal medicine Mitchell, S.D., 1948-50, Sioux City, Iowa, 1950—; instr. Coll. Medicine U. S.D., 1975-77, now clin. assoc. prof. medicine; bd. dirs. St. Joseph Mercy Hosp., 1977-80, 87-90; mem. staff St. Joseph Mercy Hosp. (now Marion Health Ctr.), 1950-91, chief of staff, 1963; bd. dirs. St. Vincent Hosp., 1977-80, 87-90, mem. staff, 1950-91, chief of staff, 1954-77, also bd. dirs.; mem. staff St. Luke's Med. Ctr.; clin. assoc. prof. medicine State U. Iowa; ret., 1991; med. vol. Project U.S.A. of AMA, 1991—; mem. Iowa Bd. Med. Examiners, 1989-95; instr. schs. nursing St. Vincent Hosp., Luth. Hosp.; co-founder, pres. Siouxland Mental Health Assn., 1968-75; vol. cons. Siouxland Cmty. Health Clinic; bd. dirs. mid-step svcs. for mentally handicapped Hospice of Siouxland, Marian Health Ctr., 1974-80, 89-91, also cofounder, 1st pres., chmn. dependency unit, founder renal dialysis unit, 1964. Contbr. articles to med. jours. Ordained deacon Cath. Ch., 1988; vol. cons. Siouxland Community Health Ctr., 1993—. Capt. M.C., U.S. Army, 1946-48. Decorated Knight of St. Gregory (Vatican); named Internist of Yr., Iowa Soc. Internal Medicine, 1987; recipient Laureate award Iowa Chpt. ACP, 1991, Humanitarian award Siouxland Community, 1991. Fellow ACP; mem. AMA, Am. Acad. Scis., Iowa State Med. Soc., Woodbury Med. Soc., Am. Soc. Internal Medicine, Iowa Soc. Internal Medicine, Am. Thoracic Soc., Iowa Thoracic Soc., Am. Heart Assn., Iowa Heart Assn., Am. Geriatric Soc., Alpha Omega Alpha. Home: 3849 Jones St Sioux City IA 51104-1447

SPELLMAN, J. R., book publishing executive. Treas., office manager Steckley Hybrid Corn Co., Lincoln, Nebr., 1954-1964; pres. Cliffs Notes Inc., Lincoln, Nebr., 1964-94; pres. emeritus Clifs Notes Inc., Lincoln, Nebr., 1995—. Office: Cliffs Notes Inc Box 80728 Lincoln NE 68501

SPELLMIRE, GEORGE W., lawyer; b. Oak Park, Ill., June 10, 1948. Attended, Brown U.; BA, Ohio State U., 1970; JD, De Paul U., 1974. Bar: Ill. 1974, U.S. Dist. Ct. (no. dist.) Ill. 1974, U.S. Tax Ct. 1984, U.S. Ct. Appeals (7th cir.) 1984, U.S. Supreme Ct. 1984. Ptnr. Hinshaw & Culbertson, Chgo.

Author: Attorney Malpractice: Prevention and Defense, 1988; co-author: Accountants' Legal Liability Guide, 1990, Illinois Handbook on Legal Malpractice, 1982, Associates Primer for the Prevention of Malpractice, 1987. Recipient Am. Jurisprudence award for contracts. Mem. ABA, Ill. State Bar Assn., Chgo. Bar Assn., Internat. Assn. Defense Counsel (legal malpractice com., defense counsel practice mgmt. com.), Soc. Trial Lawyers, Trial Lawyers Club Chgo., Fed. Trial Bar. Office: Hinshaw & Culbertson 222 N La Salle St Ste 300 Chicago IL 60601-1081

SPELTS, RICHARD JOHN, lawyer; b. Yuma, Colo., July 29, 1939; s. Richard Clark and Barbara Eve (Pletcher) S.; children: Melinda, Meghan, Richard John Jr.; m. Gayle Merves, Nov. 14, 1992. BS cum laude, U. Colo., 1961, JD, 1964. Bar: Colo. 1964, U.S. Dist. Ct. Colo. 1964, U.S. Supreme Ct. 1968, U.S. Ct. Appeals (10th cir.) 1970, U.S. Dist. Ct. (ea. dist.) Mich. 1986. With Ford Motor Internat., Cologne, Germany, 1964-65; legis. counsel to U.S. Senator, 89th and 90th Congresses, 1967-68; minority counsel to U.S. Senate Subcom., 90th and 91st Congresses, 1968-70; asst. U.S. atty., 1st asst. U.S. atty. Fed. Dist. of Colo., 1970-77; pvt. practice Denver, 1977-89; risk mgr. sheriff's dept. Jefferson County, Golden, Colo., 1990-91; owner Video Prodn. for Lawyers, 1991—. Selected for Leadership Denver, 1977; recipient cert. for outstanding contbns. in drug law enforcement U.S. Drug Enforcement Adminstrn., 1977, spl. commendation for criminal prosecution U.S. Dept. Justice, 1973, spl. commendation for civil prosecution U.S. Dept. Justice, 1976. Mem. Fed. Bar Assn. (chmn. govt. torts seminar 1980), Colo. Bar Assn. (bd. govs. 1976-78), Denver Bar Assn., Colo. Trial Lawyers Assn., Denver Law Club, Order of Coif. Republican. Methodist. Home and Office: 6697 W Hinsdale Ave Littleton CO 80123-4511

SPENCE, A. MICHAEL, economics educator, academic administrator; b. Montclair, N.J., 1943; m. Ann. BA summa cum laude, Princeton U., 1966; MA, Oxford U., 1968; PhD in Econs., Harvard U., 1972. Instr. Harvard U., Cambridge, Mass., 1971-72, prof. econs., 1976-90, prof. bus. adminstrn., 1979-90, chmn. econ. dept.; George Gund prof. of econ. and bus. adminstrn., 1983-90, dean faculty arts and scis., 1984-90; assoc. prof. econs. Stanford (Calif.) U., 1973-75, Philip H. Knight prof. econs. and mgmt., 1990—, dean Grad. Sch. Bus., 1990—; bd. dirs. BankAm. Corp., Sun Microsystems, Gen. Mills Inc., VeriFone, Inc., Bay Area Coun.; chmn. Nat. Rsch. Coun. on Sci., Tech. and Econ. Policy; mem. econs. adv. panel, NSF, 1977-79. Author: Market Signaling: Information Transfer in Hiring and Related Screening Processes, 1974; (with R.E. Caves and M.E. Porter) Competition in the Open Economy, 1980; mem. editorial bd. various jours. including Bell Jour. Econs., Jour. Econ. Theory, Pub. Policy. Rhodes scholar, 1966-68; recipient Galbraith Prize for Teaching Excellence, 1978, John Bates Clark Medal, Am. Econ. Assn., 1981. Office: Stanford U Grad Sch Bus Stanford CA 94305

SPENCE, ANDREW, artist, painter; b. Bryn Mawr, Pa., Oct. 4, 1947; s. Thomas and Elizabeth Spence; m. Mary Stewart Stoll, June 24, 1977. BFA, Temple U., 1969; MFA, U. Calif., Santa Barbara, 1971. One-man shows include TransAvant Garde Gallery, Austin, Tex., 1989, Barbara Krakow Gallery, Boston, 1989, Barbara Toll Fine Arts, N.Y.C., 1990, Compass Rose Gallery, Chgo., 1990, James Corcoran Gallery, L.A., 1990, Max Protetch Gallery, N.Y.C., 1992, 93; exhibited in group shows including Worcester (Mass.) Art Mus., 1991, Whitney Mus. Am. Art, N.Y.C., 1991, 92, Met. Mus. Art, N.Y.C., 1993; represented in permanent collections including Balt. Mus. Art, Cleve. Mus. Art, Hirshhorn Mus. and Sculpture Garden, Laguna Gloria Art Mus., Met. Mus. Art, N.Y.C., San Diego Mus. Contemporary Art, Walker Art Ctr., Whitney Mus. Am. Art, N.Y.C. Painting grantee Nat. Endowment for Arts, 1987; Guggenheim fellow, 1994.

SPENCE, BARBARA E., publishing company executive; b. Bryn Mawr, Pa., July 8, 1921; d. Geoffrey Strange and Mary (Harrington) Kantrow; m. Kenneth M. Spence Jr., June 29, 1944; children: Kenneth M. III, Christopher E., Hilary B. Grad. high sch. Movie, radio editor Parade Mag., N.Y.C., 1941-45; with Merchandising Group, N.Y.C., 1946-47; exec. dir. Greenfield Hill Congl. Ch., Fairfield, Conn., 1958-74, dir. religious edn., 1968-74; assoc. Ten Eyck-Emerich Antiques, 1974-76; personnel dir. William Morrow & Co., Inc., N.Y.C., 1976-91; ret., 1991. Chmn. pub. relations, bd. dirs. ARC, 1951-56, Family Service Soc., Fairfield, 1956-57, 61-63; chmn. pub. relations Citizens for Eisenhower, 1952, Fairfield Teens Players, 1968-71; bd. dirs. Fairfield Teens, Inc., 1965-70, Planned Parenthood of Greater Bridgeport, 1969-75, chmn. pub. affairs, 1971-72, chmn. personnel, 1972-73, chpt. vice chmn., 1973-75; pres. steering com. Am. Playwrights Festival Theatre, Inc., Fairfield, 1969-70, v.p., bd. dirs., 1971—; bd. govs. Unquowa Sch., Fairfield, 1963-69; bd. dirs. Fairfield U. Playhouse, 1971-73, Downtown Cabaret Theatre, Bridgeport, 1975-76. Mem. AAP (compensation survey com.), Fairfield Women's Exch. (bd. dirs. 1993). Home: 101 Twin Brook Ln Fairfield CT 06430-2834

SPENCE, CLARK CHRISTIAN, history educator; b. Great Falls, Mont., May 25, 1923; s. Christian Edward and Lela (Killian) S.; m. Mary Lee Nance, Sept. 12, 1953; children: Thomas Christian, Ann Leslie. B.A., U. Colo., 1948, M.A., 1951; Ph.D. U. Minn., 1955. Instr. Carleton Coll., Northfield, Minn., 1954-55; instr., then assoc. prof. Pa. State U., 1955-60; vis. lectr. U. Calif.-Berkeley, 1960-61; mem. faculty U. Ill., Champaign, 1961—; prof. history U. Ill., 1964-90, prof. emeritus, 1990—, chmn. dept., 1967-70, assoc. mem. Ctr. for Advanced Study, 1975; vis. lectr. Yale, summer 1964; vis. prof. U. Colo., summer 1967; disting. vis. prof. Ariz. State U., spring 1988. Author: British Investment and the American Mining Frontier, 1958, God Speed the Plow: The Coming of Steam Cultivation to Great Britain, 1960, Sinews of American Capitalism: An Economic History, 1964, The American West, 1966, Mining Engineers in the American West, 1970, Territorial Politics and Government in Montana, 1864-89, 1975, Montana: A Bicentennial History, 1978, The Rainmakers: American Pluviculture to World War II, 1980, The Salvation Army Farm Colonies, 1985, The Conrey Placer Mining Company, 1989. Served with USAAF, 1943-46. Fulbright fellow Eng., 1953-54; Ford Found. fellow, 1963-64; Guggenheim fellow, 1970-71; recipient ann. book award Agrl. History Soc., 1959. Mem. Western History Assn. (pres. 1969-70), Mining Hist. Assn. (pres. 1990-91), Phi Beta Kappa, Phi Alpha Theta. Home: 1107 Foley St Champaign IL 61820-6326

SPENCE, DONALD POND, psychologist, psychoanalyst; b. N.Y.C., Feb. 8, 1926; s. Ralph Beckett and Rita (Pond) S.; m. Mary Newbold Cross, June 2, 1951; children: Keith, Sarah, Laura, Katherine. AB, Harvard U., 1949; PhD, Columbia U., 1955. Lic. psychologist, N.Y., N.J. From rsch. asst. to prof. psychology NYU, 1954-74; prof. psychiatry Robert Wood Johnson Med. Sch., Piscataway, N.J., 1974—; vis. prof. psychology Stanford (Calif.) U., 1971-72, Princeton (N.J.) U., 1975—, Louvain-la-Neuve, Belgium, 1980, William Alanson White Inst., N.Y.C., 1992; mem. personality and cognition rsch. rev. com. MIMH, 1969-73. Author: Narrative Truth and Historical Truth, 1982, The Freudian Metaphor, 1987, The Rhetorical Voice of Psychoanalysis, 1994; mem. editl. bd. Psychoanalysis and Contemporary Thought, Psychol. Inquiry, Theory and Psychology; contbr. articles to profl. jours. With U.S. Army, 1944-46, ETO. Recipient rsch. scientist award NIMH, 1968-74. Mem. APA (pres. theoretical and philos. divsn. 1992-93), Am. Psychoanalytic Assn., N.Y. Acad. Sci., Sigma Xi. Democrat. Home: 9 Haslet Ave Princeton NJ 08540-4913 Office: Robert Wood Johnson Med Sch Piscataway NJ 08854

SPENCE, FLOYD DAVIDSON, congressman; b. Columbia, S.C., Apr. 9, 1928; s. James Wilson and Addie (Lucas) S.; m. Deborah Williams, July 3, 1988; children from previous marriage: David, Zack, Benjamin, Caldwell. A.B., U. S.C., 1952, J.D., 1956. Bar: S.C. 1956. Former partner firm Callison and Spence, West Columbia, S.C.; mem. S.C. Ho. Reps., 1956-62; mem. S.C. Senate, 1966-70, minority leader, 1966-70, chmn. joint com. internal security, 1967-70; mem. 92nd-103rd Congresses from 2nd S.C. dist., Washington, D.C., 1971—; chmn. nat. security com. 104th Congress, mem. subcom. mil. procurement; ranking minority mem. Armed Svcs. com., 1992-94; mem. Ho. of Reps. com. on coms. 103d Congress; mem. Rep. policy com. 104th Congress; mem. Vietnam Era Vets in Congress. Editor S.C. Law Quarterly. Past chmn. Indian Waters Coun. S.C. Boy Scouts Am., 1955-66, exec. bd., 1963—; chmn. Lexington County Mental Health Assn., 1959; former mem. bd. visitors U.S. Naval Acad. Served as capt. USNR, ret. Recipient Watchdog of the Treasury award, Order of the Palmetto award. Mem. ABA, U.S. Supreme Ct. Bar Assn., Lexington County Bar Assn., Am. Legion, VFW, Res. Officers Assn., Navy League, Kappa Alpha Order, Phi

Alpha Delta (former chief justice), Kappa Sigma Kappa, Omicron Delta Kappa. Lutheran. Office: US Ho Reps 2405 Rayburn House Office Bldg Washington DC 20515-4002

SPENCE, FRANCIS JOHN, archbishop; b. Perth, Ont., Can., June 3, 1926; s. William John and Rose Anna (Jordan) S. BA, St. Michael's Coll., Toronto, 1946; postgrad., St. Augustine's Sem., Toronto, 1946-50; JCD, St. Thomas U., Rome, 1955. Ordained to priest Roman Cath. Ch., 1950. Consecrated bishop, 1967; diocesan sec. Kingston, Ont., 1950-52; parish asst., 1955-61; mem. Marriage Tribunal, 1961-66; diocesan dir. hosp. and charities, 1961-66; pastor Sacred Heart Ch., Marmora, Ont., 1966-67; aux. bishop Mil. Vicar Canadian Forces, 1967-70; bishop of Charlottetown P.E.I. 1970-82; archbishop of Kingston Ont., 1982—; mil. vicar of Can., 1982-88. Office: Catholic Diocesan Centre, 390 Palace Rd, Kingston, ON Canada K7L 4T3

SPENCE, GLEN OSCAR, clergyman; b. Willow Springs, Mo., Jan. 20, 1927; s. John Oscar and Emma Adelia (Kentch) S.; m. Margaret Carolyn Hunter, Sept. 10, 1948; children: Rodney Glen, Randall Eugene. B.S. in Agr, U. Mo., 1950; B.A. in Bible, Oakland City (Ind.) Coll., 1957, D.Div. (hon.), 1982. Tchr. agr. Mountain View, Mo., 1950-55; instr. biology Oakland City Coll., 1955-57; ordained to ministry Gen. Bapt. Ch., 1954; pastor chs. in Evansville, Ind., 1958-65, 73-76; dir. denominational affairs Oakland City Coll., 1965-72; exec. dir. Gen. Assn. Gen. Bapts., Poplar Bluff, Mo., 1977-92; moderator Gen. Assn. Gen. Bapts., 1961, pres. gen. bd., 1963-64. Served with USNR, 1945-46. Mem. Kiwanis (lt. gov. Mo.-Ark. dist. divsn. 15 1992-93, chmn. human and spiritual values com. Mo.-Ark. dist. 1993-94).

SPENCE, JAMES ROBERT, JR., television sports executive; b. Bronxville, N.Y., Dec. 20, 1936; s. James Robert and Mary Jeffery (Grant) S.; m. Betsy Jo Viener, June 16, 1992. B.A., Dartmouth Coll. 1958. Prodn. asst. ABC Sports, Inc. (known as Sports Programs, Inc. through 1966), N.Y.C., 1960-63; asst. to exec. producer ABC's Wide World of Sports, 1963-66, coordinating producer, 1966-70; v.p. program planning ABC Sports, Inc., 1970-78, sr. v.p., 1978-86; pres. Sports Television Internat. Inc., N.Y.C., 1986—. Author: Up Close and Personal - The Inside Story of Network Television Sports, 1988. Served with U.S. Army, 1958-60. Club: Westchester Country (Rye, N.Y.). Office: Sports TV Internat Inc 545 Madison Ave New York NY 10022-4219

SPENCE, JONATHAN DERMOT, historian, educator; b. Surrey, Eng., Aug. 11, 1936; came to U.S., 1959; s. Dermot Gordon Chesson and Muriel (Crailsham); m. Helen Alexander, Sept. 15, 1962 (div. 1993); children: Colin Chesson, Ian Alexander; m. Chin Annping, Aug. 12, 1993. B.A., Cambridge (Eng.) U., 1959; Ph.D., Yale U., 1965; L.H.D. (hon.), Knox Coll., 1984, U. New Haven, 1989; Litt. D. (hon.), Wheeling Coll., 1985. Asst. prof. history Yale U., New Haven, 1966-71; prof. Yale U., 1971—, chmn. dept. history, dir. div. humanities.; Wiles lectr. Queen's U., Belfast, 1985; Gauss lectr. Princeton U., 1987; vis. prof. Peking U., 1987; chmn. Council on East Asian Studies; bd. govs. Yale U. Press, 1988—; hon. prof. Nanjing U., 1993. Author: Ts'Ao Yin and the K'Ang-Hsi Emperor, 1966, To Change China, 1969, Emperor of China, 1974, The Death of Woman Wang, 1978, The Gate of Heavenly Peace, 1981, The Memory Palace of Matteo Ricci, 1984, The Question of Hu, 1988, The Search for Modern China, 1990, Chinese Roundabout, 1992; editor: Ch'ing-Shih Wen'TI, 1965-73, (with others) From Ming to Ch'ing, 1979; em. editorial bd. Am. Hist. Revs., 1990-93, Yale Jour. Criticism, 1989, Yale Rev., 1991, China Quar., 1992. Served with Brit. Army, 1954-56. Recipient John Adison Porter prize, 1965, Christopher award, 1975, Devane teaching medal, 1978, L.A. Times book award, 1982, Vursell prize Am. Acad. and Inst. Arts and Letters, 1983, Comisso prize (Italy), 1987, Gelber prize (Can.), 1990; named to Coun. of Scholars, Libr. of Congress, 1989. Yale fellow in East Asian Studies, 1962-65, 68-70, Guggenheim fellow, 1979-80, John D. and Catherine T. MacArthur Found. fellow, 1988-93. Mem. Am. Acad. Arts and Scis., Am. Philos. Soc., Assn. Asian Studies. Home: 691 Forest Rd New Haven CT 06515 Office: Yale U History Dept PO Box 208324 New Haven CT 06520

SPENCE, MARY ANNE, geneticist, medical association executive; b. Tulsa, Sept. 8, 1944; married, 1972. BA, Grinnell Coll., 1966; PhD, U. Hawaii, 1969. NIH fellow in human genetics U. N.C., Chapel Hill, 1969-70; asst. prof. to assoc. prof. UCLA, 1970-80; prof. in psychiatry UCLA Sch. Medicine, 1980—; assoc. dean grad. divsn. UCLA, 1988—; mem. Mental Retardation Rsch. Ctr., Neuro-Psychiatric Inst., UCLA, 1974—. Co-editor: Multipoint Mapping & Linkage Based Upon Affected Pedigree Members: Genetic Analysis Workshop 6, 1989. Recipient Woman of Sci. award UCLA, 1979. Am. Soc. Human Genetics, Genetics Soc. Am., Behaviorial & Genetics Assn. Home: 1652 Benedict Canyon Dr Beverly Hills CA 90210*

SPENCE, MARY LEE, historian; b. Kyle, Tex., Aug. 4, 1927; d. Jeremiah Milton and Mary Louise (Hutchinson) Nance; m. Clark Christian Spence, Sept. 12, 1953; children: Thomas Christian, Ann Leslie. BA, U. Tex., 1947, MA, 1948; PhD, U. Minn., 1957. Instr., asst. prof. S.W. Tex. State U., San Marcos, 1948-53; lectr. Pa. State U., State College, 1955-58; mem. faculty U. Ill., Urbana-Champaign, 1973—, asst. prof., assoc. prof., 1973-81, 81-89, prof. history, 1989-90, prof. emerita, 1990—. Editor (with Donald Jackson) The Expeditions of John Charles Fremont, 3 vols., 1970-84, (with Clark Spence) Fanny Kelly's Narrative of Her Captivity Among the Sioux Indians, 1990, (with Pamela Herr) The Letters of Jessie Benton Fremont, 1993; contbr. articles to profl. jours. Mem. Children's Theater Bd., Urbana-Champaign, 1965-73. Grantee Nat. Hist. Pub. and Records Commn., Washington, 1977-78, 87-90; recipient Excellent Advisor award Liberal Arts and Sci. Coll., U. Ill., 1986. Mem. Western History Assn. (pres. 1981-82), Orgn. Am. Historians, Phi Beta Kappa (exec. sect. Gamma chpt. 1985-89, pres. 1991-92), Phi Alpha Theta. Episcopalian. Home: 1107 S Foley St Champaign IL 61820-6326 Office: U Ill Dept History 810 S Wright St Urbana IL 61801-3611

SPENCE, MICHAEL, finance educator, dean. BA in Philosophy summa cum laude, Princeton U.; BA, MA, Oxford U.; PhD in Economics, Harvard U. Assoc. prof. econs. Stanford U., 1973-75; prof. econs. and bus. adminstrn. Harvard U., 1975-90, chmn. econs. dept., George Gund prof. econs. and bus. adminstrn., 1983, dean faculty of arts and scis., 1984-90; now dean Stanford University, Stanford, CA. Recipient John Kenneth Galbraith prize, John Bates Clark medal. office: Dean of Graduate Sch of Bus Stanford University Stanford CA 94305*

SPENCE, PAUL HERBERT, librarian; b. Geraldine, Ala., Dec. 25, 1923; s. John Clardy and Leila (Carrell) S.; m. Ruth Schmidt, May 9, 1954; children—John Carrell, Peter Schmidt, Robert McCollough. A.B., Emory U., 1948, M.A., 1956; Ph.D., U. Ill., 1969. Asst. reference librarian Emory U., Atlanta, 1950-53; periodical reference librarian Air U., Maxwell AFB, 1953-56; dir. library Air Force Inst. of Tech., Wright-Patterson AFB, Ohio, 1957-58; asst. dir. social studies U. Notre Dame, South Bend, Ind., 1959-60, U. Nebr., Lincoln, 1960-63; history and polit. sci. librarian U. Ill., Urbana, 1963-66; dir. libraries U. Ga., Athens, 1966-70; dir. libraries U. Ala., Birmingham, 1970-84, collection devel. librarian, 1985-89, prof. emeritus, 1989—, libr. cons., 1990—. Bd. dirs. Southeastern Library Network, Atlanta, 1973-75. Served with U.S. Army, 1943-46, ETO. Mem. ALA (council mem. 1976-78), Ala. Library Assn. (treas. 1975-76), Southeastern Library Assn. (pres. 1980-82). Democrat. Presbyterian. Home: 614 Warwick Rd Birmingham AL 35209-4426 Office: U Ala at Birmingham 172 Sterne Libr Birmingham AL 35294

SPENCE, RICHARD DEE, paper products company executive, former railroad executive; b. Tucumcari, N.Mex., Apr. 7, 1925; s. Andrew Doke and Myrtle Hannah (Roach) S.; m. Mary Ames Kellogg, July 24, 1976; children: Mary B., James T., Richard T.; children from previous marriage: Diana, Richard N. BS, UCLA, 1949; grad., Transp. Mgmt. Program, Stanford U., 1956, Sr. Execs. Program, MIT, 1962. With So. Pacific Transp. Co., San Francisco, 1946-75, asst. v.ps.-opers., 1967-69, v.p. ops., 1969-75; pres., chief oper. officer Consol. Rail Corp., Phila., 1975-78; pres. L&N R.R. Co., Louisville, 1978-80; exec. v.p. ops. Family Lines Rail System, 1980-84; pres. Skippingdale Paper Products, Eng., 1985—. With USN, 1943-46. Mem. Ponte Vedra Club, Tournament Players Club, Sawgrass Club, Bohemian Club, Golf House Club of Elie (Scotland), Plantation Club at Ponte Vedra,

Phi Kappa Sigma. Republican. Episcopalian. Home and Office: 339 Ponte Vedra Blvd Ponte Vedra Beach FL 32082-1813

SPENCE, ROBERT DEAN, physics educator; b. Bergen, N.Y., Sept. 12, 1917; s. La Vergne Robert and Jennie (Waterman) S.; m. Helen Holbrook, June 14, 1942; children—John, Elizabeth, Janet, Barbara. B.S., Cornell U., 1939; M.S., Mich. State U., 1942; Ph.D., Yale, 1948. Asst. prof. physics Mich. State U., East Lansing, 1947-49, assoc. prof., 1949-52, prof., 1952-86, emeritus, 1986—; vis. prof. U. Bristol, Eng., 1955-56, Technische Hogesch., Eindhoven, Netherlands, 1964, Rijks universiteit, Leiden, Netherlands, 1970-71. Recipient Distinguished Faculty award Mich. State U., 1963; Guggenheim fellow, 1955-56. Mem. Nat. Soc. Profl. Engrs., Sigma Xi, Phi Kappa Phi. Research and publs. on math. physics, chem. physics, magnetism. Home: 1849 Ann St East Lansing MI 48823-3707

SPENCE, ROBERT LEROY, publishing executive; b. Carlisle, Pa., Sept. 13, 1931; s. Leroy Oliver and Esther Helen (Lau) S.; m. Barbara Amelia Hunter, Sept. 1, 1954 (div. Sept. 1978); children—Robert Roy, Bonnie Leigh; m. 2d, Maryanne Elizabeth Yacono, Jan. 10, 1979. B.A., Dickinson Coll., 1953; postgrad, Temple U., 1955-57, Rutgers U., 1956, 59-60, U. Pa., 1960. Cert. tchr., N.J. Chmn. dept. math. Haddon Heights High Sch., N.J., 1954-62; sr. editor Silver Burdett Co., Morristown, N.J., 1962-64; editor-in-chief Harcourt Brace Jovanovich, Inc., N.Y.C., 1964-81; v.p., pub. Harper & Row Publishers, Inc., N.Y.C., 1981-85; Scribner Ednl. Pubs. div. Macmillan, Inc., N.Y.C., 1985; pres. R&M Spence, Inc., Sparta, N.J., 1985—. Author textbook series: Growth in Mathematics, 1978, Excel in Mathematics, 1989-90, Mathematics Plus: Multicultural Projects, 1993. Mem. Assn. Am. Pubs. (mem. exec. com. 1981-84), Nat. Council Tchrs. Math., Internat. Reading Assn., Am. Numismatic Assn. Avocations: rare coin collecting; coin newsletter author and publisher; artist; writer. Home and Office: 37 Heather Ln Sparta NJ 07871-3538

SPENCE, SANDRA, association executive; b. McKeesport, Pa., Mar. 25, 1941; d. Cedric Leroy and Suzanne (Haudenshield) S. BA, Allegheny Coll., 1963; MA, Rutgers U., 1964. With Pa. State Govt., Harrisburg, 1964-68, Appalachian Regional Commn., Washington, 1968-75; legis. rep. Nat. Assn. Counties, Washington, 1975-77; fed. rep. Calif. Dept. Transp., Washington, 1977-78; dir. congl. affairs Amtrak, Washington, 1978-81, corp. sec., 1981-83; dir. computer svcs. Nat. R.R. Passenger Corp., Washington, 1983-84; co-owner Parkhurst-Spence Inc., 1985; owner The Spence Group, 1986-90; v.p. Bostrom Corp., Washington, 1990-92; exec. dir. Soc. Glass and Ceramic Decorators, 1992—; chmn. legis. com. Womens Transp. Seminar, 1977-79, dir., 1982-83, v.p., 1983-84, chmn. edn. com., 1982-83; com. on edn. and tng. Transp. Rsch. Bd., 1982-85. Contbr. articles to profl. jours. Dommr., sec. D.C. Commn. for Women, 1983-88; del. Ward III Dem. Com., 1982-90, 1st vice chmn., 1987-88. Fellow Eagleton Inst. Politics, 1963-64; recipient Achievement award Transp. Seminar, 1982, 83. Mem. Greater Washington Soc. Assn. Execs. (vice-chair law and legis. com. 1989-90, chmn. 1990-91, chmn. scholarship com. 1992-93, bd. dirs 1993—, Rising Star award 1989, Chmn.'s award for Govt. Rels. 1991), Am. Soc. Assn. Execs. (mgmt. cert. 1987), Phi Beta Kappa. Home: 3701 Appleton St NW Washington DC 20016 Office: Soc Glass and Ceramic Decorators 1627 K St NW Ste 800 Washington DC 20006

SPENCER, DALE A., medical products executive; b. 1945. BS in Engring., U. Maine, 1968; MBA, So. Ill. U., 1973. With Kuken Steel Co., Cin., 1973-75; sales and mktg. mgr. Baxter Travenol Labs., Mpls., 1975-80; with Scimed Life Systems Inc., Osseo, Minn., 1980—, pres., CEO, 1982, now chmn. and CEO, 1994; also, pres. (subsidiary) Scimed, Inc., Osseo, Minn. With USAF, 1968-73. Office: Scimed Life Systems Inc 1 Scimed Pl Osseo MN 55311*

SPENCER, DAVID JAMES, lawyer; b. Altadena, Calif., June 23, 1943; s. Dorcy James and Dorothy Estelle (Pingry) S.; m. Donna Rae Blair, Aug. 22, 1965; children: Daniel, Matthew. BA, Rocky Mountain Coll., 1965; JD, Yale U., 1968. Bar: Minn. 1968, U.S. Dist. Ct. Minn. 1968, U.S. Ct. Appeals (8th cir.) 1970. Mem. firm Briggs and Morgan, P.A., Mpls. and St. Paul, 1968—. Contbg. author 10 William Mitchell Law Rev., 1984; contbr. articles to profl. jours. Trustee Rocky Mountain Coll., Billings, Mont., 1980—; bd. dirs. Reentry, Inc., 1993—; pres., bd. dirs St. Croix Friends of Arts, Stillwater, Minn., 1981-84; bd. dirs. Valley Chamber Chorale, Stillwater, 1989-92; v.p. Minn. Jaycees, St. Paul, 1974; elder Presbyn. Ch. Recipient Silver Key St. Paul Jaycees, 1974; Disting. Svc. award Rocky Mountain Coll., 1981, Outstanding Svc. award, 1988, Disting. Achievement award, 1992. Fellow Am. Coll. Real Estate Lawyers; mem. ABA, Minn. Bar Assn., Hennepin County Bar Assn., Stillwater Country Club, Mpls. Athletic Club. Presbyterian. Avocations: trout fishing, game bird hunting, golf, singing. Home: 9987 Arcola Ct N Stillwater MN 55082-9523 Office: Briggs & Morgan 2400 IDS Ctr 80 S 8th St Minneapolis MN 55402-2113

SPENCER, DAVID MILLS, library administrator; b. Eugene, Oreg., Dec. 7, 1950; s. Richard J. and Adelaide (Marsh) S. BA in English Lit., Lewis & Clark Coll., 1973; M in Urban and Regional Planning, U. Oreg.; 1978; MLS, Cath. U. Am., 1988. Asst. planner Linn County Planning Dept., Albany, Oreg., 1979-80; from asst. planner to dir. Benton County Devel. Dept., Corvallis, Oreg., 1980-87; from reference libr. to br. libr. Nat. Air & Space Mus. Br. Libr. Smithsonian Instn. Librs., Washington, 1989—; ptnr. Spencer Co. Ltd. Partnership, Elmira, Oreg., 1993—. Mem. Thomas Episcopal Ch., Washington, treas., 1991-95, vestry mem., 1993-95, jr. warden, 1995—. Mem. Spl. Libr. Assn., Nat. Trust for Hist. Preservation. Democrat.

SPENCER, DOMINA EBERLE, mathematics educator; b. New Castle, Pa., Sept. 26, 1920; d. Andrew Berger and Ina May (Eberle) S.; m. Parry Moon, Aug. 17, 1961; 1 child, Euclid Eberle Moon. SB, MIT, 1939, SM, 1940, PhD, 1942. Asst. prof. physics Am. U., Washington, 1942-43, Tufts Coll., Medford, Mass., 1943-47, Brown U., Providence, 1947-50; assoc. prof. math. U. Conn., Storrs, 1950-60, prof. math., 1960—; cons. Sylvania, Salem, 1953-70, Ainsworth Lighting, L.I., 1943-53, Marlux Corp., Sommerville, Mass., 1948-61, Hollywood Light, Hollywood, Calif., 1945-58. Author: (with P. Moon) Lighting Design, 1947, Field Theory for Engineers, 1960, Field Theory Handbook, 1960, Foundations of Electrodynamics, 1960, Vectors, 1965, Partial Differential Equations, 1969, The Photic Field, 1981, Theory of Holors, 1986; co-inventor Aperture Lamp. Chmn. concert com. St. Paul's Ch., Brookline, 1988—; pres. Back Bay Manor Tenants Assn., Boston, 1985—. Recipient Disting. Alumna award Friends Select Sch., Phila., 1987. Fellow Illuminating Engring. Soc. (gold medal 1974), Optical Soc. Am.; mem. Am. Math. Soc., Math Assn. Am., Am. Phys. Soc., MIT Nautical Assn. Presbyterian. Avocations: music, photography. Home: 75 St Alphonsus St Apt 2101 Boston MA 02120-1676 Office: U Conn U-9 Storrs CT 06268

SPENCER, DONALD CLAYTON, mathematician; b. Boulder, Colo., Apr. 25, 1912; s. Frank Robert and Edith (Clayton) S.; m. Mary Jo Halley (div.); children: Maredith (dec.), Marianne; m. Natalie Robertson (dec.); 1 child, Donald Clayton Jr. BA, U. Colo., 1934; BS, MIT, 1936; PhD, Cambridge (Eng.) U., 1939, ScD, 1963; ScD (hon.), Purdue U., 1971. Instr. MIT, Cambridge, 1939-42; assoc. prof. Stanford (Calif.) U., 1942-46, prof.; 1946-50, 63-68; assoc. prof. Princeton (N.J.) U., 1950-53, prof., 1953-63, 68-78, Henry Burchard Fine prof. emeritus, 1978—. Co-author: (with A.C. Schaeffer, monograph) Coefficient Regions for Schlicht Functions, 1950, (with M. Schiffer) Functionals of Finite Riemann Surfaces, 1954, (with A. Kumpera) Lie Equations, vol. I: General Theory, 1972, (with H.K. Nickerson and N.E. Steenrod, textbook) Advanced Calculus, 1959. Recipient Bocher prize Am. Math. Soc., 1948, Nat. medal of sci. Pres. of U.S., 1989, George Norlin award U. Colo., 1990. Fellow Am. Acad. Arts and Scis.; mem. NAS. Home: 943 County Rd 204 Durango CO 81301-8547

SPENCER, DONALD SPURGEON, historian, academic administrator; b. Anderson, Ind., Jan. 29, 1945; s. Thomas E. and Josephine (Litz) S.; m. Pamela Sue Roberts, June 19, 1965; 1 child, Jennifer Wynne. BA, Ill. Coll., 1967; PhD, U. Va., 1973. Asst. prof. history Westminster Coll., Fulton, Mo., 1973-76, Ohio U., Athens, 1976-77; from asst., assoc. to full prof., assoc. dean, asst. provost U. Mont., Missoula, 1977-90; provost SUNY, Geneseo, 1990-93; pres. Western Ill. U., Macomb, 1994—. Author: Louis Kossuth and Young America, 1978, The Carter Implosion: Jimmy Carter and the Amateur Style of Diplomacy,1989; contbr. articles to jours. in field. With U.S. Army, 1968-71, Korea. Woodrow Wilson Found. fellow, 1968;

Danforth Found. univ. teaching fellow, 1971. Mem. Phi Beta Kappa. Congregationalist. Home: 2001 Wigwam Hollow Rd Macomb IL 61455-9336 Office: W Ill Univ Office of the President Sherman Hall Macomb IL 61455

SPENCER, EDGAR WINSTON, geology educator; b. Monticello, Ark., May 27, 1931; s. Terrel Ford and Allie Belle (Shelton) S.; m. Elizabeth Penn Humphries, Nov. 26, 1958; children: Elizabeth Shawn, Kristen Shannon. Student, Vanderbilt U., 1949-50; B.S., Washington and Lee U., 1953; Ph.D., Columbia U., 1957. Lectr. Hunter Coll., 1954-57; mem. faculty Washington and Lee U., 1957—, prof. geology, head dept.; 1962—, Ruth Parmly prof.; Pres. Rockbridge Area Conservation Council, 1978, 95; NSF sci. faculty fellow, New Zealand and Australia; dir. grant for humanities and pub. policy on land use planning Va. Found., 1975; dir. grant Petroleum Research Fund, 1981-82; leader field trip Cen. Appalachian Mountains Internat. Geol. Congress, 1989. Author: Basic Concepts of Physical Geology, 1962, Basic Concepts of Historical Geology, 1962, Geology: A Survey of Earth Science, 1965, Introduction to the Structure of the Earth, 1969, 3d edit., 1988, The Dynamics of the Earth, 1972, Physical Geology, 1983, Geologic Maps, 1993. Recipient Va. Outstanding Faculty award Va. Coun. of Higher Edn., 1990. Fellow Geol. Soc. Am., AAAS; mem. Am. Assn. Petroleum Geologists (dir. field seminar on fold and thrust belts 1987, 88-91), Am. Inst. Profl. Geologists, Am. Geophys. Union, Nat. Assn. Geology Tchrs., Yellowstone-Bighorn Rsch. Assn., Phi Beta Kappa (hon.), Sigma Xi. Home: PO Box 1055 Lexington VA 24450-1055

SPENCER, EDSON WHITE, computer systems company executive; b. Chgo., June 4, 1926; s. William M. and Gertrude (White) S. Student, Princeton, 1943, Northwestern U., U. Mich., 1944; B.A., Williams Coll., 1948; M.A., Oxford (Eng.) U., 1950. With Sears, Roebuck & Co., Chgo., 1951-54, Honeywell Inc., Mpls., 1954—; Far East regional mgr. Honeywell, Inc., Tokyo, 1959-65; corp. v.p. internal ops. Honeywell, Inc., Mpls., 1965-69, exec. v.p., 1969-74, pres., chief exec. officer, 1974-78, chief exec. officer, 1978-87, chmn. bd., 1978—. Mem. Phi Beta Kappa. Office: Mayo Found Bd Trustees 200 1st St SW Rochester MN 55905-0001

SPENCER, ELIZABETH, author; b. Carrollton, Miss., 1921; d. James Luther and Mary James (McCain) S.; m. John Arthur Blackwood Rusher, Sept. 29, 1956. BA, Belhaven Coll., 1942; MA, Vanderbilt U., 1943; LittD (hon.), Southwestern U. at Memphis, 1968; LLD (hon.), Concordia U. at Montreal, 1988; LittD (hon.), U. of the South, 1992. Instr. N.W. Miss. Jr. Coll., 1943-44, Ward-Belmont, Nashville, 1944-45; reporter The Nashville Tennessean, 1945-46; instr. U. Miss., Oxford, 1948-51, 52-53; vis. prof. Concordia U., Montreal, Que., Can., 1976-81, adj. prof., 1981-86; vis. prof. U. N.C., Chapel Hill, 1986-92. Author: Fire in the Morning, 1948, This Crooked Way, 1952, The Voice at the Back Door, 1956, The Light in the Piazza, 1960, Knights and Dragons, 1965, No Place for an Angel, 1967, Ship Island and Other Stories, 1968, The Snare, 1972, The Stories of Elizabeth Spencer, 1981, Marilee, 1981, The Salt Line, 1984, Jack of Diamonds and Other Stories, 1988, (play) For Lease or Sale, 1989, On the Gulf, 1991, The Night Travellers, 1991; contbr. short stories to mags. and anthologies. Recipient Women's Democratic Com. award, 1949, recognition award Nat. Inst. Arts and letters, 1952, Richard and Hinda Rosenthal Found. award Am. Acad. and Letters, 1957; Guggenheim Found. fellow, 1953, 1st McGraw-Hill Fiction award, 1960, Henry Bellamann award for creative writing, 1968; Award of Merit medal for the short story Am. Acad. Arts and Letters, 1983, Salem award for lit., 1992, Dos Passos award for fiction, 1992; Kenyon Rev. fellow in fiction, 1957; Bryn Mawr Col. Donnelly fellow, 1962; Nat. Endowment for Arts grantee in lit., 1983, Sr. Arts Award grantee Nat. Endowment for Arts, 1988, N.C. Gov.'s award for lit., 1994. Mem. Am. Acad. Arts and Letters, Fellowship of So. Writers (charter; vice chancellor 1993—). Home: 402 Longleaf Dr Chapel Hill NC 27514-3042

SPENCER, FOSTER LEWIS, newspaper editor; b. Putnam, Conn., Dec. 18, 1932; s. Ralph Washburn and Helen (Thompson) S.; m. Dorothy Virginia Purda, Aug. 18, 1956; children: Faith Elizabeth, Beth Mary. B.A., U. Mass., 1960. News editor Palmer (Mass.) Jour.-Register, 1956-60; Sunday feature editor Springfield (Mass.) Republican, 1960-65; mng. editor Buffalo News, 1966—; chmn. N.Y. State adv. bd./UPI, 1980-86. Served with USAF, 1952-56, Korea. Recipient Spl. award AP, 1979. Mem. N.Y. AP Assn. (pres. Albany 1976-77), N.Y. State Soc. Newspaper Editors (pres. 1983). Democrat. Congregationalist. Home: 292 Summer St Buffalo NY 14222-2114 Office: Buffalo News 1 News Plaza Buffalo NY 14203-2994

SPENCER, FREDERICK GILMAN, newspaper editor in chief; b. Phila., Dec. 8, 1925; s. F. Gilman and Elizabeth (Hetherington) S.; m. Isabel Brannon, July 3, 1965; 1 child, Isabel; children by previous marriage: Amy, Elizabeth Blair, F. Gilman, Jonathan. Student pub. and pvt. schs. Copyboy Phila. Inquirer, 1947-49; photographer-reporter Chester (Pa.) Times, 1949, 1952-59; photographer, sports editor Mt. Holly (N.J.) Herald, 1949-52; mng. editor Main Line Times, Ardmore, Pa., 1959-63; asst. city editor Phila. Bull., 1963-64; editorial spokesman Sta. WCAU-TV, Phila., 1964-67; editor The Trentonian, Trenton, N.J., 1967-75, Phila. Daily News, 1975-84, N.Y. Daily News, N.Y.C., 1984-89; editor-in-chief Denver Post, 1989-93, columnist, 1993—. With USNR, 1943-46. Recipient Pulitzer prize for editorials, 1974. Mem. Am. Soc. Newspapers Editors, Sigma Delta Chi. Office: Denver Post 1560 Broadway Denver CO 80202-5133*

SPENCER, GEOFFREY F., church administrator; b. Teralba, NSW, Australia; came to U.S., 1966; m. Jill Marcia Godwin; children: Paul, Mark, Shelly. Grad., Newington Coll., NSW, Australia; BA, Sydney (Australia) U.; MA in Am. History, U. Mo., Kansas City; MDiv, St. Paul Sch. Theology. Ordained to ministry, 1954; ordained high priest, 1958, ordained apostle, 1984. With dept. Christian edn. Reorganized Ch. of Jesus Christ of Latter Day Saints, 1966, commr. pastoral svcs., dir. program svcs. divsn., pres. Temple Sch., asst. to 1st pres., commr. religious edn., acting dir. program svcs. divsn., mem. Coun. Twelve Apostles; mem. ch. history commn., theology com.; pres. Quorum of High Priests, 1974-84; mem. Standing High Coun., 1976-84. Author: The Burning Bush, Strangers and Pilgrims, The Promise of Healing; contbr. articles to profl. jours. Avocations: literature, psychology, music. Office: Reorganized Ch of Jesus Christ of Latter Day Saints PO Box 1059 Independence MO 64051

SPENCER, GUY J., JR., entrepreneur; b. Huntsville, Ala., July 24, 1933; s. Guy J. and Frances (Strong) S.; m. Loretta Lee Purdy, July 30, 1960 (div. 1984); children: Sarah Frances Spencer Chappell, Guy J. III; m. Sally Martin Cox, July 20, 1986; stepchildren: Lucy Martin Legrand, John Wheeler Legrand. Student, U. Ala., 1951-54. V.p. Ala. Oil Co. Huntsville, Inc., 1956-63, pres., 1964-77; pres. Spencer Cos., Inc., Huntsville, 1978—; v.p. Ala. Oil Co. Morgan County, Inc., Ala. Oil Co. Athens, Inc.; founding dir. First Comml. Bank Huntsville, 1983—. Chmn. Huntsville Depot Mus. Bd., Huntsville, 1976—; bd. dirs. Ala. Coun. Econ. Edn., 1984—; Ala. Alliance for Bus. and Industry, 1984, Bus. Coun. Ala., 1985—; Huntsville/Madison County Conv. Visitors Bur., 1991—; So. Growth Policies Bd., Research Triangle, N.C., 1987-90; mem. Pres.'s cabinet U. Ala., Tuscaloosa; mem. state adv. bd. U. Ala., Birmingham; mem. army community rels. com. U.S. Army Missile Command, Redstone Arsenal, Ala., 1988—. With Signal Corps, U.S. Army, 1954-56. Named Man of Yr., Ala. Petroleum Marketers Assn., 1980; recipient Fletcher E. Seldon award Clean Community Systems Huntsville/Madison County, 1984; Ala. Petroleum Coun. (Outstanding Oilman award 1970, Outstanding Svc. to Petroleum Industry award 1961, 71), Better Bus. Bur. N.Am. (past exec. officer, dir. Huntsville/Madison County C. of C. (past exec. officer, dir.), Huntsville Country Club, Heritage Club (bd. govs. 1984—), Kiwanis. Avocations: travel, community service, entertaining. Home: 405 Echols Ave SE Huntsville AL 35801-3136 Office: Spencer Cos Inc PO Box 45 Huntsville AL 35804-0045

SPENCER, HARRY CHADWICK, minister; b. Chgo., Apr. 10, 1905; s. John Carroll and Jessie Grace (Chadwick) S.; m. Mary Louise Wakefield, May 26, 1935; children: Mary Grace Spencer Lyman, Ralph Wakefield. B.A., Willamette U., 1925, D.D. (hon.), 1953; M.Div., Garrett Bibl. Inst., 1929; M.A., Harvard U., 1932. Ordained to ministry Meth. Ch., 1931; pastor Washington Heights Ch., Chgo., 1931-33, Portage Park Ch., Chgo., 1933-35; rec. sec. bd. missions Meth. Ch., 1935-40, asst. exec. sec., 1940-45, sec. dept. visual edn., 1945-52, exec. sec. radio and film commn., 1952-56, gen. sec. TV, radio and film commn., 1956-68, asso. gen. sec. program council div. TV, radio and film communication, 1968-72; asso. exec.

sec. joint commn. on communications United Meth. Ch., 1972, ret., 1973; mem. exec. com. Nat. Council Chs. Broadcasting and Film Commn., 1952-73, chmn., 1960-63; mem. exec. com. Nat. Council Chs., 1960-63, mem. gen. bd., 1967-72, v.p. Cen. div. communications, 1969-72; chmn. constituting assembly World Assn. for Christian Broadcasting, 1963; mem. constituting assembly World Assn. Christian Communication, 1968, dir. assembly, 1975; mem. adminstrv. com. Ravemco, 1950-70, Intermedia, 1970-72; vis. prof. Garrett Evang. Theol. Sem., 1975; lectr. in field. Exec. producer: TV series Learning to Live; radio series Night Call; motion pictures John Wesley, etc.; Contbr. articles on films to ch. publs. Trustee Scarritt Coll., 1967-74, emeritus, 1974-88; bd. dirs. Outlook Nashville, 1977-83, sec., 1980; bd. dirs. Nashville chpt. UN Assn., 1976-83. Recipient award excellence art communications Claremont Sch. Theology, 1973, The Pioneer in Religious Communications award World assn. for Christian Communication, 1989; inducted into United Meth. Communicators Hall of Fame, 1983. Mem. United Meth. Assn. Communicators, World Assn. Christian Communications (award). Clubs: Kiwanis (Woodmont); Harvard (Nashville). Home: PO Box 150063 Nashville TN 37215-0063 *The most precious quality we know is human personality. Unfortunately, innumerable hazards constantly beset each individual even from the time of conception. Nevertheless, every person has inherited many priceless advantages. The ability to store up knowledge and the imagination to foresee future events, which make possible human communication, have enhanced the value of human personality and brightened our hope for the future—if human beings can now learn the secret of self-discipline and will use it to achieve long-range benefits for a world community.*

SPENCER, HARRY IRVING, JR., retired banker; b. Worcester, Mass., Feb. 3, 1925; s. Harry Irving and Bertha (Johnson) S.; m. Violet Virginia Bergquist, Sept. 16, 1950; children—Nancy Elaine, Harry Irving III, Carol Helen. B.A., Clark U., 1950. With Worcester County Nat. Bank, 1950-82, asst. treas., 1954-58, cashier, 1958-82, v.p., 1966-69, sr. v.p., 1969-77, exec. v.p., cashier, 1977-82, clk., dir., 1980-82; exec. v.p., cashier, sec. Shawmut Worcester County Bank, N.A., 1982-88, also bd. dirs.; sec., treas., dir. Nobility Hill Realty Corp.; dir. Worcester Capital Corp., Wornat Leasing Corp. Bd. dirs. Worcester Taxpayers Assn. Methodist (trustee). Clubs: Kiwanis; Economic (Worcester, Mass.), Plaza (Worcester, Mass.). Home: 79 Birchwood Dr Holden MA 01520-1939 Office: 446 Main St Worcester MA 01608-2302

SPENCER, HENRY BENNING, insurance industry investment advisor; b. Washington, Feb. 25, 1940; s. Samuel and Dora W. Spencer; m. Kate Hodges, June 1962 (div. June 1966); 1 child, Russell Price; m. Helen M. Walker, Dec. 12, 1966; 1 child, Samuel III. AB, Harvard U., 1962. Trust investment officer Riggs Nat. Bank, Washington, 1968-72; v.p., treas. Equitable Gen. Corp., Vienna, Va., 1973-79; fin. sec. Guardian Life Ins. Co. Am., N.Y.C., 1979-82, 2d v.p. fixed income securities, 1982-83, v.p. fixed income securities, 1983-84, v.p. investments, 1984-85, sr. v.p. investments, 1985-90; chief investment officer Head Asset Mgmt., N.Y.C., 1990—. Served to lt. USN, 1962-67, Vietnam. Fellow Life Mgmt. Inst.; mem. Washington Soc. Investment Analysts. Clubs: Chevy Chase (Md.), Metropolitan (Washington), Dunes (Narragansett, R.I.), Knickerbocker (N.Y.C.). Home: 45 E 62nd St New York NY 10021-8025 Office: 545 Madison Ave 6th Fl New York NY 10022

SPENCER, IVAN CARLTON, clergyman; b. nr. West Burlington, Pa., July 8, 1914; s. Ivan Quay and Annie Minnie (Back) S.; m. Elizabeth Garate, Apr. 14, 1935; children: David Carlton, Esther Elizabeth (Mrs. Saied Adour), John Wesley. Grad., Elim Bible Inst., 1933; D.D., Am. Bible Coll., 1966. Ordained to ministry Elim Missionary Assemblies. Pastor various chs., 1935-38; instr. Elim Bible Inst., 1938, campus pastor, 1938-44, pres., 1949-82; gen. sec. Elim Missionary Assemblies (now Elim Fellowship), 1940-54, gen. chmn., 1954-85; bd. dirs. Nat. Assn. Evangs., 1958-85, Pentecostal Fellowship of N. Am., 1961-86, treas., 1963-65, 73-81. Address: 7245 College St Lima NY 14485

SPENCER, JAMES CALVIN, SR., humanities educator; b. Detroit, Oct. 21, 1941; s. Donald and Beulah S.; m. Linda J. Voloshen, Nov. 21, 1987; children: James, Anne. BA, Calif. State U., 1966; MA, SUNY, 1970, PhD in Philosophy, 1973. NDEA fellow SUNY, Buffalo, 1968-70, SUNY fellow, 1970-71; instr. Cuyahoga C.C., Parma, Ohio, 1971-73, asst. prof., 1973-77, assoc. prof., 1977-81, prof. philosophy and art, 1981—; cons. continuing edn. divsn. Kans. State U., 1986, Case Western Res. U., Cleve., 1973, Ford Motor Co., Brookport, Ohio, 1990, Campus Planning INs., Cleve., 1991-94; pres. Spencer Enterprises, Brecksville, Ohio, 1991—; reviewer manuscripts for Wadsworth Pub. Author: The Nightmare Never Ends, 1992; contbr. articles to profl. jours. Ward com. Democratic Party, Ashland, Ohio, Libertarian Party, Buffalo; precinct com. mem. Dem. Party, Bresckville; exec. com. mem. Dem. Party, Cuyahoga County, Ohio. Grantee Nat. Sci. Found., 1979. Office: Cuyahoga Community College 11000 Pleasant Valley Rd Parma OH 44130

SPENCER, JAMES H., art director, production designer. Prodn. designer: (TV movies) Friendly Persuasion, 1975, Red Alert, 1977, King, 1978, Some Kind of Miracle, 1979, Son Rise: A Miracle of Love, 1979, Not in Front of the Children, 1982, Journey to the Center of the Earth, 1993, (films) Fire Sale, 1977, Die Laughing, 1980, King of the Mountain, 1981, Stripes, 1981, Poltergeist, 1982, The Sender, 1982, Gremlins, 1984, Innerspace, 1987, The 'Burbs, 1989, Gremlins 2: The New Batch, 1990, Lethal Weapon 3, 1992; art dir.: (films) Bound for Glory, 1976, Rocky, 1976, Twilight Zone-The Movie ("Nightmare at 20,000 Feet"), 1983. Office: care Lawrence Mirisch The Mirisch Agency 10100 Santa Monica Blvd Ste 700 Los Angeles CA 90067*

SPENCER, JAMES JEFFREY, executive director; b. Oil City, Pa., Nov. 19, 1958; s. Donald Ralph and Betty Jane (Coughlan) S. BS in Music Edn., Clarion U., 1981; MusB in Mktg., 1981. Chpt. cons. Alpha Chi Rho, Neptune, N.J., 1981-83; dir. Chpt. Svcs., 1983-86, exec. dir., nat. sec., 1986—; trustee Alpha Chi Rho Ednl. Found., Neptune, N.J., 1986—. Contbr. articles to profl. jours. Chmn., adminstrv. coun. West Grove United Meth. Ch., Neptune, N.J., 1993—. Republican. Methodist. Avocations: music, reading, skiing. Home: 301 W Aylvania Ave Apt 363B Neptune City NJ 07753 Office: Alpha Chi Rho 109 Oxford Way Neptune NJ 07753

SPENCER, JAMES R., federal judge. BA magna cum laude, Clark Coll., 1971; JD, Harvard U., 1974, MDiv, 1985. Staff atty. Atlanta Legal Aid Soc., 1974-75; asst. U.S. atty. Washington, 1978, U.S. Dist. Ct. (ea. dist.) Va., 1983; judge U.S. Dist. Ct. (ea. dist.) Va., Richmond, 1986—; adj. prof. law U. Va., 1987—. Capt. JAGC, U.S.Army, 1975-78, res. 1981-86. Mem. ABA, Nat. Bar Assn., State Bar of Ga., D.C. Bar, Va. State Bar, Richmond Bar Assn., Washington Bar Assn., Old Dominion Bar Assn., Omega Psi Phi. Office: US Courthouse PO Box 630 Richmond VA 23205

SPENCER, JOHN ANDREW, real estate development corporation executive; b. Ft. Pierce, Fla., Sept. 26, 1948; s. Andrew Jackson and Kathryn Samantha (Gray) S.; m. Maria Ester Cascante, Sept. 29, 1979; 1 child, Sarah. BS, Fla. State U., 1970; MS, Ariz. State U., 1976. CPA, Ariz. Sr. auditor Peat, Marwick, Mitchell & Co., Phoenix, 1976-79; asst. controller, controller Sahara Hotel and Casino, Las Vegas, 1979-80; asst. treas. Del Webb Hotels, Las Vegas, 1980-82; asst. controller, controller Del E. Webb Corp., Phoenix, 1982-85, v.p., controller, 1985—; mem. profl. adv. bd. Ariz. State U. Acctg. Dept., Tempe, 1985—. Served with USAR, 1970-76. Mem. Am. Inst. CPA's, Ariz. State Soc. CPA's. Republican. Methodist. Office: Del E Webb Corp 2231 E Camelback Rd Phoenix AZ 85016-9097

SPENCER, JOHN HEDLEY, biochemistry educator; b. Stapleford, Eng., Apr. 10, 1933; emigrated to Can., 1956; s. Thomas and Eva (Johnson) S.; m. Magdeliene Van Ryn, Sept. 16, 1958; children—Robin Anne, David Thomas, Mark Stewart. B.Sc. U. St. Andrews, Scotland, 1955, B.Sc. with honours, 1956; student, Montreal Cancer Rsch. Soc., 1956-59; Ph.D., McGill U., 1960. Damon Runyon Meml. Fund postdoctoral fellow Columbia U., N.Y.C., 1959-61; mem. faculty McGill U., Montreal, 1961-78, assoc. prof. biochemistry, 1966-71, prof., 1971-78; prof. biochemistry Queen's U., Kingston, Ont., 1978—, head biochemistry, 1978-90; vis. prof. U. Montreal, 1992-93. Author: The Physics and Chemistry of DNA and RNA, 1972; co-editor: Planet Earth: Problems and Prospects, 1995. Recipient Ayerst award Can. Biochem. Soc., 1972. Fellow Royal Soc. Can.; mem. AAAS, Can. Biochem.

Soc. (treas. 1966-69, pres. 1979-80), Can. Fedn. Biol. Socs. (pres. 1981-82), Biochem. Soc., Am. Soc. Biochemistry and Molecular Biology, Royal Soc. Can., Sigma Xi. Home: 21 Hillcroft Dr, Kingston, ON Canada K7L 4E8

SPENCER, JOHN M., safety engineer; b. New Martinsville, W. Va., May 14, 1950; s. Harrison J. and Frances L. (Askew) S.; m. Kathleen Ann Lafferty, July 7, 1972; children—Jennifer Kathleen, Elizabeth Ann. A.B. in Ed., Fairmont State Coll., 1972; M.S. in Safety Mgmt., W.Va. U., 1974. Safety supr. Kaiser Aluminum and Chemical Corp., Ravenswood, W.Va., 1974-77; div. safety engr. Ford Motor Co., Dearborn, Mich., 1977-81; supt. safety protection services and ins. Kaiser Aluminum and Chem. Corp., Spokane, Wash., 1981—. Mem. Am. Soc. Safety Engrs., Nat. Safety Council (exec. safety com.). Home: 5416 N Northwood Dr Spokane WA 99212-1606

SPENCER, LAVYRLE, writer; b. Browerville, Minn., Aug. 17, 1943; d. Louis Joseph and Janet Adamek (Baughman) Kulick; m. Daniel F. Spencer, Dec. 10, 1962; children: Amy Elizabeth, Beth Adair. Author: The Fulfillment, 1979, The Endearment, 1982 (Hist. Romance of Yr. award Romance Writers of Am.), Hummingbird, 1983 (Hist. Romance of Yr. award Romance Writers of Am.), Twice Loved, 1984 (Hist. Romance of Yr. award Romance Writers of Am.), Sweet Memories, 1984, The Hellion, 1984, A Heart Speaks, 1986, Tears, 1986, Years, 1986, The Gamble, 1987, Separate Beds, 1987, Vows, 1988, Morning Glory, 1988, Spring Fancy, 1989, Bitter Sweet, 1990, Forgiving, 1991, November of the Heart, 1992, Bygones, 1993, Family Blessings, 1994, Home Song, 1995. Office: 6701 79th Ave Brooklyn Park MN 55445*

SPENCER, LEWIS DOUGLAS, lawyer; b. Frankfort, Ind., Feb. 6, 1917; s. Clarence D. and Hazel (Ghormley) S.; m. Marcia Jane Maish, Jan. 29, 1947; children: Karen Jane Spencer Redman, Margo Linn Spencer Estruth. AB, DePauw U., 1939; LLB, Columbia, 1942; student, Motorola Exec. Inst., 1969. Bar: N.Y. 1942, Ind. 1943, Ill. 1947. Assoc. firm Carter, Ledyard and Milburn, N.Y.C., 1942-43, Barnes, Hickam, Pantzer & Boyd, Indpls., 1943-44, O'Connor & Farber, N.Y.C., 1944-47, Peterson, Rall, Barber, Ross & Seidel, Chgo., 1947-51; atty. Motorola, Inc. (and subsidiaries), 1951-77, asst. sec., 1956-74, sec., 1974-77, gen. atty., 1959-73, gen. counsel, 1973-77, v.p. 1965-77; lectr. sch. law Loyola U., Chgo., 1978-79, prof. sch. law, 1979-86. Contbr. articles to profl. jours. Mem. Park Ridge (Ill.) Bd. Fire and Police Commrs., 1964-67; mem. Park Ridge Zoning Bd. Appeals and Zoning Commn., 1967-75, chmn., 1968-75; bd. dirs. Park Ridge United Fund, 1966-69, pres., 1968. Mem. Chgo. Tax Club (bd. dirs. 1965-71, pres. 1969), The Nat. Soc., SAR. Mem. Park Ridge Community Ch. (bd. dirs. 1964-72, chmn. congregation 1970-71). Home: 5555 N Sheridan Rd Apt 1602 Chicago IL 60640-1628

SPENCER, MARGARET GILLIAM, lawyer; b. Spokane, Wash., Aug. 30, 1951; d. Jackson Earl and Margaret Kathleen (Hindley) Gilliam; m. John Bernard Spencer, Feb. 21, 1993. BA in Sociology, U. Mont., 1974, MA in Sociology, 1978, JD, 1982. Bar: Mont. 1982, Colo. 1982. Assoc. Holland & Hart, Denver, 1982-84; assoc. Roath & Brega, P.C., Denver, 1984-88, shareholder, dir., 1988-89; spl. counsel Brega & Winters, P.C., Denver, 1989; corp. counsel CH2M Hill, Inc., Denver, 1989—. Democrat. Episcopalian. Avocations: skiing, scuba diving. Office: CH2M Hill Inc PO Box 22508 Denver CO 80222

SPENCER, MARY EILEEN, biochemist, educator; b. Regina, Sask., Can., Oct. 4, 1923; d. John J. and Etta Christina (Hamren) Stapleton; m. Henry Anderson Spencer, July 3, 1946; 1 child, Susan Mary. AA, Regina Coll., 1942; BA with high honors in Chemistry, U. Sask., 1945; MA in Chemistry, Bryn Mawr Coll., 1946; PhD in Agrl. Chemistry, U. Calif.-Berkeley, 1951. Chemist, Ayerst, McKenna and Harrison Ltd., Montreal, Que., Can., summer 1945, full time, 1946-47, Nat. Canners Assn., San Francisco, 1948; teaching fellow U. Calif.-Berkeley, 1949-51, faculty food chemistry, 1951-53; faculty U. Alta., Edmonton, Can., 1953-61, instr., asst. prof., assoc. prof., acting head biochem. dept., 1960-61, assoc. prof. plant sci. dept., 1962, prof. plant sci., 1964-83, McCalla rsch. prof., 1983-84, univ. prof., 1984—; pres. Rootrainers Corp.; mem. NRC Can., 1970-73, 73-76, Task Force on Post-Secondary Edn., Alta. Govt. Com. on Ednl. Planning, 1970-72; chmn. nat. adv. com. on biology NRC, mem. adv. bd. NRC Prairie Regional Lab.; mem. adv. bd. NRC Atlantic Regional Lab.; mem. adv. bd. NRC Biol. Sci. Divsn.; chmn. ad hoc vis. com. in forestry rsch. NRC, 1975-76; bd. govs. U. Alta. 1976-79; mem. Agr. Can. Cons. Com. IBT Pesticides, 1981-82; mem. coun. Natural Scis. and Engring. Rsch. Coun. Can., 1986-92, mem. adv. com. Networks Ctrs. Excellence, 1989-92; mem. Premier's Coun. on Sci. and Tech., 1990-94. Recipient Queen Elizabeth II Silver Jubilee medal, 125th Ann. Can. Confedn. Commemorative medal. Fellow Royal Soc. Can., Chem. Inst. Can.; mem. Can. Soc. Plant Physiologists (pres. 1971-72, Gold medal 1990), Plant Growth Regulator Soc. Am., Am. Soc. Plant Physiologists, Can. Assn. Univ. Tchrs., Internat. Plant Growth Regulator Soc. Office: U Alta Dept Animal Food Scis, Faculty Agr & Forestry, Edmonton, AB Canada T6G 2E3

SPENCER, MELVIN JOE, hospital administrator, lawyer; b. Buffalo Center, Iowa, Jan. 2, 1923; s. Kenos W. and Jennie (Michaelsen) S.; m. Dena Joyce Butterfield, Mar. 1, 1952; children: Dennis Norman, Gregory Melvin, Shelly Lynn Spencer Goodnight. A.B., U. Mich., 1948, J.D., 1950. Bar: Iowa 1950, Mo. 1950, Okla. 1961. Practiced in Kansas City, Mo., 1950-61, Oklahoma City, 1961—; assoc., partner Watson, Ess, Marshall & Enggas, 1950-61; partner Miller & Spencer (and predecessor firm), 1961-75, of counsel, 1975-80; adminstr. Deaconess Hosp., 1975-92, cons., 1992-93; dir. Union Bank & Trust Co., Oklahoma City, 1977-88, 89—; dir., sec. Hosp. Casualty Co., 1977-92; dir., treas. VHA of Okla., Inc., 1986-92. Assoc. editor Mich. Law Rev., 1949-50. Gen. counsel Free Methodist Ch. N.Am., sec., mem. bd. adminstrn., chmn. investment com., 1986-88; chmn. Free Meth. Found.; mem. constl. council Free Meth. Ch. World Fellowship; mcpl. judge, Roeland Park, Kans., 1952; mem. City Council, Roeland Park, 1954; precinct chmn. Republican Party, 1968-69; del. Rep. State Conv., 1968; bd. dirs. Deaconess Hosp., Oklahoma City, Christian Counselling Center, 1973-75; chmn. bd. trustees Okla. Hosp. Assn., 1983, trustee, 1978-84; bd. dirs. FMC Ministries, Inc., Emergency Med. Services Central Okla. 1975-78; trustee, vice chmn. bd. Central Coll., McPherson, Kans., 1972-86; trustee Okla. Ambulance Trust, 1984-87; mem. adv. bd. Okla. State U. Tech. Inst., 1980-92. Served to capt. USAAF, 1943-46. Named Layman of Yr., Free Meth. Ch. N.Am., 1984; recipient W. Cleveland Rodgers Disting. Svc. award Okla. Hosp. Assn., 1985; fellow Cen. Coll. Acad. of Achievers, 1990. Mem. Okla. Bar Assn., Okla. County Bar Assn., Okla. Heritage Assn., Okla. Hist. Soc., Order of Coif, Phi Beta Kappa, Phi Kappa Phi. Free Methodist (bd. dirs., sec.). Club: Men's Dinner. Home: 5910 N Shawnee Ave Oklahoma City OK 73112-1627

SPENCER, MILTON HARRY, economics and finance educator; b. N.Y.C., Mar. 25, 1926; m. Roslyn Pernick; children: Darcy, Robin, Cathy. BS, NYU, 1949, MA, 1950; PhD, Cornell U., 1954. Instr. econs., fin. Queens Coll., N.Y.C., 1949-52; research asst. Cornell U., Ithaca, N.Y., 1952-54; economist Armour & Co., Chgo., 1954-55; assoc. prof. Wayne State U., Detroit, 1955-62, prof., 1962-91, prof. emeritus, 1991—; vis. prof. U. Hawaii, Honolulu, 1965-66; lectr., U.S., Australia, Europe, Asia, Africa, South Am.; cons. U.S. Dept. State, Washington, 1959—, govts. of Chile, Israel, Eng., France, Italy, Australia, Hong Kong, Japan, Rep. of China and various domestic and fgn. corps. Author: Basic Economics, 1951, Economic Thought, 1954, Business and Economic Forecasting, 1958, Managerial Economics, 3 edits., 1959-68, Contemporary Economics, 8 edits., 1971-93; various monographs; contbr. numerous articles to profl. jours. Served as cpl. U.S. Army, 1943-45. Recipient Disting. Service awards from U.S. Dept. State, Govts. of Chile, Israel, France, Spain, England, Italy, Belgium. Mem. Am. Econ. Assn., Am. Fin. Assn., Nat. Assn. Bus. Economists. Avocations: piloting vintage planes, hang gliding. Office: Wayne State U Sch Bus Adminstrn Detroit MI 48202

SPENCER, PETER SIMNER, neurotoxicologist; b. London, Nov. 30, 1946; U.S. citizen; married; 2 children. BSc, U. London, 1968, PhD in Pathology, 1971. Rsch. asst. Nat. Hosp. Nervous Disorders U. London, 1968-70, rsch. fellow Royal Free Hosp. Sch. Medicine, 1970-71; fellow pathology Albert Einstein Coll. Medicine, 1971-73, asst. prof., 1973-81, assoc. prof. neurosci., 1977-83, prof. neurosci., 1983—; assoc. prof. pathology, dir. Inst. Neurotoxicology, 1979—; dir. Oreg. Health Sci U.; cons. Nat. Inst.

Occupational Safety & Health, 1976-77, EPA, 1977—; chmn. adv. bd. Jour. Neurotoxicology, 1978—; mem. adv. bd. Rutgers U. Toxicology Program, 1984, Howe & Assocs., 1985, Peripheral Nerve Repair & Regeneration, 1985; mem. bd. toxicol. and environ. health hazards NAS, 1984, Safe Drinking Water Com., 1985; sec. Third World Med. Rsch. Found., 1985—; adj. prof. Coll. Vet. Medicine Oreg. State U. Assoc. editor Jour. Neurocytology, 1977—; author: Experimental and Clin. Neurotoxicology. Fellow Joseph P. Kennedy Jr. Found., 1974-76; recipient Silvio O. Conte Nat. prize for Neuroscience contbns. relevant to environ. health, 1993, Sr. Travel award Alzheimer Assn. Mem. AAAS, Am. Assn. Neuropathologists (Weil award 1976, Moore award), Am. Soc. Cell Biologists, Am. Neurological Assn. Anatomic Soc. Gt. Britain & Ireland, Brit. Neuropathology Soc., World Fedn. Neurology, Royal Coll. Pathologists, Pan-Am. Neuroepidiology Found. (hon.). Achievements include research in cellular relationships in the nervous system and the effects of neurotoxic chemicals. Office: Oregon Hlth Sciences Univ 3181 SW Sam Jackson Park Rd L606 Portland OR 97201

SPENCER, REX LEROY, secondary education educator; b. Kendallville, Ind., Jan. 29, 1944; s. Richard Donald and Mildred Francis (Fourman) S.; m. Diana Carole Land, Nov. 21, 1981; children: Katie Jo, Emily Paige. BS, The Defiance Coll., 1966; MA, Ball State U., 1970. Cert. tchr., Ohio. Tchr. Ansonia (Ohio) High Sch., 1966-80, Ansonia (Ohio) Middle Sch., 1982-86, Ansonia (Ohio) High Sch., 1986—; instr. Edison State C.C., Piqua, Ohio, 1983-88, Defiance (Ohio) Coll., summer 1989-92. Named Outstanding Am. History Tchr., Darke County DAR, 1992. Mem. NEA, Ohio Edn. Assn., Ansonia Edn. Assn. (pres. 1976-77, treas. 1991—), Nat. Coun. for the Social Studies, Ohio Coun. for the Social Studies, Defiance Coll. Alumni Assn. (bd. mem. 1976-79, v.p. 1979-80, pres. 1980-82). Methodist. Avocations: golf, bicycling, walking, antique collecting, singing with barbershop quartet. Office: Ansonia High Sch 200 W Canal St Ansonia OH 45303-0279

SPENCER, RICHARD HENRY, lawyer; b. Kansas City, Mo., Nov. 29, 1926; s. Byron Spencer and Helen Elizabeth (McCune) Hockaday; m. Barbara G. Rau, Aug. 2, 1952 (div. 1955) 1 child, Christina C.; m. Katherine Graham, Dec. 28, 1957; children: Elisabeth M., Katherine S. BS in Engring., Princeton U., 1949; LLB, U. Mo., 1952. Bar: Mo. 1952, U.S. Dist. Ct (we. dist.) Mo. 1955. Assoc. Spencer, Fane, Britt & Browne, Kansas City, 1952-59, ptnr., 1959—; sec. Daniels-McCray Lumber Co., Kansas City, 1975—, First Am. Fin.Corp., Kansas city, 1971—, First Am. Ins. Co., Kansas City, 1971—, bd. dirs.; bd. dirs. United Mo. City Bank, Kansas City. Co-author: Fiduciary Duties, Rights and Responsibilities of Directors, 1985. Sec. Kansas City Symphony, 1983—; sec., bd. dirs. Met. Performing Arts Fund, Kansas City, 1984—. Mem. ABA, Mo. Bar Assn., Lawyers Assn. Kansas City, Kansas City Club (pres. 1974), Kansas City Country Club (pres. 1986), Rotary. Republican. Episcopalian. Avocations: hunting, golf, tennis, traveling. Home: 77 Le Mans Ct Shawnee Mission KS 66208-5230 Office: Spencer Fane Britt & Browne 1400 Commerce Bank Bldg 1000 Walnut St Kansas City MO 64106-2123

SPENCER, RICHARD PAUL, biochemist, educator, physician; b. N.Y.C., June 7, 1929; s. David E. and Frances (Fried) S.; m. Gwendolyn Enid Williams, Apr. 7, 1956; children: Carolyn Roberts, Jennifer Holt, Priscilla James. AB, Dartmouth Coll., 1951; MD, U. So. Calif., 1954; MA (NSF fellow, Helen Hay Whitney fellow), Harvard U., 1958, PhD, 1961. Intern Beth Israel Hosp., Boston, 1954-55; practice medicine specializing in nuclear medicine; mem. faculty biophysics U. Buffalo, 1961-63; chief radioisotope service VA Hosp., Buffalo, 1961-63; assoc. prof. nuclear medicine Yale Sch. Medicine, 1963-68, prof., 1968-74; prof., chmn. dept. nuclear medicine U. Conn. Health Center, 1974—. Author: The Intestinal Tract, 1960, (with others) Biophysical Principles, 1965, Radionuclide Studies of the Spleen, 1975, Clinical Focus on Nuclear Medicine, 1977, Handbook of Nuclear Medicine, 1977, Therapy in Nuclear Medicine, 1978, Radiopharmaceuticals: Structure-Activity Relationships, 1981, Interventional Nuclear Medicine, 1984, New Procedures In Nuclear Medicine, 1988; contbr. (with others) articles to profl. jours. Mem. Am. Physiol. Soc., AAAS, Soc. Nuclear Medicine, Biophys. Soc. Achievements include discovery of functional asplenia; developed first complete description of relationship of food intake to reproductive success and to longevity in a species. Office: U Conn Health Ctr Farmington CT 06030

SPENCER, ROBERT C., political science educator; b. Chgo., Mar. 28, 1920; m. Edith Maxham McCarthy, Sept. 13, 1941; children: Margaret, Catherine, Anne, Thomas More, David. AB, U. Chgo., 1943, MA, 1952, PhD in Polit. Sci. (Univ. fellow 1952-53), 1955. Instr. polit. sci. and sociology St. Michaels Coll., 1949-51, asst., then assoc. prof. polit. sci., 1953-60, prof. govt., 1960-63, dir. summer sessions, 1960-61, asst. to pres., 1963-65; prof. polit. sci., chmn. dept., dean summer sessions U. R.I., 1965-67; grad. dean U. R.I. (Grad. Sch.), 1967-69; founding pres. Sangamon State U., Springfield, Ill., 1969-78; prof. govt. and public affairs Sangamon State U., 1978-88, prof. emeritus, 1988—; research assoc. Indsl. Relations Center, U. Chgo., 1952-53; extension lectr. N.Y. State Sch. Indsl. and Labor Relations, Cornell U., 1956-57; vice chmn. West Central Ill. Ednl. Telecommunications Consortium, 1975-77, chmn., 1977-78; chmn. task force personnel Vt. Little Hoover Commn., 1957-58; mem. Ill. adv. com. U.S. Commn. on Civil Rights, 1979-87; bd. mgrs. Franklin Life Variable Annuity Funds, 1974—; vis. prof. polit. sci., sr. rsch. assoc. local govt. ctr. Mont. State U., Bozeman, 1985, 89, 90—. Author: (with Robert J. Huckshorn) The Politics of Defeat, 1971. Bd. dirs. City Day Sch., Springfield, 1979-83, Gt. Am. People Show Repertory Co. 1980-90; vice chmn. Petersburg Libr. Bd., 1982-88; chmn. Petersburg Zoning Bd. Appeals, 1984-90; mem. Vt. Senate, 1959-63; faculty fellow Ford Found.'s Nat. Ctr. for Edn. in Politics, rsch. dir. Dem. Nat. Com., 1962-63; mem. adv. bd. Landmark Preservation Coun. Ill., 1986-89; mem., treas. Gallatin County Coun. on Aging, 1993—. Roman Catholic. Home: 2303 S 3rd Ave Bozeman MT 59715-6009

SPENCER, ROZELLE JEFFERY, moving and storage company executive; b. Memphis, July 3, 1936; s. William Arthur and Octavia (McCormack) S.; m. Winifred L. Jones, July 5, 1968; children: Jeffery Christian, Derrick Christopher. Student, DePaul U., Chgo., 1956-59; BA, Northeastern Ill. U., Chgo., 1990, MA Candidate, 1990-91. Transp. rep. Santa Fe R.R., Chgo., 1956-64; employment supr. Trans World Airlines, Chgo., 1964-70; pres., CEO Aaron Bros. Moving Systems Inc., Chgo., 1969—; pres. Aaro Medicar Transport, Chgo., 1976-85, Hyde Park Self Storage Inc., Chgo., 1990—. Mem. Chgo. Coun. Fgn. Rels., 1980's. Assn. African Historians, Chgo., 1980's and 90's, Task Force for Black Political Empowerment, Chgo., 1980's and 90's; assoc. Montford Point Marine Assn., Chgo., 1970's and 80's. Mem. Nat. Assn. Guardsmen, Plaza Club. Democrat. Baptist. Home: 10706 S Seeley Ave Chicago IL 60643-3315

SPENCER, SAMUEL, lawyer; b. Washington, Dec. 8, 1910; s. Henry Benning and Katharine (Price) S.; children from previous marriage: Henry B., Janet Spencer Dougherty, Richard A.; m. June Byrne, May 29, 1982. Student, Milton (Mass.) Acad., 1924-29; A.B. magna cum laude, Harvard U., 1932, LL.B., 1935. Bar: N.Y. 1937, D.C 1938, U.S. Supreme Ct 1950. Assoc. Shearman & Sterling, N.Y.C., 1935-37, Covington, Burling, Rublee, Acheson & Shorb, Washington, 1937- 40, 45-47; ptnr. Spencer, Graham & Holderman, 1947—; pres. bd. commrs., D.C., 1953-56; pres., chmn. bd. Tenn. R.R. Co., 1956-73. Bd. dirs. Nat. Symphony Orch., 1949-51, Garfield Hosp., 1947-53, 56-62; bd. dirs. Children's Hosp., 1948-53, sec., 1951-53; trustee Potomac Sch., 1947-53; pres. Washington Hosp. Ctr., 1958-60, bd. dirs., 1958-65; mem. Washington Nat. Monument Soc., 1958-91. Served to comdr. USNR, 1940-45. Decorated Bronze Star with combat V. Mem. ABA, Bar Assn. D.C., Am. Cancer Soc. (trustee D.C. 1951-53), AIA (hon.), Washington Inst. Fgn. Affairs (bd. dirs. 1961-89, sec. 1961-81), Jud. Council D.C. Circuit (com. on adminstrn. of justice 1966-70), Soc. of Cincinnati, Phi Beta Kappa. Episcopalian (sr. warden). Clubs: Metropolitan of Washington (bd. govs. 1949-53, 56-61, pres. 1959-60); Chevy Chase (Md.). Home: 5904 Cedar Pky Bethesda MD 20815-4251 Office: 2000 Massachusetts Ave NW Washington DC 20036-1022

SPENCER, SAMUEL REID, JR., educational consultant, former university president; b. Rock Hill, S.C., 1919; m. Ava Clark; 1948; children: Samuel Reid, Ellen Spencer Henschen, Clayton, Frank. AB summa cum laude, Davidson Coll., 1940, LLD (hon.), 1964; MA, Harvard U., 1947, PhD, 1951; LHD (hon.), Oglethorpe U., 1977, Queens Coll., 1983, Bridgewater Coll. 1986, Marymount U., 1988, Hollins Coll., 1991, Mary Baldwin Coll., 1992;

LittD (hon.), Washington and Lee U., 1991. With Vick Chem. Co., N.Y.C. 1940; research asst. to Grenville Clark, Dublin, N.H., 1947-48; asst. to pres. Davidson Coll., 1951-54, dean of students, asso. prof. history, 1954, dean of students, prof. history, 1955-57; pres. Mary Baldwin Coll., 1957-68; pres. Davidson (N.C.) Coll., 1968-83; pres. emeritus, 1983—; pres. Va. Found. for Ind. Colls., Richmond, 1983-88; sr. cons. Acad. Search Consultation Svc., 1989—; interim pres. Hollins Coll., 1990-91; dir. Piedmont Bank & Trust Co.; Fulbright lectr. U. Munich, 1965-66; mem. Bd. Fgn. Scholarships, 1980-83, chmn., 1982-83; bd. dirs. Assn. Am. Colls., 1976-83, chmn. assn., 1981-82; pres. So. Univ. Conf., 1979-80; mem. commn. govtl. relations Am. Council Edn., 1973-76. Author: Decision for War, 1917, 1953, Booker T. Washington and the Negro's Place in American Life, 1955, (with J. Garry Clifford) The First Peacetime Draft, 1986. Bd. dirs. Grenville Clark Fund, Dartmouth Coll., 1973—, Charlotte-Mecklenburg chpt. Urban League, 1979-83; trustee Agnes Scott Coll., 1975-91; trustee Union Theol. Sem., Richmond, Va., 1985-94, chmn. 1988-94. Maj. AUS, 1940-45. Austin fellow Harvard, 1947-48; Rosenwald fellow, 1948-49; Kent fellow Nat. Council on Religion in Higher Edn., 1949-51. Mem. Fulbright Assn. (bd. dirs. 1989-92), Phi Beta Kappa, Omicron Delta Kappa. Presbyterian (bd. Christian edn.). Address: PO Box 1117 Davidson NC 28036-1117

SPENCER, SCOTT, novelist; b. Washington, Sept. 1, 1945; s. Charles and Jean (Novick) S.; m. Claire Joubert Dupuy, Jan. 24, 1979; children: Celeste, Asher. BA, U. Wis., 1969. Author: Last Night at the Brain Thieves Ball, 1973, Preservation Hall, 1976, Endless Love, 1979, Waking the Dead, 1986, Secret Anniversaries, 1990, Men in Black, 1995. Mem. PEN (exec. bd. 1979-85), Authors Guild, Nat. Writers Union (exec. bd. 1986-92). Office: Alfred A Knopf Inc 201 E 50th St New York NY 10022-7703

SPENCER, STEVEN D., lawyer; b. Mar. 22, 1953. BS, Cornell U., 1975; JD, Columbia U., 1979. Bar: Pa. 1978, N.Y. 1979. Ptnr. Morgan, Lewis & Bockius, Phila.; adj. prof. Villanova U. law sch. 1991-92. Office: Morgan Lewis & Bockius 2000 One Logan Sq Philadelphia PA 19103

SPENCER, STEVEN SEARS, medical consultant; b. Phila., Aug. 27, 1929; s. Steven Murray and Mary Emma (Sears) S.; m. Joan Esther Price, June 11, 1955; children: Mary Elizabeth, Margaret Ruth, Sarah Price, Rebecca Louise. BA, Swarthmore Coll., 1951; MD, U. Pa., 1955. Diplomate Am. Bd. Internal Medicine; lic. physician Republic of Tanzania, N.Mex., Ariz.; cert. correctional health profl. Intern U. Mich., 1955-56; fellow in internal medicine Mayo Found. and Mayo Clinic, 1959-62; pvt. practice Flagstaff, Ariz., 1963-70; assoc. prof. U. Dar es Salaam, Tanzania, 1970-74; assoc. prof. U. Ariz., 1974-79, clin. lectr.; 1979-94; clin. assoc. prof. U. N.Mex., 1986-94; pvt. cons. Santa Fe, 1994—; mem. cons. staff Albert Schweitzer Hosp., 1960; mem. med. staff Flagstaff Cmty. Hosp., 1963-70, chief of staff, 1966-67, chief of medicine, 1964-67, 69-70; mem. staff Muhimbili Hosp., Dar es Salaam, 1970-74, U. Hosp., Tucson, Ariz., 1974-79, Tucson VA Hosp., 1974-79, Sage Meml. Hosp., 1979-85; med. dir. Navajo Nation Health Found., Sage Meml. Hosp., Ganado, Ariz., 1979-85, N.Mex. Corrections Dept., 1985-93; cons. in field. Contbr. numerous articles to profl. jours. Mem. Ariz. Bd. Med. Examiners, 1979-85, chmn., 1984-85, Gov.'s Task Force on HIV/AIDS, 1986-93; bd. dirs. St. Elizabeth Shelter for the Homeless, 1991—; mem. N.Mex. Com. to Stop Executions, 1994—. Sr. asst. surgeon USPHS, 1956-59. Fellow Nat. Heart Inst., 1960, NEH, 1975. Fellow ACP; mem. APHA (jail and prison health com.), Am. Correctional Health Svcs. Assn. (bd. dirs. 1991-95, chair policy and standards com.), Am. Correctional Assn., Internat. Physicians for Prevention of Nuclear War, Soc. Correctional Physicians. Democrat. Mem. Soc. of Friends. Avocations: choral singing, fly fishing, skiing. Home and Office: 2154 Calle de Sebastian Santa Fe NM 87505

SPENCER, THOMAS W., mining executive, energy executive; b. 1929. BSME, W.Va. U., 1952. Various mgmt. and exec. pos. Transco Energy Co., London, Ky., 1952—, sr. v.p., chief adminstrv. officer, 1985, now pres. With U.S. Army, 1954-56. Office: Transco Coal Co 100 Coal Dr London KY 40741*

SPENCER, W. E., oil company executive; b. 1937. BS, U. Texas, 1960. Engr. California Oil Comp., 1960-65; Coastal Corp., Houston, TX, 1965—; sr. vp, explor. prod. Coastal Corp., Houston, TX, 1983—. Office: Coastal Corp 9 E Greenway Plz Houston TX 77046-0979

SPENCER, WILLIAM COURTNEY, foundation executive, international business executive; b. Uniontown, Pa., Sept. 15, 1919; s. Clarence Ashley and Hazel (Stark) S.; m. Evelyn Van Cleve Bailey, Aug. 6, 1942; children: Courtney Lloyd, Henry Bailey, Edward Ashley. AB, Drew U., 1941; AM, Columbia U., 1946, EdD, 1952. Tchr. Scarsdale (N.Y.) Pub. Schs., 1946-49; dir. Univ. Sch. Columbia, 1949-52; prof. edn. and adminstrn. U. Del., 1952-55; prof., dir. grad. program tchr. edn. NYU, 1955-59, prof. higher edn. and internat. affairs, 1960-61; prof. adminstrn. U. Chile, Santiago, 1959-60; dir. Interam. affairs Inst. Internat. Edn. and asst. sec. gen. Coun. Higher Edn. in Am. Republics, 1961-65; assoc. dean Grad. Sch. Bus. Columbia U., 1965-67, spl. asst. to pres., 1967-69; pres. Western Coll., Oxford, Ohio, 1969-74, The Lindenwood Colls., 1974-79, Fund for Peace, 1979-80; v.p. Trans Internat. Mgmt. Corp., 1979-88; spl. adviser Fund for Higher Edn., 1979-82, pres., 1982-86; spl. asst. to pres. Internat. Exec. Svc. Corps, Stamford, Conn., 1988; dir. internat. devel. svcs. Nippon Manpower Ltd, Tokyo, 1988-91; pres. Trans Internat Exec. Svcs., 1988-92; mng. dir. Centre Internat. Edn., 1992—; UNESCO Latin Am. major project in edn., Chile, 1959-60, project edn. and econ. planning, India, 1962; cons. Am. Coun. Edn., 1960-61; del. Pan-Am Assembly on Population, 1965; mem. standing com. on internat. edn. Coll. Entrance Exam. Bd., 1972-74; cons. Am. Med. Internat. Inc., 1980, McGraw Hill Internat. Book Co., 1981, AID, Indonesia, 1982, Thermo-Electron Corp., China, 1984, Internat. Exec. Svc. Corps, Jamaica, 1989, Costa Rica, 1991, 93, Hungary, 1991. Author: Education and World Responsibility, 1965, also articles; editor: Art and the University, 1964, University and National Development, 1965, Agriculture and the University, 1965. Bd. dirs. Internat. Sch. Svc., 1963-69, chmn., 1967-69; mem. Mo. master planning com. Coordinating Bd. Higher Edn., 1975-79; pres. Ind. Colls. and Univs. of Mo., 1977-79; bd. dirs. St. Louis Coun. on World Affairs, 1977-79; mem. scholarship bd. Timken Co. Ednl. Fund, 1971-76; bd. dirs. Internat. Inst. Energy Conservation, 1984-89, Conn. River Mus., 1988—. Lt. comdr. USNR, 1942-46. Decorated Purple Heart; commendation medals from Royal Navy, U.S. Navy. Mem. Coun. Fgn. Relations, N.Y. Yacht Club, Essex (Conn.) Yacht Club, North Cove Yacht Club. Home: 18 Otter Cove Dr Old Saybrook CT 06475-1340

SPENCER, WILLIAM FRANKLIN, SR., soil scientist, researcher; b. Carlinville, Ill., Mar. 4, 1923; s. Jesse H. and Mayme (Wohlert) S.; m. Marjorie Ann Hall, June 2, 1946; children: Barbara Annette, William Franklin Jr., Gary Alan. BS in Agr., U. Ill., 1947, MS in Chemistry, 1950, PhD in Agronomy, 1952. Asst. chemist U. Fla., Lake Alfred, 1951-54; soil scientist USDA Agrl. Rsch. Svc., Laramie, Wyo., 1954-55; Brawley, Calif., 1955-57; assoc. soil chemist U. Fla., Lake Alfred, 1957-62; rsch. leader USDA Agrl. Rsch. Svc., Riverside, Calif., 1962—; mem. Western Soil & Water Rsch. Com., Riverside, 1965-75; cons. Cen. U., Maracay, Venezuela, 1979. Contbr. over 105 articles to profl. jours. With U.S. Army, 1943-46, PTO. Fellow AAAS, Am. Soc. Agronomy, Soil Sci. Am.; mem. Am. Soc. Environ. Toxicology and Chemistry, Internat. Soil Sci. Soc., Gamma Sigma Delta, Sigma Xi. Methodist. Achievements include research on behavior and fate of pesticides. Home: 2935 Arlington Ave Riverside CA 92506-4450 Office: U Calif USDA Agrl Rsch Svc Riverside CA 92521

SPENCER, WILLIAM H., ophthalmologist; b. N.Y.C., 1925. MD, U. Calif., San Francisco, 1954. Diplomate Am. Acad. Ophthalmology (exec. dir.). Intern Phila. Gen. Hosp., 1954-55; resident in ophthalmology U. Calif., San Francisco, 1955-58. Office: Calif-Pacific Med Ctr 2340 Clay St 5th Fl San Francisco CA 94115-1932*

SPENCER, WILLIAM J., engineering executive, researcher; b. 1930. AB, William Jewell Coll.; MS in Math., Kans. State U., PhD in Physics. With Bell Labs., Lincroft, N.J., 1959-72; dir. system support, dir. rsch. Sandia Nat. Labs., Livermore and Albuquerque, N.Mex., 1973-81; mgr. integrated circuit lab. Xerox Palo Alto Rsch. Ctr., Calif., 1981-90; with Sematech Inc., Austin, Tex., 1990—, pres., CEO, also bd. dirs. Office: Sematech Inc 2706 Montopolis Dr Austin TX 78741

SPENGLER, DAN MICHAEL, orthopedic surgery educator, researcher, surgeon; b. Defiance, Ohio, Feb. 25, 1941; s. Harold A. and Wilhelmina Spengler; m. Cynthia Niswonger; children: Christina, Craig. BS, Baldwin-Wallace Coll., 1962; MD, U. Mich., 1966. Diplomate Am. Bd. Orthopaedic Surgery (bd. dirs. 1988—). Intern in gen. surgery King County Hosp., Seattle, 1967-68; resident in orthopedics U. Mich., Ann Arbor, 1970-73; asst. prof. U. Wash., Seattle, 1974-78, assoc. prof., 1978-83; bd. dirs. Am. Bd. Orthopaedic Surgery. Author: Low Back Pain, 1982. Fellow Am. Acad. Orthopaedic Surgeons; mem. Am. Orthopaedic Assn., ACS, Am. Bd. Orthopaedic Surgeons (pres. 1993-94), Assn. Bone and Joint Surgeons, Internat. Soc. for Study of Lumbar Pain, U. Nashville Club. Avocations: flying, golf, running, skiing. Office: Vanderbilt U Dept Orthopaedic Rehab 1211 21st Ave S #D-4208 Nashville TN 37203-2405

SPENGLER, KENNETH C., meteorologist, professional society administrator; b. Harrisburg, Pa., BA, Dickinson Coll., 1936; MS, MIT; DSc (hon.), U. Nev., 1966. Exec. dir. Am. Meteorol. Soc., Boston, 1946-88, emeritus exec. dir., 1988—. Recipient Cleveland Abbe Disting. Svc. award Am. Meteorol. Soc., 1993. Mem. AAAS, AIAA, Am. Geophys. Union, Coun. Engring. & Sci. Soc. Home: 189 Jason St Arlington MA 02174*

SPENSER, IAN DANIEL, chemist educator; b. Vienna, Austria, June 17, 1924; m. Anita Fuchs, Sept. 5, 1951; children: Helen Ruth, Paul Andrew. B.Sc. with honors, U. Birmingham (Eng.), 1948; Ph.D. in Biochemistry, U. London, 1952, D.Sc. in Organic and Biochemistry, 1969. Demonstrator in biochemistry King's Coll., U. London, 1948-52, asst. lectr. in biochemistry Med. Coll. St. Bartholomew's Hosp., 1952-54, lectr., 1954-57; postdoctoral fellow div. pure chemistry NRC Can., Ottawa, Ont., 1953-54; asst. prof. biochemistry McMaster U., Hamilton, Ont., Can., 1957-59; assoc.prof. McMaster U., 1959-64, prof., 1964-68, prof. chemistry, 1968-89, prof. emeritus, 1989—; Akademischer Gast Laboratorium für Organische Chemie/Eidgenössische Technische Hochschule, Zürich, Switzerland, 1971, 89; vis. prof. Inst. Organic Chemistry, Tech. U. Denmark, Lyngby, 1977, Inst. Organische Chemie/Univ. Karlsruhe, Fed. Republic Germany, 1981, Institut für Pharmazeutische Biologie, Universität Bonn, Federal Republic of Germany, 1989. Research in biosynthesis of alkaloids, biosynthesis of vitamin Bl and vitamin B6. Recipient Sr. Scientist award NATO, 1980; recipient Can.-Japan Exchange award, 1982-83, Univ. Club of Hamilton award, 1990. Fellow Royal Soc. Can., Chem. Inst. Can. (John Labatt Ltd. award 1982-83), Royal Soc. Chemistry (U.K.); mem. Biochem. Soc., Am. Soc. Biochemistry Molecular Biol., Am. Soc. Pharmacognosy, Phytochem. Soc. N. Am. Office: McMaster U, Dept Chemistry, Hamilton, ON Canada L8S 4M1

SPERAKIS, NICHOLAS GEORGE, artist; b. N.Y.C., June 8, 1943; s. George and Cathren (Cokatas) S.; m. Yolanda de Carmen Mesa, Feb. 1, 1983. Student, Pratt Inst., 1960, NAD, 1960-61, Art Students League N.Y., Pratt Graphic Art Center, 1961-63. Instr. Sumitt (N.J.) Art Center, 1971, New Sch. Social Research, N.Y.C., 1972—, Fashion Inst. Tech., N.Y.C., 1977—. Exhibited one-man shows at Paul Kessler Gallery, 1963, 64, Provincetown, Mass., Hinckley and Brohel Art Gallery, Washington, 1964, N.Y.C., 1965, Mari Galleries, Woodstock, N.Y., 1966, 67, 68, Larchmont, N.Y., 1967, Eric Schindler Galleries, 1965, Richmond (Va.) Art Gallery, N.Y. U. Student Loeb Center, 1969, L.I. U., 1971, Pratt Inst., 1971, Bienville Gallery, New Orleans, 1972, 74, Pace U., N.Y.C., 1972, Lerner-Heller Gallery, N.Y.C., 1975, 76, Daedal Gallery, Balt., 1976, Reading Mus. Art, (Pa.), 1977, Bklyn. Mus., 1977, Washington Irving Gallery, N.Y.C., 1982, Museo Universitario Del Chopo, Mexico City, 1984, Forum Gallery, N.Y.C., Mus. Contemporary Art, Bogota, The Altler Gallery, Munich, 1989, Galerieverein Blankenese, Hamburg, Fed. Republic Germany, 1988, Galeria Sextante, Bogota, 1989, La Franca, Centro de Arte, Medellin, Colombia, 1989, various woodcut exhbns., others; exhibited group shows, Mercy Hurst Coll., Erie, Pa., 1963, 64, Bklyn. Mus., 1964, 77, Jewish Mus., 1964, Chrysler Mus., 1964, 65, Assoc. Am. Artists Galleries, N.Y.C., 1965, Norfolk (Va.) Mus. Arts Scis., 1965, Long Beach (Calif.) Coll., 1969, Am. Acad. and Nat. Inst. Arts and Letters, 1969, 75, Mid West Mus-Am-Art, 1981, numerous others, print exhbns., France, Italy, Spain, other European Countries, Far East, 1970-71, Lerner-Heller Gallery, 1973, 76, Amherst Coll., 1974, Worcester (Mass.) Mus. Fine Art, 1977, Reading (Pa.) Mus. Art, 1977, Galeria El Museo Santate de Bogota, Colombia, 1992, Mus. Modern Art, Rio de Janeiro, Brazil, 1992, travel Ams., Europe, 1992, Rhino Horn, N.Y.C., 1994; represented in permanent collections Bklyn. Mus., Walter P. Chrysler Mus., Norfolk, Va., Norfolk Mus. Arts and Scis., N.Y.C. Public Library, Phila. Mus. Fine Arts, Worcester Mus. Fine Art, Flint (Mich.) Art Inst., Mus. Modern Art, N.Y.C., U. Conn., Storrs, Amherst Coll., Okla. Fine Arts Center Mus., Am. Acad. and Nat. Inst. Arts and Letters, Detroit Inst. Fine Art, Corcoran Gallery of Art, Midwest Mus. Am. Art, Exeter Acad., Conn., Mus. Modern Art, N.Y.C., print collections Nat. Mus. Am. Art Smithsonian Instn., DeHunter Mus. Art, Chattanooga, Inst. of Congress, Washington, High Mus. Art, Atlanta, Free Libr., Phila., Kunst Mus., Fine Arts Mus. Bern Switzerland, Australian Nat. Gallery, Canberra, Snite Mus. Art, U. Notre Dame, Ind., Bibliotheque Royale Albert/ER, Bruxelles, Belgium, Museo Rayo, Roldanillo, Colombia, Stedelijk Mus., Amsterdam, The Netherlands, Hirshhorn Mus., Washington, Santa Fe de Bogota, Nordjyllands Kunstmus., Aalborg, Denmark, Banco Bozano Simonsen, Rio de Janeiro; organized (with others), Rhino Horn artist group, N.Y.C., 1970. Recipient First Prize Purchase award Mercy Hurst Coll., 1964; Lawrence and Hinda Rosenthal award Am. Acad. and Nat. Inst. Arts and Letters, 1969; Guggenheim graphics fellow, 1970; McDowell Colony summer residency, 1976. Mem. Soc. Am. Graphic Artists. Address: 245 W 29th St Floor 12A New York NY 10001 *Art doesn't bring out the voters for candidates X or Z. Art brings forth an experience and enters the knowledge of the viewer, so it helps the individual consider new channels and modes of behavior. One of the reasons there is so much censorship of art is due to the power art has to transform people at the roots not into some action but in a more generalized manner in terms of understanding institutions and traditions for what they really are. I think art changes emotions more than it changes specific ideas.*

SPERANDIO, GLEN JOSEPH, pharmacy educator; b. Glen Carbon, Ill., May 8, 1918; s. Henry A. and Marjorie (Dunstedter) A.; m. Dorys Bell, June 21, 1946; 1 child, James Glen. B.S., St. Louis Coll. Pharmacy, 1940; M.S., Purdue U., 1947, Ph.D., 1950. Pharmacist, 1936-41; analytical chemist Grove Labs., St. Louis, 1941-43, 45; mfg. pharmacist William R. Warner Co., St. Louis, 1944; instr. Purdue U., 1946-50, asst. prof. pharmacy, 1950-53, assoc. prof., 1953-62, prof., 1962—; head dept., 1966-78, assoc. dean, 1978-83, assoc. dean emeritus, 1984—; exec. dir. Ind. Soc. Hosp. Pharmacists, 1984—; indsl. cons., 1955-81; pharm. cons. VA Hosp., Indpls., 1963-69; mem. blue ribbon com. on standardized bd. exams. Nat. Assn. Bds. Pharmacy, 1969; cons. on clin. pharmacy Surgeon Gen., U.S. Army, 1973-80. Author: Laboratory Manual of Cosmetics, 1956, (with others) Scoville's Art of Compounding, 1959, (with others) Clinical Pharmacy, 1966; author, editor: (with others) Hosp. Pharmacy Notes, 1959-74. Served with USCGR, 1944. Named 1st prof. clin. pharmacy in U.S., Distinguished Alumnus St. Louis Coll. Pharmacy, 1969. Mem. Parenteral Drug Assn. (regional v.p. 1965-67), Nat. Formulary, Ind. Soc. Hosp. Pharmacists (pres. 1955-57, hon. mem., Disting. Educator award 1980), Am. Pharm. Assn. (sec.-treas. sect. practical pharmacy 1956), Ind. Pharm. Assn., Tipp County Pharm. Assn., Internat. Fedn. Pharmacists, Soc. Cosmetic Chemists, Am. Legion, Masons (32 deg.), Golden Key, Sigma Xi, Kappa Psi (Nat. Svc. award 1967, nat. pres. 1963-67), Rho Chi, Phi Lambda Upsilon. Research in drug, cosmetic formulation. Home: PO Box 2509 West Lafayette IN 47906-0509 Office: Purdue U Sch Pharmacy Lafayette IN 47907 *A great help in solving problems is to look at the situation from the other person's point of view.*

SPERBER, DANIEL, physicist; b. Vienna, Austria, May 8, 1930; came to U.S., 1955, naturalized, 1967; s. Emanuel and Nelly (Liberman) S.; m. Ora Yuval, Nov. 29, 1963; 1 son, Ron Emanuel. M.Sc., Hebrew U., 1955; Ph.D., Princeton U., 1960. Tng. and rsch. asst. Israel Inst. Tech., Haifa, 1954-55, Princeton U., 1955-60; sr. scientist, rsch. advisor Ill. Inst. Tech. Rsch. Inst., Chgo., 1960-67; assoc. prof. physics Ill. Inst. Tech., 1964-67, Rensselaer Poly. Inst., Troy, N.Y., 1967-72; prof. Rensselaer Poly. Inst., 1972—; Nordita prof. Niels Bohr Inst., Copenhagen, 1973-74, NATO research fellow, vis., prof., 1974-77; vis. prof. G.S.I., Darmstadt, Fed. Republic Germany, 1983; sr. Fulbright research scholar, Saha Inst. Nuclear Physics, Calcutta, India, 1987-88. Contbr. over 100 sci. papers to profl. jours. Served to capt. Israeli Army, 1948-51. Fellow Am. Phys. Soc.; mem. Israel

Phys. Soc., N.Y. Acad. Scis., Sigma Xi. Jewish. Home: 1 Taylor Ln Troy NY 12180-7162 Office: Rensselaer Poly Inst Dept Physics Troy NY 12180-3590 *My goals are to further an understanding of nature by basic research in nuclear theory and to introduce a new generation to this research.*

SPERBER, MARTIN, pharmaceutical company executive, pharmacist; b. N.Y.C., Aug. 6, 1931; s. David and Gertrude (Besen) S.; m. Ellen Claire Marx, June 7, 1953; children—Steven Jay, Susan Barbara Parnes. B.S., Columbia U., N.Y.C., 1952. Registered pharmacist. Pharmacist, dir. sales and mktg. Henry Schein, Inc., N.Y.C., 1953-65, v.p., 1965-80; pres., chief oper. officer Henry Schein, Inc., Port Washington, N.Y., 1980-89, vice chmn., 1989—, also bd. dirs.; pres., chief oper. officer Schein Pharm., Inc., Port Washington, 1985-89, chmn., chief exec. officer, 1989—, also bd. dirs.; chmn., chief exec. officer Danburg Pharm. Inc., Carmel, N.Y., 1989—, also bd. dirs.; chmn., chief exec. officer Steris Labs., Inc., Phoenix, 1989—, also bd. dirs. Mem. coun. of overseers Arnold and Marie Schwartz Coll. Pharmacy, L.I. U. Mem. Am. Pharm. Assn. Office: Schein Pharm Inc 100 Campus Dr # 375 Florham Park NJ 07932-1006

SPERELAKIS, NICHOLAS, physiology and biophysics educator, researcher; b. Joliet, Ill., Mar. 3, 1930; s. James and Arestia (Kayadakis) S.; m. Dolores Martinis, Jan. 28, 1960; children: Nicholas Jr., Mark, Christine, Sophia, Thomas, Anthony. BS in Chemistry, U. Ill., 1951, MS in Physiology, 1955, PhD in Physiology, 1957. Teaching asst. U. Ill., Urbana, 1954-57; instr. Case Western Res. U., Cleve., 1957-59, asst. prof., 1959-66, assoc. prof., 1966; prof. U. Va., Charlottesville, 1966-83; Joseph Eichberg prof. physiology Coll. Medicine U. Cin., 1983—, chmn. dept., 1983-93; cons. NPS Pharm., Inc., Salt Lake City, 1988—, Carter Wallace, Inc., Cranbury, N.J., 1988-91; vis. prof. U. St. Andrews, Scotland, 1972-73, U. San Luis Potosi, Mex., 1986, U. Athens, Greece, 1994; Rosenblueth prof. Centro de Investigacion y Avanzades, Mex., 1972; mem. sci. adv. com. several internat. meetings, editorial bd. numerous sci. jours. Editor: Handbook of Physiology on Circulation: The Heart, 1979, Physiology and Pathophysiology of the Heart, 1984, 2d edit., 1988, 3d edit., 1994, Calcium Antagonists: Mechanisms of Action on Cardiac Muscle and Vascular Smooth Muscle, 1984, Cell Interactions and Gap Junctions, vols. I and II, 1989, Frontiers in Smooth Muscle Research, 1990, Ion Channels in Vascular Smooth Muscle and Endothelial Cells, 1991, Essentials of Physiology, 1992, Cell Physiology Source Book, 1995, Electrogenesis of Biopotentials, 1995; assoc. editor Circ. Rsch., 1970-75, Molecular Cellular Cardiology; contbr. articles to profl. jours. Lectr. Project Hope, Peru, 1962. Sgt. USMC, 1951-53, Res., 1953-59. Recipient Disting. Alumnus award Rockdale (Ill.) Pub. Schs., 1958; U. Cin. Grad. fellow, 1989; NIH grantee, 1959—. Mem. Am. Physiol. Soc. (chair steering com. sect. 1981-82), Biophys. Soc. (coun. 1990-93), Am. Soc. Pharmacology and Exptl. Therapeutics, Internat. Soc. Heart Rsch. (coun. 1980-89, 92—), Am. Heart Assn. (established investigator 1961-66, Rsch. Merit award Ohio chpt. 1995), Am. Hellenic Ednl. Progressive Assn. (pres. Charlottesville chpt. 1980-82), Ohio Physiol. Soc. (pres. 1990-91), Phi Kappa Phi. Democrat. Greek Orthodox. Avocations: ancient coins, stamp collecting. Office: U Cin Coll Medicine 231 Bethesda Ave Cincinnati OH 45267-0576

SPERGEL, DAVID NATHANIEL, astrophysicist; b. Rochester, N.Y., Mar. 25, 1961; s. Martin S. and Rochelle S. (Leffert) S.; m. Laura H. Kahn, Aug. 26, 1990; 1 child, Julian J. AB summa cum laude, Princeton U., 1982; AM, Harvard U., 1985, PhD, 1986. Asst. prof. Princeton (N.J.) U., 1982-92, assoc. prof., 1993—; mem. Inst. for Advanced Study, N.J., 1986-87. Contbr. sci. articles to profl. jours. Recipient Helen B. Warner prize Am. Astron. Soc., 1994; Sloan fellow, 1987; named Presdl. Young Investigator, NSF, 1987. Office: Princeton U Peyton Hall Princeton NJ 08544

SPERGER, COURTLAND, food products executive; b. 1922. Chmn. Alto Dairy Coop, Waupun, Wis., 1944—. Office: Alto Dairy Coop N 3545 County EE Waupun WI 53963*

SPERLING, ALLAN GEORGE, lawyer; b. N.Y.C., Dec. 10, 1942; s. Saul Sperling and Gertrude (Lober) Sperling Bernstein; m. Susan Kelz, June 27, 1965; children: Matthew Laurence, Stuart Kelz, Jane Kendra. Bar: N.Y. 1969, U.S. Ct. Appeals (2d cir.) 1975. Law clk. to presiding justice U.S. Dist Ct., New Haven, 1967-68; assoc. Cleary, Gottlieb, Steen & Hamilton, N.Y.C., 1968-75, ptnr., 1976—. Editor Yale Law Jour. Bd. Merce Cunningham Dance Found., N.Y.C., 1992—, vice-chmn., 1985-92; chmn. bd. Rye (N.Y.) Arts Ctr. Inc., 1985-88, bd. dirs., 1990-94; bd. dirs. Friends of the Neuberger Mus., Purchase, N.Y., 1989—. Mem. ABA, N.Y. State Bar Assn., Order of Coif, Phi Beta Kappa. Home: Kirby Ln Rye NY 10580 Office: Cleary Gottlieb Steen & Hamilton 1 Liberty Plz New York NY 10006-1401

SPERLING, ELLIOT HARRIS, history educator; b. N.Y.C., Jan. 4, 1951; s. Solomon and Edith (Kantor) S.; m. Annie Joly, Apr. 10, 1982; 1 child, Coline Joly. BA, Queens Coll., CUNY, 1973; MA, Ind. U., 1980, PhD, 1983. Vis. asst. prof. of history U. So. Miss., Hattiesburg, 1984-85; asst. prof. of Tibetan studies dept. of Uralic and Altaic studies Ind. U., Bloomington, 1986-93; vis. asst. prof. of Tibetan and Himalayan studies, dept. Sanskrit and Indian studies Harvard U., Cambridge, Mass., 1992-93; assoc. prof. of Tibetan studies, dept. ceri. Eurasian studies Ind. U., 1993—; vis. lecturer U. Delhi and Jawaharlal Nehru U., India, 1994—. Contbr. articles to profl. jours. John D. & Catherine T. MacArthur Found. fellow, 1984-89, Fulbright scholar, 1994. Mem. The Tibet Soc., The Mongolia Soc., The Am. Oriental Soc., The Assn. for Asian Studies. Democrat. Jewish. Office: Ind U Dept Uralic and Altaic Studies Goodbody Hall Bloomington IN 47405

SPERLING, GEORGE, cognitive scientist, educator; s. Otto and Melitta Sperling. B.S. in Math., U. Mich., 1955; M.A. in Psychology, Columbia U., 1956; Ph.D. in Psychology, Harvard U., 1959. Rsch. asst. in biophysics Brookhaven Nat. Labs., Upton, N.Y., summer 1955; rsch. asst. in psychology Harvard U., Cambridge, Mass., 1957-59; mem. tech. rsch. staff Acoustical and Behavioral Rsch. Ctr., AT&T Bell Labs., Murray Hill, N.J., 1958-86; prof. psychology and neural sci. NYU, N.Y.C., 1970-92; disting. prof. cognitive scis. U. Calif., Irvine, 1992—; instr. psychology Washington Sq. Coll., NYU, 1962-63; vis. assoc. prof. psychology Duke U., spring 1964; adj. assoc. prof. psychology Columbia U., 1964-65; acting assoc. prof. psychology UCLA, 1967-68; hon. rsch. assoc. Univ. Coll., U. London, 1969-70; vis. prof. psychology U. Western Australia, Perth, 1972, U. Wash., Seattle, 1977; vis. scholar Stanford (Calif.) U., 1984; mem. sci. adv. bd. USAF, 1988-92. Recipient Meritorious Civilian Svc. medal USAF, 1993; Gomberg scholar U. Mich., 1953-54; Guggenheim fellow, 1969-70. Fellow AAAS, Am. Acad. Arts and Sci., Am. Psychol. Assn. (Disting. Sci. Contbn. award 1988), Optical Soc. Am.; mem. NAS, Assn. for Research in Vision and Opthalmology, Am. Interdisciplinary Conf. (founder, organizer 1975—), Eastern Psychol. Assn. (bd. dirs. 1982-85), Soc. for Computers in Psychology (steering com. 1974-78), Psychonomic Soc., Soc. Exptl. Psychologists, Soc. for Math. Psychology (chmn. 1983-84, exec. bd. 1979-85), Phi Beta Kappa, Sigma Xi. Office: Dept Cognitive Sciences SS Tower Univ of California Irvine CA 92717

SPERLING, GEORGE ELMER, JR., lawyer; b. Phila., Feb. 5, 1915; s. George E. and Margaret Ethel (Fulton) S.; m. Elizabeth Ruth Smollett, Feb. 3, 1945; children: Mary Elizabeth, Doris Fulton, Patricia Anne. A.B., Pa. State Coll., 1936, M.A., 1937; J.D., U. Mich., 1940. Bar: Mich. 1940. Practice in Ann Arbor, 1940-42; counsel Standard Oil Co., Cleve., 1943-45, Carnation Co., Los Angeles, 1946-82; asst. sec. Carnation Co., 1951-63, sec., 1963-82, mem. jr. bd. dirs., 1952-62; v.p. Buckley & Sperling, Monterey, Calif., 1982-85; ptnr. Buckley, Sperling & Frey, Monterey, 1985-87; ptnr. Buckley & Sperling, Santa Monica, 1987—, pres., 1992—. Chmn. Wilshire YMCA, 1952—; pres. Brentwood Protective Assn., 1958-60; trustee Bel Air Town and Country Sch.; mem. pres.' coun. San Francisco Theol. Sem., San Anselmo, Calif., 1993—; pres. Clara Schmidt Found., 1992—. Mem. Navy League, Pa. State Coll. Alumni Assn. of So. Calif. (v.p.), Mich., Ohio, Calif. Wis. bar assns., Brentwood Youth Council (pres. 1959). Presbyn. Clubs: Toastmasters, Riviera Country Presdt's (U. Mich.). Lodge: Miracle Mile Kiwanis (pres. dir.). Home: 347 25th St Santa Monica CA 90402-2521 Home: PO Box 832 Pebble Beach CA 93953-0832 *The most important thing for a person to do is to keep your mind alert at all times. You will never get old if you keep thinking of ways to help your country, your neighbors, your friends, and yourself.*

SPERLING, GODFREY, JR., journalist; b. Long Beach, Calif., Sept. 25, 1915; s. Godfrey and Ida (Bailey) S.; m. Betty Louise Feldmann, June 22, 1942; children—Mary (Mrs. John H. McAuliffe), John Godfrey. B.S., U. Ill., 1937; J.D., U. Okla., 1940. Bar: Ill. bar 1940. Practice in Urbana, Ill.; also reporter Champaign-Urbana News-Gazette, 1940-41; mem. staff Christian Sci. Monitor, 1946—, Midwest bur. chief, 1957-62, N.Y. bur. chief, 1962-65, news mgr., asst. chief Washington bur., 1965-73, nat. polit. corr., 1970-83, chief Washington Bur., 1973-83, sr. Washington columnist, 1984—; lectr. nat. affairs, 1955—, Woodrow Wilson vis. fellow, 1976—. Served to maj. USAAF, 1941-46; col. Res. Recipient Alumnus Achievement award U. Ill., 1987, Spl. Citation, Nat. Press Found. for unique contbns. to Am. journalism, 1994. Mem. Okla. Bar Assn., Ill. Bar Assn., Mass. Bar Assn., Congl. Press Corr. Assn., White House Press Corr. Assn., Nat. Press Club (Washington), Overseas Writers Club (Washington), Gridiron of Washington (pres. 1991), Sperling Breakfast Group (host 1966—), Kenwood Country Club (Bethesda, Md.), Navy Officers Club (Bethesda), Sigma Delta Chi. Christian Scientist. Office: Christian Science Monitor 910 16th St NW Washington DC 20006-2903

SPERLING, JOHN GLEN, education company executive; b. Willow Springs, Mo., Jan. 9, 1921; s. Leon Birchfield and Lena (McNama) S.; m. Virginia Vandergrift, June 1951 (div. 1965); 1 child, Peter Vandegrift. BA, Reed Coll., 1948; MA, U. Calif., 1952; PhD, U. Cambridge, Eng., 1955. Instr. U. Md., Europe, 1955-57; asst. professor Ohio State U., Columbus, 1957-76; prof. San Jose (Calif.) State U., 1960-72; pres. Inst. Profl. Devel., San Jose, 1972-76. U. Phoenix, 1976-80; pres., chief exec. officer Apollo Group Inc., Phoenix, 1980—. Co-author: Economic Concepts & Institutions, National Economic Policies, Communist Economies, Third World Economies, 1974-76, War Finance 1689-1714, New Cambridge Modern History, 1970; contbr. articles to profl. jours. Cons. Combating Juvenile Delinquency, Sunnyvale, Calif., 1972-75, Calif. Ctr. Community Schs., San Jose, 1971-73; active Open Space & Urban Devel. Commn., Santa Clara County, Calif., 1971-73, Trustee Ariz. Theater Co., Phoenix. Recipient Ehrman Studentship, Kings Coll., Cambridge U., 1953-55, Acad. Freedom award Calif. Fedn. Tchrs., L.A., 1988. Mem. Arizona Club, Internat. Club (Washington). Democrat. Home: 5290 E Exeter St Phoenix AZ 85018-3234 Office: Apollo Group Inc 4615 E Elwood St Phoenix AZ 85040-1936

SPERLING, ROBERT Y., lawyer; b. Chgo., July 14, 1947. AB, U. Ill., 1969; JD, De Paul U., 1972. Bar: Ill. 1972, U.S. Dist. Ct. (no. dist.) Ill. 1972, U.S. Ct. Appeals (7th cir.) 1975, U.S. Supreme Ct. 1978. Ptnr. Katte Muchin & Zavis, Chgo. Mem. ABA (local govt. law sect., litigation sect., antitrust law legis. com. 1977-79), Ill. State Bar Assn., Chgo. Bar Assn. (jud. com. 1972, local govt. com. 1972, young lawyers divsn.). Office: Katten Muchin & Zavis 525 W Monroe St Ste 1600 Chicago IL 60661-3693

SPERO, BARRY MELVIN, medical center executive; b. Richmond, Va., July 13, 1937; s. Stanley Leo and Jean (Marmorstein) S.; m. Merle Burns, May 29, 1960; children: Amy, Robin, Melissa. BA, U. Richmond, 1959; MHA, Med. Coll. Va., 1961. Asst. administr. Bapt. Hosp., Nashville, 1963-66, administrv. dir., 1966-68; v.p., dir. hosp. adminstrn. Hosp. Affiliates, Inc., Nashville, 1968-71; exec. dir. Bon Secours Hosp., Grosse Pointe, Mich., 1971-77; pres. The Mt. Sinai Med. Ctr., Cleve., 1977-85; pres., pres. NeWell Health Care System Newton-Wellesley Hosp., 1985-90; pres. Maimonides Med. Ctr., Bklyn., 1990-95, Masonicare, Wallingford, Conn., 1995—; bd. dirs. Premier Health Alliance, chmn., 1981-84, Premier Preferred Care, Healthfirst; bd. trustees Villa Maria Nursing Ctr./Bon Secours Hosp., 1974—, chmn. bd., 1988—; bd. dirs. League Vol. Hosps. and Homes, 1991-95, chmn.-elect, 1992-95; coun. overseers Arnold & Marie Schwartz, Coll. Pharmacy and Health Scis., 1992-95; mem. State of Ohio Gov.'s Commn. on Health Care Cost, 1984-85; mem. various coms. Coun. Teaching Hosps., 1992-95; treas. Vol. Hosps. Am., Mass., 1986-90; chmn. hosp. adv. com. Blue Cross N.E. Ohio, 1983-85; bd. trustees Med. Instrumentation Systems, 1978-84. Mem. personnel practice com. Combined Jewish Philanthropies; chmn. United Way, West Suburban Hosp. Div.; regional bd. Bay Bank Middlesex; mem. Perpetual Benevolent Fund Com., Blue Print 2000, Commonwealth Mass. Fellow Am. Coll. Healthcare Execs.; mem. Greater N.Y. Hosp. Assn. (bd. govs. 1992—), Am. Hosp. Assn. (com. on Medicare payment for outpatient svcs. 1989-90), Mass. Hosp. Assn. (bd. trustees 1987-90, com. on health systems 1986-90), Met. Boston Hosp. Coun. (chmn. 1988-90), New Eng. Healthcare Assembly (Blue Ribbon com. 1985-90), Ohio Hosp. Assn. (exec. coun., bd. trustees 1981-85), Greater Cleve. Hosp. Assn. (exec. coun., bd. trustees 1978-85), Coun. Teaching Hosps. (various coms. 1992—). Jewish. Avocations: golf, tennis, scuba diving. Office: Masonicare PO Box 70 Wallingford CT 06492

SPERO, JOAN EDELMAN, federal agency administrator; b. Davenport, Iowa, Oct. 2, 1944; d. Samuel and Sylvia (Halpern) Edelman; m. Carl Michael Spero, Nov. 9, 1969; children: Jason, Benjamin. Student, L'Inst. d'Etudes Politiques, Paris, 1964-65; BA, U. Wis., 1966; MA, Columbia U., 1968, PhD, 1973. Asst. prof. Columbia U., N.Y.C., 1973-79; ambassador of U.S. to UN Econ. and Social Council, N.Y.C., 1980-81; v.p. Am. Express Co., N.Y.C., 1981-83; v.p. internat. corp. affairs, 1983-89; treas., sr. v.p., 1989-91; exec. v.p. corp. affairs and communications Am. Express Co., 1991-93; under sec. for econ., bus. and agrl. affairs Dept. of State, Washington, 1993—; vis. scholar Fed. Res. Bank N.Y., 1976-77; mem. U.S.-Japan Bus. Coun., Washington, 1983—. Author: The Politics of International Economic Relations, 4th edit., 1990, The Failure of the Franklin National Bank, 1980; contbr. articles to profl. jours. Trustee Amherst Coll.; bd. dirs. French-Am. Found.; mem. Coun. Am. Ambassadors. Named to Acad. Women Achievers, YWCA, 1983; named Fin. Woman of Yr., Fin. Women's Assn., 1990; recipient George Washington Disting. Statesperson award, 1994; Woodrow Wilson fellow. Mem. Coun. on Fgn. Rels. (Internat. Affairs fellow), The Trilateral Commn., Svcs. Policy Adv. Com., Phi Beta Kappa. Democrat. Jewish. Avocations: writing; swimming. Office: US Dept State Econ Bus and Agt Affairs 2201 C St NW Washington DC 20520-7512

SPERO, STANLEY LEONARD, broadcast executive; b. Cleve., Oct. 17, 1919; s. Morris B. and Hermine (Harve) S.; m. Frieda Kessler, June 30, 1946; children: Laurie, Lisa, Leslie. BS cum laude, So. Calif., 1942; postgrad., Cleve. Coll., 1943. Account exec. Sta. WHKK, Akron, Ohio, 1946-48, Sta. KFAC, L.A., 1948-52; account exec. Sta. KMPC, Hollywood, 1952-53, v.p., gen. sales mgr., 1953-68, v.p., gen. mgr., 1968-78; v.p. Golden West Broadcasters, 1978-94; sr. sports cons. Cap Cities, Stas. KMPC and KABC, Hollywood, 1994—. Pres. permanent charities com. entertainment industry, 1972. With U.S. Maritime Svc., 1942-43. Mem. So. Calif. Broadcasters Assn. (chmn. 1972), Am. Advt. Fedn. (gov. 1972), Advt. Assn. West, Hollywood C. of C. (bd. dirs. 1972-90, chmn. bd. dirs. 1985-87), Hollywood Advt. Club (bd. dirs. 1972, pres. 1960-61). Home: 5027 Hayvenhurst Ave Encino CA 91436-1114 Office: Sta KMPC 5858 W Sunset Blvd Los Angeles CA 90028-6661

SPERRY, JAMES EDWARD, anthropologist; b. Weeping Water, Nebr., May 17, 1936; s. John Edward and Augusta Anna (Frandsen) S.; m. Gail Louise Killen, Sept. 26, 1964; 1 child, Patrick Reuben. Student, Bethany Coll., Lindsborg, Kans., 1953-55; A.B. in Art and Anthropology, U. Nebr., Lincoln, 1962, M.A. in Anthropology, 1965; postgrad., Mus. Mgmt. Inst., 1984. Teaching asst. U. Neb., 1961-63, instr. anthropology, 1964-65; research archeologist State Hist. Soc. N.D., Bismarck, 1965-69; supt. State Hist. Soc. N.D., 1969—; sec. N.D. Heritage Found., 1973-76; sec. N.D. Lewis and Clark Trail Council, 1970, chmn., 1971; N.D. hist. preservation officer, 1969—, N.D. State records coordinator, 1975-93; mem. Theodore Roosevelt Rough Rider award com., 1969—. Editor: North Dakota History: Journal of the Northern Plains, 1969-1973; contbr. numerous articles profl. jours. Bd. dirs. Burleigh/Morton chpt. ARC, 1987-93, chmn., 1993, mem. N.D. State svc. coun., 1993-94. Served with USAF, 1956-59. Am. Assn. State and Local History fellow, 1967; Bush summer fellow, 1984. Mem. Sigma Xi, Delta Phi Delta, Sigma Gamma Epsilon. Home: 1811 Estate Ave Bismarck ND 58504-3043 Office: State Hist Soc ND ND Heritage Ctr 612 E Blvd Bismarck ND 58505

SPERRY, SANDRA PHILLIPS, nursing administrator; b. Oak Park, Ill., May 27, 1948; d. John E. and Ruth (Haney) P. AS, Triton Coll., 1969; BA, Northeastern Ill. U., 1975; MPA, NYU, 1983, postgrad., 1987. RN, N.Y.; advanced profl. cert. in quantitative analysis and computer applications in health planning. Head nurse NYU Med. Ctr., N.Y.C., evening asst. dir.,

clin. asst. dir., C.A.D.N.; dir. nursing NYI-BDH, N.Y.C.; sr. v.p. nursing N.Y. Downtown Hosp., N.Y.C. Ill. State scholar Ill. Women's Clubs. Mem. Am. Orgn. Nursing Execs., N.Y. Nurses Assn. Home: 69 Gold St Apt 7D New York NY 10038-1882

SPERTUS, PHILIP, investment company executive; b. Chgo., 1934; grad. MIT, 1956. With Intercraft Industries Corp., Chgo., pres., 1969-79, chmn. bd., 1979-92, also chief exec. officer and dir. Office: 3321 Bee Caves Rd Ste 333 Austin TX 78746-6609

SPERZEL, GEORGE E., JR., personal care industry executive; b. 1951. BS in Bus. Adminstrn./Mgmt., U. Louisville, 1977. With General Electric Co., 1977-93; with Andrew Jergens Co., Cin., 1993—, now v.p., CFO. Office: Andrew Jergens Co 2535 Spring Grove Ave Cincinnati OH 45214*

SPETH, GERALD LENNUS, education and business educator; b. Logan, Utah, July 14, 1934; s. Fredrick William and Elizabeth LaVern (Nuttall) S.; m. Dora Goff, Aug. 11, 1955; children: Camille, Michael Gerald, Mark Alan, Janell, Doreen. BS, Utah State U., 1956; MBA, Ind. U., 1969; EdD, Ball State U., 1988. Auditor Ernst & Ernst, Salt Lake City, 1956, 58-59; officer 1st and 2d lt. U.S. Army, 1956-58, officer capt. to col., 1959-82; controller Columbia Club, Indpls., 1982-83; sr. v.p. Allied Fidelity Corp., Indpls., 1983-85; adj. faculty Ind. Cen. U., Indpls., 1982-85; prof., dir. grad. bus. progs. U. Indpls., 1985—; cons. in mgmt. and strategic planning. Counselor in stake presidency, bishop, welfare dir., mission pres., high councilor LDS Ch., 1965—. Recipient Legion of Merit, 1971-80, Bronze Star medal, 1966. Mem. Am. Soc. Mil. Comptrollers, U.S. Govt. Accts. Assn., Beta Gamma Sigma, Sigma Iota Epsilon, Alpha Kappa Psi, Kappa Delta Psi, Delta Mu Delta. Home: 8337 Goldfinch Cir Indianapolis IN 46256-1629 Office: U Indpls 1400 E Hanna Ave Indianapolis IN 46227-3697

SPETH, JAMES GUSTAVE, United Nations executive, lawyer; b. Orangeburg, S.C., Mar. 4, 1942; s. James Gustave and Amelia St. Clair (Albergotti) S.; m. Caroline Cameron Council, July 3, 1964; children: Catherine Council, James Gustave, Charles Council. BA summa cum laude, Yale U., 1964, LLB, 1969; MLitt, Oxford U., 1966. Bar: D.C. 1969. Law clk. to Justice Hugo L. Black U.S. Supreme Ct., 1969-70; sr. staff atty. Natural Resources Def. Council, Washington, 1970-77; mem. Council Environ. Quality, Washington, 1977-79, chmn., 1979-81; prof. law Georgetown U. Law Ctr., Washington, 1981-82; pres. World Resources Inst., Washington, 1982-93; adminstr. UN devel. program UN, N.Y.C., 1993—; founded World Resources Inst.; organized Western Hemisphere Dialogue environ. and devel., 1990; chaired U.S. Task Force internat. devel. and environ. security. Contbr. articles to profl. jours.; speaker in field. Bd. dirs. World Resources Inst., Keystone Ctr., Nat. Resources Def. Coun., Woods Hole Rsch. Ctr. Recipient Resources Def. award Nat. Wildlife Fedn., 1976, Barbara Swain award of honor Nat. Resources Coun. Am., 1992; named to Global 500 Honor Role United Nations Environ. Program, 1988; Rhodes scholar, 1964-66. Mem. Coun. on Fgn. Rels. (N.Y.C.), China Coun. for Internat. Coop. on Environment and Devel. Episcopalian. Home: 350 E 57th St Apt 10A New York NY 10022-2953 Office: UNDP 1 United Nations Plz New York NY 10017-3596

SPETRINO, RUSSELL JOHN, retired utility company executive, lawyer; b. Cleve., Apr. 22, 1926; s. John Anthony and Madeline Spetrino; m. Marilyn Folk, July 17, 1954 (dec.); children: Michael J., Ellen A. Spetrino Raines; m. Mildred Pilkton, June 26, 1993. B.S., Ohio State U., 1950; LL.B., Western Res. U., 1954. Bar: Ohio 1954. Asst. atty. gen. Ohio, 1954-57; atty.-examiner Public Utilities Commn. of Ohio, Columbus, 1957-59; atty. Ohio Edison Co., Akron, 1959-69, sr. atty., 1970-73, gen. counsel, 1973-78, v.p., gen. counsel, 1978-87, exec. v.p., gen. counsel, 1987-89, ret., 1989. Served with inf. U.S. Army, 1944-46. Mem. Portage County Club. Republican. Home: 333 N Portage Path Unit 34 Akron OH 44303-1252 *The importance of—and the strength that can be derived from—simple intellectual honesty never ceases to amaze me. It is so much easier to deal successfully with others when every effort is made to understand their views, and your own views are based upon thoughtful, honest conviction.*

SPEVACK, MARVIN, English educator; b. N.Y.C., Dec. 17, 1927; s. Nathan and Miriam (Propper) S.; m. Helga Husmann, May 28, 1962; 1 child, Edmund Daniel. B.A., CCNY, 1948; M.A., Harvard U., 1950, Ph.D., 1953. Instr. English CCNY, 1955-61; asst. prof. City Coll. N.Y., 1961-63; prof. English, U. Muenster, Germany, 1963-89, dir. English seminar, 1964-89, dir. Inst. Erasmianum, 1974-89; Fulbright lectr. U. Münster, Germany, 1961-62; vis. prof. U. Munich, 1962-63, NYU, summer 1966, Harvard U., summer 1973, U. N.Mex., 1985-86, Bowling Green State U., fall 1989; fellow Folger Shakespeare Libr., 1970; hon. rsch. fellow Univ. Coll., London, 1980-81, 95—; vis. fellow Wolfson Coll., Cambridge (Eng.) U., 1984; scholar-in-residence Ctr. for Renaissance and Baroque Studies, U. Md., spring 1989; vis. rsch. fellow Inst. for Advanced Studies in Humanities, U. Edinburgh, Scotland, 1991. Author: Harvard Concordance to Shakespeare, 1973, A Complete and Systematic Concordance to the Works of Shakespeare, 9 vols., 1968-80, Robert Burton, Philosophaster, 1984, Shakespeare: The second, Third, and Fourth Folios, 1985, New Cambridge Julius Caesar, 1988, New Variorum Antony and Cleopatra, 1990, A Shakespeare Thesaurus, 1993; also articles and editions. Served with AUS, 1953-55. Guggenheim fellow, 1973-74, Andrew W. Mellon Found. fellow Huntington Libr., 1992, Ctr. for Book fellow Brit. Libr., London, 1994-95. Mem. Internat. Assn. U. Profs. English, MLA, Internat. Shakespeare Assn., Deutsche Shakespeare Gesellschaft W., Shakespeare Assn., Soc. Textual Scholarship, Harvard Club (N.Y.C.), Harvard of Rhein-Ruhr Club (Germany), Phi Beta Kappa. Home: 14 Potstiege, 48161 Münster Germany Office: 12-20 Johannisstrasse, 48143 Münster Germany

SPEYER, JASON LEE, engineer, educator; b. Boston, Apr. 30, 1938; s. Joseph Louis and Ruth Sylvia (Steinmetz) S.; m. Barbara Joan Sachs, Sept. 11, 1966; children—Gil, Gavriel, Rakhel, Joseph. B.S., MIT, 1960; M.S., Harvard U., 1964, Ph.D., 1968. Registered profl. engr., Tex. Engr. Boeing Co., Seattle, 1960-61; sr. engr. Raytheon Co., Bedford, Mass., 1961-68; sr. analyst Analytical Mechanics Assocs., Inc., Cambridge, Mass., 1968-70; mem. research staff Charles Stark Draper Lab., Cambridge, Mass., 1970-76; Harry H. Power prof. engring. U. Tex., Austin, 1976-90; lectr. MIT, 1971-76; vis. scientist Weizmann Inst. Sci., 1972-73; Lady Davis prof. Technion, Haifa, Israel, 1983; Hunsaker vis. prof. aeros. and astronautics MIT, 1989-90. Recipient Hocott Disting. Engring. Rsch. award Coll. Engring., U. Tex., 1985, Exceptional Civil award USAF, 1991; Raytheon fellow, 1963-67. Fellow IEEE (bd. govs. Control Sys. Soc. 1982—, assoc. editor Transaction on Automatic Control), AIAA (Mechanics and Control of Flight award 1985, Dryden lectureship in rsch. 1995, assoc. editor Jour. Spacecraft and Rockets, Jour. Guidance and Control). Home: 11358 Chalon Rd Los Angeles CA 90049-1721 Office: UCLA Dept Mech Aerospace and Nuclear Engring Los Angeles CA 90024

SPEYRER, JUDE, bishop; b. Leonville, La., Apr. 14, 1929. Ed., St. Joseph Sem., Covington, La., Notre Dame Sem., New Orleans, Gregorian U., Rome. Ordained priest Roman Cath. Ch., 1953. Consecrated bishop Lake Charles, La., 1980—. Office: PO Box 3223 444 Iris St Lake Charles LA 70602*

SPEZIALE, A. JOHN, organic chemist, consultant; b. Rocky Hill, Conn., Nov. 3, 1916; s. Antonio and Giovina (DiMarco) S.; m. Dorothy Baumeister, May 2, 1942; children: Dona Speziale Luedde, Karen Speziale Hutcheson, Wendy Speziale Tarson. B.S. in Pharmacy, U. Conn., 1942, M.S., 1943; Ph.D., U. Ill., 1948. With Monsanto Co., St. Louis, 1948-79; sr. scientist agrl. div. Monsanto Co., 1960-63; dir. research Monsanto Agrl. Products Co., 1963-79; chem., agrl. and indsl. cons., 1979—; vis. lectr. Washington U., St. Louis, 1950-53; bd. dirs. Mycogen Corp., EOSystem, Inc. Author publs. Served with U.S. Army, 1944-46. Recipient Kenneth A. Spencer award, 1981. Mem. AAAS, Am. Chem. Soc. (chmn. com. organic div. 1974-76, mem. editorial bd. Jour. Organic Chemistry 1964-69, lectr. 1970-74, St. Louis sect. award 1973), Weed Sci. Soc. Am. (hon.), Sigma Xi. Patentee synthesis and mechanism action pesticides, phosphorus chemistry, enamines, epoxides, heterocyclics, haloamides. Home: 311 Northumberland Ave Redwood City CA 94061-3837

SPEZIALE, JOHN ALBERT, lawyer; b. Winsted, Conn., Nov. 21, 1922; s. Louis and Mary (Avampato) S.; m. Mary Kocsis, Aug. 12, 1944; children: John Albert, Marcia Jean. BA in Econs., Duke U., 1943, JD, 1947. Bar: Conn. 1948. Clk. Judiciary Com. of Conn. Gen. Assembly, 1949; judge Mcpl. Ct., Torrington, Conn., 1949-51; dir. CD, 1951-52; fed. atty. OPS, 1951-52; mem. Conn. State Jud. Council, 1955-59; sr. partner firm Speziale, Mettling, Lefebre & Burns, Torrington, 1958-61; city atty. Torrington, 1957-59; treas. State of Conn., 1959-61; judge Conn. Ct. Common Pleas, 1961-65, Conn. Superior Ct., 1965-77; presiding judge Conn. Superior Ct. (Appellate div.), 1975-77, chief judge, 1975-77, mem. exec. com., 1975-84, chmn. exec. com., 1977-81; justice Conn. Supreme Ct., 1977-81, chief ct. adminstr., 1978-81, chief justice, 1981-84; sr. ptnr. Cummings & Lockwood, Hartford, 1984-92; of counsel, 1992—; state trial referee Conn., 1986—; mem. exec. com. Nat. Conf. State Trial Judges, 1970-74; faculty advisor grad. session Nat. Coll. State Judiciary, U. Nev., 1973; mem. Conn. Jud. Rev. Coun., 1975-77; co-chmn. planning commn. criminal adminstrn. Conn. Justice Commn., 1975-78; mem. Conn. Commn. on Adult Probation, 1976-77, Adv. Coun. on Ct. Unification, 1976-78, Conn. Bd. Pardons, 1977-78; mem. exec. com. Nat. Bd. Trial Advocacy, 1983-88, dir. 1988—; mem. mediation com. Ctr. Pub. Resources, 1985—. chmn. State-Fed. Relations Com. Conf. of Chief Justices, 1983-84; chmn. adv. bd. Use of Vol. Lawyers to Supplement Jud. Resources, Nat. Inst. Justice and Nat. Ctr. for State Ctrs., 1983-87; mem. lawyers com. Nat. Ctr. for State Cts., 1985-88; chmn. subcom. jud. decisions Nat. Assn. Ins. Commrs. adv. Com. Environ. Liability Ins., 1985-87; mem. Panel of Trial and Appellate Judges, Asbestos Claims Facility, 1986—;l arbitrator Ins. Arbitration Forums, Inc., 1986—; others. Trustee Conn. Jr. Republic, 1975-83; bd. dirs. Newington Children's Hosp. 1983-86, corporator 1983—; chmn. awards com. Freedoms Found. at Valley Forge, 1982, trustee Nat. Council, 1986—; fellow Pvt. Adjudication Found. Duke U. Sch. Law, 1986—. Lt. (j.g.) USNR, 1942-46, PTO. Recipient Conn. Trial Lawyers Jud. award, 1977; 1st Unico Nat. Disting. Key award, 1977; Citizen of Yr. award Elks, 1982; Alva P. Loiselle lifetime achievement award, 1984; Disting. Service award Nat. Ctr. for State Cts., 1985; Significant Practical Achievement award Ctr. for Pub. Resources Legal Program, 1985; Conn. Law Rev. award, 1985. Fellow Am. Bar Found. (life), Conn. Bar Found. (charter); mem. ABA (vice-chmn. 1984-86, com. on stds. jud. adminstrn. jud. adminstrn. divsn.), Inst. Jud. Adminstrn., Am. Judicature Soc. (dir. 1978-82), Conn. Bar Assn. (com. on alternative dispute resolution 1985-87, com. on liaison with state cts. 1986-92), Hartford Bar Assn., Litchfield County Bar Assn., Supreme Ct. Hist. Soc., Am. Arbitration Assn. (comml. panel arbitrators 1987—, panelist large complex case program 1993—), Am. Fedn. Musicians (life), Sons of Italy of Am., Conn. State Srs. Golf Assn., Inc., Litchfield County Univ. Club, Torrington Country Club, Unico Club (life), Bear Lakes Country Club (Fla.), K.C., Phi Beta Kappa. Roman Catholic. Home: 278 Windtree Torrington CT 06790-7904 Office: Cummings & Lockwood City Place 1 Hartford CT 06103

SPEZZANO, VINCENT EDWARD, newspaper publisher; b. Retsof, N.Y., Apr. 3, 1926; s. Frank and Lucy S.; m. Marjorie Elliott, Dec. 18, 1948; children: Steve, Judy, Mark, Christine (dec.). BA in Journalism, Syracuse (N.Y.) U., 1950. Reporter Livingston Republican, Geneseo, N.Y., 1950-51, Lynchburg (Va.) News, 1951-54, St. Louis Globe-Democrat, 1954-55; polit. writer, then dir. public service and research Rochester (N.Y.) Times Union, 1955-68; dir. public service, then dir. promotion and public service Gannett Co., Inc., 1968-75; pres., publisher Cape Publs., Inc., Cocoa, Fla., 1975-84; chmn. Cape Publs., Inc., 1984-91; asst., then v.p. Gannett/South, Gannett Co., Inc., 1977-79; pres. Gannett Southeast Newspaper Group, Gannett Co., Inc., 1979-82; exec. v.p. USA Today, 1982-83, pres., 1983; sr. v.p. communications Gannett Co., 1983-84, bd. dirs.; pres., pub. Gannett Rochester Newspapers, 1984-90, chmn., 1990-91; pres. Gannett N.E. Div., 1984-86; past mem. journalism endowment adv. com. U. Fla.; bd. dirs. Marine Midland Bank. Editor handbook. Past trustee St. John Fisher Coll., Rochester; trustee Brevard Art Ctr. and Mus., Melbourne, Fla.; bd. dirs. Cape Canaveral Hosp., 1991—, Fla. Inst. Tech., 1991—, Astronauts Meml. Found., 1991—, vice-chmn., space camp adv. bd.; bd. vice-chmn. Rochester Conv. Bur., 1986-91; mem. Founder's Com. The Rochesterians, 1986—; mem. adv. bd. Space Pioneers, Inc. With A.C., USNR, 1944-46. Recipient News Ariting award Va. Press Assn., 1953, Citizen of Yr. award Citizens Club Rochester, 1960, Disting. Svc. award for non-members Kiwanis Club, 1960, Pub. Svc. Reporting award Am. Polit. Sci. Assn., 1963; named NE Kiwanis Citizen of Yr., 1987, Boss of Yr. Coca Beach chpt. Nat. Secretaries Assn., 1977, Rochester Communicator of Yr., 1987, Rochester Citizen of Yr., 1987, Cavaliere (Knight) in Order of Merit Republic of Italy, 1994. Mem. Internat. Newspaper Promotion Assn. (pres. 1970-71, Silver Shovel award 1975), Am. Newspapers Pubs. Assn., So. Newspaper Pubs. Assn. Found. (chmn.), Fla. Press Assn. (pres. 1984), N.Y. Newspaper Pubs. Assn. (bd. dirs.), Cocoa Beach Area C. of C., Rochester Area C. of C. (bd. dir. 1985—, chmn. bd. 1989-90). Roman Catholic. Home: 855 S Atlantic Ave Cocoa Beach FL 32931-2424 Office: 1 Gannett Plz Melbourne FL 32940 Office: Cape Pubs Inc PO Box 363000 Melbourne FL 32936

SPHAR, GAIL ELLEN, insurance company executive; b. LaPorte, Ind., Mar. 4, 1946; d. Edward R. and Dorothy Mae (Wallace) Trigg; 1 child. BS, U. S.C., 1966, MS, 1972; MBA, U. Ala.-Birmingham, 1984. Instr. U. S.C., Columbia, 1971-73; mgr. tng. and devel. Blue Cross and Blue Shield of S.C., 1973-76; dir. tng. and devel. Blue Cross & Blue Shield of Ala., 1976-79, mgr. dept. human resources, 1979-82, v.p. human resources 1983-87; v.p. administrn. and human resources Blue Cross & Blue Shield of Mo., 1987, sr. v.p. administrn. & corp. affairs, 1991-92, regional v.p., COO, 1993—. Childcare funding and fin. Childcare Task Force, United Way, Birmingham, 1983-84, bd. dirs., chmn. personnel com. Childcare Resources of Jefferson, Shelby and Walker counties, 1984-86, pres., 1987; v.p. membership, pres. FORUM, Birmingham, 1984; mem. adv. bd. Masters in Pub. and Pvt. Mgmt. program Birmingham So. Coll., 1985-87; vice-chmn. pers. com. Confluence St. Louis, 1988-89, chmn., 1990-93, bd. dirs., 1991-93, exec. com., 1992-93; mem. Vol. Svcs. St. Louis chpt. ARC, 1988-93; mem. partnership program com. St. Louis Art Mus., 1992; bd. dirs. The Caring Program Mo., 1988-93, Marshall Coll., 1993, 1st Unitarian Ch., 1991-93, NCCJ, St. Louis Region, 1992-93, Heart of Mo. Girl Scout Coun., 1994; chmn. workforce issues task force Gov. Commn. Mgmt. & Productivity, 1994; mem. adv. bd. St. Louis Regional Quality Inst., 1992-93. Mem. Am. Soc. Indsl. Mgmt. (bd. dirs. 1989-93, St. Louis chpt), Regional AIDS Interfaith Network (bd. dirs. 1993), Vis. Nurses Assn. Ctrl. Mo. (bd. dirs. 1994—); Birmingham C. of C. (bd. dirs. 1987). Avocations: reading, music, astronomy and astrophysics, volleyball. Office: Blue Cross-Blue Shield Mo 1000 W Nifong Columbia MO 65205

SPHAR, RAYMOND LESLIE, JR., physician, research administrator; b. Charleroi, Pa., July 27, 1934; s. Raymond Leslie and Alma Josephine (Massey) S.; m. Jean Frances Cusick, June 24, 1961 (div. 1976); 1 child, Christina Leslie. BS, Westminster Coll., 1956; MD, Jefferson Med. Coll., 1961; MPH, Yale U., 1972. Commd. lt. USN, 1961, advanced through grades to capt., 1975; resident in preventive medicine Yale U., New Haven, 1969-72; rsch. med. officer Naval Submarine Med. Rsch. Lab., Groton, Conn., 1972-73, comdg. officer, 1973-78; program mgr. med. rsch. Office of Naval Tech., 1978; dir. undersea and radiation medicine Bur. of Medicine and Surgery, Navy Dept., 1978-81; exec. officer Naval Med. Rsch. and Devel. Command, Bethesda, Md., 1981-83; comdg. officer Naval Med. Rsch. Inst., Bethesda, Md., 1983-86; asst. for med. life scis. rsch. Office of Sec. of Def., 1986-89; dir. R&D Bur. Medicine & Surgery, Washington, 1989-90; dir. med. rsch. svc. Dept. Vets. Affairs, Washington, 1991-92, dep. assoc. chief med. dir., 1992—; U.S. rep. to NATO panel, Brussels, 1986-89; DOD rep. Nat. Adv. Rsch. Resources Coun., NIH, 1986-89; VA rep. Nat Cancer Adv. Bd., NIH, 1991—. Fellow Coll. of Physicians of Phila.; mem. Am. Coll. Preventive Medicine, Am. Coll. Occupational and Environ. Medicine (master), Army and Navy Club, English-Speaking Union, Yale Club, Fgn. Svc. Club. Presbyterian. Home: 2475 Virginia Ave NW Washington DC 20037-2639 Office: Dept Vets Affairs 810 Vermont Ave NW Washington DC 20420-0002

SPHEERIS, PENELOPE, film director; b. New Orleans, 1945. MFA, UCLA Film Sch. Producer: TV series of shorts for Saturday Night Live; films include: The Decline of Western Civilization II: The Metal Years, 1988, Real Life, 1979; dir. (documentary) the Decline of Western Civilization, 1981, (films) Suburbia, 1984, (also screenwriter) The Boys Next Door, 1985, Hollywood Vice Squad, 1986, Dudes, 1987, Wayne's World, 1992, The Beverly Hillbillies, 1993, The Little Rascals, 1994; screenwriter: Summer Camp Nightmare, 1987; actress: Wedding Band, 1990; tv films directed include: Prison Stories: Women on the Inside, 1990. Office: The Gersh Agency Inc 232 N Canon Dr Beverly Hills CA 90210*

SPHIRE, RAYMOND DANIEL, anesthesiologist; b. Detroit, Feb. 12, 1927; s. Samuel Raymond and Nora Mae (Allen) S.; m. Joan Lois Baker, Sept. 5, 1953; children—Suzanne M., Raymond Daniel, Catherine J. BS, U. Detroit, 1948; MD, Loyola U., Chgo., 1952. Diplomate Am. Bd. Anesthesiology. Intern Grace Hosp., Detroit, 1952-53; resident Harvard Anesthesia Lab.-Mass. Gen. Hosp., 1953-55; attending anesthesiologist Grace Hosp., Detroit, 1955-72, dir. dept. inhalation therapy, 1968-70; sr. attending anesthesiologist, dir. dept., dir. dept. respiratory therapy Detroit-Macomb Hosps. Assn., 1970—, trustee, 1978—; chief of staff, 1980—; clin. asst. prof. Wayne State U. Sch. Medicine, 1967—; clin. prof. respiratory therapy Macomb Community Coll., Mount Clemens, Mich., 1971—; examiner Am. Registry Respiratory Therapists, 1972—; insp. Joint Rev. Com. Respiratory Therapy Edn., 1972—. Co-author: Operative Neurosurgery, 1970, First Aid Guide for the Small Business or Industry, 1978. With AUS, 1944-45; 1st lt. M.C., USAF, 1952. Fellow Am. Coll. Anesthesiologists, Am. Coll. Chest Physicians; mem. AMA, Am. Soc. Anesthesiologists, Wayne County Soc. Anesthesiologists (pres. 1967-69), Am. Assn. Respiratory Therapists, Soc. Critical Care Medicine, Detroit Athletic Club, Country Club of Detroit, Cumberland Club (Portland, Maine), Severance Lodge. Roman Catholic. Home: 373 Saint Clair Ave Grosse Pointe MI 48230-1501 Office: 119 Kercheval Ave Grosse Pointe MI 48236-3670

SPICER, ERIK JOHN, retired Canadian parliamentary librarian; b. Ottawa, Ont., Can., Apr. 9, 1926; s. Clifford and Violet (Gundersen) S.; m. Mary Helen Blair, July 4, 1953; children: Erika Anne, John Blair. B.A., U. Toronto, 1948, B.L.S., 1949, postgrad. in history, 1949-50; M.A.L.S., U. Mich., 1959. Circulation and reference librarian Ottawa Pub. Library, 1948-49, 50-53, U. Mich., 1953-54; dep. librarian Ottawa Pub. Library, 1954-60; parliamentary librarian Library of Parliament, 1960-94, parliamentary libr. emeritus, 1994—; Can. corr. Internat. Centre for Parliamentary Documentation, Inter-Parliamentary Union, 1966-94; also for parliamentary and adminstrv. libraries sect. Internat. Fedn. Library Assns., The Hague, 1962-94, mem. standing adv. com. spl. libraries sect., 1972-76, pres. parliamentary libraries sect., 1972—, mem. standing adv. com., com. on ofcl. publs., 1972-76; voting del. ann. congresses Can. Library Assn., 1966-72, Ont. Library Assn., 1973-75; observer Can. Govt. Library Com., 1971-94; ex-officio mem. Nat. Library Adv. Council, 1960-69, mem. bd., 1970-94; dir. UNESCO Workshop on Devel. Parliamentary Libraries, Nigeria, 1982. Trustee Ottawa Pub. Library Bd., 1970-73. Served with RCAF and RCIC, 1944-45. Decorated Can. Forces decoration; recipient Centennial medal, 1967; Queen's Jubilee medal, 1977; Can. 125 medal, 1993, Order of Can., 1995; Library Service fellow U. Mich., 1953-54; Can. Council fellow, 1959. Life mem. Can. Library Assn. (councillor 1964-67, alt. del. Can. Commn. on UNESCO 1972, pres. 1979-80), Ont. Hist. Soc.; mem. Can. Internat. Polit. Sci. Assn., Ont. Library Assn. (pres. 1962-63), Library Assn. Ottawa (pres. 1955-56), Royal Can. Mil. Inst. Toronto, Guards Assn., Hansard Soc., Commonwealth Parliamentary Assn. (hon. Can. br.), Can. Study of Parliament Group (sec. 1982-87), Cen. Investigative Journalism, Assn. Profl. Execs., Beta Phi Mu, Phi Kappa Phi. Club: Country (Aylmer). Home: 300 Queen Elizabeth Driveway #2A, Ottawa, ON Canada K1S 3M6

SPICER, HAROLD GLENN, chemical engineer; b. Cin., Aug. 4, 1960. BS in Chemistry, U. Dayton, 1983, BSChemE, 1983, MS, 1987. Rsch. assoc. U. Dayton, Ohio, 1982-84; mgr. R & D Isotec Inc., Dayton, 1983—. Office: Isotec Corp 3858 Benner Rd Miamisburg OH 45342-4304

SPICER, HOLT VANDERCOOK, speech and theater educator; b. Pasadena, Calif., Feb. 1, 1928; s. John Lovely and Dorothy Eleanor (Clause) S.; m. Marion Arel Gibson, Aug. 16, 1952; children: Mary Ellen, Susan Leah, Laura Alice, John Millard. B.A., U. Redlands, 1952, M.A., 1957; Ph.D., U. Okla.-Norman, 1964. Instr. speech and theatre Southwest Mo. State Coll., 1952-59, assoc. prof., 1959-64, prof., 1964—, head dept. speech and theatre, 1967-71, dean Sch. Arts and Humanities, 1971-85; chmn. Dist. 4 Nat. Debate Tournament Com., 1955, 58, 64, 68. Bd. dirs. Springfield Community Ctr., Mo., 1981—. Named Debate Coach of Decade U.S. Air Force Acad., 1965, Holt V. Spicer Debate Forum, 1988; recipient Alumni Achievement award in Speech and Debate U. Redlands, 1991; team won CEDA Nat. Debate championship, 1992. Mem. Speech Communication Assn., Am. Forensic Assn., AAUP. Episcopalian (vestryman 1981-85). Home: 2232 E Langston St Springfield MO 65804-2646 Office: SW Mo State U 901 S National Ave Springfield MO 65804-0027

SPICER, JOANEATH A., museum curator; b. Chgo., Mar. 16, 1943; d. Thomas William Spicer and Joneath (Hill) Hopkins. BA, Smith Coll., 1965; MA, Yale U., 1967, PhD, 1979. From lectr. to asst. prof. U. Toronto, Ont., Can., 1971-87; freelance cons., 1987-89; James A. Murnaghen curator Renaissance and Baroque art Walters Art Gallery, Balt., 1990—; cons. Spectrum, 1988-89. Mem. editorial adv. bd. U. Toronto Quar., 1982-86, Jour. Walters Art Gallery, 1990—; vol. editor, 1990; contbr. articles to profl. jours. Mentor Project RAISE, Balt., 1991—; active mayoral com. Balt.-üRotterdam Sister Cities, 1994—. Fullbright Rsch. fellow, 1968-70; Chester Dale fellow Nat. Gallery Art, 1970-72; grantee Humanities and Social Scis. Com. Can., 1985-86, Internat. Rsch. and Exchs. Bd., 1991; Exhibition Planning grantee Nat. Endowment for Arts, 1993-94. Mem. Renaissance Soc. Am., Am. Soc. for Study Ctrl. European Art (v.p. 1980-81), Coll. Art Assn. (Alfred Barr award com. 1993—), Historians Netherlands Art. Office: Walters Art Gallery 600 N Charles St Baltimore MD 21201

SPICER, JOHN AUSTIN, physicist; b. Rock Springs, W.Va., Sept. 25, 1930; s. Ernest Marvin and Ruth (Stevens) S.; m. Erika Gruendig, 1959; children: Cynthia, Michael, Marilynn. BS, U. Wyoming, 1956, MS, 1957; PhD, U. Freiburg, Germany, 1962. Mathematician Geotech. Corp., Laramie, Wyo., 1956-57; physicist Goodyear Aerospace Corp., Litchfield, Ariz., 1962-63; head engr. Aeroject Gen. Corp., Azusa, Calif., 1963-64; mathematical analyst North Am. Aviation Info. Systems Div., Downey, Calif., 1973-76; program mgr. Chrysler Space Systems Div., New Orleans, La., 1966-68; sr. research mathematician U. Dayton Research Inst., Ohio, 1968-70; ops. research analyst U. McCall Printing Corp. Systems Dept., Dayton, 1970-71; mathematical Systems Dyamics Br. AF Flight Dynamics La., 1971-72; physicist Radar and Microwave Tech. Br. Af Avionics lab., 1972-74, Analysis and Evaluation Br. AF Avionics Lab., 1974-89; physicist tech group, target recognition br. AF Avionics Lab., Dayton, Ohio, 1989—. Contbr. articles on neural networks, wavelets and fractal methodology to profl. jours. Achievements include inventing "exact stability," which gives a dead beat response, that is, always stable and controllable, and also reaches equilibrium in minimum time. Home: 4666 N St Rt 235 Conover OH 45317-9601 Office: WL/AARA Bldg 23 2010 5th St Wright Patterson AFB OH 45433-7001

SPICER, KEITH, federal official, journalist, educator; b. Toronto, Can., Mar. 6, 1934. BA Modern Langs. and Lit., U. Toronto, PhD Polit. Scis.; diploma French civilization, La Sorbonne, Paris; MA Internat. Rels. Inst. d'Etudes Politiques, U. Paris; HHD (hon.), York U., Ottawa U., Lauretian U. TV, radio host, interviewer, commentator Radio Can., Radio Québec, Can. Broadcasting Corp., TV Ont., TVA, CKVU, Radio-Can. Internat.; pres. Spicer Comm. Group Inc., Can., U.S. 1984-89; spl. asst. to Minister Justice, Can., 1970-77; 1st commr. Ofcl. Langs., Can.; chmn. Can. Radio-TV Comm. Commn., Can., 1989-90, 91—; editorial writer The Globe and Mail, Toronto; mag. columnist L'Actualité; prof. U. Ottawa, U. Toronto, Dartmouth Coll., New Hampshire, York U., U. B.C., Simon Fraser U. Author A Samaritan State, Cher péquiste...et néanmoins ami, The Winging It Logic System, Think on Your Feet; editor The Ottawa Citizen, 1985-89; contbr. articles to profl. jours. Mem. Order Can. (officer), Union Parlementaries of French Lang. (officer). Office: CRTC, Ottawa, ON Canada K1A 0N2

SPICER, S(AMUEL) GARY, lawyer, writer; b. Dickson, Tenn., Jan. 8, 1942; s. Clark and E. Maybelle (Hogin) S.; m. Katherine M. Stettner, May 12, 1972; children: Victoria, S. Gary Jr., Matthew, Katie, Mark David. BA, Adrian Coll., 1964; MBA, Wayne State U., 1965; JD, Detroit Coll. Law, 1969. Bar: Mich. 1969, Tenn. 1969. With pers. dept. GM Truck & Coach Detroit, 1964-66; with trust dept. Nat. Bank Detroit, 1966-69; acct. Price Waterhouse & Co., Detroit, 1969-71; pres. Law Firm of S. Gary Spicer,

Detroit, 1971—. Author: Surviving Success, 1990. Co-chmn. endowment com. Adrian (Mich.) Coll., 1980—; Don & Dolly Smith Found., Detroit, 1981—, Ernie Harwell Found.; adv. trustee Grosse Pointe (Mich.) Acad., 1983—; pres., trustee Twitty, Mislap, Sterban Found., Detroit, 1985—; mem. performing arts com. Detroit Pub. Schs.; trustee Detroit Tigers Players Home Clubhouse Scholarship Fund. With USAR, 1965-71; elder Ft. St. Presbyn. Ch. Recipient Young Alumni Achievement award Adrian Coll. Alumni Assn., 1987. Mem. Detroit Athletic Club, Country Club of Detroit. Avocations: Russian literature, squash, fitness running.

SPICER, WILLIAM EDWARD, III, physicist, educator; b. Baton Rouge, Sept. 7, 1929; s. William Edward II and Kate Crystal (Watkins) S.; m. Cynthia Stanley, June 12, 1951 (div. 1969); children: William Edward IV, Sally Ann; m. Diane Lubarsky, Apr. 24, 1969; 1 dau., Jacqueline Kate. B.S., Coll. William and Mary, 1949, MIT, 1951; M.A., U. Mo., 1953, Ph.D, 1955; D.Tech. (hon.), U. Linköping, Sweden, 1975. Scientist RCA Labs, 1955-61, Lawrence Radiation Lab., U. Calif.-Livermore, 1961-62; mem. faculty Stanford U., 1962—, prof. elec. engring. and materials sci. engring., 1965—, prof. by courtesy applied physics, 1976—, Stanford Aschermann prof. engring., 1978—, prof. Stanford Synchrotron Radiation Lab, 1992—; dir. Acad. Skills, Inc., Los Altos, Calif., 1971-73; dep. dir. Stanford Synchrotron Radiation Lab., 1973-75, cons. dir., 1975—, prof., 1992—; cons. to govt. and industry, 1962—; mem. solid state scis. panel Nat. Acad. Sci.-NRC, 1965-73; cons., lectr. Chinese univ. devel. project World Bank-Fudan U., 1983; mem. panel atomic and molecular physics div. Nat. Bur. Standards, 1966-73, chmn., 1971-73; mem. adv. group election devices Dept. Def., 1975-82; fellow Churchill Coll., Cambridge U., Eng., 1979; mem. panel Japanese tech. evaluation program U.S. Dept. Commerce and NSF, 1983-84; acting dir. Stanford Photon. Lab., 1987-99; chmn. affiliated faculty Stanford Syncrotron Radiation Lab., 1988—. Mem. editorial bd. Jour. Crystal Growth, 1981-85; author publs. theory and experiment solid state and surface physics and chemistry, photoemission, optical properties solids, electronic structure metals, semiconductors, insulators, high temperature superconductors. Bd. dirs. Princeton (N.J.) YMCA, 1960-62. Recipient Achievement award RCA, 1957, 60, mentor award Nat. Conf. Black Phys. Students, 1992; named Scientist of Yr., Indsl. Research and Devel. mag., 1981; Guggenheim fellow, 1978-79. Fellow IEEE, Am. Phys. Soc. (Oliver Buckley Solid State Physics prize 1980); mem. Am. Vacuum Soc. (chmn. electronics material div. 1978-79, dir. 1978-80, trustee 1981-82, Medard W. Welch award 1984), Phi Beta Kappa. Home: 785 Mayfield Ave Palo Alto CA 94305-1043 Office: Stanford U Mccullough Bldg Stanford CA 94305

SPICKLER, ROBERT, performing arts executive; b. Montreal, Canada, 1945. BA, U. Montreal, 1971, MLitt, 1972. Co-dir., adminstrv. dir. Théâtre d'Aujourd'hui, 1970-79; prof. theatre, 1970-78; sec. gen. CEGEP Edourd-Montpetit, Longueuil, 1979-82; dir. theatre section Can. Coun., Ottawa, 1982-85; adminstrv. dir. Théâtre du Nouveau-Monde, Montreal, 1985-87; assoc. dir., dir. Arts Divsn. Can. Coun., 1987-88; rep. govt. Can. Internat. Conf. Industrialized Countries on Cultural Policy, Tokyo; guest speaker Internat. Colloquium of French Speaking Countries. Office: Orchestre Symphonique de Montreal, 85 Ste-Catherine W Ste 900, Montreal, PQ Canada H2X 3P4

SPIEGEL, ARTHUR HENRY, III, managing director, president; b. Chgo., June 25, 1939; s. Arthur Henry II and Eleanor F. Spiegel; children: Julia M., Adam H.; m. L. Pollock; 1 child. Samuel. BA, Stanford U., 1965; MBA, Harvard U., 1967. Assoc. dir. ACCION, Venezuela, 1959-61; assoc. adminstr. N.Y.C. Housing and Devel. Adminstrn., 1967-70; dep. adminstr. N.Y.C. HRA, 1970-74; chief oper. officer for Medicaid Dept. Social Svcs. and Child Welfare, N.Y.C., 1970-74; exec. dir. Dept. Social Svcs., N.Y.C., 1970-74; pres. founder APM, Inc., N.Y.C., 1974—; bd. dirs., treas. Nat. Ctr. for Health Edn., N.Y.C., 1988—. Bd. dirs., past pres. Greater N.Y. chpt. March of Dimes, 1985—. Mem. Harvard Club, N.Y. Athletic Club. Office: APM Inc 1675 Broadway 18th Fl New York NY 10019

SPIEGEL, DANIEL L., diplomat; b. Balt., Sept. 5, 1945; s. William and Anna (Stiffman) S.; m. Marianne Albertson; 1 child, Anna. AB, Washington U., St. Louis, 1967; MPA, Harvard U., 1969; JD, Georgetown U., Washington, 1979. Legis. asst. U.S. Senate, Washington, 1969-76; spl. asst. to Sec. of State Dept. of State, Washington, 1977-78, mem. policy planning staff, 1978-79; ptnr. Akin, Gump, Strauss, Hauer, LLP, Washington, 1983-90, dir. internat. practice, 1991-93; sr. advisor Clinton-Gore transition Dept. of State, Washington, 1992-93; amb., permanent rep. U.s. Mission to UN, Geneva, 1993—. Home: US Mission to UN, Rt de Pregny 11, 1292 Chambesy-Geneva Switzerland

SPIEGEL, EDWARD A., astrophysicist, fluid dynamicist, educator; b. Simon and Gertrude Spiegel; m. Barbara Cohen, July 7, 1962. B.A., UCLA, 1952; M.A., U. Mich., 1954, M.S., 1956, Ph.D., 1958. Instr., asst. prof. astronomy U. Calif.-Berkeley, 1958-60; Peyton fellow Princeton U., N.J., 1959-60; research scientist, sr. research scientist Courant Inst. NYU, N.Y.C., 1960-65; assoc. prof. physics Courant Inst. NYU, 1965-67, prof. physics, 1965-69; prof. astronomy Columbia U., N.Y.C., 1969-80; Rutherford prof. astronomy Columbia U., 1980—; cons. NASA, 1962-68, NATO, 1965-67, ICASE, 1985—; assoc. in astrophysics Woods Hole Oceanographic Instn., 1960-72; vis. prof. math. U. Chgo. 1989. Editor: (with J.P. Zahn) Problems of Stellar Convection, 1977, (with R. Buchler and J. Perdeng) Chaotic Behavior in Astrophysics, 1985; contbr. articles to profl. jours. Hon. trustee Chaim Gross Found. NSF sr. postdoctoral fellow, 1966-67; Guggenheim fellow, 1974-75; Fulbright fellow, 1986-87. Fellow Royal Astronom. Soc.; mem. Internat. Astronom. Union, Am. Phys. Soc., N.Y. Acad. Scis., Am. Inst. Mechanics, Phi Beta Kappa. Clubs: Confreries des Chevaliers de Tastevins. Office: Columbia U Dept Astronomy New York NY 10027

SPIEGEL, EVELYN SCLUFER, biology educator, researcher; b. Phila., Mar. 20, 1924; d. George and Helen (Lauranos) Sclufer; m. Melvin Spiegel, Apr. 16, 1955; children: Judith Ellen, Rebecca Ann. BA, Temple U., 1947; MA, Bryn Mawr Coll., 1951; PhD, U. Pa., 1954. Asst. program dir. for regulatory biology NSF, Washington, 1954-55; instr. in biology Colby Coll., Waterville, Maine, 1955-59; rsch. assoc. Dartmouth Coll., Hanover, N.H., 1961-74, rsch. assoc. prof. biology, 1974-78, rsch. prof. biology, 1978-91; rsch. prof. biology emerita, 1991—; vis. scholar Calif. Inst. Tech., Pasadena, 1964-65, U. Calif.-San Diego, La Jolla, 1970, Nat. Inst. for Med. Rsch., Mill Hill, Eng., 1971, NIH, Washington, 1975-76, U. Basel (Switzerland) Bi-ocenter, 1979, 80, 81, 82, 85. Contbr. numerous articles to profl. jours., chpts. to books and book reviews. Mem. Soc. for Devel. Biology, Marine Biol. Lab. Corp. (trustee 1981-86, 88-92). Office: Dartmouth Coll Dept Biol Scis Hanover NH 03755

SPIEGEL, FRANCIS HERMAN, JR., pharmaceutical company executive; b. Bethlehem, Pa., Apr. 25, 1935; s. Francis H. and Elizabeth (Redding) S.; m. Nancy Starner; children: Todd, Tadd, Thomas. B.A. in Acctg., Lehigh U., 1957. C.P.A., Pa. Account analyst Merck & Co., Inc., Rahway, N.J., 1966, mgr. internal auditing, 1967-70, dir. acctg., 1970-72, asst. controller, 1972-76, controller, 1976-79, treas., 1979-81, v.p. corp. planning, 1981-82; v.p. planning and devel. Merck & Co., Inc., 1983-84, v.p. fin., 1985-87, sr. v.p., 1987—, exec. v.p., 1992—; bd. dirs. Arkwright Ins. Co. Chmn. vis. com. Lehigh U., Bethlehem, Pa., 1980-83, now trustee; trustee Fin. Execs. Rsch. Found. Served to capt. USMC, 1958-61. Mem. AICPA, Fin. Execs. Inst., Conf. Bd. Coun. Fin. Execs. Office: Merck & Co Inc 1 Merck Dr PO Box 100 Whitehouse Station NJ 08889

SPIEGEL, HART HUNTER, retired lawyer; b. Safford, Ariz, Aug. 30, 1918; s. Jacob B. and Margaret (Hunter) S.; m. Genevieve Willson, Feb. 12, 1946; children: John Willson, Claire Margaret Spiegel Brian, Jennifer Emily Spiegel Grellman. BA, Yale U., 1940, LLB, 1946. Bar: Calif. 1946, D.C. 1960. Assoc. Brobeck, Phleger & Harrison, San Francisco, 1947-55, ptnr., 1955-90; chief counsel IRS, Washington, 1959-61, mem. adv. group to commr., 1975. Served to lt. USMC, 1942-46, PTO. Fellow Am. Bar Found.; mem. Am. Law Inst., ABA (council mem. tax sect. 1966-68), Bar Assn. San Francisco (pres. 1983). Clubs: Pacific Union (San Francisco) Berkeley Tennis (pres. 1964-65). Home: 3647 Washington St San Francisco CA 94118-1832 Office: Brobeck Phleger & Harrison 1 Market Pla Spear St Tower San Francisco CA 94105

SPIEGEL, HERBERT, psychiatrist, educator; b. McKeesport, Pa., June 29, 1914; s. Samuel and Lena (Mendlowitz) S.; m. Natalie Shainess, Apr. 24, 1944 (div. Apr. 1965); children: David, Ann; m. Marcia Greenleaf, Jan. 29, 1989. B.S., U. Md., 1936, M.D., 1939. Diplomate: Am. Bd. Psychiatry. Intern St. Francis Hosp., Pitts., 1939-40; resident in psychiatry St. Elizabeth's Hosp., Washington, 1940-42; practice medicine specializing in psychiatry N.Y.C., 1946—; attending psychiatrist Columbia-Presbyn. Hosp., N.Y.C., 1960—; faculty psychiatry Columbia U. Coll. Physicians and Surgeons, 1960—; adj. prof. psychology John Jay Coll. Criminal Justice, CUNY, 1983—; mem. faculty Sch. Mil. Neuropsychiatry, Mason Gen. Hosp., Brentwood, N.Y., 1944-46. Author: (with A. Kardiner) War Stress and Neurotic Illness, 1947, (with D. Spiegel) Trance and Treatment: Clinical Uses of Hypnosis, 1978; subject of book: (by Donald S. Connery) The Inner Source: Exploring Hypnosis with Herbert Spiegel, M.D.; Mem. editorial bd.: Preventive Medicine, 1972; Contbr. articles to profl. jours. Mem. profl. advisory com. Am. Health Found.; mem. pub. edn. com., smoking and health com. N.Y.C. div. Am. Cancer Soc.; mem. adv. com. Nat. Aid to Visually Handicapped. Served with M.C. AUS, 1942-46. Decorated Purple Heart. Fellow Am. Psychiat. Assn., Am. Coll. Psychiatrists, Am. Soc. Clin. Hypnosis, Am. Acad. Psychoanalysis, Internat. Soc. Clin. and Exptl. Hypnosis, William A. White Psychoanalytic Soc., N.Y. Acad. Medicine, N.Y. Acad. Scis.; mem. Am. Orthopsychiat. Assn., Am. Psychosomatic Soc., AAAS, AMA, N.Y. County Med. Soc. Office: 19 E 88th St New York NY 10128-0500

SPIEGEL, JOHN WILLIAM, banker; b. Indpls., Mar. 14, 1941; s. William Sordon and Elizabeth (Hall) S.; children: W. Robert, John F., Bradley H.; m. Elizabeth Devereux Morgan, Aug. 16, 1986; stepchildren: David P. Adams III, Morgan G. Adams, E. Devereux Adams. BA, Wabash Coll., 1963; MBA, Emory U., 1965; postgrad., Nova U., 1993-95. Rsch. assoc. IMEDE (Mgmt. Inst.), Lausanne, Switzerland, 1965-66; mgmt. trainee Trust Co. Bank, Atlanta, 1966-67, bond portfolio mgr., 1967-72; data processing mgr. Trust Co. Ga., Atlanta, 1972-78, treas., 1978-85; exec. v.p., chief fin. officer SunTrust Banks Inc., Atlanta, 1985—; mem. Emory U. Bd. Visitors, 1991—; bd. dirs. Rock Tenn. Co., Sallie Mae; former mem. taxation and payment systems com. ABA; former instr. Morehouse Coll. and Banking Schs.; mem. exec. com. CFO divsn. ABA, 1987-90, chair, 1989-90. Mem. exec. com., bd. dirs. Alliance Theatre, Atlanta, 1985-92, pres., 1989-91; bd. dirs. High Mus. Art, Atlanta, 1985—; pres. Young Audiences Atlanta Inc., 1981-84, bd. dirs., 1985, mem. adv. bd., 1986—; pres. bd. visitors Grady Meml. Hosp., Atlanta, 1983-90; v.p. exec. bd. Atlanta Area coun. Boy Scouts Am., 1983-92, treas., 1989-91, mem. adv. bd., 1992; mem. adv. coun. Ga. State U. Sch. Accountancy, 1981-85, chmn. curriculum subcom., 1983-84; mem. exec. com., trustee Morehouse Sch. Medicine, 1984-93, chmn. fin. com., 1987-90, chmn., 1990-92; mem. Leadership Atlanta, 1976—, trustee, 1990-94; trustee, mem. exe. com. Robert W. Woodruff Arts Ctr. Inc., 1976—, treas., 1976-83, chmn. fin. com., 1984-89, 93—; chmn. fin. com., bd. dirs. Schenck Sch., Atlanta, 1986-88; exec. vice chmn. bd. trustees Holy Innocents Episcopal Sch., Atlanta, 1976-79, bd. dirs., treas., 1987-90; bd. dirs. Atlanta Opera, 1986—, United Way Met. Atlanta, Inc., 1994—. Mem. Bank Adminstrn. Inst. (chmn. ops. and tech. com. 1987-89, bd. dirs. 1988-92, banking svcs. steering com. 1985—), Fin. Execs. Inst., Atlanta C. of C. (pub. affairs coordinating com. 1984-87, aviation task force 1992-93), Emory U. Bus. Sch. Alumni Assn. (bd. dirs. 1985-92, pres. 1989-92), Cherokee Town and Country Club (Atlanta). Episcopalian. Home: 3043 Nancy Creek Rd NW Atlanta GA 30327-1901 Office: SunTrust Banks Inc PO Box 4418 Atlanta GA 30302-4418

SPIEGEL, LAWRENCE HOWARD, advertising executive; b. N.Y.C., Oct. 9, 1942; s. Melvin Arthur and Rose (Black) S.; m. Christy Mansfield; children from previous marriage: Robert, David. BA, NYU, 1963. Print buyer William Esty Co., N.Y.C., 1964-65, broadcast buyer, 1965-66; media planner Batten, Barton, Durstine & Osborn, Inc., N.Y.C., 1966-67, media supr., 1967-68, assoc. media dir., 1969-72, v.p., 1972-74; media group head Jack Tinker & Ptnrs., N.Y.C., 1968-69; v.p. Tracy-Locke, Dallas, 1974-80, sr. v.p., 1980-84, exec. v.p., 1984-89; prin. The Richards Group, Dallas, 1989—; Richards/Spiegel Value Added, Dallas, 1994—; pres. Tex. Coun. Advt., 1991—. Guest editor Mktg. and Media Decision mag., June 1982. Mem. Dallas Cable Bd., 1983-86; chmn. mktg. com. U. Tex., Dallas, 1984-89; pres. Cable Access Dallas, Inc., 1985-86; trustee Dallas Symphony Assn., 1978—; bd. dirs. Equest Inc., 1991-92; bd. dirs. I Have a Dream Found., 1994—. Mem. Assn. Broadcasting Execs. Tex. (pres. 1975-76), Am. Women in Radio and TV, Inc. (bd. dirs. 1992-93). Republican. Avocations: skiing, sailing. Office: The Richards Group 10000 N Central Expwy Ste 1200 Dallas TX 75231-4104

SPIEGEL, MARILYN HARRIET, real estate executive; b. Bklyn., Apr. 3, 1935; d. Harry and Sadie (Oscher) Unger; m. Murray Spiegel, June 12, 1954; children: Eric Lawrence, Dana Cheryl, Jay Barry. Grad. high sch., Bklyn. Exec. sec. S & W Paper Co., N.Y.C., 1953-54, Japan Paper Co., N.Y.C., 1954-58; salesperson Red Carpet Realtors, Los Alamitos, Calif., 1974-75, Coll. Park Realtors, Garden Grove, Calif., 1975-79; owner, broker S & S Properties, Los Alamitos, Calif., 1979—. Named Realtor of Yr., 1989. Mem. Calif. Assn. Realtors (bd. dirs. 1984—), West Orange County Bd. Realtors (bd. dirs. 1984—, 1st v.p. 1987, pres. 1988), Million Dollar Sales Club, Long Beach C. of C., Seal Beach C. of C., Orange County C. of C., Summit Orgn., Toastmasters (pres. founders group Garden Grove, Calif. 1990). Home: 4765 Candleberry Ave Seal Beach CA 90740-3035 Office: S & S Properties 3502 Katella Ave Ste 208 Los Alamitos CA 90720-3115

SPIEGEL, MELVIN, retired biology educator; b. N.Y.C., Dec. 10, 1925; s. Philip Edward and Sadie (Friedman) S.; m. Evelyn Sclufer, Apr. 16, 1955; children: Judith Ellen, Rebecca Ann. B.S., U. Ill., 1948; Ph.D., U. Rochester, 1952; M.A. (hon.), Dartmouth Coll., 1967. Research fellow U. Rochester, 1952-53, Calif. Inst. Tech., 1953-55, 64-65; asst. prof. Colby Coll., 1955-59; mem. faculty Dartmouth Coll., Hanover, N.H., 1959—, prof. biology, 1966-93; prof. emeritus Dartmouth Coll, Hanover, N.H.; chmn. dept. biol. scis. Dartmouth Coll., Hanover, N.H., 1972-74; summer investigator Marine Biol. Lab., Woods Hole, Mass., 1954—; sr. research biologist U. Calif.-San Diego, 1970-71; vis. prof. biochemistry Nat. Inst. Med. Research, Mill Hill, London, 1971; vis. prof. Biocenter, U. Basel, 1979-82, 85; Wilson Meml. lectr. U. N.C., 1975; program dir. developmental biology NSF, 1975-76; mem. cell biology study sect. NIH, 1966-70. Editorial bd.: Biol. Bull., 1966-70, 71-75, Cell Differentiation, 1979-88 ; contbr. articles to profl. jours. Trustee Marine Biol. Lab. Corp.; mem. exec. com., trustee Marine Biol. Lab. 1976-80. Served with AUS, 1943-46, ETO. Decorated Purple Heart with 2 oak leaf clusters, Combat Inf. badge. Fellow AAAS; mem. Am. Soc. Cell Biology, Am. Soc. Devel. Biology, Internat. Soc. Devel. Biologists (sec.-treas. 1977-81, bd. dirs. 1981-85). Home: 15 Barrymore Rd Hanover NH 03755-2401

SPIEGEL, S. ARTHUR, federal judge; b. Cin., Oct. 24, 1920; s. Arthur Major and Hazel (Wise) S.; m. Louise Wachman, Oct. 31, 1945; children: Thomas, Arthur Major, Andrew, Roger Daniel. B.A. in Econs., U. Cin., 1942, postgrad., 1949; LL.B., Harvard U., 1948. Assoc. Kasfir & Chalfie, Cin., 1948-52; assoc. Benedict, Bartlett & Shepard, Cin., 1952-53, Gould & Gould, Cin., 1953-54; ptnr. Gould & Spiegel, Cin., 1954-59; assoc. Cohen, Baron, Druffel & Hogan, Cin., 1960; ptnr. Cohen, Todd, Kite & Spiegel, Cin., 1961-80; judge U.S. Dist Ct. Ohio, Cin., 1980—. Served to capt. USMC 1942-46. Mem. ABA, Ohio Bar Assn., Cin. Bar Assn., Fed. Bar Assn., Cin. Lawyers Club. Democrat. Jewish. Office: US Dist Ct 832 US Courthouse 5th Walnut St Cincinnati OH 45202

SPIEGELMAN, ART, author, cartoonist; b. Stockholm, Feb. 15, 1948; s. Wladek and Andzia (Zylberberg) S.; m. Francoise Mouly, July 12, 1977; children: Nadja, Dashiell. Student, Harpur Coll. (now SUNY), Binghamton, N.Y. Creative cons., artist, designer, editor, writer Topps Chewing Gum, Inc., Bklyn., 1966-88; editor Douglas Comix, 1972; contbg. editor Arcade, the Comics Revue, 1975-76; founding editor Raw, 1980—; artist, contbg. editor New Yorker, 1992—; instr. San Francisco Acad. Art, 1974-75, N.Y. Sch. Visual Arts, 1979-87. Author, illustrator: The Complete Mr. Infinity, 1970, The Viper Vicar of Vice, Villainy, and Vickedness, 1972, Ace Hole, Midge Detective, 1974, The Language of Comics, 1974, Breakdowns: From Maus to Now: An Anthology of Strips, 1977, Work and Turn, 1979, Every Day Has Its Dog, 1979, Two-Fisted Painters Action Adventure, 1980, Maus: A Survivor's Tale, 1986 (Joel M. Cavior award for

Jewish Writing 1986, Nat. Book Critics Cir. nomination 1986, Pulitzer prize 1992), Maus, Part Two, 1992 (Nat. Book Critics Cir. nomination 1992, Pulitzer prize 1992), The Wild Party, 1994, (with F. Mouly) Read Yourself Raw, 1987; contbr. The Apex Treasury of Underground Comics, 1974; compiling editor (with B. Schneider) Whole Grains: A Book of Quotations, 1972; exhbns. include N.Y. Cultural Ctr., Inst. Contemporary Art, London, Seibu Gallery, Tokyo, Mus. Modern Art, N.Y.C., 1991, Galerie St. Etienne, N.Y.C., 1992, Ft. Lauderdale Mus. Art, 1993; creator Wacky Packages, Garbage Pail Kids and other novelties; contbr. to numerous underground comics. Recipient Playboy Editorial award for best comic strip, 1982, Yellow Kid award for best comic strip author, 1982, Regional Design award Print mag., 1983, 84, 85, Inkpot award San Diego Comics Conv., 1987, Stripschappening award for best fgn. comics album, 1987, Alpha Art award Angoulenne, France, 1993. Office: Raw Books & Graphics 27 Greene St New York NY 10013-2537 Office: care Wylie Aitken & Stone 250 W 57th St Ste 2106 New York NY 10107-0001

SPIEKERMAN, JAMES FREDERICK, lawyer; b. The Dalles, Oreg., Feb. 13, 1933; s. Oscar Frederick and Anne (Hesketh) S.; m. Rosalind Lee Somers, Dec. 27, 1962; children: Tim, Cynthia, Peter. BS, U. Oreg., 1955, LLB, 1961. Bar: Oreg. 1961. Law clk. U.S. Fed. Dist. Ct., Portland, Oreg., 1961-62; assoc., then ptnr. and sr. ptnr. Schwabe, Williamson & Wyatt, Portland, 1962—. Capt. USAF, 1956-58. Mem. ABA, Oreg. State Bar (bd. govs. 1988-91, v.p. 1989-90), Multnomah Bar Assn. (pres. 1973), Oregon Assn. of Def. Counsel (pres. 1982), Fed. Ins. and Corp. Counsel, City Club of Portland, Multnomah Athletic Club (Portland). Republican. Episcopalian. Avocations: fly fishing, tennis. Office: Schwabe Williamson & Wyatt 1211 SW 5th Ave Portland OR 97204-3713

SPIELBERG, STEVEN, motion picture director, producer; b. Cin., Dec. 18, 1947; m. Amy Irving, Nov. 27, 1985 (div.); 2 children: Max Samuel, Sasha; m. Kate Capshaw; 1 dau. Ba, Calif. State Coll., Long Beach; Hon. Doctorate in Creative Arts, Brandeis U., 1986. founder Amblin Entertainment (Universal Studios), Dreamworks SKG (with Jeffrey Katzenberg and David Geffen); directed segments of TV series Columbo; dir. TV movies Night Gallery, 1969, Duel, 1971, Savage, 1972, Something Evil, 1972; exec prodr. series: Steven Spielberg's Amazing Stories, Tiny Toon Adventures, Family Dog, seaQuest DSV; films include (dir.): The Sugarland Express, 1974 (also story), Jaws, 1975, Close Encounters of the Third Kind, 1977 (also co-writer), 1941, 1979, Raiders of the Lost Ark, 1981, Indiana Jones and the Temple of Doom, 1984, Indiana Jones and the Last Crusade, 1989, Hook, 1991, Jurassic Park, 1993; (dir., prodr.): E.T. The Extra-Terrestrial, 1982, The Color Purple, 1985, Empire of the Sun, 1987, Always, 1989, Schindler's List, 1993 (Best Drama & Best Dir. Golden Globe awards, Best Picture & Best Dir. Academy awards); (dir., exec. prodr.): Twilight Zone: The Movie, 1983; (prodr.): Poltergeist, 1982 (also co-writer), An American Tail: Fievel Goes West, 1991, Casper, 1995; (exec. prodr.): I Wanna Hold Your Hand, 1978, Used Cars, 1980, Continental Divide, 1981, Gremlins, 1984, The Goonies, 1985, Back to the Future, 1985, Young Sherlock Holmes, 1985, The Money Pit, 1986, An American Tail, 1986, Innerspace, 1987, Batteries not included, 1987, Who Framed Roger Rabbit?, 1988, The Land Before Time, 1988, Dad, 1989, Back to the Future Part II, 1989, Joe Verses the Volcano, 1990, Back to the Future Part III, 1990, Gremlins 2: The New Batch, 1990, Arachnophobia, 1990, Cape Fear, 1991, We're Back!: A Dinosaur's Story, 1993, The Flintstones, 1994, The Little Rascals, 1994; (actor): The Blues Brothers, 1980. Recipient Hasty Pudding Man of Yr. award, 1983; Outstanding Directorial Achievement award for feature films Dirs. Guild Am., 1985; film award Brit. Acad. Film and TV Arts, 1986; Irving Thalberg Mem. award Acad. Motion Picture Arts & Scis., 1987; Golden Lion award for Career Achievement, Venice Film Festival, 1993; Amer. Film Inst. Life Achievement Awd., 1995. Fellow Brit. Acad. Film and TV Arts. Won film contest with 40-minute war movie, Escape to Nowhere, at age 13; made film Firelight at age 16, and made 5 films while in coll.; became TV dir. at Universal Pictures at age 20. Office: CAA 9830 Wilshire Blvd Beverly Hills CA 90212-1804*

SPIELMAN, CHRIS, professional football player; b. Canton, Ohio, Oct. 11, 1965. Student, Ohio State U. With Detroit Lions, 1988—. Recipient Lombardi award, 1987; named to Sporting News Coll. All-Am. team, 1986, 87, Pro Bowl team, 1989-91. Office: Detroit Lions 1200 Featherstone Rd Pontiac MI 48342*

SPIELMAN, JOHN PHILIP, JR., historian, educator; b. Anaconda, Mont., June 16, 1930; s. John Philip and Lewanna (Coleman) S.; m. Danila B. Cole, Sept. 14, 1955. BA, U. Mont., 1951; MA, U. Wis., 1953, PhD, 1957; m. Danila B. Cole, Sept. 14, 1955. Instr., U. Mich., Ann Arbor, 1957-59; asst. prof. history Haverford (Pa.) Coll., 1959-65, assoc. prof., 1965-70, prof., 1970-85, Audrey Dusseau meml. prof. humanities, 1985—, dean, 1966-68. Served with U.S. Army, 1953-55. Mem. Am. Hist. Assn., Soc. French Hist. Studies, Soc. Austrian and Habsburg Historians. Author: Leopold I of Austria, 1977, The City and the Crown, 1993; co-author 2 textbooks; translator: Simplicissimus (Grimmelshausen), 1981. Home: 749 Millbrook Ln Haverford PA 19041-1210 Office: Haverford Coll 370 Lancaster Ave Haverford PA 19041-1392

SPIELVOGEL, CARL, international marketing executive; b. N.Y.C., Dec. 27, 1928; s. Joseph and Sadie (Tellerman) S.; m. Barbaralee Diamonstein, Oct. 27, 1981; children: David Joseph, Rachel Fay, Paul Abram. BBA, CUNY, 1956, LLD (hon.), 1984. Reporter, columnist N.Y. Times, 1950-60; with McCann-Erickson, Inc., Interpublic Group of Cos., Inc., N.Y.C., 1960-74; vice chmn., chmn. exec. com., dir. Interpublic Group of Cos., Inc., 1974-80; chmn., chief exec. officer Backer & Spielvogel, Inc., 1980-87; chief exec. officer, chmn. bd. dirs. Backer Spielvogel Bates Worldwide, Inc., N.Y.C. 1987-94; chmn. United Auto Group, 1994—; dir. Manhattan Industries, Franklin Corp.; bd. dirs. Hasbro, Inc. Chmn. Com. in the Public Interest, 1975-79, Tri-State United Way, 1984; pres. bd. trustees Baruch Coll. Fund, 1979; mem. Bus. Com. Arts; bd. dirs., mem. exec. com. Mt. Sinai Hosp., N.Y.C.; bd. dirs. N.Y. Council Humanities, N.Y. Philharmonic, 1987—, The Asia Soc., 1989—; bd. trustees The Lincoln Ctr. for the Performing Arts, 1987—; chmn. The Mayor's Com. for Pub.-Pvt. Partnerships; exec. com. Bus. Mktg. Corp., N.Y.C.; chmn. com. div. WNET-Public Broadcasting; bd. trustees, mem. exec. com., chmn. bus. com. Met-Mus. Art.; mem. internat. adv. bd. Bus. Coun. United Nations. With U.S. Army, 1953-55. Recipient Human Relations award Anti-Defamation League, 1972, Achievement award Sch. Bus. Alumni, CCNY, 1972, Citizens Union award, 1980, Disting. Alumni award for Outstanding Career Accomplishment Baruch Coll., 1990; named Marketer of Yr. N.Y. chpt. Am. Mktg. Assn., 1982, Outstanding Exec. Crain's N.Y. Bus., 1987. Mem. Mcpl. Art Soc. Clubs: Princeton (N.Y.C.), Yale. Office: Backer Spielvogel Bates Worldwide Inc Chrysler Bldg 405 Lexington Ave New York NY 10174-0002

SPIELVOGEL, SIDNEY MEYER, investment banker; b. N.Y.C., July 14, 1925; s. Hyman and Rae (Mandel) S.; m. Beverly Anne Gold, Dec. 18, 1960; 1 son, Peter James. B.S.S., CCNY, 1944; A.M., Harvard U., 1946, M.B.A. 1949. Economist Treasury Dept., Washington, 1946-47; assoc. dept. mgr. Alexander's Dept. Stores, 1949-53; asst. to mdse. mgr., dept. mgr. Bloomingdale's Dept. Store, 1953-56; with Prudential-Bache Securities Inc., 1956-88, 1st v.p., 1971-75, sr. v.p., 1975-86, sr. v.p., 1986-88; dir. MoneyMart Assets Inc., pres., 1981-87; lectr. Hunter Coll., N.Y.C., 1963-68. Bd. dirs. Emanu-el Midtown YM-YWHA, N.Y.C., 1975-91; mem. Harvard Grad. Soc. Coun., 1983-88, 89-92, 94—, chmn., 1985-87. Mem. Phi Beta Kappa. Clubs: Harvard (N.Y.C.), Harvard Bus. Sch. (N.Y.C.), World Trade Center (N.Y.C.). Home: 245 E 19th St New York NY 10003-2639 Office: Corp Capital Cons Inc 1185 Ave of Americas New York NY 10036

SPIER, PETER EDWARD, artist, author; b. Amsterdam, Netherlands, June 6, 1927; came to U.S., 1952, naturalized, 1958; s. Joseph Eduard and Albertine Sophie (Van Raalte) S.; m. Kathryn M. Pallister, July 12, 1958; children: Thomas P., Kathryn E. Student, Ryks Academie Voor Beeldende Kunsten, Amsterdam, 1945-47. Jr. editor Elsevier's Weekly, Amsterdam, 1950-51, Elsevier Pub. Co., Houston, 1952. Free-lance author, illustrator, N.Y.C., 1952—; speaker, lectr. schs. and libraries.; author, illustrator: 38 books, including: The Star-Spangled Banner, 1973, Fast-Slow, High-Low, 1972, Crash! Bang! Boom!, 1972, Tin Lizzie, 1975, Noah's Ark, 1977, Oh, Were They Ever Happy!, 1978, Bored—Nothing to Do, 1978, The Legend of New Amsterdam, 1979, People, 1980, Peter Spier's Village Books, 1981, Rain, 1982, Christmas!, 1983, The Book of Jonah, 1985, Dreams, 1986, We

The People, 1987, Peter Spier's Circus, 1992, Father, May I Come?, 1993; illustrator over 150 books; contbr., illustrator many nat. mags. Lt. Royal Netherlands Navy, 1947-58. Runner-up for Caldecott medal, 1960; recipient Christopher award, 1970, Boston Globe award, 1967, Caldecott medal, 1978, Christopher award, 1978, Nat. Religious Book award, 1978, Lewis Carroll Shelf award, 1978, Media award NCCJ, 1980, David McCord award, 1989. Clubs: Shoreham (N.Y.); Country; Netherlands (N.Y.C.). Address: PO Box 566 5 Warden Cliff Rd Shoreham NY 11786-0566

SPIERKEL, GREG, electronics executive; b. 1957. BA, Carleton U. With Mitel Corp., Reston, Va., 1986—, now pres., CEO. Office: Mitel Inc 11921 Freedom Dr Ste 500 Reston VA 22090*

SPIERS, RONALD IAN, diplomat; b. Orange, N.J., July 9, 1925; s. Thomas Hoskins and Blanca (De Ponthier) S.; m. Patience Baker, June 11, 1949; children: Deborah Wood, Peter, Martha, Sarah. BA, Dartmouth Coll., 1948; M in Pub. Affairs, Princeton U., 1950. With U.S. Atomic Energy Commn., 1950-54; officer-in-charge disarmament and arms control Dept. State, 1955-61; dir. NATO Affairs, 1962-66; polit. counselor London, 1966-69; asst. sec. for Bur. Politico-Mil. Affairs U.S. Dept. State, Washington, 1969-73; U.S. ambassador Nassau, Bahamas, 1973-74; dep. chief-of-mission Am. Embassy, London, 1974-77; U.S. permanent rep. to Cento Coun., 1977-79; U.S. ambassador Ankara, Turkey, 1977-80; asst. sec. for intelligence and rsch., mem. U.S. Intelligence Bd. U.S. Dept. State, Washington, 1980-81; U.S. ambassador Islamabad, Pakistan, 1981-83; under-sec. for mgmt. U.S. Dept. State, Washington, 1983-89; under-sec. gen. for polit. affairs UN, N.Y.C., 1989-92; internat. affairs cons. U.S. Dept. State, Washington, 1992—; career ambassador U.S. Fgn. Svc., 1984. Served to lt. (j.g.) USN, 1943-46, PTO. Woodrow Wilson fellow Princeton U., 1948. Fellow Nat. Acad. of Pub. Administrn.; mem. Am. Fgn. Svc. Assn., Internat. Inst. Strategic Studies, Coun. on Fgn. Rels., Am. Acad. of Diplomacy, Washington Inst. Fgn. Affairs. Home: RR 1 Box 54A South Londonderry VT 05155-9706

SPIERS, TOMAS HOSKINS, JR., architect; b. Paris, Jan. 26, 1929; s. Tomas Hoskins and Blanca Genevive (DePonthier) S. (parents Am. citizens); m. Nancy M. Fenold, Aug. 10, 1952; children: Merrick David, Jordan Henry, Corey Albert. Student Mohawk Coll., 1946-48; BA, Hobart Coll., 1951; MArch, Yale U., 1960. Registered architect, Pa., N.J., N.Y., Mass., Md., Ohio, Conn., S.C., R.I., Ind., Va., W.Va., Fla., Ga., Vt. Archtl. designer Pederson & Tilney, New Haven, 1955-60; mng. dir. Pederson & Tilney/Spiers, Milan, 1963-66; v.p. S.E. Asia, Louis Berger, Inc., Bangkok, Thailand, 1966-68; v.p. architecture Benatec Assos., Harrisburg, Pa., 1968-75, v.p. design, 1975-78, sr. v.p., 1979-87; pres., 1987-91, chief exec. officer, 1991-94, pres. Spiers, McDonald, Bharucha & Royal Inc., 1994—; lectr. archtl. restoration Pa. State U., 1975-80; cons. Pa. Hist. & Mus. Commn., Bur. Historic Sites; mem. Pa. State Hist. Preservation Bd., 1980-84, chmn. 1986-88. Prin. works include restoration of Gen. Knox quarters, Valley Forge, Pa., Eagle Hotel, Waterford, Pa., The Highlands, Whitemarsh, Pa., Washington Monument, Balt. Bd. dirs. Urban League of Harrisburg, Inc., 1977-84. Served with USN, 1951-55. Mem. AIA (com. on inst. resources 1977-94, exec. com. 1980-82, chmn. 1983), ASCE, Am. Arbitration Assn. (arbitrator 1974—), Assn. Preservation Tech.; bd. dirs., editor bull. 1979-82, v.p. 1984-87, pres. 1988-92), Soc. Am. Mil. Engrs. Home: 357 N 27th St Camp Hill PA 17011-3629 Office: Spiers McDonald Bharucha & Royal Inc 150 Corporate Ctr Dr Ste 101 Camp Hill PA 17011-1759

SPIES, CLAUDIO, composer, educator; b. Santiago, Chile, Mar. 26, 1925; came to U.S., 1942, naturalized, 1966; s. Mauricio and Gertrudis (Heilbronn) S.; m. Emmi Vera Tobias, June 10, 1953 (div. 1986); children: Caterina, Michael, Tatiana, Leah, Susanna. AB, Harvard, 1950, MA, 1954. Instr. music Harvard U., 1953-57; lectr. music Vassar Coll., 1957-58; asst. prof. music, condr. orch. Swarthmore Coll., 1958-63, assoc. prof., 1964-69, prof., 1969-70; prof. music Princeton U., 1970-95, prof. music emeritus, 1995—. Conducted 1st performances of new works, Stravinsky, Boston, 1954, Santiago, 1954, Swarthmore Coll., 1963-68, Harvard, 1968, cond. own works, Composer's Forum, N.Y.C., 1961, Los Angeles County Museum, 1965, Columbia U. Group for Contemporary Music, 1966 (recipient prize for composition U. de Chile 1948, 54, 56); (Brandeis U. Creative Arts citation 1967); composer: orch. Music for a Ballet, 1955, Descanso en jardin; woodwind quartet, tenor and baritone; text by Jorge Guillén, 1957, Il Cantico di Frate Sole; bass. and orch., 1958, Five Psalms; soprano, tenor and 6 instruments; commd. by Harvard Mus. Assn., 1959, Verses from the Book of Ruth; women's voices and piano; commd. by Phila. Art Alliance, 1959, Tempi; music 14 instruments; commd. by Fromm Music Found., 1962, Proverbs on Wisdom; male voices, piano and organ; commd. by Colgate U., 1964, Animula Vagula, Blandula; 4 part chorus, a cappella, 1964, Viopiacem; duo for viola and keyboard instruments, 1965, LXXXV, Eights and Fives; strings and clarinets, 1967, Times Two; horns, 1968, Three Songs on Poems by May Swenson, 1969, Bagatelle for piano, 1970, 7 Enzensberger-Lieder; baritone, 4 instrumentalists, 1972, Shirim le Hathunatham; soprano, 5 instruments, 1975, Five Sonnet-Settings; Shakespeare; vocal quartet and piano, 1976-77; 5 Dádivas, occasional pieces for piano, 1977-81, Half-Time; for clarinet and trumpet, 1981, Rilke: Rühmen; soprano, clarinet, trumpet, piano, 1981, Tagyr for baritone, flute, clarinet, bassoon, horn and viola, 1983, Seven Sonnets; Shakespeare/Celan; soprano, bass, clarinet, bass clarinet, string trio, 1989; Lament and a Complementary Envoi, Dylan Thomas, baritone, piano, 1990, Dreimal Sieben, oboe and piano, 1991, Insieme, flute and violin, 1994, Beisammen, 2 oboes, also English horns, 1995; contbr. numerous articles and revs. to Perspectives of New Music, Mus. Quarterly, Notes, Tempo, Coll. Music Symposium, Jour. of Arnold Schoenberg Inst., vols. essays Berg, Brahms, Mendelssohn, Stravinsky; mem. editorial bd. Perspectives of New Music. Recipient Bohemian Club prize Harvard, 1950; John K. Paine Traveling fellow, 1950-51; Lili Boulanger Meml. Fund award, 1956; grantee The Ingram Merrill Found., 1966; sr. fellow Council Humanities, Princeton, spring 1966, fall 1966-67; award Nat. Inst. Arts and Letters, 1969; fellow Nat. Endowment Arts, 1975. Mem. Am. Soc. U. Composers (mem. founding bd.), Internat. Alban Berg/Soc. Ltd. (mem. founding bd.), Phila. Composers' Forum (exec. com. 1966-67), League-ISCM (mem. bd. 1970-73), Am. Brahms Soc., Phi Beta Kappa. Office: Princeton U Music Dept Woolworth Ctr Mus Stud Princeton NJ 08544

SPIES, DENNIS J., editor; b. Hays, Kans., Dec. 20, 1941; s. Joseph A. and Germaine A. (Giebler) S.; (widowed Apr. 1985); children: Quentin, Tracy, Angie; m. Linda Yarbrough, Feb., 1990. BA, West Tex. State U., 1970. Draftsman Jeppesen and Co., Denver, 1963-65; tech. illustrator Emerson Electric, St. Louis, 1965-66; reporter Amarillo (Tex.) Globe-News, 1966-68, copy editor, 1968-80, news editor, 1980-84, night city editor, 1984-86, mng. editor, 1986—. Author: (poetry) Sharing, 1984, Kansas Moon, 1989. Bd. dirs. Adult Literacy Coun., Amarillo, 1987-91, Goodwill Industries, 1987-93, United Way, 1989-90; mem. steering com. Leadership Amarillo, 1989-90. With USAF, 1960-63. Mem. AP Mng. Editors, Lions. Avocations: poetry, music, cars, motorcycles. Office: Amarillo Globe-News 907 S Van Buren St Amarillo TX 79101-3329

SPIES, ROBERT J., manufacturing executive, light; b. 1939. BA, Syracuse U., 1960; MBA, NYU, 1966. With Berol Corp., Bremtwood, Tenn., 1974—, now sr. v.p., asst. sec., asst. treas. Office: Berol Corp 105 Westpark Dr Brentwood TN 37027*

SPIESICKE, MARGRIT HERMA, counselor; b. Hannover, L. Saxonia, Germany, Dec. 29, 1925; came to U.S. 1960; d. Louis Adolf Otto Fritz and Else Herma (Meier) Becker; m. Horst Guenther Spiesicke, Nov. 9, 1949; 1 child, Marc Anthony. Cert. English/German interpreter, Hannover (Germany) Lang. Coll., 1947; AA with hons., Broward C.C., Hollywood, Fla., 1983; BA in Humanities, Fla. Internat. U., 1989; postgrad., Nova U., 1992—. State interpreter British Mil. Govt., Hannover, 1947-49; sec., office mgr. Townsend Co., Montreal, Can., 1950-60; sec., adminstrv. asst. Wometco Enterprises, Miami, 1960-85; adminstrv. sec. Barry U., Miami, 1985-88; med. sec. Broward Correctional Instn., Pembroke Pines, Fla., 1988-90, instl. counselor, 1990—. Vol. group counselor Mancy Figueredo, M.D., Miami, 1988-89. Mem. Phi Kappa Phi. Republican. Lutheran. Avocations: music, reading, creative writing.

SPIESS, FRED NOEL, oceanographer, educator; b. Oakland, Calif., Dec. 25, 1919; s. Fred Henry and Elva Josephine (Monck) S.; m. Sarah Scott Whitton, July 25, 1942; children: Katherine Spiess Dallaire, Mary Elizabeth Spiess DeJong, John Morgen Frederick, Helen Spiess Shamble, Margaret Josephine Deligio-Spiess. A.B., U. Calif., Berkeley, 1941, Ph.D., 1951; M.S., Harvard U., 1946. With Marine Phys. Lab., U. Calif., San Diego, 1952—; dir. Marine Phys. Lab., U. Calif., 1958-80, U. Calif. Inst. Marine Resources, 1980-88; dir. Scripps Inst. Oceanography, La Jolla, 1964-65, prof. oceanography, 1961—; chair U. Calif. Acad. Coun. and Assembly U. Calif. Bd. Regents, 1988-90; Mem. Naval Research Adv. Commn., 1978-81; mem. com. on geodesy Nat. Acad. Scis., 1980-84; mem. Def. Sci. Bd., 1976-79. Capt. USNR, 1941-79. Decorated Silver Star medal, Bronze Star medal; recipient John Price Wetherill medal Franklin Inst., 1965; Compass Disting. Scientist award Marine Technol. Soc., 1971; Robert Dexter Conrad award U.S. Sec. of Navy, 1974, Navy Disting. Pub. Svc. award, 1990; Newcomb Cleveland prize AAAS, 1981. Fellow Acoustical Soc. Am. (Pioneers of Underwater Acoustics medal 1985), Am. Geophys. Union (Maurice Ewing award 1983), Marine Tech. Soc. (Lockheed award 1985); mem. Nat. Acad. Engring., Phi Beta Kappa, Sigma Xi. Home: 9450 La Jolla Shores Dr La Jolla CA 92037-1137 Office: U Calif San Diego Scripps Inst Oceanogra La Jolla CA 92093

SPIKES, JOHN JEFFERSON, SR., forensic toxicologist, pharmacologist; b. Grand Prairie, Tex., Jan. 30, 1929; s. George W. and Madge (Ballard) S.; m. Marilyn Ruth Tomlimson, Apr. 17, 1949; children: Juli Spikes Jensen, John J. Jr., James M., Jay S., Jerry D. BS, Union Coll., 1951; MS, George Washington U., 1959; PhD, U. Tex., Galveston, 1971. Diplomate Am. Bd. Forensic Toxicologists. Instr. U. Tex. Med. Br., Galveston, 1971-72; toxicologist Pathology Labs. Houston, 1972-73, Biochemical Procedures, North Hollywood, Calif., 1973-75; chief toxicologist Ill. Dept. Pub. Health, Chgo., 1975-85; forensic toxicologist Nat. Med. Svcs., Willow Grove, Pa., 1985—; mem. drug abuse adv. com. FDA, Washington, 1984-87; cons. U.S. Postal Svc., 1982-84, Chgo. Transit Authority, 1978-86; presenter in field. Coauthor: (chpt.) Progress in Clinical Pathology, vol. III, 1981; contbr. articles to profl. jours. Cpl. U.S. Army Med. Corp 1952-54. Fellow Am. Acad. Forensic Scientists; mem. Soc. Forensic Toxicologists, Am. Clin. Scientists, Sigma Xi. Office: Nat Med Svcs Inc 2300 Stratford Ave Willow Grove PA 19090

SPIKINGS, BARRY PETER, film company executive; b. Boston, Eng., Nov. 23, 1939; came to U.S., 1986; children from previous marriage: Nicolas, Rebecca. Student, Boston (Eng.) Grammar Sch. Dir. Great Western, 1969-72; ptnr. Brit. Lion Films Holdings Ltd., Eng., 1972-75; chmn. Shepperton Studios, Eng., 1975-82; joint mng. dir., chmn., chief exec. officer E.M.I. Film & Theater Corp., 1975-82, chmn., chief exec., 1982-85; ind. producer, 1982-85; dir. Galactic Films, 1985-86; pres., chief oper. officer Nelson Entertainment Group Inc., Beverly Hills, Calif., 1986-91; ptnr. Pleskow Spikings Partnership, Beverly Hills, 1991—; creator contractual arrangements with Orion, Columbia, Showtime, Viacom. Producer The Deer Hunter, 1978 (Oscar award for best picture). Office: Pleskow Spikings 335 N Maple Dr Ste 352 Beverly Hills CA 90210

SPIKOL, ART, editor, writer, illustrator; b. Phila., Mar. 22, 1936; s. Emanuel and Yetta (Levy) S.; m. Rosalind Noshay, Jan. 12, 1958 (div.); 1 child, Victoria; m. Linda Parent, May 28, 1967; 1 child, Elizabeth. Student, Phila. Coll. Art, 1959-62. Art dir. Phila. mag., 1969-74, exec. editor, 1975-78, editor, 1980-82; art dir. Boston mag.; v.p. communications Einstein Med. Ctr., Phila., 1982-85; pres. Art Spikol, Inc., Phila., 1985—. Author: Magazine Writing: The Inside Angle, 1979, The Physalia Incident, 1988; columnist Writer's Digest, 1976-94. Recipient Best Feature Writing award Sigma Delta Chi, 1972, Penney-Mo. Mag. award U. Mo., 1974, Nat. Mag. Editor award Columbia Sch. Journalism, 1982. Jewish. Avocations: sketching, painting, pocket billiards. Office: Art Spikol Inc 751 S 5th St Philadelphia PA 19147-3042

SPILERMAN, SEYMOUR, sociologist, educator; b. N.Y.C., Apr. 17, 1938; s. Nathan and Blanche (Linzer) S. B.A., Pomona Coll., 1959; M.A., Brandeis U., 1961; Ph.D., Johns Hopkins U., 1968. From asst. prof. to prof. sociology U. Wis.-Madison, 1968-77; dir. policy analysis Russell Sage Found., N.Y.C., 1977-79; Julian C. Levi prof. social scis. Columbia U., N.Y.C., 1979—; cons. Equitable Ins. Co., N.Y.C., 1979—, N.Y.C. Corp. Counsel, 1983—; sr. research fellow Brookdale Inst., Jerusalem, 1975—. Editor: Social Indicator Models, 1975. Guggenheim fellow Jerusalem, 1973-74; recipient Romnes award U. Wis. Trustees, 1975. Fellow Am. Sociol. Assn., AAAS. Jewish. Office: Columbia U Dept Sociology New York NY 10027

SPILHAUS, ATHELSTAN, meteorologist, oceanographer; b. Cape Town, Union of South Africa, Nov. 25, 1911; came to U.S., 1931, naturalized, 1946; s. Karl Antonio and Nellie (Muir) S.; m. Kathleen Fitzgerald, 1978; children by previous marriage: Athelstan F., Mary Muir, Eleanor (dec.), Margaret Ann, Karl Henry. B.Sc., U. Cape Town, 1931, D.Sc., 1948; M.S., Mass. Inst. Tech., 1933; D.Sc., Coe Coll., 1961, Hahnemann Med. Coll., 1968, U. R.I., 1968, Phila. Coll. Pharmacy and Sci., 1969, Hamilton Coll., 1970, U. S.E. Mass., 1970, U. Durham, Eng., 1970, U. S.C., 1971, Southwestern U. at Memphis, 1972; LL.D., Nova U., 1970, U. Md., 1978. Research asst. Mass. Inst. Tech., 1934-35; asst. dir. tech. services Union of South Africa Def. Forces, Pretoria, 1935-36; research asst. Woods Hole (Mass.) Oceanographic Instn., and Cambridge, Mass., 1936-37; investigator in phys. oceanography Woods Hole (Mass.) Oceanographic Instn., and Cambridge, 1938, phys. oceanographer, 1940—; asst. prof. meteorology N.Y. U., 1937, assoc. prof., 1937-42, prof., 1942, dir. research, 1946; meteorol. adviser to Union S. Africa Govt., 1947; dean Inst. Tech. U. Minn., 1949-66, prof. physics, 1966-67; pres. Franklin Inst., Phila., 1967-69, Aqua Internat. Inc., 1969-70; fellow Woodrow Wilson Internat. Center for Scholars, 1971-74; with NOAA, Dept Commerce, Washington, 1974-80; disting. scholar Annenberg Center, U. So. Calif., 1981; vis. scholar Inst. Marine and Coastal Studies, U. So. Calif., 1982-83; pres. Pan Geo, Inc., 1984—; Dir. Sci. Service, Inc., Am. Dynamics Corp., Donaldson Co., Minn.; trustee Aerospace Corp., Los Angeles; U.S. commr. Seattle World's Fair, 1961-62; chmn. nat. fisheries center and aquarium adv. bd. U.S. Dept. Interior; mem. adv. coms. for armed forces; mem. nat. com. IGY; mem. com. on oceanography, com. on polar research Nat. Acad. Scis.; mem. exec. bd. UNESCO, 1955-58; mem. sci. adv. com. Am. Newspapers and Pubs. Assn.; sr. summer fellow Woods Hole Oceanographic Instn., 1990. Contbr.: numerous articles to profl. jours. including Jour. of Meterology; author: numerous articles to profl. jours. including The Ocean Laboratory. Trustee Woods Hole Oceanographic Instn., St. Paul Inst.; mem. Nat. Sci. Bd., 1966-72; vice chmn. Invest-in-America. Served from capt. to lt. col. USAAF, 1943-46. Decorated Legion of Merit, Exception Civilian Service medal USAF; recipient Patriotic Civilian Service award Dept. Army. Fellow AAAS (pres. 1970, chmn. 1971), Am. Geog. Soc., Geog. Soc., Royal Meteorol. Soc., Am. Geophys. Union; mem. AIAA, NAS (mem. com. pollution), Am. Philos. Soc. Episcopalian. Clubs: Cosmos (Washington); Bohemian (San Francisco). Inventor of Bathythermograph, 1938. Home: PO Box 1063 Middleburg VA 22117-1063 Office: Pan Geo Inc PO Box 2000 Middleburg VA 22117-2000

SPILHAUS, KARL HENRY, textiles executive, lawyer; b. N.Y.C., July 19, 1946; s. Athelstan Frederick and Mary (Atkins) S.; m. Constance DeLaMater, Dec. 30, 1989; stepchildren: Mary Alexis Welch, Antonia Morrow Welch. BA, U. Pa., 1971; JD, New Eng. Sch. Law, 1975. Bar: Mass. 1975. Staff atty. Legal Svcs., Cape Cod and the Islands, 1975-76; with No. Textile Assn., 1976—, pres., 1982—; pres. No. Textile Export Trading Co., Boston, 1992—; pres. Cashmere and Camel Hair Mfrs. Inst., 1984—; U.S. del. Internat. Labor Orgn. Textiles Com.; mem. adv. coun. U. Mass., Dartmouth, 1979—; arbitrator Am. Arbitration Assn., Boston. Trustee Mus. Am. Textile History. Bacon Free Libr., South Natick, Mass.; mem. Eliot Ch. of South Natick. With USMC, 1966-69, Vietnam. Mem. Textile Club Boston (pres.), Soc. King's Chapel, Phi Psi (hon.). Office: No Textile Assn 230 Congress St Boston MA 02110-2409

SPILKA, MARK, English educator; b. Cleve., Aug. 6, 1925; s. Harvey Joseph and Zella (Fenberg) S.; m. Ellen Potter, May 6, 1950 (div. Dec. 1965); children: Jane, Rachel, Aaron; m. Ruth Dane Farnum, Jan. 18, 1975 (div. May 1993); stepchildren: Betsy, Polly; m. Shelly Regenbaum, July 4, 1993; stepchildren: Shir, Livi. B.A. magna cum laude, Brown U., 1949; M.A., Ind. U., 1953, Ph.D., 1956. Editorial asst. Am. Mercury, 1949-51;

instr. U. Mich., 1954-58, asst. prof., 1958-63; assoc. prof. Brown U., Providence, 1963-67, prof., 1967—; Israel J. Kapstein prof. English, 1990, chmn. English dept., 1968-73; Summer seminar dir. Nat. Endowment for Humanities, 1974; pres. Conf. Editors of Learned Jours., Modern Lang. Assn., 1974-75; vis. prof. Grad. Inst. Modern Letters U. Tulsa, summer 1975, Hebrew U., Jerusalem, 1972, Ind. U., summer 1976. Author: The Love Ethic of D.H. Lawrence, 1955, Dickens and Kafka: A Mutual Interpretation, 1963, Virginia Woolf's Quarrel with Grieving, 1980, Hemingway's Quarrel with Androgyny, 1990, Renewing the Normative D.H. Lawrence: A Personal Progress, 1992; editor: D.H. Lawrence: A Collection of Critical Essays, 1963, Towards a Poetics of Fiction: Essays from Novel: A Forum on Fiction, 1967-76, 1977, (with Caroline McCracken-Flesher) Why the Novel Matters: A Postmodern Perplex, 1990; mng. editor: Novel: A Forum on Fiction, 1967-77; editor, 1978—. Served with USAAF, 1944-46. Named Harry T. Moore Disting. D.H. Lawrence scholar MLA and D.H. Lawrence Soc., 1988; Ind. Sch. Letters fellow, 1961, 63; Guggenheim fellow, 1967-68; Nat. Endowment for Humanities fellow, 1978-79, 87. Mem. MLA (pres. Dickens Soc. 1986), AAUP, Phi Beta Kappa. Home: 294 Doyle Ave Providence RI 02906-3355

SPILKER, JAMES J., JR., electronics executive; b. 1933. PhD, Stanford U. Mgr. Lockheed Corp., 1958-63; mgr. WDL divsn. Philco Ford, 1963-73; co-founder Stanford Telecommunications, Sunnyvale, Calif., 1973—, now chmn., pres., CEO. Office: Stanford Telecommunications 1221 Crossman Ave Sunnyvale CA 94088-3733*

SPILLANE, MICKEY (FRANK MORRISON SPILLANE), author; b. Bklyn., Mar. 9, 1918; s. John Joseph and Catherine Anne S.; m. Mary Ann Pearce, 1945 (div.); children: Kathy, Ward, Mike, Carolyn; m. Sherri Malinou, Nov. 1964 (div.); m. Jane Rodgers Johnson, Oct. 1983. Attended, Kans. State Coll. Scripter, asst. editor Funnies, Inc., in 1940's; co-founder Spillane-Fellows Prodns., Nashville, 1969. Author: (mystery-suspense novels) I, the Jury, 1947, Vengeance is Mine!, 1950, My Gun Is Quick, 1950, The Big Kill, 1951, One Lonely Night, 1951, The Long Wait, 1951, Kiss Me, Deadly, 1952, Tough Guys, 1960, The Deep, 1961, The Girl Hunters, 1962, Day of the Guns, 1964, The Snake, 1964, Bloody Sunrise, 1965, The Death Dealers, 1965, The Twisted Thing, 1966, The By-Pass Control, 1967, The Delta Factor, 1967, Body Lovers, 1967, Killer Mine, 1968, Me. Hood!, 1969, Survival: Zero, 1970, Tough Guys, 1970, The Erection Set, 1972, The Last Cop Out, 1973, The Flier, 1973, Tomorrow I Die, 1984, The Killing Man, 1989, (children's books) The Day the Sea Rolled Back, 1979 (Junior Literary Guild award 1979), The Ship That Never Was, 1982; screenwriter, actor: (films) The Girl Hunters, 1963; creator: (TV series) Mike Hammer, 1984-87; editor: Murder Is My Business, 1994; appeared in Miller Lite Beer commls. Served to capt. USAAF, World War II. Address: Gen Delivery Middleburg VA 22117*

SPILLANE, ROBERT RICHARD, school system administrator; b. Lowell, Mass., Oct. 29, 1934; s. John Joseph and Catherine (Barrett) S.; children: Patricia, Robert Jr., Kathleen, Maura. BS, Ea. Conn. State Coll., 1956; MA, U. Conn., 1959, PhD, 1967. Elem. and secondary tchr. Storrs, Conn., 1956-60, Chaplin, Conn., 1960-62; elem. prin. Trumbull, Conn., 1962-63; secondary prin. Trumbull, 1963-65; asst. supt. Glassboro (N.J.) Pub. Schs., 1966-68, Roosevelt (L.I., N.Y.) Schs., 1968-70, New Rochelle (N.Y.) Pub. Schs., 1970-78; dep. commr. N.Y. State Dept Edn., Albany, N.Y., 1978-81; supt. Boston Pub. Schs., 1981-85, Fairfax (Va.) County Pub. Schs., 1985—; bd. dirs. Council Great City Schs.; mem. adv. bd. Met. Ctr. Ednl. Research, Devel. and Tng. NYU, Instr. Mag.; chmn. pres.' adv. bd. Tchrs. Coll. Columbia U.; co-chmn. adminstrs. com. study on edn. and edn. of tchrs. U.S. Office Edn., Washington; mem. N.Y. State Sch. Officers Resolutions Com. on Legislation, Westchester County Chief Sch. Officers Legis. Com.; bd. dirs. Curriculum Devel. Council So. N.J., Impact II, N.Y.C.; adj. prof. sch. edn. Fordham U., N.Y.C., Iona Coll., New Rochelle, Bank St. Coll. Edn., N.Y.C., Glassboro State Coll.; instr. NYU; vis. lectr. U. Bridgeport, Conn. Author: You and Smoking, 1970, Management by Objectives in the Schools, 1978; contbr. articles to profl. jours. Trustee Mus. Fine Arts, Boston; bd. dirs. Jr. Achievement Ea. Mass., Inc.; mem. adv. com. Boston Pub. Library, The Statue of Liberty-Ellis Island Found., Inc., commn. on Bicentennial U.S. Constitution. Recipient Disting. Alumni award Ea. Conn. State Coll., 1969, Disting. Alumni award U. Conn., 1986; named one of Outstanding Young Men of Am. Mem. Am. Assn. Sch. Adminstrs. (Nat. Supt. of the Year award 1995), Mass., Conn., N.J., N.Y. Assns. Sch. Adminstrs., Sch. Mgmt. Study Group (pres. 1971-73, Hall of Fame award 1974), Assn. Supervision and Curriculum Devel., Nat. Sch. Pub. Relations Assn., Phi Delta Kappa. Avocations: swimming, sailing, skiing, theater and the arts, entertaining. Office: Fairfax Cty Public Schools 10700 Page Ave Fairfax VA 22030-4006*

SPILLARD, ERNEST JOHN, oil company executive; b. London, June 14, 1939; came to U.S., 1981; s. Richard John and Iris Ethel (Turpy) S.; divorced; children: Dinah Susan, Mark John; m. Marray Candice Miller, July 21, 1989. MBA, U. Tex., 1989. Various exec. positions FG Minter Group, London, 1964-75; mng. dir. Ferry Works Plant Hire Ltd., London, 1975-77; v.p. Beck Arabia Ltd., Alkhobar, Saudi Arabia, 1977-79; contr. Pool Arabia Ltd., AlKhobar, 1979-81; various positions Pool Co., Houston, 1981-86, sr. v.p., 1986—. Fellow Assn. Chartered Cert. Accts. Home: 540 Wilcrest Dr Houston TX 77042-1076 Office: Pool Energy Svcs Co 10375 Richmond Ave Houston TX 77042-4124

SPILLER, EBERHARD ADOLF, physicist; b. Halbendorf, Ger., Apr. 16, 1933; came to U.S., 1968; s. Walter Richard and Ruth Elfriede (Radzey) S.; m. Marga Dietz, Dec. 18, 1964; children—Michael, Bettina. Diploma, U. Frankfurt, Ger., 1960, Ph.D., 1964. Asst. U. Frankfurt, 1960-68, mem. faculty, 1966-68; physicist IBM Research Center, Yorktown Heights, N.Y., 1968-93; emeritus physicist IBM, 1993—; guest prof. Tech. U. Denmark, 1994-95. Author: Soft X-Ray Optics, 1994. Fellow AAAS, Am. Optical Soc.; mem. German Phys. Soc., Photo-Optic Instrumentation Soc. Research in solid state physics, laser and coherence optics, nonlinear optics, thin films, soft x-rays, x-ray microscopy, lithography; inventor multilayer x-ray optics, x-ray astronomy, x-ray lithography. Home: Lakeside Rd Mount Kisco NY 10549 Office: IBM Corp TJ Watson Research Ctr Yorktown Heights NY 10598

SPILLER, HART, microbiologist; b. Berlin, Dec. 1, 1939; came to U.S., 1979; s. Helmut and Erika (Hurt) S. Degree, Pedagogical Coll. Univ., 1962, FA Univ. Erlangen, 1972; PhD, FA Univ. Erlangen, 1975. Registered primary, secondary tchr., Australia, 1963-65; supr. English schs. New Guinea, 1966; postdoctoral rsch. assoc. U. Konstanz, West Germany, 1975-78; fellow U. Calif., Davis, 1979-80; adj. postdoctoral assoc. U. Fla., Gainesville, 1981-85; postdoctoral assoc. U. Fla., 1986-87; rsch. asst. prof. biology Fisk U., Nashville, 1989-94. Active Amnesty Internat., Konstanz, Davis, 1977-79; founder, referee commr. Gainesville Recreational Soccer, 1981-88; bd. dirs. Clergy & Laity Concerned, Nashville, 1990-94; scoutmaster troop 76 Boy Scouts Am., 1990-94, scout coord.; councillor Corinthian Bapt. Ch., Nashville, 1989-94. Mem. Am. Soc. Plant Physiologists, Am. Soc. Microbiology. Avocations: human rights, biotechnology innovations, inner city Scouting. Office: Corinthian Bapt Ch 819 33d Ave N Nashville TN 37209

SPILLERS, WILLIAM RUSSELL, civil engineering educator; b. Fresno, Calif., Aug. 4, 1934; s. William Horton and Marguerite Ester (Johnson) S.; m. Priscilla Watson, Sept. 10, 1960 (div. 1981); children: Sarah, William, Lars; m. Sandra Lynn Newsome, July 15, 1983. Student, Fresno State Coll., 1951-53; BS, U. Calif, Berkeley, 1955, MS, 1956; PhD, Columbia U., 1961. Registered profl. engr., N.Y. Structural engr. John Blume Assocs., San Francisco, 1956-57; teaching asst. Columbia U. N.Y.C., 1957-61, prof. civil engring. and engring. mechanics, 1961-76; prof. civil engring. Rensselaer Poly. Inst., Troy, N.Y., 1976-90; prof., chmn. civil and environ. engring. N.J. Inst. Tech., Newark, 1990—; cons. Weidlinger Assoc., N.Y.C., 1957-76, Geiger Berger Assoc., N.Y.C., 1957-76, DeLeuw Oh Eocha, Manchester, Eng., 1974, Parsons Hawaii, Los Angeles, 1983, Horst Berger Ptnrs., N.Y.C., 1980; organizer NSF workshop on design theory, Troy, N.Y., 1988. Author: Automated Structural Analysis, 1972, Iterative Structural Design, 1975, Intro Structures, 1985, (with R. Levy) Analysis of Geometrically Nonlinear Structures, 1995; editor 4 books including Design Theory, 1988; contbr. more than 125 articles to profl. jours. NSF fellow, 1976, Guggenheim

fellow, 1968. Mem. ASCE (numerous coms., chmn. exec. com. TCCP, 1987), Internat. Assn. Bridge & Structural Engrs. Democrat. Achievements include contribution to the development of fabric structures; initiated the science of design theory; participated in development of applications of digital computers to large structural systems. Home: 571 Parker St Newark NJ 07104-1523 Office: NJ Inst Tech Dept Civil & Environ Engring Newark NJ 07102

SPILLMAN, JANE SHADEL, curator, researcher, writer; b. Huntsville, Ala., Apr. 30, 1942; d. Marvin and Elizabeth (Russell) Shadel; m. Don Lewis Spillman, Feb. 18, 1973; children: K. Elizabeth, Samuel Shadel. AB, Vassar Coll., 1964; MA, SUNY, 1965. Rsch. asst. Corning (N.Y.) Mus. Glass, 1965-70, asst. curator, 1971-73, assoc. curator Am. glass, 1974-77, curator, 1978—, head of curatorial dept., 1994—; cons. New Bedford (Mass.) Glass Mus., 1986, The White House Curator's Office, Washington, 1987-90. Author: Complete Cut and Engraved Glass of Corning, 1979, Knopf Collectors Guide to Glass, Vol. 1, 1982, Vol. 2, 1983, White House Glassware, 1989, Masterpieces of American Glass, 1990; also 6 other books, numerous articles. Mem. Am. Assn. Mus. (chairperson curators com. 1989-93), Nat. Early Am. Glass Club (bd. dirs. 1989-95), Glass Circle of London. Office: Corning Mus Glass 1 Museum Way Corning NY 14830-2253

SPILLMAN, ROBERT ARNOLD, architect; b. Bethlehem, Pa., May 21, 1931; s. Otto Henry and Ruth Meredith (Miller) S.; m. Cidney Jane Brandon, July 7, 1956; children—Catherine, Sarah, Peter. B.Arch., Cornell U., 1954. Registered profl. architect Pa., N.J., Va., Del., Ga., N.Y. Archl. designer office Douglass Orr, New Haven, 1956-58; ptnr. Lovelace & Spillman, Architects, Bethlehem, 1959-70; sr. ptnr. Spillman Farmer Architects, Bethlehem, 1971-82; pres. Spillman Farmer Shoemaker Pell Whildin, P.C, Bethlehem, 1983—. Trustee, Laros Found., Bethlehem, 1970—; pres. Bethlehem Library Bd., 1970-74, United Way Northampton and Warren Counties, 1979-81, Lehigh River Found., 1992—; v.p. Lehigh Valley Indsl. Parks, 1985—; chmn. City of Bethlehem Bd. Historic Archl. Rev., 1961-82. Recipient New Constrn. award Historic Easton, Inc. (Pa.), 1981. Mem. Pa. Soc. Architects (disting. bldg. awards 1971, 76, 78, 94), AIA, Soc. Coll. and Univ. Planners, Eastern Pa. chpt. AIA (pres. 1969-70). Democrat. Episcopalian. Served as 1st lt. USAF, 1954-56. Clubs: Bethlehem; Bay Head Yacht (N.J., rear commodore 1985-87). Office: Spillman Farmer Shoemaker Pell 1 Bethlehem Plz 1000 Bethlehem PA 18018

SPILMAN, RAYMOND, industrial designer; b. Wichita, Kans., Jan. 12, 1911; s. Robert Bruce and Willa (Wood) S.; m. Mary Jordan, May 15, 1937; children: Susan, Alden. Student, Kans. State U., 1933. Stylist Gen. Motors Corp., 1935-39; staff designer Walter Dorwin Teague, N.Y.C., 1940-42; chief designer Johnson Cushing & Nevell, N.Y.C., 1942-46; propr. Raymond Spilman Indsl. Design, N.Y.C., 1946, Stamford, Conn., 1963, Darien, Conn., 1983—; ednl. adviser, lectr. design and design curriculums, color applications in design. Mem. edit. bd., Color Rsch. and Applications Quar., 1976-80; producer films on color and design; collections included in Archives of Domestic Life Smithsonian Inst., 1950—. Recipient Elec. Mfg. Design award Gates Pub. Co., 1950, award U.S. Trade Fair Exhbns., Yugoslavia, 1955, Italy, 1957, Peru, 1959 and 63, Poland, 1964, Graphis award, Graphis mag. Italy, 1957, Internat. Triennale award Undicesima Triennale di Milano, Milan, Italy, 1957, Wescon award of merit West Cost Elec. Prodn. Mfg. Assn., 1959, Design USA award Indsl. Design Soc. Am., 1965, Product Engring. Master Design awards, 1959, 66, Housewares Design award, 1967, 68, citation for design in steel Am. Iron and Steel Inst., 1974, John Vassos award Indsl. Design Soc. Am., 1985, Personal Recognition award Indsl. Designers Soc. Am., 1993; Endowment Arts design project fellow Nat. Endowment Arts, 1977; Design Advancement grantee Nat. Endowment Arts, 1989-90. Fellow Indsl. Design Soc. Am. (Personal Achievement award 1993, Personal Recognition award 1993); mem. Am. Soc. Indsl. Designers (pres. 1960-62, chmn. bd. dirs. 1963-64), Am. Inter-Soc. Color Coun. (bd. dirs. 1970-72, 76-77), Phi Delta Theta. Home and Office: Raymond Spilman Indsl Design 1 Althea Ln Darien CT 06820

SPILMAN, ROBERT HENKEL, furniture company executive; b. Knoxville, Tenn., Sept. 27, 1927; s. Robert Redd and Lila (Henkel) S.; m. Martha Jane Bassett, Apr. 2, 1955; children: Robert Henkel Jr., Virginia Perrin, Vance Henkel. BS, N.C. State U., 1950. With Cannon Mills, 1950-57; with Bassett Table Co., Va., 1957-60; dir. Bassett Furniture Industries Inc., 1960—, exec. v.p., 1966, pres., 1966-89, CEO, 1979—, chmn., 1982—; bd. dirs. Pittston Co., Greenwich, Conn., Nations Bank Corp., Charlotte, Trinova Corp., Maumee, Ohio, Dominion Resources, Inc., Richmond, Va.; chmn. bd. dirs. Jefferson-Pilot Corp., Greensboro, N.C., Internat. Home Furnishings Ctr., High Point, N.C.; mem. adv. bd. Liberty Mut. Ins. Co. Trustee Va. Found. Ind. Colls.; bd. dirs. Blue Ridge Airport Authority. Lt. U.S. Army, WWII and Korea. Recipient Best Chief Exec. Officer in Home Furnishing Industry award Wall Street Transcript, 1981, 82; named Humanitarian of Yr., City of Hope, 1982. Mem. Am. Furniture Mgrs. Assn. (James T. Ryan award 1984), So. Furniture Mfrs. Assn. (bd. dirs., past pres.), Furniture Factories Mktg. Assn. (past chmn., bd. dirs.), Va. Mfrs. Assn. (past mem. exec. com.), Bassett Country Club, Chatmoss Country Club, Hunting Hills Country Club, Brook Club, Commonwealth Club, Linville Golf Club, Sailfish Club Fla., Waterfront Golf Club (Moneta, Va.), Grandfather Golf and Country Club (Linville, N.C.). Episcopalian. Avocation: fishing. Office: Bassett Furniture Industries Inc PO Box 626 Bassett VA 24055-0626

SPINA, ANTHONY, photojournalist; b. Detroit; s. Costan and Julia (Perry) S.; m. Frances Leto, Mar. 2, 1946; children: Costan II, Julia, Kathryn. BA, Detroit Inst. Tech., 1939; LHD (non.), Siena Heights Coll., 1988. Mem. photography staff Detroit Free Press, 1946—, chief photographer, 1952-86, spl. asst. to mng. editor, 1986-89, chief photographer emeritus, 1990—. Author: The Making of the Pope: Pope John XXIII, 1962, The Pope and The Council, 1963, This Was the President: John F. Kennedy, 1964, The Press Photographer, 1968, From A Distant Country: Pope John Paul II, 1979, On Assignment: Projects in Photo-journalism, 1982, (weekly photog. questions and answer column) Knight Ridder Newspapers Wire Service.; numerous one-man exhbns. include Detroit Art Inst., 1976, Los Angeles County Museum, 1976, Vatican Mus., 1968; mem. spl. Free Press team, 1968 (Pulitzer prize). Served with USN, World War II, Korea. Decorated Knight, St. Gregory The Great (Pope Paul VI); named to Journalist Hall of Fame, Mich. State U., 1989; recipient Gold medallion Pope John XXIII, 1962, Silver medallion, 1962, Bronze medallion, 1962, Gov.'s Media award Concerned Citizens for the Arts, 1989, also 482 nat. and internat. photog. awards; Tony Spina, Chief Photographer: Four Decades of His News Photography, pub. in his honor Detroit Free Press, 1989. Roman Catholic. Home: 3525 Squirrel Rd Bloomfield Hills MI 48304-2457 Office: 321 W Lafayette Blvd Detroit MI 48226-2703

SPINA, ANTHONY FERDINAND, lawyer; b. Chgo., Aug. 15, 1937; s. John Dominic and Nancy Mara (Ponzio) S.; m. Anita Phyllis, Jan. 28, 1961; children—Nancy M. Spina Okal, John D., Catherine M. Spina Samatas, Maria J. Spina Samatas, Felicia M. B.S. in Social Sci., Loyola U., Chgo., 1959; J.D., DePaul U., 1962. Bar: Ill. 1962. Assoc. Epton, Scott, McCarthy, & Bohling, Chgo., 1962-64; sole practice, Elmwood Park, Ill., 1964-71; pres. Anthony & Spina, P.C., 1971-84, Spina, McGuire & Okal, P.C., 1985—; atty. Leyden Twp., Ill., 1969-89, Village of Rosemont, Ill., 1971; counsel for Pres. and dir. Cook County Twp. Ofcls. of Ill., 1975—; counsel for exec. dir. Ill. State Assn. Twp. Ofcls.; counsel Elmwood Park Village Bd., 1967-89, Norwood Park St. Lighting Dist., 1988—, various Cook County Twps. (including DuPage, 1980-82, Maine, 1981—, Norwood Park, 1982—, Wayne, 1982-84), all Cook County Hwy. Commrs. Traffic Fine Litigation, Hanover Twp. Mental Health Bd., 1991—, Glen Elders Assn., 1994—; mem. Elmwood Park Bldg. Code Planning Commn. Bd. Appeals. Recipient Lacodaire medal, Dean's Key Loyola U.; Loyola U. Housing awards, 1965, 71, 76; award of appreciation Cook County Twp. Ofcls., av rating Martindale-Hubbel. Mem. Ill. Bar Assn., ABA, Chgo. Bar Assn., West Suburban Bar Assn. of Cook County (past chmn. unauthorized practice of law sect.), Am. Judicature Soc., Justinian Soc. Lawyers, Ill. State Twp. Attys. Assn. (past v.p., pres. 1982-86, dir. 1986—), Nat. Town and Twp. Attys. (past v.p., pres. 1993—, Ill. del.), Montclare/Leyden C. of C., Edgebrook C. of C. (past bd. dirs.), Nat. Assn. Italian Am. Lawyers, Blue Key, Delta Theta Phi, Tau Kappa Epsilon, Pi Gamma Mu. Roman Catholic. St. Rocco Soc. of Simbario (auditor-trustee Chgo.), KC (scribe, trustee, past grand

knight, bldg. corp. dir. 1967—, Calabresi in Am. Orgn. (bd. dirs. 1990—). Author Rosemont Village Ordinances, 1971; Elmwood Park Bldg Code, 1975, Leyden Twp. Codified Ordinances, 1987. Office: 7610 W North Ave Elmwood Park IL 60635

SPINA, DENNIS J., gas industry executive; b. Phila., Pa., 1944. Graduated, Temple U., 1969. Pres. Suburban Propane, Whippany, N.J. Office: Suburban Propane PO Box 206 Whippany NJ 07981

SPINA, HORACIO ANSELMO, physician; b. Buenos Aires, Argentina, Mar. 19, 1939; came to U.S., 1970; s. Antonio and Rosa Palma S.; m. Patricia Anne Duffy, Apr. 4, 1985; children: Alicia V., Cristina V., Mario A. MD, Universidad Nacional Cordoba, Argentina, 1968; MD in Psychiatry, U. Pittsburgh, 1974. Diplomate Am. Bd. Psychiatry and Neurology. Resident U. Pitts., 1971-74; rotating intern Shadyside Hosp., Pitts., 1970-71; med. dirs. psychiat. svcs. and chem. dependence program St. Clair Mem. Hosp., Pitts., 1980—; clin. asst. prof. psychiatry U. Pitts. Mem. APA, InterAm. Coll. Physicians and Surgeons, Psychiat. Physicians of Pa., Cordoba Soc. Pharmacology and Therapeutics, N.Y. Acad. Scis., Am. Soc. Clin. Psychopharmacology. Avocations: cooking, gardening, music, pottery. Office: 1050 Bower Hill Rd Ste 303 Pittsburgh PA 15243-1869

SPINCIC, WESLEY JAMES, oil company executive, consultant; b. New Castle, Pa., Aug. 6, 1945; s. Edward and Mary Louise (Ferk) S.; m. Gayle Sharon Burnett, June 2l, 1975; children: John Reginold, Sheri Diane. BS in Engring., U.S. Mil. Acad., 1967; postgrad. in bus., U. So. Calif., 1973. Account rep. Dupont Glore-Forgon, L.A., 1973-74; drilling engr. Mobil Oil Co., Dallas, 1974-77; drilling supt. Ranger Oil Co., Houston, 1977; drilling and engring. mgr. Kilroy Co. Tex., Houston, 1977-8l; chmn. bd. Avanti Svcs., Inc., Houston, 198l—; bd. dirs. Humble (Tex.) Nat. Bank, Cheyenne Oil and Gas Co., Houston, Avanti Internat., Drillpro Inc. Organizer Kingwood (Tex.) Emergency Med. Assn., 1978. Capt. U.S. Army, 1967-73. Mem. Soc. Petroleum Engrs., Am. Petroleum Inst., Internat. Assn. Drilling Contractors, Tex. Ind. Producers and Royalty Owners Assn., Assn. West Point Alumni. Republican. Roman Catholic. Avocations: golf, hunting. Home: 4714 Breezy Point Kingwood TX 77345 Office: 15600 JFK Blvd Ste 220 Houston TX 77032

SPINDEL, ROBERT CHARLES, electrical engineering educator; b. N.Y.C., Sept. 5, 1944; s. Morris Tayson and Isabel (Glazer) S.; m. Barbara June Sullivan, June 12, 1966; children—Jennifer Susan, Miranda Ellen. B.S.E.E., Cooper Union, 1965; M.S., Yale U., 1966, M.Phil., 1968, Ph.D., 1971. Postdoctoral fellow Woods Hole Oceanographic Instn, Mass., 1971-72, asst. scientist, 1972-76; assoc. scientist Woods Hole Oceanographic Instn., Mass., 1976-82; sr. scientist Woods Hole Oceanographic Instn, Mass., 1982-87, chmn. dept. ocean engring., 1982-87; dir. applied physics lab. U. Wash., 1987—. Contbr. articles to profl. jours.; patentee on underwater nav. Recipient A.B. Wood medal Brit. Inst. Acoustics, 1981, Gano Dunn medal The Cooper Union, 1989. Fellow IEEE (assoc. editor jour. 1982—), Acoustical Soc. Am. (exec. coun. 1985-86), Marine Tech. Soc. (pres. elect 1991-93, pres. 1993-95). Democrat. Jewish. Avocations: automobile restoration, hiking. Home: 14859 SE 51st St Bellevue WA 98006-3515 Office: U Wash Applied Physics Lab 1013 NE 40th St Seattle WA 98105-6606

SPINDEL, WILLIAM, chemistry educator, scientist, educational administrator; b. N.Y.C., Sept. 9, 1922; s. Joseph and Esther (Goldstein) S.; m. Sara Lew, 1942 (div. 1966); children: Robert Andrew, Lawrence Marshall; m. Louise Phyllis Hoodenpyl, July 30, 1967. B.A., Bklyn. Coll., 1944; M.A., Columbia U., 1947, Ph.D., 1950. Jr. scientist Los Alamos Lab, Manhattan Dist., 1944-45; instr. Poly. Inst., Bklyn., 1949-50; assoc. prof. State U. N.Y., 1950-54; research assoc., vis. prof. Columbia, 1954-57, vis. prof., sr. lectr., 1962-74; assoc. prof., then prof. Rutgers U., 1957-64; prof., chmn. dept chemistry Belfer Grad. Sch. Sci., Yeshiva U., 1964-74; exec. sec., office chemistry and chem. tech. NAS-NRC, 1974-81, also staff dir. bd. on chem. scis. and tech., prin. staff officer commn. phys. scis., math. and resources, 1982-90, sr. cons., 1990—; vis. Am. scientist, Yugoslavia, 1971-72. Contbr. articles to profl. jours. Served with AUS, 1943-46. Recipient profl. staff award NRC, 1985; Guggenheim fellow, 1961-62; Fulbright Research scholar, 1961-62. Fellow AAAS; mem. Am. Chem. Soc. Club: Cosmos. Achievements include research on separation of stable isotopes, isotope effects on chemical and biological processes; developed chemical exchange process for concentrating nitrogen-15. Home: 6503 Dearborn Dr Falls Church VA 22044-1116

SPINDLER, G. R., mining company executive. Chief oper. officer Pyxis Resources Co., Abingdon, Va. Office: Clinchfield Coal Co Inc 448 W Main St Lebanon VA 24266

SPINDLER, GEORGE DEARBORN, anthropologist, educator, author, editor; b. Stevens Point, Wis., Feb. 28, 1920; s. Frank Nicholas and Winifred (Hatch) S.; m. Louise Schaubel, May 29, 1942; 1 dau., Sue Carol Spindler Coleman. B.S., Central State Tchrs. Coll., Wis., 1940; M.A., U. Wis., 1947; Ph.D., U. Calif. at Los Angeles, 1952. Tchr. sch. in Wis., 1940-42; research asso. Stanford, 1950-51, mem. faculty, 1951—, prof. anthropology and edn., 1960-78, exec. head dept., 1963-67, 84; vis. prof. U. Wis., Madison, 1979, 80, 81, 82, 83, 84, 85; editor Am. Anthropologist, 1962-66; cons. editor Holt, Rinehart & Winston, 1965-91, Harcourt, Brce, 1991—; vis. prof. U. Calif. Santa Barbara, 1986-91. Author: Menomini Acculturation, 1955, (with A. Beals and L. Spindler) Culture in Process, 1967, rev. edit., 1973, Transmission of American Culture, 1959, (with L. Spindler) Dreamers Without Power, 1971, rev. edit., 1984, Burgbach: Urbanization and Identity in a German Village, 1973, (with Louise Spindler) The American Cultural Dialogue and its Transmission, 1990; editor: Education and Anthropology, 1955, (with Louise Spindler) Case Studies in Cultural Anthropology, 1960—, Methods in Cultural Anthropology, 1965—, Case Studies in Education and Culture, 1966—, Basic Units in Anthropology, 1970; editor, contbr.: Education and Culture, 1963, Being An Anthropologist, 1970, Education and Cultural Process, 1974, rev. edit., 1987, The Making of Psychological Anthropology, 1978, 2nd edit., 1994, Doing the Ethnography of Schooling, 1982, Interpretive Ethnography of Schooling at Home and Abroad, 1987, Pathways to Cultural Awareness: Cultural Therapy with Students and Teachers, 1994. Pres. Peninsula Sch. Bd., Menlo Park, Calif. 1954-56. Served with AUS, 1942-45. Recipient Lloyd W. Dinkelspell award Stanford U., 1978, Disting. Svc. award Soc. Internat. Diplomacy and Third World Anthropologists, 1984, Disting. Career Contbn. award Com. on Role and Status of Minorities, Am. Eden. Rsch. Assn. Nat. Acad. Edn., 1992; fellow Ctr. Advanced Study of Behavioral Scis., 1956-57; subject of Vol. 17 Psychoanalytic Study of Soc. essays, 1992. Fellow Am. Anthrop. Assn.; mem. Southwestern Anthrop. Assn. (pres. 1962-63), Coun. for Anthropology and Edn. (pres. 1982, George and Louise Spindler award for outstanding contbns. to ednl. anthropology 1987), Nat. Acad. Edn. Home: 489 Kortum Canyon Rd Calistoga CA 94515 Office: Ethnographics PO Box 38 Calistoga CA 94515-0038 *My major aims as a professional observer and interpreter of human behavior are to acquire knowledge by research and disseminate understanding to others by teaching, writing, and editing. As a person I try to keep love, work, play in balanced relationship to each other, and strive for tolerance at least, and hopefully appreciation for others who are different than myself.*

SPINDLER, GEORGE S., lawyer, oil industry executive. BCE, Ga. Inst. Tech., 1961; JD, DePaul U., 1966. Bar: Ill. 1966. Asst. gen. counsel, patents and licensing Amoco Corp., Chgo., 1979-81, gen. mgr. info. svcs., 1981-85, v.p. planning and adminstrn., 1985-87, assoc. gen. counsel, 1987-88, dep. gen. counsel, 1988-89, v.p., gen. counsel, 1989-92, sr. v.p., gen. counsel, 1992—. Office: Amoco Corp PO Box 87703 200 E Randolph Dr Chicago IL 60680

SPINDLER, JOHN FREDERICK, lawyer; b. Milw., Aug. 23, 1929; s. Howard L. and Margaret (Knauf) S.; m. Martha Murdoch, June 26, 1952; children: Susan Spindler Nelson, Elizabeth Spindler, John F. Jr. Robert P. BA, U. Mich., 1951, JD, 1953. Bar: Mich. 1953, Pa. 1954, U.S. Ct. Claims 1955, U.S. Ct. Mil. Appeals 1955, Conn. 1956, U.S. Supreme Ct. 1956, U.S. Dist. Ct. Conn. 1960, U.S. Tax Ct. 1967, Fla. 1977. Assoc. Cummings & Lockwood, Stamford, Conn., 1956-63, ptnr., 1963—. Bds. dirs. Stamford YMCA, 1987-93, Stamford Hist. Soc., 1984-90. 1st lt. JAGC, U.S. Army, 1953-56. Home: 175 Saddle Hill Rd Stamford CT 06903-2306 Office:

Cummings & Lockwood Four Stamford Plz PO Box 120 Stamford CT 06904-0120

SPINDLER, MICHAEL H., computer company executive; b. 1942. MBA, Rheinische Fachochschule. European mktg. mgr. Apple Computer Inc., 1980-88, pres. Apple Europe divsn., 1988-90, exec. v.p., COO, 1990-91, pres., COO, 1991-93, now pres., CEO, 1993—; also chmn. Claris Corp., Santa Clara, Calif. Office: Apple Computer Inc 20525 Mariani Ave Cupertino CA 95014-6201*

SPINDLER, PAUL, public relations executive; b. Chgo., May 2, 1931; s. Isaac Edward and Sophia (Stein) S.; m. Gail Klynn; children from previous marriage: Kevin, Makayla, Cyd, Jeffrey. BA in Journalism, Temple U., 1952. Reporter Akron Beacon Jour., Akron, Ohio, 1955-58, San Francisco Examiner, 1958-59; editor Santa Clara (Calif.) Daily Jour., 1959-63; dir. pub. affairs Litton Industries, Inc., Beverly Hills, Calif., 1963-68; dir. pub. relations Internat. Industries, Beverly Hills, 1968-70; pres. Paul Spindler & Co., L.A., 1970-75; exec. v.p. Manning Selvage & Lee, Inc., N.Y.C., 1975-85; pres. The Spindler Co., L.A., 1985-87; pres. Western div. GCI Group, L.A., 1987-91; pres. GCI/Spindler, L.A., 1991—; bd. dirs. Phoenix House Calif., Inc.; vis. com. mem. Sch. Bus. Adminstrn. U. So. Calif. Cpl. U.S. Army, 1952-54. Mem. Pub. Relations Soc. Am., Fin. Analysts Fedn., Mountain Gate Country Club (L.A.). Democrat. Jewish. Office: The Spindler Orgn Inc 6100 Wilshire Blvd Ste 804 Los Angeles CA 90048-5115

SPINELLA, JUDY LYNN, healthcare administrator; b. Ft. Worth, Apr. 8, 1948; d. Gettis Breon and Velrea Inez (Webb) Prothro; children: Scott Slater, Jennifer. BS, U. Tex., 1971; MS, Tex. Woman's U., 1973; MBA, Vanderbilt U., 1993. RN, Tex., Calif., Tenn. Asst. prof. U. Tex., Arlington, 1976-81; dir. emergency svcs. San Francisco Gen. Hosp., 1981-84, assoc. adminstr. for clin. svcs., 1984-88; exec. dir. for nursing svcs. Vanderbilt U. Med. Ctr., Nashville, 1988-93, dir. patient care svcs., 1993-94; dir., COO Vanderbilt U. Hosp., Nashville, 1994—. Wharton fellow Johnson & Johnson, 1987. Mem. Am. Orgn. Nurse Execs., Emergency Nurses Assn. (bd. dirs., treas. 1979-86), Tenn. Orgn. Nurse Execs. (bd. dirs. 1989-91), Sigma Theta Tau. Avocations: hiking, skiing, travel. Home: 784 Harpeth Trace Dr Nashville TN 37221-3144

SPINELLA, STEPHEN, actor. Student, NYU Grad. Acting program. Stage appearances include The Age of Assassins, La Fin de la Baleine, Heavenly Theatre, A Bright Room Called Day, Hydriota, The Illusion, Burrhead, Tartuffe, 7 By Beckett, Serious Money, Major Barbara, The Virgin Molly, King Lear, Angels in America: Millenium Approaches, 1993 (Tony award 1993), Angels in America: Peristroika, 1993 (Tony award 1994); film appearances include: Virtuosity, 1995; TV movies include: And The Band Played On, 1994. Recipient Marion Scott Actor Achievement award. Office: William Morris Agy 1350 Ave Americas New York NY 10019*

SPINELLI, JERRY, writer; b. Norristown, Pa., Feb. 1, 1941; s. Louis Anthony and Lorna Mae (Bigler) S.; m. Eileen Mesi, May 24, 1977; children: Kevin, Barbara, Lana, Jeffrey, Molly, Sean, Benjamin. BA, Gettysburg (Pa.) Coll., 1963; MA, Johns Hopkins U., 1964. Editor Chilton Co., Radnor, Pa., 1966-89. Author: Space Station Seventh Grade, 1982, Who Put That Hair in My Toothbrush?, 1984, Night of the Whale, 1985, Jason and Marceline, 1986, Dump Days, 1988, Maniac Magee, 1990 (Newbery medal 1991, Boston Globe/Horn Book award 1991), Bathwater Gang, 1990, There's a Girl in My Hammerlock, 1991, Dump Days, 1991, Fourth Grade Rats, 1991, Bathwater Gang Get Down to Business, 1992, Do the Funky Pickle, 1992, Report to the Principal's Office!, 1992, Who Ran My Underwear Up the Flagpole?, 1992, Picklemania, 1993, Tooter Pepperday, 1995. Avocations: tennis, reading, country music, travel. *

SPINGLER, FRANK JOSEPH, lawyer; b. Poughkeepsie, N.Y., Dec. 29, 1945; s. Frank J. and Catherine W. Spingler; m. Susan Hueth, Apr. 25, 1986; 1 child, Erin. BA in English, St. Bonaventure U., 1967; JD, Georgetown U., 1970. Bar: D.C. 1972. Dir. real estate So. Ry. Co., Washington, 1976-80; gen. atty. Norfolk So. Ry., Washington, 1980-84; v.p. B.F. Saul Co., Chevy Chase, Md., 1984-87, Potomac Capital Investment Corp., Washington, 1987—. Serves as capt. USAR, 1971—. Mem. ABA, D.C. Bar Assn. Office: Potomac Capital Investment Corp 900 19th St NW Washington DC 20006-2100

SPINKS, JOHN LEE, engineering executive; b. Central City, Ky., June 19, 1924; s. William Lee and Lucy Susan (Greenwood) S.; m. Marion Louisa Mutz, Dec. 24, 1951; children—Susan Marie, Douglas John. B.S.M.E., U. Ky., 1951; postgrad., U. So. Calif., 1951-52, UCLA, 1957-58; grad., Res. Police Acad., 1977; Ph.D. (hon.), World U., 1984. Diplomate: Am. Acad. Environ. Engrs.; registered profl. engr., Calif., La., Tex., Del., Wis., N.H., Okla., Ky., Miss. cert. res. police officer class I Calif.; cert. energy mgr. Aerodynamicist Rockwell Internat., Los Angeles, 1951-52, Downey, Calif., 1954-55; engr. Bell Telephone Labs., Burlington, N.C., 1952-54, Mobil Oil Corp., Torrance, Calif., 1955-56; supervising engr. II S. Coast Air Quality Mgmt. Dist., El Monte, Calif., 1956-83; pres. Environ. Emissions Engring. Co., 1983—; dep. dir. civil engring. div., space div. USAF Res., Los Angeles AFB, 1961-73; cons. nat. and internat. govt. air quality agys. Co-author: Air Pollution Engineering Manual, 1967, 2d edit., 1973. Res. police officer Hermosa Beach Police Dept., 1977—; mgr. Little League Baseball, 1966-70; instr. rock and ice mountaineering; dir. AQMD Golf League, 1968-81; lectr. marathon running; usher St. Francis Episcopal Ch., Palos Verdes Estates, Calif., 1968-81. Served to lt. col. USAF, 1943-46. Decorated Air Force Commendation medal; recipient U.S. Presdl. Sports award in running, 1977, Sierra Peaks emblem; named to Hon. Order Ky. Cols. Fellow Inst. Advancement Engring. (Coll. of fellows), Am. Biog. Inst., Internat. Biog. Assn. (Eng.); mem. Nat. Soc. Profl. Engrs., Calif. Soc. Profl. Engrs., Air Pollution Control Assn., ASME, Inst. Environ. Scis., Soc. Environ. Engrs. (London), Am. Soc Engring. Edn., Soc. Engring. Sci., Assn. Energy Engrs., N.Y. Acad. Scis., Soc. Am. Mil. Engrs., AAAS, Internat. Backpackers Assn., Am. Assn. Engring. Soc., Appalachian Trail Conf., Am. Alpine Club, Austrian Alpine Club, Alpine Club Can., Himalayan Rescue Assn., U.S. Olympic Soc., Internat. Srs. Olympic Assn., Am. Med. Joggers Assn., Nat. Joggers Assn., Aerobics Internat. Research Soc., Mountain Safety Research Soc., Am. Coll. Sports Medicine, Nat. Athletic Health Inst., Wilderness Soc., Triangle Frat., Sierra Club. Clubs: Srs. Track, Pacific Crest. Home: 26856 Eastvale Rd Palos Verdes Peninsula CA 90274-4007 Office: Engring Co Environ Emissions Palos Verdes Peninsula CA 90274 The achievement of one's personal goals in itself has little meaning. Complete fulfillment comes with guiding youngsters in their formative years, helping them reach higher levels of motivation and social behavior to insure saneness for tomorrow.

SPINKS, MICHAEL, retired professional boxer; b. 1956; s. Leon and Kay S.; m. Sandy (dec.); 1 child, Michelle. Profl. boxer, 1976—. World Boxing Assn. Light-Heavyweight champion, 1981-86; World Boxing Council Light-Heavyweight champion, 1983-85; Internat. Boxing Fedn. Heavyweight champion, 1985-87; Gold medalist 1976 Olympics, Montreal, Can. Office: care Butch Lewis 250 W 57th St New York NY 10102-0158*

SPINKS, PAUL, retired library director; b. London, Mar. 7, 1922; came to U.S., 1952; m. Clarice Ada Goode, Jan. 27, 1946; 1 child, Philip Andrew. B.A., U. Okla., Norman, 1958; M.L.S., U. Okla., 1959. Catalog asst. Brit. Mus. Library, London, 1939-52; research reports librarian Naval Postgrad. Sch., Monterey, Calif., 1959-61; assoc. librarian Naval Postgrad. Sch., 1961-74, dir. libraries, 1975-93; prof. emeritus, 1993—. Author studies in field. Recipient Civilian Svc. Meritorious award USN, 1993. Mem. ALA, Spl. Libraries Assn., Am. Soc. Info. Sci. Episcopalian. Club: Brit.-Am. (sec. Monterey 1982-85). Home: 855 Capistrano Dr Salinas CA 93901-2420

SPINNER, ROBERT KEITH, hospital administrator; b. Mpls., Nov. 2, 1942; married. B, St. John's U., 1964; M, U. Minn., 1969. Adminstrv. resident Fairview Hosps., Mpls., 1968-69; adminstrv. trainee Abbott-Northwestern Hosp., Mpls., 1966-67, asst. adminstr., 1969-72, assoc. adminstr., 1972-76, adminstr., 1976-81, v.p. ops., 1981-82, exec. v.p., 1982-88, pres., 1988—. Home: 7722 Lochmere Ter Edina MN 55439 Office: Abbott-Northwestern Hosp 800 E 28th St Minneapolis MN 55407

SPINOTTI, DANTE, cinematographer. Cinematographer: (films) Sotto, Sotto, 1984, The Berlin Affair, 1985, Manhunter, 1986, Choke Canyon, 1986, Crimes of the Heart, 1986, From the Hip, 1987, Illegally Yours, 1987, Beaches, 1988, Mamba, 1988, Torrents of Spring, 1989, True Colors, 1991, The Comfort of Strangers, 1991, Frankie and Johnny, 1992, (with Doug Milsome) The Last of the Mohicans, 1992, Nell, 1994. Office: Smith/Gosnell/Nicholson & Assoc PO Box 1166 1515 Palisades Dr Pacific Palisades CA 90272*

SPINRAD, BERNARD ISRAEL, physicist, educator; b. N.Y.C., Apr. 16, 1924; s. Abraham and Rose (Sorrin) S.; m. Marion Eisen, June 29, 1951; children: Alexander Abraham, Mark David, Jeremy Paul, Diana Esther; m. Lois Ringston Helton, Jan. 28, 1983. BS with honors, Yale, 1942, MS, 1944, PhD in Phys. Chemistry, 1945, Sterling fellow postdoctoral research, 1945-46. Physicist Oak Ridge Nat. Lab., 1946-48; mem. staff Argonne Nat. Lab., 1949-67, 70-72, dir. reactor engring. div., 1957-63, sr. physicist applied physics div., 1963-67, 70-72; dir. div. nuclear power and reactors IAEA, Vienna, Austria, 1967-70; prof. nuclear engring. Oreg. State U., Corvallis, 1972-82, prof. emeritus, 1983—; prof., chmn. dept. nuclear engring. Iowa State U., Ames, 1983-90, prof. emeritus, 1990—; adviser U.S. delegation Internat. Conf. Peaceful Uses Atomic Energy, Geneva, 1955, 58; cons. IAEA, 1961, 63, 72, 74; chmn. European-Am. Com. Reactor Physics, 1962-64; mem. com. nuclear and alternative energy systems NRC, 1974-79, com. innovative concepts and approaches to energy conservation, 1984-85, com. univ. research reactors, 1986-88; vis. researcher Internat. Inst. Applied Systems Analysis, Vienna, 1978-79, chmn. nuclear engring. dept. head orgn., 1986-87. Author books, papers and reports in field; mem. editorial bd. Annals of Nuclear Energy. Named Man of Year Chgo., 1956, Man of Year Hinsdale, Ill., 1958. Fellow Am. Phys. Soc., Am. Nuclear Soc. (past dir.); mem. AAAS, Am. Chem. Soc., UN Assn. Am., Sigma Xi. Address: 18803 37th Ave NE Seattle WA 98155-2713 *I have lived by trying to understand the rich fabric of the world and our lives, and I love the richness. All the elements should be in it, and this means that apparent contradictions are to be harmonized and resolved, rather than set against each other. I find that I have to be selectively moderate, aggressively opposing the nonsense which is bound up with the valid points in polarized ideologies. It is an attitude which is a bit lonely, for it rejects blind loyalty and blind faith, but I value the dignity of it.*

SPINRAD, HYRON, astronomer; b. N.Y.C., Feb. 17, 1934; s. Emanuel B. and Ida (Silverman) S.; m. Bette L. Abrams, Aug. 17, 1958; children—Michael, Robert, Tracy. A.B., U. Calif. at Berkeley, 1955, M.A., 1959, Ph.D. (Lick Obs. fellow), 1961. Studied galaxies U. Calif. at Berkeley, 1960-61; planetary atmospheres work Jet Propulsion Lab., Pasadena, Calif., 1961-63; investigation atmospheres of coolest stars U. Calif. at Berkeley, 1964-70. Mem. Am. Astron. Soc., Astron. Soc. Pacific. Spl. research water vapor on Mars, molecular hydrogen on Jupiter, Saturn, Uranus and Neptune, temperature measurements on Venus atmosphere, spectra of galaxies and near-infrared observations, 71-72, location of faint radio galaxies, redshifts of galaxies, galaxy evolution and cosmology, 1973, spectroscopic observations of volatile gases in comets. Home: 7 Ketelsen Ct Moraga CA 94556-1814 Office: Univ California Dept Astronomy Berkeley CA 94720

SPINRAD, ROBERT JOSEPH, computer scientist; b. N.Y.C., Mar. 20, 1932; s. Sidney and Isabel (Reiff) S.; m. Verna Winderman, June 27, 1954; children: Susan Irene, Paul Reiff. B.S., Columbia U., 1953, M.S. (Bridgham fellow), 1954; Ph.D. (Whitney fellow), MIT, 1963. Registered profl. engr., N.Y. Project engr. Bulova Research & Devel. Lab., N.Y.C., 1953-55; sr. scientist Brookhaven Nat. Lab., Upton, N.Y., 1955-68; v.p. Sci. Data Systems, Santa Monica, Calif., 1968-69; v.p. programming Xerox Corp., El Segundo, Calif., 1969-71; dir. info. scis. Xerox Corp., 1971-76, v.p. systems devel., 1976-78; v.p. research Xerox Corp., Palo Alto, 1978-83; dir. systems tech. Xerox Corp., 1983-87, dir. corp. tech., 1987-92, v.p. tech. analysis and devel., 1992-94; v.p., tech. strategy, 1994—; cons. Contbr. articles to profl. jours. Mem. IEEE, Assn. for Computing Machinery, Nat. Acad. Engring., Sigma Xi, Tau Beta Pi. Achievements include patents in field. Office: Xerox Corp 3333 Coyote Hill Rd Palo Alto CA 94304-1314

SPINWEBER, CHERYL LYNN, research psychologist; b. Jersey City, July 26, 1950; d. Stanley A. And Evelyn M. (Pfleger) S.; m. Michael E. Bruich, June 18, 1977; children: Sean Michael Bruich, Gregory Alan Bruich. AB with distinction, Cornell U., 1972; PhD in Exptl. Psychology, Harvard U., 1977. Lic. psychologist, Calif. Asst. prof. psychiatry Tufts U. Sch. Medicine, Medford, Mass., 1977-79; asst. dir. sleep lab. Boston State Hosp., 1973-79; dep. head dept. behavioral psychopharmacology Naval Health Research Ctr., San Diego, 1979-86, head dept. behavioral psychopharmacology, 1986-89; research asst. prof. dept. psychiatry Uniformed Svcs. U. of the Health Scis., Bethesda, Md., 1985—; lectr. workshop instr. U. Calif. San Diego, La Jolla, 1979-81, vis. lectr. 1979-86; assoc. adj. prof. Dept. Psychology, 1989-94, adj. prof., 1994—; courtesy clin. staff oppointee dept. psychiatry Naval Hosp., San Diego, 1984—; clin. dir. Sleep Disorders Ctr. Mercy Hosp., San Diego, 1991—; pediatric sleep specialist Children's Hosp., San Diego, 1992—. Contbr. articles to profl. jours. Scholar Cornell U., Ithaca, N.Y., 1968-72, West Essex Tuition, 1968-72, Cornell U. Fedn. Women, 1917-72, Harvard U., 1972-73, 74-76, NDEA Title IV, 1973-74; postdoctoral associateship Nat. Research Council, 1978-80, Outstanding Tchg. award U. Calif. San Diego, 1994. Fellow Am. Sleep Disorders Assn., Clin. Sleep Soc., We. Psychol. Assn. (sec.-treas. 1986—); mem. Am. Men and Women of Sci., Sleep Rsch. Soc. (exec. com. 1986-89), Calif. Sleep Soc., Sigma Xi. Office: U Calif San Diego Dept Psychology 0109 La Jolla CA 92093

SPIOTTA, RAYMOND HERMAN, consulting editor; b. Bklyn., Feb. 24, 1927; s. Michael Joseph and Olga Elizabeth (Schmidt) S.; m. Maria Theresa Attanasio, Apr. 17, 1949; children: Robert, Michael, Ronald, Mark, Sandra. B.M.E., Pratt Inst., 1953. Mfg. engr. Arma div. Am. Bosch Arma Corp., Garden City, N.Y., 1948-53; mng. editor Machinery mag., N.Y.C., 1953-65; editor Machine and Tool Blue Book, Wheaton, Ill., 1965-89; editorial dir. Machine and Tool Blue Book & Mfg. Systems, Carol Stream, Ill., 1989-90; cons. editor Cutting Tool Engring., Northbrook, Ill., 1992—. Contbr. to Am. Peoples Ency. Yearbook; contbr. articles to profl. jours. Mem. DuPage County (Ill.) area council Boy Scouts Am., 1966-73. Served with AC USNR, 1944-48. Mem. Numerical Control Soc. of AIM-Tech., Soc. Am. Value Engrs., Soc. Mfg. Engrs., Am. Inst. Indsl. Engrs., Robotics Internat. Roman Catholic. Home and Office: 1484 Aberdeen Ct Naperville IL 60564

SPIOTTO, JAMES ERNEST, lawyer; b. Chgo., Nov. 25, 1946; s. Michael Angelo and Vinnetta Catherine (Henninger) S.; m. Ann Elizabeth Humphreys, Dec. 23, 1972; children: Michael Thomas, Mary Catherine, Joan Elizabeth, Kathryn Ann. AB, St. Mary's of the Lake, 1968; JD, U. Chgo., 1972. Bar: Ill. 1972, U.S. Dist. Ct. (no. dist.) Ill. 1973, U.S.C. Appeals (3rd and 7th cir.) 1974, U.S. Supreme Ct. 1978, U.S.C. Appeals (9th cir.) 1984, U.S. Dist. Ct. (so. dist.) Calif. 1984. Exclusionary rule study-project dir. Law Enforcement Assistance Agy. Grant, Chgo., 1972; law clk. to presiding justice U.S. Dist. Ct., Chgo., 1972-74; assoc. Chapman and Cutler, Chgo., 1974-80, ptnr., 1980—; chmn. program on defaulted bonds and bankruptcy Practising Law Inst., 1982—; chmn program on troubled debt financing, 1987—. Author: Defaulted Securities, 1990; contbr. numerous articles to profl. jours. With USAR, 1969-75. Mem. Assn. Bond Lawyers, Law Club of City of Chgo., Union League. Roman Catholic. Office: Chapman and Cutler 111 W Monroe St Chicago IL 60603-4080

SPIRA, JOEL SOLON, electronics company executive; b. N.Y.C., Mar. 1, 1927; m. Ruth Rodale, Nov. 7, 1954; children: Susan, Lily, Juno. BS in Physics, Purdue U., 1948. Project engr. Reeves Instrument Corp., Paramus, N.J., 1952-59; prin. systems analyst ITT Communications Systems, Paramus, 1959-61; pres., dir. tech. Lutron Electronics Co., Coopersburg, Pa., 1961-90, chmn., 1990—. Office: Lutron Electronics Co Inc 7200 Suter Rd Coopersburg PA 18036

SPIRA, MELVIN, plastic surgeon; b. Chgo., July 3, 1925; s. Samuel and Jessie (Tivin) S.; m. Rita Silver, Nov. 27, 1952; children—Mary Ann, Joel Bennett, Pamela Beth. Student, Wright Jr. Coll, Chgo., 1942-43, Franklin and Marshall Coll., Lancaster, Pa., 1943-44; DDS, Northwestern U., 1947, MSD, 1951; MD, Med. Coll. of Ga., 1956. Diplomate Am. Bd. Plastic Surgery. Intern Duke U. Hosp., Durham, N.C., 1956-57, jr. asst. resident, 1958-59, asst. resident, 1959-60; resident Jefferson Davis Hosp, Houston, 1960-61, asst. in surgery and plastic surgery; sr. attending physician Ben Taub Gen. Hosp, Houston, chief of plastic surgery; attending physician Tex. Children's Hosp., Houston; chief plastic surgery Meth. Hosp., Houston, St. Lukes Episc. Hosp., Houston, VA Hosp., Houston; prof. Baylor Coll. Medicine, Houston, head div. plastic surgery; chmn. Am. Bd. Plastic Surgery, 1984-85. Served with USN, 1943-45, 48-50. Fellow ACS; mem. Houston Surg. Soc., Am. Soc. Maxillofacial Surgeons (pres. 1974-75), Am. Soc. Plastic and Reconstructive Surgeons, Harris County Med. Soc., Plastic Surgery Research Council, So. Med. Assn., Tex. Med. Assn., Am. Trauma Soc., G.V. Black Soc., Internat. Soc. for Burn Injuries, Am. Burn Assn., Am. Cleft Palate Assn., Am. Assn. Plastic Surgeons (pres. 1992-93), Acad. Plastic Surgery Forum, Internat. Soc. Reconstructive Microsurgery, Tex. Surg. Soc., Michael E. DeBakey Internat. Cardiovascular Soc., Baron Hardy Soc., Am. Soc. for Aesthetic Plastic Surgery, Alpha Omega Alpha, Sigma Xi. Avocations: snow skiing; photography; painting; tennis. Office: Baylor Coll Medicine Div Plastic Surgery 6560 Fannin St Ste 800 Houston TX 77030-2725

SPIRA, PATRICIA G., performing arts association executive; b. Milw.; d. Lawrence Manfred and Ruth Pauline (Miller) Goodsitt; m. Marvin Alfred Spira, July 12, 1952; children: David, James, Ann, Ellen. BA in History, U. Wis., Milw., 1967. Dir. group sales Swan Theatre and Supper Club, Milw., 1962-63; mgr. box office Performing Arts Ctr., Milw., 1969-80; dir. devel. St. Louis Conservatory and Schs., 1980-81; pres. Box Office Mgmt. Internat., N.Y.C., 1981—; tchr. Creative Dramatics, Milw., 1962-66; adv. coun. Town Hall, N.Y.C., 1989—; bd. dirs. Theatre and Dance Co., N.Y.C., 1986-89. bd. dirs. Milw. Chamber Music Soc., 1974-80. Mem. Am. Soc. Assn. Execs., N.Y. Soc. Assn. Execs. Avocations: reading, travel, theater. Office: Box Office Mgmt Internat 250 W 57th St # 722 New York NY 10107

SPIRES, ROBERT CECIL, foreign language educator; b. Missouri Valley, Iowa, Dec. 1, 1936; s. Roy C. and Ellen M. (Epperson) S.; m. Roberta A. Hyde, Feb. 2, 1963; children: Jeffrey R., Leslie Ann. BA, U. Iowa, 1959, MA, 1963, PhD, 1968. Asst. prof. Ohio U., Athens, 1967-69; asst. prof. dept. Spanish and Portuguese U. Kans., Lawrence, 1969-72, assoc. prof., 1972-78, prof., 1978—, chmn. dept., 1983-92. Author: La novela española, 1978, Beyond the Metafictional Mode, 1984, Transparent Simulacra, 1988; contbg. editor SigloXX/20th Century; editorial bd. Jour. of Interdisciplinary Literary Studies, 1993—, Ind. Jour. of Hispanic Lit., 1992— Served with U.S. Army, 1959-61. NEH fellow, 1981-82, U.S.-Spain Joint Com. fellow, 1985-86, Hall Ctr. for Humanities fellow, 1992, Program Cultural Coop. fellow, 1993. Mem. Revista de Estudios Hispánicos (editorial bd. 1985—), Anales de Literatura Contemporánea (editorial bd. 1981—), Letras Peninsulares (editorial bd. 1987—), MLA (del. assembly 1989-91), MLA 20th Century Spain (exec. com. 1983-89), 20th Century Spanish Assn. Am. (v.p. 1989-92). Home: 2420 Orchard Ln Lawrence KS 66049-2710 Office: U Kans Dept Spanish & Portuguese Lawrence KS 66045-0239

SPIRN, MICHELE SOBEL, communications professional, writer; b. Newark, Jan. 26, 1943; d. Jack and Sylvia (Cohen) Sobel; m. Steven Frederick Spirn, Jan. 27, 1968; 1 child, Joshua. BA, Syracuse U., 1965. Creative dir. Planned Communications Svcs., N.Y.C., 1966-72, EDL Prodns., N.Y.C., 1972-73; free-lance writer Bklyn., 1973-83; dir. pub. rels. Nat. Coun. Jewish Women, N.Y.C., 1983-90, dir. communications, 1990-95; freelance writer Bklyn., 1995—; adj. lectr. CUNY, Bklyn., 1977-81. Author: The Fast Shoes, 1985, The Boy Who Liked Green, 1985, The Know-Nothings, 1995; co-author: A Man Can Be..., 1981; editor, columnist Children's Entertainment Rev. mag., N.Y.C., 1982; columnist The Phoenix newspaper, Bklyn., 1983. Pres. Tenth St. Block Assn., Bklyn., 1989-91; vol. Model Media Program, Bklyn., 1985—. Recipient Silver medal for pub. svc. film N.Y. Internat. Film and TV Festival, 1972. Mem. Editl. Freelancers Assn. Avocations: reading, gardening.

SPIRO, BENJAMIN PAUL, economist, consultant; b. Concise, Switzerland, June 6, 1917; came to U.S., 1941, naturalized, 1948; s. Louis and Jeanne (Secretan) S.; m. Nelly Riveros, Oct. 2, 1963; 1 son, Cyril Sven. Lic.Sc.Pol., U. Lausanne, 1939, Lic.Sc.Ec., 1940, Dr.Sc.Pol., 1941; postgrad., Columbia U., 1941-42. Sec. to Swiss Legation, Washington, 1943-45; with Irving Trust Co., N.Y.C., 1945-46; mem. faculty Duke U., 1946-47; with World Bank, 1947-59; pres. Bank-Fund (credit union), 1959-60; with Stanford Research Inst., 1959; fgn. econ. and financial cons. to internat. orgns., govts., pvt. cos. San Francisco, 1961—; pres. Benjamin Spiro Assos., Inc., San Francisco, 1962—; Adviser Central Bank and Nat. Bank Econ. Devel., Brazil, 1965-67, Indonesian Devel. Bank, 1968; integrated regional devel. projects in, Morocco, 1969-71, Iran, 1972-75, East Africa, 1975-76, Yemen, 1977; promoted small-scale industry devel. in, Latin Am., Africa, 1978—. Contbr. to profl. lit. Active Boy Scouts Am., 1941-60. Served with Swiss Army, 1937-41. Recipient Silver Beaver award, 1953. Mem. Nat. Democratic Club. Home: Le Mazot, 1857 Huemoz Switzerland Office: 3309 Stephenson Pl NW Washington DC 20015-2451

SPIRO, HERBERT JOHN, political scientist, politician, educator, ambassador; b. Hamburg, Germany, Sept. 7, 1924; came to U.S., 1938, naturalized, 1944; s. Albert John and Marianne (Stiefel) S.; m. Elizabeth Anna Petersen, June 7, 1958 (div.); children: Peter John, Alexander Charles Stiefel; m. Marion Ballin, July 22, 1985. Student, San Antonio Jr. Coll., 1942-43; AB summa cum laude, Harvard U., 1949, MA, 1950, PhD, 1953; MA (hon.), U. Pa., 1971. Adminstrv. asst. U.S. War Dept., Vienna, Austria, 1945-46; mem. faculty Harvard U., Cambridge, Mass., 1950-61, asst. prof., 1957-61; assoc. prof. polit. sci. Amherst (Mass.) Coll., 1961-65; prof. polit. sci. U. Pa., Phila., 1965-73; mem. policy planning staff Dept. State, Washington, 1970-75; ambassador to Cameroon, 1975-77; amb. to Equatorial Guinea, 1975-76; fellow Woodrow Wilson Internat. Ctr. for Scholars, Smithsonian Instn., Washington, 1978; vis. prof. polit. sci. Def. Intelligence Sch., Washington, 1979-80; univ. prof. polit. sci. John F. Kennedy Inst. for N.Am. Studies, Free U. Berlin, 1980-89; Fulbright sr. research prof. U. Coll. Rhodesia and Nyasaland, 1959-60; cons. Brit. Commn. to Rev. Constn., Fedn. Rhodesia and Nyasaland, 1960, Japanese Commn. on Revision Constn., 1962; vis. assoc. prof. U. Chgo., 1961, Stanford (Calif.) U., 1963; chmn. Asian and African Studies program, Amherst-Smith-Mt. Holyoke Colls., U. Mass., 1964-65; vis. prof. internat. affairs Woodrow Wilson Sch., Princeton (N.J.) U., 1966; mem. adv. council polit. sci. Haverford Coll., 1966-71; affiliated with Nuffield Coll., Oxford (Eng.) U., 1967-68; resident scholar Rockefeller Found. Study Ctr., Bellagio, Italy, 1968, 78; vis. prof. govt., guest scholar Ctr. for Internat. Affairs, Harvard U., 1983; vis. scholar U. Tex., Austin, 1984-89; life mem. Brit. studies faculty seminar U. Tex., Austin, 1983—; researcher Lyndon Baines Johnson Presdl. Library, 1985-86; fellow Aspen (Colo.) Inst. Humanistic Studies, 1986; adj. prof. govt. U. Tex., Austin, 1989-91; participant internat scholarly and diplomatic confs.; lectr. various univs. Author: Politics of German Confederation, 1958, (with others) Patterns of Government, 1958, 2d edit., 1962, Government by Constitution, 1959, Politics in Africa, 1962, 2d edit., 1975, Five African States, 1963, World Politics: The Global System, 1966, (with others) Authority, Nomos I, 1958, Community, Nomos II, 1959, Responsibility, Nomos III, 1960, Privacy Nomos XIII, 1971, Why Federations Fail, 1968, Responsibility in Government, 1969, The Dialectic of Representation 1619-1969, 1969, Politics as the Master Science: From Plato to Mao, 1970, Theory and Politics, 1971, Between Sovereignty and Integration, 1974, A New Foreign Policy Consensus?, 1979, (with others) The Legacy of the Constitution, 1987, (with others) Anti-Americanism, 1988; editor, contbr.: (with others) Africa: The Primacy of Politics, 1966, Patterns of African Development, 1967; contbr. to: World Book Ency., Ency. Britannica, Intern. Ency. of the Social Scis.; host Spiro's Conversations, Austin Community TV, 1990-92; precinct chmn. Travis County; Rep. cand. for Tex. Ho. of Reps., 1991, U.S. House of Reps. 1992, 94. Decorated Bronze Star with oak leaf cluster, Purple Heart; grand officer Legion of Valor Cameroon, 1977; recipient Detur prize Harvard Coll., 1948, Bowdoin prize, 1952; John Harvard scholar, 1949-51, Holzer scholar, 1949-51; Guggenheim fellow, 1959-60, Social Sci. Research Council faculty fellow, 1962, 67-68, Rockefeller Found. fellow, 1958, Sheldon travelling fellow Harvard U., also Fulbright fellow, 1953-54; Moody grantee Lyndon Baines Johnson Found., 1985. Fellow Assn. for Diplomatic Studies; mem. African Studies Assn., Am. Polit. Sci. Assn. (coun. 1968-70, chmn. election com. 1969), Internat. Polit. Sci. Assn., Am. Soc. Polit. and Legal Philosophy, Ambs. Forum Reps. Abroad, Coun. Fgn. Rels., Internat. Rep. Inst., Am. Coun. on Germany, Coun. Am.

Ambs., Am. Fgn. Svc. Assn., Mil.rder Purple Heart, Austin Com. Fgn. Affairs (dir.), Tex. Harvard Alumni Assn. (appointed regional dir. 1994—), Signet Soc., Harvard U. Faculty Club, Harvard Club (N.Y.C.), Harvard Club Berlin (pres. 1985-89), Harvard Club Austin (pres. 1990-92), Phi Beta Kappa. Republican. Address: Towers of Town Lake 40 N I H 35 Apt 4b3 Austin TX 78701-4329

SPIRO, HOWARD MARGET, physician, educator; b. Cambridge, Mass., Mar. 23, 1924; s. Thomas and Martha (Marget); m. Marian Freelove Wagner, Mar 11, 1951; children—Pamela Marget, Carolyn Standish, Philip Marget, Martha Standish. B.A., Harvard, 1944, M.D., 1947; M.A., Yale, 1967. Intern Peter Bent Brigham Hosp., Boston, 1947-48; resident Peter Bent Brigham Hosp., 1948-51, Mass. Gen. Hosp., 1953-55; practice medicine, specializing in gastroenterology New Haven, 1955—; chief gastrointestinal unit Yale Sch. Medicine, 1955-82, prof. medicine, 1967—, dir. program for humanities in medicine, 1983—. Author: Clinical Gastroenterology, 1970, 4th edit., 1993, Doctors, Patients and Placebos, 1986; editor: Jour. Clin. Gastroenterology, 1979—, (with others) When Doctors Get Sick, 1987, Empathy and the Practice of Medicine, 1993. Served with USNR, 1943-45; Served with AUS, 1951-53. Mem. ACP (master). Club: Madison Beach. Home: 89 Middle Beach Rd Madison CT 06443-3006 Office: Box 3333 333 Cedar St New Haven CT 06520-8019

SPIRO, MELFORD ELLIOT, anthropology educator; b. Cleve., Apr. 26, 1920; s. Wilbert I. and Sophie (Goodman) S.; m. Audrey Goldman, May 27, 1950; children: Michael, Jonathan. B.A., U. Minn., 1941; Ph.D., Northwestern U., 1950. Mem. faculty Washington U., St. Louis, 1948-52, U. Conn., 1952-57, U. Wash., 1957-64; prof. anthropology U. Chgo., 1964-68; prof., chmn. dept. anthropology U. Calif., San Diego, 1968—; Bd. dirs. Social Sci. Research Council, 1960-62. Author: (with E.G. Burrows) An Atoll Culture, 1953, Kibbutz: Venture in Utopia, 1955, Children of Kibbutz, 1958, Burmese Supernaturalism, 1967, Buddhism and Society: A Great Tradition and Its Burmese Vicissitudes, 1971, Kinship and Marriage in Burma, 1977, Gender and Culture: Kibbutz Women Revisited, 1979, Human Nature and Culture, 1993; editor: Context and Meaning in Culture Anthropology, 1965, Oedipus in the Trobriands, 1982, Burmese Brother or Anthropological Other?, 1992. Fellow Am. Acad. Arts and Scis., Nat. Acad. Scis.; mem. Am. Anthrop. Assn., Am. Ethnol. Soc. (pres. 1967-68), AAAS, Soc. for Psychol. Anthropology (pres. 1979-80). Home: 2500 Torrey Pines Rd La Jolla CA 92037-3431

SPIRO, ROBERT HARRY, JR., foundation and business executive, educator; b. Asheville, N.C., Dec. 5, 1920; s. Robert Harry and Eoline Peterson (Shaw) S.; m. Terrie C. Gay, May 17, 1980; children by previous marriage: Robert Timothy, Elizabeth Susan, James Monroe. BS, Wheaton (Ill.) Coll., 1941; postgrad. Navy Supply Sch., Harvard U., 1943; postgrad., U. N.C., 1945-46; PhD, U. Edinburgh, Scotland, 1950; student, Union Theol. Sem., summers 1951-53; postdoctoral, Duke U., summer 1954; ScD (hon.), Fla. Inst. Tech. Assoc., then prof. history King Coll., Bristol, Tenn., 1946-50; prof. history Miss. Coll., 1950-57; pres. Blue Ridge Assembly, Black Mountain, N.C., 1957-60; dean Coll. Liberal Arts Mercer U., prof. history, 1960-64; pres. Jacksonville U., Fla., 1964-79; under sec. of Army, 1980-81; cons. to bus., 1981-84, 86—; nat. exec. dir. Res. Officers Assn. U.S., 1984-86; chmn. RHS Imprinted Products Inc.; v.p. Crescent Fin. Corp.; bd. mgrs. Voyager Variable Annuity of Fla., 1972-79; v.p. Am. Sec. Coun. Found.; past pres. Fla. Assn. Colls. and Univs.; trustee Southwestern Bapt. Theol. Sem., 1968-78; mem., past chmn. Ind. Colls. and Univs. Fla., 1964-79, chmn., 1967; sec.-treas. Assn. Urban Univs., 1968-76; mem. Fla.-Columbia Ptnrs.; gen. chmn. Jacksonville Sesquicentennial Commn., 1970-72; mem. N.C. Tricentennial Commn., 1962—; past mem. adv. coun. Robert A. Taft Inst. Govt., Inst. Internat. Edn. Contbr. articles to profl. publs. and encys. Trustee Southwestern Bapt. Theol. Sem., 1968-78; mem. Fla.-Columbia Ptnrs.; gen. chmn. Jacksonville Sesquicentennial Commn., 1970-72; mem. N.C. Tricentennial Commn., 1962—; chmn. bd. Bapt. Coll. and Sem., Washington. Lt. USNR, 1941-45; ret. rear adm. USNR, 1978. Decorated Palmes Academique (France); recipient Disting. Civilian Svc. award Dept. of Army, 1981. Mem. Navy League U.S. (former pres. Jacksonville coun.), Naval Res. Assn. (nat. adv. coun.), Res. Officers Assn., Ret. Officers Assn., Am. Legion, Kiwanis (pres. Georgetown, D.C. club 1991-92), Army-Navy Country Club (Arlington, Va.), Army and Navy Club (Washington), Phi Delta Kappa, Alpha Kappa Psi, Phi Alpha Theta, Phi Kappa Phi. Home: 5821 Colfax Ave Alexandria VA 22311-1013 *Esse Quam Videre—"To Be Rather than to Seem"—is an eloquent apothegm I learned in high school Latin classes. For me it has been a demanding goal for daily living, a worthy aspiration for each task in life and a challenging vision of what I wish and ought to be.*

SPIRO, THOMAS GEORGE, chemistry educator; b. Aruba, Netherlands Antilles, Nov. 7, 1935; s. Andor and Ilona S.; m. Helen Handin, Aug. 21, 1959; children—Peter, Michael. Bs, UCLA, 1956; Ph.D., M.I.T., 1960. Fulbright researcher U. Copenhagen, Denmark, 1960-61; NIH fellow Royal Inst. Tech., Stockholm, 1962-63; research chemist Calif. Research Corp., LaHabra, 1961-62; mem. faculty Princeton U., 1963—, prof. chemistry, 1974—, head dept., 1979-88, Eugene Higgins prof., 1981—. Author: (with William M. Stigliani) Environmental Issues in Chemical Perspective, 1980, Environmental Science in Perspective, 1980; contbr. articles to profl. jours. Recipient Bomem-Michelson award Bomem Corp., 1986; NATO sr. fellow, 1972, Guggenheim fellow, 1990. Fellow AAAS; mem. Am. Chem. Soc., Phi Beta Kappa, Sigma Xi. Office: Princeton U Dept Chemistry Princeton NJ 08544

SPIRO, WALTER ANSELM, advertising and public relations agency executive; b. Berlin, Germany, Aug. 10, 1923; came to U.S., 1940, naturalized, 1945; s. Harry L. and Kate (Loewenstein) S.; children: Karen Leslie, Pamela Anne, Paul David, Amy Eloise. Student, Athelton Coll., affiliate Cambridge U., Folkestone, Eng., 1938-40. Display dir. Allied Stores, N.Y.C., 1947-51; advt. dir. Gimbel Bros., Phila., 1951-58; exec. v.p. Lavenson Bur. Advt., Phila., 1958-64; chmn. Spiro & Assocs. (now Earle Palmer Brown & Spiro), Phila., 1964—. Bd. dirs. Pa. Ballet, 1982—; bd. dirs. Pa. Hosp., 1984—; trustee Phila. United Fund, 1973—, Phila. Orch. Assn., 1981—, Phila. Mus. Art, 1981—; bd. dirs., mem. exec. com. Urban Affairs Partnership; mem. founding group Global InterDependence Center, 1978—; mem. leadership com. Bus. Leaders Organized for Catholic Schs., 1981—; founding mem. Bus. Execs. for Nuclear Arms Control, 1983—; bd. dirs. Greater Phila. First Corp., 1983—, WHYY-TV & FM radio broadcasting stas. Mem. World Affairs Council Phila. (dir. 1971—, vice-chmn. 1974-78), Am. Assn. Advt. Agys. (com. of bd. agy. mgmt.). Clubs: Downtown, Urban, Vesper, Peale, Sunday Breakfast. Home: 1900 Rittenhouse Sq Philadelphia PA 19103-5735 Office: Earle Palmer Brown & Spiro 1 Liberty Pl 1650 Market St Philadelphia PA 19103-7337

SPISAK, JOHN FRANCIS, environmental company executive; b. Cleve., Mar. 27, 1950; s. Ernest Lawrence and Adele Marie (Chipko) S.; m. Barbara Ann Heisman, June 10, 1972; children: John Stefan, Theresa Rose. BS in Chemistry, Purdue U., 1972, BS in Biology with honors, 1972. Rsch. engr. Anaconda Minerals, Tucson, 1972-79; chief metallurgist Fed. Am. Uranium, Riverton, Wyo., 1979-80; v.p. ops. Anschutz Mining Corp., Denver, 1980-87; chmn. bd. dirs. Warrenton Refining (subs. of Anschutz Corp.), Denver, 1987-89; CEO SP Environ./Indsl. Compliance, Denver, 1989—; mem. Western States-U.S. Senate Coalition for Superfund Reform. Contbr. articles to profl. publs.; patentee sequential flotation of sulfide ores. Named One of Fifty Colo. Top Bus. Leaders, Colo. Assn. Commerce and Industry. Mem. AIME, Soc. Mining, Metallurgy and Exploration, Nat. Assn. Environ. Mgrs. (co-founder, bd. dirs. Washington chpg., co-chmn. govt. liaison and advocacy com.), Denver Club, Elks. Republican. Roman Catholic. Avocations: classical piano, cycling, model railroads. Home: 9570 Lacosta Ln Littleton CO 80124-8909 Office: Indsl Compliance Union Tower 165 S Union #1000 Lakewood CO 80228

SPITLER, KENNETH F., wholesale distribution executive; b. 1949. With Miesel/Sysco Food Svc. Co., Canton, Mich., 1986—, pres. Office: Miesel/Sysco Food Svc Co 41600 Van Born Rd Canton MI 48188-2797*

SPITLER, LEE WILLIAM, banker; b. Racine, Wis., Feb. 14, 1919; s. Marion Albert and Agnes Elizabeth (Lowe) S.; m. Helen Deloris Krejci, Mar. 19, 1949; children—Susan D., Lee William, Anne M., James E. B.S.,

U. Md., 1956; M.B.A., George Washington U., 1962; postgrad. advanced mgmt. program, Harvard U., 1963; grad., U.S. Air Force War Coll., 1959, U.S. Air Force Command and Staff Coll., 1955. Commd. 2d lt. U.S. Air Force, 1943, advanced through grades to col., 1956; chief personnel stats. div. Hdqrs. U.S. Air Force, Washington, 1950-54; asst. dir. statis. services U.S. Air Force, 1958-63; asst. comptroller Hdqrs. U.S. European Command U.S. Air Force, Paris, 1955-58; asst. comptroller Hdqrs. Air Tng. Command U.S. Air Force, Randolph AFB, Tex., 1963-64; ret. U.S. Air Force, 1964; v.p. Computax Corp., El Segundo, Calif., 1965-69; exec. v.p. Irving Bank Corp., N.Y.C., 1969-84; sr. exec. v.p Irving Trust Co., N.Y.C., 1969-84; ret., 1984; pres. Spitler Fin. Svcs., Monterey, Calif., 1985—; dir. Turkiye Tutunculer Bankasi AS, Izmir, Turkey, 1984-87. mem. nat. adv. bd. Am. Security Council. Decorated Legion of Merit. Mem. Internat. Assn. Fin. Planning, Am. Bankers Assn., Am. Mgmt. Assn., Soc. for Mgmt. Info. Systems, Ret. Officers Assn., Nat. Assn. Uniformed Services, Mil. Order World Wars, Am. Assn. Mil. Comptrollers, Am. Legion, Veterans of Fgn. Wars, Am. Assn. Ret. Personnel, Inst. Cert. Planners, Air War Coll. Alumni Assn., First Fighter Group Assn. Clubs: Harvard, West Point Officers. Home: 200 Glenwood Cir Apt 525 Monterey CA 93940-6747 Office: 200 Glenwood Circle Monterey CA 93940

SPITTLE, JAMES PRATT, arts administrator; b. Detroit, Feb. 4, 1952; s. Fredrick Jackson and Mary (Steiger) S.; m. Hilary Rose, Sept. 8, 1984; 1 child, Thea Charlotte. BS in Theatre, Ea. N.Mex. U., 1974. Stagehand Santa Fe (N.Mex.) Opera Co., 1972-73; tech. dir. Ea. N.Mex. U., Portales, 1974-76; scene shop foreman Meadow Brook Theatre, Rochester, Mich., 1979-82, 84-85; mng. dir. Meadow Brook Theatre, Rochester, 1985-92; prodn. coord. Birmingham (Mich.) Theatre, 1982-83; prodn. stage mgr. Detroit Inst. of Art, 1983-84; prodn. dir. Meadow Brook Music Festival, Rochester, 1982-86; exec. dir. Tibbits Opera Found. and Arts Coun. Mem. Alpha Psi Omega. Presbyterian. Avocations: reading, music, baseball, gardening. Office: Tibbits Opera House 14 S Hanchett St Coldwater MI 49036-1907

SPITTLER, JAYNE ZENATY, advertising executive; b. Chgo., July 24, 1948; d. Ernest Frederick and Mary Winifred (McEvilly) Zenaty; m. Joseph R. Spittler, Aug. 22, 1987; 1 child, Brian Joseph. BA, Clarke Coll., 1971; PhD, Mich. State U., 1980. Asst. dir. pub. rels. Clarke Coll., Dubuque, Iowa, 1974-76; asst. prof. dept. telecommunications Ind. U., Bloomington, 1979-81; supr. media rsch. Leo Burnett Co., Inc., Chgo., 1981-82, mgr. media rsch., 1982-84, v.p., dir. media rsch., 1984—; guest lectr. Northwestern U., Evanston, Il., 1981—. Vol. ARC, McHenry County, Ill.; zoo parent Brookfield (Ill.) Zoo, 1975—. Named to Media Rsch. All Star Team, Media Decisions, N.Y., 1987; recipient Excellence in Teaching award, Mich. State U., 1979, grant broadcast ownership, FCC, 1979, grant VCR Usage, Corp. for Pub. Broadcasting, 1980. Mem. Advt. Rsch. Found. (chair video electronic media coun. 1990-94, media comm. coun. mem. 1986—, radio rsch. coun. 1988—), Chgo. Advt. Fedn. (bd. dirs. 1986-91), Am. Assn. Advt. Agys. (media rsch. com. 1984—), Mich. State U. Alumni Assn. (Disting. Alumna award 1994). Roman Catholic. Avocation: skiing. Office: Leo Burnett Co Inc 17 Bougainvillea Ave Key West FL 33040-6226

SPITZ, BARBARA SALOMON, artist; b. Chgo., Jan. 8, 1926; d. Fred B. and Sadie (Lorch) Salomon; m. Lawrence S. Spitz, Mar. 19, 1949; children—Thomas R., Linda J., Joanne L. A.B., Brown U., 1947; student, Art Inst. Chgo., 1942-43, R.I. Sch. Design, 1945. One-woman exhbns. include Benjamin Galleries, Chgo., 1971, 73, Kunsthaus Buhler, Stuttgart, Germany, 1973, Van Straaten Gallery, Chgo., 1976, 80, Elca London Studio, Montreal, Que., Can., 1977, Loyola U. Chgo., 1988, Schneider, Bluhm, Loeb gallery, Chgo., 1993, The Ctr. Gallery, 1994; group exhibitions include Am. Acad. Arts and Letters, Library of Congress traveling print exhbn., Tokyo Cen. Mus. Arts, Nat. Acad. Design, N.Y.C., Pratt Graphic Ctr., Honolulu Acad. Arts, Wadsworth Atheneum, Nat. Aperture, 1986—, others; represented in permanent collections, Phila. Mus. Art, DeCordova Mus., Okla. Art Ctr., Milw. Art Ctr., Los Angeles County Mus. Art, Art Inst. Chgo., Portland Mus. Art. Vice-chmn. Chgo. area Brown U. Bicentennial Drive; treas. Hearing and Speech Rehab. Ctr., Michael Reese Hosp., 1960; fine arts patron bd. Newport Harbor Art Mus. Mem. Artists Equity, Print Club Phila., Boston Printmakers, Arts Club of Chgo., Soc. Am. Graphic Artists. Address: 1106 Somerset Ln Newport Beach CA 92660-5629

SPITZ, CHARLES THOMAS, JR., clergyman; b. Hazard, Nebr., May 26, 1921; s. Charles Thomas and Magdalene (Schneemann) S.; m. Dorothy O. Gross, June 11, 1944 (dec. 1982); children: Charles Thomas III, Gretchen Ann.; m. Karen Ankener Lucas, Aug. 25, 1983; 1 child, Garrett Richard. Grad., St. Paul's Coll., Concordia, Mo., 1939; A.B., Concordia Sem., St. Louis, Iowa, D.D., 1965; D.D., Capital U., Columbus, Ohio, 1967, Muhlenberg Coll., 1967, Gettysburg Coll., 1970; L.H.D., Luther Coll. Decorah, Iowa, 1967. Ordained to ministry Lutheran Ch., 1944; pastor in Waterloo, Iowa, 1944-46, Marengo, Iowa, 1947-53; dir. broadcasting Luth. Laymen's League, St. Louis, 1953-66; gen. sec. Luth. Council U.S., 1966-73; pastor in Manhasset, L.I., N.Y., 1974-84; exec. assoc. Fuchs, Cuthrell & Co., 1984-85; sr. ptnr. Corp. Exec. Outplacement, 1986-91; pres. Creative Energetics, 1985—; exec. asso. Evang. Lutheran in Mission, 1974-76; pres. Luth. Ch. in Mission, 1975-78; dir. Assn. Evang. Luth. Chs., 1976-83; mem. Commn. Luth. Unity, 1978-83; mem. commn. on faith and order Nat. Council Chs., 1977-83, vice chmn., 1979-82. Trustee Eger Luth. Home, 1987-92. Home: 21 Deepdale Dr Manhasset NY 11030-3303

SPITZ, LEWIS WILLIAM, historian, educator; b. Bertrand, Nebr., Dec. 14, 1922; s. Lewis William and Pauline Mary (Griebel) S.; m. Edna Marie Huttenmaier, Aug. 14, 1948; children: Stephen Andrew, Philip Mathew. AB, Concordia Coll., 1944; MDiv, Concordia Sem., 1946; MA, U. Mo., 1947; PhD, Harvard U., 1954; DD (hon.), Concordia Theol. Sem., 1977; LLD (hon.), Valparaiso (Ind.) U., 1978; LittD (hon.), Wittenberg U., 1983; DLitt (hon.), Concordia Coll., 1988. With U. Mo., Columbia, 1953-60, assoc. prof. history, 1958-60; Fulbright prof. U. Mainz, Fed. Republic of Germany, 1960-61; prof. history Stanford (Calif.) U., 1960—; William R. Kenan Jr. prof., 1974—; assoc. dean humanities and scis., 1973-77; vis. prof. Harvard U., Cambridge, Mass., 1964-65; dir. rsch. Ctr. for Reformation Rsch., Clayton, Mo., summer 1964, mem. bd. control, 1973—; sr. fellow Southeastern Medieval and Renaissance Inst., Duke U., summer 1968; vis. prof. Barnard Coll., 1980-81; sr. fellow Inst. Advance Study Princeton U., 1979-80; vis. prof. Institut für Europäische Geschichte, Mainz, Ger., 1992. Author: Conrad Celtis: The German Arch-Humanist, 1957, The Religious Renaissance of the German Humanists, 1963, Life in Two Worlds: A Biography of William Sihler, 1968, The Renaissance and Reformation Movements, 2 vols., 1987, Humanismus und Reformation in der Deutschen Geschichte, 1980, The Protestant Reformation, 1517-1559, 1985; contbr. The Harvest of Humanism in Central Europe: Essays in Honor of Lewis W. Spitz, 1993, Johann on Education, 1995; mem. editorial bd.; Soundings, 1973-79, Ch. History, 1982-86; mng. editor: Archive for Reformation History, 1968-76. Recipient Harbison award for teaching Danforth Found., 1964; Guggenheim fellow, 1956; Nat. Endowment for Humanities sr. fellow, 1965; Am. Council Learned Socs. fellow, 1971; Huntington Library fellow, 1959; Inst. Advanced Study Princeton fellow, 1979-80; Pew Found. fellow, 1983. Fellow Am. Acad. Arts and Scis.; mem. Am. Soc. Reformation Rsch. (pres. 1963-64), Am. Hist. Assn., No. Calif. Renaissance Soc. (pres. 1964-65), Am. Soc. Ch. History (pres. 1976-77). Home: 827 Lathrop Dr Stanford CA 94305-1054 Office: Stanford U Dept History Stanford CA 94305 *College teaching has enabled me to develop a career which coincides perfectly with my inner needs and goals in life, which have more to do with service than with ambition, more with love of people than wish to dominate, more with mind and spirit than with material things.*

SPITZ, SEYMOUR JAMES, JR., retired fragrance company executive; b. Milw., Nov. 17, 1921; s. Seymour James and Marie (Spinette) S.; m. Elizabeth Taylor Parks, Feb. 7, 1948 (div. Aug. 1967); children: William Taylor, Elizabeth Seymour, Anne Bellin; m. Ellen C. Flynn, July 25, 1969; 1 dau., Ellen Christina. SB, MIT, 1943. With Newport Industries div. Heyden Newport Chem. Corp., Pensacola, Fla., 1946-65; asst. chief engr., 1955-57, asst. v.p., 1957-58; v.p. Newport Industries div. Heyden Newport Chem. Corp., 1959-60, exec. v.p., 1960-61, pres., 1961-65; v.p. parent co. Heyden Newport Chem. Corp., 1962-65, became group v.p., 1965; exec. v.p. Heyden Newport Chem. Corp. (name now Tenneco Chems., Inc.), 1966; pres. Tenneco Chems., Inc., 1967-69; sr. v.p. parent co. Tenneco Inc.; pres.

and dir. Internat. Flavors & Fragrances Inc., N.Y.C., 1970-85. Mem. MIT Corp. Devel. Com., 1977-86; trustee Spence Sch., 1982-88, Savannah Symphony, 1990-95, Telfair Mus. Art, Savannah, 1993—. With USN, WWII, 1943-46. Mem. Univ. Club (N.Y.C.), Larchmont Yacht Club (N.Y., trustee 1986-89), Landings Club, Oglethorpe Club, Chatham Club. Home: 6 Brandenberry Rd Savannah GA 31411-2201

SPITZBERG, IRVING JOSEPH, JR., lawyer, corporate executive; b. Little Rock, Feb. 9, 1942; s. Irving Joseph and Marie Bettye (Seeman) S.; m. Roberta Frances Alprin, Aug. 21, 1966 (div. 1988); children—Edward Storm, David Adam; m. Virginia V. Thorndike, Dec. 24, 1988. B.A., Columbia U., 1964; B.Phil., Oxford U., 1966; J.D., Yale U., 1969. Bar: Calif. 1969, D.C. 1985, Va. 1995. Asst. prof. Pitzer Coll., Claremont, Calif., 1969-71; fellow Inst. Current World Affairs, N.Y.C., 1971-74; vis. lectr. Brown U., Providence, 1973; prof. SUNY, Buffalo, 1974-78; dean of coll. SUNY, 1974-78; gen. sec. AAUP, Washington, 1980-84; exec. dir. Coun. for Liberal Learning of Assn. Am. Colls., Washington, 1985-89; pres. The Knowledge Co., Fairfax, Va., 1985—; ptnr. Spitzberg & Drew, Washington, 1990-92; of counsel Spirer & Goldberg, Washington, 1993—; coord. Alvan Ikoku Coll., Nigeria, 1979-80; cons. Bd. Adult Edn., Kenya, 1973-74, Philander Smith Coll., Little Rock, 1978-80; co-dir. nat. study on campus life for Carnegie Found. for Advancement Teaching, 1989-90. Author and editor: Exchange of Expertise, 1978, Universities and the New International Order, 1979, Universities and the International Exchange of Knowledge, 1980; author: Campus Programs on Leadership, 1986, Racial Politics in Little Rock, 1987; co-author: (with Berdahl and Moodie), Quality and Access in Higher Education, 1991, (with Virginia Thorndike) Creating Community on College Campuses, 1992. Founder Coalition for Ednl. Excellence, Western N.Y., 1978-80; founding mem. Alliance for Leadership Devel., Washington, 1985; counsel GASP, Pomona, Calif., 1969-71; Dem. Committeeman, Erie County, N.Y., 1978-80; founding pres. Internat. Found. for St. Catherine's Coll., Oxford, 1986—; founder Coun. for Liberal Learning. Nat. winner Westinghouse Sci. Talent Search, 1960; Kellett scholar Trustees of Columbia U., 1964-66. Mem. AAAS, Internat. Soc. Ednl., Cultural, and Sci. Exchs., Washington Ethical Soc. Jewish. Clubs: Columbia, Yale (Washington). Avocations: kids, the internat. Office: The Knowledge Co 4041 University Dr Ste 105 Fairfax VA 22030

SPITZE, ROBERT GEORGE FREDERICK, agricultural economics educator; b. Berryville, Ark., Oct. 12, 1922; s. Wesley Henry and Nora Catherine (Stullken) S.; m. Hazel Cleo Taylor, Mar. 4, 1944; children—Glenna Dean Spitze Franklin, Ken Rollin. Student, Columbia U., 1944; BS (Sears Roebuck nat. fellow), U. Ark., 1947; PhD (Knapp research fellow), U. Wis., 1954. Instr. U. Wis., Madison, 1950; asst. prof. to prof. U. Tenn., Knoxville, 1951-60; prof. agrl. econs. U. Ill., Urbana, 1960-93; vis. prof. Wye Coll., U. London, 1967-68; vis. research prof. policy U.S. Dept. Agr., Washington, 1975; vis. lectr. various univs., U.S. and Eng.; cons. Fed. Intermediate Credit Bank, 1958-59, Ill. Gen. Assembly Commn. on Revenue, 1963, Tex. A&M U., 1970, Am. Farm Bur. Fedn., Chgo., 1971, Ill. Gov.'s Commn. on Farm Income, 1972, Nat. Agrl. Research Policy Adv. Com., 1975, U.S. Dept. Agr. Econs. Research Service, 1976, Wharton Econometric Forecasting Inc., 1977, Nat. Rural Center, Washington, 1979-80, Nat. Public Policy Com., 1980, Okla. State U., 1986; mem. Ill. Gov.'s Council Econ. Advisers, 1974-76. Co-author: Food and Agricultural Policy, Economics and Politics, 1994; co-editor Policy Rsch. Notes, 1975—, Food, Agriculture, and Rural Policy into the Twenty-first Century, 1994; editor: Agricultural and Food Policy: Issues and Alternatives for the 1990s, 1990; contbr. articles to profl. jours., chpts. to books. Lt. USNR, 1943-47. Recipient Funk recognition award, 1973, Excellence in Teaching award U. Ill., 1977, Outstanding Agr. Coll. Alumni award U. Ark., 1994. Mem. AAAS, Am. Econ. Assn., Am. Agrl. Econs. Assn. (Disting. Policy award 1981, Disting. Teaching award 1972, travel study grantee to France 1964), Internat. Assn. Agrl. Econs., Agrl. Econs. Soc. (U.K.), AAUP, Blue Key, Sigma Xi, Omicron Delta Kappa, Gamma Sigma Delta, Phi Eta Sigma, Alpha Zeta, Phi Sigma. Office: U Ill Dept Agr Econ 1301 W Gregory Dr Urbana IL 61801-3608

SPITZER, ADRIAN, pediatrician, medical educator; b. Bucharest, Rumania, Dec. 21, 1927; came to U.S., 1963, naturalized, 1968; s. Osias and Sophia S. S.; m. Carole Zelter, Oct. 31, 1951; 1 son, Vlad. B.S., Matei Basarab Lyceum, Bucharest, 1946; M.D., Med. Sch. Bucharest, 1952. Diplomate: Am. Bd. Pediatrics. Intern White Plains (N.Y.) Hosp., 1964; resident Hosp. Med. Coll. Pa., 1965-66; postdoctoral fellow pediatric nephrology Albert Einstein Coll. Medicine, 1966-67; postdoctoral fellow in renal physiology Cornell U. Med. Sch., 1967-68; practice medicine specializing in pediatric nephrology Bronx, N.Y., 1968—; asst. prof. pediatrics Albert Einstein Coll. Medicine, 1968-72, assoc. prof., 1972-76, prof., 1976—, dir. div. nephrology, 1973—; mem. staff Bronx Mcpl. Hosp. Ctr., high Albert Einstein Coll. Medicine/Montefore Med. Ctr.; mem. Medicine B Study sect.-NIH, 1976-80; Prof. C. Dunders rotating chmn. U. Utrecht, The Netherlands, 1990—; vis. fellow St. Catherine's Coll.; vis. fellow dept. biochemistry Oxford U., 1981-82; coord. Internat. Study Kidney Disease in Children; chmn. organizing com. 1st-6th Internat. Workshop on Devel. Renal Physiology, 1980-95; mem. renal adv. com. N.Y.C Dept. Health; sci. adv. bd. rsch. and grant com. Nat. Kidney Found., 1982; chmn. pediatric nephrology bd. Am. Bd. Pediat., 1982-83. Mem. editorial bd.: Pediatric Nephrology, Seminars in Nephrology; assoc. editor: Pediatric Renal Disease, 1979, 2d edit., 1992; editor: The Kidney Development, 1982. NIH spl fellow, 1967, John E. Fogarty Sr. Internat. fellow, 1981-82; grantee NIH, N.Y. State Health Research Council, Nat. Kidney Found.; recipient Bela Schick medal for extraordinary achievements in acad. and clin. pediatrics. Mem. Am. Soc. Nephrology, Am. Soc. Pediatric Nephrology (council 1977-80, pres. 1981-82), Am. Fedn. Clin. Research, Am. Physiol. Soc., Soc. Pediatric Research, Salt and Water Club, Am. Acad. Pediatrics, Am. Pediatrics Soc., Intersoc. Council for Kidney and Urinary Tract Research (sec.-treas. 1984-89). Office: Albert Einstein Coll Medicine 1410 Pelham Pky S Bronx NY 10461-1101

SPITZER, CARY REDFORD, avionics consultant, electrical engineer; b. New Hope, Va., July 31, 1937; s. Clyde Burke and Marion Jeanette (Redford) S.; m. Carrie Laura Ruth Logan, June 18, 1960; 1 child, Stiegel Logan. BSEE, Va. Poly. Inst. & State U., 1959; MS in Engring. Mgmt., George Washington U., 1970. Rsch. engr., engring. mgr. Langley Rsch Ctr., NASA, Hampton, Va., 1962-94; founder, pres. AvioniCon, Inc., 1993—; lectr. UCLA, 1989—, George Washington U., 1994. Author: Viking Orbiter Views of Mars, 1981, Digital Avionics Systems, 1987, 2d edit., 1993, Avionics Handbook, 1995; contbr. articles to sci. publs. 1st lt. USAF, 1959-62. Recipient Volare award Airline Avionics Inst., 1988; named Va. Peninsula Engr. of Yr., 1993. Fellow AIAA (assoc., Digital Avionics award 1994), IEEE (Centennial medal 1984), Aerospace and Electronic Systems Soc. of IEEE (pres. 1973-74), Exch. Club (pres. Williamsburg 1985). Methodist. Avocations: kite flying, car mechanics. Home/Office: 3409 Foxridge Rd Williamsburg VA 23188-2499

SPITZER, HUGH D., lawyer; b. Seattle, Feb. 14, 1949; s. George Frederick and Dorothy Lea (Davidson) S.; m. Ann Scales, Oct. 14, 1983; children: Johanna Spitzer, Claudia Spitzer, Jenny Spitzer. BA, Yale U., 1970; JD, U. Wash., 1974; LLM, U. Calif., 1982. Bar: Wash. 1974, U.S. Dist/ Ct. (ea. and we. dists.) Wash. 1975, U.S. Ct. Appeals (9th and D.C. cirs.) 1975, U.S. Supreme Ct. 1980. Program analyst N.Y.C. Health and Hosp. Corp., 1970-71; labor lawyer Hafer, Cassidy & Price, Seattle, 1974-76; legis. asst. Seattle City Coun., 1976-77; legal counsel to mayor City of Seattle, 1977-81; mcpl. bond lawyer Foster Pepper & Shefelman, Seattle, 1982—. Contbr. articles to profl. jours. bd. dirs. King County Housing Ptnrship, Seattle; vice chair Puget Sound Water Quality Authority Wash. State, 1989—; chair Seattle Law Income Housing Levy Oversight com., 1988—. Mem. Nat. Assn. Bond Lawyers. Democrat. Avocations: hiking, skiing. Office: Foster Pepper & Shefelman 1111 3rd Ave Bldg Ste 3400 Seattle WA 98101

SPITZER, JACK J., banker; b. N.Y.C., Sept. 11, 1917; s. Ira I. and Jennie (Brody) S.; m. Charlotte May Braunstein, Dec. 21, 1941; children: Jil Spitzer-Fox, Robert Braunstein. BA, UCLA, 1938; LLD (hon.), Adelphi U., 1980, Ben-Gurion U.of the Negev, 1991. Pres., chief exec. officer Spitzer Co., Los Angeles, 1951-59, Brentwood Savs. & Loan, Los Angeles, 1959-66, Sterling Savs. & Loan, Riverside, Calif., 1966-72, Security Savs. & Loan, Seattle, 1972-78; chmn. bd. dirs., chief exec. officer Cert. Reports, Kinderhook, N.Y.,

1967–, Covenant Mortgage, Mercer Island, Wash., 1982–; Pacific Linen, Bothell, Wash., 1984–; chmn. Vitritek Environ., Inc., Columbia, Mo., 1993–. Pres. United Way, Riverside, 1970; nat. chmn. David Ben-Gurion Centennial Com. of the U.S., Inc., 1985-87; mem. U.S. Del. to Inauguration of Pope John Paul II, apptd. by Pres. Carter, 1978; 1st v.p. Dem. County Cen. Com., Los Angeles, 1953-62; Vice chmn., bd. govs. Ben-Gurion Univ. of Negev, 1984–, pres. Am. Assocs., 1985; founder, chmn. Seattle-Beer Sheva (Israel) Sister City Com., 1977; exec. committeeman Am. Jewish Joint Distbn. Com., v.p., Conf. on Jewish Material Claims, 1978–; vice chmn. bd. trustees Med. Edn. for South African Blacks, 1984–. Served to 2d lt. U.S. Army, 1943-46. Spitzer dept. of Social Work at Ben-Gurion Univ. named in his honor, 1986; recipient Outstanding Communal Svc. award Wurtzweiler Sch. Social Work, 1987, Gold medal for Humanitarian Svc., B'nai B'rith, 1994. Mem. Meml. Found. for Jewish Culture (treas. 1978–, chmn. exec. com. 1990–, pres. 1994–), Alexis de Tocqueville Soc., United Way, Rainier Club (Seattle), A.Z.A. of B'nai Brith (internat. pres. 1938-39, Harry Lapidus Communal Svc. award 1936, Sam Beber Outstanding Alumnus award 1970), B'nai Brith (west coast pres. 1968-69, internat. pres. 1978-82, hon. pres. 1982–, internat. chmn. susquicentennial celebration 1992-94), Rotary (World Cmty. Svc. award 1994). Avocation: ping pong. Home: PO Box 2008 Kirkland WA 98083-2008 Office: Covenant Mortgage Corp 9725 SE 36th St Ste 304 Mercer Island WA 98040-3840

SPITZER, JOHN BRUMBACK, lawyer; b. Toledo, Mar. 6, 1918; s. Lyman and Blanche (Brumback) S.; m. Lucy Ohlinger, May 10, 1941 (dec. Oct. 13, 1971); children: John B., Molly (Mrs. Edmund Frost), Lyman, Adelbert L.; m. Vondah D. Thornbury, July 3, 1972; stepchildren: Vondah, Barbara, James R. Thornbury. Grad., Phillips Andover Acad., 1935; B.A., Yale, 1939, LL.B., 1947. Bar: Ohio 1947. Since practiced in Toledo; law clk. to U.S. Supreme Ct. Justice Stanley Reed, 1947-48; ptnr. Marshall, Melhorn, Cole, Hummer & Spitzer, Toledo, 1955-86, Hummer & Spitzer, Toledo, 1986-89; with Hummer Legal Svcs. Corp, Perrysburg, Ohio, 1990–; pres. Spitzer Box Co., 1955-63; v.p. Spitzer Bldg. Co., 1960-91, pres. 1992–. Pres. Toledo Symphony Orch., 1956-58, v.p., sec., 1958-86. Maj. AUS, World War II. Mem. Belmont Country Club. Congregationalist. Home: 29620 Gleneagles Rd Perrysburg OH 43551-3515 Office: Hummer Legal Svcs Corp 353 Elm St Perrysburg OH 43551

SPITZER, LEO, historian, educator; b. La Paz, Bolivia, Sept. 11, 1939; came to U.S., 1950; s. Eugene and Rose (Wolfinger) S.; m Manon S. Spitzer, Aug. 23, 1961 (div. 1980); 1 child, Alexander; m. Marianne Hirsch, May 9, 1981; children: Oliver, Gabriel. BA in Spanish magna cum laude, Brandeis U., 1961; MA in History, U. Wis., 1963, PhD, 1969; MA (hon.), Dartmouth Coll., 1982. Instr. dept. history Dartmouth Coll., Hanover, N.H., 1967-69, asst. prof. history, 1969-75, assoc. prof., 1975-81, prof., 1981–, chair dept., 1989-92; rsch. assoc. Inst. African Studies U. Coll. Sierra Leone, 1965-66, 70, 76; rsch. assoc. Centro de Estudos Afro-Asiaticos-CEAA, Rio de Janeiro, Brazil, 1980-82, Boston U., 1986-92; rsch. affiliate Ctr. European Studies Harvard U., Cambridge, Mass., 1984-85. Author: The Sierra Leone Creoles: Responses to Colonialism 1870-1945, 1974, Lives In Between: Assimilation and Marginality in Austria, Brazil, West Africa 1780-1945, 1990; author chpts. to books; contbr. articles to profl. jours. Recipient Ford Found. award, 1974; Am. Philos. Soc. grantee, 1970, Hewitt Presdl. Devel. grantee, 1987, Sloan Found. grantee, 1985; Social Sci. Rsch. Coun. fellow, 1972, Marion and Jasper Whiting Found. fellow, 1991, Littauer Found. fellow, 1992, Nat. Humanities Ctr. fellow, 1992-93, John Simon Guggenheim fellow, 1995. Home: RFD Box 75 East Thetford VT 05043 Office: Dartmouth Coll Dept History Hanover NH 03755

SPITZER, LYMAN, JR., astronomer; b. Toledo, June 26, 1914; s. Lyman and Blanche C. (Brumback) S.; m. Doreen D. Canaday, June 29, 1940; children: Nicholas, Dionis, Lutetia, Lydia. AB, Yale U., 1935, DSc, 1958; Henry Fellow, Cambridge (Eng.) U., 1935-36; PhD, Princeton U., 1938; Nat. Rsch. fellow, Harvard U., 1938-39; DSc, Case Inst. Tech., 1961, Harvard U., 1975, Princeton U., 1984; LLD, Toledo U., 1963. Instr. physics and astronomy Yale U., 1939-42; scientist Sub. Studies Group, Columbia U. Div. War Research, 1942-44; dir. Sonar Analysis Group, 1944-46; assoc. prof. astrophysics Yale U., 1946-47; prof. astronomy, chmn. dept. and dir. obs. Princeton U., 1947-79, Charles A. Young prof. astronomy, 1952-82, chmn. rsch. bd., 1967-72, dir. project Matterhorn, 1953-61, chmn. exec. com. Plasma Physics Lab., 1961-66, sr. rsch. astronomer, 1982–; trustee Woods Hole Oceanographic Inst., 1946-51; mem. Com. on Undersea Warfare, NRC, 1948-51; mem. Yale U. Council, 1948-51; chmn. Scientists Com. on Loyalty Problems, 1948-51; chmn. Space Telescope Inst. Council, Assoc. Univs. Rsch. Astronomy, 1981-90. Author: monograph Physics of Fully Ionized Gases, 1956, rev., 1962; Diffuse Matter in Space, 1968, Physical Processes in the Interstellar Medium, 1978, Searching Between The Stars, 1982, Dynamical Evolution of Globular Clusters, 1987; editor: Physics of Sound in the Sea, 1946; contbr. articles to Astrophysical Jour., Physics of Fluids, Phys. Rev., others. Recipient Rittenhouse medal, 1957, Exceptional Sci. Achievement medal NASA, 1972, Bruce Gold medal, 1973, Henry Draper Gold medal, 1974, James C. Maxwell prize, 1975, Karl Schwarzschild medal, 1975, Disting. Pub. Svc. medal NASA, 1976, Gold medal Royal Astron. Soc., 1978, Nat. medal sci., 1980, Janssen medal, 1980, Franklin medal Franklin Inst., 1980, Crafoord prize Royal Swedish Acad. Scis., 1985, Madison medal Princeton U., 1989, Franklin medal Am. Philos. Soc., 1991. Mem. NAS, Am. Acad. Arts and Scis., Am. Philos. Soc., Am. Astron. Soc. (past pres.), Royal Soc. (London, fgn.), Royal Astron. Soc. (assoc.), Royal Soc. Scis. Liège (fgn. corr.), Am. Phys. Soc., Astron. Soc. Pacific, Am. Alpine Club, Alpine Club (London). Unitarian. Research on interstellar matter, space astronomy, stellar dynamics, broadening of spectral lines, conductivity of ionized gases, controlled release of thermonuclear energy.

SPITZER, MARC LEE, lawyer; b. Pitts., Sept. 12, 1957; s. Richard A. and Edith (Brodie) S. BA in History and Polit. Sci. summa cum laude, Dickinson Coll., 1979; JD cum laude, U. Mich., 1982. Bar: Ariz. 1982, U.S. Dist. Ct. Ariz. 1982, U.S. Tax Ct. 1982, U.S. Ct. Appeals (9th cir.) 1985. Ptnr. Fennemore, Craig, Phoenix, 1982–; state sen. dist. 18, chmn. senate fin. com., joint legis. tax com. Bd. dirs. Ariz. Rep. Caucus, Phoenix, 1982–, Ariz. Acad., 1990; mem. devel. com. Dickinson Coll., 1985-86; mem. Soc. for the Arts; vice-chmn. Ariz. 18th Dist., 1986–; alternate del. 1988 Rep. Nat. Conv. GOP; legal counsel Ariz. Rep. Party; apptd. by pres. Ariz. Senate and speaker of house Ariz. Commn. Mcpl. Taxation. Mem. ABA (vice-chmn. tax legis. sect.), State Bar Ariz. (cert. specialist taxation), Ariz. Tax Research Found. (bd. dirs. 1984–), Ariz. Tax Research Assn., Maricopa County Bar Assn., Phi Beta Kappa, Sigma Alpha Epsilon. Jewish. Clubs: Arizona, Phoenix City, Captain's (bd. dirs.). Avocations: fishing, prospecting, classical music, racquetball. Home: 304 W Orangewood Phoenix AZ 85021

SPITZER, ROBERT RALPH, academic administrator emeritus; b. Waukesha, Wis., May 4, 1922; s. John and Ruth S.; m. Marie L. Woerfel, 1946; children: John, Jeffrey, Susan. BS in Agr, U. Wis., 1943, M.S. in Animal Nutrition and Biochemistry, 1945, Ph.D. in Animal Nutrition and Med. Physiology, 1947. With Murphy Products Co., Burlington, Wis., 1947-75; pres. Murphy Products Co., 1958-74, chmn. bd., 1974-75; coordinator Food for Peace, U.S. Dept. State, Washington, 1975-76; pres. Milw. Sch. Engring., 1977-91, pres. emeritus, 1991–; chmn., trustee Norman Vincent Peale Nat. Cabinet, Pawling, N.Y., trustee; bd. dirs. State Bank, Hales Corners, Kikkoman Foods, Inc., Maple Leaf Farms, Milford, Ind., Roundy's Inc., Pewaukee, Wis.; citizen mem. Wis. State Bar, bd. govs. 1992-94. Author: Family Organizer, 1977, The American Challenge, 1980, No Need for Hunger, 1981, The Enterprise Collection, 1991, Help the Hungry Feed Themselves, 1994. Chmn. adv. com. Milw. Billy Graham Crusade, 1979; mem. adv. com. on edn. Rickover Found., past mem. com.; pres. Nat. 4-H Coun., 1975; past trustee Farm Found., Nutrition Found., N.Y.C.; active Gov.'s Coun. on Sci. and Tech.; bd. dirs. mem. edn. com. Wis. Mfrs. and Commerce Found. Recipient Freedom's Found. award, 1964, 82, 83, Freedoms Found. award, 1987; Coll. Agr. award U. Wis., 1971; Disting. Service award, 1972; Disting. Lectr. award Mich. State U., 1976; SBA Wis. Agribus. Advocate of Yr., 1985; Disting. Service award Wis. Farm Bur. Fedn., 1984; Wis. Agri-Bus. Adv. of Yr. award U.S. Small Bus. Adminstrn., 1985; Hon. Legion of Honor award Internat. Supreme Order DeMolay, 1987; Disting. Svc. award Pub. Expenditure Survey Wis., 1987; Educator of Yr. award Sales and Mktg. Execs. Milw., 1988; Wis. Leadership Network award, 1993; Patrick Henry citation Mil. Order of World Wars, 1993. Mem. Am. Inst. Chemists, Am. Soc. Animal Prodn., Am. Chem. Soc., Am. Poultry Sci. Assn., Am. Soc. Engring. Edn., Univ. Club, Washington Club, Lake

Geneva Country Club, Milw. Athletic Club, Navy League, Rotary (club pres. 1954-55, 89-90, Vocat. Recognition award 1989, hon. mem. 1993), Sigma Xi, Phi Lambda Upsilon, Alpha Zeta, Phi Eta Sigma, Phi Sigma, Delta Phi Zeta, Phi Kappa Phi, Delta Theta Sigma, Gamma Sigma Delta. Republican. Episcopalian. Home: 1134 North Rd Burlington WI 53105-9056 Office: 706 N Jefferson St Milwaukee WI 53202-4591 *Peace and freedom from hunger will be a reality in our time with enlightened moral leadership in government and if economic and technical literacy are achieved. Service to our fellow human beings is a privilege.*

SPITZER, WILLIAM GEORGE, university dean, physicist, educator, researcher; b. L.A., Apr. 24, 1927; s. Max and May Lea (Axleband) S.; m. Jeanette Dorothy Navsky, June 23, 1949; children—Matthew Laurence, Margaret Ilene. B.A., UCLA, 1949; M.S., U. So. Calif., 1952; Ph.D., Purdue U., 1957. Mem. tech. staff Bell Telephone Lab., Murray Hill, N.J., 1957-62; mem. tech. staff Bell & Howell Research Ctr., Pasadena, Calif., 1962-63; prof. material sci. and physics U. So. Calif., Los Angeles, 1963–, chmn. dept. material sci., 1967-69, chmn. dept. physics, 1969-72, 78-81, vice provost, dean Grad. studies, 1983-85; dean Letters, Arts and Scis. U. So. Calif., 1985-89; retired, 1992; acting provost U. So. Calif., 1993. Contbr. chpts. to books, articles to profl. jours. Served with U.S. Army, 1945-46. Hon. DHL awarded by Hebrew Union Coll., Jewish Inst. of Religion, 1992. Fellow Am. Phys. Soc.; mem. IEEE (sr.). Home: 4995 Lamia Way Oceanside CA 92056-7431 Office: U So Calif Material Sci Dept Vivian Hall Engring University Park Los Angeles CA 90007

SPITZNAGEL, JOHN KEITH, microbiologist, immunologist; b. Peoria, Ill., Apr. 11, 1923; s. Elmer Florian and Anna S. (Kolb) S.; m. Anne Moulton Sirch, Feb. 2, 1947; children: John, Jean, Margaret, Elizabeth, Paul. B.A., Columbia U., 1943, M.D., 1946. Diplomate Nat. Bd. Med. Examiners, Am. Bd. Internal Medicine. Intern Johns Hopkins Hosp., Balt., 1946-47; resident in internal medicine Barnes Hosp., St. Louis, 1949-51; vis. investigator Rockefeller Inst., N.Y.C., 1952-53, Nat. Inst. Med. Research, London, 1967-68; mem. faculty U. N.C., Chapel Hill, 1957-79; prof. microbiology and infectious diseases U. N.C., 1957-79; cons. N.C. Meml. Hosp., Chapel Hill, 1974-79; ad hoc adviser NIH, 1971–; prof. microbiology and immunology, chmn. dept. Emory U., Atlanta, 1979-93, prof. emeritus microbiology and immunology, 1993–; mem. study sect. bacteriology and mycology NIH, 1975-79, 85-89, chmn., 1977-79. Editor: Infection and Immunity, 1970-80, Jour. Immunology, 1973-80, Jour. Reticuloendothelial Soc, 1973-80. Served with M.C. AUS, 1947-57. Recipient Research Career Devel. award USPHS, 1957-67, Disting. Service award Sch. Medicine U. N.C., Chapel Hill, 1987; USPHS postdoctoral fellow, 1968; USPHS and AEC grantee. Fellow ACP, Infectious Disease Soc.; mem. AAAS, AAUP, Am. Soc. Microbiology (div. group councilor 1977-79), Am. Assn. Immunologists, Reticuloendothelial Soc. (pres. 1982), Infectious Disease Soc., So. Soc. Clin. Rsch., Assn. Am. Med. Sch. Microbiology and Immunology Chmn. (pres. 1990-91), Sigma Xi. Research on cell biology of human neutrophil polymorphonuclear leukocytes, and oxygen ind. mechanisms of antimicrobial phagocytoses; first to demonstrate cationic antimicrobial proteins of polymorphonuclear leukocytes granules; co-discoverer of a cationic protein of polymorph granules with antimicrobial action and a powerful attractant for mononuclear phagocytes. Home: 2251 Brianwood Ct Decatur GA 30033-1715 Office: 1440 Clifton Rd NE Atlanta GA 30307-1053

SPIVACK, FRIEDA KUGLER, psychologist, educator, academician, researcher, company executive; b. N.Y.C., Aug. 21, 1932; d. David and Anna (Steir) Kugler; married; children: Alizah Brozgold, Ely. MA with honors, Hunter Coll., 1963; PhD, NYU, 1971. Prof. Manhattan Coll., N.Y.C., 1971-74, Queens Coll., Flushing, N.Y., 1974-76, Lehman Coll., N.Y.C., 1976-92; lectr., keynoter N.Y. State Devel. Disabilities Planning Svcs., 1995–; bd. dirs., v.p. HCHC, Inc., Bklyn.; bd. dirs., past pres. Inter-Am. Conductive Edn. for Motor Disabled; bd. dirs., pres. Family Diagnostic Treatment Ctr., Bklyn. Contbr. articles to profl. jours., chpts. to textbooks; author curriculum in field; author children's developmental assessments. Mem. exec. bd. N.Y. State Div. Early Childhood, 1981–; del. Coun. for Exceptional Children, 1981-88; chmn. Empire State Consortium of Early Childhood Grants, 1990-91; bd. dirs., sec. ACE Integration Head Start. Mem. AAUP, Nat. Assn. Sch. Psychologists, Internat. Coun. Psychologists, Coun. for Exceptional Children (lectr., keynoter 1995–), Am. Fedn. Tchrs.-Profl. Staff Congress, Internat. Coll. Pediatrics (mem. exec. bd. 1986–), N.Y.C. Reggio Emilia Program. Avocations: sculpture, writing, travel.

SPIVACK, GORDON BERNARD, lawyer, lecturer; b. New Haven, June 15, 1929; s. Jacob and Sophie (Ocheretianski) S.; m. Dolores Olivia Traversano, Jan. 16, 1956; children—Michael David, Paul Stephen. B.S. with philosophic orations and honors with exceptional distinction, Yale U., 1950, LL.B. magna cum laude, 1955. Bar: Conn. 1955, U.S. Supreme Ct. 1962, N.Y. 1970. Trial atty. antitrust div. Dept. Justice, Washington, 1955-60; asst. chief field ops. antitrust div. Dept. Justice, 1960-64, chief field ops. antitrust div., 1964-65, dir. ops. antitrust div., 1965-67; assoc. prof. law Yale U., New Haven, 1967-70; vis. lectr. Yale U., 1970-78; ptnr. Lord, Day & Lord, N.Y.C., 1970-86, Coudert Bros., N.Y.C., 1986–; speaker on antitrust law; mem. Pres.'s Nat. Commn. for Rev. Antitrust Law and Procedures, Washington, 1978-79. Contbr. numerous articles on antitrust law to profl. jours. Served with U.S. Army, 1950-52. Recipient Sustained Superior Performance award Dept. Justice, 1955-60. Fellow Am. Coll. Trial Lawyers; mem. ABA, N.Y. State Bar Assn., Bar Assn. City N.Y., Yale Club (N.Y.C.), Pine Orchard Yacht and Country Club (Conn.). Jewish. Avocation: detective stories. Home: 118 Townsend Ter East Haven CT 06512-3129 Office: Coudert Bros 1114 Ave of the Americas New York NY 10036

SPIVACK, HENRY ARCHER, life insurance company executive; b. Bklyn., Apr. 15, 1919; s. Jacob and Pauline (Schwartz) S.; m. Sadie Babe Meiseles, Jan. 1, 1941; children: Ian Jeffrey, Paula Janis. Student CCNY, 1936-42; BBA, Am. Coll., Bryn Mawr, Pa., 1965. CLU. Comptroller Daniel Jones, Inc., N.Y.C., 1947-59; field underwriter Union Cen. Life Ins. Co., N.Y.C., 1959-79, mgr. programming dept., 1966-69, assoc. agy. mgr., 1977-79; pension dir. Bleichroeder, Bing & Co., N.Y.C., 1975-77, sr. v.p. NCA Agy., Inc. (formerly New Confidence Agy.), 1979-90, Bentley Agy., Inc., 1990-92; Luxco & Assocs., 1990–; pension dir., employee benefit plan cons., estate and fin. planning, pres. Profl. Benefit Planners Inc. N.J.; instr. N.Y. State Ins. Dept., C.W. Post Coll., L.I. N.Y. Ctr. for Fin. Studies; coord. Ins. Dept. Yeshiva U., N.Y.; ins. courses instr.; also lectr., moderator. Contbr. articles to publs. Served with USN, 1943-46. Mem. Life Underwriters Assn. N.Y. (past chmn. blood bank), Am. Soc. CLU's (past chmn. N.Y. chpt. pension sect., past chmn. profl. liaison com.), Am. Soc. Pension Actuaries, Pensioneers at C.W. Post Coll., C.W. Post Coll. Tax Inst. and Fin. Planning Inst., Practising Law Inst., Internat. Assn. Fin. Planners, Internat. Assn. Registered Fin. Cons. (registered fin. cons.), Internat. Platform Assn., Greater N.Y. Brokers Assn. Lodge: K.P. (life; past dep. grand chancellor N.Y. state). Office: 500 N Broadway Jericho NY 11753-2111

SPIVAK, ALVIN A., retired public relations executive; b. Phila., Nov. 30, 1927; s. Herman and Bella (Haimovitz) S.; m. Martha Barry, Nov. 26, 1965; 1 dau., Denise. B.S., Temple U., 1949. With I.N.S., 1949-58; Senate reporter, also mem. gen. staff I.N.S., Washington, 1951-58; with U.P.I., 1958-67, White House reporter, 1960-67; pub. affairs dir. Nat. Adv. Commn. on Civil Disorders, 1967-68, Democratic Nat. Com., 1968-70; corp. pub. affairs dir. Gen. Dynamics Corp., 1970-94, ret., 1994. Served with USAAF, 1946-47. Mem. Nat. Press Club, Sigma Delta Chi, Beta Gamma Sigma. Home: 9201 Fernwood Rd Bethesda MD 20817-3315

SPIVAK, JOAN CAROL, medical public relations specialist; b. Phila., May 12, 1950; d. Jack and Evelyn Lee (Copelman) S.; m. John D. Goldman, May 17, 1980; children: Jesse, Marcus. AB, Barnard Coll., 1972; M of Health Scis., Johns Hopkins U., 1980. Freelance writer N.Y.C., 1980-84; project dir. Impact Med. Communication, N.Y.C., 1984-87; exec. v.p. Daniel J. Edelman Inc., N.Y.C., 1987–. Co-author: (pamphlet) Lead: New Perspectives on an Old Problem, 1978; contbr. The Book of Health, 1981. Bd. dirs. May O'Donnell Dance Co., N.Y.C., 1983-85, Chamber Ballet U.S.A., N.Y.C., 1985-87, Nat. Child Labor Committee, 1991&. Mem. N.Y. Acad. Sci. Democrat. Jewish. Avocations: pottery, sailing. Office: Daniel J Edelman Inc 1500 Broadway New York NY 10036-4015

SPIVAK, JONATHAN M., journalist; b. Boston, Sept. 2, 1928; s. Lawrence E. and Charlotte (Ring) S.; m. Dorothy A. Amendt, Jan. 10, 1953 (div.); children: Jennifer Lee, Timothy L.A.; m. 2d Micheline Aler, Dec. 18, 1980. B.A. magna cum laude, Harvard U. 1950. Reporter Hollister Evening Free Lance, Calif., 1954-55, UP, San Francisco, 1955, San Francisco Call Bull., 1956-57; staff corr. Wall St. Jour., San Francisco, 1957-58, Washington, 1959-78, London, 1978-83, N.Y.C., 1984; writer Paris. Served to 2d lt. U.S. Army, 1951-53. Recipient several writing awards. Mem. Inst. Medicine, Acad. Scis., Phi Beta Kappa, Athenaeum Club (London), Harvard Club (N.Y.C.). Jewish. Home: Ferme le Gres, Lauris France 84360

SPIVAK, ROBERT ELLIOT, financial consultant; b. Phila., Dec. 30, 1936; s. Philip and Helen (Kramer) S.; m. Willa Cohen, June 21, 1958 (div. 1973); children: Michael, Merri, Gregory; m. Ann Taylor Hogge, Sept. 11, 1976. BSBA, Muhlenburg Coll., 1958; postgrad., U. Pa., 1960-61; degree in fin. cons., Am. Coll., 1987. Fin. cons. CMS Cos., Phila., 1968–; lectr. in field. Pres. U.S. Com. Sports for Israel, 1981-85, 89–; chmn. So. N.J. Cystic Fibrosis, 1975; mem. Drug Edn. Info. Clinic, Cherry Hill, N.J., 1972; bd. dirs. Internat. Jewish Sports Hall of Fame, Israel, 1981–, Wingate Inst. for Phys. Fitness, 1981–, Phila. JCC Coun., 1980-88; del. U.S. Olympic Com., 1989; dir. Einstein Med. Ctr., 1992. Contbr. articles to profl. jours. Honoree Phila. Office Israel Bonds, 1988. Mem. Nat. Assn. Security Dealers, Million Dollar Round Table, Assn. Advanced Life Underwriting, Am. Soc. CLUs, Woodcrest Country Club (pres. 1975), B'rith Shalom (v.p. 1970-72), B'nai B'rith. Democrat. Jewish. Home: 2330 Pine St Philadelphia PA 19103-6415 Office: CMS Cos 1926 Arch St Philadelphia PA 19103-1444

SPIVEY, BRUCE E., integrated delivery systems management executive; b. Cedar Rapids, Iowa, Aug. 29, 1934; s. William Loranzy and Grace Loretta (Barber) S.; children: Lisa, Eric; m. Patti Amanda Birge, Dec. 20, 1987. B.A., Coe Coll., 1956; M.D., U. Iowa, 1959, M.S., 1964; M.Ed., U. Ill., 1969; hon. doctorate Sci., Coe Coll., 1978. Diplomate Am. Bd. Ophthalmology (fellow, bd. dirs. 1975-83). Asst. prof. U. Iowa Coll. Medicine, Iowa City, 1966, assoc. prof., 1966-71; dean Sch. Med. Scis. U. Pacific, San Francisco, 1971-76; prof., chmn. dept. ophthalmology Pacific Med. Ctr. (now Calif. Pacific Med. Ctr.), San Francisco, 1971-87, pres., chief exec. officer, dir., 1976-91; exec. v.p., chief exec. officer Am. Acad. Ophthalmology, San Francisco, 1978-93; pres., chief exec. officer Calif. Healthcare System, Bay area, 1986-92, Northwestern Healthcare Network, Chgo., 1992–; bd. dirs. Ophthalmic Pub. Co., Chgo., 1977–, pres., 1993–; v.p. Am. Bd. Med. Specialties, 1978-82, pres., 1980-82; chmn. bd. dirs. Vol. Hosps. of Am.-No. Calif., 1985-87, nat. bd. dirs., 1991–; mem. nat. adv. eye coun. NEI, NIH, 1987-92; mem. sci. med. advisors group Dept. Vets. Affairs, 1987-93; trustee, bd. dirs., sec. bd. Ophthal. Mut. Ins. Co., 1988–, Phoenix Alliance, Inc., 1993–. Contbr. over 110 articles to profl. jours.; inventor instruments for eye surgery. Bd. dirs. Pacific Vision Found., San Francisco, 1978–, U.S.-China Ednl. Inst., 1979–; trustee Coe Coll., 1985–, Found. AAO, 1981–. Served to capt. U.S. Army, 1964-66. Decorated Bronze Star; recipient Emile Javal Gold medal Internat. Contact Lens Council, San Francisco, 1982, Gradle medal Pan-Am. Assn. Ophthalmol., others. Fellow ACS, Am. Acad. Ophthalmology (Disting. Svc. award 1972, Sr. Honor award 1986); mem. AMA, Am. Ophthal. Soc. (Howe medal 1993, bd. dirs. 1986-91, pres. 1994-95), Academia Ophthal. Internat., Soc. Med. Adminstrs., Internat. Congress Ophthalmology (sec.-gen. 1978-82), Internat. Coun. Ophthalmology (sec.-gren. 1994–, trustee 1986–), Pacific-Union Club. (San Francisco), Chgo. Club, Chevy Chase Club, Racquet Club Chgo., Glen View Club. Republican. Presbyterian. Office: Northwestern Healthcare Network 980 N Michigan Ave Chicago IL 60611-4501

SPIVEY, JOSEPH M., III, lawyer; b. Richmond, Va., Aug. 10, 1935; s. Joseph M. and Ethel Clarke (Dorsey) S.; m. Ann Dare Davis, Feb. 1, 1958; children—Joseph M., IV, Timothy Andrew Woodland, Thomas Nelson Carpenter. B.S. in Civil Engrng., Va. Mil. Inst., 1957; LL.B., Washington and Lee U., 1962. Bar: Va. 1962, D.C. 1979, U.S. Supreme Ct. 1972, U.S. Ct. Appeals (4th cir.) 1965, U.S. Ct. Appeals (10th cir.) 1981, U.S. Ct. Appeals (D.C. cir.) 1978, U.S. Ct. Appeals (2d cir.) 1983, U.S. Dist. Ct. (ea. and we. dists.) Va. 1963, U.S. Dist. Ct. D.C. 1978. Assoc. Hunton & Williams, Richmond, 1962-69, ptnr., 1969–; now of counsel; gen. counsel Va. Mil. Inst. Found., Inc. Bd. visitors Va. Mil. Inst. Served to capt., arty. U.S. Army, 1957-59. Mem. ABA, Richmond Bar Assn. (pres. 1982-83), Va. Bar Assn., Am. Coll. Trial Lawyers. Clubs: Country of Va., Commonwealth (Richmond). Office: Hunton & Williams Riverfront Plaza East Tower 951 East Byrd St Richmond VA 23219

SPIVEY, TED RAY, English educator; b. Fort Pierce, Fla., July 1, 1927; s. Theodore Roosevelt and Etty Pearl (Sumner) S.; m. Julia Brannon Douglass, June 30, 1962; children—Mary Leta, John Andrew. A.B., Emory U., 1949; M.A., U. Minn., 1951, Ph.D., 1954. Reporter Greenville Reporter, S.C., 1949-50; instr. Emory U., Atlanta, 1954-56; mem. faculty Ga. State U., Atlanta, 1956-89, assoc. prof. English, 1960-64; prof. Ga. State U., 1964-89, Regents' prof., 1984-89, emeritus, 1989–. Author: (with Kenneth M. England) A Manual of Style, 1960, The Renewed Quest, 1969, The Coming of the New Man, 1971, The Journey Beyond Tragedy, 1980, Revival: Southern Writers in the Modern City, 1986, The Writer as Shaman: The Pilgrimages of Conrad Aiken and Walker Percy, 1986, To Die in Atlanta: Poems of the Civil War and After, 1987, Beyond Modernism: Toward a New Myth Criticism, 1988, A City Observed: Poems of the New Age, 1988, (with Arthur Waterman) Conrad Aiken: A Priest of Consciousness, 1989, Flannery O'Connor: The Woman, The Thinker, The Visionary, 1995. Served with USN, 1945-46. Urban Life Center grantee, 1977-80. Mem. So. Atlantic Modern Lang. Assn. Democrat. Episcopalian. Club: Brittany. Home: 3181 Frontenac Ct NE Atlanta GA 30319-2414

SPIZZIRRI, RICHARD DOMINIC, lawyer; b. Oak Park, Ill., Feb. 21, 1933; s. Anthony and Marie (Giraldi) S.; children: Abigail Adams Kamen, Hillary Hale McAtee, Peter Eliot, Anthony. A.B. magna cum laude, Brown U., 1955; LL.B. cum laude, Harvard U., 1958. Bar: N.Y. 1959. Assoc. firm Davis Polk & Wardwell, N.Y.C., 1958-67, mem., 1967-93; sr. counsel, 1994–; bd. dirs. Centocor, Inc., Sugen, Inc., Broadcast Ptnrs., Inc.; sec. Morgan Stanley Rsch. Ventures L.P., 1984-93. Trustee Juilliard Sch., N.Y.C., 1967–; Juilliard Found., 1980-94, Inst. Mus. Art, 1975–. Mem. ABA, Bar Assn. City N.Y., Phi Beta Kappa. Office: Davis Polk & Wardwell 450 Lexington Ave New York NY 10017

SPLANE, RICHARD BEVERLEY, social work educator; b. Calgary, Alta., Can., Sept. 25, 1916; s. Alfred William and Clara Jane (Allyn) S.; m. Verna Marie Huffman, Feb. 22, 1971. BA, McMaster U., 1940, LLD (hon.), 1990; cert. social sci. and adminstrn., London Sch. Econs., 1947; MA, U. Toronto, 1948, MSW, 1951, PhD, 1961; LLD (hon.) Wilfrid Laurier U., 1988. Exec. dir. Children's Aid Soc., Cornwall, Ont., Can., 1948-50; with Health and Welfare Can., Ottawa, 1952-72; exec. asst. to dep. minister nat. welfare Health and Welfare Can., 1959-60, dir. unemployment assistance, 1960-62, dir. gen. welfare assistance and services, 1960-70, asst. dep. minister social allowances and services, 1970-72; vis. prof. U. Alta., Edmonton, 1972-73; prof. social policy Sch. Social Work, U. B.C., Vancouver, 1973–; cons. Govt. Can., Govt. Alta., UNICEF. Author: The Development of Social Welfare in Ontario 1791-1893; (with Verna Huffman Splane) Chief Nursing Officers in National Ministries of Health, 1994. Served with RCAF, 1942-45. Recipient Centennial medal Govt. Can., 1967, Charles E. Hendry award U. Toronto, 1991, Commemorative medal for 125th anniversary of Confederation of Canada, 1992. Mem. Can. Assn. Social Workers (Outstanding Nat. Svc. award 1985), Can. Inst. Pub. Adminstrn., Can. Hist. Assn., Can. Coun. on Social Devel., Internat. Assn. Schs. Social Work, Internat. Confs. Social Devel. (pres.), World Federalists of Can. (pres. Vancouver br.). Mem. United Ch. Can. Club: Vancouver. Office: Sch Social Work U BC, Vancouver, BC Canada V6T 1W5

SPLETE, ALLEN PETERJOHN, association executive, educator; b. Carthage, N.Y., June 24, 1938; s. Howard Henry and Minnie Bertha (Peterjohn) S.; m. Marilyn Lois Detweiler, June 18, 1966; children—Heidi, Michael. BA, St. Lawrence U., 1960; MA with distinction, Colgate U., 1962; PhD, Syracuse U., 1968; LHD, Campbellsville Coll., 1990; LLD, Davis and Elkins Coll., 1990; LHD, Mt. Union Coll., 1992, St. Thomas Aquinas Coll., 1992, U. Indpls., 1994, Juniata Coll., 1994, Hastings Coll., 1994. Adminstrv. asst. to v.p. acad. affairs Syracuse U., N.Y., 1965-68, assoc. dean, exec. asst. to provost, 1968-70; v.p. for acad. planning St.

Lawrence U., Canton, N.Y., 1970-82; pres. Westminster Coll., New Wilmington, Pa., 1982-85, Council Ind. Colls., Washington, 1985—; dir. Council for Understanding Tech. in Human Affairs, 1985-91; dir. Nat. Prepaid Tuition Plan, 1988-91; cons. York Coll., Pa., 1974; mem. planning and research com. N.Y. State Com. on Ind. Colls. and Univs., 1975-82; mem. statewide higher edn. adv. com. N.Y. State Senate Com. on Higher Edn., 1979-82; mem. nat. adv. bd. Flaming Rainbow U., 1989—; mem. adv. bd. Assn. Gov. Bds. Presdl. Search Consultation Svc., 1987-94, Academic Search Consultation Svc., 1989—, mem. Harvard Sem. for new pres. adv. bd., 1990—; bd. dirs. Am. Coun. on Edn., 1991-92; mem. oversight and review com. leadership and orgnl. devel. program United Negro Coll. Fund, 1991— Co-author: Frederic Remington-Selected Letters, 1988, A Good Place To Work: Sourcebook for the Academic Workplace, 1991; editor: (with others) Confs. on Adirondack Park, 1972-82, Can.-Am. Relations, 1974-75; contbr. articles to profl. jours. Chmn. planning bd. Village of Canton, 1974-81; elder Neelsville Presbyn. Ch., 1986-89; trustee Adirondack Conservancy, Wilsboro, N.Y., 1980-82. Served to 1st lt. USAF, Army, 1960-62. Recipient Alumni citation St. Lawrence U., 1987; John Ben Snow Found. grantee, 1981. Mem. Pa. Assn. Colls. and Univs. (govt. relations com. 1983-85), Middle States Assn. (team chmn. com. on higher edn. 1976-78, 81), Assn. Am. Colls. (project rev. cons. 1981-82), Soc. Educators and Scholars (bd. editors), Assn. Am. Colls. (pres. adv. com. 1977-78, reviewer Quill project 1978-79), St. Lawrence County Hist. Assn. (pres. 1977-82), Frederic Remington Mus. Assn., Beta Theta Pi (v.p. 1980-83). Republican. Home: 10821 Longmeadow Dr Damascus MD 20872-2240 Office: Coun Ind Colls 1 Dupont Cir NW Ste 320 Washington DC 20036-1110

SPLIETHOFF, WILLIAM LUDWIG, chemical company executive; b. Matamoras, Pa., Apr. 8, 1926; s. Oscar and Louisa (Rummel) S.; m. Dorothy Coffman, June 11, 1949; children: Christina Spliethoff Hansen, Karen Spliethoff Walker, William Mark; m. Marjorie Ann Johnson, Nov. 15, 1971. BS in Chemistry, Pa. State U., 1946, MS, 1948; PhD in Organic Chemistry, Mich. State U., 1953. Rsch. chemist E.I. duPont de Nemours & Co., Wilmington, Del., 1952-60; dir. market rsch. chem. divsn. Gen. Mills, Inc., Kankakee, Ill., 1960-62, mgr. comml. devel., 1962-67; asst. mng. dir. Polymer Corp., Sydney, Australia, 1967-69; v.p. Gen. Mills Chems., Inc., Mpls., 1969-77; exec. v.p. Henkel Corp., Mpls., 1977-86; mgmt. cons. Chanhassen, Minn., 1986—; bd. dirs. Princess Soft Toys, Inc.; sr. v.p. Henkel of Am., N.Y.C., 1981-86; chmn. Habib-Ean., Ltd., Karachi, Pakistan, 1970-79, Nutralgum, S.P.A., Milan, 1972-85, Henkel Ireland Ltd., Cork, 1975-86; v.p. Chem-Plast, S.P.A., Milan, 1977-86, Poliamidas de Venezuela, S.A., Caracas, 1975-86, Gemisa, S.A. de C.V., Mexico City, 1979-86. Mem. bd. edn., Kankakee, 1964-67. Mem. Am. Chem. Soc., Chem. Market Rsch. Assn., Comml. Devel. Assn. (honor award 1982), Sigma Xi, Phi Lambda Upsilon.

SPLINTER, WILLIAM ELDON, agricultural engineering educator; b. North Platte, Nebr., Nov. 24, 1925; s. William John and Minnie (Calhoun) S.; m. Eleanor Love Peterson, Jan. 10, 1953; children: Kathryn Love, William John, Karen Ann, Robert Marvin. BS in Agrl. Engring., U. Nebr., 1950; MS in Agrl. Engring., Mich. State U., 1951, PhD in Agrl. Engring., 1955. Instr. agrl. engring. Mich. State U., East Lansing, 1953-54; assoc. prof. biology and agrl. engring. N.C. State U., Raleigh, 1954-60, prof. biology and agrl. engring., 1960-68; prof., chmn. dept. agrl. engring. U. Nebr., Lincoln, 1968-84, George Holmes Disting. prof., 1984—, head dept. agrl. engring., 1984-88, assoc. vice chancellor for rsch., 1988-90, interim vice chancellor for rsch., dean grad. studies, 1990-92, vice chancellor for rsch., 1992-93, George Holmes Disting. prof. emeritus, 1993-94; interim dean Coll. of Engring. and Tech., 1995—; cons. engr. Mem. exec. bd. Am. Assn. Engring. Socs.; hon. prof. Shengyang (People's Republic of China) Agrl. U. Contbr. articles to tech. jours.; patentee in field. Served with USNR, 1946-51. Recipient Massey Ferguson Gold medal, Kiwanis award for disting. svc., 1994, John Deere Gold Medal, 1995; named to Nebr. Hall of Agrl. Achievement. Fellow AAAS, Am. Soc. Agrl. Engrs. (pres., adminstrv. council, found. pres.); mem. Nat. Acad. Engring., Soc. Automotive Engrs., Am. Soc. Engring. Edn., Nat. Soc. Profl. Engrs., Sigma Xi, Sigma Tau, Sigma Pi Sigma, Pi Mu Epsilon, Gamma Sigma Delta, Phi Kappa Phi, Beta Sigma Psi. Home: 4801 Bridle Ln Lincoln NE 68516-3436 Office: U Nebr 202 Biol Systems Engring Labs Lincoln NE 68583

SPLITSTONE, GEORGE DALE, retired hospital administrator; b. Sharon, Pa., Oct. 10, 1925; s. Paul R. and Rose (Kelly) S.; divorced; children by previous marriage: David, Scott. B.A., Westminster Coll., 1951; M.S., Columbia U., 1953. Asst. administr. Denver Gen. Hosp., 1953-56, Reid Meml. Hosp., Richmond, Ind., 1956-59; adminstr. Reid Meml. Hosp., 1959-68; pres. Univer. Community Hosp., Tampa, Fla., 1968-87. Dist. dir. Boy Scouts Am., 1983. Served with U.S. Army, 1943-46. Kellogg Found. grantee, 1977. Mem. Am. Coll. Hosp. Adminstrs., Fla. Hosp. Assn. (dir. 1973), Tampa Area Hosp. Council (v.p. 1980-83). Democrat.

SPLITTSTOESSER, WALTER EMIL, plant physiologist; b. Claremont, Minn., Aug. 27, 1937; s. Waldemar Theodore and Opal Mae (Young) S.; m. Shirley Anne O'Connor, July 2, 1960; children: Pamela, Sheryl, Riley. B.S. with distinction (univ. fellow), U. Minn., 1958; M.S., S.D. State U., 1960; Ph.D., Purdue U., 1963. Plant breeder U. Minn., 1956-58; weed scientist S.D. State U., 1958-60; plant physiologist Purdue U., 1960-63, Shell Oil Co., Modesto, Calif., 1963-64; biochemist U. Calif., Davis, 1964-65; mem. faculty U. Ill., Urbana, 1965—; prof. plant physiology U. Ill., 1974—, head vegetable crops div., 1972-82; vis. prof. Unov. Coll., Dublin, Ireland, 1987, Univ. Coll., London, 1972, La Trobe U., Melbourne, Australia, 1995; biologist Parkland Coll., Champaign, Ill., 1974; vis. rsch. assoc. Rothamsted Exptl. Sta., Herpenden, England, 1980; disting. vis. prof. Nagoya (Jpn) U., 1982; biotechnologist U. Coll., Dublin, 1987. Author: Vegetable Growing Handbook, 1979, 2d edit., 1984, 3d edit., 1990; contbr. over 200 articles to sci. jours.; rev. editor: Analytical Biochemistry, 1976-78, NSF, 1978-79; numerous others. Recipient J.H. Gourley award Am. Fruit Grower-Am. Soc. Hort. Sci., 1974, Outstanding Grad. Educator award, 1990; NIH fellow, 1964-65. Fellow Am. Soc. Hort. Sci. (rev. editor jour. 1969—), Japanese Soc. Promotion of Sci.; mem. Am. Soc. Plant Physiologists, Japanese Soc. Plant Physiologists, Sigma Xi (pres. 1990-91), Alpha Zeta, Gamma Sigma Delta, Delta Theta Sigma, Phi Kappa Phi. Home: 2006 Cureton Dr Urbana IL 61801-6226 Office: U Ill 1102 S Goodwin Ave Urbana IL 61801-4709

SPOCK, BENJAMIN MCLANE, physician, educator; b. New Haven, Conn., May 2, 1903; s. Benjamin Ives and Mildred Louise (Stoughton) S.; m. Jane Davenport Cheney, June 25, 1927 (div. 1976); children: Michael, John Cheney; m. Mary Morgan Councille, Oct. 24, 1976. B.A., Yale U., 1925, student Med. Sch., 1925-27; M.D., Columbia U., 1929. Intern in medicine Presbyn. Hosp., N.Y.C., 1929-31; in pediatrics N.Y. Nursery and Child's Hosp., 1931-32; in psychiatry N.Y. Hosp., 1932-33; practice pediatrics N.Y.C., 1933-44, 46-47; instr. pediatrics Cornell Med. Coll., 1933-47; asst. attending pediatrician N.Y. Hosp., 1933-47; cons. in pediatric psychiatry N.Y. City Health Dept., 1942-47; cons. psychiatry Mayo Clinic and Rochester Child Health Project, Rochester, Minn.; asso. prof. psychiatry Mayo Found., U. Minn., 1947-51; prof. child devel. U. Pitts., 1951-55, Western Res. U., 1955-67. Author: Baby and Child Care, 1946, (with J. Reinhart and W. Miller) A Baby's First Year, 1954, (with M. Lowenberg) Feeding Your Baby and Child, 1955, Dr. Spock Talks with Mothers, 1961, Problems of Parents, 1962, (with M. Lerrigo) Caring for Your Disabled Child, 1965, (with Mitchell Zimmerman) Dr. Spock on Vietnam, 1968, Decent and Indecent, 1970, A Teenagers Guide to Life and Love, 1970, Raising Children in a Difficult Time, 1974, Spock on Parenting, 1988, (with Mary Morgan) Spock on Spock: A Memoir of Growing Up With the Century, 1989, A Better World for Our Children, 1994. Presdl. candidate Peoples Party, 1972, advocator Nat. Com. for a Sane Nuclear Policy (SANE), co-chmn., 1962. Served to lt. comdr. M.C., USNR, 1944-46. Home: PO Box 1268 Camden ME 04843-1268 *In pediatric practice I was trying, with difficulty, to reconcile concepts gained in psychoanalytic training with what mothers told me about their children. After ten years of that, I was able to write Baby & Child Care, which, in turn, brought invitations to research and teaching jobs. To save children from radiation I became a public supporter of a test ban treaty and co-chairman of SANE in 1962, which led, eventually to full-time opposition to the Vietnam war, conviction for conspiracy, conversion to socialism.*

SPODAK, MICHAEL KENNETH, forensic psychiatrist; b. Bklyn., Nov. 5, 1944; s. Harry and Betty (Rahn) S.; children: Lisa Beth, Brett David. B.S., Union Coll., 1966; M.D., SUNY-Syracuse, 1970. Diplomate: Nat. Bd. Med. Examiners, Am. Bd. Neurology and Psychiatry. Intern Mary Imogene Bassett Hosp., Cooperstown, N.Y., 1970-71; resident John Hopkins Hosp., Balt., 1974-77; practice medicine specializing in civil and criminal forensic psychiatry Towson, Md., 1977—; chief dept. psychiatry Balt. County Gen. Hosp., Randallstown, 1989; mem. staff Clifton T. Perkins Hosp. Ctr., Jessup, Md., 1977-92; clin. asst. prof. psychiatry U. Md. Hosp., Balt., 1983—; psychiat. cons. Bur. Disability Ins., Social Security Adminstrn., Workmen's compensation Commn., Balt., 1981—; dir. community forensic services Mental Hygiene Adminstrn., Md., 1982-92; faculty Nat. Jud. Coll., 1988—; mem. Md. Task Force on Somatic Therapies. Contbr. numerous articles on forensic psychiatry to profl. jours., chpt. to book. Served with M.C. USN, 1972-74. Mem. Am. Acad. Psychiatry and Law, Am. Psychiat. Assn., Md. Psychiat. Soc., Md. Med. Soc. (chmn. occupational health com. 1983-90), Baltimore County Med. Soc. Office: 26 W Pennsylvania Ave Towson MD 21204-5001

SPODEK, BERNARD, curriculum educator; b. Bklyn., Sept. 17, 1931; s. David and Esther (Lebenbaum) S.; m. Prudence Debb, June 21, 1957; children: Esther Yin-ling, Jonathan Chou. BA, Bklyn. Coll., 1952; MA, Columbia U., 1955, EdD, 1962. Cert. early childhood edn. tchr., N.Y. Tchr. Beth Hayeled Sch., N.Y.C., 1952-56, N.Y. City Pub. Schs., Bklyn., 1956-57, Early Childhood Ctr., Bklyn. Coll., 1957-60; asst. prof. elem. edn. U. Wis.-Milw., 1961-65; assoc. prof. early childhood edn. U. Ill., Champaign, 1965-68, prof. dept. curriculum and instrn., 1968—; dir. dept. grad. programs, 1986-87, chair dept., 1987-89, dir. hons. program, Coll. Edn., 1984-86, mem. faculty Bur. Ednl. Rsch., 1981-85; dir. insts. Nat. Def. Edn. Act, 1965-67, dir. experienced tchr. fellowship progam, 1967-69, co-dir. program for tchr. trainers in early childhood edn., 1969-74; vis. prof. Western Wash. State U., 1974, U. Wis., Madison, 1980; vis. scholar Sch. Early Childhood Studies, Brisbane (Australia) Coll. Advanced Edn., Delissa Inst. Early Childhood Studies, S. Australia Coll. Advanced Edn., 1985, Beijing Normal U., Nanjing Normal U., E. China Normal U., Shangai, People's Republic China, 1986. Author or co-author 28 books including: (with others) A Black Studies Curriculum for Early Childhood Education, 1972, 2d edit., 1976, Teaching in the Early Years, 1972, 3d edit., 1985, Early Childhood Education, 1973, Studies in Open Education, 1975 (Japanese trans.), Early Childhood Education: Issues and Perspectives, 1977, (with Nir-Janiv and Steg) International Perspectives on Early Childhood Education, 1982 (Hebrew trans.), with Saracho and Lee (Mainstreaming Young Children, 1984, (with Saracho and Davis) Foundations of Early Childhood Education, 1987, 2d edit. (Japanese trans.), 1991, (with Saracho) Right from the Start, 1994, Dealing with Individual Differences in the Early Childhood Classroom, 1994; editor: Handbook of Research in Early Childhood Education, 1982, Today's Kindergarten, 1986, (with Saracho and Peters) Professionalism and the Early Childhood Practitioner, 1988, (with Saracho) Early Childhood Teacher Education, 1990, Issues in Early Childhood Curriculum, 1991, Educationally Appropriate Kindergarten Practices, 1991, Issues in Childcare, 1992, Handbook of Research on the Education of Young Children, 1993, (with Saracho) Language and Literacy in Early Childhood Education, 1993; series editor Yearbook in Early Childhood Education, early childhood edn. publs., 1971-79; guest editor Studies in Ednl. Evaluation, 1982; also contbr. chpts to books, articles to profl. jours. Mem. Assn. for Childhood Edn. Internat. (nursery sch. com. 1964-66), Am. Ednl. Rsch. Assn. (chair early childhood and child devel. spl. interest group 1983-84, publs. com. 1984-86), AAUP, Nat. Assn. Edn. Young Children (sec. 1965-68, bd. govs. 1968-72, pres. 1976-78, editorial adv. bd. 1972-76, book rev. editor, 1972-74, cons. editor, 1985-87 Young Children jour., mem. tchr. edn. commn. 1981-88, chair commn. on appropriate edn. 4-5 yr. old children 1984-85, cons. editor Early Childhood Rsch. Quar. 1987-90)], Nat. Soc. for Study of Edn. (1972 yearbook com.), Soc. Rsch. Child Devel., Early Education and Development. Office: U Ill Dept Curriculum & Instrn 1310 S 6th St Champaign IL 61820-6925

SPOFFORD, ROBERT HOUSTON, advertising agency executive; b. N.Y.C., Apr. 3, 1941; s. Robert Knowlton and Linda Prieber (Houston) S.; m. Susan Proctor Allerton; children—Margaret, Robert Christopher. B.E.E., Cornell U., 1964. Account exec. Batten, Barton, Durstine & Osborn, Inc., N.Y.C., 1964-71, v.p., 1971-84, sr. v.p., 1984-88, exec. v.p., dir. strategic planning, 1988—. Contbr. articles to advt. and data processing jours. Mem. Westchester County Democratic Com. N.Y. 1974-78; ch. organist. First recipient Founder's medal Batten, Barton, Durstine & Osborn, Inc., 1985. Unitarian. Home: 449 35th St Manhattan Beach CA 90266-3320 Office: BBDO LA 10960 Wilshire Blvd Los Angeles CA 90024-3702

SPOFFORD, SALLY HYSLOP, artist; b. N.Y.C., Aug. 20, 1929; d. George Hall and Esther (McNaull) Hyslop; m. Gavin Spofford, Mar. 11, 1950 (dec. Jan. 1976); children: Lizabeth Spofford Smith, Leslie Spofford Russell. Student, The China Inst., N.Y.C., 1949, The Art Students League, N.Y.C., 1950; BA with high honors, Swarthmore Coll., 1952. Instr. Somerset Art Assn., Peapack, N.J., 1978-95, Hunterdon Art Ctr., Clinton, N.J., 1985—; adv. bd., lectr. Apollo Muses, Inc., Gladstone, N.J.; bd. trustees Artshowcase, Inc. One-man show Riverside Studio, Pottersville, N.J. 1985, Morris Mus., Morristown, N.J. 1989, Schering-Plough Gallery, Madison, N.J., 1989, Phoenix Gallery, N.Y.C., 1990, Robin Hutchins Gallery, Maplewood, N.J., 1992, Berlex Labs. Corp. Office, Wayne, N.J., 1992, Hunterdon Art Ctr., Clinton, N.J., 1993; exhibited in group shows at Hickory (N.C.) Mus., 1983, Purdue U., 1983, Monmouth (N.J.), 1984, Nabisco Brands Gallery, E. Hanover, N.J., 1985, 89, Hunterdon Art Ctr., Clinton, N.J., 1988, 93, Schering-Plough Gallery, Madison, 1988, Morris Mus., Morristown, 1989, Montclair (N.J. State U., 1995; represented in permanent collections N.J. State Mus., Trenton, Newark Mus. Painting residency fellow Vt. Studio Ctr., 1992. Mem. Assoc. Artists N.J. (pres. 1985-87), N.J. Watercolor Soc., Federated Art Assns. of N.J. (panel mem. 1985, demonstrator 1991). Home: PO Box 443 Bernardsville NJ 07924-0443

SPOHN, HERBERT EMIL, psychologist; b. Berlin, Germany, June 10, 1923; s. Herbert F. and Bertha S.; m. Billie M. Powell, Aug 28, 1973; children—Jessica, Madeleine. B.S.S., CCNY, 1949; Ph.D., Columbia U., 1955. Research psychologist VA Hosp., Montrose, N.Y., 1955-60; chief research sect. VA Hosp., 1960-64; sr. research psychologist Menninger Found., Topeka, 1965-80; dir. hosp. research Menninger Found., 1979-94, dir. research dept., 1981-94; ret., prof. emeritus for rsch., 1994—; mem. mental health small grant com. NIMH, 1972-76, mem. treatment assessment rev. com., 1982-85, chmn. 1986-87. Author: (with Gardner Murphy) Encounter with Reality, 1968; assoc. editor: Schizophrenia Bull, 1970-87, 91—; contbr. articles to profl. jours. Served with AUS, World War II. USPHS grantee, 1964—. Fellow Am. Psychopath. Assn.; mem. AAAS, N.Y. Acad. Sci., Soc. Psychopath. Research, Phi Beta Kappa, Sigma Xi. Office: Menninger Found PO Box 829 Topeka KS 66601-0829

SPOHR, ARNOLD THEODORE, artistic director, choreographer; b. Rhein, Sask., Can., Dec. 26, 1927. Student, Winnipeg (Can.) Tchrs. Coll., 1942-43; Assocs., Royal Conservatory Music, Toronto, Can.; cert., Royal Acad. Dance; LLD (hon.), U. Man., Can., 1970, U. Winnipeg, 1984; DFA (hon.), U. Victoria, Can., 1987. Cert. tchr. pub. schs. Tchr. piano, 1946-51; prin. dancer Winnipeg Ballet (now Royal Winnipeg Ballet), 1945-58, artistic dir., tchr. dance, 1958-88, artistic dir. emeritus, 1988—; choreographer, performer Rainbow Stage Sta. CBC-TV, 1957-60; dir. dept. dance Nelson Sch. Fine Arts, 1964-67; artistic dir. dept. dance Banff Sch. Fine Arts, 1967-81; bd. dirs. Can. Theatre Centre; vice chmn. Bd. Dance Can.; adjudicator Can. Council, Can. Dance Tchrs. Assn., N.Y. Internat. Ballet Competitions. Choreographer Ballet Premier, 1950, Intermede, 1951, E Minor, 1959, Hansel and Gretal, 1960, also 18 musicals for Rainbow Stage. Decorated Order of Can., 1970; recipient Centennial medal Govt. of Can., 1967, Manitoba's Order of Buffalo, 1969, Molson prize, 1970, Can. Actor's Equity Assn. Champagne award, 1979, Dance mag. Ann. award, 1981, Diplome D'honneur Can. Conf. of Arts, 1983, Can. Tourism medal, 1985, Royal Bank award, 1987. Mem. Dance in Can. Assn. (bd. dirs., Can. Dance award 1986). Office: Canada's Royal Winnipeg Ballet, 380 Graham Ave, Winnipeg, MB Canada R3C 4K2*

SPOLAN, HARMON SAMUEL, banker; b. Phila., Dec. 12, 1935; s. Jay and Edythe (Greenberg) S.; m. Betty Jane Evnitz, Mar. 30, 1958; children:

Michael, Suzanne. AB, Temple U., 1957, LLB, 1959; postgrad. Oxford U., 1966. Bar: Pa. 1960. Ptnr. Ravetz & Shuchman, Phila., 1960-68, Blair & Co., N.Y.C., 1968-72; v.p. Butcher & Singer, Phila., 1972-74; pres. Capital First Corp., Phila., 1974-75, State Nat. Bank, Rockville, Md., 1975-78, Jefferson Bank, Phila., 1978—; pres., bd. dirs. State Bancshares, Inc., Phila.; pres. bd. dirs. Jefferson Bank, Phila., Bryn Mawr Resources, Phila.; lectr. law U Pa., Phila., 1964-68. Author: Federal Aids to Financing, 1970; contbr. articles to profl. jours. Former chmn. bd. Huntingdon Hosp., Willow Grove, Pa., 1982-89; bd. dirs. YMHA, Phila., 1978—; dir. Anti-Defamation League, 1982. Named Man of the Yr., Nat. Assn. Women Bus. Owners, 1978; Disting. Alumnus, Central High Sch., 1975. Mem. ABA, Phila. Bar Assn., Locust Club, Oxford and Cambridge Club (London). Republican. Jewish. Office: Jefferson Bank 250 S 18th St Philadelphia PA 19103

SPOLLEN, JOHN WILLIAM, lawyer; b. Bklyn., Aug. 26, 1944. AB, Fordham U., 1966, JD, 1973. Bar: N.Y. 1974, U.S. Dist. Ct. (so. dist.) N.Y. 1975. Ptnr. Simpson, Thacher & Bartlett, N.Y.C., 1973—. 1st lt. U.S. Army, 1967-69. Mem. ABA, N.Y. State Bar Assn., N.Y. County Lawyers Assn. Club: Larchmont Shore.

SPONG, JOHN SHELBY, bishop; b. Charlotte, N.C., June 16, 1931; s. John Shelby and Doolie Boyce (Griffith) S.; m. Joan Lydia Ketner, Sept. 5, 1952 (dec. 1988); children: Ellen Elizabeth, Mary Katharine, Jaquelin Ketner; m. Christine Mary Bridger, Jan. 1, 1990. A.B., U. N.C., 1952; M.Div., Va. Theol. Sem., 1955; D.D., St. Paul's Coll., 1976, Va. Theol. Sem., 1977. Ordained to ministry Episcopal Ch., 1955, bishop, 1976; rector St. Joseph's Ch., Durham, N.C., 1955-57, Calvary Ch., Tarboro, N.C., 1957-65, St. John's Ch., Lynchburg, Va., 1965-69, St. Paul's Ch., Richmond, Va., 1969-76; bishop Diocese of Newark, 1976—; mem. governing body Nat. Episc. Ch., 1973-76. Author: Honest Prayer, 1973, This Hebrew Lord, 1974, Dialogue—In Search of Jewish-Christian Understanding, 1975, Christpower, 1976, The Living Commandments, 1977, The Easter Moment, 1980, Into the Whirlwind: The Future of the Church, 1983, Beyond Moralism, 1986, Survival and Consciousness, 1987, Living in Sin? A Bishop Rethinks Human Sexuality, 1988, Rescuing the Bible from Fundamentalism—A Bishop Rethinks the Meaning of Scripture, 1991, Born of a Woman, 1992, Resurrection: Myth or Reality?, 1994. Mem. Richmond Human Relations Commn. Club: Rotary. Home: 43 Ogden Pl Morristown NJ 07960-5248 Office: 24 Rector St Newark NJ 07102-4512

SPONG, WILLIAM BELSER, JR., lawyer, educator; b. Portsmouth, Va., Sept. 29, 1920; s. William Belser and Emily (Nichols) S.; m. Virginia Wise Galliford, June 3, 1950 (dec. May 1993); children: Martha Kingman, Thomas Nichols. Student, Hampden-Sydney Coll., 1937-40, LLD (hon.), 1968; LLB, U. Va., 1947; postgrad., U. Edinburgh, Scotland, 1947-48; LLD (hon.), Roanoke Coll., 1969, Washington and Lee U. and Coll. William and Mary. Bar: Va. 1947. Lectr. law Coll. William and Mary, 1948-49, 75-76; practice law Portsmouth, 1949-76; mem. Va. Ho. Dels., 1954-55, Va. Senate, 1956-66, U.S. Senate, 1966-73; gen. counsel Comm. for Conduct Fgn. Policy, 1973-75; U.S. Senate, 1966-73; gen. counsel Comm. for Conduct Fgn. Policy, 1973-75; dean Marshall-Wythe Sch. Law Coll. William and Mary, 1976-85, Woodbridge prof. emeritus, 1985—; pres. Old Dominion U., 1989-90; spl. master Va. Electric & Power Co., et al vs. Westinghouse Corp., 1977-80, re Dalkon Shield litigation, 1983-85, Smith vs. Morton-Thiokol, 1988; ptnr. Cooper, Spong & Davis, Portsmouth, 1990—; guest scholar Woodrow Wilson Center Smithsonian Instn.; vis. scholar U. Va. Sch. Law, 1973; adj. prof. law U. Richmond, 1974-75, Salzburg Seminar, 1979; sr. visitor Inst. Advanced Legal Studies, U. London, 1985; vis. prof. Washington and Lee U., 1986; Ewald Disting. vis. prof. U. Va. Sch. Law, 1987; Menzies lectr. Australian Nat. U. 1990. Chmn. Va. Commn. Pub. Edn., 1958-62, Gov.'s Commn. on Va.'s Future, 1982-84; mem. Va. Coun. Higher Edn., 1985-89; trustee Hampden-Sydney Coll., 1951-72, Va. Hist. Soc., 1990—; mem. bd. visitors Air Force Acad., 1970, Naval Acad., 1971, Coll. William and Mary, 1992—. With USAAF, 1942-45. Mem. Va. Bar Assn. (pres. 1976), Portsmouth Bar Assn. (past pres.), Order of Coif, Phi Beta Kappa, Phi Alpha Delta, Omicron Delta Kappa, Pi Kappa Alpha. Home: 351 Middle St Portsmouth VA 23704-2826 Office: Cooper Spong & Davis PO Box 1475 Portsmouth VA 23705-1475

SPONSLER, GEORGE CURTIS, III, research administrator, lawyer; b. Collingswood, N.J., Dec. 2, 1927; s. George Curtis and Mary Grace (Hollinberger) S.; m. Bridget Ruth Butcher, Sept. 3, 1955; children: Freda Grace, Naomi Margaret Bride, Curtis Alexander. B.S. in Engring., Princeton U., 1949, M.A., 1951, Ph.D., 1952; J.D., George Washington U., 1981. Bar: Md. 1981, D.C. 1982, U.S. Ct. Appeals (4th cir.) 1982, U.S. Ct. Appeals (fed. cir.) 1984. U.S. Supreme Ct. 1986. With Lincoln Lab., MIT, 1952-56; liaison officer Office Naval Research, London, 1956-58; head spl. projects br. Office Naval Research, Washington, 1958-59; sr. scientist Hoffman Sci. Center, Santa Barbara, Calif., 1959-60; chief sci., dir. tech. analysis and ops. research U.S. Navy Bur. Ships, 1960-63; dir. advanced planning, fed. systems div. IBM, 1963-66, dir. center exploratory studies, 1966-68; exec. sec. div. engring. Nat. Acad. Sci.-NRC, 1968-70; pres. Law Math. and Tech. Inc., 1970—; on leave, Congl. fellow U.S. Senate, Washington, 1987-88; mem. adv. com. to Office Emergency Planning, Nat. Acad. Sci., 1967-72, chmn. subcom. automation, 1966-68, mem. joint adv. com. on electromagnetic pulse, 1970-74; cons. Exec. Office of Pres., 1971-73. Contbr.: Tech. Innovation, Harper Ency. of Sci.; author articles in field. Fellow AAAS (electorate nominating com. 1980-83, chmn.-elect sect. X, 1983-84, chmn. 1984-85, mem. coun. 1985-86), Am. Physics Soc.; mem. IEEE (sr., chmn. subcom. on privacy of communications and info. policy com. 1982-85, aerospace R&D policy com. 1990-92), Phi Beta Kappa, Sigma Xi. Democrat. Episcopalian. Club: Cosmos (Washington). Home: 7804 Old Chester Rd Bethesda MD 20817-6280

SPOOLSTRA, LINDA CAROL, minister, educator, religious organization administrator; b. Hillsdale, Mich., July 11, 1947; d. Jay Carroll and Carol Elsa (Linstrom) Lehmann; m. Gerald William Spoolstra, Feb. 17, 1973. BA, Bethel Coll., 1969; MA, Fla. State U., 1970; M of Div., McCormick Theol. Sem., Chgo., 1978; DD (hon.), Cen Bapt. Theol. Sem., Kansas City, Kans., 1988. Ordained Am. Bapt. Clergywoman. Tchr. Dade County Pub. Schs., Miami, Fla., 1970-71; ins. claims adjustor Safeco Ins. Co., Chgo., 1971-72; dir. of community outreach and edn. N. Shore Bapt. Ch., Chgo., 1972-78, assoc. pastor, 1978; pastor First Bapt. Ch., Swansea, Mass., 1978-84; exec. dir. commn. on the ministry Am. Bapt. Chs. U.S.A., Valley Forge, Pa., 1984-90; exec. minister Am. Bapt. Chs. Mass., Dedham, 1990—; mem. Nat. Coun. of Chs. Profl. Ch. Leadership, N.Y.C., 1984-90; commn. on pastoral leadership Bapt. World Alliance, McLean, Va., 1984-90; mem. gen. bd. Nat. Coun. Chs. of Christ, 1990—. Trustee Andover-Newton Theol. Sch., 1990—. Avocations: sailing, tennis, travel, classical music. Office: Am Bapt Chs Mass 20 Milton St Dedham MA 02026-2954

SPOON, ALAN GARY, communications and publishing executive; b. Detroit, June 4, 1951; s. Harry and Mildred (Rudman) S.; m. Terri Alper, June 3, 1975; children: Ryan, Leigh, Randi. B.S., MIT, 1973, M.S., 1973; J.D., Harvard U., 1976. Cons. The Boston Cons. Group, 1976-79, mgr., 1979-81, v.p., 1981; v.p. The Washington Post Co., 1982-84, 85; v.p., contr. Washington Post, 1985-86, v.p. mktg., 1986-87; v.p. fin., CFO The Washington Post Co., 1987-89; pres. Newsweek mag. 1989-91; COO The Washington Post Co., 1991—, pres., 1993—; dir. Info. Industry Assn., Washington, 1982-83, 88-89; bd. dirs., trustee WETA-Pub. Broadcasting, 1987; bd. dirs. The Riggs Nat. Bank of Washington, 1991-93. Recipient award for scholarship and athletics Eastern Coll. Athletic Conf. and MIT, 1973. Mem. New Eng. Intercollegiate Sailing Assn. (pres. 1972), Fin. Execs. Inst., Internat. Newspapers Fin. Execs. Home: 7300 Loch Edin Ct Rockville MD 20854-4835 Office: The Washington Post Co 1150 15th St NW Washington DC 20071-0001

SPOONER, CHARLES EDWARD, university administrator, health educator; b. Boston, July 25, 1932; s. Charles Edward and Elizabeth Terese (Mahoney) S.; m. Beth Ann Tillman, Nov. 17, 1962; children: Allison Marie, Deanna Lynn. BA, UCLA, 1956, MS, 1961, PhD, 1963; cert. in Health Systems Mgmt., Harvard U., 1976. Pharmacologist Riker Labs., Boston and Los Angeles, 1951-59; predoctoral fellowship NIMH, 1960-63, postdoctoral fellowship, 1963-65; research pharmacologist UCLA, 1965-68, asst. prof. med. sch., 1968; from asst. prof. to prof. med. sch. U. Calif., La Jolla, Calif., 1968—, assoc. dean, prof., 1974—; cons. VA Hosp., Sepulveda, Calif., 1964-81, NIMH, Bethesda, Md., 1976-81, Bd. Med. Quality Assurance, Sacramento, Calif., 1983; vis. prof. Harvard Med. Sch., 1976. U. Oxford Med. Sch., 1992. Fulbright fellow U. Oxford Med Sch., 1986-87. Mem. AAAS,

Am. Soc. Pharmacology Exptl. Therapeutics, Assn. Am. Med. Colls., Soc. Neurosci., Sigma Xi. Clubs: Fedn. Fly Fishermen (West Yellowstone), Steamboaters (N. Umpqua River, Oreg.). Avocation: fly fishing for trout, salmon. Home: 14178 Recuerdo Dr Del Mar CA 92014-2961 Office: U Calif San Diego Sch Med La Jolla CA 92093

SPOONER, FORREST ALLEN, insurance company executive; b. Yonkers, N.Y., July 7, 1941; s. Forrest Jerd and Lucille Winifred (Paul) S.; m. Marita Constance Schellings, Sept. 23, 1967; children: Barbara, Lauren, Arlene. BA, Williams Coll., 1963. With MONY Fin. Services, N.Y.C., 1966—, 2d v.p., 1974-77, v.p., 1977-84, sr. v.p., 1984—, chief fin. officer, 1987—; mem. adv. com. N.Y. State Retirement System, Albany. Bd. dirs. Montvale (N.J.) Athletic League, 1986—. Served as 1st lt. U.S. Army, 1963-66, Vietnam. Decorated Purple Heart, Bronze Star. Fellow Soc. Actuaries; mem. Am. Acad. Actuaries. Republican. Baptist. Avocations: sports, bridge, genealogy. Home: 5 Timberland Trl Montvale NJ 07645-1518 Office: MONY Fin Services 1740 Broadway New York NY 10019-4315

SPOONER, MARK JORDAN, lawyer; b. Norfolk, Va., Nov. 11, 1945; s. David Freeland and Ann (Jordan) S.; m. Roberta A. Cunningham, June 29, 1968; children: David, Christine. AB, Georgetown U., 1967; JD, U. Va., 1970. Bar: D.C. 1970, Va. 1970, Calif. 1994, U.S. Ct. Appeals (D.C., 4th and 7th cirs.), U.S. Ct. Claims, U.S. Supreme Ct. 1977. Assoc. Arnold & Porter, Washington, 1970-77, ptnr., 1978—. Co-author: International Joint Ventures, 1988, 93. Mem. ABA, Va. Bar Assn. Republican. Roman Catholic. Avocations: running, sailing, chess, bridge. Office: Arnold & Porter 777 S Figueroa St 44th Fl Los Angeles CA 90017-2513

SPOOR, WILLIAM HOWARD, food company executive; b. Pueblo, Colo., Jan. 16, 1923; s. Charles Hinchman and Doris Field (Slaughter) S.; m. Janet Spain, Sept. 23, 1950; children: Melanie G., Cynthia F., William Lincoln. BA, Dartmouth Coll., 1949; postgrad., Denver U., 1949, Stanford U., 1965. Asst. sales mgr. N.Y. Export divsn. Pillsbury Co., 1949-53; mgr. N.Y. office Pillsbury Co., 1953-62; v.p. export divsn. Pillsbury Co., Mpls., 1962-68, v.p., gen. mgr. internat. ops., 1968-73, CEO, 1973-85, also bd. dirs., chmn. exec. com., 1987, pres., CEO, 1988, past chmn. bd. dirs.; bd. dirs. Coleman Co. Mem. regional export expansion coun. Dept. Commerce, 1966-74; bd. dirs. Exec. Coun. Fgn. Diplomats, 1976-78; mem. bd. visitors Nelson A. Rockefeller Ctr., Dartmouth Coll., 1992—; mem. exec. com. Minn. Hist. Soc., 1983, Minn. Orchestral Assn., United Negro Coll. Fund, 1973-75; chmn. Capitol City Renaissance Task Force, 1985; trustee Mpls. Found., 1985—; mem. sr. campaign cabinet Carlson Com. U. Minn., 1985; mem. corp. rels. com. Nature Conservancy, 1985; mem. Nat. Cambodia Crisis Com., Pres. Pvt. Sector Dept. Transp Task Force, 1982, Pres. Pvt. Sector Survey on Cost Control, 1983; chmn. YWCA Tribute to Women in Internat, Industry. 2nd. lt. inf. U.S. Army, 1943-46. Recipient Golden Plate award, Am. Acad. Achievement, Disting. Bus. Leadership award, St. Cloud State U., Miss. Valley World Trade award, Outstanding Achievement award, Dartmouth Coll., Horatio Alger award, 1986, Medal of Merit, U.S. Savs. Bond Program; honored with William H. Spoor Dialogues on Leadership, Dartmouth Coll., honored Fair Player Minn. Women's Polit. Caucus, 1989. Mem. Grocery Mfrs. Am. (treas., bd. dirs. 1973-84), Nat. Fgn. Trade Coun., Minn. Hist. Soc. (bd. dirs.), Minn. Bus. Partnership, River Club N.Y.C., Woodhill Country Club, Lafayette Club (Wayzata, Minn.), Mpls. Club. (bd. govs. 1985), Delray Club, Little Club, Gulf Stream Club, Gulf Stream Bath and Tennis Club, Gulf Stream Golf Club, Old Baldy Club (Saratoga, Wyo.). Home: 622 Ferndale Rd W Wayzata MN 55391-9628 Office: 4900 IDS Ctr Minneapolis MN 55402

SPORE, KEITH KENT, newspaper editor; b. Milw., May 29, 1942; s. G. Keith and Evelyn A. (Morgan) S.; divorced; children: Bradley, Julie; m. Kathy Stokebrand. BS in Journalism, U. Wis., Milw., 1967. City editor Milw. Jour. Sentinel, 1977-81, asst. mng. editor/news, 1981-89, mng. editor, 1989-91, editor, 1991-95, editl. page editor, 1995—. Author: (novels) The Hell Masters, 1977, Death of a Scavenger, 1980. With U.S. Army, 1961-64. Recipient UPI Award for Investigative Reporting, 1978. Mem. Milw. Press Club. Office: Milw Jour Sentinel 918 N 4th St PO Box 371 Milwaukee WI 53203-1500

SPORES, RONALD MARVIN, anthropology educator, ethnohistorian; b. Eugene, Oreg., Jan. 25, 1931; s. Marvin C. and Marie (Norwood) S.; children: Lisa France, Ronald Jonathan. B.S., U. Oreg., 1953; M.A., Mexico City Coll., 1960; Ph.D., Harvard U., 1964. Asst. prof. anthropology U. Mass., Amherst, 1964-65; prof. anthropology Vanderbilt U., Nashville, 1965—, dir. anthropology program, 1967-77. Author: The Mixtec Kings and Their People, 1967, The Mixtecs, 1984; co-author: The Cloud People, 1983; series editor: monograph Vanderbilt Publications in Anthropology, 1971—. Served with U.S. Army, 1953-55, Korea. Mem. Am. Soc. for Ethnohistory (pres. 1978-79). Republican. Methodist. Home: 3415 W End Ave Nashville TN 37203-1023 Office: Vanderbilt U Nashville TN 37235

SPORKIN, STANLEY, federal judge; b. Phila., 1932; m. Judith Sally Imber, Sept. 30, 1955; children: Elizabeth Michael, Daniel Paul, Thomas Abraham. AB, Pa. State U., 1953; LLB, Yale U., 1957. Bar: Del. 1958, Pa. 1958, U.S. Dist. Ct. D.C. 1963, U.S. Supreme Ct. 1964, U.S. Ct. Appeals (2d cir.) 1975, U.S. Ct. Appeals (4th cir.) 1978. Law clk. to presiding justice U.S. Dist. Ct. Del., 1957-60; assoc. Haley Woolenberg & Bader, Washington, 1960-61; staff atty. spl. study securities markets U.S. SEC, Washington, 1961-63, atty., 1963, chief atty. enforcement br., 1963-66, chief enforcement atty., 1966, asst. dir., 1967, assoc. dir., 1968-72, dep. dir. div. trading and markets, 1972-73, dir. div. enforcement, 1973-81; gen. counsel CIA, Washington, 1981-86; judge U.S. Dist. Ct. D.C., Washington, 1985—; adj. prof. Antioch Law Sch., 1974-81, Howard U., 1981—; mem. exec. com. U. Calif. Securities Regulation Inst., 1977—. Contbr. articles to profl. jours. Recipient Nat. Civil Svc. League's Spl. Achievement award, 1976, Rockefeller Pub. Svc. award, 1978, Pres.' Disting. Fed. Civilian Svc. award, 1979, Pa. State U. Alumnus of Yr. award, 1979, William O. Douglas award for lifetime achievement Assn. Securities and Exch. Commn. Alumni, 1994; honored by B'nai B'rith Hall of Fame; named Alumni Fellow Coll. Bus. Administrn. Pa. State U., 1990. Fellow Am. Bar Found.; mem. ABA, Fed. Bar Assn. (exec. council securities law sect. 1978—), Del. Bar Assn., Bar Assn. of D.C., Am. Law Inst., Am. Inst. CPA's, Fed. Legal Council, Adminstrv. Conf. of U.S., Phi Beta Kappa, Phi Kappa Phi. Office: US Dist Ct US Courthouse 3rd & Constitution Ave NW Washington DC 20001

SPORN, STANLEY ROBERT, retired electronic company executive; b. N.Y.C., Dec. 10, 1928; s. Max and Mollie (Thau) S.; m. Audrey Brandfield, June 29, 1952; children: Lawrence (dec.), David, Howard. BEE, CCNY, 1950; MSEE, U. Tenn., 1951. Devel. engr. Arma div. AMBAC Industries, N.Y.C., 1951-55, sr. engr., 1958-60, supr., then sect. head, 1960-76, dir. engring., 1976-78; sr. devel. engr. Norden Labs., White Plains, N.Y., 1955-58; dir. engring. Gull Airborne Equipment, Smithtown, N.Y., 1978-81, v.p. engring., 1981-86; v.p. advanced tech. Gull Electronic Systems Divsn. Parker Hannifin Corp., Smithtown, 1986-95; ret., 1995. Author: (with others) Mechanical Design and Systems Handbook, 1964; patentee accelerometers, servos, electronics. Mem. Tau Beta Pi, Eta Kappa Nu. Office: Gull Inc Electronic Systems Divsn 300 Marcus Blvd Smithtown NY 11787

SPOSATO, CHARLES, secondary education educator; b. Westerly, R.I., May 24, 1947; s. Patrick John and Helen Juanita (Travis) S.; m. Mary Elizabeth O'Connell, Aug. 30, 1970; children: Mary Melissa, Martha Elizabeth. BA, Boston Coll., 1970; MEd, Framingham State Coll., 1974. Tchr. Framingham (Mass.) Sch. System, 1970—; trustee Framingham Pub. Libr., 1984—, vice-chairperson, 1984—. Named Tchr. in Space Finalist NASA, 1985, Mass. Tchr. of Yr. State Dept. Edn., 1990, Man of Yr. MetroWest Newspapers, 1990. Mem. Nat. Tchr. Yr. Assn., Mass. Tchr. of Yr. Assn. (v.p. 1990), Tchr. in Space Inst. Avocations: chess writing, jogging, racquetball, reading. Home: 21 Essex St Framingham MA 01701-6405 Office: Framingham South High Sch 31 Flagg Dr Framingham MA 01701

SPOTSWOOD, ROBERT KEELING, lawyer; b. Balt., July 11, 1952; s. William Syson and Helen Marie (Fairchild) S.; m. Ashley Hayward Wiltshire, Aug. 19, 1978; children: Robert Keeling, Mary Hayward. BS with highest distinction in Applied Math., U. Va., 1974, JD, 1977. Bar: Ala. 1977, U.S. Dist. Ct. (no. dist.) Ala. 1979, U.S. Dist. Ct. (so. dist.) Ala. 1980, U.S. Ct. Appeals (5th cir.) 1979, U.S. Ct. Appeals (11th cir.) 1981, U.S. Dist.

Ct. (mid. dist.) Ala. 1986, U.S. Supreme Ct. 1987. Ptnr. Bradley, Arant, Rose & White, Birmingham, Ala., 1977—. Mem. Birmingham Bar Assn., ABA. Club: Mountain Brook. Home: 3865 Cove Dr Birmingham AL 35213-3801 Office: Bradley Arant Rose & White PO Box 830709 Birmingham AL 35283-0709

SPRAGENS, THOMAS ARTHUR, educational consultant; b. Lebanon, Ky., Apr. 25, 1917; s. William Henry and Lillian (Brewer) S.; m. Catharine Smallwood, May 24, 1941; children: Thomas Arthur, Barbara, Allen, David William. A.B., U. Ky., 1938, LL.D., 1964; Maxwell fellow pub. adminstrn., Syracuse U., 1939-40; LL.D., Westminster Coll., Fulton, Mo., 1958, Berea Coll., 1982, Centre Coll., 1982; Litt. D., U. Ala., 1967; H.H.D., Ky. State U., 1984. Research asst. Ky. Dept. Revenue, 1938-39, adminstrv. asst. to commr., 1941-42; adminstv. analyst U.S. Bur. Budget, 1940-41, sr. analyst, 1942-45; asst. chief food allocations Fgn. Econ. Adminstrn., 1945; asst. to pres. Stanford U., 1945-51; sec., treas. Fund for Advancement Edn., 1951-52; pres. Stephens Coll., 1952-57; pres. Centre Coll. of Ky., Danville, 1957-81, pres. emeritus, 1981—; pres. Spragens Assocs., Inc.; cons. in institutional devel. Mem. Ohio Valley Regional Coun., 1973-75; pres. So. Coll. Univ. Union, 1970-74, So. Univ. Conf., 1975; trustee Pikeville Coll., 1985-91; bd. dirs. Shakertown at Pleasant Hill, Ky., 1973-91, Leadership Ky., Inc., 1985—; city commr. Danville, Ky., 1990-94; del. Nat. Dem. Conv., 1968. Mem. Am. Council Edn. (dir. 1966-69), Ky. Hist. Soc. (bd. dirs.), Pendennis Club, Filson Club, Rotary, Phi Beta Kappa, Omicron Delta Kappa. Presbyterian (mem. bd. Christian edn. 1966-73). Home: 3 Charleston Greene Danville KY 40422-1800 Office: Centre Coll Library Danville KY 40422

SPRAGENS, WILLIAM CLARK, public policy educator, consultant; b. Lebanon, Ky., Oct. 1, 1925; s. Thomas Eugene and Edna Grace (Clark) S.; m. Elaine Jean Dunham, June 14, 1964. AB in Journalism, U. Ky., 1947, MA, 1953; PhD, Mich. State U., 1966. Instr. U. Tenn., Knoxville, 1962-64; part-time instr. Mich. State U., East Lansing, 1964-65; asst. prof. Millikin U., Decatur, Ill., 1965-67, Wis. State U., Oshkosh, 1967-69; assoc. prof. Bowling Green (Ohio) State U., 1969-82, prof., 1982-86, prof. emeritus, 1986—; owner Spragens Rsch./Analysis, Reston, Va., 1989—. Author: Electronic Magazines, 1995; editor-in-chief: Popular Images of American Presidents, 1988. Del. candidate McGovern for pres. campaign, Bowling Green, 1972; co-dir. Nat. Convs. Program, 1972, 76, 80, 84. Lyndon Baines Johnson Found. grantee, 1977, 78. Mem. World Affairs Coun. Washington, Am. Polit. Sci. Assn., Internat. Soc. for Polit. Sociology, Am. Soc. for Pub. Adminstrn. Democrat. Presbyterian. Avocations: coin collecting, first day cover collecting, psychology. Home and Office: PO Box 410 Herndon VA 22070

SPRAGUE, CHARLES CAMERON, medical foundation president; b. Dallas, Nov. 14, 1916; s. George Able and Minna (Schwartz) S.; m. Margaret Frederica Dickson, Sept. 7, 1943; 1 dau., Cynthia Cameron. BBA, BS, DSc, So. Meth. U.; MD, U. Tex. Med. Branch, Galveston, 1943; DSc (hon.), U. Dallas, 1983, Tulane U., 1991. Diplomate Am. Bd. Internal Medicine. Intern U.S. Naval Med. Center, Bethesda, Md., 1943-44; resident Charity Hosp., New Orleans, 1947-48, Tulane U. Med. Sch., 1948-50; Commonwealth research fellow in hematology Washington U. Sch. Medicine, St. Louis, also Oxford (Eng.) U., 1950-52; mem. faculty Med. Sch. Tulane U., 1952-67, prof. medicine, 1959-67; dean Med. Sch. Tulane U. (Sch. Medicine), 1963-67; prof., dean U. Tex. Southwestern Med. Sch., Dallas, 1967-72; pres. U. Tex. Health Sci. Center, Dallas, 1972-86; pres. SW Med. Found., 1987-88, chmn. bd., chief exec. officer, 1988—; pres. emeritus U. Tex. SW Med. Ctr.; Mem. Nat. Adv. Council, 1966-70; mem. adv. com. to dir. NIH, 1973—; chmn. Gov.'s Task Force Health Manpower, 1981, Gov.'s Med. Edn. Mgmt. Effectiveness Com.; chmn. allied health edn. adv. com., coordinating bd. Tex. Coll. and Univ. System.; mem. coordinating bd. Tex. Higher Edn., 1989—vice chmn., 1990—. Mem. adv. coun. Ctr. for Bioenviron. Rsch., Tulane U. 1991-93; adv. com. Ctr. Sci. and Soc., U. Tex., Dallas, 1991—. With USNR, 1943-47. Recipient Ashbel Smith Disting. Alumnus award U. Tex. Med. Br., 1967; Disting. Alumnus award So. Meth. U., 1965; recipient Sports Illustrated Silver Anniversary award, 1963. Mem. Assn. Am. Med. Colls. (chmn. council deans 1970, chmn. exec. council and assembly 1972-73), Am. Soc. Hematology (pres. 1966), Assn. Acad. Health Ctrs. (bd. dirs. 1982—, chmn. bd. 1985-86). Office: Southwestern Medical Found PO Box 45708 5323 Harry Hines Blvd Dallas TX 75245-0708*

SPRAGUE, EDWARD AUCHINCLOSS, retired association executive, economist; b. N.Y.C., Oct. 9, 1932; s. Irvin Auchincloss and Maude Browning (Fisher) S.; m. Patricia Ivy Cannon, Apr. 27, 1957; children: James Edward, Elizabeth Mary, Jennifer Ann. BA, Princeton U., 1954; MA, NYU, 1961. Rsch. analyst N.J. State C. of C., Newark, 1957-59; assoc. economist F.W. Dodge Corp., N.Y.C., 1959-62; economist Lehman Bros., N.Y.C., 1962-67; v.p. Nat. Assn. Mfrs., N.Y.C. and Washington, 1967-77; dir. tax policy The Tax Found., Washington, 1977-82; sr. v.p. The Tax Found., 1985-89; exec. dir. Tax Exec. Inst., 1982-85; v.p., exec. dir. The Tax Coun., 1979-82, 86-91, cons., 1991-92; cons. Employers Coun. on Flexible Compensation, Washington, 1992-93; ret., 1993. Editor: Building Business, 1961-62; jour. The Tax Executive, 1983-85. With U.S. Army, 1955-57. Mem. Nat. Tax Assn. Republican. Home: 623 Running Fox Rd Lusby MD 20657

SPRAGUE, GEORGE FREDERICK, geneticist; b. Crete, Nebr., Sept. 3, 1902; s. Elmer Ellsworth and Lucy Kent (Manville) S. B.S., U. Nebr., 1924, M.S., 1926, D.Sc., 1958; Ph.D., Cornell U., 1930. With Dept. Agr., 1924-72, leader corn and sorghum investigations, 1958-72; mem. faculty U. Ill., Urbana, 1973-86; prof. emeritus U. Ill., 1986-93. Editor: Corn and Corn Improvement, 3d edit, 1989; contbr. articles to profl. jours. Recipient Superior Svc. award USDA, 1960, Disting. Svc. award, 1970, Wolf Found. award, Nat. Coun. Plant Breeders award, DeKalb Career award; inducted into USDA-Agrl. Rsch. Svc. Sci. Hall of Fame. Fellow AAAS, Washington Acad. Scis., Am. Soc. Agronomy (pres. 1960, Crops Rsch. award 1957); mem. NAS, Crops Sci. Soc. (pres. 1951), Am. Genetics Assn., Genetics Soc. Am., Am. Soc. Plant Physiologists, Am. Naturalists, Biometrics Soc. Home: 494 W 10th Ave # 208 Eugene OR 97401-9999

SPRAGUE, JAMES MATHER, medical scientist, educator; b. Kansas City, Mo., Aug. 31, 1916; s. James P. and Lelia (Mather) S.; m. Dolores Marie Eberhart, Nov. 25, 1959; 1 son, James B. B.S., U. Kans., 1938, M.A., 1940; Ph.D., Harvard U., 1942; A.M. (hon.), U. Pa., 1971. From asst. to asst. prof. anatomy Hopkins Med. Sch., 1942-50; asst. prof. to prof. anatomy U. Pa. Med. Sch., Phila., 1950-83; chmn. dept. U. Pa. Med. Sch., 1967-76, Joseph Leidy prof. anatomy, 1973-83, emeritus Joseph Leidy prof., 1983—; dir. Inst. Neurol. Sci., 1973-80, chmn. univ. faculty senate, 1963; vis. prof. Northwestern U., 1948, U. Oxford, 1949, Rockefeller U., 1955, Cambridge U., 1956, U. Pisa, 1966, 74-75, U. Leuven, 1984—; sci. consultants. NIH, 1957-60. Co-editor: Progress in Psychobiology and Physiological Psychology, 1966-84; asso. editor: Acta Neurobiol. Exper., 1976; contbr. articles to profl. jours. Recipient Macy faculty award, 1974-75; Guggenheim fellow, 1948-49. Mem. Nat. Acad. Scis., Am. Assn. Anatomists (v.p. 1976-78), Japanese Assn. Anatomists (hon.), Soc. Neurosci. Democrat. Home: 410 Lantern Ln Berwyn PA 19312-2011 Office: Dept Cell & Devel Biology Dept Neurosci Sch Medicine U Pa Philadelphia PA 19104-6058

SPRAGUE, JOHN LOUIS, management consultant; b. Boston, 1930; s. Robert Chapman and Florence Antoinette (van Zelm) S.; m. Mary-Jane Whitney, June 19, 1952; children—John Louis, William Whitney, Catherine van Zelm, David Hyatt. A.B., Princeton, 1952; Ph.D., Stanford, 1959. With Sprague Electric Co., North Adams, Mass., 1959-87; co-dir. engring. labs., sr. v.p. engring. Sprague Electric Co., 1964-65, v.p. research and devel., 1965-66, sr. v.p. semi-condr. div., 1967-76, pres., 1976-87, chief exec. officer, 1981-87; pres. John L. Sprague Assocs. Inc., 1988—; bd. dirs. Sipex corp., State Mut. Cos., Aerovox, Inc., MRA Labs., Inc., Calif. Micro Devices. Chmn. Williamstown United Fund-ARC Campaign, 1961; trustee Pine Cobble Sch., 1978, Middlesex Sch., 1994— Served to lt. (j.g.) USNR, 1952-55. Mem. IEEE, Electrochem. Soc., Am. Chem. Soc., Sci. Research Soc. Am., Confrerie des Chevaliers du Tastevin, Confrerie de la Chaine des Rotisseurs, Mayflower Hist. Soc., Sigma Xi, Phi Lambda Upsilon. Club: Princeton (N.Y.C.). Home: 124 Chestnut Cir Lincoln MA 01773-4915

SPRAGUE, NORMAN FREDERICK, JR., surgeon, educator; b. L.A., June 12, 1914; s. Norman F. and Frances E. (Ludeman) S.; m. Caryll E.

Mudd, Dec. 27, 1941 (dec. Apr. 1978); children: Caryll (Mrs. Mingst), Norman Frederick III, Cynthia Sprague Connolly, Elizabeth (Mrs. Day); m. Erlenne Estes, Dec. 31, 1981. AB, U. Calif., 1933; MD, Harvard U., 1937. Intern Bellevue Hosp., N.Y.C., 1937, house surgeon, 1938-39; pvt. med. practice L. A., 1946—; mem. hon. staff Hosp. of Good Samaritan, L. A.; mem. staff St. Vincent Med. Ctr., L. A.; asst. clin. prof. surgery UCLA, 1951—; dir. emeritus Western Fed. Savs. & Loan Assn.; chmn. bd. dirs. Western Pioneer Co., 1961-63, Pioneer Savs. & Loan Assn., 1959-63; dir. Arden-Mayfair, Inc., 1966-69; also chmn. exec. com.; dir. mem. exec. com. Cyprus Mines Corp., 1959-79; trustee Mesabi Trust, 1964-76. Chmn. exec. com., v.p. Harvard Sch., 1954-65; mem. Community Redevel. Agy. City of L.A., 1966-69, vice chmn., 1967-69; mem. Calif. Regional Med. Programs Area IV Council, 1970-75; bd. dirs., v.p. Calif. Inst. Cancer Rsch., 1974-80, pres., 1980-82; bd. dirs. Cancer Assoc., 1975-80; trustee UCLA Found., Marlborough Sch., 1981-90, Mildred E. and Harvey S. Mudd Found., Hollywood Bowl Assn., 1962-66; hon. trustee Calif. Mus. Found.; mem. exec. com., trustee Youth Tennis Found., 1960-70; trustee, pres. mem. exec. com. S.W. Mus.; founding trustee, Harvey Mudd Coll.; chmn. bd. trustees Caryll and Norman Sprague Found., 1957—, Harvard Sch.; mem. bd. visitors UCLA Med. Sch.; nat. bd. dirs. Retonitis Pigmentosa Internat. Served to maj. M.C. AUS, 1941-46. Decorated Bronze Star; recipient Bishop's award of Merit Episc. Diocese L.A., 1966, Highest Merit award So. Calif. Pub. Health Assn., 1968. Mem. AMA, SAR, Calif. Med. Assn., L.A. County Med. Assn. (pres. jr. sect. 1953), Am. Cattlemen's Assn., Symposium Soc., Tennis Patrons Assn. (dir. 1960-70), Calif. Club, Harvard Club, L.A. Country Club, Delta Kappa Epsilon. Home: 550 S Mapleton Dr Los Angeles CA 90024-1811 Office: 2049 Century Park E Ste 2760 Los Angeles CA 90067-3202

SPRAGUE, PETER JULIAN, semiconductor company executive, lecturer; b. Detroit, Apr. 29, 1939; s. Julian K. and Helene (Coughlin) S.; m. Tjasa Krofta, Dec. 19, 1959; children: Carl, Steven, Kevin, Michael. Student, Yale U., 1961, MIT, 1961, Columbia U., 1962-66. Chmn. bd. dirs. Nat. Semiconductor Corp., Santa Clara, Calif.; chmn. Wave Sys., Inc.; bd. dirs. Software Profls., Inc. Trustee Strang Clinic. Club: Yale. Home: 399 Under Mountain Rd Lenox MA 01240-2035 Office: Wave Sys Corp 540 Madison Ave New York NY 10022 Office: Nat Semiconductor Corp 2900 Semiconductor Dr PO Box 58090 Santa Clara CA 95051

SPRAGUE, WILLIAM, insurance company executive, farmer; b. 1938. Pres. Ky Farm Bur Mutual Inc., Louisville; farmer Sturgis, Ky. Office: Ky Farm Bur Mutual Inc 9201 Bunsen Pky Louisville KY 40220*

SPRAGUE, WILLIAM DOUGLAS, lawyer, company executive; b. Houston, Dec. 23, 1941; s. William Douglas and Helen (Mims) S.; m. Marilyn Wells, Aug. 7, 1965; children: William Douglas III, Anne W., Robert L. BS, U. Wis., 1964; JD, Harvard U., 1967. Bar: Wis. 1967, Mich. 1972, Ind. 1978, Pa. 1991. Assoc. Reinhart, Boerner, Van Deuren, Norris & Rieselbach, Milw., 1967-71; lawyer Ford Motor Credit Co., Dearborn, Mich., 1971-77; various legal positions to sr. v.p. adminstrn. AMAX Coal Co., Indpls., 1977-87; assoc. gen. counsel Alumax Inc., San Mateo, Calif., 1987-88; v.p., gen. counsel Lukens Inc., Coatesville, Pa., 1988—. Gen. campaign chmn. United Way Chester County, Exton, Pa., 1990. Mem. ABA, Wis. Bar Assn., Mich. Bar Assn., Ind. Bar Assn., Pa. Bar Assn., Phi Kappa Phi, Phi Eta Sigma. Avocations: golf, bridge. Office: Lukens Inc 50 S 1st Ave Coatesville PA 19320-3418

SPRAGUE, WILLIAM WALLACE, JR., food company executive; b. Savannah, Ga., Nov. 11, 1926; s. William Wallace and Mary (Crowther) S.; m. Elizabeth Louise Carr, Oct. 3, 1953; children: Courtney, Lauren Duane, William Wallace III, Elizabeth Louise. BSME, Yale U., 1950. With Savannah Foods & Industries, Inc., 1952-94, ret., 1994, sec., 1961-62, v.p., 1962-72, pres., chief exec. officer, 1972-92, chmn. bd. dirs., CEO, 1993-94, also bd. dirs.; mem. audit quality rev. com. NationsBank Corp., Charlotte, N.C.; mem. adv. bd. NationsBank Ga., N.A., Savannah; bd. dirs. Everglades Sugar Refinery, Clewiston, Fla.; chmn. bd. dirs. Mich. Sugar Co., Saginaw, Colonial Sugars, Gramercy, La., Food Carrier, Inc., Savannah, Raceland (La.) Sugars, Inc., Savannah Foodsvc., Inc.; bd. dirs., pres. Adeline Sugar Factory Co.. Ltd., Savannah, Coastal Mgmt. Corp., Savannah. Trustee Savannah Bus. Group, Savannah Benevolent Assn.; chmn. mem. steering com. United Way Savannah; vice chmn. Savannah CEO Coun.; chmn. emeritus Youth Futures Authority, Savannah. With USN, 1945-46. Named Sugar Man of Yr. and recipient Dyer Meml. award B.W. Dyer & Co., 1985; named Industrialist of Yr. Internat. Mgmt. Coun., 1988. Mem. World Sugar Rsch. Orgn. (chmn. 1982-85), Grocery Mfrs. Assn. (bd. dirs.), The Sugar Assn. (bd. dirs.), NAM, Carolina Plantation Soc.. St. Andrews Soc., Oglethorpe Club, Century Club (Savannah). Office: Savannah Foods & Industries PO Box 339 Savannah GA 31402-0339

SPRANG, MILTON LEROY, obstetrician, gynecologist, educator; b. Chgo., Jan. 15, 1944; s. Eugene and Carmella (Bruno) S.; m. Sandra Lee Karabelas, July 16, 1966; children: David, Christina, Michael. Student, St. Mary's Coll., 1962-65; MD, Loyola U., 1969. Diplomate Am. Bd. Ob-gyn; Nat. Bd. Med. Examiners; CME accreditation. Intern St. Francis Hosp., Evanston, Ill., 1969-70, resident, 1972-75, sr. attending physician, 1985—; assoc. attending physician Evanston Hosp., 1975-79, attending physician, 1980-84, sr. attending physician, 1985—, v.p. med. staff, 1990-91, pres.-elect, 1991-92, pres., 1992-93; also bd. dirs., 1991-94; sec. coun. Evanston Hosp., 1993-94; chmn. ob-gyn Cook County Grad. Sch. Medicine, Chgo., 1983-91; instr. Northwestern U. Med. Sch., Chgo., 1975-78, assoc. prof., 1984; pres. Northwestern Healthcare Network Physician Leadership, 1994; lectr. to acad. and civic groups; program dir. postgrad. courses; chmn. Ob-Gyn Nat. CCtr. for Advanced Med. Edn., 1991—; bd. dirs. Ill. Found. Med. Rev., Nat. Ctr. for Advanced Med. Edn.; trustees Ill. State Ins. Svcs., 1991-94; bd. govs. Ill. State Med. Inter-Ins. Exch., 1987. Editor: Profl. Staff News, 1992-93; chmn. editorial bd. Jour. Chgo. Medicine, 1986—; contbr. articles to profl. jours. Bd. dirs. Am. Cancer Sooc., chmn. profl. edn. com. North Shoore unit, 1982-85; bd. dirs. Chgo. Community Info. Network, 1994-95; mem. Nat. Rep. Congrl. Com., 1981—, Ill. Med. Polit. Action Com. With USN, 1970-72. Fellow ACS, Am. Coll. Ob-Gyn (chmn. Ill. sect. 1975-76), Am. Soc. Colposcopy and Cervical Pathology; mem. AMA (Physician Recognition award 1977, 80, 83), Ill. Med. Soc. (del. to AMA 1987, 91—, ho. of dels., govt. affairs com. 1988-90, chmn. reference com. 1989, chmn. bd. trustees 1990-91, 94, chmn. fin. com. 1992-94, sec.-treas. 1994—), Chgo. Med. Soc. (v.p. 1984-85, adv. com. advt. standards 1978-84, counselor, physician's rev. com. 1980-85, sec. 1989—, exec. coun. north suburban br. 1981-82, trustee ins. bd. 1982—, nominating com. 1985-86, trustee 1986-92, treas. 1986-89, sec. 1989-90, pres.-elect 1990-91, pres. 1991-92, chmn. fin. com. 1986-89, pres. 1991-93, chmn. fin. com. physicians benefit trust 1993-94), Chgo. Found. Med. Care (nominating com. 1980-84, med. care evaluation and edn. com. 1980-83, practice guidelines com. 1984), Physicians Benefit Trust (chmn. fin. com. 1993-94). Roman Catholic. Avocations: reading, raising fish, swimming. Home: 4442 Concord Ln Skokie IL 60076-2606 Office: AGSO 1000 Central St Evanston IL 60201-2400

SPRATT, JOHN MCKEE, JR., congressman, lawyer; b. Charlotte, N.C., Nov. 1, 1942; s. John McKee and Jane Love (Bratton) S.; m. Jane Stacy, May 31, 1968; children: Susan Elizabeth, Sarah Stacy, Catherine Bratton. A.B., Davidson Coll., 1964; M.A., Corpus Christi Coll., Oxford U. 1966; LL.B, Yale U., 1969. Ops. analyst Office of Asst. Sec. of Def., 1969-71; ptnr. Spratt, McKeown & Spratt, Rock, S.C., 1971-83; pres. Spratt Ins. Agy., Ft. Mill, 1973-82, Bank of Ft. Mill, S.C., 1973-82; mem. 98th-104th Congresses from 5th S.C. dist., Washington, D.C., 1983—; mem. Armed Svcs. com., subcoms. oversight and investigations, military acquisitions, govt. opns. com., subcoms. commerce, consumer, monetary affairs, joint com. orgn. congress; former dir. Bank of York. Chmn. bd. trustees Divine Saviour Hosp., York, 1980-82; bd. dirs. Piedmont Legal Services, Inc., 1978-82; bd. visitors Davidson Coll., 1978-80; chmn. bd. visitors Winthrop Coll., 1976. Served to capt. JAGC, U.S. Army, 1969-71. Mem. S.C. Bar Assn. (ho. of dels.), ABA. Democrat. Presbyterian. Office: US Ho of Reps 1536 Longworth House Office Bldg Washington DC 20515-4005*

SPRAY, PAUL, surgeon; b. Wilkinsburg, Pa., Apr. 9, 1921; s. Lester E. and Phoebe Gertrude (Huff) S.; m. Mary Louise Conover, Nov. 28, 1943; children—David C., Thomas L., Mary Lynn (Mrs. Thomas Branham). B.S., U. Pitts., 1942; M.D., George Washington U., 1944; M.S., U. Minn., 1950.

Diplomate Am. Bd. Orthopedic Surgery. Intern U.S. Marine Hosp., S.I., 1944-45; resident Mayo Found., Rochester, Minn., 1945-46, 48-50; practice medicine specializing in orthopedic surgery Oak Ridge, Tenn., 1950—; mem. staff Oak Ridge Hosp., Park West Hosp., Knoxville, Harriman Hosp., Tenn., Bapt. Hosp. of Roane County; vol. vis. cons., CARE Medico, Jordan, 1959, Nigeria, 1962, 65, Algeria, 1963, Afghanistan, 1970, Bangladesh, 1975, 77, 79, Peru, 1980, U. Ghana, 1982; AMA voluntary physician, Vietnam, 1967, 72; vis. assoc. prof. U. Nairobi, 1973; mem. teaching team of Internat. Coll. Surgeons to Khartoum, vis. prof. orthopedic surgery U. Khartoum, 1976; hon. prof. San Luis Gonzaga U., Ica, Peru; AmDoc vol. cons., U. Biafra Teaching Hosp., 1969; vis. prof. Mayo Clinic, 1988; sec. orthopedics overseas div. CARE Medico, 1971-76, sec. medico adv. bd., 1974-76, vice chmn., 1976, chmn., 1977-79, U. CARE, Inc., 1977-79, pub. mem. care bd. dirs., 1980-90, bd. overseers, 1991—; chmn. Orthopedics Overseas, Inc., 1982-86, treas., 1986-88; mem. U.S organizing com. 1st Internat. Acad. Symposium on Orthopedics, Tianjin, China, 1983; mem. CUPP Internat. Adv. Council, 1986—; bd. dirs. East Tenn. Health Plan, 1987-90; citizen amb. to Vietnam, People to People, 1993; invited guest spkr. Japan Orthopedic Assn., 1994. Mem. editorial bd. Contemporary Orthopedics, 1984—. V.p. Anderson County Health Coun., 1975, pres., 1976-77, hon. bd. dirs., 1991; pres. health commn. Coun. Southern Mountains, 1958-65, sec. bd. dirs., 1965-66; Tenn. pres. UN Assn., 1966-67; vice chmn. bd. Camelot Care Ctr., Tenn., 1979-82, chmn., 1982-86; chmn. bd. dirs. Camelot Found., 1986-87; hon. mem. World Orthopedic Concern, 1990; with del. to Vietnam People to People, 1993, citizen ambassador to Vietnam, 1993; del. to Oak Ridge's Sister City, Obinsk, Russia, 1993; bd. dirs. Vietnam Am. Scholarship Found. Recipient Svc. to Mankind award Sertoma, 1967, Humanitarian award Lions Club, 1968, Freedom Citation, 1978, Amb. Goodwill award 1979, Medico Disting. Svc. award, 1990, 1st Ann. Vocat. Svc. award Oak Ridge Rotary, 1979, Tech. Communication award East Tenn. chpt. Soc. for Tech. Communication, 1983, Individual Achievement award Meth. Med. Ctr. of Oak Ridge, 1991, Humanitarian award Orthopaedics Overseas, 1992; Melvin Jones fellow Lions Club, 1993. Fellow ACS, Internat. Coll. Surgeons (Tenn. regent 1976-80, bd. councillors 1980-84, hon. chmn. bd. trustees 1981-83, trustee 1983-84, v.p. U.S. sect. 1982-83, mem. surg. teams com. 1983-90, Humanitarian award 1992); mem. AMA (Humanitarian Assn. award 1967, 72), Société International Chirugie Orthopédique et de Traumatologie, So. Orthopedic Assn., Western Pacific Orthopedic Assn., Orthopedic Letters Club, Am. Fracture Assn., Am. Acad. Orthopedic Surgeons (mem. com. on injuries 1980-86), Tenn. Med. Assn. (com. on emergency med. svcs. 1978-88), Peru Acad. Surgery (corr.), Peruvian Soc. Orthopedic Surgery and Traumatology (corr.), Clin. Orthopaedic Soc., Mid-Am. Orthopedic Soc., Rotary Club (Oak Ridge chpt.). Home: 507 Delaware Ave Oak Ridge TN 37830-3902 Office: Medical Arts Bldg Ste 404 123 W Tennessee Ave Oak Ridge TN 37830

SPRAYBERRY, ROSLYN RAYE, secondary school educator; b. Newnan, Ga., June 29, 1942; d. Henry Ray and Grace (Bernhard) S. BA, Valdosta State Coll., 1964; MA in Teaching, Ga. State U., 1976, EdS in Spanish, 1989; EdD, Nova U., 1993. Cert. tchr., Ga. Tchr. history Griffin (Ga.) High Sch., 1964-65; tchr. 6th grade Beaverbrook Elem Sch., Griffin, 1965-66; tchr. Spanish, chair fgn. lang. dept. Forest Park (Ga.) High Sch., 1966-77; chair fgn. lang. dept. Spanish Forest Park (Ga.) High Sch., 1969-77; tchr. Spanish, chair fgn. lang. dept. Riverdale (Ga.) High Sch., 1977—; correlator Harcourt, Brace, Jovanovich, 1989; adv. bd. So. Conf. Lang. Teaching, 1992—; lectr. and speaker in field. Contbr. articles to The Ednl. Resource Info. Ctr. Clearinghouse on Langs. and Linguistics, Ctr. for Applied Linguistics, Washington; designed courses for the Gifted, Ga. Dept. of Edn. Cnvener Acad. Alliances-Atlanta II, Clayton County, Ga., 1987; advisor, workshop leader Ga. Fgn. Lang. Camp, Atlanta, 1983; dir. Clayton County Fgn. Lang. Festival, 1990-91. Recipient STAR Tchr. award Ga. C. of C., 1982; Fulbright-Hays scholar, 1978; NEH grantee, 1977, 84. Mem. NEA, Am. Coun. Tchrs. Fgn. Langs., Am. Assn. Tchrs. Spanish and Portuguese, Ga. Assn. Educators, Fgn. Lang. Assn. Ga. (treas. 1977-85, assoc. editor jour. 1981-86, Tchr. of Yr. award 1976), Clayton County Edn. Assn., So. Conf. Lang. Teaching, KPS Leadership Specialists (co-founder 1993). Methodist. Avocations: guitar playing, traveling, reading, writing. Home: 9261 Brave Ct Jonesboro GA 30236

SPRECHER, BARON BARON WILLIAM, pianist, composer, conductor, diplomat; b. Saarbrucken, Germany, Jan. 20, 1924; came to U.S., 1952; s. Wolf and Karoline (Jung) Sprecher; m. Blossom Tag, Aug. 6, 1952. Studied piano with Prof. Wittels, Tel Aviv; studied piano with Madame Vengerova, N.Y.C.; studied composition with Paul Ben-Haim, Tel Aviv, studied conducting with Georg Singer; hon. degree, Inst. of Vocal Arts, 1957; Dr. honoris causa in Philosophy of Music, World Univ. Roundtable, 1988; MusD (hon.), London Inst. Applied Rsch., 1991, DFA (hon.), 1993, HHD, 1993; MusD (hon.), Australian Inst. Coord. Rsch., 1991; diploma, Gran Premio Am., 1990, Paladino del Tricolore, 1990; D Musicology, Somerset U.; D Music (hon.), Atlantic Southeastern U.; Diploma, Acad. Argentina de Diplomacia; Assoc. (hon.), Inst. Affairs Internat., Paris, 1993; DD (hon.) The Christian Congregation; D rerum politicarum (hon.), LittD, U. Aeterna Lucina Vitama, 1991; DD (hon.), LittD, Germany, 1994; PhD (hon.), Germany, 1994. Korrepetitor Israel Folk Opera, Tel-Aviv, 1940-43; piano soloist Israel Philharm. Orch., Tel-Aviv, 1946-48; pres., music dir. Bronx Philharm., N.Y.C., 1971-83; music dir. Sta. WEVD, N.Y.C., 1969-85; asst. pianist accompanying Lotte Lenya, Richard Tucker, Jan Peerce, Itzhak Perlman, Jan Kiepura, Ilona Massey; prof. Inst. Hautes Etudes Economiques et Sociales; rsch. prof. Alliance Universelle Paix Connaissance, Paris, 1991; prof. Haute Ecole de Recherche, Inst. des Hautes Etudes Economiques et Sociales; mem. coun. Inst. de Documentation et D'Etudes Europeennes; dep. mem., diplomat Internat. State Parliament. Composer: (Song Book) Yinglish, piano soloist 1st performance of Gershwin's Concerto in F in Israel; composer Piano Sonata, 1945, Jerusalem Concerto for Piano and Orch., 1967, (TV spl.) Great is Thy Faith, 1970; pianist-condr. 24 record albums; mem. The First Piano Quartet (Acad. award nomination, Peabody award). Consul Sovereign State Aeterna Lucina for State and City of N.Y.; comdr. fgn. rels. Island Du Caricom, 1995; diplomat World Jewish Congress. Decorated noble knight Noble House of Amena, knight order Knight Templars of Jerusalem, knight comdr. Lofsenic Ursinius Order, baron Order of Bohemian Crown, comdr. Order of Golden Lance (Australia), capt. Légion de L'Aigle de Mer, Baron of Montsalvat, knight Holy Grail, count San Ciriaco, comdr. fgn. rels. Island du Caricom, 1995, diplomat World Jewish Congress, Liard-Lord of Camster, Caithness, Scotland, 1995; recipient Diplomatic medal Internat. Parliament for Safety and Peace, 1995, Gold Cross of Honour, Albert Schweitzer Soc. Austria, Albert Einstein medal, Circulo Nobiliario Caballeros Universales, 1992, Swan Knight (Chevalier au Cygne), Order of the Swan, others. Fellow United Writers' Assn. India; mem. ASCAP, Maison Internat. des Intellectuels, Internat. Parliament for Safety and Peace, World Parliament Confedn. of Chivalry (Grand Coun.), World Acad. Assn. of the Universe (life), Bronx Philharm. Symphony Soc., Inc. (founder, pres.), Internat. Platform Assn. Am. Fedn. Musicians, Robert Stolz Soc. Gt. Britain, World Univ. Roundtable (trustee, founder), Nat. Soc. Universalists (canonist, chmn. of trustees), Internat. Cultural Corr. Inst., Circulo Nobiliario de los Caballeros Universales (grandmaster U.S.), Royal Order Bohemian Crown (baron), Légion de L'Aigle de Mer (capt.). Avocations: walking, chivalry and heraldry, cats, collecting rare musical books and recordings, collecting rare medieval coins and antique Coptic Ethiopian Crosses. Home and Office: Res Monsalvat 1D 2235 Cruger Ave Bronx NY 10467-9411

SPRECHER, DAVID A., university administrator, mathematician; b. Saarbrucken, Fed. Republic Germany, Jan. 12, 1930; s. Wolfgang and Karolina (Jung) S.; children: Lorrie, Jeannie. Student, Hebrew U., 1952-54; A.B., U. Bridgeport, 1958; Ph.D., U. Md., 1963. Instr. math U. Md., 1961-63; asst. prof. Syracuse U., 1963-66; assoc. prof. math. U. Calif.-Santa Barbara, 1966-71, prof., 1971-92; prof. emeritus, 1993—; chmn. dept., 1972-75, assoc. dean Coll. of Letters and Sci., 1975-78, dean Coll. of Letters and Sci., 1978-81, provost/dean, 1981-91. Author: Elements of Real Analysis, 1970, 2nd edit., 1987, Precalculus Mathematics, 1974, Finite Mathematics, 1976; (with P. Frank and A. Yaqub) A Brief Course in Calculus With Applications, 1971, 2nd edit., 1976; (with P. Frank) Calculus, 1975; contbr. articles to profl. jours. Served with Israeli Army, 1948-50. Mem. Am. Math. Soc., Math. Assn. Am. Office: U Calif 6709 South Hall Santa Barbara CA 93106

SPRECHER, PETER LEONARD, JR., financial services company executive; b. Indpls., Apr. 16, 1930; s. Peter Leonard Sr. and Ann (Gardner) S.; m. Phyllis Willingham, Feb. 27, 1954; children: Jeffrey C., Jill A., Karen

L. BBA, Ind. U., 1953. CLU, ChFC. Agt., supr. Provident Mut. Life Ins. Co., Indpls., 1955-58; supt. of agys. Provident Mut. Life Ins. Co., Phila., 1958; agy. mgr. Provident Mut. Life Ins. Co., Madison, Wis., 1959-67; gen. agt. Washington Nat. Ins. Co., Madison, 1967-85; pres. P.L. Sprecher & Assocs., Madison, 1985—. Contbr. articles to profl. jours. Pres. Madison Met. YMCA, 1976, Parkwood Hills Commun. Assn., Madison, 1970, Bethel Luth. Ch. Coun., Madison, 1974; mem. ins. com. Madison Tech. and Vocat. Sch., 1990-91; bd. dirs. Wis. Youth Symphony Orch., 1987, Madison Opportunity Ctr., 1991—. 1st lt. USAF, 1954-55, Korea. Recipient ins. awards. Mem. Nat. Assn. Life Underwriters (Million Dollar Round Table 1976—, Assn. for Advanced Life Underwriting 1988—, Nat. Quality award 1977-94, Disting. Svc. award 1993), Madison Assn. Life Underwriters (pres. 1989-90, Disting. Svc. award 1993), Madison Gen. Agt. Assn. (pres. 1964-65), Madison CLU Soc. (pres. 1972-74), Madison Estate Coun., Madison Club. Republican. Avocation: tournament tennis. Home: 6409 Shenandoah Way Madison WI 53705-2542 Office: PL Sprecher & Assocs 4513 Vernon Blvd Madison WI 53705-4964

SPREIREGEN, PAUL DAVID, architect, planner, author; b. Boston, Dec. 12, 1931; s. Jacob Harold and Janet Elaine (Zisman) S.; m. Rose-Hélène Bester, Oct. 17, 1961. Grad., CIAM Sch., Venice, 1954, M.I.T., 1952-54, Rensselaer Poly. Inst., 1949-51, Boston Mus. Fine Arts Sch., 1946-49. Archtl. designer Studio Architetti BBPR, Milan, Italy, 1954, Uhlin & Malm, Stockholm, 1955; Skidmore Owings & Merrill Uhlin & Malm, N.Y.C., 1956; urban designer Adams Howard & Greeley, Boston, 1958-59, Downtown Progress, Washington, 1960-62; dir. urban design programs AIA, Washington, 1962-66; dir. architecture and environ. arts programs Nat. Endowment for Arts, Washington, 1966-70; architect, planner, author Washington, 1970—; mem. Fed. Commn. for Reconstrn. and Devel. Alaska, 1964; adv. Study of profl. Edn. of Landscape Architects, Ford Found., 1969-72; host weekly radio program Places for People Nat. Public Radio, 1972-84; tchr. Boston Archtl. Center, 1959, Yale U. Sch. Planning, 1966, Catholic U. Grad. Sch. Architecture and Planning, 1967, 77, U. Hawaii, 1968, U. Pa., 1968, U. Tenn., 1969, Harvard U., 1970, Ball State U., 1973-74, Emons Distinguished prof. architecture, 1973-74; architect State of Md. Vietnam Vets. Meml., 1988; profl. adviser Vietnam Vets. Meml. Design Competition, Washington, 1981, adv. Intelsat HQ design competition, Washington, 1980; advisor Kent State U. Meml. Design Competition, 1985-86, AT&T/Bell Labs. Solid State Tech. Lab., Upper McCungie, Pa., 1982-83, Nat. Peace Garden Design Competition, 1989. Principle works include water treatment plans Washington Suburban Sanitary Commn., 1974, pumping station, 1985, Akron (Ohio) State Office Bldg., 1983, State of Md. Vets. Meml., 1988; author: Urban Design: The Architecture of Towns and Cities, 1965 (also in Japanese and Spanish); (with H. Von. Hertzen) Building a New Town: The Story of Finland's New Garden City, Tapiola, 1971, Design Competitions, 1979, William Morgan, Architect, 1987; editor: The Modern Metropolis: Its Origins, Form, Characteristics, and Planning (Hans Blumenfeld), 1967, On the Art of Designing Cities: Selected Essays of Elbert Peets, 1968, Metropolis and Beyond: Selected Essays of Hans Blumnfeld, 1979. Mem. vis. com. on arts M.I.T., 1973-76. Served to 1st lt. C.E. U.S. Army, 1956-58. Waid Edn. Fund grantee, 1967; Innisfree Found. fellow, 1966; Fulbright fellow Italy, 1954-55. Fellow AIA (design citation Potomac chpt. 1974, Student medal 1954, chmn. com. design competitions 1977-84, chmn. com. reg. devel. and natural resources 1970-74, com. urban design 1966-74), Am. Inst. Interior Designers (hon.); mem. Am. Soc. Landscape Architects (Pres.'s award Potomac chpt. 1986), Am. Planning Assn. (Spl. award 1983). Address: Paul D Spreiregen FAIA 2215 Observatory Pl NW Washington DC 20007-1813

SPREITER, JOHN ROBERT, engineering educator, space physics scientist; b. Oak Park, Minn., Oct. 23, 1921; s. Walter F. and Agda E. (Hokanson) S.; m. Brenda Owens, Aug. 7, 1953; children: Terry A., Janet L., Christine P., Hilary M. B Aero. Engring., U. Minn., 1943; MS, Stanford U., 1947, PhD, 1954. Research scientist Ames Research Ctr. NASA, Moffett Field, Calif., 1943-69, chief theoretical studies br., 1962-69; prof. applied mechanics, mechanical engring. and aeros. and astronautics Stanford (Calif.) U., 1968-92, prof. emeritus, 1992—; lectr. Stanford U., 1951-68; cons. Nielsen Engring. and Research Inc., Mountain View, Calif., 1968-85, RMA Aerospace, Mountain View, 1985—. Contbr. numerous articles to profl. jours. and books. Served with USN, 1944-46. Fellow AIAA, Royal Astron. Soc., Am. Geophys. Union; mem. AAAS, Am. Phys. Soc., The Planetary Soc., Saratoga Tennis Club (treas. 1955-65), Fremont Hills Country Club (Los Altos Hills, Calif.), Stanford Faculty Club, Sigma Xi, Tau Beta Pi, Tau Omega. Democrat. Achievements include pioneering studies in transonic aerodynamics; numerous contributions to studies of solar terrestrial relations, solar wind interaction with the earth, moon, other planets, and the local interstellar medium. Home: 1250 Sandalwood Ln Los Altos CA 94024-6739 Office: Stanford U Div Applied Mechanics Stanford CA 94305

SPRENGER, GORDON M., hospital administrator; b. Albert Lea, Minn., Apr. 30, 1937. Bachelors degree, St. Olaf Coll., 1959; masters degree, U. Minn., 1961. Registrar USAF Hosp., Hamilton AFB, Calif., 1961-64; with St. Luke's Hosp., Milw., 1964-67, Northwestern Hosp., Mpls., 1967-71; exec. v.p. Abbott-Northwestern Hosp., Mpls., 1971-75, pres., 1975—; prof. U. Minn., 1976—; acad. lectureship; preceptor. Mem. Am. Hosp. Assn., Minn. Hosp. Assn. (bd. dirs. 1978-81, chmn. 1983-84, community svc., treas., 1981. Office: Healthspan Health System Corp 2810 57th Ave N Minneapolis MN 55430

SPRENKLE, CASE MIDDLETON, economics educator; b. Cleve., Aug. 18, 1934; s. Raymond E. and Helen K. (Middleton) S.; m. Elaine Elizabeth Jensen, June 22, 1957; children: David, Peter, Amy. B.S., U. Colo., 1956; M.A., Yale U., 1957, Ph.D, 1960. Instr. econs. Yale U., New Haven, 1959-60; mem. faculty U. Ill., Urbana, 1960—, prof. econs., 1970—, chmn. dept. econs., 1976-80; asst. dean Coll. Commerce U. Ill, Urbana, 1962-65; dir. U. Ill.-U. Warsaw MBA program, 1991—; faculty Econs. Inst., Boulder, Colo., 1965, 72, 81; vis. scholar London Sch. Econs., 1967, 74, 81, 88; vis. lectr. City of London U., 1981; cons. Ill. Revenue Commn., 1962—; bd. dirs. Aggregate Equipment co. Contbr. articles to profl. jours. Bd. dirs. Champaign-Urbana Symphony, treas., 1972-74, pres., 1975-77; bd. dirs. Champaign County Arts and Humanities Coun., 1977-79; bd. dirs. Champaign-Urbana Mass Transit Dist., 1983—, vice chmn., 1985, 93-94. Am. Bankers Assn. grantee, 1970-71. Mem. Am. Econs. Assn., Am. Fin. Assn., Omicron Delta Epsilon. Presbyterian. Home: 3403 S Persimmon Cir Urbana IL 61801-7128 Office: U Ill Dept Econs 1201 S 6th St Champaign IL 61820

SPRICK, DENNIS MICHAEL, critic, copy editor; b. Passaic, N.J., Sept. 2, 1956; s. Frederick Vincent and Jeannette Mary (Claudepierre) S. BA, Lehigh U., 1978. Copy editor Daily Advance, Roxbury, N.J., 1978-80; film and Broadway critic, copy editor Times Herald-Record, Middletown, N.Y., 1980—. Mem. Am. Theatre Critics Assn., Phi Beta Kappa. Roman Catholic. Avocations: running, yoga, singing, vegetarian cooking, massage. Office: Times Herald-Record 40 Mulberry St Middletown NY 10940

SPRIESTERSBACH, DUANE CARYL, university administrator, speech pathology educator; b. Pine Island, Minn., Sept. 5, 1916; s. Merle Lee and Esther Lucille (Stucky) S.; m. Bette Rae Bartell, Aug. 31, 1946; children: Michael Lee, Ann. B.Ed., Winona State Tchrs. Coll., 1939; M.A., U. Iowa, 1940, Ph.D., 1948. Asst. dir. pers. rels. Pacific Portland Cement Co., San Francisco, 1946-47; prof. speech pathology U. Iowa, Iowa City, 1948-89, v. pres. and dean Grad. Coll., v.p. ednl. devel. and rsch., 1965-89, v. pres. and dean emeritus, 1989—; dean. Grad. Coll., 1965-89; cons., 1994—; com. mem. Nat. Inst. Neurol. Disease and Blindness; chmn. dental tng. com. Nat. Inst. Dental Research, 1967-72, chmn. spl. grants rev., 1978-82; chmn. bd. Midwest Univs. Cons. Internat. Activities, Columbus, 1978-87. Author: Psychosocial Aspects of Cleft Palate, 1973, (with others) Diagnostic Methods in Speech Pathology, 1978; co-editor: Cleft Palate and Communication, 1968, Diagnosis in Speech Language Pathology, 1994. Pres. Iowa City Community Theater, 1964, 77, 83. Served to lt. col. U.S. Army, 1941-46, ETO. Decorated Bronze Star; Nat. Inst. Dental Rsch. fellow, 1971. Fellow AAAS; mem. Assn. Grad. Schs. (pres. 1979-80), Am. Speech and Hearing Assn. (pres. 1965, honor award), Am. Cleft Palate Assn. (pres. 1961-62, disting. service award), Midwestern Assn. Grad. Schs. (chmn. 1979-80), Mortar Board, Sigma Xi. Episcopalian. Club: Cosmos (Washington). Home: 2

Longview Knl Iowa City IA 52240-9148 Office: Univ Iowa M212 Oakdale Hall Oakdale IA 52319

SPRIGGS, RICHARD MOORE, ceramic engineer, research center administrator; b. Washington, Pa., May 8, 1931; s. Lucian Alexander and Kathryn (Aber) S.; m. Patricia Anne Blaney, Aug. 1, 1953; children—Carolyn Elizabeth Spriggs Muchna, Richard Moore, Alan David. B.S. in Ceramics, Pa. State U., 1952; M.S. in Ceramic Engring., U. Ill., 1956, Ph.D. in Ceramic Engring., 1958. Sr. research engr. Ferro Corp., Cleve., 1958-59; sr. staff scientist, group leader, ceramics rsch. AVCO Corp., Wilmington, Mass., 1959-64; assoc. prof. metall. engring. Lehigh U., Bethlehem, Pa., 1964-67, prof. metallurgy and materials sci. and engring., 1967-80, adminstrv. asst. to pres., 1970-71, asst. v.p. for adminstrn., 1971-72, v.p. for adminstrn., 1972-78, dir. phys. ceramics lab., 1964-70, assoc. dir. Materials Research Ctr., 1964-70; vis. sr. staff assoc. Nat. Materials Adv. Bd. NRC, Washington, 1979-80, sr. staff officer, staff scientist, 1988, staff dir. bd. on assessment of NBS programs, 1984-87; J.F. McMahon prof. ceramic engring., dir. NYS Ctr. Advanced Ceramic Tech. N.Y. State Coll. Ceramics, Alfred (N.Y.) U., 1987—, dir. office of sponsored programs, 1988—. Contbr. articles to profl. publs. Co-patentee in field. Pres., bd. dirs. YMCA, Bethlehem, Pa., 1978-79. Served to lt. USNR, 1952-56. Fellow Armco Steel Corp., 1956-58, Am. Council on Edn., 1970-71. Fellow Am. Ceramic Soc. (disting. life, pres. 1984-85, Ross Coffin Purdy award 1965, Hobart M. Kraner award Lehigh Valley sect. 1980, trustee pension trust fund 1979-84, Orton lectr. 1988, McMahon lectr. 1988, coord. programs and meetings 1991-92), Ceramic Soc. Japan (Centennial medal 1991), Brit. Inst. of Ceramics; mem. AAAS, N.Y. Acad. Scis., Internat. Inst. for Sci. of Sintering, Nat. Inst. Ceramic Engrs., Materials Rsch. Soc. (hon.), Ceramic Ednl. Council, Brit. Ceramic Soc., Internat. Acad. Ceramics (trustee 1988—), Am. Soc. Engring. Edn., Materials Rsch. Soc., Fedn. of Materials Socs. (trustee 1978-84), Ceramic Assn. N.Y. (sec.-treas. 1988—), Serbian Acad. Scis. and Arts (fgn.). Lodge: Rotary (dir. 1982-87, pres. 1985-86). Office: Alfred U Ctr Advanced Ceramic Tech NY State College of Ceramics Alfred NY 14802

SPRING, JOHN BENHAM, car rental company executive; b. Nashua, N.H., Mar. 28, 1936; s. John D. and Ethel A. S.; m. Susan Kloster, Mar. 29, 1969; children: Jessica, Katherine, Elizabeth, Margaret. A.B., Dartmouth Coll., 1957, M.B.A., 1961. C.P.A., Calif., Mich., Minn., Ill. Mgr. Price Waterhouse & Co., San Francisco, 1961-70; mgr. fin. staff Ford Motor Co., Dearborn, Mich., 1970-74; group v.p. fin. and adminstrn. Nat. Car Rental System, Inc., subs. Household/Internat., Mpls., 1974-77; sr. v.p., chief fin. officer Household/Internat., Prospect Heights, Ill., 1977-83; exec. v.p., fin. Adminstrn. Nat. Car Rental System, Inc., subs. Household/Internat., Mpls., 1983-87; exec.v.p., chief fin. officer Nat. Car Rental System, Inc., Mpls., 1987—. Bd. govs./treas. Children's Theatre Co. Mpls. Served to capt. USMC, 1957-60. Mem. Fin. Execs. Inst. (com. on corp. fin.), Am. Inst. C.P.A.'s. Club: Econ. (Chgo.). Home: 100 2nd St SE Apt 203 Minneapolis MN 55414-2128 Office: Nat Car Rental System Inc 7700 France Ave S Minneapolis MN 55435-5296

SPRING, MICHAEL, editor, writer; b. N.Y.C., Oct. 14, 1941; s. Sol and Muriel (Roth) S.; m. Marjorie Hornblower Bauer, Mar. 1965 (div. 1980); children: Declan, Evan; m. Janis Abrahms, 1993. B.A., Haverford Coll., Pa., 1964; M.A., Columbia U., N.Y.C., 1970. Reporter Bergen Record, Hackensack, N.J., 1969-71; editor Scholastic Inc., N.Y.C., 1971-87; editorial dir. Fodor's Travel Publs., 1987-94, v.p., 1989-94; pub. Macmillan Travel, N.Y.C., 1994—; broadcaster, writer WNCN-FM, N.Y.C., 1983-84. Author: Great Weekend Escape Book, 1982, 4th rev. edit. 1990, Student's Guide to Julius Ceasar, 1984; editor: American Way of Working, 1980, 50 vol. Barron's Book Notes series, 1984, Scholastic Literature Anthologies, 4 vols., 1985, 87, Great European Itineraries, 1987, Touring Europe, 1990, 3d edit. 1994; contbg. editor Conde Nast's Traveler, 1987—; travel expert CNN Travel Show, 1991-94. Democrat. Jewish. Home: 20 Country Rd Westport CT 06880-2525 Office: Macmillan Travel 15 Columbus Cir New York NY 10023

SPRING, PAULL E., bishop. Bishop Northwestern Pa. Evang. Luth. Ch. in Am., Oil City. Office: Evang Luth Ch in Am PO Box 338 Rte 257 Salina Rd Seneca PA 16346-0338

SPRING, RAYMOND LEWIS, legal educator; b. Warsaw, N.Y., Aug. 5, 1932. AB, Washburn U., 1957, JD, 1959. Bar: Kans. 1960, U.S. Ct. Appeals (10th cir.) 1960. Assoc. Crane, Martin, Claussen & Ashworth, Topeka, 1959-65; examiner Workmen's Compensation program State of Kans., 1961-62; asst. prof. law Washburn U., Topeka, 1965-68, assoc. prof., 1968-71, acting dean Sch. of Law, 1970-71, prof., dean Sch. of Law, 1971-78, Disting. prof., 1978—; interim v.p. for acad. affairs, 1988-91; faculty Karl Menninger Sch. Psychiatry and Mental Health Scis., 1987—; mem. cts. subcom. Kans. Gov.'s Com. on Criminal Adminstrn., 1970-79; dir. Century Savs. Assn., Shawnee Mission, Kans., 1978-84, chmn., 1980-82. Author: (with Ryan) Vernon's Kansas Criminal Code Annotated, 1971, Vernon's Kansas Code of Criminal Procedure, 1973; The End of Insanity, 1983, (with Lacoursiere and Weissenberger) Patients, Psychiatrists and Lawyers: Law and the Mental Health System, 1989. Bd. dirs. Topeka Welfare Planning Coun., 1964-66, Kans. Adv. and Protective Svcs., Inc., 1987—, Shawnee Coun. Campfire Girls, 1965-68; chmn. Shawnee County Young Reps., 1962-64; leader edn. divsn. Topeka United Fund, 1972; deacon Ctrl. Congrl. Ch., 1972-74, 79-80, 85-87, trustee, 1980-81, moderator, 1988; mem. Kans. Bd. Admissions of Attys., 1979-86, Kans. Gov.'s adv. com. mental Health and Retardation Svcs., 1983-90; mem. human studies commn. Colmery-O'Neil VA Med. Ctr., 1982-89. Recipient Disting. Svc. award Washburn Law Sch. Assn., 1987, William O. Douglas Outstanding Prof. award, 1980. Mem. ABA, Kans. Bar Assn. Topeka Bar Assn., Barristers, Kans. Hist. soc. (bd. dirs. 1980-93), Phi Kappa Phi, Delta Theta Phi, Phi Sigma Kappa. Home: 1616 SW Jewell Ave Topeka KS 66604-2737 Office: 1700 SW College Ave Topeka KS 66621-1110

SPRINGEL, BARRY L., lawyer; b. Detroit, Sept. 5, 1942. BS, Drexel Inst. Tech., 1964; JD, U. Mich., 1967; LLM, George Washington U., 1968. Bar: Mich. 1968, Ohio 1969. Ptnr. Jones, Day, Reavis & Pogue, Cleve. Office: Jones Day Reavis & Pogue North Point 901 Lakeside Ave Cleveland OH 44115

SPRINGER, CHARLES EDWARD, state supreme court justice; b. Reno, Feb. 20, 1928; s. Edwin and Rose Mary Cecelia (Kelly) S.; m. Jacqueline Sirkegian, Mar. 17, 1951; 1 dau., Kelli Ann. BA, U. Nev., Reno, 1950; LLB, Georgetown U., 1953; LLM, U. Va., 1984; student Grad. Program for Am. Judges, Oriel Coll., Oxford (Eng.), 1984. Bar: Nev. 1953, U.S. Dist. Ct. Nev. 1953, D.C. 1954, U.S. Supreme Ct. 1962. Pvt. practice law Reno, 1953-80; atty. gen. State of Nev., 1962, legis. legal adv. to gov., 1958-62; legis. bill drafter Nev. Legislature, 1955-57; mem. faculty Nat. Coll. Juvenile Justice, Reno, 1978—; juvenile master 2d Jud. Dist. Nev., 1973-80; justice Nev. Suprem Ct., Carson City, 1981—; mem. Jud. Selection Commn., 1981—, Nev. Supreme Ct. Gender Bias Task Force, 1981—; trustee Nat. Coun. Juvenile and Family Ct. Judges, 1983—; mem. faculty McGeorge Sch. Law, U. Nev., Reno, 1982—; chmn. Nev. Commn. for Women, 1991—. With AUS, 1945-47. Recipient Outstanding Contbn. to Juvenile Justice award Nat. Coun. Juvenile and Family Ct. Judges, 1989, Midby-Byron Disting. Leadership award U. Nev., 1988. Mem. ABA, Am. Judicature Soc., Am. Trial Lawyers Assn., Phi Kappa Phi. Office: Nev Supreme Ct Capitol Complex 201 S Carson St Carson City NV 89701

SPRINGER, DAVID EDWARD, lawyer; b. Chgo., Jan. 20, 1952; s. Edward W. and Mildred (Bergmark) S. AB summa cum laude, Yale U., 1974, JD, 1977. Bar: Ill. 1977, U.S. Ct. Appeals (5th cir.) 1978, U.S. Dist. Ct. (no. dist.) Ill. 1978, U.S. Ct. Appeals (7th cir.) 1981, U.S. Supreme Ct. 1981, U.S. Ct. Appeals (4th cir.) 1982, U.S. Ct. Appeals (fed. cir.) 1983, Wis. 1990, U.S. Dist. Ct. (D.C. cir.) 1991, U.S. Ct. Appeals (8th cir.) 1992. Atty., ptnr. Kirkland & Ellis, Chgo., 1977-86, Skadden, Arps, Slate, Meagher & Flom, Chgo., 1986—. Mem. Chgo. Club, City Club Chgo., Phi Beta Kappa. Republican. Protestant. Office: Skadden Arps Slate 333 W Wacker Dr Ste 2100 Chicago IL 60606-1288

SPRINGER, DOUGLAS HYDE, retired food company executive, lawyer; b. Englewood, N.J., Jan. 31, 1927; s. Arthur Hyde and Melicent Katherine (Messenger) S.; m. Virginia Helen Chouinard, Nov. 23, 1949; children: Susan Compton, Debora Lee. Student, Wesleyan U. 1944-45; AB, Yale U., 1947;

LLB, Columbia U., 1950. Bar: N.Y. 1950. Atty. Port of N.Y. Authority, 1950-52; legal counsel Worthington Corp., Harrison, N.J., 1953-61, asst. sec., 1956-61; asst. counsel Campbell Soup Co., Camden, N.J., 1961-65, asst. sec., 1965, spl. assignments, 1966, dir. spl. studies, corp. planning, 1966-69, dir. corp. planning frozen foods, 1969-70, asst. treas., 1970-71, treas., 1971-73, v.p. fin. planning, 1973-75, v.p., controller, 1975-78, v.p., treas., 1978-88, v.p. investment mgmt., 1988-90; trustee Meml. Health Allience; mem. adv. bd. Pa. Liberty Mut. Ins. Co., 1971-88; mem. Eastern regional adv. bd. Arkwright-Boston Mfrs. Mut. Ins. Co., 1985-90; exec. sec. Gov.'s Interstate Adv. Com., 1966; asst. to mem. Pres.'s Commn. on Postal Orgn., 1967-68; spl. asst. to chmn South Jersey Port Corp., 1969-71; mem. N.J. Econ. Devel. Council, 1972-76; mem. adv. coun. Tax Found., 1980-89. Trustee Nat. Food Processors Assn. Retirement Plan and Trust Indenture Fund, 1976-89, Perkins Ctr. for Arts, 1979-88, Ind. Coll. Fund, N.J., 1982-88; mem. exec. bd., v.p. fin. Camden County coun. Boy Scouts Am., 1978-90; mem. Y's Men's Club, Moorestown, N.J., 1990—, v.p 1992-94, pres. 1994-95; With USNR, 1944-46. Mem. Nat. Assn. Corp. Treas. (bd. dirs. 1982-88), Phila. Treas. Club, Internat. Bus. Forum (bd. dirs. 1980-88), Phi Nu Theta, Phi Delta Phi, N.J. Soc. Pa. (pres. 1992-93). Clubs: Yale (Phila., N.Y.C.); Nassau (Princeton, N.J.). Home: 735 Mill St Moorestown NJ 08057-1803

SPRINGER, EDWIN KENT, mechanical engineer; b. Bellingham, Wash., Sept. 17, 1912; s. George Edwin and Abbie (Kent) S.; m. Frances Stewart, Oct. 19, 1940; children: Ann Bogue, Robert Edwin, Bruce Kent. BS in Mech. Engring., U. So. Calif., 1936; MS in Mech. Engring., U. Wis., 1945. Registered profl. engr., Calif., Wis. Draftsman Fluid Packed Pump Co., Los Nietos, Calif., 1935-36, plant engr., 1936-39; mech. engr. Preco, L.A., 1939-41, Consol. Western Steel Co., L.A., 1941; instr., asst. prof. U. Wis., Madison, 1941-46; successively asst. prof. mech. engring., assoc. prof., and prof. U. So. Calif., Los Angeles, 1946-77, dir. Fedn. for Cross-Connection Control and Hydraulic Research, 1965-85; emeritus dir. Fedn. for Cross-Connection Control and Hydraulic Research, 1985—; bd. dirs. Western States Symposium, Cypress, Calif., 1980—; assoc. bd. mem. So. Calif. Water Utility Assn., San Dimas, 1975—. Mem. Utility Adv. Commn. City of Pasadena, Calif., 1979-86; mem. Linda Vista Property Owners Assn., Barton Flats Cabin Owners Assn. Recipient Disting. Emeriti award U. So. Calif. 1986. Fellow ASME (life, Charles Russ Richards award 1986); mem. AAUP, Am. Soc. Engring. Edn., Am. Backflow Prevention Assn. (life), Am. Water Works Assn. (hon., George Warren Fuller award 1986). Republican. Episcopalian. Avocations: gardening, fishing. Home: 1465 Scenic Dr Pasadena CA 91103-1936

SPRINGER, FLOYD LADEAN, architect; b. Goodrich, N.D., Feb. 1, 1922; s. George Roy Springer and Louise Baumbach; m. Dorothy Mae Shepard; children: Debra Louise, Tami June. Student, U. Denver, 1948-51; BS in Archtl. Engring., U. Colo., 1952; postgrad., U. Wash., 1953-54, U. Utah, Portland, Oreg., 1980. With Seattle Delta Investment Group, 1984—. Cpl. inf. U.S. Army, 1941-44, PTO. Decorated Silver Star. Mem. Frank Lloyd Wright Conservancy (N.W. chpt.), Mason (32d degree), Union Concerned Scientists, N.Y. Acad. Sci., Internat. Platform Assn., Ctr. for Study of Dem. Instns., Heritage Found., Inst. Urban Design, Am. Arbitration Assn., Nat. Trust for Hist. Preservation, The Wilderness Soc., Sierra Club, Am. Mus. Natural History, Common Cause, Nat. Soc. Lit. and the Arts, Nat. Audubon Soc., Soc. of Am. Mil. Engrs., others. Presbyterian. Avocations: photography, landscaping, leaded art glass, skiing, golfing. Home and Office: 18548 60th Ave NE Seattle WA 98155-4453

SPRINGER, FRED EVERETT, federal agency administrator; b. Washington, June 30, 1945; s. Sidney and Janet L. (Bushlow) Kurland; m. Lola Weinberg Springer, Aug. 3, 1946; children: Eileen Gerri Frazier, Michelle Sherrie, Paul Louis. BSCE, U. Md., 1967; postgrad., George Washington U. Civil engr. Naval Facilities Engring. Command, Bur. of Stds., 1967-70, FPC, Washington, 1970-76; chief project mgmt. br. Divsn. of Lic. Projects, Office of Elec. PowerRegulation FPC/FERC, Washington, 1976-83; dep. dir. project mgmt. Office of Hydrpower Lic., Office of Elec. Power Regulation FERC, Washington, 1983-84, dir. divsn. project mgmt., 1984-87, dir. Office Hydropower Licensing, 1987—; tchr. specialty courses to numerous fed. and state agys. and U. Mich.; mem. steering com. Hydrovision 94; writer, presenter at least 25 papers or speeches related to hydropower licensing to orgns. and confs. Pres., v.p. Highland of Olney (Md.) Civic Assn.; v.p., treas. B'nai Shalom of Olney; coach Olney Boys and Girls Club. Mem. ASCE, Tau Beta Pi, Chi Epsilon. Democrat. Jewish. Office: OHL-FERC 825 N Capital St NE Washington DC 20426

SPRINGER, GEORGE STEPHEN, mechanical engineering educator; b. Budapest, Hungary, Dec. 12, 1933; came to U.S., 1959; s. Joseph and Susan (Grausz) S.; m. Susan Martha Flory, Sept. 15, 1963; children: Elizabeth Anne, Mary Katherine. B in Engring., U. Sydney, Australia, 1959; M in Engring., Yale U., 1960, MSc in Engring., 1961, PhD, 1962. Registered profl. engr., Mass. Asst. prof. mech. engring. MIT, Cambridge, Mass., 1962-67; prof. mech. engring. U. Mich., Ann Arbor, 1967-83; Paul Pigott prof., chmn. dept. aeronautics and astronautics Stanford (Calif.) U., 1983—. Author: Erosion by Liquid Impact, 1975; co-author, co-editor 12 books; contbr. over 150 articles to scholarly and profl. jours. Recipient Pub. Svc. Group Achievement award NASA, 1988. Fellow AIAA (Engr. of Yr. 1995), ASME (Worcester Reed Warner medal 1994), Soc. Advancement Materials and Process Engring. (award 1991); mem. Am. Phys. Soc., Soc. Automotive Engrs. (Ralph Teeter award 1978), Nat. Acad. Engring. Achievements include patent in field. Office: Stanford U Dept Aeronautics and Astronautics Stanford CA 94305

SPRINGER, JAMES VAN RODEN, lawyer; b. N.Y.C., July 9, 1934; s. Charles Meredith and Jeanne (Nehrbas) S.; m. Carol Murphy, Mar. 31, 1962; children: Catherine. AB, Harvard U., 1955, LLB, 1961. Bar: N.Y. 1962, D.C. 1962, U.S. Ct. Appeals (D.C. cir.) 1963, U.S. Ct. Appeals (10th cir.) 1972, U.S. Ct. Appeals (2d cir.) 1973, U.S. Ct. Appeals (5th cir.) 1976, U.S. Ct. Appeals (6th and 7th cirs.) 1977, U.S. Ct. Appeals (11th cir.) 1981, U.S. Ct. Appeals (1st cir.) 1984, U.S. Ct. Appeals (4th cir.) 1986, U.S. Ct. Appeals (9th cir.) 1990, U.S. Ct. Appeals (fed. cir.) 1991, U.S. Supreme Ct. 1968. Law clk. to chief judge U.S. Ct. Appeals for 2d Cir., N.Y.C., 1961-62; assoc. Covington and Burling, Washington, 1962-67; asst. legal advisor U.S. Dept. State, Washington, 1967-68; dep. solicitor gen. U.S. Dept. Justice, Washington, 1968-71; ptnr. Dickstein, Shapiro and Morin, Washington, 1972—. Pres. Harvard Law Rev., 1960-61; contbr. articles to profl. jours. With U.S. Army, 1955-58, Korea. Mem. ABA, D.C. Bar. Democrat. Home: 3017 44th Pl NW Washington DC 20016 Office: Dickstein Shapiro & Morin 2101 L St NW Washington DC 20037-1594

SPRINGER, JEFFREY R., bank officer; b. 1944. With Chemical Bank, N.Y., 1968-74, Md. Nat. Bank, 1974-85, Diversified Investments Assn., Balt., 1985-87; with Citizens Bancorp, Laurel, Md., 1987, now pres. Office: Citizens Bancorp 14401 Switzer Ln Laurel MD 20707*

SPRINGER, JOHN KELLEY, hospital administrator; b. Salem, Ohio, May 11, 1931; s. Wilbur Johnson and Nellie Marie (Kelley) S.; m. Jane Lee Parsons, Oct. 13, 1956; children: Kelley Lynn, Dana Lee, Susan Elizabeth, Nellie Jane. AB, Dartmouth Coll., 1953; MHA, U. Mich., 1960; LLD (hon.), Briarwood Coll., 1991. Adminstrv. resident Mary Hitchcock Meml. Hosp., Hanover, N.H., 1959-60; asst. administr. Mary Hitchcock Meml. Hosp., 1960-64, asso. adminstr., adminstr. for ops., 1969-71; assoc. exec. dir. Hartford (Conn.) Hosp., 1971-73, exec. 1974-76, pres., 1977-87, vice chmn., chief exec. officer, 1987-89, vice chmn., 1989—; pres., chief exec. officer Conn. Health System, 1986—; bd. dirs. ITT Hartford Mut. Fund; pres. Combined Hosps. Alcoholism Program, Inc., 1972-75; chmn. Capital Area Health Consortium, 1987-90; lectr. Sch. Pub. Health, Yale U., 1975. Deacon 1st Ch. of Christ Congl., West Hartford, 1975-79; bd. dirs. Urban League Greater Hartford, 1973-76, Hartford Sem. Found., Greater Hartford chpt. ARC, vice-chmn. 1978-80. Capt. USMC, 1953-58; col. USMCR, ret. Mem. Am. Coll. Healthcare Execs., New Eng. Hosp. Assembly (pres. 1972), Conn. Hosp. Assn. (chmn. bd. trustees 1982-83), Am. Hosp. Assn. (coun. on fin. 1975-78, chmn. 1981-86, del.-at-large 1979-80, bd. trustees 1992-94), Greater Hartford C. of C. (bd. dirs. 1980-82), Hartford Club, Hartford Golf Club, University Club. Home: 1844 Albany Ave West Hartford CT 06117-1701 Office: Conn Health System 55 Farmington Ave Hartford CT 06105-3711

SPRINGER, JOHN SHIPMAN, public relations executive; b. Rochester, N.Y., Apr. 25, 1916; s. Wilfred A. and Alice Jane (Grosjean) S.; m. June Alicia Reimer, June 3, 1953; children: Gary John, Alicia Ann, Cynthia Lynn. Student, U. Toronto, Ont., Can., 1935-37; Ph.B., Marquette U., 1939. Feature writer Rochester Democrat and Chronicle, 1940-41; head mag. publicity RKO Radio Pictures, N.Y.C., 1946-57, 20th Century-Fox Films, N.Y.C., 1957-59; v.p. Arthur Jacobs, Pub. Relations, 1959-60; ptnr. Jacobs & Springer (pub. relations), 1960-62; pres. John Springer Assos., Inc., N.Y.C., Los Angeles, London, Paris and Rome, 1964—. Author: All Talking! All Singing! All Dancing!, 1966, The Fondas, 1970, They Had Faces Then, 1975, Forgotten Films to Remember, 1980, They Sang, They Danced, They Romanced, 1991; contbr. to: Close Ups, Conversations with Joan Crawford; author mag. articles and newspaper features.; creator/producer "Film Segments" Night of 100 Stars; producer/host stage-screen shows starring Bette Davis, Myrna Loy, Sylvia Sidney, Joan Crawford, Rosalind Russell, Debbie Reynolds, Joanne Woodward, Lana Turner, Henry Fonda, others in, N.Y.C., US tour, Australia, Gt. Britain; writer/producer Ann. Am. Mus. Moving Image ann. tributes to Sidney Lumet, Elia Kazan, James Stewart, Sidney Poitier, Mike Nichols, Robert DeNiro, Al Pacino; producer, dir. three films/live events at 92d St. Y, New York, with in person guest stars including Ginger Rogers, Liv Ullmann, Tony Randall, Sylvia Sidney, Van Johnson, Geraldine Fitzgerald, Farley Granger, Betty Comden, Adolph Green, etc., 1991. Served with USAAF, 1942-45. Recipient Byline award Coll. Journalism, 1970, By-line award Marquette U., 1970. Democrat. Roman Catholic. Home and Office: 130 E 67th St New York NY 10021-6136

SPRINGER, MARLENE, university administrator, educator; b. Murfreesboro, Tenn., Nov. 16, 1937; d. Foster V. and Josephine Jones; children: Ann Springer, Rebecca Springer. BA in English & Bus. Adminstrn., Centre Coll., 1959; MA in Am. Lit., Ind. U., 1963, PhD in English Lit., 1969. Chair English dept. U. Mo., Kansas City, 1980-81, acting assoc. dean grad. sch., 1982; Am. Coun. of Edn. Adminstrn. fellow U. Kans., Laurence, 1982-83; dean of grad. sch. U. Mo., Kansas City, 1983-84, assoc. vice chancellor for acad. affairs & grad. studies, 1985-89; vice chancellor for acad. affairs East Carolina U., Greenville, N.C., 1989-94; pres. CUNY Coll. S.I., 1994—. Author: What Manner of Woman: Essays, 1977, Thomas Hardy's Use of Allusion, 1983, Plains Woman: The Diary of Martha Farnsworth, 1986 (Choice award 1986), Ethan Frome: A Nightmare of Need, 1993. Huntington Libr. fellow, 1988. Mem. Am. Coun. on Edn. (profl. devel. com. 1991—, invited participant Nat. Forum 1984), Am. Assn. State Colls. & Univs. (exec. com. 1992—), Acad. Leadership Acad. (exec. com. 1992—), Assn. Tchr. Educators (chair 1992), Coun. Grad. Schs. (chair 1986-88). Office: Coll Staten Island 2800 Victory Blvd Staten Island NY 10314

SPRINGER, MICHAEL LOUIS, federal agency administrator; b. Sarasota, Fla., Jan. 28, 1938; s. Stewart and Vergie (Fayard) S.; m. Afife Camila Chamas, Aug. 31, 1963; children: Elizabeth Karime, Michele Renee, John David. BA, George Washington U., 1964; MPA, The Am. U., 1978. With fin. mgmt. office Nat. Libr. Medicine, Bethesda, Md., 1969-71; dep. dir. mgmt. and orgn. div. U.S. EPA, Washington, 1971-73, dir. mgmt. info. and data systems div., 1973-75; sr. mgmt. assoc. mgmt. improvement and evaluation U.S. Office Mgmt. and Budget, Washington, 1977-82; dep. dir. Office Adminstrn. U.S. NRC, Washington, 1982-86; staff dir. Office Consolidation, Washington, 1987-88; dir. Office Consolidation U.S. Nuclear Regulatory Commn., Washington, 1988-94, dir. divsn. facilities and property mgmt., 1994—; bd. dirs. Transp. Action Partnership North Bethesda and Rockville, Md., 1988—. Mem. Citizens Adv. Com. for North Bethesda Master Plan, Montgomery County, 1990-91. Roman Catholic. Office: Nuclear Regulatory Commn Mail Stop T-7D59 Washington DC 20555

SPRINGER, PAUL DAVID, lawyer, motion picture company executive; b. N.Y.C., Apr. 27, 1942; s. William W. and Alma (Markowitz) S.; m. Mariann Frankfurt, Aug. 16, 1964; children: Robert, William. BA, U. Bridgeport, 1963; JD, Bklyn. Law Sch., 1967. Bar: N.Y. 1968, U.S. Dist. Ct. (so. and ea. dists.) N.Y. 1968, U.S. Ct. Appeals (2d cir.) 1970, U.S. Supreme Ct. 1973, Calif. 1989. Assoc. Johnson & Tannenbaum, N.Y.C., 1968-70; assoc. counsel Columbia Pictures, N.Y.C., 1970; assoc. counsel Paramount Pictures, N.Y.C., 1970-79; v.p., theatrical distbn. counsel, 1979-85, sr. v.p., chief resident counsel East Coast, 1985-87; sr. v.p., asst. gen. counsel Paramount Pictures, L.A., 1987—; Bar: N.Y. 1968, U.S. Dist. Ct. (so. and ea. dists.) N.Y. 1968, U.S. Ct. Appeals (2d cir.) 1970, U.S. Supreme Ct. 1973, Calif. 1989. Trustee West Cunningham Park Civic Assn., Fresh Meadows, N.Y., 1978—. Mem. ABA, Assn. of Bar of City of N.Y., L.A. Copyright Soc., Acad. Motion Picture Arts and Scis., Motion Picture Pioneers.

SPRINGER, ROBERT DALE, retired air force officer, consultant, lecturer; b. Millheim, Pa., Jan. 17, 1933; s. Simon Peter and Ruth Olive (McCool) S.; m. Bonnie Joan Brubaker, Aug. 30, 1953; children: Robert Dale Jr., Debra K. Springer Miller, Curtis A., Michele L. Demmy, Tania. BA in Social Sci., George Washington U., 1964, MS in Internat. Affairs, 1969. Cert. command pilot. Commd. 2d lt. U.S. Air Force; advanced through grades to lt. gen.; comdr. 435th Tactical Airlift Wing, Rhein-Main Air Base, Federal Republic Germany, 1978-80, 322d Airlift Div, Ramstein Air Base, Federal Republic Germany, 1980-81, Air Force Manpower and Personnel Ctr., Randolph AFB, Tex., 1982-84, 21 A.F., McGuire AFB, N.J., 1984-85; insp. gen. USAF, Washington, 1985-87; with DCS-personnel Mil. Airlift Command, Scott AFB, Ill., 1981-82, vice comdr.-in-chief, 1987-88; ret., 1988; media cons., lectr., 1989—; dir. Air Force Commissary Svc., San Antonio, 1982-84, Army-Air Force Exch. Svc., Dallas, 1982-84; chmn. bd. dirs. Air Force Welfare Bd., San Antonio, 1982-84; bd. dirs. Livingspan, The Aviation Channel. Exec. dir Air Force Meml. Found., 1992—; trustee Aerospace Edn. Found., 1992-94. Mem. Air Force Assn. (Presdl. Citation 1984), Airlift-Tanker Assn. (life mem., sr. v.p. 1989-94), Arnold Air Soc. (exec. dir. 1990-93, trustee 1993—), Ret. Officers Assn. (life), Daedalians (life). Lutheran. Lodge: Masons. Avocations: tennis; golf; reading.

SPRINGER, STANLEY G., lawyer; b. Newburgh, N.Y., Sept. 27, 1927; s. Allen Paul and Mabel (Thorn) S.; m. Roberta Gietz, Sept. 14, 1947 (div. 1975); children—Valerie, Beverly, Jeffrey, Gregory, Kimberly, Lindsay; m. Vallie Strong, July 2, 1979 (dec. 1987). B.A., Union Coll., 1949; LL.D. with distinction (1st Fraser scholar), Cornell U., 1953. Bar: Wis. 1953, Ill. 1958, Tex. 1970, Calif. 1988. Mem. firm Whyte, Hirschboeck, Minahan, Harding & Harland, Milw., 1953-58; atty. Libby, McNeill & Libby, Chgo., 1958-63; gen. counsel, v.p. J.I. Case Co., Racine, Wis., 1963-69; v.p., gen. counsel, dir. Mich. Gen. Corp., Dallas, 1969-83; pvt. practice Dallas, 1983-88; gen. counsel George Realty Co., Inc. and affiliated cos., San Gabriel, Calif., 1988-90; dir. J.I. Case Credit Corp., 1963-69, Colt Mfg. Co., Inc., 1967-69. Chmn. Racine Heart Fund campaign, 1964; commr. Racine Redevel. Authority, 1965-69; bd. dirs., sec., pres. Prestonwood Country Club Condominium Assn., 1981-84; dir. and legal advisor Friends of the Point Vicente Interpretive Ctr., Inc., Rancho Palos Verdes, Calif., 1988-90, also docent at ctr. Served with AC, USNR, 1945-47. Recipient 1st prize WPB Carey Exbn., Cornell U., 1953. Mem. ABA, Wis. Bar Assn., Tex. Bar Assn., Dallas Bar Assn., Calif. Bar Assn., Lawyer-Pilots Bar Assn., Order of Coif, Phi Delta Phi, Phi Kappa Phi. Home: 3721 Spring Valley Rd Apt 202 Dallas TX 75244-3311

SPRINGFIELD, JAMES FRANCIS, retired lawyer, banker; b. Memphis, Nov. 5, 1929; s. C.L. and Mildred (White) S.; m. Shirley Burdick, June 1, 1951 (div.); children: Sidney, Susan, James Francis; m. Nancy Hardwick Ragan, Feb. 8, 1987 (dec. Jan. 1988); m. Donna Thomas Moore, Feb. 22, 1989. BA with distinction in econs., Southwestern at Memphis (now Rhodes Coll.), 1951; LLB, U. Memphis, 1960. Bar: Tenn. 1960. With Union Planters Nat. Bank, Memphis, 1951-94; exec. v.p., sr. trust officer, head trust dept. Union Planters Nat. Bank, 1968-85, gen. counsel, sec. bd., 1985-94; sec. bd., exec. v.p., gen. counsel Union Planters Corp., 1985-94; ret., 1994. Mem. president's coun. Rhodes Coll., Memphis, Memphis, 1991—92; chmn. bd. trustees So. Coll. Optometry, 1978-80; trustee Plough Found., Memphis Conf. United Meth. Ch. Found., 1978-85, U. Tenn. Med. Units Found., 1975-82, MidSouth Pub. Comm. Found., 1985-87; chmn. fin. com. Hutchinson Sch.; sec. bd. trustees Vision Edn. Found., 1977-78; bd. experts Tenn. Trust Sch., chmn., 1977; mem. president's adv. coun. Lambuth Coll, 1982-85; mem. exec. bd. Chickasaw coun. Boy Scouts Am., 1983-87; bd. visitors Memphis State U. Cecil C. Humphreys Sch. Law; treas. Balmoral Civic Club, 1967-68. Served to lt. (j.g.) USNR, 1951-54. Mem. Tenn. Bar

Assn. (chmn. interprofl. rels. com. 1976), Memphis and Shelby County Bar assn. (chmn. moral fitness com. 1972), Tenn. Bankers Assn. (chmn. legis.com. trust div. 1976-77, treas. 1972-73, pres. 1976-77, bd. dirs. 1976-77), Bank Adminstrn. Inst. (chmn. trust commn. 1981-82), Estate Planning Coun. Memphis (pres. 1973-74), Sigma Nu (div. comdr. 1967-68, treas., bd. dirs. House Corp. 1966-81), Omicron Delta Kappa (Rhodes Coll. chpt.). Republican. Home: 8334 Heatherglen Dr Memphis TN 38138-6209

SPRINGSTEEL, FREDERICK NEIL, computer science educator; b. Bellingham, Wash., Aug. 8, 1940; s. Guy Stewart and Charlotte E. (Glinesky) S.; m. Karen M. Rohrbach, June 12, 1965 (div. Jan. 1975); 1 child, Ian Michael; m. Pamela Botts Reser, Aug. 3, 1985. AB in Math., U. Notre Dame, 1962; MA in Math., U. Wash., 1964, PhD, 1967. Cert. Computer Profl. Asst. prof. math. Bowdoin Coll., Brunswick, Maine, 1967-71; assoc. prof. math. U. Mont., Missoula, 1971-77; assoc. prof. computer sci. U. Mo., Columbia, 1977-90, prof. computer sci., dir. grad. studies, 1991—; guest prof. computer sci. dept. Kaiserslautern (Germany) U., 1976-77; vis. assoc. prof. computer sci. Oreg. State U., Corvallis, 1985-86, U. Wash., Seattle, 1986. Contbr. articles to profl. jours. Treas. Unitarian-Universalist Ch., Columbia, 1989-91; mem. tech. com. Columbia Pub. Schs., 1991-92; dir. Boone County Indsl. Devel. Authority, 1993—. Rsch. grantee NSF, 1985-90, Fulbright grantee, Yugoslavia, 1986. Assn. for Computing Machinery (rev. Computing Reviews, assoc. editor Sigmod Record, 1988-91). Avocations: classical ensemble singing, walking, biking. Office: U Mo Computer Sci Dept Columbia MO 65211

SPRINGSTEEN, BRUCE, singer, songwriter, guitarist; b. Freehold, N.J., Sept. 23, 1949; s. Douglas and Adele S.; m. Julianne Phillips, May 13, 1985 (div. 1988); m. Patti Scialfa; children: 1 son, Evan James, 1 daughter, Jessica Rae. Attended community coll. Performed in N.Y. and N.J. nightclubs; signed with Columbia Records in 1972; first album Greetings from Asbury Park, New Jersey, 1973; nationwide concert tours with The E-Street Band, 1974-92; albums include The Wild, The Innocent and the E-Street Shuffle, 1974, Born to Run, 1975 (Gold Record award), Darkness on the Edge of Town, 1978, The River, 1980, Nebraska, 1982, Born in the U.S.A. (Best Pop/Rock Album of Yr., Downbeat Readers Poll 1984), 1984, Bruce Springsteen and the E Street Band Live/1975-1985, 1986, Tunnel of Love, 1987, Chimes of Freedom, 1988, Human Touch, 1992, Lucky Town, 1992, Bruce Springsteen Greatest Hits, 1995; songs composed include Thunder Road, Glory Days, Rosalita, Pink Cadillac, Jersey Girl, Hungry Heart; appears on Patti Scialfa's album, Rumble Doll, 1993. Recipient Grammy award for best male rock vocalist, 1984, 87, 94; Academy Award, Golden Globe award for Best Original Song in a Film, and MTV Best Video from a Film Award for "Streets of Philadelphia" from the film, Philadelphia, 1994. Office: care Premier Talent Agy 3 E 54th St New York NY 10022-3108*

SPRINGSTEEN, DAVID FOLGER, financial consultant; b. N.Y.C., Mar. 29, 1932; s. Nelson J. and Gwendolyn (Folger) S.; BS, MIT, 1954; MBA, Harvard U., 1958; m. Nancy Neller, Oct. 22, 1955; children: Susan S. Jamieson, Page S. Vanatta. Aero. rsch. scientist Lewis Flight Propulsion Lab. NASA, Cleve., 1955-57; with Chase Manhattan Bank, N.Y.C., 1958-71, asst. treas., 1961-64, 2d v.p., 1964-68, v.p. Energy div., 1969-71; v.p. corp. fin. Stone & Webster Securities Corp., 1971-74; v.p. corp. fin. E.F. Huttons & Co., Inc., N.Y.C., 1974-78; fin. cons., corp. fin. David F. Springsteen Co., Greenwich, Conn., 1978—; Dir. Eastman Community Assn., Delta Cooling Towers, Inc. Served to lt. USAF, 1955-57. Mem. Holland Soc. Home: PO Box 248 Snow Hill Point Grantham NH 03753 Office: 205 Shore Rd Greenwich CT 06830-6329

SPRINKEL, BERYL WAYNE, economist, consultant; b. Richmond, Mo., Nov. 20, 1923; s. Clarence and Emma (Schooley) S.; m. Lory Kiefer, Aug. 29, 1993; children: Gary L., Kevin G. Student, N.W. Mo. State U., 1941-43, U. Oreg., 1943-44; BS, U. Mo., 1947; MBA, U. Chgo., 1948, PhD, 1952; LHD (hon.), DePaul U., 1975; LLD (hon.), St. Michael's Coll., 1981, U. Mo., 1985, U. Rochester, 1985, Govs. State U., 1988, U. Nebr., 1988; Doctor of Pub. Adminstrn., Marion Coll., 1988. Instr. econs. and fin. U. Mo., Columbia, 1948-49, U. Chgo., 1950-52; with Harris Trust & Savs. Bank, Chgo., 1952-81, v.p., economist, 1960-68, dir. rsch., 1963-69, sr. v.p., 1968-74, economist, 1968-81, exec. v.p., 1974-81; undersec. monetary affairs Dept. Treasury, Washington, 1981-85; chmn. Coun. Econ. Advisers, The White House, Washington, 1985-89, mem. Pres.'s Cabinet, 1987-89; pvt. cons. economist, 1989—; cons. Fed. Res. Bd., 1955-59, Bur. of Census, 1962-70, Joint Econ. Com. U.S. Congress, 1958, 62, 67, 71, Ho. of Reps. Banking and Currency Com., 1963, Senate Banking Com., 1975; econ. adv. bd. to sec. commerce, 1967-69; bd. economists Time mag., 1968-80; bd. dirs. US Life Corp., Duff and Phelps Utilities Income Fund, Inc. Author: Money and Stock Prices, 1964, Money and Markets-A Monetarist View, 1971; co-author: Winning with Money, 1977;. Pres. Homewood-Flossmoor (Ill.) Community High Sch., 1959-60. With AUS, 1943-45. Recipient Hamilton Bolton award Fin. Analysts Assn., 1968, Alexander Hamilton award U.S. Treasury, 1985. Fellow Nat. Assn. Bus. Economists; mem. Am. Econ. Assn., Nat. Assn. Bus. Economists, Beta Gamma Sigma. Home: 20140 Saint Andrews Dr Olympia Fields IL 60461-1169

SPRINKLE, CHARLES RAY, wholesale grocery company executive; b. Hutchinson, Kans., 1935. Grad., Kans. State U., 1957. Former exec. v.p. Dillon Stores div. Dillon Cos., Inc.; with United Grocers, Ltd., Richmond, Calif., 1979-84, v.p. ops., 1979-80, v.p., chief oper. officer, 1980-84, pres., chief exec. officer, 1984, also dir.; with Fleming Cos., Inc., Oklahoma City, from 1984, former exec. v.p. western region; now pres., chief oper. officer Save Mart Supermarkets, Modesto, Calif. Served with U.S. Army. Office: Save Mart Supermarkets 1800 Standiford Ave Modesto CA 95350-0180

SPRINKLE, WILLIAM MELVIN, engineering administrator, audio-acoustical engineer; b. Washington, Sept. 2, 1945; s. Melvin Cline and Gladys Virginia (Miller) S.; div.; children: Timothy William, Allison Anne. BS in Chemistry, Randolph-Macon Coll., 1967; M in Engring. Adminstrn., Va. Poly. Inst. & State U., 1990. Registered profl. engr., Va. Sr. cons. Sprinkle & Assocs., Kensington, Md., 1973-76; audio systems engr. Robertshaw Controls Co., Richmond, Va., 1976-80; sr. engr. TDFB-Engrs. & Architects, Richmond, Va., 1980-85; property mgmt. officer Signet Bank, Richmond, Va., 1985-87; asst. dir. engring. Va. Dept. Corrections, Richmond, 1987—; mem. summer adj. faculty Eastman Sch. Music, Rochester, N.Y., 1974-83. Editor newsletter Richmond Area Bicycling Assn.; contbr. Time Saver Standards for Architectural Design Data, 1982. Mem. Acoustical Soc. Am., Pi Delta Epsilon (v.p.). Methodist. Office: Dept of Corrections 6900 Atmore Dr Richmond VA 23225

SPRINSON, DAVID BENJAMIN, biochemistry educator; b. Raigorod, Ukraine, Apr. 5, 1910; came to U.S., 1921; s. Moses and Rebecca (Skolnick) S.; m. Helen Reuss Sprinson, Aug. 8, 1943; children: Joan, Mary, John. BS, CCNY, 1931; MS, NYU, 1936; PhD, Columbia U., 1946, DSc (hon.), 1991. Rsch. assoc. Columbia U., N.Y.C., 1946-51, asst. prof. biochemistry, 1951-54, assoc. prof., 1954-58, prof., 1958-78, prof. biochemistry and molecular biology emeritus, 1978—; prof. biochemistry and molecular biology emeritus St. Luke's/Roosevelt Hosp. Ctr., N.Y.C., 1979—; career investigator Am. Heart Assn., 1958-75. Contbr. articles to sci. jours. Grantee NIH, NSF, Am. Heart Assn., Am. Cancer Soc., 1950-91. Mem. NAS, AAAS, Am. Soc. for Biochemistry and Molecular Biology. Office: St Luke's/Roosevelt Hosp Ctr 1000 10th Ave New York NY 10019-1056

SPRINTHALL, NORMAN ARTHUR, psychology educator; b. Attleboro, Mass., Aug. 19, 1931; s. William Archie and Edith Jarvis (Clark) S.; m. Lois May Thies; children: Douglas, Jane, Carolyn. A.B. magna cum laude, Brown U., 1954, M.A., 1959; Ed.D., Harvard U., 1963. Dir. fin. aid Brown U., 1955-60; asst. prof., then asso. prof. psychology, program chmn. counseling Harvard U., 1963-72; mem. faculty U. Minn., Mpls., 1972-82; prof. ednl. psychology U. Minn., 1973-82, program chmn. counseling, 1972-74; prof., head counselor edn. program N.C. State U., Raleigh, 1982-87, prof., counselor, educator, 1968-75, prof. emeritus; cons. Bur. Educationally Handicapped; co-dir. Ethical Reasoning Project in Pub. Adminstrn., U.S. and Poland, 1993—. Author: Educational Psychology: Readings, 1969, Guidance for Human Growth, 1971, Educational Psychology: A Developmental Approach, 6th ed., 1994, Value Development as the Aim of Education, 2d edit., 1981, Adolescent Psychology: A Developmental View, 1984, 2d rev. edit., 1988, 3d edit., 1995; co-author: Stewart-Sprinthall Management

Survey (SSMS) Ethics and Public Administration; mem. editorial bd. profl. jours. Bd. dirs. Josephson Inst. Advancement of Ethics, 1986-90. Fellow APA; mem. ACA, Am. Edn. Rsch. Assn., Phi Beta Kappa.

SPRIZZO, JOHN EMILIO, federal judge; b. Bklyn., Dec. 23, 1934; s. Vincent James and Esther Nancy (Filosa) S.; children—Ann Esther, Johna Emily Sprizzo Bolka, Matthew John. BA summa cum laude, St. John's U., Jamaica, N.Y., 1956; LLB summa cum laude, St. John's U., 1959. Bar: N.Y. 1960. Atty. U.S. Dept. Justice, 1959-63; asst. U.S. atty. so. dist. N.Y. Dept. Justice, N.Y.C., 1963-68, chief appellate atty., 1966-68, asst. chief criminal div., 1966-68; assoc. prof. Fordham U. Law Sch., N.Y.C., 1968-72; ptnr. Curtis, Mallet-Prevost, N.Y.C., 1972-81; dist. judge U.S. Dist. Ct. (so. dist.) N.Y., N.Y.C., 1981—; cons. Nat. Com. for Reform of Criminal Laws, N.Y.C., 1971-72; mem. Knapp Commn., 1971-72; assoc. atty. Com. of Ct. on Judiciary, N.Y.C., 1971-72. Co-contbr. articles to profl. law revs. Mem. ABA, D.C. Bar Assn., Assn. of Bar of City of N.Y. Office: US Dist Ct US Courthouse Foley Sq New York NY 10007-1501

SPROAT, CHRISTOPHER TOWNSEND, artist; b. Boston, Sept. 23, 1945; s. Robert Henry and Audrey (Townsend) S.; m. Mary Lydia Bachmann. Student, Skohegan Sch., 1963, Boston U., 1964-65, Sch. of Mus. of Fine Arts, Boston, 1965-69. Solo exhbns. include Inst. of Contemporary Art, Boston, 1970, Hayden Gallery, MIT, Cambridge, 1976, Marian Goodman Gallery, N.Y., 1980, The Boston Athenaeum, 1984, Bette Stoler Gallery, N.Y., 1985, Barbara Krakow Gallery, Boston, 1985, 95; group shows include Mus. Fine Arts, Boston, 1971-72, 74, Whitney Mus. Am. Art, N.Y.C., 1973, Mus. Modern Art, N.Y.C., 1982, Newport Harbor Art Mus., Calif., 1985; work commd. by U.S. govt., Rayovac, Hyatt Hotels, Embassy Suites, Hasbro, others. Mass. Arts and Humanities Found. fellow 1975, 78; grantee NEA, 1975-76, 80-81, 84-85, N.Y. Found for the Arts. Democrat. Avocations: skiing, hiking, kyaking. Home: PO Box 2086 New York NY 10013-0875 Home: PO Box 1320 Putney VT 05346-9998

SPROAT, JOHN GERALD, historian; b. Los Angeles, Apr. 1, 1921; s. John Gerald and Grace (Elwell) Drummond S.; m. Ruth Christensen, Mar. 18, 1967; 1 child by previous marriage, Barbara. B.A., San Jose State Coll., 1950; M.A., U. Calif.-Berkeley, 1952, Ph.D., 1959. Instr. Mich. State U., 1956-57; asst. prof. Williams Coll., 1957-63; prof. Lake Forest Coll., Ill., 1963-74; prof. history U. S.C., Columbia, 1974-92, chmn. dept., 1974-83; dist. prof. emeritus, 1992—; sr. fellow Inst. for So. Studies, 1992—; Fulbright prof. Hamburg U., Fed. Republic Germany, 1961-62; vis. fellow Cambridge U., Eng., 1970; vis. prof. U. Calif.-Berkeley, 1972; Fulbright prof. U. Munich, Fed. Republic Germany, 1982, Indonesia, 1993-94; Am. participant lectr. USIA, India, Pakistan, 1987; mem. S.C. Commn. Archives and History, 1974-83, emeritus, 1979-83; mem. S.C. Bd. Rev. Hist. Places, 1974-86, chmn., 1978-83; del. Am. Council Learned Socs. Author: The Best Men: Liberal Reformers in the Gilded Age, 1988; (with others) The Shaping of America, 1972, Making Change: South Carolina Banking in the 20th Century, 1990; contbr. chpts. to books; exec. producer A Bond of Iron, S.C. ETV, 1979; gen. editor So. Classics Series. Past pres., trustee Columbia Mus. Art. Served with USAAF, 1941-45. NEH grantee, 1976, 77, 79, 85; Shell Found. grantee, 1967, 70, 73; Lilly Endowment grantee, 1966-67. Mem. Am. Hist. Assn., Orgn. Am. Historians, So. Hist. Assn. Episcopalian. Clubs: Capital City (Columbia). Home: 1686 Woodlake Dr Columbia SC 29206-4647 Office: U SC Inst For So Studies Columbia SC 29208

SPROGER, CHARLES EDMUND, lawyer; b. Chgo., Feb. 18, 1933; s. William and Minnette (Weiss) S. BA (David Himmelblau scholar), Northwestern U., 1954, JD, 1957. Bar: Ill. 1957. Practiced in Chgo., 1958—; assoc. Ehrlich & Cohn, 1958-63, Ehrlich, Bundesen, Friedman & Ross, 1963-72; partner Ehrlich, Bundesen, Broecker & Sproger, 1972-77; pvt. practice, 1977—; mem. adv. com. curriculum Ill. Inst. Continuing Legal Edn., Chgo., 1976—; v.p. Mediation Coun. of Ill., 1986-87; arbitration panelist for Cir. Ct. Cook County, 1990—. Editor: Family Lawyer, 1962-63; contbr. articles to legal pubs. Mediator Pastoral Psychotherapy Inst., 1982-86. Fellow Am. Acad. Matrimonial Lawyers (bd. examiners 1972-86, chmn. Law Day U.S.A. 1975); mem. ABA, Ill. Bar Assn. (chmn. coun. family law 1970-71), Chgo. Bar Assn. (matrimonial law com. 1958—), Am. Arbitration Assn. (divorce mediation com. 1983—), Decalogue Soc., U. Mich. Club Chgo. (pres. 1988-89), Phi Alpha Delta. Home: 2901 S King Dr Chicago IL 60616-3343 Office: 155 N Michigan Ave Chicago IL 60601-7511

SPROLE, FRANK ARNOTT, retired pharmaceutical company executive, lawyer; b. Bklyn., Sept. 13, 1918; s. Frank Newland and Eleanor Arnott (Greenberg) S.; m. Sarah Louise Knapp, Sept. 23, 1944; children—Wendy Sprole Bangs, Frank J., Anne Sprole Mauk, Jonathan K., Sarah Sprole Obregon. B.A., Yale U., 1942; LL.B., Columbia U., 1949. Bar: N.Y. 1949. Assoc. firm Winthrop Stimson, Putnam & Roberts, N.Y.C., 1949-50; atty. Bristol-Myers Co., N.Y.C., 1950-52, asst. sec., 1952-55, sec., 1955-67, v.p., 1965-73, sr. v.p., 1973-77, vice chmn. bd., 1977-84; bd. dirs. officer Proprietary Assn., Washington, 1978-84; dir., officer Knapp Fund, N.Y.C., 1960—. Pres. bd. trustees Hotchkiss Sch., Lakeville, Conn., 1980-85; trustee Internat. Inst. Rural Reconstrn., N.Y.C., and Manila, 1983-87. Served to lt. comdr. USNR, 1942-45, PTO. Mem. Assn. of Bar of City of N.Y., Yale Club of N.Y.C., Wee Burn Country Club, Bohemian Club, Mid Ocean Club, John's Island Club. Republican. Episcopalian. Avocation: golf. Home: 394 Mansfield Ave Darien CT 06820-2112

SPRONG, GERALD RUDOLPH, banker; b. Rodman, Iowa, Oct. 16, 1933; s. Earl Frank and Minnie Viola (Schroeder) S.; m. Barbara J. Sprong, Oct. 7, 1956; children: Lisa Sprong Whitacre, Bradley N., Douglas R. BS in Edn., N.W. Mo. State U., 1956. CPA, Mo. Ptnr. Peat, Marwick, Mitchell & Co. CPA's, Kansas City, Mo., 1958-73; pres., chief exec. officer Ameribanc, Inc., St. Joseph, Mo., 1973—; also bd. dirs. Ameribanc, Inc.; bd. dirs. Am. Banke, St. Joseph, Kansas City, St. Louis, St. Joseph Light and Power. Bd. dirs. St. Joseph Devel. Corp., Sch. Dist. Found., United Way, Jr. Achievement, 1956—; trustee William Jewell Coll., Liberty, Mo., 1973-88; chmn., bd. dirs. Coordinating Bd. for Higher Edn., Jefferson City, Mo., 1980-86. 1st lt. USMC, 1955-58. Recipient awards Girl Scouts Am., N.Y.C., 1987—. Mem. AICPA, St. Joseph C. of C. (bd. dirs.). Clubs: St. Joseph Country; River (Kansas City). Avocations: tennis, jogging, golfing. Office: Ameribanc Inc 1 Robidoux Ctr Saint Joseph MO 64501-4134

SPROTT, DAVID ARTHUR, statistics and psychology educator; b. Toronto, Ont., Can., May 31, 1930; s. Arthur Frederick and Dorothy (Barry) S.; m. Muriel Doris Vogel; children: Anne, Jane. BA, U. Toronto, 1952, MA, 1953, PhD, 1955. Rsch. asst. Galton Lab., London, 1955-56; biogeneticist, clin. tchr. dept. psychiatry U. Toronto, 1956-58; assoc. prof. stats. U. Waterloo, Ont., 1958-61, prof., 1961—, prof. psychology, 1964—, dean math., 1966-72, chmn. dept. stats., 1966-75; vis. prof. various univs. and colls. Contbr. numerous articles to profl. jours. Recipient Gold medal Statis. Soc. Can., 1988. Fellow Am. Statis. Assn., Inst. Math. Stats., Royal Soc. Can., Royal Photog. Soc.; mem. Internat. Statis. Inst. Avocations: photography, wine making. Office: U Waterloo Math Faculty, Waterloo, ON Canada N2L 3G1

SPROTT, JOHN T., ambassador; b. Phoenix, Apr. 6, 1933; m. Jeanne S.; 5 children. B.A., Northern Ariz. Univ.; Ph.D., Univ. of Colorado. Econ. instructor Univ. of Colorado, 1960-61; asst. econ. prof. Duquesne Univ., Penn., 1962-65; chmn., Econ. & Comml. Study Prog. Frn. Svc. Inst., 1966-67; sr. econ. adviser U.S. Econ. Mission to Chile, 1968-71; dep. coord., then coord. Econ. & Comml. Studies div. Fgn. Svc. Inst., 1971-75, dean, Sch. of Profl.Studies, 1975-81, dep. dir., 1981-93; U.S. amb. to Swaziland Mbabane, 1993—; lect. Johns Hopkins Univ., 1967-68. with U.S. Navy 1951-55. Mem. Instl. Assn. of Dirs of Diplomatic Academies, Inst. of Intl. Relations, Sr.Exec. Svc. Assn.; Aircraft Owners & Pilots Assn. Office: Am Embassy Mbabane Dept State Washington DC 20521

SPROTT, RICHARD LAWRENCE, government official, researcher; b. Tampa, Fla., Aug. 9, 1940; s. Joseph Albert and Marie Marguerite (Deborah) S.; m. Margaret Ann Weidel, June 19, 1965; children—Lynn Marie, Edward Ann. Student, Franklin and Marshall Coll., 1958-60; B.A., U. Nc., 1962, M.A. in Psychology, 1964, Ph.D in Psychology, 1965. Asst. prof. Oakland U., Rochester, Mich., 1967-69; assoc. staff scientist Jackson Lab., Bar Barbor, Maine, 1969-71, staff scientist, 1971-80; health scientist administr. Div. Research Resources, NIH, Bethesda, Md., 1980-81; br. chief Nat. Inst.

on Aging, Bethesda, 1981-84, assoc. dir., 1984—. Editor: Hormonal Correlates of Behavior, 1975, Age, Learning Ability and Intelligence, 1980; mem. editorial bd. Exptl. Aging Research jour., 1978—; contbr. articles to profl. jours. Mem. Bar Harbor Town Council, 1975-79, chmn., 1978-79; mem. bd. appeals Town of Bar Harbor, 1972-75, mem. warrant com., 1972-75. NIH fellow, 1965-67; NIH grantee, 1969-79. Fellow Am. Psychol. Assn.; mem. Behavior Genetics Assn. (membership chmn. 1979). Home: 11514 Regency Dr Potomac MD 20854-3733 Office: Nat Inst on Aging Rm 2C231 7201 Wisconsin Ave Bethesda MD 20892

SPROUL, JOHN ALLAN, retired public utility executive; b. Oakland, Calif., Mar. 28, 1924; s. Robert Gordon and Ida Amelia (Wittschen) S.; m. Marjorie Ann Hauck, June 20, 1945; children: John Allan, Malcolm J., Richard O., Catherine E. A.B., U. Calif., Berkeley, 1947, LL.B., 1949. Bar Calif. 1950. Atty. Pacific Gas & Electric Co., San Francisco, 1949-52, 56-62, sr. atty., 1962-70, asst. gen. counsel, 1970-71, v.p. gas supply, 1971-76, sr. v.p., 1976-77, exec. v.p., 1977-89, cons., 1989—; gen. counsel Pacific Gas Transmission Co., 1970-73, v.p., 1973-79, chmn. bd., 1979-89, also bd. dirs.; atty. Johnson & Stanton, San Francisco, 1952-56; bd. dirs. Oreg. Steel Mills, Inc. Bd. dirs. Hastings Coll. of Law. Served to 1st lt. USAAF, 1943-46. Mem. Calif. Bar Assn. (inactive), Pacific Coast Gas Assn., World Trade Club, Pacific-Union Club, Orinda Country Club. Home: 8413 Buckingham Dr El Cerrito CA 94530-2531 Office: Mail Code H17F PO Box 770000 123 Mission St San Francisco CA 94177

SPROULL, ROBERT LAMB, retired university president, physicist; b. Lacon, Ill., Aug. 16, 1918; s. John Steele and Chloe Velma (Lamb) S.; m. Mary Louise Knickerbocker, June 27, 1942; children: Robert F., Nancy M. AB, Cornell U., 1940, PhD, 1943; LLD (hon.), Nazareth Coll., 1983. Research physicist RCA labs., 1943-46; faculty Cornell U., 1946-63, 65-68, prof. physics, 1956-63, dir. lab. atomic and solid state physics, 1959-60, dir. materials sci. center, 1960-63, v.p. for acad. affairs, 1965-68; dir. Advanced Research Projects Agy., Dept. Def., Washington, 1963-65; v.p.; provost U. Rochester, N.Y., 1968-70; pres. U. Rochester, 1970-84, pres. emeritus, 1984—; prin. physicist Oak Ridge Nat. Lab., 1952; physicist European Rsch. Assoc., Brussels, 1958-59; lectr. NATO, 1958-59; past bd. dirs., John Wiley & Sons, Charles River Labs., United Technols. Corp., Xerox Corp., Bausch & Lomb; mem. sci. adv. com. GM Corp., 1971-80, chmn., 1973-80; mem. Def. Sci. Bd., 1966-70, chmn., 1968-70; mem. Naval Rsch. Adv. Com., 1974-76, Sloan Commn. Higher Edn., 1977-79, N.Y. Regents Commn. Higher Edn., 1992-93. Author: Modern Physics, 1956; Editor: Jour. Applied Physics, 1954-57. Trustee Deep Springs Coll., 1967-75, 83-87, Cornell U., 1972-77. Ctr. for Advanced Study in Behavioral Scis. fellow, 1973; Meritorious Civilian Svc. medal Sec. of Def., 1970. Fellow Am. Acad. Arts and Scis.; mem. Telluride Assn. (pres. 1945-47), Inst. of Def. Analysis (trustee 1984-92). Home: 16910 Bay St Jupiter FL 33477-1206 Office: U Rochester Rochester NY 14627

SPROUSE, JAMES MARSHALL, federal judge; b. Williamson, W.Va., Dec. 3, 1923; s. James and Garnet (Lawson) S.; m. June Dolores Burt, Sept. 25, 1952; children: Tracy Sprouse Ferguson, Jeffrey Marshall, Andrew Michael, Sherry Lee Sprouse Shinholser, Shelly Lynn Sprouse Schneider. A.B., St. Bonaventure (N.Y.) U., 1947; LL.B., Columbia U., 1949; postgrad. in internat. law, U. Bordeaux, France, 1950. Bar: W.Va. Asst. atty. gen. State of Va., 1949; with W.Va. CIA, 1952-57; pvt. practice W.Va., 1957-72, 75-79; justice W.Va. Supreme Ct. Appeals, 1972-75; judge U.S. Ct. Appeals (4th cir.), Lewisburg, W.Va., 1979-92, sr. cir. judge, 1992—. Served with AUS, 1942-45. Fulbright scholar. Mem. Am. Bar Assn., W.Va. State Bar, W.Va. Bar Assn., W.Va. Trial Lawyers Assn., Kanawha County Bar Assn., VFW, Am. Legion. Democrat. Presbyterian. Clubs: Shriners, Aheppa. Office: US Ct Appeals 4th Cir PO Box 401 122 N Court St Lewisburg WV 24901-1102

SPROW, HOWARD THOMAS, lawyer, educator; b. Atlantic City, Dec. 4, 1919; s. Howard Franklin and Elizabeth B. (Riley) S.; m. Mildred J. Fiske, July 22, 1945; children—Howard Hamilton, Mildred Elizabeth (Mrs. William son), Matthew Thomas. A.B. cum laude, Colgate U., 1942; J.D., Columbia, 1945; LLD (hon.), St. Lawrence U., 1987. Bar: N.Y. 1946. Mem. firm Brown, Wood, Fuller, Caldwell & Ivey, N.Y.C., 1945-70; partner Brown, Wood, Fuller, Caldwell & Ivey, 1954-70; gen. counsel, v.p. corporate and pub. affairs, sec. Merrill Lynch, Pierce, Fenner & Smith Inc., N.Y.C., 1970-77, Merrill Lynch & Co., Inc., 1973-77; mem. firm Rogers & Wells, N.Y.C., 1977-80; of counsel Rogers & Wells, 1980-87; prof. law Albany Law Sch., Union U., 1980-90, prof. emeritus, 1990—; of counsel Crane & Mackrell, Albany, 1990-92; sr. counsel Whiteman Osterman & Hanna, Albany, 1992—; adj. prof. law Fordham U., 1974-80; mem. adv. panel to Law Revision Commn. on Recodification N.Y. State Ins. Law, 1973-84, chmn., 1976-80. Mem. editorial bd. Columbia Law Rev, 1944-45; editor: Financing in the International Capital Markets, 1982. Mem. ABA, N.Y. State Bar Assn., Assn. of Bar of City of N.Y. Home: 55 Marion Ave Albany NY 12203-1820 Office: Whiteman Osterman & Hanna One Commerce Plz Albany NY 12260

SPROWL, CHARLES RIGGS, lawyer; b. Lansing, Mich., Aug. 22, 1910; s. Charles Orr and Hazel (Allen) S.; m. Virginia Lee Graham, Jan. 15, 1938; children: Charles R., Robert A., Susan G., Sandra D. A.B., U. Mich., 1932, J.D., 1934. Bar: Ill. 1935. Pvt. practice, 1934—; of counsel Taylor, Miller, Sprowl, Hoffnagle & Merletti, 1986—; Dir. Simmons Engring Corp., Busch & Schmitt, Inc., Petersen Aluminum Corp. Mem. Bd. Edn., New Trier Twp. High Sch., 1959-65, pres. 1965-66; mem. Glencoe Zoning Bd. Appeals, 1956-76, chmn., 1966-76; mem Glencoe Plan Commn., 1962-65; bd. dirs. Glencoe Pub. Libr., 1953-65, pres. 1955-56; trustee Highland Park Hosp., 1959-69; bd. dirs. Cradle Soc., 1968-92. Fellow Am. Coll. Trial Lawyers; mem. Chgo. Bar Assn. (bd. mgrs. 1949-51), Ill. Bar Assn., ABA, Juvenile Protective Assn. (dir. 1943-53), Northwestern U. Settlement (pres. 1963-70, dir.), Soc. Trial Lawyers, Delta Theta Phi, Alpha Chi Rho. Presbyn. Clubs: Law (pres. 1969-70), Legal (pres. 1953-54), Univ. Monroe, Skokie Country. Home: 558 Washington Ave Glencoe IL 60022-1837 Office: 33 N La Salle St Chicago IL 60602-2607

SPROWLS, ROBERT WAYNE, veterinarian, laboratory administrator; b. Phillips, Tex., Mar. 19, 1946; s. Charlie and Nettie Elizabeth (Green) S.; m. Linda Sue Rhoades, Aug. 11, 1966; children—Kimberly, Kari. B.S. in Vet. Sci., Tex. A&M U., 1968, D.V.M., 1969, Ph.D., 1973. NIH fellow pathology Tex. A&M U., College Station, 1969-73; asst. prof. Med. Ctr., U. Ark., Little Rock, 1973-75; head pathologists Tex. Vet. Med. Diagnostic Lab., Amarillo, 1975-81; dir. Tex. Vet. Med. Diagnostic Lab., 1981—. Contbr. articles to profl. jours. Chmn. Valley View Nazarene Ch., Amarillo, 1984—. Mem. AVMA, Am. Assn. Vet. Lab. Diagnosticians (mem. exec. bd. 1992—, mem. accreditation com. 1990—), Acad. Vet. Cons. (corr. sec. 1992—), Tex. Vet. Medicine Assn., High Plains Vet. Medicine Assn. (sec.-treas. 1980-81, 90—), Am. Assn. Bovine Practitioners, Amarillo A&M Club (v.p. 1977-78). Office: Tex A&M Vet Med Diagnostic Lab PO Box 3200 Amarillo TX 79116-3200

SPRUCE, EVERETT FRANKLIN, artist; b. Faulkner County, Ark., Dec. 25, 1908; s. William Everett and Fannie (McCarty) S.; m. Alice Kramer, Feb. 18, 1934; children: Alice Spruce Swaim and Georgia Spruce Walker (twins), William Everett, Henry Arthur. Student, Dallas Art Inst., 1925-29; pvt. study with, Olin H. Travis, Thomas M. Stell. Gallery asst. Dallas Mus. Fine Arts, 1931-34, registrar, 1935, asst. dir., 1935-40; instr. U. Tex., Austin, 1940-44; asst. prof. art U. Tex., 1944-47, chmn. dept. art, 1948-50, prof. art, mem. grad. faculty, 1954-74, prof. emeritus, 1974—, dir. grad. studio program dept. art, 1965-73. One-man shows Dallas Mus. Fine Arts, 1932, 58, Santa Barbara Mus. Art, 1945, McNay Art Inst., San Antonio, 1958, Wunderlich Gallery, Austin, Tex., 1991; exhibited Hudson D. Walker Gallery, N.Y.C., 1938-39, Levitt Gallery, N.Y.C., 1946, 48, 50, 51, ann. exhbn. painting and sculpture, Calif. Palace Legion of Honor, 1940, Mus. Fine Arts, Houston, Carnegie Inst., NAD, Corcoran Gallery, 1946, Laguna Gloria Art Mus., Austin, 1993; retrospective exhbn., Ford Found., 1959, ann. exhbn. Am. painting, Whitney Mus. Am. Art, 1959, U. Tex. Art Mus., Austin, 1979, Laguna Gloria Art Mus., Austin, 1993; represented in permanent collections: Houston Mus. Fine Arts, Des Moines Art Ctr., Walker Art Ctr., Mpls., Newark Art Mus., Phillips Gallery, Washington, Wichita Art Mus., McNay Art Inst., San Antonio, Dallas Mus. Fine Arts, Whitney Mus. Modern Art, Met. Mus., Nat. Mus. of Am. Art, Washington, Mus. Modern

Art, N.Y., Rio de Janeiro, Phila. Acad. Fine Arts, Nelson Gallery, Kansas City, Mo., Nat. Mus. Am. Art, Smithsonian Instn., Colorado Springs Fine Arts Center. (Recipient 1st prize Midwestern Artists Exhbn., Kansas City 1937, W. W. Crocker prize Calif. Palace Legion of Honor 1940, 1st prize Tex. Gen. Exhbn. Paintings and Sculpture 1946, prize Pepsi-Cola competition NAD, 1946, ann. exhbn. Am. Painting and Sculpture, Carnegie Inst., Pitts., 1946, La Tausca art exhbn. Riverside Mus., N.Y.C., 1946, 1st prize 17th exhbn. Tex. painting and sculpture 1955, biennial exhbn. Contemporary Am. Painting, Corcoran Gallery Art 1949, Venice Biennial 1950, Am. Paintings, Brussels, 1948, Bordighera, Italy 1956, U. Tex. Art Mus., Austin 1979, others); paintings reproduced in Everett Spruce, A Portfolio of Eight Paintings (By waters and Goodrich), 1958, Everett Spruce (by John Palmer Leeper), 1959, Everett Spruce Paintings and Drawings, 1950-79 (by Marian B. Davis), Texas Gulf Coast, 1979; paintings illustrated in book Pecos to Rio Grande, 1983; 50 yr. retrospective Wunderuch Gallery, Austin, 1994. Ford Found. grantee, 1958. Mem. AAUP, Tex. Fine Arts Assn. Home: 15 Peak Rd Austin TX 78746-5544

SPRUCH, LARRY, physicist, educator; b. Bklyn., Jan. 1, 1923. BA, Bklyn. Coll., 1943; PhD in Physics, U. Pa., 1948. From asst. instr. to instr. physics U. Pa., 1943-48; Atomic Energy Commn. fellow MIT, 1948-50; from asst. prof. to assoc. prof. NYU, N.Y.C., 1950-61, prof. physics, 1961—; cons. Lawrence Radiation Lab., 1959-66; vis. prof. inst. theoretical physics U. Colo., 1961, 68; mem. Inst. Advanced Study, 1981-82; del. China U.S. Physics Exam and Application, 1985, 86; mem. adv. bd. inst. theoretical atomic and molecular physics Harvard-Smithsonian Ctr. Astrophysics, 1989-91. Corr. Comments Atomic & Molecular Physics, 1972—. Recipient von Humboldt Sr. award, 1985, 88, Alumni award of Merit Bklyn. Coll., 1967; Tyndale fellow U. Pa., 1946-48, NSF sr. fellow U. London, Oxford U., 1963-64. Fellow Am. Phys. Soc. (Davisson-Germer prize 1992). Achievements include research in Beta decay, nuclear moments, isomeric transitions, internal conversion, atomic and nuclear scattering, variational principles, astrophysics, charge transfer, Thomas-Fermi theory, radiative corrections, atoms in magnetic fields, Levinson's theorem, casimir interactions, semiclassical radiation theory. Office: NYU Dept of Physics Washington Sq New York NY 10003

SPRUGEL, GEORGE, JR., ecologist; b. Boston, Sept. 26, 1919; s. George and Frances Emily (Strong) S.; m. Catharine Bertha Cornwell, Oct. 27, 1945; 1 son, Douglas George. B.S., Iowa State U., 1946, M.S., 1947, Ph.D., 1950. Instr., then asst. prof. zoology and entomology Iowa State U., 1946-54; asst. head biology br. Office Naval Research, 1951-53; spl. asst. to asst. dir., div. biology and medicine NSF, 1953-54, program dir. environ. biology, 1954-64; chief scientist Nat. Park Service, 1964-66; chief Ill. Natural History Survey, 1966-80, chief emeritus, 1980—; Cons. in field; mem. adv. com. environ. biology NSF, 1965; dir. program conservation of ecosystems U.S. Internat. Biol. Program, 1969-72; mem. study group on role lunar receiving lab. NASA, 1969-70, mem. life scis. com., 1972-78; mem. ecology adv. com. Bur. Reclamation, 1972-74; mem. Gov. of Ill. Sci. Adv. Com., 1967-80, Ill. Environ. Quality Council, 1970-73; mem. environ. studies bd. com. to devel. protocol for toxic substances Nat. Acad. Scis.-Nat. Acad. Engring., 1972-73; mem. NRC, 1968-72. Served as officer USNR, 1940-45, 51-53. Fellow AAAS (council 1961-73, v.p., chmn. sect. biol. scis. 1971); mem. Am. Inst. Biol. Scis. (mem.-at-large gov. bd. 1969-72, exec. com. 1972-75, pres. 1974), Ecol. Soc. Am. (council 1961-78, v.p. 1968), Am. Soc. Zoologists (sec. 1970-72, chmn. div. ecology 1971), Sci. Research Soc. Am., Sigma Xi. Home: 2710 S 1st St Champaign IL 61821-7114

SPRUIELL, VANN, psychoanalyst; b. Leeds, Ala., Oct. 16, 1926; s. Vann Lindley and Zada (Morton) S.; m. Iris Taylor, Sept. 20, 1951 (div. Oct. 1966); children: Graham, Fain, Garth; m. Joyce Ellis, Feb. 11, 1967; stepchildren: Sidney Reavey, Catherine Ellis, Matson Ellis. BS, U. Ala., Tuscaloosa, 1948; MD, Harvard U., 1952. Resident Bellevue Hosp., N.Y.C., 1952-53, N.Y. Hosp., N.Y.C., 1953-55; fellow Tulane Sch. Medicine, New Orleans, 1955-57; pvt. practice New Orleans, 1957—; vis. rschr. Anna Freud Ctr., London, 1972-73; co-pub. JOURLIT and BOOKREV; pres. and founding mem. Psychoanalytic Archives CD-ROM Texts, New Orleans, 1993—; clin. prof. psychiatry La. State U. Sch. Medicine, Tulane U. Sch. Medicine; sec. Ctr. for Advanced Studies in Psychoanalysis, 1989—. Editorial bd. Psychoanalytic Quarterly, 1973—; N.Am. editor Internat. Jour. Psychoanalysis, London; contbr. articles to profl. jours. and books. Sgt. U.S. Army, 1944-46. Mem. Am. Psychoanalytic Assn. (chmn., sec. bd. on profl. standards 1979-92), Wyvern Club. Avocation: sailing. Home: 215 Iona St Metairie LA 70005-4137

SPRUNG, DONALD WHITFIELD LOYAL, physics educator; b. Kitchener, Ont., Can., June 6, 1934; s. Lyall MacAulay and Doreen Bishop (Price) S.; m. Hannah Sueko Nagai, Dec. 12, 1958; children: Anne Elizabeth, Carol Hanako. BA, U. Toronto, Ont., 1957; PhD, U. Birmingham, Eng., 1961, DSc, 1977. Asst lectr. U. Birmingham, Eng., 1960-61; instr. Cornell U., Ithaca, N.Y., 1961-62; rsch. staff lab. nuclear sci. MIT, Boston, 1964-65; asst. prof. McMaster U., Hamilton, Ont., 1962-66, assoc. prof., 1966-71, physics prof., 1971—, dean faculty sci., 1975-84, mem. bd. govs., 1986-90, chair dept. physics and astronomy, 1991—; vis. prof. U. Barcelona, Spain, 1991-92, 95. Contbr. articles to profl. jours. C.D. Howe fellow, 1969-70. Fellow Royal Soc. Can.; mem. Can. Assn. Physicists (Herzberg medal 1972), Am. Phys. Soc.; mem. Inst. Physics. Avocations: bicycling, cabinet making. Office: McMaster Univ Dept Physics and Astronomy, 1280 Main St W, Hamilton, ON Canada L8S 4M1

SPUDICH, JAMES A., biology educator; b. Collinsville, Ill., Jan. 7, 1942; married, 1964; 2 children. BS, U. Ill., 1963; PhD in Biochemistry, Stanford U., 1967. USPHS trainee Stanford (Calif.) U., 1968; asst. prof. biochemistry U. Calif., San Francisco 1970-74, assoc. prof., from 1974; now prof. biochemistry and devel. biology Beckman Ctr., Stanford U. Sch. Medicine. Author: Molecular genetic Approaches to Protein Structure and Function, 1989; editor: Methods in Cell Biology, 1987, Annual Rev. Cell Biology, 1994; co-editor Annual Rev. Cell Biology, Vol. 1, 1985. USAF Sci. Rsch. fellow Cambridge U., 1969, NSF fellow, 1970; Am. Cancer Soc. rsch. grantee U. Calif., San Francisco, 1970. Mem. AAAS, NAS, Am. Soc. Cell Biologists (pres. 1989). Research in molecular basis of mitosis, amoeboid movement and other forms of cell motility. Office: Stanford U Dept Biochemistry Stanford Med Ctr Stanford CA 94305*

SPUDIS, PAUL D., geologist; b. Bowling Green, Ky., Aug. 29, 1952; s. Frank Paul and M. Erlene (Wren) S.; m. Anne M. Seaborne, Oct. 21, 1982; children: Janelle Kathryn, Diane Michelle. BS, Ariz. State U., 1976; Sc.M., Brown U., 1977; PhD, Ariz. State U., 1982. Research geologist NASA Ames Research Ctr., Mountain View, Calif., 1976-78, U.S. Geol. Survey, Flagstaff, Ariz., 1980—; com. mem. numerous NASA sci. adv. panels, 1983—. contbr. numerous articles to profl. jours. NASA grantee, 1980—. Mem. Am. Geophys. Union. Avocations: reading, tropical fish, boomeranging. Office: US Geol Survey 2255 N Gemini Dr Flagstaff AZ 86001-1698

SPUEHLER, DONALD ROY, retired lawyer, writer, mythologist; b. Elmhurst, Ill., Sept. 28, 1934; s. Ernst Albert and Elizabeth Walser; m. Jane Romm, Oct. 1, 1966; children: Sean Jason, Tracy Ariana. AB in Econs. magna cum laude, Harvard U., 1956, AM in Econs., 1958, JD magna cum laude, 1964; postgrad., Cambridge U., Eng., 1956-57. Bar: Calif. 1965, U.S. Dist. Ct. (cen. dist.) Calif. 1965. Assoc. O'Melveny & Myers, Los Angeles, 1964-72, tax ptnr., 1972-92, of counsel, 1992-95; bd. dirs. Mercury Gen. Corp., Los Angeles. Contbr. articles on tax law to profl. jours. Cons. Filer Commn. on Charitable Orgns., Washington, 1973-74; bd. dirs. Amateur Chamber Music Players Inc., End Hunger Network; pres. ACMP Found. With AUS, 1958-61. Knox fellow, 1956-57, Rockefeller Found. fellow, 1957-58; recipient John Harvard award Harvard U., 1953-56. Mem. Calif. Bar Assn., Phi Beta Kappa. Democrat. Buddhist. Avocations: spiritual study, tennis, community work. Office: O'Melveny & Myers 400 S Hope St Los Angeles CA 90071-2801

SPULBER, NICOLAS, economics educator emeritus; b. Brasov, Romania, Jan. 1, 1915; m. Pauline; Aug. 5, 1950; 1 son, Daniel Francis. MA, New Sch. Social Rsch., 1950, PhD magna cum laude, 1952. Rsch. assoc. Ctr. Internat. Studies, Mass. Inst. Tech., 1952-54; mem. faculty Ind. U., Bloomington, 1954—; prof. econs. Ind. U., from 1961, acting chmn. Inst. East European Studies, 1956-59, Disting. prof. econs., 1974-80, Disting. prof.

emeritus, 1980—; vis. prof. City Coll., City U. N.Y., 1963-64. Author: The Economics of Communist Eastern Europe, 1957, reissued 1976, The Soviet Economy: Structure, Principles, Problems, 2d edit, 1969, Soviet Strategy for Economic Growth, 1964, The State and Economic Development, 1966, Socialist Management and Planning, 1971, Organizational Alternatives in Soviet-Type Economies, 1979, Managing the American Economy from Roosevelt to Reagan, 1989, Restructuring The Soviet Economy: In Search of the Market, 1991, The American Economy: The Struggle for Supremacy in the 21st Century, 1995; co-author: Quantitative Economic Policy and Planning, 1976, Economics of Water Resources: From Regulation to Privatization, 1994; editor, co-editor 5 books; contbr. numerous articles to profl. jours. in, U.S. and fgn. countries. Halle fellow, 1951-52; grantee Am. Philos. Soc., 1956; grantee Ford Found., 1962-63; rsch. fellow Ford Faculty Found., 1960-61; sr. fellow Internat. Devel. Rsch. Ctr., Ind. U., 1969-71. Mem. Am. Econ. Assn. Office: Ind U Dept Econs Bloomington IN 47405

SPUNGIN, JOEL D., wholesale office supplies and equipment executive; b. 1937. With United Stationers Supply Co., Des Plaines, Ill., 1958—; exec. v.p. United Stationers Supply Co., Des Plaines, 1973-77; pres., COO, 1977-81; pres., COO United Stationers Inc., Des Plaines, 1981-87, vice chmn., CEO, 1987-88, chmn., pres., CEO, 1988-91, chmn., CEO, 1991—, chmn. emeritus, 1995, bd. dirs., 1995—. Office: United Stationers Inc 2200 E Golf Rd Des Plaines IL 60016-1246*

SPUNT, SHEPARD ARMIN, realty executive, management and financial consultant; b. Cambridge, Mass., Feb. 3, 1931; s. Harry and Naomi (Drooker) S.; B.S., U. Pa., 1952, M.B.A., 1956; m. Joan Murray Fooshee, Aug. 6, 1961 (dec. June 1969); children—Erica Frieda and Andrew Murray (twins). Owner, Colonial Realty Co., Brookline, Mass., 1953—, Cambridge, 1960—; sr. assoc. Gen. Solids Assocs., 1956—; chmn. bd. Gen. Solids Systems Corp., 1971-74; trustee Union Capital Trust, Boston; incorporator Liberty Bank & Trust Co., Boston; dir. clerk The Computer Co., Somerville, Mass., 1986—. Chmn., Com. for Fair Urban Renewal Laws, Mass., 1965—; Boston Area assoc. trustee U. Pa.; treas. Ten Men of Mass., 1980. Pres., New Eng. Council of Young Republicans, Mass., 1964-69, 69-71; vice chmn. Young Rep. Nat. Fedn., 1967-69, dir. region I, 1964-67, 69-71; mem. Brookline Republican Town Com., 1960—; del. Atlantic Conf. Young Polit. Leaders, Brussels, 1973; bd. dirs. Brookline Taxpayers Assn., 1964—, v.p., 1971-72, pres., 1972—. Registered profl. engr., Mass. Mem. Nat. Soc. Profl. Engrs., Rental Housing Assn., Greater Boston Real Estate Bd., Navy League, Boston Athenaeum, Copley Soc. Boston. Lodges: Masons, Shriners. Author: (with others) A Business Data Processing Service for Small Business Practitioners, 1956; A Business Data Processing Service for Medical Practitioners, 1956, rev. edit., 1959. Author, sponsor consumer protection and election law legislation Mass. Gen. Ct., 1969—. Patentee in field of automation, lasers, dielectric bonding. Home: 177 Reservoir Rd Chestnut Hill MA 02167-1426 Office: 21 Elmer St Cambridge MA 02138-6107

SPURGEON, EDWARD DUTCHER, law educator; b. Newton, N.J., June 2, 1939; s. Dorsett Larew and Mary (Dutcher) S.; m. Carol Jean Forbes, June 17, 1963; children: Michael Larew, Stephen Edward. AB, Princeton U., 1961; LLB, Stanford U., 1964; LLM in Taxation, NYU, 1968. Bar: Calif. 1965. Assoc. atty. Stammer McKnight et al, Fresno, Calif., 1964-67; assoc. atty. Paul Hastings Janofsky and Walker, L.A., 1968-70, ptnr., 1971-80; prof. law U. Utah, Salt Lake City, 1980-90, Wm. H. Leary prof. law and policy, 1990-93, assoc. dean acad. affairs Coll. Law, 1982-83, dean Coll. Law, 1983-90; dean, prof. Sch. of Law U. Ga., Athens, 1991—; vis. prof. Albert and Elaine Borchard Found., L.A., 1983—; vis. prof. law Univ. Coll. London, fall 1990, Stanford U. Law Sch., spring 1991; ex-officio mem. Utah State Bar Commn., 1984-90; cons. devel. office U. Utah, 1991-93. Co-author: Federal Taxation of Trusts, Grantors and Beneficiaries, 1st edit., 1978, 2d edit., 1989. Mem. Utah Gov.'s Task Force Officers and Dirs. Liability Ins., 1985-87, Utah Dist. Ct. Reorgn. Commn., 1986-87, Justice in 21st Century Commn., Utah, 1989-91; bd. visitors, exec. com. Stanford U. Law Sch., 1988-93. Mem. ABA (Commn. on Legal Problems of the Elderly 1991—), Am. Bar Found. Office: U of Ga Law School Athens GA 30602

SPURLING, EVERETT GORDON, JR., architect, construction specifications consultant; b. Fallston, N.C., Sept. 5, 1923; s. Everett Gordon and Vera Mae (Lattimore) S.; m. Margaret Ball Duckworth, Sept. 9, 1944; children: David Steven, Diana Lynn, Norman Kent. AS, Mars Hill Coll., 1940-42; B in Archtl. Engring. with high honors, N.C. State U., 1947, postgrad., 1948. Registered architect, N.C., Va., Md. Inspector aircraft Glenn Martin Co., Balt., 1942; draftsman, architect F. Carter Williams, Architect, Raleigh, N.C., 1947-52; staff architect C.E. Silling and Assocs., Charleston, W.Va., 1952-53, Greife and Daley, Architects, Charleston, 1953-55; ptnr. Hunter and Spurling, Architects, Charleston, 1955-57; project architect, assoc. McLeod and Ferrara, Architects, Washington, 1957-64; owner, cons. E.G. Spurling Jr., Architect, Washington and Bethesda, Md., 1964—; guest lectr. Montgomery Coll., Cath. U., U. Mo.-Rolla, George Washington U.; guest speaker, panelist numerous constrn. orgns. Contbr. articles to profl. jours. Served as sgt. C.E., U.S. Army, 1944-46, ETO. Recipient Design award GSA, 1990. Fellow AIA, Constrn. Specifications Inst. (Cert. Appreciation 1971, 93, Ben John Small Meml. award 1979, Edn. Commendation 1979, Master Format Spl. award 1983, Mid. Atlantic Region Cert. Appreciation 1990, 92, hon.); mem. ASTM, Am. Arbitration Assn. (panelist 1979-95), Specifications Cons. in Ind. Practice (pres. 1977-80), Tau Beta Pi, Phi Kappa Phi. Democrat. Baptist. Avocations: fishing, woodworking, art, fgn. travel. Home and Office: 6312 Marjory Ln Bethesda MD 20817-5804

SPURRIER, STEVE, university athletic coach, former professional football player. Quarterback San Francisco 49'ers, 1967-75, Tampa Bay Buccaneers, 1976; head football coach Duke U., 1987-89, U. Fla. Gators, 1990—. Winner Heisman Trophy, U. Fla., 1966. Office: Univ Fla PO Box 14485 Gainesville FL 32604-2485*

SPYERS-DURAN, PETER, librarian, educator; b. Budapest, Hungary, Jan. 26, 1932; came to U.S., 1956, naturalized, 1964; s. Alfred and Maria (Almasi-Balogh) S-D; m. Jane F. Cumber, Mar. 21, 1964; children: Kimberly, Hilary, Peter. Certificate, U. Budapest, 1955; M.A. in L.S, U. Chgo., 1960; Ed.D., Nova U., 1975. Profl. asst. libr. adminstrn. div. ALA, Chgo., 1961-62; assoc. dir. librs., assoc. prof. U. Wis., 1962-67; dir. librs., prof. Western Mich. U., 1967-70; dir. librs., prof. libr. sci. Fla. Atlantic U. 1970-76; dir. libr. Calif. State U., Long Beach, 1976-83; dir. libr. and info. sci., dir. libr. Wayne State U., Detroit, 1983-86, dean, prof. libr. and info. sci. program, 1986-95, dean and prof. emeritus, 1995—; cons. Spyers-Duran Assocs., 1995—; vis. prof. State U. N.Y. at Geneseo, summers 1969-70; cons. publs., libr. and info. scis.-related enterprises; chmn. bd. internat. Colls., 1970—. Author: Moving Library Materials, 1965, Public Libraries - A Comparative Survey of Basic Fringe Benefits, 1967; editor: Approval and Gathering Plans in Academic Libraries, 1969, Advances in Understanding Approval Plans in Academic Libraries, 1970, Economics of Approval Plans in Research Libraries, 1972, Management Problems in Serials Work, 1973, Prediction of Resource Needs, 1975, Requiem for the Card Catalog: Management Issues in Automated Cataloging, 1979, Shaping Library Collections for the 1980's, 1981, Austerity Management in Academic Libraries, 1984, Financing Information Systems, 1985, Issues in Academic Libraries, 1985; mem. editorial bd. Jour. of Library Adminstration, 1989-95. Mem. Kalamazoo County Library Bd., 1969-70; Bd. dirs. United Fund. Mem. ALA, Mich. Libr. Assn., Internat. Fed. Libr. Assns., Assn. Info. Sci., Fla. Libr. Assn., Calif. Libr. Assn., Fla. Assn. Community Colls., Boca Raton C of C., U. Chgo. Grad. Libr. Sch. Alumni Club (pres. 1973-75), Mich. Libr. Consortium (bd. dirs. 1983-87), Detroit Area Libr. Network (pres. bd. dirs. 1985-95), Mich. Ctr. for Book (pres. 1988-89), Am. Soc. Info. Sci., Assn. Libr. and Info. Sci. Edn. Republican. Methodist. Home: 8000 Sailboat Key Blvd St Petersburg Beach FL 33707 Office: Wayne State Univ Librs Detroit MI 48202

SQUARCIA, PAUL ANDREW, school superintendent; b. Yukon, Pa., Nov. 17, 1939; s. Paul and Lucy (Nardone) S.; m. Gena Maria Porreca, Aug. 18, 1962; children: Paul, Stephanie, Suzanne. BS, Boston U., 1961, cert. advanced studies, 1974; EdD, Boston Coll., 1987; MEd, U.N.H. 1967. Sci. tchr. Berlin (N.H.) Sch. Dept., 1961-63, asst. prin., 1963-66; prin. Oxford Hills High Sch. South Paris, Maine, 1967-70; prin. Silver Lake Regional Dist., Kingston, Mass., 1970-72, asst. supt. schs., 1972-78, supt. schs., 1978—; adj. prof. Bridgewater (Mass.) State Coll., 1980—, Lesley Coll.,

Cambridge, Mass., 1980—. Recipient Nat. Superintendent of the Yr. awd., Massachusetts, Am. Assn. of School Administrators, 1993. Mem. ASCD, Am. Assn. Sch. Adminstrs., Mass. Assn. Sch. Supts. (pres. 1992-93). Roman Catholic. Avocations: reading, traveling, spectator sports. Home: 28 Holmes Terr Plymouth MA 02360 Office: Silver Lake Regional Dist 130 Pembroke St Kingston MA 02364

SQUIBB, SAMUEL DEXTER, chemistry educator; b. Limestone, Tenn., June 20, 1931; s. Benjamin Bowman and Lou Pearl S.; m. JoAnn Kyker, Dec. 15, 1951; children—Sandra Lavanne, Kevin Dexter. B.S., E. Tenn. State U., 1952; Ph.D., U. Fla., 1956. Assoc. prof., dir. chemistry Western Carolina U., Cullowhee, N.C., 1956-60; asst. prof., dir. chemistry Eckerd Coll., St. Petersburg, Fla., 1960-63; asso. prof. Eckerd Coll., 1963-64; prof. chemistry U. N.C., Asheville, 1964-94, prof. emeritus, 1994—, chmn. dept., 1964-94; vis. prof. U. N.C., Chapel Hill, 1976-81, 83-87, 92-95, Clemson U., S.C., 1982; cons. So. Assn. Colls. and Schs., State of W.Va. Author: Experimental Organic Chemistry, 1972, Understanding Chemistry One, 1979, rev. 1990, Two, 1981, rev. 1991, Three, 1981, rev. 1992, Four, 1981, rev. 1992, Five, 1981, rev. 1989, Six, 1984, Chemistry One, 1976, rev. 1987, Two, 1980, rev. 1990, Experimental Chemistry One, 1976, rev. 1988, Two, 1981, rev. 1991; contbr. articles to profl. jours. Mem. Grose United Meth. Ch. Disting. Tchr. award U. N.C.-Asheville, 1983. Fellow Am. Inst. Chemists (life, nat. publs. bd. 1988-92); mem. Am. Chem. Soc. (Charles H. Stone award Carolina Piedmont sect. 1979, Disting. Chemist award Western Carolinas sect. 1993, chmn. Tampa Bay subsect. 1963, Western Carolina sect. 1981, editor Periodic News Western Carolina sect. 1980—, Disting. Chemist award 1993), N.C. Inst. Chemists (pres. 1977-79, sec. 1975-77, 85-91, Disting. Chemist award 1986), Skyland Twirlers Square Dance Club, Silver Spurs Advanced Square Dance Club, Skylark Round Dance Club, Phi Beta Kap. Office: U NC Dept Chemistry Asheville NC 28804

SQUIBB, SANDRA HILDYARD, special education educator; b. Kansas City, Mo., May 23, 1943; d. Victor Herbert and Vivian Aline (Henderson) Hildyard; children: Jason, Trevor. BA, So. Meth. U., 1966; MS, FHSU, 1984. Cert. early childhood, spl. edn. tchr., Kans., Tex., cert. bldg. adminstr. K-12. Speech pathologist Edinburg (Tex.) Consolidated Sch. Dist., 1971-74; owner, audiologist Northwest Kans. Hearing Svc., Colby, Kans., 1976—; supr. Northwest Kans. Ednl. Svc. Ctr., Colby, 1980-87; coord. Northwest Kans. Ednl. Svc. Ctr., Oakley, Kans., 1987-92; treas. Kans. Div. of Early Childhood, 1987-89. Precinct chmn. Dem. Party, Thomas County, 1980—, party chmn., 1988-90; mem. Parent Adv. Coun., Colby, 1984-87; mem. bd. Alcohol and Drug Abuse Coun.; cmty. rep. Head Start Policy Coun., 1994—. Recipient grants in field. Mem. Coun. for Exceptional Children (award of excellence 1991). Roman Catholic. Avocation: skiing. Home: 425 La Hacienda Dr Colby KS 67701-3912 Office: NW Kans Ednl Svc Ctr Oakley KS 67748

SQUIER, DAVID LOUIS, manufacturing executive; b. Buffalo, Oct. 30, 1945; s. Clayton L. and Ruth H. Squier; m. Sue Sampson, Aug. 12, 1967; children: Jennifer, Allison. BS in Mech. Engring., Lehigh U., 1967; MBA, Wharton Sch., U. Pa., 1971. With mfg. mgmt. program GE, various cities, 1967-70; mgr. corp. planning Howmet Corp., Greenwich, Conn., 1971-73; mgr. corp. and bus. planning Howmet Corp., Muskegon, Mich., 1973-75; plant mgr. Howmet Corp., Hampton, Va., 1976-78; gen. mgr. Howmet Corp., Wichita Falls, Tex., 1979-82; v.p Howmet Corp., Greenwich, 1983-87, sr. v.p., 1987-89, exec. v.p., 1989-91, COO, 1991-92, pres., CEO, 1992—, also bd. dirs. Mem. rev. and prioritization bd. Iacocca Inst., Bethlehem, Pa., 1990—. Home: 56 Laurel Rd New Canaan CT 06840-3206 Office: Howmet Corp 475 Steamboat Rd Greenwich CT 06830-7144

SQUIER, JACK LESLIE, sculptor, educator; b. Dixon, Ill., Feb. 27, 1927; s. Leslie Lee and Ruth (Barnes) S.; m. Jane Bugg, June 9, 1950. Student, Oberlin Coll., 1945-46; B.S., Ind. U., 1950; M/F.A., Cornell U., 1952. Instr. Cornell U., 1952, asst. prof. art, 1958-61, asso. prof., 1961-65, prof., 1965—; designer Howatt Pottery Co., N.Y.C., 1953; account exec. Jamian Advt. Co., N.Y.C., 1954-58; asst. prof. U. Calif., Berkeley, 1960; mem. Internat. Assn. Art, UNESCO, 1964-72, mem. exec. com., 1966-69, v.p., 1969-72. One-man shows include Alan Gallery, N.Y.C., 1956, 59, 62, 64, White Mus., Cornell U., 1959, 68, Instituto de Arte Contemporaneo, Lima, Peru, 1963, Landau-Alan Gallery, N.Y.C., 1966, 69, Herbert F. Johnson Mus., Corwell Univ. (retrospective of work , 1953-93); exhibited in group shows at Mus. Modern Art, N.Y.C., 1957, Whitney Mus., N.Y.C., 1952, 54, 56, 58, 62, 67, 78, Hirshhorn Mus., Washington, 1978, Mus. Fine Arts, Boston, 1958, Chgo. Art Inst., 1960, Brussel's Worlds Fair, 1956, competition, Auschwitz, Poland, 1957, Albright-Knox Mus., Buffalo, 1968, Claude Bernard Gallery, Paris, 1957, Hanover Gallery, London, 1958; represented in permanent collections Mus. Modern Art, N.Y.C., Whitney Mus. Art, Hirshhorn Mus., Instituto de Arte Contemporaneo, Everson Mus., Syracuse, N.Y., Stanford U. Mus., St. Lawrence U. Mus., SUNY at Potsdam, Ithaca Coll. Johnson Mus. at Cornell U., Houston Mus., Hood Mus.-Dartmouth (N.H.) U.; retrospective exhbn. Herbert F. Johnson Mus. Cornell U., 1993; work pub. in various, books, mags., newspapers, slide collections, catalogs. Served with AC USN, 1945-47. Office: Cornell U Dept Art 100 Tjaden Hall Ithaca NY 14850

SQUIER, LESLIE HAMILTON, psychology educator; b. San Francisco, Nov. 17, 1917; s. Leslie Hamilton and Alma Ida (Bergmann) S.; m. Anne Frances Wood, Dec. 12, 1959; children—Renata, Leslie III, Stafford, Kurt. B.A., U. Calif.-Berkeley, 1950, Ph.D., 1953. From instr. to prof. psychology Reed Coll., Portland, Oreg, 1953-88, dean of students, 1955-61, prof. emeritus, 1988—; vis. scientist Oceanic Inst., Makapuu, Oahu, Hawaii, 1969-70, 71; vis. prof. Paine Coll., Augusta, Ga., 1984; NSF fellow U. Oreg. Med. Sch., Portland, 1976, U. Hawaii Med. Sch., Honolulu, 1977. Trustee Portland Zool. Soc., 1962-68. Served with USAF, 1942-46. Mem. AAAS, APA, Am. Psychol. Soc., Oreg. Psychol. Assn. (pres. 1965), Western Psychol. Assn., Assn. for the Study of Dreaming, Phi Beta Kappa, Sigma Xi. Home: 5647 SE 38th Ave Portland OR 97202-7501 Office: Reed Coll Portland OR 97202

SQUIER, ROBERT DAVE, political consultant, documentary filmmaker; b. Brainerd, Minn., Sept. 21, 1934; s. Ralph Thomas and Lucille (Morse) S.; m. Jane McNeely, Apr. 12, 1958; children: Mark Ralph, Robert McNeely; m. 2d Prudence Bergman, Jan. 15, 1976. B.A., U. Minn., 1956; Lowell grad. fellow, Boston U., 1957-58. Program mgr. U. Tex. TV, Austin, 1961-64; dir., exec. producer Nat. Ednl. TV, N.Y.C., 1964-65; head TV and film prodn. USIA, Washington, 1966-67; spl. asst. to pres. and exec. producer Nat. Ednl. TV; dir. TV and radio Democratic Nat. Com., Washington, 1967-68; pres. Squier, Eskew, Knapp & Ochs Communications (formerly The Communications Co. and Squier-Eskew), Washington, 1968—, The Film Co., 1980—; Squier, Knapp & Ochs Comm., Washington; cons. House Dem. Campaign Com., Dem. Nat. Com. Dir.: feature documentary William Faulkner, 1979 (duPont-Columbia Gold medal N.Y. Film Festival); exec. producer: TV broadcast Our World, 1967; dir.: TV broadcast Casals in P.R., 1971; producer-dir.: feature documentary Herman Melville, Damned in Paradise. Served to sgt. Signal Corps U.S. Army, 1960-61. Recipient Columbus award Ohio State U., 1964, Emmy award Acad. TV Arts and Scis. for series Sounds of Summer, Gt. Am. Dream Machine, 1966, Disting. Alumni Award Boston U. Mem. Dirs. Guild Am. Democrat. Club: Cosmos (Washington). Home: The Moorings Millwood VA 22646 Office: Squier Knapp Ochs Comm 511 2nd St NE Washington DC 20002

SQUIRE, ALEXANDER, management consultant; b. Dumfrieshire, Scotland, Sept. 29, 1917; s. Frederick John and Lillian (Ferguson) S.; m. Isabelle L. Kerr, June 23, 1945; children: Jonathan, David, Deborah, Stephen, Philip, Martha, Timothy, Rebecca, Elizabeth. BS, MIT, 1939. Research metallurgist Handy and Harman, Fairfield, Conn., 1939-41; devel. metallurgist Sullivan Machinery Co., Michigan City, Ind., 1941-42; head powder metallurgy br. Watertown Arsenal Lab., Mass., 1942-45; mgr. metall. devel. Westinghouse Electric Corp., Pitts., 1945-50; project mgr. Bettis Atomic Power Lab., Pitts., 1950-62; gen. mgr. plant apparatus div. Westinghouse, 1962-69; dir. purchases and traffic Westinghouse Electric Corp., 1969-71; pres. Westinghouse Hanford Co., Richland, Wash., 1971-79; bus. cons. Richland, 1979-80; dep. mng. dir. Wash. Public Power Supply System, 1980-85, cons., 1985—. Mem. Nat. Acad. Engring., Am. Nuclear Soc., Am. Soc. Metals, AIME, Am. Def. Preparedness Assn. Address: 2415 Winburn Ave Durham NC 27704

SQUIRE, ANNE MARGUERITE, religious leader; b. Amherstburg, Ont., Can., Oct. 17, 1920; d. Alexander Samuel and Coral Marguerite Park; m. William Robert Squire, June 24, 1943; children: Frances, Laura, Margaret. BA, Carleton U., Ottawa, 1972, BA with honors, 1974, MA, 1975; LLD (hon.), Carleton U., 1988; DD (hon.), United Theol. Coll., 1979, Queen's U., 1985. Cert. tchr., Ont. Adj. prof. Carleton U., 1975-82; sec. div. ministry personnel and edn. United Ch. Can., Toronto, 1982-85, moderator, 1986-88. Author curriculum materials, 1959—; contbr. articles to profl. jours. Mem. bd. mgmt. St. Andrew's Coll., Saskatoon, Sask., 1982, Queens Theol. Coll., Kingston, Ont., 1980-82. Recipient Senate medal Carleton U., 1972. Mem. Can. Research Inst. for Advancement Women, Delta Kappa Gamma (pres. 1978-79). Office: 731 Weston Dr, Ottawa, ON Canada K1G 1W1

SQUIRE, JAMES ROBERT, retired publisher, consultant; b. Oakland, Calif., Oct. 14, 1922; s. Harry Edwin and Ruby (Fulton) S.; m. Barbara Lyman, Jan. 20, 1946; children: Kathryn Richard, David Whitford. BA, Pomona Coll., 1947, DLitt, 1966; MA, U. Calif., Berkeley, 1949, PhD, 1956. Tchr. secondary sch. Oakland, Calif., 1949-54; supr., lectr. English edn. U. Calif. at Berkeley, 1951-59; prof. English U. Ill., Urbana, 1959-67; exec. sec. Nat. Council Tchrs. English, 1960-67; editor-in-chief, sr. v.p. Ginn & Co., Lexington, Mass., 1968-74; sr. v.p., pub. Ginn & Co., 1975-80, sr. v.p., dir. research and devel., 1980-82, sr. v.p., cons., 1983-84; cons., 1984-94; lectr. grad. sch. edn. Harvard U., 1990-95; pres. Nat. Conf. Rsch. in English, 1982-83. Author: (with W. Loban, M. Ryan) Teaching Language and Literature, 1961, 69, (with R.K. Applebee) High School English Instruction Today, 1968, (with B.L. Squire) Greek Myths and Legends, 1967, Teaching English in the United Kingdom, 1969, A New Look at Progressive Education, 1972; editor: Teaching of English, 76th Yearbook Nat. Soc. Study Edn., 1977, Dynamics of Language Learning, 1987, Writing K-12 Exemplary Programs, 1987, (with J. Jensen, D. Lapp, J. Flood) Handbook of Research on Teaching the English Language Arts, 1991, (with E.J.. Farrell) Transactions in Literature: A Fifty Year Perspective; section editor: Ency. of English Studies and Language Arts, 1994. Bd. dirs. Am. Edn. Publ. Inst., 1968-70. With AUS, 1943-45. Recipient Creative Scholarship award Coll. Lang. Assn., 1961, Lifetime Rsch. award Nat. Conf. Rsch. in English, 1992; named Ky. col., 1966; named to Hall of Fame in reading, 1987. Mem. MLA (pres. 1995), Assn. Am. Pubs. (vice chmn. sch. divsn. 1971-73, chmn. 1974-76, 81-82, Mary McNulty award 1983), Nat. Coun. Tchrs. English (Exec. Com. award 1967,l Disting. Svc. award 1991), Internat. Reading Assn., Coll. Conf. on Composition and Communication, Phi Delta Kappa. Home: # 1 Nubanusit Rd Marlborough NH 03455 Office: Harvard Grad Sch Edn 209 Larsen Hall Cambridge MA 02138

SQUIRE, RUSSEL NELSON, musician, emeritus educator; b. Cleve., Sept. 21, 1908. B.Mus. Edn., Oberlin Coll., 1929; A.M., Case Western Res. U., 1939; Ph.D., NYU, 1942; postgrad. U. So. Calif. Dir. Oberlin Summer Music Sch., Ohio, 1929; dir. instrumental music instrn. Chillicothe Pub. Schs., Ohio, 1929-37; faculty Pepperdine U., Malibu, Calif., 1937-56, prof. music, 1937-56, now prof. emeritus, also chmn. fine arts div., 1940-56; faculty Calif. State U.-Long Beach, 1956-72, prof. music, 1964-72, now prof. emeritus; vis. prof. Pacific Christian Coll., 1970-74; prof. philosophy Sch. Edn., Pepperdine U., 1972-78; profl. theater orch. pianist, 1926-28; founder/propr./dir. Ednl. Travel Service involving study residencies in Europe, the Near East, China, India, Australia, Africa; Service: Agoura, Calif., 1958-84. Author: Studies in Sight Singing, 1950; Introduction to Music Education, 1952; Church Music, 1962; Class Piano for Adult Beginners, 1964, 4th edit., 1990; also contbr. articles to profl. jours. Founder/pres. Council for Scholarship Aid to Fgn. Students, Inc.; mem. Los Angeles County Music Commn., 1948-60; bd. dirs. Opera Guild So. Calif., 1948-60; pres. Long Beach Symphony Assn., 1963-64 (bd. dirs 1961-64). Mem. Music Tchrs. Assn. Calif. (br. pres. 1948-51), AAUP (chpt. founding pres. 1948-49), Rotary, Phi Mu Alpha Sinfonia (life). Club: Twenty (Los Angeles), Bohemians (Los Angeles). Home: 350 Robin Rd Waverly OH 45690-1521

SQUIRE, WALTER CHARLES, lawyer; b. N.Y.C., Aug. 5, 1945; s. Sidney and Helen (Friedman) S.; m. Sara Jane Abramson; children: Harrison, Russell, Zachary, Andrew. BA, Yale U., 1967; JD, Columbia U., 1971. Bar: N.Y. 1971, U.S. Dist. Ct. (so. and ea. dists.) N.Y. 1975, U.S. Ct. Appeals (2d cir.) 1974, U.S. Supreme Ct. 1977. Ptnr. Jones Hirsch Connors & Bull, N.Y.C., 1986—. Bd. govs. Arthritis Found. N.Y., Inc., 1993—; bd. dirs. MedicAlert Found. N.Y., 1990—. Mem. ABA, N.Y. State Bar Assn., Assn. of Bar of City of N.Y., Internat. Bar Assn., Licensing Execs. Soc., Am. Arbitration Assn. (arbitrator 1975—, mediator 1993—), Am. Acad. Hosp. Attys., Risk Ins. Mgmt. Soc. (lectr. 1983, 84). Office: Jones Hirsch Connors & Bull 101 E 52d St New York NY 10022

SQUIRES, ARTHUR MORTON, chemical engineer, educator; b. Neodesha, Kans., Mar. 21, 1916; s. Charles Loren and Vera Amber (Moore) S. A.B. with distinction in Chemistry, U. Mo., 1938; Ph.D., Cornell U., 1947. Design engr. M.W. Kellogg Co., N.Y.C., 1942-46; asst. dir. process devel. Hydrocarbon Research, Inc., N.Y.C., 1946-51, dir. process devel., 1951-59; cons. chem. process industries N.Y., 1959-67; prof. chem. engring. CUNY, 1967-74, disting. prof., 1974-76, chmn. dept. chem. engring., 1970-73; Vilbrandt prof. chem. engring. Va. Poly. Inst. and State U., Blacksburg, 1976-82, disting. prof., 1978-86, disting. prof. emeritus, 1986—. Author: The Tender Ship, 1986; editor: (with D.A. Berkowitz) Power Generation and Environmental Change, 1971; contbr. articles to profl. jours.; patentee in field. Mem. N.Y. Pro Musica, 1953-60. Fellow Am. Acad. Arts and Scis., AAAS; mem. Nat. Acad. Engring., Am. Inst. Chem. Engrs. (inst. lectr.), Am. Chem. Soc. (Henry H. Storch award 1973), ASME, Sigma Xi, Tau Beta Pi. Avocation: performing medieval and Renaissance music. Home: 2710 Quincy Ct Blacksburg VA 24060-4124 Office: Va Poly Inst and State U Dept Chem Engring Blacksburg VA 24061

SQUIRES, JOHN HENRY, federal bankruptcy judge; b. Urbana, Ill., Oct. 21, 1946; s. Henry Warrick and Nell Catherine (McDonough) S.; m. Mary Kathleen Damhorst, June 7, 1969; children: Jacqueline Marie, Mary Elizabeth, Katherine Judith, Emily Jean, Grace Dorothy. AB cum laude, U. Ill., 1968, JD, 1971. Bar: Ill. 1971, U.S. Dist. Ct. (cen. dist.) 1972, U.S. Tax Ct. 1978. Assoc. Brown, Hay & Stephens, Springfield, Ill., 1971-76, ptnr., 1977-87; judge U.S. Bankruptcy Ct. No. Dist. of Ill., ea. div., 1988—; trustee in bankruptcy, 1984-87; adj. prof. law John Marshall Law Sch., Chgo., 1994; lectr. Chgo. Bar Assn., Ill. Inst. Continuing Legal Edn. , Comml. Law League Am., Ill. Credit Union League; mem. lay adv. bd. St. Joseph's Home, Springfield, 1980-84, sec., 1982-83, v.p., 1983-84. With USAF, 1969. Mem. Chgo.-Lincoln Am. Inn of Ct., Am. Bus. Club, Union League of Chgo. Office: US Bankruptcy Ct No Dist Ill Ea Div Rm 656 219 S Dearborn St Chicago IL 60604-1702

SQUIRES, SCOTT WILLIAM, special effects expert, executive. With Indsl. Light & Magic, San Rafael, Calif., 1975-79, visual effects supr., 1985—; co-founder, pres. Dreamquest Visual Effects, 1979-85. Asst. cameraman (film) Close Encounters of the Third Kind, 1977; cameraman (film) Buck Rogers and the Battleship Galactica, 1977; rsch. designer (film) Star Trek I, 1979; spl. effects supr. films including Blue Thunder, Buckeroo Bonzai, End of the Century, One From the Heart, Blade Runner, Dentsu, 1988, Micronauts, 1988; tech. dir. Witches of Eastwick, 1986, Willow, 1987, Who Framed Roger Rabbit, 1988; visual effects supr. (film) The Hunt for Red October, 1990; dir. visual effects (film) Showscan, 1991; effects supr. (comml.) Disney Coke. Recipient Acad. Tech. award pioneering work on input scanners, 1995, several effects awards as effects supr. Brit. Petroleum Elevator comml. Office: Indsl Light & Magic PO Box 2459 San Rafael CA 94912-2459

SQUIRES, WILLIAM RANDOLPH, III, lawyer; b. Providence, Sept. 6, 1947; s. William Randolph and Mary Louise (Gress) S.; m. Elisabeth Dale McAnulty, Sept. 23, 1984; children: Shannon, William R. IV, Mayre Elisabeth, James Robert. BA in Econs., Stanford U., 1969; JD, U. Tex., 1972. Bar: Wash. 1973, U.S. Dist. Ct. (we. dist.) Wash. 1973, U.S. Dist. Ct. (ea. dist.) Wash. 1976, U.S. Ct. Appeals (9th cir.) 1976, U.S. Supreme Ct. 1976, U.S. Claims Ct. 1982. Assoc. Oles, Morrison, Rinker, Stanslaw, & Ashbaugh, Seattle, 1973-78; ptnr., chmn. litigation group Davis Wright Tremaine (formerly Davis, Wright, Todd, Riese & Jones), Seattle, 1978—. Mem. ABA, Wash. State Bar Assn., Seattle-King County Bar Assn. Episcopalian. Clubs: Wash. Athletic, Rainier (Seattle). Home: 1015 E Prospect

St Seattle WA 98102-4319 Office: Davis Wright Tremaine 2600 Century Sq Seattle WA 98101

SQUYRES, BARBARA HOPKINS, nursing administrator; b. Lufkin, Tex., May 12, 1938; d. Jack Phil and Catherine Elizabeth (Burris) Taylor; divorced: children: Jack, Mike, Todd; m. John F. Squyres, Dec. 10, 1987. Diploma cum laude, Meth. Hosp., 1959; student, Tex. Woman's U. Dir. nurses Woodland Heights Gen. Hosp., Lufkin, The Pavilion, McKinney, Tex.; dir. oper. rm. Meml. City Med. Ctr., Houston, asst. administr. nursing svc. Mem. HONE, AONE, ANA, Tex. Nurses Assn., Assn. Operating Rm. Nurses (bd. dirs.). Home: 9731 Derrik Dr Houston TX 77080-1228

SREBNIK, HERBERT HARRY, retired anatomy educator; b. Berlin, Germany, Mar. 25, 1923; came to U.S., 1948; s. Max and Esther (Srebrnik) S.; m. Marilyn Lorraine Fine, Sept. 2, 1951; children: David Michael. BA, U. Calif. at Berkeley, 1950, MA, 1955, PhD, 1957. Instr. anatomy U. Calif., Berkeley, 1957-59, asst. prof., 1959-65, assoc. prof., 1965-71, prof., 1971—; chmn. dept. biology, 1987—. Contbr. articles on reproductive and devel. biology, teratology, nutrition, to profl. jours. With RAF, 1943-46, MTO. Mem. Am. Assn. Anatomists, AAAS, Am. Inst. Nutrition, The Endocrine Soc., Soc. Exptl. Biology and Medicine, Phi Beta Kappa. Home: 319 Vassar Ave Kensington CA 94708-1105 Office: U Calif Dept Molecular And Bio Berkeley CA 94720

SREENIVASAN, KATEPALLI RAJU, mechanical engineering educator; b. Kolar, India, Sept. 30, 1947; married 1980; 2 children. BE, Bangalore U., 1968; ME, Indian Inst. Sci., 1970, PhD in Aeronautical Engring., 1975. JRD Tata fellow Indian Inst. Sci., 1972-74, project asst., 1974-75; fellow U. Sydney, Australia, 1975, U. Newcastle, 1976-77; rsch. assoc. Johns Hopkins U., Balt., 1977-79; from asst. prof. to assoc. prof. Yale U., New Haven, 1982-85, prof. mech. engring., 1985—, Harold W. Cheel prof. mech. engring., 1988—, prof. physics, 1990—, prof. applied physics, 1993—; vis. scientist Indian Inst. Sci., 1979, vis. prof., 1982; vis. sci. DFVLR, Gottingen, Germany, 1983; vis. prof. Calif. Inst. Tech., Pasadena, 1986, Rockefeller U., 1989, Jawaharlal Nehru Ctr. Advancement Sci. Studies, 1992, Inst. Advanced Study, Princeton, 1995; chmn. Mech. Engring. Dept., 1987-92. Recipient Narayana Gold medal Indian Inst. Sci., 1975, Disting. Alumnus award, 1992; Humboldt Found. fellow, 1983, Guggenheim fellow, 1989. Fellow ASME, Am. Phys. Soc. (Otto Laporte award), AIAA (assoc.); mem. Am. Math. Soc., Conn. Acad. Sci. and Engring., Sigma Xi. Achievements include research in origin and dynamics of turbulence; control of turbulent flows; chaotic dynamics; fractals. Office: Yale Univ Dept Mech Engring M6 ML New Haven CT 06520

SRERE, BENSON M., communications company executive, consultant; b. Rock Island, Ill, Aug. 13, 1928; s. Jacob H. and Margaret (Weinstein) S.; m. Betty Ann Cerruti, June 20, 1957; children: David Benson, Anne Michele, Peter John. BA magna cum laude, U. So. Calif., 1949. Newsman U.P., Los Angeles, 1948-56; assoc. editor Good Housekeeping mag., N.Y.C., 1956-59; sr. editor Good Housekeeping mag., 1959-67, asst. mng. editor, dir. spl. publs. div., 1967-68, mng. editor, 1968-72, exec. editor, v.p., 1972-75, v.p., editorial dir., 1975-76; v.p., gen. mgr. King Features Syndicate, 1976-81; v.p. Hearst Metrotone News, 1976-81; exec. asst. to pres. Hearst Corp., 1981—, v.p., 1983-94; dir. Hearst/ABC Video Svcs., Hearst/ABC Viacom Entertainment Svcs., A&E Cable Network, Lifetime Cable Network. Trustee Optometric Center of N.Y. Found., 1978-79. Served with U.S. Army, 1950-52. Mem. Soc. Profl. Journalists, Phi Beta Kappa, Phi Kappa Phi, Phi Eta Sigma. Home: 11 Lafayette Ct Greenwich CT 06830

SRERE, PAUL A., biochemist, educator; b. Davenport, Iowa, Sept. 1, 1925. BS in Chemistry, U. Calif., L.A., 1947; PhD in Comparative Biochemistry, U. Calif., Berkeley, 1951. Biochemist Mass. Gen. Hosp., Boston, Mass., 1951-53; postdoctoral fellow Jane Coffin Fund for Med. Rsch. Yale U., 1953-54; post doctoral fellow Pub. Health Rsch. Inst. City of N.Y., 1954-55; postdoctoral fellow U. Munich, Germany, 1955-56; asst. prof. dept. biol. chemistry U. Mich., 1956-61, assoc. prof., 1961-63; rsch. biochemist U. Calif., 1963-66; prof. dept. of biochemistry, Southwestern Med. Ctr. U. Tex., Dallas, 1966—; chief pre-clin. sci. unit Dept. V.A. Med. Ctr., Dallas, 1966—; prof. dept. internal medicine, Southwestern Med. Ctr. U. Tex., Dallas, 1973—; rsch. career scientist Dept. V.A. Med. Ctr., Dallas, 1975—; vis. scientist U. Lund, Sweden, 1972, Inst. Enzymology, Budapest, 1982, Sheffield U., England, U. Basel Biozentrum, Switzerland, 1985, U. Lund, 1992; mem. numerous editorial bds. Editor: (with others) Regulation of Cardiac Metabolism, 1976, Metabolism, Clinical, and Experimental, 1976, Microenvironments and Metabolic Compartmentation, 1978, Current Topics in Cellular Regulation, 1981, UCLA Symposia on Molecular and Cellular Biology, 1990. Recipient William S. Middleton award, 1974, Wilford T. Doherty awd., Am. Chemical Soc., 1993. Mem. AAAS, AAUP, Am. Chemical Soc. (treas. 1979-81), Am. Soc. for Cell Biology, Am. Soc. Biological Chemists, Am. Soc. Bichemistry and Molecular Biology, Protein Soc. Achievements include research in stucture and function, both chemical and biological of the three citrate lyase enzymes. Office: VA Med Ctr U Tex Southwestern Med Ctr 4500 S Lancaster Rd Dallas TX 75216

SRINIVASACHARI, SAMAVEDAM, chemical engineer; b. Visakhapatnam, India, Oct. 5, 1926; came to U.S., 1958; s. Appalachari Srinivasa and Chudamani Samavedam; m. Vasanta S. Chari, Feb. 11, 1955; children: Sarita, Roger. M of Chem. Engring., NYU, 1959; PhD in Chem. Engring., Poly. Inst. Bklyn., 1967. Registered profl. engr., Pa. Teaching fellow Poly. Inst. Bklyn., 1960-63; sr. process devel. engr. Internat. Latex & Chemical, Dover, Del., 1966-73; prin. process engr. Catalytic, Inc., Phila., 1973-75; sr. process engr. Coalcon/Union Carbide, N.Y.C., 1976-77, Foster Wheeler Energy Corp., Livingston, N.J., 1977-82; chemical and environ. engr. Duro-Test Corp., Clifton, N.J., 1987-92, mgr. environ. engring., 1992—. Mem. AICE, Am. Chem. Soc. Democrat. Hindu. Achievements include design of chem. and petroleum plants, design of synthetic fuels plants; rsch. in environ. and regulatory problems of indsl. plants, environ. clean up of indsl. plant sites. Home: 12 The Ter Rutherford NJ 07070 Office: Duro-Test Corp 185 Scoles Ave Clifton NJ 07012-1125

SRINIVASAN, VENKATARAMAN, marketing and management educator; b. Pudukkottai, Tamil Nadu, India, June 5, 1944; came to U.S., 1968; s. Annaswamy and Jambagalakshmi Venkataraman; m. Sitalakshmi Subrahmanyam, June 30, 1972; children: Ramesh, Mahesh. B Tech., Indian Inst. Tech., Madras, India, 1966; MS, Carnegie-Mellon U., 1970, PhD, 1971. Asst. engr. Larsen & Toubro, Bombay, 1966-68; asst. prof. mgmt. and mktg. U. Rochester, N.Y., 1971-73, assoc. prof., 1973-74; assoc. prof. Stanford (Calif.) U., 1974-76, prof., 1976-82, dir. PhD program in bus., 1982-85, Ernest C. Arbuckle prof. mktg. and mgmt. sci., 1982—; mktg. area coord., 1976-78, 88-93; cons. in field. Mem. editorial bd. Jour. Mktg. Rsch., 1988—, Mktg. Sci., 1980—, Mgmt. Sci., 1974-91; contbr. articles to profl. jours. Mem. Am. Mktg. Assn., Inst. Ops. Rsch./Mgmt. Scis. Hindu. Avocation: classical music.

SROGE, MAXWELL HAROLD, marketing consultant, publishing executive; b. N.Y.C., Oct. 9, 1927; s. Albert N. and Goldie (Feldman) S.; children: Roberta, David, Marc, Sarah. Student, CCNY, 1946-48, NYU, 1948, New Sch. Social Research, 1948. Dir. sales Bell & Howell Co., Chgo., 1950-60; dir. prodn. planning Bell & Howell Co., 1961-62, pres. Robert Maxwell div., 1962-63; pres. Maxwell Sroge Co., Inc., Chgo., 1965—; Telespond, Inc., Chgo., 1971—; pres. Maxwell Sroge Pub., Inc., Chgo., 1976—; chmn. JUF Comm. Industry, 1974-75, Transatlantic Catalogue Corp.; chmn. Direct Mktg. Svcs. Inc.; pub. Non-Store Mktg. Report, Inside Leading Mail Order Houses, Mail Order Industry Ann. Report, Best in Catalogs, How to Create Successful Catalogs, The Catalog Marketer, 101 Ideas for More Profitable Catalogs; bd. dirs. Tools Direct; chmn. Telespond Inc. Mem. New Ill. Com., 1965; speakers bur. Percy for Gov., 1964, Citizens for Percy, 1972; co-chmn. Percy for Pres. Exploratory Com., 1974; mem. regional adv. bd. Nat. Jewish Hosp., 1974-75; mem. devel. com. WTTW-Channel 11, 1975-76, NCCJ; founder Save the Tarryall, Inc., 1982. Served with USNR, World War II. Mem. Direct Mail Mktg. Assn. (Gold Mail Box award 1978, Internat. Gold Carrier Pigeon award 1979), Nat. Retail Merchants Assn., Retail Advt. Conf., World Futures Soc. *To succeed man must stretch himself, his mind, his heart, his grasp. Our capabilities far exceed our accomplishments. Within each of us there is the potential for greatness if we will dig deep enough to find it. Those of us who have been blessed to have discovered success owe a*

special responsibility to the world around us to make it a better place for all men to live.

SROKA, JOHN WALTER, trade association executive; b. Perth Amboy, N.J., July 24, 1946; s. John and Mary (Teliszewski) S.; m. Paula J. Devitt, Aug. 17, 1968; children: Amanda, Alexandra. BA in Psychology, Fairleigh Dickinson U., 1968, postgrad., 1968-69; postgrad. in law, Am. U., 1972-73. Asst. exec. dir. Associated Gen. Contractors of Am., Washington, 1973-87; exec. v.p. Nat. Assn. Sheet Metal and Air Conditioning Contractors, Chantilly, Va., 1987—. Sgt. U.S. Army, 1969-71. Mem. Am. Soc. Assn. Execs. Roman Catholic. Office: SMACNA 4201 Lafayette Center Dr Chantilly VA 22021-1209

STAAB, THOMAS ROBERT, textile company financial executive; b. Beaver Falls, Pa., Apr. 23, 1942; s. Henry Louis and Margaret Constance (Clarke) S.; m. Angela Maria Simon, Aug. 5, 1965; children: Thomas II, Jennifer, Thea. BBA, U. Pitts., 1964, MBA, 1965. CPA, Pa. Sr. audit mgr. Price Waterhouse & Co., Pitts., 1970-77; practice fellow Fin. Acctg. Standards Bd., Stamford, Conn., 1978-80; dir. corp. acctg. and taxes Fieldcrest Cannon Inc., Eden, N.C., 1981-85, asst. contr., 1985-86, contr., 1986-92, v.p. fin., 1992-93; CFO, 1994—; mem. adv. bd. Arkwright Mut. Ins. Co. Served to lt. USN, 1966-70. Mem. Am. Inst. CPA's, Pa. Inst. CPA's, N.C. Textile Mfrs. Assn., Am. Textile Mfrs. Inst. Republican. Roman Catholic. Avocation: farming. Home: 3726 Nc # 65 Reidsville NC 27320 Office: Fieldcrest Cannon Inc 326 E Stadium Dr Eden NC 27288

STAAR, RICHARD FELIX, political scientist; b. Warsaw, Poland, Jan. 10, 1923; s. Alfred and Agnes (Gradalska) S.; m. Jadwiga Maria Ochota, Mar. 28, 1950; children: Monica, Christina. B.A., Dickinson Coll., 1948; M.A. (Univ. fellow), Yale, 1949; Ph.D., U. Mich., 1954. Research analyst U.S. Dept. State, Washington, 1951-54; prof. polit. sci. Ark. State Coll., Jonesboro, 1957-58; lectr. overseas program U. Md., Munich, Germany, 1958-59; assoc. prof. to prof., chmn. dept. polit. sci. Emory U., 1959-69; sr. fellow Hoover Instn. on War, Revolution and Peace at Stanford, 1969—, prin. assoc. dir., 1969-81, dir. internat. studies program, 1975-81, 85-91; U.S. ambassador to Mut. and Balanced Force Reductions Negotiations, Vienna, 1981-83; Nimitz chair Naval War Coll., 1963-64; prof. polit. affairs Nat. War Coll., 1967-69; cons. Office Sec. Def., 1969-73; adj. prof. USMC Command and Staff Coll., 1971-81; sr. advisor to Comdg. Officer Politico-Mil. Affairs USNR, Treasure Island, Calif., 1975-81; disting. vis. prof. nat. security affairs Naval Postgrad. Sch., 1979; cons. U.S. ACDA, 1983-86, Sandia Nat. Labs., 1991—; mem. bd. visitors Def. Language Inst., 1988—. Author: Poland, 1944-62, The Sovietization of a Captive People, 1962, reprinted, 1975, Communist Regimes in Eastern Europe, 5th edit., 1988, USSR Foreign Policies After Detente, 1985, rev. edit., 1987, Foreign Policies of the Soviet Union, 1991; co-author; Soviet Military Policies Since World War II, 1986; contbg. author and editor: Aspects of Modern Communism, 1968; editor: Yearbook on International Communist Affairs, 1969-91, Arms Control: Myth Versus Reality, 1984, Public Diplomacy: USA Versus USSR, 1986, Future Information Revolution in the USSR, 1988, United States - East European Relations in the 1990's, 1989, East-Central Europe and the USSR, 1991, Transition to Democracy in Poland, 1993; mem. editorial bd. Current History, Orbis, Strategic Rev., Mediterranean Quar.; contbr. articles to profl. jours. Asst. dist. commr. Quapaw Area council Boy Scouts Am., 1954-57; active Profs. for Goldwater, 1964; mem. Reagan for Pres. Com., 1980; dir. for nat. security affairs Office of Pres.-Elect, 1980-81; mem. Academicians for Reagan, 1984. Served to col. USMCR, 1960-83. Decorated Legion of Merit. Mem. Am. Polit. Sci. Assn., Internat. Studies Assn., Am. Assn. Advancement Slavic Studies, Phi Beta Kappa, Kappa Sigma. Republican. Methodist. Home: 36 Peter Coutts Cir Stanford CA 94305-2503 Office: Hoover Instn Stanford CA 94305-6010

STAATS, DEAN ROY, retired reinsurance executive; b. Somerville, N.J., Sept. 18, 1924; s. Roy Theodore and Maude Ellen (Rhodes) S.; m. Marilyn Ann Hockenbury, 1947 (div. 1956; 1 child, Barry Clinton; m. Marilyn Lee Truitt, Dec. 16, 1961. B.Sc., Brown U., 1946, M.A., 1948. Asst. actuary N.Am. Reassurance Co., N.Y.C., 1959-67, data processing officer, 1967-69, v.p., actuary, 1969-71, sr. v.p., 1971-84, exec. v.p., 1984-86; pres., dir. NARe Life Mgmt. Co., N.Y.C., 1985-86; rep. Life Ins. Guaranty Corp, 1977-86; U.S. mgr. Can. Reassurance Co., 1984-86; cons. actuary, 1986-89. Served to lt. (j.g.), USN, 1943-46, PTO. Fellow Soc. Actuaries; mem. Am. Acad. Actuaries N.Y. Jr. Actuaries Club (pres. 1960-61), Soc. Actuaries (reins. adminstrn. com. 1984-85). Republican. Clubs: Anchor and Saber (pres. 1959-60). Avocations: art collectibles; tennis; gardening; travel. Home and Office: 234 Hansell Rd Newtown Square PA 19073-2509

STAATS, ELMER BOYD, foundation executive, former government official; b. Richfield, Kans., June 6, 1914; s. Wesley F. and Maude (Goodall) S.; m. Margaret S. Rich, Sept. 14, 1940; children: David Rich, Deborah Rich Staats Sanders, Catharine Rich Staats Taubman. AB, McPherson (Kans.) Coll., 1935, LLD (hon.), 1966; MA, U. Kans., 1936; PhD, U. Minn., 1939; D. in Pub. Service (hon.), George Washington U., 1971; D. in Adminstrn. (hon.), U. S.D., 1973; LLD (hon.), Duke U., 1975, Nova U., 1976, U. Pa., 1981, Lycoming Coll., 1982; LHD (hon.), Ohio State U., 1982. Research asst. Kans. Legis. Council, 1936; teaching asst. U. Minn., 1936-38; staff Pub. Adminstrn. Service, Chgo., 1937-38; staff mem. U.S. Bur. Budget, Exec. Office Pres., 1939-47, asst. to dir., 1947, asst. dir. charge legis. reference, 1947-49, exec. asst. dir., 1949-50, dep. dir., 1950-53, 58-66; comptroller gen. U.S. Washington, 1966-81; pres. Harry S. Truman Scholarship Found., 1981-84, chmn., 1984—; bd. dirs. rsch. dir. Marshall Field & Co., Chgo., 1953; exec. dir. ops. coord. bd., Nat. Security Coun., 1953-58; professorial lectr. pub. adminstrn. George Washington U., 1944-49; mem. bd. visitors Nat. Def. U., 1981-90; mem. vis. com. John F. Kennedy Sch. Govt., Harvard U., 1974-80, Grad. Sch. Mgmt., UCLA, 1976—; mem. Com. on Pub. Policy Studies U. Chgo., 1976—; trustee Nat. Inst. Pub. Affairs, 1969-77; mem. Conf. Bd., 1966; mem. dir.'s adv. coun. Met. Life Ins. Co., 1985-94, emeritus mem., 1994—; dir. Computer Data Systems, Inc., 1981—; bd. advisors Alexander Proudfoot & Co., 1981-85; mem. pub. rev. bd. Arthur Andersen & Co., 1981-91; bd. dirs. Air Products and Chems., 1981-85, Met. Life Ins. Co., 1981-85, Nat. Intergroup Inc. (formerly Nat. Steel Corp.), 1981-86; chmn. congl. panel on social security orgn., 1983-84; mem. nat. commn. on pub. svc., 1987-90; mem. commn. to rev. honor code of West Point U.S. Mil. Acad., 1988-89; mem. Govt. Acctg. Standards Bd., 1984-90; chmn. Fed. Acctg. Standards Adv. Bd., 1991—. Author: Personnel Standards in the Social Security Program, 1939; contbr. to: Am. Polit. Sci. Rev. Trustee Am. U., 1969-80; trustee McPherson Coll., 1969-79, mem. bd. trustees and research and policy com., com. for econ. devel., 1981—; bd. govs. Internat. Orgn. of Supreme Audit Instns., 1969-80; trustee Kerr Found., 1981—; bd. dirs. George C. Marshall Found., 1984—. Recipient Rockefeller Pub. Service award, 1961, Alumni achievement award U. Minn., 1964, Disting. Service citation U. Kans., 1966, Warner D. Stockberger Achievement award, 1973, Abraham O. Smoot Pub. Service award Brigham Young U., 1975, Person of Yr. award Washington chpt. Inst. Internal Auditors, 1975, Thurston award Inst. Internal Auditors, 1988, medal of honor Am. Inst. CPAs, 1980, Engr. of Yr. award San Fernando Valley Engrs. Council, 1980, Presdl. Citizens medal, 1981, Hubert Humphrey medal, 1981, Pub. Service Achievement award Common Cause, 1981; fed. exec. award Evaluation Research Soc., 1980; named to Acctg. Hall of Fame, 1981; fellow Brookings Instn., 1938-39. Mem. Nat. Acad. Pub. Adminstrn., Assn. Govt. Accountants, Am. Acad. Polit. and Social Sci. (dir. 1966—), Am. Soc. Public Adminstrn. (pres. Washington 1948-49, nat. coun. 1958-65, nat. pres. 1961-62), Am. Mgmt. Assns. (gen. mgmt. coun. 1966-85, trustee 1981-85), Cosmos Club (Washington), Chevy Chase (Md.), Phi Beta Kappa, Pi Sigma Alpha, Beta Gamma Sigma, Alpha Kappa Psi. Methodist. Office: Harry S Truman Scholarship Found 712 Jackson Pl NW Washington DC 20006-4901

STABA, EMIL JOHN, pharmacognosy and medicinal chemistry educator; b. N.Y.C., May 16, 1928; s. Frank and Marianna T. (Mack) P.; m. Joyce Elizabeth Ellert, June 19, 1954; children—Marianna, Joanna, Sarah Jane, John, Mark. B.S. cum laude, St. John's U., 1952; M.S., Duquesne U., 1954; Ph.D., U. Conn., 1957. Asst. prof. U. Nebr., 1957-60, prof., chmn. dept., 1968; prof. dept. pharmacognosy U. Minn., 1968—; cons. econ. plants and plant tissue culture U.S. Army Q.M.C.; cons. on drug plants and plant tissue culture NASA; cons. N.C.I. at N.I.H. on anti-cancer natural product production, 1991-92; cons. Govt. of Korea, food and pharm. industry; cons. NSF-Egyptian Acad. Sci. Rsch. Tech., 1984—; internat. vis. prof. Dalhousie

U., 1983; cons. on Indonesia biotech. devel. World Bank-Midwestern Univs. Consortium for Internat. Activities, 1985-90, Thailand, 1989; mem. natural products revision com. U.S. Pharmacopeia, 1980—; mem. adv. coun. on life scis. NASA, 1984-87. Mem. editorial bd.: Jour. Plant Cell, Tissue and Organ Culture, 1980-86, plant cellular and developmental biology sect. of In Vitro, 1988—. Served with USNR, 1945-46, PTO. Sr. fgn. fellow NSF, Poland, 1969; Fulbright fellow, Germany, 1970; Coun. Sci. and Indsl. Rsch.-NSF fellow, India, 1973, Pakistani Coun. Sci. and Indsl. Rsch.-NSF fellow, Pakistan, 1978; fellow U.K. Sci. Engring. Rsch. Coun., 1989. Fellow AAAS; mem. Am. Soc. Pharmacognosy (pres. 1971-72), Am. Assn. Colls. Pharmacy (chmn. tchrs. sect. 1972-73, dir. 1976-77), Tissue Culture Assn. (pres. plant sect. 1972-74), Am. Pharm. Assn. and Acad. (chmn. pharmacognosy and nat. products 1977), Soc. Econ. Botany, Am. Soc. Pharmacognosy. Home: 2840 Stinson Blvd Minneapolis MN 55418-3127 Office: U Minn Coll Pharmacy Unit F-9106 Minneapolis MN 55455

STABELL, WALTER W., chemicals executive; b. 1939. BA in Bus, Drexel U., 1962. With Rohm Haas Tex. Inc., Deer Park, Tex., 1962—, now sec., treas., 1972—. Office: Rohm Haas Texas Inc 6600 La Porte Rd Deer Park TX 77536•

STABENAU, JAMES RAYMOND, research psychiatrist, educator; b. Milw., May 24, 1930; s. Walter Frederick and Ruth Emile (Jung) S.; m. Barbara Louise Burris, Oct. 3, 1981; children: Victoria Ruth, Erik Fowler. BS magna cum laude, Marquette U., 1952, MD cum laude, 1955; grad., Washington Psychoanalytic Inst. Diplomate: Am. Bd. Neurology and Psychiatry. Intern Johns Hopkins Hosp., 1955-56; clin. assoc. lab. chem. pharmacology Nat. Cancer Inst., NIH, 1956-58; asst., asso. and chief resident psychiatry U. Rochester Sch. Medicine and Dentistry, Strong Meml. Hosp., 1958-61; research psychiatrist sect. twin and sibling studies adult psychiatry br., clin. investigations NIMH, NIH, 1961-69; research cons. Washington Sch. Psychiatry, 1964-69; prof., chmn. dept. psychiatry U. Conn., Hartford, 1969-73; dir. research U. Conn., 1973-91, prof. emeritus sch. medicine; med. dir. Psych West Corp., Sacramento, 1991; sec. Psych West Med. Group Inc., 1993—; prof. sch. medicine U. Calif. Davis; vis. scientist Genetics Unit, Inst. Psychiatry, U. London, 1980-81. Contbr. articles to med. jours. Recipient Eben J. Carey Anatomy award Marquette U. Sch. Medicine, 1952, Lakeside prize, 1955, Lt. William Milman award, 1955; scholar in residence Rockefeller Found., Bellagio, Italy, 1978. Fellow Am. Psychiat. Assn.; mem. Conn. Psychiat. Soc., Washington Artists, Alpha Omega Alpha (v.p. Marquette U. chpt. 1955), Epsilon Phi Chi. Home: 14609 Guadalupe Dr Rancho Murieta CA 95683 Office: 1792 Tribute Rd Ste 400 Sacramento CA 95815

STABILE, BENEDICT LOUIS, retired academic administrator, retired coast guard officer; b. Bklyn., Dec. 13, 1927; s. Domenic and Vita (Grillo) S.; m. Barbara Adele Thompson, June 10, 1951; children: Janet T., Bennett R., Gale V., Roderick T. BS, USCG Acad., 1950; naval engring. degree, MIT, 1956. Commd. USCG, 1950, advanced through grades to vice admiral; served aboard USCG cutters Eastwind, Unimak, Castle Rock, Reliance & Mellon; comdg. officer USCG Yard, Curtis Bay, Md., 1975-77; chief engr. USCG, Washington, 1977-79; dist. comdr. USCG (7th Dist.), Miami, Fla., 1979-82; vice comdt. USCG, Washington, 1982-86; ret. USCG, 1986; coll. pres. Webb Inst. Naval Architecture, Glen Cove, N.Y., 1986-90, ret., 1990. Decorated Meritorious Service medal (3), D.S.M. (2), Legion of Merit, Order of Merit of Italian Republic. Mem. Am. Soc. Naval Engrs., Soc. Naval Architects and Marine Engrs.

STABLER, DONALD BILLMAN, business executive; b. Williamsport, Pa., Dec. 23, 1908; s. George William and Etta Mae (Billman) S.; m. Dorothy Louise Witwer, Aug. 10, 1952; 1 dau., Beverly Anne. B.S., Lehigh U., 1930, M.S., 1932, LL.D., 1974; LL.D., Dickinson Law Sch., 1981. Owner Donald B. Stabler (Contractor), Harrisburg, Pa., 1940-55; chmn. bd., chief exec. officer Stabler Cos. Inc., 1955-91, Stabler Constrn. Co., 1955-91, Protection Services Inc., 1955—, State Aggregates Inc., DBS Transit, Inc., 1964—, Stabler Devel. Co., Harrisburg, Pa., 1983—, Stabler Land Co., Harrisburg, Pa., 1984—, Ea. Industries, Inc., Elco-Hausman Constrn. Corp., 1976—, The Center Valley (Pa.) Club Inc., 1992—, Work Area Protection Corp., St. Charles, Ill., 1986—, Precision Solar Controls Inc., Garland, Tex., 1990—; bd. dirs. Millers Mut. Ins. Co., Harrisburg., Road Info. Program, Washington, pres., 1970-74, chmn. bd., 1975-78, chmn. emeritus, 1979—. Bd. dirs. Harrisburg Polyclinic Med. Center, Miami Heart Rsch. Inst.; trustee Lehigh U. Recipient silver hard hat award Constrn. Writers Assn., 1973, Humanitarian award Lions, 1973, Nat. Automobiler Dealers award, 1978, Man & Boy award Boys' Club, 1984, Man of Yr. March of Dimes, 1994, real estate award, 1994, rebuilding Am. award CIT, 1985, master entrepreneur of yr. award Cen. Pa. 1994; named man of yr. Pa. Hwy. Info. Assn., 1992. Mem. Am. Rd. and Transp. Builders Assn. (dir., ARBA award 1974, Nello L. Teer, Jr. award 1994), Associated Pa. Constructors (dir., adv. bd., pres. 1949-50), Nat. Asphalt Pavement Assn., Pa. Asphalt Pavement Assn., U.S. C. of C., Pa. C. of C., Harrisburg C. of C. (adm. 1960), Am. Soc. Hwy. Engrs. (Industry Man of Year 1975), Harrisburg Builders Exchange, Nat. Soc. Profl. Engrs., Pa. Soc. Profl. Engrs. (Engr. of Yr. Harrisburg chpt. 1981), Com. of 100 Miami Beach (dir.), Pa. Soc. N.Y., Lehigh U. Alumni Assn. (pres. 1965-66, L-in-Life award 1972), Navy League, Chi Epsilon, Pi Delta Epsilon. Presbyterian. Clubs: Tall Cedars; Surf (Miami Beach) (pres. 1974-76, chmn. bd. of govs. 1976-78, bd. govs. 1974—); Bal Harbour (Miami); Harrisburg Country (Harrisburg); Saucon Valley Country (Bethlehem, Pa.). Lodges: Masons, Shriners, Jesters, Elks, Rotary. Home: Stray Winds Farm 4001 Mcintosh Rd Harrisburg PA 17112-1927 also: 236 Bal Bay Dr Bal Harbour FL 33154-1313 Office: 635 Lucknow Rd Harrisburg PA 17110-1644

STABLER, LEWIS VASTINE, JR., lawyer; b. Greenville, Ala., Nov. 5, 1936; s. Lewis Vastine and Dorothy Daisy S.; m. Monteray Scott, Sept. 5, 1958; children: Dorothy Monteray, Andrew Vastine, Monteray Scott, Margaret Langston. B.A., Vanderbilt U., 1958; J.D. with distinction, U. Mich., 1961. Bar: Ala. 1961. Assoc. firm Cabaniss & Johnston, Birmingham, Ala., 1961-67; assoc. prof. law U. Ala., 1967-70; ptnr. Cabaniss, Johnston, Gardner, Dumas & O'Neal (and predecessor firms), Birmingham, 1970-91, Walston, Stabler, Wells, Anderson and Bains, Birmingham, 1991—; mem. com. of 100 Candler Sch. Theology, Emory U. Bd. editors: Mich. Law Rev, 1960-61. Fellow Am. Bar Found.; mem. Am. Law Inst., Ala. Law Inst. (mem. council, dir. 1968-70), ABA, Ala. Bar Assn., Birmingham Bar Assn., Am. Judicature Soc., Am. Assn. Railroad Trial Counsel, Order of Coif. Methodist (cert. lay speaker). Clubs: Country of Birmingham, Rotary. Home: 3538 Victoria Rd Birmingham AL 35223-1404 Office: Walston Stabler Wells Anderson & Bains PO Box 83064 Birmingham AL 35283-0642

STACEY, KATHLEEN MARY, advertising and public relations executive; b. Boston, Jan. 7, 1951; d. John Robert and Catherine Mary (Gray) Young; m. Gary Ronald Stacey, Feb. 10, 1984. BA, Northeastern U., Boston, 1974. Asst. producer WGBH-TV, Boston, 1971-73; asst. editor Arlington (Mass.) Advocate Century Publs., 1973-75; mng. editor New England Pubs., Bradford, Vt., 1975-76; free-lance writer Boston, 1976-81; copywriter Berenson & Isham, Boston, 1981-82; assoc. creative dir. The Interface Group, Needham, Mass., 1983-84; pres. Young Stacey Assocs., Marshfield Hills, Mass., 1984—; pres. West End Designs, Marshfield Hills, Mass., 1992—. Scituate, Mass., 1992—; cons. Copperstone's Ltd., Boston, Circle Floors, Haufler Associates, West End CArpets, Monadnock Music. Chair Mass. Radio Reading Day, 1992, Scituate Heritage Days Festival, 1993-94, Festival of Arts, 1994. Mem. North River Arts Soc. (bd. dirs. 1989-84, treas. 1994), Scituate C. of C. (bd. dirs. 1992-95, treas. 1994), Talking Info. Ctr. (bd. dirs. 1992). Democrat. Roman Catholic. Avocations: video, photography. Home: 51 Hampstead Way Marshfield MA 02050-6237 Office: Young Stacey Assocs Inc Box 141 Marshfield Hills MA 02051-0141

STACEY, WESTON MONROE, JR., nuclear engineer, educator; b. Birmingham, Ala., July 23, 1937; s. Weston Monroe and Dorothy (Todd) S.; m. Penny Smith; children: Helen Lee, Weston Monroe III, Lucia Katherine. BS in Physics, Ga. Tech., 1969, MS in Nuclear Sci., 1963; PhD in Nuclear Engring., MIT, 1966. Nuclear engr. Knolls Atomic Power Lab., Schenectady, N.Y., 1962-64, 66-69, Argonne Nat. Lab., Chgo., 1969-77; Callaway Regents prof. Ga. Inst. Tech., Atlanta, 1977—. Author 5 books; contbr. more than 150 articles to profl. jours. 1st lt. USMC, 1959-61. Recipient Cert. Appreciation Dept. Energy, Disting. Assoc. award Dept.

Energy, 1990. Fellow Am. Phys. Soc., Am. Nuclear Soc. (bd. dirs. 1974-77, Outstanding Achievement award); mem. AAAS, Soc. Engr. Educators. Office: Ga Inst Tech Nuclear Engring Dept 0225 Atlanta GA 30332

STACHACZ, JOHN CHARLES, librarian; b. Cleve., Nov. 2, 1952; s. Charles Stanley and Caroline (Brobrowski) S.; m. Melissa Finney, Sept. 23, 1978; 1 child, Jennifer Elizabeth. BA, U. N.Mex., 1975; MA in Geography, U. Ky., 1977, MSLS, 1978. Serials libr. Washburn U, Topeka, 1978-81; libr. Dickinson Coll., Carlisle, Pa., 1981—. Rev. to book revs.; contbr. articles to profl. jours. Mem. ALA, Assn. Am. Geographers, Assn. Coll. and Rsch. Librs. Office: Dickinson Coll Carlisle PA 17013-2896

STACHO, ZOLTAN ALADAR, construction and engineering company executive; b. Budapest, Hungary, Mar. 16, 1930; came to U.S., 1957; s. Aladar and Elizabeth (Balazs) S.; m. Maria E. Belatini, July 4, 1951; children: Dorika, Carla. MSCE, U. Tech. and Ec. Sci., Budapest, 1952. Registered profl. engr. Colo., Calif., Mass., Mich., Ga., N.Y., Pa. Chief engr. U.S. Army, Air Force Exchange, 1963-65; project mgr. PBQ&D, San Francisco, Boston, 1965-70; projects mgr. Kaiser Engrs., Inc., Oakland, Calif., 1970-78, v.p., 1978-84, group v.p., 1984-86, exec. v.p., 1986-89, also bd. dirs.; sr. v.p., mgr. corp. ops. svcs. Holmes and Narver, Orange, Calif., 1989-90; with Bechtel Nat., Inc., San Francisco 1990-91; pres. Holmes and Narver, Inc., Orange, Calif., 1991—. Contbr. articles to profl. jours. Fellow ASCE; mem. Project Mgmt. Inst. Roman Catholic. Home: 210 Lille Ln Apt 214 Newport Beach CA 92663-2694 Office: Holmes & Narver Inc 999 Town Country Rd Orange CA 92668

STACHOWSKI, WILLIAM T., state senator; b. Buffalo, Feb. 14, 1949; s. Stanley J. and Pearl (Wojcik) S. BA in Polit. Sci., U. Coll. Holy Cross, 1972. Legislator Erie County Legislature, Buffalo, 1974-81; senator N.Y. State Legislature, Albany, 1981—; mem. U.S. Rte. 19 Assn., Western N.Y., 1982—, U.S. Rte. 62 Assn., Western N.Y., 1985—, City of Buffalo Auditorium Task Force. Recipient Friend of Law Enforcement award N.Y. State Sheriffs, 1990, Fellow Medal Hilbert Coll., 1993. Mem. Erie County Dem. Party, 1967—. Roman Catholic. Avocations: sports. Home: 2030 Clinton St Buffalo NY 14206-3312 Office: NY State Senate State Capital Albany NY 12207

STACK, EDWARD WILLIAM, business management and foundation executive; b. Rockville Centre, N.Y., Feb. 1, 1935; s. Edward Henry and Helen Margaret (Leitner) S.; m. Christina Carol Hunt, Aug. 19, 1967; children: Amy Alison, Kimberly Anne, Suzanne Gail. BBA, Pace U., 1956; LLD (hon.), Hartwick Coll., 1982; LHD (hon.), Pace U., 1991, L.I. U., 1994. Sec., dir. Clark Estates, Inc., fin. and bus. mgmt., N.Y.C., 1956-90, pres., bd. dirs., 1990—; v.p., dir. Leatherstocking Corp., hotels and real estate, Cooperstown, N.Y., 1961-92, pres., bd. dirs., 1992—; sec.-treas., dir. The New Republic, Inc., mag., Washington, 1974—; regional adv. bd. Chem. Banking Corp., N.Y.C., 1993—. Sec., trustee N.Y. State Hist. Assn., Cooperstown, 1961—; vice chmn., trustee Mary Imogene Bassett Hosp., 1961—; sec. Nat. Baseball Hall of Fame and Mus., Inc., Cooperstown, 1961-77, pres., chmn., 1977-93, chmn., 1993—; v.p. bd. dirs. Farmers' Mus., Inc., Cooperstown, 1964—; sec. Clark Found., N.Y.C., 1963-90, v.p., bd. dirs., 1990—; v.p., bd. dirs. Nourse Found., N.Y.C., 1976—; trustee Glimmerglass Opera, Cooperstown, Park Ave. Meth. Ch. Trust Fund, Baseball Am. Found., Inc.; trustee, treas. Bethany Deaconess Soc., Bklyn.; bd. dirs. United Meth. City Soc. of Meth. Ch., N.Y.C.; adv. coun. Salvation Army Nassau County. Mem. Downtown Assn. (N.Y.C.), Mohican Club (Cooperstown, N.Y.). Republican. Home: 25 Waverly St Glen Head NY 11545-1004 Office: 30 Wall St New York NY 10005-2201

STACK, GEOFFREY LAWRENCE, real estate developer; b. Trinidad, British West Indies, Sept. 16, 1943; s. Gerald Francis and V. Louise (Bell) S.; m. Victoria Hammack, 1970 (div. 1986); 1 child, Kathryn; m. Nancy J. Haarer, Apr. 19, 1987; children: Alexandra, Natalie. Ba., Georgetown U., 1965; MBA, U. Pa., 1972. Dir. acquisitions J.H. Snyder Co., L.A., 1972-75; from project mgr. to exec. v.p. Richards West, Newport Beach, Calif., 1975-77; pres. Regis Homes Corp., Newport Beach, 1977-93; mng. dir. Sares-Regis Group, Irvine, Calif., 1993—; bd. dirs. WJS, Inc., Newport Beach, 1988—, Arral & Ptnrs., Hong Kong, 1981—; Calif. Housing Coun., Sacramento, 1986—. Mem. adv. bd. Coro So. Calif., Santa Ana, 1991—; bd. regents Franciscan Sch. of Theology, Berkeley, Calif., 1991—; bd. advisors Grad. Sch. Bus., U. Calif., Irvine, 1992. Capt. USMC, 1967-70. Decorated 2 Bronze Stars, 21 Air medals, Navy Commendation medal, Purple Heart. Mem. Young Pres. Orgn., Big Canyon Country Club, Pacific Club, Ctr. Club. Democrat. Roman Catholic. Office: Sares Regis Group 18802 Bardeen Ave Irvine CA 92715-1521

STACK, GEORGE JOSEPH, philosophy educator; b. N.Y.C.; s. George Francis and Elizabeth (Sullivan) S. m. Claire Avena, Sept. 9, 1962 (dec.); children: Diane Joan, Christopher George. B.A., Pace U., 1960; M.A., Pa. State U., 1962, Ph.D., 1964. Instr. humanities Pa. State U., 1962-63; instr. philosophy L.I. U., 1963-64, asst. prof., 1964-67; asst. prof. SUNY, Brockport, 1967-68; assoc. prof. SUNY, 1968-70, prof., chmn., 1970-77, prof., 1977—, also advisor Center for Philosophic Exchange, 1970-82; cons. to Choice. Author: Berkeley's Analysis of Perception, 1970, 2d edit., 1992, On Kierkegaard: Philosophical Fragments, 1976, Kierkegaard's Existential Ethics, 1977, 2d edit., 1992, Japanese transl., 1985, Sartre's Philosophy of Social Existence, 1978, reprinted 1992, Lange and Nietzsche, 1983; contbg. author: Nietzsche and Modern German Thought, 1991, Nietzsche and Emerson, 1992, Nietzsche: Man, Knowledge, Will to Power, 1994; editorial advisor: Folia Humanistica, Filosofia Oggi; contbr. over 180 philos. articles to profl. jours. NDEA fellow, 1960-63; NEA fellow, 1969. Mem. United Univ. Profls. Office: SUNY Dept Philosophy Brockport NY 14420

STACK, J. WILLIAM, JR., management consultant; b. Lansing, Mich., July 13, 1918; s. Joseph William and Helen (Dodge) S.; m. Wolcott Rorick, Sept. 25, 1948; children: Christopher D., Nathan S., Joseph W., David R., Peter S. B.A., Yale U., 1940. With Gen. Motors Corp, 1945-57; dir. mktg. Gen. Motors Corp (AC Electronics div.), 1955-57; v.p. Kurth Malting Co., Milw., 1957-59; gen. sales mgr. Massey Ferguson, Inc., Toronto, Can., 1960-62; pres., founder Stancor Ltd., Toronto, 1963-68; pres. William Stack Assocs. Inc., N.Y.C., 1968—; mem. Navy and Marine Corps Acquisition Rev. Com., 1974-75. Served to lt. comdr. USNR, 1940-45. Mem. Yale Club of N.Y.C., New Canaan Country Club. Republican. Episcopalian. Home: 31 Lakeview Ave New Canaan CT 06840-5947 Office: Stack Assocs 31 Lakeview Ave New Canaan CT 06840-5947

STACK, JOHN WALLACE, lawyer; b. Chgo., May 30, 1937; s. Wallace and Irma Evelyn (Anderson) S.; m. Della Rae Melin, Feb. 15, 1975; children: James Randolph, Linnea Claire, Theodore. BBA, U. Wis., 1960; JD, U. Calif., Berkeley, 1963. Bar: Ill. 1963, D.C. 1963, U.S. C. Appeals (7th cir.) 1963, U.S. Supreme Ct. 1972. Assoc. Pattishall, McAuliffe & Hofstetter, Chgo., 1963-64; assoc. Winston & Strawn, Chgo., 1964-70, ptnr., 1970—. Contbg. editor U. Calif. Law Rev., 1963. Mem. ABA (antitrust and corp., banking and bus. law sects.), W Club of U. Wis. (Madison), Order of Coif, Phi Delta Phi, Beta Gamma Sigma. Republican. Lutheran. Avocations: sports, gardening, reading. Home: 2906 Lincoln St Evanston IL 60201-2047 Office: Winston & Strawn 35 W Wacker Dr Chicago IL 60601-1614

STACK, MAURICE DANIEL, retired insurance company executive; b. N.Y.C., Dec. 15, 1917; s. Maurice E. and Margaret (Brooks) S.; m. Catherine T. O'Connor, Nov. 25, 1943; children: Mary Jane, Eileen, Peter, Clare. Student, U. Notre Dame, 1935-36; B.B.A., Manhattan Coll., 1939; M.B.A., Harvard, 1941. Investment analyst Carnegie Corp., N.Y.C., 1946-48; adminstrv. asst. Tchrs. Ins. & Annuity Assn., 1948-49; investment analyst First Nat. Bank N.Y., 1949-54; fin. sec. Atlantic Mut. Ins. Co., N.Y.C., 1954-56; v.p. Atlantic Mut. Ins. Co., 1957-60, fin. v.p., trustee, 1961-66, chmn. fin. com. 1966-83; trustee emeritus Atlantic Mutual Ins. Co. Trustee emeritus, adviser St. Vincent's Hosp.; trustee emeritus YWCA. Served to maj. C.E., AUS, 1941-46. Mem. N.Y. Soc. Security Analysts, Soc. for Propagation of the Faith (dir.). Clubs: K.M. (N.Y.C.), Harvard (N.Y.C.). Home: 85 Lynbrook Ave Point Lookout NY 11569-0095

STACK, MAY ELIZABETH, library director; b. Jackson, Miss., Nov. 10, 1940; d. James William and Irene Thelma (Baldwin) Garrett; m. Richard

Gardiner, Apr. 15, 1962; children: Elinor, Harley David. BS, Miss. State Coll. for Women, 1962; MBA, Western New Eng. Coll., 1981; MLS, So. Conn. State U., 1989. Clk. Western New Eng. Coll., Springfield, Mass., 1965-66; acquisitions staff Western New Eng. Coll., Springfield, 1966-72, cataloger, 1972-84, asst. dir., 1984-89, acting dir., 1989-90, dir., 1990—; chair Cen./Western Mass. Automated Resource Sharing Collection Devel. Com., Paxton, Mass., 1993—, exec. bd. 1993—. mem. East Longmeadow (Mass.) Hist. Soc., 1989-92. Mem. ALA, Mass. Libr. Assn., Assn. Coll. and Rsch. Librs., Libr. and Mgmt. Assn., Libr. Info. and Technology Assn. Methodist. Avocations: horseback riding, show dogs. Office: Western New Eng Coll D'Amour Libr 1215 Wilbraham Rd Springfield MA 01119-2654

STACK, R. TIMOTHY, health facility administrator; b. 1952. BA, Bethany (W.Va.) Coll., 1952; MA, Med. Coll. Va., 1977. Asst. administr. Southside Hosp., Pitts., 1977-79; sr. v.p., COO Cen. Med. Ctr., Pitts., 1980-81; pres. Southside Hosp., 1981-87; pres., adminstr. Borgess Health Alliance Inc., Kalamazoo, Mich., 1987—. Office: Borgess Health Alliance Inc 1521 Gull Rd Kalamazoo MI 49001*

STACK, ROBERT LANGFORD, actor; b. Los Angeles, Jan. 13, 1919; s. James Langford and Elizabeth (Wood) S.; m. Rosemarie Bowe, Jan. 23, 1956; children: Elizabeth Langford, Charles Robert. Student, U. So. Calif., 1937-38. Pres. St. Pierre Prodns., Los Angeles, 1959—. Actor, co-producer: (TV series) The Untouchables, 1959-63 (2 nominations, 1 Emmy award); actor: The Name of the Game, 1968-71, Most Wanted, 1976-77, Strike Force, 1982-83, Unsolved Mysteries, 1986—; actor: (TV movies) The Strange and Deadly Occurence, 1974, The Adventure of the Queen, 1975, Murder on Flight 502, 1975, Undercover with the KKK, 1979 (narrator), Perry Mason: The Curse of the Sinister Spirit, 1987, The Return of Elliot Ness, 1991; (TV miniseries) George Washington, 1984, Hollywood Wives; (films) including First Love, 1940, When the Daltons Rode, 1940, Mortal Storm, 1940, Nice Girl, 1941, Badlands of Dakota, 1941, To Be or Not To Be, 1942, Eagle Squadron, 1942, Men of Texas Fighter Squadron, 1948, Date with Judy, 1948, Miss Tatlock's Millions, 1948, Mr. Music, 1950, The Bullfighter and the Lady, 1950, My Outlaw Brother, 1951, Bwana Devil, 1952, War Paint, 1953, The High and the Mighty, 1953, Iron Glove, 1954, Written on the Wind, 1956 (Acad. Award nomination for best supporting actor), The Last Voyage, 1959, John Paul Jones, 1959, The Caretakers, 1963, The Corrupt Ones, 1967, Story of a Woman, 1970, '1941', 1979, Airplane!, 1980, Uncommon Valor, 1983, Big Trouble, 1984, Glory Days, 1987, Caddyshack II, 1988, Joe Verses the Volcano, 1990. Served with USN, WWII. Recipient Emmy award Acad. TV Arts and Scis. Office: care Camden Artists 409 N Camden Dr Beverly Hills CA 90210-4417

STACK, STEPHEN A., JR., lawyer; b. Bryn Mawr, Pa., 1945. BA cum laude, Yale U., 1967; JD cum laude, U. Pa., 1970. Bar: D.C. 1970, Pa. 1974. Atty. Bur. Competition FTC, Washington, 1970-73; ptnr. Dechert Price & Rhoads, Phila. Mem. ABA (mem. coun. antitrust sect. 1989-92). Office: Dechert Price & Rhoads 4000 Bell Atlantic 1717 Arch St Philadelphia PA 19103-2713

STACK, STEPHEN S., manufacturing company executive; b. DuPont, Pa., Apr. 25, 1934; s. Steve and Sophie (Baranowski) Stasenko. BSME, Case Western Res. U., 1956; postgrad. Syracuse U. Registered profl. engr., Ill. Mech. engr. Kaiser Aluminum, Erie, Pa., 1956-58; instr. Gannon U., Erie, 1958-60, Syracuse (N.Y.) U., 1960-61; engring. supr. A. O. Smith Corp., Erie and Los Angeles, 1961-66; gen. mgr. Am. Elec. Fusion, Chgo., 1966-67; mgr. new products Maremont Corp., Chgo., 1967-69; dir. market planning Gulf and Western Ind., Bellwood, Ill., 1969-71; mgmt. and fin. cons. Stack & Assocs., Chgo., 1971-76; pres. Seamcraft, Inc., Chgo., 1976—; mem. Ill. Legis. Small Bus. Conf., 1980, Gov.'s Small Bus. Adv. Commn., 1984—; Ill. State House Conf. on Small Bus., 1986. chmn. West Cell, 1988—, Link Pers. Svcs. Corp., 1989—; v.p. Ind. Bus. Assn. Ill., 1993-94; mem. small bus. adv. coun. Fed. Res. Bank of Chgo., 1989-91; del. White House Conf. on Small Bus., 1986. Patentee in liquid control and metering fields. Treas. Sem. Townhouse Assn., 1993-94; active Lincoln Park Conservation Assn., Sheffield Neighbors Assn. Recipient Am. Legion award, 1948, Case Western Res. U. Honor key, 1956, Eagle Scout award, 1949. Mem. Ill. Mfrs. Assn. (bd. dirs. 1986—), Small Mfrs. Action Council (vice chmn. 1986-87, chmn. 1988-89), Mfrs. Polit. Action Com. (exec. com. 1987—, vice chmn. 1993—), Am. Mgmt. Assn., Ind. Bus. Assn. Ill. (v.p. 1993), Pres.' Assn., Blue Key, Beta Theta Pi, Theta Tau, Pi Delta Epsilon. Clubs: Chgo. Yacht, Chgo. Execs., East Bank, Singapore (Mich.) Yacht, Capitol Hill (Washington), Fullerton Tennis (pres. 1971-79, treas. 1979-83, bd. dirs. 1983-86), Lake Shore Ski (v.p. 1982, 91). Office: 932 W Dakin St Chicago IL 60613-2922

STACKELBERG, OLAF PATRICK VON, mathematician; b. Munich, Germany, Aug. 2, 1932; came to U.S., 1946, naturalized, 1947; s. Curt Frhrr. and Ellen (Biddle) von Stackelberg; m. Cora Elizabeth Sleighter, Sept. 4, 1954; children: John Sleighter, Peter Olaf, Paul Emmet. B.S in Math. M.I.T., 1955; M.S., U. Minn., 1960, Ph.D. in Math, 1963. Asst. prof. math. Duke U., Durham, N.C., 1963-68; assoc. prof. Duke U. 1968-76; prof., chmn. dept. math. Kent (Ohio) State U., 1976—; vis. assoc. prof. U. Ill., 1969-70, U. London, Eng., 1974, Wesleyan U., summers 1965-76. Mng. editor: Duke Math. Jour, 1971-74; contbr. articles U.S. and fgn. jours. Mem. State of Ohio Steering Com., Project Discovery. Served with Chem. Corps AUS, 1956-58. Alexander von Humboldt research fellow U. Stuttgart, Germany, 1965-66; NSF research grantee. Mem. AAAS, AAUP, Am. Math. Soc., Math. Assn. Am. (nat. bd. govs. 1991-94), Inst. Math. Stats., Fedn. Am. Scientists, Assn. Computer Machinery, London Math. Soc. Home: 1411 Aurora Hudson Rd Aurora OH 44202-8408 Office: Kent State U Dept Math and Computer Sci Kent OH 44242

STACKHOUSE, JOHN WESLEY, publishing executive; b. South Bend, Ind., Feb. 12, 1940; s. Zeno Walter and Mildred Ellen (Delcamp) S.; m. Patsy Ann Erickson, Sept. 14, 1963; children: John E. Joseph W., David P., Katherine A., Jason A., Ryan E., Patricia M. BS in Acctg. and Econs., U. Indpls., 1962. Auditor Ernst & Ernst (now Ernst & Young), Indpls., 1962-65; mgr. gen. acctg. Lake Cen. Airlines, Indpls., 1965-68; from mgr. gen. acctg. to dir. fin. svcs. Howard W. Sams & Co., Inc., Indpls., 1968-73; from sr. fin. analyst to asst. comptr. ITT Pub., Indpls., 1973-81; v.p. fin. treas. CFO Nixon Newspapers, Inc., Peru, Ind., 1981—, also bd. dirs. Bd. dir. Perue/Miami County Econ. Devel. Corp., 1993—. With USAR, 1963-69. Mem. Internat. Newspaper Fin. Execs. (bd. dirs. 1991—), Peru C of C. (bd. dirs. 1991, pres. elect 1992, pres., 1993, 94), Rotary (pres. Peru club 1989-90). Presbyterian. Avocations: photography, reading, fishing. Office: Nixon Newspapers Inc 35 W 3rd St Peru IN 46970-2154

STACKHOUSE, RICHARD GILBERT, retired financial company executive; b. Ottawa, Ont., Can., Nov. 26, 1929; s. A. Gilbert and Leone (Turner) S.; m. Edna Betty Fitzsimmons, July 9, 1955 (dec. July 1988); children: Brent Richard, Kerry Jane, Nancy Edna; m. Jean Elinor Stark, Nov. 3, 1990. B of Commerce, Queen's U., Kingston, Ont., 1953. Chartered acct., FCA, Ont. Contr. Goddard Enterprises Ltd., Barbados, W.I., 1964-65; staff acct. to mgr. Price Waterhouse, Toronto, Ont., 1953-64, mgr., 1965-67, ptnr., 1967-92; chmn. bd. Queen's U., 1990-95, Gov. Exhbn. Place, Toronto, 1988-94. Lt. Royal Can. Navy Res., 1949-53. Mem. Can. Nat. Exhbn. Assn. (pres. 1990-92), Donwood Inst. (chmn. 1982-86), Ont. Safety League (chmn. 1984-86), Nat. Club (pres. 1986-87), Mississaugua Golf and Country Club (pres. 1983-84), Masons (treas. 1983—). Office: Price Waterhouse, 1st Canadian Pl Box 190, Toronto, ON Canada M5X 1H7

STACKPOLE, LAURIE EVELETH, library director; b. Schenectady, N.Y., June 27, 1934; d. Lawrence Nelson and Genevieve (McCafferty) E.; m. John D. Stackpole, June 11, 1960; children: Mark L., Paul L., Jean S. Brown. AB, Trinity Coll., Washington, 1956; MA, Smith Coll., 1957; MSLS, Cath. U., 1977. Reference libr. NOAA, Rockville, Md., 1977-81, head libr. svcs., 1981-84, sys. libr. 1984-85, head libr. divsn., 1985-86; chief libr. Naval Rsch. Lab., Washington, 1986—; rep. Fed. Libr. and Info. Ctr. Com., Washington, 1992-94; mem. adv. coun. FEDLINK, Washington, 1992-94, chair, 1993. Contbr. articles to profl. jours. Mem. ALA (sec.-treas. Fed. Librs. Round Table 1992-94, bd. dirs. 1994—), Spl. Libr. Assn. (chair-elect, chair mil. libr. divsn., 1990). Office: USN Naval Rsch Lab Ruth H Hooker Rsch Libr & Tech Info Ctr Code 5220 Washington DC 20375-5334

STACY, ALAN, gas industry executive; b. 1941. Degree, Lamar U., 1965. With Phillips Petroleum Co., Odessa, Tex., 1965-69; with Enogex Inc., Okla. City, 1969—, v.p., COO, 1986—; pres. Enogex Products Corp., Okla. City. Office: Enogex Inc 515 Central Park Dr Oklahoma City OK 73105*

STACY, ANGELICA M., chemistry educator. Prof. dept. chemistry U. Calif., Berkeley. Recipient Francis P. Garvan-John M. Olin medal Am. Chem. Soc., 1995. Office: U Calif Dept Chemistry 419 Latimer Hall Berkeley CA 94720-1401*

STACY, BILL WAYNE, college president; b. Bristol, Va., July 26, 1938; s. Charles Frank and Louise Nelson (Altwater) S.; m. Sue Varnon; children: Mark, Sara, James. B.S.Ed., S.E. Mo. State U., 1960; M.S., So. Ill. U., 1965, Ph.D., 1968. Tchr. Malden High Sch., Mo., 1960-64; faculty Southeast Mo. State U., Cape Girardeau, 1967-89, dean Grad. Sch., 1976-79, interim pres., 1979, pres., 1980-89; pres. Calif. State U., San Marcos, 1989—; dir. Boatmen's Nat. Bank. Bd. dirs. San Diego United Way. Mem. Am. Assn. State Colls. and Univs. (dir.), Am. Assn. Higher Edn., PIC Policy Bd., San Diego, Rotary. Presbyterian.

STACY, CHARLES BRECKNOCK, lawyer; b. Charleston, W.Va., Sept. 2, 1924; s. George Palmer and Patti (Hubbard) S.; m. Judith Cook Willner, June 14, 1947; 1 child, Charles Brecknock. B.S., Yale U., 1948, LL.B., 1951. Bar: W.Va. 1951. Assoc. firm Spilman, Thomas & Battle, 1951-58; v.p. Lewis-Hubbard Corp., 1957; ptnr. Spilman, Thomas & Battle, Charleston, 1958—; mem. U.S. Circuit Ct. Judge Nominating Commn., 4th Circuit, 1977-79. Contbr. articles to law and tax publs. Pres. Kanawha-Charleston Vis. Nursing Assn., 1966-67; bd. dirs. Charleston Symphony Orch., 1960-70, pres., 1962-63; bd. trustees Woodberry Forest (Va.) Sch., 1970-76; pres. Woodberry Forest Alumni Assn., 1972-74; bd. dirs. Community Council of Kanawha Valley, Inc., 1971-79, pres., 1975-77; bd. dirs. United Way of Kanawha Valley, Inc., 1973-77, exec. com., 1975-77; trustee Greater Kanawha Valley Found., 1968-72, adv. bd., 1972—, chmn. bd., 1970-72; bd. dirs. W.Va. Tax Inst., 1958-67, pres., 1959-60. Served with USAAF, 1943-46. Fellow Am. Bar Found., Am. Coll. Trust and Estate Counsel, Am. Coll. Tax Counsel; mem. ABA (coun. 1977-83, vice chmn. adminstrn. sect. taxation 1980-83), Kanawha County Bar Assn., W.Va. State Bar (chmn. standing com. on state and fed. taxation 1959-70), W.Va. Bar Assn., Am. Law Inst., Am. Judicature Soc., Edgewood Country Club Charleston (gov. 1973-75, 83-86), Sea Pines Country Club (Hilton Head, S.C.), Yale Club N.Y.C., Rotary (bd. dirs. Charleston club 1979-80, 83-91, pres. 1989-90). Democrat. Presbyterian. Home: 1560 Thomas Cir Charleston WV 25314-1623 Office: Spilman Ctr 300 Kanawha Blvd E Charleston WV 25301

STACY, DENNIS WILLIAM, architect; b. Council Bluffs, Iowa, Sept. 22, 1945; s. William L. and Mildred Glee (Carlsen) S.; BArch., Iowa State U., 1969; postgrad. U. Nebr., 1972. Registered architect, Iowa, Tex., Colo., Mo.; m. Judy Annette Long, Dec. 28, 1968; 1 child, Stephanie. Designer Troy & Stalder Architects, Omaha, 1967, Architects Assocs., Des Moines, 1968-69, Logsdon & Voelter Architects, Temple, Tex., 1970; project architect Roger Schutte & Assocs., Omaha, 1972-73; architect, assoc. Robert H. Burgin & Assocs., Coun. Bluffs, 1973-75, Neil Astle & Assocs., Omaha, 1975-78; owner, prin. Dennis W. Stacy, AIA, Architect, Glenwood, Iowa, 1978-81, Dallas, 1981—. Mem. City of Dallas Urban Design Adv. Com., 1992-95; chmn., Glenwood Zoning Bd. Adjustment, 1979-81; chmn. Mills County Plant Iowa Program, 1979-81; mem. S.W. Iowa Citizen's Adv. Com., Iowa State Dept. Transp., 1977-81; regional screening chmn. Am. Field Svc. Internat./Intercultural Programs, 1974-79, Iowa-Nebr. rep., 1978-80. With U.S. Army, 1969-71. Decorated Nat. Def. Svc. medal, Vietnam Svc. medal, Vietnam Campaign medal, Army Commendation medal. Mem. AIA (recipient Iowa Design Honor award 1981, commendation awards (2) 1990, citation of honor award 1991, 92, Dallas Design awards (2) 1991, Texas Design Honor award 1992, Dallas AIA Firm of Yr. award 1992, Dallas commr. design, 1991, chmn. Dallas design awards 1992, pres-elect. Dallas AIA, 1995), Nat. Coun. Archtl. Registration Bds., Tex. Soc. Archs. (environ. resource com. 1994-95, chmn., Tex. arch. pub. com., 1992-95), The 500 Inc. (outstanding mem. 1985), Glenwood Optimist (Disting. Svc. award 1982, pres. 1980-81), Masons. Archtl. Works include: Davies Amphitheater, 1980, Addison Nat. Bank Bldg., 1985, Fairview Recreation Complex, 1984, Computer Lang. Rsch. Corp. Learning Ctr., 1987., Villa Roma, 1988, C.U. Performing Arts Ctr., 1989, Mercedes-Benz Distbn. Ctr., 1987, Dallas Chpt. AIA Offices, 1990, Janadria Festival Arena, 1994, Dallas Homeless Campus, 1994, Surg. Ctr. Pain Mgmt. Inst., 1995, Physicians Consultants Clinic, 1994. Home: 4148 Cobblers Ln Dallas TX 75287-6725 Office: 2136 N Harwood St Ste 100 Dallas TX 75201-2246

STACY, FRANCES H., judge. BA, Baylor Univ., 1977; JD, Baylor Law Sch., 1979. With U.S. Atty.'s Office (Tex. so. dist.) Criminal Divsn., 1980, Civil Rights Divsn. 1980-81, Land and Resources Divsn. 1981-87, Civil Divsn., 1987-88, Appelate Divsn., 1988-90; magistrate judge U.S. Dist. Ct. (Tex. so. dist.), 5th circuit, Houston, 1990—. Author: Federal Civil Procedure Before Trial, Lawyers Cooperative Practice Guide. Mem. Tex. Bar Found. Office: Fed Bldg 515 Rusk Rm 7727 Houston TX 77002-2600

STACY, RICHARD A., adminstrative law judge; b. Eldorado, Ark., Mar. 7, 1942; s. Jack Leonard S. and Estelle (Mabry) Carrier; m. Karen Kay King, Aug. 20, 1961; children: Mark L., Andrea L. B.A., U. Wyo., 1965, J.D., 1967. Bar: Wyo. 1967, Colo. 1967, U.S. Supreme Ct. 1972. Revisor Wyo. Statute Revision Com., Cheyenne, 1967-69; asst. atty. gen. State of Wyo., 1969-72; asst. U.S. atty. Dept. Justice, Cheyenne, 1972-75; U.S. atty. Dis. Wyo., Cheyenne, 1981-94; adminstrv. law judge Office of Hearing & Appeals, San Jose, Calif., 1994—; mem. atty. gen's adv. com. of U.S. attys. Dept. Justice, 1981-84. Mem. Gov.'s Statewide Drug Alcohol Adv. Bd., 1988-94. Mem. ABA, Wyo. Bar Assn., Colo. State Bar, Santa Clara County Bar Assn. (hon., com. on bench, bar, media, police relationships 1995—). Republican. Episcopalian. Club: Kiwanis (charter pres. Wheatland 1977). Office: Hearings & Appeals 280 S 1st St San Jose CA 95113-3086

STADDON, JOHN ERIC RAYNER, psychology, zoology, neurobiology educator; b. Grayshott, Hampshire, Eng.; came to U.S., 1960; s. Leonard John and Dulce Norine (Rayner) S.; m. Lucinda Paris. BSc, Univ. Coll., London, 1960; PhD, Harvard U., 1964. Asst. prof. psychology U. Toronto, Ont., Can., 1964-67; from asst. prof. to prof. Duke U., Durham, N.C., 1967-72, prof., 1972-83, J.B. Duke prof. psychology, prof. neurobiology and zoology, 1983—. Author: Adaptive Behavior and Learning, 1983, Behaviorism, 1993; editor: Behavioral Processes, 1979, Behavior and Philosophy, 1993; assoc. editor: Jour. Exptl. Analysis of Behavior, 1979-82. Recipient von Humboldt prize, 1985. Fellow AAAS, N.Y. Acad. Scis., Soc. Exptl. Psychology; mem. Phi Beta Kappa (hon.), Sigma Xi. Avocations: history, philosophy of science, public policy. Office: Duke U Dept Exptl Psychology PO Box 90086 Durham NC 27708-0086

STADE, GEORGE GUSTAV, humanities educator; b. N.Y.C., Nov. 25, 1933; s. Kurt Herman and Eva Bergit (Aronson) S.; m. Dorothy Louise Fletcher, Dec. 16, 1957; children: Bjorn, Eric, Nancy, Kirsten. B.A., St. Lawrence U., 1955; M.A., Columbia U., 1958, Ph.D., 1965. Tchr. Collegiate Sch., N.Y.C., 1957-58; instr. Bernard Baruch Sch. Bus., N.Y.C., 1958-59, Bklyn. Poly. Inst., 1959-60, Rutgers U.-Newark, 1960-62; instr. Columbia U., N.Y.C., 1962, asst. prof., 1965, assoc. prof., 1968, prof. English, 1971—; cons. various law firms, N.Y.C., 1960—. Author: Robert Graves, 1967, Confessions of a Lady-Killer, 1979; editor: European Writers, 13 vols., Selected Letters of E.E. Cummings, 1968, Six Modern British Writers, 1974, Six Contemporary British Writers, 1976, European Writers: Selected Authors, 3 Vols., 1992; contbr. over 100 articles to profl. jours. Mem. PEN, N.Y. Book Critics Circle, Popular Culture Assn., Alks. Home: 430 W 116th St New York NY 10027-7210 Office: Columbia U 604 Philosophy Hall New York NY 10027

STADELMAN, WILLIAM RALPH, chemical institution executive; b. Ont., Can., July 18, 1919; s. John Joseph and Lillian (Trachsell) S.; m. Jean MacLaren, Nov. 2, 1951; 1 child, Mary Laren. B.A.Sc., U. Toronto, 1941; M.B.A., U. Pa., 1949. Chief process engr. Can. Synthetic Rubber, Ltd., 1943-47; lectr. mktg. U. Pa., 1948-49; asst. to mgr. Pa. Salt Mfg. Co., 1950; sec.-treas. Ont. Research Found., Mississauga, 1950-64, pres., 1964-84; pres. WRS Assocs., 1984—; dir., sr. exec. Inst. Chem. Sci. and Tech., 1985-89; dir. Med. Tech. Investment Corp. Fellow World Acad. Art and Sci.; mem. Assn.

Profl. Engrs. Ont., Can. Rsch. Mgmt. Assn., Bd. Trade Met. Toronto, Club of Rome, Caledon Ski Club. Home and Office: WRS Assocs, 31 Rykert Crescent, Toronto, ON Canada M4G 2T1

STADELMANN, EDUARD JOSEPH, plant physiologist, educator; b. Graz, Austria, Sept. 24, 1920; s. Eduard Joseph and Josefa (Eigner) S.; m. Ok Young Lee, Mar. 22, 1975. BS, Bundesrealgymnasium, Graz, Austria, 1939; PhD, U. Innsbruck, Austria, 1953; Pvt. Docent, U. Freiburg, Switzerland, 1957; PhD (hon.), Agrl. U. Vienna, 1989. Sr. asst. U. Freiburg, 1962-63; rsch. assoc. U. Minn., Mpls., 1963, asst. prof., 1964-66, assoc. prof., 1966-72, prof. hort. sci., 1972-91, prof. emeritus, 1991—. Muellhaupt Scholar in Biology, Ohio State U., 1958-59; Humboldt Found. awardee, 1974-75; Fulbright award, Coun. Internat. Exchange, 1979-80, 87-88. Mem. Am. Inst. Biology, Am. Soc. Plant Physiologists, German Bot. Soc., Swiss Bot. Soc., Sigma Xi. Roman Catholic. Office: Univ Minn Dept Hort Sci 1970 Folwell Ave Saint Paul MN 55108-6007

STADLEN, DIANE ELIZABETH, marketing professional; b. Chgo., Nov. 10, 1953; d. Harvey O. and Regina E. (Kozlowski) Nottke; m. Richard W. Stadlen, Feb. 17, 1974; children: Jennifer Beth, Rachael Michelle. Student, Southwest Coll., Chgo., 1971-72. Traffic mgr. Sta WDAI-FM, Chgo., 1973-81; assoc. Creswell, Munsell, Fultz & Zirbel, Inc., Cedar Rapids, Iowa, 1981-88; sr. v.p., dir. Creswell, Munsell, Fultz & Zirbel, Inc., Cedar Rapids, 1988—. Mem. communications com. United Way East Cen. Iowa, 1986-88. Mem. Nat. Agr. Mktg. Assn. (vice chmn. issues forum 1990, chmn. 1991, v.p. exec. com., 1993—), Nat. Assn. Farm Broadcasters (adv. bd. 1983-90), Starch Farms (chmn. steering com. 1988—). Office: Creswell Munsell Fultz & Zirbel Inc 4211 Signal Rdg NE Cedar Rapids IA 52402-2524

STADLER, CRAIG ROBERT, professional golfer; b. San Diego, June 2, 1953; s. Donald Edwin and Betty M. (Adams) S.; m. Susan Barrett, Jan. 6, 1979; children: Kevin Craig, Christopher Barrett. Student, U. So. Calif. Profl. golfer Palm Beach Gardens, Fla.; winner Hope Classic, 1980, Greater Greensboro Open, 1980, Kemper Open, 1981-82, Tucson Open, 1982, Masters, 1982, World Series of Golf, 1982, 92, Tour Championship, 1991. U.S. amateur champion, 1973; mem. U.S. Walker Cup team, 1975; leading money winner PGA Tour, 1982. Mem. Golf Mag. (Player of Yr. 1982).

STADLER, GERALD P., transportation executive; b. 1937; married. Student, Loyola U. Sec. United Van Lines, Fenton, Mo., 1981-84, vice chmn., 1984—, also bd. dirs. Office: United Van Lines Inc 1 United Dr Fenton MO 63026-2535

STADTER, PHILIP AUSTIN, classicist, educator; b. Cleve., Nov. 29, 1936; s. John M. and Mary Louise (Jones) S.; m. Lucia Angela Ciapponi, July 6, 1963; children: Paul, Maria, Mark. B.A., Princeton U., 1958; M.A., Harvard U., 1959, Ph.D., 1963. Instr. U. N.C., Chapel Hill, 1962-64, asst. prof., 1964-67, assoc. prof., 1967-71, prof., 1971—, chmn. dept. classics, 1976-86, prof. comparative lit., 1991—, Falk prof. humanities, 1991—. Author: Plutarch's Historical Methods, 1965, The Public Library of Renaissance Florence, 1972, Arrian of Nicomedia, 1980, A Commentary on Plutarch's Pericles, 1989; editor: The Speeches of Thucydides, 1973, Plutarch and the Historical Tradition, 1992. Fulbright fellow Rome, 1960-61; Guggenheim fellow Florence, Italy, 1967-68; NEH fellow, 1974-75; fellow Am. Council Learned Socs., Oxford, Eng., 1982-83. Fellow Nat. Humanities Ctr.; mem. Am. Philol. Assn. (dir. 1977-80), Am. Assn. Ancient Historians, Soc. Promotion of Hellenic Studies, Classical Assn. Middle West and South. Democrat. Roman Catholic. Office: U NC Dept Classics Chapel Hill NC 27599-3145

STADTLER, BEATRICE HORWITZ, author; b. Cleve., June 26, 1921; d. David and Minnie (Gorelick) Horwitz; m. Oscar Stadtler, Jan. 31, 1945; children—Dona Stadtler Rosenblatt, Sander, Miriam Stadtler Rosenbaum. MS in Religious Edn., 1983, M Judaic Studies, 1988. Sec. Cleve. Dept. Pub. Health and Welfare, 1940; sec., dept. mgr. Fed. Pub. Housing Authority, Cleve., 1943; primary supr. Temple Beth Shalom Religious Sch., Cleve., 1953; registrar Cleve. Coll. Jewish Studies, 1958-83; asst. editor Israel Philatelist, 1976—; speaker on holocaust, lectr. at writer's confs. and classes; scholar-in-residence various cities; tchr. Cleve. Hebrew Schs., 1992—. Author: Once Upon a Jewish Holiday, 1963, The Story of Dona Gracia, 1969, The Adventures of Gluckel of Hamlen, 1967, Rescue From the Sky (in Hebrew), 1972, Personalities of the Jewish Labor Movement, 1972, The Holocaust: A History of Courage and Resistance, 1975 (prize outstanding juvenile book, Jewish Book Coun., Nat. Jewish Welfare Bd. 1975), The History of Israel Through Her Postage Stamps, 1993; also stories and articles for children in Chattanooga Shofar newspaper; poems in book Women Speak to God; film strip The Adventures of Mirkee Pirkee and Danny Dollar, 1963 (prize Nat. Council Jewish Audio Visual Materials 1963); libretto rock opera Solomon the King; contbr. articles to Shofar mag., Young Judaean; contbr. article on holocaust to New Book of Knowledge; author weekly column Cleve. Jewish News, 1964-70, Boston Jewish Advocate, 1970-92; contbr. articles to publs. Adviser youth group United Synagogue, 1967-70; mem. Holocaust task force Jewish Community Fedn. Cleve.; mem. Educator's Assembly, Pioneer Women., Edn. Council N. Am.; mem. U.S. Holocaust Meml. Council, chmn. adv. panel Holocaust edn., judge writing contest for students 9th-12th grades.; mem. Gov.'s commn. of the State of Ohio on Holocaust Edn.; mem. State of Ohio Holocaust Commn., Cleve. Holocaust Ctr. (chmn. edn.), Bd. Cleve. Hebrew Schs. (chmn. edn.); bd. dirs. Women's Div. Jewish Nat. Fund. Recipient Leslie Reggel award for outstanding contbns. to Israel Philately, 1994, prizes Fedn. and Welfare Funds Audio Visual Coun. of Am. Assn. Jewish Edn. Democrat. Home: 24355 Tunbridge Ln Cleveland OH 44122-1631

STADTMAN, EARL REECE, biochemist; b. Carrizozo, N.Mex., Nov. 15, 1919; s. Walter William and Minnie Ethyl (Reece) S.; m. Thressa Campbell, Oct. 19, 1943. B.S., U. Calif., Berkeley, 1942, Ph.D., 1949. With Alcan Hwy. survey Pub. Rds. Adminstrn., 1942-43; rsch. assoc. U. Calif., Berkeley, 1938-49, sr. lab. technician, 1949; AEC fellow Mass. Gen. Hosp., Boston, 1949-50; chemist lab. cellular physiology Nat. Heart Inst., 1950-58, chief enzyme sect., 1958-62, chief lab. biochemistry, 1962—; biochemist Max Planck Inst., Munich, Germany, Pasteur Inst., Paris, 1959-60; faculty mem. microbiology U. Md.; prof. biochemistry grad. program dept. biology Johns Hopkins U.; adv. com. Life Scis. Rsch. Office, Am. Fedn. Biol. Sci., 1974-77; bd. dirs. Found. Advanced Edn. Scis., 1966-70, chmn. dept. biochemistry, 1966-68; biochem. study sect. rsch. grants NIH, 1959-63. Editor Jour. Biol. Chemistry, 1960-65, Current Topics in Cellular Regulation, 1968—; Circulation Rsch., 1968-70; exec. editor Archives Biochemistry and Biophysics, 1960—, Life Scis., 1973-75; Procs. NAS, 1975-81, Trends in Biochem. Rsch., 1975-78; mem. editorial adv. bd. Biochemistry, 1969-76, 81—. Recipient medallion Soc. de Chemie Biologique, 1955, medallion U. Pisa, 1966, Presdl. Rank award as Disting. Sr. Exec., 1981, Welch Found. Award in Chemistry, 1991, Rsch. award Am. Aging Assn., 1992, Paul Glen award Am. Gerontology Soc., 1993. Mem. Am. Chem. Soc. (Paul Lewis Lab. award in enzyme chemistry 1952, exec. com. biol. div. 1959-64, chmn. div. 1963-64, Hillebrand award 1969), Am. Soc. Biol. Chemists (publs. com. 1966-70, coun. 1974-77, 82-84, pres. 1983—, Merckaward 1983), Nat. Acad. Sci. (award in microbiology 1970), Am. Acad. Arts and Scis., Am. Soc. Microbiology, Washington Acad. Scis. (award biol. chemistry 1957, Nat. medal sci. 1979, meritorious exec. award 1980, Robert A. Welch award in chemistry 1991, Paul Glenn award in aging 1993). Office: Nat Heart and Lung Inst 9000 Rockville Pike Bethesda MD 20892-0001*

STADTMAN, THRESSA CAMPBELL, biochemist; b. Sterling, N.Y., Feb. 12, 1920; d. Earl and Bessie (Waldron) Campbell; m. Earl Reece Stadtman, Oct. 19, 1943. BS, Cornell U., 1940, MS, 1942; PhD, U. Calif.-Berkeley, 1949. Rsch. assoc. U. Calif., Berkeley, 1942-47; Rsch. assoc. med. sch. Harvard U., Boston, 1949-50; biochemist Nat. Heart, Lung and Blood Inst. NIH, USPHS, HHS, Bethesda, Md., 1950—. Editor Jour. Biol. Chemistry, Archives Biochemistry and Biophysics, Molecular and Cellular Biochemistry; editor-in-chief Bio Factors; contbr. articles on amino acid metabolism, methane biosynthesis, vitamin B12 biochemistry, selenium biochemistry to profl. jours. Helen Haye Whitney fellow Oxford U., Eng., 1954-55; Rockefeller Found. grantee U. Munich, 1959-60; recipient Rose award, 1987, Klaus Schwarz medal, 1988. Mem. NAS, Am. Soc. Microbiology, Biochem. Soc., Soc. Am. Biochemists, Am. Chem. Soc., Am. Acad. Arts and Scis.,

Sigma Delta Epsilon (hon.). Home: 16907 Redland Rd Derwood MD 20855-1954 Office: Nat Heart Lung & Blood Inst HHS Bethesda MD 20892

STADTMAN, VERNE AUGUST, former foundation executive, editor; b. Carrizoso, N.Mex., Dec. 5, 1926; s. Walter William and Minnie Ethel (Reece) S.; m. Jackolyn Carol Byl, Aug. 26, 1949; children: Kristen Karen, Rand Theodore, Judith Dayna, Todd Alan. A.B., Calif.-Berkeley, 1950. AUS, 1945-47; mng. editor Calif. Monthly, Calif. Alumni Assn., Berkeley, 1950-64; centennial editor U. Calif., Berkeley, 1964-69; assoc. dir., editor Carnegie Commn. on Higher Edn., Berkeley, 1969-73, Carnegie Council on Policy Studies in Higher Edn. Berkeley, 1973-80; v.p. gen. services Carnegie Found. for Advancement Teaching, Princeton, N.J., 1980-89; trustee Editorial Projects Edn., Inc., 1957-91, pres., 1962-63, chmn. bd., 1980-86; guest scholar Hiroshima U., Japan, 1978. Author: California Campus, 1960, University of California, 1868-1968, 1970, Academic Adaptations, 1980; editor: (with David Riesman) Academic Transformation: Seventeen Institutions Under Pressure, 1973 (Book of Yr. award Am. Council Edn.); compiler-editor: Centennial Record of the University of California, 1967. Served with AUS, 1945-47. Recipient Alumnus Service award Calif. Alumni Assn. 1970. Mem. Am. Alumni Council (pres. 1963-64), Edn. Writers Assn., Friends Bancroft Library. Home: 182 St James Dr Sonoma CA 95476-8336

STADTMUELLER, JOSEPH PETER, federal judge; b. Oshkosh, Wis., Jan. 28, 1942; s. Joseph Francis and Irene Mary (Kilp) S.; m. Mary Ellen Brady, Sept. 5, 1970; children: Jeremy, Sarah. B.S. in Bus. Adminstrn., Marquette U., 1964, J.D., 1967. Bar: Wis. 1967, U.S. Supreme Ct. 1980. With Kluwin, Dunphy, Mankin and McNulty, 1968-69; asst. U.S. atty. Dept. Justice, Milw., 1969-74; 1st. asst. U.S. atty. Dept. Justice, 1974-75; with Stepke, Kossow, Trebon and Stadtmueller, Milw., 1975-76; asst. U.S. atty. Dept. Justice, 1977-78, dep. U.S. atty., 1978-81, U.S. atty., 1981-87; judge U.S. Dist. Ct. (ea. dist.) Wis., Milw., 1987—. Recipient Spl. Commendation award Atty. Gen. U.S., 1974, 80. Mem. ABA, State Bar Wis. (bd. govs. 1979-83, exec. com. 1982-83), Am. Law Inst., Univ. Club (Milw.). Republican. Roman Catholic. Club: University (Milw.). Office: 471 US Courthouse 517 E Wisconsin Ave Milwaukee WI 53202-4506

STAEHELIN, LUCAS ANDREW, cell biology educator; b. Sydney, Australia, Feb. 10, 1939; came to U.S., 1969; s. Lucas Eduard and Isobel (Malloch) S.; m. Margrit Weibel, Sept. 17, 1965; children: Daniel Thomas, Philip Roland, Marcel Felix. Dipl. Natw., Swiss Fed. Inst. Tech., Zurich, 1963, Ph.D. in Biology, 1966. Research scientist N.Z. Dept. Sci. and Indsl. Research, 1966-69; research fellow in cell biology Harvard U., Cambridge, Mass., 1969-70; asst. prof. cell biology U. Colo., Boulder, 1970-73, assoc. prof., 1973-79, prof., 1979—; vis. prof. U. Freiburg, 1978, Swiss Fed. Inst. Tech., 1984, 92; mem. cellular biology and physiology study sect. NIH, Bethesda, Md., 1980-84; mem. DOE panel on rsch. directions for the energy bioscis., 1988, 92; mem. NSF adv. panel for cellular orgn., 1994—. Editor Jour. Cell Biology, 1977-81, European Jour. Cell Biology, 1981-90, Plant Physiology, 1986-92, Plant Jour., 1991—, (with C.J. Antzen) Ency. Plant Physio., Vol. 19, Photosynthesis III, 1986; contbr. numerous articles to sci. jours. Recipient Humboldt award Humboldt Found., 1978, Sci. Tchr. award U. Colo., 1984, NIH research grants, 1971—. Mem. AAAS, Am. Soc. Cell Biology, Am. Soc. Plant Physiology, German Acad. Natural Scis. Leopoldina. Home: 2855 Dover Dr Boulder CO 80303-5305 Office: U Colo Dept Molecular Cell/Devel Biology Campus Box 347 Boulder CO 80309-0347

STAEHLE, ROBERT L., foundation executive; b. Rochester, N.Y., Apr. 22, 1955; s. Henry Carl and Isabel Montgomery S. BS in Aero. and Astronautic Engring., Purdue U., 1977. Prin. investigator Skylab Expt. ED-31 (bacteria aboard Skylab), NASA/Marshall Space Flight Center, Huntsville, Ala., 1972-74; student trainee engring. Skylab Expt. ED-31 (bacteria aboard Skylab), NASA/Marshall Space Flight Center, 1974-77; sci. observation analyst Caltech/Jet Propulsion Lab., Pasadena, Calif., 1977-78; engr. advanced projects group, 1978-83, mem. tech. staff system integration sect. of Space Sta., 1983-87, mem. tech. staff and space sta., user ops. team leader, 1987-88; tech. mgr. Jet Propulsion Lab., Pasadena, Calif., 1988—, mgr. space sta. Freedom support office Pasadena ops., 1990-92, Pluto team leader, 1992-93, mgr. Pluto preproject, 1993—; prin. founder, pres. World Space Found., South Pasadena, Calif., 1979—; founding dir. So. Calif. Space Bus. Roundtable, 1987—. Co-author: Project Solar Sail, New Am. Libr., 1990; contbr. articles to profl. jours. Bd. dirs. Caltech Y, 1987-93. Nat. Space Club Goddard scholar, 1977; Charles A. Lindbergh Fund grantee, 1986. Fellow Brit. Interplanetary Soc.; mem. AIAA, Tau Beta Pi, Sigma Gamma Tau. Avocations: photography, hiking. Office: World Space Found PO Box Y South Pasadena CA 91031-1000

STAELIN, DAVID HUDSON, electrical engineering educator, consultant; b. Toledo, May 25, 1938; s. Carl Gustav and Margaret e. (Hudson) S.; m. Ellen Mahoney, June 16, 1962; children: Carl H., Katharine E., Paul H. SB, MIT, 1960, SM, 1961, ScD in Elec. Engring., 1965. Instr. elec. engring. MIT, Cambridge, 1965, asst. prof., 1965-69, assoc. prof., 1969-76, prof., 1976—; asst. dir. Lincoln Lab. MIT, Lexington, 1990—; vis. asst. scientist Nat. Radio Astronomy Obs., Charlottesville, Va., 1968-69; cons. Jet Propulsion Lab., Pasadena, Calif., 1969, Wellesley, Mass., 1965—; dir. Environ. Rsch. and Tech., Inc., Concord, Mass., 1969-78; co-founder, chmn. PictureTel Corp., Peabody, Mass., 1984-87; mem. com. on radio frequency requirements for rsch., NAS, Washington, 1980-86, chmn. 1983-86; chmn. advanced microwave sounder working group NASA, Washington, 1981-82, mem. space applications adv. com.,NASA, 1983-85. Co-author: Made in America, 1989, Electromagnetic Waves, 1994; also articles; patentee grinding and polishing sheet glass, display of dynamic images, ribbon-beam cathode ray tube. Fellow IEEE, AAAS; mem. Am. Geophys. Union, Am. Meteorl. Soc., Internat. Union for Radio Sci. Office: MIT Rm 26-341 Cambridge MA 02139

STAELIN, RICHARD, business administration educator; b. Larchmont, N.Y., Aug. 3, 1939; s. Richard Carl and Dorothy (Potts) S.; m. Julie Ann Fischer, Aug. 24, 1963; children: Adam, Kate. BSME, U. Mich., 1961, BS in Math., 1962, M.B.A., 1963, Ph.D., 1969. Market planner IBM, Harrison, N.Y., 1963-66; prof. Carnegie-Mellon U., Pitts., 1969-82; Edward and Rose Donnell prof. Duke U., Durham, N.C., 1982—; assoc. dean faculty affairs, 1982-91; exec. dir. Mktg. Sci. Inst., Cambridge, Mass., 1991-93; vis. prof. Australian Grad. Sch., Kensington, Australia, 1980-81. Author: Consumer Protection Legislation and the U.S. Food Industry, 1980; mem. editorial bd. Jour. Mktg. Rsch., 1974-82, Jour. Consumer Rsch., 1976-87; area editor Mktg. Sci., 1983-88; editor-in-chief Mktg. Sci., 1995—. Mem. Pitts. Exec. Bd.; treas. Pitts. Arts and Crafts Ctr., 1976-79; bd. dirs. Dispute Settlement Ctr., Chapel Hill, N.C.; bd. vis. drama dept. Duke U., 1990—. Recipient Best Mktg. Paper award Inst. Mgmt. Sci., 1985, hon. mention, 1986; HEW grantee, 1972-74; NSF grantee, 1973-79. Mem. Am. Mktg. Assn., Assn. Consumer Research, Inst. Mgmt. Sci. Office: Fuqua School of Business Science Dr Rm 339 Durham NC 27706-2597

STAFF, CHARLES BANCROFT, JR., music and theater critic; b. Franklin, Ind., July 2, 1929; s. Charles Bancroft and Clara Margaret (Jennings) S. AB, Franklin Coll., 1951; BM, Ind. U., 1955. Copy editor Indpls. News, 1955-58, movie, TV critic, 1958-65, music, drama critic, 1965—; pianist dance band, Franklin, 1943-46. Composer numerous musical pieces string quartet, 1954, wind quintet, 1954, violin sonata, 1955, Deat Under A Tree, Wicked Tales for Evil Children, 1980. Organist Presbyn. Ch., Franklin, 1945-48, Bapt. Ch. Franklin, 1948-51. Recipient Best Critical Writing award Indpls. Press Club, 1977, 78. Democrat. Office: Indpls News 307 N Pennsylvania St Indianapolis IN 46204-1811

STAFFORD, BARBARA ROSE, lawyer; b. N.Y.C., July 14, 1949; d. Sol and Theresa (Tenenbaum) S.; m. Robert M. Armstrong. BA, U. Denver, 1971; JD, U. Chgo., 1990. Bar: Ill. 1990, D.C. 1992. Hearing commr. Colo. Dept. Revenue, Denver, 1974-87; assoc. Katten, Muchin & Zavis, Chgo., 1990-91; dep. asst. sec. Internat. Trade Adminstrn., U.S. Dept. Commerce, Washington, 1993—; cons., staff Dem. Nat. Com., Washington, 1992. Author: The Sunset Provisions: Mortality and the Uruguay Round, 1994, Caselaw Compendium of Colorado Motor Vehicle Law, 1985. Active Community Econ. Devel. Law Project, Chgo., 1990. Mem. ABA, D.C. Bar Assn., Women's Bar Assn. D.C. Avocation: golf. Office: 14th and Constitution Washington DC 20030

STAFFORD, DONALD GENE, chemistry educator; b. Valliant, Okla., Oct. 9, 1930; s. Otto Lewis and Rose Lavelle (Osterdock) S.; m. Jane Wright, July 5, 1951; children—Michael Royce, Robert Gene, Joel Dan. B.S., U. Okla., 1957, Ph.D., 1969; M.S., Okla. State U., 1961. Prof. sci. edn. East Cen. U., Ada, Okla., 1961-73, prof. chemistry, 1973—; adj. prof. U. Okla., Norman, 1970—. Author: The Improvement of Science in Oklahoma (7-12), 1970, Guidelines and Successful Practices in Elementary Edn, 1970, Wings for a Dinosaur, 1972, Early Childhood Resource Book, 1972, Teaching Science in the Elementary School, 1973, 3d edit., 1979, Teaching Science in the Secondary School, 1973, Research, Teaching, and Learning with the Piaget Model, 1976, Investigations in Physical Science, 1976, The Learning Science Program K-6 (7 children's books and 7 tchr.'s guides), 1976, TOP, The Oklahoma Project, Chemistry, 1987, The Learning Cycle, 1988. Served with AUS, 1948-53. Mem. Am. Chem. Soc., Nat. Sci. Tchrs. Assn., Okla. Sci. Tchrs. (pres. 1973-74, 78-79), Sigma Xi. Home: 2202 Fullview Dr Ada OK 74820-4436

STAFFORD, EARL, conductor. Began piano studies at age 8; profl. and solo debut with Thunder Bay Symphony at age 10; studied at Faculty of Music, U. Toronto, with Milton Kaye in N.Y.C., at Paris Conservatory with Franco Ferrara and Aldo Ciccolini; joined Royal Winnipeg Ballet as prin. pianist, 1975, appointed assoc. music dir., 1982, now music dir. and condr.; also music dir. dance div. Banff Ctr. Fine Arts. Orchestrator numerous ballets for Royal Winnipeg Ballet, including Five Tangos, Bluebird Pas De Deux, Giselle Pas De Deux, Tchaikovsky Pas De Deux, Nuages; guest condr. various Can. orchs. including Vancouver Symphony, Calgary Philharmonic, Regina Symphony, Winnipeg Symphony, Saskatoon Symphony Orch., Nat. Arts Ctr. Orch., Thunder Bay Symphony. Recipient Gold medal for accompanying, Internat. Ballet Competition, Varna, Bulgaria, 1980. Office: EML Internat Artist Mgmt Inc, 219 Baseline Rd East, London, ON Canada N6C 2N6*

STAFFORD, FRANK PETER, JR., economics educator, consultant; b. Chgo., Sept. 17, 1940; s. Frank Peter and Ida Gustava (Tormala) S.; m. Lilian Elisabeth Lundin, Aug. 8, 1964; children: Craig Peter, Jennifer Elisabeth, Christine Anna. BA, Northwestern U., 1962; MBA, U. Chgo., 1964, PhD, 1968. Asst. prof. econs. U. Mich., 1966-71, assoc. prof., 1971-73, 74-75, prof., 1976—, chmn. dept. econs., 1980—, rsch. scientist Inst. Social Rsch., 1995—, chair budget study com., 1995—; vis. assoc. prof. Grad. Sch. Bus.-Stanford U., 1973-74; spl. asst. for econ. affairs U.S. Dept. Labor, Washington, 1975-76; vis. prof. dept. econs. U. Saarlandes, Fed. Republic Germany, 1986; faculty rsch. assoc. Inst. Social Rsch., Ann Arbor, 1979—; vis. scholar Indsl. Inst. for Econs. and Social Rsch., Stockholm, 1979, 83, 90, Worklife Study Ctr., Stockholm, 1988, 90; Tinbergen Found. prof. U. Amsterdam, 1992, 94; panel mem. Social Sci. Rsch. Coun., N.Y.C., 1979—; rsch. assoc. Nat. Bur. Econ. Rsch., Cambridge, Mass., 1983—; prof. econs. Tinbsrgne Found. U. Amsterdam, 1992; vis. scholar U. Stockholm, 1994. Author, editor: Time Use Goods and Well Being, 1986, Studies in Labor Market Behavior: Sweden and the United States, 1981; mem. editorial bd.: Am. Econ. Rev., 1976-78; contbr. articles to profl. jours. Grantee NSF, 1973, 80, NICHD, 1995—. Mem. Am. Econs. Assn. Home: 3535 Daleview Dr Ann Arbor MI 48105-9604 Office: U Mich Dept Econs Lorch Hall Rm 312 Ann Arbor MI 48105

STAFFORD, J. FRANCIS, archbishop; b. Balt., July 26, 1932; s. F. Emmett and Mary Dorothy S. Student, Loyola Coll., Balt., 1950-52; B.A., St. Mary's Sem., Balt., 1954; S.T.B., S.T.L., Gregorian U., Rome, 1958; M.S.W., Catholic U., 1964; postgrad., Rutgers U., 1963, U. Wis.-Madison, 1969, St. Mary's Sem. and Univ., Balt., 1973-75. Spiritual moderator Ladies of Charity Ch., Balt., 1966-76; spiritual moderator Soc. St. Vincent de Paul, Balt., 1965-76; urban vicar Archdiocese of Balt., 1966-76, monsignor, 1970, vicar gen., auxiliary bishop, 1976-83; bishop Diocese of Memphis, 1983-86; archbishop Archdiocese of Denver, 1986—; dir. Assn. Cath. Charities, Balt., 1966-76; archdiocesan liaison to Md. Cath. Conf., Balt, 1975-78; Oriental Orthodox/Roman Cath. consultation Nat. Cath. Conf. Bishops, 1977-85, com. on doctrine, 1978-82, chmn. ecumenical and interreligious affairs com., 1987-90; co-chmn. bilateral dialogue Roman Cath./World Meth. Council, 1977-86; co-chmn. U.S. Roman Cath.-Luth. Dialogue, 1986—; chmn. Bishops' com. marriage and family life U.S. Cath. Conf., 1978-84; mem. gen. Synod Bishops, Vatican City, 1980. Contbr. articles to profl. jours. Trustee Good Samaritan Hosp., Balt., 1973-77, Cath. U. Am., 1990—, Blue Cross of Md., Inc., 1973-76, Balt. Urban Coalition, 1970-75; trustee, chmn., St. Thomas Theol. Sem., 1987—; bd. dirs. Sch. Social Work and Planning, U. Md., 1973-76. Recipient Father Kelly Alumni award Loyola High Sch., Md., 1973-76. Recipient Father Kelly Alumni award Loyola High Sch., 1978; Alumni Laureate, Loyola Coll., 1979. Mem. World Meth. Conf. Roman Cath. Dialogue (co-chmn. 1977-86), Oriental Orthodox Roman Cath. Consultation (co-chmn. 1977-85), Nat. Conf. Cath. Bishops, Luth. Roman Cath. Dialogue, Congregation for Doctrine of Faith. Office: 200 Josephine St Denver CO 80206*

STAFFORD, JAMES F., electronics executive; b. 1944. With Honeywell Inc., 1965-73, Bendix, 1973-76, Fairfield Camera & Instrument Corp., 1976-79, Synertek, 1979-81; dir. materials Seeq Technology, Inc., San Jose, Calif., 1981-84; pres., CEO Chips & Tech. Inc., San Jose, 1985—. Office: Chips & Tech Inc 2950 Zanker Rd San Jose CA 95134*

STAFFORD, JOHN ROGERS, pharmaceutical and household products company executive; b. Harrisburg, Pa., Oct. 24, 1937; s. Paul Henry and Gladys Lee (Sharp) S.; m. Inge Paul, Aug. 22, 1959; children—Carolyn, Jennifer, Christina, Charlotte. AB, Dickinson Coll., 1959; LLB with distinction, George Washington U., 1962, Degree (hon.), 1994. Bar: D.C. 1962. Assoc. Steptoe & Johnson, Washington, 1962-66; gen. atty. Hoffman-LaRoche, Nutley, N.J., 1966-67, group atty., 1967-70; gen. counsel Am. Home Products Corp., N.Y.C., 1970-74, v.p., 1972-77, sr. v.p., 1977-80, exec. v.p., 1980-81, pres., 1981—, chmn., chief exec. officer, 1986—; bd. dirs. Chem. Bankin Corp., Allied Signal Inc., Pharm. Rsch. and Mfrs. Am. (chmn. 1991-92), Grocery Mfrs. Am., Inc., Met. Life Ins. Co., Nynex Corp. Bd. dirs. Ctrl. Park Conservancy, Project Hope; trustee com. econ. devel. adv. bd. Am. Paralysis Assn. Recipient John Bell Larner 1st Scholar award George Washington U. Law Sch., 1962, Outstanding Achievement Alumnus award, 1981. Mem. ABA, D.C. Bar ASsn., Nat. Assn. Mfrs. (bd. dirs.), Sky Club (N.Y.C.), Essex Fells (N.J.) Country, Links Club (N.Y.C.), Baltusrol (N.J.), Robert Trent Jones (Va.). Office: American Home Products Corp 5 Giralda Farms Madison NJ 07940

STAFFORD, JOSEPHINE HOWARD, lawyer; b. San Antonio, July 27, 1921; d. Joseph and Olive Maeblume (Goodson) Howard; m. Harry B. Stafford (div. 1958); 1 child, Julie. BA, U. N.C., 1942, LLB, 1952. Bar: N.C. 1952, Fla. 1953, U.S. Dist. Ct. (mid. dist.) Fla. 1954, U.S. Ct. Appeals (11th cir.), U.S. Ct. Appeals (5th cir.); lic. real estate broker; cert. arbitrator, Hillsborough County Cir. Ct. Assoc. Fowler, White, Gillen, Yancey and Humkey, Tampa, Fla., 1952-54; pvt. practice Tampa, 1954-57, 69-72; exec. dir., atty. Legal Aid Bur., Tampa, 1957-69; atty. City of Tampa, 1972—; instr. U. South Fla., Tampa, 1971-72; adj. prof. Hillsborough Community Coll., Tampa, 1980-86; lectr. U. South Fla., Tampa, 1973, U. Tampa, U. Fla., Gainesville, 1959; atty. Housing Authority City of Tampa, 1970-72; substitute judge mcpl. ct., 1958-71, interim mcpl. ct. judge, 1971-72; mem. Grievance Com. "13C". Author: Amendments to Search Warrant Law; Tax Laws, Agencies and Ordinances; Divorce, 1979; author Mayor's Proclamation Commemorating D-Day, 1994. Precinct committeewoman Hillsborough County Dem. Exec. Com., Tampa, 1991, co-chmn., 1970; bd. mem., past pres. chmn. com. Travelers Aid Soc., Tampa, 1971-93; bd. mem., fin. com. Girl Scouts Am., Tampa, 1991—; bd. mem., exec. com., past pres. Police Athletic League, Tampa, 1984-88, 90—; mem. Fla. Commn. on Status of Women; co-chmn. Selective Svc. System, 1971-76; bd. dirs. ARC, Tampa chpt., 1954-79, Am. Cancer Soc., Hillsborough County unit, 1982-84. Recipient Svc. to Mankind award Sertoma Internat., Tampa, 1969, Outstanding Bus. and Profl. Woman of Yr. award Bus. and Profl. Women, Tampa, 1959, 69, Women Helping Women award Soroptimist Club, Tampa, 1989, Excellence award Hillsborough County Dem. Women's Club, 1991. Mem. ABA (Nat. Conf. Lawyers and Social Workers, Nat. Conf. Lawyers and Realtors, Standing Com. on Nat. Conf. Groups), Fla. Bar Assn. (chmn., legal aid com.), Tampa and Hillsborough County Bar Assns. (dir. 1958-63, chmn. elder law com. 1991-93), Nat. Legal Aid and Defender Assn. (nat. bd. dirs.), Fla. Assn. Women Lawyers (pres.), Tampa Assn. Women Lawyers (pres., named Outstanding Women Lawyers of Achievement, 1993), Fla. Fedn. Social

Workers (pres. bd. 1969), Fla. Fedn. Social Workers (pres. Hillsborough County chpt. 1964), Tampa Legal Sec. Assn., U.S. Navy League. Democrat. Methodist. Avocations: poetry, art, theatre, pottery, gardening, swimming. Home: 3402 S Gardenia Dr Tampa FL 33629-8208 Office: City of Tampa Legal Dept 315 E Kennedy Blvd Tampa FL 33602-5211

STAFFORD, REBECCA, college president, sociologist; b. Topeka, July 9, 1936; d. Frank C. and Anne Elizabeth (Larrick) S. A.B. magna cum laude, Radcliffe Coll., 1958, M.A., 1961; Ph.D., Harvard U., 1964. Lectr. dept. sociology Sch. Edn., Harvard U., Cambridge, Mass., 1964-70, mem. vis. com. bd. overseers, 1973-79; assoc. prof. sociology U. Nev., Reno, 1970-73, prof., 1973-80, chmn. dept. sociology, 1974-77, dean Coll. Arts and Scis., 1977-80; pres. Bemidji (Minn.) State U., 1980-82; exec. v.p. Colo. State U., Ft. Collins, 1982-83; pres. Chatham Coll., Pitts., 1983-91, Monmouth U., West Long Branch, N.J., 1993—; bd. dirs. First Fidelity Bancorp, N.J. Contbr. articles to profl. jours. Trustee Monmouth Med. Ctr.; bd. dirs. Univ. Presbyn. Hosp., 1985-93, Pitts. Symphyony, 1984-93, Winchester-Thurston Sch.; chmn. Harvard U. Grad. Soc. Coun., 1987-93. Recipient McCurdy-Rinkle prize for rsch. Eastern Psychiat. Assn., 1970; named Man of Yr. in Edn., City of Pitts., 1986, Woman of Yr. in Edn., YWCA Tribute to Women, 1989; grantee Am. Coun. Edn. Inst. Acad. Deans, 1979, Inst. Ednl. Mgmt., Harvard U., 1984. Mem. Harvard U. Alumni Assn. (bd. dirs. 1985-87), Phi Beta Kappa, Phi Kappa Phi. Address: Monmouth University West Long Branch NJ 07764

STAFFORD, ROBERT THEODORE, lawyer, former senator; b. Rutland, Vt., Aug. 8, 1913; s. Bert L. and Mable R. (Stratton) S.; m. Helen C. Kelley, Oct. 15, 1938; children—Madelyn, Susan, Barbara, Dianne. B.S., Middlebury Coll., 1935, LL.D., 1960; postgrad., U. Mich., 1936; LL.B., Boston U., 1938, LL.D., 1959; LL.D., Norwich U., 1960, St. Michaels Coll., 1967, U. Vt., 1970. Bar: Vt. bar 1938. City prosecutor Rutland, 1939-42; state's atty. Rutland County, 1947-51; dep. atty. gen. Vt., 1953-54, atty. gen., 1954-56, lt. gov., 1957-58, gov., 1959-60; mem. 87th to 92d Congresses, Vt.-at-large; apptd. U.S. Senate, 1971, mem., 1972-89, chmn. com. on environment and public works, 1981-87, chmn. edn. subcom., 1981-87, ranking mem., 1987-89; ptnr. Stafford, Abiatell & Stafford, 1938-46; sr. ptnr. Stafford & LaBrake, 1946-51. Chmn. UN-U.S.A. Assn. Panel UNESCO, 1989—. Lt. comdr. USNR, 1942-46, 51-52; capt. Res. Named Disting. Scholar U. Vt., 1989, Disting. Prof. Pub. Affairs Castleton State Coll., 1989. Mem. V.F.W., Am. Legion. Club: Elk. Home and Office: 1 Sugarwood Hill Rd RR 1 Box 3954 Rutland VT 05701 Office: Castleton Coll Coolidge Libr Bldg Castleton VT 05735

STAFFORD, THOMAS PATTEN, retired military officer, former astronaut; b. Weatherford, Okla., Sept. 17, 1930; m. Linda A. Dishman; children: Dionne, Karin. BS, U.S. Naval Acad., 1952; student, USAF Exptl. Flight Test Sch., 1958-59; DSc (hon.), Oklahoma City U., 1967; LLD (hon.), Western State U. Coll. Law, 1969, U. Cordoba, Argentina; D Communications (hon.), Emerson Coll., 1969; D Aero. Engring. (hon.), Embry-Riddle Aero. Inst., 1970; LHD (hon.), U. Okla., 1994; M of Humane Letters (hon.), Southwestern U., 1994; HHD (hon.), Oklahoma Christian U. Commd. 2d lt. USAF, 1952; advanced through grades to lt. gen.; chief performance br. Aerospace Research Pilot Sch., Edwards AFB, Calif.; with NASA, Houston, 1962-75; assigned Project Gemini, pilot Gemini VI, 1965, command pilot Gemini IX, 1966, comdr. Apollo X, 1969, chief astronaut office, 1969-71; dep. dir. flight crew operations, comdr. Apollo-Soyuz flight, 1975; comdr. Air Force Flight Test Ctr., Edwards AFB, 1975; lt. gen., dep. chief staff Research, Devel. and Aquisition, 1979; ret., 1979; chair The White House/NASA Com. to Independently Advise NASA How to Return to Moon and Explore Mars, 1990-91; chmn. bd. Omega Watch Co. Am.; dir. F-117A Stealth Fighter program, 1978; co-founder tech. cons. firm Stafford, Burke, Hecker, Inc., Alexandria, Va.; adv. numerous govtl. agys. including Nat. Aeronautics and Space Adminstrn., Air Force Systems command; defense adv. to Ronald Reagan during presdl. campaign; bd. dirs. numerous cos. Co-author: Pilot's Handbook for Performance Flight Testing, Aerodynamics Handbook for Performance Flight Testing. Decorated DFC with oak leaf cluster, D.S.M. (3), Disting. Flying Cross (2); recipient NASA Disting. Svc. medal (2), NASA Exceptional Svc. medal (2), Air Force Command Pilot Astronaut Wings; Chanute Flight award AIAA, 1976, VFW Nat. Space award, 1976; Gen. Thomas D. White USAF Space trophy Nat. Geog. Soc., 1976; Gold Space medal Fedn. Aeronautique Internationale, 1976, Laurel Award, Space/Missiles, Aviation Week & Space Tech., 1991, Congl. Space medal honor V.P. Dan Quayle, 1993, Rotary Nat. award Space Achievement, 1993, Goddard award Astronaut Hall of Fame, 1993, Pub. Svc. award NASA, 1994; co-recipient AIAA, 1966, Harmon Internat. Aviation trophy, 1966, Spl. Trustees award NATAS, 1969. Fellow Am. Astronautical Soc., Soc. Exptl. Test Pilots; mem. AIAA, AFTRA (hon. life). Holder all-time world speed record for space flight, 24,791.4 miles per hour. Address: 1006 Cameron St Alexandria VA 22314-2427 *As we move through life, each of us has an opportunity to make a contribution to humanity. In this respect, I have been extremely fortunate as I have been privileged to help explore new frontiers in space and aviation technology. But, it is clear to me that the most important element in a successful program is people. Their willingness to discipline their efforts and to work together to achieve important objectives remains the most important factor in a successful operation.*

STAFFORD, WILLIAM HENRY, JR., federal judge; b. Masury, Ohio, May 11, 1931; s. William Henry and Frieda Gertrude (Nau) S.; m. Nancy Marie Helman, July 11, 1959; children: William Henry, Donald Helman, David Harrold. B.S., Temple U., 1953, LL.B., 1956; J.D., 1968. Bar: Fla. 1961, U.S. Ct. Appeals (5th cir.) 1969, U.S. Supreme Ct. 1970. Assoc. firm Robinson & Roark, Pensacola, 1961-64; individual practice law Pensacola, 1964-67, state atty., 1967-69, U.S. atty., 1969-75; U.S. dist. judge No. Dist. Fla., Tallahassee, 1975—, U.S. dist. judge, chief judge, 1981-92; instr. Pensacola Jr. Coll., 1964, 68; mem. judicial council U.S. Ct. Appeals (11th cir.), 1986-89; apptd. com. on intercircuit assignments, 1987-92, subcom. on fed. jurisdiction, 1983-87. Lt. (j.g.) USN, 1957-60. Mem. Fla. Bar (mem. numerous coms., bench/bar commn. 1991-92, bench/bar implementation commn. 1993), Dist. Judges Assn. 11th Cir. (pres. 1984-85), State Fed. Judicial Council Fla., Am. Inns of Ct., Tallahassee Bar Assn., Tallahassee Inn (pres. 1989-91), Masons, Shriners, Rotary, Sigma Phi Epsilon, Phi Delta Phi. Republican. Episcopalian. Office: US Dist Ct 110 E Park Ave Tallahassee FL 32301-7750

STAFL, ADOLF, obstetrician, gynecologist, educator; b. Prague, Czechoslovakia, May 5, 1931; came to U.S., 1965; s. Adolf and Anna (Gabrielova) S.; m. Jarmila Kresl; children: Jan, Denny. MD, Charles U., Prague, 1951-57, PhD, 1964. Cert. Am. Bd. Ob-Gyn. Asst. prof. ob-gyn Charles U., Plzen, Czechoslovakia, 1962-68; instr. ob-gyn Johns Hopkins U., Balt., 1968-69; from asst. prof. to prof. ob-gyn Med. Coll. Wis., Milw., 1969-85, prof. ob-gyn, 1985—. Author: Atlas of Colposcopy, 1982; contbr. articles to profl. jours. Fellow Am. Coll. Obstetricians and Gynecologists; hon. mem. British Soc. Colposcopy and Cervical Pathology, Italian Soc. Colposcopy and Cervical Pathology, Obstet. and Gynecologic Soc. of Valencia, Spain, Obstet. and Gynecol. Soc. Paraguay; mem. Internat. Fedn. Cervical Pathology and Colposcopy (pres. 1975-78), Am. Soc. Colposcopy and Cervical Pathology (pres. 1982-84), Am. Gynecol. and Obstet. Soc., Soc. Gynecologic Oncologists. Home: 2202894 NW Maplewood Ln Waukesha WI 53186 Office: Med Coll Wis 8700 W Wisconsin Ave Milwaukee WI 53226-3512

STAGE, THOMAS BENTON, psychiatrist; b. Marietta, Ohio, July 23, 1926; s. John Douglas and Grace (Shawhan) S.; m. Doris Jeane Weinstock, Dec. 22, 1951; children: Samuel Ray, Amy Elizabeth, James Robert; m. Alicia Anderson Marsh, June 7, 1993. B.A. cum laude, Marietta Coll., 1949; M.D., Ohio State U., 1952. Diplomate: Am. Bd. Psychiatry and Neurology. Intern Detroit Receiving Hosp., 1952-53; psychiat. resident, fellow Menninger Sch. Psychiatry, Topeka, 1953-56; sect. chief, chief psychiatry VA Hosp., Topeka, 1956-62; adminstr. VA Hosp., Sheridan, Wyo., 1962-66; dir. VA Hosp., Salem, Va., 1967-72; dep. asst. chief med. dir. for ambulatory care VA Central Office, Washington, 1972-74; dir. No. Va. Mental Health Inst., Falls Church, 1974-78; asst. commr. for mental health State of Va., Richmond, 1978-79; dir. clin. services Fairfax-Falls Church Community Services Bd., Vienna, Va., 1979-82, psychiat. cons. for med. affairs, 1982—; instr. Menninger Sch. Psychiatry, 1958-62, U. Wyo. Sch. Nursing, 1963-66; assoc. prof. U. Va. Med. Sch., 1972-74; cons. surveyor Joint Commn. on

Accreditation of Hosps., 1976—; cons. Crow-No. Cheyenne USPHS Hosp., 1963-66, Ala. Dept. Mental Health (Wyatt Com.), 1986-91; psychiatric cons. on accreditation Commonwealth of Va. Dept. Mental Health, Mental Retardation and Substance Abuse, 1982—; mem. Comprehensive Mental Health Ctr. Com., 1968-73, Gov.'s Adv. Commn. on Mental Health, 1971-74; chmn. Drug Abuse Rehab. Com., 1970-73; cons. adminstrv. psychiatry NIMH, 1975-78; chmn. steering com. Asso. Faculties Program Community Psychiatry, Washington, 1975-77; mem. State Health Coordinating Coun., 1976-89. Contbr. articles to profl. jours. Served wtih USNR, 1944-46, PTO. Fellow Am. Psychiat. Assn. (life); mem. Am. Assn. Psychiat. Adminstrs., Washington Psychiat. Soc., Psychiat. Soc. Va., Am. Assn. Community Psychiatrists. Home: 11410 Hollow Timber Way Reston VA 22094-1906 Office: Office Mental Health Svcs 3340 Woodburn Rd Annandale VA 22003-1298

STAGER, DONALD K., construction company executive. Chmn., CEO, Dillingham Constrn. Corp.; Pleasanton, Calif. Office: Dillingham Constrn Corp 5960 Inglewood Dr Pleasanton CA 94588-8535

STAGER, LAWRENCE E., archaeologist, educator; b. Kenton, Ohio, Jan. 5, 1943; married; 2 children. BA, Harvard U., 1965, MA, 1972, PhD in Syro-Palestinian Archeology and History, 1975. Instr. Oriental Inst., U. Chgo., 1973-74, asst. prof., 1974-75, assoc. prof. Syro-Palestinian archeology, from 1976; Dorot prof. archeology of Israel, Dept. Near Eastern Langs. and Civilizations and Anthropology Harvard U., Cambridge, Mass., 1986—; co-dir. Am. Expdn., Idalion, Cyprus, 1972-74; dir. UNESCO Save Carthage Project, Am. Punic Archaeol. Expdn., 1975-80, Harvard Semitic Mus., 1987—, Leon Levy Expdn. to Ashkelon, Israel, 1985-95. Author: Ashkelon Discovered, 1991, Essays in Biblical Archaeology, 1995; co-author: Idalion I, Idalion II; contbr. articles to profl. publs. Mem. Am. Schs. Oriental Rsch. (editor newsletter 1975-76, assoc. trustee 1977-80, trustee 1987-90, assoc. editor bull. 1978—), Archaeol. Inst. Am. (v.p. 1986-88, trustee 1989-91), Am. Orient Soc., Soc. Bibl. Lit. Rsch. in economy, society and religion of ancient Israel; archaeology of Philistines, Canaanites and Phoenicians. Office: Harvard U Semitic Mus Dept Near Ea Langs/Civil Cambridge MA 02138-2091

STAGG, LOUIS CHARLES, English language and literature educator; b. New Orleans, Jan. 3, 1933; s. Louis Anatol and Gladys (Andrews) S.; BA in English, La. Coll., 1955; MA in English U. Ark., 1957, PhD in English, 1963; m. Mary Casner, June 5, 1959; children: Robert Charles, Helen Marie. Teaching asst. English U. Ark., 1955-59; asst. prof. William Jewell Coll., 1959-60; instr. Stephen F. Austin State U., 1960-62; asst. prof. Memphis State U. (name changed to U. Memphis), 1962-69, assoc. prof., 1969-77, prof., English language and literature 1977—, dir. grad. studies in English, 1985-88, dir. English Drama Players, 1968—, dir undergrad. advising for English, 1970-80, 88-91, chair policies and procedures com. for English, 1983—, tenure and promotion com. for English, 1978-80, 82-86, 89-94; chmn. acad. policies com. Memphis State U. Senate, 1981-82, 88-90, 93—, mem. exec. com. senate, 1987-91, 93—, parliamentarian of senate, 1987-88, 90-91, 94—, humanities rep. budget adv. com. dean coll. arts and scis., 1992-93, mem. steering com., chair of schedules, originator Alliance Creative Theatre, Edn. and Rsch. series, 1989, 90, 92, 94; cons. NEH, 1975, 76, 78, Ohio State U. Press, summer 1985, 86, U. Jordan, Aman, 1985; chair policies and procedures subdivsn. Eng. Dept. so. assn. colls., schs. self study, mem. steering com., 1992-93; cons. Memphis State U. Learning Media-Ctrs. catalogue Shakespeare holdings, 1992-93, rev., 1993-94, 94-95. Mem. Memphis Oratorio Soc. Chorus, 1969-92, diction coach, 1987, Memphis Symphony Chorus, 1993—, Memphis in May Tattoo Chorus, 1993. Recipient summer stipend NEH, 1967; Memphis State U. grantee, 1965—; travel grantee to U.S. Library of Congress, summer 1971. Mem. MLA, So. Humanities Coun. (sec.-treas. 1974-76, exec. com. 1976-83, 94—, chmn. coun. 1993-94, chmn. sect. humanities in pluralistic society 1984, ad hoc com. on crisis in teaching humanities 1977—, chmn. local arrangements for convs. 1975, 94), Tenn. Philol. Assn. (pres. 1976-77, exec. com. 1977, local arrangements chmn. 1987), Marlowe Soc. Am. (book reviewer 1984, 86, 87, 88, 93), Am. Soc. for Theatre Rsch., Samuel Beckett Soc., Conf. on Christianity and Lit., South Cen. Conf. on Christianity and Lit. Soc. for Study of Works of Harold Pinter (asst. constitution revision 1988, asst. with planning 1992, treas. 1994—, mem. exec. com. 1994—), Ark. Philol. Assn., Shakespeare Assn. Am. (local arrangements host com. 1985), Stratford-Upon-Avon Shakespeare Festival, Eng.; Eugene O'Neill Soc., Alliance for Creative Theatre, Edn. and Rsch. (chmn. schedules com., rep. for English, mem. steering com., originator of proposal 1986, 89, 90, 92, 94), Internat. Shakespeare Assn., Am. Soc. Theatre Rsch., Internat. Soc. Theatre Rsch., Medieval and Renaissance Drama Soc., Renaissance Soc. Am., South Cen. Renaissance Conf. (chmn. nominations 1976, exec. com. 1978-80, program com. 1981-83, chmn. sect. Shakespeare 1981, 85, 95, 16th Century lit. 1982, chmn. local arrangements 1983, symposium on humanism 1984, chmn. Shakespeare on film and the teaching of Brit. Drama 1986, chmn. music in Shakespeare's plays 1987, chmn. sect. Thematic Approaches to Tudor/Stuart Drama 1988, chmn. sect. Medieval influences on Renaissance drama 1993, chmn. Shakespeare's Villains: Stage and Page 1995, chmn. local arrangements for convention 1990, chmn. spl. session 1989, 95), South Cen. MLA (assoc. editor for English, South Cen. Bull. 1982-84, nominations 1985-86, 95—, book reviewer South Cen. Rev. 1983, 85, 86, sec. English I.B. Renaissance, 1986, chair, 1987, sec. spl. sect. Renaissance Drama, 1988, chair Shakespeare's Tragi-comedies and tragi-comic romances, 1989, co-chair local arrangements 1980, 92), South Atlantic MLA, South Cen. Coll. English Assn. (sec.-treas. 1980-81, v.p. 1981-82, pres. 1982-83, exec. com. 1983-90, co-host 1982, com. constitution revision 1989), Coll. English Assn., Internat. Patristic Medieval and Renaissance Conf. (sect. chmn. Medieval drama 1977, chair Shakespeare), Am. Theatre Assn. (chmn. sect. combining Brit. lit. and theatre in teaching of drama 1983, chmn. Shakespeare sect. 1994), The Stratford Can. Shakespeare Festival, AAUP (sec. treas. Memphis State U. chap. 1982-86, v.p. 1986-88, pres. 1988-90), Phi Beta Kappa (pres. Memphis alumni assn. 1985-88, mem. spl. panel The Soc. and the New Scholarship at 37th triennial coun. 1994), Alpha Chi. Democrat. Episcopalian (lay reader 1969-86). Author: (with J. Lasley Dameron) Poe's Critical Vocabulary, 1966; author series: Index To The Figurative Language of John Webster's Tragedies, 1967, of Ben Jonson's Tragedies, 1967, of Thomas Heywood's Tragedies, 1967, of George Chapman's Tragedies, 1970, of John Marston's Tragedies, 1970, of Thomas Middleton's Tragedies, 1970, of Cyril Tourneur's Tragedies, 2d edit. all 7 under title Index to the Figurative Language of the Tragedies of Shakespeare's Chief 17th Century Contemporaries 1977), 3d edit., 1982; Index to the Figurative Language of the Tragedies of Shakespeare's Chief 16th Century Contemporaries, 1984; contbr. to Great Writers of the English Language: Dramatists, 1979, 87; circulation editor Interpretations, 1976-80; contbr. articles on English and American drama to profl. jours., publs. on Shakespeare, other lit. publs. Home: 5219 Mason Rd Memphis TN 38117-2104 Office: U Memphis Dept English Memphis TN 38152 *It's time—past time— we realized we all belong to one race, human, and that we have only one world, this one, only one ecological system, this one, if we want humanity to survive beyond our own life times.*

STAGG, TOM, federal judge; b. Shreveport, La., Jan. 19, 1923; s. Thomas Eaton and Beulah (Meyer) S.; m. Margaret Mary O'Brien, Aug. 21, 1946; children: Julie, Margaret Mary. B.A., La. State U., 1943, J.D., 1949. Bar: La. 1949. With firm Hargrove, Guyton, Van Hook & Hargrove, Shreveport, 1949-53; pvt. practice law Shreveport, 1953-58; sr. ptnr. firm Stagg, Cady & Beard, Shreveport, 1958-74; judge U.S. Dist. Ct. (we. dist.) La., 1974-84, 91-92, chief judge, 1984-90, sr. judge, 1990-74; pres. Abe Meyer Corp., 1960-74, Stagg Investments, Inc., 1964-74; mng. partner Pierremont Mall Shopping Center, 1963-74; v.p. King Hardware Co., 1955-74; Mem. Shreveport Airport Authority, 1967-73, chmn., 1970-73; chmn. Gov.'s Tidelands Adv. Council, 1969-70; del. La. Constl. Conv., 1973-74; chmn. rules com., com. on exec. dept.; mem. Gov.'s Adv. Com on Offshore Revenues, 1972-74. Active Republican party, 1950-74, del. all. convs., 1956, 60, 64, 68, 72; mem. Nat. Com. for La., 1964-72, mem. exec. com., 1964-68; Pres. Shreveport Jr. C. of C., 1955-56; v.p. La. Jr. C. of C., 1956-57. Served to capt., inf. AUS, 1943-46, ETO. Decorated Bronze Star, Purple Heart with oak leaf cluster. Mem. Am., La., Shreveport bar assns., Photog. Soc. Am. Office: US Dist Ct 300 Fannin St Ste 4100 Shreveport LA 71101-3141

STAGLIN, GAREN KENT, finance and computer service company executive; b. Lincoln, Nebr., Dec. 22, 1944; s. Ramon and Darlene (Guilliams) S.; m. Sharalyn King, June 8, 1968; children: Brandon Kent, Shannon

King. BS in Engring. with honors, UCLA, 1966; MBA, Stanford U., 1968. Treas. Stanco, Inc., 1968—; assoc. Carr Mgmt. Co., N.Y.C., 1971-75; v.p. Crocker Nat. Bank, San Francisco, 1975-76; dir. fin. Itel Corp., San Francisco, 1976-77, pres. ins. services div., 1977-79; corp. v.p., gen. mgr. ADP Automotive Svcs. Group, San Ramon, Calif., 1978-91; chmn., chief exec. officer Safelite Glass Corp., Columbus, Ohio, 1991—; bd. dirs. Grimes Aerospace Corp. Bd. dirs. Peralta Hosp. Cancer Inst., 1977-78, Berkeley Repertory Theatre, 1979-85, Summa Care, Inc., 1988-90, Quick Response Svcs., Inc., 1991—, First Data Corp., 1992—; chmn. major gifts program Ea. Bay region, Stanford (Calif.) U., 1989-92. Lt. USN, 1968-71. Mem. Stanford Assocs. (bd. govs. 1985-92), Young Pres. Orgn., Internat. Inst. Soc. (bd. govs. 1985-92), Stanford Bus. Sch. (adv. bd. 1995—), Nat. Glass Assn. (govt. affairs com.). Democrat. Lutheran. Home: PO Box 680 1570 Bella Oaks Ln Rutherford CA 94573

STAHELI, DONALD L., grain company executive; b. 1931. BS, Utah State U., 1953; MS, U. Ill., 1954, PhD, 1956. With Swift & Co., 1958-69, Allied Mills (now World Meat and World Milling Groups of Continental Grain Co., 1969—; dir. Continental Grain Co., N.Y.C., 1977—, exec. v.p., 1977-84, pres., COO, 1984-88, pres., CEO, 1988—. With USAF, 1956-58. Office: Continental Grain Co 277 Park Ave New York NY 10172-0003*

STAHL, ALAN MICHAEL, curator; b. Providence, Aug. 7, 1947; s. Benjamin and Evelyn (Miller) S.; m. Pamela McAbee Dec. 28, 1968 (div. 1976). BA, U. Calif., Berkeley, 1968; MA, U. Pa., 1973, PhD, 1977. Asst. curator Am. Numismatic Soc., N.Y.C., 1980-82, assoc. curator, 1982-86, curator, 1986—; visiting prof. Universita di Venezia, Venice, Italy, 1987-88. Author: Merovingian Coinage/Metz, 1982, Venetian Tornesello, 1985, Medal in America, 1988. Recipient Research Grant G.K. Delmas Found., 1981, 83, 85. Mem. Fed. Internat. de la Medaille (USA del.), Am. Medallic Sculpture Assn., Nat. Sculpture Soc. (councillor), Medieval Acad. Am., N.Y. Numismatic Club. Home: 565 Ft Washington Ave New York NY 10033-1935 Office: Am Numismatic Soc Broadway Alley New York NY 10099

STAHL, ALICE SLATER, psychiatrist; b. Vienna, Austria, Jan. 8, 1913; came to U.S., 1938; d. Sam and Helen (Bluman) Slater; widowed; children: Kenneth Lee, June Audrey. Baccalaureate, Gymnasium, Vienna, 1932; Med. Dr., U. Vienna Med. Sch., 1938. Intern Williamsport (Pa.) Gen. Hosp., 1939-40; resident in psychiatry Gallinger Mcpl. Hosp., Washington, 1940-41, Independence State Hosp., 1941-42; resident in psychiatry Bellevue Hosp., N.Y.C., 1942-43, attending psychiatry, 1945-48; staff psychiatrist Jewish Bd. of Guardians, N.Y.C., 1943-45; attending psychiatrist Jamaica Hosp., Queens, N.Y., 1948-52; dir. adolescent psychiatry Hillside Hosp., Glen Oaks, N.Y., 1954-62, attending staff psychiatrist, 1962—; supervising psychiatrist Bergen Pines County Hosp., Paramus, N.J.; prof. psychiatry, asst. prof. clin. psychiatry Yeshiva U. Fellow AMA (life), Am. Psychiat. Assn. (life); mem. Am. Psychoanalytic Assn. (life), Am. Soc. for Adolescent Psychiatry (life). Avocations: swimming, hiking, gardening, grandmotherhood. Home and Office: 305 Joan Pl Wyckoff NJ 07481-2818

STAHL, CHARLES EUGENE, lawyer; b. Washington, Sept. 23, 1944; s. George P. Sr. and Dorothy G. (McCaffrey) S. BA, U. Notre Dame, 1967; JD, Northwestern U., 1971. Bar: Ill. 1972, Calif. 1980. Assoc. Newman & Hess, Chgo., 1971-73; ptnr. Newman & Stahl, Chgo., 1973-83, Arvey, Hodes, Costello & Berman, Chgo., 1984, Friedman & Koven, Chgo., 1985, Winston & Strawn, Chgo., 1986—; lectr. Ill. Inst. For Continuing Edn., Chgo., 1975—; speaker Infocast Banking Semminars, Santa Monica, Calif., 1987—. Bd. dirs. Chgo. Symphony Orch., 1987—, William Ferris Chorale, Chgo., 1988—. Mem. Univ. Club. Democrat. Roman Catholic. Avocations: classical music, sports collectibles, history. Office: Winston & Strawn 35 W Wacker Dr Chicago IL 60601-1614

STAHL, DAVID EDWARD, association executive; b. Chgo., Apr. 10, 1934; s. Archie Edward and Dorothy (Berning) S.; m. Carolyn Downs Stahl, June 23, 1956; children: Stephen, Michael, Kurt, Thomas. B.S., Miami U., 1956. Exec. v.p. Republic Realty Mortgage Corp., Chgo., 1963-66; dep. mayor City of Chgo., 1966-70, city comptroller, 1971-73; exec. v.p. Urban Land Inst., Washington, 1973-76, Nat. Assn. Home Builders, Washington, 1977-84; pres. Nat. Forest Products Assn., Washington, 1984-87; exec. v.p. Urban Land Inst., Washington, 1987-92; exec. dir. Young Pres.'s Orgn., Irving, Tex., 1992—; del. 6th Ill. Constl. Conv., Springfield, 1970. Served to lt. USAF, 1956-59. Mem. Am. Soc. Assn. Execs., Lambda Alpha. Roman Catholic. Clubs: Economic (Chgo.), Wayfarers; Annapolis Yacht. Home: 3801 Gilbert G Dallas TX 75219 Office: 451 S Decker Dr # 200 Irving TX 75062

STAHL, DAVID M., lawyer; b. Chgo., Sept. 22, 1946. BA, U. Ill., 1968; JD magna cum laude, U. Mich., 1971, MA, 1971. Bar: Ill. 1972, U.S. Dist. Ct. (no. dist.) Ill. 1972, U.S. Ct. Appeals (D.C. dist.) 1979, U.S. Ct. Appeals (9th cir.) 1984, U.S. Ct. Appeals (7th cir.) 1986, U.S. Dist. Ct. (ea. dist.) Mich. 1989. Ptnr. Sidley & Austin, Chgo. Office: Sidley & Austin 1 First Nat Plz Chicago IL 60603

STAHL, FRANK LUDWIG, civil engineer; b. Fuerth, Germany, 1920; came to U.S., 1946, naturalized, 1949; s. Leo E. and Anna (Regensburger) S.; m. Edith Cosmann, Aug. 31, 1947; children—David, Robert. BSCE, Tech. Inst. Zurich, Switzerland, 1945. With Ammann & Whitney, Cons. Engrs., N.Y.C., 1946-93, project engr., 1955-67, assoc., 1968-76, sr. assoc., 1977-81, chief engr. Transp. div., 1982-93; lectr. in the field. Prin. works include: Verrazano-Narrows Bridge, Throgs Neck Bridge, Walt Whitman Bridge, Improvements to Golden Gate Bridge, rehab. of Williamsburg Bridge, N.Y.C. Royal Gorge Bridge, Colo., Interstate-10 Deck Tunnel, Phoenix, Ariz.; contbr. articles to profl. jours. on bridge design and construction. Recipient Gold award The James F. Lincoln Arc Welding Found., 1986, John A. Roebling medal Internat. Bridge Conf., 1992. Fellow ASCE (Thomas Fitch Rowland prize 1967, Innovation in Civil Engring. award of merit 1983, Metro. Civil Engr. of Yr. award 1987, Roebling award 1990), ASTM (vice pres. A-1 on steel, stainless steel and related alloys 1978-83, chmn. steel reinforce-subcom. 1971-82, award of merit 1982); mem. Am. Inst. Steel Constrn., Engring. Found. (rsch. coun. on structural connections), Internat. Assn. Bridge and Structural Engring., Internat. Bridge Tunnel and Turnpike Assn. Home: 20911 28th Rd Flushing NY 11360-2412

STAHL, JACK LELAND, real estate company executive; b. Lincoln, Ill., June 28, 1934; s. Edwin R. and Edna M. (Burns) S.; m. Carol Anne Townsend, June 23, 1956; children: Cheryl, Nancy, Kellea. BS in Edn., U. N.Mex., 1957. Tchr. Albuquerque Public Schs., 1956-59; pres. House Finders, Inc., Albuquerque, 1959-65; v.p. N.Mex. Savs. & Loan Assn., Albuquerque, 1965-67; chmn. bd. Hooten-Stahl, Inc., Albuquerque, 1967-77; mem. N.Mex. Ho. of Reps., 1969-70; pres. The Jack Stahl Co., Albuquerque, 1977—; mem. N.Mex. Senate, 1981-86; lt. gov. State of N.Mex., 1987-90. Mem. N.Mex. Ho. of Reps., 1969-70; mem. exec. bd. Gt. SW coun. Boy Scouts Am., 1982-89; bd. dirs. Better Bus. Bur. N.Mex., 1968-82, pres., 1975-76; trustee Univ. Heights Hosp., 1980-85; vice chmn. N.Mex. Bd. Fin., 1987-90, N.Mex. Community Devel. Coun., 1987-90. Named Realtor of Yr., Albuquerque Bd. Realtors, 1972. Mem. Nat. Assn. Realtors, Nat. Homebuilders assn., N.Mex. Amigos, 20-30 Club (pres. 1963-64), Rotary. Republican. Methodist. Office: 1911 Wyoming Blvd NE Albuquerque NM 87112-2865

STAHL, LADDIE L., electrical engineer, manufacturing company executive; b. Terre Haute, Ind., Dec. 8, 1921; s. Edgar Allen and Martha (Llewellyn) S.; m. Thelma Mae Beasley, Dec. 11, 1942; children: Stephanie, Laddie L. Craig. B.S. in Civil Engring., Purdue U., 1942; M.S. in Engring., Johns Hopkins U., 1950. With GE, 1954-90; mgr. planning and resources, electronics sci. and engring., corp. research and devel. GE, Schenectady, N.Y., 1974-76, mgr. electronics systems programs ops., elec. sci. and engring., 1976-84, mgr. spl. programs and project devel. operation, 1984-90; dir. tech. transfer program Data Storage Systems Ctr. Carnegie Mellon U., Pitts., 1990—; chmn. adv. group U.S. Army Electronics Command, 1971-74; mem. U.S. Army Sci. Bd., 1978-87; cons. in field. Contbr. articles to profl. publs. Mem. alumni bd. dirs. Purdue U., 1979-82. Served with U.S. Army, 1942-54, ETO; maj. gen. Res. (ret.), 1954-77. Decorated D.S.M., Legion of Merit. Mem. AIAA (sr.), IEEE (life), Am. Def. Preparedness Assn., Tau Beta Pi, Chi Epsilon. Clubs: Mohawk (Schenectady); Army and Navy (Washington). Home: 29 Fairway Ln Rexford NY 12148-1225 Office: Carnegie Mellon U

Hamerschlag Hall A206 ECE Dept Hamburg Hall 2505 Pittsburgh PA 15213-3890

STAHL, LESLEY R., journalist; b. Lynn, Mass., Dec. 16, 1941; d. Louis and Dorothy J. (Tishler) S.; m. Aaron Latham; 1 dau. B.A. cum laude, Wheaton Coll., Norton, Mass., 1963. Asst. to speechwriter Mayor Lindsay's Office, N.Y.C., 1966-67; researcher N.Y. Election unit London-Huntley Brinkley Report, NBC News, 1967-69; producer, reporter WHDH-TV, Boston, 1970-72; news corr. CBS News, Washington, from 1972; moderator Face the Nation, 1983-91; co-editor, corr. CBS News, 60 Minutes, 1991—. Trustee Wheaton Coll. Recipient Tex. Headliners award, 1973, Dennis Kauff award for lifetime achievement in journalism; named Best White House Corr., Washington Journalism Rev., 1991. Office: CBS News 60 Minutes 555 W 57th St New York NY 10019*

STAHL, NORMAN H., federal judge; b. Manchester, N.H., 1931. BA, Tufts U., 1952; LLB, Harvard U., 1955. Law clk. to Hon. John V. Spalding Mass. Supreme Ct., 1955-56; assoc. Devine, Millimet, Stahl & Branch, Manchester, N.H., 1956-59, ptnr., 1959-90; dist. judge U.S. Dist. Ct. (N.H. dist.), 1990-92; cir. judge U.S. Ct. Appeals (1st cir.), Concord, N.H., 1992—. Del. to Rep. Nat. Conv., 1988. Mem. N.H. Bar Assn. Office: US Ct Appeals 55 Pleasant St Rm 220 Concord NH 03301-3938

STAHL, O(SCAR) GLENN, writer, lecturer, former government official; b. Evansville, Ind., Apr. 30, 1910; s. Oscar and Mayme (Wittmer) S.; m. Marie Jane Rueter, June 26, 1934; children: Elaine Marie, Alan G. A.B., U. Evansville, 1931, LL.D., 1984; M.A., U. Wis., 1933; PhD, N.Y. U., 1936. Instr. govt. NYU, 1933-35; personnel officer TVA, 1935-41; with Fed. Security Agy. (later HEW), 1941-51; dir. personnel, 1948-51; with U.S. CSC (now OPM), 1951-69, dir. bur. policies and standards, 1955-69; adj. prof. public adminstrn. Am. U., 1949-69; part time prof. U. Tenn., 1939, Dept. Agr. Grad. Sch., 1941-49; vis. lectr. various univs., U.S. and abroad; lectr. Salzburg Seminar in Am. Studies, 1965; tech. assistance adviser to Venezuela UN, 1958-59, 72; U.S. rep. UN Conf., Ethiopia, 1964; Ford Found. cons. to India, 1968-69, 71, Nepal, 1969, Pakistan, 1974; AID adviser, Pakistan, 1969, 71; U.S. rapporteur Internat. Congress Adminstrv. Scis., Dublin, 1968; U.S. rep. UN Seminar, Tashkent, Uzbekistan, 1969; spl. advisor to W. Ger., 1971; spl. cons. Public Adminstrn. Service-Govtl. Affairs Inst. and Internat. Personnel Mgmt. Assn., 1973-76; dir. Internat. Symposium on Public Personnel Adminstrn., Salzburg, 1973, 75; speaker Latin Am. Conf. on Civil Service Tng., Venezuela, 1982. Author: Training Career Public Servants for the City of New York, 1936, Public Personnel Administration, 8th edit, 1983, The Personnel Job of Government Managers, 1971, Frontier Mother, 1979, The Need for a Public Philosophy, 1987, Standing Up for Government, 1990; editor: Personnel Adminstrn, 1945-55, Improving Public Services, 1979, (with others) Police Personnel Administration, 1974; contbr. numerous articles to jours. Mem. Arlington County (Va.) Sch. Bd., 1948-50; pres. Arlington Com. to Preserve Public Schs., 1958-61. Recipient Disting. Service award CSC, 1960; Stockberger award Soc. Personnel Adminstrn., 1962; Career Service award Nat. Civil Service League, 1967; medal of Honor U. Evansville, 1981; hon. fellow Nat. Acad. Pub. Adminstrn., 1988. Mem. Am. Polit. Sci. Assn., Am. Soc. Public Adminstrn. (editorial bd. 1955-58), Internat. Inst. Adminstrv. Sci., Internat. Personnel Mgmt. Assn. (hon. life mem., exec. com. Public Personnel Assn. 1951-54, pres. 1965-66, Washington rep. 1971-73). Presbyterian. Home: 3600 N Piedmont St Arlington VA 22207-5333

STAHL, PHILIP DAMIEN, physiology and cell biology educator; b. Wheeling, W.Va., Oct. 4, 1941; married; 3 children. BS, West Liberty State Coll., 1964; PhD in Pharmacology, W.Va. U., 1967. From asst. to assoc. prof. Washington U. Med. Sch., St. Louis, 1971-81, prof. physiology, from 1982—, head dept., 1984—, now Edward Mallinckrodt Jr. prof. cell biology and physiology; fellow Space Sci. Research Ctr., U. Mo., 1967; Arthritis Found. fellow molecular biology, Vanderbilt U., 1968-70. Mem. Brit. Biochem. Soc., Am. Chem. Soc., Am. Physiol. Soc., Am. Soc. Biol. Chemists. Research in Lysosomes. Office: Washington Univ Sch Dept Cell Biology & Physiology 660 S Euclid Ave Box 8228 Saint Louis MO 63110-1093*

STAHL, RICHARD G. C., journalist, editor; b. Chgo., Feb. 22, 1934; m. Gladys C. Weisbecker; 1 child, Laura Ann. Student, Northwestern U. of Ill., Chgo. Editor Railway Purchases and Stores Mag., Chgo., 1960-63; editor pub. rels. dept. Sears Roebuck & Co., Chgo., 1963-68; dir pub. rels. dept. St. Joseph's Hosp. Med. Ctr., Phoenix, 1968-72; v.p. pub. rels. Consultation Svcs., Inc., Phoenix, 1972-73; creative dir. Don Jackson and Assoc., Phoenix, 1973; editor, pub. rels. mgr. Maricopa County Med. Soc., Phoenix, 1974-76; mng. editor Ariz. Hwys. mag., Phoenix, 1977—. Regional editor: (travel guides) Budget Travel, 1985, USA, 1986, Arizona, 1986; free-lance writer and editor. Mem. Soc. Profl. Journalists. Avocation: woodworking. Office: Ariz Hwys Mag 2039 W Lewis Ave Phoenix AZ 85009-2819 Personal philosophy: Follow your dream and fulfill your potentialities.

STAHLMAN, MILDRED THORNTON, pediatrics and pathology educator, researcher; b. Nashville, July 31, 1922; d. James Geddes and Mildred (Thornton) S. AB, Vanderbilt U., 1943, MD, 1946; MD (hon.), U. Goteborg, Sweden, 1973, U. Nancy, France, 1982. Diplomate Am. Bd. Pediatrics, Am. Bd. Neonatology. Cardiac resident La Rabida Sanitarium, Chgo., 1951; instr. pediatrics Vanderbilt U., Nashville, 1951-58, instr. physiology, 1954-60, asst. prof. pediatrics, 1959-64, asst. prof. physiology, 1960-62, assoc. prof. pediatrics, 1964-70, prof., 1970—, prof. pathology, 1982—, Harvie Branscomb Disting. prof., 1984, dir. div. neonatology, 1961-89. Editor: Respiratory Distress Syndromes, 1989; contbr. over 140 articles to profl. publs. Recipient Thomas Jefferson award Vanderbilt U., 1980, Apgar award Am. Acad. Pediatrics, 1987; NIH grantee, 1954—. Mem. AAAS, Am. Pediatric Soc. (pres. 1984), Soc. Pediatric Rsch., Am. Physiology Soc., So. Soc. Pediatric Rsch. (pres. 1961-62), Royal Swedish Acad. Scis., Inst. of Medicine of the Nat Acad. of Scis. Episcopalian. Home 558 Beech Creek Rd S Brentwood TN 37027-3421 Office: Vanderbilt U Med Ctr 21st Ave Nashville TN 37232

STAHMANN, ROBERT F., education educator; b. Peoria, Ill., Nov. 26, 1939; s. Fred Soeffner and Mary Emma (Thompson) S.; m. Kathleen Cook, Dec. 21, 1965; children: Benjamin C., John C., Paul C., Mark C., Anne. BA, Macalester Coll., 1963; MS, U. Utah, 1965, PhD, 1967. Research fellow U. Utah, 1966-67; sr. counselor U. Iowa, Iowa City, 1967-71; coordinator counseling service U. Iowa, 1971-72, dir. counseling service, 1972-75, asst. prof. edn., 1967-71, assoc. prof., 1971-75; prof. family scis. Brigham Young U., Provo, Utah, 1975—, chmn. dept. family scis., 1983-89, dir. Marriage and Family Counseling Clinic, 1976-83, coordinator program in marriage and family therapy, 1977-83; vis. prof. sex and marital therapy clinic Coll. Medicine, U. Utah, 1980-81; mem. Utah State Marriage and Family Therapy Licensing Bd., 1982-92; mem. Comm. Accreditation for Marriage and Family Therapy Edn., 1989-94, chair, 1990-94. Co-author: Premarital Counseling, 1980, 2d edit., 1987, Dynamic Assessment in Couples Therapy, 1993; co-editor: Ethical and Professional Issues for Marital and Family Therapists, 1980; co-editor, contbr.: Counseling in Marital and Sexual Problems: A Clinician's Handbook, 1977, 3d edit., 1984; assoc. editor: Jour. Coll. Student Pers., 1971-77; editor: Jour. Assoc. Mormon Counselors and Psychotherapists, 1977-78; contbr. chpts. to books., articles to profl. jours. Scoutmaster Boy Scouts Am., 1969-72, 83-87, commdr. 1976-79; mem. Orem City Beautification Commn., 1986-87; mem. adv. bd. Ret. Sr. Vol. Program for Utah County, 1987-89. Fellow Am. Assn. Marriage and Family Therapy (bd. dirs. 1977-79); mem. ACA, Am. Assn. Sex Educators, Counselors and Therapists (cert.), Utah Assn. Marriage and Family Counselors (pres. 1978-80), Nat. Coun. on Family Rels., Utah Coun. on Family Rels. (pres. 1987-88), Sigma Xi, Phi Kappa Phi. Mem. LDS Ch. Office: Brigham Young U Provo UT 84602

STAHR, ELVIS J(ACOB), JR., lawyer, conservationist, educator; b. Hickman, Ky., Mar. 9, 1916; s. Elvis and Mary Anne (McDaniel) S.; m. Dorothy Howland Berkfield, June 28, 1946; children: Stephanie Ann, Stuart Edward Winston, Bradford Lanier. AB, U. Ky., 1936; BA (Rhodes scholar), U. Oxford, Eng., 1938; BCL 1939, MA, 1943; diploma in Chinese Lang., Yale U., 1943; LL.D., W.Va. Wesleyan Coll., Waynesburg Coll., 1959, Concord Coll., 1960, U. Md., U. Pitts., 1961, La. State U., Tex. Christian U., U. Ky., 1962, U. Notre Dame, 1964, Ind. State U., 1966, Brown U., 1967, Northwestern U., U. Fla., 1968, U. Tampa, 1972, Ind. U.,

1976, Cumberland Coll., 1990; D.Environ. Sci., Rollins Coll., 1973; Dr.Mil. Sci., Northeastern U., 1962; D.Pub. Adminstrn., Bethany Coll., 1962; D.H.L., DePauw U., 1963, Rose Hulman Inst., 1965, Transylvania U., 1973; Litt.D., U. Cin., 1966, U. Maine, 1976; Pd.D., Culver-Stockton Coll., 1966; D.Sc., Norwich U., 1968, Hanover Coll., 1975. Bar: N.Y. State 1940, Ky. 1948, D.C. 1983, U.S. Supreme Ct. 1950, U.S. Ct. Mil. Appeals 1952. Practiced as assoc. Mudge, Stern, Williams & Tucker, N.Y.C., 1939-41; sr. assoc. Mudge, Stern, Williams & Tucker, 1946-47; assoc. prof. law U. Ky., 1947-48, prof. law, 1948-56; dean U. Ky. (Coll. Law), 1948-56, provost, 1954-56; exec. dir. Pres. Eisenhower's Com. on Edn. Beyond High Sch., 1956-57; vice chancellor professions U. Pitts., 1957-58; pres. W.Va. U., Morgantown, 1958-61; spl. asst. Sec. Army, Washington, 1951-52, cons., 1953; Sec. of the Army Dept. Def., Washington, 1961-62; pres. Ind. U., 1962-68, Nat. Audubon Soc., N.Y.C., 1968-79; sr. counselor Nat. Audubon Soc., 1979-81, pres. emeritus, 1981—; ptnr. Chickering & Gregory, San Francisco, 1982-85; of counsel Chickering & Gregory P.C., San Francisco, 1986—; dir. Acacia Mut. Life Ins. Co., 1968-85; pres. Univ. Assocs., Inc., 1981-90; exec. v.p. Pub. Resource Found., 1982—; sr. cons. Cassidy & Assocs., Inc., 1984—; chmn. Washington Conservation Roundtable, 1986-87; dir. Chase Manhattan Corp. and Bank, 1976-79, Fed. Res. Bank Chgo., 1966-68, dep. chmn., 1967, 68; Mem. Constn. Rev. Commn. Ky., 1949-56, Ind., 1967-68; mem. U.S. del. UN Conf. on Human Environment, Stockholm, 1972, Joint U.S.-USSR Com. on Cooperation for Protection of Environment, 1973, Internat. Whaling Commn., London, 1975, 78; mem. U.S. Aviation Adv. Commn., 1970-73, Nat. Commn. for World Population Yr., 1974; nat. chmn. U.S.O., 1973-76; pub. mem. Nat. Petroleum Council, 1974-79; mem. Summit Conf. on Inflation, 1974. Author: (with others) Economics of Pollution, 1971. Mem. Nat. Commn. on Accrediting, 1963-68; trustee Transylvania U., 1969-76, mem. founders bd. 1978-80; pres. Midwestern Univs. Rsch. Assn., 1963-66; incorporator Argonne Univs. Assn., 1965, trustee, 1965-67; trustee Univs. Rsch. Assn., 1965, mem. coun. pres' 1965-69, chmn. 1968; bd. dirs. Alliance to Save Energy, 1977-88, Resolve, 1977-81, Coun. Fin. Aid to Edn., 1966-69; chmn. higher edn. adv. com. Edn. Common. States, 1966-68; mem. bd. Govtl. Affairs Inst., 1968-72, Inst. Svcs. to Edn., 1965-67; chmn. Commn. on Fed. Rels., Am. Coun. on Edn., 1966-68; mem. exec. com. Nat. Assn. State Univs. and Land Grant Colls., 1965-68; mem. at-large bd. dirs. Am. Cancer Soc., 1970-76; trustee Com. Econ. Devel., 1964-82, hon.trustee, 1982—; mem. exec. bd. Nat. Assn. Ednl. Broadcasters, 1969-72; adv. coun. Elec. Power Rsch. Inst., 1971-77, Gas Rsch. Inst., 1977-83, Population Inst., 1981—, FAIR, 1982—; mem. Govtl. Affairs Com. of Ind. Sector, 1980-91; bd. dirs. Regional Plan Assn. Greater N.Y., 1970-75; evaluation panel Nat. Bur. Standards, 1975-77; adv. coun. Nat. Energy Project, Am. Enterprise Inst. Pub. Policy Rsch.1974-76; chmn. Coalit. Concerned Charities, 1972-78; mem. exec. bd. Am. Com. for Internat. Conservation, 1978-80; bd. dirs. World Environ. Ctr., 1978-85, Environ. and Energy Study Inst., 1983-90, mem. chmn.'s coun. 1990—; chmn. Green Fire Cnserv. Assn., 1988-91, com. Constnl. System, 1985—, Nat. Water Alliance, 1983, Land Betwen the Lakes Assn., 1986-89, Pvt. Trust for Pub. Edn., 1990-92, Pub. Mems. Assn. of Fgn. Svc., 1991-94. Lt. col. AUS, 1941-46, N. Africa, China. Decorated Spl. Breast Order of Yun Hui (2) Army Navy and Air Force medal 1st class (China); Bronze Star medal with oak leaf cluster (U.S.); Order of Grand Cross (Peru).; recipient Algernon Sydney Sullivan medallion of N.Y. Soc. 1936; named One of Am.'s Ten Outstanding Young Men U.S. Jr. C. of C. 1948; Meritorious Civilian Svc. medal Dept. Army, 1953, Disting. Civilian Service medal Dept. Army, 1971; Disting. Svc. award U. Ky. Alumni Assn., 1961; Disting. Service award Res. Officers Assn. U.S., 1962, Kentuckian of Year award Ky. Press Assn., 1961 and WHAS (Louisville), 1968, Conservation Service award Dept. Interior, 1979, Conservation Achievement award Nat. Wildlife Fedn., 1978, Barbara Swain Award of Honor Natural Resources Coun. Am., 1988; Sesquicentennial medal U. Mich., 1967, Centennial medal U. Ky., 1965; named Ky. Col. and gen., U. Ky. Disting. Alumni (tennis), ROTC Hall of Fame; La. and Neb. adm., Hon. Citizen of Tex., Ind. Sagamore; awarded keys to the cities of San Francisco, San Juan, New Orleans, Orlando, Louisville, others. Mem. Assn. U.S. Army (life, pres. 1965-68, chmn. coun. trustees 1969-74), Ind. Soc. of Rhodes Scholars, ABA, Fed. Bar Assn., Kentuckians (pres. N.Y.C. 1976-79, life trustee), S.R., SAR, Ky. Bar Assn., D.C. Bar Assn., Ind. Bar Assn. (hon.), Disciples of Christ Hist. Soc. (life mem.), Army-Navy (Washington), Field (Greenwich), Pilgrims of U.S., Boone and Crockett, Order of Coif, Phi Beta Kappa, Sigma Chi (Balfour Nat. award 1936, Significant Sig 1961, found bd. 1974-91, Order of Constantine 1981), Omicron Delta Kappa (dir. found. 1984-90, Laurel Crowned Circle award), Phi Delta Phi, Tau Kappa Alpha (Dist. Alumni award 1966), Merton Soc. (Oxford, Eng.), Oxford Soc.: hon. mem. Blue Key, Beta Gamma Sigma, Alpha Kappa Psi, Kappa Kappa Psi. Presbyterian. Home: 16 Martin Dl N Greenwich CT 06830-4719 Office: Chickering & Gregory PC 1815 H St NW # 650 Washington DC 20006-3604 Focus on getting good results rather than on getting credit for them.

STAIANO, EDWARD F., electronics company executive; b. N.Y.C., 1936. Student, Bucknell U., 1958, U. N.Mex., 1967. Corp. v.p. Motorola Inc., Roselle, Ill., 1981-85, corp. v.p., 1985-87, exec. v.p., 1987—. Office: Motorola Inc 1475 W Shure Dr Arlington Heights IL 60004-7810

STAIGER, RALPH CONRAD, educational consultant, former educational association executive; b. N.Y.C., Sept. 10, 1917; s. Max Frederick and Marie Anna (Scheffmacher) S.; m. Marian Carpenter, Dec. 23, 1945; children: Charles Carpenter, Joan Marie. B.A., Columbia U., 1939; M.A., Tchrs. Coll., 1942; Ed.D., Temple U., 1952. Reading cons. Utica (N.Y.) Schs., 1952-62; prof. psychology, dir. reading clinic U. So. Miss., Hattiesburg, 1952-62; exec. dir. Internat. Reading Assn., Newark, Del., 1962-84; pres. Reading Svcs. Cons., 1984—; adj. prof. edn. U. Del., Newark, 1962-84; mem. Internat. Book Com., 1974-89, chmn. 1984-89; hon. mem. nat. adv. bd. Libr. of Congress Ctr. for The Book, 1977-84; mem. U.S. Nat. Comm. for UNESCO, 1981-86; pres. U.S. Bd. on Books for Young People, 1985-86; hon. mem. Internat. Bd. on Books for Young People, 1992, exec. com. 1994—. Author: New Directions in Reading, 1967, The Teaching of Reading, 1973, Roads to Reading, 1979, Planning and Organizing Reading Campaigns, 1983, Developing the Reading Habit in Children, 1989. Bd. mgrs. Western br. YMCA, 1967-73. Mem. Nat. Conf. Rsch. English (pres.), Alliance for Advancement Edn. (pres.), Coun. Communication Svcs. (pres. 1981-83), Internat. Reading Assn. (dir.), Nat. Reading Conf. (dir.), Univ. Club Washington.

STAINE, ROSS, lawyer; b. El Paso, Tex., July 13, 1924; s. Adelbert Claire and Dennie Joe (Stowe) S.; m. Mary Louise Sibert, Aug. 15, 1947; children: Martha Louise, Julie Ann, Ross. B.A., Tex. A&M U., 1947; LL.B., U. Tex., 1950. Bar: Tex. Assoc. Baker & Botts, Houston, 1947, ptnr., 1962—. Served with AUS, 1943-46; served to 1st lt. U.S. Army, 1950-52, PTO. Mem. State Bar Tex., Houston Bar Assn., Tex. Law Rev. Assn., Order of Coif, Phi Delta Phi. Baptist. Clubs: Forest (Houston), Coronado (Houston), Univ. (Houston). Home: 5555 Del Monte Dr # 807 Houston TX 77056-4116 Office: Baker & Botts 3000 One Shell Plaza Houston TX 77002

STAINES, DAVID MCKENZIE, English educator; b. Toronto, Ont., Can., Aug. 8, 1946; s. Ralph McKenzie and Mary Rita (Hayes) S. BA, U. Toronto, 1967; AM, Harvard U., 1968, PhD, 1973. Asst. prof. English Harvard U., Cambridge, Mass., 1973-78, vis. assoc. prof., summers 1980, 82; assoc. prof. English U. Ottawa, Ont., 1978-85, prof., 1985—; vice-dean faculty of Arts U. Ottawa, Ont., 1994—. Author: Tennyson's Camelot, 1982, Beyond the Provinces: Literary Canada at Century's End, 1995; contbr. articles and revs. Arthurian lit. medieval drama and romance to profl. jours.; editor: The Canadian Imagination, 1977, The Forty-ninth and Other Parallels, 1986; editor Jour. Can. Poetry, 1984—; gen. editor New Can. Libr., 1988—; translator The Complete Romances of Chrétien de Troyes, 1990; co-editor Elements of Literature, 1990, The Short Story in English, 1991. Ind. study fellow NEH, London, 1977-78, fellow Huntington Libr., San Marino, Calif., 1979. Mem. Medieval Acad. Am. (chmn. com. on ctrs. and regional assn. 1981-87), MLA, Internat. Arthurian Soc., Assn. Can. Univ. Tchrs. English. Roman Catholic. Avocations: theater, bridge. Home: 12 Galt St, Ottawa, ON Canada K1S 4R4 Office: Univ Ottawa, Dept English, Ottawa, ON Canada K1N 6N5

STAINES, MAVIS AVRIL, artistic director, ballet principal; b. Cownsville, Que., Can., Apr. 9, 1954; d. David Russell and Betty (Knott) S.; m. Jyrki Virsunen, Feb. 4, 1988. Student, Nat. Ballet Sch., 1968-73, 81-83. Dancer Nat. Ballet of Can., 1973-78, 1st soloist, 1975-78; dancer Dutch Nat. Ballet,

1978-81; artistic dir. Nat. Ballet Sch., Toronto, Ont., Can., 1989—; mem. artistic staff Nat. Ballet Sch., 1982, assoc. artistic dir., 1984; juror Prix de Lausanne, Switzerland, 1993, 94, 95; mem. task force on classicl ballet tng. DANCE/USA, Phila., 1994; mem. dance adv. com. The Can. Coun.; mem. Dance 20/20 Com., mem. DAN/CE--The Dance Comty. of Educators; bd. dirs. Kala Nidhi Fine Arts of Can. Office: The Nat Ballet Sch, 105 Maitland St, Toronto, ON Canada M4Y 1E4

STAINROOK, HARRY RICHARD, banker; b. Phila., Jan. 11, 1937; s. Millward M. and Janet (Cruickshank-Smith) S.; m. Judith Ann Swann, May 21, 1966; children: Jennifer, Eric. B.A., Rutgers U., 1970. Mgr. bank ops. First Pa. Bank, Phila., 1956-61, asst. v.p. br. dept., 1964-73, v.p., mgr. London office, 1973-75, v.p. internat. dept., 1975-78; sr. v.p. comml. group First Pa. Bank, 1978-81, exec. v.p., trust and investments, 1981-85; exec. v.p. trust and investments Mfrs. and Traders Trust Co., Buffalo, 1985—. Chmn. bd. dirs. Greater Buffalo Opera Co.; bd. dirs. Buffalo Philharm. Orch., U. Buffalo Found.; adv. bd. Buffalo Coun. on World Affairs. With U.S. Army, 1961-64. Mem. N.Y. State Bankers Assn., Buffalo C. of C., English Speaking Union, Saturn Club. Lutheran. Office: Mfrs and Traders Trust Co One M and T Pla Buffalo NY 14240

STAIR, FREDERICK ROGERS, retired foundation executive, former seminary president; b. Knoxville, Tenn., Mar. 7, 1918; s. Fred Rogers and Cristyne (Miller) S.; m. Martha Osborne, Dec. 19, 1942; children: Mary Miller, Thomas Osborne. B.S., Davidson Coll., 1939, D.D., 1960; postgrad., U. Edinburgh, 1945-46; B.D., Union Theol. Sem., Va., 1947, Th.M. 1948; LL.D., Davis and Elkins Coll., 1969; postgrad., Advanced Mgmt. Program, Harvard, 1972-73. Ordained to ministry Presbyn. Ch., 1943; asst. to pres. Union Theol. Sem., Va., 1948-53; pastor in Hickory, N.C., 1953-59, Atlanta, 1959-67; pres. Union Theol. Sem., Va., 1967-81; exec. dir. Presbyn. Ch. (U.S.A.) Found., Charlotte, N.C., 1981-88. Trustee Davidson Coll., 1955-59, 73-85, chmn. bd., 1980-84; program coordinator Inst. for Theol. Edn. Mgmt. Served with inf. AUS, 1942-46. Moses D. Hoge fellow, 1948, rsch. fellow Yale Divinity Sch., 1973, Ecumenical Inst., U. Salamanca, Spain, 1979. Mem. Phi Beta Kappa, Phi Gamma Delta, Omicron Delta Kappa, Sigma Upsilon. Home: 5150 Sharon Rd Charlotte NC 28210-4799

STAIR, GOBIN, publishing executive, painter, graphic designer; b. S.I., N.Y., July 30, 1912; s. Gobin and Elsie (Wilson) S.; m. Julia Sitterly, Oct. 5, 1933; children—Adrian, Charlotte. A.B., Dartmouth, 1933; L.H.D., Starr King Sch. for Ministry, 1975. With Beacon Press, Boston, 1956-75, dir., 1962-75. Illustrator: Gulliver's Travels (Swift), 1957, Middle Passage (Coxe), 1960, Old Quotes at Home (Darling), 1965, The King Lear Experience, 1976, Old Tales for a New Day (Fahs and Cobb), 1980, True to Form, 1988; creator: Alphabet Mural, Kingston, Mass. Pub. Libr., 1994. Mem Bookbuilders of Boston (pres. 1961-62, William A. Dwiggins award 1965), Boston Soc. Printers. Home: 9 Wapping Rd PO Box 123 Kingston MA 02364

STAIRS, DENIS WINFIELD, political science educator; b. Halifax, N.S., Can., Sept. 6, 1939; s. Henry Gerald and Freda (Winfield) S.; m. Valerie Downing Street, Aug. 10, 1963 (div. Dec. 1986); children: Robert Woodliffe, Christopher Winfield; m. Jennifer Smith, July 18, 1987. BA, Dalhousie U., 1961, Oxford U., 1964; MA, Oxford U., 1968; PhD, U. Toronto, 1969. Asst. prof. dept. polit. sci. Dalhousie U., 1966-70, assoc. prof., 1970-75, dir. Centre Fgn. Policy Studies, 1971-75, prof. polit. sci., 1975—, chmn. dept., 1980-85, mem. adv. com. acad. relations, dept. external affairs, 1978—, v.p., acad. and research, 1988-93; bd. dirs. Atlantic Coun. Can., 1979—; mem. coun. Social Sci. and Humanities Rsch. Coun. Can., 1981-87; mem. rsch. coun. Can. Inst. Advanced Rsch., 1986—; bd. dirs. Inst. for Rsch. on Pub. Policy, 1989—. Author: The Diplomacy of Constraint: Canada, the Korean War, and the United States, 1974. Rhodes scholar, 1961; J.W. Dafoe postgrad. fellow internat. studies, 1965-66; Can. Council leave fellow, 1972-73; Social Scis. and Humanities Research Council Can. leave fellow, 1979-80. Fellow Royal Soc. Can.; mem. Can. Polit. Sci. Assn. (pres.), Can. Internat. Affairs, Internat. Studies Assn., Internat. Polit. Sci. Assn. Club: Royal N.S. Yacht Squadron. Office: Dalhousie U, Dept Polit Sci, Halifax, NS Canada B3H 4H6

STAKER, ROBERT JACKSON, federal judge; b. Kermit, W.Va., Feb. 14, 1925; s. Frederick George and Nada (Frazier) S.; m. Sue Blankenship Poore, July 16, 1955; 1 child, Donald Seth; 1 stepson, John Timothy Poore. Student, Marshall U., Huntington, W.Va., W.Va. U., Morgantown, U. Ky., Lexington; LL.B, W.Va. U., 1952. Bar: W.Va. 1952. Practiced in Williamson, 1952-68; judge Mingo County Circuit Ct., Williamson, 1969-79; U.S. dist. judge So. Dist. W.Va., Huntington, 1979-95, sr. U.S. dist. judge, 1995—. Served with USN, 1943-46. Mem. ABA, W.Va. State Bar. Democrat. Presbyterian.

STAKGOLD, IVAR, mathematics educator; b. Oslo, Dec. 13, 1925; came to U.S., 1941, naturalized, 1947; s. Henri and Rose (Wishengrad) S.; m. Alice Calvert O'Keefe, Nov. 27, 1964 (dec. Jan. 1994); 1 dau., Alissa Dent. BME, Cornell U., 1945, MME, 1946; PhD, Harvard U., 1949. Instr., then asst. prof. Harvard, 1949-56; head math. and logistics brs. Office Naval Research, 1956-59; faculty Northwestern U., 1960-75, prof. math. and engring. scis., 1964-75, chmn. engring. scis., 1969-75; prof. math. U. Del., 1975—, chmn., 1975-91; dir. Washington office Am. Math. Soc., 1994—; mem. U.S. Army basic research com. NRC, 1977-80, MS 2000 oversight com., 1989-91; mem. com. on applications of math. NAS-NRC, 1982-86; mem. adv. panel on computational and applied math. Nat. Inst. Standards and Tech., 1990—; vis. faculty Math. Inst., Oxford (Eng.) U., 1973, 92, Univ. Coll., London, 1978, Victoria U., Wellington, N.Z., 1981, Ecole Polytechnique Federale de Lausanne, Switzerland, 1981, Bari U., 1987, U. Complutense, Madrid, 1987, 92, U. Milan, 1992. Author: Boundary Value Problems of Mathematical Physics, Vols. I and II, 1967, Green's Functions and Boundary Value Problems, 1978; mem. editl. bd. Am. Math. Monthly, 1975-80, Jour. Applicable Analysis, 1977-90, Internat. Jour. Engring. Sci., 1977—, Jour. Integral Equations, 1978, Jour. Math. Analysis and Applications, 1988-94, SIAM Rev., 1989-94. Mem. Soc. Indsl. and Applied Math. (trustee 1976-85, chmn. 1979-85, pres. 1989-90, pres. 1991), Conf. Bd. Math. Sci. (chmn 1990-92), Coun. Sci. Soc. Pres. (exec. bd. 1990), Am. Math. Soc. (dir. Washington office). U.S. rep. World Bridge Championships, 1959, 60; holder 7 nat. bridge championships. Home: 13 Fairfield Dr Newark DE 19711-2767

STAKIAS, G. MICHAEL, lawyer; b. Norfolk, Va., Feb. 2, 1950; s. George and Gloria May (Hoggard) S. BA, William & Mary, 1972; JD, Thomas M. Cooley Law Sch., 1976; LLM, NYU, 1977. Bar: Mich., 1976, D.C. 1980, Pa. 1980, N.Y. 1994. Atty. U.S. SEC, Washington, 1977-80; ptnr. Blank, Rome, Comisky & McCauley, Phila., 1980—. Bd. dirs. Thomas M. Cooley Law Sch., Lansing, Mich., 1988—. Mem. ABA (bus. law sect., chmn. small bus. capital formation subcom. 1988), Patrons Found. Office: Blank Rome Comisky & McCauley 1200 Four Penn Ctr Plz Philadelphia PA 19103

STALBERG, ZACHARY, newspaper editor; b. Phila., Apr. 6, 1947; m. Deborah Lock, Sept. 2, 1990. Student polit. sci., Temple U., 1968. Reporter Bucks County Courier Times, Levittown, Pa., 1970-71; reporter Phila. Daily News, 1971-75, city editor, 1975-77, mng. editor, 1977-79, exec. editor, 1979-84, editor, 1984—. Served with U.S. Army, 1968-70. Mem. Am. Soc. Newspaper Editors. Home: 413 S 49th St Philadelphia PA 19143-1709 Office: Philadelphia Daily News 400 N Broad St Philadelphia PA 19130-4015*

STALCUP, JOE ALAN, lawyer, clergyman; b. Hooker, Okla., Feb. 13, 1931; s. Herbert I. and Ruby (Gantt) S.; m. Nancy Jo Vaughn, Sept. 3, 1950; children: Melinda, Sondra Jo, Cheri Ann. B.B.A. cum laude, So. Methodist U., 1951, J.D. magna cum laude, 1959, M.Th. magna cum laude, 1978. Bar: Tex. 1959. Tchr. Dallas Ind. Sch. Dist., 1951-57; assoc. mem. firm Locke, Purnell, Boren, Laney & Neely, Dallas, 1959-66; assoc. atty., partner firm Geary, Brice & Lewis, Dallas, 1966-67; founder, sr. partner firm Stalcup, Johnson, Meyers & Miller (and predecessor firm), Dallas, 1968-75; dean Sch. Theology for the Laity, 1978-80, 92—. Pres. Dallas County Young Democrats, 1952-54; Bd. dirs., exec. com. N. Tex. Christian Communications Commn., 1972-78; bd. dirs., v.p. Greater Dallas Council Chs., 1972-75; bd. dirs., chmn. Christian Club. Found. 1976-84, 86-91, Christian Bd. Publ., 1991—. Mem. ABA, Tex. Bar Assn., Dallas Bar Assn., Am. Judicature Soc., Phi Alpha Delta. Mem. Christian Ch. (minister). Home:

7594 Benedict Dr Dallas TX 75214-1903 Office: 6510 Abrams Rd Dallas TX 75231-7217

STALDER, FLORENCE LUCILLE, secondary education educator; b. Fairmont, W.Va., Jan. 3, 1920; d. Brooks Fleming and Sally May (Odewalt) Clayton; m. Bernard Nicholas Stalder, Sept. 14, 1946; children: Kathryn Lynn Stalder Mirto, Susan May Stalder Woodard. BA in Edn. with honors, Fairmont State Coll., 1966; MA, W.Va. U., 1973; postgrad., Kent State U., 1973, U. Va., Charlottesville, 1981. Cert. elem. tchr., W.Va. Sec. to mgr. Hall Agy., Inc., Fairmont, W.Va., 1943-43; sec. to supt. Westinghouse Electric Corp., Fairmont, 1943-47; sec. to purchasing agt. Fairmont Supply Co., 1947-48; sec. to dist. mgtr. Ea. Gas & Fuel Assoc., Gen. Stores Div., Grant Town, W.Va., 1948-50; sec. to pres., v.p. Hutchinson Coal Co., Fairmont, 1950-52; sec. to personnel mgr. Consolidation Coal Co., Fairmont, 1957-61; sec. and asst. to adminstr. Fairmont Clinic (Monongahela Valley Assoc. Health Ctrs.), 1965-70; instr. Fairmont Jr. High, Miller Jr. High Schs., 1968-85; instr., dir. W.Va. Univ. Younger Youth Sci. Camps, Fairmont, 1966-72; workshop instr. W.Va. State Bd. Edn. Energy Workshops, Fairmont, 1973-74; adult edn. instr., Fairmont, 1985—. Pres. PTA, 1958-61; troop leader Girl Scouts USA, 1961-64; sec., mem. League of Women Voters, Fairmont, 1968—. Mem. AAUW (pres. 1972-74), Marion County Edn. Assn., W.Va. Edn. Assn., NEA, W.Va. Adult Edn. Assn., Daus. of Founders and Patriots of Am. (pres. 1979-85, nat. officers club 1985—), DAR (1st v.p. regent 1986-92, regent 1992—), Daus. of Am. Colonists (vice regent 1988-91, regent 1991-94), Daus. Am. Pioneers, Alpha Delta Kappa (pres. 1979-81). Republican. Methodist. Avocations: ecology and conservation issues, humane education, food preservation, gardening. Home: 1208 Bell Run Rd Fairmont WV 26554-1400

STALEY, AUGUSTUS EUGENE, III, advertising executive; b. Decatur, Ill., Sept. 12, 1928; s. Augustus Eugene Jr. and Lenore (Mueller) S. Student, Northwestern U., 1946-49. Account exec. Ruthrauff & Ryan, Inc., 1950-52; advt. dir. A.E. Staley Mfg. Co., Decatur, Ill., 1952-58; v.p. Dancer-Fitzgerald-Sample, 1958-61, Arthur Meyerhoff Assocs., 1961; exec. v.p. Don Kemper Co., Inc., Chgo., 1961-69; pres., chmn., chief exec. officer SMY Media, Inc., Chgo., 1969—; pres. Advt. Contractors, N.Y.C., 1970-74; chief exec. officer Atwood Richards, Inc., N.Y.C., 1970-86; dir. Mueller Co., Decatur. Sgt. U.S. Army, 1950-60. Clubs: Tavern, Chgo. Athletic (Chgo.), Sky Line (Chgo); Williams (N.Y.C.). Lodges: Masons. Office: SMY Media Inc 333 N Michigan Ave Chicago IL 60601-3901

STALEY, DELBERT C., telecommunications executive; b. Hammond, Ind., Sept. 16, 1924; s. Eugene and Nellie (Downer) s.; m. Ingrid Andersen, Mar. 16, 1946; children—Crista Staley Ellis, Cynthia Staley-Ianoale, Clifford, Corinn. Student, Rose Poly. Inst., Hammond, 1943-44; grad. advanced mgmt. program, Harvard U., 1962; D. Engring. (hon.), Rose Hulman Inst. Tech., 1981; LL.D. (hon.), Skidmore Coll., 1983. With Ill. Bell Telephone, 1946-76, v.p. ops., 1972-76; pres. Ind. Bell, 1976-78; v.p. residence mktg. AT&T, 1978-79; pres. N.Y. Telephone, 1979-83, chmn. bd., chief exec. officer, 1983; chmn. bd., chief exec. officer NYNEX Corp., White Plains, N.Y., 1983-89, chmn., dir. internat. mgmt. com., 1989-91; bd. dirs. Dean Foods, Franklin Park, Ill., Ball Corp., Muncie, Ind., Bank N.Y., N.Y.C., Allied-Signal Inc., John Hancock Mut. Life Ins. Co., Polaroid Corp., Digital Equipment Corp., Maynard, Mass. With U.S. Army, 1943-46; ETO. Recipient Puerto Rican Legal Def. and Edn. Fund award, 1981, Cleveland Dodge award YMCA Greater N.Y., 1983, New Yorker for N.Y. award Citizens Com. for N.Y., 1984, Leadership in Mgmt. award Pace U., 1988, Albert Schweitzer Leadership award Hugh O'Brian Youth Found., 1988, Hammond Achievement award The Hammond Hist. Soc., 1988, Gold Medal award USO, 1988, Am. Vocation Success award Pres. George Busch, 1989. Mem. Ind. Acad. (hon.), Telephone Pioneers Am. (pres. 1983-84), Westchester Country Club, Blind Brook Club, Royal Poinciana Club. Presbyterian. Home: 32 Polly Park Rd Rye NY 10580-1927 Office: NYNEX Corp 1095 Avenue of the Americas New York NY 10036

STALEY, HENRY MUELLER, manufacturing company executive; b. Decatur, Ill., June 3, 1932; s. Augustus Eugene, Jr. and Lenore (Mueller) S.; m. Violet Lucas, Feb. 4, 1955; children—Mark Eugene, Grant Spencer. Grad., Governor Dummer Acad., 1950; B.S. in Psychology, Northwestern U., 1954, M.B.A. in Finance, 1956. Salesman Field Enterprises, Chgo., 1953; salesman A.E. Staley Mfg. Co., 1951, mgmt. trainee, 1956-57, ins. mgr., 1957-59, asst. treas., 1959-65, treas., asst. sec., 1965-73, v.p., treas., asst. sec., 1973-77, v.p. bus. and econ. analysis, 1977-87, also dir., 1969-85; pvt. investor Decatur, 1987—; dir. Staley Continental, Inc., 1985-88. Crusade chmn. Macon County unit Am. Cancer Soc., 1964-65, mem. bd. dirs., 1965-71, vice chmn. bd., 1965-66, chmn. bd., 1966-69; bd. dirs. United Way Decatur and Macon County, 1972-74; mem. adv. council Millikin U., 1968—, chmn. adv. council, 1970-71; mem. Decatur Meml. Hosp. Devel. Council, 1969-71, mem. finan. com., bd. dirs., 1970-79, mem. long-range planning com., 1976-77, mem. devel. and community relations com., 1977-78. Mem. Decatur C. of C. (dir. 1967-72), Sigma Nu. Clubs: Decatur, Decatur Country. Home and Office: 276 N Park Pl Decatur IL 62522-1952 also: 74 Ironwood Ln Lahaina HI 96761

STALEY, JAMES TROTTER, microbiology educator; b. Brookings, S.D., Mar. 14, 1938; s. Newton Clarence and Isabelle (Trotter) S.; m. Sonja Jeanne Erickson, Dec. 28, 1963; children: Greg, Wendy. Ba, U. Minn., 1960; MS, Ohio State U., 1963; PhD, U. Calif., Davis, 1967. From instr. to asst. prof. Mich. State U., East Lansing, 1967-69; asst. prof. U. N.C., Chapel Hill, 1969-71; asst. prof. U. Wash., Seattle, 1971-74, assoc. prof., 1974-82, prof. microbiology, 1982—. Mem. editorial bd. Microbial Ecology, 1977, Applied Environ. Microbiology, 1975. Microbiological Reviews, 1990-92, Geomicrobiology, 1991—; editor: Bergey's Manual, 1981, Microbiological Reviews, 1992—; contbr. articles to jours. Mem. AAAS, Am. Soc. Microbiology (vice chmn., chmn. gen. microbiology sect. 1975-76, div. lectr. 1983), Internat. Assn. Microbiology Soc. (judicial commn. 1983—), Internat. Symposium on Environ. Biogeochemistry. Office: U Wash Dept Microbiology SC 42 Seattle WA 98195

STALEY, JOSEPH HARDIN, JR., lawyer; b. Tyler, Tex., May 23, 1937; s. Joseph Hardin and Mildred Lucille (Wilkerson) S.; m. Linda Luan Best, June 20, 1959; children: Joe H. III, Stefanie Staley Rice, LuAnne Staley Hobbs. BA, Yale U., 1959; LLB, U. Tex., 1964. Bar: Tex. 1964, U.S. Dist. Ct. (no dist., so. dist., we. dist.) Tex., U.S. Ct. Appeals (5th cir.), U.S. Tax Ct., U.S. Supreme Ct. Assoc. Locke, Purnell, Boren, Laney & Neely, Dallas, 1964-68; minority counsel U.S. Senate Banking and Currency Com., Washington, 1968-70; ptnr. Locke Purnell Rain Harrell, Dallas, 1970—; mem. grievance com. State Bar Tex., Dallas, 1977-86, bd. dirs., Austin, 1983-86. Candidate U.S. Congress, 13th Dist. Tex., 1970; nat. adv. coun. U.S. Small Bus. Adminstrn., Washington, 1972-78; bd. dirs. Yale Club Dallas, 1972—; Dallas Soc. for Crippled Children, 1980-85, Dallas Area Red Cross, 1984—; FOCAS, 1985-89, Met. Dallas YMCA, 1986—; mem. Tex. Constitution Revision Com., Dallas, 1974; regent Midwestern State U., Wichita Falls, Tex., 1989—. Fellow Tex. Bar Found.; mem. Salesmanship Club Dallas, The Links, Dallas Country Club (bd. govs.). Republican. Methodist. Avocations: golf, fishing, hunting. Home: 4445 Rheims Pl Dallas TX 75205-3626 Office: Locke Purnell Rain Harrell 2200 Ross Ave Ste 2200 Dallas TX 75201-6766

STALEY, LYNN, English educator; b. Madisonville, Ky., Dec. 24, 1947; d. James Mulford and Florine (Hurt) Staley. AB, U. Ky., 1969; MA, PhD, Princeton U., 1974. Grad. asst. Princeton (N.J.) U., 1971-73; instr. English Colgate U., Hamilton, N.Y., 1974-75, from asst. to assoc. prof., 1975-86, prof., 1986—; presenter in field. Author: The Voice of the Gawain-Poet, 1984, The Shepheardes Calendar: An Introduction, 1990, Margery Kempe's Dissenting Fictions, 1990; contbr. articles to profl. jours. Mem. MLA, Medieval Acad. Am., Renaissance Soc. Am., New Chaucer Soc., Spenser Soc. Office: Colgate U Dept English 13 Oak Dr Hamilton NY 13346

STALEY, ROBERT W., mechanical engineer, electric company executive; b. 1935. BSME, Cornell U., 1958, MBA, 1959. Dir. corp. devel. Trane Co., 1960-75; v.p. corp. tech. Emerson Electric Co., St. Louis, 1975-77, internat. v.p., 1977-78, chief fin. officer, sr. v.p. fin., 1978-81, sr. v.p., group v.p., 1981-83, exec. v.p., 1983-88, vice chmn., 1988—, also bd. dirs. Capt. U.S. Army, 1959-66. Office: Emerson Electric Co 8000 W Florissant Ave Saint Louis MO 63136-8506

STALEY, THOMAS FABIAN, language professional, academic administrator; b. Pitts., Aug. 13, 1935; s. Fabian Richard and Mary (McNulty) S.; m. Carolyn O'Brien, Sept. 3, 1960; children: Thomas Fabian, Caroline Ann, Mary Elizabeth, Timothy X. A.B., Regis Coll., 1957, B.S., 1957; M.A., U. Tulsa, 1958; Ph.D., U. Pitts., 1962; D.H.L., Regis Coll., 1979. Asst. prof. English Rollins Coll., 1961-62; mem. faculty U. Tulsa, 1962-88, prof. English, 1969-88, dean Grad. Sch., 1969-77; dir. Grad. Inst. Modern Letters, Trustees prof. modern lit. U. Tulsa (Grad. Sch.), 1977—; dean Coll. Arts and Scis. U. Tulsa, 1981-83, provost, v.p. acad. affairs, 1983-88, McFarlin prof. modern lit., 1988—; prof. English, dir. Ransom Humanities Rsch. Ctr. U. Tex., Austin, 1988—, Chancellor's Centennial prof. of the Book, 1989-92, Harry Huntt Ransom chair liberal arts, 1992—; Fulbright prof., Italy, 1966-67; Fulbright lectr., 1971; Danforth assoc., 1962-67; chmn. Internat. James Joyce Symposium; dir. Grad. Inst. Modern Letters, 1970-81. Author: James Joyce Today, 1966, James Joyce's Portrait of the Artist, 1968, Italo Svevo: Essays on His Work, 1969, (with H.J. Mooney) The Shapeless God: Essays on the Modern Novel, 1968, (with B. Benstock) Approaches to Ulysses: Ten Essays, 1970, Approaches to Joyce's Portrait: Ten Essays, 1977, Jean Rhys: A Critical Study, 1979; editor: Il Punto Su Joyce, 1973, Dorothy Richardson, 1975, Ulysses: Fifty Years, 1974, Twentieth-Century Women Novelists, 1982, British Novelists, 1890-1929, Traditionalists, Dictionary of Lit. Biography, Vols. 34, 36, 70, 77, An Annotated Critical Bibliography of James Joyce, 1989, Joyce Studies: An Annual edit., 1990, Studies in Modern Literature Series, 1990, Reflections on James Joyce: Stuart Gilbert's Paris Journal, 1993, James Joyce Quar., 1963-89; adv. editor Twentieth-Century Lit., 1966—; bd. dirs. Eighteenth-Century Short Title Catalogue/North America, 1990; contbr. articles to profl. jours. Bd. dirs. Tulsa Arts Coun., 1969-76, NCCJ, 1979—; pres. James Joyce Found., 1968-72; chmn. bd. Undercroft Montessori Sch., 1968-70, Marquette Sch., 1969-70; bd. dirs. Cascia Hall Prep. Sch.; chmn. disting. authors com. Tulsa Libr. Trust, 1984; mem. bd. commrs. Tulsa City-County Libr., chmn., 1980-82; mem. adv. coun. Tex. Inst. for Humanities; trustee Regis U., 1992—; bd. dirs. Libr. Am., 1994—, Harlick Trust, 1994—. Recipient Am. Council Learned Socs. award, 1969, 80. Mem. MLA, Internat. Assn. Univ. Profs. English, Anglo-Irish Studies Assn., Am. Com. for Irish Studies, James Internat. de Bibliophilie, James Joyce Soc., Hopkins Soc., Tex. Philos. Soc. (bd. dirs. 1991—), U.S. Tennis Assn., Tulsa Tennis Club, Westwood Country Club, The Athenaeum Club (London), Grolier Club (N.Y.), Edgecomb Tennis Club (Kennebunk, Maine), Tarry House, Phi Beta Kappa. Home: 2528 Tanglewood Trail Austin TX 78703-1540

STALFORT, JOHN ARTHUR, lawyer; b. Balt., June 9, 1951; s. John Irving and Libby Jean (Adams) S.; m. Rebecca Higgins, Aug. 21, 1976 (div. 1984); m. Anne Cheesman, July 19, 1985. BA, U. Va., 1973, MBA, JD, 1977. Bar: Md. 1977. Assoc. Miles & Stockbridge, Balt., 1977-84, ptnr., 1984—. Author: Commercial Financing Forms-Maryland, 1986. Sec. Roland Pk. Rds. and Maintenance Corp., Balt., 1978-83. Mem. ABA, Md. State Bar Assn. Bond Lawyers, Roland Pk. Civic League, Balt. Country Club, Ctr. Club, Md. Club, Talbot Country Club, Phi Beta Kappa. Republican. Presbyterian. Avocations: skiing, tennis, golf, lacrosse, running. Office: Miles & Stockbridge 10 Light St Baltimore MD 21202-1435

STALKER, ANNIE ELEANOR, borough official; b. Kivalina, Alaska, Jan. 8, 1945; d. Jacob Akachak and Marie (Towksjhea) Stalker; m. Nicholaas V. Rentenaar (div.); children: Elmer, Jacob, Julian, Dominique; m. Michael J. Patkotak (div. 1981); m. Nels Martin (div. June 199). Grad. high sch., Mt. Edgecumbe, Alaska. Adminstrv. asst. Mauneluk Assocs., Kotzebue, Alaska, 1982-83; bilingual instr. North Slope Borough Sch. Dist., Point Lay, Alaska, 1986-89; exec. sec. North Slope Borough, Barrow, 1974-81; village coord. North Slope Borough, Barrow and Point Lay, 1983-86; coord. sr. citizens North Slope Borough, Point Lay, 1991-93, village coord., alt. mem. planning commn. and substance abuse treatment svcs. adv. bd., 1993—; alt. mem. health bd., 1994—; cmty. health rep. North Slope Borough Health Dept., 1983; a creator Inuit Circumpolar Conf. Mem. provincial coun. Episcopal Diocese of Alaska, 1993—. Recipient commendation North Slope Borough Health Dept., 1992. Democrat. Avocations: reading, eskimo dancing. Home: 1229 Cordova Apt A Anchorage AK 99501 Office: North Slope Borough PO Box 101 Barrow AK 99759

STALKER, JACQUELINE D'AOUST, academic administrator, educator; b. Penetang, Ont., Can., Oct. 16, 1933; d. Phillip and Rose (Eaton) D'Aoust; m. Robert Stalker; children: Patricia, Lynn, Roberta. Teaching cert., U. Ottawa, 1952; tchr. music, Royal Toronto Conservatory Music, 1952; teaching cert., Lakeshore Tchrs. Coll., 1958; BEd with honors, U. Manitoba, 1977, MEd, 1979; EdD, Nova U., 1985. Cert. tchr. Ont., Man., Can. Adminstr., tchr., prin. various schs., Ont. and Que., 1952-65; area commr. Girl Guides of Can., throughout Europe, 1965-69; adminstr., tchr. Algonquin Community Coll., Ottawa, Ont., 1970-74; tchr., program devel. Frontenac County Bd. Edn., Kingston, Ont., 1974-75; lectr., faculty advisor dept. curriculum, edn. U. Man., Can., 1977-79; lectr. U. Winnipeg, Man., Can., 1977-79; cons. colls. div. Man. Dept. Edn., 1980-81, sr. cons. programming br., 1981-84, sr. cons. post secondary, adult and continuing edn. div., 1985-88, dir. post secondary career devel. br. and adult and continuing edn. br., 1989; asst. prof. higher edn., coord. grad. program in higher edn. U. Man., 1989-92, assoc. prof., coord. grad. program in higher edn., 1992—; cons. lectures, seminars, workshops throughout Can. Contbr. articles to profl. jours.; mng. editor Can. Jour. of Higher Edn., 1989-93. Mem. U. Man. Senate, 1976-81, 86-89, bd. govs., 1979-82; Can. rep. Internat. Youth Conf., Garmisch, Fed. Republic of Germany, 1968; vol. Can. Cancer Soc.; mem. Assn. RN Accreditation Coun., 1980-85; chair Child Care Accreditation Com., Man., 1983-90; chair Task Force Post-Secondary Accessibility, Man., 1983; vol. United Way Planning and Allocations; provincial dir., mem. nat. bd. Can. Congress for Learning Opportunities for Women. Mem. Can. Soc. Study Higher Edn., Man. Tchrs. Soc., U. Man. Alumni Assn., Women's Legal Edn. and Action Fund, Am. Assn. Study Higher Edn. Home: 261 Baltimore Rd, Winnipeg, MB Canada R3L 1H7

STALLARD, HUBERT R., telecommunications industry executive; b. 1937. Degree, Hampden-Sydney (Va.) Coll. Engr. staff asst. Bell Atlantic Va. Inc., Richmond, 1959-85, pres., CEO, 1985—; mem. bd. dirs. Universal Corp., Richmond. Office: Bell Atlantic Va Inc 600 E Main St Richmond VA 23219*

STALLARD, HUGH R., telephone company executive; b. Norton, Va., Jan. 31, 1937; s. Nathaniel Winfield and Evelyn (Stewart) S.; m. Alice Cheatwood, Aug. 1, 1959; children: Craig Winston, Brian Kendrick, Mark Brian. BS, Hampden-Sydney Coll., 1959. Successively staff asst. engr., foreman svc., plant supr., foreman supr., dist. plant supr., dist. plant mgr. Chesapeake and Potomac Telephone Co. of Va., Richmond, Roanoke, Newport News, Norfolk, 1960-68; from staff supr. to div. plant mgr. Chesapeake and Potomac Telephone Co. of Va., Northern and Culpeper, 1969-73; from gen. engring. mgr. to gen. mgr. network engring. and provisioning, Richmond Chesapeake and Potomac Telephone Co. of Va., Richmond, 1977-80, asst. v.p. revenue requirements, 1980-82, asst. v.p. external affairs, 1982-85, v.p. 1985-88, pres., 1988-90, pres., chief exec. officer, 1990—; staff supr. Chesapeake and Potomac Telephone Cos., Washington, 1968-69; gen. plant mgr. Chesapeake and Potomac Telephone Co. of Washington, 1973-77. Exec. adv. bd. Jr. Achievement of Richmond, 1981; adv. bd. U. Richmond, 1982; bd. dirs. Richmond Renaissance, 1985, Va. Literacy Found., 1989; mem. Va. Bus. Coun., Richmond, 1985, corp. bd. YMCA of Greater Richmond, 1986, capital funds bd. United Way Greater Richmond, 1988—; trustee Va. Found. for Ind. Colls., 1986, Hampden-Sydney (Va.) Coll., 1987. Lt. comdr. U.S. Naval Res. Named Chief Exec. Officer of Yr. Minority Devel. Coun., 1989, Bus. Man of Yr. Va. Literacy Found., 1989. Mem. Va. Mfrs. Assn., Va. Telephone Assn. (bd. dirs. 1984-85). Presbyterian. Office: Chesapeake & Potomac Tel Co 600 E Main St Richmond VA 23219-2441

STALLINGS, CHARLES HENRY, physicist; b. Durham, N.C., Dec. 28, 1941; s. Henry Harroll and Dorothy (Powers) S.; m. Elizabeth Bright, Sept. 4, 1965; children: Deborah, Sharon. BS, N.C. State U., 1963, MS, 1964; PhD, U. Wis., 1970. Sr. physicist Physics Internat. Co., San Leandro, Calif., 1970-73, dep. dept. mgr., 1974-76, dept. mgr., 1976-79, dir. satellite X-ray test facility office, 1979-81, dir. bus. devel., 1981-83, v.p., dir. rrsch. devel., 1983—. Contbr. articles to tech. jours. Patentee in field. Mem. Gen. Plan Rev. Com., Pleasanton, Calif., 1983. Mem. Am. Phys. Soc., IEEE (assoc.).

Home: 1717 Courtney Ave Pleasanton CA 94588-2692 Office: Olin Corp Physics Internat 2700 Merced St San Leandro CA 94577-5633

STALLINGS, GENE CLIFTON, university athletic coach, former professional coach; b. Paris, Tex., Mar. 2, 1935; s. Eugene C. and Neil (Moye) S.; m. Ruth Ann Jack, Dec. 1, 1956; children: Anna Lee, Laura Nell, John Mark, Jacklyn Ruth, Martha Kate. B.S., Tex. A&M U., 1958. Asst. football coach U. Ala., 1958-64; head football coach, dir. athletics Tex. A&M U., 1964-72; asst. coach Dallas Cowboys, 1972-85; head football coach St. Louis Cardinals (now known as Phoenix Cardinals), 1986-89, U. Ala. Crimson Tide, 1990—; dir. Bank of A&M, College Station, Tex., Rolling Internat., Inc., Dallas; Spalding sports cons. Mem. Sam Houston council Boy Scouts Am.; trustee Abilene (Tex.) Christian U. Named 1983 Dallas Father of the Yr.; elected to Tex. A&M U. Hall of Fame, 1982. Mem. Nat. Assn. Collegiate Dirs. Athletics, Am. Football Coaches Assn., Fellowship Christian Athletes. Mem. Ch. of Christ. Coached NCAA divisional IA U. Ala. Nat. Champions, ranked # 1 by UPI and AP, 1992. Office: Univ Ala PO Box 870323 Tuscaloosa AL 35487-0323*

STALLINGS, (CHARLES) NORMAN, lawyer; b. Tampa, Fla., Apr. 3, 1914; s. Otto Pyromus and Minnie Henderson (Mitchell) S.; m. Mary Phillips Powell, Feb. 6, 1943; children: Charles Norman, Jean Katherine, Mary Anne. A.B., U. Fla., 1935; J.D., Harvard U., 1938, LL.M., 1940. Bar: Mo. 1939, Fla. 1940, D.C. 1941, Ga. 1946. Asso. firm Ryland, Stinson, Mag & Thomson, Kansas City, Mo., 1938-39, Sutherland, Tuttle & Brennan, Washington, 1940-41, Atlanta, 1946-49; mem. firm Shackleford, Farrior, Stallings & Evans, Tampa, Fla., 1949-84, of counsel, 1984—. Vice chmn. Hillsborough County (Fla.) Aviation Authority, 1955-61. Served to lt. col. U.S. Army, 1941-46, ETO. Decorated Bronze Star; Croix de Guerre avec Palma, Belgium). Fellow Am. Coll. Trial Lawyers; mem. ABA, Hillsborough County Bar Assn. (past pres.), Fla. Bar Assn. (past gov.), Univ. Club (past pres.), Tampa Yacht and Country Club (past gov.), Ye Mystic Krewe of Gasparilla (past capt. and king), Phi Delta Phi, Kappa Alpha. Republican. Episcopalian. Home: 1901 S Ardsley St Tampa FL 33629-5930 Office: PO Box 3324 Tampa FL 33601-3324

STALLMEYER, JAMES EDWARD, engineer, educator; b. Covington, Ky., Aug. 11, 1926; s. Joseph Julius and Anna Catherine (Scheper) S.; m. Mary Katherine Davenport, Apr. 11, 1953; children: Cynthia Marie, James Duncan, Michael John, Catherine Ann, John Charles, Gregory Edward. BS, U. Ill., 1947, MS, 1949, PhD, 1953. Jr. engr. So. Ry. System, 1947; research asst. U. Ill., Urbana, 1947-49; research assoc. U. Ill., 1951-52, asst. prof. civil engring, 1952-57, assoc. prof., 1957-60, prof., 1960—; cons. on structural problems various indsl. and govt. agys. Author: (with E.H. Gaylord Jr.), Design of Steel Structures. Served with USN, 1944-46. Standard Oil fellow, 1949-51; recipient Adams meml. award, 1964, Everitt award for teaching excellence, 1981. Mem. ASCE, Am. Concrete Inst., Am. Ry. Engring. Assn., ASTM, Am. Welding Soc., Am. Soc. Metals, Soc. Exptl. Stress Analysis, Scabbard and Blade, Sigma Xi, Chi Epsilon, Sigma Tau, Tau Beta Pi, Phi Kappa Phi. Republican. Roman Catholic. Club: KC. Office: Newmark Civil Engring 205 N Mathews Ave Urbana IL 61801-2352

STALLONE, SYLVESTER ENZIO, actor, writer, director; b. N.Y.C., July 6, 1946; s. Frank and Jacqueline (Labofish) S.; m. Sasha Czack, Dec. 28, 1974 (div.); children: Sage, Seth; m. Brigitte Nielsen, Dec. 15, 1985 (div. 1987). Student, Am. Coll. of Switzerland, 1965-67, U. Miami, 1967-69. Formerly, usher, fish salesman, horse trainer, delicatessen worker, truck driver, bouncer, zoo attendant, short order cook, pizza demonstrator, phys. edn. tchr., motel supt., bookstore detective. Appeared in motion pictures Lords of Flatbush, 1973, Capone, 1974, Rocky, 1976, (Oscar for Best Picture 1976, Golden Globe award for best picture 1976, Donatello award for best actor in Europe 1976, Christopher Religious award 1976, Bell Ringer award Scholastic Mag. 1976, Nat. Theatre Owners award 1976) F.I.S.T., 1978, Paradise Alley, 1978, Rocky II, 1979, Nighthawks, 1981, Victory, 1981, Rocky III, 1982, First Blood, 1982, Rhinestone, 1984, Rambo: First Blood Part II, 1985, Rocky IV, 1985, Cobra, 1986, Over the Top, 1987, Rambo III, 1988, Lock Up, 1989, Tango and Cash, 1989, Rocky V, 1990, Cliffhanger, 1993, Demolition Man, 1993, The Specialist, 1994, Judge Dredd, 1995; producer, dir. film Staying Alive, 1983; author: Paradise Alley, 1977, The Rocky Scrapbook, 1977; novel Rocky II. Recipient Star of the Year award 1977, named Show West actor of the year 1979, Artistic Achievement award Nat. Italian Am. Found., 1991, Order of Arts and Letters, French Ministry, 1992, Caesar award for Career Achievement, 1992. Mem. Screen Actors Guild, Writers Guild, Stuntmans Assn. (hon.), Dirs. Guild. Nomination for two Oscars (acting and writing) in same year (1976) occurred for only 3d time in history. Office: care Ron Meyer Creative Artists Agy 9830 Wilshire Blvd Beverly Hills CA 90212-1804 *Once in one's life, for one mortal moment, one must make a grab for immortality; if not, one has not lived.*

STALLWORTH, ANNE NALL, writer, writing educator; b. Birmingham, Ala., Sept. 30, 1935; d. John Martin and Lida Lucille (Crump) Nall; m. Clarke J. Stallworth Jr., Mar. 23, 1925; children: Carole Anne Stallworth, Clarke J. Stallworth III. Student, Birmingham-So. Coll., 1952-53. Tchr. U. Ala., Birmingham; tchr. Birmingham. Author: This Time Next Year, 1972 (Best Fiction award), Where the Bright Lights Shine, 1977, Go, Go, Said the Bird, 1984 (movie rights pending); (short story) Waiting (McCall's mag.), 1976. All had fgn. publ. Editor Found. for Women's Health newsletter, Birmingham; publicity dir. Birmingham Music Club. Recipient Best Fiction award Ala. Libr., 1972. Avocations: speaking at libraries, women's clubs; presenting workshops for writers. Home: 4019 Montclair Rd Birmingham AL 35213-2411

STALLWORTH-BARRON, DORIS A. CARTER, librarian, educator; b. Ala., June 12, 1932; d. Henry Lee Carter and Hattie Belle Stallworth; m. George Stallworth, 1950 (dec.); children: Annette LaVerne, Vanzette Yvonne; m. Walter L. Barron, 1989. BS, Ala. State U., 1955; MLS, CUNY, 1968; postgrad., Columbia U., St. John's U., NYU. Cert. supr. and tchr. sch. libr. media, N.Y. Libr. media specialist N.Y.C. Bd. Edn.; head libr. Calhoun County High Sch., Hobson City, Ala.; cons. Libr. Unit, N.Y.C. Bd. Edn.; cons. evaluator So. Assn. Secondary Schs., Ala.; supr., adminstr., liason rep. Community Sch. Dist. #24 N.Y.C. Sch. System; previewer libr. media Preview Mag., 1971-73; mem. ednl. svcs. adv. coun. Sta. WNET, 1987-89; mem. coun. N.Y.C. Schs. Libr. System, 1987-90; turn-key tchr. trainer N.Y. State Dept. Edn., 1988; spl. guest speaker and lectr. Queens Coll., City U., Community Sch. Dist. #24, PTA, N.Y. City Sch. System, Libr. unit, 1980-90; curriculum writer libr. unit N.Y.C. Bd. Edn., 1985-86. Contbr. articles to ednl. publs. Mem. State of Ala. Dem. Exec. Com., 1994—; active A for Kids. Mem. NAFE, ALA, Am. Assn. Sch. Librs. (spl. guest speaker and lectr. for conv. 1987), Am. Sch. Libr.'s Assn., Nat. Assn. Black Pub. Adminstrs., N.Y. State Libr. Assn., N.Y.C. Sch. Librs. Assn., Nat. Forum for Black Pub. Adminstrs., N.Y. Coalition 100 Black Women, Lambda Kappa Mu Sorority, Inc., Alpha Kappa Alpha Sorority.

STALNAKER, JOHN HULBERT, physician; b. Portland, Oreg., Aug. 29, 1918; s. William Park II and Helen Caryl (Hulbert) S.; m. Louise Isabel Lucas, Sept. 8, 1946; children: Carol Ann, Janet Lee, Mary Louise, John Park, Laurie Jean, James Mark. Student, Reed Coll., Portland, 1936-38; AB, Willamette U., Salem, Oreg., 1941; MD, Oreg. Health Scis. U., 1945. Diplomate Am. Bd. Internal Medicine. Intern Emanuel Hosp., Portland, 1945-46; resident in internal medicine St. Vincent Hosp., Portland, 1948-51; clin. instr. U. Oreg. Med. Sch., 1951-54, 60-62; staff physician VA Hosp., Vancouver, Wash., 1970-79; cons. in internal medicine, 1951-79. Contbr. articles to profl. jours. Pianist various civic and club meetings, Portland; leader Johnny Stalnaker's Dance Orch., 1936-39. Lt. (j.g.) USNR, 1946-48. Fellow ACP; mem. AMA, Multnomah County Med. Soc., Oreg. State Med. Assn., N.Am. Lily Soc., Am. Rose Soc. Avocations: music, photography, horticulture. Home: 2204 SW Sunset Dr Portland OR 97201-2068

STALOFF, ARNOLD FRED, financial executive; b. Dover, N.J., Dec. 12, 1944; s. William and Ida (Greenberg) S.; m. Sharon Marcia Teplitsky, June 10, 1967; children: Kimberly, Lindsay. BBA, U. Miami, 1967. Statistician U.S. Census Bur., Washington, 1967-68; fin. analyst SEC, Washington, 1968-71; sr. v.p. Phila. Stock Exchange, 1971-78; v.p. Securities Industry Automation Corp., N.Y.C., 1978-80; pres. Fin. Automation Corp., Phila., 1980-83, Phila. Bd. Trade, 1983-89; pres., chief exec. officer Commodity Exchange, Inc. (COMEX), N.Y.C., 1989-90; chief exec. officer Bloom Staloff Corp.,

Phila., 1990—; bd. dirs. Phila. Stock Exchange, Lehman Bros. Fin. Products, Inc. Ab. Variety Club for Handicapped Children, Phila., 1987-92; mem. adv. bd. Phila. Internat. Airport, 1988—. Mem. Nat. Futures Assn. (bd. dirs. 1987-90). Avocations: golf, skiing. Office: Bloom Staloff Corp 2000 Market St Philadelphia PA 19103-3231

STALON, CHARLES GARY, retired economics educator, institute administrator; b. Cape Girardeau, Mo., Oct. 26, 1929; s. Charles Douglas and Lucy Idell (Row) S.; m. Marie Allene Hitt, Mar. 15, 1952; children: Connie Lucille Stalon Babbitt, Donna Jean Stalon Williams. Student, Ohio State U., 1955-56; BA, Butler U., 1959; MS, Purdue U., 1963, PhD, 1966. Econs. instr. Purdue U., Lafayette, Ind., 1962-63; econs. prof. So. Ill. U., Carbondale, 1963-77; rsch. economist Fed. Power Commn., Washington, 1969-70; commr. Ill. Commerce Commn., Springfield, 1977-84, Fed. Energy Regulatory Commn., Washington, 1984-89; dir. Putnam, Hayes & Bartlett, Inc., Washington, 1989-91; dir. Inst. Pub. Utilities, prof. econs. Mich. State U., East Lansing, 1991—; pres. Mid-Am. Regulatory Commn., Chgo., 1983-84; mem. adv. coun. Gas Rsch. Inst., 1981-84, 91—. Author: (book chpt.) Papers in Quantitative Economics, 1968, The Future of Electrical Energy, 1986; contbr. articles to profl. jours. With USN, 1948-49, 52-54. Mem. Am. Econ. Assn., Transp. and Pub. Utility Group, Nat. Soc. Rate of Return Analysts (bd. dirs. 1982-90), Coun. on Econ. Regulation (bd. dirs. 1986—), Nat. Assn. Regulatory Utilities Commns., Nat. Regulatory Rsch. Inst. (bd. dirs. 1983-84, 91—), Inst. for Study of Regulation (bd. dirs. 1984-87).

STAM, DAVID HARRY, librarian; b. Paterson, N.J., July 11, 1935; s. Jacob and Deana B. (Bowman) S.; m. Deirdre Corcoran, May 15, 1963; children—Julian, Wendell, Kathryn. AB, Wheaton Coll., 1955; postgrad., New Coll., U. Edinburgh, 1955-56; MLS, Rutgers U., 1962; postgrad., CUNY, 1963-64; PhD, Northwestern U., 1978. Asst. editor library publs., reference librarian, manuscript cataloguer New York Pub. Library, 1959-64; librarian Marlboro (Vt.) Coll., 1964-67; head tech. services dept. Newberry Library, Chgo., 1967-71; assoc. librarian Newberry Library, 1969-73; librarian Milton S. Eisenhower Library, Johns Hopkins U., Balt., 1973-78; Andrew W. Mellon dir. rsch. libraries N.Y. Pub. Library, N.Y.C., 1978-86; Univ. librarian Syracuse U., 1986—; trustee Gladys K. Delmas Found. Author: Wordsworthian Criticism 1964-1973: An Annotated Bibliography, 1974, (with Rissa Yachnin) Turgenev in English: A Checklist of Works by and about Him, 1960; Contbr. articles to profl. jours. Served with USNR, 1956-58. Brit. Acad. Overseas fellow, 1975. Mem. ALA, Am. Hist. Assn., Am. Antiquarian Soc., Caxton Club (Chgo.), Princeton Club of N.Y., Grolier Club (N.Y.C.). Home: 2400 Euclid Ave Syracuse NY 13224-1811 Office: Syracuse U E S Bird Libr 222 Waverly Ave Syracuse NY 13210-2412

STAMAS, STEPHEN, investment executive; b. Salem, Mass., Apr. 26, 1931; s. Theodore and Georgia (Fotopulos) S.; m. Elaine Heidi Zervas, Apr. 24, 1955; children: Heidi, Theodore. AB, Harvard, 1953, Ph.D., 1957, B.Phil. (Rhodes scholar), Oxford U., 1955. Budget examiner Bur. Budget, Washington, 1957-59; loan officer Devel. Loan Fund, Washington, 1959-60; mgr. internat. div. treasurer's dept. Standard Oil Co. (N.J.), N.Y.C., 1960-63; dep. European financial rep. Standard Oil Co. (N.J.), London, Eng., 1963-64; govt. relations mgr. Esso Europe, 1964-67; petroleum planning mgr. Esso Internat., 1967-68; dep. asst. sec. for financial policy Dept. Commerce, Washington, 1968-69; chief economist Standard Oil Co. (N.J.), N.Y.C., 1969-70; dep. mgr. pub. affairs dept. Standard Oil Co. (N.J.), 1971; v.p. pub. affairs Exxon Corp., N.Y.C., 1973-86; pres. Wallace Funds, N.Y.C., 1986-87; pres. N.Y. Philharm., 1984-89, chmn., 1989—; pvt. investment exec. Windcrest Ptnrs., N.Y.C., 1992—. Trustee, pres. Am. Ditchley Found.; trustee, vice chmn. Rockefeller U.; chmn. Am. Assembly, Columbia U., Marlboro Sch. Music; mem. bd. overseers Harvard Coll., 1979-85; chmn. N.Y. Philharm.-Symphony Soc.; vice chmn. Lincoln Ctr. for the Performing Arts; bd. dirs. The Greenwall Found., BNY Hamilton Funds, Inc., Seacor Holdings Inc. Mem. Council Fgn. Relations (bd. dirs.), Acad. Polit. Sci., Am. Council on Germany (bd. dirs.), Phi Beta Kappa. Clubs: Harvard (N.Y.C.), Century Assn. (N.Y.C.), Manursing Island (Rye, N.Y.). Home: 325 Evandale Rd Scarsdale NY 10583-1505 Office: New York Philharm Avery Fisher Hall 10 Lincoln Center Plz New York NY 10023-6900 also: Windcrest Ptnrs 122 E 42nd St New York NY 10168-0001

STAMATAKIS, CAROL MARIE, state legislator, lawyer; b. Canton, Ohio, Apr. 27, 1960; d. Emmanuel Nicholas and Catherine Lucille (Zam) S.; m. Michael Charles Shklar, Mar. 23, 1985. BA in Criminology and Criminal Justice, Ohio State U., 1982; JD, Case Western Res., 1985. Bar: N.H. 1985, U.S. Dist. Ct. N.H. 1985. Atty. Law Office Laurence F. Gardner, Hanover, N.H., 1985-87, Law Office William Howard Dunn, Claremont, N.H., 1987-90, Elliott, Jasper & Stamatakis, Newport, N.H., 1990-93; state rep. N.H. State Legislature, 1988-94; of counsel Law office of Michael C. Shklar, Newport, 1994—; instr. Am. Inst. Banking, Claremont, 1987-88, 91-92, 95. Asst. editor: (jours.) Health Matrix: The Jour. of Health Services Mangement, 1983-85. Treas., mem. Town of Lempster N.H. Conservation Commn., 1987—; bd. dirs. Orion House, Inc., Newport, N.H., 1987-91; town chair N.H. Dem. Party, 1987—; mem. Town of Lempster Recycling Com., 1988—, Community Task Force on Drug and alcohol Abuse, 1988. Mem. ABA, N.H. Bar Assn., Sierra Club, Upper Valley Group (former vice chair and solid waste chair). Avocations: drawing, painting. Home: PO Box 807 Newport NH 03773-0807

STAMBAUGH, ARMSTRONG A., JR., restaurant and hotel executive; b. Cleve., Nov. 1, 1920; s. Armstrong Alexander and Beatrice (Snyder) S.; m. Janet Turley Marting, July 26, 1943 (div. 1958); children—Susan Reed (Mrs. Roy H. Beaton, Jr.), Sally Russell (Mrs. Michael H. Huber), Elizabeth Renshaw (Mrs. James W. Ewing); m. Aagot Hinrichsen Cain, June 10, 1972. B.A., Dartmouth, 1942; Indsl. Adminstr., Harvard, 1943, M.B.A., 1946. Research asst., then instr. bus. adminstr. Harvard Grad. Sch. Bus. Adminstrn., 1946-48; with Gulf Oil Corp., 1948-66; coord. sales devel. mktg. hdqrs. Gulf Oil Corp., Houston, 1962-63; v.p. Eastern marketing region Gulf Oil Corp., Phila., 1963-66; exec. v.p. adminstrn. Howard Johnson Co., Inc., 1966-70, exec. v.p. ops. and adminstrn., 1970-79, exec. v.p. asst. to pres., 1979-81, dir., 1969-81; operator, developer food and lodging facilities, 1981—. Pres. trustees Fox Chapel Country Day Sch., Pitts., 1955-57; div. vice chmn. Boston United Fund, 1961; bd. dirs. Houston Internat. Trade and Travel Fair, 1962-63, World Affairs Coun. Phila., 1964-65; dir. Phila. C. of C., 1964, 65, 66; bd. overseers Hanover Inn, Dartmouth Coll., 1979-85, chmn., 1984-85; trustee Old Sturbridge Village, Mass., 1979—. Served to lt. (j.g.) USNR, 1943-46. Mem. Pine Valley Golf Club (N.J.), Weston (Mass.) Golf Club, Kittansett Golf Club (Mass.), Boston Skating Club, Harvard Club (Boston), Vineyard Haven Yacht Club (Mass.), Paradise Valley Country Club (Ariz.), Delta Tau Delta. Home: 474 Concord Rd Weston MA 02193-1313 Office: 39 Main St Waltham MA 02154-6900

STAMBAUGH, RONALD, physicist, researcher; b. May 24, 1947. BS, U. Wis., 1969; MS, Yale U., 1972, PhD in Physics, 1975. Rsch. scientist Gen. Atomics, 1975—. Mem. Am. Phys. Soc. (Award for Excellence in Plasma Physics Rsch. 1994). Office: General Atomics PO Box 85608 San Diego CA 92138*

STAMBERG, SUSAN LEVITT, radio broadcaster; b. Newark, Sept. 7, 1938; d. Robert I. and Anne (Rosenberg) Levitt; m. Louis Collins Stamberg, Apr. 14, 1962; 1 child, Joshua Collins. BA, Barnard Coll, 1959; DHL (hon.), Gettysburg Coll., 1982, Dartmouth Coll., 1984, Knox Coll., U. N.H., SUNY, Brockport. Editorial asst. Daedalus, Cambridge, Mass., 1960-62; editorial asst. The New Republic, Washington, 1962-63; host, producer, mgr., program dir. Sta. WAMU-FM, Washington, 1963-69; host All Things Considered Washington, 1971-86; host Weekend Edition Nat Pub. Radio, Washington, 1987-89; spl. corr. Nat. Pub. Radio, 1990—; bd. dirs. AIA, Washington, 1983-85, PEN/Faulkner Fiction Award Found., 1985—. Author: Every Night at Five, 1982, The Wedding Cake in the Middle of the Road, 1992. Talk: NPR's Susan Stamberg Considers All Things, 1993. Recipient Honor award Ohio U., 1977, Edward R. Murrow award Corp. for Pub. Broadcasting, 1980; named Woman of Yr., Barnard Coll., 1986; Silliman Coll. Yale U., 1984—; inducted Broadcasting Hall of Fame, 1994. Avocations: sketching; piano; knitting. Office: Nat Pub Radio 635 Massachusetts Ave NW Washington DC 20001-3753

STAMELMAN, RICHARD HOWARD, French and humanities educator; b. Newark, Mar. 7, 1942; s. Louis Robert and Golda (Senzer) S.; m. Rebecca

White, June 5, 1965; children—Emily Gibson, Jeremy White. B.A., Hamilton Coll.; Ph.D., Duke U. Asst. prof. French and humanities Wesleyan U., Middletown, Conn., 1967-74, assoc. prof., 1974-79, prof., 1979-93, William R. Kenan Jr. prof. humanities, 1983-92, dean humanities, 1986-89, dir. Ctr. for the Humanities, 1976-82, dir. humanities devel., 1982-85; dir. Weston Ctr. for Fgn. Langs., Lits. and Cultures Williams Coll., Williamstown, Mass., 1992—, prof. Romance langs., 1992—; chair dept. French and Italian U. Colo., Boulder, 1991-92; organizer (study group) Ecrire le Livre: Autour d'Edmond Jabès, Cerisy-la-Salle, France, 1987; co-dir. Edouard Morot-Sir Summer Inst. for French Cultural Studies, Hanover, N.H., 1994. Author: The Drama of Self in Guillaume Apollinaire's Alcools, 1976, Claude Garache: Prints, 1965-85, 1985, Lost Beyond Telling: Representations of Death and Absence in Modern French Poetry, 1990; editor: Contemporary French Poetry, Studies in 20th Century Literature, 1989, Ecrire le Livre: Autour d'Edmond Jabès, 1989, Italian transl., 1991, French Poetry since the War, L'Esprit Créateur, 1992; editor, prin. translator: The Lure and the Truth of Painting, Selected Essays by Yves Bonnefoy, 1995; translator: The Grapes of Zeuxis and Other Fables by Yves Bonnefoy, 1987, Once More the Grapes of Zeuxis by Yves Bonnefoy, 1989, The Last Grapes of Zeuxis by Yves Bonnefoy, 1993; mem. editorial bd. French Forum; contbr. articles to profl. jours. Recipient Chevalier dans l'ordre des Palmes Académiques award French Govt., 1993; NEH fellow, 1973; Am. Council Learned Socs. grantee, 1983. Mem. MLA (regional del. 1987-90), Am. Assn. Tchrs. French, Acad. Lit. Studies. Home: 417 Main St Portland CT 06480-1523 Office: Williams Coll Weston Ctr Fgn Langs Lits Culture Williamstown MA 01267

STAMEY, THOMAS ALEXANDER, physician, urology educator; b. Rutherfordton, N.C., Apr. 26, 1928; s. Owen and Virginia (Link) S.; m. Kathryn Simmons Dec. 1, 1973; children: Fred M., Charline, Thomas A. III, Allison, Theron. BA, Vanderbilt U., 1948; MD, Johns Hopkins U., 1952. Diplomate Am. Bd. Urology. Intern, then resident Johns Hopkins Hosp. 1952-56; asst. prof. urology Johns Hopkins U. Sch. Medicine, Balt., 1958-60, assoc. prof., 1960-61; assoc. prof. Stanford (Calif.) U., 1961-64, 1964-90, prof., chmn. dept., 1991—, chmn. div. urology, 1961-90. Author: Renovascular Hypertension, 1967, Pathogenesis and Treatment of Urinary Tract Infections, 1980, Urinalysis and Urinary Sediment: A Practical Guide for the Health Science Professional, 1985; editor: Campbell's Urology, Monographs in Urology, 1980—. Capt. M.C., USAF, 1956-58. Recipient Sheen award ACS, 1990, Ferdinand C. Valentine award N.Y. Acad. Medicine, 1991. Mem. Am. Urol. Assn., Am. Surg. Assn. (sr.), Inst. Medicine of NAS. Avocation: fishing. Office: Stanford U Med Ctr 300 Pasteur Dr Stanford CA 94305-5118

STAMM, ALAN, lawyer; b. Galesburg, Ill., Nov. 22, 1931; s. Gustave Frederick and Miriam (Simon) S.; m. Shelley Lynn Ramage, Mar. 19, 1978; 1 child, Lucinda Anne. Student, Universidad Nacional de Mex., summer 1950; AB, Yale U., 1952; JD, Harvard U., 1957. Bar: Calif. 1957, U.S. Supreme Ct. 1963. Assoc. Thelen, Marrin, Johnson & Bridges, San Francisco, 1957-60; staff atty. Litton Industries Inc., Beverly Hills, Calif., 1960-66; asst. sec. Litton Industries Inc., Beverly Hills, 1963-66; sec., gen. counsel Internat. Rectifier Corp., L.A., 1966-69, v.p., 1968-69; v.p., gen. counsel Republic Corp., L.A., 1969-71, also bd. dirs., 1970-71; v.p., gen. counsel Sat. Rev. Industries, N.Y.C., 1971-72; v.p., gen. counsel Mattel Inc., Hawthorne, Calif., 1972-74, staff cons., 1974-75; of counsel Long & Levit, L.A., 1975-82, O'Donnell & Gordon, L.A., 1983-87, Hedges, Powe & Caldwell, L.A., 1988-90; pvt. practice L.A., 1990—; judge pro tem Mcpl. Ct. L.A. Jud. Dist., 1977—; arbitrator L.A. Superior Ct. 1979—, judge pro tem L.A. Superior Ct. 1989—, arbitrator Nat. Assn. Securities Dealers, 1991—. Founding trustee Ctr. for Law in the Pub. Interest; adv. trustee L.A. Ctr. for Photog. Studies; Eagle Scout. Served from ensign to lt. (J.G.) USNR, 1952-54; now lt. comdr. Res.; ret. Mem. ABA, Calif. Bar Assn., L.A. Bar Assn., Am. Jewish Com., Harvard Law Sch. Assn., L.A. County Art Mus., Greater L.A. Energy Coalition (gen. counsel), Am. Arbitration Assn. (nat. panel arbitrators), NAACP, Sierra Club, Nat. Assn. Yale Alumni (former bd. govs.), Yale Club of So. Calif. (former dir.), Harvard Club of So. Calif., Phi Beta Kappa. Home: 422 Denslow Ave Los Angeles CA 90049-3507 Office: 1840 Century Park E Fl 8 Los Angeles CA 90067-2101

STAMM, ROBERT JENNE, building contractor, construction company executive; b. Albuquerque, Nov. 17, 1921; s. Roy Allen and Elizabeth C. (Baldridge) S.; m. Florence I. Bradbury, May 14, 1943; children—R. Brad, Susan Stamm Evans. BSCE, U. N.Mex., 1942; postgrad. in Naval Architecture, U.S. Naval Acad., 1943. Registered profl. engr. and surveyor, N.Mex. With Bradbury & Stamm Constrn. Co., Albuquerque, 1946—; chmn., chief exec. officer Bradbury & Stamm Constrn. Co., 1975—, former pres. Mem. U. N.Mex. Found., 1982-94, N.Mex. Commn. on Higher Edn., 1986—; mem. centennial exec. com. U. N.Mex., chmn. devel. fund, 1984-85, 89-94; trustee Albuquerque Cmty. Found., 1983—; trustee Albuquerque Mus., 1993—; bd. dirs. N.Mex. Mus. Natural History, 1995—; bd. dirs., pres. Albuquerque Bus.-Edn. Compact, 1987-88, Albuquerque Mus. Found., 1986-91, Indsl. Found.; Albuquerque; past bd. dirs., officer United Way, Girl Scouts U.S.A., Boy Scouts Am., Presbyn. Hosp. Ctr. Found., Presbyn. Heart Inst., Greater Albuquerque Cmty. Ednl. Alliance, N.Mex. First, Albuquerque Econ. Forum, Albuquerque YMCA, Anderson-Abruzzo Internat. Balloon Mus. Comdr. USNR, 1943-69, ret. Recipient Regents Recognition medal U. N.Mex., 1986, Zimmerman award, 1988, U.N.Mex. Centennial Alumnus award Nat. Assn. State Univ. and Land Grant Colls., 1987, Disting. Pub. Svc. award State N.Mex., 1990, Award of Excellence, Presbyn. Health Fedn., 1991, Disting. Citizen award Boy Scouts-Great S.W. Coun., 1994; named Most Admired Co., N.Mex. Pvt. 100, 1990, 92, 94; named to Albuquerque Sr. Citizen Hall of Fame, 1994; named for N.Mex. Outstanding Philanthropic Leadership, 1994. Mem. NSPE (Albuquerque Engr. of Yr. 1987), Assoc. Gen. Contractors N.Mex. (pres. bldg. br. 1962), Econ. Forum Albuquerque, Exec. Assn. Greater Albuquerque. Episcopalian. Clubs: Albuquerque Country (bd. dirs. 1972-76, 87-89), Albuquerque Tennis (bd. dirs. 1978-80). Lodge: Elks. Avocations: tennis; skiing; golf. Home: 1524 Las Lomas Rd NE Albuquerque NM 87106-4532 Office: Bradbury & Stamm Constrn Co PO Box 25027 Albuquerque NM 87125-0027

STAMOS, JOHN, actor; b. Orange County, Calif., Aug. 19, 1963; s. Bill and Loretta Stamos. Drummer with various bands. Actor: (TV series) General Hospital (Emmy award, 2 Soapy awards), Dreams, 1984, You Again?, 1986-87, Full House, 1988-95, (TV movies) Daughter of the Streets, 1990, Captive, 1991, (feature film) Never Too Young to Die, 1986, Born to Ride, 1991. Recipient Youth in Film award. Mem. AFTRA, Child Help U.S.A. (nat. spokesperson). Office: William Morris Agy 151 S El Camino Dr Beverly Hills CA 90212-2704*

STAMOS, JOHN JAMES, judge; b. Chgo., Jan. 30, 1924; s. James S. and Katherine (Manolopoulos) S.; m. Helen Voutiritsas, Sept. 3, 1955 (dec. 1981); children—James, Theo, Colleen, Jana; m. Mary Sotter, March 21, 1986. LL.B., DePaul U., 1948. Bar: Ill. 1949. Since practiced in Chgo.; asst. corp. counsel City Chgo., 1951-54; asst. states atty. Cook County, 1954-61; chief criminal div. States Attys. Office, 1961-64, 1st asst. states atty., 1964-66, states atty., 1966-68; judge Appellate Ct. of State of Ill., 1968-88; Judge Ill. Supreme Ct., Springfield, 1988-90; ret., 1990; of counsel Stamos and Trucco, Chgo., 1991—. Served with AUS, 1943-45.

STAMOS, THEODOROS, artist; b. N.Y.C., 1922. Student, Am. Artists Sch. One-man shows of paintings and drawings, most recently at Athens (Greece) Gallery, 1974, Louis K. Meisel Gallery, N.Y.C., 1977, 79, Galerie Le Portail, Heidelberg, Fed. Republic of Germany, 1977, Tomasulo Gallery, Union Coll., N.J., 1978, Edwin Ulrich Mus., Wichita, Kans., 1979, SUNY, New Paltz, 1980, Munson-Williams-Proctor Inst., Utica, N.Y., 1980, Hokin Gallery, Chgo., 1980, Pierides Gallery Modern Art, Athens, Greece, 1987, Mus. Morsbroich, Leverkusen, Ger., 1988, Ileana Tounta Contemporary Art Ctr., Athens, 1991-92, ACA Galleries, N.Y.C., 1991-92; group shows, most recently at Solomon Guggenheim Mus., N.Y.C., 1977, Herbert F. Johnson Mus., Cornell U. Ithaca, N.Y., 1978, Whitney Mus. Modern Art, N.Y.C., 1978, Washington Internat. Art Fair, 1978, Louis K. Meisel Gallery, 1978, Gallery 700, Milw., 1979, Hokin Gallery, Chgo., 1980, DuBose Gallery, Houston, 1980, Munson-Williams-Proctor Inst., Utica, 1980, Mus. Knoedler, Zurich, Switzerland, 1983-85, Ericson Gallery, 1985, Kouros Gallery, 1985-86, Studio d'arte Zanuzzi, Milan, Italy, 1988, Ileana Tounta Gallery, Athens, 1989; represented in numerous collections including Met. Mus. Art, N.Y.C.,

Corcoran Gallery Art, Washington, Mus. Modern Art, N.Y.C., San Francisco Mus. Art, Va. Mus. Fine Arts, Norfolk, Art Inst. Chgo., Whitney Mus. Am. Art, N.Y.C., Smith Coll. Mus. Art, Northhampton, Mass., Museo d'Arte Moderno, Rio de Janiero, Balt. Mus. Art, Bklyn. Mus. Art, Tel Aviv Mus., Wadsworth Atheneum, Hartford, Conn., Fogg Art Mus., Harvard U., Cambridge, Mass., Nat. Picture Gallery, Athens, Nat. Mus. Greece, Wilhelm-Hack Mus., Ludwigshafen, Fed. Republic Germany, Mus. Moderner Kunst, Vienna, Austria, Guggenheim Mus., N.Y.C., others; retrospective exhbn. Mus. Morsbroich, Lever Kusen, Fed. Republic Germany, 1988; illustrator Sorrows of Cold Stone, 1951, The Hidden Airdome & Uncollected Poems, 1956. Tiffany Found. fellow, Brandeis U. Creative Arts award. Office: Louis K. Meisel Gallery 141 Prince St New York NY 10012

STAMP, FREDERICK PFARR, JR., federal judge; b. Wheeling, W.Va., July 24, 1934; s. Frederick P. Sr. and Louise (Aul) S.; m. Joan A. Corson, Sept. 20, 1975; children: Frederick Andrew, Joan Elizabeth. BA, Washington and Lee U., 1956; LLB, U. Richmond, 1959. Bar: W.Va. 1959, Va. 1959, Pa. 1986, U.S. Supreme Ct. 1973, U.S. Ct. Appeals (4th cir.) 1962, U.S. Dist. Ct. (no. dist.) W.Va. 1960, U.S. Dist. Ct. (so. dist.) W.Va. 1975, U.S. Dist. Ct. (we. dist.) Pa., U.S. Tax Ct. 1973, W.Va. Supreme Ct. Appeals 1966, Va. Supreme Ct. Appeals 1959. Assoc., then ptnr. Schrader, Stamp, Byrd, Byrum & Companion and predecessor firms, Wheeling, 1960-90; judge U.S. Dist. Ct. (no. dist.) W.Va., Wheeling, 1990-94, apptd. chief judge, 1994—; mem. ho. of dels. W.Va. Legislature, Charleston, 1966-70. Mem. W.Va. Bd. Regents, Charleston, 1970-77; trustee Linsly Sch., Wheeling, 1977—. Fellow Am. Bar Found., Am. Coll. Trial Lawyers; mem. W.Va. Bar Assn. (pres. 1981-82), W.Va. Commn. on Uniform State Laws, Nat. Conf. Commrs. on Uniform State Laws.

STAMP, NEAL ROGER, lawyer; b. Watkins Glen, N.Y., Sept. 19, 1918; s. Nelson Mathews and Mae Emma (Broderick) S.; m. Maja Stina Cavetz, Apr. 24, 1946; children: Thomas G., Gayle E. A.B., Cornell, 1940, J.D., 1942. Bar: N.Y. 1943. Pvt. practice Rochester, 1946-47; asst. corp., asso. legal counsel Cornell U., Ithaca, N.Y., 1947-59; sec. corp., asso. legal counsel Cornell U., 1959-62, sec. corp. 1959-79, univ. counsel, 1962-79, sr. counsel, 1979-84, univ. counsel emeritus, 1979—, dir. aero. lab., research found.; higher edn. cons., 1979—; lectr Practicing Law Inst.; dir. First Bank & Trust Co. Ithaca, 1971-84, chmn., 1978-84; dir Challenge Industries, Inc. Trustee Tompkins County Meml. Hosp., 1959-66, pres., 1961-62. Served to 1st lt., inf. AUS, 1942-46, MTO. Mem. ABA (ho. of dels. 1977-79), N.Y. State Bar Assn., Tompkins County Bar Assn., Assn. of Bar of City of N.Y., Nat. Assn. Coll. and U. Attys. (exec. bd. 1964-68, 72-79, life mem., pres. 1976-77). Home: Apt 14-2-F PO Box 4508 700 Warren Rd Ithaca NY 14852-4508

STAMPER, JAMES M., retired English language educator; b. Roxana, Ky., Sept. 26, 1917; s. Marion and Amanda (Combs) S.; m. Diane C. Mahoney, Aug. 12, 1967. BS in Edn., Union Coll., 1941; MA in English, U. Ky., 1946. Subs. tchr. Ermine Elem. Sch., Dry Fork Elem. Sch., 1936-37; elem. tchr. Hot Spot Premium Sch., 1937-41; h.s. Eng. tchr. Whitesburg H.S., Ky., 1941-46; instr. English U. Ky., Lexington, U. Md., College Park; instr. bus. English DePaul U., Chgo.; English tchr., cons. in high sch. English Bd. Edn., Chgo.; substitute tchr. Chgo. Area Schs., ret.; vis. instr. in English Jacksonville (Fla.) U. Co-author: A Handbook on Oral Reading Diagnosis, Resource Materials for Essential English in the Secondary Schools, A Syllabus in Basic English; contbr. articles to profl. jours. Scholar Knights of Columbus, Union Coll., U. Ky. Mem. AARP. Home: 1448 N Picadilly Cir Mount Prospect IL 60056-1028

STAMPER, JOE ALLEN, lawyer; b. Okemah, Okla., Jan. 30, 1914; s. Horace Allen and Ann (Stamey) S.; m. Johnnie Lee Bell, June 4, 1936; 1 child, Jane Allen (Mrs. Ernest F. Godlove). B.A., U. Okla., 1933, LL.B., 1935, J.D., 1970. Bar: Okla. bar 1935. Practice in Antlers, 1935-36, 46—; mem. firm Stamper, Burrage & Hadley, 1974—; atty. Pushmataha County, 1936-39; spl. justice Okla. Supreme Ct., 1948. Mem. Okla. Indsl. Commn., 1939-40; pres. Antlers Sch. Bd., 1956-67, Pushmataha Found., 1957—; mem. Okla. Bicentennial Comm., 1971—; vice chmn. bd. U. Okla. Law Center, 1975-78; mgr. Okla. Democratic party, 1946, dist. chmn., 1946-50; alt. del. Dem. Nat. Conv. 1952. Served to col. AUS, 1935-46, E O Decorated Bronze Star. Fellow Am. Bar Found., Am. Coll. Trial Lawyers, Am. Bd. Trial Advocates (announced) mem. ABA (del. 1974-91, state del. 1975-86, mem. com. on law book pub. practices 1974-76, bd. govs. 1986-89, standing com. on fed. jud. improvement 1989-92), SAR, Okla. Bar Assn. (bd. govs. 1969-73, Pres.'s award 1977, 80, 93), Okla. Bar Found. (pres. 1977), Mil. Order World Wars, Pi Kappa Alpha. Baptist (deacon). Clubs: Petroleum (Oklahoma City). Lodges: Masons, Shriners, Lions. Home: 1000 NE 2nd St Antlers OK 74523-2822 Office: PO Box 100 112 N High St Antlers OK 74523-2250

STAMPER, MALCOLM THEODORE, aerospace company executive; b. Detroit, Apr. 4, 1925; s. Fred Theodore and Lucille (Cayce) S.; m. Marion Philbin Guinan, Feb. 25, 1946; children: Geoffrey, Kevin, Jamie, David, Mary, Anne. Student, U. Richmond, Va., 1943-44; BEE, Ga. Inst. Tech., 1946; postgrad., U. Mich., 1946-49; DHumanities, Seattle U., 1994. With Gen. Motors Corp., 1949-62; with Boeing Co., Seattle, 1962-90; mgr. electronics ops., v.p., gen. mgr. turbine div. Boeing Co., 1964-66; v.p., gen. mgr. Boeing Co. (747 Airplane program), 1966-69, v.p., gen. mgr. comml. airplane group, 1969-71, corp. sr. v.p. ops., 1971-72; pres. Boeing Co., 1972-85, vice chmn., 1985-90; chief executive officer Storytellers Ink Pub., Seattle, 1990—, also chmn. bd. dirs.; bd. dirs. Nordstrom Co., Esterline Co., Chrysler Co., Whittaker Corp.; trustee The Conf. Bd., 1988—. Candidate for U.S. Ho. of Reps., Detroit, 1952; trustee, chmn. Seattle Art Mus.; nat. bd. dirs. Smithsonian Assocs. With USNR, 1943-46. Named Industrialist of Year, 1967; recipient Educator's Golden Key award, 1970, Elmer A. Sperry award, 1982, AIEE award, Ga. Inst. Tech. award, Sec. Dept. Health and Human Services award, Silver Beaver award Boy Scouts Am., 1989. Mem. Nat. Alliance Businessmen, Phi Gamma Delta.

STAMPER, ROBERT LEWIS, ophthalmologist, educator; b. N.Y.C., July 27, 1939; m. Naomi T. Belson, June 23, 1963; children: Juliet, Marjorie, Alison. BA, Cornell U., 1957-61; MD, SUNY-Downstate, 1965. Diplomate Am. Bd. Ophthalmology (assoc. examiner 1976-92, bd. dirs. 1992—, mem. glaucoma panel 1993—); lic. physician, Calif. Intern Mt. Sinai Hosp., N.Y.C., 1965-66; resident in ophthalmology Washington U.-Barnes Hosp. St. Louis, 1968-71; Nat. Eye Inst.-NIH fellow dept. ophthalmology Washington U., St. Louis, 1971-72, from instr. ophthalmology to asst. prof. dept. ophthalmology, 1971-72; asst. prof. dept. ophthalmology Pacific Presbyn. Med. Ctr., San Francisco, 1972-76, assoc. prof. ophthalmology, 1976-87; chmn. dept. ophthalmology Calif. Pacific Med. Ctr. (formerly Pacific Presbyn. Med. Ctr.), San Francisco, 1987—; asst. opthalmologist Barnes Hosp., St. Louis, 1971-72, Harkness Hosp., San Francisco 1973-74; dir. ophthalmic photography and fluorescin angiography, dept. ophthalmology Washington U., St. Louis, 1969-72; dir. resident tng. Pacific Presbyn. Med. Ctr., 1972-89, dir. glaucoma svc., vice-chmn. dept. ophthalmology, 1974-87; chief ophthalmology svc. Highland Hosp., Oakland, Calif., 1974-76; clin. instr. dept. ophthalmology U. Calif., San Francisco, 1974-77; clin. asst. prof. ophthalmology U. Calif., Berkeley, 1974-78, asst. clin. prof. ophthalmology, 1978-85; sr. rsch. assoc. Smith-Kettlewell Inst. Visual Scis., San Francisco, 1972-89; project code-dir. ophthalmic curriculum for med. students Nat. Libr. Medicine, 1973-75; commr. Joint Commn. on Allied Health Pers. in Ophthalmology, 1975-87, bd. dirs., 1978-88, sec., 1980, v.p. 1982-83, pres., 1984-85; provisional asst. chief dept. ophthalmology Mt. Zion Hosp., San Francisco, 1976-87, assoc. chief dept. ophthalmology, 1982-86; ophthalmic cons. Ft. Ord, Calif., 1976—, Oakland (Calif.) Naval Hosp., 1978-83; instr. Stanford (Calif.) U., 1977—; glaucoma cons. U.C. Davis, 1978-84; vis. lectr. dept. ophthalmology Hadassah Hebrew U. Med. Ctr., Jerusalem, 1978, Oxford (Eng.) U. Eye Hosp., 1986; ind. med. examiner State of Calif. 1979—; mem. appeals hearing panel Accreditation Coun. for Grad. Med. Edn., 1986-93, mem. residency rev. com. for ophthalmology, 1993—; mem. provisional courtesy staff Peralta Hosp., Oakland, 1988-92; mem. ophthalmic advisory com. adv. panel USFDA, 1989-92; presenter, lectr. in field. Editor Ophthalmology Clinics of North Am., 1988—; mem. editl. adv. com. Ophthalmology, 1982-89, mem. editl. bd., 1983-94; contbr. articles to profl. jours. Chmn. bd. Agy. for Jewish Edn., Oakland, 1986-89; bd. dirs. Jewish Fedn. Greater East Bay, Oakland, 1992-94; bd. dirs. Found. for Glaucoma Rsch.; mem. glaucoma adv. com. Nat. Soc. to Prevent Blindness, 1981—; mem. Am. Diabetes Assn. Surgeon USPHS, 1966-68. Recipient Nat. Soc.

for Performance and Instrn. award for self-instrnl. material in ophthalmology, 1975, Honor award Am. Acad. Ophthalmology, 1982, Statesmanship award Joint Commn. on Allied Health Pers. in Ophthalmology, 1989; N.Y. State Regents scholar, 1961, N.Y. State scholar in medicine, 1965; Blalock student fellow UCLA Sch. Medicine, 1961, Fight for Sight student fellow dept. ophthalmology N.Y. Hosp. and Cornell Med. Ctr., 1962, 63, 64. Fellow Am. Acad. Ophthalmology and Otolaryngology (rep. to joint commn. on allied health pers., faculty home study course sect. X, chmn. sect. VIII 1983-85, bd. councilors, editl. adv. com. Opthalmology jour. 1982-89, editl. bd. Ophthalmology jour. 1983-94, and many others), ACS; mem. AMA (Physician's Recognition award 1989), Am. Ophthalmologic Soc., Assn. for Rsch. in Vision and Ophthalmology, Calif. Med. Assn. (asst. sec. sect. ophthalmology, chmn., sci. bd. rep. adv. panel on ophthalmology 1985-91), Nat. Soc. Prevent Blindness (mem. glaucoma adv. com. 1981—, bd. dirs. 1986—), No. Calif. Soc. Prevent Blindness, Calif. Assn. Ophthalmology, Pan Am. Ophthalmological Soc., N.Y. Acad. Scis., Las Vegas Ophthalmological Soc. (hon.). Office: Cc Med Ctr 2340 Clay St San Francisco CA 94115

STAMPLEY, NORRIS LOCHLEN, former electric utility executive; b. Bentonia, Miss., Dec. 21, 1920; s. Orville K. and Norma Eloise S.; m. Mary Virginia Russum, May 28, 1942; children: Mary Lynn, Virginia Kaye. Registered profl. engr., Miss. Engr. U.S. Navy Dept., Washington, 1942-45; with Miss. Power & Light Co., Jackson, 1947-84, chief engr., 1968-72, v.p., 1972-80, sr. v.p., 1980-84; now ret. Miss. Power & Light Co. Pres. Met. YMCA, Jackson, 1980, 85; trustee Mcpl. Separate Sch. Dist., 1980-90, Miss. Baptist Found., 1981-85, 87-92; chmn. So. Baptist Conv. Brotherhood Commn., 1985-86. Served with Signal Corps, U.S. Army, 1945-47. Named Alumnus of Yr. Hinds Jr. Coll., 1980. Mem. Nat. Soc. Profl. Engrs., Miss. Engring. Soc. (Engr. of Yr. 1974), IEEE, Am. Nuclear Soc., Jackson C. of C. (dir.), Phi Theta Kappa (Alumnus of Yr. 1977). Clubs: Exchange (pres. 1975). Home: 343 Elms Court Cir Jackson MS 39204-4333

STAMPONE, FREDERICK ALBERT, retail executive, C.P.A.; b. Phila., Jan. 1, 1956; s. Peter Frederick and Joan Elizabeth (Kramer) S.; m. Karen Lee Bogar, Sept. 12, 1981. Student Drexel U., 1974-78. C.P.A., Calif., Pa. Supr. pub. acctg. Touche Ross & Co., Phila., 1978-82; controller The Pep Boys, Los Angeles, 1982-83, asst. v.p., controller, 1983—; sr. v.p. administrn., 1988, chief administrv. officer, 1993—. Treas., Pa. State Senate Campaign, Phila., 1981, Democratic Exec. Com. 41st Ward, Phila., 1982; bd. dirs. Coun. Better Bus. Burs., 1992. Mem. Am. Inst. C.P.A.s, Pa. Inst. C.P.A.s, Retail Fin. Execs. of So. Calif. Roman Catholic. Office: 3111 W Allegheny Ave Philadelphia PA 19132

STAMPS, DAVID M., publishing executive. Pub. Bonni Buy'rr Inc., Geneva, Ill. Office: Bonni Buy'rr Inc 2700 Keslinger Rd Geneva IL 60134*

STAMPS, GLADYS A., middle school educator; b. Boaz, Ala., Mar. 3, 1944; d. William O. and Cecile (Norris) S. AA, Snead Jr. Coll., 1964; BS, Auburn U., 1967; MA, Ala. A&M U., 1972. Cert. tchr., adminstr., Ala. Tchr. East Coweta High Sch., Newnan, Ga., 1967-68; tchr. Madison (Ala.) Sch., 1968-90, asst. prin., 1979-81, 88-89; tchr. Liberty Mid. Sch., Madison, 1990—; sch. revs. com. So. Assn. Accreditation, Ala., 1986, 88. Mem. Northwest Huntsville (Ala.) Assn., 1980-89; vol. Huntsville Botan. Gardens, 1989-92; sec. Sherwood Civic Assn., Huntsville, 1992. Mem. NEA, Ala. Edn. Assn., Madison County Edn. Assn., Ala. Assn. Social Studies, Geography Alliance, Madison County Hist. Soc., Alpha Delta Kappa (historian 1990-92). Baptist. Avocations: reading, swimming, sewing, outdoor activities. Home: 6508 Janke St Huntsville AL 35806 Office: Liberty Mid Sch 281 Dock Murphy Dr Madison AL 35758

STAMSTA, JEAN F., artist; b. Sheboygan, Wis., Nov. 2, 1936; d. Herbert R. and Lucile Caroline (Malwitz) Nagel; m. Duane R. Stamsta, Aug. 18, 1956; children: Marc, David. BS, BA, U. Wis., 1958. guest curator Milw. Art Mus., 1986; resident artist Leighton Artist Colony, Banff, Alta., Can., 1987. Solo exhbns. Am. Craft Mus., N.Y.C., 1971, Winona (Minn.) State U., 1986, Lawrence U., Appleton, Wis., 1990, Walkers Point Ctr. Arts, Milw., 1990; group shows include Milw. Art Mus., 1986, 88, Nat. Air & Space Mus. Smithsonian Instn., Washington, 1986, Madison (Wis.) Art Ctr., 1987, 90, Paper Press Gallery, Chgo., 1988, North Arts Ctr., Atlanta, 1990, Dairy Barn Cultural Arts Ctr., Athens, Ohio, 1991, Paper Arts Festival, Appleton, Wis., 1992, Fine Arts Mus., Budapest, Hungary, 1992, Tilburg Textile Mus., The Netherlands, 1993, U. Wis.- Madison Union Gallery, 1994. NEA craftsman fellow, 1974. Avocations: swimming, travel. Home and Studio: 9313 Center Oak Rd Hartland WI 53029

STANALJCZO, GREGG, computer services executive; b. 1959. Degree, Oakland U. With CDI Computer Svcs., Inc., Troy, Mich., 1982—, now pres., 1994—. Office: C D I Computer Svcs Inc 466 Stephenson Hwy Troy MI 48083*

STANBACK, BRAD, conservationist. Recipient Pres.'s Conservation Achievement award The Nature Conservancy, 1993. Mem. Nature Conservancy (Pres. Conservation Achievement Awd., 1993). Address: Route 1 PO Box 543 Canton NC 28716*

STANBACK, FRED, conservationist. Recipient of Pres.'s Conservation Achievement award. The Nature Conservancy, 1993. Mem. of Nature Conservancy (Pres. Conservation Achievement Awd., 1993). Address: 220 Stonewall Rd Salisbury NC 28144*

STANBACK, LAWRENCE, conservationist. Recipient Pres.'s Conservation Achievement award The Nature Conservancy, 1993. Mem. of Nature Conservancy (Pres. Conservation Achievement Awd., 1993). Address: 536 Royal St Apt C New Orleans LA 70130*

STANBURY, JOHN BRUTON, physician, educator; b. Clinton, N.C., May 15, 1915; s. Walter A. and Zula (Bruton) S.; m. Jean F. Cook, Jan. 6, 1945; children: John Bruton, Martha Jean, Sarah Katherine, David McNeill, Pamela Cook. A.B., Duke U., 1935; M.D., Harvard U., 1939; M.D. (hon.), U. Leiden (Netherlands), 1975; postgrad., U. Pisa, Italy, 1994. House officer Mass. Gen. Hosp., 1940-41, asst. resident, 1946, chief med. resident, 1948, mem. med. staff, 1949—; research fellow pharmacology Harvard Med. Sch., 1947; vis. prof. medicine U. Leiden, 1955; prof. exptl. medicine MIT, Cambridge, 1966-80; emeritus MIT, 1980—; cons. Pan Am. Health Orgn., WHO, UNICEF, U.S. AEC. Author: Endemic Goiter: The adaptation of man to iodine deficiency, 1954, Metabolic Basis of Inherited Disease, 5th edit., 1984, The Thyroid and Its Diseases, 5th edit., 1984, Endemic Goiter, 1969, Human Development and the Thyroid, 1972, Endemic Goiter and Endemic Cretinism, 1980, Prevention and Control of Iodine Deficiency Disorders, 1987, A Constant Ferment, 1991, The Damaged Brain of Iodine Deficiency, 1994, The Inborn Errors of the Thyroid System, 1994. Served from lt. (j.g.) to comdr. USNR, 1941-45. Recipient Delmar S. Fahrney medal Franklin Inst., 1993, Prince Mahidol award, Thailand, 1994. Mem. Am. Physicians, Soc. Clin. Investigation, Am. Thyroid Assn. (pres. 1969), Am. Acad. Arts and Scis., Endocrine Soc., Endocrine Socs. Finland, Colombia, Peru, Ecuador and Argentina, Internat. Coun. for Control of Iodine Deficiency Disorders. Democrat. Episcopalian. Home: 43 Circuit Rd Chestnut Hill MA 02167-1802

STANBURY, ROBERT DOUGLAS GEORGE, lawyer, executive; b. Exeter, Ont., Can., Oct. 26, 1927; s. James George Stuart and Elizabeth Jean (Hardy) S.; m. Miriam R. Voelker, June 21, 1952; children: Susan, Carol, Ian, Duncan. B.A. in journalism, U. Western Ont., 1950; grad., Osgoode Hall Law Sch., 1955; LLB, York U., 1991. Bar: Ont. 1955, Queen's counsel 1974. Account exec. Public and Indsl. Relations Ltd., Toronto, 1950-51; ptnr. Hollingworth & Stanbury, Toronto, 1955-65; mem. Can. Parliament, 1965-77; minister of citizenship and info. 1969-71, of communications, 1971-72, of nat. revenue, 1972-73; del. to UN Gen. Assembly, 1974-76; v.p., gen. counsel, sec. Firestone Can. Inc., Hamilton, Ont., 1977-83; ptnr., chief exec. officer Firestone Can. Inc., 1983-85; sec., dir. Dayton Tire Can. Ltd., 1977-83; dir. Workers Compensation Bd. (Ont.), 1985-88; counsel Inch Easterbrook & Shaker Barristers & Solicitors, Hamilton, Ont., 1986—; pres., CEO Can. Coun. for Native Bus., 1988-91; vice chmn. bd. dirs. Workers Compensation Bd., Ont., 1991-94. Mem. N.Y. Bd. Edn., 1961-64, chmn., 1963-64;

mem. Met. Toronto Sch. Bd., 1963-64, Met. Toronto Planning Bd., 1963; bd. dirs. Hamilton and Dist. C. of C., 1979-85, pres., 1983-84; bd. dirs. Hamilton Found., 1980-84, pres., 1982-83; bd. dirs. Art Gallery Hamilton, 1980-88, v.p., 1984-86, pres., 1986-87; bd. dirs. Can. C. of C., 1982-86, exec. com., 1983-86; mem. bus. adv. coun. McMaster U., 1983-89, chmn., 1987-88; bd. dirs. Chedoke-McMaster Hosps., 1983-92, v.p., 1987-88; bd. dirs., v.p. Inst. Corp. Dirs. in Can., 1986-87, pres., 1987-88, vice chmn., 1988-91; bd. govs. Jr. Achievement Hamilton-Wentworth, 1988-91; mem. Can. Broadcast Stds. Coun., Ont., 1990—; mem. adv. coun. U. Western Ont. Grad. Sch. Journalism, 1994—; mem. Nunavut Arbitration Bd., 1994—. Recipient Can. Centennial medal, 1967, Queen's Jubilee medal, 1977, Confedn. medal, 1993; apptd. mem. for life Queen's Privy Coun. for Can., 1969; hon. mem. InterParliamentary Union. Fellow Inst. Dirs. (U.K.); mem. Law Soc. Upper Can., Internat. Commn. Jurists, Can. Coun. Adminstrv. Tribunals, Soc. Ont. Adjudicators and Regulators, Can. Club of Hamilton (bd. dirs. 1986-89), Kappa Alpha, Phi Delta Phi. Liberal. Presbyterian. Home: 607 Edgewater Cres, Burlington, ON Canada L7T 3L8 Office: 1 King St W, Hamilton, ON Canada L8P 4X8

STANCILL, JAMES McNEILL, finance educator, consultant; b. Orange, N.J., July 30, 1932; s. James Sr. and Anne Jeanne (Sauter) S.; m. Catherine Jackson, Sept. 25, 1954; children: Martha A., Mary C., Christine E. AB, George Washington U., 1954, MBA, 1957; PhD in Fin. and Econs., U. Pa., 1965. Buyer Melpar Inc., Falls Church, Va., 1954-59; instr., adminstrv. officer U. Pa., Phila., 1959-64; prof. fin. U. So. Calif., Los Angeles, 1964—; prin. Stancill & Assocs., Pasadena, Calif., 1964—; chmn. Southwest Products Co., Irwindale, Calif. Author: Management of Working Capital, 1970; contbr. numerous articles to Harvard Bus. Rev., 1977—. Avocations: genealogy, sailing. Office: Grad Sch Bus Univ Of So Calif Los Angeles CA 90089

STANCZAK, JULIAN, artist, educator; b. Borownica, Poland, Nov. 5, 1928; came to U.S., 1950, naturalized, 1957; s. Victor and Elizabeth (Cwynar) S.; m. Barbara M. Meerpohl, June 10, 1963; children: Danuta M., Christopher. B.F.A., Cleve. Inst. Art., 1954; M.F.A., Yale U., 1956. Tchr. Art Acad. Cin., 1957-64, Cleve. Inst. Art, 1965—. One-man shows include Dayton Art Inst., 1964, Martha Jackson Gallery, N.Y.C., 1964, 65, 68, 71, 72, 75, 77, 79, Miami U., Oxford, Ohio, 1965, Feingarten Galleries, Los Angeles, 1966, Kent State U., 1968, Dartmouth, 1968, Akron (Ohio) Art Inst., 1969, Cleve. Inst. Art, 1971, London Arts Gallery, 1971, Cin. Art Mus., 1972, 80, Corcoran Gallery Art, Washington, 1972, Canton (Ohio) Art Inst., 1974, Pollack Gallery, Toronto, 1975, Ohio State U., 1976, IMF and CARE, Washington, 1978, Butler Inst. Am. Art, Youngstown, Ohio, 1980, Nat. Mus. Warsaw, Poland, 1981, Alice Simsar Gallery, Ann Arbor, Mich., 1982, 88, New Gallery, Cleve., 1983, Charles Foley Gallery, Columbus, Ohio, 1984, 88, Walker Gallery, Chgo., 1986, Carl Solway Gallery, Cin., Jane Haslem Gallery, Washington, 1986, Standard Oil Co. Hdqrs., Cleve., 1987, Alice Simsar Gallery, Ann Arbor, Mich., Boca Raton Mus. Art, Fla., 1989, Carl Solway Gallery, Cin., Charles Foley Gallery, Columbus, Ohio, Ctr. for Contemporary Art, Cleve., 1990; one man retrospective David Anderson Gallery, Buffalo, N.Y., Dennos Mus.,Traverse City, Mich.; exhibited in group shows: Mus. Modern Art, N.Y.C., 1965, Albright Knox Art Gallery, Buffalo, 1965, 68, Detroit Art Inst. 1965, Larry Alrich Mus., 1965, U. Ill., 1965, Gallery Moos, Toronto, 1965, Kranert Art Mus., Urbana, Ill., 1965, San Francisco Mus. Art, 1965, Flint (Mich.) Inst. Art, 1966, Carnegie Inst., Pitts., 1967, Japan Cultural Forum, 1967, Smithsonian Instn., Washington, 1967, 69, 85, Dept. State, Washington, 1968, Cin. Art Mus., 1968, 83, Del. Art Ctr., 1970, Seibu, Tokyo, 1971, Mansfield (Ohio) Art Ctr., 1973, Butler Art Inst., Youngstown, Ohio, 1973, Minn. Art Mus., Mpls., 1973, Akron Art Inst., 1975, Indpls. Mus. Art, 1976, Bklyn. Mus. Art, 1976, 80, Cleve. Mus. Art, 1976, 77, 83, Memphis Acad. Art, 1981, Nat. Gallery Art, 1981, 85, Hirshhorn Mus. Art, 1981, Montclair Art Mus., N.J., 1982, Art Acad. Cin., 1986, Embassies Travelling Exhbn., Madrid, 1987, Warsaw, Poland, 1991; represented in permanent collections: Nat. Mus. Am. Art, Albright Knox Art Gallery, Larry Aldrich Mus., Mus. Modern Art, Dayton Art Inst., Hirshhorn Mus., Washington, Butler Inst. Am. Art, Youngstown, Ohio, Rufino Tomajo Mus., Mex., Cleve. Art Assn., Milw. Art Inst., Canton (Ohio) Art Inst., USIA, N.Y.C., Balt. Mus. Art, San Francisco Mus. Art, Herron Mus. Art, Indpls., Okla. Art Ctr., Oklahoma City, Pa. Acad. Fine Arts, Phila., Carnegie Inst., Pitts., Cleve. Mus. Art, Cin. Art Mus., Tulsa Mus. Fine Arts, Columbus (Ohio) Art Mus., Akron Art Inst., Corcoran Art Mus., Nat. Gallery, Washington, Lowe Art Mus., Coral Gables, Fla., Contemporary Art Mus., Houston, Winnipeg Fine Arts Ctr., Man., Can., Dracket Fine Art Collection, Cin., Kalamazoo Inst. Arts, Worcester Art Mus., Phoenix Art Mus., Indpls. Mus. Art, Wasserman Devel. Corp., Cambridge, Dartmouth Coll., Hanover, N.H., Etzold Sammlung, Cologne, Fed. Republic Germany, Johnson & Johnson Fine Art Collection, Conn., Nelson Rockefeller Collection, N.Y., Chase Manhattan Bank, N.Y., Mus. Fine Arts, Los Angeles, Newport Harbor Mus., Newport Beach, Calif., N.Y. State U. at Buffalo. Recipient 1st prize Dayton Art Inst., 1964; recipient Butler Inst. Am. Art award, 1966, Cleve. Fine Arts prize, 1970, Ohio Arts Council award, 1972, Best of Show award Internat. Platform Assn., 1973-76. Mem. Abstract Artists Am., Internat. Platform Assn. Pioneer optical art. Address: 6229 Cabrini Ln Seven Hills OH 44131

STANDAERT, FRANK GEORGE, medical research administrator, physician; b. Paterson, N.J., Nov. 12, 1929; s. George Joseph and Ethel Mirene (Miller) S.; m. Joan Frances Cairns, Feb. 7, 1959; children: David, Robert, Christopher. AB, Harvard Coll., 1951; MD, Cornell U., 1955. Lic. physician Ohio, Md., D.C. N.Y. Intern in medicine Johns Hopkins Hosp., Balt., 1955-56; rsch. fellow Cornell U. Med. Coll., N.Y.C., 1956-57, instr. pharmacology, 1959-60, from asst. to assoc. prof. pharmacology, 1960-67; Schering Found. Prof., chmn. dept. pharmacology Georgetown U. Schs. Medicine and Dentistry, Washington, 1967-86, acting chmn. dept. biochemistry, 1985-86; v.p. acad. affairs, dean Coll. Medicine Med. Coll. Ohio, Toledo, 1986-89, prof. pharmacology and anesthesiology, 1986-91; assoc. v.p. for rsch. Med. Coll. Ohio, 1990-91; dir. rsch. Toledo Hosp., 1990—; adj. prof. anesthesiology U. Mich. Sch. Medicine, 1993—; active various coms. NIH, 1968-86; mem. merit rev. bd. neurobiology VA, 1974-77, chmn., 1976-77, cons., 1977; mem. Commn. Fed. Drug Approval Process U.S. Congress, 1981-82; discussion leader toxicology and safety evaluation Gordon Rsch. Conf., 1983; cons. FTC, 1971-74, 78, Occupational Safety and Health Adminstrn., 1974, FDA, initial rev. group orphan products devel., 1984—; del. U.S. Pharmacopeial Conv., 1970-86; adj. prof. anesthesiology Med. Sch. U. Mich., 1992—. Contbr. over 75 articles to profl. jours. Served to lt. USN, 1957-59. Recipient Career Devel. award USPHS, 1961-65, 66-67, Golden Apple award Georgetown Med. Sch., 1968. Fellow AAAS; mem. AMA, Am. Soc. Clin. Pharmacology and Therapeutics, Drug Info. Assn., Soc. Neurosci., The Peripatetic Soc., Am. Soc. Pharmacology and Exptl. Therapeutics (active various coms., 1966—, pres. 1990—), Fedn. Am. Socs. for Exptl. Biology (treas. 1982-84, bd. dirs. 1991—, various coms.), Assn. Med. Sch. Pharmacology (councilor 1974-75, sec. 1975-76, pres. 1982-84), Am. Assn. Med. Colls. (audit com. 1984), Soc. Toxicology (sect. mechanisms, founding mem. Nat. Capital Area chpt., 1982), Georgetown Inst. Neurosci. (bd. dirs. 1985-90, bd. scientific advisors 1985-90), Pharm. Mfr.'s Assn. Found., Nat. Bd. Med. Examiners (pharmacology com. 1983-86, comprehensive part II com. 1986-89), Nat. Research Council (div. biology and agr., various coms.), Am. Heart Assn. (nat. capital affiliate, bd. dirs. 1972-78, Exceptional Service award 1983), Sigma Xi, Alpha Omega Alpha. Clubs: Cosmos (Washington), Toledo Country. Office: The Toledo Hosp PO Box 691 Toledo OH 43697-0691*

STANDBERRY, HERMAN LEE, school system administrator, consultant; b. Oran, Mo., Feb. 22, 1945; s. Willie Standberry and Bettie Mae (Thompson) Standberry-Taylor; m. Barbara Irene Palmer, July 1, 1942; children: Donna, Zetta, Nina, Miriam, Miranda, Gretchen, Charles, Mary, Dwayne, Helena, Regina, Lakesha. BS, So. Ill. U., 1968, MA, Newport U., 1981, DHL (hon.), 1990; EdD, Walden U., 1992; D Ministry, U. Bibl. Studies and Sem., 1995. Cert. supt. gen. adminstr., curriculum, tchr. Tchr. Community H.S. Dist. 428, Blue Island, Ill., 1968-70; exec. dir. Kane County Coun. for Econ. Opportunity, Batavia, Ill., 1970-75; dep. dir./program planner, Head-Start dir., casemgr., youth supr., educator State of Ill., Dept. Pub. Aid, Dept. Corrections, Chgo., Joliet and St. Charles, Ill., 1975-85; adminstrv. asst. to prin. Bloom High Sch. Dist. 206, Chicago Heights, Ill., 1992-93; asst. prin. Rogers High Sch., Michigan City, Ind., 1994—; chmn. bd. dirs. Greater Chgo. Coun. of Religious Orgns., 1985-89; mem. George Bush's. Rep. Presdl. Task Force, Washington, 1989; nominated mem. U.S. Rep. Senatorial Inner

Cir., Washington, 1989. Author (curriculum) Business Law I & II, 1968, Career Counseling and Survival, 1978. Bd. dirs. United Way, Elgin, Ill, 1972, City of Elgin-Fremont Youth Orgn., 1971-72; host agy. rep. Dept. Human Svcs., Chgo., 1985-90; sustaining mem. Ill. Rep. Party, Springfield, 1989; host agy. Percy Julian High Sch., Chgo., 1989-90, Ill. Dept. Pub. Aid, Chgo., 1987. Recipient grant Ill. Dept. Pub. Aid, 1984-87, hon. award Christian World Affairs Conf., 1985-86. Mem. Internat. Assn. Police and Community Rel. Officers, United Evangelistic Consulting Assn. (bd. dirs., pres. 1985—). Home: 803 E 193d St Glenwood IL 60425 Office: United Evangelistic Assn 1236-42 W 103d St Chicago IL 60643

STANDBRIDGE, PETER THOMAS, insurance company executive; b. Norristown, Pa., Mar. 30, 1934; s. Henry Kay and Helen Margaret (Ballard) S.; m. Jean Ann Sire, Sept. 29, 1956; children: Kevin Scot, Keith Alan, Kathryn Ann, Steven Todd. A.B., Lafayette Coll., Easton, Pa., 1955. Regional mgr. Kemper Group, Richmond, Va., 1961-63; div. sales mgr. Kemper Group, Syracuse, Summit, N.Y., N.J., 1963-73; spl. planning officer Kemper Group, Long Grove, Ill., 1973; v.p. mktg. Kemper Group, 1973-86, sr. v.p., 1986-87, exec. v.p., 1988—; dir. Kemper County Mut. Ins., Garland, Tex., 1978-85, Am. Protection Ins. Co., Long Grove, 1976—, Acord Corp., Oradell, N.J., 1978-82. Mem. Henrico County (Va.) Rep. Com., 1960-64; trustee Village of Manlius, N.Y., 1966-68; bd. govs. Good Shepherd Hosp., Barrington, Ill., 1983-92; chmn. Marquis Soc. Lafayette Coll., 1984-86; bd. dirs. Buehler YMCA, Palatine, Ill., 1989-92; trustee Lafayette Coll., 1991-93. Republican. Episcopalian. Club: Barrington Hills Country (dir. 1983-85); Lake Zurich (Ill.) Golf, The Landings (Ga.). Home: 910 Rub Of The Green Ln Barrington IL 60010 Office: Kemper Group Long Grove IL 60049

STANDEN, MICHAEL, metal products company executive. Pres. Metallurg Inc., N.Y.C. Office: Metallurg Inc 25 E 39th St New York NY 10016-0903

STANDER, JOSEPH WILLIAM, mathematics educator, former university official; b. Covington, Ky., Dec. 2, 1928; s. Charles G. and Rosa (Kerner) S. B.S., U. Dayton, Ohio, 1949; M.S., Cath. U. Am., 1957, Ph.D. in Math, 1959. Joined Soc. of Mary Roman Cath. Ch., 1946; tchr. Hamilton (Ohio) Cath. High Sch., 1949-50, Colegio Ponceno, Ponce, P.R., 1950-55; mem. faculty U. Dayton, 1960—, prof. math., 1970—; dean U. Dayton (Grad. Sch.), 1968-74, v.p. acad. affairs, 1974-89, prof. math. dept., 1990—. Mem. Math. Assn. Am. Office: U Dayton 300 College Park Ave Dayton OH 45469-0300

STANDIFER, MONTY RAY, controller; b. Tex., Jan. 1, 1940; s. Hershel Leon and Norma (Reynolds) S.; m. Glenda Sue Richardson, June 24, 1960; children—Dee Ann, Richie Tac. B.B.A. in Acctg., Tex. Christian U. C.P.A., Tex. Staff acct. Sproles Woodard & Co., C.P.A.s, Ft. Worth, 1965-68; corp. acct. Alcon Labs., Ft. Worth, 1968-71; corp. acctg. mgr. Tandy Corp., Ft. Worth, 1971-74, controller internat. divs., 1974—. Mem. Am. Inst. C.P.A.s, Tex. Soc. C.P.A.s. Methodist. Office: Tandy Corp 1600 One Tandy Ctr Fort Worth TX 76102

STANDIFER, SABRINA, state legislator; m. Brad Barkley. Mem. Kans. Ho. of Reps., 1993—; self-employed computer cons. Democrat. Home: 317 W 41st St N North Wichita KS 67204-3203 Office: Kans Ho of Reps State Capitol Topeka KS 66612

STANDING BEAR, ZUGGUELGERES GALAFACH, criminologist, forensic scientist, educator; b. Boston, Jan. 10, 1941; m. Nancy Lee Karlovic, July 13, 1978 (div. Aug. 1985); m. Virginia Anne Red Hawk, Mar. 22, 1988. BS, U. Nebr., 1971; MS in Forensic Sci., George Washington U., 1974; postgrad. cert. in forensic medicine, Armed Forces Inst. Pathology, 1974; MSEd, U. So. Calif., 1976; MPA, Jacksonville State U., 1981; PhD in Criminology, Fla. State U., 1986. Cert. coroner, Ga., 1988-92; cert. criminal justice instr., Calif., Ga. Criminal investigator U.S. Army, 1965; dist. comdr. 7th region U.S. Army Criminal Investigation Command, Seoul, 1974-77; course mgr. U.S. Army Mil. Police Sch., Ft. McClellan, Ala., 1978-81; ret. U.S. Army, 1981; instr. Fla. State U., Tallahassee, 1981-85; asst. prof. No. Ariz. U., Flagstaff, 1985-86; program coord., prof. Valdosta (Ga.) State U., 1986-95; assoc. prof. dept. sociology Colo. State U., Ft. Collins, 1995—; v.p. Bearhawk Cons. Group, Ft. Collins, 1986—. Editor Jour. Contemporary Criminal Justice, 1992. Mem. leadership coun. Cmty. Policing Project, Valdosta, 1993-94. Decorated Bronze Star medal. Fellow Am. Coll. Forensic Examiners (life), Am. Acad. Forensic Scis. (gen. chmn. 1988-90, gen. sec. 1987-88, gen. chmn. 1988-90, gen. program co-chair 1995—); mem. ASTM (co-coord. sexual assault evidence standards task group), Am. Sociol. Assn., Acad. Polit. Sci., Am. Soc. Criminology, Acad. Criminal Justice Scis., Am. Bd. Forensic Examiners (bd. cert., diplomate of the bd.), Internat. Assn. Forensic Nurses (exec. bd. dirs., cons. and permissions exec.). Democrat. Haudenosaunee (Native Am.). Avocations: horsemanship, traditional Native American religious counseling. Office: Colo State U Dept Sociology Fort Collins CO 80523

STANDISH, JOHN SPENCER, textile manufacturing company executive; b. Albany, N.Y., Apr. 17, 1925; s. John Carver and Florence (Spencer) S.; m. Elaine Joan Ritchie, Oct. 20, 1962 (div. 1984); children: John Carver, Christine Louise; m. Patricia Hunter, Nov. 9, 1985. BS, MIT, 1945. Asst. to prodn. mgr. Forstmann Woolen Co., Passaic, N.J., 1945-52; various positions Albany Internat. Corp., 1952-72, v.p., 1972-74, exec. v.p., 1974-76, vice chmn., 1976-84, chmn., 1984—; bd. dirs. Berkshire Life Ins. Co., Pittsfield, Mass. Bd. dirs. Albany chpt. ARC, 1966-92, chpt. chmn., 1971-74, bd. govs., Washington, 1980-86; bd. dirs. United Way Northeastern N.Y., Albany, 1980—, pres., 1984-85; trustee Albany Med. Coll. and Ctr., 1984-93, Sienna Coll., Loudonville, N.Y., 1987—; chmn. U. Albany Fund, 1982-87, 89-92; pres. U. Albany Found., 1992—. Sgt. U.S. Army, 1945-46. Mem. Am. Mgmt. Assn., World Econ. Forum, Ft. Orange Club, Wolferts Roost Country Club, Schuyler Meadows Country Club, John's Island Club (Fla.). Republican. Episcopalian. Avocations: bridge, tennis, golf. Home: 1 Schuyler Meadows Rd Loudonville NY 12211-1421 Office: Albany Internat Corp PO Box 1907 Albany NY 12201-1907

STANDISH, SAMUEL MILES, oral pathologist, college dean; b. Campbellsburg, Ind., July 6, 1923; s. Irvin Arthur and Etta May (Smedley) S.; m. Gertrude Elizabeth Eberle, Aug. 6, 1949; children—Nancy Jo, Linda Sue. D.D.S., Ind. U., 1945, M.S., 1956. Diplomate: Am. Bd. Oral Pathology (dir. 1973-80), Am. Bd. Forensic Odontology. Practice dentistry, specializing in oral pathology Indpls., 1948-58; mem. faculty Sch. Dentistry Ind. U., 1958—, emeritus prof. oral pathology, 1967-88, chmn. div. clin. oral pathology, 1967-77, asst. dean sch., 1969-74, asso. dean, 1974-88; cons. Nat. Cancer Inst., 1969-73, Nat. Bd. Dental Examiners, 1966-74, ADA, 1971-77. Author: (with others) Oral Diagnosis/Oral Medicine, 1978, Maxillofacial Prosthetics: Multidisciplinary Practice, 1972, Outline of Forensic Dentistry, 1982. Served with USNR, 1945-47. Fellow Am. Acad. Oral Pathology (pres. 1972-73); mem. ADA, Internat. Assn. Dental Research and Acad. Forensic Sci., Sigma Xi, Omicron Kappa Upsilon, Xi Psi Phi. Home: 4548 Manning Rd Indianapolis IN 46208-2768 Office: Ind U Sch Dentistry Indianapolis IN 46202

STANDISH, WILLIAM LLOYD, judge; b. Pitts., Feb. 16, 1930; s. William Lloyd and Eleanor (McCargo) S.; m. Marguerite Oliver, June 12, 1963; children: Baird M., N. Graham, James H., Constance S. Bar: Pa. 1957, U.S. Supreme Ct. 1967. Assoc. Reed, Smith, Shaw & McClay, Pitts., 1957-63, ptnr., 1963-80; judge Ct. Common Pleas of Allegheny County (Pa.), 1980-87; judge U.S. Dist. Ct., Pa. we. dist., 1987—; solicitor Edgeworth Borough Sch. Dist., 1963-66. Bd. dirs. Sewickley (Pa.) Community Ctr., 1981-83, Staunton Farm Found., mem. 1984—, trustee, 1984-92; corporator Sewickley Cemetery, 1971-87; trustee Mary and Alexander Laughlin Children's Ctr., 1972-90; trustee Leukemia Soc. Am., 1978-80, trustee western Pa. chpt., 1972-80, Western Pa. Sch. for the Deaf. Recipient Pres. award Leukemia Soc. Am., 1980. Mem. ABA, Pa. Bar Assn., Allegheny County Bar Assn., Am. Judicature Soc., Acad. Trial Lawyers Allegheny County (treas. 1977-78, bd. dirs. 1979-80), Am. Inn of Ct. (Pitts. chpt. 1993—). Office: US Dist Ct 911 Us Courthouse Pittsburgh PA 15219

STANDLEY, PAUL MELVIN, chemist; b. East Liverpool, Ohio, Nov. 8, 1943; s. Paul N. and Ruth J. (Barnhart) S.; m. Rebecca S. Nentwick, Nov. 8,

1969 (div. Jan. 1988); children: Celeste N., Matthew J., Zachary P.; m. Monica Lee Sneller, July 28, 1990. BS in Chemistry, Kent State U., 1970. Compounder Gen. Tire Devel., Akron, Ohio, 1970-74; from rsch. chemist to sr. rsch. chemist Dayco Tech. Ctr., Springfield, Mo., 1974-81, mgr. tech. svc., 1981-83, mgr. adv. tech. group, 1983-86; bus. mgr. auto accessories Dayco Products Plant, Springdale, Ariz., 1986-89; v.p. R & D Dayco Products, Inc., Dayton, Ohio, 1989—. With USAF, 1962-66. Mem. Rubber Div. of Am. Chem. Soc. (chmn. symposium 1984, program planning com. 1985-88). Achievements include patents for elastomeric products, for process equipment and product applications, for pulleys, for power transmission products, for material compositions. Office: Dayco Products Inc Box 1004 1 Prestige Pl Dayton OH 45401-1004

STANEK, ALAN EDWARD, music educator, performer, music administrator; b. Longmont, Colo., July 3, 1939; s. Edward Thomas Stanek and Mary Rose (Hicks) Stanek MacDougall; m. Janette Elizabeth Swanson, Aug. 23, 1963; children: Michael Alan, Karen Leigh. B in Mus. Edn., U. Colo., 1961; MusM, Eastman Sch. Music, 1965; MusD, U. Mich., 1974. Dir. instrumental music Ainsworth Pub. Sch., Nebr., 1961-64, Cozad Pub. Sch., Nebr., 1965-67; asst. prof. music Hastings Coll., Nebr., 1967-76; prof., chmn. dept. music Idaho State U., Pocatello, 1976—. Contbr., editor, reviewer for profl. jours. including Clarinet, Idaho Music Notes, Nebr. Music Educator. Mem. Music Educators Nat. Conf., Idaho Music Educators Assn. (chmn. higher edn. 1978-86, pres. 1988-90, chair state solo contest 1990-92), Internat. Clarinet Assn. (sec. 1978-84, v.p. 1986-88, pres.-elect 1994—), Coll. Music Soc., Nat. Assn. Schs. Music (sec. N.W. region 1979-82, vis. evaluator 1990—, chair N.W. region 1991-94), Rotary (pres. Gate City chpt. 1994-95). Office: Idaho State U Dept Music PO Box 8099 Pocatello ID 83209

STANFILL, DENNIS CAROTHERS, business executive; b. Centerville, Tenn., Apr. 1, 1927; s. Sam Broome and Hattie (Carothers) S.; m. Therese Olivieri, June 29, 1951; children: Francesca (Mrs. Peter Tufo), Sara, Dennis Carothers. BS, U.S. Naval Acad., 1949; M.A. (Rhodes scholar), Oxford U., 1953; LHD (hon.), U. S.C. Corporate finance specialist Lehman Bros., N.Y.C., 1959-65; v.p. finance Times Mirror Co., Los Angeles, 1965-69; exec. v.p. 20th Century-Fox Film Corp., 1969-71, pres., 1971, chmn. bd., chief exec. officer, 1971-81; pres. Stanfill, Bowen & Co., 1981-90; chmn. bd. dirs., chief exec. officer AME, Inc., 1990-91; co-chmn., co-CEO Metro-Goldwyn-Mayer, Inc., 1992-93; sr. advisor Credit Lyonnais, 1993-95; chmn. Stanfill Enterprises (HK), 1995—; bd. dirs. Dial Corp., Weingart Found. Trustee Calif. Inst. Tech. Served to lt. USN, 1949-59; politico-mil. policy div. Office Chief Naval Ops., 1956-59.

STANFILL, SHELTON G., performing arts administrator; m. Brigitte. BA in History and Social Scis., Colo. State U., postgrad. Exec. dir. Hopkins Ctr. Dartmouth Coll.; dir. cultural programs Colo. State U.; dir. Nat. Arts Festival 12th Winter Olympic Games; ptnr. Brown, Stanfill & Brown; pres., CEO Wolf Trap Found. for Performing Arts, Vienna, Va.; pres. Music Ctr. L.A. County, 1994—; chair panels, cons. Nat. Endowment for Arts, Lincoln. Ctr., Bklyn. Acad. Music, UCLA; advisor Telluride Film Festival. Avocations: reading, wine, dancing, film, medieval history. Office: Music Ctr LA County 135 N Grand Ave Los Angeles CA 90012

STANFORD, DENNIS JOE, archaeologist, museum curator; b. Cherokee, Iowa, May 13, 1943; s. William Erle and Mary L. (Fredenburg) S.; m. Margaret Brierty, June 4, 1988; 1 dau., Brandy L. BA, U. Wyo., 1965; MA, U. N.Mex., 1967, PhD, 1972. Archeologist, curator Smithsonian Instn., Washington, 1972—; head div. archeology, 1990-92, chmn. dept anthropology, 1992—; v.p. dir. Taraxacum Press, 1981—; mem. adv. bd. Ctr. for the Study of the First Americans, 1985—; rsch. assoc. Denver Mus. Natural History, 1989—. Author: The Walakpa Site, Alaska, 1975; editor: (with Robert L. Humphrey) Pre-Llano Cultures of the Americas, 1979, (with George C. Frison) The Agate Basin Site, 1982, (with Jane Day) Ice Age Hunters of the Rockies, 1992. Mem. Anthrop. Soc. Washington (gov. 1974-77), Soc. Am. Archeology, Am. Quaternary Assn. Research, publs. on Paleo-Indian Studies, N.Am., S.Am., N.E. Asia, especially Western U.S., Arctic. Home: 1350 Massachusetts Ave SE Washington DC 20003-1556 Office: Smithsonian Instn Washington DC 20560

STANFORD, DONALD ELWIN, English educator, editor, poet, critic; b. Amherst, Mass., Feb. 7, 1913; s. Ernest Elwood and Alice (Carroll) S.; m. Edna Goodwin, July 1937 (div. 1946); 1 child, Don David; m. Maryanna Peterson, Aug. 14, 1953 (dec. Mar. 1992). BA, Stanford U., 1933, Ph.D., 1953; M.A., Harvard U., 1934. Instr. La. State U., Baton Rouge, 1949-50, asst. prof. English, 1953-54, assoc. prof., 1954-62, prof., 1962-79, Alumni prof. English, 1979-83, Alumni prof. emeritus, 1983—; vis. prof. Duke U., Durham, N.C., 1961-62, Tex. A&M U., College Station, 1984. Author: New England Earth, 1941, The Traveler, 1955, In the Classic Mode: The Achievement of Robert Bridges, 1978, Revolution and Convention in Modern Poetry, 1983; editor: The Poems of Edward Taylor, 1960, Dictionary of Literary Biography, vol. 19, 1981, Dictionary of Literary Biography, vol. 20, 1983, Selected Letters of Robert Bridges, 2 vols., 1983, Humanities Series, 1963-66, The So. Rev., 1963-83, cons. editor The So. Rev., 1987—; mem. adv. bd. Hopkins Quar., 1981—. Recipient Disting. Research Master award La. State U., 1982; Guggenheim Found. fellow, 1959-60; La. State U. Disting. Faculty fellow, 1973-74; NEH research scholar, summers 1972, 78. Mem. PEN, MLA, South Atlantic MLA, Phi Beta Kappa, Phi Kappa Phi. Democrat. Club: Athenaeum (London). Home: 776 Delgado Dr Baton Rouge LA 70808-4730

STANFORD, HENRY KING, college president; b. Atlanta, Apr. 22, 1916; s. Henry King and Annie Belle (Callaway) S.; m. Laurie Ruth King, Sept. 19, 1936; children: Henry, Lowry, Rhoda, Peyton. AB, Emory U., 1936, MA, 1940, LLD, 1962; postgrad. U. Heidelberg, Germany, 1936-37; MS in Govt. Mgmt. (Alfred P. Sloan Found. fellow 1941-43), U. Denver, 1943, LLD, 1962; (Tax Found. fellow 1943-44), NYU, 1949; DCL Jacksonville (Fla.) U., 1963; LLD, Loyola U., New Orleans, 1968, U. Akron, Kyung Hee U., Seoul, Korea, 1968, Rollins Coll., 1977, Barry Coll., 1979, DHL, U. Tampa, 1969; DLitt, U. R.I., 1970; D in Higher Edn., U. Miami, 1981; DHL, Birmingham-So. Coll., 1987. Instr., Emory U., 1937-40; asst. prof. Ga. Inst. Tech., 1940-41; instr. NYU, 1943-46; prof. pub. administrn., also dir. sch. pub. administrn. U. Denver, 1946-48; pres. Ga. Southwestern Coll., Americus, 1948-50; dir. U. Center in Ga., 1950-52; asst. chancellor U. System of Ga., 1952-53; pres. Ga. State Coll. for Women, Milledgeville, 1953-56; chief of party NYU-Internat. Cooperation Adminstrn. Contract, Ankara, Turkey, 1956-57; pres. Birmingham-So. Coll., 1957-62, U. Miami, Fla., 1962-81; pres. emeritus U. Miami, 1981—; interim pres. U. Ga., 1986-87, pres. emeritus, 1987—; bd. dirs. Avatar Holdings, 1980—DWG, Southeastern Pub. Service, Wilson Bros., 1982-86, Fischbach Corp., 1985-86, NVF, 1985-86, So. Bell, 1969-85; research asst. Tax Found., N.Y.C., 1943-44; staff N.A.M. com. exec., 1944-46; mem. bd. dirs. Birmingham br. Fed. Res. Bank Atlanta, 1960-62, Jacksonville br., Atlanta, 1967-72, chmn., 1969, 72. Trustee Knight Found., 1982—; vice chmn. Invest-in-Am., 1984-86, chmn. 1986-87; chmn. Dade County Community Relations Bd., 1969-71; bd. visitors Air U, Maxwell AFB, Ala., 1963-66; trustee Caribbean Resources Devel. Found., 1978—, pres., 1978-83, chmn., 1983-84; chmn. Jimmy Carter Hist. Site Adv. Commn., 1990—. Decorated Star of Africa medal Liberia; officer Order of Merit Fed. Republic of Germany; recipient Eleanor Roosevelt-Israel Humanitarian award, 1965, Outstanding Civilian Svc. award U.S. Army, 1966, Silver Medallion Fla. region NCCJ, 1968, Ga. region, 1987, Disting. Svc. award Ga. Coll., 1979, C.H.I.E.F. award Ind. Colls. and Univs. Fla., 1983, Sibley award Ga. Mil. Coll., 1991, Emory medal, 1991, Adrian Dominican Ednl. Leadership award Barry U., 1991, Atlanta Boys' High Alumnus award, 1992, James Blair Humanitarian award Americus, Ga., 1993, Westmeyer award pub. svc. NYU, 1993. Mem. Assn. Colls. and Schs. (chmn. commn. colls. 1960-62, pres. 1972-73), Nat. Assn. Ind. Colls. and Univs. (dir. 1976-80), Assn. Caribbean Univ. and Rsch. Insts. (v.p. 1965-79), Golden Key Honor Soc. (bd. dirs. 1982-91), Internat. Assn. Univ. Pres. (exec. com. 1977-81), Delta Phi Alpha, Phi Beta Kappa Omicron Delta Kappa, Phi Sigma Iota, Alpha Kappa Psi, Phi Mu Alpha, Phi Kappa Phi, Rotary. Methodist. Lodge: Rotary (Americus, Ga.) (pres. 1984-85). Office: PO Box 1065 510 W Lamar St Americus GA 31709-3443 The greatest literary influence on my life has been Goethe's Faust, Part I. Reading it in the original German as a college student, I was struck immediately with the demands Faust made of himself in concluding the con-

tract with Mephistopheles: he would lose his soul if he ever chose a "bed of ease," succumbed to flattery, opted for pleasure alone, or said to any one moment, "Linger awhile; you are so nice!" In other words, whenever he ceased striving, he was lost.

STANFORD, JACK ARTHUR, biological station administrator; b. Delta, Colo., Feb. 18, 1947; s. LeRoy and Wilma (Tucker) S.; children: Jake, Chriss. BS in Fisheries Sci., Colo. State U., 1969, MS in Limnology, 1971; PhD in Limnology, U. Utah, 1975. Fisheries biologist Alaska-Fish and Game, Dillingham, 1968-69; rsch. biologist and limnologist instr. U. Mont., Missoula, 1973-74; dir. Flathead Lake Biol. Sta. U. Mont., Polson, 1980—; research prof. zoology U. Mont., Missoula, 1983-86; Jessie M. Bierman prof. U. Mont., Missoula, Mont., 1986—; prof. N. Tex. State U., Denton, 1974-81; panelist div. biotic system NSF, Washington, 1985—. Editor: Ecology of Regulated Streams, 1979, Groundwater Ecology, 1994; mem. bd. editors: Regulated Rivers: Research and Management, 1985—; contbr. over 85 articles to profl. jours. Advisor Nature Conservancy, Boulder, Colo., 1982—. Named Bierman Prof. Ecology U. Mont., 1986—; grantee EPA, U.S. Army, U.S. Bur. Reclamation, NSF, U.S. Nat. Park Svc. Mem. AAAS, Mont. Acad. Sci., Am. Soc. Limnology and Oceanography, Ecol. Soc. Am. (pub. affairs com., 1994—), N.Am. Benthological Soc. (exec. com. 1979, 1988-89). Avocation: fly fishing, skiing. Office: U Mont Flathead Lake Biol Sta 311 Bio Station Ln Polson MT 59860-9659

STANFORD, JAMES M., oil company executive. BSc in Mining Engring., Loyola Coll., Montreal; BSc in Petroleum Engring., U. Alta., Can. Various engring. and mgmt. positions Mobil Oil Can. Ltd., 1959-78; gen. mgr. conventional prodn. Petro-Can., Calgary, Alta., 1978-80, v.p., sr. v.p. prodn., 1980-82; pres., COO Petro-Can. Resources, 1990-93; pres., CEO, dir. Petro-Can., Calgary, Alta., 1993—. Bd. dirs. Calgary Philharm. Soc., past chmn.; bd. dirs. Alta. Theatre Projects, Coun. for Can. Unity. Mem. Assn. Profl. Engrs., Geologists of Alta., Can., Inst. Mining and Metallurgy, Can. Assn. Petroleum Producers (bd. dirs.), Chancellor's Club. and Pres.' Cir. U. Calgary (bd. dirs.). Office: Petro Can, PO Box 2844, 150-6th Ave SW, Calgary, AB Canada T2P 3E3

STANFORD, JOSEPH STEPHEN, diplomat, lawyer, educator; b. Montreal, Que., Can., May 7, 1934; s. Walter Albert and Geraldine (O'Loghlin) S.; m. Agnes Mabelle Walker, Nov. 16, 1957; children: Kevin, Karen, Michael. BA, U. Montreal, 1953; LLB, U. Alta., Edmonton, Can., 1956. Bar: Alta. 1957; called to Queen's Counsel 1984. Mem. Greenan, Cooney & Stanford, Calgary, Alta., 1957-60; joined Fgn. Svc., Dept. External Affairs, Govt. of Can., 1960; amb. to Israel Tel Aviv, 1979-82; also Can. high commr. to Cyprus; asst. dep. min. for Africa and Mid. East Dept. External Affairs, Ottawa, Ont., 1983-85, asst. dep. min. for Europe, 1985-87, assoc. undersec. of state for external affairs, 1987-88; dep. solicitor gen. Govt. of Can., Ottawa, 1988-93; sr fellow, conflict mgr. Canadian Center Mgmt. Devel., Ottawa, 1993—; assoc. Conflict Mgmt. Group, Cambridge, Mass. Contbr. articles on internat. law, fgn. investment and conflict resolution to profl. jours. Roman Catholic. Avocations: wilderness canoeing, tennis, skiing. Home: 58 Amberwood Cres, Nepean, ON Canada K2E 7C3 Office: Canadian Center Mgnt Devel, 373 Sussex Dr, Ottawa, ON Canada K1N 8V4

STANFORD, MELVIN JOSEPH, publisher, management consultant; b. Logan, Utah, June 13, 1932; s. Joseph Sedley and Ida Pearl (Ivie) S.; m. Yvonne Watson, Feb. 8, 1951 (div. 1956); children: Connie Stanford Tendick, Cheryl Stanford Bohn; m. Linda Barney, Sept. 2, 1960; children: Joseph Barney Stanford, Theodore Barney Stanford, Emily Stanford, Charlotte Stanford Vaughan, Charles Barney Stanford, Sarah Stanford. B.S. (First Security Found. scholar), Utah State U., 1957; M.B.A. (Donald Kirk David fellow), Harvard U., 1963; Ph.D., U. Ill., 1968. CPA, Utah. Asst. audit supr. Utah Tax Commn., 1959-61, auditor, 1958-59; acct. Haskins & Sells, C.P.A.s, Boston, 1961-62; acctg. staff analyst Arabian Am. Oil Co., Dhahran, Saudi Arabia, 1963-64; teaching and rsch. asst. U. Ill., Urbana, 1966-68; mem. faculty Brigham Young U., Provo, Utah, 1968-82; dir. mgmt. devel. programs Brigham Young U., 1970-73, prof. bus. mgmt., 1974-82; dean Coll. Bus., Mankato (Minn.) State U., 1982-89, prof. mgmt., 1989-94, prof. emeritus, 1994—; mem. adv. bd. M.L. Bigelow & Co., Inc., Organ Builders; bd. dirs. Creative Machine Tools Corp.; cons. Strategic Planning, Decision Case Mgmt., New Enterprise Mgmt.; vis. mgmt. professor Boston U., Europe, 1975-76; vis. prof. agrl. mgmt. U. Minn., 1991-92. Author: New Enterprise Management, 1975, 82, Management Policy, 1979, 83; co-author: Cases in Business Policy and Strategy, 1990, Decision Cases for Agriculture, 1992, Business Plan Guidebook, 1995; also articles, mgmt. cases; founder Midwestern Jour. Bus. and Econs., 1985. Bishop, Mankato ward LDS Ch., 1987-91. With USAF, 1951-55, USAR, 1956-80. Named Amb. of City of Mankato, 1988. Fellow N.Am. Case Rsch. Assn. (v.p. for rsch. 1985-86, pres. 1987-88, Curtis E. Tate Jr. Outstanding Case Writer award 1992); mem. SAR (pres. Utah 1978-79, nat. trustee 1979-81, Meritorious Svc. medal 1981, Patriot medal 1991), Sons of Utah Pioneers, Alpha Kappa Psi, Phi Kappa Phi. Home: 1754 N Cobblestone Dr Provo UT 85604-1155

STANG, PETER JOHN, organic chemist; b. Nûrnberg, Germany, Nov. 17, 1941; came to U.S., 1956; s. John Stang and Margaret Stang Pollman; m. Christine Schirmer, 1969; children: Antonia, Alexandra. BS, DePaul U., Chicago, 1963; Ph.D., U. California, Berkeley, 1966; hon. degr., Moscow State Lomonossov U., 1992, Russian Academy of Sciences, 1992. Instr. Princeton (N.J.) U., 1967-68; from asst. to assoc. prof. U. Utah, Salt Lake City, 1969-79, prof., 1979-92, Disting. prof. chemistry, 1992—. Co-author: Organic Spectroscopy, 1971; author: (with others) Vinyl Cations, 1979; contbr. 270 articles to sci. publs. Humboldt-Forschungspreis, 1977; JSPS Fellowship, 1985; Fulbright-Hays Sr. Scholarship, 1988. Fellow AAAS; mem. Am. Chem. Soc. (assoc. editor jour. 1982—). Office: Univ Utah Dept Chemistry Salt Lake City UT 84112

STANGE, JAMES HENRY, architect; b. Davenport, Iowa, May 25, 1930; s. Henry Claus and Norma (Ballhorn) S.; m. Mary Suanne Peterson, Dec. 12, 1954; children: Wade Weston, Drew Dayton, Grant Owen. BArch, Iowa State U., 1954. Registered architect, Iowa, Nebr., Kans., Mo., Okla. Designer Davis & Wilson, Lincoln, Nebr., 1954-62, v.p., 1962-68; v.p., sec. Davis, Fenton, Stange, Darling, Lincoln, Nebr., 1968-76, pres., 1976-92, chmn., 1978-94; mem. State Bd. Examiners for Engrs. and Architects, 1989-92, chmn. region V NCARB, 1991. Prin. works include Lincoln Airport Terminal, Sq. D Mfg. Plant, Lincoln, Bryan Meml. Hosp. (masterplans and additions), 1970, 80, 90, Bryan Ambulatory Care Ctr. Med. Office Bldg., Same Day Surgery Conf. Ctr., Parking Garage, 1993—, Nebr. Wesleyan Theatre, Lincoln, Hasting (Nebr.) YMCA, various structures U. Nebr., Lincoln, ctr. and br. offices Am. Charter Fed. Savs & Loan, Southeast High Sch. (addition), 1984, U. Nebr. Animal Sci. Bldg., 1987, Beadle Ctr., UNL, 1991. Pres. Lincoln Ctr. Assn., 1979, Capitol Assn. Retarded Citizens, 1972; chmn. United Way Campaign, 1986, chmn. bd., 1988; chmn. Bryan Hosp. Found. Endowment Com., 1988-90; bd. dirs. Delta Dental, 1987-92; Downtown Lincoln Assn., 1985-94, steering com. 1989, v.p. Nebr. Jazz Orch., 1994; mem. mayor's com. Study Downtown Redevel., 1989, pub. bldg. com., masterplan rev. com., 1994; deacon Presbyn. Ch., 1960, chmn. bd. trustees, 1968-90, elder, 1972-87. Recipient Honor award Conf. on Religious Architecture, 1969, also numerous state and nat. awards from archtl. orgns. Mem. AIA (Nebr. bd. dirs. 1964-65, treas. 1965, sec. 1966, v.p. 1967, pres. Nebr. 1968, mem. com. on architecture for health, 1980-94, Regional Design award 1976, 88), Am. Assn. Health Planners, Interfaith Forum on Religion, Art, Architecture, Lincoln C. of C. (bd. dirs. 1982). Republican. Clubs: Exec. (pres. 1972), Crucible, 12, Hillcrest Country (pres. 1977), Lincoln Univ. (sec. 1992—, bd. dirs. 1991—, pres. 1994). Avocations: travel, photography, golf. Home: 3545 Calvert St Lincoln NE 68506-5744 Office: Davis/Fenton/Stange/Darling Inc 211 N 14th St Lincoln NE 68508-1616

STANGELAND, ROGER EARL, retail chain store executive; b. Chgo., Oct. 4, 1929; s. Earl and Mae E. (Shaw) S.; m. Lilah Fisher, Dec. 27, 1951; children: Brett, Cyndi Stangeland Meili, Brad. Student, St. Johns Mil. Acad., 1943-47, Carleton Coll., 1947-48; BS, U. Ill., 1949-51. With Coast to Coast Stores, Mpls., 1960-78, pres., 1972-77; sr. v.p., exec. v.p. Household Merchandising, Chgo., 1978-84; chief exec. officer, dir. The Vons Grocery Co., Los Angeles, 1984-85; past CEO The Vons Cos., Inc., Arcadia, Calif., chmn., 1986—. Chmn. Wauconda (Ill.) Bd. Edn., 1957-60, Hopkins (Minn.)

Bd. Edn., 1968-74; bd. fellows Claremont (Calif.) U. Ctr. and Grad. Sch., 1986; bd. dirs. L.A. area Boy Scouts Am.; trustee Hugh O'Brian Youth Found.; mem. CEO bd. advisors U. So. Calif. Sch. Bus. Adminstrn.; trustee St. John's Mil. Acad.; bd. visitors Peter F. Drucker Grad. Mgmt. Ctr. Mem. Am. Inst. Wine and Food (bd. dirs.), Food Mktg. Inst. (chmn. bd. dirs.), Food Employers Coun. (exec. com., bd. dirs.), Mchts. & Mfrs. Assn. (bd. dirs.), L.A. Area C. of C. (bd. dirs.), Jonathan Club (L.A.), Calif. Club. Home: 842 Oxford Rd San Marino CA 91108-1214 Office: Vons Cos Inc PO Box 3338 618 Michillinda Ave Arcadia CA 91007-6300*

STANGER, ABRAHAM M., lawyer; b. N.Y.C., Sept. 25, 1921; s. Joseph I. and Tillie (Rothfield) S.; m. Claire Y. Schwebel, Sept. 18, 1948; children: Richard, Jordan, Hope. BA cum laude, CCNY, 1941; LLB, NYU, 1948, LLM, 1952, Dr. Jud. Sci., 1958. Bar: N.Y. 1949, U.S. Tax Ct 1951, U.S. Dist. Ct. (so. dist.) N.Y. 1951, U.S. Dist. Ct. (ea. dist.) N.Y. 1953, U.S. Supreme Ct. 1958, U.S. Ct. Appeals (2d cir.) 1960, U.S. Ct. Claims 1984; CPA, N.Y. Sr. ptnr. corp. div. fin. reporting, disclosure issues and tax matters Stanger, Robson & Rothstein, N.Y.C., 1960-72, Trubin Sillcocks Edelman & Knapp, N.Y.C., 1972-83; sr. ptnr. corp. fin. reporting, disclosure issues and tax reporting Seyfarth, Shaw, Fairweather & Geraldson, N.Y.C., 1983—; adj. prof. law NYU, 1958—; mem. Fin. Acctg. Standards Adv. Council, 1979-83. Contbr. numerous articles on fin. reporting and disclosure to profl. jours; edit. staff NYU Law Rev., 1947-48; columnist Corp. Law Rev., 1978-86. Recipient Scroll Appreciation award, NYU. Fellow Am. Bar Found.; mem. AICPA (futures issues com. 1985-88), ABA (chmn. com. law and acctg. sect. bus. law 1980-85, chmn. subcom. lawyers replies to auditors 1985—, chmn. subcom. acctg. methods of com. tax acctg. problems sect. of taxation 1982-86, vice chmn. com. tax acctg. problems 1986-90, mem. nat. conf. of lawyers and CPA's 1988-91), N.Y. State Bar Assn., Assn. of Bar of City of N.Y., N.Y. County Lawyers Assn., Internat. Bar Assn. (rep. on consultative group internat. auditing practices com. 1995—), Am. Judicature Soc. Home: 605 Park Ave New York NY 10021 Office: Seyfarth Shaw Fairweather & Geraldson 900 Third Ave New York NY 10022

STANGER, ILA, writer, editor; b. N.Y.C., Oct. 13, 1940; d. Jack Simon and Shirley Ruth (Nadelson) S. B.A., Bklyn. Coll., 1961. Feature and travel editor Harpers Bazaar, N.Y.C., 1969-75; exec. editor Travel and Leisure mag., N.Y.C., 1975-85; editor in chief Food and Wine Mag., N.Y.C., 1985-89, Travel and Leisure mag., N.Y.C., 1990-93; contbg. editor Town and Country mag., 1993—; writer on arts, features and travel; consulting editor Saveur mag. Mem. N.Y. Travel Writers, Am. Soc. Mag. Editors. Home and Office: 115 W 71st St New York NY 10023-3838

STANGER, JOHN WILLIAM, finance company executive; b. Boston, Jan. 24, 1923; s. John Sawyer and Lenora (Leo) S.; m. Valerie Gudel, Apr. 14, 1951; 1 dau., Pamela Beth. Student, Boston U., 1941-43; A.B., Harvard U. 1947. With G.E. Capital Corp., N.Y.C., 1947-85; v.p., gen. mgr. comml. and indsl. fin. G.E. Capital Corp., 1962-75; pres., gen. mgr. G.E. Capital Corp. subs. G.E. Co., 1975-79, chief exec. officer, 1979-84, vice chmn., 1984-85, also bd. dirs.; chmn., dir. Signal Capital Corp., 1985-93, Stanger, Miller Inc., 1985-91; dir. Monetary Mgmt. Corp. Served to capt. USAAF, 1943-45, 51-53. Decorated D.F.C. Mem. Harvard Lower Fairfield Club, Greenwich Country Club, City Club, Jupiter Golf Club. Republican. Home and Office: 18305 Southeast Village Cir Tequesta FL 33469

STANHOPE, WILLIAM HENRY, lawyer; b. Chillicothe, Ohio, Aug. 17, 1951; s. William Wallace and Elizabeth C. Stanhope; m. Kristen A. Keirsey, July 26, 1976; children: Liesel, Sally, Kaitlyn. BA, Duke U., 1973; JD, Northwestern U. Law Sch., 1976. Bar: Minn. Supreme Ct. 1976, U.S. Dist. Ct. Minn. 1976, U.S. Dist. Ct. Ga. 1979, Ga. Supreme Ct. 1979, Ga. Ct. Appeals 1979. Assoc. Robins, Kaplan, Miller & Ciresi, Mpls., Atlanta, 1976-82; ptnr. Robins, Kaplan, Miller & Ciresi, Atlanta, 1982-91, mng. ptnr. SE Regional Office, 1991—; instr. NITA, Raleigh, N.C., 1988, Emory U., Atlanta, 1990—. Contbr. articles to profl. jours. Mem. ABA, Assn. Trial Lawyers Am., Ga. State Bar Assn., Ga. Trial Lawyers Assn. Office: Robins Kaplan Miller & Ciresi 2600 One Atlantic Plz 950 E Paces Ferry Rd NE Atlanta GA 30326-1119

STANIAR, BURTON B., television company executive; b. Summit, N.J., Jan. 30, 1942; s. George Andrew and Marion (Dreher) S.; m. Vicki Campbell, Apr. 13, 1968; children—Judson Campbell, Guy Shepard. B.A. Washington and Lee U., 1964; M.B.A., Columbia U., 1966. New products mgr. Colgate Palmolive Co., N.Y.C., 1966-70; v.p., prin. Artcraft Concepts, N.Y.C., 1970-74; dir. mktg. Church & Dwight Co., Piscataway, N.J., 1974-80; sr. v.p. mktg. Group W Cable, Inc., N.Y.C., 1980-81, sr. v.p. mktg., programming, 1981-82, pres., 1982-86, sr. exec. v.p Westinghouse Broadcasting Co., Inc., N.Y.C., 1986-87, chmn., chief exec. officer, 1987—; bd. dirs. Gibson Greetings, Inc. Trustee Mus. Broadcasting; chmn. Ctr. for Communication, Inc. Mem. Internat. TV and Radio Soc. (bd. govs.), TV Operator's Caucus (chmn.), Adv. Bd. for Rsch. Program in Telecommunications and Info. Policy at Columbia U., Met. Mus. Bus. Com. (vice chmn.), Columbia U. Bus. Sch. Alumni Assn. (bd. dirs.), Nat. Urban League (trustee). Office: Westinghouse Broadcasting Co 888 7th Ave New York NY 10106-0200

STANISLAO, JOSEPH, consulting engineer, educator; b. Manchester, Conn., Nov. 21, 1928; s. Eduardo and Rose (Zaccaro) S.; m. Bettie Chloe Carter, Sept. 6, 1960. BS, Tex. Tech. U., 1957; MS, Pa. State U., 1959; Eng.ScD, Columbia U., 1970. Registered profl. engr., Mass., Mont. Asst. engr. Naval Ordnance Research, University Park, Pa., 1958-59; asst. prof. N.C. State U., Raleigh, 1959-61; dir. research Darlington Fabrics Corp., Pawtucket, R.I., 1961-62; from asst. prof. to prof. U. R.I., Kingston, 1962-71; prof., chmn. dept. Cleve. State U., 1971-75; prof., dean N.D. State U. Fargo, 1975-94, acting v.p. agrl. affairs, 1983-85, asst. to pres., 1983—; dir. Engring. Computer Ctr. N.D. State U., 1984—; prof. emeritus indsl. engring. and mgmt. N.D. State U., Fargo, 1994—; pres. XOX Corp., 1984-90; chmn. bd., chief exec. officer ATSCO, 1989—, chief engr., 1993—; adj. prof. Mont. State U., 1994—. Contbr. chpts. to books, articles to profl. jours.; patentee pump apparatus, pump fluid housing. Served to sgt. USMC, 1948-51. Recipient Sigma Xi award, 1968; Order of the Iron Ring award N.D. State U., 1972, Econ. Devel. award, 1991; USAF recognition award, 1979, ROTC appreciation award, 1982. Mem. Am. Inst. Indsl. Engrs. (sr.; v.p. 1964-65), ASME, Am. Soc. Engring. Edn. (campus coord. 1979-81), Acad. Indsl. Engrs. Tex. Tech U., Lions, Elks, Am. Legion, Phi Kappa Phi, Tau Beta Pi (advisor 1978-79). Roman Catholic. Home: 8 Park Plaza Rd Bozeman MT 59715

STANISLAW, RICHARD JOHN, university program director; b. Phila., Nov. 29, 1939; s. Benjamin and Alma (Peterson) S.; m. Rebecca Anne Wetzel, Feb. 1, 1964; children: Richard Jr., Andrew, Natalie. BS in Bible, Music, Phila. Coll. of Bible, 1962; BMusEd in Voice, Temple U., 1966, MMus in Composition, 1968; D of Mus. Arts in Choral Conducting, U. Ill., 1976. High sch. music tchr. Phila., Quakertown, Pa., 1969-74; prof. Bloomsburg (Pa.) State Coll., 1969-82; v.p. acad. affairs Taylor U., Upland, Ind., 1982—; chmn. Commn. Higher Edn., 1989-91. Author: A Checklist of Four-Shape Tunebooks, 1978, Dictionary of Hymnology, 1992; contbr. articles to profl. jours. Choir dir. Blackford County community chorus, Hartford City, Ind., 1987—; choir dir. 1st Presbyn. Ch., Muncie, Ind., 1989—; bd. dirs. Marion (Ind.) Philharm. Orch., 1985-88. Fellow Am. Coun. Edn., 1982-83, NEH, Columbia U., 1977. Mem. Am. Assn. Higher Edn., Nat. Assn. Evangs., Music Educators Nat. Conf., Coun. Deans Christian Coll. Consortium (chmn. 1989-92), Am. Choral Dirs. Assn., Pa. Choral Dirs. Assn. (pres. 1981-82). Home: 100 Tadlock Rd Bristol TN 37620-2627

STANKEY, SUZANNE M., editor; b. Grand Rapids, Mich., Apr. 4, 1951; d. Robert Michael and Elizabeth (Rogers) Stankey; m. Homer Brickey, Jr. B.A., Ohio U., Athens, 1973; B.J., U. Mo., Columbia, 1977. Editor Living Today, The Blade, Toledo, 1980-82, Toledo Mag., The Blade, 1982-92, Living Today, Toledo, 1992—. Mem. Toledo Press Club, Toledo Sailing Club. Home: 2510 Kenwood Blvd Toledo OH 43606-3601 Office: The Blade 541 N Superior St Toledo OH 43660-0001

STANKIEWICZ, WLADYSLAW JOZEF, political scientist, educator; b. Warsaw, Poland, May 6, 1922; s. Jozef Edmund and Helena Kamilla (Pawlowicz) S. M.A., U. St. Andrews, Scotland, 1944; Ph.D., London Sch.

Econs. and Polit. Sci., 1952. Lectr. Polish U. Coll., London, 1947-52; research asso. Mid-European Studies Center, N.Y.C., 1952-54; vis. postdoctoral fellow Princeton U., 1954-55; economist Govt. of Ont., Can., 1956-57; mem. faculty U. B.C., Vancouver, 1957-87; prof. polit. sci. U. B.C., 1965-87, prof. emeritus, 1987—; lectr. in over 60 univs. in, Europe, N.Z., Australia, Africa, and Asia. Author numerous books, 1955—, latest being Canada-U.S. Relations and Canadian Foreign Policy, 1973, Aspects of Political Theory: Classical Concepts in an Age of Relativism, 1976, Approaches to Democracy, 1980, Am. edit., 1981, In Search of a Political Philosophy: Ideologies at the Close of the Twentieth Century, 1993, Jottings: Thoughts & Aplorisms, 1995; editor books, 1964—, latest being In Defense of Sovereignty, 1969, British Government in an Era of Reform, 1976, The Tradition of Polish Ideals, 1981. Served with Polish Army, 1940-46. Fellow Can. Council, 1968-69, 74-75; Social Scis. and Humanities Research Council Can., 1979-80; I.W. Killam Sr. fellow, 1969-70, 71-72, 77-78. Mem. Am. Soc. Polit. and Legal Philosophy, Am. Polit. Sci. Assn. Office: Univ BC Dept Polit Sci, Vancouver, BC Canada V6T 1Z1 *I think it is important to believe in a hierarchy of values; to eschew what is merely practical or popular; to shape one's thoughts into a coherent system of ideas reflecting a Weltanschauung; to pursue long-range goals; not to commit oneself to secondary objectives; to see a project through all its stages; to avoid the distinction between working and living; to preserve a sense of the joy of life.*

STANLEY, ARTHUR JEHU, JR., federal judge; b. nr. Lincoln, Kans., Mar. 21, 1901; s. Arthur and Bessie (Anderson) S.; m. Ruth Willis, July 16, 1927; children: Mary Louise Stanley Andrews, Carolyn Stanley Lane, Constance Stanley Yunghans, Susan Stanley Hoffman. LL.B., Kansas City Sch. Law (U. Mo.), Kansas City, 1928. Bar: Kans. bar 1928. County atty. Wyandotte County, Kans., 1935-41; U.S. dist. judge Dist. of Kans., Leavenworth, 1958-71; chief judge Dist. of Kans., 1961-71, sr. U.S. dist. judge, 1971—; mem. Jud. Conf. U.S., 1967-70, chmn. com. on operation jury system, 1973-78, mem. bicentennial com., 1975-78. Mem. Kans. Senate, 1941. Served with 7th U.S. Cav. Can. Army, World War I; with USN, 1921-25; Yangtze Patrol Force 1923-25; 9th Air Force USAAF, 1941-45; disch. to Inf. Res. as lt. col. Fellow Am. Bar Found.; mem. ABA, Kans. Bar Assn., Wyandotte County Bar Assn. (past pres.), Leavenworth County Bar Assn., Am. Judicature Soc., Kans. Hist. Soc. (pres. 1974-75), Am. Legion. Angli-can. Home: 501 N Esplanade St Leavenworth KS 66048-2027 Office: US Dist Ct 235 Fed Bldg Leavenworth KS 66048 *My goal in life has been to have and deserve the affection of my family and the respect of my professional colleagues.*

STANLEY, BOB, artist; b. Yonkers, N.Y., Jan. 3, 1932; s. Robert and Margaret (Druitz) S.; m. Marylin Herzka, 1970. B.A., Oglethorpe U., 1953; postgrad., Columbia U., 1953, Bklyn. Mus. Art Sch., 1954-56. faculty Sch. Visual Arts, N.Y.C., 1970-72, 84—; vis. artist La. State U., 1976, Syracuse U., 1978, Princeton U., 1979-80, St. Lawrence U., Canton, N.Y., 1978, New Arts Program, Kutztown, Pa., 1984. One man exhbns. include Bianchini Gallery, N.Y.C., 1965, 66, Internat. Gallery Orez, The Hague, Holland, 1966, Contemporary Art Center, Cin., 1966, Galerie Ricke, Kassel, Germany, 1966, 67, Gegenverkehr, Aachen, Germany, 1969, On 1st, N.Y.C., 1969, Warren Benedek Gallery, 1972, N.Y. Cultural Center, 1974, La. State U. Union Gallery, Baton Rouge, 1976, Hal Bromm Gallery, N.Y.C. & Elizabeth Weiner Gallery, 1978, 80, Bucklew Goehring Gallery, Tampa, Fla., 1983, Centre d'Art Contemporain, Dijon, France, 1986, John Davis Gallery, N.Y.C., 1986, 87, Galerie G. Lavrov, Paris, 1987, 88, Gallerie Bébert, Rotterdam, The Netherlands, 1989, The Painted Bride Gallery, Phila., 1990, The Greenville County (S.C.) Art Mus., 1991, Barbierato Arte Contemporanea, Asiago, Italy, 1992, Moderne Künst Dietmar Werle, Köln, Germany; retrospective exhibit at Holly Keenberg-Contemporary Art, Winnipeg, Man., Can., 1980; group exhbns. include 2 man show, P.S.I. Long Island City, 1977, Antisensitivity Show, Ohio U., 1964, Pop and Circumstance, Four Seasons, N.Y.C., 1965, Contemporary Americans, Art Inst. Chgo., 1965, John G. Powers Collection, Larry Aldrich Mus., Ridgefield, Conn., 1966, Hanford Yang Collection, Larry Aldrich Mus., Ridgefield, 1968, 29th Ann., Art Inst. Chgo., 1969, Aspects of a New Realism, Milw. Art Center, 1969, Ann. Exhbn, Whitney Mus. Am. Art, N.Y.C., 1967, 69, 72, 73, 17th, Nat. Print Exhbn, Bklyn. Mus., 1970, Monumental Art, Contemporary Arts Center, Cin., 1970, Recent Aquisitions, Washington U. Mus., St. Louis, 1967, Obsessive Image, Inst. Contemporary Art, London, Eng., 1968, Documenta 68, Kassel, Germany, Another Aspect of Pop, P.S.I. Long Island City, 1978, Milw. Art Center, 1969, Corcoran Gallery Art, 1980, Parrish Art Mus., Southampton, N.Y., 1980, Des Moines Art Center, 1980, Krannert Art Mus., Champaign-Urbana, Ill., 1980, William Paterson Coll., Wayne, N.J., 1980, Worcester Art Mus., Mass., 1981, Orozco Gallery, Mexico City, 1981, Am. Acad. and Inst. Arts and Letters, 1982, Daniel Wolf Gallery, N.Y.C., 1982, Ft. Worth Art Mus., 1984, Harcus Gallery, Boston, 1984, Fuji I, Tokyo, 1985, U.R.I. Fine Arts Ctr., 1985, Art Mus. Princeton, N.J., 1985, White Columns, N.Y.C., 1987, Lyman Allyn Mus., New London, Conn., 1987, High Mus. Art, Atlanta, 1988, Lehigh U., Bethlehem, 1988, Nelson-Atkins Mus. Art, Kansas City, 1989, Contemporay Arts Ctr., Cin., 1990, Centro Cultural La Gerneral Granada, Spain, 1990, numerous others. Recipient Casandra Found. award, 1969, Igor Found. award, 1987. Address: 3 Crosby St New York NY 10013-3102

STANLEY, DANIEL JEAN, geological oceanographer, senior scientist; b. Metz, France, Apr. 14, 1934; came to U.S., 1941, naturalized, 1946; s. Paul Emile and Madeleine (Simon) Streisguth; m. Adrienne N. Ellis, Mar. 5, 1988; children: Marc Michel, Eric Paul, Brian, Natalie Anne, Susan. B.Sc., Cornell U., 1956; M.Sc., Brown U., 1958; D.Sc., U. Grenoble, France, 1961. Research geologist French Petroleum Inst., Paris, 1958-61; asst. to dir. U.S. Waterways Expt. Sta., Vicksburg, Miss., 1961-63; asst. prof. geology Ottawa U., Ont., Can., 1963-64; research assoc. prof. Dalhousie U., Halifax, N.S., Can., 1964-66; sr. scientist, oceanographer, dir. Deltas-Global Change Program div. sedimentology Smithsonian Instn., Washington, 1966—; adj. prof. U. Québec, 1992—; cons. to govts. Mediterranean countries; sci. expert Internat. Ct. Justice, 1981—; curator Smithsonian Instn., Washington. Editor: New Concepts of Continental Margin Sedimentation, 1969, Mediterranean Sea: A Natural Sedimentation Laboratory, 1972, Marine Sediment Transport and Environmental Management, 1976, Sedimentation in Submarine Canyons, Fans and Trenches, 1978, The Shelfbreak: A Critical Interface on Continental Margins, 1983, Geological Evolution of the Mediterranean Basin, 1985; contbr. chpts to books, articles to profl. jours. Bd. dirs. Mediterranean Basin and Deltas Programs. Served to capt. C.E., U.S. Army, 1961-63. Recipient médaille Alpes Maritimes, France, 1976, F.P. Shepard medal Soc. for Sedimentary Geology, 1990; grantee in field. Fellow Geol. Soc. Am., AAAS, Geol. Soc. Belgium; mem. Internat. Assn. Sedimentologists, Am. Assn. Petroleum Geologists, Soc. Econ. Paleontologists and Mineralogists, Geol. Soc. Washington, Sigma Xi. Republican. Club: Cosmos (Washington). Office: Smithsonian Instn Sedimentology Dv Washington DC 20560

STANLEY, DAVID, retail company executive; b. Kansas City, Mo., 1935; married. Grad., U. Wis., 1955; LLB, Columbia U., 1957. Assoc. Paul, Weiss, Rifkind, Wharton & Garrison, N.Y.C., 1957-60; ptnr. Faegre & Benson, Mpls., 1960-71; exec. v.p. Piper, Jaffray & Hopwood, Mpls., 1971-80; pres. Payless Cashways, Inc., Kansas City, 1980-86, chief exec. officer, 1982—, chmn., 1985—, also bd. dirs. Local Initiaves, Support Corp., Nat. Equity Fund, Inc., Piper Jaffray Inc. Bd. dirs. Dole Found. Office: Payless Cashways Inc PO Box 419466 2300 Main St Kansas City MO 64108-2415*

STANLEY, EDMUND ALLPORT, JR., foundation administrator, philanthropist; b. N.Y.C., July 9, 1924; s. Edmund Allport and Emily (Hasslacher) S.; m. Jennifer Berger, June 5, 1976; children by previous marriage—Edmund Allport III, Eric V., Lisa. A.B., Princeton U., 1949. With Bowne & Co., N.Y.C., 1949-94; v.p. Bowne & Co., 1953-56, pres, 1956-74, chmn. bd., 1956-86, chmn. exec. com., 1986-94. Pres. Robert Bowne Found, N.Y.C., Town Creek Found.; Oxford, Md.; Served with AUS, 1943-45. Decorated Bronze Star medal, Purple Heart. Clubs: Bond of N.Y., Pilgrims. Home: South St Oxford MD 21654

STANLEY, EDWARD ALEXANDER, forensic scientist, geologist, technical and academic administrator; b. N.Y.C., Apr. 7, 1929; s. Frank and Elizabeth (Wolf) S.; m. Elizabeth Ann Allison, June 7, 1958; children: Karen (dec.), Scott. B.S., Rutgers U., 1954; M.S., Pa. State U., 1956, Ph.D., 1960.

Geologist, Amoco Petroleum Co., Tulsa, 1960-62; prof. U. Del., 1962-64, U. Ga., 1964-77; assoc. dean rsch., chmn. geology dept. Indiana (Pa.) U. , 1977-81; supr. Phillips Petroleum Co., Bartlesville, Okla., 1981-86, dir., comdg. officer N.Y.C. Police Dept. Crime Lab., 1986-94, cons. geology, forensic sci. microscopy 1994—; cons. geology, Athens, Ga., 1963-77, Indiana, Pa., 1977-81. Contbr. articles to profl. jours. Served to sgt. USAF, 1947-50. NSF grantee 1965-68, 74, Office Water Resources Rsch. grantee, 1965-68; NAS exch. prof. Soviet Union, 1968-69, 73; invited guest Moscow Forensic Labs., 1990; invited speaker FBI Internat. Symposium on Forensic Trace Evidence, 1991. Fellow AAAS, Geol. Soc. Am., Royal Microscopical Soc.; mem. Am. Assn. Petroleum Geologists, Am. Soc. Crime Lab. Dirs., Am. Acad. of Forensic Sci., Northeastern Forensic Assn., Internat. Assn. for Identification, . Am. Assn. Stratigraphic Palyologists, Am. Soc. Photogrammetry and Remote Sensing, The Biol. Photograhers Assn., N.Y. Microscopical Soc., Sigma Xi. Presbyterian. Avocations: photography, music, firearms. Home: 2004 Haverford Rd Ardmore PA 19003-3010

STANLEY, ELLEN MAY, historian, consultant; b. Dighton, Kans., Feb. 3, 1921; d. Delmar Orange and Lena May (Bobb) Durr; m. Max Neal Stanley, Nov. 5, 1939; children: Ann Y. Stanley Epps, Janet M. Stanley Horsky, Gail L. Stanley Peck, Kenneth D., Neal M., Mary E. Stanley McEniry. BA in English and Journalism, U. Kans.) State U., 1972, MA in History, 1984. Pvt. practice local/state historian, cons., writer local history Dighton, 1973—, cons. genealogy, 1980—; vice chmn. State Preservation Bd. Rev., Kans., 1980-87; area rep. Kans. State Mus. Assn., 1978-84. Author: Early Lane County History: 12,000 B.C. - A.D. 1884, 1993 (cert. of commendation Am. Assn. State and Local History); contbr. articles to profl. jours. Precinct woman com. Alamota Township, Kans., 1962-86; mem. Dem. State Affirmative Action Com., 1975. Recipient hon. mention for photography Ann. Christian Arts Festival, 1974, Artist of Month award Dane G. Hansen Mus., 1975. Mem. Kans. State Hist. Soc. (pres. 1990-91), Lane County Hist. Soc. (sec. 1970-78). Methodist. Avocations: fossil hunting, walking, photography, antiques. Home: 100 N 4th Dighton KS 67839 Office: 116 E Long St Dighton KS 67839

STANLEY, H(ARRY) EUGENE, physicist, educator; b. Norman, Okla., Mar. 28, 1941; s. Harry Eugene and Ruth S.; m. Idahlia Dessauer, June 2, 1967; children: Jannah, Michael, Rachel. BA in Physics (Nat. Merit scholar), Wesleyan U., 1962; postgrad. (Fulbright scholar), U. Cologne, W. Ger., 1962-63; PhD in Physics, Harvard U., 1967; PhD (hon.), Bar-Ilan U., Ramat-Gan, Israel, 1994. NSF predoctoral rsch. fellow Harvard U., 1963-67; mem. staff Lincoln Lab MIT, 1967-68, asst. prof. physics, 1969-71, assoc. prof., 1971-73; Miller rsch. fellow U. Calif., Berkeley, 1968-69; Hermann von Helmholtz assoc. prof. health scis. and tech. Harvard U.-MIT Program in Health Scis. and Tech., 1973-76; vis. prof. Osaka (Japan) U., 1975; univ. prof., prof. physics, prof. physiology Sch. Medicine, dir. Ctr. Polymer Studies Boston U., 1976—; Joliot-Curie vis. prof. Ecole Superieure de Physique et Chimie, Paris, 1979; vis. prof. Peking U., 1981, Seoul Nat. U., 1982, 30th Ann. Saha Meml. Lecture, 1992; dir. NATO Advanced Study Inst., Cargese, Corisca, 1985, 88, 90; dir. IUPAP Internat. Conf. on Thermodynamics and Statis. Mechanics, 1986; cons. Sandia Nat. Lab., 1983—; Dowell Schlumberger Co., 1982—, Elscint Co., 1983-85; nat. co-chmn. Com. of Concerned Scientists, 1974-76. Author: Introduction to Phase Transitions and Critical Phenomena, 1971, From Newton to Mandelbrot: A Primer in Theoretical Physics, 1990, Fractal Forms, 1991, Fractal Concepts in Surface Growth, 1995; editor: Biomedical Physics and Biomaterials Science, 1972, Cooperative Phenomena Near Phase Transitions, 1973, On Growth and Form, Fractal and Non-Fractal Patterns in Physics, 1985, Statistical Physics, 1986, Random Fluctuations and Pattern Growth, 1988, Correlations and Connectivity: Geometric Aspects of Physics, Chemistry and Biology, 1990, Fractals in Science, 1994; assoc. editor Physica A, 1988-91, editor, 1991—. Recipient Choice award Am. Assn. Book Pubs., 1972, Macdonald award, 1986, Venture Rsch. award British Petroleum, 1989, Mass. Prof. of Yr. award Coun. Advancement and Support of Edn., 1992; John Simon Guggenheim Meml. fellow, 1979-80. Fellow Am. Phys. Soc. (chmn. New Eng. sect. 1982-83), AAAS; mem. NAS (non-linear sci. panel). Home: 50 Metacomet Rd Newton MA 02168-1465 Office: Boston U Ctr for Polymer Studies Boston MA 02215 *The greatest joy of my professional life is to share in the excitement of learning something new—however minor—about the workings of Nature. The greatest joy of my personal life is to be able to imagine that I've done my very best to meet the needs of my family and my co-workers. The greatest obstacle to happiness is the persistent feeling that it is impossible to find that tortuous path whereby both joys may occasionally be experienced.*

STANLEY, HUGH MONROE, JR., lawyer; b. Ft. Lewis, Wash., Oct. 25, 1944; s. Hugh Monroe Sr. and Rita (McHugh) S.; m. Patricia Page Stanley, Aug. 17, 1968; children: Allison Michele, Matthew Monroe, Trevor, Marshall. BA magna cum laude, U. Dayton, 1966; JD, Georgetown U., 1969. Bar: Ohio 1969, U.S. Ct. Appeals (6th cir.) 1983, U.S. Supreme Ct. 1979. Assoc. Arter & Hadden, Cleve., 1969-76, ptnr., 1976—, chmn. litigation dept. Staff editor Georgetown Law Jour., bd. editors. Fellow Am. Bar Found., Bar Assn. Greater Cleve., Am. Coll. Trial Lawyers, Internat. Acad. Trial Lawyers, Internat. Soc. Barristers, Nat. Assn. R.R. Trial Counsel; mem. ABA, Fed. Bar Assn., Def. Rsch. Inst., Cleve. Assn. Civil Trial Attys., Ohio Assn. Civil Trial Attys. Republican. Roman Catholic. Avocation: reading. Office: Arter & Hadden 1100 Huntington Bldg 925 Euclid Ave Cleveland OH 44115

STANLEY, JACK H., newspaper publishing executive. V.p.- operations The Houston Chronicle, Tex. Office: Houston Chronicle Pub Co 801 Texas St Houston TX 77002-2906*

STANLEY, JAMES PAUL, printing company executive; b. Montreal, Que., Can., Aug. 15, 1915; s. Paul Garton and Florence May (Tooke) S.; m. Anne Seymour Raynsford ; children—Marie, Susan, James, Sarah. B.Engring., McGill U., Montreal, 1938. Staff engr. Stevenson, Kellogg Ltd., 1938-41; plant mgr. Dow Brewery Ltd., 1947-53; v.p., then pres. Ronalds-Federated Ltd., Montreal, 1954-77; chmn. bd., chief exec. officer Ronalds-Federated Ltd., 1977-80. Gov. Montreal Gen. Hosp. Served with RCAF, 1941-46. Fellow Graphic Arts Tech. Found. Mem. Ch. of Eng. Clubs: St. James's. Home: 799 Wartman Ave, Kingston, ON Canada K7M 4M3

STANLEY, JAMES RICHARD, lawyer; b. Williamsport, Pa., Oct. 23, 1931; s. Leslie Wright and Hazel (Stryker) S.; m. Darlene Foster, Nov. 18, 1961; children: Susan A., Sandra R., James F., Jeffrey W. BA, Pa. State U., 1953; JD, Dickinson Sch. Law, 1958. Bar: Pa. 1959, N.Y. 1963, U.S. Supreme Ct. 1967, Ill. 1983. Atty. Duquesne Light Co., Pitts., 1958-62, Hazeltine Corp., Little Neck, N.Y., 1962-64; div. counsel Sealtest Foods, Phila. and Schenectady, N.Y., 1964-71; dir. legal dept. Thiokol Corp., Newtown, Pa., 1971-82; assoc. gen. counsel specialty chems. group Morton Thiokol, Inc., Chgo., 1982-86, gen. counsel, 1986-87; v.p. legal affairs, gen. counsel Morton Internat., Inc., Chgo., 1987—; mem. adv. bd. Northwestern U. Corp. Counsel Ctr., Chgo., 1986—. Served to 1st lt. U.S. Army, 1953-55. Mem. ABA (com. on corp. law depts. 1986—), Phila. Bar Assn., Ill. Bar Assn., Chgo. Bar Assn. Republican. Presbyterian. Clubs: Met., Tower (Chgo.). Office: Morton Internat Inc 100 N Riverside Plz Chicago IL 60606-1596

STANLEY, JAY, sociologist, educator; b. Charleston, W.Va., Dec. 14, 1940. BS, U. Tenn., 1962, MA, 1963; PhD, U. Md., 1970; HHD (hon.), Lincoln Meml. U., 1990. Asst. prof. dept. social sci. George Mason U., Arlington, Va., 1970-71; assoc. prof. dept. sociology and anthropology Towson State U., 1971-78, prof. sociology, 1978—; fellow The Johns Hopkins U., Balt., 1974-78, rsch. sociologist dept. obstetrics and gynecology, 1974-80; spl. mem. grad. faculty dept. sociology U. Md., College Park, 1990—. Author: Transitions to Leisure; Conceptual and Human Issues, 1985, Social Research: Theory and Methods, 1992, Challenges in Military Health Care: Perspectives on Health Status and the Provision of Care, 1993; editor: Armed Forces and Society: An Interdisciplinary Jour., 1992—; contbr. articles to profl. jours. Recipient Nat. Outstanding Educator award, 1975; named to Educator's Hall of Fame by Lincoln Meml. U., 1987, Literary Hall of Fame by Lincoln Meml U., 1988. Fellow Inter-Univ. Seminar on Armed Forces and Soc. (mem. adv. coun. 1989—); mem. Phi Kappa Phi, Alpha Kappa Delta, Omicron Delta Kappa, Sigma Xi, Phi Sigma Kappa (bd. dirs. 1990—). Home: 1021 Breezewick Rd Baltimore MD 21286-3306

STANLEY, JOHN R., petroleum company executive; b. 1939; married. With Sonic Enterprises, United Petroleum, Valley Gas & Oil Inc., Valley Oil Co. Inc., Petroleum Products Inc., Palmer Shoppes Realty Trust, 1959-68; pres. Good Hope Refinery Inc., Norco, La., Good Hope Industries Inc., Norco; chmn. bd., chief exec. officer TransAm. Nat. Gas Corp., Houston. Office: TransAm Nat Gas Corp 140 Cypress Sta Dr #200 Houston TX 77090

STANLEY, JULIAN CECIL, JR., educator; b. Macon, Ga., July 9, 1918; s. Julian Cecil and Ethel (Cheney) S.; m. Rose Roberta Sanders, Aug. 18, 1946 (dec. Nov. 1978); 1 child, Susan Roberta Willhoft; m. Barbara Sprague Kerr, Jan. 1, 1980. B.S., Ga. So. U., 1937; Ed.M., Harvard U., 1946, Ed.D., 1950; D of Ednl. Excellence (hon.), U. North Tex., 1990. Tchr. Fulton and West Fulton high schs., Atlanta, 1937-42; instr. psychology Newton Jr. Coll., 1946-48; instr. edn. Harvard U., 1948-49; asso. prof. ednl. psychology George Peabody Coll. Tchrs., 1949-53; assoc. prof. edn., 1953-57, prof. edn., 1957-62, prof. ednl. psychology, 1962-67, chmn. dept., 1962-63; dir. lab. exptl. design U. Wis., Madison, 1961-67; prof. edn. and psychology Johns Hopkins U., 1967-71, prof. psychology, 1971—; dir. study mathematically precocious youth, 1971—; mem. rsch. adv. coun. Coop. Rsch. Br., U.S. Office Edn., 1962-64; mem. examiners for aptitude tests Coll. Entrance Exam. Bd., 1961-65, chmn., 1965-68; mem. rsch. com. Ednl. Testing Svc., 1962-67; fellow Social Sci. Rsch. Coun. Inst. Math. for Social Scientists, U. Mich., summer 1955; postdoctoral fellow statistics U. Chgo., 1955-56; Fulbright rsch. scholar U. Louvain, Belgium, 1958-59; Fulbright lectr. New Zealand and Australia, 1974; cons. U. Western Australia, 1980; fellow Ctr. for Advanced Study in Behavioral Sci., 1965-67, vis. scholar, 1983; hon. prof. Shanghai (People's Republic of China) Tchrs. U.; disting. tchr. Commn. on Presdl. Scholars, 1987, 92; disting. vis. prof. U. Ga., 1947, U. Hawaii, 1960, Harvard U., 1963, U. North Tex., 1990, U. NSW, Australia, 1992; mem. adv. bd. Tex. Acad. Maths. and Sci., 1988—; trustee Ctr. for Excellence in Edn., 1989-93; Julian C. Stanley prof. Ednl. Psychology U. Wis., Madison, 1995. Author: Measurement in Today's Schools, 4th edit, 1964, (with D.T. Campbell) Experimental and Quasi-Experimental Designs for Research, 1966, (with Gene V. Glass) Statistical Methods in Education and Psychology, 1970, (with K.D. and B. Hopkins) Educational and Psychological Measurement and Evaluation, 3d edit, 1990, (with K.D. Hopkins, G.H. Bracht) Perspectives in Educational and Psychological Measurement, 1972; Editor: Improving Experimental Design and Statistical Analysis, 1967, Preschool Programs for the Disadvantaged, 1972, Compensatory Education for Children, Ages 2-8, 1973, (with D.P. Keating, L.H. Fox) Mathematical Talent: Discovery, Description, and Development, 1974, (with W.C. George, C.H. Solano) The Gifted and the Creative: A Fifty-Year Perspective, 1977, Educational Programs and Intellectual Prodigies, 1978, (with W.C. George, S.J. Cohn) Educating the Gifted: Acceleration and Enrichment, 1979, (with C.P. Benbow) Academic Precocity: Aspects of Its Development, 1983; adv. editor jours. Served with USAAC, 1942-45. Julian C. Stanley chair in ednl. psychology created U. Wis., Madison, 1995. Fellow APA (pres.- elect edn. psychology 1965-66, div. evaluation and measurement 1972-73, Thorndike award for disting. psychol. contbns. to edn. 1978), AAAS, Am. Statis. Assn., Am. Psychol. Soc. (J. McKeen Cattell award 1994); mem. Nat. Council Measurement Edn. (pres. 1963-64), Am. Ednl. Research Assn. (pres. 1966-67, award for disting. contbns. to research in edn. 1980), Nat. Assn. for Gifted Children (2d v.p. 1977-79, Disting. Scholar award 1982), AAUP (past pres. chpt.), Psychometric Soc. (past dir.), AAUP (past chpt. pres.), Tenn. Psychol. Assn. (past pres.), Nat. Acad. Edn., Phi Beta Kappa (past chpt. pres.), Phi Beta Kappa Assocs., Sigma Xi, Phi Delta Kappa. Office: Johns Hopkins U SMPY 156A Bloomberg Ctr Baltimore MD 21218-2690 *I am deeply indebted for my graduate education to the G.I. Bill following World War II.*

STANLEY, JUSTIN ARMSTRONG, lawyer; b. Leesburg, Ind., Jan. 2, 1911; s. Walter H. and Janet (Armstrong) S.; m. Helen Leigh Fletcher, Jan. 3, 1938; children: Janet Van Wie Hoffmann, Melinda Fletcher Douglas, Justin Armstrong, Harlan Fletcher. AB, Dartmouth Coll., 1933, AM (hon.), 1952, LLD (hon.), 1983; LLB, Columbia U., 1937; LLD (hon.), John Marshall Law Sch., 1976, Suffolk U., 1976, Vt. Law Sch., 1977, Norwich U., 1977, Ind. U., 1981, Oklahoma City U., 1981, IIT-Chgo.-Kent Coll. Law, 1988, William Mitchell Coll. Law, 1989. Bar: Ill. 1937. Since practiced in Chgo.; assoc. Isham, Lincoln & Beale, 1937-48, ptnr., 1948-66; ptnr. Mayer, Brown & Platt, 1967-91; of counsel, 1991—; v.p. Dartmouth Coll., 1952-54; asst. prof. law Chgo.-Kent Coll. Law, 1938-43, prof., 1943-46; pub. mem. disputes sect. Nat. War Labor Bd., 1943-44. Trustee Presbyn.-St. Luke's Hosp., Wells Coll., 1960-69, Rockford Coll., 1962-70; trustee Ill. Childrens Home and Aid Soc., pres., 1963-64. Served as lt. USNR, 1944-46. Recipient medal for excellence Columbia U. Law Sch., 1984, Disting. Svc. award, 1994. Fellow Am. Bar Found., Am. Coll. Trial Lawyers; mem. ABA (chmn. pub. utility sect. 1970-71, ho. of dels. 1973—, pres. 1976-77, chmn. commn. on professionalism 1985-86, ABA medal 1986), Fed. Energy Bar Assn., Chgo. Bar Assn. (pres. 1967-68), Ill. Bar Assn. (Disting. Svc. award 1986), Alumni Coun. Dartmouth (pres. 1952), Am. Law Inst., Am. Judicature Soc., Supreme Ct. Hist. Soc. (pres. 1987-91, chmn. 1995—), Alpha Delta Phi. Episcopalian. Office: Mayer Brown & Platt 190 S La Salle St Chicago IL 60603-3410

STANLEY, MARGARET KING, performing arts administrator; b. San Antonio, Tex., Dec. 11, 1929; d. Creston Alexander and Margaret (Haymore) King; children: Torrey Margaret, Jean Cullen. Student, Mary Baldwin Coll., 1948-50; BA, U. Tex., Austin, 1952; MA, Incarnate Word Coll., 1959. Tchg. cert. 1953. Elem. tchr. San Antonio Ind. Sch. Dist., 1953-54, 55-56, Arlington County Schs., Va., 1954-55, Ft. Sam Houston Schs., San Antonio, 1956-57; art, art history tchr. St. Pius X Sch., San Antonio 1959-60; tchr. Trinity U., 1963-65; designer-mfr., owner CrisStan Clothes, Inc., San Antonio, 1967-73; founder, exec. dir. San Antonio Performing Arts Assn., 1976-92; founder Arts Council of San Antonio, 1962; founding chmn. Joffrey Workshop, San Antonio, 1979; originator, founding chairwoman Student Music Fair, San Antonio, 1963; radio program host On Stage, San Antonio, 1983—. Originator of the idea for a new ballet created for the City of San Antonio, "Jamboree," commd. from the Joffrey Ballet, world premiere in San Antonio, 1984. Pres. San Antonio Symphony League, 1971-74; v.p. Arts Council of San Antonio, 1975; bd. govs. Artists Alliance of San Antonio, 1982; v.p. San Antonio Opera Guild, 1974-76, founder Early Music Festival, San Antonio, 1990; mem. adv. bd. Hertzberg Circus Mus. Recipient Outstanding Tchr. award Arlington County Sch. Dist., 1954, Today's Woman award San Antonio Light Newspaper, 1980, Woman of Yr. in arts award San Antonio Express News, 1983, Emily Smith award for outstanding alumni Mary Baldwin Coll., 1973, Erasmus medal The Dutch Consulate, 1992, Sesquicentennial medallion, 1992; named to Women's Hall of Fame, San Antonio, 1984, Disting. Alumnae, St. Mary's Hall, 1995; teaching fellow Trinity U., San Antonio, 1964-66. Mem. Internat. Soc. Performing Arts Adminstrs. (regional rep. 1982-85, bd. dirs. 1991—), Met. Opera Nat. Coun., Assn. Performing Arts Presenters, Women in Comm. (Headliner award 1982, San Antonio chpt.), Jr. League of San Antonio, Battle of Flowers Assn., S.W. Performing Arts Presenters (chmn. 1988-92). Avocations: traveling, reading.

STANLEY, PAMELA MARY, cell biologist; b. Melbourne, Australia, Mar. 25, 1947; came to U.S. 1977; d. John Patrick and Edith Della (Hart) Fetherstonhaugh; m. Evan Richard Stanley, Feb. 6, 1970; children: Damian Alexander, Robert Fenton. BSc with honors, U. Melbourne, 1969, PhD, 1972. Rsch. assoc. U. Toronto, Toronto, Can., 1972-77; asst. prof. Albert Einstein Coll. Medicine, Bronx, 1977-82, assoc. prof., 1982-86, prof. of cell biology, 1986—; mem. study sect. NIH, Bethesda, 1989-93. Editorial bd. Molecular and Cellular Biology, 1980-91, Glycobiology, 1990—, Molecular Biology of the Cell, 1991-93, Jour. Biol. Chemistry, 1995—; contbr. articles to profl. jours. Bd. dirs. Kids Meeting Kids Can Make A Difference, N.Y., 1986—, Alaria Chamber Ensemble, N.Y., 1995—; mem. Educators for Social Responsibility, N.Y., 1985—; mem. review group Am. Cancer Soc., 1981-85. NSF grantee, 1977, Am. Cancer Soc. grantee, 1978, 80, NIH grantee, 1980, 83, 85, 86, 90, 91. Mem. Am. Soc. for Biochemistry and Molecular Biology, Soc. for Cell Biology, Internat. Assn. Women Biochemists. Office: Albert Einstein Coll Medicine Dept Cell Bio Bronx NY 10461

STANLEY, PETER WILLIAM, college president; b. Bronxville, N.Y., Feb. 17, 1940; s. Arnold and Mildred Jeanette (Pattison) S.; m. Joan Olivia Hersey, Sept. 14, 1963 (div. 1978); m. Mary-Jane Cullen Cosgrove, Sept. 2,

1978; 1 dau., Laura. B.A. magna cum laude, Harvard U., 1962, M.A., 1964, Ph.D., 1970; LHD (hon.), Occidental Coll., 1994. Asst. prof. history U. Ill. Chgo., 1970-72; asst. prof. history Harvard U., 1972-78, lectr. history, 1978-79; dean of coll. Carleton Coll., Northfield, Minn., 1979-84; program officer in charge edn. and culture program Ford Found., 1984-87, dir. edn. and culture program, 1987-91; pres. Pomona Coll., Claremont, Calif., 1991—; lectr. Fgn. Service Inst., Arlington, Va., 1977-89. Author: A Nation in the Making: The Philippines and the United States, 1974; co-author: Sentimental Imperialists: The American Experience in East Asia, 1981; editor, contbr.: Reappraising an Empire: New Perspectives on Philippine-American History, 1984; contbr. numerous articles to scholastic jours., 1966—. Trustee The Coll. Bd., 1991—, vice-chair, 1993-94, chair 1994—; dir. The Hitachi Found., 1993—; dir. Assn. Am. Coll. and Univs., 1995—; bd. fellows Claremont Grad. Sch. and Claremont U. Ctr., 1991—; active humanities and scis. coun. Stanford U., 1986—; nat. adv. bd. Ctr. for Rsch. on Effective Schooling for Disadvantage Students, John Hopkins U., 1989-92; nat. adv. coun. Nat. Fgn. Lang. Ctr., 1992—; mem. exec. com. Consortium Financing Higher Edn., 1992—; bd. dirs. Nat. Assn. Latino Elected Ofcls. Ednl. Fund, 1992—, Commn. on Internat. Edn., Am. Coun. Edn., 1992-95. Fellow Charles Warren Ctr. for Studies in Am. History-Harvard U., 1975-76; Frank Knox Meml. fellow Harvard U., 1962-63. Mem. AAUP, Am. Hist. Assn., Assn. Asian Studies, Coun. on Fgn. Rels., Phi Beta Kappa. Home: 345 N College Ave Claremont CA 91711-4408 Office: Pomona Coll Pres Office Claremont CA 91711-6301

STANLEY, RALPH, bluegrass musician; b. Stratton, Va., Feb. 25, 1927. Founder (with Carter Stanley) band, Stanley Bros. and Clinch Mountain Boys, 1946; albums include: Old Country Church, Hills of Home, Old Home Place, The Stanley Sound Around The World, Plays Requests, A Man and His Music, I Want to Preach the Gospel, Cry From the Cross, Let Me Rest on Peaceful Mountain, Banjo in the Hills, Best of Bluegrass, Folk Song Festival, In Person, 1983, Collector's Edition Vols. 1-6, Long Journey Home, Rank Strangers, Together for the Last Time; appeared at Royal Albert Hall, London, 1966. Grammy nomination, Best Country Vocal Collaboration for Miner's Prayer" (with Dwight Yoakam), 1994. Office: Rebel Records PO Box 3057 Roanoke VA 24015-1057*

STANLEY, RICHARD HOLT, consulting engineer; b. Muscatine, Iowa, Oct. 20, 1932; s. Claude Maxwell and Elizabeth Mabel (Holthues) S.; m. Mary Jo Kennedy, Dec. 20, 1953; children: Lynne Elizabeth, Sarah Catherine, Joseph Holt. BSEE, Iowa State U., 1955, B.S. in Mech. Engring., 1955; M.S. in San. Engring., U. Iowa, 1963. Registered profl. engr., Iowa, other states. With Stanley Cons. Inc., Muscatine, Iowa, 1955—, pres., 1971-87, chmn., 1984—; also bd. dirs. Stanley Cons. Inc.; bd. dirs. HON Industries, Inc., vice-chmn., 1979—; chmn. Nat. Constrn. Industry Coun., 1978, Com. Fed. Procurement Archtl.-Engring. Svcs., 1979; pres. Ea. Iowa C.C. Bettendorf, 1966-68; mem. indsl. adv. coun. Iowa State U. Coll. Engring., Ames, 1969—, chmn., 1979-81. Contbr. articles to profl. jours. Bd. dirs. Northeast-Midwest Inst., 1989-95, treas. 1991-93, chmn. 1993-95; bd. dirs. Stanley Found., pres. 1984—; bd. dirs. Muscatine Health Support Found., pres. 1984—; bd. dirs. Muscatine United Way, 1969-75, Iowas State U. Meml. Union, 1968-83, U. Dubuque, Iowa, 1977-93, Inst. Social and Econ. Devel.; bd. govs. Iowa State U. Achievement Found., 1982—. With C.E. U.S. Army, 1955-57. Recipient Young Alumnus award Iowa State U. Alumni Assn., 1966, Disting. Svc. award Muscatine Jaycees, 1967, Profl. Achievement citation Coll. Engring., Iowa State U., 1977, Anson Marston medal Iowa State U., 1991; named Sr. Engr. of Yr., Joint Engring. Com. Quint Cities, 1973. Fellow ASCE, Am. Cons. Engrs. Coun. (pres. 1976-77), Iowa Acad. Sci.; mem. IEEE (sr.), ASME, Am. Soc. Engring. Edn., Nat. Soc. Profl. Engrs., Cons. Engrs. Coun. Iowa (pres. 1967), Iowa Engring. Soc. (pres. 1973-74, John Dunlap-Sherman Woodward award 1967, Disting. Svc. award 1980, Voice of Engr. award 1987, Herbert Hoover Centennial award 1989), Muscatine C. of C. (pres. 1972-73), C. of C. of U.S. (constrn. action coun. 1976-91), Tau Beta Pi, Phi Kappa Phi, Pi Tau Sigma, Eta Kappa Nu. Presbyterian (elder). Club: Rotary. Home: 601 W 3rd St Muscatine IA 52761-3119 Office: Stanley Cons Inc Stanley Bldg Muscatine IA 52761

STANLEY, RICHARD P., mathematics educator; b. N.Y.C., June 23, 1944; s. Alan and Shirley (Silver) S.; m. Doris S. Skulsky, July 4, 1971; children: Kenneth, Sharon. BS, Calif. Inst. Technology, 1966; PhD, Harvard U., 1971. Math. instr. MIT, Cambridge, Mass., 1970-71; Miller research fellow Miller Inst., Berkeley, Calif., 1971-73; asst. prof. applied math. MIT, Cambridge, 1973-75, assoc. prof. applied math., 1975-79, prof. applied math., 1979—; cons. in field. Author: Combinatorics and Commutative Algebra, 1983, Enumerative Combinatorics, Vol. 1, 1986. Recipient SIAM Polya Prize Soc. Indsl. and Applied Math., Guggenheim Fellowship, Guggenheim Found., 1983-84. Fellow Am. Acad. Arts and Scis.; mem. Nat. Acad. Scis., Am. Math. Soc., Math. Assn. Am. Home: 64 Great Meadow Rd Newton MA 02159-2748 Office: MIT 77 Massachusetts Ave Cambridge MA 02139

STANLEY, ROBERT L., computer services executive; b. 1946. With Equifax, Atlanta, 1967-85; with Dateq Info. Network Inc., Norcross, Ga., 1985—, now CHB, pres. Office: Dateq Info Network Inc 5555 Triangle Pky Ste 400 Norcross GA 30092*

STANLEY, RONALD ALWIN, environmental scientist, poet; b. Edinburg, Tex., June 18, 1939; s. Hamlet Alwin and Gloria Goldie (Rinkel) S.; m. Dorothy Thibault, Aug. 29, 1963 (div. July 1982); children: Ronald Alwin Jr., David A., Catherine A. Stanley Brookes; m. Susan Absher, Sept. 25, 1982 (div. Dec. 1986); 1 child, Angela M.; m. Mary M. Aldridge, Dec. 26, 1992. AS, Coll. of the Ozarks, 1959; BS, U. Ark., 1961, MS, 1963; PhD, Duke U., 1970; MPA, U. So. Calif., 1982. Intern Oak Ridge (Tenn.) Nat. Lab., summer 1963; scientist Tenn. Valley Authority, Muscle Shoals, 1964-75; asst. prof. biology Memphis State U., 1975, U. S.D., Springfield, 1975; scientist, mgr. EPA, Washington, 1976—; dir. contracts mng. group, 1992-94, coord. trade and environment policy, 1994-95; program mgr. Agy. for Internat. Devel., Washington, 1989-90; co-mgr. Blackberry Hills Farm, Clearville, Pa., 1992—. Author: Dark Vision, 1990; co-author: Environmental Management of Water Projects, 1987; author, pub.: My Mother, The Earth, 1990, With All My Heart, 1990, Fragments of the Journey, 1991; pub.: Holding to the Light, 1991; contbr. articles to profl. jours. Overseer Potomac Appalachian Trail Club, Washington, 1990-92, One-Plus-One Social Svc. Soc., Washington, 1992—; usher Arena Stage, 1985-95; mentor Environmenters, 1994-95; Duke Club of Washington Internat. Interest Group, 1995. Mem. Ecol. Soc. Am., Am. Chestnut Found., Nature Conservancy, Soc. Wetland Scientists, Sierra Club, Phi Beta Kappa, Sigma Xi. Democrat. Office: US EPA 401 M St SW Washington DC 20460-0001

STANLEY, SCOTT, JR., editor; b. Kansas City, Kans., July 11, 1938; s. Winfield Scott and Irene Mae (Flint) S.; m. Janice Johns, Aug. 30, 1959; children: Leslie, Scott, Margaret. BA, Earlham Coll., 1960. Mng. editor Am. Opinion mag., Boston, 1961-85; editor Rev. of The News mag., Boston, 1965-85; editor-in-chief Conservative Digest, Washington, 1985-88, Am. Press Internat., Washington, 1987—; mng. editor Nutrition and Healing, 1994—; mem. nat. bd. dirs. Young Ams. for Freedom, 1960-62; public speaker and univ. lectr., 1962—. Keynote speaker Am. Party Nat. Conv., 1976; pres. Ams. Legal Def. Fund, 1977—; bd. govs. Council for Nat. Policy, 1981—; bd. dirs. Free Congress Polit. Action Com. Recipient award of merit Young Ams. for Freedom, 1970, Freedom award Nat. Congress for Freedom, 1969-79. Congregationalist. Clubs: Nat. Press, Meganset Yacht.

STANLEY, SHERRY A., lawyer; b. Buffalo, N.Y., Oct. 17, 1955; d. Arthur A. and Irene S.; m. William C. Hearon, Mar. 27, 1987. BA, U. West Fla., 1975; JD, U. Fla., 1978. Bar: Fla. 1978. Assoc. Mahoney, Hadlow & Adams, Miami, Fla., 1978-80; ptnr. Steel, Hector & Davis, Miami, 1980-87, Weil, Gotshal & Manges, Miami, 1987-92; sr. counsel Barnett Banks, Inc., Miami, 1992-94; ptnr. Coll, Davidson, Carter, Smith, Salter & Barkett, P.A., Miami, Fla., 1994—. Mem. Fla. Bar, Order of Coif, Phi Theta Kappa. Republican. Roman Catholic. Office: Barnett Banks Inc 701 Brickell Ave Miami FL 33131

STANLEY, STEVEN MITCHELL, paleobiologist, educator; b. Detroit, Nov. 2, 1941; s. William Thomas and Mildred Elizabeth (Baker) S.; m. Nell Williams Gilmore, Oct. 11, 1969. A.B. with highest honors, Princeton U., 1963; Ph.D., Yale U., 1968. Asst. prof. U. Rochester, 1967-69; asst. prof. paleobiology Johns Hopkins U., 1969-71, assoc. prof., 1971-74, prof., 1974,

chmn. Dept. Earth and Planetary Scis., 1987-88; assoc. in research Smithsonian Instn., 1972—; mem. bd. earth scis. NRC, 1985—, vice chmn., 1988, mem. bd. earth scis. resources, 1988-88, com. on solid earth scis., exec. and steering com., 1988, com. on geosciences, environ. and resources, 1990—. Author: Relation of Shell Form to Life Habits in the Bivalvia, 1970, (with D.M. Raup) Principles of Paleontology, 1971, Macroevolution: Pattern and Process, 1979, The New Evolutionary Timetable: Fossils, Genes, and the Origin of Species, 1981, Earth and Life through Time, 1986, Extinction, 1987, Exploring Earth and Life Through Time; mem. editorial bd.: Am. Jour. Sci, 1975—, Paleobiology, 1975-82, 88—, Evolutionary Theory, 1973—. Recipient Outstanding Paper award Jour. Paleontology, 1968, Allan C. Davis medal Md. Acad. Scis., 1973, Outstanding Tech. Paper award Washington Geol. Soc., 1986; Guggenheim fellow, 1981. Fellow Am. Acad. Arts and Scis., Nat. Acad. Scis., Geol. Soc. Am. (chmn. Penrose com. 1978); mem. Paleontol. Soc. (councilor 1976-77, sr. councilor 1991-93, pres. 1993-94, Charles Schuchert award 1977), Soc. for Study Evolution (councilor 1982-84), Am. Geophys. Union, Paleontol. Rsch. Inst. Office: Johns Hopkins U Dept Earth Planetary Sciences Baltimore MD 21218

STANLEY, THOMAS BAHNSON, JR., investor; b. Martinsville, Va., Jan. 9, 1927; s. Thomas B. and Anne (Bassett) S.; m. Ruth Barnes, Sept. 10, 1949; children: Thomas Bahnson III, Susan Walker, Andrew. B.S. in C.E., Va. Mil. Inst., 1946; B.S.C., U. Va., 1948; grad., Advanced Mgmt. Program, Harvard U., 1970. With Stanley Furniture Co., Stanleytown, Va., 1948-79, dir., 1950-79, exec. v.p., 1952-62, pres., 1962-71, chmn., 1971-79; pres. Mead Interiors, Stanleytown, 1969-74; group v.p. Mead Corp., Dayton, Ohio, 1969-74; also dir. Mead Corp.; dir. Piedmont Bankgroup, Inc., Martinsville, Va., Stanley Land & Lumber Co., Drakes Branch, Va.; treas., dir. Hobe Sound (Fla.) Co. Inc., 1989—. Mem. Henry County Sch. Bd., 1957-80; chmn. bd. trustees Ferrum Coll., 1977-79. Mem. So. Furniture Mfrs. Assn. (dir., pres. 1966, chmn. 1967). Methodist. Lodge: Masons (32 deg.). Home: Land's End Hunter's Green Dr Stanleytown VA 24168 Office: PO Box 26 Stanleytown VA 24168-0026

STANLEY, THOMAS EDWARD, publishing company executive; b. Springfield, Ill., June 10, 1948; m. Christine Lloreda, 1989; children: Robert, Laurel, Evan. BS in Econs., MacMurray Coll., 1971. Mgr. ops. Hertzberg New Method, Jacksonville, Ill., 1971-78; dir. sales Bantam Books, N.Y.C., 1978-82, 1978-82; v.p., dir. mktg. Avon Books, Hearst Corp., N.Y.C., 1982-84; exec. v.p. Simon & Schuster, N.Y.C., 1984-89; pres. Stanley & Assocs., N.Y.C., 1989-92; sr. v.p., pub. Merriam-Webster Inc., Springfield, Mass., 1991—. Avocations: coach youth sports, running, reading. Office: Merriam-Webster Inc PO Box 281 47 Federal St Springfield MA 01102

STANLEY, TIMOTHY WADSWORTH, economist; b. Hartford, Conn., Sept. 28, 1927; s. Maurice and Margaret Stowell (Sammond) S.; m. Nadia Leon, June 7, 1952; children: Timothy Wadsworth III, Alessandra Maria, Christopher Maurice, Flavia Margaret. Student, Choate Sch., 1943-45; B.A., Yale, 1950; LL.B., Harvard, 1955, Ph.D., 1957. Bar: Conn. 1956, U.S. Supreme Ct. 1971. Mem. staff Office Sec. Def., 1955; teaching fellow Harvard U., 1955-56; spl. asst. White House staff, 1957-59, spl. asst. to asst. sec. def. for internat. security affairs, 1959-62; vis. research fellow Council on Fgn. Relations, N.Y.C., 1962-63; dir. dir. policy planning staff Office Sec. Def., 1963-64; asst. to sec. def. for NATO force planning, Paris, 1965-67; def. adviser (minister) U.S. Mission to NATO, Paris and Brussels, 1967-69; vis. prof. internat. relations Johns Hopkins Sch. Advanced Internat. Studies, 1969-70; exec. v.p. Internat. Econ. Policy Assn., Washington, 1970-74; pres. Internat. Econ. Policy Assn., 1974-84, chmn., 1984-87; pres. Internat. Econ. Studies Inst., 1974—; profl. lectr. George Washington U., 1957-60; cons. to various govt. agys., univs., bus. orgns., 1969-70; spl. rep. ACDA in negotiations for East-West Mut. Balanced Force Reductions, 1973-74, cons., 1974-80; mem. U.S. Govt. Adv. Com. on Investment, Tech. and Devel., 1974—; mem. Nat. Strategic Materials and Minerals Program Adv. Com., 1984-88. Author: American Defense and National Security, 1955, NATO in Transition, 1965, Detente Diplomacy, 1970; co-author: U.S. Troops in Europe, 1971, The United States Balance of Payments, 1972, Raw Materials and Foreign Policy, 1977, Technology and Economic Development, 1979, U.S. Foreign Economic Strategy for the Eighties, 1982, Mobilizing U.S. Industry: A Vanishing Option for National Security?, 1987, To Unite our Strength: Enhancing the United Nations Peace and Security System, 1992; contbr. articles to profl. jours. Bd. dirs. Atlantic Coun. U.S., UN Assn. U.S., Nat. Capital Area, v.p., 1992—; mem. transition team Pres.-elect George Bush, 1988-89. Served to 1st lt. AUS, 1946-48, 51-52. Recipient Distinguished Civilian Service medal Dept. Def., 1969. Mem. Coun. on Fgn. Rels. N.Y. Inst. for Strategic Studies London, Met. Club. Congregationalist. Home: 3028 O St NW Washington DC 20007-3107 Office: Internat Econ Studies Inst 1064 Papermill Ct NW Washington DC 20007-3619

STANLEY, WILLIAM ROBERT, federal agency official; b. Bklyn., Dec. 22, 1932; s. William and Mabel Christine (Stark) S.; m. Edith Joyce Stafford, July 4, 1956 (div. July 1983); children: Donna Lynne, Susan Carole, Christopher Robert; m. Marian Kasica, Mar. 24, 1984. Student, Upsala Coll. 1951-52; BS, St. Lawrence U., 1955. With credit dept. Chase Manhattan Bank, N.A., N.Y.C., 1956-58, Fedn. Bank and Trust Co., N.Y.C., 1959-62; bank examiner State of N.Y., N.Y.C., 1962-71, sr. bank examiner, 1971-75, prin. bank examiner, 1975-86, supervising bank examiner, 1986-89; sr. trust analyst bd. govs. Fed. Res. System, 1989-94, supervisory trust analyst, 1994—; coordinator employee assistance program State of N.Y., N.Y.C., 1984-86. Vol. fireman Jackson Twp. Vol. Fire Co., N.J., 1965-67. Mem. Fundamental Christian Ch. Avocations: racquetball, swimming, reading, hiking. Home: 9425 Flowerden Ln Manassas VA 22110-6641 Office: Fed Res System Washington DC 20551

STANNERS, CLIFFORD PAUL, molecular biologist, cell biologist, biochemistry educator; b. Sutton, Surrey, Eng., Oct. 19, 1937; married; 3 children. BSc, McMaster U., 1958; MSc, U. Toronto, 1960, PhD, 1963. Fellow molecular biology MIT, Cambridge, Mass., 1962-64; from asst. prof. to prof. med. biophysics U. Toronto, Can., 1964-82; sr. sci. biol. rsch. Ont. (Can.) Cancer Inst., 1964-82; prof. biochemistry McGill U., Montreal, 1982—, dir. McGill Cancer Ctr., 1988—; mem. grants Med. Rsch. Coun. & Nat. Cancer Inst. Can., 1965—, U.S. Nat. Cancer Inst., 1973-79. Assoc. editor Jour. Cell Physiology, 1973-92, Cell, 1975-84. Mem. AAAS, Can. Biochem. Soc., Can. Soc. Cell Biology, Am. Assn. Cancer Rsch. Achievements include rsch. in growth control of animal cells; protein synthesis somatic cell genetics; cell virus interactions; intercellular adhesion molecules; human cancer; human carcinoembryonic antigen cloning and function. Office: McGill U, 3655 Drummond St, Montreal, PQ Canada H3G 1Y6

STANS, MAURICE HUBERT, retired business consultant, former government official; b. Shakopee, Minn., Mar. 22, 1908; s. J. Hubert and Mathilda (Nyssen) S.; m. Kathleen Carmody, Sept. 7, 1933 (dec. Oct. 1984); children: Steven, Maureen, Theodore, Terrell. Student, Northwestern U., 1925-28, Columbia U., 1929-30; LL.D., Ill. Wesleyan U., 1954, Northwestern U., 1960, DePaul U., 1960; D.P.A., Parsons Coll., 1960; LL.D., Grove City Coll., St. Anselm's Coll., 1969, U. San Diego, Gustavus Adolphus Coll., 1970, Pomona Coll., 1971, Maryville Coll., 1971, Rio Grande Coll., 1972, Nat. U. 1979, Pepperdine U., 1984. C.P.A. With Alexander Grant & Co. (C.P.A.'s), Chgo., 1928, exec. ptnr., 1940-55; pres., dir. Moore Corp. (stove mfrs.), Joliet, Ill., 1938-45; dir., mem. exec. com. James Talcott, Inc., N.Y.C., 1941-55; fin. cons. to postmaster gen. U.S., 1953-55, dep. postmaster gen. U.S., 1955-57; dep. dir. U.S. Bur. Budget, 1957-58, dir., 1958-61; pres. Western Bancorp., Los Angeles, 1961-62; also vice chmn. United Calif. Bank; sr. ptnr. William R. Staats & Co., 1963-64; pres. William R. Staats Co., Inc., 1964-65, Glore Forgan, William R. Staats, Inc., N.Y.C., 1965-69; syndicated columnist, 1961-62; sec. of Commerce Washington, 1969-72; Bd. dirs. Uniglobe Travel (Internat.), Vancouver; pres., bd. dirs. Farmont Corp., L.A.; bd. dirs., treas. Electronic Town Hall Meetings, Inc., 1992-93; bd. dirs. chmn. AT&D Inc., 1993—; bus. cons., L.A., 1975-92; chmn., bd. dirs. Weatherby, Inc., 1986-91. Author: The Terrors of Justice, 1978; contbr. numerous articles on govt. fin., fgn. trade and bus. to profl. pubs. Founder, past pres., now chmn. dir. Stans Found., Chgo.; chmn. Nixon Finance Com., 1968, Republican Nat. Finance Com. 1968-69, 72-73, Finance Com. to Re-Elect Pres., 1972-73; fin. chmn., bd. dirs. Nixon Presdl. Library, 1985—; trustee Pomona Coll., 1962-69; bd. dirs. Huntington Med. Rsch. Inst.; bd. dirs. Arnold and Mabel Beckman Found., Irvine, Calif., 1988-92, Eisenhower World Affairs Inst., Washington, 1987—, chmn. 1991-93; chmn.

Minority Enterprise Devel. Adv. Coun., Washington, 1989-91; founding dir. African Wildlife Found., Washington, 1958. Recipient Great Living Am. award U.S. C. of C., 1961, Tax Found. award, 1960, Free Enterprise award Internat. Franchise Assn., 1988; named to Acctg. Hall of Fame, 1968. Mem. NAM (dir. 1968-69), AICPA (pres. 1954-55, Pub. Service award 1954), Ill. Soc. CPAs (dir. 1944-46), D.C. Soc. CPAs (hon.), Hawaii Soc. CPAs (hon.), Am. Acctg. Assn. (nat. Alpha Kappa Psi award 1952), Fed. Govt. Accountants Assn., Nat. Assn. Postmasters (hon.), Iron Molders and Foundry Workers Union (hon.). Clubs: Union League, Adventurers (Chgo.), California (Los Angeles), Athenaeum (Pasadena), Shikar-Safari Club Internat. (founding 1952, trustee internat. found.), Safari Club Internat., East African Profl. Hunters (hon.), Explorers (N.Y.C.), African Safari (Washington, founding bd. dirs. 1957), Jamhuri of Garissa (Kenya) (hon.), Valley Hunt (Pasadena).

STANSBERRY, JAMES WESLEY, air force officer; b. Grafton, W.Va., Dec. 29, 1927; s. William Adrian and Phyllis Gay (Robinson) S.; m. Audrey Mildred Heinz, May 7, 1950; children: Nora G. Fitzpatrick, Amy G. Stansberry Goodhand, Lisa Stansberry De Regis. B.S., U.S. Mil. Acad., 1949; M.B.A., Air Force Inst. Tech., 1956. Advanced through grades from pvt. to lt. gen. USAF; chief prodn. (Kawasaki Gifu Contract Facility), Gifu, Japan, 1956-57; dep. asst. to Sec. of Def. for atomic energy Washington, 1970-71; dep. dir. procurement policy U.S. Air Force, 1972-73; dep. chief staff contracting and mfg. (Hdqrs. Air Force Systems Command), Andrews AFB, Md., 1977-81; comdr. Electronic Systems Div. Hanscom AFB, Mass., 1981-84; pres. Stansberry Assocs. Inc., 1984—. Decorated D.S.M. with oak leaf cluster, Legion of Merit with oak leaf cluster. Methodist. Home: 43 Monadnock Dr Westford MA 01886-3021 The real secrets are enthusiasm, competence and good luck; and it helps immensely to marry a good woman.

STANSBURY, PHILIP ROGER, lawyer; b. Milw., May 7, 1931; s. Carroll and Margaret (Manning) S.; m. Daviette Clagett Hill, Dec. 5, 1959; children: Henry Tayloe, Catherine Contee. AB, Haverford (Pa.) Coll., 1953; JD, Harvard U., 1956. Bar: D.C. 1956, U.S. Ct. Appeals (D.C. crct.) 1956. Assoc. Covington & Burling, Washington, 1958-66, ptnr., 1966—. Contbr. articles to profl. jours. Mem. Southwestern Legal Found. (adv. bd.), Soc. the Cin. Republican. Roman Catholic. Office: Covington & Burling 1201 Pennsylvania Ave NW PO Box 7566 Washington DC 20044

STANSFIELD, CHARLES W., educational administrator; m. Charlene Rivera, Sept. 6, 1989. BA in Spanish, Fla. State U., 1968, MA in Fgn. Lang. Edn., 1969, MS in Teaching English as Second Lang., 1970, PhD in Fgn. and Second Lang. Edn., 1973. Tchr. English, Centro Colombo-Americano, Bogota, Colombia, 1966; 2jr. high sch. tchr. Spanish Fla. State U. Demonstration Sch., 1968-69; instr. Spanish, U. Colo., Boulder, 1970-73, asst. prof., 1973-80, assoc. prof., 1980-81; assoc. program dir. lang. programs Ednl. Testing Svc., Princeton, N.J., 1981-86; dir. fgn. lang. edn. and testing div. Ctr. for Applied Linguistics, Washington, 1986-94, dir. ERIC Clearinghouse Lang. and Linguistics, 1986-94; pres. Second Lang. Testing, Inc., Bethesda, Md., 1993—; dir. Peace Corps Tng. Ctr., Managua, Nicaragua, 1978; mem. exec. com. Joint Nat. Com. on Langs., 1988-93; conf. coord. Interagy. Lang. Roundtable Invitational Symposium on Lang. Aptitude Testing, Rosslyn, Va., 1988; mem. adv. bd. Nat. Fgn. Lang. Resources Ctr., U. Hawaii, 1991-93; numerous presentations at profl. meetings, 1970—. Author: Cuaderno de ejercicios, 1976, rev. edit., 1981; co-author: Manual de laboratorio, 2d rev. edit., 1981, The Test of Spoken English as a Measure of Communicative Ability in the Health Professions.; Validation and Standard Setting, 1983, (with others) Multiple-Choice Cloze Items and the Test of English as a Foreign Language, 1988; co-editor: Second Language Proficiency Assessment: Current Issues, 1988, Language Aptitude Reconsidered, 1990; also numerous articles. Named Outstanding Alumnus Fla. State U., 1994; Colo. Congress Fgn. Lang. Tchrs. scholar, 1981. Mem. Am. Assn. Tchrs. Spanish and Portuguese (life), Am. Coun. on Teaching Fgn. Langs. (Paul Pinsleur award 1984), Am. Ednl. Rsch. Assn., Internat. Assn. Applied Linguistics, Nat. Assn. for Bilingual Edn., Nat. Coun. on Measurement in Edn., Internat. Lang. Testing Assn. (pres. 1992-93), Tchrs. English to Speakers Other Langs., Washington Area Tchrs. English to Speakers Other Langs., Colo. Tchrs. English to Speakers Other Langs. (Gladys Doty award 1987). Home and Office: 10704 Mist Haven Ter Rockville MD 20852

STANSKY, PETER DAVID LYMAN, historian; b. N.Y.C., Jan. 18, 1932; s. Lyman and Ruth (Macow) S. B.A., Yale U., 1953, King's Coll., Cambridge (Eng.) U., 1955; M.A., King's Coll. Cambridge (Eng.) U., 1959; Ph.D., Harvard U., 1961; D.L. (hon.), Wittenburg U., 1984. Teaching fellow history and lit. Harvard U., 1957-61, instr., then asst. prof. history, 1961-68; assoc. prof. history Stanford U., 1968-73, prof., 1973-74, Frances and Charles Field prof., 1974—, chmn. dept. history, 1975-78, 79-82, 89-90, assoc. dean humanities and scis., 1985-88; chmn. publs. com. Conf. Brit. Studies, 1970-78; pres. Pacific Coast Conf. Brit. Studies, 1974-76, N. Am. Conf. Brit. Studies, 1983-85; vis. fellow Wesleyan Center Humanities, Middletown, Conn., 1972, All Soul's Coll., Oxford (Eng.) U., 1979, St. Catherine's Coll. Oxford (Eng.) U., 1983. Author: Ambitions and Strategies, 1964, England Since 1867, 1973, Gladstone, 1979, William Morris, 1983, Redesigning the World, 1985; co-author: Journey to the Frontier, 1966, The Unknown Orwell, 1972, Orwell: The Transformation, 1979, London's Burning, 1994. Guggenheim fellow, 1966-67, 73-74; Am. Council Learned Socs. fellow, 1978-79; NEH fellow, 1983, Royal Hist. Soc. fellow Ctr. for Advanced Study Behavioral Scis., 1988-89. Fellow Am. Acad. Arts and Scis. (coun. 1994—); mem. Am. Hist. Assn. (pres. Pacific Coast br. 1988-89), Conf. on Brit. Studies, Victorian Soc., William Morris Soc., AAUP, Century Assn. Home: 375 Pinehill Rd Hillsborough CA 94010 Office: Stanford U Dept History Stanford CA 94305

STANTON, ALEXANDER, public relations executive; b. N.Y.C., Nov. 29, 1953. BA in Urban Affairs, Hobart Coll. Account exec. Dorf/MJH, 1977, v.p., 1978-79, 79-80, exec. v.p., ptnr., 1981-84; pres. Dorf & Stanton Communications, Inc., N.Y.C., 1984-90, pres., CEO, 1991—; press aide U.S. Senate; press sec./legis. aide various legislators N.Y. Legislature. Mem. Pub. Rels. Soc. Am. (pres.-elect N.Y. chpt.), Young Pres. Orgn. Office: Dorf & Stanton Communications 111 Fifth Ave New York NY 10003-1005

STANTON, DONALD SHELDON, university administrator; b. Balt., June 8, 1932; s. Kenneth Gladstone and Dorothy Erma (Hettrick) S.; m. Barbara Mae Hoot, June 25, 1955; children: Dale Richard, Debra Carol, Diane Karen. AB, Western Md. Coll., 1953, LLD, 1981; MDiv magna cum laude, Wesley Theol. Sem., 1956; MA, Am. U., 1960; Ed.D., U. Va., 1965; L.H.D., Columbia Coll., 1979; Litt.D., Albion Coll., 1983. Ordained to ministry United Methodist Ch., 1956; pastor Balt. and Va. confs. United Meth. Ch., 1953-59; dir. Richmond (Va.) Area Wesley Found., 1959-63; chaplain, dean of students Greensboro Coll., 1963-65; chaplain Wofford Coll., 1965-69; dir. office coll. services United Meth. Div. Higher Edn., Nashville, 1969-75; v.p. for devel. Wesleyan Coll., 1975-78; pres. Adrian Coll., 1978-88, Oglethorpe U., Atlanta, 1988—; administr., prof. European internat. edn. programs, summers 1960, 69-71, 73; chmn., pres. Mich. Intercollegiate Athletic Assn., 1986-87; mem. exec. com. Mich. Colls. Found., 1985-88. Contbr. articles, revs. to profl. publs. in U.S.; Japan and Argentina, chpts. to books; editor: Faculty Forum, 1972-74. Bass-baritone soloist; bd. dirs. Toledo Symphony, 1980-83, Lenawee County Jr. Achievement, 1980-83; chair bd. trustees Univ. Ctr. Ga., 1994—; chair bd. dirs. So. Collegiate Athletic Conf., 1994-95. Adminstrn. bldg. at Adrian Coll. named in honor of Stanton and his wife, 1988. Mem. Assn. Univ. Adminstrs. (bd. dirs. 1990-93), Ga. Assn. Colls. (pres. 1992), Soc. Wesley (Disting. Alumni Recognition award 1988), Ga. Found. for Ind. Colls. and Univs. (past mem. pub. rels. com.), Commerce Club, Rotary, Omicron Delta Kappa, Order of Omega, Tau Kappa Epsilon, Psi Chi, Phi Eta Sigma, Phi Beta Delta. Home: 1571 Windsor Pky NE Atlanta GA 30319-2740 Office: Oglethorpe U Office of Pres 4484 Peachtree Rd NE Atlanta GA 30319-2737

STANTON, EDWARD M., public relations company executive; b. Port Chester, N.Y., Aug. 28, 1921. BJ, Northwestern U., 1943. With Westchester-Rockland Newspapers, N.Y., 1945-47; city editor Women's Wear Daily, 1947-56; pres. Bell & Stanton, Inc., 1956-77, Bell & Stanton, 1956-77, Bell & Stanton div. Manning, Selvage & Lee, Inc., N.Y.C., since 1977; vice chmn. Manning, Selvage & Lee, since 1977, vice chmn./N.Y. gen. mgr. 1981-82, pres., since 1982, pres., chief exec. officer, 1985-87, chmn., chief exec. officer, 1987-91, chmn., 1992. Author textbook on retailing, 1955.

Mem. SDX, ASAE. Office: Manning Selvage & Lee Inc 79 Madison Ave New York NY 10016-7802

STANTON, ERIC, wholesale distribution executive. Co-chmn., sec., CFO, treas. Simon Mktg. Inc., L.A., 1974—. Office: Simon Mktg Inc 1900 Ave of the Stars Ste 400 Los Angeles CA 90067*

STANTON, FRANK, communications executive; b. Muskegon, Mich., Mar. 20, 1908; s. Frank Cooper and Helen Josephine (Schmidt) S.; m. Ruth Stephenson, 1931 (dec. 1992). BA, Ohio Wesleyan U., 1930; PhD, Ohio State U., 1935. Diplomate Am. Bd. Profl. Psychology. With research dept. CBS Inc., N.Y.C., 1935-45, pres., 1946-71, vice chmn., 1971-73, pres. emeritus, 1973—; chmn. The Rand Corp., Broadcast Internat., Inc., 1987-93, Capital Income Builder, Inc., Sony Music Entertainment, Inc., Internat. Herald Tribune (Paris), Interpub. Group of Cos.; dir. Capital World Growth & Income Fund; chmn. U.S. Adv. Commn. Info., Washington, 1964-73. Co-author: The Study of Psychology, 1935, Radio Research, 1941, 42-43; author: International Information, Education and Cultural Relations: Recommendations for the Future, 1975; co-editor Communications Rsch., 1948-49; producer films: some Physiological Reactions to Emotional Stimuli, 1932, Factors in Visual Depth Perception, 1936. Bd. overseers Harvard Coll., 1978-84, chmn. vis. com. Kennedy Sch. Govt., 1979-85; founding mem., chmn. Ctr. for Advanced Study in Behavioral Scis., Stanford, Calif., 1953-60, trustee, 1953-71; chmn. ARC, Washington, 1973-79, vice chmn. League of Red Cross Socs., Geneva, Switzerland, 1973-80; mem. Pres.'s Com. Arts and Humanities, Washington, 1983-90, Nat. Portrait Gallery Commn., Washington, 1973-92, Bus. Coun., Washington, 1956— (hon.); dir. trustee William Benton Found., Bryant Park Restoration Corp., Ednl. Broadcasting Corp. (hon.), Internat. Design Conf. in Aspen, Colo., Lincoln Ctr. Inst., Mus. of TV and Radio, Recorded Anthology Am. Music; emeritus trustee, dir. Lincoln Ctr. for Performing Arts, Rockefeller Found., Carnegie Instn. Washington. Recipient Peabody awards, 1959, 60, 61, 64, 72, Trustees award Nat. Acad. TV Arts and Scis., 1959, 72, Paul White Meml. award Radio and TV News Dirs. Assn., 1957, 71, Spl. Honor award AIA, 1967, Internat. Directorate award Nat. Acad. TV Arts and Scis., 1980, Trustees award Calif. Inst. Arts, 1994; named to TV Acad. Hall of Fame, 1986, Market Rsch. Coun. of N.Y., 1988. Fellow AAAS, Am. Psychol. Assn.; Am. Acad. Arts and Scis., N.Y. Acad. Scis., Century Assn., Harvard Club, Cosmos Club, Rockefeller Ctr. Club, Sigma Delta Chi; mem. Sigma Xi. Office: 25 W 52d St New York NY 10019

STANTON, GEORGE BASIL, JR., engineering executive, chemical engineer, consultant; b. Bklyn., Nov. 3, 1926; s. George B. and Despina Stanton. B in Chem. Engring., Poly. Inst., Bklyn., 1945, M in Chem. Engring., 1948; MBA, NYU, 1971, MA in Safety and Health, 1975. Cert. safety profl., indsl. hygienist. Chief occupational health Dept. Labor State of N.J., 1971-74; cons. engr. N.J., 1974-79; pres. Am. Hazard Control Cons., Inc., Caldwell, N.J., 1979—; adj. prof. N.J. Inst. Tech., 1974-92, Ctr. for Safety NYU, 1977-84; organizer, pres. Essex Fells Fedn. for Ednl. Excellence, Inc., 1994—. Organizer, pres. Essex Falls Found. for Ednl. Excellence, Inc., 1994—. Fellow Royal Soc. Health; mem. ASME (Centennial medal 1980), Am. Soc. Safety Engrs. (award 1980). Office: Am Hazard Control Cons Inc PO Box 231 Caldwell NJ 07006-0231

STANTON, HARRY DEAN, actor; b. Ky., July 14, 1926. Actor: (feature films) Tomahawk Trail, 1957, The Proud Rebel, 1958, Pork Chop Hill, 1959, A Dog's Best Friend, 1959, Cool Hand Luke, 1967, Kelly's Heroes, 1970, Two-Lane Blacktop, 1971, Pat Garrett and Billy the Kid, 1971, Dillinger, 1973, Zandy's Bride, 1974, The Godfather, Part II, 1974, Rancho Deluxe, 1974, Farewell, My Lovely, 1975, The Missouri Breaks, 1976, 92 in the Shade, 1976, Renaldo and Clara, 1977, Straight Time, 1977, The Rose, 1979, Wise Blood, 1979, Alien, 1979, Deathwatch, 1979, The Black Marble, 1980, UFOria, 1980, Private Benjamin, 1980, Escape from New York, 1981, Young Doctors in Love, 1982, One From the Heart, 1982, Tough Enough, 1983, Christine, 1983, Repo Man, 1984, The Bear, 1984, Red Dawn, 1984, Paris, Texas, 1984, One Magic Christmas, 1985, Pretty in Pink, 1986, Food for Love, 1986, The Last Temptation of Christ, 1988, Dream A Little Dream, 1989, Twister, 1989, The Fourth War, 1990, Wild at Heart, 1990, Man Trouble, 1992, Twin Peaks: Fire Walk With Me, 1992; (TV spl.) Faerie Tale Theatre, Showtime, 1987; (TV film) Flatbed Annie and Sweetie Pie: Lady Truckers, 1979, I Want to Live, 1983, Payoff, 1992, Hostages, 1993, Hotel Room, 1993. Mem. Screen Actors Guild. Office: Bresler Kelly Kipperman Ste 1730 15760 Ventura Blvd Encino CA 91436*

STANTON, JAMES ADKINS, technology equipment leasing company executive, consultant; b. Tallahassee, Jan. 24, 1941; s. Charles Newton and Louise (Harris) S.; m. Diane Rae Stovall, June 2, 1962; children: Nancy Rae Stanton Stamm, James Adkins Jr., Suzanne Louise. BS in Math., U. Ala., Tuscaloosa, 1963. Systems analyst Boeing Co., Huntsville, Ala., 1963-68; pres. VEE, Inc., Rosslyn, Va., 1968-70, Psi Tran Corp., Rosslyn, 1973-75, Sci. Mgmt. Systems Co., Landover, Md., 1975-80, Stanton Group, Inc., Herndon, Va., 1984-88; v.p. Computer Data Systems, Bethesda, Md., 1970-73; v.p. cons. Morino Assocs., Inc., Vienna, Va., 1980-84; sr. v.p. adminstrn. Comdisco, Inc., Rosemont, Ill., 1988—; mem. adv. bd. So. Ill. U. Coll. Bus. Adminstrn., Carbondale, 1988—, Pontikes Ctr. for Mgmt. Info., Carbondale, 1988—. Author: Bull Moose School of Modern Management, 1987; also over 30 articles. Mem. Am. Mgmt. Assn., Data Processing Mgmt. Assn., Computer Measurement Group (best mgmt. devel. paper award 1987). Avocations: Ferrari automobiles, vintage racing. Office: Comdisco Inc 6111 N River Rd Rosemont IL 60018

STANTON, JOHN JEFFREY, editor, broadcast journalist, government programs director, analyst; b. Wichita Falls, Tex., July 19, 1956; s. John Joseph Jr. and Joan (Marley) S.; m. Scylla Maria Silva, Jan. 6, 1981; 1 child, Damien Kristian. BS in Pub. Adminstrn. and Bus. Adminstrn., Nichols Coll., 1978; M in Pub. Adminstrn., U. Detroit, 1980. Rsch. asst. Am. Enterprise Inst., Washington, 1977; rep. aide R.I. Ho. of Reps., Providence, 1977-78; mng. editor Am. Politics, Washington, 1982, assoc. editor, 1983, corp. advisor, 1984, sr. editor, 1985-87; editor, govt. programs mgr. ENTEK Alexandria, Va., 1988-90; govt. programs dir., cons. Tuckerman Group, Springfield, Va., 1991; comm. industry writer Arlington, Va., 1991—; program dir. TeleStrategies, McLean, Va., 1991-93; Washington corr., editorial bd. mem. Tech. Transfer Jour., 1994—; editor Tech. Transfer Newsletter; asst. to pres., info. transfer specialist Am. Def. Preparedness Assn., Arlington, 1994—; creator, co-host (radio programs) Power Breakfast, Sta. WNTR, Washington, 1987, Am. Politics Radio, 1987; frequent guest broadcast journalist Stas. WNTR, WAMU-NPR, Washington, WBAL, Balt. and Washington areas. Polit. campaign cons. to Glenn Tenney, 1992—; commr. Arlington Little League Baseball, 1993; mem. Arlington Edn. Adv. Com. Recipient Doers Honoree The Washington Times, 1988. Roman Catholic. Avocations: coaching youth league sports programs.

STANTON, LOUIS LEE, federal judge; b. N.Y.C., Oct. 1, 1927; s. Louis Lee and Helen Parsons (La Fétra) S.; m. Berit Eleonora Rask; children: L. Lee, Susan Helen Benedict, Gordon R., Fredrik S. BA, Yale U., 1950; JD, U. Va., 1955. Assoc. Davis Polk Wardwell Sunderland & Kiendl, N.Y.C., 1955-66; assoc. Carter, Ledyard & Milburn, N.Y.C., 1966-67, ptnr., 1967-85; judge U.S. Dist. Ct. (so. dist.) N.Y., N.Y.C., 1985—. Served to 1st lt. USMCR, 1950-52. Fellow Am. Coll. Trial Lawyers, N.Y. Bar Found.

STANTON, MARSHALL P., academic administrator, clergyman; b. Satanta, Kans., Oct. 15, 1935; s. Vernon and Julia (Beatrice) S.; m. Janice Marie Duryee, Dec. 20, 1956; children: Eric, Kirsten, Nathan. BA, Friends U., 1957, DD, 1986; BD, Asbury Theol. Sem., 1960; ThM, Princeton Theol. Sem., 1961. Ordained minister United Meth. Ch. Pastor United Meth. Ch., Laurel, Ohio, 1958-60, Jewell, Kans., 1961-66, Salina, Kans., 1966-67, Colby, Kans., 1971-78; dist. supt. United Meth. Ch., Hutchinson, Kans., 1978-84; pres. Kans. Wesleyan U., Salina, 1984—, also bd. dirs. Bd. dirs. Southwestern Coll., Winfield, Kans., 1978-84. Mem. Kans. Ind. Coll. Assn. (chmn. bd. dirs. 1989-90), Assoc. Colls. Cen. Kans. (chmn. bd. dirs. 1988-89), Ministerial Assn. (pres. Salina chpt. 1969-70, pres. Colby chpt. 1973-74), Salina C. of C. (bd. dirs. 1986-90), Rotary. Avocations: jogging, bicycling, radio-control model aircraft. Home: 151 Aspen Rd Salina KS 67401-3609 Office: Kans Wesleyan U Office of Pres 100 E Claflin Ave Salina KS 67401-6196

STANTON, MICHAEL, architectural firm executive. BA, Yale Coll., 1970, MArch., 1973. Arch. Daniel Mann Johnson Mendenhall, Balt., 1973, Brook Caruthers Shaw, Toronto, Ont., Can., 1973-74, Bull Field Volkmann Stockwell, San Francisco, 1976-82, Stanton & Assocs. Archs., San Francisco, 1983—; bd. dirs. Am. Archtl. Found., Calif. Archtl. Found., Archtl. Found. No. Calif.; mem. select pub. rels. task force Calif. Bd. Archtl. Examiners, 1986. Prin. works include Hills Plaza Luxury Condominiums, San Francisco, Fillmore Marketplace, San Francisco, Oak Grove Apts., Novato, Calif., Park Dolores Townhouses, San Francisco, Ford's Dept. Store, Watsonville, Calif., Moss Landing (Calif.) Marina Village, Ellinwood Shopping Ctr., Pleasant Hill, Calif., Portland (Oreg.) Hilton Remodel, Kaufman's Deli, San Francisco, Potter Electric Bldg., San Francisco; contbr. on urban design and archtl. issues to profl. jours. Bd. dirs. Assn. Retarded Citizens, 1988—. Recipient Award of Merit, Pacific Coast Builder's Conf., 1991, 93, Watsonville C. of C. Commendation, 1990, Award of Merit, Minn. House and Home mag., Designer's Choice award Indsl. Design mag., Cert. of Merit (2) Graphic Arts Award Competition; Annie G.K. Garland fellow Yale U., 1972-73. Fellow AIA (vice-chmn. urban design com. 1989-92, bd. dirs. 1992—, Presdl. Citation 1989, Citation for Excellence in Urban Design, 1988, 90, WAID scholar 1972-73, chmn. editl. bd. Bay Arch.'s Rev. San Francisco chpt. 1980—, chmn. urban design com. San Francisco chpt. 1984-86, pres. San Francisco chpt. 1991); mem. Am. Inst. Archs. (Calif. coun., v.p. govt. affairs 1988-89, pres. 1991), Urban Land Inst. Office: Stanton & Assocs 100 Spear St Ste 939 San Francisco CA 94105

STANTON, MICHAEL JOHN, newspaper editor; b. New Britain, Conn., Mar. 30, 1944; s. John Martin and Helen (McNally) S.; m. Barbara Ann Mucha, Aug. 27, 1966; 1 child, Sean. A.B. in English, Holy Cross Coll. 1966. Reporter, editor Providence (R.I.) Jour., 1968-72; press sec. Gov. R.I. Providence, 1972-77; asst. news editor St. Louis Globe-Dem., 1977-81; news copy desk chief Detroit Free Press, 1981-83, exec. news editor, 1983-85, asst. to exec. editor, 1985-86; exec. news editor Seattle Times, 1986—. Office: The Seattle Times PO Box 70 Fairview Ave N & John St Seattle WA 98111

STANTON, PATRICK MICHAEL, lawyer; b. Phila., Sept. 8, 1947; s. Edward Joseph and Helen Marie (Coghlan) S.; m. Kathleen Ann Fama, Aug. 22, 1970; children: Cheryl Marie, Susan Elizabeth. BS in History, St. Joseph's U., 1969; JD, U. Va., 1972; MBA, Fairleigh Dickinson, 1984. Bar: Ohio 1972, U.S. Dist. Ct. (so. dist.) Ohio 1972, N.J. 1982, U.S. Dist. Ct. N.J. 1982, N.Y. 1984. Assoc. Taft, Stettinius & Hollister, Cin., 1972-80; labor counsel Union Camp Corp., Wayne, N.J., 1980-83; dir. labor relations, equal employment oppurtunity programs W.R. Grace & Co., N.Y.C., 1983-86; of counsel Shanley & Fisher, P.C., Morristown, N.J., 1986-89, ptnr., chmn. labor and employment group, 1989-95; Stanton, Hughes, Diana & Zucker, P.C., Florham Park, N.J., 1995—; adj. prof. bus. law Fairleigh Dickinson Univ.; exec. dir. Sidney Reitman employment law Am. Inn. Ct., 1993—. Pres., bd. dirs N.Y. State Adv. Coun. on Employment Law, Inc., N.Y.C., 1985-86. DuPont scholar U. Va., 1970. Mem. ABA, N.J. State Bar Assn. (exec. com. labor employment law sect. 1989—, rec. sec. 1995—), Phi Alpha Theta, Delta Mu Delta. Roman Catholic. Home: 292 Forest Ave Glen Ridge NJ 07028-1808 Office: Stanton Hughes Diana & Zucker PC 30A Vreeland Rd Ste 340 Florham Park NJ 07932

STANTON, ROBERT, historic site director. Regional dir. Ford's Theatre (Lincoln Museum) Frederick Douglas National Historic Site, and The Old Stone House, Washington, D.C. Office: Fords Theatre Lincoln Mus 511 10th St NW Washington DC 20004-1402 also: Frederick Douglass Nat Hist Site care Nat Parks-E 1900 Anacostia Dr SE Washington DC 20020-6722 also: Old Stone Ho 3051 M St NW Washington DC 20007-3702*

STANTON, ROBERT JAMES, JR., geologist, educator; b. Los Angeles, June 17, 1931; s. Robert James and Audrey (Franke) S.; m. Patricia Ann Burns, Sept. 13, 1953; children—John, Carol. B.S., Calif. Inst. Tech., 1953; Ph.D., 1960; M.A., Harvard U., 1956. Research geologist Shell Devel. Co., Houston, 1959-67; mem. faculty Tex. A&M U., 1967—, prof. geology, 1972-86, V.C. Fish prof. geology, 1986—, head dept., 1979-83; vis. prof. U. Nuremburg-Erlangen, Germany, 1984. Co-author: Paleoecology: Principles and Applications, 1981, 2d edit., 1990. Served with AUS, 1953-55. Fellow Geol. Soc. Am.; mem. Internat. Paleontol. Union, Paleontol. Soc., Paleontol. Research Inst., Soc. Econ. Paleontologists and Mineralogists (Outstanding Paper award 1970), Sigma Xi, Tau Beta Pi. Republican. Presbyterian. Home: 3609 Sunnybrook Ln Bryan TX 77802-3922 Office: Tex A&M U Dept Geology College Station TX 77843

STANTON, ROBERT JOHN, corporate bank executive, lawyer; b. Coffeyville, Kans., Jan. 25, 1913; s. William P. and LaVeta (Reilly) S.; m. Mary Locke, June 4, 1938; children: Robert John Jr., James Locke, William Clark. AB, U. Okla., 1935, LLB, 1937. Bar: Okla. 1937. Assoc. firm mem. Martin, Logan, Finney, Stanton and Moyers, Tulsa, Okla., 1937-54; gen. counsel, sr. v.p., dir. Amerada Petroleum Corp., Tulsa, N.Y.C., 1954-69; sr. v.p., dir. Amerada Hess Corp., N.Y.C., 1969-71; chmn. exec. com. First Nat. Bank and Trust, Co., Tulsa, 1971-79; rsch. fellow Southwestern Legal Found. Chmn. William K. Warren Found., Tulsa, 1973-91. Capt. (JAGD) U.S. Army, 1944-46. Mem. ABA, Okla. Bar Assn., Order of Coif, Phi Beta Kappa. Republican. Roman Catholic.

STANTON, ROGER D., lawyer; b. Waterville, Kans., Oct. 4, 1938; s. George W. and Helen V. (Peterson) S.; m. Judith L. Duncan, Jan. 27, 1962; children: Jeffrey B., Brady D., Todd A. AB, U. Kans., 1960, JD, 1963. Bar: Kans. 1963, U.S. Dist. Ct. Kans. 1963, U.S. Ct. Appeals (10th cir.) 1972, U.S. Supreme Ct. 1973. Assoc. Stanley, Schroeder, Weeks, Thomas & Lysaught, Kansas City, Kans., 1963-68; ptnr. Weeks, Thomas, Lysaught, Bingham & Johnston, Kansas City, 1968-72, Weeks, Thomas & Lysaught, 1969-80, also bd. dirs., chmn. exec. com., 1981-82, Stinson, Mag & Fizzell, 1983—; chmn. products practice group, also bd. dirs. Active Boy Scouts Am., 1973-79; pres. YMCA Youth Football Club, 1980-82; co-chmn. Civil Justice Reform Act com. Dist. of Kans., 1991-95. Fellow Am. Coll. Trial Lawyers (state chmn. 1984-86); mem. Internat. Assn. Def. Counsel, Am. Bd. Trial Adv., Def. Rsch. Inst. (state co-chmn. 1979-90, Exceptional Performance award 1979), Kans. Bar Assn. (Pres.'s award 1982), Johnson County Bar Found. (trustee), Kans. Def. Counsel (pres. 1977-78), Kans. Inn. Ct., U. Kans. Sch. Law Alumni Assn. (bd. dirs. 1972-75). Chmn. bd. editors Jour. Kans. Bar Assn., 1975-83; contbr. articles to legal jours. Office: Stinson Mag & Fizzell The Mast Bldg 7500 W 110th St Overland Park KS 66210

STANTON, RONALD P., export company executive. Chmn. Transammonia, Inc., N.Y.C. Office: Transammonia Inc 350 Park Ave New York NY 10022-6022

STANTON, THOMAS MITCHELL, lawyer, educator; b. Vicksburg, Miss., Sept. 30, 1922; s. John Francis and Hazel Florence (Mitchell) S.; m. Jean Aldrich Herron, Oct. 31, 1953; children: Lucinda S. Duddy, Amy S. Conklin, Thomas Herron. BS, Harvard U., 1943, JD, 1948. Bar: Ohio 1949, Wis. 1962. Pvt. practice law Cin., 1949-56; corp. atty. Kroger Co., Cin., 1957-61; with Kimberly-Clark Corp., Neenah, Wis., 1962-86; v.p., gen. counsel Kimberly-Clark Corp., Neenah, 1971-84, v.p., internat. counsel, 1985-86; ret. Kimberly-Clark Corp., 1986; lectr. litigation decision analysis Boston U., Northwestern U. Law Sch. U. Wis. etc., 1986—; of counsel Reinhart, Boerner, Van Deuren, Norris & Rieselbach, 1987—; v.p., sec., bd. dirs Tango, Inc.; pres., dir. Dataphon Co. of S.C. Trustee Friends of Bronze Age Archeology in the Aegean Area. Capt. AUS, 1943-46. Mem. ABA, Wis. Bar Assn. (bd. dirs. internat. practice sect.), Am. Corp. Counsel Assn. (internat. legal affairs com.), North Shore Golf Club, Univ. Club. Home: 390 Park St Menasha WI 54952-3428 Office: 101 W Canal St Ste 25 Neenah WI 54956-3045

STANTON, WALTER OLIVER, electronics company executive; b. Canton, Ohio, Sept. 29, 1914; s. Bela Hayden and Edna (Keckeley) S.; Elec. Engring., Wayne State U.; m. Mary Ann Wilcox; children—Sharon (Mrs. Robert Russell), Diana (Mrs. Grant Thornbrough), Pamela Stanton (Mrs. John O'Donnell). Pres. Pickering & Co., Inc., 1948—; Stanton Magnetics, Inc., 1966—, Pickering Impex S.A., switzerland, Stanton Impex S.A. Fellow Audio Engring. Soc. (pres. 1957); mem. Inst. Dirs. (London), Chief Exec.'s Forum. Home: 12860 Marsh Lndg Palm Beach Gardens FL 33418-7524 Office: Sunnyside Blvd Plainview NY 11803

STANTON, WILLIAM JOHN, JR., marketing educator, author; b. Chgo., Dec. 15, 1919; s. William John and Winifred (McGann) S.; m. Imma Mair, Sept. 14, 1978; children by previous marriage: Kathleen Louise, William John III. BS, Ill. Inst. Tech., 1940; MBA, Northwestern U., 1941, PhD, 1948. Mgmt. trainee Sears Roebuck & Co., 1940-41; instr. U. Ala., 1941-44; auditor Olan Mills Portrait Studios, Chattanooga, 1944-46; asst. prof., assoc. prof. U. Wash., 1948-55; prof. U. Colo., Boulder, 1955-90; prof. emeritus, 1990—; head mktg. dept. U. Colo., 1955-71, acting dean, 1963-64; assoc. dean U. Colo. (Sch. Bus.), 1964-67; vis. prof. summers U. Utah, 1946, 49, U. Calif., Berkeley, 1950, UCLA, 1957; mktg. cons. to various bus. firms and govt. agys., 1950—; lectr. univs. Austria, India, Mex., New Zealand; mem. faculty exec. devel. programs sponsored by Sales and Mktg. Execs. Internat. and by Advanced Mgmt. Rsch., 1963-71. Author: Economic Aspects of Recreation in Alaska, 1953; (with Richard H. Buskirk and Rosann Spiro) Management of a Sales Force, 9th edit., 1995 (also Spanish transl.); (with others) Challenge of Business, 1975; (with M. Etzel and B. Walker) Fundamentals of Marketing, 10th edit., 1994 (also Spanish, Portuguese and Indonesian transls.); (with M.S. Sommers and J.G. Barnes) Can. edit. Fundamentals of Marketing, 6th edit., 1992, (with K. Miller and R. Layton) Australian edit., 3d edit., 1994, (with R. Varaldo) Italian edit., 2d edit., 1990, (with others) South African edit., 1992; monographs on Alaska Tourist Industry, 1953-54; contbr. articles to profl. jours. Mem. Am., So., Southwestern, Western mktg. assns., Beta Gamma Sigma. Roman Catholic. Home: 1445 Sierra Dr Boulder CO 80302-7846

STANTON-HICKS, MICHAEL D'ARCY, anesthesiologist, educator; b. Adelaide, Australia, June 3, 1931; came to U.S., 1972; s. Cedric Stanton-Hicks and Florence (Haggett) Perrin; m. Kristina Lismarck, Aug. 4, 1969 (div. Aug. 1984); children: Erik Michael, Leif Neal; m. Ursula Koch, Aug. 27, 1985. MB, BS, Adelaide U., 1962; Dr. of medicine, U. Dusseldorf, 1984. Bd. equivalent Am. Bd. Anesthesiology, Am. Bd. Pain Medicine. Intern Queen Elizabeth Hosp., Adelaide, 1961-62, tutor, staff anesthesiologist, 1970-72; resident Royal Postgrad. Med. Sch., London and Lasarettet Köping, 1966-68; asst. dir. anesthesiology intensive care Södersjükhuset, Stockholm, 1968-69; instr. anesthesiology U. Wash. Med. Sch., Seattle, 1969-70, asst. prof., 1972-75; prof., chmn. dept. U. Mass. Med. Sch., Worcester, 1975-83; acting chmn., 1985-86; prof., dir. pain clinic and rsch. Johannes Gutenberg U., Mainz, Fed. Republic Germany, 1986-88, prof., 1986—; dir. pain mgmt. ctr. Cleve. Clinic Found., 1988—. Author, editor: Regional Anesthesia: Advances and Selected Topics, 1978, (with Boas) Chronic Low Back Pain, 1982; author: (with Raj and Nolte) Illustrated Manual of Regional Anesthesia, 1988 (Most Beautiful Book of Yr. award Frankfurt, Fed. Republic Germany Pubs. Book Conv. 1989), Pain and Sympathetic Nervous System, 1989, (with Janig and Boas) Reflex Sympathetic Dystrophy, 1989. Flight lt., squadron leader res. Royal Australian Air Force, 1962-65. Australian Univs. Commn. mature age scholar, 1953-60. Fellow Royal Coll. Surgeons (faculty anaesthetists), Royal Coll. Anesthetists, Am. Coll. Pain Medicine; mem. Internat. Assn. Study Pain (chmn. spl. interest group on sympathetically maintained pain 1990—), Am. Soc. Regional Anesthesia (bd. dirs. 1979-91, pres. 1989-90), Am. Soc. Anesthesiologists, Assn. Anesthetists Gt. Britain and Ireland, Ohio State Med. Assn., Cleve. Acad. Medicine, Am. Acad. Med. Infrared Imaging (bd. dirs. 1991—, pres. 1994-95), Am. Pain Soc., Am. Acad. Pain Medicine, Am. Neuromodulation Soc. (pres. 1994—), Army-Navy-Air Force Club. Republican. Anglican. Avocations: skiing, photography, travel, flying. Home: 198 Woodsong Way Chagrin Falls OH 44023-6703 Office: Cleve Clinic Found 9500 Euclid Ave Cleveland OH 44195-0001

STANWAY, PAUL WILLIAM, newspaper editor; b. Manchester, Eng., Apr. 22, 1950; arrived in Canada, 1976; s. William and Gladys (Wright) S.; m. Erina Danyluk, May 5, 1976; children: Scott, Nicole. Reporter Nottingham (Eng.) Post, 1969-72, Express and Star, Wolverhampton, Eng., 1972-76, Free Press, Winnipeg, Can., 1976-77; city editor Edmonton (Can.) Sun, 1978-80, news editor, 1980-81, mng. editor, 1981-84, assoc. editor, columnist, 1988-90; editor Calgary (Can.) Sun, 1988-90; European bureau chief Toronto Sun Pub., London, 1990-92; editor-in-chief Edmonton Sun, 1992—. Avocations: skiing, golf, fishing, travel. Office: The Edmonton Sun, 4990 - 92 Ave, Edmonton, AB Canada T6B 3A1

STANWICK, TAD, systems engineering and business management executive; b. Severn, Md., May 4, 1916; s. Walter L. and Mary Ann (Pfeiffer); m. Wickliffe Shackleford, Dec. 16, 1941; children: Covington Philip, Wickliffe Mary, Welb Thomas. Student, St. John's Coll., Annapolis, Md., 1935, U.S. Naval Acad., 1936. Asst. to pres. and chmn. bd. Am. Machine & Foundry Co., N.Y.C., 1952-55, v.p., 1955-57; v.p., dir. Cleve. Pneumatic Industries, Inc., 1957-62; pres. Pneumo Dynamics Corp., 1959-62; pres., chmn. bd. Stanwick Corp., 1962-92. Author: Lacrosse, 1939. Bd. dirs. U.S. Bus. and Indsl. Council. Served as comdr. USNR, 1940-53. Mem. Philos. Soc. Washington, Soc. Naval Architects and Marine Engrs., Internat. Oceanographic Found., Def. Orientation Conf. Assn., Internat. Christian Union Bus. Execs., Metaphys. Soc. Am., IEEE, Philos. Soc. Am., Holy Name Soc., Phi Sigma Kappa. Clubs: U.S. Yacht Racing Union, Chesapeake Bay Yacht Racing Assn, Annapolis Yacht, CIMAV Yacht, Army and Navy. Home: 4715 Upton St NW Washington DC 20016-2369 Office: 1800 K St NW Washington DC 20006-2202

STANZLER, JORDAN, lawyer. AB, Harvard U., 1967; JD, U. Chgo., 1972; LLM in Taxation, NYU, 1987. Bar: Calif. 1972, N.Y. 1981. Asst. U.S. atty. So. Dist. N.Y., 1982-88, chief tax unit, 1987-88; ptnr. Anderson Kill Olick & Oshinsky, San Francisco, 1988—; lectr. ins. coverage matters. Contbr. articles to profl. jours. Office: Anderson Kill Olick & Oshinsky CT Corp Ctr 1 Sansome St San Francisco CA 94104

STAPH, JACK A., corporate lawyer; b. 1945. BSBA, Youngstown State U., 1967; JD, Cleve. State U., 1973. Bar: Ohio 1973. Ins. mgr. Revco D.S. Inc., Twinsburg, Ohio, 1972-73, asst. sec., corr. counsel, 1974-86, v.p., gen. counsel, sec., 1986-87, v.p., sec., gen. counsel, 1987—; sec. Hook-Superx Inc., Twinsburg, Hook's Drug Stores, Twinsburg, Revco Discount Drug Ctrs., Twinsburg, Superx Drug Stores, Twinsburg. Office: Revco D S Inc 1925 Enterprise Pky Twinsburg OH 44087*

STAPLES, DANNY LEW, state senator; b. Eminence, Mo., Apr. 1, 1935; s. Harvey R. and Edna O. (Smith) S.; m. Barbara Ann Salisbury, 1966; children: Jeannine Shaffer Spurgin, Janet Shaffer, Robin Staples, Joe Shaffer, Richard Staples. Student Southwest Mo. State U., 1952-54, Ark. State U., 1954. Mem. Mo. State Ho. of Reps., 1977-82, Mo. State Senate, Dist. 20, 1983—. Democrat. Methodist. Mem. Sigma Pi. Office: Rte 3 Box 18 Eminence MO 65466 also: State Senate State Capitol Jefferson City MO 65101

STAPLES, JAMES G., lawyer; b. Grand Rapids, Mich., Feb. 14, 1931. BSME, Purdue U., 1953; LLB, U. Mich., 1956. Bar: D.C. 1956, Mich. 1957, Ill. 1957. Ptnr. Baker & McKenzie, Chgo. Office: Baker & McKenzie 1 Prudential Plz 130 E Randolph St Chicago IL 60601

STAPLES, O. SHERWIN, orthopaedic surgeon; b. Boston, May 19, 1908; s. Oscar S. and Nellie E. (Barnes) S.; m. Mable Hughes, Dec. 11, 1945; children—Katherine E., Thomas H. A.B., Harvard, 1930, M.D., 1935. Diplomate: Am. Bd. Orthopaedic Surgery (examiner 1964-69). Intern Boston City Hosp., 1935-37; resident Mass. Gen., Children's hosps., Boston, 1937-39; asst. orthopaedic surgery (Mass. Gen. Hosp.), 1939-46; asst. orthopaedic surgeon New Eng. Peabody Home Crippled Children, 1939-46; chmn. orthopaedic surgery sect. Hitchcock Clinic and Mary Hitchcock Meml. Hosp., 1946-73; cons. VA Hosp., White River Junction, Vt., 1947-73, chief, orthopedic sect., 1973-81, cons. orthopedics, 1981-92; asst. orthopaedic surgery Harvard Med. Sch., 1939-46; mem. faculty, chmn. orthopaedic sect. Dartmouth Med. Sch., 1946-73, clin. prof. surgery, 1967-73, emeritus, 1973—. Assoc. editor: Jour. Bone and Joint Surgery, 1961-67; Contbr. articles to med. jours. Served from capt. to lt. col. M.C. AUS, 1942-45, MTO. Mem. Aesculapian Club, N.H. Med. Soc., Grafton County Med. Soc. (pres. 1963), Boylston Med. Soc., Boston Orthopaedic Club (pres. 1960-61), Am. Acad. Orthopaedic Surgeons, A.C.S., Am. Orthopaedic Assn., New Eng. Surg. Soc., Soc. Internat. de Chirurgie Orthopédique et de Traumatologie, Am. Orthopaedic Foot Soc. (founding), Assn. Orthopaedic Chmn. (founding). Home: Hemlock Rd Hanover NH 03755

STAPLES, RICHARD CROMWELL, microbiologist, researcher; b. Hinsdale, Ill., Jan. 29, 1926; s. George Allen and Ruth Larken (Maxted) S.; children: Cynthia, Laura, Robert. BS, Colo. State U., 1950; AM, Columbia U., 1954, PhD, 1957. Asst. plant biochemist Boyce Thompson Inst., Yonkers, N.Y., 1957-61, plant biochemist, 1962-66, program dir. plant stress, 1966-76; program dir. plant stress Boyce Thompson Inst. Cornell U., Ithaca, N.Y., 1977-88, G.L. McNew scientist, 1988-92, G.L. McNew scientist emeritus, 1993-; adj. prof. plant pathology Cornell U., Ithaca, 1968-. Editor: Stress Physiology of Crop Plants, 1979, Linking Research to Crop Production, 1980, Plant Disease Control, 1981; editor FEMS Microbiology Letters, 1994-; contbr. more than 140 articles to profl. jours. Alexander von Humboldt Stiftung Sr. Scientist award, Bonn, 1981, Ruth Allen award, 1994. Fellow Am. Phytopathol. Soc.; mem. Phi Kappa Phi, Beta Beta Beta, Gamma Sigma Delta. Avocations: birding, hunting. Office: Cornell Univ Boyce Thompson Inst of Plant Res 207 Klinewoods Rd Ithaca NY 14850

STAPLES, RICHARD FARNSWORTH, lawyer; b. Providence, Nov. 24, 1919; s. Harold E. and Margaret (Smith) S.; m. Mary Kingsbury, June 20, 1942; children: Richard Farnsworth, Jr., Benjamin T., Edward K. A.B., Harvard U., 1941, LL.B., 1949. Bar: R.I. 1949. Ptnr. Tillinghast, Collins & Graham, Providence, 1949-81; ptnr. Hinckley, Allen & Snyder, Providence, 1981-87, of counsel, 1987-; mem. commn. on jud. tenure and discipline, 1987-93. Chmn. sch. com. Town of Barrington (R.I.), 1956-62, mem., 1957-62; mem. State Bd. Edn., Providence, 1964-69, chmn., 1968-69; pres. R.I. Hist. Soc., 1981-83. Served to 1st lt. U.S. Army, 1943-46. Decorated Bronze Star. Mem. ABA, R.I. Bar Assn., Soc. of Colonial Wars, Turks Head Club, Providence Art Club, Harvard Club. Home: 180 Slater Ave Providence RI 02906-5723 also: Loon Lake Rd Freedom NH 03836-0298

STAPLETON, HARVEY JAMES, physics educator; b. Kalamazoo, Dec. 22, 1934; s. Herbert James and Viola Delia (Early) S.; m. Joan Ellleen Sylvander, June 22, 1957; children: Patricia Lynne, Susan Joan, Jeffrey Denis. B.S., U. Mich., 1957; Ph.D., U. Calif., Berkeley, 1961. Faculty physics U. Ill., Urbana, 1961-; prof. U. Ill., 1969-, assoc. dean Grad. Coll., 1980-, assoc. vice chancellor for rsch., 1987-, interim dean, 1992, interim vice chancellor for rsch., 1992; Alfred P. Sloan fellow, 1962-64. Contbr. articles to profl. jours. Fellow Am. Phys. Soc.; mem. Phi Beta Kappa, Sigma Xi, Phi Sigma Kappa, Phi Kappa Phi, Phi Eta Sigma. Roman Catholic. Home: 305 Elmwood Dr Champaign IL 61821-3217 Office: U Ill 601 E John St Champaign IL 61820-5711

STAPLETON, JAMES FRANCIS, lawyer; b. Bridgeport, Conn., June 30, 1932; s. James M. and Lucy V. (Moran) S.; m. Margaret M. Daly, July 13, 1957; children: James F., Mark T., Paul and Kathleen. BSS, Fairfield U., 1954; LLB, Boston U., 1957; LLM, Georgetown U., 1958. Bar: Conn. 1957, U.S. Dist. Ct. (ea. and so. dists.) N.Y. 1959, U.S. Ct. Appeals (2d cir.) 1966, U.S. Dist. Ct. Conn. 1961, Mass. 1957, U.S. Supreme Ct. 1965, U.S. Ct. Appeals, (D.C. cir.) 1958. Atty., Appellate Sect., Antitrust Div., U.S. Dept. Justice, 1957-58; assoc., ptnr. Marsh, Day & Calhoun, Bridgeport, Conn., 1958-73; city atty. City of Bridgeport, 1971-73; legis. counsel Conn. Bankers Assn., 1971-73; judge Conn. Superior Ct., 1973-78; chmn. Criminal Justice Commn., State of Conn., 1991-; ptnr. Day, Berry & Howard, Stamford, Conn., 1978-. Mem. Bridgeport Bd. Edn., 1960-69. Fellow Am. Bar Found., Am. Coll. Trial Lawyers (chmn. state com. 1994-); mem. Conn. Bar Assn. (bd. govs., ho. of dels., v.p., pres.), Fed. Bar Council for 2d Circuit (vice-chmn.), ABA, Bridgeport Bar Assn., Stamford-Darien Bar Assn. Home: 225 Winton Rd Fairfield CT 06430-3858 Office: Day Berry & Howard One Canterbury Green Stamford CT 06901

STAPLETON, JAMES HALL, statistician, educator; b. Royal Oak, Mich., Feb. 8, 1931; s. James Leo and Dorothy May (Hall) S.; m. Alicia M. Brown, Apr. 3, 1963; children: James, Lara, Sara. B.A., Eastern Mich. U., 1952; M.S., Purdue U., 1954, Ph.D., 1957. Statistician Gen. Electric Co., 1957-58; asst. prof. stats. and probability Mich. U. East Lansing, 1958-63; assoc. prof. Mich. State U., 1963-72, prof., 1972-, chmn. dept., 1968-75; cons. Gen. Telephone Co. of Ind.; vis. prof. U. Philippines, 1978-79. Mem. USS-Mich. Swim Club, AAU, 1976-84, chmn., 1976-78; mem. Mich. AAU Exec. Bd., 1976-81. NSF fellow, 1966-67. Mem. Inst. Math. Stats., Am. Stats. Assn. (pres. Mid-Mich. chpt. 1987-89). Office: Mich State U Dept Statistics East Lansing MI 48823

STAPLETON, JEAN (JEANNE MURRAY), actress; b. N.Y.C.; d. Joseph E. and Marie (Stapleton) Murray; m. William H. Putch (dec.); 2 children. Student, Hunter Coll., N.Y.C., Am. Apprentice Theatre, Am. Actors Co., Am. Theatre Wing; student with Harold Clurman, LHD (hon.), Emerson Coll.; hon. degree, Hood Coll., Monmouth Coll. Career debut in Candide with Balt. Opera Co.; appeared in The Italian Lesson with Balt. Opera; first N.Y. stage role in The Corn is Green, Equity Library Theatre; starred as mother in Am. Gothic, Circle-in-the-Sq.; Broadway debut with Judith Anderson In The Summer House; also appeared on Broadway in Damn Yankees, Bells Are Ringing, Juno, Rhinoceros and Funny Girl; first major break in comic ingenue role as Myrtle Mae with Frank Fay in Harvey on-tour; played with nat. tour of Come Back, Little Sheba starring Shirley Booth; starred in tour of Morning's at Seven, The Show-Off, Daisy Mayme; appeared in motion pictures including Damn Yankees, 1958, Bells Are Ringin, 1960, Up the Down Staircase, 1967, Cold Turkey, 1971, The Buddy System, 1984, Klute; appeared in numerous TV shows including Studio One, Naked City, Armstrong Circle Theater, The Defenders, Jackie Gleason Show, PBS-TV appearances Grown-ups, Trying Times, The Boss, cable TV appearances Let Me Hear You Whisper, Mother Goose Rock and Rhyme, Faerie Tale Theatre: Cinderella and Jack & The Beanstalk, The Habitation of Dragons, Fee Fi Fo Fum, Mrs. Piggle-Wiggle; starred in the title role of Aunt Mary on Hallmark Hall of Fame, 1979; most famous TV role as Edith Bunker on All In The Family, 1971-79; TV films include Dead Man's Folly, Tail Gunner Joe, 1977, Isabel's Choice, 1981, Angel Dusted, 1981, Eleanor: First Lady of the World, 1982 (Emmy nomination), A Matter of Sex, Grown-Ups, Fire In The Dark, 1991 (CBS-TV), The Parallax Garden, 1993, Ghost Mom, 1993; appeared the Totem Pole Playhouse, Fayetteville, Pa., starred at Kennedy Ctr. in Daisy Mayme, 1978, The Late Christopher Bean, 1982, Bon Appetit; appeared on Broadway in Arsenic and Old Lace (also nat. tour), 1986; mem. nat. tour. co. Drood, 1986, The Birthday Party, 1989, Mountain Language, 1989 (Obie award); in CBS-TV series Bagdad Cafe, 1990, L.A. Opera's Oklahoma, 1990, The Learned Ladies (by Moliere), 1990, Bon Appetit & The Italian Lesson, 1991 (CSC Repertory), (Off-Broadway) The Road to Home U. Va. and N.Y., 1992, Night Seasons, 1993, Bon Appetit (San Francisco), The Learned Ladies (ACT San Francisco), Mrs. Piggle-Wiggle (Showtime), 1994, Romeo and Juliet, The Shakespere Co. D.C., 1994, Night Seasons, Signature Theatre N.Y., 1994, Blithe Spirit, Costa Mesa, Calif. U.S. commr. to Internat. Woman's Yr. Commn. and Nat. Conf. Women, Houston, 1977; bd. dirs. Women's Rsch. and Edn. Inst.; trustee Actors' Fund Am. Recipient Emmy award for best performance in comedy series 1970-71, 71-72, 78, Golden Globe awards Hollywood Fgn. Press Assn. 1972, 73, Obie award, 1990. Mem. AFTRA, SAG, Actors Equity Assn. Office: care Bauman & Hiller 5757 Wilshire Blvd Los Angeles CA 90036-3697

STAPLETON, JEAN, think-tank executive. Pres. Woman's Rsch. and Edn. Inst., Wash., D.C. Office: Women's Rsch and Edn Inst 1700 18th St NW Ste 400 Washington DC 20009

STAPLETON, KATHARINE LAURENCE, English educator, writer; b. Holyoke, Mass., Nov. 20, 1911; d. Richard Prout and Frances (Purtill) S. A.B., Smith Coll., 1932; postgrad., U. London, Eng., 1932-33. Registrar Mass. Pub. Employment Service, 1933-34; faculty Bryn Mawr Coll., 1934-; prof. English and polit. theory, 1948-64, chmn. dept. English, 1954-65, Mary E. Garrett prof. English, 1964-80, prof. emeritus, 1980-. Author: Justice and World Society, 1944, The Design of Democracy, 1949, H.D. Thoreau: A Writer's Journal, 1960, Yushin's Log and Other Poems, 1969, The Elected Circle: Studies in the Art of Prose, 1973, Marianne Moore: The Poet's Advance, 1978, Some Poets and Their Resources: The Future Agenda, 1995. Mem. bd. sponsors Nat. Com. for an Effective Congress. Recipient Lindback Found. award, 1980; Smith Coll. Alumnae fellow, 1932-33; Guggenheim fellow, 1947-48; Nat. Endowment for Arts fellow, 1972-73. Mem. MLA, Renaissance Soc., Thoreau Soc., Assn. Lit. Scholars and Critics, Four Chaplains Legion of Honor, Phi Beta Kappa. Home: 229 N Roberts Rd Bryn Mawr PA 19010-2817

STAPLETON, MAUREEN, actress; b. Troy, N.Y., June 21, 1925; d. John P. and Irene (Walsh) S.; m. Max Allentuck, July 1949 (div. Feb. 1959); children: Daniel, Katharine; m. David Rayfiel, July, 1963 (div.). Student, Siena Coll., 1943. Debut in Playboy of the Western World, 1946; toured with Barretts of Wimpole Street, 1947; plays include Anthony and Cleopatra, 1947, Detective Story, The Bird Cage, Rose Tattoo, 1950-51, The Sea Gull, Orpheus Descending, The Cold Wind and the Warm, 1959, Toys in the Attic, 1960-61, Plaza Suite, 1969, The Gingerbread Lady, 1970 (Tony award 1970), 27 Wagons Full of Cotton, Country Girl, 1972, Secret Affairs of Mildred Wild, 1972, The Gin Game, 1977-78, The Little Foxes, 1981; motion pictures include Lonely Hearts, 1959, The Fugitive Kind, 1960, A View from the Bridge, 1962, Bye Bye Birdie, 1963, Trilogy, 1969, Airport, 1970, Plaza Suite, 1971, Interiors, 1978, The Runner Stumbles, 1979, Reds, 1981 (Oscar award as best supporting actress), The Fan, 1981, On the Right Track, 1981, The Electric Grandmother, 1982, Mother's Day, 1984, Johnny Dangerously, 1984, Cocoon, 1985, The Money Pit, 1986, Nuts, 1987, Made in Heaven, 1987, Cocoon: The Return, 1990, Passed Away, 1992, Trading Mom, 1994, The Last Good Time, 1995; TV films include Tell Me Where It Hurts, 1974, Cat On a Hot Tin Roof, 1976, All the King's Men, 1958, For Whom the Bell Tolls, 1959, Save Me a Place at Forest Lawn, 1966, Mirror, Mirror, Off the Wall, 1969, Queen of the Stardust Ballroom, 1975, The Gathering, 1977, Part II, 1979, Letters From Frank, 1979, Little Gloria ... Happy at Last, 1982, Sentimental Journey, 1984, Private Sessions, 1985, Liberace: Behind the Music, 1988, Last Wish, 1992, Miss Rose White, 1992. Recipient Nat. Inst. Arts and Letters award, 1969. *

STAPLETON, NIGEL JOHN, finance director; b. London, Nov. 1, 1946; s. Frederick Ernest John and Katie Margaret (Tyson) S.; m. Johanna Augusta Molhoek, Dec. 21, 1982; 1 child, Henry James. BA with honors, Cambridge U., Eng., 1968; MA, Cambridge U., 1971. Internal auditor Unilever, Ltd., London, 1968-70; group mgr. internal audit Unilever, Ltd., 1970-73, sr. auditor, 1973-75; corp. planning mgr. Bocm Silcock, Hampshire, Eng., 1975-77; devel. dir. Bocm Silcock, 1977-80; comml. mem. N.Am. office Unilever PLC, London, 1980-83; v.p. fin. Unilever U.S., Inc., N.Y.C., 1983-86; fin. dir. Reed Internat. P.L.C., London, from 1986; dep. chmn., CFO Reed Elsevier, 1994-. Mem. con. for industry and fins. NEDO, London, 1988-. Fellow Chartered Inst. Mgmt. Accts.; mem. Naval and Mil. Club. Avocations: tennis, opera, classical music, gardening. Office: Reed Internat PLC, 6 Chesterfield Gardens Wiaiej, London W1A 1EJ, England

STAPLETON, RICHARD D., construction company executive; b. 1936. Grad., Lehigh U., 1958; LLM, Boston U., 1962. Bar: Conn. 1961; CPA, Conn. Tax mgr. Peat, Marwick, Mitchell & Co., Hartford, Conn., 1961-66; from various positions to exec. v.p., sec., gen. counsel Lane Constrn. Co., Meriden, Conn., 1966-. Office: Lane Constrn Corp 965 E Main St Meriden CT 06450-6006

STAPLETON, WALTER KING, federal judge; b. Cuthbert, Ga., June 2, 1934; s. Theodore Newton and Elizabeth Grantland (King) S.; m. Georgianna Duross Stapleton; children: Russell K., Theodore N., Teryl J. B.A., Princeton, 1956; LL.B., Harvard, 1959; LL.M., U. Va., 1984. Bar: Del. Assoc. mem. firm Morris, Nichols, Arsht & Tunnell, Wilmington, Del., 1959-65; dep. atty. gen. State of Del., 1963; partner Morris, Nichols, Arsht & Tunnell, 1966-70; judge U.S. Dist. Ct. Del., Wilmington, 1970-85; chief judge U.S. Dist. Ct. Del., 1983-85; judge U.S. Ct. Appeals (3d cir.), 1985-; Dep. atty. gen., Del., 1964; mem. Jud. Conf. U.S., 1984-85. Bd. dirs. Am. Bapt. Chs., U.S.A., 1978. Baptist. Office: US Ct Appeals 844 N King St Wilmington DE 19801-3519*

STAPP, DAN ERNEST, retired lawyer, utility executive; b. New Orleans, July 1, 1934; s. James Frank, Jr. and Marguerite Edna (Joubert) S.; m. Barbara Allan Wilmot, June 10, 1961; children: Marguerite Wilmot (dec.), Mary Darby, Paul Wilmot, James Andrew. B.A., Loyola U., New Orleans, 1955, LL.B., 1957. Bar: La. 1957. With New Orleans Pub. Service Inc., 1958-68, asst. to v.p., 1965-68; with Entergy Svcs. (formerly MSU System Svcs. Inc.), New Orleans, 1968-72, v.p., sec., asst. treas. Entergy Svcs., 1968-80; sr. v.p., 1980-92; sec. System Fuels, Inc., New Orleans, 1972-92, Entergy Corp. (formerly Middle South Utilities, Inc.), New Orleans, 1974-92, Systems Energy Resources, Inc., Jackson, Miss., 1974-91, Electec, Inc., 1984-91, Entergy Ops., Inc., 1990-91, Enterg Power, Inc., 1990-92. Trustee Mercy Hosp., New Orleans, 1973-80, pres., 1975, chmn. bd. devel., 1971-72; mem. pres.'s coun. Loyola U., 1975-83, chmn., 1980-82; adv. coun. Coll. Bus. Adminstrn., 1969-70; mem. adv. bd. Asso. Cath. Charities, 1979-82; gen. chmn. United Way Greater New Orleans, 1978, trustee, 1978-84; mem. exec. bd. New Orleans Area coun. Boy Scouts Am., 1980-85, pres., 1984-85. 2d lt. AUS, 1957. Mem. ABA, La. Bar Assn., New Orleans Country Club, Pickwick Club, Blue Key (past chpt. pres.), Alpha Sigma Nu, Delta Theta Phi. Republican. Roman Catholic. Home: 401 Bellaire Dr New Orleans LA 70124-1014

STAPP, JOHN PAUL, surgeon, former air force officer; b. Bahia, Brazil, July 11, 1910; s. Charles Franklin and Mary Louise (Shannon) S.; m. Lillian Lanese, Dec. 23, 1957. B.A., Baylor U., 1931, M.A. cum laude, 1932, D.Sc., 1956; Ph.D., U. Tex., 1939; M.D., U. Minn., 1943; grad., Army Field Service Sch., 1944, Sch. Aviation Medicine, 1945, Indsl. Med. Course, 1946; D.Sc., N.Mex. State U., 1979. Diplomate Am. Bd. Preventive Medicine, Am. Bd. Aerospace Medicine. Intern St. Mary's Hosp., Duluth, Minn., 1944; commd. 1st lt. U.S. Army, 1944; advanced through grades to capt. M.C. USAF, 1957; resident Lincoln Army AC Regional, 1944-45; research project officer (Aero Med. Lab.), Wright Field, Ohio, 1946; chief lab. (Aero Med. Lab.), 1958-60; chief scientist aerospace med. div. Brooks AFB, Tex., 1960-65; chief impact injury br. (Armed Forces Inst. Pathology), Washington, 1965-67; chief med. scientist Nat. Hwy. Safety Bur., 1967-70; now mem. staff N.Mex. Rsch. Inst., La Cruces; cons. Dept. Transp., Washington, 1970-; adj. prof. Safety and Systems Mgmt. Center, U. So. Calif., 1972-; Systems Mgmt. Center, Los Angeles, 1973-; cons. accident epidemiology and pathology Armed Forces, Bur. Standards, NIH, Nat. Acad. Scis., Gen. Services Adminstrn.; chief Aero Med. Field Lab., Holloman AFB, Alamogordo, N.Mex., 1953-58; cons. N.Mex. State U. Phys. Scis. Lab., Las Cruces, 1972-; mem. subcom. on flight safety NACA; permanent chmn. Ann. Stapp Car Crash Conf.; chmn. Gov.'s Commn. Internat. Space Ctr., 1986; pres. N.Mex. Rsch. Inst., 1987. Mem. N.Mex. Gov.'s Commn. Internat. Space Hall of Fame, 1974-; mem. N.Mex. Planning Bd., 1975-; Bd. dirs. Kettering Found.; v.p. Internat. Astronautical Fedn., 1959-60. Decorated D.S.M. with bronze oak leaf, Legion of Merit (for crash research) with bronze oak leaf; recipient award for outstanding research by Air Force officer Nat. Air Council, 1951; John Jeffries award for med. research Inst. Aero. Sci., 1953; Air Power award for sci. Air Force Assn., 1954; Flight Safety Found. award for contbns. Air Transp. Safety, 1954; Air Force Cheney award, 1955; Gorgas award Assn. Mil. Surgeons, 1956; Med. Tribune award for automotive safety, 1965; award for contbns. to automotive safety Am. Assn. for Automotive Medicine, 1972; Cresson medal Franklin Inst., 1973; Excalibur award safety research, 1975; cert. of achievement Nat. Space Club, 1976; Lovelace award NASA Assn. Flight Surgeons, 1982; Outstanding Service award Aviation/Space Writers Assn., 1984; Honda medal ASME, 1984; Disting. Alumnus award Baylor U., 1986, Nat. medal for tech. Pres. Bush, 1991; elected to Internat. Space Hall of Fame, 1979, Nat. Aviation Hall of Fame, 1985, Safety and Health Hall of Fame, Internat., 1991; recipient Nat. Medal Tech., 1991; annual John Paul Stapp medal biomechanics Aerospace Med. Assn., 1993—, Disting. Pub. Svc. award Nat. Aviation and Space Writers Assn., 1994. Fellow Aero. Med. Assn. (Liliencrantz award for deceleration research 1957), Am. Astronautical Soc., Am. Rocket Soc. (pres. 1959, Wyld award 1955, Leo Stevens medal 1956), Soc. Automotive Engrs.; mem. U.S. Mil. Surgeons Assn., Internat. Acad. Astronautics, Internat. Acad. Aviation Medicine, Civil Aviation Medicine Assn. (pres. 1968), Am. Soc. Safety Engrs. (hon.), Order Daedalians (hon.), Sigma Xi. Achievements include research rocket sled experiments reproducing aircraft crash forces to determine human tolerance limits, 1947-51. Home: PO Box 553 Alamogordo NM 88311-0553 Office: NMex Rsch Inst PO Box 454 Alamogordo NM 88311-0454 *Life is consciousness involved in thinking and doing; it is valued in terms of the quality of resulting contributions to the stream of human advancement. I live in hopes of always doing better and producing more.*

STAPP, OLIVIA BREWER, opera singer; b. N.Y.C., May 31, 1940; d. Henry and Jean Brewer; m. Henry Stapp III; 1 child, Henry. BA, Wagner Coll; studied with, Marjorie Mayer Steen, Ettore Campogalliani, Rodolfo Ricci and Oren Brown; Dr. honoris causa, Wagner Coll., 1988. Appeared as leading soprano in Truandot, Idomeno at La Scala, Milano; Tosca, Elektra, Macbeth, Tabarro at Met. Opera, N.Y.C.; Erani, Macbeth, Il Tabarro at Liceo Barcelona; Macbeth, Madame Butterfly, Tosca, Aida, Fanciulla del West, Lohengrin at Deutche Oper Berlin; Vespre Siciliani at Grand Theater, Geneva; Nabucco, Attila, Macbeth at Zurich Oper; Salome at The Colon Theater, Buenos Aires; Cavalleria Rusticana, Anna Bolena, Tosca, Nabucco at San Francisco; Elektra Cavalleria Rusticana at Vienna Staatsoper; Idameneo at Munich Staatsoper; Carmen, The Consul, Ariadne auf Naxos, Anna Bolena, Roberto Deveraux, Cavalleria Rusticana at City Opera, N.Y.C.; Lady Macbeth, Nabucco, Turandot at Hamburg Staatsoper; Fanciulla el West, Aida, Nabucco, Turandot at the Arena de Verona; Turandot at Seoul, Korea; Turandot in N.H.K. Tokyo; Norma in Winnipeg, Edmonto, Montreal and Vancouver, Can.; Lady Macbeth in Chatelet Theater, Paris, others. Recipient Puccini award Vissi d'Arde, 1991; Fulbright scholar. Address: Columbia Artist Mgmt Inc Zemsky Green Div 165 W 57th St New York NY 10019-2201*

STAPP, WILLIAM EDWARD, lawyer; b. Yoakum, Tex., Aug. 18, 1917; s. William Edward and Lillian (Franks) S.; m. Isabelle Pool, June 30, 1945; children: Barbara, Will. B.A., U. Tex., Austin, LL.B. Bar: Tex. 1941. Asst. atty. gen. Tex., 1946-47; securities commr. Tex. Sec. State's Office, 1948-49; ptnr. Vinson & Elkins, Houston, 1965-; mem. Tex. Gov.'s Com. Codification Sch. Laws, 1968-69. Served to lt. USNR, 1942-45, PTO. Decorated Purple Heart. Mem. Tex. Assn. Sch. Bds. (council sch. attys.), Houston Bar Assn. Democrat. Presbyterian. Club: Houston. Home: 1110 River Bend Dr Houston TX 77063-1505 Office: Vinson & Elkins 3300 First City Tower 1001 Fannin Houston TX 77002

STAPP, WILLIAM FRANCIS, museum curator, photographic historian; b. McKinney, Tex., Mar. 2, 1945; s. Richard Michael and Barbara Louise (McTee) S.; m. Carol Buchalter, Aug. 27, 1967; 1 child, Rose Anna. BA in Polit. Sci., Tulane U., 1967; MA, U. Pa., 1970, Goddard Coll., 1976. Curator photographs Nat. Portrait Gallery, Smithsonian Instn., Washington, 1976-91; sr. curator 19-20th century photography Internat. Mus. Photography, George Eastman House, Rochester, N.Y., 1991-; guest scholar J. Paul Getty Mus., Malibu, Calif., 1989. Co-author: Picture It!, Robert Cornelius, Irving Penn: Master Images, 1990. Mem. Am. Fedn. Arts (adv. com.). Office: Internat Mus Photography 900 East Ave Rochester NY 14607-2219

STAPRANS, ARMAND, electronics executive; b. Riga, Latvia, Feb. 28, 1931; s. Theodore and Elvira (Ulmanis) S.; m. Vija Spalvins, Sept. 25, 1955; children: Silvija, Armin, Erik. Student, Willamette U., 1949-52; BSEE, U. Calif., Berkeley, 1954, MSEE, 1955, PhDEE, 1959. Rsch. asst. dept. elec. engring. U. Calif., 1955-57; engr. microwave tube div. Varian Assocs., Palo Alto, Calif., 1957-60, engring. mgr., 1960-68, ops. mgr., 1978-78, 86-89, chief engr., 1978-86, gen. mgr. coupled cavity tube divsn., 1989-92, v.p., 1990—; gen. mgr. microwave power tube products, 1992—. Contbr. articles to profl. jours., chpt. to book; patentee microwave tubes field. Fellow IEEE (electron device adminstrv. com. 1983-88). Home: 445 Knoll Dr Los Altos CA 94024-4732 Office: Varian Assocs Microwave Power Tube Prod 811 Hansen Way M/S/ B-018 Palo Alto CA 94304-1031

STAR, DARREN, television writer, producer. Screenwriter: (films) Doin' Time on Planet Earth, 1989, If Looks Could Kill, 1991; creator, exec. prodr. (television series) Beverly Hills, 90210, 1991—, Melrose Place, 1992—, Central Park West, 1995—. Office: Internat Creative Mgmt 8942 Wilshire Blvd Beverly Hills CA 90211

STARBIRD, LONNIE DARRYL, producer of custom car shows, designer and builder of custom automobiles; b. Topeka, Aug. 7, 1933; s. Austin Tyler and Lucy Marie (Campbell) S.; m. Donna Mae Gray, July 5, 1953; children: Debra Marie, Clifford Dean, Cristy Mae, Rick Alan. Student, Wichita State U., 1951-54. Owner Starbird Custom Autos, Wichita, Kans., 1955-86, Starbird Prodns., Wichita, 1957-83; pres. Nat. Rod & Custom Assn. Mulvane, Kans., 1970-84, Dickens Christmas Exposition, Mulvane, 1982-83, Nat. Show Prodn., Inc., Mulvane, 1983—; Nat. Ad Agy. Inc., Mulvane, 1983—; design cons. Monogram Models, Morton Grove, Ill., 1963-67; freelance photographer leading auto mags. 1957-86. Starbird creations featured in Stern Mag. in Germany, 1986, Custom Car mags. in England and Australia, 1979, 83; L & M Custom Car tour of Europe - 6 Starbird creations over 20 major cities, 1986. Named Custom Car Builder of Yr., Nat. Hot Rod Assn., 1960, Constructer of Yr., Internat. Show Car Assn., 1986; recipient Master Builder award Grand Nat. Roadster Show, 1963; winner of 500 trophies in leading auto shows throughout US. Mem. Internat. Auto Show Producers Assn. (v.p. 1986). Roman Catholic. Home: RR 3 Box 180 Afton OK 74331-9003 Office: Nat Show Producers Inc RR 3 Box 180 Afton OK 74331-9003

STARE, FREDRICK JOHN, nutritionist, biochemist, physician; b. Columbus, Wis., Apr. 11, 1910; s. Fredrick Arthur and Susan (Seidell) S.; m. Joyce Allen, Sept. 14, 1935 (dec. May 1957); children: Fredrick Allen, David, Mary; m. Helen Haxton Foreman, June 9, 1959 (dec. Feb. 1974); m. Mary Bartlett Engle, Dec. 30, 1976 (div. 1983); m. Irene Mackey Kelsey, Sept. 15, 1984. B.S., U. Wis., 1931, M.S., 1932, Ph.D., 1934; M.D., U. Chgo., 1941; MA (hon.), Harvard U., 1945; D.Sc., Suffolk, 1963, Trinity Coll., Dublin, 1964, Muskingum Coll., 1977. Asst. biochemist U. Wis., 1931-34; Nat. Research fellow Washington U. Sch. Medicine, St. Louis, 1934-35; Gen. Edn. Bd. fellow Cambridge (Eng.) U., 1935-36, Szeged, Hungary, 1936, Zurich, 1937; research assoc. Bowman Cancer Found., Wis., 1937-39; intern Barnes Hosp., St. Louis, 1941-42; prof. nutrition Harvard Med. Sch. and Sch. Pub. Health; prof. nutrition, chmn. dept. nutrition, 1942-76; prof. nutrition emeritus Harvard Sch. Pub. Health, 1976—; jr. asso. medicine Peter Bent Brigham Hosp., 1942-44, asso. in medicine, 1944-50, sr. asso. medicine, 1950-60, cons. medicine, 1960-70; co-founder syndicated radio program Healthline; dir. Continental Group; former mem. food and nutrition bd. NRC; cons. nutrition Sec. War, USPHS; mem. health adv. com. Fgn. Operations Adminstrv.; com. health commn. on Inter-govtl. Relations; mem. Nat. Health Edn. Com. Author: Living Nutrition, Scope Manual on Nutrition, Eat OK-Feel OK, Food for Today's Teens, Food for Fitness After Fifty; The Executive Diet, Panic in the Pantry, Your Basic Guide to Nutrition, Dear Dr. Stare: What Shall I Eat?, The Harvard Square Diet; Nutrition for Good Health, The 100% Natural, Purely Organic, Cholesterol-Free, Megavitamin, Low-carbohydrate Nutrition Hoax, Balanced Nutrition Beyond The Cholesterol Scare, Adventures in Nutrition, Your Guide to Good Nutrition; nat. syndicated columnist: Food and Your Health; former editor: Nutrition Revs. Overseer emeritus New Eng. Conservatory Music; bd. dir. Lown Cardiovascular Found., Pathfinder Internat.; co-founder, bd. dirs. Am. Coun. Sci. and Health. Recipient Pub. Svc. award U. Chgo., 1982, medal of honor Internat. Found. for Nutrition Rsch. and Edn., 1989, Disting. Svc. award U. Chgo. Med. and Biol. Scis. Alumni Assn., 1992, Excellence in Med. Nutrition Edn. award Am. Soc. Clin. Nutrition, 1993, Disting. Emeritus Prof. award Harvard Sch. Pub. Health, 1993, citation for 50 yrs. of svc. Harvard U., 1993, Am. Coun. Sci. and Health award, 1994; Fredrick John Stare professorship of nutrition established by Harvard U., 1991. Fellow APHA, Royal Irish Coll. Physicians (hon.); mem. AMA (Goldberger award 1961), Am. Acad. Arts and Scis., Mass. Med. Soc., Am. Chem. Soc., Am. Soc. Biol. Chemists, Am. Inst. Nutrition (Elvehjem award 1969), Biochem. Soc. (Eng.), Am. Soc. Clin. Investigation, Am. Soc. Arteriosclerosis, Am. Dietetic Assn. (hon.), Group of European Nutritionists (hon.), Soc. Nutrition Edn., Harvard Club (Boston, N.Y.C.), Cosmos Club, Sigma Xi. Home: 267 Cartwright Rd Box 812085 Wellesley MA 02181-0013 Office: Harvard U Sch Pub Health 665 Huntington Ave Boston MA 02115-6021 *I never expect anyone to work any harder than I do. Be overly generous in giving credit to others. Never ask anyone to do anything you are not willing to do yourself.*

STARER, ROBERT, composer; b. Vienna, Austria, Jan. 8, 1924; came to U.S., 1947, naturalized, 1957; s. Nison and Erna (Gottlieb) S.; m. Johanna Herz, Mar. 27, 1942; 1 child, Daniel. Student. State Acad., Vienna, 1938-39, Jerusalem Conservatory, 1939-42; postgrad. diploma, Juilliard Sch. Music, 1949. mem. faculty Juilliard Sch. Music, 1949-74; assoc. prof. Bklyn. Coll., 1963-66, prof., 1966-91, Disting. prof., 1966-91, ret., 1991. Composer: Symphony 1, 1950, Symphony 2, 1951, Piano Concerto 1, 1947, Piano Concerto 2, 1952, Concerto a Tre, 1954, Viola Concerto, 1958, Ariel, 1959, Joseph and His Brothers, 1966; opera The Intruder, 1956, Concerto for

Violin Cello and Orch, 1967, Six Variations with Twelve Notes, 1967, On The Nature of Things (chorus), 1968, Symphony 3, 1969; ballets The Dybbuk, 1960, Samson Agonistes, 1961, Phaedra, 1963, Mutabili, 1965, Third St. Overture, 1970, (opera), Pantagleize, 1971, Concerto Piano 3, 1972, Images of Man, 1973, Stone Ridge Set, Mandala, Profiles in Brass, 1974, The Last Lover (opera), 1975, Journals of a Songmaker; text by Gail Godwin, 1975, The People, Yes; text by Carl Sandburg, 1976, Piano Quartet, 1977; song cycle Transformations, 1978; operas Apollonia, 1978, Anna Margarita's Will, 1979; chorus Voices of Brooklyn, 1980, Evanescence, 1981; Violin Concerto, 1982, Hudson Valley Suite, 1983, Concerto a Quattro, 1984, Piano Trio, 1985, Remembering Felix, 1986, Kaaterskill Quartet, 1987, Cello Concerto, 1987, Duo for violin and piano, 1988, Angel Voices for brass and organ, 1989, Night Thoughts for chorus and synthesizer, 1990, Yizkor and Anima Eterna for flute and harpsichord, 1991, Clarinet Quintet, 1992, Episodes for Viola, Cello and Piano, 1993, Concerto for Two Pianos, 1994, String Quartet No. 2, 1995; also chamber music, choral, piano music, songs.; author: Rhythmic Training, 1969, Continuo: A Life in Music, 1987; Symphonic works premiered by N.Y. Philharmonic condrs., other leading condrs. in, U.S., abroad, ballets commd. by Martha Graham, 1961-63, CBS TV for Anna Sokolow, 1964, Lincoln Center for John Butler, 1967. Served with RAF, 1943-46. Recipient award Am. Acad. and Inst. Arts and Letters, 1979; Guggenheim fellow, 1957, 63; Fulbright postdoctoral research grantee, 1964; Nat. Endowment for Arts grantee, 1974, 77. Mem. ASCAP, Am. Music Ctr. (dir. 1962-64), Am. Acad. Arts and Letters.

STARFIELD, BARBARA HELEN, physician, educator; b. Bklyn., Dec. 18, 1932; d. Martin and Eva (Illions) S.; m. Neil A. Holtzman, June 12, 1955; children—Robert, Jon, Steven, Deborah. A.B., Swarthmore Coll., 1954; M.D., SUNY, 1959; M.P.H., Johns Hopkins U., 1963. Teaching asst. in anatomy Downstate Med. Ctr., N.Y.C., 1955-57; intern in pediatrics Johns Hopkins U., 1959-60, resident, 1960-62, dir. pediatric med. care clinic, 1963-66, dir. community staff comprehensive child care project, 1966-67, dir. pediatric clin. scholars program, 1971-76, prof. health policy, head health policy div., joint appointment in pediatrics, 1975—; disting. univ. prof., 1994—; mem. Nat. Com. Vital Stats., 1994—; cons. DHHS; mem. nat. adv. coun. Agy. for Health Care Policy and Rsch., 1990-94. Editorial bd. Med. Care, 1977-79, Pediatrics, 1977-82, Internat. Jour. Health Svcs.,1 978—, Med. Care Rev. 1980-84; contbr. articles to profl. jours. Recipient Dave Luckman Meml. award, 1958; HEW Career Devel. award, 1970-75. Fellow Am. Acad. Pediatrics; mem. Nat. Acad. Sci. Inst. Medicine (governing coun. 1981-83), Am. Pediatric Soc., Soc. Pediatric Rsch., Internat. Epidemiologic Assn., Ambulatory Pediatric Assn. (pres. 1980), Am. Pub. Health Assn., Sigma Xi, Alpha Omega Alpha. Office: Johns Hopkins Sch Hygiene 624 N Broadway Baltimore MD 21205-1901

STARGELL, WILLIE (WILVER DORNEL STARGELL), professional sports team coach, former baseball player; b. Earlsboro, Okla., Mar. 6, 1941. Student, Santa Rosa Jr. Coll. Player Pitts. Pirates, 1962-82, coach, 1982-85; coach Atlanta Braves, 1985-88; player All-Star Game, 1964-66, 71-73, 78. Named Sportsman of Yr. Sports Illus. mag., 1979, co-Most Valuable Player Nat. League, 1979, Major League Player of Yr. Sporting News, 1979; inducted into Baseball Hall of Fame, 1988. Office: care Pitts Pirates 3 Rivers Stadium 600 Stadium Cir Pittsburgh PA 15212-5740*

STARING, GRAYDON SHAW, lawyer; b. Deansboro, N.Y., Apr. 9, 1923; s. William Luther and Eleanor Mary (Shaw) S.; m. Joyce Lydia Allum-Poon, Sept. 1, 1949; children: Diana Hilary Agnes, Christopher Paul Norman. Student, Colgate U., 1943-44; A.B., Hamilton Coll., 1947; J.D., U. Calif.-Berkeley, 1951. Bar: Calif. 1952, U.S. Supreme Ct. 1958. Atty. Office Gen. Counsel, Navy Dept., San Francisco, 1952-53; atty. admiralty and shipping sect. U.S. Dept. Justice, San Francisco, 1953-60; assoc. Lillick & Charles, San Francisco, 1960-64, ptnr., 1965—; titulary mem. Internat. Maritime Com.; bd. dirs. Marine Exchange at San Francisco, San Francisco Maritime Assn., 1986-88; instr. pub. speaking Hamilton Coll., 1947-48. Author: Law of Reinsurance, 1993; assoc. editor Am. Maritime Cases, 1966-92, editor, 1992—; contbr. articles to legal jours. Mem. San Francisco Lawyers Com. for Urban Affairs, 1972-90; bd. dirs. Legal Aid Soc., San Francisco, 1974-90, v.p., 1975-80, pres. 1980-82. With USN, 1943-46, comdr. USNR. Fellow Am. Bar Found., Am. Coll. Trial Lawyers; mem. ABA (chmn. maritime ins. com. 1975-76, mem. standing com. admiralty law 1976-82, 86-90, chmn. 1990, ho. dels. 1986-90), Fed. Bar Assn. (pres. San Francisco chpt. 1968), Bar Assn. San Francisco (sec. 1972, treas. 1973), Calif. Acad. Appellate Lawyers, Maritime Law Assn. U.S. (exec. com. 1977-88, v.p. 1980-84, pres. 1984-86), Brit. Ins. Law Assn., Brit.-Am. C of C. (bd. dirs. 1987—), World Trade Club San Francisco, Tulane Admiralty Inst. (permanent adv. bd.), Assocs. Maritime Mus. Libr. (dir. 1990-92, pres. 1992-94). Republican. Episcopalian. Home: 195 San Anselmo Ave San Francisco CA 94127-1513 Office: 2 Embarcadero Ctr Ste 2600 San Francisco CA 94111-3800 *"How small, of all that human hearts endure,/That part which laws or kings can cause or cure!".*

STARK, BRUCE GUNSTEN, artist; b. Queens, N.Y., Feb. 17, 1933; s. Richard M. and Karen (Gunsten) S.; m. Joan Patricia Lauer, Nov. 19, 1960; children: Robert, Ronald. Student, Sch. Visual Arts, N.Y.C., 1955-58. Artist, cartoonist N.Y. Daily News, N.Y.C., 1961—. Exhibited one-man shows Art Inst., Pitts., 1968, U. Kutztown, Pa., 1970, N.Y. Bank for Savs., N.Y.C., 1971; group shows Nat. Art Mus. Sport, N.Y.C., 1971; represented in permanent collections Everett Dirksen Library, L.D. Johnson Library, Baseball Hall Fame, Cooperstown, N.Y., Basketball Hall Fame, Mass. Served with USN, 1952-54. Recipient Nat. Cartoonist Soc.'s Rueben Catagory awards for sports, 1966, 75, spl. features, 1968; Page One award for best sports cartoon, 1970, 73 N.Y.C., 71; 3d, 4th, 6th prizes Internat. Salon de Caricatures Montreal, 1966, 68, 69; Most Outstanding Achievement award Sch. Visual Arts, 1982. Original cartoons requested by Pres. Nixon, Johnson; 1st color cartoon appearing on front page of N.Y. Daily News. Home: 212 Elm Ave Melbourne FL 32951-2420 Office: 105 S Riverside Dr Melbourne FL 32903-4365 *My goals, ideas, principles and standards of conduct are all helpfully outlined for me by God in His holy word—the Bible. I really need no other source. Whatever success has come to me, I think, is because of this, and what God has done for me, through His Son, Jesus Christ.*

STARK, CAROLINE, library director. Dir. Nashville & Davidson County Pub. Libr. Office: Public Library Nashville & Davidson County 225 Polk Ave Nashville TN 37203-3500

STARK, CHARLES H., III, architectural firm executive. BS in Architecture, U. Cin., 1959; student, Toledo Mus. Art. Registered arch., Ohio, Fla., Ind., Mich., Tenn., Conn., Ill., N.C., Okla.; cert. Nat. Coun. Archtl. Registration Bds. Assoc. Bauer Stark & Laskbrook (formerly Richards, Bauer and Moorhead), Toledo, 1963-67, sr. assoc., 1967-70, dir. design, 1970-71, ptnr., 1971-80, pres., 1980—. Pres. Maumee Valley Hist. Soc., mem. long range planning com., bd. trustees; founder Landmark Com., mem. exec. com.; bd. trustees Toledo Repertoire Theatre, mem. new bldg. com.; mem. adv. com. Owens Tech. Coll.; mem. cmty. tech. adv. com. U. Toledo; active Ohio Hist. Soc., Maumee Heritage Corridor Planning Com. Recipient 1st Pl. award Nat. Ceramic Tile Competition, Cin. Illuminating Engrings. Soc. Competition. Mem. AIA (mem. urban design com., Toledo chpt. bd. trustees, pres., v.p., treas.), Archs. Soc. Ohio (mem. legis. rev. com., bd. trustees, past chmn. design awards com.), Nat. Trust Hist. Preservation, Vistula Soc. (founder), Toledo Met. Area Coun. Govts. (mem. energy guidance com., chmn. new constrn. task force), Toledo Area Small Bus. Assn., Toledo Area C. of C., U. Cin. Alumni Assn. (pres.), Lucas County Port Authority (mem. econ. devel. focus group), Com. of One Hundred (mem. downtown planning adv. com.), The Uptown Assn. (bd. trustees. Mem. Toledo est. C.). Office: Bauer Stark & Lashbrook 1600 Madison Ave Toledo OH 43624

STARK, DAVID ETHAN, museum curator; b. Lakewood, Ohio, Mar. 19, 1953; s. Crandall Yetter and Alma Florence (Wozniak) S. B.A. in French, Oberlin Coll., 1974; M.A. in History of Art, Ohio State U., 1978, Ph.D., 1979. Asst. prof. U. Minn.-Morris, 1980-81; research assoc. Tweed Mus. Art, Duluth, Minn., 1981-82; curator mem. Munson Williams Proctor Inst., Utica, N.Y., 1982-84, R.I. Sch. Design, Providence, 1984—. Contbr. articles to profl. jours. Ohio State U. fellow, 1974-78, grantee, 1978. Mem. Coll. Art Assn. Am., Am. Assn. Museums, Phi Kappa Phi. Office: Mus Art RI Sch Design 224 Benefit St Providence RI 02903-2711

STARK, DENNIS EDWIN, banker; b. Springfield, Ill., Dec. 24, 1937; s. Edwin C. and Ida (Fentem) S. B.S., Ill. Wesleyan U., 1959; Sanxay fellow practical ethics, Princeton U., 1959-60; M.B.A., Harvard U., 1962. Adminstrv. asst. to chmn. bd. Industrial Valley Bank, Phila., 1962-64; fin. analyst E.I. DuPont de Nemours, Wilmington, Del., 1964-65; asst. treas. Old Stone Bank, Providence, 1965-68, treas., 1968-71; sr. v.p., treas., sec. Old Stone Bank and Old Stone Corp., Providence, 1971-76; exec. v.p., chief fin. officer Old Stone Corp., Old Stone Bank, 1976-86, Dime Savs. Bank, N.Y.C., 1986-88; ptnr. Bank Mgmt. Ptnrs., N.Y.C., 1988-90; sr. v.p., CFO, corp. sec Cen Fed Bank, Pasadena, Calif., 1990-92; exec. v.p., CFO, Corp. sec. Ea. Bank, Lynn, Mass., 1992—. Mem. bd. overseers Peabody Essex mus., Salem, Mass.; mem. vestry, treas. St. Stephen's Ch., Providence; mem. bd. visitors Ill. Wesleyan U., Bloomington; trustee Gilbert Stuart Meml., Saunderstown, R.I. Mem. Fin. Execs. Inst., Fin. Mgrs. Soc., Am. Soc. Corp. Secs., Harvard Bus. Sch. Assn. of Boston, Acacia (co-founder Ill. Wesleyan U. chpt.), Providence Art Club, Hope Club, Harvard Club (N.Y.C., Boston), Agawam Hunt, Dunes Club. Republican. Episcopalian. Avocations: philately, numismatics. Home (summer): 41 Courtway Narragansett RI 02882 Office: Ea Bank 270 Union St Lynn MA 01901

STARK, DONALD GERALD, pharmaceutical executive; b. Hot Springs, S.D., Dec. 25, 1926; s. Gordon Leo and Louise May (Smith) S.; m. Mary Jean Enfield, Mar. 6, 1944; children: Donald Gerald, Stevan R. B.C.S., Drake U., Des Moines, 1950, M.S. in Edn., 1952. Tchr., Missouri Valley (Iowa) High Sch., 1950-51; prin. Bayard (Iowa) High Sch., 1952-53; with Sandoz Inc., 1954—, Sandoz Ltd., Basle, Switzerland, 1967-68; pres. Sandoz Pharm. Ltd. Tokyo, 1969-72; pres. pharm. div. Sandoz Inc., 1973-81, also corp. dir.; pres. pharm. group Sterling Drug, Inc., N.Y.C., 1981-83, also corp. group v.p., chmn. bd., chief exec. officer Nova Pharm. Corp., Balt., 1983-87, vice chmn., 1988-92; treas. Am. Found. Pharm. Edn.; bd. dirs. Cert. Med. Reps. Inst.; adv. bd., lectr./speaker program Fairleigh Dickinson U. Bd. dirs. Savannah Symphony. Served with AUS, 1945-47. Mem. Pharm. Mfrs. Assn., Nat. Wholesalers Drug Assn., Internat. House of Japan, Elk River Club (Banner Elk, N.C.), Landings Club (Savannah, Ga.).

STARK, FORTNEY HILLMAN (PETE STARK), congressman; b. Milw., Nov. 11, 1931; s. Fortney Hillman Sr. and Dorothy M. (Mueller) S.; children: Jeffrey Peter, Beatrice Ann, Thekla Brumder, Sarah Gallup; m. Deborah Roderick. BS, MIT; MBA, U. Calif. Teaching asst. MIT, Cambridge, 1953-54; pres. Skaife & Co., Berkeley, Calif., 1957-61; founder Beacon Savs. & Loan Assn., Antioch, Calif., 1961; pres., founder Security Nat. Bank, Walnut Creek, Calif., 1963-72; mem. 93d-102nd Congresses from 9th Calif. dist., 1973—; chmn. ways and means subcom. on health 93d-103d Congresses from 13th dist. Calif., 1973—; mem. D.C. com., Ways and Means com., subcom. Health, Select Revenue Measures, joint econ. com. Bd. dirs. ACLU, 1971, Common Cause, 1971, Starr King Sch.; del. Dem. State Cen. Com.; trustee Calif. Dem. Coun. Capt. USAF, 1955-57. Mem. Delta Kappa Epsilon. Office: House of Representatives 239 Cannon Bldg Washington DC 20515-0513

STARK, FRANCIS C., JR., horticulturist, educator; b. Drumright, Okla., Mar. 19, 1919; s. Francis C. and Maude Salena (Crowder) S.; m. Dorothy Lucille Moore, Sept. 14, 1941; children: Carolyn P. Stark Reich, Francis C. III. BS., Okla. A&M Coll., 1940; M.S., U. Md., 1941, Ph.D., 1948. Asst. prof. horticulture U. Md., College Park, 1945-49; assoc. prof. U. Md., 1949-51, prof., 1951-80, prof. emeritus, 1980—, head dept. horticulture, 1964-74, chmn. food sci. program, 1966-73, provost agr. and life scis., 1974-80, acting vice chancellor acad. affairs, 1981-82, spl. asst. to v.p., 1982—. Contbr. articles to profl. jours. Mem. Md. Gov.'s Commn. on Migratory Labor, 1959-79, chmn., 1963-76; bd. dirs. Capital Area Christian Ch., 1961-66, 89-94, pres., 1963-66; bd. dirs. Christian Ch. Facilities for Aging, 1965—, pres., 1975-80; trustee Lynchburg (Va.) Coll., 1979-79. With USAAF, 1942-45. Recipient Hon. State Farmer award Md. Future Farmers Assn., 1966. Fellow Am. Soc. Hort. Sci., AAAS. Club: Rotary. Office: U Md Dept Horticulture College Park MD 20742

STARK, JACK LEE, college president; b. Urbana, Ind., Sept. 26, 1934; s. Lynn C. and Helen (Haley) S.; m. Jil Carolyn Harris, June 14, 1958; children: Janet, Jeffrey, Jennifer, Jonathan. BA, Claremont McKenna Coll., 1957; hon. degree, Redlands U., LDH, 1973. Asst. to pres. Claremont (Calif.) McKenna Coll., 1961-70, pres., 1970—. Active Pomona Valley Cmty. Hosp.; bd. dirs. Thacher Sch., Ojai, Calif. Capt. USMCR, 1957-60. Mem. Assn. Ind. Calif. Colls. and Univs. (chmn.), Ind. Colls. So. Calif. (bd. dirs.), Western Coll. Assn. (bd. dirs.). Club: California (Los Angeles). Home: 1679 Tulane Ave Claremont CA 91711 Office: Claremont McKenna Coll Office of Pres 500 E 9th St Claremont CA 91711-6400

STARK, JOAN SCISM, education educator; b. Hudson, N.Y., Jan. 6, 1937; d. Ormonde F. and Myrtle Margaret (Kirkey) S.; m. William L. Stark, June 28, 1958 (dec.); children: Eugene William, Susan Elizabeth, Linda Anne, Ellen Scism; m. Malcolm A. Lowther, Jan. 31, 1981. B.S., Syracuse U., 1957; M.A. (Hoadly fellow), Columbia U., 1960; Ed.D., SUNY, Albany, 1971. Tchr. Ossining (N.Y.) High Sch., 1957-59; free-lance editor Holt, Rinehart & Winston, Harcourt, Brace & World, 1960-70; lectr. Ulster County Community Coll., Stone Ridge, N.Y., 1968-70; asst. dean Goucher Coll., Balt., 1970-73; asso. dean Goucher Coll., 1973-74; assoc. prof., chmn. dept. higher postsecondary edn. Syracuse (N.Y.) U., 1974-78; dean Sch. Edn. U. Mich., Ann Arbor, 1978-83, prof., 1983—; dir. Nat. Ctr. for Improving Postsecondary Teaching and Learning, 1986-91. Editor: Rev. of Higher Education, 1991—; contbr. articles to various publs. Leader Girl Scouts U.S.A., Cub Scouts Am.; coach girls Little League; dist. officer PTA, intermittently, 1968-80; mem. adv. com. Gerald R. Ford Library, U. Mich., 1980-83; trustee Kalamazoo Coll., 1979-85; mem. exec. com. Inst. Social Research, U. Mich., 1979-81; bd. dirs. Mich. Assn. Colls. Tchr. Edn., 1979-81. Mem. Am. Assn. for Higher Edn., Am. Ednl. Rsch. Assn., Assn. Study Higher Edn. (dir. 1977-79, v.p. 1983, pres. 1984, Rsch. Achievement award 1992), Assn. Innovation Higher Edn. (nat. chmn. 1974-75), Assn. Instl. Rsch. (disting. mem.), Assn. Colls. and Schs. Edn. State Univs. and Land Grant Colls. (dir. 1981-83), Acctg. Edn. Change Commn., Phi Beta Kappa, Phi Kappa Phi, Sigma Pi Sigma, Eta Pi Upsilon, Lambda Sigma Sigma, Phi Delta Kappa, Pi Lambda Theta. Office: Univ Mich 2002 Sch of Edn Ann Arbor MI 48109-1259

STARK, MARTIN J., management consultant; b. N.Y.C., May 29, 1941; s. Nathan and Lola (Belmont) S.; m. Shigemi Matsumoto, Apr. 27, 1967; AA Glendale Coll., 1960; BA, Calif. State U., 1966; postgrad. San Fernando Valley Coll. Law, 1967-70. Systems analyst Industrial Electronic Engrs., Van Nuys, Calif., 1969-71; sales mgr., 1971-73; sales rep. Columbia Artists Mgmt., Inc., N.Y.C., 1973-78, sales mgr., 1978-79, v.p. bus. affairs, mgr. data processing, 1979-82; dir. corp. affairs Kolmar-Luth Entertainment, Inc., N.Y.C., 1982-84; pres. Oryx Corp., N.Y.C., 1984-85; exec. v.p. Asco Aerospace Products, Inc., El Segundo, Calif., 1985-87; exec. v.p. Internat. Engine Parts, Inc., Chatsworth, Calif., 1987-92; pres. Stark & Assocs., Northridge, Calif., 1985-91; owner Mail Boxes Etc., 1992—; lectr. Calif. State U., Long Beach; cons. City of N.Y., Memory Data Software, IEPO, Inc., and others. Mem. Am. Symphony Orch. League, Assn. Coll., Univ. and Cmty. Arts Adminstrs., Internat. Soc. Performing Arts Adminstrs., Am. Mgmt. Assn., The Classical Singer's Assn., Calabasas C. of C., Delta Upsilon. Avocations: sports cars, antiques, travel. Home: 18342 Chatham Ln Northridge CA 91326-3603

STARK, MAURICE GENE, research institute financial executive; b. Elyria, Ohio, Sept. 23, 1935; s. Maurice George and Florence Ann (Woiczikowski) S.; m. Judith Belle Martin, July 21, 1956; children: Susan, David, Daniel, Douglas, Dean. B.S., Ohio State U., 1957; cert. program for sr. execs., Sloan Sch. Mgmt., MIT, 1978. Supr., auditor Auditor Gen.'s Office, U.S. Air Force, Columbus, Ohio, 1961-65; mgr. corp. acctg. Battelle Meml. Inst., Columbus, Ohio, 1965-75; controller and dir. fin. Battelle Columbus div., Ohio, 1975-78; v.p.-treas. Battelle Meml. Inst. ., Columbus, 1978-92; treas. Battelle Devel. Corp., Columbus, 1978-90; bd. dirs., chmn. Research Ins. Co. Ltd., Hamilton, Bermuda, 1978—; treas., mem. Vorstand, Battelle-Institut e.V., Frankfurt, Fed. Republic Germany, 1978—; bd. dirs., sec. Tin Research Inst., Columbus, Ohio, 1982—; trustee The Sessions Group, Columbus. Trustee Ctr. Ohio Transit Authority, Columbus, 1975—; Columbus Symphony Orch., 1983-92, treas., 1984-92. With USAF, 1958-61, capt. USAR, 1961-63. Recipient Spl. Service award USAF, 1965. Mem. Fin.

Execs. Inst. (dir. 1983-84), Treas. Club (dir. 1982-84, 1991—). Lutheran. Club: Optimists (Columbus) (pres. 1975-76). Lodge: Rotary. Office: Battelle Meml Inst 505 King Ave Columbus OH 43201

STARK, MILTON DALE, sports association executive; b. Fellows, Calif., Apr. 28, 1932; s. Ernest Esco and Ruth Hazel (Keeney) S.; m. Katherine Margaret Boyd, Dec. 17, 1955 (div. June 1978); children: Mark Boyd, Kimberly Kay, Matthew Scott, Martin Dean; m. Diana Lynn Mead, July 26, 1980; 1 child, Ryan. AA, Taft Coll., 1956; BA, Whittier Coll., 1958, MEd, 1963. Cert. ednl. adminstr., Calif. Sec. Western Softball Congress, Hollywood, Calif., 1962-70; commr. Internat. Softball Congress, Anaheim Hills, Calif., 1966-75, sec., 1975-83, exec. dir., 1983—; v.p. U.S. Fastpitch Assn., Colorado Springs, Colo., 1993—; mem. coun. Amateur Softball Assn., 1994—; sports cons. Whittier (Calif.) News, 1959-70. Editor-in-chief Softball Illus. mag., 1966-69; columnist The Fastpitch Chronicle, 1993—; contbg. author: FastPitch World, 1993; contbr. articles to softball mags. Served with USAF, 1951-55. Named to Internat. Softball Congress Hall of Fame, 1981, recipient Alumni Achievement award Whittier Coll. Lancer Soc., 1989. Mem. Whittier Coll. Alumni Assn. (bd. dirs. 1989-94). Republican. Avocations: theater, wine and book collecting, traveling. Home and Office: Internat Softball Congress 6007 E Hillcrest Cir Anaheim CA 92807-3921

STARK, NATHAN JULIUS, association administrator, lawyer; b. Mpls., Nov. 9, 1920; s. Harold and Anna (Berlow) S.; m. Lucile D. Seidler, Nov. 28, 1943; children: Paul S., David H. Robert, Margaret J. AA, Woodrow Wilson Jr. Coll., Chgo., 1940; BS, U.S. Mcht. Marine Acad., 1943; JD, Ill. Inst. Tech., 1948; LLD (hon.), Park Coll., 1969, U. Mo., 1980; DHL, Scholl Coll., Hahnemann U., 1987. Bar: Ill. 1947, Mo. 1952. Plant mgr. Englander Co., Inc., Chgo., 1949-51; partner law firm Downey, Abrams, Stark & Sullivan, Kansas City, Mo., 1952-53; v.p. Rival Mfg. Co., Kansas City, 1954-59; sr. v.p. ops. Hallmark Cards, Inc., Kansas City, 1959-74; dir. Hallmark Cards, Inc., 1960-74; pres., chmn. Crown Center Redevel. Corp., 1971-74; sr. vice chancellor health scis. Schs. Health Professions, U. Pitts., until 1984, sr. vice chancellor emeritus, 1984—, also pres. Univ. Health Center, 1974-79, 81—, also prof. Grad. Sch. Public Health; undersec. HEW, Washington, 1979-81; of counsel Fort & Schlefor, Washington; pres., CEO Nat. Acad. of Social Ins., 1992—; dir. ERC Corp., 1970-79, Hallmark Continental Ltd., Ireland, 1971-73; mem. exec. bd. Nat. Bd. Med. Examiners, 1984; mem. bd. Accreditation Coun. for Continuing Med. Edn., 1991; cons., mem. adv. bd. Health Care Administration Internat. Inc., 1991—; pres. Nat. Acad. Social Ins., Washington. Contbr. articles to profl. and bus. jours. Legal counsel Lyric Opera Theatre, Kansas City, Mo., 1958-72; mem. com. undergrad. med. edn. AMA, 1966-73; vice chmn. health ins. benefits adv. com. NEW, 1965-70; sec. task force on Medicaid, 1960-70, chmn. adv. comm. incentive reimbursement experimentation, 1968-70; chmn. capital investment conf. HEW-HRA, 1976; mem. liaison com. Am. Assn. Med. Colls.-AMA, 1970-74; chmn. task force life-long learning opportunities Kellogg Found., 1975-77; chmn. cmty. hosp.-med. staff group practice program Robert Wood Johnson Found., 1974-79; mem.-at-large Nat. Bd. Med. Examiners; mem. bd. Blue Cross Western Pa., 1975-79, Am. Nurses Found., 1975-77, Health Sys. Agy. SW Pa., 1976—; v.p. Kansas City Philharm. Assn., 1954; sec. Eddie Jacobson Meml. Found., 1960—; mem. tech. bd. Milbank Meml. Fund, 1976-78; pres., chmn Kansas City Gen. Hosp. and Med. Ctr., 1962-74; trustee Kansas City Ballet Theater, 1977-79, Pitts. Chamber Opera Theater, 1978—; mem. VA Scholars Bd. Governance, 1979—; hon. fellow, trustee Hastings Ctr., 1981; v.p. Pitts. Opera; adv. bd. of trustees St. Joseph Coll., trustee, 1994. Recipient Chancellor's medal U. Mo. at Kansas City, 1969; Pro-Meritus award Rockhurst Coll., 1967; Layman award; AMA, 1974. Fellow Am. Acad. Pediatrics (hon.); mem. Inst. Medicine of NAS (coun. 1973-76), Am. Hosp. Assn. (hon. mem., Trustee award 1968), Am. Coll. Hosp. Adminstrs., Nat. Acad. Social Ins. (bd. trustees, pres. 1992-94). Home: 4343 Westover Pl NW Washington DC 20016-5554

STARK, NELLIE MAY, forest ecology educator; b. Norwich, Conn., Nov. 20, 1933; d. Theodore Banjamin and Dorothy Josephine (Pendleton) Beetham; m. Oscar Elder Stark, Oct. 1962 (dec). B.A., Conn. Coll., 1956; AM, Duke U., 1958, PhD, 1962. Botanist Exptl. Sta., U.S. Forest Svc., Old Strawberry, Calif., 1958-66; botanist, ecologist Desert Rsch. Inst., Reno, Nev., 1966-72; prof. forest ecology Sch. Forestry, U. Mont., Missoula, 1972-92; pvt. cons. Philomath, Oreg.; pres. Camas Analytical Lab., Inc., Missoula, 1987-92. Contbr. articles to profl. jours. Named Disting. Dau. Norwich, Conn., 1985; recipient Conn. award Conn. Coll., 1986, 54 grants. Mem. Ecol. Soc. Am. (chair ethics com. 1974, 76), Bot. Soc. Am., Soc. Am. Foresters (taskforce 1987-88).

STARK, RAY, motion picture producer. Student, Rutgers U. Publicity agt., lit. agt.; talent agt. Famous Artist Agy., to 1957; co-founder Seven Arts Prodn. Co., 1957; ind. film producer, 1966—. Producer: (films) The World of Suzie Wong, 1960, The Night of the Iguana, 1964, Reflections in a Golden Eye, 1967, Funny Girl, 1968, The Owl and the Pussycat, 1970, Fat Ctiy, 1972, The Way We Were, 1973, Funny Lady, 1975, The Sunshine Boys, 1975, Murder By Death, 1976, Smokey and the Bandit, 1977, The Goodbye Girl, 1977, The Cheap Detective, 1978, California Suite, 1978, Chapter Two, 1979, The Electric Horseman, 1979, Seems Like Old Times, 1980, Annie, 1982, Blue Thunder, 1983, Nothing in Common, 1986, Peggy Sue Got Married, 1986, The Secret of My Success, 1987, Biloxi Blues, 1988, Steel Magnolias, 1989, Revenge, 1990, Lost in Yonkers, 1993, Barbarians at the Gate, 1993 (Emmy award Outstanding Made for Television Movie, 1993), Mr. Jones, 1993, Dr. Jekyll and Ms. Hyde, 1995, Mariette in Ecstacy, 1995, To Gillian on Her 37th Birthday, 1995. Recipient Thalberg award Acad. Motion Picture Arts and Scis., 1980. Office: Hepburn Bldg W 10202 W Washington Blvd Culver City CA 90232-3119*

STARK, RICHARD BOIES, surgeon, artist; b. Conrad, Iowa, Mar. 31, 1915; s. Eugene and Hazel (Carson) S.; m. Judy Thornton, Oct. 31, 1967. A.B., Stanford U., 1936; postgrad., U. Heidelberg, 1936-37; M.D., Cornell U., 1941. Diplomate Am. Bd. Plastic Surgery (pres. 1967-68). Intern Peter Bent Brigham Hosp., Boston, 1941-42; asst. resident surgery Childrens Hosp., Boston, 1942; plastic surgeon Northington Gen. Hosp., Ala., 1945-46, Percy Jones Gen. Hosp., Mich., 1946; postwar fellow anatomy and embryology Stanford U., 1946-47; from asst. resident to resident in head and neck surgery VA Hosp., Bronx, N.Y., 1947-50; asst. resident, resident surgery, plastic, head and neck and gen. surgery N.Y. Hosp., 1947-50; instr. surgery Cornell U., 1950-52, asst. prof., 1952-55, assoc. prof., 1955; asst. attending surgeon N.Y. Hosp., 1950-55; asst. prof. surgery Columbia U., 1955-58, assoc. prof., 1958-73, prof. clin. surgery, 1973—; assoc. attending surgeon St. Luke's Hosp., N.Y.C., 1955-58, founding attending surgeon Dept. Plastic Surgery, 1958—; founder dept. Plastic surgery, 1955; cons. Walter Reed Med. Ctr., 1970-77. Author: Plastic Surgery, 1962, Cleft Palate, 1968, Plastic Surgery at the New York Hospital 100 Years Ago, 1952, Aesthetic Plastic Surgery, 1980, Total Facial Reconstruction, 1985, Plastic Surgery of the Head and Neck, 1986; contbr. 53 chpts. to books, 214 articles to profl. jours.; assoc. editor: Plastic Reconstructive Surgery, 1977-82; founding editor: Annals Plastic Surgery, 1978-81; 19 one-person art shows, 1946—. Chmn. Medico Adv. Bd., 1976-77; mem., v.p. CARE Bd.; v.p. Wellborn Found., N.Y.C. Served with AUS, 1943-46. Decorated Bronze Star (U.S.); Medal of Honor (2) (Vietnam); cavallero Order of San Carlos (Colombia), Dieffenbach medal (Berlin), Gold medal Nat. Inst. Social Scis. Fellow ACS; mem. Am. Assn. Plastic Surgeons, Am. Soc. Plastic and Reconstructive Surgery (pres. 1966, Spl. Achievement award), Found. Am. Soc. Plastic and Reconstructive Surgery (pres. 1961-65), Am. Surg. Assn., Soc. Univ. Surgeons, French Soc. Plastic Surgeons, Brasilian Soc. Plastic Surgeons, Colombian Soc. Plastic Surgeons, Argentina Soc. Plastic Surgeons, Brit. Assn. Plastic Surgery, Peruvian Acad. Plastic Surgery, N.Y. Surg. Soc., N.Y. Acad. Medicine (mem. Friends Rare Book Room), Plastic and Reconstructive Surgery (sec., pres. 1966), N.Y. State Med. Soc. (pres., sec., med. history), N.Y. Regional Soc. Plastic and Reconstructive Surgery (pres. 1064-65), Halsted Soc. (pres. 1973-74), James IV Assn. Surgeons, Am. Soc. Aesthetic Plastic Surgery (pres. 1974-75), Nat. Arts Club (exhibiting mem.), Century Club (profl. artist), Artist Fellowship. Home: 35 E 75th St New York NY 10021-2761

STARK, ROBERT MARTIN, mathematician, civil engineer, educator; b. N.Y.C., Feb. 6, 1930; s. Alexander and Julia (Gross) S.; m. Carol LaSage, Jan. 13, 1955 (dec. Mar. 1988); children: Bradley R., Timothy D., Steven M., Candice B. AB, Johns Hopkins U., 1951; MA, U. Mich., 1952; PhD, U.

Del., 1965. Rsch. scientist Bausch and Lomb, Rochester, N.Y., 1955; instr. Rochester Inst. Tech., 1956-57; asst. dean engring., asst. prof. math. Cleve. State U., 1957-62; instr. U. Del., 1962-64, asst. prof. civil engring. and ops. rsch., 1964-68, assoc. prof., 1968-76, prof., 1976—; pres., cons. applied sci. R.M. Stark & Co., Inc.; vis. assoc. prof. MIT, 1972-73; chmn. grad. program in ops. rsch.; cons. in field. Author: (with R.L. Nicholls) Mathematical Foundations for Design: Civil Engineering Systems, 1972, (with R.H. Mayer, Jr.) Quantitative Construction Management: Uses of Linear Optimization, 1983, (with R. Engelbrecht-Wiggans and M. Shubik) Auctioning, Bidding and Contracting, 1983, (with C. Sloyer, et al) Contemporary Applied Mathematics Series, 1987. Bd. dirs. Geriatrics Svcs. Del., Inc., 1989—; Wilmington Sr. Ctr., 1994—, Meals on Wheels Found.; bd. dirs. Del. Acad. Sci., 1990—, pres. 1994—; bd. dirs., v.p. White Clay Watershed Assn.; commr. Del. Heritage Commn., 1990—. Grantee Office Naval Rsch., 1974-81, NSF, 1969-70, U.S. Army Rsch. Office, 1966-68. Mem. AAAS, ASCE, Nat. Coun. Tchrs. Math., Inst. Mgmt. Sci., Ops. Rsch. Soc. Am., Phila. Ops. Rsch. Soc. (pres. 1970), White Clay Watershed Assn. (bd. dirs. 1992—). Avocations: research, publs. ops. rsch., applied probability. Home: One Fox Ln Newark DE 19711 Office: U Del Dept Math Sci Newark DE 19716

STARK, ROHN TAYLOR, professional football player; b. Mpls., May 4, 1959; m. Ann Stark; 1 child, Rohn Jr. BS in Finance, Fla. State U., 1982. With Indpls. Colts, 1982-84; punter Indpls. Colts (formerly Balt. Colts), 1984—. Punter on the Sporting News Coll. All-Am. Team, 1981, NFL All-Pro team, 1992; played in Pro Bowl 1985, 86, 90, 92. Office: Indpls Colts PO Box 535000 Indianapolis IN 46253-5000*

STARK, SUSAN R., film critic; b. N.Y.C., July 9, 1940; d. Albert A. and Lillian H. (Landau) Rothenberg; m. Allan F. Stark, June 26, 1968 (div. 1983); children: Allana Fredericka, Paula-Rose. B.A., Smith Coll., 1962; M.A.T., Harvard U., 1963. Film critic Detroit Free Press, 1968-79, Detroit News, 1979—. Mem. Phi Beta Kappa. Office: Detroit News 615 W Lafayette Blvd Detroit MI 48226-3197

STARK, THOMAS MICHAEL, state supreme court justice; b. Riverhead, N.Y., Feb. 13, 1925; s. John Charles and Mary Ellen (Gaynor) S.; m. Jane Claire Crabtree, Dec. 30, 1954; children: Elizabeth Mary, Ellen Gaynor. BS cum laude, Holy Cross Coll., 1945; LLB, Harvard U., 1949. Bar: N.Y. 1950. Assoc. Zaleski & Jablonka, Riverhead, 1949-51; sole practice Riverhead, 1951-63, town atty., 1953, justice of peace, mem. town bd., 1956-57; mem. Riverhead Bd. Edn., Riverhead, 1960-63; judge county ct. County of Suffolk, Riverhead, 1963-68; justice 10th Jud. Dist. Supreme Ct. N.Y., Riverhead, 1969—, assoc. justice appellate term, 1985—; supervising judge Suffolk County Superior Criminal Cts., Riverhead, 1978-92; panel discussion leader Ann. Conf. N.Y. State Trial Judges, 1970-81; criminal law subcom. N.Y. State Trial Judges Benchbook, 1970-75; vice chmn. com. on criminal jury instrns. N.Y. State Office Ct. Administrn., 1975—; lectr. N.Y. State Office Ct. Adminstrn., 1977-87; mem. N.Y. State Ct. Facilities Task Force, 1980-84. Mem. exec. bd., v.p. Suffolk County council Boy Scouts Am., 1955-58; mem. exec. com., co-leader Riverhead, Suffolk County Republican Com., 1964-62. Served as ensign USNR, World War II. Recipient Silver Beaver award Boy Scouts Am., 1957, Disting. Eagle Scout, 1974; named Judge of Yr., Suffolk County Criminal Bar Assn., 1984. Mem. ABA (jud. adminstrn. sect.), N.Y. State Bar Assn. (presiding officer jud. sect. 1988-89, ho. dels. 1989-90), Suffolk County Bar Assn. (sec. 1959-62, 3d v.p. 1962-63). Home: Bay Woods Aquebogue NY 11931 Office: Suffolk County Criminal Blvd Riverhead NY 11901

STARK, WERNER E., food broker; b. Munich, Feb. 12, 1921; came to U.S., 1938; s. Herman H. and Klara (Rosenfelder) S.; m. Betty (div. 1969); children—Jackie Odom, Larry. B.A., U. Ill., 1942. Chmn. Stark & Co., Farmington Hills, Mich. 1947—; now chmn. bd. dirs. Served with C.I.C., U.S. Army, 1943-47, ETO. Mem. Nat. Food Broker's Assn. (dir. Detroit Tennis and Squash [mem. 1975-76]. Home: 7643 Danbury Cir West Bloomfield MI 48322-3570 Office: Stark & Co Inc 30301 Northwestern Hwy Farmington MI 48334-3260

STARKE, EDGAR ARLIN, JR., metallurgist, educator; b. Richmond, Va., May 10, 1936; s. Edgar Arlin and Mary Louise (Stein) S.; m. Donna Lee Frazier, June 10, 1961; children—John Arlin, Karen Lee. B.S. in Metall. Engring., Va. Poly. Inst., 1960; M.S., U. Ill., 1961; Ph.D. in Metall. Engring., U. Fla., 1964. Metallurgist Savannah River Lab., Aiken, S.C., 1961-62; asst. prof. Ga. Inst. Tech., Atlanta, 1964-68, assoc. prof. metallurgy, 1968-72, prof., 1972-82, dir. Fracture and Fatigue Research Lab., 1978-82; Earnest Oblesby prof. materials sci. U. Va., Charlottesville, 1983—, mem. staff Ctr. Advanced Studies, 1983-84, dean Sch. Engring. and Applied Sci., 1984-94; univ. prof., Oglesby prof. materials sci. and engring., 1994—; vis. scientist Oak Ridge Nat. Lab., 1967, Max-Planck Institut for Metallforschung, Stuttgart, Fed. Republic Germany, 1971; cons. Bell Tel. Labs., 1973-75, Lockheed Ga. Rsch. Lab., 1965-82, Southwire Co., 1967-82, Reynolds Metals Co., 1983-88, Northrop Corp., 1983—, Lockheed Missiles Space Co., 1983—, Kaiser Aluminum, 1984-86, GE, 1989—; mem. aeronautic adv. com. NASA, 1990-94, AGARD Structures and Materials panel, 1992—. Author articles to profl. jours. Served with U.S. Army, 1954-56. Fellow ASM Internat.; mem. Am. Soc. Metals (sec. Atlanta chpt. 1974-75), AIME (sec.-treas. Ga. chpt. 1965-66, v.p. 1967, pres. chpt. 1968, sec'd non-ferrous metallurgy com. 1973-74, vice chmn. 1974-75, chmn. 1976-78, vice chmn. program metals sci. bd. dirs. 1978-79), NRC (natural materials adv. bd.), Sigma Xi (sec. Ga. Inst. Tech. chpt. 1974-75), Tau Beta Pi, Alpha Sigma Mu, Omicron Delta Kappa, Phi Delta Epsilon. Home: RR 5 Box 331A Charlottesville VA 22901-8949

STARKEY, RICHARD See STARR, RINGO

STARKEY, WILLIAM EDWARD, telephone company executive; b. Ridley Park, Pa., Aug. 2, 1935; s. William Lester and Miriam Starkey; m. Barbara, June 20, 1959; children: William T., Michael M., Jennifer E. B.S. in Bus. Adminstrn. U. Del., 1957; M.S. in Bus. Adminstrn, St. Francis Coll., Ft. Wayne, Ind., 1964. Trainee Bell Telephone Co. of Pa., 1957, asst. dist. traffic mgr., 1959-64; traffic engr. Gen. Telephone Co., Ind., 1964; methods mgr. Gen. Telephone Co., 1965, gen. traffic adminstrn. mgr., 1965, gen. traffic engr. mgr., 1968; system traffic engr. mgr. GTE Svc. Corp., N.Y.C., 1969-71; traffic dir. Gen. Telephone Co. S.E., 1971-74, v.p. staff, 1974-76; oper. v.p. Gen. Telephone Co. Pa., 1976-77; v.p. mktg. and customer service, 1977-78, regional v.p. mktg. and customer service No. region, 1979-80; v.p. regulatory affairs GTE Info. Svcs. Inc., Stamford, Conn., 1980-82; v.p. staff regulatory affairs GTE Telephone Ops., Stamford, Conn., 1982-85; pres. GTE Fla. Telephone, Tampa, 1985-88, GTE Info. Svcs., Tampa, 1988—. Boys basketball coach YMCA, 1971-78, bd. dirs., 1976-78; trustee Fla. Orch. U. Tampa; chmn. bd. deacons 1st Presbyn. Ch., 1975; div. chmn. United Fund, 1962-64, 75-76; bd. dirs., exec. com. United Way of Greater Tampa, Hyde Park United Meth. Ch., Fla. State Fair, Prison Crusade Bd. With AUS, 1957-58, 60-61. Mem. Fla. C. of C. (bd. dirs.), Greater Tampa C. of C. (pres.), Omicron Delta Kappa. Republican. Methodist. Office: GTE Info Svcs Inc PO Box 2924 Barnett Pla 8th Fl Tampa FL 33601

STARKMAN, GARY LEE, lawyer; b. Chgo., Sept. 2, 1946; s. Oscar and Sara (Ordman) S. AB, U. Ill., 1968; JD cum laude, Northwestern U., 1971. Bar: Ill. 1971, U.S. Dist. Ct. (no. dist.) Ill. 1972, U.S. Ct. Appeals (7th cir.) 1972, U.S. Supreme Ct. 1974, Trial Bar U.S. Dist. Ct. (no. dist.) Ill. 1982, U.S. Ct. Appeals (3d cir.) 1984, U.S. Ct. Appeals (D.C. cir.) 1984. Asst. U.S. Atty. No. Dist. Ill., 1971-75; gen. counsel, dir. research Center for Thompson Campaign Com., 1975-77; counsel to Gov. of Ill., 1977-81; ptnr. Ross & Hardies, Chgo.; mem. admissions com. U.S. Dist. Ct. (no. dist.) Ill. Chmn. state agys. divsn. Jewish United Fund Met. Chgo., 1978-81; chmn. Ill. Racing Bd., 1991—; 'bd. dirs. Internat. Assn. Racing Commn., 1992-94; mem. community adv. bd. Jr. League of Chgo., 1979-83. Recipient John Marshall award for appellate litigation, Atty. Gen. U.S., 1974, Nat. Svc. award Tau Epsilon Phi, 1968; named to Ten Outstanding Young Citizens, Chgo. Jr. C. of C., 1978. Mem. ABA (litigation sect.), Chgo. Bar Assn. (constl. law com.), Decalogue Soc., Northwestern U. Law Alumni Assn. Co-author textbook: Cases and Comments on Criminal Procedure, 1974, 2d edit., 1980, 4th edit., 1992; contbr. writings to profl. publs., book revs. to periodicals. Office: Ross & Hardies 150 N Michigan Ave Ste 2500 Chicago IL 60601-7567

STARK-RICE, PATRICIA LEE, dean, mental health nurse; b. Americus, Ga., Sept. 15, 1938; d. Ernest William Lee and Margaret (Pilcher) Rush; m. Jimmie C. Stark, Sept. 29, 1961 (div.); children: Jaime Catherine Stark Schier, Patricia Ann Stark Reitz; m. Edward J. Rice, Feb. 11, 1987. AA, Ga. Southwestern Coll., 1959; BSN, Emory U., 1960, MN, 1963; DSN, U. Ala., 1979. Diplomate logotherapy Viktor Frank Inst. Logotherapy. Rehab. cons. Liberty Mut. Ins. Co., Atlanta, 1960-61; instr. Grady Meml. Hosp., Atlanta, 1961-62, Ga. Bapt. Hosp., Atlanta, 1963-64; float pool staff nurse Weld County Meml. Hosp., Greeley, Colo., 1964-65; asst. prof. Ga. Southwestern Coll., Americus, 1966, 67-72, 75; instr. St. Petersburg (Fla.) Jr. Coll., 1972-74; dept. chair nursing Albany (Ga.) State Coll., 1975-77; dean Sch. Nursing Troy (Ala.) State U., 1979-84, U. Tex. Health Sci. Ctr., Houston, 1984—; faculty part-time Samford U., Birmingham, Ala., 1977-79; bd. dirs. Curaflex Home Health Co., Houston, 1989-90; pres., bd. dirs. Ctr. for Logotherapy, Houston, 1992. Editor: The Hidden Dimension of Illness Human Suffering, 1992. Mem. gov's. appointee to adv. com. Tex. Commr. for Ins. Utilization Rev., Austin, 1992. Named Outstanding Woman in Edn. YWCA, 1988; recipient Friend of Nursing award Houston chpt. Pediatric Nursing Practitioners, 1992. Mem. Am. Assn. Colls. Nursing (bd. dirs.), Tex. Nurses Assn. (v.p. dist. #9 1991-92), Rotary Internat. (pub. health com. 1990—). Avocations: golfing, needlepoint, quilting. Home: 13 Town Oaks Pl Bellaire TX 77401 Office: U Tex Health Sci Ctr 1100 Holcombe Blvd Houston TX 77030

STARKS, FLORENCE ELIZABETH, special education educator; b. Summit, N.J., Dec. 6, 1932; d. Edward and Winnie (Morris) S. BA, Morgan State U., 1956; MS in Edn., CUNY, 1962; postgrad., Fairleigh Dickinson U., 1962-63, Seton Hall U., 1963, Newark State Coll. Cert. blind and visually handicapped and social studies tchr., N.J. Tchr. adult edn. Newark Bd. of Edn.; ret.; tchr. N.Y. Inst. for Edn. of the Blind, Bronx; developer first class for multiple handicapped blind children in pub. sch. system, Newark, 1960; ptnr. World Vision Internat. Mem. ASCD, AFL-CIO, AAUW, Coun. Exceptional Children, Nat. Assn. Negro Bus. and Profl. Women's Club Inc., N.J. Edn. Assn., Newark Tchrs. Assn., Newark Tchrs. Union-Am. Fedn. Tchrs., World Vision Internat. (ptnr.). Home: 4 Park Ave Summit NJ 07901-3942 Office: Newark Bd Edn 2 Cedar St Newark NJ 07102-3015

STARKS, FRED WILLIAM, chemical company executive; b. Millford, Ill., Aug. 16, 1921; s. Otis Earl and Evelyn Viola S.; m. Minnie Jane Reynolds, Sept. 4, 1946; children: David F., Steven J., Daniel J. B.S., U. Ill., 1943, M.S., 1947; Ph.D., U. Nebr., 1950. Supr., U.S. Rubber Co., Torrance, Calif., 1943-44; supr. DuPont, Niagara Falls, N.Y., 1950-57; pres. Starks Assocs., Inc., Buffalo, N.Y., 1957-89, chmn., 1989—; spl. lectr. U. Buffalo, 1959-63. Lt. (j.g.) USNR, 1944-46. Avery fellow, 1948-49; USPHS fellow, 1949-50. Mem. Am. Chem. Soc., N.Y. Acad. Sci., Am. Inst. Chemists, Sigma Xi. Clubs: Buffalo, Cosmos, Chemists. Patentee in field. Home: 742 Highland Ave Buffalo NY 14223-1645 Office: Starks Assocs Inc 1280 Niagara St Buffalo NY 14213-1503

STARKS, RICHARD, newspaper publishing executive. V.p. advertising The Dallas Morning News, Tex. Office: The Dallas Morning News Communication Ctr Young & Houston Sts Dallas TX 75202*

STARKWEATHER, GARY KEITH, optical engineer, computer company executive; b. Lansing, Mich., Jan. 9, 1938; married; 2 children. BS, Mich. State U., 1960; MS, U. Rochester, 1966. Engr. Bausch & Lomb, Inc., 1962-64; area mgr. optical systems Xerox Palo Alto (Calif.) Rsch. Ctr., 1964-80, sr. rsch. fellow, 1980-88; Apple fellow advanced tech. group Apple Computer, Inc., Saratoga, Calif., 1988—; dir. Apple Computer, Inc., Cupertino, Calif.; instr. optics Monroe Community Coll., 1968-69. Recipient of David Richardson Medal, 1991, Optical Soc. Am. mem. Optical Soc. Am. (David Richardson medal 1991), Soc. Photog. Inst. Engrs. Achievements include research in optics and electronics and their specific system interaction, involving display and hard copy image systems. Home: 10243 Rapkwood Dr #2 Cupertino CA 95014-1458*

STARLEAF, DENNIS ROY, economics educator; b. Moline, Ill., Mar. 27, 1938; s. Carl Gustof and Helen Marie (Van Cleemput) S.; m. Elizabeth Ann Compton, June 3, 1961; children: Monica I., Katrina E., Christopher C. BA, U. Calif., Berkeley, 1959; MA, U. Calif., L.A., 1960; PhD, Vanderbilt U., 1967. Asst. prof. econs. Iowa State U., Ames, 1964-68, assoc. prof., 1968-71, prof., 1971—, chair of econs., 1984—; economist Fed. Res. Bd. of Govs., Washington, 1973-74; bd. dirs. Iowa State U. Press, Ames, 1987—; cons. Midwest Rsch. Inst., Kansas City, Mo., 1988—. Assoc. editor: Jour. of Fin., 1971-73; contbr. articles to profl. jours. Trustee Iowa State U. Found., Ames, 1984—. Doctoral dissertation fellow Ford Found., 1962-63; recipient Faculty Svc. award Nat. Univ. Continuing Edn. Assn., 1983, Gold Quil award Am. Soc. Farm Mgrs. and Rural Appraisers, 1989. Mem. Am. Econs. Assn., Am. Agrl. Econ. Assn., Phi Beta Kappa. Avocations: skeet, trap, scuba diving, swimming. Home: 2218 Northwestern Ave Ames IA 50010-4527 Office: Iowa State U Dept Econs Heady Hall Ames IA 50011

STARLING, JAMES LYNE, university administrator; b. Ridgeway, Va., Aug. 16, 1930; s. Leonard Anderson and Florine (Anderson) S.; m. Martha Elizabeth Lewis, Mar. 17, 1968; 1 child, Elizabeth Anne. B.S., Va. Polytech. Inst. & State U., Blacksburg, 1951; M.S., Pa. State U., 1955, Ph.D., 1958. Instr. agronomy Pa. State U., University Park, 1957-58, asst. prof. agronomy, 1958-63, assoc. prof. agronomy, 1963-69, prof., head dept. agronomy, 1969-85, assoc. dean for adminstrn., Coll. Agr., 1985-93, sr. assoc. dean, 1993—. Served to 1st lt. U.S. Army, 1951-53, Korea. Fellow AAAS; mem. Am. Soc. Agronomy (pres. N.E. br. 1980-81), Crop Sci. Soc. Am., Am. Forage and Grassland Council, Pa. Grassland Council (pres. 1968), Pa. Plant Food and Protectant Edn. Soc. (pres. 1974-75), Phi Kappa Phi, Gamma Sigma Delta, Phi Epsilon Phi, Phi Sigma. Democrat. Methodist. Club: Kiwanis (State College, pres. 1982-83). Home: 1736 Princeton Dr State College PA 16803-3261 Office: Pa State U 201 Agr Adminstrn Bldg University Park PA 16802

STARN, DOUGLAS, artist, photographer; b. Somers Point, N.J., May 18, 1961. Cert., Sch. of Mus. Fine Arts, Boston, 1985. Works with brother Mike P. Starn under name Starn Twins; exhibited in group shows at Whitney Biennial, Whitney Mus. Am. Art, N.Y.C., 1987, Saatchi Collection, London, 1988, Mus. Fine Arts, Boston, 1988, Univ. Art Mus., Berkeley, Calif., Wadsworth Atheneum, Hartford, Conn., Mus. Contemporary Art, Chgo., 1988, Contemporary Arts Ctr., Cin., 1990, Balt. Mus. Art, Akron (Ohio) Art Mus., Blackford U., 1990, Israel Mus., Jerusalem, 1990, Metropolis-Internat. Art Exhbn., Berlin, 1991, Martin-Gropius-Bau, Berlin; two-man shows include Ringling Mus. Art, Sarasota, Fla., 1987, Mus. Modern Art, San Francisco, 1988; co-contbr. art work to various books. NEA grantee; recipient Infinity award, Internat. Ctr. of Photography, 1992. Office: Stux Gallery 163 Mercer St # 1 New York NY 10012-3203

STARN, MIKE P., artist, photographer; b. Somers Point, N.J., May 18, 1961. Cert., Sch. of Mus. Fine Arts, Boston, 1985. Works with brother Douglas Starn under name Starn Twins; exhibited in group shows at Whitney Biennial, Whitney Mus. Am. Art, N.Y.C., 1987, Saatchi Collection, London, 1988, Mus. Fine Arts, Boston, 1988, Univ. Art Mus., Wadsworth Atheneum, Hartford, Conn., Israel Mus., Jerusalem, 1990, Metropolis-Internat. Art Exhbn., Berlin, 1991, Martin-Gropius-Bau, Berlin; solo mus. shows include Ringling Mus. Art, Sarasota, Fla., 1987, Mus. Modern Art, San Francisco, 1988, Berkeley, Calif., Contemporary Art, Chgo., 1988, Contemporary Arts Ctr., Cin., 1990, Balt. Mus. Art, Akron, Ohio, Blaffer, Houston, 1990, Nat. Gallery of Victoria Melbourne, Australia, 1993, Naoshima Contemporary Art Mus., Japan, 1993; author: (book) Mike and Doug Starn, 1990; co-contbr. art work to various books. NEA grantee; recipient Infinity award, Internat. Ctr. of Photography, 1992. Office: Leo Castelli Gallery 420 W Broadway New York NY 10012

STARNES, EARL MAXWELL, urban and regional planner, architect; b. Winter Haven, Fla., Sept. 14, 1926; s. Thomas Lowe and Kathryn Maxwell (Gates) S.; m. Dorothy Jean Prather, Aug. 21, 1949; children: Tom, Will, Janet, Patricia. Student, Fla. So. Coll., 1946-48; BArch cum laude, U. Fla., 1951; MS in Urban and Regional Planning, Fla. State U., 1973, PhD, 1977. Registered architect, Fla. Assoc. Courtney Stewart (Architect), Ft. Lauderdale, Fla., 1951-52, William Bigoney, Architect, Ft. Lauderdale, 1952-

53, William T. Vaughn, Architect, Ft. Lauderdale, 1953, Alfred B. Parker, Architect, Miami, Fla., 1953-55; Rufus Nims, Architect, Miami, 1955-57; ptnr. Starnes & Rentscher, Architects, Miami, 1957-63, Starnes, Rentscher & Assocs., Architects, Miami, 1963-71; dir. div. mass transp. Fla. Dept. Transp., Tallahassee, 1971-72; dir. div. state planning Fla. Dept. Adminstrn., 1972-75; engaged in research and cons. service Tallahassee, 1975; prof., chmn. urban and regional planning Coll. Architecture U. Fla., Gainesville, 1976-88; prof. urban and regional plan coordination, doctrial studies Coll. of Architecture U. Fla., 1989-93, prof. emeritus, 1993—; instr. architecture U. Miami, 1953; adj. asst. prof. dept. urban and regional planning Coll. Social Scis., Fla. State U., 1971-74; mem. adv. panel B8-15, Nat. Coop. Hwy. Research Program, Transp. Research Bd., NRC-Nat. Acad. Scis., 1974—; mem. adv. bd. Pub. Tech., Inc., 1974—; mem. North Central Fla. Regional Planning Com., 1980-85, Fla. Substate Dist. Com., 1985-87; co-chmn. Joint Liaison Com. on Div. Responsibility for Urban Services, Dade County, Fla., 1965-71; chmn. joint policy com. U. Miami-Dade County Jackson Med. Center, 1966-71; chmn. Cape Fla. State Park Adv. Council, 1966-69, Dade County Landscape Ordinance Study Com., 1967-70, South Fla. Everglades Area Planning Council, 1969-71; vis. lectr. Calif. Poly. State U., San Luis Obispo, 1988-89; cons. Urban Planning Fla. and Caribbean. Prin. works include 1st Unitarian Ch., Miami; contbr. article on archtl. planning relationship Ency. Architecture Planning, 1987, chpt. to Growth Management, 1992; contbr. articles on land use and urban devel. policies, wetland protection and state planning to profl. jours. Active South Dade Mental Health Soc., 1967-68, Cape Fla. Acquisition Com., 1966, Dade County Downtown Govtl. Center Com., 1967-71, Miami Downtown Devel. Authority, 1970, Gov.'s Task Force on Resource Mgmt., 1971-72, Nat. Task Force on Natural Resources and Land Use Info. and Tech., 1973-74, Fla. Gov.'s Commn. on Property Rights, 1993-94; county commr. Dist. 7, Dade County, 1964-71; vice mayor, 1964, 68; mem. adv. com. Legis. Council Subcom. on Constrn. Industry Study, 1966-68; bd. dirs., chmn. retirement and compensation com. State Assn. County Commrs., 1964-71; mem. Alachua County Budget Study Com., 1978, Fla. Land Use Adv. Com. for Phosphate Lands, 1978-80, Suwanee River Water Mgmt. Bd., 1982-87, 91—, chmn. 1987-88; chmn. Fla. Inst. Phosphate Research, 1984-87; bd. dirs. 1000 Friends of Fla, 1986—. With USCG, 1944-46. Fellow AIA (urban design com. 1976-80); mem. Am. Inst. Cert. Planners, Nat. Inst. Bldg. Scis. (steering com. for rsch. 1979-80), Assn. Collegiate Schs. of Planning (bd. dirs. 1986-88), Gargoyle Soc., Phi Kappa Phi. Democrat. Unitarian. Office: PO Box 234 Cedar Key FL 32625

STARNES, JAMES WRIGHT, lawyer; b. East St. Louis, Ill., Apr. 3, 1933; s. James Adron and Nell (Short) S.; m. Helen Woods Mitchell, Mar. 29, 1958 (div. 1978); children: James Wright, Mitchell A., William B. II; m. Kathleen Israel, Jan. 26, 1985. Student St. Louis U., 1951-53; LLB, Washington U., St. Louis, 1957. Bar: Mo. 1957, Ill. 1957, Fla. 1992. Assoc. Stinson, Mag & Fizzell, Kansas City, Mo., 1957-60, ptnr., 1960-90; ptnr. Mid-Continent Properties Co., 1959-90, Fairview Investment Co., Kansas City, 1971-76, Monticello Land Co., 1973—; sec. Packaging Products Corp., Mission, Kans., 1972-89; chmn., treas. Galerie of Naples (Fla.), Inc., 1990-92. Bd. dirs. Mo. Assn. Mental Health, 1968-69, Kansas City Assn. Mental Health, 1966-78, pres., 1969-70; bd. dirs. Heed, 1965-73, 78-82, pres., 1966-67, fin. chmn. 1967-68; bd. dirs. Kansas City Halfway House Found., exec. com., 1966-69, pres., 1966; bd. dirs. Joan Davis Sch. for Spl. Edn., 1972-88, v.p., 1972-73, 79-80, pres., 1980-82; bd. dirs. Sherwood Ctr. for Exceptional Child, 1977-79, v.p., 1978-79. Served with AUS, 1957. Mem. ABA, Washington U. Law Alumni Assn. (bd. govs. 1990-92). Presbyterian (deacon). Mem. adv. bd. Washington U. Law Quar., 1957-90. Home and Office: 2657 E Wildwood Rd Springfield MO 65804

STARNES, MICHAEL S., trucking executive; b. 1945. BBA, U. Miss., 1968. Terminal mgr. Western Gillette Trucking, Fresno, Calif. and El Paso, Tex., 1968-73; gen. mgr. Rebel Motor Freight Lines, 1973-78; chmn. bd. dirs., pres., CEO M.S. Carriers, Inc., Memphis, 1977—; pres. TCX, Inc. Office: M S Carriers Inc 3150 Starnes CV Memphis TN 38116*

STARNES, WILLIAM HERBERT, JR., chemist, educator; b. Knoxville, Tenn., Dec. 2, 1934; s. William Herbert and Edna Margaret (Osborne) S.; m. Maria Sofia Molina, Mar. 4, 1986. BS with honors, Va. Poly Inst., 1955; PhD, Ga. Inst. Tech., 1960. Rsch. chemist Esso Rsch. & Engring. Co., Baytown, Tex., 1960-62, sr. rsch. chemist, 1962-64, polymer additives sect. head, 1964-65, rsch. specialist, 1965-67, rsch. assoc., 1967-71; instr. and rsch. assoc. dept. chemistry U. Tex., Austin, 1971-73; mem. tech. staff AT&T Bell Labs., Murray Hill, N.J., 1973-85; prof. chemistry Poly. U., Bklyn., 1985-89, head dept. chemistry and life scis., 1985-88, assoc. dir. polymer durability ctr. 1987-89, Floyd Dewey Gottwald Sr. prof. chemistry Coll. William and Mary, Williamsburg, Va., 1989—; invited lectr. several fgn. countries and U.S.; vis. scientist Tex. Acad. Scis., 1964-67; mem. bd. doctoral thesis examiners Indian Inst. Tech., New Delhi, 1988, McGill U., Montreal, 1989, MacQuarie U., Sydney, 1991, McMaster U., Hamilton, Can., 1994; panelist, reviewer NSF Acad. Rsch. Facilities Modernization Program, 1990; cons. numerous indsl. cos.; course dir. continuing edn. Mem. adv. bd. and bd. reviewers Jour. Vinyl Tech., 1981-83; guest USSR Acad. Scis., 1990, Russian Acad. Scis., 1992; mem. editorial bd. Jour. of Chemical and Biochemical Kinetics, 1992—; contbr. articles to profl. jours., chpts. to books; patentee in field. NSF fellow 1958-60; recipient Profl. Progress award Soc. Profl. Chemists and Engrs. 1968, Disting. Tech. Staff award AT&T Bell Labs. 1982, Polymer Sci. Pioneer award Polymer News, 1988, Honor Scroll award N.J. Inst. Chemists, 1989; NSF grantee, Nat. Bur. Standards Ctr. for Fire Rsch. grantee, Internat. Copper Rsch. Assn. grantee, Va. Ctr. Innovative Tech. grantee, GenCorp Found. grantee. Fellow AAAS (Project 2061 1985-86, chmn. chemistry subpanel 1985-86, mem. panel on phys. scis. and engring., 1985-86), Am. Inst. Chemists (life); mem. Am. Chem. Soc. (bd. dirs. southeastern Tex. sect. 1970, speakers bur. div. polymer chemistry 1976—, mem.-at-large exec. com. VA. sect. 1995), Soc. Plastics Engrs., N.Y. Acad. Scis. (life), Va. Acad. Sci., Sigma Xi (MA. Ferst award Ga. Inst. Tech. chpt. 1960), Phi Kappa Phi, Phi Lambda Upsilon (pres. Va. Poly. Inst. chpt. 1954-55). Current work: Degradation, stabilization, flammability, microstructures, and polymerization mechanisms of synthetic polymers, especially poly (vinyl chloride); free radical chemistry; carbon-13 nuclear magnetic resonance and organic synthesis. Subspecialties: Organic chemistry; Polymer chemistry. Office: Coll William and Mary Dept Chemistry PO Box 8795 Williamsburg VA 23187-8795

STAROSTOVIC, EDWARD JOSEPH, JR., engineer, engineering company executive; b. Chgo., Apr. 8, 1933; s. Edward J. and Esther Ruth (Guinee) S.; m. Marilyn Ann Mucek, June 23, 1956; children: Lynn, Ann, Karen, Susanne. BA, Ill. Inst. Tech., Chgo., 1958. Registered profl. engr., Wis. Owner, Structural Plywood Co., Chgo., 1958-60; engr., mgr. Wausau Homes Inc., Wis., 1960-72; engr., exec. v.p. PFS Corp., Madison, Wis., 1972-78, engr., pres. 1978—; bd. dirs. Wood Heating Alliance, Washington, 1982-88; del. U.S.-USSR Tech. Exchange Agreement, Washington, 1977—; part-time lectr. factory-built housing U. Wis., Madison. Mem. editorial rev. bd. Automated Builder, 1973—; contbr. articles to profl. jours. Mem. Joint Coun. for Industrialized/Modular Bldgs., 1987—, Pres.'s Nat. Manufactured Housing Adv. Coun., 1988; chmn. Wausau Area Regional Plan Commn., 1967. With U.S. Army, 1953-55, Korea. Recipient E. Kurtz award Nat. Assn. Bldg. Mfrs., 1972, S.A. Walters' Chmn.'s award Building Systems Coun., 1989. Mem. Nat. Soc. Profl. Engrs., Nat. Inst. Bldg. Scis., Am. Soc. Quality Control, Forest Products Research Soc., Internat. Assn. Elec. Inspectors, ASTM, Nat. Assn. of Home Builders (bd. dirs. Bldg. Systems Councils 1985-87), Nat. Inst. Bldg. Scis. (steering and main com., modular housing com. report to congress 1988). Office: PFS Corp 2402 Daniels St Madison WI 53704-6798

STARR, ALLAN H., lawyer; b. Trenton, N.J., June 21, 1944; s. Samuel L. and Rose (Ungar) S.; m. Donna deGroat, June 10, 1967; children: Jessica L., Aaron C. BA summa cum laude, Union Coll., 1966; LLB, U. Pa., 1969. Bar: Pa., U.S. Supreme Ct., U.S. Ct. of Appeals (3d cir.), U.S. Dist. Ct. (ea. dist.) Pa. 1969. Assoc. White and Williams, Phila., 1969-75, ptnr., 1976—; chmn. exec. com. casualty litigation dept. Colon-Rectal Surg. Found., Phila., chmn. Healthcare Law Group; bd. dirs., ethics com. Quakertown Hosp., Pa. Trustee Perkiomen Sch. Pennsburg, Pa., 1990. Mem. Am. Acad. of Hosp. Attys., Am. Bd. Trial Advocates, Internat. Assn. of Defense Counsel, Soc. of Hosp. Attys. of Pa., Pa. Defense Inst., Phi Beta Kappa. Avocations: saltwater sport fishing, tennis. Office: White and Williams One Liberty Pl Ste 1800 1650 Market St Philadelphia PA 19103

STARR, ARNOLD, neurologist, educator; b. N.Y.C., Aug. 5, 1932; s. Harry and Augusta (Rubelman) S.; children: David, Jonathan; m. Bonnie Olsen; 1 child, Noah. AB cum laude, Kenyon Coll., 1953; MD, NYU, 1957. Diplomate Am. Bd. Psychiatry and Neurology. Med. intern Beth Israel Hosp., Boston, 1957-58; resident in neurology Boston City Hosp.; teaching fellow Harvard U., Boston, 1958-60; rsch. assoc. NIH, Bethesda, Md., 1960-62; NIH spl. fellow U. Copenhagen, 1962-63, Sechenov Inst. Physiology, Moscow, 1963, Centre de Recherge Neurophysiologique, Paris, 1964-65; asst. prof. medicine Stanford U., Palo Alto, Calif., 1964-71; assoc. prof. medicine and psychobiology U. Calif., Irvine, 1972-74, prof. neurology, psychobiology and physiology, 1974-77, prof. neurology, psychobiology and cognitive scis., 1977—, prof. psychiatry, 1983—, chief div. neurology, 1973-77, founding chmn. dept. neurology, 1977-86, dir. neurology residency program, 1973-90; neurologist Irvine Med. Ctr. U. Calif., Orange, 1972—; cons. Nat. Multiple Sclerosis Soc., N.Y.C.; cons. mem. bd. sci. counselors, NIH, Bethesda, Md., 1988-92; Rosenthal vis. prof. Israel Inst. Tech., Haifa, 1982, 90; vis. prof. Tanta (Arab Republic of Egypt) U., 1985, U. London, 1986-88, U. Rome, 1986-87, U. Hangzhou, People's Republic China, 1986, U. Vienna, Austria, 1989; lectr. in field. Author: Sensory Evoked Potentials, 3 vols., 1984; contbr.: Behavioral Neurosciences, 1980; editorial reviewer various jours.; contbr. numerous articles to profl. jours., book chpts. Sr. surgeon USPHS, 1960-62. Fellow Acoustical Soc. Am.; mem. Am. Neurol. Assn., Am. Acad. Neurology (therapeutics and tech. assessment subcom. 1990), Nu Sigma Nu. Avocation: pomology. Office: U Calif-Irvine Dept Neurology & Medicine Irvine CA 92717

STARR, BART (BRYAN BARTLETT STARR), former professional football coach, former professional football player; b. Montgomery, Ala., Jan. 9, 1934; s. Benjamin B. and Lula I. (Tucker) S.; m. Cherry Morton, May 8, 1934; children: Bart, Bret (dec.). BS, U. Ala., 1956. Quarterback Green Bay Packers, 1956-71, asst. coach, 1972; gen. mgr., head coach, 1975-84; chmn. Healthcare Realty Management, 1984—; bd. dirs. Sentry Ins., Stevens Point, Wis., Bruno's Inc., Birmingham, Ala., Just For Feet, Birmingham, Ala. Coauthor: Quarterbacking, 1967, Starr, 1989. Recipient as one of the Jaycees 10 Outstanding Young Men in America, 1968, Byron White Award, NFL Man of the Year award, 1969, Nat. Profl. Football Hall of Fame, 1977. player, NFL Pro-Bowl 1960-62, 66, NFL Passing Leader, 1962, 64, 66, NFL Player of the Year 1966; mem., NFL Championship teams 1961, 62, 65, 66, 67, Super Bowl Championship teams 1967, 68 (MVP 1967, 68). Office: Healthcare Realty Management 1400 Urban Center Dr Ste 400 Birmingham AL 35242

STARR, CHAUNCEY, research institute executive; b. Newark, Apr. 14, 1912; s. Rubin and Rose (Dropkin) S.; m. Doris Evelyn Debel, Mar. 20, 1938; children: Ross M., Ariel E. E.E., Rensselaer Poly. Inst., 1932, Ph.D., 1935, D.Engring. (hon.), 1964; D.Engring. (hon.), Swiss ETH, 1980; D. Sci. (hon.), Tulane U., 1986—. Research fellow physics Harvard, 1935-37; research asso. Mass. Inst. Tech., 1938-41; research physicist D.W. Taylor Model Basin, Bur. Ships, 1941-42; staff radiation lab. U. Calif., 1942-43, Tenn. Eastman Corp., Oak Ridge, 1943-46, Tenn. Eastman Corp. (Clinton Labs.), 1946; chief spl. research N. Am. Aviation, Inc., Downey, Calif., 1946-49; dir. atomic energy research dept. N. Am. Aviation, Inc., 1949-55, v.p., 1955-66; gen. mgr. N. Am. Aviation, Inc. (Atomics Internat. div.), 1955-60, pres. div., 1960-66; dean engring. U. Calif. at Los Angeles, 1966-73; cons. prof. Stanford, 1974—; pres. Electric Power Research Inst., 1973-78, vice chmn., 1978-87, pres. emeritus, 1987—; Dir. Atomic Indsl. Forum. Contbr. sci. articles to profl. jours. Decorated Legion of Honor (France); recipient Henry D. Smyth award Atomic Indsl. Forum, 1983. Fellow Am. Nuclear Soc. (past pres.), Am. Phys. Soc., AAAS (dir.); mem. AIAA (sr.), Am. Power Conf., Nat. Acad. Engring., Am. Soc. Engring. Edn., Royal Swedish Acad. for Engring. Scis., Eta Kappa Nu, Sigma Xi. Home: 95 Stern Ln Atherton CA 94027-5422

STARR, CHESTER G., history educator; b. Centralia, Mo., Oct. 5, 1914; s. Chester Gibbs and Nettie (Glore) S.; m. Gretchen Daub, July 15, 1940; children: Jennifer (Mrs. Michael Johnson), Richard G., Thomas J.J. A.B. with distinction, U. Mo., 1934, LL.D., 1981; M.A., 1935; Ph.D., Cornell U., 1938; LLD (hon.), U. Ill., 1987, St. Michaels Coll., 1992. Faculty U. Ill. at Urbana, 1940-70, prof. history, 1953-70, chmn. div. humanities, 1953-55, chmn. dept. history, 1960-61; prof. U. Mich., Ann Arbor, 1970-85; Bentley prof. U. Mich., 1973-85, Hudson prof., 1981-82; Cons. World Book, 1963-67, Ency. Americana, 1966—. Author: Roman Imperial Navy, 1941, From Salerno to the Alps, 1948, Emergence of Rome, 1950, Civilization and the Caesars, 1954, Origins of Greek Civilization, 1961, History of Ancient World, 1965, Rise and Fall of Ancient World, 1965, Awakening of the Greek Historical Spirit, 1968, Athenian Coinage, 480-449 B.C, 1970, Ancient Greeks, 1971, Ancient Romans, 1971, Early Man, 1973, Political Intelligence in Classical Greece, 1974, 94, Economic and Social Growth of Early Greece, 1977, Essays on Ancient History, 1979, Beginnings of Imperial Rome, 1980, The Roman Empire: A Study in Survival, 1982, Individual and the Community: The Rise of the Polis, 1986, Past and Future in Ancient History, 1987, Influence of Sea Power on Ancient History, 1988, The Birth of Athenian Democracy, 1990, 93, The Aristocratic Temper of Greek Civilization, 1991. Served from 1st lt. to lt. col. AUS, 1942-46, MTO. Decorated Bronze Star; Croce di Guerra Italy).; Recipient certificate as distinguished grad. U. Mo., 1963; Am. Acad. in Rome fellow, 1938-40; Guggenheim fellow, 1950-51, 58-59. Fellow Am. Acad. Arts and Scis.; mem. Am. Hist. Assn. (chmn. com. on ancient history 1961-67, Disting. scholar 1991), AAUP (chpt. pres. 1956-57), Socs. for Promotion Roman and Hellenic Studies, Royal Numis. Soc., Assn. Ancient Historians (pres. 1974-78), Phi Beta Kappa, Phi Mu Alpha. Home: 2301 Blueberry Ln Ann Arbor MI 48103-2212

STARR, DAVID, newspaper editor, publisher; b. N.Y.C., Aug. 1, 1922; s. Aaron and Helen (Simon) S.; m. Marjorie Giffen, Aug. 3, 1943; children: Pamela, Peter. B.A., Queens Coll., 1942. Reporter, rewriteman L.I. Daily Press, 1942-50; exec. editor Nassau Daily Rev. Star, 1953-55; asst. editor Newark Star-Ledger, 1954-56; assoc. editor L.I. Press, 1953-54, 56-62, mng. editor, 1962-69, editor, 1969-77; sr. editor Newhouse Newspapers, 1971—; pub. Springfield Union-News, Sunday Republican, 1977—, now pres. and pub.; pres.Springfield Central, Inc., 1978-88, chmn. 1989—. Trustee Nassau Community Coll., SUNY, 1959-66; bd. dirs. Springfield Libr. and Mus. Assn., chmn., 1988-90; mem. Mass. Cultural Coun., 1980—; bd. dirs. Am. Arts Alliance, 1988-92, chmn., 1989-92. Mem. Am. Soc. Newspaper Editors, Am. Newspaper Pubs. Assn. *

STARR, DAVID EVAN, corporate executive; b. Muscatine, Iowa, May 4, 1962; s. Walter C. and Ruth E. (Hayes) S. Grad. high sch., Marion, Iowa. Telemktg. dir. East-West Theatrical Prodns., West Port, Conn., 1983-85, WRG Enterprises, Sarasota, Fla., 1985-86; CEO Wolf Entr., 1982-84, Nat. Labyrinth Cos., Cedar Rapids, Iowa, 1989—, Megaplex Industries, Marion, Iowa, 1992—. Author: Girls of the Deep, 1989. Charter mem. Repub. Presdl. Task Force, Washington, 1982—; sustaining mem. Repub. Nat. Com., Washington, 1984—. Mem. Assn. MBA Execs., U.S. Jaycees. Methodist. Avocations: model building, reading, business. Office: Megaplex Industries PO Box 171 Marion IA 52302-0171

STARR, FREDERICK BROWN, furniture manufacturing executive; b. Westfield, Mass., Dec. 11, 1932; s. Frederick Rickaby and Virginia (Brown) S.; m. Sue Zook, June 1958; children: Jonathan, Curtis, Anne. BA in English, Trinity Coll., Hartford, Conn., 1955. Archtl. ceilings salesman Armstrong World Industries, Inc., Indpls., 1958-63, mktg. mgmt., Lancaster, Pa., 1963-73, v.p., gen. sales mgr. subs. co. Thomasville Furniture Industries, Inc., (N.C.), 1973-77, sr. v.p., gen. sales mgr. 1977-82, pres., CEO, 1982—, also dir.; bd. dirs. Furniture Libr., High Point, N.C. vice-chair U. N.C., Greensboro, 1985—, Reynolds House Mus., 1988—; pres. N.C. Shakespeare Theatre, 1987—; bd. dirs. Community Hosp., Thomasville, 1984—; chmn. TFI Found., Thomasville, 1984—. Served with U.S. Army, 1955-57. Mem. Internat. Home Furnishings Market Assn. (chmn. 1992-93). Republican. Episcopalian. Home: 5506 E Rockingham Rd Greensboro NC 27407-7242 Office: Thomasville Furniture 401 E Main St Thomasville NC 27360

STARR, GRIER FORSYTHE, retired pathologist; b. Jamestown, N.D., Oct. 6, 1926; s. Earl Grier and Grace (Forsythe) S.; m. Virginia Lucille Heidinger, June 25, 1948; children: William Grier, Joan Elizabeth Starr Barton. BS cum laude, Jamestown (N.D.) Coll., 1947; MD, Northwestern

U., 1951; MS in Pathology, U. Minn., 1956. Diplomate Nat. Bd. Med. Examiners, 1952, Minn., Mich., Oreg. and Wash. state bds., Am. Bd. Pathology in Clin. Pathology, 1956, and in Pathol. Anatomy, 1957. Intern Evanston (Ill.) Hosp., 1951-52; sr. resident in pathology Henry Ford Hosp., Detroit, 1955-56; fellow in pathology Mayo Clinic, Rochester, Minn., 1952-55, cons. surgical pathology, 1956-59; cons., pathologist Lab. Pathology and Pathology Cons., Eugene, Oreg., 1959-91, pres., 1973-85; mem. staff McKenzie-Willamette Hosp., Springfield, Oreg., 1959-91—; mem. staff Sacred Heart Gen. Hosp., Eugene, Oreg., 1959-91, chief of staff, 1969-71, dir. labs., 1973-86, emeritus staff, 1992—; chmn. bd., chief ops. officer Oreg. Consol. Labs., Eugene, Oreg., 1986-89; bd. dirs Oreg. Blue Cross-Blue Shield, Portland, 1985-94, Sisters of St. Joseph of Peace Health & Hosp. Svcs., Bellevue, Wash., 1990—; affiliate in pathology Oreg. Health Scis. Ctr., Portland, 1972-88; assoc. prof. U. Oreg., Eugene, 1986. Contbr. articles to profl. jours. Served with USN, 1944-46. Fellow Am. Coll. Pathologists, Am. Soc. Clin. Pathologists; mem. AMA, Lane County Med. Soc. (pres. 1984-85), Am. Soc. Cytology, Internat. Acad. Pathologists, Pacific NW Soc. Pathologists (pres. 1979-80), Oreg. State Soc. Pathologists, Am. Soc. Dermatopathology (chmn. 1984, peer rev. com. 1976-91). Republican. Presbyterian. Avocation: raising, training and showing Am. Quarter Horse Assn.-registered cutting horses. Home: 2455 S Louis Ln Eugene OR 97405-1026

STARR, HARVEY, political scientist; b. N.Y.C., Nov. 11, 1946; s. Nathan and Betty (Brand) S.; m. Madonna Kissel, June 1, 1969 (div. Dec. 1979); m. Dianne C. Luce, July 2, 1994. BA, SUNY, Buffalo, 1967; M of Philosophy, Yale U., 1970, PhD, 1971. Acting instr. Dept. Polit. Sci., Yale U., New Haven, Conn., 1970-71; visiting fellow in politics Dept. Politics, U. Aberdeen, Scotland, 1971-72, 78-79; asst. prof. Dept. Polit. Sci., Ind. U., Bloomington, 1972-77, assoc. prof., 1977-83, prof., 1983-89; prof. in internat. affairs Dept. Govt. & Internat. Studies, U. S.C., Columbia, 1989—; editl. bd. Am. Polit. Sci. Rev., 1985-89, 91-95, Internat. Studies Quar., 1985-90, Jour. of Politics, 1988—, Comparative Polit. Studies, 1979-82, Internat. Interactions, 1985-91, editor, 1991—; assoc. editor Teaching Polit. Sci., 1978-81. Author: Henry Kissinger: Perceptions of International Politics, 1984; co-author: Inquiry, Logic and International Politics, 1989, World Politics: Menu for Choice, 1981, 85, 89, 92, The Diffusion of War: A Study of Opportunity and Willingness, 1991; contbr. articles to profl. jours. Grantee NSF, 1982-84. Mem. Peace Sci. Soc. Midwest (pres. 1978-80), Ind. Consortium for Security Studies (dep. dir. 1980-89), Data Devel. in Internat. Rsch. (exec. coun. 1986-87, 89-92), Conflict Processes Sect., Am. Polit. Sci. Assn. (exec. coun. 1989-91, pres. 1992-95), So. Polit. Sci. Assn. (exec. coun. 1991-94). Office: U SC Dept Govt Internat Studies Columbia SC 29208

STARR, ISIDORE, lawyer, educator; b. Bklyn., Nov. 24, 1911. BA, CCNY, 1932; MA, Columbia U., 1939; LLB, St. John's U., Jamaica, N.Y., 1936; JSD, Bklyn. Law Sch., 1942; PhD, New Sch. Social Rsch., 1957. Bar: N.Y. 1937. Tchr. N.Y.C. high schs., 1934-61; assoc. prof., prof. edn. Queens Coll., 1961-75, emeritus, 1975—; dir. Inst. on Law-Related Edn., Lincoln-Filene Ctr., Tufts U., 1963; dir. Law Studies Inst., N.Y.C., 1974; adv. on Our Living Bill of Rights Film Series (6 films) Encyclopedia Britannica Ednl. Corp.; mem. Ariz. Ctr. for Law-Related Edn.; cons. in field. Bd. dirs. Phi Alpha Delta Juvenile Justice Program, 1981—. John Hay fellow, 1952-53. Recipient Outstanding Citizen award Philip Morris Cos., 1992. Mem. ABA (hon. chair adv. commn. on Youth Edn. for Citizenship, Isidore Starr award for Spl. Achievement in Law Studies, Leon Jaworski award 1989), Am. Judicature Soc., Am. Soc. for Legal History, Am. Legal Studies Assn., Nat. Coun. Social Studies (past pres.), Phi Beta Kappa, Phi Alpha Delta (cert. of appreciation 1981). Author: The Lost Generation of Prince Edward County, 1968, The Gideon Case, 1968, The Feiner Case, 1968, The Mapp Case, 1968, The Supreme Court and Contemporary Issues, 1968, Human Rights in the United States, 1969, The American Judicial System, 1972, The Idea of Libery, 1978, Justice: Due Process of Law, 1981; co-editor Living American Documents, 1971. Address: 6043 E Harvard St Scottsdale AZ 85257

STARR, KENNETH WINSTON, lawyer; b. Vernon, Tex., July 21, 1946; s. W. D. and Vannie Maude (Trimble) S.; m. Alice Jean Mendell, Aug. 23, 1970; children: Randall Postley, Carolyn Marie, Cynthia Anne. B.A., George Washington U., 1968; M.A., Brown U., 1969; J.D., Duke U., 1973; LLD (hon.), Hampden Sydney Coll., Shenandoah U., Mitchell Coll. Law. Bar: Calif. 1973, D.C. 1979, Va. 1979. Law clk. to Judge David Dyer U.S. Ct. Appeals (5th cir.), Miami, Fla., 1973-74; assoc. Gibson, Dunn & Crutcher, Los Angeles, 1974-75; law clk. to Chief Justice Warren E. Burger, U.S. Supreme Ct., Washington, 1975-77; assoc., ptnr. Gibson, Dunn & Crutcher, Washington, 1977-81; counselor to atty gen. of U.S. Dept. Justice, Washington, 1981-83; judge U.S. Ct. Appeals (D.C. circuit), Washington, 1983-89; solicitor gen. Dept. Justice, Washington, 1989-93; ptnr. Kirkland & Ellis, Washington, 1993—; ind. counsel for Whitewater, 1994—. Contbr. articles to legal jours. Legal advisor CAB transition team office of pres.-elect, 1980-81; legal advisor SEC transition team, 1980-81; bd. adv. Duke Law Jour. Recipient Disting. Alumni awards George Washington U., Duke U.; recipient Atty. Gen.'s Award for Disting. Svc., 1993, Am. Values award U.S. Indsl. Coun. Ednl. Found., 1993. Fellow Am. Bar Found. (judicial fellows com., judicial conf. com. on bicentennial of U.S. constitution); mem. ABA, Am. Law Inst., Am. Judicature Soc., Inst. Jud. Adminstrn. (pres.), Supreme Ct. Hist. Soc., Calif. Bar Assn., D.C. Bar Assn., Va. Bar Assn., Order of Coif, Phi Delta Phi (Hughes chpt. Man of Yr. 1973).

STARR, LEON, retired chemical research company executive; b. Bronx, N.Y., May 2, 1937; s. Michael and Bella (Foux) S.; m. Joan Gail Linett, June 19, 1960; children—Michael Jason, Jennifer Nicole. B.S., Poly. Inst., Brooklyn, 1958; Ph.D., U. Mo., 1962. Teaching asst. U. Mo. Columbia, 1958-62; chem. researcher Mobil Chem. Co., Edison, N.J., 1962-67; various mgmt. positions then dir. tech. Celanese Corp., N.Y.C., 1967-83, corp. v.p tech., 1983-86; pres. Celanese Research Co., N.Y.C., 1983-90; pres., corp. v.p. tech. Hoechst Celanese Corp., Chatham, N.J., 1986-90, ret., 1990; pres. Lee Starr Assocs., 1990—; adv. bd. U. Pa. 1988-90; adv. coun. Hampton U., 1988—; nat. adv. coun. Synthesis Coalition on Engring. Edn. 1991—. Contbr. chpt. to book; patentee in field. Fellow Phillips Corp., U. Mo., 1961-62, Poly. Inst. N.Y., 1985. Mem. AAAS, Assn. Rsch. Dirs., Am. Chem. Soc. (corp. assoc. 1983-90, bd. govs.), Natural Sci. Assn., N.Y. Acad. Scis., Soc. Chem. Industry, Chem. Mfrs. Assn. (chmn. chem. regulations and adv. com. 1977-82), Am. Inst. Chemists, Sales and Mktd. Execs. Internat. (v.p. 1972-73), Sigma Xi. Avocations: tennis; sailing; collecting antique scientific instruments.

STARR, MARTIN KENNETH, management educator; b. N.Y.C., May 21, 1927; s. Harry and Melanie (Krauss) S.; m. Polly Exner, Apr. 3, 1955; children: Christopher Herschel, Loren Michael. BS, MIT, 1948; MS, Columbia U., 1951, PhD, 1953. Ptnr., dir. M.K. Starr Assocs., 1956-61; prof. mgmt. sci. Columbia U., N.Y.C., 1961—; dir. Ctr. for the Study of Ops. Columbia U., 1980—, vice dean Grad. Sch. Bus., 1974-75; guest lectr. Am. U., Beirut, 1964, MIT, 1964-67, U. Cape Town, S.Africa, 1976, 80, 82, 84, 86, 88; cons. E.I. duPont de Nemours & Co., Eastman Kodak Co., Lever Brothers, TRW, R.J. Reynolds, Young & Rubicam, IBM. Author: Operations Management, 1978, (with Irving Stein) The Practice of Management Science, 1976, Systems Management of Operations, 1971, Management: A Modern Approach, 1971, Product Design and Decision Theory, 1963, Production Management: Systems and Synthesis, 2d edit, 1972, (with David W. Miller) Executive Decisions and Operations Research, 2d edit, 1969, The Structure of Human Decisions, Inventory Control-Theory and Practice, 1962, (with David G. Dannenbring) Management Science: An Introduction, 1981, (with Earl K. Bowen) Statistics for Business and Economics, 1982, (with Marion Sobol) Statistics for Business and Economics: An Action Learning Approach, 1983, Managing Production and Operations, 1989, Global Corporate Alliances and the Competitive Edge, 1991, (with Marion Sobol) Introduction to Statistics for Executives, 1993; editor: Executive Readings in Management Science, 1965, (with Milan Zeleny) Multiple Criteria Decision Making, 1977, Global Competitiveness: Getting the U.S. Back on Track, 1988; editor in chief: Mgmt. Sci, 1967-82; mem. editorial bd. Behavioral Sci., 1970—; editorial adviser: Operational Research Quar., 1970-85; cons. editor: Columbia Jour. World Business; Prodn. Decision Making, fall, 1977, Quantitative methods in mgmt., McGraw-Hill Book Co., N.Y.C.; contbr. articles to profl. jours. Mem. Inst. Mgmt. Scis. (pres. 1974-75), Prodn. and Ops. Mgmt. Soc. (pres. elect 1994—), Beta Gamma Sigma. Home: PO Box 229 Southampton NY 11969-2129 Office: Columbia U Ctr for Study of Ops Grad Sch Bus 311 Uris Hall New York NY 10027 *The ability to manage*

complex systems has become the most pressing requirement as we move to and through the year 2000. Remarkable growth of strong interdependencies has occurred since 1980. Energy, ecology, international trade, quality, and productivity are some examples of critical issues for resolution. Management science combines art and logic with advancing computer-linked technology to achieve social benefit. Perhaps a new name is needed to describe this effort. By whatever name it is called, the impact of management science will determine the character of the 21st century and will, in turn, be changed by it.

STARR, MICHAEL SETH, critic; b. Hackensack, N.J., Nov. 18, 1961; s. Ivan Lee and Zelda Libby (Ladenheim) S.; m. Gail Ellen Fleisher, June 11, 1989; 1 child, Rachel Lara. BA in Am. Lit., George Washington U., 1983. Copy and rsch. editor Broadband Comms., N.Y.C., 1984-87; reporter, film citic Daily Register, Red Bank, N.J., 1987, Daily Local News, West Chester, Pa., 1987-90; entertainment editor North Jersey hearld-News, Passaic, N.J., 1990-93, TV critic, 1993—. Author: Peter Sllers: A Film History, 1991, Works of Art: The Art Carney Story, 1995. Recipient 1st Pl. award Jersey Press assn., 1992, 3d Pl. award, 1993. Mem. TV Critics Assn. Jewish. Home: 840 Summit Ave Hackensack NJ 07601 Office: North Jersey Herald & News 988 Main Ave Passaic NJ 07055

STARR, PAUL ELLIOT, sociologist, writer, editor, educator; b. N.Y.C., May 12, 1949; s. Saul and Sarah Marion (Buzen) S.; m. Sandra Lurie Stein, Apr. 12, 1981. BA, Columbia U., 1970; PhD, Harvard U., 1978. Jr. fellow Harvard Soc. Fellows, 1975-78; asst. prof. Harvard U., Cambridge, Mass., 1978-82, assoc. prof., 1982-85; prof. sociology Princeton (N.J.) U., 1985—; founder, co-editor The Am. Prospect. Author: The Discarded Army: Veterans After Vietnam, 1974, The Social Transformation of American Medicine, 1983 (C. Wright Mills award 1983, Pulitzer prize 1984, Bancroft award 1984), The Logic of Health-Care Reform, 1992. Guggenheim Found. fellow, 1981-82. Democrat. Office: Princeton U Dept of Sociology Green Hall Princeton NJ 08544-1010

STARR, RICHARD CAWTHON, botany educator; b. Greensboro, Ga., Aug. 24, 1924; s. Richard Neal and Ida Wynn (Cawthon) S. BS in Secondary Edn., Ga. So. Coll., 1944; MA, George Peabody Coll., 1947; postgrad. (Fulbright scholar), Cambridge (Eng.) U., 1950-51; PhD, Vanderbilt U., 1952. Faculty Ind. U., 1952-75, prof. botany, 1960-76; founder, head culture collection algae U. Tex., Austin, prof. botany, 1976—; head course marine botany Marine Biol. Lab., Woods Hole, Mass., 1959-63. Algae sect. editor: Biol. Abstracts, 1959—; editorial bd.: Jour. Phycology, 1965-68, 76-78; assoc. editor: Phycologia, 1963-69; Contbr. articles to profl. jours. Trustee Am. Type Culture Collection, 1962-68, 80-85. Guggenheim fellow, 1959; sr. fellow Alexander von Humboldt-Stiftung, 1972-73; recipient Disting. Tex. Scientist award Tex. Acad. Sci., 1987. Fellow AAAS, Ind. Acad. Sci.; mem. NAS (Gilbert Morgan Smith Award 1985), Am. Inst. Biol. Scis. (governing bd. 1976-77, exec. com. 1980), Bot. Soc. Am. (sec. 1965-69, v.p. 1970, pres. 1971, Darbaker prize 1955), Phycological Soc. Am. (past pres., v.p., treas.), Soc. Protozoologists, Internat. Phycological Soc. (sec. 1964-68), Brit. Phycological Soc., Akademie Wissenschaft zu Göttingen (corr.), Sigma Xi. Office: U Tex Dept Botany Austin TX 78713

STARR, RICHARD WILLIAM, retired banker; b. Phila., Oct. 7, 1920; s. Edwin Bell and Bertha (Aurand) S.; student U. Buffalo, 1946-50; BS, U. So. Calif., evenings 1952-58; grad. Am. Inst. Banking, 1942, Pacific Coast Sch. Banking, U. Wash., 1968, Stanford Grad. Sch. Credit and Fin. Mgmt., 1958; Harvard U. Grad. Sch. Advanced Mgmt. Program, 1975; m. Evelyn Irene Johnson, Aug. 3, 1943; children—David Richard, Daniel Robert. With Marine Trust Co. of Buffalo, 1939-50, mgr. credit dept., 1947-50; with Calif. Bank, Los Angeles, 1952-61, with United Calif. Bank (formerley Calif. Bank), 1961-79, with First Interstate Bank (formerley United Calif. Bank), 1979-83; installment credit officer, 1952-53, mgr. credit dept., 1953-58, comml. lending officer, loan administr., 1958-61, br. mgr., 1961, asst. cashier, 1955, asst. v.p., 1956-63, v.p., 1963-71, sr. v.p., 1971-83, area adminstr. nat. div., 1969-70, br. adminstr., 1970-73, mgr. state div. corp. banking dept., 1973-74, mgr. so. div. Calif. Banking Group, Los Angeles 1974-76, adminstr. spl. credits div., 1976-79, with First Interstate Bank , exec. v.p., adminstr. Calif. div., 1979-80, sr. credit adminstr. bank credit policy and supervision div., 1980-83, also chmn. credit policy worldwide, pvt. practice cons., Orange, Calif., 1983-94; dir. I.C.N. Pharms., Inc., Costa Mesa, Calif. Served with USCGR, 1942-45, USNR, 1947-52. Mem. Mortgage Banking Assn. (chmn. Orange County 1962—), Robert Morris Assocs., Calif. Bankers Assn. (exec. com. 1972), Beta Gamma Sigma. Republican. Clubs: Santa Ana (Calif.) Country; Jonathan (Los Angeles), Masons. Home: 2849 N Rustic Gate Way Orange CA 92667-1709

STARR, RICK, broadcasting executive; b. Flint, Mich., Feb. 9, 1947; s. C. Dean and Barbara (Clements) S.; m. Branka Starr, Sept. 20, 1970 (div. Apr. 1985); m. Joyce Arlene Richman, July 20, 1985. Student, Lehigh U., 1964-66; BA in Communications, Curry Coll., 1969. Announcer Sta. WKBK, Keene, N.H., 1969-70; program dir. Sta. WGUY, Bangor, Maine, 1970-72, Sta. WCAS, Boston, 1972-76, Sta. KDKA, Pitts., 1977-79; v.p., gen. mgr. Sta. WBZ, Boston, 1983-89, Sta. WMAQ, Chgo., 1989—. Bd. dirs. Pitts. Wind Symphony, 1984-89, CRIS Radio, Chgo., 1992-93. Mem. Pitts. Radio Orgn. (pres. 1984-85), Radio Broadcasters Chgo. Office: Sta WMAQ-AM NBC Tower 455 N Cityfront Plaza Dr Chicago IL 60611-5503

STARR, RINGO (RICHARD STARKEY), musician, actor; b. Liverpool, Eng., July 7, 1940; s. Richard and Elsie (Gleave) Starkey; m. Maureen Cox, Feb. 11, 1965 (div. 1975); children: Zak, Jason, Lee; m. Barbara Bach, Apr. 27, 1981. Drummer, vocalist mus. group, The Beatles, 1962-69; musician with Rory Storme's Hurricanes, 1959-62; solo performer, 1970-77; toured with All-Starr Band, 1992; recs. include Ringo the 4th, Sentimental Journey, 1970, Beaucoups of Blues, 1970, Ringo, 1973, Goodnight Vienna, 1974, Blast From Your Past, 1975, Starrstruck: Ringo's Best, 1989, Ringo's Rotogravure, 1976, Ringo the Fourth, 1977, Bad Boy, 1978, Stop and Smell the Roses, 1981, Time takes Time, 1992; solo albumn It Don't Come East, 1971, Only You, 1975, No No Song, 1975, (with the Beatles) A Hard Day's Night, 1964, Rubber Seol, 1965, Sgt. Pepper's Lonely Hearts Club Band, 1967, Yellow Submarine, 1969, Let It Be, 1969, Hey Jude, 1970, Love Songs, 1977, Reel Music, 1982, numerous others; film appearances with the Beatles include A Hard Day's Night, 1964, Help!, 1965, Yellow Submarine, 1968, Let It Be, 1970, TV film Magical Mystery Tour, 1967; individual film appearances include Candy, 1968, The Magic Christian, 1969, 200 Motels, 1971, Blindman, 1971, Tommy, 1972, That'll Be the Day, 1973, Born to Boogie, also dir., producer, 1974, Son of Dracula, also producer, 1975, Lisztomania, 1975, Ringo Stars, 1976, Caveman, 1981, The Cooler, 1982, Give My Regards to Broad Street, 1984; appeared in TV miniseries Princess Daisy, 1983; star TV series Shining Time Station, PBS, 1989—. Decorated Order Brit. Empire; recipient numerous Grammy awards with The Beatles; inducted with The Beatles into Rock and Roll Hall of Fame, 1988. Office: 2 Glynde Mews, London SW3 1SB, England*

STARR, ROSS MARC, economist, educator; b. Oak Ridge, Nov. 14, 1945; s. Chauncey and Doris E. S.; m. Susan S. Strauss, July 2, 1967; children: Daniel, Diana. B.S., Stanford U., 1966, Ph.D., 1972. Cons. Rand Corp., summers 1966, 67, Western Mgmt. Sci. Inst., Grad. Sch. Mgmt., UCLA, summers 1967, 71; Cowles Found. staff research economist Yale U., New Haven, 1970; faculty Yale U., 1970-74, assoc. prof. econs., 1974; assoc. prof. econs. U. Calif.-Davis, 1975-76, prof. econs., 1976-80; prof. econs. U. Calif.-San Diego, 1980—, chmn. dept., 1987-90; vis. lectr. London Sch. Econs., 1973-74; vis. scholar U. Calif.-Berkeley, 1978-80; vis. lectr. Peoples U. of China, Beijing, 1987. Co-editor: Essays in Honor of Kenneth J. Arrow, 1986: v.1, Social Choice and Public Decision Making, v.2, Equilibrium Analysis, v.3, Uncertainty, Information and Communication; editor: Gen. Equilibrium Models of Monetary Economies, 1989; contbr. articles to profl. jours. NDEA fellow, 1966-69; Yale jr. faculty fellow, 1973-74; Guggenheim fellow, 1978-79; NSF grantee, 1979-81, 83-85. Office: U Calif San Diego Dept Econs 0508 9500 Gilman Dr La Jolla CA 92093-0508

STARR, STEVEN DAWSON, photographer; b. Albuquerque, Sept. 6, 1944; s. Richard Vernon and Carol (Harley) S.; m. Marilynne Sue Anderson, Aug. 6, 1965; 1 child, Stephen Richard. Student, Antioch Coll., 1962-63, Bethel Coll., 1963-64; B.A., San Jose State Coll., 1967. Photographer San Jose Mercury-News, Calif., 1966-67; photographer, picture editor A.P., 1968-73;

audiovisual producer Starr Productions, Inc., Coral Gables, Fla., 1974-85; photographer Picture Group Agy., 1986-88, Saba Press, N.Y.C., 1988—. Recipient Pulitzer prize for spot news photography, 1970, Nat. Headliners award, 1970, George Polk Meml. award, 1970, Pictures of Year hon. mention, 1970. Office: Saba Press 6399 Wilshire Blvd Ste 420 Los Angeles CA 90048-5716

STARR, V. HALE, communications executive; b. Winner, S.D., July 31, 1936; d. Archibald William and Alvina Lucille (Williams) Hale. BA in Drama, English, Dakota Wesleyan U., 1967, LLD (hon.), 1994; MEd in Speech, Black Hills State Coll., 1971; MA Communications Rsch., U. Iowa, 1976, PhD Communications Rsch., 1979; LLD (hon.), Dakota Wesleyan U., 1994. Personnel dir. Starr Enterprises, Mitchell, S.D., 1965-69, v.p., 1967-69; tchr. Mt. Vernon (Iowa) High Sch., 1967-68; asst. prof. English, speech, drama S.D. Sch. Mines & Tech., Rapid City, 1968-70, asst. prof. sociology, 1970-74; unwed pregnancy counselor Munson Clinic, Rapid City, 1972-74; marriage counselor N&S Assocs., Rapid City, 1973-74; div. counselor Women's Resource and Action Ctr. U. Iowa, Iowa City, 1974-76, curriculum and student teaching, supr. student tchrs., 1975-77; pres. Starr & Assocs., West Des Moines, Iowa, 1978—; fin. dir./owner KEYNOTE, Inc., West Des Moines, 1985—; owner Starr-Terry, West Des Moines, 1983—; non-legal cons. grant writing, Iowa, Nebr., 1974—. Author: Voir Dire, 1993; co-author: Jury Selection, 1985, 2d edit., 1993; mem. editorial bd. Forensics Reports Critical Reviewer, 1987-90; contr. articles to profl. jours. Pres. Common Cause Iowa, 1980-81; mem. regional bd. Common Cause, Washington, 1980-82; bd. dirs. Nat. Women's Polit. Caucus, Iowa, 1972-76. Named Greater Des Moines Woman of Achievement YWCA, 1986, Iowa Leader in Bus. Drake U. Leadership Inst., 1985, 86; recipient Communication and Leadership award Dist. 19 Toastmasters, Des Moines, 1986. Mem. Law and Soc. Assn. (bd. dirs. 1987—), Internat. Assn. Ethicists, Am. Soc. Trial Cons. (founding mem., bd. dirs. 1983-85, chair com. to develop profl. standards 1983-85), Speech Communication Assn. (conv. presenter 1983, 86, 91), Am. Sociol. Assn., Internat. Communication Assn., Cen. State Speech Assn., Iowa Communication Assn. (conv. presenter 1979), Polk County Assn. Women Attys., Consortium Club (founding mem.). Office: Starr & Assocs Inc 1201 Grand Ave West Des Moines IA 50265-3523 also: 3218 E Bell Rd #304 Phoenix AZ 85032

STARRETT, PAMELA ELIZABETH, symphony executive director, violinist, conductor; b. Concord, N.H., July 15, 1962; d. John Frederick and Nancy Elizabeth (Garland) S.; m. John Peter Ingalls, May 14, 1988; children: Hugh Starrett Ingalls, Edmund Starrett Ingalls. B of Mus. Arts, U. Mich., 1984, MusM, MBA, 1988. Orch. mgr. Ann Arbor (Mich.) Symphony Orch., 1987-88, asst. condr., 1988; mktg. dir. Kalamazoo Symphony Orch., 1989-90 music dir. Battle Creek (Mich.) Youth Orch., 1989-91; exec. dir. Battle Creek Symphony Orch., 1990—. Chair young artists competition Kalamazoo Bach Festival, 1989-90. Mem. Mich. Orch. Assn. (trustee 1990-91, 93—). Home: 153 Laurel Dr Battle Creek MI 49017-4666 Office: Battle Creek Symphony Orch 25 Michigan Ave W Ste 1206 Battle Creek MI 49017-7012

STARRFIELD, SUMNER GROSBY, astrophysics educator, researcher; b. L.A., Dec. 29, 1940; s. Harold Ernest and Eve (Grosby) S.; m. Susan Lee Hutt, Aug. 7, 1966; children: Barry, Brian, Sara. BA, U. Calif., Berkeley, 1962; MA, UCLA, 1965, PhD, 1969. From lectr. to asst. prof. Yale U., New Haven, 1967-71; rsch. scientist IBM, Yorktown Heights, N.Y., 1971-72; asst. prof. Ariz. State U., Tempe, 1972-75, assoc. prof., 1975-80, prof., 1980—; vis. assoc. prof. Steward Observatory, Tucson, 1978-79; vis. staff mem. Los Alamos (N.Mex.) Nat. Lab., 1974-94. Author numerous scientific papers. Grantee Ariz. State U., 1973, NSF, 1974-94, NASA, 1981—; Los Alamos summer fellow, 1974, 86, 88; recipient Joint Inst. Lab. Astrophysics, 1985-86. Fellow Royal Astron. Soc.; mem. Internat. Astron. Union, Am. Astron. Soc. (high energy astrophyics div., mem. publs. bd. 1978-81), Am. Physical Soc. (astrophysics div.). Achievements include discovery of thermonuclear runaway theory of nova outburst; co-discovery of hottest known class of pulsating variable stars and the cause of their pulsations, ultraviolet studies of nova cygni, 1992. Office: Ariz State U Dept Physics/Astronomy PO Box 871504 Tempe AZ 85287-1504

STARRY, DONN ALBERT, former aerospace company executive, former army officer; b. N.Y.C., May 31, 1925; s. Don Albert and Edith (Sortor) S.; m. Leatrice Hope Gibbs, June 15, 1948; children: Michael, Paul, Melissa, Melanie. B.S., U.S. Mil. Acad., 1948; M.S. in Internat. Affairs, George Washington U., 1966. Commd. 2d lt. U.S. Army, 1948, advanced through grades to gen., 1977; svc. in Europe, Korea and Vietnam; comdr. 11th armored cavalry rgt. Vietnam, Cambodia, 1969-70; assigned Dept. Army Staff, 1970-72; comdr. Armor Center and Ft. Knox, Ky., 1973-76, V Corps, Europe, 1976-77; comdr. Tng. and Doctrine Command Ft. Monroe, Va., 1977-81; comdr. in chief U.S. Readiness Command, 1981-83, ret., 1983; v.p. mission analysis and tech. affairs Ford Aerospace and Communications Corp., Detroit, 1983-84, v.p., gen. mgr. space missions div., 1984-86; exec. v.p. Ford Aerospace Corp., Arlington, Va., 1987-90; spl. asst. to pres. BDM Internat., McLean, Va., 1988-90; advisor to govt. and industry in several countries. Mem. Def. Sci. Bd., 1985-93, Order of Aaron and Hur, Friends of Fifth of May; trustee Eisenhower Found., 1995—; chmn. bd. U.S. Cavalry Meml. Found., 1995—. Decorated Def. D.S.M., Army D.S.M. with oak leaf cluster, Silver Star, Bronze Star with V, Soldier's medal, Purple Heart, Legion of Merit; French Ordre Nationale du Merite, German Knight Commander's Cross of Order of Merit with Badge and Star, Disting. Flying Cross, Air Medal with 9 oak leaf clusters; named to U.S. Army Ft. Leavenworth Command and General Staff Coll. Hall of Fame, 1993. Mem. U.S. Armor Assn., Assn. U.S. Army. Episcopalian. Office: 11401 Lilting Ln Fairfax Station VA 22039-1717

STARTUP, CHARLES HARRY, airline executive; b. Middletown, N.Y., Feb. 24, 1914; s. Charles H. and Laura Beatrice (Langan) S.; m. Jane Butler Williams, June 26, 1942; children—Charles Alan, Ann Elizabeth, Thomas Andrew. A.B., Middlebury Coll., 1936; postgrad., U. Cin., 1937-39. With Am. Airlines, N.Y.C., 1939-63, asst. v.p. customer service, 1957-59; v.p. passenger sales and service Am. Airlines, 1959-61, v.p. passenger sales, 1961-63, dir. admiralty bd., 1973-79; v.p. mktg. Nat. Car Rental System, 1963-64. Adminstr. Light Opera of Manhattan, 1981-84. Mem. Cin. Sales Execs. Council (pres. 1955), Soc. Consumer Affairs Profls. (dir.), Chi Psi. Club: Skal (N.Y.C.). Home: 221 W College St Oberlin OH 44074-1533

STARYK, STEVEN S., violinist, concertmaster, educator; b. Toronto, Ont., Can., Apr. 28, 1932; s. Peter and Mary Staryk; m. Ida Elisabeth Busch, May 17, 1963; 1 child, Natalie. Student, Royal Conservatory of Music, Toronto, 1942-48, Harbord Collegiate Inst., Toronto, 1945-48; LittD (hon.), York U., Toronto, 1980. Soloist, concertmaster CBC-Radio Can., Toronto, 1951-55, Royal Philharmonic Orch., London, 1956-59; 1st concertmaster, tchr. Concertgebouw Orch. and Amsterdam Conservatory, 1960-63; concertmaster Chgo. Symphony Orch., 1963-67; prof. of violin Oberlin (Ohio) Coll. Conservatory, 1968-72, Acad. of Music, Vancouver, B.C., Can., 1972-75, Royal Conservatory of Music, Toronto, 1975-87; concertmaster Toronto Symphony, 1982-87; prof. of violin, chair string div. U. Wash. Sch. Music, Seattle, 1987—; faculty music U. Toronto, 1980-87; vis. prof. U. Victoria, 1972, U. Ottawa, 1975, Northwestern U., 1965-66; founding mem. Quartet Can., 1975-80. Soloist, recitalist, N.Am., Europe and the Far East; recording artist on EMI-HMV, CBC, Everest, Orion, other labels. Recipient 2 Arts awards Can. Council, Ottawa, 1968, 75, Queen's Silver Jubilee medal Govt. of Can., Toronto, Shevchenko medal, Winnipeg, Man., Can. Home: 5244 17th Ave NE Seattle WA 98105-3408 Office: U Wash Sch Music Mail Stop DN-10 Seattle WA 98195

STARZINGER, VINCENT EVANS, political science educator; b. Des Moines, Jan. 12, 1929; s. Vincent and Genevieve (Evans) S.; m. Mildred Hippee Hill, June 16, 1953; children: Paige Hill, Evan. A.B. summa cum laude, Harvard U., 1950, LL.B., 1954, Ph.D., 1959; A.M. (hon.), Dartmouth Coll., 1968. Bar: Iowa 1954. Practice with firm Bannister, Carpenter, Ahlers & Cooney, Des Moines, 1954; teaching fellow, then instr. govt. Harvard, 1957-60; faculty dept. govt. Dartmouth, 1960-94, chmn. dept. govt., 1972-77, 83-85, Joel Parker prof. law and polit. sci., 1976-94, prof. emeritus, 1994—. Author: Middlingness: Juste Milieu Political Theory in England and France, 1815-48, 1965, repub. as The Politics of the Center, 1991; also articles. Served with AUS, 1955-56. Sheldon traveling fellow, 1950-51; Social Sci. Research Council fellow, 1958-59; Dartmouth faculty

fellow, 1963-64; Am. Philos. Soc. award and Earhart Found. fellow, 1970-71. Mem. Am. Polit. Sci. Assn., Am., Iowa bar assns., Phi Beta Kappa. Clubs: American, Canadian Alpine, Cambridge (Mass.) Boat. Home: Elm St Norwich VT 05055 Office: PO Box 981 Hanover NH 03755

STARZL, THOMAS EARL, physician, educator; b. Le Mars, Iowa, Mar. 11, 1926; s. Roman F. and Anna Laura (Fitzgerald) S.; m. Barbara Brothers, Nov. 27, 1954 (div.); children: Timothy, Rebecca, Thomas; m. Joy D. Conger, Aug. 1, 1981. BA, Westminster Coll., 1947, DSc (hon.), 1965; MA, Northwestern U., 1950, MD, PhD, 1952; DSc (hon.), N.Y. Med. Coll., 1970, Westmar Coll., 1974, Med. Coll. Wis., 1981, Northwestern U., 1982, Bucknell U., 1985, Muhlenberg Coll., 1985, Mt. Sinai Sch. Medicine, 1988, MD (hon.), U. Louvain, Belgium, 1985, U. Genova, 1988, U. Rennes, 1988; LLD (hon.), U. Wyo., 1971; LHD (hon.), LaRoche Coll., 1988. Intern Johns Hopkins U. Hosp., Balt., 1952-53, fellow, surg., 1953-54, resident, 1955-56; mem. faculty Northwestern U. Med. Sch., Evanston, Ill., 1958-61; mem. faculty U. Colo. Med. Sch., Denver, 1962-80, prof. surgery, 1964-80, chmn. dept. surgery, 1972-80; prof. surgery U. Pitts., 1981—; mem. staff Presbyn. Hosp., Univ. Hosp., Children's Hosp. of Pitts., Pitts. VA Hosp. Author: Experience in Renal Transplantation, 1964, Experience in Hepatic Transplantation, 1969; contbr. articles to profl. jours. Recipient award Westminster Coll., 1965, Achievement award Lund U., 1965, Eppinger award Soc. Internat. de Chirurgie, 1965, Eppinger prize, Freiburg, 1970, William S. Middleton award for outstanding research in VA system, 1968, Merit award Northwestern U., 1969, Disting. Achievement award Modern Medicine, 1969, Creative Council award U. Colo., 1971, Colo. Man of Yr. award, 1967, Brookdale award AMA, 1974, David Hume Meml. award Nat. Kidney Found., 1978, Pitts. Man of Yr. award, 1981; Markle scholar, 1958. Fellow ACS (Sheen award 1982), Am. Acad. Arts and Scis.; mem. Soc. Univ. Surgeons, Soc. Vascular Surgery, Am. Surg. Assn., Transplantation Soc., Deutsche Gesellschaft für Chirurgie, numerous others. Office: U Pitts Sch Med Dept Surgery 1084 Scaife Hall Pittsburgh PA 15261-2010*

STASACK, EDWARD ARMEN, artist; b. Chgo., Oct. 1, 1929; s. Clifford Clement and Elizabeth Frances (Mallek) S.; m. Mary Louise Walters, June 20, 1953 (div. 1972); children: Caren Marie, Jennifer Elizabeth, John Armen, Michael Clifford; m. Diane Miura Hirsch, June 26, 1993. BFA with high honors, U. Ill., Urbana, 1955, MFA, 1956. Instr. in art U. Hawaii, 1956-61, prof. art, chmn. dept. art, 1969-72, program chmn. in printmaking, 1975-83, prof. emeritus, 1988; affiliate Downtown Gallery, N.Y., 1969-70; adj. prof. Prescott Coll. Author: (with J. Halley Cox) Hawaiian Petroglyphs, 1970, (with Georgia Lee) Petroglyphs of Kaho'olawe, 1993, (with Georgia Lee) Ka'upulehu Petroglyphs, 1994; one-man shows Honolulu Acad. Arts, 1961, 66, 69, 76, 87, U.S. embassies Istanbul and Izmir, Turkey, 1976, Am. Cultural Center, Bucharest, Rumania, 1976, Cleve. Inst. Art, 1976, Hilo (Hawaii) Coll. Gallery, 1976, Amfac Plaza Gallery, 1978, Ryan Gallery, 1981, Art Loft, Honolulu, 1983; group shows include Carnegie Inst., Pitts., 1964, Krakow (Poland) Biennial, 1966, 68, Smithsonian Inst., Washington, 1967, Mexico City Mus. Modern Art, 1968, Leicester Gallery, London, 1965, Art Mus. Manila (Philippines), 1982, 2d Internat. Biennial Print Exhibit Republic of China, 1986, Yuma Art Ctr., 1990; represented in permanent collections, Mus. Modern Art, N.Y.C., Met. Mus. Art, N.Y.C., Chgo. Art Inst., Bklyn. Mus., Honolulu Acad. Arts, Hawaii State Found. Culture and the Arts, Library of Congress, Phila. Mus. Art, Boston Pub. Library. Served with U.S. Army, 1952-54. Recipient numerous prizes, including: Boston Printmakers Mems. prize, 1967; Juror's awards Honolulu Printmakers, 1957, 58, 59, 62, 63, 66, 67, 68, 74, 77, 87; Soc. Am. Graphic Artists prizes, 1956, 57, 61, 62, 63, 68, 73, 78, 79, 80, 91; Tiffany Found. fellow, 1958, 62; Rockefeller Found. grantee, 1959; MacDowell Colony fellow, 1971, 75; Hawaii State and U.S. Bicentennial Commns. fellow, 1975. Mem. Soc. Am. Graphic Artists, Australian Rock Art Rsch. Assn., Rock Art Assn. Hawaii (emeritus pres.), Am. Rock Art Rsch. Assn., Prescott Fine Arts Assn. Office: 1878 Paradise Ln Prescott AZ 86301

STASHEFF, JAMES DILLON, mathematics educator; b. N.Y.C., Jan. 15, 1936; s. Edward and Evelyn Columbia (Maher) S.; m. Ann Helen Pekarik; children: Steven, Kim. BA, U. Mich., 1956; MA, Princeton (N.J.) U., 1958, PhD, 1961; DPhil, Oxford (Eng.) U., 1961. Moore instr. MIT, Cambridge, Mass., 1960-62; asst. prof. Notre Dame U., South Bend, Ind., 1962-64, assoc. prof., 1964-68, prof., 1968-70; prof. Temple U., Phila., 1970-78, U. N.C., Chapel Hill, 1976—; vis. prof. Princeton U., 1968-69, U. Pa., Phila., fall 1992, Rutgers U., New Brunswick, N.J., spring 1987, Lehigh U., spring 1993. Author: H-Spaces from a Homotopy Point of View, 1970, (with others) Characteristic Classes, 1974. Danforth fellow, 1956-60, Sloan fellow, 1967-69; Marshall scholar, 1958-60; NSF grantee 1964-84, 85-88, 89—. Mem. Am. Math. Soc., London Math. Soc., Math. Assn. Am., Phi Beta Kappa. Roman Catholic. Avocations: dancing. Office: U NC Math CB # 3250 Chapel Hill NC 27599

STASHOWER, MICHAEL DAVID, retired manufacturing company executive; b. Cleve., July 15, 1926; s. Joseph G. and Tillie (Mirlevitz) S.; m. Gloria Goodstein, Oct. 29, 1950; children—Susan, Deborah Missal, Jon. B.A., Cornell U., 1947, M.B.A., 1949. With Ford Motor Co., 1949-57; contr. Dodge assembly plant Chrysler Corp., 1958-62; asst. contr. Am. Machine & Foundry Co., 1962-67; comptr. Perkin-Elmer Corp., 1967-76, v.p., comptr., 1976-79, sr. v.p. fin., 1979-85; v.p. fin. Softstrip, Inc., Waterbury, Conn., 1985-87, exec. v.p. 1987-90; sr. v.p. CFO Data Switch Corp., Shelton, Conn., 1990-93, exec. v.p., CFO, 1993-94, ret., 1994; dir. Data Switch Corp. Past pres. United Jewish Appeal/Fedn. Westport-Wilton-Norwalk, Conn.; v.p., treas., hon. dir. Temple Israel of Westport, Conn., 1984-91; bd. dirs. Coun. Jewish Fedns.; bd. dirs., treas. Jewish Home for the Elderly; treas. Guidance Clin. Fairfield County, Conn. With USNR, 1944-46. Mem. Cedar Point Yacht Club. Home: 14 Cardinal Ln Westport CT 06880-1714

STASIK, RANDY, health facility administrator. Treas. Borgess Health Alliance Inc., Kalamazoo, Mich. Office: Borgess Health Alliance Inc 1521 Gull Rd Kalamazoo MI 49001*

STASIOR, WILLIAM F., engineering company executive; b. 1941. BSEE, Northwestern U., MSEE. With Booz Allen & Hamilton Inc., N.Y.C., 1967—, pres., COO, 1990—; CEO, chmn. bd. dirs. Booz Allen & Hamilton Inc., McLean, Va., 1991—. Office: Booz Allen & Hamilton Inc 101 Park Ave New York NY 10178-0002*

STASSEN, JOHN HENRY, lawyer; b. Joliet, Ill., Mar. 22, 1943; s. John H. and Florence C. (McCarthy) S.; m. Sara A. Gaw, July 6, 1968; children: John C., David A. BS, Northwestern U., 1965, JD, Harvard U., 1968. Bar: Ill. 1968. Assoc. Kirkland & Ellis, Chgo., 1968, 73-76, ptnr. 1977—. Contbr. articles to legal jours. Lt. comdr., JAGC, USNR, 1969-72. Mem. ABA (past chmn. com. on futures regulation), Ill. Bar Assn., Chgo. Bar Assn., Phila. Soc. Mid America Club, Racquet Club. Home: 1310 N Astor St Chicago IL 60610-2114 Office: Kirkland & Ellis 200 E Randolph Dr Ste 5900 Chicago IL 60601-6401

STASSI, RONALD V., electric power industry executive. Pres. So. Calif. Pub. Power Authority, Pasadena, 1990—; gen. mgr. Burbank (Calif.) Pub. Svc. Dept. Office: Southern Cal Pub Power Auth 200 S Los Robles Ave Pasadena CA 91101*

STASTNY, DONALD JOSEPH, architect; b. Klamath Falls, Oreg., May 18, 1943; s. Edwin James and Mariam Francis (Chatham) S.; m. Janet Helen Dalton, June 11, 1966; children—Kimberly, Kory, Joshua. B.S., Oreg. State U., 1965, B.Arch., U. Wash., 1968; M.Arch., M.City Planning, U. Pa., 1969. Registered architect, Oreg., Wash. Designer Roche, Dinkeloo & Assoc., Hamden, Conn., 1969-70; research architect Athens Ctr. of Ekistics, Greece, 1970-71; project architect Bumgardner Architects, Seattle, 1971-73; sr. designer Campbell, Yost, Grube, Portland, Oreg., 1973-75; urban designer Ekistic Cons., Edmonton, Alta., Can., 1973-76; pres. Stastny Architects, Portland, 1975—; research, chmn. bd. trustees Oreg. Sch. of Design, Portland, 1981—; profl. advisor Beverly Hills Civic Ctr., Calif., 1982. Prin. works include: Columbia World Trade Ctr., 1982; Goose Hollow Village, 1982, Princeton Bldg., 1985. Chmn. central city planning com. City of Portland, 1984-86; mem. planning com. Monterey Design Conf., Calif., 1984-85; panel mem. Oreg. Arts Commn., Salem, 1983; mem. design rev. com. Multnomah County, Oreg., 1977; panel mem. Nat. Endowment for Arts,

Washington, 1983-84. Ford Found. fellow, 1970. Mem. AIA, Am. Inst. Cert. Planners, Am. Planning Assn. (State Planning award Oreg. chpt. 1980), Can. Inst. Planners, Inst. Urban Design. Democrat. Office: Stastny Architects PC 813 SW Alder St 200 Portland OR 97205

STASZESKY, FRANCIS MYRON, electric company consultant; b. Wilmington, Del., Apr. 16, 1918; s. Frank J. and Ruth (Jones) S.; m. Barbara F. Kearney, May 30, 1943; children—Francis Myron, John B., Barbara J., Faith A., Paul D. BSME, MIT, 1943; MSME, Mass. Inst. Tech., 1943. Mech. engr. Union Oil Co. Calif., L.A., 1943-45; with E.I. duPont de Nemours Co., Wilmington, Del., 1946-48; joined Boston Edison Co., 1948, supervising engr. design and constrn., 1948-57, supt. engring. and constrn. dept., 1957-64, v.p., asst. to pres., 1964-67, exec. v.p., 1967-79, pres., chief operating officer, 1979-83; cons., 1983—; dir. Boston Edison Co. 1968-83. Fellow ASME (life); mem. IEEE (sr., life), Nat. Acad. Engring., Engring., Soc. New Eng. (pres. 1961-62), Palm Valley Country Club (Palm Desert, Calif.), Brae Burn Country Club (West Newton, Mass.). Address: 166 Bank St Harwich Port MA 02646

STATA, RAYMOND, data processing and computer company executive; b. Coatesville, Pa., Nov. 12, 1934. BSEE, MIT, 1956, MSEE, 1958. V.p. sales Inland Controls Co., 1956-65; sr. v.p. Analog Devices, Inc., 1965-71, pres., 1971-73, chmn. bd., pres., CEO, 1973—. Office: Analog Devices Inc 1 Technology Way Norwood MA 02062-2634*

STATLER, IRVING CARL, aerospace engineer; b. Buffalo, N.Y., Nov. 23, 1923; s. Samuel William and Sarah (Strauss) S.; m. Renee Roll, Aug. 23, 1953; children—William Scott, Thomas Stuart. B.S. in Aero. Engring., U. Mich., 1945, B.S. in Engring. Math., 1945; Ph.D., Calif. Inst. Tech., 1956. Research engr. flight research dept. Cornell Aero. Lab., Inc., Buffalo, 1946-53; prin. engr. flight research dept. Cornell Aero. Lab., Inc., 1956-57, asst. head aero-mechanics dept., 1957-63, head applied mechanics dept., 1963-70, sr. staff scientist aeroscis. div., 1970-71; research scientist U.S. Army Air Mobility Research and Devel. Lab., Moffett Field, Calif., 1971-73; dir. Aeromechanics Lab. U.S. Army Air Mobility Research and Devel. Lab., 1973-85, dir. AGARD, 1985-88; sr. staff scientist NASA Ames Rsch. Ctr., 1988-92, chief Human Factors Rsch. Divsn., 1992—; research scientist research analysis group Jet Propulsion Lab., Pasadena, Calif., 1953-55; chmn. flight mechanics panel adv. group aerospace research and devel. NATO, 1974-76; lectr. U. Buffalo, Millard-Fillmore Coll., Buffalo, 1957-58. Served with USAAF, 1945-46. Fellow AIAA (Internat. Cooperation in Space Sci. medal 1992), AAAS, German Aerospace Soc., Royal Aero Soc.; mem. Am. Helicoptor Soc., Sigma Xi. Home: 1362 Cuernavaca Circulo Mountain View CA 94040-3571 Office: NASA Ames Rsch Ctr MS262-1 Moffett Field CA 94035

STATLER, OLIVER HADLEY, writer; b. Chgo., May 21, 1915; s. Oliver Isaiah and Alice Mae (Hadley) S. BA, U. Chgo., 1936; LHD (hon.), Nat. Coll. Edn., Evanston, Ill., 1966. Administr. U.S. Civil Svc., Japan, 1947-54; writer, 1954—; tchr. U. Hawaii, Honolulu, 1977, adj. prof., 1977—. Sgt. U.S. Army, 1940-45, PTO. Guggenheim Found. fellow, 1973; Ctr. for Asian and Pacific Studies, U. Hawaii scholar-in-residence fellow, 1981; Japan Found. fellow, Tokyo, 1986. Mem. PEN, Authors Guild, Assn. for Asian Studies. Democrat. Home and Office: 1619 Kamamalu Ave Apt 302 Honolulu HI 96813-1770

STAUB, AUGUST WILLIAM, drama educator, theatrical producer; b. New Orleans, Oct. 9, 1931; s. August Harry and Laurel (Elfer) S.; m. Patricia Gebhardt, Nov. 22, 1952; 1 child, Laurel Melicent. BA, La. State U., 1952, MA, 1956, PhD, 1960. Instr., tech. dir. La. State U., 1955; instr. Ea. Mich. U., 1956-58; assoc. dir. Dunes Summer Theatre, Michigan City, Ind., summers 1957-60; asst. prof., assoc. dir. univ. theatre U. Fla., 1960-64; assoc. prof. U. New Orleans, 1964-66, prof., chmn. dept. drama and communications, 1966-76; prof.; head drama dept. U. Ga., 1976-95; exec. producer Jekyll Island Mus. Comedy Festival, 1984-88, Highlands (N.C.) Playhouse, 1989—, Ga. Repertory Theatre, 1991—; exec. sec. Theatres of La.; v.p. New Orleans Internat. Jazz Festival, 1967-69; pres. S.W. Theatre Conf., 1973-74. Author: Lysistrata, 1968, The Social Climber, 1969, A Small Bare Space, 1970, Introduction to Theatrical Arts, 1971, Creating Theatre, 1973, Varieties of Theatrical Arts, 1980, 83, 94; gen. editor: Artists and Ideas in the Theatre (Peter Lang), 1989—; assoc. editor Speech Tchr., 1966-68, So. Speech Comm. Jour., 1974-77, Quar. Jour. Speech, 1977-79. Bd. dirs. Friends Ga. Mus., Ga. Symphony, Coun. Arts for Children, New Orleans, New Orleans Ctr. Creative Arts, Athens Arts. Commn., Ga. Alliance Arts Edn. Lt. AUS, 1952-54. Recipient Creativity in Rsch. medallion U. Ga., 1987, Disting. Svc. award S.W. Theater Conf., 1985; La. State U. Found. Disting. Faculty fellow, 1970-71. Fellow Coll. of Fellows of Am. Theatre; mem. Am. Theatre Assn. (pres. 1985-86, bd. dirs.), Univ. and Coll. Theatre Assn. (pres. 1974-75), Nat. Assn. Schs. Theatre (pres. 1981-83), Univ. Resident Theatre Assn. (bd. dirs.), Inst. European Theatre, Nat. Theatre Conf., Am. Soc. Theatre Rsch., Internat. Fedn. Theatre Rsch. Home: 400 Ponderosa Dr Athens GA 30605-3324 *How good it is to be able to earn a living doing what one loves to do.*

STAUB, MARTHA LOU, elementary education educator; b. Cumberland, Md., May 29, 1939; d. Walter W. and Velma Grace (Darr) McCoy; m. Paul L. Staub, Apr. 11, 1964; children: Desiree, Paul, Sharon, Lucy, Charles. BS, Frostburg State U., 1961; postgrad., We. Md. State U., 1983; MS, Towson State Coll., 1983; student, Loyola Coll., 1988. Cert. tchr. 1st-mid. sch., Md. Elem. tchr. Cumberland Valley, Bedord, Pa., Garrett County, Oakland, Md., Carroll County, Westminster, Balt. County Bd. Edn., Towson, Md.; with peer counseling, 1990-93, master learning, 1988-91. Recipient Excellence in Edn. award Baltimore County, 1990-91; honored by Randallstown Elem. PTA, 1989; donation made in her honor Christa McAuliffe scholarship fund, 1990. Mem. ASCD, NEA (Excellence in Teaching honor 1992), Md. State Tchrs. Assn., Tchr.'s Assn. of Balt. County Orgn., PTA, Md. Coun. Tchrs. Math., Women Educators of Balt. County Orgn., Delta Kappa Gamma. Home: 913 Clearview Ave Hampstead MD 21074-2327

STAUB, W. ARTHUR, health care products executive; b. Detroit, Dec. 25, 1923; s. Edward Elmer and Emma Josephine (Fleury) S.; m. Alla Elizabeth Edwards, June 26, 1948; children: James Randall, Sally Ann, David Scott. BS, Dartmouth Coll., 1944; MD, Temple U., 1947. Intern Muhlberg Hosp., Plainfield, N.J., 1947-48; resident in pediatrics Abington (Pa.) Meml. Hosp., 1950-51; practice medicine specializing in pediatrics Westfield (N.J.) Med. Group, 1948-63; assoc. med. dir. Ciba Pharm. Co., Summit, N.J., 1963-66; med. dir., v.p. life sci. div. Becton-Dickinson and Co., Rutherford, N.J., 1966-70; v.p. med. affairs C. R. Bard Co., Murray Hill, N.J., 1970—, also bd. dirs.; bd. dirs. Crestmont Fed. Savs. and Loan Assn., Edison, N.J., Colonial Trust Nat. Bank, North Palm Beach, Fla.; cons. Children's Specialized Hosp., Westfield, 1948—, Overlook Hosp., Summit, 1948—. Contbr. articles to profl. jours. Sec., treas. Westfield Med. Soc., 1961; deacon Presbyn. Ch., Westfield, 1959—. Served to capt. USAF, 1951-53. Fellow Am. Coll. Physician Execs.; mem. AAAS, Assn. Advancement Med. Instrumentation, Health Industry Mfrs. Assn. (chmn. med. and sci. steering com.). Republican. Presbyterian. Clubs: Echo Lake Country (Westfield) (bd. trustees 1984—); Lost Tree (North Palm Beach, Fla.); Skytop (Pa.). Avocations: golf, physical fitness, reading, sailing, travel. Home: 810 Village Rd North Palm Beach FL 33408-3334

STAUBACH, ROGER THOMAS, real estate executive, former professional football player; b. Cin., Feb. 5, 1942; s. Robert Joseph and Elizabeth (Smyth) S.; m. Marianne Jeanne Hoobler, Sept. 4, 1965; children: Jennifer Anne, Michelle Elizabeth, Stephanie Marie, Jeffrey, Amy Lynn. Student, Roswell (N.Mex.) Mil. Inst., 1960-61; BS, U.S. Naval Acad., 1965. Quarterback Dallas Cowboy Football Team, 1969-79; pres. Holloway-Staubach Co. (name now Staubach Co.), 1980-92; chmn., CEO, pres. Staubach Co., Dallas, 1993—; former announcer CBS Football. Author: First Down, Lifetime to Go, 1974, Time Enough to Win, 1981. Bd. dirs. Halliburton Co., Gibson Greetings, Salvation Army; active Pres. Coun. on Phys. Fitness, 1981-83. Lt. USNR, 1965-69. Recipient Heisman Trophy, 1963; played Pro Bowl, 1971, 76, 78; inducted into Nat. Football League Hall of Fame, 1985. Mem. Fellowship of Christian Athletes. Roman Catholic. Office: Staubach Co 6750 Lyndon B Johnson Fwy Dallas TX 75240-6512

STAUBER, KARL NEILL, federal executive; b. Statesville, N.C., Jan. 4, 1951; s. Van G. and Dorthea (Mills) S.; m. Hollis Scott, Aug. 14, 1971. BA, U. N.C., 1973; Program for Mgmt. Devel., Harvard U., 1983; PhD, Union Inst., Cin., 1993. Asst. dir. Reynolds Babcock Found., Winston-Salem, N.C., 1974-79; exec. dir. Needmor Found., Toledo, Ohio, 1979-83; pres. Econ. Devel., Inc., Boulder, Colo., 1983-86; v.p. program N.W. Area Found., St. Paul, 1986-93; dep. under sec. USDA, Washington, 1993—, 1994—. Contbr. editorials to newspapers. Adv. bd. mem. Found. Mid South, Jackson, Miss., 1988-93, Mpls. Found., 1991-93. Avocations: furniture building, tractor restoration. Office: USDA 14th & Independence Ave Washington DC 20250

STAUBER, MARILYN JEAN, educator, consultant; b. Duluth, Minn., Feb. 5, 1938; d. Harold Milton and Dorothy Florence (Thompson) Froehlich; children: Kenneth D. and James H. Atkinson; m. Lawrence B. Stauber, Jan. 11, 1991. BS in K-6 Edn., U. Minn., Duluth, 1969, MEd in Math., 1977. Cert. elem. and secondary reading tchr., reading and reading specialist, devel. reading tchr., reading cons. Sec. div. vocat. rehab. State Minn., Duluth, 1956-59; sec. Travelers Ins. Co., Duluth, 1962-66; lead tchr. Chpt. 1 reading and math. Proctor, Minn., 1969—. Mem. choir, comm. coord. Forbes Meth. Ch., Proctor. Mem. NEA, Nat. Reading Assn., Minn. Arrowhead Reading Coun., Elem. Coun. (pres. 1983-84, 86-87), Proctor Fedn. Tchrs. (recert. com. 1980—, treas. 1981-86), Phi Delta Kappa. Home: 6713 Grand Lake Rd Saginaw MN 55779-9782

STAUBITZ, ARTHUR FREDERICK, lawyer, healthcare products company executive; b. Omaha, Nebr., Mar. 14, 1939; s. Herbert Frederick Staubitz and Barbara Eileen (Dallas) Alderson; m. Linda Medora Miller, Aug. 18, 1962; children: Michael, Melissa, Peter. AB cum laude, Wesleyan U., Middletown, Conn., 1961; JD cum laude, U. Pa., 1964. Bar: Ill. 1964, U.S. Dist. Ct. (no. dist.) Ill. 1964, U.S. Ct. Appeals (7th cir.) 1964, Pa. 1972. Assoc. Sidley & Austin, Chgo., 1964-71; sr. internat. atty., assoc. gen. counsel, dir. Japanese ops Sperry Univac, Blue Bell, Pa., 1971-78; from asst. to assoc. dep. gen. counsel Baxter Internat. Inc., Deerfield, Ill., 1978-85, v.p., dep. gen. counsel, 1985-90; v.p. Baxter Diagnostics, 1990-91; sr. v.p., sec., gen. counsel Amgen, Inc., Thousand Oaks, Calif., 1991-92; v.p., gen. mgr. Ventures Group Baxter World Trade Corp., Deerfield, Ill., 1992-93; v.p., sec., gen. counsel Baxter Internat. Inc., Deerfield, Ill., 1993, sr. v.p., gen. counsel, 1993—. Mem. Planning Commn., Springfield Twp., Montgomery County, Pa., 1973-74, mem. Zoning Hearing Bd., 1974-78; bd. dirs. Twp. High Sch. dist. 113, Deerfield and Highland Park, Ill., 1983-91, pres. 1989-91; trustee Food and Drug Law Inst., 1991-92, 93—; bd. dirs. Music of the Baroque, 1994—; trustee Roosevelt U., 1994—. Mem. ABA, Chgo. Bar Assn. Episcopalian. Home: 232 Deerfield Rd Deerfield IL 60015-4412 Office: Baxter Internat Inc 1 Baxter Pky Deerfield IL 60015-4634

STAUBUS, GEORGE JOSEPH, accounting educator; b. Brunswick, Mo., Apr. 26, 1926; s. George Washington and Florence Lidwina (Pittman) S.; m. Sarah Mayer, Apr. 11, 1949; children: Lindsay, Martin, Paul, Janette. B.S., U. Mo., 1947; M.B.A., U. Chgo., 1949, Ph.D., 1954. C.P.A., Ill. Instr. U. Buffalo, 1947-49, U. Chgo., 1950-52; asst. prof. then assoc. prof. acctg. U. Calif.-Berkeley, from 1952, now Michael N. Chetkovich prof. emeritus; vis. prof. NYU, 1965, London Grad Sch. Bus. Studies, 1966-67, U. Kans., 1969-70; Erskine lectr. U. Canterbury, New Zealand, 1972, 91. Author: A Theory of Accounting to Investors, 1961, Activity Costing and Input-Output Accounting, 1971, Making Accounting Decisions, 1977, An Accounting Concept of Revenue, 1980, Activity Costing for Decisions, 1988, Economic Influences on the Development of Accounting in Firms, 1995—. Served with USN, 1944-46. Recipient Disting. prof. Calif. Soc. C.P.A.s, 1981. Fellow Acctg. Researchers Internat. Assn. (treas. 1981-83); mem. Am. Acctg. Assn. (disting. internat. lectr. 1982), Am. Inst. C.P.A.s, Fin. Execs. Inst. Office: U Calif-Berkeley Berkeley CA 94720

STAUDENMAIER, MARY LOUISE, banker, lawyer; b. Marinette, Wis., Apr. 13, 1938; d. Louis W. and Hildegarde C. (Schmit) S. BA, Mt. Mary Coll., Milw., 1960; JD, Marquette U., 1971; postgrad. in banking, U. Wis., 1980; postgrad. in bus., Harvard U., 1980. Bar: Wis. 1971. Tchr. math. Milw. High Sch., 1960-66; security analyst 1st Wis. Trust, Milw., 1966-68, trust adminstr., 1968-70; v.p. Am. City Bank & Trust, Milw., 1970-75; trust officer Marine Nat. Exchange Bank, Milw., 1975; v.p., trust officer Heritage Trust Co., Milw., 1975-77; pres., chief exec. officer, trust officer Stephenson Nat. Bank and Trust, Marinette, 1977—, also bd. dirs., chmn.; bd. dirs. chmn.; speaker on estate planning; bd. dirs. TYME Corp. bd. dirs. Marinette Area Econ. Devel. Corp.; mem. fin. coun. and investment com. Cath. Diocese Green Bay, Wis.; mem. Marinette Downtown Revitalization Com.; past chmn. Marinette Downtown Adv. Com.; past pres. Marinette Voyageurs Com.; chair fin. com. Holy Family Congregation; past bd. dirs. Marinette Area Indsl. Devel. Corp., United Way Marinette and others; bd. dirs. Woolsack Soc. Marquette U. Law Sch. Recipient Touhey award Marinette Cath. Cen. High Sch., 1988, Mary Neville Bielefeld award Marquette U., 1989, Madonna medal for Profl. Excellence, Mount Mary Coll., 1990. Mem. Wis. Bar Assn. (past bd. dirs. corp., banking and bus. law com.), Wis. Bankers Assn. (br. banking task force), Marinette County Bar Assn. (past pres.), Wis. Trustees Assn. (past mem. legis. com.), Ind. Bankers Assn., Marinette Area C. of C. (past bd. dirs.), Marquette U. Law Alumni Assn. (past bd. dirs.), Assn. Marquette U. Women (past bd. dirs.). Home: 2411 Riverside Ave Marinette WI 54143 Office: Stephenson Nat Bank & Trust 1820 Hall Ave Marinette WI 54143

STAUDER, ALFRED MAX, wire products company executive; b. Mexico City, May 25, 1940; s. Hans and Charlotte (Mueller) S.; m. Deanna J. Woods, June 12, 1962; children—Carl, Monique. B.A., Principia Coll., 1962. Chief exec. officer Woods Wire Products, Inc., Carmel, Ind., 1965—. Served to 1st lt. U.S. Army, 1962-65. Mem. Young Pres. Orgn. Republican. Christian Scientist. Club: Palm Beach Polo and Country (Fla.). Home: PO Box 891 Carmel IN 46032-0891 Office: Woods Wire Products Inc 510 3rd Ave SW Carmel IN 46032-2032*

STAUDER, WILLIAM VINCENT, geophysics educator; b. New Rochelle, N.Y., Apr. 23, 1922; s. William P. and Margaret (Boll) S. A.B. St. Louis U., 1943, M.S. in Physics, 1948; S.T.L., St. Mary's (Kans.) Coll., 1953; Ph.D. in Geophysics, U. Calif. at Berkeley, 1959. Joined S.J., 1939, ordained priest Roman Catholic Ch., 1952. Faculty St. Louis U., 1959-92, prof. geophysics, 1966-92, prof. emeritus, 1992—; rector Jesuit community, 1967-73, 88-91, chmn. dept. earth and atmospheric scis., 1972-75, acting dean Grad. Sch., 1974-75, dean Grad. Sch., 1975-87, dir. univ. rsch. 1975-87, assoc. acad. v.p., 1989—; vis. research assoc. U. Calif.-Berkeley, 1984-85. Contbr. articles to profl. jours. Trustee Marquette U., 1978-90. Fellow Am. Geophys. Union; mem. Seismol. Soc. Am. (bd. dirs. 1962-68, pres. 1965, chmn. Eastern sect. 1964), Phi Beta Kappa, Sigma Xi. Home: 3601 Lindell Blvd Saint Louis MO 63108-3393

STAUDERMAN, BRUCE FORD, advertising executive, writer; b. Jersey City, Mar. 17, 1919; b. Herbert Henry and Helen Ann (Jacobus) S.; m. Claude Outhier, Mar. 23; 1946. Student, Syracuse U., 1936-38, TV Workshop, N.Y.C., 1949-50, Sch. TV Technique, 1950. V.p. TV, radio, films Meldrum & Fewsmith, Inc. (advt. agy.), Cleve., 1954-62; exec. v.p., chmn. plans bd., exec. creative dir. Meldrum & Fewsmith, Inc. (advt. agy.), 1973-79; v.p., creative dir. Ogilvy & Mather (advt. agy.), N.Y.C., 1962-69, Kenyon & Eckhardt, Inc. (advt. agy.), N.Y.C., 1979-83, Barnhart & Co. (advt. agy.), Denver, 1983-84; pres. Stauderman Advt., 1984—; v.p., creative dir. Mktg. Resources Group (advt. agy.), 1985-88; dir. TV, advt. cons. Intermarco-Elvinger (advt. co.), Paris, 1969-73; TV cons. gov., Ohio, 1958; council mem., judge C.L.I.O. Festival, 1960—; chmn. Paris jury, 1969-73; jury mem. Internat. Advt. Film Festival, Cannes, Venice, 1976—. Radio, TV program writer: House of Mystery, 1946-51; writer, producer, dir., WXEL-TV, Cleve., 1951-54. Mem. men's com. Cleve. Playhouse, 1958-62; chmn. TV com. Cleve. United Fund, 1958-59. Served from pvt. to 2d lt. AUS, 1941-46; to 1st lt. N.G. Essex Troop AUS, 1948-50. Mem. Am. Assn. Advt. Agys. (TV and radio adminstrs. com. 1958-62), Am. Fedn. TV and Radio Artists, Naval Club (London). Home: 30 Water St, Lavenham, Suffolk CO10 9RN, England

STAUFF, MICHAEL FREDERICK, financial manager; b. Frankfurt, Fed. Republic Germany, Feb. 22, 1950; came to U.S., 1950; s. Ralph Thomas and Leona Marie (McMahon) S.; m. Rosemary Chere Delaware, Aug. 2, 1975;

children: Matthew, Adam. BS in Bus. Adminstrn., Northeastern U., 1972, MBA, 1983. Plant acct. Pandel Bradford, Lowell, Mass., 1972-73; fin. mgr. Modicon Corp., North Andover, Mass., 1973-75; asst. controller Simplex, Inc., Gardner, Mass., 1975-77, asst. to pres., 1977-80, materials mgr., 1980-83, mgr. corp. planning, 1983-85; v.p., chief fin. officer Internat. Marine Industries, Inc., Stamford, Conn., 1985-94; v.p., CFO TranSwitch Corp., Shelton, Conn., 1994—. Mem. Nat. Acctg. Assn., Fin. Execs. Inst. Roman Catholic. Avocations: skiing, boating, jogging. Home: 117 Settlers Farm Rd Monroe CT 06468-3324 Office: TranSwitch Corp 8 Progress Dr Shelton CT 06484

STAUFFER, CHARLES HENRY, retired chemistry educator; b. Harrisburg, Pa., Apr. 17, 1913; s. Charles C. and Hannah (Henry) S.; m. Eleanor Ramsdell, July 8, 1939; children—Charles R., Anne Elizabeth, John E. A.B., Swarthmore Coll., 1934; M.A., Harvard U., 1936, Ph.D., 1937. Instr. Worcester (Mass.) Poly. Inst., 1937-43, asst. prof., 1943-52, assoc. prof., 1952-58; assoc. prof. affiliate Clark U., Worcester, 1941; prof., chmn. dept. chemistry St. Lawrence U., Canton, N.Y., 1958-65; prof. chemistry, chmn. div. natural scis. math. Bates Coll., Lewiston, Maine, 1965—, Charles A. Dana prof. chemistry, 1968-77, prof. emeritus, 1977—; dir. chem. kinetics data project Nat. Acad. Scis., 1954-64; mem. adv. com. Office Critical Constants, 1961-64. Fellow AAAS, Am. Chem. Soc. (sec., chmn. No. N.Y. sect., councilor Maine sect.); mem. Sigma Xi, Phi Beta Kappa (Swarthmore Coll. chpt.). Clubs: Mason, Searsport Yacht. Home: 10 Champlain Ave Lewiston ME 04240-5217

STAUFFER, DELMAR J., professional association executive; b. Saybrook, Ill., Nov. 22; s. Calvin Bishop and Lillian Ruth (Hammel) S.; m. Mary Barbara Gower, Oct. 22, 1939; children: Andrew Thomas, Matthew Eric. BS in Health Edn. and Biology, U. Ill., 1963, MS in Health Edn., 1967, postgrad., 1970. Sci. tchr. Glenwood (Ill.) Sch. for Boys, 1963-65, Edgewood Jr. High Sch., Highland Park, Ill., 1965-66; grad. instr. health and safety U. Ill., Champaign, 1966-70; health edn. adminstr. AMA, Chgo., 1970-71; dir. bur. health edn. and audio svcs. ADA, Chgo., 1971-77, sec. coun. on dental health and planning, 1976-78, asst. exec. dir., 1978-86; exec. dir. Chgo. Dental Soc., 1986-89, Radiol. Soc. N.Am., Oak Brook, Ill., 1989—; cons. Am. Fund for Dental Health, Chgo., 1978-85, advisor, trustee, 1988-89; cons. Fedn. Dentaire Internat., 1983-86. Co-author, editor strategic plan Future of Dentistry, 1983; contbr. articles to profl. jours. Mem. Lake Bluff (Ill.) Sch. Bd. Caucus, 1980-86. Recipient award of merit Am. Coll. Dentists, Washington, 1985. Fellow Am. Sch. Health Assn. (fin. com. 1985—); mem. Am. Soc. Assn. Execs., Chgo. Soc. Assn. Execs., Am. Pub. Health Assn., Ill. Soc. Pub. Health Edn., Town and Tennis Club (pres. 1984). Republican. Methodist. Office: Radiol Soc N Am 2021 Spring Rd Ste 600 Oak Brook IL 60521-1860

STAUFFER, JOHN H., newspaper and broadcast executive; b. Arkansas City, Kans., Apr. 8, 1928; s. Oscar Stanley and Ethel Lucille (Stone) S.; m. Ruth Granger, June 3, 1950; children: John H. Jr., William H., Mary S. Brownback. BS Journalism, U. Kans., 1949. Reporter Topeka State Jour., 1949-54; editor The Kansan, Newton, 1954-57; pub. The Kansan, Kansas City, 1957-72, Topeka-Capital Jour., 1972-86; sr. v.p. Stauffer Comm. Inc., Topeka, 1969-86, pres., CEO, 1986-92; chmn. Topeka-Capital Jour., 1991—; also bd. dirs. Stauffer Comm. Inc., Topeka; dir. Mercantile Bank of Topeka. Pres. Kansas City Kans. United Way, 1968-69; chmn. bd. trustees Stormont-Vail Hosp., Topeka, 1984-86; mem. session 1st Presbyn. Ch., Topeka, 1986-89. Lt. U.S. Army, 1950-52. Mem. Kans. Press Assn. (pres. 1985-86), Inland Press Assn. (dir. 1980-88), Topeka Country Club (dir. 1978-83), Topeka C. of C. (pres. 1979), Kansas City C. of C. (pres. 1970-71), Top of the Tower, Phi Delta Theta. Republican. Presbyterian. Home: 2845 SW Jewell Ave Topeka KS 66611-1615 Office: Stauffer Comm Inc 616 SE Jefferson St Topeka KS 66607-1197

STAUFFER, MICHAEL KIRK, communications executive, consultant; b. N.Y.C., Nov. 25, 1944; s. George Michael and Geraldine (Kirk) S. BA, SUNY, Fredonia, 1966; MA, U. Minn., 1971, postgrad., 1971-73. Instr. U. Minn., Mpls., 1971-73; prep. sch. history tchr., 1973-74, vocat. rehab. counselor, grant writer, 1974-78; with Citibank, 1978-88, issues mgr. and pub. affairs dir.; staff dir. pub. affairs and govt. rels. NYNEX, 1990—; planned and implemented leadership task force and report State of N.Y. Info. Superhwy., 1990-92; consumer adv. coun., 1992; cons. White House Conf. on Families, 1980, Asian Mgmt. Bus. Assn., Calif. State Commn., ARC in Greater N.Y., Community Bd. 5, Queens, N.Y. V.p. Forum for Corp. Responsibility, Inc.; bd. dirs. Fredonia Coll. Found., Pub. Works Forum, Sons of the Revolution at Fraunces Tavern; alt. bd. dirs. Child Care Action Campaign. Fellow Inst. for Rsch. in History; mem. N.Y. Acad. Scis., Am. Mgmt. Assn., Pub. Rels. Soc. Am., Issues Mgmt. Assn., N.Y.C. Pub. Issues Group (a founder 1978), Masons, S.R. Avocation: history. Home: 1760 Dekalb Ave Ridgewood NY 11385-1142 Office: NYNEX 1095 Ave of the Americas New York NY 10036

STAUFFER, ROBERT ALLEN, former research company executive; b. Dayton, Ohio, Jan. 26, 1920; s. John G. and Verna G. (Theobald) S.; m. Justine M. Wells, Mar. 20, 1943 (div. 1969); children—Susan, Nancy; m. Ruth Stanley Munro, Oct. 30, 1969. B.A. in Chemistry, Harvard, 1942. With Nat. Research Corp., Cambridge, 1942-67; gen. mgr. research div. Nat. Research Corp., 1949-63, dir., 1954-67, v.p., 1949-67; with Norton Co., Worcester, Mass., 1963-71; v.p. research Norton Co., 1963-71; v.p., gen. mgr. Norton Research Corp., Cambridge, 1968-71; v.p. NRC Metals Corp., 1955-56, Environ. Research and Tech., Concord, Mass., 1971-80. Patentee in field. Home: 3208 Heatherwood at Kings Way Yarmouth Port MA 02675

STAUFFER, RONALD EUGENE, lawyer; b. Hempstead, N.Y., Jan. 22, 1949; s. Hiram Eugene and Florence Marie (Hintz) S.; m. Vicki Lynn Hartman, June 12, 1973; children: Eric Alan, Craig Aaron, Darren Adam. SB, MIT, 1970; JD magna cum laude, Harvard U., 1973. Bar: D.C. 1973, U.S. Ct. Mil. Appeals 1976, U.S. Tax Ct. 1979. Ptnr. Hogan & Hartson, Washington, 1977-87, Sonnenschein Nath & Rosenthal, Washington, 1988—. Contbr. articles to profl. publs. Capt. U.S. Army, 1970-77. Mem. ABA (chair TIPS Employee Benefits Com. 1977—), D.C. Bar Assn., Tau Beta Pi, Sigma Gamma Tau. Avocations: running, water skiing. Home: 10207 Woodvale Pond Dr Fairfax Station VA 22039-1658 Office: Sonnenschein Nath & Rosenthal 1301 K St NW Ste 600 Washington DC 20005-3317

STAUFFER, SARAH ANN, political worker; b. Lancaster, Pa., June 13, 1915; d. Charles F. and Gertrude (Frantz) S. Student, Franklin and Marshall Coll., 1957-58, Wharton Sch. Bus. Adminstrn., U. Pa., 1958-62. Office mgr. aircraft div. Armstrong Cork Co., 1941-43; mem., then capt. 45th div. Clubmobile unit ARC, Anzio, Italy and Munich, Germany, 1943-45; dir. personnel and operations U.S. Occupied Ty. ETO Clubmobile div., 1945-46; bd. dirs. Lancaster (Pa.) chpt. ARC, 1947-51, treas., 1949-51; past mem. bd. Lancaster Symphony Assn.; mem. exec. com. Pa. Health Council, 1954-55; del.-at-large Community Chest Council, 1958-72; regional dir. Assn. Jr. Leagues Am., 1951-55, treas., 1955-57; del. gov.'s conf. White House Conf. on Children and Youth, 1960; del. to U.S. Dept. Labor Women's Bur. Nat. Conf., 1970; mem. friends adv. com. Scheie Eye Inst., 1980-93; mem. bd. Young Republicans of Pa., 1937-39, 45-47; mem. Rep. Nat. Com. for Pa., 1964-74; exec. com. Rep. Nat. Com., 1964-68; mem. bd. Pa. Council Rep. Women, 1957—, hon. pres.; alt. del. Rep. Nat. Conv., 1960, del.-at-large, 1964, 68, 72, 80. Pres. Commonwealth Bd. Med. Coll., 1973-75; mem. exec. com. Nat. Bd. Med. Coll Pa., 1978; bd. visitors Franklin-Marshall Coll., 1972-84; sec. Pa. Electoral Coll., 1972; bd. dirs. Rehab. Internat. U.S.A., 1981-85, del. to world congress, Portugal, 1984; fellow Lancaster Country Day Sch., 1989. Named Disting. Dau. of Pa., 1965; mem. Legion of Honor-Chapel of Four Chaplains, 1979. Former assoc. mem. Acad. Polit. and Social Sci., Acad. Polit. Sci; charter mem. Historic Preservation Trust of Lancaster County. Clubs: Colony (N.Y.C.); Acorn (Phila.); Soroptimist (Lancaster, Pa.) (hon.), Bus./Profl. Women (Lancaster, Pa.). Home: Lime Spring Farm PO Box 6247 Rohrerstown PA 17607-6247

STAUFFER, STANLEY HOWARD, newspaper and broadcasting executive; b. Peabody, Kans., Sept. 11, 1920; s. Oscar S. and Ethel L. (Stone) S.; m. Suzanne R. Wallace, Feb. 16, 1945 (div. 1961);l children: Peter, Clay, Charles; m. Elizabeth D. Priest, July 14, 1962 (div. 1991); children: Elizabeth, Grant; m. Madeline A. Sargent, Nov. 27, 1992. AB, U. Kans.,

1942. Assoc. editor Topeka State Jour., 1946-47; editor, pub. Santa Maria (Calif.) Times, 1948-52; rewrite and copy editor Denver Post, 1953-54; staff mem. AP (Denver bur.), 1954-55; exec. v.p. Stauffer Publs., Inc., 1955-69; gen. mgr. Topeka Capital-Jour., 1957-69; pres. Stauffer Comm., Inc., 1969-86, chmn., 1986-92; bd. dirs. Stauffer Comm., Inc., Topeka/Shawnee County Devel. Corp.; chmn. bd. dirs. Stauffer Comm. Found. Past pres. Topeka YMCA; past chmn. adv. bd. St. Francis Hosp.; past chmn. Met. Topeka Airport Authority; trustee William Allen White Found., Menninger Found., Midwest Rsch. Inst., Washburn U. Endowment Assn. With USAAF, 1942-45. Named Chpt. Boss of Yr. Am. Bus. Women's Assn., 1976, Outstanding Kans. Pub. Kappa Tau Alpha, 1980, Legion of Honor De Molay, Topeka Phi of Yr., 1971. Mem. Kans. Press Assn. (past pres.), Inland Daily Press Assn. (past dir.), Air Force Assn. (past pres. Topeka), Kans. U. Alumni Assn. (past dir.), Kans. C. of C. and Industry (past chmn.), Def. Orientation Conf. Assn., Topeka Countgry Club, Top of the Tower Club, Garden of the Gods Club (Colorado Springs), Masons (32d deg.), Shriners, Phi Delta Theta (past chpt. pres.), Sigma Delta Chi (past chpt. pres.). Episcopalian (past sr. warden). Office: Stauffer Comm Inc 6th & Jefferson St Topeka KS 66607

STAUFFER, THOMAS GEORGE, hotel executive; b. Akron, Ohio, Mar. 4, 1932; s. Caldwell E. and Rose C. (Ortscheidt) S.; m. Lois Campsey, June 18, 1960. B.S., Case Western Res. U., 1954. Cert. hotel adminstr. Pres. Renaissance Hotels Internat. (Ams.), 1954—. Recipient Legion of Honor, Order of DeMolay. Mem. Am. Hotel and Motel Assn., Urban Land Inst., Nat. Restaurant Assn. (dir.), Rolling Rock Club, Clifton Club, Masons, Shriners, Sigma Chi (Significant Sigma Chi). Home: 1000 Estill Dr Cleveland OH 44107-1418 Office: Renaissance Hotels Internat 29800 Bainbridge Rd Solon OH 44139

STAUFFER, THOMAS MICHAEL, educational administrator; b. Harrisburg, Pa., Dec. 5, 1941; s. John Nisley and Louis Lee Stauffer; m. Marion Walker, Aug. 26, 1966 (div. Dec. 1989); children: Amity Juliet, Courtney Amanda, Winston Thomas; m. Deborah Whisnand, May 16, 1993; 1 stepchild, Elizabeth Stinson. Student, Juniata Coll., 1959-61; BA cum laude, Wittenberg U., Ohio, 1963; Cert. in E. European Politics, Freie U. Berlin, 1964; MA, PhD, U. Denver, 1973. Asst. dean coll., asst. prof. polit. sci. Keene State Coll., 1968-72; dir. fellows in acad. adminstrn., office leadership devel. Am. Coun. Edn., 1972-78; v.p., dir. div. external relations Am. Council on Edn., Washington, 1978-82; pres. and prof. pub. policy and internat. studies Golden Gate U., San Francisco, 1992—; exec. sec. Fedn. of Assn. of the Acad. Health Care Professions, 1975-80; chmn. task force on the future of Am. Coun. on Edn., 1978; exec. dir. Bus.-Higher Edn. Forum, 1978-81, Nat. Commn. on Higher Edn. Issues, 1980-81; pres., prof. pub. policy U. Houston, Clear Lake, 1982-91; pres., prof. pub. policy and internat. rels. Golden Gate U., 1992—; spl. asst. to adminstr. NASA, 1992; cons. NSF, U.S. Dept. State, Coun. for Internat. Exch. of Scholars, Japan External Trade Orgn.; mem. Commn. on Credit and Credentials, Am. Coun. Edn., Coun. on Competitiveness, Bay Area Internat. Forum; chair nat. bd. Challenger Ctr. for Space Sci. Edn., 1987, Ctr. for Advanced Space Studies; mem. dels. on Higher Edn. and Econ. Devel. to People's Republic of China, S.E. Asia, Japan, Rwanda, Sri Lanka, United Arab Emirates, 1978-94. Exec. editor Ednl. Record and Higher Edn. and Nat. Affairs, 1978-82; contbr. articles to profl. jours., newspapers, monographs, chpts. to books. Chmn. com. advanced tech. Tex. Econ. Devel., 1984, Houston Com. on Econ. Diversification Planning, 1984, Houston World Trade Ctr. Task Force, 1985, East Tex. 2000 Com. on Econ. Devel., S.E. Tex. Higher Edn. Coun., 1989, Clear Lake Area Econ. Devel. Found.; v.p. Inter-Am. U. Coun. for Econ. and Social Devel., Houston World Trade Assn.; vice chmn. Tex. Sci. and Tech. Coun., 1986; pres. St. John Hosp.; trustee San Francisco Consortium; bd. dirs. Houston Hosp. Coun. Found., Tex. Coun. on Econ. Edn., Tex. Senate Space Industry Tech. Commn., Tex. Innovation Info. Network System; vice-chair San Francisco World Trade Assn.; mem. steering com. Houston Econ. Devel. Coun., Calif. Ind. Edn. Coun., blue ribbon com. City Coll., Bay Area Coun. Industry Edn. Coun. of Calif., community bd. St. Mary's Hosp., San Francisco YMCA. Recipient Disting. Alumni award Grad. Sch. Internat. Studies U. Denver, 1989, Tex. Senate Resolution of Commendation, 1991; Am. Coun. on Edn. fellow in acad. adminstrn., 1972, Ford Found. and Social Sci. Found. fellow, 1963-68, sr. fellow Am. Leadership Forum. Mem. AAAS, Internat. Studies Assn. (co-chmn. ann. meeting 1978), Am. Hosp. Assn., Policy Studies Orgn., Internat. Assn. Univ. Pres., San Francisco Com. on Fgn. Rels., Oakland C. of C., San Francisco C. of C. (econ. devel. com.), Commonwealth Club, San Francisco World Trade Club, Univ. Club San Francisco. Home: 1806 Green St San Francisco CA 94123 Office: Golden Gate U Office of Pres 536 Mission St San Francisco CA 94105-2921

STAUFFER, WILLIAM ALBERT, insurance company executive; b. Maryville, Mo., June 9, 1930; s. Marion W. and Louise (Mangelsdorf) S.; m. Jean VanSlyck Shanley, Apr. 11, 1953; children—Rebecca, John, Rachel. B.J., U. Mo., 1952. Gen. mgr. York (Nebr.) Daily News-Times, 1955-61, Grand Island (Nebr.) Daily Ind., 1961-63; with Northwestern Bell Telephone Co., 1963-83, sec.-treas., 1970-72; v.p., chief exec. officer Northwestern Bell Telephone Co., Fargo, N.D., 1972-74; v.p., chief exec. officer-Iowa Northwestern Bell Telephone Co., Des Moines, 1974-83; exec. v.p., chief operating officer Blue Cross-Blue Shield Iowa, Des Moines, 1984-87; bus. cons. Des Moines, 1987—; bd. dirs. Hubbell Realty Co., Des Moines, Iowa-Des Moines Nat. Bank, Life Care Retirement Communities, Inc. (chmn., 1994—). Nat. By-Products, Inc., Des Moines, POP Radio Corp., N.Y.C. Pres. Convalescent Home Children, Des Moines, 1969; v.p. Mid-Iowa council Boy Scouts Am.; pres. Hospice of Ctrl. Iowa Found.; Regional Health Care Corp., Omaha, 1971, Mercy Hosp. Found., 1979-81; mem. adv. bd. Mercy Hosp. Des Moines.; bd. dirs., sec. Omaha Symphony Orch. Assn., 1970, Iowa Coll. Found., Des Moines Symphony Orch. Assn., YMCA, Des Moines; bd. dirs. Blue Shield Iowa, Living History Farms; trustee Drake U., Des Moines; trustee devel. coun. U. Mo., pres. 1986-90. Served with USAF, 1952-54. Named to Mo. Basketball Hall of Fame, 1990, U. Mo. Intercollegiate Athletics Hall of Fame, 1991. Mem. C. of C. Des Moines (pres. 1981), Greater Des Moines Com., Phi Delta Theta. Clubs: Wakonda (pres. 1989), Des Moines. Home: 4916 Harwood Dr Des Moines IA 50312-1833 Office: 4916 Harwood Dr Des Moines IA 50312-1833

STAUP, JOHN GARY, safety engineer; b. Cleve., May 10, 1931; m. Ellsworth Leroy and May Ann (Weisgerber) S.; m. Elizabeth Louise Friemoth, Jan. 10, 1953; children: Michael Steven, Valerie Elysa Staup Gerdemann, Timothy Karl. BA, Dayton U., 1949; student, U. Mich. Design engr. Gramm Trailer, Delphos, Ohio, 1955-57, F.C. Russell Co., Pandora, Ohio, 1957-59, Ins. Svc. Office, Lima, Ohio, 1959-65, Ctrl. Mut. Ins., Van Wert, Ohio, 1965-76, Mid. Am. Tech. Svcs., Delphos, 1980—; adminstr. safety programs and security programs for various firms. Sgt. USAF, 1951-55. Mem. Am. Single Shot Rifle Assn. (sec-treas. 1991—), Maumee Valley Soc. Safety Engr., Optimist Club (v.p.). Avocations: gun collecting, civic involvement, public speaking, target shooting, travel. Home: 709 Carolyn Dr Delphos OH 45833

STAUTH, ROBERT E., food service executive; b. 1945. Grad., Kans. State U.; student, Stanford U. Exec. Program, 1989. Joined Fleming Cos. Inc., Oklahoma City, 1977, various mgmt. positions, 1977-93, pres., COO, bd. dirs., 1993, CEO, 1993—; chmn. Fleming Cos.; bd. dirs. IGA, Inc. Adv. bd. Coll. Bus. Adminstrn., U. Okla., Kans. State U.; mem. Okla. Bus. Roundtable. Mem. Nat. Am. Wholesale Grocers Assn. (govt. rels. com., nominating com.), Food Mktg. Inst. (exec. steering com. on ECR, mem. industry rels. com.), Okla. State C. of C. Office: Fleming Cos Inc PO Box 26647 6301 Waterford Blvd Oklahoma City OK 73126-0647

STAVELY, KEITH WILLIAMS FITZGERALD, librarian; b. New Brunswick, N.J., May 13, 1942; s. Homer Eaton and Elizabeth (Williams) S.; m. Kathleen Fitzgerald, Aug. 19, 1978; 1 child, Jonathan Keith. BA, Yale U., 1964, PhD, 1969; MLS, Simmons Coll., 1980. Asst. prof. English Boston U., 1969-74, Ohio State U., 1990-91; lectr. in English Boston Coll., 1975-80; adult svcs. libr. Watertown (Mass.) Free Pub. Libr., 1979-89, br. libr. 1984-89, head adult svcs., 1989-90; reference libr. Somerville (Mass.) Pub. Libr. 1991-92; asst. adminstr. Fall River (Mass.) Pub. Libr., 1992—. Author: Puritan Legacies: Paradise Lost and the New England Tradition, 1630-1890, 1987, paperback edit., 1990, The Politics of Milton's Prose Style, 1975; co-author: Family Man: What Men Feel About Their Wives, Their Children, Their Parents, and Themselves, 1978; contbr. articles and revs. to profl.

publs. Fellow Fulbright Found., India, 1964-65, Am. Coun. Learned Socs., 1988-89, John Simon Guggenheim Meml. Found., 1989. Mem. MLA (Prize for Ind. Scholars 1987), ALA, Mass. Libr. Assn., Phi Beta Kappa.

STAVER, LEROY BALDWIN, banker; b. Portland, Oreg., Oct. 1, 1908; s. Herbert LeRoy and Grace (Baldwin) S.; m. Helene M. Matschek, Oct. 16, 1937; I son, Roger. J.D., Northwestern Coll. Law, 1930; grad., Rutgers U. Grad. Sch. Banking, 1937-39. Bar: Oreg. bar 1929. With U.S. Nat. Bank of Oreg., 1925-74, asst. trust officer, 1936-42, trust officer, 1942-58, v.p., trust officer, 1958—, exec. trust officer, 1959-63, exec. v.p., exec. trust officer, 1963-66, pres., 1966-74; chmn., 1971-74, also dir.; chmn. Commerce Mortgage Co., 1967-74; chmn., chief exec. officer U.S. Bancorp., 1969-74, also dir. Hon. trustee Med. Rsch. Found. Oreg., pres. 1975-76; life trustee Willamette U., St. Vincent Med. Rsch. Found., Oreg. Grad. Inst. Sci. and Tech.; hon. bd. dirs. World Forstrry Ctr. Named to Oreg. Bankers Assn. Hall of Fame, 1989. Mem. Am., Oreg. bar assns., C. of C. (pres. 1975), Oreg. Hist. Soc. (bd. dirs. 1978-91), Delta Theta Phi. Clubs: Arlington, Waverley Country. Home: 9908 SE Cambridge Ln Milwaukie OR 97222-7402 Office: US Nat Bank Oreg PO Box 4412 Portland OR 97208-4412

STAVERT, ALEXANDER BRUCE, bishop; b. Montreal, Que., Can., Apr. 1, 1940; s. R. Ewart and Kathleen H. (Rosamond) S.; m. Diana Greig, June 26, 1982; children: Kathleen, Rosamond, Timothy. Student, Lower Can. Coll., Montreal, 1957; BA, Bishop's U., 1961; STB, U. Toronto, Ont., Can., 1964, ThM, 1976, DD (hon.), 1986. Ordained to ministry Anglican Ch. as deacon, 1964, as priest, 1965. With Mission of Schefferville, Que., 1964-69; fellow, tutor in div. Trinity Coll., U. Toronto, 1969-70, chaplain, 1970-76; with St. Clement's Mission East, St. Paul's River, Que., 1976-81; chaplain Champlain Regional Coll., Bishop's U., 1981-84; dean, rector St. Alban's Cathedral, Prince Albert, Sask., Can., 1984-91; consecrated bishop Anglican Diocese of Que., Quebec, 1991—. Address: Diocese of Que, 31 rue des Jardins, Quebec, PQ Canada G1R 4L6

STAVES, SUSAN, English educator; b. N.Y.C., Oct. 5, 1942; d. Henry Tracy and Margaret (McClernon) S. AB, U. Chgo., 1963; MA, U. Va., 1964, PhD, 1967. Woodrow Wilson intern Bennett Coll., Greensboro, N.C. 1965-66; from asst. prof. to prof. Brandeis U., Waltham, Mass., 1967—, Paul Proswimmer prof. of Humanities, 1993—; Clark prof. UCLA, 1989-90. Author: Players' Scepters: Fictions of Authority in the Restoration, 1979, Married Women's Separate Property in England, 1660-1833, 1990; co-author: (with John Brewer) Early Modern Conceptions of Property, 1994; also articles in Modern Philology, 18th-Century Studies, Studies in Eng. Lit., Studies in Eighteenth Century Culture, Law and History. Assoc. mem. Belmont (Mass.) Dem. Town Com.; mem. ACLU, 1967—. Woodrow Wilson fellow, 1963-64, Woodrow Wilson Dissertation fellow, 1966-67, Harvard Liberal Arts fellow, 1980-81, John Simon Guggenheim fellow, 1981-82. Mem. MLA (exec. com. div. on late-18th century English lit. 1984-86), Am. Soc. for 18th-Century Studies (exec. bd. 1987-90), Am. Soc. for Legal History, AAUP, English Inst. Episcopalian. Avocations: tennis, squash. Office: Brandeis U Dept English Waltham MA 02254

STAVIG, MARK LUTHER, English language educator; b. Northfield, Minn., Jan. 20, 1935; s. Lawrence Melvin and Cora (Hjertaas) S.; m. Donna Mae Ring, July 3, 1957; children—Anne Ragnhild, Thomas Edward, Rolf Lawrence. B.A., Augustana Coll., 1956, Oxford U., 1958; M.A., Oxford U., 1962; Ph.D., Princeton U., 1961. Instr. to asst. prof. English Colo. Coll., Colorado Springs, 1968—. Author: John Ford and the Traditional Moral Order, 1968, The Forms of Things Unknown: Renaissance Metaphor in Romeo and Juliet and A Midsummer Night's Dream, 1995; editor: Ford, 'Tis Pity She's a Whore, 1966. Fellow Danforth Found., 1956-61, Woodrow Wilson Found., 1956-57; Fulbright scholar Oxford U., 1956-58. Mem. MLA, Shakespeare Assn. Am. Democrat. Home: 1409 Wood Ave Colorado Springs CO 80907-7348 Office: Colo Coll Dept English Colorado Springs CO 80903

STAVITSKY, ABRAM BENJAMIN, immunologist, educator; b. Newark, May 14, 1919; s. Nathan and Ida (Novak) S.; m. Ruth Bernice Okney, Dec. 6, 1942; children: Ellen Barbara, Gail Beth. AB, U. Mich., 1939, MS, 1940; PhD, U. Minn., 1943; VMD, U. Pa., 1946. Research fellow Calif. Inst. Tech., 1946-47; faculty Case Western Res. U., 1947—, prof. microbiology, 1962—, prof. molecular biology, 1983-89, emeritus, 1989; mem. expert com. immunochemistry WHO, 1963-83; mem. microbiology fellowship com. NIH, 1963-66; mem. microbiology test com. Nat. Bd. Med. Examiners, 1970-73; chmn. microbiology test com. Nat. Bd. Podiatry Examiners, 1978-82. Mem. editorial bd. Jour. Immunological Methods, 1979-88, Immunopharmacology, 1983—. Vice pres. Ludlow Community Assn., 1964-66. Fellow AAAS; mem. Am. Assn. Immunologists, Am. Soc. Microbiology, Sigma Xi. Home: 14604 Onaway Rd Cleveland OH 44120-2845 Office: 2119 Abington Rd Cleveland OH 44106-2333

STAVITSKY, JEFFREY, wholesale distribution executive; b. 1949. With YKK Zipper Co., N.Y.C., 1970-77; with D.B. Brown, Inc., Newark, 1977—, pres. Office: D B Brown Rte 425 Ave P Newark NJ 07105*

STAVRO, STEVE A., professional hockey team executive. Chmn. bd., chief exec. officer Toronto Maple Leafs, Ont., Can. Office: Toronto Maple Leafs, 60 Carlton St, Toronto, ON Canada M5B 1L1*

STAVROPOULOS, WILLIAM S., chemical executive; b. Bridgehampton, N.Y., May 12, 1939; m. Linda Stavropoulos; children: S. William, Angela D. BA in Pharm. Chemistry, Fordham U.; PhD in Medicinal Chemistry, U. Washington. Research chemist in pharm. research Dow Chem. Co., Midland, Mich., 1967, research chemist for diagnostics product research, 1970, research mgr. diagnostics product research, 1973, bus. mgr. diagnostics product research, 1976, bus. mgr. polyolefins, 1977, dir. mktg. plastics dept., 1979; comml. v.p. Dow Chem. Co. Latin Am., Coral Gables, Fla., 1980; pres. Dow Latin Am., 1984; comml. v.p., basics and hydrocarbons Dow Chem. Co. U.S.A., Midland, 1985-87; group v.p. Dow Chem. Co. U.S.A., 1987-90; pres. Dow U.S.A., 1990; v.p. The Dow Chemical Co., 1990; sr. v.p. The Dow Chem. Co., 1991, pres., 1992; pres., COO The Dow Chem. Co., Midland, 1993—; bd. dirs. Dow Corning Corp., The Dow Chem. Co.; CEO Essex Chem Corp, 1988-92. Office: Dow Chem Co 2030 Willard H Dow Ctr Midland MI 48674

STAVROU, NIKOLAOS ATHANASIOS, political science educator; b. Griazdani-Delvino, Albania, May 5, 1935; came to U.S., 1956, naturalized, 1962; s. Athanasios Haritos and Aristoula F. (Laiou) S.; married. B.A., Hunter Coll., 1963; M.A. in Internat. Affairs, George Washington U., 1965, Ph.D. in Polit. Sci., 1970. Research fellow Inst. Sino-Soviet Studies, George Washington U., 1963-64; lectr. govt. Howard U., Washington, 1968-70; asst. prof. Howard U., 1970-72, assoc. prof. polit. sci., 1972-77, prof. polit. sci. and internat. affairs, 1978-79, assoc. chmn. dept. polit. sci., 1979-82; adj. professorial lectr. George Washington U., 1983; guest lectr. Fgn. Service Inst. State Dept.; coordinator Eastern Mediterranean Study Group; area specialist on Yugoslav, Albanian and Greek affairs. Author: Allied Politics and Military Interventions: The Political Role of the Greek Military, 1977; contbg. author: Political Parties of Europe; contbg. author: Yearbook on International Communism; editor: Edvard Kardelj: The Historical Roots of Non-Alignment, 1980, Greece under Socialism, 1988; author, editor Greece Under Socialism, 1988; editor Mediterranean Quar., 1991—; contbr. more than 200 articles to profl. jours., chpts. to books. Howard U. Research grantee, 1973-74, 77-78, 88-89. Mem. Internat. Studies Assn. (v.p. Mediterranean affairs). Eastern Orthodox. Club: Cosmos (Washington). Office: Howard Univ Dept Polit Sci Washington DC 20059

STAW, BARRY MARTIN, business and psychology educator; b. Los Angeles, Sept. 13, 1945; s. Harold Paul and Shirley C. (Posner) S.; 1 child, Jonah Martin. BS, U. Oreg., 1967; MBA, U. Mich., 1968; PhD, Northwestern U., 1972. Asst. prof. bus. adminstrn. U. Ill., Urbana, 1972-75; assoc. prof. Northwestern U., Evanston, Ill., 1975-77, prof., 1977-80; prof. U. Calif., Berkeley, 1980—, Mitchell prof. Leadership and communication, 1986—; researcher in organizational psychology. Editor: Psychological Dimensions of Organizational Behavior; co-editor: New Directions in Organizational Behavior, (book series) Research in Organizational Behavior; editorial bd. Organizational Behavior and Human Decision Processes,

1974—, Jour. Occupational and Organizational Psychology, 1990—; contbr. numerous articles to profl. jours. Fellow APA, Am. Psychol. Soc., Acad. Mgmt. Soc. for Organizational Behavior. Democrat. Jewish. Avocations: basketball, tennis, skiing. Office: Univ of Calif Haas Sch Bus Adminstrn Berkeley CA 94720

STAWASZ, CHERIE, public relations executive; b. Chgo., Apr. 10, 1947; d. Edward Paul and Louise Antoinette (Dutka) S.; m. Francis Andre Koenig, June 18, 1983. B.A., Cardinal Stritch Coll., 1968. Traffic coordinator Sta.-WPIX-TV, N.Y.C., 1969-70; prodn. assoc. Green Dolmatch Advt., N.Y.C., 1970-73; publicity assoc. Simon & Schuster, N.Y.C., 1973-75; account exec. Siesel Co., N.Y.C., 1976-78; v.p. Rowland Co., N.Y.C., 1978-84; pres. Stawasz Pub. Relations, Inc. (subs. of Jordan, Manning, Case, Taylor & McGrath Advt., Inc.), N.Y.C., 1984—. Active C.G. Jung Found., Westchester Hist. Soc. Roman Catholic. Office: Stawasz/Drucker Comms 445 Park Ave New York NY 10022-2606

STAY, BARBARA, zoologist, educator; b. Cleve., Aug. 31, 1926; d. Theron David and Florence (Finley) S. A.B., Vassar Coll., 1947; M.A., Radcliffe Coll., 1949, Ph.D., 1953. Entomologist Army Research Center, Natick, Mass., 1954-60; vis. asst. prof. Pomona Coll., 1960; asst. prof. biology U. Pa., 1961-67; asso. prof. zoology U. Iowa, Iowa City, 1967-77; prof. U. Iowa, 1977—. Fulbright fellow to Australia, 1953; Lalor fellow Harvard U., 1960. Mem. Am. Soc. Zoologists, Am. Inst. Biol. Scis., Am. Soc. Cell Biology, Entomol. Soc. Am., Iowa Acad. Scis., Sigma Xi. Office: U Iowa Dept Biological Scis Iowa City IA 52242

STAYIN, RANDOLPH JOHN, lawyer; b. Cin., Oct. 30, 1942; s. Jack and Viola (Tomin) S.; children: Gregory S., Todd R., Elizabeth J. BA, Dartmouth Coll., 1964; JD, U. Cin., 1967. Bar: Ohio 1967, U.S. Dist. Ct. (so. dist.) Ohio 1968, U.S. Dist. Ct. D.C. 1977, U.S. Ct. Appeals (6th cir.) 1968, U.S. Ct. Appeals (fed. cir.) 1986, U.S. Supreme Ct. 1974, U.S. Ct. Appeals (D.C. cir.) 1976, U.S. Ct. Internat. Trade, 1985. Assoc. Frost & Jacobs, Cin., 1967-72; exec. asst., dir. of legislation U.S. Sen. Robert Taft, Jr., Washington, 1973-74, chief of staff, 1975-76; assoc. Taft, Stettinius & Hollister, Washington, 1977, ptnr., 1978-88; ptnr. Barnes & Thornburg, Washington, 1988—; bd. dirs. W.J.S. Holdings Ltd., W.J.S. Inc.; mem. adv. coun. U.S. and FGN. Comml. Svc., U.S. Dept. Commerce. Chmn., mem. numerous coms., chmn., worker campaigns for local politicians Rep. Party state and local orgns.; mem. Citizens to Save WCET-TV, 1967-72, Fine Arts Fund, 1970-72, Cancer Soc., 1970-72; chmn. agy. rels. com. Hamilton County Mental Health and Mental Retardation Bd., 1969-71, vice chmn., 1971, chmn., 1971-72; v.p. Recreation Commn., City of Cin., 1970-72; mem. funds mgmt. com. Westwood 1st Presbyn. Ch., 1968, v.p., 1969, pres., 1970, trustee, 1970, elder, 1971-72; bd. dirs. Evans Mill Pond Owners Assn., v.p., 1986, pres., 1987; active Washington Nat. Cathedral Fund Com. Mem. ABA (sect. on internat. law and practice, vice chmn. com. on nat. legislation 1977-79, internat. sect., anti-trust sect.), Am. Soc. Assn. Execs. (legal sect., internat. sect.), Internat. Bar Assn., D.C. Bar Assn. (com. on internat. law). Avocations: theater, tennis, skiing, travel, reading. Office: Barnes & Thornburg #500 1401 Eye St NW Washington DC 20005

STAYMAN, ALLEN PAUL, government executive; b. Phila., Oct. 19, 1953; s. Joseph Webster Jr. and Barbara Brehm (Porter) S.; m. Aurora Justine Cebreros, Aug. 4, 1988; children: Laura Brehm, Justine Cebreros. BA in Environ. Design, U. Wash., 1975, MS in Fisheries Sci., 1981. Cons. fisheries biologist Seattle, 1981-84; legis. asst. U.S. Senate, Washington, 1984, profl. staff Com. on Energy & Natural Resources, 1984-93; dep. asst. sec. U.S. Dept. of Interior, Washington, 1993—. Sea Grant fellow NOAA, U.S. Dept. of Commerce, 1978. Mem. Phi Beta Kappa. Office: US Dept of Interior 1849 C St NW Washington DC 20240

STAYTON, THOMAS GEORGE, lawyer; b. Rochester, Minn., May 1, 1948; m. Barbara Joan Feck, Aug. 8, 1970; children: Ryan, Megan. BS, Miami U., Oxford, Ohio, 1970; JD, U. Mich., 1973. Bar: Ind. 1973, U.S. Dist. Ct. (so. dist.) Ind. 1973, U.S. Ct. Appeals (7th cir.) 1977. Ptnr. Baker & Daniels, Indpls., 1973—. Recipient Sagamore of the Wabash Gov. of Ind., 1988. Mem. ABA, Ind. State Bar Assn., Indpls. Bar Assn. Club: Indpls. Athletic. Office: Baker & Daniels 300 N Meridian St Ste 2700 Indianapolis IN 46204-1782

STEAD, EUGENE ANSON, JR., physician; b. Atlanta, Oct. 6, 1908; s. Eugene Anson and Emily (White) S.; m. Evelyn Selby, June 15, 1940; children: Nancy White, Lucy Ellen, William Wallace. B.S., Emory U., 1928, M.D., 1932. Med. intern Peter Bent Brigham Hosp., Boston, 1932-33; surg. intern Peter Bent Brigham Hosp., 1934-35, assoc. medicine, 1939-42, acting physician-in-chief, 1942; research fellow medicine Harvard, 1933-34; asst. resident medicine Cin. Gen. Hosp., 1935-36, resident, 1936-37; instr. medicine U. Cin., 1935-37; resident phys. Thorndike Meml. Lab.; asst. medicine Harvard and Boston City Hosp., 1937-39; instr. medicine Harvard, 1938-41, assoc., 1941-42; prof. medicine Emory U.; physician-in-chief Grady Hosp., Atlanta, 1942-46; dean Emory U., 1945-46; physician in chief Duke Hosp., 1947-67; prof. medicine Duke U. Sch. Medicine, 1947-78; disting. physician VA, 1978-85. Editor: Circulation, 1973-78, N.C. Med. Jour., 1983-92; Contbr. numerous articles on various aspects of circulation to med. jours. Mem. N.C. Med. Soc., Am. Fedn. Clin. Research, Assn. Am. Physicians, Am. Soc. Clin. Investigation, Alpha Omega Alpha, Sigma Xi, Phi Beta Kappa. Methodist. Home: 5113 Townsville Rd Bullock NC 27507-9438 Office: Duke U Dept Medicine Durham NC 27710

STEAD, JAMES JOSEPH, JR., securities company executive; b. Chgo., Sept. 13, 1930; s. James Joseph and Irene (Jennings) S.; m. Edith Pearson, Feb. 13, 1954; children: James, Diane, Robert, Caroline. BS, DePaul U., 1957, MBA, 1959. Asst. sec. C.F. Childs & Co., Chgo., 1957-62; exec. v.p., sec. Koenig, Keating & Stead Inc., Chgo., 1962-66; 2d v.p., mgr. midwest mcpl. bond dept. Hayden, Stone Inc., Chgo., 1966-69; sr. v.p., nat. sales mgr. Ill. Co. Inc., 1969-70; mgr. instl. sales dept. Reynolds and Co., Chgo., 1970-72; partner Edwards & Hanly, 1972-74; v.p., instl. sales mgr. Paine, Webber, Jackson & Curtis, 1974-76; v.p., regional instl. sales mgr. Reynolds Securities, Inc., 1976-78; sr. v.p., regional mgr. Oppenheimer & Co., Inc., 1978-88; sr. v.p., regional mgr. fixed income Tucker Anthony, 1988—; instr. Mcpl. Bond Sch., Chgo., 1967—. With AUS, 1951-53. Mem. Security Traders Assn. Chgo., Nat. Security Traders Assn., Am. Mgmt. Assn., Mcpl. Fin. Forum Washington. Clubs: Execs., Union League, Mcpl. Bond, Bond (Chgo.); Olympia Fields Country (Ill.); Wall Street (N.Y.C.). Home: 1005 Hickory Ridge Ct Frankfort IL 60423-2114 Office: 1 S Wacker Dr Chicago IL 60606-4614

STEAD, WILLIAM WHITE, physician, educator, public health administrator; b. Decatur, Ga., Jan. 4, 1919; s. Eugene Anson and Emily (White) S.; m. Ethel Barnett, June 14, 1947 (div.); 1 child, Richard Barnett; m. Joan Jordan DeVore, Apr. 22, 1975. A.B., Emory U., 1940, M.D., 1943. Intern Grady Meml. Hosp., Atlanta, 1944; resident in medicine Emory U., 1944-45, U. Cin., 1946-48; resident in medicine U. Minn., 1948-49, faculty med. schs., 1949-57; faculty med. schs. U. Fla., 1957-60; prof. medicine Med. Coll. Wis., Milw. County Gen. Hosp., Milw., 1960-72; med. dir. Muirdale Sanatorium, Milw., 1960-72; prof. medicine U. Ark. Med. Sch., 1972—; chief pulmonary diseases service VA Hosp., Little Rock, 1972-73; cons. VA Hosp., 1973—; dir. Tb control Ark. Health Dept., Little Rock, 1973—; cons. VA Hosp., Wood, Wis., 1960-72. Author 3 books on Tb, also numerous articles. Served to lt. (j.g.) M.C. USNR, 1945-46; capt. M.C. AUS, 1953-54. Recipient Tom T. Ross award Ark. Public Health Assn., 1981; Robert S. Abernathy award for excellence in medicine Am. Coll. Physicians, 1984, James D. Bruce award Am. Coll. Physicians, 1988; research grantee in pulmonary emphysema, 1957-65. Master ACP; mem. AAAS, AMA, Am. Fedn. Clin. Rsch. (nat. sec. 1955-58, v.p. 1958-59, pres. 1959-60), Ctrl. Soc. Clin. Rsch., Am. Soc. Clin. Investigation, Am. Thoracic Soc. (Trudeau medal 1988), Am. Coll. Chest Physicians. Research on unitary concept of Tb and epidemiology of Tb; variation in susceptibility to Tb infection; history of Tb chemotherapy of Tb as a global epidemic; suggestion for genetic engineering of material to enhance resistance to initial infection with Tb. Office: Ark Dept of Health 4815 W Markham St Little Rock AR 72205-3867

STEADHAM, CHARLES VICTOR, JR., entertainment agent, producer; b. Camp LeJune, N.C., Oct. 22, 1944; s. Charles Victor Sr. and Mary Alice

(Adams) S. AA, U. Fla., 1964. Profl. musician various show bands, 1967-75; owner, agt. Blade Agy., Gainesville, Fla., 1975—; pres. Blade Software, Inc., Gainesville, 1990—. Contbr. articles to profl. jours. Mem. Orlando/Orange County (Fla.) Conv. and Visitors Bur., 1986—; Jacksonville (Fla.) Tourist and Conv. Bur., 1986—; grad. Leadership Gainesville XV, 1988; bd. dirs. Gamble Rogers Meml. Found., 1992—. Recipient C. Shaw Smith Founders award, 1988. Mem. Fla. C. of C., Country Music Assn. (assoc.) Nat. Assn. Campus Activities (assoc., bd. dirs. 1976-83, Founders award 1981, Entertainment Agy. of Yr. award 1983, 87), Am. Soc. Assn. Execs. (assoc.), Fla. Soc. Assn. Execs. (assoc.), Meeting Planners Internat. (assoc.) Democrat. Avocations: scuba diving, jogging. Office: Blade Agy PO Box 1556 Gainesville FL 32602-1556

STEADMAN, CHARLES WALTERS, lawyer, corporate executive, writer; b. Falls City, Nebr., July 25, 1914; s. William Sherman and Marie (Walters) S.; m. Dorothy Marie Fawick, Feb. 14, 1942 (dec. Sept. 1974); children: Suzanne Louise Steadman Hoerr (dec.), Carole Elaine Steadman Kinney, Charles T. W., Dorothy M. (Diana); m. Consuelo Matthews Artini, May 10, 1986. A.B., U. Nebr., 1935; J.D., Harvard U., 1938. Bar: Ohio 1939, D.C. 1956, U.S. Supreme Ct. 1950, U.S. Ct. Claims 1958. Partner Marshman, Hornbeck, Hollington, Steadman & McLaughlin, Cleve., 1946-65, Steadman, Jones & Baxter, 1956-70; chmn. bd. St. Regis Hotel Corps., 1960-63; vice chmn. Leaseway Intercontinental, 1961-65; prin. Charles W. Steadman Counselor-at-Law, 1970; chmn. com. to end govt. waste Nat. Taxpayers Union, 1979; chmn. bd., pres. Steadman Security Corp., Steadman Technology and Growth Fund, Steadman Investment Fund, Steadman Associated Fund, Steadman American Industry Fund; chief counsel Select U.S. Senate Com., 1956; spl. master commr. Matter of Dissolution of Cleve. Savs. Soc., 1959-62; spl. presdl. rep. to Oman, 1980. Author: Steadman's Revision of the Ohio Civil Practice Manual, 1950, The National Debt Conclusion: Establishing the Debt Repayment Plan, 1993; also legal and econ. articles.; editor: Charles W. Steadman Economic Review. Bd. govs. Investment Co. Inst., 1969-72; chmn. Washington met. area Rep. Nat. Fin. Com., 1980-81; mem. exec. com. Presdl. Inaugural Com., 1981; founder Presdl. Trust, 1981; trustee Tex. Wesleyan Coll., 1982. Served as lt. col. AUS, World War II; chief counsel legal div. Cleve. Ordnance Dist. Recipient Disting. Service award U. Nebr., 1960. Mem. ABA (com. corp., banking and bus. law 1958-60), Ohio Bar Assn., Cleve. Bar Assn., Ohio Bar, Bar Assn. D.C., Internat. Bar Assn., Am. Law Inst. (life), Am. Judicature Soc.; 1925 F Street Club, Union Club (Cleve.), Beach Club (Palm Beach, Fla.), Everglades Club (Palm Beach, Fla.), Racquet and Tennis Club (N.Y.C.), Sky Club (N.Y.C.). Home: 425 Worth Ave Palm Beach FL 33480-4568 also: 2500 Virginia Ave NW Washington DC 20037-1901 Office: 1730 K St NW Washington DC 20006-3868

STEADMAN, DAVID ROSSLYN AYTON, business executive, corporate director; b. Wembley, Eng., June 7, 1937; came to U.S., 1980; s. Eric and Iris Sina (Smith) S.; m. Beryl Ellen Giles, Jan. 5, 1963; children—Michael, Christopher, Timothy. B.Sc. in Engring. with honors, City U., London, 1960. Mng. dir. Cossor Electronics, Harlow, Eng., 1974-78; chmn. EMI med. Electronics, London, 1978-80; pres. Raytheon Data Systems, Norwood Mass., 1980-84, Raytheon Ventures, Lexington, 1985-87; chmn., chief exec. officer GCA Corp., Andover, Mass., 1987-88; pres. Atlantic Mgmt. Assocs., officer GCA Corp., Wolfeboro, N.H., 1988—; chmn., CEO Integra-Hotel & Restaurant Co., 1990-94; chmn. Brookwood Cos., Inc., 1989—, Aavid Theral Technologies, Inc., Tech. Svc. Group, Inc.; bd. dirs. Vitronics Corp., Telequip Corp., ElectroScan Corp. Fellow Instn. Elec. Engrs. (U.K.); mem. Brit. Inst. Mgmt. (companion), Inst. Mech. Engrs. (U.K.). Avocations: music; sailing. Office: Atlantic Mgmt Assocs Inc PO Box 1859 Wolfeboro NH 03894-1859

STEADMAN, DAVID WILTON, museum official; b. Honolulu, Oct. 24, 1936; s. Alva Edgar and Martha (Cooke) S.; m. Kathleen Carroll Reilly, Aug. 1, 1960; children: Alexander Carroll, Kate Montague. B.A., Harvard U., 1960, M.A.T., 1961; M.A., U. Calif.-Berkeley, 1966; Ph.D., Princeton U., 1974. Lectr. Frick Collection, N.Y.C., 1970-71; asst. dir., acting dir., assoc. dir. Princeton U. Art Mus., 1971-73; dir. galleries Claremont Colls., (Calif.), 1974-80; art cons. Archtl. Digest, L.A., 1974-77; rsch. curator Norton Simon Mus., Pasadena, Calif., 1977-80; dir. Chrysler Mus., Norfolk, Va., 1980-89, Toledo Mus. Art, Ohio, 1989—. Author: Graphic Art of Francisco Goya, 1975, Works on Paper 1900-1960, 1977, Abraham van Diepenbeeck, 1982. Chester Dale fellow Nat. Gallery Art, Washington, 1969-70. Mem. Coll. Art Assn., Am. Assn. Mus. Dirs. Episcopalian. Office: Toledo Mus Art PO Box 1013 Toledo OH 43697-1013

STEADMAN, JACK W., professional football team executive; b. Warrenville, Ill., Sept. 14, 1928; s. Walter Angus and Vera Ruth (Burkholder) S.; m. Martha Cudworth Steinhoff, Nov. 24, 1949; children: Thomas Edward, Barbara Ann, Donald Wayne. B.B.A., So. Methodist U., 1950. Accountant Hunt Oil Co., Dallas, 1950-54; chief accountant W.H. Hunt, Dallas, 1954-58, Penrod Drilling Co., Dallas, 1958-60; gen. mgr. Dallas Texans Football Club, 1960-63; gen. mgr. Kansas City Chiefs Football Club, 1963-76, exec. v.p., 1966-76, pres., 1976-88; also chmn. bd., 1988—; chmn. benefit com. NFL; chmn. Hunt Midwest Enterprises, Inc., Kansas City, HME Entertainment Divsn. (Worlds of Fun, Oceans of Fun), Kansas City, 1972—; dir. Commerce Bank of Kansas City, Pvt. Industry Coun., former chmn., Full Employment Coun., former chmn. Former bd. dirs. Children's Mercy Hosp., bd. dirs. Civic Council, Starlight Theatre Assn., Kansas City, Am. Royal Assn.; pres. Heart of Am. United Way, 1981; adv. trustee Research Med. Ctr., Kansas City; trustee Midwest Research Inst.; mem. Village Presbyn. Ch.; past chmn. C. of C. of Greater Kansas City. Recipient Kans. Citian of Yr. award, 1988. Mem. Indian Hills Country Club, Kansas City (pres. 1988), 711 Inner, River, Carriage, Man-of-the-Month Fraternity. Home: 6436 Wenonga Ter Shawnee Mission KS 66208-1732 Office: Kansas City Chiefs 1000 Walnut St Ste 1528 Kansas City MO 64106

STEADMAN, JOHN MARCELLUS, III, English educator; b. Spartanburg, S.C., Nov. 25, 1918; s. John Marcellus and Medora Rice (Rembert) S. AB, Emory U., 1940, MA, 1941, DHL (hon.), 1976; MA (T.W. Hunt scholar), Princeton U., 1948, PhD, 1949. Instr. English Ga. Inst. Tech., 1941-42; asst. prof. U. N.C., 1949-51; ind. study and rsch. in English lit., 1953-61; from rsch. assoc.to sr. rsch. assoc. Henry E. Huntington Libr., San Marino, Calif., 1962—; mem. faculty U. Calif., Riverside, 1966—; prof. English U. Calif., 1967—, faculty rsch. lectr., 1977, prof. emeritus, 1989—; vis. disting. prof. City U. N.Y., fall, 1974. Author numerous books including: Disembodied Laughter: Troilus and the Apothéosis Tradition, 1972, The Lamb and The Elephant: Ideal Imitation and the Context of Renaissance Allegory, 1974, Epic and Tragic Structure in Paradise Lost, 1976, Nature into Myth: Medieval and Renaissance Moral Symbols, 1979, Milton's Biblical and Classical Imagery, 1984, The Hill and the Labyrinth: Discourse and Certitude in Milton and his Near-Contemporaries, 1984, The Wall of Paradise: Essays on Milton's Poetics, 1985, Milton and the Paradoxes of Renaissance Heroism, 1987, Redefining a Period Style: "Renaissance," "Mannerist," and "Baroque" in Literature, 1990, Ryoanji Temple and Other Poems, 1993; co-editor latest being A Milton Ency. vols. I-IX, 1978-83; editor: latest being Huntington Library Quar., 1962-81. Capt. USAAF, 1942-46; capt. USAF, 1951-52. Grantee Huntington Libr., 1961-62; Procter fellow Princeton U., 1949, Guggenheim fellow, 1979. Mem. Milton Soc. Am. (pres. 1973, honored scholar 1976), So. Calif. Renaissance Conf., Phi Beta Kappa, Chi Phi, Fine Arts Club. Democrat. Home: 250 S Oak Knoll Ave Apt 109 Pasadena CA 91101-2923 Office: Henry E Huntington Libr San Marino CA 91108

STEADMAN, JOHN MONTAGUE, judge; b. Honolulu, Aug. 8, 1930; s. Alva Edgar and Martha (Cooke) S.; m. Alison Storer Lunt, Apr. 8, 1961; children—Catharine N., Juliette M., Eric C. Grad., Phillips Acad., Andover, Mass., 1948; BA summa cum laude, Yale U., 1952; LLB magna cum laude, Harvard U., 1955. Bar: D.C. 1955, Calif. 1956, U.S. Supreme Ct. 1964, Hawaii 1977. Assoc. Pillsbury, Madison & Sutro, San Francisco, 1956-63; atty. Dept. Justice, 1963-64; dep. under sec. army for internat. affairs, 1964-65; spl. asst. to sec. and dep. sec. def. Dept. Def., 1965-68; gen. counsel Dept. Air Force, 1968-70; vis. prof. law U. Pa. Law Sch., 1970-72; prof. law Georgetown U. Law Ctr., Washington, 1972-85, assoc. dean, 1979-84; assoc. judge D.C. Ct. Appeals, 1985—; instr. Lincoln Law Sch., San Francisco, 1961-62, San Francisco Law Sch., 1962-63; vis. prof. U. Mich. Sch. Law, 1976, U. Hawaii Sch. Law, 1977; of counsel firm Pillsbury, Madison & Sutro, Washington, 1979-85. Editor: Harvard Law Rev, 1953-

55. Sinclair-Kennedy Traveling fellow, 1955-56. Mem. Am. Law Inst., Phi Beta Kappa, Delta Sigma Rho, Zeta Psi. Episcopalian. Home: 2960 Newark St NW Washington DC 20008-3338 Office: DC Ct Appeals 500 Indiana Ave NW Washington DC 20001-2138

STEADMAN, LYDIA DUFF, elementary school educator, symphony violinist; b. Hollywood, Calif., Dec. 31, 1934; d. Lewis Marshall and Margaret Seville (Williams) Duff; m. John Gilford Steadman, Apr. 14, 1961 (dec.). Student, Pepperdine U., 1952-55; BA in Music Edn., U. So. Calif., 1957. Cert. spl. secondary music, edn. tchr., Calif. Instrumental music tchr. Lancaster (Calif.) Sch. Dist., 1957-62; instrumental music tchr. Simi Sch. Dist., Simi Valley, Calif., 1962-70, elem. tchr., 1970—; tchr. Polynesian culture, dances, games, 1970—; hist. play wright for elem. grades, organizer elem. sch. dance festivals; dir. All Dist. Orch., Lancaster, Simi Valley Schs., 1957-70; compile Japanese Culture Study Unit for elem. grades Ventura County. 1st violinist San Fernando Valley Symphony, Sherman Oaks, Calif., 1962-75, Conejo Valley Symphony, Thousand Oaks, 1975-81, tour concert mistress, 1980; 2d violinist Ventura County Symphony, 1981-94. Pres. San Fernando Cmty. Concerts, Van Nuys, Calif., 1982-94; free lancing with pit orch. Cabrillo Music Theatre, Conejo Players Theater; organizer ann. sch. Jump Rope-a-Thon for Am. Heart Assn., Nat. Geog. Geography Bee; bd. dirs. East Ventura County Cmty. Concert Assn. Mem. AAUW, NAFE, Bus. and Profl. Women (pres. Golden Triangle chpt. 1988-90, issues and mgmt. chair 1990, ways and means chair Coast chpt. 1990, editor Golden Triangle newsletter 1988-90, treas. 1992-93, sec. 1993-94, v.p. 1994—, pres. 1995-96), Sigma Xi-Sci. Rsch. Soc., Pacific Asia Mus., Armand Hammer Mus. Republican. Mem. Ch. of Christ. Avocations: hula dancing, walking, collecting world coins, world traveling, violin. Home: 32016 Allenby Ct Westlake Village CA 91361-4001

STEADMAN, RICHARD COOKE, retail corporate executive; b. Honolulu, Oct. 1, 1932; s. Alva Edgar and Martha (Cooke) S.; m. Jane Blaner Nuckolls, Aug. 20, 1955; children: Christopher M., Peter W., Lee H. AB, Yale U., 1955; MBA, Harvard U., 1957. Intelligence analyst U.S. Govt., Washington, 1957-59; assoc., ptnr. G.H. Walker & Co., N.Y.C., 1959-66; dep. asst. sec. def. E. Asia and Pacific affairs Dept. of Def., Washington, 1966-69; ptnr. J.H. Whitney & Co., N.Y.C., 1969-81; now chmn. Nat. Convenience Stores Inc., Houston, also bd. dirs.; bd. dirs. Storage Tech. Corp. Trustee Children's TV Workshop, N.Y.C.; co-chmn., trustee German Marshall Fund, Washington; chmn., chief transition Dept. Def., Carter-Mondale Adminstrn. Baker scholar, 1957. Mem. Council Fgn. Relations, Phi Beta Kappa. Democrat. Home: 25 Commerce St New York NY 10014-3763 Office: Nat Convenience Stores Inc 100 Waugh Dr Houston TX 77007-5850

STEAMER, ROBERT JULIUS, political science educator; b. Rochester, N.Y., Oct. 14, 1920; s. William August and Lotte (Becker) S.; m. Jean Worden, Apr. 12, 1947; children: Gregg Robert, James Worden. B.A. in Social Sci., Bucknell U., 1947; M.A. in Polit. Sci., U. Va., 1952; Ph.D., Cornell U., 1954; postgrad. law, Oxford (Eng.) U., 1968-69. Asst. prof. Oglethorpe U., 1952-55, U. Mass., 1955-56; assoc. prof. La. State U., 1956-62; prof. polit. sci., chmn. dept. Lake Forest (Ill.) Coll., 1962-72; prof. U. Mass., Boston, 1972-88, dean Coll. II, 1974-76, vice chancellor for acad. affairs, provost, 1976-79; vis. summer prof. Tulane U., 1958, Cornell U., 1960, UCLA, 1965; staff cons. La. sect. U.S. Commn. Civil Rights, 1961. Author: The Constitution: Cases and Comments, 1959, The Supreme Court in Crisis, 1971, The Supreme Court: Constitutional Revision and the New Strict Constructionism, 1973, Chief Justice: Leadership and the Supreme Court, 1986; sr. co-author: American Constitutional Law: Cases and Commentary, 1991; contbr. articles to profl. jours. Served with USAAF, 1942-46. Recipient Gt. Tchr. award Lake Forest Coll., 1965; Lilly Found. Research award, 1967; Major Research award Project 87, 1981; hon. research fellow U. Exeter, Eng., 1981. Mem. Am. Polit. Sci. Assn., Midwest Polit. Sci. Assn. (v.p. 1970-71), New Eng. Polit. Sci. Assn. (pres. 1979-80). Home: 439 Kilbourn Rd Rochester NY 14618

STEAR, EDWIN BYRON, corporate executive; b. Peoria, Ill., Dec. 8, 1932; s. Edwin Joseph and Juanita Blanche (Hoffman) S.; married; children—Brian Douglas, Linnea Susan. B.S. in Mech. Engring, Bradley U., 1954; M.S., U. So. Calif., 1956; Ph.D. (Hughes Staff fellow), UCLA, 1961. Mem. tech. staff Hughes Aircraft Co., Culver City, Calif., 1954-59; asst. research engr. U. Calif., Los Angeles, 1959-61; asst. prof. engring. U. Calif., 1964-68, assoc. prof., 1968-69; mgr. guidance and control research lab. Lear Siegler, Inc., Santa Monica, Calif., 1963-64; assoc. prof. elec. engring. U. Calif., Los Angeles and Santa Barbara, 1969-73; prof. U. Calif., 1973-79, chmn. dept., 1975-79; chief scientist USAF, 1979-82; dir. Wash. Technology Ctr., 1983-90; prof. elec. engring. U. Wash., Seattle, 1983-90, assoc. dean research Coll. Engring., 1983-85; corp. v.p. tech. assessment Boeing Co., Seattle, 1990—; mem. sci. adv. bd. USAF, 1971-79, 84-92, vice chmn., 1986-89, chmn., 1989-90; mem. aeros. adv. com. NASA, 1984-90; cons. to industry and govt., 1964-79, 82—; mem. SAE Tech. Stds. Bd., 1994—; mem. industry adv. coun. Accreditation Bd. for Engring. and Tech., Inc., 1994—; trustee Analytical Svcs., Inc., 1984-90; mem. guidance and control panel NATO Adv. Group Aerospace R & D, 1981-92, dep. chmn. panel, 1988-90, chmn., 1990-92. Editor: (with A. Kadish) Hormonal Control Systems, 1969; mem. editorial bd. Aircraft jour. AIAA, 1974-77; contbr. articles to profl. lit. Served to 1st lt. USAF, 1961-63. Named Disting. Alumnus Bradley U., 1980; recipient civilian exceptional svc. medals USAF, 1982, 92; Arnold D. Beckman lectr. on rsch. and innovation U. Ill., Urbana, 1993; Mental Health Tng. Program fellow UCLA, 1972-74. Fellow IEEE; mem. AIA, AAAS, Internat. Fedn. Automation Control, Am. Electronics Assn. (sci. and tech. com. 1988-90), Sigma Xi, Eta Kappa Nu, Pi Mu Epsilon, Tau Beta Pi, Phi Eta Sigma, Tau Sigma. Home: 14010 SE 44th Pl Bellevue WA 98006-2331 Office: The Boeing Co PO Box 3707 MS 13-43 Seattle WA 98124-2207

STEARLEY, ROBERT JAY, retired packaging company executive; b. Brazil, Ind., Sept. 6, 1929; s. Melvin George and Hila Mona (Bolin) S.; m. Helen Louise Dellacca, Nov. 25, 1950; children: Rhonda Jo, Robert Thomas. B.S. in Mech. Engring., Rose Hulman Inst. Tech., 1957; postgrad., Harvard U., 1979. Gen. mgr. Poly Tech Corp., Mpls., 1961-63; gen. mgr. plastics Gt. Plains Bag Corp., Stamford, Conn., 1963-66, v.p., 1966-71, v.p. ops., 1971-75, pres., 1975-84, dir., 1966-84; v.p. Jefferson Smurfit Corp., Alton, Ill., 1984—. Mem. Paper Shipping Sack Mfg. Assn. (dir. 1980-82), Am. Legion. Republican. Methodist. Club: Norwood Hills Country (St. Louis). Lodge: Elks. Home: 2 Country Estate Pl Saint Louis MO 63131-3411

STEARNS, CARL DAVID, architect; b. Boston, July 15, 1944; s. Donald Elmer and Catherine Marie (Weuwiesinger) S.; m. Susan Leith Bunot, Sept. 9, 1967; 1 child, Sarah Anne. BArch, Cornell U., 1967, BA in Hist. Preservation, 1977. Registered arch. N.Y. Arch.-in-tng. Myrus/Reckmeyer Group, Syracuse, N.Y., 1972, Hueber Hares Glavin, Syracuse, N.Y., 1973-75; arch. Quinlivan Pierik & Krause, Syracuse, N.Y., 1975; jr. hist. sites restoration coord. Bur. Hist. Sites N.Y. State Parks, Jamesville, 1976-77; sr. hist. sites restoration coord. Bur. Field Svcs. N.Y. State Parks, Albany, 1978-79; ptnr. Crawford Stearns Coffey, Syracuse, 1979-81, Crawford & Stearns, Archs., Syracuse, 1981—. Prin. works include Cazenovia Gothic Cottage, 1980, Hanford Mus., 1983, First Bapt. Ch., Hamilton, N.Y., 1987, A.M.E. Zion Ch., Ithaca, N.Y., 1982; inventor roof flashing product. Charter bd. dirs. Adirondack Archtl. Heritage, Raquette Lake, N.Y., 1990—; bd. dirs. state hist. site Friends of Lorenzo, Cazenovia, 1988—, Hanford Mus., East Meridith, N.Y., 1985-87; mem. archtl. panel N.Y. State Coun. on the Arts, N.Y.C., 1982-84. Lt. USN, 1967-71. Recipient Bronze medal N.Y. Soc. Archs., 1967. Mem. AIA, Assn. for Preservation Tech., Soc. for the Preservation of New Eng. Antiquities, Nature Conservancy (Adirondack chpt.), Adirondack Landowner's Assn. (dance.). Democrat. Unitarian. Avocations: restoring historic buildings, antique boats, antique cars, cross country.

STEARNS, CLIFFORD BUNDY, congressman, business executive; b. Washington, DC, Apr. 16, 1941; s. Clifford Robert and Emily Elizabeth (Newlin) S.; m. Joan Bette Moore; children: Douglas Moore, Clifford Bundy Jr., Scott Newlin. BSEE, George Washington U., 1963. Mgr. Control Data Systems, Inc., L.A., 1967-69; sr. contract adminstr. CBS, Inc., Stamford, Conn., 1969; account exec. Kutola Advt. Agy., Greenwich, Conn., 1970-71, Images 70/Wilson Haight Welch, Inc., Greenwich, 1971-72; motel owner Hatfield, Mass., 1972-77; pres., motel mgr. Stearns House, Inc., Silver Springs, Fla., 1977-88; mem. 101st-103rd Congresses from 6th Fla. dist., 1989—; mem. banking, fin. and urban affairs com., vets. affairs com. 101st Congress from 6th Fla. dist.; mem. energy and commerce com., subcoms. energy and power, commerce, consumer protection and competetiveness; 104th Congress, mem. commerce and vets. coms., subcoms. telecom. and fin., healthcare, energy and power; broker Silver Springs (Fla.) Real Estate, 1981-88. Trustee, vice chmn. Monroe Regional Hosp., Ocala, Fla., 1984-89; bd. dirs. Boys Club of Ocala, 1980-84; pres. Toastmaster Club L.A., 1962. Capt. USAF, 1963-67. Mem. Am. Hotel/Motel Assn., Fla. Hotel/Motel Assn., Am. Assn. Realtors, Fla. Assn. Realtors, Marion County Motel Assn. (pres. 1979), Marion C. of C. (bd. dirs. 1987—), Kiwanis (pres. Ocala club 1984). Republican. Presbyterian. Avocations: basketball, swimming, computers. Home: 2071 SE 54th Ter Ocala FL 34471-8702 Office: US Ho of Reps 332 Channing St NE Bldg Washington DC 20002-1028 Office: Ho of Reps 2352 Rayburn Office Bldg Washington DC 20515 also: 115 SE 25th Ave Ocala FL 34471

STEARNS, ELLIOTT EDMUND, JR., retired surgeon; b. Cleve., Jan. 11, 1923; s. Elliott Edmund and Sarah (Hoyt) S.; m. Martha Hudson Small, June 26, 1945; children: Michael Elliott, Philip Hoyt, Danial Arthur. Student, Williams Coll., 1942-43; BS, U. Calif., Berkeley, 1945; MD, U. Calif., San Francisco, 1948. Diplomate Am. Bd. Urology. Intern U.S. Pub. Health Hosp., San Francisco, 1949-50; resident Sonoma Co. Hosp., Santa Rosa, Calif., 1950-51; fellow urology Tuc Cleve. (Ohio) Clinic, 1952-54; chief resident urology Cin. (Ohio) Gen. Hosp., U. Cin., 1954-56; med. staff St. Mary's Hosp., Tucson, 1956-87, St. Joseph's Hosp., Tucson, 1956-87, Tucson (Ariz.) Med. Ctr., 1956-87, Puma County Hosp., Tucson, 1956-87; ret., 1987; exec. com. mem. Pima County Med. Ctr., Tucson 1970's; chief of surgery St. Joseph's Hosp., Tucson, 1980's. Author: Catupult, 1994. Capt. USAF, 1954-56. Fellow ACS. Home: 2926 N Cascade Cir Tucson AZ 85715

STEARNS, JAMES GERRY, retired securities company executive; b. Lapine, Oreg., Jan. 29, 1922; s. Carey Summer and Betty (Hunt) S.; m. June Elizabeth Speer, Nov. 21, 1943; children: Robert Sumner, Katherine Inga, Gerry Marshall. Student, Oreg. State U. Flight instr. U.S. AAC, 1942-45; supr. Modoc County (Calif.), Alturos, 1951-67; dir. Calif. Dept. Conservation, Sacremento, 1967-72; sec. Calif. Agr. and Services Agy., Sacremento, 1972-75; dir. office alcohol fuels U.S. Dept. Energy, Washington, 1981-82; chmn., chief exec. officer Securities Investor Protection Corp., Washington, 1982-94; ret., 1994. With USAAC, 1942-45. Republican. Lodges: Masons; Shriners; Jesters. Office: Securities Investor Protection Corp 805 15th St NW Ste 800 Washington DC 20005-2215

STEARNS, MILTON SPRAGUE, JR., financial executive; b. N.Y.C., June 3, 1923; s. Milton Sprague and Katherine (Stieglitz) S.; m. Virginia McCormick; children—Virginia Parker Stearns King, John Brackett, Barbara Ellison Stearns Terry, Kathryn Trowbridge Stearns Sergio, Elizabeth Sprague (dec.). Grad., Phillips Exeter Acad., 1942; BS cum laude, Harvard U., 1946, MBA, 1948. With The Fidelity Bank, Phila., 1948-72; group v.p. nat. lending div. The Fidelity Bank; pres. Charter Fin. Co., Radnor, Pa., 1972—; chmn., chief exec. officer Judson Infrared, Inc., 1976-87; bd. dirs. CFM Tech. Corp., Inc., West Chester, Pa., Infocore, King of Prussia, Pa.; ret. dir. The West Co., Phoenixville, Pa. Trustee Franklin Inst., Bryn Mawr Presbyn. Ch., pres. 1993-95. Served with USNR, WWII; lt. (j.g.) Res. ret. Mem. Robert Morris Assoc. (pres. Phila. chpt. 1961-62), Spee Club Cambridge, Mass., Merion Golf Club, Merion Cricket Club, Phila. Skating and Humane Soc., Union League Club of Phila., Delray Beach (Fla.) Club, Delray Beach Yacht Club, Country Club of Fla., Gulfstream Bath and Tennis Club, Pine Tree Golf Club. Home: 43 Righters Mill Rd Gladwyne PA 19035-1548 Office: 290 King Of Prussia Rd Ste 300 Radnor PA 19087

STEARNS, NEELE EDWARD, JR., diversified holding company executive; b. Chgo., Apr. 2, 1936; s. Neele Edward Sr. and Grace (Kessler) S.; m. Bonnie Ann Evans; children: Katherine Grace, Kendra Ann. BA magna cum laude, Carleton Coll., 1958; MBA with distinction, Harvard U., 1960. Audit staff Arthur Andersen Co., 1962-66, audit mgr., 1966-67; asst. gen. mgr. internat. divsn. Imperial-Eastman Corp., 1967-68; asst. treas. Allied Products Corp., 1968-69, treas., 1969-72; v.p Henry Crown (Ill.) and Co., 1972-75, v.p., controller, 1975-79; exec. v.p., chief oper. officer Henry Crown and Co., 1979-86; pres., chief exec. officer CC Industries, Inc., Chgo., 1986—. Trustee Ravinia Festival Assn., treas.; chmn. fin. com. Lakeland Health Svcs. (Highland Park Hosp.), trustee, treas. Mem. Commercial Club Chgo., Econ. Club Chgo., University Club Chgo., Chgo. Club, Skokie Country Club, Phi Beta Kappa. Office: CC Industries Inc 222 N La Salle St Chicago IL 60601-1003

STEARNS, PETER NATHANIEL, history educator; b. London, Mar. 3, 1936; (parents Am. citizens); s. Raymond P. and Elizabeth (Scott) S.; m. Nancy Driessel (div. 1976); children: Duncan, Deborah; m. Carol Zisowitz, Mar. 26, 1978; children: Clio Elizabeth, Cordelia Raymond. AB, Harvard U., 1957, MA, 1959, PhD, 1963. Instr. to assoc. prof. U. Chgo., 1962-65; prof., chmn. history dept. Rutgers U., New Brunswick, N.J., 1965-74; Heinz prof. history Carnegie Mellon U., Pitts., 1974—, chmn. dept. history, 1986-92, dean Coll. Humanities and Social Scis., 1992—; co-dir. Pitts. Ctr. for Social History, 1986-92; chmn. acad. adv. coun. N.Y.C. Coll. Bd., 1982-85; chmn. Pacesetter World History commn., Coll. Bd., 1992—. Author: European Society in Upheaval: Social History since 1800, 1967 (trans. Swedish), rev. edit., 1975, 3d edit., 1991, Priest and Revolutionary: Lamennais and the Dilemma of French Catholicism, 1967 (trans. Polish), Modern Europe, 1789-1914, 1969, Revolutionary Syndicalism and French Labor: a cause without rebels, 1971, (with Harvey Mitchell) Workers and Protest: The European Labor Movement, 1890-1914, 1971, The European Experience since 1815, 1972, 1848: The Revolutionary Tide in Europe, 1974 (pub. in Eng. as The Revolutions of 1848), Lives of Labor: Work in Maturing Industrial Society, 1975 (trans. German), Old Age in European Society, 1977, Face of Europe, 1977, Paths to Authority: Toward the Formation of Middle Class Consciousness, 1978, Be A Man! Males in Modern Society, 1979, rev. edit., 1990, (with Linda Rosenzweig) Themes in Modern Social History, 1985, (with Carol Stearns) Anger: The Struggle for Emotional Control in America's History, 1986, World History: Patterns of Change and Continuity, 1987, (with others) Makers of Modern Europe, 1987, rev. edit., 1994, (with others) Readings in World History, Vol. 1: The Great Tradition and Vol. 2: The Modern Centuries, 1987, Expanding the Past: A Reader in Social History, 1988, Life and Society in the West, The Modern Centuries, 1988, World History: Traditions and New Directions, 1988, rev. edit., 1994, (with C. Stearns) Emotion and Social Change, Toward a New Psychohistory, 1988, (with Andrew Barnes) Social History and Issues in Consciousness and Cognition, 1989, Jealousy: Evolution of an Emotion in American History, 1989, Interpreting the Industrial Revolution, 1991, (with Michael Adas and Stuart Schwartz) World Civilizations, 1991, Meaning Over Memory: Issues in Humanities Education, 1993, The Industrial Revolution in World History, 1993, (translated into Swedish), American Cool: Developing a 20th Century Emotional Style, 1994, Turbulent Passage: A Global History of the 20th Century, 1994; editor: Century for Debate, 1969, The Impact of the Industrial Revolution, 1972, (with Walkowitz) Workers in the Industrial Revolution, 1974, The Other Side of Western Civilization, 1979, rev. edit., 1984, 4th edit., 1991, The Rise of Modern Women, 1977, (with Michael Weber) The Spencers of Amberson Avenue: A Turn-of-the-Century Memoir, 1983, (with Van Tassel) Old Age in a Bureaucratic Society, 1986; editor in chief Jour. Social History, 1967—; editor: Encyclopedia of Social History, 1993, Ency. World Hist., 1994, 5th edit. Encyclopedia World History rev.; contbg. editor history of emotions series NYU Press; contbr. over 150 articles to profl. and popular jours. Guggenheim Found. fellow, 1973-74; NEH grantee, 1981-84, 86, 90, Rockefeller Found. grantee, 1982-83. Fellow Internat. Soc. for Rsch. on Emotion; mem. Am. Hist. Soc., World History Assn., Am. Hist. Assn. (v.p., head teaching div. 1995—), Nat. Bd. Profl. Teaching Standards. Democrat. Avocations: racquet sports, travel. Home: 509 S Linden Ave Pittsburgh PA 15208-2846 Office: Carnegie Mellon U History Dept Pittsburgh PA 15213-3890

STEARNS, RICHARD GAYLORE, judge; b. L.A., June 27, 1944; s. Gaylore Rhodes and Jeannetta Viola (Hofheinz) S.; m. Patricia Ann McElligott, Dec. 21, 1975. BA, Stanford U., 1968; MLitt, Oxford U., Eng., 1971; JD, Harvard U., 1976. Bar: Mass. Dep. campaign mgr. McGovern for Pres., Washington, 1970-72; spl. asst. U.S. Senate, Washington, 1972-73; asst. dist. atty. Commonwealth of Mass., Dedham, 1976-79, 80-82; del. dir. Kennedy for Pres., Washington, 1979-80; asst. U.S. atty. U.S. Dept. Justice, Boston, 1982-90; assoc. justice Superior Ct. Mass., Boston, 1990-94; U.S. dist. judge U.S. Dist. Ct. Mass., Boston, 1994—. Author: Massachusetts Criminal Law: A Prosecutor's Guide, 15th edit., 1995. Rhodes scholar, 1968. Mem. ABA, Mass. Bar Assn., Phi Beta Kappa. Office: US Dist Ct 707 PO & Courthouse Bldg Boston MA 02109

STEARNS, ROBERT LELAND, curator; b. L.A., Aug. 28, 1947; s. Edward Van Buren and Harriett Ann (Hauck) S.; m. Sheri Roseanne Lucas, Oct. 2, 1982 (div. 1994); children: Marissa Hauck, Caroline Lucas. Student, U. Calif., San Diego, 1965-68, BFA, 1970; student, Calif. Poly. State U., San Luis Obispo, 1968. Asst. dir. Paula Cooper Gallery, N.Y.C., 1970-72; prodn. asst. Avalanche Mag., N.Y.C., 1972; dir. Kitchen Ctr. for Video/Music, N.Y.C., 1972-77, Contemporary Arts Ctr., Cin., 1977-82; dir. performing arts Walker Art Ctr., Mpls., 1982-88; dir. Wexner Ctr. for Arts, Columbus, Ohio, 1988-92; mem. Wexner Ctr. Found., Columbus, 1990-92; dir. Stearns & Assocs./Contemporary Arts Svcs., Lancaster, Ohio, 1992—; adj. prof. dept. art, assoc. dean Coll. Art, Ohio State U., Columbus, 1988-92; cons. McKnight Found., St. Paul, 1978, Jerome Found., 1978-79; chmn. Artists TV Workshop, N.Y.C., 1976-77; bd. dirs., chmn. Minn. Dance Alliance, Mpls., 1983-88; bd. dirs. Haleakala, Inc. N.Y.C.; mem. various panels Nat. Endowment for Arts, Washington, 1977—; mem. pub. arts policy Greater Columbus Arts Coun., 1988-90; adv. coun. Bklyn. Acad. Music, 1982-84, Houston Grand Opera, 1991-93. Author; editor: Robert Wilson: Theater of Images, 1980, Photography and Beyond in Japan, 1995; editor: Dimensions of Black, 1970; exec. editor: Breakthroughs, 1991; author and editor numerous catalogues. Decorated chevalier Order of Arts and Letters (France); Jerome Found. travel grantee, 1986, Japan Found. travel grantee, 1991.

STEARNS, STEPHEN RUSSELL, civil engineer, forensic engineer, educator; b. Manchester, N.H., Feb. 28, 1915; s. Hiram Austin and Elisabeth Scribner (Brown) S.; m. Eulalie Moody Holmes, Jan. 1 1939; children: Marjorie Elisabeth, Stephen James, Jonathan David. A.B., Dartmouth Coll., 1937; C.E., Thayer Sch. Engring., 1938; M.S., Purdue U., 1949. Civil engr. Gannett, Eastman, Fleming, Harrisburg, Pa., 1938-40; marine egr. Bur. Ships, Phila. Navy Yard, 1940-41; engr. Dry Dock Assocs., Phila Navy Yard, 1941-43; instr. Thayer Sch. Engring., Dartmouth, 1943-45, asst. prof., 1945-53, prof. civil engring., 1953-80; UN cons., Poland, 1974, 78; engr. Ops. Research, Inc., Washington, 1963-72; phys. reconnaisance in Alaska Boston U. Phys. Research Labs., 1953; chief applied snow and ice research br. Snow, Ice, Permafrost Research Establishment, U.S. Army Engrs., 1954-55; Mem. Sch. Bd., Hanover, N.H., 1951-60, chmn., 1957-59; mem. N.H. Gov.'s Transp. Com., 1966-67, Task Force, 1969; chmn. Lebanon (N.H.) Regional Airport Authority, 1966-69; mem. N.H. Bd. Registration Profl. Engrs., 1975-83. Mem. Am. Soc. Engring. Edn., ASCE (dir. 1978-81, pres. 1983-84), Sigma Chi. Congregationalist. Home: 10 Barrymore Rd Hanover NH 03755-2402

STEBBINS, DENNIS ROBERT, environmental management consultant; b. Evergreen Park, Ill., Mar. 4, 1948; s. Daniel Mathew and Alberta Irene (Schmidt) S.; m. Ida Gattinger, Feb. 14, 1989. AA in Bus. Mgmt./Sci., Mohegan C. C., Norwich, Conn., 1983; BS in Environ. Studies, Chadwick U., 1993, MBA, 1993, MS in Environ. Mgmt., 1994. Enlisted USN, 1966, advanced through grades to commd. chief warrant officer, ret., 1989; pres., CEO Fanciful Notions, Inc., Honolulu, 1989-91; Hawaii state mgr. of field ops. Census '90 U.S. Dept. Commerce/U.S. Bur. of Census, Honolulu, 1990; pres., CEO Stebbins Internat Ltd., Honolulu; pres. The Global Environ. Mgmt. Devel. Group, Belize, 1993—; dir. project infrastructure devel. in Belize and Venezuela The Global Environ. Mgmt. Devel. Group, 1994; pres., exec. dir. Found. of Earth Resources, Scis. and Techs., Reno and Honolulu, 1994—; instr. Can. Fed. Staff Coll., B.C., 1992; assoc. prof. Chaminade U., Honolulu, 1994—; adj. prof. Chadwick U., Birmingham, Ala., 1994—, Magellan U., Birmingham, Ala., 1995—; spl. advisor UN Environ. Program, 1992—, internat. corp. adv. coun., 1992—; advisor UN Devel. Program, 1994—; mem. faculty Nat. Bus. Inst., Eau Clair, Wis., 1993—, Lincoln Grad. Ctr., San Antonio, 1994—; mem. Law Seminars Internat., Seattle, 1994—. Author of one book and co-author four books on environ. sci.; contbr. articles to internat. profl. jours. Advisor, trustee The Tanager Found., Reno, Nev., 1992-93; bd. dirs. Neighborhood Bd. Honolulu, 1992-93, Mayor's Complete County Com., Honolulu, 1990. Mem. ASTD (Hawaii chpt. bd. dirs., pres.-elect 1990-92), UN Assn. U.S. (bd. dirs. 1992-93), Nat. Soc. Environ. Cons. (nat. adv. bd. 1994—), Am. Meteorol. Soc., C. of C. of Hawaii (bd. dirs. small bus. coun. 1990-91), Ret. Officers Assn. (chpt. bd. dirs., pub. rels. dir. 1992-93), N.Am. Environ. Edn. Assn., Am. Assn. Corp. Environ. Officers, Nat. Assn. Environ. Profls. Democrat. Avocations: fencing, golf, tennis, theatre, gourmet cooking. Home: 1520 Ward Ave #1302 Honolulu HI 96822-3556 Office: Stebbins Internat Ltd The Environ Leadership Consultancy 1750 Kalakaua Ave Ste 3775 Honolulu HI 96826

STEBBINS, RICHARD HENDERSON, electronics engineer, peace officer, security consultant; b. Pittsburgh, Pa., Dec. 2, 1938; s. Earl Carlos and Esther Frances (Kusluch) S.; m. Rosemary Tanneberger, Aug. 12, 1984; children from previous marriage: Richard Earl, Susan Elizabeth. BSEE with high honors, U. Md., 1965; postgrad., Trinity U., 1973-74. cert. peace officer, Tex. Engring. tech. Nat. Security Agy., Ft. Meade, Md., 1960-65; design engr. Page Communications Engr., Washington, 1965-66, Electromechanical Rsch., Inc., College Park, Md., 1966-67, Honeywell, Inc., Annapolis, Md., 1967-68; electronics engr., intelligence rsch. specialist Fed. Civil Svc., San Antonio, 1968-91; pvt. cons. San Antonio, 1991—; comdr.'s advisor Air Force Cryptologic Support Ctr., San Antonio, 1988-91; deputy dir. countermeasures ops., intelligence rsch. specialist USAF HQ Electronic Security Command, San Antonio, 1981-88; mem. blue ribbon com. on ops. security & comm. security roles & relationships for command and svc. Author, lectr. in field; contbr. articles to profl. jours. With USN, 1956-59. Mem. NRA, Tau Beta Pi, Eta Kappa Nu, Phi Kappa Phi. Republican. Episcopalian. Avocations: hunting, fishing, target shooting, family history rsch. Home: 9602 Clear Falls San Antonio TX 78250-5067

STEBBINS, ROBERT ALAN, sociology educator; b. Rhinelander, Wis., June 22, 1938; s. William Nelson and Dorothy May (Guy) S.; m. Karin Yvonne Olson, Jan. 11, 1964; children: Paul, Lisa, Christi. B.A., Macalester Coll., 1961; M.A., U. Minn., 1962, Ph.D., 1964. Assoc. prof. Presbyterian Coll., Clinton, S.C., 1964-65; assoc. prof.to prof. Meml. U. Nfld., St. John's, Can., 1965-73; prof. U. Tex.-Arlington, 1973-76; prof. sociology U. Calgary, Alta., Can., 1976—, dept. head, 1976-82; head dept. sociology and anthropology Meml. U. Nfld., 1968-71. Author: Commitment to Deviance, 1971, The Disorderly Classroom: Its Physical and Temporal Conditions, 1974, Teachers and Meaning, 1975, Amateurs, 1979, The Magician, 1984, Sociology: The Study of Society, 2d edit., 1990, Canadian Football: The View from the Helmet, 1987, Deviance: Tolerable Differences, 1988, The Laugh-Makers: Stand-Up Comedy as Art, Business, and Life-Style, 1990, Amateurs, Professionals and Serious Leisure, 1992; co-editor: Fieldwork Experience, 1980, The Sociology of Deviance, 1982, Experiencing Fieldwork, 1991, Career, Culture, and Social Psychology in a Variety Art, 1993, Predicaments: Moral Difficulty in Everyday Life, 1993, The Franco-Calgarians: French Language, Leisure and Linguistic lifestyle in an Anglophone City, 1994. Pres. St. John's Orch., 1967-68; mem. Dallas Civic Symphony, 1973-76, Orch. Soc. of Calgary, 1978—. Can. Coun. Sabbatical Leave fellow, 1972-72, Calgary Inst. for Humanities fellow, 1988, Killam resident fellow, 1990; NEH summer stipend, 1976. Mem. Am. Sociol. Assn., Can. Sociology and Anthropology Assn. (pres. 1988-89), Internat. Sociol. Assn., Assn. for Can. Studies, Soc. for Study of Symbolic Interaction, Social Sci. Fedn. Can. (pres. 1991-92), Can. Assn. for Leisure Studies (v.p. 1993—), Internat. Soc. Bassists Club (Ann Arbor, Mich., chmn. amateur divsn. 1974-84). Home: 144 Edgemont Estates Dr NW, Calgary, AB Canada T3A 2M3 Office: U Calgary Dept Sociology, 2500 University Dr NW, Calgary, AB Canada T2N 1N4

STEC, JOHN ZYGMUNT, real estate executive; b. Stalowawola, Poland, Jan. 21, 1925; Came to U.S.A. 1947.; s. Valenty and Maria (Madej) S. m. Wanda G. Baca, Oct. 13, 1956; children: David, Maria, Monica. Student, Poland, 1941-44, Kent St. U., Oh., 1965-66, Kent St. U., Oh., 1966-67. Cert. Master of Corporate Real Estate. With The Singer Co., Cleve., 1952-54, dis.

mgr., 1954-60, sales supr., 1960-67; dir. real estate The Singer Co., Detroit and Chgo., 1967-73; v.p. Fabri Center of Am., Beachwood, Ohio, 1973—; sr. v.p. real estate Fabri-Centers of Am., Inc., Beachwood, Ohio, 1987—; With U.S. Army 1950-52. With U.S. Army, 1950-52. Mem. Nat. Assoc. of Corporate Real Estate (speaker, organizer 1974-77, audit Com. 1977-79, bd. dirs. 1970-82, Outstanding Achievement award 1982). Chagrin Valley Club. Repulican. Roman Catholic. Avocations: swimming, hiking, reading. Home: 9630 Stafford Rd Chagrin Falls OH 44023-5302 Office: Fabri-Ctrs Am Inc 5555 Darrow Rd Hudson OH 44236-4011 *Personal philosophy: Think success and you'll be successful. Perseverance of any goal leads to achievement.*

STECK, THEODORE LYLE, biochemistry and molecular biology educator, physician; b. Chgo., May 3, 1939; s. Irving E. and Mary L. S.; children: David B., Oliver M. B.S. in Chemistry, Lawrence Coll., 1960; M.D., Harvard U., 1964. Intern Beth Israel Hosp., Boston, 1964-65; fellow Beth Israel Hosp., 1965-66; research assoc. Nat. Cancer Inst., NIH, Bethesda, Md., 1966-68, Harvard U. Med. Sch., Boston, 1968-70; asst. prof. medicine U. Chgo., 1970-74, asst. prof. biochemistry and medicine, 1973-74, assoc. prof., 1974-77, prof., 1977-84, chmn. dept. biochemistry, 1979-84, prof. biochemistry and molecular biology, 1984—, chair environ. studies program, 1993—. Office: 920 E 58th St Chicago IL 60637-1474

STECK, WARREN FRANKLIN, entomology researcher, science administrator; b. Regina, Sask., Can., May 10, 1939; m. 1963; 2 children. B in Eng., McGill U., 1960; PhD in Organic Chemistry, U. Sask., 1964. Rsch. assoc. Rsch. Inst. Okla. U., 1963-64; asst. rsch. officer Nat. Rsch. Coun. Can., 1964-70, assoc. rsch. officer, 1970-76, sr. rsch. officer, 1976-80, asst. dir., 1980-81, assoc. dir., 1982-83, dir. Plant Biotech. Inst., 1983-90, dir. gen. Plant Biotech Inst., 1991—. Mem. Phytochemical Soc. N. Am., Canadian Assn. Conifer Biotechnology, Internat. Assn. Plant Tissue Culture, Internat. Soc. Chem. Ecology, Canadian Rsch. Mgmt. Assn. Achievements include rsch. in insect sex attractants and pheromones, chem. ecology. Office: Plant Biotechnology Inst, 1326 Conn, Saskatoon, SK Canada S7H 3L1*

STECKEL, BARBARA JEAN, city financial officer; b. L.A., Mar. 9, 1939; d. John Herschel and Bernice Evelyn (Selstad) Webb Banta; m. Jimmie Raeburn Lugenbeel, Feb. 16, 1957 (div. 1962); Leanna Virgina, Debra Lynn; m. Dale Robert Steckel, Mar. 16, 1962; 1 child, Richard Alan. AA in Bus., Anchorage Community Coll., 1975; BBA, U. Alaska, Anchorage, 1980. City clk., treas. City of Kotzebue, Alaska, 1973-74, city mgr., treas., 1974-76; grants adminstr. Municipality of Anchorage, Alaska, 1976-79, contr., 1979-82, mcpl. mgr., 1982-84, chief fiscal officer, 1984-87; fin. dir., treas. City of Riverside, Calif., 1988—; bd. dirs. Riverside Cmty. Ventures, Corp., Cmty. Health Corp., chmn. fin. com. Mem. adv. coun. sch. bus. and pub. adminstrn. U. Alaska, Anchorage, 1982-85; bd. dirs. Anchorage Parking Authority, 1984-87, ICMA Retirement Corp., 1985-93, Police and Fire Retirement Sys. Mcpl. of Anchorage, 1982-87, chmn., 1986; devel. com. mem. Am. Heart Assn., Anchorage, 1987. Mem. Govt. Fin. Officers U.S. and Can. (bd. dirs. 1984-87), Mcpl. Fin. Officers Alaska (pres. 1981-82), Nat. Assn. Accts. (bd. dirs. 1986-87), Am. Soc. Women Accts., Calif. Mcpl. Fin. Officers (chmn. cash mgmt. com. 1989-91, bd. dirs. 1992-95, pres. elect 1995-96), Mcpl. Treas. Assn. (R.E. Phillips award, Svc. award, debt. com. chmn. 1992—), Calif. Mcpl. Treas. Assn., Internat. City Mgrs. Assn., U. Alaska Alumni Assn., Rotary, Elks. Avocations: reading, sewing. Office: City of Riverside 3900 N Main St Riverside CA 92522-0002

STECKEL, RICHARD J., radiologist, academic administrator; b. Scranton, Pa., Apr. 17, 1936; s. Morris Leo and Lucille (Yellin) S.; m. Julie Raskin, June 16, 1960; children: Jan Marie, David Matthew. BS magna cum laude, Harvard U., 1957, MD cum laude, 1961. Diplomate: Am. Bd. Radiology. Intern UCLA Hosp., 1961-62; resident in radiology Mass. Gen. Hosp., Boston, 1962-65; clin./rsch. assoc. Nat. Cancer Inst., 1965-67; mem. faculty UCLA Med. Sch., 1967—, prof. radiol. scis. and radiation oncology, dir. Jonsson Comprehensive Cancer Ctr., 1974-94; chair dept. radiol. scis. UCLA Med. Ctr., 1994—; pres. Assn. Am. Cancer Insts., 1981. Author/editor 3 books; contbr. over 130 articles on radiology and cancer diagnosis to profl. publs. Fellow Am. Coll. Radiology; mem. Radiol. Soc. N. Am., Am. Roentgen Ray Soc., Assn. Univ. Radiologists. Office: UCLA Med Ctr Dept Radiol Scis 10833 Le Conte Ave Los Angeles CA 90095-1721

STECKLER, LARRY, publisher, editor; b. Bklyn., Nov. 3, 1933; s. Morris and Ida (Beekman) S.; m. Catherine Coccozza, June 6, 1959; children: Gail Denise, Glenn Eric, Kerri Lynn, Adria Lauren. Student, CCNY, 1951. Assoc. editor Radio-Electronics mag., N.Y.C., 1957-62, editor, 1967-85; pub., editor in chief Radio Electronics mag., 1985-92; electronics editor Popular Mechanics mag., N.Y.C., 1962-65; assoc. editor Electronic Products mag., Garden City, N.Y., 1965-67; editorial dir. Merchandising 2-Way Radio mag., N.Y.C., 1975-77; v.p., dir. Gernsback Publs., N.Y.C., 1975-84; pres., dir., 1984—; pub., editorial dir. Spl. Projects mag., 1980-84, Radio-Electronics Ann., 1982-84; pub., editor in chief Hands-On Electronics, 1984-88; Popular Electronics Mag., 1988—, Hobbyists Handbook, 1989—; pub., editor in chief Experimenters Handbook, 1986—; Radio Craft, 1993; pub., editor in chief Computer Digest, 1985-90; pres. Claggk, Inc., 1986—; Silicon Chip, 1993-94; pub., editor in chief The Magic Course, Eating In/Dining Out on Long Island, Modern Short Stories, 1987-90, GIZMO, 1988—, Video/Stereo Digest, 1989-94; pres. Sci. Probe Inc., 1989-93; pub., editor in chief Sci. Probe! mag., 1989-93, StoryMasters, 1989—, Electronics Shopper, 1990—, Electronics Market Ctr., 1991—; Radio Craft, 1993; mem. electronics adv. bd. Bd. Coop. Ednl. Services, Nassau County, N.Y., 1975-77; pres. Electronics Industry Hall of Fame, 1985—; bd. dirs. Pub. Hall of Fame, 1987-89. Author books, handbooks; pub.; contbr. articles to profl. jours. Bd. dirs. Nassau County council Camp Fire Girls, 1971-72. Served with U.S. Army, 1953-56. Recipient Coop. award Nat. Alliance TV and Electronic Services Assns., 1974, 75; inducted into Electronics Industry Hall of Fame, 1985. Mem. IEEE, Internat. Soc. Cert. Electronic Technicians (chmn. 1974-76, 79-81, 93—, Chmn.'s award 1985, dir. at large 1991-93, rep. to NESDA bd. 1991-93), Nat. Electronics Sales and Svc. Dealers Assn. (rec. sec. N.Y. state 1976-78, Man of Yr. award 1975, 85, treas. 1991-94, M.L. Finneyberg Excellence award 1994), Am. Mgmt. Assn., Radio Club Am., Internat. Underwater Explorers Soc., Am. Soc. Bus. Press Editors (sr.), Internat. Performing Magicians (assoc.). Soc. Profl. Journalists, L.A. Press. Home: 2601 Springridge Dr Las Vegas NV 89134-8848 Office: Gernsback Pub Inc 500B Bi County Blvd Farmingdale NY 11735-3931 also: Claggk Inc 4820 Alpine Pl # A101 Las Vegas NV 89107 *Do not be afraid to try the unaccepted. Do not be afraid to do the undesirable. Do what you enjoy. . .do it well. . .and after it is done. . .never regret having done it. . .only regret what you have not yet done.*

STECKLER, PHYLLIS BETTY, publishing company executive; b. N.Y.C.; d. Irwin H. and Bertha (Fellner) Schwartzbard; m. Stuart J. Steckler; children: Randall, Sharon Steckler-Slotky. BA, Hunter Coll.; MA, NYU. Editorial dir. R.R. Bowker Co., N.Y.C., Crowell Collier Macmillan Info. Pub. Co., N.Y.C., Holt Rinehart & Winston Info. Systems, N.Y.C.; pres., CEO Oryx Press, Scottsdale, Ariz., 1973-76, Phoenix, 1976—; adj. prof. history Ariz. State U., Tempe. Past chmn. Info. Industry Assn.; pres. Ariz. Ctr. for the Book; bd. dirs. Contemporary Forum of Phoenix Art Mus., Phoenix Pub. Libr. Friends; past pres. Friends of the Librs., U.S.A.; mem. edn. adv. coun. Senator John McCain. Elected to Hunter Coll. Hall of Fame, 1985. Mem. ALA, Spl. Librs. Assn., Am. Soc. Info. Soc., Ariz. Libr. Assn., Univ. Club of Phoenix (bd. dirs., sec.). Home: 6711 E Camelback Rd Unit 32 Scottsdale AZ 85251-2065 Office: Oryx Press 4041 N Central at Indian School Rd Phoenix AZ 85012

STECKLING, ADRIENNE See ADRI

STEDMAN, RICHARD RALPH, lawyer; b. Columbus, Ohio, July 18, 1936; s. Ralph Dale and Kathleen (Smith) S.; m. Elizabeth Ann Witschey, Dec. 18, 1965; children: Gretchen Kathleen, Richard Ralph II, Patrick Christopher Raymond. BBA, Ohio State U., 1958, JD, 1964. Bar: Ohio 1964; CPA, Ohio. Staff acct. Price Waterhouse Co., Columbus, 1958-60; salesman Royal McBee Co., Columbus, 1960; ptnr. Vorys, Sater, Seymour & Pease, Columbus, 1964—. Contbr. articles to profl. jours. Trustee, counsel Found. Cath. Diocese of Columbus, 1985—; trustee, sec.-treas. Nat. Soc. Cath. Founds.; trustee Ohio Dominican Coll., 1990—, St. Charles Prep. Sch., 1990—, Edward Orton, Jr. Ceramic Found., 1994—. Merson fellow Ohio

---

State U., 1963-64. Mem. Columbus Bar Assn., Fin. Execs. Inst., Athletic Club Columbus, Columbus Club, Brookside Golf and Country Club, Zanesfield Rod and Gun Club, Equestrian Order of Knights Holy Sepulchre of Jerusalem. Republican. Avocations: golfing, tennis, fishing. Office: Vorys Sater Seymour & Pease 52 E Gay St Box 1008 Columbus OH 43215-3161

STEED, ALLAN J., physical science research administrator. Dir. Space Dynamics Lab. Utah State U., Logan, Utah. Office: Utah State U Space Dynamics Lab Logan UT 84341-1942

STEED, ROBERT LEE, lawyer, humor columnist; b. Augusta, Ga., Nov. 20, 1936; s. Robert Pentecost and Doris (Roop) S.; m. Linda (Lu) Ruth McElroy, Aug. 23, 1958; children: Joshua, Georgia, Nona Begonia. AB, Mercer U., 1958, LLB, 1961, LLD (hon.), 1979. Bar: Ga. 1959. Law clk. to presiding justice Supreme Ct. of Ga., Atlanta, 1961-62; assoc. King & Spalding, Atlanta, 1962-67, ptnr., 1967—. Author: Willard Lives, 1981, Lucid Intervals, 1983, Money Power and Sex (A Self-Help Guide for All Ages), 1985; editor: The First Hundred Years: A Centennial History of King and Spalding (Della Wager Wells), 1985, The Sass Menagerie, 1988, Mail Fraud, The Laughable Letters of Robert L. Steed, 1991; columnist The Atlanta Jour.-Constn., 1978—. Mem., vice chmn. Met. Atlanta Crime Commn.; mem. bd. sponsors Atlanta Coll. Art; bd. dirs. 11 Alive Cmty. Svc. Awards, 1984—; chmn. bd. visitors Mercer Law Sch., 1970-71, 72-73, chmn. spl. gifts com. for renovation of Law Sch. Bldg., chmn. com. to select law sch. dean; trustee Mercer U., 1972-77, 79-84, 85-90, 91—, chmn. bd. trustees, 1985-90, mem. pres.'s coun., 1977-79, 84-85, mem. exec. com., 1974-77, chmn., 1982-84; bd. dirs. Walter F. George Found. for Mercer Law Sch. 1986—; trustee Walter F. George Sch. Law, George W. Woodruff Trust; bd. dirs. Clifton Corridor Coun., 1990-95. 1st lt. USAR, 1959. Recipient Journalistic Achievement award Dixie Coun. Authors, 1985, Humor award, 1985; Outstanding Alumnus award Mercer U., 1985, Disting. Alumnus award Mercer U. Coll. Liberal Arts, 1994. Mem. ABA, State Bar Ga. (bd. govs. 1967-68, pres. younger lawyers sect. 1967-68), Atlanta Bar Assn., Am. Coll. Investment Counsel, Ga. C. of C. (bd. dirs. 1982-85, chmn. Red Carpet Tour 1979-80, indsl. devel. commn. 1982-83), Bus. Coun. Ga. (bd. dirs. 1983-85), Mercer Alumni Assn. (exec. com. 1970-73), Mercer Law Alumni (pres.), U. Ga. Gridiron Secret Soc., Lawyers Club Atlanta, Old War Horse Lawyers Club, Capital City Club (bd. dirs. 1982-89, sec. 1985-87), Blue Key, Phi Delta Theta. Baptist. Home: 1058 Nawench Dr NW Atlanta GA 30327-1340 Office: King & Spalding 191 Peachtree St NE Atlanta GA 30303-1763

STEEDMAN, DORIA LYNNE SILBERBERG, advertising agency executive; b. L.A.; d. Mendel B. and Dorothy H. (Howell) Silberberg; m. Richard Cantey Steedman, Feb. 19, 1966; 1 child, Alexandra Loren. BA summa cum laude, UCLA. Producer EUE/Screen Gems, N.Y.C., 1963-66, Jack Tinker & Ptnrs., N.Y.C., 1966-68, Telpac Mgmt., N.Y.C., 1968-72; v.p. broadcast prodn. Geer DuBois Adv., N.Y.C., 1973-78, acctg. mgr., dir. ops., 1979-92; exec. v.p., dir. creative devel. Partnership for a Drug-Free America, N.Y.C., 1992—. Recipient Andy award Art Dirs. Club, 1968, 71; named one of 100 Best and Brightest Women in Advt., Advt. Age mag., 1988. Mem. Advt. Women N.Y. (pres. 1993-95), Phi Beta Kappa. Office: Partnership for a Drug-Free Am 405 Lexington Ave New York NY 10174-0100

STEEGMANN, ALBERT THEODORE, JR., anthropology educator; b. Cleve., Aug. 15, 1936; s. Albert Theodore and Frances (Boten) S.; m. Ruth Mighell, Jan. 26, 1963; children: Catherine, Thomas. B.A., U. Kans., 1958; M.A., U. Mich., 1961, Ph.D., 1965. Instr. anthropology dept. U. Mo., Columbia, 1964-65, asst. prof., 1965-66; asst. prof. anthropology SUNY-Buffalo, 1966-69, assoc. prof., 1969-74, prof., 1974—, dept. chmn., 1979-86; v.p. N.Y. Council for Evolution Edu., 1982—. Author: Physical Anthropology Workbook, 1974; Editor: Boreal Forest Adaptations, 1983, Yearbook Phys. Anthropology, 1993—. Served with Md. Corps USAR, 1961-66. NSF grantee, 1967, 70, 73, 78, 91. Fellow Am. Anthropology Assn., AAAS; mem. Am. Assn. Phys. Anthropologists (exec. com. 1974-77, sec. treas. 1985-89), Soc. for Study Human Biology, Human Biology Council. Democrat. Unitarian. Office: SUNY Buffalo Dept Anthropology 380 MFAC Buffalo NY 14261

STEEL, ADRIAN L., JR., lawyer; b. St. Louis, Jan. 2, 1950. AB, U. Mo., 1972; JD magna cum laude, U. Mich., 1975. Bar: Mo. 1975, Ill. 1976, U.S. Supreme Ct. 1979, D.C. 1981. Law clk. to Hon. William H. Webster U.S. Ct. Appeals (8th cir.), 1975-76; spl. asst. to dir. FBI, 1978-81; ptnr. Mayer, Brown & Platt, Washington. Mem. ABA, Ill. State Bar Assn., Mo. Bar, D.C. Bar Assn. Office: Mayer Brown & Platt 2000 Pennsylvania Ave NW Washington DC 20006-1812

STEEL, ALAN RICHARD, financial executive; b. Los Angeles, Apr. 28, 1945; s. Richard Frederick and Vera Ann (Szabo) S.; m. Catherine Marie McNamara, Nov. 24, 1966; children: Eric, Jeffrey, Carrie. BS, U. So. Calif., 1967. CPA. Auditor, audit mgr. Arthur Andersen & Co., Los Angeles, 1967-74; fin. mgr. Atlantic Richfield Co., Los Angeles, 1974-80; controller Data Design Labs., Cucamonga, Calif., 1980-83, v.p. fin., treas., chief fin. officer, 1983—. Republican. Roman Catholic. Avocations: skiing, jogging. Office: Data Design Labs 1244 S Claudina St Anaheim CA 92805-6232

STEEL, DANIELLE FERNANDE, author; b. N.Y.C., Aug. 14, 1947; d. John and Norma (Stone) Schuelein-Steel. Student, Parsons Sch. Design, 1963, NYU, 1963-67. Vice pres. pub. relations and new bus. Supergirls Ltd., N.Y.C., 1968-71; copywriter Grey Advt., San Francisco, 1973-74. Author novels Going Home, 1973, Passion's Promise, 1977, Now and Forever, 1978, The Promise, 1978, Season of Passion, 1979, Summers End, 1979, To Love Again, 1980, The Ring, 1981, Loving, 1980, Love, 1981, Remembrance, 1981, Palomino, 1981, Once in a Lifetime, 1982, Crossings, 1982, A Perfect Stranger, 1982, Thurston House, 1983, Changes, 1983, Full Circle, 1984, (non-fiction) Having A Baby, 1984, Family Album, 1985, Secrets, 1985, Wanderlust, 1986, Fine Things, 1987, Kaleidoscope, 1987, Zoya, 1988, Star, 1988, Daddy, 1989, Message from Nam, 1990, Heartbeat, 1991, No Greater Love, 1991, Jewels, 1992, Mixed Blessings, 1992, Vanished, 1993, Accident, 1994, The Gift, 1994, Wings, 1994, Lightning, 1995; (children's) Martha's Best Friend, Martha's New School, Martha's New Daddy, Max's New Daddy, Max and The Babysitter, Max's Daddy Goes To The Hospital; contbr. poetry to mags., including Cosmopolitan, McCall's, Ladies Home Jour., Good Housekeeping. Home: PO Box 1637 New York NY 10156-1637 Office: 598 Madison Ave New York NY 10022-1614

STEEL, DAWN, motion picture producer; b. N.Y.C., Aug. 19; m. Charles Roven; 1 child, Rebecca. Student in mktg., Boston U., 1964-65, NYU, 1966-67. Sportswriter Major League Baseball Digest and NFL, N.Y.C., 1968-69; editor Penthouse Mag., N.Y.C., 1969-75; pres. Oh Dawn!, Inc., N.Y.C., 1975-78; v.p. merchandising, cons. Playboy mag., N.Y.C., 1978-79; v.p. merchandising Paramount Pictures, N.Y.C., 1979-80; v.p. prodn. Paramount Pictures, L.A., 1980-83, sr. v.p. prodn., 1983-85, pres. prodn., 1985-87; pres. Columbia Pictures, 1987-90; formed Steel Pictures (with Touchstone Pictures and Walt Disney Film & TV), 1990-94, Atlas Entertainment, 1994; mem. dean's adv. bd. UCLA Sch. Theater, Film, TV, 1993. First woman studio pres.; prodns. for Paramount include Flashdance, Footloose, Top Gun, Star Trek III, Beverly Hills Cop II, The Untouchables, The Accused, Fatal Attraction, 1985-87; prodns. for Columbia include Ghostbusters II, Karate Kid III, When Harry Met Sally, Look Who's Talking, Casualties of War, Postcards from the Edge, Flatliners, Awakenings; prodr. Steel Pictures for Disney: Honey, I Blew Up the Kid, 1992, Cool Runnings, 1993, Sister Act 2, 1993; prodr. (benefit concert) For Our Children, Pediatric AIDS Found., 1992; author: They Can Kill You, But They Can't Eat You, 1993. Appointeee Presdl. Commn. Scholars, 1993; mem. L.A. Mayor Richard Riordan's Transition Team, 1993, U.S. Del. to Winter Olympics, 1994; chair Mayor's Entertainment Industry Task Force, 1993; bd. dirs. Hollywood Supports, 1993. Recipient Women Film Crystal award Women in Film, 1989. Mem. Acad. Motion Picture Arts and Scis. Avocations: skiing, tennis. Office: Atlas Entertainment 9169 Sunset Blvd Los Angeles CA 90069

STEEL, DUNCAN GREGORY, physics educator; b. Cleve., Jan. 11, 1951; s. Robert John and Mildred (Graham) S.; m. Nancy Elizabeth Harknett, May 3, 1975; children: Adam, Benjamin. BA, U. N.C., 1972; MS, U. Mich., 1973, 75, PhD, 1976. Physicist Exxon Rsch. and Engrng., Linden, N.J., 1977-78, Hughes Rsch. Labs., Malibu, Calif., 1975-85; prof. U. Mich., Ann

---

Arbor, 1985—; scientist Inst. Gerontology Sch. Medicine, U. Mich., Ann Arbor, 1986—; topical editor Jour. Optical Soc., Washington, 1986-92. Contbr. articles to profl. jours. Fellow Optical Soc. Am., Am. Phys. Soc.; mem. IEEE (sr.). Achievements include first phase conjugate laser, first high resolution nonlinear laser spectroscopy of semiconductor heterostructures; demonstration of collision induced resonances in atoms; demonstration of low noise (below the standard quantum limit) room temperature semiconductor lasers; demonstration of in vitro trystophan phosphorescence for studies of protein structure in solution. Office: U Mich Physics Dept 500 E University Ave Ann Arbor MI 48109-1105

STEEL, GORDON, electronics executive; b. 1944. BA, Pomona Coll., 1967; MBA, Stanford U., 1971. Divsn. mgr. Quantor, 1973-77; treas. Impell Corp.; CFO Evotek, 1980-84, Pyramid Technology, 1984-87; with Xilinx Inc., San Jose, Calif., 1987—, now v.p., CFO. Address: Xilinx Inc 2100 Logic Dr San Jose CA 95124-3450*

STEEL, HOWARD HALDEMAN, pediatric orthopaedic surgeon; b. Phila., Apr. 17, 1921; s. Howard Hinchman and Elizabeth (Haldeman) S.; m. Joan Elizabeth Clack, Aug. 16, 1964; children—Michael, Celia, Turner, Kathleen, Patrick, Townsend, Anna, Howard H. III. A.B., Colgate U., 1942; M.D., Temple U., 1945, M.S., 1951; Ph.D. in Anatomy, U. Wash., 1966. Enlisted U.S. Navy, 1941, advanced through grades to lt. comdr. M.C., 1955; ret., 1956; intern Temple U. Med. Center, Phila., 1945-46; resident in orthopaedic surgery Temple U. Med. Center, 1948-51; prof. orthopaedic surgery U. Wash., Seattle, 1965-66, Temple U., 1966—; endowed chair, prof. pediatric orthopaedics Temple U. Hosp., 1989—; clin. prof. orthopaedic surgery Med. Coll. Pa., 1985—; chief surgeon Shriners Hosp. for Crippled Children, Phila. 1966-86, emeritus chief of staff, 1986—; pres. Steel Fudge Shops, Inc., Atlantic City, 1958—; chmn. bd. Steels Fudge, Inc.; Hunterian lectr., London, 1958; med. cons. U.S Army Med. Corps, USN, 1965-85; clin. prof. emeritus U. Pa., 1985; prof. emeritus of orthopaedic surgery Temple U. 1985. Contbr. articles to profl. jours. Mem. Pine Barrens Conservation com. N.J. Legislature, Trenton, 1973-75; v.p. Colgate U. Alumni Corp., 1965-78; trustee Colgate U., 1972-78; hon. mem. Nat. Treasure of Japan, 1992. Recipient Apple Tchg. awards Sr. Class U. Wash., 1966, Temple U. Med. Sch., 1976, Disting. Alumnus award Colgate U., 1975, Humanitarian award City of Phila., 1978, Presdl. citation for rsch. in Berrylum, 1942, Humanitarian award Chapel of Four Chaplains, 1981. Fellow A.C.S.; mem. AMA (Billings Gold medal), Am. Orthopaedic Assn., Phila. Orthopaedic Soc. (pres. 1970), Am. Acad. Orthopaedic Surgeons, Pediatric Orthopaedic Soc., Orthopaedic Research Soc., Scoliosis Research Soc., Phila. Acad. Surgeons, Phila. Coll. Medicine, Eastern Orthopaedic Assn. (founder, 1st pres., Disting. Service award 1978), Jefferson Orthopaedic Soc., Phila. Roentgen Ray Soc., Am. Spinal Injury Assn., Hon. Nat. Treasure Japan, Phi Beta Kappa, Alpha Omega Alpha. Republican. Episcopalian. Clubs: Phila. Country, Phila. Skating and Humane Soc, Merion Cricket, Merion Golf, Wissahickon Skating, Wissahicon Ski, Confrerie des Chevalier du Tastevin, Union League of Phila, Orpheus Club of Phila., Ocean City Yacht, Corinthian Yacht, Masons (Columbia 91 award 1981), Shriners. Researcher, developer orthopaedic procedures. Office: Shriners Hosp for Crippled Children 8400 Roosevelt Blvd Philadelphia PA 19152-1299

STEEL, JOHN M., electronics executive; b. 1944. Gen. mgr. OEM spares and tech. devices Control Data Corp., Mpls., 1968-83; with Zytec Corp., Eden Prairie, Minn., 1983—, v.p. sales & mktg. Office: Zytec Corp 7575 Market Pl Dr Eden Prairie MN 55344*

STEEL, RONALD LEWIS, author, historian, educator; b. Morris, Ill., Mar. 25, 1931. BA magna cum laude, Northwestern U., 1953; MA, Harvard U., 1955. Vice consul U.S. Fgn. Service, 1957-58; editor Scholastic mag., N.Y.C., 1959-62; sr. assoc. Carnegie Endowment for Internat. Peace, 1982-83; fellow Woodrow Wilson Internat. Ctr. Scholars, 1984-85; prof. internat. relations U. So. Calif., Los Angeles, 1986—; fellow Wissenschaftskolleg zu Berlin, Federal Republic of Germany, 1988; vis. fellow Yale U., 1971-73; vis. prof. Wellesley Coll., 1978, U. Tex., 1977, 79, 80, 85, Rutgers U., 1980; UCLA, 1981, Dartmouth Coll., 1983, Princeton U., 1984. Author books including: The End of Alliance: America and the Future of Europe, 1964, (with G. Kimble) Tropical Africa Today, 1966, Pax Americana, 1967, Imperialists and Other Heroes, 1971, Walter Lippmann and the American Century, 1980, Temptations of a Superpower, 1995; editor various publs. for H.W. Wilson Co., 1961-67; contbr. to N.Y. Rev. Books; contbg. editor New Republic. Served with U.S. Army, 1954-56. Recipient Sidney Hillman award, 1968, Washington Monthly book award, 1980, Los Angeles Tims book award for non-fiction, 1980, Nat. Book Critics Circle award, 1981, Bancroft prize Columbia U., 1981, Am. History Bancroft prize, 1980, Am. Book award for biography, 1982; Guggenheim fellow, 1973-74. Mem. Council on Fgn. Relations. Office: U So Calif Sch Internat Rels Los Angeles CA 90089-0043

STEELE, ANA MERCEDES, government official; b. Niagara Falls, N.Y., Jan. 18, 1939; d. Sydney and Mercedes (Hernandez) S.; m. John Hunter Clark, June 2, 1979. AB magna cum laude, Marywood Coll., 1958. Actress, 1959-64; sec. Nat. Endowment for Arts, Washington, 1965-67, dir. budget and research, 1968-75, dir. planning, 1976-78, dir. program coordination, sr. exec. service, 1979-81, assoc. dep. chmn. for programs, dir. program coordination, sr. exec. service, 1982-93, acting chmn., acting sr. dep. chmn., 1993, sr. dep. chmn., sr. exec. svc., 1993—; guest lectr. George Washington U., 1987; trustee Marywood Coll., 1989—. Author, editor report: History of the National Council on the Arts and National Endowment for the Arts During the Johnson Administration, 1968; editor: Museums USA (Fed. Design Council award of Excellence 1975), 1974; National Endowment Arts 1965-1985; A Brief Chronology of Federal Involvement in the Arts, 1985. Former reader Rec. for the Blind, N.Y.C.; former tutor Future for Jimmy, Washington. Named Disting. Grad. in Field of Arts, Marywood Coll., 1976; recipient Sustained Superior Performance award Nat. Endowment for Arts, Washington, 1980, Disting. Service award, 1983, 84, 85, 89, 92. Mem. Actors' Equity Assn., Screen Actors Guild, Delta Epsilon Sigma, Kappa Gamma Pi. Office: Nat Endowment for Arts Nancy Hanks Ctr 1100 Pennsylvania Ave NW Washington DC 20506-0001

STEELE, ANITA MARTIN (MARGARET ANNE MARTIN), law librarian, legal educator; b. Haines City, Fla., Dec. 30, 1927; d. Emmett Edward and Esther Majulia (Phifer) Martin; m. Thomas Dinsmore Steele, June 10, 1947 (div. 1969); children: Linda Frances, Roger Dinsmore, Thomas Garrick, Carolyn Ann; m. James E. Beaver, Mar. 1980. BA, Radcliffe Coll., 1948; J.D., U. Va., 1971; M.Law Librarianship, U. Wash., 1972. Asst. prof. law U. Puget Sound, Tacoma, 1972-74, assoc. prof. law, 1974-79, prof. law, 1979—, dir. law library, 1972-94; prof. law, dir. law libr. Seattle U., Tacoma, 1994—. Author: (book) Martin and Carmichael Descendants in Georgia, 1811-1994, 1994; contbr. articles to profl. jours.; mem. editorial adv. bds. various law book pubs., 1980—. Treas. Congl. Campaign Orgn., Tacoma, 1978, 80; mem. adv. bd. Clover Park Vocat.-Tech. Sch., Tacoma, 1980-82. Mem. Am. Assn. Law Libraries, Internat. Assn. Law Libraries, Am. Soc. Internat. Law. Republican. Home: 1502 S Fernside Dr Tacoma WA 98465-1305 Office: Seattle U Sch Law 950 Broadway Plz Tacoma WA 98402-4470

STEELE, BETTY LOUISE, retired banker; b. Sigourney, Iowa, Nov. 20, 1920; d. Otto Orville and Freda Marie Christina (Strohman) Utterback; m. David L. Steele, Jan. 17, 1942; 1 child, David Leroy. Student pub. schs., Iowa. With N.W. Des Moines Nat. Bank, 1959-68, v.p., 1966-68; v.p., sec. Brenton Banks, Inc., Des Moines, 1968-86; mem. pension com. Brenton Banks, Inc., 1980-86, vice chmn. investment com., 1983-86, dir., 1976-83; sec. Brenton Found. 1970-83; mem. State Banking Bd., 1977-81. Author articles. Bd. dirs. Ctrl. Iowa chpt. ARC, 1984-90, mem. exec. com., asst. treas., 1984-90; mem. fin. audit com., 1985-93; mem. dean's com. Iowa State U. Coll. Home Econs., 1982-84; mem. Iowa Pub./Pvt. Sector Task Force, Gov.'s Com. for Volunteerism, 1984. Mem. Des Moines C. of C. (Nat. Leadership award 1976), Fin. Women Internat. (nat. pres. 1976-77, bd. dirs. 1970-78, trustee ednl. found. 1974-76 (Betty L. Steele award given in her honor Iowa chpt.), Am. Bankers Assn. (govt. relations council 1977-79), Iowa Bankers Assn. (legis. com. 1975-76). Republican. Mem. Ch. of Christ. Home: 6022 Terrace Dr Johnston IA 50131-1591

STEELE, CARL LAVERN, academic administrator; b. Patoka, Ill., Aug. 22, 1934; s. Boyd Alfa and Effie Jane (Corson) S.; m. Lula Irene Saliba, June

11, 1961; children: Jeffrey Van, Gregory Michael, Douglas Alan. BEd, So. Ill. U., 1956, MEd, 1960; MLS, No. Ill. U., 1971. Tchr. Shawneetown (Ill.) Community High. Sch., 1956-57; GED instr. U.S. Army, Ft. Hood, Tex. and Ulm, Fed. Republic of Germany, 1957-59; tchr. Forrest-Strawn-Wing Unit Dist., Forrest, Ill., 1959-61, Richwoods Community High Sch., Peoria, Ill., 1961-66; asst. dir. instructional materials Sauk Valley Coll., Dixon, Ill., 1966-68; dir. Ednl. Resources Ctr., Rock Valley Coll., Rockford, Ill., 1968-93; ret., 1993. Asst. World Record sec. Nat. Fresh Water Fishing Hall of Fame, Hayward, Wisc., 1977-79. Served with U.S. Army, 1957-59. Mem. ALA, Assn. Ednl. Communications and Technology, Ill. Assn. Ednl. Communications and Technology (conv. chmn. 1976), No. Ill. Media Assn. (conv. chmn.), Learning Resource Commn. ICCCA (chmn. 1981). Democrat. Presbyterian. Avocations: fishing, travel, reading, woodworking, gardening. Home: 5758 Weymouth Dr Rockford IL 61114-5547

STEELE, CHARLES GLEN, retired accountant; b. Faulkton, S.D., July 24, 1925; s. Clifford D. and Emily O. (Hanson) S.; m. Shirley June Ferguson, Nov. 9, 1947; children: Richard Alan (dec.), Deborah Ann Steele Most. B.B.A., Golden Gate U., San Francisco, 1951, M.B.A., 1962. With Deloitte Haskins & Sells, 1951-86, partner, 1963-86, partner charge Chgo. office, 1973-76; partner charge personnel and adminstrn. Deloitte Haskins & Sells, N.Y.C., 1976-78; chmn., chief exec. officer Deloitte Haskins & Sells, 1978-86; instr. evening program Golden Gate U., 1952-58. Served with USNR, 1943-48. Recipient Elijah Watts Sells Gold medal for highest grade in U.S. for C.P.A. exam., 1951. Mem. Am. Inst. C.P.A.s. Club: Honorable Company of Edinburgh Golfers. Home and Office: 26349 Rio Ave Carmel CA 93923-9101

STEELE, EARL LARSEN, electrical engineering educator; b. Denver, Sept. 24, 1923; s. Earl Harold and Jennie (Larsen) S.; m. Martha C. Hennessey, June 27, 1953; children: Karl Thomas, Earl Robert, Karen Lynn, Kevin Douglas, Lisa Louise, Colleen Carol. B.S. with honors, U. Utah, 1945; Ph.D., Cornell U., 1952. Research physicist Gen. Electric Co., 1952-56; chief device devel. Motorola, Inc., 1956-58; mgr. devel. lab. Hughes Aircraft Co., 1958-64; research scientist N.Am. Rockwell Corp., 1964-69; prof. elec. engring. U. Ky., Lexington, 1969-90, prof. emeritus, 1991—; chmn. dept. U. Ky., 1971-80, 1988-89; Affiliate prof. Ariz. State U., 1956-58, U. Calif.-Irvine, 1966-69; adviser So. Calif. Coll., Costa Mesa, 1963-64; charter mem. Orange County Academic Decathlon (Calif.); bd. dirs. Southeastern Center for Elec. Engring. Edn., 1975—, treas., 1980-81, v.p., 1981-82, resident dir., 1981-82, 89-90, pres., 1982-83, mem. coun. of pres.', 1983—. Author: Optical Lasers in Electronics; contbr. articles to profl. jours. Fellow IEEE; mem. Am. Soc. Engring. Edn. (U. Ky. Coll. Engring. rep. to ASEE, 1988-90), Am. Phys. Soc., Internat. Soc. Hybrid Microelectronics, Sigma Xi, Tau Beta Pi, Eta Kappa Nu (dir. 1974-76, v.p. 1983-84, pres. 1984-85). Mem. LDS Ch. Home: 313 Blueberry Ln Lexington KY 40503-2004

STEELE, ERNEST CLYDE, retired insurance company executive; b. Corbin, Ky., May 11, 1925; s. J. Fred and Leona (McFarland) S.; m. Cora Jones, June 17, 1944 (dec. Nov. 1988); children: Gerald R., David. P.; m. Helen LeCoultre, July 7, 1990. BS with honors, U. Ky., 1948, MS, 1950. Asst. actuary Peninsular Life Ins. Co., Jacksonville, Fla., 1950-54; actuary Pioneer Life & Casualty Co., Gadsden, Ala., 1955; v.p., actuary Guaranty Savs. Life Ins. Co., Montgomery, Ala., 1956-57; exec. v.p., actuary Am. Investment Life Ins. Co., Nashville, 1958-59; pres., actuary Appalachian Nat. Life Ins. Co., Knoxville, Tenn., 1959-67; sr. v.p., chief investment officer, ops. analyst Coastal States Life Ins. Co., Atlanta, 1968-71; exec. v.p., dir. Coastal States Life Ins. Co., 1971-74, pres., dir., 1974-79; pres., dir. Occidental Life Ins. Co. of N.C., 1979-85, chmn., 1986-88; pres., dir. Peninsular Life Ins. Co., 1981-83, chmn., 1986-88; exec. v.p. investments MCM Corp., 1985-88; past pres. Ga. Assn. Life Inst. Cos., 1976-77. Mem. devel. coun. U. Ky. Served to 2d lt. U.S. Army, 1943-45. Fellow Life Mgmt. Inst.; mem. Life Office Mgmt. Assn. (past chmn. bd.), Am. Council Life Ins. (past dir.), U. Ky. Alumni Assn. (past bd. dirs.), Am. Acad. Actuaries, Pi Mu Epsilon. Republican. Baptist. Home: 103 Newell Village Dr Seymour TN 37865-5931 *My success in life is measured by the success of those with whom I have been associated.*

STEELE, FRANK CHANNEL, sales executive; b. N.Y.C., Oct. 1, 1938; s. Ralph E. and Frances (Channell) S.; m. Karon Kay Kennelly, May 22, 1965; children: Darrin, Danielle. BA, U. Rochester, 1960. Sales rep. Scott Paper Co., Salt Lake City, 1964-66; adminstrv. asst. Scott Paper Co., Seattle, 1966-69, asst. dist. mgr., 1969-70; regional sales mgr. Airborne Freight Corp., Phila., 1970-72; regional mgr. Airborne Freight Corp., Boston, 1972-76; regional mgr. N.Y.C., 1976-78, regional mgr., v.p., 1978-80; v.p. sales Seattle, 1980-84, sr. v.p. sales, 1984—. 1st lt. USAF, 1960-63. Office: Airborne Freight Corp 3101 Western Ave Seattle WA 98121-1043

STEELE, GLENN DANIEL, JR., surgical oncologist; b. Balt., June 23, 1944; m. Diana; 1 child, Joshua; m. Lisa; children: Kirsten, Lara. AB magna cum laude, Harvard Coll., 1966; MD, NYU, 1970; PhD, Lund U., Sweden, 1975. Intern, then resident Med. Ctr. U. Colo., Denver, 1970-76; fellow NIH in immunology Univ. Lund, Sweden, 1973-75; asst. surgeon Sidney Farber Cancer Inst., Boston, 1976-78; clin. assoc. surgical oncology Sidney Farber Cancer Inst., 1978-79; jr. assoc. in surgery Peter Bent Brigham Hosp., Boston, 1976-82; instr. surgery Med. Sch. Harvard, Boston, 1976-78; asst. prof. surgery Med. Sch. Harvard Coll., 1978-81; assoc. physician surgical oncology Sidney Farber Cancer Inst., 1979-82; assoc. prof. surgery Med. Sch. Harvard Coll., 1981-84; surgeon Brigham & Women's Hosp., 1982-84; assoc. physician surgical oncology Dana-Farber Cancer Inst., 1982-84, physician surg. oncology, 1984—; chmn. dept. surgery, deaconess Harvard Surg. Svc. New England Deaconess Hosp., Boston, 1985—; William V. McDermott prof. surgery Med. Sch. Harvard Coll., 1985—; cons. surgeon Boston Hosp. for Women, 1977-80. assoc. editor Jour. of Clin. Oncology, 1986—, Jour. of Hepatobiliary-Pancreatic Surgery, 1993—; mem. editorial bd. Annals of Surgery, Annals of Surg. Oncology, British Jour. of Surgery, Surgery, Surgical Oncology; contbr. numerous articles to profl. jours. Recipient NIH fellow 1973-75, Am. Cancer Soc. fellow 1972-73, 76-79, various other rsch. grants. Fellow Am. Coll. Surgeons (chmn. patient care and rsch. com. commn. on cancer 1989-91, mem. bd. govs. 1991—, chmn. commn. on cancer 1991-93, exec. com. 1993—); mem. Am. Assn. Immunologists, Am. Bd. Surgery (dir. 1993—), Am. Bd. Med. Specialties, Am. Soc. Clin. Oncology, Am. Surg. Assn., Assn. Program Dirs. in Surgery, Assn. for Surgical Edn., Internat. Fedn. Surg. Colls., Internat. Surg. Group, New England Cancer Soc., and numerous other mems. Office: New Eng Deaconess Hosp 185 Pilgrim Rd Boston MA 02215-5501

STEELE, HARRY GERARD, diversified company executive; b. Pitts., Mar. 21, 1942; s. Albert Franklin and Josephine (Sherek) S.; m. Rita Catherine Winslade, May 24, 1944; children: Amy, Brian. BBA, U. Notre Dame, 1965; MBA, Northwestern U., Evanston, Ill., 1966. Acct. Union Carbide Corp., N.Y.C., 1966-69; mgr. corp. budgets Pfizer Inc., N.Y.C., 1969-71, controller Pfizer Labs., 1971-72; dir. budgets and planning Lone Star Industries, Greenwich, Conn., 1972-76; dir. planning and fin. controls Philip Morris U.S.A., N.Y.C., 1976-79; contr., v.p. fin. and adminstrn. N.Y.C., 1984—. Bd. dirs. Retreat Hosp., Richmond, 1982-84, Theatre IV, Richmond, 1982-83; town meeting rep. City of Darien, Conn., 1974-84. Mem. Nat. Assn. Accts. Republican. Home: 67 Dans Hwy New Canaan CT 06840-2502 Office: Philip Morris USA 120 Park Ave New York NY 10017-5523

STEELE, JAMES B., journalist; b. Hutchinson, Kans., Jan. 3, 1943; s. James B. and Mary V. (Peoples) S.; m. Nancy Saunders; 1 child, Allison E. BA, U. Mo., 1967. Reporter Phila. Inquirer, Kansas City Times, 1962-68; dir. info. Laborers' Internat. Union, AFL-CIO, Washington, 1968-69; reporter Phila. Inquirer, 1970—. Co-author: Empire: The Life, Legend and Madness of Howard Hughes, 1979, Forevermore: Nuclear Waste in America, 1985, America: What Went Wrong?, 1992. Recipient Pulitzer prize for nat. reporting, 1975, 89; numerous other journalism awards. Office: Phila Inquirer 400 N Broad St Philadelphia PA 19130-4099*

STEELE, JAMES HARLAN, former public health veterinarian, educator; b. Chgo., Apr. 3, 1913; s. James Hahn and Lydia (Nordquist) S.; m. Aina Oberg, 1941 (dec. 1969); children: James Harlan, David, Michael; m. Maria-Brigitte Meyer, 1969. DVM, Mich. State Coll., 1941; MPH, Harvard U., 1942. With Ohio Dept. Health, 1942-43; with USPHS, 1943-71; advancing through grades to asst. surgeon gen. for vet. affairs and chief vet. officer; chief vet. pub. health activities Communicable Disease Center, Atlanta, 1947-71; prof. environ. health U. Tex. Sch. Pub. Health, Houston, 1971-83, prof. emeritus, 1983—; cons. WHO, 1950—, Pan-Am. Health Orgn., 1945—, FAO, UN, 1960, German Health Svc., 1986-93; vis. prof. Tex. A&M U., 1976—, all univ. prof., 1981-82; trustee Nat. Found. Infectious Diseases. Author: Bovine Tuberculosis Control in Man and Animals, 1969, rev. (with Charles Thoen), 1995; editor-in-chief Zoonoses Handbooks, 1979-84, cons. editor, 1994; contbr. articles to profl. jours. and sects. to books on food hygiene and irradiation. Recipient Mich. State U. Alumni award, 1958, USPHS Order of Merit, 1963, Karl F. Meyer Gold Head Cane award, 1966, Disting. Svc. award USPHS, 1971, Mich. State U. Coll. Vet. Medicine award, 1972, hon. mem. Epidemic Intelligence Svc., 1975, Centennial award U. Pa., 1984, Am. Vet. Med. Assn. Internat. Vet. award, 1984, Pub. Svc. award, 1993; James H. Steele Vet. Pub. Health award World Vet. Epidemiology Soc., 1975. Fellow Am. Pub. Health Assn. (emeritus, 1984; Bronfman award 1971, Centennial award 1972), Am. Coll. Epidemiology (founding fellow); mem. Conf. Pub. Health Vets. (founder), Am. Soc. Tropical Medicine (emeritus), Am. Coll. Vet. Preventive Medicine (founder, hon. diploma 1983, Pres.'s award 1994), Nat. Acad. Health Practitioners, World Vet. Epidemiology Soc. (founder, pres. 1971), Am. Vet. Epidemiology Soc. (pres. 1966-88), World Vet. Assn. (hon.), Philippines Vet. Med. Assn. (hon.), Peru Vet. Med. Assn. (hon.), Hellenic Vet. Soc. (Athens Greece, hon. diploma, 1977), U.S. Animal Health Assn. (life), U.S.-Mex. Pub. Health Assn. (hon., life), Mil. Surgeons Assn. (hon. life), Infectious Disease Soc. Am. (emeritus), Internat. Epidemiology Soc. (emeritus), XXI World Vet. Congress (Moscow, hon. diploma 1979), German Health Svc. (hon. diploma, 1988, Order of Merit 1993), Harvard U. Alumni Assn., Mich. State U. Alumni Assn., Alpha Psi. Episcopalian. Home: 10722 Riverview Way Houston TX 77042-1121 Office: School of Public Hlth University of Texas Houston TX 77225 *I have believed firmly throughout my career that I should share my knowledge and expertise with my fellow man, be he American or citizen of the world. Those of us who are more fortunate to be endowed with intellectual advantages have an even greater responsibility to share.*

STEELE, JOHN HYSLOP, marine scientist, oceanographic institute administrator; b. Edinburgh, U.K., Nov. 15, 1926; s. Adam and Annie H.; m. Margaret Evelyn Travis, Mar. 2, 1956; 1 son, Hugh. B.Sc., Univ. Coll., London U., 1946, D.Sc., 1964. Marine scientist Marine Lab., Aberdeen, Scotland, 1951-66; sr. prin. sci. officer Marine Lab., 1966-73, dep. dir., 1973-77; dir. Woods Hole Oceanographic Instn., Mass., 1977-89, pres., 1986-91; mem. NAS/NRC Ocean Sci. Bd., 1978-88, chmn., 1986-88; mem. rsch. and exploration com. Nat. Geog. Soc.; mem. Arctic Rsch. Commn., 1988-92; trustee Univ. Corp. Atmospheric Rsch., 1987-91, Bermuda Biol. Sta., R.W. Johnson Found.; del. Internat. Coun. Exploration Sea; bd. dirs. Exxon Corp. Author: The Structure of Marine Ecosystems, 1974; Contbr. articles to profl. jours. Served with Brit. Royal Air Force, 1947-49. Recipient Alexander Agassiz medal Nat. Acad. Sci., 1973. Fellow Royal Soc. London, AAAS, Royal Soc. Edinburgh, Am. Acad. Arts and Scis. Home: PO Box 25 Woods Hole MA 02543-0025 Office: Woods Hole Oceanographic Inst Woods Hole MA 02543

STEELE, JOHN LAWRENCE, journalist; b. Chgo., June 9, 1917; s. Leo M. and Helen (Schumann) S.; m. Louise V. Stein, June 27, 1940; children: Deborah, John Lawrence, Scott. Grad. Lake Forest Acad., 1935; A.B., Dartmouth Coll., 1939; Nieman fellow, Harvard U., 1951-52. With Chgo. City News Bur., 1939; staff Chgo. bur. U.P.I., 1939-41; bur. legislative corr. U.P., Washington, 1941-42, 45-53; legis. polit. corr. Time mag., 1953-55; White House corr., 1955-58; chief Washington bur.; Time-Life mags., 1958-69; sr. corr. Time-Life News Service, 1969-79; v.p. Time Inc., Washington, 1979-82, cons., 1982-84, pub. policy cons., 1985—. Collaborator: (with A.H. Vandenberg, Jr. and Joe A. Morris) The Private Papers of Senator Vandenberg, 1952; contbr. articles to mags. and jours., chpts. to books. Mem. alumni coun. Dartmouth Coll., 1971-74; mem. Native Am. Vis. Com., 1973-78, chmn., 1975-78; bd. mem. Mag. Pubs. Assn., 1979-81; participant TV news interview programs NBC, CBS, BBC, 1950-79. Recipient The Dartmouth Alumni award for disting. svc. in journalism and pub. affairs. Mem. Burning Tree Club, Met. Club, Sigma Delta Chi (Hall of Fame 1979). Home and Office: 3100 Newark St NW Washington DC 20008-3343

STEELE, KAREN KIARSIS, state legislator; b. Haverhill, Mass., Sept. 26, 1942; d. Victor and Barbara (McFee) Kiarsis; m. Edward E. Steele, Apr. 16, 1966; children: Shawn Robert, Gretchen Garvey. BA, U. Vt., 1964. Tchr. Waterbury Sch. System, 1964-65, Burlington (Vt.) Sch. System, 1965-67; legislator State of Vt., Montpelier, 1982—. Trustee Cen. Vt. Hosp., Berlin. Mem. Am. Legis. Exch. Coun. (nat. chmn. healthcare task force). Republican. Avocations: golf, swimming, reading, skiing. Home: RR 2 Box 796 Waterbury VT 05676-9713 Office: State House Montpelier VT 05602

STEELE, KATHLEEN FRANCES, federal official; b. Kansas City, Mo., Oct. 28, 1960. Admissions counselor N.E. Mo. State U., Kirksville, 1980-83, assoc. dir. admissions, 1983-86, programming coord. dept. pub. svcs., 1986-87; Iowa, N.H. dir. Gephardt for Pres., St. Louis, 1987-88; mem. Mo. Ho. of Reps., Jefferson City, 1988-94; state dir. Clinton for Pres., 1991-92; regional dir. U.S. Dept. Health and Human Svcs., Kansas City, Mo., 1994—; chair Freshman Dem. Caucus, 1989, chair sci., tech. and critical issues com. Bd. dirs. Adair County chpt. ARC, 1987. Recipient Young Careerist award Kirksville Bus. and Profl. Women, 1988. Mem. Nat. Order Women Legislators, Women Legislators of Mo. (pres. 1989-92). Roman Catholic. Avocations: sports enthusiast, dancing, reading, politics. Home: 6 Nantucket Ct Smithville MO 64089 Office: US Dept Health and Human Svcs 601 E 12th St Room 210 Kansas City MO 64106

STEELE, KENNETH FRANKLIN, JR., hydrology educator, resource center director; b. Statesville, N.C., Jan. 16, 1944; s. Kenneth Franklin and Ruth Virginia (Wilhelm) S.; m. Sheila Kay Stumpf, Sept. 3, 1966; children: Krista Robin, Celisa Anne. BS in Chemistry, U. N.C., 1966, PhD in Geology, 1971. Registered profl. genealogist, Ark., registered hydrogeologist. From instr. to assoc. prof. geology U. Ark., Fayetteville, 1970-83, prof., 1983—, dir. Ark. Water Resources Ctr., 1988—; cons. in field. Contbr. numerous articles to profl. jours., chpts. to books. Summer faculty fellow Oak Ridge Associated Univs., 1981, 83, 85. Mem. Assn. Ground-Water Scientists and Engrs., Geol. Soc. Am. (regional bd. dirs. 1980-82, 84-86), Am. Water Resources Assn. (bd. dirs. 1991-94), Ark. Ground Water Assn. (bd. dirs. 1988-90, 93—, v.p. 1991, pres. 1992), Nat. Assn. Water Inst. Dirs. (counselor 1990-93). Achievements include research on the importance of rainstorms on spring water chemistry, nitrate contamination of ground water. Home: 1115 Valley View Dr Fayetteville AR 72701-1603 Office: U Ark Water Resources Ctr 113 Ozark Hall Fayetteville AR 72701

STEELE, KURT D., publishing company executive; b. 1945; married. BA, Colgate U., 1967; JD, Columbia U., 1971. Assoc. Brown, Wood, Ivery, Petty & Mitchell, 1971-74; atty. McGraw & Hill Inc., N.Y.C., 1974-76, asst. gen. counsel, 1976-80, asst. sec., 1980-86; v.p., gen. counsel, sec. 1980-81, v.p., assoc. gen. counsel, 1981-86; sr. v.p., gen. counsel, sec. Standard & Poor's Corp., N.Y.C., 1986—. Office: Rand McNally Inc 8255 Central Park Ave Skokie IL 60076

STEELE, LENDELL EUGENE, research scientist; b. Kannapolis, N.C., May 5, 1928; s. Robert Lee and Ina (Chapman) S.; m. Rowena Miller, Jan. 29, 1949; children—Joyce Lee Steele McCartney, Carol Ann Steele, Pamela Jane Steele Nelson, Linda Kay Steele Miller. B.S. in Chemistry, George Washington U., 1950; M.A. in Econs, Am. U., 1959. Registered profl. engr., Calif. Chemist U.S. Geol. Survey, Washington, 1949, U.S. Dept. Agr. Research Center, Beltsville, Md., 1949-50; analytical chemist U.S. Naval Research Lab., Washington, 1950-51, chemist-research physicist, 1953-58, mgr. sci. research, 1958-86; metall. engr. AEC, Germantown, Md., 1966; cons. U.S. Metal Properties Council, 1968-70, 75-85; pvt. practice tech. cons. Springfield, Va., 1986—; U.S. rep. to IAEA, Vienna, Austria, 1967-93. Author: Analysis of Reactor Vessel Radiation Effects Surveillance Programs, 1970, Neutron Irradiation Embrittlement of Reactor Pressure Vessel Steels, 1975; Editor; contbg. author: Structural Integrity of Lightwater Reactor Components, 1983, Status of U.S.A. Nuclear Reactor Pressure Vessel Surveillance, 1983, Radiation Embrittlement and Surveillance of Nuclear Reactor Pressure Vessels: An International Study, Vol. I, 1983, Vol. II, 1986, Vol. III, 1989, Vol. IV, 1993; Light Water Reactor Structural Integrity, Vol. I, 1984, Vol. II, 1988, Component Repair, Replacement and Failure Prevention in Light Water Reactors, 1986; contbr. articles to profl. jours. Served with USAF, 1951-53. Recipient Superior Civilian Service medal U.S. Navy, 1976. Fellow Am. Soc. Metals, D.C. Acad. Sci. (Engring. Sci. award 1966), ASTM (life, Dudley award and medal 1972, bd. dirs. 1980-82, vice chmn. bd. 1983-84, chmn. bd. 1985, award of merit 1979); mem. Rsch. Soc. Am. (Applied Sci. award 1962), Am. Nuclear Soc. (Spl. award and prize 1972), Fedn. Materials Socs. (pres. 1984), Sigma Xi. Home and Office: 7624 Highland St Springfield VA 22150-3931

STEELE, OLIVER, English educator; b. Birmingham, Ala., May 13, 1928; s. Oliver L. and Mary Lucile (Abernethy) S.; m. Joy Cogdell, Dec. 23, 1950; children—Christopher, Mark, Eleanor, Andrew, Paul. B.S. in English, Auburn U., 1949, M.S. in English, 1951; Ph.D., U. Va., 1965. Instr. English U. Va., Charlottesville, 1959-65, asst. prof. English, 1965-67; assoc. prof. English U. Iowa, Iowa City, 1967-74, prof. English, 1974-92, prof. emeritus English, 1992—; Editor: Ellen Glasgow: a Bibliography, 1964, The Faerie Queene: Book I & II, 1965. Served with U.S. Army, 1953-55; Germany. Mem. Renaissance Soc. Am., Bibliographical Soc. U. Va., Raven Soc. Democrat. Avocation: music. Home: 1120 E Court St Iowa City IA 52240-3232 Office: Univ Iowa Dept English Iowa City IA 52240

STEELE, RICHARD J., management consultant; b. Elkhart, Ind., Sept. 27, 1925; s. Cornelius H. and Harriett (Poel) S.; m. Martha J. Micko, July 8, 1950; children: Barbara, Cheryl, Patricia, Thomas, Richard Jr., Marjorie, Gregory, Susan, Kathleen. SB, MIT, 1946; MBA, Ind. U., 1949. Cert. mgmt. cons. V.p. Fry Cons.'s, Inc., Chgo., 1950-70; pres. Richard Steele and Ptnrs., Inc., N.Y.C., 1970-72, Richard Steele Cons.'s, Inc., Columbia, Md., 1978—; group v.p. Macro Systems, Inc., Silver Spring, Md., 1972-78; sr. v.p. Birch & Davis Assocs., Inc., Silver Spring, 1979-94; counselor Nat. Health Coun., N.Y.C., 1971-94. Author: (with others) Determinants of HMO Success, 1988. Trustee Village of Riverwoods, Ill., 1967. Lt. USNR, 1943-75, WWII, Korea. Recipient Award of Merit Am. Heart Assn., 1974. Mem. World Future Soc., Inst. Mgmt. Cons. Republican. Unitarian. Home: 5122 Durham Rd E Columbia MD 21044-1423 Office: Richard Steele Cons Inc 5122 Durham Rd East Columbia MD 21044-1423

STEELE, ROBERT EDWIN, orthopedic surgeon; b. Kansas City, Mo., Jan. 8, 1937; s. Robert Edwin and Margaret Jane (Levens) S.; m. Emily Wells Stephens, May 9, 1964; children: Edward Stephen, Thomas McKewon, Linda Katherine. AB, U. Mo., 1959; MD cum laude, Harvard U., 1963. Diplomate Am. Bd. Orthopedic Surgery; cert. Am. Acad. Orthopedic Surgeons, Assn. Arthritic Hip and Knee Surgery. Instr. in orthopedic surgery Harvard Med. Sch., Boston, 1971; mem. med. staff Good Samaritan Hosp., Corvallis, Oreg., 1971—; bd. dirs. Good Samaritan Hosp., 1984-88, pres. med. staff, 1985, chmn. peer rev. com., 1994. Author: Studies on Osteonecrosis, 1979. Lt. USNR, 1964-66, Vietnam. Recipient Kappa Delta award for Outstanding Orthopedic Rsch., Am. Acad. Orthopedic Surgeons, 1978. Mem. Corvallis Orthopedic Surgeons (pres. 1990). Achievements include performance of total knee replacement. Avocations: camping, cycling, hiking, skiing, white water boating. Office: Corvallis Orthopedic Surg 3640 NW Samaritan Dr Corvallis OR 97330

STEELE, ROBERT STEVEN, psychology educator; b. Seattle, Nov. 20, 1946; s. Clifford W. and Georgia Rose (Wilson) S. BA magna cum laude, Whitman Coll., Walla Walla, Wash., 1968; PhD with distinction, Harvard U., 1973; MA, Wesleyan U., 1992. Asst. prof. Wesleyan U., Middletown, Conn., 1973-81, assoc. prof., 1982-90, prof. psychology, 1991—, chmn. dept. psychology, 1993-94; dir. curriculum mapping project Wesleyan U., 1993-94; dir. Network Am., 1994—. Author: Freud and Jung, 1982. Photographer, Protectors of Animals, Colchester, Conn., 1989—. Rantoul fellow Carnation Co., 1964-68; NSF fellow, 1971-73. Mem. Phi Bta Kappa. Avocation: gardening. Office: Wesleyan Univ Dept Psychology Middletown CT 06459

STEELE, RODNEY REDFEARN, federal judge; b. Selma, Ala., May 22, 1930; s. C. Parker and Miriam Lera (Redfearn) S.; m. Frances Marion Blair, Aug. 1, 1964; children: Marion Scott, Claudia Redfearn, Parker Blair. AB, U. Ala., 1950, MA, 1951; LLB, U. Mich., 1954. Bar: Ala. 1954, U.S. Dist. Ct. (mid. dist.) Ala. 1959, U.S. Ct. Appeals (5th cir., now 11th cir.) 1981. Law clk. Ala. Ct. Appeals, 1956-57; assoc. Knabe & Nachman, Montgomery, Ala., 1957-61; asst. U.S. atty. Dept. Justice, Montgomery, 1961-66; staff atty. So. Bell T&T Co., Atlanta, 1966-67; judge U.S. Bankruptcy Ct., Mid. dist. Ala., Montgomery, 1967—, chief judge, 1985—; adj. prof. Jones Law Sch. Served with U.S. Army, 1954-56, Korea. Mem. ABA, Ala. State Bar, Montgomery County Bar Assn. Democrat. Episcopalian. Office: US Bankruptcy Ct PO Box 1248 1 Court Sq Montgomery AL 36104-3540

STEELE, SHELBY, writer, educator; b. Chgo., 1946; s. Shelby Sr. and Ruth S. Grad., Coe Loll., 1968; M in Sociology, So. Ill. U., 1971; PhD in English, U. Utah, 1974. Prof. dept English Calif. State U., San Jose. Author: The Content of Our Character: A New Vision of Race in America, 1991 (Nat. Book Critics Circle award 1991); contbr. essays to profl. jours. Office: San Jose State U Dept English 1 Washington Sq San Jose CA 95192*

STEELE, THOMAS MCKNIGHT, law librarian, law educator; b. Bartlesville, Okla., June 4, 1948; s. James Robert and Erna Blanche (McKnight) S.; m. Barbara Van Curen, Mar. 23, 1973 (div. 1985); children: James Robert, Ryan Thomas, David Christopher, Justin Daniel; m. Martha Bolling Swann, Apr. 1985 (div. 1990); m. LeAnn P. Joyce, Jan. 1995. BA in History, Okla. State U., 1969; MLS, U. Oreg., 1974; JD, U. Tex., 1977. Adminstrv. asst. Tarlton Law Libr. U. Tex., Austin, 1975-77; acting law librarian Underwood Law Libr. So. Meth. U., Dallas, 1977-78, asst. law librarian, 1978-79; assoc. prof. law, dir. Franklin Pierce Law Ctr., Concord, N.H., 1979-82; asst. prof., dir. U. Miss. Law Libr., University, 1982-85; assoc. prof., dir. Wake Forest U. Sch. Law Libr., Winston-Salem, N.C., 1985-91; prof., dir. Profl. Ctr. Libr. Wake Forest U., Winston-Salem, N.C., 1991; cons. in field; exec. dir. SCRIBES--Am. Soc. Writers on Legal Subjects, 1988—. Editor newsletter Scrivener, 1986-88; mng. editor Scribes Jour. Legal Writing, 1989—; editor column Pub. Librs. and Pub. Laws, 1986-88; compiler bibliography IDEA, 1981-83, Jour. Air Law and Commerce, 1977-81; author: Using Liability Insurance To Manage Risk, 1995; co-author: A Law Library Move: Planning Preparation and Execution, 1994. With U.S. Army. Mem. Am. Assn. Law Librs. Democrat. Baptist. Office: Wake Forest U Sch Law PO Box 7206 Winston Salem NC 27109-7206

STEELE, VICTORIA LEE, librarian; b. L.A., Feb. 24, 1952; d. John Wilms and Marjorie (Lee) Erpelding; m. Timothy Reid, Jan. 14, 1979. BA, UCLA, 1974, MLS, 1981; MA, U. So. Calif., 1993. Libr. Belt Libr. of Vinciana UCLA, 1981-82, head history and spl. collections Biomed. Libr., 1983-86, dir. devel. librs., 1986-88; head spl. collections U. So. Calif., L.A., 1988—; fundraising cons. Author: Becoming a Fundraiser, 1992; prodr. film: Every time I See a Patient..., 1994; contbr. articles to profl. publs. Bd. dirs. Oscar Romero Clinic, L.A., 1994—; founder L.A. Preservation Network. U. Calif. rsch. grantee, 1979; Fulbright fellow, (UK), 1995. Mem. ALA (3M/JMRT award 1982). Office: U So Calif Doheny Libr University Park Los Angeles CA 90089-0182

STEEN, CARLTON DUANE, private investor, former food company executive; b. Walnut Grove, Minn., June 12, 1932; s. Conrad Wendell and Hilda (Eng) S.; m. Dorothy Corinne Sorknes, Aug. 16, 1953; children: James, Craig, Jennifer. BA in Econs. cum laude, St. Olaf Coll., 1954; MA in Indsl. Relations, U. Minn., 1957. Job analyst Exxon Corp., Roselle, N.J., 1958-59; personnel adminstr. Kraft Inc., Chgo., 1959-65, compensation mgr., 1965-69; plant mgr. Kraft Inc., Decatur, Ga., 1969-70, Champaign, Ill., 1971-74; v.p. prodn. Kraft Inc., Chgo., 1974-76; pres. Indsl. Foods div., Memphis, 1976-82, Indsl. Foods Group, 1982-87. Served to capt. USAF, 1955-57. Republican. Lutheran.

STEEN, JOHN THOMAS, JR., lawyer; b. San Antonio, Dec. 27, 1949; s. John Thomas and Nell (Donnell) S.; m. Ida Louise Clement, May 12, 1979; children: John Thomas, Ida Louise Larkin, James Higbie Clement. AB, Princeton U., 1971; JD, U. Tex., 1974. Bar: Tex. 1974, U.S. Dist. Ct. (we. dist.) Tex. 1976, U.S. Ct. Appeals (5th cir.) 1989. Assoc. firm Matthews &

Branscomb, San Antonio, 1977-82; ptnr. firm Soules, Cliffe & Reed, San Antonio, 1982-83; sr. v.p., gen. counsel, dir. Commerce Savs. Assn., San Antonio, 1983-88; pvt. practice, San Antonio, 1988—; bd. dirs. North Frost Bank, San Antonio, 1982-84. Trustee San Antonio Acad., 1976-81, 87-93, chmn. bd., 1989-91; v.p. Bexar County Easter Seal Soc., San Antonio, 1976-77; trustee, vice chmn. San Antonio C.C. Dist., 1977-82; bd. dirs. Tex. Easter Seal Soc., Dallas, 1977-80, San Antonio Rsch. and Planning Coun., 1978-81, Community Guidance Ctr., 1983-84; vice-chmn. Leadership San Antonio, 1978-79; dir. Fiesta San Antonio Commn., 1982-83, 93—; Bexar County commr., San Antonio, 1982, Tex. Commn. on Economy and Efficiency in State Govt., 1985-89; Coliseum Adv. Bd., 1985-91, chmn. bd., 1990-91; pres. San Antonio Performing Arts Assn., 1984-85; bd. trustees World Affairs Coun. San Antonio, 1982—, chmn. bd., 1984-86; trustee United Way San Antonio, 1985-92; bd. dirs. Accord Med. Found., 1987-92; mem. adv. bd. U. Tex., San Antonio, 1987—; trustee Tex. Cavaliers Charitable Found., 1994—. 1st lt. USAR, 1973-81. Fellow San Antonio Bar Found., Tex. Bar Found. (life); mem. Tex. Bar. Assn., San Antonio Acad. Alumni Assn. (pres. 1976-77), Ivy Club (Princeton, N.J.), San Antonio German Club (pres. 1982-83), Order of Alamo, Tex. Cavaliers (bd. dirs. 1989-92, 1994—, comdr. 1994-95), San Antonio Country Club (bd. govs. 1990-93, v.p. 1992-93), Argyle Club, Conopus Club (bd. dirs. 1989-90), Princeton Club San Antonio and South Tex. (pres. 1980-81), Phi Delta Phi. Home: 207 Ridgemont Ave San Antonio TX 78209-5431 Office: 300 Convent St Ste 2440 San Antonio TX 78205-3725

STEEN, LOWELL HARRISON, physician; b. Kenosha, Wis., Nov. 27, 1923; s. Joseph Arthur and Camilla Marie (Henriksen) S.; m. Cheryl Ann Rectanus, Nov. 20, 1969; children—Linda C., Laura A., Lowell Harrison Jr., Heather J., Kirsten M. B.S., Ind. U., 1945, M.D., 1948. Intern Mercy Hosp.-Loyola U. Clinics, Chgo., 1948-49; resident in internal medicine VA Hosp., Hines, Ill., 1950-53; pvt. practice, Highland, Ind., 1953—; pres., chief exec. officer Whiting Clinic, 1960-85; mem. sr. staff St. Catherine Hosp., East Chicago, Ind; staff Community Hosp., Munster, Ind.; bd. commrs. Joint Commn. Accreditation of Hosps. Served with M.C., AUS, 1949-50, 55-56. Recipient Disting. Alumni Service award Ind. U., 1983. Fellow ACP; mem. AMA (trustee 1975, chmn. bd. trustees 1979-81), Ind. Med. Assn. (pres. 1970, chmn. bd. 1968-70), World Med. Assn. (dir. 1978-82, chmn. 1981-82, del. world assembly), Ind. Soc. Internal Medicine (pres. 1963), Lake County Med. Soc., Ind. U. Sch. Medicine Alumni Assn. (pres. 1989-90). Presbyterian. Home: 8800 Parkway Dr Hammond IN 46322-1520 also: Gateway 11481 Waterford Village Dr Fort Myers FL 33913 Office: 3641 Ridge Rd Hammond IN 46322-2053

STEEN, LYNN ARTHUR, mathematician, educator; b. Chgo., Jan. 1, 1941; s. Sigvart J. and Margery (Meyer) S.; m. Mary Elizabeth Frost, July 7, 1940; children: Margaret, Catherine. BA, Luther Coll., 1961; PhD, MIT, 1965; DSc (hon.), Luther Coll., 1986, Wittenberg U., 1991. Prof. math St. Olaf Coll., Northfield, Minn., 1965—; vis. scholar Inst. Mittag-Leffler, Djursholm, Sweden, 1970-71; writing fellow Conf. Bd. Math. Sci., Washington, 1974-75; exec. dir. Math. Sci. Edn. Bd., Washington, 1992-95. Author: Counterexamples in Topology, 1970, Everybody Counts, 1989; editor: Mathematics Today, 1978, On the Shoulders of Giants, 1990, Math. Mag., 1976-80; contbg. editor: Sci. News, 1976-82. NSF Sci. faculty fellow, 1970-71, Danforth Found. grad. fellow, 1961-65. Fellow AAAS (sec. math. sect. 1982-88); mem. Am. Math. Soc., Math. Assn. Am. (pres. 1985-86, Disting. Svc. award 1992), Coun. Sci. Soc. Pres. (chmn. 1989), Sigma Xi (Bd. Dirs. Spl. award 1989). Home: 716 St Olaf Ave Northfield MN 55057 Office: St. Olaf Coll Dept of Math Northfield MN 55057

STEEN, NORMAN FRANK, marketing executive; b. Saxton, Ky., June 27, 1933; s. Clayton Roy and Marjorie (Lawson) S.; m. Linda Lee Peterson, June 21, 1961; 1 dau., Michelle. BS, U. Oreg., 1958. Dir. Botsford, Constantine & Gardner, advt., San Francisco, 1959-60, 64-69; mng. dir. Botsford Internat., Tokyo, 1960-64; Far East mktg. dir. Foremost-McKesson Co., 1969-71; chmn., mng. dir. Needham Standard Far East, Hong Kong, 1979; dir. USP Needham, Australia, BNRR-Needham, London, Heye Needham, Ger., KHK/Needham, Malaysia; pres. Needham, Harper & Steers Internat. Inc., N.Y.C., 1980-83; dir. Needham, Harper & Steers Inc.; ptnr. Erle and Greene & Co.; co-founder Nicholson & Steen Ltd., London; chmn. Centurion Holdings Ltd.; bd. dirs. Barker, Nicholson, Lewin & Steen. Served with AUS, 1954-56. Mem. Explorers Club, Beta Theta Pi, Alpha Delta Sigma. Club: Royal Hong Kong Yacht. Office: 12 Sutton Row, London W1V 5FH, England

STEEN, PAUL JOSEPH, retired broadcasting executive; b. Williston, N.D., July 4, 1932; s. Ernest B. and Inez (Ingebrigtson) S.; m. Judith Smith; children—Michael M., Melanie. BA, Pacific Luth. U., 1954; MS, Syracuse U., 1957. Producer, dir. Sta. KNTV, San Jose, Calif., 1957-58, Sta. KVIE, Sacramento, 1958-60; asst. prof. telecommunications Pacific Luth. U., Tacoma, 1960-67; dir. ops. Sta. KPBS San Diego State U., 1967-74; gen. mgr., 1974-93, prof. telecommunications and film, 1974-93, dir. univ. telecommunications; co-chmn. Office of New Tech. Initiatives. Dir. (tel. program) Troubled Waters (winner Nat. Ednl. TV award of excellence 1970). With AUS. Named Danforth Assoc. Mem. Pacific Mountain Network (bd. dirs., chmn., bd. of govs. award 1993), NATAS, Assn. Calif. Pub. TV Stas. (pres.), Pi Kappa Delta. Home: 4930 Campanile Dr San Diego CA 92115-2331

STEEN, WESLEY WILSON, former bankruptcy judge, lawyer; b. Abbeville, La., Feb. 15, 1946; s. John Wesley and Margaret (Chauvin) S.; m. Evelyn Finch, Aug. 29, 1970; children: Anna Frances, John Wesley, Lee Wilson. BA in English, U. Va., 1968; JD, La. State U., 1974. Bar: La. 1974, Tex. 1988. Assoc. Sanders, Downing, et al, Baton Rouge, 1974-77, ptnr., 1977-80; solo practice law, Baton Rouge, 1980-83; ptnr., atty. Steen, Rubin, et al, Baton Rouge, 1983-84; bankruptcy judge U.S. Bankruptcy Ct., Middle Dist. La., part time, 1983-84, full time, Baton Rouge, 1984-87; mem. Winstead, Sechrest & Minick, Houston, 1988—; mem. La. State Law Inst. Continuous Revision Com., La. Trust Code, 1980-87; mem. Baton Rouge Estate and Bus. Planning Council, 1980-87, State Bar Com. on Bar Admissions, Baton Rouge, 1981-85; adj. asst. prof. law La. State U., 1979-87, So. U. Law Sch., 1981; congl. page U.S. Ho. of Reps., 1963-64. Adv. editor Am. Bankruptcy Law Jour.; contbr. articles to profl. jours. Vestryman, St. James Episcopal Ch., 1980-83; bd. dirs., pres. Baton Rouge Symphony Assn., 1976-87, St. James Place, 1985-87, Cerebral Palsy Ctr., 1981, Baton Rouge Gallery, 1982. Fellow Am. Coll. Bankruptcy; mem. Baton Rouge Bar Assns., La. Bar Assn., Order of Coif, Omicron Delta Kappa. Republican. Episcopalian. Avocations: jogging, computers. Office: Winstead Sechrest & Minick 910 Travis St Ste 1700 Houston TX 77002-5807

STEENBURGEN, MARY, actress; b. Newport, Ariz., 1953; m. Malcolm McDowell, 1980 (div.); children: Lilly, Charlie. Student, Neighborhood Playhouse. Films: Goin' South, 1978, Time After Time, 1979, Melvin and Howard, 1980 (Academy Award, Best Supporting Actress), Ragtime, 1981, A Midsummer Night's Sex Comedy, 1982, Cross Creek, 1983, Romantic Comedy, 1983, One Magic Christmas, 1985, Dead of Winter, 1987, End of the Line, 1987 (also exec. prodr.), The Whales of August, 1987, Miss Firecracker, 1989, Parenthood, 1989, Back to the Future III, 1990, The Long Walk Home, 1990 (narrator), The Butcher's Wife, 1991, Philadelphia, 1993, What's Eating Gilbert Grape, 1993, Clifford, 1994, It Runs in the Family, 1994, Pontiac Moon, 1994; appeared in Showtime TV's Faerie Tale Theatre prodn. of Little Red Riding Hood and (miniseries) Tender Is the Night, 1985; TV films: The Attic: The Hiding of Anne Frank, 1988; theater appearances include: Holiday, Old Vic, London, 1987, Candida, Broadway, 1993. Office: William Morris Agy Inc 151 El Camino Beverly Hills CA 90212*

STEENHAGEN, ROBERT LEWIS, landscape architect, consultant; b. Grand Rapids, Mich., July 11, 1922; s. Abraham and Rena (Vanden Broek) S.; m. Doris Brisentine, Aug. 2, 1952; children: Deborah, Cynthia, James. A.S., Grand Rapids Jr. Coll., 1942; B.S., Mich. State U., 1949. Chief landscape design Eastern design office Nat. Park Service, Phila., 1963-66; capt. planning team Nat. Park Service, Washington, 1966-71; asst. mgr. N.E. area Design Office Nat. Park Service, Denver, 1971-77, asst. mgr., 1978-80; cons. landscape architecture Lakewood, Colo., 1980—. Served to sgt. U.S. Army, 1942-45, PTO. Recipient Meritorious Service award Nat. Park Service, 1971; recipient Performance award for Nat. Bicentennial Program, 1976. Fellow Am. Soc. Landscape Architects. Home: 2473 S Carr Ct Denver CO 80227-3104

STEENSLAND, RONALD PAUL, librarian; b. Dothan, Ala., Dec. 16, 1946; s. Maurice John and Claire Folkes S.; m. Nancy Hollister, Dec. 20, 1970; 1 child, Ronald Paul. B.A., Fla. State U., 1969, M.S., 1970; postgrad., Miami (Ohio) U., 1972, U. Md., 1980, U.S. Army War Coll., 1995. Dir. Davidson County Pub. Libr., Lexington, N.C., 1970-73, Hidalgo County Libr. System, McAllen, Tex., 1973-76, Los Alamos County Libr., 1976-77, Lexington (Ky.) Pub. Libr., 1977—; chmn. John Cotton Dana Library Public Relations Awards, 1977. Treas. Hidalgo County chpt. ARC, 1975. Served to col. USAR, 1969-70. Recipient Service award United Way. Mem. Res. Officers Assn. (sec.-treas. chpt. 100), Assn. U.S. Army (sec. Bluegrass chpt.), U.S. Chess Fedn., ALA, Southeastern Library Assn., Ky. Library Assn., Lexington C. of C., Alpha Tau Omega. Baptist. Clubs: Lafayette, Pres.'s, Lexington Chess, Rotary. Office: Lexington Pub Libr 140 E Main St Lexington KY 40507-1318

STEENSMA, ROBERT CHARLES, English language educator; b. Sioux Falls, S.D., Nov. 24, 1930; s. Anton Charles and Martha (Johnson) S.; m. Sharon Hogge, Sept. 5, 1964; children: Craig, Michael, Laura, Kathryn, Rebecca. BA, Augustana Coll., Sioux Falls, 1952; MA, U. S.D., 1955; PhD, U. Ky., 1961. Instr. English Augustana Coll., 1955-57; asst. prof. of U. S.D., 1959-62; asst. prof., then assoc. prof. Utah State U., Logan, 1962-66; mem. faculty U. Utah, 1966—, prof. English, 1971—; lectr. Utah Humanities Coun., 1992-94. Author: Sir William Temple, 1970, Dr. John Arbuthnot, 1979; Editor: On The Original and Nature of Government (Sir William Temple), 1965; Contbr. articles to profl. jours. Served to capt. USNR, 1948-83. Mem. Rocky Mountain MLA, U.S. Naval Inst., Am. Soc. 18th Century Studies, South Cen. Soc. for 18th Century Studies (pres. 1994-95), Western Lit. Assn., S.D. Hist. Soc. Republican. Lutheran. Office: U Utah Dept English Salt Lake City UT 84112

STEEPLES, DOUGLAS WAYNE, university dean, consultant, researcher; b. Great Bend, Kans., Mar. 30, 1935; s. Marion Wayne and Dorothy Augusta (King) S.; children from previous marriage: Donald Bruce, John Douglas, Sheila Margaret; m. Christine Marie Webster, Dec. 8, 1990. B.A. summa cum laude, U. Redlands, 1957; M.A., U. N.C., 1958, Ph.D., 1961; cert., Inst. Ednl. Mgmt., Harvard U., 1981. Asst. prof. history Calif. State U.-Northridge, 1961-64; prof. history Earlham Coll., Richmond, Ind., 1963-80; acad. v.p. Wartburg Coll., Waverly, Iowa, 1979-80; exec. v.p. Westminster Coll., Salt Lake City, 1980-83; provost Ohio Wesleyan U., Delaware, Ohio, 1983-85, acting pres.. winter 1984; dean Coll. Liberal and Fine Arts, U. So. Colo., Pueblo, 1985-89; v.p. for acad. affairs Aurora (Ill.) U., 1989-94; dean Coll. Liberal Arts, Mercer U., Macon, Ga., 1994—; cons. higher edn. mgmt.; cons., reader advanced placement program Ednl. Testing Service, Princeton, N.J., 1976—; cons., evaluator North Central Assn. Schs. and Colls., Chgo., 1985—; bd. dirs. Western Ind. Colls. Fund, Salt Lake City, 1980-83. Editor, contbg. author: Institutional Revival: Case Histories, 1986, Successful Strategic Planning: Case Studies, 1989, Managing Change in Higher Education, 1990; contbr. articles to various pubs. Pres. Luth. Interparish Coun., Richmond, 1975-78; bd. dirs. Soc. for Use and Preservation of Resources, Richmond, 1976-79; mem. adv. bd. Pueblo Symphony Orch., 1987-89; mem. allocations com. United Way Richmond, 1976-79, Pueblo, 1988-89, Aurora, 1990-94. Scholar U. Redlands, Calif., 1953-57; Danforth fellow, 1957-61; Woodrow Wilson fellow, 1957-58; Found. for Econ. Edn. fellow in bus., 1963; Am. Philos. Soc. grantee, 1966. Mem. Am. Hist. Assn., Orgn. Am. Historians, So. Hist. Assn., Sierra Club, Phi Beta Kappa (senator united chpts. 1973-79), Omicron Delta Kappa. Republican. Lodges: Rotary (bd. dirs. 1983-84). Avocations: mountaineering, running, bagpiping. Office: Mercer U Coll Liberal Arts 1400 Coleman Ave Macon GA 31207-0001

STEER, ALFRED GILBERT, JR., foreign language educator; b. Lansdowne, Pa., May 30, 1913; s. Alfred Gilbert and Selma Elizabeth (Taber) S.; m. Elizabeth Jean Kell, Sept. 6, 1947; children: Susan Elizabeth, John Thomas. A.B., Haverford Coll., 1935; M.A., Duke U., 1938; Ph.D., U. Pa., 1954. Instr. Washington and Lee U., 1937-41, Haverford Coll., U. Pa., 1947-55; head lang. div Internat. Mil. Tribunal, Nurnberg, Germany, 1945-46; asst. prof., then assoc. prof. SUNY-Binghamton, 1955-59; assoc. prof. Columbia U., 1959-67; prof. Germanic and Slavic langs., head dept. Germanic and Slavic langs U. Ga., Athens, 1967-83, prof. emeritus, 1983—, chmn. linguistics com., 1969-83. Author: (with W.W. Pusey III and B.Q. Morgan) Readings in Military German, 1943, Goethe's Science in the Structure of the Wanderjahre, 1979, Goethe's Elective Affinities the Robe of Nessus, 1990; contbg. author: Jahrbuch des Freien Deutschen Hochstifts, 1965, Approaches to Teaching Goethe's Faust, 1986, Science Skeleton of Goethe's Works, 1987; also articles. Bd. dirs. Univ. System of Ga. Studies Abroad Programs, 1969-70, Prospective Tchr. Fellowship Program, HEW. Served with USNR, World War II. Fellow Am. Philos. Soc., 1965-66; fellow Columbia Council for Research in Humanities, 1965-66. Mem. MLA, Am. Assn. Tchrs. German (v.p., pres. chpt. 1970-71). Home: 215 Bishop Dr Athens GA 30606-4013 Office: U Ga Dept Germanic Slavic L Athens GA 30602

STEER, REGINALD DAVID, lawyer; b. N.Y.C., July 16, 1945; s. Joseph D. and Rozica (Yusim) S.; m. Marianne Spizzy, July 22, 1984; children: Derek B., Trevor A. BA, U. Minn., 1966, JD, 1969. Bar: Minn. 1969, Calif. 1973, U.S. Dist. Ct. (no., ea. and cen. dists.) Calif., U.S. Ct. Mil. Appeals 1969, U.S. Ct. Appeals (9th cir.), U.S. Ct. Appeals (11th cir.), U.S. Supreme Ct. 1981, U.S. Ct. Internat. Trade. Assoc. Pillsbury, Madison & Sutro, San Francisco, 1973-79, ptnr., 1979—; lectr. Calif. Continuing Edn. of Bar, San Francisco, 1981. Served to capt. U.S. Army, 1969-73. Mem. ABA (antitrust and litigation sects.). Club: Olympic (San Francisco). Avocations: piano, tennis, photography. Office: Pillsbury Madison & Sutro 235 Montgomery St San Francisco CA 94104-2902

STEERE, ALLEN CARUTHERS, JR., physician, educator; b. Apr. 11, 1943; m. Margaret Mercer, 1969; children: Allen Caruthers III, Margaret Hamilton, Samuel Mercer, John Summers. BA, Columbia U., 1965, MD, 1969; DSc. (hon.), Indiana U., 1992. Diplomate Am. Bd. Internal Medicine; lic. rheumatologist, N.Y., Ga., Ct., Mass. Intern St. Luke's Hosp., N.Y.C., 1969-70, asst., sr. resident, 1970-72, chief resident, instr. medicine, 1972-73; chief resident, instr. medicine Coll. Physicians and Surgeons Columbia U., N.Y.C., 1972-73; clin. instr. medicine Hosp. for Spl. Surgery Cornell U., N.Y.C., 1972-73; clin. instr. medicine Grady Meml. Hosp. Emory U., Atlanta, 1973-75; clin. fellow in rheumatology Yale U., New Haven, 1975-77, asst. prof. medicine, epidemiology and pub. health, 1977-81, assoc. prof. medicine, 1981-87; prof. medicine, chief rheumatology and immunology New Eng. Med. Ctr. Tufts U., Boston, 1987—. With USPHS, 1973-75. Recipient Citation for Elucidation of Lyme disease Infectious Diseases Soc. Am., 1984, Ciba-Geigy Rheumatology prize Internat. League Against Rheumatism, 1985, award for discovery of Lyme disease Nat. Inst. Arthritis and Musculoskeletal Skin Diseases, 1988, Richard and Hinda Rosenthal award ACP, 1990, Joseph Mather Smith prize Coll. Physicians and Surgeons, Columbia U., 1990, Zucker Faculty prize Tufts U., 1990, award for studies Lyme disease Nat. Health Coun., 1990, Lee C. Howley Sr. prize Arthritis Found., 1993; Rsch Achievement Found., 1977-80, Sr. fellow, 1981-86. Mem. Am. Assn. Clin. Investigation, Am. Fedn. Clin. Rsch., Am. Coll. Rheumatology. Office: Tufts U Sch Medicine New Eng Med Ctr # 406 750 Washington St Boston MA 02111-1526

STEERE, WILLIAM CAMPBELL, JR., pharmaceutical company executive; b. Ann Arbor, Mich., June 17, 1936; s. William Campbell and Dorothy (Osborne) S.; m. Lynda Gay Powers, Jan. 29, 1957; children: William, Mark, Christopher. BS, Stanford U., 1959. Sales rep. Pfizer & Co., Modesto, Calif., 1970-72; v.p., dir. ops. Pfizer Labs, N.Y.C., 1982-84; sr. v.p., dir. ops. Pfizer Pharms., N.Y.C., 1982-84, exec. v.p., 1984-86, pres., 1986-91; pres., CEO Pfizer Inc., 1991-92, chmn. bd., CEO, pres., 1992—; also bd. dirs., bd. dirs. Texaco Inc., NYU Med. Ctr., Minerals Techs. Inc., Fed. Res. Bank of N.Y., Sta. WNET-TV. Trustee N.Y. Bot. Garden; bd. overseers Meml. Sloan-Kettering Cancer Ctr. Mem. Pharm. Rsch. and Mfrs. Am. (bd. dirs.), Bus. Coun. (bd. dirs.), Bus. Roundtable, Univ. Club, N.Y. Yacht Club. Avocations: sailing, skiing. Office: Pfizer Inc 235 W 42nd St New York NY 10017-5755

STEFANELLI, JOSEPH JAMES (JOE STEFANELLI), artist; b. Phila., Mar. 20, 1921; s. Alessandro and Carmela (Leone) S. Student, Graphic Sketch Club, 1934-38, Phila. Mus. Coll. Art, 1938-40, Pa. Acad. Fine Arts, 1940-41, New Sch. for Social Research, 1949-50, Art Students League, N.Y.C., 1950-51, Hans Hoffman Sch. Painting, N.Y.C., 1951-52. faculty U. Calif., Berkeley, summers 1960, 63; vis. critic Cornell U., U. Ark., U. Iowa, U. W.Va., U. Wis., U. N.Mex.; artist in residence Princeton U., 1963-66; faculty Columbia U., 1966-74, New Sch. for Social Research, 1966—, Bklyn. Coll., from 1974. One-man shows, Artists Gallery, 1950, New Gallery, 1952, Artists Gallery, 1954, Poindexter Gallery, 1957, 58, 60, Hacker Gallery, 1962, Thibaut Gallery, 1963, Princeton U., 1964, U. Ark., 1965, Westbeth Galleries, 1971, Bertha Schaeffer Gallery, 1973, 74, Andre Zarre Gallery, 1977, R.H. Love Gallery, Chgo., 1989, Randall Gallery, St. Louis, 1989, Penna Acad. Fine Arts, 1989, M13 Gallery N.Y.C., 1991, Benson Gallery, Southampton, N.Y., 1992, Olaf Clasen Gallery, 1992; group shows include, Stable Gallery, Kootz Gallery, Poindexter Gallery, Tanager Gallery, Mus. Modern Art, Whitney Mus., Andre Zarre Gallery, ann. shows, Whitney Mus., Pa. Acad., Corcoran Gallery, Carnegie Internat., U. Ill., Albright Mus., Walker Art Center, Chgo. Art Inst., Mus. Modern Art; represented in permanent collections, Balt. Mus., Sarah Lawrence Coll., N.Y. U., Cornell U., U. Calif. Mus., Geigy-Ciba collection, Chase Manhattan Bank, Union Carbide Co., U. Mass., U. Mont., Norfolk Art Mus., Walker Art Center, Whitney Mus., also pvt. collections; murals include, pub. schs., Bklyn., Manhattan Community Coll.; War artist for: Yank, Army weekly. Recipient Fulbright award for Rome, 1958-59, Spear Rsch. Fund award Princeton U. for Rome, summer 1965; fellow Am. Rsch. Ctr. in Egypt, 1966-67, Esther and Adolph Gottlieb Found., 1986, 88, Kraser, Pollock Found., 1991. Studio: 463 West St Apt D1006 New York NY 10014

STEFANIAK, NORBERT JOHN, business administration educator; b. Milw., Jan. 12, 1921; s. Peter Stephen and Mary Ann (Schlaikowski) S.; m. Elizabeth Jean Horning, Aug. 27, 1949; children—John, Mary, Jane, Beth, Joel, Peter, James, Thomas, Anne, Jean. B.B.A., U. Wis., 1948, M.B.A., 1950, Ph.D., 1960. C.P.A. Instr. U. Wis., Milw., 1950-53; treas., controller Wauwatosa (Wis.) Realty Co., 1953-56; prof. bus. adminstrn. U. Wis., Milw., 1957-75, prof. emeritus. Author monograph, also articles. Past commr. West Allis (Wis.) Planning Commn.; bd. dirs. Polish Festivals, Inc., Columbus KC, West Allis, Internat. Exch. Found.-Poland and Milw. County, Wis.; condemnation commr. Milw. County; bd. review City of West Allis, Wis. With USAAF, WWII. Named Polish-Am. Man of Yr., Polish Nat. Alliance (Milw. Soc.), 1990. Mem. Am. Real Estate and Urban Econs. Assn. (past pres.), Wis. Realtors Assn. (past dir.), Wis. Real Estate Exam. Bd. (past vice chmn.), Am. Soc. Real Estate Counselors (emeritus), Polish Nat. Alliance. Home: 865 S 76th St Milwaukee WI 53214-3026 Office: S63w13680 Janesville Rd Muskego WI 53150-2713

STEFANICS, ELIZABETH T. (LIZ STEFANICS), state legislator. BA, Eastern Ky. U.; MS, U. Wis.; PhD, U. Minn. Mem. N.Mex. Senate; mem. conservation com., judiciary com., chmn. health and human svcs. com., adminstr. health and human svcs. Democrat. Address: PO Box 1301 Santa Fe NM 87504-6127 Office: N Mex State Senate State Capitol New Mexico State Capitol NM 87503

STEFANILE, LAWRENCE VINCENT, management counsulting company executive; b. Jersey City, N.J., Jan. 24, 1939; s. Angelo Anthony and Agnes Antoinette (Altomonte) S.; m. Margaret Ann Marzell, Apr. 2, 1967. AB, Seton Hall U., 1961; MA, Niagara U., 1962; doctoral equivalency, St. John's U., 1968; EdD, U. Am., 1991; D, St John's U. 1968. Cert. sch. adminstr., N.J.; cert. Am. Coll. Hosp. Adminstrs. Coord. internat. tchr. devel. program at Ohio U. U.S. Dept. State, 1963-64; vice prin. Marist High Sch., Bayonne, N.J., 1964-68; dir. coll. rels. St. peter's Coll., Jersey City, 1968-72; COO St. Francis Hosp., Jersey City, 1972-81; pres. Vanguard Mgmt. Svc., Short Hills, N.J., 1981—; with U.S. Dept. Vets. Affairs, N.Y.C., 1993—, Phila., 1993—; cons. Village of Ridgefield Park, N.J., 1968—, U.S. Dept. Vets. Affairs, Newark, 1992—, Borough of Little Ferry, N.J., 1992—. Author: The Art of The Search: A Guide to Successful Job Placement, 1991, A Systems Approach to Job Search and Placement, 1992. Trustee St. Francis Hosp., Jersey City, 1978; bd. dirs. Hudson chpt. ARC, Jersey City, 1978; commr. Manpower Commn.-Hudson, Jersey City, 1979; mem. Hosp. Reimbursement coun. N.J. Dept. Health, Princeton, 1980. Seton Hall U. scholar, 1957; fellow Niagara U., 1961, Fulbright Found., 1962, Ohio U., 1962; named to Internat. Tchr. Devel. Program, Fulbright Exch., 1962. Mem. Seton Hall U. Alumni, Niagara U. Alumni Assn., U. Am. Alumni Assn. Office: Vanguard Mgmt Svc 1 Short Hills Ave Short Hills NJ 07078-2526

STEFANKO, ROBERT ALLEN, financial executive; b. Cleve., Jan. 20, 1943; s. John and Mary (Kovach) S.; m. Barbara Jane Gittner, Feb. 12, 1963; children—Sandra Marie, Robert Todd. B.S. in Acctg., Miami U., Oxford, Ohio, 1964. Mgr. Price Waterhouse, Cleve., 1964-72; chmn. bd., chief fin. officer A. Schulman Inc., Akron, Ohio, 1972—. Bd. dirs. Akron Devel. Found., Akron Community Found., Akron Gen. Med. Ctr. Mem. AICPA, Nat. Assn. Accts. Avocations: golf; reading. Office: A Schulman Inc 3550 W Market St Akron OH 44333-2699

STEFANO, JOSEPH WILLIAM, film and television producer; author; b. Phila., May 5, 1922; s. Dominic and Josephine (Vottima) S.; m. Marilyn Epstein, Dec. 5, 1953; 1 son, Andrew Dominic. Ed. pub. schs. Pres. Villa di Stefano Prodns., 1962—. Toured as song and dance man in Student Prince, 1945, Merry Widow, 1946; composer music and lyrics popular songs, night club revues, indsl. shows, others, 1946-57; author screenplays The Black Orchid, 1958, The Naked Edge, 1960, Psycho, 1960, Anna di Brooklyn, 1962, Eye of the Cat, 1969, Futz, 1970, The Kindred, 1986, Blackout, 1989, Psycho IV: The Beginning, 1990; TV drama Made in Japan, 1959, movies for TV, 1970-78; producer, author TV series The Outer Limits, 1963-64, Swamp Thing, 1990. Recipient Robert E. Sherwood award for Made in Japan, Fund for Republic, 1959, Edgar Allen Poe award for Psycho, Mystery Writers Am., 1960, Columbian award Federated Italo-Ams. Calif., 1964, Pres.'s award Acad. Sci.-Fiction Fantasy and Horror Films, 1987; inducted into Cultural Hall Fame, South Phila. High Sch., 1994. Mem. ASCAP, Writers Guild Am., Dirs. Guild Am., Producers Guild Am., Acad. Motion Pictures Arts and Scis., Mystery Writers Am. Home: 10216 Cielo Dr Beverly Hills CA 90210-2035 *For me it has always been important to succeed first in my own eyes. This personal sense of success seems warmer and surer and more likely to maintain the spirit during those moments when worldly success dances to tunes other than my own. Goals are golden. Guidelines are lines on a street map; they show how many different ways there are to go from where to when.*

STEFANO, ROSS WILLIAM, business executive; b. Cortland, N.Y., June 18, 1955; s. Nicola Sebastian and Gloria Maria (Saltarez) S.; m. Janet Stapleton, Apr. 2, 1977; children: Nicolas J.J., Christian A., Mari Elizabeth. BS, Cornell U., 1977, MBA, 1978. CPA, Calif. Supr. Coopers & Lybrand, San Francisco, 1978-81; fin. mgr. Genstar Corp., San Francisco, 1981-83; v.p., treas., v.p. mktg. CIS Corp., Syracuse, N.Y., 1983-92; cons., 1992-94; sr. v.p. Pietrafesa Co., Liverpool, N.Y., 1994—. Bd. dirs., pres. FM Soccer Club, 1984—; bd. dirs. Syracuse YMCA, 1986-89; fund raiser Boy Scouts Am., Syracuse, 1986-89, Cath. Charities, Syracuse, 1991. Mem. AICPA, Cavalry Club.

STEFANSCHI, SERGIU, dancer; b. Komralid, Romania, Mar. 2, 1941; emigrated to Can., 1971, naturalized, 1977; s. Alexander and Lidia S. Diploma, Acad. Dance, Leningrad, 1960. Tchr. Nat. Ballet Sch. and Nat. Ballet of Can., Toronto, 1978—. Prin. dancer, Bucharest (Romania) Opera, 1960-68, Jeunesse Musicale de France, 1969-70, Theatre Francaise de la Danse, Paris, 1970, Nat. Ballet of Can., Toronto, Ont., 1971-78, appeared with, Belgrade (Yugoslavia) Opera, 1966, 68, Coob Marieta (Ga.) Ballet, 1976 (Recipient Silver medal I, Internat. Ballet Concourse, Varna, Bulgaria 1964), Internat. Guest Theater. Mem. Actors Equity Can. Mem. Romania Orthodox Ch. Home: 319 Ave Keewatin, Toronto, ON Canada M4P 2A4 Office: 111 Maitland St, Toronto, ON Canada M4Y 1E4

STEFFAN, WALLACE ALLAN, entomologist, educator, museum director; b. St. Paul, Aug. 10, 1934; m. Sylvia Behar, July 16, 1966; 1 child, Sharon. B.S., U. Calif.-Berkeley, 1961, Ph.D., 1965. Entomologist dept. entomology Bishop Mus., Honolulu, 1964-85, head diptera sect., 1966-85, asst. chmn.,

1979-85; dir. Idaho Mus. Natural History, Idaho State U., Pocatello, 1985-89, U. Alaska Mus., 1989-92; prof. biology U. Alaska Fairbanks, 1989-92; exec. dir. Great Valley Mus. Natural History, 1992-94; dir. Sun Cities Art Mus.; mem. grad. affiliate faculty dept. entomology U. Hawaii, 1969-85; reviewer NSF, 1976—; mem. internat. editorial adv. com. World Diptera Catalog, Systematic Entomology Lab., U.S. Dept. Agr., 1983-85; mem. affiliate faculty biology, Idaho State U., 1986-89; bd. dirs. Idaho State U. Fed. Credit Union, 1986-89; mem. adv. coun. Modesto Conv. & Visitors Bureau, 1992-95; mem. Ft. Hall Replica Commn., 1986-89. Acting editor Jour. Med. Entomology, 1966; assoc. editor Pacific Insects, 1980-85. Judge Hawaii State Sci. and Engring. Fair, 1966-85, chief judge sr. display div., 1982, 83, 84; advisor to bd. Fairbanks Conv. and Visitors Bur., 1989-91; mem. vestry St. Christophers Episcopal Ch., 1974-76, St. Matthew's Episcopal Ch., Fairbanks, 1990-91; pres. Alaska Visitors Assn., Fairbanks, 1991; advisor Fairbanks Conv. Visitors Bur. Bd., 1989-91; bd. dirs. Kamehameha Fed. Credit Union, 1975-77, chmn., mem. supervisory com., 1980-84. Served with USAF, 1954-57. Grantee NIH, 1962, 63, 67-74, 76-81, 83-85. U.S. Army Med. Research and Devel. Command, 1964-67, 73-74, NSF, 1968-76, 83-89, City and County of Honolulu, 1977, U.S. Dept. Interior, 1980, 81. Mem. Entomol. Soc. Am. (mem. standing com. on systematics resources 1983-87), Am. Mosquito Control Assn., Pacific Coast Entomol. Soc., Soc. Systematic Zoology, Hawaiian Entomol. Soc. (pres. 1974, chmn. coms. 1966-85, editor procs. 1966), Hawaiian Acad. (councillor 1976-78), Entomol. Soc. Wash., Fairbanks C. of C. (adv. bd. Conv. Visitors Bur. 1989), Alaska Visitors Assn. (pres. Fairbanks chpt. 1991), Sigma Xi (pres. San Joaquin chpt. 1994-95, mem. bd. cultural corrections review 1994-95). Office: Sun Cities Art Mus 17425 N 115th St Sun City AZ 85373-2501

STEFFEN, CHRISTOPHER J., bank executive; b. 1942. BA, U. Mich., 1964; MBA, Wayne State U., 1967. With Ford Motor Co., 1967-74, Unarco, Price Waterhouse; contr. IC Indsl. Corp., 1974-80; v.p., contr. Chrysler Corp., 1981-88; CFO, exec. v.p., chief adminstrn. officer Honeywell, Inc., 1989-93; CFO Eastman Kodak, 1993; exec. v.p., CFO Citicorp, N.Y.C., 1993—. Office: Citicorp 399 Park Ave New York NY 10043

STEFFEN, PAMELA BRAY, secondary school educator; b. Bessemer, Ala., Mar. 9, 1944; d. James Ernest and Margaret Virginia (Parsons) Bray; m. Ted N. Steffen, June 17, 1972; children: Elizabeth, Thor. BA, U. Louisville, 1966; MA, Spalding U., 1975. Cert. tchr., gifted tchr., Ky. Tchr. English and German Louisville (Ky.) Pub. Schs., 1967-73; tchr. English to fgn. students Internat. Ctr., U. Louisville, 1970-78; bookkeeper T.N. Steffen PSC, Louisville, 1978-85; tchr. of adults Jefferson County Pub. Schs., Louisville, 1985-87, tchr. English and German, 1987—; network participant, bd. dirs. Foxfire, Louisville, 1990—; spokesperson Coalition Essential Schs., Providence, 1990—, Ctr. for LEadership in Sch. Reform, Louisville, 1990—; group leader AAUW, Louisville, 1983-88; presenter seminars; 94 AATG summer Austrian Inst. Graz; participant Austrian Landeskunde Internat., 1994. Bd. dirs. Jefferson County Med. Soc. Aux., Louisville, 1984-88, Highland Community Ministries, Louisville, 1980-87, Highland Ct. Apts. for Elderly, Louisville, 1984-87; nat. v.p. Deafness Rsch. Found. Aux., 1984-88; mem. vestry and rector search com. St. Andrew's Episcopal Ch., Louisville, 1985-88; active Louisville Fund for Arts campaign, 1980-93; Louisville Orch. Assn. fundraiser. Fulbright fellow Goethe Inst., Munich, 1969; grantee Ky. Arts Coun., 1991-92, artist-in-residence, 1992—; grantee Ky. Humanities Coun. CES, 1993, fall forum presenter; named to Ky.'s Commonwealth Inst. Tchrs. and Vis. Tchrs. Inst.; selected for Landeskunde in Österreich, 1994. Mem. ASCD, Nat. Coun. Tchrs. English, Coalition Essential Sch., Nat. Coun. Tchrs. English, Greater Louisville Coun. Tchrs. English, Am. Assn. Tchrs. German. Avocations: swimming, travel, beagling, writing, reading. Home: 2404 Park Boundary Rd Louisville KY 40205-1620 Office: Fairdale High Sch 1001 Fairdale Rd Fairdale KY 40118-9744

STEFFENS, DONNA IRENE, gifted and talented education educator; b. Akron, Ohio, July 23, 1945; d. Harry Lee and Hazel Irene (Jay) Dye; m. Donald William Steffens, Dec. 18, 1971; children: Buddy Burgy, Jyl, Scott. BS in Edn., U. Akron, 1968, MS in Ednl. Adminstrn., 1972, postgrad., 1974. Cert. tchr., prin., supr./coord./dir. instrn., Wis. Tchr. elem. Copley (Ohio) Pub. Schs., 1966-74; inservice cons. Summit City Svcs., Akron, Ohio, 1973; tchr. Title 1 Cedarbur (Wis.) Pub. Schs., 1975, middle sch. tchr., 1988-90, dist. coord. gifted programming, 1990—; pvt. tutor Columbia, Md., 1978; day care operator Ellicott City, Md., 1978-79; instr. Cardinal Stritch Coll. of Edn., 1995 (curriculum coun. for dist., 1993-95, staff devel. com., 1993-95, assessment com., 1993-95); Christian edn. coord. Alliance Bible Ch., Cedarburg; adv. coun. chair Gifted Program, Cedarburg, 1988-92; enrichment program adv. com. U. Washington County. Mem. Libr. Bd., 1991, Cedarburg Community Scholarship Bd., 1991, Jaycettes, 1979-81; chairperson Parents Supporting Parents. Recipient Meritorious Svc. award Wis. Assn. Edn. Gifted and Talented, 1991, Jennings grant Copley Pub. Schs. Mem. ASCD, Wis. Coun. Gifted and Talented, Wis. Assn. Edn. Gifted and Talented. Avocations: singing, crafts. Office: Cedarburg Sch Dist W68 N611 Evergreen Blvd Cedarburg WI 53012-1847

STEFFENS, DOROTHY RUTH, political economist; b. N.Y.C., May 5, 1921; d. Saul M. and Pearl Y. (Reiter) Cantor; m. Jerome Steffens, Nov. 19, 1940; children: Heidi Sue, Nina Ellen. BBA, CCNY, 1941; MEd, Temple U., 1961; PhD, Anthony U., 1981. Economist Nat. War Labor Bd., Washington, 1941-44, United Elec. Radio Machine Workers, Phila., 1944-46; instr. group dynamics Temple U., Phila., 1955-57; seminar program dir. Soc. Friends, Washington, 1958-61; tng. dir. Nat. Coun. Negro Women, Washington, 1967-68; edn. cons. Peace Corps, Nigeria, 1969-70; exec. dir. Women's Internat. League for Peace and Freedom, Phila., 1971-77, Fund for Open Info. and Accountability, Inc., 1978-80; conf. dir. Haverford Coll., 1980-84; exec. sec. Nigerian Women's Com., 1968-69; del. African Women's Seminar UN, Accra, Ghana, 1969; mem. Africa panel Am. Friends Svc. Com., 1976-88, mem. internat. divsn. exec. com., 1977-84; resource lectr. Internat. Women's Seminar, Lillehammer, Norway, 1991. Author: The Day after Summer, 1966; editorial bd. The Churchman, 1977—; mem. nat. bd. Gray Panthers, 1989-91; contbr. articles to profl. jours., newspapers, mags. N.Y. C. of C. scholar, N.Y. State Regents scholar CCNY, 1941. Quaker. *Women, minorities and the economically disadvantaged have the wisdom and the capacity to bring about a world of peace and social justice and to do it non-violently.*

STEFFENS, JOHN LAUNDON, brokerage house executive; b. Cleve., July 7, 1941; m. Louise Cullen, Nov. 25, 1967; children: Drew, Julie, Wesley. B in Econs., Dartmouth Coll., 1963. Various positions Merrill Lynch, 1963—; exec. v.p. Pvt. Client Group, 1990—. Office: Merrill Lynch & Co Inc World Fin Ctr N Tower 250 Vesey St New York NY 10281-1012

STEFFENSEN, DWIGHT A., medical products and data processing services executive; b. Fresno, Calif., 1943. BA, Stanford U., 1965. Corp. contr. Synergex Corp. (merged with Bergen Brunswig Corp. 1985), Orange, Calif., 1969-72, chief fin. officer, v.p., 1972-80, chief oper. officer, chief fin. officer, exec. v.p., treas., 1980-83, pres., chief exec. officer, 1983-85, exec. v.p., 1985—; pres. Drug Service Inc., 1975-80; pres., coo, dir. Bergen Brunswig Corp. Office: Bergen Brunswig Corp 4000 W Metropolitan Dr Orange CA 92668-3510

STEFFER, ROBERT WESLEY, clergyman; b. Spokane, Wash., June 24, 1934; arrived in Can., 1987; s. Harold Wesley and Kathryne (Trumble) S.; m. Diane De'Moisey, Aug. 19, 1960; children: Erika Kirsten, Beauregard Gregory Robert. BA, Whitworth Coll., 1956; BD, Lexington Theol. Sem., 1959; MA, Ind. U., 1966, PhD, 1967. Ordained to ministry Christian Ch. (Disciples of Christ), 1959. Civilian dir. religious edn. U.S. Army Armor Ctr., Ft. Knox, Ky., 1960-64; assoc. min. Christian Ch. (Disciples of Christ), Oklahoma City, 1967-71; prof. Phillips U., Enid, Okla., 1971-76; fraternal worker div. overseas ministries Christian Ch. (Disciples of Christ), Barrow-in-Furness, Cumbria, Eng., 1976-79; Lilly vis. prof. religious edn. Christian Theol. Sem., Indpls., 1979-81; dir. edn. for mission div. homeland ministries Christian Ch. (Disciples of Christ), Indpls., 1981-87; exec. regional min. Christian Ch. (Disciples of Christ) in Can., Guelph, Ont., 1987—; sec. Coll. Chs. of Christ in Can., Guelph, 1987—. Contbr. articles to religious publs. and ency. Col. USAR, 1964—. Lilly Found. fellow in adult edn. Ind. U., 1964-66. Mem. Disciples of Christ Hist. Soc. (life, trustee 1990-94), Religious Edn. Assn. (bd. dirs. 1994—), Conf. Regional Mins. and Moderators (chmn. nominating com.), Ch. Fin. Coun. (bd. dirs. 1995—, exec. com.

1995). Democrat. Avocations: gardening, reading, travel, music. Home: PO Box 30013 2 Quebec St, Guelph, ON Canada N1H 8J5 Office: All-Can Com Christian Ch, PO Box 64, Guelph, ON Canada N1H 6J6

STEFFES, DON CLARENCE, state senator; b. Olpe, Kans., Jan. 13, 1930; s. William A. and Marie M. (Dwyer) S.; m. Janie L. Steele, Oct. 10, 1953; children: Michael, Steve, David, Andrew, Nancy, Terrence, Jennifer. BS, Kans. State Tchrs. Coll., 1952, MS, 1958. Mgr. Abilene C. of C., Kans., 1955-57; mem. staff Topeka C. of C., 1957-60; mgr. McPherson C. of C., Kans., 1960-65; exec. v.p. Kans. Devel. Credit Corp., Topeka, 1965-68, McPherson Bank & Trust, 1968-73; pres., CEO BANK IV McPherson (formely McPherson Bank & Trust), 1973-91; mem. Kans. State Senate, Topeka, 1992—. Mem. Kans. Main St. Adv. Counsel, Topeka, 1978-82; pres., bd. dirs. Mingenback Found., McPherson, Kans., 1970—; vice chmn. Nat. Commn. Agrl. Fin., Washington, 1987-89; v.p. McPherson Indsl. Devel. Co., 1970-75. Named Man of Yr. McPherson Coll., 1989. Mem. Kans. Bankers Assn. (pres. 1985), KC. Roman Catholic. Home: 1008 Turkey Creek Dr Mc Pherson KS 67460-1823

STEFFES, KENT, volleyball player; b. Pacific Palisades, Calif., June 23, 1968. Student, Stanford U.; BA in Econ., UCLA, 1993. Profl. volleyball tour player. Named AVP Rookie of Yr., 1989, Up & Coming Player of Yr., 1988, AVP Most Valuable Player by Volleyball Monthly Mag., 1992. Mem. Assn. Volleyball Profls. (sec., bd. dirs.). First and only AVP mem. to win with 3 different ptnrs. in same yr., 1990; won 8 Miller Lite Opens, 1991; first and only AVP mem. to win 2 Joe Cuervo Gold Crown Series Events with different ptnrs. in same yr., 1991; won Miller Lite Tournament of Champions with Karch Kiraly, 1992, Miller Lite U.S. Championships, 1992, Miller Lite Grand Prix, 1992, with Karch Kiraly, 1992; compiled record 18 AVP Open wins, 1992; tied all-time consecutive open wins, 1992. Office: U S Volleyball Assn 15260 Ventura Blvd Sherman Oaks CA 91003*

STEFFEY, EUGENE PAUL, veterinary medicine educator; b. Reading, Pa., Oct. 27, 1942; s. Paul E. and Mary M. (Balthaser) S.; children: Michele A., Bret E., Michael R., Brian T. Student, Muhlenberg Coll., 1960-63; D in Vet. Medicine, U. Pa., 1967; PhD, U. Calif., Davis, 1973. Diplomate Am. Coll. Vet. Anesthesiologists (pres. 1980). NIH spl. research fellow U. Calif., San Francisco, 1973; asst. prof. U. Calif., Davis, 1974-77, assoc. prof., 1977-80, prof. vet. medicine, 1980—, also chmn. dept. vet. surgery, 1980-93; mem. scientific reviewers Am. Jour. Vet. Research, Schaumburg, Ill., 1984-87. Contbr. numerous articles to profl. jours. Mem. AVMA, Am. Coll. Vet. Anesthesiologists, Am. Physiol. Soc., Am. Soc. Pharmocology Exptl. Therapeutics, Am. Soc. Anesthesiologists, Assn. Vet. Anaesthetists, Calif. Soc. Anesthesiologists, Comparative Respiratory Soc., Internat. Anesthesia Research Soc., Pa. Vet. Med. Assn., Sigma Xi, Phi Zeta. Office: U Calif Dept Surg/Radiol Scis School of Vet Medicine Davis CA 95616

STEFFY, JOHN RICHARD, nautical archaeologist, educator; b. Lancaster, Pa., May 1, 1924; s. Milton Grill and Zoe Minerva (Fry) S.; m. Esther Lucille Koch, Oct. 20, 1951; children: David Alan, Loren Craig. Student, Pa. Area Coll., Lancaster, 1946-47, Milw. Sch. Engring., 1947-49. Ptnr. M.G. Steffy & Sons, Denver, Pa., 1950-72; ship reconstructor Kyrenia Ship Project, Cyprus, 1972-73. Inst. Nautical Archaeology, College Station, Tex., 1973—; from lectr. to prof. anthropology Tex. A&M U., College Station, 1976-88, Sara W and George O. Yamani prof. nautical archaeology, 1989-90, prof. emeritus, 1990—; lectr. on ship constrn. Author: Wooden Shipbuilding and the Interpretation of Shipwrecks, 1994; co-editor: The Athlit Ram, 1991; contbr. chpts. to books and articles to profl. jours. Sec. Denver Borough Authority, Pa., 1962-72. Served with USN, 1942-45. MacArthur Found. fellow, 1985. Mem. Archaeol. Inst. Am., Soc. Nautical Research, N.Am. Soc. Oceanic History. Republican. Methodist. Office: Tex A&M U Inst Nautical Archaeology College Station TX 77843

STEFOFF, JAMES EDWARD, retired clothing company executive; b. Mishawaka, Ind., Mar. 29, 1938; s. Angelo Chono and Hildreth Mary (Slagle) S.; m. Jacqulyn Louise McDowell; children: Debra Kay, James J., Jo Ellen. BA in Econs., Kalamazoo Coll., 1953. Div. service mgr. Clark Equipment Co., Buchanan, Mich., 1960-70; dir. mgmt. info. systems Mean Services Inc., Chgo., 1970-76, v.p., ops., 1976-80, pres., 1980-83; exec. v.p. Angelica Corp., St. Louis, 1983—. Home: 1010 Thoreau Ct Saint Louis MO 63146-5540 Office: Healthcard Svcs Angelica Group 10176 Corporate Sq Dr Saint Louis MO 63132

STEG, J(AMES) L(OUIS), artist; b. Va., Feb. 6, 1922; s. Albert J. and Clara M. (Manista) S.; m. Margaret O'Brien, July 5, 1948 (dec. May 1985). Student, Rochester Inst. Tech., 1939-42; B.F.A., State U. Iowa, 1947, M.F.A., 1949. Instr. Newcomb Coll. Tulane U., 1951-53, asst. prof. art, 1953-58, assoc. prof., 1958-64, prof., 1964-92; technique cons. Perment Pigments Corp.; mem. staff cultural project High Sch. New Orleans, HEW Project Genesis. (Recipient prize 8th Lugano Internat. Print Exhbn. 1964, awards Bklyn. Mus., 1948, 52, Phila. Print Club, 1951, 64, Ark. Art Center 1969), one-man shows, Associated Am. Artists Gallery, N.Y.C., 1964, U. So. Fla., Tampa, 1964, Weyhe Gallery, N.Y.C., 1945, Phila. Art Alliance, 1955, Cushing Gallery, Dallas, 1966, Ohio State U., 1972, New Orleans Acad. Art, 1983, group shows include, Lugano (Switzerland) Exhbn., 1964, Phila. Art Alliance, 1968, Graphic Arts, Russia, 1966, U. Pitts., 1974, So. Arts Council, 1982; represented in permanent collections, Mus. Modern Art, N.Y.C., Library of Congress, Phila. Mus., Fogg Mus. of Harvard U., Cleve. Mus., Malmo Mus., Sweden, retrospective exhbn., New Orleans Mus. Art, 1978. Bd. dirs. Urban League, New Orleans, 1963. Served with U.S. Army, 1942-45. Recipient purchase prize Minn. Mus. Art, 1980; Carnegie-Tulane fellow, 1960; nominated to Printmaker Emeritus title Southern Graphic Coun., 1989. Mem. Color Print Soc. Am. Office: Hall-Barnett 320 Exchange Alley New Orleans LA 70130 *I have had two basic standards given to me by my father: "Work for the night is coming!" "Do this while you are resting!".*

STEG, LEO, research and development executive; b. Vienna, Austria, Mar. 30, 1922; came to U.S. 1941, naturalized, 1946; s. Jacob and Clara (Gellert) S.; m. Doreen Ethel Ray, June 12, 1947; children: Paula Jamie, Ellen Leslie, Audrey Leigh. B.S., City Coll. N.Y., 1947; M.S., U. Mo., 1948; Ph.D., Cornell U., 1951. Registered profl. engr., Pa. Chief engr. Fed. Design Co., N.Y.C., 1946-47; instr. mech. engring. U. Mo., Columbia, 1947-48; instr. applied mechanics and materials Cornell U., Ithaca, N.Y., 1948-51, asst. prof., 1951-55; systems engr., missile and space div. GE, Phila., 1955-56, mgr. space sci. lab., 1956-79, chief scientist, 1980-81; sr. v.p. University City Sci. Center, Phila., 1981-82; pres. Steg, Ray & Assocs., Villanova, Pa., 1980—; sci. and pub. policy fellow Brookings Inst., Washington, 1982-84; pres. Technical Applications Internat., Inc., McLean, Va., 1990—; adj. prof. Drexel U.; cons. to space scis. bd. Nat. Acad. Scis., other govt. agencies. Contbr. articles to profl. jours.; editor 2 books. Assoc. trustee U. Pa. Named Engr. of Yr. Phila., 1965. Fellow AIAA (editor-in-chief jour. 1963-67), AAAS; mem. Phila. Acad. Scis. (founding), Franklin Inst. Phila. (past mem. bd. mgrs.), Long Beach Island Found. Arts and Scis. (past chmn. bd.), Sigma Xi, Phi Kappa Phi. Clubs: Cosmos, Cornell of N.Y. Home: 1616 Hepburn Dr Villanova PA 19085-2005

STEGALL, DANIEL RICHARD, lawyer, educator; b. Portsmouth, Va., Oct. 4, 1946; s. Earl and Theresia Loyce (Barlow) S.; m. Linda Elaine Gehman, Aug. 17, 1968; children—Justin Daniel, Joshua Gehman. Student, Ga. Inst. Tech., 1964; B.S., Va. Poly. Inst., 1969; M.B.A., U. Va., 1973, J.D., 1973. Bar: Va. 1973, D.C. 1974, Calif. 1981. Assoc., Hogan & Hartson, Washington, 1974-76; ptnr. Melrod, Redman & Gartlan, 1976-80, Rose & Stegall, Los Angeles, 1982-84, Dreisen, Kassoy & Freiberg, Los Angeles, 1984—; of counsel Lawler, Felix & Hall, 1980-81; adj. prof. U. So. Calif., Los Angeles, 1983-84, Loyola Law Sch., 1982—; lectr. in field. Contbr. tax articles to law rev. jours. Mem. ABA (chmn. subcom.), Calif. State Bar, Va. State Bar, D.C. Bar, Order of Coif, Phi Kappa Phi, Tau Beta Pi. Republican. Presbyterian. Club: Riverbend Country (Great Falls, Va.).

STEGEMAN, CHARLES, fine arts educator, lecturer, consultant; b. Ede, Netherlands, June 5, 1924; s. Leendert Gerrit and Christina Anna S.; m. Françoise André, Dec. 9, 1950 (div. July 1981); children: Charles François, Marc Alexandre, Daniel John; m. Marie-Thérèse Zenner, Nov. 9, 1984. Diploma in painting, Akademie van Beeldende Kunst, The Hague, Netherlands 1945-46, Académie Royale des Beaux-Arts, Brussels, 1946-49, National Hoger Instituut van Schoone Kunsten, Antwerp, Belgium, 1949-50.

Instr. U. B.C., Vancouver, 1953-62; tchr. summer sch. U. Calgary, Banff, Alberta, 1953-75; artist-in-residence Art Inst. Chgo., 1962-69; tchr. North Shore Art League, Winnetka, Ill., 1963-69; adj. faculty mem. Roosevelt U., Chgo., 1965-67; assoc. prof. Haverford Coll., Pa., 1969—; prof. Haverford Coll., 1972—; humanities fellow Med. Coll. Pa., 1981-88, adj. faculty mem. New Sch. Music, 1982-85, Sch. Medicine U. Pa., 1986—. Author: (book) Les Cryptes de la Cathédrale de Chartres, 1993 (review) Bulletin de la Société archéologique d'Eure-et-Loir, 1992; co-author: (article in collected work): The Humanities: From a Medical Point of View, 1987. Mem. Assn. Villard de Homecourt for the Interdisciplinary Study of Medieval Tech., Sci. and Art (co-founder, pres. 1984-90, mem. bd. dirs. 1984-92), Société archéologique d'Eure-et-Loir. Home: 2 College Cir Haverford PA 19041-1312 Office: Haverford Coll 370 Lancaster Ave Haverford PA 19041-1392

STEGEMEIER, RICHARD JOSEPH, oil company executive; b. Alton, Ill., Apr. 1, 1928; s. George Henry and Rose Ann (Smola) S.; m. Marjorie Ann Spess, Feb. 9, 1952; children: Richard Michael, David Scott, Laura Ann, Martha Louise. BS in Petroleum Engring., U. Mo., Rolla, 1950, cert. petroleum engr. (hon.), 1981; MS in Petroleum Engring., Tex. A&M U., 1951; D of Engring. (hon.), U. Mo., Rolla, 1990. Registered profl. engr., Calif. Various nat. and internat. mgmt. positions with Unocal Corp. (formerly Union Oil Co.), L.A., 1951—, pres. sci. and tech. div., 1979-80, sr. v.p. corp. devel., 1980-85, pres., COO, 1985-88, CEO, also chmn. bd. dirs., 1988-94; bd. dirs. First Interstate Bancorp, Found. Health Corp., Halliburton Co., Northrop Corp., Outboard Marine Corp. Patentee in field. Bd. dirs. Calif. Econ. Devel. Corp.; bd. govs. Town Hall of Calif., The Music Ctr. of L.A. County; bd. overseers Exec. Coun. on Fgn. Diplomats, Huntington Libr.; chmn. L.A. World Affairs Coun., 1990-94; pres. World Affairs Coun. of Orange County, 1980-82; chmn. Brea (Calif.) Blue Ribbon Com., 1979-80; trustee Coun. for Econ. Devel., U. So. Calif., Harvey Mudd Coll., Loyola Marymount U.; mem. adv. bds. Northwestern U. Kellogg Grad. Sch. of Mgmt.; bd. vis. UCLA Anderson Grad. Sch. of Mgmt., U. Mo., Rolla; mem. adv. bd. Calif. State U., Fullerton, adv. coun., Long Beach; bd. dirs. YMCA of L.A., L.A. Philharm. Assn., John Tracy Clinic; chmn. L.A. area coun. Boy Scouts of Am., Calif. C. of C. chmn., 1994; gen. campaign chmn. United Way of Greater L.A., 1990-91; trustee and immediate past pres. Hugh O'Brian Youth Found., 1993-94, L.A. Archdiocese Edn. Found. Recipient Merit award Orange County Engring. Coun., 1980, Outstanding Engr. Merit award Inst. Advancement Engring., 1981, Disting. Achievement medal Tex. A&M U., Hugh O'Brian Youth Found. Albert Schweitzer Leadership award, 1990, Human Rels. award Am. Jewish Com., 1990. Mem. AIChE (Disting. Career award So. Calif. sect. 1989), NAM (bd. dirs.), Nat. Acad. Engring., Am. Petroleum Inst. (bd. dirs.), Soc. Petroleum Engrs. (lectr. 1978), Nat. Petroleum Coun., 25 Yr. Club Petroleum Industry (past pres.), Calif. Bus. Roundtable, Calif. Coun. on Sci. and Tech., Calif. Club. Republican. Roman Catholic. Office: Unocal Corp PO Box 7600 Los Angeles CA 90051-0600*

STEGEMOELLER, HARVEY A., clergy member, church administrator. Exec. dir. Evangelical Lutheran Church of America Foundation, Chgo. Office: Evangelical Lutheran Church Am 8765 W Higgins Rd Chicago IL 60631-4101

STEGENGA, PRESTON JAY, international education consultant; b. Grand Rapids, Mich., July 9, 1924; s. Minder and Dureth (Bouma) S.; m. Marcia Jean DeYoung, July 28, 1950; children: James Jay, Susan Jayne. BA, Hope Coll., 1947; MA, Columbia U., 1948; PhD, U. Mich., 1952; LHD (hon.), Northwestern Coll., Iowa, 1989. Instr. history, polit. sci. Berea Coll., Ky., 1948-50; assoc. prof. Berea Coll., 1952-55; assistantship U. Mich., 1950-52; pres. Northwestern Coll., Orange City, Iowa, 1955-66; chief Cornell U. Project, U. Liberia-U.S. AID Program, Monrovia, W. Africa, 1966-68; coordinator internat. program Calif. State U., Sacramento, 1968-71; dir. Calif. State U. (Internat. Center), 1971-88; acting v.p. acad. affairs Calif. State U., 1974-75; spl. asst. to pres. Calif. State U., Sacramento, 1988-92; mem. Calif. State Liaison Com. for Internat. Edn.; ednl. cons. to Pres. Republic of Liberia, 1973-74; cons. internat. programs Am. Assn. State Colls. and Univs., 1975-89; cons. UN Devel. Programme, 1975-88; internat. edn. cons., 1992—; v.p. Sacramento chpt. UN Assn., U.S.A., 1969-71, pres., 1971-73, bd. dirs.; mem. Calif. UN Univ. Adv. Coun., 1976-80, internat. trade com. C. of C., 1984—, chair coll.-U. com., 1995—; pres. Tri-State Coll. Conf., 1963-64; dir. Fulbright project for Chinese scholars, 1985; cons. internat. projects Calif. State Fair, 1990—. Author: Anchor of Hope, 1954; asst. to editor History of Edn. Jour.; contbr. articles to profl. jours. Trustee Western Sem., Mich., Northwestern Coll., Iowa, 1955-66, 91—, New Brunswick Sem., N.J., 1955-66, Global Calif. Coun., 1991-93; trustee, v.p. World Affairs Coun., 1976-77, 85-90, pres., 1990-92; mem. Task Force for Improving Am. Competence in World Affairs, 1980-89; mem. internat. bd. Los Rios Coll. Found., 1980-85; mem. Am. Coun. for UN U., 1979-85, Interfaith Svc. Bd., 1985-90; bd. dirs. New Zealand-Sacramento Sister City, 1989—. With AUS, 1942-45. Decorated Purple Heart; named hon. chief Kpelle Tribe, West Africa, 1973, hon. commodore Port of Sacramento, 1983; recipient Disting. Svc. award UN Assn., 1971, Republic of Venezuela Edn. award, 1979, Outstanding Svc. award Fed. Republic of Germany, 1985, Disting. Svc. award Calif. State U. Chancellor, 1988, Citation of Achievement, Calif. Sec. of State, 1988, U.S. Congl. Register Recognition Citation, 1988, President's Award, World Affairs Coun., 1992, Gov.'s award Calif. State Fair, 1993, Internat. award Sacramento C. of C., 1993; Ministry of Edn. scholar Republic of China, 1981; German Acad. Exch. Svc. fellow U. Bonn, 1981; Hon. Legis. Resolutions, Calif. State Senate and Assembly, 1988. Mem. Assn. Iowa Coll. and Univ. Pres. (v.p. 1965-66), NEA, Calif. State Univ. Student Personnel Assn., Am. Acad. Polit. and Social Sci., Assn. for Advancement of Dutch-Am. Studies, Phi Delta Kappa, Phi Kappa Phi, Phi Beta Delta. Mem. Reformed Ch. Am. Home: 545 Mills Rd Sacramento CA 95864-4911

STEGER, CHARLES WILLIAM, university administrator; b. Richmond, Va., June 16, 1947; s. Charles William and Virginia Belle (Garrett) S.; m. Janet Grey Baird, Sept. 13, 1969; children: Christopher B., David C. BArch, Va. Poly. Inst. & State U., 1970, MArch, 1971, PhD, 1978. Registered architect, Va. Project planner, architect Wiley & Wilson Inc., Lynchburg, Va., 1971-72, mgr. urban planning dept., 1973-74; dir. Environ. Design Consortium Inc., Blacksburg, Va., 1974-85; inst. grad. urban design program Coll. Architecture and Urban Studies , Va. Poly. Inst. and State U., Blacksburg, 1974-76, chmn. grad. urban design program, 1976-81; dean Coll. Architecture and Urban Studies, Va. Poly. Inst. and State U., Blacksburg, 1981-93; acting v.p. for pub. svc. Va. Poly. Inst. and State U., Blacksburg, 1990-93, v.p. for devel. and univ. rels., 1993—; bd. dirs. Va. Found. Architecture, Richmond. Contbr. articles to jours. in field. Bd. dirs. Va. Chamber Music Acad., Blacksburg, 1989—, Hollins Coll., Roanoke, Va., 1987—, Boswil (Switzerland) Found., 1986—, Ctr. in the Square, Roanoke, 1993—; v.p. Va. Tech. Found., Inc., 1993—; adv. coun. Va. Ctr. on Rural Devel., 1992—; commr. Gov.'s Commn. on Population Growth and Devel., Richmond, 1989—, ACSA Coun. on Arch. Rsch., 1987—; mem. Am. Planning Assn., Am. Inst. Cert. Planners. Avocations: cattle farming, golf, canoeing. Office: Va Poly Inst and State U VP Devel Univ Rels 315 Burruss Hall Blacksburg VA 24061

STEGER, EVAN EVANS, III, lawyer; b. Indpls., Oct. 24, 1937; s. Charles Franklin and Alice (Hill) S.; m. Suzy Gillespie, July 18, 1964; children—Cynthia Anne, Emily McKee. A.B., Wabash Coll., 1959; J.D., Ind. U., 1962. Bar: Ind. 1962, U.S. Dist. Ct. (so. dist.) Ind. 1962, U.S. Ct. Appeals (7th cir.) 1972, U.S. Tax Ct. 1982, U.S. Supreme Ct. 1982. Assoc. Ice, Miller, Donadio and Ryan, and predecessor firm Ross, McCord, Ice and Miller, Indpls., 1962-69, ptnr., 1970—. Fellow Am. Coll. Trial Lawyers; mem. ABA, Ind. Bar Assn., Indpls. Bar Assn., Internat. Assn. Def. Counsel. Democrat. Presbyn. Office: Ice Miller Donadio & Ryan Box 82001 1 American Sq Indianapolis IN 46282

STEGER, JOSEPH A., university president. Formerly sr. v.p. and provost U. Cin., pres. 1984—. Office: U Cin Office of Pres Cincinnati OH 45221-0063

STEGER, RALPH JAMES, chemist; b. Meridian, Okla., Jan. 24, 1940; s. Daniel Bose and Opal Creola (Brothers) S. BS in Chemistry and Math., Langston U., 1962. Cartographer Aeronautical Chart and Info. Ctr. ACIC

USAF, St. Louis, 1962-63; lab. technician Sigma Chem. Co., St. Louis, 1963; phys. scientist U.S. Army Chem. Corps, Edgewood Arsenal, Md., 1963-65; rsch. chemist Chem. Rsch., Devel. and Engring. Ctr. SMCCR Rsch. Lab., Analytical Div., Aberdeen Proving Ground, Md., 1965-86; chemist Chem. Rsch., Devel. and Engring. Ctr. SMCCR-Detection, Detection Technology, Aberdeen Proving Ground, 1986—; adv. com. Garrison Gents, Balt., 1980—; ACOR monitoring govt. contracts, Balt., 1987—. Contbr. articles to profl. publs. Mem. Okla. Hist. Soc. Mem. AAAS, N.Y. Acad. Sci., Okla. Hist. Soc. Office: CBDCOM-RTE Aberdeen Proving Ground MD 21010-5423

STEGER, WILLIAM MERRITT, federal judge; b. Dallas, Aug. 22, 1920; s. Merritt and Lottie (Reese) S.; m. Ann Hollandsworth, Feb. 14, 1948; 1 son, Merritt Reed (dec.). Student, Baylor U., 1938-41; LL.B., So. Meth. U., 1950. Bar: Tex. 1951. Pvt. practice Longview, 1951-53; apptd. U.S. dist. atty. Eastern Dist. Tex., 1953-59; mem. firm Wilson, Miller, Spivey & Steger, Tyler, Tex., 1959-70; U.S. dist. judge Ea. Dist. Tex. Tyler, 1970—. Republican candidate for gov. of Tex., 1960; for U.S. Ho. of Reps., 1962; mem. Tex. State Republican Exec. Com., 1966-69; chmn. Tex. State Republican Party, 1969-70. Pilot with ranks 2d lt. to capt. USAAF, 1942-47. Mem. ABA, State Bar Tex., Masons (32 degree, Shriner). Home: 801 Meadowcreek Dr Tyler TX 75703-3524 Office: US Courthouse PO Box 1109 Tyler TX 75710-1109

STEGMAYER, JOSEPH HENRY, housing industry executive; b. Teaneck, N.J., Jan. 4, 1951; s. Arthur Harry and Alicia (Ward) S. BS in Fin., U. Louisville, 1973. Spl. projects Worthington Industries Inc., Columbus, Ohio, 1973-75, dir. investor rels., 1975-77, dir. corp. rels., 1977-80, v.p. corp. devel., 1980-82, v.p., CFO, 1982-93, treas., 1983-93, also bd. dirs.; pres. Clayton Homes, Inc., Knoxville, Tenn., 1993—, also bd. dirs.; bd. dirs. Cardinal Funds Inc., Columbus. Editor: We've Only Scratched the Surface, 1981. Chmn. YMCA, Columbus, 1981-83; pres. Columbus Zoo, 1987-90, chmn., 1990-93; bd. dirs. Muskingum Coll., 1984-93, Knoxville 200, Found. of Diocese of Columbus; fin. chmn. Ronald McDonald House, Columbus. Named Citizen of Yr., Columbus Jaycees, 1984; recipient Outstanding Achievement in Fin. award Phi Beta Kappa, 1984. Mem. Fin. Execs. Inst., Knoxville C. of C. (bd. dirs.), Athletic Club. Roman Catholic. Avocations: scuba diving, travel, investing. Office: Clayton Homes Inc PO Box 15169 Knoxville TN 37901

STEHLE, EDWARD RAYMOND, secondary education educator, school system administrator; b. Pitts., May 30, 1942; s. Edward August and Mary Josephine (Veverka) S.; m. Alberta McConnell; 1 child, Christian Dollison. BA, U. Pitts., 1964; MA, Columbia U., 1966, doctoral student, 1966-68. Instr. European history C.W. Post Coll., Long Island U., Greenville, N.Y., 1967-68, Middlebury (Vt.) Coll., 1968-69; history master The Lawrenceville Sch., Lawrenceville, N.J., 1969—, dir. day students, 1978-83, asst. dir. coll. counseling, 1983-88, chmn. history dept., 1988-94; asst. dir. The N.J. Scholars Program, Lawrenceville, 1981, dir., 1982-91; cons. U. Del. Sea Grant Coll., Newark, 1981-82; cons. on history of migration Statue of Liberty-Ellis Island Nat'l., N.Y.C., 1985-88; mem. selection com. Morris County (N.J.) Summer Opportunities for Tchrs. Program, Morristown, 1985-86; bd. mem. N.J. Scholars Program, Lawrenceville, 1988—; bd. trustees Craftsbury Chamber Players, Greensboro, Vt., 1985-89; chmn. Bd. N.J. Scholar Program, 1988—. Co-author: A Guide to Programming in Basic Plus, 1975; contbr. Harper's Encyclopedia of the Modern World, 1972. Vice pres. Assoc. Mems., Ch. of Christ, Greensboro, 1974-76, pres., 1976-78. Mem. Am. Hist. Assn., Nassau Club (Princeton, N.J.), Mountainview Country Club (Greensboro, Vt.). Democrat. Episcopalian. Avocation: painting. Home: 2810 Main St Lawrenceville NJ 08648-1017 Office: The Lawrenceville Sch Main St Lawrenceville NJ 08620-2310

STEHLI, FRANCIS GREENOUGH, geologist, educator; b. Upper Montclair, N.J., Oct. 16, 1924; s. Edgar and Emily (Greenough) S.; m. Irene Comfort, June 19, 1948; children: Anne, Robert, John, Edgar. B.S., St. Lawrence U., 1949, M.S., 1950; Ph.D., Columbia U., 1953. Asst. prof. invertebrate paleontology Calif. Inst. Tech., 1953-56; tech. group supr. research dept. Am. Petroleum Corp., 1956-60; prof. geology, chmn. dept. Case Western Res. U., 1960-73, Samuel St. John prof. earth scis., 1973-80, acting dean sci., 1975, acting dean sci. and engring., 1976, dean sci. and engring., 1977-80; dean grad. studies and research U. Fla., Gainesville, 1980-82; dean Coll. Geoscis. U. Okla., Norman, 1982-86; chmn. sci. adv. com. DOSECC, Inc., 1986—; rsch. assoc. Archeol. Rsch. Team, 1993—; geol. cons., 1960—. Author articles in field. Served with USNR, 1943-46. Fellow Geol. Soc. Am., AAAS; mem. Geochem. Soc., Paleontol. Soc. (pres.), Am. Soc. Engring. Edn., No. Ohio Geol. Soc. Home: 7711 SW 103d Ave Gainesville FL 32608 Office: DOSECC Sci Adv Com 7711 SW 103rd Ave Gainesville FL 32608-6214 also: Archeol Rsch Team 1519 NW 25 Terrace Gainesville FL 32605

STEHLING, FERDINAND CHRISTIAN, physical chemist; b. Fredericksburg, Tex., Feb. 18, 1930; 4 children. BS, BA, St. Mary's U., Md., 1950; MA, U. Tex., 1957, PhD in Phys. Chemistry, 1958. Rsch. assoc. Exxon Chem. Co., Houston, 1958-80, sr. rsch. assoc., 1980—. Recipient Profl. Progress award Soc. Profl. Engrs. and Chemists, 1973. Mem. Am. Chem. Soc. (Coop. Rsch. in Polymer Sci. and Engring. award 1995), Sigma Xi. Office: Exxon Chemical Corp 13501 Katy Freeway Houston TX 77079*

STEHSEL, MELVIN LOUIS, biology educator; b. Long Beach, Oct. 3, 1924; s. Louis Joseph Stehsel and Ida Batchelder; m. Beatrice Henrietta Solli, Nov. 30, 1957; children: Dené, Craig. BS in Chemistry, U. Calif. Berkeley, 1945, MS in Plant Physiology, 1947, PhD in Plant Physiology, 1950. Research fellow Calif. Inst. Tech., Pasadena, Calif., 1948-51; chemist Mobil Oil, Los Angeles, 1951-56; sr. engr. Aerojet, Azusa, Calif., 1956-65; prof. biology Pasadena City Coll., 1965—; cons. plant tissue culture LA County Arboretum, Arcadia, Calif., 1975—. Editor: (newsletter) Foothill's Rare Fruit Growers. Rockefellow scholar U. Chgo., 1942; French Govt. fellow, 1951. Mem. AAAS, Am. Chem. Soc., Am. Botanical Soc., Am. Orchid Soc. Republican. Presbyterian. Avocations: orchid growing, hang gliding, piano studies. Home: 1049 Rancho Rd Arcadia CA 91006-2225 Office: Pasadena City Coll 1570 E Colorado Blvd Pasadena CA 91106-2003

STEIB, JAMES TERRY, bishop; b. May 17, 1940. Ordained priest Roman Cath. Ch., 1967. Titular bishop Fallaba, 1983; aux. bishop St. Louis, 1983; consecrated bishop, 1984; bishop Diocese of Mempis, 1993—. Address: Old Cathedral Rectory PO Box 41679 Memphis TN 38174-1679*

STEIG, WILLIAM, author, artist; b. N.Y.C., Nov. 14, 1907; s. Joseph and Laura (Ebel) S.; m. Elizabeth Mead, Jan. 2, 1936 (div.); children: Lucy, Jeremy; m. Kari Homestead, 1950 (div. 1963); 1 child, Margit Laura; m. Stephanie Healey, Dec. 12, 1964 (div. Dec. 1966); m. Jeanne Doron, 1969. Ed., Coll. City N.Y., 1923-25, NAD, 1925-29. Cartoonist New Yorker, N.Y.C., 1930—; author, illustrator for children's books, 1968—. artist drawings in other mags, water color in collections, Bklyn. Mus.; oneman show wood sculpture, Downtown Gallery, N.Y.C., 1939, also exhibited drawings and sculpture, Smith Coll., 1940; author: Man About Town, 1932, About People: A Book of Symbolic Drawings, 1939, The Lonely Ones, a book of drawings, 1942, All Embarrassed, 1944, Small Fry, 1944, Persistent Faces, 1945, Till Death Do Us Part, 1947, The Agony in the Kindergarten, 1950, The Rejected Lovers, 1951, The Steig Album: Seven Complete Books, 1953; Dreams of Glory, 1953, Roland, the Minstrel Pig, 1968, CDB, 1968, Sylvester and the Magic Pebble, 1969 (Caldecott medal 1970), The Bad Island, 1969, An Eye for Elephants, 1970, The Bad Speller, 1970, Amos and Boris, 1971, Male/Female, 1971, Dominic, 1972 (Christopher award 1973, Prix de la Fondation de France 1983), The Real Thief, 1973 (Best Children's Book prize, Italy 1990), Farmer Palmer's Wagon Ride, 1974, Abel's Island, 1976 (Newbery Honor book), The Amazing Bone, 1976 (Caldecott Honor book), Caleb and Kate, 1977, Tiffky Doofky, 1978, Drawings, 1979, Gorky Rises, 1980, Doctor de Soto, 1982 (Am. Book award 1983), Yellow & Pink, 1984, Ruminations, 1984, Solomon the Rusty Nail, 1984, Brave Irene, 1986, CDC?, 1986, Zabajaba Jungle, 1987, Spinky Sulks, 1988, Doctor De Soto Goes to Africa, 1992, (book of drawings) Strutters and Fretters, 1992; executed Wood sculpture R.I. Mus., Providence, Smith Coll. Mus., Northampton, Mass.; pub. Zabajaba Jungle, 1987, Shrek, 1990, Our Miserable Life, 1990. Recipient William Allen White award, 1975; Irma Simonton Black award, 1981. Home: 301 Berkeley St # 4 Boston MA 02116-2002

STEIGBIGEL, ROY THEODORE, infectious disease physician and scientist, educator; b. Bklyn., Nov. 23, 1941; s. Samuel and Lillian I. (Parker) S.; m. Julia Ann Enterline, June 10, 1967 (div. 1983); children: Keith D., Glenn N.; m. Sidonie Ann Morrison, Oct. 15, 1985; 1 child, Andrew M. BA, Carleton Coll., 1962; MD, U. Rochester, 1966. Diplomate Am. Bd. Internal Medicine, Am. Bd. Infectious Disease. Resident U. Rochester, N.Y., 1966-68; resident Stanford U., Palo Alto, Calif., 1970-71, fellow, 1971-73; from asst. to assoc. prof. U. Rochester, N.Y., 1973-83; prof. SUNY, Stony Brook, 1983—; mem. adv. bd. infectious disease U.S. Pharmacopea, Rockville, Md., 1980—; mem. adv. panels NIH, Bethesda, Md., 1985-87. Contbr. over 10 chpts. to books and over 85 articles to profl. jours. Served in USPHS, 1968-70. Fellow NIH, 1971-73, grantee, 1985—. Fellow ACP, Infectious Disease Soc. Am. Office: SUNY School of Medicine HSC-T-15-080 Stony Brook NY 11794-8153

STEIGER, GRETCHEN HELENE, marine mammalogist, research biologist; b. Williamsport, Pa., May 7, 1960; d. Robert Folk and Helene (Moltz) S.; m. John Calambokidis, July 29, 1989; 1 child, Alexei Steiger Calambokidis. BS in Zoology, U. N.C., 1982. Rsch. biologist Cascadia Rsch. Collective, Olympia, Wash., 1982—, also bd. dirs.; pres. Cascadia Rsch., 1988—; whale census technician, Barrow, Alaska, 1988; rsch. assoc. U. Alaska, Fairbanks, 1991; presenter in field. Author (with others) numerous govt. reports and publs.; contbr. articles to profl. jours. Instr. Feminists Self-def. Tng., Olympia, 1984-92. Mem. Soc. Northwestern Vertebrate Biology, Soc. Marine Mammalogy (charter), Wildlife Soc. (Wash. chpt.). Office: Cascadia Research Collective 218 1/2 4th Ave W Olympia WA 98501-1004

STEIGER, HEIDI SCHWARZBAUER, investment executive; b. Boston, July 8, 1953; d. Wilhelm Frederick and Lucille Florence (Isabelle) Schwarzbauer; m. Kenneth Jay Brine, June 5, 1977 (div. 1982); m. Paul Ernest Steiger, Nov. 23, 1985; children: Erika, Laura, Isabelle, William. Cert., U. De Poitiers, La Rochelle, France, 1974; BA in English, Boston Coll., 1975; cert. in underwriting, Bryn Mawr (Pa.) Coll., 1979; MBA in Fin., Columbia U., 1985. Advt. and sales promotion specialist New England Life, Boston, 1975-77; product mgr. retail mktg. div. Fidelity Group, Boston, 1977-80, mgr. corp. comm., 1980-81, dir. mktg., 1981-83; sr. v.p. spl. products divsn. Herzfeld & Stern, N.Y.C., 1983-85; ptnr. individual asset mgmt. Neuberger & Berman, N.Y.C., 1986—; mem. adv. bd. Fin. & Acctg. Audio Digest, Greenwich, Conn., 1988—. Contbr. articles to numerous profl. jours. Mem. fin. com. Ravitch for Mayor, N.Y.C.; chairperson assoc. bus. com. Met. Mus. Art, N.Y.C., 1989; bd. dirs., chairperson devel. com. Nat. Theatre of the Deaf, Chester, Conn., 1987—; bd. dirs. Fountain House. Mem. Boston Coll. Alumni Assn. (class corr. 1975—), Fin. Women's Assn. (pres. N.Y.C. chpt. 1988-89), Phi Beta Kappa. Republican. Episcopalian. Avocations: tennis, piano, wine, skiing. Office: Neuberger & Berman 605 3rd Ave New York NY 10158-0001

STEIGER, JANET DEMPSEY, government official; b. Oshkosh, Wis., June 10, 1939; 1 child, William Raymond. BA, Lawrence U., 1961; postgrad., U. Reading, Eng., 1961-62, U. Wis., 1962-63; LLD (hon.), Lawrence U., 1992. Legis. aide Office of Gov., Wis., 1965; v.p. The Work Place, Inc., 1975-80; commr. Postal Rate Comm., Washington, 1980-89, acting chmn., 1981-82, chmn., 1982-89; past commr., now chmn. FTC, Washington, 1989—; U.S. del. OECD, Paris, 1989—. Author: Law Enforcement and Juvenile Justice in Wisconsin, 1965; co-author: To Light One Candle, a Handbook on Organizing, Funding and Maintaining Public Service Projects, 1978, 2d edit., 1980. Chmn. Commn. on Vets. Edn. Policy, 1987-90. Woodrow Wilson scholar; Fulbright scholar, 1961. Mem. Phi Beta Kappa. Office: FTC Office of Chmn 6th & Pennsylvania Ave NW Washington DC 20580-0002*

STEIGER, PAUL ERNEST, newspaper editor, journalist; b. N.Y.C., Aug. 15, 1942; s. Ernest and Mary Agnes (Walsh) S.; children: Erika Maren, Laura Arlene, Isabelle Amanda, William Ernest. B.A., Yale U., 1964. Staff reporter Wall Street Jour., San Francisco, 1966-68; asst. mng. editor Wall Street Jour., N.Y.C., 1983-85, dep. mng. editor, 1985-91, mng. editor, 1991—, also v.p.; bus. writer Los Angeles Times, 1968-71, econ. corr. Washington bur., 1971-78, bus. editor L.A., 1978-83. Co-author: The 70's Crash, 1970. Recipient G.M. Loeb award UCLA, 1971, 74, 78, John Hancock award, 1971. Office: Wall Street Journal Dow Jones & Co Inc 200 Liberty St New York NY 10281-1003*

STEIGER, ROD, actor; b. Westhampton, N.Y., Apr. 14, 1925; s. Fredrick and Lorraine (Driver) S.; m. Sally Gracie, 1952; m. Claire Bloom, Apr. 15, 1959 (div.); 1 daughter, Anna; m. Sherry Nelson, Apr. 1973 (div. 1979); m. Paula Ellis. Ed. pub. schs., Newark. Life mem. Met. Mus. Art, N.Y.C. Theatrical appearances include Night Music, 1951, Enemy of the People, 1953, Rashomon, 1959; motion picture appearances include On the Waterfront, 1953, Big Knife, 1955, Oklahoma, 1956, Jubal, 1957, Across the Bridge, 1958, Al Capone, 1959, Seven Thieves, 1959, The Mark, 1960, World in My Pocket, 1960, The Tiger Among Us, 1961, Convicts 4, 1961, The Longest Day, 1962, The Time of Indifference, 1962, Hands on the City, 1963, The Pawnbroker, 1964 (Berlin Film Festival award), The Loved One, 1964, Doctor Zhivago, 1966, In the Heat of the Night, 1967 (Golden Globe award, Acad. award for Best Actor), Waterloo, 1971, Happy Birthday, Wanda June, 1971, Duck You Sucker, 1972, Lolly-Madonna, 1973, Lucky Luciano, 1975, Hennessy, 1975, W.C. Fields and Me, 1976, F.I.S.T, 1978, Dirty Hands, 1978, Love and Bullets, 1979, The Amityville Horror, 1979, The Lucky Star, 1980, Lion of the Desert, 1981, Cattle Annie and Little Britches, 1981, The Chosen, 1982, The Magic Mountain, 1982, Portrait of a Hitman, 1984, The Naked Face, 1985, The January Man, 1988, American Gothic, 1988, Tennessee Waltz, That Summer of White Roses, A Question of Life, Men of Respect, The Ballad of the Sad Cafe, 1991, Guilty As Charged, 1992, The Player, 1992, The Specialist, 1994; TV appearance as Marty, 1953 (Sylvania award), The Movie Maker, 1967, Jesus of Nazareth (miniseries), 1977, Cook and Peary: The Race to the Pole, 1983, Hollywood Wives (miniseries), 1985, Sword of Gideon, 1986, Desperado: Avalanche at Devil's Ridge, 1988, Passion and Paradise, 1989, In the Line of Duty: Manhunt in the Dakotas, 1991, Sinatra, 1992; appeared in play Moby Dick, 1962. Served with USNR, 1942-45. Office: c/o Gold/Marshak & Assoc 3500 W Olive Ave Burbank CA 91505-5320*

STEIGERWALDT, DONNA WOLF, clothing manufacturing company executive; b. Chgo., Apr. 2, 1929; d. Harry Hay and Donna (Currey) Wolf; m. William Steigerwaldt, Dec. 31, 1969; children: Debra, Linda. BA, U. Colo., Colo. Springs, 1950, LHD (hon.), 1987. Ins. broker Conn. Mut. Life Ins. Co., Chgo., 1950-53; vice chmn. Jockey Internat., Inc., Kenosha, Wis., 1978-80, chmn., chief exec. officer, 1980—. Pres. Donna Wolf Steigerwaldt Found., Inc.; mem. Infant Welfare Soc., Evanston Hosp.-Glenbrook Hosp. Corp., N.W. Cmty. Hosp. Aux., Aid to Animals No. Ill., Inc.; vice chmn. Carthage Coll., 1982-92, chmn., 1992—; bd. dirs. Century Club Sarasota Meml. Hosp. Paul Harris fellow, Rotary, 1984. Mem. Am. Apparel Mfrs. Assn., Navy League U.S., Glenview Hist. Soc., Exec. Women Internat. (hon.), Rotary (Paul Harris fellow 1984). Republican. Episcopalian. Clubs: North Shore Country, Plaza, Valley Lo Sports; Meadows Country (Sarasota, Fla.). Office: Jockey Internat Inc 2300 60th St Kenosha WI 53140-3889

STEIGMAN, ANDREW L., academic dean; b. N.Y.C., Aug. 30, 1933; s. Nathan and Sarah (Levine) S.; m. Meryl Fialka, June 20, 1959; children: Daria H., Jonathan S. AB summa cum laude, Princeton U., 1954; postgrad., London Sch. Econs., 1954-55, Am. U., Washington, 1958-60. Fgn. svc. officer Dept. State, various locations, 1958-69; first sec. Dept. State, U.S. Embassy, Paris, 1969-72; polit. counselor Dept. State, U.S. Embassy, Lagos, Nigeria, 1972-75; U.S. ambassador to Gabon Dept. State, U.S. Embassy, Libreville, Gabon, 1975-77; dir. nat. intelligence tasking office Intelligence Community Staff, Washington, 1978-80; dep. asst. sec. for personnel Dept. State, Washington, 1981-84; asst. dean/prof. internat. relations Georgetown U., Washington, 1985—; vis. fellow Woodrow Wilson Fellowship Found., Princeton, 1987—; mem. edn. com. Atlantic Council, Washington, 1989—. Author: The Foreign Service of the United States, 1985. With U.S. Army, 1955-57. Wilbur Carr award, U.S. Dept. State, 1985. Mem. Am. Polit. Sci. Assn., Am. Hist. Assn., Am. Fgn. Svc. Assn., Phi Beta Kappa. Avocation: philately. Office: Georgetown U Sfs Icc # 301 Washington DC 20057

STEIGMAN, GARY, physics and astronomy educator; b. N.Y.C., Feb. 23, 1941. BS in Physics magna cum laude, CCNY, 1961; MS in Physics, NYU, 1963, PhD in Physics, 1968. Rsch. asst. Brookhaven Nat. Lab., 1961; teaching asst. physics dept. Cornell U., 1961-62; rsch. scientist Aerospace Corp., 1962; teaching asst. physics dept. NYU, 1963-64, rsch. asst. physics dept., 1966-67, instr. physics dept., 1967-68; vis. fellow Inst. Theoretical Astronomy, Cambridge, Eng., 1968-70; rsch. fellow physics Calif. Inst. Tech., 1970-72; asst. prof. astronomy Yale U., 1972-78; assoc. prof. physics Bartol Rsch. Found., 1978-80, prof. physics, 1980-86; prof. physics and astronomy Ohio State U., 1986—; vis. scientist Nat. Radio Astronomy Obs., 1975-76; vis. prof. Stanford U., 1979; dir. early universe program Inst. for Theoretical Physics, U. Calif., Santa Barbara, 1981; George Ellery Hale dist. vis. prof. Enrico Fermi Inst., U. Chicago, 1983; mem. adv. bd., bd. trustees Aspen Ctr. Physics, organizing com. Astrophysics Workshops, 1973-83, 86—. Assoc. editor Nuclear Physics B, 1984—. Recipient NSF fellowship, 1963, 64, 65, 65-66, N.Y. State Regents Coll. Teaching fellowship, 1961-62, 62-63, 64-65, 1st prize Gravity Rsch. Found. Essay Competition, 1980, first E.A. Yunker Lectr. in Physics award, Oreg. State U., 1985, Alexander von Humboldt-Stiftung Sr. U.S. Scientist award, 1986, Disting. Scholar award Ohio State U., 1992; named Del. Scientist of Yr., Sigma Xi, 1979. Fellow Am. Phys. Soc.; mem. Am. Astron. Soc., Internat. Astron. Union. Home: 43 Campus View Blvd Columbus OH 43235 Office: Ohio State Univ Dept Physics 174 W 18th Ave Columbus OH 44310

STEIL, GEORGE KENNETH, SR., lawyer; b. Darlington, Wis., Dec. 16, 1924; s. George John and Laura (Donahoe) S.; m. Mavis Elaine Andrews, May 24, 1947; children: George Kenneth, John R., MIchelle Steil Bryski, Marcelaine Steil-Zimmermann. Student, Platteville State Tchrs. Coll., 1942-43; JD, U. Wis., Madison, 1950. Bar: Wis. 1950, U.S. Tax Ct. 1971, U.S. Dist. Ct. (western dist.) Wis. 1950. Assoc. J. G. McWilliams, Janesville, 1950-53; ptnr. McWilliams and Steil, Janesville, 1954-60, Brennan, Steil, Ryan, Basting & MacDougall (S.C., and predecessor), Janesville, 1960-72; pres. Brennan, Steil, Basting & MacDougall (S.C., and predecessor), 1972—; lectr. law U. Wis., 1974; bd. dirs. Heritage Mut. Ins. Co., Sheboygan, Wis., Blain Supply Inc., Blain's Farm & Fleet Stores; trustee, bd. dirs. Roman Cath. Diocese of Madison; mem. Wis. Supreme Ct. Bd. Atty. Profl. Responsibility, 1982-87, chmn., 1984-87; chmn. Gov.'s Adv. Coun. Jud. Selection, State of Wis., 1987-92; chmn. Wis. Lottery Bd., 1987-90. Bd. dirs. St. Coletta Sch. for Exceptional Children, Jefferson, Wis., 1972-76, 78-84, 86-89, chmn., 1982-83; bd. regents U. Wis., 1990—, pres., 1992-94. Recipient Disting. Svc. award U. Wis. Law Alumni, 1991. Fellow Am. Bar Found. (life), Am. Coll. of Trust and Estate Counsel; mem. ABA, Janesville Area C. of C. (pres. 1970-71), State Bar Wis. (pres. 1977-78), Wis. Bar Found. (bd. dirs. 1976—, Charles L. Goldberg Disting. Svc. award 1990). Roman Catholic. Home: 431 Apache Dr Janesville WI 53545-4305 Office: Brennan Steil Basting & MacDougall 1 E Milwaukee St Janesville WI 53545-3011

STEILEN, JAMES R., lawyer; b. Mitchell, S.D., Apr. 17, 1949; s. Ronald and Gladys M. (Aulner) S.; m. Carol Jane Scoonover, June 6, 1970; children: Matthew, Jennifer, Katherine, Daniel. BA, U. Iowa, 1971; JD, Harvard U., 1974. Bar: Minn. 1974. Shareholder Popham, Haik, Schnobrich & Kaufman Ltd., Mpls., 1974—. Capt. U.S. Army, 1971-76. Mem. Wayzata Country Club. Office: Popham Haik Schnobrich & Kaufman Ltd 3300 Piper Jaffray Tower 222 S 9th St Minneapolis MN 55402-3389

STEIN, A. C., clergy member, church administrator. Dir. of the dept of human resources Evangelical Lutheran Church in Am, Chgo. Office: Evang Luthern Ch Am 8765 W Higgins Rd Chicago IL 60631-4101

STEIN, ALAN L., investment banker; b. Phila., Nov. 21, 1930; s. Harry J. and Minnie (Kohn) S.; m. Ruth Sussman, June 7, 1953; children: Paul, Julie, Jennifer. AB, Columbia Coll., 1952; MBA, Harvard U., 1954. With Goldman Sachs and Co., 1954-68; ptnr. in charge of corp. investment banking activities West Coast Goldman Sachs and Co., San Francisco, 1968-76; dep. dir. dept. econ. and bus. devel. State of Calif., 1978, sec. Bus. Transp. and Housing Agy., 1978-80; assoc. dean exec. edn. Berkeley Sch. Bus. U. Calif., 1981-82; mem. com. Montgomery Securities, 1982—, exec. dir. investment banking, sr. mng. dir. Chmn. bd. dirs. Bridge Housing Corp.; chmn. bd. trustees Am. Conservatory Theater; dir. Bay Area Coun.; trustee, past pres. bd. trustees San Francisco Mus. Modern Art. Mem. Villa Taverna, Calif. Tennis Club, Lake Merced Golf and Country Club. Office: Montgomery Securities 600 Montgomery St San Francisco CA 94111

STEIN, ALFRED J., electronics executive, computer software company executive; b. 1933. With Tex. Instruments, 1958-76, Motorola Inc., 1976-81, Arrow Electronics, 1981-82; with VLSI Tech. Inc., San Jose, Calif., 1982—, pres., chmn. bd. dirs., CEO. Office: VLSI Tech Inc 1109 Mckay Dr San Jose CA 95131*

STEIN, ARLAND THOMAS, lawyer; b. Pitts., Nov. 19, 1938; s. Thomas Edward and Josephine Cecelia (Kiedaisch) S.; m. Helen Marie Horin, Aug. 14, 1965; children—Thomas Arland, John Andrew, Christian Michael. B.S. in Engring. Sci., Purdue U., 1961, postgrad., 1961-62; LL.B., U. Va., 1965. Bar: Pa. 1965, Ohio 1966, U.S. Patent Office 1967, U.S. Supreme Ct. 1969. Assoc. Blenko, Leonard & Buell, Pitts., 1965-71; ptnr. Yeager, Stein & Wettach, Pitts., 1971-74; Reed Smith Shaw & McClay, Pitts., 1974—. Mem. ABA, Allegheny County Bar Assn., Am. Patent Law Assn., Pitts. Patent Law Assn., Lic. Execs. Soc., Tau Beta Pi, Omicron Delta Kappa (charter mem.), Rose Ade Found. Republican. Lutheran. Clubs: Masons, K.T., Duquesne Club. Home: 144 Riding Trail Ln Pittsburgh PA 15215-1500 Office: Reed Smith Shaw & McClay Mellon Sq 435 6th Ave Pittsburgh PA 15219-1886

STEIN, ARNOLD, English educator; b. Brockton, Mass., Apr. 27, 1915; m. Bess Dworsky, June 20, 1942; children: Jonathan, Deborah. A.B., Yale U., 1936; A.M., Harvard U., 1938, Ph.D., 1942. Instr. U. Minn., Mpls., 1940-46; asst. prof. English Ohio State U., Columbus, 1946-48; assoc. prof. U. Wash., Seattle, 1948-53, prof., 1953-71; prof. English Johns Hopkins U., Balt., 1971-74; Sir William Osler prof., 1974-80; prof. U. Ill., Urbana, 1980-85, emeritus prof., 1985—; Fulbright lectr. Tel Aviv U., 1986-87. Author: Answerable Style, 1953, Heroic Knowledge, 1957, John Donne's Lyrics, 1962, George Herbert's Lyrics, 1968, The Art of Presence, 1977, The House of Death, 1987; mem. adv. bd. Poetry Northwest, 1960—; mem. editorial bd. Milton Studies, 1968—; editor: Theodore Roethke, 1965, On Milton's Poetry, 1970; editor: English Literary History, 1971—, sr. editor, 1974-80. Served as pvt. F.A. U.S. Army, 1943-45, ETO. Renaissance issue of ELH (English Lit. History) pub. in honor, 1982; Ford Found. fellow, 1953-54; Guggenheim Found. fellow, 1959-60. Mem. Renaissance Soc. Am., MLA, Milton Soc. Am. (Honored Scholar 1980), Folger Inst. Renaissance Studies (mem. central com. 1973-77).

STEIN, BENNETT MUELLER, neurosurgeon; b. N.Y.C., Feb. 2, 1931; s. Walter Charles and Marjorie Clare (Bennett) S.; m. Doreen Holmes, May 28, 1955 (dec. 1984); children: Susan, Marjorie; m. Bonita Soontit, Sept. 19, 1987; 1 child, Bennett Charles. A.B., Dartmouth Coll., 1952; M.D., C.M., McGill U., Montreal, Que., 1955. Diplomate: Am. Bd. Neurol. Surgery, Nat. Bd. Med. Examiners. Rotating intern U.S. Naval Hosp., St. Albans, N.Y., 1955-56; Fulbright scholar Inst. Neurology, Nat. Hosp., London, 1958-59; asst. resident in surgery Presbyn. Hosp., N.Y.C., 1959-60; asst. resident in neurosurgery Presbyn. Hosp., 1960-63, chief resident, 1963-64; spl. fellow neuroanatomy Nat. Inst. Neurol. Diseases and Blindness, 1964-66; asso. in neurol. surgery Columbia U. Coll. Phys. and Surgeons, 1964-68, mem. faculty, 1968—, Byron Stookey prof. neurol. surgery, 1980—; dir. service neurol. surgery Presbyn. Hosp., 1980—; prof. neurol. surgery, chmn. dept. Tufts-New Eng. Med. Center, Boston, 1971-80; dir. Am. Bd. Neurol. Surgeons, 1988—. Author articles in field; mem. editorial bds. profl. jours. Served as officer M.C. USNR, 1956-58. Fellow A.C.S.; mem. Am. Assn. Anatomists, AMA, Acad. Neurol. Surgeons, Congress Neurol. Surgeons, Am. Assn. Neurol. Surgeons, Am. Acad. Neurol. Surgeons, Soc. Neurol. Surgeons, Cajal Club, Brazilian Neurol. Soc. (corr.), N.Y. State Neurosurg. Soc., New Eng. Neurosurg. Soc., Mass. Med. Soc., Boston Surg. Soc., Boston Soc. Psychiatry and Neurology, Sigma Xi, Alpha Omega Alpha, Alpha Kappa Kappa. Lutheran. Office: Presbyn Hosp Columbia-Presbyn Med Ctr 710 W 168th St New York NY 10032-2603

STEIN, BERNARD, stockbroker; b. N.Y.C., Nov. 24, 1913; s. Abraham and Fannie (Zoob) S.; m. Marion Charlotte Holtsberg, Feb. 24, 1946; children: Robert Frederick, Ellen Frances (Mrs. Howard Lazarus). Student, Sch. Commerce, NYU, 1930-32. Ptnr. firm Ralph E. Samuel & Co., N.Y.C., 1947-70, Neuberger & Berman, Inc., 1970—; sr. v.p., treas., dir. Energy Fund, N.Y.C., 1962-80, pres., 1980-91, dir. emeritus; former vice chmn. Neuberger & Berman Mgmt. Co., N.Y.C. Served with USAAF, 1942-45. Clubs: Quaker Ridge Golf (Scarsdale); Beach Point (Mamaroneck, N.Y.). Home: 8 Split Tree Rd Scarsdale NY 10583-7900 Office: Neuberger & Berman 605 3d Ave New York NY 10158-3698

STEIN, BERNARD ALVIN, business consultant; b. Winnipeg, Can., June 4, 1923; s. Herman Louis and Rebecca (Harris) S.; m. Dorothy Lock, Jan. 1, 1942; 1 dau., Marilynn Stein Lakein. Vice-pres. food drug div. Giant Food, Inc., Washington, 1951-69; v.p., gen. mgr. Read Drug Stores, Balt., 1969-70; pres. Scotty Stores div. Sav-A-Stop, Jacksonville, Fla., 1970-71; pres., gen. mgr. Liberal Markets, Dayton, Ohio, 1971-72; pres. Pueblo Supermarkets, San Juan, P.R., 1972-74, Hills Supermarkets, Brentwood, N.Y., 1974-75, Allied Supermarkets, Detroit, 1976-78, Chatham Supermarkets, Detroit, 1978-81, Network Assocs., Chgo., 1981-92; bus. cons. Balt., 1992—. Mem. Presdl. Com. for Emergency Food Controls, 1969. Served with USAAF, 1943-45. Decorated Air medal. Home: 111 Hamlet Hill Rd # 707 Baltimore MD 21210 Office: 4 Estates Ct #3107 Baltimore MD 21208

STEIN, BOB, professional basketball team executive. Pres. Minn. Timberwolves. Office: Minn Timberwolves 600 1st Ave N Target Ctr Minneapolis MN 55403*

STEIN, CAREY M., lawyer; b. Chgo., July 15, 1947; s. Daniel and Shirley (Weinstein) S.; m. Seena R. Silverman, July 8, 1972; children: Allison, Amy. BS, So. Ill. U., 1970; JD, DePaul U., 1974. Bar: Ill. 1974, N.Y. 1988, Pa. 1990, Mo. 1992. Tax examiner IRS, Chgo., 1973-75; atty. Ill. Dept. Revenue, Chgo., 1975-77; asst. corp. counsel Hart, Schaffner & Marx, Chgo., 1977-83; Assoc. gen. counsel, asst. sec. Hartmarx Corp., Chgo., 1983-84, v.p., sec., gen. counsel, 1984—, exec. v.p., 1992, chief adminstrv. officer, 1993; adv. bd. midwest region Arkwright Mutual Ins. Co., 1993. Mem. exec. com., bd. dirs. Ctr. for Enriched Living, Deerfield, Ill., 1984—, pres. 1990-91; mem. adv. bd. Northwestern U. Corp. Counsel Ctr., Chgo., 1984—; mem. exec. com., bd. dirs. Jewish Edn. Met. Chgo., 1987—, sec.-treas., 1988-89, v.p., 1989-91; mem. bd. dirs. Better Boys Found., 1993. Mem. ABA, Ill. Bar Assn., Chgo. Bar Assn., Am. Soc. Corp. Secs., Am. Apparel Mfrs. Assn. (legal com. 1985—). Am. Arbitration Assn. (adv. com., panel 1988—). Jewish. Office: Hartmarx Corp 101 N Wacker Dr Chicago IL 60606-1718

STEIN, CARL, architect; b. N.Y.C., Jan. 27, 1943; s. Richard George and Ethel (Levy) S.; m. Nancy Ellen Jones, May 28, 1965; 1 child, Jesse Lee. BA, Middlebury (Vt.) Coll., 1964; BArch, Cooper Union Coll., N.Y.C., 1968; postgrad., Harvard U., 1966-67. With Marcel Breuer & Assocs., N.Y.C., 1968-71; assoc. Richard G. Stein & Assocs., N.Y.C., 1971-77; ptnr. The Stein Partnership, N.Y.C., 1977—; pres., bd. dirs. Westbeth Housing Corp., N.Y.C., 1988—; co-founder Parents and Friends for Children's Survival, chair, 1982-89; prin. instructor Trenton Integrated Community Energy System. Prin. works include New Hdqrs. for Rescue Co. No. 1, N.Y., New 41st Precinct, Bronx, N.Y., Walt Whitman Birthplace Vis. Ctr., Huntington Sta., N.Y., Yantai (China) Kai Gang Houses, Rockland County Courthouse Restoration, New City, N.Y., Cmty. Ch. of the Pelhams, N.Y., PS/IS 73, Bklyn., Bronx Biomed. Rsch. Park, 19th Precinct, N.Y.C., firehouse for Engine Co. 39 N.Y.C. Fire Dept. (Lucy B. Moses award 1992); reconstruction of Cen. Park Police Sta., N.Y.C., Shepard Hall, CCNY, (with R. Kinoshita and A. Marshall) Women's Rights Nat. Hist. Pk., Seneca Falls, N.Y., Energy Conscious Architecture (monograph), NW Corner master plan and Modular Units, World of Birds, Bronx Wildlife Conservation Park, Prototype Affordable Housing, Croton-on-Hudson, N.Y.; author Handbook of Energy Use for Building Construction; contbr. articles to profl. jours. Mem. Environ. Action Coalition, 1992—. Fellow AIA (chair energy profl. devel. program 1979, 81, chair N.Y.C. fellows com. 1994). Office: The Stein Partnership Architect 20 W 20th St New York NY 10011-4213

STEIN, DALE FRANKLIN, retired university president; b. Kingston, Minn., Dec. 24, 1935; s. David Frank and Zelda Jane S.; m. Audrey Dean Bloemke, June 7, 1958; children—Pam, Derek. B.S. in Metallurgy, U. Minn., 1958; Ph.D., Rensselaer Poly. Inst., Troy, N.Y., 1963. Metallurgist rsch. lab. GE, Schnectady, N.Y., 1958-67; assoc. prof. U. Minn., 1967-71; prof. metall. engring., head dept. Mich. Technol. U., Houghton, 1971-77; head mining engring. Mich. Technol. U., 1974-77, v.p. acad. affairs, 1977-79, pres., 1979-91; pres. emeritus, 1991—; chmn. NSF, Dept. of Energy, 1972-90; trustee Rensselaer Poly. Inst., 1989-95; chmn. com. on decontamination and decommissioning uranium enrichment facilities Nat. Rsch. Coun., 1993—; active Nat. Materials Adv. Bd., 1987-93; chmn. adv. com. Ctr. for Nuclear Waste Regulatory Analyses. Contbr. articles to profl. jours. Paul Harris fellow. Fellow Metall. Soc. (pres. 1979, inst. Hardy Gold medal 1965), Am. Soc. Metals (Geisler award Eastern N.Y. chpt. 1967); mem. AIME, AAAS, NAE, Sigma Xi, Phi Kappa Phi, Tau Beta Pi, Alpha Sigma Nu.

STEIN, DAVID FRED, investment executive; b. N.Y.C., May 17, 1940; s. William Howard and Phoebe Louise (Hockstader) S.; m. Susan Vail Berresford, June 17, 1963 (div. 1970); 1 child, Jeremy Vail; m. Ellen Gail Cohen, Sept. 16, 1973; children: Katharine Ellen, Nicholas David. BA, Harvard U., 1962; MBA, Harvard Grad. Sch. Bus. Adminstrn., 1965. Assoc. Bache & Co., N.Y.C., 1965-68; assoc., then gen. ptnr. Kuhn Loeb & Co., N.Y.C., 1969-77; mng. dir. Lehman Brothers Kuhn Loeb, N.Y.C., 1977-83, Shearson Lehman Am. Express, N.Y.C., 1983-86; sr. exec. v.p., dir. Am. Express Bank, N.Y.C., 1986-87; mng. dir. Shearson Lehman Hutton, N.Y.C., 1987-89; mng. dir., mem. exec. com. The Stamford Co., N.Y.C., 1989-90, J & W Seligman & Co., N.Y.C., 1990—; co-chmn. Seligman, Henderson Co., N.Y.C., 1991—; mem. Internat. Com. of Nat. Assn. Security Dealers, 1970-85. Trustee P.R. Traveling Theatre, N.Y.C., 1970-72, Altro Health and Rehab. Ctr., Bronx, N.Y., 1975-82, Blythedale Children's Home, Valhalla, N.Y., 1977—, Montefiore Med. Ctr., Bronx, 1990—; trustee, chmn. fin. com. Riverdale Country Sch., Bronx, 1988—; mem. Coun. on Fgn. Rels. With U.S. Army, 1962-63. Mem. Century Country Club (Purchase, N.Y.), River Club (N.Y.C.), Harvard Club (N.Y.C.), Edgartown (Mass.) Yacht Club, Mill Reef Club (Antigua, B.V.I.), Chappaquiddick Beach Club (Edgartown). Democrat. Avocations: reading, sailing, fishing, skiing. Home: 875 Park Ave New York NY 10021-0341 Office: J & W Seligman 100 Park Ave New York NY 10017-5516

STEIN, DONALD GERALD, psychology educator; b. N.Y.C., Jan. 27, 1939; s. Frank and Elizabeth (Bernstein) S.; m. Darel Hammer; children: Jessica, Matthew. B.A. in Exptl. Psychology, Mich. State U., 1960, M.A., 1962; Ph.D. in Physiol. Psychology, U. Oreg., 1965. NIMH Postdoctoral research fellow MIT, 1965-66; asst. prof., dir. brain research lab. Clark U., Worcester, Mass., 1966-69, assoc. prof. psychology, dir. lab., 1969-73, prof. psychology, 1973-88; prof. neurology U. Mass. Med. Ctr., Worcester, 1978-88; prof. biol. scis. and psychobiology, dean grad. sch., assoc. provost research Rutgers U., Newark, 1988-94; adj. prof. neurosci. Univ. Medicine and Dentistry N.J.; organizer 1st Internat. Conf. on Psychobiology of Aging, Luxembourg, 1979; mem. adv. com. Nat. Conf. on Future Univ. Rsch., U. Ga., 1983-84; adj. prof. biology Clark U., 1986-88; cons. Ctr. for Brain Injury Rehab., Copenhagen; profl. coun. Nat. Head Injury Found., 1988; mem. faculty Eurpean Sch. for Neurosci., Praglia/Padua, Italy 1990; pres. Winter Conf. On Brain Rsch., 1992-94. Author: (with J. Rosen) Basic Structure and Function in the Central Nervous System, 1974, Motivation and Emotion, 1974, Learning and Memory, 1974, (with S. Finger) Brain Damage and Recovery: Research and Clinical Perspectives, 1982, Plasticite Neuronale, Vieillissement et Récuperation de la Suite de Lé Cérébrales, 1983; editor: The Psychobiology of Aging: Problems and Perspectives, 1980, Plasticity and Recovery of Function in the Central Nervous System, 1974, (with J. Rosen and N. Butters) Pharmacological Approaches to the Treatment of Brain and Spinal Cord Injuries, (with B. Sabel) Theoretical and Controversial Issues in Recovery from Brain Damage, (with S. Brailowsky and B. Will) Les Dépannages du Cerveau, El Cerebro Averiado, 1992, Brain Repair, 1995; editor-in-chief Restorative Neurology and Neuroscience; contbr. over 150 articles to sci. jours. Recipient Fulbright Travel award France, 1975, Grass Found. Traveling Scientist award, 1979, Disting. Alumni award U. Oreg., 1990, Ministry of Higher Edn. Rsch. award Govt. of France, 1995; Fulbright grantee U. Lyon Med. Sch., 1971-72. Fellow AAAS (fellowship 1980-81), Congress Sci. and Engring., Am. Psychol. Soc.; mem. Soc. Neurosci., European Brain and Behavior Soc., Internat. Soc. Neuropsychology, Nat. Coalition for Sci. and Tech. (founder, chmn. exec. com. 1982-88), N.Y. Acad. Scis. (chmn. biomed. sci. 1993-94), Phi Beta Kappa, Sigma Xi. Office: Rutgers U Dept Psychology Newark NJ 07102 In science and education, one must always work to challenge dogma and dare to be different. A love of learning is the key to effective teaching and research.

STEIN, ERIC, retired law educator; b. Holice, Czechoslovakia, July 8, 1913; came to U.S., 1940, naturalized, 1943; s. Zikmund and Hermina (Zalud) S.; m. Virginia Elizabeth Rhine, July 30, 1955. JUD, Charles U., Prague, Czechoslovakia, 1937; JD, U. Mich., 1942; Dr. honoris causa, Vrije U., Brussels, 1978, U. Libre, Brussels, 1979. Bar: Ill. 1946, D.C. 1953. Practiced law Prague, 1937; with State Dept., 1946-55; acting dep. dir. Office UN Polit. Affairs, 1978; faculty U. Mich. Law Sch., Ann Arbor, 1979; prof. internat. law and orgn. U. Mich. Law Sch., 1958-76, Hessel E. Yntema prof. law, 1976-83, emeritus prof., 1983—; co-dir. internat. legal studies, 1958-76, dir., 1976-81; vis. prof. Stanford Law Sch., 1956, 77, Law Faculties, Stockholm, Uppsala and Lund, Sweden, 1969, Inst. Advanced Legal Studies U. London, 1975, U. Ariz., 1991, 92; lectr. Hague Acad. Internat. Law, summer 1971; vis. lectr. European U. Inst., Florence, Italy, 1983, Beijing, Shanghai, Wuhan, 1986, U. Tokyo, Kyoto, 1986, Coll. of Europe, Bruges, Pontificia, Madrid, 1988; Jean Monnet prof. European U. Inst., Florence, Italy, 1991, Henry Morris lectr. Kent Coll. of Law, Chgo., 1992, 93, Jeanne Kiewit Taylor disting. vis. lectr. U. Ariz., winter 1993; adviser U.S. delegation UN Gen. Assembly, 1947-55; mem. adv. panel, cons. Bur. European Affairs, State Dept., 1966-73; cons. U.S. rep. for trade negotiations, 1979; vice chmn. com. Atlantic studies Atlantic Inst., 1966-68; mem. adv. council Inst. European Studies, Free U., Brussels, Belgium, 1965-70; mem. U.S. Com. for Legal Edn. Exchange with China, 1983-91; lectr. Acad. of European Law, Florence, Italy 1990. Author: (with others) American Enterprise in the European Common Market-A Legal Profile, vols. I, II, 1960, (with H.K. Jacobson) Diplomats, Scientists and Politicians: The United States and the Nuclear Test Ban Negotiations, 1966, Harmonization of European Company Law: National Reform and Transnational Coordination, 1971, Impact of New Weapons Technology on International Law-Selected Aspects, 1971, Un Nuovo Diritto per l'Europa, 1991; editor: (with Peter Hay) Law and Institutions in the Atlantic Area Readings, Cases and Problems, 1967, (with Peter Hay and Michel Waelbroeck) European Community Law and Institutions in Perspective, 1976; co-author, co-editor: Courts and Free Markets-Perspectives From the United States and Europe, 1982; bd. editors: Am. Jour. Internat. Law, 1965—; mem. adv. bd. Common Market Law Rev., 1964—, Legal Issues of European Integration, 1974—, Rivista di Diritto Europeo, 1978—, Columbia Jour. East European Law, 1994—, Columbia Jour. European Law, 1994—; contbr. articles to profl. jours. Mem. Internat. Com. for Revision Czechoslovak Constn., 1990-92. With AUS, 1943-46. Decorated Bronze Star, Order Italian Crown, Italian Mil. Cross; Guggenheim fellow, 1962-63; Social Sci. Rsch. Coun. grantee; Rockefeller Found. scholar-in-residence, 1965, 73; Alexander von Humboldt Stiftung awardee, 1982; fellow Inst. Advanced Study, Berlin, 1984-85, IREX rsch. grant, 1995. Mem. ABA (co-chmn. European law com. 1982, mem. coun. sect. on internat. law and practice 1983-84), Internat. Law Assn. (com. on regional econ. devel.), Coun. Fgn. Rels., Am. Soc. Internat. Law (exec. coun. 1954-57, bd. rev. and devel. 1965-67, 70-75, hon. v.p. 1982—), Brit. Inst. Internat. and Comparative Law, Internat. Acad. Comparative Law (assoc.). Home: 2649 Heather Way Ann Arbor MI 48104

STEIN, GEORGE HENRY, historian, educator, administrator; b. Vienna, Austria, May 18, 1934; came to U.S., 1939, naturalized, 1948; m. Dorothy Ann Lahm, Nov. 22, 1963; 1 child, Kenneth. B.A. with honors (N.Y. State Regents scholar), Bklyn. Coll., 1959; M.A. in History (Regents fellow), Columbia U., 1960, Ph.D. in History (Pres.'s fellow), 1964. Lectr. history City Coll., CUNY, 1962-63; instr. dept. history Columbia U., N.Y.C., 1963-65; asst. prof. Columbia U., 1965-66; assoc. prof. dept. history SUNY-Binghamton, 1966-70, prof., 1970—, disting. teaching prof., 1973—, vice chmn. grad. affairs, 1974-76, v.p. acad. affairs, 1976-87, provost, 1985-87, acting pres., 1986-87; manuscript evaluator and cons. to numerous publishers, 1964—. Author: The Waffen SS: Hitler's Elite Guard at War, 1939-45, 1966, paperback edit., 1984 (transl. into German, 1967, French, 1967, Spanish, 1973, Portuguese, 1970); contbr. articles on modern European history to scholarly publs.; editor: Hitler, 1968; contbr. book revs. to hist. jours. Served with USAF, 1953-57. NEH fellow, 1970-71. Mem. Am. Hist. Assn. (mem. conf. group on cen. European history, conf. group for use of psychology in history), Acad. Polit. Sci., Assn. of Contemporary Historians, Am. Assn. Higher Edn., Nat. Assn. State Univs. and Land Grant Colls. (mem. council acad. affairs 1976-87), Am. Counc. Edn. (exec. com. nat. coun. chief acad. officers 1983-85), Com. Internat. d'Histoire de la Deuxieme Guerre Mondiale (mem. Am. com. on history of WWII). Office: SUNY Dept History Binghamton NY 13901

STEIN, GERALD, real estate and diversified holding company executive; b. Milw., Dec. 4, 1937; s. Rudolph and Mary (Uberstine) S.; m. Louise Sharon Mendelson, Sept. 6, 1959; children—Debra, Leslie, Leigh. B.B.A., U. Wis.-Milw., 1959; J.D., Marquette U., Milw., 1962. Bar: Wis. 1962; C.P.A., Wis. Exec. v.p. Towne Realty Inc., Milw., 1957-80; vice chmn. Unicare Services Inc., Milw., 1968-83; pres. Zilber Ltd., Milw., 1980—; dir. Universal Mortgage, Milw. Pres. Jewish Vocat. Service, Milw., 1982; pres. Milw. Pub. Mus., 1984, v.p. Milw. Jewish Fedn., 1984. Served as 1st lt. U.S. Army, 1962-64. Mem. Wis. Bar Assn. Club: Milw. Athletic. Office: Zilber Ltd 710 N Plankinton Ave Milwaukee WI 53203-2404

STEIN, GILBERT, professional hockey executive; b. Phila., Jan. 11, 1928; m. Barbara Stein; children: Andrew, Holly Spinner, John. Grad., Temple U.; JD, Boston U. Exec. v.p., chief exec. officer Phila. Flyers Hockey Club; vice-chmn. NHL Enterprises, Inc., N.Y.; v.p., gen. counsel NHL, N.Y., pres., 1992—. Office: NHL 650 Fifth Ave 33d Fl New York NY 10019

STEIN, HERBERT, economist; b. Detroit, Aug. 27, 1916; s. David and Jessie (Segal) S.; m. Mildred Fishman, June 12, 1937; children: Rachel (Epstein), Benjamin. AB, Williams Coll., 1935, LLD (hon.), 1980; PhD, U. Chgo., 1958; LLD (hon.), Rider Coll., 1971, Hartford U., 1973, Roanoke Coll., 1984, New Haven U., 1987, Hofstra U., 1994. Economist FDIC, 1938-40, Nat. Def. Adv. Commn., 1940-41, WPB, 1941-44, Office War Moblzn. and Reconversion, 1945; economist Com. Econ. Devel., 1945-48, assoc. dir. research, 1948-56, dir. research, 1956-66, v.p., chief economist, 1966-67; sr. fellow Brookings Instn., 1967-69; mem. Pres.'s Council Econ. Advisers, Washington, 1969-72; chmn. Pres.'s Council Econ. Advisers, 1972-74; A. Willis Robertson prof. econs. U. Va., Charlottesville, 1974-84; weekly columnist The Economy Today, Scripps-Howard and other newpapers, 1974-80; bd. contbrs. Wall St. Jour., 1974—; cons. Congl. Budget Office, 1976-89; mem. Adv. Com. Nat. Growth Policy Processes, 1976-77, Pharm. Reimbursement Adv. Bd., 1976-77; adj. scholar Am. Enterprise Inst., 1975-77, sr. fellow, 1977—; cons. U.S. Dept. State, 1983-92; mem. Pres.'s Econ. Policy Adv. Bd., 1981-89; mem. Pres.'s Blue Ribbon Commn. on Def. Mgmt., 1985-86. Author: U.S. Government Price Policy during the World War, 1938, (with de Chazeau, Hart, Means, Myers, Yntema) Jobs and Markets, 1946, The Fiscal Revolution in America, 1969, rev. edit., 1990, Economic Planning and the Improvement of Public Policy, 1975, (with W. Leontief) The Economic System in an Age of Discontinuity, 1976, (with Benjamin Stein) On the Brink, 1977, (with Benjamin Stein) Money Power, 1980, Presidential Economics, 1984, rev. edit., 1994, Washington Bedtime Stories, 1986, Governing the $5 Trillion Economy, 1989, (with M. Foss) An Illustrated Guide to the American Economy, 1992, A New Illustrated Guide to the American Economy, 1995, On the Other Hand..., 1995; editor: Policies to Combat Depression, 1956, Tax Policy for the Twenty-First Century, 1988, AEI Economist, 1977-88; contbr. to: Agenda for the Nation, 1968, Contemporary Economic Problems, 1976, 77, 78, 79, 80. Co-chmn. Economists for Ford, 1976; founding mem. Ams. for An Effective Presidency, 1980; mem. vis. comn. econs. dept. Harvard U., 1979-80; mem. Group of 1978-81. Served as ensign USNR, 1944-45. Recipient 1st prize Pabst Post-War Employment awards, 1944, Frank Seidman award polit. economy Rhodes Coll., Memphis, 1989; Center Advanced Study in Behavioral Scis. fellow, 1965-66. Mem. Am., Va. econ. assns., So. Econ. Assn. (pres. 1983-84), Nat. Economists Club (chmn., bd. govs. 1987—), Am. Acad. Arts and Scis., Phi Beta Kappa. Club: Cosmos. Office: Am Enterprise Inst 1150 17th St NW Washington DC 20036

STEIN, HERMAN DAVID, social sciences educator, past university provost; b. N.Y.C., Aug. 13, 1917; s. Charles and Emma (Rosenblum) S.; m. Charmion Kerr, Sept. 15, 1946; children: Karen Lou Gelender, Shoshi Stein Bennett, Naomi Elizabeth. B.S.S., CCNY, 1939; M.S., Columbia U., 1941, D. Social Welfare, 1958; L.H.D., Hebrew Union Coll.-Jewish Inst. Religion, Cin, 1969; LLD, Jewish Theol. Sem., 1995. Family case worker, dir. pub. relations Jewish Family Service, N.Y.C., 1941-45; mem. faculty Sch. Social Work, Columbia U., N.Y.C., 1945-47, 50-64, prof. social scis., 1958-64, dir. rsch. ctr., 1959-62; dean Sch. Applied Social Scis. Case Western Res. U., Cleve., 1964-68, provost for social and behavioral scis., 1967-71, John Reynolds Harkness prof., social adminstr., 1972-89, univ. provost, v.p. 1969-72, 86-88, univ. prof. and provost emeritus, 1990—, univ. prof., faculty Ctr. for Internat. Health, 1989—; founder, dir. Global Currents Lectures, 1983-88; vis. prof. Sch. Social Work, U. Hawaii, Honolulu, winter 1971-72; fellow ctr. for Advanced Study in Behavior Scis., 1974-75, 78-79; Dep. dir. budget and rsch. dir. welfare dept. Am. Joint Distbn. Com. (European Hdqrs.), Paris, 1947-50; sr. adviser to exec. dir. UNICEF, 1974-83; cons. UNICEF, UN Social Devel. Div., 1960-83; adv. com. NIMH, 1959-71; mem. Bd. Human Resources, Nat. Acad. Scis., 1972-74; lectr. Sch. Social Work, Smith Coll., 1951-62, Harvard U. Sch. Pub. Health, 1971-85; cons. indsl. and nonprofit orgns. Author: The Curriculum Study of the Columbia University School of Social Work, 1960; co-author: The Characteristics of American Jews, 1965; Editor: (with Richard A. Cloward) Social Perspectives on Behavior, 1958, Planning for the Needs of Children in Developing Countries, 1965, Social Theory and Social Invention, 1968, The Crisis in Welfare in Cleveland, 1969, Organization and the Human Services, 1981; mem. editorial bd.: Adminstr. in Social work, 1976—; contbr. to profl. jours. Chmn. Mayor's Commn. on Crisis in Welfare in Cleve., 1968. Recipient Disting. Svc. award Coun. on Social Welfre, 1970, René Sand award Internat. Coun. on Social Welfire, 1984, Univ. medal Case Western Res. U., 1994. Mem. NASW (chmn. commn. internat. social welfare 1964-65), Am. Sociol. Assn., Soc. Applied Anthropology, Coun. Social Work Edn. (pres. 1966-69), Internat. Assn. Schs. Social Work (pres. 1968-76), Internat. Conf. Social Welfare (exec. com. 1976-80, internat. adv. bd. 1986—, bd. dirs. coun. internat. programs 1965-92), Club of Rome (assoc. 1988—), Phi Beta Kappa. Office: Case Western Res U 436 Pardee Hall Cleveland OH 44106

STEIN, HOWARD, mutual fund executive; b. 1926. Student, Juilliard Sch. Music, 1944-46. With Seaporcel Metals Inc., 1950-53, Bache & Co., 1953-55; asst., dir. Dreyfus Investment Mgmt. of Dreyfus and Co., also gen. partner, 1965—; v.p. Dreyfus Fund Inc., 1961-65, pres., chmn. bd., 1965—; pres., dir. Dreyfus Corp., 1965-70, chmn. bd., chief exec. officer, 1970—. Office: Dreyfus Corp 200 Park Ave New York NY 10166-0039

STEIN, HOWARD S., banker; b. N.Y.C., Dec. 27, 1939; s. J. Zachary and Adele (Epstein) S. B.A., U. Mich., 1961; M.B.A., Harvard U., 1963. Mem. treas.'s staff Gen. Motors Corp., N.Y.C., 1963-69; dep. dir. fiscal ops. Human Resources Adminstrn., City of N.Y., 1969-71, dep. adminstr., 1972-74, 1st dep. adminstr., 1974-78; asst. commr. Manpower and Career Devel. Agy., N.Y.C., 1971-72; dep. commr. rent and housing maintenance Housing and Devel. Adminstrn., City of N.Y., 1972; v.p. Citicorp Credit Services Inc., N.Y.C., 1979-86; sr. v.p. Citicorp Retail Services Inc., N.Y.C., 1986-87; exec. dir. Landmark Mut. Funds Group of Citibank, N.A., N.Y.C., 1987-88; v.p. br. banking sect. devel. div. Citibank NA, 1989-91; sr. credit officer worldwide securities svcs. div. Fin. Instns. Group Citibank NA, N.Y.C., 1991—; lectr. human resources policy Nova U., Ft. Lauderdale, Fla., 1973-74; field instr. adminstrn. specialization NYU Sch. Social Work, 1976-77. Past bd. dirs., chmn. program com. Vol. Urban Cons. Group, Inc.; chmn. bd. dirs. Nova Inst; past treas., past pres., bd. dirs. Child Study Assn. Am./ Wel-Met Inc., 1963-85; past treas., bd. dirs. Career Center for Social Services Greater N.Y., Inc.; past treas., past pres. bd. dirs. Cavalier King Charles Spaniel Club U.S.A., Inc.; past bd. dirs., past sec. Child Welfare Info. Services; treas., bd. dirs., chmn. fin. com. WNYC Found.; bd. dirs. Senate Residence Owners Inc., New Goddard-Riverside Housing Devel. Fund Co., N.Y.C. Health and Hosps., Corp., 1976, Homes for the Homeless; mem. corp. Children's Mus., Boston; bd. dirs., treas., mem. fin. com. Goddard Riverside Neighborhood Houses; mem. Dept. Disciplinary com. Supreme Ct. State N.Y. Appellate Divsn. 1st Jud. Dept. Clubs: University, Harvard (N.Y.C.) (past mem. admissions com.). Home: 1158 Fifth Ave New York NY 10029-6917 Office: 111 Wall St New York NY 10043-1000

STEIN, IRVIN, orthopaedic surgeon, educator; b. Fayetteville, N.C., Oct. 17, 1906; s. Kalman and Fannie (Berman) S.; m. Dorothy Bluthenthal, Aug. 21, 1934 (dec. Sept. 1985); children: Jane (Mrs. Gerald Finerman), Margery (Mrs. Frederich Schab), Katherine (Mrs. Keith Sachs); m. Bernice Hutzler, July 1986. AB, U. N.C., 1926; MD, Thomas Jefferson U., Phila., 1930. Diplomate Am. Bd. Orthopedic Surgery. Intern Sinai Hosp., Balt., 1930-31; resident surg. pathology Johns Hopkins, 1931-32; resident Phila. Orthopaedic Hosp., 1932-33; resident orthopedic surgery Johns Hopkins Hosp. and Children's Hosp. Sch., 1933-34; chief orthopedic surgery Phila. Gen. Hosp., 1941—; dir. chmn. dept. orthopedic surgery Albert Einstein Med. Center, Phila., 1962-72; emeritus chmn. Albert Einstein Med. Center, 1972—; clin. prof. orthopedic surgery emeritus U. Pa. Sch. Medicine, Phila.; cons. dept. health svcs. Phila. Sch. System. Co-author: Living Bone in Health and Disease, 1955, Clinical Densitometry, 1971; Contbr. numerous articles to profl. jours. Chmn. Phila. Chamber Orch. Soc., 1967-70; bd. dirs. emeritus Phila. Orch. Recipient Rehab. Physician of Year award Phila. Easter Seal Soc. 1971. Fellow ACS, Am. Assn. Study Neoplastic Diseases, N.Y. Acad. Scis., Coll. Physicians Phila., Am. Med. Writers Assn., Internat. Coll. Surgeons (pres. Pa. div. 1971, regent), Phila. Orthopedic Soc. (pres. 1970), Am. Acad. Orthopedic Surgery, Am. Geriatric Assn., Am. Acad. Surgery. Club: Broken Sound Golf. Home and Office: 2066 N Ocean Blvd Boca Raton FL 33431-7802

STEIN, J. DIETER, chemical company executive; b. 1934. PhD, U. Mainz, 1961. Instr. Inst. Phys. Chemistry U. Mainz, 1961-63; rsch. chemist plastics lab. BASF AG, 1963-76, dep. dept. mgr., 1976-80, dir., head ctrl. human resources mgr., 1980-83; head coatings ops. divsn., chmn. bd. BASF Lacke & Farber AG, 1983-88; chmn. bd., pres., CEO BASF Corp., 1988—. Office: BASF Corp 3000 Continental Dr N Mount Olive NJ 07828-1234

STEIN, JAY M., planning and design educator, consultant; b. N.Y.C., Dec. 21, 1946; s. Samuel and Helen (Hershkowitz) S.; m. Karen Lee Klenberg, Aug. 18, 1987; children: Danielle Eva, Melissa Ilana. BA, Harpur Coll., 1968; MA, York U., Toronto, Ont., Can., 1971; PhD, U. Mich., 1976. Cert. planner. Lectr. U. Mich., Ann Arbor, 1974-76; asst. prof. planning Ga. Inst. Tech., Atlanta, 1976-81, assoc. prof., 1981-86; prof., chmn. dept. SUNY, Buffalo, 1986-89, acting dean, 1988; prof., chmn. dept. urban and regional planning U. Fla., 1989—; vis. prof. Stanford (Calif.) U., 1984-85; prin. Jay M. Stein Assocs.; cons. Legal Svcs. Corp. Ga., Atlanta, 1980-84, Atlanta Regional Commn., 1982, Legal Svcs. Corp. Ala., Montgomery, 1983-84, New Orleans Legal Svcs., 1986-89; affiliate Transportation Rsch. Bd. Editor: Public Infrastructure, 1988, Growth Management: The Planning Challenge of the 1990s, 1992, Classic Readings in Urban Planning, 1994, Classic Readings in Real Estate and Development, 1995; editl. bd. mem. Jour. Arch. and Planning Rsch., Jour. Infrastructure Systems; contbr. chpts. to books and articles to profl. jours. Mem. Am. Inst. Cert. Planners, Am. Planning Assn. (mem. jour. editl. bd. 1984-88, 95—), Assn. Collegiate Schs. Planning (mem. exec. com. 1980-82), Fla. Am. Planning Assn. (v.p.), Urban Land Inst. (affiliate). Avocations: tennis, photography. Office: Univ Fla Coll Architecture Dept Urban & Regional Planning Gainesville FL 32611

STEIN, JAY WOBITH, legal research and education consultant; b. Sauk Centre, Minn., June 19, 1920; s. Julius A. and Emaline (Wobith) S.; children: Holly Jayne, Navida Carol, April Jae, Andrew John, John Henry. BA cum laude, U. Minn., 1942; MA, Stanford U., 1949, Syracuse U., 1960; MS, Columbia U., 1950, PhD. 1957. Dir. CIA rsch. team, 1947-49; dir. library, asst. prof. social studies Southwestern U., Memphis, 1954-57; asst. dir. librs., adminstv. assoc. to v.p. Syracuse (N.Y.) U., 1958-61; faculty Maxwell Sch., Syracuse, 1959-61; asst. to pres. Drake U., Des Moines, Iowa, 1961-64; dir. State Higher Edn. Commn., Des Moines, 1964-67; dean Coll. Arts and Scis., prof. polit. sci. Western Ill. U., Macomb, 1967-69, prof. polit. sci. and edn., 1969-74; prof. rsch. libr. John Marshall Law Sch. Libr., Chgo., 1989-94; rsch. cons. law, libr., edn. Columbus, Ohio, 1995—; catalogue planner, econs. and govt., N.Y. Pub. Library, 1953; proposal reviewer U.S. Dept. Edn. Fund for the Improvement of Post-secondary Edn., 1982. Author: The Mind and the

Sword, 1961, How Society Governs Education, 1975, Mass Media, Education and a Better Society, 1979, Society, Culture and Education, 1984, others; editor Scholar and Educator jour., 1977-85; contbr. articles to profl. jours. Mem. Coun. of Faculties of Bd. Govs. State Colls. and Univs., 1980-86, chmn. 1984-85; Family Cultural Ensemble, 1968-71; active with ch. and civic groups. With USN, 1942-46. Coolidge Found. fellow, 1980; grantee Univ. Rsch. Coun., others; recipient various overseas grants, 1970-80, including U. Bonn Acad. Exch., Germany, Internat. Recreation Assn., Switzerland, U.S. Dept. Edn., Europe and Egypt, also Iran, USSR. Mem. ABA (assoc.), ALA (life), ASPA, Am. Arbitration Assn. (panel of arbitrators), Am. Judicature Soc., Am. Polit. Sci. Assn. Soc. Advancement Edn., Soc. Educators and Scholars (founder 1976, exec. dir. 1976-82, chmn. bd. 1980-88), Rotary, Phi Beta Kappa, Phi Kappa Phi, Phi Delta Kappa, Alpha Mu Gamma, Pi Sigma Alpha, Lambda Alpha Psi. Avocations: books, swimming, running. Office: 518 E Town # 510 Columbus OH 43215

STEIN, JEROME LEON, economist, educator; b. Bklyn., Nov. 14, 1928; s. Meyer and Ida (Shapiro) S.; m. Hadassah Levow, Aug. 27, 1950; children: Seth, Gil, Ilana. B.A. summa cum laude, Bklyn. Coll., 1949; M.A., Yale U., 1950, Ph.D., 1955. Instr. Brown U., Providence, 1953-56; asst. prof. Brown U., 1956-60, assoc. prof., 1960-62, prof., 1962-70, Eastman prof. polit. economy, 1970-94, prof. emeritus, 1994; vis. prof. Hebrew U., Jerusalem, 1965-66, 72-73, 78; Ford Found. rsch. prof. econs. U. Calif., Berkeley, 1979-80, Sorbonne, U. Paris, 1982, Tohoku U., Sendai, Japan, 1983, Haute Etudes Comml., France, 1987, Monash U., Melbourne U., Australia, 1989, U. Aix-en-Provence, Marseille, France, 1992, 95, U. Munich, 1994, La Sapienza, Rome, 1994. Author: Essays in International Finance, 1962, (with G.M. Borts) Economic Growth in a Free Market, 1964, Money and Capacity Growth, 1971, Monetarism, 1976, Monetarist, Keynesian and New Classical Economics, 1982, Economics of Futures Markets, 1986, International Finance Markets, 1991, Fundamental Determinants of Exchange Rates, 1995; bd. editors: Am. Econ. Rev, 1974-80; assoc. editor: Jour. of Finance, 1964-70. Ford Found. faculty fellow, 1961-62; Social Sci. Research Council grantee, 1965-66; Guggenheim fellow, 1972-73. Mem. Am. Econ. Assn. Home: 77 Elton St Providence RI 02906-4505 Office: Brown U 79 Waterman St Providence RI 02912-9079

STEIN, JOSEPH, playwright; b. N.Y.C.; s. Charles and Emma S.; m. Elisa Loti, Feb. 7, 1975; children by previous marriage: Daniel, Harry, Joshua; children of present marriage: John, Jenny Lyn. BSS, CCNY, 1934; MSW, Columbia U., 1937. Psychiat. social worker N.Y.C., 1938-45. Writer: radio shows, including Raleigh's Room, 1948-49, Henry Morgan Show, 1949-52; TV shows, including Your Show of Shows, 1952-54; Sid Caesar Show, 1954-55; playwright Plain and Fancy, 1955; Mr. Wonderful, 1957, Juno, 1959, Take Me Along, 1959, Enter Laughing, 1963, Fiddler on the Roof, 1964 (Am. Theatre Wing Tony award for best musical, 1965, N.Y. Drama Critics Circle award Best Musical 1965), Zorba, 1968 (Tony nomination), Irene, 1975, King of Hearts, 1978, Carmelina, 1979, The Baker's Wife, 1983, (Olivier award nomination London 1989), Rags, 1986 (Tony nomination); screenplays Enter Laughing, 1970; Fiddler on the Roof, 1972 (Screen Actors Guild award). Mem. Authors League, Screen Writers Guild (award recipient), Dramatists Guild Coun. Home: 1130 Park Ave New York NY 10128-1255 Office: 250 W 57th St New York NY 10102-0158

STEIN, MARSHALL DAVID, lawyer; b. Greensboro, N.C., Dec. 17, 1941; s. Joseph and Celia (Feuer) S.; m. Helene Sue Weiner, Mar. 20, 1965; children: Lisa D., Daniel R. BA, Brandeis U., 1964; LLB, Boston U., 1967. Bar: Mass. 1968, U.S. Dist. Ct. Mass. 1970, U.S. Dist. Ct. Vt. 1978, U.S. Ct. Appeals (1st cir.) 1971, U.S. Supreme Ct. 1981. Asst. U.S. atty. U.S. Atty.'s Office U.S. Dist. Ct. Mass., 1974-76; chief staff atty. (1st cir.) U.S. Ct. Appeals, Boston, 1976-78; ptnr. Cherwin & Glickman, Boston, 1983—. Assoc. editor Mass. Law Rev., Boston 1980-90; contbr. articles to profl. jours. Panelist issues in housing discrimination U.S. Commn. Civil Rights, Washington, 1985. Mem. Mass. Bar Assn., Boston Bar Assn. (chmn. judicial pay raise subcom. 1993—). Jewish. Office: Cherwin & Glickman 1 International Pl Boston MA 02110-2600

STEIN, MARTIN DONALD, architect; b. Phila., Jan. 1, 1931; s. Abraham and Rosella (Silverberg) S.; m. Sara Bonnett; children: Lincoln, Rafael, Joshua, Aram. BArch, Pa. State U., 1954. Architect Louis Allen Abramson Architects, N.Y.C., 1956-58, Resneck & Green Architects, N.Y.C., 1958-63; proj. mgr., dir. design, v.p. Max O. Urbahn Assocs., N.Y.C., 1963-80; pres., chief exec. officer Urbahn Assocs., Inc., N.Y.C., 1981—. Contbr. articles to profl. jours. Vol lectr., career advisor on architecture to local high schs., colls., 1976—. Served with U.S. Army, 1954-56. Recipient numerous archtl. awards. Mem. AIA, Nat. Trust for Hist. Preservation, Soc. Am. Mil. Engrs., Nat. Council of Archtl. Registration Bds. Jewish. Avocations: skydiving, gardening, landscaping. Office: Urbahn Assocs Inc 1250 Broadway New York NY 10001-3701

STEIN, MARVIN, psychiatrist, educator; b. St. Louis, Dec. 8, 1923; s. Samuel G. and Dora (Kline) S.; m. Ann Hackman, May 5, 1950; children: Leslie, David, Lisa. BS, MD, Washington U., St. Louis, 1949; grad., Phila. Psychoanalytic Inst., 1959. Intern St. Louis City Hosp., 1949-50; asst. resident in psychiatry Barnes Hosp., St. Louis, 1950-51; fellow in psychiatry Hosp. U. Pa., 1953-55; asst. prof., then assoc. prof. psychiatry U. Pa. Med. Sch., 1956-63; prof. psychiatry Cornell U. Med. Sch., N.Y.C., 1963-66; prof., chmn. dept. psychiatry SUNY Downstate Med. Ctr., Bklyn., 1966-71; chmn. dept. psychiatry Mt. Sinai Sch. Medicine, N.Y.C., 1971-87, Esther and Joseph Klingenstein prof., 1971-94, Esther and Joseph Klingenstein prof. emeritus, 1994—; mem. fellowships rev. panel NIMH, 1961-64, chmn. mental health extramural rsch. adv. com., 1968-71, chmn. rev. com. Mental Health Aspects of AIDS, 1988-90; mem. rsch. adv. com. VA, 1965-68, mem. rsch. svc. merit rev. bd. in behavioral sci., 1972-75; chmn. Mental Health Rsch. Career Award Com., 1963-67; chmn. bd. dirs. Founds. Fund for Rsch. in Psychiatry, 1967-70; mem. behavioral medicine study sect. NIH, 1981-83, geriatric rev. com., 1986-88. Contbr. articles on brain and behavior and immune function to med. jours. USPHS postdoctoral fellow, 1951-53; mental health career investigator, 1956-61; sr. fellow grantee, 1961-63. Mem. Am. Psychiat. Assn. (chmn. rsch. coun. 1981-84), N.Y. Acad. Medicine (Salmon com. 1984—). Home: 5700 Arlington Ave Bronx NY 10471-1503 Office: Mt Sinai Sch Medicine 1 Gustave L Levy Pl New York NY 10029-6504

STEIN, MICHAEL HENRY, lawyer; b. New Haven, Conn., Aug. 28, 1942; s. Joseph and Sylvia (Susman) S.; m. Eileen McGinley, June 13, 1965. BA, Swarthmore Coll., 1964; LLB, Columbia U., 1968. Bar: D.C. 1971. Lectr. law U. Botswana, Lesotho, Swaziland, Roma, Lesotho, 1968-70; trial atty. U.S. Justice Dept., Washington, 1970-77; gen. counsel U.S. Internat. Trade Commn., Washington, 1977-84; ptnr. Verner, Liipfert, Bernhard, McPherson & Hand, Chartered, Washington, 1984-85, Dewey Ballantine, Washington, 1985—. Mem. Fed. Circ. Bar Assn. (bd. dirs. 1990—). Avocations: sailing, sheep dog trialing. Office: Dewey Ballantine 1775 Pennsylvania Ave NW Ste 200 Washington DC 20006-4605

STEIN, MILTON MICHAEL, lawyer; b. N.Y.C., Sept. 18, 1936; s. Isidore and Sadie (Lefkowitz) S.; m. Jacqueline Martin, June 17, 1962; children: April, Alicia. AB, Columbia U., 1958, LLB, 1961. Bar: N.Y. 1962, Pa. 1971, U.S. Supreme Ct. 1971. Asst. dist. atty. N.Y. County, 1962-67; sr. counsel Nat. Commn. for Reform of Fed. Criminal Law, Washington, 1967-70; asst. dist. atty., chief of appeals City of Phila., 1970-73; asst. dir. Nat. Wire Tapping Commn., Washington, 1973-75; dir. D.C. Law Revision, Washington, 1975-77; spl. asst. HUD, Washington, 1977-79; asst. gen. counsel U.S. Commodity Futures Trading Commn., Washington, 1979-83; v.p. N.Y. Futures Exch., N.Y.C., 1983-89, N.Y. Stock Exch., N.Y.C., 1989—. Mem. ABA, N.Y. State Bar Assn., Assn. of Bar of City of N.Y. Democrat. Jewish.

STEIN, MYRON, internist, educator; b. Boston, May 27, 1925; s. Isador and Sara Ester (Zimble) S.; m. Pauline June Alpert, June 21, 1953 (dec. 1992); children: Lisa Jayne, Susan Jo Stein-Matthews, Amy Stein Weinberg, Laurie Jennifer. BA, Dartmouth Coll., 1948; MD, Tufts U., 1952. Diplomate Am. Bd. Internal Medicine. Assoc. medicine Med. Sch. Harvard U., Boston, 1957-65; assoc. prof. med. sci. Brown U., Providence, 1965-68, prof. med. sci., 1968-73; pvt. practice medicine Beverly Hills, Calif.; clin. prof. med. Sch. Medicine, UCLA, 1973-75, clin. prof., 1975—; cons. VA Hosp., Pro-

vidence, 1965-73, L.A., 1975-89, Wadsworth VA Med. Ctr.; mem. pulmonary study sect. NIH, Bethesda, Md., 1971-95. Editor: Pulmonary Embolic Disease, 1965, Pulmonary Thromboembolism, 1973, New Directions in Asthma, 1975, Bronchial Asthma, 1985, 3d edit., 1993; contbr. 120 articles to med. jours. Mem. bd. corp. vis. com. Sch. Medicine Tufts U., Medford, Mass., 1986; bd. overseers, 1987. With AUS, 1943-46. Recipient Maimonides award Govt. of Israel, 1982. Fellow Am. Coll. Chest Physicians (sr. editor 1971-79); mem. Calif. Thoracic Soc. (sec.-treas. 1978, pres. 1981), L.A. Trudeau Soc., New Eng. Pulmonary Soc., Calif. Lung Assn. (chmn. edn. com. 1978-82, bd. dirs. 1981, Calif. medal 1989). Democrat. Jewish. Avocations: tennis, jogging, collecting lead soldiers. Office: 414 N Camden Dr Ste 1100 Beverly Hills CA 90210-4532

STEIN, OTTO LUDWIG, botany educator; b. Augsburg, Germany, Jan. 14, 1925; came to U.S., 1939, naturalized, 1944; s. Julius and Margaret (Haas) S.; m. Diana Borut, June 15, 1958; children: Deborah Lee, Judith Ann, Suzanne Beth, Jonathan Henri Richard. B.S. with distinction, U. Minn., 1949, M.S., 1952, Ph.D., 1954. Instr. botany U. Mo. at Columbia, 1955; USPHS research fellow Brookhaven Nat. Lab., 1955-57, research collaborator, 1958-68; asst. prof. botany U. Mont., Missoula, 1957-63; asso. prof. U. Mont., 1963-64; asso. prof. botany U. Mass., Amherst, 1964-70; prof. botany U. Mass., 1970-90, prof. emeritus, 1990—, head dept., 1969-74; dir. U. Mass./U. Freiburg (Germany) Exchange Program, 1979; vis. asst. prof. botany U. Calif., Berkeley, 1961-62. Served with AUS, 1944-46. NATO sr. research fellow Imperial Coll., London, Eng., 1971-72. Fellow Linnean Soc. (London), AAAS; mem. Bot. Soc. Am. (chmn. developmental sect. 1963-65), Soc. Developmental Biology, Soc. Exptl. Biology, Sigma Xi, Gamma Sigma Delta, Alpha Zeta, Gamma Alpha. Home: 140 Red Gate Ln Amherst MA 01002-1845 Office: U Mass Dept Biology Amherst MA 01003

STEIN, PAUL ARTHUR, financial services executive; b. St. Louis, Aug. 20, 1937; s. Harry Arthur and Julia (Vandivort) S.; m. Ann Garwood, Oct. 8, 1960 (dec. 1993); children: Valerie Suzanne, Paul Garwood. AB, Dartmouth U., 1959. From trainee to dir. spl. market offices Merrill Lynch, N.Y.C. and Princeton, 1959—; dir., officer VIP, Inc. Mem. Beacon Hill Club (Summit, N.J.), N.J. Ctr. for Visual Arts (officer and trustee), Securities Industry Inst. (former trustee). Episcopalian.

STEIN, PAUL DAVID, cardiologist; b. Cin., Apr. 13, 1934; s. Simon and Sadie (Friedman) S.; m. Janet Louise Tucker, Aug. 14, 1966; children: Simon, Douglas, Rebecca. BS, U. Cin., 1955, MD, 1959. Intern Jewish Hosp., Cin., 1959-60, med. resident, 1961-62; med. resident Gorgas Hosp., C.Z., 1960-61; fellow in cardiology U. Cin., 1962-63, Mt. Sinai Hosp., N.Y.C., 1963-64; rsch. fellow Harvard Med. Sch., Boston, 1964-66; asst. dir. cardiac catheterization lab. Baylor U. Med. Ctr., Dallas, 1966-67; asst. prof. medicine Creighton U., Omaha, 1967-69; assoc. prof. medicine U. Okla., Oklahoma City, 1969-73; prof. rsch. medicine U. Okla. Coll. Medicine, Oklahoma City, 1973-76; dir. cardiovascular rsch. Henry Ford Hosp., Detroit, 1976-94, med. dir. cardiovascular rehab., 1994—; adj. prof. physics Oakland U., Rochester, Mich., 1985—; Henry Ford prof. medicine Case Western Res. U., Cleve., 1994—. Author: A Physical and Physiological Basis for the Interpretation of Cardiac Auscultation: Evaluations Based Primarily on Second Sound and Ejection Murmurs, 1981; contbr. articles to profl. jours. Coun. on Clin. Cardiology fellow Am. Heart Assn., 1971, Coun. on Circulation fellow, 1972. Fellow ACP, Am. Coll. Cardiology, Am. Coll. Chest Physicians (pres. 1993), Internat. Acad. Chest Physicians and Surgeons (pres. 1993); mem. ASME, Am. Physiol. Soc., Ctrl. Soc. Clin. Rsch. Office: Henry Ford Hosp New Center Pavillion 2921 W Grand Blvd Detroit MI 48202-2691

STEIN, PAULA JEAN ANNE BARTON, hotel real estate consultant; b. Chgo., July 29, 1929; m. Marshal L. Stein: children: George L., Guy G. BA, Lake Forest (Ill.) U., 1951; postgrad., Roosevelt U., Chgo., 1955-77, UCLA, 1978-79. Lic. internat. hotel and mgmt. cons./broker, Ill. Adminstry. asst. publicity Kefauver for Pres., Chgo., 1951; adminstry. asst. Wells Orgns., Chgo., 1952; writer Employers Assn. Am., Chgo., 1952, Woodworking Jobbers Assn., Chgo., 1953; cons. L.A., 1978-80; founder, pres., ptnr., cons. internat. hotel real estate Steinvest, Inc., Chgo., 1980—; cons. Spindrift, Inc., Chgo., 1980—; trustee St. Joseph's Coll., Renssaelaer, Ind., 1986—. Recipient Corp. Leadership award Hispanic Am. Contractors Industry, 1988, John Hyman Corp. award, 1988. Mem. Chgo. Real Estate Bd., Ill. Real Estate Bd., Nat. Assn. Realtors, Met. Planning Coun., Lambda Alpha. Clubs: Met., Standard, Northmoor. Office: Stein & Co 208 S La Salle St Ste 1630 Chicago IL 60604-1103

STEIN, RICHARD ALLEN, real estate developer; b. Chgo., Jan. 16, 1939; s. Joseph and Selma (Strauss) S.; m. Carol Katzman, Oct. 1, 1967; children: Barbara, Katherine. BS in Hotel Adminstrn., Cornell U., 1961. Cert. property mgr. Ptnr., founder The Littlestone Co., Chgo., 1961-71; chmn., chief exec. officer Stein & Co., Chgo., 1971—; bd. dirs. Exch. Nat. Bank Chgo., Evanston/Northwestern U. Research Park, Ill., Navy Pier Devel. Authority; mem. adv. com. Civic Fedn. Chgo., 1985—; mem. Urban Land Inst., 1986—. Bd. dirs. Chgo. Urban League, 1987—, The Lambs, Inc., Libertyville, Ill., 1981—; trustee Ravinia Festival Assn., Highland Park, Ill., 1985—; bd. trustees St. Joseph's Coll., Renssaelaer, Ind., 1986—. Recipient Corp. Leadership award Hispanic Am. Contrs. Industry, 1988, Developer of Yr. award Black Contractors United, 1988, John Hyman Corp. award, 1988. Mem. Chgo. Real Estate Bd., Ill. Real Estate Bd., Nat. Assn. Realtors, Met. Planning Coun., Lambda Alpha. Clubs: Met., Standard, Northmoor. Office: Stein & Co 208 S La Salle St Ste 1630 Chicago IL 60604-1103

STEIN, RICHARD PAUL, lawyer; b. New Albany, Ind., Sept. 2, 1925; s. William P. and Lillian M. (Russell) S.; m. Mary Charlotte Key, June 22, 1959; children: Richard Paul, William, Patricia. Student, Miligan (Tenn.) Coll., 1943-44, Duke, 1944-45; J.D., U. Louisville, 1950. Bar: Ind., 1950. With labor relations Goodyear Engring. Co., Charlestown, Ind., 1952-54; ptnr. Naville & Stein, New Albany, 1954-61; pros. atty. 52d Jud. Circuit Ind., 1956-61; U.S. atty. So. Dist. Ind., 1961-67; chmn. Pub. Service Commn. of Ind., 1967-70; legis. counsel Eli Lilly Co., Indpls., 1970-74; v.p. pub. affairs Pub. Service Co. Ind., 1974-90; atty., pub. affairs cons., 1990—; dir. Indpls. Indians; Co-counsel New Albany-Floyd County Bldg. Authority, 1960-62; mem. State Bd. Tax Commrs. Adv. Bd., Ind. Study Commn. Sec. New Albany Dist. Dem. Com., 1956-61; chmn. New Albany United Way, 1957. Served to lt. USNR, 1943-46, 50-51; lt. Res. Named Floyd County Young Man of Yr. Floyd County Jr. C. of C., 1955, Outstanding Young Man of Yr. New ALbany Jaycees. 1958. Mem. Ind. Bar Assn., Marion County Bar Assn., Ind. Prosecutors Assn. (pres. 1960-61), Ind. Electric Assn. (dir.), Am. Legion, Pi Kappa Alpha, Phi Alpha Delta. Roman Catholic. Clubs: Highland Country, Skyline Lodge: K.C. Avocations: tennis, golf, reading. Home: 9315 Spring Forest Dr Indianapolis IN 46260-1269

STEIN, RICHARD STEPHEN, chemistry educator; b. N.Y.C., Aug. 21, 1925; s. Isidor and Florence (Lewengood) S.; m. Judith Elma Balise, May 27, 1951; children: Linda Ann, Anne Marie, Carol Joan, Lisa Jean. BS, Poly. Inst. Bklyn., 1945; MA, Princeton U., 1948, PhD, 1949; DS (hon.), U. Ulm, Fed. Republic Germany, 1989; DSc (hon.), U. Mass., 1992. Postdoctoral fellow Cambridge U., 1948-49; research assoc. Princeton U., 1949-50; asst. prof. U. Mass., Amherst, 1950-57; asso. prof. U. Mass., 1957-59, prof., 1959-61, Commonwealth prof., 1961-80, Goessman prof. chemistry, 1980-92; Goessman prof. emeritus, 1992—; founder, dir. Polymer Research Inst. U. Mass., 1961—; cons. Monsanto Co., Exxon Corp., Polaroid Corp., Proctor and Gamble. Co-editor: Electromagnetic Scattering, 1967, Structure and Properties of Polymer Films, 1973; contbr. numerous articles to profl. jours. Recipient Internat. award Soc. Plastics Engrs., 1969, Bingham award Rheology Soc., 1972, Award for Disting. svc. for Advancement of Polymer Sci., Soc. Polymer Sci. Japan, 1988, Gordon Res. Conf. Huggins award, 1987. Mem. NAS, NAE, AAAS, AAUP, Am. Acad. Arts and Scis., chem. Soc. (Bordon award 1972, Polymer Chemistry award 1983), Am. Phys. Soc. (award in high polymer physics 1976), Rheology Soc., Sigma Xi. Founder sci. rheo-optics of polymers. Home: 5 Berkshire Ter Amherst MA 01002-1301

STEIN, ROBERT, consumer products company executive; b. Budapest, Hungary, Apr. 24, 1939; s. Lipot and Sarolta (Klein) S.; m. Elaine Ruth Slayton, July 7, 1963; children: Jeffrey, Michael. BS in Acctg., U. Bridgeport, 1962, MBA, 1977. Budget analyst McGraw-Hill, N.Y.C., 1963-

66; mgr. budget/acctg. Xerox, N.Y.C., Stamford (Conn.), 1966-72; group contr. AMF, White Plains, N.Y., 1972-78; v.p. fin., chief fin. officer Empire of Carolina, N.Y.C., 1978-80; pres., chief exec. officer Ekco Group, Nashua, N.H., 1980—; bd. dirs. Hood Enterprises, Newport, R.I. Overseer Lawrence (Mass.) Gen. Hosp., 1991; mem. fin. com. Temple Emanuel, Andover, Mass., 1991; bd. dirs. Youth Soccer, Andover, 1991. Sgt. USAR, 1963-71. Mem. Nat. Assn. Mgmt. Accts., Fin. Exec. Inst., Orgn. for Growth (Boston), Cookware Mfg. Assn. (bd. dirs.), Nat. Housewares Mfg. Assn. (bd. dirs.). Jewish. Avocations: tennis, skiing, golf. Home: 30 Blood Rd Andover MA 01810-4722 Office: Ekco Group Inc 98 Spit Brook Rd Nashua NH 03062-5737

STEIN, ROBERT ALAN, electronics company executive; b. Chgo., Oct. 18, 1930; s. Manfred and Mildred (Rosenfield) S.; m. Frances Roslyn Berger, Dec. 25, 1960; 1 dau., Marcia Beth. B.A., U. Chgo., 1950, M.B.A. 1953. C.P.A., Ill. Sr. auditor Scovell, Wellington & Co., Chgo., 1955-63; supr. corp. acctg. Mack Trucks, Inc., Montvale, N.J., 1963-65; v.p. fin., treas. Lionel Corp., N.Y.C., 1965-82; pres. ITI Electronics, Inc., Fairfield, N.J., 1982—. Served with U.S. Army, 1953-55. Mem. Am. Inst. CPAs. Home: 32 Stonewall Dr Livingston NJ 07039-1822 Office: 12 Kulick Rd Fairfield NJ 07004-3308

STEIN, ROBERT BENJAMIN, biomedical researcher, physician; b. Buffalo, Oct. 28, 1950; s. Frank and Eleanor (Bankoff) S.; m. Marcia Joan Lieberman, Aug. 10, 1975 (div.); children: Rebecca Anna, Joshua David; m. Sophia Anne Rose, Dec. 29, 1989; children: Susan Claire, Stephanie Michelle. BS, Ind. U., 1972; MD, PhD, Duke U., 1979. Diplomate Am. Bd. Anatomic and Clin. Pathology. House staff Duke U. Med. Ctr., Durham, N.C., 1980-83; sr. research fellow Dept. Virus and Cell Biology Merck Sharp & Dohme Rsch. Labs., West Point, Pa., 1983-87, assoc. dir. molecular and cardiovascular pharmacology, 1987-89, sr. dir., head dept. pharmacology, 1989-90; v.p. rsch. Ligand Pharms., Inc., San Diego, 1990—. Contbr. articles to profl. jours., chpts. to books. Ins. Med. scholar, 1977-79; James B. Duke scholar, 1976-78; Lang Med. Pub. award, 1979; NIH grantee, 1974-75. Fellow Am. Soc. Clin. Pathologists, N.Y. Acad. Scis., Am. Physiol. Soc., AAAS, Sigma Xi, Phi Beta Kappa, Alpha Omega Alpha. Avocations: piano, history, literature, windsurfing. Home: 4431 Heritage Glen Ln San Diego CA 92130-2419 Office: Ligand Pharms Inc 9393 Towne Centre Dr Ste 100 San Diego CA 92121-3016

STEIN, ROBERT WILLIAM, actuary, accountant; b. Milw., Feb. 4, 1949; s. Herbert A. and Elizabeth (Greenman) S.; children: Paul, Jennifer; m. Christine Marie Denham, May 14, 1988. BBA, Drake U., 1971. CPA, N.Y. Cons. actuary Milliman & Robertson, Inc., Milw., 1971-74, Denver, 1974-80; sr. mgr. Ernst & Whinney, Denver, 1976-80; ptnr. Ernst & Whinney, Chgo., 1980-87, N.Y.C., 1987—. Author: Universal Life, 1980; contbr. articles on fin. mgmt. Fellow Soc. Actuaries (bd. govs. 1990-93); mem. AICPA, Am. Acad. Actuaries. Avocations: raising and riding horses, skiing. Office: Ernst & Young 787 7th Ave New York NY 10019

STEIN, RONALD JAY, artist, airline transport pilot; b. N.Y.C., Sept. 15, 1930; s. William and Ruth (Krasner) S. Diploma, The Cooper Union, 1953; BFA, Yale U., 1955; MFA, Rutgers U., 1960; grad., FAA Acad. Pilot Examiner Sch., 1980. Cons. Aviation Assocs., 1988—; mem. faculty Worcester Mus. Fine Arts, Rutgers U., 1960-63; aviation cons.; pilot examiner, accident prevention safety counselor FAA. One man shows sculpture and paintings include, Mirski Gallery, Boston, 1956, Inst. Contemporary Art, Boston, 1958, Irving Gallery, Milw., 1960, 71, Mayer Gallery, N.Y.C., 1960, 61, Reighaupt Gallery, Boston, 1966, Tibor Denagy Gallery, N.Y.C., 1964, N.Y. World's Fair, 1964, Marlborough Gallery, London, 1967, Kind Gallery, Chgo., 1969, Hokin Gallery, Palm Beach, Fla., 1974, Benson Gallery, L.I., N.Y., 1988, Benton Gallery, South Hampton, N.Y., 1988, 89, Odeon Gallery, Sag Harbor, N.Y., 1993; exhibited in group shows, Inst. Contemporary Art, Boston, Corcoran Gallery, Washington, Contemporary Arts Mus., Houston, U. N.C. Raleigh, Mus. Contemporary Art, Chgo., Benton Gallery, South Hampton, N.Y., Mus. Modern Art, N.Y.C., Cornell U., Ithaca, N.Y., Finch Coll. Mus. Fine Arts, N.Y.C.; represented in permanent collections, Am. Fedn. Art, N.Y.C., Guggenheim Mus., N.Y.C., Carnegie Inst., Chgo., Tenn. Fine Arts Ctr., Nashville, Mus. Contemporary Art, Chgo., Wadsworth Atheneaum, Hartford, Conn., Finch Coll. Mus. Art, N.Y.C., Guild Hall, East Hampton, N.Y., Mus. Modern Arts, N.Y.C., Smithsonian Instn., others. Commd. spl. min. of eucharist Most Holy Trinity Roman Cath. Ch., East Hampton, N.Y., 1992—. Capt. U.S. Mcht. Marine, 1976-81. Mem. NRA, Yale Club. Republican. Home: 836 Fireplace Rd East Hampton NY 11937-1512

STEIN, RUTH ELIZABETH KLEIN, physician; b. N.Y.C., Nov. 2, 1941; d. Theodore and Mimi (Foges) Klein; m. H. David Stein, June 9, 1963; children: Lynn Andrea Stein Melnick, Sharon Lisa, Deborah Michelle. AB, Barnard Coll., 1962; MD, Albert Einstein Coll. Medicine, 1966. Diplomate Am. Bd. Pediatrics. Intern, then resident Bronx Mcpl. Hosp. Ctr., 1966-68; sr. resident, fellow Children's Hosp. Med. Ctr., Washington, 1968-69; instr. dept. pediatrics George Washington U., Washington, 1969-70; with Albert Einstein Coll. of Medicine, Bronx, 1970—, assoc. prof. pediatrics, 1977-83, prof., 1983—; vice chmn. dept. pediatrics Albert Einstein Coll., 1992—; pediatrician-in-chief, dir. pediatrics Bronx Mcpl. Hosp. Ctr., 1992—; vis. prof. pub. health dept. epidemiology Yale U. Sch. of Medicine, New Haven, 1986-87; prin. investigator Preventive Intervention Rsch. Ctr. for Child Health, N.Y., Nat. Child Health Assessment Planning Project, N.Y., Behavioral Pediatric Tng. Program, N.Y.; dir. gen. pediatrics Pediatric Div., N.Y.; apptd. to Montefiore Med. Ctr., North Ctrl. Bronx Hosp. Editor: Caring for Children with Chronic Illness: Issues and Strategies, 1989; mem. editorial bd. Jour. Behavioral and Devel. Pediatrics; contbr. articles to profl. jours. Fellow Am. Acad. Pediatrics; mem. APHA, Am. Pediatric Soc., Soc. for Pediatric Rsch., Ambulatory Pediatric Assn. (bd. dirs. 1982-89, pres. 1987-88), Soc. for Behavioral Pediatrics, Alpha Omega Alpha. Jewish. Home: 91 Larchmont Ave Larchmont NY 10538-3748 Office: Albert Einstein Coll Medicine 1300 Morris Park Ave Bronx NY 10461-1975

STEIN, SANDRA LOU, educational psychologist, educator; b. Freeport, Ill., Oct. 6, 1942; d. William Kenneth and Marien Elizabeth (Dahlgren) S. BS, U. Wis., Madison, 1964; MS in Edn., No. Ill. U., 1967, EdD, 1969. Tchr. English Rockford (Ill.) Sch. Dist., 1964-65; tchr. Russian Jefferson County Sch. Dist., Lakewood, Colo., 1965-66; asst. prof. edn. U. S.C., Columbia, 1969-71, No. Ill. U., DeKalb, 1971-72, Rider U., Lawrenceville, N.J., 1972-75; assoc. prof. edn. Rider Coll., Lawrenceville, N.J., 1975-81, prof. edn., 1981—, dept. chair, 1983-91; cons. on measurement and evaluation, women's advs., 1973—. Contbr. articles to ednl. publs. Treas. Lawrenceville Men's Breakfast Club, 1983-85; deacon Presbyn. Ch. Lawrenceville, 1984-87; contest judge N.J. Fedn. Bus. and Profl. Women, 1989; vol. Habitat for Humanity, Trenton, N.J., 1989. Recipient Disting. Teaching award Rider Coll. and Lindback Found., 1981. Mem. AAUP (Outstanding Achievement award Rider Coll. chpt. 1988), Am. Ednl. Rsch. Assn., Am. Psychol. Assn., Phi Delta Kappa (pres. 1986-87, Svc. Key award 1991, faculty advisor 1994—). Office: Rider U 2083 Lawrenceville Rd Trenton NJ 08648-3099

STEIN, SEYMOUR, electronic scientist; b. Bklyn., Apr. 4, 1928; s. Louis Harry and Clara (Roth) S.; m. Corinne Leader, Sept. 14, 1954; children: Paul M., Emily L. BEE, CCNY, 1949; MS in Applied Physics, Harvard U., 1950, PhD in Applied Physics, 1955. Sr. engring. specialist Applied Rsch. Lab., GTE Sylvania, Waltham, Mass., 1954-56, sr. scientist, 1959-64, assoc. dir., 1964-66; dir. Communications Systems Lab., GTE Sylvania, Waltham, 1966-69; staff mem. Hermes Electronics, Cambridge, Mass., 1956-59; pres. Stein Assocs. div. Adams-Russell Co. Waltham, 1969-79; pres. SCPE, Inc., Newton Centre, Mass., 1979—. Co-author: Communications Systems and Techniques, 1966, Modern Communication Principles, 1967. Fellow IEEE. Jewish. Office: SCPE Inc 56 Great Meadow Rd Newton MA 02159-2748

STEIN, SOL, publisher, writer, editor in chief; b. Chgo., Oct. 13, 1926; s. Louis and Zelda (Zam) S.; m. Patricia Day, Mar. 31, 1962; children: Kevin David, Jeffrey Lewelyn, Leland Dana, Robert Bruce, Andrew Charles, David Day, Elizabeth Day. BSS, CCNY, 1948; MA, Columbia U., 1949, postgrad., 1949-51. Lectr. social studies CCNY, 1948-51; sr. editor, ideological adv. staff Voice of Am., U.S. State Dept., 1951-53; gen. editor, originator Beacon Press Paperbacks, Boston, 1954—; cons. to pres. Harcourt, Brace,

Jovanovich, N.Y.C., 1958-59; exec. v.p. The Mid-Century Book Soc., N.Y.C., 1959-62; pres., editor in chief Stein & Day Pubs., Briarcliff Manor, N.Y., 1962-89; pres. The Colophon Corp., Scarborough, N.Y., 1983—, The WritePro Corp., 1989—, The Stein Software Corp., 1993—; lectr., playwright Columbia U., 1958-60, Dialogue for Writers, Pub., U. Calif., Irvine, 1990-93; treas. The Forensic Found., N.Y.C., 1959-62; founding mem. Playwrights Group, The Actors Studio, 1957. Author: (plays) The Illegitimist, 1953 (1st prize Dramatists Alliance), A Shadow of My Enemy, 1957, (novels) The Husband, 1969, The Magician, 1971, Living Room, 1974, The Childkeeper, 1975, Other People, 1979, The Resort, 1980, The Touch of Treason, 1985, A Deniable Man, 1989, The Best Revenge, 1991, (computer software) WritePro, The Stein Creative Writing Program, 1989—, FirstAid for Writers, 1991, FictionMaster, 1993, (nonfiction) A Feast for Lawyers, 1989; also articles, revs., poetry. Exec. dir. Am. Com. for Cultural Freedom, 1953-56; mem. exec. com. Am. Friends of Captive Nations. Served to 1st lt. AUS, 1945-47. Fellow Yaddo Found., 1952, MacDowell Colony, 1952-56. Recipient Disting. Instr. award U. Calif. at Irvine, 1992. Mem. New Dramatists Com. (coun. mem.), Internat. Brotherhood Magicians (hon. life), Writers Guild Am. East. Avocations: tennis, inventing computer software programs. Home: 43 Linden Cir Scarborough NY 10510 Office: The WritePro Corp 43 S Highland Ave Ossining NY 10562-5213

STEIN, STANLEY RICHARD, lawyer, fast food company executive; b. Boston, Apr. 17, 1942; s. Frederick J. and Minnie L. (Gilette) S.; m. Ann Debra Stein, July 2, 1967; children: Jason, Jamie. BA, Boston U., 1964; JD, Boston Coll., 1967. Bar: Mass., Ohio. Supervisory atty. NLRB, 1967-72; head labor rels. dept. Schottenstein, Garel & Zox, Columbus, Ohio, 1972-74; labor rels. counsel McDonald's Corp., Oak Brook, Ill., 1974-78, v.p. labor rels., 1978-81, v.p. pers. and labor rels., 1981—. Mem. ABA.

STEIN, STEPHEN ELLERY, research chemist, software engineer; b. N.Y.C., Dec. 13, 1948; s. Max and Rose (Zagon) S.; m. Beverly Ann Cipuzak, July 14, 1975; 1 child, Matthew. BS in Chemistry, U. Rochester, 1969; PhD in Phys. Chemistry, U. Wash., 1974. Rsch. chemist SRI Internat., Menlo Park, Calif., 1974-76; assoc. prof. chemistry W.Va. U., Morgantown, 1976-81; rsch. chemist Nat. Inst. Studies Tech., Gaithersburg, Md., 1981—. Author databases. Recipient Gold medal U.S. Dept. Commerce, 1988. Mem. Am. Chem. Soc. (councilor 1975, Storch award 1992), Am. Soc. for Mass Spectrometry. Achievments include production of data and software for technical databases (mass spectra, infrared spectra and chemical thermodynamics). Office: Nat Inst Studies Tech A260/222 Gaithersburg MD 20899

STEIN, STEPHEN WILLIAM, lawyer; b. N.Y.C., Apr. 12, 1937; s. Melvin S. and Cornelia (Jacobowitz) S.; m. Judith N., Jan. 22, 1966. AB, Princeton U., 1959; LLB, Columbia U., 1962; LLM, NYU, 1963. Bar: N.Y. 1962, Fla. 1962. Assoc. White & Case, N.Y.C., 1963-67; atty. advisor U.S. Agy. Internat. Devel., Washington, 1967-69; regional legal advisor Mission to India U.S. Agy. Internat. Devel., New Delhi, 1969-71; asst. gen. counsel U.S. Agy. Internat. Devel., Washington, 1971-73; assoc. prof. Delson & Gordon, N.Y.C., 1973-87; ptnr. Kelley Drye & Warren, N.Y.C., 1987—; mem. U.S. exec. com. Indonesian Trade, Tourism & Investment Promotion Program, 1990-92; mem. U.S.-Indonesia Trade & Investment Adv. Com., 1989-92; vis. instr. internat. Devel. Law Inst., 1993; lectr. Internat. Law Inst., Washington, 1984, 85; spkr. in field. Mem. ABA (mem. sect. internat. law, mem. com. internat. energy law, mem. com. internat. investment and devel., mem. com. Asia-Pacific law), Internat. Bar Assn. (mem. sect. energy resources law, mem. com. oil law, mem. com. gas law, mem. sect. bus. law, mem. com. internat. constrn. projects, chmn. subcom. constrn. financing and BOT projects), Assn. Bar City of N.Y. (mem. com. Asian affairs 1992—, mem. com. internat. law 1982-85, mem. com. fgn. and comparative law 1978-81), Am. Indonesian of C. (bd. dirs. 1986—, pres. 1989—). Home: 320 Central Park West New York NY 10025 Office: Kelley Drye & Warren 101 Park Ave New York NY 10178-0002

STEIN, WILLIAM WARNER, anthropology educator; b. Buffalo, Oct. 9, 1921; s. Carl and Blanche (Gutman) S.; m. Rhoda Ruth Spector, June 12, 1949 (dec. 1993); children: Daniel Julian, Susan Isabel. AB, U. Buffalo, 1949; PhD, Cornell U., 1955. Asst. prof. U. Miami, Coral Gables, Fla., 1956-61, U. Alta., Calgary, Can., 1961-63; from asst. to assoc. prof. U. Kans., Lawrence, 1963-65; from assoc. prof. to prof. SUNY, Buffalo, 1965-94, prof. emeritus, 1994—. Author: Hualcan: Life in the Highlands of Peru, 1961, El levantamiento de Atusparia, 1988, Mariátegui y Norka Rouskaya, 1989, El caso de los becerros hambrientos y otros ensayos de antropología económica peruana, 1991; editor: Peruvian Contexts of Change, 1985. Served with U.S. Army, 1941-45, ETO. Home: 131 Cadman Dr Buffalo NY 14221-6963 Office: SUNY at Buffalo Dept Of Anthropology Buffalo NY 14261

STEINBACH, SHELDON ELLIOT, lawyer; married; one child. BA, Johns Hopkins U., 1963; LLB, Columbia U., 1968; MAPA, U. Minn., 1968. Bar: Md. 1967, U.S. Dist. Ct. (D.C. dist.) 1968. Adminstrv. asst. to dean gen. extension div. U. Minn., Mpls., 1966-67; assoc. law firm Balt., 1967-69; lectr. polit. sci. Grad. Sch. George Washington U., 1973-74; gen. counsel, asst. dir. govtl. relations Am. Coun. Edn., Washington, 1974—; bd. trustees Mary Baldwin Coll., 1985—. Contbr. articles to profl. jours. Reporter law enforcement task force Mayor's Adv. Commn. on Crime, Balt., 1967-69; trustee Mary Baldwin Coll., 1985—. Mem. ABA, Md. Bar Assn., Am. Arbitration Assn. (nat. panel). Home: 6906 Tilden Ln Rockville MD 20852-4547 Office: Am Coun Edn One Dupont Ctr Ste 835 Washington DC 20036

STEINBACK, KENNETH B., computer sales company executive; b. St. Louis, Aug. 11, 1943; s. Sol Steinback and Dorothy (Millman) Steinback Vittert; m. Marilyn Ellen Dann, May 30, 1970; children: Susan Lynn, Robert Jay. BSBA, Washington U., St. Louis, 1966. Sys. analyst McDonnell Douglas Automation Co., St. Louis, 1966-67; mktg. rep. Honeywell Info. Systems, St. Louis, 1970-72; dist. sales mgr. Fabri-Tek, Inc., St. Louis, 1972-73; v.p. Computer Sales Internat., Inc., St. Louis, 1973-77, exec. v.p. 1977-80, pres., chmn., 1980-84, chmn., chief exec. officer, 1984—. Bd. dirs. Ctrl. Inst. for Deaf, 1986—, Jewish Ctr. for Aged, 1988—. 1st lt. U.S. Army, 1967-70. Mem. Am. Assn. Equipment Lessors, Computer Dealers and Lessors Assn. bd. dirs. 1982—; treas. 1984-86, chmn., chief exec. officer, 1988—). Avocations: golf, jogging, reading.

STEINBACK, ROBERT LAMONT, newspaper columnist; b. N.Y.C., Nov. 20, 1955; s. Robert Lee Jr. and Trudy Marcella (Miller) S. BA in Econs., U. Rochester, 1977; MS in Journalism, Northwestern U., 1983. Comml. credit analyst Chem. Bank N.Y. N.Am., Rochester, N.Y., 1977-81; stockbroker Merrill Lynch Pierce Fenner & Smith, Rochester, 1981-82; intern reporter Green Bay (Wis.) Press Gazette, 1982; reporter, editor, columnist Miami (Fla.) Herald, 1983—. Recipient Explanatory Journalism award Fla. Soc. Newspaper Editors, 1990, Green Shade award for best serious commentary Soc. Profl. Journalists, 1991. Office: Miami Herald 1 Herald Plz Miami FL 33132-1693

STEINBERG, ARTHUR G(ERALD), geneticist; b. Port Chester, N.Y., Feb. 27, 1912; s. Bernard Aaron and Sarah (Kaplan) S.; m. Edith Wexler, Nov. 22, 1939; children: Arthur E., Jean E. Strimling. B.S., CCNY, 1933; M.A., Columbia U., 1934, Ph.D. (Univ. fellow), 1941. Mem. genetics dept. McGill U., Montreal, Que., Can., 1940-44; chmn. dept. genetics Fels Research Inst., asso. prof. genetics Antioch Coll., Yellow Springs, Ohio, 1946-48; cons. div. biometry and med. stats. Mayo Clinic, Rochester, Minn., 1948-52; geneticist Children's Cancer Research Found. and research asso. Children's Hosp., Boston, 1952-56; prof. biology Case Western Res. U., Cleve., 1956-72; asst. prof. human genetics, dept. preventive medicine Case Western Res. U., 1956-60, asso. prof., 1960-70, prof. human genetics, dept. reproductive biology, 1970—, Francis Hobart Herrick prof. biology, 1972-82, emeritus, 1982—; prof. human genetics, dept. medicine, 1975-82; lectr. genetics dept. orthodontics Harvard Sch. Dental Medicine, 1975-78; dir. heredity clinic Lakeside Hosp., Cleve., 1958-76; vis. prof. Albert Einstein Med. Coll., N.Y.C., 1962, 64, 66, bull. U., Bloomington, 1972, NY U. Sch. Medicine, 1977; XIIth Jean. Raymond Dart lectr. U. Witwatersrand, Johannesburg, S.Africa, 1975; mem. permanent com. to arrange Internat. Congresses Human Genetics; mem. med. adv. bd. Cystic Fibrosis Found. Cleve., 1957-69; mem. sci. adv. bd. Nat. Cystic Fibrosis Research Found., 1961-63; cons. to expert adv. panel on human genetics WHO, 1961, mem. expert adv. panel,

1965-85; mem. research adv. com. United Cerebral Palsy Found. 1962-65; mem. med. adv. bd. Nat. Genetics Found., 1966-68, chmn., 1968-80; dir. WHO Collaborating Centre for Reference and Research on Genetic Factors of Human Immunoglobulins, 1966-78; cons. study of diabetes in Pima Indians NIH, 1970—. Editor: Am. Jour. Human Genetics, 1956-61; sr. editor: Progress in Med. Genetics, 1960-83; mem. internat. bd. editors: Human Genetics Abstracts, 1962—; cons. editor: Transfusion, 1964—; contbg. editor: Vox Sanguinis, 1965-79; contbr. articles to sci. jours. Bd. dirs. Cleve. Zoo; mem. Cleve. Inst. Art, Cleve. Mus. Art, Cleve. Health Mus., Mus. Natural History. Fellow Australian Acad. Sci. (sr.), AAAS; mem. Am. Soc. Human Genetics (pres. 1964, dir. 1954-66), Genetics Soc. Am., Am. Assn. Immunologists, Japanese Soc. Human Genetics (hon.), Societe Francaise d'Anthropologie et d'Ecologie Humaine (fgn. mem. sci. counsel 1972), Sigma Xi. Home: 20300 N Park Blvd Apt 4B Cleveland OH 44118-5026 Office: 405Nc Millis Sci Center Case Western Res U Cleveland OH 44106 *The motivation for my life's work (research and teaching) has been to learn more about heredity and its application to humanity. I am fortunate in that my wife has always been supportive of my efforts, while pursuing a career of her own.*

STEINBERG, ARTHUR JAY, lawyer; b. Bklyn., Sept. 25, 1955; s. Eugene and Estelle (Bzezensky) S.; m. Ninette Z. Zavelson, Oct. 19, 1980; children: Jaclyn, Lauren, Alyx. Ba cum laude in Econs., Columbia Coll., 1976; JD, N.Y.U., 1979. Bar: N.Y. 1980, U.S. Dist. Ct. (so. and ea. dists.) N.Y. 1980, U.S. Cir. Ct. (2d cir.) 1986, U.S. Cir. Ct. (4th cir.) 1991. With Kay, Scholer, Fierman, Hays, & Handler, N.Y.C., 1979-87; ptnr. Kay, Scholer, Fierman, Hays & Handler, N.Y.C., 1988—. Mem. ABA, Am. Banks Inst., N.Y.C. Bar Assn. Democrat. Jewish. Office: Kaye Scholer Fierman Hays & Handler 425 Park Ave New York NY 10022-3506

STEINBERG, BURT, retail executive; b. N.Y.C., June 2, 1945; s. Harry and Etta (Lippman) S.; m. Francine Hershkowitz, Dec. 22, 1968; children: Michael, Jessica. BA, CCNY, 1968; MBA, Columbia U., 1970. Mdse. mgr. Abraham & Straus, Bklyn., 1972-77; sr. v.p. Brooks Fashion Stores, N.Y.C., 1977-82, Dress Barn Inc., Stamford, Conn., 1982—. Mem. Columbia Alumni Assn., Am. Mktg. Assn. Avocations: coaching youth soccer and baseball, travel, sports. Office: Dress Barn Inc 88 Hamilton Ave Stamford CT 06902-5944

STEINBERG, CHARLES ALLAN, electronics manufacturing company executive; b. Bklyn., June 7, 1934; s. Joseph and Rose (Graff) S.; m. Helen Greene, June 16, 1956; children—Ruth, Steven, Bruce. B.S.E.E., CCNY, 1955; M.S.E.E., M.I.T., 1958. Mem. tech. staff Bell Telephone Labs., Whippany, N.J., 1955; research and teaching asst. MIT, 1955-58; engring. sect. mgr. Airborne Instruments Lab. div. Eaton Corp., Deer Park, N.Y., 1958-63; exec. v.p. Ampex Corp., Redwood City, Calif., 1963-86, pres., chief exec. officer, 1986-88; pres. bus. and profl. group Sony Corp. Am., Montvale, N.J., 1988—. Contbr. numerous articles on med. electronics and diagnosis, info. systems to profl. jours.; patentee computer techniques in medicine. Bd. dirs. Santa Clara County (Calif.) United Fund, 1969-71. Mem. IEEE, CCNY Alumni Assn., M.I.T. Alumni Assn., Sigma Xi, Tau Beta Pi, Eta Kappa Nu. Office: Sony Electronics Inc 3 Paragon Dr Montvale NJ 07645-1735

STEINBERG, DANIEL, preventive medicine physician, educator; b. Windsor, Ont., Can., July 21, 1922; came to U.S., 1922; s. Maxwell Robert and Bess (Krupp) S.; m. Sara Murdock, Nov. 30, 1946 (dec. July 1986); children: Jonathan Henry, Ann Ballard, David Ethan; m. Mary Ellen Stratthaus, Aug. 11, 1991; 1 stepchild: Katrin Seifert. B.S. with highest distinction, Wayne State U., 1941, M.D. with highest distinction, 1944; Ph.D. with distinction (fellow Am. Cancer Soc. 1950-51), Harvard U., 1951; M.D. (hon.), U. Gothenburg, 1991. Intern Boston City Hosp., 1944-45; physician Detroit Receiving Hosp., 1945-46; instr. physiology Boston U. Sch. Medicine, 1947-48; joined USPHS, 1951, med. dir., 1959; research staff lab. cellular physiology and metabolism Nat. Heart Inst., 1951-53, chief sect. metabolism, 1956-61, chief of lab. metabolism, 1962-68; lectr. grad. program NIH, 1955, mem. sci. adv. com. ednl. activities, 1955-61, com. chmn., 1955-60; mem. metabolism study sect. USPHS, 1959-61; chmn. heart and lung research rev. com. B Nat. Heart, Lung and Blood Inst., 1977-79; vis. scientist Carlsberg Labs., Copenhagen, 1952-53, Nat. Inst. Med. Research, London, 1960-61, Rockefeller U., 1981; pres. Lipid Research Inc., 1961-64, adv. bd., 1964-73; prof. medicine, head div. metabolic disease Sch. Medicine, U. Calif., San Diego and La Jolla; also program dir. basic scis. medicine Sch. Medicine, U. Calif., 1968—. Former editor Jour. Lipid Research; mem. editorial bd. Jour. Clin. Investigation, 1969-74, Jour. Biol. Chemistry, 1980-84, Arteriosclerosis, 1980—; exec. editor Analytical Biochemistry, 1978-80; contbr. articles to profl. jours. Bd. dirs. Found. Advanced Edn. in Scis., 1959-68, pres., 1956-62, 65-67. Served to capt. M.C. AUS, World War II. Mem. Nat. Acad. Scis., AAAS, Am. Acad. Arts and Scis., Am. Heart Assn. (mem. exec. com. coun. on arteriosclerosis 1960-63, 65-73, chmn. coun. arteriosclerosis 1967-69), Fedn. Am. Scientists (exec. com. 1957-58), Am. Soc. Biol. Chemists, Am. Soc. Clin. Investigation, Assn. Am. Physicians, Am. Fedn. Clin. Rsch., European Atherosclerosis Discussion Group, Alpha Omega Alpha. Home: 7742 Whitefield Pl La Jolla CA 92037-3810 Office: U Calif San Diego Dept Medicine 0682 9500 Gilman Dr La Jolla CA 92093-0682

STEINBERG, DAVID, comedian, author, actor; b. Winnipeg, Man., Can., Aug. 9, 1942; s. Jacob and Ruth S.; married; 2 children: Sasha, Rebecca. Student, Hebrew Theol. Coll., U. Chgo. Writer, actor Second City, Chicago; actor: Broadway appearances include Carry Me Back to Morningside Heights, Little Murders, (TV shows) Music Scene, The David Steinberg Show; dir.: (films) Paternity, 1981, Going Berserk, 1983, also The Richard Belzer Show, (TV shows) Newhart, Designing Women, Seinfeld, It Had To Be You, (commls.) Pizza Hut (with Roseanne Barr, Clio award 1987), NCR (with Dom deLuise), Jell-O (with Bill Cosby), Bartles & Jaymes; author spl. Return of Smothers Bros; rec. David Steinberg Disguised as a Normal Person; starred in film Something Short of Paradise, 1979. Office: care William Morris Agy Inc 151 S El Camino Dr Beverly Hills CA 90212-2775

STEINBERG, DAVID ISAAC, economic development consultant, educator; b. Cambridge, Mass., Nov. 26, 1928; s. Naaman and Miriam (Goldberg) S.; m. Isabel Maxwell, 1951 (div. 1962); 1 child, Christopher; m. Ann Myongsook Lee, May 15, 1964; children: Alexander I., Eric D. BA, Dartmouth Coll., 1950; MA, Harvard U., 1955; DLitt (hon.), Sungkunkwan U., Seoul, Republic of Korea. Analyst Nat. Security Coun., Washington, 1951-53; program officer Asia Found., N.Y.C., 1956-58; asst. rep. Asia Found., Burma, 1958-62, Hong Kong, 1962-63; rep. Asia Found., Republic of Korea, 1963-68, Washington, 1968-69; cons., sr. fgn. svc. officer AID, Washington and Bangkok (Thailand), 1969-86; ret., 1986; pres. Mansfield Ctr. for Pacific Affairs, Helena, Mont., 1986-87, Sr. Resources Internat., 1989-94; disting. prof. Korea Studies Georgetown U., Washington, 1990-94; rep. The Asia Found., Seoul, Korea; pvt. cons., Washington, 1987—, World Bank, 1987—, Woodrow Wilson Ctr. for Scholars of the Smithsonian Instn., Dept. of State and the Agy. for Internat. Devel., the Can. Internat. Devel. Agy., Devel. Assocs., Inc., and others; founding mem. Burma Studies Found., De Kalb, Ill., 1987. Author: Burma's Road Toward Development, 1981, Burma, 1982, The Republic of Korea Economic Transformation and Social Change, 1988, The Future of Burma, 1990. 1st lt. U.S. Army, 1953-55. Fellow Lingnan U., Canton, China, 1948, Dartmouth Coll., 1950; named Disting. Prof. of Korea Studies, Georgetown U. Mem. Assn. Asian Studies, Oriental Ceramic Soc., Asia Devel. Roundtable (chmn. 1984-86, 87—), Siam Soc., Royal Asiatic Soc. (life Korea br.), Burma Rsch. Soc. (life), Asia Soc. (cons. 1988—), Cosmos Club, Royal Bangkok (Thailand) Sports Club. Home: 6207 Goodview St Bethesda MD 20817-6101 Office: The Asia Found, KPO Box 738, Seoul 110-607, Korea

STEINBERG, DAVID JOEL, academic administrator, historian, educator; b. N.Y.C., Apr. 5, 1937; s. Milton and Edith (Alpert) S.; m. Sally Levitt (div. Dec., 1986); children: Noah, Jonah; m. Joan Diamond, Aug. 28, 1987. BA magna cum laude, Harvard U., 1959, MA, 1963, PhD, 1964; DLitt, Kyung Hee U., Seoul, Korea, 1989. Prof. history U. Mich., 1964-73; exec. asst. to pres. Brandeis U., Waltham, Mass., 1973-77, v.p., univ. sec., 1977-83; pres. L.I. U., Brookville, N.Y., 1985—; testified before Com. on Fgn. Affairs, U.S. Ho. of Reps., Fgn. Affairs Com. of U.S. Senate; cons. The Ford Found., UN Fund for Population Activities. Author: Philippine Collaboration in World War II, 1967 (Univ. Press award 1969), The Philippines: A Singular and a

Plural Place, 1982, rev. edit., 1994; author (with others) In Search of Southeast Asia: A Modern History, 1970, rev. edit., 1987, Asia in Western and World History: A Guide for Teaching, 1993. Trustee Commn. Ind. Colls. and Univs.; bd. dirs. L.I. Assn.; past pres. Cambridge (Mass.) Ctr. for Adult Edn., chmn. L.I. Group. English Speaking Union Exchange scholar, Malvern Coll., NDEA scholar, Fulbright Found. exchange scholar. Mem. Council Fgn. Relations, Assn. Asian Studies (chmn. fin. com.), Phi Beta Kappa. Democrat. Jewish. Club: Harvard (N.Y.C.). Office: LI U Northern Blvd Greenvale NY 11548

STEINBERG, DICK, professional football team executive. Gen. mgr., vice pres. N.Y. Jets. Office: NY Jets 1000 Fulton Ave Hempstead NY 11550-1009*

STEINBERG, HOWARD ELI, lawyer, holding company executive; b. N.Y.C., Nov. 19, 1944; s. Herman and Anne Rudel (Sinnreich) S.; m. Judith Ann Schucart, Jan. 28, 1968; children: Henry Robert, Kathryn Jill. A.B., U. Pa., 1965; J.D., Georgetown U., 1969. Bar: N.Y. 1970, U.S. Dist. Ct. (so. and ea. dists.) N.Y. 1973, U.S. Ct. Appeals (2d cir.) 1976. Assoc. Dewey, Ballantine, Bushby, Palmer & Wood, N.Y.C., 1969-76, ptnr., 1977-83; sr. v.p., gen. counsel, corp. sec. Reliance Group Holdings Inc., N.Y.C., 1983—; bd. dirs. Puerto Rican Legal Def. and Edn. Fund, Inc.; corp. sec. Data Resources, Inc., Lexington, Mass., 1978-79; sr. v.p., counsel to exec. com. Frank B. Hall & Co., 1987-92. Editor case notes: Georgetown Law Jour., 1968-69. Mem. bd. overseers U. Pa. Sch. Arts and Scis., 1989—. Capt. JAGC, AUS, 1972-74. Mem. ABA, N.Y. State Bar Assn., Assn. of Bar of City of N.Y. (com. on securities regulation 1984-87, com. on corp. law 1987-90, com. on fed. legis. 1990-93, chair ad hoc com. on Senate Confirmation Process 1991-92), Univ. Club. Jewish. Office: Reliance Group Holdings Inc 55 E 52nd St New York NY 10055-0002

STEINBERG, JACK, lawyer; b. Seattle, Jan. 6, 1915; s. Solomon Reuben and Mary (Rashall) S.; widower; children: Roosevelt, Mary Ann Steinberg Shulman, Quentin. BA, U. Wash., 1936, JD, 1938. Bar: Wash. 1938, U.S. Dist. Ct. (we. dist.) Wash. 1938, U.S. Ct. Appeals (9th cir.) 1938. Ptnr. Steinberg & Steinberg, Seattle, 1938—. Former editor and pub. The Washington Examiner; contbr. numerous articles to legal jours. Judge pro tem Seattle Mcpl. Ct., Seattle, 1952; past pres. Emanuel Congregation, Seattle, Seattle chpt. Zionist Orgn. Am. Recipient Scrolls of Honor award (3) The State of Israel. Mem. Assn. Trial Lawyers Am., Am. Judicature Soc., Wash. Bar Assn., Wash. Assn. Trial Lawyers, Seattle-King County Bar Assn. Jewish Orthodox. Avocation: outdoor activities. Office: Steinberg & Steinberg 1210 Vance Bldg Seattle WA 98101

STEINBERG, JAMES IAN, marketing executive; b. N.Y.C., Oct. 2, 1957; s. S. Sherman and Marian (Cohn) S.; m. Andrea F.C. Hacquoil, Feb. 28, 1984. Student, U. London, 1978; BA, Columbia Coll., 1979; MBA, NYU, 1984. Account exec. Grey Advt., N.Y.C., 1984-86; sr. product mgr. Sterling Drug Co., N.Y.C., 1986—. Mem. Am. Mktg. Assn. Club: Columbia. Avocation: squash. Home: 4 River House Irvington NY 10533-1540

STEINBERG, JANET ECKSTEIN, journalist; b. Cin.; d. Charles and Adele (Ehrenfeld) Eckstein; m. Irvin S. Silverstein, Oct. 22, 1988; children: Susan Carole Steinberg Somerstein, Jody Lynn Steinberg Lazarow. BS, U. Cin., 1964. Free-lance writer; guest appearances Braun and Co., Sta.-WLW-TV. Contbr. numerous articles to newspapers, mags. and books, U.S., Can., Singapore, Australia, N.Z.; travel columnist Cin. Post, 1978-86, Ky. Post, 1978-86, Cin. Enquirer, 1986-94; travel editor S. Fla. Single Living, 1988-92; contbr. Singles Scene and Cin. Mag., 1980—; travel columnist Eastside Weekend Mag., 1994—; contbg. editor Travel Agt., 1986-88, Birnbaum Travel Guides, 1988—; The Writer, 1988-92, Entree, 1986—; travel columnist Northeast mag., 1986-88, South Fla. Single Living, 1984-92. Recipient Lowell Thomas travel journalism award, 1985, 86, 91, Henry E. Bradshaw Travel Journalism award, 1st place, best of show, 1988, Buckeye Travel award Ohio Divsn. Travel & Tourism, 1992. Mem. Am. Soc. Journalists and Authors, Soc. Am. Travel Writers (1st place award for best newspaper story 1981, 3d place award for best mag. story 1981, 91, 1st place award for best newspaper article award 1984, 91, best mag. article 1985, 2d place award best pathos article, 1984, 88, 2d place award specific category, 1989), Midwest Travel Writers Assn. (Best Mag. Story award 1981, 95, Best Series award 1981, 94, 84 Cipriani award 1981, 1st place award best article 1989, 2d place award for best article 1982-84, 89, 95, 3d place award best article 1992, Mark Twain award 1992), Pacific Area Travel Assn., Internat. Food, Wine, and Travel Writers Assn., Losantiville Country Club, Travelers Century Club, Circumnavigators Club. Home: 900 Adams Crossing # 9200 Cincinnati OH 45202-1666

STEINBERG, JONATHAN ROBERT, lawyer; b. Phila., Jan. 3, 1939; s. Sigmund Hopkins and Hortense B. (Gottlieb) S.; m. Rochelle Helene Schwartz, May 30, 1963; children: Andrew Joshua, Amy Judith. BA, Cornell U., 1960; LLB cum laude, U. Pa., 1963. Bar: D.C. 1963, U.S. Ct. Appeals (D.C. cir.) 1964. Law clk. to judge U.S. Ct. Appeals (D.C. cir.), 1963-64; atty. advisor, then dep. gen. counsel Peace Corps, Washington 1964-69; com. on labor and pub. welfare, counsel subcom. on vets. affairs, U.S. Senate, 1969-71, counsel subcom. on R.R. retirement, 1971-73, counsel spl. subcom. on human resources, 1972-77, chief counsel com. on vets. affairs, 1977-81, minority chief counsel and staff dir. com. on vets. affairs, U.S. Senate, 1981-87, chief counsel and staff dir. com. on vets. affairs, 1987-90; assoc. judge U.S. Ct. of Vets. Appeals, 1990—. Contbr. to legal jours. Bd. dirs. Bethany West Recreation Assn., Bethany Beach, Del., 1973-84, 86-90. Mem. aba, D.C. Bar Assn., Order of Coif. Democrat. Jewish. Home: 11204 Hawhill End Potomac MD 20854-2039 Office: US Ct Vets Appeals 625 Indiana Ave NW Ste 900 Washington DC 20004-2901

STEINBERG, JOSEPH SAUL, investment company executive; b. Chgo., Feb. 5, 1944; s. Paul S. and Sylvia (Neikrug) S.; child from previous marriage, Sarah Aliza; m. Diane L. Heidt, 1987; children: Paul Steven, Rachel Catherine. A.B., NYU, 1966; M.B.A., Harvard U., 1970. Vol. Peace Corps, Kingston, Jamaica, 1966-68; v.p. Carl Marks & Co., Inc. (investment bankers), N.Y.C., 1970-78; pres. Leucadia Nat. Corp., N.Y.C., 1979—; also bd. dirs.; bd. dirs. Empire Ins. Group. Trustee NYU. Clubs: Harvard, Nat. Arts (N.Y.C.). Office: Leucadia Nat Corp 315 Park Ave S New York NY 10010-3607

STEINBERG, LAWRENCE EDWARD, lawyer; b. Dallas, Nov. 25, 1935; s. Oscar J. and Pearl L. (Soloman) S.; children: Adam Joseph, Ilana Sara. B.B.A., U. Tex., 1958; J.D., So. Methodist U., 1960. Bar: Tex. 1960. Since practiced in Dallas; partner firm Steinberg Soloman & Meer, 1971-88, Johnson & Steinberg, Dallas, 1988-93; of counsel Jenkins & Gilchrist, Dallas, 1994—. Mem. Urban Rehab. Stds. Bd., Dallas, 1975-76; mem. adv. com. affirmative action program Dallas Ind. Sch. Dist., 1974-76; regional bd. chmn. Anti-Defamation League of B'nai Brith, 1974-77, nat. exec. com., 1977—, nat. law com., 1974-87; trustee Edna Gladney Home, 1975-92, Shelton Sch., 1987-90; bd. dirs. Jewish Fedn. Greater Dallas, 1984-87, 91-94; trustee Temple Emanu-El. 2d lt. U.S. Army, 1958-59. Mem. Lincoln City Club, Columbian Club, Masons (Shriner), Zeta Beta Tau., Phi Delta Phi, Beta Gamma Sigma, Psi Tau Pi (nat. pres.). Home: 10131 Hollow Way Rd Dallas TX 75229-6634 Office: 1445 Ross Ave Ste 3200 Dallas TX 75202

STEINBERG, LEO, art historian, educator; b. Moscow, July 9, 1920; came to U.S., 1945; s. Isaac N. and Anna (Esselson) S. Ph.D., NYU Inst Fine Arts, 1960; Ph.D. (hon.), Phila. Coll. Art, 1981, Parsons Sch. Design, 1986, Mass. Coll. Art, 1987. Assoc. prof. art history Hunter Coll., CUNY, N.Y.C., 1961-66, prof., 1966-75; prof. Grad. Ctr. CUNY, 1969-75; Benjamin Franklin prof. art. history U. Pa., Phila., 1975-91, prof. emeritus 1991—. Author: Other Criteria, 1972, Michelangelo's Last Paintings, 1975, Borromini's San Carlo alle Quattro Fontane, 1977, The Sexuality of Christ in Renaissance Art and in Modern Oblivion, 1983. Recipient award in lit. Am. Acad. and Inst. Arts and Letters, 1983; fellow Am. Acad. Arts and Scis., 1978, Univ. Coll., London U., 1979, MacArthur Found., 1986; recipient Frank Jewett Mather award, 1956, 84. Mem. Coll. Art Assn. Am. Home: 165 W 66th St New York NY 10023-6546

STEINBERG, MALCOLM SAUL, biologist, educator; b. New Brunswick, N.J., June 1, 1930; s. Morris and Esther (Lerner) S.; children—Jeffery, Julie,

Eleanor, Catherine; m. Marjorie Campbell, 1983. B.A., Amherst Coll., 1952; M.A., U. Minn., 1954, Ph.D., 1956. Postdoctoral fellow dept. embryology Carnegie Instn., Washington, 1956-58; asst. prof. Johns Hopkins, Balt., 1958-64; assoc. prof. Johns Hopkins, 1964-66; prof. biology Princeton U., 1966-90, Henry Fairfield Osborn prof. biology, 1975—, prof. molecular biology, 1990—; instr.-in-charge embryology course Marine Biol. Lab., 1967-71, trustee, 1969-77; chmn. Gordon Research Conf. on Cell Contact and Adhesion, 1985; appointed to NAS/NRC Bd. on Biology, 1986-92. Mem. editorial bd. Bioscience, 1976-82; contbr. articles to profl. jours. Fellow AAAS; mem. AAUP, Am. Soc. Zoologists (program officer div. developmental biology 1966-69, chmn.-elect, then chmn. 1982-85), Am. Soc. Cell Biology, Internat. Soc. Developmental Biologists, Internat. Soc. Differentiation (bd. dirs. 1995), Soc. Developmental Biology (trustee, sec. 1970-73), Sigma Xi. Home: 86 Longview Dr Princeton NJ 08540-5642

STEINBERG, MARCIA IRENE, science foundation program director; b. Bklyn., Mar. 7, 1944; d. Solomon and Sylvia (Feldman) S.; 1 child, Eric Gordon. BS, Bklyn. Coll., 1964, MA, 1966; PhD, U. Mich., 1973. Rsch. scientist Meth. Hosp. Bklyn. Dept. Pathology, Bklyn., 1966-67, U. Mich. Dept. Surg. Rsch., Ann Arbor, Mich., 1967-68; post doctoral fellow Syracuse U. Dept. Biology, Syracuse, N.Y., 1973-76; from post doctoral fellow to assoc. prof. SUNY, Syracuse, N.Y., 1976-89; with NSF, Washington, 1990—; reviewer NATO fellowship NSF, San Francisco, 1988, Ad Hoc NSF, 1990—; reviewer NATO fellowship NSF, San Francisco, 1988, Ad Hoc NSF, Syracuse, N.Y., manuscripts in field; vis. scientist Weizmann Inst. Renal Rsch. Fund, Weizmann Inst., Israel, 1987, 1988. Contbr. articles to profl. jours. Recipient Wellcome Rsch. Travel Grant, Wellcome Found. Cambridge U., U.K., 1985, Regents scholarship SUNY Bd. Regents, Bklyn., 1960-64. Mem. AAAS, Am. Soc. Biochemistry Molecular Biology, Assn. Women Sci., Sigma Xi. Office: 1800 G St NW Washington DC 20550-0002

STEINBERG, MARK ROBERT, lawyer; b. Chgo., Aug. 23, 1945; s. Matthew and Irma (Polacek) S.; m. Marjorie Anne Scott, Sept. 3, 1966; 1 child, Matthew Martin. BA, Carleton Coll., 1966; MA, Stanford U., 1968; JD cum laude, Northwestern U., 1972. Bar: Calif. 1972, U.S. Dist. Ct. (cen. dist.) Calif. 1973, U.S. Dist. Ct. (no., ea. and so. dists.) Calif. 1980, U.S. Ct. Appeals (3d cir.) 1981, U.S. Ct. Appeals (9th cir) 1983, U.S. Ct. Appeals (fed. cir.) 1991. Ptnr. O'Melveny & Myers, L.A., 1980-93; counselor to legal adviser U.S. Dept. of State, Washington, 1993-94; dir. exec. office for nat. security, assoc. dep. atty. gen. U.S. Dept. Justice, Washington, 1994—. Articles editor Northwestern U. Law Rev., 1971-72. Trustee Carleton Coll., 1990-94; bd. dirs. Legal Aid Found., L.A., 1990-93; dep. gen. counsel Ind. Commn. on L.A. Police Dept., 1991; mem. U.S. Presdl. Transition Team, Dept. Justice, 1992-93. Mem. ABA, Los Angeles County Bar Assn., Women Lawyers' Assn. L.A., Carleton Coll. Alumni Assn. (pres. 1988-90). Office: Exec Office Nat Security US Dept Justice 10th and Constitution Ave Washington DC 20530

STEINBERG, MARSHALL, toxicologist; b. Pitts., Sept. 18, 1932; s. Harry Lionel and Eva (Goldstein) S.; m. Patricia Louise Zobac, Nov. 3, 1962; children: Leslie Renee, Michael Allan, Maureen Sara. BS, Georgetown U., 1954; MS, U. Pitts., 1956; PhD, U. Tex., 1966. Commd. U.S. Army, 1956, advanced through grades to col., 1957-74, ret., 1976; prin. investigator Tracor Jitco, Rockville, Md., 1977, v.p. chief div., 1977-78; v.p., dir. life scis. Hazleton Labs. Am., Vienna, Va., 1978-83; v.p., sci. dir. Hazleton Labs. Corp., Vienna, Va., 1983-87, v.p. Asian ops., 1987-90; v.p. health and environment Hercules, Inc., Wilmington, Del., 1990—; chmn. safety panel Fed. Working Group on Pest Mgmt., Washington, 1973-74; cons. Office of Pesticide Programs; EPA, Washington, 1975-77; mem. expert in pharmacology and toxicology French Govt., 1985-90; chmn. safety com. Internat. Pharm. Excipients Coun., 1990—, also bd. dirs.; bd. dirs. Global Environ. Svcs., Inc. Author articles, govt. reports. book chpts. Bd. dirs. Del. chpt. Am. Lung Assn.; trustee Health Environ. Scis. Inst.; mem. sci. adv. bd. Digene, 1986-89. Decorated Legion of Merit. Mem. Soc. Toxicology (sec. 1983, 85), Am. Coll. Toxicology (pres. 1986), Am. Indsl. Hygiene Assn., Toxicology Lab. Accreditation Bd. (sec. 1985-91), Acad. Toxicological Scis. (fellow, councillor 1982-85), v.p. 1990-91), Royal Soc. Medicine, Internat. Soc. Regulatory Toxicology and Pharmacology, Brandywine Valley Assn. (bd. dirs.). Jewish. Avocation: hunting. Office: Hercules Inc Hercules Plz Wilmington DE 19894

STEINBERG, MELVIN ALLEN, lieutenant governor, lawyer; b. Balt., Oct. 4, 1933; s. Irvin and Julia (Levenson) S.; m. Anita Akman, 1958; children: Edward Bryan, Susan Renee, Barbara Ellen. AA, U. Balt., 1952, JD, 1955. Bar: Md. 1955. Ptnr. Steinberg Lichter Coleman & Rogers, Towson, Md., 1978-86, Levin Gann & Hankin, Towson, 1986—; mem. Md. State Senate, 1967-87, vice chmn. jud. process, 1975-79; chmn. fin. com., 1979-82, pres. of senate, 1983-87, lt. gov., Md., 1987—. Del. Dem. Nat. Conv., 1968. Mem. Am. Judicature Soc., ABA, Md. Bar Assn., Balt. Bar Assn., Nu Beta Epsilon. Democrat. Jewish. Lodges: B'nai B'rith, Masons. Office: State House Office Lt Gov Annapolis MD 21401

STEINBERG, MEYER, chemical engineer; b. Phila., July 10, 1924; s. Jacob Louis and Freda Leah S.; m. Ruth Margot Elias, Dec. 24, 1950; children: David Martin, Jay Louis. BSChemE, Cooper Union, 1944; MSChemE, Bklyn. Poly. Inst., 1949. Registered profl. engr. N.Y. Jr. chem. engr. Manhattan dist., Kellex Corp., Oak Ridge, Los Alamos, 1944-46; asst. chem. engr. Deutsch & Loonam, 1947-50; chem. engr. Guggenheim Brothers, Mineola, N.Y., 1950-57; head process sci. div. Brookhaven Nat. Lab., Upton, N.Y., 1957—; expert in fossil and nuclear energy. Contbr. articles to profl. jours. Served with AUS, 1944-46. Recipient IR-100 award, 1970; Wasson award Am. Concrete Inst., 1972, Engr. of Year award, 1985, Ind. award Quest, 1985. Fellow Am. Nuclear Soc., Am. Inst. Chem. Engrs. (dir. L.I. sect.); mem. Am. Chem. Soc., AAAS, Am. Concrete Inst., Inst. Assos. Hydrogen Energy, Sigma Xi. Democrat. Jewish. Research on nuclear and fossil energy. Home: 15 Alderfield Ln Melville NY 11747-1724 Office: Brookhaven Nat Lab Upton NY 11973

STEINBERG, MICHAEL, music critic, educator; b. Breslau, Germany, Oct. 4, 1928; came to U.S., 1943, naturalized, 1951; s. Siegfried and Margarethe (Cohn) S.; m. Jane Bonacker, July 26, 1953 (div. 1983); children: Peter Sebastian, Adam Gregory; m. Jorja Fleezanis, July, 1983. A.B., Princeton U., 1949, M.F.A., 1951; Mus. D. (hon.), New Eng. Conservatory Music, 1966. Free-lance writer, 1952—; head history dept. Manhattan Sch. Music, N.Y.C., 1957-64; music critic Boston Globe, 1964-76; dir. publs. Boston Symphony Orch., 1976-79; artistic adviser San Francisco Symphony, 1979-89, program annotator, lectr., 1989—; artistic adviser Minn. Orch., 1989-92; artistic dir. Minn. Sommerfest, 1990-92; program annotator, lectr. N.Y. Philharmonic, 1995—; vis. mem. faculty Hunter Coll., 1954, U. Sask. (Can.), 1959, Smith Coll., 1964, Brandeis U., 1964-65; faculty New Eng. Conservatory Music, 1968-71, Wellesley Coll., 1971-72, Brandeis U., 1971-72, Mass. Inst. Tech., 1973; disting. vis. prof. McMaster U., Hamilton, Ont., 1982; cons. NEH, Nat. Endowment for Arts, Mass. Council of Arts and Humanities, Calif. Arts Council, Rockefeller Found. Served with U.S. Army, 1955-57. Recipient Sang prize for criticism in arts, 1969; citation for Excellence in Criticism Am. Guild Organists, 1972. Mem. Am. Internat. musicological assn. Home: 6828 Valley View Rd Minneapolis MN 55439-1646 Office: Davies Symphony Hall San Francisco CA 94102

STEINBERG, MICHAEL, department store executive. Pres., chief exec. officer Foley's, Houston, 1988—. Office: R H Macy & Co Inc 151 W 34th St New York NY 10001-2124 Office: Foley's 1110 Main St Houston TX 77002-6303

STEINBERG, MORRIS ALBERT, metallurgist; b. Hartford, Conn., Sept. 24, 1920; s. Abraham and Rose (Bellow) S.; m. Natlee Jean Haas, Apr. 29, 1951; children: Laurie Beth, Cathy, James J. B.S. (Competitive scholar), M.I.T., 1942, M.S. in Metallurgy (S.K. Wellman fellow), 1946, D.Sc., 1948; postgrad., Harvard Bus. Sch., 1970. Registered profl. engr.; Calif. Instr. dept. metallurgy MIT, Cambridge, Mass., 1946-48; head and dir. Horizons Inc., Cleve., 1948-58; officer and dir. Micrometric Instrument Corp., Cleve., 1949-51; sec., dir. Diwolfram Corp., Cleve., 1950-53; chief metallurgist Horizons Titanium Corp., Cleve., 1951-54; dir. material sci. lab. Lockheed Missiles & Space Co., Palo Alto, Calif., 1958-65; dep. chief scientist Lockheed Corp., Burbank, Calif., 1965-74; dir. tech. applications Lockheed Corp., 1974-83, v.p. sci., 1983-86; pres. P.V.D. Corp., 1986; adj. prof. materials dept. Sch. Engring. and Applied Sci., UCLA, 1978-88; mem. structures

tech. panel for Chief of Staff, USAF, 1971-72; mem. Air Force studies bd. NRC, 1982-85; mem. ad hoc com. of B-1 structures, sci. adv. bd., 1972-78; mem. Nat. Materials Adv. Bd., NRC, Nat. Acad. Scis., 1976-80; expert NASA Shuttle Flight Cert. Com., 1979-81; mem. Aeros. Space and Engring. Bd. NRC, NAE, 1984-88; keynote speaker 4th World Conf. on Continuing Engring. Edn., Beijing, 1989. Contbr. numerous articles on metallurgy and aerospace materials to engring. jours. Served to capt. USAF, 1942-46, ETO. Fellow Am. Soc. Metals (mem. public affairs com. 1973-75), Inst. for Advancement of Engring., AAAS, Am. Inst. Chemists, AIAA; mem. Soc. Mfg. Engring. (chmn. engring. materials com. 1969-72), Soc. Automotive Engrs., N.Y. Acad. Scis., Aerospace Industries Assn. (chmn. materials and structures com. 1973-74), NAE (elected mem. 1977, panel laser mirror reliability 1982-84, awards com. 1985-85, chmn. com. on continuing edn. 1983-85, NRC/NAE Aeros. and Space Engring. Bd. 1984-88, chmn. com. on net shape tech. Air Force Studies Bd. 1984-86), Soc. Mfg. Engrs. (mem. tech. coun. 1969-72, Indsl. Tech. Mgmt. award 1981), AIAA (chmn. materials com. 1962-64, chmn. honors and awards com. L.A. sect. 1977-79). Home: 348 Homewood Rd Los Angeles CA 90049-2712

STEINBERG, MORTON M., lawyer; b. Chgo., Feb. 13, 1945; s. Paul S. and Sylvia (Neikrug) S.; m. Miriam C. Bernstein, Aug. 25, 1974; children: Adam Michael, Shira Judith. AB with honors U. Ill., 1967; JD, Northwestern U., 1971. Bar: Ill. 1971, U.S. Dist. Ct. (no. dist.) Ill. 1971, Colo. 1995. U.S. Ct. Appeals (7th cir.) 1971, U.S. Supreme Ct. 1974; DC, 1994. Assoc. Caffarelli & Wiczer, Chgo., 1971-73; assoc. Arnstein, Gluck, Lehr, Barron & Milligan, Chgo., 1974-76, ptnr., 1977-86; ptnr., Rudnick & Wolfe, 1986—; speaker in field. Sr. editor Jour. Criminal Law and Criminology, Northwestern U., 1969-71; Bd. dirs. Camp Ramah in Wis., Inc., Chgo., 1974—, sr. v.p., 1992-94, pres., 1994—; bd. dirs., v.p. Camp Ramah in Wis. Endowment Corp., 1993—; bd. dirs. North Suburban Synagogue Beth-El, Highland Park, Ill., 1978—, corp. sec., 1983-87, pres. 1989-91, chmn. bd. trustees, 1991-93, trustee, 1991—; mem. Nat. Ramah Commn., 1987—, v.p. 1994—; bd. dirs. Found. Conservative Judaism in Israel, 1985-90; Midwest region bd. dirs. United Synagogue of Conservative Judaism, 1989-91, 94—; charter mem. U.S. Holocaust Meml. Mus., 1992. Served with USAR, 1969-75. Recipient Youth Leadership award Nat. Fedn. Jewish Men's Clubs, N.Y.C., 1963; cert. of merit U.S. Dist. Ct. Fed. Defender Program, Chgo., 1969. Mem. ABA, Internat. Wine Lawyers Assn., Ill. Bar Assn., Chgo. Bar Assn. Jewish. Home: 1320 S Lincoln Ave Highland Park IL 60035-3459 Office: Rudnick & Wolfe 203 N La Salle St Chicago IL 60601-1210

STEINBERG, ROBERT M., holding company executive; b. Bklyn., 1942; married. Student, N.C. State U., 1964. Asst. v.p. Ideal Rubber Co., 1964-65; with Reliance Group Inc., N.Y.C., 1965—, salesman, 1965-67, asst. dir. corp. devel., 1967-68, asst. v.p. computer svcs., 1968-69, v.p. adminstrn., 1969-74, sr. v.p. adminstrn., 1974-75; exec. v.p., 1978-81, pres., chief oper. officer, 1981—, also dir.; also pres., chief oper. officer, dir. Reliance Group Holdings Inc., N.Y.C.; pres., chief oper. officer Leasco Corp.; chmn., chief exec. officer Reliance Ins. Co.; dir. Empire Inc., Zenith Nat. Ins., Days Inn Corp., Frank B. Hall & Co., Telemundo Group, Inc. Bd. dirs. Jewish Guild for Blind. Office: Reliance Group Holdings Inc 55 E 52nd St New York NY 10055-0002

STEINBERG, ROBERT PHILIP, lawyer; b. Danville, Ill., Apr. 4, 1931; s. Frederick Philip and Beulah Iona (Olmsted) S.; m. Doris Elizabeth Blank, May 10, 1958; children: Susan Elizabeth, Mary Louise. BA, DePauw U., 1953; LLB, N.Y. U., 1956. Bar: N.Y. 1956, Pa. 1959. Assoc. Shearman & Sterling, N.Y.C., 1956; assoc. Drinker Biddle & Reath, Phila., 1958-65, ptnr., 1965—, chmn., 1992-94. V.p. Germantown Hist. Soc., Phila., 1991—, The Phila. Theatre Co., 1992—. With U.S. Army, 1956-58. Mem. Phila. Bar Assn. (treas. 1970-72). Home: 18 E Springfield Ave Philadelphia PA 19118 Office: Drinker Biddle & Reath Phila Nat Bank Bldg 1345 Chestnut St Philadelphia PA 19107-3496

STEINBERG, SAUL, artist; b. Ramnic-Sarat, Romania, June 15, 1914; naturalized, 1943; s. Maurice and Rosa (Jacobson) S. Ed., Bucharest High Sch., 1932; student philosophy, Bucharest U., 1932-33; Dottore Architecttura, Regio Politecnico, Faculta de Architettura, Milan, Italy, 1933-40; hon. degrees, Harvard U., 1976; NYU, 1978, Royal Coll. Arts, London, 1988, Yale U., 1989. Cartoonist for mag. Bertoldo, Milan, 1936-39; practicing architect, 1939-41; went from Italy to Dominican Rep., 1941, to U.S., 1942 free-lance artist, cartoonist, mainly for New Yorker, 1941—; artist-in-residence Smithsonian Instn., 1967. Exhibited one-man shows Betty Parsons Gallery, 1943, 52, 66, 68, 73, Mus. Modern Art, 1946, Sidney Janis Gallery, 1952, 66, 73, Inst. Contemporary Art, London, 1952, Galerie Maeght, Paris, 1953, 73, Kunstmuseum, Basel, Switzerland, 1954, Stedelijk Mus., Amsterdam, 1953, Museo de Arte, Sao Paulo, Brazil, 1952, Galerie Blanche, Stockholm, 1953, Hanover, Germany, 1954, Pace Gallery, N.Y.C., 1982, Galeria Seno Milan, 1990, John Berggruen Gallery, 1990; group shows Haus der Kunst, Munich, 1981, 82, U.N.C.-Greensboro, 1981, Okla. Art Ctr., Oklahoma City, 1982, Nelson-Atkins Mus. Art, 1982, Los Angeles County Mus. Art, 1982, Pace Gallery, 1982, 87, Harvard U., 1985, Galerie LeLong, Paris, 1986, Columbus (Ohio) Mus. Art, 1986, Kunsthalle Nurenberg, Fed. Republic Germany, 1988, Fondation Maeght, St. Paul de Venice, 1991, O'Hara Gallery, N.Y.C., 1991, others; retrospective show Whitney Mus., N.Y. travelled to Hirshorn Mus., Washington, Serpentine Gallery, London, Found. Maeght, St. Paul de Vence, France; represented in permanent collections Mus. Modern Art, N.Y.C., Met. Mus. Art, N.Y.C., Albright-Knox Gallery, Buffalo, Fogg Mus., Harvard U., Victoria and Albert Mus., London, others.; author: All in Line, 1945, The Art of Living, 1949, The Passport, 1954, The Inspector, 1973. Served to lt. USNR, 1943-45. Named Chevalier des Arts et des Lettres, France, 1968. Mem. Am. Acad. Arts and Letters (Gold medal 1974). Am. Acad. Arts and Scis. Office: Gemini G E L at Joni Moisant Weyl 375 W Broadway 2d Fl New York NY 10012-4303

STEINBERG, SAUL PHILLIP, holding company executive; b. N.Y.C., Aug. 13, 1939; s. Julius and Anne (Cohen) S.; m. Barbara Herzog, May 28, 1961 (div. 1977); children: Laura, Jonathan, Nicholas; m. Laura Sconocchia, Dec. 21, 1978 (div. Dec. 1983); 1 child, Julian; m. Gayfryd McNabb, Jan. 22, 1984; children: Rayne, Holden. BS, Wharton Sch., U. Pa., 1959. Founder, chmn., chief exec. officer, dir. Reliance Group Holdings Inc., N.Y.C.; chmn. bd. dirs. Telemundo Group Inc.; bd. dirs. Symbol Techs. Inc., Zenith Nat. Ins. Corp., N.Y.C., N.Y. Pa. bd. overseers Wharton Sch. U. Pa.; mem. bd. overseers Cornell U. Med. Coll., N.Y.C., trustee Jewish Med. Ctr., N.Y.C., U. Pa., N.Y. Pub. Libr.; bd. dirs. N.Y.C. Partnership. Mem. Glen Oaks Club. Jewish. Home: 740 Park Ave New York NY 10021-4251 Office: Reliance Group Holdings Inc 55 E 52nd St New York NY 10055-0002

STEINBERG, STEPHEN ARTHUR, information systems executive; b. Hartford, Conn., June 15, 1944; s. Morris and Irene (Lebon) S.; m. Lois Shapiro, Apr. 21, 1974; children: Beth, Meredith, Genna. B Elec. Engring., Rensselaer Poly. Inst., 1966; MBA, U. Chgo., 1968. Sr. systems cons. Mobil Oil Corp., N.Y.C., 1968-71; v.p. systems and tech. Citibank, N.A., N.Y.C., 1972-88; v.p., dir. info. systems Capital Markets Assurance Corp., N.Y.C., 1989—. Mem. IEEE Computer Soc. Avocation: jazz drummer. Office: Capital Markets Assurance Corp 885 3d Ave New York NY 10022

STEINBERG, WARREN LINNINGTON, school principal; b. N.Y.C., Jan. 20, 1924; s. John M. and Gertrude (Vogel) S.; student U. So. Calif., 1943-44, UCLA, 1942-43, 46-47, BA, 1949, MEd, 1951, EdD, 1962; m. Beatrice Ruth Blass, June 29, 1947; children: Leigh William, James Robert, Donald Kenneth. Tchr., counselor, coach Jordan High Sch., Watts, Los Angeles, 1951-57; tchr. athletic coordinator Hamilton High Sch., Los Angeles, 1957-62; boys' vice prin. Univ. High Sch., Los Angeles, 1962-67, Crenshaw High Sch., Los Angeles, 1967-68; cons. Ctr. for Planned Change, Los Angeles City Sch., 1968-69; instr. edn. UCLA, 1965-71; boys' vice prin. LeConte Jr. High Sch., Los Angeles, 1969-71, sch. prin., 1971-77; adminstrv. cons. integration, 1977-81, adminstr. student to student interaction program, 1981-82; prin. Gage Jr. High Sch., 1982-83, Fairfax High Sch., 1983-90. Pres. Athletic Coordinators Assn., Los Angeles City Schs., 1959-60; v.p. P-3 Enterprises, Inc., Port Washington, N.Y., 1967-77, Century City (Calif.) Enterprises, 1966-88. V.p. B'nai B'rith Anti-Defamation League, 1968-70; mem. adv. com. Los Angeles City Commn. on Human Relations, 1966-71, 72-76, commr., 1976—, also chmn. edn. com.; pres. Los Angeles City Human Relations Commn., 1978-87; mem. del. assembly Community Relations Conf. of So. Calif., 1975-91; mem. citizens adv. com. for student integration Los Angeles Unified Sch.

Dist., 1976-79; chmn. So. Calif. Drug Abuse Edn. Month com., 1970. Bd. dirs. DAWN, The Seedling, 1993-95. Served with USMCR, 1943-46. Recipient Beverly Hills B'nai B'rith Presdl. award, 1965, Pres.'s awardCommunity Rels. Conf. So. Calif., 1990; commended Los Angeles City Council, 1968, 88. Mem. West Los Angeles Coordinating Council (chmn. case conf., human relations), Beverly-Fairfax C. of C. (bd. dirs. 1986-88). Lodges: Lions (dir. 1960-62), Kiwanis. Contbr. articles on race relations, youth behavior to profl. jours. and newspapers. Home: 2737 Dunleer Pl Los Angeles CA 90064-4303

STEINBERGER, RICHARD LYNN, lawyer, corporate executive; b. Columbus, Ohio, Mar. 24, 1939; s. Harold V. and Dorothy Dolan (Dunn) S.; m. Nancy Sue Orewiler, Sept. 9, 1961; children: Amy, Mitchell. AB magna cum laude, Butler U., 1961; JD, Ohio State U., 1964. Bar: Ohio 1964, U.S. Supreme Ct. 1967. Assoc. Pickel, Schaeffer & Ebeling, Dayton, Ohio, 1964-74; co-founder, exec. v.p. Nord Resources Corp., Dayton, 1968-85, pres., 1985-88; vice chmn. Nord Resources Corp., Santa Rosa, Calif., 1988—, Sierra Rutile, Ltd., 1982—. Office: Nord Resources Corp 3510 Unocal Pl Ste 114 Santa Rosa CA 95403-0917

STEINBOCK, JOHN T., bishop; b. L.A., July 16, 1937. Student, Los Angeles Diocesan sems. Ordained priest Roman Cath. Ch., 1963. Aux. bishop Diocese of Orange, Calif., 1984-87; bishop Diocese of Santa Rosa, Calif., 1987-91; titular bishop of Midila, 1984; bishop Diocese of Fresno, Calif., 1991—. Office: Diocese of Fresno 1550 No Fresno St Fresno CA 93703-3788

STEINBRENNER, GEORGE MICHAEL, III, professional baseball team executive, shipbuilding company executive; b. Rocky River, Ohio, July 4, 1930; s. Henry G. and Rita (Haley) S.; m. Elizabeth Joan Zieg, May 12, 1956; children: Henry G. III, Jennifer Lynn, Jessica Joan, Harold Zeig. BA, Williams Coll., 1952; postgrad., Ohio State U., 1954-55. Asst. football coach Northwestern U., 1955, Purdue U., 1956-67; treas. Kinsman Transit Co., Cleve., 1957-63; pres. Kinsman Marine Transit Co., Cleve., 1963-67, dir., 1965—; pres., chmn. bd. Am. Ship Bldg. Co., Cleve., 1967-78, chmn. bd., 1978—; prin. owner N.Y. Yankees, Bronx, 1973-90, 93—; limited ptnr. N.Y. Yankees, 1990-93; owner Bay Harbor Inn, Tampa, Fla., 1988—; bd. dirs. Gt. Lakes Internat. Corp., Gt. Lakes Assocs., Cin. Sheet Metal & Roofing Co., Nashville Bridge Co., Nederlander-Steinbrenner Prodns. Mem. Cleve. Little Hoover Com., group chmn., 1966; chmn. Cleve. Urban Coalition; vice chmn. Greater Cleve. Growth Corp., Greater Cleve. Jr. Olympic Found. Served to 1st lt. USAF, 1952-54. Named Outstanding Young Man of Yr. Ohio Jr. C. of C., 1960, Cleve. Jr. C. of C. 1960; Chief Town Crier, Cleve., 1968; Man of Yr., Cleve. Press Club, 1968. Mem. Greater Cleve. Growth Assn. (bd. dirs.). Office: NY Yankees Yankee Stadium E 161st St & River Ave Bronx NY 10451*

STEINBRINK, WILLIAM H., lawyer; b. Richmond, Ind., Oct. 4, 1942. AB, Wittenberg U., 1964; LLB, Duke U., 1967. Bar: Ohio 1967. Ptnr. Jones, Day, Reavis & Pogue, Cleve. Mem. ABA (chair com. law firms bus. law sect. 1989—), Order of Coif. Office: Jones Day Reavis & Pogue North Point 901 Lakeside Ave Cleveland OH 44114

STEINBRONN, RICHARD EUGENE, lawyer; b. Chgo., Oct. 16, 1941; s. Eugene Frederick and Harriet (Slominski) S.; m. Patricia Burckell, June 13, 1964; children: Jeanne L., Nanette C., Richard Eugene Jr. BA in Philosophy, St. John's U., Collegeville, Minn., 1963; LLB, U. Notre Dame, 1966. Bar: Ind. 1966, U.S. Dist. Ct. (no. dist.) Ind. 1969, U.S. Ct. Appeals (7th cir.) 1969. Assoc. Thornburg, McGill & Deahl, Elkhart, Ind., 1968-72; ptnr. Thornburg, McGill & Deahl, Elkhart, 1973-81; ptnr. Barnes & Thornburg, Elkhart, 1982-85, Ft. Wayne, Ind., 1986—. Rsch. editor Notre Dame Lawyer (law rev.), 1965-66. Chmn. United Way, Elkhart, 1978-85; bd. dirs., pres. Jr. Achievement Elkart County, 1971-85; adv. bd. Leadership Ft. Wayne, 1991—. Capt. U.S. Army, 1963-68. Mem. ABA, Nat. Health Lawyers Assn., Ind. Bar Assn. (bd. dirs. litigation sect. 1984-86), Elkhart County Bar Assn. (chmn. com. 1968-85), Allen County Bar Assn. (bd. dirs. 1986-88, jud. selection com. 1987-88, sec. 1988-89), Def. Rsch. Inst., Greater Ft. Wayne C. of C. (bd. dirs.), Rotary (dist. 6540 youth exch. com. Ft. Wayne club 1986-91, chmn. internat. affairs 1991, dist. chmn. 1992-95, dir. ctrl. states youth exch. inc. exec. 1994—). Republican. Roman Catholic. Avocation: Civil War history. Office: Barnes & Thornburg 1 Summit Sq Ste 600 Fort Wayne IN 46802

STEINBRUCKNER, BRUNO FRIEDRICH, foreign language educator; b. Linz/Donau, Austria, Aug. 22, 1941; came to U.S., 1965, naturalized, 1973; s. Bruno and Michaela Maria (Wimberger) S.; m. Claudia Jane Frey, Mar. 9, 1973. Ph.D., U. Innsbruck, 1965. Asst. U. Innsbruck, spring 1965; mem. faculty Am. U., 1965—, prof. German studies, 1973—, chmn. dept. lang. and lit. studies, 1975-79; dir. The Am. U. Ctr., Vienna, 1985—. Author: Diefgn. studies, 1975-79; dir. The Am. U. Ctr., Vienna, 1985—. Author: Dialektographie des oberen Mühlviertels, 1976, Ludwig Thoma, 1978; also articles.; contbg. author: Encyclopedic Dictionary of Religion, 1979; Contbg. author: Die deutsche Literatur, Germany in World Politics, 1979; Contbg. author: Federal Republic of Germany, 2d edit., 1982. Mem. Am. Goethe Soc. (pres. 1971-73), Am. Assn. Tchrs. German (chpt. corr. sec. 1965-66), Nat. Humanities Faculty. Home: PO Box 747 Mc Lean VA 22101-0747 Office: PO Box 314, A-1191 Vienna Austria

STEINDLER, HOWARD ALLEN, lawyer; b. Cleve., June 12, 1942; s. Sidney and Lois Jean (Rosenberg) S.; m. Shirley Weinstein, Oct. 26, 1973; children: Rebecca, Allison, Daniel. B.S., Miami U.-Oxford, Ohio, 1964; J.D., Ohio State U., 1967. Bar: Ohio 1967. Mem. firm Benesch, Friedlander, Coplan & Aronoff, Cleve., 1967—. Pres. bd. trustees Cleve. Scholarship Program, 1987—. Office: Benesch Friedlander Coplan & Aronoff 2300 BP America Bldg 200 Public Sq Cleveland OH 44114

STEINDLER, MARTIN JOSEPH, chemist; b. Vienna, Austria, Jan. 3, 1928; came to U.S., 1938; s. J.P. and M.G. S.; m. Joan Long, Aug. 16, 1952; children: M.H., T.P. PhD, U. Chgo., 1947, BS, 1948, MS, 1949, PhD, 1952. Chemist Argonne (Ill.) Nat. Lab. 1953-74 sr. chemist, 1974—, assoc. dir. div. chem. engring., 1978-84, dir. chem. tech. div., 1984-93, sr. tech. advisor, 1993—; mem. adv. com. on nuclear waste NRC, Washington, 1988—, chmn. 1995; adminstrv. judge ASLBP, 1973-90. Contbr. articles to profl. publs.; patentee in field. Pres. Matteson-Park Forest (Ill.) Sch. Bd., 1959-78. Recipient Disting. Performance medal U. Chgo., 1992. Mem. AAAS, Am. Nuclear Soc., Am. Inst. Chem. Engrs. (Robert E. Wilson award 1990), Sigma Xi. Office: Argonne Nat Lab 9700 Cass Ave Argonne IL 60439-4803

STEINEM, GLORIA, writer, editor, lecturer; b. Toledo, Mar. 25, 1934; d. Leo and Ruth (Nuneviller) S. BA, Smith Coll., 1956; postgrad. (Chester Bowles Asian fellow), India, 1957-58; D. Human Justice, Simmons Coll., 1973. Co-dir., dir. ednl. found. Ind. Rsch. Svc., Cambridge, Mass. and N.Y.C., 1959-60; contbg. editor Glamour Mag., N.Y.C., 1962-69; co-founder, contbg. editor New York Mag., 1968-72; feminist lectr. 1969—; co-founder, editor Ms. Mag., 1971-87, columnist, 1980-87, cons. editor, 1987—; Active various civil rights and peace campaigns including United Farmworkers, Vietnam War Tax Protest, Com. for the Legal Def. of Angela Davis (treas. 1971-72); active polit. campaigns of Adlai Stevenson, Robert Kennedy, Eugene McCarthy, Shirley Chisholm, George McGovern; Co-founder, bd. dirs. Women's Action Alliance, 1970—; convenor, mem. nat. adv. com. Nat. Women's Polit. Caucus, 1971—; co-founder, pres. bd. dirs. Ms. Found. for Women, 1972—; founding mem. Coalition of Labor Union Women, 1974; mem. Internat. Women's Year Commn., 1977; editorial cons., Conde Nast Publications, 1962-69, Curtis Publishing, 1964-65, Random House Publishing, 1988—, McCall Publishing. Author: The Thousand Indias, 1957, The Beach Book, 1963, Wonder Woman, 1972, Outrageous Acts and Everyday Rebellions, 1983, Marilyn: Norma Jeane, 1986, Revolution from Within: A Book of Self-Esteem, 1992, Moving Beyond Words, 1994; contbg. author NBC Today Show, 1987-88; contbr. to various anthologies. Pres. Voters for Choice, 1979—. Recipient Penney-Missouri Journalism award, 1970, Ohio Gov.'s award for Journalism, 1972, Bill of Rights award ACLU of So. Calif., 1975; named Woman of the Yr. McCall's mag., 1972; Woodrow Wilson Internat. Ctr. for Scholars fellow, 1977; inducted into Nat. Women's Hall of Fame, 1993. Mem. NOW, AFTRA, Nat. Press Club, Soc. Mag. Writers, Authors' Guild, Phi Beta Kappa. Office: Ms Magazine 230 Park Ave 7th Fl New York NY 10169

STEINER, BARBARA S., lawyer; b. Highland Park, Ill., June 14, 1949. BA with high honors, U. Mich., 1970, JD with honors, 1974. Bar: Ill. 1974. Ptnr. Jenner & Block, Chgo. Mem. ABA, Ill. State Bar Assn. (mem. antitrust and unfair competition coun. 1984-92, sec. 1989, vice chmn. 1990, chair 1991). Office: Jenner & Block One IBM Plz Chicago IL 60611-3608

STEINER, DONALD FREDERICK, biochemist, physician, educator; b. Lima, Ohio, July 15, 1930; s. Willis A. and Katherine (Hoegner) S. BS in Chemistry and Zoology, U. Cin., 1952; MS in Biochemistry, U. Chgo., 1956, MD, 1956; D Med. Sci. (hon.), U. Umea, 1973, U. Ill., 1984, Technische Hochschule, Aachen, 1993, U. Uppsala, 1993. Intern King County Hosp., Seattle, 1956-57; USPHS postdoctoral research fellow, asst. medicine U. Wash. Med. Sch., 1957-60; mem. faculty med. sch. U. Chgo., 1960—, chmn. dept. biochemistry, 1973-79, A.N. Pritzker prof. biochemistry, molecular biology and medicine, 1985—, sr. investigator Howard Hughes Med. Inst. 1986—; Jacobaeus lectr., Oslo, 1970; Luft lectr., Stockholm, 1984. Co-editor: The Endocrine Pancreas, 1972, discoverer proinsulin. Recipient Gairdner award Toronto, 1971, Hans Christian Hagedorn medal Steensen Meml. Hosp., Copenhagen, 1970, Lilly award, 1969, Ernst Oppenheimer award, 1970, Diaz-Cristobal award Internat. Diabetes Fedn., 1973, Banting medal Am. Diabetes Assn., 1976, Banting medal Brit. Diabetes Assn., 1981, Passano award, 1979, Wolf prize in medicine, 1985, Frederick Conrad Koch award Endocrine Soc., 1990. Mem. Nat. Acad. Scis., Am. Soc. Biochemists and Molecular Biologists, AAAS, Am. Diabetes Assn. (50th Anniversary medallion 1972), European Assn. Study Diabetes, Am. Acad. Arts and Scis., Sigma Xi, Alpha Omega Alpha. Home: 2626 N Lakeview Ave Apt 2508 Chicago IL 60614-1821

STEINER, DUANE, religious administrator. Mgr. Ch. of the Brethren Annual Conf. Office: Church of The Brethern 1451 Kundee Ave Elgin IL 60120

STEINER, ERICH ERNST, botany educator; b. Thun, Canton Bern, Switzerland, Apr. 9, 1919; came to U.S., 1922; s. Gotthold and Emmy (Schmid) S.; m. Dorothy Aileen White, July 8, 1944; children: Kurt Edric, Karl Rolf, Kim Eric. BS, U. Mich., 1940; PhD, Ind. U., 1950. Instr. botany dept. of botany U. Mich., Ann Arbor, 1950-53, asst. prof. dept. of botany, 1953-56, assoc. prof. dept. of botany, 1956-61, prof. dept. of botany, 1961-88, prof. emeritus, 1988—, chmn. dept. botany, 1968-71, dir. Matthaei Bot. Gardens, 1971-77, 89-91. Author: Botany Laboratory Manual, 1957m 65; translator: Genetics of Fungi, 1967; mem. editorial bd. Plant Sci. Bull., 1959-71. Sec. Mich. Acad. Sci., 1957-58. 2d lt. Med. Adminstrv. Corps, U.S. Army, 1943-46; ETO. NSF Postdoctoral fellow, 1960-61. Mem. Bot. Soc. Am., Genetics Soc. Am., Am. Soc. Naturalists, Soc. for Study of Evolution, Am. Assn. Bot. Gardens and Arboreta (bd. dirs. 1979-82), Sigma Xi, Phi Beta Kappa. Avocations: gardening, woodworking, photography; achievements include research in the genetics and evolution of Oenothera. Office: U Mich Dept Of Biology Ann Arbor MI 48109

STEINER, GEORGE (FRANCIS STEINER), author, educator; b. Paris, Apr. 23, 1929; s. Frederick George and Elsie (Franzos) S.; m. Zara Shakow, 1955; children—David Milton, Deborah Tarn. BA, U. Chgo., 1949; MA, Harvard U., 1950; PhD, Oxford U., 1955; LittD (hon.), East Anglia Coll., 1976, Louvain U., 1980, Mount Holyoke Coll., 1983, Durham U., 1995; D honoris causa, U. Bristol, 1989; DLitt (hon.), U. Glasgow, 1990, U. Liège, 1990, U. Ulster, 1993; U. Durham, 1995. Mem. staff Economist, London, 1952-56; mem. staff Inst. Advanced Study Princeton (N.Y.) U., N.J., 1956-58, Gauss lectr., 1959-60; Massey lectr., 1974; First Lord Weidenfeld prof. Comp. Lit. Oxford U., 1994—; cons. and lectr. in field; Maurice lectr. U. London, 1984, Leslie Stephen lectr. Cambridge U., 1985, W.P. Ker lectr. U. Glasgow, 1986; lectr. Page-Barbour Lectures U. Va., 1987, Gifford lectr., 1990; vis. prof. Coll. France, 1992; First Lord Weidenfeld vis. prof. comparative lit., Oxford U., 1994—. Author: Tolstoy or Dostoevsky, 1958, The Death of Tragedy, 1960, Anno Domini, 1964, Language and Silence, 1967, Extraterritorial, 1971, In Bluebeard's Castle, 1971, The Sporting Scene: White Knights in Reykjavik, 1973, After Babel, 1975 (adapted for TV as The Tongues of Men, 1977), Heidegger, 1978, On Difficulty and Other Essays, 1978, The Portage to San Cristobal of A.H., 1981, Antigones, 1984, George Steiner: A Reader, 1984, Real Presences, 1989, Proofs and Three Parables, 1992; editor: The Penguin Book of Modern Verse Translation, 1966, Homer: A Collection of Critical Essays (with Robert Flagles), 1962. Decorated chevalier de la Legion d'Honneur (France); Churchill Coll. fellow, 1961—; Hon. fellow Balliol Coll., Oxford, Eng., 1995; Fulbright prof., 1958-69; recipient O. Henry Short Story award, 1958, Guggenheim fellowship, 1971-72, Zabel award Nat. Inst. Arts and Letters, U.S., 1970, King Albert medal Royal Belgian Acad., 1982, P.E.N. Internat. Fiction prize, 1993; Faulkner Fiction grantee P.E.N., 1983; Le Prix du Souvenir, 1974. Mem. Am. Acad. Arts and Scis. (hon.), English Assn. (pres. 1975), German Acad. Lit. (corr.). Office: Churchill Coll, Cambridge England

STEINER, GILBERT YALE, political scientist; b. Bklyn., May 11, 1924; s. Isidor Aaron and Fannie (Gelbtrunk) S.; m. Louise King, July 27, 1950; children: Charles King, Daniel Tod, Paula Amy. A.B., Columbia U., 1945; A.M., 1948; Ph.D., U. Ill., 1950. Faculty U. Ill., Urbana, 1950-66; prof. govt., pub. affairs U. Ill., 1959-66; asst. dean U. Ill. (Grad. Coll.), 1956-58; dir. Inst. Govt. and Pub. Affairs, 1958-66; sr. fellow Brookings Instn., Washington, 1966—; dir. govtl. studies Brookings Instn., 1968-76, acting pres., 1976-77; staff dir. Chgo. Home Rule Commn., 1954-55; research dir. Northeastern Ill. Local Govt. Area Commn., 1957-63; vis. prof. polit. sci. U. Calif.-Berkeley, 1965; Kimball lectr. Brigham Young U., 1985; study dir. Commn. to Recommend Plan for Pub. Higher Edn. in Ill., 1960; spl. asst. to gov., Ill., 1961-63; cons. Bush Found., Edna McConnell Clark Found. Author: The Congressional Conference Committee, 1951, Legislation by Collective Bargaining, 1951, (with others) Chicago's Government, 1954, (with S.K. Gove) Legislative Politics in Illinois, 1960, Social Insecurity, 1966, The State of Welfare, 1971, The Children's Cause, 1976, The Futility of Family Policy, 1981, Constitutional Inequality, 1985; editor: The Abortion Dispute and the American System, 1983. Bd. dirs. Found. for Child Devel., Manpower Demonstration and Research Corp., Governance Inst. Served with AUS, 1943-46. Social Sci. Research Council fellow, 1957; Ford Found. fellow, 1961-62. Home: 5408 Center St Chevy Chase MD 20815-7101 Office: Brookings Institute Washington DC 20036

STEINER, HENRY JACOB, law and human rights educator; b. Mt. Vernon, N.Y., 1930; s. Meier and Bluma (Henigson) S.; m. Pamela Pomerance, Aug. 1, 1967; stepchildren: Duff, Jacoba. BA magna cum laude, Harvard U., 1951, MA, 1955, LLB magna cum laude, 1955. Bar: N.Y. 1956, Mass. 1963. Law clk. to Hon. John M. Harlan, U.S. Supreme Ct., 1957-58; assoc. Sullivan and Cromwell, N.Y.C., 1958-62; asst. prof. sch. law Harvard U., Cambridge, Mass., 1962-65, prof., 1965—, founder, dir. law sch. Human Rights Program, 1984—; chair Human Rights Studies Com., Harvard U., 1994—; vis. prof. CEPED, Rio de Janeiro, Brazil, 1968-69; vis. prof. Yale U., New Haven, 1972-73, Stanford U., 1965; cons. AID, 1962-64, Ford Found. 1966-69. Co-author: (textbook) Transnational Legal Problems, 4th edit., 1994, Tort and Accident Law, 2d edit., 1989; author: Moral Argument and Social Vision in the Courts, 1987, Diverse Partners: Non-Governmental Organizations in the Human Rights Movement, 1991; author, editor: Ethnic Conflict and the UN Human Rights System, 1995; former devels. editor Harvard Law Rev.; contr. articles to profl. jours. Office: Law Sch Harvard U Cambridge MA 02138

STEINER, HERBERT MAX, physics educator; b. Goeppingen, Germany, Dec. 8, 1927; came to U.S., 1939, naturalized, 1944; s. Albert and Martha (Epstein) S. B.S., U. Calif., Berkeley, 1951, Ph.D., 1956. Physicist Lawrence Berkeley Lab., Berkeley, Calif., 1956—; mem. faculty U. Calif., Berkeley, 1958—, prof. physics, 1966—; William H. McAdams prof. physics, chmn. dept., 1992—; vis. scientist European Center Nuclear Research, 1960-61, 64, 68-69, 82-83, Max Planck Inst. Physics and Astrophysics, Munich, 1976-77; vis. prof. Japanese Soc. Promotion Sci., 1978; vis. prof. physics U. Paris, 1989-90. Author articles in field. Served with AUS, 1946-47. Recipient Sr. Am. Scientist award Alexander von Humboldt Found., 1976-77; Guggenheim fellow, 1960-61. Fellow Am. Phys. Soc. Office: U Calif Berkeley Dept Physics Berkeley CA 94720*

STEINER, JEFFREY JOSEF, industrial manufacturing company executive; b. Vienna, Austria, Apr. 3, 1937; came to U.S., 1958; s. Beno and Paula

(Bornstein) S.; m. Claude Angel, Apr. 11, 1957 (div. 1972); children: Eric, Natalia, Thierry; m. Linda Schaller, Mar. 6, 1976 (div. June 1983); children: Benjamin, Alexandra; m. Irja Bonnier, Mar. 19, 1987. Student textile design, U. London, 1956; student textile mfg., Bradford Inst. Tech., London, 1957; HHD, Yeshiva U., 1994. Mgmt. trainee Metals and Controls div. Tex. Instruments, Attleborough, Mass., 1958-59, mgr. internat., 1959-60; pres. Tex. Instruments, Argentina, Brazil, Mex., Switzerland, France, 1960-66, Burlington Tapis, Paris, 1967-72; chmn., pres. Cedec S.A. Engring. Co., Paris, 1973-84; chmn., CEO Fairchild Corp., N.Y.C., 1985—, Banner Aerospace, 1993—; bd. dirs. Copley Fund, Fall River, Mass., Franklin Corp., N.Y.C. Trustee Montefiore Med. Ctr., N.Y.C.; bd. dirs. Israel Mus., Yeshiva U. Bus. Sch. Decorated Knight of the Arts (France), Knight Indsl. Merit of France, Chevalier de L'ordre des Arts et des Lettres, 1990, Chevalier de L'order National du Merite, 1992; recipient City of Paris medal Mayor Jacque Chirac, 1990. Mem. City Athletic Club, Racing Club, Polo Club. Jewish. Avocations: tennis, sailing. Office: Fairchild Corp 110 E 59th St New York NY 10022-1304

STEINER, KENNETH DONALD, bishop; b. David City, Nebr., Nov. 25, 1936; s. Lawrence Nicholas and Florine Marie (Pieters) S. B.A., Mt. Angel Sem., 1958; M.Div., St. Thomas Sem., 1962. Ordained priest Roman Catholic Ch., 1962, bishop, 1978; asso. pastor various parishes Portland and Coos Bay, Oreg., 1962-72; pastor Coquille Ch., Myrtle Point, Powers, Oreg., 1972-76, St. Francis Ch., Roy, Oreg., 1976-77; aux. bishop Diocese of Portland, Oreg., 1977—; vicar of worship and ministries and personnel dir. clergy personnel Portland Archdiocese. Democrat. Office: 2838 E Burnside St Portland OR 97214-1830

STEINER, LEE NATHAN, lawyer; b. Newark, Nov. 10, 1922; s. Joseph and Jeanette (Stamler) S.; m. Roslyn Roth, June 28, 1948; children: Terry, Catherine Steiner Adair, Nancy Steiner-Fraiman. BA, Lafayette Coll., 1943; JD, U. Pa., 1949. Bar: N.Y. 1950, U.S. Dist. Ct. (so. dist.) N.Y. 1950, U.S. Supreme Ct. Assoc. Weil, Gotshal & Manges, N.Y.C., 1950-56; ptnr. Loeb & Loeb, N.Y.C., 1965-90; bd. dirs. Carnegie Hall, N.Y.C., 1975—. Mem. Found. For Friends of South Pacific, 1973—. Lt. Comdr. USNR, 1943-46, PTO. Mem. Cousteau Soc. (bd. dirs. 1970—), Sunningdale Country Club (pres. 1974-78). Avocation: golf. Office: Loeb & Loeb 345 Park Ave New York NY 10154-0037

STEINER, LISA A(MELIA), immunologist, educator; b. Vienna, Austria, May 12, 1933; came to U.S., 1939, naturalized, 1945; d. Herman and Stella (Hornik) S. B.A., Swarthmore Coll., 1954; M.A., Radcliffe Coll., 1956; M.D., Yale U., 1959. Intern Yale U. Med. Sch., New Haven, 1959-60, clin. fellow, 1960-62; H.H. Whitney research fellow Washington U., St. Louis, 1962-65; Am. Heart Assn. research fellow St. Mary's Hosp. Med. Sch., London, 1965-67; asst. prof. immunology MIT, Cambridge, Mass., 1967-70, assoc. prof., 1970-80, prof., 1980—; mem. study sect. NIH, Bethesda, Md., 1974-78, 84-86; mem. pers. com. Am. Cancer Soc., N.Y.C., 1979-83, 88—; chmn. bd. overseers Brandeis U., Waltham, Mass., 1979-89; mem. bd. sci. counselors Div. Cancer Biology and Diagnosis, Nat. Cancer Inst., NIH, Bethesda, 1980-83. Contbr. articles to profl. jours. Trustee Helen Hay Whitney Found., 1984—. Fellow AAAS (mem.-at-large biol. scis. com. 1985-89); mem. Am. Assn. Immunologists, Am. Soc. Biol. Chemists. Home: 100 Memorial Dr Cambridge MA 02142-1314 Office: MIT Room 68-271 77 Massachusetts Ave Cambridge MA 02139-3594

STEINER, MICHAEL, sculptor; b. N.Y.C., May 12, 1945; s. Arthur and Eleanor (Perreira) S.; m. Phyllis I. Meshover, May 4, 1979. Student, Art Students League, 1964. One-man shows include Salander-O'Reilly Galleries, N.Y.C. and Berlin, Mus. of Art, Ft. Lauderdale, Fla., Mus. of Fine Arts, Boston, Andre Emmerich Gallery, N.Y.C., Meredith Long & Co., Houston, Hart House, Univ. Toronto, Norman Mackenzie Art Gallery, Regina, Sask., Galerie Wentzel, Hamburg, Germany, Dwan Gallery, N.Y.C., Fischbach Gallery, N.Y.C., numerous others; exhibited in group shows at Whitney Mus. Am. Art, N.Y.C., Univ. Mich. Mus. Art, Ann Arbor, Mus. Contemporary Art, Chgo., Grand Palais, Paris, Am. Embassy in Madrid, Inst. Contemporary Art, Phila., Larry Aldrich Mus. Contemporary Art, Ridgefield, Conn., Edmonton (Alta.) Art Gallery, Sonoma State Univ. Art Gallery, Rohnert Park, Calif., Lowe Art Gallery, Syracuse, N.Y., numerous others; represented in permanent collections including Mus. Modern Art, N.Y.C., Solomon R. Guggenheim Mus., N.Y.C., Hirshhorn Mus. and Sculpture Garden, Washington, Mus. Fine Arts, Boston, Mus. Fine Arts, Houston, Musee d'Art Moderne et d'Art Contemporain, Nice, France, Walker Art Ctr., Mpls., numerous others. Guggenheim fellow, 1971.

STEINER, PETER OTTO, economics educator, dean; b. N.Y.C., July 9, 1922; s. Otto Davidson and Ruth (Wurzburger) S.; m. Ruth E. Riggs, Dec. 20, 1947 (div. 1967); children: Alison Ruth, David Denison; m. Patricia F. Owen, June 2, 1968. A.B., Oberlin Coll., 1943; M.A., Harvard, 1949, Ph.D. 1950. Instr. U. Calif., Berkeley, 1949-50, asst. prof. econs., 1950-57; assoc. prof. U. Wis., Madison, 1957-59, prof., 1959-68; prof. econs. and law U. Mich., Ann Arbor, 1968-91, prof. emeritus, 1991—, chmn. dept. econs., 1971-74, dean Coll. Lit., Sci. and Arts, 1981-89; vis. prof. U. Nairobi, Kenya, 1974-75; Cons. U.S. Bur. Budget, 1961-62, Treasury Dept., 1962-63, various pvt. firms, 1952—. Author: An Introduction to the Analysis of Time Series, 1956, (with R. Dorfman) The Economic Status of the Aged, 1957, (with R.G. Lipsey) Economics, 10th edit., 1993, On the Process of Planning, 1968, Public Expenditure Budgeting, 1969, Mergers: Motives, Effects, Policies, 1975, also articles. Served to lt. USNR, 1944-46. Social Sci. Research Council Faculty Research fellow, 1956; Guggenheim fellow, 1960; Ford Faculty Research fellow, 1965. Mem. Am. Econ. Assn., Econometric Soc., AAUP (mem. com. Z 1970-73, pres. 1993-94). Home: 502 Heritage Dr Ann Arbor MI 48105-2556 Office: U Mich Law Sch 625 S State St Ann Arbor MI 48109-1215

STEINER, RICHARD RUSSELL, conglomerate executive; b. Chgo., Feb. 26, 1923; s. Frank Gardner and Ruth (Cowie) S.; m. Colleen M. Kearns, Dec. 6, 1949; children—Robert C., Kevin K., Sheila M. B.A., Dartmouth Coll., 1948. With Steiner Corp., Salt Lake City, 1948—; divisonal dir., v.p. Steiner Corp., 1951-59, pres., 1959—; dir. Am. Uniform Co. Served with USAAF, 1942-46. Decorated D.F.C. Mem. Phi Beta Kappa. Clubs: Alta, Salt Lake Country. Office: 505 E South Temple Salt Lake City UT 84102-1004

STEINER, ROBERT ALAN, neuroendocrinologist, researcher; b. Chgo., Mar. 9, 1947; s. Alan Dale and Elizabeth (Ann) Smith; m. Sally Jean Hewett, Mar. 19, 1983. B.A., U. Pacific, 1969; Ph.D., U. Oreg. Med. Sch., 1975. Sr. fellow Regional Primate Research Ctr., U. Wash., Seattle, 1974-78; asst. prof. dept. ob-gyn, physiology and biophysics U. Wash., Seattle, 1978-83, assoc. prof. dept. ob-gyn and physiology and biophysics, 1983—. Contbr. articles to profl. jour. Recipient award Nat. Human Growth Found., 1977; Nat. Inst. Child Health and Human Devel. grantee, 1978—. Mem. The Endocrine Soc., Soc. Neuorsci., AAAS, Soc. Study Reprodn. Democrat. Home: 6998 Island Center Rd NE Bainbridge Is WA 98110-1618 Office: U Wash Dept Ob Gyn # Rh-20 Seattle WA 98195

STEINER, ROBERT FRANK, biochemist; b. Manila, Philippines, Sept. 29, 1926; came to U.S., 1933; s. Frank and Clara Nell (Weems) S.; m. Ethel Mae Fisher, Nov. 3, 1956; children: Victoria, Laura. A.B., Princeton U., 1947; Ph.D., Harvard U., 1950; chief lab. phys. biochemistry Naval Med. Research Inst., 1965-70; prof. chemistry U. Md., Balt., 1970—; chmn. dept. chemistry U. Md., 1974—; dir. grad. program in biochemistry, 1985; mem. bd. advisors Ctr. for Fluorescence Spectroscopy, 1992—; mem. biophysics study sect. NIH, 1976. Author: Life Chemistry, 1968, Excited States of Proteins and Nucleic Acids, 1971, The Chemistry of Living Systems, 1981, Excited States of Biopolymers, 1983; editor Jour. Biophys. Chemistry, 1972—, Jour. Fluorescence, 1991; contbr. more than 160 articles to profl. jours. Served with AUS, 1945-47. Recipient Superior Civilian Achievement award Dept. Def., 1966; NSF rsch. grantee, 1971-77, NIH, 1973-93. Fellow Washington Acad. Sci., Japan Soc. for Promotion Sci.; mem. Am. Soc. Biol. Chemists. Club: Princeton (Washington). Achievements include development of fluorescence techniques for studying proteins. Home: 2609 Turf Valley Rd Ellicott City MD 21042-2021 Office: 5401 Wilkens Ave Baltimore MD 21228-5329

STEINER, ROBERT LISLE, language consultant; b. Tehran, Iran, May 21, 1921; s. Robert Lisle and Lois (Foresman) S.; m. Margaret S. Sherrard, June 4, 1944; children—Patricia Jean, Robert Lisle III, William Sherrard, John Scott. Grad., Mercersburg (Pa.) Acad., 1938; B.A., Wooster (O.) Coll.; M.I.A., Columbia, 1948. Cons. Commn. Chs. on Internat. Affairs, 1948-49; cultural attache Am. embassy, Iran, 1950-52; educationist U.S. Office Edn., 1952-54; program dir. Am. Friends of Middle East, 1954-59; v.p. Vershire Co., Vt., 1959-62; dir. Peace Corps, Kabul, Afghanistan, 1962-66; regional dir. North Africa, Near East and South Asia, 1966-69; dir. Washington office Devel. & Resources Corp., 1969-70; dir. Ctr. for Cross-Cultural Tng. and Research, adviser to univ. pres. on internat. affairs U. Hawaii, Honolulu, 1971-72; gen. mgr. Hawaii Pub. Broadcasting Authority, 1972-73; exec. dir. N.J. Edn. Consortium, Princeton, 1973-78; pres. InterLink Lang. Ctrs., Princeton, 1979-91, chmn., 1992—; tchr. U. Kansas City, Mo., 1957, Bradford (Vt.) Acad., 1961; poultry cons. Middle East Tech. U., Ankara, Turkey, 1963. Councilman, v.p. Shanks Village Assn., Orangeburg, N.Y., 1948; chmn. Kabul Sch. Bd., 1965. Served as pilot USNR, 1943-46. Mem. Princeton Mid. East Soc. (sec. 1986-88). Democrat. Presbyterian. Home: 406 Rosedale Rd Princeton NJ 08540-2313 Office: Interlink Lang Ctrs 406 Rosedale Rd Princeton NJ 08540-2313

STEINER, ROGER JACOB, linguistics educator, author, researcher; b. South Byron, Wis., Mar. 27, 1924; s. Jakob Robert and Alice Mildred (Cowles) S.; m. Ida Kathryn Posey, Aug. 7, 1954 (dec. May 1992); children: David Posey, Andrew Posey. BA, Franklin & Marshall Coll., 1945; MDiv, Union Theol. Sem., 1947; MA, U. Pa., 1958, PhD, 1963. Ordained to ministry, Meth. Ch., 1947. Clergyman United Meth. Ch., N.Y., Wis., Pa., 1945—; lectr. U. Bordeaux, France, 1961-63; instr. dept. langs. & lit. U. Del., Newark, 1963-64, asst. prof., 1964-71, assoc. prof., 1971-80, prof., 1980-85; prof. dept. linguistics U. Del., Newark, 1985—; cons. Charles Scribner's Sons, 1972-75, Larousse, N.Y.C., 1981-84, Houghton-Mifflin, Boston, 1981-84, Macmillan, 1994—. Author: Two Centuries of Spanish and English Bilingual Lexicography (1590-1800), 1970, New College French and English Dictionary, 1972, rev. 2nd edit. 1988. Recipient fellowship Am. Philos. Soc., Phila., 1971, Lilly Found., Phila., 1979-81. Mem. MLA (founder lexicography group 1974-75, chmn. 1976, 77, 80, 85), Dictionary Soc. N.Am. (exec. bd.), Del. Coun. for Internat. Visitors (brochure chmn.), Phi Beta Kappa (pres. Alpha Delta chpt. 1975-76). Republican. Avocations: languages, photography. Office: U Del Dept Linguistics Newark DE 19716-2551

STEINER, STUART, college president; b. Balt., July 24, 1937; s. Louis and Lillian (Block) S.; m. Rosalie Weiner, Sept. 12, 1962; children—Lisa, Susan, David, Robyn. AA, Balt. Jr. Coll., 1957; B.S., U. Md., 1959; grad. cert., Fla. State U., 1962; M.S.W., U. Pa., 1963; J.D., U. Balt., 1967; M.A., Tchrs. Coll., Columbia U., 1972; EdD, Columbia U., 1987. Caseworker, then supr. and dir. juvenile ct. services Balt. Dept. Social Services, 1960-64; dir. referral center Health and Welfare Council Met. Balt., 1964; dir. admissions and placement Harford Jr. Coll., Bel Air, Md., 1965-67; dean of students Genesee Community Coll., Batavia, N.Y., 1967-68; dean of coll. Genesee Community Coll., 1968-75, pres., 1975—; pres. SUNY West; mem. coun. of pres.'s SUNY, acting dep. to chancellor for community colls., 1985, pres. of assn. Pres. of Pub. Community Colls. Contbr. articles to profl. jours. Bd. dirs. St. Jerome Hosp., Genesee County Community Chest, Health Sci. Agy., Western N.Y., N.Y. Spl. Olympicsd Com., Girl Scouts Genesee Valley, 1989-90; trustee Villa Maria Coll.; trustee, v.p. N.Y. Chiropractic Coll.; pres. Genesee County United Way, Community Coll. of Balt. Hall of Fame. Heisler scholar, 1960-61; Kellogg fellow, 1971-72; Sigma Delta scholar, 1958-59. Mem. Am. Assn. Higher Edn., Assn. Am. Pres. Pub. C.C.s (pres.), Pvt. Indsl. Coun. (bd. dirs.). Home: 33 Woodcrest Dr Batavia NY 14020-2721 Office: Genesee Community Coll One College Rd Batavia NY 14020

STEINER, WILLIAM, direct marketing advertising agency executive, consultant; b. N.Y.C., Nov. 4, 1913; s. Bernhard and Regina (Storch) S. B.S. in Mktg. and Journalism, NYU, 1936. Market research dir. Topics Pub. Co., N.Y.C., 1936-40; circulation dir. Scholastic Mags., N.Y.C., 1940-44; promotion dir. Washington Post, 1944-49; bus. mgr. The Am. Girl, N.Y.C., 1949-50; circulation dir. Young Am. Mags. and Films, N.Y.C., 1950-52; pub. Gauden mag., N.Y.C., 1952-54; pres. William Steiner Assocs., Inc., N.Y.C., 1954-85, Steiner/Mauck Direct Inc., 1985-93. Contbr. chpts. to Handbook of Magazine Publishing, 1975, Best of Catalog Age, 1982. Contbr. articles to trade publs. Mem. Direct Mktg. Assn. (judge awards competition, com. mem.), Nat. Bus. Circulation Assn. Fulfillment Mgmt. Assn. (Industry award 1980), Direct Market Creative Guild (times.), Direct Mktg. Club N.Y. (Leadership award 1982), Women's Direct Response Group (chmn. newsletter com.). Club: NYU (N.Y.C.). Died May 20, 1993. Home: New York N.Y.

STEINFALS, CHRISTIAN WERNER, hotel executive; b. Duesseldorf, Germany, Jan. 22, 1933; came to U.S., 1964; Ed., Duesseldorf Hotel and Gastronomic Sch., 1948-51. Cert. hotel adminstr. Banquet mgr. Hotel Sonesta, Hartford, Conn., 1964-68; food and beverage mgr. Euclid Charterhouse Hotel, Cleve., 1968-69, Kaanapali Beach Hotel, Maui, Hawaii, 1969-70; dir. food and beverage Carlton Tower Hotel, London, 1970-71; asst. gen. mgr. Sutton Pl. Hotel, Toronto, Ont., Can., 1971-72; gen. mgr. Bristol Pl. Hotel Group, Toronto, 1972-78; exec. v.p. ops. Resorts Internat. Hotel Casino, Atlantic City, 1978-86; dir. ops. AFRC Hotels Bavaria, Fed. Republic Germany, 1986-87; exec. v.p. pres. devel. The Bristol Group Park Plaza Hotel, Toronto, 1987-89; regional v.p., gen. mgr. Ramada Renaissance Hotel, Atlanta, 1989—; mem. South Jersey Devel. Council. Mem. Am. Hotel and Motel Assn., Atlantic City Conv. Bur., Atlantic City Hotel Assn. Maitre de Table of Confrerie de la Chaine des Rotisseurs. Office: Atlanta Renaissance Hotel 4736 Best Rd Atlanta GA 30337-5612

STEINFELD, JEFFREY IRWIN, chemistry educator, consultant, author; b. Bklyn., July 2, 1940; s. Paul and Ann (Ravin) S. B.Sc., MIT, 1962; PhD, Harvard U., 1965. Postdoctoral fellow U. Sheffield, Yorkshire, Eng., 1965-66; asst. prof. chemistry MIT, Cambridge, 1966-70; assoc. prof. MIT, 1970-79, prof., 1980—; mem. sci. adv. bd. Lasertechnics, Inc., Albuquerque, 1982—. Author: Molecules & Radiation, 1974; co-author: Chemical Kinetics and Dynamics, 1989; editor: Laser and Coherence Spectroscopy, 1977, Laser-Induced Chemical Processes, 1981; co-editor: Spectrochimica Acta, 1983—; contbr. articles to profl. jours. Treas. Ward 2 Democratic Com., Cambridge, 1972-73. NSF fellow Harvard U., Cambridge, 1962-65; NSF fellow Sheffield U., 1965-66; Alfred P. Sloan Found. research fellow MIT, 1969-71; Guggenheim fellow, 1972-73. Fellow Am. Phys. Soc.; mem. AAAS, Fedn. Am. Scientists, Sigma Xi, Phi Lambda Upsilon. Jewish. Office: MIT Room 2-221 Cambridge MA 02139

STEINFELD, MANFRED, furniture manufacturing executive; b. Josbach, Germany, Apr. 29, 1924; s. Abraham and Paula (Katten) S.; m. Fern Goldman, Nov. 13, 1949; children: Michael, Paul, Jill. Student U. Ill., 1942; BS in Commerce, Roosevelt U., 1948. Research analyst State of Ill., 1948-50; v.p. Shelby Williams Industries, Inc., Chgo., 1954-63, pres., 1964-72; chmn. bd., 1973—; bd. dirs. Amalgamated Trust & Savs. Bank. Mem. adv. bd. Sch. Human Ecology, U. Tenn., 1981-87, devel. council, 1982-87; mem. adv. bd. dept. interior design Fla. Internat. U., 1981-85. Life trustee Roosevelt U., Chgo.; past pres. Roosevelt U. Bus. Sch. Alumni Council; hon. governing mem. Art Inst. Chgo.; mem. com. 20th century decorative art; bd. dirs. Jewish Fedn. Chgo. 1986-90; gen. chmn. Jewish United Fund, 1987; nat. vice chmn. United Jewish Appeal, 1988-94. Served to 1st lt. AUS, 1942-45, 50-52. Decorated Bronze Star, Purple Heart; named Small Bus. Man of Yr., Central Region, 1967; established Manfred Steinfeld Hospitality Mgmt. Program at Roosevelt U., Chgo., 1988; recipient Horatio Alger award of disting. Ams., 1981, Outstanding Bus. Leader award Northwood Inst., 1983. Mem. Horatio Alger Assn. (bd. dirs. 1986-92), Standard Club, Bryn Mawr Country Club, Bocaire Country (Boca Raton, Fla.), Beta Gamma Sigma. Home: 1300 N Lake Shore Dr Apt 34D Chicago IL 60610-2169 Office: Mdse Mart Rm 1348 Chicago IL 60654 also: Shelby Williams Industries Inc 150 Shelby Williams Dr Morristown TN 37813

STEINFELD, RAY, JR., food products executive; b. Portland, Oreg., Nov. 21, 1946; s. Ray and June Catherine (Cox) S.; m. Janis Bowen, Nov. 11, 1978; children: Erik, Blair. Student, Wheaton Coll., 1964-66, Drew U., 1967; BS in Polit. Sci. Lewis & Clark Coll., 1968. Sales rep. Continental Can Co., L.A., 1969-72; CEO Steinfeld's Products Co., Portland, Oreg.,

1972—; chmn. Oreg. Mus. Sci. in Industry, 1992-94. Treas., bd. dirs. Portland Recycling Team, Portland, 1973—; pres. exec. bd. Stop Oreg. Litter and Vandalism, 1973-92, pres., 1976; chmn., exec. com. Oreg. Landmark of Quality, 1985-87; pres. exec. com. William Temple House, 1985-91; vestry mem. Trinity Episcopal Ch., 1987-90; chmn. Oreg. Strategic Plan Agrl. Dept., 1988, World Trade Week, Portland, 1989; mem. Gov. Robert's Task Force, Salem, Oreg., 1991-92; bd. dirs Oreg. Enterprise Forum, 1992—, chmn., 1995. Mem. Pickle Packers Internat. (mdse. com. chmn.). Democrat. Espiscopalian. Avocations: tennis, golf, bridge, handball. Office: 10001 N Rivergate Blvd Portland OR 97203-6596 also: Oregon Mus of Sci and Industry 1945 SE Water Ave Portland OR 97214-3356

STEINFELD, THOMAS ALBERT, publisher; b. N.Y.C., June 17, 1917; s. Albert and Marjorie (Lesser) S.; m. Joan Rollinson, July 29, 1945 (dec. Nov. 1973); children: Geoffrey T., Jill R.; m. Viviane Barkey, June 20, 1977. Student, G. Phillips Exeter Acad., 1934, Harvard U., 1934-35. Salesman John Orr Products, N.Y.C., 1935-36; asst. advt. mgr. Bloomingdale's, N.Y.C., 1936-37; with Playbill mag., N.Y.C., 1937—; pub. Playbill mag., 1962-65, pres., 1962-68; now v.p., nat. sales dir. Playbill. Served to capt. AUS, 1942-46, CBI. Mem. English Speaking Union, Aspetuck Valley Country Club (Weston, Conn.), The Wings Club (N.Y.C.). Home: 83 W Meadow Rd Wilton CT 06897-4722 Office: 52 Vanderbilt Ave New York NY 10017-3808

STEINFELS, MARGARET O'BRIEN, editor; b. Chgo., July 28, 1941; m. Peter Steinfels, Aug. 31, 1963; 2 children: Gabrielle, John Melville. BS, Loyola U., Chgo., 1963; MA, NYU, 1971. Editor Hastings Ctr. Report, 1974-80; social sci. editor Basic Books, 1980-81; bus. mgr., later exec. editor Christianity and Crisis, 1981-84; founding editor Church mag., dir. publs. Nat. Pastoral Life Ctr., 1984-87, dir. publications: editor Commonweal mag., 1988—. Author: Who's Minding the Children: The History and Politics of Day Care in America, 1974. Office: Commonweal 15 Dutch St New York NY 10038-3719

STEINFELS, PETER FRANCIS, newspaper correspondent, writer; b. Chgo., July 15, 1941; s. Melville Philip and Margaret Mary (Holland) S.; m. Margaret Mary O'Brien, Aug. 31, 1963; children: Gabrielle, John Melville. AB, Loyola U., 1963; MA, Columbia U., 1964, PhD, 1976. Editorial asst. Commonweal mag., N.Y.C., 1964-65, asst. editor, 1965-67, assoc. editor, 1967-71, exec. editor, 1978-84, editor, 1984-88; sr. religion corr. N.Y. Times, 1988—; assoc. for humanities Inst. of Soc., Ethics and Life Scis., Hastings-on-Hudson, N.Y., 1972-77; co-editor (with Margaret O'Brien Steinfels) Hastings Ctr. Report, Hastings-on-Hudson, 1973-77. Author: The Neoconservatives, 1979; editor (with Robert M. Veatch) Death Inside Out, 1975. Roman Catholic. Home: 924 W End Ave New York NY 10025-3534 Office: NY Times 229 W 43rd St 3d Fl New York NY 10036

STEINFINK, HUGO, chemical engineering educator; b. Vienna, Austria, May 22, 1924; s. Mendel and Malwina (Fiderer) S.; m. Cele Intrator, Mar. 21, 1948; children: Dan E., Susan D. B.S., CCNY, 1947; M.S., Columbia U., 1948; Ph.D. Bklyn. Poly. Inst., 1954. Research chemist Shell Devel. Co., Houston, 1948-51, 53-60; T. Brockett Hudson prof. chem. engring. U. Tex., Austin, 1960—. Contbr. articles to profl. jours. Served with AUS, 1944-46. Fellow Am. Mineral. Soc.; mem. AIChE, Am. Chem. Soc., Am. Crystallographic Assn. (pres.-elect 1994, pres. 1995), Materials Rsch. Soc., Phi Beta Kappa, Sigma Xi, Phi Lambda Epsilon. Home: 3811 Walnut Clay Dr Austin TX 78731-4011 Office: U Tex Coll Engring Austin TX 78712

STEINFORT, JAMES RICHARD, university program director; b. Grand Rapids, Mich., Oct. 1, 1941; s. Gerald Gene and Harriett Lois (Stauffer) S.; m. Elizabeth Ann O'Laughlin, Mar. 14, 1964; children: Dawn, Robin, Susan, Troy, Ginger. AA in Computer Sci., San Jacinto Coll., Pasadena, Tex., 1973; BS in Tech. Mgmt. cum laude, Regis Coll., 1987. Chartered cons. Am. Cons. League. Customer engr. Control Data Corp., Mpls., 1964-65; computer engr. GE, Phoenix, 1965-69; tech. analyst Manned Spacecraft Ctr., Houston, 1969-73, systems analyst, 1973-75; tech. support mgr. Ohio Med. Products, Houston, 1975-79; prodn. regional mgr. Johnson & Johnson Co., Denver, 1979-83; prin., internat. cons. J.R. Steinfort & Assocs., Boise, Idaho, 1983-90; dir. TIES Tech. and Indsl. Ext. Svc.) Boise State U., 1990—. Author: (non-fiction) Conspiracy in Dallas, 1975, rev. edit., 1992; (tech. manuals) Medical/EDP Design Applications, 1985, Factory Quality Audit, 1991; editor newsletter Industry TIES, 1992-94, ISO-9000 Guidelines & Checklist, 1994. Chmn. subcom. Gov.'s Prayer Breakfast Commn., Boise, 1988-92; v.p. Full Gospel Businessman's Internat., Boise, 1990. With USAF, 1960-64. Univ. Ctr. grantee Econ. Devel. Administrn., Boise, 1990-92. Mem. Am. Soc. for Quality Control (sr.), Nat. Assn. Mgmt. and Tech. Assistance Ctrs. (bd. dirs 1990—), Am. Mgmt. Assn., Am. Cons. League (chartered cons.), Idaho Total Quality Inst. (bd. dirs 1991—), Tech. Transfer Soc. Avocations: hiking, camping, photography, writing, hunting. Home: 11934 Ginger Creek Dr Boise ID 83704 Office: Boise State Univ 1910 University Dr Boise ID 83725

STEINGRABER, FREDERICK GEORGE, management consultant; b. Mpls., July 7, 1938; s. Frederick F. and Evelyn (Luger) S.; m. Veronika Agnes Wagner, Aug. 9, 1974; children—Karla, Frederick. B.S., Ind. U., 1960; MBA, Beta Gamma Sigma, U. Chgo., 1964. Cert. mgmt. cons. Internat. banker Harris Trust, Chgo., 1960-61; with comml. loan and credit No. Trust Co., Chgo., 1963; assoc. A.T. Kearney, Chgo., 1964-69, prin., 1969-72, officer/ptnr., 1972—, pres., chief ops. officer, 1981, chief exec. officer, 1984—, chmn. bd., CEO, treas, 1986—; also bd. dirs.; bd. dirs. Lawter Internat., Mercury Fin. Co.; mem. Inst. for Ill., 1986; bd. dirs. Maytag Corp., Southeastern Thrift & Bank Fund, The Conf. Bd. Chief Crusader United Way-Crusade of Mercy, Chgo., 1983-90, div. chmn., 1988; bd. dirs. Ill. Coalition, 1989, Northwestern Healthcare Network, 1989—, fin. rsch. and adv. com. City of Chgo., 1989—; mem., past chmn. dean's adv. coun. Ind. U., 1985—, bd. dirs. Ind. U. Found.; mem. coun. of Grad. Sch. Bus. U. Chgo.; mem. Northwestern U. Assocs.; bd. dirs. Children's Meml. Hosp., Chgo., 1985—; exec. com. Mid.-Am. Com., 1985—. Mem. NAM (bd. dirs.), Inst. Mgmt. Cons., Chgo. Coun. Fgn. Rels. (bd. dirs.), Ill. State C. of C. (bd. dirs. 1982-88, exec. com. 1984-88, chmn. Ill. Alliance for Econ. Initiatives), Exec. Club Chgo., Acad. Alumni Fellows Ind. U. (award), Chgo. Club, Econ. Club (bd. dirs.), Comml. Club, Northwestern U. Assn., Met. Club, Glenview Club, others. Home: 615 Warwick Rd Kenilworth IL 60043-1149 Office: AT Kearney Inc 222 W Adams St Chicago IL 60606-5235

STEINHARDT, HENRY, photographer; b. N.Y.C., Nov. 15, 1920; s. Maxwell and Ruth (Davis) S.; m. Elizabeth Smith, 1946 (dec. 1955); children: Elizabeth, Maxwell; m. Helene Fleck, Feb. 1, 1958; 1 child, Henry III. AB, Harvard U., 1942, MArch, 1949. Registered architect. Office mgr. R.H. Cutting, Architect, N.Y.C., 1951-53; ptnr., architect Steinhardt & Thompson, Architects, N.Y.C., 1953-61; architect The Cerny Assocs., St. Paul, 1961-63, John Graham & Co., Seattle, 1963-67, Morse/Kirk, Seattle, 1967-68, N.G. Jacobson & Assocs., Seattle, 1968-69; pvt. practice Mercer Island, Wash., 1969-75; architect USN, Bremerton, Wash., 1975-78; photographer Mercer Island, 1979—. Prin. works exhibited at Washington, Seattle and Andover, Mass.; contbr. articles to fgn. archtl. jours. 1st lt. US Army, 1943-46; capt. USAF, 1950-52. Recipient Design award Progressive Architecture, 1959, Archtl. award Fifth Ave. Assn., 1960. Fellow AIA. Democrat. Home and Office: 7825 SE 63rd Pl Mercer Island WA 98040-4813

STEINHARDT, PAUL JOSEPH, physics educator, consultant; b. Washington, Dec. 25, 1952; s. Charles Sidney and Helen (Danuff) S.; m. Nancy Riva Shatzman, July 1, 1979; children: Charles Louis, Joseph Solomon, William Martin, Cynthia Rose. BS, Calif. Inst. Tech., 1974; MA, Harvard U., 1975, PhD, 1978. Jr. fellow Soc. Fellows Harvard U., Cambridge, Mass., 1978-81; asst. prof. physics U. Pa., Phila. 1981-83, assoc. prof., 1983-85, prof., 1985—, Mary Amanda Wood chair physics, 1989—; cons. IBM Rsch., Yorktown Heights, N.Y., 1978-90, Mitre Corp., McLean, Va., 1987-92; vis. lectr. Phi Beta Kappa, 1989-90; Monell fellow Inst. for Advanced Study, Princeton, 1989-90, Dyson fellow, 1995; Harvard Loeb lectr., 1990. Author: Physics of Quasicrystals, 1988, Quasicrystals: The State of the Arts, 1991; patentee quasiperiodic screens, quasiperiodic patterns, quasicrystals. Recipient 1st prize Gravitational Rsch. Essay Competition, 1993, 2d prize 1990; Sloan Found. fellow, 1982-85, Guggenheim fellow, 1994-95; U.S. Dept.

Energy grantee, 1982. Fellow Am. Phys. Soc.; mem. Am. Astron. Soc., Materials Rsch. Soc., Sigma Xi. Democrat. Jewish. Home: 1000 Cedargrove Rd Wynnewood PA 19096-2006 Office: U Pa Dept Physics 33D Walnut St Philadelphia PA 19144

STEINHARDT, RALPH GUSTAV, III, law educator; b. Bethlehem, Pa., July 28, 1954; s. Ralph Gustav Jr. and Mary Etzler (Hawks) S.; m. Donna Scarboro, Oct. 23, 1982; children: Ruth Jackson Steinhardt, Ralph Gustav IV. BA summa cum laude, Bowdoin Coll., 1976; JD, Harvard U., 1980. Bar: D.C. 1980, U.S. Dist. Ct. D.C. 1981, U.S. Ct. Appeals (D.C. and 9th circs.) 1983, U.S. Supreme Ct. 1984. Assoc. Patton Boggs & Blow, Washington, 1980-85; prof. law Nat. Law Ctr. George Washington U., Washington, 1985—; co-dir. Oxford-GW Summer Inst. in internat. Human Rights Law, 1994; litigation advisor Internat. Human Rights Law Group, Washington, 1985—; mem. coun. advisors UN High Commr. for Refugees, Washington, 1987—. Contbg. author: Testimonial Privileges, 1983, World Justice? U.S. Courts and International Human Rights, 1991, United Nations Legal Order, 1994; contbr. articles to profl. jours. Pro bono counsel in field; bd. dirs. Hancock Point (Maine) Village Improvement Soc., 1988-92. Henry Luce Found. scholar, 1976-77; recipient Pro Bono Atty. award Internat. Human Rights Law Group, 1987; finalist Trial Lawyer of Yr., 1989. Mem. Am. Soc. Internat. Law (exec. com. 1994), Phi Beta Kappa. Mem. Soc. of Friends. Avocations: musical composition, sailing. Office: George Washington U Nat Law Ctr 720 20th St NW Washington DC 20006-4304

STEINHART, ASHLEY, lawyer; b. Sacramento, Aug. 25, 1943; s. Joseph and Betty Steinhart; m. Phyllis Bonnie Levine, Aug. 24, 1966; children: Dana Michele, Jason Gary. BA, Mich. State U., 1964; JD, Columbia U., 1967; LLM in Taxation, NYU, 1970. Bar: N.J. 1967, N.Y. 1988. Atty. Hannoch Weisman, Roseland, N.J., 1967-72, ptnr., 1972-83, dir., 1983-93, chmn. tax dept., 1976-85, chmn. estate and trust dept., 1979-87, chm. compensation com., 1987-90; ptnr. Lowenstein, Sandler, Kohl, Fisher & Boylan, Roseland, 1993—; lectr. in field; moderator seminars. Presenter TV program Insurance Matters, 1988, others; contbr. articles to jours. in field. Founder Monmouth County, N.J. Maccabiah Games, 1979; com. mem. Columbia U., 1983—; sponsor N.J. Retarded Citizens Assn., 1988—. Recipient Mission of Mercy award Israel Red Cross, 1988. Fellow Am. Coll. Trust and EstateCounsel; mem. ABA (real property and probate, tax, law firm econs. sects.), N.J. Bar Assn., Essex County Bar Assn., Mich. State U. Alumni Assn., Athletic Congress U.S.A., Mensa, Beta Gamma Sigma. Avocations: basketball, softball, racquet sports, U.S. coin collecting, Scrabble-by-Mail. Home: 25 Oswego Ln Short Hills NJ 07078-1213 Office: Lowanstein Sandler Kohl Fisher & Boylan 65 Livingston Ave Roseland NJ 07068-1734

STEINHART, RONALD G., banker; b. Beaumont, Tex., June 15, 1940; s. Werner and Marga (Steinhart); m. Phyllis Yonet; children: David Alan, Kenneth Jason, Barry Joel. BBA, U. Tex., MBA. Pres. Dallas Bank & Trust, 1965-69; chmn. bd. Town North Nat. Bank, Dallas, 1972-75, Dallas/Fort Worth Airport Bank, 1972-75; pres. Main Street Nat. Bank, Dallas, 1969-77; chmn. bd. Equitable Bank, Dallas, 1979-80; pres. Valley View Bank, Dallas, 1977-80; vice chmn. InterFirst Corp., Dallas, pres., chief operating officer, 1980-86; vice chmn. First RepublicBank Corp., Dallas, 1986-88; formerly prin. RepublicBank Assn., Dallas; pres., COO Banc One Tex. Corp. (formerly Deposit Guaranty Bank), Dallas, 1989—; prin. rep. Assn. Bank Holding Cos.; chmn., chief exec. officer Tex.-Op Bancshares Inc. Mem. Edwin L. Cox Sch. Bus. assoc. bd. So. Meth. U.; mem. exec. bd., chmn. 1983 and 1984 Scout show Circle Ten council Boy Scouts Am.; sec./treas. Dallas Citizens Council; dir. Jewish Welfare Fedn. Found., Dallas Zoolog. Soc., State Fair of Tex., United Way of Dallas; mem. Cotton Bowl Council. Served with USAF, 1958-68, with res. Mem. Tex. Bankers Assn., Tex. Assn. Bank Holders Cos., Dallas Clearing House Assn. (dir.), Tex. Soc. C.P.A.s, Assn. Res. City Bankers, Young Pres. Orgn. Office: Banc One Tex Corp 1717 Main St Dallas TX 75201

STEINHAUER, GILLIAN, lawyer; b. Aylesbury, Bucks, Eng., Oct. 6, 1938; d. Eric Frederick and Maisie Kathleen (Yeates) Pearson; m. Bruce William Steinhauer, Jan. 2, 1960; children: Alison (Humphrey) Eric, John, Elspeth. AB cum laude, Bryn Mawr (Pa.) Coll., 1959; JD cum laude, U. Mich., 1976. Bar: Mich. 1976, Mass. 1992, U.S. Dist. Ct. (ea. dist.) Mich. 1976, U.S. Ct. Appeals (6th cir.) 1982. Assoc. Miller, Canfield, Paddock & Stone, Detroit, 1976-82, sr. ptnr., 1983-92; dir. Commonwealth of Mass. Workers' Compensation Litigation Unit, Boston, 1992—; mem. Atty. Gen.'s Task Force to Reduce Waste, Fraud and Abuse in the Workers' Compensation System, 1992—. Chancellor Cath. Ch. St. Paul, Detroit, 1976-83, 91; pres. bd. trustees Cath. Cmty. Svcs. Inc., 1989-92; bd. dirs. Spaulding for Children, 1991-92, Davenport House, 1992—; mem. Vestry St. Michael's Ch., Marblehead, Mass., 1994—. Mem. Mich. State Bar Found. (life); mem. State Bar Mich., Fed. Jud. Conf. 6th Cir. (life), Bryn Mawr Club of Mich. (pres. 1970-91). Home: 510 Hale St Prides Crossing MA 01965 Office: 100 Cambridge St Rm 1801 Boston MA 02202

STEINHAUS, JOHN EDWARD, physician, medical educator; b. Omaha, Feb. 23, 1917; s. Emil F. and Pearl (Haynie) S.; m. Mila Jean Pinkerton, Feb. 21, 1943; children: Kathryn, Carolyn, Barbara, William, Elizabeth. B.A., U. Neb., 1940, M.A., 1941; M.D., U. Wis., 1945, Ph.D., 1950. Diplomate: Am. Bd. Anesthesiologists. Pvt. practice specializing in anesthesiology Madison, Wis., 1951-58, Atlanta, 1958—; faculty U. Wis., 1951-58; mem. faculty Emory U., Atlanta, 1958—; prof. anesthesiology Emory U., 1959-87, prof. emeritus, 1987—, chmn. dept., 1959-85; chief anesthesiology service Grady Meml. Hosp., 1959-77, Emory U. Hosp., 1958-85. Author: Medical Care Divided; contbr. articles to profl. jours. Pres. Anesthesia Found. Mem. Am. Soc. Anesthesiologists (past pres., Disting. Service award 1982), So. Soc. Anesthesiologists (past pres.), AMA, AAAS, Assn. U. Anesthetists (past pres.), Anesthesiology History Assn. (pres), Soc. Pharm. Exptl. Therapeutics, Phi Beta Kappa, Sigma Xi, Alpha Omega Alpha. Home and Office: 836 Castle Falls Dr NE Atlanta GA 30329-4114

STEINHAUSER, SHELDON ELI, sociology and gerontology educator; b. N.Y.C., Aug. 11, 1930; s. Charles W. and Helen (Rosenstein) S.; m. Frances Goldfarb, June 28, 1953 (div. 1963); children: Karen, Lisa Steinhauser Hackel; m. Janice M. Glass, May 2, 1965; children: Shayle, David, Susan Hirschman. BS, L.I. U., 1963; DPS, Regis U., 1994. Community cons. Anti-Defamation League, Columbus, Ohio, 1951-57; regional dir. Anti-Defamation League, Denver, 1957-85, dir. nat. field svcs., 1977-85, dir. nat. community svcs. divsn., 1979-81, western area dir., 1975-85; exec. v.p. Allied Jewish Fedn. of Denver, 1985-91; pres. Sheldon Steinhauser & Assocs., Denver, 1991—; instr. sociology Met. State Coll., Denver, 1969-71, asst. prof. sociology, 1972-94, asst. prof., 1972-94, assoc. prof., 1994—; arbitrator Am. Arbitration Assn., Denver, 1988—; pres cons EEOC. Leader Congl. Missions to Egypt and Israel, 1982, 83; staff dir. Mission to Israel, 1986, 87, 90; del. White House Conf. on Aging, 1995; cons. cmty. rels. svc. U.S. Dept. Justice, 1995; mem. cmty. working group Nat. Civilian Cmty. Corps; former mem. Denver Anti-Crime Coun.; chmn. Mountain States Inst. Judaism, Denver, 1958-59; past pres. Adult Edn. Coun. Met. Denver; past mem. cmty. adv. bd. Jr. League Denver; mem. Colo. Martin Luther King Holiday Planning Com., L.Am. Rsch. and Svc. Agy. Recipient M.L. King Jr. Humanitarian award Colo. M.L. King Commn., Denver, 1986, 1st Ann. Human Rels. award Colo. Civil Rights Commn., Denver, 1965, Humanitarian award NAACP, Denver, 1980, ADL Civil Rights Achievement award, 1989; named to Gallery of Fame, Denver Post, 1979, 80. Mem. Western Social Sci. Assn., Am. Sociol. Assn., Colo. Jewish Reconstructionist Fedn., Am. Soc. on Aging, Social. Practice Assn., B'nai B'rith (Columbus v.p., Denver). Avocations: travel, photography, tennis, running, cantorial music.

STEINHOFF, HAROLD WILLIAM, retired research institute executive; b. Ft. Morgan, Colo., Mar. 9, 1919; s. Lawrence Henry and Helen Grace (Morse) S.; m. Marian Andelea Towne, Jan. 19, 1944; children: Richard Terrell, David Lee. BS in Forestry, Colo. A&M Coll., 1941; MS in Forest Zoology, Syracuse U., 1947, PhD in Wildlife Biology, 1957. Grad. teaching asst. Syracuse (N.Y.) U., 1941-42, 46-47; timber estimator U.S. Forest Svc., Ft. Collins, Colo., 1944; ranger U.S. Nat. Park Svc., Estes Park, Colo., 1947; prof. Colo. State U., Ft. Collins, 1947-74, Centennial prof., 1970—, regional adminstr., 1974-77, dist. dir. 1977-81; project leader Four Corners Rsch. Inst., Durango, Colo., 1977—, pres., 1981-92; cons. Devel. Rsch. Assocs.,

Denver, 1971, Stanford Rsch. Inst., Menlo Park, Calif., 1971; project leader Huddelston & Buck, Denver, 1972. Author: Wildlife Ecology, 1961, Ecosystem Biology, 1976; editor: Ecological Impact of Snowpack Augmentation, 1976; contbr. The Values of the Wildlife Resource, 1987. Dean Teaching Inst. Ft. Collins Coun. Chs., 1952-56; chmn. environ. com. Durango C. of C., 1977; chmn. LaPlata County Energy Coun., Durango, 1977, Durango Uranium Tailings Task Force, 1978-91. Capt. C.E. U.S. Army, 1942-46, ETO. Recipient Oliver Pennock Disting. Svc. award Colo. State U., 1968. Mem. The Wildlife Soc. (coun. 1966-71), Coll. Forestry Alumni Assn. (pres. 1964-64, Honor Alumnus award 1976), Soc. Am. Foresters, Am. Inst. Biol. Sci., Nat. Wildlife Fedn., Toastmasters (pres. Durango chpt. 1980-81), Phi Kappa Phi (pres. Ft. Collins 1965). Avocations: photography, home construction. Home: 2705 N College Dr Durango CO 81301-4410

STEINHOFF, WILLIAM RICHARD, English literature educator; b. Chgo., Feb. 13, 1914; s. William Richard and Nellie (Mulligan) S.; m. Rosannah Jenne Cannon, Jan. 6, 1940; m. Marilyn Mason Brown, May 8, 1993. A.B., Calif.-Berkeley, 1938, M.A., 1940, Ph.D., 1948. Mem. faculty U. Mich., Ann Arbor, 1948—; prof. English lit. U. Mich., 1963—, prof. emeritus, 1985—; vis. prof. U. Aix-Marseilles, France, 1964-65; mem. exec. com. Coll. Conf. Composition and Communications, 1959-60. Author: George Orwell and the Origins of 1984, 1975 (pub. in Eng. as The Road to 1984); editor: (with others): Modern Short Stories, 1951, (with others) The Image of the Work, 1952, (With A. Carr) Points of Departure, 1960. Chmn. Mich. Commn. Tchr. Certification, 1961-62. 2d lt. AUS, 1943-46. Ford fellow, 1954-55; Fulbright lectr., Indonesia, 1984-85, Bratislava, Czechoslovakia, 1987-88. Home: 2108 Scottwood St Ann Arbor MI 48104

STEINHORN, IRWIN HARRY, lawyer, educator, corporate executive; b. Dallas, Aug. 13, 1940; s. Raymond and Libby L. (Miller) S.; m. Linda Kay Shoshone, Nov. 30, 1968; 1 child, Leslie Robin. BBA, U. Tex., 1961, LLB, 1964. Bar: Tex. 1964, U.S. Dist. Ct. (no. dist.) Tex. 1965, Okla. 1970, U.S. Dist. Ct. (we. dist.) Okla. 1972. Assoc. Oster & Kaufman, Dallas, 1964-67; ptnr. Parness, McQuire & Lewis, Dallas, 1967-70; sr. v.p., gen. counsel LSB Industries, Inc., Oklahoma City, 1970-87; v.p., gen. counsel USPCI, Inc., Oklahoma City, 1987-88; ptnr. Hastie & Steinhorn, Oklahoma City, 1988—; adj. prof. law Oklahoma City U. Sch. Law, 1979—; lectr. in field. Mem. adv. com. Okla. Securities Commn., 1986—. Served to capt. USAR, 1964-70. Mem. ABA, Tex. Bar Assn., Okla. Bar Assn. (bus. assn. sect., sec.ptreas. 1986-87, chmn. 1988-89), Com. to Revise Okla. Bus. Corp. Act, Oklahoma City Golf and Country Club, Rotary, Phi Alpha Delta. Republican. Jewish. Home: 6205 Avalon Ln Oklahoma City OK 73118-1001 Office: Hastie & Steinhorn 3000 1st Okla Tower 210 Park Ave Oklahoma City OK 73102-5601

STEINKAMP, FREDRIC, film editor. Editor: (films) The Adventures of Huckleberry Finn, 1960, Where the Boys Are, 1960, Two Loves, 1961, All Fall Down, 1962, Period of Adjustment, 1962, It Happened at the World's Fair, 1963, Sunday in New York, 1963, Quick, Before It Melts, 1964, The Unsinkable Molly Brown, 1964, Once a Thief, 1965, Duel at Diablo, 1966, Grand Prix, 1966 (Academy award best film editing 1966), Mister Buddwing, 1966, Doctor, You've Got to Be Kidding, 1967, Charly, 1968, The Extraordinary Seaman, 1969, The Shoot Horses, Don't They?, 1969 (Academy award nomination best film editing 1969), (with Marjorie Fowler and Roger J. Roth) The Strawberry Statement, 1970, The Marriage of a Young Stockbroker, 1971, (with Donald Guidice) A New Leaf, 1971, Nightmare Honeymoon, 1972, (with Michael McLean) Freebie and the Bean, 1974, (with Guidice) Three Days of the Condor, 1975, (with Thomas Stanford and Guidice) The Yakuza, 1975, (with David Bretherton and Guidice) Harry and Walter Go to New York, 1976, Bobby Deerfield, 1977, Fedora, 1979, (with Karl F. Steinkamp) Bound by Honor, 1993; (films with William Steinkamp) Hide in Plain Sight, 1980, Tootsie, 1982 (Academy award nomination best film editing 1982), Against All Odds, 1984, (also with Pembroke Herring and Sheldon Kahn) Out of Africa, 1985 (Academy award nomination best film editing 1985), White Nights, 1985, Adventures in Babysitting, 1987, Burglar, 1987, Scrooged, 1988, Havana, 1990, The Firm, 1993. Office: care Lawrence A Mirisch The Mirisch Agency 10100 Santa Monica Blvd Ste 700 Los Angeles CA 90067*

STEINKAMP, ROBERT THEODORE, lawyer; b. St. Louis, Sept. 11, 1945; s. William P. and Leona M. (Kraus) S.; m. Cheryl Sue Dunlop, Aug. 19, 1967; children: Theodore Bewick, Rebecca Anne. BA, William Jewell Coll., Liberty, Mo., 1967; JD, U. Mo., Kansas City, Mo., 1971; postgrad., U. Mo., Kansas City, 1971-72. Bar: Mo. 1971, U.S. Dist. Ct. (we. dist.) Mo. 1971, U.S. Tax Ct. 1971, U.S. Ct. Appeals (8th cir.) 1971. Assoc. Morris, Foust, Moudy & Beckett, Kansas City, 1971-76; ptnr. Morris, Foust & Beckett, Kansas City, 1976-78, Beckett & Steinkamp, Kansas City, 1978-90; v.p., gen. counsel, sec. Applebee's Internat., Inc., Kansas City, 1990—. Mem. Downtown, Inc., Kansas City, 1978-84, Friends of Art, Nelson Art Gallery, Kansas City, 1985—, Nat. Hist. Preservation Found., 1985—; bd. dirs. Kappa Alpha Order Nat. Fraternity Housing Corp., Lexington, Va., 1984-92; bd. dirs., pres. ADKASHA, Liberty, Mo., 1977—; bd. dirs. Liberty Symphony Orch., Inc., 1982-87, pres. 1984-86; committeeman Kappa Alpha Order Nat. Fraternity Housing Com., Lexington, 1984-92, Clay County Fine Arts Coun., 1991-93; sec. Heartland Franchising Assn., 1991-93. Mem. ABA (forum on franchising, corp. and tax sections), Kansas City Bar Assn., Lawyer's Assn. Kansas City, Mo. Bar Assn., Clay County Bar Assn., Kans. City Club, Liberty Hills Country Club (bd. dirs. 1985-87). Republican. Methodist. Avocations: golf, tennis, reading, travel. Office: Applebees Internat Inc Ste 100 4551 W 107th St Shawnee Mission KS 66207

STEINKAMP, WILLIAM, film editor. Editor: (films) King of the Mountain, 1981, The Fabulous Baker Boys, 1989 (Academy award nomination best film editing 1989), (with Michael Tronick and Harvey Rosenstock) Scent of a Woman, 1992, Man Trouble, 1992; (films with Fredric Steinkamp) Hide in Plain Sight, 1980, Tootsie, 1982 (Academy award nomination best film editing 1982), Against All Odds, 1984, (also with Pembroke Herring and Sheldon Kahn) Out of Africa, 1985 (Academy award nomination best film editing 1985), White Nights, 1985, Adventures in Babysitting, 1987, Burglar, 1987, Scrooged, 1988, Havana, 1990, The Firm, 1993. Office: care Motion Picture Editors 7715 Sunset Blvd #220 Los Angeles CA 90046*

STEINMAN, LISA MALINOWSKI, English literature educator, writer; b. Willimantic, Conn., Apr. 8, 1950; d. Zenon Stanislaus and Shirley Belle Malinowski; m. James A. Steinman, Apr. 1988 (div. 1980); m. James L. Shugrue, July 23, 1984. BA, Cornell U., 1971, MFA, 1973, PhD, 1976. Asst. prof. English Reed Coll., Portland, Oreg., 1976-82, assoc. prof., 1982-90, prof., 1990—, Kenan prof. English lit. and humanities, 1993—; cons. NEH, Washington, 1984-85. Author: Lost Poems, 1976, Made in America, 1987, All That Comes to Light, 1989, A Book of Other Days, 1992; editor Hubbub Mag., 1983—; editl. bd. Williams Rev., 1991—, Stevens Jour., 1994—; contbr. articles to profl. jours. Fellow Danforth Found., 1971-75, NEH, 1983, Oreg. Arts Commn., 1983-84, Nat. Endowment for Arts, 1984; Rockefeller Found. scholar, 1987-88; recipient Pablo Neruda award, 1987, Oreg. Inst. Literary Arts award, 1993. Mem. MLA, Poets and Writers, PEN (N.W. chpt., co-founder, officer 1989-93). Home: 5344 SE 38th Ave Portland OR 97202-4208 Office: Reed Coll Dept English 3203 SE Woodstock Blvd Portland OR 97202-8199

STEINMAN, ROBERT CLEETON, accountant; b. Phila., June 11, 1931; s. George Curtis and Kathryn Agnes (Johnstone) S.; m. Nancy Badri Pourian, Sept. 24, 1960; children: Shirley Kathryn, Susan Soraya, Robert Mark. B.Sc. in Bus. Adminstrn, Drexel U., 1954, M.B.A., 1970. C.P.A., Pa. Accountant Main Lafrentz & Co. (C.P.A.'s), Phila., 1956-58; asst. treas. Ostheimer and Co., Inc., Phila. 1958-62; controller Biol. Abstracts, Inc., Phila., 1962-64; budget, cost and fin. analysis mgr. PQ Chems. Co., 1964-70; v.p., group controller 1st Pa. Bank, Phila., 1970-78; sr. v.p., comptroller Phila. Savs. Fund Soc., 1978-87; controller Kravco Co., 1987-88, spl. asst. to the pres., 1988-91; chief fin. officer Lorel Mktg. Group Inc., King of Prussia, Pa., 1991-92; adj. assoc. prof. Grad. Sch. Drexel U., Phila. Co-founder Briarlin Civic Assn., 1969, treas. 1969-72, pres., 1975—; Bd. dirs. Sigma Pi Nat. Found., treas. frat. Served with AUS, 1954-56. Mem. Pa. Bankers Assn. (faculty trust tng. sch.), Fin. Execs. Inst., Pa. Inst. CPAs, Sigma Rho, Sigma

Pi, Overbrook Golf Club. Republican. Methodist. Home: 804 Lawrence Ln Newtown Square PA 19073-2610

STEINMETZ, DAVID CURTIS, religion educator, publisher, minister; b. Columbus, Ohio, June 12, 1936; s. Walter Curtis and Lucy Margaret (Binderbasen) S.; m. Virginia Ruth Verpleogh, June 20, 1959; children: Claire Elise, Matthew Eliot. BA with highest honor, Wheaton Coll., 1958; BD summa cum laude, Drew U., 1961; postgrad., U. Goettingen, Federal Republic of Germany, 1964-65; ThD, Harvard U., 1965. Ordained to ministry United Meth. Ch., 1959. Asst. and assoc. prof. Lancaster (Pa.) Theol. Sem., 1966-71; prof. Duke U. Durham, N.C., 1971-88, Amos Ragan Kearns prof. history of Christianity, 1988—; pres., pub. The Labyrinth Press, Inc., 1981—; vis. prof. Harvard U., 1977; adv. coun. Interpretation, Richmond, Va., 1979-82. Author: Misericordia Dei, 1968, Reformers in the Wings, 1971, Luther and Staupitz, 1980, Luther in Context, 1986; mem. editorial bd. Archiv für Reformationsgeschichte, 1977-93, Duke U. Monographs in Medieval and Renaissance Studies, 1972—, Brill Studies in Medieval and Reformation Thought, Leiden, Holland, 1981—. Named Scholar-Tchr. of Yr. Duke U., 1986; Rockefeller doctoral fellow Rockefeller Found., 1964-66, faculty fellow Assn. Theol. Schs., 1970, 77-78, Guggenheim fellow Guggenheim Found., 1977-78, NEH summer fellow, 1990. Mem. Medieval Acad. Am., Am. Soc. Ch. History (pres. 1985), Renaissance Soc. Am., Soc. for Reformation Rsch., Soc. for Scholarly Pub. Office: Duke U Div Sch Durham NC 27706

STEINMETZ, DEBORAH SUSAN, interior designer; b. New Orleans, Nov. 29, 1951; d. Donald Frederick and Estelle Margaret (Ulmer) Tossell; B.F.A., La. State U., 1973; m. Robert Steinmetz, Dec. 29, 1973. Interior designer David Grinnell Architect, 1973-75; interior design cons.; Columbus, Ga., 1975-77; designer Dameron-Pierson, New Orleans, 1977-79; v.p. interior design Interior Environments, Inc., New Orleans, 1979-83; pres., owner Steinmetz & Assocs., 1983—; mem. interior design curriculum com. Dominican Coll., New Orleans, 1981-82; mem. interior design adv. com. Delgado Community Coll., New Orleans, 1982—; chmn. membership Preservatin Resource Ctr., 1988. Mem. visual arts com. Contemporary Art Center, 1980-81; dir. profl. devel. Nat. Coun. Interior Design Qualification, 1994-95. Mem. Soc. Interior Designers (Presdl. citation; chmn. New Orleans assn. 1980-81, dir. La. chpt. 1982—, newsletter editor La. Chpt. 1982, chain membership/admissions La. chpt. 1984, treas. 1985-87, sec. 1988, nat. dir. 1993-94), Internat. Interior Design Assn., Nat. Trust Hist. Preservation, La. Landmarks Soc., La. State Bd. Interior Design Examiners, Interior Designers of La. (treas. 1987), La. State Interior Design Alumni (sec. 1987). Roman Catholic. Home: 2850 Annunciation St New Orleans LA 70115-1002 Office: 225 Baronne St Ste 207 New Orleans LA 70112-1790

STEINMETZ, JON DAVID, mental health facility administrator, psychologist; b. N.Y.C., June 4, 1940; s. Lewis I. and Rose (Josefsberg) S.; m. Jane Audrey Hilton, Dec. 24, 1964; children: Jonna Lynn, Jay Daniel. BA, NYU, 1962; MA, Bradley U., 1963. Lic. psychologist, Ill. Intern in psychology Galesburg (Ill.) State Rsch. Hosp., 1963-64; staff psychologist Manteno (Ill.) State Hosp., 1964-68, program dir., 1968-70, asst. dir., 1970-72; dep. dir. Manteno Mental Health Ctr., 1972-80, Tinley Park (Ill.) Mental Health Ctr., 1980-88; dir. Chgo. Read Mental Health Ctr., 1988-91; ret., 1991; cons. Jane Addams Hull House Assn., 1992—. Trustee Village of Park Forest, Cook and Will Counties, Ill.; officer, bd. dirs. various civic orgns., Park Forest. Home: 200 Hickory St Park Forest IL 60466-1016

STEINMETZ, KAYE H., state legislator; m. Bob Steinmetz; children: Mark, Steven, Richard, Stacey. Grad., Columbia Coll.; postgrad., U. Mo. Mem. Mo. Ho. of Reps., chmn. children, youth and families com., mem. social svc. and Medicaid com., edn. com., appropriations com. for social svc. and corrections, others. Alt. del. Nat. Conf. State Legis.; bd. dirs. Nat. Order Women Legislators, Mo. State Jr. Miss Scholar Progam; mem. Gov. Conf. Edn., 1976, Gov. Conf. Children and Youth, White House Conf. Aging, Mo. State Adv. Bd. Sch. Nurses and Parents as 1st Tchrs., Adv. Bd. Ct. App. Spl. Advocates, Planning Coun. United Way Greater St. Louis, Mo. PTA. Recipient Woman of Achievement award, 1975, Dem. Meritorious Svc. award St. Louis Globe; named to 10 Best Legislators List by Mo. Times. Address: 1814 Kilmory Dr Florissant MO 63031-4154 Office: Mo Ho of Reps State Capital Jefferson City MO 65101

STEINMETZ, RICHARD BIRD, JR., holding company executive, lawyer; b. Orange, N.J., Mar. 27, 1929; s. Richard Bird and Charlotte (Quinby) S.; m. Merriam Holly Miller, June 9, 1956; children: Richard Blair, Jonathan Bird, Edward Quinby. BA, Yale U., 1950; JD, Harvard U., 1955. Bar: N.Y. 1955. Assoc. Chadbourne and Parke, N.Y.C., 1955-59; with Anaconda Co., N.Y.C., 1959-79, v.p., gen. counsel, 1971-79; v.p. Colt Industries Inc., N.Y.C., 1979-82; v.p., gen. counsel Pittston Co., Greenwich, Conn., 1982-84; exec. v.p. Case, Pomeroy and Co., N.Y.C., 1984-94; bd. dirs. Case, Pomeroy and Co., Enable Software, Inc. Served to capt. USMC, 1950-52. Mem. ABA, Assn. of Bar of City of N.Y., Assn. of Gen. Counsel. Republican. Episcopalian. Home: 78 Zaccheus Mead Ln Greenwich CT 06831-3752 Office: Case Pomeroy & Co Inc 529 Fifth Ave New York NY 10017-4608

STEINMETZ, ROBERT CHARLES, architect; b. Charleston, W.Va., Oct. 16, 1951; s. Charles and Bernadine Steinmetz; m. Deborah Susan Toselle, Dec. 29, 1974. BArch, La. State U., 1974. Architect Pound Flower & Dedyler, Columbus, Ga., 1974-75, David Allan Grinnell, Atlanta, 1975, Maxwell & Lebreton, New Orleans, 1975-77; architect, assoc. Mathes Group, New Orleans, 1977-84; architect, prin. Steinmetz & Assocs., New Orleans, 1984—; value added reseller computers, software Integrated Facility Systems Corp., New Orleans, 1991—. Mem. New Orleans Mus. Art, New Orleans Preservation Res. Ctr., Nat. Trust for Hist. Preservation. Mem. AIA (chair interiors com. 1995), La. Architecture Assn., La. Landmarks Soc., Nat. Coun. Archtl. Registration Bds. (cert.), IFMA. Office: 225 Baronne St Ste 1720 New Orleans LA 70112-1710

STEINMETZ, SOL, publishing company editor; b. Velki-Bockov, Slovakia, July 29, 1930; came to U.S., 1948; s. Philip and Lea (Zwiebel) S.; m. Tzipora Mandel, June 26, 1955; children: Jacob J., Abraham A., Steven B. BA, Yeshiva Coll., N.Y.C., 1952, DD, 1956. Ordained rabbi, 1956. Asst. editor G. & C. Merriam Co., Springfield, Mass., 1957-61; gen. editor Barnhart Books, Bronxville, N.Y., 1962-89; exec. editor dictionaries Random House, Inc., N.Y.C., 1990-94, editl. dir., 1995—. Co-author: Barnhart Dictionary of New English, 1973, Second Dictionary of New English, 1980, Thhird Dictionary of New English, 1990; author: Yiddish and English: A Century of Yiddish in America, 1986. Mem. Am. Dialect Soc., Dictionary Soc. N.Am., League of Yiddish, Religious Zionists Am., Rabbinic Alumni RIETS. Avocations: reading, travel, writing, studying. Home: 1273 North Ave New Rochelle NY 10804 Office: Random House Inc 201 E 50th St New York NY 10022-7703

STEINMILLER, JOHN F., professional basketball team executive; b. Mt. Prospect, Ill.; m. Corinne Steinmiller; children: John Henry, Mary Kate. V.p. bus. ops. Milw. Bucks, 1977—. Bd. dirs. M.W. Athletes Against Childhood Cancer Fund, Milw. Big Bros.-Big Sisters, Metro Milw. YMCA; mem. Greater Milw. Com. Recipient Contardi Commitment award MACC Fund, 1991. Mem. Milw. Pen and Mike Club (pres.). Office: Milw Bucks 1001 N 4th St Milwaukee WI 53203-1314

STEINRUCK, CHARLES FRANCIS, JR., management consultant, lawyer; b. Phila., Apr. 25, 1908; s. Charles Francis and Laura (Crutchley) S.; m. Esther Sophia Schramm, June 1, 1936 (dec. Oct. 1962); children—Carol, Lisa.; m. Alice Bignell Marchese, Nov. 22, 1967. Student, U. Pa., 1925-28; LL.B., South Jersey Law Sch. (now Rutgers U.), 1937, J.D., 1972. Bar: D.C. bar 1938. Accountant J.S. Timmons, Inc., Phila., 1926-28; merged with Philco corp., 1928, asst. to sec., 1937-41, asst. sec., 1941-42, sec., 1942-61; asst. sec. Philco-Ford Corp., 1962-68; cons. 1962—; resident v.p. Togotechnique, S.A.R.L., Republique Togolaise, 1979—. Author: An Anecdotal History, 1988. Mem. John W. Westcott Law Soc., Night Watch Sr. Soc. (U. Pa.), Am. Bar Assn., Sigma Kappa Phi, Delta Sigma Pi. Republican. Presbyterian. Clubs: Germantown Cricket (Phila.); Seaview Country (Absecon, N.J.). Home: 614 E Mcdevitt Dr Absecon NJ 08201-6000

STEINWACHS, DONALD MICHAEL, public health educator; b. Boise, Idaho, Sept. 9, 1946; s. Don Peter and Emma Bertha (Weisshaupt) S.; m. Sharon Kay Carlson, Aug. 25, 1972. MS, U. Ariz., 1970; PhD, Johns Hopkins U., 1973. Asst. prof. health svcs. adminstrn. Johns Hopkins U., Balt., 1973-79, assoc. prof. health policy and mgmt., 1979-86, dir. Health Svcs. Rsch. & Devel. Ctr., 1982—, prof. health policy and mgmt., 1986—, chairperson health policy and mgmt., 1994—; sec. adv. com. Dept. Vets. Affairs, Washington, 1991-92; mem. Inst. Medicine, NAS, Washington, 1993—; bd. dirs. Health Outcomes Inst., Inc., Mathematica Policy Rsch. Inc. Contbr. articles to profl. jours. Mem. Gov's Commn. on Health Policy Rsch. and Fin., Md., 1988-90. Capt. U.S. Army, 1973. Grantee NIMH, Agy. for Health Care Policy and Rsch., Robert Wood Johnson Found. Mem. Ops. Rsch. Soc. Am., Assn. Health Svc. Rsch. (bd. dirs., pres.), Found. for Health Svc. Rsch. (bd. dirs., pres.). Achievements include development of methods for using management information systems to examine patterns of medical care, costs, and indicators of the quality of care. Office: Johns Hopkins U 624 N Broadway Baltimore MD 21205-1996

STEIR, PAT IRIS, artist; b. Newark, Apr. 10, 1940. Studies, Pratt Inst., 1956-58, 60-62; BFA, Boston U., 1961, studies, 1958-60; DFA (hon.), Pratt Inst., 1991. Art dir. Harper & Row, N.Y.C., 1968-69; tchr. Calif. Art Inst., 1973-75. One woman shows include Terry Dintenfass Gallery, N.Y., 1964, Bienville Gallery, N.Y., 1969, Graham Gallery, N.Y., 1971, Fourcade, Droll, Inc., N.Y., 1975, John Doyle Gallery, Paris, 1975, Galerie Farideh Cadot, Paris, 1976, 78, 79, 80, Morgan Thomas Gallery, Santa Monica, Calif., 1976, Otis Art Inst., L.A., 1976, Xavier Fourcade, Inc., N.Y., 1976, Carl Solway Gallery, Cin., 1977, Galeria Marilena Bonomo, Bari, Italy, 1978, Galerie d'Art Contemporain, Geneva, 1980, Art Mus. U. So. Fla., Tampa, 1990, Galerie Montenay, Paris, 1990, N.J. Ctr. for Visual Arts, Summit, 1990, Musée d'Art Contemporain, Lyon, France, Victoria Miro Gallery, London, 1990, Dennis Ochi Gallery, Sun Valley and Boise, Idaho, 1990, Robert Miller Gallery, N.Y., 1990, Landfall Press, Chgo., 1990, Gallerie Thaddeus Ropac, Paris, 1990, Linda Cathcart Gallery, Santa Monica, Calif., 1991, Galerie Franck & Schulte, Berlin, 1991, MacKenzie Art Gallery, Regina, Can., 1991, K. Kimpton Gallery, San Francisco, 1991, Bellas Artes, Sante Fe, 1991, Thaddeus Ropac, Salzburg, Austria, 1991, Galleria Fernando Alcolea, Barcelona, Spain, Whitney Mus., N.Y.C., 1991, Galerie Pfefferle, Munich, 1991, Linda Cathcart Gallery, Santa Monica, Calif., 1991, Nina Freudenheim Gallery, Buffalo, 1991, The Bklyn. Mus., 1992; 3 person installation show Le Magazine, Grenoble, Switzerland, 1990; group exhbns. include Ben Shahn Gallery William Patterson Coll., Wayne, N.J., 1990, Ecole Des Beaux Arts, Tourcoing, France, 1990, 91, Mus. Art R.I. Sch. Design, 1990, Marc Richards Gallery, L.A., 1990, Louver Gallery, N.Y., 1990, Norah Haime Gallery, N.Y., 1990, Nat. Gallery of Art, Washington, 1990; represented in permanent collections including Kunstmuseum, Bern, Switzerland, Walker Art Ctr., Mpls., Bklyn. Mus., Musee d'art Contemporain, Lyons, France, Met. Mus. Art, N.Y., Mus. Modern Art, N.Y., Nat. Gallery, Washington, Nat. Mus. Am. Art, Washington, Whitney Mus. Am. Art, N.Y. Studio: c/o Robert Miller Gallery 41 E 57th St New York NY 10022

STEISS, ALAN WALTER, research administrator, educator; b. Woodbury, N.J., Feb. 15, 1937; s. Walter and Martha (Schreoder) S.; m. Patricia Foster McClintock, June 13, 1959; children: Carol Jean, Darren C., Todd A. BA in Sociology and Psychology, Bucknell U., 1959; MA in Urban Planning, U. Wis., 1966, PhD, 1969. Statewide planning dir. State of N.J., Trenton, 1960-65; mem. faculty Va. Poly. Inst. and State U., Blacksburg, 1967-69, program chmn. environ. and urban systems, 1969-78, assoc. dean architecture, 1974-78, assoc. dean rsch. div., 1978-83, assoc. provost, 1983-88; dir. div. rsch. devel. and adminstrn. U. Mich., Ann Arbor, 1988—, prof. urban planning, prof. pub. health, 1988—; cons. various state and local govts., 1960—, Trust Territory of the Pacific, Micronesia, 1968. Author numerous book including: Management Control in Government, 1982, Governmental Accounting and Control, 1984, Strategic Management and Organizational Decision Making, 1985, Financial Management in Public Organizations, 1989, Management Planning and Control, 1991. Chair Montgomery (Va.) Pub. Svc. Authority, 1978-83; bd. dirs. Mich. Pub. Health Inst.; mem. policy and planning bd. Mich. Consortium for Enabling Tech., 1991-95. Univ. fellow U. Wis., 1959-60, NDEA fellow, 1966-67. Mem. AAUP, ASPA, Am. Inst. of Planners (prog. chmn. 1964), Assn. Collegiate Schs. of Planning (mem. exec. com. 1970-71, sec. 1971-73), Assn. Collegiate Schs. in Architecture, Nat. Assn. Schs. Pub. Affairs and Adminstrn. (inst. rep. 1975-76), Coun. of Univ. Insts. for Urban Affairs, N.J. Fed. of Planning Officials (sec. 1960-64), Urban America Inc., Nat. Urban Coalition, Psi Chi, Tau Sigma Delta, Lambda Alpha. Home: 4820 Greenway Ct Ann Arbor MI 48103-9414 Office: U Mich Div Rsch Devel & Adminstrn 3003 S State ST Ann Arbor MI 48109-1274

STEITZ, JOAN ARGETSINGER, biochemistry educator; b. Mpls., Jan. 26, 1941; d. Glenn D. and Elaine (Magnusson) Argetsinger; m. Thomas A. Steitz, Aug. 20, 1966; 1 child, Jonathan Glenn. B.S., Antioch Coll., 1963; Ph.D., Harvard U., 1967; D.Sc. (hon.), Lawrence U., Appleton, Wis., 1982, Rochester U. Sch. Medicine, 1984, Mt. Sinai Sch. Medicine, 1989, Bates Coll., 1990; DSc (hon.), Trinity Coll., 1992, Harvard U., 1992. Postdoctoral fellow MRC Lab. Molecular Biology, Cambridge, Eng., 1967-70; asst. prof. molecular biophysics and biochemistry Yale U., New Haven, 1970-74; assoc. prof. Yale U., 1974-78, prof. molecular biophysics and biochemistry, 1978—; investigator Howard Hughes Med. Inst., 1986—. Recipient Young Scientist award Passano Found., 1975, Eli Lilly award in biol. chemistry, 1976, U.S. Steel Found. award in molecular biology, 1982, Lee Hawley, Sr. award for arthritis rsch., 1984, Nat. Medal of Sci., 1986, Dickson prize for Sci. Carnegie-Mellon U., 1988, Warren Triennial prize Mass. Gen. Hosp., 1989, Christopher Columbus Disc. award in biomed. rsch., 1992, Weizmann Women and Sci. Awd., 1994, NY Acad. of Scis. Fellow AAAS; mem. Am. Acad. Arts and Sci., Nat. Acad. Arts and Sci., Am. Phil. Soc., NY Acad of Scis., (Weizmann Women & Sci. Awd. 1994). Home: 45 Prospect Hill Rd Branford CT 06405-5711 Office: Yale U Sch Medicine Dept Blochem & Biophysics 295 Congress Ave New Haven CT 06536

STELCK, CHARLES RICHARD, geology educator; b. Edmonton, Alta., Can., May 20, 1917; s. Robert Ferdinand and Florella Maud (Stanbury) S.; m. Frances Gertrude McDowell, Apr. 24, 1945; children—David, Brian, Leland, John (dec.). B.Sc., U. Alta., 1937, M.Sc., 1941; Ph.D., Stanford U., 1951. Registered profl. geologist, Alta. Field geologist B.C. Dept. Mines, Victoria, Can., 1939-41; field geologist Canol Project, Norman Wells, N.W.T., Can., 1941-43, Imperial Oil Co., Calgary, Alta., 1943-49; from lectr. to prof. emeritus geology U. Alta., Edmonton, 1946—. Contbr. numerous articles principally on biostratigraphy of Cretaceous to sci. publs. Fellow Royal Soc. Can.; mem. Assn. Profl. Engrs., Geologists and Geophysicists Alta. (Centennial award 1979), Geol. Assn. Can. (Logan medal 1982), Geol. Soc. Am., Can. Soc. Petroleum Geologists (Douglas medal 1994). Conservative. Office: U Alta, Geology Dept, Edmonton, AB Canada T6G 2E3

STELL, LANCE KEITH, philosophy educator; b. Galesburg, Ill., Dec. 18, 1943; s. Kenneth Phillip and Esther (Dethmers) S.; m. Susan Kathleen Stell, Aug. 19, 1967; children: Dean, Virginia, Audrey. AB cum laude, Hope Coll., 1966; AM, U. Mich., 1969, PhD, 1974. Asst. prof. philosophy Hope Coll., Holland, Mich., 1969-71; instr. Albion (Mich.) Coll., 1971-72; asst. prof. Ill. State U., Normal, 1972-75; vis. scholar U. Iowa, Iowa City, 1975-76; from asst. prof. to assoc. prof. Davison (N.C.) Coll., 1976-85, acting chair, 1983-85, prof., chair, 1985—, Charles A. Dana prof., 1991—; prof. clin. ethics dept. internal medicine Carolinas Med. Ctr., Charlotte, N.C., 1990—; bd. mem. Bioethics Resource Group Ltd.; mem. Bd. Forensic Examiners. Fellow Danforth Teaching, 1967, Ctr. for Chinese Studies, 1967, NEH, 1975-76, Mellon Found. Summer Rsch., 1978, 80, Nat. Humanities Ctr., 1982-83, grantee Liberty Fund, 1980, Health Svcs. Found., 1991-93; Title VI Chinese Lang. fellow NDFL, 1968, biotechology summer fellow Alfred Slone Found., 1985, teaching/rsch. med. ethics fellow Carolinas Med. Ctr., 1989-90. Mem. Am. Philosophical Assn., Am. Soc. Law and Medicine, Soc. Health and Human Values. Office: Davidson Coll PO Box 1719 Davidson NC 28036

STELL, WILLIAM KENYON, neuroscientist, educator; b. Syracuse, N.Y., Apr. 21, 1939; arrived in Can., 1980; dual citizenship Am./Can, 1992; s. Henry Kenyon and Edith Doris (Lawson) S.; m. Judith Longbotham, June 27, 1974 (separated); children: Jennifer Susan, Sarah Ruth. B.A. in Zoology with high honors, Swarthmore Coll., 1961; Ph.D. in Anatomy, U. Chgo., 1966, M.D. with honors (E. Gellhorn prize 1967), 1967. Staff fellow, then sr. staff fellow Nat. Inst. Neurol. Diseases and Stroke, NIH, 1967-72; asso. prof., then prof. ophthalmology and anatomy UCLA Med. Sch., 1972-80; assoc. dir. Jules Stein Eye Inst., UCLA, 1978-80; prof. anatomy U. Calgary (Can.) Faculty Medicine, 1980—, prof. surgery/ophthalmology, 1992—, head dept., 1980-85, prof. surgery and ophthalmology, 1992—; dir. Lions Sight Centre, Calgary, 1980—; guest rschr. in physiology Lab. Physiologie Nerveuse, Centre Nat. de la Recherche Scientifique, Gif-sur-Yvette, France, 1985-86. Served with USPHS, 1967-69. Served with USPHS, 1967-69. Grantee USPHS, Med. Rsch. Coun. Can., Alta. Heritage Found. Med. Rsch., Natural Scis. and Engring. Rsch. Coun. Can., NATO, Human Frontier Sci. Program; William and Mary Greve Internat. research scholar, 1979-80. Mem. Assn. Rsch. in Vision and Ophthalmology, Soc. Neurosci. Home: 2020 17th Ave NW, Calgary, AB Canada T2M 0S6 Office: Univ of Calgary, 3330 Hospital Dr NW, Calgary, AB Canada T2N 4N1

STELLA, FRANK DANTE, food service and dining equipment executive; b. Jessup, Pa., Jan. 21, 1919; s. Facondino and Chiara (Pennoni) S.; m. Martha Theresa Yetzer; children: Daniel, Mary Anne, William J., Philip J., Marsha, James C., Stephen P. Student, U. Detroit, 1937-41, Washington and Lee, 1944; D in Bus. and Industry (hon.), Washington and Lee, 1944; D in Bus. and Industry (hon.), Gentium Pacem U., Rome, 1979; D in Sci. and Bus. Adminstn. (hon.), Cleary Coll., 1985. Pres., chmn., CEO F.D. Stella Products Co., Detroit, 1946—; founding ptnr. The Fairlane Club (sold to Club Corp. Am., 1979); chmn. bd., CEO Stella Internat., N.Y.C.; mem. Mich. Higher Edn. Facilities Commn., Area-Wide Water Quality Bd., Fed. Statis. Commn., White House Fellows Commn. and others; chmn. Detroit Income Tax Rev. Bd.; instr. engn. and mgmt. small bus. U. Detroit; vice chmn., bd. dirs. Met. Realty Corp.; bd. dirs. Fed. Home Loan Bank Indpls., Computer Bus. Solutions Inc. Bd. dirs. March of Dimes Mich., 1976, mem. exec. com., 1984; corp. bd. dirs. Boys Club Met. Detroit., 1979; bd. dirs., exec. com. Orchestra Hall, 1974, vice chmn., 1979-82, chmn. 1982—; trustee U. Detroit, 1971-80, 82—, exec. com. 1971-77, chmn. devel. com. 1971-80, chmn. nominating com. 1971-78; chmn. Nat. Vol. Commn., Nat. Rep. Heritage Council, 1985—, chmn. 1991—; trustee Sacred Heart Rehab. Ctr., 1981—, St. Gabriel Media, Inc., 1980—; group chmn. food and drug div. United Found., 1978-79; mem. adv. bd. dirs. Bishop Borgess High Sch., 1984-88; bd. dirs. Ctr. for Ind. Living, Detroit Rehab. Inst., 1977-82, New Detroit Inc., Detroit Econ. Growth Corp., 1983, Detroit Econ. Growth Fund, 1983, Mich. Opera Exec. Com.; mem. St. John's Hosp. Guild, Friend of the Folger Libr., Washington, 1978-80; vice chmn. Detroit Symphony Orch. Hall Bd.; mem. divisional bd. trustees Mt. Carmel Mercy Hosp., 1979-90; founding chmn. 1979-82, mem. exec. com. 1979—; mem. exec. com. Nat. Rep. Com. 1985—; active Mich. Rep. Com.; apptd. Presdl. Commn. on Fed. Stats.; chmn. Nat. Vol. Svc. Comm.; presdl. commn. White House fellows; apptd. by Gov. Mich. Higher Edn. Facilities Commn.; mem. Area-wide Water Quality Bd., founding pres. Legatus Mich. chpt., internat. bd. dirs.; chmn. bd. Mercy Hosp. Detroit and Health Svcs., 1987-90; Nat. Italian Am. Found., Washington, 1992; former mem. Detroit Renaissance, Inc.; appointed by Gov. John Engler to chair Mich. Christopher Columbus Quincentenary Commn., 1991; appointed by President George Bushto Christopher Columbus Presdl. Quincentinaery Jubilee Commn., 1991; chmn. Nat. Rep. Heritage Groups Coun., 1991; bd. dirs. Oakland Children's Svcs., 1992, Metro Detroit Juvenile Diabetes, 1991. Recipient over 35 awards from local, nat. and internat. civic and profl. orgns. Mem. Alliance for Mich. (bd. dirs. 1984—), Detroit Ctrl. Bus. Dist. Assn., Nat. Comml. Refrigerator Sales Assn. (bd. dirs., pres. 1953-54, adv. bd. 1954—), Nat. Assn. Wholesaler-Distbrs. (del. 1982—), Wholesale Distbrs Assn. (bd. dirs. 1973—, v.p. 1976, pres. 1977-79), Bus. Edn. Alliance (various offices), Mich. Restaurant Assn., Food Svc. Execs. Assn., Italian-Am. C. of C. Mich., Nat. Italian-Am. Found. (charter, bd. dirs., exec. com., pres. 1979—), Hispanos Organized to Promote Entrepreneurs (bd. dirs. 1976-81), Econ. Club Detroit (bd. dirs. 1982—), Air Force Assn. (charter), Am. Soc. Legion Merit, Greater Detroit C. of C. (chmn. 1987-88, bd. dirs.), Wayne County C.C. Found. (pres.), Young Pres.'s Orgn., Detroit Club, Detroit Athletic Club, Detroit Golf Club, The Fairlane Club, Capitol Hill Club, Skyline Club (Southfield). Home: 19180 Gainsborough Rd Detroit MI 48223-1344 Office: 7000 Fenkell St Detroit MI 48238-2083

STELLA, FRANK PHILIP, artist; b. Malden, Mass., May 12, 1936; s. Frank and Constance Aida (Santonelli) S.; m. Barbara Rose, 1961 (div.); children: Rachel, Michael, Laura; m. Harriet McGurk, 1978; children: Peter, Patrick. AB in History, Princeton U., 1958, DFA (hon.), 1984; hon. degree, Mpls. Coll. Art and Design, 1974, Brandeis U., 1985, Dartmouth Coll., 1985. Represented by Leo Castelli Gallery, 1959; artist-in-residence Dartmouth Coll., 1963; instr. Brandeis U., 1969; Charles Eliot Norton prof. poetry Harvard U., Cambridge, Mass., 1983; lectr. Pratt Inst., Bklyn., 1960, Yale U., 1965, Cornell U., 1965, Seattle Art Mus., 1967, Detroit Inst. Arts, 1967, Art Inst. Chgo., 1968, 85, Bezalel Acad. Arts and Design, Jerusalem, 1981, Whitney Mus., Mus. Fine Art, Boston, 1982, San Antonio Art Inst., 1983, Harvard U., 1983-84, Musee Nat. d'Art Moderne, Paris, 1984, Coun. for U.S. and Italy, N.Y., 1984, Frick Collection, N.Y., 1985, Dartmouth Coll., 1985; instr. art U. Saskatchewan, 1967, Brandeis U., 1968; vis. critic dept. art, Cornell U., 1965. One-man shows Leo Castelli Gallery, N.Y.C., 1960, 62, 64, 66, 69, 73, 75, 79, 82, Galerie Lawrence, Paris, 1961, 64, Fergus Gallery, L.A., 1963, 65, Kasmin Ltd., London, 1964, 66, 68, M. Knoedler & Co., 1976, 81, 85, David Mirvish Gallery, London, 1966, Pasadena (Calif.) Art Mus., 1966, Seattle Art Mus., 1967, Galerie Bischofsberger, Zurich, Switzerland, 1967, Gallery Modern Art, Washington, 1968, Irving Blum Gallery, L.A., 1968, 69, 71, 73, Mus. Modern Art, N.Y.C., 1970, 1987 (retrospective); touring show Stella, since 1970, 1978, Galerie Daniel Templon, Paris, 1975, Andre Emmerich, Zurich, 1976, Galerie M Bochum, Fed. Republic Germany, 1977, Mus. Modern Art, Oxford, Eng. 1977, Galerie Valeur, Nagoya, Japan, 1978, 79, Getler/Pall Gallery, N.Y.C., 1980, Akira Ikeda Gallery, Nagoya, Japan, 1980, 81, 82, 83, 85, 86, 87, 88, 89, Koh Gallery, Tokyo, 1980, Knoedler Gallery, 1977, 80, 82, 85, 87, Galerie Hans Strelow, Dusseldorf, Fed. Republic Germany, 1981-82, 87, Mus. Modern Art, San Francisco, 1983, Inst. Contemporary Arts, London, 1985, Greenberg Gallery, St. Louis, 1985-86, Laumeier Sculpture Pk., St. Louis, 1986, Gagosian Gallery, N.Y.C., 1987, Nat. Mus. Art, Osaka, Japan, 1988, Staatsgalerie Stuttgart, Fed. Republic Germany, 1988-89, Kawamura Mem. Museum of Art, Japan, 1991; numerous group shows throughout U.S., Europe, 1959—, including 37th Corcoran Gallery Art Biennale, Washington, 1981; included in permanent collections, Addison Gallery Am. Art, Phillips Acad., Andover, Mass., Art Gallery Ont., Toronto, Can., Balt. Mus., Rose Art Mus., Brandeis U., Waltham, Mass., Bklyn. Mus., List Art Ctr., Brown U., Providence, Cleve. Art Mus., Contemporary Art Mus., Houston, Dallas Mus. Fine Art, Denver Mus. Art, Des Moines Art Ctr., 1st Nat. Bank Houston, Fogg Art Mus., Boston, Guggenheim Mus., High Mus., Atlanta, Hirshhorn Mus. and Sculpture Garden, Washington, Ind. U. Art Mus., Bloomington, Inst. Contemporary Art, Phila., Jacksonville (Fla.) Art Mus. Inc., Kitakyushu (Japan) Mcpl. Mus., Kunstmuseum, Basel, Switzerland, Stedelijk Mus., Amsterdam, Art Inst., Chgo., Detroit Inst. Art, L.A. County Mus. Art, Walker Art Center, Mpls., Mus. Modern Art, N.Y.C., San Francisco Mus. Art, Whitney Mus. Am. Art, N.Y.C., Albright-Knox Gallery, Buffalo, La. Mus., Humleback, Denmark, Met. Mus. Art, N.Y.C., Milw. Art Ctr., Mpls. Inst. Arts, Modern Art Mus. Ft. Worth, Moderna Museet, Stockholm, Musee Nat. d'Art moderne, Paris, Mus. Bochum, Fed. Republic Germany, Mus. Boymans von Beuningen, Rotterdam, The Netherlands, Mus. Contemporary Art, Chgo., Mus. Contemporary Art, L.A., Mus. Fine Arts, Houston, Nagoaka (Japan) Mus. Art, Smithsonian Instn., Washington, Nat. Gallery Art, Washington, Nationalgalerie, Berlin, Nat. Mus. Am. Art, Washington, Nelson-Atkins Mus. Art, Kansas City, Mo., Phila. Mus., Phillips Collection, Washington, Portland (Oreg.) Ctr. Visual Arts, St. Louis Art Mus., Seattle Art Mus., Seibu Art Mus., Tate Gallery, Lonon, Toledo Mus. Art, Vancouver (B.C.) Art Mus., Can., Wadsworth Atheneum, Hartford, Conn., Wallraf-Richartz Mus., Cologne, Fed. Republic Germany; author: Frank Stella: Illustrations after El Lissitzky's Had Gadya 1982-84, 1985, Working Space, 1986; work subject of numerous monographs and publs.; subject of film Frank Stella at the Fogg 1984, 1985. Bd. dirs. Coun. for U.S. and Italy. Recipient 1st prize Tokyo Internat. Biennale, 1967, Claude M. Fuess award Phillips Acad., 1979, Skowhegan Medal for Painting, 1981, Mayor's Award of Honor Mayor of N.Y.C., 1982, Award of Am. Art Pa. Acad. Fine Arts, 1985; hon. fellow Bezalel Acad. Arts and Design, 1981, Am. Acad. Arts and Letters, 1982-83. Fellow Mac. Fellows (NYU). Office: care Leo Castelli Gallery 420 W Broadway New York NY 10012-3764

STELLA, JOHN ANTHONY, investment company executive; b. Jessup, Pa., Feb. 3, 1938; s. John Anthony and Alda (Parri) S.; m. Aurelia M. Arre, Feb. 20, 1965; children—John C., Matthew A., Krista R. B.S., U. Detroit, 1960; M.B.A., NYU, 1965. Bus. evaluation cons. Allied Chem. Co., N.Y.C., 1965-70; treas. Spinnerin Yarn Co., Hackensack, N.J., 1970-72, Penn-Dixie Cement Corp., N.Y.C., 1972-74; v.p. finance Halecrest Co., 1974-76; treas. Rsch.-Cottrell, 1976-84, v.p., contr./treas., 1984-88; pres. John A. Stella & Assocs., Plainfield, N.J., 1988-91; sr. v.p. Investment Support Systems, Inc., Bloomfield, N.J., 1991—; pres. State Tax Auditing & Rsch., Inc., Plainfield. Served with AUS, 1960. Office: 300 Broadacres Dr Bloomfield NJ 07003 also: State Tax Auditing & Rsch Inc 925 Madison Ave Plainfield NJ 07060

STELLA, VALENTINO JOHN, pharmaceutical chemistry educator; b. Melbourne, Victoria, Australia, Oct. 27, 1946; came to U.S., 1968; s. Giobatta and Mary Katherine (Sartori) S.; m. Mary Elizabeth Roeder, Aug. 16, 1969; children: Catherine Marie, Anne Elizabeth, Elise Valentina. B of Pharmacy, Victorian Coll. Pharmacy, Melbourne, 1967; D of Pharmacy, U. Kans., 1971. Lic. pharmacist, Victoria. Pharmacist Bendigo (Victoria) Base Hosp., 1967-68; asst. prof. Coll. Pharmacy U. Ill., Chgo., 1971-73; from asst. prof. to assoc. prof. to prof. Sch. Pharmacy U. Kans., Lawrence, 1973-90, Univ. disting. prof., 1990—; dir. Ctr. for Drug Delivery Rsch.; cons. to 15 pharm. cos., U.S, Japan, Europe. Co-author: Chemical Stability of Pharmaceuticals, 2d edit., 1986; co-editor: Prodrugs as Novel Drug Delivery Systems, 1976, Directed Drug Delivery, 1985, Lymphatic Transport of Drugs, 1992; author numerous papers, revs., abstracts. Fellow AAAS, Am. Assn. Pharm. Scientists, Am. Acad. Pharm. Scientists. Roman Catholic. Achievements include 11 U.S. patents; rsch. in application of phys./organic chemistry to the solution of pharm. problems. Home: 1324 Lawrence Ave Lawrence KS 66049 Office: U Kans Dept Pharm Chemistry 3306 Malott Hall Lawrence KS 66045

STELLER, ARTHUR WAYNE, educational administrator; b. Columbus, Ohio, Apr. 12, 1947; s. Fredrick and Bonnie Jean (Clark) S. BS, Ohio U., 1969, MA, 1970, PhD, 1973. Tchr., Athens (Ohio) City Schs., 1969-71; curriculum coord., tchr. Belpre (Ohio) City Schs., 1971-72; prin. elem. schs., head tchr. learning disabilities South-Western City Schs., Grove City, Ohio, 1972-76; dir. elem. edn. Beverly (Mass.) Pub. Schs., 1976-78; adj. prof. Lesley Coll., Cambridge, Mass., 1976-78; coord. spl. projects and systemwide planning Montgomery County Pub. Schs., Rockville, Md., 1978-80; asst. supt. Shaker Heights (Ohio), 1980-83; supt. schs. Mercer County Pub. Schools., Princeton, W. Va., 1983-85; supt. schs. Oklahoma City Pub Schs., 1985-92; supt. schs. Cobb County, Ga., 1992-93; dep. supt. Boston Pub. Schs., 1993—; adj. faculty Harvard U., 1992-93. Author: Educational Planning for Educational Success, Effective Schools Research: Practice and Promise; editor: Effective Instructional Management; cons. editor, book rev. editor Jour. for Ednl. Pub. Rels.; mem. editorial bd. Jour. for Curriculum & Supervision; contbr. articles to profl. jours. Bd. govs. Kirkpatrick Ctr.; mem. Oklahoma City Com. for Econ. Devel.; founding bd. dirs. Oklahoma Alliance Against Drugs, Oklahoma Zool. Soc. Inc.; selected for Leadership Okla. City, 1986; bd. dirs. Leadership Oklahoma City, ARC; bd. dirs. Okla. Centennial Sports Inc.; mem. Oklahoma Acad. for State Goals, State Supt.'s Adv. Coun.; mem. clin. experiences adv. com. U. Okla. Coll. Edn.; trustee Arts Coun. Oklahoma City, Omniplex Sci. and Arts Mus., Oklahoma City Area Vocat.-Tech. Dist. 22 Found.; mem. Urban Ctr. Ednl. Adv. Bd., U.S. Dept. Edn. Urban Supt. Network, Coun. Great City Schs. Bd., Urban Edn. Clearing House Adv. com., U. Okla. Adminstrn. cert. program com., Community Literacy Coun. Bd.; chmn. bd. dirs. Langston U.; chairperson United Way Greater Okla., Sch. Mgmt. Study Group, Okla. Reading Coun. (Okla. literacy coun. reading award 1989), Okla. City PTA; bd. dirs. Oklahoma County chpt. ARC, Jr. Achievement Greater Oklahoma City Bd., Oklahoma State Fair Bd., Horace Mann League Bd., Last Frontier Coun. Bd. Charles Kettering Found. IDEA fellow, 1976, 78, 80; Nat. Endowment Humanities fellow, Danforth Found., 1987-88; recipient Silver Beaver award Boy Scouts Am., 1990, Amb. award HMC, 1995. Mem. ASCD (exec. coun., pres.-elect 1993-94, pres. 1994—), Nat. Orgn. Legal Problems in Edn., Nat. Policy Bd. Ednl. Adminstrn., Am. Assn. Sch. Adminstrs. (life, Leadership for Learning award, 1991, Coll. Bd. Advanced Placement Spl. Recognition award 1991), Nat. Assn. Elem. Sch. Prins. (life), Nat. Assn. Edn. Young Children (life), Nat. Sch. Pub. Rels. Assn. (Honor award 1991), Internat. Soc. Ednl. Planning, Nat. Soc. Study Edn., Nat. Planning Assn., Coun. Basic Edn., Am. Edn. Fin. Assn., Ohio Assn. Elem. Sch. Adminstrs., Buckeye Assn. Sch. Adminstrs., Ohio ASCD, Ohio U. Coll. Edn. (disting. alumnus award 1991), Okla. ASCD (Publ. award 1989), Okla. Assn. Sch. Adminstrs., Mass. Assn. Sch. Adminstrs., Mass. ASCD, Okla. Coalition for Pub. Edn., Okla. Commn. for Ednl. Leadership, Urban Area Supts. (Oklahoma br.), Ohio U. Alumni Assn. (nat. dir. 1975-78, pres. Cen. Ohio chpt. 1975-76, pres. Mass. chpt. 1976-78, life mem. trustee's acad.), World Future Soc. (life), Greater Oklahoma City C. of C. (exec. bd. dirs.), South Oklahoma City C. of C. (bd. dirs.), Oklahoma Heritage Assn., Heritage Hills Assn. (bd. dirs.), Victorian Soc. (New England chpt.), Nat. Eagle Scout Assn., Aerospace Found. (hon. bd. dirs.), Am. Bus. Card Club, Coca Cola Collectors Club, Internat. Club, Rotary (Boston), Mgmt. Consortium (bd. advisors), Tau Kappa Epsilon Alumni Assn. (regional officer Mass. 1976-78, named Alumni Nat. Hall of Fame 1986, Nat. Alumnus of Yr. 1993, Excellence in Edn. award 1993), Kappa Delta Pi (life, advisor Cen. Okla. chpt., nat. publs. com.), Phi Delta Kappa (life). Methodist. Home: 30 Carruth St Dorchester MA 02124

STELLER, HERMANN, neurobiologist, educator; b. Bad Nauheim, Germany, Apr. 25, 1957; came to U.S., 1985; s. Horst and Gisela (Opper) S.; m. Bettina Zirnheld, June 18, 1982; 1 child, Nicolas Sebastian. Diploma in biology, U. Frankfurt, Fed. Republic Germany, 1981; PhD, U. Heidelberg, Fed. Republic Germany, 1984; postgrad., U. Calif., Berkeley, 1985-87. Predoctoral fellow European Molecular Biology Lab., Heidelberg, 1981-84; postdoctoral fellow U. Calif., Berkeley, 1985-87; asst. prof. MIT, Cambridge, Mass., 1987-92, assoc. prof. neurobiology, rschr., 1992—; assoc. investigator Howard Hughes Med. Inst., Chevy Chase, Md., 1993—; mem. sci. adv. bd. IDUN Pharms., San Diego, 1993—, NIH, ACS, 1992—; asst. neurobiologist Mass. Gen. Hosp., Boston, 1990—. Searle scholar Chgo. Cmty. Trust, 1988, Pew Charitable Trust scholar, 1989. Mem. AAAS, Genetics Soc. Am., Soc. for Neurosci. Avocations: fly fishing, hiking, skiing. Office: MIT E25-436 Dept of Brain & Cognitive 77 Massachusetts Ave Cambridge MA 02139

STELLING, JOAN DONNA, rehabilitation nurse; b. Greenville, S.C., May 10, 1955; d. Frank Henry and Donna (Mayer) S. BSN, Med. U. S.C., 1977; MSN, U. Ala., Birmingham, 1983. RN, Ala.; Cert. Rehab. RN. Staff nurse Med. U. Hosp., Charleston, S.C., 1978-82; rehab. clin. nurse specialist Roper Hosp., Charleston, S.C., 1983-85; clin. nurse specialist spinal cord injuries U. Ala. Hosp., Birmingham, 1985-91, dir. rehab. nursing, 1991—. Bd. dirs. Ms. Wheelchair Ala., 1990—. Mem. Assn. Rehab. Nurses (pres., bd. dirs. 1989—), Am. Assn. Spinal Cord Injury Nurses, Sigma Theta Tau (Cert. of Recognition, del. 1981, Gamma Omicron chpt.), S.C. Hosp. Assn. (Outstanding Young Woman of Am. 1982). Avocations: swimming, boating, gardening. Home: 1353 Swallow Ln Birmingham AL 35213-1621 Office: U Ala Hosp 619 19th St S Birmingham AL 35233-1924

STELLRECHT, FRITZ, newspaper publishing executive; b. Ulm, Fed. Republic Germany, Jan. 6, 1941; came to U.S., 1957; s. Karl Wilhelm and Else Kaethe (Schaupp) S.; m. Priscilla Holtz, Feb. 22, 1974. BA, San Jose State U., 1968, cert. secondary teaching, 1969. Tchr. San Jose Pub. Schs., Calif., 1969-75; various mgmt. positions San Jose Mercury, 1978-82; mgr. regional circulation USA Today, Los Angeles, 1982-83; gen. mgr. USA Today, Kansas City, Mo., 1983-84, Chandler, Ariz., 1984—. Served with U.S. Army, 1963-65. Mem. Internat. Circulation Mgrs. Assn., Calif. Western Circulation Mgrs. Assn., Ariz. Newspaper Assn. (assoc.). Republican. Avocations, golf, chess, collecting stamps and WWII memorabilia. Office: USA Today 411 N Roosevelt Ave Chandler AZ 85226-2699

STELLWAGEN, ROBERT HARWOOD, biochemistry educator; b. Joliet, Ill., Jan. 6, 1941; s. Harwood John and Alma Dorothy (Handorf) S.; m. Joanne Kovacs, June 15, 1963; children: Robert Harwood, Alise Anne. AB, Harvard U., 1963; PhD, U. Calif.-Berkeley, 1968. Staff fellow NIH, Bethesda, Md., 1968-69; postdoctoral scholar U. Calif.-San Francisco, 1969-70; asst. prof. biochemistry U. So. Calif., L.A., 1970-74, assoc. prof., 1974-80, prof., 1980—; cons. abbr. 1981-86, vice chmn. dept., 1993—; vis. scientist Nat. Inst. for Med. Research, Mill Hill, Eng., 1979. Contbr. articles to profl. jours. Recipient Henderson prize Harvard U., 1963; NSF fellow,

1963-67; NIH grantee, 1971-84. Mem. AAAS, Am. Soc. Biochemistry and Molecular Biology, Sierra Club, Phi Beta Kappa. Democrat. Office: U So Calif 2011 Zonal Ave Los Angeles CA 90033-1034

STELMACK, GLORIA JOY, elementary education educator; b. Chgo., Oct. 1, 1933; d. Raymond Thomas and Bess (Henneberry) Ibison; m. Carl Francis McGarrity, Feb. 7, 1953; children: Maureen, Thomas, Stephen, John; m. Stephen Stanley Stelmack, Dec. 22, 1979. BA with honors, U. Ill., 1972; MA in Reading, Northeastern Ill. U., 1977. Cert. tchr.; Ill. Tchr., reading specialist St. Pius Sch., Chgo., 1972-82, St. Jane de Chantal Sch., Chgo., 1982—; adv. com. St. Jane de Chantal Sch., Chgo., 1986—; v.p. Nat. Coun. of Tchrs. of English, Chgo., 1980-81. Nominated for Golden Apple award, 1990. Avocations: travel, reading, flower arranging, golf. Office: Saint Jane de Chantal Sch 5201 S McVicker Chicago IL 60638

STELPSTRA, WILLIAM JOHN, minister; b. Paterson, N.J., Nov. 1, 1934; s. Duke and Nellie (Stapert) S.; m. Anna Rizkovsky, Sept. 6, 1958; 1 child, Linda Mae. BA, Alma White Coll., 1957; B. of Religion, Zarephath Bible Sem., 1958. Ordained to ministry Pillar of Fire Ch., 1954. Pastor Pillar of Fire Ch., Little Falls, N.J., 1956-60; evangelist Wesleyan Meth. Ch., 1960-64; founder, dir. Bethel Children's Home, Paterson, N.J., 1964-71, Bethel Ranch Rehab. for Men, West Milford, N.J., 1971—; founder, pres. World for Christ Crusade, Inc., N.J., Fla., 1960—; dir. fgn. missions World for Christ Crusade, Inc., Haiti, Ghana, India, 1980—; adminstr. Fellowship House, Bloomfield, N.J., 1979—, Bright Side Manor, Teaneck, N.J., 1978—. Mem. Ocean Grove C. of C. Republican. Wesleyan Ch. Avocations: painting with oils, swimming, boating, travel, gardening. Home: 1005 Union Valley Rd West Milford NJ 07480 Office: World for Christ Crusade 1005 Union Valley Rd West Milford NJ 07480

STELZEL, WALTER TELL, JR., accountant, financial company executive; b. Chgo., Aug. 23, 1940; s. Walter Tell and Kathryn (Evans) S.; m. Sarah Rauen, Jan. 5, 1963; children: William, Susan, Michael. BSBA, Xavier U., 1962; MBA, U. Chgo., 1983. CPA, Ill. Sr. acct. Ernst & Ernst, 1962-69; contr. U.S. Reduction Co., 1969-74; asst. corp. contr. Am. Nat. Can. Co. (formerly Nat. Can. Corp.), Chgo., 1974-76, corp. contr., 1976-78, v.p., contr., 1978-81, v.p., asst. to pres., 1981-84, exec. v.p. fin., 1984-93, sr. exec. v.p., bd. mem., 1993—. 1st U.S. Army, 1962-65. Germany. Office: Am Nat Can Co 8770 W Bryn Mawr Ave Chicago IL 60631-3515

STELZENMULLER, CYRIL VAUGHN, lawyer; b. Fairfield, Ala., Jan. 25, 1928; s. James Grey and Helen (Brennan) S.; m. Jeannette Faye Wood, Mar. 19, 1965; 1 child, James Wood. BA, Cornell U., 1950, LLB with distinction, 1952. Bar: Ala. 1952, U.S. Dist. Ct. (no. dist.) Ala. 1955, U.S. Ct. Appeals (5th cir.) 1955, U.S. Ct. Appeals (D.C. cir.) 1973, U.S. Ct. Appeals (6th cir.) 1975, U.S. Supreme Ct. 1980, U.S. Ct. Appeals (11th cir.) 1982. Law clk. to judge U.S. Ct. Appeals (5th cir.), New Orleans, 1954-55; assoc. Burr & Forman, Birmingham, Ala., 1955-64, ptnr., 1964—. Contbr. articles to law rev. Col. ANG. Mem. Order of Coif, Phi Beta Kappa. Avocation: stained glass. Home: 3537 Victora Rd Birmingham AL 35223 Office: Burr & Forman S Trust Towers Ste 3000 Birmingham AL 35203

STEM, CARL HERBERT, business educator; b. Eagleville, Tenn., Jan. 30, 1935; s. Marion Ogilvie and Sara Elizabeth (Jones) S.; m. Linda Marlene Wheeler, Dec. 28, 1963; children: Anna Elizabeth, Susan Kathleen, John Carl, David Leslie. BA, Vanderbilt U., 1957; AM (Woodrow Wilson fellow, Harvard scholar), Harvard U., 1960, PhD, 1969. Internat. fin. economist, bd. govs. Fed. Res. System, Washington, 1963-70; prof. econs. Tex. Tech. U., Lubbock, 1970-73; prof. internat. fin., chmn. area of fin., adminstr. grad. programs, assoc. dean, dean Coll. Bus. Adminstrn. Tex. Tech U., Lubbock, 1970—; sr. econ. adviser Office Fgn. Direct Investments, U.S. Dept. Commerce, Washington, 1973-74; cons. U.S. Dept. Treasury, 1974-75; mem. faculty Grad. Sch. Credit and Fin. Mgmt., Lake Success, N.Y., 1974-87; adj. scholar Am. Enterprise Inst. Public Policy Rsch., Washington, 1974-88; treas. Mission Jour., Inc., 1969-88. Editor (with Makin and Logue) Eurocurrencies and The Interational Monetary System; contbr. articles to profl. jours. Trustee St. Mary Plains Hosp., Lubbock, Tex., 1987-92, chmn., 1992; v.p. Tex. Coun. of Collegiate Edn. for Bus., 1977-78, pres., 1978-79. Capt. Security Agy. AUS, 1961-62. Fulbright scholar U. Reading, Eng., 1957-58. Mem. Southwestern Bus. Adminstrn. Assn. (pres. 1982-83), Nat. Assn. Bus. Economists, So. Bus. Adminstrn. Assn. (v.p. 1985-86, pres. 1986-87), Lubbock Econ. Coun. (pres. 1973), Am. Assembly Collegiate Schs. Bus. (standards com. 1981-84, bd. dirs. 1993—), Lubbock Club (pres. 1986-87), Phi Beta Kappa, Omicron Delta Kappa, Phi Kappa Phi, Beta Gamma Sigma., Tau Kappa Alpha. Mem. Ch. of Christ. Home: 6218 Louisville Dr Lubbock TX 79413-5429 Office: Tex Tech U Bus Adminstrn Lubbock TX 79409 *Most important to me are the ever timely values of our Judeo-Christian heritage- faith in God and appreciation for the inherent value of man. These values have underpinned my aspirations and sustained me through disappointments. They have generated the perseverance and continual hope so vital to me as I have worked for self-growth and to make a contribution to the institutions and people with which I have been associated in various periods of my life.*

STEMBRIDGE, VERNIE A(LBERT), pathologist, educator; b. El Paso, Tex., June 7, 1924; s. Vernie Albert and Anna Marie (Lawless) S.; m. Aileen Cofer Marston, June 14, 1944; children—Shirley (Mrs. J.P. Watkins), Ann (Mrs. Donald M. Connell), Vivian (Mrs. Lance E. Porter). B.A., U. Tex. at El Paso (formerly Tex. Coll. Mines), 1943; M.D., U. Tex., Galveston, 1948. Diplomate: Am. Bd. Pathology (trustee 1969-80, sec. 1976-79, pres. 1980). Intern U.S. Marine Hosp., Norfolk, Va., 1948-49; resident in pathology Med. Br., U. Tex., Galveston, 1949-52; asst. prof. pathology Med. Br., U. Tex., 1952-54, asso. prof., 1954-56; asso. prof. Southwestern Med. Sch., Dallas, 1959-61; prof. Southwestern Med. Sch., 1961—, Ashbel Smith prof., 1991—, chmn. dept. pathology, 1966-88; chmn. emeritus Southwestern Med. Sch., Dallas, 1992—; interim dean Allied Health Scis. U. Tex. Southwestern Med. Sch., 1988-91; assoc. dir. clin. labs. U. Tex. Med. Br. Hosps., 1952-56; sr. pathologist, chief aviation pathology sect. Armed Forces Inst. Pathology, Washington, 1956-59; dir. pathology labs. Parkland Hosp., Dallas, 1966-85; cons. VA Hosp., Dallas; cons. to surgeon gen. USAF; civil air surgeon FAA; chmn. sci. adv. bd. Armed Forces Inst. Pathology; mem. State of Tex. Radiation Adv. Bd., 1987-94. Contbr. articles to med. jours. Served with USAF, 1956-59. Decorated Legion of Merit; named Outstanding Alumnus U. Tex. at El Paso, 1978, Hon. Alumnus, U. Tex. Southwestern Med. Sch., 1964, Ashbel Smith outstanding alumnus U. Tex. Med. Br., 1982; recipient Joint Disting. Service award Am. Soc. Clin. Pathologists/Coll. Am. Pathologists, 1987. Mem. Internat. Acad. Pathology (counsellor 1970-73), Am. Soc. Clin. Pathologists (bd. dirs. 1973-79, pres. 1977-78, bd. registry, gov. 1983-90, Ward Burdick award for outstanding contbns. 1981), AMA (residency rev. com. of pathology 1972-78, chmn. 1977-78, residency rev. com. nuclear medicine 1972-78), Intersoc. Pathology Council (sec. 1979-84), Coll. Am. Pathologists, Am. Assn. Pathologists, Assn. Pathology Chairmen (mem. council, pres. 1979), Am. Assn. Blood Banks, Tex. Soc. Pathologists (pres. 1966, Caldwell award 1967), Tex. Med. Assn. (ho. of dels. 1966-86), Dallas County Med. Soc. (pres. 1985, Max Cole Leadership award 1991), Am. Registry Pathology (bd. dirs. 1986-91, chmn. 1989-90), Phi Rho Sigma, Mu Delta, Alpha Omega Alpha. Home: 10424 Marsh Ln Dallas TX 75229-5223 Office: 5323 Harry Hines Blvd Dallas TX 75235-9072

STEMMER, WAYNE J., real estate and financial services company executive; b. Elizabeth, N.J., Oct. 29, 1942; s. Jay Stemmer; m. Barbara J. Mantz, Nov. 7, 1964; children: Wayne J. Jr., Traci. BA, Rutgers U., 1964. Gen. mgr. Citibank, Sydney, Australia, 1975-78; dir. Citicorp Real Estate Inc., Dallas and Houston, 1980-82; chief real estate investment officer Citibank N.A., N.Y.C., 1982-83; pres. Unicorp Am. Corp., N.Y.C., 1983—, also bd. dirs.; pres., chief operating officer The Lincoln Savs. Bank, N.Y.C., 1988—, also bd. dirs.; bd. dirs. Unicorp Can. Corp., Toronto; pres., chief oper. officer, dir. Lincoln Savs. Bank, N.Y.C. Served to capt. arty. U.S. Army, 1965-66. Mem. Internat. Council Shopping Ctrs., N.Y. Real Estate Bd., Soc. Real Estate Appraisers. Avocation: golf. Office: Unicorp Am Corp 99 Park Ave New York NY 10016-1503

STEMMLER, EDWARD JOSEPH, physician, retired association executive, retired academic dean; b. Phila., Feb. 15, 1929; s. Edward C. and Josephine (Heitzman) S.; m. Joan C. Koster, Dec. 27, 1958; children: Elizabeth, Margaret, Edward C., Catherine, Joan. B.A., La Salle Coll., Phila., 1950,

Sc.D. (hon.), 1983; M.D., U. Pa., 1960; Sc.D. (hon.), Ursinus Coll., 1977, Phila. Coll. Pharmacy and Sci., 1989; L.H.D. (hon.), Rush U., 1986, Med. Coll. Pa., 1994; ScD (hon.), SUNY, Syracuse, 1994. Diplomate Am. Bd. Internal Medicine. Intern U. Pa. Hosp., 1960-61, med. resident, 1961-63, fellow in cardiology, 1963-64, chief med. resident, 1964-65, chief med. outpatient dept., 1966-67; chief of medicine U. Pa. Med. Svc. VA Hosp., Phila., 1967-73; mem. deans com. VA Hosp., 1974-88; instr. medicine Grad. Div. Medicine, U. Pa., 1964-66, NIH postdoctoral rsch. trainee, dept. physiology, 1965-67, assoc. in medicine, 1966-67; assoc. in physiology Grad. Div. Medicine, 1967-72, asst. prof. medicine, 1967-70, assoc. prof., 1970-74, prof., 1974—, Robert G. Dunlop prof., 1981-91, prof. emeritus, 1991—; assoc. dean Univ. Hosp., 1973, assoc. dean student affairs, 1973-75, acting dean, 1974-75, dean, 1975-88, dean emeritus, 1989—; exec. v.p. U. Pa. Med. Ctr., 1986-89; exec. v.p. Assn. Am. Med. Colls., 1990-94, sr. adv. to pres., 1994—; mem. Nat. Bd. Med. Examiners, 1974-76, nominating and ad hoc governance coms., 1985, vice chmn., 1987-89, treas., 1989-91, chmn., 1991-95; mem. exec. com.; mem. ednl. policy com. Nat Fund for Med. edn., 1975-77; mem. deans com. VA Hosp., 1974-88; bd. dirs. Rhone-Poulence Rorer, Inc.; trustee Dorothy Rider Pool Healthcare Trust, 1991; trustee Ursinus Coll., 1991—. Contbr. articles to profl. jours. Chmn. Pa. Dean's Com., 1976-87; bd. govs. Mid-Ea. Regional Med. Libr. Svcs., 1977-81, chmn., 1978-81; bd. visitors U. Pitts. Sch. Medicine, 1980-85, U. Md. Sch. Medicine, 1991-94; bd. overseers Dartmouth Med. Sch. and C. Everett Koop Inst. 1992—; adv. com. dept. medicine U. Ala., Birmingham, 1985-89; vis. com. Tufts U. Sch. Medicine, 1990—, U. Calif., Davis 1993—. Decorated Commendation medal; recipient Frederick A. Packard award, 1960, Albert Einstein Med. Ctr. staff award, 1960, Roche award, 1960. Master ACP (treas., chmn. investment com. 1975-80, Laureate award Ea. Pa. region 1986); mem. AMA (health policy agenda), Med. Soc. D.C., Am. Fedn. for Clin. Rsch., Inst. Medicine NAS, Assn. Am. Med. Colls. (ad hoc external exam. rev. com. 1980—, exec. coun. 1980—, coun. of deans adminstrv. bd. 1980—, chmn. 1983-84, nat. chmn.-elect 1985-86, chmn. assembly 1986-87, Coll. of Physicians of Phila. (bd. censors 1979-85, coun. 1979-85, 90-92), Am. Clin. and Climatological Soc., Alpha Omega Alpha. Republican. Mem. Christian Ch. Home: R1 Box 676 Roseland VA 22967 Office: Assn Am Med Colls 2450 N St NW Washington DC 20037-1167

STEMPEL, ERNEST EDWARD, insurance executive; b. N.Y.C., May 10, 1916; s. Frederick Christian and Leah Lillian S.; m. Phyllis Brooks (dec. Mar. 1993); children: Diana Brooks Bergquist, Calvin Pinkcomb, Neil Frederick, Robert Russell. A.B., Manhattan Coll., 1938; LL.B., Fordham U., 1946; LL.M., NYU, 1949, D.J.S., 1951; LL.D. (hon.), Manhattan Coll., 1986. Bar: N.Y. 1946. With Am. Internat. Underwriters Corp., N.Y.C., 1938-53; v.p., dir. Am. Internat. Co. Ltd., Hamilton, Bermuda, 1953-63, chmn. bd., from 1963; chmn., dir. Am. Internat. Assurance Co. (Bermuda) Ltd., Am. Internat. Reins. Co. Ltd., Bermuda, Philippine Am. Life Ins. Co., Manila, Australian Am. Assurance Co., Ltd., Am. Internat. Assurance Co. Ltd., Hong Kong, AIG Life Ins. Co., Del. Am. Life Ins. Co., Wilmington, Del., Am. Internat. Life Assurance Co. of N.Y.; pres., dir. Starr Internat. Co. Inc.; vice-chmn.-life div., mem. exec. com., dir. Am. Internat. Group Inc.; dir. C.V. Starr & Co. Inc., N.Y.C., Am. Life Ins. Co., Wilmington, Seguros Interamericana (S.A.), Mexico, Mt. Mansfield Co., Inc., Stowe, Vt., Seguros Venezuela (C.A.), Caracas, dir. Am. Internat. Underwriters (Latin Am.), Inc., Bermuda, Am. Internat. Underwriters Mediterranean, Inc., Bermuda, Pacific Union Assurance Co., Calif., Underwriters Adjustment Co., Panama. Served to lt. (j.g.) USNR, 1942-46. Mem. Am. Bar Assn., N.Y. State Bar. Clubs: Marco Polo (N.Y.C.), Royal Bermuda Yacht (Bermuda), Mid-Ocean (Bermuda), Coral Beach (Bermuda), Riddell's Bay Golf and Country (Bermuda). Office: Am Internat Co Ltd, PO Box HM 152, Hamilton HM AX, Bermuda

STEMPEL, GUIDO HERMANN, III, journalism educator; b. Bloomington, Ind., Aug. 13, 1928; s. Guido Hermann Jr. and Alice Margaret (Menninger) S.; m. Anne Elliott, Aug. 30, 1952; children: Ralph Warren, Carl William, Jane Louise. Student, Carnegie Tech., 1945-46; AB in Journalism, Ind. U., 1949, AM in Journalism, 1951; PhD in Mass Communication, U. Wis., 1954. Sports editor Frankfort (Ind.) Times, 1949-50; instr., asst. prof. Sch. Journalism, Pa. State U., University Park, 1955-57; from assoc. prof. to prof. Dept. Journalism, Cen. Mich. U., Mt. Pleasant, 1957-65; assoc. prof. Sch. Journalism, Ohio U., Athens, 1965-68, prof., 1968-82, Disting. prof., 1982—, dir., 1972-79; rsch. cons. Ohio Newspaper Assn., Columbus, 1985—; chmn. rsch. com. Coll. Media Advisors, 1963-69, 79-84; mem. adv. bd. dept. comm. arts U. West Fla., 1987—; survey coord. Scripps Howard News Svc., 1992—. Co-author: The Media in the 1984 and 1988 Presidential Campaigns, 1991; assoc. editor: Newspaper Rsch. Jour., 1992—; editor, co-author: The Practice of Political Communication, 1994; co-editor, co-author: Research Methods in Mass Communications, 1981, 2d edit., 1989; editor: Journalism Quar., 1972-89; contbr. articles to profl. jours. Mem. bd. visitors Def. Info. Sch., Ft. Harrison, 1985—. Served with U.S. Army, 1954-55. Recipient Chancellor's award U. Wis., 1977. Mem. Assn. for Edn. in Journalism and Mass Communication (chmn. rsch. com. 1968-71; Eleanor Blum award 1989), Soc. Profl. Journalists, Rotary (pres. Athens unit 1984-85). Democrat. Methodist. Home: 7 Lamar Dr Athens OH 45701-3730 Office: Ohio Univ Sch of Journalism Athens OH 45701

STEMPLE, JOEL GILBERT, computer company executive; b. Bklyn., Feb. 3, 1942; s. Max David and Helen (Nechamkin) S.; m. Sharon Claire Schneider, Apr. 6, 1968; children—Tracy, Allyson. BS, Bklyn. Coll., 1962; MA, Yale U., 1964, PhD, 1966. Asst. prof. Queens Coll., Flushing, N.Y., 1966-70, assoc. prof. math., 1970-82; v.p. Manchester Equipment Co. Inc., Hauppauge, N.Y., 1982—. Office: Manchester Equipment Co Inc 50 Marcus Blvd Hauppauge NY 11788

STEMPLER, JACK LEON, aerospace company executive; b. Newark, Oct. 30, 1920; s. Morris and Ida (Friedman) S.; m. J Adelaide Williams, Oct. 28, 1950; children: Mark N., Sandra J., Carrie B. BA, Montclair (N.J.) State Coll., 1943; LL.B., Cornell U., 1948. Bar: N.Y., D.C. 1949. Atty. com. uniform code mil. justice Dept. Def., 1948-49, atty. adviser legis. div., 1949-50; asst. counsel Munitions Bd., 1950-53; counsel Armed Forces Housing Agy., 1952-54, Advanced Research Projects Agy., 1958-65; asst. gen. counsel logistics Dept. Def., 1953-65, asst. to sec. def. for legislative affairs, 1965-70; gen. counsel Dept. Air Force, 1970-77; asst. to sec. of def. for legis. affairs, 1977-81; ret.; cons. in field. Served to 1st lt. USMCR, 1942-46, PTO. Recipient Outstanding Civilian Performance award Dept. Def., 1959, Distinguished Civilian Service award, 1965, Distinguished Civilian Service award USAF, 1973, 75, 77; awarded Presdl. rank of Disting. Exec., 1980; recipient Disting. Public Service award Dept. Def., 1981. Mem. Fed., D.C. bar assns., Cornell Law Sch. Assn., Air Force Aid Soc. (trustee). Home: 4701 Newcomb Pl Alexandria VA 22304-1506

STENBERG, CARL W(ALDAMER), academic program director, educator; b. Pitts., July 8, 1943; s. Carl W. and Mildred (Baggs) S.; m. Kirstin D. Thompson; children: Erik Anders, Kerry Cathryn, Kaameran Baird. BA, Allegheny Coll., 1965; MPA, SUNY, Albany, 1966, PhD, 1970. Research asst. N.Y. State Div. Budget, Albany, 1967; analyst, then sr. analyst U.S. Adv. Commn. on Intergovtl. Relations, Washington, 1968-77, asst. dir. for policy implementation, 1977-83, acting exec. dir., 1982; exec. dir. Council of State Govts., Lexington, Ky., 1983-89; prof., dir. Weldon Cooper Ctr. for Pub. Svc. U. Va., Charlottesville, 1989—; Disting. prof. pub. svc., 1991—; adj. prof. Am. Part Program USIA, 1987; adj. prof. George Washington U., mem. Am. Part Program USIA, 1971, 81, Am. U., 1972-80, 82, U. Md., 1976, U. So. Calif., 1984-87; v.p. Bureaucrat Inc., Washington, 1973-77, mng. editor, 1973-77. Feature editor Pub. Mgmt. Forum Pub. Adminstrn. Rev., 1977-83, editor U. of Va. newslatter, 1994—. Pres. Reston Home Owners' Assn., Va., 1973-74; mem. U.S. del. Ad Hoc Group on Urban Problems, OECD, 1980-82. Vivien Stewart vis. fellow Cambridge U., Eng., 1980; recipient Disting. Alumni award Polit. Sci. Dept. Rockefeller Coll., 1985. Mem. Am. Soc. Pub. Adminstrn. (pres. 1990-91, Marshall E. Dimock and Louis Brownlow awards), Va. Alliance for the Pub. Svc. (pres. 1991-92), Colonnade Club, Boars Head Sports Club, Bull and Bear Club. Home: 1839 Edgewood Ln Charlottesville VA 22901-1638 Office: U Va Weldon Cooper Ctr Pub Svc 918 Emmet St N Ste 300 Charlottesville VA 22903-4832

STENBERG, DONALD B., state attorney general; b. David City, Nebr., Sept. 30, 1948; s. Eugene A. and Alice (Kasal) S.; m. Susan K. Hoegemeyer,

June 9, 1971; children: Julie A., Donald B. Jr., Joseph L., Abby E. BA, U. Nebr., 1970; MBA, Harvard U., 1974, JD cum laude, 1974. Bar: Nebr. 1974, U.S. Dist. Ct. Nebr. 1974, U.S. Ct. Appeals (fed. cir.) 1984, U.S. Ct. Claims 1989, U.S. Ct. Appeals (8th cir.) 1989, U.S. Supreme Ct., 1991. Assoc. Barlow, Watson & Johnson, Lincoln, Nebr., 1974-75; ptnr. Stenberg and Stenberg, Lincoln, 1976-78; legal counsel Gov. of Nebr., Lincoln, 1979-82; sr. prin. Erickson & Sederstrom, Lincoln, 1983-85; pvt. practice law Lincoln, 1985-90; atty. gen. State of Nebr., Lincoln, 1991—. Mem. Phi Beta Kappa. Republican. Office: Office of Atty Gen 2115 State Capital Lincoln NE 68509

STENCHEVER, MORTON ALBERT, physician, educator; b. Paterson, N.J., Jan. 25, 1931; s. Harold and Lena (Suresky) S.; m. Diane Bilsky, June 19, 1955; children: Michael A., Marc R., Douglas A. A.B., NYU, 1951; M.D., U. Buffalo, 1956. Intern Mt. Sinai Hosp., 1956-57; resident obstetrics and gynecology Columbia-Presbyn. Med. Center, N.Y.C., 1957-60; asst. prof., Oglebey research fellow Case-Western Res. U., Cleve., 1962-66; asso. prof. dept. reproductive biology Case-Western Res. U., 1967-70, dir. Tissue Culture Lab., 1965-70, coordinator Phase II Med. Sch. program, 1969-70; prof., chmn. dept. obstetrics-gynecology U. Utah Med. Sch., Salt Lake City, 1970-77, U. Wash. Sch. Medicine, Seattle, 1977—; test com. chmn. for Ob-Gyn Nat. Bd. Med. Examiners, 1979-82. Author: Labor: Workbook in Obstetrics, 1968, 2d edit., 1993, Human Sexual Behavior: A Workbook in Reproductive Biology, 1970, Human Cytogenics: A Workbook in Reproductive Biology, 1973, Introductory Gynecology: A Workbook in Reproductive Biology, 1974; co-author: Comprehensive Gynecology, 1987, 2d edit., 1992, Caring for the Older Woman, 1991, Office Gynecology, 1992, Labor, 1993; assoc. editor Ob-Gyn, 1986—, Ob-Gyn Survey; mem. editorial bd. Western Jour. Medicine; contbr. articles to profl. jours. Served to capt. USAF, 1960-62. Fellow Am. Coll. Obstetricians and Gynecologists (com. on residency edn. 1974-80, learning resource commn. 1980-86, vice chmn. 1982-83, chmn. prolog self-assessment program 1982-86), Am. Assn. Obstetricians and Gynecologists, Am. Gynecol. Soc., Am. Soc. Ob-Gyn, Pacific Coast Ob-Gyn Soc.; mem. AAAS, AMA, Assn. Profs. Gynecology and Obstetrics (chmn. steering com. teaching methods in obstetrics and gynecology 1970-79, v.p. 1975-76, pres. 1983-84, v.p. Found. 1986-87, pres. Found. 1987-91), Pacific N.W. Ob-Gyn Soc., Wash. State Med. Assn., Seattle Gynec. Soc. (v.p. 1981, pres.-elect 1982, pres. 1982-83), Pacific Coast Obstet.-Gynecol. Soc., Am. Soc. Human Genetics, Ctrl. Assn. Obstetrics and Gynecology, Soc. Gynecologic Investigation, Wash. State Obstet. Soc., Tissue Culture Assn., N.Y. Acad. Sci., Utah Ob-Gyn Soc., Utah State Med. Assn., Teratology Soc., Am. Fertility Soc., Am. Bd. Ob-Gyn (bd. dirs. 1988—, v.p. 1990-92, treas. 1992—), mem. resident rev. com. Ob-Gyn 1993—, chmn. divsn. urogynocology of reconstructive pelvic surgery). Home: 8301 SE 83rd St Mercer Island WA 98040-5644 Office: U Wash Dept Ob-Gyn 1959 NE Pacific St Seattle WA 98195-0004

STENDAHL, KRISTER, retired bishop; b. Stockholm, Sweden, Apr. 21, 1921; came to U.S., 1954, naturalized, 1967; s. Olof and Sigrid (Ljungquist) S.; m. Brita Johnsson, Sept. 7, 1946; children: John, Anna, Daniel. Teol. kand., U. Uppsala, Sweden, 1944, teol. lic., 1949, teol.dr., 1954; Litt. D. (hon.), Upsala Coll., 1963; D.D., St. Olaf Coll., 1971, Harvard U., 1985, St. Andrews U., 1987, Calif. Luth. U., 1995; LL.D., Susquehanna U., 1973; L.H.D. (hon.), Hebrew Union Coll./Jewish Inst. Religion, 1980, Brandeis U., 1981, Loyola U., New Orleans. Ordained priest Ch. of Sweden, 1944; chaplain to students Uppsala U., 1948-50, instr. O.T., N.T. exegesis, 1951-54, docent, 1954; asst. prof. N.T. Harvard U. Div. Sch., 1954-56, asso. prof., 1956-58, John H. Morison prof. N.T. studies, 1958-63, Frothingham prof. Bibl. studies, 1963-68, dean, John Lord O'Brian prof. div., 1968-79, Andrew W. Mellon prof. div., 1981-84; pastor Luth. Ch. Am., 1968-84; bishop of Stockholm Ch. of Sweden, 1984-88; Robert and Myra Kraft and Jacob Hiatt Disting. prof. Christian studies Brandeis U., 1991-93; moderator consultation on ch. and Jewish people World Council Chs., 1975-85; co-dir. Osher Ctr. for Tolerance and Pluralism Phalom Hartman Inst., 1994—. Author: The School of St. Matthew, 1954, 2d edit., 1968, The Bible and the Role of Women, 1966, Holy Week, 1974, Paul Among Jews and Gentiles, 1976, Meanings, 1984, Energy for Life, 1990, Final Account, 1995. Recipient Disting. Service award Assn. Theol. Schs., 1988. Fellow Am. Acad. Arts and Scis.; mem. Nathan Soederblom Soc.

STENDELL, REY, ecological research director. Dir. Midcontinent Ecol. Sci. Ctr., Fort Collins, Colo. Office: Midcontinent Ecol Sci Ctr 4512 McMurry Ave Fort Collins CO 80525-3400

STENDER, LINDA DE MILT, county official; b. Fanwood, N.J., July 25, 1951; d. Kenneth E. and Shirley (Lamperti) deMilt; m. Richard Chapman Stender, June 26, 1976; children: Caroline, Niel, Tyler. BA, Am. U., 1973. Councilwoman Borough of Fanwood, 1988-90, mayor, 1992—; freeholder County of Union, Elizabeth, 1994—. Chmn. Fanwood Downtown Commn., 1984-85; mem. Fanwood Planning Bd., 1986; active Fanwood Scotch Plains PTA. Mem. N.J. Elected Women Ofcls., Union County Women's Polit. Caucus (v.p. 1989), Fanwood Scotch Plains Coll. Club. Democrat. Avocations: family, cooking, golf. Office: Office Bd Chosen Freeholders County Adminstn Bldg Elizabethtown Plaza Elizabeth NJ 07207

STENEHJEM, LELAND MANFORD, banker; b. Arnegard, N.D., May 25, 1918; s. Odin N. and Lillie (Moe) S.; m. Judith H. Johnson, July 21, 1944; children—Leland Manford, Stephen Leslie, Joan Marie. B.S., N.D. State U., 1941; grad., U. Wis. Grad. Sch. Banking, 1948. With First Internat. Bank, Watford City, N.D., 1943—; exec. v.p. First Internat. Bank, 1961-66, pres., 1966—; chmn. bd. dirs. First Internat. Bank and Trust, 1992—; chmn First Nat Bank of Fessenden, N.D., 1983—; Mem. N.D. Banking Bd., 1958-63; mem. N.D. adv. council Farmers Home Adminstrn., 1957-60; bd. dirs. N.D. State U. Found. Pres. Good Shepherd Home, 1963—; bd. dirs. N.D. State U. Alumni Assn.; pres., bd. trustees First Luth. Ch. 2d lt. USMCR World War II. Recipient Singular Achievement award Greater N.D. Assn. Mem. Am. Bankers Assn. (past mem. exec. council), N.D. Bankers Assn. (past pres.), Ind. Bankers Assn. Am. (past pres.), Watford City Assn., Commerce (pres.), Alpha Tau Omega. Lutheran. Lodges: Mason, Elk, Lion (pres. Watford City), Rotarian (pres.), Shriners. Home: 100 SW 4th St Watford City ND 58854 Office: 100 N Main St Watford City ND 58854-7100

STENEHJEM, WAYNE KEVIN, state senator, lawyer; b. Mohall, N.D., Feb. 5, 1953; s. Martin Edward and Marguerite Mae (McMaster) S.; m. Tama Lou Smith, June 16, 1978 (div. Apr. 1984); 1 child, Andrew. A.A. Bismarck (N.D.) Jr. Coll., 1972; BA, U. N.D., 1974, JD, 1977. Bar: N.D. 1977. Ptnr. Kuchera & Stenehjem, Grand Forks, N.D., 1977—; spl. asst. atty. gen. State of N.D., 1983-87; mem. N.D. Ho. Reps., 1976-80, N.D. State Senate, 1980—; mem. Senate Com. on Social Svcs., 1985-86, Interim Legis. Judiciary Com., 1987-88, Senate Judiciary Com., 1995—. Chmn. Dist. 42 Reps., Grand Forks, 1986-88; bd. dirs. N.D. Spl. Olympics, 1985-89, Christus Rex Luth. Ch., pres., 1985-86. Named Champion of People's Right to Know, Sigma Delta Chi, 1979, Outstanding Young Man of N.D., Grand Forks Jaycees, 1985, N.D. Friend of Psychology, N.D. Psychol. Assn., 1990; recipient Excellence in County Govt. award N.D. Assn. Counties, 1991. Mem. N.D. State Bar Assn., Grand Forks County Bar Assn., Mental Health Assn. (bd. dirs.). Home: 2204 12th Ave N Grand Forks ND 58203 Office: Kuchera Stenehjem Crawford & Walberg 212 S 4th St PO Box 6352 Grand Forks ND 58206-6352

STENGEL, ROBERT FRANK, mechanical and aerospace engineering educator; b. Orange, N.J., Sept. 1, 1938; s. Frank John and Ruth Emma (Geidel) S.; m. Margaret Robertson Ewing, Apr. 8, 1961; children: Brooke Alexandra, Christopher Ewing. SB, MIT, 1960; MS in Engring., Princeton U., 1965, MA, 1966, PhD, 1968. Aerospace technologist NASA, Wallops Island, Va., 1960-63; tech. staff group leader C.S. Draper Lab., Cambridge, Mass., 1968-73, Analytic Scis. Corp., Reading, Mass., 1973-77; assoc. prof. Princeton (N.J.) U., 1977-82, prof. mech. and aerospace engring., 1982—, assoc. dean engring., 1994—; cons. GM, Warren, Mich., 1995—; mem. com. strategic tech. U.S. Army NRC, 1989-92; vice chmn. Congl. Aero. Adv. Com., Washington, 1986-89; mem. com. on trans-atmospheric vehicles USAF Sci. Adv. Bd., 1984-85; mem. com. on low altitude wind shear and its hazard to aviation Nat. Rsch. Coun., 1983. Author: Optimal Control and Estimation, 1994; N.Am. editor Cambridge Aerospace Series, 1993—; Cambridge Univ. Press, 1993—; contbr. more than 100 tech. papers to profl. publs.; patentee

wind probing device. Lt. USAF, 1960-63. Recipient Apollo Achievement award NASA, 1969, Cert. of Commendation, MIT, 1969. Fellow IEEE; mem. AIAA (assoc. fellow), Soc. Automotive Engrs. (mem. aerospace guidance and control systems com.). Avocations: photography, music, bicycling. Home: 329 Prospect Ave Princeton NJ 08540-5330 Office: Princeton U D202 Engineering Quadrangle Princeton NJ 08544

STENGEL, RONALD FRANCIS, management consultant; b. Lock Haven, Pa., Oct. 18, 1947; s. Elmer S. and Elizabeth (Heivley) S.; m. Margaret Linda Dezack, Aug. 23, 1969. BSME, U. Pa., 1969, MBA, 1976. Mfg. engr. Control Data Corp., Valley Forge, Pa., 1969-70; mgr. mfg. svcs. Knoll Internat., East Greenville, Pa., 1970-75; ptnr. mgmt. cons. Touche Ross & Co., Phila., 1976-85; pres. RF Stengel & Co. Inc., Valley Forge, 1985—.

STENHOLM, CHARLES W., congressman; b. Stamford, Tex., Oct. 26, 1938; m. Cynthia Ann Watson (div.); children: Chris, Cary, Courtney Ann. Grad., Tarleton State Jr. Coll., 1959; B.S. in Agrl. Edn., Tex. Tech U., 1961, M.S. in Agrl. Edn., 1962; LL.D. (hon.), McMurry Coll., 1983, Abilene Christian U., 1991. Farmer Tex.; past pres. Rolling Plains Cotton Growers and Tex. Electric Coops.; mem. 96th-103rd Congresses from 17th Tex. dist., Washington, D.C., 1979—; apptd. deputy whip 96th-102d Congresses from 17th Tex. dist., 1989—; former mem. state Dem. Exec. Com.; dep. whip Washington, 1989—; mem. agrl. subcom. Budget Com., Conservative Dem. Forum; founder, co-chmn. Congl. Leaders United for a Balanced Budget; founder Dem. Congl. Campaign Commn.; speaker's appt. to bd.; Dem. Caucus adv. group and task force on economy; com. on orgn. study and rev. of Dem. Caucus; ranking minority mem. Gen. Farm Commodities subcom.; mem. of Subcom. for Resource Conservation, Rsch. Forestry. Active Bethel Luth. Ch., Ericksdahl, Tex.; charter trustee Cotton Producer Inst. Recipient Gerald W. Thomas Outstanding Agriculturalist award Tex. Tech U., 1979, Am. Farmer Degree Future Farmers Am., 1979, Disting. Alumnus award Tarleton State U., 1979, Pres. Coun. award Tex. Future Farmers Am., 1981, Disting. Alumnus award Tex Tech U., 1987, MORE Common Sense Sound Dollar awards, 1988, 90, Guardian of Small Bus. awards, 1980-92, Watchdogs of the Treasury awards, 1980-92, Legis. award Nat. Rural Health Assn., 1991, Disting. Svc. award Tex. Soc. Biomed. Rsch., 1993, Disting. Svc. award Tex. Med. Assn., 1993; named Legislator of Yr. Chem. Prodrs. and Distbrs. Assn., 1992, Man of Yr. Progressive Farmer, 1993. Mem. Tex. State Soc. (Washington, past pres.), Tex. Breakfast Club (Washington, past pres.), Rolling Plains Cotton Growers (past pres.), Stamford C. of C. (past pres.). Democrat. Lutheran. Office: 1211 Longworth Washington DC 20515

STENHOUSE, EVERETT RAY, clergy administrator; b. Minco, Okla., May 15, 1931; s. George E. and Jessie Loraine (Dean) S.; m. Alice Irene English, Aug. 22, 1948; children: Brenda Jones, Judy Lundberg, Stephen, Andrew. Student, U. Calif. Berkeley, U. Athens, 1969-71. Ordained to ministry Assemblies of God, 1955. Pastor Wayside Chapel, Bakersfield, Calif., 1955-59, Bethel Temple, Bakersfield, 1960-63; dist. dir. youth So. Calif. Dist. Assemblies of God, Costa Mesa, Calif., 1963-67; assoc. pastor 1st Assembly of God, San Diego, 1968-69; missionary Assemblies of God Fgn. Missions, Athens, Greece, 1969-73; pastor Bethany Ch., Alhambra, Calif., 1974-79; supt. So. Calif. Dist., Assemblies of God, Costa Mesa, 1979-85; asst. gen. supt. Gen. Coun. Assemblies of God, Springfield, Mo., 1986-94; bd. adminstrn. Nat. Assn. Evangs., Wheaton, Ill., 1986—, Pentecostal Fellowship of No. Am., Ontario, Canada, 1986-94; chmn., bd. dirs. Assemblies of God Theol. Sem., Springfield, 1991-94, Ministers Benefit Assn., Springfield, 1986-94. Contbr. articles to various mags. Home: 19 Durango Rancho Mirage CA 92270

STENICKA, CHARLES EDWARD, III, professional association executive; b. Omaha, Apr. 26, 1929; s. Charles Edward Jr. and Gladys Ann (Hoffman) S.; m. Mary Jean Rademacher, May 2, 1951 (div. June 1970); children: Mary Melissa, Mark Edward, Catherine Ann, Marcia Jane; m. France Adelle Holmsley, June 5, 1974. Student, U. Colo., 1949; JD, Creighton U., 1955. Bar: Nebr. 1955. V.p. indsl. rels. Nat. Assn. Mfg., N.Y.C., 1963-66; pres. Employers Assn. El Paso, Tex., 1962-63, 66-70; assoc. prof. mgmt. U. Tex., El Paso, 1970-80; pres. MRA-The Mgmt. Assn., Brookfield, Wis., 1980—; Trustee Roundy's Inc., Milw., 1986—. With USAF, 1951-53, Libya. Mem. Nat. Assn. Mfrs. (chmn. indsl. rels. group 1991-92), Wis. Soc. Assn. Execs. (chair, vice-chair, treas. 1981-90), Rotary. Republican. Mem. Reformed Ch. Avocations: golf, travel, reading. Home: 15375 Kata Dr Elm Grove WI 53122-1028 Office: MRA The Mgmt Assn 235 N Executive Dr Ste 100 Brookfield WI 53005-6004

STENN, KURT S., dermatology and pathology educator; b. Chgo., Apr. 6, 1940. BS, U. Chgo., 1961; MD, U. Rochester, 1965; MS (hon.), Yale U., 1985. Prof. dermatology and pathology Yale U., New Haven, Conn., 1971—; Served to capt. USAF, 1967-69. Office: Yale U Dept Dermatology Patho New Haven CT 06520

STENNETT, WILLIAM CLINTON (CLINT STENNETT), radio and television station executive, state legislator; b. Winona, Minn., Oct. 1, 1956; s. William Jessie and Carole Lee (Halsey) S. BA in Journalism, Idaho State U., 1979. Gen. mgr. Wood River Jour., Hailey, Idaho, 1979-85, pres., pub., 1985-87; pres. Sta. KWRV-TV, Ketchum, Idaho, Sta. KSKI-FM, Sun Valley, Idaho; mem. Idaho Ho. of Reps., Boise, 1990-94, state senator, 1995—. Recipient Gen. Excellence award Idaho Newspaper Assn., 1985, 86, 87. Mem. Rotary Internat., Ketchum Sun Valley C. of C. (bd. dirs. 1990-95). Democrat.

STENSLAND, LINDA L., state senator; 3 children. Student, Sioux Falls Coll., Augustana Coll. Mem. S.D. State Senate from 14th dist.; pres. Environ. Consulting Co. Author: Ground Water Protection Act, Comprehensive Recycling Act. Mem. edn. and job tng. com. State Fed. Assembly of Nat. Conf. State Legislatures; bd. dirs. Nat. Recycling Coalition, Washington. Democrat. Lutheran. Home: 1800 E Otonka Rdg Sioux Falls SD 57103-4565 Office: SD Senate Pierre SD 57501

STENSVAAG, JOHN-MARK, legal educator, lawyer; b. Mpls., July 1, 1947; s. John Monrad and Hannah (Mehus) S.; m. Nancy Kay Strommen, June 19, 1970; children: Eric Paul, Nellie Malene, Rebecca Gayle, Kirsten Elizabeth, Jonathan Michael. BA, Augsburg Coll., Mpls., 1969; JD, Harvard U., 1974. Bar: Minn. 1974, U.S. Dist. Ct. Minn. 1977, U.S. Ct. Appeals (D.C. cir.) 1978. Law clk. U.S. Ct. Appeals (8th cir.), Duluth, Minn., 1974-75, U.S. Dist. Ct. Minn., Mpls., 1975-76; spl. asst. atty. gen. Minn. Pollution Control Agy., Roseville, 1976-79; assoc. prof. law Vanderbilt U., Nashville, 1979-83, assoc. prof., 1983-87, prof., 1987-88; vis. prof. law U. Iowa, Iowa City, 1987-88, prof., 1988—. Author: Hazardous Waste Law and Practice, 1986 (vol. 1 1986, vol. 2 1989), Clean Air Act: Law and Practice, vol. 1, 1991, vol. 2, 1993; contbr. articles to legal publs. Bancroft Grad. fellow, 1969-73. Lutheran. Home: 4 Heather Dr Iowa City IA 52245-3227 Office: U Iowa Coll Law Iowa City IA 52242

STENT, GUNTHER SIEGMUND, molecular biologist, educator; b. Berlin, Germany, Mar. 28, 1924; came to U.S., 1940, naturalized, 1945; s. George and Elizabeth (Karfunkelstein) S.; m. Inga Loftsdottir, Oct. 27, 1951; 1 son, Stefan Loftur. BS, U. Ill., 1945, PhD, 1948; DSc (hon.), York U., 1984. Research asst. U. Ill., 1945-48; research fellow Calif. Inst. Tech., 1948-50, U. Copenhagen, Denmark, 1950-51, Pasteur Inst., Paris, France, 1951-52; asst. research biochemist U. Calif., Berkeley, 1952-56; faculty U. Calif., 1956—, prof. molecular biology, 1959—, prof. arts and scis., 1967-68, chmn. molecular biology, 1980-86, chmn. molecular and cell biology, 1987-92, dir. virus lab., 1980-86; document analyst U.S. Field Info. Agy. Tech., 1946-47; mem. genetics panel NIH, 1959-64, NSF, 1965-68; fellow Inst. Advanced Studies, Berlin, 1985-90. Author: Papers On Bacterial Viruses, 2d edit, 1966, Molecular Biology of Bacterial Viruses, 1963, Phage and the Origin of Molecular Biology, 1966, The Coming of the Golden Age, 1969, Function and Formation of Neural Systems, 1977, Morality as a Biological Phenomenon, 1978, Paradoxes of Progress, 1978, Molecular Genetics, 2d edit, 1978; mem. editorial bd.: Jour. Molecular Biology, 1965-68, Genetics, 1963-68, Zeitschrift für Vererbungslehre, 1962-68, Ann. Revs. Genetics, 1965-69, Ann. Revs. Microbiology, 1966-70, Jour. Neurosci., 1988—; contbr. numerous sci. papers to profl. lit. Merck fellow NRC, 1948-54; sr. fellow NSF, 1960-61; Guggenheim fellow, 1969-70; Fogarty Resident Scholar NIH, 1990-92. Mem. NAS, Am. Acad. Arts and Scis., Soc. Neurosci., Am. Philos.

Soc., Acad. Scis. and Lit. of Mainz (Germany), European Acad. Scis. and Arts, Cosmos Club. Home: 145 Purdue Ave Kensington CA 94708-1032

STENWICK, MICHAEL WILLIAM, internist, geriatric medicine consultant; b. Red Wing, Minn., 'Nov. 12, 1941; s. Vincent Ferdinand and Geraldine Frances (Veith) S.; m. Judith Ann Nelson, June 10, 1961; children: Scott Michael, Gregg William. BS cum laude, Hamline U., 1963; MD, U. Minn., 1969. Diplomate Am. Bd. Internal Medicine. Fellow dept. pharmacology U. Minn., Mpls., 1966-68; intern in internal medicine Northwestern Hosp., Mpls., 1969-70, resident in internal medicine, 1970-73; sr. internist internal medicine sect. Bloomington Lake Clinic, Mpls., 1973—; bd. dirs. Bloomington Lake Clinic, Mpls., pres., 1977, v.p. 1989—, fin. com., 1987—, chmn. properties, 1984—, chmn. trustees profit sharing; med. adviser Kimberly Quality Care, St. Paul, 1990—; internal medicine cons. Fairview Multiple Sclerosis Ctr. and Rehab. Unit, Mpls., 1986—; informal adviser internal medicine sect. Minn. Relative Value Index, Mpls., 1971; mem. task force Riverside Med. Ctr., Mpls., 1988-91, chmn. critical care com., 1986-91, reviewer quality assurance subcom., 1989-90. Contbr. articles to profl. jours. Mem., co-organizer, 1st pres. Cyrus Barnum Soc., U. Minn. Med. Sch., Mpls.; bd. dirs. Signal Inn Beach and Racquetball Club, Sanibel Island, Fla., 1983-84, 89—, Signal Inn Condominium Assn., Sanibel Island, 1983-84, 89—; co-emcee Nursing Talent Show, Northwestern Hosp., Mpls., 1969; 1st med. dir. Beltrami Health Ctr., Mpls., 1970-72. Recipient scholarship Charles and Alora Allis Found., 1960-63, Walter Kenyon award, 1963, grant U. Minn., 1963. Fellow Am. Coll. Physicians; mem. AMA, Am. Soc. Internal Medicine, Minn. Med. Assn., Hennepin County Med. Assn., Mpls. Soc. Internal Medicine. Republican. Lutheran. Achievements include research in drug specificity that could be defined even in an alkylating agent. Office: Bloomington Lake Clinic 3017 Bloomington Ave Minneapolis MN 55407

STENZEL, KURT HODGSON, physician, nephrologist, educator; b. Stamford, Conn., Nov. 3, 1932; s. Alfred B. and Aurelie C. (Hodgson) S.; m. Carolyn Briggs, Dec. 21, 1957; children—Matthew, Jennifer, Mary. BA magna cum laude, N.Y. U., 1954; M.D., Cornell U., 1958. Intern Bellevue Hosp., N.Y.C., 1958-59; resident, 1959-60, 62-63; asst. in medicine Cornell U. Med. Coll., N.Y.C., 1959-60; asst. prof. medicine Cornell U. Med. Coll., 1965-68, asso. prof. biochemistry and surgery, 1969-75, prof. biochemistry, medicine and surgery, 1976—, chief div. nephrology (medicine), 1979-92, dir. Rogosin Kidney Ctr., 1970—; attending physician, surgeon N.Y. Hosp., N.Y.C., 1976—; Diplomate Am. Bd. Internal Medicine and Nephrology. contbr. articles to profl. publs. Served to lt. M.C. USNR, 1960-62. Recipient Nat. Kidney Found. Hoenig award for excellence in renal medicine. Fellow ACP; mem. Am. Soc. Biol. Chemists, Am. Soc. Nephrology, Transplantation Soc., Am. Fedn. Clin. Research, Am. Assn. Immunologists, Am. Soc. for Artificial Internal Organs, Phi Beta Kappa. Research on cell biology, cellular immunology, transportation and dialysis. Office: Cornell Univ Med College 1300 York Ave New York NY 10021-4896

STENZEL, WILLIAM A., consulting services executive; b. Cambridge, Mass., Jan. 21, 1923; s. Herman Rheinhold and Helen (Proskurniak) S.; m. Pallie Jean Bottorff, July 25, 1952; children: Jeffrey Rheinhold, Anne Virginia, Peter Deane, Christopher James. B.A. cum laude, Harvard U., 1944, M.B.A., 1948. Advt. mgr. Waltham Watch Co., Mass., 1948-54; v.p. Tracer Lab. Inc., Waltham, 1954-62; sr. v.p. Premier Indsl. Corp., Cleve., 1962-85, Mex. Info. and Cons. Svcs., Inc., 1985—; v.p. Edn. Techs. and Cons., Inc. Bd. dirs. Greater Cleve. chpt. ARC, 1983-86, bd. dirs., mem. exec. com. Orange City chpt., Calif.; fund raiser Cleve. Orch., 1977-81; trustee Mid Town Corridor, 1985-87, Dunham Tavern Mus., 1985-87; bd. dirs., mem. exec. com., mem. fin. devel. com. Orange City chpt. ARC; bd. dirs. blood, tissue svcs. So. Calif. region ARC, 1992—, treas., 1993. Served with U.S. Army, 1942-45. Fellow Rowfant Club, 1985—. Clubs: Harvard Bus. Sch., Rowfant (Cleve.). Home and Office: 124 Avenida Cota San Clemente CA 92672-3327

STEORTS, NANCY HARVEY, international management consultant; b. Syracuse, N.Y., Nov. 28, 1936; d. Frederick William and Josephine Elizabeth (Jones) Harvey; 1 dau., Deborah Joan. BS, Syracuse U., 1959. Asst. buyer, public relations coordinator Woodward & Lothrop, Washington, 1958-61; home economist Washington Gas Light Co., 1961-64; sales assoc. real estate Summit, N.J., 1967-68; survey specialist Dept. Agr., Washington, 1968-69; chmn. U.S. Consumer Product Safety Commn., Washington, D.C., 1981-85; pres., CEO Nancy Harvey Steorts & Assocs., Dallas, 1985-88, Nancy Harvey Steorts Internat., Washington and Dallas, 1988—; cons. Exec. Reorgn. Govt., Washington, 1971; nat. dir. women's speakers' bur. Com. Re-elect Pres., Washington, 1971-72; dir. candlelight dinners Presdl. Inaugural Commn., 1972-73, 81; expns. dir. Dept. Commerce, Washington, 1973; spl. asst. for consumer affairs to sec. agr., 1973-77; pres. Nancy Harvey Steorts & Assocs., 1977-81; disting. lectr., Strom Thurmond Inst. Govt. and Pub. Affairs, Clemson U.; mem. adv. coun. to bd. dirs., Adolph Coors Co.; mem. U.S. Dept. of Commerce Nat. Adv. Com. Tex., Nat. Adv. Com., Dist. Export Coun. Tex., Nat. Adv. Com. Export Now; mem. working com. on standards between U.S. and Russia; U.S. del. NAFTA Com. on environ. standards; bd. govs. Nat. Consumers adv. com. Fed. Reserve, 1990-93; U.S. del. to COPOLCO, Am. Nat. Standards Inst., The Hague, The Netherlands, NAFTA Del. on Environ. Standards; dir. People to People Trade Mission to Spain, 1987; del. Japan-Tex. Trade Mission, Tokyo, Osaka, Japan, Moscow, Kiev, Leningrad, U.S.-Russia Bus. Devel. Com. on Stds.; chmn. Dallas del. to meet with Prince Charles; mem. nat. consumer adv. coun. Fed. Res. Bd.; official U.S. rep. to 4th Pub. Health, Med. Equipment and Drugs Expn. Moscow USSR; speaker U.S. Seminar Soviet Health Care Exhbn., Moscow; bd. dirs., corp. adv. bd. Sch. Mgmt., Syracuse U.; mem. nat. consumer adv. com. Am. Nat. Standards Inst.; bd. dirs. Mission Investment Trust Co., Tuscon; internat. lectr. and keynote speaker in field. Producer, host syndicated TV show spl. Trustee Food Safety Council Conf. Consumer Orgns.; bd. dirs. Women's Inst. Am. U.; bd. advisers Coll. Human Devel., Alumnae Assn., Syracuse U., nat. bd. dirs.; commr. Montgomery County Commn. Women; pres. Welcome Wagon Clubs from 1986, Dallas Citizens Council, 1986—; bd. dirs. Council of Better Bus. Burs.; bd. adv. Am. U. Women's Inst.; bd. dirs. Med. Coll. Pa., Tex. Women's Alliance; bd. dirs., vice-chmn. regional devel. Nat. Assn. Women Bus. Owners; mem. internat. com. Cons. 2000; bd. dirs. Jr. Achievement, United Way, Dallas, Goals of Dallas, Internat. Mayor's Ball; internat. del. 1st Women's Internat. Trade Mission to Europe for Women Entrepeneurs; chairwoman Trade Mission of Women Leaders to Taiwan, 1988; del. to USSR Internat. Women's Forum Mission; mem. adv. coun. to So. Meth. U. Dept. Economics; co-chmn. fundraising Dallas Symphony; nat. dir., coord. bicentennial presdl. inaugural dinners, 1989; pres. Dallas Citizens' Coun., 1986-88; chmn. Afternoon with Oprah Winfrey Fundraising Benefit; chmn. Women Leaders Delegation to Taiwan; mem. corp. bd. dirs. Ariz. Rehab. Systems; mem. nat. bd. overseers U.S. Dept. Commerce; mem. Am. Nat. Standards Inst., Nat. Consumer Adv. Coun.; bd. dirs. Nat. Women's Econ. Alliance Found., I Have a Dream Found.; chmn. Dallas Glass Ceiling Commn.; bd. overseers Tex. Quality Bd. Recipient George P. Arents Pioneer medal Syracuse U., 1979, spl. award for consumer concern Nat. Diet Workshop, Malcolm Baldridge award, Bd. of Overseers; named one of five outstanding pub. servants Gallagher Report, 1984. Mem. Nat. Bd. Dirs., Am. Home Econs. Assn., AAUW, Nat. Consumers League, Am. Women in Radio and TV, Exec. Women in Govt. (chmn.), Nat. Conf. Consumer Orgns., Syracuse U. Alumni Assn. (bd. dirs.). Office: 4689 S Versailles Ave Dallas TX 75209-6017

STEP, EUGENE LEE, retired pharmaceutical company executive; b. Sioux City, Iowa, Feb. 19, 1929; s. Harry and Ann (Keiser) S.; m. Hannah Scheuermann, Dec. 27, 1953; children—Steven Harry, Michael David, Jonathan Allen. BA in Econs., U. Nebr., 1951; MS in Acctg. and Fin., U. Ill., 1952. With Eli Lilly Internat. Corp., London and Paris, 1964-69; dir. Elanco Internat. Eli Lilly Internat. Corp., Indpls., 1969-70, v.p. marketing, 1970-72, v.p. Europe, 1972; v.p. mktg. Eli Lilly and Co., Indpls., 1972-73, pres. pharm. div., 1973-86, exec. v.p., 1986—, also dir.; bd. dirs. Scios-Nova Cell-Genesys, Medco Rsch. Pathogenesis. Served to 1st lt. U.S. Army, 1953-56. Mem. Pharm. Mfrs. Assn. (bd. dirs. 1980-92), Internat. Pharm. Mfrs. Assn. (pres. 1991-92). Home: 741 Round Hill Rd Indianapolis IN 46260-2917

STEPAN, ALFRED C., political science educator, author; b. Chgo., July 22, 1936; s. Alfred Charles and Mary Louise (Quinn) S.; m. Nancy Leys, Jan. 10,

1964; children: Adam, Tanya. B.A., U. Notre Dame, 1958, Balliol Coll., Oxford U., Eng., 1961; M.A., Balliol. Coll., Oxford Univ., Eng., 1963; Ph.D., Columbia U., 1969; M.A. hon., Yale U., 1976. Spl. corr. The Economist, 1964; mem. staff Rand Corp., 1966-69; asst. prof. polit. sci. Yale U., New Haven, 1970-72, assoc. prof., 1972-76, prof., 1976-83; chmn. Council Latin Am. Studies, Yale U., New Haven, 1972-74, 76-81; dir. Concilium on Internat. and Area Studies, Yale U., New Haven, 1982-83; dean, prof. Sch. Internat. and Pub. Affairs, Columbia U., N.Y.C., 1983-91; Burgess prof. polit. sci. Columbia U., 1990—; mem. internat. adv. council Centro de Estudios de Estado y Sociedad, Buenos Aires, Argentina, 1976—; bd. dirs. Ctr. Inter-Am. Relations, N.Y.C. 1977-84; mem. Commn. on U.S.-Brazilian Relations, 1979-80; mem. nat. exec. com. Americans Watch, N.Y.C., 1982—; mem. nat. adv. council W. Harriman Inst. for Advanced Study Soviet Union, N.Y.C., 1983-91; fellow Inst. Advanced Studies U. Sao Paulo, 1989; vis. prof. Juan March Inst., 1990. Author: State and Society: Peru in Comparative Perspective, 1978, The Military in Politics: Changing Patterns in Brazil, 1971, Rethinking Military Politics: Brazil and the Southern Cone, 1988; editor Authoritarian Brazil: Origins, Policies and Future, 1973, (with Bruce Russett) Military Force and American Society, 1973, (with Juan Linz) The Breakdown of Democratic Regimes, 1978, Democratizing Brazil: Problems of Transition and Consolidation, 1989. Bd. dirs. Richard Tucker Music Found., N.Y.C., 1983—; chmn. 1985-91; trustee U. Notre Dame, 1985-91. Served to 1st lt. USMC, 1960-63. Research grantee Social Sci. Research Council, 1972; fellow John Simon Guggenheim Meml. Found., 1974-75; Ford vis. fellow St. Antony's Coll., Oxford U., Eng., 1978-79; Tinker vis. scholar CEBRAP, Sao Paulo, Brazil, 1982. Fellow Am. Acad. Arts and Scis.; mem. Fgn. Policy Assn. (bd. govs. 1986—), Coun. Fgn. Rels. Office: Columbia U Rsch Inst on Internat Change 420 W 118th St New York NY 10027-7213

STEPAN, FRANK QUINN, chemical company executive; b. Chgo., Oct. 24, 1937; s. Alfred Charles and Mary Louise (Quinn) S.; m. Jean Finw, Aug. 23, 1958; children: Jeanne, Frank Quinn, Todd, Jennifer, Lisa, Colleen, Alfred, Richard. A.B., U. Notre Dame, 1959; M.B.A., U. Chgo., 1963. Salesman Indsl. Chems. div. Stepan Chem. Co., Northfield, Ill., 1961-63, mgr. internat. dept., 1964-66, v.p. corporate planning, 1967-69, v.p., gen. mgr., 1970-73, pres., 1973-84; pres., chmn., chief exec. officer Stepan Co., Northfield, Ill., 1984—, also bd. dirs. Mem. liberal arts council Notre Dame U., South Bend, Ind., 1972—; bd. dirs. Big Shoulders, Chgo. Served to 1st lt. AUS, 1959-61. Mem. Chem. Mfrs. Assn. (bd. dirs.), Soap and Detergent Assn. (bd. dirs.), Ill. Bus. Roundtable, Econ. Club Chgo., Exmoor Country Club, Bob O'Link Golf Club, Everglades Club. Home: 200 Linden St Winnetka IL 60093-3862 Office: Stepan Co Edens & Winnetka Rds Northfield IL 60093

STEPANIAN, IRA, banker; b. Cambridge, Mass., Nov. 14, 1936; s. Sarkis H. and Armenoohi (Kupelian) S.; m. Jacquelynne McLucas, Aug. 6, 1961; children: Philip, Alisa, Steven. B.A., Tufts U., 1958; M.B.A., Boston Coll., 1971. Credit investigator Dun & Bradstreet, Boston, 1958-59; rsch. assoc. Ernst Assocs., Inc., Arlington, Mass., 1959-63; with First Nat. Bank Boston, 1963—, exec. v.p., 1980, vice chmn., from 1981, pres., from 1983, now chmn., chief exec. officer, dir.; vice chmn. Bank of Boston Corp., from 1981, pres., from 1983, chief oper. officer, dir., 1983-87, chief exec. officer, 1987—, now also chmn., dir.; bd. dirs. Liberty Mut. Ins. Co., NYNEX-New Eng., Fed. Res. Bank Boston. Trustee emeritus Tufts U., Medford, Mass.; trustee Boston Mus. Sci., Boston Mus. Fine Arts, Gen. Hosp.; bd. dirs. Mass. Bus. Roundtable, Internat. Monetary Conf. Mem. Bankers Roundtable. Office: Bank of Boston 100 Federal St PO Box 2016 Boston MA 02106-2016

STEPANSKI, ANTHONY FRANCIS, JR., computer company executive; b. Jersey City, N.J., June 29, 1941; s. Anthony Francis and Gertrude Stepanski; m. Jane Ellen Schuler, Sept. 5, 1965; children—Matthew A.W., Melinda Kate. B.A., Clark U., 1963. Sales rep. IBM Corp., N.Y.C., 1964-68; from sales rep. to sr. v.p. AGS Computers, Inc., N.Y.C. and Mountainside, N.J., 1968-82; exec. v.p. AGS Computers, Inc., Mountainside, 1982—; pres., chief exec. officer AGS Info. Services, Inc., Mountainside, 1986—; also bd. dirs. AGS Computers, Inc., a NYNEX Co., Mountainside; now exec. v.p., Keane, Inc., Clark, N.J. Trustee Clark U., Worcester, Mass., 1987, Children's Specialized Hosp. Found., Mountainside, 1989; bd. dirs. Westchester Artificial Kidney Ctr., Valhalla, N.Y., 1982, Westfield Symphony Orch., N.J., 1983. Served with USAR, 1965-66. Office: Keane Inc (AGS Computers) Cali Ctr 100 Walnut Ave Ste 501 Clark NJ 07066

STEPHAN, ALEXANDER F., German language and literature educator; b. Lüdenscheid, Fed. Republic Germany, Aug. 16, 1946; came to U.S., 1968; s. Eberhard and Ingeborg (Hörnig) S.; m. Halina Konopacka, Dec. 15, 1969; 1 child, Michael. MA, U. Mich., 1969; PhD, Princeton U., 1973. German instr. Princeton U., N.J., 1972-73; asst. prof. German UCLA, 1973-77, assoc. prof., 1977-83, prof., 1983-85; prof. German U. Fla., Gainesville, 1985—, chmn., 1985-93. Author: Christa Wolf, 1976, 4th edit., 1991, Die deutsche Exilliteratur, 1979, Christa Wolf (Forschungsbericht), 1981, Max Frisch, 1983, Anna Seghers im Exil, 1993; editor: Peter Weiss, Die Ästhetik des Widerstands, 1983, 3d edit., 1990, Exil literatur und die Künste, 1990, Exil-Studien, 1993—, Christa Wolf: The Author's Dimension, 1993; co-editor: Studies in GDR Culture and Society, 1981-90, Schreiben im Exil, 1985; editl. bd. Germanic Rev., Humanities Monograph Series, U. Fla., 1985-93, Argonautenschiff Jahrbuch der Ann Seghers Gesellschaft. Peter Weiss Jahrbuch fellow Humboldt Found., 1988, 94, Guggenheim Found. fellow, 1989, VG Wort fellow, 1992, UCLA faculty fellow, 1984, U. Fla., 1986, 92; grantee Internat. Rsch. and Exchs. Bd., 1993, German Acad. Exch. Svcs., 1993, NEH, 1974, 84, Am. Coun. Learned Socs., 1976, 77, 84, Sch. Theory and Criticism, 1978, Am. Philos. Soc., 1979, 81, 92. Mem Internat. Vereinigung für Germanische Sprach und Literaturwissenschaften, Am. Assn. Tchrs. German, Soc. for Exile Studies, German Studies Assn., Deutscher Germanistenverband, Internat. PEN, Soc. for German-Am. Studies, Internat. Ann. Seghers Soc. (founding). Home: 2402 NW 27th Terr Gainesville FL 32605-2829 Office: U Fla Dept Germanic & Slavic Langs/Lit 263 Dauer Gainesville FL 32611

STEPHAN, EDMUND ANTON, lawyer; b. Chgo., Oct. 7, 1911; s. Anton Charles and Mary Veronica (Egan) S.; m. Evelyn Way, July 3, 1937; children: Miriam, Edmund Anton, Martha (Mrs. Robert McNeill), Donald, Christopher, Evelyn, Gregory, Joan (Mrs. David Nelson). A.B., U. Notre Dame, 1933; LL.B., Harvard, 1939. Bar: N.Y. 1940, Ill. 1945. Assoc. firm Carter, Ledyard & Milburn, N.Y.C., 1939-42; atty. charge N.Y. office U.S. Alien Property Custodian, 1943-45; assoc. firm Mayer, Brown & Platt (and predecessors), Chgo., 1945-47; partner Mayer, Brown & Platt (and predecessors), 1947-90, of counsel, 1991—; dir. (hon.) Brunswick Corp., Marsh & McLennan Cos. Emeritus chmn. bd. trustees U. Notre Dame. Mem. Am. Ill., Chgo. bar assns. Roman Catholic. Clubs: Legal (Chgo.), Mid-Day (Chgo.), Chicago (Chgo.), Law (Chgo.); Michigan Shores (Wilmette, Ill.), Westmoreland Country (Wilmette, Ill.); Harvard (N.Y.C.); Bob-O-Link Golf (Highland Park, Ill.). Home: 1410 Sheridan Rd Wilmette IL 60091-1840 Office: Mayer Brown & Platt 190 S La Salle St Chicago IL 60603-3410

STEPHAN, EGON, SR., cinematographer, film equipment company executive; b. Leipzig, Germany, Nov. 25, 1933; came to U.S., 1952; 1 child, Egon Jr. Engr. Reeves Sound Inc., N.Y.C., 1952-55, Camera Equipment Co., N.Y.C., 1955-57; instr. U.S. Army Signal Corps., 1957-59; camera rental mgr. F&B Ceco, Miami, Fla., 1959-66; freelance cinematographer, 1966—; owner, pres. Cine Video Tech., Inc., Miami, 1968—. Cinematography credits include: Mission Shark, Miami Blues, Police Academy 4, Flight of the Navigator, Blue City, Two Young People, Blue Lightning, Wet Gold, Next of Kin, Cayman Triangle, Spring Break, Ernest Saves Christmas, (TV series) Love Boat, Caribe, Traum Schiff, Charley Hannah, (TV commls.) Sea Escape, Holiday Cruise Lines, Chrysler, Buick, Royal Caribbean, Heinekin Beer, Miller Beer, Medallion Beer, Styveysant Cigaretts, Shel Oil, Hess Oil, KFC, and various 16mm documentaries. Recipient Cine Golden Eagle award Council on Internat. Nontheatrical Events, 1973, Gold Camera award U.S. Indsl. Film Festival, 1974, Emmy award Nat. Acad. TV Arts and Scis., Fisher Meml. award South Fla. Film and Tape Producers Assn., 1981. Mem. Soc. Motion Picture and TV Engrs., Fla. Motion Picture and TV Assn. (chmn. 1978), Internat. Assn. Theatrical Stage Employees. Office: Cine Video Tech Inc 7330 NE 4th Ct Miami FL 33138-5005

STEPHAN, JOHN JASON, historian, educator; b. Chgo., Mar. 8, 1941; s. John Walter and Ruth (Walgreen) S.; m. Barbara Ann Brooks, June 22, 1963. B.A., Harvard U., 1963, M.A., 1964; Ph.D., U. London, 1969.

Research assoc. Social Sci. Center, Waseda U., Tokyo, 1969-70; mem. faculty U. Hawaii, Honolulu, 1970—; prof. history U. Hawaii, 1977—, chmn. E. Asian studies program, 1973-74, dir. program on Soviet Union in Pacific-Asia region, 1986-88; rsch. prof. Japan Found.; fellow U. Hokkaido, 1976-77; vis. prof. Inst. of Far East, Moscow, 1982, Inst. Econ. Rsch., Khabarovsk, USSR, 1982-83, Stanford U., 1986, Kennan Inst. for Advanced Studies, 1987; adj. rsch. assoc. East-West Ctr., 1988-92; Sanwa disting. lectr. Fletcher Sch. of Law & Diplomacy Tufts U., 1989. Author: Sakhalin: A History, 1971, The Kuril Islands: Russo-Japanese Frontier in the Pacific, 1974, The Russian Fascists, 1978, Hawaii Under the Rising Sun, 1984, Soviet-American Horizons on the Pacific, 1986, The Russian Far East, 1994. Sr. assoc. mem. St. Antony's Coll., Oxford (Eng.) U., 1977; Bd. dirs. Library Internat. Relations, Chgo., 1976-87; Hawaii rep. U.S.-Japan Friendship Commn., 1980-83. Fulbright fellow, 1967-68; Asia Found. grantee, 1974. Mem. AAUP, Am. Hist. Assn., Am. Assn. Advancement Slavic Studies, Assn. Asian Studies, Authors Guild, Internat. House of Japan, Can. Hist. Assn. Address: 4334 Round Top Dr Honolulu HI 96822-5021

STEPHAN, ROBERT TAFT, state attorney general; b. Wichita, Kans., Jan. 16, 1933; s. Taft and Julia S.; m. Marilyn Stephan; children: Dana, Lisa, Constance, Kimberly, Keith. BA, Washburn U., 1954, JD, 1957; postgrad., U. Pa., 1967. Bar: Kans. 1957. Pvt. practice law, 1957-63; judge Wichita (Kans.) Mcpl. Ct., 1963-65, Kans. Dist. Ct., 18th Jud. Dist., 1965-78; atty. gen. State of Kans., 1979-95; chmn. Kans. Jud. Conf., 1977, Kans. Sentencing Commn., 1993-95; mem. adv. bd. Shawnee County Ct.-Appointed Spl. Adv. Program. Hon. crusade chmn. Kans. div. Am. Cancer Soc., 1979-81; mem. adv. coun. Kans. Spl. Olympics, chmn. Corp. Giving Club, 1985-86; mem. adv. coun. Kans. Tchrs. of Tomorrow; bd. trustees Leukemia Soc. Am., Kans. chpt.; bd. dirs. Victory in the Valley. Named Kans. Trial Judge of Yr. Kans. Trial Lawyers Assn., 1977, Big Bros. of Yr., 1984, Outstanding Big Bros. Midwest, 1985; recipient Disting. Svc. award Washburn U., 1985; Allied Profl. award Nat. Orgn. for Victim Assistance, 1993. Mem. Am. Judges Assn., Am. Judicature Soc., ABA (mem. adv. commn. youth alcohol and drug problems), Nat. Assn. Attys. Gen. (past pres., chmn. commn. car rental guidelines, mem. fed. trade commn. working group), Wagonmasters Club, Elks, Moose, Masons, Shriners. Republican. Office: 14243 W 84th Ter Lenexa KS 66215

STEPHANOFF, KATHRYN ANN, library director; b. Milton, Mass., Apr. 30, 1929; d. Edward Carlton and Kathryn (O'Brien) Grady; m. Robert Stephanoff, 1949; 1 child, Sheila Benson. BS, Boston U., 1945; MLS, Rutger U., 1969; Doctorate in Humane Letters, Allentown Coll., 1982. Dir. Allentown (Pa.) Pub. Library, 1969—; dir. First Nat. Bank, Allentown, 1980-86; advisor Meridian Bank, Reading, Pa., 1986—. Author numerous library related pubs. Trustee Trexler Found., Allentown, 1985—; dir. Indsl. Devel. Corp., Allentown, 1984—; mem. Lehigh County Indsl. Authority, 1984—; treas. United Way, Lehigh County, 1983-85; pres. Center City Assn., Allentown, 1980-83; chmn. Downtown Improvement Dist. Authority, 1992—; mem. bd. dirs. Lehigh Valley Hosp. Bd., 1992—. Named Disting. Daughter Pa. Gov. Thornburgh; recipient Disting. Svc. award Lehigh County C. of C., 1989. Mem. Am. Library Assn., Pa. Library Assn. (Disting. Svc. award, 1990), Women's Club (exec. bd.). Republican. Roman Catholic. Avocations: tennis, swimming. Home: 972 Buttonwood St Emmaus PA 18049-3202 Office: Allentown Pub Libr 1210 W Hamilton St Allentown PA 18102-4371

STEPHANOPOULOS, GEORGE ROBERT, federal official; b. Fall River, Mass., Feb. 10, 1961; s. Robert and Nikki C. Stephanopoulos. AB Polit. Sci. summa cum laude, Columbia U., 1982; M Theology, Oxford U., 1986. Adminstrv. asst. rep. Edward Feighan, Washington; dep. comm. dir. Dukakis Bentsen campaign, 1988; exec. floor mgr. to House Majority leader Gephardt, Washington; dir. comm. Clinton/Gore campaign, Little Rock; dir. comm. The White House, Washington, sr. advisor to the Pres. of U.S., 1993—. Recipient medal of Excellence Columbia U., 1993; Rhodes scholar Oxford U. Mem. Phi Beta Kappa. Democrat. Greek Orthodox. Office: The White House 1600 Pennsylvania Ave NW Washington DC 20500-0001

STEPHANOPOULOS, GREGORY, chemical engineering educator, consultant, researcher; b. Kalamata, Greece, Mar. 10, 1950; came to U.S., 1973; s. Nicholas and Elizabeth (Bitsanis) S.; m. Maria Flytzani; children—Nicholas-Odysseas, Alexander, Rona-Elisa. B.S., Nat. Tech. U., Athens, Greece, 1973; M.S., U. Fla., Gainesville, 1975; Ph.D., U. Minn., Mpls., 1978. Registered profl. engr., Greece. Asst. prof. chem. engring. Calif. Inst. Tech., Pasadena, 1978-83, assoc. prof. chem. engring., 1983-85; prof. chem. engring. MIT, Cambridge, 1985—. Editor: Kinetics and Thermodynamics of Biological Systems, 1983. Mem. editorial bd. Mathematical Biosciences, 1984—, Biotech. Progress, 1984—. Contbr. articles to profl. jours. Dreyfus Tchr. scholar Camille and Henry Dreyfus Found., 1982; recipient Pres. Young Investigator award NSF, 1984; NSF grantee, 1980—. Mem. Am. Inst. Chem. Engrs. (programming coordinator 1983), Am. Chem. Soc. Greek Orthodox. Avocations: chess; music; travel. Office: Mass Inst Tech Dept Chem Engring 66-552 77 Massachusetts Ave Cambridge MA 02139-4307*

STEPHEN, JOHN ERLE, lawyer, consultant; b. Eagle Lake, Tex., Sept. 24, 1918; s. John Earnest and Vida Thrall (Klein) S.; m. Gloria Yzaguirre, May 16, 1942; children: Vida Leslie Stephen Renzi, John Lauro Kurt. JD, U. Tex., 1941; postgrad., Northwestern U., 1942, U.S. Naval Acad. Postgrad. Sch., Annapolis, 1944; cert. in internat. law, U.S. Naval War Coll. Newport, R.I., 1945; cert. in advanced internat. law, U.S. Naval War Coll. 1967. Bar: Tex. 1946, U.S. Ct. Appeals (D.C. cir.) 1949, U.S. Tax Ct. 1953, U.S. Supreme Ct. 1955, U.S. Dist. Ct. D.C. 1956, U.S. Ct. Appeals (2nd cir.) 1959, U.S. Ct. Appeals (7th cir.) 1964, U.S. Dist. Ct. (so. dist.) N.Y. 1964, D.C. 1972, U.S. Dist. Ct. (no. dist.) Ill. 1974, U.S. Dist. Ct. (we. dist.) Wash. 1975, Mich. 1981, U.S. Dist. Ct. (we. dist.) Mich. 1981, U.S. Dist. Ct. (so. dist.) Tex. 1981. Gen. mgr., corp. counsel Sta. KOPY, Houston, 1946; gen. atty., exec. asst. to pres. Tex. Star Corp. and affiliated cos., Houston, 1947-50; ptnr. Hofheinz & Stephen, Houston, 1950-57; v.p., gen. counsel TV Broadcasting Co., Tex. Radio Corp., Gulf Coast Network, Houston, 1953-57; spl. counsel, exec. asst. Mayor, City of Houston, 1953-57; spl. counsel Houston C. of C., 1953-56; v.p., gen. counsel Air Transp. Assn. Am., Washington, 1958-70, Amway Corp. and affiliated cos., Ada, Mich., 1971-82; counsellor, cons. Austin, Tex., 1983—; chief protocol City of Houston, 1953-56; advisor Consulates Gen. of Mex., San Antonio, Houston, New Orleans, Washington, 1956-66; adv. bd. Jour. of Air Law and Commerce, 1966-72; vis. lectr. bus. sch. Harvard U., Pacific Agribus. Conf., Southwestern Legal Found., Inter-Am. Law Conf.; apptd. by Pres. legal advisor, del. U.S. Diplomatic Dels. to Internat. Treaty Confs., Paris, London, Rome, Tokyo, Mexico City, 1959-68; U.S. Del. to Internat. Air-Rte. Dels. to U.K., France, Spain, Portugal, Belgium, The Netherlands, Japan, Rep. of Korea, Mex., Australia, Argentina, Soviet Union, and Brazil, 1960-70; legal advisor, del. U.S. Dels. to United Nations Specialized Orgns., Montreal, Geneva, 1964-71; U.S. rep. Internat. Conf. on Aircraft Noise, London, 1967; hon. faculty mem. sch. of law, sch. of bus., U. Miami, 1968—. Author, editor in field. Chmn. legal com. Nat. Aircraft Noise Abatement Coun.; bd. dirs. Houston Mus. Fine Arts, 1953-57, Contemporary Arts Assn., 1953-57, Tex. Transp. Inst., 1964-72. Comdr. line USNR, 1941-46, combat PTO and S.E. Asia; mem. staff Supreme Allied Command, NATO, 1952. Recipient Jesse L. Lasky award RKO Pictures-CBS, Hollywood, Calif., 1939, H.J. Lutcher Stark award U. Tex., 1940, 41, Walter Mack award Pepsico, U. Tex., 1941, Best U.S. Pub. Svc. Broadcasts award CCNY, 1946. Mem. ABA (past chmn., mem. coun. sect. pub. utility law, standing com. on aero. law), Am. Law Inst., World Peace Through Law Ctr. Geneva (past chmn. internat. aviation law com.). Fed. Bar Assn., D.C. Bar, State Bar Tex., State Bar Mich., Fed. Communications Bar Assn., Assn. ICC Practitioners, Am. Judicature Soc., Washington Fgn. Law Soc. (vis. lectr. 1967-68), Japanese Air Law Soc. (hon. mem. 1966—), Venezuelan Air and Space Law Soc. (hon.), Internat. Club (Washington), Explorers (Washington), Houston Polo Club, Lakeshore Club (Chgo.), Nat. Aviation Club, Saddle & Cycle (Chgo.), Breakfast Club (Houston), Execs. (Houston), Ky. Cols., Ark. Travelers, Tex. Adms. Home: 6904 Ligustrum Cv Austin TX 78750-8352

STEPHEN, MICHAEL ANTHONY, insurance company executive; b. Saint John, N.B., Can., Jan. 17, 1929; m. Beatrice Bourque. B.A., U. Montreal, Que., Can., 1951; grad. Advanced Mgmt. Program, Harvard U., 1983. Agt. London Life, Saint John, 1955-60; br. mgr. London Life, Halifax, N.S., Can.,

1960-69; dir. agys. Sun Life, Montreal, 1969-74; v.p. life div. Aetna Can., Toronto, Ont., Can., 1974-81, exec. v.p. ins. ops., 1981-83, exec. v.p., chief oper. officer, 1983-85, pres., chief oper. officer, 1985-87, pres., chief exec. officer, 1987-92; pres. Aetna Internat., Inc., Hartford, Conn., 1992—, also bd. dirs.; bd. dirs. Aetna Life Ins. Co. Can., Aetna Trust, Aetna Internat. Chile S.A., Seguros Monterrey Aetna S.A. Bd. dirs. Toronto Symphony. Mem. Harvard U. Alumni Assn. (Toronto), Bd. Trade, Toronto Club, York Club. Office: Aetna Internat 151 Farmington Ave Hartford CT 06156

STEPHENS, ALBERT LEE, JR., federal judge; Judge U.S. Dist. Ct. (cen. dist.) Calif., Los Angeles. Office: US Dist Ct 312 N Spring St Los Angeles CA 90012-4701

STEPHENS, BART NELSON, former foreign service officer; b. Norfolk, Va., May 29, 1922; s. Bart Dannelly and Lura Lee (Cannon) S.; m. Barrett Krausz, Jan. 7, 1950; children: Tracey Rainier, Schuyler Barrett, Holly Cannon, Sinah Kendall Lee. A.B., Duke, 1943; A.M., Harvard, 1947; lang. tng., Fgn. Service Inst., 1962, 66, 76. Divisional asst. Greece-Turkey-Iran sect., pub. affairs overseas program staff Dept. State, 1948-49; asst. pub. affairs officer Thessaloniki, Greece, 1950; asst. info. officer Athens, 1950-51; pub. affairs officer Patras, Greece, 1951-54 and, Thessaloniki, 1954; dir. Amerika Haus, Nuernberg, Germany, 1955-59; mem. cultural council City of Nuernberg, 1958-59; mgmt. analyst USIA, Washington, 1959-61; cultural attache Am. Embassy, Warsaw, Poland, 1963-65; dir. Am. Cultural Center, Saigon, Vietnam, 1967-68; 1st sec., regional projects officer Am. Embassy, Vienna, Austria, 1968-70; consul, pub. affairs officer Am. consulate gen. Stuttgart, Germany, 1970-73; area coordinator (Europe) USIA, Washington, 1973; seminar-conf. Programming officer USIA, 1973-74; dep. dir. Office Internat. Arts Affairs, Dept. State, 1974-76; counselor cultural affairs officer Am. Embassy, Bangkok, 1977-82; counselor Sr. Fgn. Service. Contbr. articles to profl. jours. Vice chmn., bd. dirs. Thailand-U.S. Edni. Found., 1977-82; bd. dirs. John F. Kennedy Found., Thailand, 1977-82, John E. Peurifoy Found., 1979-82, Lynchburg Symphony Orch., 1992-93; exec. sec. Eisenhower Exch. Fellowship Selection Com., Thailand, 1977-82; mem. winter forums com. Sweet Briar Coll., 1990—. Lt. (j.g.) USNR, 1944-46, PTO. Decorated Bronze Star with combat V, Purple Heart.; recipient Meritorious Svc. award USIA, 1956, medal for civilian service in Vietnam, 1968, Civilian award U.S. European Command, 1973. Mem. Am. Fgn. Svc. Assn., Soc. Lees of Va., Siam Soc., Westwood Country Club (Vienna, Va.), Boonsboro Country Club, Phi Beta Kappa, Omicron Delta Kappa, Phi Eta Sigma, Pi Kappa Phi. Home: 201 St James Pl Lynchburg VA 24503-4226

STEPHENS, BOBBY GENE, college administrator, consultant; b. Glendale, S.C., Mar. 8, 1935; s. Dewey and Bertha Cordelia (Mott) S.; m. Sandra Elizabeth White, June 27, 1957; children: Elaine, Ward, Todd, Adam. B.S., Wofford Coll., 1957; M.S., Clemson U., 1961, Ph.D., 1964; LHD (hon.), MacMurray Coll., 1987. Textile chemist Reeves Bros., Fairforest, S.C., 1957-58; grad. asst. Clemson (S.C.) U., 1960-63; instr. chemistry Wofford Coll., Spartanburg, S.C., 1963-64, asst. prof., 1964-67, assoc. prof., 1967-72, prof., v.p. acad. affairs, 1972-80; pres. MacMurray Coll., Jacksonville, Ill., 1980-86; v.p. research and enrollment Wofford Coll., Spartanburg, S.C., 1986-91, v.p. sci. and tech., 1991—; project dir. Howard Hughes Med. Inst., 1992—; cons. colls. and industry. Contbr. articles to sci. jours.; inventor extractions with propylene carbonate, 1975; producer: TV series The Psychology of Interpersonal of Interpersonal Behavior, 1974. Co-chmn. Daniel Morgan Restoration Com., 1986-88; vice chmn. Spartanburg County Pollution Control Authority, 1970-74; bd. dirs. S.C. Lung Assn., Spartanburg, 1970-75, Communications Svcs., Inc., 1977-80; sect. maj. United Way, 1975-77. 1st lt. U.S. Army, 1958-60. Recipient Jefferson award S.C. Acad. Sci., 1969; recipient 1st prize graphics div. 2d Edit. Art Contest, 1971, 2d and 3d prizes Lawson's Fork Creek Photography Contest, 1978; USPHS grantee; NSF grantee. Mem. Am. Chem. Soc., Nat. Assn. Gifted Children, Assn. Edni. Communications and Tech., Phi Beta Kappa. Methodist. Home: 131 Henry Ct Spartanburg SC 29306 Office: Wofford College 429 N Church St Spartanburg SC 29303

STEPHENS, BOBBY WAYNE, nursing home administrator; b. Booneville, Ark., Dec. 4, 1944; s. Cecil L. and Estella L. Stephens; m. Mary Beth Carolan, Nov. 27, 1966; children: Travis Wayne, Matthew Samuel. BS in Bus. Adminstrn., U. Ark., 1969; postgrad., Yale U., 1986, 89, U. Pa., 1984. Acct. Beverly Enterprises, central div., Ft. Smith, Ark., 1969-71, v.p., 1971-75, exec. v.p., 1975-80, pres., 1980-89, sr. v.p., 1989—; bd. mem. Nat. Coun. Health Care Facilities, Washingotn, 1982-85, Tex. Nursing Home Assn., Austin, 1982-84, Ark. Nursing Home Assn., Little Rock, 1980-82, Ark. Health Care Assn., Little Rock, 1989; advisor Health Care Steering Com., Congressman Beryl Anthony, Washington, 1987. Bd. mem. Ark. Gerontol. Soc., Little Rock, 1985-88, Project Compassion, Ft. Smith, 1985-87, Mgmt. Dept. Adv. Bd. U. Ark., Fayetteville, 1986-89, Ark. Devel. Fin. Authority, Little Rock, 1985—. Recipient Corp. Humanitarian award Ark. Office Volunterism, Little Rock, 1984, Extra Mile award Central Ark. Area on Aging, Little Rock, 1986. Mem. Fort Smith C. of C. (bd. mem. 1984-86), Hardscrabble Country Club, Town Club. Republican. Presbyterian. Avocations: water and snow skiing, jogging, reading, golf. Home: 3700 Free Ferry Rd Fort Smith AR 72903-1760 Office: Beverly Enterprises PO Box 2765 Fort Smith AR 72913-2765

STEPHENS, DELIA MARIE LUCKY, lawyer; b. Temple, Tex., Aug. 2, 1939; d. James Richard and Mattie (Barfield) Lucky; m. Billy C. Stephens, 1962 (div. 1983); children: William Carl, James Kelley. BA, U. Mary Hardin-Baylor, 1961; JD, Thurgood Marshall Sch. Law, Houston, 1981. Bar: Tex. 1981, U.S. Dist. Ct. (so. dist.) Tex. 1981. Pvt. practice law Houston, 1981—. Writer feature stories The Jour. Newspapers, 1976-79. Elder, trustee Clear Lake Presbyn. Ch., Houston, 1985—; founding dir. East-West Cultural Inst., 1991—; bd. dirs. Palmer Drug Abuse Coun., 1986-90. Mem. AAUW, Tex. State Bar Assn., Houston Bar Assn., Houston Rose Soc., Am. Rose Soc., Houston Mus. Fine Arts, U. Mary Hardin-Baylor Alumni Assn. (nominating com. 1973), Coastal Bend Mary Hardin-Baylor Club (pres. 1972), Clear Lake Area C. of C., Houston Outdoor Nature Club. Democrat. Presbyn. Avocations: roses, swimming, golf, drama, music. Home: 482 Lost Rock Dr Webster TX 77598-2640 Office: 17000 El Camino Real Ste 104 Houston TX 77058-2632

STEPHENS, DONALD JOSEPH, retired architect; b. Albany, N.Y., Apr. 29, 1918; s. Arthur Everett and Evangeline (Cosgrave) S.; m. Jean E. Brown Clausen, Apr. 15, 1950; children—Christian, Linda, Suzanne, Marc, Paul, Thomas. B.Arch., Rensselaer Polytechnic Inst., 1940. Archtl. engr. Watervliet Arsenal, 1941-44; assoc. architect Henry L. Blatner, Albany, 1946-56; pres. Stephens Assocs. P.C., Architects, Albany, 1956-84; mng. architect C.T. Male Assocs PC, 1985-87; mem. N.Y. State Bd. Architecture, 1976-85. Chmn. Taconic Valley Planning Assn., 1967-72; chmn. Town of Berlin (N.Y.) Planning Bd., 1960-79; pres. bd. edn. Berlin Central Sch. Dist., 1971-72. Served with USN, 1944-46, PTO. Fellow AIA (regional dir. 1974-76); mem. N.Y. State Assn. Architects (Matthew Del Gaudio award 1971). Home: PO Box 301 Berlin NY 12022-0301

STEPHENS, DONALD R(ICHARDS), banker; b. San Francisco, June 28, 1938; s. Donald Lewis and Anona Marie (O'Leary) S.; m. Christina Brinkman, Sept. 11, 1971; children: Lane B., Justin H., Nicholas W., Adam H. BS, U. So. Calif., 1961; JD., Hastings Coll., 1969. Pres. Campodonico & Stephens, San Francisco, 1963-65; pres., owner Union Investment Co., San Francisco, 1966-69; assoc. Law Offices of Louis O. Kelso, 1969-72; individual practice law, San Francisco Co., 1972-77; pres. D.R. Stephens & Co., San Francisco, 1978-91, also bd. dirs.; chmn. N.Am. Trust REIT, also bd. dirs.; bd. dirs. Charles Schwab Family of Funds Inc., Skouras Pictures, Solo Serve Corp. Bd. dirs. Bay Area Coun.; trustee St. Francis Meml. Hosp., San Francisco, 1976-82; mem. policy adv. bd. U. Calif. Mem. Urban Land Inst., World Bus. Coun., Bohemian Club, Calif. Club. Republican. Presbyterian. Avocations: tennis, golf.

STEPHENS, E. BARRIE, business executive. Chmn., chief exec. officer Robertshaw Controls Co., Richmond, Va. Office: Robertshaw Controls Co 1701 Byrd Ave Richmond VA 23230-3011

STEPHENS, EDWARD CARL, communications educator, writer; b. L.A., July 27, 1924; s. Carl Edward and Helen Mildred (Kerner) S.; children:

Edward, Sarah, Matthew. AB, Occidental Coll., 1947; MS, Northwestern U., 1955. Advt. exec. Dancer-Fitzgerald-Sample Inc., N.Y.C., 1955-64; prof. Medill Sch. Journalism, Northwestern U., Evanston, Ill., 1964-76; prof., chmn. dept. advt. S.I. Newhouse Sch. Pub. Communications, Syracuse U., N.Y., 1976-80, dean, 1980-89; prof. comms. S.I. Newhouse Sch. Pub. Comms. Syracuse U., 1990-92, prof. emeritus, 1992—; cons. Foote, Cone & Belding Communications. Author: (novels) A Twist of Lemon, 1958, One More Summer, 1960, Blow Negative!, 1962, Roman Joy, 1965, A Turn in the Dark Wood, 1968, The Submariner, 1974, (nonfiction) Submarines, 1960. Mem. George Polk Awards Com. With USN, 1943-46, 1950-53. Capt. USNR (ret.). Decorated Purple Heart. Mem. Am. Acad. Advt. (pres. 1976-77), Assn. Edn. Journalism and Mass Communication, Authors League, Century Club of Syracuse, Alpha Tau Omega. Episcopalian. Office: Syracuse U Newhouse Sch Pub Communications Syracuse NY 13210

STEPHENS, ELTON BRYSON, bank executive, service and manufacturing company executive; b. Clio, Ala., Aug. 4, 1911; s. James Nelson and Clara (Stuckey) S.; m. Alys Varian Robinson, Nov. 28, 1935; children: James Thomas, Jane Stephens Comer, Elton Bryson Jr., Dell Stephens Brooke. B.A., Birmingham-So. Coll., 1932, LLD (hon.), 1977; LL.B., U. Ala., 1936, LHD (hon.), 1990; grad., Advanced Mgmt. Program, Harvard U., 1960; LHD (hon.), Faulkner U., 1992. Bar: Ala. 1936. Regional dir. Keystone Readers Service, Birmingham, 1937-43; partner, then founder and pres. Mil. Service Co., Inc. (predecessor of EBSCO Industries, Inc.), Birmingham, 1943-58; founder EBSCO Industries, Inc., and affiliates, 1958; since pres., chmn. bd. EBSCO Industries, Inc., and affiliates, Birmingham; bd. dirs. R.A. Brown Ins. Agy. Ltd., 1966—; chmn. EBSCO Investment Svc., Inc., 1959—; Canebsco Subscription Svc., Toronto, Ont., Can., 1972—; founder, chmn. Ala. Bancorp divsn. The Citizens Bank Leeds, The Fort Deposit Bank, Highland Bank; founder EBSCO Savs. and Profit Sharing Trust, Ala. Bancorp Savs. and Profit Sharing Trust. Mem. fin. and investment com., past chmn. bd. trustees, chmn. exec. com. Birmingham-So. Coll.; trustee So. Research Inst.; former pres., chmn. bd. trustee Birmingham Met. YMCA; mem. bd., chmn. econ. pension com. Tenn.-Tombigbee Waterway Authority; founder ½ Clubs of Ala., founder United Art Fund/Met. Arts Council; vice chmn., bd. dirs. hon. chmn. Elton B. Stephens Expressway named in his honor, 1970, Elton B. Stephens Library, Clio, 1979. Mem. Birmingham C. of C. (bd. dirs.) The Club, Birmingham Press Club, Summit Club, Mountain Brook Country Club (Ala.), Rotary (pres. Homewood, Ala. 1979-80, Paul Harris fellow), Alpha Tau Omega (past chmn. nat. found.), Omicron Delta Kappa, Phi Alpha Delta. Methodist. *Invest/reinvest earnings to create employment/profits for growth/expansion. Support worthwhile projects including but not limited to: education, health, religion, needy, cultural, arts, boys/girls clubs, law enforcement, conservation, nature, water resources. Share profits and protect the welfare and health of your employees with a major catastrophic medical program. These philosophies built a company I started in 1943 with capital of $5,000 and sales under $1,000,000 with under 20 employees to annual sales of over $700,000,000 and 3400 employees with adequate capital from earnings and borrowing to continue growth. EBSCO operates world wide.*

STEPHENS, FRANKLIN WILSON, transportation executive; b. Coleman, Tex., Jan. 22, 1940; s. Jacob W. and Eldora E. (Henson) S.; m. Lou Ann Birdwell; children: Brit, Chris. BBA, Tex. Lutheran Coll., 1962. Dist. sales mgr. Ryder Truck Rental Inc., Houston, 1969-73; dist. mgr. Ryder Truck Rental Inc., Oklahoma City, 1973-77, San Francisco, 1977-78; regional v.p. Ryder Truck Rental Inc., Nashville, 1978-85; sr. v.p., gen. mgr. Ryder Truck Rental, Inc., Miami, 1985-92, sr. v.p. purchasing-asset mgmt., 1992—. Served to lt. USN, 1963-69, to lt. comdr. USNR, 1969—. Republican. Lutheran. Office: Ryder Truck Rental Inc 3600 NW 82nd Ave Miami FL 33166-6682

STEPHENS, GARY RALPH, American literature and journalism educator; b. Wichita, Kans., Mar. 4, 1943; s. Hubert Hal and Iris Lenore (Edgar) S.; m. Swati Niru Desai, May 13, 1978; children: Anaar, Joshua. AB, Wichita State U., 1965; MA, Brandeis U., 1969, PhD, 1972. Asst. prof. English Queens Coll., CUNY, Flushing, 1971-75; asst. prof. English N.Y. Inst. Tech., Old Westbury, 1976-81, assoc. prof. English, 1982-88, chmn. dept. English, 1979-82; prof. English N.Y. Inst. Tech., N.Y.C., 1989—, dir. Sch. Humanities, 1982-92; assoc. in journalism Grad. Sch. Journalism Columbia U., N.Y.C., 1986—; cons. in field. Contbr. articles to profl. publs. J.W. Fulbright fellow India, 1993; fellow Woodrow Wilson Found., 1965, Rockefeller Found., 1966, NEH, 1981. Office: NY Inst Tech 1855 Broadway New York NY 10023

STEPHENS, GEORGE EDWARD, JR., lawyer; b. Lawrence, Kans., Mar. 26, 1936; s. George Edward and Mary Helen (Houghton) S.; m. Gretel Geiser, Dec. 31, 1965; children: Thaddeus Geiser, Edward Houghton, Mary Schoentgen. Student, U. Colo., Boulder, 1954-57, U. Colo. Sch. Medicine, Denver, 1957-59; LLB, Stanford U., 1962. Bar: Calif. 1963, U.S. Dist. Ct. (cen. dist.) Calif. 1963, U.S. Ct. Appeals (9th cir.) 1971. Law clk. to judge U.S. Dist. Ct., Los Angeles, 1962-64; assoc. ptnr. Pollock & Palmer, Los Angeles, 1964-69; ptnr. Gates, Morris, Merrill & Stephens, Los Angeles, 1969-72, Paul, Hastings, Janofsky & Walker, Los Angeles, 1972—; mem. Coordinating Coun. on Lawyer Competence, Conf. Chief Justices, 1983-86; chmn. probate sect. L.A. County Bar Assn., 1979-80. Nat. chmn. Stanford (Calif.) U. Law Fund Quad Program, 1980-87; mem. bd. visitors Stanford Law Sch., 1982-85; founder mus. Contemporary Art, L.A., 1982; bd. dirs. Pacific Oaks Coll., 1990—. Recipient Stanford Assocs. award, 1982. Fellow Am. Bar Found., Am. Coll. Trust and Estates Counsel, Internat. Acad. Probate and Trust, Fellows of Contemporary Art (bd. dirs. 1991-92); mem. ABA (chmn. standing com. specialization 1979-82, standing com. lawyer referral svcs., 1969-76, consortium delivery legal svcs. and the pub., 1979-82), Stanford Law Soc. (pres. 1972-73). Episcopalian. Clubs: Chancery (Los Angeles), Annandale Golf (Pasadena, Calif.), Valley Hunt (Pasadena). Office: Paul Hastings Janofsky & Walker 555 S Flower St Fl 23D Los Angeles CA 90071-2300

STEPHENS, GERALD D., insurance company executive; b. Peoria, Ill., June 17, 1932; m. Helen Marie Davis. BBA, with honors in Ins., U. Wis., 1955. V.p. H.O. Stephens & Sons, Inc., Peoria, 1958-65; pres., dir. RLI Ins. Co., Peoria, 1965—; bd. dir. numerous businesses and ins. agys. Jefferson TR& Savs. Bank. Bd. dir. adv. bd. St. Francis Hosp., 1983—; bd. dirs. Peoria Econs. Devel. Commn. 2d lt. U.S. Army, 1955-58. Mem. Peoria C. of C., Nat. Soc. CPCU (past pres. Cen. Ill. chpt.), Creve Coeur (Ill.) Club, Country Club of Peoria, Beta Theta Pi. Home: 493 E High Point Dr Peoria IL 61614-2243 Office: R L I Corp 9025 N Lindberg Dr Peoria IL 61615-1499

STEPHENS, JACKSON THOMAS, investment executive; b. Prattsville, Ark., Aug. 9, 1923; s. Albert Jackson and Ethel Rebecca (Pumphrey) S.; children: Jackson Thomas, Warren Amerine. Grad., Columbia Mil. Acad., Tenn., 1941; student, U. Ark., 1941-43; B.S. U.S. Naval Acad., 1946. Pres. Stephens, Inc., Little Rock, from 1957; chmn. Stephens, Inc., 1986—. Trustee U. Ark., 1948-57. Office: Stephens Inc PO Box 3507 111 Center St Little Rock AR 72201

STEPHENS, JAMES M., federal agency administrator; b. Rochester, N.Y., Sept. 16, 1946; married; two children. AB, Wittenberg U., 1968; JD, Case Western Reserve U., 1971. Assoc. Roetzel and Andress, Akron, Ohio, 1973-77; asst. minority labor counsel com. edn. and labor U.S. House Reps., 1977-81; majority labor counsel com. labor and human resources U.S. Senate, 1981-85; mem. Nat. Labor Rels. Bd., Washington, 1985-88, 94— chmn., 1988-94. Office: NLRB 1099 14th St NW Washington DC 20570

STEPHENS, JAMES T., publishing executive; b. 1939; married. BA in Bus. Adminstrn., Yale U., 1961; MBA, Harvard U., 1964. With Ebsco Industries Inc., Birmingham, Ala., 1961—, asst. v.p., 1966-67, v.p., 1967-70, exec. v.p., from 1970, now pres., also bd. dirs. Office: Ebsco Industries Inc PO Box 1943 Top of Oak Mountain Hwy 280 Birmingham AL 35201

STEPHENS, JAY B., lawyer; b. Akron, Iowa, Nov. 5, 1946; s. Lyle R. and Marie (Borchers) S. BA magna cum laude, Harvard U., 1968, JD cum laude, 1973. Bar: D.C. 1973. Assoc. Wilmer, Cutler & Pickering, Washington, 1973-74; asst. spl. prosecutor Watergate Spl. Prosecution Force, Washington, 1974-75; assoc. gen. counsel Overseas Pvt. Investment Corp.,

Washington, 1976-77; asst. U.S. atty. Dept. Justice, Washington, 1977-81, spl. counsel to asst. atty. gen., 1981-83, dep. assoc. atty. gen., 1983-85, assoc. dep. atty. gen., 1985-86; dep. counsel to Pres. Reagan, 1986-88; U.S. atty. for D.C. Office U.S Atty., 1988-93; ptnr. Pillsbury Madison & Sutro, Washington, 1993—. Contbr. articles to profl. publs. Knox fellow Oxford, Eng., 1968-69. Mem. D.C. Bar Assn., Supreme Ct. Bar Assn., Assn. U.S. Atty. Assn., Phi Beta Kappa. Republican. Presbyterian. Home: 8312 Simsbury Pl Alexandria VA 22308-1563 Office: Pillsbury Madison & Sutro 1050 Connecticut Ave Ste 1200 Washington DC 20026

STEPHENS, JERRY WAYNE, librarian, library director; b. Birmingham, Ala., Sept. 10, 1949; s. William Larkin and Odell (Kerr) S.; m. Lisa Brown, June 2, 1972; children—Jeramy Wayne, Elizabeth Ashley, John Larkin. BS in Acctg., U. Ala.-Birmingham, 1974, M.B.A., 1976; M.L.S., U. Ala., 1977, Ph.D. in Adminstrn. Higher Edn., 1982. Svc. mgr. Hammond Organ Studios, Birmingham, 1973-74; acct. Mervyn Sterne Libr., U. Ala., Birmingham, 1974-75, asst. to dir. 1975-76, asst. dir., 1976-85, libr., dir., 1985—; interim fiscal officer Univ. Coll. U. Ala., Birmingham, 1982, interim asst. v.p. for acad. affairs, 1989-91; vice chmn. Network Acad. Lbirs., 1985-86, chmn., 1986-88; cons. Birmingham Pub. Libr., 1977; cons. Southeastern Libr. Assn., Atlanta, 1979-80; bd. dirs. Southeastern Libr. Network, treas., 1992-93, chmn., 1993-94. Contbr. articles to profl. publs. Sponsored exec. United Way, Birmingham, 1978, sr. exec., 1982; foster parent Dept. Pensions and Securities, Birmingham, 1982-83; elder Homewood Cumberland Presbyn. Ch., Birmingham, 1982-84, 88-90. With USN, 1972-73. Named one of Outstanding Young Men Am., U.S. Jaycees, 1978, 79. Mem. ALA, SE Libr. Assn., Ala. Libr. Assn. (treas. 1977-78). Am Mgmt. Assn. Avocations: camping; softball. Home: 2621 Kemp Ct Birmingham AL 35226 Office: U Ala-Birmingham Mervyn H Sterne Libr University Station Birmingham AL 35294

STEPHENS, JOHN FRANK, association executive, researcher; b. Malone, N.Y., Nov. 9, 1949; s. J. Frank and Marjorie (Drew) S.; m. Smaroula Georgina Paraskevoudakis, Sept. 1, 1989; 1 child, Georgina Elizabeth. B.A. Harpur Coll., 1971; M.A., SUNY-Binghamton, 1973, Ph.D., 1977. Research assoc. Fernand Braudel Ctr., SUNY-Binghamton, 1977; asst. to provost U. Md., College Park, 1978; vis. instr. St. Mary's Coll. Md., St. Mary's City, 1978-79; dir. Alexandria Regional Preservation Office, Va., 1980-83; exec. dir. Am. Studies Assn., College Park, Md., 1983—; cons. (in field); reviewer U.S. Dept. Interior, NEH, HEW, USIA, PBS, Washington, 1983—. Author: (with Immanuel Wallerstein) Libraries and Our Civilizations, 1978, (with others) Archaeology in Urban America: A Search for Pattern Process, 1982. Exec. dir. Nat. Humanities Alliance, 1992—. Fulbright-Hays fellow, 1974-75; Spanish Govt. fellow, 1974-75. Mem. Am. Studies Assn., Fulbright Assn. Home: 4631 Bettswood Dr Olney MD 20832 Office: Am Studies Assn 1120 19th St Ste 301 Washington DC 20036

STEPHENS, LESTER JOHN, JR., banker; b. N.Y.C., Sept. 14, 1943; s. Lester John and Margaret (Tableman) S.; m. Suzanne M. Ekkers. BBA in Acctg., Pace U., 1966, MBA in Fin., 1970; grad. cert. Stonier Sch., Rutgers U., 1973; grad. cert. Amos Tuck Sch., Dartmouth Coll., 1983; postgrad., U. Pa., 1985. Various positions in acctg. and fin. Chase Manhattan Corp. and Chase Manhattan Bank, N.Y.C., 1966-74, v.p. dir. internat. acctg., 1974-77, v.p., dir. fin. projects, 1977-83, v.p., dir. fin. reporting, 1983-85, chief fin. officer, internat. sector, 1985-87, corp. controller, 1987—; chmn. fin. reporting com. N.Y. Clearing House; chmn. acctg., fin. com. Bank Adminstrn. Inst., 1989-91. Mem. adv. coun. Pace U. Served as sgt. USNG, 1966-71. Mem. Fin. Execs. Inst., City Midday Club, Skytop Club. Avocations: golf, boating. Office: Chase Manhattan Corp 2 Chase Manhattan Plz New York NY 10081-0001

STEPHENS, LOUIS CORNELIUS, JR., insurance executive; b. Dunn, N.C., Dec. 19, 1921; s. Louis Cornelius and Agnes (Warren) S.; m. Mary Adams, Sept. 6, 1952; children: Michael W., Mary A., Louis Cornelius III, Anne M., Suzanne G., Joan R., Melanie L., Peter W. B.S., U. N.C., 1942; M.B.A., Harvard U., 1947. With Pilot Life Ins. Co., Greensboro, N.C., 1949—; v.p., treas. Pilot Life Ins. Co., 1965-68, sr. v.p., 1968-70, exec. v.p., 1970-71, pres., chief adminstrv. officer, 1971-73, pres., chief exec. officer, 1973—, also dir.; pres., dir. JP Investment Mgmt. Co.; v.p., dir. Jefferson-Pilot Corp.; dir. Jefferson-Pilot & So. Fire & Casualty Cos., Jefferson-Pilot Title Ins. Co.; treas. JP Growth Fund, Inc. Past pres. United Community Services.; bd. dirs. Excellence Fund U. N.C. at Greensboro, N.C. Leadership Inst., Research Triangle Inst., Salem Coll. and Acad., Ecumenical Inst. Belmont Abbey Coll. Served with USNR, World War II. Office: The Duke Endowment Suite 3500 100 N Tryon St Charlotte NC 28202-3200

STEPHENS, MARTHA FOSTER, advertising executive; b. Lansing, Mich., Dec. 4, 1961; d. Richard Bailey and Gretchen (Meyer) Foster; m. Mark Burgis Stephens, Apr. 11, 1987; children: Emily Kaitlynn, Matthew Foster. BA in English, Mich. State U., 1984; postgrad., Wayne State U. Mem. editorial staff Better Investing, Royal Oak, Mich., 1986-88; with communications Holtzman and Silverman, Farmington Hills, Mich., 1988-89; tech. writer, intern Unisys, Plymouth, Mich., 1989; dir. corp. svcs. and advt. Nat. Assn. Investors Corp., Royal Oak, 1989—. Mem. Nat. Investor Rels. Inst. (sec. 1991-92, v.p. membership 1992-93, v.p. programs 1993-94, pres. 1994—). Avocations: computer layout and design, running. Office: Nat Assn Investors Corp PO Box 220 Royal Oak MI 48068

STEPHENS, MICHAEL DEAN, hospital administrator; b. Salt Lake City, May 1, 1942; married. B, Columbia U., 1966, MHA, 1970. Adminstrv. resident Mt. Sinai Med. Ctr., N.Y.C., 1969-70; asst. administr. Greenville (S.C.) Gen. Hosp., 1970-71, assoc. administr., 1971-72, adminstr., 1972-75; pres. Hosp Meml. Hosp.-Presbyn., Newport Beach, Calif., 1975—. Mem. Am. Coll. Healthcare Execs. Home: 900 Alder Pl Newport Beach CA 92660-4121 Office: Hoag Meml Hosp Presbyn Box 611 Newport Beach CA 92658-8912

STEPHENS, NORVAL BLAIR, JR., marketing consultant; b. Chgo., Nov. 20, 1928; s. Norval Blair and Ethel Margaret (Lewis) S.; m. Diane Forst, Sept. 29, 1951; children: Jill E., John G., Sandra J. (dec.), Katherine B., James N. BA, DePauw U., 1951; MBA, U. Chgo., 1959. Asst. to v.p. ops. Walgreen Drug Co., Chgo., 1953-56; with Needham, Harper Worldwide (formerly Needham, Harper & Steers), Chgo., 1956-86; v.p. Needham, Harper Worldwide (formerly Needham, Harper & Steers), Hwa-70, sr. v.p., 1970-72, exec. v.p. internat., 1972-74; exec. v.p., mng. dir. Needham, Harper Worldwide (formerly Needham, Harper & Steers), N.Y.C., 1974-75; exec. v.p. Chgo. office Needham, Harper & Steers, 1975-82, exec. v.p. internat., 1982-86; also dir.; pres. Deltacom, N.Y.C., 1971-76; pres. Norval Stephens Co., 1987—. Bd. advisors Barrington Area Arts Coun., 1985-86, bd. dirs., 1987-89; bd. dirs. N.W. Cmty. Hosp. Found., Arlington Heights, 1976-89, vice chmn., 1987-89; bd. dirs. Harper Coll. Ednl. Found., Palatine, Ill., 1977-86, pres., 1980-86; bd. dirs. Barrington Area Devel. Coun., 1978—, pres., 1994—; bd. visitors, dir. alumni bd. DePauw U., 1979-83, pres., 1981-83, trustee, 1983—. With USMCR, 1951-53. Named Young Man of Yr., Arlington Heights Jaycees, 1964; recipient Rector award DePauw U., 1976, Old Gold Goblet award for outstanding svc. DePauw U., 1994. Mem. Internat. Advt. Assn. (v.p. Midwest chpt. 1986-87), Am. Mgmt. Assn., Am. Mktg. Assn., Internat. Fedn. Advt. Agys. (exec. dir. 1988—), U. Chgo. Alumni Assn., DePauw Alumni Assn. (pres. 1977-79), Phi Beta Kappa, Delta Tau Delta (bd. dirs. edn. found. 1987—), 2d v.p. Arch chpt. 1988-90, 1st v.p. 1990-92, pres. 1992-94). Republican. Methodist. Home: 107 Fox Hunt Trl Barrington IL 60010-3418 Office: 1450 American Ln Ste 1400 Schaumburg IL 60173-6084 *I view my life not as a passage but a daily renewing challenge: to be better; to be a better father, husband, brother, son; to return each day an honest day's work; to bear witness to my beliefs and my faith; to serve my fellowman. I seek a whole life and a life of rewarding parts, each a lesson and an experience.*

STEPHENS, OLIN JAMES, II, naval architect, yacht designer; b. N.Y.C., N.Y., Apr. 13, 1908; s. Roderick and Marguerite (Dulon) S.; m. Florence Reynolds, Oct. 21, 1930; children: Olin James III, Samuel R. Student, MIT, 1926-27; M.S. (hon.), Stevens Inst. Tech.; M.A. (hon.), Brown U.; D laurea ad honorem in Arch., Universario Architetura, Venice, Italy. Draftsman Henry J. Gielow, N.Y.C., 1927-28; draftsman P.L. Rhodes, N.Y.C., 1928; formed with Drake H. Sparkman firm of Sparkman & Stephens, 1928, Inc., 1929, chief designer, 1929-78; faculty mem. Royal Designers for Ind.,

London. Yachts designed include Dorade, 1930, Stormy Weather, 1934, Lulu, Ranger, (with W. Starling Burgess), 1937, Baruna, Blitzen, Goose, 1938, Vim, Gesture, 1939, Llanoria, 1948, Finisterre, 1954, Columbia, 1958, Constellation, 1964, Intrepid, 1967, Charisma, Morning Cloud, 1971, Courageous, 1974, Enterprise, 1977, Freedom, 1979, others; design agt. U.S. Navy, 1939—. Recipient David Taylor medal Soc. Naval Architects & Marine Engrs., 1959, Beppe Crowe award Internat. Yacht Racing Union, 1992, Gibbs Bros. medal NAS, 1993. Fellow Soc. Naval Architects and Marine Engrs. (David W. Taylor medal 1959); mem. Nat. Acad. Engring., Am. Boat and Yacht Coub. (pres. 1959, 60), N.Am. Yacht Racing Union, Offshore Racing Coun. (chmn. internat. tech. com. 1967-73, 76-69), N.Y. Yacht (tech. com. 1989—), Manhassett Bay Club (hon.), Cruising Club of Am. (tech. com. 1989—), Royal Ocean Racing Club (Eng.), Royal Thames Yacht Club (London). Home: 80 Lyme Rd Apt 160 Kendal at Hanover Hanover NH 03755 Office: Sparkman and Stephens Inc 79 Madison Ave New York NY 10016-7802

STEPHENS, PHILLIP, screenwriter, producer; b. Council Bluffs, Iowa, June 25, 1940; s. Ronald Donald and Alice Margrete (Skelton) S.; m. Elaine Jensen, July 1, 1961 (div. June 1983); children: Christopher Roland, Denise Andrea. BA in Theatre/Film, U. Denver, 1973, MA in Mass Communications, 1979. Screenwriter Mary Muphy Agy., Hollywood, Calif., 1975-78, Concept Continuum, Denver, 1978-79; prof. TV and Film Studies U. Denver, 1979—; writer, producer C-Star Internat. Entertainment, 1988-89; writer, dir., exec. producer Ravenshead Communications, Denver, 1990-92. Vol. moutain search and rescue team. Recipient Bronze medal Internat. Film and TV Festival, N.Y., 1973, 79; Phillip Stephens' Libr. Collection named in his honor U. Wyo. Mem. Author's League of Am., Dramatist's Guild, U. Film and Video Assn., Broadcast Edn. Assn., Internat. Freelance Photographers Assn., Internat. Film and Video Assn. Avocations: fly fishing, camping, photography, raising horses. Office: U Denver University Blvd Denver CO 80202

STEPHENS, RICHARD BERNARD, natural resource company executive; b. Cambridge, Mass., Dec. 24, 1934; s. Theron Walter and Emma Marie (Bernard) S.; m. Anne Monique Devant, Oct. 18, 1958; children: Ann Marie, Claire Elizabeth, Jennifer Leslie. BA in Econs., Rice U., 1956; grad. exec. program bus. adminstrn., Columbia U., 1974. Landman Tenneco Oil Co., Lafayette, La., 1960-65; v.p. La. Land and Exploration Co., New Orleans, 1965-80; pres. Freeport Oil Co., New Orleans, 1980-84, McMoRan Oil and Gas Co., New Orleans, 1984-86; sr. v.p., dep. to chmn. Freeport-McMoRan, Inc., New Orleans, 1986—, office of the chmn., 1992-93; ret.; sr. advisor to chmn. Freeport, McMoran, Inc., New Orleans, 1993—. Mem. exec. bd., exec. com. New Orleans Boy Scouts Am., 1984—; trustee Mercy Hosp. New Orleans, 1977-81, La. Nature and Sci. Ctr., New Orleans, 1985-88; pres. Dad's Club St. Martin Protestant Episc. Sch., Metairie, La., 1975-76, sch. trustee, 1976-80; vice chmn. United Way New Orleans, 1976-77; dir. Eisenhower Ctr. U. New Orleans, 1989—, World Trade Ctr., 1992—; 1st lt. C.E., U.S. Army, 1956-60. Decorated The Sovereign Mil. Hospitaler Order of St. John of Jerusalem of Rhodes and of Malta, The Mil. and Hospitaler Order of St. Lazarus of Jerusalem. Mem. Nat. Gas Supply Assn. (steering com. 1982-86), Mid-Continent Oil and Gas Assn. (exec. com. 1984-88), Am. Petroleum Inst. (exec. com. 1985-88), La. Assn. Ind. Producers and Royalty Owners (dir. 1977-79), New Orleans Geol. Soc., Am. Assn. Petroleum Landmen, French-Am. C. of C. Assn. Rice Alumni (exec. bd. 1983-86, pres.-elect 1995—), Mil. Order World Wars, Rice Assocs., Brown Soc., Metairie Country Club, New Orleans Petroleum Club (bd. dirs. 1980-83), Commanderie Bordeaux sous Commanderie la Nouvelle Orleans, Pickwick Club, Laipro Wildcatters Club, Boston Club. Republican. Roman Catholic. Avocations: wildfowl wood collecting, long distance jogging, tennis, golf. Home: 800 Rue Bourbon Metairie LA 70005-3421 Office: Freeport-McMoRan Inc Box 611190004 1615 Poydras St New Orleans LA 70161

STEPHENS, ROBERT F., state supreme court chief justice; b. Covington, Ky., Aug. 16, 1927. Student, Ind. U.; LL.B., U. Ky., 1951. Bar: Ky. 1951. Asst. atty. Fayette County, Ky., 1964-69; judge Fayette County, 1969-75; atty. gen. Ky. Frankfort, 1976-79; justice Supreme Ct. Ky., Frankfort, 1979—, chief justice, 1982—; pres. Conf. of chief justices, 1992-93; chmn. Nat. Ctr. for State Ct., 1992-93. Staff: Ky. Law Jour. Bd. dirs. Nat. Assn. Counties, 1973-75; 1st pres. Ky. Assn. Counties; 1st chmn. Bluegrass Area Devel. Dist.; chmn. Ky. Heart Assn. Fund Drive, 1976-78. Served with USN, World War II. Named Outstanding Judge of Ky. Ky. Bar Assn., 1986, Outstnding County Judge, 1972; recipient Herbert Harley award Am. Judicature Soc. Mem. Order of Coif. Democrat. Office: Ky Supreme Ct Capitol Bldg Frankfort KY 40601

STEPHENS, SHAND SCOTT, lawyer; b. Pasadena, Calif., Mar. 25, 1949; s. Elmer Shand and Gladys Joy (Baker) S.; m. Marcia Pizzo, July 25, 1982 (div. Dec. 1985). BA, Yale U., 1971; JD, U. Calif., San Francisco, 1975. Bar: Calif. 1975, U.S. Dist. Ct. (no., so., ea. and cen. dists.) Calif. 1975, U.S. Ct. Appeals (9th cir.) 1975. Assoc. Bronson Bronson & McKinnon, San Francisco, 1978-82, ptnr., 1982—; gen. counsel San Francisco State U. Found., 1986—; gen. counsel Westamerica Bank, San Rafael, Calif., 1987—, Valley Bank, 1993—. Bd. dirs. Russian Arts Found. Mem. ABA, Calif. Bar Assn., Order of Coif. Avocations: American Civil War history and archaeology, skiing, tennis. Office: Bronson Bronson & McKinnon 505 Montgomery St San Francisco CA 94111-2552

STEPHENS, STEVE ARNOLD, real estate broker; b. Irby, Cheshire, Eng., May 25, 1945; came to U.S., 1983; s. Harold Dennis George and Hilda Leonora (Howell) S.; m. Lynn Williams, Apr. 14, 1983. Student, Manchester U., Eng. 1967-69. Lic. pvt. detective, Ill. From cadet to detective Cheshire (Eng.) Police, 1961-69; acting detective sgt. Merseyside (Eng.) Police, 1969-73; acting sgt. Hampshire (Eng.) Police, 1975-77; retail store owner Horsham, West Sussex, Eng., 1977-79; pvt. detective Carratu Internat., London, 1979-83, D.A.C. Stephens, Aurora, Ill., 1983-86; broker Primus Coml., Oswego, Ill., 1986—. Bd. dirs. Aurora Crimestoppers, pres., 1994—. Recipient Republican Legion of Merit award. Mem. Nat. Assn. Realtors (CCIM), Comml. Investment Real Estate Inst. (cert., bd. dirs. Ill. CCIM chpt. 1992—, sec.-treas. 1994, v.p. 1995), No. Ill. Comml. Assn. Realtors (dir. 1995—), Internat. Assn. Chiefs of Police, Ill. Assn. Realtors, Greater Aurora C. of C., Aurora Country Club. Avocations: travel, literature, golf. Home: 151 Buckthorn Ln # 103 North Aurora IL 60542-1421 Office: Primus Comml Real Estate 13 W Merchants Dr Oswego IL 60543-9454

STEPHENS, SUNNY COURINGTON, special education educator; b. Abilene, Tex., Mar. 13, 1943; d. Samuel Delmar and Delta Ree (Kniffen) Courington; m. Kenneth Edward Stephens, Apr. 6, 1967; 1 child, Lane Bradley. BS, Abilene Christian U., 1965; postgrad., U. Tex., 1972; MEd, Our Lady of the Lake Coll., San Antonio, 1977; PhD, Tex. Woman's U., 1983. Cert. secondary tchr., spl. edn. tchr., supr., bilingual tchr., early childhood tchr. Tchr. Poteet (Tex.) Ind. Sch. Dist., 1965-71, San Antonio Ind. Sch. Dist., 1971-79; tchr. South San Antonio Ind. Sch. Dist., 1979-80, dir. spl. edn., 1991—; prof. Incarnate Word Coll., San Antonio, 1978-93; cons. Advocacy, Inc., Austin, Tex., 1981—, Easter Seal Rehab., San Antonio, 1978—, Children's Hosp., San Antonio, 1978—, Sch. Dists., Tex. Ariz., Colo., La., 1978—. Author: ABC Cookery, 1980, Curriculum Guide Early Childhood, 1978, (multimedia program) Learning Thru Success, 1980; contbr. articles to profl. jours. Named Outstanding Profl. Nat. Spina Bifida Assn., 1986, Tex. Prof. of Yr. Coun. for Advancement and Support of Edn., 1987, Estee Lauder Knowing Woman, 1988. Mem. Tex. Coun. Exceptional Children (pres. 1980-81), Tex. Spina Bifida Assn. (bd. dirs. 1983-93). Avocations: quilting, barbershop quartet singing. Home: RR 1 Box 97 Poteet TX 78065-9742 Office: South San Antonio Sch Dist 2415 W Southcross San Antonio TX 78211

STEPHENS, THOMAS M(ARON), education educator; b. Youngstown, Ohio, June 15, 1931; s. Thomas and Mary (Hanna) S.; m. Evelyn Kleshock, July 1, 1955. BS, Youngstown Coll., 1955; MEd, Kent State U. 1957; EdD, U. Pitts., 1966. Lic. psychologist, Ohio. Tchr. Warren (Ohio) public schs., 1955-57, Niles (Ohio) public schs., 1957-58; psychologist Montgomery County, Ohio, 1958-60; with Ohio Dept. Edn., Columbus, 1960-66; Asso. prof. edn. U. Pitts., 1966-70; prof. edn. Ohio State U., 1970—, chmn. dept. exceptional children, 1972-82, chmn. dept. human services edn., 1982-87, assoc. dean coll. edn., 1987-92, prof., 1987-92, prof. emeritus, 1992—; clin.

prof. edn. U. Dayton, Ohio, 1993—; exec. dir. Sch. Study Coun. Ohio, Columbus, 1993—; clin. prof. U. Dayton, 1992—; mem. Higher Edn. Consortium for Spl. Edn., Chmn., 1976-77; pub., pres. Cedars Press, Inc. Author: Directive Teaching of Children with Learning and Behavioral Handicaps, 2d edit, 1976, Implementing Behavioral Approaches in Elementary and Secondary Schools, 1975, Teaching Skills to Children with Learning and Behavioral Disorders, 1977, Teaching Children Basic Skills: A Curriculum Handbook, 1978, 2d edit., 1983, Social Skills In The Classroom, 1978, 2d edit., 1991, Teaching Mainstreamed Students, 1982, 2d edit., 1988, Social Behavior Assessment Scale, 1991; dir.: Jour. Sch. Psychology, 1965-75, 80—; exec. editor: The Directive Tchr.; assoc. editor: Spl. Edn. and Tchr. Edn., Techniques, Behavioral Disorders, Spl. Edn. and Remedial Edn.; contbr. articles to profl. jours. U.S. Office of Edn. fellow, 1964-65. Mem. Am. Psychol. Assn., Nat. Assn. Sch. Psychologists (charter), State Dirs. for Gifted (pres. 1962-63), Coun. Exceptional Children (gov., Tchr. Educator of Yr. Tchr. Edn. Div. 1985), Coun. Children with Behavioral Disorders (pres. 1972-73). Home: 1753 Blue Ash Pl Columbus OH 43229-3651 Office: Sch Study Coun of Ohio 665 E Granville Dublin Rd Columbus OH 43229

STEPHENS, WARREN A., banking executive. BA, Washington & Lee U., 1979; MBA, Wake Forest U., 1981. V.p. corp. fin. dept Stephens Inc., Little Rock, 1981-86, pres., CEO, 1986—; also bd. dirs. Stephens Inc. Office: Stephens Inc Stephens Bldg 111 Center St PO Box 3507 Little Rock AR 72201-4402

STEPHENS, WILLIAM RICHARD, college president emeritus; b. Ashburn, Mo., Jan. 2, 1932; s. George Lewis and Helen S.; m. Arlene Greer, June 28, 1952; children—Richard, Kendell, Kelli. B.S., Greenville Coll., Ill., 1953; M.Ed., U. Mo., 1958; Ed.D., Washington U., St. Louis, 1964. Tchr. Sturgeon High Sch., Mo., 1955-57; asst. prof. then assoc. prof. edn. Greenville Coll., 1957-61, dir. NCATE self-study, 1960-61; spl. instr. Washington U., St. Louis, 1961-64; mem. faculty Ind. State U., 1964-70; vis. prof. Ind. U., Bloomington, 1969-70; prof. history and philosophy of edn. Ind. U., 1970-71; v.p. acad. affairs, dean of faculty Greenville Coll., 1971-77, acting pres., 1977, pres., 1977-93; pres. emeritus, 1993—; chmn., bd. dirs. Fedn. Ind. Ill. Coll. and Univs., 1991-92. Author: Social Reform and the Origins of Vocational Guidance, 1890-1925, 1970; Education of American Life (with William Van Til), 1972; also curriculum materials, reports; editor procs. ednl. meetings. Vice-chmn. Kingsbury Park Dist., Greenville, 1972-77; mem. edn. com. Bond County Mental Health Assn., 1974. Served with U.S. Army, 1953-55. Recipient Merit award Nat. Vocat. Guidance Assn., 1973; fellow Acad. Achievers, Ctrl. Coll., 1994. Mem. History of Edn. Soc. (chmn. nominating com. 1969), Midwest History of Edn. Soc. (pres. 1971-72), Philosophy of Edn. Soc., Ohio Valley Philosophy of Edn. Soc. (sec.-treas. 1967-70), Soc. Profs. Edn. (assoc. editor publs. 1968-70), Central States Faculty Colloquium (chmn. 1969—), John Dewey Soc. (pres.-elect 1978-80, pres. 1980-82, editor Insights 1973-78), North Central Assn., Assn. Free Methodist Ednl. Instns. (pres. 1980—). Office: Greenville Coll 315 E College Ave Greenville IL 62246-1199

STEPHENS, WILLIAM THOMAS, forest products manufacturing company executive; married. BS, U. Ark., 1965, MS, 1966. Various mgmt. positions Manville Forest Products Corp., from 1963; asst. v.p. fin., then sr. v.p., pres. forest products group Manville Corp., Denver, exec. v.p. fin. and adminstrn., from 1984, now pres., chief exec. officer, chmn., bd. dirs. Office: Manville Corp PO Box 5108 Manville Plz Denver CO 80202*

STEPHENS, WOODFORD CEFIS (WOODY STEPHENS), horse trainer, breeder; b. Stanton, Ky., Sept. 1, 1913; s. Lewis and Helen (Welch) S.; m. Lucille Elizabeth Easley, Sept. 11, 1937. Ed., Ky. Pub. Schs. Began as exercise boy, then trainer thoroughbred horses Ky., 1929—; jockey, 1931-40, profl. trainer thoroughbred horses, 1940—. Subject of biography: Guess I'm Lucky, 1985. Recipient profl. horse racing awards including: N.Y. Turf Writers Assn. Outstanding Trainer award, 1982, 83, Nat. Turf Writers Mr. Fitz Award, 1982, Silver Horseshoe award Ky. Derby Festival, 1983, Gold Cup award, N.Y., 1986, 87, C.V. Whitney Spl. Achievement award, 1993, Eclipse award N.Y. Turf Writers, 1993, Lifetime Achievement award 70th Ann. award N.Y. Turf Writers, 1993, Lifetime Achievement award Hialeah, 1989, others; named to Thoroughbred Racing's Hall of Fame, 1976, Horseperson of Yr. award, Fla., 1981, Legend in All Star Events, Fla., 1988, Caesars Legends of Racing, Atlantic City, 1988, Trainer of Decade AP, N.Y. Turf Writers, 1990, N.Y. Sports Mus. Hall of Fame, 1990; Ky. Col.; 1963; trainer of more than 300 stake race winners, including 2 Ky. Derbys, 1 Preakness, 5 Belmont Stakes; inducted into Hall of Fame, 1976, Saratoga, Hall of Fame, L.I.; Woody's Corner erected Belmont Race Track, 1992; inducted into the Hialeah Park Classic Club, 1994; 150 silver trophies. Mem. United Thoroughbred Trainers Am., Turf and Field Club (N.Y.), Thoroughbred Club Am., Sky Island Club. Winner of 5 consecutive Belmont Stakes ranks as one of horse racings most outstanding accomplishments; life-size sculpture erected in hometown of Stanton. Home: 15534 Cairnryan Ct Miami Lakes FL 33014-2624 Office: Belmont Race Track Hempstead Elmont NY 11003

STEPHENSON, ALAN CLEMENTS, lawyer; b. Wilmington, N.C., Nov. 7, 1944; s. Abram Clements and Ruth (Smith) S.; m. Sherri Jean Miller, Dec. 19, 1970; children: Edward Taylor, Anne Baldwin. AB in Hist., U. N.C., 1967; JD, U. Va., 1970. Bar: N.Y. 1971. Assoc. Cravath, Swaine & Moore, N.Y.C., 1970-78, ptnr., 1978-88; mng. dir. Wasserstein, Perella and Co. Inc., N.Y.C., 1988-92; ptnr. Cravath, Swaine & Moore, N.Y.C., 1992—; bd. dirs. Met. Assistance Corp., N.Y.C. Bd. dirs. Travelers Aid Soc. N.Y., N.Y.C., 1979-82. Morehead scholar John M. Moorehead Found., 1963. Mem. ABA, N.Y. State Bar Assn., Assn. of Bar of City of N.Y., The Brook Club, The Links Club, Tuxedo Club, Union Club, Phi Beta Kappa. Home: 1107 Fifth Ave New York NY 10128-0145 Office: Cravath Swaine & Moore 825 8th Ave New York NY 10010-7475

STEPHENSON, ARTHUR EMMET, JR., investment company executive, banker; b. Bastrop, La., Aug. 29, 1945; s. Arthur Emmet and Edith Louise (Mock) S.; m. Toni Lyn Edwards, June 17, 1967. B.S in Fin. magna cum laude, La. State U., 1967; M.B.A. (Ralph Thomas Sayles fellow), Harvard U., 1969. Chartered fin. analyst. Adminstrv. aide to U.S. Sen. Russell Long of La., Washington, 1966; security analyst Fidelity Funds, Boston, 1968; chmn. bd., pres. Stephenson & Co., Denver, Stephenson Mcht. Banking Inc., Circle Corp.; sr. ptnr. Stephenson Ventures, Stephenson Properties; chmn. bd. Gen. Comm., Inc., Globescope Corp., Starpak Inc.; co-founder Pub. Network, Inc.; underwriting mem. Lloyd's of London, 1978-92; founder Charter Bank and Trust, chmn., 1980-91; bd. dirs. Danaher Corp.; mem. adv. bd. First Berkshire Fund, Capital Resources Ptnrs., L.P.; pub. Law Enforcement Product News, Colo. Book, Pub. Safety Product News. Mem. assocs. coun. Templeton Coll. at Oxford U., Eng.; nat. trustee Nat. Symphony Orch. at John F. Kennedy Ctr. for Performing Arts; mem. nat. steering com. Norman Rockwell Mus., Stockbridge, Mass.; past mem. Colo. small bus. coun.; del. White House Conf. Recipient Hall of Fame award Inc. Mag., 1994. Mem. Harvard U. Bus. Sch. Assn. (internat. pres. 1987-88), Young Pres.'s Orgn. (Calif. Inland Empire chpt. chmn. 1992-93, area coun. mem.), Colo. Investment Advisors Assn. (treas., bd. dirs. 1975-76), Fin. Analysts Fedn., Denver Soc. Security Analysts (bd. dirs. 1975-77), Colo. Press Assn., Colo. Harvard Bus. Sch. Club (pres. 1980-81, chmn. 1981-82), Omicron Delta Kappa, Phi Kappa Phi, Beta Gamma Sigma, Kappa Sigma, Delta Sigma Pi. Office: 100 Garfield St Denver CO 80206-5550

STEPHENSON, BARBERA WERTZ, lawyer; b. Bryan, Ohio, Dec. 10, 1938; d. Emerson D. and Beryl B. (Barber) Wertz; m. Gerard J. Stephenson Jr., June 22, 1960; 1 child, Thomas. Student, Smith Coll., 1956-57; BSEE, MIT, 1961; JD, U. N.Mex., 1981. Bar: N.Mex. 1981. Electronic engr. Digital Equipment Corp., Maynard, Mass., 1960-66; logic analyst Librascope, Glendale, Calif., 1966; electronic engr. Md. Dept. of Def., Ft. Meade, 1966-68; mem. tech. staff Xerox Data Systems, Rockville, Md., 1968; pvt. practice cons., Silver Spring, Md., 1969-78; pvt. practice law, Albuquerque, 1981—. Author: Financing Your Home Purchase in New Mexico, 1992; patentee analog to digital converter, kitchen calculator. Mem. N.Mex. Bar Assn. Office: 4221 Silver Ave SE Albuquerque NM 87108-2720

STEPHENSON, BETTE MILDRED, physician, former Canadian legislator; b. Aurora, Ont., Can., July 31, 1924; d. Carl Melvin and Clara Mildred (Draper) S.; grad. Earl Haig Coll. Inst.; MD, U. Toronto, 1946; m. Gordon Allan Pengelly, 1948; children: J. Stephen A., Elizabeth Anne A., C.

Christopher A., J. Michael A., P. Timothy A., Mary Katharine A. Mem. med. staff Women's Coll. Hosp., 1950-90, chief dept. gen. practice, dir. outpatient dept., 1956-64; mem. med. staff N.Y. Gen. Hosp., 1967-89; elected Ont. Legislature for York Mills, 1975, 77, 81, 85; minister labor, 1975-78; minister edn. minister colls. and univs., 1978-85, treas. and dep. premier, 1985; pres. Gwillimbury Found. Post Secondary Edn.; dir. Can. Inst. Advanced Rsch.; dir. Women's Coll. Hosp.; trustee Recovery Inc. Fellow Coll. Family Physicians Can. (chmn. nat. coordinating com. on edn. 1961-64, chmn. confs. on edn. for gen. practice 1961, 63), Acad. Med. Toronto; mem. Ont. Med. Assn. (dir. 1964-72, pres. 1970-71), Can. Med. Assn. (dir. 1968-75, pres. 1974-75), Art Gallery Ont., Royal Ont. Mus., Order of St. John (officer), Order of Can. (officer).

STEPHENSON, C. GENE, academic administrator. Pres. U. Ozarks, Clarksville, Ark. Office: Univ Ozarks Office of President 415 College Ave Clarksville AR 72830

STEPHENSON, DONALD GRIER, JR., government studies educator; b. DeKalb County, Ga., Jan. 12, 1942; s. Donald Grier and Katherine Mason (Williams) S.; m. Ellen Claire Walker, Aug. 15, 1967; children: Todd Grier, Claire Walker. AB, Davidson Coll., N.C., 1964; MA, Princeton U., 1966, PhD, 1967. Research assoc. Nat. War Coll., Washington, 1968-70; asst. prof. govt. Franklin and Marshall Coll., Lancaster, Pa., 1970-73, assoc. prof. govt., 1973-81, prof. govt., 1981—; Charles A. Dana prof., 1989—; mem. adv. coun. to dean of the chapel Princeton U., 1974-85; Commonwealth lectr. Pa. Humanities Coun., Phila., 1987-88, 90, 92—. Co-author: American Constitutional Development, 1977, American Government, 1992, 94, American Constitutional Law, 1993; author: The Supreme Court and the American Republic, 1981, An Essential Safeguard, 1991; contbr. articles to profl. jours. Elder, mem. Session, First Presbyn. Ch., Lancaster, 1973-76; judge Pa. constl. competition Dickinson Coll., 1988—. Capt. U.S. Army, 1968-70. Woodrow Wilson fellow, 1964-65, 66-67; Nat. Endowment for Humanities grantee, 1972, 85-89. Mem. Am. Polit. Sci. Assn. (Corwin award com. 1978), Pa. Polit. Sci. Assn. (editorial bd. Polity 1972-78), Supreme Ct. Hist. Soc. (editorial award 1990). Presbyterian. Home: 62 Oak Ln Lancaster PA 17603-4762 Office: Franklin and Marshall Coll PO Box 3003 Lancaster PA 17604-3003

STEPHENSON, DONNAN, lawyer, former state supreme court justice; b. LaHarpe, Kans., Nov. 21, 1919; s. Ralph Duane and Zoe B. (Donnan) S.; m. Patricia Marie Ledyard, May 14, 1942; children: Mark Donnan, Bruce Ledyard. B.S. in Bus. Adminstrn., U. Kans., 1941, LL.B., 1948. Bar: Kans. 1948, N. Mex. 1949. With TWA, 1948; practice law Santa Fe, 1958-70; ptrn. Bigbee & Stephenson, Santa Fe, 1949-62, Stephenson & Olmsted, 1962-66, Stephenson, Campbell & Olmsted, 1966-70; justice N. Mex. Supreme Ct., Santa Fe, 1971-76; sr. ptnr. Bigbee, Stephenson, Carpenter, Crout & Olmsted, Santa Fe, 1976-81, of counsel, 1982-88. Established and endowed Stephenson Lectures in Law and Govt. Kans. U. Law Sch. Served to lt. USNR, WWII. Decorated Bronze Star; recipient Kans. U. Law Sch. Disting. Alumnus, 1981. Fellow N.Mex. Bar Assn. Home: 1014 Bishops Lodge Rd Santa Fe NM 87501-1009

STEPHENSON, DOROTHY GRIFFITH See GRIFFITH, DOTTY

STEPHENSON, HERMAN HOWARD, banker; b. Wichita, Kans., July 15, 1929; s. Herman Horace and Edith May (Wayland) S.; m. Virginia Anne Ross, Dec. 24, 1950; children: Ross Wayland, Neal Bevan, Jann Edith. BA, U. Mich., 1950; JD with distinction, U. Mo., Kansas City, 1958, LLD (hon.), 1993. Bar: Kans. 1958. With City Nat. Bank, Kansas City, Mo., 1952-54, City Bond & Mortgage Co., Kansas City, 1954-59, Bank of Hawaii, Honolulu, 1959-94; ret., 1994; now chmn. bd., CEO Bancorp Hawaii Inc. and subs. Bank Hawaii, Banque de Tahiti; bd. dirs. Banque de Nouvelle-Caledonie, Pacific Basin Econ. Coun. U.S. Mem. Com, Bancorp Hawaii, Inc., Bank Hawaii, bancorp Hawaii Charitable Found., Bank of Hawaii Internat. Inc., Hawaiian Trust Co. Bd. dirs. Honolulu Symphony, Maunalani Found., Aloha United Way, Pacific Fleet Submarine Meml. Assn., Pacific Basin Econ. Coun. U.S. Mem. Com.; co-chmn. Ellison Onizuka Meml. Scholarship Fund Com.; chmn. bd. regents U. Hawaii. With U.S. Army, 1950-52. Mem. ABA, Am. Bankers Assn. (past chmn. exec. com. housing and real estate fin. div., dir. 1976-77, mem. governing coun. 1976-77, mem. govt. rels. coun. 1986-89), Kans. Bar Assn., Hawaii Bankers Assn. (pres. 1991-92), U.S.-Japan Bus. Coun., Pacific Asia Travel Assn. (Hawaii chpt., assoc.), Navy League of U.S., Hawaii Bus. Roundtable, Pacific Forum/CSIS (bd. govs.), Assn. Res. City Bankers, U.S.-Korea Bus. Coun., Kappa Sigma, Pi Eta Sigma, Oahu Country Club, Pacific Club, Waialae Country Club, Rotary. Office: Bank of Hawaii PO Box 2900 Honolulu HI 96846

STEPHENSON, HUGH EDWARD, JR., retired physician, educator; b. Columbia, Mo., June 1, 1922; s. Hugh Edward and Doris (Pryor) S.; m. Sarah Norfleet Dickinson, Aug. 15, 1964; children—Hugh Edward III, Ann Dunlop. AB, BS, U. Mo., 1943; MD, Washington U., St. Louis, 1945. Diplomate Am. Bd. Surgery, Am. Bd. Thoracic Surgery. Mem. faculty U. Mo. Sch. Medicine, Columbia, 1953—, prof. surgery, 1956—, chmn. dept. surgery, 1956-60, chief div. gen. surgery, 1976-87, chief staff, 1982-94, John Growdon Disting. prof. surgery emeritus, 1987—, interim dean, 1988-89, assoc. dean, 1989-92, dist. prof. surgery emeritus, 1993; Markle scholar acad. medicine, 1954-60. Author: Immediate Care of the Acutely Ill and Injured, 2d edit, 1974, Cardiac Arrest and Resuscitation, 4th edit., 1975, The Kicks That Count; Contbr. articles to profl. jours. Named one of Outstanding Young Men of Nation, Nat. Jr. C. of C., 1956, James IV Surg. Traveler Gt. Britain, 1962, Dist. Faculty award, 1989. Mem. ACS, AMA (del., chmn. coun. on med. edn. 1994-95, co-chmn. liaison com. on med. edn 1995), Vascular Surgery Soc., Soc. Thoracic Surgeons, So. Thoracic Surgery Assn., So. Med. Assn. (coun.), Mo. Med. Assn. (chmn. jud. coun. 1986—, v.p. 1986-87), Beta Theta Pi (trustee, v.p., pres. gen. frat. 1978-81). Baptist. Home: 5 Danforth Cir Columbia MO 65201-6223 Office: U Mo Sch Medicine 1 Hospital Dr Columbia MO 65212-0001

STEPHENSON, JAN LYNN, professional golfer; b. Sydney, Australia, Dec. 22, 1951; d. Francis John and Barbara (Green) S.; m. Eddie Vossler, 1982. Student, Australian schs. Profl. golfer, 1972—; mem. Australian Ladies Profl. Golf Assn. tour, 1972-73, U.S. Ladies Profl. Golf Assn. tour, 1974—. Winner New South Wales (Australia) Jr. Championship, 1963-69; winner Australian Jr. Championship, 1968-71, Australian Title, 1973, Sarah Coventry Championship, 1976, Birmingham Championship Ala., 1976, Women's Internat., 1978, Sun City Classic, 1980, Peter Jackson Classic, 1981, Mary Kay Classic, 1981, United Va. Bank Classic, 1981, Ladies Profl. Golf Assn. Championship, 1982, Women's Tucson Open, 1983, Women's U.S. Open, 1983, Lady Keystone Open, GNA Tournament, 1985, French Open, 1985, Santa Barbara Open, 1987, Safeco Seattle Classsic, 1987, Konica San Jose Classic, 1987, 1st LPGA Skins Game, Frisco, Tex., 1990; named Rookie of Yr., U.S. Profl. Golfers Assn., 1974; Sportsman of Yr., Sportswriters Assn., Australia, 1976. Office: 7601 Della Dr # 276 Orlando FL 32819-7233*

STEPHENSON, KATHRYN BURG, performing company executive; b. York, Pa., Apr. 1, 1950; d. Joel James and Ruth Marie (Glatfelter) Burg; m. Michael Lee Stephenson, Aug. 25, 1973; children: M'Liss Kathryn, Corenn Marie. BA in Dance, Butler U., 1972, MA in Dance, 1978. Dancer Nawal, Los Angeles, 1972-73, 74-76; dancer, tchr. Arlington (Va.) Dance Theater, 1973; dancer, tchr. Indpls. Ballet Theatre, 1976-83, adminstr., exec. dir., 1983—; bd. dirs. Community Hosp. Women's Bd., Indpls. Indpls. Cultural Consortium, Performing Arts High Sch., Indpls. Tchr. North United Meth. Ch., Indpls., 1979—. Named one of Top 10 Women of Yr. Indpls. Women mag., 1985. Avocations: baking. Office: Indpls Ballet Theater 502 B N Capitol Ave Indianapolis IN 46204-1612

STEPHENSON, ROBERT BAIRD, energy company executive; b. Washington, Jan. 20, 1943; s. Orlando Worth and Martha Ann (Kostelak) S.; m. Sheryl Ann Fish, Jan. 10, 1967; children: Brie Danielle, Eric Baird. BS in Mech. Engring., Purdue U., 1965; MS in Nuclear Engring., U. Mich., 1970, MBA, 1972. Engr. Jersey Nuclear Co., Inc., Boston, 1972-74; engr., mgr. Exxon Nuclear Co., Inc., Richland, Wash., 1974-80; mng. dir. Exxon Nuclear GmbH, Lingen, Fed. Rep. Germany, 1980-83; mktg., sales staff Exxon Nuclear Co., Inc., Bellevue, Wash.,1983-85,v.p. adminstrn., 1986; v.p. comml. div. Exxon Nuclear Co., Inc., Bellevue, 1987; pres. chief exec. of-

ficer, chmn. EPID, Inc., San Jose, Calif., 1985-86; pres., chief exec. officer Advanced Nuclear Fuels Corp., Bellevue, Wash., 1988-91; pres. CEO Siemens Nuclear Power Corp., Bellevue, 1991-92; pres., CEO Siemens Power Corp., Bellevue and Milw., 1992—; also bd. dirs. Lt. U.S. Navy, 1965-70. Mem. Am. Nuclear Soc., Lakes Club. Avocations: sailing, boating, golf. Office: Siemens Power Corp 155 108th Ave NE Bellevue WA 98004-5901

STEPHENSON, ROBERT CLAY, commercial real estate developer; b. Meadville, Pa., Sept. 21, 1938; s. LeRoy Vernon and Martha Louise (Clay) S.; m. Judith Regina Trohaugh, Jan. 19, 1963; children: Robert Scott, Eric Thomas, Cynthia Lynn. BA, Allegheny Coll., 1962. Group sales rep. Conn. Gen. Life Ins., Detroit, 1962-64; salesman, broker Donovan Co., Pitts., 1964-73; v.p. Oliver Realty, Inc., Pitts., 1974-81; ptnr. Liberati/Davenport/Stephenson, Pitts., 1981, DeBartolo LDS Assocs., Pitts., 1981-85; pres. Carnegie Properties, Inc., Pitts., 1985-86; v.p. office/indsl. properties The Edward J. DeBartolo Corp., Youngstown, Ohio, 1986—. Session ruling elder Bower Hill Presbyn. Ch.; twp. committeeman Rep. Party Mt. Lebanon Twp.; troop committeeman Boy Scouts Am., Bethel Park, Pa.; real estate cons. The Children's Mus., Pitts.; treas. Ducks Unltd., Washington, County, Pa.; community amb. to Eng. Expt. in Internat. Living, Putney, Vt. Mem. Nat. Assn. Realtors, Pa. Assn. Realtors, Realtors Assn. Met. Pitts. (mem. vigilance/ethics com. 1967-69, mem. long range planning com. 1976-78, chmn. 1977-78, mem. R-day conf. com. 1981, mem. pub. rels. com. 1982, mem. Realtor of Yr. com. 1982—), Nat. Assn. Indsl./Office Parks (mem. we. Pa. chpt. 1978—, pres. 1981-82, bd. dirs. 1993—, mem. nat. com. project analysis 1985), Soc. Indsl. and Office Realtors (mem. we. Pa. chpt., pres. 1983, 84, 90, chmn. ann. dinner com. 1982, 89, mem. govt. rels. nat. com. 1982-83, mem. nat. com. office mktg. 1987-88), Nat. Assn. Corp. Real Estate Execs. (mem. Pitts. chpt., pres. 1982), Inst. Real Estate Mgmt., The Urban Land Inst., Westminster Presbyn. Ch., St. Clair County Club, Univ. Club, Bally's Scandinavian Spa, Phi Kappa Psi. Presbyterian. Avocations: fishing, snow skiing, scuba diving, golf, hunting. Home: 1895 Tilton Dr Upper Saint Clair PA 15241-2636 Office: The Edward J DeBartolo Corp 1895 Tilton Dr Pittsburgh PA 15241-2636

STEPHENSON, ROSCOE BOLAR, JR., state supreme court justice; b. Covington, Va., Feb. 22, 1922. A.B., Washington and Lee U., 1943, J.D., 1947, LL.D. (hon.), 1983. Bar: Va. 1947. Ptnr. Stephenson & Stephenson, Covington, 1947-52; commonwealth's atty. Alleghany County, Va., 1952-64; ptnr. Stephenson, Kostel, Watson, Carson and Snyder, Covington, 1964-73; judge 25th Jud. Cir. Ct. Commonwealth Va., Covington, 1973-81; justice Va. Supreme Ct., Richmond, 1981—. Recipient Covington Citizen of Yr. award, 1973; recipient Outstanding Alumni award Covington High Sch., 1973. Fellow Am. Coll. Trial Lawyers; mem. Va. State Bar (council 1969-73), Va. Bar Assn., Va. Trial Lawyers Assn., Order of Coif. Home: Clearwater Park Covington VA 24426 Office: Va Supreme Ct 100 N 9th St Richmond VA 23219-2335 also: 214 W Main St Covington VA 24426-1543

STEPHENSON, SAMUEL EDWARD, JR., physician; b. Bristol, Tenn., May 16, 1926; s. Samuel Edward and Hazel Beatrice (Walters) S.; m. Janet Sue Spotts, May 16, 1970; children: Samuel Edward III, William Douglas, Dorothea Louise, Judith Maria. B.S., U. S.C., 1946; M.D., Vanderbilt U., 1950. Intern Butterworth Hosp., Grand Rapids, Mich., 1950-51; instr. to asso. prof. surgery Vanderbilt U., 1955-67; prof. surgery U. Fla., 1967—; chmn. dept. surgery Univ. Hosp., Jacksonville, 1967-78. Asst. editor So. Med. Jour., 1968-88; contbr. articles to profl. jours. Co-chmn. Fla. Burn and Trauma Registry, 1974-77. Served with USNR, 1944-45. Fellow A.C.S.; mem. Am. Coll. Chest Physicians. Mason. Club: University (Jacksonville). Home: 10553 Scott Mill Rd Jacksonville FL 32257-6227 Office: 1501 San Marco Blvd Jacksonville FL 32207-2905

STEPHENSON, TONI EDWARDS, publisher, investment management executive; b. Bastrop, La., July 23, 1945; d. Sidney Crawford and Grace Erleene (Shipman) Little; BS, La. State U., 1967; grad. owner/pres. mgmt. program Harvard Bus. Sch.; m. Arthur Emmet Stephenson, Jr., June 17, 1967; 1 dau., Tessa Lyn. ; pres., dir. Gen. Communications, Inc., Denver; sr. v.p., founder Stephenson & Co., Denver, 1971—; Stephenson Mcht. Banking, 1980—; gen. ptnr. Viking Fund; ptnr. Stephenson Properties, Stephenson Ventures, Stephenson Mgmt. Co.; bd. dirs. Starpak Internat., Inc.; founder Charter Bank & Trust. Pub. Law Enforcement Product News, Pub. Safety Product News, Premier Expos, Inc., Globescope Corp.; sec., HBS/OPM16, former dir. The Children's Hosp., St. Joseph's Hosp. Past pres. Children's Hosp. Assn. Vols. Mem. Harvard Bus. Sch. Clubs of Colo., So. Calif. and Orange County, Colo. Press Assn., DAR, Delta Gamma. Clubs: Rancho Mirage (Calif.), Annabel's (London), Thunderbird Country, Denver Petroleum. Office: Gen Communications Inc 100 Garfield St Denver CO 80206-5550

STEPLER, RICHARD LEWIS, magazine editor; b. Norfolk, Va., Aug. 15, 1945; s. Richard Lewis and Mary Ann (Beard) S.; m. Janet Sarah Froelich, Sept. 13, 1981; children: Jesse Benjamin, Rebecca Ann. BA, NYU, 1969. From editor to sr. editor Popular Sci., N.Y.C., 1975—. Mem. Nat. Assn. Sci. Writers, Am. Soc. Mag. Editors, Internat. Motor Press Assn. (v.p. 1984-91). Office: Popular Sci 2 Park Ave New York NY 10016

STEPNER, MICHAEL JAY, architect; b. Chgo., Sept. 7, 1940; s. Lester Harry and Florence (Addison) S.; m. Rosemary Reiser, Apr. 2, 1965; children: Rachel, Jessica, Adam, Joshua, Rebekah. Student, U. Minn., 1961-62; BArch, U. Ill., 1966; postgrad., U. Calif., Berkeley, 1971; U.S. Navy Engring. Schs., 1965-66. Registered architect, Calif. Urban designer, planner Crosstown Assocs., Chgo., 1968-71; urban designer, planner planning dept. City of San Diego, 1971-81, asst. planning dir., 1981-88, acting planning dir., 1987-88, city architect, 1988-92, asst. to city mgr., spl. projects coord., 1992-94, city urban design coord., 1994—; vis. critic in urban design U. Ill, Chgo., 1970-71, San Diego State U. Grad. Sch. Planning and Pub. Adminstrn., Urban Design & Site Planning Inst., 1974-85; lectr. Urban Conservation Grad. Sch. History, U. San Diego, 1978, 81, 82, 87; asst. prof., lectr., design critic New Sch. Architecture, San Diego City U., 1980—; faculty assoc. for transp. and land use planning Lincoln Inst. Land Policy, Cambridge, Mass., 1993-95; mem. hist. bldg. code bd. State of Calif.; mem., dir. Community Planning and Design Ctr., San Diego, 1971-74. Bd. dirs. Citizens Coordinate for Century III, 1991—; mem. Regional Urban Design Assistance Team, Seattle, Washington, and Liverpool, Eng.; past bd. dirs. Californians for Preservation Action. Recipient Leadership in Planning award New Sch. Architecture, 1992, Gaslamp Pioneer award San Diego Gaslamp Quarter Found., 1993, Ellen and Roger Revelle award Citizens Coordinate for Century III, 1993. Fellow AIA (co-chair housing assistance team City of Washincton, 1990, bd. dirs. San Diego chpt. 1976-78, mem. nat. urban design com., past mem. Calif. coun., hist. preservation-urban conservation com., urban design commr. San Diego chpt. 1975-76, Spl. award for Excellence in Govt. 1983; mem. Am. Planning Assn. (Disting. Leadership award Calif. chpt. 1991), Am. Inst. Cert. Planners, Inst. for Urban Design, Urban Land Inst., Lambda Alpha. Home: 4260 Hortensia St San Diego CA 92103-1105

STEPNEY, PHILIP HAROLD ROBERT, museum director; b. Edmonton, Alta., Can., Nov. 19, 1947; s. Harold Albert and Elenor Blanche (Landals) S.; m. Donna Maureen Kelly, Sept. 4, 1967; children: Sean Philip Stuart, Erin Maureen, Lindsay Dawn. B.Sc. with honors, U. Alta., Edmonton, Can., 1969. M.Sc., U. Toronto, Ont., Can., 1971, Ph.D., 1979. Wildlife biologist Renewable Resources Cons. Svc., Edmonton, 1975, project mgr., 1976, dir. bus. devel., 1977, curator ornithology Provincial Mus. Alta., Edmonton, 1978-81, asst. dir. natural history, 1981-87, asst. dir., curatorial, 1987-89, dir., 1989—; mem. collections com. U. Alta., Edmonton, 1982-89, adj. rsch. assoc. dept. forest sci., 1987—; chmn. Lakeland Coll Curriculum Adv. Com., Vermillion, Alta., 1984—; Editor: (exhbn. catalog) The Scriver Blackfoot Collection, 1990; mem. editorial bd. Alta. Studies Jour., 1986-90; contbr. articles to jours. in field. Recipient Can. Nat. Sportsman Show award U. Toronto, 1973; collections registration grantee Mus. Assistance Program, 1972, 79, 80, 83, Alta. Hist. Resources Found. grantee, 1988, Alta. Recreation, Pks., Wildlife Found. grantee, 1989; Can. Cultural Property Export Rev. Bd. grantee, 1989; Mus. Museums Assn. grantee, 1990; U. Toronto scholar, 1972, 73, 74. Mem. Am. Ornithologists Union (co-chair collections com. 1984—), Soc. Can. Ornithologists (treas. membership sect. 1985—), Cooper Ornithol. Soc., Wilson Ornithol. Soc. Avocations: bonsai, hunting, fly fishing, taxidermy, photography. Office: Provincial Mus of

Alberta, 12845 102nd Ave, Edmonton, AB Canada T5N 0M6 *Life is like a game of golf, full of obstacles, many of our own making, that we are constantly trying to overcome. Each time one strives to perform better than before and satisfaction and sense of accomplishment come from how you play the game, not just playing it.*

STEPNICK, ARLENE ALICE, nursing education administrator; b. Phila.. MS, Old Dominion U., 1982; PhD, U. Tex., 1987. Assoc. prof. nursing Hampton (Va.) U., 1982-89; chair dept. nursing Christopher Newport U., Newport News, Va., 1989—; nursing cons. various hosps., Va., 1982—. Contbr. articles to profl. publs. Mem. ANA (coun. nurse researchers), Nat. League Nursing, So. Nursing Rsch. Soc., Sigma Theta Tau. Avocations: opera, symphony music, non-fiction books. Office: Christopher Newport U 50 Shoe Ln Newport News VA 23606-2949

STEPNOSKI, MARK MATTHEW, professional football player; b. Erie, Pa., Jan. 26, 1967. Student, U. Pitts. Center Dallas Cowboys, 1989-95, Houston Oilers, 1995—; player NFC Championship Game, 1992, Super Bowl XXVII, 1992, Super Bowl XXVIII, 1993. Named to Pro Bowl Team, 1992, 93. Office: Dallas Cowboys One Cowboys Pkwy Irving TX 75063*

STEPONAITIS, VINCAS PETRAS, archaeologist, anthropologist, educator; b. Boston, Aug. 10, 1953; s. Vincas and Elena (Povydis) S.; m. Laurie Cameron, Dec. 31, 1976; children: Elena Anne, Lillian Kazimiera. AB in Anthropology magna cum laude, Harvard U., 1974; MA in Anthropology, U. Mich., 1975, PhD in Anthropology, 1980. From lectr. to assoc. prof. dept. anthropology SUNY, Binghamton, 1979-87; assoc. prof. U. N.C., Chapel Hill, 1988-94, prof., 1995—, dir. Rsch. Labs. Anthropology, 1988—; guest worker Nat. Bur. Standards, 1979; adj. lectr. dept. anthropology SUNY, Binghamton, 1979; invited lectr. univs. U.S., Europe, 1980—. Author: Ceramics, Chronology, and Community Patterns, An Archaeological Study at Moundville, 1983; editor Southeastern Archaeology, 1984-87; regional editor Investigations in Am. Archaeology, 1987-91; mem. edit. bd. Southern Cultures, 1992—; mem. edit. adv. bd. Prehistory Press, 1990—; contbr. articles to profl. jours.; presenter papers profl. meetings, seminars; pub. book reviews; abstracts. Smithsonian Instn. fellow, 1978-79; grantee NSF, 1978-80, 83, 89-92, 94, Wenner-Gren Found., 1981, 86-88, Nat. Geographic Soc., 1987-88, Z. Smith Reynolds Found., 1992-94. Fellow Am. Anthrop. Assn.; mem. Soc. Am. Archaeology (Presdl. Recognition award 1993-94, exec. com. 1983-84, treas. 1992-94), Southeastern Archaeol. Conf. (editor 1984-87, pres. 1990-92), N.C. Archaeol. Soc. (exec. sec. 1988-91, sec. 1991—), N.C. Archaeol. Coun. (exec. com. 1988-92), Archaeol. Soc. S.C., Ala. Archaeol. Soc., Miss. Archaeol. Soc., La. Archaeol. Soc., Tenn. Anthrop. Assn. Office: U NC Rsch Labs Anthropology Alumni Bldg CB 3120 Chapel Hill NC 27599-3120

STEPP, JAMES MICHAEL, business executive; b. Huntington, W.Va., Apr. 26, 1944; s. James Dial and Helen (Shelton) S.; m. Lillian Arlene Radeker, Jan. 3, 1970; children: James Michael, Scott Adams, John Radeker. BS, U.S. Mil. Acad., 1966; MBA, Stanford U., 1972. Commd. lt. C.E. U.S. Army, 1966, advanced through grades to capt., 1968, served in Vietnam, resigned, 1970; asst. v.p. Bank of Am., San Francisco, 1972-75; v.p. Bank of Am., N.Y.C., 1975-81; v.p.; treas. Fotomat Corp., Wilton, Conn., 1981-83, Emhart Corp., Hartford, Conn., 1983-89; pres. Am. Corp. Fin. Group Inc., West Hartford, 1989-92; exec. v.p., CFO Purolator Products Co., Tulsa, Okla., 1992—, bd. dirs.; adv. dir. Conn. Nat. Bank, 1986-92. Bd. dirs. Jr. Achievement, North Cen. Conn., 1986-92. Decorated Silver Star, Bronze Star, Purple Heart, Army Commendation medal, Air medal. Mem. Fin. Execs. Inst., Stanford Bus. Sch. Alumni Assn., West Point Soc. of N.Y. Republican. Episcopalian. Avocations: tennis, fishing, jogging, golf.

STEPP, LAURA SESSIONS, journalist; b. Ft. Smith, Ark., July 27, 1951; d. Robert Paul Sessions and M. Rae Barnes; m. Carl Sessions Stepp; children: Ashli, Amber, Jeffrey. BA, Earlham Coll., 1973; MA, Columnia U., 1974. Reporter Palm Beach Times, West Palm Beach, Fla., 1974; investigative reporter, editor The Evening Bull., Phila., 1975; projects editor The Charlotte (N.C.) Observer, 1979-81, asst. editorial page editor, 1981-82; Md. editor The Washington Post, 1982-86, religion editor, 1987-92, writer Style sect., 1992—. Bd. advisors U. Md. Casey Journalism Ctr. Children and Families, College Park. Recipient Nat. Reporting award Religion Writers Am., Feature Writing award AAUW, 1994. Mem. Investigative Reporters and Editors (bd. dirs. 1986-90). Office: Washington Post Co 1150 15th St NW Washington DC 20071-0002

STEPPLER, HOWARD ALVEY, agronomist; b. Morden, Man., Can., Nov. 8, 1918; s. Alvey Morden and Sophia (Doern) S.; m. Phyllis Ivy Parsonage, May 10, 1945; 1 child, Glenn. B.S., U. Man., 1941; M.Sc., McGill U., 1948, Ph.D., 1955. Research scientist Agr. Can. Research, 1948-49; asst. prof. agronomy McGill U., 1949-57, prof., 1957-84, prof. emeritus, 1984—, chmn. agronomy dept., 1955-70, chmn. dept. plant sci., 1976-84; agrl. advisor Can. Internat. Devel. Agy., 1970-71; trustee Centro Internacional Agricultura Tropical Colombia, 1972-78, Internat. Svc. Nat. Agrl. Rsch., The Hague, 1980-84, Agrl. Devel. Coun. N.Y., 1977-85, Internat. Livestock Ctr. for Africa, Ethiopia, 1984-89; trustee Internat. Coun. Rsch. in Agroforestry, 1983-91, chmn. bd., 1984-91; interim dir. gen. Internat. Coun. for Rsch. in Agroforestry, Nairobi, 1980-81; trustee Internat. Rice Rsch. Inst., 1988-93; founding bd. dirs. So. African Ctr. Coordination in Agrl. Rsch., Botswana, 1984-85. Capt. arty. Royal Can. Arty., 1942-46. Internat. Devel. Research Centre sr. Research fellow, 1973-74. Fellow Agrl. Inst. Can. (pres. 1964-65, Internat. Agrl. Recognition award 1994); mem. Am. Soc. Agronomy, Crop Sci. Soc. Am., Can. Soc. Agronomy (pres. 1957-58, Disting. Agronomist award 1993), Rotary. Office: 21111 Lakeshore Rd, Sainte Anne de Bellevue, PQ Canada H9X 3V9

STEPTOE, MARY LOU, lawyer; b. Washington, July 15, 1949; d. Philip Pendleton and Irene (Hellen) S.; m. Peter E. Carson, Sept. 1986; children: Elizabeth Maud, Julia Grace. BA, Occidental Coll., 1971; JD, U. Va., 1974. Bar: Va., 1974, Supreme Ct., 1987. Staff atty., Bur. of Competition FTC, Washington, 1974-79, atty. advisor to commr., 1979-86, exec. asst. to chmn., 1988-89, assoc. dir., Bur. of Competition, 1989-90, dep. dir., 1990-92, acting dir., 1992—. Office: FTC Competition Bur 6th & Pennsylvania Ave NW Washington DC 20580-0002

STEPTOE, PHILIP P., III, lawyer; b. Washington, Nov. 13, 1951. AB, Princeton U., 1973; JD, U. Va., 1976. Bar: Va. 1976, Ill. 1976. Ptnr. Sidley & Austin, Chgo. Mem. ABA (sect. pub. utility 1988—), Chgo. Bar Assn. (sect. pub. utility 1976—). Office: Sidley & Austin 1 First Nat Plz Chicago IL 60603

STERBAN, RICHARD ANTHONY, singer; b. Camden, N.J., Apr. 24, 1943; s. Edward Joseph and Victoria Marie (Giordano) S.; children: Richard Alan, Douglas Scott, Christopher Patrick. Student, Trenton State Coll. coowner Silverline-Goldline Music Pub. Cos.; partner Nashville Sounds, Greensboro Hornets, baseball teams. Mem. gospel singing groups; mem. Stamps Quartet, bass singer, ptnr., Oak Ridge Boys, 1972—; albums include Y'All Come Back Saloon, 1977, Room Service, 1978, Oak Ridge Boys Have Arrived, 1979, Together, 1980, Greatest Hits, 1980, Fancy Free, 1981, Bobbie Sue, 1982, Oak Ridge Boys Christmas, 1982, American Made, 1983, Deliver, 1984, Greatest Hits II, 1984, Step On Our, 1985, Seasons, 1986, Christmas Again, 1986, Where The Fast Lane Ends, 1987, Heartbeat, 1987, Monongahela, 1988, Unstoppable, 1991, The Long Haul, 1992, Back to Back, 1994. Recipient with group: Grammy awards, Am. Music award for Country Group of Yr., 1982, Best Country Video award, Everday, 1985; named Best Vocal Group Acad. Country Music, 1977, 79, Best Country Group of Yr. AGVA, 1981, Number One Country Group Billboard mag., 1978, 80, Vocal Group of the Yr. Country Music Assn., 1978. Mem. Country Music Assn., AFTRA, Nat. Acad. Rec. Arts and Scis., Acad. Country Music. Office: care Oak Ridge Boys Jim Halsey Co 3225 S Norwood Ave Tulsa OK 74135-5400*

STERGIOS, PETER DOE, lawyer; b. Derry, N.H., Jan. 24, 1942; s. William G. and Ruthmary (Doe) S.; m. Leonides Conde, Aug. 29, 1971; children: Irene, Cathy. BA with distinction, Brown U., 1964; JD, Harvard U., 1972; sr. ptnr. Bar: N.Y. 1973, U.S. Dist. Ct. (so. and ea. dists.) N.Y. 1974, U.S. Ct. Appeals (2d cir.) 1974, U.S. Supreme Ct. 1977. Assoc. Shea &

Gould, N.Y.C., 1972-80, ptnr., 1980-87; ptnr. Epstein Becker & Green, P.C., N.Y.C., 1987—. Contbr. articles to profl. jours. Capt. U.S. Army, 1964-68, Vietnam. Mem. ABA (internat. labor rels. law com.), Fed. Bar Assn., Am. Arbitration Assn. (panel of arbitrators), N.Y. State Bar Assn., N.Y. County Lawyers Assn., Assn. Bar City N.Y., Harvard Club, Govs. Island Officers Club, Am. Legion. Office: Epstein Becker & Green PC 250 Park Ave New York NY 10177-0001

STERLING, DAVID M., graphic designer; b. Okla., Apr. 28, 1951; s. Paul J. and Roberta Myrtice (Rousseau) S. BA, Oklahoma City U., 1973; MFA, Cranbrook Acad. Art, Bloomfield Hills, Mich., 1978. Exhibit designer Omniplex, Oklahoma City, 1973-76; art dir. Indsl. Design Mag., N.Y.C., 1979-81; prin. Doublespace, N.Y.C., 1982-94; founder, prin. World Studio and World Studio Found., N.Y.C., 1992—; graphic design faculty Sch. of Visual Arts, N.Y.C., 1992—. Pub. mag., Fetish 1979-81; pub. mag. Sphere, 1994—; works included in books: Graphic Style: From Victorian to Post-Modern, 1988, New American Design, 1988, Low Budget/High Quality Design, 1990, Cranbrook Design: The New Discourse, 1990, Contemporary Graphic Design, 1991; permanent collections of Cranbrook Academy of Art, Library Congress, Michael C. Rockefeller Arts Center, Smithsonian Institution. Recipient AIGA Cover Show Am. Inst. Graphics Arts, N.Y. 1984, AIGA Communications Graphics Am. Inst. Graphic Arts, N.Y. 1986, Type Dirs. Club award 1990, 92, Best of Category award Design Review, N.Y. 1986, Am. Assn. of Mus., 1986, 88, Am. Ctr. for Design, 1990, AIGA Communication Graphic, 1990, Indsl. Design Review, 1985, 86, 88, 93, N.Y. Festivals. Democrat. Office: World Studio Ste 602 19 W 21 New York NY 10010

STERLING, DONALD JUSTUS, JR., retired newspaper editor; b. Portland, Oreg., Sept. 27, 1927; s. Donald Justus and Adelaide (Armstrong) S.; m. Julie Ann Courteol, June 7, 1963; children: Sarah, William, John. A.B., Princeton U., 1948; postgrad. (Nieman fellow), Harvard U., 1955-56. Reporter Denver Post, 1948-52; news staff mem. Oreg. Jour., Portland, 1952-82; editor Oreg. Jour., 1972-82; asst. to pub. The Oregonian, 1982-92, ret., 1992. Pres. Tri-County Community Coun., 1972-73. Recipient Izaak Walton League Golden Beaver award, 1969, Edith Knight Hill award, 1978, Jessie Laird Brodie award Planned Parenthood Assn., 1983, McCall award Women in Communications, 1987, Roger W. Williams Freedom of Info. award Oreg. Newspaper Pubs. Assn., 1989; English-Speaking Union traveling fellow, 1959. Mem. Soc. Nieman Fellows, Oreg. Hist. Soc. (pres. 1977-79), Mazamas, Lang Syne Soc. Clubs: City (Portland) (pres. 1973-74), Multnomah Athletic (Portland); Dial, Elm, Cannon (Princeton). Home: 1718 SW Myrtle St Portland OR 97201-2300

STERLING, DONALD T., professional basketball team executive; b. Chgo.. Lawyer L.A. (formerly San Diego) Clippers, Nat. Basketball Assn., owner, also chmn. bd. Office: care LA Clippers LA Meml Sports Arena 3939 S Figueroa St Los Angeles CA 90037-1207*

STERLING, KEIR BROOKS, historian, educator; b. N.Y.C., Jan. 30, 1934; s. Henry Somers and Louise Noel (de Wetter) S.; B.S., Columbia U., 1961, M.A., 1963, Profl. Diploma, 1965, Ph.D., 1973; m. Anne Cox Diller, Apr. 3, 1961; children: Duncan Diller, Warner Strong, Theodore Craig. Asst. to dean Sch. Gen. Studies, Columbia U., N.Y.C., 1959-65, rsch. grantee, Eng., 1965-66; instr. in history Pace U., N.Y.C. and Pleasantville, N.Y., 1966-71, asst. prof., 1971-74, assoc. prof., 1974-77, adj. prof., 1977—; ordnance br. historian U.S. Army Ordnance Ctr. and Sch., Aberdeen Proving Ground, Md., 1983-94, U.S. Army Combined Arms Support Command, Ft. Lee, Va., 1994—; lectr. in gen. counselling Bklyn. Coll., City U. N.Y., 1967-68; asst. acad. dean, adj. asst. prof. history, coord. Am. studies program, dir. summer session Marymount Coll., Tarrytown, N.Y., 1968-71; asst. dean Rockland Community Coll., SUNY, Suffern, 1971-73; vis. prof. Mercy Coll., Westchester Community Coll., King's Coll., Nyack Coll., U. Wis., 1975, 75, 78-80, 83, Harford (Md.) Community Coll., 1987-94; co-project dir. Am. Ornithologists Union Centennial Hist. Project, 1976-89; cons. Arno Press, Inc., 1973-78, Coun. State Colls. of N.J., 1974-75, NSF, 1983—, Am. Trust for Brit. Libr., 1986-89; active Columbia U. Seminar on History and Philosophy of Sci., 1976—, Bicentennial Com. Tarrytown, 1975-76; archivist, historian mem. steering com. sect. mammalogy Internat. Union Biol. Scis., 1985—. Served with U.S. Army, 1954-56. Grantee Theodore Roosevelt Meml. Fund, Am. Mus. Natural History, 1967, Nat. Geog. Soc., 1977, NSF/ Am. Soc. Mammalogists, 1978, NSF, 1981-82, IREX, 1982, mem. Archives and 75th Anniversary Coms. Mem. Am. Soc. Mammalogists, Am. Ornithologists Union (co-chmn. Centennial Hist. Com., mem. Archives Com., grantee, 1976, 77), Am. Soc. Environ. History (sec., mem. governing bd., editor newsletter), Rhinebeck (N.Y.) Hist. Soc. (trustee, pres. 1980-83), Harford County Com. of Md. Hist. Trust, Harford County Hist. Dist. Commn. (v.p. 1987-94), Hist. Soc. Harford County (bd. dirs. 1989-94), Assn. Bibliography of History (mem. coun. 1994—), Phi Alpha Theta, Sigma Tau Delta, Phi Delta Kappa. Democrat. Episcopalian. Author: Last of the Naturalists: The Career of C. Hart Merriam, 1974, 77, Serving the Line with Excellence: The History of the U.S. Army Ordnance Corps as Expressed through the Lives of its Chiefs of Ordnance, 1812-1987, rev. edit., 1992, Addere Flammam: Commanders of the U.S. Army Ordnance Center and School 1918-1993, 1993; editor: Notes on the Animals of North America (B.S. Barton), 1974; assoc. editor Am. Nat. Biog., 1989—; editor, contbr.: Natural Sciences in America, 1974, 68 vols., 1974, Biologists and Their World, 1978, 77 vols.; gen. editor, contbr.: The International History of Mammalogy, 1987—; editor, contbr. to numerous works in history Am. natural scis. and Am. mil. history. Home: 7104 Wheeler Rd Richmond VA 23229 Office: 10500 A Avenue Fort Lee VA 23801

STERLING, LEON SAMUEL, computer scientist, researcher, educator; b. Melbourne, Victoria, Australia, May 17, 1955; came to U.S., 1985; s. Joseph and Ruth Rita (Harris) S.; m. Miriam Camille Freilich, Aug. 1, 1982; children: Danya Z., Sara T. BSc with honors in Maths. and Computer Sci., U. Melbourne, 1976; PhD, Australian Nat. U., Canberra, 1980. Rsch. fellow dept. artificial intelligence U. Edinburgh, Scotland, 1980-83; Dov Biegun postdoctoral fellow dept. applied math. and computer sci. Weizmann Inst. Sci., Rehovot, Israel, 1983-84; asst. prof. dept. computer engring. and sci. Case Western Res. U., Cleve., 1985-89, assoc. dir. Ctr. for Automation and Intelligent Systems Rsch., 1986-89, dir., 1989-91, assoc. prof. dept. computer engring. and sci., 1989-94, prof., 1994—; gen. chmn. N.Am. Conf. on Logic Programming, Case Western Res. U., 1989; invited lectr. Advanced Sch. on Founds. of Logic Programming, Sardinia, Italy, 1988, 4th Asian Sch. on Computer Sci., Thailand, 1989; cons. ALMEX Ticket Equipment Ltd., Eng., IBM Sci. Ctr., Israel, Hal Robotics, Tel Aviv, Hadassah Hosp., Israel, Quintus Prolog, Palo Alto Calif., AI-Ware, Cleve., AT&T, Columbus, Ohio, Chi Corp., Cleve., O'Connor & Assocs., Chgo.; mem. tech. com. TC-12 Artificial Intelligence, 1991—; chair poster program Internat. Logic Programming Symposium, San Diego, 1991; co-chair programs AI '92 Australian Artificial Intelligence Conf., Hobart, 1992; reviewer, participant numerous seminars, confs.; panelist numerous symposia. Author: (with E.Y. Shapiro) The Art of Prolog: Advanced Programming Techniques, 1986, 2d edit., 1993; editor: The Practice of Prolog, 1990, (with A. Adams) AI'92, 1992, Intelligence Systems, Concepts and Applications, 1993; adv. bd. Expert Systems: Research and Applications, 1989—; reviewer Computing Reviews, Jour. Parallel Processing, Computational Intelligence, Internat. Joint Conf. on Artificial Intelligence; contbr. articles to profl. jours. Grantee NSF, 1987, 88, 88-89, 88-90, 90, Expert Systems Internat., 1986, Tex. Instruments, 1986, TRW, 1985-87, Ex-Cell-O Compressor Components Corp., 1987, Cleve. Advanced Mfg. Program, 1986-87, 87-88, Lewis Rsch. Ctr. NASA 1987, 88-89, 89-90, Systran Corp., 1989, BP Am. and Cleve. Advanced Mfg. Program, 1990-91. Mem. IEEE (reviewer jours), Assn. Computing Machinery (reviewer jour.), Am. Assn. Artificial Intelligence, Assn. Logic Programming (exec. com., area editor, guest editor Jour. Logic Programming). Office: Case Western Res U Dept Computer Engring and Sci Cleveland OH 44106

STERLING, RAYMOND LESLIE, civil engineering educator, researcher, consultant; b. London, Apr. 19, 1949; came to U.S., 1966; s. Richard Howard and Joan Valeria (Skinner) S.; m. Linda Lee Lundquist, Aug. 8, 1970 (div. Sept. 1982); children: Paul, Juliet, Erika; m. Janet Marie Kjera, Aug. 20, 1983; 1 child, Zoey. B in Civil and Structural Engring. with 1st class honors, U. Sheffield, Eng., 1970; MS in Geol. Engring., U. Minn., 1975, PhDCE, 1977. Registered civil engr., Minn.; chartered structural engr., Eng. Engr. trainee Met. Water Bd., London, 1968; civil engr. Egil Wefald and

Assocs., Cons. Engrs., Mpls., 1969-71; structural engr. Husband and Co., Cons. Engrs., Eng., 1971-73; rsch. asst. U. Minn., Mpls., 1973-77, dir. Underground Space Ctr., 1977—, asst. prof. dept. civil and mineral engring., 1977-83, assoc. prof., 1983—; project. coord., structural engr. Setter, Leach and Lindstrom, Inc., Mpls., 1976-77; prin. cons. Itasca Cons. Group, Inc., Mpls., 1981-94; vice-chmn. U.S. nat. com. on tunneling tech. NRC, NAS, 1990-92, chmn. 1992-94, mem. com. on infrastructure, 1991-93, bd. on infrastructure and constricted environment, 1994—; acting co-dir. Minn. Cold Climate Bldg. Rsch. Ctr. U. Minn., 1987-89, co-dir. Bldg. Energy Rsch. Ctr., 1986, mem. speaker's bur., active numerous other u. coms.; mem. energy adv. com. Legis. Com. on Minn. Resources, 1989—; mem. com. on moisture control in bldgs. U.S. Bldg. Thermal Envelope Coordinating Coun., 1985-86; mem. program planning com. on bldg. founds. U.S. Dept. Energy, 1985—; mem. adv. bd. for energy efficient residence demonstration project Nat. Assn. Home Builders, 1980; mem. Gov's. Exxon Oil Overcharge Adv. Task Force, 1986, Mpls. Energy Future Com., 1980-81, Scientist's Inst. for Pub. Info., N.Y.; cons. U.S. Army Corps. Engrs., UN, N.Y., Opus Corp., Mpls., Dames & Moore Internat., London, City of Mpls., Larson Engring., White Bear, Minn., Pilsburg Co., Mpls., Colgate Div. Sch., Rochester, N.Y., many others; adv. prof. Chongqing Inst. Architecture and Engring., Sichuan, People's Republic China, 1985—; vis. researcher Nat. Inst. Pollution and Resources MITI, Japan, 1991; vis. prof. U. Mo., Rolla, 1979; Shimizu prof. civil and mineral engring., U. Minn., 1988—; mem. eminent speaker program Instn. Engrs., Australia, 1993; lectr., presenter numerous profl. meetings. Author: Earth Sheltered Housing Design: Guidelines, Examples and References, 1978, transl. into Chinese, French, Spanish and Russian, 2d. edit., 1985, (with others) Earth Sheltered Community Design: The Design of Energy-Efficient Residential Communities, 1980 (award for Best Book in Architecture and Urban Planning Profl. and Scholarly div. Assn. Am. Pubs. 1981), transl. into Spanish, 1981, Underground Building Design, 1983, translated into Japanese and Russian, others, Building Foundation Handbook, 1988, Underground Space Design, 1993, others; editor: (with others) Key Questions in Rock Mechanics: Proc. 29th U.S. Symposium on Rock Mechanics, 1988; contbr. articles to profl. jours. including Jour. Agrl. Engring., Internat. Jour. Rock Mechanics and Mining Scis., Exptl. Mechanics, many others. Recipient Young Engr. of Yr. award Minn. Fedn. Engring. Soc., 1982, Applied Rsch. award in rock mechanics Nat. Rsch. Coun.; elected fgn. mem. Acad. Engring. of Russian Fedn., 1993; grantee Shimizu Constrn. Co., 1987—, Nat. Assn. Homebuilders, 1989, U.S. Dept. Energy, 1989-90, NSF, 1991, Minn. Dept. Transp., 1991, ASHRAE, 1991—, many others. Fellow ASCE (pres. Minn. sect. 1990-91, bd. dirs. 1985—, Young Civil Engr. of Yr. award 1982), Instn. Civil Engrs., Inst. Structural Engrs.; mem. NSPE, Am. Underground Space Assn., Internat. Tunneling Assn. (coordinating editor jour. 1986—), vice animateur working group on costs/benefits of subsurface utilization), Acad. Engring. Russian Fedn. (fgn.), Mpls. Engrs. Club. Achievements include research in underground construction, underground space utilization, rock mechanics, and energy use in buildings. Office: U Mound Space Ctr 790 Civil Engring 500 Pillsbury Dr SE Minneapolis MN 55455-0198

STERLING, RICHARD LEROY, English and foreign language educator; b. Atlantic City, Feb. 18, 1941; s. Richard Leroy and Anne (Bass) S. BA, Am. U., 1968; MA, Cath. U., 1971; PhD, Howard U., 1990. Tchr. French and English, adult and continuing edn. D.C. Pub. Schs., Washington, 1969-71, 76-83; instr. French Howard U., Washington, 1973-76, grad. teaching asst., 1983-85, instr., lectr. in French, 1985-89; tchr. English Community-Based Orgns., D.C. Pub. Schs., Washington, 1989-91; asst. prof. French and English Bowie (Md.) State U., 1991—; tchr. summer enrichment program for gifted children Sch. Edn., Howard U., summers 1985, 86; tchr. ESL, D.C. Pub. Schs., summer, 1989; vice chmn. World Centennial Conf.: French, Am. and Planetary Dimensions of Saint-John Perse, U. D.C., 1987. Author: The Prose Works of Saint-John Perse: Towards an Understanding of His Poetry, 1994; author articles and book reviews. Mem. Senegal friendship com. Office Cmty. and Ethnic Affairs, Prince George's County Govt., Md., 1993-94, Assn. Democratique des Francais a L'Etranger, 1988—; mem. membership com. and outreach com. St. John's Ch., Washington, 1993. With U.S. Army, 1964-66, Germany. Mem. MLA, Coll. Lang. Assn., Samuel Beckett Soc., Societe des Professeurs Francais et Francophones d'Amerique, Zora Neale Hurston Soc., Am. Assn. Tchrs. French (sec.-treas. Washington chpt. 1986-90), Pi Delta Phi, Sigma Tau Delta. Democrat. Episcopalian. Avocations: classical music, history, travel. Home: 4235 Alton Pl NW Washington DC 20016-2017 Office: Bowie State U Dept English & Modern Langs Bowie MD 20715

STERLING, ROBERT LEE, JR., investment company executive; b. Cleve., June 12, 1933; s. Robert Lee and Kathryn (Durell) S.; children from previous marriage: Robert Livingston, Wiliam Lee, Cameron Platt; m. Joyce Lanier Milner, June 4, 1994. Student, U. Edinburgh, Scotland, 1955; BA, Brown U., 1956; MBA, Columbia U., 1962. Corp. rsch. analyst Morgan Guaranty Trust, N.Y.C., 1962-63; asst. comptr. Western Hemisphere CPC Internat., N.Y.C., 1963-66; v.p. White, Weld & Co., Inc., N.Y.C., 1966-78, Merrill Lynch Asset Mgmt., 1978-80, Wood, Struthers & Winthrop Mgmt. Corp., N.Y.C., 1980-83; sr. v.p. Shearson Lehman Bros. Asset Mgmt., 1983-88; v.p.; sr. portfolio mgr. Chase Manhattan Bank, 1988-93; sr. v.p., sr. portfolio mgr. Melhado, Flynn & Assocs., Inc., N.Y.C., 1993—. Mem. adv. bd. Mus. Modern Art, Oxford U., Eng. Lt. USNR, 1956-60. Mem. New Eng. Soc. (past pres.), J.P. Morgan medal), St. Andrews Soc., St. Nicholas Soc., Pilgrims, N.Y. State Soc. of Cin. (pres.), Squadron A (N.Y.), Univ. Club (N.Y.C.), Edgartown (Mass.) Yacht Club, Bath & Tennis (Palm Beach, Fla.), Anabell's (London), Alpha Delta Phi, Alpha Kappa Psi. Home: 907 Fifth Ave Apt 5C New York NY 10021 Office: Melhado Flynn & Assocs Inc 530 Fifth Ave New York NY 10036

STERLING, SHIRLEY FRAMPTON, artist, educator; b. L.A., Oct. 9, 1920; d. James Alexander and Elizabeth Mary (Herman) F.; m. Edwin Leigh Sterling, Mar. 26, 1942; children: Michael Leigh, Marianne. BA, Occidental Coll., 1942; postgrad., La. Tech. U., 1979-89. Cert. tchr. Calif. Glendale, Calif., 1942-45; artist, tchr. Watercolor Art Soc., Houston, Pasadena, Kemah, Tex., 1973—; lectr., demonstrator various art socs. Active as Gray Lady Internat. Red Cross, Wiesbaden, Fed. Republic Germany, 1960-61, Honolulu, 1968-69. Mem. Nat. Watercolor Soc.(elected signature mem.), Knickerbocker Artists, Southwestern Watercolor Soc., Tex. Watercolor Soc. (Patron of Arts award), So. Watercolor Soc., Watercolor Art Soc.-Houston, Western Fedn. Watercolor Soc., Phi Beta Kappa. Republican. Home: 4011 Manorfield Dr Seabrook TX 77586-4209

STERN, ARTHUR PAUL, electronics company executive, electrical engineer; b. Budapest, Hungary, July 20, 1925; came to U.S., 1951, naturalized, 1956; s. Leon and Bertha (Frankfurter) S.; m. Edith M. Samuel; children: Daniel, Claude, Jacqueline. Diploma in Elec. Engring., Swiss Fed. Inst. Tech. Zurich, 1948; MSEE, Syracuse U., 1955. Mgr. electronic devices and applications lab. Gen. Electric Co., Syracuse, N.Y., 1957-61; dir. engring. Martin Marietta Corp., Balt., 1961-64; dir. ops. Bunker Ramo Corp., Canoga Park, Calif., 1964-66; v.p., gen. mgr. advanced products div. Magnavox, Torrance, Calif., 1966-79, pres. Magnavox Advanced Products and Systems Co., Torrance, 1980-90; vice chmn., bd. dirs. Magnavox Govt. and Indsl. Electronics Co., Ft. Wayne, Ind., 1987-90; pres. Ea. Beverly Hills Corp., 1991—; non-resident staff mem. MIT, 1956-59; instr. Gen. Elec. Bus. Mgmt., 1955-57. Chmn. engring. div. United Jewish Appeal, Syracuse, 1955-57; mem. adv. bd. dept. elec. engring. U. Calif., Santa Barbara, 1980-92; mem. Sch. Engring. Adv. and Devel. Council Calif. State U., Long Beach, 1985-90. Co-author: Transistor Circuit Engineering, 1957, Handbook of Automation, Computation and Control, 1961; also articles; U.S., fgn. patentee in field. Fellow AAAS, IEEE (pres. 1975, bd. dirs.-officer 1970-77, guest editor spl. issue IEEE Trans. on Circuit Theory 1956, invited guest editor spl. issue Procs. IEEE on Integrated Electronics 1964, Centennial medal 1984). Jewish.

STERN, CARL LEONARD, former news correspondent, federal official; b. N.Y.C., Aug. 7, 1937; s. Hugo and Frances (Taft) S.; m. Joy Elizabeth Nathan, Nov. 27, 1960; children: Lawrence, Theodore. A.B., Columbia U., 1958, M.S., 1959; J.D., Cleve. State U., 1966, J.D. (hon.), 1975; J.D. (hon.), New Eng. Coll. Law, 1977. Bar: Ohio 1966, D.C. 1968, U.S. Supreme Ct. 1969. Law corr. NBC News, Washington, 1967-93; dir. Office of Pub. Affairs U.S. Dept. Justice, Washington, 1993—; lectr. Nat. Coll.; adj. prof. George Washington U., Stanford U. Editorial bd.: The Dist. Lawyer. Recipient Peabody award, 1974, Emmy award, 1974, Gavel award, 1969, 74,

Headliner Club award, 1991. Mem. ABA (vice chmn. criminal justice sect. com. on criminal justice and the media, gov., forum com. on communications law, working group intelligence requirements and criminal code reform), AFTRA (nat. exec. bd. 1984-86, first v.p. Washington, Balt. chpt. 1985-87). Home: 2956 Davenport St NW Washington DC 20008-2165 Office: US Dept Justice Rm 1228 10th St & Constitution Ave NW Washington DC 20530

STERN, CARL WILLIAM, JR., management consultant; b. San Francisco, Mar. 31, 1946; s. Carl William and Marjorie Aline (Gunst) S.; m. Karen Jaffe, Sept. 7, 1966 (div. Mar. 1972); 1 child, David; m. Holly Drick Hayes, Mar. 21, 1985; 1 child, Matthew. BA, Harvard U., 1968; MBA, Stanford U., 1974. Cons. Boston Cons. Group, Inc., Menlo Park, Calif., 1974-77, mgr., 1977-78; mgr. Boston Cons. Group, Inc., London, 1978-80; v.p. Boston Cons. Group, Inc., Chgo., 1980-87, sr. v.p., 1987—. Lt. USNR, 1968-71. Office: Boston Consulting Group Inc 200 S Wacker Dr Chicago IL 60606-5801

STERN, CHARLES, foreign trade company executive; b. Germany, Dec. 2, 1920; came to U.S., 1940, naturalized, 1943; s. Julius and Else (Br) S.; m. Eve Hamburger, Sept. 20, 1947 (dec. Apr. 1980); children—Enid S., June M. Matriculation, U. London, 1937. With J. Gerber & Co., Inc., N.Y.C., 1940—; asst. v.p. J. Gerber & Co., Inc., 1960-63, v.p., 1963-68, exec. v.p., 1968-74, pres., chief exec. officer, 1974-88, chmn., 1986-89, chmn. emeritus, 1989—, cons. Served with AUS, World War II. Mem. ASTM, Am. Inst. Imported Steel (past pres.).

STERN, DANIEL, actor; b. Bethesda, Md., Aug. 28, 1957. TV movies include Samson & Delilah, Weekend War, The Court-Martial of Jackie Robinson; TV series Hometown, 1985, (narrator) The Wonder Years, 1988-93; films: Breaking Away, 1979, Starting Over, 1979, A Small Circle of Friends, 1980, Stardust Memories, 1980, It's My Turn, 1980, One-Trick Pony, 1980, Honky Tonk Freeway, 1981, I'm Dancing As Fast As I Can, 1982, Diner, 1982, Blue Thunder, 1983, Frankenweenie, 1984, Get Crazy, 1983, C.H.U.D., 1984, Key Exchange, 1985, The Boss' Wife, 1986, Hannah and Her Sisters, 1986, Born in East L.A., 1987, D.O.A., 1988, The Milagro Beanfield War, 1988, Leviathan, 1989, Little Monsters, 1989, Friends, Lovers and Lunatics, 1989, Coupe de Ville, 1990, My Blue Heaven, 1990, Home Alone, 1990, City Slickers, 1991, Home Alone 2, 1992, (also dir.) Rookie of the Year, 1993, City Slickers II: The Legend of Curley's Gold, 1994, (also prodr.) Tenderfoot, 1995. Office: CAA 9830 Wilshire Blvd Beverly Hills CA 90212*

STERN, DANIEL, author, executive, educator; b. N.Y.C., Jan. 18, 1928; s. Morris and Dora (Hochman) S.; m. Gloria Shapiro, Nov. 9, 1963; 1 son, Eric Branfman. Sr. v.p., mng. dir., mem. bd. mgmt. McCann-Erickson Advt., Inc., N.Y.C., 1964-69; v.p. advt. and publicity worldwide, also dir. Warner Bros., 1969-72; v.p. dir. mktg. Longchamps, Inc., N.Y.C., 1972-73; v.p., creative dir. Lubar-Southard, Inc., N.Y.C., 1973; fellow Ctr. for Humanities, Wesleyan U., 1969, vis. prof. letters and English, 1976-79; v.p. promotion East Coast CBS Entertainment, N.Y.C., 1979-86; pres. entertainment divsn. McCaffrey & McCall, Advt., N.Y.C., 1986; prof. English and creative writing U. Houston, 1992—; Cullen disting. prof. English, 1993—; dir. Humanities, 92nd St. YMHA, 1988. Author: Girl with Glass Heart, 1953, The Guests of Fame, 1955, Miss America, 1959, Who Shall Live, Who Shall Die, 1963 (Internat. Remembrance award for fiction Bergen Belsen Assn. 1973), After the War, 1967, The Suicide Academy, 1968, The Rose Rabbi, 1971, Final Cut, 1975, An Urban Affair, 1980, Twice Told Tales, 1989 (Richard and Hinda Rosenthal Fiction award AAAL 1990), Twice Upon a Time, 1992. With U.S. Army, 1946-47. Mem. PEN, Nat. Book Critics Circle, Author's League.

STERN, DANIEL ALAN, business management consultant; b. Bklyn., Aug. 28, 1944; s. William Joseph and Rita (Winegarten) S.; m. Gail Lynn Eddy, June 28, 1978. BS, Cornell U., 1965, PhD, 1971; MS, U. So. Calif., 1967. Cert. coll. teaching credential, Calif. Mem. sr. staff Hughes Aircraft Co., Culver City, Calif., 1965-73; mgr. digital signal processing TRW, Redondo Beach, Calif., 1973-79; pres. Martin & stern, Inc., Manhattan Beach, Calif., 1979-83; v.p. corp. devel. ROCKCOR, Inc., Redmond, Wash., 1983-85; v.p. advanced systems Rockcor group Olin Corp., Redmond, 1985-87; v.p. advanced def. systems Olin Corp., East Alton, Ill., 1987-89, v.p. tech., 1989-90; v.p. parent co. Olin Corp., Stamford, Conn., 1990-92, chief scientist, 1991-92; ind. cons., 1992—; bd. dirs. Secure Trans., Inc., Ponoma, Calif.; cons. Mertec, 1985—, United Technologies, 1993—; mem. bd. advisors U. Conn. Advanced Materials Inst., Storrs, 1991-92; mem. tech. coun. Conf. Bd., N.Y., 1992. Councilman City of Manhattan Beach, 1990-91, mayor pro tem, 1991-92, mayor, 1992-93; bd. dirs. Congregation Tifereth Jacob. Hughes fellow Hughes Aircraft Co., 1966. Mem. IEEE, Assn. U.S. Army, Assn. Old Crows, League Calif. Cities. Republican. Jewish. Avocations: motorcycle riding, shooting. Home and Office: 473 32d St Manhattan Beach CA 90266

STERN, DAVID JOEL, basketball association executive; b. N.Y.C., Sept. 22, 1942; s. William and Anna (Bronstein) S.; m. Dianne Bock, Nov. 27, 1963; children Andrew, Eric. B.A., Rutgers U., 1963; LL.B., Columbia U., 1966. Bar: N.Y. 1963. Assoc. Proskauer Rose Goetz & Mendelsohn, N.Y.C., 1966-74, ptnr., 1974-78; gen. counsel Nat. Basketball Assn., N.Y.C., 1978-80, exec. v.p. bus. and legal affairs, 1980-84, commr., 1984—. Trustee Beth Israel Med. Ctr., 1985—, Rutgers U. Found., 1987—, Columbia U., 1992—; mem. Martin Luther King, Jr. Fed. Holiday Commn., 1988—; White House Com. for a Drug-Free Am., 1988; bd. dirs. NAACP, 1990-93. Mem. ABA, N.Y. State Bar Assn., Assn. Bar City N.Y. (chmn. com. on entertainment and sports 1983-86). Office: NBA Olympic Tower 645 Fifth Ave New York NY 10022-5910

STERN, DENNIS M., lawyer; b. Amsterdam, Holland, Oct. 27, 1941; s. Henry and Henny S.; m. Barbara Freund, Sept. 5, 1965; children: Sharon L., Michelle A., Jonathan D. BA, CUNY, 1963; LLB, NYU, 1966, LLM, 1967. bar: N.Y. 1967, U.S. Dist. Ct. (so. dist.) N.Y. 1972, Pa. 1976, Conn. 1989. Assoc. Frankenthaler, Kohn & Schneider, N.Y.C., 1969-74; v.p. Wells Fargo Alarm Svcs., King of Prussia, Pa., 1974-83; exec. v.p. gen. counsel, sec. Nat. Guardian Corp., Greenwich, Conn., 1983—. Mem. ABA, The Corp. Bar Assn., Am. Soc. Corp. Secs. Avocations: skiing, racquetball, bicycling. Office: Nat Guardian Corp 777 W Putnam Ave Greenwich CT 06830-5090

STERN, EDWARD, performing company executive. Producing artistic dir. Cin. Playhouse in the Park. Office: Cincinnati Playhouse in the Park Box 6537 Cincinnati OH 45206-0537

STERN, EDWARD ABRAHAM, physics educator; b. Detroit, Sept. 19, 1930; s. Jacob Munich and Rose (Kravitz) S.; m. Sylvia Rita Steidl, Oct. 30, 1955; children: Hilary, Shari, Miri. BS, Calif. Tech., 1951, PhD, 1955. Post-doctoral fellow Calif. Tech., Pasadena, 1955-57; asst. prof. U. Md., College Park, 1957-61, assoc. prof., 1961-64, prof., 1964-65; prof. U. Wash., Seattle, 1965—. Contbr. over 200 articles to profl. jours.; editor; three books. Recipient B. Warren award Am. Crystallography Assn., 1979; named Guggenheim fellow, Cambridge, Eng., 1963-64, NSF Sr. Post-doctoral fellow, Haifa, Israel, 1970-71, Fulbright fellow, Jerusalem, Israel, 1985-86. Fellow AAAS, Am. Physical Soc. Achievements include patent for x-ray focusing device; development of x-ray absorption fine structure techniques; research on surface plasmons, nonlinear reflection from surfaces, electronic properties of alloys. Office: U Wash Physics Dept FM-15 Seattle WA 98195

STERN, ERNEST, science research executive, electrical engineer; b. Wetter, Hesse, Germany, June 5, 1928; came to U.S., 1938; s. Albert and Hilda (Katz) S.; m. Shola Jackson, May, 1955 (dec. Dec. 1960); children: Jessica, Sara; m. Phoebe M. Salten, Sept., 1962 (div. 1971); children: Hilary, Jennifer; m. Marcia Brown, May 16, 1971. BSEE, Columbia U., 1953; postgrad., Cornell U., 1953-55. Sr. engr. Sperry Gyroscope, L.I., N.Y., 1955-58; sr. researcher electronics lab. GE, Liverpool, N.Y., 1958-60; v.p. rsch. Microwave Chems. Lab., N.Y.C., 1961-64; assoc. divsn. head, sr. staff mem. MIT Lincoln Lab., Lexington, Mass., 1964-95, dir. Strategic Def. Initiative study of laser radars, 1984-85; cons., 1995—; mem. sci. and engring. adv. group to Strategic Def. Initiative Orgn., Washington, 1985-88. Co-inventor X-Ray Lithography, 1973 and ultrasonic, gyromagnetic and flat panel imaging devices. With USN, 1946-48. Fellow IEEE (sonics and ultrasonics

adminstrn. com. 1980-84); mem. AAAS, Am. Phys. Soc., Appalachian Mountain Club. Democrat. Jewish. Avocations: mountain hiking, music, ballet, reading. Office: MIT Lincoln Lab PO Box 73 244 Wood St Lexington MA 02173-6499

STERN, FRITZ RICHARD, historian, educator; b. Breslau, Germany, Feb. 2, 1926; came to U.S., 1938, naturalized, 1947; s. Rudolf A. and Catherine (Brieger) S.; m. Margaret J. Bassett, Oct. 11, 1947 (div. 1992); children: Frederick P., Katherine Stern Brennan. B.A., Columbia U., 1946, M.A., 1948, Ph.D., 1953; D.Litt. (hon.), Oxford U., 1985. Lectr., instr. Columbia U., 1946-51, faculty, 1953—, prof. history, 1963—, Seth Low prof. history, 1967-92, univ. prof., 1992—, provost, 1980-83; acting asst. prof. Cornell U. 1951-53; tchr. Free U. Berlin, 1954, Yale U., 1963; permanent vis. prof. U. Konstanz, West Germany, 1966—; sr. adviser U.S. Embassy, Bonn, 1993-94; Élie Halévy prof. U. Paris, spring 1979; Phi Beta Kappa vis. scholar, 1979-80; Tanner lectr. Yale, 1993. Author: The Politics of Cultural Despair, 1961, The Failure of Illiberalism-Essays in the Political Culture of Modern Germany, 1972, rev. edit., 1992, Gold and Iron: Bismarck, Bleichroeder and the Bldg. of the German Empire, 1977 (recipient Lionel Trilling award Columbia U.), Dreams and Delusions: The Drama of German History, 1987; editor: The Varieties of History, 1956, 71, (with L. Krieger) The Responsibility of Power, 1967; mem. editorial bd. Foreign Affairs, 1978-92; contbr. articles to profl. jours.; reviewer Fgn. Affairs, 1963—. Trustee German Marshall Fund, 1981—; Aspen Inst. of Berlin, 1983—; senator Deutsche Nationalstiftung, 1994—; mem. Trilateral Commn., 1983-90. Decorated Officer's Cross Order of Merit Fed. Republic of Germany; fellow Center Advanced Behavioral Scis., 1957-58; fellow Social Sci. Research Council, 1960-61; fellow Am. Council Learned Socs., 1966-67; fellow Netherlands Inst. Advanced Study, 1972-73; mem. Nuffield Coll., Oxford, 1966-67, Inst. Advanced Study Princeton, 1969-70; Guggenheim fellow, 1969-70; Ford Found. grantee, 1976-77; vis. scholar Russell Sage Found., 1989, spring 1993; recipient Leopold-Lucas-prize Evang. Faculty U. Tübingen, 1984. Mem. Am. Hist. Assn., Am. Acad. Arts and Scis., Am. Philos. Soc., Coun. Fgn. Rels., Deutsche Akademie für Sprache und Dichtung (corr.), Berlin Brandenburgische Akademie der Wissenschaften (corr.), Orden Pour le Mérite, Germany, Phi Beta Kappa (senator-at-large 1973-78). Club: Century (N.Y.C.). Home: 15 Claremont Ave New York NY 10027-6814

STERN, GAIL FRIEDA, historical association director; b. Atlantic City, May 18, 1950; d. Herbert and Faith (Beldegreen) Stern; m. Irwin Allen Popowsky (div.); m. Shawn Paul Aubitz, Sept. 20, 1987; 1 child, Jonathan. Student, Brown U., 1972; postgrad., U. Pa., 1973. Asst. in decorative arts Phila. Mus. Art, 1972-75; asst. curator Wheaton Mus. Glass, Millville, N.J., 1973-74; assoc. dir. Pa. Humanities Coun., Phila., 1976-79; mus. curator The Balch Inst. for Ethnic Studies, Phila., 1979-83, mus. dir., 1984-93; dir. Hist. Soc. Princeton, N.J., 1993—; chair State Task Force on Folk Arts and Culture, 1981-82; vice chmn. crafts panel Pa. Coun. on the Arts, Harrisburg, 1988-89; chair cultural conservation com., Pa. Heritage Affairs Commn., Harrisburg, 1990-92; participant Internat. Partnership in Mus., Singapore, 1991. Mem. Mus. Coun. Phila. (v.p. 1982-83), Am. Assn. Mus./Internat. Coun. Mus. (bd. dirs.), N.J. Mus. Assn. (mem. bd. dirs.) Am. Assn. for State and Local History Awards (N.J. chair 1994-95). Home: 131 E Maple Ave Morrisville PA 19067-6235 Office: Hist Soc Princeton 158 Nassau St Princeton NJ 08542-7006

STERN, GEOFFREY, lawyer, disciplinary counsel; b. Columbus, Ohio, Nov. 29, 1942; s. Leonard J. and Anastasia (Percin) S.; m. Barbara Shnider; children: Emily, Elizabeth. Student, Williams Coll., 1960-63; BA cum laude, Ohio State U., 1965, JD summa cum laude, 1968. Bar: Ohio 1968. Assoc. Alexander, Ebinger, Holschuh & Fisher, Columbus, Ohio, 1968-72; ptnr. Folkerth, Calhoun, Webster, Maurer & O'Brien, Columbus, Ohio, 1972-80, Arter & Hadden, Columbus, Ohio, 1980-93; disciplinary counsel Supreme Ct. of Ohio, 1993—; nat. coordinating counsel for asbestos litigation Combustion Engring. Inc. and Basic, Inc., 1985-93; lectr. on legal ethics; mem. Spl. Commn. to Review Ohio Ethics Rules, 1995—. Sr. editor Ohio State Law Jour., 1967-68. Pres. Bexley (Ohio) City Coun., 1977-80, mem., 1973-80, mem. Bexley Civil Svc. Commn., 1983-85; v.p., trustee Creative Living, Columbus, 1981-89, Ohio Citizens Com. for Arts, Columbus, 1982-88; mem. Nat. Def. Com. on Asbestos in Bldgs. Litigation, 1986-92; pub. mem. Ohio Optical Dispensers Bd., Columbus, 1978-82. Recipient Am. Jurisprudence Evidence award Ohio State U. Coll. Law, 1967. Fellow Am. Bar Found., Columbus Bar Found., Ohio State Bar Found.; mem. Ohio State Bar Assn. (com. on legal ethics and profl. conduct, sec. 1981-90, vice chmn. 1990-92, chmn. 1992-93), Columbus Bar Assn. (profl. ethics com 1975-86, 90-93), Order of Coif, Phi Beta Kappa, Pi Sigma Alpha. Home: 278 Crossing Creek N Columbus OH 43230-6108 Office: Disciplinary Counsel of Ohio Supreme Ct 175 S 3d St Ste 280 Columbus OH 43215

STERN, GERALD DANIEL, lawyer; b. N.Y.C., May 16, 1933; s. Solomon Stern and Stella Schoen; m. Doris Gittelman Mar. 21, 1960; children: Nelson M., Andrew L., Teri H. BA, NYU, 1954, LLB, 1957. Bar: N.Y. 1957, Calif. 1988, U.S. Ct. Appeals (2d cir.) 1959, U.S. Dist. Ct. (no. dist.) N.Y. 1965, U.S. Dist. Ct. D.C. 1969, U.S. Ct. Appeals (D.C. cir.) 1969, U.S. Dist. Ct. Md. 1970, U.S. Supreme Ct. 1970, U.S. Tax Ct. 1971, U.S. Ct. Appeals (9th cir.) 1987, U.S. Ct. Appeals (fed. cir.) 1987, U.S. Dist. Ct. (no. dist. Calif. 1987, so. dist. 1988). Assoc. Paul, Weiss, Rifkind, Wharton & Garrison, N.Y.C., 1957-67, ptnr., 1967-87; ptnr. Irell and Manella, Menlo Park, Calif., 1987-89, Brown & Bain, Palo Alto, Calif., 1989-91, Davis & Schroeder, Monterey, Calif., 1991-92; adj. prof. law NYU, 1983-87. Author: The Naked First Lady - A Humorous History of Monterey Peninsula, 1992. Chmn. legal com., trustee Westchester Reform Temple, Scarsdale, N.Y., 1983-87. Mem. ABA, N.Y. State Bar Assn., N.Y. County Bar Assn., Fed. Bar Coun., Beach Point Club, Boca West Club, Chamisol Tennis Club. Home and Office: 25493 Paseo De Cumbre Monterey CA 93940-6637

STERN, GERALD DANIEL, poet; b. Pitts. Feb. 22, 1925; s. Harry and Ida (Barach) S.; m. Patricia Miller, Sept. 12, 1952 (div.); children: Rachel, David. BA, U. Pitts., 1947; MA, Columbia U., 1949. English tchr., prin. Lake Grove (N.Y.) Sch., 1951-53; English tchr. Victoria Dr. Secondary Sch., Glasgow, Scotland, 1953-54; English instr. Temple U., Phila., 1956-63; assoc. prof. English Indiana (Pa.) U. of Pa., 1963-67; prof. English Somerset (N.J.) County Coll., 1968-82; prof. English, Writers' Workshop, U. Iowa, Iowa City, 1982—; lectr. Douglas Coll., New Brunswick, N.J., 1968; vis. poet Sarah Lawrence Coll., Bronxville, N.Y., 1978, U. Pitts., 1978; vis. prof. Columbia U., N.Y.C., 1980, Bucknell U., Lewisburg, Pa., 1988, NYU, 1989, 91, Princeton U., 1989; Fanny Hurst prof. Washington U., St. Louis, 1985; coal. chmn. creative writing U. Ala., Tuscaloosa, 1984. Author: (poetry) Pineys, 1971, The Naming of Beasts, 1972, Rejoicings: Selected Poems 1966-72, 1973, Lucky Life, 1977 (Lamont Poetry selection 1977, Nat. Book Critics Cir. award for poetry nominee 1978), The Red Coal, 1981 (Melville Caine award Poetry Soc. Am. 1982), Paradise Poems, 1984, Lovesick, 1987, New and Selected Poems 1989, Two Long Poems, 1990, Leaving Another Kingdom: Selected Poems, 1990, Bread Without Sugar, 1992, (essays) Selected Essays, 1988. Guggenheim fellow, 1980, Am. Acad. Poets fellow, 1993; NEA grantee to be master poet for Pa. 1973-75, Creative Writing grantee, 1976, 81, 87, State of Pa. Creative Writing grantee, 1979; recipient Gov. award for excellence in arts State of Pa., 1980, Bess Hokin award Poetry, 1980, Bernard F. Connor's award Paris Rev., 1981, Am. Poetry Rev. award, 1982, Jerome J. Shestack Poetry prize Am. Poetry Rev., 1984. Office: U Iowa 436 EPB Iowa City IA 52242

STERN, GERALD JOSEPH, advertising executive; b. Chgo., Nov. 1, 1925; s. Abraham and Mary (Spivak) S.; m. Sally R. Welham, May 28, 1950; children: Larry S., David J. B.S. in Journalism, U. Ill., 1949. Subscription sales promotion Esquire Mag., Chgo., 1949-50; v.p., creative dir. Marvin Gordon & Assos., Chgo., 1950-54; pres., chief exec. officer Stern, Walters/ Earle Ludgin, Inc. (advt.), Chgo., Beverly Hills, Calif. and Ft. Lauderdale, Fla., from 1954, formerly chmn. bd., chief exec. officer, now ret.; bd. dir. Advance Leasing Corp., Ted Bates Adv. Inc.; Mem. Nat. Com. Improving Advt. Bd. dirs. Off-the-St. Club. Served with USAAF, 1943-46. Mem. Am. Assn. Advt. Agys. (treas. Chgo. div. 1973), Nat. Advt. Rev. Bd., Chgo. Advt. Club. Club: Twin Orchard Country (dir.). Home: 726 Raleigh Rd Glenview IL 60025-4326

STERN, GERALD MANN, lawyer; b. Chgo., Apr. 5, 1937; s. Lloyd and Fannye (Wener) S.; m. Linda Stone, Dec. 20, 1969; children: Eric, Jesse,

Maia. B.S. in Econs., U. Pa., 1958; LL.B. cum laude, Harvard, 1961. Bar: D.C. 1961, Calif. 1991, U.S. Supreme Ct. 1971. Trial atty. civil rights div. U.S. Dept. Justice, 1961-64; assoc. firm Arnold & Porter, Washington, 1964-68; ptnr. Arnold & Porter, 1969-76; founding ptnr. Rogovin, Stern & Huge, Washington, 1976-81; exec. v.p., sr. gen. counsel Occidental Petroleum Corp., Washington, 1981-82, L.A., 1982-92; spl. counsel fin. instn. fraud and health care fraud U.S. Dept. Justice, Washington, 1993—. Author: The Buffalo Creek Disaster, 1976; co-author: Southern Justice, 1965. Mem. ABA. Home: 3322 Newark St NW Washington DC 20008-3330

STERN, GRACE MARY, former state legislator; b. Holyoke, Mass., July 10, 1925; d. Frank McLellan and Marguerite M. (Nason) Dain; m. Charles H. Suber, June 21, 1947 (div. 1959); children: Ann, Peter, Thomas, John; m. Herbert L. Stern, May 13, 1962; stepchildren: Gwen, Herbert III, Robert. Student, Wellesley Coll., 1942-45; LLD (hon.), Shimer Coll., 1984. Asst. supr. Deerfield Twp., Lake County, Ill., 1967-70; county clk. Lake County, Ill., 1970-82; mem. Ill. Ho. of Reps., Springfield, 1984-92, Ill. State Senate, 1993-95. Author: With a Stern Eye, 1967, Still Stern, 1969. Candidate lt. gov. State of Ill., 1982. Democrat. Presbyterian. Home: 291 Marshman Ave Highland Park IL 60035-4732 Office: 540 Frontage Rd Ste 1000 Northfield IL 60093

STERN, GUY, German language educator, writer; b. Hildesheim, Germany, Jan. 14, 1922; came to U.S., 1937, naturalized, 1943; s. Julius and Hedwig (Silberberg) S.; m. Judith Owens, June 16, 1979; 1 child, Mark. B.A. in Romance Langs., Hofstra Coll., 1948; M.A. with honors in Germanic Langs., Columbia U., 1950, Ph.D. with honors, 1953. Grad. asst., then instr. Columbia U., 1948-55; asst. prof., then asso. prof. Denison U., Granville, Ohio, 1955-63; prof. German, dept. head U. Cin., 1964-73, dean univ., 1973; 76; prof., chmn. Germanic and Slavic dept. U. Md., College Park, 1976-78; v.p., provost Wayne State U., Detroit, 1978-80; disting. prof. German Wayne State U., 1980—; guest prof. Goethe Inst., Freiburg U., summers 1963-66, 84, Frankfurt U., 1993; adv. editor langs. and linguistics Dover Publs. Co-author: Brieflich Erzaehlt, 1956, Listen and Learn German, 1957, Say It in German, 1958, Uebung macht den Meister, 1959, An Invitation to German Poetry, 1960, Hints on Speaking German, 1961, Quick Change Pattern Drills, vol. I, 1962, vol. II, 1963, Hoer zu und Rat mit, 1964; author: Efraim Frisch: Zum Verstaendnis des Geistigen, 1964, War, Weimar and Literature, 1971, Alfred Neumann (anthology with biography), 1979, Literatur im Exil, 1989, Nazi Book Burning and the American Response, 1989; editor: Konstellationen: Die besten Erzaehlungen des Neuen Merkur, 1964; co-editor: Nelly Sachs Ausgewaehlte Gedichte, 1968; assoc. editor: Lessing Yearbook, 1970-72, edit. bd. 1972—; sr. editor, 1979-81; contbr. articles on 18th and 20th century German lit. to profl. jours.; also chpts. to books. Bd. dirs. Kurt Weill Found., sec., 1990—; bd. dirs. Leo Baeck Inst., 1967—, mem. exec. bd., 1978—; bd. dirs., chair acad. adv. com. Holocaust Meml. Mus. Greater Detroit; co-founder, pres. Lessing Soc., 1975-77; bd. dirs. Detroit Am. Jewish Com., 1988—. With AUS, 1942-45. Decorated Bronze Star; Fulbright Rsch. grantee U. Munich, 1961-63; recipient Order of Merit 1st Class, 1968, Friendship award, 1983, Germany, 1987, Grand Order of Merit, Festschrift in Honor of Guy Stern; Exile and Enlightment, 1987, Goethe medal, 1989, Presdl. award for Excellence in Teaching, 1992, Disting. Alumni award Hofstra U., 1993. Mem. Am. Assn. Tchrs. German (pres. 1970-72, Disting. Germanist of Yr. 1985, hon. mem. 1989), AAUP, Internat. PEN Club, MLA, South Atlantic MLA, Soc. for Exile Studies (v.p. 1981—). Home: 20672 Knob Woods Dr Southfield MI 48076-4033

STERN, HERBERT JAY, lawyer; b. N.Y.C., Nov. 8, 1936; s. Samuel and Sophie (Berkowitz) S.; children: Jason Andrew and Jordan Ezekiel (twins), Samuel Abraham, Sarah Kathrine. B.A., Hobart Coll., 1958; J.D. (Ford Found. scholar), U. Chgo., 1961; LL.D. (hon.), Seton Hall Law Sch., 1973, Hobart Coll., 1974; L.H.D. (hon.), Newark State Coll., 1973; D.C.L. (hon.), Bloomfield Coll., 1973; Litt.D. (hon.), Montclair State Coll., 1973. Bar: N.Y. 1961, N.J. 1971. Asst. dist. atty. New York County, 1962-65; trial atty. organized crime and racketeering sect. Dept. of Justice, 1965-69; chief asst. U.S. atty. Dist. of N.J., Newark, 1969-70; U.S. atty. Dist. of N.J., 1971-74, U.S. dist. judge, 1974-87; ptnr. Stern & Greenberg, Newark, 1990—; mem. adv. com. U. Chgo. Law Sch. Author: Judgment in Berlin, 1984 (Valley Forge award Freedoms Found. 1984, Torch of Learning award Am. Friends of Hebrew U. 1987), Trying Cases to Win, Vol. I, 1991, Vol. II, 1992, Vol. III, 1993. Named One of America's 10 Outstanding Young Men U.S. Jr. C. of C., 1971; Swartzer scholar U. Chgo. Law Sch., 1985; recipient Dean's Club award U. Akron Sch. Law, 1986, medal of excellence Hobart Coll., 1990. Fellow ABA, Am. Law Inst. (Clarence Darrow award), Internat. Platform Assn.; mem. ABA, N.J. Bar Assn., Fed. Bar Assn. (past pres. Newark chpt., recipient William J. Brennan, Jr. award 1987), Essex County Bar Assn., Am. Judicature Soc., Phi Alpha Delta. Subject of book Tiger in the Court, 1973. Office: 75 Livingston Ave Roseland NJ 07068-3701

STERN, HOWARD ALLAN, radio disc jockey, television show host; b. Roosevelt, N.Y., 1954; s. Ben and Ray S.; m. Alison Berns, 1978; children: Emily, Debra, Ashley Jade. BA in Comm., Boston U., 1976. Disc jockey Sta. WRNW, Briarcliff Manor, N.Y., 1976-78, Sta. WCCC, Hartford, Conn., 1978-79, Sta. WWWW, Detroit, 1979-80, Sta. WWDC, Washington, 1980-82, Sta. WNBC, N.Y.C., 1982-85, Sta. WXRK, N.Y.C., 1985—, numerous other markets, 1986—. TV shows include The Howard Stern Show (WOR-TV), 1990-92, The Howard Stern Interview (E!), 1992-93, The Howard Stern Show (E!), 1994—; recordings include 50 Ways To Rank Your Mother, 1982, Crucified by the FCC, 1991; pay-per-view spls./videos include: Howard Stern's Neglige and Underpants Party, U.S. Open Sores, Butt Bongo Fiesta, The Miss Howard Stern New Year's Eve Pageant; Books include: Private Parts, 1993. Libertarian candidate for gov. State of N.Y., 1994. Rest Stop on I-295 in N.J. named in his honor, 1995. Address: The Howard Stern Show WXRK-FM 600 Madison Ave New York NY 10022 also: c/o Don Buchwald & Associates 10 E 44th St New York NY 10017-3606*

STERN, ISAAC, violinist; b. Kreminiecz, Russia, July 21, 1920; came to U.S., 1921; s. Solomon and Clara S.; m. Nora Kaye, Nov. 10, 1948; m. Vera Lindenblit, Aug. 17, 1951; children: Shira, Michael, David. Student, San Francisco Conservatory, 1930-37; numerous hon. degrees including, Dalhousie U., 1971, U. Hartford, 1971, Bucknell U., 1974, Hebrew U., Jerusalem, 1975, Yale U., 1975, Columbia U., 1977, Johns Hopkins U., 1979, U. Md., 1983, Tel Aviv U., 1983, NYU, 1989, U. Ill., 1992, Harvard U., 1992. Recital debut San Francisco, 1934; orchestral debut San Francisco Symphony Orch. (Pierre Monteux condr.), 1936; N.Y. debut, 1937; Carnegie Hall recital debut, 1943; N.Y. Philharm. debut (Arthur Rodzinski condr.), 1944; participated Prades Festival with Pablo Casals, 1950-52; soloist for first orchestral and recital performances at Kennedy Ctr., Washington; first Am. to perform in USSR after World War II, 1956; mem. Istomin-Rose-Stern trio, 1962-83 (Beethoven cycle w/Istomin & Rose 1970-71); performed in China at invitation of Chinese govt., 1979; performed world premieres of violin works by Bernstein, Dutilleux, Hindemith, Maxwell Davies, Penderecki, Rochberg and Schuman; has played with major orchestras, given countless recitals and performed at important festivals in the U.S., Europe, Israel, Far East, Australia and S. Am. Over 100 records, cassettes and CD's for CBS Masterworks, named Artist Laureate 1984 CBS Masterworks; made soundtrack for motion pictures Humoresque (Warner Bros.) and Fiddler on the Roof (United Artists); starred in soundtrack Tonight We Sing (20th Century Fox) and Journey to Jerusalem with Leonard Bernstein; documentary film From Mao to Mozart-Isaac Stern in China (Academy award 1981, Cannes Film Festival Special Mention), Carnegie Hall: The Grand Reopening, 1987 (Emmy award), Isaac Stern-A Life, 1991. Chmn. bd. Am.-Israel Cultural Found.; chmn., founder Jerusalem Music Ctr.; originating mem. Nat. Endowment for the Arts; pres. Carnegie Hall, N.Y.C., 1960—. Recipient numerous Grammy awards; Comdr. Ordre de la Couronne, 1974; Commander Legion d'Honneur, 1979, 90; J.F. Kennedy Ctr. Honors, 1984; Commander's Cross of the Order of the Dannebrog, Denmark, 1985; Musician of the Year-ABC/Musical Am., 1986; Fellow of Jerusalem, 1986; Wolf Prize, 1987; Grammy Lifetime Achievement Award, 1987; Nat. Medal of Honor, 1991; Presdl. Medal of Honor, 1992; numerous local city awards. Office: care ICM Artists Ltd 40 W 57th St New York NY 10019-4001

STERN, JAMES ANDREW, investment banker; b. N.Y.C., Oct. 1, 1950; s. Arthur and Lenore (Oppenheimer) S.; m. Jane Yusem, April 13, 1975; children: Peter, David. BS, Tufts U., 1972; MBA, Harvard U., 1974. Assoc.

Lehman Bros. Inc., N.Y.C., 1974-79, v.p.; 1979-82, mng. dir., 1982-94; chmn. The Cypress Group, N.Y.C., 1994—; dir. K & F Industries, Inc., N.Y.C., Loral Aerospace Holdings, Inc., N.Y.C., R.P. Scherer Corp., N.Y.C., Noel Group, Inc., N.Y.C., Lear Seating Corp., N.Y.C., Infinity Broadcasting Corp., N.Y.C. Trustee Tufts U., Medford, Mass., 1982—. Clubs: Quaker Ridge Golf (Scarsdale, N.Y.), Beach Point (Mamaroneck, N.Y.). Avocations: golf, reading. Office: The Cypress Group Inc 425 Lexington Ave New York NY 10017

STERN, JAN PETER, sculptor; b. Berlin, Nov. 14, 1926; came to U.S., 1938, naturalized, 1945; s. Frederick Martin and Therese Else (van Perlstein) S.; m. Irene Monat, Mar. 19, 1955; children: Daniel Martin, William Glenn. B.Indsl. Design, Syracuse U., 1953; postgrad., New Sch. Social Research, N.Y.C., 1955. Design engr. hdqrs. staff Worthington Corp., Harrison, N.J., 1953-55; product designer Donald Deskey Assos., N.Y.C., 1955-58. One-man shows: Barone Gallery, N.Y.C., 1960, Pa. State U., 1962, New Sch. Social Research, 1963, Ankrum Gallery, Los Angeles, 1968, group shows include: San Francisco Mus. Modern Art, 1974, Chgo. Mus. Contemporary Art, 1975, Marlborough Gallery, N.Y.C., 1976, Denise Rene Gallery, N.Y.C., 1978, Esther Robles Gallery, Los Angeles, 1978, Los Angeles Contemporary Inst. Art, 1982; represented in permanent collections: Stedlijk Mus., Amsterdam, Joseph H. Hirshhorn Mus., Norton Simon Mus., Walter Gropius Coll., Vera Newmann Coll., Storm King Mus., Los Angeles City Hall Mall, U. Hawaii, Capitol Mall, Washington, State Found. on Culture and Arts, Hawaii; pub. commns. include Los Angeles City Hall Mall, Golden Gateway Ctr., San Francisco. CPR instr. ARC, 1948-78. Served with U.S. Army, 1945-46. Mem. Artists Equity Physicians for Social Responsibility, Artists for Econ. Action. Club: Windsurfing Assn. Am. Home: PO Box 1972 Santa Monica CA 90406-1972

STERN, JOAN NAOMI, lawyer; b. Phila., Mar. 7, 1944; d. Clarence J. and Diana D. (Goldberg) S. BA, U. Pa., 1965; JD, Temple U., 1977. Bar: Pa. 1977. Assoc. Blank, Rome, Comisky & McCauley, Phila., 1977-83, ptnr., 1983—, co-chair pub. fin. group, 1982-93, chair pub. fin. group, 1993, co-chair pub. fin. dept., 1994—; cons. counsel Phila. Charter Commn., 1993-94. Contbr. articles to profl. jours. Mem. Sch. Dist. Task Force on Regulatory Reform, Phila., 1987, Tax Policy and Budget Com., 1989, Phila. Mayor's Fiscal Adv. Com., 1990; chair Sch. Dist. of Phila. Task Force on Alternate Financing Strategies, 1995; bd. mgrs. Moore Coll. Art and Design, Phila., 1993—; bd. dirs Police Athletic League, Phila., 1994—. Fellow Am. Bar Found.; mem. ABA, Nat. Assn. Bond Lawyers, Phila. Bar Assn., Phila. Bar Assn. (chmn. mcpl. govt. com. 1983—), Pa. Assn. Bond Lawyers. Office: Blank Rome Comisky & McCauley 4 Penn Center Plz Philadelphia PA 19103-2521

STERN, JOSEPH A., lawyer; b. Cleve., Dec. 7, 1949; s. Arthur J. and Thelma (Arnold) S. BA, Yale U., 1972, JD, 1976. Assoc. Winthrop Stimson, N.Y.C., 1976-79; assoc. Fried Frank Harris Shriver & Jacobson, N.Y.C., London, 1975-84, ptnr., 1984—. Vice chair, dir. Mex. Am. Legal Defense and Edn. Fund, L.A., 1991—; dir. Am. Friend Chamber Music of Europe, N.Y.C., 1986—. Mem. ABA, City Bar Assn. Office: Fried Frank Harris 1 New York Plz New York NY 10004

STERN, JOSEPH AARON, services contracting executive; b. N.Y.C., Apr. 24, 1927; s. Charles M. and Anna (Robinson) S.; m. Phyllis A. Swett, Aug. 26, 1950; children: Carole, Beth, Charles. BS in Food Tech., MIT, 1949, MS in Food Tech., 1950, PhD in Food Tech., 1953. Food technologist Davis Bros. Fisheries Inc., Gloucester, Mass., 1948-49; teaching and research asst. Dept. Food Tech. MIT, Cambridge, 1950-53; assoc. prof. U. Wash. Coll. of Fisheries, Seattle, 1953-55; chief biochemistry unit, chief life scis. sect.; mgr. interplanetary mission support and advanced exploration systems Boeing Co., Seattle, 1956-66; assoc. prof. U. Wash. Coll. of Fisheries, Seattle, 1963-68; asst. sect. mgr. Jet Propulsion Lab., Pasadena, Calif., 1966-69; pres. The Bionetics Corp., Hampton, Va., 1969—. Contbr. articles to profl. jours. Recipient cert. appreciation Viking Project Office, NASA, 1975, pub. svc. award NASA, 1977. Mem. Am. Inst. Biol. Sci., AIAA, Nat. Contract Mgmt. Assn., N.Y. Acad. Scis., Sigma Xi. Office: The Bionetics Corp 2 Eaton St Ste 1000 Hampton VA 23669-4053

STERN, JOSEPH SMITH, JR., former footwear manufacturing company executive; b. Cin., Mar. 31, 1918; s. Joseph S. and Miriam (Haas) S.; m. Mary Stern, June 14, 1942; children: Peter Joseph, William Frederick, Peggy Ann Graeter. AB, Harvard U., 1940, MBA, 1943; HHD (hon.), Xavier U., 1988; DSc(hon.), U. Cin., 1989. With R. H. Macy & Co., N.Y.C., 1940-41; with U.S. Shoe Corp., Cin., 1941-68; v.p. U.S. Shoe Corp., 1951-65, pres., 1965-66, chmn. bd., chief exec. officer, 1966, chmn. exec. com., 1966-68, dir., 1956-70; prof. bus. policy emeritus U. Cin. Pres. bd. trustees Cin. and Hamilton County Pub. Libr.; chmn. Cin. Bicentennial Com., Greater Cin. Tall Stacks Commn.; trustee Cin. Music Hall Assn., Cin. Hist. Soc., Children's Hosp. Med. Center, Cin. Symphony Orch., Cin Country Day Sch., 1956-72, Family Sve., Cin., 1964-82; trustee, pres. Cin. Mus. Festival Assn.; pres. bd. trustees Children's Convalescent Hosp., Cin., 1972-75; bd. overseers vis. com. univ. libr. Harvard U. Served to lt. USNR, 1943-46. Recipient Disting. Community Sve. award NCCJ, 1986, Great Living Cincinnatian award Cin. C. of C., 1989, Disting. Svc. award U. Cin. Coll. Bus., 1992. Mem. Am. Footwear Industries Assn. (life; dir.). Jewish (past pres. temple). Clubs: Literary (Cin.), Harvard (Cin.) (pres. 1965), Queen City (Cin.), Queen City Optimists, Harvard (N.Y.C.). Home: 3 Grandin Pl Cincinnati OH 45208-3402

STERN, JOYCE REUBEN, lawyer; b. Chgo., Nov. 20, 1935; d. Jacob and Libby (Kunin) Reuben; m. J. Lee Stern, June 16, 1957; children: Daniel Morris, Murray Charles, Jonathan Ralph. BA cum laude, U. Mich., 1957, MPA, 1960; JD, Catholic U., 1979. Bar: Md. 1979, D.C. 1980, U.S. Dist. Ct. Md. 1980, U.S.C. Appeals (4th cir.) 1983, U.S. Supreme Ct. 1985. Assoc. Shaffer & Davis, Rockville, Md., 1979-80, Kutak, Rock & Huie, Washington, 1980-82; asst. county atty. Montgomery County Md., Rockville, 1982-84, assoc. county atty., 1984-85, sr. asst. county atty., 1985-88; assoc. Frank, Bernstein, Conaway & Goldman, Bethesda, Md., 1988-90; asst. atty. gen. State Atty. Gen., Annapolis, Md., 1990; county atty. Montgomery County, Md., 1990—. V.p. YWCA, San Bernardino, Calif., 1967; chairperson Project Assist, Ft. Walton Beach, FL, 1967-71. Mem. ABA, AAUW (bd. dirs. 1963-67), Md. State Bar Assn., Md. Assn. County Civil Attys. (pres. 1991—), Montgomery County Bar Assn. Democrat. Jewish. Office: Montgomery County Atty 101 Monroe St Fl 3 Rockville MD 20850-2540

STERN, LEO G., lawyer; b. Mpls., Apr. 10, 1945; s. Philip J. and June I. (Monasch) S.; m. Christine E. Lamb, June 29, 1968; children: Alison M., Zachary A. BA, U. Calif., Davis, 1967; JD cum laude, U. Minn., 1970. Bar: Minn. 1970, U.S. Dist. Ct. Minn. 1971, Calif. 1971, U.S. Ct. Appeals (6th, 7th and 8th circ.) 1985, U.S. Supreme Ct. 1993; cert. mediator and arbitrator, Minn. Ptnr. Cox, King & Stern, Mpls., 1977-95, Wright, West & Diessner, Mpls., 1977-84, Fredrikson & Byron, P.A., Mpls., 1984—. Mem. Minn. Bar Assn. (governing coun. environ. and natural resources law sect. 1989—), Am. Arbitration Assn. (arbitrator, mediator). Avocations: sailing, jogging. Home: 4331 Fremont Ave S Minneapolis MN 55409-1720 Office: Fredrikson & Byron PA 1100 International Ctr 900 2nd Ave S Minneapolis MN 55402-3314

STERN, LEONARD BERNARD, television and motion picture production company executive; b. N.Y.C., Dec. 23, 1923; s. Max and Esther (Marton) S.; m. Gloria Jane Stroock, Aug. 12, 1956; children: Michael Stroock, Kate Jennifer. Student, NYU, 1944. Dir. TV L.A., 1946-53; writer, dir., producer Jackie Gleason Show/Honeymoomers, Sergeant Bilko, Steve Allen Show N.Y.C., 1953-64; founder Price-Stern-Sloan, L.A., 1959-64, v.p., 1964-69; dir. Price-Stern-Sloan, 1969—, pres. Heyday Prodns., L.A., 1962-69, 75—; v.p. Talent Assocs./Norton Simon, L.A. and N.Y.C., 1965-75. Author: (with Roger Price) Mad Libs, 1958, What Not to Name the Baby, 1960, Dear Attila the Hun, 1985; (with Roger Price and Larry Sloan) The Baby Boomer Book of Names, 1985; (with Diane L. Robison) A Martian Wouldn't Say That, 1994; writer, dir.: (motion pictures) Just You and Me, Kid, 1979, Target, 1985, Missing Pieces, 1990; creator, writer, dir. 21 TV series, including Get Smart, McMillan and Wife and He and She, 1953-89; media editor Dialogue newsletter. Mem. adv. coun. Sch. of Arts, NYU; bd. dirs. Nat. Coun. for Families and TV, Inst. for Mental Health Initiatives.

Recipient Peabody award U. Ga., Writers Guild award 1956, 66, Nat. Assn. TV Arts and Scis. award 1956, 66-67, Emmy award 1956, 1966. Mem. Writers Guild Am., Dirs. Guild Am., Caucus for Producers, Writers and Dirs. (co-chmn.), Mem. of Yr award 1987, Disting. Svc. award 1987), Producers Guild Am. (pres.), Bd. Motion Picture and TV Fund Found. Office: 5th flr east 11835 W Olympic Blvd Los Angeles CA 90064-1823

STERN, LEONARD NORMAN, pet supply manufacturing company executive; b. N.Y.C., Mar. 28, 1938; s. Max and Hilda (Lowenthal) S.; m. Allison Maher; children: Emanuel Theodore, Edward Julius, Andrea Caroline. B.S. cum laude, NYU, 1956, M.B.A. 1957. Formerly pres., dir., now chmn., chief exec. officer Hartz Group, Inc., 1959—; pres., chmn. bd. Hartz Mountain Industries, pub. Village Voice; mem. adv. bd. Chem. Bank, N.Y.C., 1970—; active real estate constrn., devel. Bd. dirs. Manhattan Day Sch., Jewish Ctr., N.Y.C.; founder Albert Einstein Coll. Medicine, 1958; mem. N.Y.C. Holocaust Meml. Comm.; founder Homes for the Homeless; trustee, chmn. fin. com. NYU. Office: Hartz Mountain Industries 667 Madison Ave New York NY 10021-8029

STERN, LESLIE WARREN, management consultant; b. N.Y.C., July 3, 1938; s. Herman and Lillian Bella (Rosenbloom) S.; m. Madeline Carol Kuttner, Jan. 23, 1966; children: Derek Alexandre, Cory Jay. BS, Cornell U., 1960; MBA, Tulane U., 1967. Catering mgr. Irish Internat. Airlines, N.Y.C., 1960-61; dir. mgmt. services Plaza Hotel Hotel Corp. Am., N.Y.C., 1961-68; pres. Stern & Watson, Inc. (formerly L.W. Stern Assocs.), N.Y.C., 1968-93; mng. dir. Ward Howell Internat., Inc., N.Y.C., 1993—; exec.-in-residence A.B. Freeman Sch. of Bus., Tulane U. Mem. Tulane U. Parents Coun.; past mem. alumni affairs and devel. com. Cornell U. Bd. Trustees; chmn. Cornell U. Coun. Mem. Internat. Assn. Corp. and Profl. Recruiters (treas., mem. exec. bd.), Cornell Alumni Assn. (pres.). Office: Ward Howell Internat 99 Park Ave New York NY 10016-1699

STERN, LEWIS ARTHUR, lawyer; b. Pitts., Apr. 28, 1934; s. John C. and Belle (Maretsky) S.; m. Chris Ertel; children: Isobel, Gillian, Emily, Thomas. B.A., Yale U., 1955, LL.B., 1958. Bar: N.Y. 1959. Law clk. to chief judge U.S. Ct. Appeals (2d cir.), N.Y.C., 1958-59; assoc. Fried, Frank, Harris, Shriver & Jacobson, N.Y.C., 1959-67, ptnr., 1967—. Office: Fried Frank Harris 1 New York Plz New York NY 10004

STERN, LOUIS WILLIAM, marketing educator, consultant; b. Boston, Sept. 19, 1935; s. Berthold Summerfield Stern and Gladys (Koch) Cohen; m. Rhona L. Grant; children: Beth Ida, Deborah Lynn. A.B., Harvard U., 1957; M.B.A. in Mktg, U. Pa., 1959; Ph.D in Mktg, Northwestern U., 1962. Mem. staff bus. research and consumer mktg. sects. Arthur D. Little, Inc., Cambridge, Mass., 1961-63; asst. prof. bus. orgn. Ohio State U., Columbus, 1963-64; assoc. prof. mktg. Ohio State U., 1966-69, prof. mktg., 1970-73; prof. mktg. Northwestern U., Evanston, Ill., 1973-75; A. Montgomery Ward prof. mktg. Northwestern U., 1975-83, chmn. dept. mktg., 1977-80, John D. Gray disting. prof. mktg., 1984—; on leave as exec. dir. Mktg. Sci. Inst., Cambridge, Mass., 1983-85; Thomas Henry Carroll Ford Found. vis. prof. Harvard U. Grad. Sch. Bus. Adminstrn., 1984-85; mem. staff Nat. Commn. on Food Mktg., Washington, 1965-66; vis. assoc. prof. bus. adminstrn. U. Calif., Berkeley, 1969-70; guest lectr. York U., U. Minn., U. Ky., UCLA, Ohio State U., U. N.C., Duke U., U. Wis., U. Pitts., U. Chgo., MIT, U. Mich., U. Pa., Cornell U., U. Mo., Norwegian Sch. Econs. and Bus. Adminstrn.; faculty assoc. Hernstein Inst., Vienna, Austria, 1976-77, Mgmt. Centre Europe, 1988—; faculty assoc. Gemini Cons., Inc., Montvale, N.J., 1977—; mem. midwest adv. bd., 1989—; Xerox research prof. Northwestern U., 1981-82; cons. to FTC, 1973, 80. Author: Distribution Channels: Behavioral Dimensions, 1969 (with Frederick D. Sturdivant and others) Managerial Analysis in Marketing, 1970, Perspectives in Marketing Management, 1971, (with John R. Grabner, Jr.) Competition in the Marketplace, 1971, (with Adel I. El-Ansary) Marketing Channels, 4th edit., 1992, (with Thomas L. Eovaldi) Legal Aspects of Marketing Strategy: Antitrust and Consumer Protection Issues, 1984; (with Adel I. El-Ansary and James R. Brown) Management in Marketing Channels, 1989; mem. editorial bd. Jour. Mktg. Research, 1976-82, Jour. Mktg., 1979-83, Mktg. Letters, 1988-94; contbr. articles on marketing to profl. jours. Mem. exec. com. Northwest Area Council on Human Relations, Columbus, 1971-72. Ohio State U. rsch. grantee, 1964-73, Mktg. Sci. Inst. rsch. grantee, 1976-77, 88-90, 92—; recipient Harold H. Maynard award for best article of 1980 Jour. of Mktg.; named Mktg. Educator or Yr. Sales and Mktg. Execs. Internat., 1989, also Chgo. chpt., 1990, Outstanding Profl. of Yr. award, 1992, and named one of Top 6 Profs. in Kellogg Sch., Northwestern U., Grad. Mgmt. Assocs., 1984—, (named 5 times Outstanding Prof. Exec. Masters Program); named one of the Top 12 Tchrs. in Bus. Schs. in U.S., Bus. Week; recipient Am. Mktg. Assn. Richard D. Irwin Disting. Mktg. Educator of Yr., 1994. Mem. AAUP, Am. Mktg. Assn. (mem. program com. educators conf. 1971, chmn. com. 1978, Paul D. Converse award 1986). Hellenic Inst. Mktg. (hon.), Beta Gamma Sigma. Home: 724 Sheridan Rd Wilmette IL 60091-1960 Office: Northwestern U JL Kellogg Grad Sch Mgmt Dept Mktg Evanston IL 60208

STERN, MADELEINE BETTINA, rare books dealer, author; b. N.Y.C., July 1, 1912; d. Moses Roland and Lillie (Mack) S. BA, Barnard Coll., 1932; MA, Columbia U., 1934. Tchr. English N.Y.C. High Schs., 1934-43; ptnr. Leona Rostenberg Rare Books, N.Y.C., 1945—; lectr. history of book, feminism, pub. history, lt. Author: The Life of Margaret Fuller, 1942, Louisa May Alcott, 1950, Purple Passage: The Life of Mrs. Frank Leslie, 1953, Imprints on History: Book Publishers and American Frontiers, 1956, We the Women: Career Firsts of Nineteenth Century America, 1962, So Much in a Lifetime: The Story of Dr. Isabel Barrows, 1965, Queen of Publishers' Row: Mrs. Frank Leslie, 1966, The Pantarch: A Biography of Stephen Pearl Andrews, 1968, Heads and Headlines: The Phrenological Fowlers, 1971, Books and Book People in 19th-Century America, 1978, Antiquarian Bookselling in the United States: A History from the Origins to the 1940s, 1985, Nicholas Gouin Dufief of Philadelphia Franco-American Bookseller, 1776-1834, 1988, The Life of Margaret Fuller: A Revised Second Edition, 1991; (with Leona Rostenberg) Old and Rare: Forty Years in the Book Business, 1974, rev. edit. 1988, Between Boards: New Thoughts on Old Books, 1978, Bookman's Quintet: Five Catalogues about Books, 1980, Quest Book-Guest Book: A Biblio-Folly, 1993, Connections: Our Selves-Our Books, 1994; editor: Women on the Move, 4 vols., 1972, Victoria Woodhull Reader, 1974, Louisa's Wonder Book-An Unknown Alcott Juvenile, 1975, Behind a Mask: The Unknown Thrillers of Louisa May Alcott, 1975, Plots and Counterplots: More Unknown Thrillers of Louisa May Alcott, 1976, Publishers for Mass Entertainment in 19th-Century America, 1980, A Phrenological Dictionary of 19th-Century Americans, 1982, Critical Essays on Louisa May Alcott, 1984, A Modern Mephistopheles and Taming a Tartar by Louisa May Alcott, 1987, Louisa May Alcott Unmasked: Collected Thrillers, 1995; co-editor: Selected Letters of Louisa May Alcott, 1987, A Double Life: Newly Discovered Thrillers of Louisa May Alcott, 1988, The Journals of Louisa May Alcott, 1989, Louisa May Alcott: Selected Fiction, 1990, (co-editor) Freaks of Genius: Unknown Thrillers of Louisa May Alcott, 1991, From Jo March's Attic: Newly Discovered Thrillers of L.M. Alcott, 1993 (Victorian Soc. award), We the Women, new edit. 1994, The Lost Stories of Louisa May Alcott, 1995. Guggenheim fellow, 1943-45; recipient Medalie award Barnard Coll., 1982, Victorian Soc. award. Mem. Antiquarian Booksellers Assn. Am. (gov. 1966-68, 78-80), Internat. League Antiquarian Booksellers, MLA, Am. Printing History Assn. (co-recipient award 1983), Authors League, Manuscript Soc. (former trustee), Phi Beta Kappa. Jewish. Home: 40 E 88th St New York NY 10128-1176 Office: Rare Books 40 E 88th St New York NY 10128-1176

STERN, MARC IRWIN, financial services executive; b. Vineland, N.J., Apr. 17, 1944; s. Albert B. and Sylvia (Goodman) S.; m. Eva Suzanne Kuhn, Aug. 14, 1966; children: Adam Bryan, Suzanne Rona. BA cum laude in Polit. Sci., Dickinson Coll., Carlisle, Pa., 1965; MA, Columbia U., 1966, JD magna cum laude, 1969. Bar: N.Y. 1969, N.H. 1975. Law clk. U.S. Ct. Appeals 2d Circuit, 1969-70; assoc. Debevoise & Plimpton, 1970-74; v.p., gen. counsel Wheelabrator-Frye Inc., Hampton, N.H., 1974-80, sr. v.p., 1980-83; sr. v.p. adminstrn. The Signal Cos., Inc., La Jolla, Calif., 1983-85, Allied-Signal Inc., Morristown, N.J., 1985-86; mng. dir., chief adminstrv. officer The Henley Group, Inc., N.Y.C. and La Jolla, 1986-88; pres. SunAmerica, Inc., L.A., 1988-90, The TCW Group, Inc., L.A., 1992—;

chmn. bd. TCW Ams. Devel., Inc., 1990—, TCW Funds, Inc., 1990—, TCW London Internat., Ltd., 1993, TCW Asia, Ltd., 1993; bd. dirs. Qualcomm, Inc. Trustee Salk Inst. for Biol. Studies, La Jolla, Dickinson Coll., Carlisle, Pa., UCLA Med. Ctr.; bd. dirs. L.A. Music Ctr. Opera. Home: 10247 Century Woods Dr Los Angeles CA 90067-6312 Office: The TCW Group Inc 865 S Figueroa St Ste 1800 Los Angeles CA 90017-2556 also: 200 Park Ave Ste 2200 New York NY 10166-0001

STERN, MARVIN, psychiatrist, educator; b. N.Y.C., Jan. 6, 1916; s. Jacob and Mary (Kappel) S.; m. Libby Rifkin, Jan. 18, 1942; children: Carol S., Robert M., Theodore A. B.S., CCNY, 1935; M.D., NYU, 1939. Diplomate Am. Bd. Psychiatry and Neurology. Intern in medicine and surgery Bellevue Hosp., N.Y.C., 1939-40, resident in medicine and psychiatry, 1940-42, fellow in psychiatry, 1946-47; practice medicine specializing in psychiatry N.Y.C., 1947—; asst. prof. psychiatry NYU Med. Ctr., N.Y.C., 1948-55, assoc. prof., 1955-62, prof., 1962-79, Menas S. Gregory prof. psychiatry, 1979-86, prof., 1986—, exec. chmn. dept. psychiatry, 1976-86; mem. staff NYU Hosp., Bellevue Hosp.; cons. psychiatrist VA Hosp.; cons. psychiatrist emeritus Brookdale Hosp. Served to maj. AUS, 1942-46. Fellow Am. Psychiat. Assn. (sec. dist. br. 1956-63, pres. dist. br. 1964, area chmn. 1962-63); mem. Am. Psychosomatic Assn., N.Y.C. Acad. Medicine, Harvey Soc., NYU Med. Alumni Assn. (pres. 1979-80), Phi Beta Kappa, Sigma Xi, Alpha Omega Alpha. Home: 300 E 33rd St Apt 12C New York NY 10016-9415 Office: NYU Sch Medicine 550 1st Ave New York NY 10016-6481

STERN, MARVIN, management consultant; b. Bklyn., Jan. 5, 1923; s. David and Regina (Harnik) S.; m. June Bronstein Wittlin, Mar. 24, 1945; children—Ellis Roy, Richard Keith; m. Patricia Wolberg, June 17, 1955; children—Valerie Ann, Gary Allen, Jody Amanda. B.S. in Mech. Engring., CCNY, 1943; M.S., NYU, 1947, Ph.D. in Math, 1954. Corp. staff exec. rsch. and devel. Gen. Dynamics Co., 1958-60; asst. dir. strategic weapons Office Sec. Def., Washington, 1960-61; dep. dir. def. rsch. and engring., weapons systems Office Sec. Def., 1961-62; v.p. rsch. and engring. N.Am. Aviation, Inc., El Segundo, Calif., 1962-63; mgmt. cons. L.A., 1963-64; pres. aero. systems div. Gen. Precision, Inc., Wayne, N.J., 1964-66; v.p. Rand Corp., Santa Monica, Calif., 1967-68; pres. Laird Systems, L.A., 1968-70, Marvin Stern, Inc., Santa Ynez, Calif., 1970—; sr. fellow UCLA Ctr. for Internat. and Strategic Affairs, 1990-92; cons. Office Sec. Def., Sec. Transp., Pres.'s Sci. Adv. Com., CIA; Def. Sci. Bd., Naval Res. Adv. Com. Author: (with George Gamow) Puzzle Math, 1958; editor: (with Morton Alperin) Vistas in Astronautics, 1958. Trustee Lycée Français de Los Angeles. Recipient Meritorious Civilian Service medal Sec. Def., 1962. Address: 4001 Long Valley Rd Santa Ynez CA 93460-9721

STERN, MILTON, chemical company executive; b. Boston, Apr. 20, 1927; s. Morris and Lily (Colton) S.; m. Roberta L. Navisky, July 10, 1949; children—Mark, Lawrence, Brian. B.S., Northeastern U., 1949; M.S. (Alcoa fellow), MIT, 1950, Sc.D. (Alcoa fellow), 1952. Postdoctoral fellow in metallurgy MIT, 1952-54; with Union Carbide Corp., N.Y.C., 1954-73; v.p. electronics div. Union Carbide Corp., 1968-69, exec. v.p. mining and metals div., 1969-73; v.p. exploration Kennecott Corp., N.Y.C., 1973-76; sr. v.p. Kennecott Corp., 1976-78, exec. v.p., 1978-82, also dir.; sr. exec. v.p. Stauffer Chem. Co., Westport, Conn., 1982-84; vice chmn. Stauffer Chem. Co., 1984—, also dir. Contbr. numerous articles in electrochemistry and metallurgy to tech. jours. Mem. vis. com. M.I.T., 1972-75; mem. corp. Northeastern U.; mem. White House Task Force on Am. Indian Affairs; chmn. Am. Indian Affairs. Served with USNR, 1945-46. Recipient Nuodex award Northeastern U., 1949; Sears B. Condit award, 1949. Mem. AIME, Nat. Assn. corrosion Engrs. (Willis R. Whitney award 1963), Am. Soc. Metals, Electrochem. Soc. (Young Authors award 1955, 58, jour. div. editor 1958-61), PGA Nat. Club, Sigma Xi, Tau Beta Pi. Patentee in field.

STERN, MORT(IMER) P(HILLIP), journalism and communications educator, academic administrator, consultant; b. New Haven, Feb. 20, 1926; s. Bernard and Louise Eleanor (Spiro) S.; m. Patricia Ruth Freeman, Jan. 10, 1946; children: Susan C., Margaret L. AB, U. Ark., 1947; MS, Columbia U., 1949; postgrad., Harvard U., 1954-55; PhD, U. Denver, 1969. Reporter S.W.-Am., Ft. Smith, Ark., 1946-47; night bur. mgr. UPI, Little Rock, 1947-48; reporter, polit. writer, state editor Ark. Gazette, Little Rock, 1949-51; reporter, rewrite man Denver Post, 1951-53, night city editor, 1953-54, asst. editor Rocky Mountain Empire sect., 1955-56, mng. editor, 1956-58, assoc. editor, 1958, editorial page editor, 1958-65, asst. to pub., 1965-70, editorial page editor, 1971-73; dean Sch. Pub. communication U. Ala., 1973-74; dean Sch. Journalism U. Colo., Boulder, 1974-77; lectr. journalism U. Denver, 1953-54, adj. prof., 1970, exec. dir. pub. affairs, 1977-78, exec. asst. to chancellor, 1978-84; prof., chmn. dept. journalism and mass communication U. No. Colo., Greeley, 1985-90; pres. P. Paty & Co., Georgetown, Colo., 1989—; Atwood prof. journalism U. Alaska, Anchorage, 1981-82. With USAAF, 1944-45. Nieman fellow Harvard U., 1954-55. Mem. Assn. for Edn. in Journalism, Phi Beta Kappa, Omicron Delta Kappa, Sigma Delta Chi. Baptist. Home: PO Box 549 Georgetown CO 80444-0549

STERN, NANCY FORTGANG, mathematics and computer science, educator; b. N.Y.C., July 15, 1944; d. Murray and Selma (Karp) Fortgang; m. Robert A Stern, Sept. 3, 1964; children: Lori Anne, Melanie. AB, Barnard Coll., 1965; MS, NYU, 1968; MA, SUNY, 1974, PhD, 1978. Programmer analyst ATT, N.Y.C., 1965-67; asst. prof. Nassau Community Coll., Garden City, N.Y., 1965-68; adj. prof. Dowling Coll. SUNY, 1968-77; disting. prof. Hofstra U., Hempstead, N.Y.; rsch. cons. Am. Inst. Physics, N.Y., 1976-77; adv. editor John Wiley & Sons, 1977—. Author 12 textbooks on computing; asst. editor in chief Annuals for the History of Computing, 1977-87; contbr. articles to profl. jours. Mem. Charles Babbage Inst., Nat. Computing Com.

STERN, PAULA, international trade advisor; b. Chgo., Mar. 31, 1945; d. Lloyd and Fan (Wener) Stern; m. Paul A. London; children: Gabriel Stern, Genevieve Stern. BA, Goucher Coll., 1967; MA in Middle Eastern Studies, Harvard U., 1969; MA in Internat. Affairs, Fletcher Sch. of Law and Diplomacy, 1970, MA in Law and Diplomacy, 1970, PhD, 1976; D of Comml. Sci. (hon.), Babson Coll., 1985; LLD (hon.), Goucher Coll., 1985. Legis. asst., then sr. legis. asst. U.S. Sen. Gaylord Nelson, Washington, 1972-74, 1976; guest scholar Brookings Inst., Washington, 1975-76; policy analyst Pres. Carter-V.P. Mondale Transition Team, Washington, 1977-78; internat. affairs fellow Council on Fgn. Relations, Washington, 1977-78; commr. Internat. Trade Commn., Washington, 1978-87, chairwoman, 1984-86; sr. assoc. Carnegie Endowment for Internat. Peace, Washington, 1986-88; pres. The Stern Group, 1988—; sr. fellow The Progressive Policy Inst., 1993—; bd. dirs. Westinghouse Corp., Harcourt Gen., Duracell Internat.; sr. adviser to Clinton Campaign; mem. Pres.'s Adv. Com. for Trade Policy and Negotiations; mem. Trilateral Commn., Commn. for Econ. Devel. Author: Water's Edge–Domestic Politics and the Making of American Foreign Policy, 1979; author numerous articles and chpts. on internat. affairs. Recipient Journalism award Alicia Patterson Found., 1970-71. Mem. Coun. Fgn. Rels., Inter-Am. Found. (bd. dirs. 1980-81). Democrat. Jewish. Avocations: sculpture, tennis, ballet. Office: The Stern Group Inc 3314 Ross Pl NW Washington DC 20008

STERN, RALPH DAVID, lawyer, county and municipal; b. Longview, Tex., June 20, 1943; m. Jane R. Cooper, Mar. 20, 1971; children: Eric, Justin. AB, Bucknell U., 1963; JD, U. Chgo., 1966. Bar: D.C. 1967, Ill. 1967, Calif. 1970, U.S. Supreme Ct. 1970. Law clk. Ill. Appellate Ct., Chgo., 1966-67; assoc. Ressman & Tishler, Chgo., 1968-70; exec. asst. Orange County Bd. Suprs., Santa Ana, Calif., 1970-71; gen. counsel San Diego City Schs., 1971-83; ptnr. Whitmore, Kay & Stevens, Palo Alto, Calif., 1983-88, Stern & Keebler, San Mateo, Calif., 1988-90; gen. counsel Schs. Legal Counsel, Hayward, Calif., 1990—; chmn. Nat. Coun. Sch. Attys., 1982-83; pres. Legal Aid Soc. San Diego, 1976-79, Nat. Orgn. on Legal Problems of Edn., 1981-82. Editor: Law and the School Principal, 1978; contbr. articles to profl. jours. Mem. exec. bd., county membership chair Boy Scouts Am., San Diego, 1981-83; vice chmn. Laurels for Leaders, San Diego, 1980-83; mem. ednl. adminstrn. adv. com. U. San Diego, 1981-86; mem. adv. com. West's Ednl. Law Reporter, 1981-85. Named Outstanding Young Citizen, San Diego Jaycees, 1977. Office: Schs Legal Counsel 313 W Winton Ave Rm 372 Hayward CA 94544-1198

STERN, RAYMOND, principal. Prin. Hebrew Acad. Indpls. Recipient Elem. Sch. Recognition award U.S. Dept. Edn., 1989-90. Office: Hebrew Acad of Ind 6602 Hoover Rd Indianapolis IN 46260-4199

STERN, RICHARD DAVID, investment company executive; b. New Rochelle, N.Y., Nov. 5, 1936; s. Leo and Grace Marjorie (Phillips) S.; m. Phyllis Marlene Edelstein, Nov. 20, 1966; children: Marjorie Anne, Andrew Howard. AB, Princeton U., 1958; MBA, Harvard U., 1962. CFA. First v.p. Newburger, Loeb & Co., N.Y.C., 1962-74, also dir., 1969-74; sr. investment officer Central Trust Co., Cin., 1974-76, owner bus. valuation cons. co., 1976-78; v.p. Gt. Western Bank & Trust Co. (now Norwest Bank Ariz. NA), Phoenix, 1978-84; pres. Stern, Ludke & Co. (now Stern Investment Mgmt. Co.), Phoenix, 1984—. Co-author: Air Cushion Vehicles, 1962. Trustee endowment trust Phoenix Chamber Music Soc., 1982-91, v.p., 1986-90, bd. dirs., 1982-91, 93-94; pres. Ctrl. Ariz. chpt. Arthritis Found., 1982-84, chmn. planned giving com., 1986-91, mem. nat. planned giving com., 1987-89; chmn. endowments and trusts com. Temple Beth Israel, Phoenix, 1980-83; dir., investment com. Endowment Found., Temple Solel, Paradise Valley, 1990—; pres. Am. Jewish Com., Phoenix, 1983-84, bd. dirs., 1983-84, adv. bd., 1985—; bd. dirs. Asian Arts Coun., Phoenix Art Mus., 1987-93, v.p., 1989-90, pres., 1990-92; trustee Ariz. Theatre Co., 1990—. Mem. Phoenix Soc. Fin. Analysts (chmn. profl. conduct com. 1980-83, membership com. 1990-91, bd. dirs.), Anti-Defamation League of B'nai B'rith (dir. Ctrl. Ariz. chpt. 1986—, exec. bd. 1989—, chair nominating com. 1990-94, chair bd. devel. 1993-94, treas. 1994—), Princeton Alumni Assn. No. Ariz. (alumni schs. com. 1992—), Univ. Club (Phoenix, bd. dirs. 1990-92, fin. com. 1990-91), Harvard Bus. Sch. Club Ariz. (bd. dirs. 1991—, pres. 1993—), Assn. for Corp. Growth (Ariz. chpt.). Republican. Home: 6013 E Donna Cir Paradise Valley AZ 85253 Office: 2930 E Camelback Rd Ste 195 Phoenix AZ 85016-4412

STERN, RICHARD GUSTAVE, author, educator; b. N.Y.C., Feb. 25, 1928; s. Henry George and Marion (Veit) S.; m. Gay Clark, Mar. 14, 1950 (div. Feb. 1972); children: Christopher Holmes, Kate Macomber, Andrew Henry, Nicholas Clark; m. Alane Rollings, Aug. 9, 1985. B.A., U. N.C. 1947; M.A., Harvard U., 1950; Ph.D., State U. Iowa, 1954. Mem. faculty U. Chgo., 1955—, prof. English, 1965—, Helen Regenstein prof. English, 1990—. Author: Golk, 1960, Europe or Up and Down with Baggish and Schreiber, 1961, In Any Case, 1962, Teeth, Dying and Other Matters, 1964, Stitch, 1965, 1968: A Short Novel, An Urban Idyll, Five Stories and Two Trade Notes, 1970, The Books in Fred Hampton's Apartment, 1973, Other Men's Daughters, 1973, Natural Shocks, 1978, Packages, 1980, The Invention of the Real, 1982, A Father's Words, 1986, The Position of the Body, 1986, Noble Rot: Stories, 1949-88, 1989 (Book of Yr. award Chgo. Sun-Times 1990), Shares and Other Fictions, 1992, One Person and Another, 1993, A Sistermony, 1995; editor: Honey and Wax, 1966. Recipient Longwood Found. award, 1960, Friends of Lit. award, 1963, fiction award Nat. Inst. Arts and Letters, 1968; Nat. Coun. Arts and Humanities fellow, 1967-68, Carl Sandburg award for fiction, 1979, Arts Coun. awards, 1979, 81, Am. Acad. and Inst. of Arts and Letters medal of Merit for Novel, 1985; Rockefeller fellow, 1965, Guggenheim fellow, 1973-74. Mem. Am. Acad. Arts and Scis. Office: Dept English U Chgo Chicago IL 60637

STERN, ROBERT ARTHUR MORTON, architect, educator; b. N.Y.C., May 23, 1939; s. Sidney S. and Sonya (Cohen) S.; m. Lynn G. Solinger, May 22, 1966 (div. 1977); 1 child, Nicholas S.G. BA, Columbia U., 1960; MArch, Yale U., 1965. Registered architect, Calif., Colo., Conn., Fla., Hawaii, Ill., Ind., Maine, Mass., Mich., Nev., N.H., N.J., Ohio, S.C., Tex., N.Y. Program dir. Archtl. League N.Y., 1965-66; designer Office Richard Meier, Architect, N.Y.C., 1966; cons. Small Parks Program, Dept. Parks, N.Y.C., 1966-70; urban designer, asst. to asst. administr. housing and devel. adminstrn. N.Y.C., 1967-70; ptnr. Robert A.M. Stern & John S. Hagmann, Architects, N.Y.C., 1969-77; prin. Robert A.M. Stern, Architects, 1977-89, prin. ptnr., 1989—; cons. Eye on New York TV documentary, CBS-TV, 1966-67; mem. architecture com. Whitney Mus. Am. Art, 1970-76, adv. commn., archtl. sect. Venice Biennale, 1980; lectr. architecture Columbia U., 1970-72, asst. prof. 1973-77, assoc. prof., 1977-82, prof. 1982—; vis. fellow Inst. for Architecture and Urban Studies, 1974-76, trustee, 1983-85; dir. Temple Hoyne Buell Ctr. for Study Am. Architecture, 1984-88, acting dir. Hist. Preservation Program, 1991—; vis. lectr. Yale U., 1972, 73; vis. critic R.I. Sch. Design, 1976, U. Pa., 1977, N.C. State U., Raleigh, 1978; William Henry Bishop vis. prof. architecture Yale U., fall 1978; editorial cons. Archtl. History Found., 1979-83. Author: New Directions in American Architecture, 1969, rev. edit., 1977, George Howe: Toward a Modern American Architecture, 1975, (with Deborah Nevins) The Architect's Eye, 1979, (with John M. Massengale) The Anglo-American Suburb, 1981, (with Thomas Catalano) Raymond Hood, 1982, East Hampton Heritage, 1982, (with John M. Massengale and Gregory Gilmartin) New York 1900, 1983, Pride of Place, 1986, (with Gregory Gilmartin and Thomas Mellins) New York 1930, 1987, (with Raymond Gastil) Modern Classicism, 1988, The House That Bob Built, 1991, The American Houses of Robert A.M. Stern, 1991, (with Thomas Mellins and David Fishman) New York 1960, 1995. Mem. N.Y.C. Mayor's Task Force on Urban Design, 1966-67, architects selection com. N.Y. Conv. Ctr., 1979; trustee Am. Fedn. Arts, 1967-79, Inst. for Architecture and Urban Studies, 1983-85; v.p. Cunningham Dance Found., 1969-73; bd. dirs. Preservation League N.Y., 1984—. Recipient numerous awards for archtl. works including Nat. Hon. awards of AIA, 1980, 85, 90, John Jay award Columbia Coll., 1991. Fellow AIA (bd. dirs. N.Y. chpt. 1976-78, Disting. archtl. award N.Y. chpt. 1982, 84, 85, 87, medal of honor 1984), Soc. Archtl. Historians (bd. dirs. 1975-78), Archtl. League N.Y. (pres. 1973-77, exec. com. 1977—), N.Y. State Assn. Architects (excellence in design cert. 1985), Am. Architecture Found. (bd. regents 1989-91), Skidmore, Owings and Merrill Found. (bd. dirs. 1984-90), Chgo. Inst. for Architecture and Urbanism (bd. dirs. 1990-93), Century Assn., Coffee House Club. Office: Robert A M Stern Arch 460 W 34th St 18th Fl New York NY 10001

STERN, ROBERT D., publishing executive; b. N.Y.C., Sept. 30, 1929; s. Morris and Jean (Gordon) S.; m. Natalie Greenberg, Sept. 5, 1952 (div. 1978); children: Mitchell, Bradley; m. Roslyne Paige, June 5, 1978. BA, Syracuse U., 1950; JD, NYU, 1953, LLM, 1958. Bar: N.Y. 1955, U.S. Dist. Ct. (D.C. cir.) 1953, U.S. Supreme Ct. 1967. Assoc. Fink, Weinberger, Levin & Gottschalk, N.Y.C., 1957-59, ptnr., 1959-72; chmn. Rudor Consol. Industries, N.Y.C., 1972—, Dance Mag., Inc., N.Y.C., 1985—; AGC/ Sedgwick Inc., Princeton, N.J., 1990—; bd. dirs. Ctr. for Graphic Communications Mgmt. and Tech., NYU, N.Y.C., 1979—; chmn. bd. dirs. AGC Sedgwick, Princeton, N.J., Rudor Consol. Ind. Inc.; pub. Stern's Performing Arts Directory, 1989—. Bd. dirs. NYU Sch. for Graphics Arts Mgmt., YMCA, N.Y.C., 1987-90; Sgt. 1st class U.S. Army, 1953-55. Mem. ABA, N.Y. State Bar Assn., Sheldrake Yacht Club (Mamaroneck, N.Y.). Avocations: tennis, skiing, sailing. Home: 2 Imperial Landing Westport CT 06880 Office: 33 W 60th St New York NY 10023

STERN, ROBERT LOUIS, lawyer; b. N.Y.C., Sept. 18, 1908; s. Albert Louis and Alma (Hays) S.; m. Terese Marks, Oct. 16, 1936 (dec. Jan. 1990); children: Lawrence K., Kenneth M., Allan H.; m. Helen Klemperer, Dec. 1, 1990. A.B., Williams Coll., 1929; LL.B., Harvard U., 1932. Bar: N.Y. 1933, Ill. 1954, D.C. 1954. Assoc. Henry F. Wolff, N.Y.C., 1932-33; atty. Petroleum Adminstrn. Bd., Dept. Interior, Washington, 1933-34, Antitrust div. Justice Dept., 1934-41; with Office Solicitor Gen., Justice Dept., 1941-54, 1st asst., 1950-54, acting solicitor gen., 1952-54; mem. firm Mayer, Brown & Platt, Chgo., 1954-93; of counsel, 1993—; vis. prof. U. Ariz. Coll. Law, 1972; mem. Fed. Adv. Com. on Appellate Rules, 1963-68, Ill. Supreme Ct. Rules Com., 1963-94; mem. study group on caseload Supreme Ct., 1972. Author: Appellate Practice in the United States, 2d edit., 1989; co-author: Supreme Court Practice, 7th edit., 1993, Illinois Civil Appellate Practice: State and Federal, 1993; contbr. articles to profl. jours. Chmn. Winnetka Community Chest, 1961-62; mem. Winnetka Caucus, 1965-67. Mem. ABA (Ross prize essay 1955, mem. various coms., mem. amicus curiae com. 1981-87), Am. Law Inst., Am. Bar Fellows (Rsch. award 1983), 7th Fed. Cir. Bar Assn., Chgo. Bar Assn., Am. Bar Found. (past dir., rsch. com.), Law Club Chgo., 49ers Country Club (Tucson). Home (summer): 706 Waukegan Rd Glenview IL 60025-4368 also (winter): 2631 E Ave de Posada Tucson AZ 85718 Office: Mayer Brown & Platt 190 S La Salle St Chicago IL 60603-3410

STERN, ROBERT MORRIS, psychology educator, researcher; b. N.Y.C., June 18, 1937; s. Irving Dan and Nellie (Wachstetter) S.; m. Wilma Olch, June 19, 1960; children—Jessica Leigh, Alison Rachel. A.B., Franklin and Marshall Coll., 1958; M.S., Tufts U., 1960; Ph.D., Ind. U., 1963. Research assoc. dept. psychology Ind. U., 1963-65; asst. prof. psychology Pa. State U., 1965-68, assoc. prof., 1968-73, prof., 1973—, disting. prof., 1992—, head dept., 1978-87; gastrointestinal psychophysiology researcher. Author: (with W.J. Ray) Biofeedback, 1977, (with W.J. Ray and C.M. Davis) Psychophysiological Recording, 1980, (with K.L. Koch) Electrogastrography, 1985; contbr. articles to profl. jours. Recipient Nat. Media award Am. Psychol. Found., 1978. Mem. Am. Psychol. Soc., Aerospace Med. Assn., Soc. Psychophysiol. Rsch., Am. Gastroent. Assn. Home: 1360 Greenwood Cir State College PA 16803-3232 Office: Pa State U 512 Moore Bldg University Park PA 16802

STERN, ROBERT STUART, dermatologist, editor; b. New Haven, Conn.. AB magna cum laude, Harvard Coll., 1966; MD, Yale U., 1970. Diplomate Am. Bd. Dermatology. Intern in internal medicine Mt. Sinai Hosp., N.Y.C., 1970-71; resident in dermatology Harvard Med. Sch., Mass. Gen. Hosp., Boston, 1973-76; rsch. assoc. clin. epidemiology and genetics Nat. Inst. Diseases and Stroke, NIH, Bethesda, Md., 1971-73; rsch. fellow dept. dermatology Mass. Gen. Hosp., Harvard Med. Sch., 1974-75; fellow Harvard Ctr. for Cmty Health and Med. Care Harvard Med. Sch., 1975-76, clin. fellow in dermatology, 1973-76, instr. dermatology, 1976-79, asst. prof. dermatology, 1979-84, assoc. prof. dermatology, 1984—; assoc. in dermatology Beth Israel Hosp., Boston, 1976-78; cons. in dermatology Boston Hosp. for Women, 1976—; asst. in dermatology Children's Hosp. Med. Ctr., Boston, 1976-80; clin. assoc. in dermatology Mass. Gen. Hosp., Boston, 1976-79; cons. div. med. oncology Sidney Farber Cancer Inst. Boston, 1977—; jr. assoc. medicine Peter Bent Brigham Hosp., Boston, 1978—; attending physician Dermatology Clinic, Beth Israel Hosp., 1976—; Physician Consultation Svc., 1976—, dir. Phototherapy Ctr., 1978—, dir. Laser Unite, 1980—; mem. Ctr. for Analysis of Health Practice, Harvard Sch. Pub. Health, 1976-83; mem. Inst. for Health Rsch., 1983—; sr. asst. surgeon USPHS, NIH, 1971-72, surgeon, 1972-73; cons. health svcs. industries com. Cost of Living Coun., Exec. Office of the Pres., 1971-73; vis. dermatologist Johns Hopkins Med. Sch., 1979, 87, NYU Sch. Medicine, 1984, U. P.R. Med. Sch., 1985, Dartmouth Med. Sch., 1989; cons. 7th edit. AMA Drug Evaluations, 1989-93; mem. sci. com. Congress on Cutaneous Drug Reactions, Paris, 1994—; mem. sci. bd. 1st Internat. Conf. on Epidemiology, Marseille, France, 1994—; lectr. in field. Reviewer Soc. of Investigative Dermatology, 1991—; mem. editl. bd.: Jour. Pharmacoepidemiology, 1988—, Archives of Dermatology, 1983—, Photodermatology, Photoimmunology and Photomedicine, 1990—, Med. and Surg. Dermatology, 1993—; contbr. over 95 articles to profl. jours. Assoc. editor Archives of Dermatology, 1984-92; co-editor Archives of Dermatology; editor Medical and Surgical Dermatology: A Critical Guide To The Literature, 1993—. Woodrow Wilson scholar, 1966; recipient Letter of Commendation, The White House, 1972, Internat. Travel award French Soc. Dermatology, Milton Fund fellowship, 1985, numerous rsch. grants, 1980—. Fellow Am. Coll. Epidemiology; mem. Soc. Investigative Dermatology (fellowship 1976-77), Am. Acad. Dermatology (co-chmn. com. on therapeutics and cosmetics 1978-81, sci. dir. adverse drug reaction reporting system 1980—, chmn. com. on govtl. rels. 1981-83, coun. on govt. liaison, 1981-83, com. on regulatory affairs 1981-84, task force on psoriasis 1982-85, task force on dermatology/pharmacy 1983-86, task force on manpower 1983-86, com. on diagnostic-related groups 1984-87, com. on psoriasis 1986-89, chmn. task force on relative value scales 1986-89, chmn. task force on dermatology/pharmacy 1986-89, task force on FDA liaison 1989-92, task force on guidelines for phototherapy 1990—, task force on accutane 1991-93), Dermatology Found., Am. Soc. for Epidemiologic Rsch., New Eng. Dermatol. Soc., Boston Dermatol. Soc. (program com. 1980-83), Am. Soc. for Photobiology, Coun. of Biology Editors, Am. Dermatol. Assn., Mass. Med. Soc., Am. Soc. for Laser Medicine and Surgery (chmn. publs. com. 1986-87), Phi Beta Kappa.

STERN, ROSLYNE PAIGE, magazine publisher; b. Chgo., May 26, 1926; d. Benjamin Gross and Clara (Sniderman) Roer; m. William E. Weber, May 3, 1944 (div. Mar. 1956); m. Richard S. Paige, June 28, 1958 (div. Apr. 1978); children: Sandra Weber Porr, Barbara Paige Kaplan, Elizabeth Paige (dec.); m. Robert D. Stern, June 5, 1978. Cert., U. Chgo., 1945. Profl. model, singer, 1947-53; account exec. Interstate United, Chgo., 1955-58; sales mgr. Getting To Know You Internat., Great Neck, N.Y., 1963-71, exec. v.p., 1971-78; pub. After Dark Mag., N.Y.C., 1978-82; assoc. pub. Dance Mag., N.Y.C., 1978-85, pub., 1985—; bd. dirs. Rudor Consol. Industries, Inc., N.Y.C., AGC/Sedgwick, Inc., Princeton, N.J. Founding pres. Dance Mag. Found., N.Y.C., 1984-86; life mem. nat. women's com. Brandeis U., Waltham, Mass., 1958—. Mem. Pub. Relations Soc. Am., LWV, Am. Theatre Wing. Democrat. Jewish. Avocations: dance, theater, opera, visual arts, travel. Home: 2 Imperial Lndg Westport CT 06880-4934 Office: Dance Mag Inc 33 W 60th St 10th Fl New York NY 10023-7905

STERN, SAMUEL ALAN, lawyer; b. Phila., Jan. 21, 1929. A.B., U. Pa., 1949; LL.B., Harvard U., 1952. Bar: Mass. 1952, D.C. 1958. Ptnr. Wilmer, Cutler & Pickering, Washington, 1962-88, Dickstein, Shapiro & Morin, Washington, 1988-92; pvt. practice law and bus. Washington and St. Petersburg, Russia, 1992-94; counsel Rogers & Wells, Washington, N.Y.C., 1994—; vis. prof. law Harvard U., Cambridge, Mass., 1976; dir. Internat. Law Inst., Georgetown U., 1971—, adj. prof. law, 1979-92; asst. counsel Warren Commn., 1964; cons. UN, 1974—; bd. dirs. Ninth Moon Inc., ADEC, Inc., Stern & Co., Norandina Holdings A.V.V., Custom Software L.L.C. Contbr. articles to legal jours. Adv. bd. Fishman-Davidson Ctr. for Study of Svc. Sector, Wharton Sch. Bus., U. Pa.; bd. dirs. Internat. Sci. Tech. Inst., Internat. Ctr., Washington; steering com. U.S.-Vietnam Trade Coun. Mem. ABA, Am. Law Inst., Am. Soc. Internat. Law, Internat. Bar Assn., D.C. Bar Assn. Home: 2336 California St NW Washington DC 20008-1637 Office: 607 14th St NW Washington DC 20005

STERN, SHERRY ANN, journalist; b. Paterson, N.J., June 27, 1954; d. Richard Norman and Norma (Davidowitz). BA, U. S. Calif., Los Angeles, 1976; MS, Northwestern U., Evanston, 1982. Reporter Ariz. Daily Star, Tucson, 1976-79, TV critic, 1979-81; news editor The Morning Press, Vista, Calif., 1982-83, mng. editor, editor in chief, 1983-84; copy editor The Orange County Register, Calif., 1984-85; asst. features news editor The Orange County Register, Santa Ana, Calif., 1985-86; features news editor Orange County Register, Santa Ana, Calif., 1986—; journalism instr. Mira Costa Coll., Oceanside, 1983-84. Vol. Lit. Vols. of Am., Huntington Beach, 1988—. Named Best Headling Portfolio Orange County Press Club, 1985, Best Student Feature Los Angeles Press Club. Mem. Orange County, Press Club. Democrat. Jewish. Office: The Orange County Register 625 N Grand Ave Santa Ana CA 92701-4397

STERN, STANLEY B., investment banker; b. Bklyn., Apr. 5, 1957; s. Emanuel and Adina (Fried) S.; m. Trudy H. Stern, Apr. 5, 1981; children: Dana A., Caroline L., Erica M. BA, CUNY, 1978; MBA, Harvard U., 1980. Assoc. Salomon Bros., N.Y.C., 1980-81; assoc. Oppenheimer & Co., Inc., N.Y.C., 1981, v.p., sr. v.p., mng. dir. Bd. dirs. Young Israel of Lawrence, L.I., N.Y., 1988—, Yeshiva U. High Sch., N.Y.C., 1992—. Mem. Am.-Israel C. of C. (bd. dirs. 1992—). Jewish. Office: Oppenheimer & Co Inc 200 Liberty St New York NY 10281-1003

STERN, STEPHEN JEFFREY, lawyer; b. L.A., Dec. 31, 1940; s. M.E. and Jane (VanDement) S.; m. Betsy Stern, June 16, 1962 (div. 1974); children: Christopher, Jeffrey; m. Sheila Stern, Apr. 23, 1976. BS in Econs., U. Calif., 1962; JD, U. San Francisco, 1965. Bar: Calif., N.Y. Ptnr. O'Melveny & Myers, L.A., 1966—; lectr., chmn. N.Y. Law Jour., Calif. League of Cities, Mcpl. Fin. Officers Assn. Mem. ABA, Calif. State Bar Assn., Nat. Assn. Bond Lawyers, Bel Air Bay Club. Office: O'Melveny & Myers 400 S Hope St Los Angeles CA 90071-2801

STERN, STEVE J., cultural organization administrator, history educator. Dir. Latin Am. and Iberian Study Program, U. Wis., Madison, Wis. Office: Univ of Wisconsin Madison Latin Am & Iberian Studies Program 1470 Van Hise Hall Madison WI 53706

STERN, T. NOEL, political scientist, educator; b. Pitts., July 7, 1913; s. Leon Thomas (LeFevre) and Elizabeth Gertrude (Limburg) S.; m. Katherine Frances Kirk, Dec. 28, 1940; children: S. Yolanda, Roland Craig, Ellen Cornog, Joan Thrush. B.A. with honors, Swarthmore Coll., 1934; postgrad., U. Lyons, France, 1934-35; M.A. in Polit. Sci, U. Pa., 1940, Ph.D. in Polit. Sci, 1942. Tchr. Lycée des Garçons, Roanne, France, 1934-35; prof. dept. govt. Boston U., 1945-53; Fulbright prof. U. Rennes, U. Strasbourg, 1952; dir. Fondation des Etats-Unis, U. Paris, France, 1953-56; acting chief UN Pub. Adminstrn. Mission to Ethiopia, 1956-57; dir. research and stats. Pa. Dept. Revenue, 1957-60; pres. West Chester State Coll., Pa., 1960-61; research prof. govt. African Studies program Boston U., 1962-63; also chief pub. adminstrn. team Boston U./US Aid, Guinea, West Africa; prof., past chmn. dept. polit. sci. U. Mass., Dartmouth, 1964-69, prof., 1969-85, prof. emeritus, 1985—, also past chmn. acad. coun. Author: Secret Family, 1988, Your Guide to Dartmouth Town Government, 1991; past mem. editl. bd. Internat. Rev. History and Polit. Sci., Revue de la Cité, Paris; contbr. to Boston U. Law Rev., Sch. and Society, New Republic, Progressive mag. Christian Sci. Monitor, Friends Jour., Quaker Life, Quaker History, Providence Jour.-Bull, New Bedford Standard-Times, U. Pa. Gazette, also others. Mem. permanent bd. New Eng. Yearly Mtg. of Friends; past mem. Dartmouth Arts Coun.; past mem. exec. com. Friends Gen. Conf., Phila.; past mem. adminstrv. bd. William Penn House, Washington; past clk. North Dartmouth Friends Mtg., past presiding clk. Sandwich Quar. Mtg. of Friends; trustee, chmn. Dartmouth Town Librs., 1992—; bd. dirs. Cmty. Ctr. for Non-Violence, New Bedford, Mass., 1994—. Mem. AAUP (past pres. U. Mass. Dartmouth chpt.), Am. Polit. Sci. Assn., LWV (acting pres. New Bedford-Fall River area 1990-91). Home: 875 Smith Neck Rd South Dartmouth MA 02748-1511

STERN, THEODORE, electric company executive; b. 1929; married. B-MechE, Pratt Inst., 1951; MS, NYU, 1956. With Westinghouse Electric Corp., Pitts., 1958—, gen. mgr. pressurized water reactor systems div., 1966-71, gen. mgr. nuclear fuel div., 1971-72, v.p. than v.p. water reactor divs., 1972-74, exec. v.p. power generation, 1974-78, exec. v.p. nuclear energy systems, 1978-86, exec. v.p. energy systems, 1986-87, exec. v.p. energy and utility systems, 1988-90; sr. exec. v.p., bd. dirs., 1990—. Office: Executive Associates Office One PPG Place, Ste 2210 Pittsburgh PA 15222

STERN, TODD DAVID, lawyer; b. Chgo., May 4, 1951; s. Richard James and Judith (Cowen) S. BA, Dartmouth Coll., 1973; JD, Harvard U., 1977. Staff atty. criminal appeals bur. Legal Aid Soc., N.Y.C., 1977-79; assoc. Paul, Weiss, Rifking, Wharton & Garrison, N.Y.C., 1979-85; gen. counsel Assoc. Mills-Pollenex, Chgo., 1985-87; dep. rsch. dir. Dukakis-Bentsen Presdl. Campaign, Boston, 1987-88; v.p. Podeste Assocs., Washington, 1989-90; sr. counsel subcom. on tech. and law Senate Judiciary Com., Washington, 1990-93; dep. asst. to pres., dep. staff sec. The White House, Washington, 1993—.

STERN, WALTER EUGENE, neurosurgeon, educator; b. Portland, Oreg., Jan. 1, 1920; s. Walter Eugene and Ida May (McCoy) S.; m. Elizabeth Naffziger, May 24, 1946; children: Geoffrey Alexander, Howard Christian, Eugenia Louise, Walter Eugene III. AB cum laude, U. Calif., MD, 1943. Diplomate: Am. Bd. Neurol. Surg. (vice chmn. 1975-80). Surg. intern, asst. resident surgery and neurol. surgery U. Calif. Hosp., 1943-46, asst. resident neurol. surgery and neuropathology, 1948; clin. clk. Nat. Hosp. Paralyzed and Epileptic, London, Eng., 1948-49; Nat. Research fellow med. sci. Johns Hopkins, 1949-50; asst. resident, resident U. Calif. Service, 1951; NIH spl. fellow univ. lab. physiology Oxford U., 1961-62; clin. instr. U. Calif., 1951; asst. prof. neurosurgery UCLA, 1952-56, assoc. prof., 1956-59, prof., 1959-87, now emeritus, chief div. neurosurgery, 1952-85, chmn. dept. surgery, 1981-87; cons. neurosurgery, Wadsworth VA Hosp. Former mem., chmn. editorial bd. Jour. Neurosurgery; contbr. articles to sci. jours., chpts. in books. Lt. to capt. M.C. AUS, 1946-48. Fellow ACS (sec.); mem. AMA, Am. Surg. Assn., Pacific Coast Surg. Assn., L.A. Surg. Soc. (pres. 1978), Am. Assn. Neurol. Surgeons (pres. 1979-80, Cushing medalist, 1992), James IV Assn. Surgeons, Western Neurosurg. Soc. (past pres.), Soc. Neurol. Surgeons (past pres.), Neurosurg. Soc. Am., Am. Neurol. Assn., Soc. Univ. Surgeons, Soc. Brit. Neurol. Surgeons (hon.), Phi Beta Kappa, Sigma Xi, Alpha Omega Alpha. Republican. Episcopalian. Home: 435 Georgina Ave Santa Monica CA 90402-1909 Office: U Calif Sch Medicine Los Angeles CA 90024

STERN, WALTER PHILLIPS, investment executive; b. N.Y.C., Sept. 26, 1928; s. Leo and Marjorie (Phillips) S.; m. Elizabeth May, Feb. 12, 1958; children: Sarah May, William May, David May. AB, Williams Coll., 1950; MBA, Harvard U., 1952. With Lazard Freres & Co., N.Y.C., 1953-54; assoc. Burnham & Co., Inc. (now Drexel Burnham Lambert Group, Inc.), N.Y.C., 1954-60, ptnr., 1960-71, sr. exec. v.p., 1972-73; vice chmn., mng. dir. eastern ops. Capital Rsch. Co., 1973—; chmn. bd. New Perspective Fund, Inc., 1973—, Fundamental Investors Inc., 1978—; chmn. Europacific Growth Fund, Inc., 1984—; chmn. bd. Emerging Markets Growth Fund; vice chmn. Income Fund Am., Inc.; pres. Growth Fund Am.; bd. dirs. Temple-Inland, Inc.; past mem. pub. Mcpl. Securities Rulemaking Bd., 1984-87; trustee Fin. Analysts Rsch. Found.; chmn. bd. trustees Hudson Inst.; dir. Jewish Community Rels. Coun. N.Y.; instr. in investment mgmt. and fin. NYU, 1956-62, 70-73. Contbr. articles to profl. jours. Chmn. fin. adv. com. Haddassah; trustee Am. Jewish Com.; gov. Anti-Defamation League; bd. dirs. Am. Friends of Tel Aviv U.; trustee Tel Aviv U., Jaffee Inst. Strategic Studies, Tel Aviv; mem. adv. bd. Competitiveness Ctr. of Hudson Inst.; v.p., exec. com. Washington Inst. Near East Policy; pres. bd. dirs. Rsch. Project on Energy and Econ. Policy; chmn. Am. steering com. Freedom Trade with Israel. Mem. N.Y. Soc. Security Analysts (bd. dirs.), Fin. Analysts Fedn. (pres. 1971-72, bd. dirs.), Inst. Chartered Fin. Analysts (pres. 1976-77, bd. dirs.), Assn. Investment and Mgmt. Rsch. (bd. dirs., exec. com. 1990—), Harvard Club, Williams Club, Econ. Club, Sunningdale Country Club, Calif. Club, Phi Beta Kappa. Jewish. Home: 450 Fort Hill Rd Scarsdale NY 10583-2413 Office: Capital Group Inc 630 Fifth Ave Ste 36 New York NY 10111 also: Capital Group Inc 333 S Hope St Los Angeles CA 90071

STERN, WILLIAM LOUIS, botanist, educator; b. Paterson, N.J., Sept. 10, 1926; s. Abram and Rose (Chrisman) S.; m. Floraet Selma Tanis, Sept. 4, 1949; children: Susan Myra, Paul Elihu. BS, Rutgers U., 1950; MS, U. Ill., 1951, PhD, 1954. Instr., then asst. prof. Yale Sch. Forestry, 1953-60; curator div. plant anatomy Smithsonian Inst., 1960-64, chmn. dept botany, 1964-67; prof. botany U. Md., College Park, 1967-79, U. Fla., Gainesville, 1979—; chmn. dept. U. Fla., 1979-85; Forestry officer FAO, 1963-64; mem. sci. adv. bd. Nat. Tropical Bot. Garden, 1969-83; mem. sci. adv. com. Winterthur Mus., 1973-86; vis. com. Arnold Arboretum of Harvard U., 1971-77; vice chmn. Arnold Arboretum of Harvard U., 1973-76; asesor cientifico U. de los Andes, Merida, Venezuela, 1975; program dir. systematic biology NSF, 1978, 79. Editor: Tropical Woods, 1953-60, Plant Sci. Bull., 1962-64, Biotropica, 1968-73; asso. editor: BioSci, 1963-65, Econ. Botany, 1966-75; mem. editorial com.: Am. Jour. Botany, 1967-69. Bd. dirs. Fairchild Tropical Garden, 1980-86; trustee Kampong Fund, 1985—. Served with USNR, 1944-46, PTO. Fellow Linnean Soc. of London; mem. Bot. Soc. Am. (pres. 1984-86), Am. Inst. Biol. Scis. (bd. dirs. 1987-89), Internat. Assn. Wood Anatomists (hon., council), Am. Soc. Plant Taxonomists (pres. 1981), Soc. Econ. Botany (treas. 1988-91), Bot. Soc. Am. (Cert. Merit 1987), Torrey Bot. Club (editor Memoirs 1971-75), Washington Bot. Soc. (pres. 1972), Internat. Soc. Tropical Foresters, Soc. Advancement Research (Philippines), Assn. for Tropical Biology, Internat. Wood Collectors Soc. (life), Phi Beta Kappa, Sigma Xi, Delta Phi Alpha, Phi Kappa Phi, Phi Sigma. Office: U Fla Dept Botany Gainesville FL 32611-8526

STERNBERG, BETTY J., school system administrator; b. N.Y., Jan. 30, 1950; d. Julius and Edith Jane (Meyer) Levin; m. Robert Jeffrey Sternberg, June 18, 1972 (div. Jan. 13, 1987); children: Seth, Sara. BA, Brandeis U., 1971; MA, Columbia U., 1972; PhD, Stanford U., 1978. Bur. chief Dept. Edn., Hartford, Conn., 1980-85, divsn. dir., 1985-92, assoc. commr., 1992—; cons. Nat. Bd. for Prof. Teaching Standards, Washington, 1992. Co-author: (textbook) Metric Multibase Mathematics, 1973, Attribute Acrobatics, 1973, People Pieces Primer, 1975; (textbook series) Math In Stride, 1987. Mem. bd. dirs. William Benton Mus. of Art U. Conn., 1989—; mem. adv. coun. Ctr. for Ednl. Excellence, 1992-93. Recipient Disting. Managerial Svc. award State of Conn., 1986. Mem. ASCD (sec. 1975-80), Conn. Assn.

Suprs. of Curriculum Devel. Avocations: tennis, interior design, gardening. Home: 2 Squirrel Hill Rd West Hartford CT 06107 Office: St Dept of Edn 165 Capitol Ave Hartford CT 06106

STERNBERG, DANIEL ARIE, musician, conductor, educator; b. Lwow, Poland, Mar. 29, 1913; came to U.S., 1939, naturalized, 1946; s. Philipp and Eva (Makowska) S.; m. Felicitas Gobineau, July 29, 1936. Baccalaureate, Realgymnasium, Vienna, 1931; student, U. Vienna, 1931-35; diploma of condr., Vienna State Acad. Music, 1935; composition study with Karl Weigl, 1931-35, conducting with Fritz Stiedry, 1935-36. Lectr., Vienna Volkshochschule, 1933-34; head piano dept. Hockaday Inst. Music, Dallas, 1940-42; dean Sch. Music, Baylor U., Waco, Tex., 1942-81; Ben H. Williams disting. prof. Sch. Music, Baylor U., 1981-82; lectr. mus. subjects. Condr. Vienna Vets. Orch., 1934-35; asst. condr. Leningrad Philharm. and Kirov Opera, 1935-36; guest condr. Leningrad and Moscow radio orchs., 1936, Dallas Symphony Orch., 1952, 65; music dir. Tbilisi (USSR) State Symphony Orch., 1936-37; mus. dir., condr. Waco Symphony Orch., 1962-87; concert accompanist. Recipient Abrams Meml. award for composition Dallas Symphony, 1948. Mem. Phi Mu Alpha, Omicron Delta Kappa. Home: 3108 Robin Rd Waco TX 76708-2275

STERNBERG, DONNA UDIN, lawyer; b. Phila., May 3, 1951; d. Jack and Frances (Osner) Udin; m. Harvey J. Sternberg; children: Zachary Samuel, Zoe Sara. Student Tel Aviv U., 1971; BA, Northwestern U., 1973; JD, Loyola U., Chgo., 1976. Bar: Ill. 1976, Pa. 1979. Profl. actress, dancer, model, 1961-76; dancer Boishoi Ballet Co., 1965, 66, 67, Leningrad Kirov Ballet Co., 1966; actress Broadway produn., 1966; appeared stage plays, TV and film roles, 1961-77; model nat. fashion mags. and publs., 1961-77; assoc. firm Ronald H. Balson & Assocs., Chgo., 1976-79, Mesirov, Gelman, Jaffe, Cramer & Jamieson, Phila., 1979-81; mem. firm Blank, Rome, Comisky & McCauley, Phila., 1981—; lectr. in field. Contbr. articles to profl. jours. Active young leadership council Fedn. Allied Jewish Appeal, 1982-84; mem. Israel Bonds New Leadership Cabinet, 1982-87, Lower Meron Planning Commn. Mem. ABA, Pa. Bar Assn., Phila. Bar Assn. Club: Radnn Valley Country Club. Office: Blank Rome Comisky & McCauley 4 Penn Center Plz Philadelphia PA 19103-2521

STERNBERG, HARRY, artist; b. N.Y.C., July 19, 1904; s. Simon and Rose (Br) S.; m. Mary Elizabeth Gosney, 1939; 1 child, Leslie Louise. Student, Art Students League, N.Y.C. tchr. Art Students League, N.Y.C.; formerly head art dept. Idyllwild Sch. Music and Art, UCLA, U. So. Calif., Idyllwild (Calif.) Arts Found., 1956-63; tchr. graphics San Diego State Coll., 1967-68; artist-in-residence Palomar Coll., San Marcos, Calif.; adj. prof. painting U. Calif., Idyllwild Sch. Music and Art. Exhibited 25 Year Retrospective show, ACA and Gorezick Galleries, 1953; one-man shows ACA Gallery, N.Y.C., 9 shows 1956-82, Brigham Young U., 58, 62, 75, Gorelick Gallery, 58, Nat. Inst. Arts and Letters, 1961, Utah State U., 1962, Salt Lake Art Ctr., Salt Lake City, 1962, Heritage Gallery, L.A., 1964, Gray Gallery, Escondido, 1970, Ulrich Mus., Art Students League, N.Y.C., 1982, Galaria Palomas, San Juan, P.R., 1982-83, Deicas Gallery, La Jolla, Calif., 1983, San Diego Print Club, 1983, Mary Ryan Gallery, N.Y.C., 1984, 89, Idyllwild Sch. Art, 1985, Todd Gallery, Idyllwild, Calif., 1985-86, 89, (graphic exhbn.) Tobey Moss Gallery, L.A., 1986, Susan Teller Gallery, N.Y.C., 1989, 90, 92, Sragow Gallery, N.Y.C., 1990, graphics retrospective Art Students League, N.Y.C., 1992, Athenium, San Diego, 1992, Susan Teller Gallery, N.Y.C., 1993; woodcut exhibition Brighton Press, San Diego, 1992; traveling show Art in the Labor Movement: West Berlin, 1983, Hamburg, Fed. Republic of Germany, 1984, Stockholm, 1985, Rome, 185, England, 1985, Midtown Gallery, N.Y.C., 1991, Worcester Art Mus., 1991, Boston Mus. Fine Art, 1991, Palomar Coll. Gallery, Vista, Calif., 1993; retrospective exhbns. Walker Art Centre, Mpls., 1973, Wichita State U., 1975, Art Students League, N.Y.C., Assoc. Am. Artists, N.Y.C., Art and Design Gallery-Bonsall, 1976, Bethesda (Md.) Art Gallery, 1980, New Vistas Gallery, Vista, Calif., 1980, Libr. of Congress, 1983, Bethesda Gallery, (Md.) Midtown Gallery, N.Y.C., 1988, 89, Avonca Internat., Rancho Bernardo, Calif., 1988, Nat. Acad. Design, 1988, Associated Am. Gallery, N.Y.C., 1989, Art Students League, N.Y.C., 1994, San Diego Mus. Art, 1994, 95; represented in permanent collections Mus. Modern Art, Met. Mus., Whitney Mus., Bklyn., Cleve., Phila. museums, Library Congress, Victoria and Albert Mus., London, Bibliothique Nationale, Paris, Syracuse U., H. de Young Meml. Mus., Wichita (Kans.) State Mus., San Francisco, Fogg Mus., Boston, Addison Gallery Am. Art, Boston, Syracuse U. Mus., Library Congress, Washington, N.Y. Pub. Library, U. Minn., Nat. Portrait Gallery, Washington, Nat. Mus., Tel Aviv, N.Z. Mus. Art, St. Lawrence U., Roberson Art Centre, Binghamton, N.Y., Cleve. Mus. Art, Ulrich Mus., Thorne Mus., Keene State Coll., Hirshorn Mus., Washington, Roanoke Mus. Fine Arts, Bklyn. Mus., 1986, La Jolla Mus. Art, San Diego Mus. Art, Nat. Acad. Design, 1988, Associated Am. Artists, N.Y.C., 1988, Wolfsonian Mus., Miami, Fla., San Diego Mus. Art; producer, dir.: motion pictures The Many Worlds of Art, 1960, Art and Reality, 1961; author: Silk Screen Color Printing, 1942, Modern Methods and Materials of Etching, 1949, Compositions, 1957, Modern Drawing, 1958, Woodcut, 1962, Short Shots and Rituals With Woodcuts, 1990, A Life, an autobiography in woodcuts, 1992. Recipient Guggenheim fellowship, 1936, 1st prize Phila. Print Club, 1942; Living Arts Found., grantee, 1960; recipient graphic prize Audubon Artists, 1955, purchase award Nat. Inst. Arts and Letters, 1972. Mem. Art Students League of N.Y.C. (hon.), Artists Equity, Artists Guild of Fine Arts Gallery (San Diego), Nat. Acad. Design, Nat. Acad. Design (N.Y.C.). Home: 2234 Hilton Head Glen Escondido CA 92026-1071 Studio: 1718 E Valley Pkwy Escondido CA 92025

STERNBERG, PAUL, retired ophthalmologist; b. Chgo., Dec. 18, 1918; s. David M. and Sarah (Kopeka) S.; m. Dorie Betty Feitler, Dec. 24, 1949; children—Daniel P., Patricia F., Paul, Susan P., David. B.S., Northwestern U., 1938, M.D., 1940. Intern Michael Reese Hosp., Chgo., 1940-41; resident ophthalmology Michael Reese Hosp., Ill. Eye & Ear Infirmary U. Ill.; spl. fellow ophthalmology Cornell U. Med. Center, N.Y. Hosp., Wilmer Inst. Johns Hopkins, 1941-44; practice medicine, specializing in ophthalmology Chgo., from 1945; attending ophthalmologist Cook County Hosp., Michael Reese Hosp., Highland Park (Ill.) Hosp., Louis Weiss Meml. Hosp.; prof. ophthalmology Chgo. Med. Sch. Contbr. sci. articles to med. and ophthal. jours. Fellow A.C.S.; mem. Assn. for Research in Ophthalmology, Am. Assn. Ophthalmology, Am. Acad. Ophthalmology, Chgo. Ophthal. Soc., Pan-Am. Congress Ophthalmology. Clubs: Standard (Chgo.); Lake Shore Country (Glencoe, Ill.). Home: 359 Surfside Pl Glencoe IL 60022-1723 Office: 225 W Washington St Ste 2150 Chicago IL 60606-3418

STERNBERG, PAUL J., lawyer; b. Nyack, N.Y., July 14, 1933; s. Paul and Helen Louise (Butler) S.; m. Barbara Patricia Boyle, Sept. 3, 1955; children: Lucinda Abbott, Alicia Boyle, Amanda Butler (dec.). AB, Harvard U., 1954; LLB, Columbia U., 1957. Bar: N.Y. 1958, Iowa 1981. Assoc. Choate, Reynolds, Huntington & Hollister, N.Y.C., 1958-61; mng. counsel The Singer Co., N.Y.C., 1963-79; sr. v.p., gen counsel, sec. Bandag Inc., Muscatine, Iowa, 1979-86; spl. counsel Hinman, Howard, and Kattell, Binghamton and Norwich, N.Y., 1986-89; v.p., gen. counsel, sec. Raymond Corp., Greene, N.Y., 1989—; bd. dirs. G.N. Johnston Equipment Co., Ltd., Dockstocker Corp., Corp. Raymond de Mexico, Broome Legal Assistance Corp.; bd. dirs., counsel So. Tier World Commerce Assn. Bd. dirs. The Chenango Found. Capt. U.S. Army, 1961-62. Mem. ABA, Assn. of Bar of City of N.Y., N.Y. State Bar Assn., Harvard Club N.Y.; Manursing Island Club. Presbyterian. Office: The Raymond Corp S Canal St Greene NY 13778

STERNBERG, ROBERT JEFFREY, psychology educator; b. Newark, Dec. 8, 1949; s. Joseph Sternberg and Lilliam Myriam (Politzer) Weingast; children: Seth, Sara; m. Alejandra Campos, 1991. BA summa cum laude, Yale U., 1972; PhD, Stanford U., 1975; D (honoris causa), Complutense U., 1994. Mem. faculty dept. psychology Yale U., New Haven, 1975—; prof. psychology Yale U., 1983-86, IBM prof. psychology and edn., 1986—. Editor-in-chief Encyclopedia of Human Intelligence, Psychol. Bull., 1991—; assoc. editor Child Development, 1981-84, Intelligence (1977-82); cons. editor Learning and Individual Differences, 1992—, Intelligence, 1977—, Devel. Rev., 1987-91, Jour. Personality and Social Psychology, 1989-91, Psychol. Rev., 1987-91; author: Intelligence, Information Processing and Analogical Reasoning, 1977, Beyond IQ, 1985, The Triarchic Mind, 1988, Metaphors of Mind, 1990, Defying the Crowd, 1995, In Search of the Mind, 1995. Recipient award for Excellence Mensa Edn. and Rsch. Found., 1989; Guggenheim Found. fellow, 1985-86. Fellow APA (past pres. divsns. 1 and

15, McCandless Young Scientist award divsn. devel. psychology 1982, Disting. Sci. award for early career contbn. 1981), Am. Acad. Arts & Scis., Am. Psychol. Soc.; mem. Am. Ednl. Rsch. Assn. (Rsch. Rev. award 1986, Outstanding Book award 1987), Soc. Multivariate Exptl. Psychology (Cattell award 1982), Nat. Assn. Gifted Children (Disting. Scholar award 1985), Assn. Portugese Psychologists (internat. award 1991), Phi Beta Kappa. Avocations: coin collecting, physical fitness, travel, reading. Home: 105 Spruce Bank Rd Hamden CT 06518-2233 Office: Yale Univ Dept Psychology PO Box 208205 New Haven CT 06520-8205

STERNBERG, SEYMOUR, insurance company executive; b. Bklyn., June 24, 1943; s. Max and Mollie Sternberg; m. Roslyn Jacobowitz, June 14, 1965 (div.); children: Jodi, Donna; m. Laurette Zolty, Sept. 14, 1980; 1 child, Matthew. BSEE, CCNY, 1965; MSEE in Computer Sci., Northeastern U., 1968. Mgr. Raytheon Co., Bedford, Mass., 1965-73; mgr. Data Architects, Waltham, Mass., 1973-75; dir. info. services Mass. Mut. Life Ins. Co., Springfield, 1975-76, 2d v.p., 1976-77, v.p. info. services, 1977-81, sr. v.p. group life and health div., 1981-84, exec. v.p. group life and health div., 1984-87, sr. exec. v.p., 1987-88; sr. v.p. group ops. N.Y. Life Ins. Co., 1989, exec. v.p., 1991, vice chmn., pres., 1995, also bd. dirs.; also bd. dirs. Mass. Mut. Life Ins. Co., Springfield; bd. dirs. Bank of New Eng. West. Vice chmn. United Way, Springfield, 1985; bd. dirs. Big Bros./Big Sisters, Springfield; trustee Springfield Coll. Mem. Am. Inst. C.L.U.s. Avocations: stamp collecting; tennis. Office: NY Life Ins Co 51 Madison Ave New York NY 10010

STERNBERGER, LUDWIG AMADEUS, neurologist, educator; b. Munich, Germany, May 26, 1921; s. Hugo and Emy (Welinger) S.; m. Nancy Jeanne Hoy, Dec. 13, 1961. B.A., Am. U. Beirut, 1941, M.D., 1945. Fellow Sloan Kettering Meml. Cancer Ctr., N.Y.C., 1948-50; sr. med. biochemist N.Y. State Dept. Health, Albany, 1950-54; asst. prof. medicine Northwestern U., Chgo., 1954-55; chief basic scis. div. Med. Research Labs., Edgewood Arsenal, Md., 1957-78; prof. brain research U. Rochester Med. Ctr. (N.Y.), 1978-86; prof. neurology, pathology and anatomy U. Md., Balt., 1986-92; sci. co-dir., treas. Sternberger Monoclonals, Inc., Balt., 1992—. Author: Immunocytochemistry, 1974, 3d edit, 1986; mem. editoral bd. Cell and Tissue Research, Histochemistry, Jour. Histochemistry and Cytochemistry, Jour. Neurosci. Methods, Jour. Neuroimmunology, Histochem. Jour., Electron Microscopy in Biology. Served to maj. M.C., U.S. Army, 1955-57. Recipient Paul A. Siple prize, 1972; recipient Humboldt prize for sci. U.S. scientists, 1980, Classic Author citation Inst. Sci. Info., 1983; Senator Jacob K. Javits neurosci. investigator award, 1984; 25th most frequently cited author in sci. lit. of 1984; author of one of 17 Newcomer Superstar papers among 100 most cited of all time. Mem. Histochem. Soc. (pres. 1977-78), Am. Soc. Neurochemistry (program com. 1983-84), Am. Assn. Immunologists, Endocrine Soc., Am. Acad. Allergy, Am. Assn. Neuropathologists. Lutheran. Home: 10 Burwood Ct Lutherville Timonium MD 21093-3502 Office: Sternberger Monoclonals Inc Alpha Ctr Bayview Rsch Campus 5210 Eastern Ave Baltimore MD 21224

STERNE, BOBBIE LYNN, city council member; b. Ohio, Nov. 27, 1919; m. Eugene Sterne (dec.); children: Lynn, Cindy. Student, Akron U., 1947-42; student, U. Cin., 1946-47. RN, Ohio. City coun. mem. City of Cin., 1971—, mayor, 1976, 79; chair human resources com., 1987-89, mem. fin. and labor com., past chair labor com., law and pub. safety com., past chair pub. works and traffic safety com., chair intergovtl. affairs and environ. com. 1990—, past chair urban devel. com. City Coun., Cin.; past chair fin. and labor com., human resources com., City Coun., Cin.; past mem. vice chair pub. wks. and traffic safety com. City Coun. Cin., also housing com.; trustee City of Cin. Retirement System, 1989—; mem. Planning Commn., City of Cin., 1989-90, others. Mem. Adult Basic Edn. Bd.; mem. adv. com. Sch. Social Work U. Cin., Parents Anonymous, YWCA Alice Paul House, Bethesda Women's Network, Big Bros. and Big Sisters; mem. Arthritis Found., Caracole Bd., Charles P. Taft Meml. Fund Com., Community Chest, Drug and Poison Info. Ctr., Friends of Cin. Parks, Friends of the William Howard Taft Birthplace, gerantology community adv. bd. Deaconess Hosp., Greater Cin. Coalition People with Disabilities; chair Emergency Svcs. Coalition. Recipient Coun. Jewish Women Hannah G. Solomon award 1972, Citizens Com. on Youth's Most Valuable Citizen award, Achievement award Greater Cin. Beautiful Com., 1982, Anniversary award for work with Housing for Older Ams., Inc. Better Housing League, 1982, Orchid award Tri-State Air Com., 1982, Citizen's award Ohio Assn. for the Edn. Young Children, Advocate award Women in Communications, 1983, Betty Blake Award for Tourism, 1985, Others award Salvation Army, 1986. Home: 4033 Rose Hill Ave Cincinnati OH 45229-1524

STERNE, JOSEPH ROBERT LIVINGSTON, newspaper editor; b. Phila., Apr. 25, 1928; s. Robert Livingston and Edith Eisner (Heymann) S.; m. Barbara Adele Greene, Feb. 10, 1951; children—Robert Greene, Paul Livingston, Edward Joseph, Adam Heymann, Lee Winslow Greene. B.A. cum laude, Lehigh U., 1948; M.S., Columbia, 1950. Reporter Salt Lake Telegram, Salt Lake City, 1948-49, Wall Street Jour., N.Y.C., 1950-51, Dallas Morning News, 1951-53; reporter Balt. Sun, 1953-72, editorial page editor, 1972—. Mem. Am. Soc. Newspaper Editors, Center Club, Hamilton Street Club, Phi Beta Kappa. Home: 215 Melanchton Ave Lutherville Timonium MD 21093-5321 Office: Baltimore Sun Baltimore MD 21278

STERNER, FRANK MAURICE, industrial executive; b. Lafayette, Ind., Nov. 26, 1935; s. Raymond E. and Maudelene M. (Scipio) S.; m. Elsa Y. Rasmusson, June 29, 1958; children: Mark, Lisa. BS, Purdue U., 1958, MS, 1959, PhD, 1962. Sr. staff specialist Gen. Motors Inst., Flint, Mich., 1962-63; dir. personnel and orgnl. research Delco Electronics, Milw., 1963-66; dir. personnel devel. and research Delco Electronics, 1966-68; partner Nourse & Sterner, Inc., Milw., 1968-69; pres., 1969-73; assoc. dean, prof. Krannert Grad. Sch. of Mgmt., Purdue U., West Lafayette, Ind., 1973-79; v.p. human resources mgmt. Johnson Controls, Inc., Milw., 1979-89; pres., chief exec. officer E.R. Wagner Mfg. Co., 1989—; pres., owner Ridgeway Devel. Inc., Milw., 1993—; bd. dirs. Wausau Homes, Inc., E.R. Wagner Mfg. Co., Children's Hosp. Health Sys. Wis., Ridgeway Devel. Inc., Am. Lung Assn. Wis. Contbr. articles to profl. jours. Club: Reamer. Home: 1440 E Standish Pl Milwaukee WI 53217-1958 Office: ER Wagner Mfg Co 4611 N 32d St Milwaukee WI 53209

STERNER, MICHAEL EDMUND, international affairs consultant; b. N.Y.C., Dec. 26, 1928; s. Harold Walther and Leonie (Knoedler) S.; m. Courtenay Read, Mar. 30, 1957; children: Lucian, Marcellin. AB, Harvard Coll., 1951. Govt. rels. rep. Arabian-Am. Oil Co., Dhahran, Saudi Arabia, 1951-54; joined Fgn. Svc., 1956; vice consul Aden, 1957-58; polit. officer Cairo, 1960-64; desk officer Near Eastern Affairs Dept. State, 1964-70, dir. Egyptian affairs, 1970-74; amb. to United Arab Emirates Abu Dhabi, 1974-76; dep. asst. sec. state for Near East and South Asian affairs, 1977-81; mng. dir. The IRC Group, Inc., 1982—. Mem. bd. govs. Mid. East Inst. With AUS, 1954-56. Mem. Coun. Fgn. Rels. Home: 2712 36th St NW Washington DC 20007-1421 Office: 1835 K St NW Washington DC 20006-1203

STERNGLASS, LILA M., advertising agency executive; b. N.Y.C., Aug. 3, 1934; d. Joseph and Sarah (Golden) Kronstadt; m. Arno E. Sternglass, Apr. 20, 1956; children: Adam, Paul. BFA, Cooper Union, 1954. Asst. art dir. Sterling Advt., N.Y.C., 1954-55; art dir. Diamond Barnett Advt., N.Y.C., 1955, I. Miller Shoes, N.Y.C., 1956, Trahey Wolf Advt., N.Y.C., 1969-70; sr. art dir. Sacks & Rosen, N.Y.C., 1970-72; assoc. creative dir. Warwick Advt., N.Y.C., 1972-80, Ketchum Advt., N.Y.C., 1980; creative dir. Rumrill Hoyt Advt., N.Y.C., 1981-88, McCaffrey and McCall Advt., 1988-90; ptnr. Hamilton/Sternglass Inc., Creative Cons., N.Y.C., 1990—. Recipient Merit award Art Dirs. Club, 1954, 56, 69, 70, 71, 74, 82, 85, Merit award Andy Advt. Club, 1971, 72, 82, 83, One Show Merit award, 1983, 84, 85, 88, 89, Clio finalist, 1983-84, 89, Clio award 1985, Internat. Radio Fest award 1984, 85, Internat. Radio Fest finalist 1984, 85, Gold Effies award, 1985, 86, 88, 89, others. Avocations: movies, museums, walking, traveling. Office: 54 W 21st St # 705 New York NY 10010-6908

STERNHAGEN, FRANCES, actress; b. Washington, Jan. 13, 1930. Student, Vassar Coll., Perry-Mansfield Sch. of Theatre; studied with Sanford Meisner, N.Y. Tchr. Milton Acad., Mass.; actress Arena Stage, Washington, 1953-54. Debut Thieves Carnival, N.Y., 1955; plays include The Carefree Tree, The Admirable Bashville (Clarence Derwent award, Obie

award), Ulysses in Night Town, Red Eye of Love, Misalliance, The Return of Herbert Bracewell, Laughing Stock, The Displaced Person, The Pinter Plays (Obie award); Broadway shows include The Skin of Our Teeth, Viva Madison Avenue, Great Day in the Morning, The Right Honorable Gentleman, The Cocktail Party, Cock-a-Doodle Dandy, Playboy of the Western World, The Sign in Sidney Brustein's Window, The Good Doctor (Tony award 1973), Equus, Angel, On Golden Pond (Drama League award), The Father, Grownups, Summer, You Can't Take It With You, Home Front, Driving Miss Daisy, Remembrance, A Perfect Ganesh, The Heiress (Tony nominee 1995); actress films include Up the Down Staircase, Starting Over, Outland, Independence Day, Romantic Comedy, Bright Lights, Big City, See You in the Morning, Communion, Misery, Doc Hollywood, Raising Cain; (TV series) Love of Life, The Doctors, Secret Storm, Cheers, Golden Years, Under One Roof, The Road Home; (TV movies) Who Will Save Our Children?, Prototype, Resting Place, Follow Your Heart, She Woke Up, Labor of Love: The Arlette Schweitzer Story, Reunion, Tales from the Crypt, Outer Limits.

STERNLICHT, SANFORD, English and theater arts educator, writer; b. N.Y.C., Sept. 20, 1931; s. Irving Stanley and Sylvia (Hilsenroth) S.; m. Dorothy Hilkert, June 4, 1950 (dec. 1977); children: David, Daniel. BS, SUNY, Oswego, 1953; MA, Colgate U., 1955; PhD, Syracuse U., 1962. Instr. SUNY, Oswego, 1959-60, asst. prof., 1960-62, prof. and dir. grad. studies in English, 1962-72, chmn. dept. theater, 1972-84; adj. prof. English Syracuse (N.Y.) U., 1984—; Leverhulme vis. prof. English U. of York, Eng., 1965-66. Author: Gull's Way, 1961, The Blue Star Commodore, 1961, Love in Pompeii, 1967, John Webster's Imagery and the Webster Canon, 1972, John Masefield, 1977, McKinley's Bulldog, 1977 (Mil. Book Club award, Saturday Evening Post Book Club award), C.S. Forester, 1981, Padraic Colum, 1985; (with E.M. Jameson) The Black Devil of the Bayous, 1971; (with E.M. Jameson) U.S.F. Constellation: Yankee Racehorse, 1981, John Galsworthy, 1986, R.F. Delderfield, 1988, Stevie Smith, 1990, Stephen Spender, 1992, Siegfried Sassoon, 1993; editor: The Selected Short Stories of Padraic Colum, 1985, The Selected Plays of Padraic Colum, 1986, The Selected Poems of Padraic Colum, 1988, In Search for Stevie Smith, 1991. Lt. (j.g.) USN, 1955-59, comdr. USNR, ret. Recipient New Poets award Writer mag., 1960, Chancellor's award SUNY, 1974; fellow Poetry Soc. Am., 1964; rsch. grantee SUNY, 1963-70; named Tchr. of Yr. Syracuse U., 1986. Mem. MLA, NAACP, PEN, Shakespeare Assn. Am., Am. Conf. Irish Studies. Democrat. Jewish. Home: 128 Dorset Rd Syracuse NY 13210-3048 Office: Syracuse U Dept English Syracuse NY 13244

STERNLIGHT, PETER DONN, economist, retired banker; b. N.Y.C., May 21, 1928; s. Morris Henry and Pearl (Donn) S.; m. Lenore Frane, Oct. 14, 1956; children: Jean Renee, Judith Ann. B.A., Swarthmore Coll., 1948; M.A., Harvard U., 1950, Ph.D., 1960. With Fed. Res. Bank N.Y., 1950-65; aide to under sec. treasury, 1961, asst. v.p. open market ops., 1964, dep. under sec. treasury monetary affairs, 1965-67; with Fed. Res. Bank N.Y., 1967-92, v.p. open market ops., 1968-77, sr. v.p., dep. mgr. system account for domestic ops., 1977-79, mgr. system account for domestic ops., 1979-92, exec. v.p., 1982-92; retired, 1992. Served with AUS, 1950-52. Recipient Exceptional Svc. award Treasury Dept., Disting. Achievement award for 1988 Money Marketers of NYU, William F. Butler award for Excellence in Bus. Econs. N.Y. Assn. Bus. Economists, 1994. Mem. Am. Econ. Assn., Am. Finance Assn., Phi Beta Kappa. Home: 301 Garfield Pl Brooklyn NY 11215-2351

STERNMAN, JOEL W., lawyer; b. N.Y.C., Oct. 20, 1943; s. Abraham and Sarah (Simon) S.; children: Mark S., Cheryl A.; m. Barbara E. Shiers, March 31, 1985; children: Matthew S., Julia S. AB, Dartmouth Coll., 1965; LLB, Yale U., 1968. Bar: N.Y. 1970, U.S. Dist. Ct. (so. and ea. dists.) N.Y. 1971, U.S. Ct. Appeals (2d cir.) 1972, U.S. Supreme Ct. 1984, U.S. Ct. Appeals (6th cir.) 1985, U.S. Ct. Appeals (9th cir.) 1994. Law clk. to judge U.S. Dist. Ct., New Haven, 1968-69; assoc Rosenman Colin Freund Lewis & Cohen, N.Y.C., 1969-77; ptnr. Rosenman & Colin, N.Y.C., 1977—. Editor Yale Law Jour., New Haven, 1966-68. Mem. Phi Beta Kappa. Office: Rosenman & Colin 575 Madison Ave New York NY 10022-2511

STERNS, JOEL HENRY, lawyer; b. N.Y.C., Apr. 13, 1934; s. Barney and Yetta S.; m. Joanne Glickman, Nov. 19, 1961; children: Rachael, Leslie, David. B.S. in Journalism, 1956; M.P.A., Princeton U., 1958; J.D., N.Y. U., 1967. Bar: N.J., D.C. Exec. asst. to comm'r. N.J. Dept. Conservation and Econ. Devel., 1958-61; exec. asst. to adminstr. Bur. Security and Consular Affairs, Dept. State, 1961-62; regional programs coordinator Alliance for Progress, 1962-64; exec. asst. to pres. Export-Import Bank U.S., 1964; dep. commr. N.J. Dept. Cmty. Affairs, 1967-68; counsel to gov. N.J., 1968-70; pres. firm Sterns, Herbert & Weinroth (P.A.), Trenton, N.J., 1970-88; mem. exec. com., compensation com. and mktg. com. Sterns, Herbert & Weinroth (merged with Hannoch-Weisman 1988), Roseland, N.J., 1988-91; pres. Hannoch-Weisman, Roseland, 1991-93, Sterns & Weinroth, Trenton, 1994—. Mem. ABA, Am. Law Inst., Am. Judicature Soc., N.J. Bar Assn. (trustee), Mercer County Bar Assn., Assn. Princeton U. Grad. Alumni (trustee 1975-77), NYU Alumni Assn. N.J. (Disting. Alumni award 1987). Home: PO Box 307 RD 1 River Rd Titusville NJ 08560 Office: Sterns & Weinroth PO Box 1298 50 W State St Ste 1400 Trenton NJ 08607

STERNSTEIN, ALLAN J., lawyer; b. Chgo., June 7, 1948; s. Milton and Celia (Kaganove) S.; m. Miriam A. Dolgin, July 12, 1970 (div. July 1981); children—Jeffery A., Amy R.; m. Beverly A. Cook, Feb. 8, 1986; children: Cheryl L., Julia S. B.S., U. Ill., 1970; M.S., U. Mich., 1972; J.D., Loyola U., 1976. Bar: Ill. 1977, U.S. Dist. Ct. (no. dist.) Ill. 1977, U.S. Dist. Ct. (no. dist.) Ohio 1977, U.S. Dist. Ct. (ea. dist) Mich. 1986, U.S. Dist. Ct. (we. dist.) Mich. 1990, U.S. Ct. Customs and Patent Appeals 1978, U.S. Ct. Appeals (7th cir.) 1979, U.S. Ct. Appeals (Fed. cir.) 1982. Patent agent Sunbeam Corp., Oak Brook, Ill., 1972-76; ptnr. Neuman, Williams, Anderson & Olson, Chgo., 1976-84; div. patent counsel Abbott Labs., North Chgo., Ill., 1984-87; ptnr. Willian Brinks Hofer Gilson & Lione, Chgo., 1987—; adj. prof. of law John Marshall Law Sch., 1989-90, DePaul Univ., 1990-92, Univ. Ill., 1992—. Legal advisor Legal Aid Soc., Chgo., 1974-76. Pub. Defender's Office, Chgo., 1974. Teaching fellow U. Mich. 1971-72; research grantee U. Mich., U.S. Air Force, 1971-72. Mem. ABA, Chgo. Bar Assn., Patent Law Assn. of Chgo. (com. chmn. 1982), Am. Intellectual Property Law Assn., Licensing Execs. Soc., Tau Beta Pi, Sigma Tau, Sigma Gamma Tau, Phi Eta Sigma. Jewish. Office: Willian Brinks Hofer Gilson & Lione 455 N Cityfront Plaza Dr Chicago IL 60611-5503

STERRETT, JAMES KELLEY, II, lawyer; b. St. Louis, Nov. 26, 1946; s. James Kelley and Anastasia Mary (Holzer) S.; m. Karen Marie Buttemer; 1 child, Brittany. AB, San Diego State U., 1968; JD, U. Calif., Berkeley, 1971; LLM, U. Pa., 1973. Bar: Calif. 1972, U.S. Dist. Ct. (so. dist.) Calif. 1972. From assoc. to ptnr. Gray, Cary, Ames & Frye, San Diego, 1972-83; ptnr. Lillick, McHose & Charles, San Diego, 1983-90, Pillsbury, Madison & Sutro, San Diego, 1991—. Contbr. articles to profl. jours. Bd. dirs. Holiday Bowl, San Diego, 1980—, Mus. Photog. Arts, San Diego, 1985-88, San Diego Internat. Sports Coun., 1980—, pres., 1990, chmn., 1992. Capt. USAFR, 1972. Fellow U. Pa. Ctr. Study Fin. Instns., 1971-72. Mem. ABA, Calif. Bar Assn., San Diego County Bar Assn., San Diego Fin. Lawyers Group. Republican. Episcopalian. Club: Fairbanks Ranch Country (Rancho Santa Fe) (bd. dirs. 1985-87). Avocation: golf. Office: Pillsbury Madison & Sutro 101 W Broadway Ste 1800 San Diego CA 92101-8219

STERRETT, JANE EVELYNE, illustrator, artist; b. N.Y.C., Jan. 3, 1942; d. Anthony H. and Frances A. Sterrett. Student, with Oskar Kokoschka, Salzburg, Austria, 1962; BFA, R.I. Sch. Design, 1963; MFA, Yale U., 1965. Chairperson art dept. Milton (Mass.) Acad./Girls Sch., 1965-68; instr. Parsons Sch. Design, N.Y.C., 1974-80; prin. Jane Sterrett Studio, N.Y.C., 1970—, freelance illustrator, 1970—; adj. prof. Pratt Inst., Manhattan, N.Y., 1972—. Free lance illustrator for various publs., corp. and advt. agys. Recipient numerous awards. Mem. Soc. Illustrators, Graphic Artists Guild. Office: 160 Fifth Ave New York NY 10010-7003

STERRETT, SAMUEL BLACK, lawyer, former judge; b. Washington, Dec. 17, 1922; s. Henry Hatch Dent and Helen (Black) S.; m. Jeane McBride, Aug. 27, 1949; children: Samuel Black, Robin Dent, Douglas McBride. Student, St. Albans Sch., 1933-41; grad., U.S. Mcht. Marine Acad., 1945; B.A., Amherst Coll., 1947; LL.B., U. Va., 1950; LL.M. in

Taxation, N.Y.U., 1959. Bar: D.C. 1951, Va. 1950. Atty. Alvord & Alvord, Washington, 1950-56; trial atty. Office Regional Counsel, Internal Revenue Service, N.Y.C., 1956-60; ptnr. Sullivan, Shea & Kenney, Washington, 1960-68; municipal coun. to office vice pres. U.S., 1965-68; judge U.S. Tax Ct., 1968-85, chief judge, 1985-88; ptnr. Myerson, Kuhn & Sterrett, Washington, 1988-89; of counsel Vinson & Elkins, Washington, 1990—. Bd. mgrs. Chevy Chase Village, 1970-74, chmn., 1972-74; 1st v.p. bd. trustees, mem. exec. com. Washington Hosp. Center, 1969-79, chmn. bd. trustees, 1979-84; chmn. bd. trustees Washington Healthcare Corp., 1982-87; chmn. bd. trustees Medlantic Healthcare Group, 1987-89; mem. Washington Cathedral chpt., 1973-81; mem. governing bd. St. Albans Sch., 1977-81; trustee Louise Home, 1979-89. Served with AUS, 1943; Served with U.S. Mcht. Marine, 1943-46. Fellow Am. Bar Found.; mem. ABA, Fed. Bar Assn., D.C. Bar Assn.; Am. Coll. Tax Counsel, Soc. of the Cincinnati, Nat. Jud. Coll. Coun. for Future, Am. Inns of Ct., Chevy Chase Club (bd. govs. 1979-84, pres. 1984), Met. Club, Lawyers Club, Alibi Club, Alfalfa Club, Ch. of N.Y. Club, Beta Theta Pi. Episcopalian. Office: Vinson & Elkins 1455 Pennsylvania Ave NW Washington DC 20004-1008

STERZER, FRED, research physicist; b. Vienna, Austria, Nov. 18, 1929; came to U.S., 1947, naturalized, 1952; s. Karl and Rosa (Trumer) S.; m. Betty Distel, Sept. 5, 1964. B.S. in Physics, CCNY, 1951; M.S. in Physics, NYU, 1952, Ph.D. in Physics, 1955. With RCA, 1954-87, RCA Labs., David Sarnoff Research Center, Princeton, N.J., 1956-87; dir. microwave tech. center RCA Labs., David Sarnoff Research Center, 1972-87; dir. microwave research lab. David Sarnoff Research Ctr., 1987-88; pres. MMTC, Inc., Princeton, 1988—; Herbert J. Kayser research prof., City Coll., CUNY, 1986-87. Contbr. numerous articles to profl. publs. Fellow IEEE; mem. Am. Phys. Soc., Nat. Acad. Engring., Sigma Xi, Phi Beta Kappa. Condr. research on optical components, microwave solid-state devices and circuits, med. microwave tech. Home: 4432 Province Line Rd Princeton NJ 08540-4368 Office: MMTC Inc 12 Roszel Rd Princeton NJ 08540-6234

STETLER, C. JOSEPH, lawyer; b. Wapaconeta, Ohio, May 13, 1917; s. Clarence Henry and Mary Frances (Kavanaugh) S.; m. Mary Norine Delaney, Aug. 16, 1941; children: Joseph James, David John, Mary Catherine, Julia Anne, Norine Teresa and Kathleen Frances (twins). LL.B., Cath. U. Am., 1938, LL.M., 1940; postgrad., Benjamin Franklin Sch. Accounting, Washington, 1940-41; D.Sc. (hon.), Mass. Coll. Pharmacy, 1978. Bar: D.C. 1940, Ill. 1951. With various agys. U.S. Govt., 1935-51; with AMA, 1951-63; gen. counsel, dir. legal and socio-econ. div., 1951-63; exec. v.p., gen. counsel Pharm. Mfrs. Assn., Washington, 1963-65; pres. Pharm. Mfrs. Assn., 1965-79, 84-85; ptnr. Munsey, Samuel & Stetler, 1979-81, Dickstein, Shapiro & Morin, 1981-84; pvt. practice Washington, 1984-86; of counsel Royer, Shacknai & Mehle, Washington, 1986-88, Hyman, Phelps & McNamara, Washington, 1988-93. Author: (with Alan Moritz) Doctor Patient and the Law, 1962, Handbook of Legal Medicine, 1964, (with Wm. Cray) Patients in Peril, The Stunning Generic Drug Scandal, 1991. Mem. staff 2d Hoover Commn., 1953-54; mem. Reagan-Bush Health Adv. Com., 1980-81, Social Security Adv. Coun., 1983. Capt. AUS, 1942-46, PTO. Mem. ABA, D.C. Bar Assn. Roman Catholic. Home: 5906 Maplewood Park Pl Bethesda MD 20814 Office: 5550 Friendship Blvd Ste 1 Chevy Chase MD 20875

STETLER, CHARLES EDWARD, English language educator; b. Pitts., Sept. 12, 1927; s. Charles Edward and Catherine (Seidel) S.; m. Ellen Donovan, June 25, 1956; (div. Jan. 1981); children: Peter, Paul, Casey; m. Kristin Jill Brown, July 17, 1984 (div. 1993); m. Mary Grace Aquino, Aug. 25, 1994. BA, Duquesne U., 1950, MA, 1962; PhD, Tulane U., 1966. Reporter Pitts. Sun Telegraph, 1957-62; instr. in English Rollins Coll., Winter Park, Fla., 1962-63; asst. prof. English Loyola U., New Orleans, 1963-67; prof. English Calif. State U., Long Beach, 1967—; exch. prof. English U. Hull, Eng., fall 1984. Author poetry; contbr. articles to profl. jours. With USN, 1945-46, 50-52. Mem. Honor Soc. for Internat. Scholars, Phi Beta Kappa. Democrat. Avocations: bridge, tennis, golf. Home: 5912 Bixby Village Dr Apt 62 Long Beach CA 90803-6314 Office: Calif State U 1250 N Bellflower Blvd Long Beach CA 90840-0004

STETLER, DAVID J., lawyer; b. Washington, Sept. 6, 1949; s. C. Joseph and Norine (Delaney) S.; m. Mary Ann Ferguson, June 18, 1971; children: Brian, Christopher, Jennifer. BA, Villanova U., 1971, JD, 1974. Bar: U.S. Supreme Ct. 1978, Ill. 1988, U.S. Ct. Appeals (7th cir.) 1988, U.S. Ct. Appeals (3d cir.) 1992, U.S. Dist. Ct. (ctrl. dist.) 1994, U.S. Ct. Appeals (8th cir.) 1994. Atty. IRS, Washington, 1974-79; spl. atty. tax divsn. Dept. Justice, Washington, 1975-79; asst. atty. U.S. Atty.'s Office, Chgo., 1979-88, dep. chief spl. prosecutions div., 1985-86, chief criminal recieving and appellate divs., 1986-88; ptnr. McDermott, Will & Emery, Chgo., 1988—; lectr. Atty. Gen. Trial Advocacy Inst., Washington, 1977—. Mem. ABA (chmn. midwest subcom. White Collar Crime com. 1991-93).

STETLER, RUSSELL DEARNLEY, JR., private investigator; b. Phila., Jan. 15, 1945; s. Russell Dearnley and Martha Eleanor (Schultz) S. B.A. with honors in Philosophy, Haverford (Pa.) Coll., 1966; postgrad., New Sch. Social Research, 1966-67. Research asst. to Bertrand Russell, 1967; lectr. Hendon Coll., London, 1968-69; pres. Archetype, Inc., Berkeley, Calif., 1971-78; pub. Westworks, Berkeley, 1977-80; pvt. investigator, 1980—; cons. dir. Ramparts Press, Palo Alto, 1971-80; editorial cons. Internews, Berkeley, 1973-78; faculty Caribbean Sch., Ponce, P.R., 1978-80. Author: The Battle of Bogside, 1970; co-editor: The Assassinations: Dallas and Beyond, 1976. Research grantee Atlantic Peace Found., 1969-70. Mem. Calif. Assn. Lic. Investigators, Nat. Assn. Legal Investigators, Calif. Soccer Referees Assn.-North (treas. Marin County chpt. 1982-90), Amigos de las Americas (pres. Marin chpt. 1985-88). Clubs: Mill Valley Soccer (dir. 1981), Albany-Berkeley Soccer (pres. 1977-78). Office: Calif Appellate Project 1 Ecker Pl San Francisco CA 94105-2752

STETSON, DANIEL EVERETT, museum director; b. Oneida, N.Y., Jan. 3, 1956; s. Robert Everett and Barbara Elizabeth (Gray) S.; m. Catherine Marie Smith; children: Kellee, Natalie, Philip. BA in Art History, Potsdam Coll. Arts and Scis., 1978; MFA in Museology, Syracuse U., 1981. Teaching asst. fine arts dept. Potsdam (N.Y.) Coll. Arts and Scis., 1977-78; grad. asst. Syracuse (N.Y.) U. Art Collections, 1979-80; acting dir. Picker Art Gallery and Colgate U. Art Collections, Colgate U., Hamilton, N.Y., 1980-81; dir. Gallery of Art U. No. Iowa, Cedar Falls, 1981-87; dir. Davenport (Iowa) Mus. Art, 1987-91; exec. dir. Austin (Tex.) Mus. Art (formerly Laguna Gloria Art Mus.), 1991—, founding exec. dir., 1994; guest curator Joe and Emily Lowe Art Gallery, Syracuse U., 1980; mem. Inter Mus. Conservation Lab., Oberlin, 1987-91; mem. design adv. com. Iowa Capitol, Des Moines, 1989-91; panel cons. Arts Midwest/Affiliated States Art Assns. of Upper Midwest, Mpls., 1983, 88; bd. dirs. Iowa Arts Coalition, 1990-91; chair Tex. Commn. on the Arts Visual Arts Review Panel, 1994; mem. planning com. Tex. Assn. of Mus., 1994; mem. art in pub. pls. com. Austin Airport, 1995. Author/curator: (exhbn. catalog) José de Creeft (1884-1982), 1983, Contemporary Icons and Explorations, 1988, (exhbn. catalog) Philip Perlstein-Painting to Watercolors, 1983, Walter Dusenbery Classical Echoes, 1985, Jaune Quick-to-See Smith and George Longfish: Personal Symbols, 1986, Reuban Nakian: Leda and The Swan, 1983, Focus 1 Michael Boyd: Paintings, 1980, 89, Focus 2 Photo Image League, 1989, Focus 3 The Art of Haiti: A Sense of Wonder, 1989, Focus 6—Contemporary Devel. in Glass, 1990, Peter Dean: Landscapes of the Mind, 1981, Joseph Raffael, 1987, Born in Iowa-The Homecoming, 1986, Stieglitz and 40 Other Photographers-The Development of a Collection, 1991-92, New Works (Austin and Central Texas Artists), 1992, Companions in Time: The Paintings of William Lester & Everett Spruce Catalogue Essay, 1993, Human Nature, Human Form Catalogue Essay, 1993, Sources and Collaborations: The Making of the Holocaust Project by Judy Chicago and Donald Woodman tour and catalog, 1994—. Bd. mem. arts coun. Cedar Arts Forum, Black Hawk County, Iowa, 1983-85; curriculum com. Leadership Investment for Tomorrow, Cedar Falls-Waterloo, Iowa, 1985-86; mem. adv. com. MBA Course of Study Styles and Strategies Non-Profit Orgns. St. Ambrose U., 1989-91, Austin BCA Arts Week Poster and Awards, 1993; mem. City of Austin Funding Process Rev. Com., 1992; Facilities Team Austin Comprehensive Arts Plan, 1991-93; mem. adv. panel Tex. Commn. Arts Visual Arts, 1993; field reviewer Inst. Mus. Svcs.-Gen. Operating Support Grant Field Reviewer, 1993; mem. arts com. Downtown Mgmt. Assn., 1995; mem. arts sub-com. Downtown Commn. Fellow N.E. Mus. Conf., Rochester, N.Y., 1979; grantee Iowa Arts Coun., Tex. Commn. Arts, NEA advancement program grant phase I & II,

1993-95; recipient mus. scholarship Am. Law Inst. ABA, Atlanta, Phila., 1984, 93. Mem. Am. Assn. Mus., Midwest Mus. Conf., Iowa Mus. Assn. (chair steering com. exhbn. workshop 1984-86, legis. action com. and indemnification com. 1981-90, bd. dirs. 1983-85), Tex. Assn. Mus. (program com., resources sharing com., 1992-94, Art Mus. Affinity group) Davenport Rotary (cultural affairs com. 1987-91). Avocations: books, music, bike riding, visual world and media. Home: 5912 Brown Rock Trail Austin TX 78749-3306 Office: Austin Mus Art at Laguna Gloria PO Box 5568 Austin TX 78763-5568

STETSON, EUGENE WILLIAM, III, film and television writer and producer; b. Norwalk, Conn., Mar. 31, 1951; s. Eugene William Jr. and Grace Stuart (Richardson) S.; m. Jane White Watson, June 14, 1993. AB, Harvard U., 1982, postgrad. in Sch. Arts and Scis., 1986. Assoc. exec. dir. Conn. River Watershed Coun., Easthampton, Mass., 1978-81; v.p. Fairhill Oil & Gas Corp. (Fairhill Oil Ltd.-Can.), N.Y.C., Calgary, Alta., Can., 1981-84; pres. Fairhill Oil & Gas Corp. (Fairhill Oil Ltd.-Can.), N.Y.C., Calgary, 1984-92; film and TV writer and producer, 1991—; bd. dirs. Piedmont Fin. Co., Greensboro, N.C., 1978-80, Chisolm Mgmt. Corp., N.Y.C., 1983—; supr. Ottauquechee Conservation Dist., Woodstock, Vt., 1978-82; pres. Boatwright Found., N.Y.C., 1981—; exec. com. Westminster Sch., Simsbury, Conn., 1984-86; gov. Smith Richardson Found., N.Y., 1984—; trustee Proctor Acad., Andover, N.H., 1985—; co-founder River Watch Network, Montpelier, Vt., 1987—. Mem. Vt. Gov.'s Coun. of Environ. Advisers, 1992—. Mem. Harvard-Radcliffe Club Vt. (v.p. 1994—), Harvard Club N.Y.C., Hasty Pudding Club. Home: RR2 Box 12 L Elm St Norwich VT 05055

STETSON, JOHN BATTERSON, IV, construction executive; b. Phila., Dec. 21, 1936; s. John Batterson Stetson III and Winifred (Walton) Todd; m. Solveig Weiland, Nov. 23, 1963; children: John Batterson V, Eric Weiland, Scott Walton. BA, Yale U., 1959, MArch, 1966; postgrad., U. Pa., 1969-73. Registered architect, Pa. Staff architect Bower & Fradley, Architects, Phila., 1966-68, Young & Exley, Architects, 1968-69; project architect Day & Zimmerman Assocs. (div. MDC Systems Corp.), Phila., 1969-71, mgr. tech. staff, 1974-76, sr. v.p. cons. services div., 1985—; project mgr. Schnadelbach & Braun, Phila., 1971-74; project exec. Bldg. Scis., Inc., Balt., Kinshasa, Zaire, 1976-77; project mgr. Bldg. Scis., Inc., Balt., 1977-78; sr. cons., v.p. MDC Systems Corp., Phila., 1978-85. Active Haverford (Pa.) Civic Assn., 1981—. Served to lt. (j.g.) USNR, 1959-81. Mem. Constrn. Mgmt. Assn. Am. (bd. dirs. 1986—), Am. Arbitration Assn., Constrn. Specifications Inst., Haverford Sch. Akumni Assn. Republican. Club: Merion Cricket (Haverford). Avocations: music, sailing. Home: 435 Berkley Rd Haverford PA 19041-1508 Office: Day & Zimmerman 208 King of Prussia Rd Radnor PA 19087

STETSON, JOHN CHARLES, corporate executive; b. Chgo., Sept. 6, 1920; s. John Charles and Dorothy H. (Eckman) S.; m. Gayle McDowell, Jan. 1, 1946; children: Sherry, Robert, Susan. B.S., Mass. Inst. Tech., 1943; postgrad., Northwestern U. Bus. Sch., 1946-48. Partner Booz Allen & Hamilton, Chgo., 1951-63; pres. pub. div. Houston Post Co., Houston, 1963-70; pres. A.B. Dick Co., Chgo., 1970-77; also dir.; sec. of the Air Force, Washington, 1977-79; nat. chmn. com. for employer support of guard and res. Dept. Def., Washington, 1980-81; pres. J.C. Stetson, Inc., 1981—; dir. Kemper Corp., NIBCO, Inc., Madison-Kipp Corp., Helene Curtis, Inc., Magna Photo Inc., Chgo. Tube and Iron, In, Laser Tech., Inc. Trustee Chgo. Symphony Orch., Falcon Found., Kemper Found. With USN, 1945-46. Recipient Disting. Service award Dept. Def., Disting. Service award also USAF. Clubs: Chicago, Knollwood, Tavern. Home: 1834 Knollwood Rd Lake Forest IL 60045-1135 Office: 900 N Shore Dr Ste 151 Lake Bluff IL 60044-2225

STETSON, PETER BRAILEY, astronomer; b. Middleboro, Mass., Aug. 30, 1952; s. George Robert and Estelle Marie (Ives) S.; m. Frances Eileen Bogucki, Aug. 5, 1979; children: Whitney Ann, Brailey Marie, Garrett Wilson, Leete Anthony. BA, Wesleyan U., 1974, MA, 1974; MS, Yale U., 1975, PhD, 1979. Postdoctoral astronomy dept. Yale U., New Haven, Conn., 1979-80; Carnegie fellow Mt. Wilson and Las Campanas Obs., Pasadena, Calif., 1980-83; rsch. assoc. Dominion Astrophys. Obs., Victoria, B.C., Can., 1983-84, asst. rsch. officer, 1984-86, assoc. rsch. officer, 1986-89, sr. rsch. officer, 1989—. Contbr. articles to Astron. Jour., Publ. Astron. Soc. of Pacific. Recipient R.M. Petrie prize lectr. Can. Astronomical Soc., 1991, Gold medal Sci. Coun. B.C., 1994. Office: Dominion Astrophys Obs, 5071 W Saanich Rd, Victoria, BC Canada V8X 4M6

STETTINIUS, WALLACE, communications executive; b. N.Y.C., Mar. 4, 1933; s. Edward Reilly Jr. and Virginia (Wallace) S.; m. Mary Gray, June 25, 1958; children: Elizabeth Stettinius Monroe, W. Gray, Gordon. BA, U. Va., 1955, MBA, 1959. Production asst. Garrett & Massie, Richmond, Va. 1959-60; office mgr., registered rep. Anderson & Strudwick, Richmond, 1960-63; v.p. Va. Capital Corp., Richmond, 1963-67; pres. William Byrd Press Inc., Richmond, 1967-87; chmn., chief exec. officer Cadmus Communications Corp., Richmond, 1984-92; chmn. Cadmus Comm. Corp. Richmond, 1992-95; instr., spkr. numerous industry and univ. seminars and courses; exec. in residence Jepson Sch., U. Richmond, 1993. Author: Management Planning and Control, 1975; co-author: The Asset Game: It's Your Move, 1982, Running in the Black, 1984. Chmn. Va. Commonwealth U. Found.; founding mem. sch. bus. coun.; former chmn. Va. Home Boys, Richmond adv. bd. Salvation Army, Friends Assn. Children; trustee Collegiate Schs., Richmond, past chmn. bd. trustees, chmn. planning com.; vice chmn. bd. trustees Va. Union U., Richmond; trustee, former chmn. Colgate Darden Sch. Sponsors U. Va., Charlottesville, Va.; trustee U. Va. Student Aid Found., George C. Marshall Found., Lexington, Va., Richmond Renaissance; past chmn., trustee Greater Richmond Found.; past bd. dirs. Printing Industry Va., Graphic Arts Tech. Found.; planning advisor various non-profit orgns. Served to capt. USMC, 1955-57. Recipient Pa. Exec. of Yr., 1993; named to Printing Hall of Fame, 1988. Mem. Soc. for Advancement of Mgmt. (mem. adv. bd. Advanced Mgmt. Jour. 1985—), Printing Industries Am. (Elmer Voight award 1982, Friedman Meml. medal 1982, exec. devel. program faculty 1970—, co-chmn. printing 2000 study, Industry Exec. of Yr. 1992). Episcopalian. Clubs: Commonwealth (Richmond), Country Club Va. Avocations: jogging, swimming, golf. Home: 206 Dryden Ln Richmond VA 23229-8205 Office: Cadmus Communications Corp 6620 W Broad St Ste 500 Richmond VA 23230

STETTLER, STEPHEN F., performing company executive; b. Phila., May 1, 1952; s. Wallace Frederick and Catherine Sue (Brill) S. AB summa cum laude, Kenyon Coll., 1974; MFA in Directing, Cath. U. Am., 1982; MLitt in Theatre, Lincoln Coll., Oxford, Eng., 1983. Dir. dramatics Westminster Sch., Simsbury, Conn., 1975-80; acting coach Hartke Conservatory Cath. U., Washington, 1982; chair drama dept. St. Albans and Nat. Cathedral Schs., Washington, 1980-84; dir., instr. acting Nat. Theatre Inst. O'Neill Theater Ctr., Waterford, Conn., 1984—; artistic dir. TNT/New Theatre Bklyn., 1987-90; producing dir. Weston (Vt.) Playhouse, 1988—; lit. asst. Arena Stage Co., Washington, 1983-84; site evaluator theatres Nat. Endowment for Arts, Washington, 1990—; panelist project grants com. Vt. Coun. Arts, Montpelier, 1993-94; mem. capital grants com. N.Y.C. Dept. Cultural Affairs, 1989; cons. various ind. schs., 1986—; guest instr. directing Teatret Vart, Norway; ednl. theatre cons., guest artist Mercersburg (Pa.) Acad., Pa. Wyoming Sem., Pa. Dir. Dancing at Lughnasa, Loot, Animal Fair, Rough Crossing, Sunday Promenade, Nora, Donkeys' Years, Into the Woods, Hay Fever, A Life in the Theatre, Spring Awakening, Mother Courage, A Midsummer Night's Dream (best play award Folger Shakespeare Libr. competition). Mem. Phi Beta Kappa. Office: Weston Playhouse PO Box 216 Weston VT 05161-0216

STETZNER, LEAH MANNING, lawyer, utilities executive; b. Hettinger, N.D., Aug. 11, 1948; d. Joseph Edward and Hazel Irene (Seymour) Manning; m. L.C. Stetzner, Mar. 20, 1970 (div. 1987); children: Autumn Lorraine, Prairie Lee. BA, U. N.D., 1970, MA, 1973; JD, U. Minn., 1977. Bar: Minn. 1977, Kans. 1985, U.S. Ct. Appeals (8th cir.) 1985, Ill. 1991. Atty. Burlington No. R.R., St. Paul, 1977-80; asst. gen. counsel Compmy and Burlington, Ft. Worth, 1981; asst. sec. No Inc., Overland Park, Kans., 1981-84, assoc. gen. counsel, 1985, counsel, 1989; gen. counsel, corp. sec. Ill. Power Co., Decatur, 1989—. Bd. dirs. Easter Seals Soc., Decatur, 1990—. Mem. ABA (bus. law com.). Office: Ill Power Co 500 S 27th St Decatur IL 62521-2200

STEUBEN, NORTON LESLIE, lawyer, educator; b. Milw., Feb. 14, 1936; s. Benjamin and Ria (Beerman) S.; m. Judith Ann Dickens, June 21, 1958; children: Sara Ann, Marc Nelson. A.B., U. Mich., 1958, J.D. with distinction, 1961. Bar: N.Y. 1962, Colo. 1975. Assoc., then ptnr. Hodgson, Russ, Andrews, Woods & Goodyear, Buffalo, 1961-68; mem. faculty U. Colo. Law Sch., Boulder, 1968—, prof. law, 1974—; of counsel Ireland, Stapleton, Pryor & Pascoe, Denver, 1980—; lectr. Law Sch., SUNY, Buffalo, 1961-68; officer Buffalo-Niagara Indsl. Devel. Corp., 1963-68, Buffalo Opportunities Devel. Corp., 1966-68; vis prof. law U. Puget Sound. Sch. Law, 1992-93. Author: Cases and Materials on Real Estate Planning, 1974, 3d edit., 1989, (with others) Problems in the Taxation of Individuals, Partnerships and Corporations, 1978, (with others) Problems in the Fundamentals of Federal Income Taxation, 1985, 3d edit., 1994, (with others) Problems in the Federal Income Taxation of Partnerships and Corporations, 1985; co-editor: Bittker, Fundamentals of Federal Income Taxation, 1983; editor Jour. Affordable Housing & Cmty. Devel. Law, 1994—; contbr. articles to profl. jours. Mem. Boulder Human Rights Commn., 1969-72, chmn., 1972-74; mem. Boulder Landlord-Tenant Com., 1973-74; trustee Boulder Open Space Bd., 1976-81, vice chmn., 1978-79, chmn., 1979-81; trustee Congregation Har Ha-Shem, Boulder, 1978-79, v.p., 1979-81, pres., 1982-84; mem. Boulder Housing Authority, 1982-89, vice chmn., 1984-85, chmn., 1985-88. Recipient S.I. Goldberg award Alpha Epsilon Pi, 1957, Disting. Svc. to Community award Buffalo Area C. of C., 1966, John W. Reed award U. Colo. Law Sch., 1970; Teaching Recognition award U. Colo.-Boulder, 1972, Teaching Excellence award, 1982; Presdl. Teaching scholar, U. Colo., 1989. Mem. ABA, N.Y. State Bar Assn., Colo. Bar Assn., Boulder County Bar Assn., Am. Law Inst., AAUP, Scribes (officer, editor Scrivener 1975-76, dir. 1979-82), Barristers Soc., Order of Coif, Tau Epsilon Rho. Democrat. Home: 845 8th St Boulder CO 80302-7408 Office: U Colo 418 Fleming Law Bldg Boulder CO 80309

STEUER, RICHARD MARC, lawyer; b. Bklyn., June 19, 1948; s. Harold and Gertrude (Vengar) S.; m. Audrey P. Forchheimer, Sept. 9, 1973; children: Hilary, Jeremy. BA, Hofstra U., 1970; JD, Columbia U., 1973. Bar: N.Y. 1974, U.S. Dist. Ct. (ea. and so. dists.) N.Y. 1974, U.S. Ct. Appeals (2nd cir.) 1974, U.S. Supreme Ct. 1979, U.S. Dist. Ct. (no. dist.) N.Y. 1984, U.S. Ct. Appeals (3rd cir.) 1987. Ptnr. Kaye, Scholer, Fierman, Hays & Handler, N.Y.C., 1973—; adj. assoc. prof. law NYU, 1985; lectr. various orgns.; neutral evaluator U.S. Dist. Ct. Ea. Dist., N.Y, 1994—. Author: A Guide to Marketing Law: Law and Business Inc., 1986; contbr. articles to profl. jours. Fellow Am. Bar Found.; mem. ABA (lectr. 1978, 85, 89, 93, editl. bd. antitrust devel. vol. 1984-86, chmn. monograph com. refusals to deal and exclusive distributorships 1983, various others, vice chmn. program com. 1988-91, chmn. spring meeting program com. 1991-92, Sherman Act sect. 1 com. 1991-93, coun. sect. antitrust law 1993—), Assn. Bar City N.Y. (chmn. antitrust and trade regulation com. 1995—, internat. trade, lectures and CLE coms., lect. 1983-94). Office: Kaye Scholer Fierman Hays & Handler 425 Park Ave New York NY 10022-3506

STEUERT, DOUGLAS MICHAEL, financial executive; b. Oklahoma City, May 21, 1948; s. Douglas Anselm and Geraldine (Sparks) S.; m. Nancy Elizabeth Ridd, Aug. 22, 1970. BS in Physics, MS in Indsl. Mgmt., Carnegie-Mellon U., 1971. Staff asst. TRW, Inc., Cleve., 1971-73, mgr. fin. research and analysis, 1973-75, dir. fin. U.S., 1975-76; dir. fin. Europe TRW, Inc., Frankfurt, Fed. Republic Germany, 1976-79; asst. treas. internat. TRW, Inc., Cleve., 1979-81, sr. fin. dir. automotive worldwide sector, 1981-84, controller valve div., 1984-86; v.p., treas. GenCorp Inc., Akron, Ohio, 1986-87; v.p. fin. and planning GenCorp Inc., Fairlawn, Ohio, 1987-90; v.p, chief fin. officer and treas., 1990-94; sr. v.p., CFO GenCorp Inc., Fairlawn, Ohio, 1994—. Dir. Mental Health Assn. Summit County, 1993—; mem. coun. on fin. Grad. Sch. Indsl. Adminstrn., Carnegie Mellon U., 1994—. Mem. Fin. Execs. Inst. (nat. chpt., N.E. Ohio chpt.), Mfrs. Alliance for Productivity and Innovation, Conf. Bd. Coun. of CFOs, Leadership Akron, Alumni Assn. Carnegie-Mellon U. Home: 505 Riverview Rd Gates Mills OH 44040-9649 Office: GenCorp Inc 175 Ghent Rd Akron OH 44333-3300

STEVASON, JOHN C., lawyer; b. Bklyn., May 18, 1946. AB in Physics, Princeton U., 1967; JD, NYU, 1973. Bar: N.Y. 1974, Oreg. 1975, U.S. Ct. Appeals (4th and 9th cirs.). Law clk. U.S. Ct. Appeals, 4th Cir., Richmond, Va., 1973-74; assoc. Lane Powell Spears Lubersky, Portland, Oreg., 1975-81, ptnr., 1982—. Mem. exec. com. of bd. mgrs., chmn. pers. com. YMCA, Columbia Wilamette, Portland, 1992—; vice chmn. human resources com. Am. Heart Assn., Oreg. chpt., Portland, 1990—. Mem. Computer Law Assn., Oreg. State Bar Assn. (computer law sect., labor rels. sect.). Office: Lane Powell Spears Lubersky 520 SW Yamhill St Ste 800 Portland OR 97204-1331

STEVENS, ADELE AMY KUBOTA, physical education educator; b. Waimea, Kauai, Hawaii, Jan. 21, 1945; d. Shigeomi and Bernice Aiko (Hamamura) Kubota; m. Donald Lynn Stevens, July 5, 1975; children: Abbie-Aiko Ke'ala, Mayumi Maile. Student, U. Hawaii, 1965-66; BA in Edn., Pacific Luth. U., 1967; postgrad., U. Hawaii, 1967-68, U. Oslo, 1970. Cert. tchr., Hawaii. Grad. teaching asst. U. Mass., Amherst, 1967-68; tchr. health, phys. edn., guidance Kauai (Hawaii) Intermediate Sch., 1968-70; exec. dir. Hawaii Motorcycle Safety Found., Honolulu, 1979-81; tchr. phys. edn. Waipahu (Hawaii) H.S., 1970-93, tchr. career guidance, 1993—; tchr. driver edn. area high schs., 1976—, coord. Project Renaissance, 1992; cooperating tchr. U. Hawaii, Honolulu, 1971-77; Brigham Young U., Laie, Hawaii, 1987; chair Sch. Climate com., 1994—. Adv. bd. Moanalua Gardens Day Care Ctr., Honolulu, 1984-87; active The Ch. at Our House, Mililani, Hawaii, 1 987—; team mom Mililani Bobby Sox Softball, 1988-90; coach, referee Mililani Am. Youth Soccer Orgn., 1988-92; participant Mililani Community Volleyball League, 1990—; asst. coach Mililani Basketball Assn., 1992. Mem. NEA, AAHPERD, ASCD, Hawaii State Tchrs. Assn. (assoc. policy coun.), Hawaii Assn. Health, Phys. Edn., Recreation and Dance, Am. Driver and Traffic Safety Edn. Assn., Leeward Oahu Tchrs. Assn. (sch. rep. 1991-92). Avocations: reading, tennis, travel. Office: Waipahu HS 94-1211 Farrington Hwy Waipahu HI 96797-3297

STEVENS, ANDREW, actor, producer, writer, director; b. Memphis, June 10, 1955; s. Noble Herman and Stella (Stevens) Stephens. BA in Psychology, Antioch U., L.A. Appeared in feature films including: Las Vegas Lady, 1974, Massacre at Central HIgh, 1974, Shampoo, 1975, Vigilante Force, 1976, Day of the Animals, 1977, The Boys in Company C, 1978, The Fury, 1978, Death Hunt, 1981, The Seduction, 1982, Ten to Midnight, 1983, Tusks, 1985, Scared Stiff, 1986, Counterforce, 1987, Fine Gold, 1987, The Ranch, 1988, The Terror Within, 1988, Bloodchase, 1989, Down the Drain, 1989, Eyewitness to Murder, 1989, Deadly Innocents, 1988, Red-Blooded American Girl, 1990; actor, writer, producer Night Eyes, 1990, Night Eyes II, 1991, Deadly Deceptions, 1991; actor, writer, dir. The Terror Within II, 1991, The Munchie, 1992, Deadly Rivals, 1992, Double Threat, 1993; writer, dir., actor Night Eyes III; prodr., actor Body Chemistry 3, Munchie Strikes Back, 1994, Body Chemistry 4; prodr. The Skate Board Kid 2; dir., prodr., actor A Woman Scorned; actor, dir. Illicit Dreams; dir. Grid Runners; prodr. Victim of Desire, Hard Bounty; appeared in TV films including: The Oregon Trail, 1975, Once An Eagle, NBC, 1977, The Bastard, 1978, Women At West Point, CBS, 1978, The Rebels, 1979, Beggarman Thief, NBC, 1979; exec. producer, actor in TV film Topper, 1979, Miracle on Ice, 1981, Forbidden Love, CBS, 1982, Journey's End, Show Time, 1983, Hollywood Wives, 1985, The Last Survivors, 1975, The Werewolf of Woodstock, 1974, Secrets, 1876; appeared in TV series: Oregon Trail, 1977, Code Red, 1981, Emerald Point NAS, CBS, 1983, Dallas, 1987, 88, Murder in Malibu: Colombo, 1990, ExtraLarge - "YoYo", 1991; also numerous specials and guest appearances, stage prodns.; dir. SwampThing, Silk Stalkings, Walker, Texas Ranger; numerous recs. Democrat. Office: Ste # 2 8285 Sunset Blvd Los Angeles CA 90046

STEVENS, ART, public relations executive; b. N.Y.C., July 17, 1935; m. Eva Sandberg, Mar. 19, 1972. B.A., CCNY, 1957. Pub. relations dir. Prentice Hall, Inc., Englewood Cliffs, N.J.; account exec. William L. Safire Public Relations Inc., N.Y.C., 1966-69; v.p. William L. Safire Public Relations Inc., 1967-68, pres., 1968-69; pres. Lobsenz-Stevens Inc., N.Y.C., 1970—; instr. Fairleigh Dickinson U.; weekly humor commentator WINK-TV, Ft. Myers, Fla. Author: The Persuasion Explosion, 1985, Sanibel Shell Shocked, 1992; weekly columnist Sanibel-Captiva (Fla.) Islander; contbr. articles to profl. jours. Bd. dirs. United Way of Putnam County, N.Y.;

trustee Gotthelf Lupus Rsch. Inst. Mem. Publicity Club N.Y. (Disting. Service award 1969), Public Relations Soc. Am. (pub. rels. com., exec com., chmn. elegibility com., counselors acad. sect.). Club: Gipsy Trail (Carmel, N.Y., pres.). Home: 201 E 21st St New York NY 10010-6401 Office: Lobsenz-Stevens Inc 460 Park Ave S New York NY 10016-7315

STEVENS, ARTHUR WILBER, JR., English literature educator, writer, editor; b. Bklyn., Aug. 16, 1921; s. Arthur Wilber and Isabella Ellen (MacGibbon) S.; m. Marjorie Athene Rogers, Feb. 15, 1955 (dec. Feb. 1979); children: Arthur Wilber III, Christopher Rivers; m. Joan Cutuly, Mar. 6, 1992. AB, Brown U., 1942; MA, U. Wash., 1956, PhD, 1957. Teaching fellow, assoc. instr. U. Wash., Seattle, 1944-54; vis. lectr., then asst. prof. Idaho State U., Pocatello, 1954-60; assoc. prof., chmn. dept. English, 1961-64; Fulbright prof. Am. and English lit. U. Mandalay (Burma) and U. Chulalongkorn, Thailand, 1956-57; Fulbright prof. Am. lit. U. Brazil, Rio de Janeiro, 1959; prof., chmn. dept. lit. Park Coll., Parkville, Mo., 1964-66; prof. English, chmn. Center Lang. and Lit. Studies; Prescott (Ariz.) Coll., 1966-69, provost, 1968-71, dir. Prescott Coll. Press., 1968-73, prof. English and comparative lit., 1972-73; prof. English and humanities U. Nev., Las Vegas, 1973-94, prof. emeritus, 1994—; dean Coll. Arts and Letters U. Nev., 1973-75, chmn. Asian Studies program, 1980-88; vis. prof. Ariz. State U., Tempe, summer 1968, SUNY, Buffalo, summer 1971, Utah Shakespeare Festival, 1972, Baylor U., summer 1976; vis. prof. U. Pa., 1983, 84; dramatic and music critic Billboard, 1947-54, Intermountain, 1954-64, Seattle Home News, 1947-53, Prescott Courier and The Paper, 1966-73, Las Vegas Rev.-Jour., 1973-77, Las Vegas Sun, 1977-84, Sta. KLAV-Radio, The Las Vegan. Author, editor: Poems Southwest, 1967, Stories Southwest, 1973; author: Pocatello; The World in Going to End Up in Burma, 1989, From the Still Empty Grave, 1995; co-editor: Indian Poetry in English, 1988, Seven Nevada Poets, Desert Wind: Anthology of Nevada Poets, 1991; contbr. poems and articles to profl. jours. and anthologies; editor, founder lit. mag. Interim, 1944-55, 85—; theatre critic Las Vegas Rev. Jour., 1984-94. Del. Theatre Libr. Assn. UNESCO Conf., San Francisco, 1957; mem. Nev. Humanities Com., 1982-88, Internat. James Joyce Found. Recipient Spanos Disting. Teaching award U. Nev., Las Vegas, 1986, Exemplary Svc. award Nev. Humanities Com., 1992; Frances Wayland scholar, 1940-42; inductee Nev. Writers Hall of Fame, Friends of Libr., U. Nev. Reno, 1992. Mem. MLA, Rocky Mountain MLA (pres. 1971), Conf. Christianity and Lit., Music Critics Assn. Am., Philol. Assn. Pacific Coast (exec. bd. 1978-80), Burma Studies Group, Am. Theatre Critics Assn., Renaissance Soc. Am., F. Scott Fitzgerald Soc., Theatre Libr. Assn., Brown Club (N.Y.C.), Princeton Club (N.Y.C.), Phi Kappa Phi, Beta Theta Pi. Home: 3770 Forestcrest Dr Las Vegas NV 89121-4909

STEVENS, BERTON LOUIS, JR., data processing manager; b. Chgo., Apr. 4, 1951; s. Berton Louis Sr. and Mary Cover (Kochavaris) S.; m. Janet Alene Madenberg, May 20, 1990. Student, Ill. Inst. Tech., Chgo., 1969-73. Systems and applications programmer Judge & Dolph, Ltd., Elk Grove Village, Ill., 1978-91, mgr. data processing, 1991—; instr. Adler Planetarium and Astron. Mus., Chgo., 1980-86. Editor and author newsletter Bert's Bull., 1987-90; editor newsletter No. Lights, 1990—. Recipient Regional award North Ctrl. Region Astron. League, 1989. Mem. Nat. Assn. Systems Programmers, Internat. Occulation Timing Assn. (sec. 1975-78), Chgo. Computer Soc., Chgo. Astron. Soc. (pres. 1977, 80, 84), Racine Astron. Soc. (pres. 1979), Astron. League (exec. sec. 1993—).

STEVENS, C. GLENN, judge; b. Rockford, Ill., Oct. 29, 1941; s. Robert W. and Mary Louise (Shaughnessy) S.; m. Suzanne Ruth Corkery, July 4, 1967; children: Robert W., Angela M. BS, St. Louis U., 1964, JD, 1966. Bar: Ill. 1966, Mo. 1966, U.S. Dist. Ct. (so. dist.) Ill. 1966, U.S. Dist. Ct. (ea. dist.) Ill. 1968. Law clk. to judge U.S. Dist. Ct. (so. dist.) Ill., Springfield, Ill., 1966-67; instr. St. Louis U., 1967-68; assoc. Pope & Driemeyer, Belleville, Ill., 1967-74; ptnr. Pope & Driemeyer, Belleville, 1974-77; judge State of Ill., Belleville, 1977—. Bd. editors St. Louis U. Law Rev., 1965-66. Arbitrator Am. Arbitration Assn., St. Clair County, Ill, 1970-77. With U.S. Army, 1958-66. Mem. Mo. Bar Assn., Ill. Judges Assn., Am. Judges Assn., Ill. State Bar Assn., St. Clair County Bar Assn., East St. Louis Bar Assn., Phi Delta Phi (pres. Murphy Inn 1965-66). Democrat. Roman Catholic. Avocations: antique cars, soccer coach. Office: Saint Clair County Courthouse Public Sq Belleville IL 62220

STEVENS, CLYDE BENJAMIN, JR., property manager, retired naval officer; b. Denver, Oct. 10, 1908; s. Clyde Benjamin and Maybelle Olive (Boot) S.; m. Lucile Lillian-Louise Kip, May 5, 1933; children: Jane Stevens White, Donald Kip, Patricia Louise Stevens Schley. BS, U.S. Naval Acad., 1930; postgrad., U.S. Naval Postgrad. Sch., Annapolis, Md., 1939, U.S. Naval War Coll., Newport, R.I., 1947. Registered profl. engr. Commd. ensign USN, advanced through grades to rear adm., 1959; comdg. officer USS R-20, S-33 Plaice and Platte, 1950-52; comdr. officer USS Platte 50-52 Destroyer Squad 6, 1954-55; with torpedo prodn. and undersea weapons div. Bur. Ordnance, Washington, 1947-59; with USS Platte, 1950-52, Destroyer squad., 1955-56; program dir. Bur. Ordnance, Washington, 1952-55, 56-59; ret., 1959; product mgr. TRW, Inc., Cleve., 1959-65; rsch. engr. Boeing Co., Seattle, 1965-74, torpedo cons., 1985; apt. owner and mgr. Seattle, 1965-; torpedo cons. Goodyear Aerospace Co., Akron, Ohio, 1965. Patentee automobile generator. Decorated Navy Cross, Silver Star with oak leaf cluster. Mem. Seattle Apt. Assn. (bd. dirs. 1967-91), Army and Navy Club, Rainier Club. Republican. Episcopalian. Home and Office: 2339 Franklin Ave E Seattle WA 98102-3356

STEVENS, DAVID, economics educator; b. Burbank, Calif., Jan. 26, 1926; s. Frederick and Alpheus (Perkins) S.; 1 child, David Fancher. B.A., Whitman Coll., 1947; M.B.A., Stanford U., 1949; LLD (hon.), Whitman Coll., 1994. Asst. prof. Okla. State U., 1949-51; asst. prof. econs. Whitman Coll., Walla Walla, Wash., 1951-54; asso. prof. Whitman Coll., 1954-56, prof., 1956-67, Roger and David Clapp prof. of econ. thought, 1958-91, prof. emeritus, 1991—, dean adminstrn., 1954-64, chmn. faculty, 1982-85; vis. prof. Glasgow U., Scotland, 1964-66, sr. research fellow, 1980—; instr. Am. Inst. Banking. Author: Adam Smith and the Colonial Disturbances, 1976; Editor: The Wedderburn Manuscript In Adam Smith: Correspondence, 1977. Commr. Regional Planning Commn., Walla Walla County, 1960-64; chmn. Walla Walla County chpt. ARC, 1961-63, 75-77. Served to lt. J.G. U.S. Navy, 1943-46. Mem. Am. Econ. Assn., Western Econ. Assn., History of Econ. Soc. Episcopalian. Home: 602 Boyer Ave Walla Walla WA 99362-2381 Office: Whitman Coll Walla Walla WA 99362

STEVENS, DWIGHT MARLYN, educational administrator; b. Wheeler, Wis., May 13, 1933; s. Clifford and Alva Orpha (Follensbee) S.; children: Patricia Lee Stevens Vanden Heuvel, Jacqueline Ann Stevens Kasper, Cynthia May Stevens Manthey, Robert Louis. B.S., Eau Claire (Wis.) State U., 1957; M.S., U. Wis., 1959, Ph.D, 1972. High sch. speech tchr. Ft. Atkinson, Wis., 1957-61; high sch. prin. Oostburg, Wis., 1961-64; prin. Arrowhead High Sch., Hartland, Wis., 1964-66; dist. adminstr. Arrowhead Sch. Dist., 1966-73; dep. state supt. Wis. Dept. Pub. Instrn., Madison, 1973-81; supt. schs. Stevens Point, Wis., 1982-93; faculty U. Wis.-Whitewater, 1971, U. Wis.-Superior, 1985, U. Wis.-Stevens Point, 1988-92, 93—. Author: (with Eye, Netzer and Benson) Strategies for Instructional Management, 1980. Dir. Ford Found., Community Planning Project for Chippewa Indians, 1970-71, Nat. Validation Team, Title III, Elementary Secondary Edn. Act; cons. HEW Workshops on Innovation, Eagle River, Wis.; chmn. Wis. sch. dist. adminstrn., 1992. Served with U.S. Army, 1953-55. Recipient Outstanding Citizenship award Waukesha County, Wis., 1974; Ford fellow John Hay Fellowship in Humanities, Williams Coll., 1963; Kettering fellow Nat. Seminar on Innovation, Honolulu, summer 1967, Outstanding Adminstrv. Practitioner award U. Wis.-Stevens Point, 1991; Disting. Alumni award U. Wis., 1980. Mem. Cen. Wis. C. of C. (pres. 1986-87), Acad. Letters and Scis. (v.p. 1987—, pres. 1988-90), Phi Delta Kappa (v.p. 1985-87), Pi Kappa Delta. Home: 3323 Echo Dells Ave Stevens Point WI 54481-5118

STEVENS, EDWARD, public relations executive; b. Cleve., Feb. 24, 1941. BA, John Carroll U., 1963. Asst. mgr., adv. constrn. dept. divsn. Warner & Swasey, 1966-69; A/E Cleve. office Dix & Eaton, 1969-71, A/E Erie office, 1971-74, v.p., gen. mgr. Erie office, 1974-79, group v.p. 1979-80, sr. v.p., gen. mgr. Erie office, 1980—, group pres., 1982; mem. bd. dirs. PRSA, Cleve. Ad. Club. Recipient Erie Ad Person of the Yr. award, 1985,

George Mead award, 1987. Office: Dix & Eaton/Public Rels 1301 E 9th St Ste 1300 Cleveland OH 44114-1502

STEVENS, EDWARD FRANKLIN, college president; b. Newcastle, Wyo., Sept. 7, 1940; s. Edward Downey and Esther Elizabeth (Watt) S.; m. Linda Elaine Loewenstein, June 3, 1962; children: Carla Sue, Cathy Lynne. Student, U. Denver, 1959-60; BA in Edn., Physics, Chemistry cum laude, Nebr. Wesleyan U., 1963; MA in Ednl. Psychology, Stats. and Measurement, U. Nebr., 1967; PhD in Higher Edn., Mktg., Mgmt., U. Minn., 1983; postdoctoral, Harvard U., 1991. Tchr., head basketball coach Alvo-Eagle (Nebr.) High Sch., 1963-64, Madison (Nebr.) High Sch., 1964-65; asst. basketball coach U. Nebr., Lincoln, 1965-67; head basketball coach, asst. prof. edn. Augustana Coll., Sioux Falls, S.D., 1967-71; v.p., gen. mgr. tng. Iseman divsn. U.S. Inds., Sioux Falls, 1971-74; chief devel. and instl. advancement officer Sioux Falls Coll., 1974-79, asst. prof. to prof., 1980-83; exec. v.p. Kearny (Nebr.) State Coll. Found., 1979-80; pres. George Fox Coll., Newberg, Oreg., 1983—. Chmn. campaign Yamhill County United Way, Newberg, 1988; bd. commrs. Newberg Community Hosp., 1988-91. NDEA fellow, 1965; recipient Young Alumni Achievement award, Nebr. Wesleyan U., 1973, Leadership Fellows award, Bush Found., St. Paul, 1976. Mem. Am. Assn. Pres. Indep. Colls. and Univs., Nat. Christian Coll. Consortium (chmn. 1987-88), Nat. Assn. Intercollegiate Athletics (council pres., exec. com. 1988-92, chmn. 1992), Nat. Assn. Evangelicals (Christian higher edn. com.), Nat. Assn. Indep. Colls. and Univs., Oreg. Ind. Colls. Assn. (bd. dirs. 1983-92, chmn. 1986-87), Oreg. Ind. Colls. Found. (bd. dirs. 1983-92, vice chmn. 1993), Coun. of Ind. Colls. (bd. dirs. 1990), N.W. Assn. Schs. and Colls. (commn. on colls.), Internat. Assn. Univs. Pres., New Life 2000 (internat. com. reference), Rotary. Republican. Mem. Soc. Friends. Office: George Fox Coll Office of Pres 414 N Meridian St Newberg OR 97132-2625

STEVENS, EDWARD IRA, information systems educator; b. York, Pa., Oct. 13, 1937; s. Francis DeHaven and Myra Jane (Foust) S.; m. Marjorie Eleanor Bisson, Aug. 29, 1959 (div. Oct. 1978); children: Mark Edward, Whitney Lynne, Kimberly Lauren; m. Kathleen Susan Berg, May 30, 1983. AB, Davidson (N.C.) Coll., 1959; MDiv, Harvard U., 1962; PhD, Vanderbilt U., 1965. Asst. prof. psychology, then assoc. prof. Eckerd Coll. (formerly Fla. Presbyn. Coll.), St. Petersburg, 1965-69, dir. research and ednl. services, 1969-73, dir. planning, exec. asst. to pres., 1977-84, prof. mgmt. info. systems, 1984—, dir. instl. rsch. and planning, 1993—; dean acad. affairs Northland Coll., Ashland, Wis., 1973-75, v.p., 1974-75; pres. Lyndon State Coll., Lyndonville, Vt., 1975-77; v.p. research St. Clair Software Systems, Inc., Clearwater, Fla., 1985-87; cons. and lectr. in field. Contbr. articles to profl. jours. Am. Council Edn. fellow, Washington, 1969-70; Fund for Improvement Post-Secondary Edn. grantee, Washington, 1976-78. Mem. Am. Assn. Higher Edn., Acad. Mgmt., Assn. Instl. Rsch., Assn. for Computer Machinery, Phi Beta Kappa. Presbyterian. Avocations: art, antiques, photography. Home: 4139 Daventry Ln Palm Harbor FL 34685-1127 Office: Eckerd Coll 4200 54th Ave S Saint Petersburg FL 33711-4700

STEVENS, EDWARD PARKER, military officer; b. Houston, Nov. 22, 1948; s. Harry Wellington and Sophia Lillian (White) S.; m. Janice Karen Morris, Sept. 6, 1969; children: Jeffery, Jennifer. BS in Health Care Adminstrn., San Jose State U., 1979; MS in Health Care Adminstrn., U. No. Colo., 1981. Enlisted U.S. Army, 1972, advanced through grades to maj., various health care positions, 1972-77; supr. orthopedics U.S. Army, San Francisco, 1977-78, infection control coordinator, 1978-80; med. platoon leader 101st Airborne div. U.S. Army, Ft. Campbell, Ky., 1980-81; exec. officer Fulda (Fed. Republic of Germany) Health Clinic, 1982-84; med. ops. officer U.S. Army, Frankfurt, Fed. Republic of Germany, 1984; med. ops. officer U.S. Army, Ft. Bragg, N.C., 1985-86, chief med. assistance team, 1986-89; chief clin. support div. Fox Army Community Hosp., Redstone Arsenal, Ala., 1989—. Asst. scout master Council Boy Scouts Am., Hope Mills, N.C., 1985-86; mem. PTA Douglas Byrd Jr. High Sch., Fayetteville, N.C., 1986—. Mem. Am. Coll. Health Execs. (various health care consumer coms. 1982—), Am. Hosp. Assn., N.C. Hosp. Assn., Assn. Mil. Surgeons, Ala. Hosp. Assn. Avocations: flying, general aviation, gardening. Home: 16002 Michelle Dr SE Huntsville AL 35803-3604

STEVENS, ELISABETH GOSS (MRS. ROBERT SCHLEUSSNER JR.), writer, journalist; b. Rome, N.Y., Aug. 11, 1929; d. George May and Elisabeth (Stryker) Stevens; m. Robert Schleussner, Jr., Mar. 12, 1966 (dec. 1977); 1 child, Laura Stevens. B.A., Wellesley Coll., 1951; M.A. with high honors, Columbia U., 1956. Editorial assoc. Art News Mag., 1964-65; art critic and reporter Washington Post, Washington, 1965-66; free-lance art critic and reporter Balt., 1966—; contbg. art critic Wall Street Jour., N.Y.C., 1969-72; art critic Trenton Times, N.J., 1974-77; art and architecture critic The Balt. Sun, 1978-86. Author: Elisabeth Stevens' Guide to Baltimore's Inner Harbor, 1981, Fire and Water: Six Short Stories, 1982, Children of Dust: Portraits and Preludes, 1985, Horse and Cart: Stories from the Country, 1990, The Night Lover: Art & Poetry, 1995; contbr. articles, poetry and short stories to jours., nat. newspapers and popular mags. Recipient A.D. Emmart award for journalism, 1980, Critical Writing citation Baot.-Washington Newspaper Guild, 1980, fiction awards Md. Poetry Rev., 1992, 93, 94, 2d prize Lite Circle, 1994, 1st prize in fiction Lite Circle, 1995, award Balt. Writers Alliance, 1994, Balt. Writers Alliance Play Writing Contest award, 1994; art critics' fellow NEA, 1973-74, fellow MacDowell Colony, 1981, Vt. Ctr. for Creative Arts, 1982-85, 88-90, 92, 93, Ragdale Found., 1984, 89, Yaddo, 1991; Work-in-Progress grantee for poetry Md. Art Coun., 1986, Creative Devel. grantee for short fiction collection Bapt. Mayor's Com. on Art and Culture, 1986. Mem. Nat. Press Club Washington, Coll. Art Assn., Balt. Bibliophiles, Authors Guild, Am. Studies Assn., Poetry Soc. Am. Home: 6604 Walnutwood Cir Baltimore MD 21212-1213

STEVENS, GARVIN L., college dean. Exec. dean U. N.D., Williston. Office: UND at Williston Office Exec Dean Williston ND 58801

STEVENS, GARY, professional jockey. Top money winner, 1991. Winner Breeder's Cup Turf Race, 1990, Breeder's Cup Juvenile, 1993, Breeder's Cup Distaff, 1994. Office: Thoroughbred Racing Assn 3000 Marcus Ave New Hyde Park NY 11042-1012*

STEVENS, GEORGE, JR., film and television producer, writer, director; b. Calif., Apr. 3, 1932; s. George Cooper and Yvonne (Shevlin) S.; m. Elizabeth Guest, July, 1965; children: Caroline, Michael, David. B.A., Occidental Coll., 1953. Asst. to George Stevens, Sr., 1951-53, motion picture prodn. asst., 1956, assoc. producer, 1957-60, TV dir., 1957-61; dir. Motion Picture Service, USIA, 1962-64, Motion Picture and TV service, USIA, 1964-67; founding dir., chief exec. Am. Film Inst., 1967-80, now co-chmn. bd.; pres. New Liberty Prodns., 1980-95; founding chmn. D.C. Arts Commn., 1969; chmn. U.S. del. Internat. Film Festivals at Moscow, Cannes, Venice, Berlin, 1963-66. Motion pictures include John F. Kennedy, Years of Lightning Day of Drums, 1964, Nine From Little Rock (Acad. award), 1965, America at the Movies, 1976; creator, prodr., writer Am. Film Inst. Life Achievement Award shows, 1973-95, TV series including AFI: A Salute to James Cagney (Emmy award), The Stars Salute America's Greatest Movies, 1977, America Entertains Vice Premier Deng Tsio Peng, 1979; creator, co-prodr., writer Kennedy Ctr. Honor series, 1978-94, (4 Emmy awards, George Foster Peabody award); creator, exec. prodr. Christmas in Washington series, 1982-94; writer, prodr., dir. George Stevens: A Filmmaker's Journey, 1985 (award Nat. Bd. of Rev. of Motion Pictures, 1986, WGA award for ABC broadcast 1988); prodr., co-writer (TV miniseries) The Murder of Mary Phagan, 1988 (Emmy award, Christopher award, George Foster Peabody award), George Stevens: D-Day To Berlin (Emmy awards for writing and narration); co-exec. prodr., dir., writer (TV miniseries) Separate But Equal, 1991 (Christopher award, Emmy award). Trustee Occidental Coll., 1980-82. Served to 1st lt. USAF, 1954-56. Named to Ten Outstanding Young Men in Fed. Govt., 1963, Ten Outstanding Young Men in U.S., 1964; recipient Jury prize Chgo. Internat. Film Film Fest., 1985, Paul Selvin award Writers Guild of Am., 1991, NAACP Legal Def. Fund award. Office: Kennedy Ctr Washington DC 20566

STEVENS, GEORGE ALEXANDER, realtor; b. Loma, Mont., Nov. 10, 1923; s. Otto Oliver and Josephine (Dale) S.; m. Martha Evie Fultz, Sept. 16, 1944 (div. 1978); children: Gary, Kathleen, Arlene, Tina; m. Arleen Dorothea Largent, Nov. 14, 1978. A in Bus Adminstrn., SUNY, 1992. Prin. George Stevens Farm, Loma, Mont., 1946-93, George Stevens, Realtor,

Loma, Mont., 1957-93; pres. George A. Stevens COrp., Loma, 1976-93, Gold and Silver Realty, Inc., Great Falls, Mont., 1993—. Trustee Sch. Dist. # 32, Loma, 1947-50; election judge Precinct # 7, Loma, 1953-88. With USN, 1944-46, PTO. Mem. Nat. Assn. Realtors, VFW (life), Am. Legion (life), Elks (life), Eagles Lodge. Democrat. Lutheran. Home: 810 8th Ave N Great Falls MT 59401-1036

STEVENS, GEORGE RICHARD, business consultant, public policy commentator; b. Chgo., Sept. 6, 1932; s. George and Irene (Kaczmarek) S.; m. Jeanne E. Sowden, Aug. 2, 1957; children: Stacey, Samantha, Pamela. B.S. with honors, Northwestern U., 1954. C.P.A., Ill. With Arthur Andersen & Co., 1954-78; mng. ptnr. Arthur Andersen & Co., Brussels, Belgium, 1957-71; partner Arthur Andersen & Co., Chgo., 1971-78; pres. Daubert Industries, Oak Brook, Ill., 1978-80, G.R. Stevens Group, 1981—; founder, pres. Stevens Center for Public Policy Studies, 1981—; Mem. Chgo. Com., 1979—; commr. Ill. Ednl. Facilities Authority, 1989—; commr. Ill. State Scholarship Commn., 1981-87; vice chmn. Ill. Ind. Higher Edn. Loan Authority, 1982-88. Mem. Better Govt. Assn. (v.p. 1972-80). Home and Office: 22615 N Las Lomas Ln Sun City West AZ 85375

STEVENS, GERALD D., secondary education educator, consultant; b. Seattle, Apr. 9, 1941; s. James Edward and Olga Rubina (Olsen) S.; children: Heather Corrine, Wendy Jeannette; m. Michele Christine Hayek, June 16, 1973; 1 child, Gerald Michael. Student, U. Wash., 1963-65; BA in Pol. Sci., Calif. State U., L.A., 1989; postgrad., U. So. Calif., 1992—. Cert. tchr., Calif. Bank auditor Nat. Bank Commerce, Seattle, 1965-72; pvt. practice GEMIC L.A., 1972-86; tchr. L.A. Unified Sch. Dist., 1986—; cons. model schs. program Fgn. Policy Assn., Washington, 1990; presenter coalition essential schs. L.A. Unified Sch. Dist., 1990-91. Author: Redistributive Econ. Justice, 1993. Vol. C.L.A.R.E. Found., Santa Monica, 1989-91. With USMC, 1960-63, PTO. Mem. So. Calif. Social Sci. Assn. (bd. dirs. 1990—, v.p.), United Tchrs. L.A., Sierra Club. Avocations: songwriting, ceramic art. Home: Unit 2 2101 Ocean Ave Santa Monica CA 90405-2228 Office: LA Unified Sch Dist 450 N Grand Ave Los Angeles CA 90012-2100

STEVENS, GLADSTONE TAYLOR, JR., industrial engineer; b. Brockton, Mass., Dec. 16, 1930; s. Gladstone Taylor and Blanche Ruth S.; m. Jane A. Crouch, July 20, 1953; children—Robert, Bartlett. B.S.M.E., U. Okla., 1956; M.S.M.E., Case Inst. Tech., 1962; Ph.D. in Indsl. Engring, Okla. State U., 1966. Registered profl. engr., Tex., Okla. Project engr. E.I. duPont, Orange, Tex., 1956-59; research engr. Thompson-Ramo-Wooldridge, Cleve., 1960-62; asst. prof. mech. and indsl. engring. Lamar U., Beaumont, Tex., 1962-64; asst. prof. to asso. prof. indsl. engring. Okla. State U., Stillwater, 1966-75; prof., chmn. dept. indsl. engring. U. Tex., Arlington, 1975—. Author: (with J.E. Shamblin) Operations Research: A Fundamental Approach, 1974, Economic and Financial Analysis of Capital Investments, 1993; Engineering Economy, 1983. Served with AUS, 1948-52. Recipient E.L. Grant award, 1974, AMOCO Teaching award, 1979, Wellington award, 1992. Mem. Am. Inst. Indsl. Engrs. (sr.), Sigma Xi, Alpha Pi Mu (nat. pres.), Tau Beta Pi, Sigma Tau, Omicron Delta Kappa. Home: 3611 Shady Park Dr Arlington TX 76013-5706 Office: U Tex Indsl Engring Arlington TX 76019

STEVENS, HENRY AUGUST, insurance agent, educator; b. Frankfurt, Main, Germany, July 21, 1921; came to U.S. 1940; m. Rosemary O'Neil, Mar. 23, 1963; children: Michael, Patrick; 1 child from previous marriage, H. Jack Fay. Student, U. Wis., 1943-44; grad., Dale Carnegie Sch., Richland, Wash., 1974. Theatre mgr. Sterling Theatres, Seattle, 1946-54, Alliance Amusement Co., Chgo., 1955-68; ins. agt. N.Y. Life Ins. Co., Richland, 1968—; regional v.p. Washington Assn. Life Underwriters, Richland, 1980; mem. adv. com. Wash. State Ins., Olympia, 1983-89. Chmn. bd. Richland YMCA, 1968; commr. Benton County Dyking Dist., Richland, 1970; chmn. Benton-Franklin Counties Bi-Centennial Commn., Tri-Cities, Wash., 1976; dist. chmn. Rep. Party, Benton County, 1980—. Staff sgt. U.S. Army 1943-46. Recipient Nat. Quality award, Nat. Sales Achievement award. Mem. Tri-Cities Life Underwriters Assn. (pres. 1975, bd. dirs.), Tri-Cities Estate Planning Coun. (pres. 1984), Kiwanis (pres. Chgo. club 1963, Richland club 1986-87, lt. gov. Pacific N.W. dist. 1983, chmn. dist. conv. 1971, 81, 91, sec. Pacific N.W. Found. 1994—). Avocations: stamp collecting, preparing family tree. Home: 712 Riverside Dr Richland WA 99352-5216 Office: NY Life Ins Co 8203 W Quinault St Kennewick WA 99336-1093

STEVENS, HERBERT FRANCIS, lawyer, law educator; b. Phila., Nov. 19, 1948; s. Herbert F. and Lois Marie (Kenna) S.; m. Jane Pickard, 1994; children: Sarah, Ben. SB, MIT, 1970; JD, Catholic U. Am., 1974; ML in Tax., Georgetown U., 1983. Bar: D.C. 1975, U.S. Supreme Ct. 1980. Law clk. to presiding justice Md. Ct. of Spl. Appeals, 1974-75; assoc. Morgan, Lewis & Bockius, Washington, 1975-78; ptnr. Lane & Edson, P.C., Washington, 1984-89; ptnr. Kelley Drye & Warren, Washington, 1989-93, Peabody & Brown, Washington, 1993—; adj. prof. Georgetown U. Law Ctr., 1983—; spkr. nat. confs., seminars, TV. Editor: Real Estate Aspects of the 1984 Tax Law, 1984; author: Real Estate Taxation: A Practitioner's Guide, 1986, A Developer's Guide to Low Income Housing Tax Credit, 1992. Chmn. bd. dirs. Ctr. for Mental Health, Inc., 1987-94; mem. exec. com., bd. dirs. Nat. Fund for U.S. Botanic Gardens, 1992—. Mem. ABA, D.C. Bar Assn. Democrat. Methodist. Home: 5309 Roosevelt St Bethesda MD 20814 Office: Peabody & Brown 1255 23rd St NW Washington DC 20037-1434

STEVENS, JAMES HERVEY, JR., financial advisor; b. Balt., June 22, 1944; s. James H. and Hilda (Pearce) S.; m. Patricia Carol Donohue, Aug. 27, 1967 (div. Mar. 1983); children: James III, Carol; m. Lisa Gay Landrum, Apr. 29, 1984. BA, Duke U., 1966; MS in Fin. Scis., Am. Coll., Bryn Mawr, Pa., 1981. CLU; ChFC; CFP; registered health underwriter. Supr. New Eng. Life, Overland Park, Kans., 1969-75, agt., 1969—; v.p., treas. Creative Planning, Inc., Overland Park, 1980—; pres. Hokanson, Lehman & Stevens, Inc., Overland Park, 1982—, Wings Over Mid-Am., Inc., 1995—. Contbg. editor monthly tax topics Kansas City Bus. Jour.; contbr. articles to profl. jours. Bd. dirs. Mo. and Am. Cancer Soc., Kans. and Mo., 1982-84, Apple Valley Homes Assn., Overland Park, 1990—, pres. 1992, Cen. United Meth. Ch., Kansas City, Mo., 1990-92., North Cross United Meth., 1991—. Recipient Outstanding Young Man award, 1977; named one of Top 200 Fin. Advisors, Money Mag., 1987, Boss of Yr., Kansas City LICOMA, 1983. Mem. Kansas City Life Underwriters (pres. 1980-82, Herbert A. Hedges award 1987), Kansas City CLU & ChFC Soc. (pres. 1981-83), Mo. Life Underwriters (pres. 1984-86), Am. Soc. CLU & ChFC (vice chmn., bd. dirs.). Republican. Avocations: model railroading, collecting post-war "Lionel", comml. pilot with IFR rating, flight instr. Home: 5200 W 98th Ter Shawnee Mission KS 66207-3221 Office: Creative Planning Inc 5340 College Blvd Shawnee Mission KS 66211-1621

STEVENS, JAMES M., food processing executive; b. 1947. With Nabisco, Bethlehem, Pa., 1968, Pepsi Cola Bottling Group, Purchase, N.Y., 1969-76; sr. v.p. Great Waters France Inc., Greenwich, Conn., 1977-81; with Premium Products Sales Corp., Greenwich, 1981-86; COO Coca Cola Enterprises, Atlanta, 1986-92; pres. Suntory Water Group Inc., Atlanta, 1992—. Office: Suntory Water Group Inc 280 Interstate North Pky Atlanta GA 30339

STEVENS, JOHN GALEN, mathematics and computer science educator; b. Kansas City, Mo., Aug. 7, 1943; s. Albert Owen and Mildred Lucille (Embree) S.; m. Mary Lou Beilstein, Dec. 27, 1966; children: Sarah, Rachel. BS in Chemistry, Ind. U., 1965; PhD, NYU, 1972. Asst. prof. Montclair State U., Upper Montclair, N.J., 1969-74; assoc. prof. Montclair State U., 1974-79, prof. math. and computer sci., 1979—; cons. Exxon Rsch. and Engring. Co., Inc., Annandale, N.J., 1975—, M.L. Energia, Inc., Princeton, N.J., 1983—. Contbr. articles to profl. jours.; patentee in field. Mem. Soc. for Indsl. and Applied Math. Am. Math. Soc., Soc. for Computer Simulation. Presbyterian. Achievements include research in mathematical modeling of physical systems, especially catalytic and photochemically enhanced combustion; applications of neural networks. Home: 130 Gallows Hill Rd Westfield NJ 07090-1107 Office: Montclair State U Dept Math & Computer Sci Montclair NJ 07043

STEVENS, JOHN PAUL, U.S. supreme court justice; b. Chgo., Apr. 20, 1920; s. Ernest James and Elizabeth (Street) S.; m. Elizabeth Jane Sheeren, June 7, 1942; children: John Joseph, Kathryn Stevens Jedlicka, Elizabeth Jane Stevens Sesemann, Susan Roberta Stevens Mullen; m. Maryan Mulholland, Dec. 1979. A.B., U. Chgo., 1941; J.D. magna cum laude, Northwestern U., 1947. Bar: Ill. 1949. Practiced in Chgo.; law clk. to U.S. Supreme Ct. Justice Wiley Rutledge, 1947-48; assoc. firm Poppenhusen, Johnston, Thompson & Raymond, 1949-52; asso. counsel sub-com. on study monopoly power, com. on judiciary U.S. Ho. of Reps., 1951; ptnr. firm Rothschild, Stevens, Barry & Myers, 1952-70; U.S. circuit judge, 1970-75; asso. justice U.S. Supreme Ct., 1975—; lectr. anti-trust law Northwestern U. Law., 1952-54, U. Chgo. Law Sch., 1955-58; mem. Atty. Gen.'s Nat. Com. to Study Anti-Trust Laws, 1953-55. Served with USNR, 1942-45. Decorated Bronze Star. Mem. Chgo. Bar Assn. (2d v.p. 1970), Am., Ill., Fed. bar assns., Am. Law Inst., Order of Coif, Phi Beta Kappa, Psi Upsilon, Phi Delta Phi. Office: US Supreme Ct 1 1st St NE Washington DC 20543

STEVENS, JOHN RICHARD, architectural historian; b. Toronto, Ont., Can., Mar. 19, 1929; came to U.S., 1954; s. Walter John and Florence Rosalie (Warr) S.; m. Marion Frances Moore, May 7, 1964. Student, Columbia U., 1966-67. Comml. artist, tech. illustrator Toronto, Ont., Can. and New Haven, Conn.; asst. to curator Mystic Seaport, 1957; curator Maritime Mus. Can., Halifax, 1960-63; with dept. no. affairs Hist. Sites Divsn., 1963-66; surveyor early bldgs. Halifax, Quebec, Fredericton, Woodstock, St. John River Valley, Ea. Twps. of Quebec; lighthouses of Great Lakes, Nova Scotia, New Brunswick; with Archtl. Heritage, Inc., 1967-70; prin. John R. Stevens Assocs., Greenlawn, N.Y., 1970—; cons. hist. restoration Old Bethpage Village Restoration, 1967-94, Soc. for the Preservation L.I. Antiquities, Roslyn Preservation Corp., Smithtown Hist. Soc., Colonial Farmhouse Restoration Soc., numerous others; restorations include Van Nostrand-Starkins House, Revolutionary War "Arsenal", two c.1900 Am.-built streetcars for City of Detroit, 1976, 80, 1878 N.Y. elevated railroad car, 1983, first electric freight locomotive, 1988, c. 1880 horsecar for Rochester Mus., 1987; lectr. Dutch-Am. bldgs., street railway history. Author: Old Time Ships, 1949, H.M. Schooner Tecumseth, 1961, Ships of the North Shore, 1963, (guidebook) Ride Down Memory Lane, 1965, 2d rev. edit., 1984, Early History of Street Railways - The New Haven Area, 1982, The Derby Horse Railway and the World's First Electric Freight Locomotive, 1987; co-author/editor: Pioneers of Electric Railroading, 1991; contbr. articles on hist. bldg. tech., book revs. to profl. publs. Bd. trustees Roslyn Landmark Soc., 1980—. With U.S. Army, 1955-57. Mem. Branford Electric Rlwy. Assn. (bd. trustees 1957, 74, 80-81, 83-85, supt. equipment 1974-75, supt. bldgs. and grounds 1980-82, chmn. bd. trustees 1983, pres. 1984, 85, contbr. articles to jour.). Home and Office: 1 Sinclair Dr Greenlawn NY 11740-2607

STEVENS, JOSEPH CHARLES, psychology educator; b. Grand Rapids, Mich., Feb. 28, 1929; s. Joseph, Jr. and Anne Katheryn (Ghysels) S.; A.B., Calvin Coll., Grand Rapids, 1950; M.A., Mich. State U., 1953; Ph.D., Harvard U., 1957. Instr., then asst. prof. psychology Harvard U., 1957-66; fellow John B. Pierce Found. Lab., also sr. research scientist Yale U., 1966—; cons. in field. Author: Laboratory Experiments in Psychology, 1965; co-editor: Sensation and Measurement, 1974; mem. editorial bds. profl. jours.; contbr. numerous articles to profl. jours. Grantee NSF; Grantee NIH; Grantee Air Force Office Sci. Research. Fellow AAAS, Am. Psychol. Soc., N.Y. Acad. Scis.; mem. Acoustical Soc. Am., Optical Soc. Am., Soc. Neurosci., Eastern Psychol. Assn., Gerontol. Soc. Am. Office: 290 Congress Ave New Haven CT 06519-1403

STEVENS, JOSEPH EDWARD, JR., federal judge; b. Kansas City, Mo., June 23, 1928; s. Joseph Edward and Mildred Christian (Smith) S.; m. Norma Jeanne Umlauf, Nov. 25, 1956; children: Jennifer Jeanne, Rebecca Jeanne. B.A., Yale U., 1949; J.D., U. Mich., 1952. Bar: Mo. 1952, U.S. Supreme Ct. 1973. Assoc. Lombardi, McLean, Slagle & Bernard, Kansas City, Mo., 1955-56; assoc. then ptnr. Lathrop, Koontz, Righter, Clagett & Norquist, Kansas City, Mo., 1956-81; judge U.S. Dist. Ct. (we. dist.) Mo., Kansas City, 1981—; chief judge, 1992—; mem. adv. com. on Fed. Rules of Civil Procedure, Washington, 1987-92; bd. trustees Harry S. Truman Scholarship Found., 1995—. Bd. govs. Citizens Assn. Kansas City, 1959-70; bd. dirs., exec. com. Truman Med. Ctr., Kansas City; trustee Central United Methodist Ch., Kansas City, 1978—, Barstow Sch., Kansas City, 1978-87. Served with USNR, 1952-55. Recipient Lon O. Hocker Meml. Trial Lawyer award Mo. Bar Found., 1963, Spurgeon Smithson award, 1987. Mem. ABA (ho. of dels. 1982-88), Kansas City Met. Bar Assn., Lawyers Assn. Mo. Bar (pres. 1980-81, bd. govs. 1976-82), Univ. Club, Carriage Club, Vanguard Club, Mercury Club. Office: US Dist Ct 811 Grand Blvd Ste 404 Kansas City MO 64106-1909

STEVENS, KENNETH NOBLE, electrical engineering educator; b. Toronto, Ont., Can., Mar. 23, 1924; came to U.S. 1948, naturalized, 1962; s. Cyril George and Catherine (Noble) S.; m. Phyllis Fletcher, Jan. 19, 1957 (div. 1979); children: Rebecca, Andrea, Michael Hugh, John Noble; m. Sharon Manuel, Jan. 14, 1994. B.A.Sc., U. Toronto, 1945, M.A.Sc., 1948; Sc.D., MIT, 1952. Inst. U. Toronto, 1946-48; faculty MIT, Cambridge, 1948—; prof. elec. engring. MIT, 1963—, Clarence J. Lebel prof., 1977—; Vis. fellow Royal Inst. Tech., Stockholm, 1962-63; cons. to industry, 1952—; vis. prof. phonetics U. Coll., London, 1969-70; mem. Nat. Adv. Council on Neurol. and Communicative Disorders and Stroke NIH, 1982-86. Author: (with A.G. Bose) Introductory Network Theory; Contbr. articles to profl. jours. Trustee Buckingham Browne and Nichols Sch., 1974-80. Recipient Quintana award Voice Found., 1992; Guggenheim fellow, 1962. Fellow IEEE, Acoustical Soc. Am. (exec. com. 1963-66, v.p. 1971-72, pres.-elect 1975-76, pres. 1976-77, gold medal 1995), Am. Acad. Arts and Scis.; mem. NAE. Home: 51 Montrose St Somerville MA 02143-1212 Office: MIT 77 Massachusetts Ave Cambridge MA 02139

STEVENS, KEVIN MICHAEL, professional hockey player; b. Brockton, Mass., Apr. 15, 1965. Student, Boston Coll. With L.A. Kings, 1983; left wing Pitts. Penguins, 1983—; mem. NHL All-Star team, 1991-92, Stanley Cup championship teams, 1991, 92; player NHL All-Star games, 1991, 92, 93. Named to NCAA All-Am. East 2nd Team, 1986-87, Sporting News All-Star 2nd Team, 1990-91, 92-93, NHL All-Star 1st Team, 1991-92. Office: Pitts Penguins Civic Arena Gate # 9 Pittsburgh PA 15219*

STEVENS, LYDIA HASTINGS, civic worker; b. Highland Park, Ill., Aug. 2, 1918; d. Rolland T.R. and Ruth Shotwell (Beebe) Hastings; m. George Cooke Stevens, Nov. 2, 1940; children: Lydia Stevens Gustin, Priscilla Stevens Goldfarb, Frederick S., Elizabeth Stevens MacLeod, George H., Ruth Stevens Stellard. BA, Vassar Coll., 1939. State rep. 151st Dist. of Conn., Greenwich, 1988-92; cons. Nat. Exec. Svc. Corps, N.Y.C., 1985. Pres. Greenwich YWCA, 1971-74, Greenwich Housing Coalition, 1982-86; v.p. planning Greenwich United Way, 1973-76; sr. warden Greenwich Christ Episcopal Ch., 1981-86; chmn. rev. commn. Episcopal Diocese of Conn., 1985-87; bd. dirs. Greenwich Libr., 1985-93; chmn. Greenwich Commn. Aging, 1986-88; pres., bd. dirs. Greenwich Broadcasting Corp., 1977-79; bd. dirs. Fairfield County Cmty. Found., 1992—. Recipient Golden Rule award J.C. Penney, 1987, President's award Greenwich YWCA, 1992. Republican. Episcopalian. Avocations: sailing, organic gardening.

STEVENS, M. ALLEN, geneticist, administrator; b. Mt. Carmel, Utah, Aug. 12, 1935; s. Joseph Merwin and Virginia (Tait) S.; m. Hermese Maw, June 6, 1960; children: Kent, Lance, Jennifer. MS, Utah State U., 1961; PhD, Oreg. State U., 1967. Asst. geneticist to prof./geneticist U. Calif., Davis, 1970-79; from regional mgr. to v.p. Campbell Soup Co., Camden, N.J., 1979-89; v.p. rsch. Petoseed Co., Inc., Woodland, Calif., 1989—; bd. dirs. Genetic Resources Comm. System, Washington, 1986—, Asian Vegetable Rsch & Devel. Ctr., Tainan, Taiwan, 1990—; mem. Nat. Plant Genetic Resources Bd., Washington, 1987-91. Contbr. chpts. to books, 1986. 1st lt. U.S. Army, 1957-59. Recipient Citation of Performance, U. Calif., Davis, 1992. Fellow AAAS, Am. Soc. Horticultural Science (pres. 1992-93, 6 outstanding paper awards 1968-83, Campbell award 1973); mem. Tomato Genetics Coop. (coord. com. 1980-90). Achievements include development of tomato varieties UC82, UC204. Home: 2 Ridgeview Pl Woodland CA 95695-6823 Office: Petoseed Co Inc 37437 State Highway 16 Woodland CA 95695-9353

STEVENS, MARILYN RUTH, editor; b. Wooster, Ohio, May 30, 1943; d. Glenn Willard and Gretchen Elizabeth (Ihrig) Amstutz; BA, Coll. Wooster (Ohio), 1965; MAT, Harvard U., 1966; JD, Suffolk U., 1975; m. Bryan J. Stevens, Oct. 11, 1969; children: Jennifer Marie, Gretchen Anna. Bar: Mass.

1975. Tchr., Lexington (Mass.) Public Schs., 1966-69; in various editorial positions Houghton Mifflin Co., Boston, 1969—, editorial dir. sch. depts., 1978-81, editorial dir. math. and scis. Sch. Div., 1981-84, mng. editor sch. pub., 1984—. Mem. LWV, Mass. Bar Assn. Office: Houghton Mifflin 222 Berkeley St Boston MA 02116

STEVENS, MARTIN, English educator; b. Hamburg, Germany, Jan. 11, 1927; came to U.S. 1939, naturalized, 1945; s. Hans Siegfried and Hertha Paula (Stern-Geiger) S.; m. Rose Zimbardo, Nov. 26, 1974; children by previous marriage: Cynthia Jean, Marc, David. B.A., Western Res. U., 1949, M.A., 1950; Ph.D., Mich. State U., 1956. Prof. English Ohio State U., Columbus, 1964-69; prof., chmn. dept. English SUNY, Stony Brook, 1969-75; prof., dean of humanities Herbert Lehman Coll. CUNY, 1975-79, dean liberal arts and scis. Baruch Coll., 1979-87, prof. English Grad. Ctr., 1975—, disting. prof. Grad. Ctr., 1986—; exec. officer PhD program in English Grad. Ctr., 1988-90. Co-author: Old English Literature, 1968, The Towneley Facsimile edit., 1977, In Print, 1983, Across the Curriculum, 1984; author: Four English Mystery Cycles, 1987, (2 vols.) The Towneley Plays, EETS edit., 1994; guest editor Mediaevalia, 1994; gen. editor Early European Drama Translation series, 1993—; contbr. articles to profl. jours. Served with USNR, 1945-46. Guggenheim fellow, 1966-67; Fulbright research scholar, 1966-67. Mem. MLA, Mediaeval Acad. Am.; Nat. Council Tchrs. English. Home: 60 Pineapple St Apt 2H Brooklyn NY 11201-6838 Office: CUNY Grad Ctr PhD Program in English 33 W 42d St New York NY 10036

STEVENS, MAY, artist; b. Boston, June 9, 1924; d. Ralph Stanley and Alice Margaret (Dick) S.; m. Rudolf Baranik, June 5, 1948; 1 child, Steven. BFA, Mass. Coll. Art, 1946; postgrad., Academie Julian, Paris, 1948-49, Art Students League, 1948. Mem. faculty Sch. Visual Arts, N.Y.C., 1964—, Skowhegan Sch. Painting and Sculpture, 1992; lectr. Royal Coll. Art, London, 1981, U. Wis.-Racine, 1973, Coll. Art Assn., Washington, 1975. One-woman shows: Terry Dintenfass Gallery, N.Y.C., 1971, Cornell U., 1973, Douglass Coll., Rutgers U., 1974, Lerner-Heller Gallery, N.Y.C., 1975, 76, 78, 81, Clark U., 1982, Boston U. Art Gallery, 1984, Frederick S. Wight Gallery, UCLA, 1985, U. Md., College Park, 1985, Real Art Ways, Hartford, Conn., 1988, New Mus. Contemporary Art, 1988, Orchard Gallery, Derry, No. Ireland, 1988, Kenyon Coll., Gambier, Ohio, 1988, Greenville County (S.C.) Art Mus., 1991, Herter Gallery, U. Mass., Amherst, 1991, U. Colo., Boulder, 1993; exhibited in group shows: Inst. Contemporary Arts, London, 1980, Gemeente Mus., The Hague, 1979, Whitney Mus., 1970, Gedok, Kunsthaus, Hamburg, Germany, 1972, Everson Mus., Syracuse, N.Y., 1976, Clocktower, N.Y.C., 1986, Guerrilla Girls Exbn. at Palladium, N.Y.C., 1985, One Penn Pla., 1985, Pentonville Gallery, London, 1986, Heckscher Mus., N.Y., 1987, Univ. Art Mus., Berkeley, Calif., 1987, Mus. Modern Art, 1988, Exit Art, N.Y.C., 1988, Sao Paulo (Brazil) Mus. Modern Art, 1989, Blum Helman Gallery, N.Y.C., 1989, Univ. Art Mus., Long Beach, Calif., 1990, Angels Gate, San Pedro, Calif., 1990, Newark Mus., 1990, Städtliche Kunsthalle, Düsseldorf, Germany, 1990, DeCordova Mus., Lincoln, Mass., 1991, Exit Art, N.Y.C., 1994, Mary Delahoyd Gallery, N.Y.C., 1995, Mary Ryan Gallery, N.Y.C., 1995, Gwenda Jay Gallery, Chgo., 1995; represented in permanent collections: Metropolitan Mus. of Art, N.Y.C., Mus. Modern Art, N.Y.C., Moca, L.A., San Francisco Mus. Art, New Mus. Contemporary Art, Whitney Mus., Bklyn. Mus., Herbert F. Johnson Mus., Cornell U., Mus. Fine Arts Boston, De Cordova Mus., Lincoln, Mass.; contbr. articles to various mags. Recipient Childe Hassam Purchase awards Nat. Inst. Arts and Letters, 1968, 69, 75, N.Y. State Coun. on Arts award, 1974; MacDowell Colony fellow, 1971, 72, 74, 75, 81, 82, 84, Bunting Inst. fellow Radcliffe Coll., 1988-89; grantee NEA, 1983, Guggenheim, 1986; honoree Women's Caucus for Art, 1990. Mem. Coll. Art Assn.

STEVENS, MILTON LEWIS, JR., trombonist; b. Gt. Barrington, Mass., Nov. 10, 1942; s. Milton Lewis and Edna Laura (Coates) S.; m. Elizabeth Mruk Stevens, June 14, 1966 (dec. June 1984); m. Priscilla Storms, Dec. 28, 1985. Mus.B. Oberlin Conservatory Music, 1965; Mus.M., U. Ill., 1966; D.M.A., Boston U., 1975. Instr. Oberlin (Ohio) Conservatory Music, 1967-68; asst. prof. Boston U., 1970-73, Ohio State U., Columbus, 1973-74; prin. trombonist Denver Symphony, 1974-78, Nat. Symphony Orch., Washington, 1978—; adj. prof. Cath. U. Am., 1978—, U. Md., College Park, 1987—. Condr. Intersvc. Trombone Choir, Washington, 1991—, Washington Symphonic Brass and Percussion Ensemble, 1993— Recipient Albert Spaulding award Berkshire Music Center, 1968. Mem. Internat. Trombone Assn. Home: 3500 Farm Hill Dr Falls Church VA 22044-1237 Office: Nat Symphony Kennedy Ctr Washington DC 20566

STEVENS, NORMAN DENNISON, retired library director; b. Nashua, N.H., Mar. 4, 1932; s. David P. and Ruth (Ackley) S.; m. Nora Bennett, Jan. 16, 1959; children: David P., Sara, Elizabeth. BA, U. N.H., 1954; MLS, Rutgers U., 1957, PhD, 1961. Acting dir. univ. librs. Howard U., Washington, 1961-63; assoc. libr. Rutgers U., New Brunswick, N.J., 1963-68; assoc. univ. libr. U. Conn., Storrs, 1968-75; univ. libr. U. Conn., 1975-87, dir. univ. librs., 1987-94, dir. emeritus univ. librs., 1994—; exec. dir. The Molesworth Inst., Storrs, 1959—; condr. librs. N.Am. Sch. for the Artsy, White Bear Lake, Minn., 1988—; pres. The Bibliosmiles, 1993—. Author: A Guide to Collecting Librariana Communications Throughout Libraries, 1983; editor: Library Humor, 1971, The Librarian, 1976. Mem. ALA, Phi Beta Kappa, Phi Kappa Phi, Pi Sigma Alpha. Avocations: collecting library memorabilia, library humor, profl. writing. Home: 143 Hanks Hill Rd Storrs Mansfield CT 06268-2315

STEVENS, PAUL EDWARD, lawyer; b. Youngstown, Ohio, July 22, 1916; s. Raymond U. and Mary Ann (Pritchard) S.; m. Janet L. Weisert, Mar. 9, 1946; 1 son, Mark O. LL.B., Ohio State U., 1941. Bar: Ohio 1941. Practiced in Youngstown, 1941—; ptnr. Green, Schiavoni, Murphy & Stevens, 1962-71, Burdman, Stevens & Gilliland, 1971-75, Stevens & Toot, 1976-77, Paul E. Stevens Co., 1977—; prof. law Youngstown Coll. Sch. Law, 1946-60; gen. counsel Animal Charity Corp., 1986—. Trustee Poland Twp., Ohio, 1960-69; Republican candidate for U.S. Congress, 1959; dist. adminstrv. asst. Congressman Charles J. Carney, 19th Ohio dist., 1970-80; pres. Welsh Nat. Gymanfa Ganu Assn., 1988-90. With AUS, 1942-46. Mem. ABA, Ohio Bar Assn. (chmn. membership com. 1955), Mahoning County Bar Assn. (pres. 1953-54), Mahoning County Planning Assn. (chmn. 1990—). Unitarian. Home: 7191 N Lima Rd Youngstown OH 44514-3749 Office: 780 Boardman Canfield Rd Youngstown OH 44512-4344

STEVENS, PAUL IRVING, manufacturing company executive; b. Lawrence, Kans., Mar. 22, 1915; s. Ira F. and Ida M. S.; m. Artie Faye Womack, Nov. 10, 1935; children: Richard Irving, Constance Irene. Student bus. adminstrn., Pasadena (Calif.) Coll., 1933-35. Indsl. engr. Consol. Aircraft Co., San Diego, 1940-49; founder, prin. stockholder, pres. United Machine Co., Ft. Worth, 1950-61; exec. v.p. Clary Corp., San Gabriel, Calif., 1962-65; pres., owner Stevens Corp., Ft. Worth, 1965-69; pres., chief exec. officer Waltham Industries, Inc., 1969-71, Stevens Industries, La Jolla, Calif., 1972—, Campbell Industries, San Diego, 1976-79; chmn., pres. Stevens Air Systems, El Cajon, Calif., 1974-81; pres. Womack Motors, Inc., El Centro, Calif., 1982-90; chmn. bd., chief exec. officer Stevens Graphics Corp., Ft. Worth, 1986—; chmn. bd. Rancho Santa Fe Nat. Bank, Calif., 1982—. Mem. Nat. Mgmt. Assn. (exec. com.), Presidents Assn., Civic Round Table, La Jolla Country Club, Colonial Country Club, Canyon Country Club, University Club, Ft. Worth Club, Shady Oaks Country Club. Republican. Methodist. Home: 2585 Calle Del Oro La Jolla CA 92037-2005 Office: PO Box 950 La Jolla CA 92038-0950

STEVENS, RAYMOND DONALD, JR., chemical company executive; b. Buffalo, Feb. 17, 1927; s. Raymond Donald and Annette (Wells) S.; m. V. Aline Larkin, Aug. 20, 1949; children—Raymond Donald III, Larkin Edgeworth, Courtney Curtis, Hunter Hubbard. Grad., Nichols Sch., Buffalo, 1945; B.S. in Econs, Wharton Sch. U. Pa., 1951. With Pierce & Stevens Chem. Corp., Buffalo, 1951—; exec. v.p. Pierce & Stevens Chem. Corp., 1958-63, pres., 1963-70, chmn. bd., 1970—; also dir.; exec. v.p. Pratt & Lambert, Inc., Buffalo, 1967-70; pres., chief exec. officer Pratt & Lambert, Inc., 1970-89, chmn., 1970—; also dir.; bd. dirs. United Paint Co. Mfrs. & Traders Trust Co., First Empire State Corp. Trustee Buffalo Gen. Hosp. Served with USNR, 1945-47. Mem. Nat. Paint and Coatings Assn. (pres.

1977-78, dir., exec. com. 1977—), Am. Legion (past post comdr.), Nova Internat. Paint Club (past pres.), Friars Sr. Soc., Phi Kappa Sigma. Club: Saturn (Buffalo). Home: 81 Hallam Rd Buffalo NY 14216-3519 Office: Pratt & Lambert Inc 75 Tonawanda St Buffalo NY 14207-3190

STEVENS, ROBERT BOCKING, lawyer, educator; b. U.K., June 8, 1933; naturalized, 1971; s. John Skevington and Enid Dorthy (Bocking) S.; m. Katherine Booth, Dec. 23, 1985; 1 child, Robin; children by previous marriage: Carey, Richard. BA, Oxford U., 1955, BCL, 1956, MA, 1959, DCL, 1984; LLM, Yale U., 1958; LLD (hon.), N.Y. Law Sch., 1984, Villanova U., 1985, U. Pa., 1987; D.Litt. (hon.), Haverford Coll., 1991. Barrister-at-law London, 1956; tutor in law Keble Coll. Oxford U., 1958-59; asst. prof. law Yale U., 1959-61, assoc. prof., 1961-65, prof., 1965-76; provost, prof. law and history Tulane U., 1976-78; pres. Haverford Coll., 1978-87; chancellor U. Calif., Santa Cruz, 1987-91; of counsel Covington and Burling, Washington and London, 1992—; master Pembroke Coll., Oxford, 1993—; vis. prof. U. Tex., 1961, U. East Africa, 1962, Stanford U., 1966, U. Coll. London, 1991-94; cons. UN, HEW, U.S. Dept. State. Author: The Restrictive Practices Court, 1965, Lawyers and the Courts, 1967, In Search of Justice, 1968, Income Security, 1970, Welfare Medicine in America, 1974, Law and Politics, 1978, The Law School, 1983, The Independence of the Judiciary, 1993. Grantee Rockefeller Found., 1962-64, Ford Found., 1962-64, 73-74, Russell Sage Found., 1967-68, NEH, 1973-74, Nuffield Found., 1975; named Hon. fellow Keble Coll. Oxford U., 1985, Socio-Legal Ctr., 1992. Mem. Marshall Aid Meml. Commn. (chair), Rsch. com., Am. Bar Found. Home: Masters Lodgings, Pembroke Coll., Oxford OX1 1DW, England Office: Covington and Burling, Leconfield House Curzon St, London W1Y 8AS, England

STEVENS, ROBERT DAVID, librarian, educator; b. Nashua, N.H., Aug. 11, 1921; s. David Philip and Ruth (Ackley) S.; m. Helen Medora Conrad, Jan. 16, 1943; children: Ruth Wilson Robertson, Hope Conrad. A.B. magna cum laude, Syracuse U., 1942; B.S. in L.S. with honors, Columbia, 1947; M.A., Am. U., 1955, Ph.D., 1965. With Library of Congress, Washington, 1947-64; coordinator pub. law 480 programs Library of Congress, 1962-64; dir. Library East West Center, Honolulu, 1966-75; dean Grad. Sch. Library Studies U. Hawaii, Honolulu, 1966-75; chief cataloging div. Copyright Office, 1975-80, coordinator copyright collections, 1980; lectr. grad. Sch. Library Studies, U. Hawaii, 1981—; chief exec. officer Molesworth Inst. West, Inc., 1984-91, chmn., 1991—; Fulbright lectr. U. Indonesia, 1971; U.S. del. Intergovtl. Conf. Planning Nat. Libraries Infrastructures, 1974. Author: Role of the Library of Congress in International Exchange of Government Publications, 1955, Toshokan Kyoryoku, 1970, Documents of International Organizations, 1974, Japanese and U.S. Research Libraries at the Turning Point, 1977, Short History of the School of Library and Information Studies, 1991; contbr. articles to profl. publs. Served to lt. USNR, 1943-46. Mem. Hawaii Library Assn. (pres. 1966-67), ALA (mem. council 1967-70, mem. U.S.-Japan adv. com. 1972—, chmn. 1974-76, Public policy and research com. 1977-81), Assocs. U. Hawaii Library (vice chmn. 1981-84), Japan Library Assn., Hui Dui, Phi Beta Kappa, Pi Sigma Alpha. Club: 15 (Honolulu). Home: 3265 Paty Dr Honolulu HI 96822-1449

STEVENS, ROBERT EDWIN, bank executive, former insurance company executive; b. Hartford, Feb. 12, 1927; s. Horace and Anna E. (Lauritzen) S.; m. Betty L. Hippler, June 30, 1951; children—Paul, Lynn, Peter. B.A., Wesleyan U., 1949. Various positions bond and common stock divs. Conn. Mut. Life Ins. Co., Hartford, 1951-71; v.p., treas. Conn. Mut. Life Ins. Co., 1972-74, sr. v.p., 1974-76, exec. v.p., 1976-89; pres. Conn. Mut. Investment Accounts, Inc., 1980-89; chmn. bd. dirs. Liberty Bank, Middletown, Conn., 1989—; bd. dirs. Freedom Fin. Svcs. Bd. dirs. Hartford Hosp.; trustee Jacob L. and Lewis Fox Scholarship Found., Wesleyan U.; corporator Middlesex Hosp. With USNR, World War II. Mem. Hartford Soc. Fin. Analysts (past pres.). Home: 46 Keighley Pond Rd PO Box 361 Cobalt CT 06414 Office: Liberty Bank Middletown CT

STEVENS, ROBERT JAY, magazine editor; b. Detroit, July 25, 1945; s. Jay Benjamin and Louise Ann (Beyreuther) S.; m. Dahlia Jean Conger, Aug. 15, 1970; children—Sandra Lee, Julia Ann. Student, Huron (S.D.) Coll., 1963-66, Wayne State U., 1968-71. Sr. staff writer Automotive News, Detroit, 1968-71; editor Excavating Contractor mag.; Cummins Pub. Co., Oak Park, Mich., 1971-78, Chevrolets, Pro Jour., Sandy Corp., Southfield, Mich., 1978-79; editor Cars and Parts mag. Amos Press, Sidney, Ohio, 1979—; truck editor Automotive Design & Devel. mag., 1971-78; lectr., speaker in field. Author: articles, poems. Served with AUS, 1966-68, Vietnam. Decorated Air medal, Bronze Star, Commendation medal; recipient Alphomega Publs. award, 1965—, Robert F. Boger Meml. award for outstanding constrn. journalism, 1975, U.L.C.C. nat. editorial award Am. Pub. Works Assn., 1978. Mem. Detroit Auto Writers (past dir.), Internat. Motor Press Assn., Soc. Automotive Historians, Antique Automobile Club Am. Republican. Presbyterian. Home: 653 Ridgeway Dr Sidney OH 45365-3432 Office: PO Box 482 911 Vandemark Rd Sidney OH 45365

STEVENS, ROGER LACEY, theatrical producer; b. Detroit, Mar. 12, 1910; s. Stanley and Florence (Jackson) S.; m. Christine Gesell, Jan. 1, 1938; 1 child, Christabel. Student, Choate Sch., 1928, U. Mich., 1928-30; DHL, U. Mich., 1964; HHD (hon.), Wayne State U., 1960; DHL, Tulane U., 1960; LLD, Amherst Coll., 1968; hon. degrees, Skidmore Coll., 1969, U. Ill., 1970, Boston U., 1970, Am. U., 1979, Boston U., 1979, Miami U., 1983, Phila. Coll. Art, 1986. Former real estate broker specializing in hotels and investment properties, 1934-60; spl. asst. to the Pres. on the arts, 1964-68; chmn. Nat. Coun. on the Arts, 1965-69, Nat. Endowment for Arts as trustee; pres. Nat. Inst. for Music Theater; chmn. Am. Film Inst., 1969-72; chmn. adv. com. Nat. Book Award, 1970-75, 1988-89; mem. Coun. for Arts, Mass. Inst. Tech.; chmn. Fund for New Am. Plays, 1986—; mem. Pres.'s Com. on Arts and Humanities, 1982-93. Producing partner in more than 200 theatrical prodns. including Old Times, West Side Story, Cat on a Hot Tin Roof, Bus Stop, The Visit, Mary, Mary, A Man for all Seasons, The Best Man, Deathtrap, Death of a Salesman; Kennedy Ctr. prodns. include Annie, First Monday in October, On Your Toes, Mass, Jumpers, Night and Day, Wings, Texas Trilogy, Bedroom Farce, Cocktail Hour, Love Letters, Metamorphosis, A Few Good Men, Artist Descending a Staircase, Shadowlands, She Loves Me. Chmn. fin. com. Dem. Party, 1956; chmn. bd. trustees John F. Kennedy Ctr. Performing Arts, 1961-88; trustee Am. Shakespeare Theater and Acad., Choate Sch., 1982-93; bd. dirs. Met. Opera Assn., 1958—, Ballet Theatre Found., 1977—, Nat. Symphony Orch., 1981-93, Filene Ctr./Wolf Trap Farm Park for Performing Arts, 1969-92, The Washington Opera, 1988-94, Peabody Conservatory, 1979-82, Folger Libr., Acad. Am. Poets. Decorated knight comdr. Brit. Empire; Royal Order of Vasa, Sweden; grand ufficiale Order of Merit Italy; comdr.'s cross Order of Merit Fed. Republic Germany; recipient award contbn. theatre Nat. Theater Conf., 1970, Presdl. Medal of Freedom, 1988, Nat. Medal of Arts, 1988; Kennedy Ctr. honoree, 1988. Fellow Royal Soc. Arts; mem. ANTA (exec. com.), Phi Gamma Delta. Clubs: Bohemian (San Francisco); Racquet and Tennis (N.Y.C.), Century Assn. (N.Y.C.), Pilgrims (N.Y.C.). Office: JFK Ctr Performing Arts Washington DC 20566

STEVENS, RON A., lawyer, public interest organization administrator; b. Indpls., Sept. 4, 1945; s. Granville Thomas and Charlotte May (Wheeler) S.; m. Judy Rohde, June 15, 1968; children: Samuel Thomas, Alison Elizabeth. BA, Okla. State U.; JD with honors, Ill. Inst. Tech., 1976. Bar: Ill. 1976. Staff atty. Legal Assistance Found. Chgo., 1976-79; staff atty., dir. housing agenda Bus. and Profl. People for Pub. Interest, Chgo., 1979-81; chief housing atty. Office of Cook County State's Atty., Chgo., 1981-82; campaign coord. north lakefront Washington for Mayor, Chgo., 1982-83; program officer The Joyce Found., Chgo., 1983-86; pres. Citizens for a Better Environment, Chgo., 1986-89; exec. dir. United Way Santa Fe County, 1989—; adv. bd. state support ctr. on environ. hazards Nat. Ctr. for Policy Alternatives, Washington, 1987-89; chair, Local Bd. EFSP, 1989—, chair Santa Fe Affordable Housing Roundtable, 1992—; steer com. Santa Fe Community Needs Assessment, 1990—. Mem. bldg. code enforcement com. Mayor's Transition Team Housing Task Force, Chgo., 1983, steering com. Chgo. Ethics Project, 1986-88; founder, chmn. Progressive Chgo. Area Network, 1981-84; bd. dirs. Uptown Recycling Sta., Chgo., 1987-89; mem. Chgo. Lawyers (chmn. housing com. 1978-81, bd. govs. 1981-83, bd. dirs. Fund for Justice, 1986-88), Chgo. Area Runners Assn. (founder, v.p. 1977-81). Home:

739 Gregory Ln Santa Fe NM 87501-4271 Office: United Way Santa Fe County PO Box 261 Santa Fe NM 87504-0261

STEVENS, ROSEMARY A., academic dean, public health and social history educator; b. Bourne, Eng.; came to U.S., 1961, naturalized, 1968; d. William Edward and Mary Agnes (Tricks) Wallace; m. Robert B. Stevens, Jan. 28, 1961 (div. 1983); children: Carey, Richard; m. Jack D. Barchas, Aug. 9, 1994. BA, Oxford (Eng.) U., 1957; Diploma in Social Adminstrn., Manchester (Eng.) U., 1959; MPH, Yale U., 1963, PhD, 1968. Various hosp. adminstrv. positions Eng., 1959-61; rsch. assoc. Med. Sch. Yale U., 1962-68, asst. prof. Med. Sch., 1968-71, assoc. prof. Med. Sch., 1971-74, prof. pub. health Med. Sch., 1974-76; master Jonathan Edwards Coll., 1974-75; prof. dept. health systems mgmt. and polit. sci. Tulane U., New Orleans, 1976-78; chmn. dept. health systems mgmt. Tulane U., 1977-78; prof. history and sociology of sci. U. Pa., Phila., 1979—, chmn. dept., 1980-83, 86-91, UPS Found. prof., 1990-91, dean Sch. Arts and Scis., Thomas S. Gates prof., 1991—; vis. lectr. Johns Hopkins U., 1967-68; guest scholar Brookings Instn., Washington, 1967-68; acad. visitor London Sch. Econs., 1962-64, 1973-74. Author: Medical Practice in Modern England: The Impact of Specialization and State Medicine, 1966, American Medicine and the Public Interest, 1971, In Sickness and in Wealth: American Hospitals in the Twentieth Century, 1989, (with others) Foreign Trained Physicians and American Medicine, 1972, Welfare Medicine in America, 1974, Alien-Doctors: Foreign Medical Graduates in American Hospitals, 1978. Bd. dirs. Am. Hosps., 1978, Ctr. for Advancement of Health. Fellow Am. Acad. Arts and Scis.; mem. Inst. Medicine of Nat. Acad. Sci., History of Sci. Soc., Am. Assn. for History of Medicine, Coll. Physicians of Phila., Cosmopolitan Club. Home: # 18 A 1900 Rittenhouse Sq Philadelphia PA 19103-9999 Office: U Pa Office of Dean 116 College Hall Philadelphia PA 19104-6377

STEVENS, ROY W., distilled spirits executive; b. Ottumwa, Iowa, Oct. 28, 1924; s. Manley O. and Ruth (Worrell) S.; m. Donna R. Borman, June 7, 1952 (dec. Jan. 1973); children: Katharine Anne Stevens Dillon, Thomas W., John M.; m. Beth A. Murphy, Apr. 20, 1974; children: Carrie Theresa, Elizabeth Mary. B.S.C., U. Iowa, 1948. With Coca-Cola Co., 1948-54, Gen. Foods Corp., 1954-67; exec. v.p. Riviana Foods, Houston, 1967-73; v.p. mktg. Hiram Walker Inc., Detroit, 1973-75; pres. Hiram Walker Inc., 1975-80, Maidstone Wine & Spirits Inc., L.A., 1980-81, Kahlua Group, 1987-91; exec. v.p. The Century Coun., Los Angeles, 1991—. Bd. dirs., past chmn. Detroit Met. YMCA; bd. dirs. L.A. Met. WMCA. St. (j.g.) USN, 1943-46. Mem. Sigma Alpha Epsilon, Jonathan Club, Annandale Golf Club (Pasadena, Calif.). Episcopalian. Home: 1221 San Marino Ave San Marino CA 91108-1228 Office: The Century Coun 550 S Hope St Ste 1950 Los Angeles CA 90071-2604

STEVENS, SHANE, novelist; b. N.Y.C., Oct. 8, 1951; s. John and Caroline (Royale) S. MA, Columbia U., 1961. mem. numerous writers confs. including Bread Loaf, Santa Barbara Writers Conf. Author: Go Down Dead, 1967, Way Uptown in Another World, 1973, Dead City, 1973, Rat Pack, 1974, By Reason of Insanity, 1979, The Anvil Chorus, 1985; (as J.W. Rider) Jersey Tomatoes, 1986, Hot Tickets, 1987; contbr. articles to pubs. including N.Y. Times, Life, Washington Post; screenwriter: By Reason of Insanity, The Me Nobody Knows. Mem. Authors Guild, Writers Guild Am. Office: William Morris Agy 1350 Ave of Americas New York NY 10019*

STEVENS, SINCLAIR MCKNIGHT, Canadian government official; b. Esquesing Twp., Ont., Can., Feb. 11, 1927; s. Robert Murray and Anna Bailey (McKnight) S.; m. Noreen Mary Charlebois, May 17, 1958. Student, Weston (Ont.) Coll., 1942-46, Oakwood Coll. Inst., Toronto, 1946-47; B.A. in Journalism, U. Western Ont., 1951; Barrister-at-law, Osgoode Hall Law Sch., 1955; LLB, 1991. Bar: Ont. 1955, Queen's Coun. 1971. Journalist Toronto Star; assoc. Fraser & Beatty; M.P. from York-Simcoe Dist. Ho. of Commons, 1972-79, M.P. from York-Peel Dist., 1979-88, minister regional indsl. expansion, 1984-86; pub. The Planet Today; sr. ptnr. Stevens & Stevens, Newmarket, Ont. Chmn. Cabinet Com. on Econ. and Regional Devel., 1984-86; pres. Treasury Bd., 1979-80. Mem. Can. Bar Assn., Delta Sigma Phi, Phi Delta Phi, Albany Club (Toronto), Met. Club (N.Y.C.). Conservative. Home: RR 2, Stevensville, ON Canada L0S 1S0

STEVENS, STANLEY DAVID, local history researcher, retired librarian; b. San Francisco, Nov. 10, 1933; s. David Franklyn and Ellen Myrtle (Wixson) S.; m. Carli Ann Lewis, Sept. 3, 1960; adopted children: Alexander Lewis, Nikolas Harriman, Brooke Cayton Stevens Rich. BA, San Jose State U., 1959. Conf. officer polit. and security com. 14th Gen. Assembly, UN, N.Y.C., 1959; map libr. U. Calif., Santa Cruz, 1965-93, ret., 1993, coord. Hihn-Younger Archive, Univ. Libr., 1994—; mem. Cartographic Users Adv. Coun., 1976-86, chmn., 1982-86; presenter in field, 1971—; adj. prof. libr. sci. San Jose (Calif.) State U., 1989, 91. Author: Catalog of aerial photos by Fairchild Aerial Surveys, Inc. now in the collections of the Department of Geography, University of California at Los Angeles, 1982; editor, Santa Cruz County History Journal; also 8 others related to Hihn-Younger Archive; contbr. over 100 articles and book revs. to profl. jours. Mem. adv. com. archaeol. program Cabrillo Coll., Aptos, Calif., 1985—; bd. dirs. Santa Cruz County Hist. Trust (formerly Santa Cruz Hist. Soc.), 1980-94, chmn. publs. com., 1980—, mem. programs adv. coun., 1994—; mem. Santa Cruz Orgn. for Progress and Euthenics, 1987—; bd. dirs. Friends of U. Calif.-Santa Cruz Libr., 1994—; mem. U. Calif.-Santa Cruz Emeriti Group. With U.S. Army, 1954-56. Recipient honors award geography and map div. for outstanding achievement in map librarianship Spl. Librs. Assn., 1981, cert. of commendation Santa Cruz Hist. Soc., 1986, appreciation cert. for svcs. Assn. Info. and Image Mgmt., 1989; grantee Librs. Assn. U. Calif., 1981-82, rsch. grantee Office of Pres., U. Calif., 1985-86. Mem. ALA (publs. com. Map and Geography Round Table 1986-86, editl. bd. Meridian 1989-92, honors award Map and Geography Round Table 1992), Western Assn. Map Librs. (hon. life, founding pres. 1967-68, treas. 1968-89, editor Info. Bull. 1969-84, Exec. Com. award 1984), Calif. Hist. Soc., Calif. Map Soc., Pajaro Valley Hist. Assn., Santa Cruz County Geneal. Soc., Capitola Hist. Soc., El Paso de Robles Hist. Soc. (life). Democrat. Avocations: resarching local history, listening to jazz and classical music. Home: 231 13th Ave Santa Cruz CA 95062 Office: U Calif Map Collection Dean E McHenry Libr Santa Cruz CA 95064

STEVENS, THEODORE FULTON, senator; b. Indpls., Nov. 18, 1923; s. George A. and Gertrude (Chancellor) S.; m. Ann Mary Cherrington, Mar. 29, 1952 (dec. 1978); children—Susan B., Elizabeth H., Walter C., Theodore Fulton, Ben A.; m. Catherine Chandler, 1980; 1 dau.; Lily Irene. B.A., U. Calif. at Los Angeles, 1947; LL.B., Harvard U., 1950. Bar: Calif., Alaska, D.C., U.S. Supreme Ct. bars. Pvt. practice Washington, 1950-52, Fairbanks, Alaska, 1953; U.S. atty. Dist. Alaska, 1953-56; legis. counsel, asst. to sec., solicitor Dept. Interior, 1956-60; pvt. practice law Anchorage, 1961-68; mem. Alaska Ho. of Reps., 1965-68, majority leader, speaker pro tem, 1967-68; U.S. senator for Alaska, 1968—, asst. Rep. leader, 1977-85; chmn. Senate Rules Com. Served as 1st lt. USAAF, World War II. Mem. ABA, Alaska Bar Assn., Calif. Bar Assn., D.C. Bar Assn., Am. Legion, VFW. Lodges: Rotary, Pioneers of Alaska, Igloo #4. Home: PO Box 100879 Anchorage AK 99510-0879 Office: US Senate 522 Hart Senate Bldg Washington DC 20510

STEVENS, THOMAS CHARLES, lawyer; b. Auburn, N.Y., Oct. 17, 1949; s. Alice (Kerlin) S.; m. Christine Eleanor Brown, June 2, 1973; children: Erin, Leigh, Timothy. BA, SUNY, Albany, 1971; JD, Duke U., 1974. Bar: Ohio 1974. Mng. prtnr. Thompson, Hine & Flory, Cleve., 1991—. Bd. trustees Greater Cleve. Growth Assn., 1993—; Greater Cleve. Roundtable, 1993—; chair profl. divsn. United Way, Cleve., 1994; active Leadership Cleve., 1992-93. Mem. ABA, Cleve. Bar Assn., Nisi Prius. Office: Thompson Hine & Flory 629 Euclid Ave Cleveland OH 44114

STEVENS, WARREN, actor; b. Clark's Summit, Pa., Nov. 2, 1919; s. Albert Clifford and Helen Dodd (Blakeslee) S.; m. Barbara Helen Fletcher, Sept. 9, 1969; children—Adam Fletcher, Matthew Dodd; 1 son by previous marriage, Laurence Blakeslee. Student, U.S. Naval Acad., 1939-40. Appeared on: New York stage in Galileo, 1947, Sundown Beach, 1948, Smile of the World, 1949, Detective Story, 1949; appeared in numerous motion pictures, since 1950, including, Barefoot Contessa, Forbidden Planet; appeared on: numerous television shows, including Richard Boone Rep. With USN, 1937-40; with USAAF, 1942-46.

STEVENS, WARREN DOUGLAS, botanist; b. Long Beach, Calif., Sept. 15, 1944; married, 1963; 1 child. AB, Humboldt State Coll., 1968; MS, Mich. State U., 1971, PhD in Botany, 1976. Asst. botany and plant pathology Mich. State U., 1971-74; cons. Cyrus William Rice divsn. NUS Corp., 1975-77; rsch. assoc. botany and plant pathology Mich. State U., 1976-78; dir. rsch. Mo. Bot. Garden, St. Louis, 1977—; collaborator Smithsonian Hassan Flora Project, 1969; cons. Ingham Co. Cir. Ctr., 1975-77. Mem. Am. Soc. Plant Taxonomists, Bot. Soc. Am., Assn. Tropical Biology, Internat. Assn. Plant Taxonomy, Sigma Xi. Achievements include research on flora of Nicaragua and systematics of Asclepiadaceae. Office: Missouri Botanical Garden PO Box 299 Saint Louis MO 63166-0299*

STEVENS, WENDELL CLAIRE, anesthesiology educator; b. Mason City, Iowa, June 28, 1931; s. Lloyd Leroy and Amy Luella (Hodson) S.; m. Lola C. Claycomb, July 27, 1958; children: Amy P., Eric C., Mitchell L. AB, Mason City Jr. Coll., 1951; MD, U. Iowa, 1956. Diplomate Am. Bd. Anesthesiology. Intern City Hosp., Cleve., 1956-57; resident in gen. surgery U. Iowa Hosp., Iowa City, 1957-58, 60-61, resident in anesthesia, 1961-63; assoc. in anesthesia U. Iowa Coll. Medicine, Iowa City, 1963, asst. prof. anesthesia dept., 1963-67; asst. prof. U. Calif. Sch. Medicine, San Francisco, 1967-72, assoc. prof., 1972-77, prof., 1977; prof., chmn. anesthesia dept. U. Iowa Coll. Medicine, Iowa City, 1978-82; prof., chmn. anesthesia dept. Oregon Health Scis. U., Portland, 1982-92, prof., 1992—. Contbr. papers and book chpts. to profl. publs. Lt. USNR, 1958-60. Recipient anesthesiology rsch. grant U. Calif., San Francisco NIH, 1969-78. Mem. Oreg. Soc. Anesthesiologists, Am. Soc. Anesthesiologists, Oreg. Med. Assn., AMA, Christian Med. Soc. Republican. Baptist. Avocations: church related activities. Office: Oreg Health Scis Ctr Dept of Anesthesiology 3181 SW Sam Jackson Park Rd Portland OR 97201-3011

STEVENS, WILBUR HUNT, accountant; b. Spencer, Ind., June 20, 1918; s. John Osburgh and Isabelle Jane (Strawser) S.; m. Maxine Dodge Stevens, Sept. 28, 1941; children: Linda Maxine Piffero, Deborah Anne Augello. BS, U. Calif., Berkeley, 1949, MBA, 1949. CPA, Calif. Staff acct. McLaren, Goode, West & Co., San Francisco, 1949-52; mng. ptnr. Fox & Co., CPAs, Salinas, 1970-73; nat. dir. banking practice Fox & Co., CPAs, Denver, 1973-80; pres., chmn. Wilbur H. Stevens, CPA, PC, Salinas, 1980-94; chmn. Stevens, Sloan & Shah, CPAs, 1994—; adj. prof. acctg. U. Denver, 1975-78; faculty mem. Assemblies for Bank Dirs., So. Meth. U., Dallas, 1976-81, Nat. Banking Sch., U. Va., Charlottesville, 1979-87; chmn., dir. Valley Nat. Bank, 1963-71. Editor Issues in CPA Practice, 1975; contbr. articles to profl. jours. Capt. AUS, 1942-53. Decorated Bronze Star, China War Meml. medal, China Victory medal; Frank G. Drum fellow U. Calif., Berkeley, 1949; Paul Harris fellow Rotary Internat., Evanston, Ill., 1978. Mem. AICPAs (v.p. 1971), Am. Acctg. Assn., Am. Assembly Collegiate Schs. Bus. (accreditation coun. 1975-78, 81-84), Nat. Assn. State Bds. Accountancy (pres. 1976-77), Calif. Soc. CPAs (pres. 1968-69, Disting. Svc. award 1988), Acctg. Rsch. Assn. (pres. 1973-75), Burma Star Assn., CBI Vets. Assn., Acad. Acctg. Historians, Commonwealth Club Calif., Masons (master 1992, grand lodge com. taxation), Knight Templar, 32 deg. Scottish Rite, Nat. Sojourners (v.p. Monterey Bay chpt. 1995), Salinas High Twelve Club (pres. 1995), QCCC London, Rotary (dist. gov. 1983, chmn. internat. fellowship accounts), Phi Beta Kappa, Beta Gamma Sigma (v.p. 1949), Beta Alpha Psi. Republican. Methodist. Home and Office: 38 Santa Ana Dr Salinas CA 93901-4136

STEVENS, WILLIAM DOLLARD, consulting mechanical engineer; b. Bayonne, N.J., Aug. 4, 1918; s. William B. and Beatrice (Dollard) S.; m. Mary E. King, Oct. 12, 1940; children: Sandra A. (Mrs. Jeffrey N. Melin), Barbara E. (Mrs. Dennis Gallagher), William K. B.Mech. Engring., Rensselaer Poly. Inst., 1940; postgrad., Case Inst. Tech., 1958; D.Sc. (hon.), N.J. Inst. Tech., 1986. Various engring. and mgmt. positions Babcock & Wilcox Co., N.Y.C., 1940-62; v.p. equipment div. Foster Wheeler Corp., Livingston, N.J., 1962-73; sr. v.p., 1972-74, exec. v.p., 1974-78, chmn. bd., 1978-81, dir., 1974-86, dir. emeritus, 1986-90; bd. of dir. Am. Soc. for Macro Engring., 1992—; instr. Pratt Inst., 1946-47; bd. overseers N.J. Inst. Tech., 1978-94. Contbr. articles to profl. jours.; patentee in field. Chmn. fund drive ARC, Hackensack, N.J., 1956; planning commr., Hackensack, 1955-58; trustee Bergen County Mental Health Consultation Ctr., 1955-58; bd. dirs. Metals Properties Coun.; mem. coun. Rensselaer Polytech. Inst., 1983—. Lt. USNR, 1943-45. Fellow ASME; mem. Nat. Acad. Engring., Sigma Xi, Tau Beta Pi, Phi Kappa Tau, Pi Tau Sigma. Methodist. Home and Office: 4 Stony Brook Rd North Caldwell NJ 07006

STEVENS, WILLIAM JOHN, management consultant, former association executive; b. Dusseldorf, Germany, Aug. 23, 1915; arrived in U.S., 1923, naturalized, 1931; s. Peter and Margaret (Kaumanns) S.; student McCall Sch. Printing, 1933; student assn. mgmt. Northwestern U., 1947; grad. Chadwick Univ., 1993; m. Dorothy V. Santangini, Feb. 14, 1937 (dec.). With Ruttle, Shaw & Wetherill, Phila., 1931-34; partner New Era Printing Co., Phila., 1934-37; plant mgr. Marcus & Co., Phila., 1937-41; supt. Edward Stern & Co., Phila., 1941-46; exec. sec. Nat. Assn. Photo-Lithographers, N.Y.C., 1946-50, exec. v.p., 1961-64, pres., 1964-71; pres., COO NPEA Exhibits, Inc., 1971-80; owner Dorval Co., pub.; pres. Opinion-3 Graphic Arts Rsch. Agy.; exec. sec. Met. Lithographers Assn., N.Y.C., 1946-50; asst. to v.p. Miehle Co., N.Y.C., 1950-56, mgr. Phila. dist., 1956-61; cons. Sales Devel. Inst., Phila., 1960-89; mem. Am. Bd. Arbitration, 1962—; chmn. adv. commn. on graphic arts N.Y.C. Tech. Coll., 1972—; bus. adminstr. St. Joseph's Parish, 1980-85. Named Industry Man of Yr. Nat. Assn. Photo-Lithographers, 1954, Man of Yr., N.Y. Litho Guild, 1962; recipient Mktg. award North Am. Pub. Co., 1967, B'nai B'rith award, 1968, N.Y. Navigators award, 1969, N.Y. Printing Craftsman Achievement award, 1989; laureate N.Y. Printers Hall of Fame, 1980, NAPL-Soderstrom award, 1984, recipient Gold Founders medal N.Y.C. Tech. Coll., 1987. Mem. Am. Soc. Assn. Execs., Graphic Arts Assn. Execs. (pres. 1969), Nat. Assn. Litho Clubs (founder, pres. 1947, Industry award 1947, 79, sec. 1964-71), N.Y. Club Printing House Craftsmen, Gamma Epsilon Tau. Clubs: Phila. Litho (pres. 1945); N.Y. Litho (N.Y.C.). Mem. Writers Inst. Author: How To Prepare Copy for Offset Lithography, 1948, Building Construction and Floor Plans for Installing Web Offset Presses; columnist for daily press; contbr. editor articles to trade pubs. Inventor Hiky-Picker, Quik-Match Color File for selection paint color samples, Stevens Foto Sizing System, Steve-O-Heat Printing Ink Dryer, "Travelr" security pocket, "Mar-Too-Nee" salad dressing. Home and Office: 4575 Barclay Crescent Lake Worth FL 33463

STEVENS, WILLIAM KENNETH, lawyer; b. Chgo., Apr. 19, 1917; s. Ernest James and Elizabeth (Street) S.; m. Anne Hughes, Jan. 4, 1943; children: Anne Elizabeth Stevens Fishman, William Hughes, Mary Carol Stevens Williams, Martha Street Stevens Gingrich. AB cum laude, U. Calif. Berkeley, 1938; MA, U. Chgo., 1940; JD, Harvard U., 1948. Bar: Ill. 1948, Fla. 1977. With First Nat. Bank Chgo., 1948-74, asst. v.p., 1958-61, v.p., 1961-74; ptnr. McDermott, Will & Emery, Chgo., 1974-85, Myers Krause & Stevens, Naples, Fla., 1986—. Author: Illinois Estate Administration, 1968. Chmn. Ill. Inst. Continuing Legal Edn., 1971-72; pres. Hinsdale (Ill.) Pub. Libr., 1977-79. Lt. USNR, 1941-45. Recipient Disting. Svc. award Chgo. Estate Planning Coun., 1981. Fellow Am. Coll. Trust and Estate Counsel; mem. ABA, Am. Law Inst., Chgo. Bar Assn., Ill. Bar Assn., Fla. Bar Assn. (bd. cert. estate planning and probate lawyer), Internat. Acad. Estate and Trust Law. Clubs: Mid-Day, Hinsdale Golf; Chikaming Country (Lakeside, Mich.), The Club at Pelican Bay (Naples). Home: 314 S Lincoln St Hinsdale IL 60521-4008 Office: Myers Krause & Stevens 5811 Pelican Bay Blvd Ste 600 Naples FL 33963-2710

STEVENS, WILLIAM LOUIS, bishop; b. Yuba City, Calif., Jan. 12, 1932; s. Ralph Fremont and Elsie Mae (Schultz) S.; B.A., San Francisco State Coll., 1953; M.Div. Gen. Theol. Sem., 1956. Ordained priest Episcopal Ch.; curate St. Luke's Ch., San Francisco; sr. curate St. Savior's, London, Order of the Holy Cross, N.Y.; rector St. Benedict's Ch., Plantation, Fla. to 1980; bishop Episcopal Diocese of Fond du Lac (Wis.), 1980—. Trustee, Nashotah Ho. Sem.; bishop visitor Sisterhood of the Holy Nativity; mem. Nat. Right to Life Com. Office: Diocese of Fond du Lac Grafon Hall 39 N Sophia PO Box 149 Fond Du Lac WI 54936-0149

STEVENS, YVETTE MARIE See KHAN, CHAKA

STEVENSON, A. BROCKIE, artist; b. Montgomery County, Pa., Sept. 24, 1919; s. Alfred Brockie and Caroline Lansdale (Sill) S.; m. Jane Merriman Mackenzie, Dec. 23, 1978. Student, Pa. Acad. Fine Arts, 1940-41, 46-50, Barnes Found., 1946-48, Skowhegan Sch., Maine, 1950. Instr. Sch. Fine Arts, Washington U., St. Louis, 1960-62; head dept. painting and drawing Corcoran Sch. Art, 1965-81, assoc. prof. to prof. design and watercolor, 1965—. One-man shows War Paintings, London and Salisbury, Eng., 1944, Instituto Cultural Peruano-Norteamericano, Lima, Peru, 1953, Art Center, Miraflores, Lima, 1958, 60, Association Cultural Peruano-Britanica, Lima, 1959, Mickelson Gallery, Washington, 1970, Pyramid Galleries Ltd., Washington, 1973, No. Va. Community Coll., 1974, Fendrick Gallery, Washington, 1978, 84, 88; group shows include, Nat. Gallery Art, London, 1944, Pa. Acad. Fine Arts, Phila., 1948, 49, 50, 51, Sociedad Bellas Artes del, Peru, Lima, 1953, 54, 55, 56, SUNY at Potsdam and Albany, 1971, Columbia (S.C.) Mus. Art, 1971, EXPO '74, Spokane, Wash., 1974, Corcoran Gallery, Washington, 1980; represented in permanent collections Corcoran Gallery Art, Washington, Dept. Def., Washington, Nat. Mus. Am. Art, Washington, Phillips Collection, Washington, Fed. Res. Bank Richmond, Va., Woodward Found., Washington, Ogunquit (Maine) Mus. Art, Brown U. Libr. Milit. Coll., Providence, R.I. Served as artist corr. U.S. Army, 1941-45, ETO. Home: 6106 Yale Ave Glen Echo MD 20812-1122 Office: Corcoran Sch Art 17 and New York Ave NW Washington DC 20006

STEVENSON, ADLAI EWING, III, lawyer, former senator; b. Chgo., Oct. 10, 1930; s. Adlai Ewing and Ellen (Borden) S.; m. Nancy L. Anderson, June 25, 1955; children: Adlai Ewing IV, Lucy W., Katherine R., Warwick L. Grad., Milton Acad., 1948; A.B., Harvard U., 1952, LL.B., 1957. Bar: Ill. 1957, D.C. 1957. Assoc. firm Mayer, Brown & Platt, Chgo., 1958-66; ptnr. Mayer, Brown & Platt, 1966-67, 81-83, of counsel, 1983-91; treas. of Ill. Springfield, 1967-70; mem. U.S. Senate from Ill., 1970-81; chmn. SCM Internat. Ltd., Chgo., 1991—. Mem. Ill. Ho. of Reps., 1965-67, Democratic candidate for gov. of Ill., 1982, 86. Capt. USMCR, 1952-54. Office: 10 S La Salle St Chicago IL 60603-1002

STEVENSON, BEN, choreographer, ballet company executive; b. Portsmouth, Eng., Apr. 4, 1936; came to U.S., 1968; s. Benjamin John and Florence May (Gundry) S.; m. Joan Toastivine, Jan. 6, 1968. Grad., Arts Ednl. Sch., London, 1955. Dir. Houston Ballet Acad.; mem. dance panel Tex. Commn. Arts, 1977; guest tchr. Am. Ballet Theatre, Joffrey Ballet, Royal Ballet, London, Beijing Dance Acad. Dancer Theatre Arts Ballet, London, 1952-54, Sadler's Wells Theatre Ballet, 1955-56, Royal Ballet, 1956-60, London Festival Ballet, 1960-62; appearances in Wedding in Paris, 1954-55, Music Man, London, 1962-63, Half a Sixpence, also, Boys in Syracuse, London, 1964; prin. dancer, ballet master, London Festival Ballet, 1964-68; artistic dir. Harkness Ballet Youth Dancers, 1968-71, Chgo. Ballet, 1974-75, Houston Ballet, 1976—; co-dir. Nat. Ballet, Washington, 1971-74; prin. ballets choreographed include Three Faces of Eve, 1965, Cast Out, 1966, Sleeping Beauty (full length), 1967, 71, 76, 78, Fervor, 1968, Three Preludes, 1968, Forbidden, 1969, Cinderella (full length), 1969, 71, 73, 74, 76, Bartok Concerto, 1970, Nutcracker (full length), 1972, 76, Symphonetta, 1972, Courant, 1973, Swan Lake (full length), 1977, L, 1978, Britten Pas de Deux, 1979, Four Last Songs, 1979, Space City, 1980, Peer Gynt (full length), 1981, Zheng Ban Qiao, 1982, The Prince of Pagodas, 1986. Recipient 1st prize London Choreographic competitions, 1965, 66, 67, 1st prize modern ballet choreography Internat. Ballet Competition, Varna, Bulgaria, 1972, Gold medal for choreography Internat. Ballet Competition, 1982. Asso. mem. Royal Acad. Dancing (Adeline Genee Gold medal 1955). Office: Houston Ballet PO Box 130487 Houston TX 77219-0487*

STEVENSON, BOBBIE LEE, education director; b. New Orleans, May 17, 1943; d. Bernice (Williams) Mayfield; widowed; 1 child, Robert Louis. BS in English Edn., So. U., 1965-66, MEd, 1974; EdD, U. Va., 1991. Tchr. New Orleans Pub. Schs., 1969-77, team mem. tchr., 1977-79, staff devel. tchr., 1979-82, dist. staff devel., 1982-83, supr. lang. arts, 1984-86, inst. specialist, 1986-92, dir., 1992—; adj. faculty Loyola U., New Orleans, 1992—. Author: Basic Communicator, 1978; editor teaching mudules African Infusion, 1991. Bd. dirs. 1st African Bapt. Ch., New Orleans, 1978, Parent Community Alliance, New Orleans, 1982, Ctr. African and African Am. Studies, So. U., New Orleans, 1993. Joint Coun. Econ. scholar, 1976; faculty fellow U. Va., 1989. Mem. ASCD, Greater New Orleans Coun. Tchrs. English, Greater New Orleans Tchrs. Writing (charter), Nat. Coun. Tchrs. English, Black Women's Assembly (charter), Future Health profl. Network (bd. dirs. 1985—), Phi Delta Kappa. Baptist. Avocations: sewing, cooking, traveling. Home: 5108 Sandhurst Dr New Orleans LA 70126-3330

STEVENSON, BRYAN ALLEN, lawyer, administrator; b. Milton, Del., Nov. 14, 1959; s. Howard Carlton and Alice Gertrude (Golden) S. BA, Eastern Coll., St. Davids, Pa., 1981; MPP, Kennedy Sch. Govt., Cambridge, Mass., 1985; JD, Harvard U., 1985. Bar: Ga. 1985, U.S. Dist. Ct. (no. dist.) Ga. 1985, U.S. Dist. Ct. (mid. dist.) Ga. 1986, Ala. 1987, U.S. Dist. Ct. (no. dist.) Ala. 1987, U.S. Dist. Ct. (mid. dist.) Ga. 1987. Staff atty. So. Prisoners Def. Com., Atlanta, 1985—; exec. dir. Ala. Capital Representation Resource Ctr., Montgomery, 1989—. Contbr. articles to publs. Recipient Nat. Human Rights award Reebol Human Rights Found., 1989, ACLU Medal of Liberty, 1991, ABA Wisdom Award for Pub. Svc., 1991; Harvard Law Sch. Pub. Interest fellow, 1985. Avocations: music, piano and keyboards.

STEVENSON, CAROL WELLS, secondary education educator; b. Richmond, Va., Feb. 14, 1942; d. Alfred Hatcher and Laura Dowdy (Hobson) Wells; m. James Pendleton Stevenson, June 23, 1962; children: James Brian Stevenson, Anne Pendleton Stevenson. BS in Home Econ. Edn., James Madison U., Harrisonburg, Va., 1962; MA in Adult Edn., Va. Commonwealth U., 1981. Cert. Home Econ., Collegiate Profl. Cert., Va. Home econ. tchr. Patrick Henry High Sch., Ashland, Va., 1962-66, Liberty Middle Sch., Ashland, Va., 1976—. Named Va. Home Econ. Tchr. of Yr., 1988, Tchr. of Yr., Liberty Mid. Sch., 1983-84, 84-85, 85-86, Most Outstanding Home Econs. Tchr. in U.S., Home Baking Assn., 1994; Check Excellence regional winner State Dept. Edn., 1990. Mem. Am. Home Econs. Assn., Va. Home Econ. Assn. (Va. Home Econs. Tchr. of Yr. award 1988), Va. Home Econ. Tchr. Assn., Am. Vocat. Assn., Va. Vocat. Assn., Nat. Assn. Vocat. Home Tchrs., Future Homemakers Am. Found. Episcopalian. Home: 202 Hanover Ave Ashland VA 23005-1815 Office: Liberty Mid Sch RR 3 Box 2500 Ashland VA 23005-9225

STEVENSON, DAVID A., materials science educator; b. Albany, N.Y., Sept. 6, 1928; married, 1958; 3 children. BA, Amherst Coll., 1950; PhD in Phys. Chemistry, MIT, 1954. Rsch. assoc. metallurgy MIT, 1953-54, asst. prof., 1955-58; prof. materials sci. Stanford (Calif.) U., 1958—; sr. rsch. fellow Max Planck Inst. Phys. Chemistry, 1968, 69. Recipient Fred Whipple award Am. Geophysical Union, 1994; Fulbright scholar U. Munich, 1954-55. Mem. Am. Inst. Mining, Metallurgy and Petroleum Engring., Electrochem. Soc., Sigma Xi. Achievements include research in synthesis and properties of semiconducting materials and device applications, solid state electrochemistry, diffusion in compound semiconductors. Office: Stanford U Dept Materials Sci Stanford CA 94305*

STEVENSON, DAVID JOHN, planetary scientist; b. Wellington, New Zealand, Sept. 2, 1948; came to U.S., 1971; s. Ian McIvor and Gwenyth (Carroll) S. BSc, Victoria U., New Zealand, 1971; PhD, Cornell U., 1976. Rsch. fellow Australian Nat. U., Canberra, Australia, 1976-78; asst. prof. UCLA, L.A., 1978-80; assoc. prof. Calif. Inst. Tech., Pasadena, 1980-84, prof., 1984—, chmn. div. geol. & planetary scis., 1989-94. Contbr. about 100 articles to profl. jours. Named Fulbright scholar, 1968, Fellow Am. Geophysical Union, Royal Soc. London, 1993; mem. AAAS, Am. Astron. Soc. (Urey prize 1984). Office: Calif Inst Tech 1201 E California Blvd Pasadena CA 91125

STEVENSON, ELIZABETH, author, educator; b. Ancon, Panama, C.Z., June 13, 1919; d. John Thurman and Bernice (Upshaw) S. BA magna cum laude, Agnes Scott Coll., 1941. With war time agys. U.S. Govt., Atlanta, 1942-47; order asst. Atlanta Pub. Library, 1948-56; asst. to coll. dean Emory U., Atlanta, 1960-74; from research assoc. to Candler prof. Grad. Inst. Liberal Arts, Emory U., Atlanta, 1974-87. Author: The Crooked Corridor: A Study of Henry James, 1949, Henry Adams, 1955 (Bancroft prize 1956), Lafcadio Hearn, 1961, Babbitts and Bohemians, 1967, Park Maker: A Life of Frederick Law Olmsted, 1977, Figures in a Western Landscape: Men and

Women of the Northern Rockies, 1994; editor: A Henry Adams Reader, 1958. Guggenheim fellow, 1950-51, 58-59; grantee Rockefeller Found., 1958-59, Am. Coun. Learned Socs., 1975; recipient Faculty Rsch. Fund award Emory U., 1960s, 70s, summer stipend NEH, 1974. Mem. Authors Guild, Phi Beta Kappa. Democrat. *Whether as a product of the era or an irritant to it, the underlying assumption is that every single life is a drama worth exploring. Biography is bound by the facts, but it is also an art, a difficult art.*

STEVENSON, ERIC VAN CORTLANDT, mortgage banker, real estate executive, lawyer; b. N.Y.C., June 27, 1926; s. Harvey and Winifred (Worcester) S.; m. Judith Kittredge Herrick, Nov. 13, 1955; children: Jonathan Herrick, Michael Kirkham, Anne Kittredge, Margaret Low, Philip Eric. B.A., Yale U., 1947, LL.B., 1950. Bar: D.C. 1951, Conn. 1954. With NLRB, 1951; practice in Hartford, Conn., 1954-55, Norwich, Conn., 1957-61; with Electric Boat Co., 1956-57; rsch. assoc. Inst. Def. Analyses, 1961-63; with Labor Dept., 1963-65; rsch. dir. George Washington U., 1965-66; gen. counsel Peace Corps, 1966-68; dir. urban affairs Life Ins. Assn. Am., N.Y.C., 1969-72; mortgage banker Sonnenblick-Goldman Corp., Washington, 1973-74, Boykin Corp., 1974-82, Stevenson and Kittredge, Inc., 1978-82; sr. v.p. Mortgage Bankers Assn. Am., Washington, 1982-91; cons. Ford Found., 1963, Conn. Housing Investment Fund, 1968-69, Carnegie Corp., 1972, HUD, 1976-77, 78-80; Housing specialist Commn. on Mental Health Svcs., D.C. Gov., 1992—. Served with USNR, 1944-46, 51-53. Home: 3502 36th St NW Washington DC 20016-3150

STEVENSON, ERNEST VAIL, retired farmer cooperative executive; b. Streator, Ill., Mar. 18, 1922; s. James Vail and Lucile (Needham) S.; m. Inez Ruth Schoellerman, Sept. 18, 1948; children: Karen Brown, Teresa (Mrs. William J. Murphy), Roger, Linda (Mrs. Brian K. Abbott). B.S., U. Ill., 1943; postgrad., 1946-47, Advanced Mgmt. Program, Harvard Bus. Sch., 1964. Research asst. U. Ill., 1946-47; with GROWMARK (formerly FS Services, Inc.), Bloomington, Ill., 1947-82, sales edn. dir., 1947-49; dist. mgr. Growmark, Inc. (formerly FS Services, Inc.), 1950-51, mgr. feed div., 1952-55, asst. gen. mgr., 1956-67, v.p. ops., 1967-68, exec. v.p., chief exec. officer, 1968-82; exec. v.p., chief exec. officer Ill. Grain Corp., 1969-80; chmn. bd. CF Industries Inc., 1967-74, dir., 1957-77; pres. St. Louis Grain Corp., 1969-82; chmn. bd. Agri-Trans. Corp., 1977-82; past dir. Farmers Export Co., Nat. Council Farmer Coops., Internat. Energy Coop., LVO Internat., Nat. Potash Co., Nat. Coop. Refinery, 1st Nitrogen Corp., Central Nitrogen Inc., St. Paul Ammonia Products, Coop. Farm Chems. Past mem. adv. com. Ill. Bd. Higher Edn.; Past bd. dirs. U. Ill. Agrl. Alumni Assn. Served as pilot USNR, 1943-45. Recipient hon. state farmer degree Future Farmers Am., award of merit U. Ill. Agrl. Alumni Assn., 1975, Bronze tablet Phi Eta Sigma. Mem. Assn. Commerce, Farmhouse Frat., Phi Kappa Phi, Gamma Sigma Delta, Alpha Zeta, Ma-Wan-Da. Presbyterian. Home: 213 Fleetwood Dr Bloomington IL 61701-2026 Office: 1701 N Towanda Ave Bloomington IL 61701-2040

STEVENSON, GALE, librarian; b. Bklyn., Oct. 8, 1942; d. Clifford Edwin and Ruth Helen (Davis) Spates; m. Andrew Kenneth Stevenson Jr., Aug. 28, 1988. B.A, Drew U., 1964; MLS, Pratt Inst., 1970. Reference asst. Purdue U., West Lafayette, Ind., 1964-68; libr. Yonkers Pub. Libr., Yonkers, N.Y., 1968-71; adminstrv. svcs. libr. Westchester Community Coll., Valhalla, N.Y., 1971-78; libr. Tompkins County Pub. Libr., Ithaca, N.Y., 1978-88; libr. Bus. Libr., Bklyn. Pub. Libr., Bklyn., 1988—, sr. bus. libr., 1988-93; divsn. chief social scis. Bklyn. Pub. Libr., Bklyn., 1993-94, asst. bus/ libr., 1994—. Office: Bklyn Pub Libr Bus Libr 280 Cadman Plz West Brooklyn NY 11201

STEVENSON, HAROLD WILLIAM, psychology educator; b. Dines, Wyo., Nov. 19, 1924; s. Merlin R. and Mildred M. (Stodick) S.; m. Nancy Guy, Aug. 23, 1950; children: Peggy, Janet, Andrew, Patricia. BA, U. Colo., 1947; MA, Stanford U., 1948, PhD, 1951. Asst. prof. psychology Pomona Coll., 1950-53; asst. to asso. prof. psychology U. Tex., Austin, 1953-59; prof. child devel. and psychology, dir. Inst. Child Devel., U. Minn., Mpls., 1959-71; prof. psychology, fellow Center for Human Growth and Devel., U. Mich., Ann Arbor, 1971—; dir. program in child devel. and social policy U. Mich., 1978-93; adj. prof. Tohoku Fukushi Coll., Japan, 1989—, Peking U. 1990—, Inst. Psychology Chinese Acad. Scis.; mem. tng. com. Nat. Inst. Child Health and Human Devel., 1964-67; mem. personality and cognition study sect. NIMH, 1975-79; chmn. com. on child devel. Nat. Acad. Scis.-NRC, 1971-73; exec. com. div. behavioral scis. NRC, 1969-72; mem. del. early childhood People's Republic of China, 1973, mem. del. psychologists, 1980; mem. vis. com. Grad. Sch. Edn., Harvard U., 1979-86; fellow Center Advanced Studies in Behavioral Scis., 1967-68, 82-83, 89-90. Recipient J.M. Cattell Fellow award in applied psychology Am. Psychol. Soc., 1994. Fellow Am. Acad. Arts and Scis., Nat. Acad. Edn.; mem. APA (pres. divsn. devel. psychology 1964-65, G. Stanley Hall award 1988), Soc. Rsch. Child Devel. (mem. governing coun. 1961-67, pres. 1969-71, chmn. long-range planning com. 1971-74, mem. social policy com. 1977-85, mem. internat. affairs com. 1991-94, Disting. Rsch. award 1993), Internat. Soc. Study of Behavioral Devel. (mem. exec. com. 1972-77, pres. 1987-91), Phi Beta Kappa, Sigma Xi. Home: 1030 Spruce Dr Ann Arbor MI 48104-2847

STEVENSON, HOWARD HIGGINBOTHAM, business educator; b. Salt Lake City, June 27, 1941; s. Ralph Shields and Dorothy Dee (Higginbotham) S.; m. Fredericka O'Connell; children: William, Charles, Andrew. BS, Stanford U., 1963; MBA, Harvard U., 1965, DBA, 1969. Asst. prof. bus. Harvard U., Cambridge, Mass., 1968-72, assoc. prof., 1972-78, Sarofim Rock prof., 1982—, sr. assoc. dean for fin. adminstrn., 1991-94; v.p. Simmons Assocs., Boston, 1970-72; v.p. fin. adminstrn. Preco Corp., West Springfield, Mass., 1978-81; dir. Landmark Comms., Norfolk, Va., Camp Dresser and McKee Inc., Cambridge, Passamaquoddy Techs., Inc., Portland, Maine, The Baupost Group, Inc., Cambridge, Sheffield Steel, Waltham, Mass. Co-author: Policy Formation and Administration, 1984, New Business Ventures and the Entrepreneur, 1985, 89, 4th edit., 1994, Entrepreneurial Ventures, 1992. Trustee Rural Land Found., Lincoln, Mass., 1973-78, Boston Ballet, Suffield Land Conservancy, Conn., 1978-82, Sudbury Valley Trustees. IBM Nat. Merit scholar, 1959; Ford Found. fellow, 1965. Mem. Fin. Execs. Inst., Acad. Mgmt., Urban Land Inst. Club: Harvard (N.Y.C.), Longwood Cricket. Office: Baker Libr 366 Harvard U Boston MA 02163

STEVENSON, IAN, psychiatrist, educator; b. Montreal, Que., Can., Oct. 31, 1918; s. John Alexander and Ruth Cecilia (Preston); m. Octavia Reynolds, Sept. 13, 1947 (dec. Nov. 1983); m. 2d, Margaret H. Pertzoff, Nov. 29, 1985. Student, St. Andrews, Scotland; BS, McGill U., 1942, MD, CM, 1943. Cert. Am. Bd. Psychiatry, 1953. Asst. prof. medicine La. State U., New Orleans, 1949-52, assoc. prof. psychiatry, 1953-57; prof. psychiatry, chmn. U. Va. Sch. Medicine, Charlottesville, 1957-67, Carlson prof. psychiatry, head div. of personality studies, 1967—; assoc. mem. Darwin Coll., U. Cambridge, 1981—. Author: The Diagnostic Interview, 1960, Twenty Cases Suggestive of Reincarnation, 1966, 10 other books; contbr. 250 articles to profl. jours. Fellow Am. Psychiat. Assn. (life); mem. AAAS, Am. Anthropol. Assn., Soc. for Psychical Rsch., London (coun. mem. and pres. 1988-89), Am. Soc. for Psychical Rsch., Soc. for Sci. Exploration (founding com.), Colonnade Club (U. Va.). Office: U of Va Health Sci Ctr PO Box 152 Charlottesville VA 22902-0152

STEVENSON, JO ANN C., federal bankruptcy judge; b. 1942. AB, Rutgers U., 1965; JD cum laude, Detroit Coll. Law, 1979. Bar: Mich. 1979. Law clk. to Vincent J. Brennan, Mich. Ct. Appeals, Detroit, 1979; law clk. to Cornelia G. Kenendy, U.S. Ct. Appeals for 6th Cir., Detroit, 1980; assoc. Hertzberg, Jacob & Weingarten, P.C., Detroit, 1980-87; judge U.S. Bankruptcy Ct., Grand Rapids, Mich., 1987—. Office: US Bankruptcy Ct 712 Ford Fed Bldg PO Box 3310 Grand Rapids MI 49503

STEVENSON, JOHN REESE, lawyer; b. Chgo., Oct. 24, 1921; s. John A. and Josephine R. S.; m. Patience Fullerton, Apr. 10, 1943 (dec. 1982); children: Elizabeth F., Sally H. Stevenson Fischer, John R. Jr., Patience Stevenson Scott; m. Ruth Carter Johnson, May 21, 1983. AB summa cum laude, Princeton U., 1942; LL.B., Columbia U., 1949, D.J.S., 1952. Bar: N.Y. 1949, D.C. 1971, U.S. Supreme Ct. 1964. Assoc. Sullivan & Cromwell, N.Y.C., 1950-55, ptnr., 1956-69, 75-87; chmn., sr. ptnr. Sullivan & Cromwell, 1979-87, counsel, 1987-92; legal adv. with rank of asst. sec. U.S.

Dept. State, 1969-72, chmn. Adv. Com. on Pub. Internat. law, 1986-90, mem. com. 1993—, U.S. Dept. State; adviser U.S. del. Gen. Assembly UN, 1969-74; chmn. U.S. del. Internat. Conf. on Air Law, The Hague, 1970; mem. U.S. del. Internat. Conf. on Law of Treaties, Vienna, 1969; amb.. spl. rep. of Pres. Law of the Sea Conf., 1973-75; U.S. mem. Permanent Ct. of Arbitration, The Hague, 1969-79, 84-90; U.S. rep. Internat. Ct. Justice, Namibia (S.W. Africa) case, 1970; spl. counsel U.S. del. Delimitation of Maritime Boundary in Gulf of Maine (Can. vs. U.S.A.), 1984; mem. OAS Inter-Am. Commn. on Human Rights, 1987-90; dir. Ctr. for Strategic and Internat. Studies; prin. Ctr. Excellence in Govt.; bd. dirs. Bank N.Y., Americas Soc. Author: The Chilean Popular Front, 1952; editor-in-chief Columbia Law Rev.; contbr. articles to legal and State Dept. jours. Trustee Andrew W. Mellon Found., 1974-94; pres., trustee Nat. Gallery Art, 1975-93. Fellow ABA (hon.); mem. Am. Soc. Internat. Law (pres. 1966-68, hon. v.p. 1968-92, hon. pres. 1992-93), N.Y. State Bar Assn. (chmn. com. on internat. law 1963-65), Internat Law Assn., Institut de Droit Internat. (v.p. 1987-89), Assn. Bar City N.Y. (chmn. com. on internat. law 1958-61), Am. Arbitration Assn. (bd. dirs. 1984-92, exec. com., chmn. internat. sect. law com.), Coun. Fgn. Rels., Am. Law Inst., Links Club (N.Y.C.), Down Town Assn. (N.Y.C.), Met. Club (Washington), Chevy Chase Club, Burning Tree Club, Phi Beta Kappa. Home: 1819 Kalorama Sq NW Washington DC 20008-4021 Office: 1701 Pennsylvania Ave NW Washington DC 20006-5801

STEVENSON, JUSTIN JASON, III, lawyer; b. Cin., Nov. 4, 1941; s. Justin Jason and Anne (Hollister) S.; m. Ann Robinson, Oct. 23, 1971; children—Justin Jason, Christopher R., Catherine F. A.B., Princeton U., 1963; LL.B., Harvard U., 1966. Bar: N.Y. 1966. Assoc. Shearman & Sterling, N.Y.C., 1966-76, ptnr., 1976—. Served to 1st lt. AUS, 1966-69. Mem. Phi Beta Kappa. Office: 599 Lexington Ave New York NY 10022-6030

STEVENSON, KENNETH LEE, chemist, educator; b. Ft. Wayne, Ind., Aug. 1, 1939; s. Willard Henry and Luella Marie (Meyer) S.; m. Virginia Grace Lowe, Dec. 26, 1959 (dec. Mar. 1991); children: Melinda Anne, Jill Marie; m. Carmen Ramona Kmety, May 9, 1992. B.S., Purdue U., 1961, M.S., 1965; Ph.D., U. Mich., 1968. Tchr. Ladoga High Sch., Ind., 1961-63; tchr. Central High Sch., Pontiac, Mich., 1963-65; prof. chemistry Ind.-Purdue U., Ft. Wayne, 1968—, chmn. dept. chemistry, 1979-86, 87—, acting dean Sch. Sci. and Humanities, 1986-87; sabbatical visitor Solar Energy Research Inst., Golden, Colo., 1980; vis. faculty N.Mex. State U., Las Cruces, 1975-76. Author: Charge Transfer Photochemistry of Coordination Compounds, 1993, also numerous rsch. papers. Mem. Am. Chem. Soc. (chmn. Northeastern Ind. sect. 1978-79, Chemist of Yr. 1979, 93), Inter-Am. Photochem. Soc., Phi Kappa Phi, Sigma Xi. Office: Ind U-Purdue U Dept Chemistry Fort Wayne IN 46805

STEVENSON, MAROLANE, counselor; b. Bottineau, N.D., Mar. 31, 1942; d. Joseph and Lillian (Paryzek) Yellen; m. June 12, 1964. BA, Coll. of Idaho, 1964; MS, U. Utah, 1969; EdD, U. Mont., 1990. cert. psychology, sociology and guidance and counseling tchr./supr., prin., supt. Counselor Missoula County High Schs., dir. career ctr.; title I, ESL, ednl. counselor dept. continuing edn. U. Utah, Salt Lake City. Author: An Experimental Analysis of the Performance of Undergraduate Students on Verbal Reasoning Problems When Tested in Solitude and In A Non-Interacting Group. Recipient Gov.'s Citation for Meritorious Svc., State of Mont., 1980, YWCA Excellence award for Pub. Svc., 1992. Mem. NEA, Am. Counseling Assn., Am. Career Guidance Assn., Am. Sch. Counselor Assn., Mont. Counseling Assn. (pres. 1973-74, v.p., editor newsletter), Mont. Edn. Assn., Mont. Sch. Counselor Assn. (legis. chair, sec. vice chair, pub. rels. chair), Mont. Adv. Coun. for Vocat. Edn. (v.p. 1980-81), Phi Delta Kappa, Delta Kappa Gamma Soc. Internat. (N.W. regional dir. 1990-92, N.W. coord. of U.S. Forum, 1988-90, state pres. 1985-87). Home: 3910 Belle Ln Missoula MT 59801-8913

STEVENSON, MICHAEL ANSON, motion picture film editor; b. Culver City, Calif., Mar. 1, 1944; s. Anson Henry and Eileen Florence (Anderson) S.; m. Sandra Lee Engelker, July 15, 1967; children: Michelle Dawn, Stacey Reneé. Student, Santa Monica Coll., 1963-64. Apprentice editor Metro Goldwyn Meyer, Culver City, 1964-69, asst. film editor, 1970-76; film editor Columbia Pictures, Burbank, Calif., 1977-84, Universal Pictures/Warner Bros., Burbank, 1985-86, Walt Disney Pictures, Burbank, 1987-90, 95, 20th Century Fox, Century City, Calif., 1991-92, Tri Star Pictures, Culver City, 1992-93, Propaganda Films, Hollywood, Calif., 1994, Topaz Enterprises Inc., Valley Village, Calif., 1994—. Staff sgt. USAR, 1965-71. Recipient Emmy nomination NATAS. Mem. Am. Cinema Editors (Eddie nomination), Acad. Motion Picture Arts and Scis. Office: Topaz Enterprises Inc 5140 Colfax Ave Ste 150 Valley Village CA 91601

STEVENSON, NIKOLAI, medical association executive; b. N.Y.C., Apr. 20, 1919; s. Milivoy Stoyan Stanoyevich and Beatrice Louise Stevenson; m. Shirley Gray, Jan. 20, 1951; children: Nanette, Matthew, Julie. BA, Columbia U., 1940. Sales mgr. Nat. Sugar Refining Co., N.Y.C., 1947-54; v.p. Olavarria & Co., N.Y.C., 1954-64; founder, sr. ptnr. Stevenson, Montgomery and Clayton, N.Y.C., 1966-82; pres. Assn. for Macular Diseases, N.Y.C., 1980—; condr. ednl. seminars in field; bd. dirs. Harper's Mag. Lectr. and contbg. author Harper's Mag., Am. Heritage, Atlantic Monthly. Col. USMCR. 1940-46. Decorated Silver Star, Bronze Star. Mem. Mayflower Descendants, Soc. of Colombia U., Sugar Club, Manhasset Bay Yacht Club, City Midday Club, Phi Gamma Delta. Episcopalian. Home: 18 Sands Ct Port Washington NY 11050 Office: Assn for Macular Diseases 210 E 64th St New York NY 10021

STEVENSON, PAUL MICHAEL, physics educator, researcher; b. Denham, Eng., Oct. 10, 1954; came to U.S., 1983; s. Jeremy and Jean Helen (Jennings) S. BA, Cambridge (Eng.) U., 1976; PhD, Imperial Coll., London, 1979. Rsch. assoc. U. Wis., Madison, 1979-81, 1983-84; fellow European Orgn. for Nuclear Rsch., Geneva, 1981-83; sr. rsch. assoc. Rice U., Houston, 1984-86, asst. prof. physics, 1986-89, assoc. prof., 1989-93; prof. physics, 1993—. Contbr. articles to profl. jours. Avocation: music.

STEVENSON, PHILIP DAVIS, lawyer; b. Canton, Republic of China, Sept. 15, 1936; s. Donald Day and Lois (Davis) S.; m. Carol Rusch, June 14, 1958 (div. 1975); children: Katherine, Ross; m. Joan Ann Lukey, Oct. 8, 1976. BA, Yale U., 1958, LLB, 1961. Assoc. Robbins, Noyes & Jansen, Boston, 1961-69; assoc. Hale and Dorr, Boston, 1969-71, jr. ptnr., 1971-75, sr. ptnr., 1975—, chmn. real estate dept., 1984-90. Contbr. articles on Mass. continuing legal edn. Mem. Weston (Mass.) Planning Bd., 1968-73, chmn., 1973. Mem. ABA, Am. Coll. Real Estate Lawyers, Mass. Bar Assn., Boston Bar Assn., N.H. Bar Assn., Abstract Club. Democrat. Unitarian. Avocations: sailing, skiing. Office: Hale & Dorr 60 State St Boston MA 02109-1816

STEVENSON, ROBERT EDWIN, microbiologist, culture collection executive; b. Columbus, Ohio, Dec. 2, 1926; s. Arthur Edwin and Mary Lucille (Beman) S. BS, Ohio State U., 1947, MS, 1950, PhD, 1954. Cert. Am. Bd. Microbiology. Virologist USPHS, Cin., 1954-58; head cell culture sect., Tissue Bank U.S. Naval Med. Sch., Bethesda, Md., 1958-60; head cell culture and tissue material sect. Nat. Cancer Inst., Bethesda, 1960-63, chief viral carcinogenesis br., 1963-67; mgr. biolog. scis., corp. devel. dept. Union Carbide Corp., Tarrytown, N.Y., 1967-72; v.p., gen. mgr., Frederick (Md.) div. Litton Bionetics, 1972-80; dir. Am. Type Culture Collection, Rockville, Md., 1980-93; dir. emeritus, 1993; dir. Large Scale Biology, Inc., Rockville, 1984—; chmn. biotech. adv. com. Dept. Commerce, Washington, 1985-93. With USN, 1944-45. Fellow Inst. for Soc., Ethics & Life Scis.; mem. Tissue Culture Assn. (pres. 1988-90), World Fedn. Culture Collections, U.S. Fedn. Culture Collections (pres. 1988-90), Am. Soc. Micrbiology, Cosmos Club (Washington). Episcopalian. Avocations: painting, cross country skiing. Home: PO Box 709 21 Ducks Head New Castle NH 03854

STEVENSON, ROBERT EVERETT, oceanography consultant; b. Fullerton, Calif., Jan. 15, 1921; s. Jeani M. Wetzel, June 29, 1988; children: Michael G., Robert K. AA, Fullerton Jr. Coll., 1941; AB, UCLA, 1946, AM, 1948; PhD, U. So. Calif. 1954. Teng. asst. UCLA, 1946; instr. Compton (Calif.) Coll., 1947-49; lectr. U. So. Calif., L.A., 1949-51, dir. inshore rsch. Hancock Found., 1953-59, 60-61; spl. rsch. oceanographer U.S. Office Naval Rsch., London, 1959; rsch. scientist dept. oceanography and meteorology Tex. A&M U., College Station, 1961-62, dir. marine lab., prof.

Grad. Sch., 1963-63; rsch. scientist Oceanographic Inst., assoc. prof. Fla. State U., Tallahassee, 1963-65; acting asst. lab. dir. Bur. Comml. Fisheries Biol. Lab., Galveston, Tex., 1965-66, asst. lab. dir., 1966-70, acting lab. dir., 1969; sci. liaison officer Office Naval Rsch., Scripps Instn. Oceanography, La Jolla, Calif., 1970-88, dep. dir. space oceanography, 1985-88; oceanography cons., Del Mar, Calif., 1988—; vis. scientist Am. Geophys. Union, 1963; disting. lectr. Am. Assn. Petroleum Geologists, 1969-72. Contbr. articles to sci. jours. With USAAF, 1941-43, 46; faculty Westminster Choir Coll., Princeton, N.Y., 1946-49. Decorated DFC, Air medal with four oak leaf clusters; recipient numerous awards Office Naval Rsch. and NASA. Fellow Geol. Soc. Am., Internat. Assn. for Phys. Scis. of Ocean (dep. sec. gen. 1985-87, sec. gen. 1987—, Marine Luftschiffer Kamradschaft (N.Y.), Order of Decibel, Sigma Xi. Home and Office: PO Box 689 Del Mar CA 92014-0689

STEVENSON, ROBERT MURRELL, music educator; b. Melrose, N.Mex., July 3, 1916; s. Robert Emory and Ada (Ross) S. AB, U. Tex., El Paso, 1936; grad., Juilliard Grad. Sch. Music, 1938; MusM, Yale, 1939; PhD, U. Rochester, 1942; STB cum laude, Harvard U., 1943; BLitt, Oxford (Eng.) U.; Th.M., Princeton U.; DMus honoris causa, Cath. U. Am., 1991; LHD (honoris causa), Ill. Wesleyan U., 1992; Litt honoris causa, Universidade Nova de Lisboa, 1993. Instr. music U. Tex., 1941-43, 46; faculty Westminster Choir Coll., Princeton, N.Y., 1946-49; faculty research lectr. UCLA, 1981, mem. faculty to prof. music, 1949—; vis. asst. prof. Columbia, 1955-56; vis. prof. Ind. U., Bloomington, 1959-60, U. Chile, 1965-66, Northwestern U., Chgo., 1976, U. Granada, 1992; cons. UNESCO, 1977; Louis Charles Elson lectr. Libr. of Congress, Washington, 1969. Author: Music in Mexico, 1952, Patterns of Protestant Church Music, 1953, La musica en la catedral de Sevilla, 1954, 85, Music before the Classic Era, 1955, Shakespeare's Religious Frontier, 1958, The Music of Peru, 1959, Juan Bermudo, 1960, Spanish Music in the Age of Columbus, 1960, Spanish Cathedral Music in the Golden Age, 1961, La musica colonial en Colombia, 1964, Protestant Church Music in America, 1966, Music in Aztec and Inca Territory, 1968, Renaissance and Baroque Musical Sources in the Americas, 1970, Music in El Paso, 1970, Philosophies of American Music History, 1970, Written Sources For Indian Music Until 1882, 1973, Christmas Music from Baroque Mexico, 1974, Foundations of New World Opera, 1973, Seventeenth Century Villancicos, 1974, Latin American Colonial Music Anthology, 1975, Vilancicos Portugueses, 1976, Josquin in the Music of Spain and Portugal, 1977, American Musical Scholarship, Parker to Thayer, 1978, Liszt at Madrid and Lisbon, 1980, Wagner's Latin American Outreach, 1983, Spanish Musical Impact Beyond the Pyrenees, 1250-1500, 1985, La Música en las catedrales españolas del Sigle de Oro, 1993; contbg. editor: Handbook Latin Am. Studies, 1976—; editor: Inter-Am. Music Rev, 1978—; contbr. to: New Grove Dictionary of Music and Musicians, 17 other internat. encys. Served to capt. U.S. Army, 1943-46, 49. Decorated Army Commendation ribbon; fellow Ford Found., 1953-54, Gulbenkian Found., 1966, 81, Guggenheim Found., 1962, NEH, 1974, Comité Conjunto Hispano-Norteamericano (Madrid), 1989; recipient Fulbright rsch. awards, 1958-59, 64, 70-71, 88-89, Carnegie Found. tchg. award, 1955-56, Gabriela Mistral award OAS, 1985, Heitor Villa Lobos Jury award OAS, 1988, OAS medal, 1986, Cert. Merit Mexican Consulate San Bernardino, Calif., 1987, Silver medal Spanish Ministry Culture, 1989, Gold medal Real Conservatorio Superior, 1994. Mem. Am. Musicol. Soc. (hon. life, Pacific SW chpt.), Real Academia de Bellas Artes, Hispanic Soc. Am., Am. Liszt soc. (cons. editor), Heterofonia (cons. editor), Brazilian Musicol. Soc. (hon.), Portuguese Musicol. Soc. (hon.), Argentinian Musicol. Soc. (hon.), Orden Andrés Bello, Primera Clase, Venezuela, 1992. Avocation: playing piano. Office: UCLA Dept Music 405 Hilgard Ave Los Angeles CA 90024-1301 *American achievements are as nothing unless they are written about and remembered. My mission has been to rescue the musical past of the Americas. Present-day composers are too busy making their own music to worry about their predecessors. As a result, every new generation of composers thinks that they are the first ones to descry Mount Olympus. Not so. The past is a succession of musical and artistic glories.*

STEVENSON, ROBERT W., technologies company executive, financial officer. BA in Econs., Stanford U., 1961; MBA, U. Pa., 1963. Analyst fin. forecasting Boeing Co., 1963, supr. accounts receivable, 1963-64, mgr. fin. statements and planning, 1964-67, project fin. mgr., 1967-68; asst. contr. Criton Techs., 1968, contr., 1968-70, asst. v.p., contr., 1970-72, asst. v.p. sec., 1972-73, asst. v.p.; sec. treas., 1973-75, sr. v.p., CFO, 1985-87, exec. v.p., CFO, 1987-89; exec. v.p., CFO Esterline Techs. Corp., Bellevue, Wash., 1987—. Mem. Fin. Execs. Inst. Office: Esterline Techs Corp 10800 NE 8th St Fl 6 Bellevue WA 98004-4428

STEVENSON, RUSSELL B., JR., lawyer; b. 1941. B.M.E., Cornell U., 1964; J.D., Harvard U., 1969. Bar: D.C. 1970. Assoc. Surrey, Karasik, Greene & Hill, Washington, 1969-71; project dir. Environ. Law Inst., Washington, 1971; assoc. prof. George Washington U. Law Ctr., Washington, 1971-75, prof., 1975-81; dep. gen. counsel SEC, Washington, 1981-83; of counsel Hale and Dorr, Washington, 1984-86, ptnr. 1886-89; ptnr. Pepper, Hamilton & Scheetz, Washington, 1989-93; now mem. Ballard, Spahr, Andrews & Ingersoll, Wash.; vis. assoc. prof. Cornell U., 1974; vis. prof., Fulbright lectr. U. Paris-I, 1977-78; chmn. City at Peace Inc.; mem. exec. com. Washington Lawyers Com. for Civil Rights Under Law; dir. D.C. Law Students in Ct. Served to lt. j.g. USN, 1964-66. Mem. ABA, Internat. Law Assn., Am. Soc. Internat. Law, Washington Council Lawyers (pres.). Co-author: Environmental Improvement through Economic Incentives, 1977; Corporations: Law and Policy, 1982; author: Corporations and Information: Secrecy, Access and Disclosure, 1980; former mng. editor Harvard Civil Rights-Civil Liberties Law Rev. Office: Ballard Spahr Andrews & Ingersoll 555 13th St NW Washington DC 20004

STEVENSON, WARREN HOWARD, mechanical engineering educator; b. Rock Island, Ill., Nov. 18, 1938; s. Joseph Howard and Camilla Irene (Darnall) S.; m. Judith Ann Fleener, June 7, 1959; children: Kathleen, Kevin, Kent. BSME, Purdue U., 1960, MSME, 1963, PhD, 1965. Engr. Martin Co., Denver, 1960-61; rsch. asst., instr. Purdue U., West Lafayette, Ind., 1961-65, asst. prof., 1965-68, assoc. prof., 1968-74, prof., 1974—; asst. dean engring., 1992—; guest prof. U. Karlsruhe, Fed. Republic Germany, 1973-74; mem. tech. conf. coms. various profl. groups. Editor: Laser Velocimetry and Particle Sizing, 1979; mem. editorial bd. Jour. Laser Applications, 1988—; contbr. articles to profl. jours.; patentee in field. U.S. sr. scientist Alexander von Humboldt Found., Fed. Republic Germany, 1973. Fellow Laser Inst. Am. (bd. dirs. 1984—, pres. 1989); mem. ASME, Optical Soc. Am. Avocations: sailing, photography. Office: Purdue U Sch Mech Engring Applied Optics Lab West Lafayette IN 47907

STEVENSON, WILLIAM ALEXANDER, retired justice of Supreme Court of Canada; b. Edmonton, Alta., Can., May 7, 1934; s. Alexander Lindsy and Eileen Harriet (Burns) S.; m. Patricia Ann Stevenson; children: Catherine, Kevin, Vivian, James. BA, U. Alta., Edmonton, 1956, LLB, 1957; LLD (hon.), U. Alta., 1992. Called to Alta. bar, 1958. Ptnr. Hurlburt Reynolds Stevenson & Agrios, Edmonton, 1957-68; prof. U. Alta. 1968-70; ptnr. Reynolds Stevenson & Agrios, Edmonton, 1970-75; judge Dist. Ct. Alta., Edmonton, 1975-79; justice Ct. of Queens Bench Alta., Edmonton, 1979-80, Ct. of Appeal Alta., Edmonton, 1980-90, Supreme Ct. Can., Ottawa, Ont., 1990-92. Co-author: Civil Procedure Guide, 1992. Mem. Can. Bar Assn., Can. Inst. for Adminstrn. Justice (pres. 1983-85, hon. dir.), Nat. Jud. Inst. (hon. dir.). Home: 7 Laurier Pl, Edmonton, AB Canada T5R 5P4

STEVENSON, WILLIAM ALEXANDER, architect; b. Wilmington, Del., Nov. 17, 1940; s. Beverly Payne and Sarah (Cobb) S.; m. Roberta Louise Porcello, Feb. 8, 1969; children: Alexander William, Christopher James. BArch, Cornell U., 1963. Registered architect Mich., Ind., Ill., Ohio, N.Y., Conn. Architect Greiner Inc., Grand Rapids, Mich., 1969-74; architect Daverman, Grand Rapids, Mich., 1974-78, v.p., dir. design, 1978-82; v.p., dir. mktg. Greiner Inc., Grand Rapids, Mich., 1982-86; v.p., dir. Greiner Inc., Grand Rapids, 1986—. Designs: Lake Hills Elementary Sch. (AIA design award 1972), Calder Plaza Office Bldg. (AIA design award 1980), Ledyard Bldg. (AIA Hist. award 1987). Bd. dirs. Camp Blodgett for underprivileged children, 1988—, Goodwill Industries, 1988—. Mem. AIA. Republican. Episcopalian. Avocations: skiing, running, gardening, cooking. Office: Greiner Inc 3950 Sparks Dr SE Grand Rapids MI 49546

STEVENSON, WILLIAM HENRI, author; b. London, June 1, 1924; s. William and Alida (Deleporte) S.; m. Glenys Rowe, July 28, 1945; children: Andrew, Jacqueline, Kevin, Sally. Student, Royal Navy Coll., 1942. Fgn. corr. Toronto (Ont., Can.) Star, 1948-58; Toronto Globe & Mail, 1958-63, Ind. TV News, London, Eng., 1964-66, CBC, 1966-77; ind. writer, broadcaster, 1977—. Author: Travels In and Around Red China, 1957, Rebels in Indonesia, 1964, Chronicles of the Israeli Air Force, 1971, A Man Called Intrepid, 1976, Ninety Minutes at Entebbe, 1976. The Ghosts of Africa, 1981; producer: TV documentaries; movie screenplays include The Bushbabies, 1970. Served as aviator Royal Navy, 1942-45. Mem. Assn. Naval Aviation U.S.A., Authors Guild, Royal Overseas League (London). Mem. Progressive Conservative Party Can. Mem. Church of England. Clubs: Royal Bermuda Yacht, Royal Hong Kong Yacht. Office: care Paul Gitlin Agy 7 W 51st St New York NY 10019-6910

STEVER, DONALD WINFRED, lawyer; b. Altoona, Pa., Jan. 25, 1944; s. Donald Winfred and June Lily (Bargfrede) S.; m. Betsy Jean Seaman, May 28, 1968 (div. Oct. 1975); 1 child, Heather Elene; m. Margo Leaman Taft, July 30, 1976; children: David Whittaker, James Taft. BA, Lehigh U., 1965; JD, U. Pa., 1968. Bar: Conn. 1968, N.H. 1969, D.C. 1983, N.Y. 1983, U.S. Dist. Ct. N.H. 1969, U.S. Dist. Ct. Conn. 1986, U.S. Dist. Ct. (so. dist.) N.Y. 1985, U.S. Dist. Ct. (no. and we. dists.) N.Y. 1990, U.S. Ct. Appeals (1st cir.) 1974, U.S. Ct. Appeals (10th cir.) 1980, U.S. Ct. Appeals (5th, 11th and Fed. cirs.) 1982, U.S. Ct. Appeals (2d cir.) 1990, U.S. Supreme Ct. 1972. Atty. Aetna Life & Casualty co., Hartford, Conn., 1968-69, Office of N.H. Atty. Gen., Concord, 1969-72; asst. atty. gen., chief environ. protection Office of N.H. Atty. Gen., 1972-77; atty. pollution control sect. U.S. Dept. Justice, Washington, 1978-79, chief pollution control sect., 1979-80; chief environ. def. sect. U.S. Dept. Justice, 1980-82; prof. Pace U. Sch. Law, White Plains, N.Y., 1982-87; adj. prof. environ. law Pace U. Sch. Law, 1987—; ptnr. Sidley and Austin, N.Y.C., 1987-93, Dewey Ballantine, N.Y.C., 1993—; bd. dirs. Environ. Law Inst., Washington, Hudson Valley Writers Ctr. Inc., Tarrytown, N.Y. Author: Seabrook and The Nuclear Regulatory Commission, 1980; Law of Chemical Reation and Hazardous Waste, 1986; editor: Environmental Law & Practice, 1992; co-editor Environmental Law & Practice, 1992. Bd. dirs. Biddeford Pool (Maine) Improvement Assn., 1989—; mem. adv. com. North Tarrytown (N.Y.) Conservation, 1989—. Mem. Biddeford Pool Yacht Club (treas. 1989-92, sec. 1992—), Sleepy Hollow Country Club, Abenakee Club, Mill Reef Club. Avocations: tennis, sailboat racing, early music. Home: 157 Millard Ave Tarrytown NY 10591-1412 Office: Dewey Ballantine 1301 Ave of the Americas New York NY 10019

STEVER, HORTON GUYFORD, aerospace scientist and engineer, educator, consultant; b. Corning, N.Y., Oct. 24, 1916; s. Ralph Raymond and Alma (Matt) S.; m. Louise Risley Floyd, June 29, 1946; children: Horton Guyford, Sarah, Margarette, Roy. A.B., Colgate U., 1938, Sc.D. (hon.), 1958; Ph.D., Calif. Inst. Tech., 1941; LL.D., Lafayette Coll., U. Pitts., 1966, Lehigh U., 1967, Allegheny Coll., 1968, Ill. Inst. Tech., 1975; D.Sc., Northwestern U., 1966, Waynesburg Coll., 1967, U. Mo., 1975, Clark U., 1976, Bates Coll., 1977; D.H., Seton Hill Coll., 1968; D.Engring., Washington and Jefferson Coll., 1969, Widener Coll., Poly. Inst. N.Y., 1972, Villanova U., 1973, U. Notre Dame, 1974; D.P.S., George Washington U., 1981. Mem. staff radiation lab. MIT, Cambridge, 1941-42; asst. prof. MIT, 1946-51, asso. prof. aero. engring., 1951-56, prof. aero. and astro., 1956-65, head depts. mech. engring., naval architecture, marine engring., 1961-65, asso. dean engring., 1956-59, exec. officer guided missiles program, 1946-48; chief scientist USAF, 1955-56; pres. Carnegie-Mellon U., Pitts., 1965-72; dir. NSF, Washington, 1972-76; sci. adviser, chmn. Fed. Council Sci. and Tech., 1973-76; dir. Office Sci. and Tech. Policy, sci. and tech. adviser to Pres., 1976-77, sci. cons., corp. trustee, 1977—; mem. secretariat guided missiles com. Joint Chiefs of Staff, 1945; sci. liaison officer London Mission, OSRD, 1942-45; mem. guided missiles tech. evaluation group Research and Devel. Bd., 1946-48; mem. sci. adv. bd. to chief of staff USAF, 1947-69, chmn., 1962-69; mem. steering com. tech. adv panel on aeros. Dept. Def., 1956-62; chmn. spl. com. space tech. NASA, chmn. research adv. com. missile and spacecraft aerodynamics, 1959-65; mem. Nat. Sci. Bd., 1970-72, mem. exofficio, chmn. exec. com., 1972-75; mem. Def. Sci. Bd., 1962-68; mem. adv. panel U.S. Ho. Reps. Com. Sci. and Astronautics, 1959-72; mem. Pres.'s Commn. on Patent System, 1965-67; chmn. U.S.-USSR Joint Commn. Sci. and Tech. Cooperation, 1973-77, Fed. Council Arts and Humanities, 1972-76; Pres. com. Nat. Sci. medal, 1973-77. Author: Flight, 1965; Contbr. articles to profl. publs. Past trustee Colgate U., Shady Side Acad., Sarah Mellon Scaife Found., Buckingham Sch.; truste Univ. Rsch Assn., 1977—, pres., 1982-85; trustee Woods Hole Oceanographic Inst., 1980—, Univ .Corp. for Atmospheric Rsch., 1980-83; bd. dirs. Saudi Arabia Nat. Ctr. for Sci. and Tech., 1978-81; bd. govs. U.S. Israel Binat. Sci. Found., 1972-76, chmn., 1972-73; mem. Carnegie Commn. on Sci., Tech. and Govt., 1988-93. Recipient Pres.'s Cert. of Merit, 1948, Exceptional Civilian Svc. award USAF, 1956, Scott Gold medal Am. Ordnance Assn., 1960, Disting. Pub. Svc. medal Dept. Def., 1969, NASA, 1988, Nat. Medal of Sci., 1991; comdr. Order of Merit Poland. Fellow AIAA (hon., pres. 1960-62), AAAS, Royal Aero. Soc., Am. Acad. Arts and Scis., Royal Soc. Arts, Am. Phys. Soc.; mem. NAS (chmn. assembly engring. 1979-83), NAE (chmn. aero. and space engring. bd. 1967-69, fgn. sec. 1984-88), Acad. Engring. of Japan (fgn. mem.), Royal Acad. of Engring. of Great Britain (fgn. mem.), Cosmos Club, Bohemian, Phi Beta Kappa, Sigma Xi, Sigma Gamma Tau, Tau Beta Pi. Episcopalian. Office: 1528 33d St NW Washington DC 20007

STEVES, GALE C., editor; b. Mineola, N.Y., Dec. 20, 1942; d. William Henry and Ruth (May) S.; m. David B. Stocher, Mar. 31, 1972 (div. Apr. 1978); Philip L. Perrone, Aug. 14, 1983. BS, Cornell U., 1964; MA, NYU, 1966. Editorial asst. Ladies Home Jour., N.Y.C., 1966-69; seafood consumer specialist U.S. Dept. Commerce, N.Y.C., 1969-73; editor food Homelife mag., N.Y.C., 1973-74; editor food and equipment Co-Ed mag., N.Y.C., 1974-76, Am. Home mag., N.Y.C., 1976-78; editor kitchen design and equipment Woman's Day mag., N.Y.C., 1978-83; editor-in-chief Woman's Day Spls., N.Y.C., 1983—; bd. dirs. Les Dames d'Escoffier, N.Y.C., Council of Sr. Ctrs. and Services of N.Y.C.; mem. editorial bd. Sr. Summary, N.Y.C., 1982-88. Author: Game Cookery, 1974, The International Cook, 1980, Creative Microwave Cooking, 1981, (with Lee M. Elman) Country Weekend Cooking. Mem. Am. Home Econs. Assn., Am. Soc. Mag. Editors, Omicron Nu. Club: Elec. Woman's Round Table. Office: Home Magazine Group 1633 Broadway New York NY 10019

STEVOS, JOYCE LOUISE, education director; b. Providence, May 22, 1943; d. Josephus Caldwell and Patricia Anita (Strong) Caldwell Smith; m. Manuel Joseph Stevos, Oct. 22, 1966 (div. Jan. 1981); 1 child, Manuel Joaquim. BEd, R.I. Coll., 1965. Cert. tchr. and prin., R.I. Tchr. Providence Sch. Dept., 1975-76, social studies dept. head, 1971-76, supr. social studies, 1976-80, dir. program and staff devel., 1990-92, dir. strategic planning and profl. devel., 1992—; cons. in field. Author: The Constitution, 1977, 87. Pres. Urban League R.I., Providence, 1983-87. Recipient Never Again award Jewish Fedn. R.I., 1983, Community Svc. award John Hope settlement House, 1987, Edn. award Providence NAACP, 1991, Nat. Educator award Milken Family Found., 1992. Mem. NCCJ (trustee, program com.), DAR, Nat. Coun. for Social Studies (membership com., sec. 1979-80, Carter G. Woodson Book Award com. 1994—), Social Studies Suprs. Assn. (sec. 1979-80), R.I. Black Heritage Soc. (pres. 1989—), Delta Sigma Theta (treas. 1989-91, scholarship). Avocations: cooking, family history, reading. Home: 57 Althea St Providence RI 02907-2801 Office: Providence Sch Dept 797 Westminster St Providence RI 02903-4018

STEWARD, H. LEIGHTON, oil company executive; b. Fairfield, Tex., Dec. 1, 1934; s. Hugh Birt and Lucille (Riley) S.; m. Lynda Brady, June 6, 1959; children; Leighton Brady, Blake Worth. B.S. in Geology, So. Meth. U., 1958, M.S. in Geology, 1960. Chief exploration ops. Shell Oil Co., Houston, 1977-79; v.p. energy and minerals Burlington No. Inc., Billings, Mont., 1979-81; exec v.p., pres. office Kilroy Co. of Tex., Houston, 1981-82; v.p.-exec., then exec. v.p. La. Land & Exploration Co., New Orleans, 1982-84, pres., chief operating officer, 1984-88, chmn., chief exec. officer, pres., 1989—; chmn. LL&E Petroleum Mktg. Inc., LL&E Pipeline Corp., LL&E (U.K.) Inc. Served to capt. USAF, 1959-62. Mem. Am. Assn. Petroleum Geologists, Am. Petroleum Inst. (bd. dirs. 1985-86), Mid Continent Oil and Gas Assn. Republican. Clubs: New Orleans Country Club; New Orleans Petroleum. *

STEWARD, JERRY WAYNE, air transportation executive consultant; b. Tulia, Tex., Mar. 22, 1945; s. Joe M. and mary Evelyn (Boggs) S.; m. Peggy L. Thomas, Nov. 18, 1978 (div. May 1993); children: Eric, Chalynda, Julie. AMT, Spartan Aeronautics, Tulsa, 1965. Dir. quality control Braniff, Dallas, Orlando, Tex., Fla., 1966-90; dir. tech. svcs. Polaris Aircraft Leasing, San Francisco, 1990-94; cons. Roanoke, Tex., 1994—. With U.S. Army, 1966-69. Avocations: hunting, fishing, travel. Home and Office: 1820 Summer Ln Roanoke TX 76262-9129

STEWARD, WELDON CECIL, architecture educator, architect, consultant; b. Pampa, Tex., Apr. 7, 1934; s. Weldon C. and Lois (Maness) S.; m. Mary Jane Nedbalek, June 9, 1956; children: Karen A., W. Craig. Cert. in architecture and planning, Ecole des Beaux Arts, Fontainebleu, France, 1956; B.Arch., Tex. A&M U, 1957; M.S. in architecture, Columbia U., 1961; LHD (hon.), Drury Coll., 1991. Registered architect, Tex., Nebr. Designer Perkins & Will, Architects, White Plains, N.Y., 1961-62; asst. prof. architecture Tex. A&M U., College Station, 1962-67, assoc. chmn. Sch. Architecture, 1966-69, assoc. dean, prof. Coll. Environ. Design, 1969-73; dean, prof. Coll. Architecture U. Nebr., Lincoln, 1973—; ednl. cons. People's Republic of China, 1979; project dir. Imo State U. Planning, Nigeria, 1981-88; vis. prof. Tong ji U., Shanghai, 1984; hon. prof. N.W. Inst. Architects Engrs., Xian, 1989; specialist Design USA, USSR, 1990; co-chmn. nat. coordination com. AIA Nat. Coun. Archtl. Registration Bd. Intership, Washington, 1980-81; bd. visitors Drury Coll., 1980—, Coll. Arch. U. Miami, Fla., 1993—; mem. nat. design rev. bd. GSA, Washington, 1994—; mem. founding bd. dirs. East/West Pacific Arch., U. Hawaii, 1995—; vice chmn. Design Futures Coun., Reston, Va., 1995—. Designer, Quinnipiac Elem. Sch., New Haven, Conn., 1961 (Am Assn. Sch. Adminstrs. Exhibit 1969), J.J. Buser Residence, Bryan, Tex., 1969, Steward Urban Residence, Lincoln, Nebr., 1994. Mem. Lincoln Architects, Engrs. Selection Bd., 1979-88; mem. Nat. Com. for U.S., China Rels., N.Y.C., 1981—, Nebr. Capitol Environ. Commn., 1989—; profl. adviser, nat. design competition Wick Alumni Ctr., Lincoln, 1981; mem. steering com. Internat. Coun. Tall Bldgs., 1992—. Grad. fellow Columbia U., 1960. Fellow AIA (pres. Brazos chpt. 1969, chmn. profl. devel. com. 1976-80, bd. dirs. 1987-90, dir. Cen. States 1987-90, nat. treas. 1991-92); mem. Nebr. Soc. Architects (bd. dirs. 1977—), Archtl. Found. Nebr. (bd. dirs. 1981—, treas. 1981—), Assn. Collegiate Schs. Architecture (bd. dirs. 1975-79), Nat. Archtl. Accrediting Bd. (bd. dirs. 1986-89, pres. 1988-89), Kazakhstan Union Architects, Aiamse Siamese Architects (hon.), Royal Inst. Canadian Architects, Fedn. Mexican Architects, Japan Inst. Architects, Tau Sigma Delta, Phi Kappa Phi, Phi Beta Delta. Home: 125 N 11th St Lincoln NE 68508-3605 Office: U Nebr Coll Architecture Lincoln NE 68588

STEWART, ALBERT CLIFTON, college dean, marketing educator; b. Detroit, Nov. 25, 1919; s. Albert Queely and Jeanne Belle (Kaiser) S.; m. Colleen Moore Hyland, June 25, 1949. BS, U. Chgo., 1942, MS, 1948; PhD, St. Louis U., 1951. Chemist Sherwin Williams Paint Co., Chgo.; rsch. asst. dept. chemistry U. Chgo., 1947-48; instr. chemistry St. Louis U., 1949-51; exec. Union Carbide Corp., Danbury, Conn., 1951-84; prof. mktg. Western Conn. State U., Danbury, 1984—, dean Sch. of Bus., 1987-90; cons. Ford Found., 1963-69, Union Carbide Corp., 1984—; bd. dirs. Exec Register, Inc., Danbury, 1985-90; assoc. Execom, Darien, Conn., 1986-90. Patentee in field. Bd. dirs. Am. Mus. Natural History, N.Y.C., 1976-85, .N.Y.C. Philharm., 1975-80; arbiter Am. Arbitration Assn., N.Y.C., Danbury; active town Coun., Oak Ridge, Tenn., 1953-57. Lt. (j.g.) USNR, World War II. Recipient Cert. of Merit Soc. Chem. Professions, Cleve., 1962. Mem. Am. Mktg. Assn., Sigma Xi. Club: Rotary (Cleve., N.Y.C.). Home: 28 Hearthstone Dr Brookfield CT 06804-3006 Office: Western Conn State U 181 White St Danbury CT 06810-6845

STEWART, ALBERT ELISHA, safety engineer, industrial hygienist; b. Urbana, Mo., Dec. 20, 1927; s. Albert E. and Maurine (Lighter) S.; m. Elizabeth O. Tice, May 31, 1958 (div.); children: Sheryl E., Mical A. BA, U. Kans., 1949; MS, U. Mo., 1958, MBA, 1970; PhD, Western States U., 1984. Registered profl. engr., Calif., cert. safety engr., cert. indsl. hygenist. Sales engr. Kaiser Aluminum and Chem. Co., Toledo, 1949-56; tchr. Kansas City (Mo.) Pub. Schs., 1959-65; indsl. hygienist Bendix Corp., Kansas City, 1960-65; safety adminstr. Gulf R&D, Merriam, Kans., 1968-71; sr. indsl. hygienist USDOL-OSHA, Kansas City, 1971-77; pres. Stewart Indsl. Hygiene, Kansas City, 1977—; adj. prof. Cen. Mo. State U. Mem. Boy Scouts Am. With U.S. Army, 1950-53. Mem. Am. Indsl. Hygiene Assn., Am. Chem. Soc., Am. Acad. Indsl. Hygiene, Am. Soc. Safety Engrs., Am. Welding Soc., Nat. Mgmt. Assn., Nat. Sci. Tchrs. Assn., Adminstrv. Govt. Soc., Am. Legion Post 596, DAV, ARC, Alpha Chi Sigma. Episcopalian. Avocations: fishing, golf, travel. Office: Stewart Indsl Hygiene & Safety Inc 8029 Brooklyn St Kansas City MO 64132

STEWART, ALEC THOMPSON, physicist; b. Windthorst, Sask., Can., June 18, 1925; s. Arthur and Nelly Blye (Thompson) S.; m. Alta Aileen Kennedy, Aug. 4, 1960; children—A. James Kennedy, Hugh D., Duncan R. B.Sc., Dalhousie U., Halifax, N.S., Can., 1946, M.Sc., 1949, LL.D. (hon.), 1986; Ph.D., Cambridge U., Eng., 1952. Research officer Atomic Energy Can., Chalk River, Ont., Can., 1952-57; assoc. prof. Dalhousie U., Halifax, 1957-60; assoc. prof. to prof. U. N.C., Chapel Hill, 1960-68; head physics Queen's U., Kingston, Ont., 1968-74, prof. physics, 1968—; vis. prof. various univs., Can., Europe, Japan, China, Hong Kong. Author 2 books; contbr. over 100 articles to profl. jours. Recipient CAP medal for achievement in physics, 1992, Canada 125 medal, 1992. Fellow Am. Phys. Soc., Royal Soc. Can. (pres. Acad. Sci. 1984-87), Japan Soc. for Promotion Sci.; mem. Can. Assn. Physicists (pres., other offices 1970-74). Achievements include research in solid state physics, behavior of phonons, electrons, positrons and postronium in crystals and liquids, public service: nuclear reactor safety, possible hazards of power frequency electric and magnetic fields. Home: 835 Wartman Ave, Kingston, ON Canada K7M 4M3 Office: Queens U, Dept Physics, Kingston, ON Canada K7L 3N6

STEWART, ALEXANDER DOIG, bishop; b. Boston, Jan. 27, 1926; s. Alexander Doig and Catherine Muir (Smith) S.; m. Laurel Gale, June 5, 1953. A.B. cum laude, Harvard U., 1948, M.B.A., 1961; M.Div. cum laude, Union Theol. Sem., N.Y.C., 1951; D.D. (hon.), Gen. Theol. Sem., N.Y.C. Ordained priest Episcopal Ch., 1951; asst. (Christ Ch.), Greenwich, Conn., 1950-52; priest-in-charge (St. Margaret's Parish), Bronx, N.Y., 1952-53; rector (St. Mark's Episc. Ch.), Riverside, R.I., 1953-70; bishop Episc. Diocese Western Mass., Springfield, 1970-83; exec. for administrn. Episcopal Ch., N.Y.C., 1983-86, exec. v.p., mgr. pension fund, 1987-91, part-time cons., 1992—; mem. faculty Barrington Coll., 1955-70; Mem. budget and program com. Episc. Ch. U.S.A.; bd. dirs. Ch. Ins. Co., Ch. Life Ins. Co., Ch. Hymnal Corp. Author: Science and Human Nature, 1960 (Wainwright House award), The Shock of Revelation, 1967; also articles. Chmn. Urban Renewal, E. Providence, R.I., 1967-70; vice chmn. United Fund Springfield, 1972; mem. schs. and scholarship com. R.I. chpt. Harvard Coll., 1960-70; A founder, 1959-87; mem. bd. dirs., sec. corp. Health Havens, Inc., E. Providence; trustee Barrington Coll., 1971-76, Episcopal Radio-TV Found., 1980—, Providence Country Day Sch., 1964-70, Ch. Pension Fund, N.Y.C., 1976-87; mem. corp. St. Elizabeth's Hosp., Providence, 1954-70, Springfield Hosp., 1970-84.—. Mem. Religious Research Assn., Union League (N.Y.C.), Harvard Western Club (Mass.), Colony Club (Springfield). Address: 75 Severn St Longmeadow MA 01106-1023

STEWART, ALLEN WARREN, lawyer; b. Manchester, N.H., Dec. 12, 1938; s. Ellwyn F. and Aelene W. (Harriman) S.; children: William, Paul, Geoffrey. BS, U.S. Naval Acad., 1961; MS, George Washington U., 1967; JD, U. Pa., 1970. Bar: Pa. 1970, U.S. Ct. Appeals (3d cir.) 1971, U.S. Supreme Ct. 1980. Morgan, Lewis & Bockius, Phila., 1970-77, ptnr., 1977-94; bd. dirs. Am. Sentinel Ins. Co., Conestoga Life Assurance Co. Editor: Reinsurance, 1991; contbr. articles to legal jours. Naval aviator, lt. comdr. USN, 1961-66. Mem. ABA, Pa. Bar Assn., Phila. Bar Assn. Club: Phila. Racquet. Avocations: sailing, fishing. Office: Conestoga Life Assurance Co 401 Parkway Blvd Broomall PA 19008

STEWART, BARBARA ELIZABETH, free-lance magazine editor, artist; b. Ft. Dodge, Iowa, June 26, 1923; d. Warren Wheeler and Christine (Hubbard) Pickett; m. Charles Crombie Stewart, Sept. 2, 1943; 1 child, Charles Crombie IV. Student, Mt. Holyoke Coll., 1940-41, Wayne State U., 1941-42, So. Conn. State U., 1944-45; AA, Mercer County Community Coll., 1970; BA, Trenton State Coll., 1972. Cert, K-I2 art tchr. Copywriter Fed. Dept.

Stores, Goodwin's, Detroit, 1942-43; dept. coord. Sears, Roebuck & Co., Trenton, N.J., 1944; sec., writer Yale U., New Haven, Conn., 1945, 46; contbg. editor Mercer Bus. Mag., Trenton, 1980—. Oil and acrylic artist. chmn. Stokes Sch. PTA, Trenton, 1952-58; pres. Rutgers coop. Extension Mercer County, Trenton, 1970-82; chmn. mem. Hillcrest Civic Assn., Trenton, 1956-83; bd. dirs. Trenton YWCA, 1975-77; chmn. women's fellowship Covenant Presbyn. Ch., Trenton, 1978-88, 90-95; vol. Art Goes to Sch. program, 1992. Mem. Nat. Art Edn. Assn., N.J. Art Edn. Assn., AAUW (local chmn. 1965, 67), Torch Club (ofcl. del. 1985-88, tchr./vol. Art Goes to Sch. Programs, Pa./N.J. chpt.). Democrat. Avocations: walking, swimming, bridge, lawn bowling. Home: 31 Clement Ave Trenton NJ 08638-1603

STEWART, BURCH BYRON, chemist, physicist; b. Chattanooga, May 7, 1929; s. Burch Dayton and Mary Elizabeth Stewart; m. Lois Mildred Speaker, June 20, 1955 (div. Mar. 1965); children: Leslie, Alyson, Kathryn; m. Shirley Elizabeth Westervelt, June 8, 1965; children: Steven, Neal, Daryl. BS in Analytical Chemistry, U. Tenn., 1955, MS in Physical Organic Chemistry, 1957, PhD in Physical Chemistry, 1959. Sr. engr. Western Electric, Princeton, N.J., 1959-60; rsch. chemist Allied Chem., Morristown, N.J., 1960-68; mgr., asst. dir. Ciba-Geigy, Ardsley, N.Y., 1968-73; dir. Applied Rsch. Labs., Miami, Fla., 1973-86; pres. Applied Consumer Svcs., Miami, 1986—; rsch. scientist Solar Reactor Corp., Miami, 1978-79; cons. BBS Assocs., Inc., Miami, 1978-81, Worth Engring., Hialeah, Fla., 1986—, All State Engring., 1986—. Inventor and patentee in field; contbr. articles to profl. jours. and encyclopedias. Vol. Askew For Pres., Miami, 1983; pres. Miami Unitarian Soc., 1984, Friends of Physics, U. Miami, 1990-91, 95—. With USN, 1950-52. Recipient Hon. Mentionship award Westinghouse Sci. Talent Search, Knoxville, 1955; AEC grantee U. Tenn., Knoxville, 1957. Mem. Am. Chem. Soc., Am. Soc. Testing Materials, Assn. Offl. Analytical Chemists, Sigma Xi. Office: Applied Consumer Svcs 9500 NW 77th Ave # 5 Hialeah FL 33016

STEWART, BURTON GLOYDEN, JR., banker; b. Clayton, N.C., Mar. 14, 1933; s. Burton Gloyden and Evelyn I. (Stallings) S.; m. Patricia Taylor, June 16, 1956; children: Burton Gloyden III, H. Taylor. AB, Duke U., 1955; grad. Sch. Banking of South, 1970; exec. program U. N.C., 1975. With Allstate Ins. Co., 1957-66, regional sales mgr., Charlotte, N.C., 1964-66; with Branch Banking and Trust Co., Wilson, N.C., 1966—, sr. v.p., mgr. corp. planning and mktg. div., 1972-81, mgr. corp. planning and investor rels., 1981-90, dir. investor rels., 1981—; dir. Branch Corp., 1974-82; dir. N.C. Payments System, 1980-89, v.p., 1983-86, chmn. bd. 1986-89; bd. dirs., chmn. Electronic Fin. Svcs., Inc., 1988-90. Bd. dirs. Wilson Heart Assn., 1968; bd. dirs., treas. Wilson Arts Coun., 1969-71; bd. dirs. Wilson United Way, 1974-80, 86-89, campaign chmn., 1977, pres., 1979, chmn. strategic planning com., 1986-90; mem. N.C. Gov.'s Efficiency Study Commn., 1985, N.C. Goals and Policy Bd., 1985-93. Lt. USNR, 1955-57. Mem. Nat. Investor Rels. Inst., Bank Investor Rels. Assn. (bd. dirs. 1984—, v.p. 1984-87), Am. Mgmt. Assn., N.C. Bankers Assn. (chmn. mktg. com. 1976), Wilson Country Club. Methodist. Office: 223 Nash St W Wilson NC 27893-3880

STEWART, CAMERON LEIGH, mathematics educator; b. Victoria, B.C., Can., Sept. 29, 1950; s. Ross and Greta Marie (Morris) S.; m. Ellen Papachristoforou, June 7, 1980; children: Elisa Maria, Andrew Ross. BSc, U. B.C., 1971; MSc, McGill U., Montreal, 1972; PhD, U. Cambridge, 1976. Rsch. assoc. Mathematical Centrum, Amsterdam, 1976-77, I.H.E.S., Bures-Sur-Yvette, France, 1977-78; asst. prof. U. Waterloo, Ont., Can., 1978-82, assoc. prof., 1982-86, prof., 1986—. Contbr. articles to profl. jours. Recipient J.T. Knight prize U. Cambridge, 1974, Killam fellow Killam Estate, 1990-92. Fellow Royal Soc. Can.; mem. Can. Math. Soc., Am. Math. Soc. Avocations: golf, ice hockey. Home: 494 Heatherhill Pl, Waterloo, ON Canada N2T 1H7 Office: U Waterloo Dept Pure Math, Waterloo, ON Canada N2L 3G1

STEWART, CARL E., judge; b. 1950. BA magna cum laude, Dillard U., 1971; JD, Loyola U., New Orleans, 1974. Atty. Piper & Brown, Shreveport, La., 1977-78; staff atty. La. Atty. Gen. Office, Shreveport, La., 1978-79; asst. U.S. atty. Office U.S. Atty. (we. dist.) La., Shreveport, 1979-83; prin. Stewart & Dixon, Shreveport, 1983-85; spl. asst. dist. atty., asst. prosecutor City of Shreveport, 1983-85; judge U.S. Dist. Ct. La., 1985-91, U.S. Ct Appeals (2nd cir.) La., 1991-94, U.S. Ct. Appeals (5th cir.) La., Shreveport, 1994—; adj. instr. dept. mgmt. and mktg. La. State U., Shreveport, 1982-85. Mem. chancellor's adv. bd. La. State U., Shreveport, 1983-89, chmn., 1988-89; mem. black achievers program steering com. YMCA, 1990; active NAACP, 1988—. Capt. JAGC, 1974-77, Tex. Mem. ABA, Nat. Bar Assn., Am. Inns. of Ct. (Harry Booth chpt. Shreveport), Black Lawyers Assn. Shreveport-Bossier, La. Conf. Ct. Appeal Judges, La. State Bar Assn. (bench/bar liaison com.), Omega Psi Phi (Rho Omega chpt.). Office: US Ct Appeals 5th Cir 300 Fannin St Ste 2299 Shreveport LA 71101*

STEWART, CARLETON M., banker, corporate director; b. Chgo., 1921; s. Carleton Merrill and Margaret (Lyon) S.; m. Alicia Dewar (dec.); 3 children; m. Kathryn White Stewart. Student, Stanford U., 1939-42; grad. in indsl. adminstrn., Harvard U., 1943, MBA, 1947. With Citibank, 1947-76; v.p. Citibank, N.Y.C., 1960-67; sr. v.p. in charge of Asia Pacific area Citibank, 1967-69, sr. v.p. in charge of S. Asia, Middle East and Africa, 1969-73; sr. officer Citibank, London, 1973-76; dir. Grindlay's Bank Ltd., London, Banque Internat. pour L'Afrique Occidentale, Paris, 1973-76; chmn. bd., chief exec. officer Am. Security Corp. and Am. Security Bank, Washington, 1976-80; chmn. bd. Internat. Bank Miami, 1983-85; dir. Travelers Asset Mgmt. Internat. Corp., N.Y.C., 1985-87. Mayor Longboat Key, Fla., 1987-88, town commr., 1984-90, chmn. ethics commn., 1990-94; mem. Planning Commn., Sarasota County, Fla., 1990-92. Capt. AUS, 1943-46.

STEWART, CHARLES EVAN, lawyer; b. N.Y.C., Mar. 4, 1952; s. Charles Thorp and Jenifer Jennings (Barbour) S.; m. Cathleen Bacich, June 26, 1982 (div. Nov. 1986); m. Patricia A. McGlothlin, Sept. 10, 1988; 1 child, Charlotte Jenifer. BA cum laude, Cornell U., 1974, JD, 1977. Bar: N.Y. 1978, U.S. dist. ct. (so. and ea. dists.) N.Y. 1978, U.S. Ct. Appeals (2d cir.) 1978, U.S. Ct. Appeals (D.C. and 7th cirs.) 1980, U.S. Ct. Appeals (3d, 9th and 5th cirs.) 1981, U.S. Supreme Ct. 1981, U.S. Ct. Appeals (10th cir.) 1982, U.S. Claims Ct. 1983, U.S. Ct. Appeals (6th cir.) 1986; arbitrator NYSE, NASD. Assoc. Donovan Leisure Newton & Irvine, N.Y.C., 1977-86; 1st v.p., assoc. gen. counsel E.F. Hutton and Co., Inc., N.Y.C., 1987-88; exec. v.p., gen. counsel Nikko Securities Co. Internat., N.Y.C., 1988—; spl. asst. dist. atty. N.Y. County, 1979-80. Contbr. articles to legal jours. Chair Cornell U. Coun.; adv. coun. Cornell U. Coll. Arts and Scis., Cornell U. Law Sch.; exec. com. Westminster Sch. Alumni Assn.; trustee YWCA Nat. Bd. Mem. ABA, Assn. of Bar of City of N.Y. (young lawyers com. 1979-83, uniform laws com. 1984-86, corp. law dept. com. 1988-91, spl. com. on Asian affairs 1989-91), Fed. Bar Coun. (com. on 2d cir. cts. 1978-93, co-chair publs. com. 1993—), Am. Soc. Internat. Law Sec. Ind. Assn. (fed regulation com. 1990—, lit. com. 1994—), Downtown Athletic Club, Univ. Club, Kennebunk River Club, Arundel Beach Club, Madison Beach Club, Chevy Chase Club. Republican. Episcopalian. Home: 122 E 82nd St New York NY 10028-0822 Office: Nikko Securities Co Internat 200 Liberty St Fl 29 New York NY 10281-1003

STEWART, CHARLES LESLIE, lawyer; b. Fayetteville, Ark., Aug. 12, 1919; s. Charles Leslie and Ruth (Want) S.; m. Edalee Esther Gastrock, Aug. 30, 1941; children: William Paul, Thomas Alan, Katherine Jean, Robert Edward. A.B., U. Ill., 1940; M.A., La. State U., 1941; student, George Washington U. Law Sch., 1944-45; J.D., U. Chgo., 1947. Bar: Ill. 1948, U.S. Supreme Ct. 1954. Economist, Dept. Agr., 1941-42; adminstrv. asst. OPA, 1942-43, Bd. Econ. Warfare, 1943; exec. dir. Chgo. div. ACLU, 1946-47; practiced law Chgo., 1948-91, Glencoe, Ill., 1991—; assoc. Mayer, Brown & Platt, Chgo., 1947-55, ptnr., 1956-67, 70-71, resident ptnr. charge European office, Paris, 1967-70; v.p., gen. counsel Hart Schaffner & Marx, Chgo., 1971-73, v.p., sec., gen. counsel, 1974-83; v.p., sec., gen. counsel Hartmarx Corp., Chgo., 1983-84, v.p., sec.; sr. counsel, 1984, of counsel legal dept., 1985-89; arbitrator Mandatory Arbitration Program Cir. Ct., Cook County, Ill., 1990—; mem. Am. Law Inst., 1983-90. Mem. Glencoe (Ill.) Bd. Edn., 1965-66; mem. planning coms. Corp. Counsel Inst., Northwestern U. Sch. Law and Ill. Inst. Continuing Legal Edn., 1981-84, vice-chmn., 1983, chmn., 1984; mem. Glencoe Union Ch. Served with OSS, AUS, 1943-45. Mem. ABA, Ill.

State Bar Assn., Chgo. Bar Assn. (com. devel. of law 1977-91, vice chmn. 1984-85, chmn. 1985-86, corp. law com. 1981-91, corp. law depts. com. 1981-83, sr. lawyers com. 1987—), Am. Soc. Corp. Secs. (adv. com. Chgo. regional group 1978-83, vice chmn. 1979-80, chmn. 1980-81, nat. dir. 1981-84, exec. com. 1983-84, corp. practices com. 1982-87, assoc. mem. 1986-91), Skokie Country Club, Delta Phi. Avocations: genealogy, history, curling. Home and Office: 745 Vernon Ave Glencoe IL 60022-1562

STEWART, CHRISTINE SUSAN, Canadian government official; b. Jan. 3, 1941; d. Morris Alexander Leishman and Laura Anne Doherty; m. David Ian Stewart, Aug. 24, 1963; children: Douglas Alexander, John David, Catherine Ann. Ed., Neuchatel Jr. Coll., Switzerland, U. Toronto, Ont., Can. Nurse; mem. Ho. of Commons, 1988—, mem. standing com. for external affairs and internat. trade, assoc. critic for human rights; official opposition critic Can. Internat. Devel. Agy.; sec. state L.Am. and Africa Cabinet of Prime Min. Jean Chrétien, Ottawa, 1993—. Founding exec. dir. Horizons of Friendship. Liberal. Roman Catholic. Office: Parliament Bldgs, 484 Confederation Bldg, Ottawa, ON Canada K1A 0A6 Office: Fgn Affairs & Internat Trade, 125 Sussex Dr, Ottawa, ON Canada K1A 0G2

STEWART, CLINTON EUGENE, adult education educator; b. Copperas Cove, Tex., Nov. 7, 1927; s. Albert Clyde and Marjorie Lee (Jones) Stewart. BA, Baylor U., 1950, MS in Edn., 1951, MA in Biology, 1964, EdD, 1970. Cert. profl. supr., administr., supt., elem., prin., driver edn. tchr. Prof. edn. Howard Payne U., Brownwood, Tex.; dean Howard Payne U., Tex.; supt. Kopperl Independ Sch. Dist., Tex.; assoc. prof. edn. Sul Ross State U., Alpine, Tex. Lt. TNG, 1954. Mem. Phi Delta KIappa (pres. 1987), Kappa Delta Pi, Beta Beta Beta, Alpha Epsilon Delta, Alpha Chi.

STEWART, CORNELIUS JAMES, II, utilities company executive; b. Houston, June 27, 1925; s. Ross and Catherine (Rial) S.; m. Gretchen Elizabeth Braun, Nov. 28, 1947; children: Cornelius James, III, Richard Ross, David Rial, Gretchen Elizabeth Stewart Anderson, Catherine Maria Stewart Carrigan. Student, U. Tex., 1945-47. With Stewart & Stevenson Svcs., Inc., Houston, 1947—; v.p. Stewart & Stevenson Svcs., Inc., 1956-73, pres., 1973-75, chmn. bd., 1975—; chmn. bd., dir. C. Jim Stewart & Stevenson, Inc., Stewart & Stevenson Realty Corp., Stewart & Stevenson Internat. Corp., Stewart & Stevenson Transp. Inc., Stewart & Stevenson Power Inc., Machinery Acceptance; bd. dirs. Reagan Commerce Bank, 1973-76, So. State Bank, 1973—, Mchts. Bank; adv. dir. Tex. Commerce Bank, 1975—, also bd. dirs. Chmn. Houston City Planning Commn., 1974-83; bd. dirs. Better Bus. Bur. Met. Houston, 1976—, vice chmn., 1981-82, chmn., 1983-85; bd. dirs. Holly Hall, 1972-76; bd. dirs., mem. fin. devel. com. Houston chpt. ARC, 1989—; bd. dirs. Kelsey Seybold Found.; bd. dirs. Salvation Army, 1989—; chmn. Houston/Grampian Region Assn., 1978—; internat. adv. dir. Up With People, 1979—; co-chmn. Houston Fundraising, 1982; mem. engring. coun. devel. com. Tex. A&M Univ., 1989—; dir. U. Tex. med. br., Galveston, 1995. Served with USAAF, 1943-45. Mem. Nat. Assn. Mfg. (bd. dirs. 1988—), Purchasing Agts. Assn. Houston (pres. 1959-60, dir. 1961-62), U.S. C of C. (internat. policy com. 1983—), Houston C of C. (dir. 1969, 76, 78, 80, 82, 84, mem. aviation steering com. 1976—, chmn. bus. devel. com. 1980-81), Nat. Indsl. Conf. Bd., Newcomen Soc. Presbyterian. Clubs: Rotary (bd. dirs. Houston club 1978—, v.p. 1980, pres. 1981, pres. found. 1991-93), Breakfast, Houston (pres. 1973, pension com. 1974—), Houston Country (bd. dirs. 1974-76). Office: Stewart & Stevenson Services Inc PO Box 1637 Houston TX 77251-1637

STEWART, C(ORNELIUS) VAN LEUVEN, lawyer; b. Balt., Sept. 22, 1936; s. Charles Morton and Lillie Emerson (Van Leuven) S.; m. Clare Wright Horsley, June 18, 1960; children: Clare Winston, Lillie Elliotte, Jenett Ten Eyck (dec.). BA, Yale U., 1958; LLB, U. Va., 1961. Bar: Md. 1962, D.C. Bar 1982. Assoc. in law U. Calif. Law Sch., Berkeley, 1961-62; assoc. Venable, Baetjer & Howard, Balt., 1962-69, ptnr., 1970-91; ptnr. Stewart, Plant & Blumenthal, Balt., 1991—. Bd. dirs., pres. Irvine Natural Sci. Ctr.; bd. dirs. Pks. and People Found.; past bd. dirs. Balt. Symphony Orch. Assn., Internat. Visitors Coun. of Balt., Roland Park Country Sch.; past pres. Md. Ballet Co., Met. Balt. Mental Health Assn. Mem. ABA, State Bar Assn., Balt. City Bar Assn., D.C. Bar Assn., Am. Coll. Trust and Estate Counsel (Md. chpt., state chair), Internat. Acad. of Estate and Trust Law, Balt. Estate Planning Coun. (mem. 1987), Magic Mê. Republican. Episcopalian. Office: 7 St Paul St Ste 910 Baltimore MD 21202-1654

STEWART, DANIEL ROBERT, retired glass company executive; b. New Kensington, Pa., July 25, 1938; s. Daniel Joseph and Sarah Madeline (Caldwell) S.; m. Marianne Colesar, Aug. 27, 1960; children—Karen Anne, Daniel John. B.S., Pa. State U., 1960, M.S., 1962, Ph.D., 1964. Research scientist Owens-Ill., Inc., Toledo, 1964-66; chief glass sci. sect. Owens-Ill., Inc., 1967-69, dir. glass and ceramic research, 1970-71, dir. corporate research labs., 1972-73, v.p corporate staff, dir. glass and ceramic tech., 1973-83; pres. Dura Temp Corp., Holland, Ohio, 1983-94; ret., 1994; U.S. rep. steering com. Internat. Congress Glass, 1980-83. Ch. treas. Ch. of the Nazarene, 1986-83; mem. local com. Boy Scouts Am., 1975-87. PPG fellow, 1961-64. Fellow Am. Ceramic Soc. (past chmn. glass div.); mem. Nat. Inst. Ceramic Engrs. (profl. achievement in ceramic engring. award 1974), Soc. Glass Tech., Sigma Xi. Republican. Patentee in field. Office: 1750 Eber Rd Holland OH 43528-9635

STEWART, DAVID MARSHALL, librarian; b. Nashville, Aug. 1, 1916; s. David and Mary (Marshall) S.; m. Gladys Carroll, June 9, 1947; 1 son, James Marshall. B.A., Bethel Coll., 1938; B.S. in LS, George Peabody Coll., 1939. Circulation asst. Vanderbilt U. Library, 1938-39; county librarian Ark. Library Commn., 1939-40; Tenn. supr. WPA library service projects, 1940-42; librarian Memphis State U., 1942-46; spl. asst. to chief card div. Library of Congress, Washington, 1947; librarian CIA, Washington, 1948-60; chief librarian Nashville Pub. Library, 1960-85; Instr. Peabody Library Sch., 1966-80. Bd. dirs. Council Community Agys., Nashville, Middle-East Tenn. Arthritis Found. (v.p. 1965), Friends Chamber Music Nashville, Travelers Aid Nashville. Served to lt. comdr. USNR, 1942-46. Mem. ALA, Tenn. Library Assn. (chmn. legislative com. 1961-65, v.p. 1965, pres. 1966, Honor award, 1983), Southeastern Library Assn., Pub. Library Assn. (chmn. standards com. 1964-65, pres. 1966-67), Alumni Assn. Bethel Coll. (dir., Disting. Alumni award 1992). Democrat. Mem. Ch. of Christ. Clubs: Kiwanian. (Nashville), Coffee House (Nashville). Home: 6342 Torrington Rd Nashville TN 37205-3157

STEWART, DORIS MAE, biology educator; b. Sandsprings, Mont., Dec. 12, 1927; d. Virgil E. and Violet M. (Weaver) S.; m. Felix Loren Powell, Oct. 8, 1956; children: Leslie, Loren. BS, Coll. Puget Sound, 1948, MS, 1949; PhD, U. Wash., 1953. Instr. U. Mont., Missoula, 1954-56, asst. prof., 1956-57; asst. prof. U. Puget Sound, Tacoma, 1957-58; head sci. dept. Am. Kiz Lisesi, Istanbul, Turkey, 1958-62; rsch. asst. prof. U. Wash., Seattle, 1963-67, rsch. assoc. prof., 1967-68; assoc. prof. Cen. Mich. U., Mt. Pleasant, 1970-72; assoc. prof. U. Balt., 1973-81, prof., 1981—. Contbr. numerous articles to profl. jours. Mem. Am. Physiol. Soc., Sigma Xi. Home: 1103 Frederick Rd Baltimore MD 21228-5032

STEWART, DOROTHY K., educator, librarian; b. Bristol, Conn., Sept. 28, 1928; d. Robert and Anna Esther (Shwirtz) Konopask; m. David Benjamin Stewart, Sept. 27, 1952 (div. Nov. 1979); children: Douglas Neil, Diane Alison. BA in Romance Langs. and Lit. cum laude, Boston U., 1950; MS in Libr. Sci., Cath. U. Am., 1959. Children's libr. Brookline (Mass.) Pub. Libr., 1953-55, Takoma Park (Md.) Libr., 1955-57; reference libr. U.S. Geol. Survey, 1961; libr. Washington Internat. Sch., 1979-80, Office Sea Grant NOAA, Rockville, Md., 1980-82; info. specialist Life Ring, Inc., Silver Spring, Md., 1983-84; pub. svc. libr. Urban Inst., Washington, 1984-85; user svcs. coord. ERIC Clearinghouse on Tchg. and Tchr. Edn., Washington, 1985—. Active, past pres. PTA, Rockville, Md., 1973-78; chmn., mem. com. Potomac (Md.) Libr. Adv. Com., 1975-85. Mem. Am. Indsl. Rsch. Assn., Spl. Librs. Assn., D.C. Libr. Assn., DiC Health Scis. Info. Network, Capital PC User Group, French lang. clubs, Phi Beta Kappa, Beta Phi Mu. Democrat. Avocations: travel, hiking, birding, microcomputers. Office: ERIC Clearinghouse on Tchg and Tchr Edn 1 Dupont Cir Ste 610 Washington DC 20036

STEWART, DUNCAN JAMES, lawyer; b. Amsterdam, N.Y., Apr. 24, 1939; s. William James and Maybelle Veronica (Matthews) S.; m. Susan Cobb Stewart, June 18, 1966; children: Benjamin Ross, Matthew Schuyler. AB, Cornell U., 1961, LLB, 1964. Bar: N.Y. 1964, U.S. Dist. C.t (no. dist.) N.Y. 1964. Assoc. Willkie Farr & Gallagher, N.Y.C., 1964, 67-72, ptnr., 1973—. Trustee Citizens Budget Commn., N.Y.; bd. dirs. Prospect Park Alliance, Bklyn., Network for Women's Svcs., N.Y. Mem. ABA, N.Y. State Bar Assn., Assn. of Bar of City of N.Y., Cornell Club. Democrat. Presbyterian. Home: 264 Berkeley Pl Brooklyn NY 11217-3904 Office: Willkie Farr & Gallagher 1 CitiCorp Ctr 153 E 53d St New York NY 10022

STEWART, EDGAR ALLEN, lawyer; b. Selma, Ala., Sept. 1, 1909; s. Edgar A. and Irma (Mallory) S.; m. Mamie V. Packer, Oct. 15, 1938; children: Edgar Allen III (dec.), Martha M. (Mrs. Edward B. Crosland, Jr.). B.A., U. South, 1929; LL.B., U. Ala., 1932. Bar: Ala. 1932. Since practiced Selma; sr. partner Reeves & Stewart, 1947-92; spl. agt. FBI, 1942-45; ret., 1993. Contbr. articles to profl. jours. Trustee Selma Scts., 1956-67; bd. dirs., pres. Selma YMCA, 1952-68; bd. dirs Indsl. Devel. Bd., Selma, YMCA Blue Ridge (N.C.) Assembly, 1983-85. Fellow Am. Coll. Trial Lawyers; mem. ABA, Ala. Bar Commn. (dir. 1970-76), Am. Coll. Probate Counsel, Internat. Assn. Ins. Counsel, Nat. Assn. R.R. Counsel, Am. Counsel Assn. (bd. dirs. Presbyn. Retirement Corp. 1993), Am. Judicature Soc., Phi Beta Kappa, Phi Delta Theta, Phi Delta Phi. Home: 500 Spanish Fort Blvd Apt 3 Spanish Fort AL 36527 Office: PO Box 457 Selma AL 36702-0457

STEWART, FRANK MAURICE, JR., federal agency administrator; b. Okalona, Miss., Apr. 1, 1939; s. Frank Maurice Stewart and Henryne Annette (Walker) Goode; m. Regina Diane Mosley, Dec. 26, 1964; children: Lisa Ann, Dana Joy. BA, Wesleyan U., 1961, MA in Teaching, 1963, diploma further study, 1963; postgrad., Am. U., 1982-84. Dir. urban edn. corps N.J. State Dept. Edn., Trenton, 1969-70; dir. urban teaching intern program Sch. Edn. Rutgers U., New Brunswick, N.J., 1970-71; staff asst. White House Conf. on Aging, Washington, 1971-73; chief program devel. U.S. Office of Equal Edn. Opportunity, Washington, 1973-74; chief policy analysis U.S. Adminstrn. on Aging, Washington, 1974-75; asst. exec. sec. U.S. HEW, Washington, 1975-77; dir. govt. programs U.S. Dept. Energy, Washington, 1977-80, dir. instnl. conservation programs, 1980-84, dir. state and local assistance programs, 1984-90, dep. asst. sec. for tech. and fin. assistance, 1990-93; acting asst. sec. for energy efficiency and renewable energy, 1993-94; mgr. Golden (Colo.) Field Office, U.S. Dept. Energy, 1994—. Recipient Svc. Recognition award Assn. Phys. Plant Adminstrs., Washington, 1982, Svc. Appreciation award Nat. Assn. State Energy Officials, Washington, 1987; named Energy Exec. of Yr. Assn. Energy Engrs., Atlanta, 1988. Mem. Sr. Execs. Assn. Episcopalian. Home: 202 S Madison St Denver CO 80206 Office: US Dept Energy Field Office 1617 Cole Blvd Golden CO 80401

STEWART, GEORGE COPE, III (SCOOP STEWART), lawyer; b. Seattle, Aug. 15, 1941; s. George Cope and Dorothy (Horsfall) S.; m. Elizabeth Dunn, Dec. 28, 1965; children: Geoffrey Cope, Jennifer Dunn. AB, U. Wash., 1963; LLM with honors, George Washington U., 1966. Bar: Va. 1966, D.C. 1966. Assoc. Steptoe & Johnson, Washington, 1966-69; exec. v.p., gen. cvounsel Quadel Corp., Washington, 1969-77; pvt. practice Washington, 1977-83; ptnr. Lewis, Mitchell & Moore, Vienna, Va., 1983-86, Arent, Fox, Kintner, Plotkin & Kahn, Washington, 1986-93; v.p., assoc. gen. counsel Marriott Internat., Inc., Washington, 1994—; lectr. in field. Bd. editors George Washington U. Law Sch., 1965-66. Chmn. Young Lawyers for Nixon-Agnew, Nat. Com. for Election of Nixon-Agnew, Washington, 1967-68; bd. dirs. Shore Owners Assn., Lake Placid, N.Y., 1987-92, ODI, Boston, 1995—. Mem. D.C. Bar Assn., Va. Bar Assn. Republican. Episcopalian. Avocations: golf, flying, reading. Home: 1841 R St NW Washington DC 20009-1644

STEWART, GEORGE RAY, librarian; b. Birmingham, Ala., Aug. 19, 1944; s. DeWitt and Ann (McCain) S.; m. Nancy Ann Norton, June 5, 1964; children: Steven Ray, Jeffery Alan. B.A., Samford U., Birmingham, 1966, M.A., 1967; M.A., Emory U., 1971. Mem. staff Birmingham Pub. Libr., 1960—, assoc. dir., 1970-76, dir., 1976-93; system dir., 1993—; part-time instr. Grad. Sch. Libr. Svc. U. Ala.; bd. dirs. Southeastern Library Network, Inc., 1986-88. Editor: Birmingham Pub. Library Press. Bd. dirs. Red Mountain Mus., 1972-79, Literacy Coun. Ctrl. Ala., 1990-94; bd. dirs. Indsl. Health Coun., Birmingham, 1972-85, sec., 1979-81, pres. bd. dirs. 1982, 83. Mem. ALA, Southeastern Libr. Assn. (trees. 1985-86, v.p. 1986-88, pres. 1989-90), Ala. Libr. Assn. (scholarship 1968, pres. 1976), Ala. Hist. Assn., Birmingham Hist. Assn. Office: Birmingham-Jefferson County Librr System 2100 Park Pl Birmingham AL 35203-2744

STEWART, GEORGE TAYLOR, insurance executive; b. N.Y.C., Dec. 29, 1924; s. Fargo Calvin and Berthe Adelle (Pelleton) S.; m. Bonnie Elizabeth Myers, Sept. 14, 1946; children: Diane Barbara Stewart Carrington, Susan Gail Stewart Dupuis. A.B., Wesleyan U., Conn., 1947; DHL (hon.), Lynchburg Coll., 1994. Analyst Geyer & Co., Inc., 1948-54, Shelby Cullom Davis & Co., 1954-56; v.p. Blyth & Co., Inc., N.Y.C., 1956-65; chmn., chief exec. officer 1st Colony Life Ins. Co., Lynchburg, Va., 1965-92, chmn. fin. com., 1992—; bd. dirs. Am. Mayflower Life Ins. Co., N.Y.; chmn. Greater Lyunchburg Cmty. Trust. Author: Investing in American Business, 1964. Trustee Lynchburg Coll., Jefferson's Poplar Forest, founder. Recipient Lynchburg Bi-Centennial award, 1976, Lynchburg Pro Opera Civica award, 1982, award Navy League, 1981, Outstanding Businessman award Lynchburg Coll. Bus. Sch., 1982. Mem. N.Y. Acad. Scis., Lynchburg C of C. (pres.), Thomas Jefferson Commemoration Commn. (presdl. apptd.), N.Y. Soc. Security Analysts, Met. Club (N.Y.C.), City Midday-Drug and Chem. Club (N.Y.C.), Calif. Club (L.A.), Boonsboro Country Club of Lynchburg (bd. dirs.), Piedmont Club, Waterfront Club. Republican. Presbyterian (elder). Office: First Colony Life Ins Co PO Box 1280 Lynchburg VA 24505-1280

STEWART, GILBERT WRIGHT, computer science educator; b. Washington, Oct. 1, 1940; s. Gilbert Wright and Ruth (Blount) S.; m. Mary Lynn Tharp, 1964; children: Michael, Laura; m. Astrid Schmidt-Nielsen, Apr. 29, 1978. A.B., U. Tenn., 1962, Ph.D., 1968. Programmer Union Carbide Nuclear Co., Oak Ridge, 1959-62, 63-64, 65-68, computer div. Gen. Electric Co., Phoenix, 1964-68; asst. prof., assoc. prof. U. Tex.-Austin, 1968-72; assoc. prof. Carnegie-Mellon U., Pitts., 1972-74, U. Md., College Park, 1974-76; prof. computer sci. Carnegie-Mellon U., 1976—; cons. Argonne Nat. Lab. (Ill.), 1974—, Nat. Bur. Standards, Gaithersburg, Md., 1979—; dir. Lab. Parallel Computation U. Md., 1983. Author: Introduction to Matrix Computations, 1974; co-author: (with Dougarra, Bunch and Moler) LINPACK Users' Guide, (with I.G. Sun) Matrix Perturbation Theory; translator: Gauss's Theoria Combinations. Woodrow Wilson fellow, 1962; NSF grantee, 1983. Mem. Soc. Indsl. and Applied Math., Am. Math. Assn., Am. Statis. Assn. Democrat. Home: 407 7th St NE Washington DC 20002-5223 Office: U Md Dept Computer Sci College Park MD 20742

STEWART, GUY HARRY, university dean emeritus, journalism educator; b. Keyser, W.Va., Feb. 12, 1924; s. Thomas R. and Martha (Mills) S.; m. Patricia Ann Groves, Dec. 27, 1948; children: Diane, Thomas, Jeffrey. B.S.J., W.Va. U., 1948, M.A., 1949; Ph.D., U. Ill., 1957. Reporter Cumberland (Md.) Evening Times, 1941-43, Mineral Daily News-Tribune, Keyser, 1941-43; asst. editor W.Va. U., Morgantown, 1949-50, dir. grad. studies and journalism, 1960-69, dean Sch. Journalism, 1969-89; dir. pub. rels., prof. Tenn. Tech. U., Cookeville, 1950-60. Author: A Touch of Charisma, 1969. Served as ensign USNR, 1944-46, PTO. Recipient P.I. Reed Achievement award W.Va. U. Journalism ALumni Assn., 1977; named to Keyser High Sch. Legion of Honor, 1991; Guy H. Stewart Journalism Endowment Fund named in his honor. Mem. W.Va. Press Assn. (life), Assn. Edn. in Journalism and Mass Communications, Rotary (dist. gov. 1983-84), Kappa Tau Alpha (nat. pres. 1980, Top Adviser award 1987). Democrat. Methodist. Home: 525 Pocahontas Ave Morgantown WV 26505-2274

STEWART, HAROLD BROWN, biochemist; b. Chatham, Ont., Can., Mar. 9, 1921; s. John Craig and Margaret Gertrude (Brown) S.; m. Audrey Pauline Blake, Oct. 14, 1950; 1 dau., Ann Margaret. M.D., U. Toronto, 1944, Ph.D., 1950; Ph.D., Cambridge (Eng.) U., 1955. Prof. biochemistry U. Western Ont., London, 1960—; chmn. dept. biochemistry U. Western Ont., 1964-72, dean grad. studies, 1972-86, prof. emeritus, 1986—; Med. Research Council Can. vis. scientist dept. biochemistry U. Cambridge, Eng., 1971-72. Contbr. articles in biochemistry to sci. jours. Served with Royal Canadian Navy, 1945-46. Mem. Canadian, U.K. biochem. socs., Canadian Physiol. Soc., Am. Soc. Biochemistry and Molecular Biology, Coll. Physicians and Surgeons of Ont. Home: 118 Baseline Rd E, London, ON Canada N6C 2N8

STEWART, HAROLD LEROY, physician, educator; b. Houtzdale, Pa., Aug. 6, 1899; s. Alexander and Lillie (Cox) S.; m. Cecelia Eleanor Finn, Sept. 30, 1929; children: Robert Campbell, Janet Eileen. Student, U. Pa., 1919-20, Dickinson Coll., 1921-22; M.D., Jefferson Med. Coll., 1926; grad., Army Med. Sch., Washington, 1929; research fellow, Jefferson Med. Coll., 1929-30, Harvard, 1937-39; Med. Sc.D. (hon.), Jefferson Med. Coll., 1964; D.Medicine and Surgery (hon.), U. Perugia, 1965, U. Turku, Finland, 1970; Doctor (hon.), Kagawa (Japan) Med. Sch., 1992. Diplomate Am. Bd. Pathology, Pan Am. Med. Assn. Intern Fitzzimmons Gen. Hosp., Denver, 1926-27; instr. to asst. prof. pathology Jefferson Med. Coll., 1930-37; asst. pathologist Jefferson Med. Coll. Hosp., Phila. Gen. Hosp., 1929-37; pathologist Office Cancer Investigations Harvard, USPHS, 1937-39; chief lab. pathology Nat. Cancer Inst., USPHS, Bethesda, Md., 1939-69; chief pathologic anatomy dept. clin. ctr. NIH, 1954-69; organizer Registry Exptl. Cancers, 1970—, Sci. emeritus, 1976—; prin. investigator, head WHO Collaborating Centre for Rsch. on Tumors Lab. Animals, 1976—; clin. prof. pathology Georgetown U., 1965—; Cons. FDA, 1969-71, Nat. Cancer Inst., 1970-76, Armed Forces Inst. Pathology, 1950—; cons., mem. study groups WHO, 1957-81, mem. expert adv. panel cancer, 1957-81; Mem. subcom. oncology NRC, 1947-65, mem. com. pathology, 1958-66, com. cancer diagnosis and therapy, 1951-57, mem. com. animal models and genetic stocks, 1972-75, chmn. histologic classification Lab. Animal Tumors, 1975-79; chmn. subcom. classification rat liver tumors NRC (Lab. Animal Tumors), 1976-79; chmn. U.S. A Com. Internat. Coun. Socs. Pathology, 1957-62, 69-75; chmn. U.S. nat. com. Internat. Union Against Cancer, 1953-59, U.S. del., 1952-74; Mem. adv. bd. Leonard Wood Meml., 1961-66; mem. com. to advance world-wide fight against cancer Am. Cancer Soc., 1963-76; mem. med. rsch. coun. Referees, New Zealand, 1987. Mem. editoral bd. Cancer Rsch., 1941-49, A.M.A. Archives of Pathology, 1957-62, Jour. Toxicology Pathology, 1988; editorial adviser Jour. Nat. Cancer Inst, 1947-56; contbr. articles to profl. jours. Trustee Thomas Jefferson U., Phila., 1969-72. Served as pvt. USMC, 1918-19; lt. M.C. U.S. Army, 1926-29; from maj. to lt. col. M.C. AUS, 1942-46. Recipient Lucy Wortham James and James Ewing Soc., 1967, Alumni Achievement award Jefferson Med. Coll., 1966, Disting. Svc. award HEW, 1966, Honors award NIH, The Dirs. award NIH, 1988, Dean's medal Jefferson Med. Coll., 1994; Dedication Jour. Exptl. Pathology, Vol. 1, No. 2, 1987; Harold L. Stewart Fund for Exptl. Pathology and Harold L. Stewart Lectureship established at Uniformed Svcs. U. of Health Scis., Bethesda, Md., 1986; honored by dedication in two books. Mem. Am. Soc. Clin. Pathologists (Ward Burdick award 1957), Am. Assn. Cancer Rsch. (pres. 1958-59), Am. Soc. Exptl. Pathology (hon.; pres. 1955), Am. Assn. Pathologists (Gold-headed Cane award 1978), Coll. Am. Pathologists, Md. Soc. Pathologists (pres. 1950-51), Washington Soc. Pathologists (sec.-treas. 1947-51), Internat. Acad. Pathology (pres. 1953-55, F.K. Mostofi award 1976), Internat. Union Against Cancer (exec. com. 1952-70, v.p. 1962), Mass. Med. Soc., Internat. Coun. Socs. Pathology (pres. 1962), Internat. Soc. Geog. Pathology, Colegio Anatomico Brasilerio (hon.), Societa Italiana di Cancerologia (hon.), Inst. Nacional de Cancerologia Mexico (hon.), Sociedad Columbiana de Patologia (hon.), Societe Belge d' Anatomie Pathologique (hon.), Sociedad Peruana Cancerologia (hon.), Soc. Cryobiology, Soc. Toxicologic Pathologists (hon.), Japanese Cancer Soc. (hon.), Purdy Stout Surg. Pathology Soc. (hon.), others. Home: 119 S Adams St Rockville MD 20850-2315 Office: NIH Nat Cancer Inst Registry Exptl Cancers Bethesda MD 20892

STEWART, HARRIS BATES, JR., oceanographer; b. Auburn, N.Y., Sept. 19, 1922; s. Harris B. and Mildred (Woodruff) S.; m. Elise Bennett Cunningham, Feb. 21, 1959; children: Dorothy Cunningham, Harry Hasburgh; 2d m. Louise Conant Thompson, Dec. 22, 1988. Grad., Phillips Exeter Acad., 1941; AB, Princeton, 1948; MS, Scripps Instn. Oceanography, U. Calif., 1952, PhD, 1956. Hydrographic engr. U.S. Navy Hydrographic Office expdn. to Persian Gulf, 1948-49; instr. Hotchkiss Sch., 1949-51; research asst. Scripps Instn. Oceanography, 1951-56; diving geologist, project mgr. Geol. Diving Cons., Inc., San Diego, 1953-57; chief oceanographer U.S. Coast & Geodetic Survey, 1957-65, dept. asst. dir., 1962-65; dir. Inst. Oceanography, Environmental Sci. Services Adminstrn., U.S. Dept. Commerce, 1965-69; dir. Atlantic Oceanographic and Meteorol. Labs., NOAA, 1969-78, cons., 1978-80; prof. marine sci., dir. Center for Marine Studies, Old Dominion U., Norfolk, Va., 1980-85; adj. prof. dept. oceanography Old Dominion U., 1986—; dir. S.E. Bank of Dadeland; chmn. Fla. Commn. Marine Sci. and Tech.; mem. exec. com., earth scis. div. Nat. Acad. Scis.; chmn. adv. bd. Nat. Oceanographic Data Center, 1965-66; chmn. survey panel interagy. com. oceanography Fed. Council Sci. and Tech., 1959-67; chmn. adv. com. underseas features U.S. Bd. Geog. Names, 1964-67; mem. sci. party No. Holiday Expdn., 1951; Capricorn Expdn., 1952-53; chief scientist Explorer Oceanographic Expdn., 1960, Pioneer Indian Ocean Expdn., 1964, Discoverer Expdn., 1968, NOAA-Carib Expdn., 1972, Researcher Expdn., 1975; mem. U.S. delegation Intergovtl. Oceanographic Commn., 1961-65; mem. Gov. Calif. Adv. Commn. Marine Resources; chmn. adv. council Dept. Geol. and Geophys. Scis. Princeton; v.p. Dade Marine Inst., 1976-77, pres., 1977-79; trustee, mem. exec. com. Assoc. Marine Insts.; mem. Fisheries Mgmt. Adv. Council Va. Marine Resources Commn., 1984-85; vice chmn. adv. council Univ. Nat. Oceanographic Lab. System, 1983-85; U.S. nat. assoc. to intergovtl. oceanographic commn. UNESCO program for Caribbean, 1964-89, vice chmn., 1974. Author: The Global Sea, 1963, Deep Challenge, 1966, The Id of the Squid, 1970, Challenger Sketchbook, 1972, No Dinosaurs on the Ark, 1988, Grungy George and Sloppy Sally, 1993. Bd. dirs. Vanguard Sch., Miami, 1974-76; trustee Metro Zoo, Miami, 1991—. Served as pilot USAAF, 1942-46, PTO. Decorated comendador Almirante Padilla (Colombia); recipient Meritorious award Dept. Commerce, 1960, Exceptional Service award, 1965. Fellow AAAS, Geol. Soc. Am., Nat. Tropical Botanical Gardens, Marine Tech. Soc. (v.p.); mem. Fla. Acad. Scis. (pres. 1978-79), Va. Acad. Sci., Am. Geophys. Union, Internat. Oceanographic Found. (v.p. 1974-80), Zool. Soc. Fla. (pres. 1970-73), Maine Hist. Soc., Marine Hist. Assn., Cape Ann Hist. Assn., Marine Coun. (Miami), Explorers Club (N.Y.), Prouts Neck Yacht Club (Maine), Cosmos Club. Presbyterian. Home (summer): 11 Atlantic Dr Scarborough ME 04074-8667 Home (winter): 720 Shadow Lake Ln Naples FL 33963

STEWART, HOMER JOSEPH, engineering educator; b. Elba, Mich., Aug. 15, 1915; s. Earl Arthur and Alta Fern (Stanley) S.; m. Frieda Klassen, June 15, 1940; children—Robert Joseph, Katherine Stanley, Barbara Ellen. Student, U. Dubuque, 1932-33; B in Aero. Engring., U. Minn., 1936; PhD, Calif. Inst. Tech., 1940. Faculty Jet Propulsion Lab. Calif. Inst. Tech., Pasadena, 1938—, prof. aeros., 1949-80, prof. emeritus, 1980—, chief research analysis sect., 1945-56, chief Liquid Propulsion Systems div., 1956-58, spl. asst. to dir., 1960-62, chief Advanced Studies Office, 1963-67, advanced studies adviser, 1967-76; dir. Sargent Industries, Inc., 1964-79, Office Program Planning and Evaluation, NASA, 1958-60; mem. tech. adv. bd. Aerojet-Gen. Corp., 1956-58, 61-70; mem. rsch. evaluation group guided missile com. Research and Devel. Bd., 1948-50, chmn., 1951; mem. sci. adv. bd. USAF, 1954-56, 1959-64; mem. sci. adv. com. Ballistics Research Lab. 1959-69, 73-77. Author: Kinematics and Dynamics of Fluid Flow, sect. VI Handbook of Meteorology, 1945; Contbr. articles to tech. jours. Recipient Outstanding Achievement award U. Minn., 1954, NASA Exceptional Service medal, 1970, I.B. Laskowitz award N.Y. Acad. Scis., 1985. Fellow AIAA; mem. Am. Meteorol. Soc., Internat. Acad. Astronautics, Sigma Xi, Tau Beta Pi. Home: 2393 Tanoble Dr Altadena CA 91001-2729 Office: Calif Inst Tech Pasadena CA 91109

STEWART, ISAAC DANIEL, JR., state supreme court justice; b. Salt Lake City, Nov. 21, 1932; s. Isaac Daniel and Orabelle (Iverson) S.; m. Elizabeth Bryan, Sept. 10, 1959; children: Elizabeth Ann, Shannon. B.A., U. Utah, 1959, J.D., 1962. Bar: Utah 1962, U.S. Ct. Appeals (4th, 8th, 9th and 10th cirs.) 1965, U.S. Supreme Ct. 1965. Atty. Dept. Justice, 1962-65; asst. prof., then assoc. prof. with tenure U. Utah Coll. Law, 1965-70, chmn. curriculum com., rsch. com., 1967-69, legal adv.; ptnr. firm Jones, Waldo, Holbrook & McDonough, Salt Lake City, 1970-79; justice Utah Supreme Ct., 1979—, assoc. chief justice, 1986-88; presiding judge 2nd dist. Utah Dist. Ct., Ogden, 1988—; lectr. in field; mem. Utah Bd. Oil, Gas and Mining, 1976-78, chmn., 1977-78; Utah rep. Interstate Oil Compact Commn., 1977-78, exec. com. 1978-79; mem. adv. com. rules of procedure Utah Supreme Ct., 1983-87;

chmn. com. on bar-press guidelines Utah Bar. Contbr. articles to legal jours. Chmn. subcom. on legal rights and responsibilities of youth Utah Gov's Com. on Youth, 1972; pres. Salt Lake chpt. Coun. Fgn. Rels., 1982; mem. Salt Lake City C. of C., 1974-79, mem. govtl. modernization com., 1976-78; missionary for Mormon Ch. in Fed. Republic Germany, 1953-56; bd. dirs. U. Utah Alumni Assn., 1986-89. Recipient Alumnus of Yr. award U. Utah Coll. Law, 1989. Mem. ABA, Utah Bar Assn. (com. on law and poverty 1967-69, com. on specialization 1977-78, pub. rels. com. 1968-69, chmn. com. on antitrust law 1977-78, com. on civil procedure reform 1968, mem. exec. com. bd. of appellate judges 1990—, Appellate Judge of Yr. 1986), Salt Lake County Bar Assn., Am. Judicature Soc., Order of Coif, Phi Beta Kappa, Phi Kappa Phi, Sigma Chi (Significant Sig award 1987). Office: Mcpl Bldg 2549 Washington Blvd Fl 6 Ogden UT 84401-3111

STEWART, J. DANIEL, air force development and test center administrator; b. Savannah, Ga., June 20, 1941; s. Benjamin F. and Bessie L. (Edenfield) S.; m. Rebecca M. Smith; children: Daniel, Laura. BS in Aero. Engring., Ga. Inst. Tech., 1963, MS in Aero. Engring., 1965, PhD in Aero. Engring., 1967; M. in Mgmt. Sci., Stanford U., 1979. Mem. tech. staff applied mechanics divsn. Aerospace Corp., El Segundo, Calif., 1967-74; br. chief tech. divsn. Air Force Rocket Propulsion Lab., Edwards AFB, Calif., 1974-78, asst. for R&D mgmt., 1979-81; divsn. chief Air Force Armament Divsn., Eglin AFB, Fla., 1981-83; dir. drone control program office 3246 Test Wing, Eglin AFB, Fla., 1983-85, joint dir. US/Allied munitions program office, 1985-86; tech. dir. rsch./devel./acquisitions Air Force Armament Divsn., Eglin AFB, Fla., 1986-88; asst. to comdr. Air Force Munitions Divsn., Eglin AFB, Fla., 1988-90; tech. dir. Air Force Devel. and Test Ctr., Eglin AFB, Fla., 1990-93, exec. dir., 1993—; mem. policy coun. Scientist and Engr. Career Program, Randolph AFB, Tex., 1994—, chmn. career devel. panel, 1994—. Bd. dirs. Internat. Found. for Telemetering, Woodland Hills, Calif., 1991—; mem. engring. adv. bd. U. Fla., Gainesville, 1988—; mem. citizens adv. com. U. West Fla., Pensacola, 1991—; mem. civilian exec. adv. bd. Air Force Materiel Command, 1990—, also former chmn.; mem. curricular adv. com. Def. Test and Evaluation Profl. Inst., 1991—. Recipient Presdl. Meritorious Rank award Pres. of U.S., 1993. Mem. Air Force Assn. (Lewis H. Brereton award 1994), Sr. Exec. Assn.; Am. Def. Preparedness Assn., Internat. Test and Evaluation Assn. (Cross medal 1994), Assn. of Old Crows, Fed. Exec. Inst. Alumni, Gulf Coast Alliance for Tech. Transfer. Avocations: tennis, golf, fishing. Office: AFDTC/CD Ste 117 101 W D Ave Eglin AFB FL 32542-5495

STEWART, JAMES B., journalist. With Wall St. Jour., N.Y.C., 1983—, now editor. Author: Holy Warriors: The Abolitionists and American Slavery, The Partners: Inside America's Most Powerful Law Firms, 1984, Wendell Phillips: Liberty's Hero, 1986, The Prosecutors, 1987. Pulitzer Prize for Explanatory Journalism, 1987. Office: Wall St Jour Dow Jones & Co 200 Liberty St New York NY 10281-1099

STEWART, JAMES BREWER, historian, author, college administrator; b. Cleve., Aug. 8, 1940; s. Richard Henry and Marion Elizabeth (Brewer) S.; m. Dorothy Ann Carlson; children: Rebecca Ann, Jennifer Lynn. BA, Dartmouth Coll., 1962; PhD, Case Western Res. U., 1968. Asst. prof. history Carrol Coll., Waukesha, Wis., 1968-69; asst. prof. history Macalester Coll., St. Paul, 1969-79, James Wallace prof. history, 1979—, provost, 1986-89; cons. Am. Coun. of Learned Socs., N.Y.C., 1988—. Author: Joshua R. Giddings & the Tactics of Radical Politics, 1970, Holy Warriors: Abolitionists & Slavery, 1976, Liberty's Hero: Wendell Phillips, 1986 (Best Biography award, Soc. Midland Authors 1986), William Lloyd Garrison and the Challenge of Emmancipation, 1992. Rsch. fellow NEH, 1973, Am. Coun. Learned Socs., 1984. Mem. Am. Hist. Assn., Orgn. Am. Historians (nom. com. 1988—), Soc. Historians of the Early Republic (exec. com. 1987—). Avocations: camping, gardening, furniture restoration. Home: 1924 Princeton Ave Saint Paul MN 55105-1523 Office: Macalester Coll Dept Of History Saint Paul MN 55105

STEWART, JAMES GATHINGS, insurance company executive; b. Fort Wayne, Ind., Oct. 5, 1942; s. Gathings and Mary (Sieber) S.; m. Janet Kartalia, Feb. 19, 1966; children: John, David, Mitchell, Rebecca. B.A., DePauw U., 1964; M.A.S., U. Mich., 1965. Various fin. positions Conn. Gen. Life Ins. Co., Hartford, Conn., 1966-77; v.p. Conn. Gen. Life Ins. Co., 1977-82; exec. v.p., chief fin. officer CIGNA Corp., Phila., 1983—. Fellow Soc. Actuaries; mem. Am. Acad. Actuaries. Republican. Office: Cigna Corp 1 Liberty Pl PO Box 7716 1650 Market St Philadelphia PA 19192-1550

STEWART, JAMES IAN, agricultural water scientist, cropping system developer, consultant; b. San Diego, Jan. 9, 1928; s. Castle Elmore and Myrtle Catherine (Hasty) S.; m. Robbie Nell Oliver, Mar. 23, 1975; children: Virginia Lane Stewart Carton, Ian Castle Stewart, Kevin Scott Overby. BSc, U. Calif., Berkeley, 1950; PhD, U. Calif., Davis, 1972. Farm advisor Agrl. Extension Svc., U. Calif., Stockton and Merced, 1950-61; extension expert Irrigation, Food and Agrl. Orgn. UN, Nicosia, Cyprus, 1962-66; assoc. rsch. water scientist U. Calif., Davis, 1966-77; supervisory soil scientist USDA/ Office for Internat. Cooperation and Devel., Nairobi, Kenya, 1977-83; team leader, agrometeorologist USAID/Kenya Mission, 1977-83; founder, pres. Found. for World Hunger Alleviation Through Response Farming (WHARF), Davis, 1984—; cons., agrometeorology AID, USDA, World Bank, FAO/UNDP, 35 countries of Ams., Europe, Asia, Africa, Australia, 1965—; sci. convocations, internat. 14 countries worldwide, 1969—. Author: Response Farming in Rainfed Agriculture, 1988; creator (computer programs) Wharf, Wharfdat, 1990; contbr. numerous articles to profl. jours. Mem. Am. Soc. Agronomy, Crop Sci. Soc. Am., Soil Sci. Soc. Am., Internat. Soil Sci. Soc., World Assn. Soil and Water Conservation, Internat. Com. for Irrigation and Drainage (life, U.S. com.), Indian Soc. Dryland Agr. (life), Internat. Platform Assn., Sigma Xi, Phi Delta Theta. Achievements include pioneering research on soil water extraction by crops; crop water requirements; relations between crop yield and water evapotranspired; impacts of water deficits in different crop growth stages; relations between season rainfall behavior and season dates of onset. Developer of FAO world standard linear and weighted growth stage models for estimating crop yields from actual evapotranscription, and contributor to four-growth-period linear model for estimating crop water requirements. Developer of "response farming" methodology for design of dryland cropping systems based on historical rainfall behavior, and seasonal flexibility in their management based on real-time rainfall season date of onset, defined to meet crop establishment requirements. Home: 640 Portsmouth Ave Davis CA 95616-2738 Office: World Hunger Alleviation Through Response Farming PO Box 1158 Davis CA 95617-1158

STEWART, JAMES M., merchant banker; b. Pitts., Jan. 21, 1943; s. Gene R. and Angela (McKnight) S.; m. Patricia Moseley, Sept. 25, 1971; children: Patricia Jr., Jason, Matthew. AB, Brown U., 1965; MBA, Stanford U., 1967. With Morgan Stanley & Co., N.Y.C., 1970-84, v.p., 1975-77, mng. dir., 1978-84; mng. dir. S.G. Warburg & Co., Inc., N.Y.C., 1985—; bd. dirs. S.G. Warburg & Co. Ltd., London; vice chmn. Securities Industries Inst., Phila., 1982-83. Trustee Green Vale Sch., Glen Head, N.Y., 1986-92; vice chmn. Brown U. Ann. Fund, Providence, R.I., 1989-90. 1st lt. U.S. Army, 1967-69, Vietnam. Mem. Bond Club (N.Y.C., gov. 1983-84), Piping Rock Club (Locust Valley, N.Y.), Stratton (Vt.) Country Club, Plantation Club (Ponte Vedre, Fla.), Brown Club N.Y. Democrat. Episcopalian. Office: S G Warburg & Co Inc 787 7th Ave New York NY 10019-6018

STEWART, JAMES MAITLAND, actor; b. Indiana, Pa., May 20, 1908; s. Alexander Maitland and Elizabeth Ruth (Jackson) S.; m. Gloria McLean, Aug. 9, 1949 (dec. Feb. 1994); children: Michael, Ronald (dec.), Judy and Kelly (twins). BS in Architecture, Princeton U., 1932; hon. degree, Indiana U. of Pa., U.S.C., Chapman Coll.; 7 other hon. degrees. Appeared in N.Y.C. in: Goodbye Again, 1932, Yellow Jack, Divided by Three and Page Miss Glory, 1934; motion pictures include Mr. Smith Goes to Washington, 1939, The Philadelphia Story, 1940, It's a Wonderful Life, 1946, Rear Window, 1954, Far Country, 1955, Man from Laramie, 1955, Strategic Air Command, 1955, The Man Who Knew too Much, 1956, Night Passage, 1957 Spirit of St. Louis, 1957, Vertigo, 1958, Bell, Book and Candle, 1959, It's a Wonderful World, 1959, Anatomy of Murder, 1959, The FBI, 1959, The Mountain Road, 1960, Two Rode Together, 1961, Mr. Hobbs Takes a Vacation, 1962, How the West Was Won, 1962, Take Her, She's Mine, 1963, Cheyenne Autumn, 1964, The Rare Breed, 1966, Flight of the Phoenix, 1966,

Firecreek, 1968, Bandolero, 1968, Cheyenne Social Club, 1970, Fool's Parade, 1971, That's Entertainment, 1974, The Shootist, 1976, Airport '77, 1977, The Big Sleep, 1978, The Magic of Lassie, 1978, Right of Way, 1983, TV show The Jimmy Stewart Show, 1971-72, Hawkins Murder, 1973-74; author: Jimmy Stewart and His Poems, 1989 (Recipient N.Y. Critics award for best male performance of 1939 in Mr. Smith Goes to Washington, Acad. award for performance in Philadelphia Story 1940, Berlin Film award 1962, Life Achievement award Am. Film Inst. 1980). Col. A.C., U.S. Army, World War II; brig. gen. USAFR, 1959. Decorated D.F.C. with oak leaf cluster, Air medal, Croix de Guerre with palm; recipient Lifetime Achievement award Screen Actors Guild, 1968, Disting. Performance award Drama League, 1970, Nat. Artist award Am. Nat. Acad. and Theatre, 1981, Kennedy Ctr. medal for lifetime achievement, 1983, Spl. Career Oscar, 1984, Presdl. medal of Freedom, 1985, Lifetime Achievement award Santa Barbara Film Festival, 1987, Lifetime Achievement award Monterey Film Festival, 1988, Lifetime Achievement award Am. Mus. of the Moving Image, 1988, Master Screen Artist award Dallas Film Festival, 1989, Ann. Spencer Tracy award UCLA, 1989, Woodrow Wilson medal Princeton U., 1990, Ann. Tribute N.Y. Film Soc., 1990, Ann. Tribute Film soc. of Lincoln Ctr., 1990, Career Achievement award Nat. Bd. Rev., 1991, Lifetime Achievement award Internat. Film Festival, 1992, Palm award Palm Springs Internat. Film Festival, 1992. Presbyterian.

STEWART, JAMES MONTGOMERY, banker; b. Detroit, May 31, 1939; s. Albert Edwin and Dagny Winter (Jensen) S.; m. Kathleen Williams, Sept. 27, 1940; children—Laura, Wendy, Kathleen. B.B.A., U. Mich., 1962, M.B.A., 1963. Asst. sec. Irving Trust Co., N.Y.C., 1966-68, asst. v.p., 1968-70, v.p., 1970-81, sr. v.p., 1981-86; regional gen. mgr. Copenhagen Handelsbank, 1986-90; gen. mgr. Den Danske Bank, N.Y.C., 1994—, pres.—. Trustee Am. Scandinavian Found. Mem. Danish Am. C. of C. (bd. dirs.), Anglers Club, Links Club, Racquet & Tennis Club, Country Club New Canaan, Beta Gamma Sigma. Republican. Avocations: trout fishing; golf; jazz; wine. Home: 130 Ramhorne Rd New Canaan CT 06840-3007 Office: Den Danske Bank 280 Park Ave New York NY 10017-1216

STEWART, JANE, psychology educator; b. Ottawa, Ont., Can., Apr. 19, 1934; d. Daniel Wallace and Jessie Stewart; m. Dalbir Bindra, Aug. 5, 1959 (dec. 1981). BA with honours, Queen's U., Kingston, Ont., 1956; PhD, U. London, 1959; DSc (hon.), Queen's U., 1992. Sr. rsch. biologist Ayerst Labs., Montreal, Que., 1959-63; part-time instr. psychology Sir George, Montreal, 1962-63; assoc. prof. psychology Williams U., Montreal, 1963-69; prof., chmn. psychology SGW Univ. (now Concordia U.), Montreal, 1969-75; prof. psychology Concordia U., Montreal, 1975—; dir. Ctr. for Studies in Behavioral Neurobiology, Concordia U., Montreal, 1990—. Fellow AAAS, APA, Can. Psychol. Assn.; mem. Soc. for Neurosci., Corp. Psychologists Province of Que., N.Y. Acad. Sci. Office: Concordia University, 1455 de Maisonneuve Blvd W, Montreal, PQ Canada H3G 1M8

STEWART, JEFF, advertising agency executive; b. N.Y.C., May 19, 1939; s. Andrew S. and Rose (Leider) S.; m. Linda Dorr McGehee, Sept. 12, 1959; children: Charles, David, Andrea. BS, Columbia Coll., 1960. Asst. prodn. mgr. Denhard & Stewart, Inc., N.Y.C., 1960-62, art dir., 1963-66, account exec., 1966-71, pres., 1971—. Author: Trade Book Mktg., 1982. Pres. Middlesex County Young Dems., 1963-64; vol. Old Bridge Vol. Fire Dept., East Brunswick, N.J., 1963-66; scoutmaster Troop 7 Boy Scouts Am., Upper Montclair, N.J., 1970-81; elder, Presbyn. Ch., Upper Montclair, 1979-84. Mem. Commonwealth Club, Players Club. Avocations: cycling, skiing, golf, canoeing, backpacking. Home: 204 Old Beach Glen Rd Boonton NJ 07005-9525 Office: Denhard & Stewart Inc 240 Madison Ave New York NY 10016-2820

STEWART, JOANNE, secondary school educator; b. Vancouver, Wash., Mar. 10, 1944; d. Edward Charles and Claudine Marie (Meilleur) Spencer; m. William Lemley Stewart, Sept. 2, 1966 (dec. June 1983); children: Amy Diane, Nicholas William. BS, Mass. State U., 1966, MA, 1973. Cert. tchr., 1966-67; tchr. home econs. Marysville (Wash.) High Sch., 1967-68, Palouse (Wash.) High Sch., 1968-73, Ennis (Mont.) High Sch., 1973-76, Genesee (Idaho) High Sch., 1976-77; instr. young family Missoula (Mont.) County High Sch., 1984-88; tchr. home econs. Woodman Sch., Lolo, Mont., 1985-86; travel cons. Travel Masters, Missoula, 1984-87; ticketing mgr. Blue Caboose Travel, Missoula, 1987-91; tchr. family and consumer scis. Victor (Mont.) High Sch., 1991—. Co-pres. Lolo PTO, 1980-81; v.p. Lolo Community Ctr., 1981; sec. Lolo Mosquito Control Bd., 1988—; mem. telecommunications com. Conrad Burns & Gov. Racicot. Marysville Edn. Assn. scholar, 1962, Future Homemakers Am. scholar, 1962. Mem. AAUW (sec. 1986, program chmn. 1987), Forestry Triangle (pres. 1981, editor cookbook 1982), Future Homemakers Am. (hon. advisor), Am. Family and Consumer Scis. Assn., Mont. Family and Consumer Scis. Assn. (bylaws chair 1994, pres. 1995-96), Mont. Vocat. Tchrs. Assn. (returning Rookie of Yr. 1992), Am. Federated Tchrs., Mont. Vocat. Family and Consumer Scis. Tchrs. (v.p. 1993-94, pres. 1994-95). Republican. Methodist. Avocations: homemaking, swimming. Home: 1200 Lakeside Dr Lolo MT 59847-9705 Office: Victor High Sch Home Econs 425 4th Ave Victor MT 59875-9499

STEWART, JOE J., manufacturing executive; b. 1938. BSChemE, Purdue U., 1959; MA, Kansas State U., 1961; PhD, N.C. State U., 1963; DEng (hon.), Purdue U., 1994. With Aerojet-Gen. Corp., 1966-72; with Babcock & Wilcox Co., New Orleans, 1972—, v.p., 1978; pres., COO Babcock & Wilcox Co., Barberton, Ohio, 1994—. Office: Babcock & Wilcox Co 20 S Van Buren Ave Barberton OH 44203-0351

STEWART, JOE R., law enforcement official; b. Arcadia, La., Apr. 5, 1952; s. Grover and Jane (Thrash) S.; m. Amanda Almeda Gunter, Aug. 24, 1974. BA in Psychology, Northeast La. U., 1974, M in Criminal Justice, 1977; student, Law Enforcement Basic Acad., La. State U., 1975; cert. basic tng., Law Enforcement Tng. Inst., 1978; field in-svc. tng., La. State U., 1980. Police officer Monroe (La.) Police Dept., 1974-90, police sgt., 1990-92, chief of police, 1992—; bd. dirs. Crime Stoppers Internat., 4th Jud. Dist. Atty. BOUNCE Program; instr. North La. Police Acad., 1989-92; co-founder, staff mem. Monroe Police Dept. Law Enforcement Tng. Sys., 1991; active Gov. Task Force on Violent Crime & Homicide, 1993—. Active St. Albans Episc. Ch., Monroe. Mem. Internat. Union Police Assn., Internat. Assn. Chiefs of Police, La. Assn. Chiefs of Police, Internat. Assn. Cult Crime Info. Network, Nat. Chief's Assn., Internat. Fraternal Order of Police, Mcpl. Police Office Assocs., N.E. La. U. Alumni Assn., N.E. La. U. Criminal Justice Alumni Assn. Avocation: hunting, home projects. Home: 1061 Angus Rd Monroe LA 71202 Office: Office of Police Chief PO Box 123 Monroe LA 71210

STEWART, JOHN DAUGHERTY, publishing company executive; b. Indiana, Pa., Oct. 16, 1915; s. Ernest Taylor and Caroline (Daugherty) S.; m. Helen Gambrill, Sept. 23, 1940 (dec. Jan. 1964); children: Caroline Leigh Stewart Estabrook, Susan Stewart Stockard; m. 2d Margret Pahl, Feb. 18, 1967. A.B., Princeton U., 1937; postgrad., Harvard U., 1938-39. Instr. Sch. Pub. and Internat. Affairs Princeton U., 1937-38; mem. editorial staff Bur. Nat. Affairs, Inc., Washington, 1939-80; v.p. Bur. Nat. Affairs, Inc, Washington, 1947-64; pres., editor-in-chief Bur. Nat. Affairs, Inc., Washington, 1964-80, chmn. bd., 1974-94; chmn. tripartite industry com. for minimum wage regulations Am. Samoa, V.I., P.R. Office Sec. Labor, 1957-60; chmn. Southeastern Econ. Devel. Found., 1970-80; chmn. disputes panel Dept. State, 1973-81. Editor: The New Labor Law, 1947, The Landrum-Griffin Act, 1959. Mem. Washington Indsl. Rels. Rsch. Assn. (pres. 1953), Swan Point Yacht and Country Club, Nat. Press Club. Home: 11280 Keokee Ct Issue MD 20645-2206 Office: Bur Nat Affairs Inc 1231 25th St NW Washington DC 20037-1157

STEWART, JOHN EZELL, educational and business consultant; b. Sand Springs, Okla., Aug. 26, 1929; m. Elsie Louise Fonville, June 18, 1954; children: Barry, Johnetta, Rhonda, Howard. BS in Vocat. Edn., Langston (Okla.) U., 1951; MS in Gen. Supervision, Calif. State U., L.A., 1964; grad. study, U. Rich., 1980, 82. Cert. collegiate profl. tchr. Staff supr. Norfolk State U.; asst. exec. v.p. Bus. Devel.; tchr.; project mgr. L.A. City Unified Sch. Dist.; edn. specialist cons. Pepperdine U., L.A.; substitute tchr. Richmond City Pub. Schs.; founder, exec. dir. Va. Adolescent Adult Rehab. Agy.; founder, prin. John Ezell Stewart Sch.; grant administr. Steamer Co., 1991—; faculty chmn. Mary McLeod Bethune Middle Sch.; spl. projects dir.

Tchr. Human rels. Workshops; pres. Pan Hellenic Coun. Mem. Am. Fedn. Tchrs., United Tchrs. L.A., Omega Psi Phi. Democrat. Buddhist. Avocations: self-development tapes, conducting business and training seminars. Office: Stewart's Consulting Svcs PO Box 70441 Richmond VA 23225

STEWART, JOHN HARGER, music educator; b. Cleve., Mar. 31, 1940; s. Cecil Tooker and Marian (Harger) S.; m. Julia Wallace, Aug. 14, 1977; children: Barbara, Cecily Bronwen. BA, Yale U., 1962; MA, Brown U., 1964; cert., New Eng. Coll., 1965. With various operas including Santa Fe Opera, N.Y.C. Opera, Met. Opera, U.S. and Europe, 1965—; lectr. Mt. Holyoke Coll., South Hadley, Mass., 1988-90; assoc. prof. music Washington U., St. Louis, 1990—; head of voice and choral program. Office: Washington U Campus Box 1032 One Brookings Dr Saint Louis MO 63130-4899

STEWART, JOHN IRWIN, JR., lawyer; b. Oklahoma City, Feb. 11, 1950; s. John Irwin and Betty Ann (Boss) S.; m. Sharon S. Stoliaroff, June 19, 1982; children: John Welling, Alexander Linzey. BA, U. Mich., 1971; JD, U. Chgo., 1975. Bar: D.C. 1975, U.S. Ct. Appeals (D.C. cir.) 1976, U.S. Supreme Ct. 1980, U.S. Ct. Appeals (2d cir.) 1986, U.S. Ct. Appeals (3d cir.) 1990. Assoc. Jones, Day, Reavis & Pogue, Washington, 1975-79; assoc. Crowell & Moring, Washington, 1979-82, ptnr., 1982—; adj. prof. Am. U. Washington Coll. Law, Washington, 1979-80. Author: (with others) Legal Guide to Broadcast Law and Regulation, 1988; topics and comment editor U. Chgo. Law Rev., 1974-75. Mem. Fed. Comm. Bar Assn. (co-chair CLE com. 1989-91). Office: Crowell & Moring 1001 Pennsylvania Ave NW Washington DC 20004-2505

STEWART, JOHN LINCOLN, university administrator; b. Alton, Ill., Jan. 24, 1917; s. Frederick William and Hilda (Donovan) S.; m. Joan Elsdon Guthridge, Sept. 23 1939 (div. 1964); children: Leslie Cythera Stewart Chalmers, Ann Guthridge Stewart Nutt; m. Ruth Peabody Quinn, July 11, 1964; stepchildren: Geoffrey Cornelius Quinn, Andrew Dean Quinn. AB, Denison U., 1938, ArtsD (hon.), 1964; MA, Ohio State U., 1939, PhD, 1947. Teaching asst. then instr. Ohio State U., Columbus, 1939-47; instr. UCLA, 1947-49; asst. prof. then prof. English Dartmouth Coll., Hanover, N.H., 1949-64; prof. Lit. U. Calif., San Diego, 1964-87, provost John Muir Coll., 1965-87. Author: Exposition for Science and Technical Students, 1950, The Essay, 1952, John Crowe Ransom, 1962, The Burden of Time, 1965, (with others) Horizons Circled, 1974, Ernst Krenek, 1990; contbr. articles to various pubs. assoc. dir. Hopkins Ctr. for Arts, 1961-64; dir. Mandeville Ctr. for Arts, 1974-76; mem. Dartmouth Community Symphony Orch., 1949-58; trustee Kinhaven Music Sch., 1960-64, Fla. West Coast Symphony, 1958; bd. dirs. Theater and Arts Found. San Diego County, 1970; pres. La Jolla (Calif.) Friends Sch. Music, 1971-73, Friends of Music, U. Calif., San Diego. Served with Aus, 1942-45. Howard Found. fellow, 1953-54, Dartmouth Coll. fellow, 1962-63. Democrat. Avocation: performer with music ensembles. Home: 9473 La Jolla Farms Rd La Jolla CA 92037-1128 Office: U Calif San Diego # 0106 La Jolla CA 92093

STEWART, JOHN MURRAY, banker; b. Summit, N.J., Apr. 2, 1943; s. Robert John Stewart and Mary Catherine (Grabhorn) Stewart Yoder; m. Sandra Meyers Frazier, Feb. 26, 1966; children: Jennifer Bricar, Catherine Dorothy. BA, U. Va., 1965; MBA, NYU, 1983. Trust officer, v.p. Bankers Trust Co., N.Y.C., 1965-82, Morgan Guaranty Trust Co., N.Y.C., 1982-83; mgr., pres., dir. Morgan Trust Co. Fla., Palm Beach, 1983-89; pres., dir. Bankers Trust Co. Fla., 1989-93; pres. pvt. capital group Sun Trust Bank, Orlando, Fla., 1993—. Campaign chmn. Palm Beach Community Chest, 1985, 86; vestryman Bethesda By the Sea Ch., Palm Beach, 1986-89, 92-94, treas. 1986-87; bd. dirs. Orlando Opera Co., 1994—. Mem. Fla. Bankers Assn. (chmn. trust bus. devel. com. 1989, planning commn.), N.Y. State Bankers Assn. (mem. trust bus. devel. com. 1978-82), N.Y. Yacht Club (N.Y.C.), Everglades Club (Palm Beach), Winter Park Racquet Club, Monmouth Boat Club (Red Bank, N.J.), Sailfish of Fla. (Palm Beach) (bd. govs. 1992—).

STEWART, JOHN WRAY BLACK, college dean; b. Coleraine, Northern Ireland, Jan. 16, 1936; s. John Wray and Margaret Reid (Black) S.; m. Felicity Ann Patricia Poole, Aug. 7, 1965; children: J.W. Matthew, Hannah Louise. BSc with honors, Queen's U., Belfast, Northern Ireland, 1958, B.Agr. with honors, 1959, PhD, 1963, DSc, 1988. Registered profl. agrologist. Sci. officer chem. rsch. div. Ministry of Agr., Belfast, 1959-64; asst. prof. soil sci. U. Sask., Saskatoon, Can., 1966-71, assoc. prof., 1971-76, prof., 1976-81; dir. Sask. Inst. Pedology U. Sask., 1981-89; dean Coll. Agr. U. Sask., Saskatoon, 1989—; tech. expert, cons. FAO/IAEA, U.N.D.P., Vienna, Austria, 1971, 1974-75; sec.-gen. Sci. Com. on Problems of Environment, Paris, 1988-92; cons. UNESCO, Paris, 1990, pres. Sci. Com on problems of the Environment, 1992; trustee Internat. Inst. Tropical Agriculture, Nigeria, 1991—; mem. sci. adv. com. Inter-Am. Inst. on Global Change Res., 1994—. Contbr. articles to profl. publs., chpts. to books. Fellow Can. Soc. Soil Sci., Berlin Inst. Advanced Study, Am. Soc. Agronomy, Soil Sci. Soc. Am.; mem. Brit. Soc. Soil Sci., Brazilian Soc. Soil Sci., Internat. Soc. Soil Sci., Agrl. Inst. Can. Avocations: squash, racquet ball, tennis. Office: U Sask, Coll Agr, Saskatoon, SK Canada S7N 0W0

STEWART, JONATHAN TAYLOR, psychiatrist, educator; b. Bethpage, N.Y., Mar. 15, 1956; s. Allen Theodore and Vivian (Dreiblatt) S.; m. Linda Sue Irvin, Oct. 27, 1984; children: Jacob Zachary, Aaron Joshua. BA with honors, Rollins Coll., 1976; MD, U. South Fla., 1979. Diplomate Am. Bd. Psychiatry and Neurology, Geriatric Psychiatry, Nat. Bd. Med. Examiners. Resident in psychiatry U. Fla. Coll. Medicine, Gainesville, 1979-83, assoc. prof. psychiatry, 1983-94; asst. chief psychiatry VA Med. Ctr., Gainesville, 1987-94; prof. psychiatry U So. Fla. Coll. Medicine, 1994—; chief geropsychiatry sect. Bay Pines (Fla.) VA Med. Ctr., 1994—. Contbr. articles to profl. jours., 1985—. Mem. Head Injury Adv. Council State of Fla., 1985-90, Gov.'s Alzheimer's Disease Registry Subcom., 1987—, VA Task Force on Extended Care, Washington, 1986. Fellow Am. Psychiat. Assn.; mem. Am. Geriatrics Soc., Fla. Psychiat. Soc. Jewish. Avocations: cooking, cycling, skin diving, traveling. flying. Office: VA Med Ctr Psychiatry Service 116A Bay Pines FL 33504

STEWART, JOSEPH LESTER, rubber company executive; b. Newton, Ala., May 31, 1915; s. Joseph Crawford and Allie (Lester) S.; m. Margaret Hines, Feb. 9, 1946; children: Margaret Allison, Barbara Lynne. B.S., Auburn U., 1937; student, Nat. War Coll., 1956-57. Commd. 2d lt. USMC 1937, advanced through grades to brig. gen., 1962; dep. dir. strategic plans dir. on staff Supreme Allied Comdr. Atlantic, 1957-59; dir. Marine Corps Command and Staff Coll., 1959-61, dep. dir. Marine Corps Ednl. Center, 1961-62; comdg. gen. Marine Corps Base 29 Palms, Calif., 1962-64; dir. Marine Corps Res., 1964-65, ret., 1965; sr. v.p. Armstrong Rubber Co., West Haven, Conn., 1965-71; chmn. bd. Armstrong Rubber Co., 1971-80, chmn. exec. com., dir., 1980-86, ret. cons. to co., 1986—. Decorated Silver Star medal, Legion of Merit with combat V and 3 Gold Stars, Bronze Star medal with combat V and 1 Gold Star, Air medal; several fgn. decorations. Episcopalian. Office: 6060 Leeland St S Saint Petersburg FL 33715-1638

STEWART, JOSEPH MELVIN, food products executive; b. Maringouin, La., Dec. 23, 1942; m. Clara St. Amant, June 18, 1967; children: Erick, Kendra. BS in Foods and Nutrition, So. U., Baton Rouge; postgrad., USDA Grad. Sch. Dir. food services, dir. child nutrition programs Washington Pub. Sch. System, 1971-80; dir. child nutrition programs div. U.S. food products Kellogg Co., Battle Creek, Mich., 1980-81, dir. corp. communications div. pub. affairs, 1981-85, v.p. pub. affairs, 1985—, sr. v.p. corp. affairs, 1988—; mem. adv. council food industry FEA, 1975. Mem. adv. council Coll. Agr. and Home Econs., So. U.; bd. govs. Pub. Affairs Council Am.; trustee Battle Creek Health System; mem. nat. agrl. rsch. and extension users adv. bd. Dept. of Agr.; bd. dirs. Battle Creek Area Urban League. Recipient Silver Plate award Foodservice Mfrs. Assn., 1974. Home: 231 Central St Battle Creek MI 49017-3346 Office: Kellogg Co 1 Kellogg Sq Battle Creek MI 49017-3534

STEWART, JOSEPH TURNER, JR., retired pharmaceutical company executive; b. N.Y.C., Apr. 30, 1929; s. Joseph Turner and Edna (Pride) S.; m. Carol Graham, Aug. 7, 1954; children: Lisa D., Alison D. BS with honors, U.S. Mcht. Marine Acad., 1951; MBA, Harvard U., 1954. Systems analyst Warner Lambert Co., Morris Plains, N.J., 1954-56; budget dir. internat. Warner Lambert Co., 1956-60, asst. div. controller consumer products group, 1960-62, div. controller group, 1962-66; dir. adminstrn. and fin. Proprietary Drug div. Warner Lamber Co., 1966; dir. Lactona Products div. Warner Lamber Co., 1967; controller Beech-Nut subs. Squibb Corp., N.Y.C., 1968; v.p. fin. Beech-Nut subs. Squibb Corp., 1968-71, v.p. planning, corp. staff parent corp., 1971-79, v.p. fin. and planning-parent co., 1979-82, sr. v.p. corporate affairs, 1982-89; also bd. dirs.; cons. Johnson & Johnson, 1990—; bd. dirs. Gen. Am. Investment Corp., Liposome Co. Pres.,, mem. exec. coun. Harvard U. Bus. Sch. Assn., 1971-76, mem. vis. com. Bus. Sch., 1976-82; trustee Tax Found., 1985-89; commr. N.J. State Commn. on Income and Expenditures, 1985-88; mem. adv. com. Grad Sch. Indsl. Adminstrn., Carnegie Mellon U., 1986-91; trustee New Sch. for Social Rsch., 1990—, U. Medicine and Dentistry of N.J. Found., 1989—; bd. dirs. Liposomie Co., 1995—; vis. coun. Madonna Biological Lab., 1995—. John Hay Whitney Opportunity fellow, 1952-54. Club: Harvard (N.Y.C.). Office: Johnson & Johnson 1 Johnson Johnson Plz New Brunswick NJ 08933

STEWART, JULIE, nonprofit organization executive; b. Pullman, Wash., Nov. 7, 1956; d. Alan M. Stewart and Carol J. Dubert Smythe; m. Paul N. Beckner, June 19, 1990. BA, Mills Coll., Oakland, Calif., 1988. Flight attendant Pan Am. World Airways, 1978-86; pub. affairs dir. Cato Inst., Washington, 1989-91; pres. Families Against Mandatory Minimums, Washington, 1991—. Mem. Phi Beta Kappa. Avocations: skiing, tennis, jogging, hiking. Office: Families Against Mandatory #200-S 1001 Pennsylvania Ave NW Washington DC 20004

STEWART, KENT KALLAM, analytical biochemistry educator; b. Omaha, Sept. 5, 1934; s. George Franklin and Grace (Sledge) S.; m. Margaret Reiber, June 10, 1956; children: Elizabeth, Cynthia, Richard, Robert. Student, U. Chgo., 1951-53; AB, U. Calif., Berkeley, 1956; PhD, Fla. State U., 1965. Guest investigator Rockefeller U., N.Y.C., 1965-67, research assoc., 1967-68, asst. prof., 1968-69; research chemist U.S. Dept. Agr., Beltsville, Md., 1970-75, lab. chief Nutrient Composition Lab., 1975-82; prof., head dept. food sci. and tech. Va. Poly. Inst. and State U., Blacksburg, 1982-85; prof. biochemistry, anaerobic microbiology, food sci./tech. Va. Poly. Inst. and State U., 1985—. Author articles and book chpts.; editor Jour. Food Composition and Analysis, also 2 books Patentee in field. Capt. USMCR, 1956-59. Fellow Inst. Food Technologist, AAAS; mem. Am. Chem. Soc., Assn. Ofcl. Analytical Chemists, Sigma Xi. Home: 517 Shawnee Trl Blacksburg VA 24060-8857 Office: Dept Biochemistry and Anaerobic Microbiology Va Poly Inst and State U Blacksburg VA 24061-0308

STEWART, KIRK T., public relations executive; b. 1951. BA in polit. sci., U. So. Calif., 1973; MA in public rels./journalism, 1976. Account exec. Burson-Marsteller, 1976-79; pub. affairs dir. Info. Svcs. Dir. TRW, 1979-81; group supr. Manning Selvage & Lee, 1981-82, v.p., 1982-83, exec. v.p., 1983-84; exec. v.p. mng. dir. Manning Selvage & Lee/L.A., Calif., 1984-89; pres. Manning, Selvage & Lee Inc., N.Y.C., 1989-91, pres., CEO, 1992; pres., CEO Manning, Selvage & Lee, Inc., N.Y.C., 1993—. Office: Manning Selvage & Lee Inc 79 Madison Ave New York NY 10016-7802

STEWART, MARGARET MCBRIDE, biology educator, researcher; b. Guilford County, N.C., Feb. 6, 1927; d. David Henry and Mary Ellen (Morrow) S.; m. Paul C. Lemon, June 1962 (div. 1968); m. George Edward Martin, Dec. 19, 1969. AB, U. N.C.-Greensboro, 1948; MA, U. N.C.-Chapel Hill, 1951; PhD, Cornell U., 1956. Instr. biology Greensboro Evening Coll. U. N.C., Greensboro, 1950-51; instr. biology Catawba Coll., Salisbury, N.C., 1951-53; extension botanist Cornell U., Ithaca, N.Y., 1954-56; asst. prof. biology SUNY, Albany, 1956-59, assoc. prof., 1959-65, prof. vertebrate biology, 1965—, Disting. Teaching prof., 1977—; faculty rsch. participant Oak Ridge Assoc. Univs., 1983. Author: (with A.H. Benton) Keys to the Vertebrates of the Northeastern States, 1964, Amphibians of Malawi, 1967; contbr. numerous articles and revs. to profl. jours. Bd. dirs. E.N. Huyck Nature Preserve, Rensselaerville, N.Y., 1976-86; bd. dirs. Ea. N.Y. chpt. Nature Conservancy, 1983-88, 90—, N.Y. State chpt. 1987-90; mem. Albany Pine Bush Commn., 1993—. Recipient Citizen Laureate award SUNY Found., 1987, Am. Philos. Soc. rsch. grantee, 1975, 81, NSF grantee, 1978-80, Oak Ridge Assocs. Univs. grantee, 1983—. Fellow Herpetologists League (bd. dirs. 1976-80); mem. Soc. for Study of Amphibians and Reptiles (pres. 1979), Am. Soc. Ichthyologists and Herpetologists (bd. govs. 1975-80, 87-90, herpetology editor 1983-85, pres.-elect 1995), Ecol. Soc. Am., Assn. for Tropical Biology, Soc. Study of Evolution, Sigma Xi, Sigma Delta Epsilon, Phi Kappa Phi. Democrat. Presbyterian. Avocations: photography, gardening, reading, travel. Office: SUNY Dept Biol Scis 1400 Washington Ave Albany NY 12222-0001

STEWART, MARK CARROLL, lawyer; b. Norwalk, Ohio, Feb. 7, 1947; s. William C. and Doris (Perry) S.; m. Sandra Jayne Fabel, June 25, 1977; children: Ellen Fabel, Ann Emily. AB, Oberlin Coll., 1969; JD, U. Minn., 1972. Bar: Minn. 1972, Ohio 1976. Law clk. to presiding judge Minn. Dist. Ct. (4th dist.), Rochester, 1972; ptnr. Saltness and Stewart, Dawson, Minn., 1973-76, Childs, Stewart, Fortney, Byer & Chambers, Van Wert, Ohio, 1976-79; gen. counsel Ohio Farmers Grain & Supply Assn., Fostoria, 1979-85; gen. counsel, sec. Country Mark Inc., 1985-91; corp. counsel Ohio/Mich. Countrymark Coop., Inc., Delaware, Ohio, 1991—; ptnr. Shumaker, Loop & Kendrick, Toledo, 1992—. Mem. ABA, Ohio Bar Assn., Nat. Soc. Accts. for Coops., Nat. Coun. Farmers Coops. (legal, tax and acctg. coms.), Sierra Club. Democrat. Avocations: gardening; outdoorsman. Office: Shumaker, Loop & Kendrick 1000 Jackson St Toledo OH 43624-1573

STEWART, MARLENE JEAN, costume designer; b. Boston, Aug. 25, 1949; d. William Edward and Germaine (Cormier) S. BA, U. Calif., Berkeley, 1972, MA; AA, Fashion Inst. Tech., N.Y.C., 1975, Fashion Inst. Design and Mdsing., Los Angeles, 1976. Fashion designer, owner Covers Inc., Calif., 1978-84. Costume designer: (films) Body Rock, 1984, Back to the Beach, 1987, Siesta, 1987, The Women's Club, 1987, Pet Sematary, 1989, Gingerale Afternoon, 1989, Wild Orchid, 1990, Side Out, 1990, The Doors, 1991, JFK, 1991, Terminator 2: Judgement Day, 1991, Pet Sematary Two, 1992, Point of No Return, 1993, I'll Do Anything, 1994, The River Wild, 1994, True Lies, 1994, (TV movies) Pair of Aces, 1990, (videos) Material Girl, Dress You Up, Would I Lie, (concert tours) Madonna's Virgin Tour, 1985, Madonna's World Tour, 1987. Cons. wardrobe Duran Duran, Earth Wind and Fire, Eurythmics, Pointer Sisters, Madonna, Janet Jackson, Grace Jones, Sylvie Vartan, Isabella Rosellini, Michael Pare. Redipient award design, Designer Bob Mackie, 1977, best costume designer Am. Video awards, 1985. Mem. Nat. Acad. Video Arts and Scics., Nat. Orgn. Female Exec., Costume Designers Guild, Am. Film Inst. (Women Film award, 1987), Mus. Contemporary Art. Home: 1416 N Havenhurst Dr #1C Los Angeles CA 90046*

STEWART, MARSHA BEACH, sales executive, entertainment executive; b. Memphis, Jan. 17, 1952; d. Bruce Charles and Marjorie Hudson (Campbell) Stewart; m. Michael G. Mushalla, Dec. 27, 1992. BBA in Internat. Bus., U. Tex., 1982; MFA in Arts Adminstrn./Dance Mgmt., Yale U., 1985. Mng. dir. Yale Cabaret, New Haven, 1984-85; agt. Columbia Artists Mgmt., Inc., N.Y.C., 1985-90; v.p. dir. sales SATRA Arts Internat. (formerly Classical Artists), N.Y.C., 1990-92; pres. Beach Internat. Enterprises, Inc., N.Y.C., 1993—; dancer with Louisville (Ky.) Ballet (formerly Civic), 1967-70, Actor's Theatre of Louisville, 1972, Arena Stage, Washington, 1972, Disney on Parade, NBC, S.Am., Europe, Africa, 1974, 75, 76, Geneva (Switzerland) Ballet Co., 1975, 76; dance chairwoman cultural entertainment com. U. Tex., Austin, 1981-82. NEA fellow, 1983, assoc., 1984. Mem. NAFE, Internat. Soc. Performing Arts Adminstrs., Assn. Performing Arts Presentors, Yale U. Alumni Assn., Yale Club of N.Y.C., Scottish Heritage Soc., N.Y. Caledonian Club, Tex. Execs. Avocations: travel, languages, ice skating.

STEWART, MARTHA KOSTYRA, caterer, author, lecturer; b. Jersey City; d. Edward and Martha (Ruszkowski) Kostyra; m. Andy Stewart, July 1, 1961 (div. 1990); 1 child, Alexis. BA in European History and Archtl. History, Barnard. Former model; former stockbroker N.Y.C.; profl. caterer; mag. owner, editor-in-chief Martha Stewart Living, 1990—; lifestyle cons. for K-Mart Corp. Author: (with Elizabeth Hawes) Entertaining, 1982, Weddings, 1987; Martha Stewart's Hors d'Oeurvres: The Creation and Presentation of Fabulous Finger Food, 1984, Martha Stewart's Pies and Tarts, 1985, Martha Stewart's Quick Cook Menus: Fifty-two Meals You Can Make in Under an Hour, 1988, The Wedding Planner, 1988, Martha Stewart's Gardening: Month by Month, 1991, Martha Stewart's New Old House:

Restoration, Renovation, Decoration, 1992, Martha Stewart's Christmas, 1993, Martha Stewart's Menus for Entertaining, 1994, Holidays, 1994; appears in weekly cooking segment on Today Show. Office: Martha Stewart Inc 10 Saugatuck Ave Westport CT 06880 also: c/o Susan Magrino Agy 167 E 73rd St New York NY 10021

STEWART, MARY FLORENCE ELINOR, author; b. Sunderland, Durham, Eng., Sept. 17, 1916; d. Frederick A. and Mary Edith (Matthews) Rainbow; m. Frederick H. Stewart, 1945. BA, Durham U., 1938, MA, 1941. Asst. lectr. English Durham U., 1941-45, part-time lectr. English, 1948-56; part-time lectr. English St. Hild's Training Coll., 1948-56. Author: Madam, Will You Talk?, 1954, Wildfire at Midnight, 1956, Thunder on the Right, 1957, Nine Coaches Waiting, 1958, My Brother Michael, 1959 (Brit. Crime Writers Assn. award 1960), The Ivy Tree, 1961, The Moonspinners, 1962, This Rough Magic, 1964 (Mystery Writers Am. award 1964), Airs Above the Ground, 1965, The Gabriel Hounds, 1967, The Wind Off the Small Isles, 1968, The Crystal Cave, 1970 (Frederick Niven award 1971), The Little Broomstick, 1971, The Hollow Hills, 1973, Ludo and The Star Horse, 1974 (Scottish Arts Coun. award 1974), Touch Not the Cat, 1976, The Last Enchantment, 1979, A Walk in Wolf Wood, 1980, The Wicked Day, 1983, Thornyhold, 1988, Frost on the Window and Other Poems, 1990, The Stormy Petrel, 1991. Fellow Newnham Coll., Cambridge, 1986. Mem. P.E.N. Office: care William Morrow 1350 Ave of the Americas New York NY 10019 also: care Hodder & Stoughton Ltd, 338 Euston Rd, London NW1 3BH, England*

STEWART, MELBOURNE GEORGE, JR., physicist, educator; b. Detroit Sept. 30, 1927; s. Melbourne George and Ottilie (Tuholke) S.; m. Charlotte L. Ford, Jan. 23, 1954; children—Jill K., John H., Kevin G. A.B., U. Mich., 1949, M.S., 1950, Ph.D., 1955. Research assoc. dept. physics AEC, Ames Lab., Iowa State U., 1955-56, asst. prof., 1956-62, assoc. prof., 1962-63; prof. Wayne State U., Detroit, 1963-94, prof. emeritus, 1994—, chmn. dept. physics, 1963-73, assoc. provost for faculty relations, 1973-86; hon. research fellow Univ. Coll., London, 1986-87,93. Editorial bd.: Wayne State U. Press, 1969-73. Served with AUS, 1946-47. Mem. Am. Phys. Soc., AAAS, Sigma Xi, Phi Beta Kappa. Home: 415 Bournemouth Rd Grosse Pointe MI 48236-2817 Office: Dept Physics Wayne State U Detroit MI 48202

STEWART, MELVIN, Olympic athlete, swimmer. Olympic swimmer Barcelona, Spain, 1992. Recipient 200m Butterfly Gold medal Olympics, Barcelona, 1992. Office: US Olympic Com 1750 E Boulder St Colorado Springs CO 80909

STEWART, MILTON ROY, lawyer; b. Clovis, N.Mex., Dec. 16, 1945; s. Virgil Maurice and E. Marie (Collins) S. BA, Ind. U., 1968, JD summa cum laude, 1971. Bar: Oreg. 1971, U.S. Ct. Appeals (9th cir.) 1971, U.S. Dist. Ct. (no. dist.) Oreg. 1971. Assoc. firm Davies, Biggs, et. al., Portland, Oreg., 1971-75; v.p., gen. counsel U.S. Datacorp, Portland, 1975-77; pvt. practice, Portland, 1977-86; ptnr. Davis, Wright Tremaine and predecessor firm, Portland, 1987—, mem. exec. com., mem. mgmt. com, chmn. firmwide bus. group. Chmn. Neighborhoods West Northwest, Portland, 1976, Oreg. chpt. Nat. Multiple Sclerosis Soc., 1994—; mem. pres. adv. bd. Portland State U.; bd. dirs., sec. YMCA of Columbia-Willamette, Portland, 1978-81; bd. vis. Ind. U. Sch. Law. Capt. U.S. Army, 1968-78. State Farm Found. fellow, 1970; John H. Edwards fellow Ind. U. Found., 1971. Mem. Oreg. State Bar, Multnomah Athletic Club, Astoria Golf and Country Club. Office: Davis Wright Tremaine 1300 SW 5th Ave Portland OR 97201-5606

STEWART, NORMAN LAWRENCE, university president; b. East St. Louis, Ill., June 20, 1942; s. Alfred and Helen (Grenard) S.; m. Nancy Lee Rosenthal, Aug. 28, 1966; children: Ian Andrew, Colin August, Brian Alfred. James scholar, U. Ill., 1960-61; B.A. with honors, diploma theology (asst. 1963-64), Wheaton (Ill.) Coll., 1963; honors scholarship, Near East Sch. Archaeology, Jerusalem, 1962; cert., Goethe Inst., W. Ger., 1964; fellow, U. Freiburg, W. Ger., 1964-65; honors fellow, Princeton Theol. Sem., 1966-67; M.A. (U.S. Steel Found. fellow), St. Louis U., 1971, Ph.D., 1972; Fulbright fellow, U. Bonn, W. Ger., 1971-72; LLD, Kobe U., Japan, 1987. Asst. dir. Dothan Archaeol. Expdn., Jenin, Israel, 1964; resident dir. Near East Sch. Archaeology, 1965-66; research asso. polit. archives W. German Fgn. Ministry, Bonn, 1971-72; mem. faculty Maryville Coll., St. Louis 1972-77; asso. prof. history, asso. acad. dean Maryville Coll., 1975-77; acad. dean. Coll. Mt. St. Joseph, Cin., 1977-79; pres. Rockford (Ill.) Coll., 1979-87, Regent's Coll., London, 1984-87; CEO, Brakeley, John Price Jones, London, 1987-91, Chancery Strategies, London, 1991—; pres. Teikyo Post U., Waterbury, Conn., 1992—; co-founder Lincoln Acad., N.Y.C., 1966; bd. dirs. Rockford Devel. Corp., 1979-87. Author: Dothan Archaeological Expedition Tomb No. 1, 1964, German Relations with the Arab East, 1937-41, 1972. Trustee Kobe Coll., 1979-90, Am. Sch. in London, 1990-92; trustee Lincoln Acad., Ill., 1979-87; bd. dirs. New Am. Theatre, Rockford, 1980-86, Swedish-Am. Hosp., 1980-87; divsn. chmn. Rockford United Way, 1981; precinct committeeman, St. Clair County, Ill., 1972-73; adv. bd. St. Louis Metro Police Acad., 1974-77; bd. dirs. Vis. Nurses Assn., Cin., 1978-79. Mem. Am. Assn. Pres. Ind. Colls. and Univs. Internat. Assn. Univ. Pres., Council Ind. Colls., Archaeol. Inst. Am., Am. Hist. Assn., Phi Beta Kappa, Alpha Sigma Nu. Presbyterian.

STEWART, PATRICIA CARRY, foundation administrator; b. Bklyn., May 19, 1928; d. William J. and Eleanor (Murphy) Carry; m. Charles Thorp Stewart, May 30, 1976. Student U. Paris, 1948-49; BA, Cornell U., 1950. Fgn. corr. Irving Trust Co., N.Y.C., 1950-51; with Janeway Rsch. Co., N.Y.C., 1951-60, sec., treas., 1955-60; with Buckner & Co. and successor firms, N.Y.C., 1961-73, ptnr., 1962-70, v.p-treas., 1970-71, pres.-treas., 1971-73; pres., treas. Knight, Carry, Bliss & Co., Inc., N.Y.C., 1971-73; pres., treas. G. Tsai & Co., Inc., 1973; v.p. Edna McConnell Clark Found., 1974-92; dir., vice chair Cmty. Found. Palm Beach and Martin Counties; bd. dirs. Melville Corp., Borden Inc., 1976-95, Continental Corp., Bankers Trust Co., Bankers Trust N.Y. Corp., Trans World Airlines, 1973-85, Morton Norivich Inc., 1979-84; allied mem. N.Y. Stock Exch., 1973-72; past mem. nominating com. Am. Stock Exch., N.Y. Stock Exch., N.Y.C. Fin. Svcs. Corp.; dir. emeritus, past chmn. Investor Responsibility Rsch. Ctr. Trustee, vice-chair Cornell U., bd. life overseers Cornell Med. Coll.; vis. com. Grad. Sch. Bus., Harvard U., 1974-80; bd. dirs. NOW Legal Def. and Edn. Fund, 1984-92, Women in Founds./Corp. Philanthropy 1980-86; vice chmn. Community Found. Palm Beach and Martin Counties, 1993—; v.p. fin. com. Women's Forum, 1982-90; vice chmn. CUNY, 1976-80; bd. dirs. United Way of Tri-State, 1977-81, Inst. for Edn. and Rsch. on Women and Work; voting mem. Blue Cross and Blue Shield Greater N.Y., 1975-82; trustee N.Y. State 4-H Found., 1970-76, Internat. Inst. Rural Reconstruction, 1974-79; mem. N.Y.C. panel White House Fellows, 1976-78; mem. bus. adv. coun. The Hosp. Chaplaincy. Recipient Elizabeth Cutter Morrow award YWCA, 1977, Catalyst award Women Dirs. in Corps., 1978, Trustee medal CUNY, 1983, Accomplishment award Wings Club N.Y., 1984, Women's Funding Coalition Innovators for Women$hare award, 1986, Banking Industry Achievement award Nat. Assn. Bank Women, 1987, Cert. Disting. Accomplishments Barnard Coll., 1989; named to YWCA Acad. Women Achievers. Mem. Fin. Women's Assn. N.Y., NOW (bd. dirs.), Coun. Fgn. Rels., Pi Beta Phi. Clubs: University (N.Y.C.); Gullane Golf (Scotland), The Glen (Scotland). Home and Office: 2613 N Ocean Blvd Delray Beach FL 33483 also: Halfland Barns, North Berwick EH395PW, Scotland

STEWART, PATRICK, actor; b. Mirfield, Eng., July 13, 1940; s. Alfred and Gladys (Barraclough) S. Trained, Bristol Old Vic Theatre Sch. Performed in (theatre) Treasure Island (U.K., debut), 1959, (U.S.) A Midsummer Night's Dream (Broadway debut), 1970, A Christmas Carol, 1991, 92, 94; (TV series) Star Trek: The Next Generation, 1987-94, (mini series) I, Claudius, 1977, Tinker, Sailor, Soldier, Spy, 1979, Smiley's People, 1982, Playing Shakespeare, 1983, When the Lion Roars, 1992, (TV movies) Little Lord Fauntleroy, 1980, John Paul II, 1984, Death Train, 1993; host on Saturday Night Live, 1994; actor (films) Hennessy, 1975, Hedda, 1975, Excalibur, 1981, The Plague Dogs (voice) 1982, Dune, 1984, Lifeforce, 1985, Code Name: Emerald, 1985, Wild Geese II, 1985, The Doctor and the Devils, 1985, Lady Jane, 1986, L.A. Story, 1991, Robin Hood: Men in Tights, 1993, Gunmen, 1994, Star Trek: Generations, 1994, The Pagemaster, 1994 (voice), Jeffrey, 1995; assoc. artist with Royal Shakespeare Co., 1967—. Office: Internat Creative Mgmt 8942 Wilshire Blvd Beverly Hills CA 90211*

STEWART, PAYNE (WILLIAM PAYNE STEWART), professional golfer; b. Springfield, Mo., 1957; m. Tracey Stewart; children: Chelsea, Aaron. Cochampion S.W. Conf., 1979; winner Indian and Indonesian Opens, 1981, Tweed Head Classic, 1981, Magnolia Classic, 1982, Quad Cities Open, 1982, Walt Disney World Classic, 1983, Hertz Bay Hill Classic, 1987, PGA Chmpionship, 1989, MCI Heritage Classic, 1989, 90, Byron Nelson Golf Classic, 1990, U.S. Open, 1991, Heineken Dutch Open, 1991, Morocco Open, 1992, 93, Skins Game Champion, 1991, 92, 93; mem. Ryder Cup U.S. team 1987, 89, 91, 93, World Cup U.S. team 1987, 90. Address: care PGA Tour 112 TPC Blvd Ponte Vedra Beach FL 32082*

STEWART, PETER BEAUFORT, retired beverage company executive; b. Montreal, Que., Can., Aug. 23, 1923; s. Harold Beaufort and Mary W. (Martin) S.; m. Yolande Winifred Powell, June 1955; children—Thomas B., Angus B. B.Comm., McGill U.; M.B.A., Harvard U. With Bldg. Products Ltd., Toronto, Ont., Can., 1947-62; ptr., v.p. mktg. Molson Breweries Ltd., Montreal, 1962-66; pres. Molson Western Breweries Ltd., Calgary, Alta., Can., 1966-70; exec. v.p., pres. Molson Breweries Ltd., Montreal, 1970-75; exec. v.p. The Molson Cos. Ltd., Toronto, 1975-88; dir. Stewart Group Ltd. Toronto.

STEWART, RICHARD ALFRED, business executive; b. Hartford, Conn., Nov. 2, 1945; s. Charles Alfred and Theresia (Procopio) S. BS, Valley Coll., 1967. Account exec. Bank Printing Inc., Los Angeles, 1967-70; pres. Carpet Closet Inc., Los Angeles, 1970-73; western sales mgr. Josten's, Los Angeles, 1973-84; pres. Western Internat. Premiums, Los Angeles, 1984-87; dir. corp. sales Tiffany and Co., Beverly Hills, Calif., 1987-90, dir. major program sales, 1990-92; dir. regional sales Tiffany and Co., N.Y.C., 1992-93, dir. major programs, 1992-93; v.p. sales & mktg. Am. Gem Corp.; recognition cons. L.A. Olympic Com., 1983-84. Contbr. articles to profl. mags.; developer medals for 1984 summer Olympics. Chmn. bd. dirs. Athletes and Entertainers for Kids. Avocations: tennis, basketball, photography.

STEWART, RICHARD BURLESON, lawyer, educator; b. Cleve., Feb. 12, 1940; s. Richard Siegfreid and Ruth Dysert (Staten) S.; m. Alice Peck Fales, May 13, 1967; children: William, Paul, Elizabeth; m. Jane Laura Bloom, Sept. 20, 1992; 1 child, Emily. A.B., Yale U., 1961; M.A. (Rhodes scholar), Oxford (Eng.) U., 1963; LL.B., Harvard U., 1966; Dr. (hon.), Erasmus U., Rotterdam, 1993. Bar: D.C. 1968, U.S. Supreme Ct 1971. Law clk. to Justice Potter Stewart, U.S. Supreme Ct., 1966-67; assoc. Covington & Burling, Washington, 1967-71; asst. prof. law Harvard U., 1971-75, prof., 1975-82, Byrne prof. adminstrv. law,, 1982-89, assoc. dean, 1984-86; asst. atty. gen. environment and natural resources div. Dept. Justice, Washington, 1989-91; prof. law NYU Law Sch., 1992-94, Emily Kempin prof. law, 1994—; of counsel Sidley & Austin, 1992—; spl. counsel U.S. Senate Watergate Com., 1974; vis. prof. law U. Calif., Berkeley Law Sch., 1979-80, U. Chgo. Law Sch., 1986-87, Georgetown U., 1991-92. Author: (with J. Krier) Environmental Law and Policy, 1978, (with S. Breyer) Administrative Law and Regulation, 1979, 3d edit., 1990, (with E. Rehbinder) Integration Through Law: Environmental Protection Policy. Fellow Am. Acad. Arts and Scis.; mem. ABA, Am. Law Inst. Office: NYU Law Sch 40 Washington Sq S New York NY 10012-1099

STEWART, RICHARD DONALD, internist, educator; b. Lakeland, Fla., Dec. 26, 1926; s. LeRoy Hepburn and Zoa Irene (Hachet) S.; m. Mary Leeuw, June 14, 1952; children: R. Scot, Gregory D., Mary E. AB, U. Mich., 1951, MD, 1955, MPH, 1962; MA, U. Wis. Milw., 1979, postgrad. Diplomate Am. Bd. Internal Medicine, Am. Bd. Med. Toxicology, Acad. Toxicol. Scis. Intern Saginaw (Mich.) Gen. Hosp., 1955-56; resident U. Mich. Med. Ctr., Ann Arbor, 1959-62; dir. med. rsch. sect. Dow Chem. Co., Midland, Mich., 1962-66; staff physician Midland Hosp., 1962-66; assoc. prof., prof. Med. Coll. Wis., Milw., 1966-78, 89-91, adj. prof. Dept. Pharmacology and Toxicology, 1978—; cons. Children's Hosp. Wis., 1990-93, Internal Medicine St. Mary's Hosp., Racine, Wis., 1983—, Dept. Emergency Medicine Milw. Regional Med. Ctr., 1993—, sr. attending staff, 1967—; staff Internal Medicine St. Luke's Hosp., Racine, 1983—; dir. Poison Ctr. Ea. Wis., 1989-93; corp. med. advisor S.C. Johnson & Son, Inc., Racine, 1971-78, dir., 1978-89. Mem. adv. med. staff Milw. Fire Dept., 1975—, Cadet USAF, 1945-46. Fellow ACP, Am. Coll. Occuptl. Medicine, Am. Acad. Clin. Toxicology, Acad. Toxicological Scis.; mem. AMA, Soc. Toxicology, Wis. State Med. Soc., Racine Acad. Medicine, Rotary Internat., Phi Theta Kappa, Phi Kappa Phi, Sigma Tau Delta. Avocations: history of medicine, wilderness hiking, literature, creative writing, inventing medical devices. Home and Office: 5337 Wind Point Rd Racine WI 53402

STEWART, RICHARD EDWIN, insurance consulting company executive; b. Washington, Nov. 4, 1933; s. Irvin and Florence Elsie (Dezendorf) S.; m. Barbara Lewis Dickson, Oct. 29, 1993. B.A., W.Va. U., 1955; B.A. (Rhodes scholar), Oxford (Eng.) U., 1957, M.A., 1961; J.D. Harvard, 1959. Bar: N.Y. 1960. Assoc. Royall, Koegel & Rogers, N.Y.C., 1960-63; asst. counsel to Gov. of N.Y., 1963-64; 1st asst. counsel, 1965-66; supr. ins. N.Y. State Ins. Dept., 1967-70; sr. v.p., gen. counsel First Nat. City Bank, N.Y.C., 1971-72; sr. v.p., dir. Chubb & Son Inc., N.Y.C., 1973-81; sr. v.p. Chubb Corp., N.Y.C., 1973-81, chief fin. officer, 1974-81; gov. N.Y. Ins. Exchange, N.Y.C., 1979-81; chmn. Stewart Econs., Inc., N.Y.C., 1981-90, Chapel Hill N.C., 1990—; mem. adv. com. HUD, 1968-72; mem. Adminstrv. Conf. U.S., 1970-74; bd. dirs. Am. Arbitration Assn., 1970-80; mem. UN panel experts on Transnational Bank failure, 1991. Co-author: Automobile Insurance....For Whose Benefit?, 1970, Watergate: Implications for Responsible Government, 1974, Medical Malpractice, 1977, Managing Insurer Insolvency, 1988, Insurance Insolvency Guarantees, 1990, A Brief History of Underwriting Cycles, 1991; author: Reason and Regulation, 1972, Insurance and Insurance Regulation, 1980. Trustee Coll. Ins., N.Y., 1970-78, Am. Coll. Life Underwriters, 1990-93; mem. Mayor's Com. on Taxi Regulation, 1979-82, ABA Com. to Improve Liability Ins. System, 1989; mem. panel experts on transnat. bank failure UN, 1991. Served with AUS, 1959. Mem. Nat. Acad. Pub. Adminstrn., Cosmos Club of Washington, Century Club of N.Y.C., Phi Beta Kappa Assn. Home and Office: 7601 Talbryn Way Chapel Hill NC 27516-7862

STEWART, ROBERT ANDREW, lawyer; b. Pueblo, Colo., Sept. 16, 1928; s. Robert James and Marie Anna (Biebl) S.; m. Mary Alyce Spiller, July 25, 1953; children: Alyson Marie, Anne Elizabeth, Robert James, Daniel Keating. LLB, U. Notre Dame, 1952; BA in History, U. Wash., 1972. Bar: Wash. 1953. Instr. in law U. Wash. Law Sch., Seattle, 1952-53; assoc. Bogle & Gates, Seattle, 1953-66, ptnr., 1966—. Chmn. bd. Am. Heart Assn. (Wash. affiliate), Seattle, 1966-68; pres. Mus. History and Industry, Seattle, 1989-91. Staff sgt. U.S. Army, 1946-47, Japan. Recipient Clint Dunagan award U.S. Jaycees, Atlanta, 1961. Fellow Am. Coll. Trust and Estate Counsel; mem. ABA (chmn. post mortem estate and tax planning com. 1987-92, chmn. marital property issues com. 1992—), Wash. Bar Assn., Seattle King County Bar Assn., Seattle Jr. C. of C. (pres. 1958), Wash. State Jr. C. of C. (pres. 1961), Wash. Athletic Club, Seattle Tennis Club. Republican. Roman Catholic. Home: 4100 E Highland Dr Seattle WA 98112-4414 Office: Bogle & Gates 5100 Two Union Sq 601 Union St Seattle WA 98101-2322

STEWART, ROBERT FORREST, JR., lawyer; b. Niagara Falls, N.Y., Oct. 25, 1943; s. Robert Forrest and Margaret Joanne (Mahoney) S.; m. Tara Campbell Mescal, Aug. 27, 1966; children: Jane Margaret, Laura Campbell, Rebecca Forrest. BS, Coll. Holy Cross, Worcester, Mass., 1965; JD, Georgetown U., 1968; LLM in Labor, Temple U., 1978. Bar: D.C. 1968, Del. 1969, Pa. 1976. Law clk. to presiding judge U.S. Dist. Ct. Del., Wilmington, 1968-69; judge adv. USAF, 1969-72; assoc. Morris, Nichols, Arsht & Tunnell, Wilmington, 1972-76; assoc. Obermayer, Rebmann, Maxwell & Hippel, Phila., 1976-80, ptnr., 1981-85; ptnr. Duane, Morris & Hecksher, Phila. and Wilmington, 1985-92, Dilworth, Paxson, Kalish & Kauffman, Phila. and Wilmington, 1992—. Author: At-Will Termination in Pennsylvania, 1983, Emerging Employee Rights, 1984, At-Will Termination in New Jersey, 1985, Legal Issues of Managing Difficult Employees in Delaware, 1988, Personnel and Employment Law in Pennsylvania/New Jersey/Delaware, 1990, Sexual Harassment, 1993. Chmn. Common Cause Del., Wilmington, 1974-75, 79-80; pub. mem. coun. Del. Assn. Profl. Engrs., Wilmington, 1981-90; pres. adv. bd. Cath. Charities, Diocese of Wilmington, 1976-90; bd. dirs., vice chmn. United Way Del. 1994—; mem. N.E. regional coun. United Way

Am., 1993—; bd. dirs. Assoc. United Ways Pa., N.J. and Del., 1993—. Named Vol. of Yr., United Way Del., 1984; recipient United Way Del. Fellowship award, 1993. Mem. ABA, ACLU (bd. dirs. Del. chpt. 1972-76, 92-95), Del. Bar Assn., Pa. Bar Assn., Phila. Bar Assn., Del. State C. of C. (labor advisor 1980—, chmn. com. employee rels. 1987—), Rodney Sq. Club, Holy Cross Varsity Club (bd. dirs. 1981—), Coun. Engring. Specialty Bd. (pub. mem. 1991—). Democrat. Roman Catholic. Office: Dilworth Paxson Kalish & Kauffman 3200 Mellon Bank Ctr 1735 Market St Philadelphia PA 19103-7501

STEWART, ROBERT GORDON, former museum curator; b. Balt., Mar. 5, 1931; s. Kenneth Elsworth and Ruth (Chambers) S. Student, Gilman Sch. 1946-49; B.F.A., U. Pa., 1954. Architect Ind. Nat. Hist. Park, Phila., 1954. Nat. Park Service, Phila., 1956-57; architect, curator Jefferson Barracks Hist. Park, St. Louis, 1958-61; dir. properties Nat. Trust for Historic Preservation, Washington, 1961-64; sr. curator Nat. Portrait Gallery, Smithsonian Instn., Washington, 1964-94, sr. curator emeritus, 1994—; cons. Loyalist Homestead, St. John's, N.B., Can., 1960; vis. lectr. George Washington U., 1967-70. Author: Nucleus for a National Collection, 1965, Recent Acquisitions, 1966, A Nineteenth-Century Gallery of Distinguished Americans, 1969, Henry Benbridge (1743-1812): American Portrait Painter, 1971, Robert Edge Pine, A British Artist in America 1784-1788, 1979. Dir. Landmarks of St. Louis, 1959-61; adjudicator Jamaican Nat. Art Competition, 1971; cons. The Papers of George Washington, 1990—. Served with U.S. Army, 1954-56. Mem. Md., Dorchester County, Lewes hist. socs., Walpole Soc., Assn. of Historians of Am. Art, Zeta Psi. Episcopalian.

STEWART, ROBERT H., III, banker; b. Dallas, 1925; married. B.B.A., So. Meth. U., 1949. Asst. cashier bus. devel., then asst. v.p. InterFirst Bank, N.A., Dallas, 1951-53, v.p. 1953-59, sr. v.p. 1959-60, pres. chief exec. officer, 1960-65, chmn. chief exec. officer, 1965—, also dir.; with InterFirst Corp. (parent), Dallas, 1972—, chmn., chief exec. officer, 1972-80, 84—, chmn. exec. com., from 1980, also dir.; dir. PepsiCo, Inc., Atlantic Richfield Co., Fidelity Union Life Ins. Co., InterFirst Investment Mgmt. Inc. Served to 1st lt. U.S. Army, 1944-46. Office: Interfirst Corp 901 Main St PO Box 83000 Dallas TX 75283-1000

STEWART, ROBERT HENRY, oceanographer, educator; b. York, Pa., Dec. 26, 1941; s. Robert Henry and Mildred June (Smith) S.; m. Hedvig Susan Bagdy, June 26, 1966 (div. Dec. 1976); 1 child, Alethea Ildico Stewart; m. Tracy Ann Bertolucci, July 19, 1986; children: Farrar Clee, Margaret Montgomery. BS, U. Tex., Arlington, 1963; PhD, U. Calif., San Diego, 1969. Asst. rsch. oceanographer Scripps Inst. Oceanography U. Calif., San Diego, 1969-78, assoc. rsch. oceanographer, 1978-79; assoc. rsch. oceanographer, assoc. adj. prof. Scripps Inst. Oceanography, U. Calif., San Diego, 1979-83, rsch. oceanographer, adj. prof., 1983-89; mem. tech. staff Jet Propulsion Lab., Calif. Inst. Tech., Pasadena, 1979-80, rsch. scientist, 1980-83, sr. rsch. scientist, 1983-89; prof. oceanography Tex. A&M U., College Station, 1989—; Topex/Poseidon project scientist Jet Propulsion Lab., 1980-88; mem. many NASA coms.; mem. coms. of Nat. Rsch. Coun., Nat. Acad. Scis.; mem. various internat. scientific coms.; cons. Univ. Corp. for Atmospheric Rsch. Author: Methods of Satellite Oceanography, 1985; editor: Radio Oceanography, 1978; contbr. articles to profl. jours. Trustee San Juan Capistrano Inst. Co-recipient Group Achievement award for Topex/Poseidon mission design NASA, 1993, NASA Pub. Svc. medal, 1994; U. Calif. Regents spl. fellow, 1963; NSF fellow, 1964. Mem. Am. Geophys. Union. Republican. Roman Catholic. Avocations: collect lepidoptera. Home: 8710 Appomattox Dr College Station TX 77845 Office: Oceanography Dept Tex A&M U College Station TX 77843-3146

STEWART, ROBERT LEE, retired army officer, astronaut; b. Washington, Aug. 13, 1942; s. Lee Olin and Mildred Kathleen (Wann) S.; m. Mary Jane Murphy; children: Ragon Annette, Jennifer Lee. BS in Math., U. So. Miss., 1964; MS in Aerospace Engring., U. Tex., 1972; grad., U.S. Army Air Def. Sch., 1964, grad. advanced course, guided missile systems officers course, 1970. Commd. 2d lt. U.S. Army, 1964, advanced through grades to brig. gen., 1986, fire team leader armed helicopter platoon 101st Aviation Bn., instr. pilot Primary Helicopter Sch., 1967-69; bn. ops. officer, bn. exec. officer 309th Aviation Bn., U.S. Army, Seoul, Korea, 1972-73; exptl. test pilot Aviation Engring. Flight Activity U.S. Army, Edwards AFB, Calif., 1974-78; astronaut candidate NASA, 1978, mission specialist Space Shuttle Mission 41-B, 1984; mission specialist STS-51J, 1985; dep. comdr. U.S. Army Strategic Def. Command, Huntsville, Ala., 1987-89; dir. of plans U.S. Space Command, 1989-92. Decorated D.S.M., (2) Legion of Merit, (4) DFC, (2) Purple Hearts, Bronze star, others; recipient NASA Space Flight medal, 1984, 85; named Army Aviator of Yr., 1984. Mem. Soc. Exptl. Test Pilots, Assn. U.S. Army, Army Aviation Assn. Am., Assn. Space Explorers. Avocations: photography, woodworking, skiing. Home: 815 Sun Valley Dr Woodland Park CO 80863-9013 Office: Nichols Rsch Corp 1525 Vapor Trail Colorado Springs CO 80916

STEWART, ROBERT WILLIAM, retired physicist, government research council executive; b. Smokey Lake, Alta., Can., Aug. 21, 1923; s. Robert Edwards and Florence May Stewart; m. Anne-Marie Robert, Apr. 19, 1973; children: Anne, Brian, Philip, Colin. B.Sc., Queens U., Kingston, Ont., Can., 1945, M.Sc., 1947; Ph.D., Cambridge (Eng.) U., 1952; D.Sc. (hon.), McGill U., 1972, Victoria U., 1993; LL.D. (hon.), Dalhousie U., 1974. Research scientist Can. Def. Research Bd., Victoria, B.C., 1950-61; prof. physics and oceanography U. B.C., Vancouver, 1960-71; dir.-gen. Inst. Ocean Scis., Sidney, B.C., Dept. Fisheries and Oceans, 1970-79; asst. dep. minister sci. and tech. B.C. Ministry Edn., Sci. and Tech., 1979; dep. minister B.C. Ministry of Univs., Sci. and Communications, 1979-84; pres. Alta. Research Council, 1984-87; dir. ctr. for earth and ocean research U. Victoria, 1987-89; global change sci. officer Internat. Coun. Sci. Union, 1990-92; vis. prof. Dalhousie U., 1960-61, Harvard U., 1964, Pa. State U., 1964; Commonwealth prof. Cambridge U., 1967-68. Contbr. articles to profl. jours. Decorated officer Order of Can.; recipient Patterson medal award Can. Meteorol. Soc., 1973, Sverdrup Gold medal Am. Meteorol. Soc., 1976, Tully medal Can. Meteorol. and Oceanographic Soc., 1989. Mem. Internat. Assn. Phys. Scis. of Ocean (pres. 1975-79), Com. on Climatic Change and the Ocean (chmn. 1983-87), Global Atmospheric Rsch. Programme (joint organizing com. 1967-79, vice chmn. 1967-71, chmn. 1971-75), Internat. Geosphere-Biosphere Programme (vice chmn. 1990-94).

STEWART, RODERICK DAVID, singer; b. North London, Eng., Jan. 10, 1945; m. Alana Collins, Apr. 6, 1979 (div. 1984); children: Alana, Sean; child with Kelly Emberg: Ruby Rachel; m. Rachel Hunter, Dec. 15, 1990, child, Renée. Singer with Jeff Beck Group, 1968-69, Faces, 1969-75; albums include (with Jeff Beck Group) Truth, 1968, Beck-Ola, 1969; (with Faces) The First Step, 1970, Long Player, 1971, A Nod Is As Good as a Wink...To a Blind Horse, 1971, Ooh La La, 1973, Coast to Coast/Overture & Beginners, 1973, Snakes and Ladders/The Best of Faces, 1976; (solo) An Old Raincoat Won't Ever Let You Down, 1969, Gasoline Alley, 1970, Every Picture Tells a Story, 1971, Never a Dull Moment, 1972, Sing it Again Rod, 1973, Smiler, 1974, Atlantic Crossing, 1975, The Best of Rod Stewart, 1976, The Best of Rod Stewart Vol. II, 1976. A Night on the Town, 1976, Foot Loose & Fancy Free, 1976, Blondes Have More Fun, 1978, Greatest Hits Vol. I, 1979, Tonight I'm Yours, 1981, Absolutely Live, 1981, Camouflage, 1984, (with Jeff Beck) Get Workin', 1985. Out of Order, 1988, Storyteller: The Complete Anthology 1964-1990, 1990, Downtown Train, 1990, Vagabond Heart, 1991, You Wear It Well, 1992, The Mercury Anthology, 1992, Once In A Blue Moon Vintage, 1993, Ridin High, The Rod Stewart Album, Unplugged...And Seated, 1993 (Grammy nomination, Best Pop Male Vocal for "Have I Told You Lately"). Named Rock Star of Year Rolling Stone mag., 1971; recipient British Rock and Pop Lifetime Achievement award, 1992; inducted into the Rock & Roll Hall of Fame, 1994. Office: care Warner Brothers 3300 Warner Blvd Burbank CA 91505-4632*

STEWART, ROSS, chemistry educator; b. Vancouver, B.C., Can., Mar. 16, 1924; s. David Methven and Jessie (Grant) S.; m. Greta Marie Morris, Sept. 7, 1946; children—Cameron, Ian. B.A., U. B.C., 1946, M.A., 1948; Ph.D., U. Wash., 1954. Lectr. chemistry Royal Roads Coll., Victoria, B.C., 1949-52, asst. prof., 1952-54, assoc. prof., 1954-55; asst. prof. chemistry U. B.C., Vancouver, 1955-59, assoc. prof., 1959-62, prof., 1962-89, hon. prof., 1989—. Author: Oxidation Mechanisms, 1964, Investigation of Organic Reactions,

1966, The Proton: Applications to Organic Chemistry, 1985, (with J.D. Roberts & M.C. Caserio) Organic Chemistry, Methane to Macromolecules, 1970; contbr. numerous articles to profl. jours. Fellow Royal Soc. Can., Chem. Inst. Can.; mem. B.C. Thoroughbred Breeders Soc. (pres. 1972-74), Can. Thoroughbred Horse Assn. (v.p. 1974-75). Club: Point Grey Golf (Vancouver). Avocations: breeding and racing thoroughbred horses; golf; gardening. Home: 4855 Paton St, Vancouver, BC Canada V6L 2H9 Office: U BC, Dept Chemistry, Vancouver, BC Canada V6T 1Y6

STEWART, RUTH ANN, public policy analyst, library administrator; b. Chgo., Apr. 4, 1942; d. Elmer Ashton and Ann (Mitchell) S.; 1 child, Allegra Gordon; m. David Levering Lewis. Student, U. Chgo., 1960-61, Simmons Coll., 1963; BA, Wheaton Coll., Norton, Mass., 1963; MS, Columbia U., 1965; postgrad., Harvard U., 1976, Fisk U., 1970, John F. Kennedy Sch. Govt., 1987. Libr. Phillips Acad., Andover, Mass., 1963-64; assoc. dir. for external svcs. N.Y. Pub. Libr., 1980-86; asst. chief Schomburg Ctr. Research in Black Culture, N.Y.C., 1968-70; asst. chief Schomburg Ctr. Research in Black Culture, N.Y.C., 1970-80; assoc. dir. for external svcs. N.Y. Pub. Libr., 1980-86; asst. Libr. of Congress for Nat. Programs, Washington, 1986-89; sr. specialist in arts and humanities, assoc. dir. for resource devel. Congl. Rsch.. Svc., Libr. of Congress, Washington, 1989—; mem. libr. vis. com. Harvard U., Cambridge, Mass., 1975-88, MIT, Cambridge, 1986-90; bd. dirs. Nat. Park Found., Washington, 1978-84; trustee, sec. Wheaton Coll., Norton, Mass., 1980—; bd. visitors Sch. Libr. and Info. Sci., U. Pitts., 1987-95; trustee, treas. Fund for Folk Culture, 1991—, The Lab. Sch. of Washington, 1992—, VOICE Internat., 1994—; bd. dirs. Women's Fgn. Policy Group, 1995—. Author: Portia, 1977; contbr. articles to profl. jours. Fellow Internat. Coun. Mus. Mem. Coun. Fgn. Rels. Office: Congls Rsch Svc RM LM 203 1st Independence Ave SE Washington DC 20540

STEWART, S. JAY, chemical company executive; b. Pineville, W.Va., Sept. 18, 1938; s. Virgil Harvey and Lena Rivers (Repair) S.; m. Judith Ann Daniels, June 3, 1961; children: Julie Annette, Jennifer Amy, Steven Jay. BSChemE, U. Cin., 1961; MBA, W.Va. U., 1966. Various positions in engring., mfg., mktg. Monsanto Co., St. Louis, 1961-73; dir. mktg. Ventron Corp. subs. Morton Thiokol, Inc., Beverly, Mass., 1973-77, gen. mgr., 1977-79; pres. Dynachem Corp. subs. Morton Thiokol, Inc., Santa Ana, Calif., 1979-82; group v.p. Thiokol Corp., Newtown, Pa., 1982; group v.p. splty. chems. Morton Internat., Inc. (formerly Morton Thiokol, Inc.), Chgo., 1983-86, pres., chief oper. officer, 1986—, also chmn., bd. dirs. Mem. Anchor Cross Soc. of Rush Presbyn.-St. Luke's Med. Ctr., 1987—, Charles McMicken Soc. U. Cin. Found., Northwestern U. Assocs., 1988—; trustee Rush Presbyn.-St. Luke's Med. Ctr., Chgo., 1987—; mem. adv. bd. Nat. Found. for History of Chemistry, 1991—. Recipient Disting. Alumnus award U. Cin., 1984. Mem. Am. Chem. Soc., Am. Inst. Chem. Engrs., Chmn. Mfrs. Assn. (bd. dirs. 1984-87), Comml. Devel. Assn., Assn. Governing Bds. Univs. and Colls., Chem. Mktg. Assn. (bd. dirs. 1990), Comml. Club Chgo., The Chgo. Club, Econ. Club Chgo. Republican. Methodist. Office: Morton Internat Inc 100 N Riverside Plz Chicago IL 60606

STEWART, SAMUEL B., banker, lawyer; b. Chattanooga, Oct. 5, 1908; s. Samuel B. and Dora (Pryor) S.; m. Celeste Dorwin, Apr. 2, 1934; children: Linda Celeste (Mrs. James F. Dickason), James Christopher Dorwin (dec.). A.B., U. Va., 1927; J.D., Columbia U., 1930; LL.D., Golden Gate U., 1965. Bar: N.Y. 1931, Calif. 1947. Assoc. Cravath, de Gersdorff, Swaine & Wood, 1930-39; partner Blake & Voorhees (and successor firm Blake, Voorhees & Stewart), 1939-47; v.p., gen. counsel Bank of Am. Nat. Trust & Savs. Assn., San Francisco, 1947-59; exec. v.p., gen. counsel Bank of Am. Nat. Trust & Savs. Assn., 1959-67, exec. v.p., chief exec. officer trust activities, 1962-67, exec. v.p., sr. adminstrv. officer, 1967-69, vice chmn. bd., 1969-70, sr. vice chmn. bd., 1970-73; also dir.; vice chmn. bd. Bank Am. Corp., 1969-70, sr. vice chmn. bd., 1970-73, also dir.; chmn. gen. trust com., 1969-70; dir. Longs Drug Stores Inc., World Corp.; spl. counsel price adjustment Truman) Spl. Com of U.S. Senate for investigation Nat. Def. Program, 1943-44; Disting. vis. prof. San Francisco State U., 1974. Editor: The Business Lawyer, 1959-60; trustee Golden Gate U.; trustee Salk Inst., chmn., 1974-85; bd. dirs. No. Calif. Presbyn. Homes Inc., 1983-89; bd. govs. San Francisco Symphony, 1974—, v.p., 1980—. Recipient Cyril Magnin award, 1979, Jefferson award Am. Inst. Public Service, 1978, Silver Spur award San Francisco Planning and Urban Research Assn., 1980. Mem. Am. Bar Assn. (past chmn. sect. corp. banking and bus. law), Legal Aid Soc. of San Francisco (pres. 1963-65), Bar Assn. San Francisco (v.p. 1967), Greater San Francisco C. of C. (pres. 1969-70, chmn. bd. 1971, lifetime contbn. award 1979), Sponsors San Francisco Performing Arts Center (pres. 1973-85), Phi Beta Kappa. Presbyn. (elder). Clubs: Bankers, Bohemian, San Francisco Golf, Silverado Country. Address: 2288 Broadway St Apt 2 San Francisco CA 94115-1287 *My philosophy of life is very simple. Do as well as you can that which you do best and that which gives you greatest satisfaction. Don't worry! If you have a problem about which you can do something—do it! If you can't do anything about it, worry won't help. My greatest satisfactions have come from doing things others could not—or would not—do, which were helpful to others.*

STEWART, SUE STERN, lawyer; b. Casper, Wyo., Oct. 9, 1942; d. Fraizer McVale and Carolyn Eliabeth (Hunt) Stewart; BA, Wellesley Coll., 1964; postgrad. Harvard U. Law Sch., 1964-65; JD, Georgetown U., 1967; m. Arthur L. Stern, III, July 31, 1965 (div.); children—Anne Stewart, Mark Alan; m. John A. Ciampa, Sept. 1, 1985 (div.). Admitted to N.Y. bar, 1968; clk. to Judges Juvenile Ct., Washington, 1967-68; mem. firm Nixon, Hargrave, Devans & Doyle, Rochester, N.Y., 1968-74, ptnr., 1975—; lectr. in field; trustee Found. of Monroe County (N.Y.) Bar, 1976-78. Sec., dir. United Community Chest of Greater Rochester, 1973-87, 92—; trustee, sec. Internat. Museum Photography at George Eastman House, Rochester, 1974—, Genesee Country Mus., Mumford, N.Y., 1976—; bd. dirs. Ctr. for Govtal. Research. Mem. Am. (chmn. task force on charitable giving, exempt orgns. com. tax sect. 1984—), N.Y. State (exec. com. tax sect., 1974-76, chmn. com. exempt orgns. 1975-76), Monroe County Bar Assn. (trustee 1974-75), BNA Portfolio, Pvt. Found. Distbns. Author: Charitable Giving and Solicitation. Office: Nixon Hargrave Devans & Doyle PO Box 1051 Clinton Sq Rochester NY 14603-1051

STEWART, THOMAS JAMES, JR., baritone; b. San Saba, Tex., Aug. 29, 1928; s. Thomas James and Gladys Naomi (Reavis) S.; m. Evelyn Lear, Jan. 8, 1955; children: Jan Lear, Bonni Lear. Mus.B., Baylor U., 1953; postgrad., Juilliard Sch. Music, 1953-54, Berlin Hochschule for Music, 1957-58. Appeared with, Met. Opera, Chgo. Opera, San Francisco Opera, Bayreuth Festival, Salzburg Festival, Vienna State Opera, Royal Opera Covent Garden, Grand Opera Paris, Deutsche Oper Berlin, La Scala, Milan, Budapest Opera, Prague Opera, 1960—, also major orchs., throughout the world. Served with USAF, 1945-49. Recipient Kammersaenger of Berlin, 1964; Richard Wagner medal, 1965; San Francisco Opera medal, 1985; Fulbright grantee, 1957-58.

STEWART, THOMAS SIMRALL, radio executive; b. Detroit, July 13, 1949; s. William Harry and Jane (Simrall) S.; m. Pamela Sohl, Jan. 17, 1976; children: Jane Sohl, Elizabeth Simrall. BS in Edn., Ohio State U., 1972. Account exec. J. Scott Corp., Columbus, Ohio, 1973-76, Sta. WBNS Radio, Columbus, 1976-77, Sta. WBNS-TV, Columbus, 1977-78; gen. sales mgr. Sta. WBNS Radio, Columbus, 1978-80, gen. mgr., 1980—, also bd. dirs., bd. dirs., pres. Ohio Assn. Broadcasters, Columbus, 1988-90. Bd. dirs. Children's Hosp., Columbus, 1990—, Arlington Edn. Fund, Columbus, 1989—; Franklin Park Conservatory, Columbus, 1988-90; chmn. 1992 Opening Ceremonies Task Force, Columbus, 1990—, Columbus Symphony Orch. Ann. Fund, 1990-91. Recipient Man of Yr. award Kappa Sigma, 1972, Outstanding Svc. award Childhood League, 1989.

STEWART, THOMAS TED, real estate developer, investment banker; b. St. Louis, July 17, 1940; s. Harold Mack and Lora Mae (Coil) S.; m. Susan Ann Schulte, Dec. 22, 1962; children: Thomas Timothy. Grad., Hindt sch., 1958. Restaurant owner and mgr., 1962-66, hotel owner and mgr., 1967-70; gen. ptnr. Sovereign Realty subs. Butcher & Co., Phila.; acquisition specialist E.G. Frances Realty; head of comml. real estate div. Sotheby Parke Bernet Internat. Realty Corp., N.Y.C., 1980s; ptnr., dir. Greenscape Devel. Corp., 1987—; pres. Stewart Capital Corp., Modesto, Calif., 1991—; prin. Thomas T. Stewart & Assocs., Jefferson City, Mo.; pres., owner, gen. mgr. Hotel

DeVille, Jefferson City, Mo.; cons. Gulf & We. Cos. in Ctrl. and S.Am.; site approval and acquisition for McDonald's Corp.; builder shopping ctrs. for Wetterau, Inc.; pres., gen. mgr. DeVille Hotel, Jefferson City, Mo., 1994—. Bd. dirs. Indsl. Devel. Comm., Jefferson City, 1986-89. With USMC, 1960-62. Mem. Harbor Club (bd. govs.), Seal Harbor Yacht Club (commodore 1986-88). Avocations: piano, flying, gardening.

STEWART, WARREN EARL, chemical engineer, educator; b. Whitewater, Wis., July 3, 1924; s. Earl Austin and Avis (Walker) S.; m. Jean Durham Potter, May 24, 1947; children—Marilyn, David, Douglas, Carol, Margaret, Mary Jean. B.S. in Chem. Engring. U. Wis., 1943, M.S. in Chem. Engring. 1947; Sc.D. in Chem. Engring. Mass. Inst. Tech., 1951. Project chem. engr. Sinclair Research Labs., Harvey, Ill., 1950-56; cons. Sinclair Research Labs., 1956-83; asst. prof. chem. engring. dept. U. Wis., Madison, 1956-58; assoc. prof. U. Wis., 1958-61, prof., 1961—, McFarland-Bascom prof., 1983—; chmn. dept., 1973-78; cons. Engelhard Industries, Inc., Newark, 1956-58; instr. spl. courses transport phenomena Chemstrand Corp., Pensacola, Fla., 1962, Nat. U. La Plata, Argentina, 1962, Esso Rsch. & Engring. Co., 1963, 66, Phillips Petroleum Co., 1963, Am. Inst. Chem. Engrs., 1965, 68, 69, Inst. Tec. Celaya (Mex.), 1983, Univ. Autonoma de Mex., 1985; Reilly lectr. Notre Dame U., 1993. Author: (with R.B. Bird and E.N. Lightfoot) Transport Phenomena, 1960, Special Topics in Transport Phenomena, 1965, (with R.B. Bird, E.N. Lightfoot and T.W. Chapman) Lectures in Transport Phenomena, 1969; editorial advisor: Latin Am. Applied Rsch.; editorial advisor: Computers and Chem. Engring. Served to ensign USNR, 1944-46. Recipient Benjamin Smith Reynolds teaching award, 1981, Byron Bird rsch. award, 1991. Fellow Am. Inst. Chem. Engrs. (Computing in Chem. Engring. award 1985); mem. NAE, Am. Chem. Soc. (Murphree award in indsl. and engring. chemistry 1989), Am. Soc. for Engring. Edn., (Chem. Engring. Lectureship award 1983), Phi Beta Kappa, Sigma Xi, Alpha Chi Sigma (research award 1981), Phi Eta Sigma, Tau Beta Pi, Phi Lambda Upsilon, Phi Kappa Phi. Conglist. (deacon, moderator). Home: 734 Huron Hl Madison WI 53711-2955

STEWART, WILLIAM GENE, broadcast executive; b. Winfield, Kans., Dec. 10, 1923; s. Everette Dewey and Mary Lee (Nace) S.; m. Lila Jean Bohlender, June 24, 1951; 1 child: Linda Jean. BA, Denver U., 1949. Mgr. KFKA radio, Greeley, Colo., 1951-56, KGHF radio, Pueblo, Colo., 1956-58, KWRL radio, Riverton, Wyo., 1958-59; owner KLMO radio, Longmont, Colo., 1959—, partner, 1988—. Sgt. USAF, 1943-46. Recipient numerous civic awards, 1959—. Mem. Longmont Am. Legion (life), Elks Club, Moose Lodge, Rotary Club (pres. 1984-85), Fox Hills Country Club. Republican. Avocations: golf, swimming, reading. Office: KLMO-AM PO Box 799 614 Kimbark St Longmont CO 80501-4911*

STEWART, ZEPH, classicist, educator; b. Jackson, Mich., Jan. 1, 1921; s. James Garfield and Harriet (Potter) S.; m. Diana Childers, Dec. 29, 1959; children: Sarah Barton, Christopher Childers, Mary Alden. BA, Yale U., 1942; AM (hon.), Harvard U., 1955. Jr. fellow Soc. Fellows, Harvard U., 1949-51; mem. faculty Harvard U., 1953—, prof. Greek and Latin, 1962—, Andrew W. Mellon prof. humanities, 1981—, chmn. dept. classics, 1977-82, Allston Burr sr. tutor Adams House, 1955-60, master Lowell House, 1963-75; dir. Ctr. for Hellenic Studies, Washington, 1985—, mem. adminstrv. com., 1979—. Author: The Ancient World, 1966; editor: Studies in Religion and the Ancient World, 1972. Trustee Bishop Rhinelander Found., 1964-70, mem. corp., 1982—; trustee Radcliffe Coll., 1972-76, Loeb Classical Library, 1973—, Inst. Advanced Study, 1979-89; trustee Hotchkiss Sch., 1964-79, 82-87, emeritus trustee, 1987—; mem. Yale U. Council, 1976-81; mem. adv. council dept. classics Princeton U., 1970-80; chmn. Harvard U. campaign United Way, 1976; bd. dirs. Aegean Inst., 1979-89; bd. advisors Dumbarton Oaks, 1985—. Served to capt. AUS, 1943-47, 51-53. Decorated Legion of Merit; Guggenheim fellow, 1965-66. Fellow Am. Acad. Arts and Scis. (councilor 1972-76, v.p. 1979-82); mem. Am. Philol. Assn. (bd. dirs. 1977-80, 1st v.p. 1982, pres. 1983), Soc. Promotion Roman Studies, Archeol. Inst. Am., Soc. Promotion Hellenic Studies, Tchrs. Classics New Eng. (pres. 1960-85), Classical Assn. U.K., Century Assn., Elizabethan Club, Signet Soc., Phi Beta Kappa, Delta Kappa Epsilon. Club: Cosmos. Home and Office: Ctr for Hellenic Studies 3100 Whitehaven St NW Washington DC 20008-3684

STEYER, ROY HENRY, retired lawyer; b. Bklyn., July 1, 1918; s. Herman and Augusta (Simon) S.; m. Margaret Fahr, Feb. 21, 1953; children: Hume R., James P., Thomas F. A.B. with honors in Govt. and Gen. Studies, Cornell U., 1938; LL.B. cum laude, Yale U., 1941. Bar: N.Y. 1941, various fed. cts. from 1947, U.S. Supreme Ct. 1955. Assoc. firm Sullivan & Cromwell, N.Y.C., 1941-42, 46-52, ptnr., 1953-88, ret., 1988. Trustee N.Y.C. Sch. Vol. Program, 1974-78. Served to lt. USNR, 1943-46. Mem. Am. Coll. Trial Lawyers, ABA (chmn. com. on antitrust problems in internat. trade antitrust sect. 1959-62), N.Y. State Bar Assn., Assn. of Bar of City of N.Y. (chmn. com. on trade regulation 1962-64), Order of Coif, Century Assn., Phi Beta Kappa, Phi Kappa Phi. Home: 112 E 74th St New York NY 10021-3562

STICE, JAMES EDWARD, chemical engineer, educator; b. Fayetteville, Ark., Sept. 19, 1928; s. F. Fenner and Charlotte (Anderson) S.; m. Patricia Ann Stroner, Sept. 22, 1951; children: Susan Emily, James Clayton. BS, U. Ark., 1949; MS, Ill. Inst. Tech., 1952, PhD, 1963. Registered profl. engr., Tex., Ark. Process engr. Visking Corp., North Little Rock, Ark., 1951-53; chem. engr. Thurston Chem. Co. div. W.R. Grace & Co., Joplin, Mo., 1953-54; asst. prof. chem. engring. U. Ark., 1954-57, assoc. prof., prof., 1962-68; instr. chem. engring. Ill. Inst. Tech., Chgo., 1957-62; dir. Bur. Engring. Teaching, assoc. prof. chem. engring. U. Tex., Austin, 1968-73; prof. engring. edn. in chem. engring., 1985-90, Bob R. Dorsey prof. engring., 1990—, dir. Ctr. for Teaching Effectiveness, 1973-89; dir. Effective Teaching Inst. U. Tex. System, summer 1970; vis. prof. U. Iberoamericana, Mexico City, summer 1977; Summer cons. E.I. duPont de Nemours & Co., Inc., Savannah River Plant, Aiken, S.C., 1955, Humble Oil & Refining Co., Baytown, Tex., 1956, Universal Oil Products Co., Des Plaines, Ill., 1957, 58, Phillips Petroleum Co., Bartlesville, Okla., 1963, Ethyl Corp., Baton Rouge, 1965, U. Wis., Eau Claire, 1970—. Author: (with B.S. Swanson) Electronic Analog Computer Primer, 1965, Computadoras Analogicas Electronicas, 1971, Expansion of Keller Plan Instruction in Engineering and Selected Other Disciplines, 1975, Developing Critical Thinking and Problem-Solving Abilities, 1987. Recipient Gen. Dynamics award for excellence in teaching, 1980, Western Electric Fund award for excellence in engring. teaching, 1981, Chester F. Carlson award for innovation in engring. teaching, 1984, Outstanding Engring. Advisor award, 1993; named Outstanding Chem. Engring. Prof., 1993; Friar Soc. Teaching fellow, 1993-94. Fellow Am. Soc. Engring. Edn. (life mem., elected dir. 1983-85, chmn. chem. engring. div. 1988-89, bd. dirs. 1990-92, v.p. 1991-92); mem. Am. Inst. Chem. Engrs., Instrument Soc. Am. (Jour. award 1966), Scabbard and Blade, Scholia (pres. 1989-90), Sigma Xi, Delta Sigma, Sigma Chi, Phi Eta Sigma, Pi Mu Epsilon, Alpha Chi Sigma, Tau Beta Pi, Omicron Delta Kappa, Phi Lambda Upsilon, Phi Kappa Phi. Home: 1503 W 32nd St Austin TX 78703-1409

STICHT, J. PAUL, retired food products and tobacco company executive; b. Clairton, Pa., 1917. BA, Grove City Coll., 1939; postgrad., U. Pitts. With U.S. Steel Corp., 1939-44; personnel dir. Trans World Airlines, 1944-48; v.p. Campbell Soup Co., 1947-57, pres. internat., 1957-60; exec. v.p. Federated Dept. Stores, Inc., 1960-65, vice chmn., 1965-67, pres., 1967-72; chmn. exec. com., COO R.J. Reynolds Industries, Inc., Winston-Salem, N.C., 1972-73, pres., CEO, 1978-79, chmn. bd., 1979-85; chmn. RJR Nabisco, Inc., Winston-Salem, 1987-89, acting chmn., CEO, 1989; Trustee Grove City Coll., Nat. Chamber Found; chmn. Caribbean/Latin Am. Action; chmn. bd. visitors Bowman Gray Sch. Medicine; mem. bd. visitors Duke U. Fuqua Sch. Bus. Office: 119 Brookstown Ave Winston Salem NC 27101-5207

STICK, ALYCE CUSHING, information systems consultant; b. N.J., July 13, 1944; d. George William and Adele Margaret (Wilderotter) Cushing; m. James McAlpin Easter, July, 1970 (div. Aug. 1986); m. T. Howard F. Stick, June, 1989. AA, Colby-Sawyer Coll., 1964; student, Boston U., 1964-65, Johns Hopkins U., 1972-74; cert., Control Data Inst. and Life Office Mgmt. Assn., 1976. Claims investigator Continental Casualty Co., Phila., 1967-69; data processing coord. Chesapeake Life Ins. Co., Balt., 1970-72; sr. systems analyst Comml. Credit Computer Corp., Balt., 1972-80; v.p. Shawmut Computer Systems, Inc., Owings Mills, Md., 1980-85; pres. Computer Relevance, Inc., Gladwyne, Pa., 1985—; cons. Sinai Hosp., Balt., 1982-85, AT&T, Reading, Pa., 1987-88, Dun and Bradstreet, Allentown, Pa., 1988, Arco Chem. Co., Newton Square, Pa., 1990-91, Rohm and Haas Co., Phila., 1992-95. Designer/author: (computer software systems) Claim-Track, 1977, Property-Profiles, 1979, Stat-Model, 1989; co-designer/author: Patient-Profiles, 1983. Treas. Balt. Mus. Art, Sales and Rental Gallery, 1984. Mem. Assn. for Systems Mgmt., Data Processing Mgmt. Assn., Ind. Computer Cons. Assn., Merion Cricket Club (Haverford, Pa.). Republican. Avocations: Am. antiques, Chinese export porcelain dealer. Office: Computer Relevance Inc 1501 Monticello Dr Gladwyne PA 19035-1206

STICKEL, FREDERICK A., publisher; b. Weehawken, N.J., Nov. 18, 1921; s. Fred and Eva (Madigan) S.; m. Margaret A. Dunne, Dec. 4, 1943; children—Fred A., Patrick F., Daisy E., Geoffrey M., James E., Bridget A. Student, Georgetown U., 1939-42; BS, St. Peter's Coll., 1943. Advt. salesperson Jersey Observer daily, Hoboken, N.J., 1945-51; retail advt. salesperson Jersey Jour., Jersey City, 1951-55; advt. dir. Jersey Jour., 1955-66, publisher, 1966-67; gen. mgr. Oregonian Pub. Co., Portland, Oreg., 1967-72, pres., 1972—, publisher, 1975—. Bd. regents U. Portland; mem. adv. bd. Portland State U.; bd. dirs. Portland Rose Festival Assn., United Way Oreg.; chmn. Portland Citizens Crime Commn.; mem. adv. bd. St. Vincent's Hosp. Capt. USMC, 1942-45. Mem. Assn. for Portland Progress (dir.), Portland C. of C. (dir.), Oreg. Newspaper Pubs. Assn. (past pres.), Pacific N.W. Newspaper Assn. (pres.), Am. Newspaper Pubs. Assn., University Club, Multnomah Athletic Waverley Country Club, Arlington Club, Rotary. Office: Oregonian Pub Co 1320 SW Broadway Portland OR 97201-3469

STICKEL, PATRICK FRANCIS, publishing executive, newspaper; b. Hoboken, N.J., Apr. 17, 1950; s. Fred A. and Margaret (Dunne) S.; m. Debra Isaak, May 10, 1986. Degree in bus. mgmt., U. Portland, 1975. With advt. dept. Jersey Jour., Jersey City, 1966-67; with Oregonian Pub. Co., Portland, 1967-68, 70-75, pressman, with retail advt. dept., 1975-77, with retail & circulation depts., 1980-86, adminstrv. asst., 1987-89, gen. mgr., 1990-94, pres., 1994—; project mgr. Times Picayune, New Orleans, 1986-87. Bd. dirs. Oreg. Symphony Assn.; exec. com. Oregon Forum, Portland. 1st lt. USMC, 1977-80. Mem. Pacific N.W. Newspapers Assn. (bd. dirs.), Waverley Country Club, Univ. Club, Multnomah Athletic Club. Avocation: golf. Office: Oregonian Pub Co 1320 SW Broadway Portland OR 97201-3469

STICKLER, DANIEL LEE, health care management consultant; b. Fairmont, W.Va., Jan. 4, 1938; s. Elmer Daniel and Ruby Lee (Ball) S.; m. Donna Lou Johnson, Apr. 16, 1960; children—Dwight Lorne, Dwayne Lee, Douglas Lynn. B.S. in Civil Engring., W.Va. U., 1960; M.P.H. in Health Adminstrn., U. Pitts., 1970. Registered profl. engr., Tex. Asst. dir. Presbyn.-Univ. Hosp., Pitts., 1970-71, assoc. dir., 1971-72, adminstr., chief operating officer, 1972-76, exec. dir., chief exec. officer, 1976-83, pres., chief exec. officer, 1983-86; pres., CEO, The Cedars Med. Ctr., Miami, Fla., 1986-91; pres. DLS Assocs., Inc., Miami, 1991—; adj. assoc. prof. Grad. Sch. Pub. Health, U. Pitts., 1976—. Fellow Am. Coll. Hosp. Adminstrn. Republican. Methodist. Clubs: LaGorce Country. Avocations: golf; gardening. Home and Office: 5335 Alton Rd Miami FL 33140-2014

STICKLER, FRED CHARLES, manufacturing company executive; b. Villisca, Iowa, Dec. 11, 1931; s. Donald H. and Martha E. (Reese) S.; m. Dorothy A. Frahm, July 10, 1955; children—Mark, Lisa, Kent. B.S., Iowa State U., 1953, Ph.D., 1958; M.S., Kans. State U., 1955. Research asst. Kans. State U., 1953-55, Iowa State U., 1955-58; asst. prof., then assoc. prof. agronomy Kans. State U., 1958-64; with Deere & Co., Moline, Ill., 1964-87; dir. Deere & Co. (Tech. Center), 1970-80, dir. product and market planning, 1980-87, ret., 1987—; crop and soils cons., 1988—. Bd. dirs. Upper Rock Island County YMCA, 1980-87, U.S. Fed. Grain Council, 1986-89. Mem. Am. Soc. Agronomy, Crop Sci. Soc. Am., Am. Soc. Agrl. Engrs.

STICKLER, GUNNAR BRYNOLF, pediatrician; b. Peterskirchen, Germany, June 13, 1925; came to U.S., 1951, naturalized, 1958; s. Fritz and Astrid (Wennerberg) S.; m. Duci M. Kronenbitter, Aug. 30, 1956; children: Katarina Anna, George David. M.D., U. Munich, Germany, 1949; Ph.D., U. Minn., Mpls., 1957. Diplomate Am. Bd. Pediat. (mem. 1965—, ofcl. examiner). Resident in clin. pathology Krankenhaus III Orden, Munich, 1950; resident in pathology U. Munich, 1950-51; intern Mountainside Hosp., Montclair, N.J., 1951-52; fellow in pediatrics Mayo Grad. Sch., Rochester, Minn., 1953-56; sr. cancer research scientist Roswell Park Meml. Inst., Buffalo, 1956-57; asst. to staff Mayo Clinic, Rochester, 1957-58; cons. in pediatrics Mayo Clinic, 1959-89, head sect. pediatrics, 1969-74; prof. pediatrics, chmn. dept. pediatrics Mayo Clinic and Mayo Med. Sch., 1974-80; mem. test com. III Nat. Bd. Med. Examiners, 1973-75; vis. prof. at various univs and instns., including U. Dusseldorf (Germany) and U. Munich, 1971, Pahlavi U., Iran, 1975, Olga Hosp., Stuttgart, Germany, 1978, Martin Luther King Hosp., Los Angeles, 1979, U. Man., 1981; mem. emeritus staff Mayo Clinic, 1989. Contbr. numerous articles to med. publs.; editorial bd. Clin. Pediatrics, 1968-76, 79—, European Jour. Pediatrics, 1976-84, Pediatrics, 1983-89. Recipient Humanitarian award Chgo. region chpt. Nat. Found. Ileitis and Colitis, 1978, award for excellence of subject matter and presentation So. Minn. Med. Assn., 1978. Mem. Am. Acad. Pediatrics, Soc. Pediatric Research, Am. Pediatric Soc., Midwest Soc. Pediatric Research (council 1967-69, pres. 1970-71), N.W. Pediatric Soc. (pres. 1973-74). Achievements include description of hereditary progressive arthropthalmopathy in 1965, now called Stickler syndrome.

STICKLER, K. BRUCE, lawyer; b. Chgo., Jan. 3, 1946. BA, So. Meth. U., 1967, JD, 1970. Bar: Tex. 1970, Ill. 1972. Ptnr. Keck, Mahin & Cate, Chgo.; clin. faculty mem. dept. hosp. and health care adminstrn. Ctr. Health Care Svcs., St. Louis U., 1987—. Mem. healthcare adv. bd. DePaul U., Chgo. Mem. ABA, Am. Acad. Hosp. Attys., Ill. State Bar Assn. (chmn. labor law sect. coun. 1983), Ill. Assn. Hosp. Attys. (bd. dirs. 1991—), Chgo. Bar Assn., State Bar Assn. Office: Keck Mahin & Cate 77 W Wacker Dr Ste 4900 Chicago IL 60601-1693

STICKNEY, DOUGLAS HENRY, biostatistician; b. Little Rock, Feb., 21, 1956; s. Henry E. and Delphine D. (Perse). B.S. in Biology, Davidson (N.C.) Coll., 1977; M.S. in Biostats., UCLA, 1980. Statis. cons. Gateways Hyperkinetic Research Clinic, Los Angeles, 1978-81; health care analyst Systemetrics Inc., Santa Barbara, Calif., 1980-81; statis. cons. Ventura (Calif.) County Air Quality Mgmt. Bur., 1982—; biostatistician Am. Edwards Labs., Irvine, Calif., 1980—, now with Quantum Health Resources, Inc. Mem. Am. Statis. Assn. Episcopalian. Contbr. articles to profl. jours. Office: Quantum Health Resources Inc 790 The City Dr S Orange CA 92668*

STICKNEY, JESSICA, former state legislator; b. Duluth, Minn., May 16, 1929; d. Ralph Emerson and Claudia Alice (Cox) Page; m. Edwin Levi Stickney, June 17, 1951; children: Claudia, Laura, Jeffrey. BA, Macalester Coll., St. Paul, Minn., 1951; PhD (hon), Rocky Mtn. Coll., Billings, Mont., 1986. Rep. State of Mont., 1989-92; mem. Gov.'s Commn. on Post-Sec. Edn., Mont., 1973-75. Mem. Sch. Bd. Trustees, Miles City, Mont., 1968-74; mem., chmn. zoning bd., Miles City, 1975-89; mem. Govt. Study Commn., Miles City, 1974-76, United Ch. Christ Bd. Homeland Ministries, 1975-81; chmn., conf. moderator United Ch. Christ Bd. Mont.-Northern Wyo. Conf., 1980-82; chmn. Town Meeting on the Air, Mont., 1980; mem., chmn. Miles Community Coll. Bd., 1975-89, chmn. 1978-80. Mem. Mont. Arts Coun. (chmn. 1982-85), Western States Arts Found. (vice chmn. 1984), Nat. Assembly State Arts Agys. (bd. dirs. 1982-88), AAUW (pres. 1964-66). Democrat. Avocations: writing, sewing, painting, reading.

STIDHAM, SHALER, JR., operations research educator; b. Washington, Dec. 4, 1941; s. Shaler and Gladys (Ruddick) S.; m. Carolyn Jean Noble, Apr. 6, 1968; children: Christiane Wilson, Dana Claire, Ann-Elise. BA, Harvard U., 1963; MS, Case Inst. Tech., 1964; PhD, Stanford U., 1968. Asst. prof. dept. ops. rsch. Cornell U., Ithaca, N.Y., 1968-75; assoc. prof., prof. dept. indsl. engring. N.C. State U., Raleigh, 1975-86; prof. dept. ops. rsch. U. N.C., Chapel Hill, 1986—, chmn. dept. ops. rsch., 1990—; lektor Aarhus (Denmark) U., 1971-72; guest prof. Tech. U. Denmark, Lyngby, 1976-77; vis. fellow Statis. Lab., Cambridge (Eng.) U., 1982-83; cons. Bell Telephone

Labs., 1981; vis. scholar Stanford (Calif.) U., 1975, 79; invited prof. Inst. Nat. Récherche en Informatique et en Automatique, Sophia Antipolis, France, 1991-92; keynote speaker to profl. confs., The Netherlands, Germany, Poland, France and Japan, 1977—. Bd. dirs. Friends of Coll., Raleigh, 1979-82, chmn. program com., 1981-82; bd. dirs. N.C. Symphony Found., Raleigh, 1990—. Overseas fellow Churchill Coll., Cambridge, 1982—. Mem. Ops. Rsch. Soc. Am. (chmn. applied probability tech. sect. 1990-91), Inst. Mgmt. Scis. (program co-chmn. internat. meeting Osaka, Japan 1989), Sigma Xi (Young Scientist Rsch. award 1978), Alpha Pi Mu. Home: 10428 Whitestone Rd Raleigh NC 27615-1236 Office: U NC Dept Ops Rsch Cb 3180 Smith Bldg Chapel Hill NC 27599

STIEBEL, GERALD GUSTAVE, art dealer; b. N.Y.C., Sept. 28, 1944; s. Eric and Irene (Sichel) S.; m. Judith Rudner, 1965 (div. 1975); children: Catherine Lynn, Daniel James; m. Penelope Hunter, Aug. 14, 1975; 1 son, Hunter Hans. BA, C.W. Post Coll., 1965; postgrad. Study Ctr. for Fine and Decorative Arts, London, Eng., 1965-66; MA, Columbia U., 1967. With Rosenberg & Stiebel, Inc., N.Y.C., 1966—, treas., 1968—, v.p., 1971-85, pres., 1985—; mem. faculty New Sch. Social Research, 1979-84; bd. dirs. Videodisc Pub., Inc., MUSE Film and TV. Apptd. Cultural Property Adv. Com., 1994—. Mem. Nat. Antique and Art Dealers Assn. Am. (v.p. 1973-77, pres. 1977-79), Art Dealers Assn. Am. (dir. 1980-89), Internat. Confedn. Dealers in Works of Art (pres. 1981-84, permanent councillor 1990—), Syndicat National Des Antiquaires. Office: 32 E 57th St New York NY 10022-2513

STIEBER, TAMAR, writer; b. Bklyn., Sept. 15, 1955; d. Alfred and Florence (Spector) S. Student, Rockland C.C., 1972-75, Rockland C.C., 1972-75, West London (Eng.) Coll., 1973-74; BA in Film cum laude, U. Calif., Berkeley, 1985, postgrad., 1985-86; grad. police reserve academycum laude, Napa Valley Coll., 1988. Office mgr., confidential sec. AP, San Francisco, 1981-83; stringer Daily Californian, Berkeley, Calif., 1983-84; film rsch. teaching asst. U. California, Berkeley, 1984-86; libr. and rsch. asst. Pacific Film Archive, Berkeley, 1984-86; intern San Francisco Examiner, 1984; reporter Sonoma (Calif.) Index-Tribune, 1987-88, Vallejo (Calif.) Times Herald, 1988-89, Albuquerque Journal, 1989-94. Recipient Pulitzer prize for specialized reporting, 1990, first place pub. svc. down. N.Mex. Press Assn., 1990, pub. svc. award Albuquerque Press Club, 1990; first place newswriting N.Mex. Press Assn., 1991; honorable mention Assn. Press Managing Editors, 1994. Mem. Soc. Profl. Journalists, Investigative Reporters and Editors, N.M. Found. Open Govt., Phi Beta Kappa. Home: PO Box 9835 Santa Fe NM 87504-9835

STIEF, LOUIS JOHN, chemist; b. Pottsville, Pa., July 26, 1933; s. Louis Norman and Dorothy Elizabeth (Bassler) S.; m. Kathleen J. Talbot, Nov. 30, 1963 (div. 1980); children—Andrew, Lorraine. B.A., La Salle Coll., 1955; Ph.D., Catholic U. Am., 1960. Nat. Acad. Scis.-NRC postdoctoral rsch. assoc. Nat. Bur. Standards, Washington, 1960-61; NATO postdoctoral fellow, ind. researcher chemistry dept. Sheffield (Eng.) U., 1961-63; sr. scientist, sr. chemist Melpar, Inc., Falls Church, Va., 1963-68; NAS-NRC sr. postdoctoral rsch. assoc. NASA/Goddard Space Flight Ctr., Greenbelt, Md., 1968-69; astrophysicist NASA/Goddard Space Flight Ctr., 1969-76, head br. astrochemistry, 1976-90, sr. scientist, 1990—; adj. prof. chemistry Cath. U. Am. Research: numerous publs., especially in Jour. Chem. Physics and Jour. Phys. Chemistry. Recipient Alumni Achievement award Cath. U. Am., 1985; NASA fellow Queen Mary Coll., U. London, 1981-82. Fellow Washington Acad. Sci.; mem. Am. Chem. Soc., Royal Soc. Chemistry, Am. Geophys. Union, Am. Astron. Soc. (div. planetary sci.), Sigma Xi. Office: NASA Goddard Space Flight Ctr Code 690 Greenbelt MD 20771

STIEFLER, JEFFREY E., financial services executive; b. 1946. BA, Williams Coll., 1968; MBA, Harvard U., 1970. Gen. mgr. Boise Cascade, 1971-75; pres. Mintz & Hoke, Inc., 1975-77; sr. v.p. Citicorp, 1977-82; exec. v.p. J.B. Coleman & Co., 1982-83; pres. Phila. Saving Fund Soc., 1986-87; sr. v.p. mktg. IDS Fin. Svcs., 1983-86; exec. v.p. sales and mktg. IDS Fin. Svcs., Am. Express subsidiary, 1987-90; pres. IDS Fin. Svcs., 1990-91, CEO, 1992-93; pres. Am. Express Co., N.Y.C., 1993—, also bd. dirs., 1993—; bd. dirs. Nat. Computer Sys. Office: Am Express Co Am Express Tower C World Fin Ctr New York NY 10285-4805

STIEHL, WILLIAM D., federal judge; b. 1925; m. Celeste M. Sullivan; children: William D., Susan M. Student, U. N.C., 1943-45; LLB, St. Louis U., 1949. Pvt. practice, 1971-78; ptnrs. Stiehl & Hess, 1978-81; ptnr. Stiehl & Stiehl, 1982-86; judge, former chief judge U.S. District Court, (so. dist.) Ill., East Saint Louis, 1986—; spl. asst. atty. gen. State of Ill., 1970-73. Mem. bd. Belleville Twp. High Sch. and Jr. Coll., 1949-50, 54-56, pres., 1956-57, Clair County, Ill., county civil atty., 1956-60. Mem. ABA, Ill. Bar Assn., St. Clair County Bar Assn. Office: US Dist Ct 212 US Courthouse East Saint Louis IL 62202

STIEHM, E. RICHARD, pediatrician, educator; b. Milw., Jan. 22, 1933; s. Reuben Harold and Marie Dueno S.; m. Judith Hicks, July 12, 1958; children: Jamie Elizabeth, Carrie Eleanor, Meredith Ellen. B.S., U. Wis., 1954, M.D., 1957. Diplomate: Am. Bd. Pediatrics, Am. Bd. Allergy and Clin. Immunology (bd. dirs. 1977-83), Am. Bd. Diagnostic Lab. Immunology. Intern Phila. Gen. Hosp., 1957-58; fellow U. Wis., 1958-59; resident in pediatrics Babies Hosp., N.Y.C., 1961-63; fellow immunology U. Calif., San Francisco, 1963-65; asst. prof. pediatrics U. Wis., 1965-68, assoc. prof., 1968-69; assoc. prof. UCLA, 1969-72, prof., 1972—, chief div. immunology and allergy, 1969—; vice chair acad. affairs dept. pediatrics, 1989—; co-dir. Ctr. for Interdisciplinary Rsch. in Immunologic Diseases UCLA, 1978-88; dir. UCLA Cystic Fibrosis Ctr., 1982-87; bd. sci. dirs. Immune Deficiency Found., 1981—, Eczema Found., 1988—, Pediatric AIDS Found., 1989—; mem. gen. clin. rsch. ctr. study sect. NIH, 1978-82, 84-88; co-dir. L.A. Pediatric AIDS Consortium, 1988—. Editor: (with V. Fulginiti) Immunologic Disorders in Infants and Children, 1972, 80, 89; Am. editor: Pediatric Research, 1984-89; assoc. editor: Pediatrics Update, 1978-85; mem. editorial bd. Pediatrics, 1972-78, Pediatrics in Rev., 1978-81, Jour. Allergy and Clin. Immunology, 1976-80, Jour. Clin. Immunology, 1985-89, Jour. Asthma Pediatric Allergy and Immunology, 1987-91, Am. Jour. Diseases of Children, 1987—, Contemporary Pediatrics, 1991—, Am. Jour. Clin. Nutrition, 1992—; contbr. articles to profl. jours. Mem. HHS Commn. on Childhood Vaccines, 1988-90; mem. clin. rsch. com. Nat. Found. March of Dimes, 1992—. Recipient Ross Research award Western Soc. Pediatric Research, 1971, E. Mead Johnson award for pediatric research, 1974, Alumni Citation award U. Wis. Med. Sch., 1988; Markle scholar, 1968-73. Mem. AAAS, Am. Assn. Immunologists, Western Soc. Pediatric Research (pres. 1983), Soc. Pediatric Research, Am. Pediatric Soc., Am. Acad. Allergy and Clin. Immunology, Am. Acad. Pediatrics, Am. Soc. Clin. Investigation, Clin. Immunology Soc., Alpha Delta Phi, Phi Beta Kappa, Alpha Omega Alpha. Home: UCLA Med Ctr 23-387 MDCC 10833 Le Conte Ave Santa Monica CA 90402-3102 Office: UCLA Cystic Fibrosis Program 10833 Le Conte Ave Los Angeles CA 90024

STIER, EDWIN H., lawyer; b. Newark, Nov. 2, 1939. B.A., Rutgers U., 1961, LL.B., 1964. Bar: N.J. 1965, U.S. Supreme Ct. 1979. Asst. U.S. atty. Fed. Ct., Newark, 1965-69; chief criminal div. U.S. Atty.'s Office, Newark, 1967-69; asst. atty. gen., dir. criminal justice State of N.J., Trenton, 1969-82; ptnr. Kirsten, Friedman & Cherin, Newark, 1982—. Author: White Collar Crime, 1981. Office: Trucking Employees 707 Summit Ave Union City NJ 07087

STIER, ROBERT H., JR., lawyer; b. Berwyn, Ill., Dec. 19, 1952; s. Robert H. and Lois (Lindahl) S.; m. Mary Ellen FitzGerald, Aug. 11, 1979; children: Meghan, Erik, Maeve. AB, Harvard Coll., 1975; postgrad., U. Gothenburg, Sweden, 1976-77; JD, Harvard U., 1980. Bar: Md. 1980, U.S. Dist. Ct. Md. 1980, D.C. 1983, U.S. Dist. Ct. D.C. 1984, U.S. Ct. Appeals (4th and D.C. cirs.) 1985, Va. 1986, U.S. Dist. Ct. (ea. and we. dists.) Va. 1986, U.S. Ct. Appeals (fed. cir.) 1986, U.S. Supreme Ct. 1986, Maine 1988, U.S. Dist. Ct. Maine 1988. Assoc. Piper & Marbury, Balt., 1980-83, Washington, 1983-87; ptnr. Bernstein, Shur, Sawyer & Nelson, Portland, Maine, 1987—. Mem. ABA, Def. Rsch. Inst. Avocations: squash, windsurfing. Office: Bernstein Shur Sawyer & Nelson PO Box 9729 Portland ME 04104-5029

STIERS, DAVID OGDEN, actor, conductor; b. Peoria, Ill., Oct. 31, 1942; s. Kenneth Truman and Margaret Elizabeth (Ogden) S. Diploma drama div., Juilliard Sch., 1973. Actor, Actors Workshop, 1962, Calif. Shakespeare Festival, 1963-68, mem., The Committee, 1968-70, San Francisco (revue)/ Broadway season City Center Acting Co., N.Y.C., 1974; Broadway appearances include Ulysses in Nighttown, 1974, The Magic Show, 1974-75; other stage appearances include King Lear, 1981; regular on TV series MASH 1977-83; other TV appearances include Mary Tyler Moore Show, Rhoda; TV film appearances include Charlie's Angels, 1976, A Circle of Children, 1977, A Love Affair: The Eleanor and Lou Gehrig Story, 1978, Sergeant Matlovich Vs. the US Air Force, 1978, Breaking Up Is Hard To Do, 1979, Damien: The Leper Priest, 1980, The Day the Bubble Burst, 1982, Anatomy of an Illness, 1984, The First Olympics-Athens 1896, 1984, The Bad Seed, 1985, North and South, 1985, North and South Book II, 1986, Mrs. Delafield Wants to Marry, 1986, Perry Mason: Case of the Notorious Nun, 1986, Perry Mason: Case of the Shooting Star, 1986, The Kissing Place, 1990; film appearances include: Drive, He Said, 1972, Oh God!, 1977, The Cheap Detective, 1978, Magic, 1978, The Man With One Red Shoe, 1985, Creator, 1985, Better Off Dead, 1985, The Accidental Tourist, 1988, Another Woman, 1988, Doc Hollywood, 1991, Beauty and the Beast, 1991 (2 voices), Iron Will, 1994, The Toolshed, 1994, Bad Company, 1995, Pocahontas, 1995 (voice), Steal Big, Steal Little, 1995; artistic assoc. The Acting Co., N.Y.C.; prin. guest condr. Yaquina Orch., 1989; now resident condr. Yaquina Chamber Orch.; guest condr. 70 orchs. including San Diego Symphony, Dallas Symphony Orch., Utah Symphony Orch., Chgo. Symphony Orch., Va. Symphony Orch., N.C. Symphony Philharm., Ft. Wayne Philharm., Calif. Symphony Orch.; also orchs. in Honolulu, Portland, Maine, Grand Rapids, Mich., Peoria, Ill. Mem. NARAS, Conductors Guild, Am. Symphony Orch. League, Internat. Horn Soc., Magic Castle, Players Club. Office: care GKAC Ste 3600 12304 Santa Monica Blvd Los Angeles CA 90025-2551*

STIFF, JOHN STERLING, development company executive; b. McKinney, Tex., Feb. 14, 1921; s. James Harrison and Elva (Boone) S.; m. Harriett Raschig, May 31, 1946; children—Mark, Justin. Student, Tex. A&M Coll., 1938-41; B.E., Yale U., 1947. Registered profl. engr., Tex. Mgmt. trainee City of Big Spring, Tex., 1938-39, 41-42; city engr. Abilene, Tex., 1947-51; city mgr. Irving, Tex., 1953-57; gen. mgr. Hardee-Pipkin Constrn.Co., Irving, 1957-58; city mgr. Garland, Tex., 1958-63, Amarillo, Tex., 1963-83; pres. Quail Creek Devel. Co., Amarillo, Tex., 1983-95. Pres. Amarillo Area Found., 1988; bd. dirs. Harrington Found., 1989. Served with USNR, 1942-46, 51-52. Mem. Internat. City Mgrs. Assn. (past pres.), Tex. City Mgrs. Assn. (past pres.), Panhandle Home Builders Assn. (past bd. dirs.), Garland Home Builders Assn., Amarillo Exec. Assn. (pres. 1988-89), Amarillo C. of C., Dallas C. of C., Amarillo A & M Club, Amarillo Yale Club, Rotary. Methodist. Home: Rte 8 Box 45-6 326 N Shore Dr Amarillo TX 79118-9339 Office: PO Box 3880 Amarillo TX 79116-3880

STIFF, ROBERT MARTIN, newspaper editor; b. Detroit, Aug. 25, 1931; s. Martin L. and Gladys (Mathews) S.; m. Cindy Rose, Aug. 30, 1980; children: David Alan, Amy Anne, Kirsten Marie. BA in Radio and Journalism, Ohio State U., 1953. Reporter, bur. chief, city editor Painesville (Ohio) Telegraph, 1953-61; deskman, asst. city editor, sports editor, city editor, day editor, state editor, asst. mng. editor St. Petersburg (Fla.) Times, 1961-67; editor St. Petersburg Evening Ind., 1967-84; dir. St. Petersburg Times Pub. Co., 1969-84; exec. editor, v.p. Tallahassee Democrat, 1985-91; pres. Bob Stiff & Assocs., Tallahassee, 1991-95; exec. editor JMT Assocs., 1991-92, 95; mng. editor About Florida, 1991-94; editor Lexington (N.C.) Dispatch, 1995—; dir. devel. and pub. rels. Fla. Taxwatch Inc., 1992-94. Mem. AP Assn. Fla. (pres. 1970-71), Am. Soc. Newspaper Editors (dir. 1981-87), Am. Soc. Newspaper Editors Found. (bd. dirs., treas. 1986-90), Fla. Soc. Newspaper Editors (pres. 1975-76, dir. 1971-84, 90-93), Fla. Bar Found. (bd. dirs. 1990-92), AP Mng. Editors Assn., Sigma Delta Chi (pres. West coast chpt. 1970-71), Tallahassee Soc. of Assoc. Execs., Tallahasse Mag. Editorial bd., Fla. Econs. Club, Capital Tiger Bay Club, 21st Century Club.

STIFFLER, JACK JUSTIN, electrical engineer; b. Mitchellville, Iowa, May 22, 1934; s. John Justin and Helen Irene (Roorda) S.; m. Ardis Ann Ackerman, Aug. 21, 1955; 1 child, Julia Alise; m. Sally Voris Burns, Apr. 20, 1989. A.B. magna cum laude in Physics, Harvard U., 1956; M.S. in E.E, Calif. Inst. Tech., 1957, Ph.D., 1962; postgrad., U. Paris, 1957-58. Engr. Hughes Aircraft Corp., Culver City, Calif., 1956-57; mem. tech. staff Jet Propulsion Lab., Pasadena, Calif., 1959-67; cons. scientist Raytheon Corp., Sudbury, Mass., 1967-81; exec. v.p. Sequoia Systems, Inc., Marlborough, Mass., 1981—; lectr. Calif. Inst. Tech., U. So. Calif., UCLA, Northeastern U. Author: Theory of Synchronous Communications, 1971; contbr. chpts. to books, articles to profl. jours. Fellow IEEE; mem. Phi Beta Kappa, Sigma Xi. Office: Sequoia Systems Inc 400 Nickerson Rd Marlborough MA 01752

STIGLER, DAVID MACK, lawyer; b. Indiana, Pa., Aug. 31, 1943; s. George Joseph and Margaret Louise (Mack) S.; m. Carolyn Ann Sawko, Sept. 30, 1990; children: Zachary, Benjamin, Julie, Joanna. AB, Oberlin Coll., 1965; JD, U. Chgo., 1968. Bar: N.Y. 1969, U.S. Dist. Ct. (so. and ea. dists.) N.Y., U.S. Tax Ct., U.S. Ct. Appeals (2d and 3d cirs.). Assoc. Rogers & Wells, N.Y.C., 1968-74; asst. gen. counsel Heublein, Inc., Farmington, Conn., 1974-86; v.p., sec. 1984-86; v.p., gen. counsel, sec. ADVO, Inc., Windsor, Conn., 1986—; sr. v.p., 1990—; staff counsel Presdl. Commn. on All-Vol. Armed Forces, Washington, 1969. Chmn. fund drive United Way, Farmington, 1980, Windsor, 1987. Mem. ABA, Am. Corp. Coun. Assn., N.Y. State Bar Assn., Am. Soc. Corp. Secs. Republican. Avocations: running, racquet sports. Office: Advo Inc 1 Univac Ln Windsor CT 06095-2629

STIGLER, STEPHEN MACK, statistician, educator; b. Mpls., Aug. 10, 1941; s. George Joseph and Margaret (Mack) S.; m. Virginia Lee, June 27, 1964; children: Andrew, Geoffrey, Margaret, Elizabeth. BA, Carleton Coll., 1963; PhD, U. Calif., Berkeley, 1967. Asst. prof. U. Wis., Madison, 1967-71, assoc. prof., 1971-75, prof. 1975-79; prof. U. Chgo., 1979—; chmn. dept., 1986-92; Ernest DeWitt Burton Disting. Svc. prof. U. Chgo., 1992—; trustee Ctr. for Advanced Study in the Behavioral Scis., Stanford, Calif., 1986-92, 93—, mem., 1995—. Author: The History of Statistics, 1986; contbr. articles to jours. in field. Guggenheim Found. fellow, 1976-77; Ctr. for Advanced Study in Behavioral Scis. fellow, 1978-79. Fellow AAAS, Am. Acad. Arts and Scis., Inst. Math. Stats. (Neyman lectr. 1988, pres. 1993-94), Am. Statis. Assn. (editor Jour. 1979-82, Outstanding Statistician award Chgo. chpt. 1993), Royal Statis. Soc. (Fisher lectr. 1986); mem. Internat. Statis. Inst., Bernoulli Soc., History of Sci. Soc., Brit. Soc. for History Sci., Quadrangle Club, Sigma Xi. Office: U Chgo Dept Statistics 5734 S University Ave Chicago IL 60637-1546

STIGWOOD, ROBERT COLIN, theater, movie, television and record producer; b. Adelaide, Australia, Apr. 16, 1934; came to Eng., 1956; s. Gordon and Gwendolyn (Burrows) S. Attended, Sacred Heart Coll., Adelaide. Worked as copywriter for advt. agy. Adelaide; held series of jobs, including mgr. provincial theater and halfway house for delinquents in Cambridge; opened talent agy. London, 1962; liquidated firm, 1965; became bus. mgr. for group Graham Bond Orgn.; became co-mng. dir. NEMS Enterprises, 1967; established own firm Robert Stigwood Orgn., 1967; formed RSO Records, 1973; became dir. of Polygram, 1976; co-founder (with Rupert Murdoch) R&R Films, 1979; founder Music for UNICEF. 1st ind. record producer in Eng. with release of single Johnny Remember Me; producer: films, including Jesus Christ Superstar, 1973, Bugsy Malone, Tommy, 1975, Survive, 1976, Saturday Night Fever, 1977, Grease I, 1978, Grease II, 1982, Moment By Moment, 1978, Sergeant Pepper's Lonely Hearts Club Band, The Fan, 1981, Times Square, 1980, Gallipoli, 1980, Staying Alive, 1983; stage musicals in Eng. and U.S.; including, Hair, Oh! Calcutta, The Dirtiest Show in Town, seeeely Pad, Pippin, Jesus Christ Superstar, Evita, Grease; TV producer in Eng. and U.S.; prodns. include The Entertainer (dramatic spl.); All in the Family (series), The Prime of Miss Jean Brodie (dramatic series). Bd. dirs. Police Athletic League, N.Y.C.; patron Australian Nat. Art Gallery. Recipient Tony award for best musical (Evita); named Internat. Producer of Yr. ABC Interstate Theatres, Inc., 1976, Knight of St. John of Jerusalem, Malta, 1985. Club: Royal Bermuda Yacht. Avocations: yachting, tennis. Home: Barton Manor Estate, Eastowes, Isle of Wight England

STILES, JOHN CALLENDER, physicist; b. Paris, Feb. 21, 1927; came to U.S., 1927; s. William Callender Irvine and Ellen Douglass (Fillebrown) S; m. Virginia Taggert, June 17, 1949; children: Janet, Susan, Judith, William, Robert. BA in Physics, Princeton U., 1950. Jr. scientist Bendix Aviation, Teterboro, N.J., 1951-52; prin. scientist Kearfott Guidance & Navigation Co., Little Falls, N.J., 1952-68, head dept. applied physics, 1972-82, dir. rsch., 1982—; chief scientist Litton Industries, Woodland Hills, Calif., 1968-72. With U.S. Army, 1944-47. Mem. Aero Club Albatross. Achievements include 35 patents in field; development of tuned rotor gyros, of ring laser gyros, of digital accelerometers, of instrumentation for use in inertial navigation systems. Home: 3000 Victorias Way Forest Hill MD 21050-1404 Office: Kearfott Guidance & Navigation Co 1150 Mcbride Ave Little Falls NJ 07424-2500

STILES, NED BERRY, lawyer; b. Mays Lick, Ky., Aug. 7, 1932; s. Andrew Jackson and Frances (Berry) S.; m. Patricia Pollard, Nov. 23, 1953 (div. 1959); 1 son, Michael P.; m. Lynn Shattuck, Apr. 16, 1966 (div. 1976); children: Andrew J., Peter S.; m. Deborah Fiedler, Dec. 2, 1978; 1 dau., Jessica B. A.B., Miami U., Oxford, Ohio, 1953; LL.M., U. Cin., 1958. Bar: Ohio 1958, N.Y. 1962. Staff atty. SEC, Washington, 1958-61; assoc. Cleary, Gottlieb, Steen & Hamilton, N.Y.C., 1961-67, ptnr., 1968-88, mng. ptnr., 1988—; pres., chmn. bd. Fir Tree Internat. Fund. mem., bd. eds., Cincinnati Law Review, 1957-58; co-author: The Silent Partners—Institutional Investors and Corporate Control, 1965; contbr. articles to legal publs. Pres., bd. dirs. Quogue Assn. Inc., N.Y.; treas. bd. dirs. Group for the South Fork, Southampton, N.Y.; bd. appeals Village of Quogue. Served to capt. USAF, 1953-55. Mem. ABA, Assn. Bar City N.Y. (former mem. securities regulation and corp. law coms.). Clubs: River (N.Y.C.), India House (N.Y.C.). Home: 1165 5th Ave New York NY 10029-6931 Office: Cleary Gottlieb Steen 1 Liberty Pla New York NY 10006*

STILES, PHILLIP JOHN, physicist, educator; b. Manchester, Conn., Oct. 31, 1934; married, 1956; 6 children. BS, Trinity Coll., 1956; PhD in Physics, U. Pa., 1961. Mem. rsch. staff Thomas J. Watson Rsch. Ctr. IBM, N.Y.C., 1963-70; prof. physics Brown U., 1970-93, chmn. dept. physics, 1974-80, dean Grad. Sch., dean of rsch., 1986-93; provost, vice chancellor, prof. physics N.C. State U., Raleigh, 1993—. U. Pa. fellow, 1961-62, NSF fellow, 1962-63; recipient Humboldt Sr. U.S. Sci. award, 1976, John Price Wetheral medal Franklin Inst., 1981. Fellow AAAS; mem. Am. Physics Soc. (Oliver E. Buckley prize 1988), Am. Astronomy Soc., Acoustical Soc. Am. Office: NC State U Office Provost/Vice Chancellor PO Box 7101 Raleigh NC 27695-7101

STILES, THOMAS BEVERIDGE, II, investment banking executive; b. Easton, Pa., Oct. 4, 1940; s. Ezra Martin and Vivien (de Fay) S.; m. Elaine Ann Patyk, July 2, 1966 (div. Oct. 1980); children—Thomas Beveridge III, Jonathan Ezra; m. Barbara Toll Alexander, Mar. 7, 1981. B.A., Yale U., 1963; M.B.A., Harvard U., 1968. V.p. Laird, Inc., N.Y.C., 1968-73; sr. v.p. dir. Smith Barney Harris Upham and Co., Inc., N.Y.C., 1973-82; exec. v.p., dir. E.F. Hutton & Co. Inc., N.Y.C., 1982-87; chmn., chief exec. officer Shearson Lehman Advisors Asset Mgmt. Co., N.Y.C., 1988-90; chmn., chief exec. officer Bernstein Macaulay, N.Y.C., also bd. dirs., 1988-90; chmn., chief exec. officer Greenwich St. Advisors, N.Y.C., 1990—; bd. dirs., treas. Cedar Lawn Cemetery, Paterson, N.J., 1973—. Served to 1st lt. M.I., U.S. Army, 1963-66. Fellow Fin. Analysts Fedn.; mem. N.Y. Soc. Security Analysts. Republican. Presbyterian. Club: Spring Lake Bath and Tennis (N.J.). Avocations: political science; tennis; swimming. Office: Greenwich St Advisors 388 Greenwich St 23 Fl New York NY 10013

STILL, CHARLES HENRY, lawyer; b. Lubbock, Tex., Sept. 22, 1942; s. Charles Alphonso and Henri Sue (Boone) S.; m. Frances Eugenia Odell, Apr. 29, 1967; children: Charles Henry Jr., Kathryn Elizabeth. BBA in Acctg., Tex. Tech. U., 1965; JD with honors, U. Tex., 1968. Bar: Tex. 1968. Assoc. Fulbright & Jaworski, Houston, 1968-75, ptnr., 1975—, head corp. dept., 1984—, mem. exec. com., 1992—; speaker numerous confs. and meetings. Comment editor Tex. Law Rev., 1967-68. Bd. dirs. Alley Theater, Houston, 1980-81, St. Luke's Episc. Hosp., Houston, 1991—; mem. vestry Christ Ch. Cathedral, Houston, 1981-84, sr. warden, 1983, chancellor, 1986—, mem. search com. for rector, 1991—. Fellow Am. Bar Found., Tex. Bar Found.; Houston Bar Assn.; mem. ABA (bus. law sect. 1968—, corp. laws com. 1983-89, fed. regulation of securities com. 1976—, subcom. on proxy statements and tender offers 1979—, com. on legal opinions 1989—, adminstrv. law sect. 1981—), Am. Law Inst., State Bar Tex. (chmn. bus. law sect. 1981-83, mem. com. on corp. laws 1985—, legislation in pub. interest com. 1983-84), Houston Bar Assn., Forest Club, Ramada-Tejas Club, Houston Ctr., Order of Coif, Phi Delta Phi, Phi Kappa Phi, Gamma Phi Beta, Beta Alpha Psi, Phi Delta Theta, Phi Eta Sigma. Avocations: jogging, reading, photography. Home: 3734 Locke Ln Houston TX 77027-4006 Office: Fulbright & Jaworski 1301 Mckinney St Ste 5100 Houston TX 77010-3036

STILL, CRAIG RUSSELL, publishing executive; b. Akron, Ohio, Oct. 10, 1969; s. Robert Barry and Susan Marie (Staub) S. AS in Culinary Arts, Culinary Inst., Am. Hyde Park, N.Y., 1988-89; BS in Hotel and Restaurant Mgmt., Berkeley Bus. Coll., N.Y.C., 1988. Cert. Am. Dietetic Assn. N.Y.; cert. chef, CIA, N.Y.; cert. Dietary Mgr.'s Assn. Ill. Pub. Beatles Connection, Tampa, Fla., 1984—; chef Marriott Internat., Tampa, Fla., 1989-91, Palm Harbor Fla., 1991-93, asst. food and beverage dir., Port St. Lucie, Fla., 1993-94; food and beverage dir. Masonic Home of Fla., St. Petersburg, 1994; pop culture editor United Pubs., L.A., 1986—, contbg. writer, 1990—. Author: Healthy Heart for Elderly, 1992; pub. Highlight books, 1990. Recipient Youngest Pub. With 10,000 Circulation award Associated Press Internat., 1985. Mem. Masons. Republican. Roman Catholic. Avocations: cooking, traveling, music, sports. Office: Beatles Conncection PO Box 1066 Pinellas Park FL 34665

STILL, GERALD G., plant physiologist, research director; b. Seattle, Aug. 13, 1933; s. Edmond N. and Clara J. (Brown) S.; m. Carole J. Hall, June 27, 1954; children: Denise K., Kirk J., Carrie R. BS in Biochemistry, Wash. State U., 1959; MS in Biochemistry, Oreg. State U., 1963, PhD in Biochemistry, 1965. Research fellow Oreg. State U., Corvallis, 1959-65; research chemist USDA Agrl. Research Service CPRB-MRRL, Fargo, N.D., 1965-76; staff scientist USDA Agrl. Research Service, Nat. Park Service, Beltsville, Md., 1976-80, nat. program dir., 1982-84; chief scientist USDA SEA-OD, Washington, 1980-82; dir. USDA Agrl. Research Service, Pacific Gas & Electric Co., Albany, Calif., 1984—; asst. prof. biochemistry N.S. State U., Fargo, 1968-76. Mem. editorial bd. Jour. Agrl. and Food Chemistry, 1978-80; contbr. numerous articles to profl. jours. Served with U.S. Army, 1952-55. Mem. Am. Chem. Soc. (numerous offices div. pesticide chemisty fellow 1977), Am. Soc. Plant Physiologists, Sigma Xi, Phi Lambda Upsilon. Office: USDA Agrl Research Service Plant Gene Expression Ctr 800 Buchanan St Berkeley CA 94710-1100

STILL, MARY JANE (M. J. STILL), mathematics educator; b. Kingsport, Tenn., Apr. 14, 1940; d. James Charles and Allie Fair (Williams) S.; m. Michael S. Golden, 1962 (div. 1971); m. Thos L. Scruggs, 1972 (div. 1975); children: Amanda Fair, Jacob Charles. AB in English, Math., Edn-Psychology, Trevecca Nazarene Coll., 1962; MEd in Math., Statistics, Auburn U., 1969. File clk. FBI, Washington, 1958; tchr. Stratford Jr.-Sr. High Sch., Nashville, 1962-63; statistician Pub. Welfare Dept. State of Tenn., Nashville, 1963-65; math. and English tchr. Smiths Sta. High Sch., Smiths, Ala., 1965-66; math., English, psychology tchr. West Point High Sch., West Point, Ga., 1966-67; math. tchr. La Grange High Sch., La Grange, Ga., 1967-68; math. and English tchr. Townsend High Sch., Townsend, Tenn., 1968-72; math., English, physical edn. tchr. Northshore High Sch., West Palm Beach, Fla., 1974-75; prof. math. Palm Beach Community Coll., Lake Worth, Fla., 1975-78, Palm Beach Community Coll.-North Campus, Palm Beach Gardens, Fla., 1978—; cons. Fla. Power & Light Co., North Palm Beach, 1989; lectr. Palm Beach Community Coll. Speakers, Palm Beach Gardens, 1986-89. Editor, advisor: College Mathematics, 1989; textbook editor, advisor Dellen Pub., Scott Foresman Pub., 1988—, Little Brown, McGraw Hill, 1989—, Wadsworth & Prindle/Weber/Smidt, 1992—; contbr. articles to profl. jours.; author math, booklets, children's stories, poetry; appeared in 2 TV commls., also producer. Scorekeeper, coach, mgr. baseball and softball leagues Palm Beach area, 1980-90; supporter Jackson polit. campaign, West Palm Beach, 1988; Children's Mus. and Turtle Soc., Juno Beach, Fla., 1986; coach, mgr. sponsor boys' baseball little league, girls'

softball, ladies' softball, Lake Park, Palm Beach Gardens, Fla., 1980-92, active softball and basketball coll. and cmty. leagues. Math. summer fellow NSF Northeastern U., Boston, 1988; grad. scholar NSF, Auburn, Ala., 1967-69, Shakespeare scholar Shakespearean Soc. Palm Beach, Stratford-on-Avon, Eng., 1975. Mem. NEA, Math. Assn. Am., Fla. Assn. Cmty. Colls., Am. Statis. Assn., Dreher Sci. Mus., Bus. Women North Palm Beach, Animal Rescue League (West Palm Beach, life), Audubon Soc., NOW, Hist. Soc., Rwy. Club, Consortium for Math. and its Applications. Nazarene. Avocations: artist, music, drama, sports, church work. Office: Palm Beach Community Coll N 3160 P G A Blvd # G A Blvd West Palm Beach FL 33410-2802

STILL, THOMAS WAYNE, newspaper editor, columnist; b. Alexandria, Va., July 9, 1953; s. Claude Richmond and Margaret Louise (Stratton) S.; m. Mary Louise Gilbert, Sept. 6, 1975 (div. Mar. 1982); 1 child, Stephanie Anne; m. Christine Ann O'Neill, June 11, 1983; children: Jason Thomas, Jessica Erin. BA in Journalism, Drake U., 1973; postgrad., U. Wis., 1980-81. Copy boy The Washington Star, 1970-71; sports reporter/copy editor The Des Moines Register, 1972-73; gen. assignment reporter The Mason City (Iowa) Globe-Gazette, 1974-76; gen. assignment reporter The Wis. State Jour., Madison, 1976-77, city hall reporter, 1977-79, chief polit. reporter, 1979-85, opinion page editor, 1985-89, assoc. editor, 1989—; polit. columnist Corp. Report/Wis., Milw., 1987-95; polit. columnist/contbr. Wis. Interest, The Wis. Policy Rsch. Inst., Milw., 1992-95; syndicated columnist "Inside Wis.", 1990-95; guest presenter/lectr. Contbr. articles to newspapers. Co-founder We the People/Wis., Madison, 1992-95; vol. Black Hawk Girl Scout Coun., Madison, 1989-95; past vol. Big Bros./Big Sisters, PTO. Recipient Midwest Regional Emmy award Nat. Acad. TV Arts and Scis., 1993, 94, Pub. Svc. Journalism award Milw. Press Club, 1980, 93, Sweepstakes award AP Mng. Editors, 1976, edit. writing award Wis. Newspaper Assn., 1986-95, grant Pew Ctr. for Civic Journalism; named one of Most Influential, Madison Mag., 1987, 91, 94. Mem. Nat. Conf. Editl. Writers (conv. com. 1995). Avocations: men's senior baseball league, fast-pitch softball, city league basketball, reading, youth coaching. Home: 218 S Segoe Rd Madison WI 53705 Office: Wis State Jour 1901 Fish Hatchery Rd Madison WI 53713

STILL, WILLIAM CLARK, JR., chemistry educator; b. Augusta, Ga., Aug. 31, 1946; s. William Clark and Ann (Smith) S. B.S., Emory U., 1969, Ph.D. in Chemistry, 1972; postgrad., Princeton U., 1972-74, Columbia U., 1974-76. Asst. prof. chemistry Vanderbilt U., Nashville, 1976-78; asst. prof. chemistry Columbia U., N.Y.C., 1978-80, assoc. prof. chemistry, 1980-81, prof. chemistry, 1981—. Contbr. numerous articles to profl. jours. Recipient Alan T. Waterman award NSF, 1981, Buchman award Calif. Inst. Tech., 1982; Cope Scholar, 1987, Stieglitz award, 1984. Mem. Am. Chem. Soc. (Computers in Chemistry award 1993), Am. Acad. Arts and Scis. Office: Columbia U Dept Chemistry New York NY 10027*

STILLER, JENNIFER ANNE, lawyer; b. Washington, May 4, 1948; d. Ralph Sophian and Joy (Dancis) S.; m. Ray Redd, Jan. 24, 1987. AB in Econs. and History, U. Mich., 1970; JD, NYU, 1973. Bar: Pa. 1973, U.S. Dist. Ct. (mid. dist.) Pa. 1977, U.S. Supreme Ct. 1978, U.S. Dist. Ct. (no. dist.) Ill. 1979, U.S. Dist. Ct. (ea. dist.) Pa. 1983, U.S. Ct. Appeals (3rd cir.) 1983. Dep. atty. gen. Pa. Dept. Justice, Harrisburg, 1973-75, Pa. Dept. Health, Harrisburg, 1975-78; sr. staff atty. Am. Hosp. Assn., Chgo., 1978-80, mgr., dept. fed. law, 1980-81; gen. counsel Ill. Health Fin. Authority, 1981-82; sr. assoc. Berriman & Schwartz, King of Prussia, Pa., 1983-85, Wolf, Block, Schorr & Solis-Cohen, Phila., 1985-88; sr. assoc. Montgomery, McCracken, Walker & Rhoads, 1988-90, ptnr., 1990—; chair health law group, 1991—. Contbr. health law articles to profl. jours. Mem. ABA mem. governing com. Health Law Forum 1994—), Nat. Health Lawyers Assn., Am. Acad. Hosp. Attys., Forum of Exec. Women, Pa. Soc. Healthcare Attys. (pres. 1994-95), Phila. Bar Assn. Avocations: gardening, bicycling, hiking, music. Office: Montgomery McCracken 3 Parkway 20th Fl Philadelphia PA 19102

STILLER, JERRY, actor; b. N.Y.C., June 8; s. William and Bella S.; m. Anne Meara, Sept. 14, 1954; children: Amy, Benjamin. BS in Speech and Drama, Syracuse U., 1950. Actor with nat. co. of Peter Pan, 1951, also at Henry St. Playhouse, 1941, Cherry Lane Theatre, N.Y.C., 1949, Billy Barnes Showboat, Chgo., 1950, Erie (Pa.) Playhouse, 1951, 52, Memphis Arena Theatre, 1952, Phoenix Theatre, 1954, 55, 56, Shakespeare Festival Theatre, Stratford, Conn., 1955, mem. Shakespeare Co. in Central Park, N.Y.C. 1957, 71, Two Gentlemen, 1971, Much Ado, 1988; Broadway appearances include The Golden Apple, 1954, The Ritz, 1975, Unexpected Guests, 1977, Hurleyburly, 1985, Three Men on a Horse, 1993, What's Wrong With This Picture?, 1994; film appearances include The Taking of Pelham 1-2-3, 1974, Airport '75, 1975, The Ritz, 1976, Those Lips, Those Eyes, 1979, Passione, 1980, Nadine, 1986, That's Adequate, 1986, Hairspray, 1986, Shoeshine (Acad. award nomination, short subject 1989), A Pair of Jokers, 1990, The Pickle, 1992; Off-Broadway appearance in Boubouroche, 1971, Prairie du Chien, 1985; co-star: TV series Joe and Sons, 1975; mem. comedy team with wife, Anne Meara, 1961—; Ed Sullivan Show; night club appearances include Compass Players, St. Louis, 1957, Happy Medium, Chgo., 1960, also Village Gate, Village Vanguard, Blue Angel, Bon Soir and, Phase Two, N.Y.C., Mr. Kelly's, Chgo., Hungry I, San Francisco, The Establishment, London, The Sands, Flamingo, Las Vegas, Harrah's, Reno and Lake Tahoe, Trump Plaza; co-star: daily TV series Take Five with Stiller and Meara, 1977-78; commercials for PBS Seize the Day; (co-recipient Voice of Imagery award Radio Advt. Bur. 1975); actor TV series, Tattinger's, 1987, The Detective, The Sunset Gang, PBS, 1991, The Hollow Boy, American Playhouse, 1991, Seinfeld, 1994. Recipient Disting. Alumnus award Syracuse U., 1973, Arents Pioneer Medal, 1979, 1st Biffy award Balt. Internat. Film Festival, Entertainment Father of Yr. award, 1977.

STILLINGER, FRANK HENRY, chemist, educator; b. Boston, Aug. 15, 1934; s. Frank Henry and Gertrude (Metcalf) S.; m. Dorothea Anne Keller, Aug. 18, 1956; children—Constance Anne, Andrew Metcalf. B.S., U. Rochester, 1955; Ph.D., Yale U., 1958. NSF postdoctoral fellow Yale U., 1958-59; with Bell Telephone Labs., Murray Hill, N.J., 1959—; head chem. physics dept. Bell Telephone Labs., 1976-79; mem. evaluation panel Nat. Bur. Standards, 1975-78; mem. adv. com. for chemistry NSF, 1980-83, mem. adv. com. for advanced scientific computing, 1984-86, mem. adv. com. Math. and Phys. Scis. Directorate, 1992—; disting. lectr. in chemistry U. Md., 1981; Karcher lectr. U. Okla., 1984; Trumbull lectr. Yale U., 1984; Washburn Meml. lectr. U. Nebr., 1986l Gucker lectr. U. Ind., 1987; W.A. Noyes lectr. U. Tex., 1988; Regents lectr. UCLA, 1990, Meek Indsl. lectr. Ohio State U., 1990, McElvane lectr. U. Wis., 1992. Assoc. editor Jour. Stat. Physics, Jour. Chem. Physics, Phys. Rev. Contbr. articles to profl. jours. Recipient Elliott Cresson medal Franklin Inst., 1978, Hildebrand award Am. Chem. Soc., 1986, Peter J. Debye award Am. Chem. Soc., 1992; Welch Found. fellow, 1974. Fellow Am. Phys. Soc. (Langmuir award 1989); mem. AAAS, Nat. Acad. Scis. Club: Early Am. Coppers Inc. Home: 216 Noe Ave Chatham NJ 07928-1548 Office: 600 Mountain Ave Murray Hill NJ 07974-0636

STILLINGER, JACK CLIFFORD, English educator; b. Chgo., Feb. 16, 1931; s. Clifford Benjamin and Ruth Evangeline (Hertzler) S.; m. Shirley Louise Van Wormer, Aug. 30, 1952; children: Thomas Clifford, Robert William, Susan, Mary; m. Nina Zippin Baym, May 21, 1971. BA, U. Tex., 1953; MA (Nat. Woodrow Wilson fellow), Northwestern U., 1954; PhD, Harvard U., 1958. Teaching fellow in English Harvard U., 1955-58; asst. prof. U. Ill., Urbana, 1958-61; assoc. prof. U. Ill., 1961-64, prof. English, 1964—; permanent mem. Center for Advanced Study, 1970—. Author: The Early Draft of John Stuart Mill's Autobiography, 1961, Anthony Munday's Zelauto, 1963, Wordsworth: Selected Poems and Prefaces, 1965, The Letters of Charles Armitage Brown, 1966, Twentieth Century Interpretations of Keats's Odes, 1968, Mill: Autobiography and Other Writings, 1969, The Hoodwinking of Madeline and Other Essays on Keats's Poems, 1971, The Texts of Keats's Poems, 1974, The Poems of John Keats, 1978, Mill: Autobiography and Literary Essays, 1981, John Keats: Complete Poems, 1982, Norton Anthology of English Literature, 1986, 1993, John Keats: Poetry Manuscripts at Harvard, 1990, Multiple Authorship and the Myth of Solitary Genius, 1991, Coleridge and Textual Instability, 1994; editor Jour. English and Germanic Philology, 1961-72. Guggenheim fellow, 1964-65. Fellow AAAS; mem. MLA, Keats-Shelley Assn. Am. (bd. dirs., editorial bd.

Jour., Disting. Scholar award 1986), Byron Soc., Phi Beta Kappa. Home: 806 W Indiana Ave Urbana IL 61801-4838

STILLINGS, DENNIS OTTO, research director; b. Valley City, N.D., Oct. 30, 1942; s. Harlow Cecil and Ruth Alice (Wolff) S. BA, U. Minn., 1965. Tchr. Henry (S.D.) Pub. Schs., 1965-66, Darby (Mont.) Pub. Schs., 1966-68; tech. rsch. libr., then mgr. hist. dept. Medtronic, Mpls., 1968-79; instr. humanities U. Minn., Mpls., 1970-72; founding dir., then curator Bakken Libr., Mpls., 1976-80; ind. antiquarian hist. cons. Mpls., 1979-81; project dir. Archaeus Project, Kamuela, Hawaii, 1981—, v.p., 1989—; cons. Ctr. for Sci. Anomalies Rsch., Ann Arbor, Mich., 1983—; bd. dirs. Dan Carlson Enterprises, Mpls., Hawaii Ctr. Integral Healing. Columnist Med. Progress Through Technology, 1974—; columnist Med. Instrumentation, 1973-76, guest editor, 1975; editor: Cyberphysiology: The Science of Self-Regulation, 1988, Cyberbiological Studies of the Imaginal Component in the UFO Contact Experience, 1989, The Theology of Electricity: On the Encounter and Explanation of Theology and Science in the 17th and 18th Centuries, 1990, Project 2010: On the Current Crisis in Health and Its Implications For the Hospital For the Future, 1992; founding editor: (jours.) Artifex, 1981-93, Archaeus, 1982-84, Healing Island. Fellow Am. Inst. of Stress; mem. Assn. Sci. Study Anomalous Phenomena, Bioelectromagnetics Soc., Soc. Sci. Exploration. Avocations: Jungian psychology, golf, fishing, travel.

STILLMAN, ELINOR HADLEY, lawyer; b. Kansas City, Mo., Oct. 12, 1938; d. Hugh Gordon and Freda (Brooks) Hadley; m. Richard S. Stillman, June 25, 1965 (div. Apr. 1975). BA, U. Kans., 1960; MA, Yale U., 1961; JD, George Washington U., 1972. Bar: D.C. 1973, U.S. Ct. Appeals (10th cir.) 1975, U.S. Ct. Appeals (9th cir.) 1976, U.S. Ct. Appeals (2d cir.) 1976, U.S. Ct. Appeals (5th cir.) 1983, U.S. Ct. Appeals (4th cir.) 1985, U.S. Supreme Ct. 1976. Lectr. in English CUNY, 1963-65; asst. editor Stanford (Calif.) U. Press., 1967-69; law clk. to judge U.S. Dist. Ct. D.C., Washington, 1972-73; appellate atty. NLRB, Washington, 1973-78; asst. to solicitor gen. U.S. Dept. Justice, Washington, 1978-82; supr. appellate atty. NLRB, Washington, 1982-86, chief counsel to mem. bd., 1986-88, 94—, chief counsel to chmn. bd., 1988-94. Mem. ABA, D.C. Bar Assn., Order of Coif, Phi Beta Kappa. Democrat. Office: Nat Labor Rels Bd 1099 14th St NW Washington DC 20005-3402

STILLMAN, JOYCE L., artist, educator, consultant; b. N.Y.C., Jan. 19, 1943; d. Murray W. and Evelyn (Berger) Stillman. BA, NYU, 1964; student, Art Students League, 1965, Pratt Inst., 1972; MFA, L.I. U., 1975; postgrad., Calif. Inst. Integral Studies, 1994—. Tchr. N.Y.C. Pub. Schs., 1964-71; artist Cen. Hall Gallery, Port Washington, N.Y., 1974-76, Louis K. Meisel Gallery, N.Y.C., 1975-84, Tolarno Gallery, Melbourne, Australia, 1976—, Allan Stone Gallery, N.Y.C., 1990—; visiting assoc. prof. Towson State U., 1982; tchr. Women in Art, Tompkins Cortland Community Coll., 1988; lectr. Cornell U., 1990. One-person shows include Cen. Hall Gallery, Port Washington, 1975, Tolarno Gallery, Melbourne, 1976, Louis K. Meisel Gallery, N.Y.C., 1977, 80, 81, 82, Heckscher Mus., Huntington, N.Y., 1980, Holtzman Gallery, Towson (Md.) State U., 1982, Roslyn Oxley Gallery, Sydney, 1976, 82, Tomasulo Gallery, Union College, N.J., 1983, Stages, Keuka Coll., Keuka Park, N.Y., 1985, New Visions, Ithaca, N.Y., 1989, Herr-Chambliss, Hot Springs, Ark., 1990, Artist on the Lake, Hector, N.Y., 1992, Mus. Modern Art Christmas Card Collection, 1994; designer Mus. Modern Art Christmas Collection, 1978-81, 94, Time-Life Poster, 1978; exhibited in over 75 group shows, corp. and mus. collections. Recipient Flower Painting award Artist's Mag., 1986, Art Dir.'s Club 58th Annual Distinctive Merit award, 1979, N.Y. State Creative Artist's Pub. Svc. grant, 1979. Mem. Nat. Assn. Women Artists, Allan Stone Gallery N.Y.C. Home and Studio: 5120 County Road 4 Burdett NY 14818-9715

STILLMAN, NINA GIDDEN, lawyer; b. N.Y.C., Apr. 3, 1948; d. Melvin and Joyce Audrey (Gidden) S. AB with distinction, Smith Coll., 1970; JD cum laude, Northwestern U., 1973. Bar: Ill. 1973, U.S. Dist. Ct. (no. dist.) Ill. 1973, U.S. Ct. Appeals (7th cir.) 1974, U.S. Dist. Ct. (ea. dist.) Wis. 1979, U.S. Supreme Ct. 1981, U.S. Dist. Ct. (no. dist. trial bar) Ill. 1983, U.S. Dist. Ct. (ctrl. dist.) Ill. 1994. Assoc. Vedder, Price, Kaufman & Kammholz, Chgo., 1973-79, ptnr., 1980—; mem. adv. bd. occupational health and safety tng. program U. Mich., Ann Arbor, 1980-83; adj. faculty Inst. Human Resources and Indsl. Rels., Loyola U., Chgo., 1983-86, mem. bd. advisors, 1986—. Author: (with others) Women, Work, and Health: Challenge to Corporate Policy, 1979, Occupational Health Law: A Guide for Industry, 1981, Employment Discrimination, 1981, Personnel Management: Labor Relations, 1981, Occupational Safety and Health Law, 1988; contbr. articles to profl. jours. Legal advisor, v.p. Planned Parenthood Assn. Chgo., 1979-81; sec. jr. governing bd. Chgo. Symphony Orch., 1983. Mem. ABA (occupational safety and health law com. 1978—), Chgo. Bar Assn. (chmn. labor and employment law com. 1986-87), Human Resources Mgmt. Assn. Chgo. (officer, bd. dirs. 1986-88), Am. Inns of Ct. (v.p. Wigmore chpt. 1988-89), Northwestern U Sch. Law Alumni Assn. (pres. 1991-92), Coun. of 100, Smith Coll. Club Chgo. (pres. 1972), Law Club, Econ. Club Chgo., The Chgo. Com. Avocations: travel, reading, the arts, collecting art. Office: Vedder Price Kaufman & Kammholz 222 N LaSalle St Chicago IL 60601-1003

STILLMAN, ROBERT DONALD, government official; b. Chgo., Sept. 27, 1929; s. Arthur Joseph and Grace Ellen (McLean) S.; m. Joan Ellen Caspersen, 1963 (dec. May 1993); children: Nancy, Barbara, John. BE in Chem. Engring., Yale U., 1950; MBA, Harvard U., 1952. With orgn. planning dept. FMC Corp., San Jose, Calif., 1954-57; assoc. Payson & Trask, N.Y.C., 1957-62, gen. ptnr., 1962-72; exec. v.p., treas., dir. AEA Investors Inc., N.Y.C., 1972-92; assoc. adminstr. for investment U.S. SBA, Washington, 1994—. Dir. St. Luke's Cmty. Svcs., Stamford, Conn., 1993—. Lt. USAF, 1952-54. Mem. Univ. Club (Washington and N.Y.C.), Yale Club (N.Y.C.), Tau Beta Pi, Sigma Xi, Alpha Chi Sigma. Office: US SBA 409 3rd St SW Washington DC 20416

STILLS, STEPHEN, musician, vocalist, composer; b. Dallas, Jan. 3, 1945. Vocalist, guitarist Buffalo Springfield band, 1966-68, Crosby, Stills & Nash, 1968-69, 77, 82, Crosby, Stills, Nash, & Young, 1969-71, solo career, 1971—. Albums include Stephen Stills, 1970, Stephen Stills II, 1971, Stephen Stills, 1975, Illegal Stills, 1976, Thoroughfare Gap, 1978, Right by You, 1984, (with Buffalo Springfield) Buffalo Springfield, 1967, (with Buffalo Springfield) Buffalo Springfield again, 1967, Last Time Around, 1969, (with Crosby, Stills, Nash & Young) Deja Vu, 1970, Four Way Street, 1972, (with Crosby, Stills, Nash, Young) So Far, 1974, American Dream, 1989, (with Crosby, Stills, Nash) Crosby, stills and Nash, 1969, Crosby, Stills and Nash, 1977, Daylight Again, Live It Up, Replay (best of), After The Storm, 1994, (with Manassas) Manassass 1972, Down The Roadm 1973; singles include (solo) Love the One You're With, 1971, Super Session, (with Buffalo Springfield) For What It's Worth, 1967, (with Crosby, Stills, Nash, & Young) Woodstock, Ohio, Teach Your Children, 1970. Office: Sony Music Entertainment Inc. 550 Madison Ave New York NY 10022-3211*

STILLWELL, G(EORGE) KEITH, physician; b. Moose Jaw, Sask., Can., July 11, 1918; came to U.S., 1947, naturalized, 1964; s. George B. and Muriel (Bolster) S.; m. Mildred Ethel Cameron, Mar. 12, 1943; children: Paul, Craig. B.A., U. Sask., 1939; M.D., Queen's U., Kingston, Ont., Can., 1942; Ph.D., U. Minn., 1954. Diplomate: Am. Bd. Phys. Medicine and Rehab. Intern Gen. Hosp., Kingston, 1942-43; resident Gen. Hosp., 1945, U. Minn., Mpls., 1947-51; pvt. practice medicine specializing in phys. medicine and rehab. Mpls., 1951-54; cons. dept. phys. medicine and rehab. Mayo Clinic, Rochester, Minn., 1954-83; chmn. dept. phys. medicine and rehab. Mayo Clinic, 1973-81; instr. U. Minn. 1950-54; instr. Mayo Grad. Sch. Medicine, 1955-60, asst. prof. phys. medicine and rehab., 1960-67, assoc. prof., 1967-73; prof. Mayo Med. Sch., 1973-83; vis. prof. Ohio State U. 1970. Contbr. numerous articles to med. publs. Served with M.C. Royal Can. Army, 1943-46. Mem. AMA, Am. Acad. Phys. Medicine and Rehab. (editorial Bd. Archives Phys. Medicine and Rehab. 1960-81, chmn. editorial bd. 1972-77, bd. govs. acad. 1963-70), Am. Congress Rehab. Medicine (Gold Key award 1973), Assn. Acad. Physiatrists. Unitarian. Office: Mayo Clinic Rochester MN 55905

STILLWELL, WALTER BROOKS, III, lawyer; b. Whitehall, Wis., July 30, 1946; s. Walter Brooks Jr. and Selpha T. (Everson) S.; m. Carolyn E. Laws, Dec. 20, 1992; children: Walter, Haviland. BA cum laude, Wake

Forest U., 1968; JD, U. Ga., 1971. Bar: Ga. 1971, U.S. Dist. Ct. (so. dist.) Ga., U.S. Ct. Appeals (11th cir.). Assoc. Hunter, Maclean, Exley & Dunn, P.C., Savannah, Ga., 1971-74, ptnr., 1974—. Alderman City of Savannah, 1974-92, mayor-pro-tem, 1990-92. Mem. State Bar Assn. Ga. (real property sect., exec. com. 1986-93, chmn. 1992), Am. Coll. Real Estate Lawyers. Democrat. Baptist. Office: Hunter Maclean Exley & Dunn PC 200 E Saint Julian St Savannah GA 31401

STILSON, WALTER LESLIE, radiologist, educator; b. Sioux Falls, S.D., Dec. 13, 1908; s. George Warren and Elizabeth Margaret (Zager) S.; m. Grace Beall Bramble, Aug. 15, 1933 (dec. June 1984); children: Carolyn G. Palmieri, Walter E., Judith A. Stirling; m. Lula Ann Birchel, June 30, 1985. BA, Columbia Union Coll., 1929; MD, Loma Linda U., 1934. Diplomate Am. Bd. Radiology, Nat. Bd. Med. Examiners. Intern White Meml. Hosp., Los Angeles, 1933-34; resident radiology Los Angeles County Gen. Hosp., 1934-36; instr. radiology Loma Linda (Calif.) U. Sch. Medicine, 1935-41, asst. prof., 1941-49, exec. sec. radiology, 1945-50, assoc. prof., 1949-55, head dept. radiology, 1950-55, prof. radiology, 1955-83, chmn. dept. radiology, 1955-69, emeritus prof., 1983—; chief radiology service White Meml. Hosp., Los Angeles, 1941-65, Loma Linda U. Med. Ctr., 1966-69; chmn. dept. radiologic tech. Sch. Allied Health Professions, 1966-75, med. dir. dept. radiologic tech., 1975-83. Contbr. articles to health jours. Fellow Am. Coll. Radiology; mem. AAAS, Los Angeles Radiol. Soc. (sec. 1960-61, treas. 1961-62, pres. 1963-64), Radiol. Soc. N.Am., Am. Roentgen Ray Soc., N.Y. Acad. Sci., Inland Radiol. Soc. (pres. 1971), Alpha Omega Alpha. Republican. Adventist. Avocations: photography, classical music, travel. Home: 25045 Crestview Dr Loma Linda CA 92354-3414 Office: Loma Linda Radiol Med Group 11234 Anderson St Loma Linda CA 92354-2870

STILWELL, JOHN QUINCY, lawyer; b. Columbia, S.C., Sept. 20, 1933; s. James Raymond and Edna (Douglass) S.; m. Regina Besman, Apr. 18, 1965 (div. Mar. 1977); 1 child, Laura Douglass; m. Nancy O'Neil, Mar. 20, 1987; children: William S. Rogers, Richard Blake Rogers, Stephen J. Rogers, Stewart D. Rogers. AB, U. N.C., 1954; LLB, Columbia U., 1961; MA, U. Tex., Dallas, 1988, PhD, 1994. Bar: N.Y. 1962, Tex. 1990. Assoc. atty. Winthrop, Stimson, Putnam & Roberts, N.Y.C., 1961-68; v.p., gen. counsel Total Energy Leasing Corp., N.Y.C., 1968-70, pres., 1970-72; ptnr. Gibbons, Green & Rice, N.Y.C., 1972-74; chmn. Transcable Inc., N.Y.C., 1974-77, John Stilwell Assocs., Inc., Fairfield, Conn., 1977-79; sr. v.p. Kidde, Inc., Saddle Brook, N.J., 1979-83; assoc. gen. counsel Mut. of N.Y. Life, N.Y.C., 1985-87; ptnr. Akin, Gump, Strauss, Hauer & Feld, L.L.P., Dallas, 1987—. Bd. dirs., sec. Shared Housing Ctr., Inc., Dallas, 1993—; trustee Consensus Found., Dallas, 1990. Served to lt. USN, 1954-58. Mem. Assn. Bar City N.Y., Dallas Bar Assn. Avocation: philosophy and communication theory. Home: 4808 Byron Ave Dallas TX 75205-3254 Office: Akin Gump Strauss 1700 Pacific Ave Ste 4100 Dallas TX 75201-4618

STILWELL, RICHARD DALE, baritone; b. St. Louis, May 6, 1942; s. Otho John Clifton and Tressie Fern (Parrish) S.; m. Elizabeth Louise Jencks, Mar. 21, 1967 (div.); m. Kerry M. McCarthy, Oct. 22, 1983. Student, Anderson Coll., 1960-62; MusB, Ind. U., 1966; MusD (hon.), Knox Coll., 1980. With Met. Opera Co., N.Y.C., 1970—. Appearances in major roles with Met. Opera, N.Y.C., Washington Opera Soc., Marseilles (France) Opera Co., Sante Fe Opera, San Francisco Opera Co., Paris Opera Co., Teatro Alla Scala, Covent Garden, Hamburg (Fed. Republic of Germany) State Opera, Glyndebourne Opera Festival, Eng., Vancouver (B.C.) Opera Co., Chgo. Opera Co., Tanglewood Festival, Israel Philharm., San Jose (Calif.) Opera, others; soloist with Nat. Symphony, Washington, Chgo. Symphony, Am. Symphony, Carnegie Hall, N.Y.C., St. Louis Symphony, Double Arts Chorale at Philharm. Hall, Met. Opera Studio at Tully Hall, N.Y.C., Boston Symphony, Los Angeles Philharm., Presl. dinner in honor of Apollo 11 astronauts, Los Angeles, 1969. Served with AUS, 1966-69. Recipient Nat. Soc. Arts and Letters award, 1963, Young Artist award St. Louis, 1963, Fisher Found. award Met. Opera Auditions, 1965. Mem. Am. Guild Musical Artists. Office: care Columbia Artists Mgmt Arbib Div 165 W 57th St New York NY 10019*

STIMMEL, BARRY, cardiologist, internist, educator, university dean; b. Bklyn., Oct. 8, 1939; s. Abraham and Mabel (Bovit) S.; m. Barbara Barovick, June 6, 1970; children: Alexander, Matthew. BS, Bklyn. Coll., 1960; MD, SUNY, Bklyn., 1964. Diplomate: Nat. Bd. Med. Examiners, Am. Bd. Internal Medicine. Resident Mt. Sinai Hosp., N.Y.C., 1964-65, 67-69; asst. dean admissions and student affairs Mt. Sinai Sch. Medicine, CUNY, 1970-71, assoc. dean, 1971—; asst. prof. medicine, 1972-75, assoc. prof., 1975-84, prof. medicine and med. edn., 1984—, assoc. dean acad. affairs, 1975-81, dean admissions, acad. affairs and student affairs, 1981—, assoc. attending physician, 1981-94, dean grad. med. edn., 1994—, attending physician, 1984—, acting chmn. dept. med. edn., 1980-94; mem. com. planning, priorities and evaluation N.Y. Met. Regional Med. Program, 1971-73; adv. com. Nat. Ctr. Urban Problems, City U. N.Y., 1970-71; adv. com. methadone maintenance Office of Drug Abuse Services State of N.Y., 1976-79; sci. adv. bd. Nat. Coun. Drug Abuse, 1976—. Author: Heroin Dependency: Medical Social and Economic Aspects, 1975, Cardiovascular Effects Mood Altering Drugs, 1979, Pain, Analgesia, Addiction, 1982, Ambulatory Care, 1983, The Facts about Drug Use, 1991; editor Advances in Alcohol and Substance Abuse, 1980-91, Jour. Advances in Alcohol and Substance Abuse, Jour. Addictive Diseases, 1991—; assoc. editor Am. Jour. Drug and Alcohol Abuse, 1974-85; contbr. chpts. to books, articles to profl. jours. Served with M.C. USNR, 1965-67. Mem. AAUP, Am. Assn. Physicians Assts. (adv. bd. 1972-73), Am. Assn. Higher Edn., Soc. Study of Addiction to Alcohol and Other Drugs, Assn. Med. Edn. and Rsch. Substance Abuse, Inst. Study of Drug Addiction, Am., N.Y. heart assns., Am., N.Y. State socs. internal medicine, Soc. Internal Medicine County of N.Y. (dir.), Am. Coll. Cardiology, Greater N.Y. Coalition on Drug Abuse, NYS Coun. on Grad. Medical Edn., N.Y. Acad. Medicine, Nat. Coun. Alcoholism, Rsch. Soc. on Alcoholism, Am. Ednl. Research Assn., Am. Fedn. Clin. Rsch., Am. Soc. Addiction Medicine. Office: Mt Sinai Sch Med 100th St and Fifth Ave New York NY 10029

STIMPERT, MICHAEL ALAN, agricultural products company executive; b. Madisonville, La., Aug. 21, 1944; s. Warren Eugene and Louisa (Beale) S.; m. Kim Kathleen Agee, Apr. 17, 1970 (div. 1983); 1 child, Kelly Kathleen; m. Helen Marie Evans, June 27, 1987; children: Katherine Helen, Michael Adam. Student, Washburn U., 1962-64, U. Copenhagen, 1964; BA, Western Res. U., 1967; MBA, Harvard U., 1974. Asst. to group v.p. Gold Kist Inc., Atlanta, 1974, mgr. internat. div., 1975-80, dir. spl. markets and staff services, 1980-81, group v.p., 1982-86; v.p. ops. and govt. affairs Golden Peanut Co., Atlanta, 1986-89, exec. v.p., 1989—; bd. dirs. Ag Tech Co., Atlanta, GPX, Guam, Universal Blanchers, Blakely, Ga., GP Blanching Inc., Atlanta, Alimentos Panamericanos, Inc., Nat. Peanut Coun., Peanut Found. Mem. adv. bd. dirs. Internat. Svc. Assn. for Health Devel. Edn. Project, 1982-91; bd. dirs. Global Health Action. Lt. (j.g.) USN, 1967-72, Vietnam. Mem. Assn. for Corp. Growth, Japan-Am. Soc. Ga., Harvard Bus. Sch. Club Atlanta, Cherokee Town and Country Club. Democrat. Roman Catholic. Office: Golden Peanut Co 1100 Johnson Ferry Rd NE Atlanta GA 30342-1707

STIMPSON, CATHARINE ROSLYN, English language educator, writer; b. Bellingham, Wash., June 4, 1936; d. Edward Keown and Catharine (Watts) S. A.B., Bryn Mawr Coll., 1958; B.A., Cambridge U., Eng., 1960, M.A., 1960; Ph.D., Columbia U., 1967. Mem. faculty Barnard Coll., N.Y.C., 1963-80; prof. English, dean of grad. sch., vice provost grad. edn. Rutgers U., New Brunswick, N.J., 1980-92, Univ. prof., 1991—; chmn. bd. scholars Ms. Mag., N.Y.C., 1981-92; dir. fellows program MacArthur Found., 1994—. Author: Class Notes, 1979, Where the Meanings Are, 1988; founding editor: Signs: Jour. Women in Culture and Society, 1974-81; book series Women in Culture and Society, 1981; columnist Change Mag., 1992-93. Chmn. N.Y. Council Humanities, 1984-87, Nat. Council Research on Women, 1984-89; bd. dirs. Stephens Coll., Columbia, Mo., 1982-85; trustee Bates Coll., 1990—. Hon. fellow Woodrow Wilson Found., 1958; Fulbright fellow, 1958-60; Nat. Humanities Inst. fellow New Haven, 1975-76; Rockefeller Humanities fellow, 1983-84. Mem. MLA (exec. coun., chmn. acad. freedom com., 1st v.p., pres. 1990), PEN, AAUP, NOW, Legal Def. and Edn. Fund (bd. dirs. 1991—), PBS (bd. dirs. 1994—). Democrat. Home: 62 Westervelt Ave Staten Island NY 10301-1432 Office: Rutgers U 172 College Ave New Brunswick NJ 08903-1157

STIMPSON, RITCHIE PLES, retired United States air force officer; b. Black Mountain, N.C., Mar. 22, 1917; s. David Ples and Lydia Hinson Stimpson; m. Marjorie Spruce, May 3, 1942; children: Richie P. Jr., David Fleming. BS in Physics, Fusman U., 1940. Commd. 2nd lt. U.S. Air Force, 1941, advanced through grades to col., 1953; squadron comdr. 13th Tactical Reconnaissance Squadron, 1942-44; dir. ops. 24 Composite Wing, Borinquen Field, P.R., 1946-47; liaison officer Armed Forces Spl. Weapons Project Armed Forces Spl. Weapons Project to Strategic Air Command, Offutt AFB, Nebr., 1950-52; dir. plans and negotiations Joint U.S. Asst. Adv. Group, Madrid, Spain, 1957-59; staff officer Joint Chiefs Staff, Washington, 1960-61, Weapons System Evaluation Group/Office of Sec. of Def., 1964-67; comdt. Air Force ROTC detachment Auburn (Ala.) U., 1967-71; ret. 1971; owner Ritch Stimpson Co., Inc., College Station, Tex., 1975-82; ind. writer, Dallas, 1982-93. Author: The Protestant Church and Bible Disregard the Truth, 1989, "Is It True?" Answers to Questions About the Bible, 1992. Decorated Commendation medals (2), Identification Badge, Outstanding Unit award. Mem. Air Force Assn., Greater Dallas Ret. Officers Assn., Greater Dallas Ret. Officers Assn. Investment Club, Oakridge Country Club, Furman U. Paladin Club. Republican. Methodist. Avocations: golf, travel, reading, bridge, gardening. Home: 2729 Laurel Oaks Dr Garland TX 75044

STIMSON, FREDERICK SPARKS, Hispanist, educator; b. Newark, Ohio, Jan. 1, 1919; s. Fred Samuel and Leah Kate (Sparks) S. B.A., Ohio State U., 1940; postgrad., Harvard U., 1940-41; Jr. fellow in Archaeology, Princeton U., 1941-42; M.A., U. Mich., 1948, Ph.D. (Ford Found. grantee), 1952. Dir. Cultural Center for Dept. State, Medellin, Colombia, 1944-46; asst. public affairs officer Am. embassy, San Salvador, El Salvador, 1947; instr. to prof. dept. Spanish Northwestern U., Evanston, Ill., 1954-81; prof. emeritus Northwestern U., 1981—, chmn. dept., 1976-79. Author: Cuba's Romantic Poet, 1964, New Schools of Spanish American Poetry, 1970, Literatura de la América Hispánica, 3 vols, 1971-75, Los poemas más representativos de Plácido, 1976. Mem. MLA, Phi Beta Kappa. Home: 3300 S Ocean Blvd Apt 819C Highland Beach FL 33487

STINCHCOMB, ROBERT G., lawyer; b. Cleve., May 5, 1929. AB, Denison U., 1951; LLB, Ohio State U., 1955. Bar: Ohio 1956. Ptnr. Baker & Hostetler, Cleve. Office: Baker & Hostetler 3200 National City Ctr 1900 E 9th St Cleveland OH 44114-3485

STINE, GEORGE HARRY, consulting engineer, author; b. Phila., Mar. 26, 1928; s. George Haeberle and Rhea (Matilda) (O'Neill) S.; m. Barbara Ann Kauth, June 10, 1952; children: Constance Rhea Stine Molde, Eleanor Anne Stine, George Willard. B.A. in Physics, Colo. Coll., 1952. Chief controls and instruments sect., propulsion br. White Sands (N.Mex.) Proving Grounds, 1952-55; chief range ops. div. U.S. Naval Ordnance Missile Test Facility at proving grounds, 1955-57; design specialist Martin Co., Denver, 1957; chief engr., pres. Model Missiles, Inc., Denver, 1957-59; design engr. Stanley Aviation Corp., Denver, 1959-60; asst. dir. research Huyck Corp., Stamford, Conn., 1960-65; sci. cons. CBS-TV, 1969, CBC, Toronto, 1969; sci. reporter Metromedia Radio News, N.Y.C., 1968; cons. Young & Rubicam Inc., N.Y.C., also Gen. Electric Co., Valley Forge, Pa., 1966-69; lectr. Franklin Inst., Phila., 1966-72; mktg. mgr. Flow Technology, Inc., Phoenix, 1973-76; cons. curator Internat. Space Hall of Fame, 1976; cons. astronautical history Nat. Air and Space Museum, Smithsonian Instn., 1965—; cons. mktg. research and surveys Talley Industries, Inc., Mesa, Ariz., 1977; cons. mktg. and comm. Flow Tech., Inc., 1976-79; cons. Sci. Applications, Inc. 1976-81, Visions of the Future, 1982-86, McDonnell Douglas Corp., 1988-90, Sci. Applications Internat. Corp., 1990, Quest Aerospace Edn., Inc., 1992—, Aero Tech., Inc., 1991; expert witness fireworks injury cases, 1984—; pres. The Enterprise Inst., Inc., 1987—; cons., writer Discover Space Computer Program, Broderbond Software, Inc., 1992-93; moderator aviation and sport rocketry conf., Bix on-line computer network, 1986—; cons. Quest Aerospace Edn., Inc., 1994—. Freelance writer, 1951—; author more than 50 books on astronautics and sci., including The Model Rocketry Manual, 1975, The Third Industrial Revolution, 2d edit, 1979, The New Model Rocketry Manual, 1977, Shuttle Into Space, 1978, The Space Enterprise, 1980, Space Power, 1981, Confrontation in Space, 1981, The Hopeful Future, 1983, The Untold Story of the Computer Revolution, 1984, The Silicon Gods, 1984, Handbook for Space Colonists, 1985, The Corporate Survivors, 1986, Thirty Years of Model Rocketry, A Safety Report, 1988, Mind Machines You Can Build, 1991, ICBM, The Making of the Weapon That Changed the World, 1991, The Handbook of Model Rocketry sixth edit., 1994; author: (as Lee Correy) sci. fiction novels and stories, including, Starship Through Space, 1954, Rocket Man, 1955, Contraband Rocket, 1956, Star Driver, 1980, Shuttle Down, 1981, Space Doctor, 1981, The Abode of Life, 1982, Manna, 1984, A Matter of Metalaw, 1986; (under own name) Warbots, 1988, Operation Steel Band, 1988, The Bastaard Rebellion, 1988, Sierra Madre, 1988, Operation High Dragon, 1989, The Lost Battalion, 1989, Operation Iron Fist, 1989, Force of Arms, 1990, Blood Siege, 1990, Guts and Glory, 1991, Warrior Shield, 1992, Judgement Day, 1992, Starsea Invaders # 1, First Action, 1993, Star-sea Invaders # 2, Second Contact, 1994, Star-sea Invaders # 3: Third Encounter, 1995; contbr. numerous articles to jours. Charter mem. citizen's adv. coun. Nat. Space Policy, 1981—; Ariz. Space Commn., 1992—. Recipient Silver medal Assn. U.S. Army, 1967, Spl. award Hobby Industry Assn., 1969; Paul Tissandier diploma Fedn. Aeronautique Internationale, 1985. Fellow AIAA (assoc.)Explorers Club, Brit. Interplanetary Soc., Am. Rocket Soc.; mem. Nat. Assn. Rocketry (hon. trustee 1978-81, founder 1957, pres. 1957-67, trustee 1978-81, Spl. Founder's award 1967, Howard Galloway Svc. award 1978, 83, 85, 87), Nat. Fire Protection Assn. (chmn. com. pyrotechnics 1974-94, Svc. award 1993, emeritus mem. 1994), N.Y. Acad. Scis., Aircraft Owners and Pilots Assn., Ariz. Pilots Assn. (dir. 1980-93, v.p. 1981-84), L-5 Soc. (v.p. 1984). Home: 2419 W Saint Moritz Ln Phoenix AZ 85023-5041 *The most interesting data are the points that fall "off the curve" because they lead to unsuspected new discoveries. I grew up on a vanishing frontier and intend to spend my life opening new frontiers—in space, because the world is no more closed than it is flat. Because of this, we do not live in a world of limits, but a limitless universe, and have a limitless future.*

STINE, JEANNE M., mayor, educator; b. Detroit, June 18, 1929; d. William Lyle and Eleanor Laura (Abele) Goodwin; m. Cornelius Robert Powers, Oct. 3, 1952 (div. Feb. 1956); 1 child, Sheila Maureen Powers; m. John Follett Stine, Feb. 1962. BS in Edn., Wayne State U., 1960, MA in Edn., 1965. cert. K-8 Elem. edn., K-12 counseling. Telephone operator Mich. Bell, Detroit, 1946-51; clerk typist McGregor Meml. Conf., Detroit, Detroit Pub. Libr., 1950-52; display advertiser Daily Tribune, Royal Oak, Mich., 1952-54; elem. sch. tchr. Guardian Angels Sch., Clawson, Mich., 1958; elem. sch. tchr. Clawson Pub. Schs., 1959-66, middle sch. counselor, 1966-92; sec. Clawson Edn. Assn., 1960-63; pres. Clawson Youth Assist., 1968-74. initiator Troy youth bur. Police Dept., 1977; pres. Troy Youth Svcs. Activities Commn., 1977-80; v.p. Troy Profl. Women's Club, 1978-84, pres. Troy Youth Svcs. Forum, 1980-84, chair Troy Consortium on Drug and Alcohol Abuse; city councilwoman City of Troy, 1976-92; pres. Troy Vol. Firefighters Women's Aux., 1989-92; mayor City of Troy, 1992—; mem. bd. dirs. Boys and Girls Club of Troy, Traffic Improvement Assn. Oakland County. Recipient Dist. Citizen award Troy C. of C., 1985, Community Svc. award Clawson-Troy Elks, 1985. Mem. Nat. League of Cities (mem. transp. steering com. 1978-86, trans. policy com. 1989-92), Am. Legion Aux., Mich. Mcpl. League (chmn. region IV transp. and pub. works 1990, meritorius svc. award 1988), Tri County Mayors Assn. (mem. steering com.), Zontas. Republican. Roman Catholic. Home: 1915 Boulan Troy MI 48084 Office: 500 W Big Beaver Rd Troy MI 48084

STINE, R(OBERT) L(AWRENCE), children's book author; b. Columbus, Ohio, Oct. 8, 1943; s. Lewis and Anne (Feinstein) S.; m. Jane Waldhorn, June 22, 1969. BA, Ohio State U., 1965. Assoc. editor Jr. Scholastic, N.Y.C., 1969-71; editor Search, N.Y.C., 1972-75, Barnas, N.Y.C., 1972-83, Maniac, N.Y.C., 1984-85. Author: The Time Raider, 1982, The Golden Sword of Dragonwalk, 1983, Horrors of the Haunted Musuem, 1984, Instant Millionaire, 1984, Through the Forest of Twisted Dreams, 1984, Indiana Jones and the Curse of Horror Island, 1984, Indiana Jones and the Giants of the Silver Tower, 1984, Indiana Jones and the Cult of the Mummy's Crypt, 1985, The Badlands of Hark, 1985, The Invaders of Hark, 1985, Demons of the Deep, 1985, Challenge of the Wolf Knight, 1985, Conquest of the Time Master, 1985, Cavern of the Phantoms, 1986, Operation: Deadly Decoy, 1986, Mystery of the Imposter, 1986, Blind Date, 1986, Twisted, 1986, The Baby-Sitter, 1989, Phone Calls, 1990, Curtains, 1991, Broken Date, 1991,

Baby-Sitter II, 1991, Beach House, 1992, Dead Girlfriend, 1993, Halloween Night, 1993, Hitchhiker, 1993, Be Careful What You Wish For, 1993, Baby-Sitter III, 1993, Call Waiting, 1994, The Beast, 1994; (series) Fear Street, Fear Street Super Chiller, Fear Street Saga, Fear Street Cheerleaders, Ninety-Nine Fear Street: The House of Evil, Thrillers, Space Cadets, Goose Bumps; (as Jovial Bob Stine) The Absurdly Silly Encyclopaedia and Flyswater, 1978, How to Be Funny: An Extremely Silly Guidebook, 1978, The Complete Book of Nerds, 1979, The Dynamite Do-It-Yourself Pen Pal Kit, 1980, Dynamite's Funny Book of the Sad Facts of Life, 1980, Going out! Going Steady! Going Bananas!, 1980, The Pigs' Book of World Records, 1980, The Sick of Being Sick Book, 1980, Bananas Look at TV, 1981, The Beast Handbook, 1981, The Cool Kids' Guide to Summer Camp, 1981, Ghastly Gnomes, 1981, Don't Stand in the Soup, 1982, Bored with Being Bored!: How to Beat the Boredom Blahs, 1982, Blips! The First Book of Video Game Funnies, 1983, Everything You Need to Survive: Brothers and Sisters, 1983, Everything You Need to Survive: First Dates, 1983, Everything You Need to Survive: Homework, 1983, Everything You Need to Survive: Money Problems, 1983, Jovial Bob's Computer Joke Book, 1985, Miami Mice, 1986, One Hundred and One Silly Monster Jokes, 1986, The Doggons Dog Joke Book, 1986; (as Eric Affabee) G.I. Joe and the Everglades Swamp Terror, 1986, Attack of the King, 1986; (as Zachary Blue) The Petrova Twist, 1987, The Jet Fighter Trap, 1987.

STINEBRING, WARREN RICHARD, microbiologist, educator; b. Niagara Falls, N.Y., July 31, 1924; s. Clifford Thomas and Signe (Arvidson) S.; m. Delores Jean Zakes, June 12, 1948; children: Dan R., Beth E., Eric. B.A., U. Buffalo, 1948; M.S., U. Pa., 1949, Ph.D., 1951. With U. Pa., Phila., 1949-55; asso. U. Pa., 1953-55; asst. prof. U. Tex. Med. Br., Galveston, 1955-57; asso. research prof. Inst. Microbiology, Rutgers U., New Brunswick, N.J., 1957-60; asst. prof. U. Pitts. Coll. Medicine, 1960-65, asso. prof., 1965-66; prof., chmn. med. microbiology U. Calif. Coll. Medicine at Irvine, 1966-68; prof. U. Vt. Coll. Medicine, Burlington, 1968-86, prof. emeritus, 1986—; chmn. med. microbiology U. Vt. Coll. Medicine, 1968-78; sabbatical leave Royal Postgrad. Med. Sch., London, 1974-75. Served with inf. AUS, 1943-45, ETO. Decorated Purple Heart.; Recipient Golden Apple award Student AMA, 1966-67, award for outstanding research and diagnosis in brucellosis eradication in U. Vt. Vt. Med. Assn., 1983. Mem. AAAS, Tissue Culture Assn. (ednl. com. 1970-72, chmn. 1970-72), Reticuloendothelial Soc., Am. Soc. Microbiology, Am. Soc. Mammalogy, Soc. Exptl. Biol. Medicine, Brucellosis Research Conf. (hon. patron). Research on host-parasite interactions delayed hypersensitivity, interferon stimulation by non-viral agts., brucellosis. Home: 139 North Prospect St Oberlin OH 44074

STINEHART, ROGER RAY, lawyer; b. Toledo, Jan. 27, 1945; s. Forrest William and Nettie May (Twyman) S.; m. Martha Jean Goodnight, Sept. 19, 1970; children: Amanda Jean, Brian Scott. BS, Bowling Green (Ohio) State U., 1968; JD, Ohio State U., 1972. Bar: Ohio 1972. Fin. analyst GE, Detroit, 1968-69; assoc. Gingher & Christensen, Columbus, Ohio, 1972-76, ptnr., 1976-80; sr. v.p., gen. counsel, sec. G.D. Ritzy's, Inc., Columbus, 1983-85; ptnr. Jones, Day, Reavis & Pogue, Columbus, 1980-83, 85—; adj. prof. law Capital U., Columbus, 1976-79; mem. adv. com. Ohio securities divsn. Dept. Commerce, Columbus, 1979—; fellow Columbus Bar Found., 1992—; adv. bd. The Entrepreneurship Inst., 1992-95. Contbr. Ohio State U. Coll. Law Jour., 1970-72. Gen. counsel, trustee Internat. Assn. Rsch. on Leukemia and Related Diseases, 1975—; v.p. trustee Hospice of Columbus, 1978-80; mem. Cen. Ohio chpt. Leukemia Soc. Am., Columbus, 1983-93, v.p., 1985-87; trustee Ohio Cancer Rsch. Assocs., Columbus, 1983—, v.p., 1990—. With USMCR, 1963-68. Mem. ABA (bus. law com., franchise law com.), Ohio State Bar Assn. (corp. law com.), Columbus Bar Assn. (securities law com., chmn. 1981-83, bus. law com., franchise law com.), Sigma Tau Delta, Beta Gamma Sigma. Home: 2155 Waltham Rd Columbus OH 43221-4149 Office: Jones Day Reavis & Pogue 1900 Huntington Ctr Columbus OH 43215

STINEHART, WILLIAM, JR., lawyer; b. L.A., Dec. 15, 1943; s. William Sr. and Martha T. S.; m. Patricia Kidney, June 22, 1968; children: Jacqueline Elaine, William III. Ba, Stanford U., 1966; LLB, UCLA, 1969. Bar: Calif. 1970, U.S. Dist. Ct. (cen. dist.) Calif. 1970. Assoc. Gibson, Dunn & Crutcher, L.A., 1969-76, ptnr., 1977—. Trustee Harvard Westlake Sch., N. Hollywood, 1983-89, S.W. Mus., 1986-89. Mem. L.A. County Bar Assn., Order of Coif, L.A. Country Club, Beach Club of Santa Monica, Calif., L.A. Tennis Club. Republican. Episcopalian. Office: Gibson Dunn & Crutcher 333 S Grand Ave Los Angeles CA 90071

STINER, CARL WADE, army officer; b. LaFollette, Tenn., Sept. 7, 1936; s. Emmit Clyde and Hassie Delma (Bullard) S.; m. Carolyn Sue Reeves, Nov. 28, 1959; children: Carla, Laurie. BS, Tenn. Poly. Inst., 1958; MPA, Shippensburg (Pa.) State Coll., 1975. Commd. 2d lt. U.S Army, 1958, advanced through grades to gen., 1990; inf. bn. officer, then brigade ops. officer 4th Inf. Div., Vietnam, 1967; comdr. 2d bn., 325 Airborne Inf. Rgt., div. ops. officer 82d Airborne Divsn., 1970; comdr. 1st Inf. Tng. Brigade, Ft. Benning, Ga., 1975; chief of staff Rapid Deployment Joint Task Force, 1980; asst. div. comdr. 82d Airborne Div.; asst. dep. dir. for politico-mil. affairs Joint Staff, Washington, until 1984; comdg. gen. Joint Spl. Ops. Command, Ft. Bragg, N.C., 1984-87, 82d Airborne Div., 1987-88, XVIII Airborne Corps, Ft. Bragg, 1988; comdr. of all forces Operation JUST CAUSE, Panama, 1989; comdr. in chief Hdqrs. U.S. Spl. Ops. Command, MacDill AFB, Fla.; ret. from active duty, 1993. Decorated D.S.M. with two oak leaf cluster, Def. D.S.M. with two oak leaf cluster, Legion of Merit with oak leaf cluster, Purple Heart, Def. Superior Svc. medal. Baptist. Avocations: golf, hunting, boating. Office: Holding Detachment OCSA USA Washington DC 20310-0200

STINES, FRED, JR., publisher; b. Newton, Iowa, Mar. 16, 1925; s. Fred and Nella (Haun) S.; m. Dorothy G. McClanahan, Sept. 5, 1953; children: Steven, Scott, Ann. B.C.S., U. Iowa, 1949. With Meredith Corp., Des Moines, 1949-90; sales promotion and mdse. mgr. Meredith Corp., 1955-63, advt. dir., 1963-66, pub., 1966—, pub. dir. mag. div., 1973-76, v.p., gen. mgr. books and newspapers, 1976-83, sr. v.p., 1983—, pres. book pub., 1986—, corp. v.p. spl. projects, 1988-90; pres., prin. Concepts in Mktg., 1990—; cert. instr. Dale Carnegie courses, 1958-63. Bd. dirs. Des Moines Ballet Assn. North Am. Outdoor Group, Mpls., 1992—; bd. dirs. v.p. Jr. Achievement of Ctrl. Iowa. Served with AUS, 1946-49. Named Farm Marketing Man of Year, 1972. Mem. Future Farmers Am. Found. (nat. chmn. 1971), Rotary Internat., Des Moines Golf and Country Club, Phi Gamma Delta (sect. chief 1983, nat. bd. dirs. 1985-86), Alpha Kappa Psi, Alpha Delta Sigma,. Club: Des Moines Golf and Country (dir., pres. 1981).

STING (GORDON MATTHEW SUMNER), musician, songwriter, actor; b. Newcastle Upon Tyne, Eng., Oct. 2, 1951; s. Ernest Matthew and Audrey (Cowell) S.; m. Frances Eleanor Tomelty, May 1, 1976 (div. Mar. 1984); children: Joseph, Katherine; m. Trudie Styler, Aug. 22, 1992; children: Brigette Michael, Jake, Eliot Pauline. Schoolmaster Newcastle Upon Tyne, Eng., 1975-77; songwriter, singer, bass player with rock group The Police, 1977-86; mng. dir. Kaliedescope Cameras, London, from 1982. Albums recorded with The Police include Outlandos D'Amour, 1977, Reggatta De Blanc, 1979, Zenyatta Mondatta, 1980, Ghost in the Machine, 1981, Synchronicity, 1983, The Singles; Every Breath You Take, 1986; stage appearance: (Broadway) Three Penny Opera, 1989; solo albums include The Dream of the Blue Turtles, 1985, Bring On The Night, 1986, Nothing Like the Sun, 1987, The Soul Cages, 1991, Ten Summoner's Tales, 1993 (Grammy award, Best Long Form Music Video, 1994), Demolition Man (soundtrack), 1993; appeared in films Quadrophenia, 1980, The Secret Policeman's Other Ball, 1982, Brimstone and Treacle, 1982, Dune, 1984, The Bride, 1985, Plenty, 1985, Julia and Julia, 1988, Stormy Monday, 1988; rec. soundtracks for films including Brimstone and Treacle, 1982, Party, Party, 1982, The Secret Policeman's Other Ball, 1982. Recipient Grammy awards with The Police, 1980-81, 83; other Grammy awards, 1983, 87, Downbeat mag. Readers' Poll Pop/Rock Musician of Yr. award, 1989, Downbeat mag. Readers' Poll Pop/Rock group award, 1989. Mem. Performing Rights Soc. Office: SFirstars, Bugle House 21A Noel St, London W1V 3PD, England also: Firstars 3520 Hayden Ave Culver City CA 90232*

STINGEL, DONALD EUGENE, management consultant; b. Pitts., Jan. 31, 1920; s. Eugene E. and Ruth I. (Liddell) S.; m. Rita Marie Sweeney, June 14, 1942; children—Donald M., Scott M., Janice L. B.S., Carnegie-Mellon U.,

1941. Metall. engr. Union Carbide Corp., Alloy, W.Va., 1941; metall. engr. to works mgr. Union Carbide Corp., N.Y.C., 1946-65; pres. Alloys and Carbide div. Airco, Inc., 1965-68, Pullman Swindell, Pitts., 1969-77; chmn. Rodeway Inns Internat. and Lodging Systems, Inc., 1982-83; dir. Export-Import Bank U.S., Washington, 1977-81, Wean-United, Pitts., 1981-93. Trustee Carnegie-Mellon U. Served to maj., Ordnance Dept., AUS, 1941-46; to lt. col., Transp. Corps, U.S. Army, 1950. Mem. Country Club of N.C. Republican. Home: 1600 Morganton Rd Box X-29 Pinehurst NC 28374

STINGELIN, VALENTIN, research center director, mechanical engineer; b. Basel, Switzerland, Apr. 22, 1933; s. Paul and Hulda (Tobler) S.; m. Hedwig Wagner, Oct. 18, 1963; children: Matthias, Sibylle, Thomas. Diploma, Swiss Fed. Inst. Tech. (ETH), Zurich, 1957, Ph.D. (Silver medal 1963) 1963. Sci. co-worker Swiss Fed. Inst. Tech., 1958-63; research scientist, project leader Ingersoll Rand Corp., Princeton, N.J., 1964-67; mem. staff Battelle Research Centers, Geneva, 1967—; head engring. dept.; then assoc. dir. Battelle Research Centers, 1973-75, dir. gen., 1975—; v.p. Battelle Meml. Inst., Columbus, Ohio, 1984—; v.p. indsl. bus. planning Europe and Japan Battelle Meml. Inst., 1986—; pres. Castolin & Eutectic Inst., St. Sulpice/Lausanne, Switzerland, 1986—. Mem. Swiss Soc. Physics, ASME, Swiss-Am. C. of C. (dir.). Office: Castolin & Eutectic Inst, PO Box 360, CH-1001 Lausanne Switzerland

STINI, WILLIAM ARTHUR, anthropologist, educator; b. Oshkosh, Wis., Oct. 9, 1930; s. Louis Alois and Clara (Larsen) S.; m. Mary Ruth Kalous, Feb. 11, 1950; children—Patricia Laraine, Paulette Ann, Suzanne Kay. B.B.A., U. Wis., 1960, M.S., 1967, Ph.D., 1969. Planner cost acct. Kimberly-Clark Corp., Niagara Falls, N.Y., 1960-62; asst. prof. Cornell U., Ithaca, N.Y., 1968-71, assoc. prof., 1971-73; assoc. prof. U. Kans., Lawrence, 1973-76; prof. anthropology U. Ariz., Tucson, 1976—; head dept. anthropology U. Ariz., 1980-89; panelist anthropology program NSF, 1976-78; cons. NIH, 1974—; mem. Ariz. Cancer Ctr., 1994—; panelist NRC/NSF Grad. Fellowship Program, 1991—. Author: Ecology and Human Adaptation, 1975, Nature, Culture and Human History - A Biocultural Introduction to Anthropology, (with Davydd J. Greenwood), 1977, Physiological and Morphological Adaptation and Evolution, 1979 (with Frank E. Poirier and Kathy B. Wreden) In Search of Ourselves: An Introduction to Physical Anthropology, 1990, 5th edit., 1994; field editor for phys. anthropology The Am. Anthropologist, 1980-83; editor in chief Am. Jour. Phys. Anthropology, 1983-89; assoc. editor Nutrition and Cancer, 1981—; cons. editor Collegium Antropologicum, 1985—; contbr. articles. Mem. Gov.'s Adv. Council on Aging, State of Ariz., 1980-83. Nat. Inst. Dental Rsch. tng. grantee, 1964-68; Clark Found. grantee, Cornell U., 1973; Nat. Dairy Coun. grantee, 1985-88; Wenner-Gren Found. grantee, 1991—; fellow Linacre Coll., Oxford, 1985; vis. fellow U. London, 1991. Fellow AAAS (steering group sect. H 1987-91), Am. Anthrop. Assn., N.Y. Acad. Scis.; mem. Am. Assn. Phys. Anthropologists (exec. com. 1978-81, pres. 1989-91), Soc. for Study Human Biology, Human Biology Coun. (exec. com. 1978-81), Soc. for Study Social Biology, Am. Inst. Nutrition, Am. Soc. on Aging, Sigma Xi. Home: 6240 N Camino Miraval Tucson AZ 85718-3025 Office: U Ariz Dept Anthropology Tucson AZ 85721

STINNETT, LEE HOUSTON, newspaper association executive; b. Madisonville, Ky., Jan. 8, 1939; s. James Houston and Eolia Frances (Hutchings) S. B.A., U. Ky., 1961, M.A., 1963. Reporter Times-Picayune, New Orleans, 1963-64; med. reporter The News, Charlotte, N.C., 1965-66; devel. writer Emory U., Atlanta, 1966-67, univ. editor, 1968-69; assoc. dir. So. Newspaper Pubs. Assn. and Found., Atlanta, 1970-80; project dir. Am. Soc. Newspaper Editors, Washington, 1981-82, exec. dir., 1983—. Contbr. articles to profl. jours. Del. Arlington Civic Fedn.; active civil rights groups and polit. orgns., Washington and No. Va., Whitman-Walker Clinic, Washington; pres. Arlington Gay and Lesbian Alliance, 1989-90. Mem. Newspaper Assn. Mgrs., Four Seasons Garden (pres. 1983), ACLU of No. Va. (bd. dirs. 1992-94). Democrat. Avocations: gardening, swimming, music.

STINO, FARID K.R., biostatistician, educator, researcher, consultant; b. Cairo, Sept. 1, 1943; came to U.S., 1988; s. Kamal Ramzi and Farida (Shenouda) S.; m. Zandra Hargrove, 1968; children: Ramzi, Farida, Karim, Magdi. BSc, Cairo U., 1964; MSc, U. Ga., 1968, PhD, 1971. Instr. Cairo U., 1964-66; rsch. asst., teaching asst. U. Ga., Athens, 1966-68, 68-71, postdoctoral fellow, 1971-72; asst. prof. Cairo U., 1972-77, assoc. prof., 1977-82, prof., 1982-88; prof. biostats. Fla. A&M U., Tallahassee, 1988—; pres. Stino Agroconsult, Giza, Egypt, 1977-78. V.p. Coptic Orthodox Ch., Tallahassee, 1990—. Mem. Am. Statistical Assn., Biometric Soc., Sigma Xi, Gamma Sigma Delta. Home: 6579 Montrose Trl Tallahassee FL 32308-1607 Office: Fla A&M U Coll Pharmacy Tallahassee FL 32307

STINSON, EDWARD BRAD, surgery educator; b. San Diego, May 19, 1938; s. Elias Bradford and Gladys Evelyn (Beaty) S.; m. Donna S. Shirk, Aug. 19, 1960; children: Bret Alan, Colin Edward. A.B., Stanford U., 1960, M.D., 1965. Intern Hennepin County Gen. Hosp., Mpls.; resident Stanford Hosp., Palo Alto, Calif.; assoc. prof. surgery dept. cardiovascular surgery Stanford U. Sch. Medicine, 1972-79, Thelma and Harry Doelger prof. cardiovascular surgery, 1979—. Contbr. articles to profl. jours. Serves to lt. comdr. USPHS, 1970-72. Recipient Giannini award Bank Am., 1969. Mem. AMA, Am. Coll. Surgeons, Alpha Omega Alpha. Republican. Office: Stanford Med Ctr Room 239 CVRB Stanford CA 94305

STINSON, GEORGE ARTHUR, lawyer, former steel company executive; b. Camden, Ark., Feb. 11, 1915; s. John McCollum and Alice (Loving) S.; m. Betty Millsop, May 31, 1947; children: Thomas, Peter, Joel. A.B., Northwestern U., 1936; J.D., Columbia U., 1939; LL.D., W.Va. Bethany Coll., Theil Coll., Salem Coll. Bar: N.Y. 1939. Partner Cleary, Gottlieb, Friendly & Hamilton, N.Y.C., 1951-61; spl. asst. to atty. gen., acting asst. atty. gen. tax div. Dept. Justice, 1947-48; v.p., sec. Nat. Steel Corp. (now Nat. Intergroup, Inc.), Pitts., 1961-63; pres. Nat. Steel Corp., 1963-75, bd. dirs., 1963-86, CEO, 1966-80, chmn., 1972-81; dir. Birmingham Steel Co., Pathe Techs. Inc.; trustee emeritus Mut. Life Ins. Co. N.Y. Trustee emeritus U. Pitts.; mem. Presdl. Commn. on Internat. Trade and Investment Policy, 1970-71; chmn. U.S. Indsl. Payroll Savs. Com., 1976; trustee George C. Marshall Found. Served to lt. col. USAAF, 1941-45. Decorated Legion of Merit. Mem. Am. Iron and Steel Inst. (chmn. bd. 1969-71), Internat. Iron and Steel Inst. (bd. dirs., chmn. 1975-77), Am. Law Inst.; Bus. Coun., Links Club (N.Y.C.), Duquesne Club (Pitts.), Laurel Valley Golf Club (Pitts.), Phi Beta Kappa. Home: Hunting Country Rd Tryon NC 28782

STINSON, JAMES R., lawyer; b. Evanston, Ill., Mar. 21, 1952. AB, DePauw U., Ind. U., 1973; JD magna cum laude, U. Ill., 1977. Ptnr. Sidley & Austin, Chgo. Mem. ABA (vice chair and. rels. ins. co.), Order of Coif. Office: Sidley & Austin 1 First Nat Plz Chicago IL 60603

STINSON, RICHARD JAMES, editor; b. Gardner, Mass., Apr. 2, 1929; s. Richard and Marguerite Electra (Foye) S.; m. Felina Mijares, Sept. 28, 1956; 1 dau., Suzanne. B.A., U. Chgo., 1956, M.B.A, NYU, 1958. Research analyst Standard & Poor's Corp., N.Y.C., 1958-66; mng. editor Financial World, N.Y.C., 1958-66, mng. editor, 1966-70, editor, 1970-72, sr. editor, 1972-81, contbg. editor, 1981-86; editor Money and Credit, 1975-81. Served with USAF, 1951-55. Mem. N.Y. Soc. Security Analysts, Fin. Analysts Fedn. Republican. Unitarian. Home: 53 Greenway S Forest Hills NY 11375-5941

STINSON, ROBERT CHARLES, lawyer; b. Cleve., Apr. 28, 1946; s. Robert Charles and Cathleen Ann (Neuhold) S.; m. Sara Ann Koma, July 26, 1969; children: Robert Jeffrey, Jennifer Cathleen. BA, Mt. Union Coll., 1968; JD, U. Cin., 1971. Bar: Ohio 1971. Assoc. Calfee, Halter & Griswold, Cleve., 1974-78; ptnr. Seikel & Stinson, Cleve., 1978-86; prin. Burke, Haber & Berick Co., L.P.A., Cleve., 1986-89; v.p., gen. counsel, sec. Bearings, Inc., Cleve., 1989-90, v.p., gen. counsel, sec., 1990—. Mem. ABA (v.p. adminstrn., human resources, gen. counsel, sec. 1994—), Ohio Bar Assn. (corp. law com.), Cleve. Bar Assn., Am. Soc. Corp. Secs., Am. Corp. Counsel Assn. Office: Bearings Inc 3600 Euclid Ave Cleveland OH 44115-2515

STINSON, WILLIAM W., transportation executive; b. Toronto, Ont., Can., Oct. 29, 1933. B.A., U. Toronto, 1954; diploma in bus. adminstrn., U. W.

Ont., 1955. Various positions Can. Pacific Rail, Toronto, 1950-66, supt. Toronto div., 1966-69; asst. gen. mgr. ops. and maintenance Pacific Region Can. Pacific Rail, Vancouver, 1969-71; gen. mgr. ops. and maintenance Pacific Region Can. Pacific Ltd., Vancouver, 1971, gen. mgr. ops. and maintenance Eastern Region, 1972-74; asst. v.p. ops. and maintenance Can. Pacific Rail, Montreal, 1974-76, exec. v.p., 1979-81; v.p. ops. and maintenance Can. Pacific Ltd., Montreal, 1976-79, pres., 1981-90, chief exec. officer, 1985—, chmn., chief exec. officer, 1989—; bd. dirs. Can. Pacific Enterprises Ltd., ADT Ltd., Pan. Can. Petroleum Ltd., Sun Life Assurance Co., Laidlaw, Inc., Unitel Comms. Inc., United Dominion Industries Inc., The Van Horne Inst.; mem. Bus. Coun. on Nat. Issues. Mem. Mt. Royal Club, Mt. Bruno Country Club. Office: Can Pacific Ltd, Succ Centre Ville PO Box 6042, Montreal, PQ Canada H3C 3E4 also: Can Pacific Ltd, 1010 de Gauchetiere St W Ste 800, Montreal, PQ Canada H3B 2N2

STIPANOVIC, ROBERT DOUGLAS, chemist, researcher; b. Houston, Oct. 28, 1939. BS, Loyola U., 1961; PhD, Rice U., 1966. Rsch. technician Stauffer Chem. Co., Houston, 1961; teaching asst. Rice U., Houston, 1961-62, rsch. asst., 1962-66; rsch. assoc. Stanford (Calif.) U., 1966-67; mem. grad. faculty Tex. A&M U., College Station, 1967—, asst. prof. chemistry, 1967-71; rsch. chemist Cotton Pathology Rsch. Unit USDA, College Station, 1971-87; rsch. leader USDA, College Station, 1987—; vis. rsch. scientist Agr. Can., Rsch. Ctr. London, Ont., 1985. Welch fellow Rice U., 1963-65, Grad. fellow, 1965-66. Mem. Sigma Xi. Home: 1103 Esther Blvd Bryan TX 77802-1924 Office: USDA Agrl Rsch Svc So Crops Rsch Lab 2765 F&B Rd College Station TX 77845-9593

STIPE, MICHAEL, musician; b. Decatur, Ga., 1960. Student, U. Ga. Singer R.E.M., 1980—; owner C-OO. Albums with R.E.M. include Chronic Town, 1982, Murmur, 1983 (Gold record, Rolling Stone Critics Poll Best Album of Yr. 1983), Reckoning, 1984 (Gold record), Fables of the Revolution, 1985 (Gold record), Life's Rich Pageant (Gold record), 1986, Dead Letter Office (Gold record), 1987, Document, 1987 (Platinum record), Eponymous, 1988 (Platinum record), Green, 1988 (Platinum record), Out of Time, 1991 (Platinum record, 7 Grammy nominations, Best Pop Vocals Grammy award for group 1992), Automatic for the People, 1992 (Platinum record, 4 Grammy nominations), Monster, 1994; guest artist for following groups: 10,000 Maniacs, 1987, Indigo Girls, 1989; exec. prodr. film Desperate Angels, 1992. Recipient MTV Video Music Video of Yr. award, 1992; named Rolling Stone Critics Poll Best New Group, 1983, Rolling Stone Group Artist of Yr., 1992, Rolling Stong Male Vocalist of Yr., 1992; MTV Best Direction, Best Editing, Best Cinematography, and Breakthrough Video awards for "Everybody Hurts", 1994. Office: Warner Bros Records 3300 Warner Blvd Burbank CA 91505-4694*

STIPE, ROBERT EDWIN, design educator; b. Easton, Pa., July 18, 1928; s. J. Norwood and Ethel M. Stipe; m. Josephine Davis Weedon, 1952; children: Daniel W. Stipe, Frederick Norwood Stipe. AB in Econ., Duke U., 1950, LLB, 1953; MRP, U. N.C., 1959. Urban planning cons. City and Town Planning Assocs., Chapel Hill, N.C., 1956-57; asst. dir., prof. pub. law and govt. U. N.C. Inst. Govt., Chapel Hill, N.C., 1957-74; sr. Fulbright rsch. fellow London U., 1968-69; dir. Divsn. Archives and History N.C. Dept. Cultural Resources, Raleigh, N.C., 1974-75; vis. prof. U. N.C., Chapel Hill, 1975-77; prof. design N.C. State U., Raleigh, 1976-89; emeritus prof. design, part time prof. design N.C. State U., 1989—; lectr. Inst. Advanced Studies, Bratislava, Slovak Republic, 1992-95; bd. trustees U.S. com. Internat. Coun. on Monuments and Sites, Preservation Action, Nat. Coun. on Preservation Edn., Hist. Preservation Fund N.C., Alliance for Preservation Hist. Landscapes, Old Salem Inc., Stagville Ctr. for Preservation Tech.; trustee Nat. Trust for Hist. Preservation; bd. counsellors Conservation Trust for N.C.; mem. bd. adv. Nat. Alliance Preservation Commn. Author, editor more than 150 articles and publs. in fields of historic preservation, landscape conservation, design, urban planning, and planning law. Mem. Chapel Hill Design Review Bd.; trustee Chapel Hill Preservation Soc.; founder, bd. mem. Chapel Hill Preservation Soc. Fellow U.S. Com. Internat. Coun. on Monuments and Sites, 1986; recipient Disting. Svc. award Ruth Coltrane Cannon award, N.C. Soc. for Preservation of Antiquities, 1973, Sec. of Interior's Disting. Conservation Svc. award, 1978, Louise DuPont Crowninshield award for Superlative Lifetime Achievement in Historic Preservation, Nat. Trust for Historic Preservation, 1988, Dist. Svc. and Profl. Leadership award Nat. Coun. for Preservation Edn., 1989. Mem. Cosmos Club (Washington), Pi Kappa Sigma (First Disting. mem. 1994). Home: 100 Pine Ln Chapel Hill NC 27514

STIPP, JOHN EDGAR, financial consultant, lawyer; b. Watseka, Ill., Feb. 10, 1914; s. George Y. and Stella M. (Tubbs) S.; m. Janet E. Miller, June 4, 1938; 1 child, Thomas John. J.D., Drake U., 1936; LL.D., Lincoln Coll., 1961. Bar: Ill., Iowa, U.S. Supreme Ct. Practiced in Danville, Ill., 1936-50; dir. Bldg. & Loan Dept., Ill. State, 1949; gen. claims atty. Continental Casualty Co., Chgo., 1950, v.p., sec., mem. fin. com., dir.; v.p., sec., mem. fin. com., dir. Continental Assurance Co., Chgo.; pres. Fed. Home Loan Bank of Chgo., 1953-74; fin. cons., 1974—; bd. dirs., mem. fin. com. CNA Fin. Corp.; trustee retirement fund Fed. Home Loan Bank System, 1953-74; bd. dirs., mem. fin. investment coms. Chgo. Title, Chgo. Title Ins., 1961-78; bd. dirs. Transp. Ins. Co. Speaker, author articles on econs., fin. Mem. Chgo. Crime Commn., Fed. Savs. and Loan Adv. Council, created by 74th Congress, 1951; commr. Vermillion Co. Airport Authority, 1946-49; bd. govs., sec., treas., chmn. fin. and investment com. Alpha Tau Omega Found., 1978—; bd. dirs. Goodwill Industries, Cook County chpt. ARC; mem. Mayor's Com. on Econ. and Cultural Devel. Chgo. Served as lt. USNR, 1943-45. Mem. Chgo. Hist. Soc., Chgo. Mus. Natural History, Newcomen Soc., Alpha Tau Omega (past nat. treas.). Lutheran. Clubs: Elks; Executives (Chgo.) (past pres.), Economic (Chgo.), Tavern (Chgo.), University (Chgo.); Restless Weasels of Lac du Flambeau (Wis.); Wisconsin (Milw.); Minocqua (Wis.) Country (Minocqua). Home and Office: 817 Westerfield Dr Wilmette IL 60091-1809 also: 9458 Country Club Rd Box 536 Minocqua WI 54548

STIRITZ, MARETTE MCCAULEY, English language educator, consultant; b. Center Point, Ark., Dec. 9, 1931; d. Edrie Delos and Lucyle Virginia (Dautrieve) McCauley; m. Charles Wayne Jackson, July 1, 1950 (dec. June 1986); children: Charles, Retta, Shelia; m. John David Stiritz Dec. 3, 1992. BSE, Ark. State U., 1962; MA, U. Ark., 1965, PhA, 1986. Tchr. elem. Plum Bayou (Ark.) Pub. Schs., 1950-52; tchr. Laura Connor H.S. Augusta, Ark., 1955-59, Swifton (Ark.) Elem. Sch., 1959-60, Swifton H.S. 1962-63; prof. English So. Ark. U., Magnolia, 1965-78, U. Cen. Ark., Conway, 1978—; cons. high schs., Conway, Morrilton, Vilonia, 1983—, Ark. Dept. Edn., Little Rock, 1982, 84; lectr. U. Chile, Santiago, 1989, Moscow Pedagogical U., 1991, 92, Academica Inst. Chileno-Norteamericano, Santiago, 1994; speaker 8th Bi-ann. Conf. Profs. Fgn. Langs., Chile, 1992, 9th Conf., Chile, 1994. Contbr. articles to profl. jours.; book reviewer Ark. Elem. Coun., 1980—. Del. Faulkner County Dems., Conway, 1984; exec. sec., founder Columbia Tchrs. Eng., Magnolia, 1974-78. Mem. Ark. Coun. Tchrs. English (pres. 1979-80, bd. dirs. 1989-93), Ark. Philol. Assn., Nat. Coun. Tchrs. English, Ark. Coll. Tchrs. English (pres. 1992-93), Conway Rotary Internat. Breakfast Club (charter), Alpha Chi (region II v.p. 1992-93. Democrat. Methodist. Home: 3414 Rhonda Ct Conway AR 72032-9168

STIRITZ, WILLIAM P., food company executive; b. Jasper, Ark., July 1, 1934; s. Paul and Dorothy (Bradley) S.; m. Susan Ekberg, Dec. 4, 1972; children—Bradley, Charlotte, Rebecca, Nicholas. B.S., Northwestern U., 1959; M.A., St. Louis U., 1968. Mem. mktg. mgmt. staff Pillsbury Co., Mpls., 1959-62; account mgmt. staff Gardner Advt. Co., St. Louis, 1963—; with Ralston Purina Co., 1981—; bd. dirs. Angelica Corp., Ball Corp., Boatmen's Bancshares, Inc., Gen. Am. Life Ins. Co., May Dept. Stores, S.C. Johnson & Son. With USN, 1954-57. Mem. Grocery Mfrs. Assn. (dir.). Office: Ralston Purina Co Checkerboard Sq Saint Louis MO 63164

STIRLING, ELLEN ADAIR, retail executive; b. Chgo., June 21, 1949; d. Volney W. and Ellen Adair (Orr) Foster; m. James P. Stirling, June 6, 1970; children: Elizabeth Ginevra, Diana Leslie, Alexandra Curtiss. Student, U. Chgo., 1970-71; BA, Wheaton Coll., Norton, Mass., 1971; postgrad., U. London, 1974. Pres., CEO, The Lake Forest Shop, 1986—; bd. dirs. Lake Forest Bank and Trust. Founder, v.p. aux. bd. Art Inst. Chgo., 1972-91; dir. Friends of Ryerson Woods, 1992—; mem. women's bd. Lyric Opera, Chgo., 1992—, Lake Forest Coll., 1989—; mem. costume com. Chgo. Hist. Soc.

Mem. Onwentsia Club, Racquet Club. Office: The Lake Forest Shop 165 E Market Sq Lake Forest IL 60045

STIRLING, ISABEL ANN, science librarian; b. San Jose, Calif., Dec. 4, 1948; d. James H. and Betty Stirling. BA, U. Calif., Riverside, 1970; MLS, Western Mich. U., 1977. Head bio-agrl. library U. Calif., Riverside, 1977-82; head sci. libr., prof. U. Oreg., Eugene, 1982—. Author: Self-Paced Library Instruction Workbook for the Sciences, 1981; contbr. articles to jours. Mem. ALA (Libr./Book fellow Ankara, Turkey 1988-89), Assn. Coll. and Rsch. Libr. of ALA (various coms.), Internat. Fedn. Libr. Assn., Oreg. Library Assn. Avocations: handloom, fiber arts. Office: U Oreg Sci Library Eugene OR 97403-5201

STIRLING, JAMES PAULMAN, investment banker; b. Chgo., Mar. 30, 1941; s. Louis James and Beverly L. (Paulman) S.; m. Ellen Adair Foster, June 6, 1970; children—Elizabeth Ginevra, Diana Leslie, Alexandra Curtiss. A.B., Princeton U., 1963; M.B.A., Stanford U., 1965. Chartered fin. analyst. Vice pres. corp. fin. Kidder, Peabody & Co. (now PaineWebber), N.Y.C. and Chgo., 1965-71, 84-86; sr. v.p. corp. fin. Kidder, Peabody & Co. (now PaineWebber), 1987—; dir. internat. investments Sears Roebuck Co., Chgo. and London, 1971-75, 77-84; asst. to sec. U.S. Dept. Commerce, Washington, 1976-77; chmn. bd. Northwestern Meml. Mgmt. Corp., Chgo., 1989—; trustee Northwestern Meml. Hosp., Chgo., 1985—. Pres. jr. bd. Chgo. Symphony, 1968-70, trustee, 1970-75; trustee Tchrs. Acad. for Math. Sci., 1991—. Mem. Investment Analysts Soc., Bond Club of Chgo., Nat. Econ. Hon. Soc. Clubs: Chicago, Racquet, Quadrangle (Chicago), Onwentsia (Lake Forest, Ill.). Office: PaineWebber 125 S Wacker Dr Chicago IL 60606-4402

STISKA, JOHN C., lawyer; b. Chgo., Feb. 14, 1942; s. Rudolph and Elsie Sophie (Nelson) S.; m. Janet Hazel Osuch, Aug. 8, 1964; children: Julie, Thomas, Michael, Matthew. BBA, U. Wis., 1965, JD, 1970. Bar: Wis. 1970, Calif. 1971. Assoc., ptnr. Luce, Forward, Hamilton & Scripps, San Diego, 1970-81; ptnr. Aylward, Kintz & Stiska, San Diego, 1981-86; pres., CEO Triton Group Ltd., La Jolla, Calif., 1986-88; ptnr. Brobeck, Phleger & Harrison, San Diego, 1988-90; pres., COO Intermark, Inc., La Jolla, Calif., 1990-92; pres., CEO Triton Group Ltd., 1993-94; chmn., CEO, 1994—. 1st lt. U.S. Army, 1965-67. Mem. ABA. San Diego County Bar Assn., Calif State Bar Assn. Lutheran. Home: 5307 Soledad Rancho Ct San Diego CA 92109-1535 Office: Triton Group Ltd 550 West C St San Diego CA 92101

STITES, BEVERLY R., judge; b. Ft. Smith, Ark., Nov. 26, 1941; d. Floyd Paul and Alice Marie Rickman; children: Scott Douglas, Shane Patton. BA, Ark. Tech. Univ., 1964; BS, Okla. Baptist Univ., 1977; JD, Univ. of Ark., 1981. Bar: Ark. 1981. Law clk. pvt. practice, 1980-81; law clk. to Chief Judge A. Franklin Waters U.S. Dist. Ct. (we dist.) Ark., 1981, clk. of ct., 1985, magistrate judge, 1987—. Office: US Courthouse PO Box 1525 S 6th St & Rogers Ave Rm 240 Fort Smith AR 72902

STITES, C. THOMAS, journalist, publisher; b. Kansas City, Mo., July 6, 1942; s. Harold Edward and Wilma Joyce (Simmons) S.; m. Helen Marie Oakey, Sept. 9, 1967 (div. 1983); children—Mary Hannah, Harold William; m. Alexandra Mezey, May 8, 1983. Student, Williams Coll., 1960-62. Night city editor Chgo. Sun-Times, 1968-70; regional editor Phila. Inquirer, 1970-72; news editor Newsday, L.I., N.Y., 1972-79; asst. nat. editor N.Y. Times, N.Y.C., 1979-1983; mng. editor Kansas City Times, Mo., 1983-85; nat. editor, assoc. mng. editor Chgo. Tribune, 1985-90; v.p. UniMedia div. Universal Press Syndicate, Kansas City, Mo., 1990—. Unitarian. Avocations: squash; music, especially jazz; reading non fiction. Office: Universal Press Syndicate 4900 Main St # 900 Kansas City MO 64112-2644

STITES, RAY DEAN, minister, college president; b. Herington, Kans., Oct. 13, 1946; s. George Darby and Edna Myrtle (Anderson) S.; m. Merelyn Kay Rich, Sept. 2, 1966; children: Ross Mitchell, Brian Darby. BA, Manhattan Christian Coll., Manhattan, Kans., 1968; MDiv, Emmanuel Sch. Religion, Johnson City, Tenn., 1974. Ordained to ministry Christian Ch., 1968. Min. Bozoo (W.Va.) Christian Ch., 1968-72; min. Cen. Christian Ch., Richardson, Tex., 1972-78, First Christian Ch., Abilene, Kans., 1979-88, Newton (Kans.) Christian Ch., 1988-91; pres. Nebr. Christian Coll., Norfolk, 1991—; instr. Ch. History, Dallas Christian Coll., 1974-76; pres. North Tex. Evangelizing Assn., 1975-77, Manhattan Christian Coll. Alumni Assn., 1983-85, Christian Evangelizing Assn. of Kans., 1987-89, 91, Kans. Christian Conv., 1989. Bd. dirs. Abilene United Way, 1981-84; mem. Dickinson County Health Dept. Adv. Bd., 1983-88, Dickinson County Coun. on Aging, 1984-88; pres. Abilene Optimist Club, 1983-84. Office: Nebr Christian Ch 1800 Syracuse Ave Norfolk NE 68701-2400

STITH, FORREST CHRISTOPHER, bishop; b. Marshall, Tex., May 18, 1934; s. Forrest M. and Daisy (Haynes) S.; m. Josephine Mitchell, June 19, 1960; 1 child, Lori Crystal. BD, Drew U., 1948; BS in Edn., U. Nebr., 1955; DD, Western Md. Coll., 1979, Nebr. Wesleyan U., 1986. Pastor Douglas Meml. Ch. United Meth. Ch., Washington, from 1958; resident bishop N.Y. West Area United Meth. Ch., 1984-92, resident bishop N.Y. area, 1992—. Trustee Drew U.; pres. gen. coun. on fin. and adminstrn. United Meth. Ch.; trustee Colgate Rochester Div. Sch. Recipient Grass Roots award D.C. Fedn. Civic Assns. for Vol. Svc., 1967. Home: 9 Rosehill Ave New Rochelle NY 10804-3614 Office: 252 Bryant Ave White Plains NY 10605-2103

STITH, KATE, legal educator; b. St. Louis, Mar. 16, 1951; d. Richard Taylor and Ann Carter (See) Stith; m. José A. Cabranes, Sept. 15, 1984; children: Alejo, Ben José. B.A., Dartmouth Coll., 1973; M.P.P., Kennedy Sch. Govt., Harvard U., 1977, J.D., 1977. Bar: D.C. Law clk. U.S. Supreme Ct., Washington, 1978-79; economist, Council of Econ. Advisers, Exec. Office of Pres.; spl. asst. Dept. Justice, Washington, 1980-81; asst. U.S. atty., U.S. Atty. So. Dist. N.Y., N.Y.C., 1981-84; assoc. prof. Yale U. Law Sch., New Haven, 1984-90; prof. of law, 1990—. Contbr. chpts. to books, articles to legal rev. Bd. Trustees, Dartmouth Coll.; commr. Conn. Permanent Commn. on the Status of Women. Mem. Phi Beta Kappa. Home: 65 Sperry Rd Bethany CT 06524-3519 Office: Yale Law School New Haven CT 06520

STITT, DAVID TILLMAN, lawyer; b. St. Louis, Apr. 9, 1943; s. David Leander and Jane Wilkinson (Dupuy) S.; m. Elizabeth Celia Santino, Apr. 30, 1981; children: Rachel Elizabeth Botkin, Samuel Thornton. AB, Davidson Coll., 1964; JD, U. Tex., 1969. Assoc. Galland, Kharasch, Calkins & Brown, Washington, 1969-71; asst. corp. counsel D.C., Washington, 1971-73, asst. U.S. atty., 1973-74; asst. county atty. Fairfax County, Va., 1975-80; county atty. Fairfax County, 1980-91; ptnr. Venable, Baetjer & Howard, McLean, Va., 1991—. Lt. U.S. Army, 1964-66, Vietnam. Mem. Va. State Bar Coun. (exec. com. 1991-93), Local Govt. Attys. of Va. (pres. 1983-84, Disting. Svc. award 1991), Conf. of Local Bar Assn. (chmn. 1990-91), Fairfax Bar Assn. (pres. 1987-88). Presbyterian. Home: 6503 Smoot Dr McLean VA 22101 Office: Venable Baetjer & Howard 2010 Corporate Ridge Ste 400 Mc Lean VA 22102

STITT, SUSAN, historical society executive; b. East Liverpool, Ohio, Jan. 1, 1942; d. Wilson Montgomery and Cora Blanche (Link) S. BA in American History, Coll. William and Mary, 1964; MA in American Civilization, U. Pa., 1966; postgrad. student, Wake Forest U., 1968, U. Del., 1970. Asst. to the dir. Historical Soc. Pa., Phila., 1966; first dir. Museum of the Albemarle, Elizabeth City, N.C., 1967-68; adminstr. Museum of Early Southern Decorative Arts, Winston-Salem, N.C., 1969-71; asst. to the dir. The Bklyn. Museum, 1971-72; project dir. Old Sturbridge (Mass.) Village, 1972-74; dir. The Museums at Stony Brook, N.Y. 1974-88; pres. Historical Soc. Pa., Phila., 1990—; mem. museum aid panel N.Y. State Coun. on the Arts, 1976-79; panelist and reviewer Nat. Endowment for the Humanities, Nat. Endowment for the Arts, Inst. Museum Svcs., 1975—. Mem. editorial bd. Museum Studies Jour., 1984-89; contbr. articles to profl. jours. Mem. advisory com. Long Island Community Found., 1986-88; mem. nonprofit subcom. advisory bd. SUNY, Stony Brook, 1987-88. Named N.C. Young Career Woman of Yr. Bus. and Profl. Womens Club, 1968, Woman of Yr. Village Times, Setauket, N.Y., 1979; recipient First Ann. Recognition award N.C. Mus. Coun., 1968, Katherine Coffey award Mid-Atlantic Assn. Museums, 1987, Ward Melville Community award Three Village Hist. Soc. 1988. Mem. Am. Assn. Museums (coun. mem. 1976-79, 1982-85, ethics com. mem. 1976-79, women's caucus mem. 1975-78, pres. 1977, v.p. 1985-86), Am. Assn. State and Local History (nat. steering com. 1987—), Mid

Atlantic Assn. Museums (v.p. 1982-85), L.I. Museum Assn. (nominating com. 1977-79), Kappa Delta Pi, Chi Delta Phi, Theta Alpha Phi. Office: Historical Soc Pa 1300 Locust St Philadelphia PA 19107-5661

STITT, WILLIAM C., engineering executive; b. 1941. BS, Rensselaer Polytechnic Inst., 1963; MBA, Harvard U., 1967. With Office of Chief Analysis Group, U.S. Dept. of Def., Washington, 1967-69; spl. asst. to Asst. Sec. Health, Edn. and Welfare Washington, 1969-71; with ICF Inc., Fairfax, Va., 1971—, pres., now mem. bd. dirs. Office: ICFCORP Internat Inc. 9300 Lee Hwy Fairfax VA 22031-1200*

STIVEN, ALAN ERNEST, population biologist, ecologist; b. St. Stephen, N.B., Can., Nov. 12, 1935; came to U.S., 1962, naturalized, 1977; s. Alan J. and Edith G. S.; m. Julia Ann Heeb, Aug. 18, 1972; 1 son, Alan; children by previous marriage: Terry, Kim. B.S., U. N.B., 1957; M.A., U. B.C., 1959; Ph.D., Cornell U., 1962. Asst. prof. zoology U. N.C., 1962-66, asso. prof., 1966-71, chmn. biology curriculum, 1968-70, prof., 1971—, chmn. ecology curriculum, 1971-86, chmn. dept. zoology, 1967-72, acting chmn., 1979-80, assoc. chmn. dept. Biology, 1992—; mem., chmn. NRC pre-doctoral fellowship panel, 1984-88, NRC rsch. associateship panel, 1990-93; bd. chmn. Highlands Biol. Sta., 1987—. Editor: Ecology and Ecol. Monographs, 1967-73; editorial bd. Jour. Invertebrate Pathology, 1967-71; contbr. articles scholarly jours. Mem. Chapel Hill Bd. Adjustment, 1973-76. NSF research grantee, 1962-82; NIH tng. grantee, 1966-70; U.S. Forest Service grantee, 1982-85, NC Wildlife Commn. grantee, 1988—. Mem. Ecol. Soc. Am., Am. Soc. Naturalists, Soc. Study Evolution. Office: U NC Dept Biology Cb 3280 Coker Hall Chapel Hill NC 27599

STIVENDER, DONALD LEWIS, mechanical engineering consultant; b. Chgo., May 8, 1932; s. Paul Macon and Grace (Larsen) S.; m. Margaret Ann Lourim, Apr. 14, 1956; children—Anne, Robert, Carole. B.S. in Engring, U.S. Coast Guard Acad., 1954; M.S., U. Mich., 1959. Registered profl. engr., Mich. R & D engr. Rsch. Labs, GM Corp., Warren, Mich., 1959-92, sr. rsch. engr., 1968-92, owner, consulting engr. Stivender Engring. Assoc., 1980—; cons. systems engring. disciplines. Contbr. articles tech. jours. on diesel, gas turbine and spark ignition engine combustion, emission, constrn. and electronic control aspects. Engring. officer USCG, 1950-58. Fellow Soc. Automotive Engrs. (Arch T. Colwell award 1968, 69, 79, governing bd. 1971-73); mem. NAS (naval studies bd. 1990-92), ASME, Combustion Inst., Sigma Xi. Achievements include invention of internal combustion engines and electronic control systems. Home: 1730 Hamilton Dr Bloomfield Hills MI 48302-0221

STIVER, WILLIAM EARL, retired government administrator; b. Madison, Ind., Mar. 30, 1921; s. John Virgil and Anna Lynne (Ryker) S.; student Hanover Coll., 1947-49; B.S., U. Calif. at Berkeley, 1951, M.B.A., 1952; m. Norma A. Cull, June 11, 1944; children—Vicki, Raymond, Gena, John. With Fed. Ser., Bur. Census, Commerce Dept., Suitland, Md., 1952-79, chief budget and finance div., 1963-73, dep. assoc. administr. Social and Econ. Stats. Administrn., 1973-75, spl. asst., assoc. dir. for adminstrn. and field ops. Bur. of Census, 1975-77, electronic data processing staff coordinator, 1977-78, ret., 1979. Served with AUS; 1942-43, 45-46. Recipient Silver medal Commerce Dept., 1969. Mem. Phi Beta Kappa, Beta Gamma Sigma. Home: 8104 Kerby Pky Ct Fort Washington MD 20744-4756

STIVERS, WILLIAM CHARLES, forest products company executive; b. Modesto, Calif., June 22, 1938; s. William P. and Helen Louise (Cummings) S.; m. Karen L. Gaspar, Aug. 6, 1961; children: William, Gregory, Michael, Kristy, Kelly, John, Jeffrey. BA, Stanford 1960; MBA, U. So. Calif., 1963; certificate, U. Wash., 1969; grad., Advanced Mgmt. Program, Harvard U., 1977. Asst. cashier, asst. v.p., v.p. First Interstate Bank, San Francisco and Los Angeles, 1962-70; finance mgr. treas. dept. Weyerhaeuser Co., Tacoma, 1970; asst. treas. Weyerhaeuser Co. 1971, treas., 1972—, v.p., 1980-91, sr. v.p., chief fin. officer, 1991—; treas. Weyerhaeuser Real Estate Co., 1970; bd. dirs., exec. com. mem. Protection Mut. Ins. Co., Park Ridge, Ill.; bd. dirs., audit com. mem. 1st Interstate Bank; bd. dirs., pres. S&S Land and Cattle Co.; nat. adv. bd. mem. Chem. Banking Corp. Chmn. bd. trustees St. Francis Community Hosp., Federal Way; bd. dirs. Ctr. Study Banking and Fin. Mkts. U. Wash., Seattle; fin. mgmt. com. mem. Am. Forest and Paper Assn. Mem. Financial Execs. Inst.

STIX, THOMAS HOWARD, physicist, educator; b. St. Louis, July 12, 1924; s. Ernest William and Erma (Kingsbacher) S.; m. Hazel Rosa Sherwin, May 28, 1950; children—Susan Sherwin Fisher, Michael Sherwin. B.S., Calif. Inst. Tech., 1948; Ph.D., Princeton U., 1953. Mem. staff Plasma Physics Lab. Princeton U., 1953—, co-head exptl. div., 1961-78, asst. dir. acad. affairs, 1978-80, assoc. dir. acad. affairs, 1980-93; prof. astrophys. sci., 1962—, assoc. chmn. dept. astrophys. sci., 1981-91; acting dir. Ctr. for Jewish Life Princeton U., 1994-95. Author: The Theory of Plasma Waves, 1962, Waves in Plasmas, 1992; mem. adv. bd. McGraw-Hill Advanced Physics Monograph Series, 1963-70; bd. editors: Physics of Fluids, 1966-68, Internat. Jour. Engring. Sci, 1969-77, Nuclear Fusion, 1975-80; assoc. editor: Phys. Rev. Letters, 1974-77. Chmn. Princeton United Jewish Appeal, 1954-55, 63-64, Princeton Hillel Found., 1972-76, pres., 1994—. Served with AUS, 1942-45. Recipient award for disting. teaching Princeton U., 1991; NSF sr. postdoctoral fellow physics Weizmann Inst. Sci., Rehovot, Israel, 1960-61; Guggenheim Meml. Found. fellow, 1969-70. Fellow Am. Phys. Soc. (chmn. div. plasma physics 1962-63, com. internat. freedom of scientists 1983-87, chmn. 1985; James Clark Maxwell prize 1980); mem. AAUP, Sigma Xi, Tau Beta Pi. Home: 231 Brookstone Dr Princeton NJ 08540-2405

STOB, MARTIN, physiology educator; b. Chgo., Feb. 20, 1926; s. Cornelius and Theodora (Sluis) S. B.S., Purdue U., 1949, M.S., 1951, Ph.D., 1953. Mem. faculty Purdue U., Lafayette, Ind., 1953—, assoc. prof. animal scis., 1958-63, prof., 1963-92; ret., 1992—. Contbr. articles to profl. jours. Patentee prodn. of fermentation estrogen. Served with USN, 1944-46; ETO, PTO. Name Best Tchr. Sch. Agr., 1970, Best Counselor Sch. Agr., 1977, Best Counselor Purdue U., 1977. Fellow AAAS; mem. Am. Inst. Biol. Scis., Am. Soc. Animal Sci., Soc. Study of Reprodn., Soc. Study of Fertility. Episcopalian. Home: 6218 W Rd 75 N Lafayette IN 47906

STOBAUGH, ROBERT BLAIR, business educator, business executive; b. McGehee, Ark., Oct. 15, 1927; s. Robert B. and Helen (Parris) S.; m. Beverly Ann Parker, Oct. 18, 1947 (dec. 1990); children: Blair, Susan, William, Clay; m. June Gray Milton, Dec. 7, 1991. B.S. in Chem. Engring., La. State U., 1947; D. Bus. Adminstrn., Harvard Bus. Sch., 1968. Refinery engr. Exxon Corp., Baton Rouge and Venezuela, 1947-52; engring. mgr. Caltex Oil Co., N.Y., Bahrain, London, 1952-59; mgr. econ. evaluation Monsanto Co., Houston, 1959-65; lectr. Harvard Bus. Sch., Boston, 1967-70, assoc. prof., 1970-71, prof., 1972-83, Charles E. Wilson prof., 1984—; chmn. doctoral programs Harvard Bus. Sch., 1984-89; dir. energy project Harvard Bus. Sch., Boston, 1972-83; chmn. tech. and ops. mgmt. area Harvard Bus. Sch., 1981-83; dir. Ashland Inc., K., Nat Convenience Stores Houston; chmn. adv. bd. to pres. Montedison, Milan, 1981-87. Co-author: Money in the Multinational Enterprise, 1973; Energy Future (best-seller list N.Y. Times and Time mag.), 1979; author: Nine Investments Abroad and Their Impact at Home, 1976, Innovation and Competition, 1988; co-editor: Technology Crossing Borders, 1984. Mem. bd. advisors Instituto de Estudios Superiores de la Empresa, Barcelona, Spain, 1973-80; co-chmn. the Dumbarton Oaks Symposium on Energy Efficiency, Washington, 1979; bd. dirs. Alliance to Save Energy, Washington, 1979-94; chmn. Blue Ribbon Commn. on Dir. Compensation, Nat. Assn. Corp. Dirs., 1995; expert testimony Congress; advisor to cabinet-level depts. of White House and UN; trustee French Libr. and Cultural Ctr., Boston, 1995. Fellow Acad. Internat. Bus. (pres. 1979-80), Council on Fgn. Relations. Am. Econ. Assn. Episcopalian. Clubs: Belmont Hill (Mass.); Harvard (N.Y.). Office: Harvard Bus Sch Soldiers Field Rd Boston MA 02163

STOBER, WILLIAM JOHN, II, economics educator; b. Boston, Mar. 24, 1933; s. Ralph William and Marjorie Cairncross (Duthie) S.; m. Jeannine Lynn Defries, Sept. 10, 1955. B.Sc., Washington and Lee U., 1955; M.A., Duke U., 1957, Ph.D., 1965. Instr., then asst. prof. econs. N.C. State U., Raleigh, 1959-65; asst. prof., then asso. prof. La. State U., 1965-69, acting head dept. econs., 1968-69; mem. faculty U. Ky., 1969—, prof. econs., 1974—, chmn. 1979-86, 90—, dir. grad. studies, 1987-90. Mem. Am. Econs. Assn., AAUP, Nat. Tax Assn., So. Econ. Assn. (exec. com. 1969-71),

Beta Gamma Sigma. Democrat. Home: 516 Mundy's Landing Rd Rte 4 Versailles KY 40383 Office: U Ky 345H B&E Lexington KY 40506

STOBO, JOHN DAVID, physician, educator; b. Somerville, Mass., Sept. 1, 1941. BA, Dartmouth Coll., 1963; MD, SUNY, Buffalo, 1968. Intern Osler Med. Services, Johns Hopkins, Balt., 1968-69, asst. med. resident, 1969-70, chief med. resident, 1972-73; research assoc. NIH, Bethesda, 1970-72; asst. prof. Mayo Clinic and Research Found., Rochester, Minn., 1973-76; assoc. prof. Moffitt Hosp., San Francisco, 1976-82, prof., head section rheumatology, clin. immunology, 1982-85; William Osler prof. medicine, chmn. dept. medicine John Hopkins Hosp. and Univ., Balt., 1985-94, vice dean clin. sci., assoc. v.p. medicine, 1994—; v.p. Johns Hopkins Health System, Balt., 1994—; chmn., CEO Johns Hopkins Healthcare LLC, Balt. Mem. editorial bds. Jour. Immunology, 1981-86, Jour. Lab. and Clin. Investigation, 1977-82, Arthritis and Rheumatism 1980-85, Jour. Reticuloendothelial Soc., 1982-84, Jour. Clin. Investigation, 1981-86, Jour. Clin. Immunology, 1982-87, Jour. Molecular and Cellular Immunology, 1984-86, Rheumatology Internat., 1984-86, Jour. Immunology, 1985-87; contbr. numerous articles to profl. jours. Transp. and immunobiology adv. com. NIAID, 1976-81; vice chmn. research com. Arthritis Found., 1982-84, chmn., 1984-86, sr. investigator, 1974-77; bd. scientific counselors Nat. Cancer Inst., 1982—; scientific adv. bd. exec. com. Lupus Research Inst.; research adv. bd. DuPont Co., 1987-94. Recipient Merck award 1967, Maimonides Med. Soc. award 1968; SUNY fellow, 1965-66. Fellow ACP, Am. Clin. and Climatol. Assn., Balt. City Med. Soc., Interurban Clin. Club, Md. Soc. Internal Medicine; mem. AAAS, Inst. Medicine, Am. Coll. Rheumatology (pres. 1989-90), Am. Rheumatism Assn. (sec., treas., 1st v.p. 1985-89), Am. Soc. Immunologists, Am. Assn. Physicians, Am. Fedn. Clin. Rsch., Am. Soc. Clin. Investigation, Assn. Profs. Medicine (sec.-treas. 1991-92, pres. 1994-95), Alpha Omega Alpha. Office: Johns Hopkins Outpatient Ctr 601 N Caroline St Ste 2080 Baltimore MD 21287-0764

STOCK, DAVID EARL, mechanical engineering educator; b. Balt., Feb. 2, 1939; s. Walter E. and Minnie H. (Bauer) S.; m. Mary W. Wilford, Aug. 4, 1962; children: Joseph W., Katherine W. BS, Penn State U., 1961; MS, U. Conn., 1965; PhD, Oreg. State U., 1972. Test engr. Pratt & Whitney Aircraft, East Hartford, Conn., 1961-65; vol. Peace Corps, Ghana, 1965-68; prof. Wash. State U., Pullman, 1972—. Contbr. articles to profl. jours. Mem. ASME (chair multiphase flow com. 1988-90, Freeman scholar 1994). Office: Wash State U Dept Mech & Materials Engr Pullman WA 99164-2920

STOCK, GREGG FRANCIS, retired association executive; b. Kansas City, Mo., Jan. 30, 1925; s. Arthur Robert and Verna Marie (Prawitz) S.; m. Sarah Ellen Smart, Nov. 8, 1947; children: Gregory Francis, Heidi Frances, Peter Huston. B.A. in Journalism; B.S. in Advt, U. Kans., 1948. Pres. Wayne-Fastock Equipment Co., Kansas City, Mo., 1953-65; dir. Kansas City Mus. 1971-82, dir. emeritus, 1982—; exec. dir. Old Santa Fe Assn., 1983-84, dir., 1984-87; exec. dir. Southwestern Assn. on Indian Affairs, Santa Fe, 1984-87, dir., 1987-90. Served to lt. (j.g.) USNR, 1943-46, PTO. Fellow Explorers Club. Home: 8345 Somerset Dr Prairie Village KS 66207

STOCK, LEON MILO, chemist, educator; b. Detroit, Oct. 15, 1930; s. J.H. Frederick and Anna (Fischer) S.; m. Mary K. Elmblad, May 6, 1961; children: Katherine L., Ann V. BS in Chemistry, U. Mich., 1952; PhD in Chemistry, Purdue U., 1959. Instr. U. Chgo., 1958-61, asst. prof., 1961-65, assoc. prof., 1965-70, prof. dept. chemistry, 1970—, master Phys. Scis. Collegiate div., 1976-81, assoc. dean div. Phys. Scis., 1976-81, assoc. dean, 1976-81, chmn. dept. chemistry, 1985-88; faculty assoc. Argonne (Ill.) Nat. Lab., 1984—, joint appointment chemistry div., 1985—, dir. chemistry div., 1988—; exploratory rsch. assoc. Electric Power Rsch. Inst., 1989; adv. bd. Ctr. for Applied Rsch. U. Ky., 1990—; Brown lectr. Purdue U., 1992; Given lectr. Pa. State U., 1995. Recipient LJ. and H.M. Quantrell prize, 1974, H.H. Storch award Am. Chem. Soc., 1987. Mem. NAS (energy engring. bd.), Am. Chem. Soc. (com. on sci. 1990-92), Coun. of Gordon Rsch. Confs. (chmn. Gordon Conf. on Fuel Sci. 1983), NRC (mem. panel on coop. rsch. in fossil energy 1984, energy engring. bd. 1984-90, mem. panel on strategic petroleum rsch. 1985, panel on rsch. needs of advanced process tech. 1992-93), Ill. Coal Bd. (program panel 1986-90, panel on prodn. techs. for transp. fuels 1990, editl. bd. Jour. Organic Chemistry 1981-86, Energy and Fuels, 1986—). Office: U of Chicago Dept of Chemistry 5801 S Ellis Ave Chicago IL 60637-1404 also: Argonne Nat Lab Chem Div Argonne IL 60439

STOCK, STUART CHASE, lawyer; b. St. Louis, July 19, 1946; s. Sheldon Harry and Muriel Cecile (Lovejoy) S.; m. Judith Ann Stewart, July 18, 1970; 1 child, Frederick Chase. BS with highest distinction, Purdue U., 1968; JD magna cum laude, Harvard U., 1971. Bar: Mo. 1971, Ind. 1973, D.C. 1974. Law clk. to Chief Judge Henry J. Friendly U.S. Ct. Appeals 2d cir., New York, 1971-72; law clk. to Justice Thurgood Marshall U.S. Supreme Ct., Washington, 1972-73; assoc. Covington & Burling, Washington, 1974-78, ptnr., 1978—; lectr. law U. Va., Charlottesville, 1987-90. Mem. Am. Law Inst. Office: Covington & Burling PO Box 7566 1201 Pennsylvania Ave NW Washington DC 20044

STOCKARD, JAMES ALFRED, lawyer; b. Lake Dallas, Tex., Aug. 4, 1935; s. Clifford Raymond and Thelma Gladys (Gotcher) S.; m. Mary Sue Hogan, Aug. 17, 1956; children—Bruce Anthony, James Alfred, Paul Andrew. BA with honors, N. Tex. State U., Denton, 1956; LLB magna cum laude, So. Methodist U., 1959. Bar: Tex. 1959. Pvt. practice Dallas, 1959-62; with Employers Casualty Co., Dallas, 1962-65; v.p. Southland Life Ins. Co., Dallas, 1965-77; sr. v.p., gen. counsel, dir. Southland Life Ins. Co., 1977-87; exec. v.p., gen. counsel, sec. Southland Fin. Corp., Dallas, 1978-87; dir. Tex. Life, Accident, Health and Hosp. Svc. Ins. Guaranty Assn., 1978-84, chmn. bd., 1980-84; ptnr. Butler & Binion, Dallas, 1987—; bd. dirs. Ins. Systems Am., Atlanta; pres., bd. dir. Dallas County Municipal Utility Dist. 1, Irving, Tex.; gen. counsel, bd. dirs. Lone Star Life Ins. Co., 1988—. Contbr. legal jours. Mem. exec. com., precinct chmn. Dallas County Dem. Com., 1971. Mem. Am., Tex., Dallas Bar Assn., Assn. Life Ins. Counsel. Methodist. Home: 4300 Druid Ln Dallas TX 75205-1029 Office: 750 N St Paul St Ste 1800 Dallas TX 75201

STOCKARD, ROBERT THOMAS, secondary school administrator; b. Alton, Ill., Jan. 29, 1940; s. John Charles and Girtha Isabelle (Smith) S.; m. Christle S. Foster, Apr. 2, 1966; 1 child, Gina Foster. BS, So. Ill. U., 1963, MS, 1967; postgrad., Butler U., 1972. Cert. indsl. arts educator, guidance counselor, secondary adminstr. Tchr. Indpls. Pub. Schs., 1963-69, dean of student, 1969-70, vice prin., 1970-80, vice prin., dir. 1980-93, dir. adult edn., 1993—; rsch. cons. Ill. Dept. Edn., Springfield, 1969; cons. Ind. Classroom Tchrs. Assn., 1969-70, Warren Twp. Schs., Indpls., 1971-72; proposal writing Indpls. Pub. Schs., 1969—, recruiter, 1965-69; workshop conel. leader IPS, 1981—; developer partnership between Ind. Career Edn. Ctr. and Auto Zone Corp. Asst. youth dir. Fall Creek YMCA, Indpls., 1963-65; bd. dirs. Near Eastside Multi-Svc. Ctr., Indpls., 1980-82, mem. adv. coun., 1982-84; adv. coun. Boy Scouts Am.; active Indpls. Urban League, Ind. Black Expo. Recipient Bus. Partnership Disting. Svc. award Indpls. C. of C., 1981, 85, Ptnrs. in Edn. Leadership award, 1983, 84, 85, 86, Disting. Recommender award Ind. U., 1986, Cmty. Svc. award Positive Change Network, 1995; grantee State of Ind., 1991, Nat. Ctr. for Rsch. in Vocat. Edn., 1992. Mem. ASCD, NAACP, Kiwanis (youth com. bd. 1990—), Am. Vocat. Assn., Ind. Vocat. Assn., Ind. Coun. of Vocat. Adminstrs., Ind. Urban League, Ind. Black Expo., 100 Black Men of Indpls., North Ctrl. Assn. Sch. Dists. (program reviewer 1975-81, mem. several sch. evaluation teams), Kappa Alpha Psi (polemarch 1992-94, bd. dirs. Indpls. chpt. 1994—, Disting. Svc. 1986, 87, 90, 91, 94, found. guide right program grantee 1993), Phi Delta Kappa, Iota Lambda Sigma. Avocations: bowling, woodworking, home maintenance, spectator sports. Home: 6565 Sunset Ln Indianapolis IN 46260 Office: Indpls Pub Schs 2405 S Madison Indianapolis IN 46225

STOCKARD, SUSAN See CHANNING, STOCKARD

STOCKBURGER, HAROLD ELLIS, JR., state legislator, insurance agency executive; b. Ft. Oglethorpe, Ga., July 9, 1960; s. Harold E. and Rebecca Ann (Queen) S.; m. Carol Lynn Bunch, Nov. 25, 1983; children: Elizabeth Marie, Jonathan Daniel. Diploma, Walker County Tech. Sch., Rock Spring, Ga., 1981. Retail mgr., 1981-86; agt. Life of Ga., Chattanooga, 1986-87, sales mgr., 1987-89; owner, mgr. Stockburger Ins., Cleveland, Tenn. 1989—; mem. Tenn. Ho. of Reps. Nashville, 1992—. Pres. Crisis Pregnancy Ctr.

Bradley County, Cleveland, 1989-92; mem. Salt and Light Com., Nashville, 1991—. Fellow Life Underwriters Am. Republican. Home: 275 Sara Dr SE Cleveland TN 37323 Address: PO Box 23 Cleveland TN 37364-0023

STOCKDALE, JAMES BOND, writer, research scholar, retired naval officer; b. Abingdon, Ill., Dec. 23, 1923; s. Vernon Beard and Mabel Edith (Bond) S.; m. Sybil Elizabeth Bailey, June 28, 1947; children: James Bond, Sidney Bailey, Stanford Baker, Taylor Burr. BS, U.S. Naval Acad., 1946; MA, Stanford U., 1962; LLD (hon.), Brown U., 1979; LHD (hon.), U. R.I., 1980; 9 other hon. degrees. Commd. ensign USN, 1946, advanced through grades to vice admiral, served as naval aviator, test pilot sch. instr., squadron comdr. of supersonic fighters, air wing comdr.; prisoner of war (sr. naval service POW) North Vietnam, 1965-73; pres. Naval War Coll., Newport, R.I., 1976-79; retired USN, 1979; pres. The Citadel, Charleston, S.C., 1979-80; sr. research fellow The Hoover Instn., Stanford U., 1981—; independent candidate V.P. U.S. running mate of Ross Perot, 1992. Author: A Vietnam Experience, 1985 (Freedoms Found. at Valley Forge hon. prize 1985); author: (with Sybil Stockdale) In Love and War, 1984. Mem. acad. adv. bd. U.S. Naval Acad., Annapolis, 1981—. Decorated D.F.C. (2), D.S.M. (3), Silver Star (4), Medal of Honor; inducted Carrier Aviation Hall of Fame, 1993. Fellow Soc. Exptl. Test Pilots (hon.); mem. Lincoln Acad. Ill. (laureate), Congl. Medal of Honor Soc., Assn. Naval Aviation, Soc. of Cincinnati, SAR, Bohemian Club (San Francisco). Episcopalian. Home: 547 A Ave Coronado CA 92118-1917 Office: Stanford U Hoover Institute Stanford CA 94305

STOCKDALE, RONALD ALLEN, grocery company executive; b. Aplington, Iowa, Apr. 28, 1934; s. Carl Robert and Mildred Louise (Gerhardt) S.; m. Carol Ann Hermeier, Dec. 23, 1956; children—Bryan Ross, Russell Allen, Paul Roderick. B.S. in Commerce, State U. Iowa, 1958. C.P.A. Auditor Arthur Andersen & Co., Chgo., 1958-63; controller Super Food Services, Bellefontaine, Ohio, 1963-66, Mountain States Wholesale Co., Boise, Idaho, 1966-69; exec. v.p., sec. West Coast Grocery Co., Tacoma, 1969-82, pres., COO, 1982-87, CEO, 1988—; bd. dirs. Profit Sharing Council Am., Chgo., 1977-83. Trustee Humana Hosp.-Tacoma, 1985-87, San Francisco Theol. Sem., 1987—; mem. adv. bd. Bus. Adminstrn., Pacific Luth. U., 1986—. Served with U.S. Army, 1954-56. Mem. AICPA, Fin. Execs. Inst. Republican. Presbyterian. Home: 2720 Soundview Dr W Tacoma WA 98466-1700 Office: W Coast Grocery Co 1525 E D St Tacoma WA 98421-1609

STOCKER, ARTHUR FREDERICK, classics educator; b. Bethlehem, Pa., Jan. 24, 1914; s. Harry Emilius and Alice (Stratton) S.; m. Marian West, July 16, 1968. A.B. summa cum laude, Williams Coll., 1934; A.M., Harvard U., 1935, Ph.D., 1939. Instr. Greek Bates Coll., 1941-42; asst. prof. classics U. Va., 1946-52, assoc. prof., 1952-60, prof., 1960-84, prof. emeritus, 1984—, chmn. dept., 1955-63, 68-78, assoc. dean Grad. Sch. Arts and Scis., 1962-66; Servi-vis. asst. prof. classics U. Chgo., summer 1951. Editor: (with others) Servianorum in Vergilii Carmina Commentariorum Editio Harvardiana, Vol. II, 1946, Vol. III, 1965; assoc. editor: Classical Outlook. Served with USAAF, 1942-46; col. (ret.). Sheldon traveling fellow from Harvard, 1940-41. Mem. Va. Classical Assn. (pres. 1949-52), Mid. West and South Classical Assn. (pres. So. sect. 1960-62, pres. 1970-71), Nat. Huguenot Soc. (pres. gen. 1989-91), Am. Philol. Assn., Mediaeval Acad. Am., Poetry Soc. Va. (pres. 1966-69), S.A.R. (chpt. pres. 1972, 91), Huguenot Soc. Va. (pres. 1981-83), Raven Soc. (Raven award 1977), Phi Beta Kappa, Omicron Delta Kappa. Republican. Presbyterian (elder). Clubs: Masons, Internat. Torch, Colonnade (Charlottesville, Va.), Farmington Country (Charlottesville, Va.), Commonwealth (Richmond, Va.), Williams (N.Y.C.), Army and Navy (Washington). Home: 1434 Grove Rd Charlottesville VA 22901-3126

STOCKER, JOYCE ARLENE, retired secondary education educator; b. West Wyoming, Pa., May 13, 1931; d. Donald Arthur and Elizabeth Mae (Gardner) Saunders; m. Robert Earl Stocker, Nov. 26, 1953; children: Desiree Lee Stocker Stackhouse, Rebecca Lois Stocker Genelow, Joyce Elizabeth Stocker Scrobola. Grad. cum laude, Coll. Misericordia, Dallas, 1953; Master's equivalency diploma, Pa. Dept. Edn., 1991. Cert. tchr., Pa. Tchr. music and lang. arts West Pittston (Pa.) Sch. Dist., 1953-60; tchr. music and choral Wyoming Area Sch. Dist., Exeter, Pa., 1970-78, tchr. English composition, 1978-93, chmn. lang. arts dept., 1982-90, dir. nat. history day activities, 1982-93; state cons. Nat. History Day. Organist, choir dir. United Meth. Ch., Wyo., 1958—; choir dir. Wyo. Centenial Choir, Wyo. 1983; mem. com., sec. Continuing Profl. Devel. Com. Pa., Exeter, 1988-93, Long Range Plan Wyo. Area Sch. Dist., Exeter 1990-91; tutor, judge Nat. History Day; judge regional, state, and nat. events for Nat. History Day. Recipient DAR Tchr. of Yr. award, 1992-93, Wilkes U., 1990; named Outstanding Educator, Times Leader, 1993. Mem. NEA, Pa. Edn. Assn., Wyo. Edn. Assn., N.E. Pa. Writing Coun., Nat. Coun. Tchrs. English, Women Educators Internat., Orgn. Am. History, PMEA, MENC, NCSS, PASR, PSERS, Pa. Coun. Social Studies, Delta Kappa Gamma (recording sec. 1991—), Phi Mu Gamma. Methodist. Avocations: reading, writing, sewing, hunting, fishing. Office: Wyoming Area Sch Dist 20 Memorial St Exeter PA 18643-2659

STOCKER, JULE E(LIAS), lawyer; b. Detroit, Sept. 16, 1906; s. David R. and Hattie V. (Gerber) S.; m. Beatrice H. Klipstein, Mar. 26, 1932; children: Maida (Mrs. George S. Abrams), Michael. AB magna cum laude, Harvard U., 1926, JD magna cum laude, 1929. Bar: N.Y. 1929, U.S. Supreme Ct. 1950. Since practiced in N.Y.C.; mem. Chadbourne, Parke, Whiteside & Wolff (name changed to Chadbourne and Parke), 1950-56; assoc. counsel, law dept.-investments Equitable Life Assurance Soc. of U.S., 1956-62, 2d v.p., asso. gen. solicitor, 1962-65, v.p., asso. gen. counsel, 1965-70, v.p., gen. atty., 1970-73, cons., 1974-79, 1985—; counsel Gruber & Gruber, N.Y.C., 1977—; lectr. Practicing Law Inst., N.Y.C., 1942—; mem. adv. com. N.Y. State Commn. Estates, 1961-66; drafting cons. N.Y. State Joint Legis. Com. Revision Corp. Laws, 1960-61; project dir. N.Y. State Law Revision Com., Recodification N.Y. Ins. Law, 1979-83; cons. N.Y. State Ins. Dept., 1983-84. Author: Wills for Servicemen, 1944, Stocker on Drawing Wills, 10th edit. 1987, lead author Supplement, 1990, 11th edit. 1993; lead author codification notes McKinney's N.Y. Ins. Law, 1985; co-author Legislators Update, 1993, supplement, 1994; editor Harvard Law Rev., 1927-29. Mem. Assn. of Bar of City of N.Y. (chmn. com. real property law 1946-49), N.Y. County Lawyers Assn. (sec. com. surrogates' ct. 1946-57), Assn. Life Ins. Counsel, ABA, N.Y. State Bar Assn., Am. Law Inst. (various coms.), Am. Coun. Life Ins. (com. ins. co. fed. income tax 1972-73, legal sect. mem. emeritus), Phi Beta Kappa and Assocs. Home: 17 W 54th St New York NY 10019-5412

STOCKHAM, THOMAS GREENWAY, JR., electrical engineering educator; b. Passaic, N.J., Dec. 22, 1933; s. Thomas Greenway and Dorothy (Post) S.; m. Martha Goodman, June 22, 1963; children: Thomas Greenway III, Carol H., John M., David W. SB, MIT, 1955, SM, 1957, ScD, 1959. Instr. elec. engring. MIT, 1957-59, asst. prof., 1959-66, mem. staff Lincoln Lab., 1966-68; assoc. prof. computer sci. U. Utah, Salt Lake City, 1968-70, prof., 1970-80; prof. elec. engring. U. Utah, 1970—; pres., chmn. Soundstream, Inc., Salt Lake City, 1975-82; cons. in field. Contbr. articles on digital signal processing, digital sound recording to profl. jours. 1st lt. USAF, 1959-62. Recipient Alexander M. Poniatoff gold medal for tech. excellence, Utah Engr. of Yr. award, Utah Engrs. Council, 1986, Emmy award NATAS, 1988, Grammy award NARAS, 1993. Fellow IEEE Audio Engring Soc. (pres. 1982-83, Gold medal); mem. Assn. for Computing Machinery, Sigma Xi, Eta Kappa Nu, Tau Beta Pi. Republican. Developer tech. and equipment for digital mastering of sound. Office: U Utah Meb # 3280 Salt Lake City UT 84112-1180

STOCKING, GEORGE WARD, JR., anthropology educator; b. Berlin, Dec. 8, 1928; came to U.S., 1929; s. George Ward and Dorothé Amelia (Reichhard) S.; m. Wilhelmina Davis, Aug. 19, 1949 (div. 1965); children: Susan Hallowell, Rebecca, Rachel Louise, Melissa, Thomas Shepard; m. Carol Ann Bowman, Sept. 29, 1968. BA, Harvard U., 1949; PhD, U. Pa., 1960. From instr. to assoc. prof. history U. Calif., Berkeley, 1960-68; assoc. 1960. From. instr. to assoc. 1960. From instr. to assoc. prof. anthropology and history U. Chgo., 1968-74, prof. anthropology, 1974—, Stein-Freiler Disting. Svc. prof., 1990—, dir. Fishbein Ctr. for History Sci. and Medicine, 1981-92; vis. prof. U. Minn., 1974, Harvard U., Cambridge, Mass., 1977, Stanford U., Palo Alto, Calif. 1983. Author: Race, Culture and Evolution, 1968, Victorian Anthropology, 1987, The Ethnographer's Magic, 1992, After Tylor, 1995; author-editor: The Shaping of American Anthropology, 1974; editor (jour.) History of Anthropology, 1983—. Fellow Ctr. for Advanced Study in Behavioral Scis., 1976-77, John Simon Guggenheim Meml. Found., 1984-85, Inst. for Advanced Study, 1992-93; Getty Ctr. for History of Art and Humanities scholar, 1988-89. Fellow Am. Anthropol. Assn., Am. Acad. Arts and Scis.; mem. Royal Anthropol. Inst. (Huxley medal 1993), History Sci. Soc. Avocations: gardening, needlepoint, bicycling. Office: Dept Anthropology 1126 E 59th St Chicago IL 60637-1580

STOCKMAN, DAVID ALLEN, former federal official, congressman, financier; b. Ft. Hood, Tex., Nov. 10, 1946; s. Allen and Carol (Bartz) S. BA in Am. History cum laude, Mich. State U., East Lansing, 1968; postgrad., Harvard U. Div. Sch., 1968-70; fellow, Inst. Politics, 1974. Spl. asst. to Congressman John Anderson, 1970-72; exec. dir. Republican Conf., Ho. of Reps., 1972-75; mem. 95th Congress from 4th Dist. Mich., Interstate and Fgn. Commerce Com., Adminstrn. Com.; chmn. Rep. Econ. Policy Task Force, 1977-81; dir. Office of Mgmt. and Budget, Washington, 1981-85; mng. dir. Salomon Bros., N.Y.C., 1985-88; gen. ptnr. The Blackstone Group, N.Y.C., 1988—; Mem. Nat. Commn. on Air Quality, 1978. Author: The Triumph of Politics: Why the Reagan Revolution Failed, 1986. Mem. Coun. on Fgn. Rels. Office: The Blackstone Group 345 Park Ave New York NY 10154-0004

STOCKMAN, GERALD RICHARD, lawyer; b. Trenton, N.J., Mar. 31, 1935; s. Julius and Alice (Robinson) S.; m. Audrey Lenore; children—Maura, Melissa, Julie, Jeffrey, Robert, Monica, Chad. B.S., Holy Cross Coll., 1956; J.D., Villanova Law Sch., 1959. Bar: Pa., 1960, N.J., 1960. Clk. to chief judge U.S. Dist. Ct. (ea. dist.) Pa., 1961, to chief judge U.S. Dist. Ct. N.J.; assoc. Albridge C. Smith, Esquire, Princeton, N.J.; assoc., ptnr. George Y. Schoch, Trenton; now pres. Stockman & Gilman; state senator N.J., 1981-91, active numerous coms.; lectr. in law; participant various panels for Inst. for Continuing Legal Edn. Mem. N.J. Gen. Assembly, from 1978; mem. Mercer County Charter Study Commn., 1974; chmn. Del. River Joint Toll Bridge Commn., 1977-78; active Heart Fund, Am. Cancer Soc., Mercer County chpt. Big Bros.; mem. exec. bd. NAACP; chmn. Del. Valley United Way; advance gifts chmn. Hamilton Hosp. Expansion Fund Drive. Recipient Brotherhood award NCCJ, 1980, Polit. Action award NAACP, 1984, Community Devel. award Middlesex, Somerset and Mercer Regional Study Council, 1984. Fellow Am. Coll. Trial Lawyers; mem. Mercer County Bar Assn., N.J. Assn. on Corrections, N.J. State Bar Assn., Assn. Trial Lawyers Am. Democrat. Roman Catholic. Office: Stockman & Gilman 2211 White Horse-Mercerville Rd Trenton NJ 08619

STOCKMAN, JAMES ANTHONY, III, pediatrician; b. Phila., 1943. MD, Jeffersib Med. Coll., 1969. Diplomate Am. Bd. Pediatrics (pres.). Intern Childrens Hosp. Pa., 1969-70, resident in pediatrics, 1970-72; fellow in pediactic hematology/oncology SUNY, Syracuse, 1972-74; now cons. prof. Duke U.; also with U. N. C., Chappel Hill. Office: Am Bd Pediatrics 111 Silver Cedar Ct Chapel Hill NC 27514-1513*

STOCKMAN, STEPHEN E., congressman; b. Bloomfield Hills, Mich., Nov. 14, 1956; m. Patti Stockman. BS in Acctg., U. Houston, 1990. Acct., tech. McKee Environ. Health, Inc., 1991-93; mem. 104th Congress from 9th Tex. dist., 1995—. Republican. Office: US House Reps 2449 Rayburn House Office Bldg Washington DC 20515-4309

STOCKMAR, TED P., lawyer; b. Denver, May 9, 1921; s. Theodore Paul and Elda Marie (Robinson) S.; m. Suzanne Louise Harl, Feb. 14, 1947; children: Stephen Harl, John Brian, Anne Baldwin Stockmar Upton. BS in Petroleum Engring., Colo. Sch. Mines, Golden, 1943; LLB, U. Denver, 1948. Bar: Colo. 1948. Ptnr. Holme Roberts & Owen Denver, 1951-91; of counsel, 1991—. Co-author: Law of Federal Oil and Gas Leases 1964, 1981; also articles. Trustee Colo. Sch. Mines, Golden, 1948-82, bd. pres., 1970-80. 1st lt. USAF, 1943-45. Mem. Denver Bar Assn., Colo. Bar Assn., Rocky Mountain Oil and Gas Assn. (dir., exec. com. 1982-93, chmn. legal com. 1986-88), Denver Country Club, Univ. Club, Law Club, Rotary (bd. dirs. 1969-71). Republican. Avocations: bird watching; skiing; tennis; golf; reading; gardening. Home: 2552 E Alameda Ave Unit # 8 Denver CO 80209 Office: Holme Roberts & Owen LLC 1700 Lincoln St Ste 4100 Denver CO 80203-4541

STOCKMAYER, WALTER H(UGO), chemistry educator; b. Rutherford, N.J., Apr. 7, 1914; s. Hugo Paul and Dagmar (Bostroem) S.; m. Sylvia Kleist Bergen, Aug. 12, 1938; children—Ralph, Hugh,. S.B., MIT, 1935, Ph.D., 1940; B.Sc. (Rhodes scholar), Oxford U., 1937; D.Sc., U. Louis-Pasteur, Strasbourg, France, 1972; L.H.D., Dartmouth Coll., 1983. Instr. M.I.T., 1939-41, asst. prof., 1943-46, assoc. prof., 1946-52, prof.; 1952-61; prof. chemistry Dartmouth, 1961-79, prof. emeritus, 1979—; instr. Columbia, 1941-43; cons. E.I. duPont de Nemours & Co., Inc., 1945—; vis. com. Nat. Bur. Standards, 1978-80. Contbr. articles on phys. and macromolecular chemistry to sci. jours. Recipient Nat. Medal of Sci., 1987, MCA Coll. Chemistry Tchr. award 1960, ; Guggenheim fellow, 1954-55, hon. fellow Jesus Coll., Oxford, Eng., 1976, Alexander von Humboldt fellow, 1978-79. Fellow Am. Acad. Arts and Scis., Am. Phys. Soc. (Polymer Physics prize 1975); mem. NAS, Am. Chem. Soc. (assoc. editor Macromolecules 1968-74, 76-94, chmn. polymer chem. divsn. 1968, Polymer Chemistry award 1965, Peter Debye award 1974, T. W. Richards medal 1988, polymer divsn. award 1988, Oesper award 1992), Soc. Plastics Engrs. (Internat. award 1991), Soc. Polymer Sci., Japan (hon. 1991), Appalachian Mountain Club, Sigma Xi (William Procter prize 1993). Office: Dartmouth Coll Chemistry Dept Hanover NH 03755

STOCKMEYER, NORMAN OTTO, JR., law educator, consultant; b. Detroit, May 24, 1938; s. Norman O. and Lillian R. (Hitchman) S.; m. Marcia E. Rudman, Oct. 1, 1966; children: Claire, Kathleen, Mary Frances. AB, Oberlin Coll., 1960; JD, U. Mich., 1963. Bar: Mich. 1963, U.S. Ct. Appeals (6th cir.) 1964, U.S. Supreme Ct. 1974. Legis. grad. fellow Mich. State U., 1963; legal counsel Senate Judiciary Com., Mich. Legislature, 1964; law clk. Mich. Ct. Appeals, 1965, commr., research dir.. 1969-76; assoc. prof. law Thomas M. Cooley Law Sch., 1977-78, prof., 1978—; vis. prof. Mercer U. Sch. Law, 1986, Calif. Western Sch. Law, 1993. Editor Mich. Law of Damages, 1989; contbr. numerous articles to state and nat. legal jours. Named one of 88 Greats Lansing State Jour., 1988. Fellow Am. Bar Found. (life); mem. ABA (chmn. Mich. membership 1972-73, lectr. Appellate Judges Conf. jud. seminars 1972-76, ho. del. 1988-92, editorial bd. Compleat Lawyer 1990—), Nat. Conf. Bar Founds. (trustee 1985-90, sec. 1988-89), Mich. State Bar Found. (pres. 1982-85, trustee 1971-92), State Bar Mich. (chmn. Young Lawyers sect. 1971-72, rep. assembly 1972-79, bd. commrs. 1985-93), Ingham County Bar Assn. (bd. dirs. 1981-85), Mich. Professions (bd. dirs. 1981-84, Profl. of Yr. 1988), Thomas M. Cooley Legal Authors Soc. (pres. 1982-83), Scribes (dirs. award 1994—), Delta Theta Phi (dean Christiancy Senate 1992; Outstanding Prof. 1984). Address: PO Box 13038 Lansing MI 48901-3038

STOCKSTILL, JAMES WILLIAM, secondary school educator; b. Springfield, Mo., Aug. 28, 1945; s. Arley Ian and Elma Jean Stockstill; m. Vicki Bell, Aug. 20, 1966 (div. 1970); 1 child, Michelle LaDawn; m. Meredith Jeanine Spencer, Dec. 26, 1974; 1 child, Danielle. BS in Edn., S.W. Mo. State U., 1969. Head football coach, phys. edn. tchr. Golden City (Mo.) High Sch., 1969-70; coach, tchr. Mountain View (Mo.) High Sch., 1970-71; journeyman bricklayer Fort Lauderdale (Fla.) BMPI Union, 1971-74; masonry contractor Waynesville, N.C., 1974-86; masonry contractor, master stone and brick masonry contractor Hillsborough, N.C., 1986—; masonry instr. Orange High Sch., Hillsborough, 1986—; owner Athenian Lady Fitness Ctr., Waynesville, 1984-86; gymnastics instr. Canton (N.C.) YMCA, 1976-80; pres. Trade and Industry Adv. Coun. Hillsborough, 1988-90; rep. VICA Skill Contest Orange High Sch., 1986-88. Author: A Collection of Poems, 1992, 93. Mem. Com. to Increase and Diversify Tax Base, Hillsborough, 1992. Mem. AFT. Avocations: weightlifting, karate, jogging, hiking, landscaping. Home: 2801 Canter Dr Hillsborough NC 27278 Office: Orange High Sch 500 Orange High Rd Hillsborough NC 27278

STOCKTON, ANDERSON BERRIAN, electronics company executive, consultant, genealogist; b. Lithonia, Ga., Oct. 7, 1943; s. Berrian Henry and Mary Grace (Warbington) S.; m. Linda Arlene Milligan, June 9, 1963; 1 child, Christopher Lee. Cert. in cryptographic engring., USAF Acad., Wichita Falls, Tex., 1963. Supr. Western Union Telegraph Co., East Point, Ga., 1965-67; mgr. RCA Corp., Cherry Hill, N.J., 1967-72; v.p. Universal Tech., Inc., Verona, N.J., 1972-76; v.p. engring. Siemens Ag., Anaheim, Calif., 1976-84, Concorde, El Toro, Calif., 1984-85, Data Card Troy, Inc., Santa Ana, Calif., 1985-86; dir. laser engring. div. ITT, San Jose, Calif., 1986-87; v.p. S.T.A.R. Ricoh Corp., San Jose, 1988-93; v.p. mktg. QMS, Inc., Mobile, Ala., 1993-94; mng. gen. dir. IDT, Inc., Santa Clara, Calif. 1994—; cons. Hutchinson (Minn.) Tech. Corp., 1984-87, Xerox, 1993, Hewlett Packard, 1993. Author: Polled Network Communications, 1976, A Quest for the Past, 1991; patentee in field. With USAF, 1961-65. Mem. IEEE, Am. Electronics Assn. Avocations: classic car collecting, genealogical and historical research, sword, coin and stamp collecting. Home: 2086 Silence Dr San Jose CA 95148 Office: IDT Inc 2972 Stender Way Santa Clara CA 95054

STOCKTON, DAVID KNAPP, professional golfer; b. San Bernardino, Calif., Nov. 2, 1941; s. Gail Rufus and Audrey (Knapp) S.; m. Catherine Fay Hales, Feb. 27, 1965; children—David Bradley, Ronald Edwin. B.S. in Gen. Mgmt., U. So. Calif., 1964. Mem. Golf's All Am. Team, 1974-76. Republican. Roman Catholic. Club: Elk. Winner 11 tour tournaments including: Profl. Golf Assn., 1970, 76, Los Angeles, 1974, Hartford, 1974, Colonial, 1967, Cleve., 1968, Milw., 1968-73, Pleasant Valley, 1971, Quad Cities, 1974, Haig and Haig Open, 1968, 6 Sr. Tour tournaments, 1992 TPC Winner (sr. rookie of the yr.), 5 Sr. Tour events-Dallas Murata Reunion, Kansas City, Park City, Seattle, Transamerica at Napa; named Sr. Player of Yr. and Arnold Palmer award Dupont Cup; rep. U.S. in 2 World Cups, 1970, 76, Ryder Cup, 1971, 77; shares former record for fewest putts for 18 holes (19); U.S. Ryder Cup capt., 1991. Office: 32373 Tres Lagos St Mentone CA 92359-9611*

STOCKTON, JOHN HOUSTON, professional basketball player; b. Spokane, Wash., Mar. 26, 1962; m. Nada Stepovich, Aug. 16, 1986; 1 child, John Houston. Grad., Gonzaga U., 1984. With Utah Jazz, Salt Lake City, 1984—; mem. U.S. Olympic Basketball Team, 1992. Named to NBA All-Star team, 1989-94; holder NBA single season rec. most assists, 1991; NBA Assists leader, 1987-1992; NBA Steals leader, 1989, 92; named NBA All-Star Co-MVP, 1993, All-NBA First Team, 1994. Led NBA in most assists per gaem, 1988,93; led NBA with highest steals per game avg., 1989,1992; shares single-game playoff record for most assists, 24, 1988. Office: Utah Jazz 301 W South Temple Salt Lake City UT 84101-1219*

STOCKTON, ROBERT STANDEFORD, writer, real estate development, construction, sales and management consultant; b. St. Louis, Aug. 20, 1939; s. George Oliver and Naomi Fleeta (Standeford) S.; m. Sharon Laurise Smith, Oct. 28, 1961 (div.); children: Debra Dianne, Virginia Kathleen; m. Bonnie Le Blanc, July 6, 1974 (div.); 1 child, Katharine Elizabeth. AA, Hannibal (Mo.) LaGrange Coll., 1959; BS, Mo. U., 1961; grad. with distinction, USAF Squadron Officer Sch., 1967, USAF Air Command and Staff Coll., 1976; MA, Cen. Mo. U., 1969; grad., Nat. Def. U., 1980. Commd. 2d lt. USAF, 1961, advanced through grades to lt. col., 1978, mem. Minuteman Missile Intercontinental Ballistic Missile combat crew, 1963-72, comdr., vice comdr. RAF bases, 1979-83; mem. resident faculty USAF Command and Staff Coll., 1976-79; ret. USAF, 1982; asst. prof. Pan Am U., Edinburg, Tex., 1972-75; dir. conf. ctr. U. S.W. La., Lafayette, 1983-85; owner Stockton Homes, Lafayette, 1987-92; owner Stockton Real Estate, Inc., Lafayette, 1987-92, also bd. dirs.; bd. dirs. Stockton Homes, Lafayette; cons. Mgmt. Concepts, Lafayette, 1983-92. Author: Countdown II: Hiroshima. Pres. La. Jr. Miss, Inc., Lafayette, 1984-85, dir. emeritus, 1983-84. Recipient Community Rels. award U.S. Amb. to Eng., 1980, Lifesaving Recognition award House of Commons/Eng. Ministry of Def., 1982. Mem. Nat. Assn. Realtors, La. Assn. Realtors, Ret. Officers Assn., DAV, Lafayette C. of C. (pres.'s club 1984-85). Republican. Roman Catholic. Avocations: computers, writing, real estate devel. projects. Home: 1000 Renaud Dr # 35 Scott LA 70583-9122

STOCKTON, THOMAS B., bishop; b. Winston-Salem, N.C., July 26, 1930; s. Norman V. and Emorie (Barber) S.; m. Jean Stevens, Aug. 22, 1953; children: Lisa S. Stockton Howell, Thomas B. Jr., Shannon Stockton Miller. BA, Davidson Coll., 1952; MDiv, Duke U., 1955; DD (hon.), Pfeiffer Coll., 1973. Ordained to ministry United Meth. Ch., 1956. Min. Thrift United Meth. Ch., Paw Creek, N.C., 1956-60, 1st United Meth. Ch., Reidsville, N.C., 1960-64, Dilworth United Meth. Ch., Charlotte, N.C., 1964-70, Cen. United Meth. Ch., Asheville, N.C., 1970-75, Myers Pk. United Meth. Ch., Charlotte, N.C., 1975-83, Wesley Meml. United Ch., High Point, N.C., 1983-88; bishop Va. Conf., United Meth. Ch., Richmond, 1988—. Trustee Duke U., Durham, N.C., 1981—, all United Meth. colls. and homes in Va. Ann. Conf., 1988—; mem. gen. bd. discipleship U. Meth. Ch., Nashville, 1988—. Home: 12923 Fox Meadow Dr Richmond VA 23233-2239 Office: United Meth Ch Va Conf PO Box 11367 Richmond VA 23230-1367

STOCKWELL, DEAN, actor; b. Hollywood, Calif., Mar. 5, 1936; s. Harry and Betty Veronica Stockwell; m. Millie Perkins; m. Joy Marchenko; 2 children. Performances include: (feature films) The Valley of Decision, 1945, Abbott and Costello in Hollywood, 1945, The Green Years, 1946, Home Sweet Homicide, 1946, The Mighty McGurk, 1946, The Arnelo Affair, 1947, The Romance of Rosy Ridge, 1947, Song of the Thin Man, 1947, Gentlemen's Agreement, 1947, Deep Waters, 1948, The Boy with Green Hair, 1948 (Golden Globe award), Down to the Sea in Ships, 1949, The Secret Garden, 1949, The Happy Years, 1950, Kim, 1950, Stars in my Crown, 1950, Cattle Drive, 1958, Compulsion, 1959 (Cannes Film Festival award 1959), Sons and Lovers, 1960, Long Day's Journey into Night, 1962 (Cannes Film Festival award 1961), Psych-Out, 1968, The Dunwich Horror, 1970, The Last Movie, 1971, The Loners, 1972, Tracks, 1976, Eadweard Muybridge, Zoopraxographer, 1976, Alsindo and the Condor, 1981, Wrong is Right, 1982, Human Highway, 1982, Sweet Scene of Death, 1983, Paris, Texas, 1984, Dune, 1984, The Legend of Billie Jean, 1985, To Live and Die in L.A., 1985, Blue Velvet, 1986, Gardens of Stone, 1987, Beverly Hills Cop, II, 1987, Blue Iguana, 1987, Tucker: The Man and His Dream, 1988, Married to the Mob, 1988, Limit Up, 1989, Buying Time, 1989, The Time Guardian, 1989, The Player, 1992, Chasers, 1993; (stage prodns.) Innocent Voyage, Theatre Guild, Belasco Theatre, N.Y.C., 1943, Compulsion, Ambassador Theatre, N.Y.C., 1958;(TV movies) Paper Man, 1971, The Failing of Raymond, 1971, The Adventures of Nick Carter, 1972, The Return of Joe Forrester, 1976, A Killing Affair, 1977, The Gambler III: The Legend Continues, 1991, Son of the Morning Star, 1991, Back Track, 1991, Shame, 1992, Fatal Memories, 1992, The Langoliers, 1995; appeared in TV series Quantum Leap, 1988-1993 (Emmy award nominee for best supporting actor in a drama 1993); appeared on radio shows Death Valley Days, Dr. Christian. Mem. SAG, AEA. Office: UTA 9560 Wilshire Blvd 5th fl Beverly Hills CA 90212*

STOCKWELL, ERNEST FARNHAM, JR., banker; b. Boston, Dec. 18, 1923; s. Ernest Farnham and Beatrice Burr (Beach) S.; m. Fiona Munro, May 24, 1952; children: Ernest Farnham III, Diana, Elizabeth. Grad., Phillips Acad., 1941; BA, Yale U., 1945. Asst. to mgr. First Nat. Bank Boston, 1950-55, br. mgr., 1955-56, asst. v.p., 1956-60, v.p., 1960-71; pres. Harvard Trust Co., Cambridge, Mass., 1971-77; chief exec. officer Harvard Trust Co., 1973-77; pres. Bay Banks Assocs., Inc., 1977-78; v.p. First Nat. Bank Boston, 1978-80, sr. v.p., 1980-88, ret., 1988. Bd. dirs. Yale Alumni Fund, chmn., 1980; trustee Episcopal Diocesan Investment Trust. With USNR, 1943-46. Mem. Yale Club (Boston and N.Y.C.), Dedham (Mass.) Country and Polo Club. Home: 36 Dover Rd Dover MA 02030-2020

STOCKWELL, RICHARD E., journalist, business executive; b. Neillsville, Wis., Mar. 12, 1917; s. Arthur Raymond and Ella (Stelloh) S. B.S., U. Wis., 1940; M.A., U. Minn., 1945; Nieman fellow, Harvard U., 1945-46. Farm editor Sta. WIBA, Madison, Wis., 1939-40; news staff WLW, Cin., 1940-41; program dir. Wis. Network, Wisconsin Rapids, 1941-42; asso. news editor WMT, Cedar Rapids, Iowa, 1942-43, WCCO-CBS, Mpls., 1943-45; editorial writer Mpls. Star, 1946-49; editor Aviation Age, N.Y.C., 1949-52, Monsanto Mag., Monsanto Internat. Mag., St. Louis, 1952-54; editorial dir. Am. Aviation Publs., Inc., Washington, 1954-55; cons., mgmt. information analyst Flight Propulsion Lab., Gen. Electric Co., Cin., 1956-58; group dir. pub. relations and advt., electronics, ordnance and aerostructures divs. Avco Corp., Cin., 1958-68; v.p. comml. and indsl. products group Avco Corp., Nashville, 1968-74; v.p. products and research group Avco Corp., 1974-76. Author: Soviet Air Power, 1956; also numerous mag. articles. Sta. WLW scholar, 1940. Mem. Royal, Am. econs. assns., Am. Polit. Sci. Assn. Clubs: Wings (N.Y.C.); Nat. Press (Washington). Home: 10 Clay St Neillsville WI 54456-2145

STOCKWELL, ROBERT PAUL, linguist, educator; b. Oklahoma City, June 12, 1925; s. Benjamin P. and Anna (Cunningham) S.; m. Lucy Louisa Floyd, Aug. 29, 1946; 1 child, Paul Witten. B.A., 1946, M.A., 1949, Ph.D., 1952. Instr. English, Oklahoma City U., 1946-48; mem. linguistics staff Sch. Langs., Fgn. Service Inst., State Dept., 1952-56; mem. faculty UCLA, 1956—, prof. English, 1962-66, prof. linguistics, 1966—, chmn. dept., 1966-73, 80-84; mem. com. lang. programs Am. Council Learned Socs., 1965-69. Author: (with J.D. Bowen) Patterns of Spanish Pronunciation, 1960, Sounds of English and Spanish, 1965, (with J. D. Bowen, J.W. Martin) The Grammatical Structures of English and Spanish, 1965, The Major Syntactic Structures of English, 1973, (with P.M. Schachter, B.H. Partee) Foundations of Syntactic Theory, 1977, Workbook in Syntactic Theory and Analysis, 1977; also numerous articles.; editor: (with R.S.K. Macaulay) Linguistic Change and Generative Theory, 1972, ; assoc. editor: Lang., 1973-79, Festschrift: rhetorica, Phonologica, Syntactica: A Festschrift for Robert P. Stockwell, 1989. Served with USNR, 1943-45. Am. Council Learned Socs. fellow, 1963-64. Mem. Linguistic Soc. Am. (exec. com. 1965-68), Philol. Assn. Great Britain. Home: 4000 Hayvenhurst Ave Encino CA 91436-3850 Office: UCLA Los Angeles CA 90024

STODDARD, BRANDON, film and television company executive; b. Bridgeport, Conn., Mar. 31, 1937; s. Johnson and Constance (Brandon) S.; married, Feb. 1984; children: Alexandra, Brooke. B.A. in Am. Studies, Yale U., 1958; postgrad., Columbia U. Law Sch., 1963. Program asst. Batten, Barton, Durstine and Osborn, N.Y.C., 1960-61; program ops. supr. Grey Advt., N.Y.C., 1962-66; dir. daytime programs Grey Advt., 1966, v.p. in charge of radio and television programs, 1968-70; dir. daytime programs ABC-TV, 1970-72, v.p. daytime programs, 1972-74, v.p. motion pictures for television, 1974-79; pres. ABC Motion Pictures, Los Angeles, 1979-85; sr. v.p. ABC Entertainment, 1979-85, pres., 1985-89; pres. ABC Prodns., 1989—. Served with U.S. Army, 1960-61. Mem. Hollywood Radio and TV Soc., Am. Film Inst., Acad. Motion Pictures Arts and Scis. Episcopalian. Club: Bel Air Bay. Office: ABC Prodns 2020 Avenue Of The Stars Fl 5 Los Angeles CA 90067-4704

STODDARD, ELLWYN R., sociology and anthropology educator; b. Garland, Utah, Feb. 16, 1927; s. Roscoe and Mary Lloyd (Redford) S.; m. Judith Mae DeGriselles, May 10, 1951 (div. 1964); children: Ellwyn R. Jr., Michael Valin, Dawn D.; m. Elaine Kirby, Aug. 28, 1964; children: Jared Evan, Sunday, Summer; stepchildren: Laura Jane Packham, George H. Packham, R. Kirby Packham. BS, Utah State U., 1952; MS, Brigham Young U., 1955; PhD, Mich. State U., 1961. Instr. sociology Drake U., Des Moines, 1959-61, asst. prof., 1962-63, assoc. prof., 1964-65; assoc. prof. Tex. Western Coll., El Paso, 1965-69; prof. sociology and anthropology U. Tex., El Paso, 1970—; field researcher, dir. rsch. cons. numerous projects, Mich., Iowa, Tex., Nigeria, 1955—. Author: Mexican Americans, 1973, Maquila, 1987; sr. co-author: Patterns of Poverty along U.S.-Mexico Border, 1987; sr. editor: Borderlands Sourcebook, 1983 (SW Book award 1984); contbr. chpts. to books and over 100 articles to profl. jours. Scoutmaster troop 158, Boy Scouts Am., El Paso, 1965-68, asst. commr. Yucca coun., 1968-71. With USCG, 1944-46, PTO; 2d lt. arty. U.S. Army, 1952-53. Recipient Diamond Jubilee Disting. Achievement award in rsch. U. Tex., El Paso, 1990; numerous rsch. grants including U. Tex., El Paso, U.S. Army, Econ. Devel. Adminstrn., 1967-86, Tex. Com. for Humanities, 1979, Hoover Instn.-Stanford U., 1984. Mem. Assn. Borderlands Scholars (founder, pres. 1976-79, Outstanding Scholarship and Svc. award 1987), Phi Kappa Phi (chpt. charter, pres. U. Tex. 1982-84). Mem. LDS Ch. Office: U Tex El Paso Dept Sociology El Paso TX 79968-0558

STODDARD, GEORGE EARL, investment company financial executive; b. Perry, Oreg., Jan. 7, 1917; s. G. Earl and Elthira (Thomas) S.; m. Elma Skelton, Feb. 4, 1942; children—Evan, Jean, Robert, Patricia. A.B., Brigham Young U., 1937; M.B.A., Harvard U., 1939; LL.B., Fordham U., 1954. Investment analyst Central Hanover Bank & Trust Co., N.Y.C., 1939-42; v.p. investment ops. Equitable Life Assurance Soc. U.S., N.Y.C., 1945-79; chmn. fin. com. W. P. Carey & Co., N.Y.C., 1979—; also dir. W. P. Carey & Co. Bd. dirs. United Fund of Bronxville-Eastchester, N.Y., 1960-61; pres. Home Sch. Assn., Eastchester, 1962. Served to lt. USNR, 1942-45. Clubs: Harvard (N.Y.C.), Harvard Bus. Sch. (N.Y.C.), Univ. (N.Y.C.). Home: 11 Cedar Pl Eastchester NY 10709-1703 Office: 50 Rockefeller Plz New York NY 10020

STODDARD, LAURENCE RALPH, JR., advertising executive; b. Mt. Kisco, N.Y., Feb. 8, 1936; s. Laurence Ralph and Alice Cary (Martin) S. BA, Colgate U., 1958; postgrad., U. Calif., Berkeley, 1958. Audience research supr. NBC, N.Y.C., 1960-66; audience measurement chief Young & Rubicam, N.Y.C., 1966-69, v.p. supr.-group supr. media planning, 1969-78, v.p dir. communications service, 1978-81, sr. v.p. communication services, group supt. media planning, 1981-86; sr. v.p., dir. media research Advt. Research Found., N.Y.C., 1986—. Served with N.G., 1960. Mem. Advt. Rsch. Found.. (chmn. mag. rsch. devel. com., mem. mag. rsch. coun. and new electronic media rsch. workshop 1994, chmn. single source symposium com.), Am. Advt. Agy. Assn. (media rsch. coun.), Advt. Computer Users Assn. (media rsch. coun.), Advt. Computer Users Assn. (bd. dirs. 1988-93, market rsch. coun. 1993—). Democrat. Episcopalian. Home: 344 W 72nd St Apt 4-E New York NY 10023-2636 Office: Advt Rsch Found 641 Lexington Ave New York NY 10022-4503

STODDARD, ROGER ELIOT, librarian; b. Boston, Dec. 2, 1935; s. Merton Edgar and Helen (Bonney) S.; m. Helen Louise Heckel, May 24, 1958; children—Alison Louise, Christopher Paine. A.B., Brown U., 1957. Asst. curator Harris Coll. Am. Poetry and Plays, Brown U., Providence, R.I., 1961-63, curator, 1963-65; asst. to librarian Harvard U. Houghton Library, Cambridge, Mass., 1958-61, asst. librarian, 1965-69, assoc. librarian, 1969-85; curator rare books Harvard Coll. Library, Cambridge, Mass., 1985—; lectr. English Harvard U., Cambridge, Mass., 1984-86, sr. lectr., 1986—; sec. Friends of Harvard Coll. Library, Cambridge, Mass., 1983—; faculty mem. Columbia U. Rare Book Sch., N.Y.C., 1984-85. Author: Catalogue of Books & Pamphlets Unrecorded in Wegelin's Early Am. Poetry, 1969; The Houghton Library 1942-82, 1982; Poet & Printer in Colonial & Federal America, 1983; The Parkman Dexter Howe Library, part 1: Early New England Books, 1983, Marks in Books, Illustrated and Explained, 1985 (N.E. Book Show award, 1986, Am. Library Assn. award, 1987), Put a Resolute Hart to a Steep Hill: William Gowans Antiquary and Bookseller, 1990; editor A Glance at Private Libraries, 1991; contbr. articles to profl. jours. Mem. Records and Archives Com., Concord, Mass., 1985-87; bd. dirs. Louisa May Alcott Meml. Assn., Concord, 1983—. Huntington Library fellow, San Marino, Calif., 1978; W. F. Milton fellow Harvard U. Med. Sch., Boston, 1978-80; D.W. Bryant fellow Harvard U., 1992. Mem. Bibliog. Soc. Am. (coun. mem. 1982-88), Bibliography of Am. Lit. (supervisory com. chmn. 1982—), Am. Antiquarian Soc. (coun. mem. 1989-93), Assn. Internat. de Bibliophilie, Book Club Calif., Colonial Soc. Mass. (corr. sec. 1993—), The Johnsonians, Bibliog. Soc. London (hon. sec. for Am. 1992—), Bibliog. Soc. Va., Grolier Club (N.Y.C.), Odd Vols. Boston Club (exec. com. 1985-87). Home: 9 Birchwood Ln Lincoln MA 01773-4907 Office: Harvard Univ Houghton Library Harvard Yard Cambridge MA 02138

STODDARD, STEPHEN DAVIDSON, ceramic engineer, former state senator; b. Everett, Wash., Feb. 8, 1925; s. Albert and Mary Louise (Billings) S.; m. JoAnn Elizabeth Burt, June 18, 1949 (div. 1993); children: Dorcas Ann, Stephanie Kay; m. Barbara L. Seitz, Feb. 1995. Student, Tacoma Coll., 1944, Conn. Coll., 1946; B.S., U. Ill., 1950. Asst. prodn. supr., asst. ceramic engr. Coors Porcelain Co., Golden, Colo., 1950-52; ceramics-powder metallurgy sect. leader Los Alamos (N.Mex.) Sci. Lab., U. Calif., 1952-80; pres., treas. Materials Tech. Assocs., Inc., 1978-94; cons. Ceramic Age Mag., 1958-60; Cons. Nuclear Applications for Ceramic Materials, 1958-60; Jury commr. Los Alamos County, 1969; justice of peace, 1956-62; mem. Los Alamos Sch. Adv. Council, 1966; mcpl. judge, 1976-77; chmn. Los Alamos Ordinance Rev. Com., 1958; Mem. Republican County and State Central Com., 1955—; county commr. Los Alamos, N.Mex., 1966-68; mem. Los

Alamos County Planning Commn., 1962-63, N.Mex. Senate, 1981-92; bd. dirs. Mountain Cmty. Bank of Los Alamos (formerly Bank of Los Alamos), Los Alamos Econ. Devel. Corp.; mem. N.Mex. State Commn. on Nat. & Cmty. Svc., 1993—. Patentee in field. Bd. dirs. Sangre de Cristo coun. Girl Scouts U.S.A., 1965-71, N.Mex. chpt. Nature Conservancy, 1987—, v.p., 1993-94; bd. dris. Southwestern Assn. on Indian Affairs, Inc., 1987-91; active Gov.'s Commn. in Nat. & Cmty. Svc., 1993—. With AUS, 1943-46. Decorated Bronze Star, Purple Heart, Combat Infantry Badge; recipient disting. alumni award U. Ill. Coll. Engring., 1986, Leopold Conservation award N.Mex. Nature Conservancy, 1988. Fellow Am. Inst. Chemists, Am. Ceramic Soc. (treas. 1972-74, pres. 1976-77, disting. life 1984); mem. Nat. Inst. Ceramic Engrs. (PACE award 1965, Greaves Walker award 1984), Am. Soc. Metals, Los Alamos C. of C. (Citizen of Yr. award 1992), Masons, Shriners, Elks (dist. dep. grand exalted ruler 1968-69), Kiwanis (pres. 1963-64, lt. gov. 1968-69), Los Alamos Golf Assn. (dir. 1964-66), Am. Legion (nat. legis. coun. 1992—), Sigma Xi, Alpha Tau Omega. Episcopalian. Home: 44 Timber Ridge Rd Los Alamos NM 87544-3528 Office: PO Box 4611 Los Alamos NM 87544-4611

STODDER, JOHN WESLEY, jewelry company executive; b. N.Y.C., 1923. Grad., Coll. Holy Cross, 1945, Harvard U., 1950. Owner Stodder Corp. Fin., Palos Verdes Estates, Calif.; vice chmn., dir. Jostens Inc., Mpls.; bd. dirs. Tally Industries Inc., Palm Beach Co., Trans Leasing Internat. Inc. Office: Jostens Inc 5501 Norman Center Dr Minneapolis MN 55437-1088

STODGHILL, RONALD, school system administrator; b. White Plains, N.Y., Dec. 21, 1939; s. Joseph and Marian (Wynn) Stodghill; children: Kimberly, Denise, Ronald. BS, Ea. Mich. U., 1961; MS, We. Mich. U., 1967; EdD, Wayne State U., 1981. Dir. edn. New Detroit, Detroit; deputy supt. St. Louis Pub. Schs., Mo.; supt. Wellston Pub. Schs., Mo. Mem. ASCD (sec.), Am. Assn. Advancement of Sci., Nat. Assn. Bilingual Edn. Home: 6574 Saint Louis Ave Saint Louis MO 63121-5798 Office: Wellston SD 6574 Saint Louis Ave Saint Louis MO 63121

STOECKER, DAVID THOMAS, banker; b. St. Louis, June 8, 1939; s. John Garth and Marie (Zahler) S.; m. Ann E. Conrad, Aug. 18, 1962; children—Lisa Ann, Susan Jane. B.S, U. Mo. U., 1963. Sr. v.p. comml. loans Mercantile Trust Co. N.Am., St. Louis, 1965-80; pres. Gravois-Merc. Bank, St. Louis, 1980-87; pres., chief exec. officer Bank of South County, St. Louis, 1987—. Served to 1st lt. AUS, 1963-65. Mem. Robert Morris Assos. (pres. St. Louis 1980). Methodist. Club: Sunset Country. Office: 9100 Gravois Rd Saint Louis MO 63123-4560

STOELTING, ROBERT K., anesthesiologist, medical association executive; b. Indpls., 1939. MD, Ind. U., 1964. Diplomate Am. Bd. Anesthesiology. Intern Blodgett Hosp., Grand Rapids, Mich., 1964-65; resident U. Calif., San Francisco, 1965-68; resident anesthesiologist Ind. U. Med. Sch., Indpls., 1968—; pres. Am. Bd. Anesthesiology. Mem. Am. Surg. Assn., Internat. Anesthesia Rsch. Soc. Office: Ind U Med Sch 1120 South Dr Indianapolis IN 46202-5135

STOER, ERIC F., lawyer; b. Pa., 1944. BA, U. Md., 1966, JD, 1969. Bar: Md. 1969, D.C. 1970, U.S. Supreme Ct. 1973, U.S. Ct. Appeals (3d cir.) 1976, U.S. Ct. Appeals (10th cir.) 1979, U.S. Ct. Appeals (6th cir.) 1980. Trial atty. FTC, Washington, 1969-70; ptnr. Bryan Cave, Washington. Mem. ABA (chmn. Robinson-Patman subcom. price discrimination 1973-78, mem. subcom. practice and jurisdiction 1978-80, mem. antitrust sect.), Md. State Bar Assn. Office: Bryan Cave 700 13th St NW Washington DC 20005-3960

STOERMER, EUGENE FILMORE, biologist, educator; b. Webb, Iowa, Mar. 7, 1934; s. Edward Filmore and Agnes Elizabeth (Ekstrand) S.; m. Barbara Purves Ryder, Aug. 13, 1960; children: Eric Filmore, Karla Jean, Peter Emil. BS, Iowa State U., 1959, PhD, 1963. Assoc. rsch. scientist, rsch. scientist U. Mich., Ann Arbor, 1965-79, assoc. prof., 1979-85, prof., 1985—; reviewer Jour. Paeleolimnology; contbr. more than 150 articles to profl. jours. Contbr. over 150 articles to profl. jours. Fellow Acad. Natural Scis., 1980; Darbaker prize, Bot. Soc. of Am., 1993. Mem. Phycological Soc. Am. (pres. 1988-89), Am. Microscopical Soc. (bd. reviewers), Internat. Assn. for Diatom Rsch. (1992-94). Home: 4392 Dexter Ave Ann Arbor MI 48103-1636 Office: U Mich Ctr for Great Lakes Ann Arbor MI 48109

STOFFER, TERRY JAMES, advertising executive; b. Alexander, Iowa, May 28, 1946; s. Jacob John and Almeda Juanita (Roe) S.; m. Linda Rosburg, Apr. 11, 1966 (div. Mar. 1980); m. Catherine S. Jewell, Dec. 28, 1984 (div. Dec. 1990); 1 child, Alan J. BS in Journalism, Iowa State U., 1968, MS in Journalism, 1970. Instr. Iowa State U. Sch. Journalism, Ames, 1969-70; pubis. mgr. Express Communications, West Des Moines, Iowa, 1970-72; sr. v.p. Creswell, Munsell, Fultz and Zirbel, Des Moines, 1972—. Mem. Nat. Adv. Bd. Iowa State U. Sch. Journalism, Ames, 1985-88; bd. dirs. Better Bus. Bur., Des Moines, 1983. Mem. Des Moines Advt. Club (v.p. 1974-75, Cliff DePuy award 1978), Advt. Profls. of Des Moines (pres. 1982-83, Ad Person of Yr. 1980), Am. Advt. Fedn. (nat. standards com. 1984-85). Republican. Methodist. Avocations: literature, cooking. Home: 325 34th St West Des Moines IA 50265-4021 Office: Creswell Munsell Fultz & Zirbel 600 E Court Ave Des Moines IA 50309-2091

STOFFLE, CARLA JOY, dean university library; b. Pueblo, Colo., June 19, 1943; d. Samuel Bernard and Virginia Irene (Berry) Hayden; m. Richard William Stoffle, June 12, 1964; children: Brent William, Kami Ann. AA, So. Colo. State Coll., Pueblo, 1963; BA, U. Colo. 1965; MLS, U. Ky., 1969; postgrad., U. Wis., 1980. Head govt. publ. dept. John G. Crabbe Library, Eastern Ky. U., Richmond, 1969-72; head. pub. services U. Wis.-Parkside Library, Kenosha, 1972-76, exec. asst. to chancellor, 1978, asst. chancellor edn. services, 1979-85; assoc. dir. U. Mich. Library, Ann Arbor, 1985-91, dep. dir., 1986-91; mem. advisor commn. Sch. Library Sci. U. Mich., Ann Arbor, 1986-92; dean librs. U. Ariz., Tucson, 1991—; vol. Peace Corps, Barbados, W.I., 1965-67; with Bowker Libr. Adv. Bd., N.Y., 1985-90. Coauthor: Administration Government Documents Collection, 1974, Materials and Method for History Research, 1979, Materials and Methods for Political Science Research, 1989; assoc. editor Collection Building, 1986-91, editorial bd., 1986-95; mem. editorial bd. The Bottom Line, 1989-95; contbr. numerous articles to profl. jours. Recipient Most Outstanding Quar. Article award Reference Svc. Press, 1986; named Outstanding Alumnus Coll. of Library and Info. Sci., U. Ky., 1989. Mem. ALA (treas. 1988-92, exec. bd. dirs. 1985-92, councilor 1983-92, recipient Miriam Dudley Bibliog. Libr. award 1991), Assn. Coll. Rsch. Librs. (pres. 1982-83, Acad./Rsch. Libr. of Yr. 1992). Home: 6801 N Montezuma Dr Tucson AZ 85718-2431 Office: U Arizona Main Libr Tucson AZ 85721

STOFFT, WILLIAM A., career officer; b. Minn., May 22, 1937; s. William R. and Lorraine (Raddatz) S.; m. Pat Gates, Oct. 19, 1960; children: Bruce, Elizabeth, Pamela. BS History, U. S.D., 1959; MA History, NYU, 1969; grad., Harvard U., 1992. Command, staff assignments U.S. Army, Europe, Vietnam, U.S., 1959-79; dir. Combat Studies Inst., asst. dep. commandant Command and Gen. Staff Coll., Ft. Leavenworth, Kans., 1979-85; chief mil. history office, chief of staff U.S. Army, Washington, 1985-89, dir. mgmt. office, chief of staff, 1989-91; with U.S. Army War Coll., Carlisle Barracks, Pa., 1991-94; chmn. bd. Armed Forces Coop Assn., 1980-85. Editor America's First Battles: 1776-1965. Major gen. U.S. Army, 1991-94. Decorated D.S.M. with oak leaf cluster, Legion of Merit with oak leaf cluster, Bronze Star with V device with two oak leaf clusters. Fellow Inter-Univ. Seminar; mem. Assn. U.S. Army, Coun. on Fgn. Rels., Armor Assn. Protestant. Avocations: fishing, hunting, golf, reading, history. Home: 133 Woodlawn Dr Custer SD 57730

STOGNER, JAMES, airport executive. Dir. ops., safety and maintenance Atlanta City Dept. Aviation; dir. ops. and maintenance William B. Hartsfield Atlanta Internat. Airport. Office: Hartsfield Atlant Internat Airpt Airport Commissioner's Office Atlanta GA 30320

STOHR, DONALD J., federal judge; b. Sedalia, Mo., Mar. 9, 1934; s. Julius Leo and Margaret Elizabeth (McGaw) S.; m. Mary Ann Kuhlman, July 31, 1957 children: Elizabeth M., Anne M., Jane C., Sara M., Ellen R. BS, St. Louis U., 1956, JD, 1958. Bar: Mo. 1958, U.S. Dist. Ct. (ea. dist.) Mo.

1958, U.S. Ct. Appeals (8th cir.) 1966, U.S. Supreme Ct. 1969. Assoc. Hocker Goodwin & MacGreevy, St. Louis, 1958-63, 66-69; asst. counselor St. Louis County, 1963-65, counselor, 1965-66; U.S. atty. Ea. Dist. Mo., St. Louis, 1973-76; ptnr. Thompson & Mitchell, St. Louis, 1969-73, 76-92; judge U.S. Dist. Ct. (ea. dist.) Mo., St. Louis, 1992—. Mem. ABA, Mo. Bar Assn., Am. Judicature Soc., St. Louis Met. Bar Assn. Office: US Court & Custom House Rm 813 1114 Market St Saint Louis MO 63101

STOIBER, CARLTON RAY, government agency official; b. Vallejo, Calif., July 5, 1942; s. Raymond F. and Grace (Fairhurst) S.; m. Susanne Alexander, Sept. 10, 1966. BA summa cum laude, U. Colo., 1964, LLB, 1969; diploma cum laude, Hague Acad. Internat. Law, 1975. Bar: Colo.1969, D.C.1970, U.S. Supreme Ct. 1973. Atty. U.S. Dept. Justice, Washington, 1969-71, dir. Office of Indian Rights, 1972-74; asst. gen. counsel U.S. NRC, Washington, 1975-80, U.S. Arms Control and Disarmament Agy., Washington, 1980-81; dir. Office Nuclear Export Control U.S. Dept. State, Washington, 1981-85, dir. Office Nuclear Non-Proliferation Policy, 1988-91, dir. Office Nuclear Tech. and Safeguards, 1991-93; counselor U.S. Mission to UN Agys., Vienna, Austria, 1985-88; dir. Internat. Programs USNAC, 1993—. Rhodes scholar, 1964, Norlin award for disting. achievement U. Colo., 1994. Mem. Reform Club, Phi Beta Kappa. Avocations: cartooning and caricaturing, mountaineering, birding. Office: US NRC 11555 Rockville Pike Rockville MD 20852

STOICHEFF, BORIS PETER, physicist, educator; b. Bitol, Macedonia, June 1, 1924; s. Peter and Vasilka (Tonna) S.; m. Lillian Joan Ambridge, May 15, 1954; 1 child, Richard Peter. B.A.Sc., U. Toronto, 1947, M.A., 1948, Ph.D., 1950, DSc (hon.), 1994; DSc (hon.), U. Skopje, Macedonia, 1981, York U., 1982, U. Windsor, 1989. McKee-Gilchrist postdoctoral fellow U. Toronto, Ont., Can., 1950-51; postdoctoral fellow NRC Can. 1951-53, sr. research officer, 1954-64; vis. scientist MIT, 1963-64; prof. physics U. Toronto, 1964-89, Univ. prof., 1977-89, Univ. prof. emeritus, 1989—, chmn. engring. sci., 1972-77, H.L. Welsh lectr., 1984; sr. fellow Massey Coll., 1979—; exec. dir. Ont. Laser and Lightwave Rsch. Ctr., 1988-91; mem. NRC Can., 1977-83; govt. appointee to coun. Assn. Profl. Engrs. Ont., 1985-91; vis. sci. Stanford U., 1978; Walter E. Kaskan lectr. SUNY-Binghamton, 1980; Elizabeth Laird Meml. lectr. U. Western Ont., 1985; U.K./Can. Rutherford lectr., 1989; v.p. Internat. Union Pure and Applied Physics, 1994—. Contbr. numerous articles to tech. jours. Decorated officer Order of Can., 1982; I.W. Killam scholar, 1977-79; Geoffrey Frew fellow Australian Acad. Sci., 1980. Fellow Royal Soc. Can. (Henry Marshall Tory medal 1989), Royal Soc. London, Am. Phys. Soc., Optical Soc. Am. (pres. 1976, William F. Meggers award 1981, Frederic Ives medal 1983), Indian Acad. Sci. (hon.), Macedonian Acad. Sci. and Arts (hon.), Am. Acad. Arts and Scis. (fgn. hon.); mem. Can. Assn. Physicists (pres. 1984, gold medal for achievement in physics 1974). Achievements include development of techniques for high resolution Raman spectroscopy of gases and determination of geometrical structures many molecules; use of lasers in spectroscopic investigations including Brillouin and Raman scattering and two photon absorption; observation of stimulated Raman absorption and stimulated Brillouin scattering resulting in generation of intense hypersonic waves in solids; use of Brillouin spectra to measure elastic constants of rare gas crystals; generation of tunable coherent VUV radiation for use in atomic and molecular spectroscopy. Home: 66 Collier St Apt 6B, Toronto, ON Canada M4W 1L9 Office: U Toronto, Dept Physics, Toronto, ON Canada M5S 1A7

STOJANOWSKI, WIKTOR J., mechanical engineer; b. Filipow, Poland, June 3, 1936; arrived in Canada, 1986; s. Stanislaw and Bronislawa (Mentel) S.; m. Danuta A. Wrona, Oct. 19, 1958; children: Dorota, Anna, Robert. MS, Acad. Mining and Metallurgy, 1958, PhD in Mech. Engring., 1973. Chief engr. design Food Industry Equipment Plant, Cracow, Poland, 1958-63; sr. design engr. Chemistry Machine and Process Design, Cracow, 1963-65; tutor Acad. Mining and Metallurgy, Cracow, 1965-80, asst. prof., 1981-87; vis. lectr. U. Wis., Madison, 1980-81; project engr. Vibron Ltd., Mississauga, Ontario, Canada, 1988-90; assoc. J.E. Coulter Assocs. Engring., Willowdale, Ontario, 1991—; noise control expert Assn. Polish Mechanics Engring., Cracow, 1973-87. Co-author: Legacie of AMM #454, 1974; contbr. articles to Jour. Mech. Engring., Inter-Noise. Achievements include patent for noise eliminator of gas stream flow into atmosphere, valve for gas expansion. Home: 1 Markburn Ct, Etobicoke, ON Canada M9C 4Y6

STOKELY, JOAN BARBARA, elementary school educator; b. Cleve., May 6, 1945; d. Paul Warner and Florence Leona (Sorensen) S. BS, Lamar U., 1967, M Elem. Edn., 1974. Cert. tchr., adminstr., Tex. 4th grade tchr. Vidor (Tex.) Ind. Sch. Dist., 1967-74, 88-94, 5th grade tchr. 1974-77, 7th and 8th grade tchr., 1979-88, Apple computer and sci. lab. tchr., 1994—; grad. equivalency diploma tchr. Beaumont Ind. Sch. Dist., Vidor, 1977-81. Pres. Vidor Tchrs. Fed. Credit Union, 1985—; mem. troop com. Boy Scouts Am., Vidor, 1972-83; tchr. Roman Cath. Chs., Beaumont, Tex., 1967-87. Mem. AAUW, DAR, Am. Bus. Women Assn. (Vocat./Woman of Yr. chmn. 1977-78), Tex. State Tchrs. Assn. (pres. Vidor chpt. 1990-94, chmn. univserv adv. coun. region 15 1991-92, sec. region 15, 1993—), Tex. Computer Edn. Assn. Avocations: genealogy, handicrafts, writing, simple computer programs, travel. Office: Oak Forest Elem Sch 2400 Highway 12 Vidor TX 77662-3497

STOKER, THOMAS M., economics educator; b. Elmhurst, Ill., Dec. 29, 1953; s. Jerome Martin Stoker and Mary Jean (Hammersmith) Rybus; m. Deborah Jean Wahl, July 12, 1975; children: Elizabeth, Jonathan. BS in Math., U. Ariz., 1974; MS in Econs., Harvard U., 1978, PhD, 1979. Prof. applied econs. Sloan Sch. Mgmt., MIT, Cambridge, 1979—; vis. rsch. fellow Nuffield Coll., Oxford U., Eng., 1987; vis. prof. U. Bonn (West Germany), 1986-87. Contbr. articles to profl. jours. NSF grantee, 1983-87, 88-90, MIT Ctr. for Energy Policy Rsch. grantee, 1984-85. Mem. Am. Econ. Assn., Am. Statis. Assn., Econometric Soc., Inst. Math. Stats., Phi Beta Kappa, Phi Kappa Phi. Avocations: fishing, woodworking. Office: Sloan Sch Mgmt MIT 50 Memorial Dr # 455 Cambridge MA 02142-1347

STOKER, WARREN CADY, university president; b. Union Springs, N.Y., Jan. 30, 1912; s. Ray W. and Dora Maude (Cady) S.; m. Ruth Eleanor Gabb, Aug. 30, 1934; children: Robert Warren, W. Lance, Lois Ruth. E.E. Rensselaer Poly. Inst., 1933, M.E.E., 1934, Ph.D., 1938. Instr. to asso. prof. elec. engring. Rensselaer Poly. Inst., 1934-51, prof., 1951—, head computer lab., 1952-55; dir. Hartford Grad. Center, 1955-57; dean Hartford Grad. Center (Grad. Center), 1957-70; asso. dean Rensselaer Poly. Inst. Grad Sch., 1957-69; v.p. Rensselaer Poly. Inst. Conn., 1961-74, pres., 1974-75, also trustee; pres. Hartford Grad. Center (formerly Rensselaer Poly. Inst. Conn.), 1975-76, pres. emeritus, 1976—, trustee, 1975—; trustee Mechanics Savs. Bank, Hartford, 1969-82, incorporator, 1969—. Mem. Sci. Research Soc. Am., IEEE, Newcomen Soc. N.Am., Am. Soc. Engring. Edn., Conn. Acad. Sci. and Engring., Sigma Xi, Tau Beta Pi, Eta Kappa Nu. Club: Hartford (Conn.). Home: 4 Neptune Dr Groton CT 06340-5423 Office: 275 Windsor St Hartford CT 06120-2910

STOKES, ARNOLD PAUL, mathematics educator; b. Bismarck, N.D., Jan. 24, 1932; s. Joel Edward and Elizabeth (Bauer) S.; m. Gaye Teresa Wims, Oct. 19, 1957; children: Michael, Jonathan, Thomas, Katherine, Christopher, Peter. Student, St. Martin's Coll., 1949-53; B.S. (RCA scholar), U. Notre Dame, 1955, Ph.D., 1959. Mathematician Research Inst. Advanced Study, Balt., 1958-60; NSF post-doctoral fellow Johns Hopkins U., 1960-61; asst. prof. Cath. U. Am., Washington, 1961-63; asso. prof. Cath. U. Am., 1963-64; prof. Georgetown U., Washington, 1965—; chmn. math. dept. Georgetown U., 1967-70; Cons. NASA, Goddard Space Flight Center, Greenbelt, Md., 1962-67, NRC sr. research asso., 1974-75; sr. mathematician Ocean Sci. div. Sci. Applications, Inc., McLean, Va., 1979—. Trustee Consortium D.C. Univs., 1970-75. Research ordinary, functional differential equations, scattering theory, acoustic tomography. Home: 9916 Derbyshire Ln Bethesda MD 20817-1535 Office: Georgetown U Math Dept Washington DC 20057

STOKES, B. R., transportation consultant; b. Anadarko, Okla., Feb. 20, 1924; s. Robert Allan and Ethel Nan (James) S.; m. Joan Pringle, Oct. 22, 1950; children: Timothy, Leigh, Lindsey, Celia. Student, U. Okla., 1941-44; B.A., U. Calif., Berkeley, 1947. Reporter, writer Oakland (Calif.) Tribune, 1946-58; dir. info. San Francisco Bay Area Rapid Transit Dist., 1958-61, asst. gen. mgr., 1961-63, gen. mgr., 1963-74; exec. v.p. Am. Public Transit

Assn., Washington, 1974-80; sr. v.p. internat. ATE Mgmt. and Service Co., Inc., 1980—; dir. gen. Saudi Arabian Public Transport Co., 1980-81. Served with USNR, 1942-46. Reid Found. fellow, 1954; Recipient Salzberg medal Syracuse U., 1975. Office: 1911 Ft Myer Dr Arlington VA 22209-1603

STOKES, CARL BURTON, ambassador, judge, former mayor, former state legislator; b. Cleve., June 21, 1927; s. Charles and Louise (Stone) S.; m. Shirley Joann Edwards, Jan. 28, 1958 (div. Oct. 1974); children: Carl Burton, Cordi, Cordell; m. Raija Kostadinov, Jan. 3, 1980 (div. 1993); 1 child, Cynthia. B.S. in Law, U. Minn., 1954; LL.B. Cleve. Marshall Law Sch., 1956, also LL.D.; LL.D., Tufts U., U. Cin., St. Francis Coll., Central State U., Wilberforce U., Lincoln U., Union Coll., Livingston Coll., Boston U., Oberlin Coll. Bar: Ohio 1957, N.Y. State bar 1974. Probation officer Cleve. Municipal Ct., 1954-58; presiding and adminstrv. judge Cleve. Mcpl. Ct., 1983-86; asst. prosecutor City Cleve., 1958-62; mayor, 1967-71; mem. Ohio Ho. of Reps., 1962-67; ptnr. Stokes & Stokes, Cleve., 1962-67, Stokes & Character Law Offices, 1980-83, Stokes & Green Law Offices, 1981-83; corr. WNBC, N.Y.C., 1972-80; mem. exec. com. Nat. League Cities, 1968-71, pres. elect, 1970-71; mem. adv. bd. U.S. Conf. Mayors, 1968-71; mem. steering com. Nat. Urban Coalition, 1968—; adv. com. Urban Am., 1969-71; mem. Ohio Ho. of Reps., 1962-67; mem. policy com. Nat. Democratic Com., 1969-71; hon. chmn. 21st Congl. Dist. caucus, 1970-72; amb. to Republic of Seychelles Dept. of State, 1994—; adj. prof. dept. polit. sci. Case Western Reserve U., 1991—. Author: The Quality of Our Environment, Promises of Power, 1973; Contbr. articles to profl. jours. Served with AUS, 1945-46, ETO. Recipient numerous awards including Equal Opportunity award Nat. Urban League; fellow Commn. Phila.; Mass. Com. Protestants, Caths. and Jews; Horatio Alger award; Pacesetter award Young People div. Jewish Community Fedn. Chgo.; Chubb fellow Yale. Mem. Elks, Gamma Eta Gamma, Kappa Alpha Psi. Club: Elks. Office: Box 148 APO AE 09815-2501

STOKES, CHARLES JUNIUS, economist, educator; b. Washington, Aug. 17, 1922; s. Francis Warner and Vivienne E. (Cooke) S.; m. Anne Richardson Wood, June 13, 1946; children—Kevin Barrett, Keith Warner. A.B. with honor and distinction, Boston U., 1943, A.M., 1947, Ph.D., 1950. Mem. faculty Atlantic Union Coll., South Lancaster, Mass., 1946-60, dean coll., 1954-56; Charles A. Dana prof. econs. U. Bridgeport, Conn., 1960-94, univ. prof., 1990-94; chmn. dept. U. Bridgeport, 1960-72; prof. econs. Andrews U., Berrien Springs, Mich., 1990-94; prof. Orientador Inst. Superior de Econ. e Gestão Univ. Tecnica Lisbon, Portugal, 1992—; dir. econ. rsch., region I OPS, 1951-53; dir. Latin Am. case studies Brookings Instn., 1963-64; Fulbright prof., Ecuador, 1958-59, Argentina, 1960, Peru, 1964; lectr. Inter-Am. Def. Coll., 1977-78; Staley Disting. lectr. Andrews U., 1983, founder, dir. Chan Shun Ctr. for Bus. Rsch., 1991-94; E.A. Johnson Disting. lectr., 1989; vis. prof., lectr. U. Colo., U. Conn., Clark U., Andrews U., U.S. Naval Postgrad. Sch., Yale U., Columbia U., So. Conn. State U., Atlantic Union Coll., and numerous overseas univs.; founder, dir. Conn. Small Bus. Devel. Ctr., U. Bridgeport, 1985-90; chmn., dir. Monroe Bank & Trust Co.; cons. to industry, founds. Author: Crecimiento Economico (Economic Growth), 1964, Transportation and Economic Development in Latin America, 1968, Managerial Economics: A Case Book, 1968, Managerial Economics: A Textbook, 1969, Historic Fairfield County Churches, 1969, Urban Housing Market Performance, 1975, Economics for Managers, 1978; editor: THRUST, 1978-89; columnist Christian Sci. Monitor; also articles to profl. jours., columns in regional newspapers. Chmn. Lancaster (Mass.) Housing Authority, 1957-61; chmn. econ. com. Greater Bridgeport Regional Planning Agy., 1961-72; dir. U.S. GAO, 1972-73; mem. Instn. for Social and Policy Studies, Yale U., 1977-85; Trustee Pioneer Valley Acad., 1966-69, Andrews U., 1967-72, Atlantic Union Coll., 1968-73, Conn. Grand Opera Assn., 1980-86; mem. Conn. com. Regional Plan Assn., 1977—; bd. dirs. Greater Bridgeport Symphony Soc., 1978—, Adventist Living Ctrs., Inc., Adventist Health System/North, 1980-85, New England Trade Adjustment Assistance Ctr., Inc.; chmn. bd. dirs., chief exec. officer Geer Meml. Hosp., 1983-89.; Served with AUS, 1943-46; assoc. Kellogg Ctr., U. Notre Dame, 1990—. Decorated Medal of Honor Argentina; named to Collegium of Disting. Alumni Boston U. Coll. Liberal Arts, 1974; Sears Found. Fed. faculty fellow, 1972-73. Fellow New Eng. Bd. High Edn.; mem. Nat. Economists Club, Am. Econ. Assn. (pres. Conn. Valley 1966), Nat. Assn. Bus. Economists (pres. Fairfield County chpt. 1980-81), Phi Beta Kappa, Phi Kappa Phi, Phi Beta Kappa Assos., Delta Sigma Rho, Beta Gamma Sigma. Home: 264 Pepper Crossing Stepney CT 06468 Success is fleeting. If only the good remains from what I have done, even that is not mine but God's.

STOKES, DONALD ELKINTON, political science educator; b. Phila., Apr. 1, 1927; s. Joseph, Jr. and Frances Deborah (Elkinton) S.; m. Sybil Langbaum, May 18, 1955; children—Elizabeth Ann, Susan Carol. A.B., Princeton, 1951; Ph.D., Yale, 1958. Purser Grace Line, Inc., 1946-47; instr. polit. sci. Yale, 1952-54; prof. polit. sci. U. Mich., Ann Arbor, 1958-74; program dir. U. Mich. (Inst. Social Research), 1958-74, chmn. dept. polit. sci., 1970-71; dean U. Mich. (Grad. Sch.), 1971-74, Woodrow Wilson Sch. Pub. and Internat. Affairs Princeton U., N.J., 1974-92; prof. pub. and internat. affairs Princeton U., 1974—; vis. prof. Australian Nat. U., U. W.I. 1969. Co-author: The American Voter, 1960, Elections and the Political Order, 1966, Political Change in Britain, 1969. Assoc. mem. Nuffield Coll. Oxford, 1963-64; Sr. Fulbright scholar to Britain, 1963; fellow Social Sci. Rsch. Coun., 1955-57; fellow Guggenheim Found., 1964-65; vis. rsch. fellow Royal Inst. Internat. Affairs, 1980, Brookings Inst., 1987, 89. Fellow Am. Acad. Arts and Scis., AAAS, Nat. Acad. Pub. Adminstrn.; mem. Am. Polit. Sci. Assn. (Woodrow Wilson award 1970), Coun. Fgn. Rels., Am. Assn. Pub. Opinion Rsch., Phi Beta Kappa. Home: 150 Fitzrandolph Rd Princeton NJ 08540-7224 Office: Princeton Univ Woodrow Wilson Sch Pub & Internat Affairs Princeton NJ 08544

STOKES, DONALD GRESHAM, vehicle company executive; b. London, Mar. 22, 1914; s. Harry Potts and Marie Elizabeth (Yates) S.; m. Laura Elizabeth Courteney Lamb, May 25, 1939 (dec. Apr. 1995); 1 child, Michael Donald. Grad. mech. engring. Harris Inst. Tech., Preston, Eng., 1933; LL.D., U. Lancaster, 1967; Ph.D. in Tech, U. Loughborough, 1968; D.Sci., U. Southampton, 1969, U. Salford, 1971. Student apprentice Leyland Motors Ltd., London, 1930; export mgr. Leyland Motors Ltd., 1946-49, gen. sales and service mgr., 1949-53, dir., 1963-67; mng. dir., dep. chmn. Brit. Leyland Motor Corp. Ltd., 1967, chmn., mng. dir., 1968-73, chmn., chief exec., 1973-75; pres. Brit. Leyland Ltd., 1975-79; chmn. Brit. Arabian Adv. Co. Ltd., 1977-85; pres. Jack Barclay Ltd., 1980-90; Dutton-Forshaw Motor Group Ltd., 1980-90; v.p. Empresa NAcional de Autocamiones S.A., Spain, 1965-73; bd. dirs. KBH Communications Ltd., GWR Group PLC; chmn. Reliant Group, 1990-94, Tow Counties Radio Ltd., 1990-94. Dep. lt. for County Palatine of Lancashire; v.p. Inst. Sci. and Tech., U. Manchester, 1968-72, pres., 1972-75. Lt. col. R.E.M.E., 1939-45. Created knight, 1965, baron (life peer), 1969; decorated Territorial Decoration; officier de l'ordre de la Couronne Belgium; comdr. de l'Ordre de Leopold II. Fellow Inst. Mech. Engrs. (coun.), v.p. 1971, pres. 1972), Inst. Road Transport Engrs., Inst. Civil Engrs.; mem. Nat. Econ. Devel. Com. (chmn. electronics com. 1966-68), Soc. Motor Mfrs. and Traders (coun., pres. 1961-62), Worshipful Company Carmen. Home: Branksome Cliff, Westminster Rd, Poole BH13 6JW, England

STOKES, GALE, history educator; b. Orange, N.J., Sept. 5, 1933; s. Howard Gale and Ida Jane (Bassett) S.; m. Roberta Black, May 5, 1958; children: John Gale, Karen E. BA, Colgate U., 1954; MA, Ind. U., 1965, PhD, 1970. Asst. prof. Rice U., Houston, 1968-75, assoc. prof. 1975-80, prof., 1980—; mem. adv. bd. East Europe program Wilson Ctr., Washington, 1986-89; chmn. Joint Com. on Ea. Europe, N.Y.C., 1984-89. Author: Legitimacy Through Liberalism, 1975, Politics as Development, 1990, From Stalinism to Pluralism, 1991, The Walls Came Tumbling Down: The Collapse of Communism in Eastern Europe, 1993 (Vucinich prize Am. Assn. Advancement of Slavic Studies 1994); mem. editorial bd. Slavic Rev., Problems of Post-Communism; contbr. articles and revs. to profl. publs. Capt. USAF, 1954-63. Grantee Fulbright Found., 1967, 77, 80, Internat. Rsch. Exch. Bd., 1980, Am. Coun. Learned Soc., 1983, Woodrow Wilson Ctr., 1990, Nat. Coun. Soviet Ea. European Rsch., 1990. Mem. Am. Hist. Assn., Am. Assn. Advancement Slavic Studies. Democrat. Home: 3746 Georgetown St Houston TX 77005-2822 Office: Rice University History Dept 6100 S Main Houston TX 77251

STOKES, HENRY ARTHUR, journalist; b. Jacksonville, Fla., Dec. 9, 1944; s. Henry Jasper and Waneta Marian (Lord) S.; m. Carolyn Elizabeth Morley, Aug. 6, 1966; children: Elizabeth, Virginia, Katherine. AA, St. Johns River Jr. Coll., Palatka, Fla., 1966; BS in Journalism with high honors, U. Fla., 1969. Reporter Daytona Beach (Fla.) News-Jour., 1966, Palatka (Fla.) Daily News, 1966-69; reporter Fla. Times-Union, Jacksonville, 1969-71, night city editor, 1972; various editing positions Detroit News, 1972-88; asst. mng. editor Comml. Appeal, Memphis, 1988-92, mng. editor, 1992—. Mem. Memphis Literacy Coun., 1989—, chmn., 1993, 94; bd. dirs. Friends Memphis/Shelby Co. Libr., 1991—; mem. pres.' adv. coun. LeMoyne-Owen Coll., 1992—. Recipient Emig award Coll. Journalism U. Fla., 1970. Mem. AP Mng. Editors Assn., Soc. Profl. Journalists, Investigative Reporters and Editors, The Egyptians, Rotary. Mem. Unitarian-Universalist Ch. Avocations: orinthology, fly fishing. Office: Comml Appeal 495 Union Ave Memphis TN 38103

STOKES, JAMES CHRISTOPHER, lawyer; b. Orange, N.J., Mar. 19, 1944; s. James Christopher and Margaret Mary (Groome) S.; m. Eileen Marie Brosnan, Sept. 7, 1968; children: Erin Margaret, Michael Colin, Courtney Dorothy. AB, Holy Cross Coll., 1966; JD, Boston Coll., 1975. Bar: Hawaii 1975, U.S. Ct. Appeals (1st and 9th cirs.) 1976, Mass. 1977, U.S. Ct. Internat. Trade 1988. Officer USMC, 1966-72; assoc. Carlsmith, Carlsmith, Wichman & Case, Honolulu, 1975-76, Bingham, Dana & Gould, Boston, 1976-82; ptnr. Bingham, Dana & Gould, London, 1980-84, Boston, 1982—. Contbr. articles to profl. jours. Active personnel bd. Town of Wellesley, Mass., 1984-89, chmn. bd., 1988-89, town moderator, 1992—. Capt. USMC, 1966-72, Vietnam. Mem. Hawaii Bar Assn., Mass. Bar Assn., Internat. Bar Assn., Boston Bar Assn., Traveller's Club (London), Union Club (Boston), Wellesley Club, German-Am. Bus. Club (Boston) (bd. dirs.). Roman Catholic. Office: Bingham Dana & Gould 150 Federal St Boston MA 02110-1726

STOKES, JAMES SEWELL, lawyer; b. Englewood, N.J., Jan. 24, 1944; s. James Sewell III and Doris Mackey (Smith) S.; m. Esther Moger, Aug. 19, 1967; children: Jessica Neale, Elizabeth Sewell. BA, Davidson (N.C.) Coll., 1966; LLB, Yale U., 1969. Bar: Ga. 1969. Asst. to gen. counsel Office Gen. Counsel of the Army, Washington, 1969-72; assoc. Alston, Miller & Gaines, Atlanta, 1972-77; ptnr. Alston & Bird (previously Alston, Miller & Gaines), Atlanta, 1977—, lead environ. lawyer, 1978—, chmn. environ. group, 1987—, chmn. client svcs. com., 1983-85, chmn. hiring com., 1986-87, chmn. mktg. com., 1993—, mem. ptnr.'s com., 1995—; speaker on environ. matters to various seminars and meetings; mem. Gov.'s Environ. Adv. Coun., 1991—. Contbr. articles to profl. jours. Co-chmn. Spotlight on Ga. Artists V, 1986; mem. City of Atlanta Zoning Rev. Bd., 1978-85, chmn., 1984-85; bd. dirs. Brookwood Hills Civic Assn., 1975-77, pres., 1977; bd. dirs. Nexus Contemporary Arts Ctr., Atlanta, 1987-92, vice chmn. capital campaign, 1989, chmn. nominating com., 1993, chmn. fundraising com., 1987-88; bd. dirs. Butler St. YMCA N.W. Br., 1973-75, Dynamo Swim Club, 1988-91, Arts Festival Atlanta, 1994—; trustee Inst. Continuing Legal Edn., Athens, 1980-81, Trinity Sch., Atlanta, 1988, Arts Festival Atlanta, 1994—, Charles Loridaus Found., 1994—; mem. session Trinity Presbyn. Ch., 1986-89, clk. of session, 1988-89, chmn. community concerns com., 1987-88, chmn. pers. com., 1989-90, chmn. assoc. pastor search com., 1991-92; bd. dirs. Park Pride, 1992; chmn. environ. affairs com. Ga. C. of C., Bus. Coun. Ga., 1987-92, environ. legal counsel, 1981-87; mem. spl. program Leadership Atlanta, 1979-80, Leadership Ga., 1987; mem. Ga. bd. advisors Trust for Pub. Land, 1990—. Capt. U.S. Army, 1969-72. Decorated D.S.M.; recipient Spl. award Atlanta chpt. AIA, 1988, Mayor Andrew Young, 1985. Mem. ABA (natural resources sect.), State Bar Ga. (chmn. environ. law sect. 1979-82), Atlanta Bar Assn., Ga. Conservation (policy steering com. 1989), Atlanta C. of C. (water resources task force 1982-87, solid waste task force 1989, air quality task force 1993—), Ga. Indsl. Developers Assn. (hazardous waste com. 1983-84), Phi Beta Kappa, Omicron Delta Kappa. Avocations: swimming, bird watching, community activities. Home: 129 Palisades Rd NE Atlanta GA 30309-1532 Office: Alston & Bird One Atlantic Ctr 1201 W Peachtree St NW Atlanta GA 30309-3424

STOKES, JOHN LEMACKS, II, clergyman, university administrator; b. Songdo, Korea, Aug. 23, 1908; s. Marion Boyd and Florence Pauline (Davis) S.; m. Alda Grey Beaman, June 20, 1933; children: John Lemacks III, Mary Anne (foster dau.). A.B., Asbury Coll., 1930; postgrad., Asbury Theol. Sem., 1930-31; M.Div., Duke U., 1932; Ph.D., Yale U., 1936; LL.D., Pfeiffer Coll., 1975. Ordained to ministry Meth. Ch., 1931. Pastor Meth. chs., Randleman, Franklin and Elkin, N.C., 1936-45, Rock Hill, St. John's, S.C., 1945-50; sec. religion higher edn., div. edni. instns. Bd. Edn. Meth. Ch., Nashville, 1950-53; del. jurisdictional conf. Meth. Ch., 1952, 60, 68; pres. Pfeiffer Coll., Misenheimer, N.C., 1953-68; exec. sec. Quadrennial Emphasis, United Meth. Ch., 1968-69; assoc. dir. N.C. Bd. Higher Edn., Raleigh, 1969-71; acting dir. N.C. Bd. Higher Edn., 1972; assoc. v.p. N.C. Assn., Chapel Hill, 1972-75; spl. asst. in acad. affairs U. N.C., 1976-93; dir. numerous out-of-state programs in health professions, 1972-94; mem. Govs. Commn. Citizens for Better Schs. N.C., 1956-60, N.C. Higher Edn. Facilities Edn., 1964-68, N.C. Com. on Drug Abuse, 1970-76, N.C. Com. on Aero. Edn., 1971-86; chmn. N.C. adv. com. Farmers Home Adminstrn., 1967-69, Marine Sci. Coun., 1969-72; dir. N.C. Inst. Undergrad. Curricular Reform, 1972-78; coordinator Fort Bragg-Pope Grad. Program, 1973-77; adv. com. Nat. Four-year Servicemens Opportunity Coll., 1973-78. Contbr. articles to religious publs. Bd. dirs. ARC, 1940-48, YMCA, 1946-50; vice chmn. Western N.C. Conf. Bd. Missions, 1960-64; trustee Asbury Coll., 1945-51. Recipient Outstanding Svc. award N.C. Optometric Assn., 1988, Merit award So. Coun. Optometrists, 1990. Mem. Aircraft Owners and Pilots Assn., U.S. Lawn Tennis Assn., Am. Assn. Higher Edn., So. Srs. Golf Assn., NEA, Nat. Christian Edn. Assn., So. Philos. Soc., Woman's Soc. Christian Service, Junaluska Country Club, Inland Greens Golf Club, Masons, Shriners, Rotary Civitan. Address: PO Box 368 Lake Junaluska NC 28745-0368

STOKES, LOUIS, congressman; b. Cleveland, Ohio, Feb. 23, 1925; s. Charles and Louise (Stone) S.; m. Jeanette Frances, Aug. 21, 1960; children: Shelley, Louis C., Angela, Lorene. Student, Case Western Res. U., 1946-48; JD, Cleve. Marshall Law Sch., 1953; LLD (hon.), Wilberforce U., 1969, Shaw U., Livingstone Coll., Morehouse Coll., Meharry Coll. Medicine. Bar: Ohio 1953. Mem. 91st-104th Congresses from 21st (now 11th) Ohio dist., Washington, D.C., 1969—; ranking minority mem. appropriations subcom. on Vets. Affairs, HUD and Ind. Agys.; guest lectr., 1960—. Mem. adv. council African-Am. Inst. Internat.; mem. exec. com. Cuyahoga County Democratic Party, Ohio State Dem. Party; bd. dirs. Karamu House; trustee Martin Luther King, Jr. Center for Social Change, Forest City Hosp., Cleve. State U. Served with AUS, 1943-46. Recipient numerous awards for civic activities including Distinguished Service award Cleve. br. NAACP; Certificate of Appreciation U.S. Commn. on Civil Rights. Fellow Ohio State Bar Assn.; mem. Am., Cuyahoga County, Cleve. bar assns., Nat. Assn. Def. Lawyers Criminal Cases Fair Housing (dir.), Urban League, Citizens League, John Harlan Law Club, ACLU, Am. Legion, Kappa Alpha Psi. Clubs: Masons (Cleve.), Plus (Cleve.). Office: US Ho of Reps 2365 Rayburn House Bldg Washington DC 20515*

STOKES, MACK (MARION) BOYD, bishop; b. Wonsan, Korea, Dec. 21, 1911; came to U.S., 1929; s. Marion Boyd and Florence Pauline (Davis) S.; m. Ada Rose Yow, June 19, 1942; children: Marion Boyd III, Arch Yow, Elsie Pauline. Student, Seoul Fgn. High Sch., Korea; A.B., Asbury Coll., 1932; B.D., Duke, 1935; postgrad., Boston U. Sch. Theol., 1935-37, Harvard, 1936-37; D.D., Millsaps Coll., 1974. Resident fellow systematic theology Boston U., 1936-38, Bowne fellow in philosophy, 1938-39; ordained to ministry Meth. Ch., deacon, 1938, elder, 1940; vis. prof. philosophy and religion Ill. Wesleyan U., 1940-41; prof. Christian doctrine Candler Sch. Theology, Emory U., 1941-56, assoc. dean, Parker prof. systematic theology, 1956-72, chmn. exec. com. div. of religion of grad. sch., 1956-72; acting dean Candler Sch. Theology, Emory U. (Candler Sch.), 1968-69; faculty mem. Inst. Theol. Studies, Oxford U., 1958; Del. Meth. Ecumenical Conf., 1947, 52, 61, 71, Holston. Gen. confs.; S.E. Jurisdictional Conf., 1956, 60, 64, 68, 72; chmn. com. ministry Gen. Conf. Meth. Ch., 1960; nat. com. Nature Unity We Seek, 1956—; mem. gen. com. ecumenical affairs theol. study com. United Meth. Ch., 1968-72, com. on Cath.-Meth. relations, 1969—, bishop, 1972—. Author: Major Methodist Beliefs, 1956, rev. 15th edit., 1990, also Chinese transl., The Evangelism of Jesus, 1960, The Epic of Revelation,

1961, Our Methodist Heritage, 1963, Crencas Fundamentals Dos Methodistas, 1964, Study Guide on the Teachings of Jesus, 1970, The Bible and Modern Doubt, 1970, Major United Methodist Beliefs, 1971, Korean transl., 1977, rev. 16th edit., 1990, The Holy Spirit and Christian Experience, 1975, Korean transl., 1985, Twelve Dialogues on John's Gospel, 1975; Jesus, The Master-Evangel, 1978, Can God See the Inside of an Apple?, 1979, Questions Asked by United Methodists, Philippine transl., 1980; The Bible in the Wesleyan Heritage, 1981, Respuestas A Preguntas Que Hacen Los Metodistas Unidos, 1983, The Holy Spirit in the Wesleyan Heritage, 1985, Spanish translation, 1992, Korean translation, 1992, Scriptural Holiness for the United Methodist Christian, 1988, Talking with God: A Guide to Prayer, 1989, Theology for Preaching, 1994. Trustee Emory U., Millsaps Coll., Rust Coll., Wood Jr. Coll. Mem. Am. Philos. Assn., Am. Acad. Religion, Metaphys. Soc. Am., Theta Phi (nat. sec.), Pi Gamma Mu. Home: Peachtree House 306 2637 Peachtree Rd NE Atlanta GA 30305 *Faith in God and basic trust in people. Knowing the direction in which to go, and moving toward it with persistence, resourcefulness, imagination and patience.*

STOKES, PATRICK T., brewery company executive; b. Washington; 1942; married. BS, Boston Coll., 1964; MBA, Columbia U., 1966. Fin. analyst Shell Oil Co., 1966-67; v.p. materials acquisitions Anheuser-Busch Cos. Inc., St. Louis, 1979-81, v.p., group exec., 1981—; pres. Anheuser-Busch Inc., St. Louis, 1990—; chief operating officer Campbell Taggart Inc. (subs. Anheuser-Busch Cos. Inc.), Dallas, 1986-90, chief exec. officer, 1990—. Served to 1st lt. U.S. Army, 1967-69. Office: Anheuser-Bush Co Inc 1 Busch Pl Saint Louis MO 63118*

STOKES, PAUL MASON, lawyer; b. Miami Beach, Fla., July 16, 1946; s. Walter Johnson and Juanita (Hemperley) S.; m. Carol Crocker, Sept. 12, 1970; children: Macon Lanford, Walter Ashley, Mary Juanita. BA, Duke U., 1968; JD, U. Chgo., 1971. Bar: Fla. 1971. Law clerk to hon. Milton Pollack U.S. Dist. Ct. (so. dist.) N.Y., N.Y.C., 1971-72; assoc. Smathers and Thompson, Miami, Fla., 1972-77, ptnr., 1977-88; ptnr. Kelley Drye & Warren, Miami, 1988—; adj. prof. law U. Miami, Coral Gables, Fla., 1987—; pub. defender Miami Springs, Fla., 1974, City of Hialeah, Fla., 1974-75. Mem. Code Enforcement Bd. Miami Springs, 1990-92; trustee Trinity Coll., Deerfield, Ill., 1988—. Fellow Am. Coll. Trust and Estate Coun.; mem. Dade County Bar Assn. (probate and guardianship ct. com. 1988—, bd. dirs. 1989-92, 94—), Fla. Bar (cert. wills, trusts and estates). Democrat. Presbyterian. Office: Kelley Drye & Warren 201 S Biscayne Blvd Miami FL 33131

STOKES, ROBERT ALLAN, science research facility executive, physicist; b. Richmond, Ky., June 25, 1942; s. Thomas Allan Stokes and Callie Mae (Ratliff) Watson; m. Elizabeth Ann Efkeman, Nov. 25, 1963 (div. 1992); m. Amy Hawthorne Carney, 1993. BS in Physics, U. Ky., 1964; MA in Physics, Princeton U., 1966, PhD, 1968; Exec. Program, U. Mich. Bus. Sch., 1991. Asst. prof. physics U. Ky., Lexington, 1968-72, assoc. prof. 1972-76; sr. scientist Battelle, Pacific N.W. Labs., Richland, Wash., 1972-74, mgr. space scis. sect., 1974-83, assoc. mgr. geophysics rsch. and engring. dept., 1983-86, mgr. engring. physics dept., 1986-87, mgr. Applied Physics Ctr., 1987-88; dep. dir. rsch. Solar Energy Rsch. Inst., Golden, Colo., 1988-90; dep. dir. NREL, Golden, Colo., 1990—; v.p. Midwest Rsch. Inst., Kansas City, Mo., 1990—; mem. adv. bd. Geophysics Inst., U. Alaska, Fairbanks. Contbr. articles to profl. jours. Woodrow Wilson fellow, Princeton U., 1964, NASA fellow, 1966-68. Mem. Am. Phys. Soc., Am. Astron. Soc., Am. Geophys. Union, AAAS, Am. Solar Energy Soc., Phi Beta Kappa. Home: 24967 Foothills Dr N Golden CO 80401-9170 Office: Nat Renewable Energy Lab 1617 Cole Blvd Golden CO 80401-3305

STOKES, THOMAS EDWARD, librarian; b. Canton, Ohio, Oct. 17, 1942; s. Thomas Edward and Elsie Mae (Groves) S.; m. Barbara Ann Wise, Aug. 19, 1967; children—Andrew Thomas, Ian Philip. B.A., Malone Coll., 1968; M.Div., Emmanuel Sch. Religion, 1974; M.L.S., George Peabody Coll. for Tchrs., 1974. Ordained to ministry Christian Ch., 1969; youth minister Calvary Evang. United Brethren Ch., Canton, 1966-67; resident counselor Malone Coll., Canton, 1967-69; student union mgr. Milligan Coll. (Tenn.), 1969-74; library asst. George Peabody Coll. for Tchrs., Nashville, 1974-75; librarian, mem. faculty Emmanuel Sch. Religion, Johnson City, Tenn., 1975—, asst. prof., 1979-81, assoc. prof. bibliography and research, 1981-89, prof., 1989—; treas. Chaplaincy Endorsement Commn., Christian Chs. and Chs. of Christ, Johnson City, 1976—. Chaplain, Tenn. Army N.G., 1974—; scoutmaster Boy Scouts Am., Johnson City, 1983-87. Served with USNR, 1960-63. Named An Outstanding Young Man of Am., Johnson City Jaycees, 1971. Mem. ALA, Am. Theol. Library Assn., Tenn. Theol. Library Assn. (v.p. pres.-elect 1982-85, pres. 1985-87), Disciples of Christ Hist. Soc. Club: Johnson City Optimist (pres. 1979-80, 81-82, sec.-treas. 1982-83). Office: Emmanuel Sch Religion One Walker Dr Johnson City TN 37601

STOKLOS, RANDY (STOKEY), volleyball player; b. Pacific Palisades, Calif., Dec. 13, 1960; m. Carrie Stoklos. Student, UCLA. Profl. volleyball tour player, 1982—; mem. U.S.A. Nat. Team, 1979-80; pres. Audio Spkrs. of Am.; model, actor. Actor: Side Out, 1990; model mag. covers. Voted AVP Most Valuable Player 1988, 89, 91; named Italian, Brazilian and Australian tour Most Valuable Player, 1991. Mem. Assn. Volleyball Profls. Won Miller Lite Chgo. Open with Brian Lewis, 1993, Nestea Open with Adam Johnson, Manhattan Beach, 1994, San Francisco, 1994; placed 2d FIVB Beach Volleyball World Championships with Sinjin Smith; ranked 1st AVP Career Earnings list and 2d on Career Open Wins; registered 100th career open, 1991, 2d player to reach that mark; won World Championships during 1st yr. on tour, 1982. Office: c/o Assn Volleyball Profls 15260 Ventura Blvd Ste 2250 Sherman Oaks CA 91003*

STOKOE, PHILLIP MICHAEL, physical education educator, school board member; b. Hollywood, Calif., July 8, 1942; s. Robert Russell and Julie Patricia S.; m. Karen Mae Hick, Apr. 2, 1969; children: Christopher Lee, Leslie Ann. BS in Phys. Edn., Zoology, Brigham Young U., 1970; MA in Ednl. Adminstrn., La Verne U., 1977. Phys. edn. tchr., coach Jurupa Unified Sch. Dist., Riverside, Calif., 1970—, dept. chmn., 1975—; football coach Rubidoux High Sch., Jurupa Unified Sch. Dist., Riverside, 1975, 76. Trustee bd. edn. Alvord Unified Sch. Dist., Riverside, 1979—, pres. bd. edn., 1982, 88, 92. With USN, 1963-65, Vietnam. Recipient Dick Bethe award YMCA, North Hollywood, 1963, Svc. award PTA, Riverside, 1981, Master of Boardmanship award Calif. Sch. Bds. Assn., 1988. Mem. NEA, VFW, Nat. Sch. Bds. Assn., Calif. Tchrs. Assn., Calif. Sch. Bd. Del. Assembly, Calif. State Legis. Network, Riverside County Sch. Bds. Assn. (del. dir. 1986—, pres. 1994—). Home: 5444 Peacock Ln Riverside CA 92505-3158

STOKSTAD, MARILYN JANE, art history educator, curator; b. Lansing, Mich., Feb. 16, 1929; d. Olaf Lawrence and Edythe Marian (Gardiner) S. B.A., Carleton Coll., 1950; M.A., Mich. State U., 1953; Ph.D., U. Mich., 1957; postgrad., U. Oslo, 1951-52. Instr. U. Mich., Ann Arbor, 1956-58; mem. faculty U. Kans., Lawrence, 1958—; assoc. prof. U. Kans., 1961-66, prof., 1966-80, Univ. Disting. prof. art history, 1980-94, Judith Harris Murphy disting. prof. art, 1994—, dir. mus. art, 1961-67, research assoc., summers 1965-66, 67, 71, 72; assoc. dean Coll. Liberal Arts and Scis., U. Kans., 1972-76; research curator Nelson-Atkins Mus. Art, Kansas City, Mo., 1969-80, consultative curator medieval art, 1980—; bd. dirs. Internat. Ctr. Medieval Art, 1972-75, 81-84, 88—, v.p., 1990-93, pres., 1993—; cons., evaluator North Cntrl. Assn. Colls. and Univs., 1972—, commr.-at-large, 1984-89. Author: Santiago de Compostela, 1978, The Scottish World, 1981, Medieval Art, 1986. Recipient Disting. Service award Alumni Assn. Carleton Coll., 1983; Fulbright fellow, 1951-52; NEH grantee, 1967-68. Fellow AAUW; mem. AAUP (nat. coun. 1972-75), Archeol. Inst. Am. (pres. Kans. chpt. 1960-61), Midwest Coll. Art Conf. (pres. 1964-65), Coll. Art Assn. (bd. dirs. 1970-80, pres. 1978-80), Soc. Archtl. Historians (chpt. bd. dirs. 1971-73). Home: 4703 Balmoral Dr Lawrence KS 66047-1801

STOKVIS, JACK RAPHAEL, urban planner and developer, government agency administrator; b. Hartford, Conn., Dec. 10, 1944; s. John and Ivette (Korda) S.; m. Evelyn Noether, May 11, 1980. A.B., Union Coll., 1967; postgrad. in bus., Boston U., 1968; M.U.P., NYU, 1973; MPhil, Columbia U., 1995. Lic. planner, N.J. Project planner Jersey City Redevel. Agy., 1970-73; sr. planner City of Jersey City, 1973-75; prin. planner City of Paterson, (N.J.), 1975-76; spl. project mgr. Gt. Falls Hist. Dist., Dept. Community Devel. City of Paterson, N.J., 1976-80; dir. Dept. Planning and

Grants, East Orange, N.J., 1980-81; gen. dep. asst. sec. community planning and devel. HUD, Washington, 1981-88, asst. sec. community planning and devel., 1988-89; pres. Stokvis Assocs., Inc., Haworth, N.J., 1989—; dir. Gt. Falls Devel. Corp., Paterson, 1975-80; project dir. Revitalization of Jersey City Italian Village, 1974-79; lectr. George Washington U., Washington; adj. prof. Rutgers U. New Brunswick, N.J., Columbia U. N.Y.C., 1981—. Author numerous articles in field. Founder Friends of Paterson Parks; v.p. Jersey City Preservation and Restoration Assn. Recipient Outstanding Student of Yr. award Am. Inst. Planning, NYU; recipient Environ. Quality award U.S. Dept. Environ. Protection, N.Y.C., Outstanding Grant Recognition Program award Nat. Endowment Arts, Program Implementation award Am. Planning Assn., Princeton, N.J., Secretary's award, 1989. Mem. Am. Inst. Cert. Planners, Urban Land Inst., Am. Planning Assn., Nat. Trust Hist. Preservation. Office: PO Box 93 Haworth NJ 07641-0093

STOLAR, HENRY SAMUEL, corporate lawyer; b. St. Louis, Oct. 29, 1939; s. William Allen and Pearl Minnette (Schukar) S.; m. Mary Goldstein, Aug. 26, 1962 (dec. Nov. 1987); children: Daniel Bruce, Susan Eileen; m. Suzanne Chapman Jones, June 2, 1989. AB, Washington U., 1960; JD, Harvard U., 1963. Bar: Mo. 1963, U.S. Supreme Ct. 1972. Assoc. then ptnr. Hocker, Goodwin & MacGreevy, St. Louis, 1963-69; v.p., sec., gen. counsel LaBarge Inc., St. Louis, 1969-74; v.p., assoc. gen. counsel then sr. v.p., gen. counsel Maritz Inc., St. Louis, 1974—. Sec., bd. dirs. The New City Sch. Inc., St. Louis, 1968-75; mem. St. Louis Bd. Aldermen, 1969-73; mem. Bd. of Freeholders City and County of St. Louis, 1987-88; v.p., bd. dirs. Ctrl. West End Assn., 1993—; sec., bd. dirs. Forest Park Forever, Inc., 1988—. Mem. ABA, Mo. Bar, Bar Assn. Met. St. Louis, Frontenac Racquet Club, Triple A Club, Phi Beta Kappa. Home: 59 Kingsbury Pl Saint Louis MO 63112-1824 Office: Maritz Inc 1375 N Highway Dr Fenton MO 63099-0002

STOLARIK, M. MARK, history educator; b. St. Martin, Slovak Republic, Apr. 22, 1943; s. Imrich and Margita (Vavro) S.; m. Anne Helene Ivanco, June 15, 1968; children: Roman Andrej, Matthew Mark. BA, U. Ottawa, 1965, MA, 1967; PhD, U. Minn., 1974. Asst. prof. history Cleve. State U., 1972-76; hist. researcher Nat. Mus. of Man., Ottawa, Ont., Can., 1977-78; pres. Balch Inst. for Ethnic Studies, Phila., 1979-91; prof. history, chair dept. Slovak history and culture U. Ottawa, Ont., Can., 1992—; cons. Harvard Ency. Ethnic Groups, Cambridge, Mass., 1976-80; advisor State Hist. Records Bd., Harrisburg, Pa., 1982-91; cons. Ency. Canada's Ethnic Groups, 1991—. Author: film documentary Vianoce-Slovak Christmas, 1978 (2d prize 1979), Slovaks in Bethlehem, Pa., 1985, The Slovak Experience, 1870-1918, 1989. Mem. Pa. adv. com. to U.S. Commn. on Civil Rights, 1985-91. Lehigh U. fellow, 1976. Mem. 1st Cath. Slovak Union, Nat. Slovak Soc., Canadian Slovak League (pres. 1994—). Roman Catholic.

STOLBERG, IRVING J., state legislator, consultant; b. Phila., Sept. 24, 1936; s. Ralph B.; 1 son. Roehr. BA, UCLA, 1958; MA, Boston U., 1964, postgrad., 1964-66; JD (hon.), U. Hartford, 1987. Internat. campus adminstr. Nat. Student Assn., Cambridge, Mass., 1958-59; program dir. Internat. Student Ctr., Cambridge, 1959-60; Midwest dir. World Univ. Service, Chgo., 1960-63; asst. prof. So. Conn. State U., New Haven, 1966-78; mem. Conn. Gen. Assembly, 1971-93; speaker Ho of Reps., 1983-84, 87-88, minority leader, 1985, 86, speaker-at-large, 1989, 90; prin. Internat. Solutions, 1994—; del. numerous internat. disarmament and conflict resolution confs. Del. Dem. Nat. Convs., 1968, 72, 76, 84, 88, 92; founder Conn. Caucus Dems.; chmn. Caucus New Eng. State Legislatures, 1985; mem. bd. overseers Regional lab. for Edn. in New Eng. and the Islands; bd. dirs. Dem. Nat. Com., 1986-89. Named Conn. Caucus Dems. Outstanding Legislator, 1974; recipient Disting. Alumni award Boston U., 1984, Presdl. medal for Community Service, So. Conn. State U., 1987. Mem. Nat. Conf. State Legislators (pres. 1987, pres. Found. 1989), Nat. Assn. Jewish Legislators (pres. 1990-91), Ctr. for Policy Alternatives (bd. dirs., CPA lifetime achievement award), Conn. Tennis Found. (bd. dirs. 1991-94). Home: 50 Roydon Rd New Haven CT 06511-2807

STOLBERG, SHERYL GAY, journalist; b. N.Y.C., Nov. 18, 1961; d. Irving and Marcia Dawn (Papier) S. BA, U. Va., 1983. Reporter Providence Jour. Bulletin, 1983-87, L.A. Times, 1987—. Recipient Unity award Lincoln U., 1987. Office: LA Times Times Mirror Sq Los Angeles CA 90012

STOLGITIS, WILLIAM CHARLES, professional society executive; b. Ware, Mass., Jan. 9, 1941; s. Vincent Charles and Doris (Dansereau) S.; m. Helen Elizabeth Dermody, Apr. 18, 1969. BS, U.S. Naval Acad., 1962; MS, U.S. Naval Postgrad. Sch., 1969; JD, Georgetown U., 1977. Bar: N.J. 1977, D.C. 1977. Commd. ensign USN, 1962, officer, 1962-82; exec. dir. Soc. Tech. Comm., Arlington, Va., 1982—. Mem. ABA, D.C. Bar Assn., N.J. Bar Assn., Am. Soc. Assn. Execs., Am. Legion. Republican. Roman Catholic. Home: 3711 N Military Rd Arlington VA 22207 Office: Society for Tech Comm 901 N Stuart Ste 904 Arlington VA 22203

STOLL, HOWARD LESTER, JR., dermatologist; b. Buffalo, June 13, 1928; s. Howard L. and Margaret (Kahler) S.; m. Jacklyn Fay Straight, June, 1948; children—Shelley, Margaret, Amy, Howard III. A.B., Harvard U., 1948; M.D., U. Pa., 1952. Diplomate Am. Bd. Dermatology. Intern E.J. Meyer Hosp., Buffalo, 1952; resident in dermatology E.J. Meyer Hosp., 1953-55; sr. cancer research surgeon Roswell Park Meml. Inst., Buffalo, 1958-59, assoc. cancer research dermatologist, 1959-67, chief, sect. dermatology, 1984-92; mem. courtesy staff Mercy Hosp., Buffalo, 1958-70; asst. in dermatology E.J. Meyer Meml. Hosp., Buffalo, 1962-72; clin. assoc. prof. dermatology Sch. Medicine, SUNY-Buffalo, 1976-91, clin. prof., 1991—. Served to capt. USArmy, 1955-57. Mem. Am. Acad. Dermatology, Soc. Investigative Dermatology, Buffalo-Rochester Dermatologic Soc. Office: Roswell Park Meml Inst Elm & Carlto Sts 666 Elm St Buffalo NY 14263-0001

STOLL, JOHN ROBERT, lawyer, educator; b. Phila., Nov. 29, 1950; s. Wilhelm Friedrich and Marilyn Jane (Kremser) S.; m. Christine Larson, June 24, 1972; children: Andrew Michael, Michael Robert, Meredith Kirstin, Alison Courtney. BA magna cum laude, Haverford Coll., 1972; JD, Columbia U., 1975. Bar: Ind. 1975, U.S. Dist. Ct. (no. and so. dists.) Ind. 1975, U.S. Ct. Appeals (7th cir.) 1978, U.S. Dist. Ct. (no. dist.) Ill. 1980, (so. dist.) N.Y. 1993, Ill. 1981, N.Y. 1989. Atty. Barnes & Thornburg, South Bend, Ind., 1975-80, Mayer, Brown & Platt, Chgo., 1980—; adj. prof. law Northwestern U., Chgo., 1985—, DePaul U., Chgo. 1987; lectr. in bus. St. Mary's Coll., Notre Dame, Ind., 1977-78. Contbr. articles to profl. jours. Mem. ABA, Ind. State Bar Assn., Am. Bankruptcy Inst., Phi Beta Kappa. Office: Mayer Brown & Platt 190 S La Salle St Chicago IL 60603-3410

STOLL, LOUISE FRANKEL, federal official; b. N.Y.C., June 6, 1939; d. Abraham H. and Ruth C. (Flexo) Frankel; m. Marc H. Monheimer, Dec. 22, 1978; children: Miriam F., Malaika S., Abraham D. BA, MA in Philosophy with honors, U. Chgo., 1961; PhD, U. Calif., Berkeley, 1978. High sch. English tchr. Nairobi, Kenya, 1964-65; transp. berkeley Unified Sch. Dist. 1971-78; mgr. govt. affairs Clear Water Program San Francisco, 1978-80, budget dir. Pub. Utilities Commn., 1980-83; sr. v.p., No. Calif. regional mgr. O'Brien-Kreitzberg and Assoc., Inc., San Francisco, 1985-93; CFO and asst. sec. budget and programs Office of Sec. Dept. Transp., Washington, 1993—; mem. Nat. Legal Affairs Com., Mid. East. Com. Active Anti-Defamation League of B'nai B'rith. Recipient Mayor's Fiscal Adv. award, City of San Francisco, 1984. Jewish. Avocation: bicycle riding. Office: Office of Sec Dept Transp 400 7th St SW Rm 10101 Washington DC 20590

STOLL, NEAL RICHARD, lawyer; b. Phila., Nov. 7, 1948; s. Mervin Stoll and Goldie Louise (Serody) Stoll Wilf; m. Linda G. Seligman, May 25, 1972; children: Meredith Anne, Alexis Blythe. BA in History with distinction, Pa. State U., 1970; JD, Fordham U., 1973. Bar: N.Y. 1974, U.S. Dist. Ct. (ea. dist.) N.Y. 1974, U.S. Ct. Appeals (2d cir.) 1974, U.S.Ct. Appeals (11th cir.) 1982, U.S. Dist. Ct. (ea. dist.) Mich. 1983, U.S. Dist. Ct. (so. dist.) N.Y. 1974, U.S. Supreme Ct. 1986. Assoc. Skadden, Arps, Slate, Meagher & Flom, N.Y.C., 1973-81, mem., 1981—; lectr. Practicing Law-Inst., N.Y.C. Contbr. articles to profl. publs. Author: (with others) Aquisitions Under the Hart Scott Rodino Antitrust Improvements Act, 1980. Mem. Assn. Bar City of New York (mem. trade regulation com. 1983-85), ABA, N.Y. State Bar

Assn. Democrat. Office: Skadden Arps Slate 919 3rd Ave New York NY 10022-3903

STOLL, RICHARD EDMUND, retired manufacturing executive; b. Dayton, Ohio, Aug. 5, 1927; s. George Elmer and Mary Francis (Zimmerle) S.; m. Vera Mae Cohagen, Sept. 2, 1950; children: Richard Edmund, Linda Ann, Donna Gail. Student in mech. engring., MIT, 1945-47; MetE. Ohio State U., 1950. Registered profl. engr. Ill., Tex. Various staff and operating positions U.S. Steel Corp., Pitts., Chgo., Houston, 1952-78; gen. mgr. metall. services U.S. Steel Corp., Pitts., 1978-84, dir. quality mgmt. program and tech., 1984-85; corp. chief metallurgist Wheeling-Pitts. Steel Corp., Wheeling, W.Va., 1985-86, v.p., gen. mgr. flat rolled steel, 1986-87, v.p., gen. mgr., interim chief ops. officer, 1987-89, exec. v.p., 1989-91, ret., 1991; cons. McElrath & Assocs., Mpls., 1984. Contbr. articles to profl. jours.; patentee in field. Served with C.E., U.S. Army, 1950-52. Fellow Am. Soc. Metals (chmn. 1963); mem. Am. Iron and Steel Inst., Am. Inst. Mining and Metallurgy (Nat. Open Hearth award 1957, bd. dirs. 1961-68), Am. Inst. Steel Engrs., Am. Soc. Metals, Dolphin Head Golf Club. Republican. Roman Catholic. Avocation: golf. Home: 3 Kinglet Lagoon Rd Hilton Head Island SC 29926-2548

STOLL, RICHARD G(ILES), lawyer; b. Phila., Oct. 2, 1946; s. Richard Giles and Mary Margaret (Zeigler) S.; m. Susan Jane Nicewonger, June 15, 1968; children: Richard Giles III, Christian Hayes. BA magna cum laude, Westminster Coll., 1968; JD, Georgetown U., 1971. Bar: D.C. 1971, U.S. Dist. Ct. D.C. 1971, U.S. Ct. Appeals D.C. 1971, U.S. Ct. Appeals (4th cir.) 1977. Assoc. Arent, Fox, Kintner, Plotkin & Kahn, Washington, 1971-73; atty. Office of Gen. Counsel EPA, Washington, 1973-77, asst. gen. counsel, 1977-81; dep. gen. counsel Chem. Mfrs. Assn., Washington, 1981-84; ptnr. Freedman, Levy, Kroll & Simonds, Washington, 1984—; instr. environ. law and policy U. Va., Charlottesville, 1981-90. Author: Handbook on Environmental Law, 1987, 88, 89, 91, Practical Guide to Environment Law, 1987; contbr. articles to profl. jours. Served to capt. USAR, 1968-76. Mem. ABA (sect. natural resources, energy and environ. law; chmn. water quality com. 1980-82, hazardous waste com. 1983-85, coun. mem. 1985-88, sect. chmn. 1990-91). Avocations: piano, golf. Office: Freedman Levy Kroll & Simonds 1050 Connecticut Ave NW Ste 82 Washington DC 20036-5303

STOLL, ROBERT W., principal. Prin. Harrison (Ohio) Elem. Sch. Recipient Elem. Sch. Recognition award U.S. Dept. Edn., 1989-90. Office: Harrison Elem Sch 600 E Broadway St Harrison OH 45030-1323

STOLL, ROGER G., health insurance company executive; b. 1942. BS, Ferris State Coll., 1965; PhD in Bio-Pharmacetics, U. Conn., 1970. With Upjohn Co., Kalamazoo, Mich., 1970-76, Am. Critical Care divsn., Baxter Internat. Inc., Deerfield, Ill., 1976-86; exec. v.p., gen. mgr. Diagnostics Bus. Group, Miles, Inc., Pitts., 1986-91; pres. Ohmeda, Liberty Corner, N.J., 1991—. Office: Ohmeda 110 Allen Rd Liberty Corner NJ 07938

STOLL, WILHELM, mathematics educator; b. Freiburg, Germany, Dec. 22, 1923; came to U.S., 1960; s. Heinrich and Doris (Eberle) S.; m. Marilyn Jane Kremser, June 11, 1955; children: Robert, Dieter, Elisabeth, Rebecca. Ph.D. in Math, U. Tübingen, Fed. Republic Germany, 1953, habilitation, 1954. Asst. U. Tübingen, 1953-59, dozent, 1954-60, ausserplanmässiger prof., 1960; vis. lectr. U. Pa., 1954-55; temp. mem. Inst. Advanced Study, Princeton, 1957-59; prof. math. U. Notre Dame, 1960-88, Vincent J. Duncan and Annamarie Micus Duncan prof. math., 1988-94, prof. emeritus, 1994—, chmn. dept., 1966-68, co-dir. Ctr. for Applied Math., 1992; vis. prof. Stanford U., 1968-69, Tulane U., 1973, U. Sci. and Tech., Hefei, Anhui, People's Republic of China, summer, 1986; adviser Clark Sch., South Bend, Ind., 1963-68; Japan Soc. Promotion Sci. fellow, vis. prof. Kyoto U., summer 1983. Publs. in field. Research complex analysis several variables. Home: 54763 Merrifield Dr Mishawaka IN 46545-1519 Office: U Notre Dame Dept Math Notre Dame IN 46556

STOLLER, CLAUDE, architect; b. N.Y.C., Dec. 2, 1921; s. Max and Esther (Zisblatt) S.; m. Anna Maria Oldenburg, June 5, 1946 (div. Oct. 1972); children: Jacob, Dorothea, Elizabeth; m. Rosemary Raymond Lax, Sept. 22, 1978. Student, Black Mountain Coll., N.C., 1942; M.Arch., Harvard U., 1949. Architect Architects Collaborative, Cambridge, Mass., after 1949, Shepley, Bulfinch, Richardson & Abbot, Boston, 1951; co-founder, partner firm Marquis & Stoller, San Francisco, 1956; pvt. practice architecture N.Y.C. and San Francisco, 1974-78; founder, partner Stoller/Partners, Berkeley, Calif., 1978, Stoller, Knoerrr Architects, 1988—; mem. faculty Washington U., St. Louis, 1955-56, U. Calif., Berkeley, 1957-91, prof. architecture, 1968—, acting chmn. dept., 1965-66, chair grad. studies, 1984-91; mem. Berkeley Campus Design Rev. Bd., 1985-91, chmn., 1992-93; commr. Calif. Bd. Archtl. Examiners, 1980-90, mem. exam. com., 1985-88; mem. diocesan commn. architecture Episcopal Diocese Calif., 1961—; vis. architect Nat. Design Inst., Ahmedabad, India, 1963; planning commr. City of Mill Valley, 1966-67; mem. pub. adv. panel archtl. services GSA, 1969-71; citizens urban design adv. com. City of Oakland, Calif., 1968; vis. com. nat. archtl. accrediting bd. U. Minn. and U. Wis., Milw., 1971; council Harvard Grad. Sch. Design Assn., 1976—; mem. design rev. com. The Sea Ranch, Calif., 1990—. Prin. works include St. Francis Sq. Coop. Apts., San Francisco, 1961, Pub. Housing for Elderly, San Francisco, 1974, Learning Resources Bldg, U. Calif., Santa Barbara, 1975, Menorah Park Housing for Elderly, San Francisco, 1979, San Jose State U. Student Housing Project, 1984, Delta Airlines Terminal, San Francisco Internat. Airport, 1988. Served with AUS, 1943-46. Recipient numerous awards including AIA Honor awards, 1963, 64, AIA Bay Region Honor award, 1974, Concrete Reinforced Steel Inst. award, 1976, AIA award, 1976, CADA Site I Solar Housing award Sacramento, Calif., 1980, State of Calif. Affordable Housing award, 1981, PG&E Suntherm award, 1981, San Francisco Housing Authority award, 1983, Orchid award City of Oakland, 1989, Citation for achievement and svc. U. Calif. Berkeley, 1991. Fellow AIA. Home: 2816 Derby St Berkeley CA 94705-1325 Office: Stoller Knoerr Architects 1818 Harmon St Berkeley CA 94703-2472

STOLLER, ERIC CHESTER, stockbroker; b. Balt., Oct. 29, 1943; s. Philip and Mollie (Estner) S.; m. Phyllis Sue Rosenstein, July 23, 1967; children: Nicholas, Matthew. BBA, U. Miami, 1964; JD, Harvard U., 1967. Bar: N.Y., Fla. Tax atty. Exxon Corp., N.Y.C., 1967-70; mng. dir. Fin. Assurance Co. Ltd. London, 1970-81; first v.p. sales Prudential Securities, Miami, Fla., 1981—. Active community bd. and investment com. New World Symphony; founder, donor Children's Home Soc. Mem. Harvard Club of Miami (bd. dirs., treas. 1988—), Miami Film Soc. (bd. sponsors), Greater Miami C. of C., Rotary Club Miami. Avocations: hiking, tennis, travel, photography, reading. Home: 8180 Erwin Rd Miami FL 33143-6208 Office: Prudential Securities Inc 1st Union Ctr 200 S Biscayne Blvd Ste 3200 Miami FL 33131-2310

STOLLER, EZRA, photojournalist; b. Chgo., May 16, 1915; s. Max and Esther (Zistblatt) S.; m. Helen Rubin, Sept. 23, 1938; children: Erica, Evan, Lincoln. B.F.A., NYU, 1938. Guest lectr. U. Okla., U. Kans., U. Notre Dame, 1971, Ga. Inst. Tech., U. Wis. Med. Sch., U. State U., 1972, Columbia Coll., 1974, 76, U. N.C., Smithsonian Instn., Harvard U., 1984-86, Harvard Grad. Sch. Design, 1985, 86, 88, U. Ariz., 1985, U. Pa., 1987, U. Orange Free State, 1995, Nat. Inst. Archtl. Edn., 1995. Exhbns. include, Max Protetch Gallery, N.Y.C., 1980, Bonafant Gallery, San Francisco, 1981, Bannenford Books, Toronto, 1981, Mpls. Art Inst., 1981, Nat. Gallery Johannesburg, 1983, Harvard GSD, 1991; author: Modern Architecture Photographs By Ezra Stoller, 1990. Recipient 1st medal for archtl. photography AIA, 1960. Mem. AIA (hon.), Am. Soc. Mag. Photographers (past pres., lifetime achievement award 1982), Archtl. League N.Y. (Gold medal 1955). Home: Kirby Ln N Rye NY 10580

STOLLER, MITCHELL R., non-profit organization administrator; b. Washington, Aug. 1, 1953; s. Sidney and Goldie (Berman) S.; m. Sheri Ann Stutsky, June 15, 1980; children: Betsy, Lauren. BS, Frostburg State Coll., 1975; postgrad., George Washington U., 1983. Tchr. Charles County Bd. Edn., Waldorf, Md., 1976-81; dir. devel. Ctrl. Md. chpt. Easter Seal Soc. Balt., 1981-83, March of Dimes Birth Defects Found., Balt., 1983-86; nat. dir. spl. projects and field ops. Retinitis Pigmentosa Found., Balt., 1986-88; exec. dir. Sudden Infant Death Syndrome Assn., Landover, md., 1988-91;

exec. v.p., COO Sudden Infant Death Syndrome Alliance, Columbia, md.; 1991-93; pres., CEO Am. Paralysis Assn., Springfield, N.J., 1993—; bd. dirs. Bd. dirs. C.J. Found. for Sudden Infant Death Syndrome Alliance, Hackensack, N.J., 1994; fundraiser Warren (N.J.) Synagogue, 1993—. Mem. Am. Soc. Assn. Execs. Avocations: golf, basketball league, coach children's soccer. Home: 11 Surrey Ln Basking Ridge NJ 07920 Office: Am Paralysis Assn 500 Morris Ave Springfield NJ 07081

STOLLERMAN, GENE HOWARD, physician, educator; b. N.Y.C., Dec. 6, 1920; s. Maurice William and Sarah Dorothy (Mezz) S.; m. Corynne Miller, Jan. 21, 1945; children: Lee Denise Stollerman Meyburg, Anne Barbara Stollerman DiZio, John Eliot. AB summa cum laude, Dartmouth Coll., 1941; MD, Columbia U., 1944. Diplomate Am. Bd. Internal Medicine. Clin. tng. Mt. Sinai Hosp. N.Y.C, 1944-46; chief med. resident Mt. Sinai Hosp., 1948; Dazian research fellow microbiology NYU Med. Sch., 1949-50, mem. dept. medicine, 1951-55; med. dir. Irvington House for Cardiac Children, 1951-55; prin. investigator Sackett Found. Research in Rheumatic Diseases, 1955-64; asst. prof. medicine Northwestern U., 1955-57, assoc. prof., 1957-61, prof. medicine, 1961-65; prof., chmn. dept. medicine U. Tenn., 1965-81, Goodman prof., 1977-81; physician-in-chief City of Memphis Hosps., 1965-81; prof. medicine Boston U. Sch. Medicine, 1981—, prof. pub. health, 1991—; chief sect. gen. internal medicine Univ. Hosp., Boston U. Med. Ctr., 1983-86; Disting. physician VA Med. Ctr., Bedford, Mass., 1986-89; assoc. chief of staff Geriatrics and Extended Care, 1989-92; clin. dir. Bedford div. Geriatric Rsch., Ednl. and Clin. Ctr., 1989-92; dir. VA Health & Human Svcs. Field Program, 1990-93; chmn. research career program com. NIAMD-NIH, 1967-70; mem. commn. streptococcal and staphylococcal diseases U.S. Armed Forces Epidemiol. Bd., 1956-74; adv. bd. immunization practices Center for Disease Control, 1968-71; expert adv. panel cardiovascular disease WHO, 1966—; mem. Am. Bd. Internal Medicine, 1967-73, chmn. cert. exam. com., 1969-73, mem. exec. com., 1971-73; chmn. Panel on Bacterial Vaccines, FDA, 1973-80; mem. nat. adv. council Nat. Inst. Allergy and Infectious Diseases, NIH, 1978-82; mem. Dept. Health & Human Services nat. vaccine adv. com.; Contbr. chpts. to Braunwald's Textbook of Cardiology, Harrison's Textbook of Medicine, Cecil & Lobe Textbook of Medicine, others, also articles to profl. jours.; editor-in-chief Advances in Internal Medicine, 1968-93, Jour. Am. Geriatric Soc., 1984-88; co-editor Hosp. Practice. Served as capt. M.C., AUS, 1946-48. Recipient Disting. Alumnus award Mt. Sinai Hosp., 1989, Thewlis award Am. Geriatric Soc., 1990, Bicentennial award in internal medicine Columbia U., 1977. Fellow ACP (master 1976, bd. regents 1978, v.p. 1984, Bruce medal for preventive medicine 1985); mem. Am. Heart Assn. (mem. exec. com., pres. council on rheumatic fever and congenital ACP disease 1965-67), Am. Fedn. Clin. Research, Am. Rheumatism Assn., Am., So. socs. clin. investigation, Central Soc. Clin. Research (v.p. 1973-74, pres. 1974-75), Assn. Profs. Medicine (pres. 1975—), Am. Assn. Immunologists, Assn. Am. Physicians, Infectious Disease Soc. Am. (council 1968-70), Phi Beta Kappa, Alpha Omega Alpha. Office: Sect Gen Int Med 1108 Boston U Med Ctr 720 Harrison Ave Boston MA 02118

STOLLERY, ROBERT, construction company executive; b. Edmonton, Alta., Can., May 1, 1924; s. Willie Charles and Kate (Catlin) S.; m. Shirley Jean Hopper, June 11, 1947; children: Carol, Janet, Douglas. B.Sc. Eng., U. Alta., 1949, LL.D. (hon.), 1985; hon. LL.D., Concordia U., Montreal, Que., 1986. Field engr. Poole Constrn. Ltd., Edmonton, 1949-54, project mgr., 1954-64, v.p., 1964-69, pres., 1969-81; chmn. bd. PCL Constrn. Group Inc., Edmonton, 1979-93; chmn. PCL Constrn. HOldings, Edmonton, 1993—; bd. dirs. TransCanada Pipelines, Fed. Industries Ltd., Winnipeg, Man., Toronto Dominion Bank. Chmn. bus. adv. coun. U. Alta., gov. of trustees; chmn. Edmonton Community Found. Recipient Exec. of Yr. award Inst. Cert. Mgmt. Cons. of Alta., 1988, Can. Businessman of Yr. award U. Alta., 1993. Fellow Can. Acad. Engring.; mem. Assn. Profl. Engrs. (Frank Spragins Meml. award 1981), Engring. Inst. Can. (Julian C. Smith medal 1990), Conf. Bd. Can. (vice chmn. 1980-82), Constrn. Assn. Edmonton (pres. 1972, Claude Alston Meml. award), Can. Constrn. Assn. (v.p. 1970, Can. Businessman of the Yr. award 1993). Conservative. Mem. United Ch. of Canada. Club: Mayfair Golf and Country (Edmonton). Office: PCL Construction Group Inc, 5410 99 St, Edmonton, AB Canada T6E 3P4

STOLLEY, ALEXANDER, advertising executive; b. Coethen Anhalt, Germany, May 12, 1922; came to U.S., 1923, naturalized, 1929; s. Mihail and Tatiana (Rainich) Stolarevsky; m. Patricia Martin, June 26, 1944 (dec. Aug. 1970); children: Christopher, Peter, Laura Stolley Smith, Annabel Stolley Hetzer, Megan Stolley Berry; m. Bette Scott Vogt, June 15, 1973. M.E., U. Cin., 1948. With Cin. Milacron, Inc., 1941-50, dir. employee relations, 1948-50, with Northlich, Stolley, Inc., Cin., 1950-89, exec. v.p., 1959-67, pres., 1967-84; chmn. Northlich, Stolley, LaWarre, Inc. (formerly Northlich, Stolley, Inc.), Cin., 1984-89. Mem. exec. com. Cincinnatus Assn., 1968-73, sec., 1970-71, v.p., 1971-72, pres., 1972-73; mem. Cin. Council on World Affairs, 1969—; chmn. Contemporary Arts Center, Cin., 1966-67; mem. exec. com. Cin. Conv. and Visitors Bur., 1975, chmn. long range planning com., 1983; trustee Cin. Symphony Orch., 1969-75. Served to 1st lt. AUS, 1943-46. Mem. Bus., Profl. Advt. Assn., Greater Cin. C. of C. (exec. com. 1982-83). Clubs: Cincinnati Country, Cincinnati Tennis, University, Gyro., Literary, Gasparilla Beach, Lemon Bay Golf, Boca Bay Pass. Home: 2363 Bedford Ave Cincinnati OH 45208-2656 Home (winter): PO Box 1339 Boca Grande FL 33921-1339

STOLLEY, JAMES S., manufacturing executive; b. Peoria, Ill., Oct. 3, 1928; s. George Brockway and Stella (Sherman) S.; m. Margaret Moynahan, Feb. 14, 1953; children: Karen Stolley Drucker, James Jr., Elizabeth. BSME, MIT, 1952. With Procter & Gamble Co., Cin., 1952-55; engr., asst. supt. Beckett Paper Co., Hamilton, Ohio, 1955-62; with Hammermill Paper Co., Erie, Pa., 1963-80, sr. v.p., 1980—; bd. dirs. Gen. Telephone Co. of Ind. Corporator, trustee Hamot Med. Ctr., Erie; corporator St. Vincent Health Ctr., Erie; trustee Villa Maria Coll., Erie. With USN, 1946-48. Mem. Pa. C. of C. (bd. dirs.), Pa. Council on Econ. Edn. (bd. dirs.). Home: 4711 Wolf Rd Erie PA 16505-1335 Office: Hammermill Paper Co E Lake Rd PO Box 16533 Erie PA 16504

STOLLEY, PAUL DAVID, medical educator, researcher; b. Pawling, N.Y., June 17, 1937; s. Herman and Rosalie (Chertock) S.; m. Jo Ann Goldenberg, June 13, 1959; children: Jonathan, Dorie, Anna. B.A., Lafayette Coll., 1957; M.D., Cornell U., 1962; M.P.H, Johns Hopkins U., 1968; M.A. hon., U. Pa., 1976. Diplomate: Am. Coll. Preventive Medicine, Am. Coll. Epidemiology. Intern U. Wis. Med. Ctr., 1962-63, resident in medicine, 1963-64; med. officer USPHS, Washington, 1964-67; asst. prof. Johns Hopkins Sch. Pub. Health, Balt., 1968-71, assoc. prof., 1971-76; Herbert C. Rorer prof. medicine U. Pa. Sch. Medicine, Phila., 1976-91; prof. and chmn. dept. epidemiology U. Md. Sch. Medicine, Balt., 1991—. Co-author: Foundations of Epidemiology, 3d edit., 1994, Epidemiology: Investigating Disease, 1995; contbg. author: Case-Control Studies, 1982; mem. editl. bd. New Eng. Jour. Medicine, 1989-93, Milbank Quar., Health and Soc., 1986—; assoc. editor Clin. Pharmacology and Therapeutics, 1987-93; contbr. articles to med. jours. Mem. Physicians for Social Responsibility, 1961—. Served to lt. comdr. USPHS, 1964-67. Fellow ACP; mem. Am. Coll. Epidemiology (pres. 1987-89), Inst. Medicine of NAS, Soc. Epidemiol. Rsch. (pres. 1982-84), Am. Epidemiol. Soc. (pres. 1994—), Internat. Epidemiol. Assn. (treas. 1982-84) Johns Hopkins Soc. Schoalrs. Home: 6424 Brass Knob Columbia MD 21044-4019 Office: Univ of Md Sch Medicine 660 W Redwood St Baltimore MD 21201-1596

STOLLEY, RICHARD BROCKWAY, journalist; b. Peoria, Ill., Oct. 3, 1928; s. George Brockway and Stella (Sherman) S.; m. Anne Elizabeth Shawber, Oct. 2, 1954 (div. 1981); children—Lisa Anne, Susan Hope, Melinda Ruth, Martha Brockway. B.S. in Journalism, Northwestern U., 1952, M.S., 1953; LL.D. (hon.), Villa Maria Coll., 1976. Sports editor Pekin (Ill.) Daily Times, 1944-46; reporter Chgo. Sun-Times, 1953; mem. staff weekly Life mag., 1953-73; bur. chief weekly Life mag., Los Angeles, 1961-64, Washington, 1964-68; sr. editor weekly Life mag., Europe, 1968-70; asst. mng. editor weekly Life mag., N.Y.C., 1971-73; mng. editor monthly Life mag., N.Y.C., 1982-86; founding mng. editor People mag., N.Y.C., 1974-82, Picture Week mag., N.Y.C., 1985-86; dir. spl. projects Time Inc., N.Y.C. 1987-89; editorial dir. Time Inc. Time Warner Inc., N.Y.C., 1989-93, sr. editorial advisor, 1993—. Introd. to Leigh A. Wiener, Marilyn: A Hollywood Farewell: The Death and Funeral of Marilyn Monroe, 1990; editor

People Celebrates People: The Best of 20 Unforgettable Years, 1994. Bd. dirs. Dirksen Congl. Rsch. Ctr., Pekin, Ill.; chmn. Twins Found., Providence; bd. govs. Nat. Parkinson Found., Miami, Fla.; pres. Child Care Action Campaign, N.Y.C.; bd. trustees N.Y.C. Citizens Crime Commn. With USN, 1946-48. Recipient Alumni merit award Northwestern U., 1977, Alumni medal Northwestern U., 1994. Mem. Am. Soc. Mag. Editors (pres. 1982-84), Nat. Press Club, Overseas Press Club, Century Assn., Kappa Tau Alpha, Sigma Delta Chi.

STOLLMAN, ISRAEL, city planner; b. N.Y.C., Mar. 15, 1923; s. Philip and Yetta (Strelchik) S.; m. Mary Florence Callahan, Dec. 27, 1953; children—Susan Elisabeth, Katharine Rachel, Sarah Ellen. B.S. in Social Sci, CCNY, 1947; M. City Planning, MIT, 1948. Planner Cleve. Planning Commn., 1948-51; planning dir. Youngstown, Ohio, 1951-57; prof., chmn. div. city and regional planning Ohio State U., 1957-68; exec. dir. Am. Soc. Planning Ofcls., 1968-92. Am. Planning Assn., Washington, 1978-93, cons., 1994—; lectr. Western Res. U., 1949-51, U. Chgo., 1968-69, U. Va., 1994—; pres. Assn. Collegiate Sch. Planning, 1966-67; chmn. Charles E. Merriam Center Pub. Adminstrn., 1977-93. Trustee Alfred Bettman Found.; bd. govs. Met. Housing and Planning Council Chgo., v.p., 1969-79. Served with USAAF, 1943-45. Mem. Am. Inst. Cert. Planners (exec. dir.), Internat. Fedn. Housing and Planning (bur. mem.). Avocation: stereoscopy. Home and Office: 1708 Swann St NW Washington DC 20009-5535

STOLLSTEIMER, JOHN F., food company executive; b. 1932; married. With J.I. Case Co., U.S. Dept. Agr., 1953-61; with econ. research, commodity trading, refinery ops. depts. Beatrice Grocery Group Inc. (subs. Beatrice Cos. Inc.), Fullerton, Calif., from 1962—, v.p. ops. planning logistics distbn., 1969; now exec. v.p. Beatrice/Hunt-Wesson Foods (subs. Beatrice Foods Cos. Inc.), Fullerton; formerly prof. agrl. econs. N.C. State Coll. Office: Beatrice/Hunt-Wesson Foods 1645 W Valencia Dr Fullerton CA 92633-3860

STOLNITZ, GEORGE JOSEPH, economist, educator, demographer; b. N.Y.C., Apr. 4, 1920; s. Isidore and Julia (Jurman) S.; m. Monique Jeanne Delley, Aug. 26, 1976; children: Cindy, Wendy, Dia. BA, CCNY, 1939; MA, Princeton U., 1942, PhD, 1952. Statistician U.S. Bur. Census, 1940-41; rsch. assoc. Princeton U. Office of Population Rsch., 1948-56; asst. prof. Princeton U., 1953-56; vis. rsch. scholar Resources for the Future, 1965-67; prof. econs. Ind. U., Bloomington, 1956-90, prof. emeritus, 1990—; dir. Ind. U. Internat. Devel. Rsch. Ctr., Bloomington, 1967-72, Ind. U. Population Inst. for Rsch. and Tng., Bloomington, 1986-91; prin. officer Population and Econ. Devel. UN, N.Y.C., 1976-78; cons. Ford Found., U.S. Congress, Rockefeller Found., UN, U.S. Dept. Commerce, U.S. Dept. Energy, U.S. Dept. HHS, U.S. Dept. State; vis. scholar Population Reference Bur., 1987-88. Author books; contbr. numerous articles in population and devel. fields, testimonies on pub. utility costs of capital. Capt. USAF, 1942-46. Nat. Sci. Found. fellow, 1959-60. Mem. Population Assn. Am. (pres. 1983), Am. Econ. Assn., Am. Statis. Assn., Econometric Soc., Internat. Union Sci. Study of Population, Cosmos Club. Home: 2636 E Covenanter Ct Bloomington IN 47401-5408 Office: Ind U Population Inst Poplars # 738 Bloomington IN 47405 Challenges are rarely more forbidding in fact than in anticipation. Early coping often pays off; faintheartedness has higher risk of loss.

STOLOFF, NORMAN STANLEY, metallurgical engineering educator, researcher; b. Bklyn., Oct. 16, 1934; s. William F. and Lila (Dickman) S.; m. Helen Teresa Arcuri, May 15, 1971; children: Michael E., Linda M., David M., Stephen L. BMetE, NYU, 1955; MS, Columbia U., 1956, PhD, 1961. Metall. engr. Pratt & Whitney Aircraft, East Hartford, Conn., 1956-58; prin. rsch. scientist Ford Sci. Lab., Dearborn, Mich., 1961-65; asst. prof. materials engring. Rensselaer Polytechnic Inst., Troy, N.Y., 1965-68, assoc. prof., 1968-71, prof., 1971—; cons. Electric Boat div. Gen. Dynamics, New London, Conn., 1987-89, Martin Marietta Rsch. Labs., Balt., 1990, Rockwell Internat., Thousand Oaks, Calif., 1989, Cummins Engine Co., Columbus, Ind., 1991. Editor: (with others) High Temperature Ordered Intermetallic Alloys, 1985, Superalloys II, 1987, others; contbr. articles to profl. jours. Recipient Fulbright Rsch. award U.S. State Dept., 1968-69. Fellow Am. Soc. Materials Internat.; mem. AIME, ASTM, The Minerals, Metals and Materials Soc., Materials Rsch. Soc. Avocations: hiking, fishing, reading. Office: Rensselaer Polytechnic Inst Materials Engring Dept MRC Bldg Troy NY 12180

STOLPEN, SPENCER, professional sports team executive. Pres. Charlotte Hornets. Office: Charlotte Hornets 100 Hive Dr Charlotte NC 28217*

STOLPER, EDWARD MANIN, geology educator; b. Boston, Dec. 16, 1952; s. Saul James and Frances A. (Liberman) S.; m. Lauren Beth Adoff, June 3, 1973; children: Jennifer Ann, Daniel Aaron. AB, Harvard U., 1974; M Philosophy, U. Edinburgh, Scotland, 1976; PhD, Harvard U., 1979. Asst. prof. geology Calif. Inst. Tech., Pasadena, 1979-82, assoc. prof. geology, 1982-83, prof. geology, 1983-90, William E. Leonhard prof. geology, 1990—, chmn. divsn. geol. and planetary sci., 1994—. Marshall scholar Marshall Aid Commemoration Commn., 1974-76, recipient Newcombe Cleve. prize AAAS, 1984, F.W. Clarke medal Geochem. Soc., 1985. Fellow Meteoritical Soc. (Niniger Meteorite award 1976), Am. Geophys. Union (James B. Macelwane award 1986), Mineral Soc. Am., Am. Acad. Arts and Scis.; mem. NAS, Geol. Soc. Am., Sigma Xi. Office: Calif Inst Tech Div Geol Planetary Sci Pasadena CA 91125

STOLPER, PINCHAS ARYEH, religious organization executive, rabbi; b. Bklyn., Oct. 22, 1931; s. David Bernard and Nettie (Rosch) S.; m. Elaine Liebman, Nov. 22, 1955; children: Akiva Psachia, Michal Hadassah Cohen, Malka Tova Kaweblum. B.A. Bklyn. Coll., 1952; M.A., New Sch. for Social Research, 1971. Rabbinical ordination Chaim Berlin-Gur Aryeh Rabbinical Acad., 1956; dir. L.I. Zionist Youth Commn., 1956-57; dir. public relations, adminstrv. dean, adviser to English-speaking students Ponevez Yeshiva, Bnai Brak, Israel, 1957-59; also prin.; instr. English and Talmud Gimnazia Bnei Akiva High Sch., 1959-77; nat. dir. youth div. Union Orthodox Jewish Congregations Am., Nat. Conf. Synagogue Youth, N.Y.C., 1959-76; founder NCSY, Torah Fund, Ben Zakai Honor Soc. Union Orthodox Jewish Congregations Am., Nat. Conf. Synagogue Youth, 1959-76; editor Jewish Youth Monthly, 1967—; exec. v.p. Union Orthodox Jewish Congregations Am., 1976—; adj. prof. Jewish studies Touro Coll., N.Y., 1975—; mem. publs., Israel, campus commns., staff mem. responsible for cable tv, Talmud Torah, day sch. comms. Union Orthodox Jewish Congregations Am., 1965—; del. White House Conf. on Children and Youth, 1961; cons. N. Am. Jewish Youth Conf., 1967—. Author: Tested Teen Age Activities, 1961, rev. edit., 1964, Day of Delight, 1961, Tefilah, Text and Source Book, 1963, Revelation, What Happened on Sinai, 1966, Prayer, The Proven Path, 1967, The Road to Responsible Jewish Adulthood, 1967, Jewish Alternatives in Love, Dating and Marriage, 1985, Love, Dating and Marriage, The Jewish View, 1994, Beyond Belief, Revelations for the Modern Jew, 1994; contbr. over 140 articles, plays and revs. to Jewish publs. Bd. dirs. Chaim Berlin Torah Schs.-Mesivta Rabbi Chaim Berlin-Rabbinical Acad., 1965—. Recipient Alumi Amudim award Mesivta Rabbi Chaim Berlin-Gur Aryeh Inst., 1967, award Assn. Orthodox Jewish Tchrs., 1975, citation Rabbinical Coun. Am., 1984, Jabotinsky medal, 1990, Alumnus of Yr. award Flatbush Yeshiva, 1989, Joseph K. Miller Achdut Yisrael award Shaalvim Yeshiva, 1993. Mem. Rabbinical Coun. Am. Home: 954 E 7th St Brooklyn NY 11230-2706 Office: Union Orthodox Jewish Cong of Am 333 7th Ave New York NY 10001-5004

STOLPER, WOLFGANG FRIEDRICH, retired economist, educator; b. Vienna, Austria, May 13, 1912; came to U.S., 1934, naturalized, 1940; s. Gustav and Paula (Deutsch) S.; m. Marta Voegeli, Aug. 11, 1938 (dec. July 1972); children: Thomas E., Matthew W.; m. Margot Kaufmann, 1979. M.A., Harvard U., 1935, Ph.D, 1938. Dr. honoris causa, U. Saarbrücken, Grosses Verdienstkreuz, Fed. Republic Germany, 1984. Instr. Harvard U., 1936-41; asst. prof. econs Swarthmore Coll., 1941-48, assoc. prof., 1948-49; assoc. prof. U. Mich., 1949-53, prof., 1953-82; dir. U. Mich. (Center for Research on Econ. Devel.), 1963-70; guest prof. U. Zurich, summers, 1952, 69-79; head econ. planning unit Fed. Ministry for Econ. Devel., Lagos, Nigeria., 1960-62; cons. USAID, Ford Found., IBRD, UN; vis. prof. Inst. F. Weltwirtschaft, Kiel, 1987. Author: (with P.A. Samuelson) Protection and Real Wages, 1941, The Structure of the East German Economy, 1960, Planning Without Facts, 1966, Joseph A. Schumpeter 1883-

1950. The Public Life of the Private Man, 1994; contbr. articles to profl. jours. Guggenheim fellow, 1947-48; Fulbright prof. Heidelberg, 1966; recipient Bernhard Harms medal U. Kiel, 1985. Mem. Am. Econ. Assns., Internat. Schumpeter Soc. (founding pres.). Home: 1051 Lincoln Ave Ann Arbor MI 48104-3526 Office: U Mich Dept Econs Ann Arbor MI 48109

STOLTZ, ERIC, actor; b. American Samoa, 1961. Studied with Peggy Fury, William Traylor, U. So. Calif. Actor: (stage prodns.) One Flew Over the Cuckoo's Nest, 1978, Hello, Dolly!, 1979, The Seagull, 1980, The Widow Claire, 1987, Our Town, 1988 (Tony award nomination Drama Desk nomination), The American Plan, 1990, Two Shakespearean Actors, 1992, Down the Road, 1993; (feature films) Fast Times at Ridgemont High, 1981, Wild Life, 1983, Mask, 1984 (Golden Globe award nomination 1985), Lionheart, 1986, Some Kind of Wonderful, 1987, Sister, Sister, Haunted Summer, Code Name Emerald, 1988, Say Anything, 1989, Manifesto, 1989, The Fly II, 1989, Memphis Belle, 1990, Singles, 1991, The Waterdance, 1991, (actor, prodr.) Bodies, Rest and Motion, 1993, Naked in New York, 1993, Killing Zoe, 1993, Sleep With Me, 1993, God's Army, 1993, Pulp Fiction, 1994, Little Women, 1994, Rob Roy, 1995, Fluke, 1995, Kicking and Screaming, 1995, Grace of My Heart, 1995; (TV movies(the Grass Is Greener, 1980, The Violation of Sarah McDavid, 1982, Thursday's Child, 1982, Paper Dolls, 1982, A Killer in the Family, 1983, Foreign Affairs, 1993, Roommates, 1994; (TV episodes) St. Elsewhere, 1983, Fallen Angels, 1994, (13 episodes) Mad About You, 1995. Office: 9830 Wilshire Blvd Beverly Hills CA 90212-1804

STOLTZFUS, VICTOR EZRA, academic administrator; b. Martinsburg, Pa., Mar. 24, 1934; s. Ira Mark and Elsie Rebecca (Shenk) S.; m. Marie Histand Althouse, June 19, 1955; children: Kristina, Rebecca, Malinda. BA in Social Sci., Goshen Coll., 1956; BD, Goshen Bibl. Sem., 1959; MA in Sociology, Kent State U., 1964; PhD in Sociology, Pa. State U., 1970. Pastor North Lima (Ohio) Mennonite Ch., 1959-66; instr. Youngstown (Ohio) U., 1964-66, Pa. State U., University Park, 1966-70; prof. Eastern Ill. U., Charleston, 1970-81; dean Goshen (Ind.) Coll., 1981-84, pres., 1984—. Contbr. articles to profl. jours. Mem. Am. Assn. Higher Edn. Lodge: Rotary. Avocation: raquetball. Home: 305 Reservoir Pl Goshen IN 46526-5231 Office: Goshen Coll Office of Pres Goshen IN 46526

STOLTZMAN, RICHARD LESLIE, clarinetist; b. Omaha, July 12, 1942; s. Leslie Harvey and Dorothy Marilyn (Spohn) S.; m. Lucy Jean Chapman, June 6, 1976; children: Peter John, Margaret Anne. MusB summa cum laude, Ohio State U., 1964; MusM magna cum laude, Yale U., 1967; postgrad., Columbia U. Tchrs. Coll., 1967-70. Mem. faculty Calif. Inst. Arts, 1970-75; Western regional dir. Young Audiences, 1972-74, mem. nat. adv. bd. Appeared in concerts throughout U.S., Europe, Japan, Hong Kong, Australia, 1976—; rec. artist, 1974—; debut LaScala, Milan, 1981, Carnegie Hall, N.Y.C., 1982; appeared in world premiere of Einar Englund concerto Helsinki Festival, 1991, Toro Takemitsu concerto (Fantasma/Cantos) Wales BBC, 1991, U.S. premiere of Lukas Foss concerto L.A. Philharm. Orch., 1991, Copland concert, 1993 (Emmy award for best performing arts video 1993), world premiere of Leonard Bernstein sonata for clarinet and orch. Pacific Music Festival, Sapporo, Japan, 1994. Recipient Horatio Parker award Yale U., 1966, Avery Fisher prize, 1977, Martha Baird Rockefeller award, 1973, Grammy award, 1983, Avery Fisher artist award 1986, Disting. Alumnus award Ohio State U., 1990. Home: 6 Lincolnshire Way Winchester MA 01890-3048 Office: 201 W 54th St # 4C New York NY 10019-5563 *Be mindful of the breath. It gives life to the sound which sends music to the soul.*

STOLWIJK, JAN ADRIANUS JOZEF, physiologist, biophysicist; b. Amsterdam, Netherlands, Sept. 29, 1927; came to U.S. 1955, naturalized, 1962; s. Leonard and Cornelia Agnes (Van Der Bijl) S.;m. Deborah Rose, 1990. B.S., Wageningen U., Netherlands, 1948, M.S., 1951, Ph.D., 1955. Biophysicist John B. Pierce Found., New Haven, 1957-61; asso. fellow John B. Pierce Found. Lab., 1961-64, fellow, 1964, asso. dir., 1974-89; instr. dept. physiology Yale U. Sch. Medicine, New Haven, 1962-63, asst. prof., 1964-68, asst. prof. epidemiology, 1968-69, asso. prof., 1969-75, prof., 1975—; dir. grad. studies, dept. epidemiology and public health, 1992—; chmn. dept. epidemiology and pub. health, 1982-89; research fellow Harvard U., 1955-56; cons. divsn. disease prevention Conn. Health Dept., 1977—; cons. vehicle inspection program Dept. Motor Vehicles, 1979-83; mem. sci. adv. bd. EPA, 1985-93; mem. tech. adv. bd. Dept. Commerce, 1977-77. Mem. Am. Physiol. Soc., Biophys. Soc., Aerospace Med. Soc., Am. Public Health Assn., AAAS, Internat. Biometeorol. Soc., Soc. Occupational and Environ. Health, Am. Conf. Govt. Indsl. Hygienists, ASHRAE, Conn. Acad. Sci. and Engring. Club: Cosmos. Home: 165 Dromara Rd Guilford CT 06437-2391 Office: PO Box 8034 60 College St New Haven CT 06520

STOLZ, BENJAMIN ARMOND, foreign language educator; b. Lansing, Mich., Mar. 28, 1934; s. Armond John and Mabel May (Smith) S.; m. Mona Eleanor Seelig, June 16, 1962; children: Elizabeth Mona, John Benjamin. A.B., U. Mich., Ann Arbor, 1955; certificat, U. Libre de Bruxelles, Belgium, 1956; A.M., Harvard U., 1957, Ph.D., 1965. Mem. faculty U. Mich., 1964—; prof. Slavic langs. and lits., 1972—; chmn. dept., 1971-85, 89-91; cons. in field. Editor: Papers in Slavic Philology, 1977; co-editor: Oral Literature and the Formula, 1976, Cross Currents, 1982-85, Language and Literary Theory, 1984, Mich. Slavic Publs., 1990—; co-editor, translator: (Konstantin Mihailovic): Memoirs of a Janissary, 1975; contbr. articles to profl. pubs. Served to lt. (j.g.) USNR, 1957-60. Recipient Orion E. Scott award humanities U. Mich., 1954, Fulbright scholar, 1955-56; Fgn. Area fellow Yugoslavia, 1963-64; Fulbright-Hays rsch. fellow Eng. and Yugoslavia, 1970-71; grantee Am. Coun. Learned Socs., 1968-70, 73, Internat. Rsch. and Exchs. Bd., 1985, 87, Woodrow Wilson Ctr., 1992. Mem. Am. Assn. Advancement Slavic Studies, Am. Assn. Tchrs. Slavic and East European Langs., Midwest MLA (pres. 1976), Huron Valley Tennis Club, Phi Beta Kappa, Kappa Phi Kappa, Delta Upsilon. Democrat. Home: 1060 Baldwin Ave Ann Arbor MI 48104-3504 Office: Univ Mich 3040 Mlb Ann Arbor MI 48109

STOLZ, NEIL N., financial services company executive; b. Ottawa, Kans., June 28, 1935; s. Norbert E. and Vida M. Stolz; m. Patricia L. Stolz, June 22, 1963; children: Sherilyn, Darryl. BS, U. Ariz., 1961. Personnel asst. Am. Savs. and Loan Assn., Whittier, Calif., 1962-66; asst. v.p. personnel Equitable Savs. and Loan Assn. (now Gt. Western Bank), L.A., 1968-83; sr. v.p. corp. planning Gt. Western Bank, Beverly Hills, Calif., 1983-84; exec. v.p., chief adminstrv. officer Fin. Corp. of Am., Irvine, Beverly Hills, 1985—. Mem. adv. bd. U. of Pacific Bus. Sch., Stockton, Calif., 1986—. Mem. Stockton C. of C. (bd. dirs. 1986—), Palos Verdes Golf Club (bd. dirs. 1982-86), Palos Verdes Tennis Club. Republican. Home: 2512 Via Amador Palos Verdes Peninsula CA 90274-2749 Office: Fin Corp Am 18401 Von Karman Ave Irvine CA 92715-1542

STOLZ, WALTER SARGENT, health scientist administrator; b. Milw., Dec. 12, 1938; s. Harold Lewis and Ruth Alice (Sargent) S. B.S., U. Wis., 1960, M.S., 1962, Ph.D., 1964. Asst. prof. psychology U. Tex., Austin, 1965-71; assoc. prof., chmn. dept. psychology Earlham Coll., Richmond, Ind., 1971-75; sr. research assoc. Ctr. for Applied Linguistics, Washington, 1975-76; health scientist adminstr. Nat. Inst. Arthritis, Diabetes, Digestive and Kidney Diseases, NIH, Bethesda, Md., 1976-84, dir. div. extramural activities, 1983—. Recipient merit award NIH, 1983; NSF fellow Harvard U., 1964-65. Mem. Am. Psychol. Assn., Sigma Xi. Avocations: sailing, travel. Office: NIH Nat Inst Diabetes Digestive & Kidney Diseases 5333 Westbard Ave Bethesda MD 20892-0001

STOLZER, LEO WILLIAM, bank executive; b. Kansas City, Mo., Oct. 14, 1934; s. Leo Joseph and Lennie Lucille (Hopp) S.; m. Eleanor Katherine Griffith, Aug. 17, 1957; children: Joan Ellen Stolzer Bolen, Mary Kevin Stolzer Giller. BS in Acctg., Kans. State U., 1957. Teller Union Nat. Bank & Trust Co., Manhattan, Kans., 1960-62, asst. cashier, 1962-63, asst. v.p., 1963-64, v.p., 1964-69, exec. v.p., 1969-72, pres., 1972-80, chmn., CEO, 1980—; bd. dirs. State Mut. Life Inst. Co. Commerce Bank, Kansas City, Ft. Riley Nat. Bank, Commerce Bank-Manhattan; chmn., CEO Griffith Lumber Co.; chmn. corp. for Am. Banking; v.p. Commerce Bancshares, Inc. Mem. exec. com., treas. Kans. State U. Found.; trustee Midwest Rsch. Inst.; chmn. Riley County Savs. Bond. Capt. USAF, 1957-60. Recipient Disting.

Service award Manhattan Jr. C. of C., 1968, Kans. State U. Advancement award. Mem. Am. Bankers Assn. (past treas., past exec. com., past bd. dirs.), Assn. of U.S. Army (bd. dirs. Ft. Riley cntrl. Kans. chpt.), Kansas U. Alumni Assn. (devel. com.), Newcomen Soc. in N.Am. (past Kans. chpt.), Rotary, KC, Beta Theta Pi. Avocation: skiing. Office: Commerce Bank 727 Poyntz Ave Manhattan KS 66502-6077

STONE, ALAN, container company executive; b. Chgo., Feb. 5, 1928; s. Norman H. and Ida (Finkelstein) S.; children: Christie-Ann Stone Weiss, Joshua. B.S.E., U. Pa., 1951. Trainee, salesman Stone Container Corp., Chgo., 1951-53, dir. mktg. service, 1954-64, gen. mgr., regional mgr., 1964-72, sr. v.p. adminstrn., gen. mgr. energy div., 1972—; also dir.; pres. Atlanta St. Andrews and Bay Line R.R., Abbeville-Grimes R.R., Apache R.R. Pres. Jewish Vocat. Service, Chgo., 1975-77; v.p. Sinai Temple, Chgo., 1077-84; vice chmn. Roycemore Sch., Evanston, Ill., 1982-87; trustee Brewster Acad., Wolfeboro, N.H. Mem. Standard Club, Tavern Club, Bryn Mawr Country Club, Tamarisk Country Club, Long Boat Key Club, Beta Alpha Psi, Phi Eta Sigma, Zeta Beta Tau. Avocations: golf; sports; reading. Office: Stone Container Corp 150 N Michigan Ave Chicago IL 60601-7508

STONE, ALAN A., law and psychiatry educator, psychiatrist; b. 1929. A.B., Harvard U., 1950; M.D., Yale U., 1955. Dir. resident edn. McLean Hosp., 1962-68; lectr. Harvard U., 1966-72, asst. prof. psychiatry, 1966-69, assoc. prof., 1969-72, prof. law and psychiatry, 1972—; Touroff-Glueck prof. Law and Psychiatry, 1982—; mem. adv. com. Am. Bar Found. Project on Mentally Ill, 1967-71; mem. Mass. Gov.'s Com. for Revision Criminal Code, 1968-72; mem. com. on mentally disabled ABA, 1973-77; chmn. Mass. Com. on Psychosurgery, 1974—; fellow Ctr. Advanced Study in Behavioral Scis., Stanford U., 1980-81; Tanner lectr. Stanford U., 1982. Served as capt. M.C., U.S. Army, 1959-61. Recipient Manfred S. Guttmacher award; Isaac Ray award, 1982. Mem. Group Advancement Psychiatry, Am. Psychiat. Assn. (trustee, v.p.; pres.; chmn. com. jud. action 1974-9). Author: (with Onque) Longitudinal Studies of Child Behavior, 1961; Mental Health and Law: A System in Transition, 1975; Law, Psychiatry and Morality: Essays and Analysis, 1984; editor: (with Sue Stone) Abnormal Personality through Literature, 1966; Office: Harvard U Law Sch Cambridge MA 02138

STONE, ALAN JAY, college administrator; b. Ft. Dodge, Iowa, Oct. 15, 1942; s. Hubert H. and Bernice A. (Tilton) S.; m. Jonieta J. Smith; 1 child, Kirsten K. Stone Morlock. BA, Morningside Coll., 1964; MA, U. Iowa, 1966; MTh, U. Chgo., 1968, DMin, 1970; PhD (hon.), Kyonggi U., Korea, 1985; LLD, Stillman Coll., 1991, Sogong U., Korea, 1992. Admissions counselor Morningside Coll., Sioux City, Iowa, 1964-66; dir. admissions, asso. prof. history George Williams Coll., Downers Grove, Ill., 1969-73; v.p. coll. relations Hood Coll., Frederick, Md., 1973-75; v.p. devel. and fin. affairs W.Va. Wesleyan Coll., Buckhannon, 1975-77; dir. devel. U. Maine, 1977-78; pres. Aurora (Ill.) U., 1978-88, Alma (Mich.) Coll., 1988—; bd. dirs. Bank of Alma. Chmn. bd. Mich. Intercollegiate Athletic Assn.; bd. dirs. Mich. Coll. Found., Assn. Ind. Colls. and Univs. of Mich., Mich. Campus Compact, Korean Social Policy Inst., Seoul; chmn. United Way Gratiot County, Strategic Planning Group Gratiot County. Named Outstanding Tchr. George Williams Coll., 1973; U. Chgo. fellow, 1966-70. Mem. Am. Assn. Higher Edn., Am. Assn. Colls., Renaissance Club, Alma Country Club. Home: 313 Maple Ave Alma MI 48801-2234 Office: Alma Coll Alma MI 48801

STONE, ALLAN BARRY, art gallery director; b. N.Y.C., Feb. 6, 1932; s. Herbert Daniel and Ruth (Klein) S.; m. Marguerite Cullman, Jan. 6, 1956 (div. 1965); children: Allison M., Jeremy, Claudia, Heather; m. Clare Chester, Sept. 3, 1965; children: Jessie Chester, Posy Merriweather. BA, Phillips Acad., 1950, Harvard U., 1954; LLB, Boston U., 1958. Atty. Legal Aid Soc., Boston, 1956-57; atty. civil frauds Dept. Justice, Washington, 1958-59; assoc. Wicks, Riddell, Bloomer, Jacoby & McQuire, N.Y.C., 1959-60; pres. Allan Stone Gallery, N.Y.C., 1960—; cons. in field. Pres. Purchase Environ. Protection Assn., N.Y., 1978-85; fellow Woodrow Wilson Found., 1982; mem. Presdl. Fellowship Com., 1980. Avocations: gardening, tennis. Home: Purchase St Purchase NY 10577-1102 Office: 48 E 86th St New York NY 10028-1009

STONE, ALLAN DAVID, economics educator; b. Joliet, Ill., Jan. 9, 1937; s. William E. and Leona V. (Frieh) S.; m. Peggy J. Carter, Jan. 11, 1958; children: David, Richard. BA, Beloit Coll., 1961; MA, U. Okla., 1964, PhD, 1973. Asst. prof. econs. U. Tex., El Paso, 1963-65; instr. econs. Wartburg Coll., Waverly, Iowa, 1965-66; asst. prof. econs. Oklahoma City U., 1966-72; prof. econs. S.W. Mo. State U., Springfield, 1972—; dept. head, 1985-87. Served with U.S. Army, 1956-58. NSF grantee. Mem. Am. Econ. Assn., Mo. Coun. Econ. Edn. (bd. dirs. 1977-80), Phi Beta Kappa, Phi Kappa Phi. Home: 820 E Cherokee St Springfield MO 65807-2708

STONE, ANDREW GROVER, lawyer; b. L.A., Oct. 2, 1942; s. Frank B. and Meryl (Pickering) S.; divorced; 1 child, John Blair. BA, Yale U., 1965; JD, U. Mich., 1969. Bar: D.C. 1970, U.S. Dist. Ct. D.C. 1970, U.S. Ct. Appeals (D.C. cir.) 1972, Mass. 1981. Assoc. Rogers & Wells, Washington, 1969-71; atty. Bur. Competition, FTC, Washington, 1971-80; antitrust counsel Digital Equipment Corp., Maynard, Mass., 1980-83, mgr. N.E. law group, 1983-86, mgr. headquarters sales law group, 1986-88; asst. general counsel U.S. (acting), 1987, 88; corp counsel Washington, 1988-90; corp. counsel, pub. sect. mktg. Digital Equipment Corp., 1990-91; corp. counsel Thinking Machines Corp., Cambridge, Mass., 1992—. Corp. mem. Tenacre Country Day Sch., Wellesley, Mass., 1981-88. Mem. ABA (antitrust sect., bus. law sect., sci. tech. sect., pub. contracts sect., communs. coml. products and svcs. com. 1983-84), Mass. Bar Assn. (internat. law steering com. 1993-94), Boston Bar Assn., Licensing Execs. Soc., Am. Intellectual Property Law Assn., New Eng. Corp. Counsel Assn. Office: Thinking Machines Corp 245 First St Cambridge MA 02142

STONE, ARTHUR HAROLD, mathematics educator; b. London, Sept. 30, 1916; came to U.S., 1959; s. Aurel P. and Rosa (Schekter) S.; m. Dorothy Maharam, Apr. 12, 1942; children: David A., Ellen R. BA, Cambridge (Eng.) U., 1938, MA, 1939; PhD, Princeton U., 1941. Mem. Inst. Advanced Study, Princeton, N.J., 1941-42; instr. Purdue U., 1942-44; with Geophys. Lab., Washington, 1944-45; fellow Trinity Coll. Cambridge U., 1946-48; lectr. Manchester (Eng.) U., 1948-57, sr. lectr., 1957-61; prof. math. U. Rochester, 1961-87, prof. emeritus, 1987—; adj. prof. Northeastern U., Boston, 1988—; vis. prof. Columbia U., 1961, Yale U., 1965-66; vis. rsch. assoc. U. Calif., Berkeley, 1971-72; vis. fellow Australian Nat. U., Canberra, 1978. Mem. editorial adv. bd. Topology and Its Applications, 1971-93; mem. internat. adv. bd. Mathematica Japonica, 1991—; contbr. articles to profl. jours. Mem. AAUP, Am. Math. Soc., Math. Assn. Am., London Math. Soc. Jewish. Office: Northeastern U Dept Math Boston MA 02115

STONE, ARTHUR JOSEPH, judge; b. St. Peters, N.S., Can., 1929; s. George and Charlotte S.; m. Anna M., 1956. B.A., St. Francis Xavier U., Antigonish, N.S., 1952; LL.B., Dalhousie Law Sch., 1955; LL.M., Harvard U., 1956. Assoc., Wright & McTaggart and successor firms, 1957-83; justice Fed. Ct. Appeal, Ottawa, Ont., Can., 1983—; justice faculty of law U. Toronto, Ont., 1971-74. Contbr. articles to profl. publs. Mem. N.S. Barristers Soc., Law Soc. of Upper Can., N.B. Barristers Soc., Law Soc. of B.C., Can. Bar Assn. (nat. exec. com. 1971-73), Can. Tax Found. (gov. 1977-79), Can. Maritime Law Assn. (pres.), Harvard U. Law Sch. Assn. Ont. (chmn. law sch. fund) Club: Toronto Marine (pres. 1977-78). Office: Fed Ct, Kent & Wellington Sts, Ottawa, ON Canada K1A 0H9

STONE, BEVERLEY, former university dean, former dean of students; b. Norfolk, Va., June 10, 1916; d. James L. and Clara (Thompson) S. B.A. in Chemistry, Randolph-Macon Woman's Coll., 1936; M.A. in Student Personnel Adminstrn., Columbia U., 1940, profl. diploma, 1956; L.H.D. (hon.), Purdue U., 1986. Tchr. Norfolk High Sch., 1936-41; instr. Tusculum Coll., 1941-43; asst. dean women U. Ark., 1946-50, assoc. dean women, 1952-54, dean women, 1954-55; asst. dean women Purdue U., 1956-67, assoc. dean women, 1967-68, dean women, 1968-74, dean students, 1974-80, ret., 1980. Author (with Barbara Cook); monograph Counseling Women, 1973. Mem. president's coun. Purdue U., 1985—; trustee Katherine S. Phillips Trust Fund, 1978-84; mem. lay bd. St. Elizabeth's Hosp., 1974-80, Salvation Army, Lafayette Art Mus., 1982-85, Crisis Ctr.; mem. Tippecanoe County Bd.

Zoning Appeals, 1982-83, West Lafayette City Coun., 1984-88; past mem. adminstrv. bd., found. bd. 1st United Meth. Ch., West Lafayette. Lt. comdr. USNR, 1943-46, 52-55. Recipient Outstanding Woman in Edn. award Coalition of Women's Orgns. in Greater Lafayette Area, 1978, Disting. Alumni award Purdue Bus.'s Coun., 1980, Disting. Woman award Purdue U., 1980; named Sagamore of the Wabash Gov. Ind., 1980, 85; Nat. Mortar Bd. Fellowship named in honor, 1994-95. Mem. AAUW (past pres. Fayetteville, Ark.), Nat. Assn. Women Deans and Counselors (treas., chmn. hdqs. adv. com. 1973-75, mem. 1975-79), Ind. Assn. Women Deans and Counselors, Mental Health Assn., Purdue Women's Club, Parlor Club, Randolph-Macon Women's Coll. Conway Club, Mortar Bd. (nat. fellowship named in her honor 1994-95), Phi Beta Kappa, Kappa Delta Pi, Omicron Delta Kappa, Pi Lambda Theta, Alpha Lambda Delta (v.p. 1975-79), Zeta Tau Alpha. Home: 1807 Western Dr West Lafayette IN 47906-2239

STONE, BONNIE CAROL, healthcare executive; b. Bklyn., Aug. 9, 1945; d. Michael and Sylvia (Silberling) S.; m. Peter Jeffrey Kaplan, Oct. 30, 1976 (div. 1987); m. John P. Deacy, Sept. 1989. BA, U. Wis., 1966; MA, Columbia U., N.Y.C., 1968; M in Urban Planning, NYU, 1974. Various positions N.Y.C., 1968-72; with N.Y.C. Health Dept., 1972-78, 86, dep. asst. commr., 1977-78, dep. commr., 1986; 1st asst. dep. commr. N.Y.C. Human Resources Adminstrn., 1978-85, dep. commr., 1985-86; v.p. L.I. R.R., Jamaica, N.Y., 1986-90; exec. dir. Selfhelp Community Svcs., Inc., N.Y.C., 1990—. NDEA fellow U. Wis., 1966. Mem. Women's Transp. Seminar. Democrat. Jewish. Home: 395 Broadway New York NY 10013 Office: Selfhelp Community Svcs Inc 440 9th Ave New York NY 10001-1620

STONE, CHARLES RIVERS, apparel manufacturing company executive; b. Greenville, S.C., July 9, 1936; s. Eugene Earle III and Allene Lawton (Wyman) S.; m. Frances Patterson Owings, Mar. 6, 1971; children—Charles Rivers, Frances Rebecca, Rosalie Wyman. Indsl. mgmt. degree, Clemson U., 1960. With Stone Mfg. Co., Greenville, 1960—; pres. Stone Mfg. Co., 1976—; CREE Co.; chmn., chief exec. officer House of Stone, Rivers of Air; mem. adv. bd. S.C. Nat. Bank, 1977—; dir. Sea Pines Plantation Co., 1965-69. Bd. dirs. Greenville Charity Bd., Greenville Community Corp., 1977—; trustee Faith Meml. Episcopal Chapel, Cedar Mountain, N.C.; charter mem. Leadership Greenville; mem. Blue Ridge Community Coll. Found. Bd. Served with USAF, 1959-60. Mem. Am. Apparel Mfrs. Assn., Young Pres. Orgn., World Bus. Coun., Chief Execs. Orgn., Greenville County Hist. Soc., Greater Greenville C. of C., Exptl. Aircraft Assn., Clemson U. Alumni Assn. Clubs: Cotillion, Poinsett, Metropolitan, Greenville Country, Commerce Club. Office: Stone Mfg Co 1500 Poinsett Hwy PO Box 3725 Greenville SC 29608

STONE, DANIEL HUNTER, metallurgical engineer, researcher; b. Pitts., Dec. 29, 1938; s. Daniel Stewart and Julia Ann (Argue) S.; m. Irene Ann Juber, Aug. 8, 1965; children: Susan Irene, Mary Lynn, Michael David, Matthew Daniel. BS, U. Pitts., 1962; MS, UCLA, 1966. Rsch. engr. N.Am. Aviation, Canoga Park, Calif., 1962-66, U.S. Steel Applied Rsch. Lab., Monroeville, Pa., 1966-72; rsch. engr. Chgo. Terminal Ctr. Assn. Am. R.R., 1972-78, dir. metallurgy, 1978-88, exec. dir., 1988—; chmn. com. on direction Internat. Wheelset Congress, 1986—; trustee Internat. Conf. on Contact Mechanisms of Rail/Wheel Systems, Cambridge, Eng., 1991—. Editor: Rail Steels, 1978; contbr. numerous articles to profl. publs. Fellow ASME (Rail Transp. award 1987, gen. commn. RTO 1991—); mem. Am. R.R. Engring. Assn. Achievements include 1 patent. Home: 433 Darrow Ave Evanston IL 60202-3248 Office: Assn Am R R AAR Chgo Tech Ctr 3140 S Federal St Chicago IL 60616-3731

STONE, DAVID BARNES, investment advisor; b. Brookline, Mass., Sept. 2, 1927; s. Robert Gregg and Bertha L. (Barnes) S.; m. Sara Cruikshank, June 16, 1951 (div. July 1976); children—David Stevenson, Benjamin Barnes, Peter Cruikshank, Jonathan Fitch, Andrew Hasbrouck; m. Ellen J. Desmond, Feb. 16, 1980; 1 son, Daniel Desmond. Grad., Milton (Mass.) Acad., 1945; A.B., Harvard, 1950, M.B.A., 1952; D.C.S. (hon.), Suffolk U., 1969; LL.D., Northeastern U., 1974; L.H.D., Curry Coll., 1981. Vice pres. Hayden, Stone Inc. (and predecessor), 1962-65, chmn. exec. com., 1965-67; pres. N.Am. Mgmt. Corp., 1968-78, chmn., 1978—; trustee Mass. Fin. Svcs. Group of Mut. Funds, 1989—; pres. Stonetex Oil Corp., Dallas. Pres. bd. trustees New Eng. Aquarium, 1959-70, chmn. bd. trustees, 1970-76; bd. overseers Boys Club Boston, 1956-61, treas., 1961-67; trustee Charles Hayden Found., 1966-92, Wellesley Coll., vice chmn. bd., 1992—; chmn. Meml. Dr. Trust; mem. Woods Hole Oceanographic Instn. With U.S. Mcht. Marines, 1945-47. Mem. Investment Bankers Assn. (chmn. New Eng. group 1963, bd. govs. 1964-67). Clubs: Kittansett (Marion, Mass.); Country (Brookline, Mass.). Home: Great Hill Marion MA 02738 also: 282 Beacon St Boston MA 02116-1152 Office: North American Mgmt Ten Post Office Sq Ste 300 Boston MA 02109

STONE, DAVID DEADERICK, physician, educator; b. Bristol, Va., Feb. 8, 1932; s. Albert Wallace and Margaret Clifton (Deaderick) S.; children: Margaret E., Caroline A., Jennifer R., Shannon D. BA cum laude, Vanderbilt U., 1954; MD, U. Va., 1958. Diplomate Am. Bd. Internal Medicine, Am. Bd. Gastroenterology. Intern N.Y. Hosp., 1958-59, resident, 1959-61; chief resident U. Va. Hosp., Charlottesville, 1961-62; fellow in gastroenterology Barnes Hosp., St. Louis, 1962-63; inst. in internal medicine U. Va. Sch. Medicine, Charlottesville, 1963-66, asst. prof., 1966-71, assoc. prof., 1971-76, prof., 1976-85, Disting. prof., 1985—; dir. Out-Patient Dept. U. Va. Hosp., 1968-72, pres. clin. staff clerkship, 1971-72; dir. Internal Medicine U. Va. Sch. Medicine, 1971-75, Physical Diagnosis Program, 1972-75, vice chmn. Dept. Internal Medicine, 1979, dir. Med. Intensive Care Unit, 1982-88, assoc. chmn. for Clin. Affairs, 1989. Contbr. articles to jours. in field. Recipient Robley Danglison award U. Va. Sch. Medicine, 1972, 78. Fellow ACP; mem. Am. Gastroent. Assn., Soc. Critical Care Medicine, Alpha Omega Alpha. *

STONE, DAVID KENDALL, financial executive; b. Natick, Mass., Dec. 7, 1942; s. Harold Hamilton and Mary (Perkins) S.; m. Patricia Donahue, June 12, 1965; children: Jonathan, Andrew, Timothy. AB, Franklin & Marshall Coll., 1964. CPA, N.Y. Acct Gilfoil & McNeal, Syracuse, N.Y., 1967-69, Ernst & Whinney, Cleve., 1969-83; sr. v.p., comptroller Fiduciary Trust Co. Internat., N.Y.C., 1983-87, sr. v.p. dir. ops., 1987-92, exec. v.p., 1992—. Treas. Cerebral Palsy and Handicapped Children's Assn., Syracuse, N.Y., 1972-75. 1st lt. U.S. Army, 1964-67, Vietnam. Mem. AICPA, N.Y. State Soc. CPAs (com. on banking and savs. instns. 1983-87), Com. Banking Instns. on Taxation, N.Y. State Bankers Assn. (com. on trust ops.). Office: Fiduciary Trust Co Internat 2 World Trade Ctr New York NY 10048-0203

STONE, DAVID PHILIP, lawyer; b. N.Y.C., Sept. 11, 1944; s. Robert and Laura Stone; m. Arlene R. Stone, June 11, 1966; children: Aaron J., Rachel E. AB, Columbia U., 1967; JD, Harvard U., 1970. Bar: N.Y. 1971. Assoc. Cahill, Gordon & Reindel, N.Y.C., 1970-74, Baer & McGoldrick, N.Y.C., 1974-76; assoc. Weil, Gotshal & Manges, N.Y.C., 1976-79, ptnr., 1979—. Office: Weil Gotshal & Manges 767 Fifth Ave New York NY 10153-0001

STONE, DENNIS J., law librarian, educator; b. Sacramento, May 25, 1948; s. Edward F. and Irene V. (Johnson) S. BA, U. Calif., Berkeley, 1970, MLS, 1971; JD, U. of Pacific, 1977. Bar: Calif. 1977. Asst. law librarian McGeorge Sch. of Law, Sacramento, 1974-77, lectr., asst. law librarian, 1977-79; law librarian, asst. prof. Gonzaga Sch. of Law, Spokane, 1979-83; law librarian, assoc. prof. law U. Conn Law Library, Hartford, 1983—. Founder Can.-Am. Law Jour., 1983; founder, editor Trends in Law Library Mgmt. and Tech. Jour., 1987; contbr. articles to profl. jours. Mem. Am. Assn. Law Libraries (exec. bd. 1983-87), New Eng. Law Library Consortium (bd. dirs. 1983—, pres. 1986-88), Law Librarians of New Eng., So. New Eng. Law Libraries, Am. Assn. Law Libraries (spl. interest sect.). Office: U Conn Sch Law Library 55 Elizabeth Hartford CT 06105

STONE, DON CHARLES, computer science educator; b. Passaic, N.J., Sept. 5, 1942; s. Robert Porter and Catherine Cook (Lanman) S. B degree Physics, Cornell U., 1965; MS in Engring., U. Pa., 1967, PhD in Instnl. Systems, 1985. Asst. prof. Glassboro State Coll. (now Rowan Coll. of N.J.), 1968-89, assoc. prof., 1989—, chair computer sci. dept., 1992—; sr. sys. analyst Intelligent Micro Sys., Inc., Narberth, Pa., 1985—. Contbr. articles to profl. jours.; lecturer in field. Mem. IEEE Computer Soc., Assn. for Computing Machinery, Geneal. Computing Assn. Pa. (v.p. 1992—). Avocations: genealogy, graphic design, typography. Home: Apt 9B-28 2401 Pennsylvania Ave Philadelphia PA 19130-3034 Office: Rowan Coll of NJ Computer Sci Dept Glassboro NJ 08028

STONE, DONALD CRAWFORD, public administrator, educator; b. Cleve., June 17, 1903; s. Alfred William and Mary Rebecca (Crawford) S.; m. Alice Kathryn Biermann, June 10, 1928; children: Nancy Leland Stone Dickinson, Alice Crawford Stone Ilchman, Elizabeth Stone Britton, Donald Crawford Stone Jr. AB, Colgate U., 1925, LLD (hon.), 1960; MS, Syracuse U., 1926; postgrad., U. Cin., 1927-28, Columbia, 1928-30; LLD (hon.), George Williams Coll., 1953. Asst. to city mgr. City of Cin., 1926-28; mem. staff Inst. Pub. Adminstrn., N.Y.C., 1928-29; dir. research internat. city mgmt. assn., research assoc. U. Chgo., 1930-33; exec. dir. Pub. Adminstrn. Service, 1933-39; asst. dir. Bur. of Budget, Exec. Office of Pres., 1939-48; dir. adminstrn. ECA (Marshall Plan), 1948-51, Mut. Security Agy., 1951-53; pres. Springfield (Mass.) Coll., 1953-57; dean Grad. Sch. Pub. and Internat. Affairs, U. Pitts., 1957-69, prof., 1969-74; Disting. Pub. Service prof. Carnegie-Mellon U., Pitts., 1975-92; dir. coalition to improve mgmt. in state/local govt., 1984-92; coalition sr. advisor Ind. U., Indpls., 1992—; Green Honors Chair prof. Tex. Christian U., 1976; exec. dir. Am. Pub. Works Assn., 1934-36; spl. asst. to Fed. WPA adminstr., 1935; lectr. pub. adminstrn. Syracuse U., 1933-37; adj. prof. Am. U., 1943-53; pres. Internat. Assn. Schs. and Insts. of Adminstrn., 1962-82; cons. Fed. PWA, 1932, Civil Works Adminstrn., 1933, Fed. Relief Adminstrn., 1934-36, TVA, 1934, Fed. Social Security Bd., 1936, U.S. Pub. Housing and R.E.A., 1938, Fgn. Ops. Agy., 1954, Nat. Council Chs., 1956, Am. Council on Edn., 1957, OAS, 1957-58, 60-61, Nat. Security Orgn., 1957-58, NASA, 1960, 73, 74-75, Com. for Econ. Devel., 1966-74, UN, 1969-73, NSF, 1974-75, 79-80, OMB, 1974; cons. Saudi Arabia, 1976, Kuwait, 1977-80; cons. GAO, 1977-80; adviser U.S. del. to UN confs., San Francisco, 1945, London, 1945-46, Lake Success, 1947, Paris, 1948; mem. UN Gen. Assembly standing com. on budget and adminstrn., 1946-48; U.S. rep. to UNESCO Preparatory Commn., London, 1945-46; Mem. Commn. on Edn. and Internat. Affairs, Am. Coun. on Edn., 1954-63; com. on internat. affairs Nat. Coun. Chs., 1966-67; past pres. Am. Consortium for Internat. Pub. Adminstrn. Author books, monographs, articles in profl. jours. Recipient numerous nat. pub. svc. awards. Mem. Cosmos Club (Washington). Mem. Disciples of Christ Ch. Home: Robin Run Village 5354 W 62d St Apt 270 Indianapolis IN 46268 also: 17765 Whispering Trail Traverse City MI 49684

STONE, DONALD JAMES, retired retail executive; b. Cleve., Mar. 5, 1929; s. Sidney S. and Beatrice (Edelman) S.; m. Norma Fay Karchmer, Oct. 26, 1952; children—Michael, Lisa, Angela. BBA, U. Tex., Austin, 1949. With Foley's, Houston, 1949-75; v.p., gen. mdse. mgr. Foley's, 1960-75; chmn., chief exec. officer Sanger-Harris, Dallas, 1975-80; vice chmn. Federated Dept. Stores, Inc., Cin., 1980-88; bd. dirs. M Corp., Fossil, Inc., Bloom Agy., Dallas, XTEC Corp., Cin. Pres. Dallas Symphony Soc., 1980-82, 88—, chmn. Found. bd., 1989—; chmn. exec. com. Dallas Ballet, 1979; bd. dirs. Dallas Mus. Fine Art, 1979-81; mem. adv. coun. Coll. Bus. Adminstrn. U. Tex., 1981—, chmn., 1990-92; bd. dirs. Cin. Ballet, 1982-87, Cin. Symphony, 1983-88, pres., 1987; bd. Cin. overseers, chmn., 1988-92; bd. govs. Hebrew Union Coll., 1988—; bd. dirs. Aspen Inst. Humanistic Studies, 1988—. Mem. Chamber of C. (chmn. cultural com. 1979-81), Assoc. Mdse. Corp. (bd. dirs., exec. com.). Democrat. Jewish. Home: 3601 Turtle Creek Blvd Dallas TX 75219-5522 Office: 3601 Turtle Creek Blvd Apt 502 Dallas TX 75219-5503

STONE, DONALD RAYMOND, lawyer; b. Madison, Wis., Mar. 6, 1938; s. Donald Meredith and June Dorothy (Graffenberger) S.; m. Dorothy Tetzlaff, June 23, 1962; children—Randall, Brian. BS in Physics, U. Wis., 1960, J.D., 1963. Bar: Minn. 1963, D.C. 1987, U.S. Supreme Ct. 1987. Patent atty. Honeywell, Inc., Mpls., 1963-66; patent atty. firm Burd, MacEachron, Braddock, Bartz & Schwartz, Mpls., 1966-68; with Medtronic, Inc., Mpls., 1968-87, v.p., then sr. v.p. product assurance and regulation, 1973-77, sr. v.p., sec., gen. counsel, 1977-80, sr. v.p., 1980-85, v.p. 1985-87; ptnr., mem. Burditt, Bowles & Radzius, Chartered, Washington, 1987-90; ptnr. McKenna & Cuneo, Washington, 1990—; condr. seminars, 1974—. Contbr. articles to profl. jours. Bd. dirs., 1st v.p. East Side Neighborhood Services, Inc., Mpls., 1976-80; bd. dirs. Guthrie Theater Found., 1979-85; mem. allocations com. United Way Mpls., 1979-86, chmn. allocations com., 1985, bd. dirs. 1985-86; mem. Citizens League of Twin Cities, 1965-86. Mem. ABA, D.C. Bar Assn., Fed. Bar Assn., Hennepin County Bar Assn., Am. Soc. Quality Control, Am. Intellectual Property Law Assn., Health Industry Mfrs. Assn. (past chmn. legal and regulatory sect., standard sect., 1975-87), Nat. Elec. Mfrs. Assn. (past chmn. med. electronics sect., 1970-76), Assn. Advancement Med. Instrumentation, Minn. State Bar Assn., Minn. Intellectual Property Law Assn. (past sec.), Minn. Corp. Counsel Assn., Regulatory Affairs. Profls. Soc., Order of Coif, Phi Delta Phi, Kappa Sigma. Episcopalian. Clubs: Mpls. Office: McKenna & Cuneo 1575 I St NW Washington DC 20005-1105

STONE, EDMUND CRISPEN, III, banker; b. Charleston, W.Va., Nov. 29, 1942; s. Edmund C. and Sallie Ragland (Thornhill) S.; m. Annette Margarethe Isaksen, Nov. 26, 1965; 1 child, Kristine Margarethe. BS, U.S. Mil. Acad., 1964; MBA, U. Va., 1972. V.p. Wachovia Bank, Winston-Salem, N.C., 1972-81; exec. v.p. First Am. Corp., Nashville, from 1981; vice chmn. First Am. Nat. Bank Nashville, 1988; exec. v.p. Regions Fin. Corp. (formerly First Ala. Bancshares, Inc.), Birmingham, 1988—. Contbg. author: The International Banking Handbook, 1983. Mem. export policy task force U.S. C. of C., 1980-81. With inf. U.S. Army, 1964-70, Vietnam, Iran. Decorated Bronze Star (Valor) with oak leaf cluster, Vietnamese Cross of Gallantry, others; hon. mem. Imperial Iranian Spl. Forces, 1968. Mem. Assn. of Grads. U.S. Mil. Acad. (trustee 1992-93). Republican. Avocations: sailing; hunting; fishing. Office: Regions Fin Corp PO Box 10247 Birmingham AL 35202-0247

STONE, EDWARD CARROLL, physicist, educator; b. Knoxville, Iowa, Jan. 23, 1936; s. Edward Carroll and Ferne Elizabeth (Baber) S.; m. Alice Trabue Wickliffe, Aug. 4, 1962; children: Susan, Janet. AA, Burlington Jr. Coll., 1956; MS, U. Chgo., 1959, PhD, 1964; DSc (hon.), Washington U., Saint Louis, 1992, Harvard U., 1992, U. Chgo., 2002. Rsch. fellow in physics Calif. Inst. Tech., Pasadena, 1964-66, sr. rsch. fellow, 1967, mem. faculty, 1967—, prof. physics, 1976-94, David Morrisroe prof. physics, 1994—, v.p. for astron. facilities, 1988-90, v.p., dir. Jet Propulsion Lab., 1991—; Voyager project scientist, 1972—; cons. Office of Space Scis., NASA, 1969-85, mem. adv. com. outer planets, 1972-73; mem. NASA Solar System Exploration Com., 1983; mem. com. on space astronomy and astrophysics Space Sci. Bd., 1979-82; mem. NASA high energy astrophysics mgmt. operating working group, 1976-84, NASA Cosmic Ray Program Working Group, 1980-82, Outer Planets Working Group, NASA Solar System Exploration Com., 1981-82, Space Sci. Bd., NRC, 1982-85, NASA Univ. Relations Study Group, 1983, steering group Space Sci. Bd. Study on Major Directions for Space Sci., 1995-2015, 1984-85; mem. exec. com. Com. on Space Research Interdisciplinary Sci. Commn., 1982-86; mem. commn. on phys. scis., math. and resources NRC, 1986-89; mem. adv. com. NASA/Jet Propulsion Labs. vis. sr. scientist program, 1986-90; mem. com. on space policy NRC, 1988-89; chmn. adv. panel for The Astronomers, KCET, 1989—. Mem. editrl. bd. Space Sci. Instrumentation, 1975-81, Space Sci. Rev., 1982-85, Astrophysics and Space Sci., 1982—, Sci. mag. Bd. dirs. W.M. Keck Found. Recipient medal for exceptional sci. achievement NASA, 1980, Disting. Svc. medal, 1981, Outstanding Leadership medal, 1986, 95, Disting. Pub. Svc. medal, 1985, Am. Edn. award, 1981, Dryden award, 1983, Space Sci. award AIAA, 1984, Aviation Week and Space Tech. Aerospace Laureate, 1989, Sci. award Nat. Space Club, 1990, Sci. Man of Yr. award ARCS Found., 1991, Pres.'s Nat. medal of Sci., 1991, Am. Philos. Soc. Magellanic award, 1992, Am. Acad. Achievement Golden Plate award, 1992, COSPAR award for outstanding contbn. to space sci., 1992, LeRoy Randle Grumman medal, 1992, Disting. Pub. Svc. award Aviation/Space Writers Assn., 1993; Sloan Found. fellow, 1971-73. Fellow AIAA (assoc.), AAAS, Am. Phys. Soc. (chmn. cosmic physics div. 1979-80, exec. com. 1974-76), Am. Geophys. Union; mem. NAS, Internat. Astron. Union, Internat. Acad. Astronautics, Am. Astron. Soc. (com. mem. div. planetary scis. 1981-84), Am. Assn. Physics Tchrs., Am. Philos. Soc., Calif. Assn. Rsch. in Astronomy (bd. dirs. 1985—, vice chmn. 1987-88, 91-94, chmn. 1988-91, 94—), Astron. Soc. Pacific (hon.), Nat. Space Club (bd. govs.). Office: Jet Propulsion Lab 4800 Oak Grove Dr M/S 180-904 Pasadena CA 91109

STONE, EDWARD DURELL, JR., landscape architect; b. Norwalk, Conn., Aug. 30, 1932; s. Edward Durell and Orlean (Vandiver) S.; m. Jacqueline Marty, Dec. 15, 1954 (div.); children: Edward D. III, Patricia Marty; m. Jean Herrell Weaver, May 13, 1978 (div.). B.A. in Architecture, Yale U., 1954; M.Landscape Architecture, Harvard U., 1959. Pres. Edward D. Stone, Jr., & Assos. (P.A.), Ft. Lauderdale, Fla., 1960-89, chmn., 1989—; vis. critic, lectr. Tex. A&M U., Lawrence Inst. Tech., U. Ga., U. Fla., U. Mich., U. Ill., U. Va., U. Tenn.; adj. prof. landscape architecture U. Miami, Fla.; cons. First Lady's Com. More Beautiful Capital, 1965-68, Fla. Gov.'s Conf. Environ. Quality, 1968-69; mem. Commn. Fine Arts, Washington, 1971-85; Mem. vis. com. Harvard U. Sch. Design; guest lectr. Chautaqua Inst., 1989, Golf Course Europe '89, Wiesbaden, Fed. Republic Germany, 1st Internat. Resort Conf., Tokyo, 1989, Symposium on European Recreational and Leisure Devel., Opio, France, 1989. Landscape archtl. designer: Pepsico World Hdqrs., Purchase, N.Y., 1972, Bal Harbour Shops (Fla.), 1971, El Morro Resort, Puerto La Cruz, Venezuela, 1972—, Profl. Golf Assn. Hdqrs. Master Plan, Palm Beach, Fla., 1978-79, Grand Cypress Resort, Orlando, Fla., 1983, Carambola Beach and Golf Club, St. Croix, V.I., 1988, Ft. Lauderdale (Fla.) Beach Revitalization, 1989, Onagawa, Japan, 1989, Pont Royal, Aix-en-Provence, France, 1989, Treyburn, Durham N.C., 1984, Euro Disney, Marne la Vallee, France, 1990, Riverwalk, Ft. Lauderdale, FL, 1989, El Conquistador, P.R., 1990. V.p. Landscape Architecture Found.; bd. dirs. Fla. Trust for Hist. Preservation, 1985-88. Capt. USAF, 1954-57. Recipient Profl. Landscape Architecture award HUD, 1968, awards Am. Assn. Nurserymen, 1967, 69, 70, 71, 77, 83, 88, 90, 91, Fla. Nurserymen and Growers Assn., 1982, 83, 85, 86, 88, 90, 91, 92, Am. Resort and Residential Devel. Assn., 1984, 85, 88, 89, 90, 91, 92, Interior Landscape Assn., 1984, 85. Fellow Am. Soc. Landscape Architects (13 awards 1963-88, 8 awards Fla. chpt. 1981-89, awards N.C. chpt. 1987, 88, 9, 92, Am. Soc. Landscape Artists medal 1994). Office: Stone Edward D Jr & Assocs 1512 E Broward Blvd Ste 110 Fort Lauderdale FL 33301-2126

STONE, EDWARD HARRIS, II, landscape architect; b. Lanesboro, Pa., Aug. 28, 1933; s. Frank Addison and Beth Lee (Brennan) S.; m. Diane Gertrude Berg, June 11, 1955; children: Randel Harris, Deborah Dee. B.S., SUNY, 1955. Landscape architect Harmon, O'Donnell & Henninger, Denver, 1955-56, U.S. Forest Service, Colo., 1958-61; regional landscape architect Alaska, 1961-64, Colo., 1964-65; chief landscape architect U.S. Forest Service, U.S. Dept. Agr., Washington, 1966-79; asst. dir. for recreation U.S. Forest Service, U.S. Dept. Agr., 1979-85; ret., 1985; with C-3 Co., Bowie, Md., 1986—. Served with AUS, 1956-57. Recipient Arthur S. Flemming award for outstanding fed. govt. service U.S. Jr. C. of C., 1969. Fellow Am. Soc. Landscape Architects (pres. 1975-76); mem. Sigma Lambda Alpha (hon.). Home and Office: 13200 Forest Dr Bowie MD 20715-4390

STONE, ELIZABETH WENGER, retired educator; b. Dayton, Ohio, June 21, 1918; d. Ezra and Anna Bess (Markey) Wenger; m. Thomas A. Stone, Sept. 14, 1939 (dec. Feb. 1987); children: John Howard, Anne Elizabeth, James Alexander. A.B., Stanford U., 1937, M.A., 1938; M.L.S., Catholic U. Am., 1961; Ph.D., Am. U., 1968. Tchr. pub. schs. Fontana, Calif., 1938-39; asst. state statistician State of Conn., 1939-40; libr. New Haven Pub. Librs., 1940-42; dir. pub. relations, asst. to pres. U. Dubuque, Iowa, 1942-46; substitute libr. Pasadena (Calif. Pub. Libr. System), 1953-60; instr. Cath. U. Am., 1962-63, asst. prof., asst. to chmn. dept. libr. sci., 1963-67, assoc. prof., asst. to chmn., 1967-71, prof., asst. to chmn., 1971-72, prof., chmn. dept., 1972-80, dean Sch. Libr. and Info. Scis., 1981-83, prof. and dean emeritus, 1983—, lectr., 1990; libr. cons. U.S. Inst. of Peace, 1988-90; libr. Nat. Presbyn. Ch., Washington, 1991—, archivist, 1994—; founder, exec. dir. Continuing Libr. Edn. Network and Exchange, 1975-79; regional Nat. Rehab. Info. Ctr., 1977, project mgr., 1977-83; co-chmn. 1st World Conf. on Continuing Edn. for the Libr. and Info. Sci. Professions, 1984-85, 2nd World Conf., Barcelona, 1993. Author: Factors Related to the Professional Development of Librarians, 1969, (with James J. Kortendick) Job Dimensions and Educational Needs in Librarianship, 1971, (with R. Patrick and B. Conroy) Continuing Library and Information Science Education, 1974, Continuing Library Education as Viewed in Relation to Other Continuing Professional Movements, 1975, (with F. Peterson and M. Chobot) Motivation: A Vital Force in the Organization, 1977, American Library Development 1600-1899, 1977, (with others) Model Continuing Education Recognition System in Library and Information Science, 1979, (with M.J. Young) A Program for Quality in Continuing Education for Information, Library and Media Personnel, 1980, (with others) Continuing Education for the Library Information Professions, 1985, The Growth of Continuing Education, 1986, Library Education: Continuing Professional Education, 1993, (with others) ALA World Encyclopedia of Library and Information Science, 3d edit., 1993; author, editor: Continuing Professional Education for Library and Information Science Personnel: Papers from Seminar at Matica Slovenska, Martin Czechoslovakia, 1989; editor: D.C. Libraries, 1964-66; contbr. articles to profl. jours. Mem. Pres.'s Com. on Employment of Handicapped, 1972-88; Establishment of Elizabeth W. Stone Lectureship Cath. U. Am., 1990; pres. D.C. chpt. Am. Mothers, Inc., 1984-86, nat. v.p., 1989-91. Recipient Presdl. award Cath. U. Am., 1982, Spl. Librs. Profl. award, 1988, DCLA Ainsworth Rand Spofford Pres.'s award, 1990, Hon. Life Mem. 1994, Alumni Achievement award in libr. and info. sci. Cath. U. Am., 1990; named D.C. Mother of Yr., 1980. Mem. ALA (coun. 1976-83, v.p. 1980-81, pres. 1981-82, chmn. Nat. Libr. Week 1983-85, founder ALA Nat. Ptnrs. for Librs. and Literacy 1984, Lippincott award 1986, Hon. Life award 1986), Assn. Libr. Info. and Sci. Edn. (pres. 1974), Am. Soc. Assn. Execs., Am. Assn. Adult and Continuing Edn., Internat. Fedn. Libr. Assns. and Instns. (chmn. Continuing Profl. Edn. Roundtable 1986—), D.C. Libr. Assn. (hon. life, pres. 1966-67, hon. chair centennial com. 1992-94, hon. life 1994), Spl. Librs. Assn. (hon. life, pres. D.C. chpt. 1973-74), Cath. Libr. Assn. (hon. life), Continuing Profl. Edn. Libr. and Info Sci. Pers., Cosmos Club, Phi Sigma Alpha, Beta Phi Mu, Phi Lambda Theta. Presbyterian. Home: 4000 Cathedral Ave NW # 15B Washington DC 20016-5249 Office: Cath U Am Washington DC 20064

STONE, F. L. PETER, lawyer; b. Wilmington, Del., Feb. 24, 1935; s. Linton and Lorinda (Hamlin) S.; m. Therese Louise Hannon, Apr. 7, 1969; 1 child, Lisa Judith. AB, Dartmouth Coll, 1957; LLB, Harvard U., 1960. Bar: Del. Supreme Ct. 1960, U.S. Ct. Appeals (3d cir.) 1964, U.S. Supreme Ct. 1965, U.S. Ct. Appeals (fed. cir.) 1983. Assoc. Connolly, Bove & Lodge, Wilmington, 1960-64; dep. atty. gen. State of Del., Wilmington, 1965-66; atty. Del. Gen. Assembly, Dover, 1967-68; counsel Gov. Del., Dover, 1969; U.S. atty. Dist. of Del., Wilmington, 1969-72; ptnr. Connolly, Bove, Lodge, & Hutz, Wilmington, 1972—; mem. Del. Agy. to Reduce Crime, 1969-72, Del. Organized Crime Commn., 1970-72, State Drug Abuse Coun., 1990-93, State Judicial Nominating Commn., 1991-93, State Coun. Corrections, 1992—; co-founder, adj. prof. criminal justice progra, West Chester (Pa.) U., 1975-79; chmn. Gov.'s Harness Racing Investigation Com., 1977, Del. Jai Alai Commn., 1977-78, Corrections Task Force, 1986-88. Author numerous articles. Chmn. UN Day, Del., 1989; Rep. candidate for atty. gen. Del., 1990; mem. Del. Gov.'s Task Force on Prison Security, 1994-95; trustee Leukemia Soc. Am., N.Y.C., 1972-74, Marywood Coll., Scranton, Pa., 1974-79, Ursuline Acad., Wilmington, 1974-80. Mem. Wilmington Country Club, Rodney Square Club, Lincoln Club Del. (pres. 1994), Rotary (bd. dirs. 1995—), Port of Wilmington Maritime Soc. (v.p. 1995—), nat. Assn. of Former U.S. Attys. (bd. dirs. 1995—). Roman Catholic. Avocations: hiking/mountaineering, tennis, music. Office: Connolly Bove Lodge & Hutz 1220 Market St PO Box 2207 Wilmington DE 19899

STONE, FRANZ THEODORE, retired fabricated metal products manufacturing executive; b. Columbus, Ohio, May 11, 1907; s. Julius Frederick and Edna (Andress) S.; m. Katherine Devereux Jones, Feb. 23, 1935; children: Franz Theodore, Thomas Devereux Mackay, Raymond Courtney (dec.), Catherine Devereux Diebold. AB magna cum laude, Harvard U., 1929; hon. degrees, Canisius Coll., 1975, Ohio State U., 1976. Chmn. bd. Columbus McKinnon Corp., Amherst, N.Y., 1935-86. Chmn. emeritus Arts Council in Buffalo and Erie County, 1973-86; pres. Buffalo Philharmonic Orch. Soc., 1959-61, also life dir.; chmn. emeritus Studio Arena Theatre, Buffalo, 1968-86; Nat. Conf. of Christians and Jews Brother Sisterhood citation, 1986; First Arts award Arts Council and Greater Buffalo C. of C. Recipient Gold Key award Buffalo YMCA, 1966, Red Jacket award Buffalo & Erie County Hist. Soc., 1976, Disting. Citizen award SUNY, Buffalo, 1985, Conductor's award Buffalo Philharm. Orch., 1993. Mem. Gulfstream Bath & Tennis Club, Ocean Club of Fla., Boca Raton Country Club, Pundits Club, The Greenbrier Club (W. Va.), Buffalo Country Club,

Buffalo Club, Saturn Club (Buffalo), The Little Club (Gulfstream). Home: 1171 N Ocean Blvd Apt 4CS Delray Beach FL 33483

STONE, FRED MICHAEL, lawyer; b. Bklyn., Jan. 20, 1943; s. Nathan and Rose (Silverman) S.; m. Bonnie B. Dobkin, Aug. 14, 1965; children—Jonathan, Jennifer. A.B. cum laude, Bklyn. Coll., 1964; J.D., Harvard U., 1967; LL.M., N.Y. U., 1971. Bar: N.Y. 1968. Assoc. Cadwalader, Wickersham & Taft, N.Y.C., 1967-69; asst. gen. counsel Standard & Poor's/Intercapital, Inc., N.Y.C., 1969-71; v.p., gen. counsel Neuwirth Funds, 1971-73, Mocatta Metals Corp., N.Y.C., 1973-76; sr. v.p., gen. counsel Am. Stock Exchange, Inc., N.Y.C., 1976-86; exec. v.p., gen. counsel Jamie Securities Co., Caronan Ptnrs., N.Y.C., 1986-88; sr. v.p., gen. counsel, sec. M.D. Sass Assocs., Inc., N.Y.C., 1989—; chmn. exec. com. Amex Commodities Exch., 1980-81; dir. Am. Gold Coin Exchange, Inc., 1981-85; exec. v.p., dir. Revere Copper and Brass, Inc., 1986-88; dir. Ea. Electric Motor Co., Inc., 1987-88; ocfl. adv. Drafting Com. to Reivse Uniform Securities Act of Nat. conf. Uniform State Law Commrs., 1981-85; chmn. options and futures regulation subcom. of fed. regulation of securities com. ABA, 1989-91, mem. task force on Hedge Funds, 1994—; lectr. various legal seminars; sec. rules com. Investment Co. Inst., 1989-92; sec., treas. steering com. Taxable Mcpl. Bondholders Protective Com., 1990—. Mem. Manalapan (N.J.) Twp. Zoning Bd. Adjustment, 1975-86; vice-chmn. Manalapan Dem. Com., 1988—; Dem. candidate for Manalapan Twp. Com., 1989, 93; mem. N.J. regional exec. com. Anti-Defamation League of B'nai Brith, 1991—. Mem. ABA, Assn. of Bar of City of N.Y., Harvard U. Law Sch. Assn., Am. Stock Exch., Inc. (arbitrator 1986—), Nat. Assn. Securities Dealers Inc. (arbitrator 1986—), Nat. Futures Assn. (nominating com. 1986-88). Democrat. Jewish. Home: 15 Kingsley Dr Manalapan NJ 07726-3134

STONE, GEOFFREY RICHARD, law educator, lawyer; N.Y.C.; b. Jan. 20, 1946; s. Robert R. and Shirley (Weliky) S.; m. Nancy Spector, Oct. 8, 1977; children: Julie, Mollie. BS, U. Pa., 1968; JD, U. Chgo., 1971. Bar: N.Y. 1972. Law clk. to Hon. J. S. Kelly Wright, U.S. Ct. Appeals (D.C. cir.), 1971-72; law clk. to Hon. William J. Brennan, Jr., U.S. Supreme Ct., 1972-73; asst. prof. U. Chgo., 1973-77, assoc. prof., 1977-79, prof., 1979-84, Harry Kalven Jr. disting. svc. prof., 1984-93; dean Law Sch., 1987-93, provost, 1994—. Author: Constitutional Law, 1986, 2d edit., 1991, The Bill Of Rights In The Modern State, 1992; editor The Supreme Ct. Rev., 1991—; contbr. articles to profl. jours. Bd. dirs. Ill. div. ACLU, 1978-84; bd. advisors Pub. Svc. Challenge, 1989. Fellow AAAS; mem. Chgo. Coun. Lawyers (bd. govs. 1976-77), Assn. Am. Law Schs. (exec. com. 1990-93), Legal Aid Soc. (bd. dirs. 1988), Order of Coif. Office: U Chgo 5801 S Ellis Ave Chicago IL 60637

STONE, GEORGE ELIOT, textile executive; b. Phila., Oct. 10, 1934; s. James K. and Betty (Kays) S.; m. Charotte Critz Harper, Oct. 3, 1959; children: Ruth Gray, Lucy Hull, Eliot. BA, Harvard U., 1956. V.p. State Street Bank, Boston, 1956-65; mgr. Milliken & Co., Spartanburg, S.C., 1965-70; chief exec. officer, chmn. bd. Baxter, Kelly & Faust Inc., Anderson, S.C., 1970-76; chmn. bd. Jackson Mills, Inc., Wellford, S.C., 1976—. Mem. adv. bd. Spartanburg Salvation Army; trustee Converse Coll, Spartanburg, Mary Black Meml. Hosp., Spartanburg. Mem. Am. Textile Mfg. Inst. (nat. bd. dirs.), Inst. Textile Tech. (nat. trustee), S.C. Textile Mfg. Assn. (past bd. dirs.). Republican. Episcopalian. Office: Jackson Mills Inc 1 Railroad St Wellford SC 29385

STONE, HARRY H., business executive; b. Cleve. May 21, 1917; s. Jacob and Jennie (Kantor) Sapirstein; m. Lucile Tabak, Aug. 10, 1960; children: Phillip, Allan, Laurie (Mrs. Parker), James Rose, Douglas Rose. Student, Cleve. Coll., 1935-36. With Am. Greetings Corp., Cleve., 1936—, v.p., 1944-58, exec. v.p., 1958-69, vice chmn. bd., chmn. finance com., chmn audit com., 1969-78, now dir.; mem. Ofcl. U.S. Mission to India and Nepal, 1965; cons. 1969-78, now dir.; mem. U.S. Dept. Commerce, U.S. Dept. State; adviser U.S. del. 24th session UN Econ. Commn. for Asia and Far East, Canberra, Australia, 1968; cons. Nat. Endowment for Arts, Nat. Council on Arts. Treas. Criminal Justice Coordinating Council., 1968-82; trustee emeritus Brandeis U., also univ. fellow. Mem. Rotary. Home: Suite 9D Bratenahl Pl # 2 Cleveland OH 44108 Office: The Courtland Group Inc 1540 Leader Bldg Cleveland OH 44114

STONE, HARVEY H., civil engineer, executive; b. N.Y.C., Mar. 24, 1942; s. George and Sylvia (Stein) S.; m. Carol Lucia Piccirillo; children: Margarida Stone Kondak, Dan, Deborah, Jim, Marco. BCE, Rensselaer Polytech., 1963. Registered profl. engr., Vt., Pa.; registered surveyor, Pa. Engr. U.S. Army Corps of Engrs., N.Y.C., 1964-66; project engr. A.W. Cross & Co., Burlington, N.J., 1966-68, George Atkin Jr. Profl. Engr. Tidoute, Pa., 1968-69; v.p. engring. Northwest Engring. Inc., Tidoute, 1969-75, exec. v.p., 1975-79, pres., 1979—. Supr. Glade Twp. Warren County, Pa., 1983-88. Mem. NSPE (pres. Buctails chpt. Pa. 1975-77), Am. Consulting Engrs. Coun. (Outstanding Engring. Achievement, Pa. Coun., 1980, 82, 93), Am. Assn. State Hwy. Engrs. Office: Northwest Engring Inc PO Box Q RR 1 Tidioute PA 16351-9801

STONE, HERBERT MARSHALL, architect; b. N.Y.C., July 12, 1936; s. Irving and Rose (Gelb) S.; m. Linda Ann Baskind, May 30, 1960; children: Ian Howard, Matthew Lloyd. BArch, Pratt Inst., N.Y.C., 1958, postgrad., 1958-59. Registered architect, N.Y., Iowa, Kans., Ill., Wis., Minn. Designer Henry Dreyfuss Indsl. Design, N.Y.C., 1960-63; architect Max O. Urbahn Architect, N.Y.C., 1963-66; project architect Brown Healey Bock, P.C., Cedar Rapids, Iowa, 1966-73; ptnr. Brown Healey Stone & Sauer, Cedar Rapids, Iowa, 1973—; guest lectr. U.S. Inst. Theatre Tech., Seattle, 1978; speaker on design of pub. libs. ALA Nat. Conv., Miami, Fla., 1994. Prin. works include Strayer-Wood Theatre, 1978, KUNI radio sta. U. No. Iowa, 1978, Cedar Rapids Pub. Libr., 1984, Greenwood Terr. Sr. Citizen Housing, 1986, Iowa State Hist. Mus., 1988, Nat. Hot Air Balloon Mus., 1988 (Spectrum Ceramic Tile Grand award 1989), Student Ctr. Grinnell Coll., 1992. Pres. Cedar Rapids Trust for Hist. Preservation, 1981—; bd. dirs. Art in Pub. Places Com., Cedar Rapids, 1988, Cedar Rapids/Marion Arts Coun., 1988, Jane Boyd Community House, Cedar Rapids, 1988. Mem. AIA, Am. 1988, Jane Boyd Community House, Cedar Rapids, 1988. Mem. AIA, Am. Mus. Assn., Greater Downtown Assn. Cedar Rapids. Avocations: bicycling, skiing, reading, ceramics. Home: 3730 Terrace Hill Dr NE Cedar Rapids IA 52402-2846 Office: Brown Healey Stone & Sauer PC 800 1st Ave NE Cedar Rapids IA 52402-5002

STONE, HOWARD LAWRENCE, lawyer; b. Chgo., Sept. 16, 1941; s. Jerome Richard Stone and Ceale (Perlik) Stone Tandet; m. Susan L. Saltzman, June 2, 1963; children—Lauren, David. Student U. Ill., 1960-61; B.S.B.A., Roosevelt U., 1963; J.D., DePaul U., 1972. Bar: Ill. 1972, U.S. Tax Ct. (no. dist.) Ill. 1972, U.S. Tax Ct. 1972, U.S. Supreme Ct. 1982; C.P.A., Ill. Agt. IRS, Chgo., 1964-72; spl. asst. U.S. atty. and chief fin. auditor and investigator No. Dist. Ill., Dept. Justice, Chgo., 1972-76; sr. ptnr. Stone, McGuire & Benjamin, Chgo., 1976—; lectr. in taxation. Author: Defending the Federal Tax Case: What To Do When the IRS Steps In, 1978; Client Tax Fraud—A Practical Guide to Protecting Your Rights, 1984. Coeditor, co-author: Handling Criminal Tax Cases: A Lawyers Guide, 1982, 87; co-author: Federal Civil Tax Law, 1982, 88; co-author: Negotiating to Win, 1985. Bd. dirs. Israel Bonds, Chgo., 1982, U. Chgo.; chmn. U. Ill. Found. Fund for Gerontology Rsch., 1984—; bd. dirs. Gastro Intestinal Research Found. U. Chgo., 1978—. Mem. Chgo. Bar Assn., Ill. State Bar Assn., Fed. Bar Assn., ABA, Decalogue Soc. Lawyers, Am. Inst. C.P.A.'s, Ill. C.P.A. Found., Am. Assn. Atty.-C.P.A.s, Ill. C.P.A. Soc. (resident lectr. in tax fraud 1976-84, 90, 91, chmn. Investment Advisers Act task force 1983-84, co-chair accts. liability annual conf.). Jewish. Lodges: B'nai B'rith, Shriners. Office: Altschuler Melvoin & Glasser 30 Wacker St Ste 2600 Chicago IL 60606

STONE, HUBERT DEAN, editor, journalist; b. Maryville, Tenn., Sept. 23, 1924; s. Archie Hubert and Annie (Cupp) S.; student Maryville Coll., 1942-43; B.A., U. Okla., 1949; m. Agnes Shirley, Sept. 12, 1953 (dec. Mar. 1973); 1 son, Neal Anson. Sunday editor Maryville-Alcoa Daily Times, 1949; mng. editor Maryville-Alcoa Times, 1949-78, editor, 1978—; v.p. Maryville-Alcoa Newspapers, Inc., 1960-90; pres. Stonecraft, 1954—. Photographer in field. Vice chmn. Tenn. Great Smoky Mountain Park Commn.; co-chmn. 175th anniversary com. Maryville Coll.; mem. mayor's adv. com. City of Maryville; mem. air service adv. com. Knoxville Met. Airport Authority; bd. dirs. United Fund of Blount County, 1961-63, 74-76, vice chmn. campaign, 1971-72, chmn. campaign, 1973, v.p., 1974, pres. 1975; vice chmn. bd. dirs.

Maryville Utilities Bd.; bd. dirs. Sam Houston Meml. Assn., Alcoa City Sch. Found., Blount County Hist. Trust, Nat. Hillbilly Homecoming Assn., Friendsville Acad., 1968-73, Alkiwan Crafts, Inc., 1970-73, Middle East Tenn. Regional Tourism Group; dir. Foothills Land Conservancy, Smoky Mountains Passion Play Assn., Blound County History Mus.; mem. adv. com. Blount County Alternative Center for Learning, Overlook Center, Inc., Sr. Citizens Home Assistance Svcs.; chmn. Blount County Long Range Planning for Sch. Facilities; mem. adv. bd. Harrison-Chilhowee Bapt. Acad, mem. Leadership Knoxville; co-founder, vice pres., pres. Leadership Blount County; founder, chmn. Townsend-in-the-Smokies Art Show/Sale, 1984—; mem. bd. govs. Maryville-Alcoa C.C. Orch. Soc; trustee, pres. bd. trustees, deacon, chmn. evangelism, fin. & pers. coms. Bapt. Ch.; mem. Blount County Bicentennial Task Force. Served from pvt. to staff sgt. AUS, 1943-45. Decorated Bronze Star; named Outstanding Sr. Man of Blount County, 1970, 77, Hon. Order Ky. Cols., Commonwealth of Ky.; recipient Pride of Tenn. award for vol. work, 1993, Outstanding Leadership award Maryville Ch. of Christ, First Tourism Pioneer award Smoky Mount. Vis. Bur. and Blount C. of C., 1994. Mem. VFW, Profl. Photographers of Am., Internat. Post Card Distbrs. Assn., Great Smoky Mountains Natural History Assn., Ft. Loudoun Assn., Tenn. Jaycees (dir. 1954-55, sec.-treas. 1955-56), Blount County Arts/ Crafts Guild, Jr. Chamber Internat. (senator) Maryville-Alcoa Jaycees (life mem., pres. 1953-54), Blount County (v.p. 1971, 76, pres. 1977), Townsend (dir. 1969-71, 83-85, pres. 1983) chambers commerce, Tenn. Associated Press News Execs. Assn. (v.p. 1973, pres. 1974), Assoc. Press Mng. Editors Assn., Tenn. Profl. Photographers Assn., Am. Legion, Foothills Pkwy. Assn. (v.p., pres.), Chilhowee Bapt. Assn. (chmn. history com.) U. Okla. Alumni Assn. (life mem., pres. East Tenn. chpt. 1954-55), Sigma Delta Chi (life, dir. E. Tenn. chpt.), Mason, Kiwanian (pres. Alcoa 1969-70); Club: Green Meadow Country. Contbr. articles to profl. publs. Home: 1510 Scenic Dr Maryville TN 37803-5634 Office: 307 E Harper Ave Maryville TN 37801-4040

STONE, ILEANE GERTRUDE, gerontologist; b. Detroit, Jan. 5, 1933; d. Joseph and Edith (Shecter) Mosten; m. Ted Stone, Dec. 25, 1952; children: Paul, Randall, Howard. BS, Wayne State U., 1954; MA, U. Mich., 1978. Counselor-ex-inst. mentally ill elderly Well Being Svcs., Detroit, 1979-81; dir. social svcs., programs, vol. svc. St. Paul's Manor & Health Ctr., San Diego, 1981-88; dir. programs and spl. projects Villa Pomerado Health Ctr., Poway, Calif., 1988-89; dir. Alzheimer adult day care Redwood Sr. Svcs., Escondido, Calfi., 1989-90, dir. social svc. activities, vol. svc., 1990—; instr. gerontology Wayne County C.C., Detroit, 1980-81; cons. Nu Age Counseling Svcs., San Diego, 1984—, Dist. Atty. San Diego Spl. Team Cons., 1986-88; lectr. Soc. Clin. Social Work, San Diego, 1987, Svc. Ctr. for Blind, San Diego, 1987, Am. Assn. Homes for Aged, 1987. Author: Success with Seniors, 1989. Charter mem. City of San Diego Coun. on Aging. Mem. Am. Soc. Aging (lectr. 1985, 88), Nat. Coun. on Aging, Am. Bus. Womens Assn. Avocations: singing, dancing, golf, lecturing, theatre. Home: 17790 Fonticello Way San Diego CA 92128-1849 Office: Redwood Terr 710 W 13th Ave Escondido CA 92025-5599

STONE, IRENE MILDRED, county commissioner; b. Chgo., July 6, 1928; d. Leopold and Anastazie (Klepsa) Macha; m. Robert James Stone, Mar. 1, 1946 (div. Apr. 1974); children: Linda Rae Stone Buziecki, Robert Leo, Michael Wayne. AA, Wright Coll., 1966; BA, U. Ill., Chgo., 1984; postgrad., U. Ill., 1984-85. Cert. real estate broker, med. technologist. Rsch. technologist Loyola U., Maywood, Ill., 1968-71; med. asst. Dr. Robert Cliche, Oak Park, Ill., 1971-73; toxicological cont and liaison Sunbeam Rsch. & Engring., Oak Brook, Ill., 1974-77; assoc. broker and appraiser Thorsen Realtors, Oak Brook, 1977-80; rsch. biologist West Side Vets. Adminstrv. Hosp., Chgo., 1980-81; lab. mgr. U. Ill., Chgo., 1981-85; bd. mem., forest res. commr. DuPage County, Wheaton, Ill., 1986—, also vice-chmn. solid waste com., mem. coms. sound waste and recycling, fin. and land acquisition, legis., ops. and devel., mem. reforestation subcom.; Forest Preserve Commr., mem. numerous coms. including Pub. Safety Com., Health & Human Svcs. Com. Crime Lab Com., Legis. Com., Reforestation Com.; legis. com. DuPage Bd. Realtors, Wheaton, 1985-87. Precinct committeeman York Twp. Rep. Committeemen's Assn., Lombard, Ill., 1970-88, mem. legis. com. 1974-76; mem. Lombard's Bldg. & Zoning Commn., 1973-81, adv. bd. Citizen's Alliance Party, Lombard, 1973-76, Lombard's zoning revisions, 1975-76, Lombard Rep. Women's Club (pres. 1984-86). Mem. Am. Legion Aux. (pres. 1961-62), Broadview Club, Nat. Assn. Counties (mem. environ. engring. com., steering com. for environ. energy and land use 1980—). Episcopalian. Avocations: breeding, training and showing Borzois, painting, golfing, tennis, sailing. Home: 326 N Lombard Ave Lombard IL 60148-2013 Office: DuPage County Board DuPage County Ctr 421 N County Farm Rd Wheaton IL 60187-2409

STONE, IRVING I., greeting card company executive; b. Cleve., Apr. 5, 1909; s. Jacob and Jennie (Canter) Sapirstein; m. Helen K. Sill, Dec. 12, 1976; children: Hensha (Mrs. Hirsch Gansbourg), Neil, Myrna (Mrs. Harold Tatar), Judith (Mrs. Morry Weiss). Student, Case-Western Res. U., Cleve. Inst. Art. With Am. Greetings Corp., Cleve., 1923—, pres., 1960-78, chmn. bd., 1978—, chief exec. officer, 1978-87, also chmn. exec. com. Chmn. bd. Hebrew Acad. Cleve.; bd. dirs. Cleve. Inst. Art, Young Israel of Cleve., Yeshiva U.; trustee Simon Wiesenthal Ctr. for Holocaust Studies; 1st v.p. Telshe Yeshiva; life mem. bd. dirs. Jewish Community Fedn. of Cleve.; v.p. Am. Assn. for Jewish Edn., Bur. Jewish Edn., Cleve., Am. Friends of Boys Town Jerusalem; founder Kiryat Telshe Stone, Israel. Office: Am Greetings Corp 1 American Rd Cleveland OH 44144-2301

STONE, JACK, religious organization administrator. Gen. sec., hdqs. ops. officer Ch. of the Nazarene, Kansas City, Mo. Office: Ch Nazarene 6401 The Paseo Kansas City MO 64131

STONE, JAMES HOWARD, management consultant; b. Chgo., Mar. 4, 1939; s. Jerome H. and Evelyn Gertrude (Teitelbaum) S.; m. Carole Marlen David, Apr. 21, 1972; children: Margaret Elisa, Emily Anne, Phoebe Jane. AB cum laude, Harvard U., 1960, MBA, 1962. Cert. mgmt. cons., CMC, 1977. Staff analyst Stone Container Corp., Chgo., 1962-64, gen. mgr., Kansas City Div., 1964-66, asst. treas., 1966-68, dir., 1969—, with exec. com., 1983—; founder, owner, CEO Stone Mgmt. Cons., 1969—; mem. strategic alliance Boston Cons. Group, 1990—; trustee exec. com. Roosevelt U., Chgo., 1983—, exec. com. edn. alliance, 1994—; co-chmn. commn. fgn. and domestic affairs Northwestern U., Evanston, Ill., 1981-86; mem. vis. com. U. Chgo., 1980—, The Chgo. Com., 1986—, Mid-Am. Com., Chgo., 1993—; bd. overseers IIT Stuart Sch. of Bus., 1994—; bd. dirs. Fullerton Metals Corp. Mem. Chgo. Coun. Fgn. Rels., 1967, bd. dirs. 1974-78; bd. dirs., mem. exec. com. NCCJ, Chgo., 1985, presiding co-chmn., 1990—; trustee Hadley Sch. Blind, Winnetka, Ill., 1985, mem. exec. com., chmn. planning com., 1989—. Mem. Warehousing Edn. and Rsch. Coun., Inst. Mgmt. Cons. (pres. Chgo. chpt. 1981-83, regl. dir. 1983-86), Coun. Ogistics Mgmt. (dir. Roundtable-Chgo. 1990-94), Assn. of Corporate Growth, The Exec. Club Chgo., Econs. Club, Harvard Club Chgo., Harvard Bus. Sch. Assocs. Chgo. (dir. 1992), Traffic Club Chgo., Standard Club, Northmoor Country Club. Avocations: family-centered activities, reading, golf, travel, coaching girls' softball. Home: 83 Woodley Rd Winnetka IL 60093-3746 Office: Stone Mgmt Corp 208 S La Salle St Chicago IL 60604-1103

STONE, JAMES J., photographer; b. Los Angeles, Dec. 2, 1947; s. Charles S. and Sylvia S. S.B in Arch, M.I.T., 1970; M.F.A. in Photography, R.I. Sch. Design, 1975. Mem. faculty R.I. Sch. Design, Providence, 1975-78, 93—, Boston Coll., Chestnut Hill, Mass., 1973-88. Author: A User's Guide to the View Camera, 1987, Stranger than Fiction, 1993; editor: Darkroom Dynamics, 1979; one-man shows, Anchorage Fine Arts Mus., 1977, Polaroid Gallery, Cambridge, Mass., 1978, Carl Siembab Gallery, Boston, 1979, Wesleyan U., Middletown, Conn., 1980, Visual Studies Workshop, Rochester, N.Y., 1986, San Francisco Camera Work, 1985, Robert Klein Gallery, 1987, Mitchell Mus., 1989, Huntington Mus. Art, 1990, Rice U., Houston, 1992; exhibited in group shows, De Cordova Mus., Lincoln, Mass., 1972, Fogg Art Mus., Cambridge, 1974, 76, Corcoran Gallery Art, Washington, 1978, 79, Mpls. Inst. Arts, 1987, Phila. Mus. Art, 1987, Nat. Mus. Am. Art, 1992; represented in permanent collection, Nat. Mus. Am. Art, Washington, Corcoran Gallery Art, Fogg Art Mus., George Eastman House, Rochester, L.A. County Mus. Art, Mus. Modern Art, N.Y.C. Pres. bd. dirs. Photog. Resource Ctr., Boston. Mass. Artists Found. artists fellow, 1976, 88, New

Eng. Found. for the Arts/NEA Regional Artists' fellow, 1993; artist-in-residence Alaska State Arts Coun., 1977; NEA photographic survey grantee, 1980. Office: care Robert Klein Gallery 38 Newbury St Boston MA 02116

STONE, JAMES ROBERT, surgeon; b. Greeley, Colo., Jan. 8, 1948; s. Anthony Joseph and Dolores Concetta (Pietrafeso) S.; m. Kaye Janet Friedman, May 16, 1970; children: Jeffrey, Marisa. BA, U. Colo., 1970; MD, U. Guadalajara, Mex., 1976. Diplomate Am. Bd. Surgery, Am. Bd. Surg. Critical Care. Intern Md. Gen. Hosp., Balt., 1978-79; resident in surgery St. Joseph Hosp., Denver, 1979-83; practice medicine specializing in surgery Grand Junction, Colo., 1983-87; staff surgeon, dir. critical care Va. Med. Ctr., Grand Junction, 1988-88; dir. trauma surgery and critical care, chief surgery St. Francis Hosp., Colorado Springs, Colo., 1988-91; pvt. practice Kodiak, Alaska, 1991-92; with South Denver Surg. Cons., Englewood, Colo., 1992-93, Summit Surg. Assocs., 1993—; asst. clin. prof. surgery U. Colo. Health Sci. Ctr., Denver, 1984—; pres. Stone Aire Cons., Grand Junction, 1988—; owner, operator Jjnka Ranch, Flourissant, Colo.; spl. advisor CAP; mem. advisor med. com. unit, 1990-92. Contbr. articles to profl. jours.; inventor in field. Bd. dirs. Mesa County Cancer Soc., 1988-89, Colo. Trauma Inst., 1988-91. Colo. Speaks out on Health grantee, 1988; recipient Bronze medal of Valor Civil Air Patrol. Fellow Denver Acad. Surgery, Southwestern Surg. Congress, Am. Coll. Chest Physicians, Am. Coll. Surgeons (trauma com. Colo. chpt.), Am. Coll. Critical Care; mem. Am. Coll. Physician Execs., Soc. Critical Care (task force 1988—). Roman Catholic. Avocations: horse breeding, hunting, fishing.

STONE, JEFFREY JAY, film critic, journalist, writer; b. Toronto, Ont., Can., Oct. 2, 1946; s. Philip Maurice and Mildred (Walton) S.; m. Sandra Patricia Ridob, May 2, 1970; children: Benjamin Matthew, Laura Noelle. Editor The Record-News, Smith Falls, Ont., 1972-73; reporter, columnist The Brampton (Ont.) Times, 1973-76; copy editor The Ottawa (Ont.) Citizen, 1976-80, asst. sports editor, 1980-81, asst. city editor, 1981-84, design editor, 1984-85, entertainment editor, 1985-90, entertainment columnist, 1990-94, film critic, 1994—. Patron Coun. for Arts in Ottawa, 1994. Mem. Variety Club of Can., Laurentian Jr. Music Club, Elvis Sighting Soc. Avocations: bridge, reading, chess. Office: The Ottawa Citizen, 1101 Baxter Rd, Ottawa, ON Canada K2C 3M4

STONE, JEREMY JUDAH, association executive; b. N.Y.C., Nov. 23, 1935; s. I.F. and Esther (Roisman) S.; m. Betty Jane Yannet, June 16, 1957. B.S. magna cum laude, Swarthmore Coll., 1957, LL.D. (hon.), 1985; Ph.D., Stanford U., 1960. Research mathematician Stanford Research Inst., 1960-62; mem. profl. staff Hudson Inst., Croton-on-Hudson, 1962-64; research assoc., arms control and disarmament Harvard Ctr. Internat. Affairs, 1964-66; asst. prof. math., lectr. polit. sci. Pomona Coll., Claremont, Calif., 1966-68; CEO Fedn. Am. Scientists, Washington, 1970—. Author: Containing the Arms Race; Some Concrete Proposals, 1966, Strategic Persuasion, 1967. Recipient award for pub. svc. Forum on Physics and Soc., Am. Phys. Soc., 1979, Fedn. of Am. Scientists Pub. Svc. award, 1994; Social Sci. Rsch. Coun. fellow in econs. Stanford U., 1968-69, Coun. Fgn. Rels. internat. affairs fellow, 1969-70. Mem. Coun. Fgn. Rels., Internat. Inst. Strategic Studies, Phi Beta Kappa. Home: 5615 Warwick Pl Bethesda MD 20815-5503 Office: Fedn Am Scientists 307 Massachusetts Ave NE Washington DC 20002-5701

STONE, JOE ALLAN, economics educator; b. Seminole, Tex., Mar. 17, 1948; s. Richard Elick and Ivy Lillian (Childs) S.; m. Crystal Lee Barnes, Aug. 30, 1969; children: Christopher Dylan, Elizabeth Ivy. BA, U. Tex., El Paso, 1970; MA, Mich. State U., 1974, PhD, 1977. Research economist U.S. Bur. Labor Stats., Washington, 1977-79; asst. prof. U. Oreg., Eugene, 1979-82, assoc. prof., 1982-84, W.E. Miner prof. econs., 1985—, head dept., 1988-92, assoc. dean Coll. Arts and Scis., 1992—; sr. economist Pres.' Council Econ. Advisors, Washington, 1984-85; vis. scholar Fed. Res. Bank Cleve., 1986. Author: (with others) Unions and Public Schools, 1984, Wage and Employment Adjustment in Local Labor Markets, 1992; contbr. articles to profl. jours. Served with U.S. Army, 1970-72. Mem. AAUP (pres. U. Oreg. chpt. 1986-87), Am. Econ. Assn., Western Econ. Assn., So. Econ. Assn., Indsl. Rels. Rsch. Inst. Episcopalian. Home: 3820 Onyx St Eugene OR 97405-4515 Office: U Oreg Dept Econs Eugene OR 97403

STONE, JOHN FLOYD, soil physics researcher and educator; b. York, Nebr., Oct. 13, 1928; s. Harry Floyd and Anastasia (Klima) S.; m. Carol Ottilie Youngson, Aug. 2, 1953; children: Mary, Margaret, David, Jana. BS, U. Nebr., 1952; MS, Iowa State U., 1955, PhD, 1957. Lab. technician U. Nebr., 1954-55; from rsch. asst. to rsch. assoc. Iowa State U., 1953-57; from asst. to assoc. prof. Okla. State U., Stillwater, 1957-69, prof. soil physics, 1969—; mem. adv. agrl. panel U.S. Dept. Def., 1977-78; mem. grant evaluation panel Water Quality Grant Program, USDA, 1989, Small. Bus. Initiative Rsch. Grant Program, 1990. Editor: Plant Modification for More Efficient Water Use, 1975, Plant Production and Management under Drought Conditions, 1983; contbr. chpts. to books, rsch. articles to profl. jours.; co-patentee apparatus for measuring water content of soil; co-discoverer Nova-Cygni, 1975. Commr. Stillwater City, 1974-75; mem. Stillwater Housing Appeals Bd., 1975-79; com. mem. troop 14 Boy Scouts Am., 1976-83, merit badge counselor, 1974—; del. to jurisdictional conf. United Meth. Ch., 1968, alt. del. to gen. conf., 1968. Grantee USDA, 1980, 83, 89, 90, 91, 92, NSF, 1961, U.S. Dept. Interior, 1968, 73, 79, 89, 91, Okla. Dept. Commerce, 1988, Okla. Coun. for Applied Sci. and Tech., Energy Efficient Irrigation, 1990. Fellow Am. Soc. Agronomy (editl. bd., assoc. editor Agronomy jour. 1982-85); mem. ASCE (com. on irrigation water requirements 1979—, chmn. task com. on calibration and use of neutron moisture meters 1990—, State-of-the-Art of Civil Engring. award 1992), Internat. Soil Sci. Soc., Am. Geophys. Union (vis. scientist lectr. 1972), Sigma Xi, Am. Radio Relay League, Stillwater Amateur Radio Club. Democrat. Methodist. Avocations: photography, amateur astronomy, music, amateur radio. Office: Okla State U Dept Agronomy 264 Agrl Hall Stillwater OK 74078

STONE, JOHN MCWILLIAMS, JR., electronics executive; b. Chgo., Nov. 4, 1927; s. J. McWilliams and Marion (Jones) S.; m. Cheryl Johansen Cullison, Dec. 18, 1976; children: Jean Stone Savanyu, Lee Stone Nelson, John III, Michael (dec.), Shannon, Tammy. BA, Princeton U., 1950. Salesman A.B. Dick Co., Milw., 1950-51; prodn. supr. Dukane Corp., St. Charles, Ill., 1951-56, exec. v.p., 1956-62, pres., 1962-70, pres., chmn. bd., 1970—, chmn. bd., chief exec. officer, 1991—; bd. dirs. Harris Bank St. Charles. Trustee The Elgin (Ill.) Acad., recipient Elgin medal 1984, emeritus, 1985—; Phillips Exeter (N.H.) Council, 1985—, Two Rivers Council Boy Scouts Am., St. Charles; mem. Delnor Hosp. Men's Found., St. Charles. Served with USNR, 1950-52. Named Exec. of Yr. Valley chpt. Profl. Secs. Internat., Aurora, 1981. Mem. Commonwealth Club of Chgo., Econ. Club of Chgo., Princeton Club of Chgo., Execs. Club of Chgo., Dunham Woods Riding Club (pres. 1967-68, 78-79, 89-90). Republican. Episcopalian. Avocation: tennis. Home: PO Box 755 Wayne IL 60184-0755 Office: Dukane Corp 2900 Dukane Dr Saint Charles IL 60174-3395

STONE, JOHN WARE, management consultant; b. Framingham, Mass., May 4, 1940; s. Henry Bowditch and Laura (Bement) S.; m. Sarah McClenny, Apr. 20, 1963 (div. 1979); m. Maribeth Kershaw, Oct. 10, 1981; children: Amy Elizabeth, Richard Taliaferro. BSBA, Charter Oak Coll., 1985. Mgmt. trainee Framingham Trust Co., 1963-65, mgr. data processing, 1964-65; asst. v.p. Essex County Bank, Lynn, Mass., 1965-68, v.p., 1968-71; v.p. Vt. Nat. Bank, Brattleboro, 1971-76, v.p., 1976-78; dir. mktg. Fin. Industry Systems, Hartford, Conn., 1978-80; mgr. KPMG Peat Marwick, Hartford, 1980-85; ptnr. KPMG Peat Marwick, Boston, 1985—. Contbg. editor: Bank Systems and Tech., 1983-90. Founder Brattleboro Hockey Assn., 1976; class corr. Northfield Mt. Hermon (Mass.) H.S., 1989-92. Mem. Data Processing Mgmt. Assn. (pres. 1969-70), Jaycees (pres. Greater Lynn chpt. 1970, founder Rowley, Mass. chpt. 1971), Holliston Newcomers (chmn. fund raising 1987-88). Avocations: sailing, golf, skiing. Office: KPMG Peat Marwick 1 Boston Pl Boston MA 02108

STONE, LAWRENCE, historian; b. Epsom, Surrey, Eng., Dec. 4, 1919; came to U.S., 1963, naturalized, 1970; s. Lawrence Frederick and Mabel Julia Annie (Read) S.; m. Jeanne Caecilia Fawtier, July 24, 1943; children: Elizabeth Caecilia, Robert Lawrence Fawtier. Student, U. Paris-Sorbonne, 1938; BA, MA, Christ Church, Oxford (Eng.) U., 1946; LHD, U. Chgo., 1979, U. Pa., 1986; LittD, U. Edinburgh, 1983, U. Glasgow, 1993; Oxford

U., 1994. Bryce research student Oxford U., 1946-47; lectr. Oxford U. (Univ. Coll.), 1947-50; fellow Wadham Coll., 1950-63; mem. Inst. Advanced Study, Princeton, 1960-61; Dodge prof. history Princeton, 1963-90, chmn. dept. history, 1967-70; dir. Shelby Cullom Davis Ctr. Hist. Studies, 1968-90. Author: Sculpture in Britain: The Middle Ages, 1955, An Elizabethan: Sir Horatio Palavicino, 1956, The Crisis of the Aristocracy, 1558-1641, 1965, The Causes of the English Revolution 1529-1642, 1972, rev. edit., 1986, Family and Fortune: Studies in Aristocratic Finance in the Sixteenth and Seventeenth Centuries, 1973, Family, Sex and Marriage in England 1500-1800, 1977, The Past and the Present, 1981, An Open Elite England: 1540-1880, 1985, The Past and the Present Revisited, 1987, Road to Divorce: England 1530-1987, 1990, Uncertain Unions: Marriage in England 1660-1753, 1992, Broken Lives: Marital Separation and Divorce in England 1660-1857, 1993, also numerous articles.; mem. editorial bd. Past and Present, 1959—. Served as lt. Royal Naval Vol. Res., 1940-45. Fellow Am. Acad. Arts and Scis.; Corr. mem. Brit. Acad.; mem. Am. Philos. Soc. Home: 266 Moore St Princeton NJ 08540-3476

STONE, LAWRENCE, retail executive. Chmn. Sterns Dept. Store, Paramus, N.J. Office: Stern's Bergen Mall Shopping Ctr Rte 4 Paramus NJ 07652 also: Allied Stores Corp 1114 Ave of the Americas New York NY 10036

STONE, LAWRENCE MAURICE, lawyer, educator; b. Malden, Mass., Mar. 25, 1931; s. Abraham Jacob and Pauline (Kurtz) S.; m. Anna Jane Clark, June 15, 1963; children: Abraham Dean, Ethan Goldthwaite, Katharine Elisheva. AB magna cum laude, Harvard U., 1953, JD magna cum laude, 1956. Bar: Mass. 1956, Calif. 1958. Rsch. asst. Am. Law Inst., Cambridge, Mass., 1956-57; assoc Irell and Manella, L.A., 1957-61, ptnr., 1963, 79—; internat. tax coordinator U.S Treasury Dept., Washington, 1961-62, tax. legis. counsel, 1964-66; prof. law U. Calif., Berkeley, 1966-78; vis. prof. law Yale U., New Haven, 1969, Hebrew U. Jerusalem, 1973-74, U. So. Calif., L.A., 1984; mem. adv. group to commr. IRS, Washington, 1973-74; mem. President's Adv. Commn. on Tax Ct. Appointments, Washington, 1976-80; tax advisory bd. Little Brown Co., 1994—. Author: (with Doernberg) Federal Income Taxation of Corporations and Partnerships, 1987, (with Klein, Bankman and Bittker) Federal Income Taxation, 1990; bd. editors Harvard Law Rev., 1955-56. Fellow Am. Coll. Tax Counsel; mem. ABA, Am. Law Inst., Internat. Fiscal Inst., Am. Arbitration Assn., Phi Beta Kappa. Office: Irell & Manella 1800 Ave Of The Stars Ste 900 Los Angeles CA 90067

STONE, LEON, banker; b. Rockdale, Tex., Feb. 27, 1914; s. Harley J. and Ella (Strelsky) S.; m. Bess Northington, Aug. 19, 1939; children—Pebble Stone Moss, Cherry J. Stone Wallin. Student, Blinn Coll., Brenham, Tex, 1932, Sul Ross Coll., Alpine, Tex., 1934, U. Tex., 1935, Rutgers U., 1954. With Brown & Root, Houston, 1936-37; Guggenheim-Goldsmith, Austin, Tex., 1937-38; with Austin Nat. Bank, 1938—, pres., 1963-84; also dir.; bd. dirs. First State Bank, Burnet, Tex.; chmn. Southwestern Grad. Sch. Banking, So. Meth. U. Dallas. Vice chmn. Tchr. Retirement System Tex., 1956-77; Bd. dirs. Presbyn. Theol. Sem., 1958—, Seton Hosp., 1966—, Mental Health and Mental Retardation Assn., 1965—. Served to lt. col. U.S. Army, ETO. Named Boss of Year, Credit Women of Austin, 1966. Mem. Am. Bankers Assn. (regional v.p. 1965—, exec. com. 1966—), Tex. Bankers Assn. (v.p. 1973), Am. Inst. Banking (past pres.), Austin C. of C. (pres. 1968), Tex. Taxpayers Assn. (pres.). Clubs: Rotarian, Mason, Shriner (Jester). Office: Nations Bank PO Box 908 Austin TX 78781-0001

STONE, LEWIS BART, lawyer; b. Bklyn., Mar. 5, 1938; s. Michael and Sylvia (Silberling) S.; m. Gretchen E. Haug, Dec. 23, 1964; children: Pamela Kendall, Lewis Bart. B.Ch.E., Rensselaer Poly. Inst., 1958; LL.B., Harvard U., 1962 Bar: N.Y. 1963, U.S. Dist. Ct. (so. dist.) N.Y. 1964, U.S. Dist. Ct. (ea. dist.) N.Y. 1964, U.S.C. Ct. Appeals (5th and 2d cirs.) 1964, U.S. Supreme Ct. Assoc. Strasser, Spigelberg, Fried & Frank, N.Y.C., 1962-65; assoc. Valicenti, Leighton Reid & Pine, N.Y.C., 1965-67; asst. counsel to gov. of N.Y., Albany, 1967-71; spl. asst. to gov. 1971; assoc. Carb, Luria, Glassner, Cook & Kufeld, N.Y.C., 1972-75, ptnr., 1975-83; ptnr. Rogers & Wells, N.Y.C., 1983—; bd. dirs. Brooks Brothers Inc. Treas. N.Y. Rep. Party, 1986—; sec., counsel citizens budget commn., 1987—. Mem. Am. Coll. Real Estate Lawyers, Sky Club, Sigma Xi, Tau Beta Pi, Phi Lambda Upsilon, Lambda Alpha. Republican. Office: Rogers & Wells 200 Park Ave Ste 5200 New York NY 10166-0153

STONE, MARVIN JULES, physician, immunologist educator; b. Columbus, Ohio, Aug. 3, 1937; s. Roy J. and Lillian (Bedwinek) S.; m. Jill Feinstein, June 29, 1958; children: Nancy Lillian, Robert Howard. Student, Ohio State U., 1955-58; SM in Pathology, U. Chgo., 1962, MD with honors, 1963. Diplomate Am. Bd. Internal Medicine, (Hematology, Med. Oncology). Intern ward med. svc. Barnes Hosp., St. Louis, 1963-64, asst. resident, 1964-65; clin. assoc. arthritis and rheumatism br. Nat. Inst. Arthritis and Metabolic Diseases, NIH, Bethesda, Md., 1965-68; resident in medicine, internal medicine U. Tex. Southwestern Med. Sch., Dallas, 1969-70, instr. dept. internal medicine, 1970-71, asst. prof., 1971-73, assoc. prof., 1974-76, clin. prof., 1976—, chmn. bioethics com., 1979-81; mem. faculty and steering com. immunology grad. program, Grad. Sch. Biomed. Scis., U. Tex. Health Sci. Ctr., Dallas, 1975, adj. mem., 1976—; dir. Charles A. Sammons Cancer Ctr., chief oncology, dir. immunology, co-dir. divsn. hematology-oncology, attending physician Baylor U. Med. Ctr., Dallas, 1976—; v.p. med. staff Parkland Meml. Hosp., Dallas, 1982. Contbr. chpts. to books, articles to profl. jours. Chmn. com. patient-aid Greater Dallas/Ft. Worth chpt. Leukemia Soc. Am., 1971-76, chmn. med. adv. com., 1978-80, bd. dirs., 1971-80; mem. v.p. Dallas unit Am. Cancer Soc., 1977-78, pres., 1978-80; mem. adv. bd. Baylor U. Med. Ctr. Found. Member With USPHS, 1965-68. Named Outstanding Full Time Faculty Mem. Dept. Internal Medicine, Baylor U. Med. Ctr., 1978, 87. Fellow ACP (gov. No. Tex. 1993—); mem. AMA, Am. Assn. Immunologists, Am. Soc. Hematology, Internat. Soc. Hematology, N.Y. Acad. Scis., Coun. Thrombosis, Am. Heart Assn. (established investigator 1970-75), Am. Soc. Clin. Oncology, Am. Osler Soc., Am. Assn. for Cancer Rsch., So. Soc. Clin. Investigation, Tex. Med. Assn., Dallas County Med. Soc., Clin. Immunology Soc., Phi Beta Kappa, Sigma Xi, Alpha Omega Alpha. Office: Baylor U Med Ctr Charles A Sammons Cancer Ctr 3500 Gaston Ave Dallas TX 75246-2088

STONE, MARVIN LAWRENCE, journalist, government official; b. Burlington, Vt., Feb. 26, 1924; s. Samuel and Anita (Abrams) S.; m. Sydell Magelaner, Nov. 20, 1949; children—Jamie Faith, Stacey Hope, Torren Magelaner. Student, Emory and Henry Coll., 1943, U. Vt., 1948; B.A., Marshall Coll., 1947; M.S., Columbia U., 1949; Litt.D., Marshall U., 1968; LL.D., Emory and Henry Coll., 1981; D.H.L., Elon Coll., 1982. Assignment reporter Huntington (W.Va.) Herald-Dispatch, 1941-43, 46-48; European corr. Internat. News Service, 1949-52, Far Eastern dir., 1952-58; Sloan Found. fellow in sci. Columbia U., 1958-59; cons. chief army research and devel., 1959-60; assoc. editor U.S News & World Report mag., 1960-66, gen. editor, 1966-68, exec. editor, 1969-70, sr. asso. exec. editor, 1971-72, exec. editor, 1973-76, v.p., editor-in-chief, 1976-85, chmn. bd., 1984-85; chmn. bd. Madana Realty Co., 1984-85; dep. dir. USIA, 1985-89; U.S. commr. gen. Seville '92' Expo, 1989-90; mem. adv. com. U.S. Patent Office, 1976-78; adj. fellow Coun. on Strategic and Internat. Studies, 1989-90; mem. adv. bd. Univ. Pubs., 1989—, Corp. for Pub. Broadcasting program adv. bd., 1992; chmn. and pres., Internat. Media Fund, 1990-95. Author: Man in Space. Vice pres., trustee, bd. dirs Washington Opera; chmn. bd. dirs. USN Meml. Found., 1981-82, vice chmn., 1983-84, bd. dirs., 1991—; nat. adv. bd. Am. U.; bd. dirs. Pub. Diplomacy Found., Am. Women's Found., 1991. Lt. (j.g.) USNR, 1943-46. Recipient Columbia Journalism 50th Anniversity Honor award, 1963, Marshall U. Disting. Alumnus award, 1973, Nat. Disting. Alumnus award Am. Assn. State Colls. and Univs., 1977, Freedoms Found. award, 1978, 79, 80, 81, Legion of Honor Chapel of Four Chaplains, 1980, Am. Eagle award, 1983, Silver Gavel award ABA, 1983, Gold Mercury Internat. award, Rome, Nat. Communication award Boys Clubs Am., Gill Robb Wilson award U.S. Air Force Assn., Disting. Honor award USIA; named to Washington Journalists' Hall of Fame, 1990; Fulbright traveling fellow, Columbia, Austria, 1950, Knight fellowship, 1995. Fellow Ctr. for Security and Internat. Studies (adj.); mem. White House Corrs. Assn., Am. Soc. Mag. Editors (exec. com. 1985), Nat. Press Club, Omicron Delta Kappa, Sigma Delta Chi. Clubs: Fgn. Corrs. of Japan (pres. 1956-57);

Internat. (Washington), Cosmos (Washington), Caribao (Washington). Home: 6318 Crosswoods Circle Lake Barcroft Falls Church VA 22044

STONE, MERRILL BRENT, lawyer; b. Jersey City, N.J., Aug. 16, 1951; s. Leonard and Claire (Orlean) S.; m. Geri Ellen Satkin, Nov. 24, 1976; children: Jacqueline Blair, Erica Lauren. AB summa cum laude, Rutgers U., 1973; JD, Columbia U., 1976. Bar: N.J. 1976, N.Y. 1977, Fla. 1981, U.S. Dist. Ct. N.J. 1976, U.S. Dist. Ct. (so. dist.) N.Y. 1977, U.S. Dist. Ct. (so. dist.) Fla. 1983. Assoc. Kelley, Drye & Warren, N.Y.C., 1976-84; resident Kelley, Drye & Warren, Miami, 1983-85; ptnr. Kelley, Drye & Warren, N.Y.C., 1985-92, mng. ptnr., 1992—. Editor: (comments section) Columbia Human Rights Law Rev., N.Y.C., 1975-76. Trustee Greater Miami C. of C., 1984-85. Named Harlan Fiske Stone Scholar, Columbia Law Sch., N.Y.C., 1975-76. Mem. ABA (bus. bankruptcy com. sect. on bus. law, banking law com.), Am. Soc. Corp. Secs., Fla. Bar Assn., Club 101, Weston Field Club, Phi Beta Kappa, Pi Sigma Alpha. Office: Kelley Drye & Warren 101 Park Ave New York NY 10178-0002

STONE, MICHAEL P. W., former federal official; b. London, June 2, 1925; married; 2 children. BA, Yale U., 1948; postgrad. law sch., NYU, 1949. Various positions Sterling Vineyards, Napa Valley, Calif., 1964-68, v.p., gen. mgr., dir., 1968-73, pres., dir., 1973-82; dir. U.S. AID Mission in Cairo, 1982-84; dir. Caribbean basin intitiative affairs AID, asst. sec. Dept. of Army, Washington, 1986-88, undersec., 1988-89, sec., 1989-93; bd. dirs. BEI Electronics, Inc.; chmn. Projects Internat. Assocs., Can. Marconi Co. Home: 3047 Divisadero St San Francisco CA 94123-3228

STONE, NORMAN R., JR., state senator; b. Balt., Sept. 8, 1935; B.A., U. Balt., LL.B., 1960. Admitted to Md. bar, 1960; practice law, Balt.; mem. Md. Ho. of Dels., 1963-67; mem. Md. State Senate, 1967—, chmn. legis. rev. com., chmn., vice-chmn. adminstrv., exec. and legis. rev. Com., vice-chmn. constl. and pub. law com., 1975-82, chmn. constl. and pub. law com., 1982-84, chmn. econ. and environ. affairs com., 1985-86, vice chmn. judicial proceeding com., 1987-94, pres. pro tem, 1995—. chmn. Balt. County Senate Del., 1968-72. Mem. Gov.'s Study Commn. on Workmen's Compensation Laws; pres. North Point Improvement Assn.; mem. North Point Peninsula Community Coordinating Council. Democrat. Roman Catholic. Clubs: K.C., Moose. Office: 6905 Dunmanway Baltimore MD 21222 Office: 2322 Lodge Forest Dr Baltimore MD 21219

STONE, OLIVER WILLIAM, screenwriter, director; b. N.Y.C., Sept. 15, 1946; s. Louis and Jacqueline (Goddet) S. Student, Yale U., 1965; B.F.A., NYU Film Sch., 1971. Tchr. Cholon, Vietnam, 1965-66; wiper U.S. Mcht. Marine, 1966; taxi driver N.Y.C., 1971. Screenwriter, dir.: Seizure, 1973, Midnight Express, 1978 (Acad. award for screenplay, Writers Guild Am. for screenplay), The Hand, 1981, (with John Milius) Conan, the Barbarian, 1982, Scarface, 1983, (with Michael Cimino) Year of the Dragon, 1985, (with David Lee Henry) 8 Million Ways to Die, 1986, (with Richard Boyle) Salvador, 1986, Platoon (also dir.), 1986 (Acad. award, Dirs. Guild award, British Acad. award); co-writer, dir.: Wall Street, 1987, Talk Radio, 1988, The Doors, 1991; screenwriter, prodr., dir.: Born on the Fourth of July, 1989 (Acad. award), JFK, 1991, Heaven & Earth, 1993, Natural Born Killers, 1994; prodr.: South Central, 1992, Zebrahead, 1992, New Age, 1994, The Joy Luck Club, 1993, (TV mini-series) Wild Palms, 1993; exec. prodr. Killer: A Journal of Murder, 1995, (HBO) Indictment: The McMartin Preschool, 1995, Nixon, 1995. Served with inf. U.S. Army, 1967-68, Vietnam. Decorated Purple Heart with oak leaf cluster, Bronze Star. Mem. Writers Guild Am., Dirs. Guild Am., Acad. Motion Picture Arts and Scis. Office: Ixtlan 201 Santa Monica Blvd 6th fl Santa Monica CA 90401

STONE, PETER, playwright, scenarist; b. Los Angeles, Feb. 27, 1930; s. John and Hilda (Hess) S.; m. Mary O'Hanley, Feb. 17, 1961. BA, Bard Coll., 1951, DLitt, 1971; MFA, Yale U., 1953. Ind. stage and screen writer, 1961—. Author: (musical comedies) Kean, 1961, Skyscraper, 1965, 1776, 1969 (Tony award Best Musical Book, 1969, N.Y. Drama Critics Circle award 1969, London Plays and Players award 1969, Drama Desk award Best Musical book writer 1969), Two by Two, 1970, Sugar, 1972, Woman of the Year, 1981 (Tony award Best Musical book 1981), My One and Only, 1983, Grand Hotel, 1989, The Will Rogers Follies, 1991 (Tony award Best Musical 1991, N.Y. Drama Critics Circle award Best New Musical 1991, Grammy award 1991), (play) Full Circle, 1973, (films) Charade, 1963 (Writers Guild award Best Comedy Film 1964, Mystery Writers Am. award Best Mystery film 1964), Father Goose, 1964 (Acad. award Best Original Screenplay 1964), Mirage, 1965, Arabesque, 1966, Secret War of Harry Frigg, 1968, Sweet Charity, 1969, Skin Game, 1971, 1776, 1972 (Christopher award for Best Film), Taking of Pelham 123, 1974, Silver Bears, 1978, Who is Killing the Great Chefs of Europe?, 1978, Why Would I Lie?, 1980, Just Cause, 1995, (TV spl.) Androcles and the Lion, 1968; (TV episodes) Studio One, 1956, Brenner, 1959, Witness, 1961, Asphalt Jungle, 1961, The Defenders, 1961-62 (Emmy award 1962), The Benefactors, 1962, Espionage, 1963, Adam's Rib, 1973-74, Ivan the Terrible, 1976, Baby on Board, 1988, Grand Larceny. Mem. Dramatists Guild (pres.), Authors League, Writers Guild Am. Home: 160 E 71st St New York NY 10021-5119 also: Stony Hill Rd Amagansett NY 11930

STONE, PETER GEORGE, lawyer, publishing company executive; b. N.Y.C., July 29, 1937; s. Leo and Anne S.; m. Rikke Linde, Dec. 26, 1974; children: Adam, Rachel. BS in Econs., L. Pa., 1959; JD, Columbia U., 1962. Bar: N.Y. 1963. Assoc. Ballon Stoll & Itzler, N.Y.C., 1963-65, Raphael, Searles & Vischi, N.Y.C., 1965-67; v.p., counsel Firedoor Corp. Am., N.Y.C., 1967-69; ptnr. Cahill, Stone & Driscoll, N.Y.C., 1969-75; v.p. fin. and law, gen. counsel Ottaway Newspapers, Inc., Campbell Hall, N.Y., 1975—; lectr., columnist on media law many univs. including Jud. Coll. U. Nev., Hartwick Coll., Bucknell U., U. N.C., Western Conn. State U., SUNY. Bd. dirs. Daily Pennsylvanian Alumni Assn. With USAR, 1962-63. Mem. ABA (forum com. on comm. law), N.Y. State Bar Assn. (ct. and cmty., pub. events and edn., pub. info. through TV coms., com. media law), N.Y. Bar Found., N.Y. State Fair Trial Free Press Newspaper Assn. Am. (com. on employee rels., chmn. com. on legal affairs, del. 1st amendment congress, com. on pub. policy), Am. Arbitration Assn., Soc. Human Resource Mgmt., Internat. Newspaper Fin. Execs., Newspaper Pers. Rels. Assn. (chmn. legal task force), Penn Club. Office: PO Box 401 Campbell Hall NY 10916-0401

STONE, RANDOLPH NOEL, law educator; b. Milw., Nov. 26, 1946; s. Fisher and Lee Della Stone; children: Sokoni, Rahman. BA, U. Wis., Milw., 1972; JD, Madison, 1975. Bar: D.C., 1975, Wis. 1975, Ill. 1977. Staff atty. Criminal Def. Consortium of Cook County, Chgo., 1976-78; clin. fellow U. Chgo. Law Sch., 1977-80; ptnr. Stone & clark, Chgo., 1983-88; pub. defender dep. dir. Pub. Defender Svc. for D.C., Washington, 1983-88; pub. defender Cook County Pub. Defender's Office, Chgo., 1988-91; lectr. U. Chgo. Law Sch., 1990, clin. prof. law, dir. Mandel Legal Aid Clinic, 1991—; adj. prof. Ill. Inst. Tech.-Chgo.-Kent Coll. Law Sch., 1991, bd. overseers, 1990; lectr. law Harvard U., 1991—; mem. Ill. Bd. Admissions to the Bar, 1994—; bd. dirs. The Sentencing Project,1986—; instr. trial advocacy workshop Harvard Law Sch., 1985-89; mem. faculty Nat. Coll. Criminal Def., Mercer Law. Sch. Adv. bd. Neighborhood Defender Svc. (Harlem), N.Y.C. Reginald Heber Smith fellow Neighborhood Legal Svcs. Program, Washington, 1975-76. Mem. ABA (sect. criminal justice coun. 1989—, chair 1993), Ill. State Bar Assn. (sect. criminal justice coun. 1989-92), Chgo. Bar Assn. (bd. dirs. 1990-92), Nat. Legal Aid and Defender Assn. (def. com.). Office: U Chgo Law Sch Mandel Legal Aid Clinic 6020 S University Ave Chicago IL 60637-2704

STONE, RICHARD B., legal educator; b. 1943. A.B., Harvard U., 1963, LL.B., 1967. Bar: La. 1967. Assoc. Covington & Burling, Washington, 1967-69; asst. to solicitor gen. Office Solicitor Gen., Dept. Justice, Washington, 1969-73; now prof. law Columbia U., N.Y.C. Office: Columbia U Sch Law 435 W 116th St New York NY 10027-7201

STONE, RICHARD B., ambassador; b. N.Y.C., Sept. 22, 1928; m. Marlene Lois Singer; children: Nancy, Amy, Elliott. AB cum laude, Harvard U., 1949; LLB, Columbia U., 1954. Bar: Fla. 1954. Pvt. practice, 1954-66; atty. City of Miami, 1966-67; state senator State of Fla., 1967-70, sec. of state, 1970-74; U.S. senator, 1975-81; mem. U.S. Senate from Fla., Washington, 1981-82; vice chmn. Capital Bank of Washington, 1982-83; amb.-at-larrge, Presdl. spl. envory for C.Am. affairs, 1983-84; vice chmn. Capital Bank, N.A., Washington, 1984-91, COO, 1989-91; U.S. amb. to Denmark, Dept. of State, Copenhagen, Denmark, 1991—; vice chmn., bd. dirs. Capital Bank Calif., 1985-91. Office: Am Embassy Dag Hammarskjolds Alle # 24 APO AE 09716 also: Am Embassy, Dag Hammarskjolds Alle 24, 2100 Copenhagen O Denmark

STONE, RICHARD JAMES, lawyer; b. Chgo., Apr. 30, 1945; s. Milton M. and Ruth Jean (Manaster) S.; m. Lee Lawrence, Sept. 1, 1979; children: Robert Allyn, Katherine Jenney, Grant Lawrence. B.A. in Econs., U. Chgo., 1967; J.D., UCLA, 1970. Bar: Calif. 1971, Oreg. 1994. Assoc. O'Melveny & Myers, L.A., 1971-77; dep. asst. gen. counsel U.S. Dept. Def., Washington, 1978-79; asst. to sec. U.S. Dept. Energy, Washington, 1979-80; counsel Sidley & Austin, L.A., 1981, ptnr., 1982-88; ptnr., head litigation dept. Milbank, Tweed, Hadley & McCloy, 1988-94; mng. ptnr., Zelle & Larson, L.A., 1994—; gen. counsel and staff dir. Study of L.A. Civil Disturbance for Bd. Police Commrs., 1992. Mem. Pub. Sector Task Force, Calif. State Senate Select Com. on Long Range Policy Planning, 1985-86, U.S. del. Micronesian Polit. Status Negotiations, 1978-79; mem. adv. panel Coun. Energy Resource Tribes, 1981-85; mem. Bishop's com. St. Aidan's Episcopal Ch., 1990—; dir. Legal Aid Found., 1991—, treas. 1994—. Recipient Amos Alonzo Stagg medal and Howell Murray Alumni medal U. Chgo., 1967; honoree Nat. Conf. Black Mayors, 1980; recipient spl. citation for outstanding performance Sec. Dept. Energy, 1981. Fellow Am. Bar Found.; mem. ABA, Calif. Bar Assn., Oreg. Bar Assn., L.A. County Bar Assn. (trustee 1986-88), Assn. Bus. Trial Lawyers, Phi Gamma Delta. Editor-in-chief UCLA Law Rev., 1970. Office: Zelle & Larson 10990 Wishire Blvd 15th Fl Los Angeles CA 90024

STONE, ROBERT A., airport administrator. Mgr. Greater Buffalo Internat. Airport. Office: Greater Buffalo Internat Airport Genesee St Buffalo NY 14225

STONE, ROBERT ANTHONY, author; b. N.Y.C., Aug. 21, 1937; s. C. Homer and Gladys Catherine (Grant) S.; m. Janice G. Burr, Dec. 11, 1959; children: Deidre M., Ian A. Student, N.Y. U., 1958-59; Stegner fellow, Stanford, 1962. Editorial asst. N.Y. Daily News, N.Y.C., 1958-60; former actor New Orleans; former advt. copywriter N.Y.C.; writer Nat. Mirror, N.Y.C., 1965-67; novelist, 1960—; mem. faculty Johns Hopkins U., Balt., 1993-94, Yale U., 1994—; free-lance writer London, Hollywood, Calif., South Vietnam, 1967-71; writer-in-residence Princeton U., 1971-72; faculty Amherst Coll., 1972-75, 77-78, Stanford U., 1979, U. Hawaii-Manoa, 1979-80, Harvard U., 1981, U. Calif.-Irvine, 1982, NYU, 1983, U. Calif.-San Diego, 1985, Princeton U., 1985. Author: (novels) A Hall of Mirrors, 1967, Dog Soldiers, 1974 (Nat. Book award 1975), A Flag for Sunrise, 1981, Images of War, 1986, Children of Light, 1986, Outerbridge Reach, 1992, (screenplays) WUSA, 1970, (with Judith Rascoe) Who'll Stop the Rain, 1978; contbg. author: Best American Short-stories, 1970, 88. Served with USN, 1955-58. Recipient William Faulkner prize, 1967, John Dos Passos prize for lit., 1982; award in lit. Am. Acad. and Inst. Arts and Letters, 1982, grantee, 1988-92; Guggenheim fellow, 1971, NEH fellow, 1983. Mem. PEN (exec. bd.). Office: care Donadio & Ashworth 121 W 27th St New York NY 10001-2765

STONE, ROBERT B., automotive company executive; b. Reading, Mich., July 22, 1930; s. Wilmer Edgar and Helen Lorene (Tearney) S.; m. Carley A. Crandall, Feb. 2, 1952; children—Tiena, Jill, Tim, Beth, Jennie, Amy, Keith. B.S. in Indsl. Arts, Eastern Mich. U., 1953; grad., Advanced Mgmt. Program, Harvard U. Bus. Sch., 1976. With Gen. Motors Corp., 1953—; dir. purchasing and prodn. control Gen. Motors Corp. (AC Spark Plug div.), Flint, Mich., 1970-74; exec. in charge purchasing activities Gen. Motors Corp. (Gen. Motors materials mgmt. staff), 1974-80, v.p. in charge materials mgmt. staff, 1980—. Bd. dirs. Eastern Mich. U.; mem. bus. adv. council Northwestern U.; bd. dirs. Met. Detroit YMCA, Genesee County Traffic Commn., 1970-74, Nat. Minority Supplier Devel. Council; pres. Flint YMCA, 1972-74. Mem. Nat. Assn. Purchasing Mgmt., Am. Mgmt. Assn. Republican. Christian Scientist. Clubs: Flint Golf, Recess. Office: GM Gen Motors Bldg 3044 W Grand Blvd Detroit MI 48202-3091 also: GM do Brazil SA, PO Box 8200, Sao Paulo 01000, Brazil *I believe in and follow this principle—that our greatest challenge is to be as creative in humanizing our corporation as we have been in mechanizing it. This begins with the assumption that intelligence or creativity or wisdom are not rare qualities found only in high places. They exist in every man and woman in the corporation. Our challenge is to develop an atmosphere to set these qualities free.*

STONE, ROBERT ELDRED, small business owner, museum director; b. Chester, N.H., July 26, 1929; s. Harold I. and Anna L. (Ahlberg) S.; m. Dorothy Harriette Fullonton, Feb. 3, 1951 (div. 1977); children: Dennis Wayne, Kathy Ann. Electronic Technician, USCG Tng. Ctr., Groton, Conn., 1952; A. in Electronic Engring., Merrimac Coll., Andover, Mass., 1957. Crew chief N.H. Permastone Corp., Londonderry, 1948, 49; quality assurance technician Western Elec. Corp. (AT&T), Lawrence, Mass., 1953-57, assoc. engr., 1957-83; owner, pres. America's Stonehenge, North Salem, N.H., 1957—. Coach, Little League Basketball, Derry, N.Y.; chmn. Cub Scouts, Derry; past mem. vestry Episc. Ch. of Transfiguration, Derry, past chmn. fin. com. With USCG, 1949-52. Mem. N.H. Archaeol. Soc., New England Antiquities Rsch. Assn. (founder, pres. 1964-76, rsch. dir. 1976-78), The Gungywamp Soc., La. Mound Soc. Avocations: archaeology, history, oil painting, reading, TV documentarys. Office: Am's Stonehenge PO Box 84 North Salem NH 03073-0084

STONE, ROBERT RYRIE, financial executive; b. Toronto, Ont., Can., Mar. 25, 1943; s. Frank R. and Norah I. (Varey) S.; m. Jacqueline P. Cogan, July 8, 1966; children: Charlie, Tracy. B.Sc., U. Toronto, 1964. Chartered acct., Can Inst. Chartered Accts. Treas., dir. fin. Gt. No. Capital Corp., Toronto, 1969-73; various positions Cominco Ltd., Vancouver, B.C., Can., 1973-78, treas., 1978-80, v.p. fin., chief fin. officer, 1980—; also bd. dirs.; bd. dirs. Cominco Fertilizers Ltd., Highland Valley Copper, Union Bank of Switzerland, Can., Global Stone Corp., chmn.; mem. adv. bd. Allendale Ins. Bd. dirs. Jr. Achievement Can., Jr. Achievement B.C. Mem. B.C. Inst. Chartered Accts., Fin. Execs. Inst. (pres. 1983-84). Office: Cominco Ltd, 200 Burrard St # 500, Vancouver, BC Canada V6C 3L7

STONE, ROGER DAVID, environmentalist; b. N.Y.C., Aug. 4, 1934; s. Patrick William and Kathleen Mary Stone; married; 1 child. BA in English, Yale U., 1955. Asst. to pub. Time Mag., 1959-61; corr., new bur. chief Time Mag., San Francisco, Rio, Paris, 1961-68; asst. to pres. Time Inc., N.Y.C., 1968-70; v.p. internat. dept. Chase Manhattan Bank, N.Y.C., 1970-74; pres. Ctr. for Inter-Am. Rels., N.Y.C., 1975-82; v.p. World Wildlife Fund, 1982-86, sr. fellow, 1986—; vice chmn. ECO Inc., Washington, 1992—; pres. Sustainable Devel. Inst., Washington, 1993—; vis. lectr. Yale Ctr. for Internat. and Area Studies, 1994-95. Author: Dreams of Amazonia, 1985, The Voyage of the Sanderling, 1990, Wildlands and Human Needs, 1991, The Nature of Development: Reports from the Rural Tropics on the Quest for Sustainable Economic Growth, 1992; contbr. chpts. to books; contbr. articles to Time, Life, Life en Espanol, Fgn. Affairs, N.Y. Times, Internat. Herald Tribune, Christian Sci. Monitor, Harvard Bus. Rev., USA Today Mag., Cruising World, Conservation Found. Letter, numerous others. Bd. dirs. Asian Inst. of Tech. Found., Caribbean Conservation Corp., Cintas Found., Armand G. Erpf Fund, Scenic Hudson, Inc.; former bd. dirs. U. Andes Found.; former bd. dirs. and exec. com. World Wildlife Fund-U.S., Ctr. for Inter-Am. Rels., Ams. Found., Accion Internat., Arts Internat., others. Lt. (j.g.) USN, 1956-59. Mem. Coun. on Fgn. Rels., Century Assn. Democrat. Episcopalian. Avocation: sailing. Home and Office: 3403 O St NW Washington DC 20007-2817

STONE, ROGER WARREN, container company executive; b. Chgo., Feb. 16, 1935; s. Marvin N. and Anita (Masover) S.; m. Susan Kesert, Dec. 24, 1955; children: Karen, Lauren, Jennifer. BS in Econs., U. Pa., 1957. With Stone Container Corp., Chgo., 1957—, dir., 1968-77, v.p., gen. mgr. container div., 1970-75, pres., chief operating officer, 1975-79, pres., chief exec. officer, 1979—, chmn. bd., chief exec. officer, 1983—; bd. dirs. First Nat. Bank Chgo./First Chgo., Morton Internat., McDonald's Corp., Option Care, Inc. Past trustee Glenwood (Ill.) Sch. for Boys; trustee Chgo. Symphony Orch. Assn.; fellow Lake Forest (Ill.) Acad.; mem. bd. overseers Wharton Sch. Bus., U. Pa.; mem. adv. coun. Econ Devel. Named Best or Top CEP in firm's industry Wall St. Transcript, 1981-86; recipient Top CEO award in Forest & Paper Specialty Products Industry, Fin. World Mag., 1984. Mem. Am. Forest and Paper Assn. (chmn. bd. 1985-86, bd. dirs), Chief Execs. Orgn., Corrugated Industry Devel. Corp. (past pres.), Inst. Paper Sci. and Tech. (former trustee), The Chgo. Com., Mid-Am. Com., Chgo. Coun. Fgn. Rels., Standard Club, Tavern Club, Comml. Club, Econ. Club, Lake Shore Country Club. Republican. Office: Stone Container Corp 150 N Michigan Ave Chicago IL 60601-7568

STONE, ROSE MARIE, vocational educator; b. Emporia, Kans., Sept. 9, 1945; d. Sherman Albert and Martha Marie (Brough) Kellum; m. Walter Lee Stone, July 18, 1965; children: Leah Marie, Zenetta Ann. Diploma in cosmetology, St. John's Sch., 1963, Capitol Beauty Sch., 1964; AAS, DelMar Coll., 1985; BA in Occupational Edn., Corpus Christi State U., 1989. Cert. cosmetology instr., Tex. Mgr. Rose Marie's Beauty Salon, Bellaire, Ohio, 1964-66; asst. mgr. Linden Lady Wigs, Columbus, Ohio, 1966-68; owner, mgr. Rose Marie's, Mt. Vernon, Ohio, 1969-76; hairstylist Clara's North Pole Beauty Salon, Corpus Christi, Tex., 1976-80; tchr. cosmetology Flour Bluff Ind. Sch. Dist., Corpus Christi, 1981-85, S.W. Ind. Sch. Dist., San Antonio, 1985-86, Carrollton (Tex.) Farmers Br. Ind. Sch. Dist., 1986-92; ednl. dir. Concept Chem., Houston, 1992; owner, ednl. dir. Rose Marie's Hair Salon, Corpus Christi, 1993—; mem. legis. com. Tex. Hairdressers and Cosmetology Assn., Corpus Christi, 1985-86. Mem. Nat. Cosmetology Cosmetology Assn., Cosmetology Instrs. in Pub. Schs. (chmn. 1987-88, chair workshop 1989), Tex. Hairdressers Assn., Tex. Indsl. Vocat. Assn., Vocat. Indsl. Clubs Am. (dist. adv. com. 1983-88, state adv. com. 1986-88, Texan award for Statesman 1990, State Leader 1985, Judging award 1985), Christian Bus. and Profl. Women's Club Corpus Christi, Corpus Christi Bus. and Profl. Women's Club, Inc., Iota Lambda Sigma. Democrat. Mem. Ch. of Christ. Avocations: fishing, sewing, hunting. Home: PO Box 18486 Corpus Christi TX 78418 Office: Rose Marie's Hair Salon 5925 McArdle Corpus Christi TX 78412

STONE, RUSSELL A., sociology educator; b. Medicine Hat, Alta., Can., Feb. 8, 1944; came to U.S., 1966; s. Ben and Clara G. (Gibbs) S.; m. S. Rala Stollar, Aug. 18, 1965; children: Peter H., Mira Beth. BA, McGill U., Montreal, Que., Can., 1965; PhD, Princeton U., 1971. Asst. to assoc prof. sociology SUNY, Buffalo, 1970-84, prof., 1984-91, chmn. dept. sociology, 1985-88; prof. sociology Am. U., Washington, 1991—, assoc. dean for grad. affairs, 1991—; vis. rsch. assoc. Israel Inst. Applied Social Rsch., Jerusalem, 1977-78; vis. assoc. prof. Ben Gurion U. of the Negev, Beersheba, Israel, 1978; vis. prof. Hebrew U., Jerusalem, 1977-78. Author: Social Change in Israel: Attitudes and Events, 1982; co-author: Political Elites on Arab North Africa, 1982; editor: OPEC and the Middle East, 1977; co-editor: Change in Tunisia, 1976, Critical Essays on Israeli Social Issues and Scholarship, 1994; chmn. editorial bd. SUNY Press, 1987-90, series editor; contbr. articles to profl. jours. Mem. Am. Sociol. Assn., Middle East Studies Assn., World Future Soc., Assn. for Israel Studies (sec., treas. 1989-93). Office: Am U Coll of Arts and Scis 4400 Massachusetts Ave NW Washington DC 20016-8012

STONE, SHARON, actress; b. Meadville, Pa., Mar. 10, 1958; d. Joe and Dorothy S; m. Michael Greenburg, 1984 (div. 1987). Student, Edinboro U. Model Eileen Ford Modeling Agy. Appeared in films Stardust Memories, 1980, Deadly Blessing, 1981, Irreconcilable Differences, 1984, King Solomon's Mines, 1985, Allan Quatermain and the Lost City of Gold, 1986, Cold Steel, 1987, Police Academy 4, 1987, Action Jackson, 1988, Above the Law, 1988, Total Recall, 1990, He Said/She Said, 1991, Scissors, 1991, Basic Instinct, 1991, Where Sleeping Dogs Lie, 1992, Sliver, 1993, Intersection, 1994, The Specialist, 1994, The Quick and the Dead, 1995, Casino, 1995; TV appearances include Not Just Another Affair, 1982, Bay City Blues, 1983, Calendar Girl Murders, 1984, The Vegas Strip Wars, 1984, War and Remembrance, 1988, (guest) The Larry Sanders Show, 1994; narrator: Harlow: The Blond Bombshell, 1993. Office: c/o ICM 8942 Wilshire Blvd Beverly Hills CA 90211*

STONE, STEVEN MICHAEL, sports announcer, former baseball player; b. Cleve., July 14, 1947. BS in Edn., Kent State U. Baseball player San Francisco Giants, 1971-72, Chgo. Cubs, 1974-76, Chgo. White Sox, 1977-78, Balt. Orioles, 1979-82; baseball announcer WGN Continental Broadcasting Co., Chgo., 1982—; owner restaurant Scottsdale, Ariz. Recipient Cy Young award Am. League, 1980. Mem. Am. League All-Star Team, 1980. Office: WGN TV 2501 W Bradley Pl Chicago IL 60618*

STONE, SUSAN RIDGEWAY, marketing educator; b. Coronado, Calif., Oct. 30, 1950; d. Lester Jay and Marguerite Ridgaway (King) Stone; m. Martin Zachary Sipkoff, Oct. 27, 1984; 1 child, Benjamin. AB, Wilson Coll., 1977; MBA, Shippensburg U., 1980; DBA, George Washington, U., 1992. Assoc. prof. mgmt. and mktg. Shippensburg (Pa.) U., 1983—; dir. mktg. VSP Wastewater Tech., Gettysburg, Pa., 1982; mktg. cons. Svcs. Unltd., Gettysburg, 1975—; lectr. in field. Author: (with Stephen J. Holoviak) Managing Human Productivity: People are Your Best Investment, 1987; contbr. articles to profl. jours.; asst. editor mag. USN Acad. Alumni Assn., 1973-74; pres. Shippensburg U. Press. Former land use chair League of Women Voters, Gettysburg; mem. fund raising com. for local candidates; pers. chair, bd. dirs. Survivors', Inc. Am. Mktg. Assn. fellow, 1986. Mem. Acad. Mktg. Sci., Am. Mktg. Assns., Mensa, Adams County Literacy Coun., Beta Gamma Sigma, Kappa Kappa Gamma. Republican. Episcopalian. Avocations: gardening, writing, sailing. Office: Shippensburg Univ Mgmt And Mktg Dept Shippensburg PA 17257

STONE, THOMAS EDWARD, defense consultant, retired rear admiral; b. Selfridge, Mich., Oct. 21, 1939; m. Lucy Lee, June 9, 1962. BS, U.S. Naval Acad., 1962; MS in Elec. Engring., Naval Postgrad. Sch., 1968; postgrad., Destroyer Dept. Head Sch., 1969. Advanced through grades to rear adm. USN, 1990, ops. officer USS Sampson, 1970; aide, flag sec. to commdr. Attack Carrier striking Force /CTF 77, 7th Fleet Vietnam, 1971-72; communications/ops. officer to comdr. in chief U.S. Naval Forces, Europe, 1972-75, exec. officer USS Mitscher, 1976-78, asst. chief of staff for communications, comdr. Naval Surface Force Atlantic, 1978-80; comdg. officer USS Preble, 1980-82; surface ops. officer, staff of comdr. Cruiser Destroyer Group 12, 1982-83; dir. Space, Command and Control Devel. Div. USN, 1984-85; comdr. U.S. Naval Communications Master Sta., Western Pacific, Guam, Marianas Island, 1985-87; comdr. Naval Telecommunications Command, 1988-90; dir. Naval Commns. info systems of Naval opers. staff, 1990-91; dir. communication programs Space & Naval Warfare Systems Command, 1991-93. Decorated Legion of Merit with three gold stars. Roman Catholic. Office: American Systems Corp 14200 Park Meadow Dr Chantilly VA 22021

STONE, WARREN R., book publishing executive. Chmn., ceo. Addison-Wesley Pub. Co. Inc., Reading, Mass. Office: Addison-Wesley Pub Co Inc 1 Jacob Way Reading MA 01867

STONE, WILLARD JOHN, retired lawyer; b. Toledo, May 19, 1913; s. Willard John and Charlotte Hall (Walker) S.; m. Mabel-June Lindauer, June 15, 1940 (div. Jan. 1952); 1 child, Arthur Walter (dec. May 1991); m. Juanita Marian Hammond, June 22, 1952 (dec. Apr. 1976); children: Willard Andrew, Stewart Hall, Marian Louise Stone Neuhouser; m. Charlotte Deane drew, 1977. A.B., U. Mich., 1936, J.D. cum laude, 1936. Bar: Calif. 1937, U.S. Supreme Ct. 1942; cert. specialist in taxation law. Sole practice Los Angeles, 1937-41, 45-51; sole practice Pasadena, Calif. 1951-86; mem. firm Stone & Doyle and predecessor firms, 1975-86; atty. war div. Dept. Justice, 1941-43; asst. prof. law Southwestern U., 1937-41. Mem. editorial bd. Mich. Law Rev., 1934-36. Contbr. articles to profl. jours. Bd. dirs. San Gabriel Valley council Boy Scouts Am. Served as lt. USNR, 1943-46. Decorated Bronze Star. Fellow Am. Coll. Trust and Estate Counsel; mem. ABA, L.A. County Bar Assn., Pasadena Bar Assn., State Bar Calif., Am. Arbitration Assn. (nat. panel arbitrators 1963—), Am. Judicature Soc., Order of Coif. Republican. Episcopalian. Clubs: Fine Arts (pres. 1969-70), University (Pasadena) Oneonta. Lodge: Masons. Home: 700 S Lake Ave Apt 314 Pasadena CA 91106-3940

STONE, WILLIAM EDWARD, association executive; b. Peoria, Ill., Aug. 13, 1945; s. Dean Proctor and Katherine (Jamison) S.; m. Deborah Ann Duncan; children: Jennifer, Allison, Molly. A.B., Stanford U., 1967, M.B.A., 1969. Asst. dean Stanford U., 1969-71, asst. to pres., 1971-77; exec. dir. Stanford Alumni Assn., 1977-90, pres., chief exec. officer, 1990—; pres., dir. Alpine Chalet, Inc., Alpine Meadows, Calif., 1987—; dir. Coun. Alumni

Assn. Execs., 1989-93, v.p., 1990-91, pres., 1991-92; trustee Coun. for Advancement and Support of Edn., 1988-91; bd. dirs. Univ. ProNet, Inc., chmn., 1990-92. Bd. dirs. North County YMCA, 1975-76; bd. dirs., chmn. nominating com. faculty club Stanford U., 1979-81; trustee Watkins Discretionary Fund, 1979-82; mem. community adv. bd. Resource Ctr. for Women. Recipient K.M. Cuthbertson award Stanford U., 1987, Tribute award Coun. for Advancement and Support of Edn., 1991. Mem. Stanford Hist. Soc., Stanford Assocs. Club: Stanford Faculty. Home: 1061 Cathcart Way Stanford CA 94305-1048 Office: Stanford Alumni Assn Inc 416 Santa Teresa St Stanford CA 94305-4005

STONE, WILLIAM HAROLD, geneticist, educator; b. Boston, Dec. 15, 1924; s. Robert and Rita (Scheinberg) S.; m. Elaine Morein, Nov. 24, 1947; children: Susan Joy, Debra M.; m. Carmen Maqueda, Dec. 22, 1971; 1 son, Alexander R.M. A.B., Brown U., 1948; M.S., U. Maine, 1949; Ph.D., U. Wis., 1953; Sc.D. (hon.), U. Cordoba, Spain, 1984. Research asst. Jackson Meml. Lab., Bar Harbor, Maine, 1947-48; faculty dept. genetics U. Wis., Madison, 1949-83; prof. U. Wis., 1961-83, prof. med. genetics, 1964-83; Cowles Disting. prof. dept. biology Trinity U., San Antonio, 1983—; staff scientist S.W. Found. for Biomed. Research, San Antonio, 1983—; adj. prof. Cellular and Structural Biology U. Tex., San Antonio, 1983—; mem. panel blood group experts FAO, 1962-67, program dir. immunogenetics research, Spain, 1971-74; adj. prof. dept. cellular and structural Biology, U. Tex. Health Sci. Ctr., San Antonio, 1983—; mem. Community Health Services Research Adv. Com., 1987—, Council Inst. Lab. Animal Resources, NRC; mem. competitive research grants panel USDA; bd. dirs. and v.p. So. Tex. Blood and Tissue Ctr., 1986—, v.p. bd., 1989-92, pres. 1995—; bd. dirs. Tex. Research and Tech. Found., 1986-90, Mind Sci. Found., 1988—, Winston Sch., 1989-91, Bexar County Women's Ctr., Inst. Lab. Animal Sci., 1977-89; mem. rev. panel NSF; mem. primate study sect. Comparative Medicine Program NIH. Author: Immunogenetics, 1967; contbr. articles to profl. jours. Bd. dirs Bexar County Women's Ctr., Alamo Theatre Arts Coun. Recipient I.I. Ivanov medal USSR, 1974, Disting. Tex. Geneticist award, 1992; Calif. Inst. Tech. NIH fellow, 1960-61. Mem. NRC, AAAS, Am. Inst. Biol. Scis., Assembly Life Scis., Am. Soc. Immunologists, Am. Genetics Assn., Am. Aging Soc., Tex. Genetics Soc. (editor newsletter, pres. elect, 1995), Am. Soc. Human Genetics, Rsch. Soc. Am., Internat. Soc. Transplant, Am. Soc. Animal Sci., Internat. Soc. Devel. Comparative Immunology, Internat. Primatological Soc., Am. Soc. Primatology, Internat. Soc. Immunology Reproduction, Fedn. Am. Soc. Exptl. Biology Soc. Devel. and Comparative Immunology (pub. affairs com.), Sigma Xi, Gamma Alpha, Beta Beta Beta. Office: Trinity U Dept Biology San Antonio TX 78212 *Some things are better never than late. We need more education and less legislation. I can't believe I get paid for something I have so much fun doing. In science you don't know what the truth is until you have read what you have written. Quite often, bad luck is really good luck gone unrecognized.*

STONE, WILLIARD EVERARD, accountant, educator; b. Phila., Aug. 28, 1910; s. Theodore Williard Jr. and Blanche (Patton) S.; m. Louise Cousins Harder, May 19, 1934; children: Theodore Williard III, Donald Edwin, Richard Patton. A.B., Pa. State U., 1933; M.A., U. Pa., 1950, Ph.D., 1957. C.P.A., Pa. Auditor Pa. Liquor Control Bd., 1934-43, U.S comptroller gen. 1943-47; partner Stone & Fisher (C.P.A.'s), Phila., 1947-50; asst. prof. accounting U. Pa. Wharton Sch. Finance and Commerce, Phila., 1951-57; assoc. prof. U. Pa. Wharton Sch. Finance and Commerce, 1957-60; prof. U. Fla., Gainesville, 1960-80; head dept. accounting U. Fla., 1960-74; bd. mgrs. U. Fla. Press, 1961-80; vis. prof. U. New South Wales, 1966; Carman G. Blough chair of acctg. U. Va., 1972-73; vis. prof. U. Port Elizabeth, 1975, Va. Poly. Inst. and State U., 1977, U. Ky., 1980-81; cons. editor Chilton Book div. Chilton Co., Phila., 1957-61, Holt, Rinehart & Winston, Inc., 1961-70; cons. to U.S. Comptr. Gen., 1963-69. Author: (with MacFarland, Ayars) Accounting Fundamentals, 1957; Co-editor: Accounting Historian's Jour.; Contbr. articles to profl. jours. Gordon Fellow Deakin U., Australia, 1981. Mem. Nat. Assn. Accountants (dir. Phila. 1954-55), Am. Inst. C.P.A.'s, Fla. Inst. C.P.A.'s, Pa. Inst. C.P.A.'s (dir. 1954-55), Am. Accounting Assn. (v.p. 1963), Acad. Accounting Historians (editor Acctg. Historians Jour. 1974-79), Beta Alpha Psi (past pres), Beta Gamma Sigma. Home: 1717 NW 23d Ave PhA Gainesville FL 32605

STONECIPHER, DAVID A., insurance company executive; b. 1941. Degree, Vanderbilt U.; M Agrl. Sci., Ga. State U., 1967. With Life Ins. Co. Ga., Altanta, 1967-92; also pres. Ga. U.S. Corp., Altanta, until 1992; pres., CEO Jefferson-Pilot Corp., Greensboro, N.C., 1992—, also bd. dirs. Office: Jefferson-Pilot Corp 100 N Greene St Greensboro NC 27401*

STONECIPHER, HARRY CURTIS, manufacturing company executive. BS, Tenn. Polytech Inst., 1960. With GE, 1960-61, 62-86, Martin Aircraft Co., 1961-62; exec. v.p Sundstrand Corp., 1987, pres., chief operating officer, 1987-88, pres., chief exec. officer, 1988-94, chmn., 1991-94, also past bd. dirs.; pres. McDonnell-Douglas Corp., St. Louis, 1994—. Office: McDonnell-Douglas Corp PO Box 516 Saint Louis MO 63166

STONEHILL, ERIC, lawyer; b. Rochester, N.Y., Feb. 27, 1950. BA with distinction, Northwestern U., 1970; JD, Cornell U., 1973, MBA, 1981, cert. hosp. and health svc. administr., 1981. Bar: N.Y. 1974, D.C. 1981, U.S. Dist. Ct. (we. dist.) N.Y. 1974, U.S. Dist. Ct. (no. dist.) N.Y. 1976. Assoc. Harris, Beach & Wilcox, Rochester, 1973-81, ptnr., 1982—. Contbr. articles to profl. jours. Bd. dirs. Rochester Eye and Human Parts Bank, 1983-91, 92—, pres., 1987-90. Mem. Nat. Health Lawyers Assn., Am. Soc. of Hosp. Attys., N.Y. State Bar Assn., D.C. Bar Assn., Monroe County Bar Assn., Sloan Alumni Assn., Phi Beta Kappa. Office: Harris Beach & Wilcox Granite Building 130 E Main St Rochester NY 14604

STONEHILL, ROBERT MICHAEL, federal agency administrator; b. N.Y.C., Oct. 29, 1949; s. Frederick and Olga (Berkowitz) S.; m. Ilene Laven, June 1, 1975 (div. Nov. 1983); 1 child, David; m. Camille Recchia, Oct. 12, 1985; children: Eric, Elizabeth, Matthew. BA, CUNY, Queens, 1971; MA, U. Colo., 1973, PhD, 1976. Teaching and rsch. asst. U. Colo., Boulder, 1972-76; evaluation specialist U.S. Office Edn., Washington, 1976-83; acting dir. state and local grants div. U.S. Dept. Edn., Washington, 1984-86, dir. Ednl. Resources Info. Ctr., 1987-94, mem. program effectiveness panel, 1982—, dir. State and Local Svcs. divsn., 1995—; del. Fed. Litter. Pre-Conf., The White House Conf. on Librs. and Info. Scis., 1990. Mem. editorial adv. bd. various jours., contbr. articles. Regents scholar, 1966-70. Mem. Am. Ednl. Rsch. Assn., Assn. Soc. for Info. Sci., Nat. Coun. for Measurement in Edn. Jewish. Avocations: skiing, popular cultural history. Office: US Dept Edn Ednl Resources Info Ctr 555 New Jersey Ave NW Washington DC 20208-5720

STONEHOUSE, JAMES ADAM, lawyer; b. Alameda, Calif., Nov. 10, 1937; s. Maurice Adam and Edna Sigrid (Thuesen) S.; m. Marilyn Jean Kotkas, Aug. 6, 1966; children: Julie Aileen, Stephen Adam. AB, U. Calif., Berkeley, 1961; JD, Hastings Coll. Law, U. Calif. San Francisco, 1965. Bar: Calif. 1966; cert. specialist probate, estate planning & trust law. Assoc. Hall, Henry, Oliver & McReavy, San Francisco, 1966-71; ptnr. firm Whitney, Hanson & Stonehouse, Alameda, 1971-77; pvt. practice, Alameda, 1977-79; ptnr. firm Stonehouse & Silva, Alameda, 1979—; judge adv. Alameda council Navy League, 1978—. Founding dir. Alameda Clara Barton Found., 1977-80; mem. Oakland (Calif.) Marathon-Exec. Com., 1979; mem. exec. bd. Alameda council Boy Scouts Am., 1979—, pres., 1986-88; mem. Nat. council Boy Scouts Am., 1986—; trustee Golden Gate Scouting, 1986-95, treas. 1989-91, v.p. 1991-92, pres. 1993-95, v.p. area III western region, 1990-95, bd. dirs. western region, 1994-95; dir. Lincoln Child Ctr. Found., 1981-87, 94—, pres., 1983-85; sch. bd. mem. St. Joseph Notre Dame, 1994—. Recipient Lord Baden-Powell Merit award Boy Scouts Am., 1988, Silver Beaver award, 1991; named Boss of Yr. Alameda Jaycees, 1977; Coro Found. fellow in pub. affairs, 1961-62. Mem. ABA, State Bar Calif., Alameda County Bar (vice chmn. com. office execs., 1977-78). Republican. Roman Catholic. Club: Commonwealth. Lodges: Rotary (dir. club 1976-78, trustee Alameda Rotary Found. 1991—, treas., 1994—). Elks (past exalted ruler, all state officer 1975-76, all dist. officer 1975-77, 78-79, Alameda). Home: 2990 Northwood Dr Alameda CA 94501-1606 Office: Stonehouse & Silva 512 Westline Dr Ste 300 Alameda CA 94501-5870

STONEKING, JERRY EDWARD, dean; b. Cin., July 12, 1942; s. Charles E. and Esther H. (Holmeyer) S.; m. Linda Kaye Parnell, Dec. 30, 1967; children: Jennifer, Jeffrey. BS in Engring. Mechanics cum laude, Ga. Inst. Tech., 1965; MS in Theoretical and Applied Mechanics, U. Ill., 1966, PhD in Theoretical and Applied Mechanics, 1969. Registered profl. engr., Tenn. Grad. student instr. theoretical and applied mechanics dept. U. Ill., Urbana, 1969-70; asst. prof. civil and environ. engring. Clarkson U., Potsdam, N.Y., 1970-74; asst. prof. dept. civil engring. and mechanics U. S.C. Columbia, 1974-75; assoc. prof. dept. engring. sci. and mechanics U. Tenn., Knoxville, 1975-78, prof., 1978-92, Internat. Bus. Machines prof., 1981-84, head dept. engring. sci. and mechanics, 1983-92, interim dean coll. engring., 1992-93, dean, 1993—; mem. various coms. U. Tenn., 1976—, mem. faculty senate, 1980-83, 94—, mem. Saturn core team, 1991—, mem. policy adv. bd., 1992—; cons., rschr. in field. Author: Hydraulics, 1975; editor: Developments in Theoretical & Applied Mechanics, 1980; reviewer Internat. Jour. Structures and Solids, Applied Mechanics Revs., Jour. Applied Mechanics, others; contbr. articles to profl. jours. Recipient Outstanding Teaching and Rsch. award IBM, 1981-84, Best Tech. Presentation award Tenn. Dental Assn., 1990; fellow NSF, 1965-69. Mem. ASME, ASCE, Am. Soc. Engring. Edn., Soc. Engring. Sci. (bd. dirs. 1990—), Southeastern Conf. Theoretical and Applied Mechanics (chmn. editorial com. 10th conf. 1979-80, organizer, conf. chmn. 10th conf. 1980, chmn. ops. com. 1987-88), mem. policy com. 1988—), Phi Kappa Phi, Sigma Xi, Tau Beta Pi. Avocations: golfing, fishing, house renovation, paddle ball. Office: U Tenn Coll Engring 124 Perkins Hall Knoxville TN 37996-2000

STONEMAN, SAMUEL SIDNEY, cinema company executive; b. Boston, Dec. 18, 1911; s. David and Anne (Fleisher) S.; m. Miriam Helpern, Sept. 2, 1934; children: Jane Stein, Elizabeth Deknatel. A.B., Dartmouth Coll., 1933; J.D., Harvard U., 1936. Bar: Mass. 1936. Ptnr. Singer, Stoneman & Kirland, Boston, 1936-42; pres. Bretton Woods Co., (N.H.), 1946-56; vice chmn. bd. Gen. Cinema Corp., Chestnut Hill, Mass., 1969-84, also dir.; vice-chmn. Harcourt Gen.; dir. Shawmut Bank of Boston, N.A., Purity Supreme, Inc., Billerica, Mass., Donlevy's Inc., Boston. Vice pres., trustee Boston Symphony Orch., 1970-83; bd. overseers Hopkins Ctr. and Hood Mus., Dartmouth Coll., 1982-88; trustee Dana-Farber Cancer Inst., Boston, 1978; pres. Combined Jewish Philanthropies, 1946-66, Beth Israel Hosp., 1970-73; mem. Dartmouth Coll. Alumni Council, 1963-66; bd. dirs. Massachusetts Bay United Fund, 1966-77, Community Found. Palm Beach and Martin Counties, Fla., Kravis Performing Arts Centre, Palm Beach; mem. adv. bd. St. Mary's Hosp., Palm Beach; regional co-chmn. NCCJ, Boston, 1969-73. Served to maj. Q.M.C. AUS, 1942-46. Fellow Brandeis U., 1956—; recipient Brotherhood Human Relations citation NCCJ, 1968, Alumni award Dartmouth Coll., 1972, Disting. Grad. award Noble and Greenough Sch., 1982. Home: 200 Via Pelicano Palm Beach FL 33480-5017

STONEMAN, WILLIAM, III, physician, educator; b. Kansas City, Mo., Sept. 8, 1927; s. William and Helen Louise (Bloom) S.; m. Elizabeth Johanna Wilson, May 19, 1951; children: William Laurence, Sidney Camdon (dec.), Cecily Anne Erker, Elizabeth Wilson, John Spalding. Student, Rockhurst Coll., 1944-46; B.S. St. Louis U., 1948, M.D., 1952. Diplomate: Am. Bd. Surgery, Am. Bd. Plastic Surgery. Intern Kansas City Gen. Hosp., 1952-53; resident in surgery St. Louis U., 1953-57, resident in plastic surgery, 1957-59, mem. faculty, 1959—, assoc. prof. surgery, assoc. prof. community medicine, 1975-84, prof. surgery, community medicine, 1984-94, prof. surgery, community medicine emeritus, 1994, assoc. dean Sch. Medicine, 1973-76; exec. assoc. dean St. Louis U. (Sch. Medicine), 1976-82, dean, 1982-95, dean emeritus, 1995—, assoc. v.p. med. ctr., 1983-95; mem. adj. faculty Washington U. Sch. Medicine, St. Louis, 1968-74; chief exec. officer Bi-State Regional Med. Program, 1968-74; bd. dirs. St. Louis Office Mental Retardation/Developmentally Disabled Resources, 1980-82, Combined Health Appeal of Mo., 1990-94. Editor: Parameters, 1976-94; contbr. articles on plastic surgery, health care delivery planning to profl. jours. Served with AUS, 1946-47. Fellow ACS; mem. AMA (chmn. sect. on med. schs. 1987-88, sect. alt. del. 1989-91, del. 1992-94), Mo. Med. Assn., Mem. St. Louis Met. Med. Soc., St. Louis Surg. Soc., Am. Soc. Plastic and Reconstructive Surgeons, Midwestern Assn. Plastic Surgeons. Roman Catholic. Club: Racquet. Office: St Louis U Sch Medicine 1316 Carr Lane Ave Saint Louis MO 63104-1004

STONEMAN, WILLIAM HAMBLY, III, professional baseball team executive; b. Oak Park, Ill., Apr. 7, 1944; s. William Hambly Jr. and Kathryn Jane (Hennessey) S.; m. Diane Falardeau, Dec. 6, 1969; children: Jill Helene, Jeffrey Alan. BS in Edn., U. Idaho, 1966; MEd, Okla. U., 1969. Baseball player Chgo. Cubs, 1967-68, Montreal (Que., Can.) Expos, 1969-73, Calif. Angels, 1974; mktg. mgr. Royal Trust Corp., Montreal and Toronto, Ont., Can., 1975-79, br. mgr., 1980-82; asst. to pres. Montreal Expos, 1983, v.p., 1984—; now v.p. baseball ops. Mem. All-Star Team Nat. League, 1972; no-hit games vs. Phila. Phillies, 1969, N.Y. Mets, 1972. Home: 17 Willow, PO Box 386, Hudson, PQ Canada J0P 1H0 Office: Montreal Baseball Club Inc Olympic Stadium, Montreal, PQ Canada H1V 3N7*

STONER, ALLAN L., science foundation director. Acting dir. U.S. National Arroretum, Washington, D.C. Office: US Nat Arboretum 3501 New York Ave NE Washington DC 20002-1958

STONER, GLENN EARL, science educator; b. Springfield, Mo., Oct. 26, 1940; s. Glenn Rees and Betty (Pearce) S.; m. Marlene Arlen, Dec. 29, 1962; children: Kevin, Brian, Steven. BS, Mo. Sch. Mines, 1962, MS, 1963; PhD, U. Pa., 1968. Sr. scientist U Va., Charlottesville, 1968-74, rsch. assoc. prof. 1974-77, assoc. prof., 1977-83, prof., 1983—, dir. Ctr. for Electrochem. Scis. and engring. 1987—; cons. in field. Contbr. articles to profl. publs.; patentee in field. Recipient awards NASA, rsch. grants. Roman Catholic. Avocations: fishing, jogging. Office: U Va Thornton Hall Ctr Electrochem Scis Charlottesville VA 22903

STONER, JAMES LLOYD, retired foundation executive, clergyman; b. Point Marion, Pa., Apr. 23, 1920; s. Martin Clark and Bess (Hare) S.; m. Janice Faller Evans, Aug. 28, 1943; children: Thomas Clark, James Douglas and Geoffrey Lloyd (twins). B.S., Bethany Coll., 1941, D.D. (hon.), 1958; B.D., M.A., Yale U., 1944. Ordained to ministry Christian Ch., 1943; minister in Hamden, Conn., 1942-44; assoc. exec. sec. U. Tex., YMCA, 1944-45; dir. Student Christian Fellowship, Bowling Green State U., 1945-47, Univ. Christian Mission, Fed. Council Ch. and Nat. Council Chs., 1947-56; minister North Christian Ch., Columbus, Ind., 1956-66; asst. gen. sec. for exec. operations Nat. Council Chs., 1966-72; sr. minister Central Christian Ch., Austin, Tex., 1972-80; dep. exec. dir. Found. for Christian Living, Pawling, N.Y., 1980-83, exec. dir., 1983-87; Chmn. com. recommendations Internat. Conv. Christians Chs., 1962-65; bd. mgrs. United Christian Missionary Soc., 1956-63; mem. adv. bd. Am. Bible Soc., 1966-72; life mem. coun. Christian Unity, Christian Ch.; a founder, 1st pres. LINK Award, Ridgewood, N.J., 1966-72; mem. Austin Conf. Chs., pres., 1973-75; rep. Tex. Conf. Chs. 1976-80; mem. goals com. Austin Tomorrow; mem. adv. bd. 1st Comml. Bank of Lakeway, Austin, Tex., 1990—. Contbr. articles to profl. publs. A founder, bd. dirs. Fellowship Christian Athletes, Kansas City, Mo., 1956-68; trustee Tougaloo (Miss.) Coll., 1968-74; v.p., mem. exec. com. Ecumenical Center Continuing Edn., Yale, 1966-72; mem. exec. com. Boy Scouts Am., Austin, 1980, Dutchess County council, 1981-82; bd. mgrs. New Milford Hosp., 1983-88; bd. dirs. Holiday Hills YMCA, 1983-87; com. mem. Town of Pawling 200th Anniversary, 1985-88, Lakeway Ecumenical Ch. Mem. Pawling C. of C. (exec. com. 1984-87), Greater Austin Fellowship of Christian Athletes (nat. adv. bd. 1994—), Masons (32 degree), Rotary (spl. lifetime mem., pres. 1983-84, dist. gov.-elect 1991-92, dist. gov. 1992-93, Paul Harris fellow), Shriners, Austin Rotary Club (hon.), Lake Travis/Lakeway Rotary Club, Alpha Psi Omega, Beta Pi. Home: 1134 Challenger St Austin TX 78734-3802 *Fill every day with rainbow colors, and punctuate life with a positive outlook... Even the Cross of Christ is a positive sign.*

STONER, JOHN RICHARD, federal government executive; b. Ypsilanti, Mich., May 11, 1918; s. Richard P. and Marjorie G. Stoner; m. Diane Leslie Snow. BA in Govt., B in Music Edn., Lawrence U., 1981. Staff asst. Senator Robert Kasten Jr., Washington, 1981-82; staff assoc. Wis. Office Fed.-State Rels., Washington, 1982-83; intergovtl. rels. officer U.S. Dept. Transp., Washington, 1983-86; congl. rels. officer, 1986-93; dir. Office of Program and Policy Support, Rsch. and Spl. Programs Adminstrn., Dept. Transp., Washington, 1991-93; exec. dir. Republican Nat. Lawyers Assn., 1993—; rep. Primerica Fin. Svcs., 1993—; state govt. rels. mgr. Am. Trucking Assn., Inc., Alexandria, Va., 1986-88; researcher George Bush for

Pres. Com., 1988; staff asst. Office of Pres.-Elect, Washington, 1988-89. Admissions contact Washington area Lawrence U., 1986-87; softball team mgr. Montgomery County Recreation League. Recipient Eagle Scout award Boy Scouts Am., 1972; Mortar Bd. scholar, 1980; Senate Rep. Policy Com. Legis. fellow, 1993—. Republican. Mem. Ch. of Christ, Scientist. Avocation: water skiing, organ. Home: 10409 Brunswick Ave Silver Spring MD 20902-4845 Office: Rep Nat Lawyers Assn 310 First St SE Washington DC 20003

STONER, PHILIP JAMES, hospital administrator; b. Brookline, Mass., Mar. 5, 1943; s. Philip and Beatrice Margaret (Murphy) S.; m. Allison Fern Leighton, Aug. 28, 1971; children: Jennifer Marie, Andrew Leighton. AS in Engring., Wentworth Inst., Boston, 1963; BS in Indsl. Engring., Millikin U., 1966; MS, Northeastern U., 1973; MBA, Western New Eng. Coll., 1980. Prodn. mgr. Goodwill Industries, Boston, 1971-72; indsl. engr. Ea. Air Lines, Boston, 1973-74; mgmt. engr. Baystate Med. Ctr., Springfield, Mass., 1974-80; v.p. for profl. svcs. Farren Meml. Hosp., Turners Falls, Mass., 1980-85; adminstr. Taylor Hosp., Bangor, Maine, 1985-87, Massena (N.Y.) Meml. Hosp., 1987-89, Falls Meml. Hosp., International Falls, Minn., 1990-93; CEO Tyrone (Pa.) Hosp., 1993—; mem. adv. bd. Rainy River Community Coll., International Falls, 1990-93. Author: (monograph) Resource Based Relative Value System, 1991. Capt. USMC, 1966-69, Vietnam. Fellow Am. Coll. Healthcare Execs.; mem. Inst. Indsl. Engrs. (sr.). Avocations: reading, jogging, making bread, boat building. Home: 416 Shorewood Dr International Falls MN 56649-2110 Office: Tyrone Hosp 1 Hosp Dr Tyrone PA 16686

STONER, R(ICHARD) B(URKETT), manufacturing company executive, member of Democratic national committee; b. Ladoga, Ind., May 15, 1920; s. Edward Norris and Florence May (Burkett) S.; m. Virginia B. Austin, Feb. 22, 1942; children—Pamela T., Richard Burkett, Benjamin Austin, Janet Elizabeth, Rebecca Lee, Joanne Jeannea. BS, Ind. U., 1941; JD, Harvard U., 1947; LLD, Butler U., 1975, Ind. U., 1994. With Cummins Engine Co., Inc., Columbus, Ind., 1947—, various adminstry., exec. positions, 1947-66, exec. v.p., corporate gen. mgr., 1966-69, vice. chmn. bd., 1969-88, vice chmn. emeritus, 1989—; dir. Cummins Engine Found. Dem. nat. committeeman for Ind.; del. Dem. Nat. Conv., 1956-92; pres., bd. dirs. Irwin-Sweeney-Miller Found.; bd. dirs. Christian Found., Columbus. Capt. AUS, 1942-46. Mem. Ind. C. of C. (dir.) Office: Cummins Engine Co Inc Box 3005 MC-60909 Columbus IN 47202

STONESIFER, RICHARD JAMES, retired humanities and social science educator; b. Lancaster, Pa., June 21, 1922; s. Paul Tobias and Esther (Wittlinger) S.; m. Nancy Jane Weaver, June 28, 1947; 1 dau., Pamela Ann. A.B., Franklin and Marshall Coll., 1946; M.A., Northwestern U., 1947; Ph.D., U. Pa., 1953. Mem. faculty Franklin and Marshall Coll., 1947-63, asso. prof. English, 1954-63, asst. to dean, 1957-60, asst. pres., 1960-63; asst. to provost, also dir. coll. gen. studies U. Pa., 1963-65; assoc. prof. communications Annenberg Sch. Communications, 1963-65; dean. Coll. Liberal Arts, prof. English Drew U., Madison, N.J., 1965-71; pres. Monmouth U., West Long Branch, N.J., 1971-79; Woodrow Wilson prof. humanities and social sci. Monmouth U., 1979-82; moderator TV discussion series, 1954-60. Author: W.H. Davies: A Critical Biography, 2d edit, 1965, also articles in profl. jours.; newspaper columnist and commentator weekly; free lance journalist. Mem. Pa. Adv. Com. Ednl. Broadcasting, 1963-65; Bd. dirs. Harrisburg Area Center Higher Edn., 1963-65; trustee N.J. Cancer Inst., 1975—. Served with USAAF, 1943-46. Mem. Phi Beta Kappa. Home: PO Box 906 306 Sanders St Mullins SC 29574-4214 *My life has been devoted to higher education, and to keeping the liberal arts at the center of the enterprise, even as of necessity we put new emphases on professional and career matters. In teaching and in administration I take as fundamental guidance the teaching from ancient Greece: moderation in all things.*

STONESTREET, ROBERT, library director. Dir., clk., treas. Pub. Libr. of Cin. Office: Pub Lib of Cin & Hamilton County Library Sq 800 Vine St Cincinnati OH 45202

STONICH, TIMOTHY WHITMAN, financial executive; b. Evanston, Ill., July 30, 1947; s. Joseph and Joyce (Whitman) S.; m. Joy Anne Harrison, June 14, 1969 (dec. Apr. 1986); m. Tamara L. Tierney, Nov. 13, 1987. B.A. in Econs., Denison U., 1969; M.B.A. in Fin., U. Chgo., 1972. Comml. banking officer Harris Bank, Chgo., 1969-74; asst. treas. Pullman Inc., Chgo., 1974-77, treas. Pullman Standard div., 1977-80; v.p. fin. Pullman Leasing Co., Chgo., 1977-80; v.p., gen. mgr. Pullman Leasing Co. Pullman Inc., 1980-83; treas. The Marmon Group, 1984-86; sr. v.p. fin. Lease Investment Corp., 1986-87; sr. v.p. fin., CFO U.S. Can Co., Oakbrook, Ill., 1987-91, exec. v.p., 1991—. Office: US Can Co 900 Commerce Dr Oak Brook IL 60521-1967

STONIER, DARYLE L., agricultural supplies company executive; married. Vice-chmn. Growmark, Inc., Bloomington, Ill., also dir.; vice-chmn. bd. Ill. Grain Corp. Served with USN, 1953-57. Mem. Ill. Agrl. Auditing Assn. (bd. dirs.). Office: Growmark Inc 1701 N Towanda Ave Bloomington IL 61701-2040

STONIER, TOM, educator, author; b. Hamburg, Fed. Republic Germany, Apr. 29, 1927; came to U.S. 1939; BA, Drew U., 1950; MS, Yale U., 1951, PhD, 1955. Jr. rsch. assoc. Brookhaven Nat. Lab. Upton, N.Y., 1952-54; postdoctoral fellow Rockefeller U., N.Y.C., 1954-57, rsch. assoc., 1957-62; assoc. prof. biology Manhattan Coll., N.Y.C., 1962-71, prof. biology, 1971-75; dir. Pacem/in Terris Inst., N.Y.C., 1971-75; prof., head sci. and soc. U. Bradford, U.K., 1975-90, prof. emeritus, 1990—; chmn. Valiant Tech., London, 1985—. Author: Nuclear Disaster, 1964, The Wealth of Information, 1983, The Three Cs: Children, Computers and Communication, 1985, Information and the Internal Structure of the Universe, 1990, Beyond Information, 1992; contbr. numerous articles to profl. jours. Sec. Fedn. of Am. Scientists, Washington, 1967-68, mem. coun., 1965-68. With USNR, 1945-46. H.D. Hooker fellow Yale U., 1950-51, Damon Runyon Meml. fellow Rockefeller U., 1956-57, postdoctoral fellow NIH Rockefeller U., 1954-56, Inst. Advanced Studies in Humanities fellow U. Edinburgh, 1989. Fellow Royal Soc. of Arts (life); mem. AAAS, N.Y. Acad. Scis., Phi Beta Kappa, Sigma Xi. Home and Office: 5 The Ave Great Barrington MA 01230

STOODT, BARBARA DERN, education educator, magazine editor; b. Columbus, Ohio, June 12, 1934; d. Millard Fissel and Helen Lucille (Taes) Dern; divorced; children: Linda Stoodt Neu, Susan Stoodt Price. BS in Edn., Ohio U., 1956; MA in Edn., Ohio State U., 1965; PhD, 1970; postgrad., U. Chgo., 1967. Tchr. North Charleston (S.C.) Schs., 1956-57, Cleveland Heights (Ohio) U., 1957-58, Mansfield (Ohio) Bd. Edn., 1958-59, 65-68; dir. reading, 1968; teaching assoc. Ohio State U., 1968-70; prof. edn. U. Akron, Ohio, 1970-77, U. N.C., Greensboro, 1977—. Author: Reading Instruction, 1981, 2d edit., 1989, Teaching Language Arts, 1988; co-author: Secondary School Reading Instruction, 1987, 5th edit., 1994, Riverside Rading Program. U.S. Office Edn. research grantee, 1970. Mem. Nat. Conf. on Research in English, Internat. Reading Assn. (Outstanding Dissertation award), Am. Ednl. Research Assn., Nat. Council Tchrs. English (outstanding research award 1971), Assn. for Supervision and Curriculum Devel., Assn. for Childhood Edn. Internat. Methodist. Avocations: gardening, travel, golf. Home: 5011 Manning Dr Greensboro NC 27410-4310 Office: Learning Mag 1607 Battleground Ave Greensboro NC 27412

STOOKEY, JOHN HOYT, chemical company executive; b. N.Y.C., Jan. 29, 1930; s. Byron and Helen Phelps (Hoyt) S.; m. Katherine Elizabeth Emory, Sept. 3, 1954; children: Helen Hoyt, Laura Emory, Hunt Emory, Anson Greene Phelps. Student, Amherst Coll., 1952, Columbia U., 1955. Asst. v.p. S.Am. Gold & Platinum Co., N.Y.C., 1956-59; officer, dir. various pvt. corps. for Investor Syndicate, 1959-69; U.S. rep. Financiera Metropolitana S.A., N.Y.C., 1962-75, Pub. Works Bank of Mexican Fed. Govt., N.Y.C., 1964-75; pres. Wallace Clark, Inc., N.Y.C., 1970-75, also bd. dirs., 1962-80; pres. Quantum Chem. Corp.(formerly Nat. Distillers & Chem. Corp.), N.Y.C., 1975-86, chmn. bd. dirs., pres., 1986-93, chmn. bd. dirs., 1993—, dir.; bd. dirs. Riegel Textile Corp., Rexham Corp. Founder, pres. Berkshire Boy Choir, Inc., from 1967; pres. Canterbury Choral Soc., 1968; chmn. health manpower com. United Hosp. Fund, 1966-71; bd. dirs. Assn. For A Better N.Y., from 1976; trustee Boston Symphony Orch., 1969-84, trustee emeritus, 1984—, Northfield-Mt. Hermon Schs., 1974-79, Council of Ams., from 1977, Bio-Energy Council, from 1977, James Weldon Johnson Community Ctr., Inc., 1965-70, Oratorio Soc. N.Y., 1965-75, Kodaly Musical Tng. Inst., 1973-75; trustee Coll. for Human Services, 1964-90, treas., 1964-75; trustee Stowe Sch., Inc., 1960-76, pres., 1960-73; mem. adv. bd. Grosvenor Neighborhood House, from 1970, Music in Old Deerfield, 1977; mem. choral panel NEA, 1993; founder, pres. Landmark Vol., 1992—. Mem. Council on Fgn. Relations, Alpha Pi Mu, Delta Kappa Epsilon. Clubs: Union, Down Town Assn., Pinnacle, Century Assn., Met. Opera, Pequot Yacht, Ctr. Harbor Yacht, Lenox, Weston Gun. Office: Quantum Chem Corp 99 Park Ave New York NY 10016-1503 Office: Petrolane Inc 240 State Rt 10 Whippany NJ 07981

STOOKEY, LAURENCE HULL, clergyman, theology educator; b. Belleville, Ill., Apr. 8, 1937; s. Loyd Leslie and Gladys E. (Hull) S.; m. Peggy Ann Reynolds, June 8, 1963 (div. 1990); children: Laura, Sarah. B.A., Swarthmore Coll., 1959; STB. magna cum laude, Wesley Theol. Sem., Washington, 1962; Th.D. with honors, Princeton Theol. Sem., 1971. Ordained to ministry United Meth. Ch., 1962. Pastor Peninsula-Del. Ann. Conf., United Meth. Ch., 1962-67, 71-73; instr. preaching and worship Princeton (N.J.) Theol. Sem., 1967-71; mem. faculty Wesley Theol. Sem., Washington, 1973—, Hugh Latimer Elderice prof., 1979—; guest lectr. Union Theol. Sem., Richmond, Va., McCormick Theol. Sem., Duke U. Div. Sch., Garrett-Evangel. Theol. Sem., Shenandoah (Va.) U.; vis. prof. U. Auckland, New Zealand, Melbourne Coll. Divinity; mem. Nat. Lutheran-United Meth. Bi-Lateral Theol. Dialogue, 1977-80; bd. dirs. Ctr. for Art and Religion, 1983-87, Liturgical Conf., 1983-91; officer Hymnal Revision Com. United Meth. Ch., 1984-88; cons. in field. Author: Living in a New Age: Sermons for the Season of Easter, 1978, Baptism-Christ's Act in the Church, 1982; co-author: Handbook of the Christian Year, 1986 (rev. 1992), Eucharist- Christ's Feast with the Church, 1993; mem. editorial bd.: Homiletic, 1974-86; contbr. articles to profl. jours. Fellow Assn. Theol. Schs. in U.S. and Can., 1979-80. Fellow N. Am. Acad. Liturgy, Acad. Homiletics; mem. Fellowship United Methodists in Worship, Music and Other Arts (officer 1981-83). Home: 13500 Justice Rd Rockville MD 20853-3268 Office: 4500 Massachusetts Ave NW Washington DC 20016-9990 *The pursuit of happiness can be dangerous. To ask ourselves whether we are happy may only fasten our attention upon those demons of discontent and frustration that plague us all. The proper query is, "How best can we contribute to the welfare of others?" Individuals-and nations-do well to abandon both oppressive practices of dependency and the destructive illusion of absolute independence. True happiness comes only with the discovery that we are designed to be constructively interdependent.*

STOOKEY, NOEL PAUL, folksinger, composer; b. Balt., Dec. 30, 1937; s. George William and Dorothea (St. Aubrey) S.; m. Mary Elizabeth Bannard, Sept. 4, 1963; children: Elizabeth Drake, Katherine Darby, Anna St. Aubrey. Student, Mich. State U., 1955-58; HHD (hon.), Husson Coll., 1978. prodn. mgr. Cormac Chem. Corp., N.Y.C., 1959-60. Released album of songs Birds of Paradise, 1954; sang professionally, master ceremonies events, Mich. State U., 1955-58; profl. singer, Greenwich Village, N.Y.C., 1960-61; mem. folksinging group, Peter, Paul and Mary, 1961—; solo rec. artist for Warner Bros., 1971-74; producer folk albums for Scepter Records, Verve/Folkway Records; founder, Neworld Media, rec. studio Neworld Records, 1977-81; rec. artist: Paul And, 1971, One Night Stand, 1972, Real to Reel, 1976, Something New and Fresh, 1978, Band and Bodyworks, 1979, Wait'll You Hear This, 1982, There is Love, 1985, State of the Heart, 1985, In Love Beyond Our Lives, 1990, Peter Paul and Mommy Too, 1993, Life-lines, 1995. Mem. AFTRA, Screen Actors Guild, ASCAP, Delta Upsilon. Club: St. Botolph's (Boston). Home: Rt 175 Blue Hill Falls ME 04615

STOPHER, PETER ROBERT, civil and transportation engineering educator, consultant; b. Crowborough, Eng., Aug. 8, 1943; came to U.S., 1968; s. Harold Edward and Joan Constance (Salmon) S; m. Valerie Anne Alway, Apr. 11, 1964 (div. Feb. 1989); children: Helen Margaret Anne, Claire Elizabeth; m. Catherine Coville Jones July 7, 1990. BSCE, U. Coll., London, 1964, PhD, 1967. Research officer Greater London Council, London, 1967-68; asst. prof. transp. planning, applied statistics, math. modeling Northwestern U., Evanston, Ill., 1968-70, from assoc. prof. to prof., 1973-79, vis. prof.1980-81; asst. prof. McMaster U., Hamilton, Ontario, 1970-71; assoc. prof. Cornell U., Ithaca, N.Y., 1971-73; tech. v.p. Schimpeler Corradino Assoc., Miami, Fla., and Los Angeles, 1980-84, v.p., 1984-87; dir., CFO Evaluation and Tng. Inst., 1987-90; prin., co-founder Applied Mgmt. and Planning Group, 1988-90; prof. civil engring. La. State Univ., Baton Rouge, 1990—, dir. La. Transp. Rsch. Ctr. 1990-93; co-founder, ptnr. PlanTrans, 1994—; spl. advisor Nat. Inst. Transp. and Rd. Research, Pretoria, S. Africa, 1976-77; vis. prof. U. Syracuse, N.Y., 1971-73, U. Louvain, Belgium, 1980. Co-author Urban Transportation Planning and Modeling, 1974, Transportation Systems Evaluation, 1976, Survey Sampling and Multivariate Analysis, 1978; contbr. articles to profl. jours. Active Stephen Ministry. Recipient Fred Burgraaf prize Hwy. Research Bd., 1968, Jules Dupuit prize World Conf. on Transp. Rsch., 1992. Mem. ASCE, Am. Stats. Assn., Transp. Rsch. Bd. (com. chmn. 1970-77, 1995—), Transp. Rsch. Forum (Joyce Yaeger prize 1994), Inst. Transp. Engrs. Democrat. Methodist. Avocations: working out, gardening, photography, reading, classical music. Home: 3533 Granada Dr Baton Rouge LA 70810 Office: La State U Dept Civil and Environ Engring Baton Rouge LA 70803-6405

STOPPARD, TOM (TOMAS STRAUSSLER), playwright; b. Zlin, Czechoslovakia, July 3, 1937; s. Eugene and Martha (Stoppard) Straussler; m. Jose Ingle, 1965 (div.); m. Miriam Moore-Robinson, 1972; 4 children. MLitt (hon.), U. Bristol, Eng., 1979, Brunel U., Eng., 1979, U Sussex, Eng., 1980. Journalist Western Daily Press, Bristol, Eng., 1954-58, Evening World, Bristol, 1958-60; free-lance reporter, 1960-63; bd. dirs. Royal Nat. Theatre, London, 1989—. Author: (plays) The Gamblers, 1965, Rosencrantz and Guildenstern are Dead, 1966 (Plays and Players Best Play award 1967, Best Play Tony award 1968), Enter a Free Man, 1968, The Real Inspector Hound, 1968, Albert's Bridge, 1969 (Prix Italia 1968), If You're Glad I'll Be Frank, 1969, After Magritte, 1970, Dogg's Our Pet, 1971, Jumpers, 1972 (Evening Standard Best Play award 1972, Plays and Players Best Play award 1972), Travesties, 1974 (Evening Standard Best Play award 1974, Best Play Tony award 1976), Dirty Linen and New-Found-Land, 1976, Every Good Boy Deserves Favor, 1974, Night and Day, 1978 (Evening Standard Best Play award 1978), Dogg's Hamlet, Cahoot's Macbeth, 1979, The Real Thing, 1982 (Evening Standard Best Play award 1982, Best Play Tony award 1984, Best Fgn. Play Tony award 1984), Hapgood, 1988, Artist Descending a Staircase, 1988, Arcadia, 1993 (Evening Standard Best Play award 1993, Oliver award 1994), Indian Ink, 1995; (play adaptations) Tango by Slawomir Mrozek, 1966, The House of Bernarda Alba by Federico Garcia Lorca, 1973, Undiscovered Country (based on Das Weite Land by Arthur Schnitzler), 1979, On the Razzle (based on Einen Jux will er sich machen by Johann Nestroy), 1981, Rough Crossing (based on The Play's the Thing by Ferenc Molnar), 1984, Dalliance (based on Liebelei by Arthur Schnitzler), 1986; (radio plays) The Dissolution of Dominic Boot, 1964, M is for Moon Among Other Things, 1964, If You're Glad I'll Be Frank, 1966, Albert's Bridge, 1967, Where Are They Now?, 1970, Artist Descending A Staircase, 1972, The Dog It Was That Died, 1982, In the Native State, 1991, also episodes of radio serials The Dales, 1964, A Student's Diary, 1965; (screenplays) The Romantic Englishwoman, 1975, Despair, 1978, The Human Factor, 1980, (with Terry Gilliam and Charles McKeown) Brazil, 1985 (Best Screenplay Acad. award nominee 1985, Best Screenplay L.A. Critics Circle award 1985), Empire of the Sun, 1987, The Russia House, 1990; (author, dir.) Rosencrantz and Guildenstern Are Dead, 1990 (Grand prize Venice Film Festival 1990), Billy Bathgate, 1991; (teleplays) A Walk on the Water, 1963, A Separate Peace, 1966, Teeth, 1967, Another Moon Called Earth, 1967, Neutral Ground, 1968, The Engagement (based on his radio play The Dissolution of Dominic Boot), 1970, One Pair of Eyes, 1972, (with Clive Exton) Boundaries, 1975, Three Men in a Boat, 1975, Professional Foul, 1977, Squaring the Circle: Poland 1980-81, 1985; (translator) Largo Desolato by Vaclav Havel, 1987; (novel) Lord Malquist and Mr. Moon, 1966; contbr. short stories to Introduction 2, 1964. Decorated comdr. Order Brit. Empire; Ford Found. grantee, 1964; recipient John Whiting award Arts Coun. Great Britain, 1967, Evening Standard Most Promising Playwright Drama award, 1972, Shakespeare prize Hamburg, Germany, 1979. Fellow Royal Soc. Literature. Office: Peters Fraser Dunlop, The Chambers 5th fl, Lots Rd, London SW10 OXF, England

STOPPLEMOOR, CHERYL See LADD, CHERYL

STORANDT, MARTHA, psychologist; b. Little Rock, June 2, 1938; d. Farris and Floy (Montgomery) Mobbs; m. Duane Storandt, Dec. 15, 1962; 1 child, Eric. AB, Washington U., St. Louis, 1960, PhD, 1966. Lic. psychologist, Mo. Staff psychologist VA, Jefferson Barracks, Mo., 1967-68; asst. prof. to prof. Washington U., St. Louis, 1968—; mem. nat. adv. council on aging Nat. Inst. on Aging, 1984-87; editor-in-chief Jour. Gerontology, 1981-86. Author: Counseling and Therapy with Older Adults, 1983; co-author: Memory, Related Functions and Age, 1974; co-editor: The Clinical Psychology of Aging, 1978, The Adult Years: Continuity and Change, 1989, Neuropsychological Assessment of Dementia and Depression in Older Adults: A Clinician's Guide, 1994. Recipient Disting. Service award Mo. Assn. Homes for the aging, 1984, Disting. Sci. Contbn. award Am. Psychol. Assn. div. Adult Devel. and Aging, 1988. Fellow Am. Psychol. Assn. (pres. div. 20 1979-80, council rep. 1983-84, 86-88), Gerontol. Soc. Am. Office: Washington U Dept Psychology Saint Louis MO 63130

STORARO, VITTORIO, cinematographer; b. Rome, June 24, 1940; s. Renato and Teodolinda (Laparelli) S.; m. Antonia Cafolla, Dec. 29, 1962; children: Francesca, Fabrizio, Giovanni. Student, Duca D'Aosta, Rome, 1951-56, Centro Italiano Addestramento Cinematografico, Rome, 1956-58; Degree in Cinematography, Centro Sperimentale di Cinematografia, Rome, 1958-60. Cinematographer Titanus, 1968, Paramount, 1970, 81, 87, United Artist, 1972, 76-77, 20th Century Fox, 1976, 78, Columbia, 1981, 84-86, Cronard Communications, 1982, Warner Bros., 1983, NBC, 1984-85. Cinematographer films including Youthful Youthful, 1968, The Bird With The Crystal Plummage, 1970, The Conformist, 1970, Last Tango in Paris, 1972, Nineteen Hundred, 1976, Scandalo Submission, 1977, Luna, 1978, Apocalypse Now, 1979 (Academy Award, 1980), Reds, 1981 (Acad. award 1982), One From the Heart, 1981, Wagner, 1982, Lady Hawke, 1983, Peter the Great, 1985, Ishtar, 1986, The Last Emperor, 1987 (Acad. award 1988), Tucker, 1987, New York Stories, 1988, Dick Tracy, 1990, The Sheltering Sky, 1990, Little Buddha, 1994. Recipient Best Cinematography award N.Y. Film Critics, 1971. Mem. Acad. Motion Picture Arts and Scis., Italian Assn. of Cinematographers (pres.). Home: Via Divino Amore 2, 00040 Rome Italy

STORB, URSULA BEATE, molecular genetics and cell biology educator; b. Stuttgart, Germany, July 6, 1936; came to U.S., 1966; d. Walter M. Stemmer and Marianne M. (Kämmerer) Nowara. MD, U. Freiburg, Fed. Republic Germany, 1960; Germany. Asst. prof. dept. microbiology U. Wash., Seattle, 1971-75, assoc. prof., 1975-81, prof., 1981-86, head. div. immunology, 1980-86; prof. dept. molecular genetics and cell biology U. Chgo., 1986—. Mem. editorial bd. Ann. Rev. Immunology, Current Opinion in Immunology, Internat. Immunology; contbr. articles to sci. jours. Grantee NIH, NSF, Am. Cancer Soc., 1973—. Fellow Am. Acad. Arts and Scis.; mem. Assn. Women in Sci., Am. Assn. Immunology, Am. Soc. Cell Biology. Office: U Chgo 920 E 58th St Chicago IL 60637-1432

STORCH, ARTHUR, theater director; b. Bklyn., June 29, 1925; s. Sam and Bessie (Goldner) S.; children: Max Darrow, Alexander English, Bess Martin. B.A., New Sch. Social Research, 1949. Actor in Broadway prodns. End as a Man, 1953, Time Limit, 1955, Girls of Summer, 1956, Look Homeward, Angel, 1957, Night Circus, 1958, The Long Dream, 1960, The Best Man, 1961; motion pictures The Strange One, 1956, Girls of the Night, 1959, The Exorcist, 1974; dir. off-Broadway Two by Saroyan, 1961, Three by Three, 1962, Talking to You (London debut), 1962, The Typists and the Tiger, 1963, The Owl and the Pussycat, 1964, The Impossible Years, 1965, The Local Stigmatic, 1970, Under the Weather, 1965, Golden Rainbow, 1967, The Chinese and Dr. Fish, 1969, Promenade All, 1970, 42 Seconds from Broadway, 1973, Tribute, 1978, Twice Around the Park, 1982, Clarence, 1986; Of Mice and Men, 1988; dir. nat. tour The King and I, 1989; dir. Syracuse Stage Waiting for Lefty, Noon, Of Mice and Men, 1974, 75, La Ronde, The Butterfingers Angel. Mornings at Seven, Dynamo, 1975-76, A Quality of Mercy, The Seagull, 1976-77, 1976-77; dir. Love Letters on Blue Paper, End of the Beginning, 1977-78, Loved, 1978, Naked, 1979, The Comedy of Errors, 1980, The Impromptu of Outremont, 1982, The Double Bass, 1984, Arms and the Man, Handy Dandy, Cyrano de Bergerac, Romeo and Juliet, 1986, Of Mice and Men, N.Y.C., 1987, Fugue, 1988, Seven By Beckett, 1988, Look Homeward Angel, Wait Unitl Dark, Dangerous Corner, 1990, A Walk in the Woods, 1989, Finding Donis Ann, 1990, Androcles and the Lion, 1991; Lend Me a Tenor, 1992, Awake and Sing, 1993; dir., actor Love Letters, 1992; producing artistic dir. Syracuse Stage; chmn. drama dept. Syracuse U., 1974-92, Arthur Storch Theatre, 1992; artistic dir. Berkshire Theatre Festival, Stockbridge, Mass., 1995—. Office: Berkshire Theatre Festival Stockbridge MA 01262

STOREN, THOMAS, JR. See DOHERTY, TOM

STORER, DONALD EDGAR, corporate executive; b. Wilkinsburg, Pa., Jan. 1, 1939; s. John William and Nelle (Forsythe) S.; m. Yvonne E. Doney, June 8, 1958 (div. Nov. 1983); m. Joanne E., Aug. 29, 1985 (children: Douglas, Gerald, Mark. BA, Otterbein Coll., 1960; MA, Ohio State U., 1968. Tchr. Cleveland Schs./Wesley Coll., Dover, Del., 1960-66; sales rep. IBM Corp., Columbus, Ohio, 1966-69; dir. mktg. IBM Corp., Chgo., 1969-72; regional mgr. IBM Corp., Hershey, Pa., 1972-75; nat. sales mgr. CBS, Inc., L.A., 1975-80; v.p. sales ARA, Inc., Phila., 1980-83; v.p. mktg. Seiler Corp., Waltham, Mass., 1983-85, sr. v.p. mktg., 1985-87, pres. Dietary Div., 1987-92; exec. v.p. Seiler Corp., 1993—. Office: The Seiler Corp 153 Second Ave Waltham MA 02254

STORER, JOHN W., lawyer, consultant; b. Washington, June 22, 1922; s. John W. and Nellie Grace (Mudd) S.; m. Harriet S. Trembecki, Oct. 2, 1945; children: Margaret, John III, Mark, Susan. JD, Loyola U., Chgo., 1949. Bar: Ill. 1949, U.S. Dist. Ct. (no. dist.) Ill. 1950, U.S. Supreme Ct. 1956. Atty. Continental Gas Co., Chgo., 1949-54, Law Offices Wyatt Jacobs, Chgo., 1954-60; founding, sr. ptnr. McKenna Storer et al., Chgo., 1960-84; mng. ptnr. McKenna Storer, Chgo., 1970-84; of counsel McKenna Storer Rowe White & Farrug, Chgo., 1984—; founder, faculty mem. transp. law inst. U. Denver, 1969; lectr. in field. Contbr. articles to profl. jours. Founder, dir. Timber Lakes (Ill.) Civic Assn., 1956; pres. Wildwood Community Assn., Chgo., 1960; organizer, past pres. Edgebrook Civic Orch.; former trustee sch. bd. St. Mary Woods Ch. Lt. AC, USN, 1942-46, PTO. Fellow Am. Bar Found.; mem. ABA (chair sr. lawyers divsn. 1990), Am. Arbitration Assn. (comml. arbitrator), Am. Soc. Metals, Am. Mgmt. Assn., Ill. State Bar (chair law practice mgmt. 1954—), Ill. Assn. Def. Counsel, Chgo. Bar Assn. (chair law practice mgmt., arbitration, 1954—, aviation law 1976—), Aviation Ins. Assn., Internat. Assn. Def. Counsel (dir., sec., treas. 1975-81, organizing advisor alternative dispute resolution com.), Transp. Lawyers Assn. (Disting. Svc. award 1989), Def. Rsch. Inst., Soc. Trial Lawyers, Trial Lawyers, Club, Ridgemoor Country Club (pres. 1967), Rio Verde Country Club (gen. counsel 1985—), Attic Club (Chgo. 1982-92), Rotary. Home: 26231 N Tonto Trl Rio Verde AZ 85263 Office: McKenna Storer Row Shite & Farrug 200 N La Salle St Ste 3000 Chicago IL 60601-1083

STORER, MARYRUTH, law librarian; b. Portland, Oreg., July 26, 1953; d. Joseph William and Carol Virginia (Pearson) Storer; m. David Bruce Bailey, Jan. 1, 1981; children: Sarah, Allison. BA in History, Portland State U., 1974; JD, U. Oreg., 1977; M in Law Librarianship, U. Wash., 1978. Bar: Oreg. 1978. Assoc. law librarian U. Tenn., Knoxville, 1978-79; law librarian O'Melveny & Myers, Los Angeles, 1979-88; dir. Orange County Law Library, Santa Ana, Calif., 1988—. Mem. Am. Assn. Law Libraries, So. Calif. Assn. Law Libraries (pres. 1986-87), Coun. Calif. County Law Librs. (sec.-treas. 1990-94, pres. 1994—). Democrat. Episcopalian. Office: Orange County Law Library 515 N Flower St Santa Ana CA 92703-2354

STORER, MORRIS BREWSTER, retired philosophy educator; b. Pitts., Nov. 14, 1904; s. Norman Wilson and Mary Elizabeth Wyman (Perry) S.; m. Gretchen Geuder Schneider, Aug. 18, 1935; children: John Winthrop, Christopher Martin, Thomas Perry. B.S., Dartmouth Coll., 1926; postgrad., Columbia U., 1930; A.M., U. Chgo., 1929, Harvard U., 1932; Ph.D., Harvard U., 1937. Asst. in philosophy U. Chgo., 1927, U. Pitts., 1927-28; corr. N.Mex. State Tribune, 1928; instr. philosophy Lafayette Coll., 1929-30; instr. philosophy, comparative religion Dartmouth Coll., 1932-35; asst. philosophy Harvard, Radcliff Coll., 1935-36; social scientist in field of conf. orgn., discussion leader tng. Bur. Agrl. Econs., Dept. Agr., 1936-41, sr. social scientist extension service, 1941-46, chmn. post-war planning subcom.

on agrl.-indsl. relations, 1942-43, acting dir., fgn. student tng. program, 1945-46; dean of instrn. Mt. Vernon Jr. Coll., Washington, 1946-47; prof. humanities and philosophy U. Fla., 1947-73, prof. emeritus, 1973—; pres. Santa Fe Telephone Co., R.E.A. Coop., 1950-52. Author: Toward a Theory of Moral Debt, 1971, Let's Discuss World Peace Organization, other public affairs discussion guides, U.S. Dept. Agr., 1940-46; editor: Humanist Ethics: Dialogue on Basics, 1980, The Larger Storer-Perry Family, Vol. I 1986, Vol. II, 1988, Vol. III, 1989. Pres. Unitarian-Universalist Fellowship of Gainesville, Fla., 1965-67. Capt. AUS, 1943-44. Mem. Am., Fla. philos. assns., Am. Fedn. Tchrs. (sec. U. Fla. chpt. 1941-42), Am. Humanist Assn. (dir. 1975-80), Humanist Soc. Gainesville (pres. 1975-76), Fellowship of Religious Humanists, Delta Upsilon. Democrat. Unitarian. Club: Melrose Civic (pres. 1949-50). Home: 915 Menlo Ave Unit A Menlo Park CA 94025

STORER, NORMAN WILLIAM, sociology educator; b. Middletown, Conn., May 8, 1930; s. Norman Wyman and Mary Emily (House) S.; m. Ada Joan Van Valkenburg, Aug. 19, 1951; children: Martin Wilson, Thomas Wyman; m. Mary Ashton Pott Hiatt, Mar. 7, 1975. A.B., U. Kans., 1952, M.A., 1956; Ph.D., Cornell U., 1961. Lectr., asst. prof. Harvard U., Cambridge, Mass., 1960-66; staff assoc. Social Sci. Research Council, N.Y.C. 1966-70; prof. sociology CUNY-Baruch Coll., N.Y.C., 1970-88; prof. emeritus CUNY-Baruch Coll., 1989—; dept. chmn. CUNY-Baruch Coll., N.Y.C., 1970-85, chmn. faculty senate, 1981-84. Author: The Social System of Science, 1966, Focus on Society, 1973, 2d edit., 1980, A Leer of Limericks, 1990, (with William Flores) Domestic Violence in Suburban San Diego, 1994; editor: The Sociology of Science, 1973; column editor San Diego Writers' Monthly, 1992-94. Served to sgt. AUS, 1953-55. Mem. AAAS, Phi Beta Kappa, Sigma Xi. Democrat. Home: 1417 Van Buren Ave San Diego CA 92103-2339

STORER, THOMAS PERRY, lawyer; b. Washington, July 14, 1944; s. Morris Brewster and Gretchen Geuder (Schneider) S.; m. Julia Manganip Owek, Dec. 22, 1966; children: Lingbawan Frederick, Allinnawa Elizabeth, Gessingga Nathaniel. BA in Math., Harvard U., 1965, JD, 1979; MPA, Woodrow Wilson Sch. Pub. and Internat. Affairs, 1969. Bar: Mass. 1979, U.S. Dist. Ct. Mass. 1979. Program officer U.S. Peace Corps, Kuala Lumpur, Malaysia, 1969-72; analyst, unit chief Bur. of Budget State of Ill., Springfield, 1972-74, dep. dir. Dept. Pub. Aid, 1974-76; cons. Mass. Medicaid Program, Boston, 1976-79; assoc. Goodwin, Procter & Hoar, Boston, 1979-87, ptnr., 1987—. Vol. U.S. Peace Corps, Bontoc, Mountain Prov., Philippines, 1965-67; elder Newton (Mass.) Presbyn. Ch., Mass., 1987—. Mem. ABA, Mass. Bar Assn. Avocations: music, computers. Home: 114 Waban Hill Rd N Chestnut Hill MA 02167-1026 Office: Goodwin Procter & Hoar Exchange Pl Boston MA 02109

STORETTE, RONALD FRANK, lawyer; b. N.Y.C., June 20, 1943; m. Monique Storette; 1 child, Ronald. BA summa cum laude, U. Va., 1966; JD, Harvard U., 1969; Diploma of Internat. Law, Stockholm Faculty of Law, 1970. Bar: D.C. 1973, U.S. Ct. Appeals (D.C. cir.) 1976, U.S. Supreme Ct. 1976, U.S. Dist. Ct. (so. and ea. dists.) N.Y. 1977, U.S. Dist. Ct. D.C. 1977, U.S. Ct. Appeals (2d cir.) 1978, U.S. Ct. Internat. Trade. 1978. Lectr. law Stockholm Faculty of Law, 1970-71; assoc. Jean-Pierre De Bandt, Brussels, 1971-73; chief legal counsel Textron Atlantic S.A., Brussels, 1973-75; assoc. Donovan, Leisure, Newton & Irvine, N.Y.C., 1975-79; ptnr. Fragomen, Del Rey & Bernsen, P.C., N.Y.C., 1979-88, Baker & McKenzie, N.Y.C., 1988-91, Proskauer Rose Goetz & Mendelsohn, N.Y.C., 1991—. Author: The Politics of Integrated Social Investment; An American Study of the Swedish LAMCO Project in Liberia, 1971, The Administration of Equality; An American Study of Sweden's Bilateral Development Aid, 1972; also articles. Cassal Found. fellow U. Stockholm, Sweden, 1969. Mem. ABA, N.Y. State Bar Assn.. Assn. of Bar of City of N.Y., Am. Immigration Lawyers Assn., Phi Beta Kappa. Office: Proskauer Rose Goetz & Mendelsohn 1585 Broadway New York NY 10036-8200

STOREY, BRIT ALLAN, historian; b. Boulder, Colo., Dec. 10, 1941; s. Harold Albert and Gladys Roberta (Althouse) S.; m. Carol DeArman, Dec. 19, 1970; 1 child, Christine Roberta. AB, Adams State Coll., Alamosa, Colo., 1963; MA, U. Ky., 1965, PhD, 1968. Instr. history Auburn (Ala.) U., 1967-68, asst. prof., 1968-70; dep. state historian State Hist. Soc. Colo., Denver, 1970-71, acting state historian, 1971-72, rsch. historian, 1972-74; hist. preservation specialist Adv. Coun. on Hist. Preservation, Lakewood, Colo., 1974-88; sr. historian Bur. Reclamation, Lakewood, 1988—. Contbr. articles to profl. publs. Mem. Fed. Preservation Forum (pres. 1990-91), Nat. Coun. Pub. History (sec. 1987, pres.-elect 1990-91, pres. 1991-92), Orgn. Am. Historians (com. 1983-86, chmn. 1985-86), Victorian Soc. Am. (bd. dirs. 1977-79), Western History Assn. (chmn. com. 1982-86), Colo.-Wyo. Assn. Mus. (sec. 1974-76, pres. 1976-77), Cosmos Club (Washington). Avocations: fishing, birding. Home: 7264 W Otero Ave Littleton CO 80123-5639 Office: Bur Reclamation D 5300 Bldg 67 Denver Fed Ctr Denver CO 80225-0007

STOREY, CHARLES PORTER, lawyer; b. Austin, Tex., Dec. 4, 1922; s. Robert Gerald and Frances Hazel (Porter) S.; m. Helen Hanks Stephens, Oct. 14, 1950; children: Charles Porter, Harry Stephens, Frederick Schatz. BA, U. Tex., 1947, LLB, 1948; LL.M.. So. Methodist U., 1952. Bar: Tex. 1948. Pvt. practice law Dallas, 1948—; assoc. Storey Armstrong Steger & Martin P.C., 1972—. Pres. Dallas Day Nursery Assn., 1958, Greater Dallas Coun. Chs., 1970-71; chmn. Internat. Com. YMCA, 1969-71; nat. bd. dirs. U.S. YMCA, 1964-75; pres. Children's Devel. Ctr., Dallas, 1959; trustee Baylor Coll. Dentistry, 1981-90, Hillcrest Found.; trustee Southwestern Legal Found., chmn. 1980-90. 1st lt., pilot USAAF, 1943-45, ETO. Decorated Air medal. Master Dallas Inn of Ct. (pres. 1991-93); fellow Am. Coll. Trial Lawyers, Am. Bar Found., Tex. Bar Found.; mem. ABA, Tex. Bar Assn. (bd. dirs. 1976-79), Dallas Bar Assn. (pres. 1975), Philos. Soc. Tex., Dallas Country Club, Crescent Club, Idlewild Club, Phi Delta Phi, Phi Delta Theta. Mem. Christian Ch. (Disciples of Christ). Home: 4400 Rheims Pl Dallas TX 75205-3627 Office: 4600 First Interstate Bank Tower 1445 Ross Ave Dallas TX 75202-2711

STOREY, FRANCIS HAROLD, business consultant, retired bank executive; b. Calgary, Alberta, Can., June 20, 1933; s. Bertwyn Morrell and Hilda Josephine (Masters) S.; m. Willomae Saiter, Apr. 25, 1954; children: Daryl, Elizabeth, Brian, Shelley. Student, Gonzaga U., 1953, Pacific Coast Bankers Sch., 1974-76. Designated Certified Profl. Cons. Bank trainee Wash. Trust Bank, Spokane, 1950-56; owner Storey & Storey, Spokane, 1956-64; agt. Bankers Life Nebr., Spokane, 1964-67; sr. v.p. Old Nat. Bank, Spokane, 1967-87, U.S. Bank of Wash., Spokane, 1987-90; pvt. practice cons. Spokane, 1990—; bd. dirs. Alloy Trailers Inc., Output Tech. Corp. Bd. dirs. United Way of Spokane, 1987-95; bd. dirs., treas., fin. chair, gen. conv. dep. Episcopal Diocese Spokane Dep., 1969—; trustee Spokane Symphony Soc., 1986-93, Spokane Area Devel. Coun., 1982-89; mem. adv. bd. Intercollegiate Ctr. Nursing Edn.; bd. dirs. Spokane Bus. Incubator. Mem. Acad. Profl. Cons. and Advisors, Spokane Rotary, Spokane Country Club, Spokane Club. Episcopalian. Avocations: golf, reading, travel. Home: 214 E 13th Ave Spokane WA 99202-1115

STOREY, JAMES MOORFIELD, lawyer; b. Boston, Apr. 12, 1931; s. Charles Moorfield and Susan Jameson (Sweetser) S.; m. Adair Miller, Aug. 28, 1954 (div. 1973); children: Barbara Sessums Storey McGrath, Mary Sweetser Storey Meley, Susan Adair Storey Frank, Eliza Allison Tebo Storey Anderson, Alice Leovy Storey Thorpe; m. Isabelle Helene Boeschenstein, May 17, 1973. A.B., Harvard U., 1953, LL.B., 1956. Bar: Mass. 1956. Atty. SEC, Washington, 1956-57, legal asst. to chmn., 1957-59; assoc. Gaston, Snow, Motley & Holt, Boston, 1959-62; ptnr. Gaston, Snow, Motley & Holt (name changed to Gaston Snow & Ely Bartlett), Boston, 1962-87, Dechert Price & Rhoads, Boston, 1987—; trustee Mt. Auburn Cemetery, Cambridge, Mass., 1980—. Mem. ABA, Boston Bar Assn., Tavern Club Boston (pres. 1985-87), City Club Corp. (pres. 1987-89), Century Assn. of N.Y. Unitarian. Home: 89A Mt Vernon St Boston MA 02108 Office: Dechert Price & Rhoads 10 Post Office Sq S 12th Fl Boston MA 02109

STOREY, KENNETH BRUCE, biology educator; b. Taber, Alta., Can., Oct. 23, 1949; s. Arthur George and Madeleine Una (Mawhinney) S.; m. Janet Margaret Collicutt, June 6, 1975; children: Jennifer, Kathryn. BSc with honors, U. Calgary, Alta., 1971; PhD, U. B.C., Vancouver, Can., 1974. Asst. prof. Duke U., Durham, N.C., 1975-79; assoc. prof. Carleton U., Ottawa, Ont., Can., 1979-85, prof., 1985—; invited lectr. at various confs., univs. Mem. editl. bd. Cryo-Letters, 1983—, Environ. Revs., 1993—; Am. Jour. Physiology, 1994—; contbr. over 300 articles to profl. jours. Recipient E.W.R. Steacie award Nat. Sci. and Engring. Rsch. Coun. Can., 1984-86, Killam sr. rsch. fellow, 1993—; Killam fellow Can. Coun., Sheffield, Eng., 1975-77. Fellow Royal Soc. Can.; mem. Am. Soc. Biol. Chemists, Can. Biochem. Soc. (Ayerst award 1989), Can. Soc. Zoology, soc. Cryobiology. Avocations: movies, music, Renaissance art. Office: Carleton U Dept Biology, 1125 Colonel By Drive, Ottawa, ON Canada K1S 5B6

STOREY, NORMAN C., lawyer; b. Miami, Fla., Oct. 11, 1943. BA cum laude, Loyola U., L.A., 1965; JD, U. Ariz., 1968. Bar: Ariz. 1968. Law clk. to Hon. James A. Walsh U.S. Dist. Ct. Ariz.; ptnr. Squire, Sanders & Dempsey, Phoenix. Mem. ABA (corp., banking and bus. law, real property, probate, trust law sects., task force pub. rels.), State Bar Ariz., Maricopa County Bar Assn., Am. Arbitration Assn. (panelist). Office: Squire Sanders & Dempsey 40 N Central Ave Ste 2700 Phoenix AZ 85004-4441

STOREY, ROBERT, lawyer; b. Tuskegee, Ala., Mar. 28, 1936; s. Dewitt Herald and Katie Pearl (Johnson) S.; m. Juanita Kendrick Cohen, May 9, 1959; children: Charles Kendrick, Christopher Robert Ransom, Rebecca Kate. AB, Harvard U., 1958; JD, Case Western Res. U., 1964. Bar: Ohio. 1964. Atty. East Ohio Gas Co., Cleve., 1964-66; asst. dir. Legal Aid Soc., Cleve., 1966-67; assoc. Burke, Haber & Berick, Cleve., 1967-70, ptnr., 1971-93; ptnr. Thompson, Hine & Flory, Cleve., 1994—; bd. dirs. GTE Corp., Stamford, Conn., Procter & Gamble Co., Cin., May Dept. Stores Co., St. Louis, Bank One, Cleve.; trustee The Kresge Found., Case Western Res. U., Univ. Sch., Great Lakes Sci. Ctr.; trustee Cleve. State U., 1971-80, chmn., 1979-80; trustee Phillips Exeter Acad., 1968-83; overseer Harvard U., 1978-84; dir. Fed. Res. Bank Cleve., 1987-90, Louisville Courier-Journ., 1984-86. Served to capt. USMC, 1958-61. Recipient Charles Flint Kellog award Assn. Episcopal Colls., 1984; named Chief Marshal, 25th Reunion, Harvard Class of 1958, 1983. Mem. Soc. Benchers, Union Club, Rowfant Club, Univ. Club, Ponce de Leon Club. Episcopalian. Home: 2385 Coventry Rd Cleveland Heights OH 44118 Office: Thompson Hine and Flory 1100 National City Bank Bld Cleveland OH 44114

STORHOFF, DONALD C., agricultural products company executive; b. 1935; married. Supr. Meadowland Dairy, 1953-69; asst. plant mgr. Associated Milk Producers Inc., 1969-72; plant mgr. Wis. Dairies Coop., Baraboo, 1972-74, product mgr., 1974-77, 1977-84, pres., 1984—, also bd. dirs.; pres. Wis. Fedn. Coop. Dairy Div. & Whey Products Inst.; bd. dirs. Am. Dry Milk Inst., Nat. Milk Producers Fedn., Nat. Cheese and Butter Inst. Office: Wis Dairies Coop RR 3 Baraboo WI 53913-9803

STORIN, MATTHEW VICTOR, newspaper editor; b. Springfield, Mass., Dec. 24, 1942; s. Harry Francis and Blanche Marie S.; m. Keiko Takita, Aug. 1, 1975; 1 child, Kenyatta; children by previous marriage: Karen, Aimee, Sean. BA, U. Notre Dame, 1964. Reporter Springfield Daily News, 1964-65, Griffin-Larrabee News Bur., Washington, 1965-69; Washington corr., city editor, Asian corr., nat. editor, asst. mng. editor, dep. mng. editor, mng. editor Boston Globe, 1969-85; dep. mng. editor U.S. News & World Report, Washington, 1985-86; editor, sr. v.p. Chgo. Sun-Times, 1986-87; editor The Maine Times, Topsham, 1988-89; mng. editor N.Y. Daily News, 1989-91, exec. editor, 1991-92; exec. editor Boston Globe, 1992-93, editor, 1993—. Recipient Disting. Polit. Reporting award Am. Assn. Polit. Sci., 1969. Office: The Boston Globe 135 Morrissey Blvd Boston MA 02107

STORING, PAUL EDWARD, foreign service officer; b. Ames, Iowa, Oct. 24, 1929; s. James Alvin and Edith Nora (Ryg) S.; children: Mimi Storing Harlan, Felice Storing Kite. Student, U Oslo, Norway, 1950-51; B.A., Allegheny Coll., 1952; M.A. with honors, Colgate U., 1956; postgrad.: U. Wis., Madison, 1955-59. Fgn. service officer Dept. State, Washington, Mex. and Scandinavia, 1960-80; spl. asst. U.S. Sect. Internat. Boundary and Water Commn. U.S. And Mex., Washington, 1980—. Contbr. articles to profl. jours. Served to cpl. U.S. Army, 1953-55. Fellow U. Wis., 1957-58; Fulbright fellow U. Oslo, 1959-60. Mem. Am. Fgn. Svc. Assn., Fulbright Assn., Phi Beta Kappa, Delta Tau Delta (pres. 1949-50). Baptist. Avocations: swimming; travel. Office: Dept State Office of Mexican Affairs 2201 C St NW Washington DC 20520-0001

STORK, DONALD ARTHUR, advertising executive; b. Walsh, Ill., June 17, 1939; s. Arthur William and Katherine Frances (Young) S.; m. Joanna Gentry, June 9, 1962; 1 child, Brian Wesley. B.S., So. Ill. U., 1961; postgrad. St. Louis U., 1968-69. With Naegele Outdoor Advt., Mpls., St. Louis, 1961-63; account exec. Richard C. Lynch Advt., 1963-64; media exec. Gardner Advt. Co., 1964-69; v.p. mktg. Advanswers Media/Programming divsn. Wells Rich Greene, N.Y.C., 1975-79; pres. Advanswers divsn. WRG/BDDP, N.Y.C., 1979—. Bd. dirs. Trailblazers, Inc.; pres. Signal Hill Sch. Assn. Parents Tchrs. Recipient Journalism Alumnus of Yr. award So. Ill. U., 1971, Alumni Achievement award, 1983. Served to capt. USAFR, 1961-67. Mem. St. Louis Advt. Club, Mensa, Alpha Delta Sigma (Aid to Advt. Edn. award 1971). Clubs: Mo. Athletic (St. Louis); St. Clair Country (Belleville).(St. Louis); St. Clair Country (Belleville). Home: 34 Symonds Dr Belleville IL 62223-1905 Office: Advanswers Media/Programming 10 S Broadway Saint Louis MO 63102-1712 also: 1740 Broadway New York NY 10019-4315

STORK, GILBERT (JOSSE), chemistry educator, investigator; b. Brussels, Belgium, Dec. 31, 1921; s. Jacques and Simone (Weil) S.; m. Winifred Stewart, June 9, 1944 (dec. May 1992); children: Diana, Linda, Janet, Philip. B.S., U. Fla., 1942; Ph.D., U. Wis., 1945; D.Sc. (hon.), Lawrence Coll., 1961, U. Paris, 1979, U. Rochester, 1982, Emory U., 1988, Columbia U., 1993. Sr. research chemist Lakeside Labs., 1945-46; instr. chemistry Harvard U., 1946-48, asst. prof., 1948-53; assoc. prof. Columbia U., N.Y.C., 1953-55, prof., 1955-61, Eugene Higgins prof., 1967-92, prof. emeritus, 1992—, chmn. dept., 1973-76; plenary lectr. numerous internat. symposia, named Lectureships in U.S. and abroad; cons. Syntex, Internat. Flavors and Fragrances; chmn. Gordon Steroid Conf., 1958-59. Guggenheim fellow, 1959; recipient Baekeland medal, 1961, Harrison Howe award, 1962, Edward Curtis Franklin Meml. award Stanford, 1966, Gold medal Synthetic Chems. Mfrs. Assn., 1971, Nebr. award, 1973, Roussel prize in steroid chemistry, 1978, Edgar Fahs Smith award, 1982, Willard Gibbs medal, Chgo. section Am. Chem. Soc., 1982, National Medal of Sci., 1982, Linus Pauling award, 1983, Tetrahedron prize, 1985, Remsen award, 1986, Cliff S. Hamilton award 1986, Mony Ferst award Sigma Xi, 1987, George Kenner award, 1992, Chemical Pioneer award Am. Inst. of Chemistry, 1992, Welch Found. Award in Chemistry, 1993, Allan R. Day award Phila. Chemists Club, 1994. Fellow NAS (award in chem. sci. 1982), French Acad. Scis., Am. Acad. Arts and Scis., Am. Philos. Soc.; mem. Am. Chem. Soc. (chmn. organic chemistry divsn. 1967, award in pure chemistry 1957, award for creative work in synthetic organic chemistry 1967, Nichols medal 1980, Arthur C. Cope award 1980, Roger Adams award in organic chemistry 1991), Royal Soc. Chemistry (hon., London), Pharm. Soc. Japan (hon.), Chemists Club (hon.). Home: 459 Next Day Hill Dr Englewood NJ 07631-1921 Office: Columbia U Dept of Chemistry Havemeyer Hall New York NY 10027

STORKE, DWIGHT CLIFTON, JR., government official; b. Fredericksburg, Va., Sept. 6, 1939; s. Dwight Clifton and Shirley Williams (King) S.; m. Sylvia Hitch Clark, Oct. 25, 1963; children: Theresa Storke Freeman, David Wallace, John Benjamin. BS, Richmond Profl. Inst., 1962; MEd, Va. Commonwealth U., 1973; PhD with honor, Internat. Sem., Plymouth, Fla., 1990. Instr. Dept. Navy, Dahlgren, Va., 1971-93; interpreter Nat. Park Svc., Washington's Birthplace, Va., 1971-74, park ranger, 1974-87, instr., 1984-86; supt. Nat. Park Svc., Richmond, Va., 1987-89, Washington's Birthplace, 1989—; fed. firearms instr. Nat. Park Svc., Va., 1980—; adj. instr. Nat. Park Svc. Tng. Acad., Grand Canyon, Ariz., 1972-75; mem. ports. mgmt. rev. bd. Nat. Park Svc., Phila., 1993—. Author: Communication Skills, 1975. Facility and program facilitator DAR, Westmoreland, Va., 1980—; capt. Va. State Guard, Fredericksburg, 1985—; dir. Shenandoah Valley Civil War Task Force, Va., 1993. Recipient Interpreter of Yr. award Mid-Atlantic region Nat. Park Svc., 1981, 82, Superior Performance award, 1986, Supt. of Yr. award Mid-Atlantic region, 1993, Meritorious Svc. award Dept. Interior, 1993. Mem. Va. Assn. Mus., No. Neck Va. Hist. Soc., Masons (master), Kappa Delta Pi. Baptist. Avocations: history, archaeology. Office: George Washington Birthplace Nat Monument Rt 1 Box 717 Washingtons Birthplace VA 22443

STORKE, WILLIAM FREDERICK JOSEPH, film producer; b. Rochester, N.Y., Aug. 12; s. Legrand Frederick Sommerfeldt and Patricia Louise S.; children: Victoria Jane, Adam John, William MacKenzie; m. Georgette MacKenzie Edwards, Feb. 22, 1970. B.A. in Econs., UCLA, 1948. With NBC, N.Y.C., 1948—, comml. editor, then comml. supr. network sales West Coast and participating program sales, dir. participating program sales, dir. program administra., v.p. program adminstrn., 1948-57, v.p. programs East Coast, 1967-68, v.p. spl. programs East Coast, 1968—; pres. Claridge Group, Ltd. div. Trident TV Ltd., London, 1979—; exec. v.p Entertainment Ptnrs., Inc., N.Y.C., 1982-87; pres. Storke Enterprises Inc., 1987—. Producer: (films) Oliver Twist, 1982, To Catch a King, 1983, A Christmas Carol, 1984, The Last Days of Patton, 1985, The Ted Kennedy Jr. Story, 1986, A Special Friendship, 1986, (TV series) Buck James, 1987, The Old Man and the Sea, 1989, Hands of a Murderer (Sherlock Holmes), 1990. Served with USNR, 1943-46. Mem. University Club, Nat. Endowment for Arts (theatre panel 1976-78). Home: 1060 Fifth Ave New York NY 10128-0104 Office: Leavy Rosensweig & Hyman care Sidney Feinberg Esq 11 E 44th St New York NY 10017-3608

STORM, DONALD JOHN, archaeologist, historian; b. Bradford, Pa., Nov. 20, 1947; s. John Ross and Jean Lamar (Frederick) S. AA, Yuba Coll., 1967; BA, Sacramento State U., 1972; postgrad., Calif. State U., Sacramento, 1972-74, Calif. State U., Chico, 1980, U. Nev., Reno, 1988-89. Instr. Marysville (Calif.) Joint Unified Sch. Dist., 1977-78; state archaeologist Calif. Dept. Parks and Recreation, Sacramento, 1981-84; owner North Yuba Contracting, Oregon House, Calif., 1984-87; archaeologist Elko dist. Nev. Bur. Land Mgmt., Elko, 1988; asst. forest archaeologist Sierra Nat. Forest, Clovis, Calif., 1990-91; archaeol. tech. Tahoe Nat. Forest, Camptonville, Calif., summer 1980; archaeol. cons. Oregon House, 1976-81, 88—; instr. Yuba Coll., Marysville, Calif., 1976-78, 88-93. Activist various conservation/environ. groups; candidate for Yuba County Supr., 1992. With U.S. Army, 1967-70. Mem. Soc. Am. Archaeology, Soc. Hist. Archaeology, Soc. for Calif. Archaeology, Calif. Hist. Soc., Nat. Trust for Historic Preservation, So. Pacific Hist. and Tech. Soc. Avocations: stamp collecting, model railroading, history. Home and Office: PO Box 552 Oregon House CA 95962

STORM, JONATHAN MORRIS, television critic; b. N.Y.C.; s. Thomas Walton and Martha Louise (Morris) S.; m. Kathleen Jo Pottick, Oct. 13, 1979. BA, Williams Coll., 1969. Reporter, city editor Rutland (Vt.) Herald, 1970-76; copy editor, assoc. editor Detroit Free Press, 1976-82; copy editor, feature editor Phila. Inquirer, 1982-89, TV critic, 1989—. Recipient Benjamin Franklin award Nat. Press Found., 1987. Mem. Hopewell Valley Golf Club, Soc. Profl. Journalists (treas. Phila. chpt. 1993—). Office: Phila Inquirer 400 N Broad St Philadelphia PA 19130-4099

STORMER, HORST LUDWIG, physicist; b. Frankfurt-Main, Fed. Republic Germany, Apr. 6, 1949; came to U.S., 1977; s. Karl-Ludwig and Marie (Ihrig) S.; m. Dominique A. Parchet, 1982. Ph.D., U. Stuttgart, 1977. Mem. tech. staff AT&T Bell Labs., Murray Hill, N.J., 1977-83, head dept., 1983-91, dir. phys. rsch. lab., 1992—. Recipient Otto Klung prize Fed. Republic of Germany, 1985; Bell Labs. fellow, 1983. Fellow Am. Phys. Soc. (Buckley prize 1984), Am. Acad. Arts and Scis. Office: AT&T Bell Labs 600 Mountain Ave New Providence NJ 07974-2010

STORMER, JOHN CHARLES, JR., geology educator, mineralogist; b. Englewood, N.J., Oct. 28, 1941; s. John Charles and Malvene Olive (Cushmore) S.; m. Jane McNair, June 17, 1963; children: Karen, Eric. BA, Dartmouth Coll., 1963; PhD, U. Calif., Berkeley, 1971. Registered geologist, Ga. Asst. geologist Climax (Colo.) Molybdenum Co., 1967; asst., then assoc. prof. U. Ga., Athens, 1971-83; geologist U.S. Geol. Survey, Reston, Va., 1982-83; prof. geology Rice U., Houston, 1983—; Carey Croneis chair in geology, 1983, chmn. dept. geology and geophysics, 1989-92; cons. various mining cos., 1975—. Contbr. articles to profl. jours.; editor: (guidebook) Elberton Batholith, 1977. Lt. USN, 1963-67, Vietnam. Grantee NSF, 1973-89. Fellow Mineral. Soc. Am.; mem. Am. Geophys. Union, Geochem. Soc., Internat. Assn. for Volcanology and Chemistry of Earth's Interior, Geol. Soc. Washington. Avocations: sailing, drawing, printmaking. Home: PO Box 1277 Kemah TX 77565-1277 Office: Rice U Dept Geology & Geophysics PO Box 1892 6100 Main St Houston TX 77005-1827

STORMONT, RICHARD MANSFIELD, hotel executive; b. Chgo., Apr. 4, 1936; s. Daniel Lytle and E. Mildred (Milligan) S.; m. Virginia Louellen Walters, Nov. 21, 1959; children: Stacy Lee Freeman, Richard Mansfield, John Frederick. B.S., Cornell U., 1958. Cert. hosp. adminstrn.; cert. hosps. industry profl. Food cost analyst, sales rep. Edgewater Beach Hotel, Chgo., 1957-58; asst. sales mgr. Marriott Hotels, Inc., Washington, 1962-64; dir. sales Marriott Hotels, Inc., Atlanta, 1964-68; resident mgr. Marriott Hotels, Inc., 1969-71; gen. mgr. Marriott Hotel, Dallas, 1971-73, Phila., 1973-74, Atlanta, 1974-79; pres. Hardin Mgmt. Co., 1979-80; v.p Marriott Franchise div. Marriott Corp., Washington, 1981-84, v.p. ops. Courtyard by Marriott, 1981-84; pres. The Stormont Cos. Inc., Atlanta, 1984-92; chmn. bd. dirs. Stormont Trice Corp., Atlanta, 1993—; cons. to mgmt. Walters & Co., 1975-82. Pres. Atlanta Conv. and Visitors Burs., 1975-76, chmn. bd., 1976-77; bd. dirs. Better Bus. Bur.; exec. com. Central Atlanta Progress, 1979-80; exec. council Boy Scouts Am. Served to lt. (j.g.) USNR, 1959-62. Recipient Disting. Salesman of Yr. award Marriott, 1967, Obi T. Brewer award for Decade of Outstanding Svc., 1979. Mem. Sales and Mktg. Execs. (exec. v.p 1969-70, pres. Atlanta 1970-71), Am. Hotel-Motel Assn. (exec. com., bd. dirs. 1993—), Ga. Hospitality and Travel Assn. (founder, dir. 1985—, pres. 1989-90, chmn. bd. 1991-92, Hotelier of Yr. award 1977), Ga. Bus. and Industry Assn. (bd. dirs.), Atlanta Hotel Assn. (pres. 1976), So. Innkeepers Assn., Atlanta C of C. (v.p. 1978-79), Gwinnett C of C. (bd. dirs.), Cornell Soc. Hotelmen (pres. Ga. chpt. 1976, regional v.p. 1989-91). Home: 2980 Nancy Creek Rd NW Atlanta GA 30327-2000 Office: Ste 1800 3350 Cumberland Cir NW Atlanta GA 30339-3360

STORMS, CLIFFORD BEEKMAN, lawyer; b. Mount Vernon, N.Y., July 18, 1932; s. Harold Beekman and Gene (Pertak) S.; m. Barbara H. Grave, 1955 (div. 1975); m. Valeria N. Parker, July 12, 1975; children: Catherine Storms Fischer, Clifford Beekman. BA magna cum laude, Amherst Coll., 1954; LLB, Yale U., 1957. Bar: N.Y. 1957. Assoc. Breed, Abbott & Morgan, N.Y.C., 1957-64; with CPC Internat., Inc., Englewood Cliffs, N.J., 1964—, v.p. legal affairs, 1973-75, v.p., gen. counsel, 1975-88, sr. v.p., gen. counsel, 1988—; bd. dirs. Atlantic Legal Found.; mem. NJ Alternate Dispute Resolution panel Ctr. for Pub. Resources. Trustee Food and Drug Law Inst.; bd. dirs. CPC Ednl. Found. Mem. ABA (com. on corp. law depts.), Assn. Gen. Counsel (pres. 1992-94), Assn. Bar City N.Y. (sec., com. on corp. law depts. 1979-81), Indian Harbor Yacht Club, Econ. Club N.Y., Sky Club, Yale Club, Phi Beta Kappa. Home: 19 Burying Hill Rd Greenwich CT 06831-2604 Office: CPC Internat Inc Box 8000 International Plz Englewood Cliffs NJ 07632-1300

STORMS, LOWELL HANSON, psychologist; b. Schenectady, Feb. 14, 1928; s. Charles Arba and Afton Miriam (Hanson) S.; married, June 16, 1955 (div.); children: Christopher, Karen, Bruce; m. Joan McEvoy Endres, Nov. 21, 1993. B.A. in Biostats, U. Minn., 1950, M.S., 1951, Ph.D. in Psychology, 1956. Clin. psychologist Hastings (Minn.) State Hosp., 1954-56; mem. faculty Neuropsychiat. Inst., UCLA, 1957-71, prof. psychiatry, 1970-71, supervising psychologist, 1963-71; prof. psychiatry Sch. Medicine, U. Calif., San Diego, 1971—; head med. psychology Sch. Medicine, U. Calif., 1971-80; v.p., dir. Clin. Psychol. Services, L.A., 1972—. Program chmn. Westwood Dem. Club, 1962-65. Served with U.S. Army, 1946-48. Fulbright grantee, 1956-57. Fellow Am. Psychol. Assn., AAAS; mem. Western Psychol. Assn., Calif. Psychol. Assn., Sigma Xi. Discoverer priming effect in verbal assns.; co-developer theory of schizophrenic behavioral disorganization. Office: 2022 Camino Del Rio N San Diego CA 92108-1508 *I try to live with full respect for the depth, richness, beauty and power of nature and with love and respect for my fellow creatures who share with me the human condition.*

STORR, ROBERT, curator painting and sculpture, artist, writer; b. Portland, Maine, Dec. 28, 1949; s. Richard J. and Virginia V. Storr; m. Rosamund Helen Morley, Sept. 1, 1979; children: Katharine, Susannah. BA, Swarthmore Coll., 1972; postgrad., Sch. Art Inst. of Chgo., 1975-78; MFA, Skowhegan (Maine) Sch. Painting and Sculpture, 1978. Assoc.

dean N.Y. Studio Sch., N.Y.C., 1987-88; asst. prof. Tyler Sch. Art, Phila., 1989—; Avery prof. Bard Coll., Annandale On Hudson, N.Y., 1990-91; curator painting and sculpture Mus. Modern Art, N.Y.C., 1991—; vis. artist Cooper Union, N.Y.C., 1988-89; vis. artist, critic R.I. Sch. Design, Providence, 1988; lectr. art mus., univs. and art schs. in U.S. and abroad. Author: Philip Guston, 1986; co-author: Chuck Close, 1987; also exhbn. catalogues; contbg. editor Art in Am.; mem. editorial bd. Art Jour.; contbr. articles to profl. jours. Penny McCall Found. grantee, 1988, Peter Norton Family Found. grantee, 1990. Mem. Internat. Assn. Art Critics. Office: Mus Modern Art 11 W 53rd St New York NY 10019-5401

STORRS, ALEXANDER DAVID, astronomer; b. Idaho Falls, Idaho, May 30, 1960; s. Charles Lysander and Betty Lou (Wood) S.; m. Jean Elizabeth Seitzer, Nov. 4, 1989; 1 child, Matthew. BS, MIT, 1982; MS, U. Hawaii, 1985, PhD, 1987. Postdoctoral fellow NASA/Goddard Space Flight Ctr., Greenbelt, Md., 1987-89, U. Tex., Austin, 1989-91; assoc. scientist Space Telescope Sci. Inst., Balt., 1991—. Mem. AAAS, Am. Astron. Soc. (divsn. planetary scis.), Smithsonian Air and Space Mus. Office: Space Telescope Sci Inst 3700 San Martin Dr Baltimore MD 21218

STORRS, ELEANOR EMERETT, research institute consultant; b. Cheshire, Conn., May 3, 1926; d. Benjamin Porter and Alta Hyde (Moss) S.; m. Harry Phineas Burchfield, Jr., Nov. 29, 1963; children: Sarah Storrs, Benjamin Hyde. B.S. with distinction in Botany, U. Conn., 1948; M.S. in Biology, NYU, 1958; Ph.D. in Chemistry, U. Tex., 1967. Asst. biochemist Boyce Thompson Inst. for Plant Research, Yonkers, N.Y., 1948-62; research scientist Clayton Found. Biochem. Inst., U. Tex., Austin, 1962-65; biochemist Pesticides Research Lab., USPHS, Perrine, Fla., 1965-67; dir. dept. biochemistry Gulf South Research Inst., New Iberia, La., 1967-77; adj. prof. chemistry U. Southwestern La., Lafayette, 1974-77; research prof. biology, dir. comparative mammalogy lab. Fla. Inst. Tech., Melbourne, 1977-94, cons. on leprosy-armadillo programs, 1994—, mem. Faculty Senate, 1979-84; cons. in rehab. and prevention deformities leprosy Pan Am. Health Orgn., WHO, Venezuela, Argentina, Brazil, Mex., 1972-90; dep. v.p. Coll. Hansenology in Endemic Countries, 1980-85. Author: (with H.P. Burchfield) Biochemical Applications of Gas Chromatography, 1962, (with Burchfield, D.E. Johnson) Guide to the Analysis of Pesticide Residues, 2 vols, 1965; also articles, book chpts. NIH grantee, 1968—; Center for Disease Control grantee, 1969-73; WHO grantee, 1973-93; leprosy program grantee, 1978-93; German Leprosy Relief Assn. grantee, 1973-78; Nat. Council Episcopal Ch. grantee, 1975-77; Brit. Leprosy Relief Assn. grantee, 1981-88; recipient plaque La. Health Dept., 1972, Distinguished Alumni award U. Conn., 1975; gold award Am. Coll. Pathologists and Am. Soc. Clin. Pathologists, 1974; Gerard B. Lambert award, spl. recognition, 1975. Fellow AAAS, N.Y. Acad. Scis.; mem. AAUW, Internat. Leprosy Assn., Am. Soc. Mammalogy (legislation and regulations com. 1983—), Am. Assn. Lab. Animal Sci. (Charles A. Griffin award 1975), Wildlife Disease Soc., East Coast Zool. Soc. (bd. dirs. 1998-92), Am. Recorder Soc., Sigma Xi. Episcopalian (vestryman). Clubs: Appalachian (Boston); Green Mountain (Bear Mountain, N.Y.); Mystik Krewe of Iberians (mem. ct. 1972, queen 1974). Pioneer devel. leprosy in exptl. animal (armadillo) reproduction. Home: 72 Riverview Ter Melbourne FL 32903-4640 Office: Fla Inst Tech 150 W University Box 6075 Melbourne FL 32901-6988 *Children display interests early in their lives, and in my life, this early interest - in animals, and the beauty of nature - is one which I have never lost, but one which seems to become more important now with the passing of years. Parents can help mold a child, but should mold the child in the child's interests as my parents did, not in a mold designed by them.*

STORRY, JUNIS OLIVER, retired engineering educator; b. Astoria, S.D., Mar. 16, 1920; s. Ole Jensen and Betsey (Ruttum) S.; m. Laurel Helen Davis, June 15, 1950; children: Cheryl Ann, David Junis. B.S. in Elec. Engring., S.D. State U., 1942, M.S., 1949; Ph.D., Iowa State U., 1967. Registered profl. engr., S.D. Engr. trainee Westinghouse Electric Co., 1942; elec. engr. Bur. Ships, Navy Dept., 1942-46, Reliance Electric Co., Cleve., 1946; mem. faculty S.D. State U., Brookings, 1946-85; prof. elec. engring. S.D. State U., 1955-85, Amdahl Disting. prof. engring., 1982-85, dean engring., 1972-82, prof., dean emeritus, 1985—; mem. S.D. Elec. Bd., 1972-77. Mem. founding bd. Assn. Christian Chs. S.D., 1972-73. NSF Sci. Faculty fellow, 1964-65. Mem. IEEE (life sr. mem.), NSPE, Am. Soc. Engring. Edn., S.D. Engring. Soc. Lutheran. Home: 105 Sunnyview RR 3 Box 26 Brookings SD 57006

STORSTEEN, LINDA LEE, librarian; b. Pasadena, Jan. 26, 1948; d. Oliver Matthew and Susan (Smock) Storsteen. AB cum laude in History, UCLA, 1970, MA in Ancient History, 1972, MLS, 1973. Librarian, L.A. Pub. Library, 1974-79; city librarian Palmdale City Library (Calif.), 1979—. Adv. bd. So. Calif. Inter-Library Loan Network, L.A., 1979-80; commr. So. Calif. Film Circuit, L.A., 1980—; council South State Coop. Library System, 1981—, chmn., 1982-83, 85-86, 87-88, 89-90, 92-93; pres. So. Calif. Film Circuit, 1985-86; rec. sec. So. Antelope Valley Coordinating Council, Palmdale, 1983-84. Mem. ALA, Calif. Library Assn., Pub. Libraries Exec. Assn. So. Calif., Am. Saddle Horse Assn., Pacific Saddlebred Assn., So. Calif. Saddle Bred Horse Assn. (bd. dirs.), Chinese Shar-Pei Club of Am. Home: PO Box 129 Palmdale CA 93590-9971 Office: Palmdale City Libr 700 E Palmdale Blvd Palmdale CA 93550-4795

STORY, JIM LEWIS, neurosurgeon, educator; b. Alice, Tex., July 30, 1931; s. Edwin Booth and Martha (Williams) S.; m. Joanne Beverly Nessly, Dec. 31, 1958; children: Kristin Kae, Mary Elizabeth, Jane Martha, James Durward. BS, Tex. Christian U., 1952; MD, Vanderbilt U., 1955. Diplomate Am. Bd. Neurol. Surgery. Intern in surgery U. Minn. Hosps., 1955-56; resident in neurosurgery U. Minn. Grad. Sch. Medicine, 1956-61; instr., asst. prof. neurosurgery div. U. Minn. Med. Sch., 1961-67; prof., head div. neurosurgery U. Tex. Health Sci. Ctr., San Antonio, 1967—. Contbr. articles to profl. publs. Mem. Am. Acad. Neurol. Surgery (v.p. 1988-89), Soc. Neurol. Surgery (chmn. membership adv. com. 1981, v.p. 1990—), Am. Assn. Neurol. Surgery (profl. practice com. 1979), Neurosurg. Soc. Am. (sec. 1978-82, pres. 1985-86), Soc. Univ. Neurosurgeons (pres. 1968-69), Congress Neurol. Surgeons (v.p. 1975-76). Office: U Tex Health Sci Ctr 7703 Floyd Curl Dr San Antonio TX 78284-6200

STOSKOPF, MICHAEL KERRY, educator; b. Garden City, Kans., Mar. 21, 1950; s. Cleve William and Doris Janet (Griffis) S.; m. Suzanne Kennedy, May 30, 1981. BS, Colo. State U., 1973, DVM, 1975; PhD, Johns Hopkins Sch. Hygiene and Pub. Health, 1986. Staff vet. Overton Park Zoo and Aquarium, 1975-77; instr. divsn. comparative medicine Johns Hopkins U., 1977-79; staff vet. Balt. Zool. Soc., 1977-81; biochemist JFK Inst., Balt., 1986-88; asst. prof. divsn. comparative medicine Johns Hopkins U., 1979-87; chief medicine Nat. Aquarium Balt., 1981-88; assoc. prof. dept. radiology Johns Hopkins U., 1986-89; assoc. prof. divsn. comparative medicine, 1987-89; dept. head, prof. companion animal & spl. species medicine N.C. State U. Coll. Vet. Medicine, 1989-93, prof. aquatic and wildlife medicine 1989—; adj. prof. dept. biology Memphis State U., 1976-77; adj. instr. dept. pathology U. Md., 1982-89; adj. prof. radiology and comparative medicine Johns Hopkins U., 1989-91; rsch. assoc. Smithsonian Inst., Washington, 1986—; coord. environ. medicine consortium N.C. State U., 1993—. Author: A Diagnostic Pathologist's Introduction to Fish, 1989, (with S. Citino) Marine Tropical Fish Medicine, 1987; editor: Tropical Fish Medicine, 1988, Fish Medicine, 1992; contbr. articles to profl. jours. Recipient AAZK Nat. award for Edn., 1978, Mark Morris Found. award, 1974, AAZV Pres.'s Svc. award, 1990; U. Helsinki Jalanka medal, 1993. Mem. AVMA, Am. Assn. Zoo Vets. (edn. com. 1989—, edit. bd. 1979-93, sect. editor 1987-93, chmn. coms. 1979-87), Am. Coll. Zool. Medicine (v.p. 1993—, sec. 1991-93, chmn. 1986-87), Am. Fisheries Soc., Am. Assn. Wildlife Vets., European Assn. Aquatic Mammals, Internat. Assn. Aquatic Animal Medicine (pres. 1988-89, bd. dirs. 1985-90, newsletter editor 1987-89), Acad. Zoo Medicine (chmn. 1979-85), Soc. Study of Reptiles & Amphibians (Rsch. award 1985), Marine Mannal Soc., Wildlife Disease Assn. Avocations: painting, photography, sculpture, water sports. Office: NC State Universtiy College of Veterinary Med 4700 Hillsborough St Raleigh NC 27606

STOSKOPF, WILLIAM HOWARD, retired music educator; b. Baxter Springs, Kans., Mar. 1, 1918; s. William Edward and Lulu Grace (Hall) S.; m. Bonnie Jean Miller, Dec. 18, 1943 (dec. 1955); children: Robert Lynn, Julie Ann Larson; m. Viola Maude Clendenen, Aug. 12, 1959. BS, Pittsburg (Kans.) State U., 1943; M of Music Edn., Northwestern U., 1940; postgrad.,

Eastman Sch. Music, Kans. U., Western State Coll., Kans. State U., U. Mo. Tchr. music McCune (Kans.) Pub. Schs., 1941-42, Ft. Scott (Kans.) Pub. Schs., 1945-46, Rosedale High Sch., Kansas City, Kans., 1947-66; coord. instrumental music Kansas City Pub. Schs., 1966-81; instr. brass Midwestern Music Camp, Lawrence, Kans., 1947-50. Dir. music Rosedale United Meth. Ch., Kansas City, 1947-76, mem. chair various coms. and adis., 1947—; chmn. Hanover Heights Neighborhood Assn., Kansas City, 1981-84. Recipient citation for outstanding musical svc. to community Kans. Music Clubs, 1973, Friend of Arts award Sigma Alpha Iota, 1989; named to Kans. Tchrs. Hall of Fame, 1991, Kans. Music Educators Hall of Fame, 1992. Mem. Phi Delta Kappa, Phi Mu Alpha. Republican. Avocations: travel, gardening, photography, reading. Home: 4134 Cambridge St Kansas City KS 66103-3319

STOSSEL, JOHN, news analyst. BA in Psychology, Princeton U., 1969. Prodr., reporter Sta. KGW-TV, Portland, Oreg.; consumer editor WCBS-TV, N.Y.C., Good Morning Am.; consumer corr. 20/20, 1981—; weekly consumer reporter ABC Radio Info. Network,. Recipient 19 Emmy awards, 5 awards for Excellence in Consumer Reporting Nat. Press Club, award Nat. Environment Devel. Assn., award Retirement Rshc. Found., George Polk award Outstanding Local Radio and Television Reporting. Office: 20/20 147 Columbus Ave Fl 10 New York NY 10023-5900

STOTERAU, H. PETER, lawyer; b. Coeur d'Alene, Idaho, June 2, 1938. BS, San Fernando Valley State Coll., 1964; JD, UCLA, 1967. Bar: Calif. 1968. Ptnr. Baker & Hostetler, L.A. Mem. ABA, L.A. County Bar Assn., State Bar of Calif. Office: Baker & Hostetler 600 Wilshire Blvd Los Angeles CA 90017

STOTHERS, JOHN B., chemistry educator; b. London, Ont., Can., Apr. 16, 1931; s. John Cannon and Florence L. (Sleigh) S.; m. Catherine Ruth Smith, June 6, 1953; children—Marta L., Margot E. B.Sc., U. Western Ont., 1953, M.Sc., 1954; Ph.D., McMaster U., 1957. Research chemist Imperial Oil Ltd., Sarnia, Ont., 1957-59; lectr. U. Western Ont., London, 1959-61, asst. prof. dept. chemistry, 1961-64, assoc. prof., 1964-67, prof., 1967—. Author: 13C NMR Spectroscopy, 1972; also over 200 research articles. Recipient award Merck, Sharpe & Dohme, 1971; Royal Soc. Can. fellow, 1976. Fellow Chem. Inst. Can.; mem. Am. Chem. Soc. Club: Sunningdale (London). Avocations: golf; traditional jazz. Office: Univ of Western Ontario, Dept of Chemistry, London, ON Canada N6A 5B7

STOTLER, ALICEMARIE HUBER, federal judge; b. Alhambra, Calif., May 29, 1942; d. James R. and Loretta M. Huber; m. James Allen Stotler, Sept. 11, 1971. BA, U. So. Calif., 1964, JD, 1967. Bar: Calif. 1967, U.S. Dist. Ct. (no. dist.) Calif. 1967, U.S. Dist. Ct. (cen. dist.) Calif. 1973, U.S. Supreme Ct., 1976; cert. criminal law specialist. Dep. Orange County Dist. Atty.'s Office, 1967-73; mem. Stotler & Stotler, Santa Ana, Calif., 1973-76, 83-84; judge Orange County Mcpl. Ct., 1976-78, Orange County Superior Ct., 1978-83, U.S. Dist. Ct. (cen. dist.) Calif., L.A., 1984—; assoc. dean Calif. Trial Judges Coll., 1982; lectr., panelist, numerous orgns.; standing com. on rules of practice and procedure U.S. Jud. Conf., 1991—; chair, 1993—; mem. exec. com. 9th Cir. Jud. Conf., 1989-93, Fed. State Jud. Coun., 1989-93, jury com., 1990-92, planning com. for Nat. Conf. on Fed.-State Judicial Relationships, Orlando, 1991-92, planning com for We. Regional Conf. on State-Fed. Judicial Relationships, Stevens, Wash., 1992-93; chair dist. ct. symposium and jury utilization Ctrl. Dist. Calif., 1985, chair atty. liason, 1989-90, chair U.S. Constitution Bicentennial com., 1986-91, chair magistrate judge com., 1992-93; mem. State Adv. Group. on Juvenile Justice and Delinquency Prevention, 1983-84, Bd. Legal Specilizaations Criminal Law Adv. Commn., 1983-84, victim/witness adv. com. Office Criminal Justice Planning, 1980-83, U. So. Calif. Bd. Councilors, 1993—; active team in tng. Leukemia Soc. Am., 1993, 95; legion lex bd. dir. U. So. Calif. Sch. Law Support Group, 1981-83. Winner Hale Moot Ct. Competition, State of Calif., 1967; named Judge of Yr., Orange County Trial Lawyers Assn., 1978, Most Outstanding Judge, Orange County Bus. Litigation Sect., 1990; recipient Franklin G. West award Orange County Bar Assn., 1985. Mem. ABA (jud. adminstrn. divsn.and litigation sect. 1984—, nat. conf. fed. trial judges com. on legis. affairs 1990-91), Am. Law Inst., Am. Judicature Soc., Fed. Judges Assn. (bd. dirs. 1989-92), Nat. Assn. Women Judges, U.S. Supreme Ct. Hist. Soc., Ninth Cir. Dist. Judges Assn., Calif. Supreme Ct. Hist. Soc., Orange County Bar Assn. (mem. numerous coms., Franklin G. West award 1984), Calif. Judges Assn. (mem. com. on judicial coll. 1978-80, com. on civil law and procedure 1980-82, Dean's coll. curriculum commn. 1981), Calif. Judges Found. Office: US Dist Ct PO Box 12339 751 W Santa Ana Blvd Santa Ana CA 92701-4509

STOTT, BRIAN, software company executive; b. Eccles, Eng., Aug. 5, 1941; came to U.S., 1983; s. Harold and Mary (Stephens) S.; m. Patricia Ann Farrar, Dec. 3, 1983. BSc, Manchester U., 1962, MSc, 1963, PhD, 1971. Asst. prof. Middle East Tech. U., Ankara, Turkey, 1965-68; lectr. Inst. Sci. and Tech., U. Manchester (Eng.), 1968-74; assoc. prof. U. Waterloo (Ont., Can.), 1974-76; cons. Electric Energy Rsch. Ctr. Brazil, Rio de Janeiro, 1976-83; prof. Ariz. State U., Tempe, 1983-84; pres. Power Computer Applications Corp., Mesa, Ariz., 1984—; cons. in field. Contbr. numerous articles to rsch. publs. Fellow IEEE. Office: Power Computer Applications 1921 S Alma School Rd # 207 Mesa AZ 85210

STOTT, GRADY BERNELL, lawyer; b. Bailey, N.C., Sept. 19, 1921; s. William Willard and Zettie Harriett (Bissette) S.; m. Mays Beal, May 9, 1952; children: Sue J., Caroline Beal. A.B., Duke U., 1947, J.D., 1952. Bar: N.C. 1952. Dist. atty. 27th Jud. Dist., Gastonia, N.C., 1957-62; partner firm Stott, Hollowell, Palmer & Windham, Gastonia, 1960—. Served with USMC, 1943-48. Fellow Am. Bar Found., Am. Coll. Trial Lawyers; mem. N.C. State Bar (pres. 1978-79), Am. Bar Assn. (del. 1980), N.C. Bar Assn., Assn. Ins. Attys. Democrat. Methodist. Club: Masons. Office: 110 W Main Ave Gastonia NC 28052-2306

STOTT, PETER WALTER, forest products company executive; b. Spokane, Wash., May 26, 1944; s. Walter Joseph and Rellalee (Gray) S. Student Portland State U., 1962-63, 65-68, U. Americas, Mexico City, 1964-65. Founder, chmn. bd. dirs. Market Transport Ltd., Portland, Oreg., 1969—; bd. dirs., pres., CEO, prin. Crown Pacific. Bd. dirs. Sunshine divsn. Portland Police Bur. (hon.), Liberty Northwest; assoc. mem. adv. bd. Pacific Crest Outward Bound Sch.; mem. pres.'s adv. bd. for athletics Portland State U. With USAR, 1966-72. Mem. Nat. Football Found. and Hall of Fame, Oreg. Sports Hall Fame (lifetime), Oreg. Trucking Assn., Arlington Club, Astoria Golf and Country, Mazamas Club, Multnomah Athletic Club, Portland Golf Club, Univ. Club. Republican. Roman Catholic. Office: Crown Pacific 121 SW Morrison St Ste 1500 Portland OR 97204-3139

STOTT, THOMAS EDWARD, JR., engineering executive; b. Beverly, Mass., May 14, 1923; s. Thomas Edward and Mildred (Ayers) S.; m. Mary Elizabeth Authelet, Feb. 26, 1944; children: Pamela, Randi, Wendy, Thomas E., Diana. BS, Tufts U., 1945. Design engr. Bethlehem Steel, Quincy, Mass., 1956-59; project engr. Bethlehem Steel, 1959-64, sr. engr. basic ship design, 1960-63, project coordinator, 1963-64; pres. Stal-Laval, Inc., Elmsford, N.Y., 1964-84, Thomas Stott & Co., Cummaquid, Mass., 1984-88; ret., 1988. Bd. dirs., treas. Friends of Prisoners, Inc.; deacon West Parish Barnstable, Mass., 1944—. With USNR, 1944-46. Fellow ASME (chmn. marine com., chmn. gas turbine div. exec. com., chmn. nat. nominating com., exec. sec. gas turbine div., Centennial medal 1980, R. Tom Sawyer award 1981, Dedicated Svc. award 1989), Soc. Naval Architects and Marine Engrs. Republican. Home: 51 Kates Path Yarmouth Port MA 02675-1448

STOTT, WILLIAM ROSS, JR., college president; b. Paterson, N.J., July 20, 1935; s. William Ross and Irene (Kearns) S.; m. Margaret Ann Lawler, July 25, 1959; children—William III, Stasia, Christopher, Rachel, Alex-a. BSS in English Lit. and Philosophy, Georgetown U., 1957, LHD (hon.), 1985; MA, Columbia U., 1963; DHL (hon), Fisk U. 1994. Faculty Fordham U., N.Y.C., 1964-73, asst. dean Coll. Arts and Scis., 1973-77; dean of students Georgetown U., Washington, 1977-80, v.p., dean of student affairs, 1980-85; pres., trustee Ripon Coll., Wis., 1985—; councilor-at-large Wis. Acad. Scis. Arts and Letters, 1987-91; bd. dirs. M & I Cen. State Bank, Cornell Lab. Ornithology. Contbr. poetry to various publs., chpt. to book; art works exhibited and pub. Served to lt. USN, 1959-62. Recipient teaching award Fordham U., 1973, Project Quill award Am. Assn. Colls.

1978. Fellow Explorers Club; mem. Associated Colls. Midwest (bd. dirs.), Wis. Found. Ind. Colls. (bd. dirs.), Wis. Policy Rsch. Inst. (adv. bd.), Nat. Audubon Soc., Am. Birding Assn. (bd. dirs.), Defenders of Wildlife (bd. dirs.), Bird Conservation Alliance (bd. dirs.), Soc. Tympanuchus Cupido Pinnatus (bd. dirs.), Urner Ornithology Club Newark. Avocations: ornithology, poetry, drawing. Office: Ripon Coll PO Box 248 Ripon WI 54971-0248

STOTTER, DAVID W., marketing executive; b. Chgo., May 17, 1904; s. Max and Lena (Wolfson) S.; m. Lucille Guild, Nov. 28, 1930; 1 child, Michael David. Student, U. Chgo., 1925. Advt. writer Campbell-Ewald Co., Detroit, 1929-34; sr. writer Lord & Thomas, Chgo., 1935-42; v.p., advt. dir. MacFarland, Aveyard & Co., 1942-51; account exec. MacFarland, Aveyard & Co., 1951-62, sr. v.p. 1959-62; pres., dir. Drewrys Ltd. U.S.A., Inc., S. Bend, Ind., 1962-64; marketing dir. Campbell-Mithun, Inc., Chgo., 1964-65; v.p. Arthur Meyerhoff Assos., Inc., Chgo., 1965—. Bd. dirs. Jewish Welfare Fund Chgo., 1954-61, Alfred Adler Inst., Chgo., 1975—; chmn. pub. relations com. Jewish United Fund, 1969. Home: 2960 N Lake Shore Dr # 2303 Chicago IL 60657-5661 Office: 410 N Michigan Ave Chicago IL 60611-4211

STOTTER, HARRY SHELTON, banker, lawyer; b. N.Y.C., Aug. 28, 1928; s. Jack and Adele (Sgel) S.; m. Marilyn H. Knight, Nov. 7, 1954; children: Jeffrey Craig, Cheryl Dee. Student, L.I. U., 1948-49; JD, St. John's U., 1952; postgrad., N.Y. U. Law Sch., 1956-57. Bar: N.Y. 1952, N.J. 1974. Pvt. practice in N.Y.C., 1952-53, 54-56; atty. Dept. Def., 1953; with trust div. Bank of N.Y., 1956-63; exec. v.p., sr. mgmt. com. United Jersey Bank, Hackensack, 1963-84; div. exec. v.p. Chase Manhattan Bank, N.Y.C., 1984-94; div., chmn. Chase Manhattan Trust Co. Fla., Palm Beach, Fla., 1984-87; pvt. trust and estates law practice N.J., 1974—; former mem. probate com. N.J. Supreme Ct. Jud. Conf. Mem. N.Y.C. and Bergen County estate planning couns.; former pres. bd. dirs. Bergen County coun. Girl Scouts Am.; bd. dirs., pres., chief exec. officer Bergen County United Way; treas. 2d Century Fund, Hackensack Hosp.; bd. dirs. Holy Name Hosp., Teaneck, N.J. With USN, World War II; brig. gen. Army N.G. Mem. ABA (co-chmn. nat. conf. lawyers and corp. trustees 1991-93), Am. Bankers Assn. (chmn. trust counsel com. 1991-93), N.Y. Bar Assn., N.J. Bar Assn., N.Y. County Lawyers Assn., Bergen County Bar Assn. (former trustee, former chmn. probate and estate planning com.), Fed. Bar Assn., N.Y. Militia Assn.

STOTTER, LAWRENCE HENRY, lawyer; b. Cleve., Sept. 24, 1929; s. Oscar and Bertha (Lieb) S.; m. Ruth Rapoport, June 30, 1957; children: Daniel, Jennifer, Steven. BBA, Ohio State U., 1956, LLB, 1958, JD, 1967. Bar: Calif. 1960, U.S. Supreme Ct. 1973, U.S. Tax Ct. 1976. Pvt. practice San Francisco, 1963—; ptnr. Stotter and Coats, San Francisco, 1981—; mem. faculty Nat. Judicial Coll.; mem. Calif. Family Law Adv. Commn., 1979-80. Editor in chief: Am. Bar Family Advocate mag. 1977-82; TV appearances on Phil Donahue Show, Good Morning America. Pres. Tamalpais Conservation Club, Marin County, Calif.; U.S. State Dept. del. Hague Conf. Pvt. Internat. Law, 1979-80; legal adv. White House Conf. on Families, 1980—. Served with AUS, 1950-53. Mem. ABA (past chmn. family law sect.), Am. Acad. Matrimonial Lawyers (past nat. v.p.), Calif. State Bar (past chmn. family law sect.), San Francisco Bar Assn. (past chmn. family law sect.), Calif. Trial Lawyers Assn. (past chmn. family law sect.). Home: 2244 Vistazo St E Tiburon CA 94920-1970 Office: 1255 Columbus Ave Ste 200 San Francisco CA 94133

STOTTLEMYER, DAVID LEE, government official; b. Waynesboro, Pa., June 1, 1935; s. Omar Samuel and Miriam (Noll) S.; m. Jane Ann Hembree, Aug. 26, 1961; children: Todd Andrew, Kristen Elizabeth, Kathryn Ann. A.B., Miami U., Oxford, Ohio, 1959; M. Pub. and Internat. Affairs (NDEA fellow), U. Pitts., 1964, also postgrad. Program and budget analyst Exec. Office of Pres., Office of Mgmt. and Budget, Washington, 1964-69; sr. mgmt. officer UN, N.Y.C., 1969-70; adviser internat. orgn. affairs U.S. Mission to UN, N.Y.C., 1971-72; counsellor internat. orgn. affairs U.S. Mission to UN, 1973-75, counsellor UN resources mgmt., 1976-77; also mem. U.S. del. 26th-31st gen. assemblies, mem. UN Com. on Contbns., 1971; mem. UN Adv. Com. on Adminstrv. and Budgetary Questions, 1973-77; dir. policy mgmt. staff Bur. Internat. Orgn. Affairs, U.S. Dept. State, Washington, 1977-80; exec. asst. to asst. sec. of state for internat. orgn. affairs Bur. Internat. Orgn. Affairs, U.S. Dept. State, 1980; mem. staff Office of Vice-Pres., Washington, 1981-83; dir. adminstrv. mgmt. service UN, N.Y.C. 1984-85; exec. asst. dir. Office of Under-Sec.-Gen. for Adminstrn. and Mgmt., UN, N.Y.C., 1986-87; pvt. practice as cons., 1987-90; dir. industry rels. NASA, Washington, 1990-91, dir. office nat. svc., 1992-93; retired, 1993; cons. pvt. practice, 1993—. Served with AUS, 1953-56. Recipient Superior Honor award State Dept., 1975. Mem. Am. Fgn. Svc. Assn. Home and Office: 5920 Sherborn Ln Springfield VA 22152-1035

STOTTS, MICHAEL W., theatrical producer; b. Calgary, Alta., Can., Mar. 23, 1961; came to U.S., 1984; s. Gerald G. and Marcella J. (Schamber) S. BA with honors, Queens U., Kingston, Ont., Can., 1984; MFA, Columbia U., 1987. Co. mgr. Manhattan Theatre Club, N.Y.C., 1986-90; mng. dir. N.J. Shakespeare Festival, Madison, N.J., 1990—; mem. faculty Drew U., Madison, 1992—; treas. N.J. Theatre Group, Florham Park, N.J., 1992—. Home: 54 Brookwood Dr Maplewood NJ 07040 Office: NJ Shakespeare Festival 36 Madison Ave Madison NJ 07940-1434

STOUGHTON, W. VICKERY, healthcare executive; b. Peoria, Ill., Mar. 1, 1946; s. Warner Vickery and Mary Olive (McNamara) S.; m. Christine Mary Kreder, Aug. 9, 1969; children: Zachary Benjamin, Samantha. B.S., St. Louis U., 1968; M.B.A., U. Chgo., 1973. Asst. dir. Boston Hosp. for Women, 1973-74; asst. dir. Peter Bent Brigham Hosp., Boston, 1975-77, dir., 1978-80; pres. The Toronto Hosp., Ont., Can.; asst. prof. U. Toronto, 1982-90, assoc. prof., 1991; vice chancellor health affairs, chief exec. officer Duke U. Hosp., Durham, N.C., 1991-92; pres. Smithkline Beecham Clin. Labs., Collegeville, Pa., 1992—; bd. dirs. Sun Life Assurance Co. Bd. dirs. Toronto Symphony, 1983-86, Toronto United Way, 1988-91. Served to capt. AUS, 1969-72. Fellow Am. Coll. Hosp. Adminstrs. Home: 7 Harford Ln Radnor PA 19087 Office: Smithkline Beecham Clinic Labs 1201 S Collegeville Rd Collegeville PA 19426

STOUT, ANTHONY CARDER, publisher; b. N.Y.C., May 20, 1939; s. Harry Howard and Maxine (Carder) S.; m. Julie Jeppson, May 24, 1965 (div. 1986); children: Craig Fitzhugh, Carder Jeppson, Antonia Armstrong, Julie Shellabarger. B.A., Williams Coll., 1961; LL.B., Harvard U., 1964. Bar: N.Y. 1966. Assoc. Milbank, Tweed, Hadley & McCloy, N.Y.C., 1965-69; pres. Ctr. for Polit. Research, Washington, 1969-72; chmn. Govt. Pub. Corp./Nat. Jour., Washington, 1972-89; pres. Govt. Investment Mgmt. Corp., Washington, 1990—; dir. World Affairs Coun., Washington, 1989-89, Nat. Press Found., 1981-89; pres. The Battle of Normandy Found., 1985-94. Trustee St. Paul's Sch., Concord, N.H., 1980-86. Mem. Phi Beta Kappa. Clubs: Brook (N.Y.); Metropolitan (Washington), Chevy Chase (Washington). Office: Govt Investment Mgmt Corp 1730 Rhode Island Ave NW Washington DC 20036-3101

STOUT, ERNEST RAY, molecular biology educator, research biochemist, botanist; b. Boone, N.C., Oct. 31, 1938; married, 1961; 3 children. BS, Appalachian State U., 1961; PhD in Botany and Biochemistry, U. Fla., 1965. Nat. Cancer Inst. fellow in biochem. genetics U. Md., 1965-67; from asst. to assoc. prof. Va. Polytech. & State U., 1967-84, prof. molecular biology, 1984—, asst. dean Coll. Arts & Sci., 1978-79, head dept. biology, 1980—. Mem. AAAS, Am. Soc. Plant Physiology. Achievements include research on mechanism of nucleic acid synthesis in higher plants, control of nucleic acid synthesis, and parovirus macromolecular synthesis. Address: RR 4 Christiansburg VA 24073 Office: Va Polytechnic Inst & State Univ Research Division Amonate VA 24601*

STOUT, GLENN EMANUEL, water resources center administrator; b. Fostoria, Ohio, Mar. 23, 1920. AB, Findlay U., 1942, DSc, 1973. Sci. coord. NSF, 1969-71; asst. to chief Ill. State Water Survey, Champaign, 1971-74; prof. Inst. Environ. Studies, Urbana, Ill., 1973-94, dir. task force, 1975-79; dir. Water Resources Ctr. U. Ill., Urbana, 1973-94; rsch. coord. Ill.-Ind. Sea Grant Program, 1980-94; emeritus, 1994—; Mem. Ill. Gov.'s Task Force on State Water Plan, 1980-94; bd. dirs. Univ. Coun. Water Resources, 1983-86, chmn. internat. affairs, 1989-92; mem. nomination com. for

Stockholm Water Prize, 1994—. Contbr. articles to profl. jours. Mem. Am. Water Resources Assn., Internat. Water Resources Assn. (sec. gen. 1985-91, v.p. 1992-94, exec. dir. 1984-95, pres. 1995—), Am. Meteorol. Soc., Am. Geophys. Union, N.Am. Lake Mgmt. Soc., Ill. Lake Mgmt. Assn. (bd. dirs. 1985-88), Internat. Assn. Rsch. Hydrology, Am. Water Works Assn., Kiwanis (pres. local club 1979-80, lt. gov. 1982-83), Sigma Xi (pres. U. Ill. chpt. 1985-86). Home: 920 W John St Champaign IL 61821-3907 Office: Internat. Water Resources Assn 1101 W Peabody Dr Urbana IL 61801-4723

STOUT, GREGORY STANSBURY, lawyer; b. Berkeley, Calif., July 27, 1915; s. Verne A. and Ella (Moore) S.; m. Virginia Cordes, Apr. 23, 1948; 1 son, Frederick Gregory. A.B., U. Calif. 1937, LL.B., 1940. Bar: Calif. 1940. Practice law San Francisco, 1946, 52—; asst. dist. atty., 1947-52; mem. Penal Code Revision Commn. Calif.; chmn. com. State Bar Calif. Contbr. articles to profl. jours. Served to master sgt. AUS, 1942-45. Fellow Am. Coll. Trial Lawyers, Am. Bar Found.; mem. ABA, Fed. Bar Assn., Am. Bd. Trial Advocates, Nat. Assn. Criminal Def. Lawyers (sec. 1958-59, pres. 1962-63). Democrat. Episcopalian. Club: Bohemian. Home and Office: 100 Thorndale Dr San Rafael CA 94903-3590

STOUT, JUANITA KIDD, judge; b. Wewoka, Okla., Mar. 7, 1919; d. Henry Maynard and Mary Alice (Chandler) Kidd; m. Charles Otis Stout, June 23, 1942. BA, U. Iowa, 1939; JD, Ind. U., 1948, LLM, 1954; LLD (hon.), Ursinus Coll., 1965, Ind. U., 1966, Lebanon Valley Coll., 1969, Drexel U., 1972, Rockford (Ill.) Coll., 1974, U. Md., 1980, Roger Williams Coll., 1984, Morgan State U., 1985, Russell Sage Coll., 1966, Fisk U., 1988, Del. State Coll., 1990. Bar: D.C. 1950, Pa. 1954. Tchr. pub. schs. Seminole and Sand Springs, Okla., 1939-42; tchr. Fla. A&M U., Tallahassee, 1949, Tex. So. U., Houston, 1949; adminstrv. asst. to judge U.S. Ct. Appeals (3d cir.), Phila., 1950-54; pvt. practice law Turner & Stout, Phila., 1954-55; chief of appeals Dist. Atty.'s Office City of Phila., 1955-59, judge mcpl. ct., 1959-69; judge Ct. Common Pleas, Phila., 1969-88, sr. judge, 1989—; justice Supreme Ct. Pa., Phila., 1988-89; sitting as sr. judge Ct. Common Pleas. Recipient Jane Addams medal Rockford Coll., 1966, Disting. Svc. award U. Iowa, 1974, MCP/Gimbel award for humanitarianism, 1988, 89—, John Peter Zenger award John Peter Zenger Soc., 1994; named to Hall of Fame of Okla., Okla Heritage Soc., 1981; named Disting. Dau. of Pa., 1988, Disting. Alumni Svc. award Ind. U., Bloomington, 1992. Mem. ABA, Pa. Bar Assn., Phila. Bar Assn. (Sandra Day O'Connor award 1994), Nat. Assn. Women Judges, Nat. Assn. Women Lawyers. Democrat. Episcopalian. Home: 1919 Chestnut St Apt 2805 Philadelphia PA 19103-3451

STOUT, LONNIE JAMES, II, restaurant operations company executive; b. Detroit, Jan. 11, 1947; s. Lonnie James and Ester J. (Andis) S.; m. Victoria Joy, Feb. 10, 1948; 1 child, Elizabeth Ramsay. BS, Tenn. Tech. U., 1973. CPA, Tenn. Acct. McCord Corp., Cookeville, Tenn., 1968-72; mgr. Ernst & Whinney, Nashville, 1973-79; exec. v.p. Winners Corp., Brentwood, Tenn., 1979-84, pres., chief exec. officer, 1986—; chmn., chief exec. officer Dinerite Corp., Atlanta, 1984-85; mem. young execs. council Nashville CityBank, 1984-85; bd. dirs. H.B. Brown Co., Nashville, Pro Parking Corp., Nashville. Mem. exec. com. Mid. Tenn. chpt. March of Dimes, Nashville, 1986-87. Mem. Fin. Exec. Inst., Am. Inst. CPAs, Tenn. Soc. CPAs, Phi Delta Theta. Republican. Presbyterian. Avocations: bridge, cooking, running. Office: Winners Corp PO Box 24300 Nashville TN 37202-4300

STOUT, RICHARD ALAN, museum director; b. Lenoir City, Tenn., 1941; m. Linda Ellen Canipe; 1 child, Shane. Grad., Carson-Newman Coll., 1963; postgrad., N.C. State U., 1964. Former asst. dir. Schiele Mus., Gastonia, N.C., 1965-74, now exec. dir., from 1974; one of 17 dept. heads City of Gastonia; mem. faculty South Point Sr. High Sch., Belmont, N.C., 1963-64; former instr. art Dept. Adult and Continuing Edn. Gaston Coll. in Dallas, N.C.; bd. dirs. N.C. Museums Council, Gaston County Mus. Art and History, United Arts and Scis. Council of Gaston County. Numerous one-man shows throughout U.S.; contbr. over 700 articles on natural history to profl. jours. Cultural advisor Gaston County C. of C.; mem. Mayor's Blue Task Force; mem. adv. council and found. Look Up Gaston. Recipient Silver Cup for Notable Achievement in Mus. Profession N.C. Museums Council, 1978, also named Mus. Dir. of Yr., 1978, Catlin Peace Pipe award Am. Indian Lore Assn., Confederation of Adopted Indians of Am., 1981, Medal of Honor for Professionalism Carson-Newman Coll. Pres.'s Adv. Council and Bd. Alumni, 1985; recipient numerous Commendations Gastonia City Council, Gaston County C. of C., Bd. dirs. Schiele Mus. Mem. Watercolor Soc. of N.C. (past v.p.), Southern Watercolor Soc. (charter mem.). Office: Schiele Mus Natural History and Planetarium Inc PO Box 953 Gastonia NC 28053-0953*

STOUT, THOMAS MELVILLE, control system engineer; b. Ann Arbor, Mich., Nov. 26, 1925; s. Melville B. and Laura C. (Meisel) S.; m. Marilyn J. Koebnick, Dec. 27, 1947; children: Martha, Sharon, Carol, James, William, Kathryn. BSEE, Iowa State Coll., 1946; MSE, U. Mich., 1947, PhD, 1954. Registered profl. engr., Calif. Jr. engr. Emerson Electric Co., St. Louis, 1947-48; instr., then asst. prof. U. Wash., Seattle, 1948-54; rsch. engr. Schlumberger Instrument Co., Ridgefield, Conn., 1954-56; dept. mgr. TRW/Bunker-Ramo Corp., Canoga Park, Calif., 1956-65; pres. Profimatics, Inc., Thousand Oaks, Calif., 1965-83; pvt. practice cons. Northridge, Calif., 1984—; active profl. engring. registration and certification. Contbr. articles, revs., papers to profl. publs., chpts. to books. Ens. USN, 1943-46. Fellow, hon. mem. Instrument Soc. Am.; mem. IEEE (sr. mem.), NSPE, Am. Inst. Chem. Engrs., Am. Soc. for Engring. Edn., Calif. Soc. Profl. Engrs. Achievements include four patents in computer control of industrial processes; participant in early digital computer installations for industrial process control. Home and Office: 9927 Hallack Ave Northridge CA 91324-1120

STOUT, WILLIAM JEWELL, department store executive; b. Bloomington, Ind., Dec. 14, 1914; s. Selatie Edgar and Frances M. (Blodgett) S.; m. Harriet Cracraft, June 15, 1940; children—David Bruce, Karen Louise. A.B., Ind. U., 1937. With L.S. Ayres & Co., Indpls., 1937-78, v.p., 1958-64, v.p. operation, 1964-65, v.p., 1965-78; pres., dir. Citizens Gas & Coke Utility. Mem. Ind. Personnel Bd., 1952-66; dir. devel. Wabash Coll., Crawfordsville, Ind., 1978-84, cons. capital fund drives; chmn. United Fund drive, 1953; pres., bd. dirs. Flanner House; bd. dirs. St. Vincent Hosp. Found.; pres., 1972-73; bd. dirs. St. Richard's Day Sch. Served to lt. comdr. USNR, 1942-46. Mem. Indpls. Personnel Assn. (past pres.), Nat. Retail Mchts. Assn., Indpls. Mchts. Assn. (pres. 1970-72), Ind. Indpls. chambers commerce. Home: 1903 Seaport Dr Indianapolis IN 46240-2832

STOVALL, CARLA JO, state official, lawyer; b. Hardner, Kans., Mar. 18, 1957; d. Carl E. and Juanita Jo (Ford) S. BA, Pittsburg (Kans.) State U., 1979; JD, U. Kans., 1982. Bar: Kans. 1982, U.S. Dist. Ct. Kans. 1982. Pvt. practice, Pittsburg, 1982-85; atty. Crawford County, Pittsburg, 1984-88; gov. Kans. Parole Bd., Topeka, 1988-94; attorney general State of Kansas, Topeka, 1995—; lectr. law Pittsburg State U. 1982-84 pres. Gilston Internat. Mktg., Inc., 1988—. Bd. dirs., sec. Pittsburg Family YMCA, 1983-88. Mem. ABA, Kans. Bar Assn., Crawford County Bar Assn. (sec. 1984-85, v.p. 1985-86, pres. 1986-87), Kans. County and Dist. Attys. Assn., Nat. Coll. Dist. Attys., Pittsburg State U. Alumni Assn. (bd. dirs. 1983-88), Pittsburg Area C. of C. (bd. dirs. 1983-85, Leadership Pitts. 1984), Bus. and Profl. Women Assn. (Young Careerist 1984), Kans. Assn. Commerce and Industry (Leadership Kans. 1983), AAUW (bd. dirs. 1983-87). Republican. Methodist. Avocations: travel, photography, tennis. Home: 3561 SW Mission Ave Topeka KS 66614-3637 Office: Atty Gen Office Jud Bldg 301 W Tenth St Topeka KS 66612-1220

STOVALL, JERRY (COLEMAN STOVALL), insurance company executive; b. Houston, July 31, 1936; s. Clifford Coleman and Maxine (Lands) S.; m. Elsie Hostetter, June 20, 1959; 1 child, Brent Allen. BBA, U. Houston, 1968. Home office adminstr. Am. Gen. Life, Houston, 1955-63, agt., agy. mgr., 1963-66, agy. mgr., regional dir. agys., regional v.p., 1969-74; sr. brokerage cons. Conn. Gen. Life, Houston, 1966-69; sr. v.p., dir. mktg. Capitol Life Ins. Co., Denver, 1974-78; v.p. dir. mktg. Integon Life Ins. Corp., Winston-Salem, N.C., 1978-81; pres. Life of Mid-Am Ins. Co., Topeka, 1981-85; pres. Victory Life Ins. Co., Topeka, 1981-85, chmn., pres., chief exec. officer, 1981-85, pres., retired chief exec. officer Integon Life Ins. Co., Winston-Salem, N.C., 1987-91, Winston-Salem.; vice-chmn. Mktg. One Inc.; bd. dirs., vice-chmn. Ga. Internat. Life; pres., Lamar Life Ins. Co., 1992—. Bd. dirs. Winston-Salem Symphony, Jr. Achievement Miss. Inc.,

Andrew Jackson Coun., Boy Scouts Am.; mem. Miss. Econ. Coun.; bd. govs. Univ. Club. With U.S. Army, 1955-57. Mem. Nat. Assn. Life Cos., Nat. Assn. Life Underwriters, Am. Soc. CLUs (Gold Key Soc.)ACI Exec. Round Table (chmn. 1995). The Country Club of Jackson, Rotary Club Jackson, Rotary Internat. Home:.115 Winged Foot Cir Jackson MS 39211-2528 Office: Lamar Life Ins Co 317 E Capitol St Jackson MS 39201-3405

STOVALL, RICHARD L., academic administrator; b. Springfield, Mo., Mar. 28, 1944; s. Wilbern Lee and Ernestine Patricia (Putman) S.; m. Susannah K. Young; children: Richard Christopher, Stacy Suzanne. BA, SW Mo. State U., 1966; MA, C.W. Post Coll. L.I. U., 1969; PhD, Ohio State U., 1975. Instr. SW Mo. State U., Springfield, 1969-72; asst. prof. U. S.C., Columbia, S.C., 1975-77; prof., asst. dept. head SW Mo. State U., Springfield, 1977—; cons. Cedar Hills High Sch., Dallas, 1986, Andrews Ins. Agy., 1984, Mo. Cosmetology Assn., 1983-84, Springfield Pers. Assn., 1982, Syntex Corp. 1981-82; pub. rels. Halcyon of Dallas, 1988-89. Contbr. articles to profl. jours. Tabulation room coord. for MSHSAA Dist. Speech Festival; lectr. Springfield Pub. Schs., City Utilities Citizens Adv. Bd.; pres. Boy Scouts Am. With ES USNR-TAR, 1962-69. Mem. Am. Forensics Assn., Speech Communication Assn. Am., So. Speech Communication Assn., Speech Communication Assn. Ohio, Cen. States Speech Assn., Speech and Theatre Assn. Mo., Cherokee Homeowners Assn. (pres.). Episcopal. Home: 1131 E Meadowlark St Springfield MO 65810-2961 Office: SW Mo State U 901 S National Ave Springfield MO 65804-0027

STOVALL, ROBERT H(ENRY), money management company executive; b. Louisville, 1926; s. Harold Samuel and Agnes C. (Hinkle) S.; m. Inger Bagger; children: Sten Torben, Harold Samuel II, Inger Benedikte, Robert Henry. B.S. in Econs., U. Pa., 1948; postgrad. in polit. economy, U. Copenhagen, 1948-49; M.B.A., N.Y. U., 1957. With E. F. Hutton & Co., 1953-67; mgr. dept. investment research E. F. Hutton & Co., N.Y.C., 1958-60, gen. partner responsible for research, 1961-67, chmn. com. investment policy, 1966-68; research dir. Nuveen Corp., N.Y.C., 1968-69; partner in mktg. and research Reynolds & Co., N.Y.C., 1969; dir. research Reynolds & Co., 1970-73; sr. v.p., dir. investment policy Dean Witter Reynolds Inc. (merger Reynolds & Co. and Dean Witter & Co., acquired by Sears, Roebuck and Co. 1981), N.Y.C., 1978-85, pub. comments on market column, 1961-85; pres. Stovall/Twenty-First Advisers, Inc., 1985—; lectr., tchr. in field; commentator Nat. Pub. Radio, 1982—; prof. fin. NYU, 1985—; regular commentator Bus. Morning, Turner Broadcasting System, 1985-88, "This Morning's Business", CBS-TV, 1988-91, "Market Wrap", Sta. CNBC/FNN-TV; governing mem. Com. on Developing Am. Capitalism. Fairfield, Conn. Columnist Forbes, 1968-76, Fin. World, 1979—; contbr. articles to profl. publs.; panelist: Wall St. Week, Public Broadcasting System, 1977—. Bd. overseers Grad. Sch. Bus. Adminstrn. NYU, 1984-90, U. Pa. Librs., 1992—; chmn. Security Industry Inst., 1986-88, life trustee, 1989—; trustee St. Clare's-Riverside Health Care Ctr. Found., Denville, N.J., 1980-93, Wayne County (Pa.) Meml. Hosp., mem. found. bd. 1989—; bd. overseers Seton Hall Prep. Sch., West Orange, N.J., 1985-93; bd. sponsors Loyola Coll. in Md. Schs. Bus., 1990—; mem. coun. com on librs. U. Pa., 1991—; dir. Sarasota Opera Assn., 1993—. With U.S. Army, World War II, Italy. Mem. Inst. Chartered Fin. Analysts (CFA), N.Y. Soc. Security Analysts (past dir., vice chmn. program com.), Mensa, Beta Gamma Sigma, Union League (N.Y.C.), S.R., Kentuckians of N.Y. (pres. 1988-90). Clubs: Down Town Assn. (N.Y.C.), Union League (N.Y.C.); S.R., Kentuckians of N.Y. (pres. 1988-90). Home: 888 Blvd Of The Arts Sarasota FL 34236 Office: Stovall/Twenty-First Advisers Inc 780 3rd Ave New York NY 10017-2024

STOVER, CARL FREDERICK, foundation executive; b. Pasadena, Calif., Sept. 29, 1930; s. Carl Joseph and Margarete (Müller) S.; m. Catherine Swanson, Sept. 3, 1954; children: Matthew Joseph, Mary Margaret Stover Marker, Claire Ellen; m. Jacqueline Kast, Sept. 7, 1973. B.A. magna cum laude, Stanford U., 1951, M.A., 1954. Instr. polit. sci. Stanford U., 1953-55; fiscal mgmt. officer Office Sec. Dept. Agr., 1955-57; asso. dir. conf. program pub. affairs Brookings Instn., 1957-59, sr. staff mem. govtl. studies, 1960; fellow Center Study Democratic Instns., Santa Barbara, Calif., 1960-62; asst. to chmn. bd. editors Ency. Brit., 1960-62; sr. polit. scientist Stanford Research Inst., 1962-64; dir. pub. affairs fellowship program Stanford U., 1962-64; pres. Nat. Inst. Pub. Affairs, Washington, 1964-70, Nat. Com. U.S.-China Relations, 1972, Cultural Resources, Inc., Washington, 1978-85; pres., dir. Federalism Seventy-Six, 1972-74; dir. cultural resources devel. Nat. Endowment for Arts, 1974-78; bd. dirs. H.E.A.R. Found., 1976-86, treas., 1976-80, pres., 1980-86; bd. dirs. Ctr. for World Lit., pres., 1987-90, chmn., 1990-92; pvt. profl. cons., 1970—; scholar-in-residence Nat. Acad. Pub. Adminstrn., 1980-82; cons. to govt., 1953—. Author: The Government of Science, 1962, The Technological Order, 1963; Founding editor: Jour. Law and Edn., 1971-73; pub. Delos mag., 1987-92. Treas. Nat. Com U.S.-China Rels., 1966-71, 82-87, 89-94, bd. dirs., 1966-74, 79-94; bd. dirs. Coord. Coun. Lit. Mags., 1966-68; trustee Inst. of Nations, 1972-76, Nat. Inst. Pub. Affairs, 1967-71, Kinesis Ltd., 1972-78; vol. Nat. Exec. Svc. Corps, 1984-89. Fellow AAAS; mem. Am. Soc. Pub. Adminstrn., Fedn. Am. Scientists, Soc. Internat. Devel., Jordan Soc. (dir. 1982-84), Nat. Acad. Pub. Adminstrn. (hon.), Md. U. Club, Internat. Soc. Panetics (pres., founding mem. 1991—), Phi Beta Kappa Assocs. (hon., lectr. 1972-87), Phi Beta Kappa. Democrat. Presbyterian. Home and Office: 4109 Metzerott Rd College Park MD 20740-2082

STOVER, DAVID FRANK, lawyer; b. Phila., May 15, 1941; s. Emory Frank and Beatrice Norah (Spinelli) S. A.B., Princeton U., 1962; J.D., U. Pa., 1965. Bar: D.C. 1966, U.S. Ct. Appeals (D.C. cir.) 1968, U.S. Ct. Appeals (9th cir.) 1969, U.S. Ct. Appeals (4th cir.) 1972. Atty. FPC, Washington, 1965-71, Tally & Tally, Washington, 1972-75; asst. gen. counsel Postal Rate Commn., Washington, 1975-79, gen. counsel, 1979-92, regulatory cons. 1992—. Author: (with Bierman, Lamont, Nelson) Geothermal Energy in the Western United States, 1978. Mem. Fed. Bar Assn. Episcopalian. Home and Office: 2970 S Columbus St # 1-b Arlington VA 22206-1450

STOVER, HARRY M., corporate executive; b. 1926; married. BS, U. So. Calif., 1947. Engr. Stone & Webster Corp., 1947-48; chief engr. Raymond Internat., 1948-51, Standard Vacuum Corp., 1951-54; with A.P. Green Refractories, 1954-76, pres., 1972-76, chief exec. officer, 1974-76, chmn. 1976; group v.p. USG Corp., 1976-79; exec. v.p. USG Corp., Chgo., 1979-85, vice chmn., 1985; chmn., chief exec. officer A.P. Green Industries Inc., Mexico, Mo., 1989-93. Served to ensign USN, 1944-46. Office: A P Green Industries Inc Green Blvd Mexico MO 65265-2980

STOVER, JAMES HOWARD, real estate executive; b. Forest Hill, W.Va., Oct. 20, 1911; s. Charles William and Zora (Goode) S.; m. May Simmons, Oct. 21, 1939 (dec.). children: Ann, Robert Bruce; m. Elizabeth J. Cobb, Dec. 27, 1977 (dec.). Student, Benjamin Franklin U., 1936-38; grad. Advanced Mgmt. Program, Harvard U., 1959, Exec. Devel. Program Ind. U., 1960, Inst. Mgmt. Northwestern U., 1960. Asst. purchasing agt. Woodward & Lothrop, Washington, 1932-35; asst. chief field supervision div., central accounts office Bur. Accounts Treasury Dept., 1935-41, asst. chief Treasury Budget sect., 1941-42, fiscal acct. Office Commr. Pub. Debt, 1946-51, chief treasury mgmt. analysis staff, 1951-63, dir. Office Mgmt. and Orgn., 1963-66, regional commr. customs Miami Region IV, 1966-72; real estate sales assoc., mgmt. cons., 1972-75; pres. Bay Realty of Fla., Inc., 1975—; Chmn. Inter-agy. Mgmt. Analysis Conf., 1958-59; mem. orgn. and mgmt. adv. com. Dept. Agr. Grad. Sch., 1956-63. Chmn. adv. cons. orgn. and procedure and legislative program Arlington (Va.) County Bd., 1958-63; pres. Tuckahoe Recreation Club, 1957; chmn. Greater Miami Fed. Exec. Coun., 1968-69; mem. exec. adv. coun. Coll. Bus. and Pub. Adminstrn., Fla. Atlantic U., 1969-80. 2d lt. to maj. AUS, 1942-46. Recipient Rockefeller Pub. Svc. award, 1959, Spl. Svc. award Treasury Dept., 1963, Exceptional Svc. award, 1965, other treasury awards, 1969, 70, 71, 72. Home: 707 Vilabella Ave Coral Gables FL 33146-1733 Office: 2335 Biscayne Blvd Miami FL 33137-4513

STOVER, JOHN FORD, railroad historian, educator; b. Manhattan, Kans., May 16, 1912; s. John William and Maud (Ford) S.; m. Marjorie Ellen Filley, Aug. 21, 1937; children: John Clyde, Robert Vernon (dec.), Charry Ellen Stover Olin. A.B., U. Nebr., 1934, M.A., 1937; Ph.D., U. Wis., 1951. Instr. social studies Arcadia (Nebr.) High Sch., 1936-37; instr. history and govt. Bergen (N.J.) Jr. Coll., 1937-41; grad. asst. history U. Wis., 1941-42,

46-47, Univ. fellow, 1946; faculty Purdue U., Lafayette, Ind., 1947—; prof. history Purdue U., 1959-78, prof. emeritus, 1978—, Purdue Research Found. XL grantee, summer 1957, 59, fellow in Coll.-Bus. Exchange Program, I.C. R.R.., summer 1962; chmn. Pres.'s adv. coun. on retirement Purdue U., 1981-82. Author: The Railroads of the South, 1865-1900, 1955, American Railroads, 1961, A History of American Railroads, 1967, Turnpikes, Canals and Steamboats, 1969, The Life and Decline of the American Railroad, 1970, Transportation in American History, 1970, History of Illinois Central Railroad, 1975, Iron Road To The West, 1978, Sixty-Five Years of Kiwanis in Indiana, 1981, History of the Baltimore & Ohio Railroad, 1987, Seventy-Five Years of Kiwanis and Indiana, 1990; contbr. to hist. jours., books, numerous encys. and biog. works. Chmn. edn. com., mem. exec. com. Ind. Sesquicentennial Commn., 1962-67; hon. mem. Indiana Am. Revolution Bicentennial commn., 1972-82; mem. adv. council Centennial History of Ind. Gen. Assembly, 1979-83; pres. Lafayette Kiwanis Found., 1977-78. Served to capt. USAAF, 1942-46. Res., ret. Named Sagamore of the Wabash Gov. Ind., 1978; recipient Alumni Achievement award U. Nebr., 1985. Fellow Soc. Am. Historians; mem. Ind. Acad. Social Scis., Western History Assn., Bus. History Conf. (trustee 1973-76), Am. Hist. Assn., So. Ind. Hist. Assn. (com. on library), Nebr. Hist. Assn., Tippecanoe County Hist. Assn. (pres. 1972-74), Lexington Group (r.r. historians), AAUP, Ind. History Tchrs. Assn. (pres. 1958-59), Orgn. Am. Historians, Newcomen Soc. N.Am., Ry. and Locomotive Hist. Soc. (editorial adv. bd. for Railroad History jour. 1970-94, Sr. Achievement R.R. History award 1983), Soc. Ind. Pioneers, Civil War Round Table of Nebr., Nat. Ry. Hist. Soc., Phi Beta Kappa (hon.), Phi Alpha Theta, Delta Sigma Rho. Republican. Methodist. Club: Fortnightly, Lincoln Open Forum. Lodge: Kiwanis (local pres. 1973-74, disting. lt. gov. 1978-79, historian Ind. dist. 1980-81, 83-90. 91-92). Avocations: golf, model railroading, stamps. Home: 2114 Heritage Pines Ct Lincoln NE 68506-2866

STOVER, LEON (EUGENE), anthropology educator, writer, critic; b. Lewistown, Pa., Apr. 9, 1929; s. George Franklin and Helen Elizabeth (Haines) S.; 1 dau. by previous marriage, Laren Elizabeth; m. 2d Takeko Kawai, Oct. 12, 1956. BA, Western Md. Coll., 1950, LittD (hon.), 1980; MA, Columbia U., 1952, PhD, 1962. Instr. Am. Museum Natural History, N.Y.C., 1955-57; asst. prof. Hobart and William Smith Colls., Geneva, N.Y., 1957-63; vis. asst. prof. Tokyo U., 1963-65; assoc. prof. Ill. Inst. Tech., Chgo., 1966-74, prof. anthropology, 1974-94, prof. emeritus, 1995—; founder, 1st chmn. John W. Campbell Meml. Award, 1972; guest lectr. Brit. Film Inst., 1986; humanities cons. Champaign (Ill.) Pub. Library H.G. Wells Traveling Exhbn., 1986; commd. as Robert A. Heinlein's authorized biographer, 1988. Author: La Science Fiction Americaine, 1972, The Cultural Ecology of Chinese Civilization, 1974, China: An Anthropological Perspective, 1976, The Shaving of Karl Marx, 1982, The Prophetic Soul: A Reading of H.G. Wells's "Things to Come", 1987, Robert A. Heinlein fot Twaune's United States Authors Series, 1987, Harry Harrison for Twayne's United States Authors Series, 1990; sr. author: Stonehedge: The Indo-European Herigate, 1979; co-author: Stonehedge: Where Atlantis Died, 1983; sr. editor: Apeman, Spaceman, 1968; co-editor: Above the Human Landscape, 1972; sci. editor: Amazing. Stories, 1967-69; cons. editor: Contemporary Authors, 1987. Recipient Chris award for best edni. film, 1974; recipient Cine award Internat. Council Non-Theatrical Events, 1973; named Disting Faculty Lectr. Sigma Xi, 1978; honored with Stover Day Western Md. Coll., 1981. Mem. H.G. Wells Soc., Sci. Fiction Writers Am. Home: 3100 S Michigan Ave Apt 602 Chicago IL 60616-3825

STOVER, MATTHEW JOSEPH, communications company executive; b. Palo Alto, Calif., May 5, 1955; s. Carl Frederick and Catherine (Swanson) S.; m. Elizabeth Biddle Richter, Apr. 27, 1985; children: Katharine Elizabeth, Madeleine Westbrook. BA, Yale U., 1976; postgrad., U. Va., 1987. Gen. mgr. K&S Assocs., Beltsville, Md., 1977-78; dir. outreach programs U.S. Office Personnel Mgmt., Washington, 1978-81; exec. asst. to chmn. Fed. Maritime Commn., Washington, 1981; exec. dir. STN Computer Services, Inc., Alexandria, Va., 1981-82; dir. corp. communications Norton Simon, Inc., N.Y.C., 1982-83; dist. mgr. corp. communications N.Y. Telephone Co., N.Y.C., 1983-86, dist. mgr. customer services, 1986-87; v.p. corp. communications Am. Express Co., N.Y.C., 1987-90, sr. v.p. communications, 1990; v.p. pub. affairs and corp. communications NYNEX Corp., White Plains, N.Y., 1990-92; pres., CEO AGS Computers, Inc., 1993-94, NYNEX Info. Resources Co., Middleton, Mass., 1994—; bd. dirs. Nat. Assn. Mfrs., Yellow Pages Pubs. Assn., Computer and Comms. Industry Assn.; trustee Com. for Econ. Devel. Editor, pub.: (lit. mag.) Buffalo Stamps, 1971-74. Mem. Nat. Com. U.S.-China Rels. Coun. for Excellence in Govt., Nat. Advt. Rev. Bd., Arthur W. Page Soc., Yale Club (N.Y.C.). Office: NYNEX Info Resources Co 35 Village Rd Middleton MA 01949

STOVER, PHIL SHERIDAN, JR., investment consultant; b. Tulsa, Jan. 23, 1926; s. Phil Sheridan and Noma (Smith) S. Student, Yale, 1943-44, Denison U., 1944-45; B.S., U. Pa., 1948. With Nat. Bank Tulsa, 1948-70, v.p., 1956-64, sr. v.p., 1964-65, sr. v.p., cashier, 1965-70; owner Phil Stover & Assocs., Tulsa, 1970—; pres., treas. Tulsalite, Inc. (mag. pubs.), 1973-79; vice chmn., dir. Tulsa Oiler Baseball Club, 1975-82, Springfield (Ill.) Redbirds Baseball Club; pres. Macon (Ga.) Baseball Club, 1980; dir. Redbirds Baseball Club, Louisville, 1982-86; ptnr. A Hotel, The Frenchmen, New Orleans, 1982-94. Chmn. Tulsa County chpt. Nat. Found, 1956-59, Tulsa Met. Water Authority, 1961-70; vice chmn. Tulsa Utility Bd., 1957-70; Treas. adv. bd. Salvation Army. Served with USNR, 1944-46. Named Okla. Jr. C. of C. Outstanding Young Man, 1954. Republican. Presbyterian. Office: 111 E 41st St Tulsa OK 74105-3830

STOVER, W. ROBERT, lay worker, temporary services executive; b. Phila., June 26, 1921; s. Robert William Stover and Jane Horton; m. Joan Cote; children: Stephen R., Susan J., Amy J. BS, Waynesburg Coll., 1942, LHD (hon.), 1991; postgrad., U. Ill., 1942-43, U. Pa., 1946. Founder, chief exec. officer Western Temporary Svcs., Walnut Creek, Calif., 1948—; also chmn. bd. dirs.; chmn., chief exec. officer Prebyn. Lay Com., Phila.; mem. Latin Am. Missions Gen. Coun., Miami, Fla., Luis Palau Adv. Com., Portland, Oreg.; past chmn. Oakland Billy Graham Crusade. Trustee, former chmn. Fuller Theol. Sem., Pasadena, Calif.; mem. adv. bd. San Francisco State Sch. Bus., African Enterprise, L.A.; mem. nat. bd. Internat. Students, Inc., Colorado Springs; former mem. Calif. State Bd. Wage and Hour Com.; life mem., former nat. chmn. Young Life Campaign, Colorado Springs. Lt. USN, WWII. Office: Western Staff Svcs Inst 301 Lennon Ln Walnut Creek CA 94598-2418

STOVER, WILLIAM RUFFNER, insurance company executive, retired; b. Washington, Aug. 31, 1922; s. Daniel I. and Carrie E. (Brubaker) S.; m. Carolyn McKean, July 19, 1947; children—Deborah Ann Stover Bowgren, Wendi Lee Stover Mirretti, Sheree Kay. Student, Northwestern U., 1941-45. Sales rep. Old Republic Life Ins. Co., 1945-1949, v.p., 1949-60, sr. v.p., 1960-68, pres., 1968-69, also bd. dirs.; ret., 1994; pres. Old Republic Internat. Corp. 1969-90, chmn. bd., chief exec. officer, 1990—; dir. Old Republic Life N.Y., Old Republic Ins. Co., Internat. Bus. and Merc. Reassurance Co., Home Owners Life Ins. Co. and subs., Minn. Title Fin. Corp., Bitco Corp., Founders Title Group, Inc., Republica Mortgage Ins. Co. Republican. Home: 907 N Sheridan Rd Waukegan IL 60085-2051

STOWE, BRUCE BERNOT, biology educator; b. Neuilly-sur-Seine, France, Dec. 9, 1927; came to U.S., 1935; s. Leland and Ruth Florida (Bernot) S.; m. Elizabeth Louise Kwasny, June 23, 1951 (dec. June 1983); children: Mark Kwasny, Eric Bernot. BSc, Calif. Inst. Tech., 1950; MA, Harvard U., 1951, PhD, 1954; MA (hon.), Yale U., 1971. Instr. biology Harvard U., Cambridge, Mass., 1955-58, tutor biochem. scis., 1956-58, lectr. botany, 1958-59; asst. prof. Yale U., New Haven, 1959-63, assoc. prof., 1963-71, prof. biology and forestry, 1971—; dir. bot. garden, 1975-78; rsch. professor Japan Soc. Promotion Sci. U. Osaka Prefecture, 1973; vis. investigator Nat. Inst. for Basic Biology, Okazaki, Japan, 1985-86. Mem. editorial bd. Plant Physiology, Waltham, Mass., 1965-89; mem. editorial com. Ann. Rev. Plant Physiology, Palo Alto, Calif., 1968-73; cons. editor Am. Scientist, New Haven, 1985-90; contbr. sci. papers to Nature, Biochem. Jour., Analytical Biochemistry, others. With U.S. Army, 1946-47. Predoctoral fellow Atomic Energy Commn. Harvard U., 1951-53, postdoctoral fellow NSF, U. Coll. North Wales, 1953-54; fellow John Simon Guggenheim Found., 1965-66; travel grantee U. Adelaide, Waite Inst., South Australia, 1972-73. Fellow AAAS; mem. AAUP, Am. Assn. Plant Physiologists (sec. 1963-65, trustee

1970-72, 75), Bot. Soc. Am. Am. Soc. Biol. Chemistry, Phytochem. Soc. N.Am., Biochem. Soc., Société Française de Physiologie Végétale, Conn. Acad. Arts and Scis. (chair publs. com. 1992-94). Democrat. Achievements include research in analysis and metabolism of plant hormones, lipid activation of plant hormone action, biochemistry of secondary plant products. Home: 161 Grand View Ave Hamden CT 06514-3518 Office: Yale U Dept Biology PO Box 208103 New Haven CT 06520-8103

STOWE, DANIEL HARDING, SR., textile executive; b. Charlotte, N.C., Mar. 6, 1956; s. Robert Lee Jr. and Ruth Link (Harding) S.; m. Pamela Allen, June 19, 1984; children: Palmer, Daniel Harding Jr. BA, Clemson (S.C.) U., 1978. V.P. R.L. Stowe Mills, Inc., Belmont, S.C., 1978-84, pres., chief operating officer, 1984—; pres. Robert Lee Stowe Jr. Found., Belmont, 1988—. Advisor Belmont Abbey Coll.; trustee N.C. Vocat. Textiel Sch., Belmont; bd. dirs. N.C. Textile Mfrs. Assn., Inc., Raleigh, N.C., 1987, U. N.C. Found., Charlotte. Mem. Young Pres.'s Orgn., Rotary. Republican. Presbyterian. Avocations: sports, music. Office: Stowe R L Mills Inc 100 N Main St Belmont NC 28012-3104

STOWE, DAVID HENRY, arbitrator; b. New Canaan, Conn., Sept. 10, 1910; s. Ansel Roy Monroe and Marjorie (Henry) S.; m. Mildred Walker, June 7, 1932; children—David H., Richard W. Student, Washington and Lee U., 1927-30; A.B., Duke, 1931, M. Ed., 1934. Tchr. N.C., 1931-37; asst. state dir. N.C. state Employment Service, 1937-41; chief examiner Bur. Budget, Washington, 1941-47; dep. to asst. to Pres. U.S., 1947-49; administ. asst. to Pres., 1949-53; arbitrator Washington, 1953-70; mem. Nat. Mediation Bd., 1970-79, chmn., 1972-75, 78; mem. atomic energy-labor mgmt. relations panel, 1962—; pub. mem. Pres.'s Missile Sites Labor Commn., 1961-67; mem. bd. Harry S. Truman Library Inst., 1981—. Recipient distinguished service award Dept. Labor, 1965. Mem. Nat. Acad. Arbitrators, Lambda Chi Alpha, Alpha Kappa Psi. Democrat. Episcopalian. Home: 717 Maiden Choice Ln Apt 417 Catonsville MD 21228-6115

STOWE, DAVID HENRY, JR., agricultural and industrial equipment company executive; b. Winston-Salem, N.C., May 11, 1936; s. David Henry and Mildred (Walker) S.; m. Lois Burrows, Nov. 28, 1959; children: Priscilla, David Henry. BA in Econs., Amherst Coll., 1958. V.p. First Nat. Bank Boston, 1961-68; mgr. Deere & Co., Moline, Ill., 1968-71; dir. Deere & Co., Moline, 1971-77, v.p., 1977-82, sr. v.p., 1982-87, exec. v.p., 1987-90, pres., chief oper. officer, 1990—. Home: 4510 5th Ave Moline IL 61265-1904 Office: Deere & Co John Deere Rd Moline IL 61265

STOWE, DAVID METZ, clergyman; b. Council Bluffs, Iowa, Mar. 30, 1919; s. Ernest Lewellyn and Florence May (Metz) S.; m. Virginia Ware, Nov. 25, 1943; children: Nancy F. (Mrs. Thomas Inui), Elizabeth A. (Mrs. Charles Hambrick-Stowe), Priscilla B. (Mrs. Thomas Nelson), David W. BA, UCLA, 1940; BD, Pacific Sch. Religion, 1943, ThD, 1953, DD (hon.), 1966; postgrad., Yale U., 1945-46. Ordained to ministry Congl. Ch., 1943; assoc. min. Congl. Ch., Berkeley, Calif., 1943-45, 51-53; missionary, univ. prof. Peking, China, 1947-50; chaplain, chmn. dept. religion Carleton Coll., 1953-56; ednl. sec. Am. Bd. Commnrs. and Congl. Ch. for World Ministries, 1956-62; prof. theology Beirut, 1962-63; exec. sec. div. fgn. missions Nat. Coun. Chs., 1963-64, assoc. gen. sec. overseas ministries, 1965-70; also bd. govs.; exec. v.p. United Ch. Bd. for World Ministries, 1970-85; cons. mission and religious china, 1985—; adj. prof. Andover Newton Theol. Sch., 1987—; mem. exec. coun. World Conf. on Religion and Peace, 1988—; bd. dirs. Congl. Christian Hist. Soc.; del. 2nd, 3rd and 4th Assemblies of World Coun. of Chs.; mem. Divsn. of World Mission & Evangelism, 1963-75. Author: The Churches' Mission in the World, 1963, When Faith Meets Faith, 1963, Ecumenicity and Evangelism, 1970; also articles in religious books and periodicals. Mem. Am. Soc. Missiology (sec.-treas. Ea. fellowship 1986—), Internat. Assn. Mission Studies, Nat. Soc. Values in Higher Edn. Phi Beta Kappa, Pi Gamma Mu, Blue Key. Home: 54 Magnolia Ave Tenafly NJ 07670

STOWE, LELAND, journalist, writer; b. Southbury, Conn., Nov. 10, 1899; s. Frank Philip and Eva Sarah (Noe) S.; m. Ruth F. Bernot, Sept. 27, 1924; 1 son, Bruce B.; m. Theodora F. Calauz, June 17, 1952. A.B., Wesleyan U., Conn., 1921, M.A. (hon.), 1936, LL.D., 1944; M.A. (hon.), Harvard U., 1945; LL.D., Hobart Coll., 1946. Reporter Worcester Telegram, 1921-22, N.Y. Herald, 1922-24; fgn. editor Pathe News, 1924-26; Paris corr. N.Y. Herald Tribune, 1926-35; roving reporter in N.Y. Herald Tribune, North and South Am., 1936-39; reporter (League of Nations' councils and assemblies), 1927-31, (World Disarmament Conf. Geneva), 1932, (World Econ. Conf.), London, 1933, (Reichstag fire trial), Germany, 1933, (end of Spanish dictatorship and founding of Spanish Republic), 1929-31, (Spanish Civil War), 1937-38, (Pres. Roosevelt's visit to Brazil and Argentina and Inter-American Peace Conf.), Buenos Aires, 1936, (Pan-Am. Conf. at Lima), Peru, 1938; war corr. Chgo. Daily News, from London, 1939; war corr. Chgo. Daily News, in Finland throughout Russo-Finnish war, 1939-40, Norway, 1940, Hungary, Yugoslavia, Rumania, Bulgaria and Turkey, 1940, Greece and Albania, 1940-41, Malaya, Thailand, Indo-China and China, 1941, Burma, 1942, Russia, 1942; commentator Am. Broadcasting Co., 1944-45; war corr. in France, Belgium, Germany, 1944, Italy and Greece, 1945; radio commentator A.B.C. and M.B.S., 1945-46; fgn. editor The Reporter Magazine, 1949-50; dir. News and Information Service of Radio Free Europe, Munich, 1952-54; roving reporter Reader's Digest, 1955-76; prof. journalism U. Mich., 1956-69, prof. emeritus, 1989—. Lectr., free-lance writer, 1947-48; Author: Nazi Means War, 1933, No Other Road to Freedom, 1941, They Shall Not Sleep, 1944, While Time Remains, 1946, Target: You, 1949, Conquest by Terror: The Story of Satelite Europe, 1952, Crusoe of Lonesome Lake, 1957, The Last Great Frontiersman; The Remarkable Adventures of Tom Lamb, 1982. Recipient Pulitzer prize for coverage of Paris (1929) Reparations Com. and formation of Young Plan and Bank for Internat. Settlements, 1930; Legion of Honor France, 1931; U. of Mo. Sch. of Journalism medal for outstanding war correspondence, 1941; Sigma Delta Chi medal and award for 1940 dispatches revealing German conquest of So. Norway, 1941; awarded Mil. Cross of Greece, 1945; Wesleyan U.'s James L. McConaughty Meml. award, 1963. Home: 801 Green Rd Ann Arbor MI 48105-3055

STOWE, MADELEINE, actress; b. L.A., Aug. 18, 1958; m. Brian Benben. Films: Stakeout, 1987, Worth Winning, 1989, Revenge, 1990, The Two Jakes, 1990, Closetland, 1991, Unlawful Entry, 1992, The Last of the Mohicans, 1992, Another Stakeout, 1993, Short Cuts, 1993, China Moon, 1993, Blink, 1994, Bad Girls, 1994; TV movies: The Gangster Chronicles: An American Story, The Nativity, Beulah Land, Black Orchid (miniseries). Office: c/o UTA 9560 Wilshire Blvd 5th Floor Beverly Hills CA 90212*

STOWE, NEAL P., architect; b. Odgen, Utah, July 21, 1943; m. Peggy L. Leininger, Aug. 1965; children: Brett Phillip, Amy Lynn, Christopher William. Student, Weber State Coll., 1963-64; BS, U. Utah, 1971, MArch, 1973; cert., Duke U., 1987. Registered architect, Utah. Project mgr. Richardson Assocs. AIA, Salt Lake City, 1974-78, assoc. ptnr., 1978-83, ptnr.-prin., 1983-86; dir. divsn. facilities constrn. and mgmt. State of Utah, Salt Lake City, 1986—; dir. facilities devel. Utah Sports Authority, Salt Lake City; mem. Regional Urban Design Com., Olympia, Wash., 1990; mem. rev. exec. com. Salt Palace Conv. Ctr., 1991—. Voting dist. chmn., county and state del. to polit. convs., 1972, 74, 76; mem. Utah Gov.'s Com. Hist. and Cultural Sites, 1978-86; mem. Ridgecrest Sch. Community Coun., 1988-89; mem. adv. bd. Salt Lake City Downtown Alliance, 1991; officer bd. trustees Assist Inc., 1976-80, pres. bd. trustees, 1980-84. With USAR, 1961-69. Recipient Award for Outstanding Svc., United Way Salt Lake City, 1977, Disting. Achievement award Dixie Coll., 1989, Pub. Svc. award Utah State Dept. Corrections, 1989, Award of Recognition, Air Force Heritage Mus. Found. Utah, 1991; named Hon. Adm., Nebr. State Navy, 1991, Outstanding Constrn. Person of Yr., Intermountain Contractor Mag. and Panel, 1993. Fellow AIA (chmn. united fund dr. Utah soc. 1976-77, chmn. ann. meeting 1985, pres. elect 1985, pres. 1986, v.p., mem. founding com. Salt Lake chpt. 1986, pres. 1979, organizing chmn. ann. meeting western mountain region 1986, chmn. pres. commn. 1986, vice chmn./chmn. elect nat. com. pub. architecture 1990, chmn. 1991, co-chmn. nat. symposium restoration states capitol bldgs. 1991, juror Thomas Jefferson award 1992, Award of Distinction western mountain region 1982); mem. Am. Soc. Pub. Adminstrs., Nat. Assn. State Facilities Adminstrs. (v.p. western states 1989, 90, sr. v.p. 1991, pres. 1992-93, past pres., sr. dir. 1993), Nat. Owners,

Contractors, and Designers Adv. Coun. (mem. steering com. 1992), Nat. Com. Design, Nat. Com. Pub. Architecture, Urban Design Com. Office: State of Utah 8819 Hidden Oak Dr Salt Lake City UT 84121

STOWE, ROBERT ALLEN, catalytic and chemical technology consultant; b. Kalamazoo, July 26, 1924; s. Allen Byron Stowe and Doris Alfreda (Wood) Stowe Weber; m. Dorothea May Davis, Aug. 23, 1947 (div. 1973); children: Michael, Randall, Catherine, Robert; m. Marion June Smith, Oct. 20, 1973 (div. 1980). AB, Kalamazoo Coll., 1948; PhD, Brown U., 1953. Phys. chemist Dow Chem. Co., Midland, Mich., 1952-58; rsch. chemist Dow Chem. Co., Ludington, Mich., 1958-64, sr. rsch. chemist, 1964-69; sr. rsch. chemist Dow Chem. Co., Midland, 1969-72, assoc. scientist, 1972-88; ret. 1988; pres. Bobcat Techs. Ltd., Cross Village, Mich., 1988—; sr. consulting assoc. Omnitech Internat. Ltd., Midland, 1989—; chief exec. scientist Environmental Assessments Ltd., Midland, 1990—; chief scientist VanTek Corp., Midland, 1993—; chief exec. scientist Environ. Assessments Ltd., Midland, 1990—; chief scientist VanTek Corp., Midland, 1993—. Contbr. articles to sci. jours.; numerous patents in U.S. and fgn. countries. Treas. Ludington Bd. Edn., 1960-63, pres., 1963-68. With USAAF, 1943-45; mem. Nat. Ski Patrol. Recipient Victor J. Azbe award Nat. Lime Assn., 1964. Fellow Am. Inst. Chemists (cert. prof. chemist); mem. Am. Chem. Soc. (program sec. divsn. indsl. and engring. chemistry 1972-82, chmn. 1982-83, councilor 1986—; sec. gen. Catalysis Secretariat 1990, 94, Joseph P. Steward award 1984), N.Am. Catalysis Soc., N.Am. Thermal Analysis Soc., Mich. Catalysis Soc. (sec.-treas. 1987-88, pres. 1988-89). Avocations: tennis, skiing, sailing. Home and Office: Box 173 5680 Chippewa Dr Cross Village MI 49723-0173

STOWE, ROBERT LEE, III, textile company executive; b. Charlotte, N.C., July 3, 1954; s. Robert Lee Jr. and Ruth Link (Harding) S.; m. Christine Ruth Edwards, Jan. 15, 1983; children: Christine Ruth, Lillian Rhyne. BA, Davidson (N.C.) Coll., 1976. Dir., mgmt. trainee R.L. Stowe Mills, Inc., Belmont, N.C., 1976-77, v.p., 1977-79, exec. v.p., 1979-84, chmn. bd., 1984—; bd. dirs Belmont Converting Co.; pres. Robert Lee Stowe Jr. Found., Belmont, 1978—; bd. mgrs. Wachovia Bank of N.C., Gaston County. Trustee Belmont Abbey Coll, 1987-90, Mint Mus. Art, Charlotte, 1989-92, Crossnore (N.C.) Sch., 1987, Sci. Museums, Charlotte, 1989-91. Daniel Jonathan Stowe Conservancy, 1990—, Gaston Day Sch., 1994—; mem. bd. Gaston Day Sch., Daniel Jonathan Shaw Conservancy, Gaston County C. of C., 1992—; deacon, elder local Presbyn. Ch. Named one of Outstanding Young Men Am., 1979. Mem. Am. Textile Mfrs. Inst. (bd. dirs. 1989-92), Newcomen Soc. U.S., N.C. Textile Found. (bd. dirs. 1986—), Met. Club N.Y., Charlotte City Club, Charlotte Country Club, Grandfather Golf and Country Club. Republican. Avocations: golf, boating, church activities. Home: 135 N Main St PO Box 232 Belmont NC 28012 Office: RL Stowe Mills Inc 100 N Main St Belmont NC 28012-3104

STOWE, WILLIAM WHITFIELD, English language educator; b. New Haven, Dec. 7, 1946; s. Arthur Clifford Jr. and Barbara (Borst) S.; m. Karin Ann Trainer, May 8, 1976. BA magna cum laude, Princeton U., 1968; MPhil, Yale U., 1977, PhD, 1978; MA ad eundem gradum, Wesleyan U., 1992. Tchr. Coleytown Jr. High Sch., Westport, Conn., 1968-73; lectr. Princeton (N.J.) U., 1976, 77; instr. Rutgers U., New Brunswick, N.J., 1977; asst. prof. Wesleyan U., Middletown, Conn., 1979-84, assoc. prof., 1984-90, prof., 1990—; chair English dept., 1992—; vis. lectr. Yale U., New Haven, 1978; vis. asst. prof. Wesleyan U., 1978-79. Author: Balzac, James and the Realistic Novel, 1983, Going Abroad: European Travel in Nineteenth-Century American Culture, 1994; editor: The Poetics of Murder, 1983 (Edgar Allen Poe award nominee 1983); contbr. articles to profl. jours. Yale U. fellow, 1973-77. Home: 50 Miller Rd Middlefield CT 06455 Office: Wesleyan U Dept English Middletown CT 06459

STOWELL, CHRISTOPHER R., dancer; b. N.Y.C., June 8, 1966; s. Kent and Francia (Russell) S. Student, Pacific N.W. Ballet Sch., 1979-84, Sch. Am. Ballet, 1984-85. Entered corps de ballet San Francisco Ballet, 1986, promoted to soloist, 1987, prin., 1990—; guest artist Ballet Met, Ohio, Pacific N.W. Ballet, Seattle, and with Jean Charles Gil, Marseilles, France. Created leading roles in Handel-A Celebration, Con Brio, The Sleeping Beauty, New Sleep, Connotations, Pulcinella, Meistens Mozart; other roles include Calcium Light Night, Rubies, The Sons of Horus, The Four Temperaments, Hearts, Tarantella, Flower Festival, La Fille Mal Garde, Haffner Symphony, Forgotten Land, The End, Agon, In the Middle Somewhat Elevated, Le Quattro Stagioni, Swan Lake, Job, Company B, Tchaikousky Pas de Deux, Maelstrom, Mercutio in Romeo and Juliet, The Dance House, Stars and Stripes; performed in Reykjavik Arts Festival, Iceland, 1990, San Francisco Ballet at the Paris Opera Garnier, 1994. Avocations: cooking, reading, camping. Office: San Francisco Ballet 455 Franklin St San Francisco CA 94102-4471

STOWELL, JOSEPH, III, academic administrator. Head Moody Bible Inst., Chgo. Office: Moody Bible Inst 820 N La Salle Dr Chicago IL 60610-3214 Office: Sta WKES-FM PO Box 8888 Saint Petersburg FL 33738

STOWELL, KENT, ballet director; b. Rexburg, Idaho, Aug. 8, 1939; s. Harold Bowman and Maxine (Hudson) S.; m. Francia Marie Russell, Nov. 19, 1965; children: Christopher, Darren, Ethan. Student, San Francisco Ballet Sch., Sch. Am. Ballet; Lead dancer San Francisco Ballet, 1957-62, N.Y.C. Ballet, 1962-68; ballet dir., ballet master Frankfurt (Fed. Republic Germany) Opera Ballet, 1973-77; artistic dir. Pacific N.W. Ballet, Seattle, 1977—; prof. dance Inst. U. Bloomington, 1969-70; bd. dirs. Dance/USA, Washington, 1986—. Choreographer: Cinderella, Carmina Burana, Coppelia, Time & Ebb, Fauré Requiem, Hail to the Conquering Hero, Firebird, Over the Waves, Nutcracker, The Tragedy of Romeo and Juliet, Delicate Balance, Swan Lake. Bd. dirs. Sch. of Am. Ballet, N.Y.C., 1981—; mem. Goodwill Games Arts Com., Seattle, 1987—; chmn. dance panel NEA, 1981-85. Grantee NEA, 1980, 85; fellow NEA, 1979. Recipient Arts Service award King County Arts Commn., 1985, Outstanding Contbn. to Pacific N.W. Ballet State of Was., 1987, Best Dance Co. award The Weekly Newspaper, Seattle, 1987, Gov. Arts award, 1988. Office: Pacific NW Ballet 301 Mercer St Seattle WA 98109-4600*

STOWELL, ROBERT EUGENE, pathologist, retired educator; b. Cashmere, Wash., Dec. 25, 1914; s. Eugene Francis and Mary (Ward) S.; m. Eva Mae Chambers, Dec. 1, 1945; children: Susan Jane, Robert Eugene Jr. Student, Whitman Coll., 1932-33; BA, Stanford U., 1936, MD, 1941; PhD, Washington U., 1944. Fellow in cytology Wash. U. Sch. Medicine, St. Louis, 1940-42; rsch. fellow Barnard Free Skin and Cancer Hosp., St. Louis, 1940-42, rsch. assoc., 1942-48; asst. resident in pathology Barnes, McMillan, St. Louis Children's Hosps., St. Louis, 1942-43, resident in pathology, 1943-44, asst. pathologist, 1944-48; instr. in pathology Washington U. Sch. Medicine, St. Louis, 1943-45; asst. prof. Washington U. Sch. Medicine, St. Louis, 1945-48; assoc. prof. Washington U. Sch. Medicine, St. Louis, 1948; advanced med. fellow Inst. for Cell Rsch., Stockholm, 1946-47; chmn. dept. oncology U. Kansas Med. Ctr., Kansas City, Kans., 1948-51, prof. pathology and oncology, dir. cancer rsch., 1948-59, chmn., 1951-59; sci. dir. Armed Forces Inst. Pathology, Washington, 1959-67; chmn. dept. pathology Sch. of Medicine U. Calif., Davis, 1967-69, asst. dean Sch. Medicine, 1967-72, prof. pathology Sch. Medicine, 1967-82, prof. emeritus, 1982—; dir. div. pathology Sacramento (Calif.) Med. Ctr., 1967-69; vis. prof. U. Md. Sch. Medicine, Balt., 1960-67; acting dir. Nat. Ctr. for Primate Biology, U. Calif., Davis, 1968-69, dir., 1969-71; cons. U.S. Atomic Energy commn., Los Alamos, N.Mex., 1949-54, NIH, 1949-74, Cancer Control Div. USPHS, 1949-59, others; mem. adv. med. bd. Leonard Wood Meml. found., Washington, 1965-67, numerous others.; prin. investigator, chmn. Expert Panel on Assessment of the Practical risk to Human Health from Nitrilotriacetic Acid in Household Laundry Product, 1984-85. Contbr. 120 articles, 30 abstracts to jours. in field; editor 32 biomed. books, monographs and conf. reports, 1941-88; mem. editorial bd. Cancer Rsch., 1949-59, Lab. Investigation, 1952-71, editor, 1967-71. Recipient Meritorious Svc. award Dept. Army, 1963, Exceptional Civilian Svc. award Dept. Army, 1965, Disting. Svc. award U. Calif. Sch. Medicine, 1988; Robert E. Stowell ann. lectureship established U. Calif. Sch. Medicine, 1991 and Am. Registry of Pathology, Washington, 1991. Mem. AMA, Am. Registry of Pathology (bd. dirs. 1976-83, exec. com. 1976-82, v.p. 1976-78, pres. 1978-79), Am. Assn. for Cancer Rsch., Am. Assn. Pathologists (Gold-headed Cane award 1990), Am. Assn. Pathologists and Bacteriologists (councilor 1965-72, v.p. 1969-70, pres. 1970-

71), Am. Soc. Clin. Pathologists, Am. Soc. for Exptl. Pathology (councilor 1962-66, v.p. 1963-64, pres. 1964-65), Calif. Med. Soc., Calif. Soc. Pathologists, Binford-Dammin Soc. Infectious Disease Pathologists, Coll. Am. Pathologists, Histochem. Soc., Internat. Acad. Pathology (councilor 1954-61, pres.-elect 1958-59, pres. 1959-60, Disting. Svc. award 1970, Diamond Jubilee award 1981,Stowell-Orbison award established 1982—), Soc. Cryobiology (bd. govs. 1968-71), Soc. for Exptl. Biology and Medicine, U.S. and Can. Acad. Pathology, Yolo County Med. Soc., Assn. Mil. Surgeons U.S. (sustaining membership award 1965), Univs. Associated for Rsch. and Edn. in Path. (bd. dirs. 1975-90, sec.-treas., 1978-82, hon. dir. 1990—), Sigma Xi, Alpha Omega Alpha. Office: Univ of Calif Sch Medicine Dept of Pathology Davis CA 95616

STOWERS, CARLTON EUGENE, writer; b. Brownwood, Tex., Apr. 14, 1942; s. Ira Milton and Fay Eloise (Stephenson) S.; m. Patricia Ann Folks, Mar. 2, 1981; children: Anson, Ashley. Student, U. Tex., Austin, 1961-63. Sportswriter Abilene (Tex.) Reporter News, 1963-64; sports editor Roswell (N.Mex.) Daily Record, 1964-65; sportswriter Lubbock (Tex.) Avalanche Jour., 1965-67; sports editor Amarillo (Tex.) Globe News, 1967-72; reporter, columnist Dallas Morning News, 1972-81; freelance writer Cedar Hill, Tex., 1981—; contbg. editor Dallas Observer, 1986—; editor Dallas Cowboys Weekly, 1985-89. Author: (non-fiction) The Randy Matson Story, 1971, Spirit, 1973, (with E.B. Hughes) Doc, 1976, (with Trent Jones) Where the Rainbows Wait, 1978, pub. softcover as Terlingua Teacher, 1982, (with Wilbur Evans) Champions, 1978, The Overcomers, 1978, (with Roy Rogers and Dale Evans) Happy Trails, 1979 (book clubs awards, Christian Herald Family Bookshelf main selection, selected for talking book program Nat. Library Svc. for Blind and Handicapped), The Unsinkable Titanic Thompson, 1982, softcover, 1988, Journey to Triumph, 1988 (also in Spanish), (with Steve Perkins and Greg Aiello) Dallas Cowboys Bluebook III, 1982 (Spanish lang. edit. 1982), Partners in Blue: The 100-Year History of the Dallas Police Department, 1983, Friday Night Heroes, 1983, Just One Kiss Baby, 1983, (with Greg Aiello) Dallas Cowboys Bluebook IV, 1983 (Spanish lang. edit. 1983), (with Billy Olson) Reaching Higher, 1984, The Dallas Cowboys: The First 25 Years, 1984, The Cowboy Chronicles, 1984, (ghosted for Ralph Carmichael) He's Everything To Me, 1986, (ghosted for Pam Lontos) Don't Tell Me It's Impossible Until I've Already Done It, 1988, Careless Whispers, 1986 (Edgar Allen Poe award Mystery Writers Am. 1986, Oppie award S.W. Booksellers Assn. 1986, other awards and included in talking book program), The Cotton Bowl: The First 50 Years, 1986, (with Jarret Bell) Dallas Cowboys Bluebook IX, 1988, (with William C. Dear) Please...Don't Kill Me: The True Story of the Milo Murder, 1989 (Literary Guild selection), (with Larry Wansley) The FBI Undercover: The True Story of Special Agent 'Mandrake', 1989, Innocence Lost, 1990, (childrens book) A Hero Named George, 1991, (childrens book) Hard Lessons, 1994, Open Secrets, 1994; gen. editor series 8 collections sports columns Sportswriters' Eye Series, 1988, 89; writer, producer 79-week, 30 minute news feature show Countdown to '84, official show of U.S. Olympic Com., documentary African Stars '84 for African Nat. TV., football halftime feature Greatest of the Great; writer cable TV show Polaroid's Sports Camera Internat.; coproducer TV show Texas by Land: The Story of the Sesquicentennial Wagon Train; script writer syndicated radio shows Faith Made Them Great, Inside the NFL. Bd. dirs. Cedar Hill (Tex.) Libr. Assn., 1989-92; mem. adv. bd. Kevin Curnutt Found. for Brain Injury Rsch., Arlington, Tex., 1988-89. Recipient Katie awards Dallas Press Club, 1985-92, Oppie award S.W. Booksellers, 1986, Edgar Allen Poe award for best fact crime book Mystery Writers Am., 1986, Stephen Philben awards Dallas Bar Assn., 1987-92, other journalism awards Tex. HEadliners Club, William Randolph Hearts Found., UPI, other; named Best Local Writer in the 1988's, reader's poll Dallas Observer. Mem. Authors Guild Am., Mystery Writers Am., Internat. Assn. Crime Writers, Profl. Football Writers Am., Tex. Sportswriters Assn. Home: 1015 Randy Dr Cedar Hill TX 75104-3035 Office: care Janet W Manus Lit Agy Inc 417 E 57th St Ste 5D New York NY 10022

STOWERS, JAMES EVANS, JR., investment company executive; b. Kansas City, Mo., Jan. 10, 1924; s. James Evans Sr. and Laura (Smith) S.; m. Virginia Ann Glasscock, Feb. 4, 1954; children: Pamela, Kathleen, James Evans III, Linda. A.B., U. Mo., 1946, B.S. in Medicine, 1947. Pres. Twentieth Century Svcs., Kansas City, 1956—, Survivors Benefit Ins. Co., Kansas City, 1956-80, 20th Century Investors, Inc., Kansas City, 1957—, Investors Research Corp ., Kansas City, 1958—, Twentieth Century Cos. Inc., Kansas City, 1984—; chmn. bd., CEO Twentieth Century Svcs., 20th Century Investors, Investors Rsch. Group, Twentieth Century Cos. Inc., Kansas City, 1993—. Author: Why Waste Your Money on Life Insurance, 1967, Principles of Financial Consulting, 1971, Yes, You Can....achieve financial independence, 1992. Served to capt. USAAF, 1943-45; with USAFR, 1945-57. Mem. Kansas City C. of C., Sigma Chi. Republican. Office: Twentieth Century Svcs 4500 Main St Kansas City MO 64111-1800

STOYANOV, MILAN, lumber products company executive; b. 1933. BA, U. Oreg., 1955. With Oreg. Pacific Forest Products Corp., Portland, 1964-70, Am. Internat. Forest Products Inc., Beaverton, Oreg., 1970-74; with Buckeye Pacific Corp., 1974-86, pres.; pres. Forest City Trading Group Inc., Portland, 1986—, also bd. dirs. Served to 1st lt. USAF, 1955-58. Office: Forest City Trading Group PO Box 4209 Portland OR 97298

STRAATSMA, BRADLEY RALPH, ophthalmologist, educator; b. Grand Rapids, Mich., Dec. 29, 1927; s. Clarence Ralph and Lucretia Marie (Nicholson) S.; m. Ruth Campbell, June 16, 1951; children: Cary Ewing, Derek, Greer. Student, U. Mich., 1947; MD cum laude, Yale U., 1951; DSc (hon.), Columbia U., 1984. Diplomate Am. Bd. Ophthalmology (vice chmn. 1979, chmn. 1980). Intern New Haven Hosp., Yale U., 1951-52; resident in ophthalmology Columbia U., N.Y.C., 1955-58; spl. clin. trainee Nat. Inst. Neurol. Diseases and Blindness, Bethesda, Md., 1958-59; assoc. prof. surgery/ophthalmology UCLA Sch. Medicine, 1959-63, chief div. ophthalmology, dept. surgery, 1959-68, prof. surgery/ophthalmology, 1963-68, prof. ophthalmology, 1968—; dir. Jules Stein Eye Inst., 1964-94, chmn. dept. ophthalmology, 1968-94; ophthalmologist-in-chief UCLA Med. Ctr., 1968-94; lectr. numerous univs. and profl. socs. 1971—; cons. to surgeon gen. USPHS, mem. Vision Research Tng. Com., Nat. Inst. Neurol. Diseases and Blindness, NIH, 1959-63, mem. neurol. and sensory disease program project com., 1964-68; chmn. Vision Research Program Planning Com., Nat. Adv. Eye Council, Nat. Eye Inst., NIH, 1973-75, 75-77, 85-89; mem. med. adv. bd. Internat. Eye Found., 1970-79; mem. adv. com. on basic clin. research Nat. Soc. to Prevent Blindness, 1971-87; mem. med. adv. com. Fight for Sight, 1960-83; bd. dirs. So. Calif. Soc. to Prevent Blindness, 1967-77, Ophthalmic Pub. Co., 1975—, v.p. 1990-93, Pan-Am. Ophthalmol. Found., 1985—; chmn. sci. adv. bd. Ctr. for Partially Sighted, 1984-87; mem. nat. adv. panel Found. for Eye Research, Inc., 1984—; mem. cons. com. Palestra Oftalmologica Panamericana, 1976-81; coord. com. Nat. Eye Health Edn. Program, 1989; mem. sci. adv. bd. Rsch. to Prevent Blindness, Inc., 1993—; mem. Internat. Coun. Opthalmology, 1993—. Editor-in-chief Am. Jour. Ophthalmology, 1993—; mem. editorial bd. UCLA Forum in Med. Scis. 1974-82, Am. Jour. Ophthalmology, 1974-91, Am. Intra-Ocular Implant Soc. Jour., 1978-79, EYE-SAT Satellite-Relayed Profl. Edn. in Ophthalmology, 1982-86; mng. editor von Graefe's Archive for Clin. and Exptl. Ophthalmology, 1976-88; contbr. over 400 articles to med. jours. Trustee John Thomas Dye Sch., Los Angeles, 1967-72. Served to lt. USNR, 1952-54. Recipient William Warren Hoppin award N.Y. Acad. Medicine, 1956, Univ. Service award UCLA Alumni Assn., 1982, Miguel Aleman Found. medal, 1992, Benjamin Boyd Humanitarian award Pan Am. Assn. Ophthalmology, 1991, Lucian Howe medal, Am. Ophthalmological Soc., 1992. Fellow Royal Australian Coll. Ophthalmologists (hon.); mem. Academia Ophthalmologica Internationales, Am. Acad. Ophthalmology (bd. councillors 1981), Found. of Am. Acad. Ophthalmology (trustee 1989, chmn. bd. trustees 1989-92), Am. Acad. Ophthalmology and Otolaryngology (pres. 1977), Am. Soc. Cataract and Refractive Surgery, AMA (asst. sec. ophthalmology sect. 1962-63, sec. 1963-66, chmn. 1966-67, council 1970-74), Am. Ophthalmol. Soc. (coun. 1985-90, v.p. 1992, pres. 1993), Assn. Research in Vision and Ophthalmology (Mildred Weisenfeld award 1991), Assn. U. Profs. of Ophthalmology (trustee 1969-75, pres.-elect 1973-74, pres. 1974-75), Assn. VA Ophthalmologists, Calif. Med. Assn. (mem. ophthalmology adv. panel 1972-94, chmn. 1974-79, sci. bd. 1973-79, ho. of dels. 1974, 77, 79), Chilean Soc. Ophthalmology (hon.), Columbian Soc. Ophthalmology (hon.), Glaucoma Soc. Internat. Congress of Ophthalmology (hon.), Heed Ophthalmic Found. (chmn., bd. dirs. 1990—), Hellenic Ophthalmol. Soc. (hon.), Internat. Coun. Ophthalmology (bd. dirs. 1993—), Los Angeles

County Med. Assn., Los Angeles Soc. Ophthalmology, The Macula Soc., Pacific Coast Oto-Ophthalmol. Soc., Pan-Am. Assn. Ophthalmology (council 1972—, pres. elect 1985-87, pres. 1987-89), Peruvian Soc. Ophthalmology (hon.), The Retina Soc. Republican. Presbyterian. Clubs: Internat. Intra-Ocular Implant, The Jules Gonin, West Coast Retina Study. Avocations: music, tennis, scuba diving. Home: 3031 Elvingeles CA 90049-1107 Office: UCLA Jules Stein Eye Inst 100 Stein Pla Los Angeles CA 90024-7000

STRACHAN, DAVID E., trade association executive; b. Pitts., June 3, 1947; s. Edward Adam and Helen Joanna (Beatty) S.; m. Judith Mary Squires, Mar. 14, 1970; children: Sarah Duff, Matthew Squires. BS, W.Va. U., 1969. Cert. assn. exec. Fin. asst. SEC, Washington, 1970-71; fin. analyst Fed. Deposit Ins. Corp., Washington, 1971-72; assoc. dir. Am. Bankers Assn., Washington, 1972-78; exec. v.p. Nat. Assn. Pers. Cons., Washington, 1978-83, D.C. Assn. Realtors, Washington, 1983-89; pres. Am. Wholesale Marketers Assn., Washington, 1989—; pres. Mgmt. and Svcs. Corp., Washington, 1991—. Contbr. articles to mags. Pres. Dist. Edn. Found., Washington, 1990—. Mem. Am. Soc. Assn. Execs., Nat. Assn. Wholesale Distbrs. Republican. Presbyterian. Avocations: boat bldg., fishing. Office: Am Wholesale Marketers 1128 16th St NW Washington DC 20036

STRACHAN, DONALD M., financial company executive; b. Cleve., June 24, 1923; s. Harry Morris and Eva (Maffett) S.; m. Suzanne Merion, June 27, 1953; children—William, Paul. Student, St. Catherine's Coll., Cambridge (Eng.) U., 1945; BS, U. Pa., 1947. CPA, Ohio, W.Va. With Ernst, CPA, 1947-70; staff acct. to mgr. Ernst, CPA, Cleve., 1947-63; ptnr. Ernst, CPA, Charleston, W.Va., 1964-70; v.p. fin., treas. Cleve. Electronics, Inc., 1970-74; with Barnes, Wendling & Cook, Cleve., 1974-77; treas. McGean-Rohco, Inc., Cleve., 1977-88; pvt. practice CPA Chagrin Falls, Ohio, 1989—. Mem. Orange Sch. bd., 1994—. Served with AUS, World War II. Mem. Delta Kappa Epsilon. Mem. United Ch. Christ. Club: Chagrin Valley Country. Home: 135 Mill Creek Ln Chagrin Falls OH 44022

STRACHAN, GLADYS, executive director; b. N.Y.C., Dec. 10, 1929; d. Jacob Allen and Annie Mae (Alston) McClendon; m. Eugene S. Callender (div. 1963); 1 child, Renee Denise; m. John R. Strachan (dec. 1982). Student, NYU, 1947-49. Dep. asst. Presbyn. Ch. of East Africa, Nairobi, Kenya, 1964-67; assoc. for women's program Presbyn. Ch. of U.S., N.Y.C., 1970-83; exec. United Presbyn. Women, N.Y.C., 1983—; cons. Peace Corps, Nairobi, 1964-67, Operation Crossroads Africa, Nairobi, 1964-67, Afro-Am. Ednl. Inst., Teaneck, N.J., 1977-79, various women's orgns. in Asia, Australia, Europe, Africa. V.p. Addicts Rehab. Ctr. Bd., N.Y.C., 1957—; mem. N.Y. Coalition of 100 Black Women, N.Y.C., 1972—; sec. Harlem Dowling Children's Svc. Bd., N.Y.C., 1983—; bd. dirs., treas. Bread for the World, Washington, 1983—. Recipient Cert. of citation borough pres. N.Y.C., 1977, Harlem Peacemaking award Harlem Peacemaking Com., 1983. Avocations: music, reading, travel, needlepoint, theater. Office: Presbyn Women 100 Witherspoon St Louisville KY 40202-1396

STRACHAN, GRAHAM, pharmaceutical company executive; b. Dundee, Scotland, Sept. 12, 1938; arrived in Can., 1968; s. Roualyn and Ellen Strachan. BSc, Glasgow U., 1961, MA, 1963. Registered patent and trade agt. Licensing officer Schering Inc., Switzerland, 1963-66; v.p. bus. devel. John Labatt Ltd., Can., 1967-82; pres., chief exec. officer Allelix Biopharms., Inc., Mississauga, Ont., Can., 1982—; chmn. Nat. Biotech. Adv. Com. Patentee in field. Fellow Patent and Trademark Inst. Can.; mem. Am. Chem. Soc., Licensing Execs. Soc., Indsl. Biotech. Assn. Can. (bd. dirs.), Assn. Biotech. Cos. (bd. dirs. 1985—, past pres.). Achievements include several patents relating to biotechnology. Home: 118 W Deane Park Dr, Islington, ON Canada M9B2S3 Office: Allelix Biopharmaceuticals Inc, 6850 Goreway Dr, Mississauga, ON Canada L4V1P1

STRACHER, ALFRED, biochemistry educator; b. Albany, N.Y., Nov. 16, 1930; s. David and Florence (Winter) S.; m. Dorothy Altman, July 4, 1954; children: Cameron, Adam, Erica. BS in Chemistry, Rensselaer Poly. Inst., 1952; MA in Chemistry, Columbia U., 1954, PhD in Chemistry, 1956. Asst. prof. SUNY Health Sci. Ctr. at Bklyn., 1959-62, assoc. prof., 1962-68, prof. biochem., 1968—, chmn. dept., 1972—; assoc. dean for research and devel., 1982-88; cons. Nat. Inst. Neurol. Communicative Disorders and Stroke NIH, 1981-84, 85-89. Editor: Muscle and Non-Muscle Motility, 1983; editorial bd. 3 jours.; editor-in-chief: Drug Targeting and Delivery; contbr. 95 articles to profl. jours. Fellow Nat. Found. for Infantile Paralysis Rockefeller Inst. for Med. Rsch., 1956-58 and Carlsberg Lab., 1958-59, Commonwealth Fund Kings Coll. U. London, 1966-67, Guggenheim Found. Oxford U., 1973-74; career scientist grantee Health Rsch. Coun. N.Y., 1962-69. Fellow AAAS; mem. Am. Soc. for Biochemistry and Molecular Biology, Harvey Soc. (treas. 1978-83), Marine Biol. Labs. (corp. mem.). Avocations: tennis, travel. Home: 47 The Oaks Roslyn NY 11576 Office: SUNY Health Sci Ctr Bklyn 450 Clarkson Ave Brooklyn NY 11203-2012

STRACK, HAROLD ARTHUR, retired electronics company executive, retired air force officer, planner, analyst, author, musician; b. San Francisco, Mar. 29, 1923; s. Harold Arthur and Catheryn Jenny (Johnsen) S.; m. Margaret Madeline Decker, July 31, 1945; children: Carolyn, Curtis, Tamara. Student, San Francisco Coll., 1941, Sacramento Coll., 1947, Sacramento State Coll., 1948, U. Md., 1962, Indsl. Coll. Armed Forces, 1963. Commd. 2d lt. USAAF, 1943; advanced through grades to brig. gen. USAF, 1970; comdr. 1st Radar Bomb Scoring Group Carswell AFB, Ft. Worth, 1956-59; vice comdr. 90th Strategic Missile Wing SAC Warren AFB, Cheyenne, Wyo., 1964; chief Studies, Analysis and Gaming Agy. Joint Chiefs of Staff, 1965-67; dep. asst. to chmn. for strategic arms negotiations Joint Chiefs Staff, 1968; comdr. 90th Strategic Missile Wing SAC Warren AFB, Cheyenne, 1969-71; chief Studies, Analysis and Gaming Agy. Joint Chiefs Staff, Washington, 1972-74, ret., 1974; v.p., mgr. MX Program Strategic Planning, Northrop Electronics, Hawthorne, Calif., 1974-88; ret., 1988. 1st clarinetist, Cheyenne Symphony Orch., 1969-71. Mem. Cheyenne Frontier Days Com., 1970-71. Decorated D.S.M., Legion of Merit, D.F.C., Air medal, Purple Heart, Order Pour le Merite. Mem. AIAA (sr. mem.), Inst. Nav., Am. Def. Preparedness Assn., Air Force Assn. (nt. dir.), Aerospace Edn. Found., Am. Fedn. Musicians, Cheyenne Frontier Days "Heels." Home: 707 James Ln Incline Village NV 89451-9612 *The precepts which have guided me recognize the dignity of the individual and human rights. I believe that living by the Golden Rule contributes to the quality of life by making us better and more useful citizens while favorably influencing others. Integrity, ideals, and high standards reinforce one's own character. While taking pride in accomplishment, show gratitude for opportunity and humility for success. Lead by example and always do your best. Service to humanity and country is the highest calling, and the satisfaction of a job well done, approbation, respect and true friendship are one's greatest rewards.*

STRACK, J. GARY, hospital administrator; b. Orlando, Fla., Aug. 1, 1945; married. Bachelors degree, U. Fla., 1967, masters degree, 1969. Adminstrv. rschr. Va. Med. Ctr., Gainesville, Fla., 1969; program mgr. Fla. Regional Med. Program, Gainesville, 1969-70; asst. prof. program in hosp. adminstrn. U. Fla., Gainesville, 1970-74; assoc. dir. Holiday Hosp., Orlando, 1974-77; assoc. exec. dir. Orlando Regional Med. Ctr., 1977-80; pres., CEO Orlando Regional Healthcare System, 1980—. Contbr. articles to profl. jours. Mem. AHA, Fla. Hosp. Assn. (bd. dirs. 1979-80). Home: 6305 Gibson Dr Orlando FL 32809 Office: Orlando Regional Healthcare System 1414 Kuhl Ave Orlando FL 32806-2093

STRADER, JAMES DAVID, lawyer; b. Pitts., June 30, 1940; s. James Lowell and Tyra Fredrika (Bjorn) S.; m. Ann Wallace, Feb. 8, 1964; children: James Jacob, Robert Benjamin. Ms. Math. State U., 1962; JD, U. Pitts., 1965. Bar: Pa. 1966, U.S. Dist. Ct. (we. dist.) Pa. 1966, U.S. Dist. Ct. (ea. dist.) Pa. 1973, U.S. Dist. Ct. (mid. dist.) Pa. 1985, U.S. Ct. Appeals (4th and 5th cirs.) 1977, U.S. Ct. Appeals (3d and 11th cirs.) 1981, U.S. Supreme Ct. 1982. Assoc. Peacock, Keller & Yohe, Washington, 1967-68; atty. U.S. Steel Corp., Pitts., 1968-77, gen. atty. workmen's compensation, 1977-84; assoc. Caroselli, Spagnolli & Beachler, Pitts., 1984—; ptnr. Dickie, McCamey & Chilcote, Pitts., 1987—. Del. Dem. Mid-Yr. Conv., 1974; mem. Dem. Nat. Platform Com., 1976; commr. Mt. Lebanon Twp., Pa., 1974-78. Served to capt. U.S. Army, 1965-67. Mem. ABA (sr. vice-chmn. worker's compensation com. 1978-94), Pa. Bar Assn. (chair worker's compensation law sect.), Allegheny County Bar Assn., Valley Brook Country Club.

Democrat. Presbyterian. Office: Dickie McCamey & Chilcote Ste 400 2 PPG Pl Pittsburgh PA 15222

STRADLEY, WILLIAM JACKSON, lawyer; b. Houston, Oct. 27, 1939; s. Samuel H. and Mary Stradley; m. Emmalee H. Stradley, Apr. 16, 1960; children—Lisa D., William M. B.S., U. Houston, 1964; J.D., 1967. Bar: Tex. 1967, U.S. Dist. Ct. (so. dist.) Tex. 1967, U.S Ct. Appeals (5th cir.)1967, U.S. Supreme Ct. 1970. Cert. Civil Trial Law, Personal Injury Trial Law Tex. Bd. of Legal Specialization; of coun. Mithoff & Jacks, L.L.P. mem. faculty trial advocacy course Law Sch. U. Houston, 1982. Pres., Police Adv. Com. 1981-84, sec., 1980-81; bd. dirs Houston Council Human Relations, 1982-84; mem. adminstrv. bd. St. Luke's United Meth. Ch.; co-chair fed. judiciary appointments com. State Bar Tex., 1991, mem. continuing legal edn. com., 1991, adminstrn. justice com., spl. com. professionalsm. Recipient Pub. Service award Houston Police Dept., 1984. Mem. Houston Bar Found. (charter), Am. Bd. Trial Advocates (pres., treas. 1980-82 v.p. 1983-84 Houston), State Bar of Tex. (chmn. grievance com.), Supreme Ct. Tex. (mem. profl. ethics com 1984-94), Houston Trial Lawyers Assn. (bd. dirs. 1980-82, v.p. 1983-84, pres. 1985-86), Houston Bar Assn. (chmn. tort and compensation sect. 1980-81, chmn. continuing legal edn. com., com. on professionalism), Tex. Trial Lawyers Am. (dir. emeritus, chmn. ethics com., by-laws com.), Assn. Trial Lawyers Am., Houston Club, Met. Racquet Club. Home: 64 E Broad Oaks Dr Houston TX 77056-1202 Office: 3450 One Allen Ctr Houston TX 77002

STRAFFON, RALPH ATWOOD, urologist; b. Croswell, Mich., Jan. 4, 1928; s. Lloyd Atwood and Verle R. (Rice) S.; m. Cary Arden Higley, Feb. 13, 1954; children: David, Daniel, Jonathan, Peter, Andrew; m. Shirley Louise Gilmore, June 20, 1987; children: Scott, Leslie. M.D., U. Mich., 1953. Diplomate: Am. Bd. Urology. Intern, then resident in surgery Univ. Hosp., Ann Arbor, 1953-56, resident in urology, 1956-59; mem. staff Cleve. Clinic, 1956—, head dept. urology, 1963-83, chmn. div. surgery, 1983-87, vice chmn. bd. govs. and chief of staff, 1987—; practice medicine specializing in urology Cleve., 1959—. Contbr. articles to med. jours. Served with AUS, 1946-48. Fellow A.C.S.; mem. Am. Assn. Genitourinary Surgeons, AMA, Am. Urol. Assn., Cleve. Acad. Medicine, Cleve. Urol. Assn., Clin. Soc. Genitourinary Surgeons, Soc. Univ. Urologists, Frederick A. Coller Surg. Soc., Am. Soc. Nephrology, Transplantation Soc., Soc. Pelvic Surgeons, Soc. Pediatric Urology, Am. Fertility Soc., Am. Assn. Clin. Urologists, Soc. Internat. d'Urologie, Am. Assn. Genitourinary Surgeons Edinburgh (hon. fellow), Coll. Medicine South Africa (hon. fellow). Home: 19701 Shelburne Rd Cleveland OH 44118-4959 Office: 9500 Euclid Ave Cleveland OH 44195-0001

STRAHM, SAMUEL EDWARD, veterinarian; b. Fairview, Kans., Feb. 9, 1936; s. Silas Tobias and Martha Mary (Beyer) S.; m. Barbara Jean Wenger, June 1, 1958; children: Gregory Lee, Bryan Scott, Andrea Marie Enloe. BS, DVM, Kansas State U., 1959. Diplomate Nat. Acad. Practice. Owner, ptnr. Osage Animal Clinic Inc., Pawhuska, Okla., 1959—, pres., 1985—; bd. 1st Nat. Bank, Pawhuska, Okla.; mem. bd. cons. Profl. Exam Svc., 1990—; mem. adv. bd. USDA Users, 1991—; mem. adv. com. Pew Nat. Health Profession Vet. Medicine, 1991. Mem. Okla. State Sch. Bd. Assn., 1977-94, 2d v.p., 1993, 1st v.p., 1994, pres.-elect, 1994; mem. Okla. All-State Sch. Bd., 1993; mem. Pawhuska Sch. Bd., 1974—, pres., 1991-94; mem. Pawhuska Planning Commn., 1965-70; mem. Okla. State U. Centennial Commn., Stillwater, 1986-91. Recipient Disting. Alumni award Coll. Vet. Medicine Kans. State U., 1994. Mem. Am. Vet. Med. Assn. (pres. elect 1988-89, pres. 1989-90, AVMA award 1986, Coun. on Govt. Affairs, 1992—), Am. Assn. Theriogenealogy, Am. Assn. Bovine Practitioners, Am. Assn. Vet. State Bds., Nat. Bd. Vet. Med. Examiners, Okla. Vet. Med. Assn. (all offices from 1959, Veterinarian of Yr. 1990), Kans. Vet. Med. Assn., Okla. Bd. Vet. Med. Examiners (pres.), Pawhuska C. of C. (pres. 1968), Pawhuska Jaycees (all offices 1959-69), Toastmasters Club. Republican. Baptist. Avocations: gardening, fishing, flying. Home: PO Box 1256 Pawhuska OK 74056-1256 Office: Osage Animal Clinic Inc PO Box 1209 Pawhuska OK 74056-1209

STRAIGHT, BEATRICE WHITNEY, actress; b. Old Westbury, L.I., N.Y., Aug. 2, 1918; d. Willard and Dorothy (Whitney) Dickerman; m. Peter Cookson, June 2, 1949; children: Gary, Anthony. Studied with, Tamara Daykarhanova, with Michael Chekhov at Chekhov Theatre Sch. A founder Theatre, Inc. (producing orgn.), 1945. Appeared in Broadway plays including Bitter Oleander, 1935, The Possessed, 1939, Twelfth Night, 1941, Land of Fame, 1943, The Wanhope Bldg, 1947, Eastward in Eden, 1947, Macbeth, 1948, The Heiress, 1948, The Innocents, 1950, The Grand Tour, 1951, Heartbreak House, 1952, The Crucible, 1953 (Antoinette Perry award), Sing Me No Lullaby, 1954, The River Line, 1957, Twelfth Night, King Lear, Phèdre, 1966, A Streetcar Named Desire, 1967, 69-70, Everything in the Garden, 1967, The Palace at 4 A.M, 1972, Ghosts, 1972, All My Sons, 1974; toured in: Broadway plays including The Right Honourable Gentleman, 1971; mem. Broadway plays including, L.I. Festival Repertory Co., 1968; film appearances include Phone Call for a Stranger, 1952, Patterns, 1956, The Silken Affair, 1957, The Nun's Story, 1959, The Young Lovers, 1964, Network, 1976 (Acad. award for best supporting actress), Bloodline, 1979, The Promise, 1979, The Formula, 1980, Poltergeist, The Power, 1986, Deceived, 1991; TV performances include The Magnificent Failure, 1952, The Borrowers, 1973, The Garden Party, 1974, Strangers in the Homeland, 1976; mini-series The Dain Curse, 1978; also guest roles on Lamp Unto My Feet; regular on: TV series Beacon Hill, 1975; operates, Young World Found.; producing: children's plays, including Who Am I?, 1971-73; conducted own radio program on, Sta. WMCA, N.Y.C., during World War II, appeared as Rose Kennedy in mini-series Robert Kennedy, His Life and Time, 1984, Run Till You Fall, 1989, People Like Us, 1990; founder Michael Chekov studio, Eng., U.S., reopened 1982—; co-founder Theatre Inc., 1946. Mem. Actors Equity, AFTRA, Screen Actors Guild. Home: 30 Norfolk Rd Southfield MA 01259 Office: care Mark Levy Mgmt 23826 Hartland St West Hills CA 91307-3022

STRAIGHT, RICHARD COLEMAN, photobiologist; b. Rivesville, W.Va., Sept. 8, 1937. BA, U. Utah, 1961, PhD in Molecular Biology, 1967. Asst. dir. radiation biology summer inst. U. Utah, 1961-63; supervisory chemist med. svc. VA Hosp., 1965—; dir. VA Venom Rsch. Lab., 1975—; adminstrv. officer rsch. svc. VA Ctr., 1980—; dir. Dixon laser inst. U. Utah, Salt Lake City, 1985-90; pres. Western Inst. for Biomed. Rsch., Salt Lake City, 1990—; dir. Utah Ctr. for Photo Medicine, Salt Lake City, 1993—. Assoc. editor Lasers in Surgery and Medicine, 1990-95, Jour. Biomed. Optics, 1995—. Mem. AAAS, Am. Chem. Soc., Am. Soc. Photobiology, Biophysics Soc., Am. Soc. for Laser Medicine and Surgery, Utah Life Sci. Industries Assn. (charter). Achievements include research in photodynamic action of biomonomers and biopolymers, tumor immunology, effect on antigens on mammary adenocarcinoma of C3H mice, ageing, biochemical changes in ageing, venom toxicology, mechanism of action of psychoactive drugs. Office: VAMC/Univ of Utah Western Inst Biomed Rsch 500 Foothill Dr Salt Lake City UT 84148

STRAIN, DOUGLAS CAMPBELL, precision instrument company executive; b. Spokane, Wash., Oct. 24, 1919; s. Clayton Preston and Edith (Crockatt) S.; m. Leila Cleo Karicofe, June 10, 1943; children: James Douglas, Barbara Joanne, Gordon Campbell. BSEE, Calif. Inst. Tech.; 1948; PhD (hon.), Internat. Coll. of the Cayman Islands, 1979. Registered profl. engr., Oreg. Design engr. Nat. Tech. Labs. Beckman Instruments, South Pasadena, Calif., 1948-49; v.p. research and engring. Brown Electro Measurements Corp., Portland, Oreg., 1949-53; pres. Electro Sci. Industries, Inc., Portland, 1953-80, chmn. bd., 1953-85, vice chmn. bd., 1985—; pres. Sunset Sci. Park, Inc., Portland, 1963-70; bd. dirs. Org. Software Inc., Portland, U.S. Bancorp/U.S. Nat. Bank, Portland, Optical Data, Inc., Lattice, Portland, Oreg. Grad. Ctr.; bd. overseers The Org. Health Sci. U. Portland. Patentee optical and electronic devices. Chmn. Tri-County Colls. for Oreg.'s Future, 1964-68, treas., 1968—; mem. Gov.'s Adv. Council for Oreg. Tech. Services, 1966-70; chmn. adv. panel to electricity div. Nat. Bur. Standards, Nat. Acad. Sci., 1971-74; mem. nat. metric adv. panel Commerce Dept., 1969-70; trustee Internat. Coll. of Caymans, 1971—; Scis. of Tomorrow, Pacific U. (past pres.; assoc. Calif. Inst. Tech., 1975—; chmn. Oreg. Alumni Fund, 1975—; bd. dirs. Vols. Internat. Tech. Assistance. Recipient Bausch and Lomb Sci. award, 1938, Reed Coll. award, 1975, Wildhack award Nat. Conf. Standards Labs., 1977, Disting. Alumni award Calif. Inst. Tech., 1986; Menninger Found. fellow. Fellow Instrument Soc. Am. (nat. pres. 1970-71); mem.

IEEE (sr.), Sci. Apparatus Makers Assn. (chmn., indsl. instrument sect. 1966-68, bd. dirs. 1973-76), Nat. Mgmt. Assn. (pres. Portland chpt. 1956-57, v.p. West Coast 1962-63), AAAS, Western Electronic Mfrs. Assn. (bd. dirs. 1956-57), Nat. Soc. Profl. Engrs., Precision Mgmt. Assn. (sr.), Electron Microscope Soc. Am. Clubs: City (research bd.), Multnomah (Portland). Home: 1710 SW Harbor Way Portland OR 97201-5153 Office: Electro Scientific Industries Inc 13900 NW Science Park Dr Portland OR 97229-5411

STRAIN, JAMES ELLSWORTH, pediatrician, retired association administrator; b. Lincoln, Nebr., Apr. 23, 1923; s. Elmer Ellsworth and Tessa Elizabeth (Stevens) S.; m. Ruby Lee Shepard; children: James A., John D., Janet M. Strain McKinney, Jeffrey Lee Phillips-Strain. AB, Phillips U., Enid, Okla., 1945; MD, U. Colo., Denver, 1947. Diplomate Am. Bd. Pediatrics (examiner 1984-89, mem. 1989-93, emeritus mem. 1993—). Intern Mpls. Gen. Hosp., 1947-48; resident in pediatrics Denver Children's Hosp., 1948-50, pres. med. staff, 1964, dir. genetic unit, 1982-86; pvt. practice specializing in pediatrics, Denver, 1950-86; exec. dir. Am. Acad. Pediatrics, Elk Grove Village, Ill., 1986-93, ret., 1993; mem. exec. bd. Denver Children's Hosp., 1977-81; pres. med. bd. Colo. Gen. Hosp., 1969-70; clin. prof. pediatrics U. Colo. Med. Ctr., 1969-86, 93—, U. Chgo., 1987-93; mem. Colo. Med. Adv. Coun. for Title 19, 1968-75, chmn., 1968-71; mem. Task Force on Iowa Health Care Standards Project, 1984-85; presenter numerous profl. confs. Mem. editorial bd. Pediatrics in Rev.; reviewer Jour. Pediatrics; contbr. articlest to profl. publs. Mem. Colo. Commn. on Children and Youth, 1971-75; trustee Phillips U., 1974—. Capt. U.S. Army, 1953-55. Recipient Disting. Alumnus award Phillips U., 1974, Florence Sabin award U. Colo., 1984, Excellence in Pub. Svc. award U.S. Surgeon Gen., 1988, Abraham Jacobi award AMA and Am. Acad. Pediatrics, 1994; James E. Strain Child Advocacy award established in his name Denver Children's Hosp., 1983. Fellow Am. Acad. Pediatrics (numerous offices and com. memberships at chpt., dist. and nat. level, including pres. 1982-83, Clifford Grulee award 1985); mem. APHA, AMA (mem. coun. sect. pediatrics 1971-93, chmn. coun. 1974-79, sect. del. 1978-79), Colo. Med. Soc. (mem. coun. dels. 1964-80), Denver Med. Soc. (mem. coun. dels. 1964-80), Can. Pediatric Soc., Ambulatory Pediatric Assn., Inst. Medicine, Alpha Omega Alpha. Republican. Mem. Disciples of Christ. Avocations: fishing, sports, reading.

STRAIT, BRADLEY JUSTUS, electrical engineering educator; b. Canandaigua, N.Y., Mar. 17, 1932; s. Clifford Norman and Marjory (Pratt) S.; m. Nancy Elaine Brown, Sept. 14, 1957; children: Andrew W., Martha S. BS, Syracuse U., 1958, MS, 1960, PhD, 1963. Engr. Eastman Kodak Co., Rochester, N.Y., 1960-61; asst. prof. Syracuse (N.Y.) U., 1965-69, assoc. prof., 1969-74, prof. elec. engring., 1974—, chmn. dept. elec. engring., 1974-79, dean engring., 1981-84, 1989-92; pres. Northeast Consortium Engring. Edn., Syracuse, N.Y., 1975—; cons. Southeastern Ctr. Elec. Engring. Edn., Orlando, Fla., 1978—; dir. Syracuse Ctr. Advanced Tech., Syracuse U., 1983-91. Editor: Application of the Method of Moments to Electromagnetic Fields, 1980. Active Community Mus., Jamesville, N.Y., PTA, Jamesville-DeWitt, N.Y. Served with USN, 1951-55. Recipient Teaching Excellence award Gen. Electric Co., 1981, Data Processing Person of Yr. award CNY, 1986. Fellow IEEE (chmn. Syracuse sect. 1980, Centennial medal and cert.); mem. AAUP, Am. Soc. Engring. Edn. (Western Electric Fund award 1981). Republican. Methodist. Home: 4460 Carriage Cir Jamesville NY 13078-9511 Office: Syracuse U 2-212 Ctr Frst Syracuse NY 13244

STRAIT, EDWARD J., research physicist. Prin. scientist Stability Physics Group Gen. Atomics, San Diego. Recipient Excellence in Plasma Physics Rsch. award Am. Phys. Soc., 1994. Office: General Atomics PO Box 85608 San Diego CA 92186*

STRAIT, GEORGE, country music vocalist; b. Pearsall, Tex., 1952; m. Norma. Degree in Agr., S.W. Tex. State U. Albums include Easy Come, Easy Go, Right or Wrong, Strait from the Heart, Strait Country, Does Ft. Worth Ever Cross Your Mind, 1985 (Country Music Assn. Album of Yr. 1985), Pure Country, 1986, No. 7, Something Special, 1986, Ocean Front Property, 1987, If You Aint Lovin' (You Aint Livin'), 1988, Beyond the Blue Neon, 1989, Livin' It Up, 1990; Ten Strait Hits, 1991, Chill of An Early Fall, 1991, Greatest Hits Volume I, II, Lead On, other platinum albums; #1 country hits include Fool Hearted Memory, 1982, Amarillo By Morning, 1983, You Look So Good in Love, 1984, The Chair, 1986, Baby Blue, 1989, Beyond the Blue Moon, 1989, Baby's Gotten Good At Goodbye, 1989, Love Without End, Amen, 1990, I've Come to Expect It From You, 1990, Chill of An Early Fall, 1991, If I Know Me, 1991, The Big One, 1995; (movie) Pure Country, 1992. Served with U.S. Army, until 1975. Recipient Entertainer of Yr. award Country Music Assn., 1989, 90, Entertainer of Yr. award Acad. Country Music, 1990; named Male Vocalist of Yr. Country Music Assn., 1985, 86, Male Vocalist of Yr. Acad. Country Music, 1984, 85, 89, SRO Touring Artist of Yr., 1990, Top Country Vocalist Am. Music Awards, 1991. *

STRAIT, LORAINE HALL, lawyer; b. Utica, N.Y., Jan. 3, 1944; d. Wendell Rippon Strait and Ruth Aline (Russell) Lally. BA, Hobart & William Smith Colls., 1965; JD, George Washington U., 1968; LLM in Taxation, U. Miami, 1984. Bar: Fla., N.Y. Asst. atty. in charge Brownsville Legal Services Corp., Bklyn., 1969-71; staff atty. Legal Services of Greater Miami, Fla., 1971; prosecutor Dade County Domestic Relations Ct., Miami, 1972; police legal advisor City of Miami Polic Dept., 1973-74, asst. city atty., 1974-78; v.p. law asst. sec. Storer Communications, Inc., Miami, 1978-86, v.p., asst. gen. counsel, 1986-87, gen. counsel, 1987—. Co-author: On Fencing; co-editor, contbr. (mag.) The Chief's Counsel. Mem. Dade County Bar Assn. Home: 922 Obispo Ave Miami FL 33134-3646 Office: Storer Communications Inc 12000 Biscayne Blvd Miami FL 33181-2742

STRAIT, VIOLA EDWINA WASHINGTON, librarian; b. El Paso, Tex., Aug. 29, 1925; d. Leroy Wentworth and Viola Edwina (Wright) Washington; m. Freeman Adams, Mar. 6, 1943; 1 child, Norma Jean (Mrs. Louis Lee James); m. Clifford Moody, Jan. 8, 1950; 1 child, Viola Edwina III (Mrs. Paul M. Cunningham); m. Amos O. Strait, Dec. 9, 1972. Bus. cert., Tillotson Coll., 1946, BA, 1948; MS in Libr. Sci., U. So. Calif., 1954. Substitute tchr. El Paso Pub. Schs., 1948; sec., bookkeeper U.S.O.-YWCA, El Paso, 1948-50; libr. asst. Spl. Svcs. Libr., Ft. Bliss, Tex., 1950-53, libr., 1954-71; equal employment opportunity officer Ft. Bliss, 1971-72; dep. equal employment opportunity officer Long Beach (Calif.) Naval Shipyard, 1972-85; with Temporary Job Mart, Torrance, Calif., 1986-87; substitute tchr. Ysleta Ind. Sch. Dist., 1988-89; profl. libr. Eastwood Hts. Elem. Sch., 1989-90; sec. Shiloh Bapt. Ch., El Paso, 1991-92; br. mgr. El Paso Pub. Libr., 1992—. Sec. Sunday sch. Bapt. Ch., 1956-66, min. music, 1958-72, supr. young adult choir, 1966-72, pres. sr. choir, 1969-71; disc jockey Sta. KELP, El Paso, 1970-72; host radio show Sta. KTEP, U. Tex., El Paso, 1994—. Mem. Am. Libr. Assn., Border Region Libr. Assn. (chmn. scholarship com. 1970), Fed. Bus. Assn., Equal Opportunity Assn., Toastmasters Internat., NAACP, Alpha Kappa Alpha, Order Ea. Star. Democrat. Baptist. Avocations: playing the piano and organ, public speaking, reading, ocean view dining. Home: 1667 Nancy Lopez Ln El Paso TX 79936-5410 Office: El Paso Pub Libr Vets Park Br 5303 Salem Dr El Paso TX 79924-1801

STRAITON, ARCHIE WAUGH, electrical engineering educator; b. Arlington, Tex., Aug. 27, 1907; s. John and Jeannie (Waugh) S.; m. Esther McDonald, Dec. 28, 1932; children: Janelle (Mrs. Thomas Henry Holman), Carolyn (Mrs. John Erlinger). BSEE, U. Tex., 1929, MA, 1931, PhD, 1939. Engr. Bell Telephone Labs., N.Y.C., 1929-30; from instr. to assoc. prof. Tex. Coll. Arts and Industries, 1931-41, prof., 1941-43, head dept. engring., 1941-43; faculty U. Tex., Austin, 1943—; prof. U. Tex., 1948-63, dir. elec. engring. research lab., 1947-72, Ashbel Smith prof. elec. engring., 1963-89, Ashbel Smith prof. emeritus, 1989—, chmn. dept., 1966-71, acting v.p., grad. dean, 1972-73. Contbr. articles to profl. jours. Fellow IEEE (Thomas A. Edison medal 1990); mem. NAE, Sigma Xi, Tau Beta Pi, Eta Kappa Nu. Home: 4212 Far West Blvd Austin TX 78731-2804

STRAITS, BEVERLY JOAN, gynecologist; b. Aurora, Ill., Jan. 29, 1939; d. Ernest Joseph and Mildred Betty (Shobe) S.; children: Kell Donald, Jill Elizabeth. BA, Carleton Coll., 1961; MD, Northwestern U., 1965. Diplomate in gynecology and obstetrics. Intern Passavant Hosp., Chgo., 1965-66; residency Lutheran Hosp., Milw., 1966-69; pvt. practice Wheat Ridge, Colo.,

1969—. Fellow Am. Coll. Obstetrics & Gynecology. Avocations: skiing, camping. Office: 7855 W 38th Ave Wheat Ridge CO 80033-6109

STRAKA, LASZLO RICHARD, publishing consultant; b. Budapest, Hungary, June 22, 1934; came to U.S., 1950, naturalized, 1956; s. Richard J. and Elisabeth (Roeck) S.; m. Eva K. von Viczian, Jan. 20, 1962 (div. May 1981); children: Eva M., Monika E., Viktoria K. B.A. cum laude, NYU, 1959. Acct. Greatrex Ltd., N.Y.C., 1952-53; pres. Maxwell Macmillan Internat. Pub. Group, N.Y.C., 1991-92; with Pergamon Press, Inc., Elmsford, N.Y., 1954-90, v.p., 1964-68, exec. v.p., treas., 1968-74, pres., 1974-75, 80-88, chmn. bd., 1975-77, 88-90, vice chmn. bd., 1977-80, 88-89, also dir.; vice chmn. bd. Pergamon Books Ltd., Oxford, Eng., 1986-88; group v.p Macmillan Inc., N.Y.C., 1989-91; pub. cons., 1992—; treas. Brit. Book Centre, Inc., N.Y.C., 1956-67; pres. Pergamon Holding Corp., 1981-86; chmn. bd. Microforms Internat., Inc., 1971-87. d. dirs, sec. Szechenyi Istvan Soc., N.Y.C., 1967-80, 89-93. Mem. Phi Beta Kappa. Club: K.C. Home and Office: 80 Radnor Ave Croton On Hudson NY 10520-2610

STRALEM, PIERRE, retired stockbroker; b. Chappaqua, N.Y., Oct. 17, 1909; s. Casimir Ignace and Edithe (Neustadt) S.; m. Nancy Lou D.A. Coffyn, June 11, 1936. A.B., Princeton, 1932. With Hallgarten & Co. (mems. N.Y. Stock Exchange), 1933—, partner, 1941-74; v.p., dir. Moseley Hallgarten Estabrook & Weeden Inc., 1974-79. Bd. dirs. George Jr. Republic. Mem. Court Club (Princeton, N.J.), Princeton Club (N.Y.C.). Home: 651 Bering Dr Houston TX 77057

STRALING, PHILLIP FRANCIS, bishop; b. San Bernardino, Calif., Apr. 25, 1933; s. Sylvester J. and Florence E. (Robinson) S. BA, U. San Diego, 1963; MS in Child and Family Counseling, San Diego State U., 1971. Ordained priest Roman Catholic Ch., 1959, consecrated bishop, 1978. Mem. faculty St. John Acad., El Cajon, Calif., 1959-60, St. Therese Acad., San Diego, 1960-63; chaplain Newman Club, San Diego State U., 1960-72; mem. faculty St. Francis Sem., San Diego, 1972-76; pastor Holy Rosary Parish, San Bernardino, 1976-78; bishop Diocese of San Bernardino, 1978-95; pub. Inland Cath. newspaper, 1979—; bishop Diocese of Reno, 1995—; bd. dirs. Calif. Assn. Cath. Campus Mins., 1960s; exec. sec. Diocesan Synod II, 1972-76; Episcopal vicar San Bernardino Deanery, 1976-78. Office: PO Box 1211 Reno NV 89504-1211

STRAM, HANK LOUIS, former professional football coach, television and radio commentator; b. Chgo., Jan. 3, 1923; s. Henry L. and Nellie (Boots) S.; m. Phyllis Marie Pesha, Nov. 27, 1953; children: Henry Raymond, Dale Alan, Stuart Madison, Julia Anne, Gary Baxter, Mary Nell. Grad., Purdue U., 1948. Offensive football coach, head baseball coach Purdue U., 1948-55; offensive football coach So. Meth. U., 1956, Notre Dame U., 1958, U. Miami, 1959; head football coach Kansas City Chiefs, 1960-74, New Orleans Saints, 1976-77; color commentator CBS Sports, N.Y.C., 1978—, CBS Radio Football Broadcasts, 1978-85. Served with USAAF, 1943-46. Recipient Big 10 medal for athletes and scholarship Big 10 Conf., 1948; named Profl. Football Coach of Year Knute Rockne Club Am. and Ft. Lauderdale Touchdown Club, 1962. Office: care CBS Sports 51 W 52nd St New York NY 10019-6165*

STRANAHAN, ROBERT PAUL, JR., lawyer; b. Louisville, Oct. 29, 1929; s. Robert Paul and Anna May (Payne) S.; m. Louise Perry, May 12, 1956; children: Susan Dial, Robert Paul, Carol Payne. A.B., Princeton U., 1951; J.D., Harvard U., 1954. Bar: D.C. 1954, Md. 1964. Assoc. Wilmer & Broun, Washington, 1957-62; ptnr. Wilmer, Cutler & Pickering, Washington, 1963-94, of counsel, 1995—; professorial lectr. Nat. Law Ctr., George Washington U., 1969-72. Served to 1st lt. USMCR, 1954-57. Mem. ABA, Fed. Bar Assn., D.C. Bar Assn. Clubs: Metropolitan (Washington), Gridiron (Washington); Chevy Chase (Md.). Home: 5316 Cardinal Ct Bethesda MD 20816-2908 also: Figure Eight Island 286 Beach Rd N Wilmington NC 28405 Office: Wilmer Cutler & Pickering 2445 M St NW Washington DC 20037-1435

STRAND, CURT ROBERT, hotel executive; b. Vienna, Austria, Nov. 13, 1920; naturalized Am. citizen, 1943; m. Fleur Lillian Emanuel, June 14, 1946; 1 child, Karen. B.S., Cornell U., 1943. Supt. service Plaza, N.Y.C. 1947-49; asst. to v.p. Hilton Hotels Corp., 1949-53; v.p. Hilton Internat. Co., N.Y.C., 1953-64, exec. v.p., 1964-67, pres., chief exec. officer, 1967-86; chmn. Hilton Internat. Co., 1986-87; sr. v.p., dir. Trans World Air Lines, Inc.; lectr. Cornell U. Sch. Hotel Adminstrn., Ecole Superieure de Scis. Econs., Paris, NYU, Houston U.; sr. cons. Am. Express; mem. adv. panel com. Am. Hotel and Motel Assn. Mem. coun. Cornell U.; adv. bd. Aspen Found.; bd. govs. Snowmass Resort Assn., also pres.; fellow Aspen Inst. Mem. Cornell Soc. Hotelmen (Hotelier of Yr. 1986). Home: 340 E 64th St New York NY 10021 Office: Am Express Tower World Fin Ctr New York NY 10285

STRAND, DAVID AXEL, university executive; b. Evanston, Ill., Dec. 30, 1935; s. Axel C. and Margaret E. (Burham) S.; m. Gertrude Lane Nadler; children—Douglas Harold, Sarah Lynn. B.A., Carroll Coll., 1958; M.S., Ind. U., 1959, Ed.D., 1967. Dean S.E. Mo. State U., Cape Girardeau, 1961-65, 70-76, v.p., 1976-78; exec. officer Ill. State U., Normal, 1978-80, v.p.-bus. and fin., 1980-83, v.p., provost, 1983-94; v.p. bus. and fin., 1994—; cons. Southeastern Christian Coll., Winchester, Ky., 1967-68, Danville Area Community Coll., Ill., 1982-83, Met. State Univ., St. Paul, 1990. Author: Articulation Agreement, 1973; (with others) Out of State Students in Public Higher Education, 1967, To Secure the Blessings of Liberty, 1986, Managing the Academic Enterprise: Case Studies for Deans and Provosts, 1988, Defining the Missions of AASCU Institutions, 1990; contbr. articles to profl. jours. Elder Presbyn. Ch., Mo., Ill., 1968; pres. bd. dirs. United Way, Cape Girardeau, 1971; pres. bd. trustees Cape Girardeau Pub. Library, 1975; state crusade chmn. Am. Cancer Soc., Mo., 1975; dist. chmn. Boy Scouts Am., S.E. Mo., 1976. Mem. N. Cen. Assn. Acad. Deans (pres. 1973-74, 86-87), Am. Assn. Higher Edn., Phi Delta Kappa, Alpha Phi Omega. Lodge: Lions (bd. dirs. 1972-75). Avocation: photography. Office: Ill State U Campus Box 1100 Campus Box 1100 Hovey Hall Rm 302 Normal IL 61790-1100

STRAND, MARK, poet; b. Summerside, P.E.I., Can., Apr. 11, 1934; came to U.S., 1938; s. Robert Joseph and Sonia (Apter) S.; m. Antonia Ratensky, Sept. 14, 1961 (div. June 1973); 1 dau., Jessica; m. Julia Rumsey Garretson, Mar. 15, 1976; 1 son, Thomas Summerfield. BA, Antioch Coll., 1957; BFA, Yale, 1959; MA, U. Iowa, 1962. Instr. English U. Iowa, 1962-65; asst. prof. Mt. Holyoke Coll., 1967; assoc. prof. Bklyn. Coll., 1971-72; Bain-Swiggett lectr. Princeton, 1973; Hurst prof. poetry Brandeis U., 1974-75; prof. U. Utah, 1981-93; U.S. poet laureate Library of Congress, Washington, 1990-91; prof. Johns Hopkins U., 1994—; Fulbright lectr. U. Brazil, Rio de Janeiro, 1965-66; adj. assoc. prof. Columbia U., 1969-72; vis. prof. U. Wash., 1968, 70, U. Va., 1977, Wesleyan U., 1979, Harvard U., 1980; vis. lectr. Yale, 1969-70, U. Va., 1976, Calif. State U., Fresno, 1977, U. Calif., Irvine, 1979. Author: Sleeping with One Eye Open, 1964, Reasons for Moving, 1968, Darker, 1970, The Story of Our Lives, 1973 (Edgar Allan Poe award Acad. Am. Poets 1974), The Sargeantville Notebook, 1974, The Monument, 1978, Elegy for My Father, 1978, The Late Hour, 1978, Selected Poems, 1980, The Planet of Lost Things, 1982, The Night Book, 1983, Mr. and Mrs. Baby and Other Stories, 1985, Rembrandt Takes a Walk, 1986, William Bailey, 1987, The Continuous Life, 1990, Dark Harbor, 1993, Hopper, 1994; editor: The Contemporary American Poets, 1968, New Poetry of Mexico, 1970, 18 Poems from Quechua, 1971, The Owl's Insomnia, 1973, The Best American Poetry 1991, The Golden Ecco Anthology, 1994; co-editor: Another Republic: Seventeen European and South American Writers, 1976, The Art of the Real, 1983, Traveling in the Family, 1987; translator: Souvenir of the Ancient World, 1976. Recipient award Am. Acad. and Inst. Arts and Letters, 1975, Utah Gov.'s award in arts, 1992, Bobbitt Nat. prize for poetry, 1992, Bollingen prize for poetry Yale Univ. Libr., 1993; Fulbright scholar in Italy, 1960-61; Ingram Merrill Found. grantee, 1966; Nat. Endowment for Arts grantee, 1967-68, 78-79, 86-87; Rockefeller Found. grantee, 1968-69; Guggenheim fellow, 1975-76; Acad. Am. Poets fellow, 1979; MacArthur Found. fellow, 1987. Fellow Acad. Am. Poets; mem. Am. Acad. and Inst. Arts and Letters. Office: c/o Harry Ford Knopf Publishers Inc 201 E 50th St New York NY 10022*

STRAND, RAY WALTER, general contractor; b. Seattle, July 23, 1924; s. Arvid O. and Antonia (Sjogren) S.; m. Luella Oak, Oct. 1948 (div. 1959); m. Ruby Good, Jan. 8, 1960; children: Timothy Ray, Donald Brent. Student,

U. Wash., 1945-48. Ptnr. Strand & Sons, Seattle, 1939-54; CEO, pres. Strand Inc., Seattle and Bellevue, Wash., 1954-92; chmn., CEO Strand Hunt Constrn., Kirkland, Wash., 1992—. Staff sgt. U.S. Army Air Corps, 1943-45. Mem. Assn. Gen. Contractors, Wash. Athletic Club, Bellevue Athletic Club, Lakes Club, Broadmoor Golf Club. Republican. Congregational. Avocations: golf, fishing, hunting. Home: 5800 Princeton Ave NE Seattle WA 98105-2134

STRAND, ROGER GORDON, federal judge; b. Peekskill, N.Y., Apr. 28, 1934; s. Ernest Gordon Strand and Lisabeth Laurine (Phin) Steinmetz; m. Joan Williams, Nov. 25, 1961. AB, Hamilton Coll., 1955; LLB, Cornell U., 1961; grad., Nat. Coll. State Trial Judges, 1968. Bar: Ariz. 1961, U.S. Dist. Ct. Ariz. 1961, U.S. Supreme Ct. 1980. Assoc. Fennemore, Craig, Allen & McClennen, Phoenix, 1961-67; judge Ariz. Superior Ct., Phoenix, 1967-85, U.S. Dist. Ct. Ariz., Phoenix, 1985—; assoc. presiding judge Ariz. Superior Ct., 1971-85; lectr. Nat. Jud. Coll., Reno, 1978-87. Past pres. cen. Ariz. chpt. Arthritis Found. Lt. USN, 1955-61. Mem. ABA, Ariz. Bar Assn., Maricopa County Bar Assn., Nat. Conf. Fed. Trial Judges, Phi Delta Phi, Aircraft Owners and Pilots Assn. Lodge: Rotary. Avocations: computer applications, golf, fishing. Home: 5825 N 3rd Ave Phoenix AZ 85013-1537 Office: US Dist Ct Courthouse and Fed Bldg 230 N 1st Ave Ste 3013 Phoenix AZ 85025-0002

STRANDBERG, JOHN DAVID, comparative pathologist; b. Alexandria, Minn., Aug. 28, 1939; s. Winfred Carl and Evelyn Joyce (Studlien) S. AB, Johns Hopkins U., 1960; DVM, Cornell U., 1964, PhD, 1968. Diplomate Am. Coll. Vet. Pathologists. USPHS-NIH postdoctoral fellow Cornell U., Ithaca, N.Y., 1964-67; fellow, resident in pathology Sch. Medicine, Johns Hopkins U., Balt., 1966-67; instr. dept. pathology/divsn. animal medicine Sch. Medicine Johns Hopkins U., Balt., 1967-68, asst. prof. pathology/divsn. lab. animal medicine, 1968-75, dir. comparative pathology tng. program Sch. Medicine, 1973—, asst. prof. pathobiology Sch. Hygiene and Pub. Health, 1974-77, acting dir. divsn. lab. animal medicine Sch. Medicine, 1974-76, assoc. prof. pathology and comparative medicine, 1975—, assoc. prof. pathobiology Sch. Hygiene and Pub. Health, 1977—, dir. divsn. comparative medicine Sch. Medicine, 1983—; vis. scientist Marine Biol. Lab., Woods Hole, Mass., 1993; cons., panelist, presenter in field; mem. peer rev. group Nat. Zool. Park, 1987, 88, 90; chmn. Md. Coun. on Sci. Use of Animals, 1989—; mem. adv. com. Nat. Ctr. for Rsch. Resources NIH, 1991—; mem. adv. bd. Nat. Aquarium in Balt., 1986—, Ctr. for Alternatives to Animal Testing, Balt., 1985—. Mem. editorial rev. bd. The Biomedical Investigator's Handbook, 1987; contbr. articles to profl. publs. V.p. Balt. Zool. Soc., 1978-82, chmn. med. com., 1973-86. Mem. AAAS, AMVA, Am. Coll. Vet. Pathologists (com. on tng. programs 1976-82), U.S. and Can. Acad. Pathology, Am. Assn. Pathologists, Md. State Vet. Med. Assn. (com. on liaison to humane orgns. 1986-88, com. on registration of vet. technicians 1977—), Am. Soc. Microbiology, Electron Microscopy Soc. Am., Am. Zool. Soc., Wildlife Disease Assn., Am. Soc. Lab. Animal Practitioners, Phi Beta Kappa, Phi Kappa Phi, Phi Zeta.

STRANDBERG, MALCOM WOODROW PERSHING, physicist; b. Box Elder, Mont., Mar. 9, 1919; s. Malcom and Ingeborg (Riestad) S.; m. Harriet Elisabeth Bennett, Aug. 2, 1947 (dec.); children—Josiah R.W., Susan Abby, Elisabeth G. Malcom B. S.B., Harvard Coll., 1941; Ph.D., M.I.T., 1948. Research asso. M.I.T., Cambridge, 1941-48; asst. prof. physics M.I.T., 1948-53, asso. prof., 1953-60, prof., 1960—. Author: Microwave Spectroscopy, 1954. Fellow Am. Phys. Soc., Am. Acad. Arts and Scis., IEEE, AAAS; mem. Am. Assn. Physics Tchrs. Episcopalian. Patentee in field. Home: 82 Larchwood Dr Cambridge MA 02138-4639 Office: Mass Inst Tech 26-353 Cambridge MA 02139

STRANDJORD, MARY JEANNINE, telecommunications executive; b. Kansas City, Mo., Dec. 21, 1945; d. Vincent Stanley and Clara Lucille (Aylward) Kerwin; m. David Christian Strandjord, June 24, 1978; 1 child, Katie Marie. BSBA, Kans. U., 1968; postgrad., U. Mo., Kansas City, 1976. CPA, Mo. Mem. audit staff Ernst & Whinney, Kansas City, 1968-71; with Kansas City Power & Light, 1971-81, dir., asst. controller, 1979-81; dir., asst. controler Macy's Midwest, 1981-82, v.p. acctg., budget and expense, 1982-85; v.p. fin. and ops. Amerisource subs. United Telecom, Westwood, Kans., 1986; v.p., controller United Telecommunications, Inc., Westwood, 1986—. Treas. St. Health Ctr. Found., Kansas City, 1986—; mem. exec. com., acct. adv. coun. Kans. U., Lawrence, 1989—. Named Woman of Yr., YMCA, 1987. Mem. AICPA, Fin. Exec. Inst., Blue Hills Country Club. Roman Catholic. Avocations: reading, walking, interior design, skiing. Home: 908 W 121st Kansas City MO 64145-1013

STRANDJORD, PAUL EDPHIL, physician, educator; b. Mpls., Apr. 5, 1931; s. Edphil Nels and RuBelle Pearl (Corneliusen) S.; m. Margaret Thomas, June 27, 1953; children: Thomas Paul, Scott Nels. BA, U. Minn., 1951, MA, 1952; MD, Stanford U., 1959. Intern U. Minn., Mpls., 1959-60; resident U. Minn., 1960-63, dir. div. chemistry, dept. lab. medicine, 1963-69, asso. dir. clin. labs. dept. lab. medicine, 1967-69; asso. prof. lab. medicine U. Wash., 1969, prof., chmn. dept. lab. medicine, 1969—; prof. emeritus, 1994—; cons. VA Hosps. Author: (with E.S. Benson) Multiple Laboratory Screening, 1969, (with G. Schmer) Coagulation-Current Research and Clinical Applications, 1973. Pres. U. Wash. Physicians. With USN, 1952-55. Recipient Borden award Stanford U., 1959, Watson award U. Minn., 1962, Gerald T. Evans award Acad. Clin. Lab. Physicians and Scientists, 1976. Fellow Am. Soc. Clin. Pathologists; mem. AAAS, Acad. Clin. Lab. Physicians and Scientists (pres.), Am. Assn. Clin. Chemistry, Am. Chem. Soc., Am. Fedn. Clin. Research, Internat. Acad. Pathology, Assn. Pathology Chmn. Home: 9410 Lake Washington Blvd NE Bellevue WA 98004-5409 Office: U Wash Dept Lab Medicine SB-10 Seattle WA 98195

STRANDNESS, DONALD EUGENE, JR., surgeon; b. Bowman, N.D., Sept. 22, 1928; s. Donald Eugene and Merinda Clarine (Peterson) S.; m. Edith Victoria Olund, June 30, 1957; children: Erik, Tracy, Jill, Sandra. B.A., Pacific Luth. U., 1950; M.D., U. Wash., 1954. Rotating intern Phila. Gen. Hosp., 1954-55; resident U. Wash. Sch. Medicine Integrated Program, 1955-57, 59-62; research fellow Nat. Heart Inst., 1959-60; clin. investigator VA Hosp., Seattle, 1962-65; NIH Career Devel. awardee VA Hosp., 1965-68; pvt. practice medicine specializing in surgery Seattle, 1962—; instr. surgery Sch. Medicine, U. Wash., Seattle, 1962-63, asst. prof., 1963-66, assoc. prof., 1966-70, prof., 1970—, head peripheral vascular div., 1971; mem. VA Merit Rev. Com. in Surgery, 1984; mem. cardiology com. Nat. Heart, Lung Blood Inst., 1985. Author: Duplex Scanning in Vascular Disorders, 1990; co-author: Hemodynamics for Surgery, 1975, Ultrasonic Techniques in Angiology, 1975, Selected Topics in Venous Disorders, 1981; editor: Collateral Circulation in Clinical Surgery, 1960, Peripheral Arterial Disease— A Physiologic Approach, 1969; co-editor: Vascular Diseases, 1987,Duplex Doppler Ultrasound, 1989; asssoc. editor Jour. Vascular surgery, 1979; mem. editorial adv. bd. Vascular Diagnosis and Therapy, 1980; mem. editorial bd. Jour. Vascular Surgery, 1983, Jour. Clin. Physiology, 1981, VASA, 1983, Jour. Vascular Medicine and Biology, 1989, Stroke, 1985; sect. editor Echocardiography, 1985; adv. editor Jour. Cardiovascular Surgery, 1984, Circulation, 1991. Served with USAF, 1957-59. Recipient Alumnus award Pacific Luth. U., 1980, Cid Dos Santos prize, 1980, Merit award Nat. Heart, Lung and Blood Inst., 1987, Albion O. Bernstein award, 1955. Fellow ACS; mem. Internat. Soc. Thrombosis and Haemostasis, Am. Surg. Assn., North Pacific Surg. Assn., Soc. for Vascular Surgery (pres. 1988), Western Vascular Soc. (pres. 1988), Soc. Univ. Surgeons, Internat. Cardiovascular Soc., Am. Inst. Ultrasound in Medicine (bd. govs. 1990-92), Will C. Sealy Surg. Soc. (hon.), So. Assn. for Vascular Surgery (hon.), Am. Venous Forum (founding). Home: 105 Cedar Crest Ln Bellevue WA 98004-6725 Office: U Wash Sch Medicine 1959 NE Pacific St Seattle WA 98195-0001

STRANDQUIST, JOHN HERBERT, association executive; b. Menominee, Mich., June 29, 1929; s. John H. and Mary A. (Van Calligan) S.; m. Mary Gabrielle Thomas, Nov. 22, 1952; children: John H. III, Mark J., Michael T., Julie P. Headland, Bridget M. Mills, Blaise R., Skye M. Kirby, Peter S. BA, George Washington U., 1968. Cert. assn. exec. Am. Soc. Assn. Execs.; sr. profl. in human resources, Soc. Human Resource Mgmt. Enlisted USMC, 1948, advanced through ranks to lt. col., 1967, retired, 1972; asst. v.p. George Washington U., Washington, 1973-77; sr. v.p. Soc. for Human Resource Mgmt., Alexandria, Va., 1977-90; pres. Am. Assn. of Motor Vehicle Adminstrs., Arlington, Va., 1990—, also bd. dirs.; bd. dirs. IRP, Inc., Arlington. Mem. Rotary (Paul Harris fellow 1992), Belle Haven Country Club. Avocations: golf, sailing. Office: Am Assn Motor Vehicle Admns Ste 1100 4200 Wilson Blvd Arlington VA 22203

STRANG, CHARLES DANIEL, marine engine manufacturing company executive; b. Bklyn., Apr. 12, 1921; s. Charles Daniel and Anna Lincoln (Endner) S. B.M.E., Poly. Inst. Bklyn., 1943. Mem. mech. engring. staff MIT, 1947-51; v.p. engring., exec. v.p. Kiekhaefer Corp. div. Brunswick Corp., Fond du Lac, Wis., 1951-64; v.p. marine engring. Outboard Marine Corp., Waukegan, Ill., 1966-68; exec. v.p. Outboard Marine Corp., 1968-74, pres., gen. mgr., 1974-80, pres., CEO, 1980-82, chmn. bd., CEO, 1982-90, chmn., 1990-93; bd. dirs., chmn. mgmt. rev. com. Outboard Marine Corp., Waukegan, 1993—. Patentee engine design and marine propulsion equipment; contbr. research papers to sci. publs. Bd. dirs. Poly. Inst. N.Y. Served with USAAF, 1944-47. Mem. Am. Power Boat Assn. (past pres.), Soc. Automotive Engrs., Union Internat. Motorboating (continental v.p. N.Am.), Sigma Xi. Club: Waukegan Yacht. Home: 25679 W Florence Ave Antioch IL 60002-8734

STRANG, JAMES DENNIS, editor; b. Ashtabula, Ohio, June 23, 1945; s. Delbert Devoe and Mildred Edith (Green) S.; m. Margaret Florence Littell, Aug. 25, 1974; children: Megan Lisbeth, Amy Colleen, Benjamin Jefferson. BS in Journalism, Kent State U., 1969. Cert. firearms instr. Reporter The Star-Beacon, Ashtabula, Ohio, 1966, The Record-Courier, Kent, Ohio, 1966-69, The Cleve. Press, 1969-71; cons. Tom Rall & Assocs., Washington, 1971-72; reporter, editor The Plain Dealer, Cleve., 1973—; instr. journalism Lorain County C.C., Elyria, Ohio, 1973-74. Recipient Nat. Comdrs. award DAV, 1980, Best Editorial award AP Soc. Ohio, 1988. Mem. Nat. Conf. Editorial Writers, Soc. Profl. Journalists, Nat. Rifle Assn. (life). Unitarian-Universalist. Avocation: shooting sports. Office: The Plain Dealer 1801 Superior Ave E Cleveland OH 44114-2107

STRANG, MARIAN BOUNDY, librarian; b. Gibson City, Ill., May 5, 1918; d. Ralph Edward and Edna Blackburn (Washburn) Boundy; m. Tom H. Strang, Sept. 27, 1943; children—Terry H., Bruce B., David R. B.A. U. Wis., 1940, M.L.S., 1941. Libr. Richland Center, Wis., 1941-42; children's libr. Dearborn (Mich.) Pub. Libr., 1942-43; asst. libr. Rapides Parish Libr., Alexandria, La., 1943-45, Beloit (Wis.) Pub. Libr., 1945-46, Fort Knox (Ky.) Libr., 1952-54; libr. Sukiran Libr., Okinawa, 1962-64; chief libr. Fort Leonard Wood, Mo., 1964-70; med. libr. U.S. Gen. World Army Hosp., Fort Leonard Wood, 1970-88, Med. Libr. Med. Ctr., Independence, Mo., 1989—, VA Med. Ctr. Med. Libr., Kansas City, Mo., 1989—, Independence (Mo.) Regional Health Ctr., 1990—. Mem. ALA, Mo. Library Assn., Fed. Librarian's Assn., Med. Library Assn., AAUN, Bus. and Profl. Women, Delta Zeta. Home: 17711B E 29th St Independence MO 64057-2669

STRANG, RUTH HANCOCK, pediatric educator, pediatric cardiologist, priest; b. Bridgeport, Conn., Mar. 11, 1923; d. Robert Hallock Wright and Ruth (Hancock) S. BA, Wellesley Coll., 1944, postgrad., 1944-45; MD, N.Y. Med. Coll., 1949; MDiv, Seabury Western Theol. Sem., 1993. Diplomate Am. Bd. Pediat.; ordained deacon Episc. Ch., 1993, priest, 1994. Intern Flower and Fifth Ave. Hosp., N.Y.C., 1949-50, resident in pediatrics, 1950-52; mem. faculty N.Y. Med. Coll., N.Y.C., 1952-57; fellow cardiology Babies Hosp., N.Y.C., 1956-57, Harriet Lane Cardiac Clinic, Johns Hopkins Hosp., Balt., 1957-59, Children's Hosp., Boston, 1959-62; mem. faculty U. Mich., Univ. Hosp., Ann Arbor, 1962-89, prof. pediatrics, 1970-89, prof. emeritus, 1989—; priest-in-charge St. Johns Episcopal Ch., Howell, Mich., 1994—; dir. pediatrics Wayne County Gen. Hosp., Westland, Mich, 1965-85; mem. staff U. Mich. Hosps.; mem. med. adv. com. Wayne County chpt. Nat. Cystic Fibrosis Rsch. Found., 1966-80, chmn. med. adv. com. nat. found., Detroit, 1971-78; cons. cardiology Plymouth (Mich.) State Home and Tng. Sch., 1970-81. Author: Clinical Aspects of Operable Heart Disease, 1968; contbr. numerous articles to profl. jours. Mem. citizen's adv. coun. to Juvenile Ct., Ann Arbor, 1968-76; mem. med. adv. bd. Ann Arbor Continuing Edn. Dept., 1968-77; mem. Diocesan Com. for World Relief, Detroit, 1970-72, Am. Heart Assn. Mich. (v.p. 1989, pres. 1991); trustee Episcopal Med. Chaplaincy, Ann Arbor, 1971—; mem. bishop's com. St. Aidan's Episc. Ch., 1966-69, sec., 1966-68, vestry, 1973-76, 78-80, 84-86, 90-91, sr. warden, 1975, 76, 78, 80, 86, 90; del. Episc. Diocesan Conv., 1980, 91; bd. dirs. Livingston Cmty. Hospice, 1995—. Mem. AMA, Am. Acad. Pediatrics, Am. Coll. Cardiology, Mich. Med. Soc., Washtenaw County Med. Soc., N.Y. Acad. Medicine, Am. Heart Assn., Women's Rsch. Club (membership sec. 1966-67), Ambulatory Pediatric Assn., Am. Assn. Child Care in Hosps., Am. Assn. Med. Colls., Am. Faculties of Pediatric Nurse Assn./Practitioners Programs (pres. 1978-81, exec. com. 1981-84), Episc. Clergy Assn. Mich., Northside Assn. Ministries (pres. 1975, 76, 79-80). Home: 4500 E Huron River Dr Ann Arbor MI 48105-9335

STRANG, SANDRA LEE, airline official; b. Greensboro, N.C., Apr. 22, 1936; d. Charles Edward and Lobelia Mae (Squires) S.; BA in English, U. N.C., 1960; MBA, U. Dallas, 1970. With American Airlines, Inc., 1960—, mgr. career devel. for women, N.Y.C., 1972-73, dir. selection and tng., 1974-75, sr. dir. selection, tng. and affirmative action, 1975-79, sr. dir. compensation and benefits, Dallas/Ft. Worth, Tex., 1979-84, dir. passenger sales tng. and devel., 1984—; regional sales mgr. Rocky Mountain Region, Denver, 1985—; pres. The SLS Group, Inc., (DBAs) Sales Leadership Seminars, Inc., Sr. Leadership Svcs., Inc., Svc. Leadership Seminars, Inc., Speakers, Lectrs., and Seminars, Inc, 1988—. AARP. Mem. Am. Mgmt. Assn., Assn. Advancement of Women into Mgmt., Am. Soc. Tng. and Devel., Am. Compensation Assn., Internat. Platform Assn. Home: 3493 E Euclid Ave Littleton CO 80121-3663

STRANG, STEPHEN EDWARD, magazine editor, publisher; b. Springfield, Mo., Jan. 31, 1951; s. A. Edward and Amy Alice (Farley) S.; m. Joy Darlene Ferrell, Aug. 19, 1972; children: Cameron Edward, Chandler Stephen. BS in Journalism, U. Fla., Gainesville, 1973; LittD (hon.), Lee Coll., 1995. Reporter Orlando Sentinel Star, Fla., 1973-76; editor Charisma mag. Calvary Assembly, Winter Park, Fla., 1976-81; pres. Strang Comm. Co., Lake Mary, Fla., 1981—; owner Creation House Books, 1986, Christian Retailing mag., 1986. Founding editor Charisma mag., 1975, Ministries Today mag., 1983; founding pub. CharismaLife Learning Resources, 1990, New Man mag., 1994. Mem. steering com. N.Am. Renewal Svcs. Com., 1985—; trustee Internat. Charismatic Bible Ministries, 1986—; pres. Christian Life Missions, 1991—, Christian Writer's Inst., 1991—. Recipient First Place award Nat. Writing Championship, William Randolph Hearst Found., 1973, Alumnus of Distinction award U. Fla. Coll. of Journalism and Comm., 1994, Industry of Yr. award for Seminole County, Fla., Econ. Devel. Commn. of Mid-Fla., 1994. Mem. Internat. Pentecostal Press Assn., Christian Booksellers Assn., Fla. Mag. Assn. (pres. 1979-80), Evang. Christian Pubs. Assn., Evang. Press Assn. Republican. Mem. Assemblies of God. Avocations: racquetball, golf. Office: Strang Comm Co 600 Rinehart Rd Lake Mary FL 32746-4868

STRANG, WILLIAM GILBERT, mathematician, educator; b. Chgo., Nov. 27, 1934; s. William Dollin and Mary Catherine (Finlay) S.; m. Jillian Mary Shannon, July 26, 1958; children—David, John Robert. S.B., MIT, 1955; B.A. (Rhodes scholar), Oxford (Eng.) U., 1957; Ph.D. (NSF fellow), UCLA, 1959. Asst. prof. mathematics MIT, 1959-63, assoc. prof., 1963-66, prof., 1966—; pres. Wellesley-Cambridge Press; hon. prof. Xian Jiaotong U., People's Republic of China, 1980. Author: An Analysis of the Finite Element Method, 1973, Linear Algebra and Its Applications, 1976, Introduction to Applied Mathematics, 1986, Calculus, 1990, Introduction to Linear Algebra, 1993, Wavelets and Filter Banks, 1995. Recipient Chauvenet prize Math. Assn. Am., 1977; Sloan fellow, 1966-67; Fairchild scholar, 1981. Home: 7 Southgate Rd Wellesley MA 02181-6606 Office: MIT Rm 2-240 Cambridge MA 02139

STRANGE, CURTIS NORTHROP, professional golfer; b. Norfolk, Va., Jan. 30, 1955; s. Thomas Wright Strange Jr. and Nancy (Ball) Neal; m. Sarah Jones; children: Thomas Wright III, David Clark. Student, Wake Forest U., 1974-76. Winner of Southeastern Amateur, 1973, NCAA, 1974, Western Amateur, 1974, Eastern Amateur, 1975, 76, North and South Amateur, 1975, 76, Va. State Amateur, 1976, World Amateur Cup, 1975, Walker Cup, 1974, Pensacola Open, 1979, Michelob-Houston Open, Mfrs. Hanover Westchester Classic, 1980, Panama Open, 1980, Sammy Davis Jr.- Greater Hartford Open, 1983, LaJet Classic, 1984, Honda Classic, Panasonic-Las Vegas Invitational, Canadian Open, 1985, Houston Open, 1986, Canadian Open, Fed. Express-St. Jude Classic, NEC World Series of Golf, 1987, Ind. Ins. Agent Open, Meml. Tournament, U.S. Open, 1988, 89, Nabisco Championships, 1988. Named to Collegiate Golf Hall of Fame, 1987, Wake Forest Hall of Fame, 1988, PGA Player-of-the-Yr., 1988; recipient Golf Writers Player-of-the-Yr. award, 1985, 87, 88, ABC Cup Japan, 1986, PGA Leading Money Winner 1985, 87-88. Avocation: hunting, fishing. Office: care IMG 1 Erieview Plz Ste 1300 Cleveland OH 44114-1715*

STRANGE, DONALD ERNEST, health care company executive; b. Ann Arbor, Mich., Aug. 13, 1944; s. Carl Britton and Donna Ernestine (Tenney) S.; m. Lyn Marie Purdy, Aug. 3, 1968; children: Laurel Lyn, Chadwick Donald. BA, Mich. State U., 1966, MBA, 1968. Asst. dir. Holland (Mich.) City Hosp., 1968-72, assoc. dir. 1972-74; exec. dir. Bascom Palmer Eye Inst./Anne Bates Leach Eye Hosp., U. Miami, Fla., 1974-77; v.p. strategic planning and rsch. Hosp. Corp. Am., Nashville, 1977-80; group v.p. Hosp. Corp. Am., Boston, 1980-82, regional v.p., 1982-87; chmn., chief exec. officer HCA Healthcare Can., 1985-87; exec. v.p. Avon Products, Inc., 1987-89; chmn. Sigecom, Ltd., 1989—, U.S. HomeCare Corp., 1990-91; exec. v.p., COO, dir. EPIC Healthcare Group, Dallas, 1991-93; chmn., CEO TransCare Corp., 1993—; bd. dirs. Curaflex, Genica Pharms. Corp., KBL Healthcare Acquisitions Corp. Adv. Bd., NEPHROGNIX, Inc., Access Radiology, Inc. Author: Hospital Corporate Planning, 1981. Mem. Am. Coll. Healthcare Execs., Fedn. Am. Hosps./Washington Bus. Group on Health, Harvard Club. Republican. Episcopalian. Office: TransCare Corp 3232 McKinney Ave Ste 1160 Dallas TX 75204

STRANGE, J. LELAND, computer company executive; b. Dallas, May 15, 1941; s. James Alton and Ola (Johnson) S.; m. Jane Hendrix Strange, Aug. 28, 1965; children—Mark, Cary, Ryan. BS Indsl. Mgmt., Ga. Tech. U., 1965, MBA, Ga. State U., 1968. Gen. mgr. Colonial Film & Equipment Co., Atlanta, 1967-69; pres. Cheese Villa Stores, Inc., 1969-74, Quadram Corp., 1981-83, Intelligent Systems Corp., 1983—(all Atlanta); prof. mktg. Mercer U., 1976-83; bd. dirs. Healthdyne Corp., Atlanta, Intelligent Systems Corp., Wave Air Corp, IQ Software Corp. Republican. Baptist. Office: Intelligent Systems Master L P 4355 Shackleford Rd Norcross GA 30093-2931

STRANGWAY, DAVID WILLIAM, university president; b. Can., June 7, 1934. BA in Physics and Geology, U. Toronto, 1956, MA in Physics, 1958, PhD, 1960; DLittS (hon.), Victoria U., U. Toronto, 1986; DSc (hon.), Meml. U. Nfld., 1986, McGill U., Montreal, Que., Can., 1989, Ritsumeikan U., Japan, 1990; D.Ag.Sc. (hon.), Tokyo U. Agr., 1991; DSc (hon.), U. Toronto, 1994. Sr. geophysicist Dominion Gulf Co. Ltd., Toronto, 1956; chief geophysicist Ventures Ltd., 1956-57, sr. geophysicist, summer 1958; research geophysicist Kennecott Copper Corp., Denver, 1960-61; asst. prof. geology U. Colo., Boulder, 1961-64; asst. prof. geophysics MIT, Cambridge, Mass., 1965-68; mem. faculty U. Toronto, 1968-85, prof. physics, 1971-85, chmn. dept. geology, 1972-80, v.p., provost, 1980-83, pres., 1983-84; pres. U. B.C., 1985—; chief geophysics br. Johnson Space Ctr., NASA, Houston, 1970-72, chief physics br., 1972-73, acting chief planetary and earth sci. divsn., 1973; vis. prof. geology U. Houston, 1971-73; interim dir. Lunar Sci. Inst., Houston, 1973; vis. com. geol. scis. Brown U., 1974-76, Meml. U. St. John's Nfld., 1974-79, Princeton U., 1981-86; v.p. Can. Geosci. Coun., 1977; chmn. proposal evaluating program Univs. Space Rsch. Assocs., 1977-78, Ont. Geosci. Rsch. Fund; Pahlavi lectr. Govt. Iran, 1978; cons. to govt. and industry, mem. numerous govt. and sci. and investigative panels; hon. prof. Changchun Coll. Geology, People's Republic of China, 1985, Guilin Coll. Geology, People's Republic China, 1987; bd. dirs. MacMillan Bioedel Ltd., Echo Bay Mines, Ltd., BC Gas Ltd., Corp.-Higher Edn. Forum, Internat. Inst. for Sustainable Devel., The Japan Soc. Can. Author numerous papers, reports in field. Adv.(hon.) Urasenke Found., Kyoto, Japan. Recipient Exceptional Sci. Achievement medal NASA, 1972; named Kil-Sly, Haida Nation (West Coast Indians of Can.), 1993, hon. advisor Urasenke Found., Kyoto, Japan, 1994; hon. fellow Green Coll., Oxford (Eng.) U., 1994. Fellow Royal Astron. Soc., Royal Soc. Can.; mem. AAAS, Soc. Exploration Geophysicists (Virgil Kauffman Gold medal 1974), Geol. Assn. Can. (pres. 1978-79, Logan Gold medal 1984), Can. Geophys. Union (chmn. 1977-79, J. Tuzo Wilson medal 1987), Am. Geophys. Union (planetology sect. 1978-82), European Assn. Exploration Geophysicists, Soc. Geomagnetism and Geoelectricity (Japan), Can. Geosci. Council (pres. 1980), Can. Exploration Geophysicists, Soc. Exptl. Geophysics (hon.), Canada-Japan Soc., (founding dir.), Internat. House Japan, Inc., Japan Soc. of Can.; alumnus (hon.) U. British Columbia.

STRASBAUGH, WAYNE RALPH, lawyer; b. Lancaster, Pa., July 20, 1948; s. Wayne Veily and Jane Irene (Marzolf) S.; m. Carol Lynne Taylor, June 8, 1974; children: Susan, Wayne T., Elizabeth. AB, Bowdoin Coll., 1970; AM, Harvard U., 1971, PhD, 1976, JD, 1979. Bar: Ohio 1979, Pa. 1983, U.S. Tax Ct. 1980, U.S.Ct. Fed. Claims 1980, U.S. Ct. Appeals (fed. cir.) 1982, U.S. Dist. Ct. (no. dist.) Ohio 1979, U.S. Dist. Ct. (ea. dist.) Pa. 1983. Assoc. Jones Day Reavis & Pogue, Cleve., 1979-82, Morgan Lewis & Bockius, Phila., 1982-84; assoc. Ballard Spahr Andrews & Ingersoll, Phila., 1984-88, ptnr., 1988—. Mem. ABA (tax sect., chair com. 1992-94), Phila. Bar Assn. (tax sect., chair fed. tax com. 1992, mem. coun. 1995—). Episcopalian. Office: Ballard Spahr Andrews & Ingersoll 1735 Market St Philadelphia PA 19103-7599

STRASBERG, SUSAN, actress, writer, educator; b. N.Y.C., May 22, 1938; d. Lee and Paula (Miller) S.; m. Chris Jones, Sept. 25, 1965; 1 dau., Jennifer. Stage debut off-Broadway prodn. Maya, 1952; appeared in role of Juliet TV prodn. Romeo and Juliet, 1953; role of daughter TV series The Marriage, 1953; also Omnibus prodn. Duchess and the Smugs, 1953; (with Helen Hayes) Dear Brutus, 1954; film debut Cobweb, 1954; Ceasar and Cleopatra (Shaw), 1956; motion pictures Picnic, 1954, Stagestruck, 1957, Time Remembered, 1957-58, Shadow of a Gunman, 1958, The Lady of the Camillas, 1962, Adventures of a Young Man, 1962, Disorder, 1964, High Bright Sun, 1965, The Trip, 1967, Psych-Out, 1968, The Name of the Game Is Kill, 1968, Roller Coaster, 1977, The Manitou, 1978, In Praise of Older Women, 1979, The Delta Force, 1986, Prime Suspect, also Kapo, Scream of Fear, The Brotherhood, The Marriage, Catch a Falling Star, The Immigrants; co-star with Franchot Tone in Time of Your Life, Brussels World's Fair; created role of Anne in Diary of Anne Frank, 1955-56; appeared in TV series Toma, 1973-74; TV movies include Beggarman, Thief; numerous other TV appearances include (series) Owen Marshall, (drama special) Frankenstein, 1973, Night Gallery, 1980, Rona Jaffe's Mazes and Monsters, 1982, (film) Schweitzer, 1990, The Cherry Orchard, 1992; author: autobiography Bittersweet, 1980, Second Book Memoir, Marilyn and Me, Sisters, Rivals, Friends, 1992. Office: care William Morris Agy 151 S El Camino Dr Beverly Hills CA 90212-2704

STRASBURGER, JOSEPH JULIUS, retired lawyer; b. Albia, Iowa, Aug. 29, 1913; s. Joseph and Elsa (Gottlieb) S.; m. Lucile C. Lapidus, Oct. 11, 1957; 1 dau., Susan A. (dec. Jan. 1970). A.B., Knox Coll., 1934; J.D., Harvard, 1937. Bar: Ill. 1937. Assoc. firm Moses, Kennedy, Stein & Bachrach, Chgo., 1939-39; assoc. gen. counsel's office Middle West Service Co., Chgo., 1939-44; ptnr. Altheimer & Gray (and predecessor firms), Chgo., 1944-87; chmn. lawyer's handbook editorial com. Jewish Fedn. Chgo., 1968-73; mem. adv. council Ill. Inst. Continuing Legal Edn., 1970-76, exec. com., 1971-76, chmn., 1974-75; lectr. probate and tax subjects. Contbr. articles to legal jours. Mem. devel. com. Knox Coll., 1964-70, trustee, 1982-87, life trustee, 1987—; trustee Latin Sch. Chgo., 1978-84. Fellow Am. Bar Found.; mem. ABA, Ill. Bar Assn., Chgo. Bar Assn. (chmn. probate practice com. 1960-61, chmn. continuing legal edn. com. 1968-69, chmn. legal edn. com. 1972-73), Chgo. Estate Planning Council (pres. 1975-76), Phi Beta Kappa, Delta Sigma Rho, Beta Theta Pi. Jewish. Clubs: Tavern (Chgo.), Standard (Chgo.). Home: 1335 N Astor St Chicago IL 60610-2152 Office: 10 S Wacker Dr Chicago IL 60606-7407

STRASFOGEL, IAN, stage director; b. N.Y.C., Apr. 5, 1940; s. Ignace and Alma (Lubin) S.; m. Judith Hirsch Norell, Feb. 15, 1973; children: Daniella Elizabeth, Gabrielle Sandra. BA, Harvard U., 1961. Administ. asst. N.Y.C. Opera Co., 1962-64, stage dir., 1964—; tchr. music Julliard Sch. Music, N.Y.C., 1965-66, Augusta (Ga.) Coll., 1967-68; founder, previous artistic dir. Augusta Opera Co., from 1967; chmn. dept. opera New Eng.

Conservatory, Boston, 1968-72; prof. opera U. Mich., Ann Arbor, 1980; stage dir. Balt. Civic Opera, Kansas City Lyric Theatre, Netherlands Opera Co., 1973—; N.Y.C. Opera, San Francisco Opera, Stuttgart Opera, Alte Oper Frankfurt, Edinburgh Festival, Aix-en-Provence Festival, Aspen Music Festival; dir. music theatre project Tanglewood Festival, Lenox, Mass., 1971-73; gen. dir. Opera Soc. Washington, 1972-75; artistic cons. Phila. Lyric Opera, 1973; dir. New Opera Theatre, Bklyn. Acad. Music, 1976-79. Author: Il Musico (music by Larry Grossman), 1990-91; editor: Ba-Ta-Clan, 1970. Served with AUS, 1966-68. Henry Russell Shaw travelling fellow, 1961-62; Ford Found. internship in performing arts, 1962-64; Internat. Inst. Edn. grantee, 1965. Mem. Phi Beta Kappa. Home: 915 West End Ave New York NY 10025-3535 Office: Sardos Artist Mgmt Corp 180 West End Ave New York NY 10023-4902*

STRASMA, JOHN DRINAN, economist, educator; b. Kankakee, Ill., Mar. 29, 1932; s. Roy and Charlotte Wilkins (Deselm) S.; m. Judith Feaster, Mar. 18, 1956 (div. 1983); children: Anne, Patricia, Susan, Kenneth, Mary; m. Anne Corry, July 21, 1984. AB, DePauw U., 1953; AM, Harvard U., 1958, PhD, 1960. Research asst. Fed. Res. Bank of Boston, 1958-59; prof. Econs. Inst., U. Chile, Santiago, 1959-72; economist UN Secretariat, 1964-65; advisor Ministry of Economy and Fin., Lima, Peru, 1970; prof. econs. and agrl. econs. U. Wis., Madison, 1972—; cons. in field; v.p. dir. Latin Am. Scholarship Program of Am. Univs., 1970-74; chmn. fin. com. Wesley Found. of Wis., 1978-87; public mem. Wis. Legis. Council Com. on Mining, 1975-90. Author: State and Local Taxation of Manufacturing Industry, 1969, Agrarian Reform in El Salvador, 1982, Agricultural Land Taxation in Developing Countries, 1987, Land Tax Reform Alternatives in Zimbabwe, 1990, Options for Redistributing Land in the New South Africa, 1993, Market-Based Land Redistribution in the new South Africa, 1993. Served with U.S. Army, 1954-56. Danforth fellow, 1956-60; Recipient Outstanding Public Service award Wis. Environ. Decade, 1978. Mem. Am. Econs. Assn., Am. Agrl. Econs. Assn., Internat. Agrl. Econs. Assn., Latin Am. Studies Assn., Soc. Internat. Devel. Methodist. Office: U Wis 427 Lorch St Madison WI 53706-1503

STRASSBURGER, JOHN ROBERT, academic administrator; b. Sheboygan, Wis., Apr. 6, 1942; s. J Robert and Elizabeth (Mathewson) S.; m. Gertrude Hunter Mackie, Aug. 24, 1968; children: Sarah Electa, Gertrude Hunter. BA, Bates, 1964; Honours degree, Cambridge (Eng.) U., 1966; PhD, Princeton U., 1976. Faculty Hiram (Ohio) Coll., 1970-82; program officer NEH, Washington, 1982-84; prof. history, v.p. acad. affairs, exec. v.p., dean Coll., Knox Coll., Galesburg, Ill., 1984-94; pres. Ursinus Coll., Collegeville, Pa., 1995—. Contbr. articles to profl. jours. Trustee Knox Galesburg Symphony. Mem. Am. Conf. Acad. Deans (chair 1990-91), Associated Coll. of the Midwest (chair deans adv. coun. 1989-90), Ill. State Hist. Soc. (bd. dirs. 1988-91), Sunday Breakfast Club (Phila.). Office: Ursinus Coll Office of Pres Collegeville PA 19426-1000

STRASSER, GABOR, priest, management consultant; b. Budapest, Hungary, May 22, 1929; s. Rezso and Theresa (Seiler) S.; m. Linda Casselman Pemble, Aug. 16, 1958 (div. 1976); children: Claire Margaret, Andrew John; m. Joka Verhoeff, Feb. 2, 1978; children: Steven Verhoeff, Tessa Christina. BCE, City Coll. N.Y., 1954; MS, U. Buffalo, 1959; PMD, Harvard, 1968; MDiv, Va. Theol. Sem., 1992. Research engr. Bell Aircraft Co., Buffalo, 1956-61; project leader Boeing Airplane Co., Seattle, 1961-62; dept. head Mitre Corp., Bedford, Mass., Washington, 1962-68; v.p. Urban Inst., Washington, 1968-69; tech. asst. to pres.'s sci. adviser White House, 1969-71, exec. sec. pres.'s sci. and tech. policy panel, 1970-71; dir. planning Battelle Meml. Inst., Columbus, Ohio, 1971-73; pres. Strasser Assocs., Inc., Washington, 1973-92; priest Va. Diocese, 1992—. Author, editor: Science and Technology Policies-Yesterday, Today, Tomorrow, 1973; Contbr. articles to profl. jours. Served to 1st lt., C.E. USAR. Recipient 1st nat. award Gravity Research Found., 1952. Mem. Am. Inst. Aeros. and Astronautics, IEEE, AAAS (chmn. indsl. sci. sect. 1974), Sigma Xi. Clubs: Cosmos (Washington), Harvard (Washington).

STRASSER, JOSEPH C., career military officer, academic administrator. Rear admiral USN; pres. Naval War Coll. Office: Office of the President Naval War College Newport RI 02841

STRASSER, WILLIAM CARL, JR., retired college president, educator; b. Washington, Feb. 4, 1930; s. William Carl and Minnie Elizabeth (Saxton) S.; m. Jeanne Carol Peake, Sept. 17, 1954 (div.); children: Sheryl Lynn, Keith Edward, Robert Carl; m. Jane Ann Gunn, Nov. 25, 1978. BA with first honors, U. Md., 1952, MA, 1954; PhD, 1961; Carnegie postdoctoral fellow in coll. administry. U. Mich., 1961-62. High sch. tchr. Cin. and Balt., 1955-57; v.p. W.C. Strasser Co., Inc., 1957-59; pub. info. specialist Balt. County (Md.) Pub. Schs., 1960-61; asst. dean, asst. prof. Sch. Edn., State U.N.Y. at Buffalo, 1962-64; rsch. asst. U.S. Office Edn., 1959-60; specialist ednl. adminstrn. U.S. Office Edn., Washington, 1964-65; asst. dir. profl. personnel Montgomery County (Md.) Pub. Schs., 1965-66; acting pres., exec. dean Montgomery Community Coll., Rockville, Md., 1966-67, pres., 1967-79, prof., 1978-86, pres. emeritus, prof. emeritus, 1986—; vis. scholar U. Calif., Berkeley, 1977-79; vice pres. Md. Council Community Coll. Presidents, 1971-72, 75-77; pres., v.p. Jr. Coll. Council Middle Atlantic States, 1969-72; founder Council Chief Exec. Adminstrs., 1973-75; mem. exec. com. Pres.'s Acad., 1975-77; mem. Gov.'s Adv. Council, Md. Higher Edn. Facilities, 1977-79; Del. UNESCO Conf. on Africa, 1961; participant 50th Anniversary Conf. Fgn. Policy Assn. U.S., 1968; mem. Congl. Internship Adv. Com., 1969-78; chmn. Montgomery County Community White Ho. Conf. on Aging, 1971; cons. Middle States Assn. Colls. and Secondary Schs., 1975—. Author: For The Community: Continuing General Education, 1979, A College For a Community, 1988; co-author: Dual Enrollment in Public and Non-Public Schools, 1965; contbr. poetry and articles to jours. Served with AUS, 1954-55. Recipient Gov. Md. Cert. Disting. Citizenship, 1979; Danforth Found. study grantee, 1972; Ford Found. grantee, 1974-75; Silver medallion for Outstanding Service, Bd. Trustees of Montgomery Coll., 1986. Mem. Am. Assn. Jr. Colls. (chmn. nat. commn. on instrn. 1969-71, mem. nat. assembly 1973, founder Pres. Acad. 1973-77), AAUP, Am. Assn. Higher Edn., Am. Mgmt. Assns., Nat. Soc. Sons. and Daus of the Pilgrims, Montgomery County C. of C. (Disting. Svc. award 1979), Rotary, Phi Kappa Phi, Omicron Delta Kappa, Pi Delta Epsilon, Phi Eta Sigma, Phi Delta Kappa. Democrat. Unitarian-Universalist. Home: 180 Woodside Dr Provo UT 84604

STRASSMANN, W. PAUL, economics educator; b. Berlin, July 26, 1926; s. Erwin Otto and Ilse (Wens) S.; m. Elizabeth Marsh Fanck, June 27, 1952; children—Joan, Diana, Beverly. B.A. magna cum laude, U Tex., Austin, 1949; M.A., Columbia U., 1950; Ph.D., U. Md., 1956. Econ. analyst Dept. Commerce, 1950-52; instr. U. Md., 1955; mem. faculty Mich. State U., East Lansing, 1956—, assoc. prof. econs. 1959-63, prof., 1963—; sr. research dir. ILO, Geneva, 1969-70, 73-74; cons. World Bank, AID. Author: Risk and Technological Innovation, 1959, Technological Change and Economic Development, 1968, The Transformation of Housing, 1982, (with Jill Wells) The Global Construction Industry, 1988. Served with USN, 1944-46. Mem. Am. Econ. Assn., Latin Am. Studies Assn., Phi Beta Kappa. Office: Mich State Univ Dept Econs East Lansing MI 48824

STRASSMEYER, MARY, newspaper columnist; b. Cleve., Aug. 5, 1929; d. Frederick H. and Katherine (Mullally) S. A.B., Notre Dame Coll., 1951; postgrad., Toledo U., 1952; J.D., Cleve. Marshall Coll. Law, Cleve. State U., 1981. Bar: Ohio 1983. Reporter Cleve. News, 1956-60; contbr. Cleve. Plain Dealer, 1957-60, feature writer, 1960-65, beauty editor, 1963-65, travel writer, 1963—, society editor, 1975-77, 85—; columnist, 1977—; co-creator syndicated cartoon Sneakers; co-owner Gerry's Internat. Travel Agy., Cleve., 1991—. Author: Coco: The Special Delivery Dog, 1979. Mem. Soc. Am. Social Scribes (founder, 1st pres.), Notre Dame Coll. Alumnae Assn. Women in Comm. Club: Press (Cleve.) (inducted into Hall of Fame 1994). Home: 2059 Broadview Rd Cleveland OH 44109-4145 Office: The Plain Dealer 1801 Superior Ave E Cleveland OH 44114-2107

STRATAS, NICHOLAS EMANUEL, psychiatrist; b. Toronto, Ont., Can., Aug. 9, 1932; came to U.S., 1957; s. Emanuel Nicholas and Argero (Terezaki) S.; m. Irene Printezi, Dec. 14, 1955; children: Nicholas Andrew, Byron Aristotle, Andrew James. BA, U. Toronto, 1953, MD, 1957. Diplomate Am. Bd. Psychiatry and Neurology, Internat. Acad. Behavioral Medicine, Fedn. State Med. Bds. U.S. Rotating intern Meml. hosp., Danville, Va., 1957-58; resident in psychiatry Ea. State Hosp., Williamsburg, Va., 1958-60; chief resident in psychiatry Dorothea Dix Hosp., Raleigh, N.C., 1960-61; dir. residency tng. Dorothea Dix Hosp., Raleigh, 1961-63; dir. profl. edn. and tng. State Dept. Mental Health, N.C., 1963-66, dir. research, 1965-66, dep. commr., 1966-73; asst. clin. prof. psychiatry U. N.C. Med. Sch., 1964-69, assoc. clin. prof. psychiatry, 1969-73, clin. prof., 1984—; assoc. clin. prof. Duke U. Med. Ctr., 1980—; pvt. practice, 1960—; lectr. William & Mary U., Williamsburg, Va., 1960, U. N.C. Sch. Pub. Health, 1964-65, U. W.Va. Med. Sch., Charleston, 1968, Vanderbilt U. Sch. Med., Nashville, 1970, U. N.C. Sch. Social Work, Chapel Hill, 1973, et. al.; organizer, pres. med. staff Ea. State Hosp., Williamsburg, 1958-59; cons. pvt. orgns. 1960—, Peace Corps, 1964-69, W. Va. State Dept. Mental Health state office program devel., 1968, Nationwide Ins. Co. mgmt. devel., 1970, Drug Action of Wake County mgmt. devel., 1970-74, The Human Ecology Inst., 1973-75, U.S. Fed. Ct. of N.C. ea. dist. expert witness, 1975-76, IBM personal devel. seminars, 1978—, Finley-Dillon Realty, 1983—, The Aviation, 1986; bd. dirs. Wake County Mental Health Assn., 1964-65; staff Wake Med. Ctr., 1973—, Rex Hosp., 1973—, Raleigh Community Hosp., 1978—; founder, med. dir. Holly Hill Hosp. 1978—, Raleigh Stress & Pain Clin., 1980-84. Author: N.C. Local Mental Health Programs-A Manual, 1968, A Multi-Discipline Approach to Consultation-Edn., 1969; contbr. articles to profl. and scholarly jours. Awards dir. Boy Scouts Am., Raleigh, N.C., Webelos coord., 1968; bd. trustees Holy Trinity Greek Orthodox Ch., 1971, Sunday sch. coord., 1975-77; mem. N.C. State Art Gallery, Raleigh Cultural Ctr., 1974. Recipient Gov. N.C. awards, 1968, 70, 84, Univ. Toronto award, 1957. Fellow APA, APHA, Am. Soc. Clin. Hypnosis, Am. Acad. Psychosomatic Medicine, Am. Coll. Forensic Psychiatry, Am. Orthopsychiat. Assn., Am. Acad. Pain; mem. AMA, AAAS, Biofeedback Cet. Inst. Am. (cert.), Wake County Med. Assn., N.C. Med. Assn., Bd. of Med. Examiners of N.C. (mem. 1987-93, pres. 1992-93). Democrat. Home: 304 Foxhall St Raleigh NC 27609-5604 Office: Raleigh Psychiat Assocs PA 3900 Browning Pl Ste 201 Raleigh NC 27609-6555

STRATAS, TERESA (ANASTASIA STRATAKI), opera singer, soprano; b. Toronto, Ont., Can., May 26, 1938. Student, of Irene Jessner, 1956-59; grad., Faculty Music, U. Toronto, 1959; LLD (hon.), McMaster U., 1986, U. Toronto, 1994. Winner Met. Opera auditions, 1959; major roles in opera houses throughout world include: Mimi in La Bohème; Tatiana in Eugene Onegin; Susanna in The Marriage of Figaro; Nedda in Pagliacci; Marenka in The Bartered Bride; Three Heroines in Il Trittico; Violetta in La Traviata; title role in Rusalka; Jennie in Mahagonny; created title role in completed version of Lulu (Alban Berg), Paris Grand Opera, 1979; film appearances Kaiser von Atlantis, Seven Deadly Sins; Zefirelli's La Traviata, Salome, Lulu, Paganini, Zarewitsch, Eugene Oregin; Broadway debut in Rags, 1986; creator the role of Marie Antoinette Ghosts of Versailles world premiere Met. Opera, 1992; sang both female leading roles Il Tabarro, Pagliacci double bill opening Met. Opera, 1994, numerous recs. including Richard Strauss' Salomé, Songs of Kurt Weill. Decorated Order of Can.; recipient 3 Grammy awards, Emmy award, Drama Desk award, 1986, 3 Grammy nominations, Tony nomination, 1986, Tiffany award, 1994; named Performer of Yr., Can. Music Council, 1979. Office: care Met Opera Co Lincoln Center Plz New York NY 10023 also: Vincent & Farrell Associates 157 West 57th St Ste 502 New York NY 10019*

STRATFORD, RAY PAUL, electrical engineer, consultant; b. Pocatello, Idaho, Feb. 26, 1925; s. Ray Percy and Olive Eudora (Jenson) S.; m. Claire Elizabeth Dennery, Sept. 2, 1949 (div. July 1969); children: Bruce Ballentyne, James Lowell, Susanne Dennery; m. Nancy Lorraine Long, Apr. 24, 1974; 1 child, Heather Lyn; stepchildren: Deborah Lorraine, David Paul. Student, Idaho State U., 1946-47; BSEE, Stanford U., 1950. Registered profl. engr. N.Y. Test engr. GE, Schenectady, N.Y., 1950-52; application GE, Schenectady, 1954-62, project engr., 1963-73, cons. engr., 1974-85; proposal engr. GE, Phila., 1952-54, application engr., 1962-63; pvt. cons. Island Park, Idaho, 1991—; adj. prof. Rensselaer Poly. Inst., Troy, N.Y., 1988, 90. Co-author: Handbook of Industrial and Commercial Electric Power System Designs, 1995; contbr. articles to profl. jours. Mem. bldg. com. LDS Sch., Schenectady, 1962-64, coord. phys. facilities, 1980-84; mem. bldg. com. Burnt Hills Sch. Bd., Glenville, N.Y., 1963-64, YMCA, Schenectady, 1965. Fellow IEEE (life mem., chairperson static power converter com. 1972, chairperson task force standard 1973-84, co-chairperson task force standard 1984-92, contbg. author Red Book 1993, Best Paper award 1981, Outstanding achievement award 1994), Rotary Internat. Avocations: woodworking, family, travel. Office: PO Box 186 Island Park ID 83429

STRATHAIRN, DAVID, actor; b. San Francisco, CA, 1949. numerous stage appearances including: I'm Not Rappaport, Salonika, A Lie of the Mind, The Birthday Party, Danton's Death, Mountain Language, L'Atelier, A Moon for the Misbegotten, Temptation; television appearances include:Miami Vice, 1985, The Equilizer, 1988, The Days and Nights of Molly Dodd, 1988-91, Day One, 1989, Son of the Morning Star, 1991, Heat Wave, 1990, Judgment, 1990, Without Warning: The James Brady Story, 1991, O Pioneers!, 1992, The American Clock, 1993; films include: Return of the Secaucus Seven, 1980, Lovesick, 1983, Silkwood, 1983, The Brother From Another Planet, 1984, Iceman, 1984, Enormous Changes at the Last Minute, 1985, When Nature Calls, 1985, At Close Range, 1986, Matewan, 1987, Eight Men Out, 1988, Stars and Bars, 1988, Dominick and Eugene, 1988, Call Me, 1988, The Feud, 1989, Memphis Belle, 1990, City of Hope, 1991, Big Girls Don't Cry...They Get Even, 1992, Bob Roberts, 1992, Shadows and Fog, 1992, A League of Their Own, 1992, Sneakers, 1992, Passion Fish, 1992, Lost in Yonkers, 1993, The Firm, 1993, A Dangerous Woman, 1993, The River Wild, 1994, Dolores Claiborne, 1995, Losing Isaiah, 1995. Office: Abrams Artists & Assoc Suite 625 9200 Sunset Blvd Los Angeles CA 90069*

STRATI, TONY J., accountant. BBA in Acctg., U. Notre Dame, MBA in Acctg. CPA, N.Mex. With Peat Marwick Main & Co., Albuquerque, ptnr., 1981—; conductor practice groups on local government and education. Bd. dirs. Greater Albuquerque C. of C. (mem. fin. com., vice-chmn. membership affairs div.), active United Way, Rehabilitation Ctr. Mem. AICPA, N.Mex. Soc. CPAs (past. bd. dirs.), Rotary. Office: Peat Marwick Main & Co 20 First Plaza Ctr NW Albuquerque NM 87102-3338

STRATING, SHARON L., elementary school educator; b. Jamestown, N.D., Jan. 20, 1949; d. Walter and Evelyn Darlene (Lang) Remmick; m. Rick Donald Strating, Dec. 24, 1978; children: Heather Dawn, Amber Nicole, Ashley Renee. BS in Secondary Edn., So. Mo. State U., 1971; MEd in Sci. Edn., N.W. Mo. State U., 1992. Cert. elem. tchr., Mo. Tchr. Cassville R-III Schs., 1971-76, Savannah R-III Sch. System, Mo., 1976-91; instr. 4th grade Horace Mann Lab Sch., Maryville, Mo., 1991—; facilitator for Environ. Edn. Pilot Project Kans. U., Lawrence; co-chair EPA Pollution Prevention Adv. Task Force; mem. biol. sci. curriculum study Elem. Tchr. Module Project, 1993; instr. for coll. practicum students. Author: Living the Constitution Through the Eyes of the Newspaper, 1987, Tabloid Teaching Tool, 6 edits., 1986-91. Chairperson March of Dimes, 1972-76, Cystic Fibrosis, 1972-78; scout leader Brownies, 1976-77; exec. bd. dirs. PTA, 1976-82, fund raising chairperson, 1976-83; program chairperson presch. PTA, 1976-80;chairperson community environ. activities, 1976—, Adopt a Hwy. Program, 1976-91; mem. Mo. Stream Team Effort, 1976—. Recipient Nat. Pres. Environ. Youth award, 1989, 89, Presdl. award State of Mo., 1992, 93, Nat. Presdl. award, 1992-93; named Mo. State Tchr. of Yr., 1990-91. Mem. Nat. Hist. Soc., Internat. Reading Assn., Nat. Bd. for Profl. Teaching Standards and Mid.-Age Child in Sci., Nat. Sci. Tchrs. Assn., Sci. Tchrs. Mo. Lutheran. Avocations: travel, ecology, creative writing, motivational speaking, arts and crafts. Office: Northwest Mo State U Horace Mann Lab Sch Brown Hall Rm 167 Maryville MO 64468

STRATMAN, JOSEPH LEE, petroleum refining company executive, consultant, chemical engineer; b. Louisville, Oct. 15, 1924; s. Dominic Herman and Mary Ann (Wolf) S.; m. Elizabeth Jewell Doyle, July 1, 1950; children—Joseph Lee, Mary Elizabeth, Sharon Ann, Judith Ann. BChemE, U. Louisville, 1947. Registered profl. engr., Tex. Chem. engr. Pan Am. Refining Corp. (doing bus. as Amoco Oil Co.), Texas City, Tex., 1947-55, operating supr., 1955-61; mgr. Texas City Refining, Inc., Texas City, Tex., 1961-69, v.p., 1969-80, sr. v.p., 1980—. Bd. dirs., mem. exec. com., treas. chmn. Galveston County ARC, 1966-73; bd. dirs., mem. exec. com., chmn. Texas City Jr. Achievement, 1966-73; treas. Texas City Refining Good Govt. Fund, 1983-88. Served with USNR, 1945-46. Mem. Am. Inst. Chem. Engrs. Roman Catholic.

STRATON, JOHN CHARLES, JR., investment banker; b. Warwick, N.Y., Apr. 18, 1932; s. John Charles and Helen (Sanford) S.; m. Sally M. Strawhand (div. Mar. 1970); children: John Charles III, Sara; m. Marion S. Holder, Feb. 18, 1974; 1 child, Ashley Holder Straton. B.A., U. Va., 1954. With Jas. H. Oliphant and Co., N.Y.C., 1956—; gen. ptnr. Jas. H. Oliphant and Co., 1962—, 1st v.p., 1972-75; v.p. Spencer Trask & Co., Inc., N.Y.C., 1975-77, Hornblower, Weeks, Noyes & Trask, N.Y.C., 1977-78, Loeb Rhoades, Hornblower & Co., 1978-79, Shearson Loeb Rhoades, 1979-81; v.p., fin. cons. Shearson Lehman Bros., N.Y.C., 1981-93; sr. v.p. Smith Barney Shearson, N.Y.C., 1993—; assessor Village of Tuxedo Park, 1963-70. Vestryman St. Mary's in Tuxedo. Served to maj. AUS, 1954-56; ret. Mem. U. Va. Alumni Assn. N.Y. (pres., treas. 1973-90), Mil. Order Fgn. Wars (comdr. 1981-86, treas. 1986—), Pilgrims of U.S., Tuxedo Pk. Club, Sigma Phi Epsilon. Home: Ledge Rd Tuxedo Park NY 10987 Office: 250 Park Ave New York NY 10177-0001

STRATOS, KIMARIE ROSE, lawyer, sports agent; b. Miami, Fla., Aug. 24, 1960; d. Jack Sloshower and Charmaine (McDougal) S. BS with high honors, U. Fla., 1981, JD with honors, 1984. Bar: Fla. 1985, U.S. Dist. Ct. (so. and mid. dist.) Fla. 1987. Ptnr. Shutts & Bowen, Miami, 1984-85, 86—; chair sports law dept., law clk. to judge U.S. Dist. Ct. (so. dist.) Fla., Miami, 1985-86; mem. bd. dirs. Fla. Sports Found., 1992—. Co-author, asst. editor: Facility Development and the Sports Authority, Law of Professional and Amateur Sports; asst. editor: Clark Boardmen, 1990; contbr. articles to profl. jours. mem. ABA, Fla. Bar (bd. govs. young lawyers sect. 1987-93, exec. coun. entertainment, arts and sports law sect. 1988—), Fla. Assn. Women Lawyers, Sports Lawyers Assn. (nat. v.p. 1988-90, 93—, bd. dirs. 1990—). Avocation: running, travel. Office: Shutts & Bowen 100 Chopin Plz Ste 1500 Miami FL 33131-2382

STRATT, RICHARD MARK, chemistry educator; b. Phila., Feb. 21 1954; s. Stanford Lloyd and Florence Clair (Sussman) S. SB in Chemistry, MIT, 1975; PhD, U. Calif.-Berkeley, 1979. Postdoctoral rsch. assoc. U. Ill., Champaign, 1979-80, NSF postdoctoral research assoc., 1980; asst. prof. chemistry Brown U., Providence, 1981-85, assoc. prof., 1986-88, prof., 1988—. Contbr. articles to profl. jours. Alfred P. Sloan fellow, 1985-89; Fulbright scholar Oxford U., 1991-92. Mem. Am. Phys. Soc., Am. Chem. Soc., Sigma Xi, Phi Lambda Upsilon. Office: Brown U Dept Chemistry Providence RI 02912

STRATTON, FREDERICK PRESCOTT, JR., manufacturing executive; b. Milw., May 25, 1939; married. B.S., Yale U.; M.B.A., Stanford U., 1963. With Arthur Andersen & Co., 1963-65, Robert W. Baird & Co., Inc., 1965-73; with Briggs & Stratton Corp., Wauwatosa, Wis., 1973—, asst. service mgr., 1973-75, asst. sales mgr., 1975-76, group sales and service adminstrn., 1976-77, v.p. adminstrn., 1977; formerly pres. Briggs & Stratton Corp., Wauwatosa to 1987; chmn. bd., chief exec. officer Briggs & Stratton Corp., Wauwatosa, Wis., 1987—, chmn. bd. dirs.; bd. dirs. Banc One Corp., Columbus, Ohio, Wis. Energy Corp., Milw., Weyenberg Shoe Man Co., Milw. Office: Briggs & Stratton Corp PO Box 702 12301 W Wirth St Milwaukee WI 53222-2110

STRATTON, GREGORY ALEXANDER, computer specialist, administrator, mayor; b. Glendale, Calif., July 31, 1946; s. William Jaspar and Rita Phyllis (Smith) S.; m. Yolanda Margot Soler, 1967 (div. 1974); 1 child, Tiffany; m. Edith Carter, Sept. 27, 1975; stepchildren: John Henkell, Paul Henkell, D'Lorah Henkell. Student, Harvey Mudd Coll., 1964-65; BS in Physics, UCLA, 1968; MBA, Calif. Luth U., 1977. Elec. engr. Naval Ship Weapon System Engring. Sta., Port Hueneme, Calif., 1968-73; sr. staff mem. Univac, Valencia, Calif., 1973-74; v.p. Digital Applications, Camarillo, Calif., 1974-75; cons. Grumman Aerospace, Point Mugu, Calif., 1975-76; F-14 software mgr. Pacific Missle Test Ctr., Pt. Mugu, 1976-84; software mgr. Teledyne Systems, Northridge, Calif., 1984-92, dir. engring. software dept., 1992-93; dep. dir. software engring. Teledyne Electronic Systems, Northridge, Calif., 1993-94; software mgr. Litton Guidance and Controls, Northridge, Calif., 1995—. Mem. City Coun., City of Simi Valley, Calif., 1979-86, mayor, 1986—; alt. Rep. County Cen. Com., Ventura County, 1986-88; mem. Rep. State Cen. Com., Calif., 1990—; bd. dirs. Simi Valley Hosp., 1987—. Mem. Assn. Ventura County Cities (chair 1990-91), Rotary (Paul Harris award Simi Sunrise chpt. 1989), Jaycees (pres. Simi Valley chpt. 1974-75, nat. bd. dirs. 1975—), v.p. Calif. state 1976-77). Republican. Lutheran. Home: 254 Goldenwood Cir Simi Valley CA 93065-6771 Office: Office of Mayor 2929 Tapo Canyon Rd Simi Valley CA 93063-2199

STRATTON, MARIANN, former director USN nurse corps; b. Houston, Apr. 6, 1945; d. Max Millard and Beatrice Agnes (Roemer) S.; m. Lawrence Mallory Stickney, nov. 15, 1977 (dec.). BSN, BA in English, Sacred Heart Dominican Coll., 1966; MA in Mgmt., Webster Coll., 1977; MSN, U. Va., 1981. Cert. adult nurse practitioner. Ensign USN, 1966, advanced through grades to rear adm., 1991; patient care coord. Naval Regional Med. Ctr., Charleston, S.C., 1981-83; nurse corps plans officer Naval Med. Command, Washington, 1983-86; dir. nursing svcs. U.S. Naval Hosp., Naples, Italy, 1986-89, Naval Hosp., San Diego, 1989-91; chief pers. mgmt. Bur. Medicine & Surgery, Washington, 1991-94; dir. USN Nurse Corps, Washington, 1991-94. Decorated Disting. Svc. medal, Meritorious Svc. medal with two stars, Naval Achievement medal. Mem. ANA, Assn. Mil. Surgeons of U.s., Interagy. Inst. of Fed. Health Car Execs.

STRATTON, RICHARD JAMES, lawyer; b. Sandwich, Ill., May 17, 1946; s. James L. and Dorothy (Olson) S.; m. Michele Disario, June 13, 1970; children: Matthew A., Laura D. AB, Harvard U., 1968, JD, 1972; MS, London Sch. of Econs., 1969. Bar: Calif. 1972, U.S. Dist. Ct. (no. dist.) Calif. 1972, U.S. Ct. Appeals (9th cir.) 1972, U.S. Dist. Ct. (cen. dist.) Calif. 1978, U.S. Dist. Ct. and ea. dists.) Calif. 1979, U.S. Supreme Ct. 1979. Assoc. Bronson, Bronson & McKinnon, San Francisco, 1972-79, ptnr., 1980—; early neutral evaluator, mediator U.S. Dist. Ct. Co-author: Real Property Litigation, 1994. Trustee San Francisco Day Sch., 1987-94; bd. dirs. Legal Aid Soc. of San Francisco 1989—. Fellow Am. Bar Found.; mem. ABA, Bar Assn. of San Francisco (bd. dirs. 1988-90), Calif. Bar Assn. Def. Rsch. Inst. (chmn. subcom. real estate brokers and agts. 1986-87), No. Calif. Assn. Def. Counsel, No. Calif. Assn. Bus. Trial Lawyers, San Francisco Barristers Club (pres. 1980), City Club, Harvard Club (San Francisco). Office: Bronson Bronson & McKinnon 505 Montgomery St San Francisco CA 94111-2514

STRATTON, ROBERT, electronics company executive; b. Vienna, Austria, Aug. 14, 1928; came to U.S., 1959, naturalized, 1966; s. Kenneth Kurt and Eugenie (Schwatzer) S.; m. Elfriede Karlberger, Jan. 11, 1980; children: David Alexander, Valerie Pam. B.Sc. in Physics, Manchester U., 1949, Ph.D. in Theoretical Physics, 1952. Rsch. physicist Met. Vickers Elec. Co. Manchester, Eng., 1952-59; with Tex. Instruments, Inc. Dallas, 1959-94; dir. physics rsch. lab. Tex. Instruments, Inc., 1959-94, assoc. dir. cen. rsch. labs., 1971-72, dir. semiconductor R & D, 1972-75, dir. cen. rsch. labs., 1975-77, asst. v.p. dir. cen. rsch. labs., 1977-82, v.p. corp. staff, dir. cen. rsch. labs., 1982-94; dir. Indsl. Outreach Elec. Materials Sci. and Tech. Ctr., Engring. and Tech. Inst. U. Tex., Austin, 1994—. Contbr. articles to profl. jours. Bd. dirs. Indsl. Rsch. Inst., 1985-88, Coun. on Superconductivity for Am. Competitiveness, 1987-90; adv. bd. dirs. Tex. Ctr. for Superconductivity, 1989—. Fellow IEEE, Inst. Physics (U.K.), Am. Phys. Soc.; mem. NAE. Office: JJ Pickle Rsch Ctr U Tex MER 1 606J Austin TX 78758

STRATTON, THOMAS OLIVER, investment banker; b. Los Angeles, Feb. 14, 1930; s. Oliver Clarke and Ethel (Savage) S.; m. Carol Joyce Wilson, Feb. 21, 1953; children: Brentley Clarke, James Morris, Thomas Oliver Jr. Student, Taft Sch., 1944-48, Stanford, 1948-50; B.S., U. Calif. at Los Angeles, 1956; M.B.A., Boston U., 1960. With Security Pacific Nat. Bank, Los Angeles, 1955-56; security analyst New Eng. Mut. Life Ins. Co., Boston, 1956-60; exec. v.p., dir. Bankers Leasing Corp., Boston, 1960-64; treas. Montgomery Ward & Co., Chgo., 1964-67; pres. Investco Assoc., Inc., 1967-75, Monterey Capital, Inc., 1975—; bd. dirs. MCI Securities, Inc. Served with AUS, 1952-55. Republican. Congregationalist. Clubs: Old Capital (Monterey); Beach and Tennis (Pebble Beach); World Trade (San Francisco).

Home: PO Box 3713 Carmel CA 93921-3713 Office: PO Box 7370 Carmel CA 93921-7370

STRATTON, WALTER LOVE, lawyer; b. Greenwich, Conn., Sept. 21, 1926; s. John McKee and June (Love) S.; children: John, Michael, Peter (dec.), Lucinda; m. DeAnna Weinheimer, Oct. 1, 1994. Student, Williams Coll., 1943; A.B., Yale U., 1948; LL.B., Harvard U., 1951. Bar: N.Y. 1952. Assoc. Casey, Lane & Mittendorf, N.Y.C., 1951-53; assoc. Donovan, Leisure, Newton & Irvine, N.Y.C., 1956-63; ptnr. Donovan, Leisure, Newton & Irvine, 1963-84, Gibson, Dunn & Crutcher, 1984-93, Andrews & Kurth, N.Y.C., 1994—; asst. U.S. atty. So. Dist. N.Y., N.Y.C., 1953-56; lectr. Practising Law Inst. Served with USNR, 1945-46. Fellow Am. Coll. Trial Lawyers; mem. ABA, Fed. Bar Coun., N.Y. State Bar Assn. Clubs: Indian Harbor Yacht, Colo. Arlberg, Yale (N.Y.C.). Home: 434 Round Hill Rd Greenwich CT 06831-2639 Office: Andrews & Kurth 425 Lexington Ave New York NY 10017

STRATTON-CROOKE, THOMAS EDWARD, financial consultant; b. N.Y.C., June 28, 1933; s. Harold and Jeanne Mildred (Stifft) children: Karen, John Ryland; m. Suzanne Williams, Oct. 21, 1989. Student, Hunter Coll., 1951-52; BS in Marine Engring. and Transp., U.S. Maritime Acad., 1952-56; student, Washington U., St. Louis, 1961; MBA in Internat. Mktg., Banking and Fin., NYU, 1967. Commd. ensign USN, 1956, advanced through grades to lt., 1967; with Goodyear Internat. Corp., Akron, Ohio, 1956-58, Esso Internat., N.Y.C., 1958-60; dir. market info. and devel. Hotel Corp. Am., Boston, 1960-63; with Continental Grain Co. N.Y.C., 1960-64; dir. charter contracts Conoco, Stamford, Conn., 1969-70; cons. A. T. Kearney, Cleve., 1970-81; investment banker E. F. Hutton, Cleve., 1981-83, AG Edwards and Sons, Inc., Cleve., 1983-89; sr. fin. cons., registered investment advisor Merrill Lynch, Cleve., 1989-95, asst. v.p., sr. fin. cons., 1995—; chmn. Indsl. Devel. Resch. Coun., Atlanta, 1970, Indsl. Devel. Resch. Coun., Snow Mass, Colo., 1971; lectr. bus. U. R.I., Kingston, 1968-70, tchr. Bus. Coll. Internat., 1986-89. Contbr. articles to profl. jours. Mem. Findley Lake (N.Y.) Hist. Soc.; mem. Nat. Task Force Reps. for Pres. Reagan, Cleve., 1982—. Mem. Naval Res. Officers Assn., Great Lakes Hist. Soc., Soc. Naval Architects/Engrs., Navy League, U.S. Coast Guard Club (Cleve.), Univ. Club, Circumnavigators Club (life), Internat. Shipmasters Assn., Propeller Club, Army Club, Navy Club, French Creek Hist. Soc., Town Club (Jamestown, N.Y.), Masons, Shriners. Avocations: sailing, skiing, bird watching, gardening, sports car enthusiast. Office: Merrill Lynch 1 Cleveland Ctr 1375 E 9th St Cleveland OH 44114-1798

STRAUB, CHESTER JOHN, lawyer; b. Bklyn., May 12, 1937; s. Chester and Ann (Majewski) S.; m. Patricia Morrissey, Aug. 22, 1959; children: Chester, Michael, Christopher, Robert. AB, St. Peter's Coll., 1958; JD, U. Va., 1961. Bar: N.Y. State 1962, U.S. Dist. Ct. (so. and ea. dists.) N.Y. 1963, U.S. Ct. Appeals (2d cir.) 1967, U.S. Supreme Ct. 1978. Assoc. Willkie Farr & Gallagher, N.Y.C., 1963-71; ptnr. Willkie Farr & Gallagher, 1971—; mem. N.Y. State Assembly, 1967-72, N.Y. State Senate, 1973-75, Dem. Nat. Com., 1976-80; mediator U.S. Dist. Ct. (so. dist.) N.Y.; neutral evaluator U.S. Dist. Ct. (ea. dist.) N.Y.; chmn. N.Y. State statewide jud. screening com., 1988-94, first dept. jud. screening com., 1983-94; mem. Senator Moynihan's jud. selection com., 1976-95. Mem. Cardinal's Com. of Laity for Cath. Charities N.Y.; trustee Lenox Hill Hosp., Collins Found. With U.S. Army, 1961-63. Mem. Am. Bar Assn., N.Y. State Bar Assn., Assn. of Bar of City of N.Y.C., Kosciuszko Found., Assn. Sons of Poland. Home: 35 Prescott Ave Bronxville NY 10708-1727 Office: Willkie Farr & Gallagher 1 Citicorp Ctr 153 E 53rd St New York NY 10022

STRAUB, CHESTER JOHN, JR., government official; b. Charlottesville, Va., Oct. 4, 1960; s. Chester John and Patrecia (Morrisey) S.; m. Erin Mary Norton, Apr. 21, 1990. BA, Tufts U., 1982. Asst. to exec. dir. Friends of Mario M. Cumo, Inc., N.Y.C., 1986; dep. exec. dir. N.Y. State Dem. Com., N.Y.C., 1987-89, exec. dir., 1989-90; corp. sec. Battery Park City Authority, N.Y.C., 1990-93; dep. asst. sec. Econ. Devel. Adminstrn., Washington, 1993—. Dir. campaign ops. Clinton/Gore Coordinated Campaign, N.Y.C., 1992. Democrat. Roman Catholic. Home: Prog Support 1228 C St SE Washington DC 20003 Office: Econ Devel Adminstrn Rm 7844 14th St and Constitution Washington DC 20230

STRAUB, PETER FRANCIS, novelist; b. Milw., Mar. 2, 1943; s. Gordon Anthony and Elvena (Nilsestuen) S.; m. Susan Bitker, Aug. 27, 1966; children: Benjamin Bitker, Emma Sydney Valli. BA, U. Wis., 1965; MA, Columbia U., 1966. English tchr. Univ. Sch., Milw., 1966-68. Author: Marriages, 1973, Julia, 1975, If You Could See Me Now, 1977, Ghost Story, 1979, Shadow Land, 1980, Floating Dragon, 1983, Lesson Park and Belsize Square, 1984, Wild Animals, 1984, Blue Rose, 1985, Koko, 1988, Mystery, 1989, Houses Without Doors, 1990, Mrs. God, 1991, The Throat, 1993, (with Stephen King) The Talisman, 1984; editor: Peter Straub's Ghosts, 1995. Recipient Brit. Fantasy award, August Derleth award, 1983, World Fantasy awards World Fantasy Conv., 1989, 93. Mem. PEN, Mystery Writers Am., Horror Writers Assn (award 1994). Avocations: jazz, opera, classical music.

STRAUB, PETER THORNTON, lawyer; b. St. Louis, Mar. 27, 1939; s. Ralph H. and Mary Louise (Thornton) S.; m. Wendy B. Cubbage, Dec. 19, 1964; children: Karl Thornton, Philip Hamilton, Ellen Elizabeth. A.B., Washington and Lee U., 1961, J.D., 1964. Bar: Mo. 1964, Va. 1964, U.S. Dist. Ct. (ea. dist.) Mo. 1967, U.S. Circuit Ct. Appeals (8th cir.) 1969, U.S. Supreme Ct. 1970, U.S. Circuit Ct. Appeals (D.C. cir.) 1971, Ct. Mil. Appeals 1970, U.S. Tax Ct. 1971, U.S. Bankruptcy Ct. 1991. Assoc. Evans & Dixon, St. Louis, 1966-68; asst. pub. defender St. Louis County, St. Louis, 1968-69; asst. U.S. Atty. St. Louis, 1969-71; trial atty. internal security div. Dept. Justice, Washington, 1971-72; atty.-adviser office of dep. atty. gen. Dept. Justice, 1972-73, dir. office criminal justice, 1974; minority counsel com. on judiciary U.S. Ho. of Reps., Washington, 1973-74; gen. counsel SSS, Washington, 1974-76; sole practice Alexandria, Va., 1976—. Pres., gov. bd. Alexandria Cmty. Mental Health Ctr., 1982—; mem. No. Va. Estate Planning Coun., 1981—; mem. pres.'s coun. Trinity Coll., Washington, 1980-87; mem. adv. bd. Salvation Army, 1991—, Am. Heart Assn., Alexandria, 1991-92; Va. escheat atty., City of Alexandria, 1994—. Capt. USAR, 1964-66. Recipient certificate of award Dept. Justice, 1970, certificate of appreciation Law Enforcement Assistance Adminstrn. Dept. Justice, 1974, Silver Beaver award Boy Scouts Am., Washington, 1987. Mem. ABA, Fed. Bar Assn., Va. Bar Assn., Bar Assn. Met. St. Louis, Mo. Bar Assn., Alexandria Bar Assn., Va. Trial Lawyers Assn., Nat. Eagle Scout Assn., Nat. Lawyers Club, Optimists (bd. dirs., pres. Alexandria chpt. 1984—), Sigma Nu. Republican. Congregationalist. Avocations: scouting, reading, bicycling. Office: 1225 Martha Custis Dr Alexandria VA 22302-2017

STRAUB, SYLVIA ANN, association executive; b. Dearborn, Mich., May 27, 1938; d. Thurman Andrew and Dorothy Inez (Pinnow) Clarke; m. Duane Gene Straub, July 27, 1960. BA with high distinction, Valparaiso U., 1960; MAT, Mich. State U., 1963; MA, Ind U., 1967, PhD, 1972. Cert. assn. exec. Instr. French Ohio U., Athens, 1963-65; dir. communications Agy. for Instructional Technol., Bloomington, Ind., 1974-82; publicity mgr. news dept. Nat. Pub. Radio, Washington, 1983-86; dir. info. and mktg. svcs. Am. Speech-Lang. Hearing Assn., Rockville, Md., 1986-89; exec. dir. Registry of Interpreters for the Deaf, Silver Spring, Md., 1989—; task force on instrnl. TV PBS, Washington, 1977-79; speaker mktg. seminar for instrnl. TV execs. Corp. for Pub. Broadcasting and U. of Lowell, Washington, 1987; writer, cons. Corp. Pub. Broadcasting, Washington, 1983. Bd. dirs. Valparaiso U. Alumni Assn., 1989—; ch. coun. mem. Luther Pl. Meml. Ch., Washington, 1985-87; task force job placement MLA, N.Y.C., 1977-78; pres. Brown County Humane Soc., Nashville, Ind., 1973-74. Recipient scholarship Valparaiso U. 1968. Mem. Am. Soc. Assn. Execs., Greater Washington Soc. of Assn. Execs., Women in Comms., Inc., Am. Assn. Tchrs. French, Am. Disabilities Found. and Channel. Office: Registry Interpreters Deaf 8719 Colesville Rd Ste 310 Silver Spring MD 20910-3919 Office: Financial Women Internat. 7910 Woodmont Ave Bethesda MD 20814

STRAUBER, DONALD I., lawyer; b. Bklyn., Dec. 28, 1936; s. Jacob N. and Hannah (Lebedinsky) S.; m. Rachel Leah Sklaroff, Aug. 14, 1960; 1 child, Jocelyn Emily. A.B., U. Pa., Phila., 1957; LL.B., Harvard U., 1960. Bar: N.Y. 1961, U.S. Supreme Ct. 1965. Law clk. to Judge William Herlands U.S. Dist. Ct., So. Dist. N.Y., N.Y.C., 1960-61; assoc. Cravath, Swaine

& Moore, N.Y.C., 1962-70; ptnr. Chadbourne & Parke and predecessor, N.Y.C., 1971—. Mem. ABA, N.Y. State Bar Assn., Assn. of Bar of City of N.Y. Home: 1160 Park Ave New York NY 10128-1212 Office: Chadbourne & Parke 30 Rockefeller Plz New York NY 10112-0127

STRAUCH, GERALD OTTO, surgeon; b. Three Rivers, Mich., July 26, 1932; s. Gerald Otto and Helen Jeanette (Zierle) S.; m. Margaret Mary Spindler, Aug. 20, 1955; children—David Mark, Susan Mary, Jean Ellen. Grad., U. Mich. M.D. 1957. Diplomate: Am. Bd. Surgery. Intern R.I. Hosp., Providence, 1957-58; resident in surgery, 1958-62; practice medicine specializing in surgery Stamford, Conn., 1964-79; chief of surgery New Britain (Conn.) Gen. Hosp., 1979-87; clin. prof. surgery N.Y. Med. Coll., 1979-80; prof. surgery U. Conn. Sch. Medicine, 1980-87; clin. prof. surgery Uniformed Svcs. Univ. Health Scis., 1984—, U. Chgo., 1988—; dir. trauma and assembly depts. Am. Coll. Surgeons, 1988—; adj. prof. surgery Northwestern U., 1988—. Contbr. numerous articles to profl. jours. Served to capt. AUS, 1962-64. Fellow ACS; mem. New Eng., Frederick A. Coller surg. socs., Soc. for Surgery of Alimentary Tract, Collegium Internationale Chirurgiae Digestivae, Conn. Soc. Am. Bd. Surgeons, Am. Assn. Surgery of Trauma, Cen. Surg. Assn., Chgo. Surg. Soc., Assn. Advancement Automotive Medicine, Shock Soc., Corr. Soc. Surgeons (editor), Sociedad de Cirujanos de Chile (hon.), Assn. Mejicana de Cirujanos Generales (hon.), Assn. Francaise de Chirurgie (hon.). Republican. Roman Catholic. Clubs: Wee Burn Country. Home: 633 Sheridan Rd Winnetka IL 60093-2323 Office: Am Coll Surgeons 55 E Erie St Chicago IL 60611-2731

STRAUCH, JOHN L., lawyer; b. Pitts., Apr. 16, 1939; s. Paul L. and Delilah M. (Madison) S.; m. Gail Lorraine Kohn, Dec. 5, 1991; children: Paul L., John M., Lisa E. BA, U. Pitts., 1960; JD magna cum laude, NYU Sch. Law, 1963. Law clk. to Judge Sterry Waterman U.S. Ct. Appeals (2d cir.), St. Johnsbury, Vt., 1963-64; assoc. Jones, Day, Reavis & Pogue, Cleve., 1964-70, ptnr., 1970—; mem. adv. com., partnership com., chmn. litigation group; mem. Statutory Com. on Selecting Bankruptcy Judges, Cleve., 1985-88; mem. lawyers com. Nat. Ctr. for State Cts. Editor-in-chief: NYU Law Rev., 1962-63. Pres., trustee Cleve. Task Force on Violent Crimes, 1985-88; trustee Legal Aid Soc., Cleve., 1978, Cleve. Greater Growth Assn., 1985-86, Citizens Mental Health Assembly, 1989-90, lawyers com. Nat. Ctr. for State Cts., 1989—. Fellow Am. Coll. Trial Lawyers (state); mem. ABA, Ohio Bar Assn., Cleve. Bar Assn. (trustee 1980-83, pres. 1985-86), Fed. Bar Assn. (trustee Cleve. chpt. 1978-79, v.p. Cleve. chpt. 1979-80), Sixth Fed. Jud. Conf. (life), Ohio Eighth Jud. Conf. (life), Order of Coif, Inns of Ct., Oakmont Club, Cleve. Racquet Club, 13th St. Racquet Club, The Country Club, Phi Beta Kappa. Home: 28149 N Woodland Rd Cleveland OH 44124-4522 Office: Jones Day Reavis & Pogue N Point 901 Lakeside Ave E Cleveland OH 44114-1190

STRAUCH, KARL, physicist, educator; b. Germany, Oct. 4, 1922; came to U.S., 1939, naturalized, 1944; s. Georg and Carola (Bock) S.; m. Maria Sadron, June 10, 1951; children—Roger A., Hans D. A. B in Chemistry and Physics, U. Calif. at Berkeley, 1943, Ph.D in Physics, 1950. Jr. fellow Soc. Fellows, Harvard U., 1950-53; asst. prof. Harvard U., Cambridge, Mass., 1953-57, assoc. prof., 1957-62, prof., 1962—; dir. Cambridge Electron Accelerator, 1967-74, George Vasmer Leverett prof. physics, 1976—; researcher in high energy physics. Contbr. articles to profl. jours. Served with USNR, 1944-46. Mem. Am. Phys. Soc., Am. Assn. Physics Tchrs., Am. Acad. Arts and Scis., Phi Beta Kappa, Sigma Xi. Home: 81 Pleasant St Lexington MA 02173 Office: Harvard U Dept Physics Cambridge MA 02138

STRAUMANIS, JOHN JANIS, JR., psychiatry educator; b. Riga, Latvia, Apr. 22, 1935; came to U.S., 1950; s. Janis and Ella (Fredrichson) S.; m. Carol A. Sharar, Aug. 8, 1959; children: John, Susan. BA, U. Iowa, 1957, MD, 1960, MS, 1964. Intern Georgetown U. Hosp., Washington, 1960-61; resident U. Iowa, Iowa City, 1961-64; asst. prof. Temple U., Phila., 1966-71, assoc. prof., 1971-77, prof., 1977-85; prof. psychiatry La. State U., Shreveport, 1985-92; prof. psychiatry, dir. rsch. Tulane U. Med. Sch., New Orleans, 1992—; cons. Camden County Hosp., Blackwood, N.J., 1967-85, VA Hosp., Shreveport, 1985-92, VA Hosp., New Orleans, 1992—. Contbr. articles to profl. jours. Lt. comdr. USN, 1964-65. Rsch. Career Devel. award NIMH, 1966. Fellow Am. Psychiat. Assn.; mem. ACP, Am. Psychopathol. Assn., Soc. Biol. Psychiatry, Am. EEG Assn., Phi Eta Sigma, Phi Beta Kappa, Alpha Omega Alpha. Avocations: travel, music, photography. Office: Tulane U Med Ctr Dept Psychiatry & Neurology 1430 Tulane Ave New Orleans LA 70112-2699

STRAUS, ALAN GORDON, lawyer; b. Washington, Nov. 1, 1952; s. Richard and Elaine (Scharroff) S.; m. Katherine Way Schoonover, June 16, 1979. BA with honors, U. Wis., 1974; JD, NYU, 1978. Bar: N.Y. 1978. Assoc. Skadden, Arps, Slate, Meagher & Flom, N.Y.C., 1977-84, 85-88, ptnr., 1988—; ptnr. Brown, Raysman & Milstein, N.Y.C., 1984-85. Co-author: Federal Regulation of Campaign Finance and Political Activity, 1982. Office: Skadden Arps Slate Meagher 919 3d Ave New York NY 10022

STRAUS, DAVID A., architectural firm executive; b. Medford, Oreg., 1943; m. Sherry Straus, 1974; 2 children. BArch, U. Oreg., 1967. Registered architect, Oreg. Founding ptnr. Skelton, Straus & Seibert, Medford, 1989—. Past bd. dirs. Medford YMCA, Rogue Valley Art Assn.; past pres. Medford Arts Commn., Arts Coun. So. Oreg.; coach Rogue Valley Soccer Assn.; leader Boy Scouts Am.; bd. dirs., past pres. Schneider Mus. Art SOSC. Ret. lt. USNR, Vietnam. Mem. AIA (past pres. So. Oreg. chpt.), Archtl. Found. Oreg. (bd. dirs.), Univ. Club Medford (past pres.), Oreg. Club So. Oreg. (past pres.), U. Oreg. Alumni Assn., Medford/Jackson County C. of C. (bd. dirs.), Rotary. Office: Skelton Straus & Seibert Arch 26 Hawthorne St Medford OR 97504-7114

STRAUS, DONALD BLUN, retired company executive; b. Middletown, N.J., June 28, 1916; s. Percy S. and Edith (Abraham) S.; m. Elizabeth Allen, Sept. 7, 1940; children: David Allen, Robert Beckwith, Sara Elizabeth. AB, Harvard U., 1938, M.B.A., 1940. Exec. dir. labor relations panel AEC, 1948-53; v.p. Health Ins. Plan of Greater N.Y., 1953-61; pres. Am. Arbitration Assn., 1963-72, pres. research inst., 1972-81; cons. Internat. Inst. of Applied Systems Analysis, 1982-85; mem. N.Y. State Bd. Mediation, 1956-59. Chmn. bd. Planned Parenthood Fedn. Am., 1962-65; emeritus bd. dirs. Internat. Council Comml. Arbitration, Population Resources Commn., Soc. Human Ecology; emeritus trustee Carnegie Endowment for Internat. Peace, Inst. Advanced Study, Princeton, Coll. of Atlantic. Mem. Coun. Fgn. Rels. Clubs: Century Assn., Knickerbocker, Harvard of N.Y.C., Pot and Kettle (Bar Harbor, Maine). Home: 1 E 66th St New York NY 10021

STRAUS, HELEN LORNA PUTTKAMMER, biologist, educator; b. Chgo., Feb. 15, 1933; d. Ernst Wilfred and Helen Louise (Monroe) Puttkammer; m. Francis Howe Straus II, June 11, 1955; children: Francis Howe III, Helen E., Christopher M., Michael W. AB magna cum laude, Radcliffe Coll., 1955; MS in Anatomy, U. Chgo., 1960, PhD in Anatomy, 1962. With U. Chgo., 1964—, asst. prof. anatomy, 1967-73, dean of students, 1971-82, assoc. prof., 1973-87, dean of admissions, 1975-80, prof. anatomy and biol. scis., 1987—; bd. govs. U. Chgo. Internat. House, 1987—. Trustee Radcliffe Coll., Cambridge, Mass., 1973-83. Recipient Quantrell Award for Excellence in teaching, U. Chgo., 1970, 87, Silver medal Case Outstanding Tchr. Program, 1987. Mem. AAAS, NCAA (acad. requirements com. 1986-92, chmn. 1990-92), Nat. Sci. Tchrs. Assn., Am. Assn. Anatomists, Harvard U. Alumni Assn. (bd. dirs. 1980-83), Phi Beta Kappa (sec., treas. U. Chgo. chpt. 1984—). Avocations: gardening, crafts, travel. Home: 5642 S Kimbark Ave Chicago IL 60637-1606 Office: U Chgo 5845 S Ellis Ave Chicago IL 60637-1404

STRAUS, IRVING LEHMAN, public relations executive; b. N.Y.C., Apr. 1, 1921; s. Nathan and Helen (Sachs) S.; m. Anna Straus, Jan. 27, 1977; children: Daniel, William. Student, Amherst Coll. (Mass.), 1939-41. Ptnr. Ralph E. Samuel & Co., N.Y.C., 1954-65; v.p. Energy Fund Inc., N.Y.C., 1958-65; pres., founder Straus Comms., Inc., N.Y.C., 1965-80; ptnr. Fin. Rels. Board Inc., N.Y.C., 1980-88, sr. cons., 1986—; dir. Arnold Constable Corp., N.Y.C., 1979-88; chmn. bd. Straus Corp. Communications, N.Y.C., 1989—; founder, pres. Mut. Fund Coun., 1989—, Westchester Aquarium, Inc., White Plains, N.Y., 1947-55; pres. Inst. Systems Corp. N.Y.C., 1983—. Served with U.S. Navy, 1942-45. Decorated Air medal; recipient Silver Anvil Pub. Rels. Soc. Am., 1979. Mem. Anvil Pub. Rels. Soc. Am., Intrepid

Mus. Pilot's Assn. (chmn. N.Y.C. chpt. 1985-89). Office: Straus Corp Communications 1501 Broadway New York NY 10036-5502

STRAUS, KENNETH HOLLISTER, former retail store executive; b. N.Y.C., Feb. 18, 1925; s. Jack Isidor and Margaret (Hollister) S.; m. Elizabeth Browne, Apr. 14, 1945 (dec. 1991); children: Melinda Straus Schwartz, Timothy; m. Brenda Newbauer Murphy, June 28, 1993. Grad., Milton Acad., 1943; student, NYU Sch. Retailing, 1945-46; grad. advanced mgmt. program, Harvard Bus. Sch., 1957. With R.H. Macy & Co., Inc., N.Y.C., 1947-85, v.p. men's and boy's wear, 1963-67, sr. v.p. domestic and internat. corp. buying, 1967-78, pres. corp. buying, 1978-80, chmn., chief exec. officer corp. buying, 1980-85, also dir., ret., 1985; cons. Nat Exec. Svc. Corp., 1985—. Hon. dep. commr., 1985-93, trustee, hon. commr. 1993—; honor emergency fund N.Y.C. Fire Dept., 1966—, chair, hon. officer adv. com., 1988—; bd. dirs. N.Y. Fire Safety Found., 1984—; pres. Fire Found. of N.Y. Inc., 1968—; mem. adv. bd. John Jay Coll. Criminal Justice, 1987—; mem. pub. safety com. The Partnership, 1987-89; bd. dirs. Police Found. 1987—, chair crime stoppers program, 1987—; vice-chair St. James' Ch., 1988-94, chmn. bldgs. and grounds com., 1988-94, grants com., Michel Fund com., 1989-90; trustee St. Luke's/Roosevelt Hosp. Ctr., 1988—; mem. exec. com., 1994—; trustee, v.p. Bd. Fgn. Parishes, 1988—, exec. com., 1989—; mem. coun. Episcopal Diocese of N.Y., 1988-91, chair comm. task force, 1989-90; bd. dirs. Episcopal Mission Soc., 1989-91, Crime Stoppers Internat., 1993—; v.p., bd. dirs. Eastside Community Ctr., Inc., 1988-91. With AUS, 1943-45. Decorated Order of Crown (Belgium); recipient Good Scout award Boy Scouts Am., 1965; named to Soc. St. John Jerusalem, 1987—. Mem. Piping Rock Club, Union Club, Harvard Club, Honor Legion FDNY (hon. 1992—). Home: 60 E End Ave Apt 40-c New York NY 10028-7908

STRAUS, LEON STEPHAN, physicist; b. Takoma Park, Md., May 29, 1943; s. Sidney and Ruth Straus; m. Cheryl Sarran Straus, Apr. 4, 1970; children: Jonathan, Jennifer. BS in Physics, Antioch Coll., Yellow Springs, Ohio, 1965; M Physics, Georgetown U., 1970, PhD in Physics, 1971. Mem. rsch. staff Ctr. Naval Analyses, Alexandria, Va., 1973-75; field rep. CTF 69 Ctr. Naval Analyses, Naples, Italy, 1975-77; project mgr. Ctr. Naval Analyses, Alexandria, 1977-79; field rep. CTF 66/67 Ctr. Naval Analyses, Naples, Italy, 1979-82; assoc. dep. dir. Ctr. Naval Analyses, Alexandria, 1982-85; field rep. CTF 72 Ctr. Naval Analyses, Kamiseya, Japan, 1985-87; program mgr. Ctr. Naval Analyses, Alexandria, 1987-90; field rep. COMSIXTHFLT Ctr. Naval Analyses, Gaeta, Italy, 1990-92; project mgr. Ctr. Naval Analyses, Alexandria, 1992—; asst. AEC, Germantown, Md., 1968-71. Contbr. articles to profl. jours. Vol. Jewish lay leader USN, Naples, 1975-77, 79-82. Recipient Fellowship Georgetown U., Washington, 1965-68. Mem. Acoustical Soc. Am., Navy Submarine League. Jewish. Achievements include evaluating U.S. Navy and Joint strategy, tactics, comm. and tech. Office: Ctr Naval Analyses 4401 Ford Ave Alexandria VA 22302-1432

STRAUS, MELVILLE, investment company executive; b. Mar. 16, 1939; s. Milton Straus and Laura DeRoy; m. Susan S. Paull (div. 1984); 1 child, Scott; m. Leila Mau, Sept. 26, 1986; children: Alexandra, Benjamin.. AB, Dartmouth Coll., 1960; MBA, Harvard U., 1967. V.p.Am. Toiletries, 1963-65; security analyst Donaldson, Lufkin & Jenrette, 1963-65; dir. rsch., exec. com. Standard & Poor's InterCapital fund, 1969-72; ptnr. Weiss, Peck & Greer Investments, 1973—; bd. dirs. Independent Curators, Inc., N.Y.C.; mem. exec. com. Weiss, Peck & Greer Investments, mgmt. com., pres., trustee Tudor Fund, Growth Fund, exec. v.p. Growth and Income Fund. Bd. dirs. Guild Hall, East Hampton, N.Y.; chmn. emeritus bd. governing trustees Am. Ballet Theatre, N.Y.C.; treas. contemporary arts coun., Mus. Modern Art, N.Y.C., chmn. bd. overseers Positive Ctr./Hood Mus., Dartmouth Coll.; mem. East Hampton Fire Dept., Am. Heart Assn., Save the Children; active Conn. Pub. Radio. Mem. Lower Manhattan Cultural Coun., Robin Hood Found., East Hampton Hist. Soc., South Fork Hist. Soc., Harmonie Club, 500 Club. Avocations: tennis, squash, golf, bridge, the arts. Office: Weiss Peck & Greer One New York Plz New York NY 10004

STRAUS, OSCAR S., II, foundation executive; b. N.Y.C., Nov. 6, 1914; s. Roger Williams and Gladys (Guggenheim) S.; m. Marion Miller Straus, 1941 (div. 1982); 1 child, Oscar S. III.; m. Joan Sutton, 1982. A.B., Princeton U., 1936; postgrad., U. Dijon, summer 1936, Sch. Bus. Adminstrn. Harvard U., 1938. Pvt. sec. Internat. Labor Office, Geneva, Switzerland, 1937-38; U.S. fgn. service officer, 1940-42; divisional asst. Dept. State, 1942-43, 44-45; treas., dir., v.p., chmn. finance com. Am. Smelting & Refining Co., 1945-59; partner Guggenheim Bros., 1959-83; pres., dir. Guggenheim Exploration Co., Inc., 1963-73; gen. ptnr. Straus Minerals, 1973-88; pres., bd. dirs. Daniel and Florence Guggenheim Found., N.Y.C.; pres., bd. dirs. Fred L. Lavanburg Found.; bd. dirs. Mutual of Omaha, Companion Life Ins. Co., United of Omaha. Trustee emeritus Am. Mus. Natural History, Mystic Seaport, Conn.; hon. chmn. Rensselaerville (N.Y.) Inst.; trustee Congregation Emanu-El. Mem. Coun. Fgn. Rels., Royal Nova Scotia Yacht Squadron Club, Cruising Club Am., River Club, Megantic Fish and Game Club, Doubles Club, Knickerbocker Club. Jewish. Home: 7 Gracie Sq New York NY 10028-8030 Office: Daniel & Florence Guggenheim Found 950 3d Ave 30th Fl New York NY 10022

STRAUS, R. PETER, communications company executive, broadcasting executive; b. N.Y.C., Feb. 15, 1923; s. Nathan and Helen (Sachs) S.; m. Ellen Louise Sulzberger, Feb. 6, 1950; children: Diane (Mrs. Carl Tucker), Katherine (Mrs. Blair Caple), Jeanne (Mrs. Richard Tofel), Eric. B.A. cum laude, Yale U., 1943. Chief sec. manpower div. U.S. Office Mil. Govt., Berlin, 1946-47; pub. relations exec. Edward L. Bernays, N.Y.C., 1947-48; program dir. spl. features radio sta. WMCA, N.Y.C., 1948-50; exec. asst. to dir. gen. ILO, Geneva, 1950-55; dir. U.S. office, 1955-58; pres. Straus Broadcasting Group, 1958-67; asst. adminstr. for Africa AID, 1967-69; pres. Straus Communications Inc., 1970-77, chmn., 1979—; chmn. Radio Sta. WMCA, N.Y.C., 1979-87, Radio Sta. WFTR, Front Royal, Va., 1980—, Radio Sta. WELV, Ellenville, N.Y., 1982—; pub. Advertiser Group Newpapers, Monroe, N.Y., 1986—, Pointer View, West Point, N.Y., Sparta (N.J.) Independent, 1988—; dir. Voice of Am., 1977-79; pres. Straus Comm., Inc., Stas. WELV-AM, WWWK-Fm, Ellenville, N.Y., 1993—; mem. faculty Johns Hopkins U. Sch. Advanced Internat. Studies, Washington, 1979-80; pub. Straus Editor's Report, 1970-72, Cranford (N.J.) Citizen and Chronicle, 1976-78; Spl. cons. USIA, 1966; Co-chmn. Interracial Council Bus. Opportunity N.Y., 1966-67; chmn. Com. Constl. Issues, N.Y., 1966-67; mem. N.Y.C. Commn. on State-City Relations, 1972-73; advisory com. Ministry of Tourism, Israel, 1972-75 N.Y.C. Aux. Policeman, 1974-77; lectr. Boston U. Sch. Pub. Communication, 1975-76; host internat. radio program Hotline, 1974-77; vis. prof. Woodrow Wilson Sch., Princeton U., 1981-82; moderator Aspen Inst. Exec. Seminar, 1982-83; founder, chmn. Com. Decent Unbiased Campaign Tactics Conduct, 1982—. Author: How To Keep Albany from Milking The City Dry, 1968, Is The State Department Color Blind, 1971, The Buddy System in Foreign Affairs, 1973, The Father of Anne Frank, 1975, The Risks and Rewards of Candor, 1979. Chmn. N.Y. State Democratic Campaign Com., 1964; N.Y. del. Nat. Dem. Convs., 1960, 64; mem. fgn. affairs task force Dem. Nat. Com., 1975-77; bd. govs. Am. Jewish Com., 1982—; pres. N.Y. chpt., 1984-87; founding mem. Black/Jewish Coalition, 1982—; v.p. Jewish Community Relations Council N.Y., 1987—; adv. bd. Nat. Inst. Against Prejudice and Violence, 1987—; bd. dirs. Golda Meir Assn., 1987—; mem. The Ctr. for Excellence in Govt.; pres. Jewish Edn. in Media, 1990. Served to 1st lt. USAAF, 1943-45. Decorated Air medal with 5 oak leaf clusters; recipient award Harlem Lawyers Assn., 1964. Mem. Council Fgn. Relations, N.Y. State Broadcasters Assn. (pres. 1964), Assn. for Edn. in Journalism and Mass Communication. Clubs: Federal City (Washington), Nat. Press (Washington); Yale (N.Y.C.). Office: Straus Communications 22 N Main St Ellenville NY 12428-1019

STRAUS, ROBERT, behavioral sciences educator; b. New Haven, Jan. 9, 1923; s. Samuel Hirsh and Alma (Fleischner) S.; m. Ruth Elisabeth Dawson, Sept. 8, 1945; children: Robert James, Carol Martin, Margaret Dawson, John William. BA, Yale U., 1943, MA, 1945, PhD, 1947. Asst. prof. Yale U., 1948-51, research asso. applied psychology, 1951-53; acting dir. Conn. Child Study and Treatment Home, New Haven, 1952-53; assoc. prof. preventive medicine SUNY Upstate Med. Center, 1953-56; prof. med. sociology U. Ky., Lexington, 1956-59; prof. dept. behavioral sci. Coll. Medicine, also chmn. dept. U. Ky., 1959-87; dir. for sci. devel. Med. Rsch. Inst. San Francisco, 1991-93; vis. fellow Yale U., 1968-69; vis. prof. U. Calif., Berkeley, 1978, 86; sec. Com. Med. Sociology, 1955-57; chmn. Coop. Com.

Study Alcoholism, 1961-63; chmn. Nat. Adv. Com. on Alcoholism, 1966-69; mem. Nat. Adv. Coun. on Alcohol Abuse and Alcoholism, 1984-87; trustee Med. Rsch. Inst. San Francisco, 1988-93; mem. Calif. Pacific Med. Ctr. Rsch. Coun., 1993. Author: Medical Care for Seamen, 1950, (with S.D. Bacon) Drinking in College, 1953, Alcohol and Society, 1973, Escape From Custody, 1974; co-editor: Medicine and Society, 1963; mem. editorial bd.: Jour. Studies on Alcohol. Pres., Bluegrass R.R. Mus., 1980. Mem. Inst. Medicine NAS, Am. Sociol. Assn. (chmn. med. sociology sect. 1967-68), Assn. Behavioral Scis. and Med. Edn. (pres. 1974), Am. Pub. Health Assn. (lifetime achievement award sect. on alcohol, tobacco and other drugs 1993), Acad. Behavioral Medicine Rsch., Phi Beta Kappa, Sigma Xi. Home: 656 Raintree Rd Lexington KY 40502-2874

STRAUS, R(OBERT) JAMES, lawyer; b. New Haven, Aug. 17, 1946; s. Robert and Ruth (Dawson) S.; m. Donna Craig, Dec. 27, 1968; children—Leigh Elisabeth, Amanda Craig, Emily Dawson, Robert Benjamin. B.A. cum laude, Yale U., 1968; J.D. U. Chgo., 1974. Bar: Ky. 1974, U.S. Dist. Ct. (we. dist.) Ky. 1974. Assoc., Brown, Todd & Heyburn, Louisville, Ky., 1974-79, ptnr., 1979—. Chmn. Legal Aid Soc., Inc. Louisville, 1981-85. Served to capt. USMC, 1968-71; Vietnam. Mem. Louisville Bar Assn., Ky. Bar Assn., ABA. Democrat. Presbyterian. Clubs: Jefferson, Louisville Boat. Home: 2517 Top Hill Rd Louisville KY 40206-2830 Office: 3200 Providian Ctr Louisville KY 40202-3363

STRAUS, ROGER W., JR., publishing company executive; b. N.Y.C., Jan. 3, 1917; s. Roger Williams and Gladys (Guggenheim) S.; m. Dorothea Liebmann, June 27, 1938; 1 son, Roger W. III. Student, Hamilton Coll., 1935-37; B.J. U. Mo., 1939, Litt.D. (hon.), 1976. Reporter Daily Reporter, White Plains, N.Y., 1936; feature writer Daily Reporter, 1939-40; editorial writer, reporter Columbia Missourian, 1937-39; editor, pub. Asterisk, 1939; editorial asst. Current History, 1940, assoc. editor, 1940-45; assoc. editor Forum, 1940-45; pres. Book Sales, Inc., 1943-46; founder Farrar, Straus & Co., Inc. (now Farrar, Straus & Giroux, Inc.), 1945; pres. Farrar, Straus & Giroux, Inc., N.Y.C., 1987—; chmn. adv. bd. Partisan Rev. mag., 1959-69. Co-editor: The Sixth Column, 1941, War Letters from Britain, 1941, The New Order, 1941; Chmn. publ. bd.: Am. Judaism mag, 1955-65. Vice pres. Fred L. Lavanburg Found., 1950-80, Daniel and Florence Guggenheim Found., 1960-76; bd. dirs. Harry Frank Guggenheim Found., Manhattanville Coll., 1970-76, John Simon Guggenheim Found.; fellow N.Y. Inst. for Humanities. Served to lt. USNR, 1941-45. Mem. P.E.N., Union Am. Hebrew Congregations (pub. com. 1955-65), Sigma Delta Chi. Clubs: Lotos, Westchester Country, Players. Office: Farrar Straus & Giroux Inc 19 Union Sq W New York NY 10003-3304

STRAUS, ROGER W, III, book publishing executive, photographer; b. N.Y.C., Nov. 13, 1943; s. Roger Williams and Dorothea (Leibman) S.; m. Nina Pelikan, June 4, 1965; children: Laura, Rachel, Tamara; m. Doris Ann Borowski, Mar. 3, 1987. BA, Columbia Coll., 1967. Dir. sales, mktg. Farrar, Straus & Giroux, N.Y.C., 1967-75; dir. mktg. Harper & Row, N.Y.C., 1976-79, editorial dir., 1979-81, assoc. pub., 1981-82; dir. sales Times Books, N.Y.C., 1982-84; exec. editor Avon Books, N.Y.C., 1984-85; mng. dir. Farrar, Straus & Giroux, 1986—; dir. Beacon Press, Boston, The Godine Press, Boston. Democrat. Jewish. Avocation: kayaking. Home: 730 King Ave Bronx NY 10464 Office: Farrar Straus & Giroux Inc 19 Union Sq W New York NY 10003

STRAUSBAUGH, SCOTT DAVID, Olympic athlete, canoeist. Olympic slalom doubles canoeist Barcelona, Spain, 1992. Recipient Gold medal canoe slalom doubles Olympics, Barcelona, 1992. Office: c/o US Olympic Com 1750 E Boulder St Colorado Springs CO 80909

STRAUSER, ROBERT WAYNE, lawyer; b. Little Rock, Aug. 28, 1943; s. Christopher Columbus and Opal (Orr) S.; m. Atha Maxine Tubbs, June 26, 1971 (div. 1991); children: Robert Benjamin, Ann Kathleen. B.A, Davidson (N.C.) Coll., 1965; postgrad., Vanderbilt U., Nashville, 1965-66; LLB, U. Tex., 1968. Bar: Tex. 1968, U.S. Ct. Mil. Appeals 1971. Staff atty. Tex. Legis. Coun., Austin, 1969-71; counsel Jud. Com., Tex. Ho. of Reps., Austin, 1971-73; chief counsel Jud. Com., Tex. Constl. Conv., Austin, 1974; exec. v.p. and legis. counsel Tex. Assn. Taxpayers, Austin, 1974-85; assoc. Baker & Botts, Austin, 1985-87; ptnr. Baker & Botts, 1988—. Assoc. editor Tex. Internat. Law Jour., 1968. Mem. Tex. Ho. Speakers Econ. Devel. Com., Austin, 1986-87; mem. adv. com. Tex. Employment Commn., 1984-85; mem. Austin Coun. Fgn. Affairs, 1987—; dir. McDonald Obs. Bd. Visitors, 1988—; mem. exec. com. Tex. Lyceum Assn., 1980-81, 84-88; elder Presbyn. Ch.; mem. exec. com. Austin Symphony Orch. Soc., 1985—, v.p. 1993-94. Capt. USNR, 1970. Named Rising Star of Tex., Tex. Bus. Mag., 1983. Mem. State Bar of Tex. (coun. mem. tax sect.), Travis County Bar Assn. Headliners Club (dir.). Home: 3312 Gilbert St Austin TX 78703-2102 Office: Baker & Botts 1600 San Jacinto Blvd Austin TX 78701

STRAUSFELD, NICHOLAS, neurobiology and entomology educator; b. Claygate, England, Oct. 22, 1942. BSc, U. Coll. London, 1965, PhD in Neurophysiology, 1986. Prof. U. Ariz., Tucson. Author: (books) Atlas of an Insect Brain, 1976, Functional Neuroanatomy, 1983. MacArthur fellow, 1995. Office: U Arizona Dept Ecology Tucson AZ 85721*

STRAUSS, ALBRECHT BENNO, English educator, editor; b. Berlin, May 17, 1921; came to U.S., 1940; s. Bruno and Bertha (Badt) S.; m. Nancy Grace Barron, July 30, 1978; 1 child, Rebecca Ilse; stepchildren: Carolyn, Kathryn. BA, Oberlin Coll., 1942; MA, Tulane U., 1948; PhD, Harvard U., 1956. Instr. English Brandeis U., 1951-52; teaching fellow gen. edn. Harvard U., 1952-55; instr. English Yale U., 1955-59; asst. prof. English U. Okla., Norman, 1959-60; asst. prof. English U. N.C., Chapel Hill, 1960-64, assoc. prof., 1964-70, prof., 1970-91, prof. emeritus, 1991—. Editor Studies in Philology, 1974-80; sec. editorial com. Yale Edit. of Works of Samuel Johnson, 1975—; mem. editorial com. Ga. edit. works of Tobias Smollett, 1973—; contbr. articles to lit. publs. Served with U.S. Army, 1942-46. Recipient Tanner Teaching award U. N.C., 1966; Fulbright fellow, Germany, 1983-84. Mem. MLA, South Atlantic MLA, Am. Soc. Eighteenth-Century Studies (pres. Southeastern group 1980-81), Coll. English Assn., Johnsonians. Republican. Jewish. Home: 396 Lakeshore Ln Chapel Hill NC 27514-1728 Office: U NC 401 Greenlaw Bldg Chapel Hill NC 27599

STRAUSS, AUDREY, lawyer; b. Phila., Oct. 7, 1947; m. John R. Wing; children: Carlin, Matthew. AB, Barnard Coll., 1968; JD, Columbia U., 1971. Bar: N.Y. 1972, U.S. Dist. Ct. (so. and ea. dists.) N.Y. 1972, U.S. Ct. Appeals (2d cir.) N.Y. 1972. Law clk. to Hon. Lawrence W. Pierce, N.Y.C., 1971-72; asst. atty. U.S. Atty's Office (So. Dist of N.Y.), N.Y.C., 1975-82, chief appellate atty., 1977-78, chief, Fraud Unit, 1980-82; assoc. counsel Office of Independent Counsel, 1987-89; ptnr. Fried, Frank, Harris, Shriver & Jacobson, N.Y.C., 1990—. James Kent Scholar Columbia U., 1970-71, Harlan Fiske Stone Scholar, Columbia U., 1968-69. Fellow Am. Coll. Trial Lawyers. Office: Fried Frank Harris Shriver & Jacobson One NY Plz 24th Fl New York NY 10004

STRAUSS, DAVID, Vice Presidential Office official; b. Fargo, N.D., Apr. 2, 1950. BA in Sociology, Moorhead State U., 1973; BS Polit. Sci. and Edn. magna cum laude, Morehead State U., 1973; postgrad., Harvard U., 1992. Exec. dir. N.D. Dem. Party, 1975-76; dir. N.D. Agrl. Stblzn. and Conservation Svc., 1977-81; adminstrv. asst. Senator Quentin Burdick of N.D., 1988-92; staff dir. U.S. Senate Com. on Environment and Pub. Works, Washington, 1988-92; chief of staff U.S. Senator Jocelyn Birch Burdick of N.D., Washington, 1992-93, Senator John Breaux of La., Washington, 1993; dep. chief of staff Office of Vice Pres., Washington, 1993. Office: Vice Pres Old Executive Ofc NW Bldg Washington DC 20501

STRAUSS, DAVID J., lawyer; b. Chgo., Jan. 26, 1943. BBA, U. Iowa, 1964, JD, 1967. Bar: Iowa 1967, Ohio 1967. Ptnr. Baker & Hostetler, Cleve. Mem. Phi Delta Phi, Order of Coif. Office: Baker & Hostetler 3200 Nat City Ctr 1900 E 9th St Cleveland OH 44114-3485

STRAUSS, EDWARD ROBERT, carpet company executive; b. Jersey City, June 14, 1942; s. Abraham and Elsie Alice (Goldstein) S.; m. Martha Ann Patmore, Oct. 30, 1966; children: Jeffrey Aaron, Craig Michael. BSBA, Rutgers U., 1973. Dept. systems mgr. Port of N.Y. Authority, N.Y.C.,

1961-68; account exec. Steiner Rouse & Co., N.Y.C., 1968-70; purchasing mgr. N.Y. State Urban Devel. Corp., N.Y.C., 1970-73; sales mgr. Siracco's, Staten Island, N.Y., 1973-76; carpet and TV buyer Hahnes Dept. Stores, Newark, 1976-80; sales mgr. Clodan Carpets, N.Y.C., 1980-83; regional mgr. Deans Carpets, Manchester, N.H., 1983-85; pres. Carpet Contractors Inc., N.Y.C., 1985-95; v.p. contact sales Simon Manges/Patterson Flynn Martin & Manges, N.Y.C., 1995—. Bd. dirs. Marlboro (N.J.) Little League, 1979-87, Marlboro Pop Warner Football, 1979-83. Mem. Free Sons of Israel (trustee, v.p.), Marlboro Mcpl. Swim Club (bd. dirs. 1989-91), Free and Accepted Masons (Menorah lodge # 249 1970-81). Jewish. Avocations: electric trains, sports. Office: Simon Manges/Patterson Flynn The D&D Bldg Martin & Manges 979 3rd Ave New York NY 10022

STRAUSS, ELLIOTT BOWMAN, economic development consultant, retired naval officer; b. Washington, Mar. 15, 1903; s. Joseph and Mary (Sweitzer) S.; m. Beatrice Phillips, Feb. 12, 1951; children by previous marriage: Elliott MacGregor, Armar Archbold, Lydia S. (Mme. Delaunay); 1 child, Christopher Joseph. B.S., U.S. Naval Acad., 1923; student, Imperial Def. Coll., London, 1948. Commd. ensign USN, 1923, advanced through grades to rear adm., 1955; assigned ships at sea, 1923-30, 32-35; asst. naval attache London, 1935-37; staff comdr. Atlantic Squadron, 1937-40; spl. naval observer London, 1941; staff Chief Brit. Combined Ops., 1942-43; U.S. ops. officer Allied Naval Comdr.-in-Chief for Normandy Invasion, 1944; comdr. Attack Transport, Pacific, 1944-45; naval adviser 1st Gen. Assembly UN, staff Mil. Staff Com., UN, 1946; comdg. officer USS Fresno, 1946-47; staff div. strategic plans Office Chief Naval Ops., 1948-51; comdr. Destroyer Flotilla 6, 1951-52; dir. def. programs div. Office Spl. Rep. in Europe, Dept. Def. rep. econ. def., 1952-55; ret., 1955; dir. engring. Bucknell U., 1956-57; dir. U.S. ops. Mission to Tunisia, 1957-60; spl. asst. to dir. ICA, 1960; dir. AID Missions to Madagascar, 1961-63; pub. mem. Fgn. Service Inspection Corps, 1965; assoc. Laidlaw & Co., N.Y.C., 1963-66; econ. devel. cons. Gen. Electric Co., 1966-69; chmn. bd. Interplan Corp., 1969-81; rep. overseas of Interplan.; cons. Dept. State, 1970. Author profl. and newspaper articles. Bd. dirs. Am. Econ. Found.; chmn. Naval Hist. Found. Decorated Bronze Star; comdr. Order Brit. Empire; Croix de Guerre with palm France). Mem. U.S. Naval Inst., English Speaking Union (nat. bd. dirs.), Order of St. John of Jerusalem (assoc.). Mem. Ch. of England. Clubs: The Pilgrims; Army-Navy (Washington), Chevy Chase (Washington), Metropolitan (Washington); New York Yacht. Home: 2945 Garfield Ter NW Washington DC 20008-3507

STRAUSS, HARLEE SUE, environmental consultant; b. New Brunswick, N.J., June 19, 1950; d. Robert Lemuel and Helene (Marcus) S. BA, Smith Coll., 1972; PhD, U. Wis., 1979. Postdoctoral fellow dept. biology MIT, Cambridge, 1979-81; congrl. sci. fellow U.S. House of Reps., Washington, 1981-83; spl. asst. Am. Chem. Soc., Washington, 1983-84; spl. cons. Environ. Corp., Washington, 1984-85; rsch. assoc. Ctr. for Tech., Policy and Indsl. Devel. MIT, Cambridge, 1985-86, rsch. affiliate, 1986—; sr. assoc. Gradient Corp., Cambridge, 1986-88; pres. H. Strauss Assocs., Inc., Natick, Mass., 1988—; pres., exec. dir. Silent Spring Inst., Inc., 1994—; adj. assoc. prof. Sch. of Pub. Health, Boston U., 1990; lectr. Tufts U. Sch. of Medicine, Boston, 1988—; steering com. Boston Risk Assessment Group, 1986—. Co-editor; author: Risk Assessment in Genetic Engineering, 1991; author: Biotechnology Regulations, 1986; author book chpts. in field. Active Instl. Biosafety Com., Army Rsch. Lab., Natick, 1989—, Army Sci. Bd., 1994—. Mem. AAAS, Am. Chem. Soc., Am. Soc. Microbiology, Assn. for Women in Sci. (chmn. com. New Eng. chpt. 1986-88, co-chmn. legis. com. 1985—), Biophys. Soc. (chmn. com. 1983-84, Congl. Sci. fellow 1981-83), Soc. for Risk Analysis (pres. New Eng. chpt. 1991—). Mem. AAAS, Am. Chem. Soc., Am. Soc. Microbiology, Assn. for Women in Sci. (chmn. mem. com. New Eng. chpt. 1986-88, co-chmn. legis. com. 1985—), Biophys. Soc. (chmn. com. 1983-84, Congrl. Sci. fellow 1981-83), Soc. for Risk Analysis. Jewish. Avocations: travel, hiking. Office: H Strauss Assocs Inc 21 Bay State Rd Natick MA 01760-2942

STRAUSS, HERBERT LEOPOLD, chemistry educator; b. Aachen, Germany, Mar. 26, 1936; came to U.S., 1940, naturalized, 1946; s. Charles and Joan (Goldschmidt) S.; m. Carolyn North Cooper, Apr. 24, 1960; children: Michael Abram, Rebecca Anne, Ethan Edward. A.B., Columbia U., 1957, M.A., 1958, Ph.D., 1960; postgrad, Oxford U., 1960-61. Mem. faculty U. Calif., Berkeley, 1961—, prof. chemistry, 1973—, vice chmn. dept. chemistry, 1975-81, 92-95, asst. dean. Coll. Chemistry, 1986-92, assoc. dean, 1995—; vis. prof. Indian Inst. Tech., Kanpur, 1968-69, Fudan U., Shanghai, 1982, U. Tokyo, 1982, U. Paris du Nord, 1987; chmn. IUPAC Commn. I.I. Author: Quantum Mechanics, 1968; assoc. editor Am. Rev. Phys. Chemistry, 1976-85, editor, 1985—. Recipient Bomen-Michaelson award Coblentz Soc., 1994, Ellis Lippincott award Optical Soc. Am., 1994; Alfred P. Sloan fellow, 1966-70. Fellow Am. Phys. Soc., AAAS; mem. Am. Chem. Soc., Sigma Xi, Phi Beta Kappa, Phi Lambda Upsilon. Achievements include research in elucidation of vibrational spectra associated with large amplitude molecular motion in gases, liquids and solids. Home: 2447 Prince St Berkeley CA 94705-2021 Office: U Calif Dept Chemistry 419 Latimer Hall Berkeley CA 94720-1460

STRAUSS, JEROME MANFRED, lawyer, banker; b. Milw., Nov. 7, 1934; s. Emanuel and Loraine (Goetz) S.; m. Mary Beth Johnson, June, 1959 (div. Nov. 1964); 1 child, Martha Lynn; m. Susan Jean Kauffman, Dec. 30, 1967; children: Jared Lee, David Aaron. BA with honors, Ind. U., 1956; JD, NYU, 1959. Bar: Ind. 1959, U.S. Dist. Ct. (so. dist.) Ind. 1959, U.S. Tax Ct. 1965, U.S. Ct. Appeals (7th cir.) 1969. Assoc. Ice Miller Donadio & Ryan, Indpls., 1959-69, ptnr., 1969-93; sr. v.p. and regional trust mgr. Merrill Lynch Trust Co., 1993—. Co-author: Marital Deduction Trusts, 1963, Real Estate in an Estate, 1963; contbr. articles to profl. jours., others. Pres. Indpls. chpt. ACLU, 1960-64; bd. dirs. Orton Soc., Indpls., 1970-72, Indpls., 1970-72, Indpls. Hebrew Congregation, 1979-85, Planned Giving Group of Ind., Indpls., 1988-95, Ind. Continuing Legal Edn. Forum, 1989-94. Fellow Am. Coll. Trust and Estate Counsel; mem. ABA (vice chmn. marital deduction com. real estate property, probate and trust sect. 1988-93), Internat. Acad. Estate and Trust Law (academician 1987—), Ind. State Bar Assn. (sec. 1979-80, chmn. probate, trust and real property sect. 1970-71), Ind. Estate Planning Coun. (pres. 1970-71), Skyline Club, Columbia Club. Home: 6441 Park Central Dr W Indianapolis IN 46260-4512 Office: Merrill Lynch Trust Co Fl 42 111 Monument Circle Indianapolis IN 46204

STRAUSS, JOHN, public relations executive; b. N.Y.C., Apr. 2, 1913; s. Nathan and Bertha Dorothy (Heineman) S.; m. Renee Valensi, Oct. 15, 1947; children: Susan Strauss Koenig, John Jay. Grad., Phillips Exeter Acad., 1931; BA, Yale U., 1935. Securities analyst Mabon & Co., N.Y.C., 1935-41; sales rep. Warner Bros. Pictures, Buffalo, 1941-45; publicist Warner Bros. Studios, Burbank, Calif., 1945-46, Columbia Studios, Hollywood, Calif., 1946-48; founder, pres. Cleary, Strauss & Irwin, 1948-64; pres. McFadden, Strauss & Irwin, Inc., 1964-75, ICPR, L.A., 1975-80, Communifax, Inc. L.A., 1980—. Trustee Oakwood Schs., 1967-70, Acad. TV Arts, 1967-70, Columbia Coll., L.A., 1979-83. Mem. Acad. Motion Picture Arts and Scis. Home and Office: 4205 Stansbury Ave Sherman Oaks CA 91423-4233

STRAUSS, JOHN STEINERT, dermatologist, educator; b. New Haven, July 15, 1926; s. Maurice Jacob and Carolyn Mina (Ullman) S.; m. Susan Thalheimer, Aug. 19, 1950; children—Joan Sue, Mary Lynn. B.S., Yale U., 1946; M.D., 1950. Intern U. Chgo., 1950-51; resident in dermatology U. Pa., Phila., 1951-52, 54-55; fellow in dermatology U. Pa., 1955-57, instr., 1956-57; mem. faculty Boston U. Med. Sch., 1958-78, prof., 1966-78; prof., head dept. dermatology U. Iowa, Iowa City, 1978—. Mem. editorial bd. Archives of Dermatology, 1970-79, Jour. Am. Acad. Dermatology, 1979-89, Jour. Investigative Dermatology, 1977-82; contbr. articles to profl. jours. Served with USNR, 1952-54. James H. Brown jr. fellow, 1947-48; USPHS fellow, 1955-57; USPHS grantee. Fellow Am. Acad. Dermatology (pres.); mem. Soc. Investigative Dermatology (sec.-treas., pres.), Dermatology Found. (sec.), Am. Bd. Dermatology (bd. dirs., pres.), Am. Dermatol. Assn. (sec., pres.), Assn. Am. Physicians, Central Soc. Clin. Rsch., Am. Fedn. Clin. Rsch. Coun. Med. Splty. Socs. (pres.). 18th World Congress Dermatology (pres.), Internat. League Dermatol. Socs. (pres. 1992—), Internat. Com. Dermatology (pres. 1992—), others. Research in sebaceous glands and pathogenesis of acne. Office: U Iowa Hosp & Clinics Dept of Dermatology 200 Hawkins Dr # Bt2045 I Iowa City IA 52242-1009

STRAUSS, JON CALVERT, medical research administrator; b. Chgo., Jan. 17, 1940; s. Charles E. and Alice C. (Woods) S.; m. Joan Helen Bailey, Sept. 19, 1959 (div. 1985); children: Susan, Stephanie; m. Jean Anne Sacconaghi, June 14, 1985; children: Kristoffer, Jonathon. BSEE, U. Wis., 1959; MS in Physics, U. Pitts., 1962; PhD in E.E., Carnegie Inst. Tech., 1965. Assoc. prof. computer sci., elec. engring. Carnegie Mellon U., Pitts., 1966-70; dir. computer ctr., prof. computer sci. Tech. U. Norway, Trondheim, Norway, 1970; vis. assoc. prof. elec. engring. U. Mich., Ann Arbor, 1971; assoc. prof. computer sci. Washington U., St. Louis, Mo., 1971-74, dir. computing facilities, 1971-73; dir. computing activities U. Pa., Phila., 1974-76, faculty master Stouffer Coll. House, 1978-80, prof. computer, info. scis., prof. decision sci. Wharton Sch., 1974-81, exec. dir. Univ. Budget, 1975-78, v.p. for budget, fin., 1978-81; prof. elec. engring. U. So. Calif., Los Angeles, 1981-85; sr. v.p. adminstrn. U. So. Calif., 1981-85; pres. Worcester Poly. Inst., Mass., 1985-94; v.p., chief fin. officer Howard Hughes Med. Inst., Chevy Chase, Md., 1994—; cons. Electronics Assocs., Inc., 1965, IBM Corp., 1960-64, Westinghouse Elec. Corp., 1959-60; bd. dirs. Wyman Gordon Co., Computervision Corp. Contbr. articles on computer systems and university mgmt. to profl. jours.; co-holder patent. Bd. dirs. Presbyn.-U. Pa. Med. Ctr., Phila. 1980-81, U. So. Calif. Kenneth Norris Jr. Cancer Hosp., L.A., 1981-85, Med. Ctr. of Ctrl. Mass., 1986-94, Worcester Acad., 1986-91, Mass. Biotech. Rsch. Inst., 1985-94. Mem. New Eng. Assn. Schs. and Colls., Inc., Commn. on Instns. of Higher Edn., Nat. Collegiate Athletic Assn. (pres.'s commn. 1990-94). Avocations: rowing, running, sailing, swimming. Office: Howard Hughes Med Inst 4000 Jones Bridge Rd Chevy Chase MD 20815-6789

STRAUSS, JUDITH FEIGIN, physician; b. N.Y., Mar. 7, 1942; d. Milton M. and Blanche (Tobias) Feigin; m. Harry William Strauss, June 14, 1964; children: Cheryl, Marcy. BS, Cornell U., Ithaca, 1963; MD, SUNY, 1967. Pediatrics. Pediatric resident SUNY, N.Y.C., 1976-68, Sinai Hosp., Balt., 1968-69; fellow pediatrics and psychiatry Johns Hopkins Hosp., Balt., 1969-70; pvt. practice in pediatrics Sacramento; cons. in pediatrics Bur. of Disability Ins. Social Security, Balt., 1973-74; pediatrician East Balt. Med. Plan, 1974-76; dir. USPHS Hosp., Boston, 1976-80; pvt. practice in pediatrics Boston, 1980-87; dir. med. svcs. Mediqual Systems, 1988—. Fellow Am. Acad. of Pediatrics; mem. Mass. Med. Soc., Am. Med. Women's Orgn., Alpha Lamda Delta. Office: Mediqual Systems 1900 W Park Dr Westborough MA 01581-3919

STRAUSS, PETER, actor; b. Croton-on-Hudson, N.Y., Feb. 20, 1947; m. Nicole S.; children: Justin, Tristen. Student, Northwestern U. Performances include (films) debut in Hail Hero, 1969, Soldier Blue, 1970, The Trial of the Catonsville Nine, The Last Tycoon, 1976, Spacehunter, 1983; (TV dramas) Rich Man, Poor Man, 1976, Rich Man, Poor Man-Book II, 1976-77, Masada, 1981, Tender is the Night, 1985, Kane and Abel, 1986; (TV spls.) The Man Without a Country, 1973, A Whale for the Killing, 1981; (TV movies) The FBI Story: The FBI Vs. the Ku Klux Klan, 1975, Attack on Terror, 1975, Young Joe, the Forgotten Kennedy, 1978, The Jericho Mile, 1979 (Emmy award), Angel on My Shoulder, 1980, Heart of Steel, 1983, Under Siege, 1986, Penalty Phase, 1986, The Proud Men, 1987, Brotherhood of the Rose, 1989, Peter Gunn, 1989, 83 Hours Till Dawn, 1990, Flight of the Black Angel, 1991, Fugitive Among Us, 1992, Trial: The Price of Passion, 1992, Men Don't Tell, 1993, The Yearling, 1994. Office: care William Morris Agy 151 S El Camino Dr Beverly Hills CA 90212-2775*

STRAUSS, PETER L(ESTER), law educator; b. N.Y.C., Feb. 26, 1940; s. Simon D. and Elaine Ruth (Mandle) S.; m. Joanna Burnstine, Oct. 1, 1964; children: Benjamin, Bethany. AB magna cum laude, Harvard U., 1961; LLB magna cum laude, Yale U., 1964. Bar: D.C. 1965, U.S. Supreme Ct., 1968. Law clk. U.S. Ct. Appeals D.C. Cir., 1964-65, U.S. Supreme Ct., 1965-66; lectr. Haile Selassie U. Sch. Law, Addis Ababa, Ethiopia, 1966-68; asst. to solicitor gen. Dept. Justice, Washington, 1968-71; assoc. prof. law Columbia U., 1971-74, prof., 1974—, Betts Prof., 1985—; gen. counsel NRC, 1975-77; sr. fellow Adminstrv. Conf. U.S.; Byrne vis. prof. Sch. Law Harvard U., Cambridge, Mass., 1994. Recipient John Marshall prize Dept. Justice, 1970, Disting. Svc. award NRC, 1977. Mem. ABA (chair sect. adminstrv. law and regulatory practice 1992-93, Disting. Scholarship award 1988), Am. Law Inst. Author: (with Abba Paulos, translator) Fetha Negast: The Law of the Kings, 1968; (with others) Administrative Law Cases and Comments, 1995; Introduction to Administrative Justice in the United States, 1989; (with Paul Verkuil) Administrative Law Problems, 1983; contbr. articles to law revs. Office: Columbia U Sch Law 435 W 116th St New York NY 10027-7201

STRAUSS, PHYLLIS R., biology educator; b. Worcester, Mass., Mar. 19, 1943. BA, Brown U., 1964; PhD, The Rockefeller U., 1971. Rsch. fellow med. sch. Harvard U., Boston, 1971-73; asst. prof. biology Northeastern U., Boston, 1973-78, assoc. prof., 1978-84, prof., 1984—, Matthews Disting. prof., 1987—; sr. scientist Sealy Ctr. Molecular Sci., Galveston, Tex., 1994—; vis. scholar Harvard U., Cambridge, Mass., 1988; reviewer NSF, NIH, Nat. Rsch. Coun., Alberta Heritage Found., U.S. Dept. Agrl. and numerous jours. and books. Author, editor: The Euraryotic Nucleus, 1990; contbr. articles to profl. jours. Grantee Am. Cancer Soc., 1973, NIH, 1977, Office Naval Rsch., 1981, WHO, 1989, 93, 94, also others. Mem. AAAS, Am. Soc. for Cell Biology (coun. 1989-91), Am. Soc. Protozoologists, Am. Soc. Biol. Chemists, Am. Women in Sci. Office: Northeastern U 360 Huntington Ave Boston MA 02115-5096

STRAUSS, ROBERT C., manufacturing executive; b. Chgo., June 1, 1941; s. Henry K. and Clara (Santi) S; children: Jennifer, Morgan. BS in Engring. and Physics, U. Ill., 1963; NS in Physics, U. Idaho, 1965. Systems analyst Eastman Kodak Co., Rochester, N.Y., 1965-68, GE, Phila., 1968-70; dir. mgmt. consulting Touche Ross & Co., Phila., 1973-79; sr. v.p. fin. Pantry Pride Inc., Ft. Lauderdale, Fla., 1979-83; pres., CEO Cordis Corp., Miami Lakes, Fla., 1983—; also dir. Bd. dirs. U. Miami Venture Coun. Forum, 1989—, Coral Gables, Miami Children's Hosp., 1990—; mem. campaign com. United Wade Dade County; chmn. biomed. devices subcom. under rsch. com. Fla. High Tech. and Industry Coun., 1989—; trustee U. Miami, 1991—. Avocations: sailing, running. Office: Cordis Corp PO Box 025700 Miami Lakes FL 33014*

STRAUSS, ROBERT DAVID, lawyer; b. Cambridge, Mass., Oct. 20, 1951; s. Walter Adolf and Lilo (Teutsch) S.; m. Deborah Mackall, Feb. 15, 1986; 1 child, Benjamin Walter. Ba, Emory U., 1973, JD, 1976. Bar: Ga. 1976. Assoc. Gambrell & Russell, Atlanta, 1976-81; ptnr. Smith, Gambrell & Russell, Atlanta, 1981-89, Trotter Smith & Jacobs, Atlanta, 1989-92, Troutman Sanders, Atlanta, 1992—. Contbr. articles to profl. jours. Mem. ABA (chmn. leasing subcom. 1988-94, uniform comml. code com.), State Bar of Ga., Equipment Leasing Assn. Am. Home: 1159 Morningside Pl NE Atlanta GA 30306-3061 Office: Troutman Sanders 5200 NationsBank Plz 600 Peachtree St NE Atlanta GA 30308-2214

STRAUSS, ROBERT PHILIP, economics educator; b. Cleve., May 11, 1944; s. Harry and Carrie S.; m. Celeste G. Meade, Jan. 11, 1980; children—Sarah Elizabeth, David Anthony, Elena Nicole. A.B. in Econs., U. Mich., 1966; M.A., U. Wis., 1968, Ph.D. in Econs., 1970. Fellow Inst. Research on Poverty, 1968-69; asst. prof. econs. U. N.C., Chapel Hill, 1969-73, assoc. prof., 1973-79; econ. policy fellow Brookings Instn., Washington, 1971-72; economist U.S. Congress Joint Com. Taxation, 1975-78; prof. econs. and pub. policy Carnegie-Mellon U., Pitts., 1979—, assoc. dean Sch. Urban and Pub. Affairs, 1981-83, dir. Ctr. for Pub. Fin. Mgmt., 1984-91; dir. research Pa. Tax Commn., 1979-81; vis. prof. econs. and pub. policy U. Rochester, 1992-94. Mem. Pa. Local Tax Reform Commn., 1987; sec. faculty Carnegie-Mellon U., 1991-92. Recipient Exceptional Service award U.S. Treasury, 1972, Disting. Service award Pitts. Tax Execs. Inst., 1987; grantee NSF, U.S. Dept. Labor, U.S. Treasury, HUD, Social Security Adminstrn. Mem. Am. Econ. Assn., Econometric Soc., Am. Statis. Assn., Nat. Tax Assn., Pub. Choice Soc., Assn. for Pub. Policy and Mgmt., Am. Soc. for Pub. Adminstrn., Am. Acctg. Assn. Club: Cosmos. Home: 2307 Country Pl Export PA 15632 Office: 5000 Forbes Ave Pittsburgh PA 15213-3815

STRAUSS, ROBERT SCHWARZ, lawyer, former ambassador; b. Lockhart, Tex., Oct. 19, 1918; s. Charles H. and Edith V. (Schwarz) S.; m. Helen Jacobs, 1941; children: Robert A., Richard A., Susan. LL.B., U. Tex., 1941. Bar: Tex. 1941, D.C. 1971. Spl. agt. FBI, 1941-45; ptnr. Akin, Gump, Strauss, Hauer & Feld, Dallas, 1945-77, 81—; Dem. nat. committeeman from

Tex., 1968-72; mem. exec. com. Dem. Nat. Com., 1969-77, treas., 1970-72, chmn., 1972-77; spl. rep. for trade negotiations with rank of ambassador Office of Pres., 1977-79; chmn. Pres. Carter's reelection campaign, 1979-81; Pres.'s personal rep. for Mid. East negotiations, 1979-81, U.S. amb. to Russia, 1991-93; bd. dirs. Archer-Daniels-Midland Co., Decatur, Ill., Gulf Stream Corp., Savannah, Ga., Gen. Instruments, N.Y.C. Co-chmn. Nat. Econ. Commn., 1988—. Recipient Presdl. medal of freedom, 1980. Mem. ABA, Dallas Bar Assn., D.C. Bar Assn. Jewish. Office: care Akin Gump Strauss Hauer & Feld 4100 First City Ctr Dallas TX 75201 also: Ste 400 1333 New Hampshire Ave NW Washington DC 20036

STRAUSS, SIMON DAVID, manufacturing executive; b. Lima, Peru, July 24, 1911; s. Lester W. and Bertha (Miller) S.; m. Elaine Ruth Mandle, Sept. 1, 1936 (dec.); children: Peter Lester, Susan Dee (Mrs. Samuel Carson Orr); m. Janet McCloskey Robbins, Dec. 19, 1982. Student, Mackay Sch., Valparaiso, Chile, 1919-21, Townsend Harris Hall, N.Y.C., 1924-27; LL.D., U. Ariz., 1981. Asst. editor Engring. and Mining Jour., 1927-32; editor Madison Eagle, N.J., 1932-34; economist Standard Statistics Co., 1935-41; asst. to dep. adminstr. Fed. Loan Agy., 1941; asst. v.p., v.p. Metals Res. Co., 1942-45; sales dept. Asarco, Inc., 1946; sales mgr. Am. Smelting & Refining Co., 1947-71, v.p., 1949-71, exec. v.p., 1971-77, vice chmn., 1977-79, also dir., 1953-81; cons. indsl. firms, 1981—; bd. dirs. Magma Copper Co.; gov. N.Y. Commodity Exchange Inc., 1947-63; dir., mem. exec. com. Zinc Inst., 1953-77, pres., 1957-59, 73-75; cons. Def. Materials Procurement Agy., 1951-52, Office Def. Moblzn., 1954-55; mem. adv. coms. Munitions Bd.; mem. advisory com. Nat. Growth Policies, 1976; vis. lectr. MIT, 1977-84, Columbia U., 1988; lectr. Pa. State U., 1978, Poly. Inst. N.Y., 1978, U. Ariz., 1979, 80, Columbia U., 1982, U. Calif., Berkeley, 1986. Author: (with L.H. Sloan) Two Cycles of Corporation Profits, 1936, (with E.H. Robie) Mineral Economics, 1959, (with W.H. Vogeley) 1976, Trouble in the Third Kingdom, 1986; contbr. articles on mining to trade jours. Trustee Manhattan Sch. Music, 1958-79, v.p., 1966-79; bd. dirs. Internat. Copper Research Assn.; mem. bd. govs. Nat. Mining Hall of Fame and Mus., Leadville, Colo., 1987—. Mem. Lead Industries Assn. (pres. 1964-66, exec. com., dir.) v.p. 1967-69, 1970-71), Silver Inst. (dir., pres. 1971-73, chmn. bd. 1974-76), Am. Bur. Metal Stats. (chmn. 1975-77), Copper Club (pres. 1967-68), Mining and Metall. Soc. Am. (Gold medal 1984), Am. Inst. Mining and Metall. Engrs. (hon.), Council Fgn. Relations. Clubs: Mining, Stockbridge Golf.

STRAUSS, STANLEY ROBERT, lawyer; b. N.Y.C., June 3, 1915; s. Maurice M. and Blanche Anna (Danciger) S.; m. Margaret Inglis Forbes, Mar. 13, 1944 (div. 1950); m. Helen Anne Cummings, Dec. 31, 1975 (dec. 1980). BA cum laude, Williams Coll., 1936; LLB, Columbia U., 1940. Bar: N.Y. 1941, D.C. 1964, U.S. Ct. Appeals (1st cir.) 1977, U.S. Ct. Appeals (3d cir.) 1986, U.S. Ct. Appeals (4th cir.) 1974, U.S. Ct. Appeals (5th cir.) 1970, U.S. Ct. Appeals (6th cir.) 1977, U.S. Ct. Appeals (8th cir.) 1975, U.S. Supreme Ct. 1965. Assoc. Howard Henig, N.Y.C., 1940-41; atty. NLRB, Washington, 1946-52, supervising atty., 1953-59, chief counsel, 1959-63; assoc. Vedder, Price, Kaufman & Kammholz, Washington, 1963-65, ptnr., 1965-90; of counsel Ogletree, Deakins, Nash, Smoak & Stewart, Washington, 1990—. Co-author: Practice and Procedure Before the National Labor Relations Board, 3d edit., 1980, 4th edit., 1987. Officer U.S. Army, 1941-45, PTO. Decorated Bronze Star; Horn scholar Columbia U. Law Sch., 1937-40. Mem. ABA, Fed. Bar Assn., D.C. Bar Assn., Kenwood Country Club. Avocations: golf, tennis. Home: 4956 Sentinel Dr Bethesda MD 20816-3594 Office: Ogletree Deakins Nash 2400 N St NW Fl 5 Washington DC 20037-1153

STRAUSS, ULRICH PAUL, educator, chemist; b. Frankfurt, Germany, Jan. 10, 1920; s. Richard and Marianne (Seligmann) S.; m. Esther Lipetz, June 30, 1943 (dec. Sept. 1949); children—Dorothy, David; m. Elaine Greenbaum, Nov. 23, 1950; children—Elizabeth, Evelyn. A.B., Columbia U., 1941; Ph.D., Cornell U., 1944. Sterling fellow Yale U., 1946-48; faculty Rutgers U., New Brunswick, N.J., 1948—, prof. phys. chemistry, 1960-90, prof. emeritus, 1990—; also dir. Sch. Chemistry, 1965-71, chmn. dept. chemistry, 1974-80; prof. emeritus Rutgers U., 1990—. Mem. editorial bd. Macromolecules, 1990-93; contbr. articles to profl. jours. Recipient Sci. achievement award Johnson Wax Co., 1986; NSF sr. fellow Nat. Center Sci. Research, Strasbourg, France, 1961-62; Guggenheim fellow U. Oxford, Eng., 1971-72. Fellow N.Y. Acad. Scis.; mem. Am. Chem. Soc. (chmn. phys. chemistry group N.J. sect. 1956, councillor 1961-72, honored by 1-day symposium at nat. meeting N.J. sect. 1986, recipient Excellence in Edn. awrd N.J. sect. 1994). Home: 227 Lawrence Ave Highland Park NJ 08904-1837 Office: Dept Chemistry Rutgers U New Brunswick NJ 08903

STRAUSS, WALTER ADOLF, foreign languages educator; b. Mannheim, Germany, May 14, 1923; came to U.S. 1936, naturalized, 1944; s. Ludwig and Fanny (Haas) S.; m. Lilo Teutsch, Sept. 8, 1946 (div. 1966); children: Robert D., Joan E., Charles L.; m. Nancy Reed Shirley, Oct. 18, 1966; children: Philip R., Matthew C. B.A., Emory U., 1944; M.A., Harvard, 1948, Ph.D., 1951. Instr. Romance langs. and gen. edn. Harvard, 1951-54; mem. faculty Emory U., 1954-70; asso. prof. Romance langs., 1958-63, prof., 1963-70; William C. Treuhaft prof. Case Western Res. U., Cleve., 1970-93, Treuhaft prof. emeritus, 1993—, chmn. dept. modern langs., 1979-91, William C. Treuhaft prof. emeritus, 1993—. Author: Proust and Literature, 1957, Descent and Return, 1971, On the Threshold of a New Kabbalah: Kafka's Later Tales, 1988. Served with AUS, 1944-47. Guggenheim fellow, 1962-63; Bollingen Found. fellow, 1962-63; NEH summer grantee, 1977—; Am. Philosophical Soc. grantee, 1986-87. Mem. MLA, Kafka Soc., Beckett Soc., AAUP, Phi Beta Kappa. Home: 2861 Berkshire Rd Cleveland Hts OH 44118-2401 Office: Dept Modern Langs and Lit Case Western Res U Cleveland OH 44106

STRAUSSLER, TOMAS See STOPPARD, TOM

STRAUSZ-HUPÉ, ROBERT, ambassador, author; b. Vienna, Austria, Mar. 25, 1903; emigrated to U.S., 1923, naturalized, 1938; s. Rudolph and Doris (Hedwig) Strausz-H.; m. Eleanor deGraff Cuyler, Apr. 26, 1938 (dec. 1976); m. Mayrose Ferreira Nugara, Aug. 22, 1979. A.M., Ph.D., U. Pa., 1944. Investment banker, 1927-37; assoc. editor Current History, 1939-41; assoc. prof. polit. sci. U. Pa., 1946-52, former prof.; spl. lectr., 1940-46; dir. Fgn. Policy Rsch. Inst., 1955-69; U.S. amb. Ceylon, 1970-72, Belgium, 1972-74, Sweden, 1974-76, NATO, 1976-77, Turkey, 1981-89; disting. fellow U.S. Inst. Peace, 1992-93. Author: The Russian-German Riddle, 1940, Axis-America, 1941, Geopolitics, 1942, The Balance of Tomorrow, 1945, International Relations, 1950, The Zone of Indifference, 1952, Power and Community, 1956, (with Kintner, Cottrell, Dougherty) Protracted Conflict, 1959, (with W. Kintner, Stefan Possony) A Forward Strategy for America, 1961, (with others) Building the Atlantic World, 1963, In My Time, 1965, Dilemmas Facing the Nation, 1979; editor: The Idea of Colonialism, 1958, Orbis, 1957-69. Lectr. Air War Coll., 1953. Served to lt. col. AUS. Mem. Coun. Fgn. Rels., Merion Cricket Club, Met. Club, Knickerbocker Club. Lutheran. Address: White Horse Farm 864 Grubbs Mill Rd Newtown Square PA 19073

STRAW, EDWARD M., naval officer; b. Marysville, Pa., Mar. 7, 1939; s. Edward Walter and Nina (McCown) S.; 1 child, Silvana Rhea; m. Christine Dusel, Sept. 9, 1989; children: Margaret Ray, Katherine Grace. BS, U.S. Naval Acad., 1961; MBA, George Washington U., 1972; grad., Nat. War Coll., 1981. Commd. ensign USN, 1961, advanced through grades to vice adm.; with Navy Supply Corps Sch., Athens, Ga., Aviation Supply Office, Phila., Naval Supply Depot, Subic Bay, The Philippines, Naval Air Sta., Corpus Christi, Tex., USS Forrestal; supply officer USS Dwight D. Eisenhower; with Naval Material Command, Washington, Office of Dep. Chief of Naval Ops. Logistics, Washington; vice comdr. Naval Supply Systems Command, 1991-92; dir. Def. Logistics Agy., Alexandria, Va., 1992—; bd. dirs. Navy Fed. Credit Union. Bd. dirs. nat. capital region Boy Scouts Am., Washington, 1992—. Decorated D.S.M., Legion of Merit with gold star. Mem. Soc. Logistics Engrs., Nat. Eagle Scout Assn. (life), Nat. War Coll. Alumni Assn. (3d v.p.), VFW (life), Masons. Avocation: largemouth bass fishing. Home: Quarters D Washington Navy Yard Washington DC 20374-0001 Office: Def Logistics Agy Cameron Station Alexandria VA 22304-6100

STRAWBRIDGE, FRANCIS REEVES, III, department store executive; b. Bryn Mawr, Pa., Dec. 14, 1937; s. Francis Reeves Strawbridge Jr. and Elizabeth Ann (Schwarz) Strawbridge Grange; m. Patricia Webb, Jan. 13, 1962 (div. 1967); children: Cynthia, Pamela; m. Mary Jo Beatty, Jan. 25, 1969; children: Elisabeth, Margaret. A.B., Princeton U., 1959. With exec. tng. program Bloomingdale's, N.Y.C., 1960-61; with Strawbridge & Clothier, Phila., 1961—, chmn. bd., 1984—; dir. Mellon Bank, Phila.; chmn. bd. trustees Princeton U. Store, 1978—. Vice chmn. bd. mgrs. Germantown Hosp., Pa., 1975—. Served to pfc. U.S. Army, 1959-60. Mem. Nat. Retail Merchants Assn. (bd. dirs. 1976—), Am. Retail Fedn. (bd. dirs. 1984—), Associated Merchandising Corp. (bd. dirs. 1984—), Greater Phila. C. of C. (bd. dirs. 1985—). Republican. Quaker. Office: Strawbridge & Clothier 801 Market St Philadelphia PA 19107-3199

STRAWBRIDGE, G. STOCKTON, retail executive; b. 1913; married. With Strawbridge and Clothier, Phila., 1934—, v.p., 1948-51, exec. v.p., 1951-55, pres., 1955-67, chmn., chief exec. officer, 1967-79, chmn. exec. com., 1979—, also bd. dirs. Lt. comdr. USN, 1941-46. Office: Strawbridge & Clothier 801 Market St Philadelphia PA 19107-3109

STRAWBRIDGE, PETER S., department store executive; b. Phila., 1938; married. B.A., Hamilton Coll., 1960. Exec. trainee Abraham & Straus, Bklyn., 1960-61; with Strawbridge & Clothier, Phila., 1961—, buyer men's sportswear, 1963-68; mgr. Neshaminy Br. Store-Strawbridge & Clothier, Phila., 1968-69; v.p., gen. mgr. Clover Store div. Strawbridge & Clothier, Phila., 1969-76, corp. exec. v.p. mdse. and publicity, 1976-79, pres., 1979—; dir.; bd. dirs. Associated Merchandising Corp., CoreStates Fin. Corp., Greater Phila. First Corp. Mem. bd. mgrs. Pa. Hosp., 1971-94; bd. dirs. Phila. Orch. Assn., 1990—. Office: Strawbridge & Clothier 801 Market St Philadelphia PA 19107-3199

STRAWBRIDGE, STEVEN LOWRY, retail executive; b. Miami, Fla., Nov. 2, 1943; s. G. Stockton and Mary (Lowry) S.; m. Elizabeth Billings, May 4, 1968; children: Steven, Whitney, Allison. BA, Hobart Coll., 1966. Mgmt. trainee Bloomingdale's, N.Y.C., 1967-68; asst. dept. mgr. jr. dresses Strawbridge & Clothier, Phila., 1968-70, mgr. women's hosiery dept., 1970-73, mgr. men's mdse. div., 1976-82, v.p., treas., sec., 1982—, also bd. dirs.; mgr. br. store div. ready-to-wear mdse. Strawbridge & Clothier, Exton, Pa., 1973-74, mgr. store, 1974-76. Bd. mgrs. Travelers Aid Soc., Phila., 1979; mem. adv. bd. Salvation Army, Phila, 1984; bd. dirs. Children's Hosp. Phila., 1986. Served with Army NG, 1966-72. Mem. Gladwyne Sports Assn. (v.p., treas), Zool. Soc. Phila. (bd. dirs.). Republican. Episcopalian. Club: Merion Cricket (Pa.). Office: Strawbridge & Clothier 801 Market St Philadelphia PA 19107-3199

STRAWDERMAN, WILLIAM E., statistics educator; b. Westerly, R.I., Apr. 25, 1941; s. Robert Lee and Alida Browning (Dow) S.; m. Susan Linda Grube; July 20, 1985; children: Robert Lee, William Edward, Heather Lynne. BS, U. R.I., 1963; MS, Cornell U., 1965, Rutgers U., 1967; PhD, Rutgers U., 1969. Mem. tech. staff Bell Telephone Labs., Holmdel, N.J., 1965-67; prof. Stanford (Calif.) U., 1969-70; instr. Rutgers U., New Brunswick, N.J., 1967-69, prof. stats., 1970—. Contbr. over 90 articles to profl. jours. Fellow Inst. Math. Stats., Am. Stats. Assn. Office: Rutgers U Statistics Dept Hill Ctr-Busch Campus New Brunswick NJ 08903

STRAWN-HAMILTON, FRANK, jazz musician, folksinger, composer and arranger, educator; b. N.Y.C., Aug. 3, 1934; s. Frank Strawn and Gladys (Bley) Hamilton; m. Sheila Lofton, Nov. 7, 1954 (div. Nov. 1971); children: Cameron, Auguste, Evan Baird, Liam Christopher, Heather Alexa; m. Deeanne Lee Walter, May 5, 1972 (div. Oct. 1980); m. Mary Doyle, Jan. 15, 1983. Student, Los Angeles City Coll., 1952-53, Chgo. Mus. Coll., 1959-62, L.A. Valley Coll., 1963-64. Organizer, head teaching staff, v.p. Old Town Sch. Folk Music, Chgo., 1957-62; ho. musician Gate of Horn, Chgo., 1959-61; mem. The Weavers, 1962-63. Appeared Asheville (N.C.) Folk Festival, 1953, Newport Folk Festival, 1959; motion picture appearance in Subterraneans, 1958; performed with trio Meridian for spl. children's programs Young Audiences in Atlanta Pub. Sch. System, 1987-94; rec. artist Folkways, Vanguard records; devel. method annotation folk guitar and 5 string banjo; film score: A Time Out of War, 1952; TV score: Survival. Mem. Irish Arts Atlanta. Mem. ACLU, UN Assn., Dramatist Guild, Chgo. Hist. Soc. (hon.). Home: 852 Cinderella Ct Decatur GA 30033-5812

STRAYHORN, RALPH NICHOLS, JR., lawyer; b. Durham, N.C., Feb. 16, 1923; Ralph Nichols and Annie Jane (Cooper) S.; m. Donleen Carol MacDonald, Sept. 10, 1949; children: Carol Strayhorn Rose, Ralph Nichols III. BS in Bus. Adminstrn., U. N.C., 1947, LLB, 1950. Bar: N.C. 1950, U.S. Dist. Ct. (mid. and ea. dists.) N.C. 1950, U.S. Ct. Appeals (4th cir.) 1950. Assoc. Victor S. Bryant, Sr., Durham, 1950-55; ptnr. Bryant, Lipton, Strayhorn & Bryant, Durham, 1956-62; sr. ptnr. Newson, Graham, Strayhorn & Hedrick, Durham, 1962-78; gen. counsel Wachovia Corp., Wachovia Bank and Trust Co., N.A., Winston-Salem, N.C., 1978-88; of counsel Petree Stockton Winston-Salem N.C., 1988—; mem. legal adv. com. to N.Y. Stock Exch., 1986-89; adv. dir. Wachovia Bank and Trust Co., Durham, 1973-78; chmn. bd. 1st Fed. Savs. & Loan Assn., Durham, 1976-78; mem. N.C. Gen. Assembly, 1959-61; bd. of visitors U. N.C., Wake Forest U. Law Sch. Lt. comdr. USNR, 1943-46. Fellow Am. Coll. Trial Lawyers, Am. Bar Found.; internat. Assn. Def. Counsel; mem. ABA, N.C. Bar Assn. (pres. 1971-72), Newcomen Soc. of U.S., 4th Jud. Conf. Episcopalian. Clubs: Old Town Club (Winston-Salem). Office: Petree Stockton 1001 W 4th St Winston Salem NC 27101

STRAYTON, ROBERT GERARD, public communications executive; b. Bklyn., Aug. 4, 1935; s. George Andrew and Kathryn Loretta (Monahan) S.; m. Patricia Cecelia Hand, Aug. 16, 1958 (div. Aug. 1972); children—Jennifer Anne, Melissa Marie, Robert Hand, Bruce Andrew; m. Jayne Helene Kramer, Mar. 4, 1983. B.A. in English, Villanova U., 1957. Accredited in pub. relations. Account exec. Carl Byoir & Assocs., Inc., N.Y.C., 1962-65; dir. pub. relations and advt. EDP div. Honeywell Inc., Wellesley, Mass., 1966-69; pres. Strayton Corp., Wellesley, Mass., 1969-84; pres., chief operating officer Gray Strayton Internat., Waltham, Mass., 1984-86; exec. v.p., vice chmn. bd. dirs. Gray and Co., Washington; exec. v.p., mng. dir. Advanced Technology Inc. Hill and Knowlton, Inc., 1986-89; pres. The Strayton Group Inc., 1990—. Mem. NCCJ, Boston, 1984—. Lt. (j.g.) USNR, 1958-61. Fellow Pub. Rels. Soc. Am. (Silver Anvil award 1968, 89, counselor, mem. exec. com. Counselors Acad. 1983-84, disting. service award 1984); mem. Nat. Investors Relations Inst., Assn. Nat. Advertisers, Advt. Club Boston (trustee 1982-87), Trout United, Inc. (v.p. 1984-93), Atlantic Salmon Task Force (bd. dirs. 1988—), Blue Water Sailing Club, Red Brook Harbor Yacht Club, Wellesley Country Club, Flycasters Club. Republican. Roman Catholic. Avocations: sailing; flyfishing; tennis; golf. Home: 18 Phillips Pond Natick MA 01760-5620 Office: The Strayton Group Inc 8 Pleasant St Natick MA 01760

STRAZIS, CYNTHIA W., nurse, administrator. BSN, Fla. State U., 1960; MEd, U. Fla., 1963; postgrad., Emory U., 1972. Vice pres. patient care svcs. Lee Meml. Hosp., Ft. Myers, Fla. Contbr. to profl. publs. Mem. Am. Hosp. Assn., Fla. Hosp. Assn., Am. Orgn. Nurse Execs., Fla. Orgn. Nurse Execs.

STREAM, ARNOLD CRAGER, lawyer, writer; b. N.Y.C., Feb. 8, 1918; s. Mervyn and Sophia (Hyams) S.; m. Barbara Bloom, Oct. 1, 1967; children by previous marriages: Jane, Abigail. BA, CCNY, 1936; LLD, St. Lawrence U., 1940. Bar: N.Y. 1940, D.C. 1942. Asst. U.S. Atty. N.Y.Dist., 1940-43; ptnr. Amen, Weisman & Butler, N.Y.C., 1948-55; exec. v.p., gen. counsel C & TV Corp., 1955-60, Hazel Bishop, Inc., 1955-60; trial lawyer, 1960-91; sr. ptnr. Monasch, Chazen & Stream, N.Y.C., 1973-82, Blum, Gersen & Stream, N.Y.C., 1982-93; ret., 1993; formerly trial counsel Gulfstream Aerospace Corp., Twentieth Century-Fox Film Corp., French Embassy, N.Y.C.; spl. counsel to TV industry; vis. lectr. Touro Coll. Law; speaker on lit. topics for Gt. Neck Libr.; archivist Palace of the Govs., Santa Fe; lit. tutor Santa Fe Community Coll. Author: (novels) The Third Bullet, Until Proven Guilty, Nemo; (short story) Sudi, others; contbr. book revs., tax series, series on constl. law, articles to profl. jours. Served to lt. col. JAGD, AUS, 1943-46. Mem. Bar of Assn. of City of N.Y. A lawyer standing in the courtroom provides the ultimate balance between excess government and excess liberty.

STREAM, JAY WILSON, financial consultant; b. Farlan, Iowa, Apr. 17, 1921; s. Adrian M. and Theo (Bennett) S.; m. Dorothy McCullough, May 20, 1960; children: Carol, James, Cindy, Linda. Student, Milw. State Tchrs. Coll., 1943. Casualty ins. underwriter R.A. Napier & Co., Chgo., 1939-41; with Wallace Supply Mfg. Co., Chgo., 1941-42; quality control specialist Am. Torpedo (Amertorp), Franklin Park, Ill., 1945-47; home office rep. John Hancock Life Ins. Co., Chgo., 1946-48; partner ready-mix concrete co. Chgo., 1949-52; owner, operating officer Jay W. Stream Assocs., Midwest Land Corp., Hydrostructures; founder, builder others; founder Village of Carol Stream, Ill., 1952-64; founder, pres., chmn. bd. Hawthorne Bank of Wheaton, Ill., 1961-68; dir. Hawthorne Bank of Wheaton, 1961—; cons. San Luis Obispo, Calif., 1970—; founder, chmn. steering com. World Arabian Horse Assn., 1967-72, 1st pres., 1972—. Head career devel., Wayne Newton, 1971-80; exec. producer several films and TV prodns. Mem. U.S. Trade Relations-U.S. Dept. Agr. Policy Adv. Com. for Trade. Served to 2d lt. USAAC, 1942-45. Republican. Home: 300 Greengate Rd San Luis Obispo CA 93401-7947 Office: 1026 Chorro St Suite 1 San Luis Obispo CA 93401

STREAN, BERNARD M., retired naval officer; b. Big Cabin, Okla., Dec. 16, 1910; s. Ralph Lester and Maude (Hopkins) S.; m. Janet Lockey, June 12, 1935; children: Bernard M., Richard Lockey, Judy (Mrs. William S. Graves). B.S., U.S. Naval Acad., 1933; grad., Armed Forces Staff Coll., 1949, Nat. War Coll., 1958. Commd. ensign USN, 1933, advanced through grades to vice adm., 1965, designated naval aviator, 1935, assigned USS Pennsylvania, 1933-35; assigned Naval Air Sta. USN, Pensacola, Fla., 1935-36; assigned USS Saratoga USN, 1936-38, assigned San Diego Naval Sta., 1938-39; assigned Pearl Harbor Naval Air Sta. USN, Hawaii, 1939-40; assigned Naval Air Sta. USN, Jacksonville, Fla., 1940-42; comdr. Fighter Squadron 1, USS Yorktown USN, 1943-44, comdr. Air Group 98, 1944-45, comdr. Air Group 75, 1945-46, head tech. tng. program sect. Office Chief Naval Ops., 1950-51, comdg. officer Air Transp. Squadron 8, 1951-54, comdg. officer Pre-Flight Sch., 1954-56, comdg. officer USS Kenneth Whiting, 1956-57, comdg. officer USS Randolph, 1958-59, chief staff, aide to comdr. Naval Air Force, U.S. Atlantic Fleet, 1959-60, comdr. Fleet Air Whidbey, 1960-61, comdr. Patrol Force 7th Fleet, also U.S. Taiwan Patrol Force, 1961-62, asst. chief naval ops. for fleet ops., 1962-64, comdr. Carrier Div. 2, Atlantic Fleet, 1964-65, comdr. World's 1st All-Nuclear Naval Task Force, 1964, comdr. round the world cruise; dep. asst. chief for pers., Bur. Naval Pers. Dept. Navy, Washington, 1965-68; chief naval air tng. Naval Air Sta. Dept. Navy, Pensacola, Fla., 1968-71; ret., 1971; v.p. O.S.C. Franchise Devel. Corp., 1971-75; chmn. bd. Solaray Corp., 1975-80; v.p. Huet-Browning Corp., Washington. Bd. dirs. U.S. Olympic Com., 1965-68; trustee No. Va. Community Colls., 1978-82. Decorated Navy Cross, (2) D.F.C. with 2 gold stars, Air medal with 7 gold stars, Legion of Merit, D.S.M., numerous area and campaign ribbons; Disting. Svc. medal (Greece); medal of Pao-Ting (Republic of China). Mem. Mil. Order World Wars, Loyal Order Carabao, Early and Pioneer Naval Aviators Assn. (pres. 1977-79), Arlington County Tax Assn. (vice chmn. 1978-80), Md. Aviation Hist. Soc. (founder, bd. dirs. 1978-82), U.S. Naval Acad. Alumni Assn. (pres. Class 1933, 1973-88), Army Navy Club (Washington), N.Y. Yacht Club, Washington Golf and Country Club (Arlington), L.A. Country Club. Address: 1200 N Nash St # 846 Arlington VA 22209 also: 804 N Camden Dr Beverly Hills CA 90210

STREAR, JOSEPH D., public relations executive; b. N.Y.C., Nov. 5, 1933; s. Morris and Betty (Birenbaum) S. B.A., CCNY, 1955. Pres. AC&R Pub. Relations, Inc., N.Y.C., 1972-82; mng. ptnr. Kanan, Corbin, Schupak & Aronow, Inc., N.Y.C., 1982-84; pres. Strear, David & Mitchell, Inc., N.Y.C., from 1984; now prin. Joseph Strear Pub. Rels., N.Y.C. Served to 1st lt. U.S. Army, 1955-57. Mem. Pub. Relations Soc. Am. Avocation: sports. Office: 408 W 57th St New York NY 10019-3053

STREATOR, EDWARD, diplomat; b. N.Y.C., Dec. 12, 1930; s. Edward James and Ella (Stout) S.; m. Priscilla Craig Kenney, Feb. 16, 1957; children: Edward James, III, Elinor Craig, Abigail Merrill. A.B., Princeton U., 1952. Commd. fgn. service officer Dept. State, 1956; assigned LCA, 1956-58; 3d sec. embassy Addis Ababa, Ethiopia, 1958-60; 2d sec. embassy Lome Togo, 1960-62; intelligence research specialist Office Research and Analysis for Africa, Dept. State, Washington, 1962-63, staff asst. to sec. state, 1964-66, chief polit.-mil. affairs unit, 1966-67; dep. dir. polit.-mil. affairs Office Polit.-Mil. Affairs, 1967-68; dep. dir. polit. affairs U.S. Mission to NATO, 1968-69; dep. dir. Office NATO and Atlantic Polit.-Mil. Affairs, Dept. State, 1969-73; dir. office, 1973-75, dep. U.S. permanent rep. to NATO, dep. chief U.S. Mission to NATO, 1975-77; minister, dep. chief of mission Am. embassy, London, 1975-84; ambassador, U.S. rep. OECD Paris, 1984-87; bd. dirs. South Bank. Mem. U.S. dels. to NATO and OECD Ministerial Meetings, 1964, 66, 69-75, 85-87; mem. 10th SEATO Council Ministers Meeting, 1965; 2d spl. Inter-Am. Conf., 1965, Conf. Security and Coop., in Europe, 1973; mem. Coun. Royal United Svcs. Inst., 1987-91, vice patron 1993—; mem. devel. com. Nat. Gallery, London; exec. com. The Pilgrims; mem. exec. com. Internat. Inst. Strategic Studies; gov. Ditchley Found.; pres. Am. C. of C. U.K., 1988-94; chmn. European Coun. Am. C. of C., 1992-94; bd. dirs. Brit-Am. Arts Assn.; gov. English Speaking Union, 1988-94; dir. Brit. Mus. Natural History Internat. Found.; mem. adv. bd. Inst. U.S. Studies-U. London; mem. coun. Oxford Inst. Am. Studies; mem. adv. com. Fulbright Commn., 1995—. Recipient Presdl. Meritorious Svc. award, 1986, Wilbur Carr award Dept. of State, 1987, Benjamin Franklin medal Royal Soc. Arts, 1992. Episcopalian. Clubs: Met. (Washington); Buck's, Beefsteak, Garrick, White's (London); Mill Reef (Antigua). Address: 9 St Albans Mansion, Kensington Court Pl, London W8 5QH, England also: Chateau de St Aignan, 32480 La Romieu France

STRECKER, IGNATIUS J., archbishop; b. Spearville, Kans., Nov. 23, 1917; s. William J. and Mary B. (Knoeber) S. Student, St. Benedict's Coll., Atchison, Kans., 1931-37, Kenrick Sem., St. Louis, 1937-42, Cath. U. Am., 1944-45. Ordained priest Roman Cath. Ch., 1942; aux. chaplain USAAF, Great Bend, Kans., 1942-44; chancellor Diocese Wichita, 1948-62; bishop Diocese Springfield-Cape Girardeau, Mo., 1962-69; archbishop Archdiocese of Kansas City, Kans., 1969—. Office: Chancery Office 12615 Parallel Ave Kansas City KS 66109-3748*

STRECKFUSS, JAMES ARTHUR, lawyer, historian; b. Cin., Apr. 28, 1951; s. Arthur James and Ruby Carolyn (Meyer) S.; m. Sharon Lynn Betz, Nov. 18, 1977; 1 child, Erich. BA in Polit. Sci., U. Cin., 1973; JD, Woodrow Wilson Coll. Law, 1981. Bar: Ind. Field rep. Ohio Lottery Commn., Cin., 1974-78; adminstrv. staff Powell, Goldstein, Frazer & Murphy, Atlanta, 1979-80; bailiff U.S. Ct. Appeals 11th Cir., Atlanta, 1980-81; spl. asst. Congressman Thomas Luken, Cin., 1982-84; job svc. employer com. staff Ohio Bur. Employment Svcs., Cin., 1984—. Contbr.: Encyclopedia of World War I, 1995; mng. editor Over the Front, 1986—. Chmn. Progressive Young Dems., Cin., 1974-75. Mem. Ind. State Bar Assn., League of W.W. I Aviation Historians (pres. 1993—), Cross and Cockade Internat. Home: 3127 Penrose Pl Cincinnati OH 45211

STREEB, GORDON LEE, diplomat, economist; b. Windsor, Colo., Dec. 24, 1935; s. Gerhard O. and Amelia (Martin) S.; m. Alice Junette Thomas, Aug. 11, 1962; children: Kurt, Kent, Kerry-Lynn. BSBA, U. Colo., 1959, BSChemE, 1959; PhD in Econs., U. Minn., 1978. Fgn. service officer U.S. Dept. State, Berlin, 1963-65; vice consul Am. Consulate, Guadalajara, Mex., 1965-67; instr. econs. U. Minn., 1968; examiner Bd. Examiners, 1972-73; internat. economist for trade policy Bur. Econ. and Bus. Affairs, Washington, 1977-79; econ. counselor U.S. mission European Office of the UN and other internat. orgns., Geneva, 1977-80; exec. asst. to undersec. of state on econ. affairs Washington, 1980-81; dep. asst. sec. state for internat. Am. Embassy, New Delhi, India, 1984-88; sr. inspector Dept. State, Washington, 1988-90; amb. to Zambia Am. Embassy, Lusaka, 1990-93; diplomat-in-residence The Carter Ctr., Atlanta, 1994—. Home: 2680 Churchwell Ln Atlanta GA 30084-2402 Office: The Carter Ctr One Copenhill Atlanta GA 30307

STREEP, MERYL (MARY LOUISE STREEP), actress; b. Madison, N.J., June 22, 1949; d. Harry Jr. and Mary W. Streep; m. Donald J. Gummer, 1978. BA, Vassar Coll., 1971; MFA, Yale U., 1975. DFA (hon.), 1983; DFA (hon.), Dartmouth Coll., 1981. Ind. actress stage, screen, 1975—.

Appeared with Green Mountain Guild, Woodstock, Vt.; Broadway debut in Trelawny of the Wells, Lincoln Center Beaumont Theater, 1975; N.Y.C. theatrical appearances include 27 Wagons Full of Cotton (Theatre World award), A Memory of Two Mondays, Henry V, Secret Service, The Taming of the Shrew, Measure for Measure, The Cherry Orchard, Happy End, Wonderland, Taken in Marriage, Alice in Concert (Obie award 1981); movie appearances include Julia, 1977, The Deer Hunter, 1978 (Best Supporting Actress award Nat. Soc. Film Critics), Manhattan, 1979, The Seduction of Joe Tynan, 1979, Kramer vs. Kramer, 1979 (N.Y. Film Critics' award, Los Angeles Film Critics' award, both for best actress, Golden Globe award, Acad. award for best supporting actress), The French Lieutenant's Woman, 1981 (Los Angeles Film Critics award for best actress, Brit. Acad. award, Golden Globe award 1981), Sophie's Choice, 1982 (Acad. award for best actress, Los Angeles Film Critics award for best actress, Golden Globe award 1982), Still of the Night, 1982, Silkwood, 1983, Falling in Love, 1984, Plenty, 1985, Out of Africa, 1985 (Los Angeles Film Critics award for best actress 1985), Heartburn, 1986, Ironweed, 1987, A Cry in the Dark, 1988 (named Best Actress N.Y. Film Critics' Circle, 1988, Best Actress Cannes Film Festival, 1989), She-Devil, 1989, Postcards From the Edge, 1990, Defending Your Life, 1991, Death Becomes Her, 1992, The House of the Spirits,1994, The River Wild, 1994, The Bridges of Madison County, 1995; TV film The Deadliest Season, 1977; TV mini-series Holocaust, 1978 (Emmy award); TV dramatic spls. Secret Service, 1977, Uncommon Women and Others, 1978;TV (narrator) The Velveteen Rabbit, 1985, A Vanishing Wilderness, 1990. Recipient Mademoiselle award, 1976, Woman of Yr. award B'nai Brith, 1979, Woman of Yr. award Hasty Pudding Soc., Harvard U., 1980, Best Supporting Actress award Nat. Bd. of Rev., 1979, Best Actress award Nat. Bd. of Rev., 1982, Star of Yr. award Nat. Assn. Theater Owners, 1983, People's Choice award, 1983, 85, 86, 87. Office: Creative Artists Agy 9830 Wilshire Blvd Beverly Hills CA 90212-1825*

STREET, DANA MORRIS, orthopedic surgeon; b. N.Y.C., May 7, 1910; s. William Dana and Elizabeth (Clark) S.; m. Elna Alice Clare, June 18, 1940; children: Rosalyn Clare (Mrs. David R. Sprague), Dana Clark, Steven Morris, William Milo. B.S., Haverford Coll., 1932; M.D., Cornell U., 1936. Diplomate: Am. Bd. Orthopaedic Surgery. Intern pathology Duke Hosp., 1936-37, Duke Hosp. (orthopedics), 1937-38; asst. resident phys. medicine Albany (N.Y.) Hosp., 1938-39; fellow Nemour Found., 1939-40; intern orthopedics Boston City Hosp., 1940; asst. resident surgery Albany Hosp., 1940-41; intern, asst. resident orthopedics Johns Hopkins Hosp., 1941-42; fellow N.Y. Orthopaedic Hosp., 1942; chief orthopedic sect. Kennedy VA Hosp., Memphis, 1946-59; prof. surgery, chief orthopedic div. U. Ark., 1959-62; prof. surgery in residence UCLA, 1962-75; head orthopedic div. Harbor Gen. Hosp., Torrance, Calif., 1962-75, Riverside (Calif.) Gen. Hosp., 1975-77; chief orthopedic sect. Jerry L. Pettis Meml. VA Hosp., Loma Linda, Calif., 1977-80; prof. orthopedics Loma Linda U., 1975-80, emeritus 1980—. Author: (with others) Evolution of Intramedullary Nailing, 1995; contrb. articles on medullary nailing and joint replacement to med. jours; also book chpts. Served to maj. M.C. USAAF, 1942-46. Mem. AMA, Am. Acad. Orthopaedic Surgeons, Am. Orthopaedic Assn., Calif. Med. Assn., Calif. Orthopaedic Assn., Western Orthopaedic Assn., Assn. Bone and Joint Surgeons (treas. 1953-56, v.p. 1956-58, pres. 1959), Am. Fracture Assn. Presbyn. (elder, deacon, clk. sessions). Home: 44201 Village 44 Camarillo CA 93012-8935

STREET, DAVID HARGETT, investment company executive; b. Oklahoma City, Dec. 4, 1943; s. Bob Allen and Elizabeth Anne (Hargett) S.; m. Betty Ann Nichols, Oct. 1, 1966; children: Elizabeth Ann, Randall Hargett, Jeffrey David. BA in English, U. Okla., 1965; MBA in Fin., U. Pa., 1970. Vice pres. SEI Corp., 1970; v.p., prin. Street & Street, Inc., N.Y.C., 1970-74; v.p., mgr. San Francisco regional office First Nat. Bank Chicago, 1974-78; sr. v.p., CFO, treas. Bangor Punta Corp., Greenwich, Conn., 1978-84; v.p., treas. Penn Cen. Corp., Greenwich, 1984-86, v.p. fin., 1986-87; sr. v.p. fin. Penn Cen. Corp., Cin., 1987-92; exec. v.p. Gen. Cable Corp., Highland Heights, Ky., 1992-94, also bd. dirs.; pres., CEO Street Capital Group, Cin., 1994—; mem. adv. bd. Mfrs. Hanover Trust Co., 1982-88. Vice chmn. bd. dirs. Greenwich Acad. for Girls, 1984-87, chmn. bd. trustees, treas., 1987-88; trustee Cin. County Day Sch., 1990-91; mem. cmty. bd. Sta. WGUC-FM, 1987-94; trustee Bethesda Hosp., Inc., 1993—, treas. 1994-95; trustee Cin. Classical Pub. Radio, Inc. 1994—, Cmty. Chest Cin. Area, Inc., 1993—, treas. 1994-95. 1st lt. M.I. U.S. Army, 1966-67. Mem. Greenwich Country Club. Presbyterian. Home and Office: 6475 Given Rd Cincinnati OH 45243-3326

STREET, JOHN CHARLES, linguistics educator; b. Chgo., Apr. 3, 1930; s. Charles Larrabee and Mary Louise (Rouse) S.; m. Eve Elizabeth Baker, June 4, 1975. BA, Yale, 1951, MA, 1952, PhD, 1955. Asst. prof. English Mich. State U., 1957-59; asst. prof. linguistics and Mongolian langs. Columbia, 1959-62; vis. asst. prof. linguistics U. Wash., 1962-63; assoc. prof. linguistics U. Wis., Madison, 1963-65; prof. linguistics U. Wis., 1965-92; prof. emeritus U. Wis., Madison, 1992—. Author: The Language of the Secret History of the Mongols, 1957, Khalkha Structure, 1963, The Journal of Oliver Rouse, 1983, An Ellis Family of Devon and Newfoundland, 1994. Research assoc. Am. Council Learned Socs., 1959-62. Served with AUS, 1955-57. Mem. Linguistic Soc. Am., Am. Oriental Soc., Soc. Uralo-Altaica, Mongolia Soc., Internat. Assn. for Mongol Studies, Phi Beta Kappa.

STREET, PATRICIA LYNN, secondary education educator; b. Lillington, N.C., May 3, 1940; d. William Banks and Vandalia (McLean) S.; m. Col. Robert Gest, June 2, 1962 (div. 1985); children: Robert, Roblyn Renee. BS Livingstone Coll., 1962; MEd, Salisbury State U., 1974; postgrad., various, 1968—. Tchr. Govt. of Guam Marianas Island, Agana, Guam, 1962-64; sec., typist USAF, Glasgow AFB, Mont., 1964-65, Syracuse (N.Y.) U. AeroSpace Engring., 1966-67; tchr. Syracuse (N.Y.) City Sch. System, 1967-69; lectr. U. of Md., Eastern Shore, Princess Anne, Md., 1970-72; tchr. Prince George's County Pub. Schs., Upper Marlboro, Md., 1973—; instr. U. Guam, Anderson AFB, 1963, U.S. Armed Forces Inst., Anderson AFB, 1963, Yorktowne Bus. Inst., Landover, Md., 1987-90, Chesapeake Bus. Inst., Clinton, Md., 1983-89; asst. advisor student tchrs. U. Md. Ea. Shore, Princess Anne, 1972; adj. instr. Bowie State U., 1990—; conv. speaker. Mem. AAUW, NEA, ASCD, Am. Vocat. Assn., Md. Bus. Edn. Assn. (pres.-elect 1987-88, pres. 1988-89, Educator of Yr. 1989), Md. Vocat. Assn. (regional rep. 1986-89, audit chmn. 1987-89, Vocat.-Tech. Educator of Yr. 1989), Ea. Bus. Edn. Assn. (co-editor newsletter 1990-91, secondary exec. dir. 1991-94), Md. State Tchrs. Assn., D.C. Bus. Edn. Assn., Nat. Bus. Edn. Assn., Data Processing Mgmt. Assn., Internat. Soc. for Bus. Edn., Nat. Bus. Edn. Com., Prince George's County Edn. Assn., New Eng. Bus. Educators Assn. Democrat. Baptist. Avocations: sewing, singing, modern creative dancing. Home: 10107 Welshire Dr Upper Marlboro MD 20772 Office: Prince George's Pub Sch Upper Marlboro MD 20772

STREET, PICABO, Olympic athlete; b. Triumph, Idaho, 1971. Silver medalist, women's downhill alpine skiing Olympic Games, Lillehammer, Norway, 1994; professional downhill skier, 1994—. Named World Cup Downhill Women's Champion, 1995. Office: US Olympic Com 1750 E Boulder St Colorado Springs CO 80909*

STREET, ROBERT A., research physicist. Rsch. scientist Xerox Corp., Palo Alto, Calif. Recipient David Adler Lectureship award Am. Phys. Soc., 1992. Office: Palo Alto Rsch Ctr Xerox Corp 3333 Coyote Hill Rd Palo Alto CA 94304-1314*

STREET, ROBERT LYNNWOOD, civil and mechanical engineer; b. Honolulu, Dec. 18, 1934; s. Evelyn Mansel and Dorothy Heather (Brook) S.; m. Norma Jeanette Ensminger, Feb. 6, 1959; children: Brian Clarke (dec.), Deborah Lynne, Kimberley Anne. Student, USN ROTC Program, 1952-57; M.S., Stanford U., 1957, Ph.D. (NSF grad. fellow 1960-62), 1963. Mem. faculty sch. engring. Stanford U., 1962—, prof. civil engring., assoc. chmn. dept., 1970-72, chmn. dept., 1972-80, 94-95, prof. fluid mechanics and applied math., 1972—, dir. environ. fluid mechanics lab., 1985-91, assoc. dean research, 1971-83, vice provost for acad. computing and info. systems, 1983-85, vice provost and dean of research and acad. info. systems, 1985-87, v.p. for info. resources, 1987-90, acting provost, 1987, v.p. libre. and info. resources, 1990-92; vice provost, dean of librs. and info. resources Stanford U., 1992-94; vis. prof. U. Liverpool, Eng., 1970-71; trustee Univ. Corp. Atmospheric Rsch., 1983-94, chmn. sci. programs evaluation com., 1981,

treas. corp., 1985, vice chmn. bd., 1986, chmn. bd., 1987-91; bd. dirs., sec.-treas. UCAR Found., 1987-91; bd. govs. Rsch. Libr. Group, 1990-91; chmn. Com. Preservation Rsch. Libr. Materials, Assn. Rsch. Librs., 1993; mem. higher edn. adv. bds. computer corps., 1983-94; mem. basic energy sci. adv. com. U.S. Dept. Energy, 1993—; bd. dirs. Stanford U. Bookstore, Inc. Author: The Analysis and Solution of Partial Differential Equations, 1973; co-author: Elementary Fluid Mechanics, 7th edit., 1996; assoc. editor Jour. Fluids Engring., 1978-81; contrb. articles to profl. jours.; mem. editl. bds. profl. jours. With C.E.C., USN, 1957-60. Sr. postdoctoral fellow Nat. Center Atmospheric Research, 1978-79; sr. Queen's fellow in marine sci., Australia, 1985; fellow N.E. Asia-U.S. Forum on Internat. Policy at Stanford U., 1985-89. Fellow AAAS; mem. ASCE (chmn. publs. com. hydraulics divsn. 1978-80, Walter Huber prize 1972), ASME (R.T. Knapp award 1986), Am. Geophys. Union, Oceanographic Soc., Am. Phys. Soc., Phi Beta Kappa, Sigma Xi, Tau Beta Pi. Office: Environ Fluid Mechs Lab Dept Civil Engring Stanford U Stanford CA 94305-4020

STREET, WILLIAM MAY, beverage company executive; b. Louisville, 1938. Grad., Princeton U., 1960; MBA, Harvard U., 1963. V.p. Brown-Forman Corp., Louisville, 1980—; mem. exec. com., 1971, sr. v.p., 1977, vice chmn., 1983—; pres., COO Brown-Forman Beverage Co. Divsn., Louisville, 1986—; pres., CEO Brown-Forman Beverages Worldwide Divsn., 1994—; vice chmn. Brown-Forman Corp., 1983—. Office: Brown-Forman Beverages Worldwide PO Box 1080 850 Dixie Hwy Louisville KY 40210-1091

STREETER, ANNE PAUL, state senator; b. Phila., July 21, 1926; s. Henry Neill and Marianne (Harris) Paul; m. Ronald Mather Streeter; children—Jean, Deborah, Stephen, Richard, Jonathan. B.A., Smith Coll., 1948. Tchr. Springdale Sch., Phila., 1948-1949, Oxford Sch., West Hartford, Conn., 1949-1950; mem. Conn. Senate, Hartford, 1982-87, dep. majority leader, 1985-87. Mem. West Hartford Town Council, 1973-81, mayor, 1975-81. Named Woman of Year, Jr. C. of C., West Hartford, 1979, Hartford, 1981. Mem. LWV (pres. 1966-67, 1969-72). Republican. Congregationalist. Home: 31 Brookmoor Rd West Hartford CT 06107-3104

STREETER, HENRY SCHOFIELD, lawyer; b. N.Y.C., May 2, 1920; s. Thomas Winthrop and Ruth (Cheney) S.; m. Mary Ann Dexter, May 16, 1959; children—Frank Sherwin, Cornelia Van Rensselaer, Natalie Thayer. B.A., Harvard U., 1942, J.D. magna cum laude, 1949. Bar: Mass. Law clk. Judge A.N. Hand, N.Y.C., 1950-51; mem. firm Ropes & Gray, Boston, 1949—. Chmn. Bd. Appeals, Wenham, Mass., 1983—; trustee, v.p. Peabody Mus. Salem, 1968—; corporator Mass. Gen. Hosp., 1976, Beverly Hosp., 1972. Served to lt. USNR, 1941-46. Mem. Mass. Hist. Soc., Am. Antiquarian Soc. (sec., trustee 1972), Club of Odd Volumes (pres.), Somerset Club, Myopia Hunt Club, Cruising of Am. Club, Walpole Soc., Tobique Salmon Club (pres.), St. Andrew Lodge. Episcopalian. Avocations: sailing; shooting; fishing. Home: Old Farm Maple St Wenham MA 01984 Office: Ropes and Gray 1 International Pl Boston MA 02110-2600

STREETER, RICHARD BARRY, academic official; b. Albany, N.Y., Aug. 6, 1940; s. Lyle Tyler and Marion Downey S.; m. Janet Grace Marsteller, July 31, 1971; children—Jonathan Lyle, Stephanie Lyne. BA, U. Fla., 1962, MEd, 1963; EdD, U. Miami, 1972. Assoc. dir. fin. aid U. Miami, Coral Gables, Fla., 1970-73; dir. fin. aid Portland (Oreg.) State U., 1973-76, asst. dean grad. studies, dir. sponsored research, 1976-80; dir. office of research Lehigh U., Bethlehem, Pa., 1980-90; asst. v.p. rsch., dir. U. South Fla., Tampa, 1990—; dir. USDOE/USF Tech. Deployment Ctr., 1994—; bd. trustees Northampton County Area C.C., 1986-90; del. to Pa. Fed. of C.C. Trustees; mem. Easton area Sch. Bd. 1984-90; bd. dirs. Oak Ridge Associated Univs. Bus. mgr. Quality of Life Maintenance Orgn., 1976-80. Mem. AAAS, Nat. Coun. Univ. Rsch. Adminstrs., Soc. Rsch. Adminstrs., Coun. on Rsch. and Tech. (rsch. policy com., commercialization task force), Archontes, Omega, Phi Delta Kappa. Republican. Presbyterian. Home: 507 Cliff Dr Temple Ter FL 33617-3807 Office: U South Fla 4202 E Fowler Ave Tampa FL 33620-9951

STREETER, RICHARD EDWARD, lawyer; b. Mpls., Aug. 6, 1934; s. Donald Stivers and Beatrice Louise (Gibbs) S.; m. Charlotte Mae Tharp; children—Christopher A., Joanna G., Matthew J., Jonathan R. B.A., Yale U., 1956; LL.B, Yale Law Sch., 1959. Bar: Ohio 1960, D.C. 1964, U.S. Supreme Ct. 1964. Assoc. Thompson, Hine and Flory, Cleve., 1960-63, 65-68, ptnr., 1968—; atty. State Dept. Legal Advisors Office, Washington, 1963, Justice Dept. Antitrust Div., Washington, 1964; asst. gen. counsel Senate Democratic Policy Com., Washington, 1964-65. Contbr. article to profl. jour. Mem. Leadership Cleve., 1981; v.p. Youth Opportunities Unltd., Cleve., 1983—; pres. Fedn. Community Planning, Cleve., 1980-82, Cleve. Legal Aid Soc., 1974-76, Plan of Action for Tomorrow's Housing, Cleve., 1987-88; chmn. Ctr. for Human Svcs., 1990-93; trustee City Club, Cleve., 1987-91, St. Vincent Quadrangle Inc., 1991—, Lake Erie Coll., 1993—; bd. dirs. United Way Svcs. Cleve., 1992—. Recipient Cleve. 10 Outstanding Young Men award Jr. C. of C., 1968. Mem. ABA, Bar Assn. Greater Cleve. (trustee 1971-74, chmn. securities law sect. 1979-80, chmn. corps. banking and bus. law sect. 1983-85), Ohio State Bar Assn. (corp. law com.). Home: 472 Greenhaven Dr Chagrin Falls OH 44022-3323 Office: Thompson Hine & Flory 1100 Nat City Bank Bldg 629 Euclid Ave Cleveland OH 44114-3070

STREETER, RICHARD HENRY, lawyer; b. Paris, Tex., Aug. 11, 1943; s. Vernon Brackin and Amy (Anderson) S.; m. Lucille Clayton Anderson, Aug. 28, 1971; 1 child, Thomas Clayton Anderson. BA, U. Tex., 1965, MA, 1969, JD, 1970. Bar: Tex. 1970, U.S. Dist. Ct. (no. dist.) Ohio 1972, U.S. Dist. Ct. (we. dist.) Tex. 1972, U.S. Dist. Ct. (no. dist.) Tex. 1973, U.S. Ct. Appeals (2nd, 4th and 5th cirs.) 1974, U.S. Ct. Appeals (D.C. cir.) 1975, D.C. 1976, U.S. Ct. Claims, 1986, U.S. Ct. Appeals (6th and 11th cirs.) 1988, U.S. Ct. Appeals (8th cir.) 1995, U.S. Ct. Internat. Trade, 1995. Atty. Gen. Counsel ICC, Washington, 1971-75; assoc. Wheeler & Wheeler, Washington, 1975-78, ptnr., 1978-87; ptnr. Barnes & Thornburg, Washington, 1987—. Mem. Transp. Lawyers Assn., Assn. Transp. Practitioners, Met. Club (house com. 1986—), Chevy Chase Club, Harbor Club. Episcopalian.

STREETER, TAL, sculptor; b. Oklahoma City, Aug. 1, 1934; s. Paul Waller and Pauline Viola (Roberts) S.; m. Dorothy Ann Romig Sheets, June 26, 1957; 1 child, Lissa. B.F.A., U. Kans., 1956, M.F.A., 1961. Prof. SUNY, Purchase, 1973—; fellow Ctr. for Advanced Visual Studies MIT, 1988—, vis. prof., 1991—; curator exhbn. The Art of the Japanese Kite, Japan Soc., N.Y.C., 1980, Ice and Air Show NEA/N.Y. Arts Coun., Lake Placid, 1983, Dayton Art Inst., 1990; Fulbright lectr., Korea, 1971; conferee Internat. Design Conf., Aspen, Colo., 1979. Exhibited in group and one-man shows N.Y. World's Fair, 1965, Whitney Mus., N.Y.C., 1965, Larry Aldrich Mus., Ridgefield, Conn., 1968, 70, Sheldon Art Mus., Lincoln, Nebr., 1970, Sculpture in Environment, Parks Dept., N.Y.C., 1970, Minami Gallery, Tokyo, 1971, Neuberger Mus., Purchase, N.Y., 1977, U. Ky. Mus., 1982, Bruckner Festival, Linz, Austria, 1982, Dayton Art Inst., 1982, AG Mus., Munich, 1983, Cleve. Art Mus., Eng., 1985, Milton Avery Mus., Bard Coll., N.Y., 1985, Citicorp Plz., Queens, N.Y., 1991, MIT Mus., 1994; represented in permanent collections Mus. Modern Art, N.Y.C., San Francisco Mus. Contemporary Art, Wadsworth Atheneum, Newark Mus., Neuberger Mus., Purchase, N.Y., Contemporary Arts Mus., Houston, Smith Coll. Mus. Art, High Mus., Atlanta, Storm King Art Center, Ark. Art Ctr., Little Rock, Milw. Art Ctr.; vis. artist-in-residence Dartmouth Coll., 1963, Bennett Coll., 1964-70, U. N.C., 1970, 72, 73, Queens Coll., 1973, Penland Sch. of Crafts, 1974, 75, 76, Arcosanti Festival, Phoenix, 1978, 80, 81, Artpark, 1978, Lakefront Festival, Milw., 1981, Sun Valley Arts Ctr., Idaho, 1986, Walker Art Ctr., Minn., 1986; commns.: Morris Coll., N.J., 1981, N.J. State Library for Blind, 1982-84, Nat. Mus. Contemporary Art, Seoul (Republic of Korea) Olympics, 1988, Gyewon Coll. of Arts, Seoul, 1991, Total Contemporary Art Mus., Seoul, 1992; author: The Art of the Japanese Kite, 1974; co-editor: Art That Flies, 1991; also articles; contbr. to Ency. of Japan, 1981; profiled in Arts Mag., Dec., 1977, U & lc Mag., Nov., 1984, An American Portrait, CBS TV, 1986, Sky, Moon, Dragons, Kites and Smiles: Tal Streeter, An American Artist in Asia, 1994, From the Place at the Far End of the Sky, 1994. Collaborations in Art, Sci. and Tech./N.Y. State Coun. on Arts grantee, 1978.

STREETMAN, BEN GARLAND, electrical engineering educator; b. Cooper, Tex., June 24, 1939; s. Richard E. and Bennie (Morrow) S.; m.

Lenora Ann Music, Sept. 9, 1961; children: Paul, Scott. BS, U. Tex., 1961, MS, 1963, PhD, 1966. Fellow Oak Ridge Nat. Lab., 1964-66; asst. prof. elec. engring. U. Ill., 1966-70, asso. prof., 1970-74, prof., 1974-82; rsch. prof. Coordinated Sci. Lab., 1970-82; prof. elec. engring. U. Tex., Austin, 1982—; dir. Microelectronics Rsch. Ctr., 1984—, Dula D. Cockrell Centennial chair engring., 1989—; cons. in field. Author: Solid State Electronic Devices, 4th edit., 1995. Recipient Frederick Emmons Terman award Am. Soc. Engring. Edn., 1981, AT&T Found. award Am. Soc. Engring. Edn. 1987. Fellow IEEE (Edn. medal 1989), Electrochem. Soc.; mem. NAE, Tau Beta Pi, Eta Kappa Nu, Sigma Xi. Home: 3915 Glengarry Dr Austin TX 78731-3835 Office: U Tex Microelectronics Rsch Ctr BRC/MER Austin TX 78712

STREETT, JOHN WILLIAM, III, museum official; b. Marion, N.C., Jan. 19, 1941; s. John William, Jr. and Emily Elaine (Carver) S.; children: Katherine Drake, Leah Farrior, Burgin Eaves. BA in English and Theatre History, Western Carolina U., 1963; cert. in Shakespeare studies, Lincoln Coll., Oxford (Eng.) U., 1963. Founding dir. Jewett Creative Arts Ctr., Berwick Acad., South Berwick, Maine, 1964-70; exec. dir. Polk Mus. Art, Lakeland, Fla., 1970-75; dir. Mus. Arts and Sci., Evansville, Ind., 1975—; chmn. mus. adv. panel Ind. Arts Commn., 1977-78. Mem. Am. Assn. Museums, Assn. Ind. Museums (bd. dirs.). Episcopalian. Office: Evansville Mus Arts & Scis 411 SE Riverside Dr Evansville IN 47713-1098

STREETT, WILLIAM BERNARD, university dean, engineering educator; b. Lake Village, Ark., Jan. 27, 1932; s. William Bernard and Marie Louise (Pfeffer) S.; m. Jackie Lou Heard, June 8, 1955; children—Robert Stuart, David Alexander, Kathleen Ann, Michael Richard. B.S., U.S. Mil. Acad., 1955; M.S., U. Mich., 1961, Ph.D., 1963. Commd. 2d lt. U.S. Army, 1955; founder, first dir. Sci. Research Lab. U.S. Mil. Acad., West Point, N.Y., 1968-78; asst. dean U.S. Mil. Acad., West Point, N.Y., 1968-78, ret. col., 1978; sr. research assoc. Cornell U., Ithaca, 1978-81, prof. chem. engring., 1981—, dean engring., 1984-93. Contbr. articles to profl. jours. Postdoctoral fellow NATO, 1966, Guggenheim fellow Oxford U., 1974. Mem. AIChE, Tau Beta Pi, Sigma Xi. Home: 105 Oak Hill Pl Ithaca NY 14850-2323 Office: Cornell U Coll Engring Olin Hall Ithaca NY 14850

STREFF, WILLIAM ALBERT, JR., lawyer; b. Chgo., Aug. 12, 1949; s. William Albert Streff Sr. and Margaret (McKeough) Streff Fisher; m. Kathleen Myslinski, Sept. 29, 1984; children: Amanda, William III, Kimberly. BSME, Northwestern U., 1971, JD cum laude, 1974. Bar: Ill. 1974, U.S. Dist. Ct. (no. dist.) Ill. 1974, U.S. Dist. Ct. (no. dist.) N.Y. 1987, U.S. Dist. Ct. (no. dist.) Calif. 1988, U.S. Ct. Appeals (7th cir.) 1980, U.S. Ct. Appeals (9th cir.) 1988, U.S. Ct. Appeals (fed. cir.) 1982. Legal writing instr. Law Sch. Northwestern U., Chgo., 1973-74; assoc. Kirkland & Ellis, Chgo., 1974-80, ptnr., 1980—; lectr. Ill. Inst. Continuing Legal Edn., 1984; adj. prof. Northwestern U. Law Sch., 1992—. Contbr. articles to profl. jours. Mem. adv. bd. Ill. Inst. Tech./Chgo.-Kent, 1983-86; trustee Northwestern U., Evanston, 1984-86, mem. vis. com. Law Sch., Chgo., 1988-94. Mem. ABA, Intellectual Property Law Assn. Chgo. (chmn. antitrust com. 1987-91). Office: Kirland & Ellis 200 E Randolph Dr # 6100 Chicago IL 60601-6401

STREIBEL, BRYCE, state senator; b. Fessenden, N.D., Nov. 19, 1922; s. Reinhold M. and Frieda I. (Broschat) S.; m. June P. Buckley, Mar. 23, 1947; 1 child, Kent. Attended U. N.D., Grand Forks; BS, San Francisco State Coll., 1947. Engr. U.S. Govt., Napa, Calif., 1943-46; dir. Martin Funeral Home, Stockton, Calif., 1946-55; owner Streibel Twin Oaks Farm, Fessenden, N.D., 1955—; state sen. State of N.D., Bismarck, 1981—, state rep., 1957-75. Author: Pathways Through LIfe, 1983. Chmn. N.D. Legis. Coun., Bismarck, 1969-75; councilman Town of Fessenden, 1976-84; former pres. 20-30 Internat. Group, Sacramento, trustee, 1952-54; dir. World Coun., Sacramento, 1951-53; bd. dirs. U. N.D. Fellows, Grand Forks, 1982-86; pres. Fessenden Airport Authority, 1980—; mem. N.D. Bd. Higher Edn., 1977-81; chmn. N.D. adv. commn. U.S. Commn. on Civil Rights, 1988-93. Recipient Sioux award U. N.D. Alumni Assn., 1976, Benefactor award U. N.D. Found., 1982, William Budge award, 1983, Outstanding Svc. award Jaycees, 1988; named Outstanding Alumnus Theta Chi, 1987. Mem. Masons (Master), Elks, Kiwanis, Shriners, Farm Bur. Republican. Baptist. Avocations: golf, philately. Home and Office: 226 2nd St N Fessenden ND 58438-7204 Office: PO Box 467 Fessenden ND 58438-0467

STREIBICH, HAROLD CECIL, lawyer; b. Baton Rouge, June 19, 1928; s. Frederick Franklin and Margaret Rose (Foley) S.; m. Theresa Ann Grimes, Apr. 25, 1973; 1 dau. by previous marriage, Margaret Ann; stepchildren: John B. Snowden, IV, Kathryn Snowden. Bar: Tenn. 1949; LL.B, U. Va., 1953; Spl. Honors, U. Memphis, 1972. Bar: Miss. 1954, Tenn. 1960. Ptnr. Streibich & Seale and predecessor firms, Memphis, 1960—; vis. lectr. Vanderbilt U. Sch. Law, 1968-74, Brigham Young U., summer 1971, Harvard U. Law Sch., 1979, 92; prof. music, prof. entertainment law U. Memphis, 1973-91; pres. Am. Rec. Inst., 1979—. Comm. Tenn. Athletic Commn., 1970, 74. Served with U.S. Army, 1945-47, 50-52; ret. brig. gen. Tenn. N.G., 1980. Recipient World Boxing Assn. award as outstanding commr., 1972, various civic awards for Easter Seal, Heart Fund. Mem. ABA, NARAS (nat. v.p. 1980-81, bd. dirs., treas. 1978-79, pres. 1979-80, Gov.'s award Nashville chpt. 1972, Memphis chpt. 1976), Tenn. Bar Assn. (ho. of dels. 1978-83, v.p., bd. govs. 1983-85, chmn. copyright, entertainment and sports law sect. 1979), Miss. Bar Assn., Memphis Bar Assn. (bd. dirs. 1975-76), Am. Coll. Intellectual Property Law (pres. 1994—), Am. Judicature Soc., Internat. Assn. Music Pubs., Summit Club, Rotary, Phi Kappa Phi, Kappa Sigma, Omega Delta Kappa, Phi Delta Phi. Home: 5475 Crescent Ln Memphis TN 38120-2449 Office: Bryton Tower Ste 101 1271 Poplar Ave Memphis TN 38104-7265

STREIBICH, RONALD LELAND, fundraising executive; b. Peoria, Ill., May 5, 1936; s. Leland Roy and Evelyn (Moffatt) S.; m. Donna Jane Matthews, Sept. 14, 1958 (div. Jan. 1980); children: John, James; m. Elinor Sue Gaines, Apr. 23, 1988. BA, Knox Coll., 1958. Regional pub. rels. dir. GE, Winston Salem, N.C., 1959-66; dir. devel. Northwestern U., Evanston, Ill., 1966-76; exec. v.p. Meth. Med. Found., Peoria, Ill., 1976-79; v.p. Knox Colll., Galesburg, Ill., 1979-82; exec. v.p. Meml. Hosp. Found., Houston, 1982-84; v.p. St. Louis Children's Hosp., 1984-88; asst. vice chancellor Tex. A&M U., College Station & Houston, 1988—. 1st lt. U.S. Army, 1958-59. Republican. Presbyterian. Avocation: golf. Home: 15710 Greencourt Houston TX 77062 Office: Tex A&M U 2121 Holcombe Ste 1107 Houston TX 77030

STREICHER, JAMES FRANKLIN, lawyer; b. Ashtabula, Ohio, Dec. 6, 1940; s. Carl Jacob and Helen Marie (Dugan) S.; m. Sandra JoAnn Jennings, May 22, 1940; children: Cheryl Ann, Gregory Scott, Kerry Marie. BA, Ohio State U., 1962; JD, Case Western Res. U., 1966. Bar: Ohio 1966, U.S. Dist. Ct. (no. dist.) Ohio 1966. Assoc., Calfee, Halter & Griswold, Cleve., 1966-71, ptnr., 1972—; bd. dirs. The Mariner Group Inc., Ft. Myers, Fla., Spectra-Tech Inc., Stamford, Conn., Cuyahoga Bolt & Screw, Cleve.; mem. Div. Securities Adv. Bd., State of Ohio; lectr. Case Western Res. U., Cleve. State U., Ctr. for Venture Devel.; mem. pvt. sector com. John Carroll U. Trustee Achievement Ctr. for Children. Mem. ABA, Fed. Bar Assn., Ohio State Bar Assn., Assn. for Corp. Growth, Ohio Venture Assn., Greater Cleve. Bar Assn., Ohio State U. Alumni Assn., Case Western Res. U. Alumni Assn., Newcomen Soc., Bluecoats Club (Cleve.), Mayfield Country (bd. dirs. 1985-89), Tavern Club, Union Club, Rotary, Beta Theta Pi, Phi Delta Phi. Roman Catholic. Republican. Home: 50 Windrush Dr Chagrin Falls OH 44022-6841

STREICHLER, JERRY, human and technology resource development consultant; b. N.Y.C., Dec. 8, 1929; s. Samuel and Mirel (Waxman) S.; m. Rosalind Fineman, Feb. 25, 1951; children: Stuart Alan, Seth Ari, Robin Cheryl. Spl. courses cert., Newark Coll. Engring., 1951; BS magna cum laude, Kean Coll. N.J., 1956; MA, Montclair State Coll., 1958; PhD, NYU, 1963. Cons. machine designer to materials handling and auto wash cos., Montclair, N.J., 1950-67; mem. faculty dept. indsl. edn. Montclair (N.J.) State Coll., 1958-65, Trenton (N.J.) State Coll., 1965-67; prof., chmn. dept. indsl. edn. and tech. Bowling Green (Ohio) State U., 1967-78, dir. Sch. Tech., 1978-85, dean Coll. Tech., 1985-91; trustee prof., 1992, dean emeritus, trustee prof. emeritus, 1993—; pres. Tng. and Edn. Mgmt. Cons. Group, 1993—; vis. prof. S.I. Community Coll., CCNY, 1965, Rutgers U., 1967, U. Mo., 1967, U. Mich., Saginaw, 1971; cons., tchr. Newaygo Vocat. Ctr., Saginaw Career Opportunities Ctr., 1971; cons. indsl. tng., pub. schs., colls.;

cons. human resource tng. and quality scis., 1984—; disting. vis. dean, spl. cons. to pres. Calif. State U., San Marcos, 1991. Asst. editor: Jour. Indsl. Tchr. Edn., 1968-70; co-editor: The Components of Teacher Education, 20th Yearbook Am. Council on Indsl. Arts Tchr. Edn.; editor: Jour. of Technology studies; contbr. articles to profl. jours. Founding com. chmn. Ohio Coun. on Indsl. Arts Tchr. Edn., 1968-69; dir. Homeowners Assn., 1993—. With USAF, 1951-52. Univ. honors scholar, 1963. Mem. NEA, Internat. Tech. Edn. Assn., Am. Vocat. Assn., Am. Tech. Edn. Assn., Am. Soc. Engring. Edn., Nat. Assn. Indsl. Tech., Miss. Valley Indsl. Tchr. Edn. Conf., Epsilon Pi Tau (exec. dir. 1976—, Laureate citation 1972, Disting. Svc. citation 1989), Omicron Delta Kappa, Phi Delta Kappa, Kappa Delta Pi. Office: TeMac Training & Edn Mgmt Cons PO Box 12332 La Jolla CA 92039-2332

STREISAND, BARBRA JOAN, singer, actress, director; b. Bklyn., Apr. 24, 1942; d. Emanuel and Diana (Rosen) S.; m. Elliott Gould, Mar. 1963 (div.); 1 son, Jason Emanuel. Grad. high sch., Bklyn.; student, Yeshiva of Bklyn. N.Y. theatre debut Another Evening with Harry Stoones, 1961; appeared in Broadway musicals I Can Get It for You Wholesale, 1962, Funny Girl, 1964-65; motion pictures include Funny Girl, 1968, Hello Dolly, 1969, On a Clear Day You Can See Forever, 1970, The Owl and the Pussy Cat, 1970, What's Up Doc?, 1972, Up the Sandbox, 1972, The Way We Were, 1973, For Pete's Sake, 1974, Funny Lady, 1975, The Main Event, 1979, All Night Long, 1981, Nuts, 1987; star, prodr. film A Star is Born, 1976; prodr., dir., star Yentl, 1983, The Prince of Tides, 1991; exec. prodr.: (TV movie) Serving in Silence: The Margarethe Cammermeyer Story, 1995; TV spls. include My Name is Barbra, 1965 (5 Emmy awards), Color Me Barbra, 1966; rec. artist on Columbia Records; Gold record albums include People, 1965, My Name is Barbra, 1965, Color Me Barbra, 1966, Barbra Streisand: A Happening in Central Park, 1968, Barbra Streisand: One Voice, Stoney End, 1971, Barbra Joan Streisand, 1972, The Way We Were, 1974, A Star is Born, 1976, Superman, 1977, The Stars Salute Israel at 30, 1978, Wet, 1979, (with Barry Gibb) Guilty, 1980, Emotion, 1984, The Broadway Album, 1986, Til I Loved You, 1989; other albums include: A Collection: Greatest Hits, 1989, Just for the Record, 1991, Back to Broadway, 1993. Recipient Emmy award, CBS-TV spl. (My Name Is Barbra), 1964, Acad. award as best actress (Funny Girl), 1968, Golden Globe award (Funny Girl), 1969, co-recipient Acad. award for best song (Evergreen), 1976, Georgie award AGVA 1977, Grammy awards for best female pop vocalist, 1963, 64, 65, 77, 86, for best song writer (with Paul Williams), 1977, 2 Grammy nominations for Back to Broadway, 1994; Nat. Acad. of Recording Arts & Sciences Lifetime Achievement Award, 1994. Office: Creative Artists Agy care Fred Spector 9830 Wilshire Blvd Beverly Hills CA 90212*

STREITWIESER, ANDREW, JR., chemistry educator; b. Buffalo, June 23, 1927; s. Andrew and Sophie (Morlock) S.; m. Mary Ann Good, Aug. 19, 1950 (dec. May 1965); children—David Roy, Susan Ann; m. Suzanne Cope Beier, July 29, 1967. A.B., Columbia U., 1949, M.A., 1950, Ph.D., 1952; postgrad. (AEC fellow), MIT, 1951-52. Faculty U. Calif., Berkeley, 1952-92, prof. chemistry, 1963-92, prof. emeritus, 1993—; researcher on organic reaction mechanisms, application molecular orbital theory to organic chemistry, effect chem. structure on carbon acidities; cons. to industry, 1957—. Author: Molecular Orbital Theory for Organic Chemists, 1961, Solvolytic Displacement Reactions, 1962, (with J.I. Brauman) Supplemental Tables of Molecular Orbital Calculations, 1965, (with C.A. Coulson) Dictionary of Pi Electron Calculations, 1965, (with P.H. Owens) Orbital and Electron Density Diagrams, 1973, (with C.H. Heathcock and E.M. Kosower) Introduction to Organic Chemistry, 4th edit., 1992; also numerous articles; co-editor: Progress in Physical Organic Chemistry, 11 vols., 1963-74. Recipient Humboldt Found. Sr. Scientist award, 1976, Humboldt medal, 1979, Berkeley citation, 1993. Fellow AAAS; mem. NAS, Am. Chem. Soc. (Calif. sect. award 1964, award in Petroleum Chemistry 1967, Norris award in phys. organic chemistry 1982, Cope scholar award 1989), Am. Acad. Arts and Scis., German Chem. Soc., Bavarian Acad. Scis. (corr.), Phi Beta Kappa, Sigma Xi. Office: U Calif Dept Chemistry Berkeley CA 94720-1460

STREKOWSKI, LUCJAN, chemistry educator; b. Grabowo, Poland, June 21, 1945; came to U.S., 1981; s. Antoni and Janina (Chrapowicz) S.; m. Alewtina Smirnova, Oct. 14, 1967; children: Rafal, Anna. BS in Organic Chemistry with distinction, Mendeleev Inst. Chemistry, Moscow, 1967; PhD in Organic Chemistry, Polish Acad. Scis., 1972; DSc in Chemistry, Adam Mickiewicz U., Poznan, Poland, 1976. Instr. organic chemistry Adam Mickiewicz U., Poznan, 1971-72, asst. prof. dept. chemistry, 1972-78, assoc. prof. dept. chemistry, 1978-81; rsch. assoc. dept. chemistry U. Fla., Gainesville, 1981-84; asst. prof. dept. chemistry Ga. State U., Atlanta, 1984-89, assoc. prof. dept. chemistry, 1989—; vis. prof. U. Fla., Gainesville, 1979-80, 81, Australian Nat. U., 1980, U. Kans., Lawrence, 1972-73. Editor: Pyridine-Metal Complexes, Vol. 14, Part 6, 1985; contbr. over 130 articles to profl. jours.; patentee in field. Recipient award Polish Ministry Sci., 1977, Polish Chem. Soc., 1973, Polish Acad. Scis., 1972, Ga. State U., 1993; grantee Am. Chem. Soc.-Poetroleum Rsch. Fund, 1985—, Solvay Pharms., 1992-93, Nat. Diagnostics, 1991-93, NIAID/NIH, 1988—, Rohm and Hass Co., 1988, Am. Cancer Soc., 1987-89, Rsch. Corp., 1985-94, Milheim Foundn. Cancer Rsch., 1985-86, numerous others. Mem. Am. Chem. Soc., Internat. Soc. Heterocyclic Chemistry. Avocation: classical music. Office: Ga State Univ Dept Chemistry Atlanta GA 30303

STRELZER, MARTIN, religious organization administrator; b. N.Y.C., Oct. 17, 1925; s. Samuel Strelzer and Sadie Rothman; m. Florence Moskowitz, Jan. 30, 1947; children: Stuart, Amy. BBS, NYU, 1953. Pres. Harry D. Spielberg, Inc., N.Y.C., 1967-70, Amstrel Textiles, Inc., N.Y.C., 1970-83, Temple Beth-El, Closter, N.J., 1971-83; pres. N.J. West Hudson Valley region Union of Am. Hebrew Congregations, Paramus, N.J., 1976-80; trustee Union of Am. Hebrew Congregations, N.Y.C., 1976-83, mem. exec. com., 1982-83, chmn. new congregations com., 1979-83; N.Am. dir. World Union for Progressive Judaism, N.Y.C., 1984—; arbitrator Am. Arbitration Assn., N.Y.C., 1970-83. Chmn. Israel Bonds Campaign, Bergen County, N.J., 1971-72, United Jewish Appeal campaign, No. Valley, N.J., 1973-74, Community Rels. Com., Bergen County, 1980-81. Recipient Circle of Light Israel Bonds Testimonial Closter, N.J., 1980. Democrat. Office: World Union for Progressive Judaism 838 Fifth Ave New York NY 10021-7064

STREM, MICHAEL EDWARD, chemicals executive; b. Pitts., Apr. 1, 1936; married, 1967. AB, Brown U., 1958; MS, U. Pitts., 1961, PhD in Chemistry, 1964. Pres. Strem Chem., Inc., 1964—. Mem. Am. Chem. Soc. Research in organometallic chemistry, including its use in organic synthesis. Office: Strem Chem Inc 7 Mulliken Way Newburyport MA 01950-4098*

STRENG, WILLIAM PAUL, lawyer, educator; b. Sterling, Ill., Oct. 17, 1937; s. William D. and Helen Marie (Conklen) S.; m. Louisa Bridge Egbert, July 8, 1967; children: Sarah, John. BA, Wartburg Coll., 1959; JD, Northwestern U., 1962. Bar: Iowa 1962, Ill. 1962, Ohio 1964, Tex. 1975. Law clk. to U.S. circuit judge Lester L. Cecil, Cin., 1963-64; asso. firm Taft, Stettinius & Hollister, Cin., 1964-70; atty.-advisor Office Sec. Tax Policy, Office Tax Legis. Counsel Dept. Treasury, Washington, 1970-71; dep. gen. counsel Export-Import Bank U.S., Washington, 1971-73; prof. law Sch. Law, So. Methodist U., Dallas, 1973-80; vis. prof. Coll. Law Ohio State U., Columbus, 1977; partner firm Bracewell & Patterson, Houston, Washington and London, 1980-85; Vinson & Elkins prof. of law U. Houston Law Ctr, 1985—; vis. prof. Rice U., NYU Law Sch., 1990; disting. vis. prof. U. Hong Kong Law Faculty, 1992; Fulbright prof. U. Stockholm Law Faculty, 1993; cons. Bracewell & Patterson, 1985—; lectr. various confs. Am. Law Inst., Practicing Law Inst., World Trade Inst., Internat. Fiscal Assn. Author: International Business Transactions—Tax and Legal Handbook, 1978, Estate Planning, 1991, International Business Planning: Law and Taxation, 6 vols., 1982, 95, Tax Planning for Retirement, 1989, 93, 94, 95, Doing Business in China, 1990, 93, 94, Federal Income Taxation of Corporations and Shareholders—Forms, 1995, Choice of Entity, 1994; contbr. articles to profl. jours. Served with USMC, 1962. Lutheran. Home: 1903 Dunstan Rd Houston TX 77005-1619 Office: U Houston Law Ctr Houston TX 77204-6372

STRENGTH, JANIS GRACE, management executive, educator; b. Ozark, Ala., Jan. 31, 1934; d. James Marion and Mary Belle (Riley) Grace; m. Robert Samuel Strength, Sept. 12, 1954; children: Stewart A., James Houston (dec.), Robert David (dec.), James Steven (dec.). BS in Home

Econs. and Edn., Auburn U., 1956; MA in Edn., Washington U., St. Louis, 1978, MA in Adminstrn., 1980. Home economist Gulf Power Co., Pensacola, Fla., 1956-59; tchr. sci. Northside Jr. High Sch., Greenwood, S.C., 1961-68; tchrs. home econs. Greenwood High Sch., 1968-70; chairperson dept. sci. Parkway West Jr. High Sch., Chesterfield, Mo., 1975-82; tchr. sci. Parkway West High Sch., Chesterfield, 1982-88; v.p.-sec. Product Safety Mgmt. Inc., Gulf Breeze, Fla., 1989—; chairperson dist. Phys. Scis. Curriculum Com., 1978-85, Sci. Fair Placement Com., 1978-82, Gifted Edn., 1983-84; leader Phys. Sci. Summer Workshops, Safety Sci. Lab. Workshop; sponsor Nat. Jr. Honor Soc., Parkway West Jr. Class. Supt. youth dept. Sunday sch. Greentrails Meth. Ch., sponsor summer camp; vol. fundraiser March of Dimes, Cerebral Palsy, Multiple Schlorosis, Cancer funds; judge Parkway/Monsanto/St. Louis Post Dispatch Sci. Fairs, 1978—; mem. citizens action com. Parkway Sch. Bd., 1980-84. Mem. NEA, Nat. Sci. Tchrs. Assn., Santa Rosa Women's Club, Tiger Point Country Club (Gulf Breese), Raintree Country Club (Hillsboro, Mo.). Republican. Methodist. Office: Product Safety Mgmt Inc Gulf Breeze FL 32561

STRENSKI, JAMES B., communications executive; b. Jan. 2, 1930; m. Jane E.; 5 children. Grad., Marquette U. Pub. info. officer USN, NATO; with Pub. Communications Inc., Chgo.; chmn., chief exec. officer Pub. Communications Inc, Tampa, Fla.; cons. to nonprofit, health care and social agys., pub. and pvt. corps., firm and acad. instns.; lectr. to industry groups, trade assns., bus. orgns. Contbr. more than 70 articles on pub. rels. to jours. in field. Mem. Tampa Jesuit High Sch. Found., Tampa Downtown Partnership Bd., Hillsborough County Affordable Housing Com., Bus. Adv. Coun., Coll. of Journalism of Marquette U.; bd. dirs. Chgo. Leadership Coun. for Met. Open Communities, Tampa Goodwill Industries-Suncoast; program chmn. Tampa Pkwy. Assn.; pub. rels. chmn. Paint Your Heart Out, Tampa, U. Tampa Bd. Fellows. Mem. Worldcom Group, Inc. (founder, exec. com.). Office: Public Communications Inc 35 E Wacker Dr Chicago IL 60601-2102

STRETCH, JOHN JOSEPH, social work educator, management and evaluation consultant; b. St. Louis, Feb. 24, 1935; s. John Joseph and Theresa Carmelita (Fleming) S.; children: Paul, Leonmarie, Sylvan, Adrienne, Sharonalice; m. Barbara Ann Stewart, Mar. 16, 1985; children: Margaret, Thomas. AB, Maryknoll Coll., Glen Ellyn, Ill., 1957; MSW, Washington U., St. Louis, 1961; PhD, Tulane U., 1967; MBA, St. Louis U., 1980. Lic. clin. social worker, 1990. Instr. Tulane U., 1962-67, assoc. prof., 1967-69; mem. faculty St. Louis U., 1969—, prof. social work, 1972—, asst. dean Sch. Social Service, 1976-87, dir. doctoral studies, 1976-94, dir. M.S.W. program, 1985-86; dir. rsch. Social Welfare Planning Coun. Met. New Orleans, 1962-69; cons. to United Way Met. St. Louis, Cath. Charities of Archdiocese of St. Louis, Cath. Svcs. for Children and Youth, Full Achievement, Mo. Province of S.J., Cath. Family Svcs., Youth Emergency Svcs., Mo. State Dept. Social Svcs., U. Mo. Extension Svc., St. Joseph's Home for Boys, Marian Hall Ctr. for Adolescent Girls, Boys Town, A World of Difference, Anti Defamation League of B'nai Brith, Prog. Youth Ctr.; expert witness on homeless U.S. House Select Com. on Families, Children and Youth, 1987; mem. resource spl. task force on homeless Office of Sec. U.S. Dept. Housing and Urban Devel., 1989; survey design cons. U.S. Office of The Insp. Gen., 1990; methodology expert on homelessness U.S. Census Bur., 1989; expert homeless policy General Acctg. Office hearings, 1992; chair Mo. Assn. for Social Welfare Low Income Housing; mem. Comprehensive Housing Affordabiltiy Strategies (CHAS) Mo. Statewide Planning Group, Missouri Housing Devel. CHAS citizen's com., Missouri Inst. of Psychiatry, Univ. City sch. dist.; mgmt. cons. People's Issues Task Force Agricultural div. Monsanto Chemical Inc., Nat. Conf. of Christians and Jews, vis. prof. Nat. Catholic U. of Am. Sch. of Soc. Svcs., 1991, U. Bristol, England, 1992, U. Calif. Sch. of Pub. Health, Berkeley, 1990; cons. Mo. Speaker of the Ho. statewide legislative task force, 1990-92; statewide grant project reviewer emergency shelter grant program Mo. Dept. of Social Svcs., 1989—; homeless svcs. grant reviewer City of St. Louis, 1994—. Editl. bd. Social Work, 1968-74, Health Progress, 1988—; manuscript referee Jour. Social Svc. Rsch., 1977—; mgmt. and evaluation content referee Wadsworth Press, Human Svcs. Press, Allyn and Bacon Press; contbr. articles profl. jours. and books. Bd. dirs. Ecumenical Housing Produ. Corp., 1985—, pres. bd. dirs., 1993-95; pres. bd. dirs. Mo. Assn. Social Welfare; mem. Dunbourg Soc. of St. Louis U.; mem. adv. bd. Salvation Army Family Haven, 1988-92; chmn. United Way of Greater St. Louis venture grant com., 1988-91, mem. allocation com., 1985—, mem. process and rev. com., 1991-93, inter-orgnl. priorities com., 1991-93; organizer Mo. State Nat. Coalition for the Homeless and Poverty. With M.C. AUS, 1958-60, capt. M.C. USAR, 1961-72. NIMH Career Leadership Devel. fellow, 1965-67; recipient Scholar of Yr. award Sch. Social Svc., St. Louis U., 1987; named Vol. of Yr. Ecumenical Produ. Corp., 1990; Presdl. scholar Sch. Social Svc., 1992. Mem. AAUP, ACLU, Acad. Cert. Social Workers, Nat. Assn. Social Workers , Mo. Assn. for Social Welfare (bd. dirs., Outstanding State-Wide Mem. of Yr. 1987), Coun. on Social Work Edn., Common Cause, Amnesty Internat., Nat. Com. on Vital and Health Stats. (subcom. on health stats. for minorities and other spl. populations of U.S. 1988—). Democrat. Roman Catholic. Home: 9100 Litzsinger Rd Saint Louis MO 63144-2214 Office: 3550 Lindell Blvd Saint Louis MO 63103-1021 *My entire professional life has been in the field of social work. My personal and professional values are derived from a dual commitment to empower the uniqueness of individuals and to enhance the development of caring communities. These goals have organized and directed my professional practice, teaching and writing. I believe that the profession of social work has a unique and singular mission in society. That mission is to advocate for and consciously bring about the social development of all people.*

STRETTON, ROSS, ballet dancer; b. Canberra, Australia; came to U.S., 1979; Student, Australian Ballet Sch. Mem. corps de ballet Australian Ballet, 1972-74, soloist, 1974-78, prin. dancer, 1978-79; with Joffrey Ballet, 1979-81; joined No. Ballet Theatre, Manchester, Eng.; guest artist Am. Ballet Theatre, 1980-81, soloist, 1981-83, prin. dancer, 1983-90, asst to the dirs., 1990-91, regisseur, 1991-93, asst. dir., 1993—. Created role in Martine van Hamel's Amnon V'Tamar; other repertoire includes: Bach Partita, La Bayadere, Bouree Fantastique, Giselle, Duets, Pillar of Fire, La Sylphide, The Wild Boy, Cinderella, Don Quixote, The Nutcracker, Swan Lake, The Sleeping Beauty, others. Office: care Am Ballet Theatre 890 Broadway New York NY 10003-1211*

STREU, RAYMOND OLIVER, financial planner, securities executive; b. Hereford, Tex., July 7, 1931; s. William Urlin and Yetta May (Hackworth) S.; m. Joan Eliz Hardwick, Nov. 24, 1953 (div. Oct. 1963); children: William Raymond, Ronald Hardwick, Russell Francis; m. Wanda Mae Daves, Sept. 2, 1964 (div. Sept. 1990); children: Rodney Jack, Randall Oliver; m. Doris Francis Wright, Mar. 6, 1993. BBA, Tex. Tech U., 1952. CFP. Co-owner Streu Hardware Co., Hereford, 1948-60; agt., broker Justice Real Estate, Hereford, 1960-62; pres. Mark IV Realtors, Hereford, 1962-73; rep., div. mgr. Waddell & Reed, Inc., Hereford, 1965-73, divsn. mgr., 1973-78; br. mgr. E.F. Hutton Fin. Svcs., Amarillo, Tex., 1978-83, Pvt. Ledger Fin. Svc., San Diego, 1983-85, Associated Planners Soc. Corp., L.A., 1985-87; pres. Asset Planning Group, Amarillo, Tex., 1983—; br. mgr. Sun Am. Securties Corp., Phoenix, 1987—; dir. regional mktg. Assoc. Investment Mgmt., Omaha, 1990—. Leadership chmn. Llano Estacado coun. Boy Scouts Am., 1972-73. Lt. comdr. USNR, 1952-66. Mem. Internat. Assn. Fin. Planning (pres. local chpt. 1988-89), Inst. Cert. Fin. Planners, High Plains Eye Bank (life), Jaycees, Lions (pres. Amarillo chpt. 1975-76). Republican. Presbyterian. Avocations: sailing, dry fly fishing. Office: Asset Planning Group 1616 S Kentucky St Ste C-350 Amarillo TX 79102-2249

STREVEY, TRACY ELMER, JR., army officer, surgeon; b. Shorewood, Wis., Apr. 24, 1933; s. Tracy Elmer and Margaret (Rees) S.; m. Victoria Crowley (div.); children: Virginia Ann, Tracy Elmer III, Andrew Victor; m. Elizabeth Sommers. Student, Pomona Coll., 1951-54; MD, U. So. Calif., 1958; student, Armed Forces Staff Coll., 1970-71, U.S. Army War Coll., 1977-78. Diplomate Am. Bd. Surgery, Am. Bd. Thoracic Surgery. Intern Los Angeles County Gen. Hosp., 1958-59; commd. officer U.S. Army, 1959, advanced through grades to maj. gen., 1983; resident in gen. surgery Letterman Gen. Hosp., San Francisco, 1962-66; resident in thoracic and cardiovascular surgery Walter Reed Gen. Hosp., Washington, 1968-70; comdg. officer 757 Med. Detachment OA, Ludwigsburg, Fed. Republic Germany, 1959-61; ward officer orthopaedic svc. 75th Sta. Hosp. Stuttgart, Fed. Republic Germany, 1961-62; chief profl. svc., chief surgery 85th Evacuation Hosp., Qui Nhon, Vietnam, 1967; comdg. officer 3d Surg. Hosp., Dong Tam, Vietnam, 1967-68; asst. chief thoracic and cardiovascular surgery service

Fitzsimons Army Med. Ctr., Denver, 1971-73, chief thoracic and cardiovascular surgery service, 1973-75; asst. dir. med. activities and dir. Profl. Edn. Gorgas Hosp., Panama Canal Zone, 1975-77; chief dept. surgery Walter Reed Army Med. Ctr., Washington, 1978-81; comdr. Brooke Army Med. Ctr., Ft. Sam Houston, Tex., 1981-83, Tripler Army Med. Ctr., Hawaii, 1983-86, U.S. Army Health Svcs. Command, San Antonio, 1986-88; ret. U.S. Army, 1988; CEO Nassau County Med. Ctr., 1988-93; pres., CEO N.Y. Hosp Med. Ctr. Queens, N.Y.C., 1993-94; v.p. N.Y. Hosp. Care Network, N.Y.C., 1994—; asst. clin. prof. surgery U. Colo. Med. Ctr., Denver, 1973-75; prof. surgery Uniformed Services U. Health Scis., Bethesda, 1978—, vice chmn. dept. surgery, 1978-81. Contbr. articles to profl. jours. Decorated D.S.M., Legion of Merit, Meritorious Service medal with 2 oak leaf clusters, Purple Heart, Army Commendation Medal for Valor, Vietnam Cross of Gallantry with Palm; recipient Outstanding Service award U. So. Calif. Med. Alumni Assn., 1983. Fellow ACS, Am. Coll. Chest Physicians, Am. Coll. Cardiology, Am. Coll. Physician Execs. (disting.); mem. Assn. Mil. Surgeons U.S., Soc. Thoracic Surgeons, Western Thoracic Surg. Assn., Am. Assn. Thoracic Surgery, Am. Cancer Soc., Bexar County Med. Soc., ARC (bd. dirs. 1984-86), Honolulu-Pacific Fed. Exec. Bd., Masons, Rotary. Avocations: ham radio; scuba diving; golf; computer science. Office: 525 E 68th St HT 703 New York NY 10021 Home: 170 Mount Tom Rd Pelham Manor NY 10803

STREW, SUZANNE CLAFLIN, choreographer, dance educator; b. Canton, Ohio, May 31, 1935; d. William Jenney and Mildred Mae (McClellan) Claflin; m. Rudolph John Strew, Aug. 15, 1964. BS, Bowling Green (Ohio) State U., 1957; postgrad., U. Wis., summer 1962; MEd, Kent (Ohio) State U., 1964; postgrad., Ohio State U., summer 1967. Tchr. Deerfield Beach (Fla.) Pub. Sch., 1959-60; instr. dance Baldwin-Wallace Coll., Berea, Ohio, 1957-59, prof., dir., choreographer, 1961—, chairperson divsn., 1992—; choreographer Berea Summer Theatre, 1965—; dir. dance concert Baldwin-Wallace Coll., 1961—. Choreographer numerous prodns. including The Sound of Music, Cleve. Opers, 1992, and over 100 prodns. Advisor Laurels Hon. Soc.; sponsor Dance Cleve. Recipient Cleve. Critics Circle award Cleve. Critics Circle, 1980, 81, 83, 84. Mem. AAHPERD (nat. dance sect.), Ohio Dance, Mortar Bd., Chi Omega, Omicron Delta Kappa (advisor). Office: Baldwin-Wallace Coll Berea OH 44017

STRICKLAND, ANITA MAURINE, retired business educator, librarian; b. Groom, Tex., Sept. 24, 1923; d. Oliver Austin and Thelma May (Slay) Pool; m. LeRoy Graham Mashburn, Aug. 12, 1945 (dec. Mar. 1977); 1 child, Ronald Gene; m. Reid Strickland, May 27, 1978. BBA, West Tex. State U., 1962, MEd, 1965; postgrad. in library sci., Tex. Women's U., 1970. Cert. tchr., Tex.; cert. librarian. Employment interviewer Douglas Aircraft Co., Oklahoma City, 1942-45; cashier, bookkeeper Southwestern Pub. Services, Groom and Panhandle, Tex., 1950-58; acct. Gen. Motors Outlet, Groom, 1958-62; tchr. bus., lang. arts Groom Pub. Schs., 1962-68; bus. tchr., librarian Amarillo (Tex.) Pub. Schs., 1968-81. Vol. Amarillo Symphony, 1980—, Amarillo Rep. Com., 1981—, Lone Star Ballet, 1981-92; docent Amarillo Mus. Art, 1987—, sec., 1987-90, 93-94, Amarillo Art Alliance, 1989-93; vol. Amarillo Alliance, 1989—, sec., 1989-90. Mem. AAUW (legis. com. 1986-88, sec. 1988-90, bd. dirs. 1989-91), Amarillo C. of C. (vol. women's divsn. 1981-86), Amarillo Christian Women's Club (asst. prayer advisor 1989-90, treas. 1995—). Baptist. Avocations: piano, reading, swimming, tennis. Home: 6513 Roxton Dr Amarillo TX 79109-5120

STRICKLAND, ARVARH EUNICE, history educator; b. Hattiesburg, Miss., July 6, 1930; s. Eunice and Clotiel (Marshall) S.; m. Willie Pearl Elmore, June 17, 1951; children: Duane Arvarh, Bruce Elmore. BA, Tougaloo Coll., 1951; MA, U. Ill., 1953, PhD, 1962. Tchr. Hattiesburg Schs., 1951-52; instr. Tuskegee Inst., 1955-56; prin. supr. Madison County Schs., Canton, Miss., 1956-59; asst. prof. history Chgo. State U., 1962-65, assoc. prof. history, 1965-68, prof., 1968-69; prof. U. Mo., Columbia, 1969—, chmn. dept. history, 1980-83, interim dir. black studies program, 1986, 94-95, sr. faculty assoc., Office of V.P. acad. affairs, 1987-88, assoc. v.p. acad. affairs, 1989-91. Author: History of the Chicago Urban League, 1966, (with Reich and Biller) Building the United States, 1971, (with Reich) The Black American Experience to 1877, 1974, The Black American Experience since 1877, 1974; editor: Working with Carter G. Woodson, the Father of Black History: A Diary, 1928-1930 (Lorenzo J. Greene), 1989. Commr. Planning and Zoning, Columbia, Mo., 1977-80, Boone County Home Rule Charter, 1982, Mo. Peace Officers Standards and Tng. Commn., 1988-89; co-chmn. Mayors Com. to Commemorate Contbns. of Black Columbians, Columbia, 1981; mem. exec. subcom. Mayor's Ad Hoc Election '82 Com., 1982; bd. dirs. Harry S. Truman Library Inst., 1987—. Recipient Disting. Svc. award Ill. Hist. Soc., 1957, Byler Disting. Prof. award U. Mo., 1994, St. Louis Am.'s Educator of Yr. award, 1994; Fellow Woodrow Wilson Found., 1959, Danforth Found. assoc., 1973. Mem. Orgn. Am. Historians, Am. Hist. Assn., Assn. Study Afro-Am. Life and History, So. Hist. Assn., State Hist. Soc. Mo., Kiwanian, Alpha Phi Alpha, Phi Alpha Theta (internat. v.p. 1991-93, pres. 1994—). Democrat. Methodist. Home: 4100 Defoe Dr Columbia MO 65203-0252 Office: U Mo Dept History 101 Read Hall Columbia MO 65211

STRICKLAND, BONNIE RUTH, psychologist, educator; b. Louisville, Nov. 24, 1936; d. Roy E. and Billie P. (Whitfield) S. BA, Ala. Coll., 1958; M.S., Ohio State U., 1960, Ph.D. (USPHS fellow), 1962. Diplomate: clin. psychology Am. Bd. Examiners in Profl. Psychology. Research psychologist Juvenile Diagnostic Center, Columbus, Ohio, 1958-60; from asst. to asso. prof. psychology Emory U., Atlanta, 1962-73; dean of women Emory U., 1964-67; prof. psychology U. Mass., Amherst, 1973—; chmn. dept. psychology U. Mass., 1976-77, 78-82, assoc. to chancellor, 1983-84; mem. adv. coun. NIMH, 1984-87; Sigma Xi nat. lectr., 1991-93. Adv. editor numerous psychology jours., acad. pub. houses; contbg. author texts personality theory.; contbr. of numerous articles on social personality and clin. psychology to profl. jours.; contbg. author of two citation classics. Recipient Outstanding Faculty award Emory U., 1968-69; Chancellor's medal disting. service U. Mass., 1983. Fellow APA (pres. divsn. clin. psychology 1983, chmn. bd. profl. affairs 1980-83, chmn. policy and planning bd. 1983-85, pres. 1987, bd. dirs. 1986-87, Outstanding Leadership award 1992), Am. Psychol. Soc. (founder 1988, bd. dirs. 1989-93), Am. Assn. Applied and Preventive Psychology (founder 1990, bd. dirs. 1990-94, pres. 1992-94), Acad. Clin. Psychology, Coun. Grad. Depts. Psychology (pres. 1982-83). Home: 558 Federal St Belchertown MA 01007-9754 Office: U Mass Dept Psychology Amherst MA 01003-7710

STRICKLAND, GEORGE THOMAS, JR., physician, researcher, educator; b. Goldsboro, N.C., Apr. 20, 1934; s. George Thomas and Flora Ross (Bridgers) S.; m. Anne Belle Garst, Feb. 13, 1960; children: George Thomas III, Paul Garst, James Kelly. BA in History, U. N.C., 1956, MD, 1960; DCMT, London Sch. Hygiene and Tropical Medicine, Eng., 1971, PhD in Parasitology, 1974. Diplomate Am. Bd. Internal Medicine. Head dept. immunoparasitology Naval Med. Rsch. Inst., Bethesda, Md., 1972-74, program mgr. infectious diseases rsch., naval med. R&D com., 1974-76; prof., dir. rsch. and edn., dept. medicine Uniformed Svcs. U. Health Scis., Bethesda, 1976-81; staff pathologist Armed Forces Inst. Pathology, Washington, 1981-82; dir. Internat. Health Program, Sch. Medicine U. Md., Balt., 1982—, prof. microbiology, medicine, epidemiology and preventive medicine Sch. Medicine, 1982—; dir. Internat. Ctr. Med. Rsch. and Tng., Lahore, Pakistan, 1983-85; chmn., vice-chmn. Nat. Coun. Internat. Health, Washington, 1977-80; Am. co-investigator Egyptian Schistosomiasis Rsch. Project, 1990—; prin. investigator rsch. project on Lyme disease, Md., 1993—, hepatitis C, Egypt, 1995—. Editor: Hunter's Tropical Medicine, 6th edit., 1984, 7th edit., 1991. Capt. USN, 1960-82. Fellow ACP, Infectious Diseases Soc. Am., Am. Coll. Tropical Medicine Hygiene, Royal Coll. Tropical Medicine Hygiene. Democrat. Avocations: tennis, gardening, travel, classical music. Home: 220 Hawthorne Rd Baltimore MD 21210-2504

STRICKLAND, HUGH ALFRED, lawyer; b. Rockford, Ill., May 3, 1931; s. Hugh and Marie (Elmer) S.; m. Donna E. McDonald, Aug. 11, 1956; children: Amy Alice, Karen Ann. A.B., Knox Coll., 1953; J.D., Chgo. Kent Coll. Law, 1959. Bar: Ill. 1960. Partner firm McDonald, Strickland & Clough, Carrollton, Ill., 1961—; asst. atty. gen. Ill., 1960-67, spl. asst. gen., 1967-69; pres. McDonald Title Co. Mem. Greene County Welfare Services Com., 1963—, Ill. Heart Assn., 1961-65; Trustee Thomas H. Boyd Meml. Hosp., 1972—. Served with AUS, 1953-55. Recipient award for meritorious service Am. Heart Assn., 1964. Fellow Ill. Bar Found. (charter); mem. ABA, Ill. Bar Assn., Greene County Bar Assn. (past pres.), Southwestern Bar Assn. (past pres.), Ill. Def. Counsel, Am. Judicature Soc., Def. Rsch. Inst., Elks Club, Westlake Country Club (v.p. 1968-70, dir.), Big Sand Lake Country Club, Phi Delta Theta, Phi Delta Phi. Methodist. Home: 827 7th St Carrollton IL 62016-1421 Office: 524 N Main St Carrollton IL 62016-1027

STRICKLAND, MARSHALL HAYWARD, bishop; b. Rome, Ga., Oct. 8, 1933; s. Albert A. Strickland and Elzie Greer Strickland Morton; 1 child, Marshall H. 2d. BA, Livingstone Coll., 1951; PhD, St. Mary's Theol. Sem., Balt.; MDiv, Hood Theol. Sem., 1955, DD (hon.); DD (hon.), Allen U. Ordained deacon AME Ch. Pastor Patten Meml. AME Zion Ch., Chattanooga, David Stan AME Zion Ch., Lancaster, S.C., Hood Meml. AME Zion Ch., Bristol, Tenn., Big Zion AME Ch., Mobile, Ala., Pa. Ave. AME Zion Ch., Balt.; bishop AME Ch.; bd. bishops AME Zion Ch., chmn. commn. judiciary, chmn. Am. Bible Soc., 1st vice chair brotherhood pension svc., 1st vice chair Christian edn., 2d vice chair bicentennial commn., trustee Livingstone Coll.; past mem. Ala. Consultation Union; guest pastor Gen. Conf. AME Ch., St. Paul Cathedral, others; speaker in field; guest on various radio and TV stas. Author: William E. Fine: Kennedy-The Dreamer, Church and Stae: Not Separate, Our Heritage is Our Religion, The Black Church: Black America's Salvation, The Black Church: Solving Black America's Crisis, Health Care: Preaching Prevention from the Pulpit, Rebuilding Our Cities in Partnership with the Black Church: A Master Plan; contbr. articles to profl. jours. Former chmn. bd. dirs. Mobile Community Action Authority; past mem. Commn. Organic Union; founder Zion Outreach Ctr., Balt. Recipient Humanitarian award Zion Outreach Svcs. Associated Black Charities, Econ. Devel. award HUB, Flood Relief Support award Jamaican Assn. Md. Mem. NAACP (past pres. Bristol chpt., Recognition awards Bristol and Balt. chpts.). Office: 2000 Cedar Circle Dr Baltimore MD 21228-3743

STRICKLAND, NELLIE B., library program director; b. Belmont, Miss., Dec. 12, 1932. BS, Murray State U., 1954; MLS, George Peabody Coll., 1971. Ref. libr. Murray State Coll., Murray, Ky., 1954; asst. libr. Dept. Army, Ft. Stewart, Ga., 1955-56; field libr. U.S. Army Japan, 1957-59; area libr. U.S. Army, Europe, 1960-66; staff libr. U.S. Army So. Command, C.Z., 1966-67; area libr. U.S. Army, Vietnam, 1967-68, staff libr., 1971-72; chief libr. U.S. Army, Ft. Benning, Ga., 1970-71; dir. library program U.S. Army Pacific, 1973-74; dir. Army libr. program Washington, 1974-94. Recipient Outstanding Performance award Ft. Benning, 1970, Armed Forces Achievement citation, 1982, 94, Order of the White Plume; Dept. of Army Tng. grantee 1971; Dept. of Addy decoartion for Exceptional Civil Svc., 1994. Mem. ALA, Kappa Delta Phi, Alpha Sigma Alpha. Home: 203 S Yoakum Pky Apt 614 Alexandria VA 22304-3716

STRICKLAND, R. MICHAEL, bank executive; b. 1950; married. BA, Rollins Coll., 1973, MBA, 1973; postgrad., Rutgers Univ., 1981. Pres. Barnett Bank Cen. Fla.; pres. Barnett Bank Palm Beach County, 1973-85, chmn. bd., pres., CEO, 1985—. Office: Barnett Bank Palm Beach County 625 N Flagler Dr West Palm Beach FL 33401-4025

STRICKLAND, ROBERT LOUIS, business executive; b. Florence, S.C., Mar. 3, 1931; s. Franz M. and Hazel (Eaddy) S.; m. Elizabeth Ann Miller, Feb. 2, 1952; children: Cynthia Anne, Robert Edson. AB, U. N.C., 1952; MBA with distinction, Harvard U., 1957. With Lowe's Cos., Inc., North Wilkesboro, N.C., 1957—, sr. v.p., 1970-76, exec. v.p., 1976-78, chmn. bd., 1978—, chmn. exec. com., 1988—, mem. office of pres., 1970-78, also bd. dirs.; founder Sterling Advt., Ltd., 1966; v.p. mem. adminstrv. com. Lowe's Profit-Sharing Trust, 1961-87, chmn. ops. com., 1972-78; mgmt. com. Lowe's ESOP Plan, 1978—; bd. dirs. Summit Communications, Atlanta, 1987—, T. Rowe Price Assocs., Balt., 1991—, Hannaford Bros., Portland, 1994—; panelist investor rels. field, 1972—; speaker, panelist employee stock ownership, 1978—; speaker London Instnl. Investor Conf., 1980; speaker on investor rels., London, Edinburgh, Glasgow, Paris, Zurich, Frankfurt, many other cities, 1980—. Author: Lowe's Cybernetwork, 1969, Lowe's Living Legend, 1970, Ten Years of Growth, 1971, The Growth Continues, 1972, 73, 74, Lowe's Scoreboard, 1978, also articles. Mem. N.C. Ho. Reps., 1962-64, Rep. Senatorial Inner Circle, 1980—; mem. exec. com. N.C. Rep. Com., 1963-73; trustee U. N.C., Chapel Hill, 1987—, chmn. bd., 1991-93; mem. com. on bus. laws & the economy N.C., 1994—; dir. U.S. Coun. of Better Bus. Burs., 1981-85; bd. dirs., v.p. Nat. Home Improvement Coun., 1972-76; bd. dirs. N.C. Sch. Arts Found., 1975-79, N.C. Bd. Natural and Econ. Resources, 1975-76; bd. dirs., mem. govt. affairs com. Home Ctr. Inst.; trustee, sec. bd. Wilkes Community Coll., 1964-73; chmn., pres. bd. dirs. Do-It-Yourself Rsch. Inst., 1981-89; pres. Hardware Home Improvement Council City of Hope Nat. Med. Ctr., 1987-89. With USN, 1952-55, lt. Res. 1955-62. Named Wilkes County N.C. Young Man of Yr., Wilkes Jr. C. of C., 1962; recipient Bronze Oscar of Industry award Fin. World, 1969-74, 76-79, Silver Oscar of Industry award, 1970, 72-74, 76-79, Gold Oscar of Industry award as best of all industry, 1972, 87, Excellence in corp. reporting Fin. Analysts Fedn., 1970, 72, 74, 81-82, cert. of Distinction Brand Names Found., 1970, Retailer of Yr. award, 1971, 73, Disting. Mcht. award, 1972, Spirit of Life award City of Hope, 1983, Free Enterprise Legend award Students Free Enterprise, 1994; named to Home Ctr. Hall of Fame, 1985. Mem. Nat. Assn. Over-the-Counter Cos. (bd. advisers 1973-77), Newcomen Soc., Employee Stock Ownership Assn. (pres. 1983-85, chmn. 1985-87), Scabbard and Blade, Phi Beta Kappa, Pi Kappa Alpha. Clubs: Twin City, Forsyth Country, Piedmont City (Winston-Salem, N.C.); Hound Ears (Blowing Rock, N.C.); Elk River (Banner Elk, N.C.); Roaring Gap (N.C.). Home: 226 N Stratford Rd Winston Salem NC 27104-3132 Office: Lowes Cos Inc 604 Two Piedmont Plz Winston Salem NC 27104

STRICKLAND, SAMUEL RAY, controller; b. Norfolk, Va., Sept. 15, 1950; s. Algrin Perry and Ruth Jordan (Furlough) S.; m. Paula Katherine Parkinson, Jan. 7, 1984; children: Katherine Elizabeth, Sarah Clayton. AB in Bus. Adminstrn., Coll. William and Mary, 1972. CPA. Acct. Price Waterhouse Inc., Washington, 1972-78; fin. project mgr. Arabian Bus. and Mgmt. Services, Dhahran, Saudi Arabia, 1978-79; v.p., controller BDM Internat. Inc., McLean, Va., 1979—. Mem. Am. Inst. CPAs, Fin. Execs. Inst. Office: CACI Inc 1100 N Glebe Rd Arlington VA 22201

STRICKLAND, THOMAS JOSEPH, artist; b. Keyport, N.J., Dec. 27, 1932; s. Charles Edward and Clementine Maria (Grasso) S.; m. Ann DeBaun Browne, Apr. 28, 1992. Student, Newark Sch. Fine and Indsl. Arts, 1951-53, Am. Art Sch., 1956-59, Nat. Acad. Sch. Fine Arts with Robert Philipp, 1957-59. Judge local and nat. art shows; TV guest; instr. painting and pastels Grove House; lectr. Exhibited in one man shows at, Hollywood (Fla.) Art Mus., 1972-76, Elliott Mus., Stuart, Fla., 1974, others; exhibited in group shows at, Am. Artists Profl. League, N.Y.C., 1958, 61, Parke-Bernet Galleries, N.Y.C., 1959, 61, 64, Exposition Intercontinentale, Monaco, 1966-68, Salon Rouge du Casino Dieppe, 1967, 7e Grand Prix Internat. de Peinture de la Cote d'Azur, Cannes, 1971, Hollywood Art Mus., 1972-76, Art Guild of Boca Raton, 1973, Stagecoach Gallery, 1973, Am. Painters in Paris, 1975; represented in permanent collections, St. Vincent Coll., Elliott Mus., Martin County Hist. Soc., Hollywood Art Mus., Salem Coll., Winston-Salem, N.C., St. Hugh Catholic Ch., Fla.; (Recipient Digby Chandler prize Knickerbocker Artists 1965, Best in Show Blue Dome Art Fellowship 1972, 1st Place, Fine Arts League, La Junta, Colo. 1973, Blue Ribbon award Cape Coral Nat. Art Show 1973, 1st prize Hollywood Art Mus. 1973, Charles Hawthorne Meml. award Nat. Arts Club Exhbn. 1977, 1st prize Miami Palette Club 1978, others.). Contbr. articles to profl. jours. Served with AUS, 1953-55. Mem. Blue Dome Art Fellowship, Pastel Soc. Am., Nat. Soc. Lit. and Arts, Grove House, Miami Palette Club. Roman Catholic. Home: 2595 Taluga Dr Miami FL 33133-2433 *My aim in life has been to find, capture, and communicate the beauty I see in the world to others by means of painting in my Impressionistic style. To achieve this goal I have developed my talent, been dedicated to art and its disciplines. I have been uncompromising in my choice of what I paint as I paint only what I want to, preferring people and always striving to do my best.*

STRICKLAND, WILLIAM JAMES, air force officer, research psychologist; b. Boston, Apr. 12, 1948; s. Harry Gunnard and Barbara Anne (Rusk) S.; m. Martha Cecile Williams, Sept. 11, 1971; children: Adam Gregory, Aaron Christopher. BS, USAF Acad., 1970; MA, Ohio State U., 1971, PhD, 1979. Commd. 2d lt. U.S. Air Force, 1970, advanced through grades to col., 1992;

test constrn. psychologist USAF Occupational Measurement Ctr., Lackland AFB, Tex., 1971-74; chief instnl. rsch. div. USAF Acad., Colorado Springs, Colo., 1980-83; chief pers. testing policy USAF Hdqrs., Pentagon, Washington, 1983-87; comdr. 3568 USAF Recruiting Squadron, Ft. Douglas, Utah, 1987-90; chief rsch. and market analysis USAF Recruiting Svc., Randolph AFB, Tex., 1990-92; dir. human resources rsch. Air Force Armstrong Lab, Brooks AFB, Tex., 1992—. Assoc. editor Jour. Mil. Psychology, 1987—; mem. editorial bd. Pers. Psychology, 1985-90. Vol. mediator Bexar County Dispute Resolution Ctr., San Antonio, 1991—. Grad. fellow Mershon Ctr. for Nat. Security, 1970, NSF, 1970. Mem. APA, Soc. for Indsl. and Orgnl. Psychology, Alamo Area Mediators Assn. Home: 15502 Cloud Top San Antonio TX 78248 Office: Armstrong Lab AL/HR 7909 Lindbergh Dr Brooks AFB TX 78235

STRICKLAND, WILLIAM JESSE, lawyer; b. Newport News, Va., Mar. 21, 1942. BSBA, U. Richmond, 1964, JD, 1970. Bar: Va. 1969, U.S. Dist. Ct. (ea. and we. dists.) Va., U.S. Ct. Claims, U.S. Tax Ct., U.S. Ct. Appeals (4th cir.). Exec. com., coord. bus. devel. McGuire, Woods, Battle & Boothe, Richmond, Va., 1969—; bd. dirs. Cableform Inc., Zion Crossroads, Va., Va. Coll. Bldg. Authority. Capt. USMC 1964-67, Vietnam. Mem. ABA, Va. Bar Assn., Richmond Bar Assn., Nat. Assn. Bond Lawyers, Va. Govt. Fin. Officers Assn., Local Govt. Attys. Assn., Va. Bond Club. Office: McGuire Woods Battle & Boothe 1 James River Plz Richmond VA 23219-3229

STRICKLER, FRANK HUNTER, lawyer; b. Washington, Jan. 20, 1920; s. Charles Brennerman and Minnie (Hunter) S.; married; children: Nancy, Elizabeth Ann, Frank, Charles. LLB, George Washington U., 1941, JD, 1947. Bar: D.C. 1947, U.S. Ct. Appeals (D.C. cir.) 1947, U.S. Dist. Ct. D.C. 1947, U.S. Supreme Ct. 1953, U.S. Ct. Mil. Justice 1956, U.S. Ct. Appeals (4th cir.) 1964, U.S. Dist. Ct. Md. 1984, U.S. Tax Ct. 1984. Asst. U.S. atty. Dept. of Justice, Washington, 1949-56; atty. Whiteford, Hart, Carmody and Wilson, Washington, 1956-85, Ober, Taylor, Grimes and Shriver, Washington, 1985; gen. counsel Washington Gas & Light Co., 1985—. Mem. ABA, Am. Coll. Trial Lawyers, D.C. Bar Assn., Md. Bar Assn. Republican. Presbyterian. Club: Congl. Country (Bethesda, Md.). Lodge: Kiwanis. Avocation: golf. Office: Washington Gas & Light Co 1100 H St NW Washington DC 20080-0001

STRICKLER, IVAN K., dairy farmer; b. Carlyle, Kans., Oct. 23, 1921; s. Elmer E. and Edna Louise (James) S.; m. Madge Lee Marshall, Aug. 7, 1949; children—Steven Mark, Thomas Scott, Douglas Lee. B.S., Kans. State U., 1947. Owner, mgr. dairy farm Iola, Kans., 1947—; tchr. farm tng. to vets. World War II, 1947-54; judge 1st and 2d Nat. Holstein Show, Brazil, 1969-70, Internat. Holstein Show, Buenos Aires, 1972, Nat. Holstein Show, Ecuador, 1978, 10th Nat. Holstein Show, Brazil, 1980; judge Holstein Show, Australia, Mex. and Argentina, 1981, Lang Lang, 1984; judge Adelaide (Australia) Royal Show, 1987; pres Mid-America Dairymen, Inc., Springfield, MO, 1981—; appointed chmn. Nat. Dairy Bd., 1985-90; dairy leader 4-H Club, 1962-75; dir. Iola State Bank; rep. U.S. Internat. Dairy Symposium, 1994, Belo Horinzote, Brazil. Trustee Allen County Community Jr. Coll.; mem. agr. edn. and rsch. com. Kans. State U., U.S. Agrl. Trade and Devel. Mission, Algeria and Tunisia, 1989. With USN, 1942-46, PTO. Recipient Silver award Holstein Friesian Assn. Brazil, 1969, Top Dairy Farm Efficiency award Ford Found., 1971, Master Farmer award Kans. State U. and Kans. Assn. Commerce and Industry, 1972, Gold award Holstein Friesian Assn. Argentina, 1972, Richard Lynng award Nat. Dairy Bd., 1990, award of merit Gamma Sigma Delta, 1987; named Man of Yr. World Dairy Exposition, 1978; portrait in Dairy Hall of Fame Kans. State U., 1974; Guest of Hon. Nat. Dairy Shrine, 1985. Mem. Mid Am. Dairymen (sec. corporate bd. 1971-81, pres. 1981—), Holstein Friesian Assn. Am. (nat. dir. 1964-72), Dairy Shrine (nat. dir. 1971-81), United Dairy Industry Assn. (dir. 1971—), Nat. Holstein Assn. Am. (pres. 1979-80), Alpha Gamma Rho. Mem. Christian Ch. (elder, bd. dirs.). Club: Nat. Dairy Shrine (pres. 1978). Home: RR 2 Iola KS 66749-9802 Office: Mid America Dairymen Inc 3253 E Chestnut Expy Springfield MO 65802-2584

STRICKLER, JEFF, newspaper movie critic. Movie critic Mpls Star Tribune. Office: Minneapolis Star Tribune 425 Portland Ave Minneapolis MN 55488-0001

STRICKLER, MATTHEW M., lawyer; b. Bryn Mawr, Pa., June 27, 1940; s. Charles S and Mary Webster (Cornman) S.; m. Margaret Renshaw, Sept. 3, 1966; children: Matthew David, Andrew Kellogg, Timothy Webster, Edward Charles. AB, Haverford Coll., 1962; JD, Harvard U., 1965. Bar: Pa. 1965, U.S. Supreme Ct. 1975. Assoc. Ballard, Spahr, Andrews & Ingersoll, Phila., 1965-74, ptnr., 1974—; lectr. in law Temple U. Sch. Law, Phila., 1993—. Editor: Representing Health Care Facilities, 1981. Bd. dirs. Phila. chpt. Girl Scouts Am., 1978—, v.p., 1984-90, 94—. Mem. Union League Phila. Office: Ballard Spahr Andrews & Ingersoll 51st Fl 1735 Market St Fl 51 Philadelphia PA 19103-7501

STRICKMAN, ARTHUR EDWIN, retired retail executive; b. N.Y.C., July 12, 1924; s. Samuel W. and Lee (Light) S.; m. Rosemary C. Lawson, Sept. 13, 1947; children: Ellen Sue, Wendy Lee, Nancy Ann. B.A. in Bus. Adminstrn., Duke U., 1945. Exec. tng., asst. buyer Bloomingdales, 1946-47; sr. buyer Bond Stores, N.Y.C., 1948-50; pres. Sandra Post, N.Y.C., 1951-58; with Lerner Stores, N.Y.C., 1959-85; v.p. mdse. Lerner Stores, 1973-74, exec. v.p., 1975-81, pres., 1982-85, chmn. bd., chief exec. officer, 1982-85. Served as officer USN, 1942-46, PTO. Home: 136 Yale Dr Rancho Mirage CA 92270-3677

STRICKON, HARVEY ALAN, lawyer; b. Bklyn., Nov. 9, 1947; s. Milton and Norma (Goodhartz) S.; m. Linda Carol Meltzer, July 2, 1972; children: Joshua Andrew, Meredith Cindy, Erica Stacey. BBA, CCNY, 1968; JD, NYU, 1971. Bar: N.Y. 1972, U.S. Dist. Ct. (so. and ea. dists.) N.Y. 1973, U.S. Ct. Appeals (2d cir.) 1973, U.S. Supreme Ct. 1975, U.S. Dist. Ct. (no. dist.) N.Y. 1980, U.S. Dist. Ct. (we. dist.) N.Y. 1981, U.S. Dist. Ct. Ariz. 1991. Law clk. U.S. Dist. Ct. (ea. dist.) N.Y., Bklyn., 1971-73; assoc. Moses & Singer, N.Y.C., 1973-80; from assoc. to ptnr. Kaye, Scholer, Fierman, Hays & Handler, N.Y.C., 1980-91; ptnr. Paul, Hastings, Janofsky & Walker, N.Y.C., 1991—; mem. complaint mediation panel, departmental disciplinary com. appellate div., 1st dept. Supreme Ct. State N.Y. Mem. Nassau County Rep. Com., Great Neck, N.Y., 1982—; chmn. bd. dirs. Flushing Community Vol. Ambulance Corps. Inc., N.Y., 1981-86, vice chmn., 1987-92. Mem. ABA, N.Y. State Bar Assn., Assn. Bar City N.Y. (chmn. complaint mediation panel com. on profl. discipline), Am. Judicature Soc., Assn. Commerl. Fin. Attys., N.Y. Law Inst., Bankruptcy Lawyers Bar Assn., (bd. govs. 1987-89, corr. sec. 1989—), Am. Bankruptcy Inst. Republican. Jewish. Home: 11 West Brook Rd Great Neck NY 11024-1219 Office: Paul Hastings Janofsky & Walker 399 Park Ave New York NY 10022-4697

STRIDER, MARJORIE VIRGINIA, artist, educator; b. Guthrie, Okla.; d. Clifford R. and Marjorie E. (Schley) S. BFA, Kansas City Art Inst., 1962. Mem. faculty Sch. Visual Arts, N.Y.C., 1970—; artist-in-residence City U. Grad. Center Mall, N.Y.C., 1976, Fabric Workshop, Phila., 1978, Grassi Palace, Venice, Italy, 1978. One-woman shows of sculpture, drawings and/ or prints include Pace Gallery, N.Y.C., 1963-64, Nancy Hoffman Gallery, N.Y.C., 1973, 74, Weather Spoon Mus., U. N.C., Chapel Hill, 1974, City U. Grad. Center Mall, 1976, Clocktower, N.Y.C., 1976, Sculpture Center, N.Y.C., 1983, Steinbaum Gallery, N.Y.C., 1983, 84, Andre Zarre Gallery, 1993, 95; one-woman travelling shows to numerous mus. across USA; exhibited in group shows The Sculpture Center, N.Y.C., 1981, Drawing Biennale, Lisbon, Portugal, 1981, Newark Mus., 1984, William Rockhill Nelson Mus., Kansas City, 1985, Danforth Mus., Framingham, Mass., 1987, Delahoyd Gallery, N.Y.C., 1992l; represented in permanent collections Guggenheim Mus., N.Y.C., U. Colo., Boulder, Albright-Knox Mus., Buffalo, Des Moines Art Center, Storm King (N.Y.) Art Center, Larry Aldrich Mus., Ridgefield, Conn., City U. Grad. Center, N.Y.C., Hirschhorn Mus. and Sculpture Garden, Washington, also pvt. collections. Nat. Endowment for Arts grantee, 1973, 80, Longview Found. grantee, 1974, Pollock-Krasner Found. grantee, 1990, Florsheim Art Fund grantee, 1991; Va. Ctr. for Creative Arts fellow, 1974, 92, MIllay Colony for the Arts fellow, 1992.

STRIEDTER, JURIJ, foreign language educator; b. Novgorod, Russia, Jan. 18, 1926; arrived in Germany; came to U.S., 1977; s. Georg and Gertrud (Zilchert) S.; m. Hildegard Temps, May 17, 1956 (dec. Apr. 1972); children:

Georg, Christoph; m. Emanuela Horstein, Aug. 23, 1974; children: Kornelia, Annette. Dr.Phil, U. Heidelberg, Germany, 1953; habilitation, Free U. Berlin, 1960; MA (hon.), Harvard U., 1977. Prof. Slavic lit., co-dir. Ost-Europa Inst. Free U., Berlin, 1961-66; prof. lit. U. Konstanz, Germany, 1967-76, dean Philosophy faculty, 1970-71; prof. Slavic and Comp. Lit. Harvard U., Cambridge, Mass., 1977—; master Cabot Ho. Harvard Coll., Cambridge, 1988—. Author: Der Schlemenroman in Russland, 1961, Die Fragment des Novalis, 1985; author, editor: Russischer Formalismus, 1969, 2d edit., 1971, Literary Structure, Evolution and Value, 1989; editor, co-editor various profl. pubs. Fellow Soc. Fellows (sr. 1978-89); mem. Am. Acad. Arts and Scis., German Rsch. Soc. (pres., main bd. 1970-76), German Soc. Slavists (chmn. 1968-70). Office: Harvard Univ Slavic Dept Cambridge MA 02138

STRIEFSKY, LINDA A(NN), lawyer; b. Carbondale, Pa., Apr. 27, 1952; d. Leo James and Antoinette Marie (Carachilo) S.; m. James Richard Carlson, Nov. 3, 1984; children: David Carlson, Paul Carlson, Daniel Carlson. BA summa cum laude, Marywood Coll., 1974; JD, Georgetown U., 1977. Bar: Ohio 1977. Assoc., Thompson, Hine and Flory, Cleve., 1977-85, ptnr., 1985—. Loaned exec. United Way of Northeast Ohio, Cleve., 1978; adv. trustee Cleve. Music Sch. Settlement. Mem. Am. Bar Found., ABA (mem. real estate fin. com. 1980—, vice-chair lender liability com. 1993—), Am. Coll. Real Estate Lawyers bd. govs. 1994—), Internat. Coun. of Shopping Centers, Nat. Assn. Office and Indsl. Parks, Ohio State Bar Assn. (bd. govs. real property sect. 1985—), Urban Land Inst., Greater Cleve. Bar Assn. (chmn. bar applicants com. 1983-84, exec. council young lawyers sect. 1982-85, chmn. 1984-85, mem. exec. council real property sect. 1980-84, Merit Svc. award 1983, 85), Pi Gamma Mu. Democrat. Roman Catholic. Home: 2222 Delamere Dr Cleveland OH 44106-3204 Office: Thompson Hine and Flory 1100 Nat City Bank Bldg 629 Euclid Ave Cleveland OH 44114-3070

STRIEGEL, PEGGY SIMSARIAN, advertising executive; b. Phila., July 12, 1941; d. Robert Ernest Samuel and Margaret (Miller) Thompson; m. James P. Simsarian, Sept. 4, 1965 (div. Sept. 1976); children: Catherine Ann, Sheila Thompson; m. Louis E. Striegel, Sept. 14, 1976 (div. June 1984); m. Andrew H. Schmeltz Jr., Dec. 4, 1991. BA, Sarah Lawrence Coll., 1963. Asst. editor Oxford U. Press, N.Y.C., 1963-64; picture editor Western Pub. Co., N.Y.C., 1964-66; art editor Houghton-Mifflin, Inc., Boston, 1966-68; pres. Peggy's Graphics, McLean, Va., 1968-78, Striegel Advt. and Graphics, Inc., Broken Arrow, Okla., 1978—. Lower Merion (Pa.) area coord. Shapp for Congress, Phila., 1970; area coord. and graphic designer Phillips for U.S. Congress, McLean, 1972; pres. bd. dirs. Gatesway Found., Broken Arrow, 1987-89; chmn. Cmty. Playhouse Broken Arrow, 1979-81; mktg. bd. chair Tulsa Philharmonic, 1995-95. Recipient numerous advt. awards including several Addies and citations Tulsa Advt. Club, 1990-91, Gold Quill, 1990, cert. Merit Printing Industries Am., 1983, award of Excellence Am. Inst. Graphic Arts, 1983, Am. Corp. Identity Graphics award, 1994. Mem. Advt. Fedn. Tulsa, Bus. and Profl. Advt. Assn. (Gold Ring award 1986, 87), Women in Communications (prpg. chmn. 1991), Builders Assn. Met. Tulsa, Direct Mktg. Assn., Met. Tulsa C of C., Broken Arrow C of C., Bus. Profl. Advt. Assn., Jr. Achievement of Tulsa (bd. dirs. 1990-94). Democrat. Presbyterian. Club: Art Directors. Avocations: tennis, swimming, sailing, jogging. Home: 6110 S 221st East Ave Broken Arrow OK 74014-2017 Office: 716 S Main St Broken Arrow OK 74012-5502

STRIER, KAREN BARBARA, anthropology educator; b. Summit, N.J., May 22, 1959; d. Murray Paul and Arlene Strier. BA, Swarthmore Coll., 1980; MA, Harvard U., 1981, PhD, 1986. Lectr. anthropology Harvard U., Cambridge, Mass., 1986-87; asst. prof. Beloit (Wis.) Coll., 1987-89; asst. prof. U. Wis. Madison, 1989-92, assoc. prof. anthropology, 1992-95, prof., 1995—; panel mem. U.S. Dept. Edn., Washington, 1989-92. Author: Faces in the Forest, 1992; mem. editorial bd. Internat. Jour. Primatology, 1990—, Primates, 1991—. Recipient Presdl. Young Investigator award NSF, 1989—. Fellow Am. Anthropol. Assn.; mem. AAAS, Am. Assn. Phys. Anthropologists, Internat. Primatological Soc., Animal Behavior Soc. Office: U Wis Dept Anthropology 5440 Social Sci Bldg 1180 Observatory Dr Madison WI 53706-1393

STRIFFLER, DAVID FRANK, dental public health educator; b. Pontiac, Mich., Oct. 24, 1922; s. Harry Charles and Gemma Scia (Romine) S.; m. Ruth Winifred Lyle, Feb. 5, 1949; children: Stephanie Lynn, Geoffrey David. Student, U. Mich., 1940-43, D.D.S., 1947, M.P.H., 1951. Diplomate Am. Bd. Dental Pub. Health; lic. dentist, Mich., N.Mex. Ctr. sch. health Dearborn (Mich.) Pub. Schs., 1951-53; dir. dental health N.Mex. Dept. Pub. Health, Santa Fe, 1953-61; assoc. prof. to prof. dental pub. health and dentistry Sch. Pub. Health and Sch. Dentistry, U. Mich., Ann Arbor, 1961-86; chmn. dept. community dentistry Sch. Dentistry, U Mich., Ann Arbor, 1962-67; chmn. dept. community health programs Sch. Pub. Health, Ann Arbor, 1978-85; prof. emeritus Sch. Dentistry and Sch. Pub. Health, 1986—; cons. USPHS, Washington, 1959—, NIH, Bethesda, Md., 1959—, Blue Cross and Blue Shield Mich., 1986-90; bd. dirs. Delta Dental Plans of Mich., Lansing, 1971-77, corp. mem., 1977-86; mem. commn. on dental accreditation ADA, Chgo., 1987-89, cons., 1989-90. Co-author: The Dentist, His Practice, and His Community, 1964, 2d edit., 1969, Dentistry, Dental Practice and the Community, 3d edit., 1983; editor: Jour. Pub. Health Dentistry, 1975-86. Served with AUS, 1943-44. Recipient Disting. Service award N.Mex. Pub. Health Assn., 1960, Disting. Service award Am. Assn. Pub. Health Dentists, 1977, Spl. Merit award Am. Assn. Pub. Health Dentistry, 1986. Fellow Am. Pub. Health Assn. (John W. Knutson Disting. Service award Dental Health sect. 1984); mem. N.Mex. Dental Hygienists Assn. (hon.), Mich. Dental Hygienists Assn. (hon.), Am. Bd. Dental Pub. Health (pres. 1969), Phi Kappa Phi, Delta Omega, Sigma Xi. Democrat. Unitarian. Home: 2217 Vinewood Blvd Ann Arbor MI 48104-2763

STRIFLER, SUSAN VICTORIA, nursing administrator; b. Ocala, Fla., Oct. 7, 1951; d. George Spontak and Agnes Victoria (Toffaletti) S. BS in Nursing, U. Fla., 1973, MS in Nursing, 1982, postgrad., 1990—. Cert. critical care nurse. Asst. head nurse ICU Orlando (Fla.) Regional Med. Ctr., 1976-78, patient care coord., 1978-85; quality assurance mgr. Sand Lake Hosp., Orlando, 1985-88, assoc. exec. dir., dir. nursing, 1990-94; bus. sys. analyst Orlando Regional Healthcare Sys., 1995—. Mem. AACN, Am. Hosp. Assn., Fla. Nurses Assn., Am. Orgn. of Nurse Execs., Fla. Orgn. Nurse Execs., Cen. Fla. Orgn. Nurse Execs., Nat. Quality Assurance Profession, Fla. Utilization Rev. Assn., Am. Coll. Healthcare Execs., Sigma Theta Tau (award for rsch.), Phi Kappa Phi. Home: PO Box 681133 Orlando FL 32868-1133

STRIGHT, I. LEONARD, educational consultant; b. Mercer, Pa., May 7, 1916; s. Fred L. and Martha (Dight) S.; m. Virginia Minser, July 24, 1940; children—Suzanne (Mrs. L. David York), Robert, William (dec.). B.A., Allegheny Coll., 1935, M.A., 1938, LL.D., 1978; Ph.D., Case-Western U., 1946; postgrad., U. Chgo., 1963. Math. tchr. Freedom (Pa.) High Sch., 1935-39, Indiana (Pa.) Joint High Sch., 1939-42; prof. math. Baldwin-Wallace Coll., Berea, Ohio, 1942-46, No. Mich. U., Marquette, 1946-47, Indiana (Pa.) U., 1947-57; dean Indiana (Pa.) U. (Grad. Sch.), 1957-71; acad. v.p. Ohio No. U., 1971-78; cons. in higher edn., 1978—; adj. prof. Gettysburg (Pa.) Coll., Shippensburg (Pa.) U. Contbr. articles profl. jours. Mem. Nat. Council Tchrs. Math., Am. Assn. U. Profs., N.E.A., S.A.R., Phi Delta Kappa, Phi Kappa Phi, Delta Tau Delta. Methodist. Clubs: Kiwanian (pres. 1960), Mason. Home: C-224 300 Willow Valley Lakes Dr Willow Street PA 17584

STRIKER, CECIL LEOPOLD, archaeologist, educator; b. Cin., July 15, 1932; s. Cecil and Delia (Workum) S.; m. Ute Stephan, Apr. 27, 1968. BA, Oberlin Coll., 1956; MA, NYU, 1960, PhD, 1968; MA (hon.), U. Pa., 1972. Instrr., asst. prof. Vassar Coll., 1962-68; assoc. prof. U. Pa., Phila., 1968-78; prof. history of art U. Pa., 1978—; chmn. dept. history of art, 1980-87; field archaeologist Dumbarton Oaks Center for Byzantine Studies, 1966—; fellow, 1972-73; dir. survey and excavation, Myrelaion, Istanbul, 1965-66; co-dir. Kalenderhane Archaeol. Project, Istanbul, 1966-78, Aegean Dendrochronology Project, 1977-88; gen. archeol. cons. Istanbul Metro and Bosphorus Tunnel Project, 1985-87; dir. archtl. Dendrochronology Project, 1988—; cons. Integrated Study of Hagia Sophia Structure, 1991—. Mem. editorial bd. Architectura: Zeitschrift für Geschichte der Architektur, 1986—. Mem. adv. bd. Ctr. for Advanced Study in the Visual Arts, 1986-88, Samuel H. Kress Found. Art History Fellowship Program, 1986-87. Served with U.S.

Army, 1954-57. Fulbright grantee in Germany, 1960-62; art historian in residence Am. Acad. in Rome, 1973; NEH grantee, 1985-86. Mem. Archaeol. Inst. Am., Coll. Art Assn.; Am. Research Inst. in Turkey (fellow 1965-66, pres. 1978-84), Council Am. Overseas Research Ctr. (chmn. 1980-84), Soc. of Archtl. Historians, Turkish Studies Assn., U.S. Nat. Com. for Byzantine Studies, Koldewey Gesellschaft, German Archaeol. Inst. (corr.), Oriental Club of Phila.

STRIKER, GARY E., scientist, research institution administrator; b. Mar. 7, 1934; m. Liliane Zeligson Morel-Maroger. MD, U. Seattle, 1959. Diplomate Am. Bd. Pathology, Nat. Bd. Med. Examiners (pathology test com. 1980-83). Rotating intern U. Wash. Hosp., Seattle, 1959-60; pathology resident UCLA, Wadsworth Gen. Hosp., VA Ctr., 1960-62; postdoctoral trainee in exptl. pathology, dept. pathology U. Wash., Seattle, 1962-64, asst. prof. dept. pathology, 1966-71, assoc. prof., 1971-75, prof., 1975-84, dean for curriculum Sch. Medicine, 1971-77; dir. div. kidney, urologic and hematologic diseases Nat. Inst. Diabetes, and Digestive and Kidney Diseases, NIH, Bethesda, Md., 1984—; attending physician Univ. Hosps. of U. Wash., 1966-84, VA Hosp., Seattle, 1969-84; cons. Children's Orthopedic Hosp., Seattle, 1966-84, Madigan Hosp., Tacoma, 1971-84, Clin. Ctr. NIH, 1985—; conf. chmn. exptl. pathology sect. U. Pierre and Marie Curie, Paris, 1981-82; guest reviewer for NSF, Juvenile Diabetes Found., VA; chmn. or mem. of multiple site visits for Nat. Inst. Gen. Med. Scis., and Nat. Heart, Lung and Blood Inst.; lectr. various univs., med. orgns., sci. meetings, confs., worldwide. Mem. editorial bd. Lab. Investigation, Am. Jour. Kidney Diseases, Am. Jour. Pathology, Am. Jour. Nephrology, Clin. Nephrology, Nephron, Diabetes and Metabolism Revs.; guest reviewer Kidney Internat., In Vitro, Am. Jour. Physiology, Jour. Clin. Investigation, Jour. Clin. Immunology and Immunopathology, Infection and Immunity, Diagnostic Immunology, Diabetes Care; contbr. numerous articles to profl. jours. With M.C., U.S. Army, 1964-66. Recipient Disting. Leadership award Am. Urol. Assn., 1987, Louis Pasteur award U. Strasbourg; fellow Macy Found., Fogarty Internat.; grantee NIH, 1975-88. Mem. AAAS, Nat. Kidney Found. (Sci. Leadership award 1986), Am. Assn. Physicians, Am. Assn. Pathologists, Am. Fedn. Clin. Rsch., Am. Soc. Nephrology, Internat. Soc. Nephrology, Am. Soc. Cell Biology, Am. Heart Assn., King County Med. Soc., Wash. State Med. Soc., Italian Soc. Nephrology (hon.).

STRIKER, GISELA, philosophy educator; b. Gütersloh, Germany, 1943; arrived in U.S., 1986; Student, Tübingen U., 1962, Hamburg U., 1962-64, Göttingen U., 1964-69, Oxford U., 1966-67; PhD, Göttingen U., 1969, Habilitation for philosophy, 1978. Asst. prof. philosophy Göttingen (Germany) U., 1971-83, prof. philosophy, 1983-86; prof. philosophy Columbia U., N.Y.C., 1986-89; prof. philosophy Harvard U., Cambridge, Mass., 1989—; George Martin Lane prof. philosophy and the classics, 1990—; vis. asst. prof. philosophy Stanford (Calif.) U., 1974; vis. assoc. prof. philosophy Princeton (N.J.) U., 1979; Nellie-Wallace-lectr. Oxford U., 1984; vis. prof. philosophy Harvard U., 1985; Tanner lectr. Stanford U., 1987. Author: (with others) Doubt and Dogmatism, 1980, Klassiker der Philosophie I, 1981, The Skeptical Tradition, 1983, The Norms of Nature, 1985, Epistemology, 1990, Encyclopedia of Ethics, 1992, Passions and Perceptions, 1993; contbr. articles to profl. jours.; pub. papers and monographs. Rsch. fellow Deutsche Forschungsgemeinschaft, 1970-71, 82-84, fellow Wissenschaftskolleg zu Berlin, 1990-91. Mem. Am. Philos. Assn., Am. Acad. Arts and Scis., N.Y. Acad. Scis. Office: Harvard U Dept Philosophy Cambridge MA 02138

STRIMBU, VICTOR, JR., lawyer; b. New Philadelphia, Ohio, Nov. 25, 1932; s. Victor and Veda (Stancu) S.; m. Kathryn May Schrote, Apr. 9, 1955; children: Victor Paul, Michael, Julie, Sue. BA, Heidelberg Coll., 1954; postgrad. Western Res. U., 1956-57; JD, Columbia U., 1960. Bar: Ohio 1960, U.S. Supreme Ct. 1972. With Baker & Hostetler, Cleve., 1960—, ptnr., 1970—. Bd. dirs. North Coast Health Ministry; mem. Bay Village (Ohio) Bd. Edn., 1976-84, pres., 1978-82; mem. indsl. rels. adv. com. Cleve. State U., 1979—, chmn., 1982; mem. Bay Village Planning Comm., 1967-69; life mem. Ohio PTA; mem. Greater Cleve. Growth Assn.; bd. trustees New Cleve. Campaign, 1987—; North Coast Health Ministry, 1989—. With AUS, 1955-56. Recipient Service award Cleve. State U., 1980. Mem. ABA, Ohio Bar Assn., Greater Cleve. Bar Assn., Ohio Newspaper Assn. (minority affairs com. 1987—), Ct. of Nisi Prius Club, Cleve. Athletic Club, The Club at Soc. Ctr. Republican. Presbyterian. Office: Baker & Hostetler 3200 National City Ctr 1900 E 9th St Cleveland OH 44114

STRINER, HERBERT EDWARD, economics educator; b. Jersey City, Aug. 16, 1922; s. Harry and Pearl (Strynar) S.; m. Erma Steinert, Dec. 9, 1943 (div. 1970); children: Richard Alan, Deborah Jane; m. Iona V. Meredith. A.B., Rutgers U., 1947, M.A., 1948; Ph.D., Syracuse U., 1951. Asst. prof. Syracuse U., 1951; economist Interior Dept., 1951-54; program dir. NSF, 1954-55, Nat. Planning Assn., 1955-57; sr. analyst Operations Research Office, Johns Hopkins, 1957-59; program dir. Brookings Inst., 1959-61, Stanford Research Inst., 1961-62; dir. Upjohn Inst., Washington, 1962-69; dean Coll. Continuing Edn. Am. U., Washington, 1969-72; dean Coll. Bus. Am. U., 1974-81, prof. econs. and mgmt., 1981-89; cons. Los Alamos Nat. Lab., 1990-91; chief planning and policy NIH, 1972-73; pres. U. Research Corp., 1973-74. Author: Toward a Fundamental Program for the Training, Employment and Economic Equality of the American Indian, 1968, Continuing Education as a National Capital Investment, 1972, Regaining The Lead: Policies for Economic Growth, 1984; co-author: Local Impact of Foreign Trade, 1960, Civil Rights, Employment and the Social Status of American Negros, 1966; Contbr. profl. jours. Mem. rev. panel Pres.'s Cabinet Com. Juv. Delinquency, 1961-63, D.C. Youth Employment Com., 1963, Pres.'s Task Force Am. Indians, 1967, White House Conf. Aging, 1971; bd. dirs. Opportunities Industrialization Ctr., NAACP, Washington. Officer inf. U.S. Army, 1943-46. Decorated Govt. China medal of merit, 1945. Home: 4979 Battery Ln Bethesda MD 20814-2634

STRINGER, GAIL GRIFFIN, information systems administrator; b. Montgomery, Ala., July 31, 1941; d. Leonard and Margaret (Wade) G.; m. Orum David Stringer, Jan. 25, 1964; 1 child, Odessa. BFA, U. Fla., 1963; MLS, Pratt Inst., 1968; M of City Planning, U. Pa., 1976; postgrad., Drexel U., 1989—. Sect. administr. Fla. State Libr., Tallahassee, 1969-73; exec. dir. Germantown Homes, Inc., Phila., 1977-80; community devel. specialist II Office Housing/Comm Devel. City of Phila., 1981-82; coord. computer svcs. Ctr. for Social Policy/Comm. Devel. Temple U., Phila., 1982-87; divsn. dir. accts. receivable/client infosystems John F. Kennedy Comm. Mental Health/ Mental Retardation Ctr., Phila., 1987—. Editor: Introduction to Computers: A Manual for Social Service Agencies, 1984; head start data mgr. (software package) User Manual, 1986; contbr. articles and papers to profl. jours. Mem. AAUW, Network of Women in Computer Tech. (bd. dirs. 1990-92), World Future Soc. (pres. Phila. chpt. 1981-82, editor newsletter Phila. chpt. 1981-82), Bus. and Profl. Women's Club (chair past legis. com.). Avocations: music, women's issues, reading, entertaining. Home: 1109 Gloria Ln Yardley PA 19067-4711 Office: John F Kennedy Ctr 112 N Broad St Philadelphia PA 19102-1510

STRINGER, HOWARD, television executive; b. Cardiff, Wales, U.K., Feb. 19, 1942; came to U.S. 1965, naturalized 1985; s. Harry and Marjorie Mary (Pook) S.; m. Jennifer Kinmond Patterson, July 29, 1978. B.A., M.A., Oxford U., 1964. Producer, dir. CBS News, N.Y.C., 1973-76, exec. producer CBS Reports, 1976-81, Evening News, 1981-84; exec. v.p., 1984-86, pres., CBS News, 1986-88, pres., CBS Broadcast Group, 1988-95; chmn., CEO Tele-TV, 1995. Vice-chmn American Film Inst.; trustee Presbyn. Hosp.; bd. govs. Nature Conservancy, Ctr. for Comm. Served to sgt. U.S. Army, 1965-67, Vietnam. Recipient Emmy awards Nat. Assn. TV Arts and Scis., 1973, 79 (2), 81 (2), 83 (4); Columbia Dupont award Columbia Journalism Sch., 1979, 81; Overseas Press Club awards, 1974, 82, 79. Presbyterian. Office: BNP Ptnrs 875 3d Ave New York NY 10022

STRINGER, JOHN, materials scientist; b. Liverpool, Eng., July 14, 1934; came to U.S., 1977; s. Gerald Hitchen and Isobel (Taylor) S.; m. Audrey Lancaster, Feb. 4, 1957; children: Helen Caroline, Rebecca Elizabeth. BS in Engring., U. Liverpool, 1955, PhD, 1958, D in Engring., 1974. Chartered engr., U.K. Lectr. Univ. Liverpool, Eng., 1957-63; fellow Battelle Columbus (Ohio) Labs., 1963-66; prof. materials sci. Univ. Liverpool, 1966-77; sr. project mgr. Electric Power Rsch. Inst., Palo Alto, Calif., 1977-81; sr.

program mgr. Electric Power Rsch. Inst., Palo Alto, 1981-87, dir. tech. support, 1987-91, dir. applied rsch., 1991-94; tech. exec. Applied Sci. and Tech., 1994—; chmn. Sci. and Tech. Edn., Merseyside, Liverpool, 1971-74; pres. Corrosion and Protection Assn., London, 1972. Editorial bd.: Oxidation of Metals Jour., 1971—; author: An Introduction to the Electron Theory of Solids, 1967; editor: (book) High Temperature Corrosion of Advanced Materials, 1989, Chlorine in Coal, 1991, Applied Chaos, 1992; contbr. over 300 articles to profl. jours. Recipient U.R. Evans award Inst. Corrosion, U.K., 1993. Fellow AAAS, NACE Internat., AIME, Inst. Energy, Royal Soc. Arts; mem. ASM Internat., Materials Rsch. Soc. Office: Electric Power Rsch Inst 3412 Hillview Ave Palo Alto CA 94304-1395

STRINGER, L. E. DEAN, lawyer; b. Sayre, Okla., June 22, 1936; s. Rex Herman and Bessie (Morris) S.; m. Carol Ann Woodson, Aug. 31, 1963; children: Craig Woodson, Laura DeAnn. BA, Okla. State U., 1958; LLB, Harvard U., 1961. Bar: Okla. 1961, U.S. Ct. Appeals (10th cir.) 1962, U.S. Dist. Ct. (we. dist.) 1963, U.S. Supreme Ct. 1972. Assoc. Crowe, Boxley, et al (now Crowe & Dunlevy), Oklahoma City, 1961-68, mem., dir., 1968—; pres. Crowe & Dunlevy, P.C., 1979-81, chmn. litigation dept., 1987—. Bd. regents Okla. State U. and A&M Colls., Stillwater, 1986-94, vice chmn., 1989-90, chmn., 1990-91; chmn. Okla. State U. Found., Stillwater, 1982-85. Maj. Okla. N. G., 1961-71. Recipient Disting. Alumnus award Okla. State U., 1979. Fellow Am. Bar Found.; mem. ABA, Okla. Bar Assn., Okla. County Bar Assn., Internat. Assn. of Def. Counsel, Okla. Assn. Def. Counsel. Democrat. Methodist. Home: 325 NW 17th St Oklahoma City OK 73103-3424 Office: Crowe & Dunlevy 20 N Broadway Ave Oklahoma City OK 73102-9200

STRINGER, MARY EVELYN, art historian, educator; b. Huntsville, Mo., July 31, 1921; d. William Madison and Charity (Rogers) S. A.B., U. Mo., 1942; A.M., U. N.C., Chapel Hill, 1955; Ph.D. (Danforth scholar), Harvard U., 1973. Asst. prof. art Miss. State Coll. for Women (now Miss. U. for Women), Columbus, 1947-58; assoc. prof. Miss. State Coll. for Women (now Miss. U. for Women), 1958-73, prof. emeritus, 1973—; regional dir. for Miss., Census of Stained Glass Windows in Am., 1840-1940. Bd. dirs. Mississippians for Ednl. Broadcasting; mem. Miss. com. Save Outdoor Sculpture, 1992-93. Fulbright scholar W.Ger., 1955-56; Harvard U. travel grantee, 1966-67; NEH summer seminar grantee, 1980. Mem. AAUW, Coll. Art Assn., Southeastern Coll. Art Conf. (dir. 1975-80, 83-89, Disting. Svc. award 1992, Miss. Hist. Soc. (award of merit, 1995), Internat. Ctr. Medieval Art, Aududon Soc., The Nature Conservancy, Sierra Club, Phi Beta Kappa, Phi Kappa Phi. Democrat. Episcopalian. Office: Dept Art Miss U for Women Columbus MS 39701

STRINGFELLOW, GERALD B., engineering educator; b. Salt Lake City, Apr. 26, 1942; s. Paul Bennion and Jean (Barton) S.; m. Barbara Farr, June 9, 1962; children: Anne, Heather, Michael. BS, U. Utah, 1964; PhD, Stanford U., 1968. Staff scientist Hewlett Packard Labs., Palo Alto, Calif., 1967-70, group mgr., 1970-80; prof. elec. engring., materials sci. U. Utah, Salt Lake City, 1980—; chmn., 1994—; adj. prof. physics U. Utah, Salt Lake City, 1988—; cons. Tex. Instruments, Dallas, 1995—, AT&T-Bell Labs., Holmdel, N.J., 1986-90, Brit. Telecom., London, 1989-92; editor-in-chief Phase Diagrams for Ceramics, Vol. IX. Author: Organometallic Vapor Phase Epitaxy, 1989; editor: Metal Organic Vapor Phase Epitaxy, 1986, 92, American Crystal Growth, 1987, Alloy Semiconductor Physics and Electronics, 1989, Phase Equilibria Diagrams-Semiconductors and Chalcogenides, 1991; U.S. sr. editor: Jour. Crystal Growth; letters editor: Jour. Electronic Materials; contbr. over 260 articles to profl. jours. Recipient U.S. Sr. Scientist award Alexander von Humboldt Soc., Bonn, Germany, 1979; guest fellow Royal Soc., London, 1990. Fellow IEEE; mem. Am. Phys. Soc., Electronic Materials Com. (pres. 1985-87). Achievements include pioneering development of organometallic vapor phase epitaxy, development of theories of thermodynamic properties of alloy semiconductors; discovery of phenomenon of compositional latching in alloy semiconductor layers grown by epitaxial techniques. Home: 960 Donner Way Salt Lake City UT 84108-2167 Office: Dept Materials Sci Univ Utah 304 EMRO Salt Lake City UT 84104-2356

STRINGFIELD, CHARLES DAVID, hospital administrator; b. Nashville, May 11, 1939; s. Ernest Jake Stringfield and Lucille (Lovelace) Birthright; m. Ruth Dvorak, Aug. 25, 1962; children—David Fisher, John Lovelace. B.A., Vanderbilt U., 1961; cert. tchr., George Peabody Coll., 1962, M.A. in Sch. Adminstrn., 1964; M.A. in Hosp. Adminstrn., Washington U., St. Louis, 1966. Tchr. Sch. Dist. No. 11, Colorado Springs, Colo., 1962-64; adminstrv. asst., adminstrv. resident Milwaukee County Instns., Milw., 1965-66; exec. dir. Tenn. Nursing Home Assn., Nashville, 1966-67; asst. dir. Tenn. Hosp. Assn., Nashville, 1966-68; adminstrv. dir. Bapt. Hosp., Inc., Nashville, 1968-70, exec. v.p., 1970-82, exec. v.p., chief exec. officer, 1981-82, pres., chief exec. officer, 1982—; pres. dedication of C. David Springfield Bldg. to Bapt. Hosp.; mem. governing bd. Mid.-Tenn. Eye Bank Found.; bd. dirs. NationaBank/Ctrl. South, Nashville Health Care Mgmt. Found./Comprehensive Care Ctr., 1993. Author: Hospital Administrator - Physician Relationships. Recipient 1st Ann. Arthritis Found. Tribute, 1989, C. David Stringfield Dedicatory plaque Bapt. Women's Pavillion East at Mid. Tenn. Med. Ctr., Disting. Svc. award Tenn. Secondary Sch. Athletic Assn., 1993; named one of Nashville's 100 Most Influential Leaders, SOURCEBOOK, 1991, 92. Fellow Am. Coll. Hosp. Adminstrs.; mem. Am. Hosp. Assn., Am. Nursing Home Assn., Southeastern Hosp. Assn., Vol. Hosps. of Am. (bd. dirs.) Lodge: Kiwanis. Office: Bapt Hosp 2000 Church St Nashville TN 37236-0002

STRINGFIELD, HEZZ, JR., contractor, financial consultant; b. Heiskell, Tenn., Oct. 4, 1921; s. Hezz and Cecil Willie (Williams) S.; m. Helen Louise Hinton, Mar. 20, 1939; children—Carolyn Mae Joyce (Mrs. James M. Corum), Don Wayne, Gail Louise (Mrs. John D. Gamble), Debra June (Mrs. Patrick T. Cassidy). Grad. bus. adminstr., Draughon Coll., 1939; student finance and bus., U. Tenn. Fin. and bus. adminstrn. exec. Clinton Engr. Works, E.I. duPont de Nemours & Co., 1943-44; Manhattan Dist. metall. project U. Chgo., 1944-45, Monsanto Chem. Co., 1945-48; nuclear div. Union Carbide Corp., 1948-77; indl. bldg. contractor, real estate developer, 1946—, cons. gen. bus., real estate financing, 1946—; pres. FBF, Inc., 1977—; with U.S. AID Mission to Middle East; cons. with industry, govt. and edn. in developing nations, 1965; bd. dirs. Found. Mgmt. Edn., Advanced Mgmt. Council, Council for Internat. Progress in Mgmt., Inc., Found. for Internat. Progress in Mgmt.; mem. Adv. Council Univs. and Colls. Fellow Soc. Advancement Mgmt. (Profl. Mgr. citation 1963, v.p. 1958-62, exec. v.p 1962-63, pres. 1963-64, chmn. bd. 1964-65); mem. Am. Mgmt. Assn., Am. Inst. Accountants. Methodist. Home: 921 Laurel Hill Rd Knoxville TN 37923-2024 Office: 1201 Hilton Rd Knoxville TN 37921-5902

STRINGHAM, LUTHER WINTERS, economist, administrator; b. Colorado Springs, Colo., Dec. 14, 1915; s. Luther Wilson and Fern (Van Duyn) S.; m. Margret Ann Pringle, Dec. 1, 1942; 1 child, Susan Jean. B.A. summa cum laude, U. Colo., 1938, M.A. in Econs, 1939; Rockefeller fellow pub. adminstrn., U. Minn., 1939-40, Nat. Inst. Pub. Affairs, 1940-41. Economist Dept. Commerce, also OPA, 1941-43; intelligence officer Def. Dept., 1946-55; program analysis officer Office of the Sec. HEW, 1956-63, chmn. sec.'s com. mental retardation, 1961-63; exec. dir. Nat. Assn. for Retarded Children, 1963-68; intergovtl. relations officer HEW, 1968-77; planning dir. Central Va. Health Systems Agy., 1977-83. Dir. TV series Healthy Virginians, 1981-83. Mem. Pres.'s Com. Employment Handicapped, 1963-68; pres. Music for People, Inc., 1971-74; lectr. CUNY, 1971-76; mem. nat. coun. Boy Scouts Am., 1963-83; co-founder Older Virginians for Action, 1983-84; bd. dirs. Capital Area Agy. Aging, 1984-87; Midlothian Dist. rep. Keep Chesterfield Clean Corp., 1992-94; mem. Quality Coun. Greater Richmond, 1993—. Capt. AUS, 1943-46; lt. col. USAFR., 1946-56. Mem. Am. Econ. Assn., Am. Soc. Pub. Adminstrn., Phi Beta Kappa, Pi Gamma Mu, Delta Sigma Rho. Home: 3101 Mount Hill Dr Midlothian VA 23113-3932

STRINGHAM, RENE, physician; b. Mpls., July 16, 1940; d. Clifford Leonard and Helen Pearl (Marcineak) Heinrich; children: Lars Eric, Leif Erik, Lance Devon. BS, St. Lawrence U., 1962; MD, U. Ky., 1972. Diplomate Am. Bd. Family Practice. Intern U. Fla., Gainesville, 1972-73; physician Lee County Coop. Clinic, Marianna, Ark., 1973-74; pvt. practice Coastal Health

Practitioners, Lincoln City, Oreg., 1975-84; county health officer Lincoln County Health Dept., Newport, Oreg., 1986-90; trustee Coast Home Nursing, Lincoln County, 1984-86; expert witness EPA, 1980—. Facilitator Exceptional Living, 1984-86. Fellow Am. Acad. Family Practice; mem. Lincoln County Med. Soc. (pres. 1984). Avocations: spontaneous music, folk dancing, sailing.

STRISIK, PAUL, artist; b. Bklyn., Apr. 21, 1918; s. Abraham Roger and Reine Rose (Rehbock) S.; m. Nancy Susan Samaras, Nov. 16, 1968; children: Peter, John Catherine, Ellen. Student, Art Students League, N.Y.C., 1946-48. Tchr. workshops, lectr. throughout, U.S. and, Europe; tchr. Scottsdale (Ariz.) Artists Sch., Nov. 1986, 88; mng. dir. Hall Line Co., Highland Mills, N.Y., 1937-40; dir. Empire Twine & Yarn Co., N.Y.C., 1945-69. Author: The Art of Landscape Painting, 1980, Capturing Light in Oils, 1995; One-man exhbns. include, Grand Central Art Galleries, N.Y.C., 1971-84, Doll & Richards, Boston, 1965, 76, Rockport (Mass.) Art Assn., 1964-69, 75, Andover (Mass.) Gallery Fine Arts, 1969, Gordon Coll., Wenham, Mass., 1972, Johnson-Welch Gallery, Kansas City, Mo., 1978, Francesca Anderson Gallery, Boston, 1986, Dodson Gallery, Oklahoma City, 1990, So. Vt. Art Ctr., Manchester, 1994; group exhbns. include, Nat. Acad. Art, 1955-93, Allied Artists Am., N.Y.C., 1971-94, Salmagundi Club, N.Y.C., 1962-88, Knickerbocker Artists, N.Y.C., 1963-95, Am. Watercolor Soc., N.Y.C., 1963-91, Rockport Art Assn., 1956-95, North Shore Arts Assn., Gloucester, Mass., 1956-95, Am. Artists Profl. League, N.Y.C., 1960-95, Cowboy Hall of Fame, Oklahoma City, 1978-95, Artists of Am., Denver, 1981-95, NAD, 1970-93, Catto Gallery, London, 1992, Royal Watercolor Soc., London, 1992; rep. permanent collections, Parrish Mus. Art, Southampton, N.Y., Percy H. Whitney Mus., Fairhope, Ala., Mattatuck Mus., Conn., Utah State U., Peabody Mus., Salem, Mass.; appeared on NBC Today Show (TV), July, 1987. Bd. govs. Rockport Bd. Trade, 1958-60. Served with USN, 1941-45. Recipient over 170 awards, including 15 gold medals; Windsor and Newton award Knickerbocker Artists, 1965; medal of merit, 1972; FAS award Allied Artists Am., 1965; Lehrer Meml. award, 1970; Wick award Salmagundi Club, 1967; Chandler award, 1967; AWS award, 1970; Salmagundi award, 1970-73; gold medal Marsh ann. exhbn., 1967, 71; gold medal Rockport Art Assn., 1967, 72, 87, 90; Best in Show award Am. Artists Profl. League grand. nat., 1968, 72; A. Dedn award Am. Watercolor Soc., 1969; Lehman award, 1970; gold medal Hudson Valley Art Assn., 1970, Bohnert award, 1989; Ray Jones Gold medal Am. Vets. Soc. Artists, 1970; Watercolor prize Nat. Arts Club, 1970; bronze medal, 1960; Obrig prize Nat. Acad., 1972; silver medal Arts Atlantic, Mass., 1972; Gold medal Franklin Mint Gallery Am. Art, 1974; Arthur T. Hill Meml. award Salmagundi Club, 1974; Helen Gould Kennedy award Acad. Artists Ann., 1974; Claude Parsons Meml. award Am. Artists Profl. League, 1975; Grumbacher award Acad. Artists, 1975; Philip G. Shumaker award Rockport Art Assn., 1975; honored by Rockport Art Assn., 1988; Elizabeth Schlemm award, 1975; Canelli Gold Medal for oils, 1975; Isabel Steinschneider Meml. award Hudson Valley Art Assn., 1980, also Dumond award 1990; spl. tribute to Paul Strisik Hudson Valley Art Assn., 1982, 88; Silver medal Acad. Artists Assn., Springfield, Mass., 1980, Rockport Art Assn., 1993; Gold medal Academic Artists Assn., 1986, Frank Vincent Dumond Meml. award Hudson Valley Art Assn., N.Y., 1990, 94, Frank Vincent Dumond $1,000 award Hudson Valley Art Assn., N.Y., 1995; named Artist of Yr. Santa Fe, N.Mex. Rotary, 1986, over 160 awards including 15 Gold medals. Mem. NAD (academician), Nat. Acad. Western Art (gold medal 1981, 84), Oil Painters Am., Rockport Art Assn. (pres. 1968-71), Am. Watercolor Soc., Allied Artists Am., Knickerbocker Artists, Internat. Soc. Marine Painters, Am. Artists Profl. League (award 1980), Am. Acad. Taos, N. Shore Arts Assn., Santa Fe Watercolor Soc., Rockport C. of C. Club: Salmagundi. Home: 123 Marmion Way Rockport MA 01966-1928

STRITTMATTER, PETER ALBERT, astronomer, educator; b. London, Eng., Sept. 12, 1939; came to U.S. 1970.; s. Albert and Rosa S.; m. Janet Hubbard Parkhurst, Mar. 18, 1967; children—Catherine D., Robert P. B.A., Cambridge U., Eng., 1961, M.A., 1963, Ph.D., 1967. Staff scientist Inst. for Astronomy, Cambridge, Eng., 1967-70; staff scientist dept. physics U. Calif.-San Diego, La Jolla, 1970-71; assoc. prof. dept. astronomy U. Ariz., Tucson, 1971-74, prof. dept. astronomy, 1974—; Regent's prof., 1994—; dir. Steward Observatory, Tucson, 1975—; mem. staff Max Planck Inst. Radioastronomy, Bonn, W. Germany, 1981—. Contbr. articles to profl. jours. Recipient Sr. award Humboldt Found., 1979-80. Fellow Royal Astron. Soc.; mem. Am. Astron. Soc., Astronomische Gesellschaft. Office: U Ariz Steward Observatory Tucson AZ 85721

STROBEL, DAVID ALLEN, psychology educator; b. Madison, Wis., Jan. 17, 1942; s. Carl Herbert and Anita (Wells) S.; m. Harriet Hartshorne, June 12, 1964 (div.); 1 child, Laura Wells; m. Linda Zimmermann, Mar. 31, 1982. B.A., Lake Forest Coll., 1964; M.A., U. Wis., 1967; Ph.D., U. Mont., 1972. Asst. prof. Northwestern U., Evanston, Ill., 1972-73; asst. prof., assoc. prof. then prof. psychology, U. Mont., Missoula, 1973—, chmn. dept., 1981, 83-90, assoc. dean Grad. Sch., 1990—; dir. Ft. Missoula Primate Lab., 1973-92. Contbr. chpts. to books. Cons. Missoula Drug Treatment Program, 1978, Missoula Spl. Edn. Coop., 1983. Grantee NIH, 1973-77, Dept. Agr./Agrl. Research Service, 1977-84. Mem. Mont. Psychol. Assn., Rocky Mountain Psychol. Assn., Western Psychol. Assn., Am. Assn. Primatologists, Internat. Soc. Primatologists, Missoula Humane Soc., Mont. Wilderness Assn., N. Rocky Mountain Assn. Lab. Animal Sci., Psychologists for Ethical Treatment Animals, Phi Beta Kappa, Sigma Xi. Home: 11284 Grant Creek Rd Missoula MT 59802-9345 Office: U of Montana Dept Psychology Missoula MT 59812

STROBEL, MARTIN JACK, motor vehicle and industrial component manufacturing and distribution company executive; b. N.Y.C., July 4, 1940; s. Nathan and Clara (Sorgen) S.; m. Hadassah Orenstein, Aug. 15, 1965; children: Gil Michael, Karen Rachel. BA, Columbia U., 1962; JD, Cleve. Marshall Law Sch., 1966; completed advanced bus. mgmt. program, Harvard U., 1977. Bar: Ohio bar 1966. Counsel def. contract adminstrn. services region Def. Supply Agy., Cleve., 1966-68; with Dana Corp., Toledo, 1968—; gen. counsel Dana Corp., 1970—, dir. govt. relations, 1970-71, asst. sec., 1971—, v.p., 1976—, sec., 1982—. Mem. ABA, Fed. Bar Assn., Machinery and Allied Products Inst., Ohio Bar Assn., Toledo Bar Assn. Office: Dana Corp PO Box 1000 Toledo OH 43697-1000

STROBEL, PAMELA B., lawyer; b. Chgo., Sept. 9, 1952. BS highest honors, U. Ill., 1974, JD cum laude, 1977. Bar: Ill. 1977, U.S. Dist. (ctrl. and no. dists.) Ill. 1977, U.S. Ct. Appeals (7th cir.) 1981, U.S. Claims Ct. 1983, U.S. Ct. Appeals (fed. cir.) 1985. Ptnr. Sidley & Austin, Chgo. Mem. Kappa Tau Alpha (staff 1975-77). Office: Commonwealth Edison Co PO Box 767 Chicago IL 60690

STROBEL, RUSS M., lawyer; b. N.Y.C., May 2, 1952. BA, Northwestern U., 1974; JD magna cum laude, U. Ill., 1977. Bar: Ill. 1977. Ptnr. Jenner & Block, Chgo. Mem. ABA, Ill. State Bar Assn., Chgo. Bar Assn. Office: Jenner & Block 1 E Ibm Plz Chicago IL 60611-3608

STROBER, MYRA HOFFENBERG, education educator, consultant; b. N.Y.C., Mar. 28, 1941; d. Julius William Hoffenberg and Regina Scharer; m. Samuel Strober, June 23, 1963 (div. Dec. 1983); children: Jason M., Elizabeth A.; m. Jay M. Jackman, Oct. 21, 1990. BS in Indsl. Rels., Cornell U., 1962; MA in Econs., Tufts U., 1965; PhD in Econs., MIT, 1969. Lectr., asst. prof. dept. econs. U. Md., College Park, 1967-70; lectr. U. Calif., Berkeley, 1970-72; asst. prof. grad. sch. bus. Stanford (Calif.) U., 1972-86, assoc. prof. sch. edn., 1979-90, prof., 1990—, assoc. dean acad. affairs, 1993—; organizer Stanford Bus. Conf. Women Mgmt., 1974; founding dir. ctr. rsch. women Stanford U., 1974-76, 79-84, dir. edn. policy inst., 1984-86, dean alumni coll., 1992, mem. policy and bd., 1992-93, chair program edn. administrn. and policy analysis, 1991-93, chair provost's com. recruitment and retention women faculty, 1992-93, chair faculty senate com. on coms., 1992-93; mem. adv. bd. State of Calif. Office Econ. Policy Planning and Rsch., 1978-80; mem. Coll. Bd. Com. Develop Advanced Placement Exam. Econ., 1987-88; faculty advisor Rutgers Women's Leadership Program, 1991-93. Author: (with others) Industrial Relations, 1972, Sex, Discrimination and the Division of Labor, 1975, Changing Roles of Men and Women, 1976, Women in the Labor Market, 1979, Educational Policy and Management: Sex Differentials, 1981, Women in the Workplace, 1982, Sex Segregation in the Workplace: Trends, Explanations, Remedies, 1984, The New Palgrave: A Dictionary of Economic Theory and Doctrine, 1987, Computer Chips and Paper Clips: Technology and Women's Employment, Vol. II, 1987, Gender in the Workplace, 1987; editor: (with Francine E. Gordon) Bringing Women Into Management, 1975, (with others) Women and Poverty, 1986, (with Sanford M. Dornbusch) Feminism, Children and the New Families, 1988; mem. bd. editors Signs: Jour. Women Culture and Soc., 1975-89, assoc. editor, 1980-85; mem. bd. editors Sage Ann. Rev. Women and Work, 1984—; mem. editorial adv. bd. U.S.-Japan Women's Jour., 1991—; assoc. editor Jour. Econ. Edn., 1991—; contbr. chpt. to book. Mem. rsch. adv. task force YWCA, 1989—; chair exec. bd. Stanford Hillel, 1990-92; bd. dirs. Resource Ctr. Women, Palo Alto, Calif., 1983-84; pres. bd. dirs. Kaider Found., Mountain View, Calif., 1990—. Fellow Stanford U., 1975-77, Schiff House Resident fellow, 85-87. Mem. NOW (bd. dirs. legal def. and edn. fund 1993—), Am. Econ. Assn. (mem. com. status of women in the profession 1972-75), Am. Ednl. Rsch. Assn., Indsl. Rels. Rsch. Assn. Office: Stanford U School of Education Stanford CA 94305

STROBER, SAMUEL, immunologist, educator; b. N.Y.C., May 8, 1940; s. Julius and Lee (Lander) S.; m. Linda Carol Higgins, July 6, 1991; 1 child, William; children from previous marriage: Jason, Elizabeth. AB in Liberal Arts, Columbia U., 1961; MD magna cum la, de Harvard U., 1966. Intern Mass. Gen. Hosp., Boston, 1966-67; resident in internal medicine Stanford U. Hosp., Calif., 1970-71; research fellow Peter Bent Brigham Hosp., Boston, 1962-63, 65-66, Oxford U., Eng., 1963-64; research assoc. Lab. Cell Biology, Nat. Cancer Inst., NIH, Bethesda, Md., 1967-70; instr. medicine Stanford U., 1971-72, asst. prof., 1972-78, assoc. prof. medicine, 1978-82, prof. medicine, 1982—; Diane Goldstone Meml. lectr., John Putnam Merrill Meml. lectr., chief div. immunology and rheumatology, 1978—; investigator Howard Hughes Med. Inst., Miami, Fla., 1976-81. Assoc. editor Jour. Immunology, 1981-84, Transplantation, 1981-85, Internat. Jour. Immunotherapy, 1985—, Transplant Immunology, 1992—; contbr. articles to profl. jours. bd. dirs. La Jolla Inst. for Allergy and Immunology; founder Activated Cell Therapy, Inc. Served with USPHS, 1967-70. Recipient Leon Reznick Meml. Research prize Harvard U., 1966. Mem. Am. Assn. Immunology, Am. Soc. Clin. Investigation, Am. Rheumatism Assn., Transplantation Soc. (councilor 1986-89), Am. Soc. Transplantation Physicians, Western Soc. Medicine, Am. Assn. Physicians, Clin. Immunology Soc. (pres. elect. 1995), Alpha Omega. Home: 435 Golden Oak Dr Menlo Park CA 94028-7734 Office: Stanford U Sch Medicine 300 Pasteur Dr Palo Alto CA 94304-2203

STROBERT, BARBARA, principal. Prin. Watchung Sch., Montclair, N.J. Recipient Elem. Sch. Recognition award U.S. Dept. Edn., 1989-90. Office: Watchung Sch 14 Garden St Montclair NJ 07042

STROCK, ARTHUR VAN ZANDT, architect; b. Los Angeles, Sept. 14, 1945; s. Arthur and Eileen (Cortelyou) S.; m. Hallie vonAmmon, Mar. 22, 1969. BArch, U. Calif., Berkeley, 1971. Registered profl. architect. Asst. dean Sch. Architecture and Fine Arts U. So. Calif., Los Angeles, 1970-71; designer Allied Architects, Long Beach, Calif., 1971-73; architect Langdon and Wilson, Newport Beach, Calif., 1973-77, Lee & Strock Architects, Newport Beach, 1978-82, Strock Architects, Inc., Newport Beach, 1982-91, Pacmar Strock Group, Newport Beach, Calif., 1992—; guest lectr. u. Calif., Irvine; guest speaker Pacific Coast Deisgn Conf., Monterey, Calif. Prin. works include I.R.W.D. Bldg., 1979 (Merit award 1982), Newport/Irvine Ctr., 1980 (Merit award 1982), Bay Corp. Ctr., 1982 (Merit award 1984), Scripps Ctr., 1985, Long Beach Airport Bus. Park, 1986, Orange County Register Hdqrs., 1986. Pres. Beacon Bay Cmty. Assn., Newport Beach, 1985-86; bd. dirs. Nat. History Found. of Orange County, 1982; bd. dirs. Bowers Mus., 1987—, pres., 1988-90, chmn., 1991-92, 93—. Fellow AIA; mem. Urban Land Inst.(internat. coun.), Newport Harbor yacht Club, Sigma Chi, U.S. Sailing (sr. judge). Republican. Avocations: yachting, fishing, tennis. Home: 23 Beacon Bay Newport Beach CA 92660-7218 Office: Pacmar Strock Group 1111 Bayside Dr Ste 130 Newport Beach CA 92695-3109

STROCK, DAVID RANDOLPH, brokerage house executive; b. Salt Lake City, Jan. 31, 1944; s. Clarence Randolph and Francis (Hornibrook) S.; m. Phyllis A. Tingley, Dec. 13, 1945 (div. June 15, 1982); children: Sarah, Heidi. AA, San Mateo Coll., 1967; BS, San Jose State U., 1970. Investment exec. Paine Webber, San Jose, Calif., 1970-78; corp. trainer Paine Webber, N.Y.C., 1978-79, rsch. coord., 1979-82; br. mgr. Paine Webber, Northbrook, Ill., 1982-84, Palos Verdes, Calif., 1984-89, Napa, Calif., 1989-90; investment exec. Paine Webber, Napa, 1990—. Contbr. articles to profl. jours. Mem. San Jose Jr. C. of C. (chmn. 1977, v.p. 1978), North Napa Rotary (pres.), Moose. Republican. Avocations: reading, Indy car racing, formula one racing, biking, whitewater rafting. Home: 3324 Homestead Ct Napa CA 94558 Office: Paine Webber 703 Trancas St Napa CA 94558

STROCK, GERALD E., school system administrator. Supt. Hatboro-Horsham (Pa.) Sch. Dist. State finalist Nat. Supt. Yr., 1993. Office: Hatboro-Horsham Sch Dist 229 Meetinghouse Rd Horsham PA 19044-2192

STROCK, HERBERT LEONARD, motion picture producer, director, editor, writer; b. Boston, Jan. 13, 1918; s. Maurice and Charlotte Ruth (Nesselroth) S.; m. Geraldine Polinger, Dec. 25, 1941; children: Leslie Carol, Gail Ellen, Candice Dell. B.A., U. So. Calif., 1941, M.A., 1942. Asst. editor Metro-Goldwyn-Mayer, Culver City, Calif., 1941-42; producer IMPPRO, Culver City, 1946-51; film editor Hal Roach Studios, Culver City, 1951-53; dir.; film editor Ian Tors Prodns., Culver City, 1951-58; dir. ZIV Prodns., Hollywood, Calif., 1956-61, Warner Bros., Burbank, Calif., 1958-63; ind. dir., pres. Herbert L. Strock Prodns., Hollywood, Calif., 1963—; pres., chmn. bd. Hollywood World Films Inc., lectr. U. So. Calif. Producer, dir.: I Led Three Lives, Mr. District Attorney, Favorite Story, Corliss Archer, Science Fiction Theater, Highway Patrol, Dr. Christian, Man Called X, Harbor Command, 1954; dir. Battle Taxi; assoc. producer, dir.: Tom Swift series,(TV shows) Mann of Action, Red Light and Siren Sky King; Maverick, Alaskans, Colt 45, Bronco, Cheyenne, 77 Sunset Strip, Bonanza, Hans Brinker Spl., Decisions-Decisions, (feature pictures) Perfect World of Rodney Brewster, I Was a Teenage Frankenstein, Blood of Dracula, How to Make a Monster, Rider on a Dead Horse, Strike Me Deadly, Search the Wild Wind, Magnetic Monster, Riders to the Stars, Gog - Storm Over Tibet; editor, dir.: The Crawling Hand, One Hour of Hell; editorial supr. Shark; writer, dir. Brother on the Run; editor: So Evil My Sister, Chamber-Mades; co-producer Small Miracle; editor, dir. (documentary) They Search for Survival; supervising film editor Hunger Telethon; editor (spl.) The Making of America, co-writer, film editor Hurray for Betty Boop; dir., chief prodn. coordinator for Miss World, 1976; editor (documentary) UFO Journals, UFO Syndrome, Legends, all 1979; co-dir., film editor Witches Brew, 1979; writer, film editor (TV series) Flipper, 1981. Editor post prodn. services: China--Mao to Now, Eucatastrophe, Tibet, El Papa, Night Screams, King Kung Fu; dir., editor Deadly Presence; producer, writer, dir. (med. documentary) A New Lease on Life; editor Snooze You Lose, Olympic Legacy, Water You Can Trust, Directions, Fish Outta Water; dir., editor Gramma's Gold; co-editor Infinity, Peaceful Sabbath; producer, writer, dir. (fund raising documentary) Combined Federal Campaign; co-dir., film editor Gramma's Gold; editor Detour; editor (experimental film) This Old Man..., Sidewalk Motel, line producer, editor, The Visitors; dir. Electric God. Served with U.S. Army, 1940-41. Mem. Acad. Motion Picture Arts and Scis., Dirs. Guild Am., Am. Cinema Editors (dir., bd. mem. 1984-85), Motion Picture Editors Guild, Delta Kappa Alpha (pres. 1941-65), Film and Videotape Editors Guild. Democrat. Avocation: photography. Office: Herbert L Strock Prodns 6311 Romaine St Hollywood CA 90038-2523

STROCK, JAMES MARTIN, state agency administrator, lawyer, conservationist; b. Austin, Tex., Aug. 19, 1956; s. James Martin Strock Sr. and Augusta (Tenney) Mullins. AB magna cum laude, Harvard U., 1977, JD, 1981; postgrad. New Coll. Oxford U., 1981-82. Bar: Colo. 1983. Teaching fellow dept. govt. Harvard U., 1980-81; spl. cons. to majority leader U.S. Senate, Washington, 1982-83; spl. asst. to administr. EPA, Washington, 1983-85, asst. administr. for enforcement, 1989-91; spl. counsel U.S. Senate Com. on Environment and Pub. Works, Washington, 1985-86; environ. atty. Davis, Graham & Stubbs, Denver, 1986-88; acting dir., gen. counsel U.S. Office Pers. Mgmt., Washington, 1988-89; sec. for environ. protection State of Calif., Sacramento, 1991—; mem. bd. advisors CALSTART, 1993—, The Environ. Tech. Export Coun., 1993—; Toxics Law Reporter, 1987-89,

Greenwire, 1991—; mem. Intergovtl. Policy Adv. Com., rep. U.S. Trade, 1991—. Contbr. articles to profl. jours.; moderator, producer Lay It On The Line, Sta. WDSU-TV, New Orleans, 1973-74. Bd. dirs. Youth Svc. Am., Washington, 1988-89, Environ. Law Inst., 1992—; nat. chair Bush Campaign Environ. Coalition, 1992. Capt. JAGC USAR, 1987-95. Recipient Retsie Arco Future award, 1992, Ross Essay award ABA, 1985, Environ. Leadership award Calif. Environ. Bus. Coun., 1994; Charles Joseph Bonaparte scholar Harvard U., 1976, Rotary Internat. scholar, 1981-82. Mem. Coun. on Fgn. Rels., University Club (Washington), Phi Beta Kappa. Republican. Office: 555 Capitol Mall Ste 235 Sacramento CA 95814-4503

STROCK, WILLIAM C., lawyer; b. Cleve., Sept. 22, 1942; s. Harry Kenneth and Mabel T. (Moseley) S.; m. Anne B. Turner, June 26, 1965; children: William Matthew, Anne Elizabeth. BA, So. Meth. U., 1964, JD, 1967. Bar: Tex. 1967. Labor rels. atty. Gen. Dynamics Co., Ft. Worth, 1967-70; ptnr. Seay, Gwinn, Crawford, Mebus & Blakeney, Dallas, 1970-82, Haynes & Boone, Dallas, 1982—; mem. adj. faculty sch. law So. Meth. U., 1983-90, employment law, 1990, labor law, 1990. Contbg. editor: Developing Labor Law, 2d edit., 1983; assoc. editor: Employment Law Handbook, 1989. Mem. ABA (labor and employment law sect.), Tex. Bar Found., Tex. Assn. Bus. (chmn. employment law subcom. 1988), Labor Law Tex. Bd. of Legal Specialization (adv. com.). Republican. Presbyterian.

STRODE, GEORGE K., sports editor; b. Amesville, Ohio, Nov. 10, 1935; s. Mac and Edith M. (Murphey) S.; m. Jennifer Lanning (div. 1973); m. Ruth E. Wingett, July 15, 1973. BJ, Ohio U., 1958. Sports editor Zanesville (Ohio) Times Reporter, 1958, Athens (Ohio) Messenger, 1958-62; sports reporter Dayton (Ohio) Daily News, 1962-63, Columbus (Ohio) Citizen Jour., 1963-69; Ohio sports editor AP, Columbus, 1969-85; sports editor Columbus Dispatch, 1985—. Mem. Ohio AP Sports Writers Assn. (v.p. 1984—), U.S. Golf Writers Assn., U.S. Harness Writers Assn. (pres. Ohio chpt. 1968-69). Republican. Methodist. Avocations: golfing, horse racing. Office: Columbus Dispatch 34 S 3rd St Columbus OH 43215-4241*

STRODE, WILLIAM HALL, photojournalist, publisher; b. Louisville, Aug. 6, 1937; s. William Hall and Margaret (Diehl) S.; m. Elizabeth Ann Wheeler, Nov. 26, 1960 (div. 1973); children: Alissa Michelle, Erin Hall; m. Hope Powel Alexander, Nov. 12, 1977; children: Hope Ives, Charlotte Alexander. B.S., Western Ky. U., 1959. News photographer Courier Jour. and Louisville Times, 1960-64, asst. dir. photography, 1968-75; photographer Courier Jour. mag., 1964-77; formed William Strode Assocs., photog. and pub. co., Louisville, 1978—, Harmony House pubs., 1984—. Author 16 books; exhbns. include Fine Arts III, 1961, Profile in Poverty, Smithsonian Instn., 1966, Documerica, in Corcoran Gallery, Washington, 1972, 73, Picture of the Year Traveling Exhibits; one man show includes Speed Mus. Active local Boy Scouts Am.; founder Nat. Press Photographers Found., 1975. Served with AUS, 1959. Recipient Headliners best photojournalism award, 1965; award for excellence for best mag. photog. reporting Overseas Press Club, 1967; co-recipient Pulitzer Prize for pub. service Courier Jour., 1967, for feature photography, 1976; Art Dirs. Gold medal, 1980, World Press Photog. Arts and Scis. award, 1985. Mem. Nat. Press Photographers Assn. (Photographer of Yr. award 1966, Newspaper Mag. Picture Editor of Yr. 1968, nat. ednl. chmn. 1966-68, v.p. 1973, pres. 1974). Am. Soc. Mag. Photographers, Soc. Profl. Journalists, Sigma Chi, Kappa Alpha Mu. Methodist. Home and Office: 1008 Kent Rd Goshen KY 40026-9768

STRODEL, ROBERT CARL, lawyer; b. Evanston, Ill., Aug. 12, 1930; s. Carl Frederick and Imogene (Board) S.; m. Mary Alice Shonkwiler, June 17, 1956; children: Julie Ann, Linda Lee, Sally Payson. B.S., Northwestern U., 1952; J.D., U. Mich., 1955. Bar: Ill. 1955, U.S. Supreme Ct. 1970; diplomate Am. Bd. Profl. Liability Attys.; cert. civil trial specialist Am. Bd. Trial Advocacy. Mem. firm Davis, Morgan & Witherell, Peoria, Ill., 1957-59; sole practice Peoria, 1959-69; prin. Strodel, Kingery & Durree Assoc., Peoria, Ill. 1969-92, Law Offices of Robert C. Strodel, Ltd., Peoria, 1992—; asst. state's atty. Peoria, 1960-61; instr. bus. law Bradley U., Peoria, 1961-62; lectr. Belli seminars, 1969-87; lectr. in trial practice; mem. U.S. Presdl. Commn. German-Am. Tricentennial, 1983. Author books and articles in med.-legal field. Gov. appointee Ill. Dangerous Drugs Advisory Council, 1970-73; gen. chmn. Peoria-Tazewell Easter Seals, 1963, Cancer Crusade, 1970; pres. Peoria Civic Ballet, 1969-70; mem. Mayor's Commn. on Human Relations, 1962-64; chmn. City of Peoria Campaign Ethics Bd., 1975; Peoria County Rep. Sec., 1970-74; campaign chmn. Gov. Richard Ogilvie, Peoria County 1972, Sen. Ralph Smith, 1970; treas. Michel for Congress, 1977—, campaign coordinator, 1982; bd. dirs. Crippled Children's Center, 1964-65, Peoria Symphony Orchestra, 1964-68. Served with AUS, 1956-57. Decorated Officer's Cross of Order of Merit (Fed. Republic Germany), 1984; named Outstanding Young Man Peoria Peoria Jr. C. of C., 1963. Mem. Assn. Trial Lawyers Am. (bd. govs. 1987—), Ill. Trial Lawyers Assn. (bd. mgrs. 1985—), ABA, Ill. Bar Assn. (Lincoln awards for legal writing 1961, 63, 65), Am. Coll. Legal Medicine, Am. Soc. Law and Medicine, Am. Inns of Ct. (charter master of bench, Lincoln Inn-Peoria, Ill.). Club: Mason (Shriner). Home: 3908 N Pinehurst Ct Peoria IL 61614-7246 Office: Commerce Bank Bldg Ste 927 Peoria IL 61602 *The pursuit of professional excellence has been a lifetime goal, coupled with contributions to public, political and civic affairs. He who takes from his community must also contribute to it.*

STROESENREUTHER, GEORGE DALE, financial executive; b. Milw., Aug. 13, 1954; s. George Dale and Alice Marie (Raisler) S.; m. Karen Lee Daniels, Aug. 29, 1981 (div. Oct. 1984); 1 child, Jason Dale; m. Lynn Louise Lloyd, Feb. 2, 1985 (div. Feb. 1995); children: Timothy George, Steven Douglas; m. LiLi Xin, Apr. 13, 1995. BBA, U. Wis., 1976. CPA, Wis., N.C., Ill. Internal auditor Allis Chalmers Corp., Milw., 1977-79, sr. fin. analyst, 1979-80, mgr. cost acctg., inventory control, 1980-82; supr. cost acctg. Abbott Labs., Rocky Mount, N.C., 1982, bus. unit controller, 1982-84; sr. div. analyst Abbott Labs., North Chicago, Ill., 1984-85, plant controller, materials mgr., 1985-87; dir. internal audit Outboard Marine Corp., Waukegan, Ill., 1987-88, Asea Brown Boveri, Inc., New Berlin, Wis., 1988-90; v.p. fin., chief fin. officer ABB Process Automation, Inc., Columbus, Ohio, 1990-91; v.p. fin., CFO ABB Traction Inc., Elmira Heights, N.Y., 1991; fin. contr. Ams.-Pacific and Far East, Cleve., 1992—; contr., CFO Bailey Fischer & Porter of Elsag Bailey Process Automation, Cleve., 1995—; dir. Harbor West Assn., Rocky Mount, 1983-84. Treas. Students for an Accessible Soc., Whitewater, 1976-78. Mem. AICPA, Il. CPA Soc. (industry com. 1986-88), Ohio Soc. CPAs (industry com. 1991), Inst. Internal Auditors. Republican. Lutheran. Avocations: fishing, golf, volleyball. Office: Elsag Bailey Process Automation 29801 Euclid Ave Wickliffe OH 44092 *There is a lot of truth to the statement "The only thing constant in life is change". Those that recognize this fact and respond accordingly are best prepared to meet the challenges of the future.*

STROH, PETER WETHERILL, brewery executive; b. Detroit, Dec. 18, 1927; s. Gari Melchers and Suzanne (Suddards) S.; m. Nicole Elizabeth Fauquet-Lemaitre, June 30, 1964; children—Pierre Alexander, Frederic Charlton. B.A., Princeton U., 1951. Asst. to pres. Stroh Brewery Co., Detroit, 1952-65, v.p., 1965-66, dir. ops., 1966-68, pres., 1968-82, chmn., chief exec. officer, 1982—, also bd. dirs.; dir. NBD Bancorp., Inc.; chmn. Detroit Renaissance, Inc., Atlantic Salmon Fedn.; vice chmn. Detroit Econ. Growth Corp.; trustee New Detroit, Inc., Solomon Guggenheim Found. With USN, 1945-46. Mem. Nat. Audubon Soc. (bd. dirs.), Conservation Internat. (bd. dirs.), Econ. Alliance Mich. (bd. dirs.). Clubs: Detroit (Country of Detroit (Grosse Pointe Farms, Mich.), Grosse Pointe; Yondotega; Anglers of N.Y.; Island of Hobe Sound (Fla.). Office: Stroh Brewery Co 100 River Place Dr Detroit MI 48207-4291

STROH, RAYMOND EUGENE, personnel executive; b. Bloomington, Ill., Aug. 13, 1942; s. Harry William and Felcie Cleo (Weaver) S.; m. Peggy Jane Whitacre, June 12, 1966; children: Rebecca Jane, David Ray. BA, So. Ill. U., 1966, U. Ill., 1977. Pers. technician Ill. Dept. Mental Health, Springfield, Ill., 1966-67; pers. officer Andrew McFarland Mental Health Ctr., Springfield, 1967-68, Manteno (Ill.) State Hosp., 1968-69; chief pers. officer Ill. Dept. Law Enforcement, Springfield, 1969-75, Ill. Dept. Revenue, Springfield, 1975-81, Ill. Dept. Mental Health, Springfield, 1981-82; pers. exec. Ill. Dept. Cen. Mgmt. Svcs., Springfield, 1982—; state govt. chmn. U.S. Savs. Bond Campaign, Springfield, 1978-82. Bd. dirs. Consumer Credit Counseling Svc., Springfield, 1988-94, sec., 1994; coun. exec. bd. Boy Scouts Am., Springfield, 1987—, v.p., 1987-95, dist. commr., 1979-86, unit commr.,

1970-79. Recipient Patriotic Svc. awards U.S. Treasury Dept., 1979-82, Silver Beaver award Boy Scouts Am., 1987, Dist. award of merit, 1981, Area Pres. awards, 1985, 86, Scouters Key award, 1976. Mem. NRA, U. Ill. Alumni Assn., So. Ill. U. Alumni Assn., Exptl. Aircraft Assn., Aircraft Owners and Pilots Assn., Ponce De Leon Inlet Lighthouse Assn., Nat. Geog. Soc., Cornell U. Ornithology Project Feederwatch, Abraham Lincoln Gun Club, Appalachian Trail Conf., Union County (Tenn.) Hist. Soc., Bass Anglers Sportsman Soc., Lionel Railroader Club, Wabash R.R. Hist. Soc., Theta Delta Chi. Republican. Lutheran. Avocations: aviation, hunting, fishing, bird watching, model railroading. Home: 2111 Warwick Dr Springfield IL 62704-4147 Office: Ill Dept Cen Mgmt Svcs 501 Stratton Ofc Bldg Springfield IL 62706

STROHBEHN, JOHN WALTER, engineering science educator; b. San Diego, Nov. 21, 1936; s. Walter William and Gertrude (Powell) S.; children from previous marriage: Jo, Kris, Carolyn; m. Barbara Ann Brungard, Aug. 30, 1980. BS, Stanford U., 1958, MS, 1959, PhD in Elec. Engring., 1964. Assoc. prof. engring. sci. Dartmouth Coll., Hanover, N.H., 1968-73, prof., 1973-94, assoc. dean, 1976-81, adj. prof. medicine, 1979-90, Sherman Fairchild prof., 1983-91, acting provost, 1987-89, provost, 1989-93; provost, prof. biomed. engring. Duke U., Durham, N.C., 1994—; disting. lectr. IEEE Antennas and Propagation Soc., 1979-82; vis. fellow Princeton (N.J.) U., 1993-94. Editor: Laser Propagation in the Clear Atmosphere, 1978; assoc. editor Trans. Ant. and Propagation, 1969-71, Trans. Biomed. Engring., 1981-87; contbr. articles to profl. jours. Scoutmaster Boy Scouts Am., Norwich, Vt., 1971-73; bd. dirs. Norwich Recreation and Conservation Council. Fellow AAAS, IEEE, Optical Soc. Am., Am. Inst. Med. Biol. Engring. (founding); mem. Radiation Rsch. Soc., Bioelectromagnetics Soc. (bd. dirs. 1982-85), N.Am. Hyperthermia Group (pres. 1986). Avocations: jogging; hiking; skiing. Home: 3806 Chippenham Rd Durham NC 27707 Office: Duke U Provost's Office 220 Allen Durham NC 27708

STROHMEYER, JOHN, writer, former editor; b. Cascade, Wis., June 26, 1924; s. Louis A. and Anna Rose (Saladunas) S.; m. Nancy Jordan, Aug. 20, 1949; children: Mark, John, Sarah. Student, Moravian Coll., 1941-43; A.B., Muhlenberg Coll., 1947; M.A. in Journalism, Columbia, 1948; L.H.D. (hon.), Lehigh U., 1983. With Nazareth Item, 1940-41; night reporter Bethlehem (Pa.) Globe-Times, 1941-43, 45-47; investigative reporter Providence Jour.-Bull., 1949-56; editor Bethlehem Globe-Times, 1956-84, v.p., 1961-84, dir., 1963-84; African-Am. journalism tchr. in Nairobi, Freetown, 1964; Atwood prof. journalism U. Alaska Anchorage, 1987-88, writer-in-residence, 1989—. Author: Crisis in Bethlehem: Big Steel's Struggle to Survive, 1986, Extreme Conditions: Big Oil and The Transformation of Alaska, 1993. Lt. (j.g.) USNR, 1943-45. Pulitzer Traveling fellow, 1948; Nieman fellow, 1952-53; recipient Comenius award Moravian Coll., 1971; Pulitzer prize for editorial writing, 1972; Alicia Patterson Found. fellow, 1984, 85. Mem. Am. Soc. Newspaper Editors, Pa. Soc. Newspaper Editors (pres. 1965-66). Club: Hiawatha Hunting and Fishing (E. Stroudsburg, Pa.). Home: 6633 Lunar Dr Anchorage AK 99504-4550

STROHSAHL, GEORGE HENRY, JR., retired rear admiral, consultant; m. Marvalyn Fiske; children: Bethany, David, Laurie. BS, Naval Acad., 1959; MS in aerospace physics, Naval Postgrad. Sch., 1967. Air officer USS Nimitz USN, vice comdr. NAVAIR, comdr. Pacific Missile Test Ctr., Naval Air Warfare Ctr. Decorated Disting. Svc. medal, Legion of Merit with two gold starts, Merit. Svcs. medal, Strike-Flight Air medal with numeral seven, Navy Commendation medal with Combat V and gold star, Navy Achievement medal.

STROKE, HINKO HENRY, physicist, educator; b. Zagreb, Yugoslavia, June 16, 1927; came to U.S., 1943, naturalized, 1949; s. Elsa and Edith (Mechner) S.; m. Norma Bilchick, Jan. 14, 1956; children: Ilana Lucy, Marija Tamar. BEE, N.J. Inst. Tech., 1949, MS, MIT, 1952, PhD, 1954. Rsch. asst. Princeton (N.J.) U., 1954-57, rsch. assoc., 1957; mem. research staff. Sponsored Research div., lectr. dept. physics MIT, 1957-63; asso. prof. physics NYU, N.Y.C., 1963-68, prof., 1968—; dept. chmn., 1988-91; prof. associé U. Paris, 1969-70, Ecole Normale Supérieure, 1976; vis. scientist Max Planck Inst. für Qunateноptik, Garching. U. Munich, 1977-78, 81, 82, 93; cons. Atomic Instrument Co., MIT Sci. Translation Svc., Tech. Rsch. Group, Cambridge Air Force Rsch. Ctr., Am. Optical Corp., ITT Fed. Labs., NASA, others; mem. com. on-line spectra of elements NAS-NRC, 1976-82; sci. assoc. CERN, Geneva, 1983—. Contbg. author: Nuclear Physics, 1963, Atomic Physics, 1969, Hyperfine Interactions in Excited Nuclei, 1971, Francis Bitter: Selected Papers, 1969, Atomic Physics 3, 1973, Nuclear Moments and Nuclear Structure, 1973, A Perspective of Physics, Vol. 1, 1977, Atomic Physics 8, 1983, Lasers in Atomic, Molecular, and Nuclear Physics, 1989; editor: Comments on Atomic and Molecular Physics, The Physical Review-The First Hundred Years. Mem. Chorus Pro Musica, Boston, 1951-54, 57-63, Münchener Bach-Chor, Munich, 1977-82, 92, Collegiate Chorale, N.Y., 1964—; Dessoff Choirs, N.Y., 1994—; Choeur pro Arte, Lausanne, 1983-92. With AUS, 1946-47. Recipient Sr. U.S. Scientist award Alexander von Humboldt Found., 1977; NATO sr. fellow in sci., 1975. Fellow Am. Phys. Soc. (publs. oversight com. 1991-93), Optical Soc. Am.; mem. AAAS, IEEE, European Phys. Soc., Société Française de Physique, Tau Beta Pi, Sigma Xi, Omicron Delta Kappa. Home: 271 Old Army Rd Scarsdale NY 10583-2619 Office: NYU Dept Physics 4 Washington Pl New York NY 10003-6621

STROLL, BEVERLY MARIE, elementary school principal; b. Akron, Ohio, Aug. 22, 1936; d. Michael Dzatko, William DeVille (stepfather) and Marie Elizabeth (Stock) Dzatko-DeVille; m. Harold E. Stroll, Aug. 22, 1959; 1 child, James. BS, Kent State, 1958, MEd, 1980, Ednl. Specialist, 1988. Cert. elem. principal, elem. supr., tchr. Elem. edn. tchr. Cleve. Pub. Schs., 1958-59; elem. edn. tchr. Akron (Ohio) Pub. Schs., 1959-80, chpt. I math tchr., 1980-85, curriculum specialist, 1985-87, program specialist, 1987-91; prin. Zion Lutheran Sch., Akron, 1991—; bd. mem. Zion Lutheran Sch., 1983—, State Supt. Adv. Bd., 1984-89. Co-chair vol. com. Nat. Inventors Hall of Fame, 1990. Named Jennings educator Martha Holden Jennings Found., 1978-79. Mem. Ohio Assn. Adminstrs. of State and Fed. Programs (exec. bd. 1989-91), Akron Women Adminstrs. (sec. 1988-90), Zion Lutheran Ch. (sec. 1988—). Avocations: boating, water sports, traveling, bible study. Office: Zion Lutheran Sch 139 S High St Akron OH 44308-1410

STROM, BRIAN LESLIE, internist; b. N.Y.C., N.Y., Dec. 8, 1949; s. Martin and Edith (Singer) S.; m. Elaine Marilyn Moskowitz, June 4, 1978; children: Shayne Lee, Jordan Blair. BS, Yale U., 1971; MD, Johns Hopkins U., 1975; MPH, U. Calif., Berkeley, 1980. Diplomate Am. Bd. Internal Medicine, Am. Bd. Epidemiology. Intern in medicine U. Calif., San Francisco, 1975-76; resident in medicine U. Calif., 1976-78, research fellow in clinical pharmacology, 1978-80; from asst. prof. to assoc. prof. medicine and pharmacology U. Pa., Phila., 1980-93, prof. medicine, 1993—, prof. biostatistics & epidemiology, 1995—; adj. asst. prof. clin. pharmacy Phila. Coll. of Pharmacy and Sci., 1981—; mem. U. Pa. Cancer Ctr., 1981—; attending staff Hosp. U. Pa., 1980—, co-dir. Clin. Epidemiology Unit, 1980—; dir. Clin. Pharmacology Cons. Svc., 1981-82; dir. Ctr. for Clin. Epidemiology and Biostatistics, 1993—, chair dept. biostatistics and epidemiology, 1995—; lectr. in field; cons. CDC, 1981, Coun. for Internat. Orgn. of Med. Scis., Geneva, Switzerland, 1981-83, Office of Tech. Assessment, Congress of U.S., 1980-81, Aging Rev. Com., Nat. Inst. Aging, 1982, Ministry of Pub. Health, State of Kuwait, 1982, Royal Trop. Inst., Amsterdam, 1983, many others. Editl. cons. Johns Hopkins U. Press, J.B. Lippincott; referee Annals of Internal Medicine, Archives of Internal Medicine, Clin. Pharmacology and Therapeutics, Digestive Diseases and Sci., Internat. Jour. Epidemiology, Internat. Jour. Epidemiology, Jour. AMA, Jour. Gen. Internal Medicine, Med. Care, Primary Care Tech., Sci.; assoc. editor Jour. Gen. Internal Medicine; mem. editl. bd. 7 jours.; contbr. numerous articles to profl. jours. Nat. Acad. Scis. grantee, Rockefeller Found. grantee, NIH grantee, many others. Fellow ACP, Am. coll. Epidemiology, Am. Epidemiology Soc.; mem. Am. Fedn. Clin. Rsch., Am. Pub. Health Assn., Am. Soc. Clin. Pharmacology and Therapeutics, Am. Soc. Clin. Investigation, Assn. of Tchrs. of Preventive Medicine, Internat. Epidemiol. Assn., Soc. for Clin. Trials, Soc. for Epidemiologic Rsch., Soc. Group Internal Medicine. Democrat. Jewish. Avocations: hiking, biking, camping, skiing. Home: 332 Hidden River Rd Narberth PA 19072-1111

STROM, LYLE ELMER, federal judge; b. Omaha, Nebr., Jan. 6, 1925; s. Elmer T. and Eda (Hanisch) S.; m. Regina Ann Kelly, July 31, 1950; children: Mary Bess, Susan Frances, Amy Claire, Cassie A., David Kelly, Margaret Mary, Bryan Thomas. Student, U. Nebr., 1946-47; AB, Creighton U., 1950, JD cum laude, 1953. Bar: Nebr. 1953. Assoc. Fitzgerald, Brown, Leahy, Strom, Schorr & Barmettler and predecessor firm, Omaha, 1953-60, ptnr., 1960-63, gen. trial ptnr., 1963-85; judge U.S. Dist. Ct. Nebr., Omaha, 1985-87, chief judge, 1987-95; adj. prof. law Creighton U., 1959—; mem. com. pattern jury instrns. and practice and proc. Nebr. Supreme Ct., 1965-91; spl. legal counsel Omaha Charter Rev. Commn., 1973. Mem. exec. com Covered Wagon Coun. Boy Scouts Am., 1953-57, bd. trustees exec. com. Mid-Am. Coun., 1988—; chmn. bd. trustees Marian High Sch., 1969-71; mem. pres. coun. Creighton U., 1990—. Ensign USNR and with U.S. Maritime Svc., 1943-46. Fellow Am. Coll. Trial Lawyers, Internat. Acad. Trial Lawyers; mem. ABA, Nebr. Bar Assn. (ho. of dels. 1978-81, exec. coun. 1981-87, pres. 1989-90), Omaha Bar Assn. (pres. 1980-81), Am. Judicature Soc., Midwestern Assn. Amateur Athletic Union (pres. 1976-78), Alpha Sigma Nu (pres. alumni chpt. 1970-71). Republican. Roman Catholic. Lodge: Rotary (pres. 1993-94). Office: US Dist Ct PO Box 607 Omaha NE 68101-0607

STROM, MILTON GARY, lawyer; b. Rochester, N.Y., Dec. 5, 1942; s. Harold and Dolly (Isaacson) S.; m. Barbara A. Simon, Jan. 18, 1975; children: Carolyn, Michael, Jonathan. BS in Econs., U. Pa., 1964; JD, Cornell U., 1967. Bar: N.Y. 1968, U.S. Dist. Ct. (we. dist.) N.Y. 1968, U.S. Ct. Claims 1969, U.S. Ct. Mil. Appeals 1969, U.S. Ct. Appeals ((D.C. cir.) 1970, U.S. Supreme Ct. 1972, U.S. Dist. Ct. (so. dist.) N.Y. 1975. Atty. SEC, Washington, 1968-71; assoc. Skadden, Arps, Slate, Meagher & Flom, N.Y.C., 1971-77, ptnr., 1977—. Served with USCGR, 1967-68. Mem. ABA, N.Y. State Bar Assn. (corp. law sect.), Assn. of Bar of City of N.Y. Republican. Jewish. Club: Beach Point, Marco Polo. Avocations: tennis, skiing. Office: Skadden Arps Slate Meagher & Flom 919 3rd Ave New York NY 10022-3903

STROM, STEPHEN ERIC, astronomer; b. Bronx, N.Y., Aug. 12, 1942; s. Albert William and Beatrice (Reisinger) S.; m. Karen Marie Lewallen, Mar. 31, 1960; children: Robert Charles, Kathy Marie, David Michael, Julie Eileen. A.B., Harvard U., 1962, A.M., Ph.D., 1964. Lectr. Harvard U., 1964-68; astro-physicist Smithsonian Astrophysical Obs., Cambridge, Mass., 1964-68; assoc. prof. astronomy SUNY, Stony Brook, 1969-71; prof. SUNY, 1971-72, coordinator astronomy and astrophysics, 1969-72; astronomer Kitt Peak Nat. Obs., Tucson, 1972-83; chmn. galactic and extragalactic program Kitt Peak Nat. Obs., 1975-79; prof. physics and astronomy U. Mass., Amherst, 1983—; chmn. Five Coll. Astronomy Dept., 1984—; assoc. mng. editor Astrophys. Jour., 1979-85; vis. prof. U. Calif., Berkeley, 1979; mem. Space Sci. Bd., 1980-83; chmn. com. on Space Astronomy and Astrophysics, 1980-83; chmn. large deployable reflector sci. coordination group NASA, 1983-86, mem. space and earth scis. adv. com., 1984-87, chmn. Infrared Processing and Analysis Ctr. Users Com., 1986-88; chmn. com. on future dirs. of nat. optical astronomy observatories Assn Univs. Research in Astronomy, chmn. optical panel, astronomy and astrophysics survey (decade rev.). Author: (with Joy Harjo) Secrets From The Center Of The World, 1989. Recipient Bok prize Harvard, 1970; Warner prize Am. Astronom. Soc., 1975; Woodrow Wilson fellow (hon.), 1962; Sloan Found. fellow, 1970-72. Mem. Am. Astronom. Soc. (councilor 1980-83, v.p. 1987-89), Astronom. Soc. Pacific, Internat. Astron. Union, AAAS (councilor 1983-85), Phi Beta Kappa, Sigma Xi. Home: 163 Heatherstone Rd Amherst MA 01002-1638 Office: U Mass Five Coll Astronomy Dept GRC Tower B Amherst MA 01003

STROM, TERRY BARTON, physician, immunologist; b. Chgo., Nov. 30, 1941; s. David and Sylvia (Abelson) S.; m. Margot Stern, Aug. 2, 1964; children: Adam, Rachel. Student U. Ill.-Chgo./Urbana, 1959-62; M.D., U. Ill. Coll. Medicine, Chgo., 1966; MA (hon.) Harvard U., 1989; DSc (hon.) Hahnemann U., 1990. Diplomate Am. Bd. Internal Medicine. Intern/jr. resident U. Ill. Hosp., Chgo., 1966-68; sr. resident in internal medicine Beth Israel Hosp., Boston, 1970-71; research fellow in medicine Peter Bent Brigham Hosp. and Harvard Med. Sch., Boston, 1971-73; asst. prof. medicine Harvard Med. Sch., 1974-78, assoc. prof. medicine, 1978-88, prof. medicine, 1988—; med. dir. renal transplant svc. Peter Bent Brigham Hosp., 1973-83, assoc. dir. lab. immunogenetics and transplantation; sr. physician Beth Israel Hosp., med. dir. renal transplant service, 1983—; dir. div. clin. immunology, 1983—; Lilly lectr. Royal Coll. Physicians, London, 1991; Clarke lectr. U. Pa., 1995; Billingham vis. prof. Vanderbilt U., 1990. Author: 4 books, contbr. 400 articles to profl. jours. Campaign worker polit. campaigns and peace orgns.; mem. U.S. Congl. Task Force on Transplantation, 1985-87, adv. panel for allergy and transplantation NIAID, 1988-91, NIH; cons. FDA, 1993—. Served to capt. USAF, 1968-70. Recipient Rsch. Career Devel. award NIH, 1976-81; Acad. Honors Day award U. Ill., 1959-61; Ill. State scholar, 1959-66. Mem. Internat. Soc. Nephrology (councillor), Assn. Am. Immunologists, Internat. Transplant Soc., Am. Soc. Clin. Investigation, Am. Soc. Transplant Physicians (founding pres. 1981), Assn. Am. Phys., Clin. Immunol. Soc. (pres. 1990), Inter Urban Clin. Club. Democrat. Jewish. Office: Beth Israel Hosp 330 Brookline Ave Boston MA 02215-5491

STROMAN, SUSAN, choreographer; d. Charles and Frances S. Grad., U. Del. Dancer: Chicago, 1977-78, Whoopee!, 1979, Richard III, 1980, Peter Pan, 1981, Dickens' Reflections on the Carol, 1983; asst. dir., asst. choreographer: (off-Broadway) Musical Chairs, 1980; co-conceiver: Trading Places, Equity Library Theatre Informals, 1983; dir., co-conceiver: (off-Broadway) Living Color, 1986; choreographer: (off-Broadway) Broadway Babylon, 1984, Sayonara, 1987, Flora, the Red Menace, 1987, Shenandoah, 1988, Slasher, 1988, Rhythm Ranch, 1989, The Roar of the Greasepaint-The Smell of the Crowd, 1990, Gypsy, 1991, And the World Goes 'Round, 1991 (Outer Critics' Circle award 1991), A Christmas Carol, 1994; (Broadway) Crazy for You, 1992 (Tony award best choreography 1992, Drama Desk award 1992, Outer Critics' Circle award 1992, Laurence Olivier award 1993), Picnic, 1993, Show Boat, 1994 (Tony award best choreography 1995, Astaire award Theatre Development Fund 1995); (New York City Opera) Don Giovanni, 1989, A Little Night Music, 1990, 110 in the Shade, 1992; (other) Liza Minnelli: Stepping Out at Radio City Music Hall, 1991 (Emmy award nomination for HBO presentation); dir.: (TV spl.) A Evening with the Boston Pops-A Tribute to Leonard Bernstein, 1989; co-conceiver, choreographer: (TV spl.) Sondheim-A Celebration at Carnegie Hall, 1992. *

STROMBERG, ARTHUR HAROLD, retired professional services company executive; b. Los Angeles, July 17, 1928; s. Walter John and Ingfrid Christine (Olsen) S.; m. Fredna B. Copeland, Aug. 29, 1953. B.A. in Econs, U. So. Calif., 1952. Broker Francis I. duPont & Co., San Francisco, 1953-59; ptnr. Glore Forgan & Co., Chgo., San Francisco, 1959-67; v.p., dir. Eaton & Howard, San Francisco, 1967-70; chief exec. officer, chmn. bd. Thortec Internat., San Mateo, Calif., 1970-89; chmn. bd. URS Internat., Arlington, Va., 1986-91. Served with USNR, 1945-48. Mem. Bohemian Club, Burlingame Country Club. Republican.

STROMBERG, CLIFFORD DOUGLAS, lawyer; b. N.Y.C., June 1, 1949; s. George M. and Greta (Netzow) S.; m. Ava S. Feiner, June 25, 1972; children: Kimberly, Eric. BA summa cum laude, Yale U., 1971; JD, Harvard U., 1974. Bar: N.Y. 1975, D.C. 1975, U.S. Dist. Ct. (so. and ea. dists.) N.Y. 1975, U.S. Ct. Appeals (D.C. cir.) 1975, U.S. Ct. Appeals (2nd cir.) 1975, U.S. Supreme Ct. 1980. Law clk. to judge U.S. Dist. Ct. (ea. dist.) N.Y., 1974-75; assoc. Arnold & Porter, Washington, 1975-78, 80-83; dep. exec. sec. HHS, Washington, 1978-80; cons. FTC, Washington, 1980; ptnr. Dorsey & Whitney, Washington, 1983-84, Hogan & Hartson, Washington, 1984—; adj. asst. prof. emergency medicine George Washington U. Sch. Medicine, 1991—. Co-author: Mental Health and Law: A System in Transition, 1975, Alternatives to the Hospital: Ambulatory Surgery Centers and Emergicenters, 1984, Entrepreneurial Health Care: How to Structure Successful New Ventures, 1985, The Psychologist's Legal Handbook, 1988, Access to Hospital Information: Problems and Strategies: 4 Frontiers of Health Services Management 3-33, 1987, Healthcare Provider Networks: Antitrust Issues and Practical Considerations in devels. in antitrust law; editorial bd. Health Business and Law, 1984-87; contbr. articles to profl. jours. Bd. dirs. Nat. Children's Eye Care Found., Washington, 1985-87. Teaching fellow in govt. Harvard U., 1973-74. Fellow Am. Bar Found.; mem. ABA

(chair working group health care reform 1993—, state membership chmn. 1984, forum com. health lawk 1987-90, adv. com. govt. affairs 1993—, governing bd., individual rights and responsibilities sect., exec. coun., 1980-90, sec. 1984-87, chair-elect 1987-88, chair 1988-89, legal aid and indigent defendants com. 1982-87), Nat. Health Lawyers Assn., Phi Beta Kappa. Office: Hogan & Hartson 555 13th St NW Washington DC 20004-1109

STROMBERG, ROLAND NELSON, historian; b. Kansas City, Mo., July 5, 1916; s. Clarence Rol and Harriet (Ridgell) S.; m. Mary R. Gray, June 10, 1939; children: Eric, Juliet. AB, U. Kansas City, 1939; MA, Am. U., 1946; PhD, U. Md., 1952. With U.S. Dept. Justice, 1940-45; instr., then asst. prof., asso. prof., prof. U. Md., College Park, 1949-66; prof. So. Ill. U., Carbondale, 1966-67; prof. history U. Wis., Milw., 1967—; acting chmn. dept. art history U. Wis., 1977-78. Author: Collective Security and American Foreign Policy, 1963, An Intellectual History of Modern Europe, 1966, European Intellectual History Since 1789, 1966, 6th edit., 1993, After Everything, 1975, Religious Liberalism in Eighteenth Century England, 1954, Heritage and Challenge of History, 1971, 2d edit., 1989, Arnold J. Toynbee, 1972, Europe in the Twentieth Century, 1979, 3d edit, 1991, Redemption by War: The European Intellectuals and the 1914 War, 1982, Five Twentieth Century Thinkers, 1990, Men, Women, and History, 1994, others. Rockefeller Found. grantee, 1957-58; recipient Disting. Alumnus award U. Mo., Kansas City, 1966; fellow Woodrow Wilson Internat. Center for Scholars, 1974. Mem. History of Sci. Soc., Soc. Historians of Am. Fgn. Relations. Home: 7033 N Fairchild Cir Milwaukee WI 53217-3851 Office: U Wis Holton Hall Milwaukee WI 53201 *It would be more edifying to say that, as historian, I have sought an understanding of the past in order to help mankind master its future. It is probably truer to say that I have simply been fascinated by the amazing record of human actions and thoughts and by the problem of making sense of them.*

STROMBERG, ROSS ERNEST, lawyer; b. Arcata, Calif., May 5, 1940; s. Noah Anders and Anne Laura (Noyes) S.; m. Toni Nicholas, Dec. 16, 1961; m. Margaret Telonicher, Oct. 3, 1965; children: Kristin, Matthew, Gretchen, Erik. BS, Humboldt State U., 1962; JD, U. Calif., Berkeley, 1965. Bar: Calif. 1966, U.S. Dist. Ct. (no. dist.) Calif. 1966, U.S. Ct. Appeals (9th cir.) 1966. Assoc. Hanson Bridgett, San Francisco, 1965-70, ptnr., 1970-85; ptnr. Epstein Becker Stromberg & Green, San Francisco, 1985-90, Jones Day Reavis & Pogue, L.A., 1990—; chmn. Jones Day's Healthcare Specialized Industry Practice. Author: Economic Joint Venturing, 1985, Acquisition and Enhancement of Physician Practices, 1988. Pres. East Bay AHEC, Oakland, Calif., 1984-87; bd. dirs. Am. Cancer Soc., Oakland, 1984—; bd. dirs. U.S.-China Ednl. Inst., San Francisco, 1985—, chmn., 1988—; pres. Am. Acad. Hosp. Attys. of Am. Hosp. Assn., Chgo., 1978. Mem. Health Fin. Mgmt. Assn., Nat. Health Lawyers Assn., Am. Acad. Hosp. Attys., Richmond (Calif.) Yacht Club, Commonwealth Club, World Trade Club, Ingomar Club. Democrat. Clubs: Richmond (Calif.) Yacht; Commonwealth San Francisco); Ingomar (Eureka). Office: Jones Day Reavis & Pogue 555 W 5th St Ste 4600 Los Angeles CA 90013-1025

STROME, STEPHEN, distribution company executive; b. Lynn, Mass., June 20, 1945; s. David and Rose (Cantor) S.; m. Phyllis Ruth Fields, Jan. 14, 1967; children: Michael, Rochelle. BA, Hillsdale (Mich.) Coll., 1967; MBA, Wayne State U., 1968. Trainee KMart Corp., Detroit, 1968-69; mgr. work measurement KMart Corp., Troy, Mich., 1970-73; mgr. tng., edn. Fruehauf Corp., Detroit, 1974-76, regional mgr. labor relations, 1976-78; dir. ops. Handleman Co., Clawson, Mich., 1978-80, account exec., 1980-82; v.p. computer software div. Handleman Co., Troy, 1983-85, pres. computer software/video div., 1986-87, exec. v.p., 1987-89, exec. v.p., chief oper. officer, 1990, pres., CEO, 1991—. Home: 4597 Kiftsgate Bend Bloomfield Hills MI 48302-2331 Office: Handleman Co 500 Kirts Blvd Troy MI 48084-4142

STROMMEN, CLIFFORD H., headmaster; b. Gilby, N.D., May 2, 1935; m. Bette Ann Freeman, Dec. 22, 1963; children: Clint K., Emily A. BS in English, Moorhead State U., 1958; MEd in Ednl. Administrn., U. Houston, 1975, EdD in Ednl. Administrn., 1981. Cert. Eng. tchr., superintendent, dist. administr., N.Y., tchr. English, Phys. Edn., Calif. Tchr. English various sr. and jr. high schs., 1958-70; dir. athletics Seaside High Sch., Monterey, Calif., 1968; dir. dormitories Am. Internat. Sch., New Delhi, India, 1970-72, vice-prin., 1971-72; dir. Am. Embassy Sch. (formerly Am. Internat. Sch.), New Delhi, India, 1972-74; supt. Internat. Sch Lusaka, Zambia, 1976-84, Escola Graduada de São Paulo, Brazil, 1984-90; headmaster Internat. Sch. Nido de Aguilas, Santiago, Chile, 1990—. Recipient Nat. Superintendent of the Yr. awd., Overseas, Am. Assn. of School Administrators, 1993. Mem. Assn. Am. Sch. Administrs. (Internat. Superintendent of Yr. 1993), Assn. Advancement of Internat. Edn. (bd. dirs. 1983-84, 87-89, v.p. 1991-92, pres. 1993-94), Assn. Am. Schs. Brazil (treas. 1984-88, pres. 1989-90), Assn. Am. Schs. S.Am.(treas. 1985-86, v.p. 1986-87, pres. 1987-88), So. Assn. Colls. and Schs. (Latin Am. com. 1993), Assn. Internat. Schs. Africa (v.p. 1976, pres. 1976-78). Office: Internat Sch Nido de Aguilas, Casilla 16211 Correo 9, Santiago Chile

STRONACH, FRANK, automobile parts manufacturing executive. Chmn., dir. Magna Internat. Inc., Markham, Ont., Can., 1971—. Founder The Fair Enterprise Inst. Office: Magna Internat Inc, 36 Apple Creek Blvd, Markham, ON Canada L3R 4Y4

STRONE, MICHAEL JONATHAN, lawyer; b. N.Y.C., Feb. 26, 1953; s. Bernard William and Judith Semel (Sogg) S.; m. Andrea Nan Acker, Jan. 27, 1979; children: Noah Gregory, Joshua Samuel. BA cum laude, Colby Coll., 1974; JD, Fordham Law Sch., 1978. Bar: N.J. 1978, N.Y. 1979, U.S. Ct. Appeals (2d and 3d cirs.) 1979, U.S. Dist. Ct. (so. and ea. dists.) N.Y. 1979 U.S. Dist. Ct. N.J. 1979, Conn. 1988. Assoc. Ratheim Hoffman et al, N.Y.C., 1978-80, Botein Hays et al, N.Y.C., 1980-84; v.p., assoc. gen. counsel, asst. sec. GE Investment Corp., Stamford, Conn., 1984—; v.p., asst. sec. GE Investment Mgmt. Inc., 1988—; v.p., gen. counsel Gindoff Enterprises Inc., 1989-90. Bd. dirs. N.Y. chpt. Juvenile Diabetes Found., N.Y.C., 1987-89, vice-chmn., 1981-88; mem. fin. com. Juvenile Diabetes Found. Internat., 1981-86; asst. prin. bassist Westchester Symphony Orch., Scarsdale, N.Y., 1982—, pres., 1982-87, chmn. bd., 1982-90, exec. mng. dir., 1990-93; vice-chmn. ann. dinner NCCJ, 1987; bd. dirs. Parkinson's Disease Found., 1989—, v.p., 1991—; active steering com. Parkinson's Disease Soc. Am., 1991—, merger com., 1991—; bd. dirs Parkinson's Action Network, 1994—. Mem. ABA (chmn. pension plan investments 1989-91, chmn. asset mgmt., 1992-94, 95—, significant legis. com. 1985-92, chmn. subcom. on joint ventures 1988-90), Am. Coll. Real Estate Lawyers, The Corp. Bar Assn., Internat. Assn. Atty's and Execs. in Corp. Real Estate, Nat. Assn. of Real Estate Investment Mgrs. (mem. sr. legal officers assn. 1992—). Republican. Jewish. Home: 10 Genesee Trail Harrison NY 10528-1802 Office: Gen Electric Investment Corp 3003 Summer St Stamford CT 06905-4317

STRONG, CHARLES ROBERT, waste management administrator; b. Bklyn., Aug. 9, 1935; s. Charles Stanley and Ida May (Brower) S.; m. Melba Janice Cochran, July 8, 1961; children: William Charles, Colin Brower. BSME, Yale U., 1957. Registered profl. engr., Tex. Equipment engr. Remington Arms Co., Bridgeport, Conn., 1957-60; prodn. supr. Johnson & Johnson, Decatur, Ill., 1960; prodn. and maintenance dept. mgr. Johnson & Johnson, New Brunswick, N.J., 1961-66; maintenance supt. Johnson & Johnson, Chgo., 1966-70; from maintenance & engr. plant mgr. to facility engring. mgr Johnson & Johnson, Sherman, Tex., 1970-80; cons. engr. Acurex Solar Corp., Mountainview, Calif., 1980-83; tech. v.p. Young-Montenay, Inc., Sherman, Tex., 1983-85, Metro Energy Co., Miami, 1985-86; pres. Airko Svc. Co., Miami, 1986-87; v.p., adminstr. Montenay Power Corp., Miami, 1987—. Contbr. articles to profl. jours. Dir. Greater Texoma Utility Dist., Sherman, 1982-85; pres. Texoma Valley Coun. Boy Scouts Am., Sherman, 1980-82, Salvation Army, Sherman, 1983; chmn., bd. dirs. 1st United Meth. Ch., Sherman, 1982-84; bd. dirs. United Meth. Ch., Plantation, Fla., 1995. With U.S. Army, 1959. Recipient Silver Beaver award Boy Scouts Am., 1982. Mem. ASME, N.W. Dade, Hialeah, Miami Springs C. of C. (bd. dirs. 1995), Rotary (program chmn. 1976-85). Republican. Methodist. Avocations: watching sports, financial planning, home projects, exercising. Office: Montenay Power Corp 6990 NW 97th Ave Miami FL 33178

STRONG, DAVID F., university administrator; b. Botwood, Nfld., Can., Feb. 26, 1944; m. Lynda Joan Marshall; children: Kimberley, Joanna. B.Sc., Meml. U. Nfld., 1965; M.Sc., Lehigh U., 1967; PhD, U. Edinburgh, 1970. NRC postgrad. scholar U. Edinburgh, Scotland, 1970-72; assoc. prof. teaching and rsch. Meml. U. Nfld., 1972-74, prof., acting dept. head, 1974-75, E.W.R. Steacie fellow, 1975-77, prof. dept. earth scis. univ. rsch., 1985-90, spl. adv. to pres., 1985-87, v.p. (acad.), 1987-90; W.F. James prof. pure and applied scis. St. Francis Xavier U., N.S., 1981-82; pres., vice-chancellor U. Victoria, B.C., Can., 1990—; Swiney lectr. U. Edinburgh, 1981; mem. rsch. coun. Can. Inst. Advanced Rsch., 1986—. Editor or co-editor several books; contbr. more than 200 papers to sci. lit. Recipient Atlantic Provinces Young Scientist award (Frazer medal), 1973; NRC Can. E.W.R. Steacie fellow, 1975-77; Fgn. Exch. fellow to Japan, 1976, France, 1976-77. Fellow Geol. Assn. Can. (Past Pres.'s medal 1980), Geol. Soc. Am., Royal Soc. Can.; mem. Can. Inst. Mining and Metallurgy (Disting. Svc. award 1979, Disting Llctrs. award 1983-84), Soc. Econ. Geologists. Office: U Victoria, PO Box 1700, Victoria, BC Canada V8W 2Y2

STRONG, GARY EUGENE, librarian; b. Moscow, Idaho, June 26, 1944; s. Authur Dwight and Cleora Anna (Nirk) S.; m. Carolyn Jean Roetker, Mar. 14, 1970; children: Christopher Eric, Jennifer Rebecca. BS in Edn., U. Idaho, 1966; AMLS, U. Mich., 1967. Adminstrv. and reference asst. U. Idaho, 1963-66; extension librarian Latah County Free Library, Moscow, 1966; head librarian Markeley Residence Library, U. Mich., 1966-67; library dir. Lake Oswego (Oreg.) Public Library, 1967-73, Everett (Wash.) Public Library, 1973-76; asso. dir. services Wash. State Library, Olympia, 1976-79; dep. state librarian Wash. State Library, 1979-80; state librarian Calif. State Library, Sacramento, 1980-94; dir. Queens Borough Pub. Libr., Jamaica, 1994—; dir. emeritus Calif. State Library Found., 1994—; chief exec. Calif. Library Services Bd., 1980-94; founder, bd. dirs. Calif. State Library Found., 1982-94, Calif. Literary Campaign, 1984-94, Calif. Rsch. Bureau, 1992; bd. dirs. No. Regional Library Bd., 1983-94; mem. adv. bd. Ctr. for Book in Libr. of Congress, 1983-86; mem. nat. adv. com. Libr. of Congress, 1987-89; chmn. adv. bd. Calif. Libr. Constrn. and Rennovation Bond Act Bd., 1989-94; vis. lectr. Marylhurst Coll., Oreg., 1968, Oreg. Div. Continuing Edn., 1972, San Jose State U. State Libr. Svc., 1990; lectr. and cons. in field. Host, producer: cable TV Signatures Program, 1974-76, nationwide videoconfs. on illiteracy, censorship, 1987; author: On Reading-in the Year of the Reader, 1987; editor Calif. State Library Found. Bull., 1982-94 (H.W. Wilson Periodical award 1988), Western Americana in the Calif. State Library, 1986, On Reading-In the Year of the Reader, 1987, Chinatown Photographer: Louis J. Stellman, 1989, Local History Genealogical Resources, 1990, Literate America Emerging, 1991; contbr. articles to profl. jours.; editor, designer and pub. of various books. Bd. dirs., v.p. Pacific N.W. Bibliog. Ctr., 1977-80; bd. dirs. Thurston Mason County Mental Health Ctr., 1977-80, pres., 1979-80; bd. dirs. Coop. Library Agy. for Systems and Services, 1980-94, vice chmn., 1981-84; bd. dirs. Sr. Services Snohomish County, 1973-76, HISPANEX (Calif. Spanish lang. database), 1983-86; bd. govs. Snohomish County Hist. Assn., 1974-76; mem. Oreg. Coun. Pub. Broadcasting, 1969-73; mem. psychiat. task force St. Peters Hosp., Olympia, 1979-80; co-founder Calif. Ctr. for the Book, bd. dirs., 1987-94; mem. adv. bd. Calif. State PTA, 1981-86, Gov.'s Tech. Conf., 1993-94; mem. adv. com. Sch. Libr. Sci., UCLA, 1991-94, Sch. Libr. and Info. Studies, U. Calif., Berkeley, 1991-94; mem. Calif. Adult Edn. Steering Com., 1988-94; chmn. collaborative coun. Calif. State Literacy Resource Ctr., 1993-94; bd. dirs. Queens coun. Boy Scouts of Am., 1994—. Recipient Disting. Alumnus award U. Mich., 1984, Disting. Svc. award Calif. Literacy Inc., 1985, Spl. Achievement award Literacy Action, 1988, Assn. Specialized and Coop. Libr. Agys. Exceptional Achievement award, 1992, Gov.'s Award of Achievement Govt. Tech. Conf., 1994, Advancement of Literacy award Pub. Libr. Assn., 1994, Jim Cotton Dana award Libr. Adminstrn. and Mgmt. Assn., 1994; named Libr. of Yr. Calif. Assn. Libr. Trustees and Commrs., 1994; Oreg. Libr. scholar, 1966. Mem. ALA (legis. com. 1980-82, Commn. on Freedom and Equality of Access to Info. 1983-86), Libr. Adminstrn. and Mgmt. Assn. (dir. 1980-88, pres. 1984-85), N.Y. Libr. Assn., Oreg. Libr. Assn. (hon. life mem., pres. 1970-71), Pacific N.W. Libr. Assn. (hon. life mem., pres. 1978-79), Calif. Libr. Assn. (govt. rels. com. 1980-94), Chief Officers of State Libr. Agys. (pres. 1984-86), Western Coun. State Librs. (pres. 1988—), Assn. Specialized and Coop. Libr. Agys., Everett Area C. of C. (bd. dirs. 1974-76). Clubs: Book of Calif., Sacramento Book Collectors, The Book Collectors (L.A.). Office: Queens Borough Pub Libr 89-11 Merrick Blvd Jamaica NY 11432

STRONG, HENRY, foundation executive; b. Rochester, N.Y., Oct. 6, 1923; s. L. Corrin and Alice (Trowbridge) S.; m. Malan Swing, June 30, 1951; children: Sigrid Anne, Barbara Kirk, Dana Elizabeth, Henry Lockwood. A.B., Williams Coll., 1949. Joined Fgn. Service, 1950; with State Dept., 1950-51; vice consul The Hague, 1951-54, Washington, 1954-55; 2d sec. U.S. Embassy, Copenhagen, 1955-58, State Dept., 1958-62, Djakarta, Indonesia, 1962-64; resigned, 1968; chmn. bd., pres. Hattie M. Strong Found., 1968—. Mem. D.C. Commn. Arts, 1968-75; mem. D.C. Bd. Higher Edn., 1973-76; vice chmn. bd. trustees J.F. Kennedy Ctr. for Performing Arts, 1975-90, hon. trustee, 1991—; bd. dirs. Nat. Symphony Orch., Pomfret Sch., Fed. City Coun., A.M. Post Found. D.C., Community Found. of Greater Washington, 1974-91, Mt. Vernon Coll., 1969-88, 91—, Nat. Capital chpt. ARC, 1994—. Republican. Episcopalian. Clubs: Chevy Chase; Metropolitan (Washington); Gibson Island (Md.). Home: 5039 Overlook Rd NW Washington DC 20016 Office: Hattie M Strong Found 1620 Eye St NW Ste 700 Washington DC 20006-2402

STRONG, JOHN DAVID, insurance company executive; b. Cortland, N.Y., Apr. 12, 1936; s. Harold A. and Helen H. S.; m. Carolyn Dimmick, Oct. 26, 1957; children: John David Jr., Suzanne. BS, Syracuse U., N.Y., 1957; postgrad. Columbia U., 1980. With Kemper Group, 1957-90, Kemper Corp., 1990—, Empire div. sales mgr., 1972-74, exec. v.p. Fed. Kemper Ins. Co., Decatur, Ill., 1974-79, pres., bd. dirs., 1979-93, CEO, 1988-93, chmn. bd., 1989-93; vice chmn. Millikin Assocs., 1993—; bd. dirs. First of Am. Bank, Decatur, 1994. Mem. adv. council Sch. Bus. Millikin U., 1975-79, 84—; bd. dirs. United Way of Decatur and Macon County, Ill., 1976-83, campaign chmn., 1978-79, pres. bd. dirs., 1979-81; pres. United Way of Ill., 1981-83; chmn. DMH Commn. Svcs. Corp., 1988, 90; bd. dirs. Decatur-Macon County Econ. Devel. Found., 1983-88, DMH Health Systems, 1987-94, Richland Community Coll. Found., 1987-90, Symphony Ord. Guild of Decatur, 1992—; bd. dirs. Ill. Ednl. Devel. Found., 1983-90, pres., 1986-87; bd. dirs. Decatur Meml. Hosp., 1985-94, vice-chmn., 1988, chmn. 1990-92; bd. dir. Ctrl. Ill. Health Assocs., Inc., 1994, vice chmn. 1994—; mem. steering com. Decatur Advantage, 1981-93, pres., 1983-93. Capt. USAR, 1958-69. Mem. Metro Decatur C. of C. (bd. dirs. 1977-80, 2d vice chmn. 1981-82, 1st vice chmn. 1982-83, chmn. 1983-84), Alpha Kappa Psi. Club: Decatur (bd. dirs. 1980-83, pres. 1983), Country of Decatur (bd. dirs. 1993—). Office: First of Am Ctr 250 N Water St Ste 366 Decatur IL 62523

STRONG, JOHN SCOTT, finance educator; b. Phila., Aug. 28, 1956; s. John S. and Thelma J. (Willard) S.. BS, Washington & Lee U., 1978; M of Pub. Policy, Harvard U., 1981, PhD in Bus. Econs., 1986. Rsch. fellow Harvard U., Cambridge, Mass., 1983-85, 89-90, 93, vis. asst. prof. econs., 1989-90; dir. exec. MBA program, assoc. prof. fin. Coll. William and Mary, Williamsburg, Va., 1985—, dir. Exec. MBA program, 1994—; cons. on econs. and fin. Republic of Indonesia, 1987—, MITI, Japan, 1988-89, European Bank for Reconstruction and Devel., 1993, Govt. of Bolivia, 1994. Author: Why Airplanes Crash: Aviation Safety in a Changing World, 1992; Restructuring Transport in the Former Soviet Union, 1995; co-author 2 books on airline deregulation; contbr. articles to profl. jours. Fulbright scholar, 1978-79; grad. fellow NSF, 1979-82. Office: Coll William & Mary Sch Bus Williamsburg VA 23187

STRONG, JOHN WILLIAM, lawyer, educator; b. Iowa City, Aug. 18, 1935; s. Frank Ransom and Gertrude Elizabeth (Way) S.; m. Margaret Waite Cleary, June 16, 1962; children—Frank Ransom, Benjamin Waite. B.A., Yale U., 1957; J.D., U. Ill., 1962; postgrad, U. N.C. 1966-67. Bar: Ill. 1963, Oreg. 1976. Assoc. firm LeForgee, Samuels, Miller, Schroeder & Jackson, Decatur, Ill., 1963-64; asst. prof. law U. Kans., 1964-66; assoc. prof. Duke U., 1966-69; prof. U. Oreg., 1969-75; legal counsel Oreg. Task Force of Med. Malpractice, 1976; prof. U. Nebr., 1977-84, dean, 1977-82, vice chancellor for acad. affairs, 1981-84; Rosenstiel Disting. prof. law U. Ariz., 1984—; nat. sec.-treas. Order of the Coif, 1992—; cons. Nat. Judicial Coll. Author: (with others) Handbook on Evidence, 4th edit., 1992. Served with U.S. Army, 1957-59. Mem. Ill. Bar Assn., Oreg. Bar Assn., ABA, Am. Law Inst., Phi

Delta Phi. Republican. Congregationalist. Home: 3220 E 3rd St Tucson AZ 85716-4233 Office: U Ariz College of Law Tucson AZ 85721

STRONG, ROBERT S., banker; b. N.Y.C., Jan. 27, 1949; s. Henry William and Ida Anna (Krone) S.; m. Virginia Hala, June 11, 1994; children: Lauren, Jennifer, Tracy, Emily. BA in Econs., Columbia U., 1971; MBA in Fin., NYU, 1977. Lending officer Chase Manhattan Bank, N.Y.C., 1973-77, v.p., 1977-88, sr. v.p., 1988-91, sector exec., 1991—, exec. v.p., 1993—. Episcopalian. Office: Chase Manhattan Bank NA 1 Chase Manhattan Plz New York NY 10081

STRONG, ROGER LEE, mathematics educator; b. Sturgis, Mich., May 22, 1936; s. Ronald George and Mildred (Hamacher) S.; m. Shirley Anne Knight, Apr. 20, 1958 (div. Apr. 1984); children: Rachelle, Kevin, Todd, David; m. Beverly Ann Stoops, July, 1984. BA, Eastern Mich. U., 1961; MA, U. Mich., 1964, PhD, 1975. Cert. secondary tchr., Mich. Tchr. high sch. math. Livonia (Mich.) Pub. Sch.s, 1961-88; assoc. prof. math. Francis Marion U., Florence, S.C., 1988—; adj. asst. prof. math. U. Mich., Dearborn, 1984-88; cons. Sumter (S.C.) Pub. Schs., 1990, Darlington (S.C.) Pub. Schs., 1992. Author: Numerical Trigonometry, 1969. With USMC, 1956-58. Fellow NSF, 1968-69; named Golf Coach of Yr., Mich., 1985, Optimist Collegiate Educator of Yr., 1993. Mem. Math. Assn. Am., Nat. Coun. Tchrs. Math., S.C. Coun. Tchrs. Math., Country Club S.C. Episcopalian. Avocations: golf, gardening, bird watching. Home: 3728 Palmer Dr Florence SC 29506 Office: Francis Marion U Dept Math Florence SC 29501

STRONG, WARREN ROBERT, construction company executive; b. N.Y.C., Oct. 1, 1933; s. Joseph and Anna (Thompson) S.; m. Eleanor M. Mendes, Mar. 31, 1931; children: Douglas J, Stuart W. AAS, N.Y.C. Community Coll., 1961; grad., U.S. Army Command and Gen. Staff Coll., 1971, Indsl. Coll. Armed Forces, 1973. Traffic engr. Parsons, Brinckerhof, Hall & MacDonald, N.Y.C., 1952-54; asst. civil engr. Borough Pres. Queens, N.Y.C., 1954-62; project mgr. Granger Bros. Inc., Worcester, Mass., 1962-69; v.p., regional mgr. Gilbane Bldg. Co., Providence, 1969-80; pres. Zapata Constructors Inc., Houston, 1980-81; pres. John. W. Cowper Co. Inc., Buffalo, 1981-86, also bd. dirs.; sr. v.p. Macco Constructors Inc., Paramount, Calif., 1986-90, pres., 1990—; chief exec. officer, 1992—; also bd. dirs. Macco Constructors Inc., Paramount, Calif.; v.p. N.Y. state bldg. chpt. AGC, Albany, 1982-86; trustee Ind. Contractors Grievance and Arbitration Trust Fund. Vol. United Way Buffalo and Erie County, 1983, chmn. constrn., 1984. Served to col., USAR, 1949-86. Recipient Founders Day award Medaille Coll., 1985. Mem. Res. Officers Assn. (pres. R.I. chpt. 1976-77), Bus. Coun. N.Y. State (bd. dirs.), Soc. Am. Mil. Engrs., Assn. U.S. Army, Buffalo Club, Sea Cliff Tennis Club, Long Beach Navy Yacht Club, L.A. Athletic Club. Republican. Roman Catholic. Avocations: skiing, photography. Office: Macco Constructors Inc 14409 Paramount Blvd Paramount CA 90723

STRONG, WILLIAM L., III, investment executive; b. Plainfield, N.J., Nov. 27, 1932; s. William Lord Jr. and Elizabeth (Burke) S.; m. Beverly Carter Brand, Sept. 17, 1955; children: William L. IV, Peter B., Catherine B. BA, Yale U., 1955; postgrad., NYU, 1958-61. Security analyst Franklin Cole & Co., N.Y.C., 1958-64; investment officer Fiduciary Trust Internat., N.Y.C., 1965-67, asst. v.p., 1967-69, v.p., 1969-71, sr. v.p., 1971—. Bd. dirs. Muhlenberg Hosp., Plainfield, 1969-74; trustee Oceanic Free Libr., Rumson, N.J. Republican. Episcopalian. Office: Fiduciary Trust Internat 2 World Trade Ctr New York NY 10048

STRONG, WILLIAM SUTHERLAND, lawyer; b. Cin., Mar. 1, 1951; s. Robert Livingston and Mary Johnston (Sutherland) S.; m. Ann Reinke, Mar. 31, 1984; 1 child, Mary Sutherland Reinke Strong. AB, Harvard U., 1973, JD, 1977. Bar: Mass. 1977, U.S. Dist. Ct. Mass. 1979, U.S. Ct. Appeals (1st cir.) 1980, U.S. Supreme Ct. 1984. Assoc. Herrick & Smith, Boston, 1977-82; ptnr. Kotin, Crabtree & Strong, Boston, 1982—; adj. prof. copyright law Franklin Pierce Law Ctr., Concord, N.H., 1987—. Author: The Copyright Book: A Practical Guide, 1981, rev. 3d edit., 1990. Trustee Boston Athenaeum, 1987—. Mem. ABA (com. chmn. 1988-90, div. chmn. 1990-91), Boston Bar. Assn. Office: Kotin Crabtree & Strong 61 Chatham St Boston MA 02109-2503

STRONGIN, THEODORE, journalist; b. N.Y.C., Dec. 10, 1918; s. Isadore and Ida (Slevin) S.; m. Ruth Klein, Aug. 13, 1947 (dec. 1954); children: Deborah, Daniel Otto; m. Harriet Stern Rosenberg, Oct. 4, 1969 (dec. 1991). Student, Harvard, 1935-37; A.B., Bard Coll., 1941; postgrad., Juilliard Sch. Music, summers 1940, 41, fall 1946, Columbia, 1947-49. Dir. music East Woods Sch., Oyster Bay, N.Y., 1947-54; mem. music faculty Bennington (Vt.) Coll., 1954-56, Dartmouth, spring 1955; arts editor Chattanooga Times, 1957-61, Albany (N.Y.) Knickerbocker News, 1961-63; music critic, reporter, record reviewer N.Y. Times, 1963-65, music critic, reporter, recs. editor, 1965-71; columnist East Hampton (N.Y.) Star, 1972-77; Cons. Music in Our Time series, N.Y.C., 1972-73, N.Y. State Council on Arts, 1970, various art instns., 1971-77. Composer: Suite for Unaccompanied Cello, 1951, Quartet for Oboe and Strings, 1952; author: Cabals, 1966. Mem. Amagansett Village Improvement Soc., 1974-86; mem. Amagansett Residents Assn., 1975-86, bd. dirs., pres., 1975-77; dir. pub. relations Ind. Voters of East Hampton, 1971. Served to capt. AUS, 1941-46. Recipient Broude Publ. prize for piano piece, 1948. Democrat. Address: 204 Woodland Dr Osprey FL 34229-9551

STRONG-TIDMAN, VIRGINIA ADELE, marketing and advertising executive; b. Englewood, N.J., July 26, 1947; d. Alan Ballentine and Virginia Leona (Harris) Strong; m. John Fletcher Tidman, Sept. 23, 1978. BS, Albright Coll., Reading, Pa., 1969; postgrad. U. Pitts., 1970-73, U. Louisville, 1975-76. Exec. trainee Pomeroy's div. Allied Stores, Reading, 1969-70; mktg. rsch. analyst Heinz U.S.A., Pitts., 1970-74; new products mktg. mgr. Ky. Fried Chicken, Louisville, 1974-76; dir. Pitts. office M/A/R/C, 1976-79; assoc. rsch. dir. Henderson Advt., Inc., Greenville, S.C., 1979-81; sr. v.p. dir. rsch. Bozell, Jacobs, Kenyon & Eckhardt, Inc., Dallas, 1981-86, sr. v.p. dir. rsch. and strategic planning Atlanta, 1986-88; sr. v.p. dir. mktg. svcs. Bozell, Inc., Atlanta, 1988—; cons. mktg. rsch. Greenville Zool. Soc., 1981; adj. prof. So. Meth. U., 1984-85. Mem. Am. Mktg. Assn. (Effie award N.Y. chpt. 1982). Republican. Episcopalian. Home: 1835 Johnson Ferry Rd Atlanta GA 30319-1922 Office: Bozell Inc 3490 Piedmont Rd NE Ste 1400 Atlanta GA 30305-1745

STROOCK, DANIEL WYLER, mathematician, educator; b. N.Y.C., Mar. 20, 1940; s. Alan Maxwell and Katherine (Wyler) S.; m. Lucy Barber, Nov. 21, 1962; children: Benjamin, Abraham. AB, Harvard Coll., 1962; PhD, Rockefeller U., 1966. Vis. mem. Courant Inst., N.Y., 1966-69, asst. prof., 1969-72; asso. prof. math. U. Colo., Boulder, 1972-75; prof. U. Colo., 1975-84, chmn. dept. math. 1979-81; prof. math. MIT, 1984—; adj. prof. U. Colo., Beijing Normal U. Author: (with S.R.S. Vanadhan) Multidimensional Diffusion Processes, 1979, (with J.D. Deuschel) Large Deviations, 1989, Probability Theory, An Analytic view, 1993; editor Math. Zeitschrift, 1992—, Ill. Jour. Math, 1982-84; Transcripts of Am. Math. Soc., 1974-80, Annals Probability, 1988-93, Advances in Math., 1994—, Jour. Functional Analysis, 1994—; contbr. articles on probability theory to profl. jours. Guggenheim fellow, 1978-79. Mem. Am. Acad. Arts and Scis., N.Y. Acad. Scis., Sigma Xi. Democrat. Jewish. Home: 55 Frost St Cambridge MA 02140-2225 Office: MIT Dept Math Cambridge MA 02139

STROOCK, MARK EDWIN, II, public relations company executive; b. N.Y.C., Nov. 6, 1922; s. Irving Sylvan and Blanche (Loeb) S.; m. Hanna Marks Eiseman, June 24, 1945; children—Mark E., Carolyn E. BA, Bard Coll., 1947. Reporter The New York Journal of Commerce, 1947-50; writer Barrons, N.Y.C., 1950-51; mng. editor Fairchild Publication, N.Y.C., 1952-53; bus. editor World Mag., N.Y.C., 1953-54; contbg. editor Time Mag., N.Y.C., 1954-56; with Young & Rubicam Inc., N.Y.C., 1956-87, v.p., corporate rels., cons., 1987—. Bd. trustee N.Y. Urban League, 1971-78, Alvin Ailey Dance Theatre, N.Y.C., 1977-84, Friends of the Theatre Mus. City N.Y., 1977-85; vice chmn. Covenant House, N.Y.C., 1978-90; exec. com., mktg. and communications com. Anti-Defamation League. Served with U.S. Army, 1943-46. Democrat. Jewish. Home: 50 Park Ave New York NY 10016-3000 Office: Young & Rubicam Inc 285 Madison Ave New York NY 10017-6486

STROOCK, THOMAS FRANK, business executive; b. N.Y.C., Oct. 10, 1925; s. Samuel and Dorothy (Frank) S.; B.A. in Econs., Yale U., 1948; m. Marta Freyre de Andrade, June 19, 1949; children: Margaret, Sandra, Elizabeth, Anne. Landman Stanolind Oil & Gas Co., Tulsa, 1948-52; pres. Stroock Leasing Corp., Casper, Wyo., 1952-89, Alpha Exploration, Inc., 1980-89; ptnr. Stroock, Rogers & Dymond, Casper, 1960-82; dir. Wyo. Bancorp., Cheyenne, First Wyo. Bank, Casper; mem. Wyo. Senate, 1967-69, 71-75, 79-89, chmn. appropriations com. 1983, co-chmn. joint appropriations com., 1983-89, mem. mgmt. and audit com. P; mem. steering com. Edn. Commn. of States; ambassador to Guatemala, 1989-92; pres. Alpha Devel. Corp., 1992—. Rep. precinct committeeman, 1950-68; pres. Natrona County Sch. Bd., 1960-69; pres. Wyo. State Sch. Bds. Assn., 1965-66; chmn. Casper Community Recreation, 1955-60; chmn. Natrona County United Fund, 1963-64; chmn. Wyo. State Republican Com., 1975-78, exec. com. 1954-60; delegate Rep. Nat. Convetion, 1956, 76; regional coord. campaign George Bush for pres., 1979-80, 87-88; chmn. Western States Rep. Chmn. Assn., 1977-78; chmn. Wyo. Higher Edn. Commn., 1969-71; mem. Nat. Petroleum Council, 1972-77; chmn. trustees Sierra Madre Found. for Geol. Research, New Haven; chmn. Wyo. Nat. Gas Pipeline Authority 1987-88; bd. dirs. Ucross Found., Denver; mem. Nat. Pub. Lands Adv. Council, 1981-85. Served with USMC, 1943-46. Mem. Rocky Mountain Oil and Gas Assn., Petroleum Assn. Wyo. Republican. Unitarian. Lodge: Kiwanis. Clubs: Casper Country; Casper Petroleum; Denver. Home and Office: PO Box 2875 Casper WY 82602-2875

STROPNICKY, GERARD PATRICK, theater director, consultant; b. Teaneck, N.J., Aug. 25, 1953; s. John F. and Elizabeth M. (Novotny) S.; m. Kathleen Horkay Baas, Aug. 16, 1987; children: Diane, William. BSc in Speech, Northwestern U., 1976. Founding mem. Bloomsburg (Pa.) Theatre Ensemble, 1978—; cons. Fedapt, N.Y.C., 1984-89; cons. theatre design Bristol (Pa.) Riverside Theatre, 1986-87, F.M. Kirby Ctr., Wilkes Barre, Pa., 1988; guest dir. Fla. Shakespeare Festival, Coral Gables, 1986-87, Touchstone Theatre, Bethlehem, Pa., 1989, 91. Pa. Playwright fellow, 1991. Mem. Theatre Assn. Pa. (bd. dirs. 1991-94), Bucknell Univ. Assn. Arts (bd. dirs. 1989—). Office: Bloomsburg Theatre Ensemble 226 Center St Bloomsburg PA 17815-1752

STROPP, ROBERT H., JR., lawyer; b. Balt., Sept. 21, 1947; s. Robert H. and Elizabeth A. (Brown) S.; m. Mary J. Worden, Oct. 9, 1970; children: Emily S., Mary K. BA, U. Md., 1969; JD, Samford U., Birmingham, Ala., 1975. Bar: Ala. 1975, D.C. 1991, U.S. Dist. Cts. (no., mid. and so.) Ala., U.S. Supreme Ct., U.S. Ct. Appeals (1st, 2d, 3d, 4th, 5th, 6th, 10th and 11th cirs.). Tchr. psychology Prince George's County Bd. Edn., Suitland, Md., 1969-72; assoc. Cooper, Mitch & Crawford, Birmingham, 1975-80; ptnr. Cooper, Mitch & Crawford, 1980-84, Stropp & Nakamura, Birmingham, 1984-88; gen. counsel United Mine Workers Am., Washington, 1988—; Mem. lawyers coordinating com. AFL-CIO, Washington, 1982—, mem. adv. coun., 1989—. Mem. ABA (labor and employment sect.), Birmingham Bar Assn., Am. Trial Lawyers Assn., Indsl. Rels. Rsch. Assn. (past. v.p. Birmingham chpt.). Democrat. Avocations: sports, travel, family. Home: 10103 Mill Wheel Ln Vienna VA 22182-1338 Office: Internat Union United Mine Workers Am 900 15th St NW Washington DC 20005-2503

STROSAHL, WILLIAM AUSTIN, artist, art director; b. N.Y.C., June 11, 1910; s. William August and Margaret Theresa (Peterson) S.; m. Rosemary Rachel Jordan, May 28, 1949 (dec. Dec. 1989); children: Timothy, Brian, William, Jordan, Margaret. Student, Parsons Sch. Design, 1926-27. Cub cartoonist N.Y. Evening Graphic, N.Y.C., 1927-28; art dir. Ohio Match Co., N.Y.C., 1928-29, Lindsay Assoc. Artists, N.Y.C., 1929-30; asst. art dir. J. Walter Thompson, N.Y.C., 1930-32, art dir., 1932-42; exec. art dir. William Esty Co., N.Y.C., 1942-55, creative dir., exec. v.p., 1956-69, watercolor painter, 1969—. Recipient Gold medal Allied Artist Am., 1965, 88; recipient Hallmark Audubon Artists, 1959, Gold and Silver medal Audubon Artists, 1980, Nat. Acad. Design, John Pike Meml. award, 1985, Ogden Pleisner Meml. award, 1987, William A. Paton Meml. prize, 1988, Creative Watercolor awards, 1990-91, 200 Yrs. Watercolor Painting award Met. Mus. Art, N.Y.C., 58 other awards for watercolor painting, 1946-90. Fellow Dolphin Fellowship; mem. Am. Watercolor Soc. (v.p. 1950), Am. Watercolor Soc. (hon. pres. 1983—), Nat. Art Dirs. Assn. (v.p. 1954), Nat. Acad. Design, Academician 1994—, Silvermine Guild, Allied Artists Am., Audubon Artists. Republican. Home: 301 Haviland Rd Stamford CT 06903-3324

STROSCIO, MICHAEL ANTHONY, physicist, educator; b. Winston-Salem, N.C., June 1, 1949; s. Anthony and Norma Lee (Sidbury) S.; children: Elizabeth de Clare, Charles Marshall Sidbury. B.S., U. N.C., 1970; M.Phil. in Physics, Yale U., 1972, Ph.D. in Physics, 1974. Physicist Los Alamos Sci. Lab., N.Mex., 1975-78; sr. staff mem. Johns Hopkins U. Applied Physics Lab., Laurel, Md., 1978-80; prof. mgr. for electromagnetic research Air Force Office of Sci. Research, Washington, 1980-83; spl. asst. to research dir. Office of Under Sec. Def., Washington, 1982-83; policy analyst White House Office of Sci. and Tech. Policy, Washington, 1983-85; prof. dir. for microelectrons and sr. scientist U.S. Army Research Office, Research Triangle Park, N.C., 1985—; adj. prof. depts. physics and elec. and computer engring. N.C. State U., Raleigh, 1985—; adj. prof. depts. elec. engring. and physics Duke U., Durham, 1986—; mem. Congl. Coun., 1989-91; lectr. UCLA, 1987, U. Mich., 1988; cons. U.S. Dept. Energy, Washington, 1985—; vice chmn. White House Panel on Sci. Communication, Washington, 1983-84; chmn. Dept. Def. Research Instrumentation Com., Washington, 1982, assoc. mem. Adv. Group on Electron Devices, 1985-91, liaison Nat. Laser Users Facility, Rochester, N.Y., 1984; liaison Panel on Sci. Communication and Nat. Security, NAS, 1982, Panel on Materials for High-Density Electronic Packaging, 1987-90; U.S. Army liaison to JASON, 1991—; mem. U.S. Govt. coord. com. of Semiconductor Rsch. Corp., 1992—. Author: Positronium: A Review of the Theory, 1975, Onslow Families, 1977; reviewer NSF, Office of Naval Rsch., Dept. Commerce and the Natural Scis., Engring. Rsch. Coun. Can., 1981—; referee jours.; contbr. articles to profl. jours.; patentee in field. Served to capt. USAF, 1974-75. Los Alamos Sci. Lab. grantee, 1977. Fellow IEEE (exec. com. for plasma sci. 1983—), Yale Sci. and Engring. Assn. (exec. bd. dirs. 1983—); mem. Am. Phys. Soc., Phi Beta Kappa, Nat. Geneal. Soc. Home: 206 E Woodridge Dr Durham NC 27707-3908 Office: US Army Research Office PO Box 12211 Durham NC 27709-2211

STROSS, JEOFFREY KNIGHT, physician, educator; b. Detroit, May 2, 1941; s. Julius Knight and Molly Ellen (Fishman) S.; m. Ellen Nora Schwartz, May 22, 1965; children: Wendy, Jonathan. BS in Pharmacy, U. Mich., 1962, MD, 1967. Diplomate Am. Bd. Internal Medicine. Intern Univ. Mich. Hosp., Ann Arbor, 1967-68, resident in internal medicine, 1971-73; instr. internal medicine U. Mich., Ann Arbor, 1973-74, asst. prof., 1974-79, assoc. prof., 1979-87, prof., 1987—; cons. Merck Sharp Dohme Co., West Point, Pa., 1982—, U.S. Dept. State, Washington, 1976—. Contbr. numerous articles to med. jours. Served to maj. USAF, 1969-71. Nat. Heart, Lung and Blood Inst. grantee, 1975—. Fellow ACP; mem. Soc. for Gen. Internal Medicine (regional chmn. 1984-86). Jewish. Home: 3541 Larchmont Dr Ann Arbor MI 48105-2853 Office: Univ of Mich Med Sch 4106 Med Sci I Ann Arbor MI 48109

STROSSEN, NADINE, law educator, human rights activist; b. Jersey City, Aug. 18, 1950; d. Woodrow John and Sylvia (Simicich) S.; m. Eli Michael Noam, Apr. 25, 1980. AB, Harvard U., 1972, JD magna cum laude, 1975. Jud. clk. Minn. Supreme Ct., St. Paul, 1975-76; assoc. Lindquist & Vennum, Mpls., 1976-78, Sullivan & Cromwell, N.Y.C., 1978-83; prof. clin. law, supervising atty. Civil Rights Clinic, Sch. Law, NYU, 1984-88; prof. law N.Y. Law Sch., N.Y.C., 1988—. Editor Harvard Law Rev., 1975; contbr. book chpts., articles to profl. jours.; author: In Defense of Pornography: Free Speech and the Fight for Women's Rights, 1995. Bd. dirs. The Fund for Free Expression, 1990—. Recipient Outstanding Young Person award Jaycees Internat., 1986, Outstanding Contbn. to Human Rights Jour. Human Rights, N.Y. Law Sch., 1989; named one of Ten Outstanding Young Ams., U.S. Jaycees, 1986. Mem. ACLU (exec. com. 1985—, gen. counsel 1986-91, pres. 1991—), Nat. Coalition Against Censorship (bd. dirs. 1989—), Coalition to Free Soviet Jews (bd. dirs. 1986—), Human Rights Watch (exec. com. 1989-91), Asia Watch (vice chair 1989-91), Mid. East Watch (bd. dirs. 1989-91), Harvard Club (N.Y.C.). Avocations: travel, skiing, singing. Home: 450 Riverside Dr # 51 New York NY 10027-6821 also: Sedgewood

Club RD 12 Carmel NY 10512 Office: NY Law Sch 57 Worth St New York NY 10013-2959

STROTE, JOEL RICHARD, lawyer; b. N.Y.C., Apr. 19, 1939; s. Jack and Fortuna (Benezra) S.; children: Jared, Noah; m. Elisa Ballestas, Dec. 14, 1991. BA, U. Mich., 1960; JD, Northwestern U., 1963. Bar: N.Y. 1964, D.C. 1965, Calif. 1967, U.S. Dist. Ct. (cen. dist.) Calif. 1967, U.S. Supreme Ct. 1971. Assoc. Damman, Blank, Hirsh & Heming, N.Y.C., 1966-65, ICC, Washington, 1965-66, Capitol Records, Hollywood, Calif., 1966-67; ptnr. Strote & Whitehouse, Beverly Hills, Calif., 1967-89; of counsel Selvin, Weiner & Ruben, Beverly Hills, Calif., 1989-94; ptnr. with Cohen, Strote & Young, 1992-94; sole practice law, 1994—; judge pro tem, L.A. County Mcpl. Ct., 1973—; probation monitor, Calif. State Bar Ct., L.A., 1985—; pres. Liberace Found., Las Vegas, Nev., 1987—; bd. chmn. Tuesday's Child, L.A., 1989—. Cpl. USMC, 1963-64. Mem. Calif. State Bar Assn., L.A. County Bar Assn., L.A. Copyright Soc., Beverly Hills Bar Assn. Democrat. Jewish. Avocations: swimming, bicycling, hiking, opera, travel. Office: Joel R Strote Profl Corp 21700 Oxnard St Ste 540 Woodland Hills CA 91367

STROTHMAN, JAMES EDWARD, editor; b. Pitts., Mar. 27, 1939; s. Edward Charles and Harriet Hope (Jones) S.; m. Eleanor Shawfield Jacobs, Sept. 9, 1961; children:—Joseph, Jill, Stuart. B.A. in Journalism, Pa. State U., 1961. Asst. city editor, city hall reporter Williamsport Grit, Pa., 1961-64; with Miami Herald, Fla., 1964-67; aerospace writer AP, Cape Kennedy, Fla., 1967-69; reporter Los Angeles bur. Electronic News, 1969-71, sr. editor computer news sect., 1971-73, mng. editor, 1973; sr. info. rep. corp. hdqrs., then program adminstr. data processing div. hdqrs. IBM Corp., 1973-77, mgr. eastern area communications data processing div., 1977-79, field communications mgr. data processing div., 1979-81, mgr. communications research div., 1981; free-lance writer and cons. Strothman Assocs., 1981-82; editor-in-chief MIS Week, N.Y.C., 1982-88; free-lance writer, cons., 1988-89; editor-in-chief Computer Pictures, Chappaqua, N.Y., 1989—; sr. editor Intech Mag. Instrument Soc. Am., Research Triangle Park, N.C., 1994—. Episcopalian.

STROTHMAN, WENDY JO, book publisher; b. Pitts., July 29, 1950; d. Walter Richard and Mary Ann (Hodtum) S.; m. Mark Kavanaugh Metzger, Nov. 25, 1978; children: Andrew Richard, Margaret Ann. Student, U. Chgo., 1979-80; AB, Brown U., 1972. Copywriter, mktg. U. Chgo. Press, 1973-76, editor, 1977-80, gen. editor, 1980-83, asst. dir., 1983; dir. Beacon Press, Boston, 1983—; trustee Brown U., 1990—. Edtl. adv. bd. Scholarly Pub., 1993-94; bd. editors Brown Alumni Monthly, 1983-89; chmn., 1986-89. Bd. dirs. Editorial Project for Edn., trustee, 1987-91, treas., 1988-90. Mem. Renaissance Soc. (bd. dirs. 1980-83), Assn. Am. Pubs. (freedom to read com.), Assn. Am. Univ. Presses (1st amendment com.), Lunch Club (N.Y.C.), Union Club, PEN New Eng. (adv. bd.), Examiner Club, NacRe Reins. Corp. (bd. dirs.). Office: Beacon Press 25 Beacon St Boston MA 02108-2892

STROTTMAN, DANIEL DAVID, physicist; b. Waverly, Iowa, Apr. 15; s. Arnold and Alice (Schwake) S.; m. Theresa Anne Short, Dec. 22, 1966; 1 child, Nissa. BA, U. Iowa, 1964; MA, SUNY, Stony Brook, 1966, PhD, 1969. Fellow Niels Bohr Inst., Copenhagen, 1969-70; research officer Oxford (Eng.) U., 1970-73; asst. prof. physics SUNY, Stony Brook, 1974-78; mem. staff Los Alamos (N.Mex.) Nat. Lab., 1978-87, group leader, 1987-92, dep. divsn. dir., 1992—; vis. prof. U. Oslo, 1973-74; mem. adv. com. Los Alamos Meson Physics Facility (now Clinton P. Anderson Meson Physics Facility at Los Alamos) program, 1986-89. Mem. editorial bd. Internat. Rev. Nuclear Physics, 1982—, Modern Physics A., 1986—; editorial bd. Phys. Rev. C, 1993—, Acta Physica Hungarica; contbr. articles to profl. jours. Pres. Los Alamos Youth Soccer League, 1985-87. Fellow Am. Phys. Soc., Humboldt; mem. AAAS, No. N.Mex. Soccer Referees Assn. (pres. 1981-84). Home: 613 47th St Los Alamos NM 87544-1825 Office: Los Alamos Nat Lab Theoretical Div MS B210 Los Alamos NM 87545

STROUD, JAMES STANLEY, retired lawyer; b. Wimbledon, N.D., Jan. 26, 1915; s. Herbert Montgomery and Amanda Getchell (Longfellow) S.; m. Marjorie Marsh Hovey, Sept. 11, 1940; children: Jay Stanley, Steven Hovey. AB, Jamestown Coll., 1936; JD, U. Chgo., 1939. Bar: Ill. 1939, U.S. Supreme Ct. 1945, D.C. 1972. Counsel Ill. Mcpl. Code Commn., Chgo., 1939-40; bill drafter Ill. Legis. Ref. Bur., Springfield, 1941; from assoc. to ptnr. Mayer, Brown & Platt, Chgo., 1941-71; ptnr.-in-charge Mayer, Brown & Platt, Washington, 1972-80. Bd. dirs. Chgo. Community Renewal Found., 1962-70; mem. adminstrv. bd. Nat. United Meth. Ch., Washington, 1982-84; coord. Extended Family Program, 1981-82. Capt. AUS, 1943-46. Home: Cottage 304 3300 Darby Rd Haverford PA 19041-1063

STROUD, JOE HINTON, newspaper editor; b. McGehee, Ark., June 18, 1936; s. Joseph Hilliard and Marion Rebecca (McKinney) S.; m. Janis Mizell, Aug. 21, 1957; children: Rebecca McKinney, Joseph Scott, Alexandra Jane; m. Kathleen M. Fojtik, Nov. 1, 1981; children: Jonathan Rudolph, Anna Marion. BA, Hendrix Coll., Conway, Ark., 1957; MA, Tulane U., 1959; LLD (hon.), Eastern Mich. U., 1977, Kalamazoo Coll., 1984, Adrian Coll., 1985; D Communicating Arts (hon.), Cen. Mich. U., 1986; LittD (hon.), Mich. State U., 1987. Reporter, then editor editorial page Pine Bluff (Ark.) Comml., 1959-60; editorial writer Ark. Gazette, Little Rock, 1960-64; editorial writer then editor editorial page Winston-Salem (N.C.) Jour.-Sentinel, 1964-68; assoc. editor Detroit Free Press, 1968-73, editor, 1973—; sr. v.p., 1978—. Mem. gen. bd. publs. United Meth. Ch., 1975-76; adv. bd. Mich. Christian Advocate, 1975-79; bd. govs. Cranbrook Inst. Sci., 1978—; trustee Cranbrook Ednl. Community, 1989—; bd. dirs. S.E. Mich. chpt. ARC, 1972-88, Detroit Symphony, 1978-83; chmn. adv. com. Svc. to Mil. Families, 1974-77, chmn. program evaluation com. 1978-80; bd. assocs. Adrian Coll., 1985—; trustee Starr Commonwealth Schs., 1989—. Recipient N.C. Sch. Bell award, 1967; Mich. Sch. Bell award, 1973; William Allen White award Inland Daily Press Assn., 1973, 76, 77; citation Overseas Press Club, 1974; Paul Tobenkin award Columbia U., 1976; Disting. Service award Mich.'s Women's Commn., 1984; Laity award Detroit Ann. Conf. United Meth. Ch., 1985. Mem. Am. Soc. Newspaper Editors, Nat. Conf. Editorial Writers (program chmn. 1978, v.p. 1987-88, pres. 1988-89), Detroit Econ. Club, Detroit Com. Fgn. Relations, Sigma Delta Chi. Clubs: Detroit, Renaissance, Nat. Press. Office: Detroit Free Press 321 W Lafayette Blvd Detroit MI 48231

STROUD, JOHN FRED, JR., state supreme court justice; b. Hope, Ark., Oct. 3, 1931; s. John Fred and Clarine (Steel) S.; m. Marietta Kimball, June 1, 1958; children: John Fred III, Ann Kimball, Tracy Steel. Student, Hendrix Coll., 1949-51; BA, U. Ark., 1959, LLB, 1960. Bar: Ark. 1959, Tex. 1988, U.S. Supreme Ct. 1963. Ptnr. Stroud & McClerkin, 1959-62; city atty. City of Texarkana (Ark.), 1961; legislative asst. to U.S. Senator John L. McClellan, 1962-63; ptnr. Smith, Stroud, McClerkin, Dunn & Nutter, 1963-79, 1981—; assoc. justice Ark. Supreme Ct., Little Rock, 1980-81. Chmn. Texarkana Airport Authority, 1966-67, Texarkana United Way Campaign, 1988; pres. Caddo area coun. Boy Scouts Am., 1971-73; former trustee Ark. Nature Conservancy; bd. dirs. Ark. Community Found.; pres. Red River Valley Assn.; commr. Red River Compact Commn.; past vice chmn. Ark. Water Code Study Commn.; chmn. bd., chmn. coun. ministries Meth. Ch. Lt. col. USAF, 1951-56, Res. ret. Recipient award of exceptional accomplishment Ark. State C. of C., 1972, 86, Silver Beaver and Disting. Eagle awards Boy Scouts Am.; named Outstanding Young Man of Texarkana, 1966, One of Five Outstanding Young Men of Ark., 1967, Outstanding Alumnus of U. Ark. Law Sch., 1980. Fellow Am. Bar Foun.; mem. ABA, Ark. Bar Assn. (chmn. exec. coun. 1979-80, pres. 1987-88), Four States Area Estate Planning Coun. (past chmn.), State Bar Tex., Miller County Bar Assn. (past pres.), Texarkana Bar Assn. (pres. 1982-83), Ark. Bar Found. (chmn. 1974-75), Am. Coll. Trust and Estate Counsel (chmn. Ark. chpt. 1986-94), S.W. Ark. Bar Assn., N.E. Tex. Bar Assn., Texarkana C. of C. (pres. 1969, C.E. Palmer award 1979), Texarkana Country Club (pres. 1990-92), Rotary (pres. Texarkana 1965-66). Democrat. Avocations: tennis, golf, hunting. Office: Box 8030 Ste 6 State Line Plaza Texarkana AR 75502

STROUD, JUNIUS BRUTUS, III, mathematics educator; b. Greensboro, N.C., June 9, 1929; s. Junius Brutus Jr. and Rachel (Witherington) S.; m. Ruby Lee Masincup, Aug. 27, 1955; children: Timothy Brion, Jonathan McIver, Cynthia Lee. BS cum laude, Davidson (N.C.) Coll., 1951; MA, U.

Va., 1962, PhD in Math., 1965. Instr./coach Fishburne Mil. Sch., Waynesboro, Va., 1953-57; tchr./coach Robert E. Lee High Sch., Staunton, Va., 1957-58; instr. math. Davidson (N.C.) Coll., 1960-63, asst. prof. math., 1965-67, assoc. prof. math., 1967-76, prof. math., 1976—, chmn. dept. math. 1983-89, Richardson prof. math., 1985-94; Richardson prof. emeritus math., 1994—; lectr. N.C. Gov's Sch., Winston-Salem, 1983, 85; vis. prof. Dartmouth Coll., 1973, St. Andrews U., Scotland, 1987. 1st lt. U.S. Army, 1951-53. Decorated Army Commendation medal; Danforth Found. grantee, 1963, NSF Sci. Faculty fellow, 1964, Smithsonian fellow, 1979; Thomas Jefferson award, Davidson Coll., 1987. Mem. Math. Assn. Am., N.C. Council Tchrs. Math., Scabbard and Blade, Sigma Xi, Sigma Pi Sigma, Phi Beta Kappa. Democrat. Presbyterian. Avocations: travel, reading, furniture repair and restoration. Home: 207 Pine Rd PO Box 94 Davidson NC 28036-9048

STROUD, RICHARD HAMILTON, aquatic biologist, scientist, consultant; b. Dedham, Mass., Apr. 24, 1918; s. Percy Valentine and Elizabeth Lillian (Kimpton) S.; m. Genevieve Cecelia DePol, Dec. 20, 1943; children: William DePol, Jennifer Celia Trivett. B.S., Bowdoin Coll., 1939; M.S., U. N.H., 1942; postgrad., Yale U., 1947-48, Boston U. Sch. Edn., 1948-49. Asst. aquatic biologist N.H. Fish and Game Dept., Concord, 1940-41; jr. aquatic biologist TVA, Norris, Tenn., 1942, asst. aquatic biologist, 1946-47; chief aquatic biologist Mass. Div. Fisheries and Game, Boston, 1948-53; asst. exec. v.p. Sport Fishing Inst., Washington, 1953-55; exec. v.p. Sport Fishing Inst., 1955-81; sr. scientist Aquatic Ecosystems Analysts, Fayetteville, Ark., 1983-88; founder, trustee Sport Fishery Rsch. Found., Washington, 1987-88; cons. aquatic resources, 1981-89, cons. editor fish sci. publs., 1982—; rsch. adv. bd. Sport Fishing Inst. Fund, 1988-94; Pentelow lectr. U. Liverpool, Eng., 1975. Author Fisheries Report for Massachusetts Lakes, Ponds, and Reservoirs, 1955; editor (ann. series) Marine Recreational Fisheries Symposia, 1982—; National Leaders of American Conservation, 1985, World Angling Resources and Challenges, 1985, Fish Culture in Fisheries Management, 1986, Multi-Jurisdictional Management of Marine Fisheries, 1986, Management of Atlantic Salmon, 1988, Planning the Future of Billfishes, Part 1, 1989, Part 2, 1990, Stemming The Tide of Coastal Fish Habitat Loss, 1991, Fisheries Management and Watershed Development, 1992, Conserving America's Fisheries, 1994; co-editor The Biological Significance of Estuaries, 1971, Black Bass Biology and Management, 1975, Predator Prey Systems in Fisheries Management, 1979; contbr. articles to various publs. Bd. dirs. Nat. Coalition Marine Conservation, 1977—; treas. Natural Resources Coun. Am., 1961-68, chmn., 1969-71, hon. mem., 1981—. Served with U.S. Army, 1942-46. Decorated Croix de Guerre with cluster.; recipient Conservation Achievement award Nat. Wildlife Fedn., 1975, 81, SOAR award Boy Scouts Am., 1972; named to Nat. Fishing Hall of Fame, 1984. Fellow Am. Inst. Fishery Research Biologists (emeritus, Outstanding Achievement award 1981), Am. Fisheries Soc. (pres. 1979-80, hon. life mem., Outstanding Achievement award 1990); mem. Internat. Fish and Wildlife Agys., Freshwater Biol. Assn. (U.K.), Fisheries Soc. Brit. Isles, Moore County Wildlife Club, Country Club (Pinehurst, N.C.). Office: PO Box #1772 Pinehurst NC 28374

STROUD, ROBERT EDWARD, lawyer; b. Chester, S.C., July 24, 1934; s. Coy Franklin and Leila (Caldwell) S.; m. Katherine C. Stroud, Apr. 8, 1961; children: Robert Gordon, Margaret Lathan. AB, Washington and Lee U., 1956, LLB, 1958. Bar: Va. 1959, U.S. Ct. Appeals (4th cir.) 1967. Assoc. McGuire, Woods, Battle and Boothe, Charlottesville, Va., 1959-64; ptnr. McGuire, Woods, Battle & Boothe, Charlottesville, Va., 1964—; mem. exec. com. McGuire, Woods, Battle & Boothe, 1978-89; lectr. math. Washington and Lee U., 1957-59; lectr. bus. tax Grad. Bus. Sch., U. Va., Charlottesville, 1969-87, lectr. corp. taxation law sch., 1985-91; lectr. to legal edn. insts., lectr. in corp. law Washington and Lee Law Sch., 1984. Co-author: Buying, Selling and Merging Businesses, 1975; editor-in-chief Washington and Lee Law Rev., 1959; editor: Advising Small Business Clients, Vol. 1, 1978, 4th edit., 1994, Vol. 2, 1980, 3d edit., 1990; contbr. articles to profl. jours. Pres. Charlottesville Housing Found., 1968-73; mem. mgmt. coun. Montreat Conf. Ct., N.C., 1974-77; trustee Presbyn. Found., 1972-73, Union Theol. Sem., Va., 1983-91; bd. dirs. Presbyn. Outlook Found., 1974—, pres., 1985-88; mem. governing council Presbyn. Synod of the Virginias, 1973-78, moderator, 1977-78; trustee, v.p. Va. Tax Found., 1984—; adv. bd. Westminster Orgn. Concert Series, 1989-93; adv. bd. Ashlawn-Highland Summer Festival, 1989-93, pres. 1994—; mem. gov. coun. Presbyn. Presbytery of the James, 1993—, moderator of coun., 1995—. Capt. inf. U.S. Army, 1958, with res. 1958-70. Fellow Am. Bar Found.; mem. ABA, Va. State Bar, Va. Bar Assn., Nat. Tax Inst., Am. Judicature Soc., Washington and Lee Law Sch. Assn. (mem. governing coun. 1974-80, pres. 1979-80), Redland Club, Bull and Bear Club, Phi Eta Sigma, Omicron Delta Kappa, Phi Delta Phi. Democrat. Presbyterian. Home: 345 Terrell Ct Charlottesville VA 22901-2171 Office: McGuire Woods Battle & Boothe PO Box 1288 Bldg Charlottesville VA 22902-1288

STROUP, ELIZABETH FAYE, librarian; b. Tulsa, Mar. 25, 1939; d. Milton Earl and Lois (Buhl) S. BA in Philosophy, U. Wash., 1962, MLS, 1964. Intern Libr. of Congress, Washington, 1964-65; asst. dir. North Cen. Regional Libr., Wenatchee, Wash., 1966-69; reference specialist Congl. Reference div. Libr. of Congress, Washington, 1970-71, head nat. collections Div. for the Blind and Physically Handicapped, 1971-73, chief Congl. Reference div., 1973-78, dir. gen. reference, 1978-88; city libr., chief exec. officer Seattle Pub. Libr., 1988—; cons. U.S. Info. Svc., Indonesia, Feb. 1987. Mem. adv. bd. KCTS 9 Pub. TV, Seattle, 1988—; bd. visitors Sch. Librarianship, U. Wash., 1988—; bd. dirs. Wash. Literacy, 1988—. Mem. ALA (pres. reference and adult svcs. div. 1984-85, bd. dir. 1985-88), Wash. Libr. Assn., D.C. Libr. Assn. (bd. dirs. 1975-76), City Club, Ranier Club. Avocations: gardening, mountain climbing, reading. Office: Seattle Pub Libr 1000 4th Ave Seattle WA 98104-1193

STROUP, KALA MAYS, university president. BA in Speech and Drama, U. Kans., 1959, MS in Psychology, 1964, PhD in Speech Communication and Human Rels., 1974. V.p. acad. affairs Emporia (Kans.) State U., 1978-83; pres. Murray State U., Ky., 1983-90, S.E. Mo. State U., Cape Girardeau, 1990—; pres. Mo. Coun. on Pub. Higher Edn.; mem. pres.'s commn. NCAA; cons. Edn. Commn. of States Task Force on State Policy and Ind. Higher Edn.; adv. bd. NSF Directorate for Sci. Edn. Evaluation; adv. com. Dept. Health, Edn. and Welfare, chair edn. com.; citizen's adv. coun. on state of Women U. S. Dept. Labor, 1974-76. Mem. mem. nat. exploring com., nat. exec. bd., former chair profl. devel. com. Boy Scouts Am.; former chair nat. adv. bd. SBA Devel. Ctrs., regional exec. bd. north ctrl. region, exec. bd. Greater St. Louis area coun., nat. personnel group com., profl. devel. com., exploring com., Young Am. awards com., north ctrl. region strategic planning com., bd. trustees, nat. mus. chair; former chair ACE L eadership Commn.; mem. Air U. Bd. Visitors; v.p. Missourians for Higher Edn.; mem. St. Francis Med. Cen. Found. Bd., bd. dirs. Cape Girardeau C. of C.; dir. U. Kans. Alumni Assn. Pres. Forum on Excellence Carnegie Found.; adv. bd. World Trade Cen. St. Louis. ACE fellow; recipient Alumni Honor Citation award U. Kans. and U. Kans. Womans Hall of Fame. Mem. Am. Assn. State Colls. and Univs. (past bd. dirs., mem. Pres.'s Commn. on Tchr. Edn., Task Force on Labor Force Issues and Implications for the Curriculum), Mortar Board, Phi Beta Kappa, Omicron Delta Kappa, Phi Kappa Phi, Rotary (found. Ednl. awards com.). Office: SE Mo State U Office of the President 1 University Plz Cape Girardeau MO 63701-4799

STROUP, RICHARD LYNDELL, economics educator, writer; b. Sunnyside, Wash., Jan. 3, 1943; s. Edgar Ivan and Inez Louise (Kellet) S.; m. Sandra Lee Price, Sept. 13, 1962 (div. Sept. 1981); children—Michael, Craig; m. Jane Bartlett Steidemann Shaw, Jan. 1, 1985; 1 child, David. Student, MIT, 1961-62; B.A., M.A., U. Wash., 1966, Ph.D. in Econs., 1970. Asst. prof. econs. Mont. State U., Bozeman, 1969-74; assoc. prof. econs. Mont. State U., 1974-78, prof. econs., 1978—; dir. Office Policy Analysis, Dept. Interior, Washington, 1982-84; vis. assoc. prof. Fla. State U., Tallahassee, 1977-78; sr. assoc. Polit. Economy Research Ctr., Bozeman, 1980—/lectr. summer univ., U. Aix (France), 1985—. Co-author: Natural Resources, 1983, Economics: Private and Public Choice, 7th edit., 1995, Basic Economics, 1993, What Everyone Should Know About Economics and Prosperity, 1993; also articles, 1972—; mem. editorial adv. bd. Regulation, 1993—. Adj. scholar Cato Inst., 1993—. Mem. Am. Econ. Assn., Western Econ. Assn. (exec. com. 1985-88), So. Econ. Assn., Mont Pelerin Soc., Phila. Soc., Pub. Choice Soc. Episcopalian. Home: 9 W Arnold St Bozeman MT

59715-6127 Office: Polit Economy Rsch Ctr 502 S 19th Ave Bozeman MT 59715-6827

STROUP, SHEILA TIERNEY, columnist; b. Aurora, Ill., Nov. 28, 1943; d. Lawrence Clifford and Dorothy (Vilven) Tierney; m. Merwin F. Stroup, Sept. 4, 1965; children: Keegan, Shannon, Claire. BA in Liberal Arts, U. Ill., 1965; MA in English, Southeastern La. U., 1982. Cert. secondary tchr., La. Tchr. English Great Mills (Md.) High Sch., 1966-69; feature writer St. Tammany News, Covington, La., 1974-75; grad. asst. Southeastern La. U., Hammond, 1981-82, instr. English, 1982-85; ednl. cons. Custom Computer Systems, Hammond, 1985-86; tchr. English William Pitcher Jr. High, Covington, 1987; community news writer Times-Picayune, New Orleans, 1988-90; met. page columnist New Orleans Times-Picayune, 1990—; free-lance writer, Covington, La., 1986-88; speaker and workshop leader in field. Author newspaper column Sheila Stroup, 1990 (1st Pl. award La. Press Assn. 1990); author adult and juvenile short stories included in Woman's World, Cricket, Reader's Digest, others. Recipient 1st Pl. award Deep South Writers Competition, 1979, 2d Pl. award, 1987-90; 1st Pl. award for column New Orleans Press Club, 1989, 93. Fellow AAUW (bd. dirs. 1978-88, various chairwoman positions); mem. Nat. Soc. Newspaper Columnists (v.p. 1991-93, pres. 1994—). Avocations: bike riding, reading, loves animals. Office: The Times-Picayune 1001 N Highway 190 Covington LA 70433-8963

STROUP, STANLEY STEPHENSON, lawyer, educator; b. Los Angeles, Mar. 7, 1944; s. Francis Edwin and Marjory (Weimer) S.; m. Sylvia Douglass, June 15, 1968; children—Stacie, Stephen, Sarah. A.B., U. Ill. 1966; J.D., U. Mich., 1969. Bar: Ill. 1969, Calif. 1981, Minn. 1984. Atty. First Nat. Bank Chgo., 1969-78, asst. gen. counsel, 1978-80, v.p., 1980; sr. v.p., chief legal officer Bank of Calif., San Francisco, 1980-84; sr. v.p., gen. counsel Norwest Corp., Mpls., 1984-93, exec. v.p., gen. counsel, 1993—; mem. adj. faculty Coll. Law, William Mitchell Coll., St. Paul, 1985—. Mem. ABA, Ill. Bar Assn., State Bar Calif., Minn. Bar Assn. Office: Norwest Corp 6th & Marquette Sts Minneapolis MN 55479-1026

STROUPE, HENRY SMITH, university dean; b. Alexis, N.C., June 3, 1914; s. Stephen Morris and Augie (Lineberger) S.; m. Mary Elizabeth Denham, June 2, 1942; children—Stephen Denham, David Henry. Student, Mars Hill Jr. Coll., 1931-33; B.S., Wake Forest Coll., 1935, M.A., 1937; Ph.D., Duke U., 1942. Faculty Wake Forest U., Winston-Salem, N.C. 1937—; assoc. prof. history Wake Forest U., 1949-54, prof., 1954-84, prof. emeritus, 1984—, chmn. dept. history, 1954-68, dir. evening classes, 1957-61, dir. div. grad. studies, 1961-67, dean grad. sch., 1967-84, dean emeritus, 1984—; Vis. prof. history Duke U., summer 1960. Author: The Religious Press in the South Atlantic States, 1802-1865: An Annotated Bibliography with Historical Introduction and Notes, 1956; Mem. editorial bd.: N.C. Hist. Rev, 1963-69. Mem. N.C. Civil War Centennial Commn., 1959-60. Served from ensign to lt. USNR, 1943-46. Recipient Christopher Crittenden award N.C. Lit. and Hist. Assn., 1982. Mem. Am. Hist. Assn., N.C. Hist. Soc. (pres. 1965), N.C. Lit. and Hist. Assn. (pres. 1974), Phi Beta Kappa, Omicron Delta Kappa. Democrat. Baptist. Home: 2016 Faculty Dr Winston Salem NC 27106-5221

STROUT, SEWALL CUSHING, JR., humanities educator; b. Portland, Maine, Apr. 19, 1923; s. Sewall Cushing and Margaret Deering S.; m. Jean Philbrick, June 12, 1948; children: Nathaniel Cushing, Benjamin Philbrick, Nicholas Lockey. B.A., Williams Coll., Williamstown, Mass., 1947; M.A., Harvard U., 1949, Ph.D., 1952. Instr. English and history Williams Coll. 1949-51; instr. history Yale U., 1952-56, asst. prof., 1956-59; asso. prof. humanities Calif. Inst. Tech., 1959-62, prof., 1962-64; faculty Cornell U., 1964-89, Ernest I. White prof. Am. studies and humane letters, 1975-89, emeritus. Author: The Pragmatic Revolt in American History: Carl L. Becker and Charles A. Beard, 1958, The American Image of the Old World, 1963, The New Heavens and New Earth: Political Religion in America, 1974, The Veracious Imagination: Essays on American History, Literature, and Biography, 1981, Making American Tradition: Visions and Revisions from Ben Franklin to Alice Walker, 1990. Served with U.S. Army, 1943-46. Morse fellow, 1956-57; Am. Philos. Soc. grantee, 1961; Fulbright fellow, spring 1967; Soc. Humanities fellow, 1971-72; resident scholar Rockefeller Study and Conf. Center, Bellagio, Italy, 1978; Nat. Humanities Ctr. fellow, 1984-85. Mem. Am. Studies Assn., Tocqueville Soc., Phi Beta Kappa. Home: 204 Cayuga Heights Rd Ithaca NY 14850-2155 Office: Cornell University Ithaca NY 14853

STROYD, ARTHUR HEISTER, lawyer; b. Pitts., Sept. 5, 1945; s. Anne (Griffiths) S.; m. Susan Fleming, July 21, 1973; 1 child, Elizabeth. AB, Kenyon Coll., 1967; JD, U. Pitts., 1972. Bar: Pa. 1972, U.S. Dist. Ct. (we. dist.) Pa. 1972, U.S. Ct. Appeals (3d cir.) 1972. Law clk. to judge U.S. Ct. Appeals (3d cir.), Phila., 1972-75; ptnr., head litigation group Reed, Smith, Shaw & McClay, Pitts., 1975—; mem. Nat. Adv. Council on Child Nutrition, U.S. Dept. Agriculture, 1984-85. Treas Mt. Mebanon Zoning Hearing Bd., 1978-81; pres. bd. dirs. Mt. Lebanon Sch. Dist., 1981-87; solicitor Allegheny County Rep. Com., 1988-95; pres. bd. dirs. Ctr. for Theater Arts, Pitts., 1984-93; participant Leadership Pitts., 1991-92; bd. dirs. Mt. Lebanon Hosp. Auth., 1993—; coun. Pitts. Cancer Inst., 1993—. Lt. USNR, 1969-71. Mem. Pa. Bar Assn., Allegheny County Bar Assn., Acad. Trial Lawyers (bd. govs.), Duquesne Club. Episcopalian. Avocations: skiing. Home: 17 St Clair Dr Pittsburgh PA 15228-1830 Office: Reed Smith Shaw & McClay 435 6th Ave Pittsburgh PA 15219-1809

STRUBBE, JOHN LEWIS, retired food chain store executive; b. Cin., June 27, 1921; s. John August and Emma Katherine (Coleman) S.; m. Nancy Richards Baer, Sept. 16, 1950; children: William Burrows, Laura, John Charles, Mary. B.S. in Gen. Engring. U. Cin., 1947, J.D., 1948. Bar: Ohio 1948, U.S. Supreme Ct. 1960, U.S. Patent Office 1950. Assoc. Wood, Arey, Herron & Evans, Cin., 1948-50; with The Kroger Co., Cin., 1950-86, sec., 1959-65, gen. atty., 1956-62, v.p., 1961-77, group v.p., 1977-85, sr. v.p., 1985-86. Gen. chmn. United Appeal Greater Cin., 1967; mem. Food Industry Productivity Task Force, 1972; past pres. Dan Beard coun. Boy Scouts Am.; past pres. bd. trustees Cmty. Chest and Coun. of Cin. Area; past trustee Greater Cin. Found., James Gamble Inst. Med. Rsch., Meth. Union; trustee Cin. Ballet Co.; vice chmn. emeritus, trustee U. Cin. Found.; past chmn. bd. The Christ Hosp., Elizabeth Gamble Deaconess Home Assn.; mem. bd. advisors to dean U. Cin. Coll. Bus. Adminstrn. With USMCR, 1943-46, 50-52. Recipient U. Cin. Distinguished Alumnus award, chmn. award for devel. new food tech. Supermarket Inst., 1976, Brotherhood citation NCCJ, 1982; named Great Living Cincinnatian, Greater Cin. C. of C., 1986. Mem. Cincinnatus Assn. (past pres., chmn.), Uniform Grocery Products Code Coun., Queen City Club (past trustee), Cin. Country Club (past trustee), Commonwealth Club, Delta Tau Delta. Methodist. Home: 661 Chardonnay Rdg Cincinnati OH 45226-1732

STRUBBE, THOMAS R., diagnostic testing industry executive; b. Ft. Wayne, Ind., Mar. 30, 1940; s. Rudolph C. and Maverne E. (Wagoner) S.; children: Tracy Lynn, Patrick Thomas, Christina Lee. B.S., Ind. U., 1962; J.D., Tulane U., 1965. Bar: Ind. 1965, Ill. 1969. Atty. Lincoln Nat. Life Ins. Co., Ft. Wayne, 1965-66; asst. counsel Lincoln Nat. Life Ins. Co., 1967-68; with Washington Nat. Corp., Evanston, Ill., 1968-90; gen. counsel Washington Nat. Corp., 1973-79, sec., 1970-84, v.p., 1975-79, sr. v.p., 1979-83, exec. v.p., 1983-84, pres., 1984-90, also bd. dirs., mem. exec. com.; pres., chief exec. officer Osborn Labs. Inc., Olathe, Kans., 1990—, also bd. dirs. Trustee Glencoe (Ill.) Union Ch., 1983-87; v.p., bd. dirs., exec. com. Chgo. chpt. Epilepsy Found., 1975-79; bd. dirs. Assn. Retarded Citizens Ill., 1985-89, Northlight Theater, 1984-89. Lt. USNR, 1965-71. Lincoln Found. grantee, 1964. Mem. ABA, Assn. Life Ins. Counsel, Nat. Investor Rels. Inst., Am. Soc. Corp. Secs., Home Office Life Underwriters Assn., Ind. Bar Assn., Ill. Bar Assn., Skokie Country Club (Ill.), Shadow Glen Golf Club (Kans.). Office: Osborn Labs Inc PO Box 2920 Shawnee Mission KS 66201-1320

STRUBEL, RICHARD PERRY, manufacturing company executive; b. Evanston, Ill., Aug. 10, 1939; s. Arthur Raymond and Martha (Smith) S.; m. Linda Jane Freeman, Aug. 25, 1961 (div. 1974); children: Douglas Arthur, Craig Tollerton; m. Ella Doyle G'sell, Oct. 23, 1976. B.A., Williams Coll., 1962; M.B.A., Harvard U., 1964. Assoc. Fry Cons., Chgo., 1964-66, mng. prin., 1966-68; with N.W. Industries, Inc., Chgo., 1968-83, v.p. corp. devel., 1969-73, group v.p., 1973-79, exec. v.p., 1979-83, pres., 1983; chmn. bd.,

pres. Buckingham Corp., N.Y.C., 1972-73; pres., chief exec. officer Microdot Inc., Chgo., 1983—; mng. ptnr. Tandem Ptnrs. Inc., Chgo., 1991—; trustee Benchmark Funds, Instl. Liquid Assets and Associated Funds. Trustee Better Govt. Assn., Chgo., U. Chgo.; bd. dirs. Children's Meml. Hosp., Children's Meml. Med. Ctr.; mem. vis. com. Divinity Sch., U. Chgo. Presbyterian. Clubs: Mid-Day, Casino, Chicago, Comml., Racquet of Chgo., Commonwealth (Chgo.). Office: Microdot Inc 70 W Madison St Ste 1400 Chicago IL 60602

STRUDLER, ROBERT JACOB, real estate development executive; b. N.Y.C., Sept. 22, 1942; m. Ruth Honigman, Aug. 29, 1965; children: Seth, Keith, Craig. BS in Indsl. and Labor Relations, Cornell U., 1964; LLB, Columbia U., 1967. Bar: N.Y. 1967, Fla. 1973. Assoc. firms in N.Y.C., 1967-71; v.p., chmn. operating com. U.S. Home Corp., Clearwater, Fla., 1972-76, v.p. legal affairs, 1976-77, v.p. ops., 1977-79; sr. v.p. ops. U.S. Home Corp., Houston, 1979-81, sr. v.p. acquisitions, 1981-84, pres., chief operating officer, 1984-86, chmn., chief exec. officer, 1986—. Pres., trustee Sch. for Young Children; mem. pres.' adv. coun. U. St. Thomas. Mem. ABA, N.Y. State Bar Assn., Fla. Bar Assn., Cornell Real Estate Coun., Nat. Assn. Homebuilders (chmn. high prodn. coun. 1991-93). Home: 11110 Greenbay St Houston TX 77024-6729 Office: US Home Corp 1800 West Loop S Houston TX 77027-3210

STRUEBING, ROBERT VIRGIL, retired oil company executive; b. Winfield, Kans., Nov. 8, 1919; s. Walter Charles and Jettie Marie (Hetherington) S.; m. Helen L. Harrington, Aug. 19, 1943; children: Gloria Struebing West, Steven R., William S. B.S. in Chem. Engring. U. Nebr., 1949. With Skelly Oil Co., El Dorado, Kans., 1949-76, refinery mgr., 1971-76; mgr. gas plants Getty Oil Co., Tulsa, 1977-80, v.p. mfg., 1980-85; sr. v.p. mfg. Getty Refining & Mktg. Co., Tulsa, 1980-85; ret., 1985. Mem. El Dorado Bd. Edn., 1965-75, pres., 1967-68. Served to capt. USAAF, 1940-45. Mem. Sigma Tau. Club: Cedar Ridge Country.

STRUELENS, MICHEL MAURICE JOSEPH GEORGES, political science educator, foreign affairs consultant; b. Brussels, Belgium, Mar. 10, 1928; m. Godelieve de Wilde, Aug. 2, 1949; children: Alain, Patricia, Brigitte, Bernard, Jean Paul (dec.). B.A., Coll. St. Pierre, Brussels, 1944; M.A., Antwerp U., Belgium, 1949; Ph.D., Am. U., Washington, 1968. Insp. econ. affairs Congo Govt., Leopoldville, 1950-54, chief insp. econ. affairs, 1954-55, dep. commr. transp., 1955-57; dir. Info. and Public Relations Office for Congo, Brussels, 1957-58, Congo Tourism Pavillion, Internat. World's Fair, Brussels, 1958-59; dir. gen. Belgian Congo and Ruanda Urundi Tourist Office, Congo, 1959; chmn. African Commn. Internat. Union Ofcl. Travel Orgns., Geneva, 1959-60; ofcl. Katanga rep. in U.S., N.Y.C., 1960-63; dir. gen. Internat. Inst. for African Affairs in Can., 1963-64; spl. asst. to prime minister Democratic Republic Congo; fgn. affairs minister, adviser to Congo UN del., adviser Congo embassy Democratic Republic Congo, Washington, N.Y.C., 1966-64; dir. Eurafrica, Consultants on Fgn. Affairs, Washington, 1966—; prof. polit. sci., French, internat. bus. Am. U., 1968-93; prof. emeritus, 1993; dir. Ctr. Rsch and Documentation on European Community Am. U., 1971—, chmn. faculty rels. com., 1986-87, chmn. grad. studies com., SIS, 1989-90; dir. E.C. Inst. in Europe, 1978-93, U. Antwerp Exchange Program, 1979-83; dir. EPSCI/ESSEC (France) Exchange Program, 1980-84, chmn. internat. bus. dept., 1980-84; dir. exchange program Bus. Sch. of Poly., U. Madrid, 1981-84; investment adviser, 1977—; adminstr. French Parish, Ctr. Studies on Internat. Relations, Econs. and Bus., La Rochelle, France, 1987—; exec. v.p. Eglise St. Louis Corp., French-Speaking Union, Washington, 1974-75; mgr. by agreement with European Communities, European Documentation Ctr. (CERDEC), accessing by satellite EC Data Banks, 1985— and providing through WCL Libr. of Am. U., On Line Pub. Access Cataloging, 1991—. Author: (with Inforcongo) Congo Belge et Ruanda-Urundi, 1958; monograph Le Canada à l'Heure de l'Afrique, 1964; The United Nations in the Congo - or ONUC and International Politics, 1976. Recipient Internat. Union Ofcl. Travel Orgns. Poster award Brussels, 1958, Etoile de Service en Argent King of Belgium, 1956; chevalier de l'Ordre Royal du Lion, 1957; Faculty award for outstanding contbn. to acad. program devel. Coll. Bus. Adminstrn., Am. U., 1979; Faculty award for outstanding teaching, 1980, 82, 84; Faculty award for outstanding service to Am. U., 1981. Mem. Golden Key, Phi Sigma Alpha. Clubs: Cosmos (Washington); Bukavu Royal Sports (founder 1950, pres. 1951-54, hon. pres. 1957) (Congo). Lodge: Rotary. Home: 1374 Woodside Dr Mc Lean VA 22102-1536 "Ad Augusta per Angusta". Using Latin, French writer Victor Hugo said it all! Nothing comes easy and "success," a very personal perception indeed, requires a great deal of luck, perseverance and hard work. True success, though, is directly related to the pursuit of happiness, which in turn is a state of mind. If and when I reach eternity, I'll then be able to tell how successful I was during my passage on earth.

STRUGGLES, JOHN EDWARD, management consultant; b. Wilmette, Ill., Nov. 29, 1913; s. William George and Sarah Adell (Chambers) S.; m. Dorothy Eloise Goetz, Oct. 23, 1937; 1 child, John Kirk. Student, Miami U., Oxford, Ohio, 1932-34. Supt. Consol. Biscuit Co., Chgo., 1934-37; sales rep. Pillsbury Mills, Chgo., 1937-41; various personnel and operating positions Montgomery Ward & Co., Chgo., Kansas City, Denver, 1941-50; v.p. personnel Montgomery Ward & Co., 1950-53; co-founder, co-chmn. Heidrick & Struggles, Inc., Chgo., 1953—. With USNR, World War II. Republican. Home: 505 Sheridan Rd Winnetka IL 60093-2639 Office: Heidrick Struggles Inc 125 S Wacker Dr Chicago IL 60606-4402

STRUIF, L. JAMES, lawyer; b. Alton, Ill., Sept. 18, 1931; s. Leo John and Clara Lillie (Bauer) S.; m. Shirley Ann Spatz, Mar. 24, 1965; children: Scott B., Jamie Lynn, Susan Marie, Jeffrey James. BS, Northwestern U., 1953; JD, U. Ill., Champaign, 1960. Bar: Ill. 1960, U.S. Dist. Ct. (so. Dist.) Ill. 1960. Gen. counsel So. Ill. U., 1960-64; pvt. practice Struif Law Offices, Alton, Ill., 1964—; lectr. So. Ill. U., Edwardsville, 1960-65. Author: Guide to Law for Laymen, 1987, Field Guide to 150 Prairie Plants of S.W. Ill., 1989. Scoutmaster Boy Scouts Am., Alton, 1966-69; active civil rights worker, Miss., 1964. With USN, submarines 1953-57, Pacific. Recipient Chmns. award Madison County Urban League, 1989, Blazing Star award The Nature Inst., 1990. Mem. Assn. Trial Lawyers Am., Ill. Trial Lawyers Assn., Ill. Bar Assn. Democrat. Mem. United Ch. of Christ. Avocations: nature, gardening, science, piano. Office: The Struif Law Offices 2900 Adams Pky Alton IL 62002-6535

STRUKOFF, RUDOLF STEPHEN, music educator; b. Rostov, Don, Russia, July 18, 1935; came to U.S., 1951; s. Stephen and Olga (Flemming) S.; m. Donna Lee Hill, May 31, 1959; children: Rudolf Stephen, Jr., Robbin Stanley, Regan Stuart. B Music Edn., Andrews U., 1960; MusM, Mich. State U., 1964, PhD in Music, 1970. Instr. music Mich. State U., East Lansing, 1963-65; asst. prof. Ind. State U., Terre Haute, 1966-69; assoc. prof. Andrews U., Berrien Springs, Mich., 1969-76; prof. music Gov's. State U., Univ. Park, Ill., 1977—; chorus master Ill. Philharm. Chorus, Park Forest, Ill., 1982-84; music dir. Univ. Community Chorale, Univ. Park, Ill., 1978—; Chamber Orch., Univ. Park, 1978—. Composer: The Greatest of These, 1970, Childhood Sketches, 1973; singer (opera) Attila by Verdi, 1979; condr. Christmas Oratorio by Saint-Saens, 1986, Stabat Mater by Rossini, 1988, German Requiem by Brahms, 1989, Requiem by Mozart, 1990, Mass in C by Beethoven, 1991, Mass in E Flat by Schubert, 1992, Requiem in C Minor by Cherubini, 1993, Cathedral Series, Joliet, Ill., Mass in B Flat by Haydn, St. Liborius, Steger, Ill., 1994, Symphony #2 (Hymn of Praise), Temple Anshe Sholom, 1994, Olympia Fields, Ill., Requiem by Mozart, St. Liborius, Steger, Ill., 1995. Lectr. Lyric Opera, Chgo., 1979—, Library Lecture Series, Park Forest, 1982, Career Days, Chgo., 1982—, Symposium on Soviet Russia, Univ. Park, 1985, Ill. Philharmonic Workshop Series, 1991—. Mem. ASCAP, Chgo. Singing Tchrs. Guild (pres. 1984-86, 91-93, bd. dirs. 1986—), Am. Choral Dirs. Assn., Nat. Assn. Tchrs. Singing, Nat. Assn. Schs. Music, Pi Kappa Lambda. Avocations: antiques, golf, reading. Office: Govs State U University Pky University Park IL 60466

STRULL, GENE, technology consultant, retired electrical manufacturing company executive; b. Chgo., May 15, 1929; s. Albert and Helen (Wolf) S.; m. Joyce Landsbaum, July 6, 1952; children—David Jay, Brian Lee. B.S.E.E., Purdue U., 1951; M.S., Northwestern U., 1952, Ph.D. in Elec. Engring. 1954. With Westinghouse Electric Corp., 1954-93; supervisory engr., adv. engr., mgr. solid state tech.-aerospace Westinghouse Electric Corp., Balt., 1958-68; mgr. sci. and tech. systems devel. div., mgr.

advanced tech. labs. Westinghouse Electric Corp., 1968-78, dep. gen. mgr. systems devel. div., 1979-81, gen. mgr. advanced tech. div., 1981-93, exec. dir. tech., 1987-93; cons. Army Sci. Bd., 1979-83, NRC-NAS, 1980-82, Def. Sci. Bd., 1981-83, NSF, 1992-93; cons. NASA, 1967-87, com. chmn., 1976-78; adv. com. panel USNR, 1989. Contbg. author: Integrated Electronic Systems, 1970, Integrated Circuit Technology, 1967; contbr. articles to profl. jours. Gene Strull Tech. Ctr. at Westinghouse Electric Corp. Advanced Tech. Labs. named in his honor, Balt., 1993; named Outstanding Elec. Engr. award Purdue U., 1994. Fellow IEEE (Govt. Industry Svc. award 1987, Frederik Philips award 1991); mem. Md. Acad. Scis. (chmn. 1978-80). Patentee in field. Home: One Gristmill Ct # 606 Baltimore MD 21208

STRUM, BRIAN J., real estate executive; b. Bklyn., Nov. 27, 1939; s. Max J. and Beatrix (Galitzky) S.; m. Mickey Weiss, Nov. 19, 1966; children: Ira, Howard, Beth. BA, Bklyn. Coll., 1960; LLB, NYU, 1963. Bar: N.Y. 1964, N.J. 1969; CLU; counselor of real estate. Atty. Gilbert, Segall and Young, N.Y.C., 1963-65; assoc. res. atty. Prudential Ins. Co. Am., N.Y.C., 1965-67, various positions, law dept., 1967-75, v.p. real estate investments, 1975-86; chmn. Prudential Property Co., Newark, 1986-92; CEO Prudential Realty Group, N.Y.C., 1992-94; Silverstein chair of real estate devel. NYU, 1995—; pres., trustee Prudential Realty Trust, 1985-94; mem. adv. bd. Chgo. Title & Trust Co., N.Y.C., 1982—. Editor: Financing Real Estate in the Inflationary Eighties, 1981; contbr. articles to profl. jours. With USAR, 1963-69. Recipient Disting. Community Svc. award Brandeis U., 1983, Urban Leadership award NYU, 1990. Fellow Anglo Am. Real Property Inst. (charter); mem. ABA (chmn. real property, probate and trust law sects. 1984-85), N.Y. State Bar Assn. (chmn. real property sect. 1975-76), Urban Land Inst. (coun. mem.), Am. Coll. Real Estate Lawyers (charter), Am. Soc. Real Estate Counselors. Office: NYU Rm 518 11 W 42nd St New York NY 10036-8083

STRUM, JAY GERSON, lawyer; b. N.Y.C., July 6, 1938; s. John and Dorothy (Chaikind) S.; m. Patricia Ann Burtis, Jan. 25, 1969; children: Daniel, Jennifer. BA in polit. sci. magna cum laude, CCNY, 1959; LLB, Harvard U., 1962. Bar: N.Y. 1963, U.S. Dist. Ct. (so. and ea. dists.) N.Y. 1963, U.S. Ct. Appeals (2d cir.) 1965, U.S. Supreme Ct. 1979. Trial atty. SEC, N.Y.C., 1963-65; ptnr. Coon, Dubow, Kleinberg & Strum, N.Y.C., 1965-67; assoc. Kaye, Scholer, Fierman, Hays & Handler, N.Y.C., 1967-70, ptnr., 1971—. Mem. ABA, Assn. of Bar of City of N.Y., Phi Beta Kappa. Club: Harvard (N.Y.C.). Office: Kaye Scholer Fierman Hays & Handler 425 Park Ave New York NY 10022-3506

STRUNK, BETSY ANN WHITENIGHT, education educator; b. Bloomsburg, Pa., May 28, 1942; d. Mathias Clarence and Marianna (Naunas) Whitenight; children: Robert J. Jr., Geoffrey M. BS in Edn., Bloomsburg U., 1964; MEd, West Chester U., 1969; cert. mentally/physically handicapped, Pa. State U., 1981; postgrad., Wilkes U., Joseph's U., Drexel U., Western Md. Coll. Cert. elem. edn., spl. edn. Tchr. Faust Sch., Bensalem (Pa.) Twp., 1964, Eddystone (Pa.) Elem. Sch., 1964-66, Lima Elem. Sch., Rose Tree Media Sch. Dist., 1966-69, Rose Tree Media (Pa.) Sch. Dist., 1977—; adj. prof. Wilkes Coll., Wilkes-Barre, Pa., 1981-86; instr. Delaware Community Coll., Media, 1986; instr., dir. ground sch. edn. Brandywine Airport, West Chester, Pa., 1986-88; instr. Drexel U., Phila., 1989—, Performance Learning Systems, Inc., Emerson, N.J., 1981—; rep. FAA, Phila., 1986-88; spl. edn. resource rm. specialist, tchr. cons. Media Elem. Sch., Rose Tree Media Sch. Dist.; tchr. trainer, designer Performance Learning Systems; curriculum designer pvt. pilot ground sch.; instr. introduction to flying and pilot companion course; chairperson profl. devel. com. Rose Tree Media Sch. Dist., 1992. Inservice Coun. of Del. County, 1992—; cons. ednl. programs, 1988—; keynote presenter, designer, editor, author Performance Learning Systems, Inc., Emerson, N.J., Nevada City, Calif., 1988—; owner, designer Betsy's Belts, Del., N.J., Pa., 1970-74; bd. dirs. Lead Tchr. Ctr. West Chester (Pa.) U., 1992—; presenter State of Pa. Lead Tchr. Conf., 1994; project dir. video documentary Performance Learning Systems, Calif., 1994. Program dir. video documentary, Nevada City, Calif., 1994; contbr. articles to profl. jours. Mem. Middletown Free Libr. Bd., 1977-79; officer Riddlewood Aux. to Riddle Meml. Hosp., Media, 1973-78; chairperson Lima (Pa.) Christian Nursery Sch., 1973, March of Dimes, Middletown, 1973; pres. Roosevelt PTG (Elem. Sch.), Media, 1982; com. person, v.p. Middletown Twp. Dem. Com., 1974; capt. March of Dimes, Media, 1987-91, Diabetes Assn., Media, 1989-91; mem. Vietnamese refugee com. Media Presbyn. Ch., 1975, mem., 1967—; vol. Tyler Arboretum, Middletown Twp., 1980-82. Recipient 1st pl. Color Divsn. Photography award Pa. Colonial Plantation, PLS 500 Club award; Fine Arts in Spl. Edn. grantee Pa. Dept. Edn., 1993-94. Mem. NEA, ASCD, Pa. ASCD, Rose Tree Media Edn. Assn. (profl. devel. com. chairperson 1992-93, profl. devel. com. rep. 1990-93, Exceptional Svc. award), Pa. State Edn. Assn., Nat. Staff Devel. Coun., Aircraft Owners and Pilots Assn., Tyler Arboretum, Media Soc. Performing Arts. Democrat. Avocations: reading, writing, interior decorating, nature walking, antiquing. Home: 203 Cohasset Ln West Chester PA 19380 Office: Rose Tree Media Sch Dist Glenwood Elem Sch Pennell Rd Media PA 19063

STRUNK, ORLO CHRISTOPHER, JR., psychology educator; b. Pen Argyl, Pa., Apr. 14, 1925; s. Orlo Christopher and Katherine Elizabeth (Glasser) S.; m. Mary Louise Reynolds, July 3, 1947; children: Laura Louise, John Christopher. Certificate, Churchman Bus. Coll., Easton, Pa., 1948; A.B., W. Va. Wesleyan Coll., Buckhannon, 1953; S.T.B., Boston U., 1955, Ph.D., 1957. Exec. sec. Inst. Pastoral Care, Mass. Gen. Hosp., 1955-57; grad. asst. Boston U., 1955-57, instr. psychology of religion, 1956; instr. Boston U. (Sch. Theology), 1957-58, 62; assoc. prof. psychology W. Va. Wesleyan Coll., 1957-60, dean, 1959-69; prof. psychology of religion Boston U., 1969-86; also faculty counselor, supr. Albert V. Danielsen Inst.; part-time faculty Webster U., 1994—; pastoral psychotherapist Grand Strand Pastoral Counseling Svc., Myrtle Beach, S.C., 1986—; assoc. dir., staff psychologist Ecumenical Counseling Svc., Inc., Melrose, Mass.; rsch. cons. Religion in Edn. Found., Calif. Author: Readings in the Psychology of Religion, 1959, Religion: A Psychological Interpretaton, 1962, Mature Religion: A Psychological Study, 1965, The Choice Called Atheism, 1969, The Psychology of Religion, 1971, Dynamic Interpersonalism for Ministry, 1973, The Secret Self, 1976, Privacy: Experience, Understanding, Expression, 1983; mng. editor: Jour. Pastoral Care. Served with USAAF, 1943-46. Decorated Air medal with five oak leaf clusters. Fellow Am. Psychol. Assn.; mem. W.Va. Assn. Acad. Deans (pres.) Methodist (elder). Home: 1068 Harbor Dr SW Calabash NC 28467-9503 *It is my conviction that life is a mystery to be lived more than it is a problem to be solved. As such, I have tried to develop a style of life which permits me to be open to a wide range of experiences guided by a simple principle which requires me to do battle with all those conditions which disrupt my and others freedom to live an authentic life of openness and continuous growth. The central principle guiding the openness to life is found in the spirit of Jesus Christ which includes love of Self, others, and my God. The task of working out these abstractions in a concrete manner is difficult and mysterious - but never, never dull.*

STRUNK, ROBERT CHARLES, physician; b. Evanston, Ill., May 29, 1942; s. Norman Wesley and Marion Mildred (Ree) S.; m. Alison Leigh Gans, Apr. 3, 1971; children: Christopher Robert, Alix Elizabeth. BA in Chemistry, Northwestern U., 1964, MS in Biochemistry, 1968, MD, 1968. Lic. MD, Ariz., Colo., Mass., Mo. Resident in pediatrics Cin. Children's Hosp., 1968-70; pediatrician Newport (R.I.) Naval Hosp., 1970-72; rsch. fellow in pediatrics Harvard Med. Sch., Boston, 1972-74; asst. prof. pediatrics U. Ariz. Health Sci. Ctr., Tucson, 1974-78; dir. clin. svcs. Nat. Jewish Ctr. for Immunology and Respiratory Med., Denver, 1978-87; sabbatical leave Boston Children's Hosp., 1984-85; dir. divsn. allergy and pulmonary diseases Children's Hosp., St. Louis, 1987—; pediatrician Barnes and Allied Hosp., St. Louis, 1987—; prof. pediatrics Sch. Medicine Washington U., St. Louis, 1987—. Recipient Allergic Disease Acad. award Nat. Inst. Allergy and Infectious Disease of NIH. Mem. Am. Acad. Allergy and Immunology, Soc. Pediatric Rsch., Am. Assn. Immunologists, Western Soc. Pediatric Rsch., Am. Bd. Allergy and Immunology (bd. dirs. 1990-95). Office: Washington U Sch Med Dept Pediatrics 400 S Kingshighway Blvd Saint Louis MO 63110-1014

STRUPP, DAVID JOHN, lawyer; b. Terre Haute, Ind., Feb. 28, 1938; s. Fares John and Mary (Stark) S.; m. Elizabeth Ann Sullivan, Aug. 22, 1959;

children: Sally Katherine, David John Jr. BS, Ind. U., 1960; JD, U. Mich., 1963; LLM in Taxation, NYU, 1968. Bar: N.Y. 1964. Mem. firm Shearman & Sterling, N.Y.C., 1963-73, ptnr., 1973-81; pres. Shorenstein Co., San Francisco, 1981-82; ptnr. Davis Polk & Wardwell, N.Y.C., 1982—; bd. dirs. MEPC Am. Properties Inc., European Investors Inc. Chmn. South St. Seaport Corp., N.Y.C., 1987; trustee South St. Seaport Mus., N.Y.C., 1985—, Miriam Osborne Home Assn., Rye, N.Y., 1973-81. Served to capt. U.S. Army, 1963-65. Avocations: sailing, golf, tennis. Office: Davis Polk & Wardwell 450 Lexington Ave New York NY 10017-3911

STRUPP, HANS HERMANN, psychologist, educator; b. Frankfurt am Main, Germany, Aug. 25, 1921; came to U.S., 1939, naturalized, 1945; s. Josef and Anna (Metzger) S.; m. Lottie Metzger, Aug. 19, 1951; children: Karen, Barbara, John. AB with distinction, George Washington U., 1945, AM, 1947, PhD, 1954; MD (hon.), U. Ulm, Fed. Republic of Germany, 1986. Diplomate in clin. psychology Am. Bd. Profl. Psychology; lic. clin. psychologist, Tenn. Research psychologist Human Factors Ops. Research Labs., Dept. Air Force, Washington, 1949-54; supervisory research psychologist, personnel research br. Adj. Gen.'s Office, Dept. of Army, Washington, 1954-55; dir. psychotherapy research project Sch. Medicine, George Washington U., Washington, 1955-57; dir. psychol. services, dept. psychiatry U. N.C. Sch. Medicine, Chapel Hill, 1957-64; asso. prof. psychology U. N.C. Sch. Medicine, 1957-62, prof., 1962-66; prof. dept. psychology Vanderbilt U., Nashville, 1966-76, dir. clin. tng., dept. psychology, 1967-76, disting. prof., 1976-94, disting. prof. emeritus, Harvie Branscomb disting. prof., 1985-86; disting. prof. emeritus, 1994—. Mem. editorial adv. bd. Psychotherapy: Theory, Research and Practice, 1963—, Jour. Cons. and Clin. Psychology, 1964—, Jour. Nervous and Mental Disease, 1965—, Jour. Am. Acad. Psychoanalysis, 1972—, Jour. Contemporary Psychotherapy, 1972-86, Psychiatry Research, 1979-86, Jour. Profl. Psychology, 1976-89, others; contbr. chpts. to books, articles and revs. to profl. jours. Recipient Helen Sargent meml. prize Menninger Found., 1963; Alumni Achievement award George Washington U., 1972; Disting. Profl. Achievement award Am. Bd. Profl. Psychology, 1976, Disting. Profl. Contbns. to Knowledge award Am. Psychol. Assn., 1987; others. Fellow Am. Psychol. Assn. (mem. exec. council 1964, exec. bd. 1969-72, council of reps. 1970-73, chmn. com. on fellows div. psychotherapy 1970-74, pres. div. clin. psychology 1974-75; recipient Disting. Profl. Psychologist award 1973, Disting. Scientist award 1979), Tenn. Psychol. Assn., AAAS; mem. Eastern Psychol. Assn., Southeastern Psychol. Assn., Am. Psychopathol. Assn., Soc. for Psychotherapy Research (pres. 1972-73, Career Contbr. award 1986). Psychologists Interested in Advancement of Psychoanalysis, Phi Beta Kappa, Sigma Xi. Home: 4117 Dorman Dr Nashville TN 37215-2404 Office: Vanderbilt U Dept Psychology Nashville TN 37240 *Scientific and professional work is a very personal endeavor. It is the pursuit of meaning and the search for answers to the existential questions that have occupied mankind through the ages. Thus, the motivation to do one's best within one's limited powers is nothing altruistic although it counts as a great reward to kindle a spark in others. As a refugee from Nazi Germany, I remain deeply grateful for the opportunities my adopted country has provided me.*

STRUTTON, LARRY D., newspaper executive; b. Colorado Springs, Colo., Sept. 12, 1940; s. Merril and Gladys (Sheldon) S.; m. Carolyn Ann Croak, Dec. 3, 1960; children—Gregory L., Kristen. A.A. in Electronics Engring., Emily Griffith Electronics Sch., 1968; B.S. in Bus. Mgmt. and Systems Mgmt., Met. State Coll., 1971; diploma in Advanced Mgmt. Program, Harvard U., 1988. Printer Gazette Telegraph, Colorado Springs, Colo., 1961-64; prodn. dir. Rocky Mountain News, Denver, 1964-80, pres., 1990, pres. and CEO, 1991—; exec. v.p. ops. and advt. Detroit Free Press, 1981-83; v.p. ops. Los Angeles Times, 1983-85, exec. v.p. ops., 1986-90. Mem. adv. com. Rochester Inst. Tech., 1984—. Mem. Am. Newspaper Pubs. Assn. (chmn. 1987, chmn. TEC com. 1985-86), R&E Council (research and engring. council of the Graphic Arts Industry Inc.). Club: Lakeside Golf (Los Angeles). Home: 50 Glenmoor Cir Englewood CO 80110-7121 also: Rocky Mountain News 400 W Colfax Ave Denver CO 80204*

STRUTZ, WILLIAM A., lawyer; b. Bismarck, N.D., May 13, 1934; s. Alvin C. and Ina Vee (Minor) S.; m. Marilyn Seagly, Aug. 31, 1957; children: Heidi Jane Mitchell, Colin Christopher, Nathaniel Paul. Student, Drake U., 1952-53; BA, N. Cen. Coll., 1956; postgrad., Washington and Lee U., 1956-57; JD, U. N.D., 1959. Bar: N.D. 1959, U.S. dist. Ct. N.D. 1959, U.S. Ct. Appeals (8th cir.) 1961. Atty. Fleck, Mather & Strutz, Ltd., Bismarck, N.D., 1959—; mem. grievance com. N.D. Supreme Ct., Bismarck, 1974-77, chmn. supreme ct. svcs. com., 1979—. Bd. dirs. Vets. Meml. Pub. Libr., Bismarck, Shiloh Christian Sch., Bismarck, 1978—. Recipient Herbert Harley award Am. Judicature Soc., 1991. Mem. ABA, Am. Bd. Trial Advocates (advocate), Lions Club. Methodist. Avocations: reading, rare book collecting, music, sports. Home: 1234 N Highland Acres Rd Bismarck ND 58501-1259 Office: Fleck Mather Strutz Ltd 400 E Broadway Ave Bismarck ND 58501-4038

STRUVE, GUY MILLER, lawyer; b. Wilmington, Del., Jan. 5, 1943; s. William Scott and Elizabeth Bliss (Miller) S.; m. Marcia Mayo Hill, Sept. 20, 1986; children: Andrew Hardenbrook, Catherine Tolstoy, Frank Leroy Hill, Guy Miller, Beverly Marcia Wise Hill (dec.), Elena Wise Struve-Hill. A.B. summa cum laude, Yale U., 1963; LL.B. magna cum laude, Harvard U., 1966. Bar: N.Y. 1967, D.C. 1986, U.S. Dist. Ct. (so. dist.) N.Y. 1970, U.S. Dist. Ct. (ea. dist.) N.Y. 1973, U.S. Dist. Ct. (no. dist.) Calif. 1979, U.S. Dist. Ct. D.C. 1987, U.S. Ct. Appeals (2d cir.) 1969, U.S. Ct. Appeals (D.C. cir.) 1973, U.S. Ct. Appeals (8th cir.) 1976, U.S. Ct. Appeals (9th cir.) 1979, U.S. Supreme Ct. 1971, U.S. Dist. Ct. (we. dist.) N.Y. 1991. Law clk. Hon. J. Edward Lumbard, Chief Judge United States Ct. Appeals for 2d Circuit, 1966-67; assoc. firm Davis Polk & Wardwell, 1967-72, ptnr., 1973—; ptnr. Ind. Counsel's Office, 1987-94. Mem. ABA, N.Y. State Bar Assn., Assn. of Bar of City of N.Y. (chmn. com. antitrust and trade regulation, 1983-86), Am. Law Inst. Home: 116 E 63rd St New York NY 10021-7343 Office: Davis Polk & Wardwell 450 Lexington Ave New York NY 10017-3911

STRUYK, ROBERT JOHN, lawyer; b. Sanborn, Iowa, May 17, 1932; s. Arie Peter and Adriana (VerHoef) S.; m. Barbara Damon, Sept. 7, 1963; children: Arie Franklin, Damon Nicholas, Elizabeth Snow. BA, Hope Coll., 1954; MA, Columbia U., 1957; LLB, U. Minn., 1961. Bar: Minn., U.S. Dist. Ct. Minn. Secondary tchr. Indianola (Iowa) Pub. Schs., 1957-58; assoc., then ptnr. Dorsey & Whitney, Mpls., 1961—. Episcopalian. Clubs: Mpls., Minikahda. Office: Dorsey & Whitney 220 S 6th St Minneapolis MN 55402

STRYER, LUBERT, biochemist, educator; b. Tientsin, China, Mar. 2, 1938. B.S. with honors, U. Chgo., 1957; M.D. magna cum laude, Harvard U., 1961; DS (hon.), U. Chgo., 1992. Helen Hay Whitney fellow Harvard U., also Med. Research Council Lab., 1961-63; from asst. prof. to assoc. prof. biochemistry Stanford U., 1963-69; prof. molecular biophysics and biochemistry Yale U., 1969-76; Winzer prof. neurobiology Stanford U. Sch. Medicine, 1976—, chmn. dept. structural biology, 1976-79; cons. NIH, NRC; pres., sci. dir. Affymax Rsch. Inst., Palo Alto, Calif., 1989-90; mem. sci. adv. bd. Jane Coffin Childs Fund, 1982-90, Rsch. to Prevent Blindness, 1984-93, Pew Scholars Profs. in BIomed Scis. Mem. editorial bd.: Jour. Molecular Biology, 1968-72, Jour. Cell Biology, 1981—; assoc. editor: Annual Revs. Biophysics and Bioengineering, 1970-76. Recipient Am. Chem. Soc. award in biol. chemistry Eli Lilly & Co., 1970, Alcon award in vision Alcon Rsch. Inst., 1992. Fellow AAAS (Newcomb Cleveland prize 1992), Am. Acad. Arts and Scis.; mem. NAS, Am. Chem. Soc., Am. Soc. Biol. Chemists, Biophys. Soc., Phi Beta Kappa. Office: Stanford Sch Medicine Fairchild Ctr D133 Stanford CA 94305

STRYKER, JAMES WILLIAM, automotive executive, former military officer; b. Grand Rapids, Mich., Apr. 20, 1940; s. John Alvin and Marian (Anderson) S.; m. Eleanor Marie Finger, Sept. 26, 1964; children: James William II, Marian Marie, Kathryn Alison Greenbauer. BS, U.S. Mil. Acad., 1963; MA, U. Mich., 1972; postgrad., U.S. Army Command and Gen. Staff Coll., 1978. Commd. 2d lt. U.S. Army, 1963, advanced through grades to lt. col., 1979; battery exec. officer 6th/20th field arty. U.S. Army, Ft. Carson, Colo., 1964-65; advisor U.S. Army, Vietnam, 1965-66; battery comdr. 4th/3d field arty. U.S. Army, Ft. Hood, Tex., 1967-68; advisor U.S. Army, Thailand, 1969-70; S-3 ops. officer 1st/7th F.A., Ft. Riley, Kans., 1972-73; assoc. prof. history U.S. Mil. Acad., West Point, N.Y., 1973-77; chief nuclear ops. Ctrl. Army Group NATO, Heidelberg, Germany, 1978-81;

dir., project mgr. tank-automotive command U.S. Army, Warren, Mich., 1981-86; ret. U.S. Army, 1986; program mgr. military vehicles operation GMC Truck, Pontiac, Mich., 1987—. Author: (with others) Encyclopedia of Southern History, 1977; co-author: Early American Wars, 1978. Decorated Legion of Merit, Bronze Star medal, Def. Meritorious Svc. medal, Meritorious Svc. medal with oakleaf cluster, Army Commendation medal with oakleaf cluster, U.S. Army/Vietnamese Cross of Gallantry with palm and gold star. Mem. NRA (life), Am. Def. Preparedness Assn. (dir. Detroit chpt. 1991-92, 94—, 2nd v.p. Detroit chpt.), Assn. U.S. Army (dir. Detroit chpt. 1990—), Gordon Setter Club Am., Nodrog Setter Club Mich. Avocations: hunting, skeet shooting, trout fishing, field training gordon setters. Home: 168 First St Romeo MI 48065-5000 Office: GMC Truck Mil Vehicles Operation Ste 130 2619 Product Dr Rochester Hills MI 48309

STRYKER, RICHARD RIPLEY, JR., museum director; b. Anchorage, Aug. 7, 1948; s. Richard Ripley Sr. and Rogene (Garvin) S.; m. Catherine Connell, Aug. 23, 1970; children: Amanda Connell, Alan Connell, Julia Connell. BA in History, Austin Coll., 1971; MA in Am. History, U. Del., 1976. Curator Hist. Soc. of Del., Wilmington, 1976-79; asst. dir. Grand Rapids (Mich.) Pub. Mus., 1979-85; dir. Corpus Christi (Tex.) Mus., 1985—. Author articles, manuals, guides in field. Mem. legis. adv. com. to state rep., Del., 1977; mem. Greater Wilmington Area Devel. Council, 1978. Mem. Am. Assn. Museums, Am. Assn. State and Local History, Mus. Assn. South Tex. (pres. 1987-88), Navy League. Republican. Episcopalian. Avocation: golf.

STRYKER, SHELDON, sociologist, educator; b. St. Paul, May 26, 1924; s. Max and Rose (Moskevitz) S.; m. Alyce Shirley Agranoff, Sept. 7, 1947; children: Robin Sue, Jeffrey, David, Michael, Mark. B.A. summa cum laude, U. Minn., 1948, M.A., 1950, Ph.D., 1955. Mem. faculty Ind. U., 1951—, prof. sociology, 1964—, disting. prof. sociology, 1985—; dir. Inst. Social Research, 1965-70, 89-94, chmn. dept. sociology, 1969-75; co-dir. Ctr. for Social Rsch., 1989-94; cons. in field; mem. social scis. research rev. com. NIMH, 1974-79, chmn., 1976-79, mem. research scientist devel. award com., 1981-85. Author books, monographs, articles, chpts. in books.; Editor: Sociometry, 1966-69, Rose Monograph Series of Am. Sociol. Assn. 1971-73, Am. Sociol. Rev. 1972—; assoc. editor: Social Problems, 1957-59. Served with AUS, 1943-46. Fellow Social Sci. Research Council, 1959-60, Ctr. Advanced Behavioral Scis., 1986-87; Fulbright research scholar Italy, 1966-67. Mem. Am. Sociol. Assn. (nat. coun. 1965-67, 80-81, chmn. social psychology sect. 1978-79, chmn. pubns. com. 1991—, Cooley-Mead award), Ohio Valley Sociol. Soc. (coun. 1965-67), North Cen. Sociol. Assn. (pres. 1978-79), Sociol. Rsch. Assn. (coun. 1978-84, pres. 1983-84), Phi Beta Kappa. Home: 3710 Saint Remy Dr Bloomington IN 47401

STRYKER, STEVEN CHARLES, lawyer; b. Omaha, Oct. 26, 1944; s. James M. and Jean G. (Grannis) S.; m. Bryna Dee Litwin, Oct. 20, 1972; children: Ryan, Kevin, Gerrit, Courtney. BS, U. Iowa, 1967, JD with distinction, 1969; postgrad., Northwestern Grad. Sch. Bus., 1969-70, DePaul U., 1971. Bar: Iowa 1969, Tex. 1986; CPA, Ill., Iowa. Sr. tax acct. Arthur Young & Co., Chgo., 1969-72; fed. tax mgr. Massey Ferguson, Des Moines, 1972-74; fed./state tax mgr FMC Corp., Chgo., 1974-78; gen. tax atty. Shell Oil Co., Houston, 1978-81, asst. gen. tax counsel, 1981-83, gen. mgr., 1983-86, v.p., gen. tax counsel, 1986—. Mem. ABA, Texas Bar Assn., Iowa Bar Assn., Am. Inst. CPA's, Ill. Soc. CPA's, Iowa Soc. CPA's., Tax Execs. Inst., Am. Petroleum Inst. Republican. Home: 10819 Everwood Ln Houston TX 77024-5416 Office: Shell Oil Co 1 Shell Plz Ste 4570 Houston TX 77001

STUART, ANNE ELIZABETH, journalist, freelance writer, educator; b. Lansing, Mich., Nov. 4, 1956. BA in English and Journalism with honors, Mich. State U., 1979; MS in Journalism, Columbia U., N.Y.C., 1986. Mng. editor Mich. Nurse, East Lansing, Mich., 1979-80; reporter, editor StarGazette/Sunday Telegram, Elmira, N.Y., 1980-83; reporter Knickerbocker News, Albany, N.Y., 1983-85; intern Newsday, Long Island, N.Y., 1985; freelance writer N.Y.C. and Boston, 1985-87; reporter The Patriot Ledger, Quincy, Mass., 1987-90, AP, Boston, 1990-94; sr. writer CIO, WebMaster Mags., Framingham, Mass., 1994—; instr. adult edn. programs, Boston, Brookline, Mass., Cambridge, Mass.; instr. Northeastern U., 1990-91, Emerson Coll., 1989. Contbr. chpts. to books; contbr. articles to Boston Mag., Boston Woman Mag., Women's Day, Mass. Health Care, Boston Herald, Northeastern Mag., CIO, WebMaster, and other publs.; mng. editor Mich. State U. newspaper The State News, 1978-79; other state news reporting and editing, 1975-78. Knight Found. for Specialized Journalism fellow, 1988; Brookdale Inst. scholar, Scripps-Howard Found. Jacqueline Radin Newsday scholar, 1985-86, The State News scholar, 1976-79; recipient nat. 1st pl. in-depth reporting Sigma Delta Chi Mark of Excellence Competition, 1986, 1st pl. in-depth reporting and feature writing, statewide 3d pl. N.Y. State Assn. Press Competition. Am. Acad. Family Physicians, 1983, Nat. Well-Done award Gannett Co., 1982, statewide 2d pl. in news Detroit Press 1979, La Nacion Press award, 1990. Home: 10 Azel Rd Braintree MA 02184-6201 Office: CIO Comm Old Conn Path Framingham MA 01701

STUART, BEN R., manufacturing company executive. Sr. v.p. Dresser Industries Inc.; chmn. Dresser-Rand, Corning, N.Y. Office: Dresser Rand Co Baron Steuben Pl Corning NY 14830

STUART, CAROLE, publishing executive; b. N.Y.C., Feb. 22, 1941; d. Frank and Sally (Stern) Rose: m. Lyle Stuart, Feb. 4, 1982; 1 child, Jennifer Susan Livingston. Student, Bklyn. Coll. Pub. Lyle Stuart, Inc., Secaucus, N.J.; assoc. pub. Carol Pub. Group, N.Y.C.; pub. Barricade Books, Inc., N.Y.C. Author: Why Was I Adopted?, To Turn You On, 39 Sex Fantasies for Women, (with Claire Ciliotta), Why Am I Going to the Hospital?, I'll Never Be Fat Again, How To Lose 5 Pounds Fast, The Affair. Mem. Authors Guild, Women's Media Group, Wine and Food Soc. N.Y., Emily's List. Home: 1530 Palisade Ave Apt 6L Fort Lee NJ 07024-5421 Office: Barricade Books 150 Fifth Ave New York NY 10011

STUART, CHARLES EDWARD, electrical engineer, oceanographer; b. Durham, N.C., Feb. 9, 1942; s. Charles Edward and Wilma Kelly Stuart; m. Margaret Ann Robinson, Jan. 9, 1982; children: Marjorie Kelly, Heather Alison. BSEE, Duke U., 1963. Engr. Westinghouse Electric Corp., Balt., 1963-65; sr. engr. Booz Allen Hamilton, Chevy Chase, Md., 1966-68; rsch. dir. B-K Dynamics Inc., Huntsville, Ala., 1969-78; oceanographer Office of Naval Rsch., Arlington, Va., 1979-84; dir. maritime system office Advanced Rsch. Projects Agy., Arlington, 1985—. Contbr. 12 papers on ocean acoustics to profl. jours. Mem. IEEE (sr., ad. com. 1991-93), Assn. Unmanned Vehicle Systems (trustee 1989-93), Acoustical Soc. Am. Methodist. Achievements include leading work in development of unmanned undersea vehicle technology. Home: 4718 N 17th St Arlington VA 22207 Office: Advanced Rsch Projects Agy 3701 N Fairfax Dr Arlington VA 22203

STUART, DERALD ARCHIE, aerospace company consultant; b. Bingham Canyon, Utah, Nov. 9, 1925; s. Muryel Archie and Ida Marie (Grow) S.; m. Isabel Cordova, Aug. 25, 1948; children: Ronald Muryel Sturtevant-Stuart, Ryda Marie Stuart Houser. B.S., U. Utah, 1947, M.S., 1948, Ph.D. in Physics, 1950. Assoc. prof. engring. mechanics and materials Cornell U., Ithaca, N.Y., 1950-58; engr. mechanics and materials Lockheed Missiles and Space Co., Sunnyvale, Calif., 1958-64, tech. mgmt. positions, 1958-66, gen. mgr., 1966-86, asst. to group pres., 1986-87; v.p. Lockheed Corp., Sunnyvale, 1970-86; cons. Cornell Aero. Lab., Buffalo, 1952-54, Lincoln Lab.-MIT, 1954-56, Allegheny Ballistics Lab., Cumberland, Md., 1952-58. Co-author: Engineering Mechanics, 1959; contbr. articles to profl. jours. Mem. Army Sci. Bd., 1982-87. Recipient S.B. Jr. award Am. Ceramic Soc., 1954; recipient Meritorious Pub. Service award Dept. Navy, 1961, cert. of commendation Dept. Navy, 1961, John J Montgomery award Nat. Soc. Aerospace Profls., 1964, Extraordinary Service award Am. Soc. Quality Control, 1983, Silver Knight of Mgmt. Nat. Mgmt. Assn., 1980, ann. award Reliability Soc., IEEE, 1986. Fellow AIAA (Wyld Propulsion award 1979, Disting. Service award, 1985); mem. U.S. Naval Inst. (assoc.), Assn. U.S. Army (life), Navy League (Disting. Service award 1985), Soc. Women Engrs. (adv. bd. 1983-85), Nat. Acad. Engring., Nat. Contract Mgmt. Assn. (adv. bd. 1981-87), Reliability and Maintainability Symposium (adv. bd. 1975-86). Republican. Mormon. Office: 9841 N 107th St Scottsdale AZ 85258-6090

STUART, EVE LYNNE, elementary education educator; b. Atlantic City, N.J., Nov. 25, 1942; d. Berned Edward and Amelia Louise (Lieteau)

Creswell; m. Henry E. Stuart, June 21, 1963 (div. Mar. 1978); children: Lisa Marie, Nanette Cecilia. Student, Cen. State U., Wilberforce, Ohio, 1960-63; BS, Glassboro State U., 1968. Cert. elem. tchr., N.J. Tchr. Head Start, Atlantic City, 1965-66, Atlantic City Pub. Schs., 1967—; tchr.-cons. N.J. Geog. Alliance, Montclair, N.J., 1990—; mentor tchr. project invest, multicultural tchr., trainer, 1992—; mem. leadership com. N.J. Geographic Alliance, 1992—. Founder, coord. Project Campsite/Summer Breeze, Atlantic City, 1989-90; mem. com. United Negro Coll. Fund, Atlantic City, 1988-89. Recipient Outstanding cert. Nat. Geog. Soc., 1990, Cape May (N.J.) Schs., 1991; Atlantic City Bd. Edn. grantee, 1989-90. Fellow Delta Sigma Theta; mem. NEA, NCCJ, N.J. Coun. for Social Studies (bd. dirs. 1991—), Atlantic City Edn. Assn. (officer 1984-88, award 1985, 86), A.C.C.E.A., A.C.E.A., Phi Delta Kappa (officer 1988-89). Democrat. Roman Catholic. Office: Atlantic City Pub Schs Indiana Ave Sch 117 N Indiana Ave Atlantic City NJ 08401-4209

STUART, FRANK ADELL, county official; b. Tahoka, Tex., Dec. 18, 1928; s. John Franklin and Mary Elizabeth (Reed) S.; m. Mary Louise Wheat Crelia, Feb. 2, 1962; children: Rita, Donna, Franklin, Burce, Susan, Mary, Chris. BBA, Tex. Tech U., 1979. Asst. cashier Am. State Bank, Lubbock, Tex., 1949-52, Citizen Nat. Bank, Lubbock, 1953-59; acct. in pvt. practice Lubbock, 1960-63; asst. mgr. Gibson Discount Ctr., Lubbock, 1964-77; tax assessor and collector Lubbock County, Lubbock, 1979-94, ret., 1994. Served to lt. col. Tex. State Guard, 1988—. Mem. Tax Assessor-Collectors Assn. Tex., Lubbock C. of C., Masons, YorkRite, Scottish Rite, Shriners, Yellow House Lodge, Daylight Lodge. Baptist. Home: 2704 57th St Lubbock TX 79413-5605

STUART, GARY MILLER, railroad executive; b. Normal, Ill., May 8, 1940; s. Henry Woodward and Ruth Amy (Miller) S.; m. Sylvia Georgeades, Oct. 10, 1965; children: David, Peter, Paul, Michael. BS, MIT, 1962; MA, Harvard U., 1965. With Ford Motor Co., Dearborn, Mich., 1965-74, Gen. Foods Corp., White Plains, N.Y., 1974-81; dir. operational rsch. Union Pacific Corp., Bethlehem, Pa., 1981-83, asst. treas., 1983-87, 1987-89, v.p., treas., 1990—; bd. dirs. ACE Ltd., Hamilton, Bermuda, 1988—. Bd. govs. Lehigh Valley Cmty. Found., 1992—; bd. dirs. Sta. WLVT-TV/Lehigh Valley Pub. TV, 1992-94. NSF fellow, 1962-65, Hon. Woodrow Wilson fellow, 1962. Mem. Fin. Execs. Inst., Assn. Am. Railroads (chmn. comm. div. 1992-93). Office: Union Pacific Corp 8th & Eaton Aves Bethlehem PA 18018

STUART, HAROLD CUTLIFF, lawyer, business executive; b. Oklahoma City, July 4, 1912; s. Royal Cutliff and Alice (Bramlitt) S.; m. Joan Skelly, June 6, 1938 (dec. 1994); children: Randi Stuart Wightman, Jon Rolf. J.D., U. Va., 1936. Bar: Okla. 1936, D.C. 1952. Ptnr. Doerner, Stuart, Saunders, Daniel, Anderson & Brolchime, Tulsa; judge Common Pleas Ct., 1941-42; asst. sec. air force, 1949-51; chmn. bd. 1st Stuart Corp., radio, oil, real estate and investments, Tulsa; dir. Lowrance Electronics, Inc., Tulsa; spl. cons. to sec. Air Force, 1961-63; mem. Okla. Hwy. Commn., 1959-63; bd. dirs. Great Empire Broadcasting Inc., Wichita, Kans. Trustee emeritus Lovelace Found., Albuquerque; trustee N.Am. Wildlife Fedn; mem. Nat. Eagle Scout Coun. Boy Scouts Am., Disting. Eagle Scout; past pres. Air Force Acad. Found., chmn. bd. Served from 1st lt. to col. USAAF, 1942-46, ETO. Decorated Bronze Star (U.S.); comdr. Order of St. Olav; King Haakon 7th Victory medal; medal of Liberation (Norway); Croix de Guerre (Luxembourg); named to Okla. Aviation and Space Hall of Fame, Okla. Hall of Fame. Mem. Am., Okla., D.C. bar assns., Air Force Assn. (dir., nat. pres., chmn. bd. 1951-52), Tulsa C. of C., Tulsa Headliner, Falcon Found. (vice chmn.), Ducks Unltd. (trustee), Delta Kappa Epsilon. Democrat. Clubs: Southern Hills Country, The Boston (Tulsa); Burning Tree (Washington); Willoughby Golf, The Amb. (Stuart, Fla.). Home: 2121 S Yorktown Tulsa OK 74114 also: 2460 Palmer Rd Jensen Beach FL 34958 Office: 4590 E 29th St Tulsa OK 74114-6205

STUART, JAMES, banker, broadcaster; b. Lincoln, Nebr., Apr. 11, 1917; s. Charles and Marie (Talbot) S.; m. Helen Catherine Davis, July 24, 1940; children: Catherine, James, William Scott. BA, BS, U. Nebr., 1940, HHD (hon.), 1990; HHD (hon.), U. Nebr., 1990. Chmn. bd. Stuart Mgmt. Co.; mng. ptnr. Stuart Enterprises; chmn. exec. com., bd. dirs. Nat. Bank Commerce, Lincoln; pres. Stuart Found. Founder, trustee Nebr. Human Resources Rsch. Found., 1948—; trustee Bryan Meml. Hosp., 1952-58, U. Nebr. Found., 1956—, Nebr. U. Endowment Fund for Disting. Tchrs.; mem. Lincoln Found., 1955—, Lincoln Sch. Bd., 1961-64, pres., 1964; chmn. bd. trustees 1st Plymouth Ch., Lincoln, 1956; pres. Lincoln Community Chest, 1960. With AUS, 1942-45. Recipient Disting. Svc. award U. Nebr., 1961, Alumni Achievement award, 1980. Mem. U. Nebr. Alumni Assn. (past pres.), Lincoln U. Club, Country Club of Lincoln, Gitchigami Club (Duluth, Minn.), Sunrise Country Club (Rancho Mirage, Calif.), Thunderbird Country Club. Home: 2801 Bonacum Dr Lincoln NE 68502-5723 Office: 852 Nbc Ctr Lincoln NE 68508

STUART, JAMES FORTIER, musician, artistic director; b. Baton Rouge, Dec. 22, 1928; s. Evander Morgan and Jeanne (Fortier) S. Mus.B., La. State U., 1950, B.Music Edn., 1950, Mus.M., 1954; Mus.D., U. Rochester, 1968. Asst. prof. voice, dir. opera Boston U.; also Boston Conservatory, 1964-68; prof. music, dir. opera Kent (Ohio) State U., 1968—; founder, artistic dir. Kent Light Opera Co., 1969—, Nat. Light Opera Co., 1977—; artistic dir. Ohio Light Opera Co., Wooster, 1979—; pres. Stuart Prodns., Ltd., Cleve., 1974—; mus. cons. Internat. Hospitality Mgmt., Inc., Cleve., 1974. Tenor soloist maj. opera cos. and symphonies, N.Y.C., Boston, Phila., Atlanta and New Orleans, 1950-70; leading tenor Am. Savoyards, 1956-60, Martyn Green Gilbert and Sullivan Co., 1961-67; translator into English from original French text: Auber's Fra Diavolo, 1988, Lecoq's La Fille de Madame Angot, 1989, Ciboulette (Reynaldo Hahn), 1990. Recipient Significant Sig Outstanding Achievement in Lyric Theatre award Sigma Chi, 1995. Office: Ohio Light Opera Wooster Coll Wooster OH 44691 A man's greatest contribution to society is developing himself to the fullest. Only after he has accomplished this can he be of service to his fellow human beings.

STUART, JOHN MALCOLM, public defender; b. Appleton, Wis., Dec. 1, 1946; s. John Armstead and Wilda Unise (Miessner) S.; m. Sallie P. Sheldon (div. 1982); m. Carla Kjellberg, Sept. 2, 1989; 1 child, Jeanne Marie Kjellberg. BA, Haverford Coll., 1968; MEd, Temple U., 1972; JD, SUNY, Buffalo, 1976. Asst. pub. defender Hennepin County Pub. Defender, Mpls., 1978-90; state pub. defender Minn. Bd. Pub. Defenders, Mpls., 1990—. Coauthor: Felony Sentencing In Minnesota, 1985. Sec., bd. dirs. Turning Point, Inc., Mpls., 1982-91; mem. Minn. Internat. Human Rights Lawyers Com. Mem. Minn. State Bar Assn., Minn. Assn. Criminal Def. Lawyers (bd. dirs. 1990—), Nat. Assn. Crimnal Def. Lawyers, Nat. Lawyers Guild (v.p. 1981-82). Avocations: jogging, cooking. Office: State Pub Defender U Minn Law Sch Rm 95 Minneapolis MN 55455

STUART, JOHN MCHUGH, JR., public relations consultant, retired foreign service officer; b. Albany, N.Y., Apr. 21, 1916; s. John McHugh and Marie (Fitzgerald) S.; m. Ruth Sherman, June 24, 1944 (dec. May 1977). Student, U. Santa Clara, 1934-35; B.A., Georgetown U., 1939; M.A., George Washington U., 1966; grad., Air War Coll., 1966. Reporter, editor, 1938-44; fgn. service officer Office Mil. Govt. U.S., Germany, 1945-50, USIA, 1954-71; press attache Am. embassy, New Delhi, 1962-65; pub. affairs officer U.S. Mission in Geneva, 1956-61; fgn. corr. Voice of Am., Korea and Germany, 1950-56; press counselor Am. embassy, Saigon, 1966-67; sr. adviser pub. affairs U.S. Mission to UN, N.Y.C., 1967-71; spl. adviser U.S. del. 26th UN Gen. Assembly, 1971; spokesman U.S. del. conf. on human environment, Stockholm, 1972; adviser 31st Gen. Assembly, 1976, 3d UN Law of Sea Conf., N.Y., 1977, VIth and Xth Spl. Gen. Assemblies on Disarmament, 1978, 82; now cons. internat. pub. affairs N.Y.C., also Washington; adviser European Security Conf., USIA, 1973, Agri-Energy Roundtable, Geneva, 1981. Served with SHAEF, World War II. Mem. Nat. Press Club. Home: 7060 Peninsula Dr Traverse City MI 49684-1746 Office: 180 West End Ave 27-L New York NY 10023

STUART, JOSEPH MARTIN, art museum administrator; b. Seminole, Okla., Nov. 9, 1932; s. Arch William and Lillian (Lindsey) S.; B.F.A. in Art, U. N.Mex., 1959, M.A. in Art, 1962; m. Signe Margaret Nelson, June 18, 1960; 1 dau., Lise Nelson Stuart. Dir., Roswell (N.Mex.) Museum and Art Center, 1960-62; curator U. Oreg. Mus. Art, 1962-63; dir. Boise (Idaho)

Gallery Art, 1964-68, Salt Lake (City) Art Ctr., 1968-71, S.D. Art Mus., Brookings, 1971-93; prof. art S.D. State U., 1971-93; represented in permanent collections: Coll. Idaho, Eureka Coll., Salt Lake Art Ctr., Sioux City (Iowa) Art Ctr., U. N.Mex. Art Mus., West Tex. State U. With USN, 1951-55. Mem. Am. Assn. Museums, Artists Equity, Coll. Art Assn., Phi Kappa Phi. Unitarian. Author: Index of South Dakota Artists, 1974; Art of South Dakota, 1974, The South Dakota Collection, 1988; author numerous exhbn. catalogs.

STUART, KENNETH JAMES, illustrator, art director; b. Milw., Sept. 21, 1905; s. William Pope and Jennie (Ballinger) S.; m. Katharine Moos, June 12, 1937 (dec. Mar. 1992); children—Kenneth James, William Alan, Jonathan. Student, Pa. Acad. of Fine Arts, 1924-25; pupil, Arthur Carles, 1925-26; student, Academie Colarossi, Paris, France, 1929-30. Art editor Saturday Evening Post, Phila., 1943-62; art dir. Reader's Digest Assn., 1962-77, cons. for graphics, new pub. ventures, 1977—; graphics dir. Am. Hist. and Cultural Soc., Washington, 1976-88; gen. ptnr. Stuart & Sons, Wilton, Conn., 1991—; cons. art dir. to Country Gentleman, 1949, Ahlen and Akerlunds, and Bonniers, Stockholm, 1949, NSRB, 1950. Illustrator mag. covers; cartoonist, 1930-43. Trustee Moore Coll. Art, Phila., 1944-50. Recipient Salmagundi Gold medal award, 1960. Office: 454 Danbury Rd Wilton CT 06897-2125

STUART, LYLE, publishing company executive; b. N.Y.C., Aug. 11, 1922; s. Alfred and Theresa (Cohen) L.; m. Mary Louise Strawn, Sept. 26, 1946; children: Sandra Lee, Rory John.; m. Carole Livingston, Feb. 4, 1982; 1 dau., Jenni. Student pub. schs., N.Y.C.; PhD (hon.), State of Calif. Reporter Internat. News Service, 1945, Variety, 1945-46; script writer Dept. State, Voice of Am., 1946; editor Music Bus. mag., 1946-48; founder Expose, 1951; pub. The Independent, 1951-75; bus. mgr. MAD mag., 1952-54; pres. Citadel Press, 1970-89; founder Lyle Stuart, Inc., 1956; pres. University Books, Inc., 1983—, Hot News, 1983, Barricade Books, 1990—; Founder North Bergen (N.J.) Pub. Library. Prodr. Chinese Festival of Music, 1952-62; author: God Wears A Bowtie, 1999, The Secret Life of Walter Winchell, 1953, Mary Louise, 1970, Casino Gambling for the Winner, 1978, Lyle Stuart on Baccarat, 1983, 2d edit., 1995, Map of Life, 1995, Winning at Casino Gambling, 1995. Served with AUS, 1942-44. Mem. Am. Booksellers Assn., Silurians, Nat. Acad. TV Arts. and Scis., N.Y. Zool. Soc., Soc. Ky. Cols. Home: 1530 Palisade Ave Apt 6L Fort Lee NJ 07024-5421 Office: Barricade Books Inc 150 Fifth Ave New York NY 10011

STUART, MARTY, country music singer, musician, songwriter; b. Philadelphia, Miss., Sept. 30, 1958; m. Cindy Cash (div.). With The Sullivan Family, 1970, Lester Flatt & the Nashville Grass, 1972-79, Johnny Cash, 1980-86; studio musician on albums with Willie Nelson, Emmylou Harris, Neil Young, Billy Joel, Bob Dylan, George Jones others; co-prodr. album A Joyful Noise, 1991; albums include Marty, With A Little Help From My Friends, 1977, Busy Bee Cafe, 1982, Marty Stuart, 1986, Hillbilly Rock, 1989, Tempted, 1991, This One's Gonna Hurt You, 1992, Let There Be Country, 1992, Love & Luck, 1994, Marty Party Hit Park, 1995. Recipient (with Travis Tritt) Grammy award for The Whiskey Ain't Workin', 1993, Country Music Assn. Vocal Event of Yr. (with Travis Tritt), with Asleep at the Wheel 1994 Grammy for Instrumental Performance "Red Wing." Office: 119 17th Ave S Nashville TN 37203

STUART, MARY, actress; b. Miami, Fla., July ; d. Guy M. and Mary (Stuart) Houchins; m. Richard Krolik, Aug. 1, 1951 (div.); children: Cynthia, Jeffrey M.; m. Wolfgang Neumann, 1986. Student pub. schs., Tulsa. Appears in leading role: Search For Tomorrow, NBC-TV, N.Y.C., 1951-86; songwriter, singer, Columbia Records, 1956, Bell Records, 1973; Author: (autobiography) Both of Me, 1980 (Lit. Guild selection). Mem. Actors Equity Assn., AFTRA, Screen Actors Guild, ASCAP. Episcopalian.

STUART, NORTON ARLINGTON, JR., data processing manufacturing executive; b. Cin., Feb. 5, 1935; s. Norton A. and Olga I. (Hess) S.; m. Julia Ann (Sue) Sullivan, June 29, 1957; children: Norton A. III, Douglas S., Mark S. BBA, U Mich., 1957; postgrad., U. Ga., 1960. Account rep. IBM, Atlanta, 1961-65; industry mgr. EDS, Dallas, 1966-67; regional sales mgr., v.p. Recognition Equipment, Chgo., 1967-70; internat. sales v.p. Recognition Equipment, Frankfurt, Fed. Republic of Germany, 1971-72; industry group v.p. Recognition Equipment, Dallas, 1972-73; industry v.p., mktg. v.p., exec. v.p. Docutel Corp., Dallas, 1973-84; sr. v.p., exec. v.p. BancTec Inc., Dallas, 1984-87, pres., chief operating officer, 1987—. Served to lt. USN, 1957-60. Mem. Am. Mgmt. Assn., Am. Mktg. Assn., Am. Electonic Assn. Republican. Presbyterian. Avocations: tennis, golf, fishing, travel. Office: Banctec Inc 4435 Spring Valley Rd Dallas TX 75244-3704

STUART, RAYMOND WALLACE, lawyer; b. Chattanooga, Feb. 13, 1941; s. Raymond Newton and Mary Vance (Wallace) S.; m. Peggy Woodward, Dec. 19, 1965; children: Raymond Warren, Laura Wallace. BS in Physics, U. Cin., 1963, JD, 1972. Bar: Ohio 1972. Pvt. practice Cin., 1972-74; atty. USIA, Washington, 1975-89, dep. gen. counsel, 1989—. Exec. editor Univ. Cin. Law Review, 1971-72. Capt. U.S. Army, 1963-66. Avocations: hunting, fishing, reading. Home: 9894 Becket Ct Fairfax VA 22032-2412 Office: US Information Agy Office of Gen Counsel 301 4th St SW Washington DC 20547-0009

STUART, ROBERT, container manufacturing executive; b. Oak Park, Ill., Aug. 3, 1921; s. Robert S. and Marie (Vavra) Solinsky; m. Lillian C. Kondelik, Dec. 5, 1962 (May 1978); m. Lila Winterhoff Peters, May 21, 1982. BS, U. Ill., 1943. Sec.-treas., gen. mgr. Warren Metal Decorating Co., 1947-49; asst. to gen. mgr. Cans, Inc., 1950-52; asst. to v.p., then v.p. Nat. Can Corp., Chgo., 1953-59, exec. v.p., 1959-63, pres., 1963-69, chief exec., 1966-69, chmn. bd., chief exec. officer, 1969-73, chmn. bd., 1973-83, chmn. fin. com., 1983, mem. corp. devel. com., until 1986, chmn. emeritus, 1986—; bd. dirs. Corp. Responsiblity Group of Greater Chgo. Past pres., bd. dirs. Chgo. Crime Commn., Nat. Crime Prevention Coun., founding chmn., Nat. Minority Supplier Devel. Coun., 1972-73, Lloyd Morey Scholarship Fund, Freedoms Found. at Valley Forge, trustee; bd. assocs. Chgo. Theol. Sem.; trustee Ill. Masonic Med. Ctr.; mem. adv. bd. Salvation Army, Broader Urban Involvement and Leadership Devel.; chmn. emeritus World Federalist Assn.; trustee Ctrl. Ch. Chgo. Congregationalist; chmn. Assn. to Unite the Dems.; numerous other civic activities. Capt. AUS, 1943-46. Mem. Pres.'s Assn. of Ill. (founding chmn. 1972-73), Naples Yacht Club, Capitol Hill Club (Washington), Chgo. Club, Econ. Club, Comml. Club, Yacht Club, Met. Club, Mason (32 degree), Rotary (past pres. Chgo. club, past dist. gov.), Alpha Kappa Lambda (past nat. pres.). Home and Office: 400 E Randolph # 6B Chicago IL 60601

STUART, ROBERT CRAMPTON, economics educator; b. Chemainus, B.C., Can., Oct. 22, 1938; s. Alexander Graham Robert and Olive C. (Chalk) S.; m. Beverly Joy, June 12, 1964; children: Craig Robert, Andrea Joy. BSc in Econs., U. of B.C., Vancouver, 1961; MSc in Econs., U. Wis., 1961, cert. in Russian studies, 1965, PhD in Econs., 1969. Vis. prof. econs. Princeton U., 1977—; prof. econs. Rutgers U., 1976—, chmn. dept., 1986-89. Mem. Am. Econ. Studies (exec. bd.), Mid Atlantic Slavic Conf. (pres.), Am. Assn. Advancement of Slavic Studies, Miata Club of Am. (nat. dir.), Photographic Soc. Am. Democrat. Avocations: antique auto collecting, photography. Home: 34 Sturwood Dr Belle Mead NJ 08502-3124 Office: Rutgers U Dept Of Econs New Brunswick NJ 08403

STUART, SANDRA KAPLAN, federal official; b. Greensboro, N.C.; d. Leon and Renee (Myers) Kaplan; children: Jay Jr., Timothy. BA, U. N.C.; JD, Monterey Coll. Law. Chief legis. asst. Rep. Robert Matsui, Washington, 1979-81; legis. dir., assoc. staff Ho. of Appropriations and Budget Coms., Washington, 1981-87; administrv. asst. Rep. Vic Fazio, Washington, 1987-89, chief of staff, 1990-93; asst. sec. legis. affairs Dept. Def. The Pentagon, Washington, 1993—. Office: Office Legis Affairs Dept Def The Pentagon Washington DC 20301-1300

STUART, WALKER DABNEY, III, poet, author, English language educator; b. Richmond, Va., Nov. 4, 1937; s. Walker Dabney Jr. and Martha (vonSchilling) S.; m. Sandra Wentzel, Jan. 20, 1983; children—Chatha, Nathan vonSchilling, Darren Wynne. A.B., Davidson Coll., 1960; A.M., Harvard U., 1962. Instr. Coll. William and Mary, Williamsburg, Va., 1961-

65; prof. English Washington and Lee U., Lexington, Va., 1965—, S. Blount Mason Jr. prof. English, 1991—; vis. prof. Middlebury (Vt.) Coll., 1968-69, Ohio U., Athens, 1975, U. Va., Charlottesville, 1981-83. Author: The Diving Bell, 1966, A Particular Place, 1969, The Other Hand, 1974, Friends of Yours, Friends of Mine, 1974, Round and Round, 1977, Nabakov: The Dimensions of Parody, 1978, Rockbridge Poems, 1981, Common Ground, 1982, Don't Look Back, 1987, Narcissus Dreaming, 1990, Sweet Lucy Wine, 1992, Light Years: New and Selected Poems, 1994; poetry and rev. editor Shenandoah, 1966-76, editor, 1988-95; bd. editors Poets in the South, 1974-82. Recipient Dylan Thomas prize Poetry Soc. Am., 1965, Gov.'s award State of Va., 1979; Nat. Endowment for Arts lit. fellow, 1975, 82; Guggenheim fellow, 1987-88. Mem. Authors Guild Am., Poetry Soc. Am. Avocations: food, travel. Home: 30 Edmondson Ave Lexington VA 24450-1904 Office: Washington and Lee U Dept English Lexington VA 24450

STUART, WALTER BYNUM, III, banker; b. Baton Rouge, Oct. 5, 1922; s. Walter Bynum and Rosa (Gauthreaux) S.; m. Rita Kleinpeter, May 20, 1944; children—Walter Bynum IV, Robert, Douglas, Ronald, Scott. B.S., La. State U., 1943. Adminstrv. mgr. Kaiser Aluminum & Chem. Corp., 1946-63; v.p. First Nat. Bank Commerce, New Orleans, 1963-65, sr. v.p., 1965, exec. v.p., 1965-73; vice chmn. bd., dir. 1st Nat. Bank Commerce, New Orleans, 1973-78; exec. v.p. 1st Commerce Corp., New Orleans, 1972-73, pres., 1973-75, vice-chmn. bd., 1975-78, dir., 1973-78; pres. Am. Bank & Trust Co., Lafayette, La., 1978-86, cons.; assoc. dir., mem. faculty Sch. Banking La. State U., 1973-75, dir., 1975-78; mem. Faculty Assemblies for Bank Dirs. Campaign group chmn. industry com., mem. United Fund for Greater New Orleans Area, 1974; mem. research com. Pub. Affairs Research Council La., 1973-76, v.p., trustee, 1973-76; bd. dirs. Bur. Govtl. Research, 1973-77, Council Better La., 1975—; pres. New Orleans Indsl. Devel. Bd., 1973-75. Served to lt. (j.g.) USNR, 1943-46. Mem. C. of C. of Greater New Orleans Area (v.p. 1973-75, bd. dirs.), Am. Bankers Assn., La. Bankers Assn. (pres. 1977), Am. Mgmt. Assn., Kappa Alpha, Delta Sigma Pi, Beta Gamma Sigma. Democrat. Roman Catholic. Office: Jefferson at Lee Lafayette LA 70501 Recognizing that life is the experiencing of reality, and that reality is simply a continuing series of problems, I long ago decided that I would treat a problem as an opportunity. Every incident of difficulty has always invited my intense interest as a challenge, and my thoughts have been immediately marshalled for positive effort. My life has been most rewarding because I believe that "a problem is an opportunity!".

STUART, WALTER BYNUM, IV, lawyer; b. Grosse Tete, La., Nov. 23, 1946; s. Walter Bynum III and Rita (Kleinpeter) S.; m. Lettice Lee Binnings May 18, 1968; children: Courtney Lyon, Walter Burke V. Student Fordham U., 1964-65; BA, Tulane U., 1968, JD, 1973. Bar: La. 1973, U.S. Dist. Ct. (ea. and we. dists.) La. 1974, U.S. Tax Ct. 1974, U.S. Supreme Ct. 1981, U.S. Dist Ct. (so. dist.) N.Y. 1983, Colo. 1987, U.S. Dist. Ct. (so. dist.) Tex. 1989. Ptnr. Stone, Pigman, Walther, Wittman and Hutchinson, New Orleans, 1973-78, Singer Hutner Levine Seeman and Stuart, New Orleans, 1978-81, Gordon, Arata, McCollam and Stuart, New Orleans, 1981-88, Vinson & Elkins, Houston, 1988—; instr. Tulane U. Law Sch., 1978-82; mem. faculty Banking Sch. of the South; bd. dirs. Inst. Politics; mem. adv. bd. City Atty.'s Office, New Orleans, 1978-79. Bd. dirs. Houston Grand Opera, 1992—. Mem. ABA, N.Y. State Bar Assn., La. Bar Assn., Tex. Bar Assn. (pres. 1994—), Tex. Assn. Bank Counsel (pres. 1994—), La. Bankers Assn. (chmn. bank counsel com.). Office: Vinson & Elkins 2500 First City Tower 1001 Fannin Houston TX 77002-6760

STUART, WILLIAM CORWIN, federal judge; b. Knoxville, Iowa, Apr. 28, 1920; s. George Corwin and Edith (Abram) S.; m. Mary Elgin Cleaver, Oct. 20, 1946; children: William Corwin II, Robert Cullen, Melanie Rae, Valerie Jo. BA, State U. Iowa, 1941, JD, 1942. Bar: Iowa 1942. Pvt. practice Chariton, 1946-62, city atty., 1947-49; mem. Iowa Senate from, Lucas-Wayne Counties, 1951-61; justice Supreme Ct. Iowa, 1962-71; judge U.S. Dist. Ct., So. Dist. of Iowa, Des Moines, 1971-86, sr. judge, 1986—. With USNR, 1943-45. Recipient Outstanding Svc. award Iowa Acad. Trial lawyer, 1987, Iowa Trial Lawyers Assn., 1988, Spl. award Iowa State Bar Assn., 1987, Disting. Alumni. U. Iowa Coll. Law, 1987. Mem. ABA, Iowa Bar Assn., Am. Legion, All For Iowa, Order of Coif, Omicron Delta Kappa, Phi Kappa Psi, Phi Delta Phi. Presbyterian. Club: Mason (Shriner). Home: 216 S Grand St Chariton IA 50049-2139 Office: US Dist Ct 103 US Courthouse E 1st & Walnut Sts Des Moines IA 50309

STUBBE, JOANNE, chemistry educator. Ellen Swallow prof. chemistry MIT, Cambridge. Arthur C. Cope scholar award Am. Chemistry Soc., 1993. Mem. NAS. Office: MIT Dept Chemistry 77 Massachusetts Ave Cambridge MA 02139-3594*

STUBBERUD, ALLEN ROGER, electrical engineering educator; b. Glendive, Mont., Aug. 14, 1934; s. Oscar Adolph and Alice Marie (LeBlanc) S.; m. May B. Tragus, Nov. 19, 1961; children: Peter A., Stephen C. B.S. in Elec. Engring., U. Idaho, 1956; M.S. in Engring, UCLA, 1958, Ph.D., 1962. From asst. prof. to assoc. prof. engring. UCLA, 1962-69; prof. elec. engring. U. Calif., Irvine, 1969—; assoc. dean engring. U. Calif., 1972-78, dean engring., 1978-83; chief scientist U.S. Air Force, 1983-85; dir. Electrical Communications and Systems Engring. div. NSF, 1987-88. Author: Analysis and Synthesis of Linear Time Variable Systems, 1964, (with others) Feedback and Control Systems, 2d edit., 1990, (with others) Digital Control System Design, 2d edit., 1994; contbr. articles to profl. jours. Recipient Exceptional Civilian Svc. medal USAF, 1985, 90. Fellow IEEE (Centennial medal 1984), AIAA, AAAS; mem. Ops. Research Soc. Am., Sigma Xi, Sigma Tau, Tau Beta Pi, Eta Kappa Nu. Home: 19532 Sierra Soto Rd Irvine CA 92715-3841 Office: U Calif Dept Elec Engring & Computer Sci Irvine CA 92717

STUBBINS, HUGH A(SHER), JR., architect; b. Birmingham, Ala., Jan. 11, 1912; s. Hugh Asher and Lucile (Matthews) S.; m. Diana Hamilton Moore, Mar. 3, 1938 (div. 1960); children: Patricia, Peter, Hugh Asher III, Michael; m. Colette Fadeuilhe, Sept. 1960 (dec. 1992); m. June M. Kootz, 1994. BS in Architecture, Ga. Inst. Tech., 1933; MArch, Harvard U., 1935. Pvt. practice Boston, 1935-38, 41—; formed partnership, 1938-40; pvt. practice Birmingham, 1940; assoc. prof. Grad. Sch. Design Harvard U., 1946-52, chmn. dept. architecture, 1953, mem. vis. com. Grad. Sch. Design, 1958-72; pres. Hugh Stubbins & Assocs., Inc., 1957-83, also chmn. bd. dirs., 1983-92; vis. critic-in-residence, Yale U., 1948-49, U. Oreg., 1950; sec. Rotch travelling Scholarship, 1971-80; Thomas Jefferson prof. architecture U. Va., 1979; mem. adv. coun. Sch. Architecture, Princeton U., 1962-65; mem. Harleston Parker Medal Com., 1973. Designer Berlin Congress Hall, 1957, Countway Libr. Medicine, Harvard U., Fed. Res. Bank, Boston, U. Va. Law Sch., Citicorp Ctr., N.Y.C., St. Peter's Ch., N.Y.C., Fifth Ave. Pl., Pitts., 1988, Bank One, Indpls., 1989, Landmark Tower, Minoto-Mirai 21, Yokohama, Japan, 1989, Ronald Reagan Presdl. Libr., 1990, numerous other bldgs.; exec. architect Phila. Stadium. Hon. mem. Boston Archtl. Ctr.; chmn. design adv. com. Boston Redevel. Authority, 1964-76; mem. design rev. panel Worcester Redevel. Authority, 1966-70; mem. adv. com. Office Fgn. Bldgs. Ops., U.S. Dept. State, 1979-82; bd. dirs. Benjamin Franklin Found.; mem. arts and archtl. com. Kennedy Meml. Libr.; mem. Fgn. Bus. Coun., Commonwealth of Mass., 1978-79; mem. nat. adv. bd. Ga. Inst. Tech., 1978-81; trustee Tabor Acad., 1974-78; mem. adv. bd. Whitney Libr. Design, 1976-78. Recipient Alpha Rho Chi medal, 1933, 3d prize at competition Nat. Smithsonian Gallery of Art, 1939, Progressive Architecture 1st Design award, 1954, Arcadia Achievement award, 1957, Rodgers and Hammerstein award, 1961, award Am. Inst. Steel Constrn., 1970, award Archtl. Record, 1971, award Prestressed Concrete Inst., 1971, award of merit Inst. So. Affairs and So. Acad. Letters, Arts and Scis., 1973, citation Am. Assn. Sch. Adminstrs., 1974, award for environ. design, 1975, award of merit Libr. Bldgs. award for Nathan Marsh Pusey Libr., Harvard U./AIA/ALA, 1976, Spl. Energy award for Shiraz Tech. Inst., Am. Assn. Sch. Adminstrs./AIA, N.E. Regional Coun. award Fed. Res. Bank, 1979, Thomas Jefferson Meml. medal U. Va., 1979, R.S. Reynolds Meml. award Citicorp, 1981, numerous other awards. Fellow AIA (v.p. 1964-65, jury fellows 1974-75, chmn. Nat. Honor award com. 1966, 79, 80, award of merit 1970, honor award 1979), Mexican Soc. Architects (hon.); mem. NAD (academician), Mass. Assn. Architects. Boston Soc. Architects (pres. 1969-70, award of honor 1988), Archtl. League N.Y. (silver medal 1958), Harvard Club, Laurel Brook Club, Malapan Yacht Club, The Little Club (Gulf Stream, Fla.), Quail Ridge (Fla.) Country Club, Century Club (N.Y.C.), Beta Theta Pi, Omicron Delta Kappa. Home: 6110

N Ocean Blvd Boynton Beach FL 33435-5241 Home (summer): 199 Brattle St Cambridge MA 02138

STUBBLEFIELD, JAMES BERT, JR., army officer; b. Charleston, Ark., Oct. 9, 1934; s. James Bert and Violet Hettie (Clevenger) S.; m. Patsy Jane Alley, June 24, 1956; children—James Bert III, Kelly Jane. B.S., Ark. Tech. U., 1956; M.H.A., Baylor U., 1969. Commd. 2d lt. U.S. Army, 1956, advanced through grades to col.; chief Supply and Services div. Noble Army Hosp., Ft. McClellan, Ala., 1962-64; med. advisor III Corps Tactical Zone, Vietnam, 1964-65; project officer Combat Devel. Command Inst. Combined Arms and Support, Ft. Leavenworth, Kans., 1966-67; sect. and br. chief Acad. Health Scis., Ft. Sam Houston, Tex., 1970-74; asst. chief health care adminstrn. div., dep. dir. U.S. Army-Baylor U. Grad. Program in Health Care Adminstrn., Acad. Health Scis., Ft. Sam Houston, 1974-75, chief, assoc. prof., 1978-80; exec. officer, chief adminstrv. services Letterman Army Med. Ctr., Presidio of San Francisco, 1980-83, chief of staff Brooke Army Med. Ctr., Ft. Sam Houston, 1983—. Decorated Bronze Star, Air medal. Fellow Am. Coll. Hosp. Adminstrs.; mem. Am. Hosp. Assn., Tex. Hosp. Assn., Am. Mgmt. Assn., Alamo Hosp. Adminstrs. Council, Trinity U. Health Care Adv. Council, Baylor U. Adv. Council. Baptist. Office: Army Residence Comm 7400 Crestway San Antonio TX 78239

STUBBLEFIELD, PAGE KINDRED, banker; b. Bloomington, Tex., Aug. 28, 1914; s. Edwin Page and Vinnye L. (Kindred) S.; m. Dorothea Mock, July 7, 1940; children—Edwin Mark, Bob Lynn. Student, Southwestern U., Georgetown, Tex., 1931; B.B.A., U. Tex., Austin, 1936. Mgr. Page Stubblefield Gen. Mdse., 1936-42; owner-operation P.K. Stubblefield Ins. Agy., 1946-51; asst. v.p. pub. relations Victoria (Tex.) Bank & Trust Co., 1951-52, v.p., 1952-58, sr. v.p., 1958-69, pres., 1969-81, chmn. bd., from 1977, chmn. bd. dirs., 1984-88; pres. Victoria Bankshares, Inc., 1974-84; past chmn. bd. dirs. Victoria Bankshares, Inc., current bd. dirs.; past chmn. bd. dirs. Victoria Bank and Trust Co., current bd. dirs.; mem. devel. bd. U. Houston-Victoria. Hon. mem. U. Tex. Centennial Commn. With fin. dept. USAAF, 1942-45. Mem. Am. Bankers Assn., Tex. Bankers Assn., Plaza Club, Victoria Country Club. Home: 2402 N De Leon St Victoria TX 77901-4814 Office: 120 S Main St Ste 414 Victoria TX 77901-8144

STUBBS, CHRISTOPHER W., physics educator. Asst. prof dept. physics U. Calif., Santa Barbara. Packard fellow David & Lucile Packard Found., 1994. Office: U Calif Dept Physics 552 University Ave Santa Barbara CA 93106-0002*

STUBBS, DONALD CLARK, secondary education educator; b. Providence, Mar. 6, 1935; s. Donald A. and Margaret Eleanor (Clark) S.; m. Lorraine Alice Thivierge, Apr. 3, 1969 (dec. Jan. 1986); 1 child, Derek C.; m. Jean Elizabeth Stubbs. AB, Cath. U. Am., Washington, 1959, MS, 1966; postgrad., St. John's U., N.Y.C., 1960. Tchr. Bishop Loughlin Meml. High Sch., Bklyn., 1959-61, Bishop Bradley High Sch., Manchester, N.H. 1961-66; tchr., sci. dept. chair LaSalle Mil. Acad., Oakdale, N.Y., 1966-69, Ponaganset Regional High Sch., Glocester, R.I., 1969—. Home: 51 Woodland Ave Smithfield RI 02917-4117 Office: Ponaganset High Sch Anan Wade Rd North Scituate RI 02857

STUBBS, GERALD, biochemist, educator; b. Hobart, Australia, May 9, 1947; came to the U.S., 1976; m. Rebecca Lynn Harris; children: Andrew, Tamsin, Anneliese, Rachel. BSc, Australian Nat. U., 1968; DPhil, Oxford U., 1972. Sci. asst. Max Planck Inst., Heidelberg, Fed. Republic of Germany, 1973-76; rsch. assoc. Brandeis U., Waltham, Mass., 1976-83; asst. prof. Vanderbilt U., Nashville, 1983-87, assoc. prof., 1987-90, prof., 1990—. Contbr. articles to profl. jours. Achievements include determination of molecular structure of tobacco mosaic virus. Office: Vanderbilt U Dept Molecular Biology PO Box 1820 Nashville TN 37235-1820

STUBBS, JAMES CARLTON, retired hospital administrator; b. MaGee, Miss., Jan. 26, 1924; s. James Sylvester and Katie Lucille (Grayson) S.; m. Essie Geraldine Shows, June 17, 1949; 1 child, James Hilton. Mgr. R. & A. Appliance store, MaGee, Miss., 1950; field insp. Miss. Mental Instn. Bd., Jackson, 1950-52; dir. Miss. Eleemosynary Bd., Jackson, 1952-75, Miss. State Hosp., Whitfield, 1975-88. Chmn. Miss. Reimbursement Commn., 1965-85; pres. Jackson-Vicksburg Hosp. Coun., 1977-79, 79—; mem. Miss. Coun. on Aging; chmn. Miss. Mental Health Planning Coun., 1988-90, chmn., 1988-89; bd. dirs. Goodwill Industries, 1989—; chmn. bd. dirs., 1993, elected vice chmn. Cmty. Mental Health/Mental Retardation Commn., 1995; mem. exec. com., 1991—; mem. Friends of Miss. State Hosp., 1986—, bd. dirs., 1988—; deacon Broadnoor Bapt. Ch., 1990. Charter mem. Sports Hall of Fame U. S. Miss. Mem. Nat. Assn. Reimbursement Officers, Miss. Mental Health/MentalRetardation Coun., Epilepsy Found., Miss. Mental Health Assn. Miss. Pub. Health Assn., Hinds County Mental Health Assn. (apptd. commr. to mental health commn. 1993—), Assn. Mental Health Adminstrs., Am. Coll. Hosp. Adminstrs., Am. Acad. Health Adminstrs., Miss. Hosp. Assn. (fin. com., dir., bd. govs. 1979-82, 85-87, chmn. 1986-87, speaker ho. of dels. 1987-88), Capital Area Mental Health Assn. (bd. dirs. 1988-90, life bd. dirs. emeritus 1994—), Colonial Country Club (bd. dirs.), Quarter Century Club, M Club, Big Gold Club, Hardwood Club (U. So. Miss.). Home: 5430 Pine Lane Dr Jackson MS 39211-4016

STUBBS, JAN DIDRA, travel industry executive; b. Waseca, Minn., June 19, 1937; d. Gordon Everett and Bertha Margaret (Bertsch) Didra; m. James Stewart Stubbs, Nov. 24, 1962; children: Jeffrey Stewart, Jacqueline Didra. BA in Speech/English, U. Minn., 1961; cert. travel counselor, Inst. Cert. Travel Agts., 1988. Sales agt. United Airlines, Mpls., 1961-64; interior decorator Lloyd and Assocs., St. Paul, 1964-66; v.p. Stubbs and Assocs., Textiles, St. Paul, 1966-83; account exec. Twin Cities Mag., Mpls., 1983-85; account exec. Internat Travel Arrangers, St. Paul, 1985-86; dir. sales, 1986-88; mgr. Dayton's Group Holidays, Mpls., 1988—; writer for Mgmt. Assistance Project. V.p. Jr. Women's Assn. of Minn. Symphony Orch.; chairperson 60th anniversary Jr. League of St. Paul, sec., 1967—, sustaining mem.; deacon Ho. of Hope Presbyn. Ch., St. Paul, 1970. Named Outstanding Alumni, Coll. Liberal Arts, U. Minn., 1995. Mem. AAUW, Inst. Cert. Travel Agts., Am. Soc. Travel Agts., Minn. Exec. Women in Tourism (publicity com. 1987-88, by-laws chmn. 1989-90, sec. 1988-89, 90, fedn. dir. 1990—, v.p., 1993, pres. 1993-94), Internat. Fedn. Women in Travel (alt. gov. Mid-Am. region, standing com. dir. historian, gov. mid-Ams. area I 1994, 95), Jr. Assistance League, St. Paul Pool and Yacht Club, Alpha Omicron Pi (pres. 1958-59, alumni pres. 1962), Whitefish Chain Yacht Club (sec.), U. Minn. Alumni Assn. Republican. Avocations: reading, water sports, travel, photography, cooking, skiing, classical music, writing. Home: 1575 Boardwalk Ct Saint Paul MN 55118-2747 Office: Dayton's Group Holidays 320 Plymouth Bldg 12 S 6th St Minneapolis MN 55402-1508

STUBBS, KENDON LEE, librarian; b. Washington, Apr. 6, 1938; s. Donald Harrison and Rosalee Adelia (Brown) S.; m. Patricia Townsend, June 3, 1961; children—Christopher, Peter, Timothy. B.A., St. John's Coll., Annapolis, Md., 1960; M.A., U. Va., 1964; M.S., Columbia U., 1965. Sr. asst. in manuscripts U. Va. Library, Charlottesville, 1965, reference librarian, 1966-76, acting acquisitions librarian, 1967-68, assoc. univ. librarian, 1976-87, assoc. univ. libr. for pub. svcs., 1987-92; acting univ. libr., 1993, assoc. univ. libr., 1994—; cons. U.S. Dept. Edn., Washington, 1982-84. Author: Quantitative Criteria for Academic Research Libraries, 1984; editor: Cumulated Assn. Research Libraries Statistics, 1981, Rsch. Libr. Statistics, 1990, ARL Statistics, 1992-94; contbr. articles on library stats., research to profl. publs. Mem. Am. Stats. Assn., Assn. of Rsch. Librs. (mem. stats. com., vis. program officer 1995—), Bibliog. Soc. U. Va. (pres. 1975-78, v.p. 1978—). Avocations: rhododendrons and azaleas. Office: U Va Libr Charlottesville VA 22903

STUBBS, THOMAS HUBERT, company executive; b. Americus, Ga., Aug. 16, 1944; s. Hubert F. and Elizabeth (Askew) S.; m. Mary Louise Quarles, Mar. 19, 1965; children: Thomas C., Chad P. BS, Auburn U., 1966. CPA, Ala., Ga., Miss. Sr. acct. Peat, Marwick, Mitchell and Co., Birmingham, Ala., 1966-72; supr. L. Paul Kassauf and Co., CPA's, Birmingham, 1972-73; staff mem. Snow, Stewart and Bradford, Birmingham, 1973-75; v.p. Cen. Computer Svcs., Inc., Birmingham, 1975-79, Cen. Bancshares of the South, Birmingham, 1979-81; ptnr. Bradford and Co., CPA's, Gulf Shore, Ala., 1981-82; v.p. trust officer Deposit Guaranty Nat. Bank, Jackson, Miss., 1983; treas. Data Supplies, Inc., Norcross, Ga., 1983-88; treas. Stevens

Graphics, Inc., Atlanta, 1988-89, v.p., 1989-90, pres. bus. products div., 1990-93, CFO, 1994—. Served with USNG, 1966-72. Mem. Am. Inst. CPA's, Ala. Soc. CPA's, Ga. Soc. CPA's, Miss. Soc. CPA's. Republican. Presbyterian. Avocations: tennis, jogging, golf. Home: 4672 Bentley Pl Duluth GA 30136-6126 Office: 713 RD Abernathy Blvd SW Atlanta GA 30310

STUBER, CHARLES WILLIAM, genetics educator, researcher; b. St. Michael, Nebr., Sept. 19, 1931; s. Harvey John and Minnie Augusta (Wilks) S.; m. Marilyn Martha Cook, May 28, 1953; 1 child, Charles William Jr. BS, U. Nebr., 1952, MS, 1961; PhD, N.C. State U., 1965. Vet., agrl. instr. Broken Bow (Nebr.) H. S., 1956-59; research asst. U. Nebr., Lincoln, 1959-61; research geneticist Agrl. Rsch. Svc., USDA, Raleigh, N.C., 1962-75, supervisory research geneticist, research leader, 1975—; prof. genetics & crop sci. N.C. State U., Raleigh, 1975—. Assoc. editor Crop Sci. Jour., 1979-82, tech. editor, 1984-86, editor, 1987-89; author, co-author over 170 articles to profl. jours., chpts. to books. Chmn. coun. on ministries and numerous offices Highland United Meth Ch., Raleigh. Lt. USN, 1952-56. Named Outstanding Scientist of Yr., USDA-ARS, 1989. Fellow Am. Soc. Agronomy, Crop Sci. Soc. Am. (editor-in-chief 1987-91, pres. 1992-93); mem. AAAS, Genetics Soc. Am., Am. Genetic Assn. (sec. 1984-86), Sigma Xi, Phi Kappa Phi. Avocations: windsurfing, water skiing, sailing. Home: 1800 Manuel St Raleigh NC 27612-5510 Office: USDA-ARS NC State U Dept Genetics PO Box 7614 Raleigh NC 27695

STUCHINS, CAROL MAYBERRY, nursing executive; b. Melrose, Mass., May 19, 1946; d. Robert Morton and Marion Evelyn (Fairchild) Mayberry; m. Robert Frederick Stuchins, Nov. 9, 1986. BS in Nursing, Boston U., 1969, MS, 1979, RN, Fla., Mass.; cert. rehab. RN. Staff nurse Univ. Hosp., Boston, 1969-70, head nurse, 1970-74, 76-79, nursing supr., 1974-75, nurse mgr., 1979-81; clin. coord. Mt. Auburn Hosp., Cambridge, Mass., 1975-76; dir. nursing Meml. Hosp. Santa Barbara, Calif., 1981-84; v.p. nursing Bon Secours Hosp., North Miami, Fla., 1984-92; nurse mgr. Mercy Hosp., Miami, Fla., 1992—; mem. Commn. for Future Nursing in Fla., 1987-90. Author: Coping with Neurologic Problems Proficiently, 1979. Mem. Mass. Nurse Execs., Assn. Rehab. Nurses, Dade County Assn. Rehab. Nurses (pres. 1988-90), Sigma Theta Tau. Office: Mercy Hosp 3663 S Miami Ave Miami FL 33133-4237

STUCKEMAN, HERMAN CAMPBELL, architectural engineer; b. Pitts., Aug. 7, 1914; s. Herman Sydney and Alma (Campbell) S.; m. Margaret Eleanor Rockwell, Aug. 28, 1940; children: Ellen Campbell, Alan Rockwell, Joyce Thayer. B.S. in Architecture, Sch. Engring. Pa. State U., 1937. Architect Edward B. Lee, Pitts., 1938-39, Gen. State Authority, Harrisburg, Pa., 1940-41, Prack & Prack, Texarkana, Tex. and Pitts., 1941-42; ptnr. Delta Mfg. Co., Milw., 1942-45; gen. mgr. Delta Mfg. Co., 1945-50; v.p. Rockwell Mfg. Co., Pitts., 1950-73; dir. real estate Rockwell Internat. Corp. (merger Rockwell Mfg. Co. and N.Am. Rockwell), 1973-75; chmn. Precise Corp., 1975—. Clubs: Duquesne, Pittsburgh Athletic, Longue Vue (Pitts.). Lodge: Rotary. Home: 300 Fox Chapel Rd Pittsburgh PA 15238-2327 Be fair with those with whom you work and associate. At all times, be honest and truthful. Give credit for work well done. Develop enthusiasm in the organization and set the goals high. Set an example by working hard. Get the work done on time.

STUCKEY, SCOTT SHERWOOD, editor; b. Wichita Falls, Tex., May 17, 1956; s. Norman Sherwood and Joanne Corinne (Scott) S. Student, Washburn U., 1974-75, U. Ibero-Am., Mexico City, 1978; BA, Kans. State U., 1979; MA, U. Mo., 1982. Reporter McPherson (Kans.) Sectinel, 1979, Topeka Capital Jour., 1980; assoc. editor Boy's Life mag., Irving, Tex., 1983-86, mng. editor, 1986—. Contbr. articles to profl. jours. Mem. Soc. Profl. Journalists, Amnesty Internat., Phi Beta Kappa, Kappa Tau Alpha. Democrat. Avocations: canoeing, running, backpacking, bicycling, racquetball. Home: 2217 Lake Sharon Dr Denton TX 76205-2211 Office: Boy's Life mag PO Box 152079 Irving TX 75015-2079

STUCKWISCH, CLARENCE GEORGE, university administrator; b. Seymour, Ind., Oct. 13, 1916; s. William Henry and Clara Sophia (Bernart) S.; m. Esther Elizabeth Ebert, Dec. 19, 1942; children: William, Stephen, David, Deborah, Stephanie. B.A. magna cum laude, Ind. U., 1939; Ph.D., Iowa State U., 1943. Mem. faculty U. Wichita, Kans., 1943-60; prof. chemistry U. Wichita, 1958-60; prof., chmn. dept. N.Mex. Highlands U., Las Vegas, 1960-64; prof., exec. officer dept. chemistry SUNY, Buffalo, 1964-68; prof., chmn. dept. U. Miami, Coral Gables, Fla., 1968-72; assoc. v.p. advanced studies and research, dean Grad. Sch. U. Miami, 1972-81, exec. v.p., provost, 1981-82; mem. council Oak Ridge Assn. Univs. Contbr. articles to profl. jours. Mem. AAAS, Am. Chem. Soc., Lions, Phi Beta Kappa, Sigma Xi, Phi Kappa Phi. Democrat. Lutheran. Patentee in chem. intermediates and pharms.

STUCKY, KEN, clergy member, religious publication editor, church organization administrator. Dir. Stewardship of the Missionary Church, Fort Wayne, Ind.; editor Priority. Office: The Missionary Ch PO Box 9127 3811 Vanguard Dr Fort Wayne IN 46899-9127

STUCKY, STEVEN (EDWARD), composer; b. Hutchinson, Kans., Nov. 7, 1949; s. Victor Eugene and Louise Doris (Trautwein) S.; m. Melissa Jane Whitehead, Aug. 22, 1970; children: Maura Catharine, Matthew Steven. MusB, Baylor U., 1971; MFA, Cornell U., 1973, DMA, 1978. Vis. asst. prof. Lawrence U., Appleton, Wis., 1978-80; prof. Cornell U., Ithaca, N.Y., 1980—, chmn. dept. music, 1992—; composer-in-residence L.A. Philharm. Orch., 1988—. Author: Lutoslawski and His Music, 1981 (Deems Taylor award ASCAP 1982); composer: Voyages, 1984, Boston Fancies, 1985, Dreamwaltzes, 1986, Concerto for orch., 1987, Son et lumière, 1988, Angelus, 1990, Impromptus, 1991, Four Poems of A.R. Ammons, 1992, Ancora, 1994, Double Flute Cto., 1994, Fanfares and Arias, 1994; received commn. from Nat. Endowment for the Arts, 1982, Koussevitzky Found. 1991. Bd. advisors Barlow Endowment, 1993—; bd. dirs. MacDowell Colony, 1993—. Fellow Guggenheim Found., Nat. Endowment for the Arts. Avocation: gardening. Office: Theodore Presser Co Care One Presser Pl Bryn Mawr PA 19010

STUDDS, GERRY EASTMAN, congressman; b. Mineola, N.Y., May 12, 1937; s. Eastman and Beatrice (Murphy) S. B.A., Yale U., 1959, M.A.T., 1961. Fgn. service officer State Dept., Washington, 1961-63; exec. asst. to presdl. cons. for a nat. service corps White House, 1963; legis. asst. to Sen. Harrison Williams U.S. Senate, 1964; tchr. St. Paul's Sch., Concord, N.H., 1965-69; mem. 93d-97th Congresses from 12th Mass. dist., 1973-83, 98th-103rd Congresses from 10th Mass. dist., 1983—; chmn. com. Merchant Marine and Fisheries, 1993; mem. com. Energy and Commerce; mem. commerce comm., ranking minority of Fisheries, Wildlife and Oceans Subcomm. Candidate for U.S. Congress from 12th Dist. Mass., 1970; del. Democratic Nat. Conv., 1968. Office: US House of Reps 237 Cannon House Office Bureau Washington DC 20515

STUDE, EVERETT WILSON, JR., rehabilitation counselor, educator; b. Fresno, Calif., Dec. 27, 1939; s. Everett Wilson and Vera Mae (Williams) S.; m. Mary-Ann Meadows, June 11, 1960; children: Susan, Sandra. B.A., Pasadena (Calif.) Coll., 1961; M.S., Calif. State U., Los Angeles, 1963; cert. psychiat. intern, U. Oreg. Med. Sch., 1965; Ed.D., U. So. Calif., 1972. Counseling psychol. trainee VA Hosp., Long Beach Calif., 1963; rehab. counselor Calif. Dept. Rehab., Pasadena, 1963-66; asst. to regional adminstr. Calif. Dept. Rehab., Los Angeles, 1966-67; vocat. rehab. coordinator, dir. tng. Rehab Research and Tng. Center, U. So. Calif. Sch. Medicine, 1967-71, instr., fieldwork coordinator Sch. Edn. rehab. counseling masters degree program, 1967-71; mem. faculty Calif. State U., Fresno, 1971—; prof. rehab. counseling Calif. State U., 1976, 1976 program coordinator, 1980-92; vocat. expert, social security disability ins. program Bur. Hearing and Appeals, 1972—; contract rehab. counselor VA, 1981-85; vocat. econ. analyst Vocat. Econs., Inc., 1990—. Author: Ethics and the Counselor, 1975; also articles. Chmn. Pasadena Jaycees Jr. Golf Tournament, 1964; bd. dirs. Day Care Center, Friends Community Ch., Fresno, 1976-77, mem. ministry and cousel, 1977-80, chmn., 1980. Recipient numerous grants; selected to give First Ann. Andrew F. Marrin Meml. lecture, 1978. Mem. Am. Coun. Assn. (senator 1975-78, chmn., treas. Western Region br. assembly, 1979-81, bd. dirs. 1981-84, mem. Ethical Stds. and Practice Com. 1985-88), Nat. Rehab.

Assn. (exec. bd. So. Calif. 1969-71, pres. San Joaquin Valley chpt. 1978-79), Calif. Rehab. Counselors Assn. (pres. 1971-72, 1985-86, newsletter editor 1975-77, 1986-93, Outstanding Contbn. to Profession award 1977, Citation Merit 1978), Calif. Assn. for Coun. and Devel. (pres. 1973-74, mem. Profl. Stds. and Ethical Practices Com. 1987-92, mem. editorial bd. 1990-94), Nat. Coun. on Rehab. Edn. (mem. editorial bd. 1987—, 2d v.p. 1989-90, 1st v.p. 1990-91, pres. 1991-92, past pres. 1992-93). Address: 2727 W Bluff # 117 Fresno CA 93711

STUDEBAKER, IRVING GLEN, engineering educator, researcher; b. Ellensburg, Wash., July 22, 1931; s. Clement Glen and Ruth (Krause) S.; (widowed); children: Ruth, Betty, Raymond, Karl, Donna. BS in Geol. Engring., U. Ariz., 1957, MS in Geology, 1959, PhD in Geol. Engring., 1977. Registered profl. engr., Wash., Nev., Ariz., Colo., Mont. Geophys. engr. Mobil, 1959-61; civil engr. City of Yakima, Wash., 1964-66; instr. Yakima Valley Coll., 1962-67; sr. rsch. geologist Roan Selection Trust, Kalulushi, Zambia, 1967-72; sr. mining engr. Occidental Oil Shale, Grand Junction, Colo., 1974-81; prof. Mont. Coll. Mining Sch., Butte, 1982—; cons. in field. Sgt. U.S. Army, 1951-54, Korea. Mem. N.W. Mining Assn., Geol. Soc. Am., Soc. for Mining and Metall. Engring., Soc. Econ. Geologists, Mont. Mining Assn., Sigma Xi (pres. Mont. tech. chpt. 1990-91). Avocations: golf, travel. Home: 5 Cedar Lake Dr Butte MT 59701-4337 Office: Mont Tech Mining Dept West Park Butte MT 59701

STUDEBAKER, JOHN MILTON, utilities engineer, consultant, educator; b. Springfield, Ohio, Mar. 31, 1935; s. Frank Milton and Monaruth (Beatty) S.; m. Virginia Ann Van Pelt, Mar. 12, 1960; 1 child, Jacqueline Ann Allcorn. BS, LaSalle U., 1969; MS, Columbia Pacific U., 1984; BS in Law, Lasalle U., 1969, LaSalle U., Chgo., 1969; MS in Engring., Columbia Pacific U., San Rafael, Calif., 1984. Cert. plant engr. Am. Inst. Plant Engrs., profl. cons. Acad. Profl. Cons. & Advisors. Indsl engr. Internat. Harvest Co., 1957-60, supr. indsl. engring., 1960-66, gen. supr. body assembly, 1967-68, mgr. indsl. engring., 1968-70; mgr. manufacturing engring. Lamb Electric Co., 1970-72, Cascade Corp., 1972-78; engring. mgr. Bundy Tubing Corp., Winchester and Cynthia, Ky., 1978-84; utility cons. engr., 1989—; instr. numerous univs. including Boston U., Clemson U., Cornell U., Harvard U., Duquesne U., U. Ala., U. Ill., U. Wis., Ga. State U., James Madison U., Tex. Tech. U., U. Calif., Calif. State U., Pacific Lutheran U., Fairleigh Dickinson U., San Francisco State U.; instr. Am. Mgmt. Assn., Rochester Inst. Tech., Ctr. for Profl. Advancement. Author: Slashing Utility Costs Handbook, 1992, Natural Gas Purchasing Handbook, 1993, Electricity Purchasing Handbook, 1995, Electricity Retail Wheeling Handbook, 1995. Mem. NSPE, Am. Inst. Plant Engrs. (cert.), Assn. Energy Engrs. (instr.), Doctorate Assn. N.Y. Educators. Republican. Office: Studebaker Group Inc 5109 Leesburg Pike Ste 210 Falls Church VA 22041

STUDEMAN, WILLIAM OLIVER, naval officer; b. Brownsville, Tex., Jan. 16, 1940; s. Oliver Jennings and Gail (McDavitt) S.; m. Gloria Diane Jeans, Sept. 12, 1964; children: Kimberly, Michael, Kate. BA, U. of S. Sewanee, 1962; student, Def. Intelligence Sch., 1966-67; M in Internat. Affairs, George Washington U., 1973; postgrad., Naval War Coll., 1973, Nat. War Coll., 1981; DSc in Strategic Intelligence (hon.), Def. Intelligence Coll., 1987. Commd. ensign USN, 1963, advanced through grades to admiral, 1992; analyst Naval Intelligence Support Ctr., Washington, 1974-75; exec. asst. Office Naval Intelligence, Washington, 1975-76; officer in charge FOSIC Norfolk, CINLANTFLT, Norfolk, Va., 1976-78; asst. chief of staff COMSIXTHFLEET, Gaeta, Italy, 1978-80; exec. asst. Office of VCNO, Washington, 1981-82; comdg. officer Navy Operational Intel Command, Washington, 1982-84; dir. long range planning USN, Washington, 1984-85; dir. Naval Intelligence, Washington, 1985-88, Nat. Security Agy., MD, 1988-92; deputy dir. Ctrl. Intelligence, 1992—. Decorated Legion of Merit with 2 gold stars, D.S.M. Mem. Armed Forces Comm. and Electronics Assn., Nat. Mil. Intelligence Assn., Naval Intelligence Profls. Episcopalian. Avocations: sailing, rebuilding cars. Office: Dep Dir Cen Intelligence CIA Washington DC 20505

STUDER, GINNY, college dean; b. Aurora, Ill., Mar. 11, 1943; d. Claron J. and Paula (Hopper) Studer. BS, U. Ill., 1965, MS, 1966; PhD, Ohio State U., 1971. Instr. U. Wash., Seattle, 1966-68; lectr. Ohio State U., 1970-71; asst. prof. kinesiology SUNY, Brockport, 1971-76, assoc. prof. kinesiology, 1977-81, prof. kinesiology, 1981—, assoc. v.p., 1982-85, dean Sch. of Arts and Performance, 1985—. Contbr. articles to profl. jours. Mem. Nat. Assn. Women Deans, Adminstrs. and Counselors, Nat. Assn. Phys. Edn. in Higher Edn. (editor 1974-76), Am. Assn. Higher Edn., AAHPERD (editor 1977-79), NCAA (coms. 1991—), Phi Kappa Phi, Alpha Chi, Mortar Bd., Torch. Office: SUNY Sch Arts and Performance Holley St Brockport NY 14420

STUDER, WILLIAM ALLEN, county official; b. Chgo., July 27, 1939; s. William Gotlieb and Annette Elizabeth (Bruzek) S.; m. Donna Barnes Bray, Dec. 26, 1961; children: Scott, Shannon. BS in Indsl. Mgmt., Ga. Inst. Tech., 1961; MS in Guidance and Counseling, Troy State U., 1975, MS in Mgmt., 1978; student, Air War Coll., Maxwell AFB, Ala., 1980-81. Commd. 2d lt. USAF, 1961, advanced through grades to maj. gen., 1989; legis. liaison U.S. Senate, Washington, 1981-83; dir. fighter ops./tng. USAF Hdqrs. Europe, Ramstein AB, Fed. Republic Germany, 1983-84; vice comdr. 10th Tactical Reconnaissance Wing RAF USAF, Alconbury, Eng., 1984-85, comdr. 10th Tactical Reconnaissance Wing RAF, 1985-86; cmdr. 81st Tactical Fighter Wing RAF USAF, Bentwaters, Eng., 1986-87; comdr. 316th Air Div/Kaiserslautern USAF, Ramstein AB, Fed. Republic Germany, 1987-88; vice comdr. 12th Air Force/U.S. So. Command USAF, Bergstrom AFB, Tex., 1988-90; comdr. 13th Air Force USAF, Clark AFB, The Philippines, 1990-91; dir. ops. CENTCOM/J-3, MacDill AFB, Fla., 1992-94; ret. USAF, 1994; dir. pub. safety dept. Hillsborough County, Tampa, Fla., 1994—. Decorated Legion of Merit with oak leaf cluster, DFC with 3 oak leaf clusters, Bronze Star, Air Medal with 35 oak leaf clusters, Legion of Honor (The Philippines), Bronze Cross medal (The Philippines), Def. Disting. Svc. medal, Air Force Disting. Svc. medal. Mem. Air Force Assn., Daedalians, Quiet Birdmen. Avocations: golf, reading. Home: 5312 S Crescent Dr Tampa FL 33611 Office: Hillsborough County Pub Safety Dept Tampa FL 33601

STUDER, WILLIAM JOSEPH, library director; b. Whiting, Ind., Oct. 1, 1936; s. Victor E. and Sarah G. (Hammersley) S.; m. Rosemary Lippie, Aug. 31, 1957; children: Joshua E., Rachel Marie. B.A., Ind. U., 1958, M.A., 1960, Ph.D. (Univ. fellow), 1968. Grad. asst. div. Library Sci., Ind. U., 1959-60, reference asst., 1960-61; spl. intern Library of Congress, 1961-62, reference librarian, sr. bibliographer, 1962-63; dir. regional campus libraries Ind. U., Bloomington, 1968-73; assoc. dean univ. libraries Ind. U., 1973-77; dir. libraries Ohio State U., Columbus, 1977—; mem. Library Services and Constrn. Act Adv. Com. of Ind., 1971-76, Adv. Coun.on Fed. Library Programs in Ohio, 1977-85, chmn. 1983-86; mem. ARL Office Mgmt. Studies Adv. Com., 1977-81, ARL Task Force on Nat. Library Network Devel., 1978-83, chmn., 1981-83, com. on preservation, 1985-88, vice-chmn., 1989-90, chmn., 1991-92, task force on scholarly communication, 1983-87, bd. dirs., 1981-84, com. stats. and measurement, 1993—; mem. network adv. com. Library of Congress, 1981-88; mem. library study com. Ohio Bd. Regents, 1984-89; mem. steering com. Ohio Library and Info. Network (Ohio Link), 1987-90; bd. dirs. Ctr. Rsch. Librs., 1989—, vice-chmn. 1993-94, chmn. 1994-95, sec., chmn. membership com. 1990-93; mem. adv. coun. Ohio Link Libr., 1990—, chmn. 1991-92, policy adv. coun., governing bd., 1991-92. Contbr. articles to profl. jours. Trustee On Line Computer Libr. Ctr. Inc., 1977-78; del. On Line Computer Libr. Ctr. Users Coun., 1983-91; mem. rsch. libres. adv. com. OnLine Computer Libr. Ctr., 1989-95, vice chair, chair-elect, 1993-94, chair, 1994-95; bd. dirs. Ohio Network of Librs. Ohionet, 1977-87, chmn., 1980-82, 86-87, treas., 1983-86; mem. Columbia U. Sch. Library Svc. Conservation Programs, vis. com., 1987-90; mem. nat. adv. coun. to comm. on preservation and access, 1989-92; treas. Monroe County (Ind.) Mental Health Assn., 1968-76; active Mental Health Social Club, 1971-73; budget rev. com. United Way, 1975-77; bd. dirs. Mental Health Assn. Recipient citation for participation MARC Inst., 1968-69; Louise Maxwell award Ind. U., 1978. Mem. ALA, Ohio Libr. Assn. (bd. dirs. 1980-83), Assn. Coll. and Rsch. Librs. (bd. dirs. 1977-81, com. on activities model for 1990, 1981-82, chmn. libr. sch. curriculum task force 1988-89), Acad. Libr. Assn. Ohio, Phi Kappa Phi (pub. rels. editor 1982-83, sec. 1983-85), Torch Club (pres. 1993-94), Phi Eta Sigma, Alpha Epsilon Delta, Beta Phi Mu. Home: 724 Olde Settler Pl Columbus OH 43214-2924 Office: Ohio

State U William Oxley Thompson Meml Libr 1858 Neill Ave Mall Columbus OH 43210

STUDIER, FREDERICK WILLIAM, biophysicist; b. Waverly, Iowa, May 26, 1936; s. Frederick William and Maudine Modelle (Shoesmith) S.; m. Susan Sarah Cook, Jan. 26, 1962; children: Frederick, Carol. B.S., Yale U., 1958; Ph.D., Calif. Inst. Tech., 1963. Postdoctoral fellow dept. biochemistry Stanford U. Med. Sch., 1962-64; asst. biophysicist dept. biology Brookhaven Nat. Lab., Upton, N.Y., 1964-67; asso. biophysicist Brookhaven Nat. Lab., 1967-70, biophysicist, 1970-74, sr. biophysicist, 1974—, chair dept. biology, 1990—; adj. prof. biochemistry SUNY, Stony Brook. Recipient Ernest Orlando Lawrence Meml. award U.S. Dept. Energy, 1977. Mem. NAS, AAAS, Am. Acad. Arts and Scis., Am. Soc. for Biochemistry and Molecular Biology, Am. Soc. Microbiology, Biophys. Soc., Am. Soc. Virology. Achievements include research on nucleic acid physical chemistry, molecular genetics bacteriophage T7. Office: Biology Dept Brookhaven Nat Lab Upton NY 11973

STUDLEY, JAMIENNE SHAYNE, lawyer; b. N.Y.C., Apr. 30, 1951; d. Jack Hill and Joy (Cosor) S.; m. Gary J. Smith, July 14, 1984. BA magna cum laude, Barnard Coll., 1972; JD, Harvard U., 1975. Bar: D.C. 1975, U.S. Dist. Ct. D.C. 1978. Assoc. Bergson, Borkland, Margolis & Adler, Washington, 1976-80; spl. asst.; sec. U.S. HHS, 1980-81; assoc. Weil, Gotshal & Manges, Washington, 1981-83; assoc. dean law sch. Yale U., New Haven, 1983-87; lectr. law, 1984-87; syndicated columnist Am. Lawyer Media, 1990-91; exec. dir. Nat. Assn. for Law Placement, Washington, 1987-90, Calif. Abortion Rights Action League, 1992-93; dep. gen. counsel U.S. Dept. Edn., 1993—; vis. scholar adj. faculty U. Calif., Berkeley, 1990-93. Pres. Conn. Women's Ednl. and Legal Fund, Hartford, 1986-87; mem. bd. advisors Nat. Assn. Pub. Interest Law Pub. Svc. Challenge. Mem. ABA (Common. on Women in the Profession 1991-94, editl. bd. Perspectives), D.C. Bar Assn., Bar Assn. San Francisco, Women's Bar Assn., Assn. Alumnae Barnard Coll. (bd. dirs. 1978-81), Barnard in Washington (pres. 1977-78), Phi Beta Kappa. Home: 3701 Clay St San Francisco CA 94118-1857 Office: Office of the Gen Coun Dept of Edn 600 Independence Ave SW Washington DC 20202

STUDWELL, THOMAS W., lawyer; b. New Haven, Conn., Aug. 12, 1949. BA with honors, Haverford Coll., 1971; JD magna cum laude, U. Ill., 1977. Bar: Ill. 1978. Ptnr. Baker & McKenzie, Chgo. Office: Baker & McKenzie 1 Prudential Plz 130 E Randolph Dr Chicago IL 60601

STUEART, ROBERT D., university information services director, educator. B.A., So. Ark. U., 1956; cert. Russian lang., 1958; M.S.L., La. State U., 1962; library sci. advanced cert., U. Pitts., 1969, Ph.D., 1971. Library asst. in reference and cataloging So. State Coll., Magnolia, Ark., 1953-56; librarian, tchr. Desha County (Ark.) Public Schs., 1956-57; library asst. microforms room, serials and Russian cataloging La. State U. Library, 1960-62; with U. Colo. Libraries, 1962-66, head circulation dept., 1964-65, instr., adminstrv. asst. to dir. libraries, 1965-66; asso. prof. library sci., asst. dir. libraries for systems and processes Pa. State U., 1966-68; vis. lectr. U. Pitts. Grad. Sch. Library and Info. Scis., 1968-71, Coll. Librarianship Wales, 1971-72; asso. prof., asst. dean U. Denver Grad. Sch. Librarianship, 1972-74; dean, prof. library and info. sci. Simmons Coll. Grad. Sch. Library and Info. Sci., Boston, 1974-94; prof., dir. LRDC Asian Inst. Tech., Bangkok, 1994—; cons., speaker in field. Author: The Area Specialist Bibliographer: An Inquiry Into His Role, 1972, (with John T. Eastlick) Library Management, 1975, 3d edit, 1987, (with Barbara Moran) Library and Information Center Management, 4th edit., 1993, Michelle My Chelle, 1987, (with Maureen Sullivan) Performance Appraisal and Evaluation, 1991; editor: (with George Miller) Collection Development, 1980, (with Richard Johnson) New Horizons for Academic Libraries, 1979; gen. editor Founds. of Library and Info. Sci., 1979-87; contbr. articles and revs. to profl. publs. Mem. Mass. Gov.'s Planning Com. for White Ho. Conf. on Librs., 1976-79, Mass. Br. Libr. Commrs., 1989—, chair, 1993-94; mem. ALA Internat. Rels. Roundtable, China Programs com., United Bd. for Christian Higher Edn. in China; chair U.S.-USSR Commn. on Libr. Cooperation, 1987-92, US-CIS/BALTIC Com. on Archives and Librs. Recipient Melville Dewey medal, 1980, Blackwell NA award, 1980, Disting. Alumni award So. Ark. U., 1984, Disting. Grad. award U. Pitts., 1985, ALISE Svc. award 1987, Beta Phi Mu award, 1990, Outstanding Alumni award La. State U., 1991; John F. Kennedy Found. fellow, 1991-92, Humphrey OCLC Forrest Press Internat. award, 1994. Mem. ALA (coun. 1978-81, 84—, exec. bd. 1987-91, chmn. pub. com. 1983-84, chmn. internat. rels. com. 1991-92), Assn. Libr. and Info Sci. Edn. (pres. 1983-84), Assn. Coll. and Rsch. Librs. (editorial bd. Coll. and Rsch. Librs. 1973-74), Libr. Adminstrn. and Mgmt. Assn. (chmn. stats. com. for libr. edn. 1978-81, Libr. Edn. Div. pres. 1977-78), Rsch. Roundtable, Am. Soc. Info. Scis., Spl. Librs. Assn., New Eng. Libr. Assn., Mass. Libr. Assn. (Libr. Advocate award 1994), Internat. Fedn. Libr. Assns. (standing com. on libr. edn. 1986-90, mem. exec. bd. 1991—), New Eng. Hist. Geneal. Soc. (bd. dirs.). Office: Asian Inst Tech, P O Box 2754, Bangkok 10505, Thailand

STUEBNER, JAMES CLOYD, real estate developer, contractor; b. Phila., Dec. 15, 1931; s. Erwin A. and Frances (Quinn) S.; children: Kathleen, Stephen, James, Susan; m. Susan Rae Peterson, June 16, 1990. BA, Dartmouth Coll., 1953. Sales engr. Rohm & Haas Co., Phila., 1956-69; pres. Structural Plastics Corp., Mpls., 1961-69; pres., chief exec. officer Northland Devel. Co., Mpls., 1969—; pres. Northland Inn and Exec. Conf. Ctr., 1988—, Northland Fitness Ctrs., 1990—. Mem. Minn. Conv. Ctr. Commn., St. Paul, 1988; commr. Minn. Econ. Devel. Commn., St. Paul, 1985; bd. dirs. Bach Soc. of Minn., Mpls., 1986—, Minn. Orchestral Assn., Mpls., 1988-91. Sgt. U.S. Army, 1953-55. Mem. Nat. Assn. Office and Indsl. Parks (bd. dirs. Minn. chpt. 1976-85, 81-90, pres. 1978-80, 92-83, nat. pres. 1983-84, v.p. 1981-82, Developer of Yr. award 1987, Minn. Bus. Person of Yr. award 1990). Avocations: road running, singing. Office: Northland Devel Co 7000 Northland Dr N Minneapolis MN 55428-1502

STUEHRENBERG, PAUL FREDERICK, librarian; b. Breckenridge, Minn., Mar. 14, 1947; s. Henry Ernest Frederick and Marian Violet (Sandberg) S.; m. Suzanne Elaine Draper, June 14, 1969 (div. Apr. 1982); m. Carole Lee DeVore, Aug. 1, 1983. BA, Concordia Sr. Coll., 1968; MDiv, Concordia Sem., 1972; STM, Christ Sem., 1974; MA, U. Minn., 1978, PhD, 1988. Asst. libr. U. Minn., Mpls., 1974-82; monographs libr. Yale Divinity Libr., New Haven, 1982-91, div. libr., 1991—; adj. assoc. prof. in theol. tit. Yale Divinity Sch., New Haven, 1993—; asst. pastor Christ Meml. Luth. Ch., Plymouth, Minn., 1974-82; adj. pastor Bethesda Luth. Ch., New Haven, 1984—; sec. Luth. Student Found., Mpls., 1978-81. Contbr. articles to profl. jours. Sec. North Haven (Conn.) Libr. Bd., 1989—. Mem. Am. Theol. Libr. Assn., Soc. Bibl. Lit., Am. Acad. Religion, North Haven Meml. Libr. Assn. Home: 280 Bayard Ave North Haven CT 06473-4307 Office: Yale U Div Sch Libr 409 Prospect St New Haven CT 06511-2167

STUELAND, DEAN THEODORE, emergency physician; b. Viroqua, Wis., June 24, 1950; s. Theodore Andrew and Hazel Thelma (Oftedahl) S.; m. Marlene Ann McClurg, Dec. 30, 1972; children: Jeffrey, Michael, Nancy, Kevin. BSEE, U. Wis., 1972, MSEE, 1973, MD, 1977. Diplomate Am. Bd. Internal Medicine, Am. Bd. Geriatric Medicine, Am. Bd. Emergency Medicine; cert. in addictions medicine, cert. med. rev. officer. Resident Marshfield (Wis.) Clinic, 1977-80, emergency physician, dir. emergency svc., 1981-93; emergency physician Riverview Hosp., Wisconsin Rapids, Wis., 1980-81; med. dir. Nat. Farm Medicine Ctr., Marshfield, 1986—, alcohol and other drug abuse unit St. Joseph's Hosp., Marshfield, 1988—; exec. com. Marshfield Clinic, 1989-91, 93-95, treas., 1993-95, ACLS state affiliate faculty Am. Heart Assn., 1984—, nat. faculty, 1992—; mem. emergency med. svcs. adv. bd. State of Wis., 1994—. Contbr. articles to profl. jours. Charter mem., pres. Hewitt (Wis.) Jaycees, 1984; bd. dirs. Northwood County chpt. ARC, 1988—. Fellow ACP, Am. Coll. Emergency Physicians (bd. dirs. Wis. chpt. 1984-90, v.p. 1990-91, pres. 1991-92, counselor 1993—), Am. Coll. Preventive Medicine; mem. Biomed. Engring. Soc. (sr. mem.), Am. Soc. Addictions Medicine. Mem. Missionary Alliance Ch. (bd. govs., treas. 1991—). Office: Marshfield Clinic 1000 N Oak Ave Marshfield WI 54449-5703

STUENKEL, WILLIAM C., airport administrator. Dir. engring. and ops. Pitts. Internat. Airport. Office: Pitts Internat Airport PO Box 12370 Dept of Aviation Pittsburgh PA 15231-0370

STUFFLEBEAM, DANIEL LEROY, education educator; b. Waverly, Iowa, Sept. 19, 1936; s. LeRoy and Melva Stufflebeam; m. Carolyn T. Joseph; children: Kevin D., Tracy Smith, Joseph. BA, State U. Iowa, 1958; MS, Purdue U., 1962, PhD, 1964; postgrad., U. Wis., 1965. Prof., dir. Ohio State U. Evaluation Ctr., Columbus, 1963-73; prof. edn., dir. Western Mich. U. Evaluation Ctr., Kalamazoo, 1973—. Author monographs; contbr. chpts. to books, articles to profl. jours. Served with U.S. Army, 1960. Recipient Paul Lazersfeld award Evaluation Rsch. Soc., 1985. Mem. Am. Ednl. Rsch. Assn., Nat. Coun. on Measurement in Edn., Am. Evaluation Assn. Baptist. Office: Western Michigan Univ The Evaluation Ctr Kalamazoo MI 49008-5178

STUHAN, RICHARD GEORGE, lawyer; b. Braddock, Pa., July 1, 1951; s. George and Pauline Madeline (Pavlocik) S.; m. Mary Ann Cipriano, Aug. 23, 1975; children: Brendan George, Sara Katherine, Brian Christopher, Caitlin Emily. BA summa cum laude, Duquesne U., 1973; JD, U. Va., 1976. Bar: Va. 1976, D.C. 1977, U.S. Ct. Appeals (D.C. cir.) 1977, U.S. Ct. Appeals (4th cir.) 1977, U.S. Claims Ct. 1979, U.S. Supreme Ct. 1980, U.S. Ct. Appeals (3d cir.) 1981, U.S. Ct. Appeals (11th cir.) 1982, U.S. Dist. Ct. (no. dist.) Ohio 1985, Ohio 1986. Assoc. Arnold & Porter, Washington, 1976-84; of counsel Jones, Day, Reavis & Pogue, Cleve., 1984-86, ptnr., 1987—. Mem. Va. Law Review, 1974-76. Pres., Malvern Citizens Assn., Shaker Heights, Ohio, 1993—, v.p. and corr. sec., 1988-92; mem. bd. trustees, fin. com. and fund raising com. WomanKind Maternal and Child Care Ctr., 1991—; chmn. Shaker Open Space Com., 1990-91; coach youth baseball Shaker Heights, 1990-92, 94; coach youth soccer Cleveland Heights Recreation League, 1990; mem. religious edn. com. St. Dominic Ch., Shaker Heights, 1987-90, 92—, tchr. parish religion sch., 1984-90, eucharistic minister, 1992—; coach youth soccer Shaker Heights Recreation League, 1988; program dir., treas. Ravenwood Park Citizens Assn., Falls Church, Va., 1981-83; del. Fairfax (Va.) County Fedn. Civic Assns., 1983-84; tchr. Confrat. of Christian Doctrine St. Anthony Ch., Falls Church, 1979-84; lectr. St. Mary's Ch., Alexandria, Va., 1976-78. Recipient Gold Medal for Gen. Excellence, Duquesne U., 1973, Debating scholar, 1969-73, Univ. scholar, 1969; DuPont scholar U. Va., 1973, Hardy Cross Dillard teaching fellow, 1975-76. Mem. Order of Coif. Democrat. Roman Catholic. Avocations: tennis, swimming, basketball, home repair. Home: 2865 Falmouth Rd Cleveland OH 44122-2838 Office: Jones Day Reavis & Pogue 901 Lakeside Ave N Point Cleveland OH 44114-1116

STUHL, OSKAR PAUL, scientific and regulatory consultant; b. Wilhelmshaven, Fed. Republic Germany, Dec. 23, 1949; s. Johannes Alexander and Johanna Wilhelmine (Hoelling) S. Dipl. Chem., U. Duesseldorf, 1976, Dr.rer.nat., 1978. Tutor, Institut fuer Organische Chemie, U. Duesseldorf, 1975-76, sci. assoc., 1976-79; mgr. product devel. Drugofa GmbH, Cologne, Fed. Republic Germany, 1980; mgr. sci. rels. R.J.R. Nabisco, Cologne, 1981-88, mgr. sci. svcs., 1989-94; cons. in field, 1995—. Mem. editorial bd. Beitraege zur Tabakforschung Internat. Mem. Dusseldorf Museums Verein, Verein der Freunde des Hetjens-Museums, Verein der Freunde und Foerderer der U. Dusseldorf, Verein der Freunde des Stadtmuseums Dusseldorf, Met. Mus. Art (N.Y.C.), Friends Royal Acad. Arts, London, Art Soc. of Rheinlande and Westfalen, Gesellschaft der Freunde der Kunstsammlung NRW; Gesellschaft der Freunde und Foerderer der Univ. Dusseldorf; Zuercher Kunstgesellschaft, Freundeskreis Theatermuseum, Dusseldorf, Foerderverein NRW-Stiftung, Forum fuer Film (Duesseldorf), Deutsch-Japanische-Gesellschaft, Verein zur Foerderung Deutsch-Japanischer Beziehungen. Mem. Gesellschaft Deutscher Chemiker, Gesellschaft Deutscher Naturforscher und Aerzte, Max-Planck-Gesellschaft, Deutsche Gesellschaft fuer Arbeits hygiene, Am. Chem. Soc. (including various divs.), Chem. Soc. Japan, N.Y. Acad. of Scis., Royal Soc. Chemistry, Am. Pharm. Assn., Acad. Pharm. Rsch. and Sci., AAAS, Internat. Union Pure and Applied Chemistry, Am. Soc. Pharmacognosy, Fedn. Internat. Pharmaceutic, Christlich Demokratische Union, CDU-Wirtschaftsvereinigung. Roman Catholic. Clubs: Vereinigung AC Dusseldorf; PCL (London); KDStV Burgundia-Leipzig (Zu Dusseldorf) im CV, Golf Club Velbert. Contbr. articles to profl. jours.; patentee in field. Office: RJR Nabisco, PO Box 140544, D-40075 Dusseldorf Germany

STUHLINGER, ERNST, physicist; b. Niederrimbach, Germany, Dec. 19, 1913; came to U.S., 1946, naturalized, 1955.; s. Ernst and Pauline (Werner) S.; m. Irmgard Lotze, Aug. 1, 1950; children: Susanne, Tilman, Hans Christoph. PhD, U. Tuebingen, Germany, 1936. Asst. prof. Technische Hochschule, Berlin, Germany, 1936-41; guidance and control equipment rocket Devel. Center, Peenemunde, Germany, 1943-45; with Guided Missile Devel. Office, Ft. Bliss, Tex., 1946-50; physicist Ordnance Missile Labs., Huntsville, Ala., 1950-56, Army Ballistic Missile Agy., 1956-60; dir. Space Scis. Lab., George C. Marshall Space Flight Center, NASA, Huntsville, Ala., 1960-68; assoc. dir. for sci. George C. Marshall Space Flight Center, NASA, 1968-76; sr. research scientist, adj. prof. U. Ala. at Huntsville, 1976—; sr. research assoc. Teledyne Brown Engring. Corp., Huntsville, 1984-88; cons. aerospace cos.; vis. scientist Tech. U. Munich, W. Germany, 1978, Max Planck Inst. Nuclear Physics, Heidelberg, 1983-85; cons. Teledyne-Brown Engring., 1984-90. Author: Ion Propulsion for Space Flight, 1964; co-author: Skylab, A Guidebook, 1973, Project Viking, 1976, Wernher von Braun, Crusader for Space, 1994. Served with German Army, 1941-43, Russian Campaign. Fellow Am. Astronautical Soc., Am. Rocket Soc. (dir.), AIAA (tech. dir.), Brit. Interplanetary Soc.; mem. Internat. Acad. Astronautics, Von Braun Astron. Soc. (dir.), Austrian Astron. Soc. (hon.), Am. Optical Soc., Deutsche Roentgengesellschaft (hon.), Deutsche Physikalische Gesellschaft, Deutsche Gesellschaft Fuer Luft und Raumfahrt (hon.), Hermann Oberth Gesellschaft (hon.), Sigma Xi. Rsch. cosmic rays, nuclear physics, 1934-41, electric space propulsion, 1947—, studies on manned missions to Mars, 1954—. Home: 3106 Rowe Dr SE Huntsville AL 35801-6151

STUHLREYER, PAUL AUGUSTUS, III, cultural organization administrator; b. Cin., Oct. 7, 1952; s. Paul Augustus Stuhlreyer Jr. and Genevieve Adams (Edwards) Hilmer; m. Janet Barbara Vidal, May 21, 1977; children: Hillary Brooke, Erica Adams, Ryan Edwards. BS, Miami U., Oxford, Ohio, 1974; MBA, U. Va., 1976. Dir. investor relations Baldwin-United Group, Cin., 1976-78; treas. Diem-Wing Paper Co., Cin., 1978-85; pvt. practice venture capitalist Cin., 1985-87; mng. dir. Cin. Opera Assn., 1987—; exec. dir. Cin. Ballet Co., 1991—; chmn. Uvonics Co. Inc., Columbus, Ohio, 1985-88; adj. instr. Coll. of Mt. St. Joseph, Cin., 1981—. Exec. dir. Cin. Ballet, 1991. Mem. Am. Ballet Assn. Republican. Episcopalian. Club: Cin. Country. Avocations: hunting, swimming, golf. Home: 5740 Lengwood Dr Cincinnati OH 45244-3866 Office: Cin Opera Assoc 1241 Elm St Cincinnati OH 45210-2267

STUHR, DAVID PAUL, business educator, consultant; b. Ridgewood, N.J., Oct. 10, 1938; s. Edward Philip and Theresa Alma (Derny) S. B Engring., Yale U., 1960; MS, Rensselaer Poly. Inst., 1962; PhD, NYU, 1972. Research fellow Fed. Res. Bank of N.Y., N.Y.C., 1968-69, cons. economist, 1969-92; assoc. in bus. Columbia U. Grad. Sch. Bus. Adminstrn., N.Y.C., 1969-72; asst. prof. fin., 1972-73; assoc. prof. fin. Rutgers U. Grad. Sch. Bus. Adminstrn., Newark, N.J., 1973-77; assoc. prof. fin. Fordham U., Faculty of Bus., N.Y.C., 1977—; acting dean faculty, 1984-85; assoc. dean Fordham U. Coll. Bus. Adminstrn., Bronx, N.Y., 1980-83, dean, 1983-87; pres. faculty senate Fordham U., Bronx, N.Y., 1994—; mem. bus. faculty com. Regents Coll. degrees SUNY, Albany, 1987—. Contbr. articles to profl. jours. Mem. exec. bd. Bergen council Boy Scouts Am., 1979—; mcpl. chmn. Ho-Ho-Kus (N.J.) Rep. Com., 1968—; chair fin. com. St. Gabriel the Archangel Ch., Saddle River, N.J., 1986—. Mem. Am. Econ. Assn. (life), Am. Fin. Assn. (life), Fin. Mgmt. Assn., Phila. Soc. (founding mem., trustee 1977-80, treas. 1979—). Republican. Roman Catholic. Avocations: backpacking, camping, skiing. Office: Fordham Univ Faculty Of Bus Bronx NY 10458

STUHR, WALTER M., seminary educator, clergyman; b. Mpls., June 4, 1932; s. Walter M. and Norma (Bodenschatz) S.; m. Barbara Jean Gordon, June 13, 1953; children—Deborah Jean, Rebecca Ann, Philip Martin. B.A., Yale U., 1954; B.D., Pacific Lutheran Sem., 1958; M.A., U. Chgo., 1965, Ph.D., 1970. Ordained to ministry United Lutheran Ch. Am. 1958. Pastor Luth. Ch. of our Redeemer, Sacramento, Calif., 1958-63; interim pastor various chs., Chgo., 1963-67; prof. ethics Pacific Luth. Theol. Sem., Berkeley, Calif., 1967—; pres., 1979-88. Mem. Richmond-Shimada Sister City Program, Calif., 1975—. Mem. Soc. Christian Ethics. Democrat. Office: Pacific Luth Theol Sem 2770 Marin Ave Berkeley CA 94708-1530

STUIVER, MINZE, geological sciences educator; b. Vlagtwedde, Groningen, The Netherlands, Oct. 25, 1929; came to U.S., 1959; s. Albert and Griet (Welles) S.; m. Annie Hubbelmeyer, July 12, 1956; children: Ingrid, Yolande. D.Sc. in Physics, U. Groningen, 1953, Ph.D. in Biophysics, 1958. Research assoc. Yale U., New Haven, 1959-62; sr. research assoc., dir. Radiocarbon Lab. Yale U., 1962-69; prof. geol. sci. and zoology U. Wash. Seattle, 1969-82, prof. geol. sci. and quaternary scis., 1982—, dir. Quaternary Isotope Lab, 1972—. Editor: Radiocarbon, 1976-88; mem. editorial bd.: Quaternary Research, 1974—, Isotope Geoscience, 1983—. Named Alexander von Humboldt sr. scientist Fed. Republic Germany, 1983. Mem. Geol. Soc. Am., Am. Quaternary Assn. Office: U Wash Box 351360 Seattle WA 98195-1360

STUKEL, JAMES JOSEPH, university official, mechanical engineering educator; b. Joliet, Ill., Mar. 30, 1937; s. Philip and Julia (Mattivi) S.; m. Mary Joan Helping, Nov. 27, 1958; children: Catherine, James, David, Paul. B.S. in Mech. Engring. Purdue U., 1959; M.S., U. Ill., Champaign-Urbana, 1963, Ph.D., 1968. Research engr. W.Va. Pulp and Paper Co., Covington, Va., 1959-61; mem. faculty U. Ill., 1968—, prof. mech. engring., 1975—, dir. Office Coal Research and Utilization, 1974-76, dir. Office Energy Research, 1976-81, dir. pub. policy program Coll. Engring., 1981-84, assoc. dean Coll. Engring. and dir. Expt. Sta., 1984-85; dean Grad. Coll., vice chancellor for research U. Ill. at Chgo., 1985-86, exec. vice chancellor, vice chancellor academic affairs, 1986-91, interim chancellor, 1990-91, chancellor, 1991-95; pres., 1995—; v.p. Chgo. Tech. Park Corp., 1985-88, pres., 1990-91; exec. sec. midwest Consortium Air Pollution, 1972-73, chmn. bd. dirs., 1973-75; mem. adv. bd. regional studies program Argonne (Ill.) Nat. Lab., 1975-76; adv. com. Energy Resources Commn., 1976; chmn. panel on dispersed electric generating techs. Office Tech. Assessment, U.S. Congress, 1980-81; chmn. rev. adv. bd. tech. rev. dist. heating and combined heat and power systems Internat. Energy Agy, OECD, Paris, 1982-83; cons. in field. Contbr. articles to profl. jours. Pres. parish council Holy Cross Roman Cath. Ch., Urbana, 1967-68. Mem. ASCE (State-of-the-Art of Civil Engring. award 1975), ASME, AAAS, Sigma Xi, Phi Kappa Phi, Pi Tau Sigma. Home: 2650 N Lakeview Ave Apt 1610 Chicago IL 60614-1819 Office: PO Box 4348 2233 Univ Hall M/C 105 Chicago IL 60680-4348

STULBERG, NEAL HOWARD, conductor, pianist; b. Detroit, Apr. 12, 1954; s. Samuel and Judith (Victor) S.; m. Leah Shahmoon, July 12, 1987. B.A. magna cum laude, Harvard Coll., 1976; M.Mus., U. Mich., 1978; postgrad., Juilliard Sch. Music, 1979-80. Condr. MIT Symphony Orch., Cambridge, 1980-82, Young Musicians Found. Debut Orch., Los Angeles, 1981-84; Exxon Arts Endowment asst. condr. Los Angeles Philharm. Orch., 1983-85; music dir., condr. N.Mex. Symphony Orch., 1985—. Recipient 2d prize Balt. Symphony Orch. Young Condrs. Competition, 1980, Seaver/Nat. Endowment Arts Conductor award, 1988; Henry Russell Shaw fellow, 1976-77. Office: NMex Symphony Orch PO Box 769 Albuquerque NM 87103-0769

STULCE, MIKE, Olympic athlete, track and field. Olympic track and field participant Barcelona, Spain, 1992. Recipient Shotput Gold medal Olympics, Barcelona, 1992. Office: US Olympic Com 1750 E Boulder St Colorado Springs CO 80909-5746*

STULL, DANIEL RICHARD, research thermochemist, educator, consultant; b. Columbus, Ohio, May 28, 1911; s. Lucius Walter and Irene Mabel (Haldeman) S.; m. Ruth Louise Keck, Sept. 26, 1936 (dec. 1982); children: Louise Irene Stull Hassman, Richard Walter; m. Mary Morton Lowe, Apr. 28, 1984. BS in Chemistry, Math., Baldwin-Wallace Coll., 1933; PhD in Chemistry, Johns Hopkins U., 1937. Asst. prof. chemistry East Carolina U., Greenville, N.C., 1937-40; rsch. crew leader Dow Chem. Co., Midland, Mich., 1940-50, rsch. tech. expert, 1950-60, dir. thermal lab., 1960-69, rsch. scientist, 1969-76, cons., 1976-77; ret., 1976; cons. in field; rsch. adv. com. Mfg. Chemists Assn., Washington, 1958-65, Nat. Rsch. Coun. rev. bd. Nat. Bur. Standards, Washington, 1959-70; rsch. mem., commr. Internat. Union Pure and Applied Chemistry, 1963-72; printer Hobby Print Shop, Alembic Press, 1954-92. Author: Fundamentals of Fire and Explosion, 1976; author, editor books Joint Army Navy Airforce Rocket Propulsion Group, 1958-76; co-author: Chemical Thermodynamics of Organic Compounds, 1948-69; contbr. to more than 70 sci. rsch. publs. Fin. chmn. 1st United Meth. Ch., Midland, 1948-58; mem. Cosmos Club, Washington, 1967-72; mem. ch. choir various communities, 1928-90. Recipient Hugh Huffman Meml. award Calorimetry Conf., Ames, Iowa, 1965, Alumni Merit award Baldwin-Wallace Coll., Berea, Ohio, 1968, Book award Rsch. Soc. Am., 1969. Fellow Am. Inst. Chemists; mem. AAAS, Am. Chem. Soc. (local sect. award 1980), Sigma Xi, Phi Beta Kappa, Phi Lambda Upsilon. Achievements include extensive compilation of vapor pressure data, development of automatic strip chart recorder for platinum resistance thermometry, 1st automatic recording low temperature calorimeter, computer program to calculate thermodynamic functions, thermal equilibria. Home: 1113 W Park Dr Midland MI 48640-4277

STULL, DEAN P., chemical company executive; b. Denver, Jan. 18, 1950; s. Donald Gordon and Dorothy Alice (Pilcher) S.; m. Nora Jo Nesbitt, June 11, 1971; children: Rebecca Lucile, Valerie Jo. BS in Chemistry, Colo. State U., Ft. Collins, 1972; MS in Organic Chemistry, U. Colo., 1974, PhD in Phys. Chemistry, 1976. Chief chemist Hauser Labs, Boulder, Colo., 1976—; chief exec. officer Hauser Chem. Research, Boulder, Colo., 1983—; vis. asst. prof. organic chemistry U. Colo., Boulder, 1981. Contbr. papers presented to sci. meetings and conventions. Mem. Am. Chem. Soc., Rocky Mountain Chromatography Discussion Group, Rocky Mountain Soc. of Applied Spectroscopy, Am. Soc. Lubrication Engrs., Fedn. Socs. Coatings Tech., Steel Structures Painting Council. Home: 6225 Niwot Rd Longmont CO 80503-8755 Office: Hauser Chem Rsch Inc 5555 Airport Blvd Boulder CO 80301-2339

STULL, DONALD LEROY, architect; b. Springfield, Ohio, May 16, 1937; s. Robert Stull and Ruth Branson; m. Patricia Ann Ryder, Dec. 29, 1959 (div. Dec. 1985); children: Cydney Lynn, Robert Branson, Gia Virginia. BArch, Ohio State U., 1961; MArch, Harvard U., 1962. Registered architect, Calif., Conn., Fla., Ky., Maine, Md., Mass., Mich., Mo., N.H., N.J., N.Y., R.I., Tenn., Tex., Va., D.C. Pres. Stull Assocs., Inc., Boston, 1966-83; pres. Stull and Lee, Inc., Boston, 1983—; mem. Loeb fellowship com. Harvard Grad. Sch. Design, Cambridge, 1969-80; mem. adv. bd. Boston Archtl. Ctr., 1972-80, Mus. Nat. Ctr. of Afro-Am. Artists, Boston, 1978—, Ohio State U. Sch. Architecture, 1980—; design prof. Harvard Grad. Sch. Design, 1974-81; mem. vis. design studio, Rice University, Houston, Tex., spring 1993; bd. dirs. Mus. of Afro-Am. History, Boston, 1975-85; mem. vis. com. Yale Sch. Art and Architecture, New Haven, Conn., 1972-76, William Henry Bishop chair Yale Sch. Architecture, 1975; mem. nat. presdl. design award jury Nat. Endowment for Arts, 1984, 88. Trustee Shaw U., 1973-75, Boston Found. for Architecture; mem. design adv. Panel, Balt., 1976-80; chmn. Mass. Art Commn., Boston, 1978-80; commr. Boston Art Commn., 1980-92; mem. Design Adv. Group, Cambridge MA 90, 94—; commr. Boston Civic Design Commn., 1987—; adv. com. Suffolk Sch. Bus. Mgmt., 1989—; bd. dirs. Historic Boston, 1990—. Recipient Presdl. Design award Nat. Endowment for Arts, 1988; named one of Outstanding Young Men Boston, 1969, Outstanding Young Men Am., 1970, Centennial Yr. Outstanding Alumnus Ohio State U., 1970. Fellow AIA (nat. design com. 1972-84); mem. Boston Soc. Architects (bd. dirs. 1969, AIA Regional Design awards 1975, 80, 89), Mass. Soc. Architects. Office: Stull and Lee Inc 38 Chauncy St Ste 1100 Boston MA 02111

STULL, FRANK WALTER, educator; b. Easton, Pa., June 4, 1935; s. George Washington and Minnie Elizabeth S.; m. Darlene Joy Hunsicker, Aug. 2, 1958; children: James, Ronald, Wendy. BS, East Stroudsburg State Coll., 1956; MEd, Lehigh U., 1966. Cert. tchr., N.J. Tchr. Korea Heung-Up Bank, Seoul, Korea, 1957-58; Howell Twp. Elem. Sch., Freehold, N.J., 1958-59, Holland Twp. Elem. Sch., Milford, N.J., 1959-91; lectr. Friends of U.S. Navy, 1992—. Bd. dirs. sec., treas, mgr. Hunterdon County Sch. Employees Fed. Credit Union, Phillipsburg, N.J., 1969-87/mem. adv. com. Hunterdon County Sch. Employees Fed. Credit Union, Lebanon, N.J., 1995; merit badge counselor Boy Scouts Am., 1970-84, cubmaster, 1971-72; active Holland Friends of USN, 1992—; treas., mem. Hist. Preservation Commn. Holland Twp., 1993—. With U.S. Army, 1956-58, Korea. Recipient Meritorious Svc. award N.J. Credit Union League, 1988, Tchr. Recognition award State

N.J. Gov., 1987, Disting. Achievement award for rsch. and preservation of history of Holland Twp. and surrounding areas; named Outstanding Elem. Tchr. Am., 1972; Experienced Tchr. in Geography fellow Pa. State U., 1967. Mem. NEA, Holland Twp. Edn. Assn., Hunterdon County Edn. Assn., N.J. Edn. Assn., Phi Delta Kappa (chartered mem. Zeta Gamma chpt.). Avocations: photography, travel. Home and Office: 806 Rugby Rd Phillipsburg NJ 08865-2033

STULL, G. ALAN, university dean, health professions educator; b. Easton, Pa., Jan. 26, 1933; s. George Washington and Minnie Elizabeth (Walter) S.; m. Joan Carolyn Gittings, July 30, 1955 (div. 1981); children—Bobbi Ann, John David; m. Jeanine Joosten, Nov. 23, 1984. Student, Lafayette Coll., Easton, Pa., 1950-51; B.S., East Stroudsburg U., 1955; M.S., Pa. State U., 1957, Ed.D., 1961. From instr. to asst. prof. Pa. State U., State College, 1958-66; from assoc. prof. to prof. U. Md., College Park, 1966-72; prof., assoc. dean U. Ky., Lexington, 1972-77; prof., dir. U. Minn., Mpls., 1977-85; prof., dean Sch. Allied Health Professions U. Wis., Madison, 1985-88; prof., dean Sch. Health Related Professions SUNY, Buffalo, 1988—. Co-author: Statistical Principles and Procedures with Applications for Physical Education, 1975; editor: Ency. of Physical Education, Fitness, and Sports, 1980; contbr. articles to profl. jours. Served with U.S. Army, 1956-58. Recipient Disting. Alumni Svc. award East Stroudsburg U., 1974; recognition award Am. Corrective Therapy Assn., 1981. Fellow Am. Acad. Kinesiol. Phys. Edn. (sec.-treas. 1982-84, pres. 1985-86), Am. Coll. Sports Medicine (chmn. position stands 1979-81); mem. AAHPERD (pres. rsch. consortium 1981-82, honor award 1981), Nat. Assn. Phys. Edn. in Higher Edn. (chmn. rsch. com. 1976-77), Assn. for Rsch., Adminstrn., Profl. Couns. and Socs. (pres. 1976-77, honor award 1980), Am. Assn. Schs. Allied Health Professions, Phi Epsilon Kappa. Republican. Methodist. Avocations: athletics; photography; travel; boating; fishing. Office: SUNY Sch Health Related Professions 435 Stockton Kimball Tower Buffalo NY 14214

STULTS, LAURENCE ALLEN, airline pilot; b. Evanston, Ill., Nov. 2, 1940; s. Allen Parker and Elizabeth Van Horne; m. Karen Frashure, Feb. 13, 1965 (div. 1986); m. Takako Yajima, Mar. 25, 1986; children: Rex Allen, Mark Edwin. AB in Econs., Colgate U., 1962; MS, George Washington U., 1978; postgrad., Cath. U., 1977; cert. in Japanese Lang., U. Guam, Manigao, 1991. Commd. 2d lt. U.S. Marine Corps, 1962, fighter pilot, 1962-83; test pilot, mgr. fighter Naval Air Test Ctr., 1972-76; advanced through grades to lt. col. commdg. officer USMC, 1980; capt. Continental Air Micronesia, 1984-91; chief pilot World Fish and Agriculture, 1991; capt. B-727 Continental Airlines, Denver, 1991-94; capt. B-757 Continental Airlines, Newark, 1994—; cons. real estate sales, Honolulu, 1983-86. Pres. Mariners Ridge Homeowners, Honolulu, 1980-86, Tumon View (Guam) Homeowners, 1987-91; Eagle Scouts. Decorated Disting. Flying Cross, Bronze Star, Cross of Gallantry. Mem. Soc. Exptl. Test Pilots (life), Ind. Assn. Continental Pilots, Continental Ops. Group, Marine Corps Assn., Order of Arrow, B.S.A. Republican. Congregationalist. Avocations: sailing, running, bicycling, tennis, golf. Home: Redondo Vista Apt 204 28602 16th Ave S Federal Way WA 98003-3134 Office: Continental Airlines Chief Pilot's Office Gate 103 Newark Internat Airport Terminal C Newark NJ 07114

STULTS, WALTER BLACK, management consultant, former trade organization executive; b. Hightstown, N.J., Oct. 25, 1921; s. C. Stanley and Nettie M. (Black) S.; m. Ann D. Haynes, June 28, 1947; children: Andrew Haynes, Thomas Stanley. BA, Williams Coll., 1943; MA (Woodrow Wilson fellow), Princeton U., 1949. Teaching asst. Princeton (N.J.) U., 1946-49; legis. asst. to U.S. Senator Robert Hendrickson, Washington, 1949-50; staff dir. U.S. Senate Small Bus. Com., 1950-61; pres. Nat. Assn. Small Bus. Investment Cos., Washington, 1961-86; prin. W.B. Stults, Cons., Chapel Hill, N.C., 1979—; dir. Pardee & Curtin Lumber Co., Pardee Resources Co., Phila.; chmn. Coun. Small and Ind. Bus. Assns., 1976-81. Pres. Carol Woods Residents Assn.; dir. Carol Woods Retirement Comty. With USAAF, 1943-46. Mem. Am. Soc. Assn. Execs. Republican. Congregationalism. Clubs: The Exchequer, Masons, Chapel HIll Country.

STULTZ, NEWELL MAYNARD, political science educator; b. Boston, June 13, 1933; s. Irving Washburn and Marjorie May (MacEachern) S.; m. Elizabeth Petronella Olckers, Apr. 6, 1958; children: Elliot Andries, Amy Elizabeth. A.B., Dartmouth Coll., 1955; M.A., Boston U., 1960, Ph.D., 1965; M.A. hon., Brown U., 1968. Fulbright exchange scholar U. Pretoria, South Africa, 1955-56; asst. prof. polit. sci. Northwestern U., Evanston, Ill., 1964-65; asst. prof. to prof. polit. sci. Brown U., Providence, 1965—, assoc. grad. dean, 1970-74, assoc. dean of faculty, 1993—; vis. fellow Yale U.-South African Research Program, 1977; vis. prof. U. South Africa, Pretoria, 1980; James Gathings lectr. Bucknell U., Lewisburg, Pa., 1980. Author: Afrikaner Politics in South Africa, 1974, Who Goes to Parliament?, 1975, Transkei's Half Loaf, 1979, (bibliography) South Africa, 1989, 2d edit., 1993; co-author: South Africa's Transkei, 1967; co-editor: Governing in Black Africa, 1970, 2d edit., 1986. V.p. World Affairs Council R.I., 1983. Served as lt. (j.g.) USN, 1956-59. Fulbright fellow, 1955-56; NDEA grantee, 1959-62; Ford Found. fellow, 1962-64; Rockefeller Found. fellow, 1976-77. Unitarian. Home: 371 New Meadow Rd Barrington RI 02806-3729 Office: Brown U Dept Polit Sci PO Box 1844 Providence RI 02912-1844

STULTZ, THOMAS JOSEPH, newspaper executive; b. Ironton, Ohio, July 28, 1951; s. Riley Frederick and Mary (Leslie) S.; m. Patricia Ann Conley, Dec. 18, 1971; children: Leslie Faye, Jessica Kristin. Student, Ohio U., 1969-71, Marshall U., 1971, U. N.C., Chapel Hill. Reporter Ashland (Ky.) Daily Ind., 1970-73, Orlando (Fla.) Sentinel, 1973; owner/pub. Greenup County Sentinel, Greenup, Ky., 1973-80; editor, writer Bob Jones U., Greenville, S.C., 1980; advt. dir. Daily Adv., Greenville, 1980-81; dir. community publs. Anderson (S.C.) Ind. Mail, 1981-84; v.p., gen. mgr. Leader Newspapers, Inc., Charlotte, N.C., 1984-86; mktg. dir. Suburban Newspapers Greater St. Louis, 1986-88; v.p. Multimedia Newspaper Co., Greenville, 1988—; pres., dir. Worldwide Tentmakers, Inc., Greenville, 1987—; pres., owner Internat. Employment Gazette, Greenville, 1989—. Deacon, tchr. Temple Bapt. Ch., Flatwoods, Ky., 1978-80; tchr. Sunday sch. Oakwood Bapt. Ch., Anderson, 1981-84, 88-90. Republican. Avocations: golf, travel, reading, church and missions activities. Home: No 6 Titleist Ct Taylors SC 29687 Office: Multimedia Newspaper Co 305 S Main St Greenville SC 29601-2640

STUMBO, RICHARD WILLIAM, JR., mining company financial executive; b. Atwood, Kans., Oct. 13, 1933; s. Richard William and W. Garnet (Crihfield) S.; m. Kathleen Ann Berry, Sept. 7, 1957; children: David, Elizabeth, Karen. BSCE, U. Wis., 1958; MBA in Acctg. and Fin., U. Pa., 1968; grad. advanced mgmt. program, Harvard U., 1983. Structural engr. and indsl. sales engr. Rilco div. Weyerhaeuser Co., St. Paul, 1958-60; div. engr., promotion dir. Plywood Fabricator Service, Chgo., 1961-63; div. v.p., gen. mgr., controller Berry Industries, Birmingham, Mich., 1963-67; new venture mgr. Conwed Corp., St. Paul, 1968-69; asst. v.p. fin. planning Burlington Northern Inc., St. Paul, 1969-71; div. controller Agrl. Equipment div. Allis-Chalmers Corp., Milw., 1971-74; v.p., sr.v.p. fin., corp. dir. Western Pacific R.R. Co., San Francisco, 1974-83; v.p. fin., chief fin. officer Homestake Mining Co., San Francisco, 1983—. With Signal Corps U.S. Army, 1954-56. Mem. Fin. Execs. Inst., Fin. Officers of No. Calif., Am. Mining Congress (chmn. fin. adv. exec. com. 1988—, exec. com. 1983—, chmn. communications workshop 1987, 89, chmn. communications com. 1983—, chmn. ins. com. 1986-87), Beta Gamma Sigma. Office: Homestake Mining Co 650 California St Fl 9 San Francisco CA 94108-2702

STUMP, BOB, congressman; b. Phoenix, Apr. 4, 1927; s. Jesse Patrick and Floy Bethany (Fields) S.; children: Karen, Bob, Bruce. B.S. in Agronomy, Ariz. State U., 1951. Mem. Ariz. Ho. of Reps., 1957-67; mem. Ariz. Senate, 1967-76, pres., 1975-76; mem. 95th-104th Congresses from 3rd Dist.Ariz., 1976—; mem. Nat. Security Com. With USN, 1943-46. Mem. Am. Legion, Ariz. Farm Bur. Republican. Seventh-day Adventist. Office: 211 Canon House of Representatives Washington DC 20515-0303 also: 230 N 1st Ave Rm 5001 Phoenix AZ 85025*

STUMP, JOHN EDWARD, veterinary anatomy educator, ethologist; b. Galion, Ohio, June 3, 1934; s. Clarence Willard and Mabel Katherine (Pfeifer) S.; m. Patricia Anne Auer, Aug. 7, 1955; children—Karen, James. D.V.M. summa cum laude (Borden award for acad. excellence 1958),

Ohio State U., 1958; Ph.D., Purdue U., 1966. Pvt. practice vet. medicine Bucyrus, Ohio, 1958-61; mem. faculty Purdue U., West Lafayette, Ind., 1961-91; prof. vet. anatomy Purdue U., 1976-91, prof. emeritus vet. anatomy, 1991; vis. prof. dept. physiol. scis. Sch. Vet. Medicine, U. Calif.-Davis, fall 1980; vis. prof. Coll. Vet. Medicine, Tex. A&M U., spring 1981. Recipient Autotutorial Excellence award Student AVMA, 1974, Amoco Found. Purdue undergrad. teaching award, 1979, Norden Disting. Tchr. award Purdue U., 1977, Outstanding Tchr. award Purdue U. Alumni Found., 1978; named Outstanding Tchr. Freshman Vet. Students, Purdue U., 1987. Mem. AVMA, Ind. Vet. Med. Assn., Ind. Acad. Vet. Medicine, World Assn. Vet. Anatomists, Am. Assn. Vet. Anatomists (pres. 1977-78), Am. Assn. Anatomists, Am. Vet. Soc. Animal Behavior, Assn. Am. Vet. Med. Colls. (Purdue del. to council of educators 1982-84), Ind. Acad. Sci., Sigma Xi, Phi Zeta, Gamma Sigma Delta. Republican. Presbyterian. Club: Tecumseh Kiwanis (pres. 1973). Office: Dept Anatomy Sch Vet Medicine Purdue U West Lafayette IN 47907

STUMP, JOHN SUTTON, lawyer; b. Clarksburg, W.Va., Aug. 7, 1929; s. John Sutton and Helen (Mannix) S.; m. Elaine Claire Scammahorn, Sept. 14, 1968; children—John Sutton IV, James Felix. Student, Washington and Lee U., 1946-47, LL.B., 1957; B.S. in Commerce, U. N.C., 1951. Bar: W.Va. 1957, Va. 1957. Assoc. Jackson, Kelly, Holt & O'Farrell, Charleston, W.Va., 1957-58, Boothe, Dudley, Koontz & Boothe, Alexandria, Va., 1958-61, Boothe, Dudley, Koontz & Blankingship, Fairfax and Alexandria, Va., 1962-63; ptnr. Boothe, Dudley, Koontz, Blankingship & Stump, Fairfax and Alexandria, 1963-71, Boothe, Prichard & Dudley, 1971-87, McGuire, Woods, Battle & Boothe, 1987—. Served to lt. comdr. USNR, 1951-54, 61-62. Fellow Am. Coll. Trial Lawyers; mem. Am. Law Inst. Home: 8329 Weller Ave Mc Lean VA 22102-1717 Office: 8280 Greensboro Dr Mc Lean VA 22102-3807

STUMP, TROY ELWOOD, zoo director; b. Lebanon, Pa., Dec. 23, 1954; s. Gerald E. and Erma J. (Bomgardner) S.; m. Linda Jean Gamby, Mar. 27, 1992; children: Christopher, Amanda, Bailey. AS in Wildlife Tech., Pa. State U., 1974. Exhibits preparator Hershey (Pa.) Mus. Am. Life; curator ZooAm. Wildlife Park, Hershey, 1977-81; dir. ZooAmerica Wildlife Park, Hershey, 1981—. Fellow Am. Assn. Zool. Parks and Aquariums (profl.), vice chmn. govtl. affairs com. 1987-92). Lutheran. Avocations: volleyball, scuba diving, spelunking, hiking, camping. Office: ZooAmerica N Am Wildlife Park 100 W Hershey Park Dr Hershey PA 17033

STUMPE, WARREN ROBERT, scientific, engineering and technical services company executive; b. Bronx, N.Y., July 15, 1925; s. William A. and Emma J. (Mann) S.; children: Jeffrey, Kathy, William. B.S., U.S. Mil. Acad., 1945; M.S., Cornell U., 1949; M.S. in Indsl. Engring., N.Y. U., 1965; grad., Command and Gen. Staff Coll., 1972, Army War Coll., 1976; Ph.D. (hon.), Milw. Sch. Engring., 1982. Registered profl. engr., N.Y., Fla., Wis. Commd. 2d lt., C.E. U.S. Army, 1945, advanced through grades to capt., 1954; with (65th Engr. Bn.), 1945-48; asst. prof. mechanics U.S. Mil. Acad., 1951-54; resigned, 1954; from capt. to col. Res., 1958-79; dep. gen. mgr., gen. engring. div. AMF, Stamford, Conn., 1954-63; exec. v.p. Dortech, Inc., Stamford, 1963-69; dir. systems mgmt. group Mathews Conveyor div. REX, Darien, Conn., 1969-71; dir. research and devel. Rexnord, Inc., Milw., 1971-73, v.p. corp. research and tech., from 1973, v.p. bus. devel. sector, 1981-83, v.p., chief tech. officer, 1983-86; pres. Rexnord Techs., Milw., 1986-87; v.p. Radian Corp., Milw., 1987-90; civilian aide to sec. army for State of Wis., 1981-85; mem. adv. bd. technology transfer program U. Wis.-Whitewater. Contbr. articles to profl. jours. Founder, pres. No Little League, Stamford, 1965-69; pres. Turn of River Jr. High Sh. PTA, 1967-68; vice chmn. for Wis. Dept. Def., Nat. Com. Employer Support Guard and Res.; bd. regents Milw. Sch. Engring.; mem. liaison coun. Coll. Engring., U. Wis., also mem. indsl. adv. coun.; mem. adv. coun. Marquette U.; mem. Wis. Gov.'s Task Force on Energy, Coun. Great Lakes Govs.' Regional Econ. Devel. Commn., 1987-88; bd. dirs. MRA-Inst. Mgmt., Inc. Mem. Am. Water Pollution Control Fedn., Indsl. Rsch. Inst. (pres., dir.), Wis. Assn. Rsch. Mgrs. (founder), West Point Soc. Wis., Tau Beta Pi, Phi Kappa Phi. Clubs: Wis., Ozaukee Country.

STUMPF, MARK HOWARD, lawyer; b. Chgo., Jan. 25, 1947; s. Samuel Enoch and Jean (Goodman) S.; m. Elizabeth Bruce, Nov. 18, 1972; children: Nicholas, Anna, Lawrence, Gillian. AB, Harvard U., 1969, JD, 1972. Bar: N.Y. 1973, D.C. 1977, U.S. Dist. Ct. (so. and ea. dists.) N.Y. 1973. Assoc. Paul, Weiss, Rifkind, Wharton & Garrison, N.Y.C., 1972-76; assoc. Arnold & Porter, Washington, 1976-80, ptnr., 1981-92, sr. ptnr., 1993—; bd. dirs. Martha's Table, Washington. Co-author: Shark Repellents and Golden Parachutes; author: (with others) Latin American Sovereign Debt Management, 1990. Decorated Order of Generalissimo Francisco de Miranda, 1st Class (Republic of Venezuela) 1991. Mem. ABA, Harvard Club N.Y.C. Democrat. Episcopalian. Home: 3820 Jocelyn St NW Washington DC 20015 Office: Arnold & Porter 555 12th St NW Washington DC 20004

STUMPF, PAUL KARL, biochemistry educator emeritus; b. N.Y.C., N.Y., Feb. 23, 1919; s. Karl and Annette (Schreyer) S.; married, June 1947; children: Ann Carol, Kathryn Lee, Margaret Ruth, David Karl, Richard Frederic. AB, Harvard Coll., 1941; PhD, Columbia U., 1945. Instr. pub. health U. Mich., Ann Arbor, 1946-48; faculty U. Calif., Berkeley, 1948-58, prof., 1956-58; prof. U. Calif., Davis, 1958-84, prof. emeritus, 1984—; chief scientist Competitive Rsch. Grants Office USDA, Washington, 1988-91; cons. Palm Oil Rsch. Inst., Kuala Lumpur, Malaysia, 1982-92; mem. sci. adv. bd. Calgene, Inc., Davis, 1990-93; mem. sci. adv. panel Md. Biotech. Inst., 1990-92. Co-author: Outlines of Enzyme Chemistry, 1955, Outlines of Biochemistry, 5th edit., 1987; co-editor-in-chief Biochemistry of Plants, 1980; exec. editor Archives of Biochemistry/Biophysics, 1965-88; contbr. over 250 articles to profl. jours. Mem. planning commn. City of Davis, 1966-68. Guggenheim fellow, 1962, 69; recipient Lipid Chemistry award Am. Oil Chemists Soc., 1974; Sr. Scientist award Alexander von Humboldt Found., 1976, Superior Svc. Group award USDA, 1992. Fellow AAAS; mem. NAS, Royal Danish Acad. Scis., Am. Soc. Plant Physiologists (pres. 1979-80, chmn. bd. trustees 1986-90, Stephen Hales award 1974, Charles Reid Barnes Life Membership award 1992), Yolo Fliers Country Club (Woodland, Calif.). Avocation: golf. Home: 764 Elmwood Dr Davis CA 95616-3517 Office: Univ of Calif Molecular/Cellular Biology Davis CA 95616

STUMPF, SAMUEL ENOCH, philosophy educator; b. Cleve., Feb. 3, 1918; s. Rev. Louis and Elizabeth (Jergens) S.; m. Jean Goodman, July 3, 1943; children—Paul Jergens, Mark Howard, Samuel Enoch. B.S., U. Calif. at Los Angeles, 1940; B.D., Andover Newton Theol. Sch., 1943; postgrad., Columbia, 1946; Ph.D., U. Chgo., 1948. Asst. prof. ethics Vanderbilt U., 1948-49, assoc. prof., 1949-52, prof. philosophy, chmn. dept., 1952-67, prof. philosophy emeritus, 1984—; vis. prof. med. ethics Vanderbilt U. (Med. Sch.), 1973-74; research prof. jurisprudence Vanderbilt U. (Law Sch.), 1974-77; research prof. med. philosophy Vanderbilt U. (Med. Sch.), 1974—; prof. law, 1977-84, prof. law emeritus, 1984—, also asst. to chancellor, 1966-67; pres. Cornell Coll., Mt. Vernon, Iowa, 1967-74; Gates lectr. Grinnell Coll. 1951; Keese lectr. U. Chattanooga, 1962; Decell lectr. Millsaps Coll., 1963; Louttit-George lectr. Washington Coll., 1967; Willson lectr. Southwestern U., 1970. Author: Philosophical Problems; Elements of Philosophy, A Democratic Manifesto, Socrates to Sartre, Morality and the Law, Philosophy: History and Problems; Contbr. articles to profl. jours. Trustee Food Safety Coun., 1976-80, Food and Drug Law Inst., 1978—. Lt. USNR, 1943-46. Carnegie research grantee, 1949; Ford fellow Harvard, 1955-56; Rockefeller fellow Oxford (Eng.) U., 1958-59. Mem. Am. Council on Legal and Polit. Philosophy, Am. Philos. Assn., Phi Beta Kappa. Home: 424 Page Rd Nashville TN 37205-4244

STUMPF, WALTER ERICH, cell biology educator, researcher; b. Oelsnitz, Sachsen, Germany, Jan. 10, 1927; came to U.S., 1963; m. Ursula Emily Schwinge, May 20, 1961; children: Andrea, Martin, Carolin, Silva. MD summa cum laude, Humboldt U., Berlin, 1952; PhD, U. Chgo., 1967; D in Biol. Humanities (hon.), U. Ulm, Germany, 1987. Resident in neurology and psychiatry Humboldt U., Berlin, 1954-57; resident in neurology and psychiatry U. Marburg, 1957-61, resident in radiobiology, 1961-62; rsch. assoc. U. Chgo., 1963-67, asst. prof., 1967-70; assoc. prof. U. N.C., Chapel Hill, 1970-73, prof., 1973—; mem. labs. for reproductive biology and neurobiology program, mem. Cancer Rsch. Ctr., Carolina Population Ctr., mem. curriculum in toxicology; vis. psychiatrist Maudsley Hosp., London, 1959; vis. prof. Max-Plank Inst. for Cell Biology, Wilhelmshaven, Germany,

1975, U. Ulm, 1981; rsch. advisor Chugai Pharm. Co., Ltd., Tokyo, 1993, 94; cons. Harris Mfg., Co. North Billerica, Mass., Rsch. Triangle Inst., Chemistry and Life Scis. Divsn., Rsch. Triangle Park, N.C., Merk Sharp and Dome, Westpoint, Pa.; exec. com. NRC, Inst. of Lab. Animal Resources, Nat. Acad. Scis., 1979-81, coun. Inst. of Lab. Animal Res., 1978-81, com., Soc. for Exptl. Biology and Med., 1987—. Editor: Autoradiography of Diffusible Substances, 1969, Anatomical Neuroendocrinology, 1975, Autoradiography and Correlative Imaging, 1995; mem. editl. bd. Neuroendocrinology Letters, 1979-87, Exptl. Aging Rsch., 1975-85, Jour. Histochemistry and Cytochemistry, 1982—, Cell and Tissue Rsch., 1982—, Molecular and Cellular Neurosci., 1989—, Biomed. Rsch., 1991—, Histochemistry, 1992—; contbr. more than 500 articles to profl. jours. Recipient Humboldt Found. award, 1989. Mem. AAAS, Am. Assn. Anatomists, N.Y. Acad. Scis., Soc. for Exptl. Biology and Medicine, Soc. for Neurosci., Endocrine Soc., Internat. Brain Rsch. Orgn., Am. Soc. Zoologists, Histochem. Soc. (coun. 1970—), Histochem. Gesellschaft (Feulgen lectrship. 1982), Internat. Soc. Xenobiotics (charter). Home: U NC Sch Medicine 2612 Damascus Church Rd Chapel Hill NC 27516 Office: Internat Inst Drug Distribution Cytopharmacology & Cytotoxicology Chapel Hill NC 27516

STUMPFF, ROBERT THOMAS, academic administrator; b. Lewistown, Pa., June 25, 1945; s. Harry Clarence and Marjorie Louise (Bossinger) S.; m. Sylvia Simmons, Apr. 22, 1972; children: Robert Dale, Cherie Lynn Stumpff Zimmer. BS, U. Md., 1968; cert., U. Ky., 1978. Adminstrv. asst. to dir. athletics U. Md., College Park, 1968-69, asst. dir. Md. student union, 1969-72, assoc. dir. Md. student union, 1973-80, acting dir. Md. student union, 1974-75, bus. mgr. athletics 1980-81, asst. athletic dir., 1982-88, mgr. gen. svcs. phys. plant, 1988—; cons. U.S. Naval Acad. Athletic Assn., Annapolis, Md., 1984. Author, editor: Maryland Wrestling, 1964-65, 68-69 (Nation's Best award); asst. editor: Maryland Football Guide, 1965-69, Maryland Basketball, 1964-65, 68-69. Mem. ch. coun. Abiding Savior Lutheran Ch., Columbia, Md., 1986-87. Mem. Am. Pub. Works Assn., Solid Waste Assn. N.Am. (bd. dirs. mid-Atlantic chpt. 1992-94), Nat. Solid Wastes Mgmt. Assn., Assn. Phys. Plant Adminstrs., Md.-Del. Solid Waste Assn., Md. Ednl. Found., Terrapin Club, U. Md. M Club Found. (life, bd. dirs. 1970—, past pres., Outstanding Wrestling Publ. 1967-68, Outstanding Awards Banquet chmn. 1990), U. Md. Alumni Assn. (life), Omicron Delta Kappa (Sigma Circle, faculty sec.-treas. 1972-76, faculty advisor 1976-91, faculty coord. 1991—). Avocations: reading, sight-seeing. Home: 8206 Bubbling Spg Laurel MD 20723-1079 Office: Univ Md Phys Plant Svc Bldg College Park MD 20742

STUNDZA, THOMAS JOHN, journalist; b. Lawrence, Mass., Mar. 4, 1948; s. John Anthony and Matilda (Stanulonis) S. BA, Merrimack Coll., 1970; MA, Valparaiso U., 1975. Reporter Eagle-Tribune, Lawrence, 1968-70, Post-Tribune, Gary, Ind., 1970-73; bus. editor Post-Tribune, Gary, 1974-78; steel editor Am. Metal Market, Pitts., 1978-80; news editor Am. Metal Market, N.Y.C., 1981-83; sr. editor Purchasing mag., Boston, 1984-94, exec. editor, 1995—; editor Purchasing's Buying Strategy Forecast newsletter, Boston, 1988—; editor audiotape news programming Purchasing's MetalsWatch!, 1994—; instr. journalism Valparaiso (Ind.) U., 1976, U. Pitts., 1980. Pres. Porter County (Ind.) Youth Svc. Bur., 1976-78. Recipient Honor Roll award U.S. Izaak Walton League, 1973, Paul Tobenkin award Columbia U., 1974; Pub. Affairs Reporting award Am. Polit. Sci. Assn., 1971, Ind. Reporting award AP Mng. Editors, 1976, Newswriting awards Ind. Pub. Health Assn., 1972-74, Amos Tuck Media award Dartmouth Coll., 1977. Mem. Soc. Am. Bus. and Econ. Writers, Soc. Profl. Journalists. Home: 144 Shore Dr Winthrop MA 02152 Office: 275 Washington St Newton MA 02158

STUNKARD, ALBERT JAMES, physician, educator; b. N.Y.C., Feb. 7, 1922; s. Horace Wesley and Frances (Klank) S. BS, Yale U., 1943; MD, Columbia U., 1945; MD (hon.), U. Edinburgh, 1992. Intern in medicine Mass. Gen. Hosp., Boston, 1945-46; resident physician psychiatry Johns Hopkins Hosp., 1948-51, rsch. fellow psychiatry, 1951-52; rsch. fellow medicine Columbia U. Svc., Goldwater Meml. Hosp., N.Y.C., 1952-53; Commonwealth rsch. fellow, then asst. prof. medicine Cornell U. Med. Coll., 1953-57; mem. faculty U. Pa., 1957-73, 76—, prof. psychiatry, 1962-73, 76—, Kenneth Appel prof. psychiatry, 1968-73, chmn. dept., 1962-73; prof. psychiatry Med. Sch., Stanford U., 1973-76. Contbr. articles on psychol., physiol., social and genetic aspects of obesity to profl. jours. Capt. M.C., AUS, 1946-48. Ctr. for Advanced Study in Behavioral Scis. fellow, 1971-72. Mem. Inst. Medicine of NAS, Am. Assn. of Chmn. of Depts. of Psychiatry (past pres.), Acad. Behavioral Medicine Rsch. (past pres.), Am. Psychosomatic Soc. (past pres.), Assn. Rsch. in Nervous and Mental Diseases (past pres.), Soc. Behavioral Medicine (past pres.). Achievements include contributions to the behavioral and pharmacological treatment of obesity and to understanding of sociological, physiological, psychological and genetic contributions to the disorder. Office: U Pa Sch Medicine Dept Psychiatry 3600 Market St Fl 734 Philadelphia PA 19104-2648

STUNTEBECK, CLINTON A., lawyer; b. Hibbing, Minn., May 25, 1938; s. Robert F. and S. Mary (Conti) S.; m. Mary Joan Carmody, Nov. 23, 1963; children: Robin, M. Alison, Susan, John, William. BA in Psychology, U. Minn., 1960; LLB, U. Maine, 1968. Bar: Pa. 1969, U.S. Dist. Ct. (ea. dist.) Pa. 1969. Ptnr. Schnader, Harrison, Segal & Lewis, Phila., 1968—; bd. dirs. Markel Corp., Greater Phila. First Partnership for Econ. Devel.; lectr. corp. and securities law. Contbr. articles to profl. jours. Pres. Radnor (Pa.) Twp. Bd. Commn., 1981-83, 92—; trustee Cabrini Coll. Capt. USAF, 1960-65. Mem. ABA, Am. Law Inst., Pa. Bar Assn., Phila. Bar Assn., Securities Industry Assn. (law and compliance com.), U. Maine Law Alumni Assn. (pres. 1974-76), Union League Phila., Phila. Country Club, Sunday Breakfast Club, Corinthian Yacht Club. Avocations: sailing, skiing, golf, tennis. Home: 371 Rose Glen Dr Wayne PA 19087-4410 Office: Schnader Harrison Segal Ste 3600 1600 Market St Philadelphia PA 19103-4247

STUNTZ, LINDA GILLESPIE, government official, lawyer; b. Bellefontaine, Ohio, Sept. 11, 1954; d. J. Bradshaw Gillespie and Freda Taylor; m. Reid P.F. Stuntz, May 23, 1981; children: Joseph Gillespie, Grace Reid. AB, Wittenberg U., 1976; JD, Harvard U., 1979. Bar: D.C. 1979, U.S. Dist. Ct. D.C. 1980, U.S. Temp. Emergency Ct. Appeals 1980, U.S. Ct. Appeals (D.C. cir.) 1980, U.S. Supreme Ct. 1983. Assoc. Jones, Day, Reavis & Pogue, Washington, 1979-81, 87-89; assoc. minority counsel Energy and Commerce Com., U.S. Ho. of Reps., Washington, 1981-86, minority counsel, staff dir., 1986-87; dep. under sec. for policy, planning and analysis U.S. Dept. Energy, Washington, 1989-92, acting asst. sec. for fossil energy, 1991, acting asst. sec. for domestic and internat. energy policy, 1992, dep. sec. energy, 1992—. Mem. Fed. Energy Bar Assn. Republican. Office: US Dept Energy Office of Dep Sec 1000 Independence Ave SW Washington DC 20585-0001

STUPAK, BART T., congressman, lawyer; b. Feb. 29, 1952; m. Laurie Ann Olsen; children: Ken, Bart Jr. AA in Criminal Justice, Northwestern Mich. C.C., Traverse City, 1972; BS in Criminal Justice, Saginaw Valley State Coll., 1977; JD, Thomas M. Cooley Law Sch., 1981. Patrolman Escanaba City Police Dept., 1972-73; state trooper Mich. Dept. State Police, 1973-84; instr. State Police Tng. Acad., 1980-82; atty., 1981-84, Hansley, Neiman, Peterson, Beauchamp, Stupak, Bergman P.C., 1984-85; ptnr. Stupak, Bergman, Stupak P.C., 1985-88; mem. Mich. Ho. of Reps., 1989-90; prin. Bart T. Stupak P.C., 1991—; mem. 103rd-104th Congresses from 1st Mich. dist., 1993—; mem. commerce subcom. on health & environment. Nat. committeeman Boy Scouts Am., coach Menominee Youth Baseball Assn., Little League; active Wildlife Unltd., Menominee Woods and Streams Assn., Menominee County Hist. Soc.; adv. com. Bay Pines Juv. Detection Ctr. Mem. Nat. Rifle Assn., Sons of the Am. Legion, Knights of Columbus, Elks Club, State Employees Retirees Assn., fin. com. Holy Spirit Catholic Ch. Democrat. Office: US Ho of Reps 317 Cannon Ho Ofc Bldg Washington DC 20515*

STUPAK, RONALD JOSEPH, dean, management educator, researcher; b. Allentown, Pa., Nov. 28, 1934; s. Frank John and Rose (Sisko) S.; m. Dolores Barbara Stupak, June 14, 1958; 1 child, Valeska Celina. BA summa cum laude, Moravian Coll., 1961; MA, Ohio State U., 1964, PhD, 1967; Exec. Cert., Fed. Exec. Inst., Charlottesville, Va., 1973. Sales planner Pa. Power and Light Co., Allentown, 1961-63; instr. to assoc. prof. Miami U., Oxford, Ohio, 1966-74; prof. to assoc. dir. Fed. Exec. Inst., Charlottesville, 1974-84;

prof. and dir. U. So. Calif., L.A./Washington, 1984-95; disting. scholar-in-residence Nat. Ctr. for State Cts., Williamsburg, Va., 1994-95; dean Ctr. for Effective Orgnl. Leadership Mt. Vernon Coll., 1995—, disting. faculty rsch. scholar, 1995—; exec. v.p. Sydron Corp., Bethesda, Md., 1993—; dean Ctr. Effective Orgnl. Leadership, disting. faculty rsch. scholar of mgmt. Mt. Vernon Coll., 1995—. Author: The Shaping of Foreign Policy, 1968, American Foreign Policy, 1979, The Assistant Secretaries, 1979. Chmn. Students for Kennedy, Bethlehem, Pa., 1960-61; coord. Ethnics for Johnson, Columbus, Ohio, 1963-64; mem. Va. Strategic Coun., Richmond, 1990-94; advisor Lt. Gov.'s Office, Richmond, 1990-94. With U.S. Army, 1955-57. Recipient Commenius award Moravian Coll., 1974, Outstanding Tchg. award U. So. Calif. Sch. Pub. Adminstrn., 1992; named Disting. Scholar, Nat. Ctr. for State Cts., 1994; Mershon fellow, 1963-67. Mem. Am. Soc. for Pub. Adminstrn. (life, Nat. Capital chpt. dir. 1985-88), Travelers Protective Assn., Fed. Exec. Inst. Alumni Assn. Democrat. Avocations: sports, film, food, poetry, aerobics. Home: 663 Bradford Ln Earlysville VA 22936 Office: Sydron Corp 7508 Coddle Harbor Ln Potomac MD 20854

STUPSKI, LAWRENCE J., investment company executive; b. 1945. JD, Yale U., 1970. V.p. Bradford Nat. Corp., N.Y.C., 1971-78; with Western Bradford Tr. Inc., San Francisco, 1978-80; pres., COO, CEO Charles Schwab & Co. Inc. (formerly Charles Schwab Corp.), 1980—, also bd. dirs. Office: Charles Schwab & Co Inc 101 Montgomery St San Francisco CA 94104-4122

STURDIVANT, FREDERICK DAVID, consultant, business educator; b. Whitewright, Tex., Oct. 17, 1937; s. Wyatt A. and Juanita P. (Phillips) S.; m. Patricia A. Robinson, Dec. 22, 1959 (div. 1981); children—Kaira, Lisha, Brian.; m. Teresa A. Mobley, Feb. 3, 1982. B.S., San Jose State Coll., 1959; M.B.A., U. Oreg., 1960; Ph.D., Northwestern U., 1963. Asst. prof. U. So. Calif., 1964-67; assoc. prof. U. Tex. at Austin, 1967-70, Harvard U., 1970-72; M. Riklis prof. bus. and its environment Ohio State U., Columbus, 1972-84; mng. dir. Gemini Mgmt. Consulting, San Francisco, 1984—; dir. Progressive Corp., Cleve., 1973-81, State Savs., Columbus, 1975-86, Actmedia, N.Y.C., 1977-80, Fel-Pro, Inc., Chgo., 1987—; bd. trustees Mktg. Sci. Inst., Cambridge, Mass., 1992—; mem. Task Force on Mktg. and Low-Income Consumers, Nat. Mktg. Adv. Com., Dept. Commerce, 1967-70; cons. Office Calif. Atty. Gen., 1966, Sen. Charles Percy, 1968; mem. adv. coun. on urban affairs to lt. gov., Tex., 1969-70; dir. rsch. Robert N. Shamansky of Ohio Congl. Campaign, 1980. Author: (with others) Competition and Human Behavior, 1968, The Ghetto Marketplace, 1969, Managerial Analysis in Marketing, 1970, Growth Through Service: The Story of American Hospital Supply Corporation, 1970, Perspectives in Marketing Management, 1971, (with O. Smalley) The Credit Merchants: A History of Spiegel, Inc, 1973, (with A. Andreasen) Minorities and Marketing: Research Challenges, 1977, Business and Society: A Managerial Approach, 4th edit, 1990, The Corporate Social Challenge, 4th edit, 1990; Contbr. articles to profl. jours. Recipient CBA Teaching Excellence award, 1968, Jack G. Taylor Teaching Excellence award, 1969, Cactus Teaching Excellence award, 1970. Mem. Am. Mktg. Assn., Assn. for Consumer Research, Southwestern Social Sci. Assn., Bus. and Society Initiative Council, Acad. of Mgmt., Beta Gamma Sigma. Democrat. Home: 10130 Oakwood Cir Carmel CA 93923-8004 Office: Gemini Mgmt Consulting One Montgomery St 17th fl San Francisco CA 94104

STURGE, MICHAEL DUDLEY, physicist; b. Bristol, Eng., May 25, 1931; came to U.S., 1961, naturalized 1991; s. Paul Dudley and Rachel (Graham) S.; m. Mary Balk, Aug. 21, 1956; children: David Mark, Thomas Graham, Peter Daniel, Benedict Paul. BA in Engring. and Physics, Gonville and Caius Coll., Cambridge, Eng., 1952; PhD in Physics, Cambridge U., Eng., 1957. Mem. staff Mullard Rsch. Lab. (now Philips), Redhill, Eng., 1956-58; sr. rsch. fellow Royal Radar Establishment, Malvern, Eng., 1958-61; mem. tech. staff Bell Labs., Murray Hill, N.J., 1961-83, Bellcore, Red Bank, N.J., 1984-86; prof. dept. physics Dartmouth Coll., Hanover, N.H., 1986—; rsch. assoc. Stanford U., 1965, U. B.C., Vancouver, Can., 1969; vis. prof. Technion, Haifa, Israel, 1972, 76, 81, 85, Williams Coll., Williamstown, Mass., 1982, 84, Trinity Coll., Dublin, 1989, 93, U. Fourier, Grenoble, France, 1989, 91; exch. scientist Philips Rsch. Lab., Eindhoven, The Netherlands, 1973-74. Contbr. over 100 papers in solid state physics to profl. publs.; co-editor: Excitons, 1982; editor Jour. of Luminescence, 1984-90. Fellow Am. Phys. Soc.; mem. Am. Assn. Physics Tchrs. Office: Dartmouth Coll Dept Physics Wilder Lab Hanover NH 03755-3528

STURGEN, WINSTON, photographer, printmaker, artist; b. Harrisburg, Pa., Aug. 27, 1938; s. George Winston and Gladys Erma (Lenker) S.; m. Nancy Kathryn Otto, Jan. 23, 1959 (div. 1981); 1 child, Bruce Eugene Sturgen; m. Jessica Sheldon, Mar. 15, 1988. BS in Forestry, Pa. State U., 1960; postgrad., U. N.H., 1961-62; M of Forestry, Pa. State U., 1964; postgrad., U. Oreg., 1966-68. Cert. profl. photographer. Devel. engr. Weyerhaeuser Co., Longview, Wash., 1964-66; mgr. Wickes Lumber Co., Elkhorn, Wis., 1968-70; dir. ops. Wickes Wanderland, Inc., Delavan, Wis., 1970-72; owner, mgr. Sturgen's Cleaners, Delavan, 1972-80, Images by Sturgen, Delavan, 1980-84; instr. photography continuing edn. dept. Western N.Mex. U., 1988-90; juror numerous orgns., 1982—. One-man shows include Artesia (N.Mex.) Mus. and Art Ctr., 1992, Delavan Art Mus., 1984, Donnell Libr., N.Y.C., 1992; exhibited in group shows at Carlsbad (N.Mex.) Mus., 1992, Sister Kenny Inst., 1992, (3rd Pl.), 93 (1st Pl.), 94, Deming Ctr. for the Arts, N.Mex., 1991, Shellfish Collection, Silver City, N.Mex., 1989, 90, 91, 92, 93, Thompson Gallery, U. N.Mex., 1989, Profl. Photographers Assn. of N.Mex., 1985, 86, 87, 88 (awards), Union Gallery, U. N.Mex., 1987, Gallery Sigala, Taos, N.Mex., 1986, World Trade Ctr., N.Y.C., 1992, 93, 94, Internat. Exposition of Photography, 1983, 84, 85, 87, Beyond Photography Touring Exhibit, 1991-92, An Am. Collection Touring Exhibit, San Francisco, Washington, Brussels, Tokyo, 1993-95, Sapporo (Japan) Internat. Print Biennial, 1993, Very Spl. Arts/N.Mex. Touring Exhibit, 1993-94, Ctr. Contemporary Art, St. Louis, 1994 (Purchase award), many others; pub. poetry, numerous articles in field. Founder, chmn. Winter Arts Festival, Silver City, N.Mex., 1988-90; com. mem. Taos Fall Arts Festival, 1985; com. chair Oktoberfest, Delavan, 1976-80. Residency grant Wurlitzer Found., 1987, 89. Mem. Very Spl. Artists N.Mex., Very Spl. Artists Washington, Enabled Artists United, Fuller Lodge Art Ctr. Avocations: painting, printmaking, photography. Home: c/o Gardner 3211 Elm St Harrisburg PA 17109

STURGEON, CHARLES EDWIN, management consultant; b. Cherryvale, Kans., May 30, 1928; s. William Charles and Lucile Myrtle (Gill) S.; children by previous marriage: Carol Ann, John Randolph, Richard Steven; m. Karen B. Riggan, May 21, 1988. A.A., Independence Jr. Coll., 1948; B.S., U. Kans., 1951; postgrad., U. Tulsa Grad. Sch., 1953-56; grad., Advanced Mgmt. Program, Harvard Bus. Sch., 1977. Research engr. Stanoline Oil and Gas, Tulsa, 1953-56; production supr. Vulcan Materials Co., Wichita, Kans., 1956-62; maintenance supt. Vulcan Materials Co., 1962-64, mgr. tech. services, 1964-69; plant mgr. Vulcan Materials Co., Newark, N.J., 1969-71; gen. mktg. mgr., v.p mktg. Vulcan Materials Co., Wichita, 1971-73; v.p. mfg. Vulcan Materials Co., Birmingham, Ala., 1974-77, pres. chem. div., 1977-87, pres., sr. v.p., 1987-90; prin. CESCO Cons. Co., Birmingham, 1990—; Birmingham, Ala., 1990. Adv. U. Kans. Sch. Chem. Engring. Served with U.S. Army, 1951-53. Mem. Am. Inst. Chem. Engrs., Nat. Mgmt. Assn., Chlorine Inst. (bd. dirs.), Chem. Mfg. Assn., Soc. Chem. Industries, Soc. of Materials, The Club Inc., Tau Theta Pi, Tau Beta Pi, Sigma Tau. Republican. Presbyterian. Office: CESCO Cons Co 2628 Apollo Cir Birmingham AL 35226-2664

STURGES, HOLLISTER, III, museum director; b. Kingston, N.Y., July 1, 1939; s. Hollister Jr. and Elizabeth (Betz) S.; m. Caroline Berg (div.); children: Kimberly, William Steele.; m. Judith Layson; 1 child, Elizabeth Layson. BA in Comparative Lit., Cornell U., 1962; MA in Art History, U. Calif., Berkeley, 1969, MPh in Art History, 1972. Cert. tchr., Calif. Tchr. English Placer High Sch., Auburn, Calif., 1963-66; instr. U. Mo., Kansas City, 1972-80; curator European art Joslyn Art Mus., Omaha, 1980-84; chief curator Indpls. Mus. Arts, 1984-87; dir. Springfield (Mass.) Mus. Fine Arts, 1988—, George Walter Vincent Smith Art Mus., 1988—; Panelist NEA, 1982, 86, 90; organizer art exhbns. Author: (exhbn. catalogue) Angels and Urchins: Images of Children at the Joslyn, 1980, (exhbn. catalogue) Jules Breton and the French Rural Tradition, 1982, (exhbn. catalogue) New Art from Puerto Rico, 1990; co-author: (exhbn. catalogue) Art of the Fantastic:

Latin America, 1920-87, 1987; author, editor: The Rural Vision: France and Americans in the late Nineteenth Century, 1987; author, co-editor: (mus. catalogue) Joslyn Art Museum Paintings and Sculptures from the Permanent Collections, 1987, (mus. handbook) Indianapolis Museum of Art: collections handbook, 1988. Bd. dirs. World Affairs Coun., 1989. Kress Found. fellow, 1974. Mem. Assn. Art Mus. Dirs., Coll. Art Assn., Am. Assn. Mus., New Eng. Mus. Assn. Avocations: squash, canoeing, chess. Office: Mus of Fine Arts 49 Chestnut St Springfield MA 01103

STURGES, JOHN SIEBRAND, consultant; b. Greenwich, Conn., Feb. 12, 1939; s. Harry Wilton and Elizabeth Helen (Niewenhous) S.; AB, Harvard U., 1960; MBA, U. So. Calif., 1965; cert. EDP, N.Y.U., 1972; cert. exec. program. Grad. Sch. Bus., U. Mich., 1982. Cert. sr. profl. in human resources, mgmt. cons.; m. Anastasia Daphne Bakalis, May 6, 1967; children: Christina Aurora, Elizabeth Athena. With Equitable Life Assurance Soc. U.S., N.Y.C., 1965-79, mgr. systems devel., 1965-70, dir. compensation and benefits, 1971-75, v.p., personnel and adminstrv. svcs., 1975-79; sr. v.p. personnel Nat. Westminster Bank U.S.A., N.Y.C., 1979-82; corp. sr. v.p. adminstrn. and human resources Willis-Corroon Corp., N.Y.C., 1982-84; mng. dir. human resources Marine Midland Bank, N.Y.C., 1984-87; mng. dir. Siebrand-Wilton Assocs., N.Y.C., 1986-87, pres., 1987—. Lay reader St. Peters Episcopal Ch., Freehold, N.J., 1972—. Lt. USNR, 1960-65. Mem. Internat. Found. Employee Benefit Plans, Commerce Assocs., Soc. for Human Resource Mgmt. (dir. 1979—), Am. Compensation Assn., Human Resources Planning Soc., Inst. Mgmt. Cons. (bd. dirs. 1992—), Employment Mgmt. Assn. (bd. dirs. 1993—), Monmouth-Ocean Devel. Coun. (dir. 1989—), Beta Gamma Sigma (dir. N.Y. 1978—), Phi Kappa Phi. Republican. Clubs: India House, Nat. Press Club, Harvard (N.Y.C.), Boston, Princeton, N.J. (dir. 1991—), Nassau Club. Office: Siebrand-Wilton Assocs Inc PO Box 2498 New York NY 10008-2498

STURGESS, GEOFFREY J., aeronautical research engineer. Sr. rsch. engr. Pratt & Whitney Engring., Hartford, Conn. Recipient Energy Systems award AIAA, 1994. Home: 26 Forest-View Dr Vernon Rockville CT 06066-4807*

STURGIS, ROBERT SHAW, architect; b. Boston, July 8, 1922; s. George and Rosamond Thomas (Bennett) S.; m. Chiquita Mitchell, Dec. 20, 1947; children: Susanna Jordan, Roger Bennett, John Hanson, Ellen Shaw. Grad. St. Mark's Sch., Southboro, Mass., 1939; AB, Harvard, 1947, MArch, 1951. Architect Kilham, Hopkins, Greeley & Brodie, Boston, 1952-55, Shepley, Bulfinch, Richardson & Abbott, Boston, 1955-64, Robert S. Sturgis, Boston, 1964-68; ptnr. Feloney & Sturgis (architects), Cambridge, 1969-75, Robert Sturgis, FAIA, 1975—; head critic Boston Archtl. Ctr., 1955-66, instr., 1988—, chair edn. com., 1989—; vis. lectr. Va. Poly. Inst., Blacksburg, 1970, Boston U., Yale U., 1975; urban design cons. Haverhill, Lynn and Cambridge, Mass., also Atlanta.; mem. overseers' vis. com. Sch. Design Harvard, 1965-70; chmn. Gov.'s Task Force and Cultural Facilities, 1972; chmn. bd., lectr. Boston Archtl. Center, 1981-85; cons. Maine State Capitol com., 1989-90. Prin. works include Cotting House, Harvard Bus. Sch., 1968, Architects' Plan for Boston, 1961, AIA Urban Design Assistance Team Program, 1967; urban designs for, Atlanta, Haverhill, Kendall Sq., Cambridge; contbr. articles to profl. jours. Served with USAAF, 1942-45. Fellow AIA (chmn. urban planning and design com. 1970, mem. planned growth task group 1988-92, Presdl. citation 1988); mem. Boston Soc. Architects (pres. 1972, chmn. civic design com. 1959-67, chmn. regional design com. 1988—), regional joint regional transp. com. 1994—). Home and Office: 5 Doublet Hill Rd Weston MA 02193-2304

STURGIS, WILLIAM BEAUFORT, packaging company executive; b. Rock Hill, S.C., Dec. 23, 1934; s. Beaufort Monroe and Corene (Clinton) S.; m. Martha Elizabeth Blackmon, Jan. 30, 1935; children: Randolph, Richard, Scott, Mark. BSChemE, Clemson U., 1957; cert. advanced mgmt. program, Harvard U., 1977. Research and devel. mgr., CRYOVAC Div. W.R. Grace and Co., Duncan, S.C., 1962-66; mfg. mgr. CRYOVAC Div. W.R. Grace and Co., Mississaugan, Ont., 1966-70; v.p. mktg. and product planning CRYOVAC Div. W.R. Grace and Co., Duncan, S.C., 1972-76, v.p mktg., 1976-84, pres., 1984—; v.p W. R. Grace and Co., N.Y.C., 1984—; dir. Nat. Broiler Council, Washington, 1972—. Bd. dirs. Clemson U. Found. With USAR, 1954-60. Mem. Am. Inst. Chem. Engrs., Soc. Plastic Industry. Presbyterian. Lodge: Rotary. Avocations: golf, hunting, fishing.

STURLEY, MICHAEL F., law educator; b. Syracuse, N.Y., Feb. 14, 1955; s. Richard Avern and Helen Elizabeth (Fisher) S.; m. Michele Y. Deitch, July 2, 1989. BA, Yale U., 1977, JD, 1981; BA in Jurisprudence, Oxford U., 1980, MA, 1985. Bar: N.Y. 1984, U.S. Dist. Ct. (so. and ea. dists.) N.Y. 1984, U.S. Supreme Ct. 1987. Law clk. to Judge Amalya L. Kearse, U.S. Ct. Appeals for 2d Cir., N.Y.C., 1981-82; law clk. to Justice Lewis F. Powell, Jr. U.S. Supreme Ct., Washington, 1982-83; assoc. Sullivan & Cromwell, N.Y.C., 1983-84; asst. prof. law U. Tex. Law Sch., Austin, 1984-88, prof., 1988—; external examiner U. London, 1987, vis. prof. Queen Mary and Westfield Coll. U. London, 1990, adviser Restatement (3d) of Property (servitudes), 1989—. Compiler, editor: The Legislative History of the Carriage of Goods by Sea Act and the Travaux Préparatoires of the Hague Rules, 3 vols., 1990; editorial bd. Jour. Maritime Law and Commerce, 1989—, book review editor, 1993—; contbg. author Benedict on Admiralty, 1990—; contbr. articles to legal jours. Mem. Am. Law Inst., Maritime Law Assn. (acad.). Office: U Tex Sch Law 727 E 26th St Austin TX 78705-3224

STURM, DONALD L., construction executive; b. 1932; married. BA, CCNY, 1954; LLB, U. Denver, 1958; LLM, NYU, 1959. Atty. IRS, 1959-62; with Peter Kiewit Sons Inc., Omaha, 1963—, v.p., 1969-82, sr. v.p., 1982-86, vice chmn., 1986—, also bd. dirs.; sr. v.p. Kiewit U.S. Co. subs. Peter Kiewit Sons Inc., Omaha, from 1982, also bd. dirs.; chmn. Kiewit Holdings Group Inc., Norwalk, Conn., 1986—. Office: Kiewit Holdings Group Inc 800 Connecticut Ave Norwalk CT 06854-1631

STURM, FRED GILLETTE, philosopher, educator; b. Batavia, N.Y., Oct. 15, 1925; s. Fred William and Eleanor Louise (Gillette) S.; m. Margaret Schaeffer (dec. Nov. 1953); children: Margaret Louise Sturm Almony, Fred Schaeffer; m. Hilda Lowd (dec. July 1963); m. Julienne Mullette (div. July 1970); m. Katharine Ehrgood, Oct. 16, 1971. AB, Allegheny Coll., 1946; MDiv, Union Theol. Sem., N.Y.C., 1948; AM, U. Rochester, 1950; PhD, Columbia U., 1961; postgrad., Vanderbilt U., 1949, Tunghai U., Taichung, Rep. of China, 1963, Chinese U., Hong Kong, 1972. Prof. Greek and N.T. Faculdade de Teologia da Igreja Metodista do Brasil, São Paulo, 1950, 51; prof. religion Inst. Pôrto Alegre, Brasil, 1952; prof. philosophy Western Coll., Oxford, Ohio, 1954-74, coord. intercultural emphasis, 1966-70; prof. philosphy U. N.Mex., Albuquerque, 1975—, acting chair dept., 1978-79, chair dept., 1982-90, interim dean Coll. Arts and Scis., 1986-87; vis. prof. religion Miami U., Oxford, Ohio, 1957-58; vis. prof. philosophy Sem. Teológico da Igreja Episcopal do Brasil, São Paulo, 1965; vis. prof. fgn. langs. and lits. Shaanxi Tchrs. U., Xi'an, People's Republic China, 1982, hon. prof., 1982—; adj. assoc. prof. philosophy, SUNY, Buffalo, 1974-75; dir. Inst. for Pueblo Indian Studies, Indian Pueblo Cultural Ctr., Albuquerque, 1976-88, assoc. dir. for R&D— 1988—. Author: Introduction to Logic, 1961, Existence in Search of Essence: The Philosophy of Spirit of Raimundo de Farias Brito, 1961, Chinese Culture, Non-Western Studies, and the Liberal Arts College, 1962, O Significado Atual do Pensamento Britiano, 1962; translator: Panorama of the History of Philosophy in Brazil, 1962; editor: Fuentes de la Filosofia Latinoamericana, 1967, Brazilian Studies: A Guide to the Humanities Literature, 1986, Pueblo Style and Regional Architecture, 1990; editor in chief Jour. Chinese Studies, 1983—; contbr. book chpts., articles to profl. jours. Fulbright rsch. grantee, Republic of China, 1963, Brasil, 65, 88, Social Sci. Rsch. Coun. grantee, Mexico, 1966, Calouste Gulbenkian Found. rsch., Portugal, 1981. Fellow Soc. Philosophers in Am. (bd. dirs. 1990—), Royal Asiatic Soc. (fgn.), Internat. Ctr. for Asian Studies, Centro de Estudos do Pensamento Luso-Brasileiro; mem. Am. Assn. for Chinese Studies (bd. dirs. 1964-87), Am. Philos. Assn., Am. Soc. for Aesthetics,Inst. Brasileiro de Filosofia (hon.), Academia Brasileira de Filosofia (effective mem. in perpetuity), Internat. Husserl and Phenomenological Soc., Internat. Soc. for Chinese Philosophy (co-dir. rsch. group on Chinese and comparative aesthetics), Latin Am. Indian Lits. Assn., Rsch. Inst. for Global Philosophy (adv. bd. 1967—), Soc. for Iberian and Latin Am. Thought (exec. com. 1976-78, v.p., 1978-80, pres 1980-82, pres.-elect 1992-94, pres. 1994—), Soc. for Advancement Am. Philosophy, The China Acad. (intenat. Sinological rsch.

com. 1969—), N.Am. Soc. for Social and Polit. Philosophy (editorial bd. 1987—), Phi Beta Kappa. Socialist. Methodist, United Ch. of Christ. Home: 7709 Midge St NE Albuquerque NM 87109-5229 Office: U NMex Dept Philosophy Albuquerque NM 87131 *In a global age of conflict when the importance of improved communication is being stressed, we need to give priority to the neglected art of listening: listening attentively and sympathetically to the viewpoints of others—essential to any true and useful dialogue; as well as listening patiently and expectantly to the voice of the Spirit without and the daemon within—necessary to know what we are called to be and do in the here-and-now.*

STURMON, PATRICIA MONTGOMERY, public relations executive; b. Springfield, Ill., Aug. 27, 1945; d. David Thomas and Mary Jane (McBride) Montgomery; m. Daniel Eugene Sturmon, Nov. 16, 1991. BA, U. Ky., 1967; EdM, U. Cin., 1970. Mgr. edn. rels. Ill. Bell, Homewood, 1971-72; mgr. comm. rels. Ill. Bell, Chicago Heights/Wheaton, 1972-75; editor Telenews Ill. Bell, Chgo., 1975-76; mgr. comm. rels. Ill. Bell, Joliet, 1976-78; mgr. media rels. Ill. Bell, Chgo., 1978-83, dir. media rels., 1983-90; sr. dir. external rels. Ameritech, Chgo., 1990-94; dir. corp. comm. ANTEC Corp., Rolling Meadows, Ill., 1994—; bd. dirs. Ill. Telecomm. Access Corp. Bd. dirs. Girl Scouts of Chgo., pres. 1988-90, Vol. Network, chair, 1992-93; bd. dirs. United Cerebral Palsy, 1990-93, Abraham Lincoln Ctr., 1990-94, Ada S. McKinley Community Ctrs., 1990-94, Girl Scouts of DuPage, 1992—. Mem. PRSA, Chgo. Pub. Rels. Forum, Women in Communications, Phi Alpha Theta, Delta Delta Delta. Avocations: snow skiing, tennis. Office: ANTEC 2850 W Golf Rd Ste 600 Rolling Meadows IL 60008

STURNS, VERNELL, airport terminal executive. Exec. dir. Dallas/Fort Worth Internat. Airport; exec. bd. dir., Dallas/Fort Worth Internat. Airport. Office: Dallas/Fort Worth Intl Airport PO Drawer 619428 Airport Admin 3200 E Airfield Dr Dallas TX 75261-9428

STURROCK, PETER ANDREW, space science and astrophysics educator; b. South Stifford, Essex, England, Mar. 20, 1924; came to U.S., 1949; s. Albert Edward and Mabel Minnie (Payne) S.; m. Marilyn Fern Stenson, June 29, 1963; children: Deirdre, Colin; 1 child from previous marriage, Myra. BA, Cambridge (Eng.) U., 1945, MA, 1948, PhD, 1951. Scientist Telecommunications Rsch. Establishment, Malvern, Eng., 1943-46, Nat. Bur. Standards, Washington, 1949-50, Atomic Energy Rsch. Establishment, Harwell, 1951-53; fellow St. John's Coll., Cambridge U., 1952-55; rsch. assoc. Stanford (Calif.) U., 1955-61, prof. applied physics and engring. sci., then prof. space sci. and astrophysics, dept. applied physics, 1961—, dir. for plasma rsch., 1964-74, 80-83; dep. dir. Ctr. for Space Sci. and Astrophysics, 1983-92, dir., 1992—. Author: Static and Dynamic Electron Optics, 1955, Plasma Physics, 1993; editor: Plasma Astrophysics, 1967, Solar Flares, 1980, Physics of the Sun, vols. I, II, III, 1986. Recipient Gravity prize Gravity Found., 1967, Hale prize Am. Astron. Soc., 1986, Henryk Arctowski medal NAS, 1990, Space Sci. award AIAA, 1992; European Ctr. for Nuclear Rsch. fellow, 1957-58. Fellow AAAS, Royal Astron. Soc., Internat. Astron. Union, Am. Phys. Soc.; mem. Soc. for Sci. Exploration (pres 1982—). Office: Stanford U Ctr Space Sci & Astrophys ERL 306 Stanford CA 94305*

STURROCK, THOMAS TRACY, botany educator, horticulturist; b. Havana, Cuba, Dec. 9, 1921; s. David and Ruth Esther (Earle) S. (parents U.S. citizens); m. Jeanne Norquist, June 30, 1948; children—Nancy Elizabeth, John David, Barbara Jeanne Sturrock Morris, Catherine Ann Sturrock Hilliard, Robert Charles. B.S in Agr. with honors, U. Fla., Gainesville, 1943, M.S. in Agr, 1943, Ph.D., 1961. Ptnr. Sturrock Tropical Fruit Nursery, Homes. Ye; insp. Fla. State Plant Bd., 1956-57; instr. Palm Beach (Fla.) High Sch., 1957-58; research assist. U. Fla., 1958-60; instr. Palm Beach Jr. Coll., 1960-64; asst. prof. botany Fla. Atlantic U., 1964-68, assoc. prof., 1968-74, prof., 1974-89, prof. emeritus 1989—; asst. dean Coll. Sci., 1971-89. Pres. West Palm Beach Jaycees, 1951-52; scoutmaster Gulf Stream council Boy Scouts Am., 1946-55, cubmaster, 1960-62, dist. chmn., 1961-63, exec. bd., 1961—, v.p., 1969-70, 80—. Served with USAAF, 1943-46. Recipient Silver Beaver award, 1951, Disting. Eagle Scout award Boy Scouts Am., 1989. Mem. Fla. Hort. Soc., Fla. Acad. Scis., Sigma Xi. Presbyterian. Home: 1010 Camellia Rd West Palm Beach FL 33405-2408

STURTEVANT, BRERETON, retired lawyer, former government official; b. Washington, Nov. 24, 1921; d. Charles Lyon and Grace (Brereton) S. B.A., Wellesley Coll., 1942; J.D., Temple U., 1949; postgrad., U. Del., 1969-71. Bar: D.C. 1949, Del. 1950. Research chemist E.I. duPont DeNemours & Co., 1942-50; law clk. Del. Supreme Ct., 1950; gen. practice law Wilmington, Del., 1950-57; partner Connolly, Bove & Lodge, Wilmington, 1957-71; examiner-in-chief U.S. Patent and Trademark Office Bd. Appeals, Washington, 1971-81; Adj. prof. law Georgetown U., 1974-79. Trustee Holton-Arms Sch., Bethesda, Md., 1977—, chmn. or mem. all coms., mem. trustee com. and bldgs./grounds com., 1994—. Mem. Am., Del. bar assns., Exec. Women in Govt. (charter mem., chmn 1978-79). Episcopalian. Clubs: Wellesley College, Washington-Wellesley (pres. 1982-84). Home: 1227 Morningside Ln Alexandria VA 22308-1042

STURTEVANT, JULIAN MUNSON, biophysical chemist, educator; b. Edgewater, N.J., Aug. 9, 1908; s. Edgar Howard and Bessie Fitch (Skinner) S.; m. Elizabeth Reihl, June 8, 1929; children—Ann Sturtevant Ormsby, Bradford. AB, Columbia U., 1927; PhD, Yale U., 1931; ScD, Ill. Coll., 1962; Sc.D. (hon.), Regensberg U., 1978. Instr. chemistry Yale U., New Haven, 1931-39, asst. prof., 1939-46, assoc. prof., 1946-51, prof., 1951-77, sr. research scientist, 1977—; staff mem. Radiation Lab., MIT, Cambridge, 1943-46; vis. prof. U. Calif.-San Diego, 1966-67, 69-70; vis. fellow Battelle Seattle Research Ctr. and U. Wash., 1972-73, Stanford U., 1976-77. Contbr. numerous articles to profl. jours. Recipient Huffman award Calorimetry Conf. U.S.A., 1964; William DeVane award Yale U., 1978; Innovator in Biochemistry award Med. Coll. Va., 1984, Wilbur Cross medal Yale U., 1987; Guggenheim fellow Cambridge U., 1955-56; Fulbright scholar U. Adelaide, Australia, 1962-63; vis. scholar, Stanford U., 1975-76; Alexander von Humboldt sr. scientist award, 1978-79. Fellow AAAS, Am. Acad. Arts and Scis.; mem. Nat. Acad. Sci., Am. Chem. Soc., Am. Soc. Biol. Chemists, Conn. Acad. Sci. and Tech.

STURTEVANT, MARGARET D., retail executive; b. Wrangell, Alaska, Jan. 9, 1929; d. Orlando K. and Margaret (Gunyah) Bakke; m. Clark B. Sturtevant, Sept. 25, 1948; children: Andra Jane, Andrew J. Student, Peterson Bus. Sch., Seattle, 1962-63. Owner The Alley Cat, Wrangell. Mem. tourism adv. bd. City of Wrangell, 1992—; v.p., bd. dirs. Wrangell Mus., 1987-93, bd. dirs., 1993—; treas. 1st Presbyn. Ch., Wrangell, 1990—; pres. The Sno Bldg., Inc., Wrangell, 1993—; pres. Wrangell Coop. Assn.; dir. Tribal House of the Bear, Wrangell, 1990—; pres. Wrangell Cultural Heritage Commn., 1989-94. Named Woman of the Yr., Beta Sigma Phi, 1991. Mem. Wrangell Emblem Club (pres. 1992). Avocations: gardening, crafts. Home: PO Box 253 225 Cassiar St Wrangell AK 99929 Office: Wrangell Coop Assoc PO Box 868 Wrangell AK 99929

STURTEVANT, PETER MANN, JR., television news executive; b. Northampton, Mass., Feb. 27, 1943; s. Peter Mann and Katharine Bryan (Hobson) S.; m. Anne Elizabeth Fitzpatrick, July 12, 1969 (div. Dec. 1984); 1 child, Amanda Hadden; m. Toni E. Siegel, Apr. 14, 1985; 1 child, Gillian Lee. BA, Wilmington Coll., 1965; MA, U. Iowa, 1967. Assoc. prodr. CBS News, Washington, 1967-71; bur. chief Viet Nam CBS News, Saigon, 1971-73; nat. news editor CBS News, N.Y.C., 1974-80, asst. v.p. devel. news events, 1981-83, producer 60 Minutes, 1984-85; exec. news editor CNN, N.Y.C., 1985-86; prodr. Today's Bus. Buena Vista TV, N.Y.C., 1987; dir. news coverage CNBC, N.Y.C., 1988-90; v.p., mng. editor CNBC, Ft. Lee, N.J., 1991-94; sr. v.p. Internat. Bus. News NBC, 1994—. Named Disting. Alumnus, Wilmington Coll., 1975; named to Journalism Hall of Fame, U. Iowa Sch. Journalism, 1988. Mem. Nat. Acad. Cable Programming (nominated ACE award 1992, 93, 94), Soc. Profl. Journalists, Deadline Club N.Y. Episcopalian. Avocations: racquet sports, landscaping, travelling, philately, parenting. Home: 90 Riverside Dr New York NY 10024 Office: NBC 30 Rockefeller Plz New York NY 10112

STURTEVANT, WILLIAM CURTIS, anthropologist; b. Morristown, N.J., July 26, 1926; s. Alfred Henry and Phoebe (Reed) S.; m. Theda Maw (div. 1986); children: Kinthi D.M., Reed P.M., Alfred B.M. (dec.); m. Sally McLendon, 1990. B.A., U. Calif.-Berkeley, 1949; Ph.D., Yale U., 1955.

Instr. dept. anthropology, asst. curator anthropology Peabody Mus., Yale U., 1954-56; ethnologist, gen. anthropologist Bur. Am. Ethnology Smithsonian Instn., Washington, 1956-65, curator N.Am. ethnology dept. anthropology Nat. Mus. Natural History Smithsonian Instn., 1965—; Fulbright lectr. U. Oxford, 1967-68; Regents lectr. U. Calif., Berkeley, 1981; vis. fellow Worcester Coll., U. Oxford, 1986-87; adj. prof. anthropology Johns Hopkins U., 1974-89; ethnol. fieldwork Seminole, Fla., 1950-67, 85 (18 months), Burma, 1955, 63-64 (12 months), Iroquois, 1952-65 (8 months), others. Author monographs, chpts. in books; Gen. editor: Handbook of N.Am. Indians; Contbr. articles to profl. jours. Trustee Mus. Am. Indian, Heye Found., N.Y.C., 1976-82, 84-86; bd. dirs. Survival Internat. USA, 1982-88; mem. internat. exec. Survival Internat., 1986-88. Served with USNR, 1945-46. Fellow Royal Anthrop. Inst. Gt. Britain and Ireland, Am. Anthrop. Assn. (book rev. editor 1962-66, exec. bd. 1974-77, pres. 1981), AAAS (del. coun. 1974-77, mem. coun. affairs 1974-75), Soc. des Américanistes, Am. Soc. Ethnohistory (pres. 1965-66), Coun. Mus. Anthropology (pres. 1979-81), Am. Ethnol. Soc. (pres. 1976-77), Soc. Am. Archaeology, Soc. Study Indigenous Langs. Ams., Royal Geog. Soc.; mem. Hakluyt Soc., Champlain Soc., Anthrop. Soc. Washington (pres. 1992-93). Home: 418 F St NE Washington DC 20002-4908 Office: MRC 112 Smithsonian Instn Washington DC 20560

STURTZ, DONALD LEE, physician, naval officer; b. Coshocton, Ohio, Apr. 18, 1933; s. Walter Raymond and Helene Josephine (Kubic) S.; m. Alice Marie McGuire, June 11, 1955; children: Jimalee, Janel. BS, U.S. Naval Acad., Annapolis, Md., 1955; MD, U. Pa., 1965. Diplomate Am. Bd. Surgery. Surg. resident USN, Phila., 1965-70; ship's surgeon USN, 1970-71; staff surgeon Bethesda Naval Hosp., USN, 1971-80; chief of surgery San Diego Naval Hosp., USN, 1980-84; exec. officer Oakland (Calif.) Naval Hosp., USN, 1984-85; prof. clin. surgery USN, Bethesda, Md., 1985-87; commd. Naval Med. Command USN, 1987-88; fleet surgeon USN, Norfolk, Va., 1989-91; surgeon USUHS, Bethesda, Md., 1991—. Contbr. articles to profl. jours. Recipient B.D. Larrey award for Surgical Excellence, Surgical Dept. USUHS, Bethesda, 1988. Fellow ACS (gov. 1985-88); mem. Am. Assn. for Surgery of Trauma, Assn. Mil. Surgeons, USN Inst. Republican. Methodist. Avocations: travel, antiquing, music, reading. Office: USUHS Dept Surgery 4301 Jones Bridge Rd Bethesda MD 20814-4712

STURTZ, RONALD M., lawyer; b. Bayonne, N.J., July 12, 1930; s. Eugene and Margaret (Altman) S.; m. Bernice Winter, nov. 30, 1952; children: Judith Sturtz Karp, Bonnie Sturtz Romberg. BS, Tulane U., 1951; JD, Am. U., Washington, 1957. Bar: N.J. 1958, U.S. Dist. Ct. N.J. 1958, U.S. Dist. Ct. D.C. 1957, U.S. Supreme Ct. 1965. Law sec. Superior Ct. N.J. Appellate Div., Trenton, 1957-58; assoc. Riker Danzig & Emery, Newark, 1958-61, Hannoch Weisman Stern & Besser, Newark, 1961-63; ptnr., dir. Hannoch Weisman, Roseland, N.J., 1963—; draftsman N.J. Alt. Procedure for Dispute Resolution Act, 1987; mem. N.J. Supreme Ct. Standing Com. on Complementary Dispute Resolution, 1990—. Nat. patroller Nat. Ski Patrol System, Denver, 1970-95. Sgt. U.S. Army, 1951-54. Mem. ABA (nat. chmn. creditor's rights com. sect. litigation 1985-88, arbitration com. 1990-94, bylaws, resolutions and blanket authority com. 1994—), Assn. Fed. Bar State N.J. (pres. 1983-84, trustee 1984—), Essex County Bar Assn. (chmn. equity jurisprudence com. 1984-87), N.J. Bar Assn. Democrat. Jewish. Avocations: boating, skiing. Home: 27 Badger Dr Livingston NJ 07039-4621 Office: Hannoch Weisman 4 Becker Farm Rd Roseland NJ 07068-1734

STUTZ, ANGELA LYNN, health facility administrator; b. Rossville, Ga., July 13, 1957; d. James Henry and Nancy Ann (Young) Davis; divorced; 1 child, Brandon. AS, Dalton Jr. Coll., Ga., 1977; BSN, So. Coll., 1985; postgrad., St. Francis U. RN, Ga. Staff nurse Critical Care Unit Hutcheson Med. Ctr., Ft. Oglethorpe, Ga., 1977-79, supr. ICU, 1980-85, dir. quality assurance, RM, 1985-90, v.p., med. staff liaison, 1990—; interim pres. Hutcheson Md. Ctr., Ft. Oglethorpe, Ga., 1994, v.p., 1994—; part time instr. So. Collegedale, Tenn., 1985-86, Walker Tech. Sch. Rockspring, Ga., 1980's; adv. bd. dirs. chairperson LPN program Walker Tech. Sch., Rockspring, 1990—. Chairperson, past pres. Am. Cancer Soc., Ft. Oglethorpe, 1985-86. Mem. Nat. Quality Assurance Soc. (dist. rep. 1992). Baptist. Avocation: reading. Home: Rt 12 Box 12418 Patty Rd Ringgold GA 30736 Office: Hutcheson Med Ctr 100 Gross Crescent Cir Fort Oglethorpe GA 30742

STUTZMAN, WARREN LEE, electrical engineer, educator; b. Elgin, Ill., Oct. 22, 1941; s. James Earl and Christina Louise (Steidinger) S.; m. Claudia Janeanne Morris, Dec. 20, 1964; children: Darren Morris, Dana Lynn. BEE, U.Ill., 1964, AB in Math., 1964; MEE, Ohio State U., 1965, PhD in Elec. Engring., 1969. Asst. prof. U. Poly. Inst. and State U., Blacksburg, 1969-74, assoc. prof., 1974-79, prof., 1979—, Thomas Phillips prof. engring., 1992—. Author: (with G. Thiele) Antenna Theory and Design, 1981, Polarization in Electromagnetic Systems, 1993. Fellow IEEE. Office: Va Poly Inst & State U Elec Engring Dept Blacksburg VA 24061-0111

STUTZMANN, NATHALIE, classical vocalist; b. Paris. Student piano, bassoon and chamber music, Ecole de l'Opéra de Paris. Performer: (operatic prodns.) Debussy's Pelleas et Mélisande, Florence and Bonn, Mussorgsky's Boris Godunov at the Liceu, Barcelona, Bordeaux, Gounod's Romeo et Juliette, Zurich, Mozart's Die Zauberflöte, Opéra de Paris Bastille, Aix-en-Provence Festival; apperances in recitals include: London Wigmore Hall, Amsterdam Concertgebouw, Salle Gaveau, St. Denis Festival, Alte Oper; vocal performances include: Mahler Third Symphony, Weisbaden, (with Gary Bertini) Knaben Wunderhorn, Stuttgart, Kindertotenlieder, Paris, Lugano, (with Nicolas Harnoncourt) Bach's St. Matthew's Passion, (with Maestro Wolfgang Sawallisch) Bach's St. John's Passion, Italy, Ombra Felice, London Symphony Orchestra; participated in numerous audio and video recordings. Recipient Deutsche Schallplattenkritik prize for Schumann recording, 1993. Office: care Herbert H Breslin Inc 119 West 57th St Rm 1505 New York NY 10019

STUVER, FRANCIS EDWARD, former railway car company executive; b. Greenville, Pa., Aug. 22, 1912; s. Willard Seeley and Anna Katherine (Henry) S.; m. Jessie Lucile Bright, Jan. 26, 1938; children: Robert Edward, Nancy (Mrs. Randolph Patrick Mutdosch). Grad. high sch. With Greenville Steel Car Co. (subsidiary Pitts. Forgings Co.), 1937—, chief accountant, 1944-46, asst. treas., 1946-54, asst. sec., 1948-56, treas., 1956-61, v.p., 1956-61, exec. v.p., 1961-75, ret., 1975; pres. Greenville Savs. & Loan Assn., 1977-83, dir., 1949-83; dir. Greenville Steel Car Co., 1961-74, Pitts. Forgings Co., 1975-80. Bd. dirs. Municipal Authority Borough Greenville, 1946-74, treas., 1946-73; bd. dirs., mem. exec. com. Mercer County br. Pa. Economy League, 1949-64; bd. dirs., treas., chmn. finance com. Greenville Hosp., 1953-59. Mem. Am. Ry. Car Inst. (dir. 1964-75). Clubs: Masons, Elks, Moose, KP, Greenville Country. Home: 46 Chambers Ave Greenville PA 16125-1856 Office: Foot Of Union St Greenville PA 16125

STUX, IVAN ERNEST, financial executive; b. Temesvar, Romania, July 27, 1945; came to U.S., 1965; s. George Stux. PhD in Math., Courant Inst., 1973; MBA, Columbia U., 1977. Asst. prof. math. dept. Columbia U. N.Y.C., 1973-77, assoc. prof. Sch. Bus., 1977-79; mgmt. cons. McKinsey & Co., N.Y.C., 1979-84; prin. Morgan Stanley & Co., Inc., N.Y.C., 1984—. Home: 27 W 69th St New York NY 10023 Office: Morgan Stanley & Co Inc 1251 Ave of the Americas Flr 33 New York NY 10020

STUZIN, CHARLES BRYAN, savings and loan association executive; b. Miami, Fla., 1942. Grad., Univ. Fla., 1964, postgrad., 1967. With Stuzin and Camner, Miami, 1973—; pres. Citizens Savs. and Fin. Corp. (CSF Holdings Inc.), Miami, 1980—, chmn. 1982—, also chief exec. officer, bd. dirs.; chmn. Citizens Mortgage Corp.; chmn., pres. Citizens Fed. Savs. and Loan; chmn., chief exec. officer Loan Am. Fin. Corp.; v.p., sec. Moore Ins. Agy.; ptnr. Webster Park Assocs., Sarasota Properties. Office: Citizens Savs Fin Corp 1221 Brickell Ave Miami FL 33131

STWALLEY, WILLIAM CALVIN, physics and chemistry educator; b. Glendale, Calif., Oct. 7, 1942; s. Calvin Murdoch and Diette Clarice (Hanson) S.; m. Mauricette Lucille Frisius, June 14, 1963; children—Kenneth William, Steven Edward. B.S., Calif. Inst. Tech., 1964; Ph.D., Harvard U., 1968. Asst. prof. U. Iowa, Iowa City, 1968-72, assoc. prof., 1972-75, prof. dept. chemistry, 1975-93, prof. dept. physics and astronomy, 1977-93, dir. Iowa Laser Facility, 1979-93, dir. Ctr. for Laser Sci. and Engring., 1987-89, George Glockler prof. physical scis., 1988-93; program dir. NSF, Wash-

ington, 1975-76 (leave of absence); prof. and head dept. physics, prof. chemistry U. Conn., Storrs, 1993—; program chmn. Internat. Laser Sci. Conf., 1985, co-chmn., 1986, chmn., 1987; lectr. Chinese Acad. Scis., 1986. Editor books in field; contbr. more than 220 articles to profl. publs. Japan Soc. for Promotion of Sci. fellow, 1982; Sloan fellow, 1970-72; numerous grants in field, 1970—. Fellow Am. Phys. Soc. (sec.-treas. div. chem. physics 1984-90, vice chair/chair/past chair Topical Group on Laser Sci. 1989-92), Optical Soc. Am.; mem. AAAS, Am. Chem. Soc. Democrat Avocations: comic books and cartoons, philately. Home: 21 Britony Dr Mansfield CT 06250 Office: Dept Physics U-46 U Conn Storrs CT 06269-3046

STYAN, JOHN LOUIS, English literature and theater educator; b. London, July 6, 1923; came to U.S., 1965; s. Louis and Constance Mary (Armstrong) S.; m. Constance W. M. Roberts, Nov. 17, 1945; children: Leigh, Day Campbell, Kim, Valentina Ebner. B.A., Cambridge (Eng.) U., 1947, M.A., 1948. Staff tutor lit., drama U. Hull, Eng., 1950-63; sr. staff tutor U. Hull, 1963-65; prof. English U. Mich., Ann Arbor, 1965-74, chmn. dept. English, 1973-74; Andrew Mellon prof. English U. Pitts., 1974-77; Franklyn Bliss Snyder prof. English lit. Northwestern U., 1977-87, prof. emeritus, 1987—; prof. theater, 1984-87, prof. theater emeritus, 1987—; chmn. acad. coun. Shakespeare Globe Theatre Ctr. (N.A.), 1981-87. Author: The Elements of Drama, 1960, The Dark Comedy, 1962, The Dramatic Experience, 1965, Shakespeare's Stagecraft, 1967, Chekhov in Performance, 1971, The Challenge of the Theatre, 1972, Drama Stage and Audience, 1975, The Shakespeare Revolution, 1977, Modern Drama in Theory and Practice, 3 vols, 1981, Max Reinhardt, 1982, All's Well That Ends Well, Shakespeare in Performance series, 1984, The State of Drama Study, 1984, Restoration Comedy in Performance, 1986. Served to lt. Royal Arty., 1941-45, Eng. Recipient Robert Lewis medal for lifetime achievement in theatre rsch. Kent State U., 1995; sr. rsch. fellow NEH, 1978-79, Guggenheim Found. fellow, 1983. Mem. Guild Drama Adjudicators, Brit. Drama League, MLA, Internat. Shakespeare Assn., Royal Over-Seas League. Home: Oak Apple Cottage, Barnes Ln, Milford on Sea Hampshire S041 0RP, England

STYCOS, JOSEPH MAYONE, demographer, educator; b. Saugerties, N.Y., Mar. 27, 1927; s. Stravos and Clotilda (Mayone) S.; m. Maria Nowakowska, Nov. 25, 1964; children: Steven Andrew, Christina Mayone (by previous marriage), Marek. AB, Princeton U., 1947; PhD, Columbia U., 1954. WithBur. Applied Social Rsch. Columbia U., 1948-50, lectr. sociology, 1951-52; project co-dir. U. P.R., 1952-53; postgrad. PC fellow U. N.C., 1954-55; assoc. prof. sociology St. Lawrence U., 1955-57; faculty Cornell U., Ithaca, N.Y., 1957—, prof. sociology, 1963—, chmn. dept., 1966-70, dir. Latin Am. program, 1962-66, dir. internat. population program, 1962-88, prof. rural sociology, 1987—, dir. population and devel. program, 1988-92; Fulbright-Hayes Disting. prof. U. Warsaw, Poland, 1979; external examiner U. Ife, Nigeria, 1973; Cons. AID, 1962-64; sr. cons. Population Council, 1963-74, 77-79; cons. Airlie Found., 1972-73, Inst. for Research in Social Behavior, 1974, Clapp & Mayne, Inc., 1974, Ford-Rockefeller Population Program, 1977, Nat. U. Costa Rica, 1979, U. P.R., 1979; trustee Population Reference Bur., 1964-68, cons., 1968-74; mem. exec. com. Internat. Planned Parenthood Fedn., West Hemmis, 1965-71, cons., 1971-77; adv. com. population and devel. OAS, 1968-70; mem. bd. Population Assn. Am., 1968-71, editorial cons. demography, 1965-69; adv. panel population Nat. Inst. Child Health and Human Devel., Dept. Health, Edn. and Welfare, 1969; co-chmn. population task force U.S. Nat. Commn. for UNESCO, 1972-73; adv. council, interdisciplinary communications program Smithsonian Instn., 1974-76; cons. Pan Am. Health Orgn., WHO, 1975; cons. steering com., acceptability task force WHO, 1978-85; cons. UNESCO, 1978-79, UN Fund for Population Activities, 1979-82, WHO, 1987-90; co-dir. Spanish family life project U. Complutense de Madrid, 1978-80; Fulbright-Hays prof. Nat. U. Costa Rica, spring 1986; chmn. U.S. Census Adv. Com. on Population Stats., 1983-84; mem. Fulbright-Hays program Nat. Screening Com. Cen. Am., 1989-92. Author: (with Hussein Abdel Aziz Sayed, Roger Avery and Samuel Firdman) Community Development and Family Planning: An Egyptian Experiment, 1988; mem. editl. bd. Human Orgn., 1962-64; gen. editor Irvington Population and Demographic Series, 1978; cons. editor Studies in Family Planning, 1977—; editor: Demography as an Interdiscipline, 1989. Mem. council Cornell U., 1969-70. Mem. Rural Sociological Soc. Home: 28 Twin Glens Rd Ithaca NY 14850-1041 Office: Cornell U Population & Devel Program Warren Hall Ithaca NY 14853-7801

STYLES, MARGRETTA MADDEN, nursing educator; b. Mount Union, Pa., Mar. 19, 1930; d. Russell B. and Agnes (Wilson) Madden; m. Douglas F. Styles, Sept. 4, 1954; children: Patrick, Michael, Megan. B.S., Juniata Coll., 1950; M. in Nursing, Yale U., 1954; Ed.D., U. Fla., 1968; hon. doctorate, Valparaiso U., 1986, U. Athens, Greece, 1991. Staff nurse VA Hosp., West Haven, Conn., 1954-55; instr. Bklyn. Hosp. Sch. Nursing, 1955-58; supr. North Dist. Hosp., Pompano Beach, Fla., 1961-63; dir. nursing edn. Broward Community Coll., Ft. Lauderdale, Fla., 1963-67; assoc. prof. Sch. Nursing Duke U., Durham, N.C., 1967-69, dir. undergrad. studies, 1967-69; prof., dean Sch. Nursing U. Tex., San Antonio, 1969-73; dean, prof. Coll. Nursing Wayne State U., Detroit; prof. nursing U. Calif., San Francisco, 1977—; dean Sch. Nursing, 1977-87; chairperson Com. for Study of Credentializing in Nursing, 1976-79; mem. adv. group div. nursing HEW, 1977; asst. dir. nursing svcs. U. Calif. Hosps. and Clinics, 1978-87; mem. Nat. Commn. Nursing, 1980—; mem. Calif. Bd. Registered Nursing, 1985—; mem. Sec.'s Commn. on Nursing HHS, 1988—. Author: On Nursing: Toward a New Endowment (Am. Jour. Nursing Book of Yr. award 1982); co-author (with A. Affara) From Principle to Power: A Guidebook to Regulation in Nursing, 1992. Recipient Disting. Alumna award Yale U. Sch. Nursing, 1979; Am. Nurses' Found. 1st disting. scholar, 1983. Fellow Am. Acad. Nursing; mem. Nat. Acad. Scis., Am. Nurses Assn. (pres. 1986-88), Internat. Coun. Nurses (bd. dirs. 1989—), Sigma Theta Tau. Office: U Calif Sch Nursing N531C-D Box 0608 San Francisco CA 94143

STYLES, RICHARD GEOFFREY PENTLAND, retired banker; b. Regina, Sask., Can., Dec. 3, 1930; s. Alfred G. and C. Ila (Pentland) S.; m. Jacqueline Joyce Frith, Oct. 31, 1959; children: Leslie Diane, David Patrick. B. in Commerce, U. Sask., 1951; Program for Mgmt. Devel., Harvard U., 1964. With Royal Bank Can., 1951-87, various domestic and internat. positions; vice chmn. Royal Bank Can., Toronto, Ont., until 1987; ret., 1987; formerly involved with Orion Royal Bank and bank's internat. subs., London, 1961-64; chmn., bd. dirs. Grosvenor Internat. Holdings Ltd., Drivers Jonas (Can.) Ltd.; bd. dirs. Echo Bay Mines Ltd., Fairwater Capital Corp., Fortis Inc., The Geon Co., Onex Corp., ProSource Distbn. Svcs., The Royal Trust Co., Scott's Hospitality Inc., Working Ventures Can. Fund Inc. Chmn. Toronto Symphony Found.; bd. govs. Mt. Sinai Hosp. Mem. Toronto Club, Rosedale Golf Club. Office: Royal Bank Plz Ste 3115, Toronto, ON Canada M5J 2J5

STYNES, STANLEY KENNETH, retired chemical engineer, educator; b. Detroit, Jan. 18, 1932; s. Stanley Kenneth and Bessie Myrtle (Casey) S.; m. Marcia Ann Meyers, Aug. 27, 1955; children: Peter Casey, Pamela Kay, Suzanne Elizabeth. B.S., Wayne State U., 1955, M.S., 1958; Ph.D., Purdue U., 1963. Lab. asst. U. Chgo., 1951; instr. Purdue U., 1960-63; asst. prof. chem. engring. Wayne State U., Detroit, 1963-64, assoc. prof., 1964-71, prof., 1971-92, dean engring., 1973-92, prof. emeritus, 1992—; dir. Energy Conversion Devices, Inc., Troy, Mich.; cons. Schwayder Chem. Metallurgy Co., 1965; chemistry dept. Wayne State U., 1965-66, Claude B. Schneible Co., Holly, Mich., 1968. Contbr. engring. articles to profl. jours. Mem. coun. on environ. strategy S.E. Mich. Coun. Govts., 1976-81; bd. dirs. Program for Minorities in S.E. Mich.; sec.-treas. Mich. Ednl. Rsch. Info. Triad; bd. dirs. Sci. and Engring. Fair of Met. Detroit, pres., 1983; bd. dirs. Midwest Program for Minorities in Engring., Sci. Ctr. Met. Detroit. Ford Found. fellow, 1959-63; DuPont fellow, 1962-63; Wayne State U. faculty research fellow, 1964-65. Fellow AIChE (past chmn. Detroit sect.), Engring. Soc. Detroit (past bd. dirs.), Mich. Soc. Profl. Engrs. (pres. 1987-88); mem. AAAS, Am. Chem. Soc., Engring. Soc. Devel. Found. (pres. 1992—), Argonne Univs. Assn. (del.), Adult Learning Inst. (bd. dirs. 1994—), Sigma Xi, Tau Beta Pi, Omicron Delta Kappa, Phi Lambda Upsilon. Presbyterian. Home: 20161 Stamford Dr Livonia MI 48152-1246 Office: Coll Engring Wayne State U Detroit MI 48202

STYRON, WILLIAM, writer; b. Newport News, Va., June 11, 1925; s. William Clark and Pauline Margaret (Abraham) S.; m. Rose Burgunder, May 4, 1953; children: Susanna Margaret, Paola Clark, Thomas, Claire

Alexandra. Student, Christchurch Sch., Davidson Coll.; Litt.D., Davidson Coll., 1986; A.B., Duke U., 1947, Litt.D., 1968. Fellow Am. Acad. Arts and Letters at Am. Acad. in Rome, 1953; fellow Silliman Coll., Yale, 1964—; jury pres. Cannes Film Festival, 1983. Author: novels Lie Down in Darkness, 1951, The Long March, 1953, Set This House on Fire, 1960, The Confessions of Nat Turner, 1967 (Pulitzer prize 1968, Howells medal Am. Acad. Arts and Letters 1970), Sophie's Choice, 1979 (Am. Book award 1980), In the Clap Shack (play), 1972, This Quiet Dust, 1982, Darkness Visible, 1990, A Tidewater Morning, 1993; also articles, essays, revs.; editor: Best Stories from the Paris Rev., 1959; adv. editor: Paris Rev., 1953—; mem. editorial bd. The Am. Scholar, 1970-76. Decorated Commandeur de l'Ordre des Arts et des Lettres, Commandeur Legion d'Honneur (France); recipient Duke U. Disting. Alumni award, 1984, Conn. Arts award, 1984, Prix Mondial del Duca, 1985, Elmer Holmes Bobst award for fiction, 1989, Edward MacDowell medal for excellence in the arts, 1988, Nat. Mag. award, 1990, Nat. medal of Arts, 1993, Medal of Honor, Nat. Arts Club, 1995, Common Wealth award, 1995. Mem. Am. Acad. Arts and Scis., Am. Acad. Arts and Letters, Soc. Am. Historians, Signet Soc., Harvard, Académie Goncourt, Phi Beta Kappa. Democrat.

STYSLINGER, LEE JOSEPH, JR., manufacturing company executive; b. Birmingham, Ala., June 28, 1933; s. Lee Joseph and Margaret Mary (McFarl) S.; m. Catherine Patricia Smith, Apr. 30, 1960; children—Lee Joseph III, Jon Cecil, Mark Joseph. Student, U. Ala., 1952. Pres., chief exec. officer Altec Industries, Inc. and predecessors, truck equipment mfrs., Birmingham, 1956-89, chief exec. officer, chmn. bd., 1989-92, chmn., 1992—; bd. dirs. Regions Fin., Mead Corp., So. Rsch. Tech., Inc., Jemison Investment Coo., Birmingham, Ala. Pres. cabinet U. Ala. Tuscaloosa; bd. dirs. Boy Scouts Am., St. Vincent's Hosp. Mem. Nat. Assn. Mfrs. (bd. dirs.), Newcomen Soc., Operation New Birmingham, U.S.C. of C., Birmingham C. of C., Bus. Coun. Ala., Country Club Birmingham, Mountain Brook Club, Shoal Creek Club, Willow Point Golf and Country Club, Rotary. Roman Catholic. Home: 3260 E Briarcliff Rd Birmingham AL 35223-1305 Office: 210 Inverness Center Dr Birmingham AL 35242-4808

STYVE, ORLOFF WENDELL, JR., electrical engineer; b. Winnebago, Minn., Feb. 1, 1936; s. Orloff Wendell and Katharine (Drake) S.; m. Jane Carol Meister, Feb. 25, 1961 (div. 1981); children: Elizabeth Anne, David John, Robert Peter, Susan Katharine. BEE, U. Minn., 1959. Registered profl. engr., Wis. Elec. distbn. engr. Wis. Electric Power Co., Menomonee Falls, 1959-69; div. distbn. engr., then svc. ctr. engring. supr. Wis. Electric Power Co., West Bend, 1969-73; planning engr. Wis. Electric Power Co., Milw., 1973-76, sr. underground dist. engr., 1976-84, elec. engr. underground dist., 1984-94; mem. elec. bd., West Bend, 1972-94. Mem. IEEE (voting mem. 1993, insulated conductors com. 1991—), Assn. of Edison Illuminating Cos. (cable engring. sect. 1991-94), Am. Nat. Stds. Inst. (distbn. transformer stds. com. 1985-88), Masons, Scottish Rite (chmn. state properties & elec. effects com. 1986—, Wis. Player's award Valley of Milw., 1989, svc. award 1991), Shriners (potentate's aide emeritus Tripoli Shrine 1986). Avocations: amateur theater, camping. Office: Cable Engring Cons 1404 Sandra Ln West Bend WI 53095-4944

SU, HELEN CHIEN-FAN, research chemist; b. Nanping, Fujian, China, Dec. 26, 1922; came to U.S. 1949; d. Ru-chen and Sieu-Hsien (Wong) Su. BA, Hwa Nan Coll., China, 1944; MS, U. Nebr., Lincoln, 1951; PhD, U. Nebr., 1953. Cert. profl. chemist. Asst. instr. in chemistry Hwa Nan Coll., Fuzhou, Fujian, China, 1944-49; prof. chemistry Lambuth Coll., Jackson, Tenn., 1953-55; rsch. asst. Auburn Rsch. Found., Auburn, Ala., 1955-57; sr. chemist, project ldr. Borden Chem. Co., Phila., 1957-63; scientist Lockheed-Ga. Rsch. Lab., Marietta, Ga., 1963-67; rsch. chemist Agrl. Rsch. Svc., USDA, Savannah, Ga., 1968-90. Contbr. numerous articles to profl. jours., chpts. in books; patentee in field. Recipient IR-100 award, Indsl. Research Mag., 1966. Fellow Am. Inst. Chemists, Ga. Inst. Chemists; mem. ACS, AAAS, N.Y. Acad. Sci., Entomol. Soc. Am., Ga. Entomol. Soc., Sigma Xi, Sigma Delta Epsilon. Methodist. Avocations: reading, gardening. Home: 5978 Robin Hood Ln Norcross GA 30093-3804 Office: USDA-ARS 3401 Edwin Ave Savannah GA 31405-1607

SU, JUDY YA HWA LIN, pharmacologist; b. Hsinchu, Taiwan, Nov. 20, 1938; came to U.S., 1962; d. Ferng Nian and Chiu-Chin (Cheng) Lin; m. Michael W. Su; 1 child, Marvin. BS, Nat. Taiwan U., 1961; MS, U. Kans., 1964; PhD, U. Wash., 1968. Asst. prof. dept. biology U. Ala., Huntsville, 1972-73; rsch. assoc. dept. anesthesiology U. Wash., Seattle, 1976-77, acting asst. prof. dept. anesthesia, 1977-78, rsch. asst. prof., 1978-81; rsch. assoc. prof., 1981-89, prof., 1989—; mem. surg. anesthesiology & trauma study sect. NIH, 1987-91; vis. scientist Max-Planck Inst. Med. Rsch., Heidelberg, West Germany, 1982-83; vis. prof. dept. anesthesiology Mayo Clinic, Rochester, Minn., Med. Coll. Wis., 1988; editorial bd. cons. Jour. Molecular & Cellular Cardiology, London, 1987—; European Jour. Physiology, Berlin, Germany, Muscle & Nerve, Kyoto, Japan, 1989—; Anesthesiology, Phila., 1987—; Molecular Pharmacology, 1988—; Jour. Biol. Chemistry, 1989—; Am. Jour. Physiology, 1990—; mem. rsch. study com. Am. Heart Assn., 1992-95. Contbr. articles to profl. jours. Grantee Wash. Heart Assn., 1976-77, 1985-87, Pharm. Mfrs. Assn. Found., Inc., 1977, Lilly Rsch. Labs, 1986-88, Anaquest, 1987—, NIH, 1978—; recipient Rsch. Career Devel. award NIH, 1982-87; rsch. fellowship San Diego Heart Assn., 1970-72, Max-Planck Inst., 1982-83. Mem. AAAS, Biophys. Soc., Am. Soc. for Pharmacology and Exptl. Therapeutics, Am. Physiol. Soc., Am. Soc. Anesthesiologists. Home: 13110 NE 33rd St Bellevue WA 98005-1318 Office: U Wash Dept Anesthesiology Box 356540 Seattle WA 98195-6540

SU, KENDALL LING-CHIAO, engineering educator; b. Fujian, China, July 10, 1926; came to U.S., 1948; s. Ru-chen and Sui-hsiong (Wang) S.; m. Jennifer Gee-tsone Chang, Sept. 10, 1960; children: Adrienne, Jonathan. BEE, Xiamen U., Peoples Republic China, 1947; MEE, Ga. Inst. Tech, 1949; PhD, Ga. Inst. Tech., 1954. Jr. engr. Taiwan Power Co., Taipei, Republic China, 1947-48; asst. prof. Ga. Inst. Tech., Atlanta, 1954-59, assoc. prof., 1959-65, prof., 1965-70, Regents prof., 1970-94, Regents' prof. emeritus, 1994—; mem. tech. staff Bell Labs., Murray Hill, N.J., 1957. Author: Active Network Synthesis, 1965, Time-Domain Synthesis of Linear Networks, 1969, Fundamentals of Circuits, Electronics, and Signal Analysis, 1978, Handbook of Tables for Elliptic-Function Filters, 1990, Fundamentals of Circuit Analysis, 1993; mem sci. adv. com. Newton Graphic Sci. mag., 1987—. Fellow IEEE; mem. Sigma Xi (pres. Ga. Inst. Tech. chpt. 1968-69, 72-73, Faculty Rsch. award 1957), Phi Kappa Phi, Eta Kappa Nu. Methodist. Office: Ga Inst Tech Sch Elec & Comp Engring Atlanta GA 30332-0250

SU, SHIAW-DER, nuclear engineer; b. Tainan, Republic of China, Jan. 20, 1945; came to U.S., 1969; s. Hsin-Chun and King-New (Chen) S.; m. Shi-Ju Wang, June 30, 1968; children: Eastor Y., Wesley Y. BS, Nat. Tsing Hua U., Republic of China, 1968; MS, Purdue U., 1971. Registered profl. nuclear engr., Calif. Engr. Burns & Roe Inc., Oradell, N.J., 1971-72; prin. Gen. Atomics, San Diego, Calif., 1972—; pres. China Nuclear Corp., Taiwan, 1990-91. Mem. Am. Nuclear Soc., Chinese Inst. Engrs. (life), Sigma Xi (assoc.). Avocations: tennis, swimming, ping-pong, bridge. Home: 5093 Zimmer Cove San Diego CA 92130 Office: Gen Atomics PO Box 85608 San Diego CA 92186-9784

SU, STEPHEN Y. H., computer science educator, consultant; b. Anchi, Fukien, China, July 6, 1938; came to U.S., 1962; s. Sing and Shu-hwei (Tasy) Su; children: Lu, Yeemay. BS in Elec. Engring., Taiwan U. 1960; MS in Computer Engring., U. Wis., 1963, PhD in Computer Engring., 1967. Asst. prof. NYU, 1967-69, U. Calif.-Berkeley, 1969-71; assoc. prof. Case Western Res. U., Cleve., 1972-73, CUNY, 1973-75; prof. Utah State U., Logan, 1975-78; prof. computer sci. SUNY-Binghamton, 1978—; logic designer Fabri-Tek Inc., Madison, Wis., 1965; mem. Tech. staff Bell Telephone Lab., 1969; cons. Sperry UNIVAC, Blue Bell, Pa., 1973-74; engr. IBM, Poughkeepsie, N.Y., 1974; cons. Standard Electric Lorenz, Stuttgart, Fed. Republic Germany, 1985, various others; participant numerous confs. Contbr. over 100 articles to profl. jours., conf. proceedings, chpts. to books. Chmn. 1984 Family Conf., Mt. Bethel, Pa., pres. Binghamton Christian Fellowship, 1983-84, v.p., 1981-82; pres. Susquehanna Valley Assn., Southern Tier, N.Y., 1980. Recipient Humboldt award Alexander Humboldt Found., 1984-85, Commemorative medal of honor, Disting. Leadership award for outstanding svc. in teaching profession; named Sr. Engr. of Yr., 1981. Mem. IEEE (assoc.

editor Trans. Computers 1974-77, vice chmn. test tech com. 1982-83, advisor Computer Soc. disting. visitor program 1976-83), Eta Kappa Nu, Tau Beta Pi, Sigma Xi. Baptist. Clubs: Tai Chi (pres. 1973-75) (Bergenfield, N.J.); Kung Fu (pres. 1971-72) (Cleve.). Avocations: tennis; skiing; jogging; sightseeing; swimming. Office: SUNY Dept Computer Sci Binghamton NY 13902-6000

SUARD, PIERRE HENRI ANDRE, power company executive; b. Lons le Saunier, Jura, France, Nov. 9, 1934; s. Gaston and Jeanne (Gaillard) S.; m. Michele Sender, Aug. 22, 1959; children: Brigitte, Bruno. Diploma in engring., Ecole Polytechnique, Paris, 1954, Ecole Ponts & Chaussees, Paris, 1959. With Min. Pub. Works, Paris, 1960-63; dir. ops. Paris Airport Authority, 1963-70; ceo Setec Economie & Informatique, Paris, 1971-73, Sogelerg-Sedim, Paris, 1973-76, Cables de Lyon, Paris, 1976-84; from mng. dir. to vice chmn. Cit Alcatel, Paris, 1984-85; chmn., ceo Alcatel NV, 1987—, Alcatel Alsthom, Paris, 1986—, Alcatel U.S.A. Corp., N.Y.C., 1985—; bd. dirs. Credit Commercial de France, Paris, 1987—, Societe Generale, 1987—, La Farge Coppee—, Compagnie General des Eaux—. Named Chevalier de la Legion d'Honneur, French Govt., 1987. Office: Alcatel Alsthom Co Gen d'Electricite, 54 rue de la Boetie, 75382 Paris Cedex 08, France

SUAREZ, ROBERTO, newspaper publishing executive; b. Havana, Cuba; came to U.S., 1961; m. Pitucha Campuzano; children: 7 sons, 5 daughters. Student, Colegio de Belén, Cuba; grad., Villanova Coll., 1949. Various postions in real estate, constrn., fin. Havana, 1950-60; from part-time mailer to contr. The Herald's subs., 1962-72; contr. Knight Pub. Co., Charlotte, N.C., 1972-78; v.p., gen. mgr. The Miami (Fla.) Herald, 1978-86, pres., 1986—; pub. El Nuevo Herald Knight Ridder Pub. Co., 1987—. Past pres. Art and Sci. Coun., Spirit Sq. Arts Ctr., Charleston; chair Kids Voting/Dade County; bd. dirs. United Way. Recipient Gold medal Knight-Ridder Pub. Co., 1989, Heritage award HIspanic Alliance, 1990, Leadership award AS-PIRA, 1991, Marion Guastella award Asociacion de Publicitarios Latinoamericanos, 1993. Mem. Inter Am. Press Assn. (pres. exec. com.), N.C. Press Assn. (former treas.), Interam. Businessmen Assn. Office: Miami Herald Pub Co 1 Herald Plz Miami FL 33132-1609

SUAREZ, XAVIER LOUIS, lawyer, former mayor; b. Las Villas, Cuba, May 21, 1949; m. Rita Suarez; 4 children. BE, Villanova U., 1971, hon. degree, 1988; M of Pub. Policy, JD, Harvard U., 1975. Bar: Fla. 1975. Instr. bus. law Biscayne Coll., 1977-78; mayor City of Miami, 1985-93; ptnr. Jorden, Schulte & Burchette, Miami, 1988-93, Shutts & Bowen, Miami, 1993—; mem. criminal justice coun. Dade County, Miami, Fla., 1980. Chmn. Miami Affirmative Action Bd., 1981, Downtown Devel. Authority, 1985—; chmn. bd. regents Cath. Univ., 1988-89; bd. advisors Harvard U. Kennedy Sch. Govt. Inst. Politics, Cambridge, Mass., St. Thomas U. Sch. Law. Mem. Fla. Bar Assn., Cuban Bar Assn. Office: Shutts and Bowen 1500 Miami Ctr 201 S Biscayne Blvd Miami FL 33131

SUAREZ-MURIAS, MARGUERITE C., retired language and literature educator; b. Havana, Cuba, Mar. 23, 1921; came to U.S., 1935, naturalized, 1959; d. Eduardo R. and Marguerite (Vendel) S.-M. A.B., Bryn Mawr Coll., 1942; M.A., Columbia U., 1953, Ph.D., 1957. Lectr. in Spanish Columbia U., 1954-56; pub. relations officer med. div. Johns Hopkins U., 1957-58; asst. prof. Spanish and French Sweet Briar Coll., 1958-59, Hood Coll., 1960-61; lectr. Cath. U., 1960-63, asst. prof., summers 1960-62, asso. prof., summers 1964-66; asst. prof. dept. langs. and linguistics Am. U., 1961-63, asso. prof., 1963-66; prof. dept. classical and modern langs. Marquette U., Milw., 1966-68; prof. Spanish and Portuguese U. Wis., Milw., 1968-83; chmn., 1972-75; guest prof. U. South Africa, Pretoria, 1980. Author: La novela romántica in Hispanoamérica, 1963, Antologia estilistica de la prosa modern española, 1968, Essays on Hispanic Literature/Ensayos de literatura hispana, 1982; contbr. articles to profl. jours.; editor: Gironella's Los cipreses creen en Dios, 1969, 87-93; designed, built homes. Mem. Nat. Trust for Historic Preservation. Roman Catholic. Home: 1315 Cold Bottom Rd Sparks MD 21152-9518

SUBA, ANTONIO RONQUILLO, surgeon; b. Philippines, Apr. 25, 1927; came to U.S., 1952, naturalized, 1961; s. Antonio Mesina and Valentina Cabais (Ronquillo) S.; m. Sylvia Marie Karl, June 16, 1956; children—Steven Antonio, Eric John, Laurinda Ann, Gregory Karl, Timothy Mark, Sylvia Kathleen. M.D., U. St. Thomas, Philippines, 1952. Diplomate: Am. Bd. Surgery. Intern St. Anthony's Hosp., St. Louis, 1952-53; resident St. Louis County Hosp., St. Louis, 1953-57; trainee Nat. Cancer Inst., Ellis Fischel State Cancer Hosp., Columbia, Mo., 1957-59; chief surg. services U.S. Army, Bremerhaven, Germany, 1959-61; practice medicine specializing in gen. and hand surgery St. Louis, 1961-89; ret., 1989; pres., prin. ARS (P.C.), 1971-84. Contbr. feature articles to Philippine publs., 1944-51, articles to med. jours. Fellow A.C.S.; mem. AMA, Pan-Pacific, Mo. surg. assns., St. Louis Surg. Soc., Am. Assn. Hand Surgery. Club: K.C. Home: 12085 Heatherdane Dr Saint Louis MO 63131-3119

SUBAK, JOHN THOMAS, lawyer; b. Trebic, Czechoslovakia, Apr. 19, 1929; came to U.S., 1941, naturalized, 1946; s. William John and Gerda Maria (Subakova) S.; m. Mary Corcoran, June 4, 1955; children—Jane, Kate, Thomas, Michael. BA summa cum laude, Yale U., 1950, LLB, 1956. Bar: Pa. 1956. From assoc. to ptnr. Dechert, Price & Rhoads, Phila., 1956-76, v.p., gen. counsel, dir., 1976-77; group v.p., gen. counsel, dir. Rohm and Haas Co., 1977-93; counsel Dechert Price & Rhoads, Phila., 1994—; bd. dirs. Newport Corp. Editor: The Bus. Lawyer, 1982-83. Bd. dirs. Am. Cancer Soc.; trustee Smith Coll. Lt.(j.g.) USN, 1950-53. Mem. ABA (chmn. corp. and bus. law sect. 1984-85), Am. Law Inst. (coun. mem.), Defender Assn. of Phila. (v.p., bd. dirs.). Democrat. Roman Catholic. Clubs: Merion Cricket, Phila. Home: 214 Ivy Ln Haverford PA 19041-1745 Office: Dechert Price & Rhoads 1717 Arch St Philadelphia PA 19103

SUBAK-SHARPE, GENELL JACKSON, editor, writer; b. Great Falls, Mont.; m. Gerald Subak-Sharpe; children: David, Sarah and Hope (twins). BA, Butler U., 1959; MS in Journalism with honors, Columbia U., 1961. Reporter Indpls. Star, 1958-61; copy editor N.Y. Times, 1962-70; exec. editor Family Health mag., 1970-74; editor Modern Opinion mag., 1974-77; v.p., editor Biomed. Info. Corp., 1977-84; pres. G.S. Sharpe Communications Inc., N.Y.C., 1981—. Co-editor: The Physicians' Drug Manual, 1981; editor: The Compendium of Drug Therapy, 1982, The Compendium of Patient Information, 1982, The Physicians' Manual for Patients, 1984, (with Victor Herbert) Mount Sinai School of Medicine Guide to Complete Nutrition, 1990 (revised as Complete Nutrition, 1995); author: (with Kathryn Schrotenboer) Freedom From Menstrual Cramps, 1981, Living with Diabetes, 1983, Overcomming Breast Cancer, 1987, Breathing Easy, 1988, (with James V. Warren) Frontiers in Medicine series: Surviving Your Heart Attack, 1984, Controlling Hypertension, 1984-87, Living with Diabetes, 1985, (with Joan Ness) The Calcium-Requirement Cookbook, 1985, (with Lois Jovanovic) Hormones: The Woman's Answerbook, 1987, (with Robert Weiss) Columbia University School of Public Health Complete Guide to Health and Well-Being After 50, (with Edward Frohlich) Take Heart, 1990, (with Raul Artal) Exercise and Pregnancy, 1992, (with S.J. Winawer and M. Shike) Cancer Free, 1995; editoral dir.: Columbia University College of Physicians and Surgeons Complete Home Medical Guide, 1985, Columbia University College of Physicians and Surgeons Complete Guide to Pregnancy, 1988, Columbia University College of Physicians and Surgeons Complete Guide to Early Child Care, 1990, Yale University Coll. Medicine Heart Book, 1992, The Good Housekeeping Illustrated Guide to Women's Health, 1995, Disney Encyclopedia of Baby and Child Care, 1995; founding editor: Being Well Magazine, 1983; Off Hours, 1983; Health and Nutrition Newsletter, 1984, Physicians Lifestyle Magazine, 1989; mng. editor Home Health Handbook, 1988—. Pulitzer Traveling fellow Columbia U., 1961-62; recipient Russell L. Cecil Writing award Arthritis Found., 1972, Mag. Writing award Am. Dental Soc., 1977, Blakeslee award Am. Heart Assn., 1985. Mem. Authors Guild, Women's Press Club, Nat. Assn. Sci. Writers, Newswomens Club N.Y. Avocations: restoration historic houses, antique collecting. Home: 606 W 116th St New York NY 10027-7011 Office: 19 W 34th St Ste 1009 New York NY 10001

SUBAK-SHARPE, GERALD EMIL, electrical engineer, educator; b. Vienna, Austria, June 15, 1925; came to U.S., 1959, naturalized, 1967; s. Robert and Nelly (Brull) S.; m. Genell Jackson, Nov. 23, 1963; children: David, Sarah and Hope (twins). BS with 1st class honors, Univ. Coll.,

London, 1951; PhD, U. London, 1965; ScD, Columbia U., 1969. Rsch. engr. Brit. Telecommunications Rsch., Taplow, Eng., 1951-58; mem. tech. staff Bell Labs., Murray Hill, N.J., 1959-64, cons., 1977-78; assoc. prof. elec. engring. Manhattan Coll., Bronx, N.Y., 1966-68; prof. elec. engring. CCNY, N.Y.C., 1968—; v.p. G.S. Sharpe Communications Inc., 1981—. Author: (with A.B. Glaser) Integrated Circuit Engineering, 1978; contbr. articles on network structure and semicondr. theory to profl. jours. Served as lt. Royal Warwickshire Regt., 1944-47. Recipient Prof. of Yr. award Eta Kappa Nu/CCNY, 1985-86. Fellow Instn. Elec. Engrs. (London); mem. IEEE (sr.), N.Y. Acad. Scis., Nat. Trust for Historic Preservation. Home: 606 W 116th St Apt 71 New York NY 10027-7024 also: Knollcroft New Concord NY 12060 Office: CCNY Convent Ave New York NY 10027

SUBLER, EDWARD PIERRE, advertising executive; b. Shelby, Ohio, Mar. 24, 1927; s. Leo John and Dorotha (Armstrong) S.; m. Alice Ellen Carpenter, Sept. 8, 1956; children: Leo, Scott, Dorotha. B.A., Denison U., 1950; grad. advanced mgmt. course, Emory U. Mgr. product advt. Westinghouse Electric Co., Mansfield, Ohio, 1950-65; mgr. advt. and sales promotion Bell & Howell Co., Chgo., 1965-69; v.p. mdsg. Westinghouse Consumer Products Co., 1969-76; sr. v.p. Ketchum Advt., Pitts., 1976-92, ret., 1992. Served with USN, 1945-46. Mem. Am. Mktg. Assn., Am. Assn. Advt. Agencies (regional chmn.), Catawba Island Club. Presbyterian. Home: 2881 N Firelands Blvd Port Clinton OH 43452

SUBLETT, CARL CECIL, artist; b. Johnson County, Ky., Feb. 4, 1919; s. Tandy and Beulah (Fitzpatrick) S.; m. Helen C. Davis, Aug. 20, 1942; children: Carol, Eric. Student, Western Ky. U., 1938-40, Univ. Center, Florence, Italy, 1945, U. Tenn., 1955-56. Indsl. engr. draftsman Enterprise Wheel & Car Corp., Bristol, Va., 1946-49; staff artist Bristol, Va.-Tennesean & Herald Courier, 1950-52; artist, asst. mgr. Bristol Art Engravers, 1952-54; art dir. Advt., Knoxville, 1954-65; prof. art U. Tenn., Knoxville, 1966-82; juror Watercolor Soc. Ala., Birmingham, 1979, Jacksonville U. Ann., 1980; juror Bristol Art Guild 8th ann. juried exhbn., 1993. Artist: prize winning water colors, 1964, drawing Soc. Nat. Exhbn., 1965, Artists U.S.A., 1971-72, 73-74, 74-75; numerous exhbns. art in embassies program, 1964—; numerous exhbns. featured in publs. including Allied Publs. Inc.; numerous exhbns. in catalogues Tenn. State Mus., Nashville, Artist U.S.A. and others; retrospective exhbn.: Knoxville Mus. Art, 1991; invitational show Hampton III Gallery, Ltd., Taylors, S.C., 1992, Union U., Jackson, Tenn., 1991, Bennett Galleries, Knoxville, 1992-93. Hon. mem. Oak Ridge Tenn.Community Art Ctr. Served with U.S. Army, 1943-45. Recipient Purchase Mead Corp. Painting of Yr., Atlanta, 1963, Grumbacher Washington Watercolor Gold, 1964, Rudolph Leach Am. Watercolor Soc., N.Y.C., 1972, Purchase Watercolor U.S.A., Springfield, Mo., 1975, Lifetime Achievement award Knoxville Arts Coun. and Knoxville Mus. of Art, 1994. Mem. NAD (Alfred Easton poor prize 1995), Bristol Art Guild (treas. 1951-54), Tenn. Watercolor Soc. (gold medal 1973, award of merit 1974, 75, 77, 78, 81, 84, 85), Knoxville Watercolor Soc., Port Clyde (Maine) Arts and Crafts Soc., Watercolor USA Soc., Knoxville Mus. Art. Methodist. Home and Studio: 2104 Lake Ave Knoxville TN 37916 Address (summer): Port Clyde ME 04855

SUBLETTE, WILLIAM EDWARD, state representative; b. Walnut Creek, Calif., Apr. 12, 1963. BA in History with honors, U. Fla., 1985, JD, 1988. Atty. Kelaher & Wieland, P.A., Orlando, Fla.; mem. Fla. Ho. of Reps., Tallahassee, 1992—; vice chmn. Orange County Legis. Del., 1992-93, chmn., 1993-94; mem. higher edn. com., mem. ethics and elections com., mem. aging and human svcs. com., mem. tourism and econ. devel. com., mem. ho. select. com. on juvenile justice reform, mem. Rep. policy com.; active Fla. Task Force to Investigate the Use of Secured Detention, 1993; co-chmn. Orange County Juvenile Justice Task Force, 1993-94. Founder, advisor Chickasaw Dist. Law Explorers Post Boy Scouts Am., 1988-90, chmn. Chickasaw Dist. Activities & Program Com., 1989-90; pres. Orange County Young Reps., 1991-92; mem. open heart program 1st Presbyn. Ch. of Orlando. Mem. ABA, Orange County Bar Assn. (young lawyers sect., treas. 1989-90, pres.-elect 1990-91, chmn. talent showcase 1990, 91, chmn. habitat for humanity project 1992, pres. 1991-92, bd. dirs. ednl. fund 1992-93, chmn. Bill of Rights project 1992, chmn. scholarship fund 1993, 94), Tiger Bay Club, Orlando Kiwanis Club. Avocations: golf, running, history, reading. Office: 2901 Curry Ford Rd Ste 208 Orlando FL 32806-3359

SUBOTNICK, MORTON, composer, clarinetist; b. L.A., Apr. 14, 1933; m. Joan La Barbara, Dec. 18, 1979. U. Denver; M.A., Mills Coll.; pupil of, Milhaud and Kirchner. Dir. Ctr. for Experiments in Art, Info. and Tech. Calif. Inst. Arts, 1969—, also co-chmn. composition dept.; vis. prof. composition Yale U., 1982-83, U. Md., 1968; bd. dirs. Am. Music Ctr.; co-dir. composition program Ctr. for Experiments in Art, Info. and Tech., Calif. Inst. Arts; music dir. Electric Circus. Formerly mem. Denver and San Francisco symphonies, chamber and solo performances; asst. prof., also co-founder Mills Coll. Performing Group; co-founder San Francisco Tape Center, 1961; formerly mus. dir. Repertory Theatre, Lincoln Center, 1966; artist-in-residence intermedia program, Sch. Arts, NYU, 1966-68; worked with magnetic tape, 1960-85; creator performances combining music, theatre and cinema, game-playing, light-shows and ritualistic phenomena suggestive of contemporary society into a new total art form (happenings) and based on indeterminacy Play Number 4; composed for electronic music synthesizer especially for the record medium Silver Apples of the Moon, 1967; composer for electronic music synthesizer The Wild Bull, 1968, 2: Touch, 1969, Sidewinder, 1971, 4 Butterflies, 1973, Until Spring, 1975, Return, 1984; all electronic music 2: Game for Two Players and No Audience, 1973; 2 Butterflies for Amplified Orchestra, The Balance Room, Before the Butterfly, 1974; Bicentennial Commn., 1976; commd. by Los Angeles Philharmonic, Boston Symphony, N.Y. Philharmonic, Phila. Orch., Chgo. Symphony, Cleve. Symphony for piano and electronic ghost score Liquid Strata, 1977, The Wild Beasts; for trombone and ghost score, 1978; The Last Dream of the Beast; for solo voice, ghost score and electronic sounds, 1978; electronic music Score for Ice Floe, 1978, A Sky of Cloudless Sulphur, 1978; Axolotl; for cello and ghost score, 1981, Parallel Lines; for solo piccolo, 9 instruments ghost score, 1979; After the Butterfly; for solo trumpet, 8 instruments and ghost score The First Dream of Light; for tuba and ghost score, 1980; The Double Life of Amphibians: Part One, Ascent into Air; for 10 instruments and live computer sounds, 1981; The Fluttering of Wings; for string quartet and ghost score for Juilliard String Quartet, 1981; An Arsenal of Defense for viola and ghost score, 1982, Trembling, for violin, piano and ghost score, 1983 (commd. by Library of Congress), The Double Life of Amphibians, 90 minute staged tone-poem (premiered at L.A. Olympic Arts Festival), 1984, The Key to Songs, for chamber orch. and synthesizer (commd. by Fromm Found.), 1985; Deutscher Akademischer Austauschdienst Künstler program composer-in-residency, West Berlin, 1981; In Two Worlds concerto for saxophone, electronic wind controller and orch., 1987-88; and The Butterflies Begin to Sing for computer and chamber ensemble commd. by Sante Fe Chamber Music Festival, 1988; Jacob's Room for voice and string quartet, 1984, Jacob's Room chamber opera for cello, computer, and 2 Voices, 1990-93, Jacob's Room for 1 cello, 1 voice and computer Wergo Recs., also choreographed for premier Ballet British Columbia, 1991, as chamber opera-premiered Am. Music Theatre Festival, Phila., 1993; Hungers-A Collaboration with video artist Ed Emschwiller, 1987, commd. by L.A. Arts Festival, A Desert Flowers for chamber orch. and computer, 1989, commd. Cleve. Chamber Orch.; pub.: European/American, All My Hummingbirds Have Alibis for Midi Pno, Midi Mallets, flute, cello, computer (commd. by NEA and Santa Fe Chamber Music Festival, first composed for CD-ROM), 1991; pub. European-American; author CD-ROM composition program Making Music, 1995. Recipient Am. Acad. Arts and Letters award, 1979, Brandeis Arts award, 1981; Guggenheim fellow, 1975; NEA grantee, 1973, 76, 85, 87, 89, 92. Address: c/o European-Am PO Box 850 Valley Forge PA 19482-0850

SUBOTNICK, STUART, food service executive; b. 1942. JD, Bklyn. Law Sch., N.Y., 1968; LLM, NYU, 1974. With Medromedia, Inc., 1967-82, sr. v.p. fin., 1982-86, bd. dirs., exec. v.p. 1986; gen. ptnr., exec. v.p. Metromedia Co., 1986—; vice chmn. bd. Metromedia Steakhouses, Inc., Vandalia, Ohio, 1988—; bd. dirs. Metromedia Steakhouses, Inc. Office: Metromedia Steakhouses Inc Dayton Internat Airport Vandalia OH 45377

SUBRAMANIAM, SHIVAN SIVASWAMY, insurance company executive; b. Madras, India, Feb. 15, 1949; came to U.S., 1970; s. Kodaganullor

Sivaswamy and Seethalakshmi S. B.E. in Mech. Engring. with honors, Birla Inst. Tech., Pilani, India, 1970; M.S. in Ops. Research, Poly. Inst. Bklyn., 1972; S.M. in Mgmt., MIT, 1978. Indsl. engr. Midland Container Corp., Ridgewood, N.J., 1971-74; mgmt. sci. analyst Allendale Ins. Co., Johnston, R.I., 1974-76; sr. mgmt. sci. analyst, 1976-77, sr. fin. staff officer, 1978-80, v.p., treas., 1980-83, v.p. fin., chief fin. officer, 1983-91, exec. v.p., 1991-92, pres., 1992-93; chmn. Allendale Ins. Co., Johnson, R.I., 1995—. Mem. Fin. Execs. Inst. (membership chmn. 1982-84, Providence chpt. pres. 1985-86), Nat. Assn. Corp. Treas. Office: Allendale Ins Co PO Box 7500 Johnston RI 02919-0750

SUCHECKI, LUCY ANNE, elementary education educator; b. East Cleveland, Ohio, May 3, 1945; d. Ben and Adelaide V. (Maneri) Urban; m. Robert K. Suchecki, Aug. 19, 1972. BS, Bowling Green State U., 1967; MA, Oakland U., 1981. Cert. elem. tchr., Mich. Elem. tchr. L'Anse Creuse Pub. Schs., Mt. Clemens, Mich., 1967—; grade cons. (book) Michigan, 1991. Active Immaculate Conception Ch., 1969—; Anchor Bay Women's Pool League, 1972—. Mem. NEA, MEA, MEA-NEA (local 1), L'Anse Creuse Ednl. Assn. (sec. 1968—), New Baltimore Hist. Soc. Roman Catholic. Avocations: boating, swimming, pool. Home: 8504 Anchor Bay Dr Clay MI 48001-3507 Office: Marie C Graham Elem Sch 25555 Crocker Blvd Harrison Township MI 48045-3443

SUCHENEK, MAREK ANDRZEJ, computer science educator; b. Warsaw, Poland, May 2, 1949; came to U.S., 1986; s. Tadeusz Aleksander and Barbara Krystyna (Zych) S.; m. Ewa Aleksandra Czerny, July 30, 1974 (div. 1991). MSc in Math. Engring., Warsaw Tech. U., 1973, PhD in Tech. Scis. with distinction, 1979. Instr. Warsaw (Poland) Tech. U., 1973-79, asst. prof., 1979-88; vis. asst. prof. Wichita (Kans.) State U., 1986-88; assoc. Nat. Inst. for Aviation Rsch., Wichita, 1987-90; vis. asst. prof. Wichita (Kans.) State U., 1986-88, assoc. prof., 1988-89, assoc. prof., chair, 1989-90; prof. Calif. State U.-Dominguez Hills, Carson, 1990—; mem. organizing com. Internat. Symposium on Methodologies for Intelligent Sys., 1989-90; program com. Ann. Ulam Math. Conf., 1990-91, Internat. Conf. on Computing and Info., 1992—; referee NSF, 1990—, Annals of Math. and Artificial Intelligence, 1992—, Jour. Logic Programming, 1992—; presenter in field. Author: (with Jan Bielecki) ANS FORTRAN, 1980, (with Jan Bielecki) FORTRAN for Advanced Programmers, 1981, 2d edit., 83, 3d edit., 88 (Minister of Sci. Higher Edn. and Techs. prize 1982); reviewer Zentralblatt fur Mathematik, 1980-89, Math. Reviews, 1989-91; mem. editorial bd.: Ulam Quarterly, 1990—; contbr. articles to profl. jours. Recipient rsch. grants Polish Govt., 1974-76, 85-86, FAA, 1988-90. Mem. AAUP, The Assn. for Logic Programming, Computer Soc. IEEE, Assn. for Computing Machinery, Assn. Symbolic Logic, Sigma Xi (chpt. pres.). Avocations: travel, modern music, cats, collectibles, target shooting. Home: 830 N Juanita Ave Redondo Beach CA 90277-2229 Office: Calif State Univ Dominguez Hills 1000 E Victoria St Carson CA 90747-0001

SUCKIEL, ELLEN KAPPY, philosophy educator; b. Bklyn., June 15, 1943; d. Jack and Lilyan (Banchefsky) Kappy; m. Joseph Suckiel, June 22, 1973. A.B., Douglass Coll., 1965; M.A. in Philosophy, U. Wis., 1969, Ph.D. in Philosophy, 1972. Lectr. philosophy U. Wis., Madison, 1969-71; asst. prof. philosophy Fla. State U., Tallahassee, 1972-73; asst. prof. philosophy U. Calif., Santa Cruz, 1973-80, assoc. prof., 1980—; provost Kresge Coll., 1983-89. Author: The Pragmatic Philosophy of William James, 1982, also articles. Mem. Am. Philos. Assn., Soc. for Advancement Am. Philosophy. Office: U Calif Cowell Coll Santa Cruz CA 95064

SUCKLING, ROBERT MCCLEARY, architect; b. Hollidaysburg, Pa., Feb. 27, 1932; s. Melvin E. and Rosanna B. (McCleary) S.; m. MaryLou Morris, Feb. 12, 1956; children: Dawn Morden, Kevin, Scott, Lisa Cronin. BArch, Carnegie-Mellon U., 1955. Registered architect, Pa., Ohio, N.Y., W.Va., N.C., Md., Ky., Va. Designer, job capt. Hayes Large Architects, Altoona, Pa., 1957-61, Nicholas J. Fiore, AIA, Altoona, 1861-62; designer, project mgr. N. Grant Nicklas, AIA, Altoona, 1962-64; project architect Pietrolungo & Kimball, Ebensburg, Pa., 1964-66; project coord. and mgr. Hayes Large Architects, Altoona, 1966-74, ptnr., 1974—; dir.-at-large Coun. Ednl. Facility Planners, Phoenix, 1987—. Neighborhood commr. Boy Scouts Am., Altoona; pres. 1st Luth. Ch., Altoona, 1984-85. Served to 1st lt. U.S. Army, 1955-57. Recipient Disting. Svc. award CEFPI, 1993. Mem. Rotary, Masons, Shriners, Order Ea. Star, Alpha Phi Omega. Republican. Avocations: travel, photography, reading. Home: 2500 Walton Ave Altoona PA 16602-3375 Office: Hayes Large Architects PO Box 1784 Logan Blvd and 5th Ave Altoona PA 16603

SUDAK, HOWARD STANLEY, physician, psychiatry educator; b. Cleve., Nov. 13, 1932; s. Sol and Leona (Simms) S.; m. Diane M. Ressler, Dec. 25, 1955 (div.); children: Ellen, Nancy, Janet, David; m. Donna M. Miller, Mar. 25, 1995. AB in Chemistry magna cum laude, Case Western Res. U., 1954, MD, 1958. Diplomate Am. Bd. Psychiatry and Neurology (sr. examiner 1991—). Intern in medicine Univ. Hosps. Cleve., 1958-59, resident in psychiatry, 1959-62; clin. assoc. NIMH, Bethesda, Md., 1962-64; chief psychiatry Cleve. VA Med. Ctr., 1964-84; asst. prof. psychiatry Case Western Res. U., Cleve., 1964-74, assoc. prof., 1974-82, prof., 1982—, vice dean Med. Sch., 1985-92; chmn. dept. psychiatry The Pa. Hosp., Phila., 1992—; psychiatrist-in-chief Inst. of Pa. Hosp., Phila., 1992—; clin. prof. psychiatry U. Pa. Sch. Medicine, 1993-94; clin. prof. psychiatry, vice chmn. psychiatry/human behavior Thomas Jefferson U., Phila., 1994—; mem. profl. adv. coun. Youth Suicide Nat. Ctr., Washington, 1986—; com. mem. Ctrs. for Disease Control, Atlanta, 1990-91. Editor: Suicide in the Young, 1984, Clinical Psychiatry, 1985; cons. editor Suicide and Life Threatening Behavior, 1988—; contbr. numerous articles to profl. jours., chpt. to books. Dir. Inst. for Urban Health, Cleve., 1990-92. Grantee NIMH, 1972-73, 83-86. Fellow Am. Psychiatry Assn., Am. Coll. Psychiatrists, Am. Coll. Psychoanalysts; mem. Am. Assn. Suicidology (trustee 1988-90), Am. Suicide Found. (trustee 1989-91), Phi Beta Kappa, Alpha Omega Alpha. Avocations: biking, sailing, reading, tennis, jazz and classical music. Home: 321 Lawrence St Philadelphia PA 19106 Office: Inst of Pa Hosp 111 N 49th St Philadelphia PA 19139

SUDAN, RAVINDRA NATH, electrical engineer, physicist, educator; b. Chineni, Kashmir, India, June 8, 1931; came to U.S., 1958, naturalized, 1971; s. Brahm Nath and Shanti Devi (Mehta) S.; m. Dipali Ray, July 3, 1959; children: Rajani, Ranjeet. B.A. with first class honors, U. Punjab, 1948; diploma, Indian Inst. Sci., 1952, Imperial Coll., London, 1953; Ph.D., U. London, 1955. Engr., Brit. Thomson-Houston Co., Rugby, Eng, 1955-57; research assoc. Cornell U., Ithaca, N.Y., 1958-59; asst. prof. elec. engring. Cornell U., 1959-63, assoc. prof., 1963-68, prof., 1968-75, IBM prof. engring., 1975—; dir. Lab. Plasma Studies, 1975-85, dep. dir. Cornell Theory Ctr., 1985-87; cons. Lawrence Livermore Lab., Los Alamos Sci. Lab., Sci. Applications Inc., Physics Internat. Co.; vis. research asso. Stanford U., summer 1963; cons. U.K. Atomic Energy Authority, Culham Lab., summer 1965; vis. scientist Internat. Center Theoretical Physics, Trieste, Italy, 1965-66, summers 1970, 73, Plasma Physics Lab. Princeton U., 1966-67, spring 1989, Inst. for Advanced Study, Princeton, N.J., spring 1975; head theoretical plasma physics group U.S. Naval Research Lab., 1970-71, sci. adviser to dir., 1974-75; chmn. Ann. Conf. on Theoretical Aspects of Controlled Fusion, 1975, 2d Internat. Conf. on High Power Electron and Ion Beam Research and Tech., 1977. Mem. editorial bd. Physics of Fluids, 1973-76, Comments on Plasma Physics, 1973—, Nuclear Fusion, 1976-84, Physics Reports, 1990—; co-editor Handbook of Plasma Physics; contbr. over 200 articles to sci. jours. Recipient Gold medal Acad. Scis. of the Czech Republic, 1993. Fellow IEEE, AAAS, Am. Phys. Soc. (Maxwell prize 1989), Nat. Rsch. Coun. (chmn. Plasma Sci. com. 1993—). Achievements include patents (with S. Humphries, Jr) intense ion beam generator. Office: Cornell Univ 369 Upson Hall Ithaca NY 14853-7501

SUDARSKY, JERRY M., industrialist; b. Russia, June 12, 1918; s. Selig and Sara (Ars) S.; m. Mildred Axelrod, Aug. 31, 1947; children: Deborah, Donna. Student, U. Iowa, 1936-39; B.S., Poly. U. Bklyn., 1942; D.Sc. (hon.), Poly. U. 1979. Founder, chief exec. officer Bioferm Corp., Wasco, Calif., 1946-66; cons. to Govt. of Israel, 1966-67; founder, chmn. Israel Chems., Ltd., Tel Aviv, Israel, 1967-72; chmn. I.C. Internat. Cons., Tel Aviv, 1971-73; vice chmn., bd. dirs. Daylin, Inc., Los Angeles, 1972-76; pres., chmn. J.M.S. Assocs., Los Angeles, 1976-82; vice chmn. bd. Jacobs

Engring. Group Inc., Pasadena, Calif., 1982-94; chmn., CEO Health Sci. Properties, Inc., Pasadena, 1994—. Patentee in field of indsl. microbiology. Bd. govs. Hebrew U., Jerusalem; trustee Polytechnic U. N.Y., 1976—; bd. dirs. Arthritis Found.; L.A., 1989-94, Mgmt. Edn. Assn., UCLA, 1990—. Served with USNR, 1943-46. Mem. AAAS, Am. Chem. Soc., Sigma Xi. Clubs: Brentwood Country (Los Angeles). Office: Health Sci Properties Inc 251 S Lake Ave Pasadena CA 91101-3003

SUDBURY, JOHN DEAN, religious foundation executive, petroleum chemist; b. Natchitoches, La., July 29, 1925; s. Herbert J. and Mary Flora S.; m. Jean Elizabeth Jung, July 18, 1947; children: John Byron, James Vernon (dec.), Linda Gail. BS, U. Tex., Austin, 1943, MA, 1947, PhD, 1949. Registered profl. engr., Okla. With Conoco Inc., various locations, 1949-83; asst. to v.p. tech. Conoco Inc., N.Y.C., 1970-72; v.p. coal research Conoco Coal Devel. Co. subs. Conoco Inc., Pitts., 1972-83; pres. Ea. European Mission & Bible Found., Houston, 1983—. Author: Oil Well Corrosion, 1956; contbr. articles to profl. jours. Mem. Ponca City (Okla.) Sch. Bd., 1965-67; trustee Okla. Christian Coll., 1968—. Served with USN, 1943-45. Recipient Frank Newman Speller award Nat. Assn. Corrosion Engrs., 1967. Mem. Am. Chem. Soc., N.Y. Acad. Scis., AAAS, Sigma Xi. Republican. Mem. Ch. of Christ. Club: Woodlands Country (Tex.). Patentee in energy field. Home: 42 Cascade Springs Pl Spring TX 77381-3101 Office: PO Box 90755 Houston TX 77290-0755

SUDDICK, PATRICK JOSEPH, defense systems company executive; b. London, Ont., Can., Sept. 27, 1923; s. Percy Edward and Eva Isobel (Jones) S.; m. Mary Agnes Walsh, July 7, 1951; children: Paul, Peter, Michael Jane Suddick Reynolds, Mark. BA in Sci., U. Toronto, 1949. With Honeywell Ltd., 1953-84; project mgr. comml. div. Honeywell Ltd., Scarborough, Ont., Can., 1953-57, asst. mgr. mil. products, 1957-58, market mgr. EDP div., 1958-65, gen. mgr. EDP div., 1965-68; v.p. EDP div. Honeywell Ltd., Willowdale, Ont., Can., 1968-70, v.p. and dir., 1970-84. Served with Can. Arty., 1942-46. Mem. Assn. Profl. Engrs., Ont., NATO Indsl. Adv. Group. Roman Catholic. Address: 25 Austin Dr Ste 419, Unionville, ON Canada L3R 8H4

SUDHAUS, WILLIAM S., petroleum company executive. Pres., chief operating officer, dir. Coral Petroleum Inc., Houston. Office: Indian Refining Partnership S 7th St Lawrenceville IL 62439

SUDLER, BARBARA WELCH, retired historical society administrator; b. Honolulu, Apr. 20, 1925; d. Leo F. and Barbara Lloyd (Petrikin) Welch; m. James Stewart Sudler, Dec. 30, 1950 (dec. 1982); children—Eleanor, James S.; m. William H. Hornby, Oct. 22, 1983. BA, U. Colo., 1944. Exec. administr. Historic Denver, 1974-79; exec. dir. Colo. Hist. Soc., Denver, 1979-81, pres., 1981-89, ret.; historic preservation officer State of Colo., Denver, 1983—; dir. Women's Bank, Denver. Editor: Nothing Is Long Ago, 1975. Recipient Soroptimist award, 1980, Contbn. to Arts award Big Sisters, 1981, Contbns. to Community award AIA, 1982, Community Service award U. Colo., 1986, James Grafton Rogers award, 1987. Mem. Am. Antiquarian Soc., Nat. Conf. State Historic Preservation Officers. Republican. Episcopalian. Clubs: Denver Country, University. Lodge: Rotary. Home: 180 High St Denver CO 80218-4018 Office: State Hist Soc Colo 1300 Broadway Denver CO 80203-2104

SUDWEEKS, WALTER BENTLEY, explosives company scientist; b. Buhl, Idaho, May 22, 1940; s. Leslie Laban and Rinda (Bentley) S.; m. Dorothy Agnes Peterson, June 1, 1965; children—Laura, Paul. B.S., Brigham Young U., 1965, Ph.D. 1970. Research chemist Du Pont Co., Wilmington, Del., 1969-72, sr. research chemist, Martinsburg, W. Va., 1972-76; sr. research scientist Ireco Chemicals, Inc., West Jordan, Utah, 1976-80, dir. product devel., 1980-84, research and devel. dir., 1984—. Holder 9 patents on emulsion explosives. Mem. Am. Chem. Soc. Republican. Mormon. Home: 734 Woodmore Dr Orem UT 84058-6104 Office: 3000 W 8600 S West Jordan UT 84084-9699 also: IRECO Inc Cross Rds Tower 11th Fl Salt Lake City UT 84144

SUE, ALAN KWAI KEONG, dentist; b. Honolulu, Apr. 26, 1946; s. Henry Tin Yee and Chiyoko (Ohata) S.; m. Ginger Kazue Fukushima, Mar. 19, 1972; 1 child, Dawn Marie. BS in Chemistry with honors, U. Hawaii, 1968; BS, U. Calif., San Francisco, 1972, DDS, 1972. Film editor, photographer Sta. KHVH-TV ABC, Honolulu, 1964-71; staff dentist Strong-Carter Dental Clinic, Honolulu, 1972-73; dentist Waianae Dental Clinic, Honolulu, 1972-73; pvt. practice Pearl City, Hawaii, 1973—; chief exec. officer Dental Image Specialists, Pearl City, 1975—; dental dir. Hawaii Dental Health Plan, Honolulu, 1987—; dental cons. Calif. Dental Health Plan, Tustin, 1987—; Pacific Group Med. Assn., The Queen's Health Care Plan, Honolulu, 1993—; dental cons. Pacific Group Med. Assn., 1994—; bd. dirs. Kula Bay Tropical Clothing Co.; mem. exec. bd. St. Francis Hosp., Honolulu, 1976-78, chief dept. dentistry, 1976-78; mem. expert med. panel Am. Internat. Claim Svc., 1995—. Mem. adv. bd. Health Svcs. for Elder Citizens, 1976—; mem. West Honolulu Sub-Area Health Planning Coun., 1981-84; mem. dental task force Hawaii Statewide Health Coordinating Coun., 1980, mem. plan devel. com., 1981-84; vol. oral cancer screening program Am. Cancer Soc.; v.p. Pearl City Shopping Ctr. Merchants Assn., 1975-84, 92-93, pres., 1994—. Regents' scholar U. Calif., San Francisco, 1968-72. Fellow Pierre Fauchard Acad., Acad. Gen. Dentistry; mem. ADA, Acad. Implants and Transplants, Am. Acad. Implant Dentistry, Hawaii Dental Assn. (trustee 1978-80), Honolulu County Dental Soc. (pres. 1982), Am. Acad. and Bd. Head, Facial, Neck Pain and TMJ Orthopedics, Intertel, Internat. Platform Assn., Mensa, Porsche Club, Pantera Owners Club, Mercedes Benz Club. Democrat. Avocations: cars, tennis, photography, gardening. Office: Dental Image Specialists 850 Kam Hwy Ste 116 Pearl City HI 96782

SUEDFELD, PETER, psychologist, educator; b. Budapest, Hungary, Aug. 30, 1935; emigrated to U.S. 1948, naturalized, 1952; s. Leslie John and Jolan (Eichenbaum) Field; m. Gabrielle Debra Guterman, June 11, 1961 (div. 1980); children: Michael Thomas, Joanne Ruth, David Lee; m. Phyllis Jean Johnson, Oct. 19, 1991. Student, U. Philippines, 1956-57; B.A., Queens Coll., 1960; M.A., Princeton U., 1962, Ph.D., 1963. Research assoc. Princeton U.; lectr. Trenton State Coll., 1963-64; vis. asst. prof. psychology U. Ill., 1964-65; asst. prof. psychology Univ. Coll. Rutgers U., 1965-67, assoc. prof., 1967-71, prof., 1971-72, chmn. dept., 1967-72; prof. psychology U. B.C., Vancouver, 1972—; head dept. U. B.C., 1972-84, dean faculty grad. studies, 1984-90; cons. in field; chmn. Can. Antarctic Rsch. Program. Author: Restricted Environmental Stimulation: Research and Clinical Applications, 1980; editor: Attitude Change: The Competing Views, 1971, Personality Theory and Information Processing, 1971, The Behavioral Basis of Design, 1976, Psychology and Torture, 1990, Restricted Environmental Stimulation: Theoretical and Empirical Developments in Flotation REST, 1990, Psychology and Social Policy, 1991; editor Jour. Applied Social Psychology, 1975-82; assoc. editor Environment and Behavior, 1992—; contbr. articles to profl. jours. Served with U.S. Army, 1955-58. NIMH grantee, 1970-72; Can. Council grantee, 1973—; Nat. Research Council Can. grantee, 1973-90; NIH grantee, 1980-84. Fellow Royal Soc. Can., Can. Psychol. Assn., Am. Psychol. Assn., Am. Psychol. Soc., Acad. Behavioral Medicine Research, Soc. Behavioral Medicine, N.Y. Acad. Scis.; mem. AAAS, Psychonomic Soc., Soc. Exptl. Social Psychology, Phi Beta Kappa, Sigma Xi. Office: U BC, Dept Psychology, Vancouver, BC Canada V6T 1Z4

SUELFLOW, AUGUST ROBERT, historical institute consultant, educator; b. Rockfield, Wis., Sept. 5, 1922; s. August Henry and Selma Hilda (Kressin) S.; m. Gladys I. Gierach, June 16, 1946; children: August Henry, Kathryn Lynn Du Bois. BA, Concordia Coll., Milw., 1942; BDiv, MDiv, Concordia Sem., St. Louis, 1946, fellow, 1947, STM, 1947; DivD, Concordia Sem., Springfield, Ill., 1967. Asst. curator Concordia Hist. Inst., St. Louis, 1946-48, dir., 1948-95, cons., 1995—; guest lectr. Concordia Sem., St. Louis, 1952-69, 74-75, adj. prof., 1975—; asst. pastor Luther Meml. Ch., Richmond Heights, Mo., 1948-56, Mt. Olive, St. Louis, 1958-75; archivist Western Dist. Luth. Ch.-Mo. Synod, 1948-66, archivist Mo. Dist., 1966-87, 88—; instr. Washington U., St. Louis, 1967-82. Hist. Mem. Am. Assn. Museums, Nat. Trust for Hist. Preservation, Soc. Am. Archivists, Orgn. Am. Historians, Western History Assn., Luth. Hist. Conf. Lutheran. Author: A Preliminary Guide to Church Records Depositories, 1969, Religious Archives: An Introduction, 1980, Heart of Missouri, 1954; cons., contbr. Luth. Cyclopedia; contbr. Moving Frontiers, 1964, Ency. of the Luth. Ch., 1965, The Luths. in N.Am.,

1975, C.F.W. Walther: The American Luther, 1987; mng. editor Concordia Hist. Inst. Quar., 1950-95, assoc. editor., 1950—; Archives & History: Minutes and Reports, 1952-89; editor: Directory of Religious Hist. Depositories in America, 1963, Microfilm Index and Bibliography, vol. I, 1966, vol. II, 1978, Luth. Hist. Conf. Essays and Reports, 1964-92; series editor: Selected Writings of C.F.W. Walther, 6 vols., 1981; vol. editor, translator: Walther's Convention Essays, vol. III, 1981; sec., mem. editorial com. Concordia Jour., 1976-81; mem. editorial/adv. com. Luth. Higher Edn. in N.Am., 1980; mem. editorial com., contbr. Moving Frontiers, 1964. Office: Concordia Hist Inst 801 De Mun Ave Saint Louis MO 63105-3199

SUELTENFUSS, SISTER ELIZABETH ANNE, university president; b. San Antonio, Apr. 14, 1921; d. Edward L. and Elizabeth (Amrein) S. BA in Botany and Zoology, Our Lady of Lake Coll., San Antonio, 1944; MS in Biology, U. Notre Dame, 1961, PhD, 1963. Joined Sisters of Divine Providence, Roman Catholic Ch., 1939; tchr. high schs. Okla. and La., 1942-49; mem. summer faculty Our Lady of Lake U. (formerly coll.), 1941-49, mem. full-time faculty, 1949-59, chmn. biology dept., 1963-73, pres., 1978—; mem. administv. staff to superior gen. Congregation Divine Providence, 1973-77. Author articles in field. Bd. dirs. Am. Cancer Soc., San Antonio chpt. ARC, Mind Sci. Found., YWCA, Alamo Pub. Telecom. Bd., S.W. Rsch. Found., I Have a Dream Found., Inst. Ednl. Leadership, Trim and Swim; bd. dirs., chmn. San Antonio Pub. Libr.; bd. dirs., pres. San Antonio Edn. Partnership. Recipient Achievement and Leadership awards U. Notre Dame, 1979, Svc. to Community award, 1991, Headliner award Women in Comms., 1980, Good Neighbor award NCCJ, 1982, Brotherhood award, 1992, Today's Woman award San Antonio Light, 1982, Outstanding Women award San Antonio Express-News, 1983, Spirit of Am. Woman award J.C. Penney, 1992, Lifetime Achievement award, 1993, Svc. to Edn. award Ford Found., 1993; named to San Antonio Women's Hall of Fame, 1985. Mem. AAUP, AAUW, San Antonio 100 Tex. Women's Forum, San Antonio Women's C. of C., Hispanic Assn. Colls. and Univs., Greater San Antonio C. of C. (past vice chmn.), San Antonio Coun. Pres. (past pres.), San Antonio Women's Hall of Fame (pres.). Home and Office: Our Lady of the Lake U Office of Pres 411 SW 24th St San Antonio TX 78207-4689

SUEN, CHING YEE, computer scientist and educator, researcher; b. Chung Shan, Kwang Tung, China, Oct. 14, 1942; s. Stephen and Sin (Kan) S.; m. Sheung Ling Chan, May 12, 1970; children: Karwa, Karnon. BSc in Engring., U. Hong Kong, 1966, MSc in Engring., 1968; M.A.Sc., U. B.C., 1970, PhD, 1972. Asst. prof. computer sci. Concordia U., Montreal, Can., 1972-76, assoc. prof., 1976-79, prof., 1979, chmn., 1980-84, dir. Centre for Pattern Recognition and Machine Intelligence, 1988—; vis. scientist Rsch. Lab. of Electronics, MIT, Cambridge, 1975, 76, 78-79; invited prof. Ecole Polytechnique Fédérale de Lausanne, Switzerland, 1979, Institut de Recherche d'Informatique et d'Automatique, Rocquencourt, France, 1976, 78, 79; co-founder, co-chmn. Internat. Conf. on Document Analysis and Recognition, St.-Malo, France, 1991, Tsukuba Sci. City, Japan, 1993, chmn., Montreal, Can., 1995; founder, chmn. Internat. Workshop on Frontiers in Handwriting Recognition, Montreal, 1990; organizer numerous confs. Author: Computational Analysis of Mandarin, 1979, Computational Studies of the Most Frequent Chinese Words and Sounds, 1986, (with Z.C. Li, T.D. Bui, Y.Y. Tang) Computer Transformation of Digital Images and Patterns, 1989; editor: (with R. De Mori) Computer Analysis and Perception Vol. 1, Visual Signals, 1982, Computer Analysis and Perception Vol. 2, Auditory Signals, 1982, (with R. De Mori) New Systems and Architectures for Automatic Speech Recognition and Synthesis, 1985, (with R. Plamondon and M.L. Simner) Computer Recognition and Human Production of Handwriting, 1989, Frontiers in Handwriting Recognition, 1990, Operating Expert System Applications in Canada, 1992, (with P.S.P. Wang) Thinning Methodologies for Pattern Recognition, 1994; assoc. editor Signal Processing, 1979—, Pattern Recognition Letters, 1982—, Pattern Recognition, 1983—, IEEE Transactions on Pattern Analysis and Machine Intelligence, 1986-89, Internat. Jour. Pattern Recognition and Artificial Intelligence, 1986—; founder, editor-in-chief Computer Processing of Chinese and Oriental Langs., 1982-93; adviser IEEE Transactions on Pattern Analysis and Machine Intelligence, 1989—; author more than 300 publs.; patentee in field. Recipient award Fedn. Chinese Can. Profls., 1988; Swire scholar U. Hong Kong, 1967, ITAC/NSERC award info. Tech. Assn. Can. and Natural Scis. and Engring. Rsch. Coun. Can., 1992. Fellow IEEE (advisor Computer Soc.), Internat. Assn. for Pattern Recognition (gov.); mem. Chinese Lang. Computer Soc. (pres. 1990-93, award 1988), Can. Image Processing and Pattern Recognition Soc. (pres. 1984-90). Office: Concordia U Dept Computer Sci, 1455 Maisonneuve W Ste GM-606, Montreal, PQ Canada H3G 1M8

SUEN, JAMES YEE, otolaryngologist, educator; b. Dermott, Ark., Oct. 9, 1940; s. Yee Gow and Mary (Chaing) S.; m. Karen Hannahs; children: Brent, Tiffany, Bradley, Brennan. BA in Zoology, U. Tex., 1962; BS, MD, U. Ark., 1966. Diplomate Am. Bd. Otolaryngology. Rotating intern San Francisco Gen. Hosp., 1966-67; resident in otolaryngology U. Ark. Med. Ctr., Little Rock, 1969-70, resident in otolaryngology, 1970-73; advanced sr. fellow M.D. Anderson Hosp. and Tumor Inst., Houston, 1973-74, faculty assoc., 1974; asst. prof. U. Ark. Coll. Medicine, Little Rock, 1974-76, assoc. prof., 1976-78, prof. otolaryngology, 1978—; chief div. otolaryngology, 1974-78, chmn. dept. otolaryngology and head and neck surgery, 1978—. Author, editor: Cancer of the Head and Neck, 1981, 2d edit., 1989, Emergencies in Otolaryngology, 1986. Capt. USAF, 1967-69. Named Chinese Man of Yr. Chinese Soc. Ark., 1983, Disting. Citizen of Yr., 1991, Disting. Faculty award U. Ark. Coll. Medicine, 1990. Fellow ACS, Am. Acad. Otolaryngology and Head and Neck Surgery, Am. Soc. Head and Neck Surgery (pres. 1993-94, coun. 1988-92); mem. Soc. Univ. Otolaryngologists. Methodist. Avocation: sculpturing. Office: U Ark Coll Medicine 4301 W Markham St Little Rock AR 72205-7101

SUENHOLZ, HERMAN HARRY, banker; b. Jamaica, N.Y., Aug. 6, 1924; s. Herman and Johanna (Gassler) S.; m. Helen J. Andrews, July 16, 1949; children: Elaine, Robert, Mary Jo, Claire, Margaret, Laura. B.S. magna cum laude, Fairleigh Dickinson U., 1959; postgrad., N.Y. U., 1960-64. With Nat. Westminster Bank N.J. (formerly First Jersey Nat. Bank), Jersey City, 1953-90; cashier Nat. Westminster Bank N.J. (formerly First Jersey Nat. Bank), 1962-65, v.p., 1965, sr. v.p., cashier, 1966-67, exec. v.p., 1967-75, pres., 1975-88, vice chmn., also bd. dirs.; vice chmn. Nat. Westminster Bancorp N.J., 1988-90, also bd. dirs., ret., 1990. Trustee Fairleigh Dickinson U.; treas., trustee Aviation Hall of Fame of N.J., 1992-94. With USNR, 1943-46. Mem. Am. Bankers Assn. (govt. relations council), N.J. Banker Assn. (exec. com.,treas., 1987-88, vice-chmn. 1988-89, chmn. 1989-90).

SUER, MARVIN DAVID, architect; b. Phila., Apr. 4, 1923; m. Gertrude Litvin, 1947; children: Marsha Suer Clark, Sharon, Deborah Suer Berman. BArch, U. Pa., 1950. Registered architect, N.J., Pa. Ptnr. Suer & Livingston, 1961-62, Suer, Livingston & Demas, 1962-69; dir. tech. prodn. Eshbach, Pullinger, Stevens & Bruder, Phila., 1969-74; assoc. Ballinger, Phila., 1974-79, Bartley Long Mirenda, Phila., 1979-85, S.T. Hudson Internat., Phila., 1986—. Archtl. works include State Hosp. for Crippled Children addition, 1964, Huey Elem. Sch., Phila., 1964, Dist. No. 4 Health Ctr., Phila., 1967, Stephen Smith Towers, 1969, Foxchase Br. Libr., 1969. Chmn. bd. trustees Phila. Found. for Architecture, 1980-81. With C.E., AUS, 1943-46. Fellow AIA (pres. Phila. chpt. 1978, 125th Yr. citation 1982); mem. Tau Sigma Delta. Home: 305 Overlook Ave Willow Grove PA 19090-2806 Office: 595 E Swedesford Rd Wayne PA 19087-1615

SUFIT, ROBERT LOUIS, neurologist, educator; b. Washington, July 16, 1950; s. Herbert and Alice Elizabeth (Rotzsch) S.; m. Diana Dills, Apr. 17, 1976 (div. Dec. 1988); children: Ben, Jessica, Alexandra. BA, Johns Hopkins U., 1972, MA, 1972; MD, U. Va., 1976. Diplomate Am. Bd. Psychiatry and Neurology, Am. Bd. Electrodiagnostic Medicine. House officer U. Pitts., 1977-80; post doctoral fellow U. Colo., Denver, 1980-82; asst. prof. U. Wis., Madison, 1982—. Contbr. 40 articles to profl. jours. and chpts. to books. Grantee NIH. Fellow Am. Acad. Neurology. Home: 564 Toepfer Ave Madison WI 53711-1666 Office: U Wis 600 Highland Ave Madison WI 53792-0001

SUGAR, PETER FRIGYES, historian; b. Budapest, Hungary, Jan. 5, 1919; s. Peter S. and Margit (Pongor) S.; m. Sally Bortz, June 18, 1955; children: Steven P., Klari A., Karen L. B.A., CCNY, 1954; M.A., Princeton, U.,

1956, Ph.D., 1959. Instr. history Princeton U., 1957-59; asst. prof. history U. Wash., Seattle, 1959-63; assoc. prof. U. Wash., 1963-69, prof., 1969-89, now prof. history emeritus; assoc. dir. U. Wash. (Inst. Comparative and Foreign Area Studies). Author: The Industrialization of Bosnia-Hercegovina, 1878-1919, 1963, Southeastern Europe under Ottoman Rule, 1354-1804, 1977, A History of Hungary, 1990, and others. Guggenheim Found. fellow, 1964-65; Woodrow Wilson fellow, 1954-55; Fulbright fellow, 1984. Mem. Am. Hist. Assn. Am. Assn. Advancement of Slavic Studies, Western Slavic Assn., Am. Assn. Study of Hungarian History. Home: 11737 12th Ave NE Seattle WA 98125-5007 Office: U Wash Dept History Seattle WA 98195

SUGARMAN, ALAN WILLIAM, educational administrator; b. Boston, Sept. 26, 1924; s. Henry and Dorothy (Adams) S.; m. Alice Mulhall, 1974; children: Michael, Susan, Ellen, William, Jane, James. BS, Boston U., 1948; MA, Columbia U., 1949, EdD, 1967; postgrad., SUNY, Albany, 1954-56. Entrance examiner Boston U., 1947-48; tchr. Public Schs. Hudson, N.Y., 1950-54; prin. jr. high sch. Public Schs. Hudson, 1954-56, prin. sr. high sch., 1956-61; prin. Spring Valley (N.Y.) Sr. High Sch., 1961-67; dir. secondary edn. Ramapo Central Sch. Dist. No. 2, Spring Valley, 1967-69; asst. supt. instrn. Ramapo Central Sch. Dist. No. 2, 1969-73; prin. Ramapo Sr. High Sch., Spring Valley, 1969; supt. schs. Connetquot Central Sch. Dist. Islip, Bohemia, N.Y., 1973-80, Ft. Lee (N.J.) Sch. Dist., 1980—; adj. prof. N.Y. U., N.Y.C., U. P.R., Rio Piedras, Hofstra U., 1967—; prof. Fordham U., N.Y.C., 1969. Athletic dir. East River Day Camp, N.Y.C., summer 1949; group worker St. John's Guild, summer 1950; asst. dir. Tenn. Work Camp, Unitarian Service Com., summer 1951; dir. spl. activities Hudson Youth Bur., Hudson, N.Y., summer 1952; exec. dir. Jewish Community Center, Hudson, 1953-56; chmn. vis. coms. Middle States Commn. Colls. and Secondary Schs., 1958-76; chmn. county leadership tng. com., mem. Rockland County exec. council Boy Scouts Am., 1956; bd. dirs. Bergen County Red Cross; corr. sec. Rockland County Negro Scholarship Fund, Inc.; pres. Spring Valley Youth Activities Com., 1956-58; bd. dirs., past campaign cochmn. Greater Hudson Community Chest; bd. dirs., 2d v.p. Hudson Youth Recreation Center, 1958-61; bd. dirs. Rockland County br. Am. Cancer Soc., 1958-61, Columbia Meml. Hosp., 1959-61; chmn. Town of Islip Health Usage Com., 1973; bd. dirs. Am. Heart Assn. N.J. affiliate, 1993—. Served with AUS, 1944-46, ETO. Recipient Disting. Svc. award Hudson Jr. C. of C., 1960, Ft. Lee Citizen of Yr. award VFW, Bergen County Citizen of Yr. award VFW, 1989, N.J. State Elks Alcohol and Drug Prevention award, 1989, St. Michael's award, 1992, PBA Silver Life Card award, 1993, EIA award Greek Orthodox Archdiocese, 1993; named Administr. of Yr., Fordham U., 1990, B'nai Brith Man of Yr., 1995. Mem. Nat. Honor Soc. Secondary Schs. (hon.), Nat. PTA (hon. life), Am. Assn. Sch. Administrs., Assn. Supervision and Curriculum Devel., Nat. Sch. Public Relations Assn., Assn. Sch. Bus. Ofcls., Nat. Soc. Study Edn., DAV, VFW, Jewish War Vets., Rotary (bd. dirs.), Phi Delta Kappa (Adminstr. of Yr. award 1990), Kappa Delta Pi, Pi Gamma Mu. Jewish (bd. edn.). Home: Shelter Bay Club 1225 River Rd Apt 7B Edgewater NJ 07020-1461 Office: 255 Whiteman St Fort Lee NJ 07024-5629

SUGARMAN, GEORGE, artist; b. N.Y.C., May 11, 1912; s. Herman and Rachel S. B.A., CCNY, 1935. adj. prof. art Hue Hunter Coll., 1961-68, also Yale U., Princeton U. One-man shows Widdifield Gallery, N.Y.C., 1958, Radich Gallery, N.Y.C., 1961, 64, 65, 66, Phila. Art Alliance, 1965, Dayton's Gallery 12, Mpls., 1966, Galerie Schmela, Dusseldorf, Germany, 1967, Galerie Ziegler, Zurich, Switzerland, 1967, 70, Kaiser Wilhelm Mus., Krefeld, Germany, 1969, Staditsches Mus., Leverkusen, 1969, Kunsthalle, Basel, Switzerland, 1970, Haus Am Waldsee Mus., Berlin, 1970, Stedelijk Mus., Amsterdam, 1970, Gallery 118, Mpls., 1971, Zabriskie Gallery, N.Y.C., 1974, Dag Hammarskjold Plaza Sculpture Garden, N.Y.C., 1974, Robet Miller Gallery, N.Y.C., 1977, 78, Galerie Liatowitsch, Basel, 1979, Rudolf Zwirner Gallery, Cologne, W. Ger., 1981, Joslyn Art Mus (retrospective), Omaha, 1981-82, Fuller-Goldeen Gallery, San Francisco, 1984, Robert Miller Gallery, N.Y.C., 1985, Whitney Mus. Am. Art, N.Y.C., 1985, Contemporary Sculpture Ctr., Tokyo, 1993; group shows include, São Paulo (Brazil) Biennale, 1963, Whitney Mus. Am. Art, 1966, Los Angeles County Mus. Art, 1967, Internat. Pavilion, Biennale, Venice, Italy, 1968, Mus. Modern Art, N.Y.C., 1969, Whitney Mus., 1976; represented in permanent collections, Walker Art Center, Mpls., Kunstmuseum, Zurich, Mus. Modern Art, Whitney Mus. Am. Art, Art Inst. Chgo., Met. Mus., N.Y.C.; sculpture commns., World Trade Center, Brussels, Albert M. Greenfield Sch., Phila., Empire State Mall, Albany, N.Y., Fed. Ct. Bldg., Balt., Akron (Ohio) Public Library, Lincoln Nat. Life Found., Ft. Wayne, Ind., Internat. Airport, Miami, Fla., Detroit Gen. Hosp., Wills Eye Hosp., Phila., Summer-Best Sta., Buffalo, Southland Life Bldg., Dallas, Columbia Plaza, Cin., Allegheny Landing, Pitts., Joslyn Sculpture Garden, Omaha, Bellevue Park, Wichita Falls, Tex., VA Hosp., Martinsburg, W.Va., Columbia Plaza, Cin., Storm King Art Ctr., Mountainville, N.Y., Mercantile Bank, San Antonio, GTE, Irving Tex., NCNB Pla., Tampa, Fla., Koll Ctr. Irvine, North Irvine, Calif., The Pavillions at Buckland Hills, Manchester, Conn., Crystal Tower, Kobe, Japan, Mitsui Marine Co., Chiba, Japan, Cultural Ctr., Miyazaki, Kyushu, Japan, Suderman Sq., Jakarta, Indonesia. Served with USN, 1941-45. Recipient 2d prize Pitts. Internat., 1961-62; Am. Acad. and Inst. Arts and Letters award; Longview Found. grantee, 1961, 62, 63; Ford Found. grantee, 1965; Nat. Found. Arts grantee, 1966, special award Sculpture Triennale Osaka, Japan, 1992. Home: 21 Bond St New York NY 10012-2451

SUGARMAN, IRWIN J., lawyer; b. Dayton, Ohio, June 17, 1943; s. Nathan and Esther (Goldstein) S.; 1 child, Alexander David Skigen Sugarman. BA, Rutgers U., New Brunswick, N.J., 1965; JD, Rutgers U., Newark, 1968. Bar: N.Y. 1968. Law clk. to Judge Edmund Palmieri U.S. Dist. Ct. for So. Dist. N.Y., N.Y.C., 1968-69; assoc. Debevoise Plimpton Lyons & Gates, N.Y.C., 1969-79; ptnr. Schulte Roth & Zabel, N.Y.C., 1979—. Bd. dirs. Santa Fe Opera, 1989-94. Office: Schulte Roth & Zabel 900 3rd Ave New York NY 10022-4728

SUGARMAN, JULE M., children's services consultant, former public administrator; b. Cin., Sept. 23, 1927; s. Melville Harty and Rachel Wolf (Meyer) S.; m. Sheila Mary Shanley, May 20, 1956 (dec.); children: Christopher, Maryanne, Jason, James; m. Candace Sullivan, Apr. 2, 1989. Student, Western Res. U., 1945-46; A.B. with highest distinction, Am. U., 1951. Dir. Head Start, 1965-69; adminstr. Human Resources Adminstrn., N.Y.C., 1970-73; chief adminstrv. officer City of Atlanta, 1974-76; vice chmn. CSC, Washington, 1977-78; dep. dir. Office Personnel Mgmt., 1979-81; mng. dir. Human Service Info. Ctr., 1981-83; v.p. Hahnemann U., 1983-86; sec. Wash. State Dept. Social and Health Services, 1986-89; exec. dir. Spl. Olympics Internat., Washington, 1989-91; chmn. Ctr. on Effective Svcs. for Children, Washington, 1991—. Served with U.S. Army, 1946-48. Recipient Meritorious Service award Dept. State, 1963, Alumni Service award Am. U., 1977, Disting. Pub. Svc. award Nat. Acad. Pub. Adminstrn., 1988. Home: 2555 Pennsylvania Ave NW Washington DC 20037-1646 Office: PO Box 27412 Washington DC 20038

SUGARMAN, MYRON GEORGE, lawyer; b. San Francisco, Nov. 7, 1942; s. Irving Carden and Jane Hortense (Weingarten) S.; m. Cheryl Ann Struble, June 8, 1968 (div. 1993); children: Andrew, Amy, Adam; m. Cynthia Wilson Woods, Apr. 16, 1994. BS, U. Calif., Berkeley, 1964, JD, 1967. Assoc. Cooley, Godward, Castro, Huddleson & Tatum, San Francisco, 1972-77, ptnr., 1977—. Served to capt. U.S. Army, 1968-71. Fellow Am. Coll. Trust and Estate Counsel, Am. Coll. Tax Counsel, Am. Bar Found.; mem. U. Calif. Alumni Assn. (bd. dirs. 1985-88), San Francisco Tax Club (pres. 1990), San Francisco Grid Club. Avocations: skiing, tennis. Office: Cooley Godward Castro Huddleson & Tatum 1 Maritime Plz San Francisco CA 94111-3404

SUGARMAN, PAUL RONALD, lawyer, educator, academic administrator; b. Boston, Dec. 14, 1931; m. Susan J. Sugarman; children: Amy J., Ellen J. AA, Boston U., 1951, JD cum laude (Law Week award 1954, assoc. editor law rev. 1952-54), 1954; LLD (hon.), Suffolk U., 1989. Bar: Mass. 1954, U.S. Supreme Ct. 1965. Ptnr. Sugarman & Sugarman, Boston, 1967-90, 94—; prof. law, dean Suffolk U. Law Sch., Boston, 1990-94; mem. Atty. Gen. Mass. Hwy. Law Study Commn., 1965, Mass. Gov.'s Select Com. on Jud. Needs, 1976; bd. bar overseers Supreme Jud. Ct., 1984-88, chmn., 1985-88; advocate Am. Bd. Trial Advocates; spl. master, commr. Boston Mcpl. Ct. Report Supreme Jud. Ct. of Mass., 1990. Trustee Mass. Bar Found., 1980-81. Served as officer AUS, 1955-58. Recipient Courageous Adv. award,

Mass. Acad. Trial Attys., 1984, William O. Douglas First Amendment Freedom award, Anti-Defamation League, 1986, Silver Shingle award for svc. to legal profession Boston U. Sch. Law, 1989, Jurisprudence award Am. Orgn. for Rehab. through Tng. Fedn., 1991, Civil Justice award Am. Bd. trial Adv., 1993. Fellow Am. Coll. Trial Lawyers, Am. Bar Found., Mass. Bar Found., Internat. Soc. Barristers; mem. Am. Bar Assn., Mass. Bar Assn. (pres. 1976-77, chmn. com. on recall of ret. judges 1982-86, Gold Medal award 1991), Am. Trial Lawyers Assn. (gov. 1966-68, pres. Mass. chpt. 1968-70), Boston Bar Assn., Boston U. Sch. Law Alumni Assn. (pres. 1979-80). Office: Sugarman and Sugarman PC One Beacon St Boston MA 02108

SUGARMAN, PAUL WILLIAM, lawyer; b. Cambridge, Mass., July 31, 1947; s. Louis Edward and Natalie (Waldman) S.; m. Susan Lee Richard, July 16, 1978; children: Sarah, Emily, Hannah. BA, Harvard U., 1969; JD, Yale U., 1975. Bar: Calif. 1976, U.S. Dist. Ct. (no. dist.) Calif. 1976, U.S. Ct. Appeals (9th cir.) 1976. Law clk. to judge U.S. Dist. Ct. (no. dist.) Calif., San Francisco, 1975-76; assoc. Heller, Ehrman, White & McAuliffe, San Francisco, 1976-81, ptnr., 1982—. Vol. U.S. Peace Corps, Ethiopia, 1969-72. Mem. ABA, Calif. Bar Assn., San Francisco Bar Assn., Phi Beta Kappa. Home: 907 Longridge Rd Oakland CA 94610-2878 Office: Heller Ehrman White & McAuliffe 333 Bush St San Francisco CA 94104-2806

SUGARMAN, ROBERT GARY, lawyer; b. Bronx, N.Y., Sept. 3, 1939; s. Eugene Leonard and Frances (Solomon) S.; m. Brenda Harrison, Sept. 8, 1963 (div. 1984); children: Dana, Alison; m. Surie Rudoff, June 16, 1985; children: Amanda, Jason. BA, Yale U., 1960, LLB, 1963. Bar: N.Y. 1963, Fla. 1963, U.S. Supreme Ct. 1971, U.S. Dist. Ct. (so. dist.) N.Y. 1966, U.S. Dist. Ct. (ea. dist.) N.Y. 1982, U.S. Ct. Appeals (2d cir.) 1970, U.S. Ct. Appeals (10th cir.) 1971. Assoc. Sugarman, Kuttner & Fuss, N.Y.C., 1966, Sullivan & Cromwell, N.Y.C., 1966-72; assoc. Weil, Gotshal & Manges, N.Y.C., 1972-75, ptnr., 1975—. Author: (with others) Litigation Strategy and Tactics , 1979, Deposition Strategy Law and Forms, 1980, Masters of Trial Practice, 1988; contbr. articles on intellectual property law to profl. jours. Assoc. counsel N.Y. State Constl. Conv., Albany, N.Y., 1967; pres. B'nai Brith Hillel-Jewish Assn. Coll. Youth, 1986-88. Served to capt. U.S. Army, 1963-65. Fellow Am. Coll. Trial Lawyers; mem. ABA, Assn. of Bar of City of N.Y. (chmn. comm. and media law com. 1989-92), B'nai Brith (internat. bd. govs. 1975-85), Anti-Defamation League (nat. commn. 1981—, nat. exec. com. 1988—, vice-chmn. 1990-92, chmn. intergroup rels. com. 1992-94, chmn. civil rights com. 1994—). Democrat. Jewish. Office: Weil Gotshal & Manges 767 Fifth Ave New York NY 10022

SUGARMAN, ROBERT JAY, lawyer; b. Meriden, Conn., May 29, 1938; s. Lester Holman and Ruth Frieda (Kalman) S.; children—Karen Elizabeth, Kenneth John, Jane Alexandra, Lily Anna. A.B., Brown U., 1960; postgrad. (Ford Found. fellow), Stanford U., 1960-61; LL.B. magna cum laude, Harvard U., 1964. Law clk. to Hon. Abraham L. Freedman, U.S. Ct. Appeals, Phila., 1965-66; ptnr. Dechert Price and Rhoads, Phila., 1964-65, 66-78, Sugarman & Assocs., Phila., 1982—; lectr. in environ. law, adj. prof. planning; legal cons. Nat. Water Quality Commn. Author: (with T. Reiner) The Crosstown Expressway: A Case Study, 1970, (with D. DeVaul and T. Keating) Trading in Power, 1985; editor: Harvard Law Rev, 1963-64; contbr. articles to profl. jours. U.S. chmn. Internat. Joint Commn., U.S. and Can., Washington, 1978-81. Office: Sugarman & Assocs 100 N 17th St 7th fl Philadelphia PA 19103

SUGARMAN, SAMUEL LOUIS, retired oil transportation and trading company executive, horse breeder; b. Montague, Mass., Apr. 18, 1927; s. Julius William and Minnie S.; m. Marlene Rodenz, Mar. 3, 1958; children—Jord Ann, Shawn, Jay Scott, Robin. B.S., U.S. Merchant Marine Acad., 1947; postgrad., N.Y. State Sch. Indsl. and Labor Relations, Cornell U., 1950; M.B.A. with distinction, Harvard U., 1953. Dir. market research and spl. projects Gulf Oil U.S., Houston, 1968-70; mgr. new venture investments Gulf Oil Corp., Pitts., 1972-74; exec. v.p. Gulf Trading & Transp. Co., Pitts., 1974-86; sr. v.p. Gulf Exploration and Prodn. Co., Houston; pres. Gulf Overseas Commodities Ltd. Served with USNR, 1953-55.

SUGG, HARRY LEE, JR., dentist; b. Memphis, June 29, 1940; s. Harry Lee Sugg and Marguerite (Stephens) Richardson; m. Claire Joyner, Dec. 19, 1965 (div. 1969); m. Kerry Jane Brown, Nov. 30, 1980. BS, Memphis State U., 1965; DDS, U. Tenn., Memphis, 1969. Rotating dental intern VA Hosp., Memphis, 1969-70; gen. practice dentistry Dallas, 1970—. Mem. ADA, Tex. Dental Soc., Dallas County Dental Soc. Republican. Mem. Bible Ch. Club: Mastermind Study (charter). Avocations: flying, photography, travel, reading. Office: Red Bird Dental Assocs 1201 W Camp Wisdom Rd Dallas TX 75232-3405

SUGG, JOHN LOGAN (JACK SUGG), advertising executive; b. Hillsboro, Ill., June 2, 1914; s. Norman J. and Clythera (McDavid) S.; m. Jean Ellen Morrison, Feb. 7, 1942; children: Michael L., Patrick M., Terry Jean. B.A., Lake Forest Coll., 1938. Engaged in newspaper work, 1938-41; with Cole & Weber, Inc., 1946—, pres., 1968-72, chmn. bd., 1972-76, chmn. exec. com., 1976-80; ret., 1981; pres. Assoc. Oreg. Industries, 1968-69. Bd. dirs. Emanuel Med. Center Found.; chmn. bd. dirs. Portland Better Bus. Bur., 1975—. Served to lt. comdr. USN, 1941-45. Named Oreg. Advt. Man of Year, 1965. Mem. Portland C. of C. (dir.), Am. Assn. Advt. Agys. (chmn. Western region 1970-71). Clubs: Arlington (pres. 1975—), Multnomah Athletic, Portland Golf. Home: 2415 SW Timberline Dr Portland OR 97225-4129 *When young people seek my advice concerning careers in the advertising agency field, this is what I tell them: "Advertising can be rich and rewarding for one who has an understanding of human motivation, basic skills in communication, capacity for plain hard work and the ability to shrug off disappointment. But if you're not confident that you can achieve management status by age 40, go into another field. Advertising's daily firing-line is for the young and venturesome.".*

SUGG, ROBERT PERKINS, former state supreme court justice; b. Eupora, Miss., Feb. 21, 1916; s. Amos Watson and Virgie Christian (Cooper) S.; m. Elizabeth Lorraine Carroll, June 23, 1940; children: Robert Perkins, Charles William, John David. Student, Wood Jr. Coll., 1933-34, Miss. State U., 1935-37, Jackson Sch. Law, 1939-40. Bar: Miss. Practice law, 1940-51, chancery judge, 1951-71; asso. justice Miss. Supreme Ct., 1971-83; county pros. atty. Webster County, Miss., 1949-50; spl. chancery judge Hinds, Scott and Jasper counties, Miss., 1989, sr. judge, 1990—; mem. adv. council Nat. Ctr. for State Cts., 1973-79. Bd. govs. Miss. Jud. Coll., 1973-80; literacy missions assoc. Home Mission Bd. of So. Bapt. Conv., 1983—. Served with USAAF, 1942-43. Named Outstanding Citizen, Eupora Jr. C. of C., 1970, Alumnus of Year, Wood Jr. Coll., 1973; recipient Service to Humanity award Miss. Coll., 1976. Mem. Miss. State Bar, Am. Judicature Soc., CAP (Miss. Wing, squadron comdr. 1974-76), Am. Legion (post comdr. 1950). Democrat. Baptist (chmn. bd. deacons 1964). Home: 1067 Meadow Heights Dr Jackson MS 39206-6021

SUGGS, JAMES C., publishing executive. Pres. Christian Bd. Publ. (CBP), St. Louis. Office: Christian Bd Publication PO Box 179 1316 Convention Plaza Dr Saint Louis MO 63166

SUGGS, LEO H., transportation executive. Sr. v.p. Yellow Freight System Inc.; CEO Preston. Office: Preston 151 Easton Blvd Preston MD 21655-9751

SUGGS, MARION JACK, minister, college dean; b. Electra, Tex., June 5, 1924; s. Claude Frank and Lottie Maye (Gibson) S.; m. Ruth Barge, Nov. 13, 1943; children: Adena Ruth Suggs Beck, James Robert, David Nathan. BA, U. Tex., 1946; BD, Tex. Christian U., 1949; PhD, Duke U., 1954. Ordained to ministry Christian Ch. (Disciples of Christ), 1948. Min. First Christian Ch., Gladewater, Tex., 1948-50, Wendell Christian Ch., N.C., 1950-52; asst. prof. Brite Div. Sch. Tex. Christian U., Ft. Worth, 1952-54, assoc. prof., 1954-56, prof., 1956-89, dean Brite Div. Sch., 1977-89; emeritus dean and prof. Tex. Christian U., Fort Worth, 1989—; mem. coun. on ministry Christian Ch. in S.W., 1976-89; chmn. coun. on theol. edn. Div. Higher Edn., 1987-88, mem. ch. fin. coun., 1985-89, bd. dirs.; mem. gen. bd. Christian Ch. (Disciples of Christ), 1986-87; lectr. min.'s week Tex. Christian U., 1961, Lexington Theol. Sem., 1966, S.W. Mo. State U., 1977; mem.

Disciples-Roman Cath. Internat. Bilateral Conv., 1978-87. Author: The Layman Reads His Bible, 1957, The Gospel Story, 1960 (Adult Book of Yr. Christian Lit. Com. 1960), Wisdom, Christology and Law in Matthew's Gospel, 1970 (Christian Rsch. Found. award 1967); also articles ; co-editor: Studies in the History and Text of the New Testament, 1967, New English Bible: Oxford Study Edition, 1976 (Religious Book award 1977), The Oxford Study Bible, Revised English Bible, 1992. Bd. dirs. Granville T. Walker Found. G.H. Kearns fellow, 1951, Am. Coun. Learned Socs. fellow, 1963-64, Assn. Theol. Schs. fellow, 1963-64; recipient Disting. Alumnus award Tex. Christian U., 1973. Mem. Soc. Bibl. Lit., Studiorum Novi Testamenti Societas, Internat. Greek N.T. Project, Phi Beta Kappa, Alpha Kappa Delta, Pi Gamma Mu, Theta Phi. Democrat. Home: 5605 Winifred Dr Fort Worth TX 76133-2501

SUGIHARA, KENZI, publishing executive; b. Kearny, N.J., Oct. 4, 1940; s. Kyuichi and Shinobuko (Yamaguchi) S.; m. Roslyn Forbes, Dec. 1966 (div. Mar. 1981); children: Kenichi, Takeo, Akira, Fumio; m. Nancy Elizabeth Kirsh, June 8, 1981; 1 child, Toshiro. BA, NYU, 1963. Supr. McGraw Hill, Inc., N.Y.C., 1965-67; assoc. dir. coll. product dept. Harcourt Brace Jovanovich Inc., N.Y.C., 1978-82, dir. electronic pub., 1982-83; v.p., pub. Bantam Electronic Pub. div., pub. Bantam Reference Books, Bantam Profl. Books, Bantam Doubleday Dell, N.Y.C., 1983-93; v.p., pub. Random House Reference & Electronic Pub. (Random House Inc.), 1993-95; pres. Sugihara and Rose, 1995—. Democrat. Presbyterian. Home: 585 W End Ave # 15D New York NY 10024-1715

SUGIMOTO, YOSHIHISA, import/export company executive. Exec. v.p. Nichimen America Inc., N.Y.C. Office: Nichimen America Inc 1185 Ave Of The Americas New York NY 10036-2601

SUGIOKA, KENNETH, anesthesiologist educator; b. Hollister, Calif., Apr. 19, 1920; s. Seigiro and Kameno (Takeda) S.; m. Mary Trabue Hinternhoff, June 18, 1966; children—Stephanie, Colin, Kimi (by previous marriage), Nathan, Brian. B.S., U. Denver, 1945; M.D., Washington U., St. Louis, 1949. Intern, resident U. Iowa, 1949-52, instr. anesthesiology, 1952; asst. prof. surgery N.C. Meml. Hosp., Chapel Hill, 1954-62, assoc. prof. surgery, 1962-64; prof. surgery, chmn. div. anesthesiology U. N.C., 1964-69, prof., chmn. dept. anesthesiology, 1969-83; prof. anesthesiology and physiology Duke U., 1985—; vis. prof. Physiol. Inst., U. Göttingen, Fed. Republic of Germany, 1963, Kings Coll. Med. Sch., London, Max-Planck Inst. Physiology, Dortmund, Fed. Republic of Germany, 1976-77; vis. prof. Royal Coll. Surgeons, Eng., 1983-84; dir. Morgan Creek Land Co.; mem. adv. com. on anesthetic and life support drugs FDA; bd. alumni U. Denver. Author textbook of clin. anesthesiology; contbr. articles to profl. jours. Pres. Triangle Opera Theater. Served to capt., M.C. USAF, 1952-54. Recipient spl. research fellowship NIH, 1961-62. Fellow Faculty Anaesthesiologists Royal Coll. Surgeons (Eng.) (hon.); mem. Soc. Acad. Anesthesia Chairmen (past pres.). Home: 319 Bayberry Dr Chapel Hill NC 27514-9116

SUGRUE, THOMAS JOSEPH, lawyer; b. Bklyn., Feb. 9, 1947; s. Francis J. and Elizabeth W. (Connolly) S.; m. Patricia A. Mannion, Aug. 5, 1972; children: Erin, Kerry. BS magna cum laude, Boston Coll., 1968; M in Pub. Policy and JD magna cum laude, Harvard U., 1975. Bar: Mass. 1975, D.C. 1982, U.S. Dist. Ct. D.C. 1982, U.S. Ct. Appeals (D.C. cir.) 1982, U.S. Supreme Ct. 1982. Law clk. to presiding justice Mass. Supreme Ct., Boston, 1975-76; atty., advisor FTC, Washington, 1976-78; assoc. Wilmer, Cutler & Pickering, Washington, 1978-83; spl. counsel for competition policies FCC, Washington, 1983-84, chief policy div. common carrier bur., 1985—. Mem. ABA, D.C. Bar Assn. Avocations: running, music, N.Y. Giants fan. Home: 1218 Knox Pl Alexandria VA 22304-1529 Office: FCC 1919 M St NW Washington DC 20554-0002

SUH, DAE-SOOK, political science educator; b. Hoeryong, Korea, Nov. 22, 1931; came to U.S. 1952; s. Chang-Hee and Chong-Hee (Paek) S.; m. Yun-Ok Park, Oct. 29, 1960; children: Maurice, Kevin. BA, Tex. Christian U., 1956; MA, Ind. U., 1958; PhD, Columbia U., 1964. Asst. prof. U. Houston, 1965-67, assoc. prof., 1968-71; prof. polit. sci., dir. Ctr. for Korean Studies, U. Hawaii, Honolulu, 1972—; prof. policy studies Korea Found., 1994—. Author: The Korean Communist Movement, 1967, Documents of Korean Communism, 1970, Korean Communism, 1980, Kim Il Sung, 1988. Mem. Conv. Ctr. Authority, Honolulu, 1989-94. Grantee Social Sci. Rsch. Coun.-Am. Coun. Learned Socs., 1963, East-/West Ctr., Columbia U., 1971, The Wilson Ctr. for Scholars, 1985, Fulbright, 1988. Mem. Am. Polit. Sci. Assn. (life), Assn. for Asian Studies. Avocations: tennis, golf. Home: 7122 Niumalu Loop Honolulu HI 96825 Office: U Hawaii at Manoa Ctr Korean Studies 1881 East-West Rd Honolulu HI 96822

SUH, NAM PYO, mechanical engineering educator; b. Seoul, Apr. 22, 1936; came to U.S.A., 1954, naturalized, 1963; s. Doo Soo and Joon Joo (Lee) S.; m. Young Ja Surh; children: Mary M., Helen H., Grace J., Caroline Y. SB, MIT, 1959, SM, 1961; PhD, Carnegie-Mellon U., 1964; D of Engring. (hon.), Worcester Poly. Inst., 1986; LHD (hon.), U. Mass., Lowell, 1988. Devel. engr. Guild Plastics Inc., Cambridge, Mass., 1958-60; sr. research engr., project mgr. USM Corp., Beverly, Mass., 1961-65; asst. prof. U. S.C., Columbia, 1965-68, assoc. prof., 1968-69; assoc. prof. mech. engring. MIT, Cambridge, 1970-75, prof., 1975—; Ralph E. and Eloise F. Cross prof., 1989—, head dept. mech. engring., 1991—, dir. Lab. Mfg. and Productivity, 1977-84, dir. industry polymer processing program, 1973-84, dir. Mfg. Inst. 1989—; asst. dir. for engring. NSF, Washington, 1984-88; chmn. Axiomatics corp., Cambridge; former chmn. bd. Sutek Corp., Hudson, Mass.; bd. dirs. SVG Industries, SVG, Inc.; cons. Lawrence Livermore Nat. Lab.; former mem. sci. and tech. rev. bd. Idaho Nat. Engring. Lab., NRC rev. panel of Nat. Engring. Lab., 1986-90; mem. vis. com. (statutory) Nat. Ins. Standards and Tech., 1990-94; mem. tech. adv. com. Alcan Aluminum Corp., 1989-90. Author: (with A.P.L. Turner) Mechanical Behavior of Solids, 1975, Tribophysics, 1986, The Principles of Design, 1990; (with others) Manufacturing Engineering, 1990; editor: (with N. Saka) Fundamentals of Tribology, 1980, with N. Sung) Science and Technology of Polymer Procs., 1979, The Delamination Theory of Wear, 1977, (with B.M. Kramer) University: Industry Cooperation, 1982; co-editor in chief Robotics and Computer Aided Mfg.; contbr. over 200 papers to profl. jours.; holder 40 U.S. patents. Former chmn. bd. Korean-Am. Soc. New Eng., 1979. USM Corp. fellow, 1962-63; recipient Best Paper award Soc. Plastics Engrs., 1981, citation Classic Inst. for Sci. Info., 1981, F.W. Taylor Research award Soc. Mfg. Engrs., 1986, Disting. Svc. award NSF, 1988, Mainstream Am. award, 1991; named Fed. Engr. of Yr., NSF/NSPE, 1987. Fellow ASME (Gustus L. Larson Meml. award 1976, Blackall award 1982, W.T. Ennor Mfg. Tech. award 1993, Best Tribology Paper award 1993); mem. AAAS, Am. Soc. for Engring. Edn. (Centennial medal 1993, KBS award for scholarly achievement 1994), Internat. Instn. for Prodn. Engring., Royal Swedish Acad. Engring. Sci. (fgn.), Sigma Xi, Pi Tau Sigma, Phi Kappa Phi. Office: MIT Rm 3-174 Dept of Mechanical Engineering Cambridge MA 02139

SUHL, HARRY, physics educator; b. Leipzig, Fed. Republic Germany, Oct. 18, 1922; s. Bernhard and Klara (Bergwerk) S.; widowed. BSc, U. Wales, 1943; PhD, U. Oxford, 1948, DSc (hon.), 1970. Temp. exptl. officer British Admiralty, England, 1943-46; mem. tech. staff Bell Labs., Murray Hill, N.J., 1948-60; prof. physics U. Calif.-San Diego, La Jolla, 1961—; cons. Aerospace Corp., El Segundo, Calif., 1961—, Exxon Research & Engring., Clinton Twp., N.J., 1977—. Editor (with others) book series: Magnetism, 1961-74; editor (mag.): Solid State Communication, 1961—. Guggenheim fellow, 1968-69, NSF fellow, 1971. Fellow Am. Phys. Soc.; mem. Nat. Acad. Scis., Calif. Catalysis Soc. Office: U Calif Dept Physics 9500 Gilman Dr La Jolla CA 92093

SUHOWATSKY, STEPHEN JOSEPH, distribution company executive; b. Troy, N.Y., Feb. 7, 1939; s. Stephen Alexander and Mary Elizabeth (Hasko) S.; m. Edna Gale Hartness, Aug. 10, 1968; children—Stephanie, Allison, Jennifer. BS., Delta State U., 1964; M.B.A., U. Pa., 1965. Asst. to treas. Eagle-Picher Industries, Cin., 1966-69; v.p. Markey Bronze, Lima, Ohio, 1969-75, pres., 1976-78; pres. Masten Corp., Chgo., 1975-78, Eagle Picher Bearings, Toledo, 1978-82, Syracuse Supply, N.Y., 1982—; dir. Met. Bancorp, Lima, Citizens Found., Key Bank N.Y., Met. Devel. Assn. Syracuse, Assoc. Gen. Contractors Am.; pres. Prima Care Health Resources (subs. Syracuse Supply, Inc.), 1986. Active fundraising Friends of the Zoo, Syracuse, Crouse Hinds Meml. Hosp. Found., Syracuse; bd. dirs. Onondaga

Indsl. Corp., Scholarship Fund Delta State; bd. dirs. WCNY Pub. TV. Recipient Outstanding Alumnus award Delta State U., 1984. Mem. Syracuse C. of C. (bd. dirs., chmn.). Republican. Roman Catholic. Clubs: Century, Onandaga, Golf (Syracuse). Avocations: golf, boating. Home: 7271 Wakefield Dr Fayetteville NY 13066-9769 Office: Syracuse Supply Co 5921 Court Street Rd Syracuse NY 13206-1734

SUHR, J. NICHOLAS, lawyer; b. N.Y.C., Nov. 14, 1942; s. Rev. Dr. Heinrich P. and Anna H. (Isenschmid) S.; m. Anne Aylett Stone, July 6, 1965; children: John Nicholas Jr., Erika Christl. BA, U. Va., 1964; JD, Am. U., 1967. Bar: N.Y. 1967, N.J. 1969, U.S. Supreme Ct. 1989. Assoc., ptnr. Topken & Farley, N.Y.C., 1967-73, Conboy, Hewitt, O'Brien & Boardman, N.Y.C., 1973-86; counsel Hunton & Williams, N.Y.C., 1986-87, Quinn, Cohen, Shields & Bock, N.Y.C., 1987-88; ptnr. Quinn & Suhr, White Plains, N.Y., 1988-95, Herzfeld & Rubin, P.C., N.Y.C., 1995—; arbitrator U.S. Dist. Ct. N.J., Trenton, 1985—, Am. Arbitration Assn., N.Y.C., 1976—. Contbr. articles to profl. jours.; commentator Ct. TV network. Mem. ABA, N.Y. State Bar Assn., N.J. State Bar Assn., U.S. Supreme Ct. Bar, Internat. Law Soc., Consular Law Soc., Product Liability Adv. Coun., German Soc. of N.Y.C. (v.p., sec., trustee 1976—), German-Am. Sch. Assn. (v.p., trustee 1986—), German Seamen's Mission N.Y. (pres., dir. 1972—). Lutheran. Avocations: fishing, woodworking. Office: Herzfeld & Rubin PC 40 Wall St New York NY 10005

SUHR, PAUL AUGUSTINE, lawyer; b. Sonwunri, Chonbuk, Korea, Jan. 20, 1940; came to U.S. 1966; s. Chong-ju and Oksuk (Pang) So; m. Angeline M. Kang Suhr; 1 child, Christopher. BA, Campbell Coll., Buies Creek, N.C., 1968; MA, U. N.C., Greensboro, 1970; MS, U. N.C., Chapel Hill, 1975; JD, N.C. Cen. U., 1988. Bar: N.C. 1989, U.S. Dist. Ct. (ea. and mid. dist.) N.C. 1989, U.S. Dist. Ct. D.C. 1990, U.S. Ct. Appeals (4th cir.) 1992. Bibliographer N.C. Div. of State Libr., Raleigh, 1975-78; dir. Pender County Pub. Libr., Burgaw, N.C., 1978-80; libr. Tob. Lit. Svc., N.C. State U., Raleigh, 1980-85; pvt. practice law Law Office of Paul A. Suhr, Raleigh & Fayetteville, 1989—. Author short stories and novelettes various lit. mags., jours. and revs. Mem. Human Resources and Human Rels. Adv. Commn., City of Raleigh, 1990—, chmn., 1994—. N.C. Humanities Com. grantee, 1979-80; recipient Presdl. award President of Korea, 1992. Mem. ABA, N.C. Bar Assn., N.C. Trial Lawyers Assn., Assn. Trial Lawyers of Am., Wake County Bar Assn., D.C. Bar Assn. Democrat. Roman Catholic. Avocations: gardening, fishing, writing. Office: 1110 Navaho Dr # 605 Raleigh NC 27609

SUHRBIER, KLAUS RUDOLF, hydrodynamicist, naval architect; b. Gnoien, Germany, Sept. 12, 1930; arrived in U.K., 1966; s. Ulrich Julius and Dora Auguste (Elsaesser) S.; m. Inge Ursula Koepke, Oct. 1, 1955; children: Andreas, Karin. Dipl. Ing., U. Rostock, Germany, 1955; Dr-Ing., Tech. U. Berlin, 1995. Chartered engr. Hydrodynamicist Institut fuer Schiffbau, Berlin, 1955-60, Versuchsanstalt fuer Binnenschiffbau e.V., Duisburg, Fed. Republic of Germany, 1960-63; sci. officer Inst. fuer Schiffbau U. Hamburg, Fed. Republic of Germany, 1963-66; sr. hydrodynamicist Vosper Ltd., Portsmouth, Eng., 1966; chief hydrodynamicist Vosper Thornycroft (U.K.) Ltd., Portsmouth, Eng., 1966-92; cons. ship hydrodynamics, 1992—; mem. cavitation com. 16th and 17th Internat. Towing Tank Conf., Leningrad, USSR, 1978-81, Gothenburg, Sweden, 1981-84; chmn. cavitation com. 18th Internat. Towing Tank Conf., Kobe, Japan, 1984-87; chmn. high speed marine vehicles com. Internat. Towing Tank Conf., Madrid, 1987-90. Co-author: (book) Dhows to Deltas, 1971; inventor reduction of cavitation erosion, 1974, 92; contbr. numerous articles and papers to profl. jours. and procs. Fellow Royal Soc. Naval Architects; mem. Soc. Naval Architects and Marine Engrs., Schiffbautechnische Ges. e.V. Avocations: sailing, skiing, history. Home and Office: 30A Beach Rd, Emsworth Hampshire PO10 7HR, England

SUHRE, WALTER ANTHONY, JR., retired lawyer and brewery executive; b. Cin., Jan. 17, 1933; s. Walter A. and Elizabeth V. (Heimbuch) S.; m. Judy Lee Carrington, June 7, 1975. B.S. in Bus. Adminstrn., Northwestern U., 1956; LL.B. with honors, U. Cin., 1962. Bar: Ohio 1962, Mo. 1982. Assoc. Taft, Stettinius & Hollister, Cin., 1962-65; with Eagle-Picher Industries, Inc., Cin., 1965-82, gen. counsel, 1970-82; v.p., gen. counsel Anheuser-Busch Cos., Inc., St. Louis, 1982-94; ret., 1993. Served with USMC, 1956-59. Mem. ABA, Mo. Bar Assn., Old Warson Country Club. Republican. Presbyterian. Home: 48 Woodcliffe Rd Saint Louis MO 63124-1336

SUHRHEINRICH, RICHARD FRED, federal judge; b. 1936. B.S., Wayne State U., 1960; J.D. cum laude, Detroit Coll. Law, 1963. Bar: Mich. Assoc. Moll, Desenberg, Purdy, Glover & Bayer, 1963-67; asst. prosecutor Macomb County, 1967; ptnr. Rogensues, Richard & Suhrheinrich, 1967; assoc. Moll, Desenberg, Purdy, Glover & Bayer, 1967-68; ptnr. Kitch, Suhrheinrich, Saurbier & Drutchas, 1968-84; judge U.S. Dist. Ct. (ea. dist.) Mich., Detroit, 1984-90, U.S. Ct. Appeals (6th Cir.). Detroit, 1990—. Mem. State Bar Mich., Ingham County Bar Assn. Office: US Ct Appeals 6th Cir Rm 241 USPO & Fed Bldg 315 W Allegan Lansing MI 48933

SUI, ANNA, fashion designer; b. Dearborn Heights, Mich., 1955; d. Paul and Grace S. Grad., Parsons Sch. Design. Founder, designer Anna Sui, 1992—; boutique Macy's Herald Sq., 1992—, N.Y.C.; opened outlet SoHo dist., 1992, N.Y.C. First runway show, 1991. Recipient Perry Ellis award new fashion talent Coun. Fashion Designers Am., 1992. Studio: 214 West 39th St Ste 800 New York NY 10018 also: c/o Keeble Cavaco & Duka Ste 10A 853 7th Ave New York NY 10019

SUINN, RICHARD MICHAEL, psychologist; b. Honolulu, May 8, 1933; s. Maurice and Edith (Wong) S.; m. Grace D. Toy, July 26, 1958; children: Susan, Randall, Staci, Bradley. Student, U. Hawaii, 1951-53; B.A. summa cum laude, Ohio State U., 1955; MA in Clin. Psychology, Stanford U., 1957, PhD in Clin. Psychology, 1959. Lic. psychologist, Colo.; diplomate Am. Bd. Profl. Psychology. Counselor Stanford (Calif.) U., 1958-59, rsch. assoc. Med. Sch., 1964-66; asst. prof. psychology Whitman Coll., Walla Walla, Wash., 1959-64; assoc. prof. U. Hawaii, Honolulu, 1966-68; prof. Colo. State U., Ft. Collins, 1968—, head dept. psychology, 1972-93; cons. in field; psychologist U.S. Ski Teams, 1976, Olympic Games, U.S. Women's Track and Field, 1980 Olympic Games, U.S. Ski Jumping Team, 1988, U.S. Shooting Team, 1994; mem. sports psychology adv. com. U.S. Olympic Com., 1983-89; reviewer NIMH, 1977-80, 94—. Author: The Predictive Validity of Projective Measures, 1969, Fundamentals of Behavior Pathology, 1970, The Innovative Psychological Therapies, 1975, The Innovative Medical-Psychiatric Therapies, 1976, Psychology in Sport: Methods and Applications, 1980, Fundamentals of Abnormal Psychology, 1984, 88, Seven Steps to Peak Performance, 1986, Anxiety Management Training, 1991; editorial bd.: Jour. Cons. and Clin. Psychology, 1973-86, Jour. Counseling Psychology, 1974-91, Behavior Therapy, 1977-80, Behavior Modification, 1977-78, Jour. Behavioral Medicine, 1978-83, Behavior Counseling Quar., 1979-83, Jour. Sports Psychology, 1980—, Clin. Psychology: Science and Practice, 1994—, Professional Psychology, 1994—; author: tests Math. Anxiety Rating Scale, Suinn Test Anxiety Behavior Scale, Suinn-Lew Asian Self-identity Acculturation Scale. Mem. City Council, Ft. Collins, 1975-79, mayor, 1978-79; mem. Gov.'s Mental Health Adv. Council, 1983, Colo. Bd. Psychologist Examiners, 1983-86. Recipient cert. merit U.S. Ski Team, 1976; NIMH grantee, 1963-64; Office Edn. grantee, 1970-71. Fellow APA (chmn. bd. ethnic minority affairs 1982-83, chmn. edn. and tng. bd. 1986-87, policy and planning bd. 1987-89, bd. dirs. 1990-93), Behavior Therapy and Rsch. Soc. (charter); mem. Assn. for Advancement Psychology (trustee 1983-86), Assn. for Advancement Behavior Therapy (sec.-treas. 1986-89, pres.-elect 1991, pres. 1992-93), Asian Am. Psychol. Assn. (bd. dirs. 1983-86). Am. Bd. Behavior Therapy (bd. dirs. 1987—), Phi Beta Kappa, Sigma Xi. Home: 808 Cheyenne Dr Fort Collins CO 80525-1560 Office: Colo State U Dept Psychology Fort Collins CO 80523

SUISSA, MIREILLE RENEE, company executive, computer consultant; b. Grenoble, France, Feb. 18, 1942; came to U.S., 1965; d. Henri Andre Ptachnik and Cecile (Sceneebaum) Lewenszpil; m. Charles Suissa (div. Jan. 1991); 1 child, Henri. Bookkeeper Comgraphix, Inc., El Paso, Tex., 1972-74; acct. El Paso Cancer Treatment Ctr., 1974-80; corp. exec. Chez Carlos, Inc., 1980—; cons. Econ. Mgmt. Cons., El Paso, 1989—. Mem. Smithsonian Inst. Recipient Outstanding Svc. awards, Special Olympics, Muscular Dystrophy, Missing Children Network, Say No To Drugs, El Paso. Mem. Nat. Sporting

Goods Assn., Nat. Fedn. Ind. Bus., U.S. C. of C., El Paso C. of C., Right to Work, B'Nai Zion Congregation Sisterhood. Republican. Jewish. Avocations: needlepoint, cooking, doll collecting, reading. Office: Chez Carlos Inc 600 S Santa Fe St El Paso TX 79901-2232

SUITER, JOHN WILLIAM, industrial engineering consultant; b. Pasadena, Calif., Feb. 16, 1926; s. John Walter and Ethel May (Acton) S.; B.S. in Aero. Sci., Embry Riddle U., 1964; m. Joyce England, Dec. 3, 1952; children—Steven A., Carol A. Cons. indsl. engr., Boynton Beach, Fla., 1955—. Instr. U. S.C. Tech. Edn. Center, Charleston, 1967-69. Served as pilot USAF, 1944-46. Registered profl. engr., Fla. Mem. Am. Inst. Indsl. Engrs., Soc. Mfg. Engrs. (sr.), Computer and Automated Systems Assn., Methods-Time Measurement Assn. (assoc.), Soc. Quality Control. Home: PO Box 5262 Englewood FL 34224-0262

SUITS, BERNARD HERBERT, philosophy educator; b. Detroit, Nov. 25, 1925; s. Herbert Arthur and Helen Dorothy (Carlin) S.; m. Nancy Ruth Berr, July 3, 1952; children—Mark, Constance. B.A., U. Chgo., 1944, M.A., 1950; Ph.D., U. Ill., 1958. Investigator venereal disease USPHS, 1950-51; personnel officer Detroit Civil Service Commn., 1952-54; instr. philosophy U. Ill., Urbana, 1958-59; asst. prof. Purdue U., 1959-66; asso. prof. U. Waterloo, Ont., 1966-72; prof. philosophy, chmn. dept. U. Waterloo, 1972—; asso. dean arts for grad. affairs, 1981—; vis. prof. U. Lethbridge, Alta., Can., 1980, U. Bristol, Eng., 1980. Author: The Grasshopper: Games, Life, and Utopia, 1978, paper, 1990; Contbr. to profl. jours. and books. Served with USNR, 1944-46. Mem. Canadian, Am. philos. assns., Philos. Soc. for Study of Sport (pres. 1975—). Office: U Waterloo, Dept Philosophy, Waterloo, ON Canada

SUITS, DANIEL BURBIDGE, economist; b. St. Louis, June 27, 1918; s. Hollis Emerson and Dorothy Dandridge (Halyburton) S.; m. Adelaide Evens Boehm, Feb. 14, 1942; children—Evan Halyburton, Holly Boehm Suits Kazarinoff. A.B. in Philosophy, U. Mich., 1940, M.A. in Econs., 1942, Ph.D. in Econs, 1948. Asst. prof. econs. dept. U. Mich., 1950-55, assoc. prof., 1955-59, prof., dir. research seminar in quantitative econs., 1959-69; dir. Am. Studies Ctr., Kyoto, Japan, 1958; prof. econs. U. Calif., Santa Cruz, 1969-74; prof. econs. Mich. State U., East Lansing, 1974-86, prof. emeritus, 1986—; vis. prof. People's U., Beijing, 1985, Fudan U., Shanghai, 1987, Swarthmore Coll., 1988; disting. vis. prof. Kalamazoo Coll., 1989; cons. to various state and fed. agys.; rsch. assoc. Ctr. Econ. Rsch., Athens, Greece, 1962-63. Author: Statistics: An Introduction to Quantitative Economic Research, 1963, Theory and Application of Econometric Models, 1963, Principles of Economics, 1970, rev. edit., 1973; originator Suits Index tax progressivity; contbr. articles to tech. jours. Served alt. mil. duty 1942-46. Recipient Disting. Faculty award Mich. State U., 1980; sr. fellow East-West Population Inst., 1978—. Fellow Econometric Soc., Am. Statis. Assn.; mem. Am. Econ. Assn. Mem. Soc. of Friends. Home: 1446 Karlin Ct East Lansing MI 48823-2333 Office: Mich State U Econs Dept East Lansing MI 48824

SUKO, LONNY RAY, lawyer; b. Spokane, Wash. Oct. 12, 1943; s. Ray R. and Leila B. (Snyder) S.; m. Marcia A. Michaelsen, Aug. 26, 1967; children—Jolynn R., David M. B.A., Wash. State U., 1965; J.D., U. Idaho, 1968. Bar: Wash. 1968, U.S. Dist. Ct. (ea. dist.) Wash. 1969, U.S. Dist. Ct. (we. dist.) Wash. 1978, U.S.C. appeals (9th cir.) 1978. Law clk. U.S. Dist. Ct. Ea. Dist. Wash., 1968-69; assoc. Lyon, Beaulaurier & Aaron, Yakima, Wash., 1969-72; ptnr. Lyon, Beaulaurier, Weigand, Suko & Gustafson, Yakima, 1972-91, Lyon, Weigand, Suko & Gustafson, P.S., 1991—; U.S. magistrate, Yakima, 1971-91. Mem. Wash. State Trial Lawyers Assn., Wash. Council Sch. Attys., Phi Delta Kappa, Phi Kappa Phi, Phi Eta Sigma. Office: PO Box 1689 Yakima WA 98907-1689

SULCER, FREDERICK DURHAM, advertising executive; b. Chgo., Aug. 28, 1932; s. Henry Durham and Charlotte (Thearle) S.; m. Dorothy Wright, May 2, 1953; children—Thomas W., Ginna M., David T. B.A., U. Chgo., 1949, M.B.A., 1963. Reporter UP Assn., Chgo., 1945-46; reporter AP, 1947; with Needham, Harper & Steers Advt., Chgo., 1947-78, dir., 1965-78, sr. account dir., 1965-66, mem. exec. com., 1966-78, exec. v.p., 1967, dir. N.Y. div., 1967-78; pres. N.Y. div. Needham, Harper & Steers Advt., 1974-75; chmn. bd. NH & S Internat., 1975-76; pres. Sulcer Communication Co., Inc., 1977-78; group exec., dir. Benton & Bowles (advt.), 1978-85; dir. bus. devel. D'Arcy Masius Benton & Bowles, advt., N.Y.C., 1985-90; vice-chmn. bd. dirs. DDB Needham Worldwide, N.Y.C., 1990-95; Schering-Plough disting. vis. prof. corp. commn. Fairleigh Dickinson U., Madison, N.J., 1993-96. Served to capt. C.E. AUS, 1950-53. Mem. Am. Assn. Advt. Agys. (bd. govs. N.Y. chpt.), Internat. Advertisers Assn., Alpha Delta Phi. Home: 350 W 50th St New York NY 10019-6668 Office: DDB Needham 437 Madison Ave New York NY 10022-7099

SULG, MADIS, corporation executive; b. Tallinn, Estonia, May 25, 1943; came to U.S., 1950; s. Hand Eduard and Erika (Turk) S.; m. Mary Diane Detellis, Dec. 30, 1967; children: Danielle Marie, Michaella Erika. SB in Indsl. Mgmt., MIT, 1965, SM in Mgmt., 1967. Cons. Barss, Reitzel & Assocs., Cambridge, Mass., 1970-71; mgr. planning and research Converse Rubber Co., Wilmington, Mass., 1971-75; dir. bus. planning and devel. AMF, Inc., Stamford, Conn., 1975-79; sr. v.p. planning and devel. Bandag, Inc., Muscatine, Iowa, 1978-88; pres. Prime Investments, 1988—; Muscatine Natural Resources Corp., 1981-88; chmn., chief exec. officer Sieg Auto Parts, Davenport, Iowa, 1989-93; COO Hammer's Plastic Recycling, Iowa Falls, Iowa, 1994, Purethane, Inc., West Branch, Iowa, 1994—. With U.S. Army, 1968-70. Presbyterian. Avocations: bridge; jogging; swimming. Home: 4855 Rambling Ct Bettendorf IA 52722-5839 Office: Purethane Inc One Purethane Pl West Branch IA 52358

SULGER, FRANCIS XAVIER, lawyer; b. N.Y.C., Sept. 3, 1942; s. John J. and Regina (Slawkowska) S.; m. Helga Nelsen, July 23, 1968; children: Derek N., Justin D. BA, Fordham U., 1964; JD, Harvard U., 1967. Bar: N.Y. 1970, U.S. Dist. Ct. (so. dist.) N.Y. 1979. Atty. F.I. duPont & Co., N.Y.C., 1968-70; assoc. Townsend & Lewis, N.Y.C., 1970-73, Thacher Proffitt & Wood, N.Y.C., 1973-78; ptnr. Thacher Proffitt & Wood, 1978—. Trustee Wildcliff Mus., New Rochelle, N.Y., 1970-74; mem. U.S. Olympic Rowing Com., Colorado Springs, Colo., 1980-84. Mem. U.S. Rowing Assn. (bd. dirs. 1979-84), N.Y. Athletic Club (rowing chmn. 1979—), Larchmont (N.Y.) Yacht Club. Avocations: rowing, collecting antiques, computers. Home: 10 Meadow Ln Greenwich CT 06831-3709 Office: Thacher Proffitt & Wood 2 World Trade Ctr New York NY 10048-0002

SULIK, EDWIN (PETE SULIK), health care administrator; b. Bryan, Tex., Feb. 1, 1957; s. Edwin Peter and Bonny Jo (Robertson) S.; m. Kolleen Marie Stevens, Aug. 8, 1981; 1 child, Laine Sheridan. Student, Blinn Jr. Coll., 1977-78, U. Tex., 1977, Tex. A&M U., 1977-83; BBA, Ky. Western. U., 1990; MBA, Ky. Western U., 1994. Lic. long term care adminstr. Sr. v.p. ops. Sherwood Health Care, Inc., Bryan, 1976-90, pres., 1990—; sec.-treas. Sherwood Health Care, Inc., Lubbock, Tex., 1987-89; pres. Sherwood Health Care, Inc., Bryan, 1990, Lubbock, 1990; pres., owner Brazos Mgmt. Health Care, Inc., Bryan, 1991. Mem. Lt. Gov. Bullock's Nursing Home Work Group, 1991-92; participant state debate with Lt. Gov. Hobby, Austin, Tex., 1987; mem. Legis. Oversight Com. Fellow Am. Coll. Health Care Adminstrs., Am. Health Care Assn., Tex. Health Care Assn. (bd. dirs. 1987-90, chair, chpt. pres. 1987-88, facility standards com. 1987—; payment for svcs. com. 1987—, Medicare com. 1989—, Omnibus Budget Reconciliation Act of 1987 com. 1987—, patient admission screening and resident rev. com. 1989—, legis. com. 1987-89, co-chair budget and fin. com. 1990-91, automation com. 1990-91, pilot project site NHIC automation 1990-91), Bryan Coll. C. of C. Inner Circle, Am. Assn. Retired Persons (Medicare/Medicaid steering com.), Tex. A&M U. Century Club, KC, Elks. Republican. Roman Catholic. Avocations: racquetball, golf, bowling, bow fishing, water skiing. Home: PO Box 3553 Bryan TX 77805-3553 Office: Sherwood Health Care Inc 1401 Memorial Dr Bryan TX 77802-5218

SULIMIRSKI, WITOLD STANISLAW, investment company executive; b. Lwow, Poland, May 18, 1933; came to U.S., 1957; s. Tadeusz and Olga (Lepkowska) S.; m. Teresa Maria Boniecka, Dec. 28, 1957; children: Elizabeth Sulimirski Blakeslee, Adam Edward. BA with honors, Cambridge U., 1953, MA, 1957. With Irving Trust Co., N.Y.C., 1957-89, exec. v.p., 1986-89; pres. Servus Assocs., Inc., N.Y.C., 1989—; chmn. exec. com.

Intercap Investments, Inc., N.Y.C., 1989—; chmn. Am. Bank in Poland, Warsaw, 1989-91, LBS Bank N.Y., 1990—; exec. dir. Am. Investment Initiative in Poland, Warsaw, 1992-94; bd. dirs. Bank Pekao S.A. Warsaw. Treas. Polish Inst. Arts and Scis., Inc., N.Y.C., 1976—; vice chmn. Kosciuscko Found., Inc., N.Y.C., 1983—; chmn. Polish Assistance, Inc., N.Y.C., 1984-92; bd. dirs. Middle East Policy Coun., Washington, 1984—, Nat. U.S.-Arab C. of C., Washington, 1987-93. Mem. Bronxville Field Club, Williams Club, Knights of Malta. Roman Catholic. Office: Intercap Investments Inc 430 Park Ave 10th Fl New York NY 10022

SULKIN, HOWARD ALLEN, college president; b. Detroit, Aug. 19, 1941; s. Lewis and Vivian P. (Mandel) S.; m. Constance Annette Adler, Aug. 4, 1963; children—Seth R., Randall K. PhB, Wayne State U., 1963; MBA, U. Chgo., 1965, PhD, 1969; LHD (hon.), De Paul U., 1990. Dir. program rsch., indsl. rels. ctr. U. Chgo., 1964-72; dean Sch. for New Learning, De Paul U., Chgo., 1972-77; v.p. De Paul U., Chgo., 1977-84; pres. Spertus Inst. Jewish Studies, Chgo., 1984—; St. Paul's vis. prof. Rikkyo U., Tokyo, 1970—; cons., evaluator North Central Assn., Chgo., 1975—. Contbr. articles to profl. jours. Sec.-treas. Grant Park Cultural and Ednl. Cmty., Chgo., 1984—; bd. dirs. Chgo. Sinai Congregation, 1972—, pres., 1980-83; bd. dirs. S.E. Chgo. Commn., 1980—, United Way, 1984—, Crusade of Mercy United Way, 1990—; Bd. dirs., chmn. World Parliament of Religion, 1989—. Mem. Adult Edn. Assn. U.S.A., Acad. Internat. Bus. Club: Cliff Dwellers (Chgo.). Office: Spertus Inst of Jewish Studies 618 S Michigan Ave Chicago IL 60605-1901

SULKIN, SIDNEY, editor, writer; b. Boston, Feb. 2, 1918; s. Frank Sam and Celia (Glazer) S.; m. Naomi Ann Levenson, Oct. 4, 1950; 1 child, Jonathan Leigh. Grad., Boston Pub. Latin Sch., 1935; B.A. cum laude, Harvard Coll., 1939. Editorial asst. Howell-Soskin Pub. Co., N.Y.C., 1940-41; chief World Wide English Programs, Voice of Am., N.Y.C., 1943-44; chief news Am. Broadcasting Sta. in Europe, SHAEF, London, 1945; with psychol. warfare divsn. SHAEF, The Hague, The Netherlands, 1945; dir. No. and Eastern Europe U.S. Internat. Book Assn., N.Y.C. and Stockholm, 1945-47; spl. Scandinavian corr. CBS-News, Stockholm, 1945-47; cons. U.S. Mil. Govt. in Germany, 1947; commentator Sta. WCCO, Mpls., 1947; chief Washington bur. Voice of Am., 1949-53; editorial dir. Nat. Issues Com., Washington, 1953-55; asso. editor Changing Times Mag., Washington, 1955-62; sr. editor Changing Times Mag., 1962-71, mng. editor, 1971-75, editor, 1975-81; dir. Kiplinger Washington Editors, 1975-81; playwright-in-residence Shakespeare-under-Stars festival, Tucson, 1981; instr. creative writing Writer's Ctr., Bethesda, Md., 1987—, U. Md., College Park, 1989-91. Author: (novel) The Family Man, 1962, Complete Planning for College, 1962, rev. edit., 1968, (play) Gate of the Lions, 1976 (Quar. Rev. Lit. Contemporary Poetry Publ. award 1980), (play) The Other Side of Babylon, 1979, (play) No More to Prophesy, 1981, (play) Summer Storm, (play) If I Lie, 1992, (stories and poems) The Secret Seed, 1983; included in anthologies: O. Henry Prize Stories, 1948, Best American Short Stories, 1948, These Your Children, Fiction of the Eighties, 1990; co-editor: For Our Freedom and Ours, 1943; co-translator: Matthew the Young King (by Korczak), 1945; contbr. short stories, articles, poetry to numerous periodicals. One-man show (paintings) Friendship Gallery, 1991; exhibited in group show at Provincetown Art Mus., 1990. Adv. com. Jewish Pub. Libr.; bd. mem. Writers Ctr. Mem. PEN, Authors Guild, Poetry Soc. Am., Dramatists Guild, Writers Watch (past pres.), Provincetown Art Assn., Nat. Press Club, Harvard Club. Democrat. Jewish. Home and Office: 5012 Elsmere Pl Bethesda MD 20814-2826 Summer Address: 9 Bobolink Ln Harwich MA 02645-2051

SULKIN, STEPHEN DAVID, marine biology educator; b. Topeka, Aug. 14, 1944; s. Norman Manuel and Dorothy (Fine) S.; m. Shelly Sinclair Turpin, June 6, 1970; children: Kimberly, Tracy, Matthew. AB, Miami U., Oxford, Ohio, 1966; MS, Duke U., 1971, PhD, 1971. Rsch. asst. prof. Chesapeake Biol. Lab. U. Md., Solomons, 1971-82; asst. prof., head Horn Point Environ. Lab. U. Md., Cambridge, 1976-82, prof., 1984-85; prof. dir. Shanna Point Marine Ctr. Western Wash. U., Bellingham, 1985—. Editor Estuarian Coastal Shelf Sci., 1990—; contbr. articles to sci. publs. Recipient Olscamp Outstanding Rsch. award WWR, 1990. Mem. AAAS, Estuarian Rsch. Fedn. Home: 3605 Illinois Ln Bellingham WA 98226-4364 Office: Shannon Point Marine Ctr 1900 Shannon Point Rd Anacortes WA 98221-4042

SULLENBERGER, ARA BROOCKS, mathematics educator; b. Amarillo, Tex., Jan. 3, 1933; d. Carl Clarence and Ara Frances (Broocks) Cox; m. Hal Joseph Sullenberger, Nov. 2, 1952; children: Hal Joseph Jr., Ara Broocks Sullenberger Switzer. Student, Randolph-Macon Woman's Coll., 1951-52, So. Meth. U., 1952, U. Tex., Arlington, 1953, Amarillo Coll., 1953-54; BA in Math., Tex. Tech. U., 1955, MA, 1958; postgrad., Tex. Christian U., 1963-67, U. N. Tex., 1969-80, Tarrant Jr. Coll., Fort Worth, Tex., 1972-83. Cert. tchr., Tex. Math. tchr. Tom S. Lubbock (Tex.) High Sch., 1955-56; instr. math. Tex. Tech U., Lubbock, 1956-63; teaching fellow math. Tex. Christian U., Ft. Worth, 1963-64; chmn. dept. math. Ft. Worth Country Day Sch., 1964-67; instr. math. Tarrant County Jr. Coll.-South, Ft. Worth, 1967-70, asst. prof. math., 1970-74, assoc. prof. math., 1974-95; prof. emeritus, 1995—, ret., 1995; cons. Project Change, Ft. Worth, 1967-68; math. scis. advisor Coll. Bd., Princeton, N.J., 1979-83; math. book reviewer for various pub. cos. including Prentice-Hall, McGraw Hill West, D.C. Heath, Prindle, Weber & Schmidt, MacMillan, Harcourt, Brace Jovanovich, Wadsworth, Worth Pub., West Pub. Contbr. article, book revs. to profl. publs.; author book suppplement to Intermediate Algebra, 1990. Active mem. Jr. League of Ft. Worth, 1954-73, sustaining mem., 1973—; editor newsletter Crestwood Assn., Ft. Worth, 1984, 86, 91, membership sec., 1985, 90, 91, pres., 1988-89, crime patrol capt., 1993, v.p., 1993. Recipient award for excellence in teaching Gen. Dynamics, 1968. Mem. Math. Assn. Am. (life), Nat. Coun. Tchrs. Math. (life), Am. Math. Assn. Two-Yr. Colls. (life), Tex. Math. Assn. Two-Yr. Colls. (charter), Tex. Jr. Coll. Tchrs.' Assn., Pi Beta Phi. Republican. Episcopalian. Avocations: grandchildren, reading, pets, walking, writing. Home: 600 Eastwood Ave Fort Worth TX 76107

SULLIVAN, ADÈLE WOODHOUSE, organization official; b. Trenton, N.J.; d. William and Adaline Dearth (Fox) Woodhouse; m. Harold E. Erb, May 27, 1929 (dec. Nov. 1957); m. William H. Sullivan, Jr., Mar. 17, 1960 (dec. Dec. 1985); 1 child, Nancy Elizabeth (Mrs. Joseph P. Thorne). Student, Rider Coll., 1925-27; LHD, Lincoln Meml. U., 1968. Mem. DAR, 1931—; state regent DAR, N.Y., 1953-56, hon. state regent for life, 1956—, nat. rec. sec. gen., 1956-59, 1st v.p. gen., 1959-62, nat. pres. gen., 1965-68, hon. pres. gen. for life, 1968—; organizing chmn. Centennial Jubilee, 1983-89; founder, pres. Nat. DAR Exec. Club, 1962-64; pres. Nat. DAR Officers Club, 1978-80; past trustee DAR Schs. Kate Duncan Smith, Grant, Ala., Tamassee, S.C., Crossnore, N.C.; sec. Air Corps office Keystone Aircraft Corp., 1927-29; sec., treas. Power Machinery Corp., N.Y.C., 1961-65. Pres. Woodhull Day Sch. PTA, Hollis, N.Y., 1942-44; chmn. student loan fund women's aux. ASME, 1946-48; v.p. N.Y. colony New Eng. Women, 1963-65; mem. Women's Nat. Adv. Commn. for Nixon, 1968; chmn. N.Y. Women for Buckley, 1970, Women's Nat. Rep. Campaign Com., 1972; mem. nat. adv. bd. Am. Security Coun.; vis. U.S. Troops, Vietnam, Jan., 1968; bd. dirs. Nat. Symphony Orch. Assn., 1965-68, Friends of Historic St. George's Ch., Hempstead, L.I., 1960-67; bd. dirs., exec. v.p. nat. affairs Cultural Laureat Found., Inc., 1973-77 ; mem. awards jury Freedoms Found., 1966-67; mem. nat. honors com. Women's Hall of Fame, Inc.; program chmn. Women's Soc., Scarsdale Community Bapt. Ch., 1977-80, trustee, 1980-86. Recipient commendation award U.S. Navy for work with DAR, World War II. award for outstanding svc. to nation Am. Coalition Patriotic Socs., 1967, Freedom Found. medal of honor, 1967, Gold medal Nat. Soc. New Eng. Women, 1969, Nat. Capital USO Disting. Svc. cert., 1968. Mem. Am. Friends of Lafayette (exec. coun.), Hon. Soc. Ky. Cols., Ams. for Patriotism, Inc. (organizing past pres.). Club: Scarsdale Women's, Scarsdale Golf. Home and Office: 10 Scarsdale Ave Scarsdale NY 10583-4045 *To aid in promoting a sense of responsible citizenship through education. To do each task undertaken to the best of my ability. To endeavor to do unto others as I would have them do unto me. To have the satisfaction of having a young woman say she had been favorably influenced by me.*

SULLIVAN, ALFRED DEWITT, university administrator; b. New Orleans, Feb. 2, 1942; s. Dewitt Walter and Natalie (Alford) S.; m. Marilyn Janie Hewitt, Sept. 1, 1962 (div. May 1989); children: Alan, Sean; m. Dorothy

Madeleine Hess, Apr. 1993. BS, La. State U., 1964, MS, 1966; PhD, U. Ga., 1969. Asst. prof. Va. Poly. Inst. and State U., Blacksburg, 1969-73; assoc. prof., then prof. Miss. State U., Starkville, 1973-88; dir. Sch. Forest Resources Pa. State U., University Park, 1988-93; dean coll. natural resources U. Minn., St. Paul, 1993—. Contbr. articles to profl. jours. Fellow Am. Coun. on Edn., 1987-88, NDEA fellow U. Ga., 1966-69; assoc. Danforth Found., 1981. Mem. Soc. Am. Foresters. Office: U Minn 235 Natural Resources Adminstrn Bldg 2003 Upper Buford Cir Saint Paul MN 55108-6146

SULLIVAN, ALLEN TROUSDALE, securities company executive; b. Nashville, Dec. 16, 1927; s. William Albert and Eleanor (Allen) S.; m. Barbara Oman, Nov. 12, 1955; children: Merida, Louise. Mgr. Ralph Nichols Co., Nashville, 1949-56; ptnr. J.C. Bradford & Co., Nashville, 1956—. Bd. dirs. Opportunity House, Nashville. Chmn. Nashville Children's Home. With USN, 1943-46. Mem. Nashville Security Dealers Assn. (pres. 1989). Clubs: Belle Meade (Nashville), Nashville City (Nashville). Home: 7 Valley Forge Nashville TN 37205-4725 Office: JC Bradford & Co 330 Commerce St Nashville TN 37201-1899

SULLIVAN, ANNE DOROTHY HEVNER, artist; b. Boston, Mar. 17, 1929; m. James Leo Sullivan, Jan. 20, 1951; children: Maura, Mark, Lianne, Christopher. Student, Northeastern U., 1973-75; BA, U. Mass., Lowell, 1977; postgrad., De Cordova Mus., Lincoln, Mass., 1987-88. Art dir., instr. Whistler House Mus., Lowell, Mass., 1971-73; art instr., dir. alternatives for individual devel. program U. Mass., Lowell, 1976-84; incorporator Depot Square Artists Gallery, Lexington, Mass., 1981-84; dir., art cons. Abbey Art Gallery, Boston, 1987-88; juried artist Emerson Umbrella Ctr. for Arts, Concord, Mass., 1989-92, Brush with History Gallery, Lowell, Mass., 1992—; juror, lectr., demonstrator, tchr. to art groups and assns., 1971—. Exhibited in juried group shows at Fed. Res. Gallery, Boston, 1990-94, Brush with History Gallery, 1990, Lowell Urban Nat. Pk., 1990, Midwest Mus. of Am. Art, Elkhardt, Ind., 1991, Cahoon Mus., Cotuit, Mass., 1991, Sumner Mus., Washington, 1992, Whistler Mus., 1992, Duxbury Mus., 1992, Attleboro (Mass.) Mus., 1992, C.L. Wolfe Art Club, N.Y.C., 1992, N.E. Ctr.-U. N.H., 1992, Emerson Umbrella at Fed Res. Boston, 1993, Bentley Coll., Waltham, Mass., 1993, Fitchburg (Mass.) Mus., 1994, U. Mass. Med. Sch., Worcester, 1994; represented in permanent collections at Neil Sulier Art Collection, Lexington, Ky., The New Eng. Bank, Shawmut Bank, Bay Banks, Concord Nat. Bank, Amoskeag Banks, N.H., 1st Capital Bank of Concord, N.H., Sheraton Corp., Boston, Calif., New Orleans. Bd. dirs. Human Svcs. Corp., Lowell, 1971-72; v.p. Whistler Mus. Art, 1972-73; chmn. Lowell Arts Coun., 1980-81; mem. Mass. Arts Advocacy Coun., Boston, 1982. Recipient M.M. Rines award for outstanding contemporary painting N.Am. Open Competition, Fed. Res. Gallery, Boston, 1994, Catharine Lorillard Wolfe Art Club, Inc. award, 1992, hon. mention All New Eng. Competition, 1989, Fitchburg Mus. 59th Ann., 1994, 2d prize Cahoon Mus., 1991. Mem. Nat. Assn. women Artists (Martha Reed Meml. award 1988, Leila Sawyer Meml. award 1994), New Eng. Watercolor Soc. (bd. dirs. 1984-92), Monotype Guild New Eng. (pres. 1992-93), Nat. League Am. Penwomen (award of excellence 1990), Copley Soc. (Copley Artist award). Home: 28 Rindo Park Dr Lowell MA 01851-3413 Studio: Brush Gallery & Studio Urban Nat Park 256 Market St Lowell MA 01852

SULLIVAN, ANNE ELIZABETH, publishing executive; b. N.Y.C., Oct. 23, 1942; d. Eugene Redmond and Anne (Rigney) S.; m. Alan H. Bomser, Oct. 11, 1984. BA, Newton (Mass.) Coll., 1964; JD, Fordham U., 1980. Bar: N.Y. 1981. With permissions dept. Farrar, Straus & Giroux, N.Y.C., 1967-74, dir. contract and copyright dept., 1988—. Office: Farrar Straus Giroux 19 Union Sq W New York NY 10003-3304

SULLIVAN, AUSTIN P(ADRAIC), JR., diversified food company executive; b. Washington, June 26, 1940; s. Austin P. Sullivan and Janet Lay (Patterson) Gemmell; m. Judith Ann Raab, June 8, 1968; children: Austin P. III, Amanda, Alexander. AB cum laude, Princeton U., 1964. Spl. asst. to dep. dir. N.J. Office Econ. Opportunity, Trenton, 1965-66; prof. staff mem. Com. on Edn. and Labor, U.S. Ho. of Reps., Washington, 1967-71, legis. dir., 1971-76; dir. govt. relations Gen. Mills, Inc., Mpls., 1976-77, corp. dir. govt. relations, 1977-78, v.p., corp. dir. govt. relations, 1978-79, v.p. public affairs, 1979-93, v.p. corp. comms. and public affairs, 1993-94, sr. v.p. corp. rels., 1994—; lectr. labor market policies Harvard U., 1972-76, Boston U., 1972-76. Bd. dirs., exec. com. Guthrie Theatre, Mpls., 1978-84, Minn. Citizens for the Arts, 1980-83, Mpls. Cmty. Bus. Employment Alliance, 1982-84, Urban Coalition Mpls., 1978-80; bd. dirs. Pub. Affairs Coun., 1985—; chmn. Mpls. Pvt. Industry Coun., 1983-87; mem. nat. Commn. on Employment and Tng., 1979-81; chmn. Minn. Gov.'s Coun. on Employment and Tng., 1976-82; mem. Gov.'s Job Tng. Coun., Mpls., 1987-91, co-chmn. Commn. on Dislocated Workers, 1988-89; mem. steering com. Minn. Meeting, 1982—; bd. advisors Dem. Leadership Coun., 1986—; bd. dirs. Minn. C. of C., 1993—; prin. the Coun. for Excellence in Govt., 1988—; chair Found. Pub. affairs, 1992-93, Pub. Affairs Coun., 1993-94. With USMC, 1957-59. Eleanor Roosevelt fellow in interracial relations, 1964-65. Mem. Coun. fo Pub. Affairs Execs. (chmn.-emeritus conf. bds. 1993, chmn. pub. affairs rsch. coun. 1989-90, mem. polit. action com. 1990-91), Grocery Mfrs. Assn. (chmn. state govt. task force 1985-92, govt. affairs coun. 1991—), Bus. Roundtable (pub. infor. com. 1987-92), U.S. C. of C. (internat. policy com. 1987-89), Greater Mpls. C. of C. (bd. dirs. 1980-86, 90-93). Home: 17830 County Rd 6 Minneapolis MN 55447-2905 Office: Gen Mills Inc One Gen Mills Blvd Minneapolis MN 55426

SULLIVAN, BARBARA BOYLE, management consultant; b. Scranton, Pa., Apr. 12, 1937; d. Edmund F. and Mary R. (O'Connell) Boyle; m. John L. Sullivan Jr. BS in Bus. Adminstrn., Drexel U., 1958; PhD (hon.), Newton Coll., 1975, Gwynedd Mercy Coll., 1975. With IBM, 1959-72; systems engring. mgr. La. and Cen. Europe IBM, Vienna, Austria, 1967-70; mgmt. devel. mgr. IBM, 1970, mgr. spl. programs, 1970-71, sales mgr., asst. br. mgr., 1971-72; pres. Boyle/Kirkman Assocs., N.Y.C., 1972-88; mng. ptnr. Innovation Assocs., Framingham, Mass., 1988-92; bd. dirs. Equitable Resources, Inc., 1974—; chair compensation com., 1989-92, nominating com., 1991, mem. audit, pension trust, and compensation com.; cons. major corps. on human resource devl. programs, organizational change programs, changing work force; condr. exec. leadership and visionary and strategic planning awareness seminars Harvard Bus. Sch., Internat. Mgmt. Conf. Trustee Drexel U.; mem. Pres.'s adv. com. Gwynedd Mercy Coll., adv. com. Drexel U. Coll. Bus. Adminstrn.; vice chmn. bd. trustee Marymount Manhattan Coll., N.Y., bd. regents Mt. St. Mary's Coll., L.A., 1982-88. Featured in numerous mags., books, radio and TV programs, including CBS 60 Minutes; named Bus. Person of Yr. St. Johns U., 1973, One of 50 Leaders for Future, Time mag., 1979. Mem. AAUW, Women's Forum, Weston Womens' League, Boston Club. Home: PO Box 505 Weston MA 02193-1311

SULLIVAN, BARRY, lawyer, educator; b. Newburyport, Mass., Jan. 11, 1949; s. George Arnold and Dorothy Bennett (Furbush) S.; m. Winnifred Mary Fallers, June 14, 1975; children: George Arnold, Lloyd Ashton. AB cum laude, Middlebury Coll., 1970; JD, U. Chgo., 1974. Bar: Mass. 1975, Ill. 1975, U.S. Dist. Ct. (no. dist.) Ill. 1976, U.S. Ct. Appeals (7th cir.) 1976, U.S. Ct. Appeals (10th cir.) 1977, U.S. Supreme Ct. 1978, U.S. Ct. Appeals (11th cir.) 1986, U.S. Ct. Appeals (5th and 9th cirs.) 1987, U.S. Ct. Appeals (D.C. cir.) 1994, U.S. Ct. Appeals (Fed. cir.) 1993. Law clk. to judge John Minor Wisdom U.S. Ct. Appeals (5th cir.), New Orleans, 1974-75; assoc. Jenner & Block, Chgo., 1975-80; asst. to solicitor gen. of U.S. U.S. Dept. of Justice, Washington, 1980-81; ptnr. Jenner & Block, Chgo., 1981-94; dean, prof. law Washington and Lee U., Lexington, Va., 1994—; spl. asst. atty. gen. State of Ill., 1989-90; lectr. in law Loyola U., Chgo., 1978-79; adj. prof. law Northwestern U., Chgo., 1990-92, 93-94, vis. prof., 1992-93; Jessica Swift Meml. lectr. in constnl. law Middlebury Coll., 1991. Assoc. editor U. Chgo. Law Rev., 1973-74; contbr. articles to profl. jours. Trustee Cath. Theol. Union at Chgo., 1993—; mem. vis. com. U. Chgo. Divinity Sch., 1987—; Yeats Soc. scholar, 1968; Woodrow Wilson fellow, Woodrow Wilson Found., 1970. Mem. ABA (chmn. coord. com. on AIDS 1988-94, mem. standing com. on amicus curiae briefs 1990—, mem. coun. of sect. of individual rights and responsibilities 1993—), Va. Bar Assn., Bar Assn. 7th Fed. Cir. (vice chmn. adminstrv. justice com. 1985-86), Am. Law Inst., Phi Beta Kappa. Democrat. Roman Catholic. Home: 201 Jackson Ave Lexington VA 24450 Office: Washington and Lee U Sch Law Lewis Hall Lexington VA 24450

SULLIVAN, BARRY MICHAEL, finance executive; b. Bethesda, Md., Apr. 10, 1945; s. Edward Daniel and Eleanor (Harrold) S.; m. Elizabeth Ann Thompson, Dec. 21, 1967; children: Scott Douglas, David Andrew. BA, Bucknell U., 1967. Asst. v.p. Chase Manhattan Bank, N.Y.C., 1970-75; v.p. Chem. Bank, N.Y.C., 1975-84; treas. Varity Corp., Toronto, Can., 1984-88; v.p., treas. Alfa-Laval, Inc., Park Ridge, N.J., 1989-92; treas. Tetra Laval U.S. Holdings and Fin., Inc., Chgo., 1992-93; v.p., treas. Harsco Corp., Camp Hill, Pa., 1993—. Lt. (j.g.) USN, 1967-70. Mem. Fin. Execs. Inst., Nat. Assn. Corp. Treas. Home: 1816 Silver Pine Cir Mechanicsburg PA 17055 Office: Harsco Corp PO Box 8888 Camp Hill PA 17001-8888

SULLIVAN, BERNARD JAMES, accountant; b. Chgo., June 25, 1927; s. Bernard Hugh and Therese Sarah (Condon) S.; m. Joan Lois Costello, June 9, 1951; children: Therese Lynn Scanlan, Bernard J., Geralyn M. Snyder. BSC, Loyola U., Chgo., 1950. CPA, Ill. Staff Bansley and Kiener, Chgo., 1950-66, ptnr., 1966-82, mng. ptnr., 1982—; bd. dirs. Associated Acctg. Firms, Internat.; exec. com. Moore Stephens and Co., U.S.A., 1984—. Arbitrator Nat. Assn. Security Dealers. Served with USN, 1945-46. Mem. Am. Inst. CPA's, Ill. Soc. CPA's, Govt. Fin. Officer Assn., Internat. Found. Employee Benefit Plans, Delta Sigma Pi. Clubs: Beverly Country (Chgo.), Metropolitan (Chgo.). Lodges: Elks, K.C. Avocations: golf, sports, travel. Home: 9636 S Kolmar Ave Oak Lawn IL 60453 Office: Bansley & Kiener 125 S Wacker Dr Chicago IL 60606

SULLIVAN, BILL, church administrator. Dir. Church Growth Division of the Church of the Nazarene, Kansas City, Mo. Office: Church of Nazarene 6401 The Paseo Kansas City MO 64131

SULLIVAN, BRENDAN V., JR., lawyer; b. Providence, Mar. 11, 1942. AB, Georgetown U., 1964, JD, 1967. Bar: R.I. 1967, D.C. 1970, U.S. Dist. Ct. D.C. 1970, U.S. Ct. Appeals (D.C. cir.) 1970, U.S. Supreme Ct. 1972, U.S. Dist. Ct. Md. 1974, U.S. Ct. Appeals (4th cir.) 1978, U.S. Ct. Appeals (3d cir.) 1979. Mem. Williams & Connolly, Washington; lectr. Practicing Law Inst., 1981—, Md. Inst. for Continuing Profl. Edn. of Lawyers, Inc., 1979—, D.C. Criminal Practice Inst., 1975-81. Author: Grand Jury Proceedings, 1981, Techniques for Dealing with Pending Criminal Charges or Criminal Investigations, 1983, White Collar Criminal Practice Grand Jury, 1985. Fellow Am. Coll. Trial Lawyers; mem. ABA, R.I. Bar Assn., D.C. Bar. Office: Williams & Connolly 725 Twelfth St NW Washington DC 20005

SULLIVAN, CARLEY HAYDEN, political party executive; b. Elko, Nev.; student U. Oreg., 1945-47; m. Will Sullivan; children—Blaine Hayden Sullivan Rose, Valerie Sullivan Mitchell, Dan, Peggy Sullivan Hagen. Mgmt. asst. State of Nev., Elko, 1967—; sec. Elko County (Nev.) Democratic Central Com., 1972—; treas. Nev. Dem. Com., 1980-82, co-chmn. state conv., 1980 mem. state cons. planning com., 1982; mem. state hosp. adv. bd., 1964-66, adv. council on children and youth, 1970-80; mem. gov.'s State Sch. Survey Com., 1975-77, Gov.'s Drug Abuse Adv. Bd., 1974-76; gov.'s del. to Nev. Library Conf., 1981; alt. del. White House Conf. on Libraries, 1982; Nev. del. to Presdl. White House Conf. on Children and Youth, 1970; life mem. Gov.'s Youth Traffic Safety Assn.; exec. sec., interim mgr. Elko C. of C., 1961-68. Pres. Elko Dem. Women, 1970; bd. dirs. Elko Dem. Club, 1970-82; chmn. Rural Nev. Mental Health Adv. Bd., 1973-78; Nev. PTA, 1962-72, pres., 1972-74; v.p. Am. Lung Assn. of Nev., 1972-82, pres.-elect, 1982-84, pres., 1984—; coordinator Youth Traffic Safety Confs., 1968-78; bd. mgrs. Nat. Com. Health and Welfare, PTA, 1972-74; adv. bd. Nat. Council Juvenile Ct. Judges, 1972-74; mem. 8 state project Designing Edn. for the Future, 1965-68; Nev. rep. to nat. ALA conv., 1981; vol. Elko Hosp. Aux.; co-chmn. 1st Rural Nev. Women's Conf., 1980; mem. Nev. Adv. Council for Vocat. Tech. Edn., 1982—; mem., Nev. commr./Nat. Council, Future of Women In The Workplace, 1983-1985; Nev. rep. to Nat. Commn. for Eleanor Roosevelt Centennial, 1984-85; del. to Dem. Nat. Conv., 1984; sec./treas. Elko County Dem. Central Com., 1984-86; mem. Nev. State Bd. Edn., 1984—; apptd. to Nev. U.S. Service Acad. Selection Com., 1987; apptd. by Gov. of Nev. to recommendation com. for Nev. Legislature; mem. Nev. State Dem. Central Com. Recipient honors Am. Lung Assn. Nev., C. of C., Nev. Dept. Edn. Gov.'s Office State of Nev.; Citizen of Year Elko County Mental Health Assn., 1985. Mem. Elko Bus. and Profl. Women (state legis. chmn., scholarship award com., del. to nat. conv.), Sigma Kappa. Office: St Bd of Education 400 W King St Carson City NV 89710

SULLIVAN, CHARLES, university dean, educator, author; b. Boston, May 27, 1933; s. Charles Thomas and Marion Veronica (Donahue) S.; divorced; children: Charles Fulford, John Driscoll, Catherine Page. BA in English, Swarthmore Coll., 1955; MA, NYU, 1968, PhD in Social Psychology, 1973; MPA, Pa. State U., 1978. Predoctoral fellow NYU, 1964-68; postdoctoral fellow Ednl. Testing Svc., Princeton, N.J., 1973-74; asst. prof. psychology Ursinus Coll., Collegeville, Pa., 1977-78; mgmt. cons., 1978-86; adj. prof. Pa. State U., Radnor, Pa., 1978-80; prof., head dept. pub. adminstrn., dir. student svcs. Southeastern U., Washington, 1986-89; asst. dean Grad. Sch. Arts and Scis. Georgetown U., Washington, 1989-92, assoc. dean Grad. Sch. Arts and Scis., 1992—; professorial lectr. dept. psychology, 1994—; exec. dir. Doylestown Found., Doylestown, Pa., 1958-73; adj. prof. social and behavioral scis. U. Md., 1984—; lectr., spkr. on lit. and art Cooper-Hewitt Mus., N.Y.C., Nat. Soc. Arts and Letters, Washington, Martin Luther King Jr. Libr., Washington, Met. Mus. Art, N.Y.C., Smithsonian Instn., Washington, Children's Book Fair, N.Y.C., Nat. Mus. Women in Arts, Lombardi Cancer Rsch. Ctr., Georgetown U., Arts Club of Washington, Phillips Collection, Corcoran Gallery of Art. Author: Alphabet Animals, 1991, The Lover in Winter, 1991, Numbers at Play, 1992, Circus, 1992, Cowboys, 1993, A Woman of a Certain Age, 1994; editor: America in Poetry, 1988, 2nd edit., 1992, Imaginary Gardens, 1989, Ireland in Poetry, 1990, Children of Promise, 1991, Loving, 1992, American Beauties, 1993, Here Is My Kingdom, 1994, Fathers and Children, 1995. Mem. bd. trustees Am. Acad. Liberal Edn., 1995—. Mem. Am. Poetry Soc., Nat. Soc. Arts and Letters, Folger Poetry Bd., Cosmos Club. Office: Georgetown U Grad Sch 302 Intercultural Ctr Washington DC 20057

SULLIVAN, CHARLES A., food products executive. BBA, U. Toledo, 1959. With Seven-Up Co., Los Angeles, 1966-70; v.p. strategic planning Pepsi-Cola Co., Los Angeles, 1966-70; pres. Seven Up of Ind.; with Westinghouse Electric Corp., 1970-79; pres. Can. Dry of New Eng. subs. Norton Simon Co., 1979-82; sr. v.p. pres. Merita div. Am. Bakeries Co. subs. BCA Corp., N.Y.C., 1982-86; exec. v.p. BCA Corp., N.Y.C.; pres., exec. v.p. Merita div. Am. Bakeries Co., 1986-89; pres., chief exec. officer Interstate Bakeries Corp., 1989—; pres., chief exec. officer Interstate Brands Corp. Office: IBC Holdings Corp 12 E Armour Blvd Kansas City MO 64111-1202

SULLIVAN, CHARLES BERNARD, hospital administrator; b. Darby, Pa., Jan. 5, 1945; married. BA, Manhattan Coll., 1966; MA, L.I.U. 1969; MHA, Columbia U., 1971. Adminstrv. resident Montefiore Med. Ctr., Bronx, N.Y., 1970-71; asst. administr. Mt. Sinai Med. Ctr., Milw., 1971-73, assoc. administr., 1973-75; exec. v.p. Reading (Pa.) Hosp. and Med. Ctr., 1975-86, pres., CEO, 1986—. Contbr. articles to profl. jours. Recipient awards. Office: Reading Hosp & Med Ctr 6th Ave Spruce St Reading PA 19603

SULLIVAN, CLAIRE FERGUSON, marketing educator; b. Pittsburg, Tex., Sept. 28, 1937; d. Almon Lafayette and Mabel Clara (Williams) Potter; m. Richard Wayne Ferguson, Jan. 31, 1959 (div. Jan. 1980); 1 child, Mark Jeffrey Ferguson; m. David Edward Sullivan, Nov. 2, 1984. BBA, U. Tex., 1958, MBA, 1961; PhD, U. North Tex., 1973; grad., Harvard Inst. Ednl. Mgmt., 1991. Instr. So. Meth. U., Dallas, 1965-70; asst. prof. U. Utah, Salt Lake City, 1972-74; assoc. prof. U. Ark., Little Rock, 1974-77, U. Tex., Arlington, 1977-80, Ill. State U., Normal, 1980-84; prof., chmn. mktg. Bentley Coll., Waltham, Mass., 1984-89; dean sch. bus. Met. State Coll. Denver, 1989-92, prof. mktg., 1992—; cons. Denver Partnership, 1989-90, Gen. Tel. Co., Irving, Tex., 1983, McKnight Pub. Co., Bloomington, Ill., 1983, dental practitioner, Bloomington, 1982-83, Olympic Fed., Berwyn, Ill., 1982 Denver Partnership Econ. Devel. Adv. Coun., 1989-91; mem. African-Am. Leadership Inst. Gov. Bd. Contbr. mktg. articles to profl. jours. Direct Mktg. Inst. fellow, 1981; Ill. State U. rsch. grantee, 1981-83. Mem. Am. Mktg. Assn. (faculty fellow 1984-85), So. Mktg. Assn., Southwestern Mktg. Assn., Denver World Trade Ctr., Denver Partnership (econ. devel. adv. bd.), Rotary, Beta Gamma Sigma. Republican. Methodist. Home: 4715 11th St

Greeley CO 80634-2318 Office: Met State Coll Dept Mktg MSCD Box 79 PO Box 173362 Denver CO 80217-3362

SULLIVAN, COLLEEN ANNE, physician, educator; b. Lucknow, India, Feb. 11, 1937; came to U.S., 1961; d. Douglas George and Nancy Irene (MacLeod) S.; m. Alexander Walter Gotta, July 17, 1965; 1 child, Nancy Colleen. MB ChB, U. St. Andrews, Scotland, 1961. Diplomate Am. Bd. Anesthesiology, Am. Coll. Anesthesiologists. Rotating intern Nassau Hosp., Mineola, N.Y., 1961-62; clin. instr. Cornell U., N.Y.C., 1962-64; resident in anesthesiology N.Y. Hosp./Cornell U., 1962-64; fellow in anesthesiology Meml. Sloan-Kettering Cancer Ctr., N.Y.C., 1964-67, asst. prof. Cornell U. Med. Coll., 1978-79; assoc. dir. anesthesia St. Mary's Hosp.-Cath. Med. Ctr., Bklyn., 1968-78; clin. assoc. prof. SUNY, Bklyn., 1979-90, clin. prof. anesthesiology, 1990—, clin. dir. anesthesia, 1990-93; clin. dir. anesthesia Kings County Hosp., Bklyn., 1983-90, med. dir. ambulatory surg. unit, 1993—. Author numerous chpt. in anesthesiology textbooks; contbr. articles to profl. jours. Mem. N.Y. State Soc. Anesthesiologists (house dels. 1983—, asst. editor Sphere 1990—, com. sci. program 1990—). Republican. Roman Catholic. Avocations: reading, cooking. Home: 29 Ascot Ridge Great Neck NY 11021 Office: Kings County Hosp Dept Anesthesia 450 Clarkson Ave Brooklyn NY 11203

SULLIVAN, CONNIE CASTLEBERRY, artist, photographer; b. Cin., Jan. 8, 1934; d. John Porter and Constance (Alf Castleberry; m. John J. Sullivan, June 6, 1959; children: Deirdre Kelly, Margaret Graham. BA, Manhattanville Coll., 1957. spl. lectr. Cin. Contemporary Art Ctr., 1984, Toledo Friends of Photography, 1991, U. Ky. Art Mus., 1993, Dennison U. Sch. Art, 1993, El Instituto de Estudios Norte Americanos, Barcelona, 1994. One-woman shows include Contemporary Art Ctr. Cleve., 1982, Cin. Contemporary Arts Ctr., 1983, Fogg Art Mus., Cambridge, Mass., 1983, 90, Camden Arts Ctr., London, 1987, Jean-Pierre Lambert Galerie, Paris, 1988, David Winton Bell Gallery, Brown U., Providence, 1989, Toni Burckhead Gallery, Cin., 1989, Rochester Inst. Tech., 1991, Fotomus. im Münchner Stadtmus., Munich, 1992, U. Ky. Art Mus., Lexington, 1993, Internat. Photography Hall, Kirkpatrick Mus. complex, Oklahoma City, 1993, Institut d'Estudios Fotografics de Catalunya, Barcelona, Spain, 1994, Cheekwood Art Mus., Nashville, 1994, Museo Damy di Fotografia Contemporanea, Brescia, Italy, 1995, Photography Gallery U. Notre Dame, Ind., 1995, Louisville Visual Art Assoc., Watertower, Louisville, KY, 1995; exhibited in numerous group shows including Dayton (Ohio) Art Inst., 1987, J.B. Speed Art Mus., Louisville, 1988, Ohio U., Athens, 1989, Centre Nat. Photographie, Paris, 1989, Cleve. Ctr. for Contemporary Art, 1991, Tampa Mus. Art, 1991, 93, Images Gallery, 1991, Dayton Art Inst./Mus. Contemporary Art Wright State U., Dayton, 1992, Bowling Green State U. Sch Art, 1992, Carnegie Arts Ctr., Covington, Ky., 1993, Cin. Art Mus., 1993, POLK Mus. Art, Lakeland, Fla., 1993, Tampa (Fla.) Mus. Art, 1993, Adams Landing Fine Art Ctr., Cin., 1995, Checkwood Mus. Art, Nashville, 1995; represented in numerous permanent collections Tampa Mus. of Art, Münchner Stadt Mus., Munich, Germany, Museo Damy, Brescia, Italy, numerous mus., Ctr. Creative Photography, Tucson, Detroit Inst. Arts, Biblioteque National, Paris; represented in numerous public collections Internat. Photography Hall of Fame and Mus., Kirkpatrick Ctr. Mus. Complex, Okla. City, Ctr, Creative Photography, Tucson, Ariz., Detroit Inst. Arts, Nelson Gallery-Atkins Mus., Kansas City, Ctr. for Photography, Bombay, Milw. Art Mus., Mus. Photography Arts, San Diego, Bibliotheque Nat., Paris, Musee Nat. D'Art Modern, Centre Georges Pompidou, Paris, Denver Art Mus., Boston Mus. Fine Arts, Stanford U. Mus. Art, Palo Alto, Indpls. Art Mus., New Orleans Mus. Art, numerous others; also pvt. collections; author: Petroglyphs of the Heart, Photographs by Connie Sullivan, 1983; work represented in numerous publs. Trustee Images Ctr. for Fine Photography, Cin., 1986-94. Arts Midwest fellow NEA, 1989-90; recipient award Toledo Friends Photography Juried Show, 1986, Best of Show award, 1988, Images Gallery, 1986, Pres.'s Coun. for Arts award Manhattanville Coll., 1991, Treasure of the Month award Mus. Fine Arts St. Petersburg, Fla., 1995; Aid to Individual Artists grantee Summerfair, 1987. Mem. McDowell Soc. Avocations: travel, reading, gardening, music. Home and Studio: 9 Garden Pl Cincinnati OH 45208-1056

SULLIVAN, CORNELIUS FRANCIS, JR., banking executive; b. Plainfield, N.J., Aug. 16, 1960; s. Cornelius Francis and Ruth Theresa (Ray) S. AB, Duke U., 1982, MBA, 1985. Youth campaign coord. Jim Johnson for Congress, Madison, 1982; founder, ptnr. Raleigh Sports Venture, Durham, N.C., 1985-86; corp. planning analyst Midlantic Banks Inc., Edison, N.J., 1986-87, corp. planning officer, 1988-89, asst. v.p., 1990-93; v.p. corp. fin. and comm. Midlantic Corp., Edison, 1993—. Councilman Town of Westfield, 1995—; press chmn. LPGA Charity Golf Tournament, N.J., 1978-89; asst. press sec. Bo Sullivan for Gov., Fairfield, 1981. Mem. S.R., Duke U. Fuqua Sch. of Bus. Alumni Coun. Home: 335 Sycamore St Westfield NJ 07090-1645 Office: Midlantic Corp 499 Thornall St Edison NJ 08837-2235

SULLIVAN, CORNELIUS J., lawyer; b. Chgo., June 25, 1943. AB, Coll. Holy Cross, 1965; JD, U. Mich., 1968. Bar: Ill. 1968, Fla. 1977. Ptnr. McDermott, Will & Emory, Chgo. Mem. ABA, Fla. Bar, Chgo. Bar Assn. Office: McDermott Will & Emery 111 W Monroe St Chicago IL 60603-4003

SULLIVAN, CORNELIUS WAYNE, marine biology researcher, educator; b. Pitts., June 11, 1943; s. John Wayne and Hilda Sullivan; m. Jill Hajjar, Oct. 28, 1966; children: Shane, Preston, Chelsea. BS in Biochemistry, Pa. State U., 1965, MS in Microbiology, 1967; PhD in Marine Biology, Scripps Inst. Oceanography, 1971. Postdoctoral fellow Scripps Inst. Oceanography, La Jolla, Calif., 1971-74; asst. prof. marine biology U. So. Calif., L.A., 1974-80, assoc. prof., 1980-85, prof., 1985—, dir. marine biology sect., 1982-91; dir. Hancock Inst. Marine Studies, L.A., 1991-93; dir. Office of Polar Programs Nat. Sci. Found., Washington, 1993—; vis. prof. U. Colo., Boulder, 1981-82, MIT, Cambridge, 1981-82, U.S. Army Cold Regions Rsch. & Engring. Lab., Hanover, 1989, Goddard Space Flight Ctr., Greenbelt, Md., 1990; field team leader Sea Ice Microbial Communities Studies, McMurdo Sound, Antarctica, 1980-86; chief scientist/cruise coord. Antartic Marine Ecosystem Rsch. at the Ice Edge Zone Project, Weddell Sea, 1983, 86, 88; mem. BIOMASS Working Party on Pack-Ice Zone Studies, 1983-86, ecol. rsch. rev. bd. Dept. Navy, 1982-85; So. Ocean Ecology Group Specialist Sci. Com. on Antarctic Rsch.; chmn. SCOR working group 86 "Sea Ice Ecology" sci. com. on oceanic rsch; mem. polar rsch. bd. NAS, 1983-86; chmn. com. to evaluate polar rsch. platforms Nat. Rsch. Coun., 1985; mem. dir. policy group NSF, 1993—. Mem. editl. bd. Jour. Microbiol. Methods, 1982-85, Polar Biology, 1987—; contbr. over 100 articles to profl. jours. With USPHS, 1969-71. Fellow USPHS, 1969-71; recipient Antarctic Svc. medal of U.S., NSF, 1981. Fellow AAAS. Office: NSF 4201 Wilson Blvd Ste 755 Arlington VA 22230-1030

SULLIVAN, DANIEL J., artistic director; b. Wray, Colo., June 11, 1940's. John Martin and Mary Catherine (Hutton) S.; children: Megan, John, Rachel M. BA, San Francisco State U. Actor, Actor's Workshop, San Francisco, 1963-65; actor, dir. Lincoln Center Repertory, N.Y.C., 1965-73; dir. (broadway) I'm Not Rapaport, also numerous regional theatres, 1973-79; resident dir. Seattle Repertory Theater, 1979-81, artistic dir., 1981—. Recipient Drama Desk award N.Y. Theatre Critics, 1972. Mem. Nat. Endowment for Arts. Democrat. Office: Seattle Repertory Theatre 155 Mercer St Seattle WA 98109-4639*

SULLIVAN, DANIEL JOSEPH, writer; b. Worcester, Mass., Oct. 22, 1935; s. Daniel and Irene Ann (Flagg) S.; m. Helen Faith Scheid, 1965; children: Margaret Ann, Benjamin, Kathleen. AB, Holy Cross Coll., 1957; postgrad., U. Minn., 1957-59, U. So. Calif., 1964-65, Stanford U., 1978-79. Reporter Worcester Telegram, Mass., 1957; reporter Red Wing Republican Eagle, Minn., 1959, St. Paul Pioneer Press, 1959-61; music and theater critic Mpls. Tribune, 1961-64; comedy writer Dudley Riggs' Brave New Workshop, 1961-64; music writer/theater reviewer N.Y. Times, 1965-68; theater critic L.A. Times, 1969-90; dramaturge Eugene O'Neill Theatre Ctr., Waterford, Conn., 1972, 73, 93, 94; instr. Nat. Critics Inst., Waterford, 1977-92, assoc. dir., 1993—; adj. prof. U. Minn., Mpls., 1990—; juror theater panel Nat. Endowment for Arts, 1983; juror Pulitzer Prize for Drama, 1985, 89, 92; pres. L.A. Drama Critics Circle, 1970-71, Ctr. for Arts Criticism, St. Paul, 1992—. Mem. Am. Theater Critics Assn. (founding mem.).

SULLIVAN, DANIEL JOSEPH, III, transportation executive; b. Fall River, Mass., May 1, 1946; s. Daniel Joseph and Alberta Teresa (Molt) S.; m. Victoria Della-Guistina, Apr. 16, 1977; children: Daniel Joseph IV, Conor Donald. BA in Psychology, Amherst Coll., 1969. Terminal mgr. Roadway Express, Fall River, 1974-75, Albany, N.Y., 1975-76, Stroudsburg, Pa., 1976-79; breakdown mgr. Roadway Express, Inc., Chattanooga, Tenn., 1979-81; dist. mgr. Roadway Express, Inc., Atlanta, 1981-83; asst. to pres. Roadway Express, Inc., Akron, Ohio, 1983-84; pres. Roadway Package System, Pitts., 1984-90; v.p., group exec. Roadway Svcs., Inc., Akron, 1990-92, pres. nat. carrier group, 1992—. Contbr. articles to profl. jours. Sgt. USAR, 1970-75. Mem. Am. Trucking Assn., Nat. Assn. Small Trucking Assn., Nat. Indsl. Traffic League, Edgewood Club (Pitts.), Gallery Country Club. Republican. Roman Catholic. Avocations: reading, gardening, children's activities. Office: Roadway Svcs Inc 1077 Gorge Blvd Akron OH 44309

SULLIVAN, DANNY, professional race car driver; b. Mar. 9, 1950; 1 child, Driscoll. Winner Indpls. 500, 1985. Office: 434 E Cooper # 201 Aspen CO 81611

SULLIVAN, DENNIS F., transportation company executive, engineer; b. Fall River, Mass., Jan. 7, 1943; s. Dennis F. Sullivan and Mary Quinn; m. Billie L. Adams; children: Ann, Denise, Jill. BSCE, U. Mass., 1964; postgrad., Harvard U., 1984. Registered profl. engr. Asst. chief engr., chief engr. TLS Amtrak, Phila., 1977-78, acting chief engr., 1978, dep. chief engr., 1978-81; asst. v.p. engring. Amtrak, Washington, 1981-82, v.p., chief engr., 1982-85, v.p. ops. and maintenance, 1985-88, exec. v.p., COO, 1988—; chmn. Washington Terminal Co., 1985—. Mem. Am. Ry. Engring. Assn., Roadmasters and Maintenance of Way Assn. Am. Roman Catholic. Office: Nat RR Passenger Corp 60 Massachusetts Ave NE Washington DC 20002-4225

SULLIVAN, DENNIS JAMES, JR., public relations executive; b. Jersey City, Feb. 23, 1932; s. Dennis James and Mary Theresa (Coyle) S.; m. Constance Rosemary Shields, Jan. 31, 1953; children: Denise Sullivan Morrison, Mary Agnes Sullivan Wilderotter, Colleen Sullivan Bastkowski, Andrea Sullivan Doelling. AB, St. Peters Coll., 1953; postgrad., U. Md., 1955; MBA, U. Pa., 1973. Various line and staff positions N.J. Bell, 1955-61, N.Y. Telephone Co., 1961-64, 67-68; various line and staff positions AT&T, N.Y.C., 1964-67, 68-76, dir. mktg., 1972-74, asst. v.p., 1974-76; v.p. mktg. Ohio Bell Telephone Co., Cleve., 1976-78; v.p. consumer info. services AT&T-Am. Bell, Parsippany, N.J., 1978-83; exec. v.p. Cin. Bell Telephone Co., 1983-84, pres., 1984-87, also bd. dirs.; exec. v.p., chief fin. officer Cin. Bell Inc., 1987-93; ret., 1993; bd. dirs. Fifth Third Bancorp & Bank; vice chmn. Community Mutual Ins. Co., Access Corp., The Future Now. Author: Videotex, IEE Nat. Conf., 1981. Mem. bd. dirs. Salvation Army, Cin. Bd. Edn., 1993—; gen. chmn. United Way, 1990—. Served as lt. (j.g.) USN, 1953-55, ret. as comdr. USNR, 1976. Mem. Cin. Country Club, Queen City Club, Bankers Club (Cin.). Roman Catholic. Office: DP Pub Relsc Hist Cable House 2245 Gilbert Ave Cincinnati OH 45206-1872

SULLIVAN, DENNIS W., power systems company executive; b. Chgo., 1938. Grad., Purdue U., 1960, Case Western Res. U., 1969. Exec. v.p., bd. dirs. Parker Hannifin Corp., Cleve.; bd. dirs. Soc. Bat. Bank. Office: Parker Hannifin Corp 17325 Euclid Ave Cleveland OH 44112-1290

SULLIVAN, DONALD, college president; b. Bklyn., Oct. 22, 1930; s. John T. and Catherine (Lane) S. B.S., Fordham U.; M.A., N.Y. U.; Ph.D., St. John's U.; LittD, St. Francis Coll., 1979. Former asst. prof., dean students St. Francis Coll., Bklyn.; now pres. St. Francis Coll.; mem. Commn. Ind. Colls. and Univs.; bd. dirs. Ridgewood Savs. Bank. Trustee Helen Keller Svcs. for the Blind. Mem. C. of C. (dir.), Downtown Bklyn. Dirs. Assn. (bd. dirs.). Clubs: Brooklyn. Office: St Francis Coll 180 Remsen St Brooklyn NY 11201-4398

SULLIVAN, DONALD BARRETT, physicist; b. Phoenix, June 13, 1939. BS, Tex. Western Coll., 1961; MA, Vanderbilt U., 1963, PhD in Physics, 1965. Rsch. assoc. physics Vanderbilt U., 1965; physicist, br. chief radiation physics br. U.S. Army Nuclear Def. Lab., 1965-67; Nat. Rsch. Coun. assoc. Nat. Bur. Stds., 1967-69, physicist, chief cryoelectronic metrol. sect., 1969-84, chief time and frequency divsn., 1984—. Mem. Am. Phys. Soc. Office: Nat Inst of Stds Tech Physics Lab Time Frequency Divsn 4036 Radio Bldg 325 Broadway Boulder CO 80303

SULLIVAN, DONALD JOHN, corporation executive, health care management consultant, publisher; b. Ont., Can., Apr. 18, 1939; s. John Donald and Mary (Mintenko) S.; m. Kate Hoisington, Oct. 27, 1962; children—Jeffrey, Daniel, Jennifer. B.S. in Indsl. Engring., Mich. Tech. U., 1965; M.S.A., Wayne State U., 1966. Project dir. NASA, 1963; Ohio rep. Am. Hosp. Assn., 1968; pres. Health Care Systems Inc., Columbus, Ohio, 1969-75; v.p. Chi Systems, Ann Arbor, Mich., 1973-75; pres. D. J. Sullivan & Assocs. Inc., Ann Arbor, Mich., 1975—, Health Care Pub., DJS Properties & Investments. Bd. dirs. Adventure Sch. for Learning Disabilities, Bloomfield Hills, Mich. Recipient awards for activities in field. Mem. Am. Coll. Hosp. Adminstrs., Hosp. Systems Mgmt. Soc., Hosp. Fin. Mgmt. Assn., Nat. League Nurses, Am. Assn. Hosp. Cons., Nat. Hosp. Planning Assn. Developer physician-hosp. programs. Office: D J Sullivan & Assocs Inc 2155 Jackson Ave Ann Arbor MI 48103-3917

SULLIVAN, EDWARD JOSEPH, lawyer, educator; b. Bklyn., Apr. 24, 1945; s. Edward Joseph and Bridget (Duffy) S.; m. Patte Hancock, Aug. 7, 1982; children: Amy Brase, Molly Elsesser, Mary Christine. BA in Polit. Sci., St. John's U., 1966; JD, Willamette U., 1969; MA, cert. Urban Studies, Portland State U., 1974; LLM, Univ. Coll., London, 1978; diploma in law, Univ. Coll., Oxford, 1984. Bar: Oreg. 1969, D.C. 1978, U.S. Dist. Ct. Oreg. 1970, U.S. Ct. Appeals (9th cir.) 1970, U.S. Supreme Ct. 1972. Counsel Washington County, Hillsboro, Oreg., 1969-75; legal counsel Gov. of Oreg., Salem, 1975-77; ptnr. O'Donnell, Sullivan & Ramis, Portland, Oreg., 1978-84, Sullivan, Josselson, Roberts, Johnson & Kloos, Portland, Salem and Eugene, Oreg., 1984-86, Mitchell, Lang & Smith, Portland, 1986-90, Preston Gates & Ellis, Portland, 1990—; bd. dirs., pres. Oreg. Law Inst. Contbr. numerous articles to profl. jours. Chmn. Capitol Planning Commn., Salem, 1975-77, 78-81. Mem. ABA (local govt. sect., com. on planning and zoning, adminstrv. law sect.) Oreg. State Bar Assn., D.C. Bar Assn., Am. Judicature Soc., Am. Polit. Sci. Assn. Democrat. Roman Catholic. Office: Preston Gates & Ellis 111 SW 5th Ave Ste 3200 Portland OR 97204

SULLIVAN, EUGENE JOHN JOSEPH, manufacturing company executive; b. N.Y.C., Nov. 28, 1920; s. Cornelius and Margaret (Smith) S.; m. Gloria Roesch, Aug. 25, 1943; children: Eugene John Joseph, Edward J., Robert C., Elizabeth Ann Hansler. BS, St. John's U., 1942, D.Commerce, 1973; M.B.A., N.Y. U., 1948. With chem. div. Borden, Inc., N.Y., 1946—; beginning as salesman, successively asst. sales Borden, Inc., 1957-58, exec. v.p., 1958-64; pres. Borden Chem. Co. div. Borden, Inc.; v.p. Borden, Inc., 1964-67, exec. v.p., 1967-73, pres., chief operating officer, 1973-79, chmn., pres., chief exec. officer, 1979-86; former adj. prof., now prof. St. John's U., 1987—; bd. dirs. W.R. Grace & Co.; chmn. bd. dirs. Hamilton Fund; trustee Atlantic Mut. Ins. Co. Trustee, vice chmn., past sec. St. John's U.; trustee N.Y. Med. Coll., Cath. Health Assn.; chmn. Commn. on Cath. Health Care. Served as lt. USNR, 1942-46; lt. Res. Mem. Coun. Fgn. Rels., Knights of Malta, Knights of Holy Sepulchre, Knights of St. Gregory, Univ. Club, Plandome Country Club, Westhampton Country Club. Office: Borden Inc 277 Park Ave New York NY 10172

SULLIVAN, EUGENE JOSEPH, food service company executive; b. Phila., Sept. 30, 1943; s. Eugene Joseph and Helen Patricia (Gartland) S.; m. Judith Ann Heller, June 12, 1965; children: Christine, Kimberly, Gregg. BS in Acctg., U. Scranton, 1965. Mgr. Swift & Co., 1965-72; with Dobbs Houses, Inc., Memphis, 1972-85, v.p., gen. mgr., 1977-82, sr. v.p., 1982-84, pres., 1984-85; pres. CKG Enterprises, Inc., Memphis, 1986—. Office: CKG Enterprises Inc 1642 E Shelby Dr Memphis TN 38116-7228

SULLIVAN, EUGENE RAYMOND, federal judge; b. St. Louis, Aug. 2, 1941; s. Raymond Vincent and Rosemary (Kiely) S.; m. Lis Urup Johansen, June 18, 1966; children—Kim, Eugene II. BS, U.S. Mil. Acad., 1964; JD, Georgetown U., 1971. Bar: Mo. 1972, D.C. 1972. Law clk. to judge U.S.

Ct. Appeals (8th cir.), St. Louis, 1971-72; assoc. Patton Boggs & Blow, Washington, 1972-74; asst. spl. counsel The White House, Washington, 1974; trial counsel U.S. Dept. of Justice, Washington, 1974-82; dep. gen. counsel U.S. Air Force, Washington, 1982-84; gen. counsel U.S. Air Force, 1984-86; gov. Wake Island, 1984-86; judge U.S. Ct. Appeals (Armed Forces), Washington, 1986-90, chief judge, 1990—. Served to capt. U.S. Army, 1964-69, Vietnam. Decorated Bronze Star, Air medal, others. Republican. Roman Catholic. Home: 6307 Massachusetts Ave Bethesda MD 20816-1139 Office: US Ct Appeals Armed Forces 450 E St NW Washington DC 20442-0001

SULLIVAN, FRANCIS EDWARD, research administrator; b. Bklyn., May 12, 1941; s. Francis and Beatrice (DeLucca) S.; m. Mary Alyce Lennon, May 10, 1969. BS, Pa. State U., 1962; MS, U. Pitts., 1964, PhD, 1968. Assoc. engr. Westinghouse Astronuclear Lab., Pitts., 1962-63; mathematician Gulf R & D Co., Pitts., 1963-66; asst. prof. U. Pitts., 1966-71; dir. Computing and Applied Math. Lab. Nat. Inst. Standards and Tech., Gaithersburg, Md., 1986-93; dir. Supercomputing Rsch. Ctr., IDA, Bowie, Md., 1993—; vis. prof. computer sci. Chalmers Tekniska Hogskola, Sweden, 1971-73; vis. prof. math. U. Nijmegen, The Netherlands, 1980-81; adj. prof. The Cath. U. Am., Washington, 1982—; lectr. Jones Hopkins U., Balt., 1988—. Author: (with A. Peresinni, J.J. Uhl Jr.) The Mathematics of Non-Linear Programming, 1988; editor: 3 profl. jours.; contbr. approximately 45 articles to profl. jours. Recipient Gold medal U.S. Dept. Commerce, 1987. Mem. Soc. Indsl. and Applied Math. (com. on sci. policy 1988—), Am. Math. Soc. Office: IDA Supercomputing Rsch Ctr Bowie MD 20715

SULLIVAN, FRANK, JR., judge; b. Mar. 21, 1950; s. Frank E. and Colette (Cleary) S.; m. Cheryl Gibson, June 14, 1972; children: Denis M., Douglas S., Thomas R. AB cum laude, Dartmouth Coll., 1972; JD magna cum laude, Ind. U., 1982. Bar: Ind. 1982. Mem. staff Office of U.S. Rep. John Brademas, 1974-79, dir. staff, 1975-78; with Barnes & Thornburg, Indpls., 1982-89; budget dir. State of Ind., 1989-82; exec. asst. Office of Gov. Evan Bayh, 1993; assoc. justice Ind. Supreme Ct., 1993—. Mem. ABA, Ind. State Bar Assn., Indpls. Bar Assn. Home: 6153 N Olney Indianapolis IN 46220 Office: Statehouse Rm 311 Indianapolis IN 46204

SULLIVAN, FRANK VICTOR, academic dean, industrial arts educator; b. Wichita, Mar. 5, 1931; s. Frank Townsend and Olive (Knisely) S.; m. Mary-Kate Larson, June 2, 1956; children: Mark Kenneth, Olive Louise. BS, Friends U., 1953; MA, U. No. Colo., 1957; EdD, U. Ill., 1964. Tchr., indsl. edn. Minnena Sch., Wichita, 1953-56; instr. Friends U., Wichita, 1956-60, U. Ill. High Sch., Urbana, 1960-63; prof. Pittsburg (Kans.) State U., 1963—, chmn. dept. indsl. arts and tech., 1978-85, dean Sch. Tech. and Applied Sci., 1985—; vis. prof. Ball State U., Muncie, Ind., 1968, Meml. U., St. John, Nfld., Can., 1978; lectr. U. Alta., Edmonton, Can., 1967-68; draftsman R.K. Blunk A.I.A., Wichita, 1952. Bd. dirs. Kans. Tech. Enterprise Corp.; mem. Kans. Advanced Tech. Council; dir. Mid-Am., Inc. Mem. Am. Soc. Engring. Edn., Internat. Tech. Edn. Assn. (life), Kans. Tech. Edn. Assn., Nat. Assn. Indsl. Tech. Tchr. Edn., Ptnrs. Ams. (bd. dirs., Kans.-Paraguay com.), Rotary, Phi Delta Kappa, Epsilon Pi Tau. Republican. Methodist. Avocations: photography. Office: Pittsburg State U Sch Tecn And Applied S Pittsburg KS 66762

SULLIVAN, G. CRAIG, chemical executive; b. 1940. BS, Boston Coll., 1964. With Proctor & Gamble Co., 1964-69, Am. Express Co., 1969-70; regional sales mgr. Clorox Co., Oakland, Calif., 1971-76, v.p. mktg., 1976-78, mgr. food svc. sales devel., mgr. bus. devel., 1978-79, gen. mgr. food svc. products divsn., 1979-81, v.p. food svc. products divsn., 1981, v.p. household products, 1981-89, group v.p. household products, 1989-92, chmn. bd., CEO, 1992—. Office: The Clorox Co 1221 Broadway Oakland CA 94612-1837*

SULLIVAN, GEORGE EDMUND, editorial and marketing company executive; b. N.Y.C., Feb. 3, 1932; s. Timothy Daniel and Helen Veronica (Danaher) S.; m. Carole Ann Hartz, Sept. 4; 1954; children—Patricia Lynn, George Edmund, Michael Frank. B.A., Iona Coll., 1957; M.Ed., Rutgers U., 1961; Ph.D., Walden U., 1980. Tchr. English Holmdel Twp. and Keyport (N.J.) Pub. Schs., 1957-62; field mgr. regional mktg. Harcourt, Brace & World, Inc., N.Y.C., 1962-69; v.p. sales Noble & Noble, Publishers, Inc., 1969-72, sr. v.p., chief exec. officer, 1972-78; pres. Sullivan Ednl. Assos., Inc., Scottsdale, Ariz., 1978—; cons. to pub. and pvt. sects. on improving writing instruction and scholastic aptitude test scores. Author numerous books on English lang., writing and map reading skills. Served with USAF, 1950-52. Mem. Assn. Am. Publishers (ofcl. rep. 1972-82), Keyport Edn. Assn. (pres. 1960-62), Am. Mgmt. Assn. Home: 7714 E 1st Ave Scottsdale AZ 85251 *The world is full of people who don't really care. Any person who chooses a worthy activity and really cares about doing it the right way, the best way, the most perfect way despite all adversity, will succeed. Really caring is the fuel that generates miracles.*

SULLIVAN, GEORGE EDWARD, author; b. Lowell, Mass., Aug. 11, 1927; s. Timothy Joseph and Cecilia Mary (Shea) S.; m. Muriel Agnes Moran, May 24, 1952; 1 son, Timothy. B.S., Fordham U., 1952. Pub. relations mgr. Popular Library, N.Y.C., 1952-55; pub. relations dir. AMF, N.Y.C., 1955-63; adj. prof. Fordham U. Author numerous books including: Discover Archaeology, 1980 (Jr. Lit. Guild selection); Superstars of Women's Track, 1981, The Supercarriers, 1981 (Jr. Lit. guild selection), The Gold Hunter's Handbook, 1981 (Outdoor Life Book Club and Popular Sci. Book Club selections), The Art of Base Stealing, 1982 (Jr. Lit. Guild selection), Great Imposters, 1982, Quarterback, 1982, Inside Nuclear Submarines, 1982, Anwar el-Sadat: The Man Who Changed Mid-East History, 1982, Pope John Paul, The People's Pope, 1984, Mr. President, 1984, Work When You Want to Work, 1985, The Thunderbirds, 1986, Work Smart, Not Hard, 1987, How the White House Really Works, 1988, Mikhail Gorbachev, 1988, The Day Man Walked on the Moon, 1989, All About Basketball, 1990, The Day They Bombed Pearl Harbor, 1991, Racing Indy Cars, 1992, Mathew Brady, His Life and Photographs, 1993, The Day Women Got the Vote, 1994. Served with USN, 1945-48. Mem. PEN, Authors Guild, Am. Soc. Journalists and Authors. Roman Catholic.

SULLIVAN, GEORGE MURRAY, transportation consultant, former mayor; b. Portland, Oreg., Mar. 31, 1922; s. Harvey Patrick and Viola (Murray) S.; m. Margaret Eagan, Dec. 30, 1946; children: Timothy M., Harvey P., Daniel A., Kevin Shane, Colleen Marie, George Murray, Michael J., Shannon Margaret, Casey Eagan. Student pub. schs.; D.P.A. (hon.), U. Alaska, 1981. Line driver Alaska Freight Lines, Inc., Valdez-Fairbanks, 1942-44; U.S. dep. marshal Alaska Dist., Nenana, 1946-52; mgr. Alaska Freight Lines, 1952-56; Alaska gen. mgr. Consol. Freightways Corp. of Del., Anchorage, 1956-67; mayor of Anchorage, 1967-82; sec. mgr. Alaska Bus. Council, 1968; sr. cons. to pres. Western Air Lines Inc., 1982-87; former legis. liaison for Gov. of Alaska; past mem. Nat. Adv. Com. on Oceans and Atmosphere, Joint Fed.-State Land Use Planning Commn.; past chmn. 4-state region 10 adv. com. OEO; mem. Fairbanks City Council, 1955-59, Anchorage City Council, 1965-67, Greater Anchorage Borough Assembly, 1965-67, Alaska Ho. of Reps., 1964-65. Trustee U. Alaska Found.; chmn. Anchorage Conv. and Visitors Bur.; bd. dirs. Western council Boy Scouts Am., 1958-59. Served with U.S. Army, 1944-46. Mem. Nat. Def. Transp. Assn. (life mem., pres. 1962-63), Nat. League Cities (dir.), Pioneers of Alaska, Alaska Mcpl. League (past pres.), Anchorage C. of C. (exec. com. 1963-65, treas. 1965-66, dir.), Alaska Carriers Assn. (exec. com.), Alaska Transp. Conf. (chmn.), U.S. Conf. Mayors (exec. com.), VFW (comdr. Alaska 1952). Club: Elks. Office: George M Sullivan Co 1345 W 12th Ave Anchorage AK 99501-4252 *America is truly the land of opportunity, and I feel that the success with which God has blessed my life attests to this fact. I have been blessed four times. Not only was I born in America, but I have lived my life in Alaska. My other two blessings are my wonderful and supportive wife and our nine healthy children.*

SULLIVAN, GORDON R., career officer; b. Boston, Sept. 25, 1937; s. Russsell Edgar and Penuel Edith (Gordon) S.; m. Miriam Gay Loftus, June 20, 1965; children: John, Mark, Elizabeth. BA in History, Norwich U., 1959, D Mil. Sci. (hon.), 1991; MA in Polit. Sci., U. N.H., 1974. Commd. 2d lt. U.S. Army, 1959, advanced through grades to gen., 1990; student Armor Officer Basic Course U.S. Army Armor Sch., Ft. Knox, Ky., 1959-60; platoon leader Co. B, 1st Medium Tank Bn., 66th Armor, 2d Armored Div., Ft. Hood, Tex., 1960; student Armor Communication Class U.S. Army Armor Sch., Ft. Knox, 1960; communications officer 1st Medium Tank Bn.,

66th Armor, 2d Armored Div., Ft. Hood, 1960-61; comdr. Co. A, 1st Medium tank Bn., 66th Armor,. 2d Armored Div., Ft. Hood, 1961; bn. communications officer 3d Medium Tank Bn. (Patton), 40th Armor, U.S. Army Pacific, Republic of Korea, 1961-62; platoon leader Co. A 3d Medium Tank Bn., 40th Armor, U.S. Army Pacific, Korea, 1962; asst. civil guard/self def. corps advisor 21st Inf. Div., Mil. Assistance Group, Vietnam, 1962-63; adminstrv. officer, later exec. asst. Office of Asst. Chief of Staff, J2 Div., Mil. Assistance Command, Vietnam, 1963-64; student Armor Officer Advanced Course U.S. Army Armor Sch., Ft. Knox, 1964-65; S-4 (Logistics) 3d Bn., 32d Armor, 3d Armored Div., U.S. Army Europe, 1965-66; comdr. Co.A, 3d Bn., 32d Armor, 3d Armored Div., U.S. Army Europe, 1966; assignment officer, later staff officer Combat Arms Sect., Mil. Pers. Div., Office of Dep. Chief of Staff for Pers., U.S. Army Europe, 1966-68; student U.S. Army Command Gen. Staff Coll., Ft. Leavenworth, Kans., 1968-69; pers. svcs. officer Plans and Ops. Div., G-1, Hdqrs., I Field Force, Vietnam, 1969-70; pers. mgmt. officer Pers. Actions Sect., Armor Br., Office of Pers. Ops., Washington, 1970-73; student Internat. Rels. U. N.H., Durham, 1973-74; comdr. 4th Bn., 73d Armor, 1st Inf. Div. (Forward), U.S. Army Europe, 1975-76; chief of staff 1st Inf. Div. (Forward), U.S. Army Europe, 1976-77; student U.S. Army War Coll., Carlisle Barracks, Pa., 1977-78; asst. chief of staff G-3 (Ops.)/Dir. Plans and Tng., 1st Inf. Div. and Fort Riley, Kans., 1978-79, G-3 (Ops.), VII Corps, U.S. Army Europe, 1980-81; comdr. 1st Brigade, 3d Armored Div., U.S. Army Europe, 1981-83; chief of staff 3d Armored Div., U.S. Army Europe, 1983; asst. comdt. U.S. Army Armor Sch., Ft. Knox, 1983-85; dep. chief of Staff for support Cen. Army Group, Europe, 1985-87; dep. comdt. U.S. Army Command and Gen. Staff Coll., Ft. Leavenworth, 1987-88; comdg. gen. 1st Inf. Div. (Mechanized), Ft. Riley, 1988-89; dep. chief of staff for ops. and plans U.S. Army/Army Sr. Mem., Mil. Staff Com. UN, Washington, 1989-90; vice chief of staff Office of the Chief of Staff, U.S. Army, Washington, 1990-91; chief of staff U.S. Army, Washington, 1991—. Editor: Portrait of an Army, 1991. Decorated D.S.M., Def. Superior Svc. medal, Legion of Merit, Bronze Star, Purple Heart, Meritorius Svc. medal with oak leaf cluster, Joint Svc. Commendation medal, Army Commendation medal with oak leaf cluster, Army Achievement medal, Combat Infantryman badge. Mem. Assn. of U.S. Army, Armor Assn. Home: Quarters One Fort Myer VA 22211 Office: Chief of Staff Army 200 Army Pentagon Washington DC 20310

SULLIVAN, JAMES FRANCIS, university administrator; b. Pitts., Sept. 15, 1930; s. Francis P. and Leona C. (Patterson) S.; m. Carol Rea, Sept. 10, 1955; children—Leslie Ann, Daniel Paul. B.A., Dartmouth Coll., 1953; M.S., U. Colo., 1956; Ph.D., U. Pitts., 1965. Asst. city mgr. Monterey, Calif., 1957-60; city mgr. Ojai, Calif., 1960-62; asst. prof. U. Pitts., 1965-67, vice-chancellor U. Calif. at Riverside, 1966-74; assoc. prof. Grad. Sch. Adminstrn., 1970-78; assoc. dir. Dry Lands Research Inst., 1974-78; vice chancellor U. Calif. at Davis, 1978-91, dean univ. extention, 1980-91. Served with USAF, 1954-55. Home: 1005 Rodeo Rd Pebble Beach CA 93953-2720

SULLIVAN, JAMES JEROME, lawyer, consultant; b. Fargo, N.D., Feb. 23, 1943; m. Roberta Jean Ranes, Nov. 8, 1980; children: Kristen, Jason, Eric, Amy. PhB, U. N.D., 1966, JD, 1970. Bar: N.D. 1970, Wash. 1982. Atty. Northwestern Nat. Life Ins. Co., Mpls., 1970-73; regional counsel Econ. Devel. Admin. of U.S. Dept. Commerce, Seattle, 1973-90; law pvt. practice Bellevue and Issaquah, Wash., 1986—. Editor, contbr. articles to numerous periodicals. Recipient numerous legal awards. Mem. ABA, Wash. State Bar Assn., Wash. State Trial Lawyers Assn. Avocations: skiing, sailing, fishing, hunting, chess, reading. Home: 11110 NE 38th Pl Bellevue WA 98004-7653 Office: 800 Bellevue Way NE Bellevue WA 98004-4229 Office: 385 Front St N Issaquah WA 98027-2929

SULLIVAN, JAMES KIRK, forest products company executive; b. Greenwood, S.C., Aug. 25, 1935; s. Daniel Jones and Addie (Brown) S.; m. Elizabeth Miller, June 18, 1960; children: Hal N., Kim J. BS in Chemistry, Clemson U., 1957, MS, 1964, PhD, 1966; postgrad. program for sr. execs., MIT, 1975; DSc (hon.), U. Idaho, 1990. Prodn. supr. FMC Corp., South Charleston, W.va., 1957-62; tech. supt. FMC Corp., Pocatello, Idaho, 1966-69; mktg. mgr. FMC Corp., N.Y.C., 1969-70; v.p. govtl. and environ. affairs Boise (Idaho) Cascade Corp., 1971—; bd. dirs. Key Bank Idaho, chmn. trust and investment com., 1983-90, exec. com., 1983—; bd. dirs., chmn. audit com. Key Trust Co. of the West; chmn. adv. bd. U. Idaho Coll. Engring., 1966-70, 80-87, centennial campaign, 1987-89, rsch. found., 1980-82; mem. Accreditation Bd. Engring. and Tech., Inc., 1994. Contbr. articles to profl. jours.; patentee in field. Mem. Coll. of Forest and Recreation Resources com. Clemson U., Idaho Found. for Pvt. Enterprise and Econ. Edn., Idaho Rsch. Found., Inc., Idaho Task Force on Higher Edn.; bd. dirs. Idaho Found. for Excellence in Higher Edn., Exptl. Program to Stimulate Competitive Rsch. NSF, N.W. Nazarene Coll., 1988-90, active Len. B. Jordan Pub. Affairs Synposium; trustee Idaho Children's Emergency Fund, 1984—; Bishop Kelly High Sch., chmn. 1987-89; chmn. Bishop Kelly Found., 1972-79, 85-89; chmn. adv. bd. U. Idaho Coll. Engring., Am. Forest and Paper Assn., Govtl. Affairs Com., Environ. Com., Future options Group; pub. affairs com. NAM; active Idaho Found. Pvt. Enterprise and Econ. Edn., 1988—; chmn. centennial campaign U. Idaho, U, Idaho Found., others; mem. environ. com. Future Options Group. 1st lt. U.S. Army, 1958-59. Recipient Presdl. Citation U. Idaho, 1990. Mem. Am. Chem. Soc., Am. Inst. Chem. Engrs., Bus. Week Found. (chmn. Bus. Week 1980), Am. Paper Isnt. (environ. steering com.), Bus. Roundtable (environ. com.), Idaho Assn. Commerce and Industry (chmn. bd. dirs.), C. of C. of U.S. (pub. affairs com.). Republican. Home: 5206 Sorrento Cir Boise ID 83704-2347 Office: Boise Cascade Corp One Jefferson Sq Boise ID 83728

SULLIVAN, JAMES LENOX, clergyman; b. Silver Creek, Miss., Mar. 12, 1910; s. James Washington and Mary Ellen (Dampeer) S.; m. Velma Scott, Oct. 22, 1935; children: Mary Beth (Mrs. Bob R. Taylor), Martha Lynn (Mrs. James M. Porch, Jr.), James David. B.A., Miss. Coll., 1932, D.D., 1948; Th.M., So. Bapt. Theol. Sem., 1935. Ordained to ministry of Baptist Ch., 1930; pastor Baptist Ch., Boston, Ky., 1932-33, Beaver Dam, Ky., 1933-38, Ripley, Tenn., 1938-40, Clinton, Miss., 1940-42; pastor First Bapt. Ch., Brookhaven, Miss., 1942-46, Belmont Heights, Nashville, 1946-50, Abilene, Tex., 1950-53; exec. sec., treas. Bapt. Sunday Sch. Bd., Nashville, 1953-73; pres. Bapt. Sunday Sch. Bd., 1973-75; exec. sec. Broadman Press, 1953-75, Convention Press, 1955-75; pres. So. Bapt. Conv., 1977. Author: Your Life and Your Church, 1950, John's Witness of Jesus, Memos for Christian Living, Reach Out, Rope of Sand with Strength of Steel, God Is My Record, Baptist Polity As I See It, Southern Baptist Polity at Work in a Church; also articles and manuals. Trustee Union U., Cumberland U., So. Bapt Theol. Sem., Hardin-Simmons U., Midstate (Tenn.) Bapt. Hosp., Hendrick Meml. Hosp., Tex. Recipient E.Y. Mullins Denominational Service award, 1973; named Miss. Bapt. Clergyman of Century. Mem. Baptist World Alliance (exec. com. 1953-80, v.p. 1970-75). Clubs: Rotary (Ripley, Tenn.); Lions (Brookhaven, Miss.); Kiwanis (Abilene, Tex.).

SULLIVAN, JAMES LEO, organization executive; b. Somerville, Mass., Dec. 11, 1925; s. James Christopher and Anna Agnes (Kilmartin) S.; m. Anne Dorothy Hevner, Jan. 20, 1951; children: Maura, Mark, Lianne, Christopher. BS in History and Govt. cum laude, Boston Coll., 1950, MEd in Adminstrn. and Fin., 1958; DCS (hon.), Suffolk U., 1990. Asst. town mgr. Arlington, Mass., 1957-62; town mgr. Watertown, Conn., 1962-65; chief adminstrv. officer Town of Milton, Mass., 1965-68; city mgr. Cambridge, Mass., 1968-70, 74-81, Lowell, Mass., 1970-74; sr. research asst. MIT, 1970-71; pres. Greater Boston C. of C., 1981-91, H.M.S. Mktg., Boston, 1991—; chmn. Mass. Gov.'s Local Govt. Adv. Com., 1978; del. to Orgn. Econ. and Cooperative Devel., Paris, 1979; mem. New Eng.-Can. Bus. Coun., 1983; pres. Careers for Later YEars, 1983; bd. dirs. Input-Output Computer Svcs., Imugen Inc., Mass. Bus. Devel. Corp. Trustee Emerson Coll., 1984-88, mem. fin. and investment com., 1985-88; bd. dirs. Bunker Hill Community Coll. Found., 1988—; mem. Adv. Com. on Reorgn. of Mass. Ct. System, 1991—; chmn. budget subcom. 1991—; bd. overseers Univ. Hosp. Boston. With USN, 1943-46. Mem. Mass. League of Cities and Towns (pres. 1978), Mass. Mayors Assn., Internat. City Mgmt. Assn., Nat. League Cities, Am. C. of C. Execs. (bd. dirs. 1988—). Club: World Trade (bd. govs. 1986—). Office: HMS Mktg 65 Franklin St Boston MA 02110-1303

SULLIVAN, JAMES N., fuel company executive; b. San Francisco, 1937. Student, U. Notre Dame, 1959. Formerly v.p. Chevron Corp., until

1988, now vice chmn., dir., 1988—. Office: Chevron Corp 225 Bush St San Francisco CA 94104*

SULLIVAN, JAMES STEPHEN, bishop; b. Kalamazoo, July 23, 1929; s. Stephen James and Dorothy Marie (Bernier) S. Student, St. Joseph Sem.; BA, Sacred Heart Sem.; postgrad., St. John Provincial Sem. Ordained priest, Roman Cath. Ch., 1955, consecrated bishop, 1972. Assoc. pastor St. Luke Ch., Flint, Mich., 1955-58; assoc. pastor St. Mary Cathedral, Lansing, Mich., 1958-60, sec. to bishop, 1960-61; assoc. pastor St. Joseph (Mich.) Ch., 1961-65, sec. to bishop, 1965-69; assoc. pastor Lansing, 1965, vice chancellor, 1969-72; aux. bishop, vicar gen. Diocese of Lansing, 1972-85, diocesan consultor, 1971-85; bishop Fargo, N.D., 1985—. Mem. Nat. Conf. Cath. Bishops (bishop's liturgical commn.). Office: Chancery Office PO Box 1750 608 Broadway Fargo ND 58102-4419*

SULLIVAN, JAMES THOMAS, printing company executive; b. N.Y.C., Jan. 9, 1939; s. James A. and Mary Sullivan; m. Hildegard Reif, Apr. 6, 1959; children—Kathleen, Sean Michael. Student, U. Md., 1959-62; A.M.P., Harvard U., 1985. With R.R. Donnelley & Sons, 1969—; sales rep. N.Y.C., 1969-74, sales mgr., 1974-75, v.p., 1975-76, sr. v.p., 1976-79, pres. book group, 1980-83, pres. mag. group, 1983-86; pres., CEO Maxwell Communications, 1986-88; chmn., CEO Sullivan Comm., Stamford, Conn., 1988—. Served with U.S. Army, 1956-62. Mem. Union League Club (N.Y.C.), Richland Country Club (Nashville). Republican. Congregationalist. Home: 160 Round Hill Rd Greenwich CT 06831 Office: Sullivan Graphics 225 High Ridge Rd Stamford CT 06905-3000

SULLIVAN, JAY MICHAEL, medical educator; b. Brockton, Mass., Aug. 3, 1936; s. William Dennis and Wanda Nancy (Kelpsh) S.; m. Mary Suzanne Baxter, Dec. 30, 1964; children: Elizabeth, Suzanne, Christopher. B.S. cum laude, Georgetown U., 1958, M.D. magna cum laude, 1962. Diplomate Nat. Bd. Med. Examiners, Am. Bd. Internal Medicine. Med. intern Peter Bent Brigham Hosp., Boston, 1962-63; resident Peter Bent Brigham Hosp., 1963-64, 66-67, chief resident, 1969-70, fellow in cardiology, 1964-66, dir. hypertension unit, 1970-74; Nat. Heart Inst. fellow, 1984, Med. Found. research fellow, 1967; preceptorship in biol. chemistry Harvard U. Med. Sch., Boston, 1967-69; asst. prof. medicine Harvard U. Med. Sch., 1970-74; dir. med. services Boston Hosp. for Women, 1973-74; prof. medicine, chief div. cardiovascular diseases U. Tenn. Coll. Medicine, Memphis, 1974—; vice-chmn. dept. medicine U. Tenn. Coll. Medicine, 1982-85; mem. staff Regional Med. Ctr., Memphis, VA, Bapt. Meml. hosps., U. Tenn. Medical Center-Wm. F. Bowld Hosp., Le Bonheur Children's Hosp., Saint Jude Children's Rsch. Hosp.; fellow Council for High Blood Pressure Research; cons. Nat. Heart, Lung and Blood Inst., 1974—, VA, 1983—. Contbr. articles to sci. jours. Served with M.C., U.S. Army, 1963-70. Fellow ACP, Am. Coll. Cardiology (bd. govs., Pres. Tenn. chpt.); mem. AAAS, Am. Heart Assn. (fellow coun. on circulation, chpt. pres. 1982-83, affiliate pres. 1994-95), Assn. Univ. Cardiologists, Assn. Profs. Cardiology, Internat. Soc. Hypertension, Am. Fedn. Clin. Rsch., Racquet Club Memphis, Sigma Xi, Alpha Omega Alpha, Alpha Sigma Nu. Roman Catholic. Home: 6077 Maiden Ln Memphis TN 38120-3104 Office: 951 Court Ave Rm 353D Memphis TN 38163-2813

SULLIVAN, JEREMIAH DAVID, physicist, educator; b. Norwood, Mass., Nov. 15, 1938; s. Jeremiah Francis and Doris Ellen (Nutton) S.; m. Mary Sheila Bonar, June 12, 1962; children: Maureen Elizabeth, Jeremiah James. B.S., Carnegie Inst. Tech., 1960; M.A. (NSF fellow), Princeton U., 1964, Ph.D. (NSF fellow), 1964. Research asso. Stanford Linear Accelerator Center, 1964-67; acting asst. prof. Stanford, 1966-67; asst. prof. physics U. Ill., Urbana, 1967-69; assoc. prof. U. Ill., 1969-73, prof., 1973—; cons. in field; mem. com. internat. security and arms control Nat. Acad. Scis., 1980-83; A.P. Sloan Research fellow, 1968-70; mem. high energy physics adv. panel ERDA/Dept. Energy, 1975-78. Contbr. numerous articles to profl. jours. Mem. Am. Phys. Soc. (directed energy weapons study group 1985-86), Am. Assn. Physics Tchrs., Fedn. Am. Scientists, Sigma Xi. Home: 604 Burkwood Ct E Urbana IL 61801-5908 Office: JF Kennedy Sch Govt Ctr Sci and Internat Affairs 79 JF Kennedy St Cambridge MA 02138

SULLIVAN, BROTHER JEREMIAH STEPHEN, former college president; b. Boston, June 25, 1920; s. John Joseph and Bridget Claire (Quirke) S. BA, Cath. U. Am., 1943, STL, 1957, STD, 1959; MA in Classics, Manhattan Coll., 1950; MA in Philosophy, Boston Coll., 1955; LLD (hon.), La Salle U., 1979; LHD (hon.), Coll. Mt. St. Vincent, 1987. Tchr. St. Peters High Sch., S.I., N.Y., 1943-48, St. Marys High Sch., Waltham, Mass., 1948-53; instr. theology and classics De La Salle Coll., Washington, 1953-59; asst. prof. theology Manhattan Coll., N.Y.C., 1959-63, assoc. prof., 1963, acad. v.p., 1963-70, exec. v.p.; provost, 1970-75, pres., 1975-87; La Salle provincialate, dir. devel. programs Christian Bros. Acad., Lincroft, N.J., 1988—. Contbr. articles to profl. jours. Chmn. N.Y.C. com. on Ind. Colls. and Univs., 1978-79; chmn. com. on Sci. and Tech., 1981; trustee African Med. Rsch., LaSalle U.; bd. dirs. chmn., FSC Found. Mem. Coll. Theology Soc. (dir., nat. treas. 1960-71), Cath. Theol. Soc. Am., Cath. Bibl. Assn., Nat. Cath. Ednl. Assn., Nat. Cath. Devel. Coun., AAUP, Phi Beta Kappa, Delta Mu Delta. Address: Christian Bros Acad Lincroft NJ 07738

SULLIVAN, JIM, artist; b. Providence, Apr. 1, 1939; s. James Henry, Jr. and Frances Winifred (Welch) S.; m. Marie-Louise Paulson. B.F.A., R.I. Sch. Design, 1961; postgrad., Stanford, 1962-63. Prof. art Bard Coll., Annandale-on-Hudson, N.Y., 1966—. One-man shows Paley and Lowe Gallery, N.Y.C., 1971, 73, Henri Gallery, Washington, 1974, Fischback Gallery, N.Y.C., 1974, Willard Gallery, N.Y.C., 1978, Nancy Hoffman Gallery, N.Y.C., 1980, 82, 84, 86, 88, Foker Skulima Gallery, Berlin, Germany, Anne Jaffe Gallery Bay Harbor Islands, Fla. 1990; exhibited in group shows including, Whitney Mus., Mus. Modern Art, Columbus Gallery Fine Arts, Worcester Art Mus., Corcoran Gallery Art, Washington; pub. collections including Met. Mus., Whitney Mus., Albany State Mus., Wadsworth Atheneum, Philip Morris INc., Owens Corning Coll., Amerada Hess. Recipient Hinda and Richard Rosenthal award Am. Acad. Arts and Letters, 1973; Stanford grantee, 1962-63; R.I. Sch. Design European Honors program Rome, 1960-61; Fulbright fellow, Paris; Fulbright fellow, 1961-62; Guggenheim fellow, 1972-73; grantee Nat. Endowment for Arts, 1982. Home: 59 Wooster St New York NY 10012-4349 Office: Bard Coll Annandale On Hudson NY 12504

SULLIVAN, JOHN, theater administrator. Mng. dir. Am. Conservatory Theatre, San Francisco. Office: Am Conservatory Theatre 30 Grant Ave Fl 6 San Francisco CA 94108-5800

SULLIVAN, JOHN FOX, publisher; b. Phila., Oct. 19, 1943; s. Neil Joseph S. and Mary (Fox) Cullumbine; m. Beverly Knight Lilley, June 10, 1978; stepchildren: Buchanan, Brooke, Whitman, Justin Lilley. BA, Yale U., 1966; MBA, Columbia U., 1968. Staff econ. analyst U.S. Dept. Def., Washington, 1968-69; asst. to pub. Newsweek Internat., N.Y.C., 1970-73, asst. mng. dir., 1974-75; pres., pub. Nat. Jour., Washington, 1975—. Mem. editl. adv. bd. Who's Who. Bd. dirs. Arena Stage. Episcopalian. Clubs: 1925 F Street; Yale (N.Y.C.). Home: 1412 28th St NW Washington DC 20007-3145 Office: Nat Jour 1501 M St NW Washington DC 20005

SULLIVAN, JOHN LOUIS, JR., retired search company executive; b. Macon, Ga., Aug. 27, 1928; s. John Louis and Elizabeth (Macken) S.; m. Barbara Boyle, Aug. 17, 1974; children: John, Katherine, Betsy, Ted. A.B. in Econs., Duke U., 1950; M.B.A., U. Pa., 1957; postgrad. Advance Mgmt. Program, Harvard U., 1975. Br. mgr. IBM, Phila., 1962-63; dep. edn. IBM, Endicott, N.Y., 1963-64; asst. to pres. Data Procesing Div. IBM, White Plains, N.Y., 1965-67; dist. mgr. Data Processing Div. IBM, Washington, 1967-69; mgr. eastern and fed. regions Memorex Corp., 1969-71; v.p. mktg. Infonet div. Computer Sci. Corp., El Segundo, Calif., 1971-75; exec. v.p. Fin. Service Group-ADP Inc., Clifton, N.J., 1975-77; sr. v.p. Heidrick & Struggles Inc., San Francisco and Los Angeles, 1977-82, dir., 1977-82, office mgr., 1979-82; v.p., mng. dir. Korn-Ferry Internat., Los Angeles, 1982-87; v.p., mng. ptnr. Korn-Ferry Internat., Boston, 1987-94; ret., 1994. Bd. dirs., mem. exec. com. March of Dimes, Los Angeles County; bd. regents Mount St. Mary's Coll., Los Angeles. Served with U.S. Army (lt. j.g.) USN, 1950-53. Mem. Harvard U. Bus. Sch. Alumni Assn. (dir.). Democrat. Clubs: Regency (Los Angeles), Bankers (San Francisco), Atheneum (Pasadena), Mission Hills (Rancho Mirage), Calif. Yacht (Los Angeles), Harvard (Boston). Office:

Korn Ferry Internat 101 Federal St Boston MA 02110-1800 also: Korn Ferry Internat 1800 Century Park E Los Angeles CA 90067

SULLIVAN, JOHN MARK, manufacturing company executive; b. Stamford, Conn., June 22, 1935; m. Helen Curtis Sachs, Sept. 6, 1959; children: Kelly Irene, Mark Michael, Kimberly Ann, Kerry Ann. BS in Mktg., NYU, 1959, postgrad., 1959-62. Regional mgr. St. Regis Paper, N.Y.C., 1959-65; dir. sales food div. Squibb-Beech Nut, N.Y.C., 1965-71; mgr. NE div. Gallo Winery, Framingham, Mass., 1971-72; gen. product mgr. Lorrilard div. Loews Internat., N.Y.C., 1972-73; pres. Lego Systems, Inc., Enfield, Conn., 1973-84; chmn., chief exec. officer Prince Mfg., Inc., Princeton, N.J., 1984—. Served with U.S. Army, 1953-55. Named Outstanding Leader, Toy Mfrs. Am.; recipient First Prize Grand Nat. award Antique Automobile Club Am. Mem. Tennis Hall of Fame (dir.), Tennis Industry Council (exec. com.), Am. Tennis Fedn. (bd. dirs., chmn. membership com. 1984—), U.S. Tennis Assn. (mfg. com.). Republican. Roman Catholic. Club: Hartford (Conn.). Home: 43 Rosedale Ln Princeton NJ 08540-2417 also: 440 Prospect St E Longmeadow MA 01028 Office: Prince Mfg Inc PO Box 2031 Princeton NJ 08543-2031

SULLIVAN, JOHN VINCENT, life insurance company executive; b. Malden, Mass., Feb. 11, 1929; s. John Vincent and Jennie Helen (Marshall) S.; student Burdett Coll., 1947-49, Williams Coll., 1968; m. Mildred E. Goddard, Aug. 21, 1971; children—John, Patricia, Richard, Charles, Alyssa. Purchasing clk. City of Revere (Mass.), 1950; office mgr., bookkeeper Monroe Products, Chelsea, Mass., 1951; with John Hancock Mut. Life Ins. Co., Boston, 1951—, assoc. controller, 1966-68, 2d v.p., 1969-74, v.p., 1975-81, sr. v.p., controller, 1982-87, ret., 1987; dir. John Hancock Variable Life Ins. Co.; adviser to Gov.'s Task force on Capital Formation for Econ. Devel., 1976-77. Chmn. fin. com. Town of Saugus (Mass.), 1963-65, treas. Saugus Housing Authority, 1962-64; pres. Saugus PTA, 1961-63. Mem. Life Ins. Assn. Mass. (treas. 1975—, mem. exec. com 1975—, chmn. 1978-79), Mass. Taxpayers Found. (dir.), Blair Industry Tax Discussion Group, Am. Council Life Ins., Life Office Mgmt. Assn. (chmn. panel 1971), Am. Mgmt. Assn. (chmn. and panel mem. at seminar 1973). Home: 37 Lincoln Cir Andover MA 01810-2946 *I am probably more optimistic than most about the outcome of events, but not so much so that I allow things to happen totally by themselves.*

SULLIVAN, JOSEPH B., retired judge; b. Detroit, May 30, 1922; s. Joseph A. and Winifred R. (Bruin) S.; m. Mary Sullivan, June 6, 1946; children: Kathleen (Mrs. Thomas Lewand), Timothy. PhB, U. Detroit, 1947, JD, 1957. Bar: Mich. 1958. Mem. firm Sullivan, Sullivan, Ranger & Ward, Detroit, after 1958; head criminal div. Atty. Gen.'s Office State of Mich., 1963-64; exec. sec. to mayor City of Detroit, 1962, commr. purchasing, 1967-69; clk. Wayne County, 1970-74; judge Wayne County Cir. Ct., 1975-86, Mich. Ct. Appeals, 1986-93; ret., 1993. Mem. Detroit Charter Revision Com., 1970-73, past bd. dirs. Mercy Coll., Detroit. With AUS, 1943-46. Mem. Soc. Irish-Am. Lawyers, Mich. Bar Assn., U. Detroit Alumni Assn., Cath. Lawyers Assn. Democrat. Home: 842 Park Ln Grosse Pointe MI 48230-1853 Office: 900 First Federal Bldg Detroit MI 48226

SULLIVAN, JOSEPH M., bishop; b. Bklyn., Mar. 23, 1930. Ed. Immaculate Conception Sem., Huntington, N.Y., also, Fordham U. Ordained priest Roman Catholic Ch., 1956; consecrated titular bishop of Suliana and aux. bishop of Bklyn., 1980—. Office: Diocese of Bklyn 378 Clermont Ave Brooklyn NY 11238-1002*

SULLIVAN, JOSEPH PATRICK, agricultural product company executive; b. Newton, Mass., Apr. 10, 1933; s. Joseph Patrick and Ruth Ann (Kelter) S.; m. Jeanne Marie Baldi, Oct. 19, 1957; children: Deirdre, Barbara, Mark. B.A. cum laude, Harvard U., 1954, M.B.A., 1956. With Swift & Co., Chgo., 1959-73; pres. Swift Chem. Co., 1972-73, Estech Inc., Chgo., 1973-80; pres., chief exec. officer Swift & Co., Chgo., 1980-83; chmn. bd. Vigoro Industries Inc., Fairview Heights, Ill., 1983—; dir. Vigoro Industries Inc.; mem. bus. adv. com. Coll. Commerce and Bus. Adminstrn., U. Ill. Bd. dirs. Chgo. Opera Theater, Am. Refugee Com.; trustee Mundelein Coll., Chgo. Acad. Scis.; trustee, mem. fin. com. Farm Found., Oak Brook, Ill.; past pres. trustees Latin Sch., Chgo., 1977—; co-chmn. Emergency Task Force for Indochinese Refugees. Served with AUS, 1956-59. Mem. Presidents Assn. Roman Catholic. Clubs: Chicago (Chgo.), Economic (Chgo.), Union League (Chgo.), Saddle and Cycle (Chgo.), Harvard (Chgo.); Harvard (Boston). Home: 6145 N Sheridan Rd Chicago IL 60660-2863 Office: Vigoro Industries Inc 207 West Highway 50 Fairview Heights IL 62208

SULLIVAN, JOSEPH PETER, insurance broker; b. Boston, Sept. 8, 1939; s. Joseph Francis and Mary Anna S.; m. Rachael Anne Cullen, Dec. 22, 1974; children: Philip, Sandra, Susan, Frederick. B Gen. Studies, U. Nebr. 1968; MA, U. No. Colo., 1973, Cen. Mich. U., 1976. Sr. acct. exec. Arkwright Ins., Greenwich, Conn., 1977-83; v.p. Frenkel & Co., N.Y.C., 1983-84; sr. account exec. Republic Hogg Robinson, N.Y.C., 1984-85; v.p. Alexander & Alexander, N.Y.C., 1985-92, Hugh Wood Inc., N.Y.C., 1992-93, Thomas Howell Group, N.Y.C., 1993—; assoc. Miller-Heiman Internat., 1986—; instr. Dale Carnegie and Assocs., 1980-87; adj. prof. ins. The Coll. of Ins., N.Y.C., 1991—. Mem. membership com. Met. Rep. Club; bd. advisors The Salvation Army. With U.S. Army, 1956-77, ETO, Korea and Vietnam. Decorated Bronze Star. Mem. Soc. Human Resource Mgmt., Assn. Former Intelligence Officers (life), Ret. Officers Assn. (bd. dirs. Knickerbocker chpt.), Soc. CPCU's, Am. Soc. CLU's, Nat. Assn. Health Underwriters, Profl. Liability Underwriting Soc., N.Y. Soc. Security Analysts, Soc. Competitive Intelligence Profls., Advt. Club N.Y., Toastmasters, N.Y. Athletic Club, Rotary, Masons, Shriners. Republican. Roman Catholic. Avocations: American history, photography, collecting old photographic prints and antique photographic equipment. Home: 105 Oldfield Rd Fairfield CT 06430-6660 Office: Thomas Howell Group 17 State St New York NY 10004-1501

SULLIVAN, JOSEPH ROBERT, financial service company executive, lawyer; b. Ridley Park, Pa., Jan. 1, 1931; s. Joseph Oswald and Catherine Patricia (McCallen) S.; m. Mary Patricia Gough, Aug. 14, 1954; children: Brian Patrick, Daniel Paul. Bar: Ind. 1963, Tex. 1977. Staff atty. Assocs. Corp. N. Am., South Bend, Ind., 1963-66; govt. relations counsel, 1964-66, asst. v.p. govt. affairs, 1966-72, v.p. govt. affairs, 1972-76; sr. v.p. govt. affairs Assocs. Corp. N. Am., Dallas, 1976—; pres. Tex. Cons. Fin. Assn., Austin, 1982-85; chmn. bd. Consumer Credit Ins. Assn., Chgo., 1986-87, pres., 1985-86. Served to 1st lt. USMC, 1950-57, Korea. Recipient Disting. Service award Am. Fin. Services Assn. Mem. ABA, Tex. Bar Assn., Ind. Bar Assn. Roman Catholic. Home: 1814 Burr Oak St Arlington TX 76012-5601 Office: Assocs Corp of N Am 250 E Carpenter Fwy Irving TX 75062

SULLIVAN, JOSEPH THOMAS, chemical executive, chemical engineer; b. Monroe County, Iowa, Mar. 10, 1940; s. James Leo and Mary Cecelia (Barron) S.; m. Marcia Jean Uttley, May 22, 1965; children: Michael, Paul, Daniel. BS in Chem. Engring., Iowa State U., 1962; PhD, U. Minn., 1966. Mech. supr. Exxon Chem., Linden, N.J., 1966-68; engring. devel. mgr. Gen. Mills Inc., Mpls., 1968-71; with Ciba-Geigy Corp., St. Gabriel, La., Cranston, R.I., Toms River, N.J. and Ardsley, N.Y., 1971-86; sr. v.p. prodn. and tech. services Ciba-Geigy Corp., Ardsley, 1986—; also bd. dirs.; chmn. bd. dirs. Ilford Inc., Paramus, N.J., 1987—. Home: 49 Bittersweet Trl Wilton CT 06897-3902 Office: Ciba-Geigy Corp 444 Saw Mill River Rd Ardsley NY 10502-2600

SULLIVAN, KATHRYN D., geologist, astronaut; b. Paterson, N.J., Oct. 3, 1951; d. Donald P. and Barbara K. Sullivan. BS in Earth Scis., U. Calif., Santa Cruz, 1973; PhD in Geology, Dalhousie U., Halifax, N.S., Can., 1978; Dr. (hon.), Halhousie, Halifax, N.S., Can., 1985, SUNY, Utica, 1990, Stevens Inst., 1992. Astronaut NASA, 1978-93, mission specialist flight STS-41G, 1984, mission specialist flight STS-31, 1990, payload comdr. flight STS-45, 1992; chief scientist NOAA, Washington, 1993—; adj. prof. Rice U., Houston, 1985-92; mem. Nat. Commn. on Space, 1985-86; mem. exec. panel Chief of Naval Ops., 1988—; first Am. woman to perform extra-vehicular activity. Comdr. USNR. Recipient Space Flight medal NASA, 1984, 90, 92, Exceptional Svc. medal, 1985, 91, Outstanding Leadership medal, 1992, Nat. Air and Space Mus. trophy Smithsonian Instn., 1985, Haley Space Flight award AIAA, 1991, AAS Prather Eva award, 1992, Flight Achievement award, 1990. Mem. AIAA, Geol. Soc. Am., Am. Geophys. Union,

Soc. Women Geographers, Explorers Club. Office: Dept Commerce NOAA 14th & Constitution Ave NW Washington DC 20230-0002

SULLIVAN, LAURA PATRICIA, lawyer, insurance company executive; b. Des Moines, Oct. 16, 1947; d. William and Patricia (Kautz) S. BA, Cornell Coll., Iowa, 1971; JD, Drake U., 1972. Bar: Iowa 1972. Various positions Ins. Dept. Iowa, Des Moines, 1972-75; various legal positions State Farm Mut. Auto Ins. Co., Bloomington, Ill., 1975-81, sec. and counsel, 1981-88, v.p., counsel and sec., 1988—; v.p., sec., dir. State Farm Cos. Found., 1985—; sec. State Farm Lloyd's, Inc., 1987—; v.p., counsel and sec. State Farm Fire and Casualty Co., 1988—; v.p., counsel and sec. State Farm Gen. Ins. Co., 1988—, also bd. dirs.; v.p. counsel, sec., dir. State Farm Life and Accident Assurance Co.; v.p. counsel, sec. State Farm Annuity and Life Assurance Co.; sec. State Farm Life Ins. Co.; dir. State Farm Indemnity Co., Bloomington, Ill., 1995—; bd. dirs. Ins. Inst. for Hwy. Safety, Nat. Conf. Ins. Guaranty Funds, chmn., 1995—. Trustee John M. Scott Indsl. Sch. Trust, Bloomington, 1983-86; bd. dirs. Scott Ctr., 1983-86, Bloomington-Normal Symphony, 1980-85, YWCA of McLean County, 1993—; chmn. Ins. Inst. for Hwy Safety, 1987-88. Mem. ABA, Iowa State Bar Assn., Am. Corp. Counsel Assn., Am. Soc. Corp. Secs. Office: State Farm Mut Automobile Ins Co 1 State Farm Plz Bloomington IL 61710

SULLIVAN, LAWRENCE MATTHEW, lawyer; b. Wilmington, Del., Sept. 5, 1937. AB in Philosophy, King's Coll., 1959; LLB, Cath. U. Am., 1964. Bar: U.S. Supreme Ct., Del. 1965, U.S. Dist. Ct. Del. 1966. Pvt. practice, 1965—; asst. county atty., New Castle County, 1966-67; register of wills, New Castle County, 1966-70; pub. defender, State of Del., 1970—; instr. bus. and real estate law, Wilmington Coll., 1976-78, Del. Tech. and Community Coll., 1978-80, Del. State Coll., 1980-82, Brandywine Coll; vice chmn. and mem. various coms. Criminal Justice Coun. Del.; mem. Del. Supreme Ct.'s Planning and Long Range Ct.'s Planning Coms., Del. Supreme Ct. Commn. on Del. Cts. 2000, Del. Agy. to Reduce Crime, Gov.'s Crime Reduction Task Force, Sentencing Accountability Commn., various other coms. Co-author: Delaware Fundamentals of Real Estate, University of Delaware Press, 1980. Sec. Rep. City Com; pres. Active Young Reps. of Wilmington; vice chmn. Young Rep. Nat. Fedn; vice chmn. Moot Ct. Bd. Govs, 1963-64; pres. Student Bar Assn., 1963-64. With U.S. Army, Del. Nat. Guard. Named Del.'s Outstanding Young Rep. of Yr., 1965, Wilmington's Young Man of Yr., 1966, one of Outstanding Young Men of Am., 1968. Mem. ABA, Am. Arbitration Assn., Assn. Trial Lawyers Am., Del. Bar Assn., Del. Trial Lawyers Assn., New Castle County Officials Assns. (pres. 1968-70), Phi Alpha Delta. Office: Sullivan & Bartley 913 Market St Ste 900 Wilmington DE 19801-3552

SULLIVAN, LEON HOWARD, clergyman; b. Charleston, W.Va., Oct. 16, 1922; m. Grace Banks, Aug. 1945; children—Howard, Julie, Hope. B.A., W.Va. State U., 1943, H.H.D. (hon.), 1956; student, Union Theol. Sem., N.Y.C., 1943-45; M.A. in Religion, Columbia U., 1947; D.D. (hon.), Va. Union U., 1956, Dartmouth Coll., 1968, Princeton U., 1969, Yale U., 1971; D.H.L. (hon.), Del. State Coll., 1966; D.Social Scis. (hon.), Villanova U., 1968; LL.D. (hon.), Beaver Coll., 1967, Swarthmore Coll., 1968, Bowdoin Coll., 1968, Denison U., 1968, Gannon Coll., 1969, Temple U., 1969; Ed.D. (hon.), Judson Coll., 1967. Ordained to ministry Bapt. Ch., 1941. Pastor Zion Bapt. Ch., Phila., 1950-88, now pastor emeritus; founder, chmn. bd. Zion Home for Ret., 1960—; Opportunities Industrialization Ctrs. Am., 1964—; Zion Investment Assocs., Inc., Progress Aerospace Inc.; dir. Girard Bank Phila., Gen. Motors Corp. Pres. Internat. Found. for Edn. and Self-Help, 1984—. Named One of Ten Outstanding Young Men Am., U.S. Jr. C. of C., 1955; One of 100 Outstanding Young Men Am., Life mag., 1963; recipient Freedom Found. award, 1960; Russwarm award Nat. Pubs. Assn.; 1963; Edwin T. Dahlberg award Am. Bapt. Conv., 1968; Am. Exemplar medal, 1969; Phila. Book award; Phila. Fellowship Commn. award; Presdl. Medal of Freedom, 1991; Disting. Svc. award Pres. Cote d'Ivoire, 1991.

SULLIVAN, LOUIS WADE, former secretary health and human services, physician; b. Atlanta, Nov. 3, 1933; s. Walter Wade and Lubirda Elizabeth (Priester) S.; m. Eve Williamson, Sept. 30, 1955; children: Paul, Shanta, Halsted. B.S. magna cum laude, Morehouse Coll., Atlanta, 1954; M.D. cum laude, Boston U., 1958. Diplomate: Am. Bd. Internal Medicine. Intern N.Y. Hosp.-Cornell Med. Ctr., N.Y.C., 1958-59, resident in internal medicine, 1959-60; fellow in pathology Mass. Gen. Hosp., Boston, 1960-61; rsch. fellow Thorndike Meml. Lab. Harvard Med. Sch., Boston, 1961-63; instr. medicine Harvard Med. Sch., 1963-64; asst. prof. medicine N.J. Coll. Medicine, 1964-66; co-dir. hematology Boston U. Med. Ctr., 1966; assoc. prof. medicine Boston U., 1968-74; dir. hematology Boston City Hosp., 1973-75; also prof. medicine and physiology Boston U., 1974-75; dean Sch. Medicine, Morehouse Coll., Atlanta, 1975-89, pres., until 1989, 1993—; sec. Dept. of Health and Human Svcs., Washington, 1989-93; non-exec. dir. GM, 1993—; mem. sickle cell anemia adv. com. NIH, 1974-75; ad hoc panel on blood diseases Nat. Heart, Lung Blood Disease Bur., 1973, Nat. Adv. Rsch. Coun., 1977; mem. med. adv. bd. Nat. Leukemia Assn., 1968-70, chmn., 1970; researcher suppression of hematopoiesis by ethanol, pernicious anemia in childhood, folates in human nutrition. John Hay Whitney Found. Opportunity fellow, 1960-61; recipient Honor medal Am. Cancer Soc., 1991. Mem. Am. Soc. Hematology, Am. Soc. Clin. Investigation, Inst. Medicine, Phi Beta Kappa, Alpha Omega Alpha. Episcopalian. Office: Morehouse Sch Medicine Office of the Pres 720 Westview Dr SW Atlanta GA 30310

SULLIVAN, MARCIA WAITE, lawyer; b. Chgo., Nov. 30, 1950; d. Robert Macke and Jacqueline (Northrop) S.; m. Steven Donald Jansen, Dec. 20, 1975; children: Eric Spurlock, Laura Macke, Brian Northrop. BA, DePauw U., 1972; JD, Ind. U., 1975. Assoc. Arnstein, Gluck, Weisenfeld & Minow, Chgo., 1975-76; ptnr. Greenberger and Kaufmann, Chgo., 1976-86, Katten Muchin & Zavis, Chgo., 1986—; adj. prof. Kent Coll. Law, ITT, 1991—. Mem. ABA, Ill. Bar Assn., Chgo. Bar Assn. Avocations: bicycling, cross country skiing, gardening, camping. Office: Katten Muchin & Zavis 525 W Monroe St Ste 1600 Chicago IL 60661-3693

SULLIVAN, SISTER MARIE CELESTE, health care executive; b. Boston, Mar. 18, 1929; d. Daniel John and Katherine Agnes (Cunniff) S. BBA, St. Bonaventure U., 1965. Joined Order Franciscan Sisters Roman Cath. Ch., 1952; bus. mgr. St. Joseph's Hosp., Providence, 1954-62; asst. adminstr. St. Joseph's Hosp., Tampa, Fla., 1965-70, adminstr., 1970-83, chief exec. officer, 1983-93; pres., chief exec. officer Allegany Health Sys., Tampa, Fla., 1994—; coord. health affairs Diocese of St. Petersburg, 1980-93; mem. Fla. Cancer Control and Research Bd., 1980-90; bd. dirs. First Fla. Bank, N.A., Barnett Bank of Tampa; gen. councillor Franciscan Sisters of Allegany, 1984-92. Contbr. articles to profl. jours. Trustee St. Francis Med. & Health Ctr., Miami Beach, Fla., 1986-92; bd. dirs. local chpt. Am. Cancer Soc. Recipient Humanitarian award Judeo-Christian Health Clinic, Tampa, 1977, Athena award Fla. West Coast chpt. Women in Communications, 1978, Exec. Woman of Yr. award Tampa Bay chpt. Network Exec. Women, 1987. Fellow Am. Coll. Health Care Execs. (life); mem. Fla. Hosp. Assn. (trustee 1983-87), Am. Mgmt. Assn., Greater Tampa C. of C. (bd. govs. 1982-87). Democrat. Club: Centre (Tampa) (founding bd. govs.). Home: 2924 W Curtis St Tampa FL 33614-7102 Office: Allegany Health Sys 6200 Courtney Campbell Csway Tampa FL 33607 *I believe success is guaranteed when there is dedication to high standards, when there is respect for the dignity and worth of the human person, and when one believes in the goodness of God.*

SULLIVAN, MARTIN EDWARD, museum director; b. Troy, N.Y., Feb. 9, 1944; s. John Francis and Helen Edna (Lynch) S.; m. Katherine Mary Hostetter, May 9, 1981; children: Abigail, Bethany. BA in History, Siena Coll., 1965; MA in History, U. Notre Dame, 1970, PhD in History, 1974. Exec. dir. Ind. Commn. for Humanities, Indpls., 1972-75; dir. pub. programs NEH, Washington, 1976-81; pres. Inst. on Man and Sci., Rensselaerville, N.Y., 1981-83; dir. N.Y. State Mus., State Edn. Dept., Albany, N.Y., 1983-90, The Heard Mus., Phoenix, 1990—; trustee Am. Indian Ritual Object Repatriation Found., N.Y.C., 1992—; chair U.S. Govt. Cultural Property Adv. Com., 1995—. Author: Museums, Adults and the Humanities, 1981; contbr. articles to profl. jours. Trustee Arizonians for cultural Devel., Phoenix, 1990—; Phoenix Cmty. Alliance, 1991—; Am. Fedn. of Arts, 1994—; mem. Nativ Am. Repatriation Act. Adv. Com., 1992—. With U.S. Army, 1966-68. Mem. Am. Assn. Mus. (v.p. 1990-93, mem. exec. com. internat. com. 1992—). Democrat. Home: 4601 E Solano Dr Phoenix AZ 85018 Office: The Heard Mus 22 E Monte Vista Rd Phoenix AZ 85004-1480

SULLIVAN, MARY MARGARET, state legislator; b. Marlborough, Mass., Sept. 9, 1952; d. Robert Patrick and Eileen Frances (Lawless) S.; m. Donald W. Meals; 1 child. BA in History, Trinity Coll., 1974; MS in Journalism, Boston U., 1979. Legis. asst. Office of Senator Patrick Leahy, 1975-78; reporter News Tribune, Waltham, Mass., 1979-81; reporter, editor News Limited, Sydney, Australia, 1981-82; copy editor Washington (D.C.) Post, 1982-88; legis. aide Office of Senator Doug Racine, Montpelier, Vt., 1989; writer U. Vt. Office of Pub. Rels., Burlington, 1989-91; comm. dir. Vt. Housing Fin. Agy., Burlington, 1991-92; state rep. Vt. State Legis., 1991—. Chair Chittenden County Dem. Com., 1991—; sec. Dem. State Com., Vt., 1991—; bd. dirs. Burlington (Vt.) Cmty. Land Trust, 1992—. Mem. Amnesty Internat. Home: 368 Flynn Ave Burlington VT 05401

SULLIVAN, MARY ROSE, English educator; b. Boston, May 13, 1931; d. John Joseph and Elinor Mary (Crotty) Sullivan. BA, Emmanuel Coll., Boston, 1952; MA, Cath. U. Am., 1957; PhD, Boston U., 1964. Tchr. Woburn Pub. Schs., Mass., 1957-60; faculty Emmanuel Coll., Boston, 1960-66; prof. English U. Colo., Denver, 1966—; mem. book reviewing staff San Diego Mag., 1980-90. Author: Browning's Voices in the Ring and the Book, 1969; co-editor: (3 vols.) letters of E.B. Browning to M.R. Mitford, 1836-54, 1983, Women of Letters: Selected Letters of E.B. Browning to M.R. Mitford, 1987, Crime Classics, 1990, Elizabeth Barrett Browning: Selected Poetry and Prose, 1993; editorial bd. English Lang. Notes, 1970—. Served to capt. USNR, 1952-83. Am. Council Learned Socs. fellow, 1973. Mem. MLA, AAUP, Browning Inst., Denver Woman's Press Club, P.E.N. West U.S.A. Office: U Colo Box 175 PO Box 173364 Denver CO 80217-3364

SULLIVAN, MICHAEL DAVID, state supreme court justice; b. Hattiesburg, Miss., Dec. 2, 1938; s. Curran W. and Mittie (Chambers) S.; m. Catherine Ainsworth Carter; children: David Paul, Rachel Michel, Margaret Elizabeth, Sarah Catherine. BS, U. So. Miss., 1960; JD, Tulane U., 1966; LLM in Jud. Process, U. Va., 1988. Atty. Hattiesburg, Miss., 1967-75; chancellor Miss. Chancery Ct. Dist. 10, 1975-84; justice Miss. Supreme Ct., Jackson, 1984—. Office: Miss Supreme Ct PO Box 117 Jackson MS 39205

SULLIVAN, MICHAEL FRANCIS, III, executive; b. DuBois, Pa., Mar. 11, 1948; s. Michael F. and Mary Jane (Borger) S.; m. Janice Marie Calame, May 30, 1969; children: Courtney, Shannon, Michael IV. BS in English & Speech, Bowling Green State U., 1969; MEd in Curriculum Devel., Wright State U., 1971; EdD in Instructional Technology, Va. Polytech Inst. & State U., 1976. Specialist in instructional design Md. State Dept. Edn., Balt., 1974-80, asst. state supt. in instructional technology, 1980-86; sr. edn. cons. UNISYS Corp., Bluebell, Pa., 1986-87, product mktg. mgr., 1987-88, dir. strategic planning and devel., 1988-90; exec. dir. Agy. for Instructional Technology, Bloomington, Ind., 1990—. Contbr. articles to profl. jours. Office: Agency for Instructional Tech Box A Bloomington IN 47402

SULLIVAN, MICHAEL MAURICE, lawyer; b. Hartford, Conn., Mar. 14, 1942; s. Charles John and Katherine (Moriarity) S.; m. Tina Noel Petro, Oct. 8, 1966; children: Tara Noel, Megan Alexandra. BA in Govt., Fairfield U., 1965; JD, Cath. U., 1972. Bar: N.Y. 1972, U.S. Dist. Ct. (so. and ea. dists.) N.Y. 1972, U.S. Ct. Appeals (2d cir.) 1972. Assoc. Sullivan & Cromwell, N.Y., 1972-75; dir. legal and govt. affairs Allied Stores Corp., N.Y., 1975-78; counsel U.S. div. Singer Co., N.Y., 1978-80; counsel internat. group Singer Co., Stamford, Conn., 1980-84; v.p., gen. counsel ITEC Inc., Huntsville, Ala., 1984—. Contbr. articles to profl. jours. V.P. Internat. Juvenile Diabetes Found., Fairfield, Conn., 1982-84. Served to lt. USN., 1965-69. Mem. ABA, N.Y. Bar Assn., Assn. Bar City of N.Y., Westchester-Fairfield County Corp. Counsel Assn. Avocations: running, tennis, golf. Home: 1321 Chandler Rd SE Huntsville AL 35801-1405 Office: ITEC Inc 520 Green Cove Rd SE Huntsville AL 35803-3012

SULLIVAN, MICHAEL PATRICK, marine officer; b. L.A. Aug. 22, 1933; s. Charles Gardner and Ann (May) S.; m. Nicole Marie St. Germaine; children: Steven, John, Byron. BA, San Diego State U., 1971; MS, Col. Naval Warfare, 1976. Commd. 2d lt. USMC, 1956, advanced through grades to maj. gen.; comdg. officer VMFA-323 and MAWTU USMC, El Toro, Calif., 1973-75, comdg. officer Marine Aircraft Group II, 1980-83; with Group 3A 1st Marine Aircraft Wing USMC, Okinawa, Japan, 1976-77; AVN evaluator Combat Readiness Evaluation System USMC, Washington, 1977-80; comdg. officer Marine Aircraft Group-41, Dallas, 1983-85; comdg. gen., asst. wing comdr. 2d Marine Aircraft Wing MCAS, Cherry Point, N.C., 1985-88; dep. comdr. War Fighting Ctr. Marine Corps Combat Devel. Command Devel. Command, Quantico, Va., 1988-90; dep. comdr. Fleet Marine Force, Atlantic Norfolk, Va., 1990-91; asst. v.p. First Citizens Bank, N.C. Mem. Marine Corps Aviation Assn. (A.A. Cunninghamaward, Aviator of Yr. 1974, Silver Hawk award 1990), Marine Corps. Assn., Marine Corps Mustang Assn., Golden Eagles.

SULLIVAN, MICHAEL PATRICK, food service executive; b. Mpls., Dec. 5, 1934; s. Michael Francis and Susan Ellen (Doran) S.; m. Marilyn Emmer, June 27, 1964; children: Katherine, Michael, Maureen, Bridget, Daniel, Thomas. BS, Marquette U., 1956; JD, U. Minn., 1962. Bar: Minn. 1962, U.S. Dist. Ct. Minn. 1962, U.S. Supreme Ct. 1975, U.S. Ct. Appeals (8th cir.) 1978. Assoc., Gray, Plant, Mooty, Mooty & Bennett, Mpls., 1962-67, ptnr., 1968-87, mng. ptnr., 1976-87; pres., chief exec. officer Internat. Dairy Queen, Inc., 1987—; bd. dirs. The Valspar Corp., Allianz Life Ins. Co. N.Am., Opus U.S. Corp.; instr. U. Minn. Law Sch., 1962-67; lectr. continuing legal edn.; spl. counsel to atty. gen. Minn., 1971-79, 82-84. Contbr. articles to profl. jours. Bd. dirs. Legal Aid Soc. Mpls.; bd. trustees Coll. St. Catherine, St. Paul Sem; bd. govs. Children's Miracle Network; bd. dirs. Met. Mpls.YMCA; pres. Uniform Law Commn. 1987-89. Served with USN, 1956-59. Mem. ABA (ho. of dels., 1984-89), Minn. Bar Assn. (gov. 1974-86), Hennepin County Bar Assn. (pres. 1978-79), Am. Bar Found., Am. Law Inst., Order of Coif. Roman Catholic. Office: Internat Dairy Queen 7505 Metro Blvd Minneapolis MN 55439

SULLIVAN, MORTIMER ALLEN, JR., lawyer; b. Buffalo, Sept. 19, 1930; s. Mortimer Allen Sr. and Gertrude (Hinkley) S.; m. Maryanne Calella, Nov. 20, 1965; children: Mark Allen, Michael John. BA, U. Buffalo, 1954. Bar: N.Y. 1964, U.S. Dist. Ct. (we. dist.) N.Y. 1966, U.S. Dist. Ct. (no. dist.) N.Y. 1967, U.S. Supreme Ct. 1970. Counsel liability claims Interstate Motor Freight System, Grand Rapids, Mich., 1964-82; v.p. J.P.M. Sullivan, Inc., Elmira, N.Y., 1959-67; govt. appeal agt. U.S. Selective Service System, 1967-71; dep. sci. div. Erie County (N.Y.) Sheriff's Office, 1971—, 1986—. Inventor (with others) in field; creator, dir. video depiction JudiVision, 1969; composer High Flight, 1983. Chmn. com. on constrn. and canons Episcopal Diocese of Western N.Y., 1975—; bd. dirs. Erie County Sheriff's Found., Inc., 1987—; bd. dirs. Orchard Park (N.Y.) Symphony Orch., 1975—, v.p., 1977-79, 91-94. With USAF, 1954-57; spl. agt. Air Force Office of Spl. Investigations, 1972-87, col. res. ret. Decorated Legion of Merit. Mem. N.Y. State Bar Assn., Erie County Bar Assn. (chmn. law and tech. com. 1970-81), Transp. Lawyers Assn., Kappa Alpha Soc. Republican. Clubs: Saturn (Buffalo); Wanakah (N.Y.) Country. Avocation: aviation. Home: 888 S Davis PO Box 1003 Orchard Park NY 14127-3917 Office: PO Box 1003 88 S Davis St Orchard Park NY 14127-2651

SULLIVAN, NICHOLAS G., science educator, speleologist; b. Phila., Dec. 20, 1927; s. Edward James and Florence (Delaney) S. BS, Cath. U. Am., 1950; MSc, U. Pitts., 1954; PhD, U. Notre Dame, 1961. Asst. prof. U. Notre Dame (Ind.), 1961-63; asst. prof., assoc. prof. prof. La Salle Coll., Phila., 1963-78, asst. to pres., 1972-74; prof. sci. Manhattan Coll., Riverdale, N.Y., 1979—; vis. prof. U. Alaska, Anchorage, 1961, U. NSW, Sydney, Australia, 1963; chmn. U.S. Deep Caving Team. Author: Speleology, the Study of Caves, 1962; contbr. over 200 articles on speleology to profl. jours. Trustee Gwynedd (Pa.) Mercy Coll., 1963-75, Nat. Speleological Found., Washington, 1985-87. Charles Lindberg Found., 1989—. Fellow Nat. Speleological Soc. (hon. life, trustee 1955-79, pres. 1957-63), Royal Geog. Soc., AAAS, N.Y. Acad. Scis., Explorers Club (pres. 1989-92, trustee 1968—, Explorer's medal Phila. chpt. 1978, Sweeney medal 1979); mem. Sydney Speleogical Soc. (hon. life), South African Speleogical Soc. (hon. life), Rittenhouse Club, Bankstown Sports Club (Sydney).

SULLIVAN, PATRICIA CLARE, hospital administrator; b. Cortland, Nebr., July 2, 1928. R.N. diploma, Mercy Hosp. Sch. Nursing, Denver, 1954; B.S.N., Coll. St. Mary, Omaha, 1955; M.H.A., St. Louis U., 1971, cert.

for internal resources for renewal, 1971; cert. in gerontology, U. Nebr., Omaha, 1976. Instr. Mercy Hosp. Sch. Nursing, Des Moines, 1955-58; dir. Mercy Hosp. Sch. Nursing, 1960-64; nursing supr. pediatrics Mercy Hosp., Des Moines, 1955-58; adminstr. Mercy Hosp., 1977-93; pres. Mercy Health Ctr. of Central Iowa, 1982-93, Mercy Hosp. Med. Ctr., 1993—; Mercy Found., Mercy Health & Human Services, Mercy Properties, ShareCare Ltd, Mercy Geriatric Services; coordinator rural hosp. nursing, nursing supr. ob-gyn Mercy Hosp., Durango, Colo., 1958-60, nursing supr., Williston, N.D., 1964-65; adminstr. St. Joseph's Mercy Hosp., Centerville, Iowa, 1965-69; resident Peter Bent Brigham Hosp., Boston, 1970-71; dir. Cen. Nat. Bancshares, First Interstate Bank Corp. Des Moines (formerly Bancshares), 1979—; in organizational renewal Province of Omaha, 1971-74; dir. community relations Archbishop Bergan Mercy Hosp., Omaha, 1974-77; mem. Province of Omaha Health Services Council, 1958—; provincial chpt. del. Province Omaha, 1970-74. Dir. film depicting tornado strike to Archbishop Bergan Mercy Hosp., 1975, numerous showings, including at Congl. hearing at Pentagon. Del. Mercy Gen. Chpt., 1981—; bd. dirs. Mercy Hosp., Devils Lake, N.D., 1977-81, Sub-Area IV, Iowa Health Systems Agy., 1977—, NCCJ, 1979-85, Health System of Mercy, 1979-83, Grand View Coll., Des Moines, 1982-87, Des Moines Better Bus. Bur., 1983-85; regional rep. Diocesan Pastoral Council, 1978-80; mem. Mercy Health Conf., 1979-83, Iowa Network Mercy Hosps. 1979—, IHA Coun. on Profl. Affairs, 1980—; bd. dirs. Convalescent Home for Children, 1980-84, Health System of Midlands, Omaha, 1984-86, Greater Des Moines Com., 1987—; chair Iowa Caucus Project, 1987-88; mem. pres.'s coun. Iowa State U., 1988—. Recipient Leadership award NCCJ, 1984, People of Vision award Iowa Soc. to Prevent Blindness, 1985; named Adminstr. of Yr. Des Moines Consortium of Family Practice Physicians, 1980-81; named to Iowa Women's Hall of Fame Iowa Commn. on Status of Women, 1988, Equestrian Order of Holy Sepulchre of Jerusalem, 1989. Mem. Nat. League for Nursing, Iowa League for Nursing (pres. 1966-69), Iowa Assn. Bus. Industry, Am. Acad. Med. Adminstrs. (pres. Iowa chpt. 1986-87, Adminstr. of Yr. 1984), Omaha League for Nursing (dir. 1976-77), Am. Hosp. Assn., Iowa Hosp. Assn., Soc. Advancement Mgmt., Des Moines C. of C. (bd. dirs.), Cath. Health Assn. (bd. dirs. 1987-93), Trendleaders of Ryan Club (advisor to chief exec. officers). Office: Mercy Health Ctr Ctrl Iowa Ste 3265 411 Laurel St Des Moines IA 50314

SULLIVAN, PATRICIA W. (TERRY SULLIVAN), real estate trainer; b. Hempstead, N.Y., July 25, 1936; d. Gilbert Hudson and Vera (Morgan) Wehmann; m. Richard J. Sullivan, June 8, 1957 (div. Apr. 1982); children: Katherine Sullivan-Irwin, Gillian Stewart, Adam W. BS, Skidmore Coll., 1958; MS, Syracuse U., 1965. Mgr. Purtell & Wigdale, Inc., Cedarburg, Wis., Merrill Lynch Real Estate, Cedarburg; office mgr. Coldwell Banker Real Estate, Cedarburg; owner, trainer, cons. Terry Sullivan Tng. and Seminars, Cambridge, N.Y., 1991—. Contbr. articles to profl. jours. Named Wis. Cert. Real Estate Brokerage Mgr. of Yr., 1990. Mem. Nat. Assn. Realtors (bd. dirs. 1989-90, Omega Tau Rho award 1983, Outstanding Educator of the Year award for medium states, 1989), Nat. Women's Coun. Realtors (pres. 1990), Women's Coun. Realtors (pres. Milw. chpt. 1982, bd. dirs. 1983-90, named WCR of Yr. 1983, LTG 1985), Ozaukee Bd. Realtors (pres. 1979, bd. dirs. 1977-79, Realtor of Yr. 1979), Realtors Nat. Mktg. Inst. (dir. RS coun. 1983-86, CRS 1978, CRB 1981), Wis. Realtors Assn. (v.p. 1982-83, bd. dirs. 1983-86, Instr. of Yr. 1988, Disting. Svc. award 1992, GRI 1975), Wis. Cert. Residential Specialists (cert.; pres. 1982, Cert. Residential Specialist of Yr. 1983), Wis. Cert. Residential Brokers (cert.; pres. 1988). Address: Terry Sullivan Tng & Seminars RR 2 Little Colfax Rd Cambridge NY 12816

SULLIVAN, PAUL J., legal administrator; b. Little Rock, Mar. 6, 1943; s. Paul J. and Margaret M. Sullivan; m. Deanna M. Ebel, June 20, 1964; children: Kelly, Katie (dec.), Edward. AA, Springfield Coll., 1963; postgrad., So. Ill. U., 1963-64; BS, Western Ill. U., 1990. Acct. Federated Funeral Dirs., Springfield, Ill., 1964-66; sales rep. Burroughs Corp., Quincy, Ill., 1966-74; sales mgr. Burroughs Corp., Peoria, Ill., 1974-77; owner Mid-Ill. Ceramic Supply, Metamora, 1977-85; gen. mgr. Svc. Network Inc., Metamora, 1985-87; legal adminstr. Quinn, Johnston, Henderson & Pretorious, Peoria, 1987—; mem. Ala. Info. Sys. and Tech. Edn. Team, 1993-94; freelance writer. Contbr. articles to profl. jours. Bd. dirs. Germantown Hills (Ill.) Sch. Bd., 1976-78. Mem. Assn. Legal Adminstrs. (nat. editl. adv. bd. 1992-94, pres. Ctrl. Ill. chpt. 1991-92), St. Jude Runner's Assn. (treas. 1991-94), Kiwanis. Republican. Roman Catholic. Avocations: running marathons, Civil War historian. Home: 252 E Audubon Hills Dr Metamora IL 61548-9436 Office: Quinn Johnson Henderson 227 NE Jefferson Ave Peoria IL 61602-1281

SULLIVAN, PAUL WILLIAM, communications specialist; b. Brockton, Mass., Dec. 7, 1939; s. Augustus Henry and Pearl Irene (Chisholm) S.; children: Todd Andrew, Geoffrey Scott, Dustin Raymond; m. Frances Tina Brown, Jan. 23, 1989. BA cum laude, Yale U., 1961; MA, U. Fla., 1971; PhD, So. Ill. U., 1977. Gen. mgr. Chronicle Pub. Co., Stoughton, Mass., 1962-67; editor Easton Bull., N. Easton, Mass., 1963-70; pub., editor Associated Weekly Newspapers, Stoughton, 1967-70; instr. dept. mass comm. Moorhead (Minn.) State U., 1971-73; assoc. prof., chmn. dept. comm. U. Evansville, Ind., 1973-78; prof., chmn. dept. journalism Temple U., Phila., 1978-87; pvt. practice comm. cons. Indian Rocks Beach, Fla., 1986-89; sales tng. cons. Met. Life Ins. Co., 1989-92; pvt. practice comm. and fin. cons. Sullivan Comms., Indian Rocks Beach, 1992—; mem. rev. panel Harry S. Truman Scholarship Found., 1981-86. Author: The Modern Free Press Fair Trial Precedent, 1987, monograph News Piracy, 1978; co-author, editor: The Teaching of Graphic Arts, 1977, The Art of Consulting, 1989; contbr. articles to profl. jours. Mem. Gov.'s Commn. for Pa. Lottery, 1981. Mem. Assn. for Edn. in Journalism and Mass Communications, Soc. Profl. Journalists, Pa. Soc. Newspaper Editors (bd. dirs. 1980-87), Phila. Bar Assn. (media rels. com. 1982-87), ACLU. Avocations: photographer, landscape gardening. Office: PO Box 1049 Indian Rocks Beach FL 34635-1049

SULLIVAN, PEGGY (ANNE), librarian; b. Kansas City, Mo., Aug. 12, 1929; d. Michael C. and Ella (O'Donnell) S. A.B., Clarke Coll., 1950; M.S. in L.S, Cath. U. Am., 1953; Ph.D. (Tangley Oaks fellow, Higher Edn. Act Title II fellow), U. Chgo., 1972. Children's public librarian Mo., Md., Va., 1952-61; sch. library specialist Montgomery County (Md.) public schs., 1961-63; dir. Knapp Sch. Libraries Project, ALA, 1963-68, Jr. Coll. Library Info. Ctr., 1968-69; asst. prof. U. Pitts., 1971-73; dir. Office for Library Personnel Resources, ALA, Chgo., 1973-74; dean of students, assoc. prof. Grad. Library Sch., U. Chgo., 1974-77; assoc. commr. for extension services Chgo. Public Library, 1977-81; dean Coll. Profl. Studies, No. Ill. U., DeKalb, 1981-90; dir. univ. librs. No. Ill. U., 1990-92; exec. dir. ALA, 1992-94; assoc. Tuft & Assocs., 1995—; instr. several grad. libr. edn. programs, 1958-73, UNESCO cons. on sch. librs., Australia, 1970; trustee Clarke Coll., 1969-72; sr. ptnr. Able Cons., 1987-92. Author: The O'Donnells, 1956, Impact: The School Library and the Instructional Program, 1966, Many Names for Eileen, 1969, Problems in School Media Management, 1971, Carl H. Milam and the American Library Association, 1976, Opportunities in Library and Information Science, 1977, Realization: The Final Report of the Knapp School Libraries Project, 1968; (with others) Public Libraries: Smart Practices in Personnel, 1982. Mem. ALA, Cath. Libr. Assn. Roman Catholic. Home and Office: Apt # 816 2800 N Lake Shore Dr Chicago IL 60657 Opportunities to use my abilities in a variety of public services have enriched my life, as I hope the results have enriched and empowered others.

SULLIVAN, PETER M., lawyer; b. Evanston, Ill., Nov. 9; s. Harold W. and Mildred (Dolan) S.; m. Michele H. Chermak, Aug. 30, 1986. BA, U. Notre Dame, 1980; JD, Loyola U., 1983. Assoc. atty. Hinshaw, Culbertson, Moelmann, Hoban & Fuller, Chgo., 1983—. Contbr. articles to profl. jours. Mem. ABA, Ill. State Bar Assn. Roman Catholic. Office: Gibson Dunn & Crutcher 333 S Grand Ave Los Angeles CA 90071

SULLIVAN, RICHARD CYRIL, retired transportation executive; b. Pa., Oct. 25, 1928; m. Harriet Walters, June 13, 1953; children: Elizabeth, Nancy, Richard, Harriet, Matthew. BA in Polit. Sci., Allegheny Coll., 1950; MA in Polit. Sci., U. Pa., 1951; AMP, Harvard U., 1984. Asst. to exec. dir. U.S. Dept. State, Brussels, 1956-59; various positions then dir. pub. affairs Port Authority N.Y./N.J., Phila., 1951-74; v.p. pub. and govt. affairs U.S. Ry. Assn., Washington, 1975-76; various positions, then v.p. resource devel. Consol. Rail Corp., Phila., 1976-93; pres. Ind. Harbor Belt R.R., 1986-92.

Mem. Bd. Edn., Ridgewood, N.J., 1970-73; mem. High Speed Intercity Rail Commn.-Pa., 1982-87. Mem. Soc. Human Resource Mgmt., R.R. Personnel Assn. (exec. com.). Home: 1 Browns Ln Villanova PA 19085-1303

SULLIVAN, ROBERT EDWARD, lawyer; b. San Francisco, May 18, 1936; s. Edward C. S. and Mary Jane (Sullivan); m. Maureen Lois Miles, June 14, 1958 (dec. 1972); children: Teresa Ann, Andrew Edward, Edward Braddock. BS, U. San Francisco, 1958; LLB, U. Calif-Berkeley, 1961. Bar: Calif. 1962. Assoc. Pillsbury, Madison & Sutro, San Francisco, 1963-70, ptnr., 1971—; lectr. bus. law Calif. Continuing Edn. Bar and Practicing Law Inst.; v.p., treas., dir. MPC Ins., Ltd., 1986-93. Contbr. articles to profl. jours. Bd. dirs., exec. com. mem., sec. San Francisco Opera Assn., 1993—. 1st lt. U.S. Army, 1961-63. Mem. ABA, State Bar Calif. (com. corps. 1979-82, chmn. 1981-82, mem. exec. com. bus. law sect. 1982-85, vice chmn. 1983-84, chmn. 1984-85, advisor 1985-86, mem. partnership com. 1990-92, chmn. ltd. liability co. drafting com. 1992-93), San Francisco Bar Assn., Bankers Club San Francisco (bd. dirs.). Democrat. Roman Catholic. Office: Pillsbury Madison & Sutro 235 Montgomery St San Francisco CA 94104-2902

SULLIVAN, RUTH ANNE, librarian; b. Portland, Maine, Jan. 15, 1955; d. Lawrence P. and Mary Louise (Gilman) S.; m. Charles H. Sullivan, May 1, 1982; children: Nora J., Ian J. BA, Wheaton Coll., 1979; MLS, U. Ariz., 1980. Serials ref. Mass. Bay Community Coll., Wellesley, 1980-81; asst. dir. Bristol Community Coll., Fall River, Mass., 1981-86, chief libr., 1986—. Office: Bristol Community Coll 777 Elsbree St Fall River MA 02720

SULLIVAN, SELBY WILLIAM, lawyer, business executive; b. Houston, Oct. 8, 1934; s. John Francis and Lois Blanch (Selby) S.; children: Selby William, Tricia, Lisa, Terry, Jack. B.A., Rice U., 1956; postgrad., Stanford U., 1956-57; LL.B. with honors, U. Tex., 1963. Bar: Tex. 1963, Fla. 1971. Ptnr. Andrews, Kurth, Campbell & Jones, Houston, 1963-72; pres. Fla. Gas Co., 1973-79, chief exec. officer, 1974-79, chmn. bd., 1977-79; exec. v.p., chief fin. and adminstrv. officer, dir., mem. exec. office Continental Group Inc., N.Y.C., 1979-80; ptnr. Maguire Vooris & Wells, Orlando, Fla., 1982-83; owner, chmn., chief exec. officer Hubbard Constrn. Co., 1984-89; chmn. bd. Orange Paving and Constrn. Co., 1984-89, Orlando Paving Co., 1984-89; owner, chmn., pres. Diamond S. Ranch, Inc., Meridian Homes, 1989—; chmn., pres. Summit Land Co., 1989—, Sullivan Investments, 1989—; dir. Sun Banks of Fla., Electric Fuels Corp., Fla. Progress Corp. Bd. dirs. Orange Bowl Com., Rice U., Fla. Bus. Forum, 1974-80; chmn. Rollins Coll. Sch. Bus., 1985-88; vice chmn. bd. dirs. Fla. Coun. 100. Mem. ABA, Fla. Bar Assn., Tex. Bar Assn., Interstate Natural Gas Assn. Am. (dir. 1975-79), Am. Natural Gas Assn. (bd. dirs. 1978-79), So. Gas Assn. (bd. dirs. 1976-79), Fla. C. of C., Interlachen Country Club (chmn., pres., bd. dirs. 1984—), Blind Brook Club, River Club, Beaver Creek Country Club, Country Club of the Rockies (bd. dirs.), Eldorado Country Club, Eagle Springs Golf Club. Home: PO Box 1740 Eagle CO 81631

SULLIVAN, STUART FRANCIS, anesthesiologist, educator; b. Buffalo, July 15, 1928; s. Charles S. and Kathryn (Duggan) S.; m. Dorothy Elizabeth Faytol, Apr. 18, 1959; children: John, Irene, Paul, Kathryn. BS, Canisius Coll., 1950; MD, SUNY, Syracuse, 1955. Diplomate Am. Bd. Anesthesiology. Intern Ohio State Univ. Hosp., Columbus, 1955-56; resident Columbia Presbyn. Med. Ctr., 1958-60; instr. anesthesiology Columbia U. Coll. Physicians and Surgeons, N.Y.C., 1961-62, assoc., 1962-64, asst. prof., 1964-69, assoc. prof., 1969-73; prof. dept. anesthesiology UCLA, 1973-91, vice chair anesthesiology, 1974-77, exec. vice chair, 1977-90, acting chmn., 1983-84, 87-88, 90-91, prof. emeritus, 1991—. Served to capt. M.C., USAR, 1956-58. Fellow NIH, 1960-61; recipient research career devel. award NIH, 1966-69. Mem. Assn. Univ. Anesthetists, Am. Physiol. Soc., Am. Soc. Anesthesiologists. Home: 101 Foxtail Dr Santa Monica CA 90402-2047 Office: UCLA Sch Medicine Dept Anesthesiology Los Angeles CA 90024

SULLIVAN, TERESA ANN, law and sociology educator, academic administrator; b. Kewanee, Ill., July 9, 1949; d. Gordon Hager and Mary Elizabeth (Finnegan) S.; m. H. Douglas Laycock, June 14, 1971; children: Joseph Peter, John Patrick. BA, Mich. State U., 1970; MA, U. Chgo., 1972, PhD, 1975. Asst. prof. sociology U. Tex., Austin, 1975-76, assoc. prof. sociology, 1981-87, dir. women's studies, 1985-87, prof. sociology, 1987—, prof. law, 1988—, assoc. dean grad. sch., 1989-90, 1992—, chair dept. sociology, 1990-92, vice provost, 1994—; asst. prof. sociology U. Chgo., 1977-81; pres. Southwestern Sociol. Assn., 1988-89; mem. faculty adv. bd. Hogg Found. Mental Health, 1989-92; mem. sociology panel NSF, 1983-85. Author: Marginal Workers Marginal Jobs, 1978; co-author: As We Forgive Our Debtors, 1989 (Silver Gavel 1990), Social Organization of Work, 1990; contbr. articles and chpts. to profl. jours. Bd. dirs. Calvert Found., Chgo., 1978, CARA, Inc., Washington, 1985; mem. U.S. Census Bur. Adv. Com., 1989-95, chmn. 1991-92; mem. sociology panel NSF, 1983-85. Grantee NSF, 1983-95, U.S. Dept. Labor, 1983-85, Leadership Tex. 1994. Fellow AAAS (liaison to Population Assn. Am. 1989-91), Sociol. Rsch Assn., Law and Soc. Assn., Am. Sociol. Assn. (sec. 1995—, editor Rose Monograph Series 1988-92), Soc. Study of Social Problems (chair fin. com. 1986-87), Population Assn. Am. (bd. dirs. 1989-91, chair fin. com. 1990-91). Roman Catholic. Avocations: volksportings, sci. fiction. Office: U Tex Office Grad Studies Main Bldg 101 Austin TX 78712

SULLIVAN, THOMAS CHRISTOPHER, coatings company executive; b. Cleve., July 8, 1937; s. Frank Charles and Margaret Mary (Wilhelmy) S.; m. Sandra Simmons, Mar. 12, 1960; children: Frank, Sean, Tommy, Danny, Kathleen, Julie. B.S., Miami U., Oxford, Ohio, 1959. Div. sales mgr. Republic Powdered Metals, Cleve., 1961-65; exec. v.p. Republic Powdered Metals, 1965-70; pres., chmn. bd. RPM, Inc., Medina, Ohio, 1971-78; chmn. bd. RPM, Inc., 1978—; bd. dirs. Pioneer Standard Electronics, Inc., Cleve., Nat. City Bank, Cleve.; dir. Cleve. Clinic Found., Cleve. Trustee Culver (Ind.) Ednl. Found., Cleve. Tomorrow; bd. dirs. Urban Community Sch., Cleve., Malachi House, Cleve., bd. dirs., adv. com. May Dugan Ctr. Cleve. Lt. (j.g.) USNR, 1959-60. Mem. Nat. Paint and Coatings Assn. (bd. dirs., exec. com.), Nat. Assn. Securities Dealers (bd. govs. 1986-88, long-range strategic planning com.). Roman Catholic. Office: RPM Inc 2628 Pearl Rd Medina OH 44256-9099

SULLIVAN, THOMAS JOHN, communications company executive; b. Jersey City, N.J., Apr. 11, 1935; s. Patrick J. and Angel (Minihane) S.; m. Frances D. Gibbons, Oct. 28, 1961; children: Kelly Ann, Thomas J. B.S. in Acctg., St. Peter's Coll., 1957; J.D., Seton Hall U., 1969. With Merck & Co., Inc., Rahway, N.J., 1957-65; mgr. fin. systems McGraw-Hill Info. Systems Co., N.Y.C., 1965-67, budget dir., 1967-68; controller McGraw-Hill Info. Systems, 1968-71, sr. v.p. product devel., 1971-73; v.p. planning systems McGraw-Hill Info., N.Y.C., 1973-76, v.p. fin. analysis, 1976-77, sr. v.p. corp. planning, 1977-83, sr. v.p. exec. asst. to pres., 1983-86, exec. v.p. adminstrn., 1986—. Mem. N.J. Bar Assn., ABA, Fin. Execs. Inst., Nat. Assn. Accts. Office: McGraw-Hill Inc 1221 Ave Of The Americas New York NY 10020-1001

SULLIVAN, THOMAS PATRICK, college president; b. Detroit, July 8, 1947; s. Walter James and Helen Rose (Polosky) S.; m. Barbara Jean Fournier, Aug. 9, 1968; children: Colleen, Brendan. BA in English, U. Dayton, 1969; M. Edn. and Adminstrn., Kent State U., 1971; postgrad., U. Mich., 1988. Tchr. Resurection Elem. Sch., Dayton, Ohio, 1968-69; administr. residence hall Kent (Ohio) State U., 1969-71; program mgr. residence hall Ea. Mich. U., Ypsilanti, 1971-73, adminstrv. assoc., 1973-76, dir. housing, 1976-83; assoc. provost Wayne County Community Coll., Belleville, Mich., 1983-84; dir. budget and mgmt. devel. Wayne County Community Coll., Detroit, 1984-86, sr. v.p. acad. affairs, acting provost, 1986; acting exec. dean Wayne County Community Coll., Belleville, 1986-88; dir. mgmt. and mgmt. devel. Wayne County Community Coll., Detroit, 1988-89; pres. Cleary Coll., Ypsilanti, 1989—; part-time instr. English and math. School-craft Coll., Livonia, Mich., 1980-90. Home: 44954 Patrick Dr Canton MI 48187-2551 Office: Cleary Coll 2170 Washtenaw Ave Ypsilanti MI 48197-1788

SULLIVAN, THOMAS PATRICK, lawyer; b. Evanston, Ill., Mar. 23, 1930; s. Clarence M. and Pauline (DeHaye) S.; divorced; children—Margaret Mary, Timothy Joseph, Kathleen Ann Student, Loras Coll., Dubuque, Iowa, 1947-49; LL.B. cum laude, Loyola U., Chgo., 1952. Bar: Ill. 1952, Calif. 1982. Asso. firm Jenner & Block, Chgo., 1954-62; partner Jenner &

Block, 1963-77, 81—; U.S. atty. for No. Dist. Ill., Chgo., 1977-81. Contbr. articles to profl. jours. Served with U.S. Army, 1952-54. Decorated Bronze Star.; Recipient medal of excellence Loyola U. Law Sch., 1965; Ill. Pub. Defender Assn. award, 1972. Fellow Am. Coll. Trial Lawyers; mem. Am., Ill., Fed. Seventh Circuit, Chgo. bar assns., Fed. Bar Assn., Am. Law Inst., Am. Judicature Soc., Chgo. Council Lawyers. Office: Jenner & Block 1 E IBM Plz Chicago IL 60611-3608

SULLIVAN, TIMOTHY, lawyer; b. Detroit, May 16, 1948; s. Paul Gilmary and Virginia (Rosier) S.; m. Marsha Rosenberg Sullivan, June 19, 1971; children: Eileen A., Hugh V. BA Journalism, U. Mich., 1970; JD, Georgetown U., 1975. Bar: Va. 1975, D.C. 1976. Contract negotiator CIA, Washington, 1973-75; assoc. Fried, Frank, Harris, Shriver & Kampelman, Washington, 1975-78; ptnr. Capell, Howard, Knabe & Cobbs P.A., Washington, 1978-83, Dykema Gossett, Washington, 1983—; lectr. in field. Narrator (audio cassette) How to Negotiate Government Contracts, 1986. Citizen mem. Alexandria Commn. Persons with Disabilities, Va., 1992—. Sgt. U.S. Army, 1970-73. Mem. ABA, Nat. Contract Mgmt. Assn., Univ. Club Washington, Congl. Country Club (bd. dirs.). Roman Catholic. Avocations: reading, sports. Office: Dykema Gossett 1300 I St NW Ste 300 West Washington DC 20005-3306

SULLIVAN, TIMOTHY JACKSON, law educator, academic administrator; b. Ravenna, Ohio, Apr. 15, 1944; s. Ernest Tulio and Margaret Elizabeth (Caris) S.; m. Anne Doubet Klare, Jan. 21, 1973. AB, Coll. William and Mary, 1966; JD, Harvard U., 1969; LLD (hon.), U. Aberdeen, Scotland, 1993. Asst. prof. law Coll. William and Mary, Williamsburg, Va., 1972-75, assoc. prof., 1975-78, prof., 1978-85, Bryan prof. law, dean, 1985-92, pres., 1992—; exec. asst. for policy Office of Gov. Charles S. Robb, Richmond, Va., 1982-85; atty. Freeman, Drapers' Co., London, 1992; vis. prof. law U. Va., Charlottesville, 1981; exec. dir. Gov.'s Commn. on Va.'s Future, Richmond, 1982-84; vice-chmn. Gov.'s Commn. on Fed. Spending, Richmond, 1986; mem. Gov.'s Fellows Selection Com., 1985-90, Gov.'s Commn. on Sexual Assault and Substance Abuse on the Coll. Campus (chmn. enforcement subcom.), 1991-92; counsel Commn. on Future of Va.'s Jud. System, 1987-89. Mem. Va. State Bd. Edn., Richmond, 1991-92; chair Gov.'s Task Force on Intercollegiate Athletics, 1992-93. Decorated Bronze Star. Fellow Am. Bar Fedn., Va. Bar Fedn.; mem. ABA, Va. State Bar, Va. Bar Assn., Bull and Bear Club, Phi Beta Kappa, Omicron Delta Kappa, Univ. Club (N.Y.C., Washington). Democrat. Avocations: wine, swimming, reading. Home: Pres House Williamsburg VA 23185 Office: Coll William & Mary PO Box 8795 Williamsburg VA 23187-8795

SULLIVAN, WALTER FRANCIS, bishop; b. Washington, June 10, 1928; s. Walter Francis and Catherine Jeanette (Vanderloo) S. B.A., St. Mary's Sem. U., Balt., 1947; S.T.L., St. Mary's Sem. U., 1953; J.C.L., Catholic U. Am., 1960. Ordained priest Roman Catholic Ch., 1953; asst. pastor St. Andrews Ch., Roanoke St. Mary's, Star of Sea, Ft. Monroe, 1956-58; sec. Diocesan Tribunal, 1960-65; chancellor Diocese of Richmond, Va., from 1965; rector Sacred Heart Cathedral, Richmond, from 1967; ordained aux. bishop of Richmond, 1970, bishop of Richmond, 1974—. Office: Chancery Office 811 Cathedral Pl Ste B Richmond VA 23220-4801*

SULLIVAN, WALTER J., school system administrator. Supt. Skaneateles (N.Y.) Ctrl. Sch. Recipient Nat. Superintendent of the Yr. awd., New York, Am. Assn. of School Administrators, 1993. Office: Skaneateles Ctrl Sch 49 E Elizabeth St Skaneateles NY 13152-1398

SULLIVAN, WALTER LAURENCE, writer, educator; b. Nashville, Jan. 4, 1924; s. Walter Laurence and Aline (Armstrong) S.; m. Jane Harrison, Aug. 30, 1947; children: Pamela Sullivan Chenery, Walter Laurence, John Harrison. BA, Vanderbilt U., 1947; MFA, U. Iowa, 1949; Litt.D., Episc. Theol. Sem., Lexington, Ky., 1973. Instr. dept. English Vanderbilt U., Nashville, 1949-52, asst. prof., 1952-57, assoc. prof., 1957-63, prof., 1963—; lectr. on pub. TV. Author: Sojourn of a Stranger, 1957, The Long, Long Love, 1959, Death by Melancholy: Essays on Modern Southern Fiction, 1972, A Requiem for the Renascence: The State of Fiction in the Modern South, 1976, In Praise of Blood Sports and Other Essays, 1990, Allen Tate: A Recollection, 1988, A Time to Dance, 1995; co-author: Southern Fiction Today: Renascence and Beyond, 1969, Southern Literary Study: Problems and Possibilities, 1975, Writing From the Inside, 1983; writer, narrator film for pub. TV; author articles. 1st lt. USMC, 1943-46. Ford Found. fiction fellow, 1951-52; Rockefeller Found. fiction fellow, 1957-58. Fellow Fellowship of So. Writers. Roman Catholic. Home: 6104 Chickering Ct Nashville TN 37215-5002 Office: Vanderbilt U Dept English Nashville TN 37235

SULLIVAN, WALTER SEAGER, editor, author; b. N.Y.C., Jan. 12, 1918; s. Walter Seager and Jeanet E. (Loomis) S.; m. Mary E. Barrett, Aug. 17, 1950; children: Elizabeth Anne, Catherine Ellinwood, Theodore Loomis. B.A., Yale U., 1940, H.L.D., 1969; H.L.D., Newark Coll. Engring., 1973; D.Sc., Hofstra U., 1974, Ohio State U., 1977, U. Ala., 1987, Muhlenberg Coll., 1987. Mem. staff N.Y. Times, 1940-87, fgn. corr. Far East, 1948-50, UN corr., 1951-52, fgn. corr., Germany, 1952-56, chief sci. writer, 1960-62, sci. news editor, 1962-63, sci. editor, 1964-87. Author: Quest for a Continent, 1957, White Land of Adventure, 1957, Assault on the Unknown, 1961, We Are Not Alone, 1964, rev. edit. 1993 (internat. Non-Fiction Book prize 1965), Continents in Motion, 1974, rev. edit. 1991, Black Holes, The Edge of Space, The End of Time, 1979, Landprints, 1984; co-author: The New York Times Guide to the Return of Halley's Comet, 1985; editor: America's Race for the Moon, 1962. Served to lt. comdr. USNR, 1940-46, PTO. Recipient George Polk Meml. award in journalism, 1959, Westinghouse-AAAS award, 1963, 68, 72, Am. Inst. Physics-U.S. Steel Found. award, 1969, James T. Grady award Am. Chem. Soc., 1969, Bradford Washburn award Boston Mus. Sci., 1972, Ralph Coats Roe medal ASME, 1975, Sci. in Soc. journalism award Nat. Assn. Sci. Writers, 1976, Disting. Public Service award NSF, 1978, Public Welfare medal NAS, 1980, Walter Sullivan award Am. Geophys. Union, 1989, Disting. Pub. Svc award Conn. Bar Assn., 1990, John Wesley Powell award U.S. Geol. Survey, 1990. Fellow AAAS, Am. Acad. Arts and Scis., Arctic Inst. N.Am.; mem. Am. Geog. Soc. (Daly medal 1973). Office: NY Times Times Sq New York NY 10036-1520

SULLIVAN, WILLIAM BEAUMONT, lawyer; b. Kansas City, Mo., May 12, 1945; s. Raymond Sidney and Georgia Belle (Sykes) S.; m. Donna Ray Daniel, Nov. 25, 1966; 1 child, Georgia Marie. BA, U. Va., 1967; JD, Harvard U., 1970. Bar: D.C. 1970, U.S. Dist. Ct. D.C. 1970, U.S. Ct. Appeals (D.C. cir.) 1970, U.S. Dist. Ct. Md. 1971, U.S. Supreme Ct. 1974, U.S. Ct. Appeals (11th cir.) 1981, N.C. 1990, U.S. Dist. Ct. (mid. dist.) N.C. 1990, U.S. Ct. Appeals (4th cir.) 1990. Assoc. Arent, Fox, Kintner, Plotkin & Kahn, Washington, 1970-77, ptnr., 1978-90, head bankruptcy dept., 1982-90; ptnr., head bankruptcy dept. Womble, Carlyle, Sandridge & Rice, Winston-Salem, N.C., 1990—; mem. Chapt. 7 Trustee Panel, Md., 1988—. Pres., bd. dirs. Atrium Condominium, Rosslyn, Va., 1988—. Fellow Am. Coll. Bankruptcy; mem. ABA, D.C. Bar Assn., N.C. Bar Assn., Am. Bankruptcy Inst., Harvard U. Law Sch. Assn. Avocations: word puzzles, music, golf. Home: 1901 Runnymeade Rd Winston Salem NC 27104-3111 Office: Womble Carlyle Sandridge & Rice 1600 One Triad Pk PO Box 84 Winston Salem NC 27102-0084

SULLIVAN, WILLIAM COURTNEY, retired communications executive; b. Webster Groves, Mo., Aug. 26, 1928; s. William J. and Corinne (Courtney) S.; m. Valerie Blaes, June 20, 1953; children: William C. Jr., Kathleen M., Margaret M. Stonecipher. Student, St. Louis U., 1946-49. J.D. cum laude, 1952. Atty. Southwestern Bell Telephone Co., St. Louis, 1956-58, atty. Mo.-Ill. area, 1958-64, gen. atty. Kans. area, 1964-70, gen. atty. Mo.-Ill., 1970-74, gen. solicitor Mo.-Ill., 1974-75, gen. solicitor gen. headquarters, 1975-84, v.p., assoc. gen. counsel, 1984-91, 1991. Bd. dirs. Sea & Sky Found., Miami, 1985—, Town and Country Police Commn., Mo., 1986—, Corp. Disputes Resolution, Inc., 1990—. Capt. USAF, 1952-55. Mem. ABA, Mo. Bar Assn., Kans. Bar Assn., St. Louis Bar Assn., Bellerive Country Club, The Club, Pelican Bay Country Club. Roman Catholic. Avocations: golf, tennis, reading, sailing, travel.

SULLIVAN, WILLIAM E., public relations executive; b. Janesville, Wis., Dec. 7, 1948. BS, U. Wis., 1971, MA, 1977; MA in Polit. Behavior, U. Essex, England, 1974. Sr. rep. pub. rels. Riker Labs/3M, 1982-83; mgr.

corp. media rels.; pub. rels. Minn. Mining and Mfg., 1983-87; pres. Videocare, 1987-89, Sullivan Comm. Group, Inc., 1989-91, Rowland Co., St. Paul, 1989—; mem. Minn. Motion Picture and TV Bd. Mem. Pub. Rels. Soc. Am., Internat. Pub. Rels. Assn. Sci. Writers. Office: The Rowland Company 420 Summit Ave Saint Paul MN 55102-2624

SULLIVAN, WILLIAM FRANCIS, lawyer; b. San Francisco, May 6, 1952; s. Francis Michael and Jane Frances (Walsh) S.; m. Joanne Mary Nebeling; children: Matthew, Meghan, Kathleen. AB, U. Calif., Berkeley, 1974; JD, UCLA, 1977. Bar: Calif. 1977, U.S. Dist. Ct. (no. dist.) Calif. 1977, U.S. Ct. Appeals (9th cir.) 1977, U.S. Dist. Ct. (ea. dist.) Calif. 1978, U.S. Ct. Appeals (D.C. cir.) 1979, U.S. Ct. Appeals (fed. cir.) 1985, U.S. Dist. Ct. (so. dist.) Calif. 1986, U.S. Dist. Ct. (cen. dist.) Calif. 1990, U.S. Supreme Ct. 1986. Assoc. Chickering & Gregory, San Francisco and Washington, 1977-81; assoc. Brobeck, Phleger & Harrison, San Diego, San Francisco, 1981-84, ptnr., 1984—; panelist Calif. Continuing Edn. Bar; instr. Fed. Practice Program, U.S. No. Dist., chair Litigation sect., 1992—, U.S. Dist. Ct. (no. dist.) Calif., 1980; instr. Coll. of Advocacy, Hastings Law Sch.; adv. bd. AMICUS Info. Svcs. Mem. ABA, Assn. Bus. Trial Lawyers (bd. govs. San Diego chpt. 1993—), Calif. Bar Assn. (litigation sect.), San Francisco Bar Assn., San Diego Bar Assn., Barristers Club San Francisco (bd. dirs. 1984-86, pres. 1985), Calif. Young Lawyers Assn. (bd. dirs. 1986-89, sec. 1987-99, 1st v.p. 1988-89). Democrat. Roman Catholic. Office: Brobeck Phleger & Harrison 550 W C St Ste 1300 San Diego CA 92101-3532

SULLIVAN, WILLIAM HALLISEY, JR., professional football team executive; b. Lowell, Mass., Sept. 13, 1915; s. William H. and Vera F. (Sullivan); m. Mary K. Malone, Dec. 29, 1941; children: Charles W., Kathleen Marie, Mary Jeannie, Nancie Vera, William Hallissey III, Patrick Jerome. A.B., Boston Coll., 1937, postgrad., 1938-39; postgrad., Harvard U. (summer 1938). Publicity dir. Boston Coll., 1938-40; spl. asst. to dir. athletics U. Notre Dame, 1941-42; with U.S. Naval Aviation Tng. Program, 1942-45; dir. pub. relations U.S. Naval Acad., 1946, Boston Braves, 1946-52; owner All Star Sports, Inc., 1952-55; asst. to pres. Met. Coal & Oil Co., Dorchester, Mass., 1955-56; v.p. Met. Coal & Oil Co., 1956-58, pres., 1958-76; group v.p. Met. Petroleum Co., 1977-84; owner New Eng. Patriots Football Club, 1975-88; pres. U.S. Naval Aviation Tng. Program; pres. Am. Football League, 1963-65; chmn. TV com., merger com. Nat. and Am. football leagues; bd. dirs. Brynwood Ptnrs., Air Express Internat., Dana-Farber Inst.; chmn. bd. NFL Properties, Inc.; incorporator Union Savs. Bank. Chmn. Greater Boston Stadium Authority, 1962-64; chmn. Christmas Seal campaign Mass. TB Assn., 1963-64; bd. dirs. Cath. Counseling Svc., Mass. Eye Rsch. Corp., Stonehill Coll.; mem. Pres.'s Coun. Boston Coll. With USNR, 1942-46. Mem. New Eng. Fuel Dealers Assn., Knight of Malta. Clubs: Indian Creek Country, Hundred of Mass. (dir.), Algonquin (Boston), Woodland Golf, Vesper Country, Fort Hill, Oyster Harbors, Atlantis Country Club (Fla.). Office: care New England Patriots Sullivan Stadium RR 1 Foxboro MA 02035

SULLIVAN, WILLIAM JAMES, university president; b. Freeport, Ill., Dec. 20, 1930; s. Arlend Eugene and Bessie (Burton) S. BA in Philosophy, St. Louis U., 1954, M.A. in Philosophy, 1956, Ph.L., 1956; S.T.L., Faculté de Theologie, Lyons, France, 1962; M.A., Yale U., 1966, M.Phil. in Religious Studies, 1967, Ph.D. in Religious Studies, 1971; D.D. (hon.), Concordia Sem. in Exile, 1977. Joined S.J., Roman Cath. Ch. Tchr. classical lang. Creighton Prep. Sch., 1955-58; asst. prof. theology Marquette U., 1967-71; dean Sch. Div., St. Louis U., 1971-75; provost Seattle U., 1975-76, pres., 1976—; bd. dirs. Internat. Fedn. Catholic Univs., 1978-88, Maryville Coll., 1972-75, Am. Council Edn., 1978-81, U. San Francisco, 1976-84; founder, bd. dirs. Wash. Student Loan Guaranty Assn.; trustee Carnegie Found. Advancement of Teaching, 1985—; mem. Wash. State Higher Edn. Facilities Authority, 1984—, Wash. State Math. Coalition, co-chair with Gov. Gardner, 1990—, Wash. State Coalition for Student Svc., 1990—; bd. dirs. U.S. Bank of Wash. Contbr. articles on theology, edn. and cultural topics to profl. jours., popular publs. Bd. dirs. World Without War Council, Seattle, 1978-81; bd. dirs. Seattle United Way, 1979-81, Creighton U., 1982-86, Loyola U. Chgo., 1983-87; chmn. host com. 1990 Goodwill Games, 1986-90. Recipient Edmund Campion award Campion High Sch., 1970; Pope John XXIII award Viterbo Coll., 1979; Brotherhood award NCCJ, 1981; Torch of Liberty award Anti-Defamation League, B'nai Brith; named Seattle First Citizen, 1990. Mem. Assn. Cath. Colls. and Univs. (bd. dirs. 1986—), Nat. Assn. Ind. Colls. and Univs. (bd. dirs. 1983-86), Assn. Jesuit Colls. and Univs. (bd. dirs. 1986—), Wash. Friends Higher Edn., Ind. Colls. Wash., Seattle C. of C. (dir. 1979-82, 88—). Catholic Clubs: Rainier, Seattle Yacht, Columbia Tower (bd. dirs.), University (Seattle). Lodge: Rotary (Seattle). Home and Office: Seattle U Broadway and Madison Seattle WA 98122

SULLIVAN, WOODRUFF TURNER, III, astronomy educator, science historian, researcher, gnomonicist; b. Colorado Springs, Colo., June 17, 1944; s. Woodruff Turner Jr. and Virginia Lucille (Ward) S.; m. Barbara Jean Phillips, June 8, 1968; children: Rachel, Sarah. SB in Physics, MIT, 1966; PhD in Astronomy, U. Md., 1971. Astronomer Naval Research Lab., Washington, 1969-71; postdoctoral fellow U. Groningen, The Netherlands, 1971-73; mem. faculty U. Wash., Seattle, 1973—, prof. astronomy, 1986—; mem. NASA Search of Extraterrestrial Intelligence Group, Ames Rsch. Ctr., Calif., 1980-94. Editor: Classics in Radio Astronomy, 1982, The Early Years of Radio Astronomy, 1984; contbr. articles to profl. jours. Grantee NSF, NASA. Mem. Internat. Astron. Union, Am. Astron. Soc., History of Sci. Soc. Club: Astron. Unit (Seattle). Avocations: hiking, softball, pardating, scrabble.

SULLOWAY, FRANK JONES, historian; b. Concord, N.H., Feb. 2, 1947; s. Alvah Woodbury and Alison (Green) S.; 1 child, Ryan. AB summa cum laude, Harvard U., 1969, AM in History of Sci., 1971, PhD History of Sci., 1978. Jr. fellow Harvard U. Soc. Fellows, 1974-77; mem. Sch. Social Sci. Inst. for Advanced Study, Princeton, N.J., 1977-78; rsch. fellow Miller Inst. for Basic Rsch. in Sci., U. Calif., Berkeley, 1978-80; rsch. fellow MIT, Cambridge, 1980-82, vis. scholar, 1989—; postdoctoral fellow Harvard U., Cambridge, 1981-82, vis. scholar, 1984-89; rsch. fellow Univ. Coll. London, 1982-84; Vernon prof. biography Dartmouth Coll., Hanover, N.H., 1986. Author: Freud, Biologist of the Mind, 1979 (Pfizer award History Sci. Soc. 1980); contbr. numerous articles on Charles Darwin and Sigmund Freud to profl. jours. Fellow NEH, 1980-81, NSF, 1981-82, John Simon Guggenheim Meml. Found., 1982-83, MacArthur Found., 1984-89. Fellow AAAS (mem. electorate nominating com. sect. L 1988-91, 94—); mem. History of Sci. Soc. (fin. com. 1987-92, com. on devel. 1988-92). Home: 18 Traymore St Cambridge MA 02140-2214 Office: MIT Bldg E51-128 Cambridge MA 02139

SULTAN, DONALD KEITH, artist, printmaker; b. Asheville, N.C., May 5, 1951; s. Norman and Phyllis (Galembeck) S.; m. Susan Osborne Reynolds, May 19, 1978; children: Frances Neal, Penn Reynolds. B.F.A., U. N.C., 1973; M.F.A., Sch. Art Inst. Chgo., 1975. Artist, N.Y.C., 1975—; one-man shows include: N.A.M.E. Gallery, Chgo., 1976, Artists Space, N.Y.C., 1977, Willard Gallery, N.Y.C., 1979, 80, Young Hoffman Gallery, Chgo., 1979, Daniel Weinberg Gallery, San Francisco, 1981, Blum Helman Gallery, N.Y.C., 1982, 84, 85, Hans Strelow Gallery, Dusseldorf, Germany, 1982, Akira Ikeda Gallery, Tokyo, 1983, Mus. Contemporary Art, Chgo., 1987, L.A. Mus. Contemporary Art, 1987, Ft. Worth Art Mus., 1988, Bklyn. Mus., 1988, Galena Trauma, Barcelona, Spain, 1992, Meredith Long & Co., Houston, 1992, Knoedler & Co., N.Y.C., 1992; exhibited in group shows: Mus. Modern Art, N.Y.C., 1984, Margo Leavin Gallery, Los Angeles, 1984, Walker Art Ctr., Mpls., 1984, The Bklyn. Mus., 1983, Boston Mus. Fine Arts, 1983, Palacio de Velasquez, Madrid, 1983, Palais Luxembourg, Paris, 1983, Indpls. Mus. Art, 1982, Art Inst. Chgo., 1981, Adelson Galleries, N.Y.C., 1990, Nippon Conv. Ctr., Makuhari Meese, Japan, 1990, Art Inst. Chgo., 1992, Bibliotechque Nationale, Paris, 1992; represented in permanent collections Art Inst. Chgo., Met. Mus. Art of N.Y.C., Mus. Modern Art, N.Y.C., Solomon R. Guggenheim Mus., N.Y.C., Australian Nat. Gallery, Dallas Mus. Fine Art, and others. Creative Artists Pub. Service grantee, 1978-79, Nat. Endowment Arts grantee, 1980-81. Club: Players. Office: Knoedler & Co 19 E 70th St New York NY 10021

SULTAN, TERRIE FRANCES, curator; b. Asheville, N.C., Oct. 28, 1952; d. Norman and Phyllis Ellen (Galumbeck) Sultan; m. Christopher French, June, 1988. BFA, Syracuse U., 1973; MA, John F. Kennedy U., 1985. Exhbn. dir. Source Gallery, San Francisco, 1982-83; adj. curator Oakland

(Calif.) Mus., 1984-85; dir. pub. affairs and pub. programs New Mus. Contemporary Art, N.Y.C., 1985-88; curator contemporary art Corcoran Gallery Art, Washington, 1988—. Author: Representation and Text in the Work of Robert Morris, 1990, Redefining The Terms of Engagement: The Art of Louise Bourgeois, 1944; also exhbn. catalogues. Mem. Am. Assn. Museums, Coll. Art Assn., ArTable. Democrat. Office: The Corcoran Gallery Art 17th St New York Ave N Washington DC 20006

SULTZER, BARNET MARTIN, microbiology and immunology researcher, educator; b. Union City, N.J., Mar. 24, 1929; s. Moses Joseph and Florence Gertrude (Fischer) S.; m. Judith Ray Moreinis, Aug. 26, 1956; 1 child, Steven Bennett. BS, Rutgers U., 1950; MS, Mich. State U., 1951, PhD, 1958. Rsch. assoc. Princeton (N.J.) Labs., Inc., 1958-64; from asst. prof. to prof. microbiology SUNY, Bklyn., 1964-94, prof. emeritus, 1994—, interim chmn. dept. microbiology, 1980-82; vis. scientist Karolinska Inst., Stockholm, 1971-72; vis. prof. Pasteur Inst., Paris, 1979-80; adj. prof. Fels Inst. of Cancer Rsch. and Molecular Biology, Temple U., Phila, 1995—. Assoc. editor Jour. of Immunology, 1983-86; contbr. book chpts. and over 50 articles to profl. jours. on microbiology and immunology; mem. editl. bd. Infection and Immunity, 1980-94. Pres. Tenants Assn. Gateway Plz., Manhattan, N.Y., 1990-92; mem. Cmty. Bd. #1, Manhattan, 1989-94. 1st lt. USMC, 1952-55. Pres.'s fellow Am. Soc. Microbiology, 1957; grantee USPHS, NIH, Office of Naval Rsch., 1967-94. Mem. AAAS, Am. Soc. Microbiology, Am. Assn. Immunologists, N.Y. Acad. Sci., Harvey Soc., Internat. Endotoxin Soc., Reticuloendothelial Soc., Sigma Xi. Achievements include patent for chemical detoxification of endotoxins including immunological and pathophysiological effects; developed first commercial immunological pregnancy test. Office: SUNY Health Sci Ctr 450 Clarkson Ave Brooklyn NY 11203-2012

SULYK, STEPHEN, archbishop; b. Balnycia, Western Ukraine, Oct. 2, 1924; s. Michael and Mary (Denys) S. Student, Ukrainian Cath. Sem. of Holy Spirit, Fed. Republic Germany, 1945-48, St. Josaphat's Sem., 1948-52; Licentia in Sacred Theology, Cath. U. Am., 1952. Ordained priest Ukrainian Cath. Ch., 1952. Assoc. pastor Omaha, 1952, Bklyn., 1953, Minersville, Pa., 1954, Youngstown, Ohio, 1955; pastor Ch. Sts. Peter and Paul, Phoenixville, Pa., 1955, St. Michael's Ch., Frackville, Pa., 1957-61, Assumption of Blessed Virgin Mary Ch., Perth Amboy, N.J., 1962-81; sec. Archeparchy Chancery, 1956-57; adminstr. St. Nicholas, Phila., 1961; archbishop Met. of Ukraine-Rite Catholics of Archeparchy, Phila., 1981—; vice chmn. Priests Senate, 1977-78; bd. dirs. Diocesan Adminstrn., 1972-79; pres. Ascension Manor, Inc.; archbishop Ukranian Rite Caths. Archeparchy Phila., Met. Ukranian-Rite Caths. U.S.A.; chmn. Priest's Senate; chmn. ad-hoc inter-rite com. Nat. Cath. Conf. Bishops/U.S. Cath. Conf., 1991. Mem. Providence Assn. Am. (Supreme Protector), Coll. Bishops of Roman Cath. Ch., Presidium of Synod of Ukranian Cath. Bishops (treas.). Office: Archdiocese of Philadelphia Chancer Office 827 N Franklin St Philadelphia PA 19123-2004*

SUMANTH, DAVID JONNAKOTY, industrial engineer, educator; b. Machilipatnam, India, Jan. 28, 1946; came to U.S., 1972; s. John Devraj and Nancy (David) Jonnakoty; m. Chaya J. Victor, June 26, 1974; children: John J., Paul J. B in Mech. Engring., Osmania U., India, 1967, M in Mech. Engring., 1969; MS in Indsl. Engring., Ill. Inst. Tech., 1974, PhD in Indsl. Engring., 1979. Teaching/research asst. Ill. Inst. Tech., Chgo., 1973-78, instr., 1979; asst. prof. indsl. engring. U. Miami, Coral Gables, Fla., 1979-83, founding dir. productivity research group, 1979—, dir. grad. studies, 1980-83, assoc. prof. indsl. engring., 1983-88, Coll. Engring. coordinator MBA/MSIE, 1984-93; prof. indsl. engring. U. Miami, Coral Gables, 1988—; chmn. 1st and 2d Internat. Conf. on Productivity Rsch., 3d, 4th, 5th Internat. Conf. on Productivity and Quality Rsch. Author: Productivity Engineering and Management, 1984, internat. student edit., 1985, Spanish edit., 1990, Indian edit., 1990, coll. custom series edit., 1994, also instrs. manual, (script) Total Productivity Management, 1985; editor: Productivity Management Frontiers I, 1987, II, 1989, Productivity and Quality Management Frontiers III, 1991, IV, 1993, V, 1995. Recipient over 60 honors, awards and recognitions including YMCA Edn. Gold medal, 1969, Freedoms Found., 1987; fellow U. Miami Eaton Honors Coll., 1986, fellow World Acad. Productivity Sci., 1989; gov.'s appointee as sr. judge Fla. Sterling award, 1992-93, judge, 1993-94, 94-95. Mem. Am. Inst. Indsl. Engrs. (sr. mem., pres. Miami chpt. 1982-83, bd. dirs. 1983-84, nat. indsl. productivity mgmt. 1984—, chairperson rsch. com. 1987, Outstanding Indsl. Engr. of Yr. Miami chpt. 1983, 84); Productivity Ctr. (trustee 1985-89), Internat. Soc. for Productivity and Quality Rsch. (founder 1993, founding pres. 1993-95, chmn. 1995—). Republican. Baptist. Avocations: reading, writing, people. Office: U Miami Productivity Rsch Group Coral Gables FL 33124

SUMARSAM, music educator; b. Bojonegoro, East Java, Indonesia, July 27, 1944; came to U.S., 1972; s. Samidi and Diwati Partoredjo; m. Urip Sri Maeny; children: Tistha, Dwi. Teaching diploma, Indonesian Nat. Music Conserv., Surakarta, 1964; BA, Indonesian Nat. Acad. Music, Surakarta, 1968; MA, Wesleyan U., Middletown, Conn., 1976; PhD, Cornell U., 1992. Tchr. Indonesian Nat. Conservatory of Music, Surakarta, 1966-71; vis. artist dept. music Wesleyan U., Middletown, Conn., 1972-76; artist in residence Wesleyan U., Middletown, 1976-90, adj. assoc. prof. music, 1990-92, adj. prof. music, 1992—; instr. Gamelan, Kasatriyan Jr. High Sch., Surakarta, 1965-69; Indonesian Embassy, Canberra, Australia, 1971-72; asst. lectr. Indonesian Nat. Acad. of Music, Surakarta, 1967-71; 1977 (summer) dir. U. Wis. Gamelan Ensemble, Madison, 1977, 1979; vis. instr. Javanese music, Brown U.; co-dir. Cornell U. Gamelan Ensemble, 1983-84, dir. (spring) 84; vis. instr. Javanese music, Winter Study Program, Williams Coll., Williamstown, Mass., 1991; cons. Art of Indonesia: Tales from Shadow World, 1990, others. Composer: Ladrang Panggayuh, 1968, Gendhing Wulan Sih, 1968, Pambuka and Panutup, 1969, Swimming, 1974, Celebration, 1982, Gendhing Hayu Rahayu, 1982, Comtemplation, 1987; musician and puppeteer since 1952 has performed in Indonesia, Japan, Australia and in many edni. instns. in the U.S; contbr. numerous articles to profl. jours. Recipient scholarships Cornell U., 1983-87. Mem. Soc. for Ethnomusicology, Koninklijk Inst. voor Taal-Land-en Volkenkunde, Soc. for Asian Music, Assn. for Asian Studies, Masyarakat Seni Pertunjukan Indonesia, Internat. Coun. Traditional Music. Home: 516 Millbrook Rd Middletown CT 06457 Office: Wesleyan U Dept Music Middletown CT 06459

SUMAYA, CIRO VALENT, pediatrician, educator; b. Brownsville, Tex., Aug. 1, 1941; s. Jorge Longoria and Irene (Valent) S.; m. Carmen Gonzalez, Apr. 8, 1967; children: Ciro II, Jaimes Andres. BA, U. Tex., Austin, 1962; MD, U. Tex., Galveston, 1966; MPH, M in Tropical Medicine, Tulane U., 1973. Specialist in pediatrics and infectious diseases. Clinical physician health dept. Tb Control, New Orleans, 1972-73; asst. prof. sch. medicine U. Calif., Los Angeles, 1973-74; asst. prof. pediatrics and pathology U. Tex. Health

Sci. Ctr., San Antonio, 1976-77, prof., 1983-94, assoc. dean affiliated programs, continuing med. edn., 1986—; dir. South Tex. Health Research Ctr., 1989—; program dir. Area Health Edn. Ctr. for South Tex., 1990—; adminstr. health resources and svcs. adminstrn. PHS HHS, 1994—; mem. Presdl. Task Force Health Care Reform, 1994. Contbr. articles to profl. jours. Med. liaison Juvenile Diabetes, San Antonio, 1980-82; bd. dirs. San Antonio Library Found., 1985-89. Capt. USAF, 1967-69. Mem. Infectious Disease Soc. of Am., Soc. for Pediatric Research, Soc. of Med. Dirs. of Continuing Med. Edn., Am. Acad. Pediatrics, Am. Soc. for Virology, Mex.-Am. Physicians Assn. of S. Tex. (v.p. 1986-87), San Antonio Pediatric Soc. (sec.-treas. 1985, v.p. 1986, pres.), Phi Beta Kappa, Alpha Omega Alpha. Roman Catholic. Avocations: classical piano, gardening. Office: Health Res & Svc Admin Parklawn Bldg Rm 14-05 5600 Fishers Lane Rockville MD 20857

SUMICHRAST, JOZEF, illustrator, designer; b. Hobart, Ind., July 26, 1948; s. Joseph Steven and Stella Sumichrast; m. Susan Ann Snyder, June 22, 1972; children—Kristin Ann, Lindsey Ann. Student, Am. Acad. Art, Chgo. Illustrator Stevens Gross, Chgo., 1971-72; illustrator Eaton & Iwen, Chgo., 1972-73, Graphique, Chgo., 1973-74; pres. Jozef Sumichrast, Deerfield, Ill., 1975—. Author; illustrator: Onomatopoeia, Q is For Crazy; exhbns. include: 200 Years of Am. Illustration, N.Y. Hist. Soc. Mus., Chgo. Hist. Soc., Finland Lath Mus., Library of Congress, Los Angeles County Mus. Art, Md. Inst. Graphic Art, State Colo. Community Coll., Tokyo Designers Gakiun Coll.; represented in permanent collections: Soc. Illustrators, Chgo. Hist. Soc., Milw. Art Dirs. Club, Phoenix Art Dirs. Club, Columbia Coll., U. Tex., contbr. numerous articles to profl. periodicals. Recipient award for children's book Chgo. Book Clinic, 1978; Gold medal Internat. Exhibition of Graphic Arts, Brazil, 1981; Gold medal Chgo. Artist Guild, 1980, 81; Silver medal N.Y. Art Dirs. Club, 1983; numerous others. Mem. Soc. Illustrators.

SUMME, GREGORY LOUIS, management consultant; b. Ft. Mitchell, Ky., Nov. 25, 1956; s. James Augustine and Mary Elizabeth (McQueen) S.; m. Susan Louise Stevie, Aug. 1, 1981; children: Heather, Erin. BSEE, U. Ky., 1978; MS, U. Cin., 1980; MBA with distinction, U. Pa., 1983. Design engr. Mostek Corp., Dallas, 1980-81; mktg. specialist Gen. Electric Plastics Europe, The Netherlands, 1982; ptnr. McKinsey & Co. Inc., Atlanta and Hong Kong, 1983-90; gen. mgr., comml. motors GE, 1991-93; sr. v.p. and gen. mgr. Allied Signal Avionics, 1993—. Contbr. articles to profl. jours. Alex Proudfoot fellow Wharton Sch., U. Pa., 1981-83. Mem. IEEE, Eta Kappa Nu. Roman Catholic. Avocations: running, squash, golf. Office: Allied Signal Avionics Inc 400 N Rogers Rd Olathe KS 66062

SUMMER, HARRY HARMON, marketing educator and consultant; b. Jackson, Tenn., Apr. 6, 1929; s. Harmon Dewey and Lillian Ruth (Carter) S.; m. Nina Mae Williams, Jan. 7, 1950; children: Lillian Anne, Linda Alice. BBA, Memphis State U., 1958; MS, U. Ill., 1961, PhD, 1966. Cert. sales exec. In sales Fischer Lime & Cement Co., Memphis, 1949-58; prof. Memphis State U., 1961—; v.p., pres. Mktg. Conss., Inc., 1967-76; pres. Research Am., Inc., 1982—; mem. Sales and Mktg. Execs. Internat. Cert. Inst., Cleve., 1986—; vice chmn. bd. trustees, 1993—. Bd. dirs. Mid-South Christian Found., Inc., 1987—. Sgt. U.S. Army, 1952-54. Mem. Am. Mktg. Assn. (chpt. pres. 1977-78). Mem. Church of Christ. Office: Rsch Am Inc 4746 Spottswood Ave Ste 193 Memphis TN 38117-4815

SUMMERALL, PAT (GEORGE ALLAN SUMMERALL), sportscaster; b. Lake City, Fla., May 10, 1931; m. Katherine Summerall; children: Susan, Jay, Kyle. Degree in Education, U. Ark., M. in Russain History. Football player Detroit Lions, 1952-53, Chgo. Cardinals, 1953-57, N.Y. Giants, 1958-61; played briefly in St. Louis Cardinals baseball orgn.; with CBS Sports, 1962—; dir. sports Sta. WCBS-Radio, N.Y.C., 1964-71; host morning program Sta. WCBS-TV, 1964-67; sportscaster early news Sta. WCBS-TV, N.Y.C.; with CBS Radio Network; sportscaster Sports Time, Predictions, Profiles; host CBS Sports Spectacular; lead play-by-play announcer NFL Football coverage CBS Sports, anchor golf and tennis coverage; sports commentator, football analyst Fox Network, 1994—. Named Sportscaster of Yr., 1977. Office: care FOX Network PO Box 900 Beverly Hills CA 90213*

SUMMERFIELD, HERBERT GIBSON, JR., bank executive; b. Newbrighton, Pa., May 29, 1940; s. Herbert Gibson Sr. and Helen Gertrude (Sebring) S.; m. Darla Jeanne Homesley, Aug. 18, 1962 (div. July 1972); m. Martha Maria Beckstein, Oct. 14, 1972. BA, Washington and Jefferson Coll., 1962; JD, Dickinson Sch. Law, 1965. Bar: Pa. 1965. Assoc. Panner, Holland & Autenreith, Beaver, Pa., 1965-70; staff atty. Pitts. Nat. Bank, 1970-72, asst. sec., 1972-74, v.p., group mgr., 1974-85, sr. v.p., div. mgr., 1985—; advisor Buchanan, Ingersoll, Pitts., 1987—; trustee Washington and Jefferson Coll., Washington, 1987—. Author: (with others) Bank Credit, 1981. Served to capt. U.S. Army, 1966-68. Mem. Pa. Bar Assn., Allegheny County Bar Assn. Republican. Clubs: Pitts. Press, Duquesne, Allegheny (Pitts.). Avocations: hunting, fishing. Home: 3006 Hartswood Dr Allison Park PA 15101-3121 Office: Pitts Nat Bank 5th Avenue St Pittsburgh PA 15265

SUMMERFIELD, JOHN ROBERT, textile curator; b. St. Paul, Feb. 21, 1917; s. Isaac and Irene (Longini) S.; m. Anne Benson, July 14, 1945. S.B. in Mech. Engring., MIT, 1938; M.B.A., U. Calif.-Berkeley, 1947, Ph.D. in Econs., 1954. Asst. prof. Sloan Sch. Mgmtg., MIT, 1952-54; br. chief CIA, Washington, 1954-56; project leader The Rand Corp., Santa Monica, Calif., 1956-62; corp. economist Douglas Aircraft Co., Santa Monica, 1962-66; v.p. econ. planning Western Airlines, Los Angeles, 1966-70; staff v.p. econ. planning Pan Am. Airways, N.Y.C., 1970-71; pres. Summerfield Assocs., Pacific Palisades, Calif., 1972-92; vis. curator Fowler Mus. Cultural History, UCLA, 1993—. Co-curator exhbns. of antique Minangkabau ceremonial textiles from West Sumatra, Textile Mus., Washington, 1990-91, Santa Barbara (Calif.) Mus. Art, 1991, Bellevue (Wash.) Art Mus., 1992, Utah Mus. Fine Art, 1992. Served to lt. USNR, 1942-45.

SUMMERFIELD, MARTIN, physicist; b. N.Y.C., Oct. 20, 1916; s. Jacob and Augusta (Tobias) S.; m. Eileen Budin, Aug. 31, 1945; 1 dau., Jacqueline. B.S., Bklyn. Coll., 1936; M.S., Calif. Inst. Tech., 1938, Ph.D., 1941. Asst. chief Air Corps Jet Propulsion Project, Calif. Inst. Tech., 1940-43, chief, rocket research div., 1945-49; chief, rocket devel. div. Aerojet Engring. Corp., Azusa, Calif., 1943-45; mem. subcom. on fuels NACA, 1948-49, subcom. on combustion, 1949-50; prof. jet propulsion Princeton U., 1951-78, prof. emeritus, 1978—; Astor prof. applied sci. N.Y. U., 1978-80; tech. dir. Project Squid, 1949-51; chief scientist Flow Industries Inc., 1975-78; pres. Princeton Combustion Research Labs., 1978-94; editor Aeros. Publ. Program, 1949-52; editor in chief Jour. Am. Rocket Soc., 1951-57; editor Jet Propulsion; also tech. editor Astronautics, 1957-63; editor in chief AIAA series on Progress in Astronautics and Aeros., 1960-90, mem. editorial bd., 1990—; editor in chief Astronautica Acta, 1964-69; cons. U.S. Army Rsch. Office, 1968-71; mem. adv. com. chem. propulsion NASA, 1968-71, Inst. of Aerospace and Astronautics, Cheng-Kung Univ., Tainan, Taiwan, 1985—; chmn. com. on toxicity hazards of materials NRC, 1984-86, mem. com. on energetic materials, 1984-87. Patentee on rocket motors and related devices. Recipient Pendray award, 1954; Wyld award, 1977. Fellow AAAS, AIAA (v.p. 1963-65), Am. Rocket Soc. (pres. 1962-63), Inst. of Advanced Tech., U. Texas, 1991—; mem. Inst. Aeronautics and Astronomy, Internat. Acad. Astronautics, Nat. Acad. Engring., ASME (Heat Transfer award 1978), Internat. Astronautical Fedn. (v.p. 1963-65), Sigma Xi. Office: Martin Summerfield Assoc Inc 6 Marvin Ct Trenton NJ 08648

SUMMERFORD, BEN LONG, retired artist, educator; b. Montgomery, Ala., Feb. 3, 1924; s. Ben Long and Ollie Jo (Gilchrist) S.; m. Christene Morris, Jan. 30, 1951; children: Jeffrey(dec.), Rebecca, James. Student, Birmingham-Southern Coll., 1942-43; B.A., Am. U., 1948, M.A., 1954; student, Ecole des Beaux Arts, Paris, 1949-50. Staff art dept. Am. U., 1950-88, chmn. dept., 1957-66, 70-86, prof. emeritus, 1988—; artist in residence Dartmouth Coll., 1993. One-man shows include, Balt. Mus. Art, Goucher Coll., Franz Bader Gallery, Washington, Jefferson Place Gallery, Washington; one-man show include Phillips Collection, Washington; represented in permanent collection, Watkins Gallery, Phillips Gallery Art, Corcoran Gallery Art, all Washington, numerous group shows of paintings. Served to ensign USNR, 1943-46. Fulbright fellow, France, 1949-50; J. Paul Getty scholar, Phillips Collection, 1990-91. Home: PO Box 2086 Shepherdstown WV 25443-1924 Office: Am U Washington DC 20016

SUMMERLIN, GLENN WOOD, advertising executive; b. Dallas, Ga., Apr. 1, 1934; s. Glenn Wood and Flora (Barrett) S.; student Ga. Inst. Tech., 1951-52; BBA, Ga. State U., 1956, MBA, 1967; m. Anne Valley, Oct. 16, 1971; 1 child, Wade Hampton; children by previous marriage: Glenn Wood III, Edward Lee. Prodn. mgr. Fred Worrill Advt., Atlanta, 1956-65; v.p. sales Grizzard, Atlanta, 1965-74, pres., 1974-94, vice chmn., 1994—. Vice chmn. Polaris dist. Boy Scouts Am., 1967. Vice chmn. Ga. State U. Found., 1974; chmn. distributive edn. adv. com. DeKalb Coll., 1974-76; bd. founders Geo. M. Sparks Scholarship Fund; bd. dirs. Atlanta Humane Soc., 1971—; treas., 1973, 81-82, 84-86, asst. treas. for capital devel., 1987—; mem. steering com. Com. to Honor Hank Aaron, 1982; lay rep. animal care com. Emory U., 1984-85; mem. adv. bd. Families in Action, 1985-86, Soc. Nonprofit Orgns.; bd. dirs. Travelers Aid Metro. Atlanta, 1989-90; mem. Atlanta Sr. Marketers Coun. 100; chmn.'s coun., mem. mktg. adv. com. Crow Canyon Archeol. Ctr., 1993—. Recipient C.S. Bolen award So. Council Indsl. Editors, 1967; named Outstanding Young Man in DeKalb County, DeKalb Jaycees, 1967, Alumnus of Year, Ga. State U., 1973; recipient Direct Mail Spokesman award Direct Mktg. Assn., 1973. Mem. Mail Advt. Svc. Assn. (pres. N.Ga. chpt. 1959-60), Ga. State U. Alumni Assn. (pres. 1966-67), Am. Mktg. Assn. (pres. Atlanta chpt. 1973-74), Ga. State U. Alumni Assn. (pres. 1971-72, dir. 1966-78), Sales and Mktg. Execs. Atlanta (dir. 1969-71), Ga. Bus. and Industry Assn. (bd. govs. 1974-76), Asso. Mail Advt. Agys. (pres. 1975-77), Nat. Soc. Fund Raising Execs. (bd. dirs. Ga. chpt. 1984, cert. 1983), Ga. Arms Collectors Assn. (dir. 1974-76, Pres.'s award 1973), Southeastern Antique Arms Collectors (charter; bd. dirs. 1978—), Tenn. Gun Collectors Assn., Tex. Gun Collectors Assn., Assn. Am. Sword Collectors (charter), Mid-Am. Antique Arms Soc. (charter), Mensa, Soc. Animal Welfare Adminstrs., Travelers Aid of Atlanta (bd. dirs. 1989-90), Am. Humane Assn., Omicron Delta Kappa. Home: 1133 Ragley Hall Rd NE Atlanta GA 30319-2511 Office: Grizzard 1144 Mailing Ave SE Atlanta GA 30315-2500

SUMMERS, ANDY (ANDREW JAMES SOMERS), popular musician; b. Poulton-Fylde, England, Dec. 31, 1942; m. Kate Unter (div.); 1 child, Layla. Attended, UCLA, 1969-73. Performed with Zoot Money's Big Roll Band, Dantalion's Chariot, The Soft Machine, The Animals; worked in bands led by Neil Sedaka, Kevin Coyne, Kevin Ayers, Strontium 90; lead guitarist The Police, 1977-84; solo artist, 1984—; albums: (with The Police) Outlandos D'Amour, 1978, Reggatta De Blanc, 1979, Zenyatta Mondatta, 1980, Ghost in the Machine, 1981, Synchronicity, 1983, The Singles; Every Breathe You Take, 1986; (with Robert Fripp) I Advance Masked, 1982, Bewitched, 1984; (solo) XYZ, 1987, Mysterious Barricades, 1988, The Golden Wire, 1989, Charming Snakes, 1990, World Gone Strange, 1991; film soundtracks: Down & Out in Beverly Hills, 1986, Out of Time, 1988, End of the Line, 1988, Weekend at Bernies, 1989. Office: Private Music 220 E 23d St New York NY 10010*

SUMMERS, ANITA ARROW, public policy and management educator; b. N.Y.C., Sept. 9, 1925; d. Harry I. and Lillian (Greenberg) Arrow; m. Robert Summers, Mar. 29, 1953; children: Lawrence H., Richard F., John S. BA, Hunter Coll., 1945; MA, U. Chgo., 1947. Sr. econ. analyst Standard Oil Co. N.J., N.Y.C., 1947-54; asst. in econs. Yale U., New Haven, Conn., 1956-59; lectr. dept. econs. Swarthmore (Pa.) Coll., 1965-71; sr. economist Fed. Res. Bank Phila., 1971-75, research officer, 1975-79; adj. prof. pub. policy U. Pa., Phila., 1979-82, prof. pub. policy and mgmt., 1982—, dept. chair, 1983-88, co-dir Wharton Urban Decentralization Project, 1987—, sr. scholar Nat. Ctr. on the Edn. Quality of the Workforce, 1991—; expert witness schs. fin. Md., Mass., Va., 1980-85; bd. dirs. Meridian Bancorp Inc., Reading, Pa., William Penn Found., Phila.; chair bd. dirs. Mathomatica Policy Rsch., Inc., Princeton, N.J. Author: Economic Report on the Philadelphia Metropolitan Area, 1985, Economic Development within the Philadelphia Metropolitan Area, 1986, Local Fiscal Issues in the Philadelphia Metropolitan Area, 1987; editor: Urban Change in the United States and Western Europe, 1992; contbr. articles to profl. jours. Chair econ. subcom. Pa. Three Mile Island Commn., Harrisburg, 1979; mem. Lower Merion (Pa.) LWV, 1963-65; mem. Mayor's Econ. Roundtable, Phila., 1984-88; mem. rsch. policy coun., 1992—, Com. for Econ. Devel.; chmn. bd. dirs. Math. Policy Rsch. Inc., 1993—; bd. dirs. William Penn Found., 1993—. Rockefeller Found. resident scholar, Bellagio, Italy, 1986. Mem. Am. Econ. Assn., Assn. for Pub. Policy and Mgmt. (policy coun. 1986), Phi Beta Kappa. Avocations: needlepoint, cooking. Home: 641 Revere Rd Merion Station PA 19066-1007 Office: U Pa Wharton Sch Dept Pub Policy and Mgmt Philadelphia PA 19104

SUMMERS, CAROL, artist; b. Kingston, N.Y., Dec. 26, 1925; s. Ivan Franklin and Theresa (Jones) S.; m. Elaine Smithers, Oct. 2, 1954 (div. Aug. 1967); 1 son, Kyle; m. Joan Ward, May 6, 1974. B.A., Bard Coll., 1951, D.F.A. (hon.), 1974. Tchr. Hunter Coll., Sch. Visual Arts, Haystack Mountain Sch. Crafts, Bklyn. Mus. Art Sch., Pratt Graphic Art Ctr., Cheltenham Twp. Art Ctr., Valley Stream Community Art Ctr., U. Pa., Columbia Coll., U. Calif., Santa Cruz, San Francisco Art Inst., U. Utah, Logan, Art Study Abroad, Paris, Casa de Espiritus Allegres Marfil, Mex., USIS workshop tour, India, 1974, 79. Represented in permanent collections at, Mus. Modern Art, Bklyn. Mus., N.Y. Pub. Library, Library of Congress, Nat. Gallery, Victoria and Albert Mus., London, Bibliotheque Nationale, Paris, Kunstmuseum, Basil, Lugano (Switzerland) Art Mus., Grenchen (Switzerland) Art Mus., Malmo (Sweden) Mus., Los Angeles County Mus., Phila. Mus., Balt. Mus., Seattle Mus., Boston Mus., Art Inst. Chgo., Am. embassies in Russia, Can., India, Thailand, Fed. Republic Germany and Eng.; traveling exhibit, Mus. Modern Art, 1964-66; retrospective exhbn., Brooklyn Mus., 1977, Nassau County Mus. Art, 1990, Belles Artes, San Miguel de Allende, Mex., 1992. Served with USMCR, 1944-48, PTO. Italian govt. study grantee, 1954-55; Louis Comfort Tiffany Found. fellow, 1955, 60; John Simon Guggenheim Found. fellow, 1959; Fulbright fellow, Italy, 1961; Coun. for Internat. Exch. Scholars rsch. grantee, India, 1993-94. Mem. Phila. Print Club. Address: 2817 Smith Grade Santa Cruz CA 95060-9764

SUMMERS, CLYDE WILSON, law educator; b. Grass Range, Mont., Nov. 21, 1918; s. Carl Douglas and Anna Lois (Yontz) S.; m. Evelyn Marie Wahlgren, Aug. 30, 1947; children: Mark, Erica, Craig, Lisa. B.S., U. Ill., 1939, J.D.; LL.M., Columbia, 1946, J.S.D., 1952; LL.D., U. Leuven, Belgium, 1967, U. Stockholm, 1978. Bar: N.Y. 1951. Mem. law faculty U. Toledo, 1942-49, U. Buffalo, 1949-56; prof. law Yale U., 1956-66, Garver prof. law, 1966-75; Jefferson B. Fordham prof. law U. Pa., 1975-90; prof. emeritus, 1990—; Hearing examiner Conn. Commn. on Civil Rights, 1963-71. Co-author: Labor Cases and Material, 1968, 82, Rights of Union Members, 1979, Legal Protection for the Individual Employee, 1989; co-editor: Labor Relations and the Law, 1953, Employment Relations and the Law, 1959, Comparative Labor Law Jour. Chmn. Gov.'s Com. on Improper Union Mgmt. Practices N.Y. State, 1957-58; chmn. Coun. Adv. Council on Unemployment Ins. and Employment Service, 1960-72; mem. Conn. Labor Relations Bd., 1964-70, Conn. Bd. Mediation and Arbitration, 1964-72. Guggenheim fellow, 1955-56; Ford fellow, 1963-64; German-Marshall fellow, 1977-78; NEH fellow, 1977-78, Fullbright fellow, 1984-85. Mem. Am. Arbitration Assn. (nat. chmn.), Internat. Soc. Labor Law and Social Legislation. Congregationalist. Home: 753 N 26th St Philadelphia PA 19130-2429 Office: U Pa Sch Law 3400 Chestnut St Philadelphia PA 19104-6204

SUMMERS, DAVID ARCHIBALD, research mining engineer, engineering educator and director; b. Newcastle-on-Tyne, Eng., Feb. 2, 1944; married, 1972; 2 children. BSc, U. Leeds, 1965, PhD in Mining, 1968. Asst. prof. mining U. Mo., Rolla, 1968-74, assoc. prof. mining, 1974-77, prof. mining, 1977-80, prof., 1980—, sr. investor Rock Mech. & Explosives Rsch. Ctr., 1970-76, dir. Rock Mech. & Explosives Rsch. Ctr., 1976-84, dir. High Pressure Water Jet Lab., 1984—. Recipient Rock Mechanics award Soc. Mining, Metallurgy & Exploration, 1993. Fellow Brit. Inst. Mining Engrs.; Brit. Inst. Mining and Metallurgy, Brit. Tunneling Soc., Cleaning Equipment Mfr. Assn., Water Jet Technol. Assn. (pres. 1986-87); mem. ASME, Am. Inst. Mining, Metall. and Petroleum Engrs., Brit. Hydromech. Rsch. Assn. (hon.). Achievements include research in water jet cutting, surface energy of rock and minerals, novel methods of excavation, cavitation at high pressure, coal mining, geothermal development, strata control. Home: 808 Cypress Dr Rolla MO 65401 Office: U Mo High Pressure Waterjet Lab Rock Mech Facility #213 Rolla MO 65401*

SUMMERS, EDWARD LEE, accounting educator; b. Houston, Aug. 24, 1937; s. Elmer L. and Elizabeth B. S.; m. Kathryn Frances Beke, 1963; children: Michael, Pamela. BA, Rice U., 1959, BSChemE (Hohenthal scholar), 1960; MBA (Univ. fellow), U. Tex., 1962, PhD (Ford Found. fellow), 1965. CPA. Staff acct. Haskins & Sells, Houston, 1962; asst. prof. acctg. Rice U., 1965-68; assoc. prof. Grad. Sch. Bus. U. Tex., 1968-71, prof. Grad. Sch. Bus., 1971—; Arthur Young Disting. prof. acctg. Grad. Sch. Bus., 1977-92, chmn. dept. acctg. Grad. Sch. Bus., 1975-80, grad. adviser acctg. Grad. Sch. Bus., 1980-84, 87-90, Thomas prof. acctg., 1992—. Author: Accounting Information Systems, 1989, revised edit., 1991; (with K.E. Knight) A Study of Knowledge Used in Management Advisory Services by Accounting Profession, 1977, (with R. Hicks) The Aurora Company: An Accounting Systems Case, 1989; contbr. articles, revs. to profl. publs.; editorial bd. Acctg. Rev., 1969-70. Bd. dirs. Univ. Fed. Credit Union, 1983-85, vice chmn. bd., 1984-85. Recipient Best Article award Witte Found., 1970, Distinguished Faculty award U. Tex. Ph.D. Students in Bus. Adminstrn., 1971; Arthur Andersen Faculty fellow, summer 1965; Rice U. grantee, 1967. Mem. AICPA (elected to coun. 1990—), Tex. Soc. CPAs (pres. Austin chpt. 1980-81, CPA of Yr. 1976, Outstanding Acctg. Educator award 1993, pres. elect 1994, 95; mem. editl. adv. bd. 1971-75, v.p. state chpt. 1983-84, exec. com. 1987-90, 94—), Am. Acctg. Assn. (chmn. Southwestern sect. 1968-69), Nat. Assn. State Bds. Accountancy (CPA exam rev. bd. 1986-89), Beta Alpha Psi, Beta Gamma Sigma (pres. U. Tex. chpt. 1969), Pi Kappa Phi. Office: U Tex Austin Dept Acctg Cba 4M # 202 Austin TX 78712

SUMMERS, FRANK WILLIAM, librarian; b. Jacksonville, Fla., Feb. 8, 1933; s. Frank Wesley and Kathleen (Gilreath) S.; 1 son, William Wesley. B.A., Fla. State U., 1955; M.A., Rutgers U., 1959, Ph.D., 1973. Libr. Jacksonville Pub. Libr., 1955, 57; sr. libr. Linden (N.J.) Pub. Libr., 1958-59; dir. Cocoa (Fla.) Pub. Libr., 1959-61; assoc. libr. Providence Pub. Libr., 1961-65; libr. Fla. State Libr., 1965-69; research fellow Rutgers U., New Brunswick, N.J., 1969-70; asst. dean, prof. Coll. Librarianship, U. S.C., 1971-76, dean, 1976-85; dean Sch. Libr. and Info. Studies Fla. State U., Tallahassee, 1985-94, prof., 1994—; lectr. Libr. Sch., U. R.I., 1964-65; libr. surveys in Fla., Ohio, N.Y., S.C., N.C., Ky., Tex. Contbr. articles profl. jours. Mem. R.I. Bd. Library Commrs., 1964-65. Served to lt. (j.g.) USNR, 1955-57. Mem. ALA (exec. bd., v.p., pres.-elect 1987-88, pres. 1988-89), R.I. Libr. Assn. (pres.), S.C. Libr. Assn. (pres.), Assn. Am. Libr. Schs. (pres.), Beta Phi Mu. Home: 505 Live Oak Plantation Rd Tallahassee FL 32312-2335 Office: Fla State Univ Sch Libr & Info Studies 2048 Tallahassee FL 32306-2048

SUMMERS, HARDY, state supreme court justice; b. Muskogee, Okla., July 15, 1933; s. Cleon A. and Fern H. Summers; m. Marilyn, Mar. 16, 1963; children: Julia Clare, Andrew Murray. BA, U. Okla., 1955, LLB, 1957. Asst. county atty. Muskogee County, 1960-62; pvt. practice law Muskogee, 1962-76; dist. judge 15th dist. Okla. Dist. Ct., 1976-85; justice Okla. Supreme Ct., Oklahoma City, 1985—. Sec. Muskogee County Election Bd., 1965-72. Capt. JAGC, USAF, 1957-62. Mem. ABA, Okla. Bar Assn., Okla. Jud. Conf. (pres. 1984). Avocations: fishing, hunting, classical music. Office: Okla Supreme Ct 242 State Capital Bldg Oklahoma City OK 73105

SUMMERS, JAMES IRVIN, retired advertising executive; b. Lexington, Mo., July 10, 1921; s. William E. and Elizabeth (Hoeflicker) S.; m. Priscilla Barstow West, Jan. 15, 1948 (div. 1985); children: Susanne Cornelia, Elizabeth Barstow, James Irvin, Daniel Edward; m. Jane Browning Beckwith, Oct. 4, 1986. With Harold Cabot & Co. Inc., Boston, 1946-86, exec. v.p., 1960-77, pres., chief exec. officer, dir., chmn. exec. com., 1977-86; mem. editorial bd. Sta. WEEI, Boston, 1985-90, also bd. dirs. Mem. exec. com., bd. dirs., v.p., chmn. Pub. Info. Com., Mass. Bay United Way, 1979-84; chmn. Swampscott Rep. Fin. Com., 1964-75; trustee, bd. mgrs., exec. com. Mass. Eye & Ear Infirmary; trustee Family Svc. Assn. Greater Boston, 1952-62; bd. dirs. Mass. Taxpayers Com., 1984-87; pres. Lit. Vols. Mass., 1987-88; pub. rels. bd. USS Constn. Mus., 1988-91. With USAAF, 1941-45. Decorated Bronze Star. Mem. Greater Boston Advt. Club (bd. dirs. 1984-86), Internat. Fedn. Advt. Agys. (bd. dirs. 1985-86), Am. Assn. Advt. Agys. (bd. dirs., treas. 1985-86), New. Eng. Broadcasters Assn. (bd. dirs. 1985-86), Bay Club, Madison Square Garden Club, Tedesco Country Club, Boca Raton Resort and Club. Home: Boca Highlands 4748 S Ocean Blvd PH 3 Highland Beach FL 33487

SUMMERS, JOHN DAVID, art history educator; b. Sandpoint, Idaho, May 28, 1941; s. John J. and Ellen (Harris) S.; m. Nancy Ellen Levine, Mar. 22, 1970; children: Benjamin, Timothy, Mary. AB, Brown U., 1963; MA, PhD, Yale U., 1969. Lectr. Bryn Mawr (Pa.) Coll., 1968-70; from asst. prof. to prof. art history U. Pitts., 1970-81; mem. Ctr. for Advanced Studies U. Va., Charlottesville, 1981-84, William R. Kenan Jr. prof. history of art, 1984—; mem. Inst. Advanced Study, Princeton, 1978-79. Author: The Sculpture of Vincenzo Danti, 1979, Michelangelo and the Language of Art, 1981, The Judgement of Sense, 1986 (M.D. Forkasch prize for best book in intellectual history Jour. History of Ideas 1987); contbr. articles to profl. jours. Recipient Younger Humanist award NEH, 1974-75, Arthur Kingsley Porter prize for articles Coll. Art Assn.,, 1974, 79; Emmy co-nomination for excellence in TV graphics, 1977; Guggenheim fellow, 1981. Home: 1201 Blue Ridge Rd Charlottesville VA 22903-1207 Office: U Va Dept Art Fayerweather Hall Charlottesville VA 22903

SUMMERS, JOSEPH FRANK, author, publisher; b. Newnan, Ga., June 26, 1914; s. John Dawson and Anne (Blalock) S.; B.A. in Math., U. Houston, 1942; profl. cert. meteorology, U. Calif. at L.A., 1943, U. Chgo., 1943; postgrad., U. P.R., 1943-44; M.A. in Math., U. Tex. at Austin, 1947; postgrad. Rice U., 1947-49; m. Evie Margaret Mott, July 8, 1939 (dec. May 1989); children: John Randolph, Thomas Franklin, James Mott. With Texaco Inc., Houston, 1933-42, 49-79, mgr. data processing, 1957-67, asst. gen. mgr. computer svcs. dept., 1967-79, automation cons., 1979-83; pres. Word Lab Inc., Houston, 1983—; instr. math. AAC, Ellington Field, Tex., 1941-42, U. Tex. at Austin, 1946-47. Pres. Houston Esperanto Assn., 1934-39; vol. tutor Thousand Points of Light, 1991—. Capt. AAC, 1942-46. Rice U. fellow, 1947-49. Mem. Assn. Computing Machinery (pres. 1956-58), Nat. Assn. Accts. (past bd. dir.), Am. Petroleum Inst. (mem. data processing and computing com. 1955-59). Author: Mathematics for Bombadiers and Navigators, 1942, Wholly Holey Holy, An Adult American Spelling Book, 1984. Contbg. author: American Petroleum Institute Drilling and Production Practices. Home and Office: 5517 Tilbury Dr Houston TX 77056-2017

SUMMERS, LAWRENCE, under secretary treasury department; b. New Haven, 1954; m. Victoria Summers; 2 daughters (twins), 1 son. SB, MIT, 1975; PhD, Harvard U., 1982. Faculty MIT, 1979-82; domestic policy economist Pres'. Coun. Econ. Advisors, 1982-83; Nathaniel Ropes prof. Harvard U., Cambridge, Mass., 1983-93; v.p. devel. econs., chief economist World Bank, 1991-93; under sec. for internat. affairs dept. U.S. Dept. Treasury, Washington, 1993—. Author Understanding Unemployment; co-author Reform in Eastern Europe; editor series Tax Policy and the Economy; contbr. numerous articles to profl. jours. Recipient John Bates Clark medal, 1993, Alan Waterman award NSF. Fellow Econometric Soc., Am. Acad. Arts and Scis. Office: Dept of the Treasury Under Secretary for Intl Affairs 15th Pennsylvania Ave NW Washington DC 20220

SUMMERS, LORRAINE DEY SCHAEFFER, librarian; b. Phila., Dec. 14, 1946; d. Kenneth William and Hilda Lorraine (Ritchey) Dey; m. F. William Summers, Jan. 28, 1984. B.A., Fla. State U., 1968, M.S., 1969. Extension dir. Santa Fe Regional Library, Gainesville, 1969-71; pub. library cons. State Library of Fla., Tallahassee, 1971-78, asst. state librarian, 1978-84; dir. adminstrv. services Nat. Assn. for Campus Activities, Columbia, S.C., 1984-85; asst. state librarian State Library of Fla., Tallahassee, 1985—; cons. in field. Contbr. articles to profl. jours. Del. Pres.'s Com. on Mental Retardation Regional Forum, Atlanta, 1975; del. Fla. Gov.'s Conf. on Library and Info. Services, 1978, 90. Mem. ALA (orgn. com. 1979-83, council 1982-84, 93—, resolutions com. 1983-85, mem. legislation com. 1993—), Assn. Specialized and Coop. Library Agys. (dir. 1964-82, chmn. planning and organ. com. 1976-80, chmn. nominating com., 1980-81, chmn. by laws com. 1985-86, exec. bd. state library agy sect. 1983-86, pres. 1987-88, chmn. standards rev. com. 1990-92), Southeastern Library Assn. (exec. bd. 1976-80, v.p., elected 1994—), Fla. Library Assn. (sec. 1978-79, dir., 1976-80), Zonta (dir. 1992-95). Democrat. Methodist. Office: State Library Fla Ra Gray Bldg Tallahassee FL 32399

SUMMERS, MAX (DUANNE), entomologist, scientist, educator; b. Wilmington, Ohio, June 5, 1938; s. John Williams Summers and Helen Jane (Rolfe) Summers Kantner; children, Mark William, Keith Dwayne; m. Sharon Braunagel, Dec. 28, 1991. AB magna cum laude, Wilmington Coll., 1962; PhD, Purdue U., 1968. Asst. prof. U. Tex., Austin, 1969-73, assoc. prof., 1973-75; prof. entomology Tex. A&M U., College Station, 1977-83, Disting. prof., 1983—, chair agrl. biotech., dir. Ctr. for Advanced Invertebrate Molecular Scis., Inst. Bioscis. and Tech., 1988—; vis. prof. U. Calif., Berkeley, 1976. Editor Virology Jour., 1983—; exec. editor Protein Expression and Purification; contbr. more than 200 articles to profl. jours.; patentee baculovirus expression vector system. Recipient J.V. Osmun Profl. Achievement award, 1988, President's award of honor Tex. A&M U., 1988, Alumni award Wilmington Coll., 1988; Alumni award Purdue U., 1989, Disting. Alumni award, 1992. Fellow AAAS, Am. Acad. Microbiology; mem. NAS, Am. Soc. for Virology (councilor 1982-85, pres. 1991-92), Am. Soc. Microbiology (lectr. Found. for Microbiology 1986-87), Soc. for Invertebrate Pathology, Genetics Soc. Am., Internat. Com. on Taxonomy of Viruses (exec. com., chair invertebrate virus subcom. 1988-93), Am. Soc. for Biochemistry and Molecular Biology, Entomol. Soc. of Am., Am. Acad. Microbiology, Sigma Xi. Home: 1908 Streamside Way Bryan TX 77807-2715 Office: Tex A&M U Dept Entomology 324 Minnie Belle Heep College Station TX 77843-2475

SUMMERS, ROBERT, economics educator; b. Gary, Ind., June 20, 1922; s. Frank and Ella (Lipton) Samuelson; m. Anita Arrow, Mar. 29, 1953; children: Lawrence Henry, Richard Fredric, John Steven. B.S., U. Chgo., 1943; Ph.D., Stanford, 1956; postgrad. (Social Sci. Research Council fellow), King's Coll., U. Cambridge, Eng., 1951-52. Instr. Stanford, 1949-50; mem. faculty Yale, 1952-59, asst. prof., 1956-59; staff mem. Cowles Found., 1955-59; economist RAND Corp., Santa Monica, Calif., 1959-60; cons. RAND Corp., 1960-80; mem. faculty U. Pa. Wharton Sch., 1959—, prof., 1967—, chmn. grad. group in econs., 1967-70, 73-76. Author: (with Lawrence R. Klein) The Wharton Index of Capacity Utilization, 1966, (with others) Strategies for Research and Development, 1967, (with others) A System of International Comparisons of Gross Product and Purchasing Power, 1975, International Comparisons of Real Product and Purchasing Power, 1978, (with others) World Product and Income, 1982; contbr. articles to profl. jours. Served with AUS, 1944-46. Ford Found. faculty rsch. fellow London Sch. Econs., 1966-67; NSF grantee 1957-59, 63-66, 80-82, 86-88, 89-91, 92-94, 94—; resident scholar Rockefeller Found. Study Ctr., 1986. Fellow Econometric Soc.; mem. AAUP, Am. Econs. Assn., Am. Statis. Assn. Home: 641 Revere Rd Merion Station PA 19066-1007 Office: U Pa Dept Econs Philadelphia PA 19104-6297

SUMMERS, ROBERT SAMUEL, lawyer, author, educator; b. Halfway, Oreg., Sept. 19, 1933; s. Orson William and Estella Bell (Robertson) S.; m. Dorothy Millicent Kopp, June 14, 1955; children: Brent, William, Thomas, Elizabeth, Robert. BS in Polit. Sci., U. Oreg., 1955; postgrad. (Fulbright scholar), U. Southampton, Eng., 1955-56; LLB, Harvard U., 1959; postgrad. rsch., Oxford U., 1964-65, 74-75, 81-82, 88-89; LLD (hon.), U. Helsinki, Finland, 1990, U. Göttingen, Germany, 1994. Bar: Oreg. 1959, N.Y. 1974. Asso. King, Miller, Anderson, Nash and Yerke, Portland, Oreg., 1959-60; asst. prof. law U. Oreg., 1960-63, asso. prof., 1964-68; vis. asso. prof. law Stanford U., 1963-64; prof. U. Oreg., 1968-69; prof. Cornell U., 1969-76, McRoberts prof. law, 1976—; summer vis. prof. Ind. U., 1969, U. Mich., 1974, U. Warwick, Eng., 1975, Australia Nat. U., U. Sydney, Australia, 1977; vis. prof. U. Vienna, Austria, 1985; Goodhart vis. prof. Cambridge U., Eng., 1991-92; H. Hurst Eminent vis. scholar U. Fla., 1995; rsch. fellow Merton Coll., Oxford U., 1981-82, Exeter Coll., Oxford U., 1988-89; cons. Cornell Law Project in public schs., N.Y., 1969-74, Law in Am. Soc. project Chgo. Bd. Edn., 1968-69; instr. Nat. Acad. Jud. Edn., 1976—; mem. faculty Salzburg Seminar in Am. Studies, 1990; ofcl. advisor Drafting Commn. on New Civil Code for Russian Fedn., 1994-95. Author: Law, Its Nature, Functions and Limits, 1986, (with Hubbard and Campbell) Justice and Order Through Law, 1973, (with Bozzone and Campbell) The American Legal System, 1973, (with Speidel and White) Teaching Materials on Commercial Transactions, 1987, Collective Bargaining and Public Benefit Conferral—A Jurisprudential Critique, 1976, The Uniform Commercial Code, 1988, (with White) Het Pramatisch Instrumentalisme, 1981, Instrumentalism and American Legal Theory, 1982, Lon L. Fuller—Life and Work, 1984, (with Atiyah) Form and Substance in Anglo-American Law, 1987, (with Hillman) Contract and Related Obligation, 1987, (with MacCormick and others) Interpreting Statutes—A Comparative Study, 1991, Nature of Law and Legal Reasoning, 1993; contbr. book revs. and articles to profl. jours.; editor: Essays in Legal Philosophy, vol. 1, 1968, vol. 2, 1971. Social Sci. Research Council fellow, 1964-65. Mem. Am. Law Inst., Assn. Am. Law Schs. (chmn. sect. jurisprudence 1972-73), Am. Soc. Polit. and Legal Philosophy (v.p. 1976-78), Internat. Assn. of Legal and Social Philosophy Am. Soc. (pres. 1989-91), Phi Beta Kappa. Republican. Congregationalist. Office: Cornell U Sch Law Myron Taylor Hall Ithaca NY 14853

SUMMERS, WILLIAM COFIELD, science educator; b. Janesville, Wis., Apr. 17, 1939; s. Crosby Hungerford and Rebecca Delores (Cofield) S.; m. Wilma Jean Poos, July 24, 1965; 1 child, Emily Alexandra. BS, U. Wis., 1961, MS, 1963, Phd, MD, 1967; MA, Yale U., 1977. Post-doctoral fellow MIT, Cambridge, Mass., 1967-68; asst. prof. Yale U., New Haven, 1968-70, assoc. prof., 1970-77, prof., 1977—; cons. NIH, Bethesda, Md., 1976—. Editor Nucleic Acids Research Jour., 1977-79, Gene jour., 1984-91; contbr. articles to profl. jours. Cons. Anna Fuller Fund, New Haven, 1973-88, Searle Scholars Program, Chgo., 1980-84; trustee Leukemia Soc. Am., N.Y.C., 1981-85, Yale-China Assn., New Haven, 1982-88, 94—. Mem. Am. Soc. Biochemistry and Molecular Biology, Am. Soc. for Microbiology, History Sci. Soc., Am. Assn. Hist. Medicine. Office: Yale U Sch Medicine 333 Cedar St New Haven CT 06520-8040

SUMMERSELL, FRANCES SHARPLEY, organization worker; b. Birmingham, Ala.; d. Arthur Croft and Thomas O. (Stone) Sharpley; m. Charles Grayson Summersell, Nov. 10, 1934. Student U. Montevallo, Peabody Coll. Ptnr., artist, writer Assoc. Educators, 1959—. Vice chmn. Ft. Morgan Hist. Commn., 1959-63; active DAR, Magna Charta Dames, U. Women's Club (pres. 1957-58), Daus. Am. Colonists (organizing regent Tuscaloosa 1956-63). Recipient Algernon Sidney Sullivan award U. Ala., 1994. Mem. Tuscaloosa County Preservation Soc. (trustee 1965-78, exec. award 1975), Birmingham-Jefferson Hist. Soc., Ala. Hist. Assn. (exec. bd. Ala. Review 1991—), Omicron Delta Kappa, Iota Circle, Anderson Soc. Clubs: University (Tuscaloosa). Co-author: Alabama History Filmstrips, 1961; Florida History Filmstrips, 1963; Texas History Filmstrips, 1965-66; Ohio History Filmstrips, 1967 (Merit award Am. Assn. State and Local History 1968); California History Filmstrips, 1968; Illinois History Filmstrips, 1970. Home: 1411 Caplewood Dr Tuscaloosa AL 35401-1131

SUMMERSETT, JAMES A., III, health care executive, hospital administrator; b. San Antonio, Jan. 11, 1957; s. James A. Jr. and Mary Joan (Becker) S.; m. Allison Elaine Fink, May 30, 1981; children: James A. IV, Anna Rebekah, Andrew Becker. BSBA, Trinity U., San Antonio, 1978; MS in Hosp. and Health Adminstrn., U. Ala., Birmingham, 1980. Adminstr. George W. Truett Meml. Hosp., Baylor U. Med. Ctr., Dallas, 1980-84; exec. dir. Baylor Med. Ctr. at Gilmer (Tex.), 1984—. Bd. dirs. Upshur County United Way, 1984—; campaign chmn., 1986, pres., 1987; bd. dirs. Upshur County unit Am. Cancer Soc., 1985—; East Tex. Yamboree Assn. 1988-89; deacon, dir. adult dept. Sunday sch., mem. com. on coms. lst Bapt. Ch., Gilmer, 1986—; bd. dirs. Gilmer Indsl. Found., 1986—, v.p., 1988—; bd. dirs. Gilmer Civic Ctr. Found., 1988—, v.p., 1988—. Mem. Am. Hosp. Assn., Am. Coll. Healthcare Execs., Tex. Hosp. Assn. (small careers com. 1986-87), Upshur County C. of C. (membership com. 1987-88, civic affairs com. 1988—), U. Ala. at Birmingham Grad. Program Hosp. and Health Adminstrn. Alumni Assn., Rotary (dir. vocat. svc. Gilmer 1985-87, Paul Harris fellow 1988). Republican. Avocations: flying, hot air ballooning, hunting, camping, racquetball. Home: 2107 H Cassia Circle Kissimmee FL 34741 Office: Conway Reg Med Ctr 2302 College Ave Conway AR 72032

SUMMERTREE, KATONAH See WINDSOR, PATRICIA

SUMMERVILLE, DAVID, pediatrician, chemist. Pediatrician Children's Hosp., Boston. Office: Children's Hosp Boston MA 02202

SUMMITT, (WILLIAM) ROBERT, chemist, educator; b. Flint, Mich., Dec. 6, 1935; s. William Fletcher and Jessie Louise (Tilson) S.; m. Nancy Jo Holland, Apr. 2, 1956; children: Elizabeth Louise, David Stanley. A.S., Flint Jr. Coll., 1955; B.S. in Chemistry, U. Mich., 1957; Ph.D., Purdue U., 1961. Research asso.; instr. chemistry Mich. State U., 1961-62, asst. prof. metallurgy, mechs. and materials, 1965-68, asso. prof., 1968-73, chmn. dept. metallurgy mechs. and materials sci., 1972-78, prof., 1973-92, prof. emeritus, 1992; research chemist Corning Glass Works, 1962-65; cons. in field. NRC Sr. Research asso. Air Force Materials Lab., Fairborn, Ohio, 1974-75. Research, publs. in corrosion, failure analysis, optical properties of materials, spectroscopy, and color sci. Mem. ASTM, Am. Chem. Soc., Am. Phys. Soc., Am. Soc. Metals, Nat. Assn. Corrosion Engrs., Sigma Xi. Home: RR4 8535 Clough Dr Grayling MI 49738 Office: Dept Materials Sci & Mechs Michigan State Univ East Lansing MI 48824

SUMMITT, ROBERT LAYMAN, pediatrician, educator; b. Knoxville, Tenn., Dec. 23, 1932; s. Robert Luther and Mary Ruth (Layman) S.; m. Joyce Ann Sharp, Dec. 23, 1955; children: Robert Layman Jr., Susan Kelly Summitt Pridgen, John Blair. Student, Davidson Coll., 1950-51; MD, U. Tenn., 1955, MS in Pediatrics, 1962. Diplomate Am. Bd. Pediatrics, recert. in pediatrics, 1983, 92, Am. Bd. Med. Genetics (bd. dirs. 1985-89). Rotating intern U. Tenn. Meml. Research Ctr. and Hosp., Knoxville, 1956; asst. resident in pediatrics U. Tenn. Coll. Medicine and City of Memphis Hosp., 1959-60, chief resident, 1960-61; USPHS fellow in pediatric endocrinology U. Tenn. Coll. Medicine, Memphis, 1961-62; fellow in med. genetics U. Wis.-Madison, 1963; asst. prof. pediatrics, child devel. U. Tenn., Memphis, 1964-68, assoc. prof., 1968-71, prof. pediatrics and anatomy, 1971—, dean Coll. Medicine, 1981—, provost, 1988-91; cons. President's Commn. on Mental Retardation, 1979-80; CEO U. Tenn. Med. Group, 1983-93, chmn., 1983—; mem. Coun. on Grad. Med. Edn., 1990—. Lt. M.C., USN, 1957-59, rear admiral USNR, ret. 1992. NIH grantee, 1965—; recipient Alumni Pub. Service award U. Tenn. Alumni Assn., 1980-81, U. Tenn. Coll. Medicine Student Body Disting. Tchr. award, 1981-82, 82-83, 83-84, 84-85, 85-86, Outstanding Alumnus award U. Tenn. Coll. of Medicine, 1984. Fellow Am. Coll. Med. Genetics, Am. Acad. Pediatrics; mem. AMA, Tenn. Med. Assn. Memphis-Shelby County Med. Soc., Am. Soc. Human Genetics (bd. dirs. 1980-82), Am. Pediatric Soc., Soc. Pediatric Rsch., Coun. of Deans of AAMC, Jour. Rev. Club (Memphis). Office: U Tenn Coll Medicine 800 Madison Ave Memphis TN 38163

SUMMITT, ROBERT MURRAY, circuit judge; b. Sweetwater, Tenn., Jan. 14, 1924; s. Murray Dyer and Vina Mae (Brakebill) S.; m. Florence Varnell, May 14, 1955; children: Virginia Anne Sharber, Robert M. Jr., Laura Stephens, Martin Dyer. JD, U. Tenn., 1949; postgrad., Nat. Jud. Coll., 1972, 79, 82, Am. Acad. Jud. Edn., 1974, 75, 76, 77, U. Tenn., 1978. Bar: Tenn. 1949, U.S. Supreme Ct. 1956. Pvt. practice Chattanooga, 1949-68; cir. judge Tenn. Jud. 1st Div. 11th Jud. Dist. Ct., Tenn., 1968—; served on Tenn. Supreme Ct., 1990; pres. Tenn. Jud. Conf., 1980, ec., v.p., exec. com. mem., 1980-84, past chmn. nominating com., continuintg edn. com., past chmn.; mem. Tenn. Ct. of the Judiciary; past chmn. ad hoc fed. diversity com. National Conf. State Trial Judges, past chmn. task force on jud. support, past chairman State Jud. Assn., chmn. fin. and budget com., Tenn. rep. to nat. conf. Author: (with others) Tenn. Trial Judges Benchbook; contbr. articles to profl. jours. State chmn., nat. rep., Inner City com. chmn., Boy Scouts Am. (Silver Beaver award 1976); bd. dirs. Salvation Army; mem. Freedom's Found.; bd. dirs., trustee, past Sunday Sch. tchr. First Centenary United Meth. Ch. Decorated Red Cross of Constantine; recipient Nat. Heritage award Downtown Sertoma Club, 1984; named Young Man of Yr., Jaycees, 1959. Mem. ABA (past chmn. Nat. Conf. State Trial Judges 1991-92, mem. judicial adminstrn. divsn. coun., judicial coun. House of Dels.), Tenn. Bar Assn., Chattanooga Bar Assn. (bd. govs.), Am. Judicature Soc., Am. Judges Assn., Internat. Acad. Trial Judges, Silver Falcon Assn., Air Force Assn., Res. Officers Assn., Retired Res. Officers Assn., U. Tenn. Alumni Assn. Century Club, Order of the Arrow, City Farmers Club, Half-Century Club, SAR (chancellor), Mason, Royal Order Jesters, Royal Order Scotland, Eastern Star, Alhambra Temple, Rotary, Phi Delta Phi, Sigma Alpha Epsilon. Avocations: gardening, beekeeping, hunting. Home: 957 Ravine Rd Signal Mountain TN 37377 Office: 11th Jud Dist Hamilton County Courthouse Chattanooga TN 37402

SUMNER, DANIEL ALAN, economist, educator; b. Fairfield, Calif., Dec. 5, 1950. B.S. in Agrl. Mgmt., Calif. State Poly. U., 1971; M.A. in Econs., Mich. State U., 1973; M.A. in Econs., U. Chgo., 1977, Ph.D., 1978. Post-doctoral fellow, labor and population group, econ. dept. Rand Corp., Santa Monica, Calif., 1977-78; asst. prof. N.C. State U., Raleigh, 1978-83, assoc. prof., 1983-87, prof. 1987-92; resident fellow, Resources for the Future, Washington, 1986-87; sr. economist Pres.'s Council of Econ. Advisers, 1987-88; dep. asst. sec. for econs. USDA, 1990-91, asst. sec. for econs., 1992-93. Frank H. Buck Jr. prof. dept. agrl. econs. U. Calif., Davis, 1993—. Author and editor books and monographs; contbr. chpts. to books, articles in profl. jours.; assoc. editor Am. Jour. Agrl. Econs. Named Alumnus of Yr., Calif. State Poly. U., 1991. Mem. Am. Econ. Assn., Econometric Soc., Am. Agrl. Econs. Assn., Internat. Assn. Agrl. Economists. Office: U Calif Davis Dept Agrl Econs Davis CA 95616

SUMNER, DAVID GEORGE, association executive; b. Norwich, Conn., Apr. 22, 1949; s. Raymond W. and Ruth M. (Crooks) S.; m. Linda Ann Churma, June 27, 1980; 1 child, Deryn Anne. MA in Polit. Sci., Mich. State U., 1970; MBA, U. Conn., 1979. Corr. Travelers Ins. Co., Hartford, Conn., 1971-72; asst. sec. Am. Radio Relay League, Newington, Conn., 1972-76, asst. gen. mgr., 1976-82, gen. mgr., 1982-85, exec. v.p., 1985—. Bd. dirs. Windham Regional Planning Agy., Willimantic, Conn., 1991—. Recipient Calcutta Key, Radio Soc. Gt. Britain, 1989, Region I award Internat. Amateur Radio Union, 1989; Radio Club Am. fellow, 1991. Mem. Newington C. of C. (bd. dirs. 1988-90). Democrat. Congregationalist. Avocation: amateur radio. Office: Am Radio Relay League 225 Main St Newington CT 06111-1400

SUMNER, GORD, electronics research executive. Treas BNR, Inc., Research Triangle Park, N.C., 1987—. Office: BNR inc 35 Davis Rd Durham NC 27709*

SUMNER, GORDON MATTHEW See STING

SUMNER, WILLIAM MARVIN, anthropology and archaeology educator; b. Detroit, Sept. 8, 1928; s. William Pulford Jr. and Virginia Friel (Umberger) S.; m. Frances Wilson Morton, June 21, 1952 (div. 1975): children: Jane DeVault, William Morton; m. Kathleen A. MacLean, Apr. 7, 1989. Student, Va. Mil. Inst., 1947-48; B.S., U.S. Naval Acad., 1952; Ph.D., U. Pa., 1972. Dir. Am. Inst. Iranian Studies, Tehran, Iran, 1969-71; asst. prof. Ohio State U., Columbus, 1971-73, assoc. prof., 1974-80, prof. anthropology, 1981-89, prof. emeritus, 1989—; dir. Oriental Inst., prof. Near Eastern langs. and civilizations U. Chgo., 1989—; dir. excavations at Tal-e Malyan (site of Elamite Anshan) sponsored by Univ. Mus., U. Pa., 1971—; v.p. Am. Inst. Iranian Studies, 1983-86. Contbr. chpts. to books, articles and essays to profl. jours. Served to lt. comdr. USN, 1952-64. Grantee NSF, 1975, 76, 79, NEH, 1988. Office: Univ Chgo Oriental Inst 1155 E 58th St Chicago IL 60637-1540

SUMRALL, HARRY, journalist; b. Palestine, Tex., Oct. 15, 1950; s. Harry Glenn and Sherea Sue (Selden) S.; m. Leslie Leizear, Dec. 19, 1954; 1 child, Samuel Harry. BA, George Mason U., 1974. Writer, critic The Washington Post, 1978-81; contbg. writer The New Republic, Washington, 1979; assoc. editor Rock Concert Mag., Washington, 1979; music writer San Jose (Calif.) Mercury News/Knight Ridder News Svc., 1982—; advisor New Music Am., Washington, 1983; lectr., guest San Francisco State U., 1991; guest critic Sta. KGO, San Francisco, 1991—. Author: Pioneers of Rock and Roll, 1994; contbg. author: New Grove Dictionary of American Music, 1983; broadcaster: (radio program) Rockology, 1989. Panelist Chatauquas for Congress, Washington, 1979. Fellow New Music Am., 1980. Office: San Jose Mercury News 750 Ridder Park Dr San Jose CA 95190

SUMRALL, LESTER FRANK, missionary, evangelist; b. Feb. 15, 1913; s. George William and Betty Elizabeth (Chandler) S.; m. Louise Margaret Layman, Sept. 30, 1944; children: Frank Lester Jr., Stephen Philip, Peter Andrew. DD, Berea Bible Co. 1964; LittD, Ind. Christian U. 1974; PhD in Religious Studies, Golden State U., 1983; DD (hon.), Oral Roberts U., 1983. Founder, chmn. LeSEA Ministries, South Bend, Ind., 1959—; founder, pastor Christian Ctr. Cathedral of Praise, South Bend, 1965—; founder, owner 9 TV stas., South Bend, 1972—, LeSea Brodcasting, South Bend, 1972—; founder, pres. World Harvest Bible Coll., South Bend, 1975—; pres. Ind. Christian U., South Bend, 1989—. Author numerous books; pub., founder World Harvest Mag., WHRI Short Wave Radio, 1988. Founder Feed the Hungry, 1987—. Named Hon. Citizen of Knoxville, Tenn., Mayor of Knoxville, 1984, Leader of Yr., Internat. Christian Bus. Leaders, 1988; recipient Congl. award U.S. Ho. of Reps., 1980, Honor Citation Nat. Religious Broadcasters, 1982, award of merit Nat. Religious Broadcasters, 1983, Meritorious Achievement award Internat. Assn. Christian Clin. Counselors, 1983, Meritorious Hoosier award Ind. Sec. State, 1983, Outstanding Community Svc. award FaithAm. Found., 1984. Mem. Full Gospel Ch. Office: LeSea Broadcasting 530 E Ireland Rd South Bend IN 46614-2660

SUMRELL, GENE, research chemist; b. Apache, Ariz., Oct. 7, 1919; s. Joe B. and Dixie (Hughes) S. BA, Eastern N.Mex. U., 1942; BS, U. N.Mex., 1947, MS, 1948; PhD, U. Calif., Berkeley, 1951. Asst. prof. chemistry Eastern N.Mex. U., 1951-53; sr. rsch. chemist J. T. Baker Chem. Co., Phillipsburg, N.J., 1953-58; sr. organic chemist Southwest Rsch. Inst., San Antonio, 1958-59; project leader Food Machinery & Chem. Corp., Balt., 1959-61; rsch. sect. leader El Paso Natural Gas Products Co. (Tex.), 1961-64; project leader So. utilization research and devel. div. U.S. Dept. Agr., New Orleans, 1964-67, investigations head, 1967-73, rsch. leader Oil Seed and Food Lab., So. Regional Rsch. Ctr., 1973-84, collaborator, 1984—. Contbr. numerous papers to profl. jours. Served from pvt. to staff sgt. AUS, 1942-46. Mem. AAAS, Am. Chem. Soc., Am. Acad. Scis., Am. Inst. Chemists, Am. Oil Chemists Soc., Am. Assn. Textile Chemists and Colorists, Rsch. Soc. Am., Phi Kappa Phi, Sigma Xi. Achievements include patents in field. Home: PO Box 24037 New Orleans LA 70184-4037 Office: 1100 Robert E Lee Blvd New Orleans LA 70124-4305

SUN, CHIEH, electronics company executive; b. China, Mar. 3, 1943; came to U.S., 1966, naturalized, 1975; s. Chin-Hwa and Jean Y. (Yeh) S.; m. Lin Lynn, June 17, 1967; children—Andrew, Christina. Ph.D., U. So. Calif. 1972. Chmn., Chung-Hwa Picture Ltd., Taiwan, 1969—; pres. Tatung Co. Am., Inc., Long Beach, Calif., 1972—; dir. Am. Asia Bank, San Francisco. Chmn. elec. engring. dept. Chinese Culture U., Taiwan, 1979—. Baptist. Office: Tatung Co Am Inc 2850 E El Presidio St Long Beach CA 90810-1178

SUN, COSSETTE TSUNG-HUNG WU, law library director; b. Taipei, Taiwan, July 14, 1937; came to U.S., 1960, naturalized, 1972; d. Lin Tsung and Chiu Ching (Wu) Hsieh; m. Stanley Siann-Shyang Sun, Nov. 23, 1961; children: Carol Sun Crowe, Marina Sheree, Olivia Cossette. LLB, Nat. Taiwan U., Taipei, 1960; MA, U. Houston, 1963; MS, Simmons Coll., Boston, 1965. Asst. prof. law, assoc. libr. St. Louis U., 1965-73; assoc. libr.U. Calif.-Berkeley, 1974-75; br. libr. Alameda County Law Libr., Hayward, Calif., 1975-77, law libr. dir., Oakland, 1978—; chmn. law libr. svcs. to instl. residents, 1979-80; pres. Coun. Calif. County Law Librs., 1982-84. Editor: State Ct. County Law Libraries Newsletter, 1979; contbr. articles to law revs. Mem. Castro Valley Mcpl. Adv. Coun., Castro Valley Libr. Adv. Commn. W.H. Anderson scholar, 1966; Matthew Bender scholar, 1971. Mem. Am. Assn. Law Librs. (cert. 1969), Spl. Librs. Assn., Asian-Pacific Libr. Assn., Alameda County Bar Assn. Office: Alameda County Law Libr Courthouse Rm 200 Oakland CA 94612

SUN, LI-TEH, economics educator; b. Hong Kong, Dec. 5, 1939; s. Beh-Yu and Ruey-Jeng (Wang) S.; m. Ping Zhong, June 1, 1991. BA in Econs., Chung Hsing U., Taipei, Taiwan, 1962; MS in Econs., Okla. State U., 1968, PhD in Econs., 1972. Rsch. assoc. U. Mont., Missoula, 1969-70; lectr. Humboldt State U., Arcata, Calif., 1972-75; acad. resource specialist Chancelor's Office Calif. State U. and Colls., Long Beach, Calif., 1975-77; assoc. prof., prof. econs. Nat. Chung Hsing U., Taipei, 1977-81, chair dept. pub. fin., 1978-82; prof. econs. Moorhead (Minn.) State U., 1982—; coord. China programs Moorhead State U., 1987-89. Contbr. articles to profl. jours. Mem. adv. bd. Centre of Humanomics, 1985—. Named Prof. of Yr., Humboldt State U., Arcata, Calif., 1974. Mem. Moorhead Cen. Lions (newsletter editor 1990-93, bd. dirs. 1983—, pres. 1987-88, Lion of Yr. 1984, 85, 90, 91). Avocations: table tennis, biking, travel. Home: 823 23rd Ave S Moorhead MN 56560-4315 Office: Moorhead State U Dept Econs Moorhead MN 56563

SUND, ELDON HAROLD, chemistry educator; b. Plentywood, Mont., June 6, 1930; s. Lawrence and Ethel May (Andersen) S.; m. Roberta Faulkner, May 30, 1957; children: Sharon Ellen, Elizabeth Dianne, Phillip Lawrence, Nancy Annemarie. BS, U. Ill., 1952; PhD, U. Tex., 1960. Rsch. chemist E.I. du Pont de Nemours & Co., Wilmington, Del., 1959-66; asst. prof. Ohio No. U., Ada, 1966-67; asst. prof. Midwestern State U., Wichita Falls, Tex., 1967-70, assoc. prof., 1970-73, prof., 1973—, chmn. dept. chemistry, 1984-90; Fulbright exchange prof. Hatfield Poly. Herts., Eng., 1985-86; vis. prof. U. Hawaii, Honolulu, 1989-90. Patentee: 1967; contbr. articles to profl. jours. 1st lt. USAF, 1952-56. Recipient Rsch. grant Robert A. Welch Found., Houston, 1970—; named Hardin prof. Hardin Found., Wichita Falls, Tex., 1975. Fellow Tex. Acad. of Sci.; mem. Am. Chem. Soc. (organ chemistry div., chem. edn. div.), Internat. Soc. of Hetrocyclic Chemistry, Sigma Xi. Lutheran. Avocations: reading, sailing, hiking. Office: Midwestern State U 2C 483rd # Mh- Wichita Falls TX 76308

SUND, JEFFREY OWEN, publishing company executive; b. Bklyn., June 19, 1940; children: Catherine, Meredith. BA, Dartmouth Coll., 1962. Sales rep. Prentice-Hall, Englewood Cliffs, N.J., 1967-73; sales rep. Houghton Mifflin, Boston, 1973-74, coll. div. editor, 1974-77, editor-in-chief, 1977-86, v.p.; editorial dir. 1986-89; pres., chief exec. officer Richard D. Irwin, Burr Ridge, Ill., 1989—. Lt. USN, 1962-66. Office: Richard D Irwin 1333 Burr Ridge Pkwy Burr Ridge IL 60521

SUNDARESAN, MOSUR KALYANARAMAN, physics educator; b. Madras, India, Sept. 2, 1929; parents Mosur Ramanathan and Kanakavalli Kalyanaraman; m. Bharathy Sundaresan, June 7, 1957; children: Sudhir, Sujata. BSc with honors, Delhi U., 1947, MSc, 1949; PhD, Cornell U., 1955. With Atomic Energy Establishment, Bombay, 1955-57; postdoctoral fellow NRC, Can., 1957-59; reader in physics Punjab U., Chandigarh, India, 1959-61; prof. physics Carleton U., Ottawa, Can., 1961—. Mem. Can. Assn. Physicists, Am. Phys. Soc., Am. Assn. Physics Tchrs., Inst. Particle Physics Can. Avocations: tennis, badminton.

SUNDBERG, ALAN CARL, former state supreme court justice, lawyer; b. Jacksonville, Fla., June 23, 1933; s. Robert Carl and Gertrude Harriet (Rudd) S.; children: Allison, Angela, Laura, Alan, William. BS, Fla. State U., 1955; LLB, Harvard U., 1958; LLD (hon.), Stetson U., 1977. Bar: Fla. 1958. Practiced in St. Petersburg, 1958-75; justice Supreme Ct. Fla., 1975-82, chief justice, 1980-82; sr. atty. Carlton, Fields, Ward, Emmanuel, Smith & Cutler, P.A., Tallahassee, 1982—; com. mem. on rules of practice and procedure of Judicial Conf. of U.S. Author: Process and Appearance, Civil Practice Before Trial, 1963. Mem. Salvation Army Adv. Bd.; chmn. bd. trustees Canterbury Sch. Fla., Inc.; bd. dirs. Fla. Gulf Coast Symphony, St. Petersburg Symphony; trustee Pinellas County Law Library; mem. Fla. Sentencing Guidelines Commn., 1982-89; chmn. Fla. Bench Bar Commn. Mem. ABA, Fla. Bar Found. (past 2d v.p.), St. Petersburg Bar Assn., Fla. Bar Assn. (spl. commn. referall contingency fees), Pinellas Trial Lawyers Assn., Internat. Acad. Trial Lawyers, Am. Coll. Trial Lawyers, Best Lawyers in Am., Phi Beta Kappa, Phi Kappa Phi, Omicron Delta Kappa, Phi Delta Phi, Dragon, Suncoasters. Democrat. Episcopalian. Office: Carlton Fields Ward Emmanuel Smith & Cutler PC PO Box 190 Tallahassee FL 32302-0190

SUNDBERG, CARL-ERIK WILHELM, telecommunications executive, researcher; b. Karlskrona, Sweden, July 7, 1943; came to U.S., 1984; s. Erik Wilhelm and Martha Maria (Snaar) S. MEE, U. Lund, Sweden, 1966, PhD, 1975. Tchr., rsch. asst.; lectr. U. Lund, 1966-75, rsch. prof. (docent) 1975-76, 1977-84; rsch. fellow European Space Agy., Noordwijk, The Netherlands, 1975-76; disting. mem. tech. staff AT&T Bell Labs., Murray Hill, N.J., 1984—; cons. L.M. Ericsson, Gothenburg, Sweden, 1976-77; Bell Labs., Crawford Hill, N.J., 1981-82; instr. Carl Cranz Gesellschaft, Oberpfaffenhofen, Fed. Republic Germany, 1990-93. Co-author: Digital Phase Modulation, 1986, Source-Matched Digital Communication Systems, 1995; contbr. articles to profl. jours.; patentee in field. Served in Swedish Navy, 1968. Fellow IEEE (Best Paper award 1986, guest editor Jour. on Selected Areas in Comm. 1988-89), IEE Marconi Premium; mem. Swedish Union Radio-Scientifique Internationale, Svenska Electric Engrs. Riksförening (Sweden), CF Civil Engrs. förbundet (Sweden). Lutheran. Avocations: travel, history, photography. Home: Apt A11 25 Hickory Pl Chatham NJ 07928 Office: AT&T Bell Labs Rm MH-2C-480 600 Mountain Ave New Providence NJ 07974

SUNDBERG, R. DOROTHY, physician, educator; b. Chgo., July 29, 1915; d. Carl William and Ruth (Chalbeck) S.; m. Robert H. Reiff, Dec. 24, 1941 (div. 1945). Student, U. Chgo., 1932-34; B.S., U. Minn., 1937, M.A., 1939, Ph.D., 1943, M.D., 1953. Diplomate: Am. Bd. Pathology. Instr., asst. prof. anatomy U. Minn., 1939-53, asso. prof., 1953-60, prof., 1960-63, prof. of lab. medicine and anatomy, 1963-73, prof. lab. medicine, pathology and anatomy, 1973-84, emeritus prof., 1984—; hematologist, dir. Hematology Labs., 1945-74, hematologist, co. dir., 1974-84. Editorial bd.: Soc. Exptl. Biology and Medicine, until 1975; mem. editorial bd.: Blood, 1960-67; assoc. editor, 1967-69. Recipient Lucretia Wilder award for research in anatomy, 1943. Mem. Am. Assn. Anatomists, Internat. European Soc. Hematology, Sigma Xi. Home: 1255 Shenandoah Ct Marco Island FL 33937 also: 2618 158th Ave NE Ham Lake MN 55304

SUNDBERG, RICHARD, architectural firm executive; b. Seattle, Oct. 10, 1942. BArch, U. Wash., 1966. Registered arch., Wash., Mont., Idaho, Wyo.; cert. Nat. Coun. Archtl. Registration Bd. Arch. Ibsen Nelsen & Assocs., 1967-74; assoc. Olson/Walker Assocs., Seattle, 1975-76, ptnr., 1976-85; prin. Olson/Sundberg Archs., Seattle, 1985—; guest juror U. Wash. Sch. Architecture; mem. hist. bldg. code tech. adv. group State of Wash. Prin. works include Overlake Park Presbyn. Ch. (Seattle chpt. Merit award AIA 1989), Evergreen State Coll. (Seattle chpt. Merit award AIA, 1993, Pacific N.W. Regional Honor award, 1993, Architecture and Energy Honor award AIA, 1993), Wash. State Hist. Soc. Mus., Hill Climb Ct. (Honor award AIA, 1983), Zoo Store-Woodland Park Zool. Gardens, 98 Union/South Arcade (Honor award AIA, 1985), Pike & Virginia Bldg. (Honor award AIA, 1979), Seattle Art Mus. Downtown, Seattle's Best Coffee-various locations, Seattle Univ. Chapel, Frye Art Mus., Antioch U., others. Mem. AIA, Nat. Trust Hist. Preservation. Office: Olson Sundberg Architects 108 1st Ave S Fl 4 Seattle WA 98104-2502

SUNDBERG, RICHARD JAY, chemistry educator; b. Sioux Rapids, Iowa, Jan. 6, 1938; s. Ernest Julius and Rosa Paulina Christina (Christensen) S.; m. Lorna Swift, 1962 children—Kelly, Jennifer. B.S., U. Iowa, 1959; Ph.D., U. Minn., 1962. Mem. faculty dept. chemistry U. Va., Charlottesville, 1964—, prof., 1974—. Author monograph: Chemistry of Indoles, 1970; author (with F. A. Carey) Advanced Organic Chemistry, 1990. Served to 1st lt. U.S. Army, 1962-64. Mem. Am. Chem. Soc., Internat. Soc. Heterocyclic Chemistry. Lutheran. Home: 2001 Greenbrier Dr Charlottesville VA 22901-2916 Office: U Va Dept Chemistry Mccormick Rd Charlottesville VA 22904

SUNDBY, SCOTT EDWIN, law educator; b. Aurora, Ill., Oct. 24, 1958; s. Elmer Arthur and Marilyn Edruth (Koeller) S.; m. Katie Louise Rees, June 15, 1980; children: Russell Taylor, Christopher Scott, Kelsey Kathleen. BA, Vanderbilt U., 1980; JD, Cornell U., 1983. Bar: Calif. 1985, U.S. Dist. Ct. (no. dist.) Calif. 1985. Law clk. to judge U.S. Ct. Appeals for IIth Cir., Savannah, Ga., 1983-84; prof. law U. Calif. Hastings Coll. Law, San Francisco, 1984-92; prof. Washington and Lee U., Lexington, Va., 1992—. Editor-in-chief Cornell Law Rev., 1982-83. Mem. Order of Coif, Phi Beta Kappa. Office: Washington and Lee Univ Sch Law Lexington VA 24450

SUNDEL, MARTIN, social work educator, psychologist; b. Bronx, N.Y., Sept. 22, 1940; s. Louis and Pauline (Brotman) S.; m. Sandra Stone, Aug. 22, 1971; children: Adam Daniel, Jenny Rebecca, Ariel Pauline. B.A. cum laude, St. Mary's U., 1961; M.S.W., Worden Sch. Social Service, 1963; M.A., U. Mich., 1968, Ph.D., 1968. Social group work supr. Valley Cities Jewish Community Ctr., Van Nuys, Calif., 1963-65; asst. prof. U. Mich. Sch. Social Work, Ann Arbor, 1968-71; postdoctoral fellow Harvard U. Lab. Community Psychiatry, Boston, 1971-72; dir. research and evaluation River Region Mental Health-Mental Retardation Bd., Louisville, 1972-77; adj. prof. Kent. Sch. Social Work-U Louisville, 1972-77, assoc. clin. prof. dept. psychiatry and behavioral scis., 1974-77, assoc. in psychology, 1975-77; sr. research assoc. The Urban Inst., Washington, 1977-80; pvt. practice psychology Dallas; Dulak Disting. prof. U. Tex., Arlington, 1980-89, prof., 1980—; mental health cons. UN High Commn. for Refugees in Cyprus, 1993—; mem. profl. adv. coun. Dallas Geriatric Rsch. Inst., 1980-89; mem. long-range planning com. Dallas Jewish Coalition for the Homeless, 1986—; mem. coordinating com. Arlington Human Svcs. Project, 1981-90, Mayor's Forum on Human Svc. Needs Assessment, Ft. Worth, 1983-86; vis. prof. U. So. Calif. Sch. Social Work, spring 1985. Author: (with Sandra Stone Sundel) Behavior Modification in the Human Services, 1975, 3d edit., 1993; Be Assertive, 1980; co-editor: Assessing Health and Human Service Needs, 1983, Individual Change Through Small Groups, 2d edit., 1985, Midlife Myths, 1989; mem. editorial bds. and cons. to profl. jours. Mem. APA, Nat. Assn. Social Workers (mem. futures commn. 1979-85, mem. steering com. Dallas 1986-90), Behavior Therapy and Rsch. Soc. (charter clin. fellow), Assn. Asvancement of Behavior Therapy, Acad. Cert. Social Workers, Coun. Social Work Edn., Internat. Soc. for the Sys. Scis. Home: 4343 Shady Bend Dr Dallas TX 75244-7448 Office: U Tex Arlington Sch Social Work PO Box 19129 University of Texas TX 76019

SUNDELIUS, HAROLD W., geology educator; b. Escanaba, Mich., July 6, 1930; s. Herbert A. and Caroline (Johnson) S.; m. Charlene P. Swanson, May 2l, 1955; children: Karin, Kristine. AB, Augustana Coll., Rock Island, Ill., 1952; MS, U. Wis., 1957, PhD, 1959. Geologist U.S. Geol. Survey, Washington, 1959-65; asst. prof. geology Wittenberg U., Springfield, Ohio, 1965-67, assoc. prof., 1967-74, prof., 1974-75, assoc. dean Coll., 1971-75; v.p., dean Coll., Augustana Coll., 1975-88, prof. geology, 1988—; cons. Dow Chem. Co., Midland, Mich., 1957, minerals dept. Exxon, Houston, 1968-75. Contbr. articles to geol. jours., chpt. to book. Bd. dirs. Luth. Hosp., Moline, Ill., 1984-89, Swenson Swedish Immigration Rsch. Ctr., Rock Island, 1984—. With U.S. Army, 1953-55, Korea. Fulbright fellow, Oslo, 1952-53, C.K. Leith fellow, 1955-57, Univ. fellow, 1957-58. Fellow Soc. Econ. Geologists, Geol. Soc. Am.; mem. Nat. Assn. Geology Tchrs., Rock Island C. of C. (bd. dirs.), Rotary (bd. dirs. Rock Island chpt.), Phi Beta Kappa, Sigma Xi. Lutheran. Home: 4310 26th Ave Rock Island IL 61201-5723 Office: Augustana College 600 38th St Rock Island IL 61201

SUNDERLAND, RAY, JR., retired insurance company executive; b. N.Y.C., Nov. 12, 1913; s. Ray and Rose (Goehl) S.; m. Melva Joyce Mace, June 13, 1943; 1 son, Joel Wayne. Grad., Sch. Profl. Accountancy Practice, Pace Coll., 1948, Sch. Bus. Adminstrn., Columbia U., 1968. CPA, N.Y. With comptroller's dept. Brown Bros. Harriman & Co., N.Y.C., 1934-40; sr. auditor Price Waterhouse & Co., N.Y.C., 1940-50; with N.Y. Life Ins. Co., N.Y.C., 1950-79; gen. auditor N.Y. Life Ins. Co., 1969-71, comptroller, 1971-79, v.p. 1971-75, sr. v.p., 1975-79; comptroller N.Y. Life Fund, Inc., 1972-79. Author and publisher: The Descandants of William Sunderland and Allied Families, 1988. Pres. community scholarship fund local sch. dist., Locust Valley, N.Y., 1958-62; bd. dirs., parents club, 1958-62; bd. dirs. Vis. Nurse Assn. L.I., N.Y., 1982-93, Vis. Nurse Assn. of Oyster Bay-Glen Cove, N.Y., 1982-92; mem. Locust Valley Libr. (long range planning com. 1992, nominating com. for bd. trustee mems. 1992—). Served to capt. USAAF, 1942-45; active duty USAR, 1946-52. Fellow Am. Coll. Genealogists (v.p. N.Y. area 1990—); mem. NRA (life), SAR (Huntington, N.Y. chpt.), Am. Coun. Life Ins. (fin. reporting principles com. 1977-78), Nat. Geneal. Soc., Geneal. Soc. Southwestern Pa., Locust Valley Hist. Soc. (N.Y.). Home: 3 Wood Ln Locust Valley NY 11560-1628

SUNDERLAND, ROBERT, cement company executive; b. Omaha, Dec. 21, 1921; s. Paul and Avis Marie (Peters) S.; m. Terri Reed, Nov. 21, 1959; children—Sharon Marie, Lori Diane. B.S.N in Bus. Adminstrm, Washington U., St. Louis, 1947; LL.D. (hon.), Bethany Coll., Lindsborg, Kans., 1980. With Ash Grove Cement Co., Overland Park, Kans., 1947—; sec., asst. treas. Ash Grove Cement Co., 1953-57, treas., 1957-61, v.p., treas., 1961-67, chmn.

bd., 1967-91, hon. chmn., 1992—; bd. dirs. T.K. Communications, Inc. Trustee Lester T. Sunderland Found., Kansas City. Served with USAAF, 1942-46, Philippines. Mem. Kansas City Club, Shadow Glen Golf Club, Sigma Chi. Republican. Presbyterian. Office: Ash Grove Cement Co 8900 Indian Creek Pky Ste 600 Shawnee Mission KS 66210-1513

SUNDERMAN, DUANE NEUMAN, chemist, research institute executive; b. Wadsworth, Ohio, July 14, 1928; s. Richard Benjamin and Carolyn (Neuman) S.; m. Joan Catherine Hoffman, Jan. 31, 1953; children: David, Christine, Richard. BA, U. Mich., 1949, MS, 1954, PhD in Chemistry, 1956. Researcher Battelle Meml. Inst., Columbus, Ohio, 1956-59; mgr. Battelle Meml. Inst., Columbus, 1959-69, assoc. dir., 1969-79, dir. internat. programs, 1979-84; sr. v.p. Midwest Rsch. Inst., Kansas City, Mo., 1984-90, exec. v.p., 1990-94; exec. v.p. Midwest Rsch. Inst., Golden, Colo., 1990-94; dir. Nat. Renewable Energy Lab., Golden, Colo. 1990-94, dir. emeritus, 1994—. Contbr. numerous articles to profl. jours. Bd. dirs. Mid-Ohio chpt. ARC, 1982-83, U. Kansas City, 1985-90, Mo. Corp. for Sci. and Tech., Jefferson City, 1986-90. Mem. AAAS, Am. Chem. Soc., Am. Mgmt. Assn. Republican. Presbyterian. Avocation: computers.

SUNDERMAN, FREDERICK WILLIAM, physician, educator, author, musician; b. Altoona, Pa., Oct. 23, 1898; s. William August and Elizabeth Catherine (Lehr) S.; m. Clara Louise Baily, June 2, 1925 (dec. 1972); children—Louise (dec.), F. William, Joel B. (dec.); m. Martha-Lee Taggart, May 3, 1980. B.S., Gettysburg Coll., 1919, Sc.D. (hon.), 1952; M.D., U. Pa., 1923, M.S., 1927, Ph.D., 1929. Diplomate Am. Bd. Internal Medicine, Am. Bd. Pathology (v.p. 1944-50 life trustee 1950—), Nat. Bd. Med. Examiners. Intern, then resident Pa. Hosp., 1924-26; assoc. rsch. med. U. Pa., Phila.; 1925-48; assoc. in chem. divsn. William Pepper Lab. U. Pa. Hosp., Phila., 1929-48; physician U. Pa. Hosp., 1929-48; med. dir. Office of Sci. Rsch and Devel., 1943-46; physician, hon. pathologist Pa. Hosp., 1988—; mem. faculty U. Pa. Sch. Medicine, Phila., 1925-47; assoc. prof. research medicine, also lectr. U. Pa. Sch. Medicine; acting head med. dept. Brookhaven Nat. Lab., Upton, N.Y., 1947-48; chief chem. div. William Pepper Lab. Clin. Medicine, U. Pa. Med. Sch., 1933-47; prof. clin. pathology, dir. Temple U. Lab. Clin. Medicine, 1947-48; med. dir. govt. explosives lab. Carnegie Inst. Tech. and Bur. Mines, 1943-46; head dept. clin. pathology Cleve. Clinic Found., 1948-49; dir. clin. research M.D. Anderson Hosp. Cancer Research, Houston, 1949-50; dir. clin. labs. Grady Meml. Hosp., Atlanta, 1949-51; prof. clin. medicine Emory U. Sch. Medicine, 1949-51; chief clin. pathology Communicable Disease Center, USPHS, 1950-51; med. adviser Rohm & Haas Co., 1947-71; med. cons. Redstone Arsenal, U.S. Army Ordnance Dept., Huntsville, Ala., 1947-49; cons. clin. pathology St. Joseph's Hosp., Tampa, Fla., 1965-66; attending physician Jefferson Hosp., Phila., 1951—, dir. div. metabolic research, clin. prof. medicine, 1951-67, clin. prof. medicine, 1951-74, hon. clin. prof. medicine, 1975—; dir. Inst. Clin. Sci., 1965—; prof. pathology Hahnemann U. Med. Coll., 1970—, co-chmn. dept. lab. medicine, 1970-75, prof. emeritus, 1989; med. adviser and cons. bus. and industry, 1947—; dir. internat. seminars on clin. chemistry and pathology, 1947—; guest lectr. Beijing (People's Republic of China) Med. U., 1989. Author, editor 36 books on clin. chemistry and pathology; author: Our Madeira Heritage, 1979, Musical Notes of a Physician, 1982, Painting with Light, 1993; editor-in-chief Annals Clin. Lab. Sci., 1970—; mem. editorial bd. Am. Jour. Clin. Pathology, 1973-77, Am. Jour. Indsl. Medicine, 1979-85; cons. editor Am. Jour. Occupational Medicine 1979-85; also over 350 articles. Trustee Gettysburg Coll., 1967-69, chmn., 1972-74, hon. life trustee, 1979—; Bermuda Biol. Sta. for Rsch., 1960-86, trustee, 1960-86, hon. life trustee, 1986; bd. dirs. Musical Fund Soc. of Phila., 1938—, hon. life, 1993; bd. dirs. Dwight D. Eisenhower Soc., 1984—, German Soc. Pa., 1986—, Geog. Soc. Phila., 1994—; violin soloist Chautauqua Summer Series, eastern U.S., 1919-20; guest soloist Concerto Soloists of Phila., 1979, 83, 84, Pa. String Tchrs. Assn., Gettysburg, 1959, Westchester, 1962, 63, 67, 68, Trenton (N.J.) Tchrs. Coll. Orch., 1965, Internat. String Conf. soloist World Congress on Arts & Medicine, Carnegie Hall, N.Y.C., 1992. Recipient Naval Ordnance Devel. award, 1946, certificate appreciation War Dept., 1947, Honor medal Armed Forces Inst. Pathology, 1964; recipient Meritorious Service award, 1979, Honor award Latin Am. Assn. Clin. Biochemistry, 1976, Disting. Svc. award Am. Soc. Clin. Pathology-Coll. Am. Pathologists, 1988, Life-time Achievement award in clin. chemistry Joint Congresses of IX Congresso Nacional de la Sociedad Espanola de Quimica Clin., 2d Internat. Congress Therapeutic Drug Monitoring and Toxicology, and 4th Internat. Congress on Automation and New Tech., Spain, 1990, John Gunther Reinhold award Phila. Sect. Am. Assn. for Clin. Chemistry, 1991, Jacob Ehrenzeller award Res. Assn. Pa. Hosp., 1993; named Disting. Alumnus Gettysburg Coll., 1963; Sunderman Seminar Rm. dedicated at Bermuda Biol.ta. for Rsch., 1992. Fellow ACP (life); mem. Am. Assn. History Medicine, Am. Diabetes Assn., AMA, Am. Soc. Clin. Investigation, Royal Soc. Health, AAUP, Endocrine Soc., Am. Assn. Biol. Chemistry, AAAS, Am. Chem. Soc., Internat. Union Pure and Applied Chemistry (nickel subcom. Commn. on Toxicology), Inst. Occupational Health (Finland), Outokumpu Oy (Finland), Am. Assn. Clin. Chemists (award for outstanding efforts in edn. and tng. 1981, John Gunther Reinhold award 1991), Coll. Am. Pathologists (founding gov., Pathologist of Yr. award 1962, Pres.'s Honor award 1984), Am. Soc. Clin. Pathology (pres. 1951, archives com. 1977—, Ward Burdick award 1975, Continuing Edn. Distinguished Service award 1976), Assn. Clin. Scientists (pres. 1957-59, dir. edn. 1959—, diploma honor 1960, ann. goblet award 1964, Gold-headed cane 1974), Coll. Physicians of Phila. (sec. 1946-48, Disting. Service award 1980), Knight of Order of St. Vincent of Portugal (Disting. Svc. cross, Order of merit, (das Verdienstkreuz), Bundesrepublik Deutschland, 1989), Am. Indsl. Hygiene Assn., Am. Occupational Medicine Assn., Am. Soc. Med. Research, Nat. Acad. Clin. Biochemistry, Pan Am. Med. Assn., Pa. Assn. Clin. Pathology, Philadelphia County Med. Soc., Mus. Fund Soc. Phila. (hon. life), Soc. Toxicology, Brit. Assn. Clin. Biochemists (hon.), Soc. Pharm. and Environ. Pathologists (hon.), Internat. Union Pure and Applied Chemistry, Inst. Occupational Health Finland (nickel subcom. commn. toxicology), Phi Beta Kappa, Sigma Xi, Alpha Omega Alpha, Phi Sigma Kappa, Alpha Kappa Kappa. Lutheran. Club: Union League (Phila.). Spl. symposium given in honor for lifetime achievement, Internat. Union Pure and Applied Chemistry, Finland, 1988. Home: 1833 Delancey Pl Philadelphia PA 19103-6606 Office: Pa Hosp Inst for Clin Sci 301 S 8th St Duncan Bldg 3A Philadelphia PA 19106-4014

SUNDQUIST, DONALD KENNETH (DON SUNDQUIST), governor, former congressman, sales corporation executive; b. Moline, Ill., Mar. 15, 1936; s. Kenneth M. and Louise (Rohren) S.; m. Martha Swanson, Oct. 3, 1959; children: Tania, Andrea, Donald Kenneth. BA, Augustana Coll., 1957. Div. mgr. Josten's, Inc., 1961-72; exec. v.p. Graphic Sales of Am., Memphis, 1972, pres., 1973-82; mem. 98th-103rd Congresses from 7th Tenn. dist., Washington, 1983-94; gov. State of Tenn., Nashville, 1995—; vice chmn. bd. Bank of Germantown, Tenn. Past mem. White House Comm. Presdl. Scholars; past chmn. Jobs for High Sch. Grads. of Republican Nat. Congl. Steering Com. George Bush for Pres., 1988, 92; nat. campaign mgr. Howard Baker for Pres., 1979; dir. com. ops., alt. del. Republican Nat. Conv., 1980; chmn. Shelby County Rep. Party, 1975-77; alt. del. Rep. Nat. Conv., 1976; exec. com. Rep. Nat. Com., 1971-73; nat. chmn. Young Rep. Nat. Fedn., 1971-73; sec. Bedford County Election Commn., 1968-70; chmn. Tenn. Young Rep. Fedn., 1969-70; dir. Mid-South Coliseum, Am. Council Young Polit. Leaders, 1972-74, U.S. Youth Council, 1972-75; bd. govs. Charles Edison Meml. Youth Fund; nat. adv. bd. Distributive Edn. Clubs Am.; mem. U.S. del. study tour, People's Republic of China, 1978, study tour, USSR, 1975. Served with USN, 1957-59. Lutheran. Lodge: Kiwanis. Office: Office of Gov State Capitol Bldg Nashville TN 37243-0001

SUNDQUIST, JAMES LLOYD, political scientist; b. West Point, Utah, Oct. 16, 1915; s. Frank Victor and Freda (Carlson) S.; m. Beth Ritchie, Dec. 25, 1937 (dec. 1982); children: Erik L., Mark L., James K.; m. Geraldine Coote, Dec. 3, 1983. Student, Weber Coll., 1932-34, HHD (hon.), 1990; student, Northwestern U., 1934-35; BS, U. Utah, 1939; MS in Pub. Admnstrn, Syracuse U., 1941; DDS (hon.), Carthage Coll., 1987. Reporter Salt Lake Tribune, 1935-39; admnstrv. analyst U.S. Bur. Budget, 1941-47, 49-51; reports and statistics officer Office Def. Moblzn., 1951-53; dir. mgmt. control European Command, U.S. Army, Berlin, 1947-49; asst. to chmn. Democratic Nat. Com., 1953-54; asst. sec. to gov. N.Y. State, 1955-56; asst. to U.S. Senator Clark, 1957-62; dep. under sec. agr., 1963-65; sr. fellow Brookings Instn., 1965-85, emeritus, 1985—, dir. govtl. studies, 1976-78; adj. prof. Smith Coll., 1975-78; Sec. platform com. Dem. Nat. Conv., 1960, 68. Author: Politics and Policy: The Eisenhower, Kennedy and Johnson Years,

1968, Making Federalism Work, 1969 (Louis Brownlow award for best pub. adminstrn. book), Dynamics of the Party System, 1973, 2d edit., 1983, Dispersing Population: What America Can Learn from Europe, 1975, The Decline and Resurgence of Congress, 1981 (Hardeman prize for best book on Congress); Constitutional Reform and Effective Government, 1986, 2d ed., 1992; editor Internat. Rev. Adminstrv. Scis, 1980-89, Beyond Gridlock?, 1993. Mem. Gov.'s Commn. on Va.'s Future, 1983-84. Recipient Exceptional Civilian Service award War Dept., 1945, Lifetime Achievement award Maxwell Sch. (Syracuse U.) Alumni Assn., 1994; sr. Research fellow U. Glasgow, Scotland, 1972-73. Mem. Nat. Acad. Pub. Adminstrn., Am. Soc. Pub. Adminstrn., Am. Polit. Sci. Assn. (treas. 1980, Charles E. Merriam award 1985), Am. Acad. Arts and Scis. Home: 3016 N Florida St Arlington VA 22207-1808 Office: 1775 Massachusetts Ave NW Washington DC 20036-2188

SUNDQUIST, JOHN A., religious organization executive. Exec. dir. Internat. Ministries Am. Bapt. Chs. U.S.A., Valley Forge, Pa.; chair Bapt. World Aid. Trustee No. Bapt. Sem., Lombard, Ill., Internat. Bapt. Sem., Prague. Office: Am Bapt Chs Internat Ministries PO Box 851 Valley Forge PA 19482-0851

SUNDQUIST, MARIA ALEXANDRA, diplomat; b. Buenos Aires, Argentina, Feb. 4, 1943; came to U.S., 1962; d. Alberto Oscar and Filomena (Cacciavillani) Garcia; m. Ralph H. Gunther, Oct. 10, 1964 (div. 1970); m. Erik Lindon Sundquist, Mar. 1, 1975; 1 child, Karin Alexandra. BA, Smith Coll., 1964; MA in Econs., NYU, 1969. Economist Chase Manhattan Bank, N.Y.C., Chem. Bank, N.Y.C.; asst. commml. attache Am. Embassy, Jeddah, Saudi Arabia, 1980-82; 1st sec. Am. Embassy, Paris, 1982-86; econ. officer U.S. Dept. of State, Washington, 1986-90; legis. asst. U.S. Senate, Washington, 1990-91; consul gen. U.S. Dept. of State, Bordeaux, France, 1991-94. Pearson fellow, 1990-91. Avocations: history, mysteries, opera, gastronomy. Office: US Dept State 2201 C St NW Rm 1252 Washington DC 20520

SUNDRY, ARTHUR P., business executive; b. 1928. BS, U.S. Naval Acad., 1951. Exec. v.p. Motorola, Inc.; v.p. communications and electronics Motorola, Inc., Roselle, Ill., 1971-77, past pres., dir.; now pres., gen. mgr. comm. sector Motorola, Inc., Schaumburg, Ill. *

SUNDSTROM, HAROLD WALTER, public relations executive; b. Chgo., Jan. 26, 1929; s. Elmer A. and Rosalind Lillian (Busse) S.; m. Mary Olin, Oct. 1, 1955; children: Geoffrey Lee, Lori Lynn, Deborah Barron. AA, Wright Jr. Coll., 1949; BA, Mich. State U., 1952; MA, 1954. Fgn. svc. info. officer USIA, Tokyo, Jakarta, Seoul, 1955-61; sr. pub. rels. assoc. Eli Lilly and Co., Indpls., 1962-66; v.p., dir. pub. rels. Eisenhower People to People Program, Kansas City, Mo., 1966-68; govt. and pub. affairs rep. North Ctrl. States Automobile Mfrs. Assn., Kansas Cityand Copenhagen, 1968-69; speechwriter, pub. rels. cons. Commdr.-in-Chief U.S. Pacific Forces, Aiea, 1969-75; pres. No. Ariz. Comm., Inc., Flagstaff, 1975-79; asst. sec., dir. pub. affairs U.S. Internat. Trade Commn., Washington, 1979-87; v.p. pub. affairs amd publs. Export-Import Bank U.S., Washington, 1987-89; pres. Halamar, Inc., Manassas, Va. and Easley, S.C., 1983—; freelance writer and poet. Author: The American West, 1956, Garuda, Introducing Indonesia, 1957, Politics and Nationalism in Indonesia, 1962, Faces of Asia: Korea, 1965, The North Arizona Scene, 1976, American Collie Champions, Vol. I, 1979, Vol. II, 1980, Vol. III, 1987, Collies - A Complete Pet Owners Manual, 1994; editor, pub. Hawaiian Dog Rev., 1972-76, Collie Cues, The Alaska Cir., The Ariz. Cir., Internat. Lhasa Apso Rev., Sandwich Isles Dog Gazette, Travel Writer, Honolulu Sun Press, 1972-76. With U.S. Army, 1947-48, 52-53, Tokyo. Recipient George Washington Honor medal Freedom Found., 1968, Silver Beaver award Aloha coun. Boy Scouts Am., 1975. Fellow Japan Soc. N.Y.; mem. Pub. Rels. Soc. Am. (Silver Anvil award 1973), Dog Writers' Assn. Am. (pres. 1984-92, Disting. Svc. award 1993), Dog Writers' Ednl. Trust (vice chmn.), Collie Club Am. (pres. 1984-86), Collie Club Am. Found. (pres. 1990-92), Pi Sigma Alpha, Phi Kappa Sigma. Republican. Avocations: pure-bred dog breeding and showing, power boating, travel, photography. Home and Office: 401 Watson Rd Easley SC 29642

SUNDT, HARRY WILSON, construction company executive; b. Woodbury, N.J., July 5, 1932; s. Thoralf Mauritz and Elinor (Stout) S.; m. Dorothy Van Gilder, June 26, 1954; children: Thomas D., Perri Lee Sundt Touche, Gerald W. BS in Bus. Adminstrn., U. Ariz., 1954, postgrad., 1957-59. Salesman ins. VanGilder Agys., Denver, 1956-57; apprentice carpenter M.M. Sundt Constrn. Co., Tucson, 1957-58, estimator, 1958-59; admnstrv. asst. M.M. Sundt Constrn. Co., Vandenberg AFB, 1959-62; sr. estimator M.M. Sundt Constrn. Co., Tucson, 1962-64, div. mgr., 1964-65, exec. v.p., gen. mgr., 1965-75, pres., chmn., 1975-79; pres., chmn. Sundt Corp., Tucson, 1980-83, chmn., chief exec. officer, 1983—; bd. dirs. Tucson Electric Power Co., Magma Copper Co., 1987—. Pres. Tucson Airport Authority, 1982; bd. dirs. U. Ariz. Found. 1981. 1st lt. U.S. Army, 1954-56. Recipient Disting. Citizen award U. Ariz., 1982, Centennial Medallion award, 1989. Mem. Tucson Country Club, Old Pueblo Club. Republican. Episcopalian. Avocation: tennis. Home: 6002 E San Leandro Tucson AZ 85715-3014 Office: Sundt Corp PO Box 26685 4101 E Irvington Rd Tucson AZ 85714-2118

SUNDT, ROBERT STOUT, construction company executive; b. Phila., Nov. 23, 1926; s. Thoralf M. and Elinor S. Sundt; m. Frances Schmidt; children: Eric, Thea Cummins. Student, Swarthmore Coll., 1944, 46-47; BS, U. Ariz., 1950. With M.M. Sundt Constrn. Co., Tucson, 1948-83, div. mgr. bldg., 1965-75, exec. v.p. constrn. ops., 1975-79, pres., chief exec. officer, 1980-83; pres. Sundt Corp., Tucson, 1983-92; bd. dirs. S.W. Gas Corp., Las Vegas, PriMerit Savs. and Loan Bank Las Vegas. Mem. Constrn. Industry Pres. Forum, adv. com. Ariz. Coun. Econ. Edn. Tucson. Served with USN, 1944-46. Mem. Tucson Met. C. of C. (bd. dirs., chmn. 1989-90), Am. Inst. Constructors, Cons. Constructors Coun. Am., Assoc. Gen. Contractors Am. (bd. dirs., past pres., bd. dirs. Ariz. Bldg. chpt., nat. exec. com. 1991-92). Office: Sundt Corp 4101 E Irvington Rd Tucson AZ 85714-2192

SUNELL, ROBERT JOHN, retired army officer; b. Astoria, Oreg., June 5, 1929; s. Ernest and Grace L. S.; m. JoAnn L. Toikka, Dec. 29, 1951; children—Perry Sunell Peterson, Patti Sunell Sigl, Robert P. Student, U. Oreg., 1949-53; B.E., U. Nebr., 1963; M.S., Shippensburg State Coll., 1973. Commd. U.S. Army, 1953, advanced through grades to maj. gen. 1983, ret., 1987; exec. officer 1st Brigade, 4th Inf. div. U.S. Army, Vietnam, 1966-67, comdr. 2d Bn., 8th Inf., 4th Inf. div., 1969-70; chief Bn. and Brigade Tactical Ops. div. Armor Sch. U.S. Army, Ft. Knox, Ky., 1973-74, dep. dir. Armored Reconnaissance Scout Vehicle Task Force, 1974-76; dep. program mgr. XM1 Tank Systems U.S. Army, Warren, Mich., 1976-78; comdr. 11th Armored Cav. Regt. U.S. Army, Germany, 1978-79; comdr. Army Tng. Support Ctr. U.S. Army, Ft. Eustis, Va, 1980-83; program mgr. Tank Systems U.S. Army, Warren, Mich., 1983-86; dir. Armored Family of Vehicles Task Force, Fort Eustis, Va., 1986-87; pres. Suonperra Inc. Mgmt. and Def. Cons., Williamsburg, Va., 1987—. Decorated Silver Star, Legion of Merit, Bronze Star, Meritorious Service award, Disting. Service medal. Mem. U.S. Army Assn., Armor Assn. Republican.

SUNG, EDWARD, physician; b. Tiensin, China, Nov. 26, 1942; came to U.S., 1959; s. Herbert and T.C. (Chao) S.; m. Sha P., Oct. 10, 1965; children: Jay, Gia. BS, Coll. William & Mary, 1963; MD, Med. Coll. Va., 1967. Resident George Washington U. Hosp. Ctr., Washington, 1974; physician pvt. practice, Atlantic City, N.J., 1975—. Maf. USPHS, 1969-71. Fellow Am. Coll. Obs-Gyn., Am. Coll. Surgeons. Office: Ctrl Obghn Assn 72 Jim Leeds Rd Pomona NJ 08240

SUNG, NAK-HO, science educator; b. Seoul, Republic of Korea, Sept. 30, 1940; s. K.Y. and B.S. (Lee) S.; m. Chong Sook Paik, May 13, 1972; 1 child, Andrew J. BS, Seoul Nat. U., 1964; MS, U. Chgo., 1967; ScD, MIT, 1972. Process engr. Hanil Nylon Industry, Republic of Korea, 1963-66; teaching asst. U. Chgo., 1966-67; rsch. asst. MIT, Cambridge, Mass., 1967-72, rsch. assoc., 1972-74, asst. prof., 1974-78; asst. prof. Tufts U., Medford, Mass., 1978-80, assoc. prof., 1980-85, prof., 1985—; dir. Lab. for Materials Interfaces Lab. for Materials and Interfaces, Medford, Mass., 1989—; vis. prof. Chengdu (China) U. Sci. and Tech., 1983; U. Conn., Storrs, 1985; cons. Sunkyong Group, Seoul, 1976—, U.S. Army Material and Mech. Rsch. Ctr., Watertown, Mass., Johnson and Johnson, W.R. Grace; pres. northeast chpt. Korean Scientists and Engrs. Assn. in Am., Boston, 1977-78. Editor:

Science and Technology of Polymer Processing, 1979; also over 80 publs. and one patent. Bd. dirs. Korean Lang. Sch., Lexington, Mass., Korean Am. Soc. of New Eng. Mem. Am. Chem. Soc., Am. Phys. Soc., Soc. Plastic Engrs., Adhesion Soc., Am. Inst. Chem. Engrs. Office: Tufts Univ Lab for Materials Interfaces Dept Chem Engring Medford MA 02155

SUNIA, TAUESE, government official. Lt. gov. Pago Pago, AS. Office: Lieutenant Gov's Office Pago Pago AS 96799*

SUNLEY, EMIL MCKEE, economist; b. Morgantown, W.Va., July 30, 1942; s. Emil McKee and Nelle Berniece (Traer) S.; m. Judith Evelyn Steere, Dec. 23, 1966; children: Rachel Anne, Gillian Traer, Neil Steere. B.A., Amherst Coll., 1964; M.A., U. Mich., 1965, Ph.D., 1968. Economist office tax analysis Dept. Treasury, Washington, 1968-73; assoc. dir. office tax analysis Dept. Treasury, 1973-75, dep. asst. sec. for tax policy, 1977-81; sr. fellow Brookings Instn., Washington, 1975-77; dir. tax analysis Deloitte & Touche, Washington, 1981-92; asst. dir. fiscal affairs dept. Internat. Monetary Fund, 1992—. Mem. editorial bd. Nat. Tax Jour. Mem. Commn. on RR Retirement Reform, 1987-90. Mem. Am. Econ. Assn., Nat. Tax Assn. (1st v.p. 1994-95), Tax Analysts (bd. dirs. 1982-93). Episcopalian. Office: Fiscal Affairs Dept Rm I53-214 Internat Monetary Fund Washington DC 20431

SUNSTEIN, CASS R., law educator. AB, JD, Harvard U. Bar: D.C. 1980. Prof. Law. Sch. U. Chgo. Author: The Partial Institution, 1993, Democracy and the Problem of Free Speech, 1993 (Goldmsith Book award Harvard U.). Office: U Chgo Sch Law 1111 E 60th St Chicago IL 60637-2702

SUNUNU, JOHN H., former chief of staff President of U.S., former governor; b. Havana, Cuba, July 2, 1939; m. Nancy Hayes, 1958; children—Catherine, Elizabeth, Christina, John, Michael, James, Christopher, Peter. B.S., MIT, 1961, M.S., 1962, Ph.D., 1966. Founder, chief engr. Astro Dynamics, 1960-65; pres. J. H. S. Engring. Co. and Thermal Research Inc., Salem, N.H., 1965-82; assoc. prof. mech. engring. Tufts U., 1966-82; assoc. dean Coll. Engring., Tufts U., 1968-73; mem. N.H. Ho. of Reps., 1973-74, Gov.'s Energy Council, 1973-78; chmn. Gov.'s Com. on N.H. Future, 1977-78; mem. Gov.'s Adv. Com. on Sci. and Tech., 1977-78; gov. State of N.H., Concord, 1983-89; chief of staff White House, Washington, 1989-91, counsellor to the President, 1991-92; co-host pub. affairs TV show Crossfire, CNN, 1992; cons.; pub. speaker, pres. JHS Assoc. Ltd, 1992. Chmn. Coalition of Northeastern Govs., 1985-86; vice chmn. Alliance for Acid Rain Control. Mem. Nat. Govs.' Assn. (vice chmn. 1986-87, chmn. task force on tech., task force on acid rain, chmn. 1987-88), Rep. Govs.' Assn. (chmn. 1985-86), New England Govs.' Assn. (chmn. 1984-85, vice chmn. adv. commn. on intergovtl. relations). Republican. Roman Catholic. Office: 24 Samoset Dr Salem NH 03079-1532 also: JHS Assoc Ltd Ste 1200 815 Connecticut Ave NW Washington DC 20006

SUOJANEN, WAINO W., management educator; b. Maynard, Mass., Jan. 12, 1920; s. Waino I. and Milma (Lindroos) S.; m. Doris G. Stinson, Dec. 24, 1948; children—Wayne William, James Norman. BS, U. Vt., 1942; MBA, Harvard U., 1946; PhD, U. Calif. at Berkeley, 1955. Chief acct. UARCO Inc., Oakland, Calif., 1947-49; div. acct. Chris-Craft Corp., Salem, Oreg., 1949-50; Asst. prof. Sch. Bus. Adminstrn., U. Calif. at Berkeley, 1950-59; assoc. prof. U.S. Naval Postgrad. Sch., Monterey, Calif., 1959-61; dir. research and devel. mgmt. program Air Proving Ground Center, Eglin AFB, Fla., 1961-64; prof. chmn. dept. mgmt. U. Miami, Fla., 1964-70; prof. mgmt. Ga. State U., Atlanta, 1970-90, prof. emeritus, 1990—; adv. editor Chandler Pub. Co., 1965-71; mem. mgmt. adv. panel NASA, 1968-71; cons. U.S. Army Mgmt. Engring. Tng. Activity, 1954-89, U.S. Office Pers. Mgmt., 1964-84; fin. mgmt. cons. to comptr. Office Asst. Sec. Def., 1957-61; cons. in logistics mgmt. tng. Office Assn. Sec. Def. for Installations and Logistics, 1964-66; cons. in mgmt. edn. and tng. Office Asst. Sec. Def. for Manpower, 1966-67; lectr. mgmt. Royal Victorian Chamber Mfrs., Melbourne, Australia, summer 1968; bd. dirs. Russian-Am. Tech. Assocs., 1993—; bd. dirs. Internat. Learning Sys., Inc., 1994—. Author: The Dynamics of Management, 1966, (with others) The Operating Manager-An Integrative Approach, 1974, Perspectives in Job Enrichment and Productivity, 1975, Management and the Brain: An Integrative Approach to Organizational Behavior, 1983. Treas. Alameda County Mental Health Assn., 1953-56; bd. dirs. Vol. Atlanta, 1971-76. Served to capt. AUS, 1943-46; lt. col. USAF Res.; ret. Recipient McKinsey Found. Book award, 1966. Mem. Acad. Mgmt, AAAS, Phi Beta Kappa, Alpha Kappa Psi, Beta Alpha Psi, Beta Gamma Sigma, Pi Gamma Mu, Sigma Iota Epsilon. Home: 1270 Mayflower Ave Melbourne FL 32940-6722

SUOMI, VERNER EDWARD, meteorologist, administrator, inventor; b. Eveleth, Minn., Dec. 6, 1915; s. John E. and Anna Emelia (Sundquist) S.; m. Paula Meyer, Aug. 10, 1941; children: Lois, Stephen, Eric. BE, Winona Tchrs. Coll., 1938; PhD, U.Chgo., 1953; DS (hon.), SUNY, Albany, 1983. Tchr. sci. and math. Minn. Schs., 1938-42; instr. meteorology U. Chgo., 1943-45; prof. meteorology U. Wis., Madison, 1948-86, prof. emeritus, 1986—, founder, dir. Space Sci. and Engring. Ctr., 1966-88, Wexler prof. meteorology, 1972-87; dir. Coop. Inst. for Meteorological Satellite Studies, 1980-84; assoc. program dir. for atmospheric sci. NSF, Washington, 1962; chief scientist U.S. Weather Bur., 1964. Patentee in field: developed flat-plate radiometer, 1957-60, satellite spin-scan weather camera, 1963, balloon-borne radioaltimeter (with N. Levanon), 1968, video display/processing computer system (with staff Space Sci. and Engring. Ctr.), 1972; contbr. articles, books. Recipient Am. Meteorological Soc. awards, 1961, 1968-69, 1980, 88, Losey award AIAA, 1971 NSF Nat. Medal of Sci., 1977, NASA Exceptional Scientist Achievement medal, 1980, Franklin Inst. medal, 1984, NOAA silver medallion, 1985, commemorative medal Soviet Geophysical Comm., 1985, Nat. Scholar award Phi Kappa Phi, 1986, Nev. medal, 1988, Walter Ahlstrom prize Finnish Acads. Tech., 1990, 38th Internat. Meteorological prize WMO, 1993; named Sr. Disting. Research Prof. Wis. Alumnae Research Found., 1984; recognized by Soc. of Exploration Geophysicists/Pecora for application of remote sensing, 1980. Fellow Acad. Arts and Scis.; mem. Am. Meteorol. Soc. (hon.), pres. 1969-70, Meisinger award 1961, Carl-Gustav Rossby Research medal 1968, Charles Franklin Brooks award 1980; hon.), Nat. Acad. Engring., Am. Fedn. Scientists, Am. Geophys. Union, AAUP, Wis. Acad. Sci., Arts and Letters (hon.), Am. Philos. Soc., Finnish Acad. Sci. Deutsch Akademie der Naturforscher Internat. Acad. Astronautics Paris, Phi Beta Kappa, Sigma Xi, Phi Kappa Phi, Sigma Pi Sigma. Home: 10 Rosewood Cir Madison WI 53711-2723 Office: U Wis Space Sci and Engring Ctr 1225 W Dayton St Madison WI 53706-1695*

SUOZZO, FRANK VINCENT, insurance company executive; b. New Haven, Mar. 14, 1928; s. Harry and Lina (Del Grippo) S.; m. Cecilia Margaret Honan, Oct. 22, 1955; children: Frank Vincent, James Harry, Edward John, Elizabeth. B.A., U. Conn., 1952. C.L.U. cert. mgmt. acct. With U.S. Life Ins. Co., N.Y.C., 1952—; 2d v.p. U.S. Life Ins. Co., 1970-74, treas., 1974—, v.p., 1976-83; v.p. fin. ops. USLIFE Corp. (parent co. U.S. Life Ins. Co.), 1983—. Author papers in field. Active local Boy Scouts Am., Little League Baseball. Served with AUS, 1946-47. Recipient Scouters award Boy Scouts Am., 1971. Fellow Life Office Mgmt. Inst.; mem. Inst. Mgmt. Acctg. Roman Catholic. Home: 171 Dewey Ave Staten Island NY 10308 Office: 3600 Rte 66 Neptune NJ 07754

SUPER, ROBERT HENRY, English educator; b. Wilkes-Barre, Pa., June 13, 1914; s. John Henry and Sadie (Rothermel) S.; m. Rebecca Ragsdale, Jan. 25, 1953; children: David Allen, Paul Eric. A.B., Princeton U., 1935, Ph.D., 1941; B.Litt., U. Oxford, Eng. 1937. Instr. English Princeton 1938-42; asst. prof. Mich. State Normal Coll., Ypsilanti, 1942-47; from asst. prof. to prof. U. Mich., Ann Arbor, 1947-84, prof. emeritus, 1984—; vis. prof. Rice U., 1965-66, U. Chgo., summer 1954, UCLA, 1967, U. Calif., Berkeley, 1973, Tex. A&M U., Winter 1984; field intelligence officer Fgn. Econ. Adminstrn., 1945; Harris Found. lectr. Northwestern U., 1968. Author: Walter Savage Landor: A Biography, 1954, The Publication of Landor's Works, 1954, The Time-Spirit of Matthew Arnold, 1970, Trollope in the Post Office, 1981, The Chronicler of Barsetshire: A Life of Anthony Trollope, 1988; Editor: The Complete Prose Works of Matthew Arnold, 11 vols. 1960-77, Anthony Trollope's Marion Fay, 1982, (with Miriam Allott) The Oxford Arnold, 1986, Anthony Trollope's The Fixed Period, 1990, Anthony Trollope's The Landleaguers, 1992. Fulbright research fellow, 1949-50; Am. Council Learned Socs. fellow, 1959-60; Guggenheim fellow, 1962-63, 70-71;

NEH fellow, 1978-79. Fellow Brit. Acad. (corr.). Home: 1221 Baldwin Ave Ann Arbor MI 48104-3623

SUPERKO, H. ROBERT, research physician; b. Bethesda, Md., Jan. 1, 1949; s. Harold Robert and Earlene (Winand) S.; m. Alison. BS, U. Calif., San Diego, 1970; MD, SUNY, 1975. Intern then resident fellow U. Calif. Davis, 1976-80; dir. Sacramento Cardiac Rehab. Clinic, 1980-81; med. dir. Lipid Rsch. Clinic Stanford (Calif.) U., 1981—; med. dir. cholesterol rsch. Lawrence Berkeley Lab. U. Calif., Berkeley, 1991—; dir. Ctr. Progressive Atherusclerosis Mgmt. Alta Bates-Herrick Hosp., Berkeley, 1990—; bd. dirs. Am. Coll. Sports medicine, Mpls., 1988—. Contbr. 12 chpts. to books and over 50 articles to profl. jours. Recipient numerous sci. rsch. grants. Mem. Am. Heart Assn. (pres. San Mateo chpt. 1988-90, bd. dirs. Dallas chpt. 1990—), Am. Assn. Cardiac Rehab. (bd. dirs. 1988—). Achievements include discovery that decaffeinated coffee causes increased LDL-cholesterol. Home: 730 Welch Rd Ste B Palo Alto CA 94304-1505 Office: Ctr Prog Atherusclerosis Mgmt 3030 Telegraph Ave Berkeley CA 94705-2037

SUPLEE, DENNIS RAYMOND, lawyer; b. Phila., Jan. 20, 1943; s. Raymond C. and Miriam C. (Morris) S.; m. Patricia H. Hickey; children: David A., Christopher D., Richard C. BS, St. Joseph's U., 1964; LLB, U. Pa., 1967. Bar: Pa. 1967. Assoc. Schnader, Harrison, Segal & Lewis, Phila., 1967-74, ptnr., 1975—; mem. exec. com., 1986-89, 91-92, chmn. exec. com., 1992—; mem. Sec. Navy's Adv. Bd. on Edn. and Tng., Washington, 1985-87. Author: (with others) The Dep. Handbook, 2d edit., 1992, Expert Witness: Law and Practice, 1993; contbr. articles to profl. jours. Mem. Pres.'s Council St. Joseph's U., Phila., 1983—; pres. North Ardmore Civil Assn., Ardmore, Pa., 1987-88. Mem. Pa. Bar Assn. (ho. of dels. 1988-89), Phila. Assn. Def. Counsel (pres. 1994-95), Phila. Country Club, Union League. Democrat. Roman Catholic. Avocations: tennis, badminton. Home: 127 St Georges Rd Ardmore PA 19003-2505 Office: Schnader Harrison Segal & Lewis 1600 Market St Philadelphia PA 19103-7240

SUPPE, JOHN, geology educator; b. L.A., Nov. 30, 1942. BA, U. Calif., Riverside, 1965; PhD, Yale U., 1969; postgrad, UCLA, 1969-71. From asst. to full prof. Princeton U., 1971—, Blair prof. of geology; now dept. chmn.; vis. prof. Nat. Taiwan U., 1978-79, 83-84, Calif. Inst. Tech., 1988-89. Guggenheim fellow. Office: Princeton U Dept Geology Princeton NJ 08544

SUPPES, PATRICK, statistics, education, philosophy and psychology educator; b. Tulsa, Mar. 17, 1922; s. George Biddle and Ann (Costello) S.; m. Joan Farmer, Apr. 16, 1946 (div. 1970); children: Patricia, Deborah, John Biddle; m. Joan Sieber, Mar. 29, 1970 (div. 1973); m. Christine Johnson, May 26, 1979; children: Alexandra Christine, Michael Patrick. B.S., U. Chgo., 1943; Ph.D. (Wendell T. Bush fellow), Columbia U., 1950; LL.D., U. Nijmegen, Netherlands, 1979; Dr. honoris causa, Académie de Paris, U. Paris V, 1982. Instr., Stanford U., 1950-52, asst. prof., 1952-55, assoc. prof., 1955-59, prof. philosophy, statistics, edn. and psychology, 1959-92, prof. emeritus; founder, chief exec. officer Computer Curriculum Corp., 1967-90. Author: Introduction to Logic, 1957, Axiomatic Set Theory, 1960, Sets and Numbers, books 1-6, 1966, Studies in the Methodology and Foundations of Science, 1969, A Probabilistic Theory of Causality, 1970, Logique du Probable, 1981, Probabilistic Metaphysics, 1984, Estudios de Filosofia y Metodologí de la Ciencia, 1988, Language for Humans and Robots, 1991, Models and Methods in the Philosophy of Science, 1993; (with Davidson and Siegel) Decision Making, 1957, (with Richard C. Atkinson) Markov Learning Models for Multiperson Interactions, 1960, (with Shirley Hill) First Course in Mathematical Logic, 1964, (with Edward J. Crothers) Experiments on Second-Language Learning, 1967, (with Max Jerman and Dow Brian) Computer-assisted Instruction, 1965-66, Stanford Arithmetic Program, 1968, (with D. Krantz, R.D. Luce and A. Tversky) Foundations of Measurement, Vol. 1, 1971, (with M. Morningstar) Computer-Assisted Instruction at Stanford, 1966-68, 1972, (with B. Searle and J. Friend) The Radio Mathematics Project: Nicaragua, 1974-75, 1976 (with D. Krantz, R.D. Luce and A. Tversky) Foundations of Measurement, Vol. 2, 1989, Vol. 3, 1990, (with Colleen Crangle) Language and Learning for Robots, 1994. Served to capt. USAAF, 1942-46. Recipient Nicholas Murray Butler Silver medal Columbia, 1965, Disting. Sci. Contbr. award Am. Psychol. Assn., 1972, Tchrs. Coll. medal for disting. service, 1978, Nat. medal Sci. NSF, 1990; Center for Advanced Study Behavioral Scis. fellow, 1955-56; NSF fellow, 1957-58. Fellow AAAS, Am. Psychol. Assn., Am. Acad. Arts and Scis., Assn. Computing Machinery; mem. NAS, Math. Assn. Am., Psychometric Soc., Am. Philos. Assn., Am. Philos. Soc., Assn. Symbolic Logic, Am. Math Soc., Académie Internationale de Philosophie des Scis. (titular), Nat. Acad. Edn. (pres. 1973-77), Am. Psychol. Assn., Internat. Inst. Philosophy, Finnish Acad. Sci. and Letters, Internat. Union History and Philosophy of Sci. (div. logic, methodology and philosophy of sci., pres. 1975-79), Am. Ednl. Research Assn. (pres. 1973-74), Croatian Acad. Scis. (corr.), Russian Acad. Edn. (fgn.), Norwegian Acad. Sci. and Letters (fgn.), European Acad. Scis. and Arts, Chilean Acad. Scis., Sigma Xi.

SUPPLE, JEROME H., university president; b. Boston, Apr. 27, 1936; m. Catherine Evans; 3 children. BS in Chemistry, Boston Coll., 1957, MS in Organic Chemistry, 1959; PhD in Organic Chemistry, U. New Hampshire, 1963. Asst. prof. chemistry SUNY Coll., Fredonia, 1964-69, assoc. prof., 1969-76, prof., 1976-78, acting dept. chair, 1975-76, assoc. dean for arts and scis., 1972-73, assoc. v.p. for acad. affairs, 1973-78, acting v.p. for acad. affairs, 1977, dean for gen. and spl. studies, 1977-78; assoc. provost for undergrad. edn. SUNY Cen. Adminstrn., 1974-75; prof. chemistry, v.p. for acad. affairs SUNY Coll., Plattsburgh, acting pres., 1978-89, on leave 1988-89; acting provost, v.p. for acad. affairs SUNY Coll., Postdsam, 1988-89; prof. chemistry, pres. S.W. Tex. State U., San Marcos, 1989—; Faculty fellow NSF, vis. rsch. faculty U. East Anglia, Norwich, Eng., 1970-71. Author books; contbr. numerous articles to profl. jours. Mem. Tex. Gov.'s total quality mgmt. steering com. Eastman Kodak rsch. fellow. Mem. AAAS, Am. Chem. Soc., Am. Assn. Higher Edn., Am. Assn. State Colls. and Univs., Am. Coun. on Edn. (bd. dirs.), Am. Assn. State Colls. and Schs. Common. on Colls., Tex. Coun. on Econ. Edn. (bd. dirs.), Tex. Assn. Coll. Tchrs., Tex. Higher Edn. Master Plan Adv. Com., San Marcos of C. Econ. Devel. Coun., San Marcos Rotary, Golden Key, Sigma Xi (past pres. Fredonia club), Phi Eta Sigma (hon.), Omicron Delta Kappa (hon.). Office: SW Tex State U Office of Pres 1020 J C Kellam Bldg San Marcos TX 78666

SUPUT, RAY RADOSLAV, librarian; b. Columbus, Ohio, May 13, 1922; s. Elias and Darinka (Balac) S.; m. Mary Grace Hansen, May 23, 1953 (dec. Nov. 1980); children: David Ray, Dorothy Mary; m. Milana Preradov, July 12, 1986. B.A., Ohio State U., 1950; M.S.L.S., Case Western Res. U., 1951, Ph.D., 1972; M.A., U. Chgo., 1955. Librarian Northwestern U., Evanston, Ill., 1951-52; reference and circulation librarian Law Library, U. Chgo., 1952-54, cataloger, 1954-57; asso. librarian Garrett-Evang. Theol. Sem., Evanston, 1957-58; head librarian Garrett-Evang. Theol. Sem., 1958-64; asst. dir. libraries and adj. lectr. dept. Slavic and E. European langs. Sch. Library Sci. Case Western Res. U., Cleve., 1964-67; acting dir. libraries Case Western Res. U., 1967-68; adj. instr. Case Western Res. U. (Sch. Library Sci.), 1965-69; librarian Case Western Res. U. (Freiberger Library), 1968-69; dir. univ. library, head dept. and prof. library sci. Ball State U., Muncie, Ind., 1969-78; univ. librarian, head dept. and prof. library service Ball State U., 1978-81, prof. library service, also adj. prof. library sci., 1981-82, chmn. dept. library and info. sci., prof. library sci., 1982-87, prof. library sci., info. sci. emeritus, 1987—. Contbr. articles to profl. jours. Nat. Endowment for Humanities and Council on Library Resources Inc. grantee. Mem. ALA, AAUP, African Violet Soc. Am., Am. Theol. Libr. Assn., Serb Nat. Fedn., Ohio Hist. Soc. Eastern Orthodox.

SURACE, RONALD J., real estate executive; b. Little Falls, N.Y., Feb. 13, 1944; s. John Paul and Mary Ann (Mastromameo) S.; m. Mary Jane Vasquez, Nov. 10, 1973; children: James Anthony, Stephanie Lee. BS in Sociology, Iowa State U., 1963; MA in Sociology, U. No. Colo., 1972. Cert. C.C. instr., Calif. Adminstrv. mgr. Comml. Union Ins., Denver and Fresno, 1981-84, Hanover Ins., Sacramento, 1984-90; ops. mgr. AIG Corp., L.A., 1990-93; COO Am Indsl. Real Estate Assn., L.A., 1993—. Mem. human rels. com. City of Aurora, Colo., 1980; com. mem. Lottery Commn. for Edn., Moorpark, Calif., 1992-94; soccer coach AYSO, Moorpark, 1994. Capt. USAF, 1965-70, Vietnam. Mem. Phi Kappa Tau (v.p. 1964-65). Republi-

can. Roman Catholic. Avocations: philately, soccer, bridge, writing, jogging. Home: 4160 Shady Point Dr Moorpark CA 93021 Office: Am Indsl Real Estate Assn 345 S Figueroa St Los Angeles CA 90071

SURACI, CHARLES XAVIER, JR., retired federal agency administrator, aerospace education consultant; b. Washington, Feb. 10, 1933; s. Charles Xavier and June Celcia (Hunter) S.; m. Florence Patricia De Mino, May 23, 1970. Cadet, Penn Mil. Coll. (now Widener U.), 1951-53; grad., Nat. Acad. Broadcasting Sch. Washington, 1959; student, Columbia Union Coll., 1962-63, 72, Catholic U., 1969; grad. extension course, CAP Staff Coll., 1974; BA, Calif. Christian Coll., 1977, HHD (hon.), 1977; grad., USAF Inspectors Gen. Sch., Eglin AFB, Fla., 1982; also grad. numerous other govt. schs. and courses. Served with USAF, 1953-57; enlisted CAP, 1957, commd. 1st lt., 1961; advanced through ranks to Col. CAP USAF Aux, 1974; co-founder Wheaton-Silver Spring Cadet Squadron; comdr. Nat. Capital Wing, 1973-76; dep. chief of staff cadet activities Middle East region, 1977-79, dir. cadet tng., 1979-82, insp. gen., 1982—; with Harry Diamond Lab., U.S. Army, Adelphi, Md., 1963—, material publs. asst., 1963-68, later asst. to motor transp. officer, now supply specialist, logistics sect. Mem. youth com. YMCA, Silver Spring, Md., 1962-69, mem. bd. mgmt., 1967—; bd. dirs. Am. Youth Com.; mem. Commn. on Children and Youth Bd. Montgomery County, Md.; mem. Montgomery County Juvenile Ct. Com., 1978-86; choir mem. Blessed Sacrament Cath. Ch., Washington; co-chmn. Right to Life Com. K.C.-Rosensteel Coun. Recipient Leader and Svc. award Silver Spring YMCA, 1968, 69, CAP Meritorious Svc. award Dept. Def., 1969, 1977, cert. of commendation from Pres. Richard Nixon, 1970, CAP Exceptional Service award Congressman Lester Wolff of N.Y., 1972, award Montgomery County C. of C., 1973, commendation Gov. of Tenn., 1975, letter of commendation Washington Mayor Walter Washington, 1977, Dept. Outstanding Patriotic Civilian Service award, 1977, Md. Vol. Cmty. honor award Montgomery County, 1981, Vol. Activist award, 1984; named Air Man of Month USAF, 1956; grand marshall Rockville, Md., Meml. Day parade, 1971; honored by Md. Ho. Dels., 1974, D.C. Govt., 1977; recipient numerous AF and CAP ribbons and medals, Dept. of Army Spl. Act or Svc. award, Dept.of the Army Superior Performance award, 1987, Pres.'s Vol. Action award nomination Pres. of the U.S., 1988, 1991, Cmty. Svc. award Wheaton-Kensington News, Bethesda Chevy Chase Current, Montgomery County Press Assn., 1990, Outstanding support Aviation Career Day Tuskegee Airmen and Commdg. Gen. of D.C. Air Nat. Guard, 1992, spl. award State of Md. for training over 1000 youth cadets in the CAP in 31 yrs., 1986, plaque name displayed at U.S. Army-Harry Diamond Lab, Adelphi, Md., Pro-Life award Knights of Columbus-Rosensteel Coun., 1992, Frank G. Brewer Meml. Aerospace award-CAP Middle East Region HQ, 1984, 1991, 1992, CAP-U.S. Air Force Auxiliary Meritorious Svc. award Middle East Region HQ, 1993, Man of the Year award State of Md. Air Force Assn., 1993, Cert. Appreciation Md. Air Force Assn. Aerospace Edn., 1993-95, Exceptional Svc. award U.S. Air Force Auxiliary, 1994-95. Mem. Air Force Assn. (bd. dirs., v.p. aerospace edn. Thomas W. Anthony chpt. Andrews AFB, Md., medal of Merit 1990, Exceptional svc. award 1991, 94, Disting. Svc. as Inspector Gen. 1991), Nat. Aerospace Assn., Navy League, Army Aviation Assn., Fed. Ret. Employees Assn., Tuskegee Airmen Inc., Mil. Order of World Wars, Nat. Officers Assn., Md. Press Assn. Montgomery County, Md. Private Industry Coun. (bd. dirs. Opportunity Skyway program), Knights of Columbus (chmn. Pro-Life Father Rosensteel coun., Outstanding Leadership Pro-Life activities 1990-91, Outstanding Svc. award 1993-94), Alumni Assn. Widener U. Democrat. Club: Andrews AFB Officers (Md.). Lodge: KC. 2 plaques in his name displayed at Columbia Union Coll., Takoma Park, Md., Widener U. (formerly Pa. Mil. Coll.), Chester. Home: Rock Creek Hills 9817 La Duke Dr Kensington MD 20895-3156 Office: USAF Aux CAP Mid East Region Hdqrs Office of Insp Gen 9817 La Duke Dr Kensington MD 20895-3156

SURATT, PAUL MICHAEL, physician, researcher; b. Ft. Lewis, Wash., Jan. 5, 1944; s. Theodore Paul and Ruth (Habink) S. BA, Columbia U., 1966; MD, Case Western Res. U., 1970. Diplomate Am. Bd. Internal Medicine. Intern, then resident in internal medicine U. Va. Sch. Medicine, Charlottesville, 1970-75, asst. prof. internal medicine, 1975-80, assoc. prof., 1980-88, prof., 1988—; organizer 1st Internat. Symposium on Sleep Apnea, 1989, 2d, 1991. Contbr. articles to med. jours. Maj. Va. N.G., 1971-77. Fellow Am. Coll. Internal Medicine, Am. Coll. Chest Physicians; mem. Am. Thoracic Soc., Am. Sleep Apnea Assn. (pres. 1989-93). Avocations: hiking, cycling, skiing, reading. Office: U Va Health Sci Ctr PO Box 546 Charlottesville VA 22902-0546

SURBECK, LEIGHTON HOMER, retired lawyer; b. Jasper, Minn., Oct. 8, 1902; s. James S. and Kathryn (Kilpatrick) S.; m. Margaret H. Packard, 1976. B.S., S.D. State Sch. Mines, 1924; J.D. magna cum laude, Yale, 1927; L.H.D., S.D. Sch. Mines and Tech., 1957; LL.D., Central Coll., 1973; D.Humanitarian Services, Northwestern Coll., Iowa, 1980; LL.D., Hope Coll., 1986. Bar: N.Y. 1929. Law sec. to Chief Justice Taft, 1927-28; assoc. Hughes, Schurman & Dwight, N.Y.C., 1928-34; mem. firm Hughes, Schurman & Dwight, 1934-37; mem. firm Hughes, Hubbard & Reed, N.Y.C., 1937-70, counsel, 1981-70. Author: Success on the Job, 1957, The Success Formula that Really Works, 1986. Trustee Pacific Sch. Religion, Berkeley, Calif., 1962-80, Golden Gate U., San Francisco, 1979-91, Central Coll., Pella, Iowa, 1966-78, Collegiate Boy's Sch., N.Y.C., 1975-78; chmn. Yale Law Sch. Fund, 1971-75. Served as col. AUS, 1942-45; chief econ. br. M.I. 1944-45. Recipient Yale medal Yale Alumni, 1975, Distinguished Service award Yale Law Sch., 1976; Horatio Alger award, 1977; named Centennial Alumnus State of S.D., 1989. Mem. ABA, N.Y. State Bar Assn., N.Y. County Bar Assn., Assn. of Bar of City of N.Y., Siwanoy Country Club, Univ. Club (N.Y.C.), Menlo Country Club (Woodside, Calif.), Masons, Order of Coif, Sigma Tau, Delta Theta Phi. Mem. Marble Collegiate Ch. (elder 1962-78). Home: 88 Faxon Rd Menlo Park CA 94027-4046 *Every honest, best effort prayerfully and with enthusiasm toward noble purposes useful beyond self always pays off handsomely, often at the most unexpected time, in the most unexpected ways and from the most unexpected sources.*

SURBER, EUGENE LYNN, architect; b. Hagerstown, Md., May 15, 1938; s. Eugene Wicker and Kathryn Gertrude (Hunt) S.; m. Margaret Ann Sparks, May 7, 1983; 1 child, James Eugene. BArch, Ga. Inst. Tech., 1964. Registered architect, Ga. Intern architect Edwards & Portman Architects, Atlanta, 1964-65, J. Robert Carlton & Assocs., Richmond, Va., 1965-66; assoc. architect Jova/Daniels/Busby Architects, Atlanta, 1966-71; prin. Surber & Barber Architects, Inc., Atlanta, 1971—; mem. bldg. com. Cath. Archdiocese Atlanta, 1990—, chmn., 1994—. Prin. works include N.E.-Intown YWCA (Ga. Trust award 1992), Newman Presbyn. Ch. (Ga. Trust award 1992), The Buggyworks (Fulton City Devel. award 1987), The Castle (Atlanta Urban Design award 1991), Wade Hampton Clubhouse and Cottages (So. Home awards 1990), Hillcrest Chapel (Ga. Trust award 1991), Byron Depot (Ga. Trust award 1991), Upson House (Ga. Trust award 1980), Franklin House (Ga. Trust award 1986), Acad. of Medicine (Ga. Assn. AIA award 1983, Ga. Trust award 1985). Past chmn. Ga. Nat. Register Rev. Bd., 1990; trustee Ga. Trust for Historic Preservation, Atlanta, chmn. restoration com., v.p. Atlanta Med. Heritage. Lt. USN, 1961-64. Fellow AIA (sec. Atlanta chpt. 1989-90, v.p. 1990-91, Hist. Preservation award 1986, Ivan Allen Sr. award 1992, Bronze medal 1974), Ga. Assn. AIA (state preservation coord. 1986—, Excellence in Architecture award 1983, Bronze medal 1993). Avocation: gardening. Office: Surber & Barber Archs Inc 1389 Peachtree St NE Ste 350 Atlanta GA 30309-3038

SURDAM, ROBERT MCCLELLAN, retired banker; b. Albany, N.Y., Oct. 28, 1917; s. Burke and LeMoyne (McClellan) S.; m. Mary Caroline Buhl, July 8, 1946; children—Peter Buhl, Robert McClellan, Mary Caroline. B.A. cum laude, Williams Coll., 1939. With Nat. Bank Detroit, 1947-88, exec. v.p., 1964-66, pres., 1966-72, chmn. bd., 1972-82, also bd. dirs., 1966-88. Served to lt. comdr. USNR, 1941-46. Mem. Detroit Club, Country Club of Detroit, Yondotega Club, Jupiter Island Club (Hobe Sound Fla.), Little Traverse Yacht Club (Harbor Springs, Mich.), Rolling Rock Club (Ligonier, Pa.), Hobe Sound Yacht Club. Home: 396 Provencal Rd Grosse Pointe MI 48236-2959 Office: 333 W Fort St Detroit MI 48226-3115

SURDOVAL, DONALD JAMES, accounting and management consulting company executive; b. N.Y.C., Aug. 26, 1932; s. Donald J. and Catherine A. (Slevin) S.; m. Patricia Fitzpatrick, May 28, 1955; children: Donald, Lisa,

John, Catherine, Brian. B.B.A., Manhattan Coll., 1954. C.P.A., N.Y., N.J. Mgr. Touche Ross & Co., 1956-63; treas. Mohican Corp., 1963-65; asst. controller, then v.p., controller Litton Industries, 1965-68; v.p., controller Norton Simon Inc., N.Y.C., 1968-81; owner Donald J. Surdoval, C.P.A. and Mgmt. Cons. Co., Waldwick, N.J., 1982—; dir. Fuller O'Brien Paint Co. Bd. dirs. Calvary Hosp., N.Y.C., Our Lady of Mercy Hosp. Served to 1st lt. USMCR, 1954-56. Mem. Fin. Execs. Inst., Hackensack Golf Club, Saddle River Valley Lions (treas.). Home: 12 Warewoods Rd Saddle River NJ 07458-2713 Office: 20 Franklin Tpke Waldwick NJ 07463-1749

SURJAATMADJA, JIM BASUKI, research engineer; b. Malang, Indonesia, Apr. 17, 1945; came to U.S., 1971; s. Rudolph and Gwat Nio (Oei) S.; m. Agnes Irmawati Said, Aug. 26, 1971; children: Sylvia Michelle, Amy Lynn. MS, Inst. Technol. Bandung, Bandung, Indonesia, 1970, Okla. State U., 1972, PhD, Okla. State U., 1976. Registered profl. engr., Okla. System engr. IBM, Jakarta, Indonesia, 1970-71; rsch. asst. Okla. State U., Stillwater, 1972-76; project engr. Fluid Power Rsch., Stillwater, 1972-76; from engr. to prin. engr. Halliburton Energy Svcs., Duncan, Okla., 1976—. Author: Introduction to Fluid Logic, 1976; contbr. articles to profl. jours; patentee in field. Recipient Young Engrs. award S.W. region Okla. Soc. Profl. Engrs., 1979, Okla. Soc. Profl. Engrs., 1980. Fellow ASME; mem. Soc. Petroleum Engrs., U.S. Water Jet Tech. Assn. Avocations: mechanics, music. Home: 1105 Timbercreek Dr Duncan OK 73533-3235 Office: Halliburton Energy Svcs 2600 S 2d Duncan OK 73536

SURKS, MARTIN I., medical educator, endocrinologist; b. N.Y.C., May 21, 1934. A.B., Columbia U., 1956; M.D., NYU, 1960. Diplomate Nat. Bd. Med. Examiners, Am. Bd. Internal Medicine, Am. Bd. Endocrinology and Metabolism; lic. physician, N.Y. State. Intern Montefiore Hosp., N.Y.C., 1960-61, jr. asst. resident in medicine, 1961-62; sr. asst. resident VA Hosp., Bronx, 1962-63; postdoctoral research fellow Nat. Inst. Arthritis and Metabolic Diseases, 1963-64; assoc. in medicine Albert Einstein Coll. Medicine, Bronx, 1967-69, asst. prof. medicine, 1969-72, assoc. prof., 1972-78, prof., 1978—, assoc. prof. lab. medicine, 1978-85, prof., 1985—, prof. pathology, 1994—; co-dir. endocrine rsch. lab. Montefiore Hosp., Bronx, 1969-76, head div. endocrinology and metabolism, 1976—, attending, 1981—; attending N. Cen. Bronx Hosp., 1976—; Van Meter lectr. Am. Thyroid Assn., Seattle, 1973; mem. merit rev. bd. VA, 1976-79; mem. endocrine study sect. NIH, 1981-85. Editorial bd. Endocrinology, 1974-78, Endocrine Research Communications, 1974—, Am. Jour. Physiology: Endocrinology and Metabolism, 1982-85, Jour. Clinical Endocrinol Metabolism, 1991—; assoc. editor Endocrinology, 1986-87. Contbr. articles to profl. jours. Served to capt. M.C., U.S. Army, 1964-66. Grantee U.S. Army, Am. Cancer Soc., USPHS, Nat. Cancer Inst.; Schering fellow, 1968. Fellow ACP; mem. Am. Thyroid Assn. (Van Meter prize, 1973; program com. 1975-77, 3d v.p. 1976-77, chair membership com. 1977-78, 80-81, dir. 1982-83, 87-90, nominating com. 1982-85, chair awards and prizes com. 1983-84, sec. 1993—), Endocrine Soc. (manpower liaison com. 1983-86), N.Y. Zool. Soc., Am. Fedn. Clin. Rsch., Am. Bd. of Internal Medicine (sect. of endocrinology and metabolism 1987-91, chmn. 1991-95, bd. dirs. 1991-95), Harvey Soc., Am. Physiology Soc., AAAS, Am. Soc. Clin. Investigation, European Thyroid Assn. (corr.), Assn. Am. Physicians, Am. Soc. Cell Biology, Interurban Clin. Club (councillor 1987-89), Phi Beta Kappa, Alpha Omega Alpha. Office: Montefiore Med Ctr 111 E 210th St Bronx NY 10467-2490

SURLES, CAROL D., university president; b. Pensacola, Fla., Oct. 7, 1946; d. Elza Allen and Versy Lee Smith; divorced; children: Lisa Surles, Philip Surles. BA, Fisk U. 1968; MA, Chapman Coll., 1971; PhD, U. Mich., 1978. Personnel rep. U. Mich., Ann Arbor, 1973-78; vice chancellor-adminstrn. U. Mich., Flint, 1987-89; exec. asst. to pres. U. Ctrl. Fla., Orlando, 1978-84, assoc. v.p. for human resources, 1984-87; v.p. acad. affairs Jackson State U., Miss., 1989-92; v.p. adminstrn. and bus. Calif. State U., Hayward, 1992-94; pres. Tex. Woman's U., Denton, Dallas, Houston, 1994—. Bd. trustees Pub. Broadcasting Ch. 24, Orlando, 1985-87. Am. Assn. Colls. and U., Golden Key Honor Soc., Dallas Citizen's Coun., Dallas Women's Found., U. Coll. Press., Austin, Tex.; bd., ex-officio Denton C. of C., Tex., 1994—. Methodist. Avocation: playing piano and oboe. Office: Tex Woman's U 1322 Oakland ACT 15 Denton TX 76201

SURLES, RICHARD HURLBUT, JR., law librarian; b. Norfolk, Va., Mar. 28, 1943; s. Richard H. and Elda Florine (Belvin) S.; m. Judith Louise Coffin, May 29, 1964; children—Stephanie Anne, Richard H. B.A., Tex. A&M U., 1963; J.D., U.Houston, 1967; M.L.L., U.Wash., 1969. Bar: Colo. 1971. asst. to law librarian U. Houston, 1966-68; asst. to law librarian King county Law Library, Seattle, 1968-69; dir. of law library, prof. law U. Denver, 1969-71, U. Tenn., Knoxville, 1971-76, U. Oreg., Eugene, 1976-81; dir. of law library, prof. law U. Ill., Champaign, 1981—, prof. libr. adminstrn., 1991. Author: Legal Periodical Management Data, 1977. Mem. Am. Assn. Law Libraries. Republican. Office: Ill Coll of Law 504 E Pennsylvania Ave Champaign IL 61820-6909

SURO, DARIO, artist, diplomat; b. La Vega, Dominican Republic, June 13, 1917; s. Jaime and Isabel Emilia (Garcia-Godoy) S.; m. Ada Maruxa Franco; children: Federico, Rosa. Studied with, Enrique Garcia Godoy, 1935-37, Diego Rivera, Agustin Lazo, Mexico City, 1943-46. Cultural attache Embassy of Dominican Rep., Mexico City, 1943-47, Madrid, 1950-63; cultural attache Embassy of Dominican Rep., Washington, 1963-65, cultural counselor, 1965-67, minister counselor of cultural affairs, 1967-70, minister plenipotentiary, dep. chief of mission, 1970—; delegate Congress of Latin Am. Intellectual Cooperation, Madrid, 1947; dir. gen. of fine arts Govt. of the Dominican Rep., Santo Domingo, 1947-50; attache permanent mission of the Dominican Rep. to the OAS, 1963-65, minister counselor, 1967-80; counselor permanent mission of the OAS, Washington, 1965-67; ambassador, alternate rep. of the Dominican Rep. to the OAS, Washington, 1980—; mem. jury 1st Caribbean Biennial, 1992; lectr. in art. Author: Arte Dominicano, 1969, several other books and catalogues; one-man shows include Palace Fine Arts, Mexico City, 1946, Galería Caralt, Barcelona, 1952, Poindexter Gallery, N.Y.C., 1962, Nat. Gallery Modern Art, 1981, La Galeria, Santo Domingo, 1985, 87, numerous others; exhibited in numerous group shows, including Salon de los Once, Madrid, 1951, Carnegie Inst., Pitts., 1952, Martin Luther King Meml. Libr., Washington, 1981, Casa de Bastidas, Santo Domingo, 1982, La Galeria, 1986, Cuban Mus., Miami Fla., 1988, Montclair Mus., 1992, Noyes Mus., 1993; paintings reproduced in numerous publs. Recipient Silver medal 2d Nat. Biennial Fine Arts, Santo Domingo, 1944, Gold medal, 1946, Eloy Alfaro Internat. Found. medal Panama, 1954, First Nat. Fine Arts Achievement award Santo Domingo, 1993. Roman Catholic. Home: 5211 Western Ave NW Washington DC 20015-2126 Office: Embassy of Dominican Rep 1715 22nd St NW Washington DC 20008-1998

SUROVELL, EDWARD DAVID, real estate company executive; b. Washington, Mar. 20, 1940; s. Samuel and Florence Deborah (Starfield) S.; m. Barbara Ann Bartelmes, Apr. 26, 1958 (div. Jan. 1974); children: David Alexander, Claire Katherine. AB, Columbia Coll., 1962; postgrad., U. Mich., 1968-71. Lic. real estate broker, Mich. Copy editor Harcourt, Brace & World, Inc., N.Y.C., 1963-65; editor Princeton (N.J.) U. Press, 1965-67, Scott, Foresman Co., Glenview, Ill., 1967-68, U. Mich., Ann Arbor, 1970-73; real estate agt. Fletcher & Klein, Inc., Ann Arbor, 1973-75; sales mgr. Charles Reinhart Co., Ann Arbor, 1975-82; pres. Edward Surovell Co., Realtors, Ann Arbor, 1982—. Chmn. Ann Arbor City Planning Commn., 1988; active Downtown Devel. Authority, Ann Arbor, 1991—, vice chair, 1994-95. Mem. Nat. Assn. Realtors (bd. govs. RB coun. 1987-91), Mich. Bd. Profl. Community Planners, Hist. Soc. Mich. (bd. dirs. 1992—), Ann Arbor Bd. Realtors (v.p. 1984, pres. 1985, Realtor of Yr. 1990), Univ. Mus. Soc. (bd. dirs. 1992—). Democrat. Jewish. Avocations: book collecting, arts philanthropy. Home: Box 2024 Vinewood Blvd Ann Arbor MI 48104-3614 Office: Edward Surovell Co/Realtors 1886 W Stadium Blvd Ann Arbor MI 48103-7007

SURPRENANT, MARK CHRISTOPHER, lawyer; b. Providence, Oct. 12, 1951; s. William and Margaret Surprenant; m. Monica Tufano; children: Christopher, Jennifer, Jeffrey. BA, Fordham U., 1973; JD, Loyola U., New Orleans, 1977. Ptnr. Adams & Reese, New Orleans, 1977—. Contbr. to vols. 22, 24, 26 Loyola Law Rev., 1977-80. Pres. Southwest Edn. Devel. Lab, Austin, Tex., 1986—. Mem. ABA, La. Bar Assn., New Orleans Def. Counsel (bd. dirs. 1983-87), Loyola Law Alumni Assn. (pres. 1983-84), Loyola U. Alumni Assn. (pres. 1986-87), Greater New Orleans Athletic

League, New Orleans C. of C. (met. edn. com.). Office: Adams & Reese One Shell Sq Ste 4500 New Orleans LA 70139

SURRENCY, ERWIN CAMPBELL, librarian, educator; b. Jesup, Ga., May 11, 1924; s. H.W. and Mary (Campbell) S.; m. Ida E. Winn, Sept. 2, 1945; children—Robert Erwin, Ellen Gwinn Surrency Orwig. Student, N.Ga. Coll., 1940-41; A.B., U. Ga., 1947, LL.B., 1948, M.A., 1949; M.A. in Library Sci, George Peabody U., 1950. Law librarian Temple U., Phila., 1950-78; asst. prof. law Temple U. 1951-54, asso. prof., 1954-60, prof., 1960-72, asst. dean, law librarian, 1972-78; prof. law, law librarian U. Ga., Athens, 1979—; vis. prof. Queen's U., Belfast, No. Ireland, 1963-64; library cons. Am. Bar Found., 1953-54; cons. Nigerian Inst. Advanced Legal Studies, 1975-76. Author: The Marshall Reader, 1955, (with Carrol C. Moreland) Research in Pennsylvania Law, 1953, 2d edit., 1965, A History of Federal Courts, 1987; editor: History of American Legal Literature, 1989; editor Am. Jour. Legal History, 1957—. Mem. Am. Assn. Law Libraries (v.p. 1972-73, pres. 1973-74), Am. Soc. Legal History (pres. 1957-58, 66-69), Ga. Hist. Soc., Selden Soc. Home: 1320 Hickory Hill Dr Watkinsville GA 30677-2127 Office: U Ga Law Sch Law Libr Athens GA 30602 *It is imperative that a successful person avoid superficiality and approach all duties presented him meticulously, with humility and with a faith in his own ability to cope with these challenges and with an abiding faith in the future.*

SURREY, MILT, artist; b. N.Y.C., Mar. 18, 1922; s. Leopold and Pauline (Zipper) Schleifer; m. Eleanor Gallant, Sept. 15, 1946; children—Elaine, Robert, David. Student, Coll. City N.Y., 1939-42. Represented in permanent collections, Allentown (Pa.) Art Mus., Butler Inst. Am. Art, Youngstown, Ohio, Cin. Art Mus., Coll. Mus., Hampton (Va.) Inst., Columbia (S.C.) Mus. Art, Davenport (Iowa) Mus., Detroit Inst. Arts, Evansville (Ind.) Mus. Art, Hickory (N.C.) Mus. Art, Jacksonville (Fla.) Art Mus., Lowe Art Center, Syracuse (N.Y.) U., Massillon (Ohio) Mus., Miami (Fla.) Mus. Modern Art, Springfield (Mo.) Art Mus., Telfair Acad. Arts and Scis., Savannah, Ga., Holyoke (Mass.) Mus. Natural History, Theodore Lyman Wright Art Center, Beloit (Wis.) Coll., Treat Gallery, Bates Coll., Lewiston, Maine. Served with AUS, 1942-45. Mem. Am. Fedn. Arts. Home: 425 E 58th St New York NY 10022-2300

SURREY, PHILIP HENRY, artist, educator; b. Calgary, Alta., Can., Oct. 8, 1910; s. Henry Philip and Kate Alice (de Guerin) S. Student, Winnipeg (Man., Can.) Sch. Art, 1927-29, Vancouver (B.C., Can.) Sch. Art, 1930-33, Art Students' League, N.Y.C., 1936-37; LL.D. (hon.), Concordia U., Montreal, 1981. Exhibited numerous one man shows, Montreal, Toronto, Ottawa, Quebec and Windsor, Ont., including retrospective, Musée d'Art Contemporain, Montreal, 1971, Canadian Cultural Centre, Paris, France, 1972; represented in permanent collections, Nat. Gallery Can., Ottawa, Art Gallery Ont., Toronto, Musée du Quebec, other pub., pvt. collections. Decorated Order of Can. Mem. Royal Can. Acad. Club: Montreal Press. *Art is a comment on life, on its beauty, ugliness and variety, with poetic color and harmonious composition. I believe my work helps me to understand and accept my world.*

SURRIDGE, STEPHEN ZEHRING, lawyer, writer; b. N.Y.C., Dec. 12, 1940; s. Robert George and Florence Elizabeth (Zehring) S.; m. Helen Frances McKenna, Mar. 15, 1969; children: Christopher S., Jonathan R., Matthew W., Martha H. BA magna cum laude, Yale U., 1962; MBA, JD, U. Mich., 1969. Bar: Wis. 1969, Mich. 1969. Assoc. Quarles & Brady, Milw., 1969-76, ptnr., 1977-89; freelance writer, 1990—. Author: (monograph) Seven Thunders of Revelation, 1985, Revelation Revisited, 1995. 1st U.S. Army, 1963-65. Mem. Phi Beta Kappa. Mem. Christian Ch. Home: 4480 N Ardmore Ave Shorewood WI 53211-1418

SURSA, CHARLES DAVID, banker; b. Muncie, Ind., Nov. 5, 1925; s. Charles Vaught and Ethel Fay (Schukraft) S; m. Mary Jane Palmer, Feb. 2, 1947; children: Ann Elizabeth, Janet Lynne, Charles Vaught, Laura Jane. BSChemE, Purdue U., 1946; MBA, Harvard, 1948. Executive NBD Bank N.A. (formerly Summit Bank, Indsl. Trust & Savings), Muncie, Ind., 1946-51, pres., 1951-80; chmn. bd., pres. NBD Bank N.A. (formerly Summit Bank, Indsl. Trust & Savings), Muncie, 1980-88, chmn. bd., CEO, 1988-90, chmn. bd., 1990-94, chmn. emeritus, 1994—; bd. dirs. Old Rep. Life Ins. Co., Chgo., Home Owners Life Ins. Co., Chgo., Old Rep. Internat. Corp., Chgo., Ball Meml. Hosp., Inc., Old Rep. Ins. Co., Greensburg, Pa., Old Rep. Life Ins. Co. N.Y.C., Am. Bus. & Merc. Ins. Group, Chgo., Am. Bus. & Merc. Reassurance Co., Chgo., bd. dirs., pres. Com. Svcs. Coun. of Del. County, 1973-74. Treas. Muncie Symphony Assn., 1949-62, pres., 1962-72, 2d v.p., 1978-80, dir., 1991—; bd. dirs., pres. The Community Found. of Muncie and Del. County, Inc., 1985—. Recipient Outstanding Young Man award Ind. Jr. C. of C., 1956, Hon. Jaycees award, 1974. Mem. Ind. Banker's Assn., Ind. Pres.'s Orgn. (treas. 1980-86), Ind. Soc. of Chgo., Internat. Wine and Food Soc., Delaware County C. of C., Ind. State C. of C., Muncie C. of C. (pres. 1959-60), Rotary (pres. 1964-65), Delaware Country Club (pres., bd. dirs. 1964), Elks, Phi Gamma Delta. Republican. Presbyterian. Home: 3410 W University Ave Muncie IN 47304-3970 Office: NBD Bank NA 220 Walnut Plz Muncie IN 47305-2804

SURWILL, BENEDICT JOSEPH, JR., college dean, educator; b. Chgo., Oct. 8, 1925; s. Benedict Joseph and Emily (Zemgolis) S.; m. Frances May Welling, Oct. 16, 1948; children: Thomas, Benedict, Robert, Patricia; m. Charlene R. McClintock, Feb. 17, 1990; 1 child, Michael McClintock. BS in Edn., Ariz. State Coll., 1951, MS in Edn., 1954; EdD, U. Colo., 1962. Elem. tchr. Winnetka (Ill.) Pub. Schs., 1958-61; jr. high sch. prin. Champaign (Ill.) Pub. Schs., 1961-63; dir. Campus Sch. SUNY, Buffalo, 1963-68; dean. Sch. Edn. Ea. Mont. Coll., Billings, 1968-88, asst. to pres., 1988-91, dean Sch. Edn., prof. edn. emeritus, 1991—; chmn. dean's coun. Mont. Univ. System, 1974; mem. Mont. Supts. Adv. Com. on Tchr. Edn. and Cert., 1969-76, chmn., 1972-73; mem. ednl. forum State Supt. Pub. Instrn., 1977-83, Mont. Rural Youth Adv. Coun., Billings, 1979-81; lectr. in field. Editor: A Critical Examination of American Education, 1985; mem. editorial bd., contbg. editor Jour. Creative Behavior, 1966-93. Co-chmn. cancer drive Billings chpt. Am. Cancer Soc., 1988-89, Mont. State Cancer Crusade, 1989. With inf. U.S. Army. Recipient Am. Assn. of Coll. for Tchr. Edn. award, 1972, Presdl. citation Ill. Assn. Sch. Adminstrs., 1973. Mem. Nat. Coun. Accreditation Tchr. Edn. (mem. standards com., mem. multicultural edn. com. 1977, bd. appeals 1980-83, bd. examiners 1988-90), Elks, Yellowstone Country Club, Phi Delta Kappa, Kappa Delta Pi. Home: 5864 Sam Snead Trl Billings MT 59106-1021

SURWIT, RICHARD SAMUEL, psychology educator; b. Bklyn., Oct. 7, 1946; s. David and Ethel (Turetsky) S.; m. Sandra E. Cummings, May 23, 1982; children: Daniel Alan, Sarah Jeanne. AB, Earlham Coll., 1968; PhD, McGill U., Montreal, Que., Can., 1972; postgrad., Harvard U. Boston. Postdoctoral fellow Harvard Med. Sch., 1972-74, instr., 1974-76, asst. prof., 1976-77; assoc. prof. psychiatry Duke U. Med. Ctr., Durham, N.C., 1977-83, prof., 1983—, vice chmn., 1993—; prof. psychology Duke U., 1991—. Author: Fear and Learning To Cope, 1978, Behavioral Approaches to Cardiovascular Diseases, 1982. Recipient rsch. scientist award NIMH, 1993. Fellow APA, Soc. Behavioral Medicine (pres. 1994), Acad. Behavioral Medicine. Home: 3804 Sweeten Creek Rd Chapel Hill NC 27514-9706 Office: Duke U Med Ctr PO Box 3842 Durham NC 27710

SUSANKA, SARAH HILLS, architect; b. Bromley, Kent, England, Mar. 21, 1957; d. Brian and Margaret (Hampson) Hills; m. Lawrence A. Susanka, July 4, 1980 (div. May 1984); m. James Robert Larson, Sept. 4, 1988. BArch, U. Oreg., 1978; MArch, U. Minn., 1983. Registered architect. Prin. Mulfinger, Susanka & Mahady (formerly Mulfinger and Susanka), Mpls., 1983—; Contbr. articles to profl. jours. Mem. AIA Minn. Avocation: writing. Home: 2345 Doswell Ave Saint Paul MN 55108-1630 Office: Mulfinger Susanka & Mahady Archs 43 Main St SE Minneapolis MN 55414

SUSCHITZKY, PETER, cinematographer. Cinematographer: (films) It Happened Here, 1962, The War Game, 1966, Privilege, 1967, A Midsummer Night's Dream, 1968, Charlie Bubbles, 1968, Leo the Last, 1970, Melody/ Swalk, 1971, The Pied Piper, 1972, Henry VIII and His Six Wives, 1972, That'll Be the Day, 1974, All Creatures Great and Small, 1975, Lisztomania, 1975, The Rocky Horror Picture Show, 1976, Valentino, 1977, The Empire Strikes Back, 1980, Krull, 1983, Falling in Love, 1984, Dead Ringers, 1988, Where the Heart Is, 1990, Naked Lunch, 1992, The Public Eye, 1992, The Vanishing, 1993, M. Butterfly, 1993. Office: Sandra Marsh Mgt 9150 Wilshire Blvd Ste 220 Beverly Hills CA 90210*

SUSKIND, DENNIS A., investment banker; b. Staten Island, N.Y., Dec. 13, 1942; s. Morris and Ida (Levine) S.; m. Cynthia Ann Leverenz, Sept. 14, 1968; children—Brian, John Paul, Pamela Claire, Audrey Elizabeth. Student, Pace Coll., N.Y.C. Vice pres. J. Aron & Co., N.Y.C., 1962-81; ptnr. Goldman Sachs & Co., N.Y.C., 1981—; bd. dirs. Merc. Exchange, 1972-80, Gold Inst., Washington, 1980-90; bd. dirs. Commodity Exchange, Inc., N.Y.C., 1980-87, 1st vice chmn., 1989-91; lectr. Fin. Times Conf., 1983, 84, 86—. Bd. dirs. Mt. Sinai Hosp. Assocs., N.Y.C., East End chpt. Nature Conservancy, Arthur Ashe Inst. for Urban Youth; trustee Collegiate Sch., N.Y.C. Mem. AIME, Silver Inst., Futures Industry Assn. (bd. dirs.),Southampton Golf Club, Atlantic Golf Club (Bridgehampton, N.Y., bd. dirs.). Home: 136 E 79th St New York NY 10021-0328 Office: Goldman Sachs & Co 85 Broad St New York NY 10004-2434

SUSKIND, RAYMOND ROBERT, physician, educator; b. N.Y.C., Nov. 29, 1913; s. Alexander and Anna (Abramson) S.; m. Ida Blanche Richardson, Dec. 27, 1944; children: Raymond Robert, Stephen Alexander. AB, Columbia U., 1934; student medicine, Edinburgh, Scotland, 1938-39; MD, SUNY, Bklyn., 1943. Intern Cin. Gen. Hosp., 1944; resident in dermatology, 1944-46, 48-49; research fellow in indsl. health U. Cin., 1948-50; research asst. bacteriology N.Y. U., 1934-36; research asst. pharmacology, 1936-37; practice medicine specializing in dermatology Cin., 1949-62; mem. faculty U. Cin., 1948-62, asso. prof. dermatology, 1952-62, dir. dermatol. research program Kettering Lab., 1948-62, Jacob G. Schmidlapp prof., chmn. dept. environ. health, dir. Kettering Lab., 1969-85, Jacob G. Schmidlapp prof. emeritus Inst. Environ. Health, 1985—, prof. medicine and dermatology, 1969-85, prof. emeritus medicine and dermatology, 1985—; attending physician U. Hosps., Cin., 1969—; dir. environ. and occupational dermatology program Ctr. for Occupational Health, U. Cin. Hosp., Cin., 1985—; prof., head div. environ. medicine, prof. dermatology U. Oreg. Med. Sch., 1962-69; chmn. standards adv. com. on cutaneous and eye hazards OSHA, 1978; Gehrmann lectr. Am. Acad. Occupational Medicine, 1977; founding mem. certifying bd. Am. Bd. Toxicology, 1978-83; mem. nat. air quality adv. com. EPA, 1970-73; mem. com. on health related effects of herbicides VA, 1979-83; cons. on Agt. Orange studies; mem. panel on human health effects of stratospheric change Nat. Acad. Scis., 1977-85; trustee Dermatology Found., 1975-80; master, trustee Fernald Settlement Fund Program, Long Term Health Effects of Ionizing Radiation Exposure from Nuclear Fuel Processing Plant, 1989—; cons. Accreditation Coun. for Grad. Med. Edn.; advisor Sch. of Pub. Health, Mahidol U., Bangkok. Contbg. editor Am. Jour. Indsl. Medicine, 1979-89, now reviewer; mem. editorial bd. Annals Internal Medicine, 1983-86, Chemosphere, 1987—; reviewer Archives Internal Medicine, Jour. AMA, Am. Jour. Pub. Health; contbr. articles to profl. jours., chpts. to books. Mem. Cin. Air Pollution Bd., 1972-76, chmn., 1974-75; bd. dirs. Cin. Chamber Music Soc. Served to capt. M.C. AUS, 1946-48. Recipient award Project Hope, 1984, Robert A. Kehoe award of merit Am. Acad. Occupational Medicine, 1987, Presdl. citation for outstanding contbns. to occupational medicine Am. Acad. Dermatology, 1988, Daniel Drake medal U. Cin., 1985, Disting. Alumni Achievement award SUNY Coll. Medicine, 1993, fellow U. Cin. Grad. Sch., 1971—. Fellow A.C.P.; mem AMA (adv. panel on toxicology council sci. affairs 1980-85), Am. Occupational Med. Assn. (chmn. dermatology com. and policy group 1958-66, dir. 1969-75, Health Achievement in Industry award 1977), Soc. Investigative Dermatology (dir., v.p., hon. mem. 1984—), Am. Acad. Dermatology (chmn. edn. com.), N.Y. Acad. Scis., Am. Indsl. Hygiene Assn., Soc. for Occupational and Environ. Health (councillor), AAAS, Am. Dermatol. Assn., Japanese Dermatol. Assn. (hon.), Chilean Dermatol. Soc. (hon.), Sigma Xi, Alpha Omega Alpha. Achievements include first description of inhibiting effect of ultraviolet radiation on allergic skin reactions; research on cutaneous toxicology, on effects of exposure to chlorinated dioxins, on effects of ionizing radiation on populations living in the vicinity of nuclear fuel processing plants. Office: Dept Environ Health U Cin Coll Medicine 3223 Eden Ave Cincinnati OH 45267-0001

SUSKIND, RONALD STEVEN, journalist; b. Kingston, N.Y., Nov. 20, 1959; s. Walter Burton and Shirley Lila (Berman) S.; m. Cornelia Kennedy, May 4, 1986; children: Walter Kennedy, Harry Owen. BA in Govt. and Fgn. Affairs, U. Va., 1981; MS in Journalism, Columbia U., 1983. No. Va. field coord. Charles Robb for Gov., Alexandria, Va., 1981; campaign mgr. John Downey for U.S. Senate, New Haven, 1982; news asst., interim reporter The New York Times, 1983-85; city/state reporter The St. Petersburg (Fla.) Times, 1985-86; sr. editor Boston Bus. Mag., 1987-88, editor, 1988-90; staff reporter The Wall Street Jour., Boston, 1990-93; sr. nat. affairs writer The Wall Street Jour., Washington, 1993—; instr. advanced journalism Harvard U., Cambridge, Mass., 1987-93; mng. cons. Big Ideas, Inc., Boston, 1988-90; commentator Sta. WBUR, Boston, 1989-93. Recipient Pulitzer prize for feature writing, 1995, Benjamin Fine award Nat. Assn. Secondary Sch. Prins., 1995, Nat. Writing award Ball State U., 1995. Office: The Wall Street Jour 1025 Connecticut Ave NW Washington DC 20036

SUSKIND, SIGMUND RICHARD, microbiology educator; b. N.Y.C., June 19, 1926; s. Seymour and Nina Phillips S.; m. Ann Parker, July 1, 1951; children: Richard, Mark, Steven. A.B., NYU, 1948; Ph.D, Yale U., 1954. Research asst. biology div. Oak Ridge Nat. Lab., 1948-50; USPHS fellow NYU Med. Sch., N.Y.C., 1954-56; mem. faculty Johns Hopkins U., Balt., 1956—; prof. biology Johns Hopkins U., 1965—, Univ. prof., 1983—, Univ. ombudsman, 1988-91, dean grad. and undergrad. studies, 1971-78, dean Sch. Arts and Scis., 1978-83; head molecular biology sect. NSF, 1970-71; cons. NIH, 1966-70, Coun. Grad. Schs., Mid States Assn. Colls. and Secondary Schs., 1973—, NSF, 1986; vis. scientist Weizmann Inst. of Sci., Israel, 1985; trustee Balt. Hebrew U., 1985-93; mem. adv. bd. La. Geriatric Ctr., 1990—. Author: (with P.E. Hartman) Gene Action, 1964, 69, (with P.E. Hartman and T. Wright) Principles of Genetics Laboratory Manual, 1965; editor: (with P.E. Hartman) Foundations of Modern Genetics series, 1964, 69 mem. sci. editorial bd. Johns Hopkins U. Press, 1973-76, 88-91. With USNR, 1944-46. NIH grantee, 1957-76. Fellow AAAS; mem. Am. Soc. Microbiology, Genetics Soc. Am., Am. Assn. Immunology, Am. Soc. Biol. Chemistry and Molecular Biology, Coun. Grad Schs., Assn. Grad. Schs., Northeastern Assn. Grad. Schs. (exec. com. 1975-76, pres. 1977-78). Research in microbial biochemical genetics and immunogenetics. Office: Johns Hopkins U Dept Biology and McCollum-Pratt Inst 34th and Charles Sts Baltimore MD 21218

SUSLICK, KENNETH SANDERS, chemistry educator; b. Chgo., Sept. 16, 1952; s. Alvin and Edith (Paul) S.; m. Adele Mazurek; 1 child, Benjamin Adam. BS with honors, Calif. Inst. Tech., 1974; PhD, Stanford U., 1978. Rsch., teaching asst. Stanford (Calif.) U., 1974-78; chemist Lawrence Livermore (Calif.) Lab., 1974-75; asst. prof. U. Ill., Urbana, 1978-84, assoc. prof., 1984-88, prof. of chemistry, 1988—; prof. Beckman Inst. for Advanced Sci. and Tech., Urbana, 1989-92; prof. of materials sci. and engring. U. Ill., Urbana, 1993—; vis. fellow Balliol Coll., Inorganic Chemistry Lab., Oxford U., Eng., 1986; bd. dirs. Ney Ultrasonics, Inc., 1993—; scientific bd. dirs. VivoRx, Inc., 1994; cons. in field. Editor: High Energy Processes in Organometallic Chemistry, 1987, Ultrasound: Its Chemical, Physical, and Biological Effects, 1988; editorial bd. Ultrasonics, 1992—; patentee isotope separation by photochromatography; contbr. articles to profl. jours. Fellow DuPont Found., 1979-80, Sloan Found., 1983-87; recipient Rsch. Career Devel. award NIH, 1985-90, NSF Spl. Creativity award, 1992-94. Fellow AAAS, Royal Soc. Arts, Mfrs. and Commerce (silver medal 1974); mem. Am. Chem. Soc. (chmn. sect. 1987-89, nobel laureate signature award 1994), Nat. Rsch. Soc. (medal 1994), Am. Acoustical Soc. Avocations: sculpting, folk music. Office: U Ill Dept Chemistry 505 S Mathews Ave Urbana IL 61801-3664

SUSMAN, ALAN HOWARD, lawyer; b. Buffalo, Apr. 7, 1945; m. Jo Ellen Fisher, Aug. 8, 1970; children: Stephanie, Jennifer. BA, Hobart Coll., 1967; JD, SUNY, Buffalo, 1970. Bar: N.Y. 1971, Ariz. 1973, U.S. Dist. Ct. Ariz. 1973, U.S. Ct. Appeals (9th cir.) 1973, U.S. Supreme Ct. 1978. Assoc. Brizdle & Hankin, Buffalo, 1971-72; appellate law clk. Ariz. Ct. Appeals, Phoenix, 1972-73; atty. Maricopa County Atty.'s Office, Phoenix, 1973-75; ptnr. Schwartz & Susman, P.A., Phoenix, 1975-81; asst. atty. gen. State of Ariz., Phoenix, 1981-84; ptnr. Storey & Ross, P.C., Phoenix, 1984-88, Jaburg & Wilk, Phoenix, 1988—; judge pro tem Superior Ct. State of Ariz., Phoenix, 1986—; instr. Phoenix Coll, 1982, 83. Bd. dirs. Phoenix Jewish Community Ctr., 1985-87. Mem. N.Y. Bar Assn., Assn. Trial Lawyers Am., Ariz. Trial Lawyers Assn., Ariz. Bar Assn. (exec. com. young lawyers sect. 1976-77), Maricopa County Bar Assn., Am. Arbitration Assn. (mem. panel arbitrators). Democrat. Avocations: golf, reading. Office: Jaburg & Wilk PC 3200 N Central Ave Ste 2000 Phoenix AZ 85012-2440

SUSMAN, MILLARD, geneticist, educator; b. St. Louis, Sept. 1, 1934; s. Albert and Patsy Ruth S.; m. Barbara Beth Fretwell, Aug. 18, 1957; children: Michael K., David L. A.B., Washington U., St. Louis, 1956; Ph.D., Calif. Inst. Tech., 1962. With microbial genetics research unit Hammersmith Hosp., London, 1961-62; asst. prof. genetics U. Wis., Madison, 1962-66, assoc. prof., 1966-72, prof., 1972—, chmn. lab. genetics, 1971-75, 77-86, assoc. dean med. sch., 1986-95, acting dean Sch. Allied Health Professions, 1988-90, vice dean med. sch., 1994-95; phage course instr., Cold Spring Harbor, N.Y., 1965. Co-author: Life on Earth, 2d edit., 1978, Human Chromosomes: Structure, Behavior, Effects, 3d edit., 1992; contbr. articles to sci. jours. Mem Genetics Soc. Am., AAAS, Sigma Xi, Phi Beta Kappa, Phi Eta Sigma, Omicron Delta Kapp. Home: 2707 Colgate Rd Madison WI 53705-2234 Office: U Wis Med Sch 1220 Medical Science Ctr Madison WI 53706

SUSMAN, MORTON LEE, lawyer; b. Detroit, Aug. 6, 1934; s. Harry and Alma (Koslow) S.; m. Nina Meyers, May 1, 1958; 1 child, Mark Lee. BBA, So. Meth. U., 1956, JD, 1958. Bar: Tex. 1958, D.C. 1988, N.Y. 1990, U.S. Dist. Ct. (so. dist.) Tex. 1961, U.S. Ct. Appeals (5th cir.) 1961, U.S. Supreme Ct. 1961, U.S. Ct. Appeals (11th cir.) 1981, U.S. Ct. Appeals (D.C. cir.) 1988. Asst. U.S. atty., Houston, 1961-64, 1st asst. U.S. atty., 1965-66, U.S. atty., 1966-69; ptnr. Weil, Gotshal & Manges and predecessor firm Susman & Kessler, Houston, 1969—. Lt. USNR, 1958-61. Fellow Am. Coll. Trial Lawyers, Tex. Bar Found.; mem. ABA, Fed. Bar Assn. (dir., Younger Fed. Lawyer award 1968), Tex. Bar Assn., Houston Club, Houstonian Club, Crescent Club. Democrat. Jewish. Home: 3238 Ella Lee Ln Houston TX 77019-5924 Office: Weil Gotshal & Manges 700 Louisiana St Ste 1600 Houston TX 77002-2727

SUSMAN, RANDALL L., anatomy educator, anthropologist; b. Jan. 19, 1948. BA in Anthropology, U. Calif., Davis, 1970; MA in Anthropology, U. Chgo., 1972, PhD in Anthropology, 1976; JD, Touro Coll., 1988. Lectr., postdoctoral fellow Dept. of Anat. Scis. SUNY, Stony Brook, 1976-77, asst. prof. Dept. Anat. Scis., 1977-83, assoc. prof. Dept. Anat. Scis., 1983-88, prof. Dept. Anat. Scis., 1988—; cons. Etonic Athletic Shoes, 1983-87, Detroit Zool. Soc., 1989-91. Author: The Pygmy Chimpanzee: Evolutionary Biology and Behavior, 1984; editor: The Evolution of Human Behavior: Primate Models, 1987, SUNY Press Series in Primatology, 1984-89; contbr. numerous articles to profl. jours., spkr. in field. Rsch. grantee NATO, 1972, Chgo. Zool. Soc., 1972, 79, N.I.H. 1978-79, 93-94, L.S.B. Leakey Found., 1976, 79, 91, Nat. Geog. Soc., 1980, 1990-91, Nat. Sci. Found., 1980-82, 83, 1984-86, 1989-92, World Wildlife Fund, 1983-84, 1985-86. Mem. AAAS, Am. Assn. Anatomists, Am. Assn. Physical Anthropologists, Am. Soc. Biomechanics, Soc. Vertebrate Paleontologists. Avocations: research on early human evolution, evolution of tool making, and field studies of African apes. Office: SUNY Stony Brook Sch Medicine Dept Anat Scis Stony Brook NY 11794-8081

SUSMAN, STEPHEN DAILY, lawyer; b. Houston, Jan. 20, 1941; s. Harry and Helene Gladys (Daily) S.; m. Karen Lee Hyman, Dec. 26, 1965; children: Stacy Margraeta, Harry Paul. B.A. magna cum laude, Yale U., 1962; LL.B. summa cum laude, U. Tex. Austin, 1965. Bar: Tex. 1965, U.S. Supreme Ct 1960. Law clk. U.S. Ct. Appeals (5th cir.), New Orleans, 1965-66, U.S.Supreme Ct., Washington, 1966-67; ptnr. Fulbright & Jaworski, 1966-75; spl. counsel to atty. gen. Austin, Tex., 1975; sr. ptnr. Susman Godfrey, Houston, 1980—; vis. prof. law U. Tex., Austin, 1975; chmn. adv. com. on discovery Tex. Supreme Ct. Bd. dirs. Contemporary Arts Mus., Assn. Yale Alumni, Yale Devel. Fund, Southwest Legal Found., Inns of Ct. Recipient ADL Jurisprudence award, 1995; named one of Best Trial Lawyers in Am., Nat. Law Jour., 1989. Mem. ABA (antitrust sect., mem. coun. litigation sect., chmn. task force on fast track litigation), State Bar Tex., Am. Law Inst., Assn. Trial Lawyers Am., Houston Bar Assn., Yale Club (Houston, N.Y.C.), Houston Trial Lawyers Assn., Tex. Assn. Civil Trial Specialists (pres.), Houston Club, Houstonian Club, Century Club, Petroleum Club (Dallas), Quinnipiac Club (New Haven). Avocations: jogging, skiing. Office: 1st Interstate Bank 1000 Louisiana St 5100 Houston TX 77002-5013

SUSMAN, THOMAS MICHAEL, lawyer, lobbyist; b. Houston, Feb. 24, 1943; s. Harry and Helene Gladys (Daily) S.; m. Julia Turitz (div. 1980); children: Tara Marie, Shana Raissa, Micah Joseph; m. Susan G. Braden, May 31, 1981; 1 child, Daily Lacey. BA, Yale U., 1964; JD, U. Tex., 1967. Bar: Tex. 1967, U.S. Ct. Appeals (D.C. cir.) 1968, D.C. 1972, U.S. Dist. Ct. D.C. 1972, U.S. Supreme Ct. 1973, U.S. Ct. Appeals (5th cir.) 1980, U.S. Ct. Appeals (1st cir.) 1982, U.S. Dist. Ct. Mass. 1982, U.S. Ct. Claims 1983, Mass. 1985. Law clk. to judge U.S. Ct. Appeals for 5th Cir., Washington, 1967-68; spl. asst. to asst. atty. gen. Office Legal Counsel, U.S. Dept. Justice, Washington, 1968-69; counsel, chief counsel subcom. on adminstrv. practice and procedure U.S. Senate, Washington, 1969-76, gen. counsel antitrust subcom., 1977-78, judiciary com., 1979-80, legis. asst. to Senator Edward Kennedy, 1980; ptnr. Ropes & Gray, Washington, 1981—; pub. mem. Adminstrv. Conf. U.S., 1980—; gen. counsel adv. coun. U.S. Ct. Claims, Washington, 1988. Contbr. numerous articles on freedom of info., antitrust and intellectual property to legal publs.; editor: The Lobbying Manual, 1993. Am. participant USIA, 1985, 88, 92. Eisenhower Found. exchange fellow, 1977. Mem. ABA (chair adminstrv. law sect. 1991-92), D.C. Bar Assn. (chmn. steering coms., Cert. of Appreciation), Am. Jewish Com. (mem. exec. bd. Washington chpt.). Jewish. Home: 3901 Argyle Ter NW Washington DC 20011-5328 Office: Ropes & Gray Ste 1200 S 1001 Pennsylvania Ave NW Washington DC 20004

SUSSENGUTH, EDWARD HENRY, computer company executive, computer network designer; b. Holyoke, Mass., Oct. 10, 1932; s. Edward Henry and Mary Frances (Murphy) S.; m. Ann Paula Coughlin, Jan. 31, 1959; children—Edward Henry III, John Andrew. A.B., Harvard U., 1954, Ph.D., 1964; M.S., MIT, 1959. Researcher IBM Corp., Poughkeepsie, N.Y., 1959-64; mem. research and devel. staff IBM Corp., Menlo Park, Calif., 1964-70; mgr. IBM Corp., Raleigh, N.C., 1970-77; div. dir. IBM Corp., White Plains, N.Y., 1977-80; fellow IBM Corp., Raleigh, 1980-91; pres. IBM Acad. Tech., 1989-91; cons., 1991—. Contbr. articles to profl. jours.; patentee in field. Bd. dirs. Wake County Hosp. System, Raleigh, 1985—. Served to lt. USN, 1954-57. Recipient Interface award Data Communications, 1988. Fellow IEEE (Simon Ramo medal, 1989); mem. NAE, Assn. Computing Machinery, Sigma Xi. Club: MacGregor Downs Country (Cary, N.C.) (gov. 1980-85), Amelia Island. Avocations: golf; photography. Home and Office: 411 Rutherglen Dr Cary NC 27511-6436

SUSSER, ALLEN, restaurateur, chef; b. Bklyn., Dec. 25, 1956. Grad. in hotel-restaurant mgmt., N.Y.C. Tech. Coll., 1976; BS in Restaurant Mgmt. with honors, Fla. Internat. U., 1978; grad. advanced classic cuisine course, Le Cordon Bleu, Paris, 1981; hon. doctorate in Culinary Arts, Johnson & Wales U. Line cook Kutchers Country Club, Monticello, N.Y., 1975; garde manger Le Bristol Hotel, Paris, 1976; chef Hilton Internat. World Trade Ctr., N.Y.C., 1977, Whiffenpoof Restaurant, Coral Gables, Fla., 1977-78, Turnberry Isle Yacht and Racquet Club, Aventura, Fla., 1980-85; tournant Le Cirque Restaurant, N.Y.C., 1978-80; owner, mgr., chef Chef Allen's Restaurant, North Miami Beach, Fla., 1986—; instr. Fla. Internat. U. Sch. Hospitality Mgmt., 1989-90; lectr. Johnson and Wales U.; lectr. in field, 1985—; tchr., trainer apprenticeship program Culinary Inst. Am., 1986—; tchr. Chef Allen's Cooking Sch., 1987—; Ariana's Cooking Sch., 1987—; William Sonoma Cooking Series, 1987-89; creator, developer wine and food program for cable TV, 1985-86; cons. Gourmet Rapide, Calif., Arion MasterCook PC, Tex., 1991—; Royal Viking Cruise Line, Coral Gables, Fla., 1991—; Cunard Cruise Line, 1992—. Chmn. Share Strength's Taste of Nation, Miami; mem. Miami Conv. and Visitors Bur., Miami Host Com.; active numerous fund raising events for civic orgns., including Am. Cancer Soc., Easter Sels, Muscular Dystrophy Found., Mt. Sinai Hosp., Cedars Med. Ctr., Meals on Wheels, March of Dimes, Scottish Rite Children's

Hosp., Atlanta, Miami Feeding Miami, Metrozoo, Miami Project To Cure Paralysis, James Beard Scholarship, Victims of Hurricane Andrew, Sta. WGBH-TV, pub. TV, Miami Symphony. Recipient Ward Arbury award for gt. potential in mgmt., 1978, silver medal Miami Culinary Show, 1981, gold medal Miami Internat. Culinary Show, 1983; named Rising Star in Am. Cuisine, James Beard Found., 1989, Gt. Regional Chef, 1990; Best New Chef, Food and Wine mag., 1991, Best Miami Chef South Fla. mag., 1992, Alumni of Yr., N.Y.C. Tech. Coll. Restaurant Mgmt. Sch., 1993; Chef Allen Day named is his honor Dade County Commrs., 1993; also others. Mem. Internat. Assn. Culinary Profls., Internat. Rare Fruit Coun., Nat. Restaurant Assn., Fla. Restaurant Assn.. Fla Restaurant Assn., Chaine de Rotisseurs (award of excellence 1987-91), Am. Inst. Wine and Food, Chefs in Am., Soc. for Cuisine in Am., Somellier Guild, Greens Rest. Assn. Avocations: scuba. Office: Chef Allen's 19088 NE 29th Ave Aventura FL 33180

SUSSER, MERVYN WILFRED, epidemiologist, educator; b. Johannesburg, South Africa, Sept. 26, 1921; came to U.S., 1965; s. Solomon and Ida Rose (Son) S.; m. Zena Athene Stein, Mar. 28, 1949; children: Ida, Ezra, Ruth. MB, BChir, U. Witwatersrand, Union of South Africa, 1950; diploma pub. health, London Conjoint Bd., 1960; DMS (hon.), U. Witwatersrand, 1993. Med. officer, then supt. Alexandra Health Centre and Univ. Clinic, Johannesburg, 1952-55; successively lectr., sr. lectr., reader, head dept. social and preventive medicine Manchester (Eng.) U., 1957-65; also med. officer div. mental health Salford, Eng.; prof., chmn. div. epidemiology Sch. Pub. Health, Columbia U., N.Y.C., 1966-78; Gertrude H. Sergievsky prof. epidemiology, dir. Sergievsky Ctr., 1977-91; Sergievsky prof. emeritus, spl. lectr., 1992—; cons. WHO, 1962, 66-72, 79, 90, NIH, NAS. Author: (with W. Watson) Sociology in Medicine, 1962, 2d edit., 1971, (with W. Watson and K. Hopper), 3d edit., 1985, Community Psychiatry: Epidemiologic and Social Themes, 1968, Causal Thinking in the Health Sciences: Concepts and Strategies of Epidemiology, 1973, (with others) Famine and Human Development: Studies of the Dutch Hungerwinter 1944-45, 1975, (with D. Rush and Z. Stein) Diet in Pregnancy: A Randomized Controlled Trial of Nutritional Supplements, 1980, Epidemiology, Health and Society: Selected Essays, 1987, (with Jennie Kline and Zena Stein) Conception to Birth: Epidemiology of Prenatal Development, 1989. With South African Defence Force, 1940-45. Belding scholar Assn. Aid Crippled Children, 1965-66; Guggenheim fellow, 1972. Fellow Royal Coll. Physicians (Edinburgh), Am. Pub. Health Assn. (John Snow award 1994), Am. Epidemiol. Soc., Am. Coll. Epidemiol., N.Y. Acad. Medicine; mem. Internat. Epidemiol. Assn., World Psychiat. Assn., Soc. Epidemiol. Rsch., Soc. Pediatric Epidemiol. Rsch., Physicians Forum. Home: 100 Pinecrest Dr Hastings Hdsn NY 10706-3702 Office: 630 W 168th St New York NY 10032-3702

SUSSEX, JAMES NEIL, psychiatrist, educator; b. Northcote, Minn., Oct. 2, 1917; s. Rollo and Florence (Bartholomew) S.; m. Margaret Ann Garty, Apr. 25, 1943; children: Margaret Eileen, Mary Patricia, Barbara Lorraine, Teresa Virginia. A.B. U. Kans., 1939, M.D., 1942. Diplomate: Am. Bd. Psychiatry and Neurology (dir. for child psychiatry 1966-70, dir. 1975-83, pres. 1982). Commd. It. (j.g.), M.C. U.S. Navy, 1943, advanced through grades to comdr., 1955; intern (Naval Hosp.), Chelsea, Mass., 1942-43; resident psychiatry (Naval Hosp.), Vallejo, Calif., 1946-49; fellow child psychiatry Phila. Guild Guidance Clinic, 1949-51; asst. chief neuropsychiatry Naval Hosp., Bethesda, Md., 1951-55; resigned, 1955; mem. faculty Med. Coll. Ala., 1955-68, prof. psychiatry, chmn. dept., 1959-68; psychiatrist-in-chief U. Ala. Hosps. and Clinics, 1959-68; faculty U. Miami Sch. Medicine, Fla., 1968—; prof. psychiatry U. Miami Sch. Medicine, 1970—, chmn. dept., 1970-83, spl. asst. to v.p. for med. affairs for geriatric medicine program, 1983-86; mem. adv. bd. Nat. Psychiat. Residency Selection Plan, 1965—; mem. Med. Adv. Bd. Ednl. Film Prodn., 1966—; cons. Bur. Rsch., U.S. office Edn., 1966-72; dir. Ala. Planning for Mental Retardation, 1964—; mem. psychiatry tng. rev. com. NIMH; mem. exec. com. Am. Bd. Med. Spltys., 1980-83. Editor: Jour. Ala. Soc. Med. History, 1957-63; editorial bd.: Jour. Am. Acad. Child Psychiatry, 1966-70. Mem. Am. Assn. Psychiat. Svcs. for Children (coun. 1966—, pres. 1972-74), Coun. Med. Specialty Socs. (pres. 1988-89), Accreditation Coun. for Grad. Med. Edn. (exec. com. 1989-94, chmn. 1992-93), Phi Beta Kappa, Nu Sigma Nu. Home: 6950 SW 134th St Miami FL 33156-6975

SUSSKIND, CHARLES, engineering educator, author, publishing executive; b. Prague, Czech Republic; came to U.S., 1945, naturalized, 1946; s. Bruno Bronislav and Gertruda (Seger) S.; m. Thelma Gabriel, May 1, 1945; children: Pamela Susskind Pettler, Peter Gabriel, Amanda Frances. Student, City U., London, 1939-40; B.S., Calif. Inst. Tech., 1948; M.Engring., Yale U., 1949, Ph.D., 1951. Research asst. Yale U., 1949-51; research assoc. Stanford U., 1951-55, lectr., asst. dir. Microwave Lab., 1955-59; mem. faculty U. Calif., Berkeley, 1955—; prof. U. Calif., 1964—, asst. dean Coll. Engring., 1964-68, also statewide administr., 1969-74; Vis. prof. U. London, 1961-62, U. Geneva, Switzerland, 1968-69; mem., cons. EPA Sci. Adv. Bd., 1982—; cons. electronics industry, govt., publishers; dir. San Francisco Press, Inc. Author: (with M. Chodorow) Fundamentals of Microwave Electronics, 1964, (with L. Schell) Exporting Technical Education, 1968, Understanding Technology, 1973, 74, 85 (transl. into Dutch, French, Italian, Korean, Spanish), Twenty-five Engineers and Inventors, 1976, (with F. Kurylo) Ferdinand Braun, 1981, (with M. E. Rowbottom) Electricity and Medicine: History of their Interaction, 1984, Jan&aposcek and Brod, 1985; editor: (with M. Hertz) Heinrich Hertz: Memoirs, Letters, Diaries, bilingual edit., 1977; editor-in-chief: Ency. Electronics, 1962. Served with USAAF, 1942-45. Named to Hon. Order Ky. Cols. Fellow IEEE; mem. AAAS, History of Sci. Soc., Soc. for History of Tech., Instn. Elec. Engrs. (London), Yale Club of N.Y.C., Faculty Club of Berkeley (bd. dirs. 1972-73), Sigma Xi (pres. Berkeley chpt. 1972-73), Tau Beta Pi. Office: U Calif Coll Engring Berkeley CA 94720-1770

SUSSKIND, HERBERT, biomedical engineer, educator; b. Ratibor, Germany, Mar. 23, 1929; came to U.S., 1938; s. Alex and Hertha (Loewy) S.; m. E. Suzanne Lieberman, June 18, 1961; children: Helen J., Alex M., David A. BChE cum laude, CCNY, 1950; MChE, NYU, 1961. Engr., sect. supr. Brookhaven Nat. Lab., Upton, N.Y., 1950-77, biomed. engr., 1977-94; assoc. prof. medicine SUNY, Stony Brook, 1979—, asst. to the chmn. med. dept., 1989-94. Co-inventor 3 patents in field. Co-founder, 1st pres. Huntington Twp. Jewish Forum, Huntington, N.Y., 1970-73; trustee Huntington Hebrew Congregation, 1970-78. Mem. Biomed. Engring. Soc., Soc. Nuclear Medicine, Am. Thoracic Soc., Am. Nuclear Soc. (exec. com., treas. L.I. Sect. 1978-83), Am. Inst. Chem. Engrs., CCNY Alumni Assn. (pres. 1982-84), CCNY Engring. & Architecture Alumni Assn., N.Y.C. (pres. 1963-65). Office: Brookhaven Nat Lab Box 5000 Bldg 490 Upton NY 11973-5000

SUSSKIND, LAWRENCE ELLIOTT, urban and environmental planner, educator, mediator; b. N.Y.C., Jan. 12, 1947; s. David J. and Marjorie H. (Friedman) S.; m. Miriam Mason, June 8, 1968 (div. Dec. 1982); m. Leslie Webster Tuttle, Dec. 12, 1982; children: Noah Gates, Lily Webster. A.B. in Sociology, Columbia U., 1968; M.C.P., MIT, 1970, Ph.D. in Urban Planning, 1973. Asst. prof. urban and environ. planning MIT, Cambridge, 1971-74, assoc. prof., 1974-82, prof., 1982—, head dept., 1978-82, dir. MIT-Harvard Pub. Disputes Program, 1980—; exec. dir. program on negotiation Harvard U. Law Sch., Cambridge, 1984-87; chmn. Consensus Bldg. Inst.; prin. assoc. Environ. Resources Mgmt., London. Author: Paternalism, Conflict and Co-Production, 1983, Proposition 2 1/2: Its Impact on Massachusetts, 1983, Resolving Environmental Regulatory Disputes, 1983, Breaking the Impasse, 1987, Environmental Diplomacy, 1994, Reinventing Congress for the 21st Century, 1995; sr. editor, founder Environ. Impact Assessment Rev., 1980—; mem. editl. policy bd. Negotiation Jour., 1984—. Mem. Am. Inst. Cert. Planners, Soc. for Profls. in Dispute Resolution. Jewish. Home: 32 Jericho Hill Rd Southborough MA 01772-1007 Office: MIT 3-411 Cambridge MA 02139

SUSSKIND, TERESA GABRIEL, publisher; b. Watford, Eng., came to U.S., 1945, naturalized, 1948; d. Aaron and Betty (Fox) Gabriel; m. Charles Susskind, May 1, 1945; children: Pamela Pettler, Peter Gabriel, Amanda. Ed. U. London, 1938-40. Profl. libr. Calif. Inst. Tech., Pasadena, 1946-48, Yale U., New Haven, Conn., 1948-51, Stanford U., Calif., 1951-52, SRI Internat., Menlo Park, Calif., 1953; founder, pres. San Francisco Press, Inc., 1959—. With Women's Royal Naval Svc., 1943-45. Author: A Room of One's Own Revisited, 1977. Active in cultural affairs; bd. govs. San

Francisco Symphony, 1986-89. Mem. Town and Gown Club (Berkeley, Calif., pres. 1984-85). Office: PO Box 426800 San Francisco CA 94142-6800

SUSSMAN, ALEXANDER RALPH, lawyer; b. Bronx, N.Y., Sept. 24, 1946; s. Herman R. and Claire (Blumenson) S.; m. Edna Rubin, Mar. 24, 1973; children: Jason, Carl, Matthew, Eric. AB cum laude, Princeton U., 1968; JD, Yale U., 1972. Bar: N.Y. 1973, U.S. Dist. Ct. (so. and ea. dists) N.Y. 1974, U.S. Ct. Appeals (2d, 3d, 5th, 6th, 8th and 10th cirs.) 1983, U.S. Supreme Ct. Law clk. to justice U.S. Dist. Ct., N.Y.C., 1972-73; assoc. Cravath, Swaine & Moore, N.Y.C., 1974-76; assoc. Fried, Frank, Harris, Shriver & Jacobson, N.Y.C., 1977-79, ptnr., 1979—. Author: (with A. Fleischer, Jr.) Takeover Defense, 3 vols., 1995. Vice pres. litigation, exec. com., bd. dirs. N.Y. Lawyers for the Pub. Interest, 1983—; bd. dirs., exec. com. Legal Aid Soc., 1987-93. Fulbright scholar U. Bordeaux, 1969. Mem. ABA, Am. Law Inst., N.Y. State Bar Assn., Assn. of Bar of City of N.Y. (fed. cts. com. 1984-87, jud. com. 1987-90, Marden lectr. com. 1991—, chmn. legal assistance com. 1988-91). Home: 20 Oak Ln Scarsdale NY 10583-1627 Office: Fried Frank Harris Shriver & Jacobson 1 New York Plz New York NY 10004

SUSSMAN, ARTHUR M., law educator; b. Nov. 17, 1942; m. Rita Padnick; children: Eric, Johanna. BS, Cornell U., 1963; LLB magna cum laude, Harvard U., 1966. Bar: Ill., N.Y., U.S. Dist. Ct. (no. dist) Ill., U.S. Supreme Ct. Assoc. atty. Cahill, Gordon, Reindel & Ohl, N.Y.C., 1966-67; assoc. atty. Jenner & Block, Chgo., 1970-75, ptnr., 1975-77; univ. legal counsel So. Ill. U., Carbondale, 1977-79; gen. counsel, v.p. legal affairs and govt. rels. U. Chgo., 1979-84, gen. counsel, v.p. adminstrn., 1984—; exec. dir. Borman Commn. U.S. Mil. Acad., 1976; lectr. law Grad. Bus. U. Chgo., 1986—; master Broadview Hall, 1986-87, resident master Woodward Ct., 1987—; bd. dirs. Lab. Schs., 1985; presenter in field. Contr. articles to profl. jours. Mem. fin. com. South Cook County Coun. Girl Scouts USA, 1971-77; mem. Carbondale Com. on Human Subjects Rsch., 1977-79; Ad hoc com. on Solomon Amendment Am. Coun. Edn., 1984, Ill. Sec. of State's Com. on Not-for-Profit Corp. Act, 1984-85; mem. regional selection panel Harry S. Truman Scholarship Found, 1984, Ill.; vice-chmn. pub. policy com. Chgo. Heart Assn., 1974-76; bd. dirs. Chapin Hall for Children, 1985. Capt. JAGC U.S. Army. Burton-Hudson Ct. fellow U. Chgo, 1982—; Fulbright fellow, London, 1987. Mem. ABA, Am. Assn. Univ. Adminstrs., Nat. Assn. Coll. and Univ. Attys., Am. Coun. Edn., Coun. for Advancement and Support Higher Edn. Office: U Chgo Office of Legal Counsel 5801 S Ellis Ave Rm 503 Chicago IL 60637-1404

SUSSMAN, BARRY, author, public opinion analyst and pollster, journalist; b. N.Y.C., July 10, 1934; s. Samuel and Esther (Rosen) S.; m. Peggy Earhart, Jan. 20, 1962; children: Seena, Shari. BA, Bklyn. Coll., 1956. Reporter Herald Courier, Bristol, Va., 1960-62, mng. editor, 1962-65; editor Washington Post, 1965-69, city editor, 1970-73, spl. Watergate editor, 1972-74, pollster, pub. opinion analyst, 1975-87; co-founder, co-dir. Washington Post-ABC News poll, 1981-87; columnist Washington Post Nat. Weekly, 1983-87; mng. editor nat. affairs UPI, Washington, 1987; ind. pub. opinion analyst and pollster, 1988—. Author: The Great Coverup: Nixon and the Scandal of Watergate, 1974, What Americans Really Think, 1988, (with Lowell P. Weicker, Jr.) Maverick, 1995. Recipient Drew Pearson award for Nat. Reporting, 1972, 1st Prize award Washington Newspaper Guild, 1973, Editor of Yr. award Washington Newspaper Guild, 1973. Mem. Am. Assn. for Pub. Opinion Rsch. (exec. coun. 1985-87). Jewish. Avocation: chess.

SUSSMAN, DAVID WILLIAM, lawyer; b. N.Y.C., Aug. 7, 1954; s. Leonard Richard and Frances Grace (Rukeyser) S.; m. Ruth Ellen Levine, Mar. 16, 1985; children: Jane, Rebecca. BA, U. Pa., 1976, MA, 1976; JD, Columbia U., 1980. Bar: N.Y. 1981, U.S. Dist. Ct. (so. and ea. dist.) N.Y. 1981, U.S. Ct. Appeals (2d cir.) 1989, U.S. Supreme Ct. 1987. Assoc. Marshall, Bratter, Greene, Allison & Tucker, N.Y.C., 1980-81; law clk. to judge David N. Edelstein U.S. Dist. Ct. (so. dist.) N.Y., 1981-83; assoc. Simpson Thacher & Bartlett, N.Y.C., 1983-87, Cole & Deitz, N.Y.C., 1987-89; gen. counsel N.Y. Yankees, Bronx, 1989-92, exec. v.p., gen. counsel, 1992—; bd. dirs., gen. counsel Historic Dists. Coun., N.Y.C., 1988-93. Mem. Community Bd. #2, N.Y.C., 1988-90. Mem. ABA, Assn. of the Bar of the City of N.Y., Phi Beta Kappa. Office: NY Yankees Yankee Stadium E 161st St & River Ave Bronx NY 10451

SUSSMAN, GERALD, publishing company executive; b. Balt., Feb. 21, 1934; s. Hyman Jacob and Sylvia (Applebaum) S.; m. Arla Ilene Ellison, Aug. 25, 1963; children: Daniel Leonard, Andrew Louis. B.A., U. Md., 1956. Co-founder, prin. Investors Service of Md., Balt., 1956-60; coll. traveller Oxford U. Press, Inc., N.Y.C., 1961-62; coll. sales mgr. Oxford U. Press, Inc., 1962-69, gen. advt. mgr., 1970-73, v.p., dir. mktg., 1974-79, sr. v.p., dir. mktg., 1979-83, sr. v.p., dir. adminstrn. and planning, 1983—. Mem. Assn. Am. Pubs. (chmn mktg. com.), Assn. Am. Univ. Presses (chmn. mktg. com. 1980-81), Pubs. Advt. Club, Phi Alpha Theta. Democrat. Jewish. Home: 8 Opatut Ct Edison NJ 08817-2923 Office: Oxford U Press Inc 200 Madison Ave New York NY 10016-3901

SUSSMAN, LEONARD RICHARD, foundation executive; b. N.Y.C., Nov. 26, 1920; s. Jacob and Carrie (Marks) S.; m. Frances Rukeyser, May 9, 1942 (div. 1958); m. Marianne Rita Gutmann, May 28, 1958; children: Lynne, David William, Mark Jacob. A.B., NYU, 1940; M.S. in Journalism, Columbia U., 1941. Copy editor N.Y. Morning Telegraph, news editor radio sta. WQXR, 1941; cable editor San Juan (P.R.) World Jour., also corr. Business Week mag., 1941-42; editor fgn. broadcast intelligence svc. FCC, 1942; press sec. to Gov. of P.R., 1942-43; dir. info. in N.Y. for Govt. of P.R., 1946-49; regional dir., then nat. exec. dir. Am. Coun. Judaism, 1949-66; cons. pub. affairs cons. Nationwide Ins. Cos. (and indsl. subs.), 1955-57; mem. editorial com. Coun. Liberal Chs., 1956-59; exec. dir. Freedom House, 1967-88, sr. scholar in internat. communications, 1988—; evaluator Fulbright Program Bd. Fgn. Scholarships, 1990-92; exec. dir. Willkie Meml., 1970-88; adj. prof. journalism and mass communication NYU, N.Y.C., 1990—; organizer, dir. Freedom House/Books USA, 1968-85; editor Freedom at Issue, bimonthly, 1970-81; mem. U.S. Dels. to Conf. World Communicaiton Yr./ 83, 1982-83; organizer acad. confs.; participant Internat. Conf. on Press Freedom, Venice, Italy, 1976, 77, Cairo, 1978, Talloires, 1981, 83, San Jose, Costa Rica, Johannesburg, and Santiago Chile, 1987, also others; mem. panel competition in space Congl. Office Tech. Assessment, 1982-83. Author: American Press-Under Siege?, 1973, Mass News Media and the Third World Challenge, 1977, Glossary for International Communications: Warning of a Bloodless Dialect, 1983, Spanish version, 1987, Power, The Press and the Technology of Freedom: The Coming of Age of ISDN, 1990, The Culture of Freedom: The Small World of Fulbright Scholars, 1992, Good News Bad News, 1994, Can a Free Press Be Responsible? To Whom? 1995, The Press: Pressed and Oppressed, 1995; editor: Three Years at the East-West Divide, 1983, Today's American: How Free?, 1986; contbr. sects. to books, articles to profl. jours. and newspapers; project dir.: Big Story-How the American Press and Television Reported and Interpreted The Crisis of Tet-1968 in Vietnam and Washington, 1977; editor: textbook series, also quar. mag. Issues, 1953-66; editl. bd. Polit. Comm. and Persuasion. Trustee Internat. Coun. on Future of Univ., 1973-84; bd. dirs. World Press Freedom Com., 1977—; chmn. Friends of Survey Mag. Charitable Trust, London, 1978-92; mem. U.S. Nat. Commn. for UNESCO, 1979-85, vice-chmn., 1983-85; mem. U.S. dels. to internat. conf. on space, African Aid, UNESCO, London Info. Forum. Decorated Legion of Merit; recipient Am. First Amendment award N.Y. br. Soc. Profl. Journalists, 1988. Mem. Internat. Inst. Comm., Internat. Press Inst., Internat. Assn. Mass Comm. Rsch., Century Club. Home: 215 E 73d St New York NY 10021 Office: 120 Wall St 26th Fl New York NY 10005

SUSSMAN, MARTIN VICTOR, chemical engineering educator, inventor, consultant; b. N.Y.C.; s. Samuel and Selma (Bagno) S.; m. Jeanne Fowler, Aug. 22, 1953; children: Ann M., Eve Leslie, David Fowler. B.S., CCNY, M.S., Columbia U., Ph.D., 1958. Registered profl. engr. Mass.; lic. marine engr. Instr., research assoc. chem. dept. Fordham U., N.Y.C., 1949-50; research fellow chem. engring. dept. Columbia U., 1951-53; sr. engr., research engr. Pioneering Lab., DuPont, Del., 1953-58; co-founder, 1st dept. chem. engring in Turkey Robert Coll., Istanbul, Turkey, 1958-61; prof. chem. engring. dept. Tufts U., Medford, Mass., 1961—; dept. chmn., established PhD and MS programs Tufts U., 1961-71; cons. engring. edn. U.S. AID, Brazil and Uruguay, 1963, Ethiopia, 1965; cons. engring. edn. Ford

Found., India, 1971, 72, 73, 74, 79; coord. engring. edn. NSF, New Delhi, 1967-68; vis. prof. MIT, 1976, U. Capetown, Republic South Africa, 1990; Disting. vis. scholar Va. Poly. Inst., 1980; hon. rsch. fellow U. Exeter, 1990. Author: Elementary General Thermodynamics, 1972, 89, Availability (Exergy) Analysis, 1980; patentee in field. Mem. Town Meeting, Lexington, Mass., 1971-78. Served with U.S. Maritime Service, 1945-47, U.S. Coast Guard. NIH Spl. Research fellow, 1968; AEC fellow, 1951; Fulbright Hays lectr., 1977; Erskine fellow U. Canterbury (N.Z.), 1983; Meyerhoff fellow Weizman Inst. Sci., 1984-85. Fellow Am. Inst. Chem. Engrs., Am. Inst. Chemists; mem. Am. Chem. Soc., Sigma Xi, Tau Beta Pi (eminent engr. 1974). Achievements includ invention of "Incremental Draw Process" for synthetic fiber manufacture now in use by industry, "Fibra-Cel" tissue culture matrix. Office: Tufts U Dept Chem Engring Medford MA 02155

SUSSMAN, MONICA HILTON, lawyer; b. N.Y.C., Apr. 2, 1952. BA cum laude, Syracuse U., 1973; JD, Hofstra U., 1977. Bar: Va. 1977, D.C. 1978. Legis. coun. N.Y. State Gov's. Office, Washington, 1977-79; spl. asst. to under sec. U.S. Dept. HUD, Washington, 1979-80, br. chief office State Agy. and Bond Fin. programs, 1980-82, office gen. counsel, 1982-83, also bd. dirs., 1988—, v.p., 1989—, treas. Nat. Housing Conf., 1990—, also programs and regulations dep. gen. counsel; ptnr. McDermott, Will & Emery, Washington; bd. dirs. Nat. Leased Housing Assn. Mem. ABA, Mortgage Bankers Assn. (insured project subcom.), D.C. Bar (govtl. assisted programs for real estate com. 1985—), Va. State Bar. Office: Dept Housing and Urban Devel Office Gen Counsel 451 7th St SW Washington DC 20410*

SUSSMAN, STEVEN DAVID, management consulting executive; b. N.Y.C., Nov. 29, 1946; s. Max and Lillian Sussman; m. Sally Parker, Feb. 1979. BS, NYU, 1969, MS, 1973, LLB, 1976. Pres. SRI, Princeton, N.J., 1982—; bd. dirs. Spartan Industries, N.Y.C. Author: Effective Negotiations, 1977. Mem. Inst. Mgmt. Cons. Avocations: tennis, drums. Office: SRI 210 Carnegie Ctr Princeton NJ 08540-6233

SUSSNA, EDWARD, economist, educator; b. Phila., Nov. 26, 1926; s. Louis and Manya (Prytzycka) S.; m. Sylvia Fishman, Mar. 8, 1953; children: Audrey Francine, Ellen Sondra. B.A., Bklyn. Coll., 1950; M.A., U. Ill., 1952, Ph.D., 1954. Instr. U. Ill., 1952-54; asst. prof. Lehigh U., 1956-57; prof. bus. adminstrn. and econs. U. Pitts., 1957—; dir. ctr. for exec. edn. Grad. Sch. Bus. U. Pitts., 1983-89; dir. mgmt. program for execs. Center for Econ. Edn., Grad. Sch. Bus., acad. dir. study program in Hong Kong and Peoples Republic China, spring 1989, 95; vis. Fulbright prof. U. Tehran, Iran, adviser, 1972-73; cons. Bur. of Budget, Dept. HEW, Dept. Transp., UN Indsl. Devel. Orgn., Bell Telephone Co., Alcoa, Westinghouse Corp., NSF, Pitts. Nat. Bank, Japanese Regional Bankers Assn., others; vis. prof. UCLA, 1970, Ecole Superieure des Scis. Economiques et Commerciales, Paris, 1976-77, U. East Asia, Hong Kong and Macau, winter 1986; vis. scholar Internat. Inst. Mgmt., Berlin, spring 1982. Contbr. articles to profl. jours. Served with U.S. Mcht. Marine, 1944-47; Served with AUS, 1954-56. Vis. prof. under Ford Found. fellowship Harvard, 1960-61; guest scholar under Ford Found. fellowship Brookings Instn., Washington, 1962-63. Mem. Am. Econ. Assn., Am. Fin. Assn., Strategic Mgmt. Inst., Beta Gamma Sigma, Omicron Delta. Home: 1538 S Negley Ave Pittsburgh PA 15217-1420

SUSSNA, ROBERT EARL, architect; b. Lakewood, N.J., Mar. 21, 1939; s. Harry D. and Emma (Tarshish) S.; m. Deborah Sarah Beilin, Nov. 5, 1960; 1 child, Jeffrey Eric. BArch, Cornell U., 1963. Registered architect N.Y., N.J., Pa., Va. Designer Holt, Morgan, Short & Agle, Princeton, N.J., 1966-68; architect Burton F. Weisbecker AIA, Princeton, 1968; prin. Weisbecker & Sussna AIA, Princeton, 1969-70, Robert Earl Sussna AIA, Princeton, 1970-90; pres. Sussna Architects PA, Princeton, 1990—. Prin. works include Chem. Bank, Princeton U., Bristol-Myers Squibb, Rhone-Poulenc Inc., Trenton State Coll., Expansion of U. Medicine and Dentistry of N.J. Med. Edn. Bldg., Mobil Rsch. & Devel. TSL/Engring. Court, Lawrenceville Sch. Circle Houses Renovation, J&J Cafeteria Renovation Design, Rahway Hosp. Emergency Ctr. Renovation, Inst. for Advanced Study Facility Audit, Newton Meml. Hosp. Facility Audit and Master Plan, Exec. Square One and Two Axiom interior design; numerous one-man shows for photography including Trenton State Mus., Newark Mus. and Jersey City Mus., 1974—. Mem. Hopewell (N.J.) Twp. Planning Bd., 1976. Grantee in photography N.J. Coun. on the Arts. Mem. AIA (treas. N.J. chpt. 1994), Am. Hosp. Assn., N.J. Soc. Archs. (Spl. award of merit 1988), Rotary (bd. dirs.), Nassau Club. Office: Sussna Architects PA 53 State Rd Princeton NJ 08540-1318

SUSTAR, T. DAVID, religious organization executive. Dir of youth and christian edn. Ch. of God, Cleve., Tenn. Office: Ch of God PO Box 2430 Cleveland TN 37320

SUTCH, RICHARD CHARLES, economics educator; b. St. Paul, Dec. 8, 1942; s. G. Charles and Marjorie Jane S.; m. Susie Speakman, Oct. 31, 1968; 1 child, Cordelia Speakman Sutch. B.A. in Econs., U. Wash., 1963; Ph.D. in Econs., MIT, 1968. Acting asst. prof. econs. U. Calif.-Berkeley, 1967-68, asst. prof. econs., 1968-72, assoc. prof. econs., 1972-77, prof. econs., 1977—; prof. history, 1987—; dir. econ. history research program, 1987, vice chmn. dept., 1975-77; vis. prof. econs. Calif. Inst. Tech., 1985-86; mem. grad. group in demography, 1977—; mem. grad. group in demography, 1977—; mem. adminstrv. com. grad. div., 1980-83, chmn. adminstrv. com. Inst. Bus. and Econ. Research, 1983-84, bd. dirs., chmn. grad. council Acad. Senate, 1982-83, mem. com. on courses of instrn., 1980-81, mem. vis. rev. com. Sch. Social Sci., 1981, Ford faculty research prof., dept. econs., 1977-78, exec. com. Coll. Arts and Letters, 1987-93, chmn. faculty, 1989-93; Berkeley div. rep. coordinating com. grad. affairs, acad. senate U. Calif. systemwide, 1981-82. Co-author: Reckoning with Slavery, 1976 (Choice Outstanding Acad. Book award), One Kind of Freedom, 1977 (Choice Outstanding Acad. Book award). Co-editor: Explorations in the New Economic History: Essays in Honor of Douglass C. North, 1982. Guggenheim fellow, 1984—; recipient Disting. Teaching award, acad. senate U. Calif.-Berkeley, 1980, award of appreciation Class of 1979. Ford Found. Jr. faculty fellow, 1970-71; prin. investigator NSF grants 1969-70, 70-73, 74-77, 84-85, 89-93, Council on Ednl. Devel. grant, U. Calif.-Berkeley, 1974; grantee Nat. Inst. on Aging, 1990-94. Mem. Agrl. History Soc., Am. Econ. Assn. Am. Econ. History Assn. (Arthur H. Cole prize 1986), Am. Hist. Assn., Cliometric Soc. (Clio award 1986, bd. trustees 1985—, bd. editors Explorations in Economic History 1985—), Internat. Econ. History Assn. (U.S. rep. 1990—), Econ. History Soc. (bd. editors Jour. Econ. History 1980-83, com. chmn. 1981, Coale award, 1987, pres. 1989-90), Nat. Assn. for Ethnic Studies, Orgn. Am. Historians, Population Assn. Am., Social Sci. History Assn. (assoc. editor Research in Econ. History). Office: Univ Calif Berkeley Dept Econs 156 Barrows Hall Berkeley CA 94720

SUTCLIFFE, ERIC, lawyer; b. Calif., Jan. 10, 1909; s. Thomas and Annie (Beare) S.; m. Joan Basché, Aug. 7, 1937; children: Victoria, Marcia, Thomas; m. Marie C. Paige, Nov. 1, 1975. AB, U. Calif. at Berkeley, 1929, LLB, 1932. Bar: Calif. 1932. Mem. firm Orrick, Herrington & Sutcliffe, San Francisco, 1943-85, mng. ptnr., 1947-78. Trustee, treas., v.p. San Francisco Law Libr., 1974-88; founding fellow The Oakland Mus. of Calif.; bd. dirs. Merritt Peralta Found., 1988. Fellow Am. Bar Found (life); mem. ABA (chmn state regulation securities com. 1960-65), San Francisco Bar Assn. (chmn. corp. law com., 1964-65), San Francisco C. of C. (past treas., dir.) State Bar Calif., Pacific Union Club, Bohemian Club, Phi Gamma Delta, Phi Delta Phi, Order of Coif. Home: 260 King Ave Oakland CA 94610-1231 Office: Old Fed Reserve Bank Bldg 400 Sansome St San Francisco CA 94111-3308

ŠUTEJ, VJEKOSLAV, conductor; b. Rijeka, Croatia, July 31, 1951; s. Josip and Alemka (Stefanini) S.; m. Linela Malici; 1 child Alemka. Degree, Music Acad., Zagreb, Croatia, 1975. Music dir. Opera Split, Split, Croatia, 1985-90, La Fenice, Venice, Italy, 1990-93, Orquesta Simfonica de Sevilla, Seville, Spain, 1991—, Houston Grand Opera, Houston, Tex., 1994—. Home: 510 Preston HGO Houston TX 77002-1954 Office: Houston Grand Opera 510 Preston St Houston TX 77002-1504

SUTER, ALBERT EDWARD, manufacturing company executive; b. East Orange, N.J., Sept. 18, 1935; s. Joseph Vincent and Catherine (Clay) S.; m. Michaela Sams Suter, May 28, 1966; children: Christian C., Bradley J.,

Allison A. BME, Cornell U., 1957, MBA, 1959. Pres., chief exec. officer L.B. Knight & Assocs., Chgo., 1959-79; v.p. internat. Emerson Electric Co., St. Louis, 1979-80, pres. motor div., 1980-87, group v.p.; 1981-83, exec. v.p., 1983-87, vice chmn., 1987; pres., chief operating officer, dir. Firestone Tire & Rubber Co., Akron, Ohio, 1987-88; pres., chief operating officer Whirlpool Corp., Benton Harbor, Mich., from 1988; exec. v.p. Emerson Electric Co., St. Louis, until 1990, pres., COO, 1990-92, sr. vice chmn., COO, 1992—; bd. dirs. Boatmen's Bancshares, Inc., St. Louis U. Bd. dirs. Jr. Achievement Nat. Bd., Colorado Springs, Colo., Jr. Achievement Miss. Valley, St. Louis Sci. Ctr. Bd.; chmn. Torch div. St. Louis chpt. United Way, 1982-86. Mem. Glenview (Ill.) Country Club, St. Louis Club, Old Warson Country Club , Log Cabin Club. Republican. Episcopalian. Office: Emerson Electric Co PO Box 4100 Saint Louis MO 63136-8501

SUTER, JON MICHAEL, academic library director, educator; b. Holdenville, Okla., Oct. 30, 1941; s. Franklin Hyatt and Erma (Abee) S. BA cum laude, East Cen. State Coll., 1963; MLS, U. Okla., 1964; PhD, Ind. U. 1973. Asst. libr. East Cen. State Coll., Ada, Okla., 1964-76; assoc. libr. East Cen. U., Ada, Okla., 1976-84; dir. librs. Houston Bapt. U., 1984—; chmn. Libr. Edn. Div. Okla. Libr. Assn., 1981, Coll. Rsch. Libr. Div., Okla., 1982. Contbr. articles to profl. jours. Pres. Ada Camp Gideons Internat., 1980-82. Higher Edn. Act fellow Ind. U., 1969-71. Mem. Popular Culture Assn., Richard III Socl., Med. Acad., Renaissance Soc., Patristics Soc. Republican. Baptist. Avocations: comic books, medieval history. Home: 8271 Wednesbury Ln Houston TX 77074-2918 Office: Houston Bapt U - Moody Libr 7502 Fondren Rd Houston TX 77074-3204

SUTERA, SALVATORE PHILIP, mechanical engineering educator; b. Balt., Jan. 12, 1933; s. Philip and Ann (D'Amico) S.; m. Celia Ann Fielden, June 21, 1958; children: Marie-Anne, Annette Nicole, Michelle Cecile. B.S. in Mech. Engring, Johns Hopkins, 1954; postgrad., U. Paris, 1955-56; M.S., Calif. Inst. Tech., 1955; Ph.D., Cal. Inst. Tech., 1960; M.A. (hon.), Brown U., 1965. Asst. prof. mech. engring. Brown U., Providence, 1960-65; assoc. prof. Brown U., 1965-68, exec. officer div. engring., 1966-68; prof. dept. mech. engring. Washington U., St. Louis, 1968—; chmn. dept. Washington U., 1968-82, 86—; vis. prof. U. Paris VI, 1973. Assoc. editor: Jour. Biochem. Engring.; mem. editorial bd. Circulation Rsch., 1975-82. Fulbright fellow Paris, 1955. Fellow ASME, Am. Inst. of Med and Biol. Engring. (founding); mem. ASHRAE, Biomed. Engring. Soc., Am. Acad. Mechanics, Internat. Soc. Biorheology, N.Am. Soc. Biorheology (pres.-elect 1986-89, pres. 1989-90), Am. Soc. Artificial Internal Organs, Am. Soc. Engring. Edn., AAAS, AIAA (Lindbergh award St. Louis sect. 1988), Tau Beta Pi, Pi Tau Sigma. Republican. Roman Catholic. Research in fluid mechanics, heat transfer, blood flow, rheology of suspensions. Home: 830 S Meramec Ave Saint Louis MO 63105-2539

SUTHERLAND, ALAN ROY, association executive; b. N.Y.C., Jan. 15, 1944; s. Arthur Abbott and Margaret Louise (Schweitzer) S. BFA, Pratt Inst., Bklyn., 1964; MPA, NYU, 1969, PhD, 1984. Personnel dir. Manhattan Psychiat. Ctr., N.Y.C., 1966-72; dep. dir. Rockland Children's Psychiat. Ctr., Orangeburg, N.Y., 1972-74; dep. dir. L.I. Devel. Ctr., Melville, N.Y., 1974-78, dir., 1978-80; personnel dir. Kiamesha (N.Y.) Concord, Inc., 1982-83; program dir. Vols. Am., N.Y.C., 1983-86; sr. staff officer Nat. Acad. Scis., Washington, 1986-88; dep. dir. U.S. Interagy. Coun. on Homeless, Washington, 1988-89; exec. dir. Travelers Aid Internat., Washington, 1989-91, AIDS Ctr. of Queens County, Rego Park, N.Y., 1992—. Editor: Homlessness, Health and Human Service Needs. Recipient Citation, N.Y.C. Coun., 1986. Mem. Am. Soc. Pub. Adminstrn., N.Y. State Assn. Mental Health Adminstrs. (pres. 1975). Lutheran. Avocation: weight lifting. Home: Apt 2A 355 W 29th St New York NY 10001 Office: AIDS Ctr of Queens County 97-45 Queens Blvd Ste 1220 Flushing NY 11374-2101

SUTHERLAND, DENISE JACKSON, ballerina; b. N.Y.C., July 19, 1951; d. John Henry and Audrey Kepple J.; m. Donald James Sutherland, July 22, 1985; 1 child, Conor. Grad., Profl. Children's Sch., 1969; student, Am. Ballet Ctr.; studied with, Robert Joffrey, Maggie Black, David Howard. Joined Joffrey Ballet, 1969, leading ballerina; ret., 1986; artistic cons., trustee Dance Notation Bur., 1986—, Profl. Children's Sch., 1987—;cons. to dance program Nat. Endowment for Arts, 1991—; trustee Joffrey Ballet, 1986-90, bd. of Vistors N.C. Sch. Arts, 1993—. Featured in three Dance in Am. programs PBS; video dictionary of Classical Ballet, guest artist with N.Y.C. Opera, Detroit Symphony, numerous regional ballet cos., in fundraising galas Met. Opera House. Home: PO Box 154 Glen Head NY 11545-0154

SUTHERLAND, DONALD, actor; b. St. John, N.B., Can., July 17, 1935; m. Lois Hardwick; m. 2d, Shirley Douglas; children: Kiefer, Rachel; m. 3d, Francine Racette; children: Roeg, Rossif, Angus. Grad., U. Toronto, 1958. Actor: Manhattan London Acad. Music and Dramatic Art, Perth Repertory Theatre, Scotland, also Nottingham, Chesterfield, Bromley, Sheffield, (plays) The Spoon River Anthology, The Male Animal, The Tempest, August for People (London debut), On a Clear Day You Can See Canterbury, The Shewing Up a Blanco Posnet, (films) The World Ten Times Over, 1963, The Castle of the Living Dead, 1964, Dr. Terror's House of Horrors, 1965, Fanatic, 1965, The Bedford Incident, 1965, Promise Her Anything, 1966, The Dirty Dozen, 1967, Sebastian, 1968, Oedipus the King, 1968, Interlude, 1968, Joanna, 1968, The Split, 1968, Start the Revolution Without Me, 1969, The Act of the Heart, 1970, M*A*S*H, 1970, Kelly's Heroes, 1970, Little Murders, 1970, Alex in Wonderland, 1971, Klute, 1971, Johnny Got His Gun, 1971, Steelyard Blues, 1972, Lady Ice, 1972, Alien Thunder, 1973, Don't Look Now, 1973, S*P*Y*S, 1974, The Day of the Locust, 1975, End of the Game, 1976, Casanova, 1976, 1900, 1976, The Eagle Has Landed, 1977, Animal House, 1978, Invasion of the Body Snatchers, 1978, The Great Train Robbery, 1979, The Kentucky Fried Movie, 1978, Murder by Decree, 1979, Bear Island, 1979, A Man, A Woman and a Bank, 1980, Nothing Personal, 1980, Ordinary People, 1980, Eye of the Needle, 1981, Gas, 1981, The Disappearance, Blood Relative, Threshold, 1983, Max Dugan Returns, 1983, Crackers, 1984, Heaven Help Us, 1985, Revolution, 1985, The Trouble with Spies, 1987, The Wolf at the Door, 1987, Apprentice to Murder, 1988, The Rosary Murders, 1988, Lock Up, 1989, Lost Angels, 1989, A Dry White Season, 1989, Backdraft, 1991, JFK, 1991, Eminent Domain, 1991, Buffy the Vampire Slayer, 1992, Younger and Younger, 1993, Shadow of the Wolf, 1993, Six Degrees of Separation, 1993, The Puppet Masters, 1994, Quicksand, Disclosure, 1994, Citizen X, 1995, Outbreak, 1995, Bethune: The Making of a Hero, FTA; TV shows and movies include Marching to the Sea, The Death of Bessie Smith, Hamlet at Elsinore, The Saint, The Avengers, Gideon's Way, The Champions, The Winter of Our Discontent, 1984, Ordeal By Innocence, 1985, Buster's Bedroom. Decorated officier dans l'Ordre des Artes et des Lettres (France); officer Order of Can. Office: Creative Artists Agy Inc 9830 Wilshire Blvd Beverly Hills CA 90212-1825 also: 760 N La Cienega Blvd Los Angeles CA 90069-5231*

SUTHERLAND, DONALD GRAY, lawyer; b. Houston, Jan. 19, 1929; s. Robert Gray and Elizabeth (Cunningham) S.; m. Mary Reynolds Moodey, July 23, 1955; children: Stuart Gray, Elizabeth Dana. BS, Purdue U., 1954; LLB, Ind. U., Bloomington, 1954. Bar: Ind. 1954, U.S. Dist. Ct. (so. dist.) Ind. 1954, U.S. Tax Ct. 1956, U.S. Ct. Claims 1957, U.S. Dist. Ct. Appeals (7th cir.) 1981, U.S. Ct. Appeals (3d cir.) 1984, U.S. Ct. Internat. Trade 1987, U.S. Supreme Ct. 1987. Assoc Ice Miller Donadio & Ryan, Indpls., 1954-64, ptnr., 1965—; practitioner in residence Ind. U. Sch. of Law, Bloomington, 1987; bd. dirs. Woodward Funds, Detroit; pres. Bison Money Market Fund., Indpls., 1982-92, chmn. bd. Contbr. articles to numerous profl. jours. Bd. dirs., v.p. Japan-Am. Soc. of Ind., Inc., Indpls., 1988—; mem. Conner Prairie Inc., Fishers, Ind., dir. 1988—, v.p. 1989-90. pres. 1990-92, chmn. bd. 1992-93; tennis ceremonies 10th Pan-Am. Games, Indpls., 1987; bd. dirs. The Children's Bur. Indpls., 1962-73, v.p., 1968-70, pres., 1970-72; bd. dirs Orchard Country Day Sch., Indpls., 1970-73, Episcopal Community Svcs., Indpls., 1965-73, v.p., 1968, pres., 1969; trustee United Episcopal Charities, Indpls, 1970-71, pres. 1971. Cpl. USMC, 1946-48. Mem. ABA, Internat. Bar Assn., Ind. State Bar Assn., Indpls. Bar Assn., Woodstock Club, Skyline Club, Econ. Club (bd. dirs. Ind. chpt. 1988—). Republican. Avocations: tennis, opera. Office: Ice Miller Donadio & Ryan 1 American Sq Box 82001 Indianapolis IN 46282

SUTHERLAND, DONALD JAMES, investment company executive; b. Teaneck, N.J.; Jan. 2, 1931; s. Conrad James and LaVinia Marie (Peters) S.; m. Denise Jackson, July 22, 1985; children: Paige, Donald, Shelley, Julie,

Conor. A.B., Princeton U., 1953; M.B.A., Harvard U., 1958; LH.D (hon.), St..Michael's Coll., 1981. Regional sales mgr. Dahlstrom Corp., Jamestown, 1958-60; assoc. McKinsey & Co., N.Y.C., 1961-64; v.p. Laird, Inc., N.Y.C., 1965-67, New Court Securities Corp., N.Y.C., 1968-70; pres. Quincy Assocs., Inc., N.Y.C., 1970-75; pres., corp. gen. ptnr. Quincy Ptnrs., Glen Head, N.Y., 1975—; chmn. bd. Crane Hoist Engring. Corp., 1975-79; chmn. bd., pres. Ala. Metal Products Co. Inc., 1976-77; chmn. bd. Am. Spring & Wire Splty. Co., Inc., 1977-82, Muehlhausen Bros. Spring & Mfg. Co., Inc., 1977-82, Lewis Spring & Mfg. Co., Inc., 1979-82, Ohio Locomotive Crane Co., Inc., 1981-86, Water Products Co., 1988-89, Publix Shirt Co., L.P., 1979-91, Quincy Packaging Group, L.P., 1984-91, Will & Baumer, Inc., 1984-94, Quincy Spring Group, Inc., 1986-94, Quincy Techs., Inc., 1987—, PCI Group, Inc., 1987-93, Perfection Forms Corp., 1990-94, Tectron Tube Corp., 1991-95, The Lion, Inc., 1993—, Cavertwire Co., Inc. 1994—. Contbr. articles to profl. jours. Trustee Sheltering Arms Children's Svc., 1973-75, St. Michael's Coll., 1972—, Cancer Rsch. Inst., 1984—, Joffrey Ballet, 1982-91, pres. 1985-87, Barry Goldwater Scholarship and Excellence in Edn. Found., 1991—, Hofstra U., 1992—; mem. vis. com. Fordham Bus. Sch., 1987—, Villa I Tatti Coun., 1991—; The New Sch., 1992—, Muhlenberg Coll., 1992—, Nassau County (N.Y.) Planning Commn., 1965-68, Internat. Coun. of World Monuments Fund, 1991—. Lt. (j.g.) USN, 1953-56. Mem. The Creek (gov. 1987—, treas. 1991-93), Cap and Gown (trustee 1981—), The Links, Econ. Club of N.Y.C. Democrat. Roman Catholic. Office: PO Box 154 Glen Head NY 11545-0154

SUTHERLAND, DOUGLASS B., tent and awning company executive, mayor; b. Helena, Mont., May 2, 1937; s. Chris and Marie Sutherland; m. Grace Sutherland, Sept. 5, 1986; children: Karen, Scott. B.A., Central Wash. U., 1959. Program specialist Boeing Co., Tacoma, Wash., 1960-71; owner, pres. Tacoma Tent & Awning, Inc., 1971—. Bd. dirs., chmn. Puget Sound Air Pollution Control Agy.; bd. dirs. Tacoma-Pierce County Bd. Health, Tacoma-Pierce County Employment and Tng. Consortium; mayor City of Tacoma, 1982—. Mem. Assn. Wash. Cities, Tacoma-Pierce County C. of C. Republican. Lodge: Rotary. Avocation: sailing. Office: Tacoma Tent and Awning Inc 121 N G St Tacoma WA 98403-2226 Office: Office of the Mayor 747 Market St Suite 1220 Tacoma WA 98402

SUTHERLAND, FRANK, publishing executive, editor; b. Mount Juliet, Tenn., May 31, 1945; s. Ernest Franklin Sr. and Fontelle (Moore) S.; m. Natilee Duning; children: Kate, Daniel. BA, Vanderbilt U., 1970. Reporter The Tennessean, Nashville, Tenn., 1963-77, zone editor, 1977-78, city editor, 1978-82, editor, 1989—; editor The Shreveport (La.) Times, 1988-89; mng. editor The Hattiesburg (Miss.) Am., 1982-86; exec. editor, v.p. The Jackson (Tenn.) Sun, 1986-88. Mem. Profl. Journalists (middle Tenn. chpt. pres. 1974-81, nat. bd. dirs. 1974, nat. treas. 1981, sec. 1982, pres.-elect 1983, pres 1984-85), Am. Soc. Newspaper Editors (mem. steering com., reporters com. for freedom of press 1979-82). Office: The Tennessean 1100 Broadway Nashville TN 37203-3116

SUTHERLAND, GAIL RUSSELL, retired industrial equipment manufacturing company executive; b. Rush Lake, Wis., Dec. 20, 1923; s. Gail Marion and Edith (Grueb) S.; m. Leone Marie Witkowski, Mar. 10, 1945; children: Keith Allan, Glenn Elliott. BS in Agr., U. Wis., Madison, 1947, BSME, 1948, MS in Agrl. Engring., 1949. Div. engr. Deere & Co., Ottumwa, Iowa, 1949-63; mgr. product engring. Deere & Co., Des Moines, 1963-77; dir. product planning Deere & Co., Moline, Ill., 1977-80, dir. product engring. planning, 1980-83, dir. product engring., 1983-84 v.p. engring., 1984-86, v.p. engring. and tech., 1986-87. Mem. editorial adv. bd. Mfg. Engring. Mag., 1987; inventor: cotton harvester blower discharge, combine soybean header, beet harvester flail feeder, pasture renovator cutter. Served as ensign USN, 1943-46. Mem. Nat. Acad. Engring., Am. Soc. Agrl. Engrs. (Engr. of Yr. 1980, Disting. Engr. of Yr. 1983), Soc. Automotive Engrs., Am. Nat. Standards Inst. (bd. dirs. 1984-86). Republican. Home and Office: 16 Mason Ln Bella Vista Village Hiwasse AR 72739

SUTHERLAND, GEORGE LESLIE, retired chemical company executive; b. Dallas, Aug. 13, 1922; s. Leslie and Madge Alice (Henderson) S.; m. Mary Gail Hamilton, Sept. 9, 1961 (dec. Mar. 1984); children: Janet Leslie, Gail Irene, Elizabeth Hamilton; m. Carol Brenda Kaplan, Feb. 19, 1986. BA, U. Tex., Austin, 1943, MA, 1947, PhD, 1950. With Am. Cyanamid Co., various locations, 1951-87; asst. dir. research and devel. Princeton, N.J., 1969-70, dir. research and devel. agr. div., 1970-73; v.p. med. research and devel. Pearl River, N.Y., 1973-86, dir. med. research div., 1978-86, dir. chem. research div., 1980-81; v.p. corp. research tech. Pearl River, 1986-87. Served with USN, 1944-46. Mem. Research Dirs. (pres. 1975-76), AAAS, Am. Chem. Soc. Home: 42 Sky Meadow Rd Suffern NY 10901-2519

SUTHERLAND, DAME JOAN, retired soprano; b. Sydney, Australia, Nov. 7, 1926; d. McDonald S.; m. Richard Bonynge, 1954; 1 son. Student, Royal Coll. Music, London, 1951. Appeared concert and oratorio performances, Australia; appeared in: opera Judith, Syndey Conservatory of Music; debut Covent Garden in Magic Flute, 1952; Italian debut in Handel's Alcina, Teatro la Fenice, Venice, 1960, Bellini's Puritani, Glyndebourne Festival, Sussex, Eng., 1960, Bellini's Beatrice di Tenda, La Scala, 1961, Rossini's Semiramide, La Scala, 1962, Meyerbeer's Les Huguenots, La Scala, 1962, N.Y. debut, Carnegie Hall, 1961; Opera debut Lucia, 1961; opened Sutherland-Williamson Opera Co. tour, Australia, 1965; appeared: Handel's Julius Caesar, Hamburg Opera, 1969, Bellini's Norma, Met Opera, 1970, opened, Lyric Opera Chgo. with, Semiramide, 1971, San Francisco Opera with, Norma, 1972, San Francisco Opera with Trovatore, 1975, Met. Opera with, I Puritani, 1976, Vancouver Opera with, Le Roi de Lahore, 1977; premiered new prodn., Met. Opera in, Tales of Hoffmann, 1973; 1st prodn. in Am. in 80 years Esclarmonde, Massenet, San Fancisco Opera, 1974; author: (with Richard Bonynge) The Joan Sutherland Album, 1986. Decorated Order of Merit, comdr. and dame comdr. Order Brit. Empire, 1991; Companion, Order Australia, 1991; recipient Grammy award for best classical vocal soloist, 1981. Fellow Royal Coll. Music. Office: care Ingpen & Williams, 14 Kensington Ct, London W8 5DN, England also: care Colbert Artist Mgmt 111 W 57th St New York NY 10019-2211

SUTHERLAND, JOE ALLEN, lawyer; b. Bowie, Tex., Mar. 4, 1934; s. Armour Rand and Ruby Lee (Smith) S.; m. Paisley Ball Butler, June 28, 1958 (div. Dec. 1972); children: David B., Janet P., Clare S.; m. Lynn Marjorie Harmer, Apr. 27, 1973 (div. Aug. 1991); children: Joseph F., Christopher A. BA in Govt., Tex. Christian U., 1955; JD, U. Chgo., 1958. Bar: U.S. Dist. Ct. (no. dist.) Ill. 1959, U.S. Dist. Ct. Md. 1969, U.S. Ct. Appeals (4th cir.) 1970, U.S. Ct. Appeals (7th cir.) 1971, U.S. Supreme Ct. 1975. Assoc. Sidley & Austin, Chgo., 1959-62; assoc. Gardner, Carton & Douglas, Chgo., 1962-67, ptnr., 1967—. Mem. ABA, Ill. Bar Assn., Chgo. Bar Assn. Democrat. Office: Gardner Carton & Douglas 321 N Clark St Chicago IL 60610-4714

SUTHERLAND, JOHN BEATTIE, radiologist, health center administrator; b. Cultus Lake, B.C., Can., Apr. 21, 1932; s. George William and Annie Ethylwynne (Nicholson) S.; m. Eva Freko, Dec. 23, 1956; children: Ian Scott, Evan Michael, Karen Elaine, Eric Neil. BSc in Physics, U. Man., Winnipeg, Can., 1954, MSc in Physics, 1956, MD, 1960, postgrad. in radiology, 1966-69. Rotating intern Winnipeg Gen. Hosp., 1960-61; rsch. asst. dept. physiology U. Man., 1961-62; staff advisor Atomic Energy Control Bd., Ottawa, Ont., Can., 1962-64, rsch. officer, Pinawa, Man., 1964-66; radiology resident Winnipeg Gen. Hosp., 1966-69; head sect. nuclear medicine Health Scis. Centre, Winnipeg, 1970-82, acting head radiology, 1982-84, head radiology, v.p., 1990—; chmn. medicale scis. Med. Adv. Com., Winnipeg, 1987—. Fellow Royal Coll. Physicians and Surgeons Can. (mem. diagnostic radiology 1969, nuclear medicine 1976), Am. Coll. Radiology; mem. Can. Med. Assn., Can. Assn. Radiologists (pres. 1994—), Can. Assn. Nuclear Medicine, Radiol. Soc. N.Am., Man. Med. Assn. (pres. 1986-87, chmn. bd. dirs. 1987-89). Office: Health Scis Centre Med 820 Sherbrook St, Winnipeg, MB Canada R3A 1R9

SUTHERLAND, KIEFER, actor; b. London, Eng., Dec. 21, 1966; s. Donald and Shirley Douglas S.; m. Camelia Kath, Sept. 12, 1986 (div.); children: Michelle Kath, Sarah. Appearances include (theater) debut in Throne of Straw, 1977, (films) Max Dugan Returns, 1983, The Bay Boy, 1984 (Genie award nominee 1984), At Close Range, 1986, Crazy Moon, 1986, Stand By Me, 1986, The Lost Boys, 1987, The Killing Time, 1987,

Promised Land, 1987, 1969, 1988, Bright Lights, Big City, 1988, Young Guns, 1988, Renegades, 1989, Chicago Joe and the Showgirl, 1990, Flashback, 1990, Flatliners, 1990, The Nutcracker Prince (voice), 1990, Young Guns II, 1990, Article 99, 1991, Twin Peaks: Fire Walk With Me, 1992, A Few Good Men, 1992, The Vanishing, 1993, The Three Musketeers, 1993, The Cowboy Way, 1994; (TV movies) Trapped in Silence, 1986, Brotherhood of Justice, 1986, Last Light, 1993. *

SUTHERLAND, LEWIS FREDERICK, diversified services company executive; b. Charleston, W.Va., Jan. 1, 1952; s. Lewis Frederick and Dorothy Louise (Droddy) S.; m. Barbara Hall Hoover, Aug. 24, 1974; children—Matthew, Mark. B.S. in Physics, Duke U., 1973; M.B.A., U. Pitts., 1974. Credit trainee Chase Manhattan Bank, N.Y.C., 1974-76, asst. treas., 1976-78, 2nd v.p., 1978-80, v.p., 1980; asst. treas. Aramark Corp., Phila., 1980-83, v.p., treas., 1983-87, v.p. corp. fin. and devel., 1987-91, sr. v.p. fin. and corp. devel., 1991-93, pres. uniform svcs. group, 1993—. Trustee People's Light and Theatre Co. Named Treas. of Yr., Cash Flow mag., 1987. Mem. Phila. Treas.' Club (past pres.), Beta Gamma Sigma. Office: Aramark Corp 1101 Market St Philadelphia PA 19107-2934

SUTHERLAND, MALCOLM READ, JR., clergyman, educator; b. Detroit, Nov. 11, 1916; s. Malcolm Read and Edith Ione (Osborne) S.; m. Mary Anne Beaumont, Dec. 23, 1943; children: Malcolm Read III, Maryanne B. AB, Miami (Ohio) U., 1938; MS, Western Res. U., 1941; BD, Fed. Theol. Faculty U. Chgo., 1945; LLD, Emerson Coll. 1963; LHD, Meadville-Lombard Theol. Sch., 1975. Ordained to ministry Unitarian Universalist Assn., 1945. Dir. boys work Goodrich Social Settlement, Cleve., 1938-40; housing mgr. Cleve. Met. Housing Authority, 1940-41; regional housing supr. Farm Security Adminstrn., 1941-42; housing mgmt. supr. FPHA, 1942-43; pastor in Ill., Va., Mass., 1944-60; exec. v.p. Am. Unitarian Assn., 1959-61; Robert Collier prof. ch. and soc., pres., dean faculty Meadville Theol. Sch. of Lombard Coll., Chgo., 1960-75; minister Harvard (Mass.) Unitarian Ch., 1975-94, min. emeritus, 1994—; minister emeritus Thomas Jefferson Meml. Ch., Charlottesville, Va., 1985—; adj. prof. dept. ministry Andover Newton Theol. Sch., 1992—; exec. dir. U.S. Com. World Conf. on Religion and Peace, N.Y.C., 1980-83, internat. coun., 1984—, also v.p. U.S. exec. coun.; bd. dirs. Unitarian Universalist Svc. Com., Beacon Press; chmn. editorial adv. com. bd. Christian Register, 1955-60; field rep. Unitarian Svc. Com., Mex., 1950-51; mem. sr. secretariat World Conf. Religion and Peace, Kyoto, 1970 and del. to Louvain, 1974, Princeton, 1979, Nairobi, 1984, Melbourne, Australia, 1989, Reva del Garda, Italy, 1994, hon. pres., 1994—; cons. Niwano Peace Found., Tokyo, 1982—; lectr., del. Japan-U.S. consultation on peace Internat. Assn. for Religious Freedom, 1970' trustee emritus, Dana McLean Greeley Found. for Peace and Justice, 1986-94; Thomas Minns lectr., Boston, 1955, Charlottesville, Va., 1978, Berry St., lectr., Boston, 1956; Harvard chair lectr. Warner Free Lectrs., 1985, 93; chmn. common. coun. Chgo. Cluster of Theol. Schs., Inc., 1970-74; pres. Inst. on Religion in an Age of Sci., 1969, 75-77, hon. v.p., 1980—, acad. fellow, 1988; bd. dirs., sec. Ctr. for Advanced Study Religion and Sci., Chgo., 1965—. Author: Personal Faith, 1955, Creators of the Dawn, 1979, Star Light, Star Bright, 1993; co-chmn. publs. bd. jour. religion and sci. Zygon, 1964—; also articles. Bd. govs. Manchester Coll., Oxford U., also hon. fellow, 1974—. Recipient Disting. Svc. award Charlottesville (Va.) Jr. C. of C., 1949, Disting. Svc. award Internat. Assn. Religious Freedom, 1975, Disting. Svc.award Konko Kyo Chs. Am., 1975. Mem. Unitarian Universalist Ministers Assn., Phi Delta Theta, Phi Mu Alpha, Alpha Kappa Delta, Omicron Delta Kappa. Club: Bucks Harbor Yacht (Maine) (commodore 1979-81). Home: 21 Woodside Rd Harvard MA 01451-1616

SUTHERLAND, MICHAEL CRUISE, librarian; b. Morgantown, W.Va., Aug. 29, 1938; s. Charles Fish and Mildred (Haymond) S. BA in English, San Fernando Valley State U., 1967, postgrad., 1968-69; postgrad., UCLA, 1967, MLS, 1970. Office asst., clk. Lindsay & Hall, L.A., 1959-60; libr. asst. I, bindery clk. Biomed. Libr. UCLA, 1961-65; jr. administrv. asst. Dept. Pub. Works City of L.A., 1967; intermediate clk. typist San Fernando Valley State U., Northridge, Calif., 1967-69; libr. I, tchg. asst. Grad. Sch. Libr. and Info. Sci. UCLA, 1970; spl. collections libr. Occidental Coll., L.A., 1970—; attendee numerous workshops and seminars; organizer Western Books Exhbn. at various librs. throughout the Western U.S., 1992, 94, judging organizer, 1993. Author numerous exhbn. catalog booklets; author: (with others) Encyclopedia of Library and Information Sciences, 1979, Western Books Exhibition Catalog, 1986, Striking Research Gold: Distinguished Collections in California Independent Academic Libraries, 1988; contbr. articles to profl. jours. Active Neighborhood Watch, AIDS Quilt Program. Mem. ALA (rare books and mag. divsn.), Rounce and Coffin club (sec., treas.). Office: Occidental Coll Mary Clapp Libr 1600 Campus Rd Los Angeles CA 90041

SUTHERLAND, RAYMOND CARTER, clergyman, English educator emeritus; b. Horse Cave, Ky., Nov. 5, 1917; s. Raymond Carter and Nellie Ruth (Veluzat) S. A.B., U. Ky., 1939, M.A., 1950, Ph.D., 1953; grad., Gen. Theol. Sem., N.Y.C., 1942; postgrad., St. John's Theol. Sem., Camarillo, Calif., 1948, Gen. Theol. Sem., N.Y.C., 1979. Ordained priest Episcopal Ch., 1942, reactivated, 1985; curate St. Luke's Ch., Anchorage, Louisville, 1942-44; prof. English U. Tenn., Knoxville, 1953-57; mem. faculty Ga. State U., Atlanta, 1957-84; prof. English Ga. State U., 1965-84, dir. English grad studies, 1978-84, prof. emeritus, 1985—; lectr. Oriental ceramics. Author: Medieval English Conceptions of Hell as Derived from Biblical, Patristic, and Native Germanic Sources, 1953, The Religious Background of Swift's Tale of a Tub, 1958, The Mechanics of Versification, 1963, 64; contbr. articles to profl. jours. Served as chaplain AUS, 1944-47. Omicron Delta Kappa disting. prof., 1979-80. Mem. Alumni Assn. Gen. Theol. Sem., Am. Assn. Advancement Humanities, Medieval Acad. Am., MLA, New Chaucer Soc., Heraldry Soc. Eng., Oriental Ceramics Soc. Eng., Ky. Hist. Soc., Hart County Hist. Soc., Phi Kappa Phi, Omicron Delta Kappa. Office: care Episcopal Diocese of Atlanta 2744 Peachtree Rd NW Atlanta GA 30305-2937

SUTHERLAND, ROBERT L., engineering company executive, educator; b. Fellsmere, Fla., May 15, 1916; s. John Alexander and Georgia Myrtle (Legg) S.; m. Mary-Alice Reed, May 18, 1945; children—Robert Hynes, Wayne Muzzy, Connie Anne, Nancy Lee, John Gary. B.S., U. Ill., 1939, M.S., 1948. Registered profl. engr., Ill., Iowa, Wyo. Devel. engr. Firestone Tire & Rubber Co., Akron, Ohio, 1939-41; research engr. Borg & Beck div. Borg-Warner Corp., Chgo, 1941; test engr. Buick Motor Div. Gen. Motors Corp., Melrose Park, Ill., 1942-43; sr. engr. research dept. Aeronca Aircraft Corp., Middletown, Ohio, 1943-45; research assoc. Coll. Engring., U. Ill., 1945-48; asst., then assoc. prof. mech. engring. State U. Iowa, Iowa City, 1948-58; city engr. Coralville, Iowa, 1950-53; prof. mech. engring. U. Wyo., Laramie, 1958-80; prof. emeritus U. Wyo., 1980—, head dept., 1960-70, rsch. assoc., 1989-92; pres. Skyline Engring. Co. Inc., Laramie, 1972—; research engr. Collins Radio Co., Cedar Rapids, Iowa, summer 1954, cons. engr., 1950-56; staff engr. Environ. Test Lab., Martin Co., Denver, summer 1960; dir. Hunter Mfg. Co., Iowa City, 1955-58, sec. bd., 1956-58. Author: Engineering Systems Analysis, 1958, History of the University of Wyoming College of Engineering 1893-1993, 1993; contbr. articles to profl. jours. Bus. adviser mfg. group Jr. Achievement, Middletown, 1943-44; mem. Iowa City Sch. Study Council, 1956-58; Mem. Civil Air Patrol, Chgo., 1941-43; legis. fellow to Nat. Conf. State Legislatures, 1982-84. Co-recipient Richard L. Templin award ASTM, 1952. Fellow ASME (life, regional v.p. 1965-67); mem. Soc. Automotive Engrs., Sigma Xi, Sigma Tau, Pi Tau Sigma, Tau Beta Pi. Methodist (steward, chmn. ofcl. bd. 1964-65, trustee 1966-69, pres. bd. 1967-69, lay leader 1969-72, chmn. council ministries 1973-75, chmn. finance com. 1975-79). Club: Kiwanian (dir. Laramie chpt. 1963-65, 79-82, pres. 1966, div. lt. gov. 1970-71, life mem. 1978). Home: 1420 Sanders Dr Laramie WY 82070-4710

SUTHERLAND, ROBERT MELVIN, life sciences professional, educator; b. Moncton, N.B., Can., Oct. 21, 1940; came to U.S., 1976; s. Hubert Alan and Florence Irene (Forbes) S.; m. Karen Jeanette Webb, June 30, 1962; children: Kathleen Anne, William Robert, Jeffrey Alan. BSc with honors, Acadia U., Wolfville, Nova Scotia, 1961, DSc (hon.), 1985; PhD, U. Rochester, 1966. Asst. prof. biophysics U. Western Ont., London, 1968-72, asst. prof. therapeutic radiology, 1972-74, assoc. prof. therapeutic radiology 1974-76, assoc. prof. biophysics, 1972-76; assoc. prof. biophysics U. Rochester, 1976-79, prof. radiation oncology, 1980-88, prof. biophysics, 1979-88, assoc. dir. Cancer Ctr., 1984-88; v.p. life sci. SRI Internat., Menlo

Park, Calif., 1988—; cons. prof. Stanford (Calif.) U., 1988—; rsch. cons. NIH, 1976—, Am. Cancer Soc., 1979-83, Nat. Cancer Inst. Can., 1974—; prin. investigator NIH and others, 1961—. Editor, assoc. editor, hon. adv. editor Internat. Jour. Radiation Oncology, 1978—; contbr. more than 400 articles to profl. jours. Recipient Sr. U.S. Scientist award Alexander von Humboldt Found., U. Mainz, Germany, 1983. Mem. AAAS (Radiation Rsch. award 1977), Am. Assn. Cancer Rsch., Am. Soc. Cell Biology, Radiation Rsch. Soc. (councillor-at-large, exec. com. 1979-82, identification com. for ann. rsch. award 1980, membership com. 1979-81), Am. Soc. for Therapeutic Radiology and Oncology (com. on radiation biology 1984-88, ann. meeting program 1988-91). Office: SRI Internat Life Scis Div 333 Ravenswood Ave Menlo Park CA 94025

SUTHERLAND, WILLIAM OWEN SHEPPARD, English language educator; b. Wilmington, N.C., Jan. 19, 1921; s. William Owen Sheppard and Mary Owen (Green) S.; m. Madeline Ethel Cooley, Sept. 12, 1947; children: Madeline, William, John, Thomas. A.B. in English with honors, U. N.C. 1942, M.A., 1947, Ph.D., 1950. Instr. English U. N.C. Chapel Hill, 1950-51; instr. Northwestern U., Chgo., 1951-54; asst. prof. U. Tex., Austin, 1954-58, assoc. prof., 1958-65, prof., 1965—, chmn. dept., 1983-90, faculty humanist rep. Deans of Humanities of Southwest Conf.; cons. Ednl. Testing Svc. and Coll. Bd., Princeton, N.J., 1961-62; NEH, Washington, 1978—. Author: Art of the Satirist, 1965; co-editor: The Reader, 1960, Six Contemporary Novels, 1961; index An Index to 18th Century Periodicals, 1800, 1956. Served to capt. C.E. U.S. Army, 1942-45. Recipient Scarborough Excellence in Teaching award U. Tex., Austin, 1959; recipient Pres. Assocs. Teaching award, 1982; NEH grantee, 1978-79. Mem. MLA, South Central MLA (exec. com. 1967-69), AAUP (state v.p. 1970-71), Nat. Council Tchrs. English (dir. 1974-78). Democrat. Episcopalian. Home: 3610 Highland View Dr Austin TX 78731-4033 Office: U Tex Dept English Austin TX 78712

SUTHERLUND, DAVID ARVID, lawyer; b. Stevens Point, Wis., July 20, 1929; s. Arvid E. and Georgia M. (Stickney) S. B.A, U. Portland, 1952; JD, U. N.Mex., 1957; postgrad., U. Wis., 1957. Bar: D.C. 1957, U.S. Supreme Ct. 1961. Atty. ICC, Washington, 1957-58; counsel Am. Trucking Assn., Washington, 1958-62; assoc. and ptnr. Morgan, Lewis & Bockius, Washington and Phila., 1962-72; ptnr. Fulbright & Jaworski, Washington and Houston, 1975-83; sr. ptnr. Zwerling, Mark & Sutherlund, Washington and Alexandria, Va., 1987-91; spl. counsel LaRoe, Winn, Moerman & Donovan, Washington, 1983—; prin. Sutherlund & Assocs., Washington, 1989—; bd. dirs., gen. counsel Nat. Film Svc., 1962-75; mem. family div. panel Pub. Defender Svc. for D.C., 1972-76. Founder, chmn. bd. govs. Transp. Law Jour, 1969-74. Vice chmn. Nat. Capitol Area coun. Boy Scouts Am., 1975-78; mem. bd. regents U. Portland, 1985-91. Spl. agt. CIC, U.S. Army, 1952-54. Mem. ABA, Fed. Bar Assn., D.C. Bar Assn., Transp. Lawyers Assn., Am. Arbitration Assn. (nat. panel arbitrators 1970—), Am. Judicature Soc., Nat. Lawyers Club, Internat. Club, Balboa Bay Club (Newport Beach, Calif.). Office: 2600 Virginia Ave NW Ste 1000 Washington DC 20037-1905

SUTHREN, VICTOR J. H., museum director; b. Montreal, Que., Can., Mar. 2, 1942; s. Joseph William and Emily Anne (Roberts) S.; m. Lindsay Jean Scott, July 12, 1969; children: Scott, Caedi, Amy. BA in Psychology, Bishop's Univ., 1965; MA in History, Concordia Univ., 1970. Mem. hist. site staff St. Lawrence Parks Commn., Kingston, Ont., 1965-67; schooner seaman Halifax, N.S., 1967; freelance writer Montreal, 1970-71; staff historian Fortress of Louisbourg, Cape Breton, N.S., Can., 1971-73; research historian Nat. Hist. Parks Can., Halifax, N.S., 1973-75; curator of art Can. War Mus., Ottawa, Ont., 1975-76, chief pub. programs, 1976-85, dir., 1985—; mem. adv. bd. Am. Clipper Trust, Balt., 1985—. Author: (novels) The Black Cockade, 1977, A King's Ransom, 1980, In Perilous Seas, 1983, Royal Yankee, 1986, The Golden Galleon, 1987, Admiral of Fear, 1990, Captain Monsoon, 1992. Fellow Royal Soc. Arts, Co. of Mil. Historians; mem. Can. Nautical Research Soc., N.Am. Soc. Oceanic History, Can. Mus. Assn., Can. Sail Train Assn. Unitarian. Avocations: ski touring, sailing, Gilbert & Sullivan operettas, writing. Home: 36 Bellwood Ave, Ottawa, ON Canada K1S 1S7 Office: Can War Mus, 330 Susses Dr, Ottawa, ON Canada K1A 0M8

SUTIN, NORMAN, chemistry educator, scientist; b. Ceres, Republic of South Africa; came to U.S., 1956; s. Louis and Clara (Goldberg) S.; m. Bonita Sakowski, June 29, 1958; children: Lewis Anthony, Cara Ruth. B.Sc., U. Cape Town (S. Africa), 1948, M.Sc., 1950; Ph.D., Cambridge U. (Eng.), 1953. Research fellow Durham U. (Eng.), 1954-55; research assoc. Brookhaven Nat. Lab., Upton, N.Y., 1956-57, assoc. chemist, 1958-61; chemist Brookhaven Nat. Lab., 1961-66, sr. chemist, 1966—, dept. chmn., 1988-95; affiliate Rockefeller U., N.Y.C., 1958-62; vis. fellow Weizmann Inst., Rehovoth, Israel, 1965; vis. prof. SUNY-Stony Brook, 1968, Columbia U., N.Y.C., 1968-69, Tel Aviv U., Israel, 1973-74, U. Calif.-Irvine, 1977, U. Tex. Austin, 1979. Editor: Comments on Inorganic Chemistry Jour., 1980-87; mem. editorial bd. Jour. Am. Chem. Soc., 1985-89, Inorganic Chem., 1986-89, Jour. Phys. Chem., 1987-92; contbr. articles to profl. jours. Mem. NAS, Am. Acad. Arts and Scis., Am. Chem. Soc. (recipient award for disting. svc. in advancement of inorganic chemistry 1983). Office: Brookhaven Nat Lab Dept of Chemistry Upton NY 11973

SUTMAN, FRANCIS XAVIER, university dean; b. Newark, Dec. 20, 1927; s. Joseph L. and Ella (Joyce) S.; m. Mabel Ranagan, Apr. 1, 1956; children—Frank J., Catherine J., Elizabeth A. A.B., Montclair State Coll., 1949, M.A., 1952; Ed.D., Columbia U., 1956. Instr. pub. secondary schs. N.J., 1949-55; instr. chemistry Upsala Coll., 1953-55; asst. prof. Wm. Paterson Coll., 1955-57; chmn., assoc. prof. natural scis. Union U. P.R., 1957-58; prof. gen. edn., chmn. SUNY at Buffalo, 1958-62; prof. sci. edn., chmn. dept. secondary edn., dir. Merit Bilingual Center Temple U. 1962-82; dean Coll. Edn., Fairleigh Dickinson U., 1982-87; mem. tech. rsch. staff Exxon Engring. & Rsch. Lab., Linden, N.J., 1955—; vis. lectr. Rutgers U.; cons. India AID Project; vis. prof., scientist Hebrew U, Israel; sr. scholar Temple U., 1988—; vis. sci. educator and program dir. edn. and human resources NSF, 1988-93; exec. dir. curriculum devel. coun. Rowan Coll., N.J., 1993—; del. OAS Coun. Sci. Edn. and Culture, 1971; co-dir. Environ. Edn. Conf. Protection Svc., Jerusalem, 1975; cons. fed., state, local sch. dists.; vis. prof. Huazhong U., People's Republic China, 1980, 87, Tianjin Normal U., 1984, 85; co-dir. chem. edn. conf., Tianjin Normal U., People's Republic China, 1984. Author: Concepts in Chemistry, 1st edit., 1962, 2d edit., 1968, What Kind of Environment Will Our Children Have?, 1971, Educating Personnel for Bilingual Settings: Today and Beyond, 1979, Teaching English Through Science, 1985, Teaching Science to Limited English Proficient Students: Excellence Through Reform, 1994. mem. Haddonfield (N.J.) Bd. Edn.; v.p. alumni bd. Montclair State Coll., 1988. Recipient N.J. Gov.'s Edn. award, 1987, award Hispanic Congress of Pa., 1980, Alumni Citation Montclair State Coll., 1988. Fellow AAAS; mem. NSTA, Am. Chem. Soc., Am. Chem. Colls. Tchr. Edn. (chief instnl. rep. 1968-87), Nat. Assn. Rsch. Sci. Teaching (pres.), N.J. Gov.'s Acad., Phi Delta Kappa (4 rsch. awards). Home: 128 Stratton Ln Mount Laurel NJ 08054-3301 Office: Temple U 456 Ritter Hall Philadelphia PA 19122 also: CDC Rowan Coll Glassboro NJ 08028 *Professional success comes after one accepts the paradoxes of life, willing to accept conflict and willing to give of one's self for a cause. But even then timing must be right.*

SUTNICK, ALTON IVAN, dean, educator, researcher, physician; b. Trenton, N.J., July 6, 1928; s. Michael and Rose (Horwitz) S.; m. Mona Reidenberg, Aug. 17, 1958; children: Amy, Gary. A.B., U. Pa., 1950, M.D., 1954; postgrad. studies in biomed. math., Drexel Inst. Tech., 1961-62; postgrad. studies in biometrics, Temple U., 1969-70. Diplomate Am. Bd. Internal Medicine. Rotating intern Hosp. U. Pa., 1954-55, resident in anesthesiology, 1955-56, resident in medicine, 1956, USPHS postdoctoral research fellow, 1956-57; asst. instr. anesthesiology, then asst. instr. medicine U. Pa. Sch. Medicine, 1955-57; resident in medicine Wishard Meml. Hosp., Indpls., 1957-58; chief resident in medicine Wishard Meml. Hosp., 1960-61; resident instr. medicine Ind. U. Sch. Medicine, Indpls., 1957-58; USPHS postdoctoral research fellow Temple U. Hosp., 1961-63; instr., then assoc. in medicine Temple U. Sch. Medicine, 1962-65; mem. faculty U. Pa. Sch. Medicine, 1964-75, assoc. prof. medicine, 1971-75; clin. asst. physician Pa. Hosp., 1966-71; research physician, then assoc. dir. Inst. Cancer Research, Phila., 1965-75; vis. prof. medicine Med. Coll. Pa., Phila., 1971-74; prof. medicine Med. Coll. Pa., 1975—, dean, 1975-89, sr. v.p., 1976-89; v.p. Ednl.

Commn. Fgn. Med. Grads, 1989—; dir. clin. devel. Am. Oncological Hosp., Phila., 1973-75; attending physician Phila. VA Hosp., 1967—, Hosp. Med. Coll. Pa., 1971—; cons. in field. Mem. U.S. nat. com. Internat. Union Against Cancer, 1969-72; mem. Nat. Conf. Cancer Prevention and Detection, 1973, Nat. Workshop Profl. Edn. in High Blood Pressure, 1973, Nat. Cancer Control Planning Conf., 1973; vice chm. Gov. Pa. Task Force Cancer Control, 1974-76, chmn. com. cancer detection, 1974-76; mem. health rsch. adv. bd. State of Pa., 1976-78; mem. diagnostic rsch. adv. group Nat. Cancer Inst., 1974-78; chmn. coordinating com. comprehensive cancer center program Fox Chase Cancer Ctr., U. Pa. Cancer Ctr., 1975; cons. WHO, Govt. of India, 1979, Govt. of Indonesia, 1980, entire S.E. Asia region, 1981, U. Zimbabwe, 1989, Ministry of Health of Poland, 1992, Israel Sci. Coun., 1992, U. Autonomade Guadalajara, Mex., 1993, Generalitat de Catlunya, Spain, 1993, Ministry of Health Russian Fedn., 1993, Instituto de Pos-Graduacao Medica Carlos Chagas, Brazil, 1994-95; mem. Nat. Conf. on Med. Edn. Author numerous articles in field.; Asst. editor: Annals Internal Medicine, 1972-75; editorial bd. other med. jours. Bd. dirs. Phila. Coun. Internat. Visitors, 1972-77, Israel Cancer Rsch. Fund, 1975-95, Am. Assocs. Ben Gurion U., Phila. Divsn., 1986—, assoc. chair, 1993—, 1993—, nat. bd. dirs., 1991—, Internat. Med. Scholars Program, 1988-89, Sight Savers Internat., 1988-91; trustee Ednl. Commn. Fgn. Med. Grads, 1987-89; adv. commn. Internat. Participation Phila. '76, 1973-76. Capt. M.C. AUS, 1958-60. Recipient Arnold and Marie Schwartz award in medicine AMA, 1976, Torch of Learning award Am. Friends of Hebrew U., 1981, medal Ben Gurion U. Negev, Israel, 1985, medal U. Cath. de Lille, France, 1987, medal U. Belgrade, Yugoslavia, 1988, Founder's award and medal Med. Coll. Pa., 1989, St. Thomas Aquinas award Santo Tomas U. Med. Alumni Assn., The Philippines, 1989, medal Kiev Med. Inst., Ukraine, 1991, Benjamin Albagli medal Inst. de Pos-Graduacao Medica Carlos Chagas, Brazil, 1993, shield Coll. Physicians and Surgeons, Pakistan, 1993, medal Ukrainian State Med. U., 1994, medal Universidad de Cantabria, Spain, 1994. Fellow ACP, Coll. Physicians Phila. (censor 1977-86, councillor 1977-86); mem. AMA, AAAS, Am. Fedn. Clin. Research (pres. Temple U. chpt. 1964-65), Am. Assn. Cancer Research, Am. Soc. Clin. Oncology, Am. Dermatoglyphics Assn., Assn. Am. Cancer Insts., Assn. Am. Med. Colls., Northeast Consortium on Med. Edn. (treas. 1983-89, chmn. 1986-87), Council of Deans of Pvt. Free-Standing Med. Schs. (co-founder, nat. chmn. 1983-85), Pa. Council Deans (chmn. 1987-89), Am. Cancer Soc. (vice chmn. service com. Phila. div. 1974-76, bd. dirs. 1974hmn. awards com. 1976), Am. Lung Assn., Am. Heart Assn., NAFSA-Assn. Internat. Educators, Pan Am. Med. Assn., Phila. Coop. Cancer Assn., N.Y. Acad. Scis., Pa. Heart Assn., Heart Assn. Southeastern Pa., Pa. Med. Soc., Phila. County Med. Soc. (chmn. com. internat. med. affairs 1964-72), Pa. Lung Assn., Phila. Assn. for Clin. Trials (bd. dirs. 1980-81), Health Systems Agy. Southeastern Pa. (gov. bd., exec. com. 1983-87, sec. 1985-87), Am. Assn. Ben Gurion U. (bd. dirs. 1986—), Soc. des Medecins Militaires Français, Assn. Med. Edn. in Europe, Sociedad Española de Educacion Medica, Internat. Med. Sch. Affiliates Consortium (co-founder, vice chmn. 1985-87), Phi Beta Kappa, Sigma Xi, Alpha Omega Alpha (councillor 1963-65). Discovered assn. of hepatitis B surface antigen with hepatitis; performed 1st studies of pulmonary Surfactant in adult human lung disease; developed cancer screening system based on risk status; pioneer in describing non-A non-B hepatitis, pioneer in showing relationship of body iron stores to cancer susceptibility and life expectancy; organized first symposium on problems of foreign medical graduates; coined word "ergasteric" for lab.-contracted disease; responsible for advances in assessment of clinical competence. Home: 2135 St James St Philadelphia PA 19103-4804

SUTOWSKI, THOR BRIAN, choreographer; b. Trenton, N.J., Jan. 27, 1945; s. Walter X. and Kathryn (Tang) S.; m. Sonia Arova, Mar. 11, 1965; 1 dau., Ariane. Student San Diego Ballet, 1958-63, San Francisco Ballet, 1963-64, Nat. Ballet, 1964. Cert. solotanzer (solo dancer), Genossenschaft Deutscher Buhnen-Angehorigen, West Germany. Soloist, Norwegian State Opera, Oslo, 1965-70; 1st soloist Hamburgische Staatsoper, Hamburg, Ger., 1970-71; dir. San Diego Ballet, 1971-76, Ballet Ala., Birmingham, 1978-81; dir. State of Ala. Ballet, Birmingham, 1982-83; chmn. Ala. Sch. Fine Arts, Birmingham, 1976—; artistic advisor, choreographer Asami Maki Ballet, Toyko, 1976-79; choreographer Atlanta Ballet, 1980-87, resident choreographer Atlanta Ballet Co., 1987-93; dance advisor Ala. State Arts Council, Montgomery, 1977-78; advisor Tenn. Ballet Co.; dance advisor Miss. Arts Council; choreographer Ballet South and State of Ala. Ballet; mem. City of Atlanta Mayor's Review Fellowship panel, 1987; adj. prof. choreography U. Ala., Tuscaloosa, 1988—; commd. choreographer Bavarian State Ballet-State Opera, Munich, 1994. Recipient Pub. TV Emmy award, 1976; Obelisk award for Choreography, 1977, 78, 79, 80; grantee Ford Found., 1964, Nat. Endowment Arts, 1973-74. Mem. Am. Guild Mus. Artists. Republican. Lutheran. Office: 1800 8th Ave N Birmingham AL 35203

SUTPHEN, HAROLD AMERMAN, JR., retired paper company executive; b. Verona, N.J., Feb. 13, 1926; s. Harold Amerman and Marion Esther (Mason) S.; m. Greta May Peterson, June 24, 1950; children—Judith Amerman, Peter Lehmann, Pamela Torrance. Grad., Phillips Exeter Acad., 1944; B.S. in Mech. Engring. Princeton, 1950. With Universal Oil Products Co., Chgo., 1950-51, Texaco, Inc., 1951-52; bus. research analyst Arthur D. Little, Inc., 1952-56; asst. div. mgr. adminstrn., fine papers div. W.Va. Pulp and Paper Co. (name now changed to Westvaco Corp.), 1956-60, v.p., 1967-80, sr. v.p., 1980-88, mgr. fine papers div., 1974-88, dir., 1975-88; v.p., treas. U.S. Envelope Co., Springfield, Mass., 1960-62, pres., CEO, 1962-67, chmn. bd., 1974-76, also dir.; bd. dirs. Tax Rev., Fairfield, Conn., 1993—, vice-chmn. Served with AUS, 1944-46. Mem. Holland Soc. N.Y., Phi Beta Kappa. Clubs: Country of Fairfield (Conn.), Weston (Conn.) Gun. Home: 33 Hill Brook Ln Fairfield CT 06430-7136

SUTRESNA, NANA S., ambassador; b. Ciamis, Indonesia, Oct. 21, 1933; m. Megawati Sutresna, Nov. 21, 1951; children: Danni, Pattiawaty, Harris. Student, Acad. Fgn. Svc., Jakarta, Indonesia, 1953; cert. in internat. law and rels., U. Wales, Aberystwyth, 1963; MA in Internat. Rels., U. Wales, 1964. Fgn. news editor Nat. News Agy. ANTARA, Jakarta, 1955-57; with Dept. Fgn. Affairs, Jakarta, 1957-67; from 3d to 2d sec. Indonesian Embassy, Washington, 1967-70; 1st sec. Indonesian Embassy, Mexico City, 1970-72; head pub. rels., spokesman Dept. Fgn. Affairs, Jakarta, 1972; min. counselor Indonesian Embassy, Vienna, Austria, 1976-79; min. Indonesian Embassy, Vienna, 1979; dir. European affairs Dept. Fgn. Affairs, Jakarta, 1979-81; head Indonesian del. to disarmament conf., amb./dep. rep. Indonesian Mission to UN, Geneva, 1981-84; dir.-gen. polit. affairs Dept. Fgn. Affairs, Jakarta, 1984-88; amb., permanent rep. Indonesian Mission UN, N.Y.C., 1988—. Decorated Grosses Verdienstkreuz Mit Stern (Fed. Republic Germany); Grand Orrice Ofder of Al-istiqlal (Kingdom of Jordan); comdr. Legion of Honor (France); Satya Lencana Karya Satya (Indonesia). Mem. Internat. Assn. Permanent Reps. to the UN (bd. dirs. 1988—). Avocation: golfing. Office: Indonesian Mission to UN 325 E 38th St New York NY 10016-2745

SUTTE, DONALD T., JR., real estate executive; b. Oak Park, Ill., Nov. 20, 1933. BS, Fla. So. Coll., 1955. Pres. Real Property Analysts, Inc., Ft. Lauderdale, Fla., 1972—. Mem. Am. Inst. Real Estate Appraisers, Soc. Real Estate Appraisers, Am. Right-of-Way Assn., Am. Soc. Real Estate Counselors, Ft. Lauderdale Bd. Realtors. Office: Real Property Analysts Inc 6700 N Andrews Ave Ste 603 Fort Lauderdale FL 33309

SUTTENFIELD, NANCY DEZORT, financial executive; b. Mt. Pleasant, Pa., Feb. 1, 1950; d. James Joseph and Alice Mae (Roofner) Dezort; m. Charlie W. Suttenfield, May 1, 1982. BS, Indiana U. of Pa., 1971; MA, Va. Commonwealth U., 1978. Rsch. asst. Va. Dept. Taxation, Richmond, 1973-74, asst. economist, 1975-77, economist, 1977-78, sr. economist, dep. rsch. dir., 1978-81; instr. econs. John Tyler C.C., Chester, Va., 1979-80; sr. budget analyst Va. Dept. Planning and Budget, Richmond, 1981-83, budget mgr., 1983-86; dir. office planning and budget Smithsonian Instn., Washington, 1986-90, acting under sec., 1990, CFO, 1990—. Contbr. articles to profl. jours. Co-founder Va. Higher Edn. Budge Officers Com.; mem. governing bd. Nat. Postal Mus. Mem. ASPA (mem. exec. com. 1993-94), Nat. Assn. Coll. and Univ. Bus. Officers, Planning Forum (past bd. dirs. Washington chpt.), Am. Assn. Mus., Fed. Exec. Inst. Alumni Assn. Office: Smithsonian Instn Finance & Adminstrn 1000 Jefferson Dr SW Rm 230 Washington DC 20560

SUTTER, ELEANOR BLY, diplomat; b. N.Y.C., Oct. 21, 1945; d. Samuel M. and Sylvia Gertrude (Ferber) Bly; children: Deborah, Willis. BA, Swarthmore Coll., 1966; MA, Am. U., 1978. Instr. English Thammasat U., Bangkok and Udornthani Tchr. Tng. Coll., 1967-71, Lomonosov State U., Moscow, 1973-74; rschr. Kennan Inst. for Advanced Russian Studies, 1977-79; fgn. svc. officer Office Soviet Internal Affairs, Dept. of State, 1979-80; fgn. svc. officer U.S. Embassy, Kinshasa, 1980-82, London, 1982-85; fgn. svc. officer Office of Strategic Nuclear Policy, Dept. of State, 1986-88, Office of Soviet Union Affairs, Dept. of State, 1988-90, U.S. Embassy, Moscow, 1990-92; charge d'affaires ad interim U.S. Embassy, Bratislava, 1993, dep. prin. officer, 1993-95, dep. chief of mission, 1995—; exec. dir., exec. sec., advisor U.S. Del. to Nuclear and Space Talks, Geneva, 1987-91; teaching fellow Russian lit. The Am. U., 1976-77; escort interpreter and translator Dept. of State, 1976. Co-author: Final Report of the Kennan Institute's Soviet Research Institutes Project, 1981. Founder Camp Wocsom, Moscow, 1974. Mem. Am. Fgn. Svc. Assn. Avocations: music, folk dance. Office: Dept of State Fgn Svc Lounge Washington DC 20520

SUTTER, HARVEY MACK, consultant, engineer; b. Jennings, La., Oct. 5, 1906; s. Josiah Harvey and Effie Relief (Murray) S.; AB, U. Wichita, 1932; m. Julia Genevieve Wright, Sept. 19, 1936; children: James Houston, Robert Mack, Julia Ann Boyd, John Norman. Design and prodn. engr. Boeing Aircraft, Wichita, Kans., 1936-38; supr. arts, crafts and coop. activities Bur. Indian Affairs, U.S. Dept. of Interior, 1938-42, chief procurement br. Bur. of Reclamation, Washington, 1946-54, chief div. procurement and property mgmt., 1954-58; asst. to adminstr. Bonneville Power Adminstrn., 1958-61, asst. to chief engr., 1962-66; cons. engr., 1967—; analyst, chief prodn. service WPB, Denver, 1942-44; chief div. supply C.E., Denver, 1944-46. Mem. exec. bd. Portland area Boy Scouts Am. Recipient Silver Beaver award. Presbyterian. Mem. Nat., Western woodcarvers assns., Internat. Wood Collectors Soc., Electric of Oreg. Author or co-author books and articles on woodcarving. Home: 3803 SE Carlton St Portland OR 97202-7635

SUTTER, JOSEPH F., aeronautical engineer, consultant, retired aircraft company executive; b. Seattle, Wash., Mar. 21, 1921; m. Nancy Ann French, June 14, 1943. B.A., U. Wash., 1943. Various engring. positions Boeing Comml. Airplane Co., Seattle, 1946-65, dir. engring. for Boeing 747, 1965-71, v.p., gen. mgr. 747 div., 1971-74, v.p. program ops., 1974-76, v.p. ops. and product devel., 1976-81, exec. v.p., 1981-86, cons., 1986-87; cons. Boeing Comml. Airplane Co., 1987—; chmn. aerospace safety adv. panel NASA, 1986; mem. Challenger Accident Commn., 1986. Served to lt. j.g. USN, 1943-45. Recipient Master Design award Product Engring. mag., 1965, Franklin W. Kolk Air Transp. Progress award Soc. Aero. Aerospace Coun., 1980, Elmer A. Sperry award, 1980, Nuts & Bolts award Transport Assn., 1983, Nat. Medal Tech., U.S. Pres. Reagan, 1985, Sir Kingsford Smith award Royal Aero. Soc. in Sydney, 1980, Wright Bros. Meml. Trophy, 1986; Joseph F. Sutter professorship established in his honor at U. Wash., Boeing Co., 1992. Fellow Royal Aero Soc. (hon.), AIAA (Daniel Guggenheim award 1990); mem. Internat. Fedn. Airworthiness (pres. 1989). Office: Boeing Comml Airplane Co PO Box 3707 Mail Stop 13-43 Seattle WA 98124

SUTTER, LAURENCE BRENER, lawyer; b. N.Y.C., Feb. 5, 1944; s. Meyer and Beatrice (Weinberger) S.; m. Betty A. Satterwhite, June 9, 1979. AB, Columbia Coll., 1965; JD, N.Y.U., 1976. Bar: N.Y. 1977, U.S. Dist. Ct. (so. and ea. dists.) N.Y. 1977. Assoc. atty. Shea & Gould, N.Y.C., 1976-80, Meyer, Suozzi, English & Klein P.C., Mineola, N.Y., 1980-82; assoc. counsel pubs. Gen. Media Internat., Inc., N.Y.C., 1982—. with N.Y. Army N.G., 1966-72. Mem. ABA, Assn. Bar of City of N.Y. (mem. com. civil rights, 1986-89, comm. and media law 1989-92, copyright and lit. property 1994-97). Democrat. Jewish. Avocation: music. Office: Gen Media Internat Inc 277 Park Ave 4th Fl New York NY 10172

SUTTER, MORLEY CARMAN, medical scientist; b. Redvers, Sask., Can., May 18, 1933; s. Christian Benjamin and Amelia (Duke) S.; m. Virginia Frances Mary Laidlaw, June 29, 1957; children—Gregory Robert, F. Michelle, Brent Morley. M.D., U. Man., 1957, B.Sc., 1957, Ph.D., 1963. Intern Winnipeg (Man.) Gen. Hosp., 1956-57, resident, 1958-59; teaching fellow pharmacology U. Man., 1959-63; supr. Downing Coll., Cambridge U., 1963-65; asst. prof. pharmacology U. Toronto, 1965-66; asst. prof. pharmacology U. B.C., 1966-68, asso. prof., 1968-71, prof., 1971—, head dept. pharmacology, 1971-87; mem. staff Vancouver (B.C.) Hosp. & Health Sci. Ctr., St. Paul's Hosp.; mem. Minister of Health's Adv. Com. on Drugs, Province of B.C., 1971-87. Contbr. articles to sci. jours. Recipient Gov. Gen. medal, 1950; Med. Research Council of Can. fellow, 1959-63; Wellcome Found. Travelling fellow, 1963; Imperial Chem. Industries fellow, 1963-65; Med. Research Council scholar, 1966-71. Mem. Pharmacol. Soc. Can. (treas. 1969-72, sec. 1986-89), British Pharmacol. Soc., Am. Soc. Pharmacology of Exptl. Therapeutics, Can. Med. Assn., N.Y. Acad. of Scis. Office: U BC Faculty Medicine Therapeutics, 2176 Health Scis Mall/Dept Pharmacology, Vancouver, BC Canada V6T 1Z3

SUTTER, RICHARD ANTHONY, physician; b. St. Louis, July 20, 1909; s. John Henry and Molly Louisa (Schuchman) S.; m. Elizabeth Henby, June 15, 1935; children—John Richard, Jane Elizabeth; Judith Sutter Hinrichs. AB, Washington U., St. Louis, 1931, MD, 1935. Diplomate Am. Bd. of Preventive Medicine, Am. Bd. of Occupational Medicine. Intern St. Louis City Hosp., 1935-36; asst. to Otto Sutter, M.D., 1937; founder, med. dir. Sutter Clinic, St. Louis, 1947-84; mem. faculty Washington U. Sch. Medicine; apptd. physician mem. nat. adv. com. on occupational safety and health OSHA, 1971-75; med. dir. St. Louis Internat. Airport, 1964-84, emeritus med. dir., 1988—; mem. Mo. Gov.'s Council on Occupational Health and Safety, Gov's Adv. Com. on Worker's Compensation, Com. on Vocat. Rehab.; cons. Barnes/Sutter Health Care, 1984-91; hon. cons. St. Mary's Hosp. East St. Louis, Ill., 1991—; mem. staff Barnes, Lutheran, Deaconess hosps.; dir. Blue Cross/Blue Shield. Contbr. articles to med. publs. Bd. dirs. Downtown St. Louis, Inc. (hon. chmn. membership com., Leadership award 1994); past dir. Blue Cross/Blue Shield; mem. St. Louis Merc. Libr. Assn., Jefferson Nat. Expansion Commn., Commn. on Future of Washington U., mem. aviation com. Regional Commerce and Growth Assn. Served to lt. col. M.C., U.S. Army, 1941-46, ETO. Decorated Bronze Star; recipient Man of Yr. award St. Louis chpt. Beta Theta Pi, 1974; Alumni Achievement award Washington U. Med. Sch., 1985; Richard A. and Elizabeth H. Sutter chair Occupational, Indsl. and Environ. Medicine named in honor, Washington U. Sch. Medicine, 1993. Fellow APHA, Am. Coll. Occupational and Environ. Medicine (Health Achievement in Industry award 1978), Am. Coll. Preventive Medicine, Am. Indsl. Hygiene Assn. (emeritus, mem. Internat. com. occupational health); mem. AMA (coun. on occupational health), St. Louis Met. Med. Soc. (hon. pres. 1947, Dr. Robert Schlueter award for Leadership 1994), Am. Assn. Ry. Surgeons (past pres.), Cen. States Soc. Ind. Medicine and Surgery (past pres.), Univ. Club, Old Warson Country Club, Washington U. Faculty Club, Eliot Soc. (founder, life), Yachting Club Am. (founder), Bradenton Country Club. Avocations: hunting, golf, fishing, estate management. Home: 7215 Greenway Ave Saint Louis MO 63130-4126 Office: Sutter Mgmt Co 7215 Greenway Ave Saint Louis MO 63130-4126 also: Condo # 321 6701 Gulf of Mexico Dr Longboat Key FL 34228

SUTTER, WILLIAM PAUL, lawyer; b. Chgo., Jan. 15, 1924; s. Harry Blair and Elsie (Paul) S.; m. Helen Yvonne Stebbins, Nov. 13, 1954; children: William Paul, Helen Blair Sutter Doppelheuer. A.B., Yale U., 1947; J.D., U. Mich., 1950. Bar: Ill. 1950, Fla. 1977, U.S. Supreme Ct. 1981. Assoc. Hopkins & Sutter (and predecessors), Chgo., 1950-57; ptnr. Hopkins & Sutter (and predecessors), 1957-89, of counsel, 1989—; mem. Ill. Supreme Ct. Atty. Registration Commn., 1975-81. Contbr. articles on estate planning and taxation to profl. jours. Chmn. Winnetka Caucus Com., 1966-67; pres., trustee Lucille P. Markey Charitable Trust, 1983—; precinct capt. New Trier Twp. (Ill.) Rep. party, 1960-68; asst. area chmn. New Trier Rep. Orgn., 1968-72; trustee Gads Hill Center, pres., 1962-70, chmn., 1971-80; trustee Northwestern Meml. Hosp., 1983—; bd. dirs. Chgo. Hort. Soc., 1982—; mem. dean's coun. Sch. Medicine, Yale U., 1991—. Served to 1st lt. AUS, 1943-46. Fellow Am. Bar Found., Am. Coll. Trust and Estate Counsel (bd. regents 1977-83, exec. com. 1981-83); mem. ABA (ho. dels. 1972-81, chmn. com. on income estates and trusts, taxation sect. 1973-75), Ill. Bar Assn. (bd. govs. 1964-75, pres. 1973-74), Chgo. Bar Assn. (chmn. probate practice com. 1963-64), Am. Law Inst., Internat. Acad. Estate and Trust Law, Am. Judicature Soc., Ill. LAWPAC (pres. 1977-83), Order of Coif, Phi Beta Kappa, Phi Delta Phi, Chi Psi, Tavern Club, Mid-Day Club, Indian Hill Club, Law Club, Legal Club, Gulf Stream Golf Club, Country Club Fla., Ocean Club (Fla.) (bd. govs. 1993—, sec. 1993—). Episcopalian. Home: 96 Woodley Rd Winnetka IL 60093 also: 6110 N Ocean Blvd #36 Ocean Ridge FL 33435 Office: Hopkins & Sutter 3 First National Pla Chicago IL 60602

SUTTLE, DORWIN WALLACE, federal judge; b. Knox County, Ind., July 16, 1906; s. William Sherman and Nancy Cordelia (Hungate) S.; m. Anne Elizabeth Barrett, Feb. 1, 1939 (dec.); children: Stephen Hungate, Nancy Joanna Suttle Walker (dec.); m. Lucile Cram Whitecotton, Aug. 21, 1956; stepchildren: Fred and Frank Whitecotton. JD, U. Tex., 1928. Bar: Tex., U.S. Supreme Ct. 1960. Practiced law Uvalde, Tex., 1928-64; U.S. dist. judge Western Dist. Tex., 1964—. Fellow Tex. Bar Found., Am. Judicature Soc.; mem. ABA, Fed. Bar Assn., Border Dist. Bar Assn., Tex. Bar Assn., San Antonio Bar Assn., Soc. for U.S. Constn. (founding mem.). Democrat. Methodist. Office: US District Court Hemisfar Plz 655 E Durango Blvd San Antonio TX 78206-1102

SUTTLES, WILLIAM MAURRELLE, university administrator, clergyman; b. Ben Hill, Ga., July 25, 1920; s. Wiley Maurrelle and Eddie Lou (Campbell) S.; m. Julia Lanette Lovern, Jan. 28, 1950. B Comml. Studies, Ga. State U., 1942; M Religious Edn., Emory U., 1953, ThM, 1947; MDiv, Yale U., 1946; EdD, Auburn U., 1958; DD, Mercer U., 1972; D Humanities, Tift Coll., 1978; LLD, Atlanta Law Sch., 1978. Ordained to ministry Baptist Ch., 1938. Asst. registrar Ga. State U., 1942-44, asst. prof. English and speech, 1946-55, assoc. prof. speech, 1955-57, prof., 1957—, prof. ednl. adminstrn. and higher edn., 1970—, also chmn. dept. speech, 1955-62, dean students, 1956-62, v.p. acad. affairs, 1964-69, exec. v.p. provost, 1970—, acting pres., exec. v.p., provost, 1987—; pres. emeritus, 1989; exec. asst. to Gov. Joe Frank Harris Ga., 1989-91; pastor Haralson (Ga.) Bapt. Ch., 1950—, Luthersville (Ga.) Bapt. Ch., 1951-62; v.p., pres. dir. Rich's, Inc., Atlanta, 1962-64; dir. Ga. Fed. Bank; adv. dir. First Union Nat. Bank of Ga. (ret.). Chmn. Joint Citizens Adv. Com. to Study Atlanta/ Fulton County Govts., 1967-69, State Adv. Com. on Consol. Edn. Progs., 1983-90, Christmas Seal Tribute Dinner, Am. Lung Assn., 1985; mem. S.E. regional manpower adv. com. U.S. Dept. Labor, 1972-74, Ga. Adv. Coun. Edn., 1985-87; trustee John and Mary Franklin Found., Ga. State U. Found., George M. Sparks Scholarship Fund, Ga. Coun. Moral/Civic Concerns, 1981—, Christian Coun. Met. Atlanta, Ga. Bapt. Homes; dir. John Mercer Found. With USN, 1944-46. Recipient medal of St. Paul, Greek Orthodox Archdiocese N. and S.Am., 1976, Community Svc. award Christian Coun. Met. Atlanta, 1985, Christmas Seal Tribute Am. Lung Assn., 1988, Gold medal award Religious Heritage Am., 1989, Medal of Honor DAR, 1990, Nat. Edn. award Am. Legion, 1992; co-recipient Abe Goldstein human rels. award Anti Defamation League B'nai Brith, 1984; named Rural Min. of Yr. for Ga., Progressive Farmer mag. and Emory U., 1959, Clergyman of Yr. for Ga., Ga. region NCCJ, 1971, One of 300 Who Have Shaped Atlanta, Atlanta mag., 1976, Ga. State U. Disting. Alumnus, 1989; selected as Exemplary Disting. Bivocational Minister in Town and Country area Nat. Coun. Bivocational Ministries, 1988. Mem. Atlanta C. of C., Ga. State U. Athletic Assn. (trustee 1982-89), Ga. State U. Alumni Assn. (pres. 1967, bd. dirs. 1963-74), Masons (33 degree, grand chaplain of grand masonic lodge of Ga. 1994-95), Shriners, Kiwanis (pres. 1966), Commerce Club, Blue Key, Mortar Bd., Phi Kappa Phi, Beta Gamma Sigma, Phi Eta Sigma, Omicron Delta Kappa, Kappa Delta Pi, Kappa Delta Pi, Kappa Phi Kappa, Phi Delta Kappa, Kappa Delta Pi, Sigma Pi Alpha, Sigma Tau Delta, Sigma Nu (grand chaplain 1979-82, 86-92, 94—, vice regent 1992—), Alpha Lambda Delta. Home: 2734 Piney Wood Dr East Point GA 30344-1956 Office: Ga State U Univ Plaza Atlanta GA 30303

SUTTON, BARRETT BOULWARE, former insurance company executive; b. Forsyth, Ga., July 6, 1927; s. James Phinazee and Katherine Woodward (Boulware) S.; m. Mary Terecia Wade, Sept. 1, 1948; children: Katherine (Mrs. John P. Apel), Barrett Boulware, Wade. AB, Vanderbilt U., 1949, LLB, 1950. Bar: Tenn. 1950. With Life and Casualty Ins. Co. Tenn., Nashville, 1950-85; gen. counsel Life and Casualty Ins. Co. Tenn., 1970-83, sr. v.p., 1972-85, also dir. Pres. Nashville Council Community Services, 1968-70, Nashville Travelers Aid Soc., 1970-72; chmn. Nashville U.S.O. Com., 1960-62; treas. Nashville Sr. Citizens, 1980; bd. dirs., sec. Oak Hill Sch., 1983-88, chmn., 1988-90; bd. dirs., treas. Exchange Club Charities, Inc., 1984-87. With USNR, 1945-46. Mem. Assn. Life Ins. Counsel, Order of Coif, Phi Beta Kappa. Presbyterian (elder). Clubs: Belle Meade Country, Nashville Exchange. Home: 750 Greeley Dr Nashville TN 37205-2634

SUTTON, BERRIEN DANIEL, beverage company executive; b. Axson, Ga., Jan. 24, 1926; s. Frank and Commie (Brooker) S.; m. Verda Lee Adams, June 6, 1953; 1 child, Kathryn. B.B.A., U. Ga., 1948. From traveling auditor to St. Louis dist. mgr. Coca-Cola Co., 1948-62; from v.p. sales to pres., gen. mgr. Coca-Cola Bottling Co., St. Louis, 1962-66; pres. Assoc. Coca-Cola Bottling Co., Inc., Daytona Beach, Fla., 1966-82; past mem. pres.'s adv. coun. Coca-Cola Co.; past. pres., bd. govs. Coca-Cola Bottlers Assn. Past gen. campaign chmn., v.p., dir., mem. exec. com. United Fund East Volusia County; past mem. exec. com. Civic League Halifax Area; past trustee Bethune Cookman Coll.; past mem. bd. dirs. Daytona Beach Symphony Soc. Served with USNR, 1944-46. Mem. 49ers, Young Pres. Orgn., Rotary (past bd. dirs., treas., pres. Daytona Beach club). Methodist. Home: 20 Habersham Park NW Atlanta GA 30305-2856

SUTTON, BETTY SHERIFF, elementary education educator; b. Orangeburg, S.C., Jan. 16, 1933; d. Luther Doyle and Mattie (White) Sheriff; m. William Bryan Nunn, June 19, 1954; 1 child, Lisbeth Sheriff Nunn (Mrs. William Reid Clark); m. James Carlton Sutton, Dec. 28, 1979. Student, Columbia Coll., 1949-52; BS, U.S.C., 1953. Tchr. grade 4 State of S.C. Pub. Schs., Blackville, 1953-54; tchr. grade 2 Dream Lake Elem. Sch., Apopka, Fla., 1954-64; tchr. spl. edn. Leon County Sch., Tallahassee, Fla., 1965-66; page mother Fla. Ho. Reps., Tallahassee, 1966-67; tchr. grade 3 Timberlane Elem. Sch./Leon County Schs., Tallahassee, 1967-71; tchr. grades 3 and 4 Golfview Elem. Sch./Brevard County Schs., Rockledge, Fla., 1972-86; tchr. grade 1 Cambridge Elem. Sch./Brevard County Schs., Cocoa, Fla., 1987-95; pres. Bits of Brevard, Inc., Rockledge. Chmn. Democrats for Conner, 1988, Keep Brevard Beautiful, 1990; active Brevard Symphony Orch. Guild, Brevard Mus. Guild, 1973-93, Brevard Heritage Coun., Inc., Episcopal, St. Marks Guild. Recipient S.C. Forestry award State of S.C. Forestry Commn., 1977; ART grantee J. Paul Getty Ctr. for Edn. in the Arts, 1990. Apopka Woman's Club (pres. 1960-62), mem. Apopka Garden Club, AAUW (pres. 1968-70), Brevard Reading Coun. (v.p. 1980-82), Am. Mothers, Inc., Columbia Coll. Column Club, Columbia Club. Alumni Club Ctrl. Fla., U.S.C. Alumni Club (life), Cocoa Elk's Ladies Aux. (chmn. fund raising), Country Club of Rockledge, Delta Kappa Gamma (pres. 1992-93, 93-94). Avocations: volunteering, reading, swimming, travel, farming. Home: 1807 Rockledge Dr Rockledge FL 32955

SUTTON, BEVERLY JEWELL, psychiatrist; b. Rockford, Mich., May 27, 1932; d. Beryl Dewey and Cora Belle (Potes) Jewell; m. Harry Eldon Sutton, July 7, 1962; children: Susan, Caroline. MD, U. Mich., 1957. Diplomate Am. Bd. Pediatrics, Am. Bd. Psychiatry and Neurology. Rotating intern St. Joseph Mercy Hosp., Ann Arbor, Mich., 1958; resident in child psychiatry Hawthorne Ctr., Northville, Mich., 1958-62; resident in pediatrics U. Hosp./ U. Mich. Med. Ctr., Ann Arbor, 1959-61; resident in psychiatry Austin (Tex.) State Hosp., 1962-64, dir. children's svc., 1964-89, dir. psychiatric residency prof., 1989—; cons. in field. Contbr. articles to profl. jours. Active numerous civic orgns. Recipient Outstanding Achievement award, YWCA, 1989, Jackson Day award, Tex. Soc. Child and Adolescent Psychiatry, 1989, Showcase award, Tex. Dept. Mental Health/Mental Retardation, 1990, Disting. Svc. award, Tex. Soc. Psychiatric Physicians, 1990. Fellow Am. Acad. Child and Adolescent Psychiatry, Am. Psychiatric Soc., Am. Pediatric Assn.; mem. Tex. Soc. Child and Adolescent Psychiatry (pres. 1979-80), Tex. Soc. Psychiatric Physicians, AMA, Tex. Med. Assn. Am. Genetics Soc. Office: Austin State Hospital 4110 Guadalupe St Austin TX 78751-4223

SUTTON, CHARLES RICHARD, architect, designer; b. Sand Springs, Okla., June 25, 1927; s. Charles A. and Violet L. Sutton; m. Jean Rector, Dec. 18, 1949; children: John Isaac, Adam Franklin. BArch, Okla. State U., 1950; MArch, Cranbrook Acad. Art, Bloomfield Hills, Mich., 1954.

Draftsman Parr & Aderhold, Oklahoma City, 1950-53; draftsman/designer Coston, Frankfurt & Short, Oklahoma City, 1954-55; designer I.M. Pei & Assocs., N.Y.C., 1957-62; designer/office dir. John Carl Warnecke & Assocs., Washington, Honolulu, 1962-68; pres. Charles R. Sutton & Assocs. Inc., Honolulu, 1968-85; prin. Sutton Candia Ptnrs., Honolulu, 1985—; lectr. in design Columbia U., 1958-62; cons. Honolulu Waterfront Master Plan, 1984; mem. design rev. bd. Kaanapali Resort, Maui, Hawaii, 1985, Kapolei New Town, Oahu, Hawaii, 1991. Archtl. designer East West Ctr., 1961, Hawaii State Capitol, 1962-68; planning designer Honolulu Capitol Dist., 1965-68; architect Aloha Tower Pla,1974-78. Founding mem., v.p. Hist. Hawaii Found.; bd. dirs. Kakaako Improvement Assn., Hawaii, 1990—. Recipient 1st prize Kalakaua Comml. Area Competition (Bishop Estate), 1971; Lloyd Warren fellow Nat. Inst. for Archtl. Edn., N.Y., Paris, 1955-56. Fellow AIA (pres. Hawaii sect. 1973, fellowship 1980); mem. Waikiki Yacht Club (commodore 1984). Mem. Christian Ref. Ch. Avocations: sailing, painting, photography. Home: 3077 Wailani Rd Honolulu HI 96813-1005 Office: Sutton Candia Ptnrs 680 Iwilei Rd Ste 420 Honolulu HI 96817-5014

SUTTON, DANA FERRIN, classics educator; b. White Plains, N.Y., Oct. 10, 1942; s. Joseph Guy Jr. and Eleanor Sutton; m. Kathryn A. Sinkovich, Aug. 16, 1975. BA, The New Sch. for Social Rsch., N.Y.C., 1965; MA, U. Wis., 1966, PhD, 1970. Lectr. Herbert Lehman Coll., CUNY, 1969-72; postdoctoral rsch. Darwin Coll., Cambridge, Eng., 1972-74, U. Auckland, New Zealand, 1974-75; asst. prof. U. Ill., Urbana, 1975-79; prof. U. Calif. Irvine, 1979—, dept. chair., 1986-94; assoc. dir. Thesaurus Linguae Graecae Project, Irvine, 1991—. Author: The Greek Satyr Play, 1975, numerous other books and monographs; editor: William Gager: The Complete Works, 1994; contbr. articles to profl. jours. John Guggenheim fellow, 1975-76. Mem. Am. Philol. Assn., Calif. Classical Assn. Office: U Calif Dept of Classics 156 Humanities Hall Irvine CA 92717

SUTTON, DOLORES, actress, writer; b. N.Y.C. BA in Philosophy, NYU. Appeared in plays Man with the Golden Arm, 1956, Career, 1958, Machinal, 1960, Rhinoceros, Liliom, She Stoops to Conquer, Hedda Gabler, Anna Karenina, Eccentricities of a Nightingale, Brecht on Brecht, Young, Gifted and Black, Luv, The Friends, The Web and the Rock, The Seagull, Saturday, Sunday, Monday, The Little Foxes, What's Wrong with This Picture, The Cocktail Hour, My Fair Lady (Broadway revival), 1994, My Fair Lady (nat. tour), 1993-94; films include The Trouble with Angels, Where Angels Go, Trouble Follows, Crossing Delancey, Crimes and Misdemeanors, Tales of the Darkside; TV appearances include Studio One, Hallmark Hall of Fame prodn. An Wilderness, Theatre Guild of the Air: Danger, Suspense, Gunsmoke, Valiant Lady, General Hospital, From These Roots, As the World Turns, Edge of Night, F. Scott Fitzgerald in Hollywood, Patty Hearst Story, All in the Family, Bob Newhart Show, All My Children, others; TV writer Lady Doc, The Secret Storm, Loving; playwright: Down at the Old Bull and Bush, The Web and the Rock, Company Comin', 1995. Mem. League of Profl. Theatre Women (bd. dirs.), Ensemble Studio Theatre.

SUTTON, FRANCIS XAVIER, social scientist, consultant; b. Oneida, Pa., July 7, 1917; s. Frank James and Rose Marie (Burns) S.; m. Ruth Jacqueline Young, Aug. 24, 1948; children: Peter, Sean, Philip, Elizabeth. BS, Temple U., 1938; MA, Princeton U., 1940, Harvard U., 1941; PhD, Harvard U., 1950. Jr. fellow, Soc. Fellows Harvard U., Cambridge, Mass., 1946-49, asst. prof., lectr., 1949-54; program officer, overseas rep. Ford Found., N.Y.C., 1954-67, dep. v.p., acting v.p., 1968-83; cons. Ford Found. and Harvard U., 1983-85; acting pres. Social Sci. Research Council, N.Y.C., 1985-86, also bd. dirs., chmn., 1988-92; cons. Rockefeller Found, U.S. Agy. for Internat. Devel. and World Bank, N.Y.C. and Washington, 1987-92; acting dir. Rockefeller Study and Conf. Ctr., Bellagio, Italy, 1990-92; cons. Aga Khan U., 1992—. Author: The American Business Creed, 1956; editor: A World to Make/Development in Perspective, 1989; contbr. articles to profl. jours. and chpts. to books. Pres. Am. Found. for Intellectual Freedom in Europe, N.Y.C., 1987-93; mem. bd. fgn. scholarships Dept. State, Washington, 1961-63; bd. dirs. Nat. Ctr. on Adult Literacy, U. Pa., Phila., 1990—; mem. adv. bd. Ctr. on Philanthropy, City Univ., N.Y.C., 1988—; mem. Coun. Internat. Partnerships in Sci. and Tech., N.Y. Acad. Scis., 1995—. Capt. U.S. Army Air Corps, 1941-45. Fellow AAAS; mem. Council on Fgn. Relations, African Studies Assn., Assn. for Asian Studies (disting. service award 1984). Democrat. Club: Century Assn. (N.Y.C.). Avocations: piano playing, dancing, snorkeling. Home: 80 Bellair Dr Dobbs Ferry NY 10522-3504

SUTTON, GEORGE W., aerospace company executive. BME, Cornell U., 1952; PhD, Calif. Inst. Tech., 1955. Mgr. GE, King of Prussia, Pa., 1956-63; scientific advisor USAF, Washington, 1963-65; v.p. AVCO, Everett, Mass., 1965-82, Heliotronics, San Diego, Mass., 1983-85, Jaycor, San Diego, 1985-90; dir. Kaman Aerospace Corp., Tucson, Ariz., 1990-92; chief scientist Aero Thermo Tech., Arlington, Va., 1992—. Author: Engineering Aspects of MHD, 1964, Engineering Magnetohydrodynamics, 1965, Direct Engery Conversion, 1967; editor-in-chief AIAA Jour., 1968—; contbr. 87 papers to refereed tech. jours. Fellow AAAS, AIAA (Thermophysics award 1980, Disting. Svc. award 1988), Nat. Acad. Engring. Achievements include pioneering development of ablation heat protection for hypersonic flight (inorganic reinforced plastic) and successful flight test, aero-optics; conceptual design of high power laser; design of high-energy laser mounted in military vehicle, kinetic energy interceptors. Office: Aero Thermo Tech Inc PO Box 15627 Arlington VA 22215-0627

SUTTON, GEORGE WALTER, research laboratory executive, mechanical engineer; b. Bklyn., Aug. 3, 1927; s. Jack and Pauline (Aaron) S.; m. Evelyn D. Kunnes, Dec. 25, 1952; children—James E., Charles S., Richard E., Stewart A. B. Mech. Engring. with honors, Cornell U., 1952; M.S., Calif. Inst. Tech., 1953, Ph.D. magna cum laude, 1955. Rsch. scientist Lockheed Missile Co., 1955; rsch. engr. Space Sci. Lab. GE, 1955-61, mgr. magnetohydrodynamic power generation, 1962-63; vis. Ford prof. MIT, 1961-62; sci. adviser Hdqrs. USAF, 1963-65; with Avco Rsch. Lab., 1965-83, dir. laser devel., 1971-82, v.p., 1972-82, v.p., tech. dir. Heliontics Laser div., 1983-85; v.p. JAYCOR, San Diego, 1985-90; dir. E-O tech. Kaman Aerospace Corp., Tucson, 1990-92; chief scientist Aero Thermal Tech., Inc., Arlington, Va., 1993—; cons. Energy Agy., 1977-79, Arms Control Agy., 1986; lectr. magnetohydrodynamics U. Pa., 1960-63, Stanford, 1964; developer of ablation heat protection for ICBM and high energy lasers, pioneer aero-optics, missile interceptor tech. Author: Proc. 4th Symposium Engring. Aspects of Magnetohydrodynamics, 1964, (with A. Sherman) Engineering Magnetohydrodynamics, 1965, Direct Energy Conversion, 1966; editor in chief Jour. Am. Inst. Aeros. and Astronautics, 1967—; contbr. 85 articles to profl. jours. Served with USAAF, 1945-47. Recipient Arthur Flemming award for outstanding govt. service, 1965. Fellow AIAA (chmn. plasmadynamics tech. com., Thermophysics award 1980, Disting. Svc. award 1988), ASME, AAAS, Nat. Acad. Engring. Avocations: tennis, travel, sailing. Office: PO Box 15627 Arlington VA 22215-0627

SUTTON, HARRY ELDON, geneticist, educator; b. Cameron, Tex., Mar. 5, 1927; s. Grant Edwin and Myrtle Dovie (Fowler) S.; m. Beverly Earlene Jewell, July 7, 1962; children: Susan Elaine, Caroline Virginia. B.S. in Chemistry, U. Tex., Austin, 1948, M.A., 1949; Ph.D. in Biochemistry, U. Tex., 1953. Biologist U. Mich., 1952-56, instr., 1956-57, asst. prof. human genetics, 1957-60; asso. prof. zoology U. Tex., Austin, 1960-64; prof. U. Tex., 1964—, chmn. dept. zoology, 1970-73, asso. dean Grad. Sch., 1967-70, 73-75, v.p. for research, 1975-79; mem. adv. council Nat. Inst. Environ. Health Scis., 1968-72, council sci. advs., 1972-76; mem. various coms. Nat. Acad. Scis.-NRC; cons. in field; bd. dirs. Associated Univs. for Research in Astronomy, 1975-79, Argonne Univs. Assn., 1975-79, Univ. Corp. for Atmospheric Research, 1975-79, Associated Western Univs., 1978-79. Author: Genes, Enzymes, and Inherited Disease, 1961, An Introduction to Human Genetics, 1988, Genetics: A Human Concern, 1985; editor: First Macy Conference on Genetics, 1960, Mutagenic Effects of Environmental Contaminants, 1972, Am. Jour. Human Genetics, 1964-69. Trustee S.W. Tex. Corp. Public Broadcasting, 1977-80, sec., 1979-80; bd. dirs. Ballet Austin, 1978-84; mem. Austin Arts Commn., 1991-95. Served with U.S. Army, 1945-46. Mem. AAAS, Am. Human Genetics (dir. 1961-69, pres. 1979) Genetics Soc. Am., Am. Soc. Biochem. and Molecular Biology, Am. Chem. Soc., Tex. Genetics Soc. (pres. 1979), Am. Genetic Assn. Club: Headliners (Austin). Achievements include research and publications in

human genetics. Home: 1103 Gaston Ave Austin TX 78703-2507 Office: U Tex Dept Zoology 528 Patterson Laboratories Austin TX 78712

SUTTON, JAMES ANDREW, diversified utility company executive; b. Gary, Ind., June 29, 1934; s. Winfield Alexander and Margaret (Aulwurm) S.; m. Beverly Joan McCorkle, Aug. 27, 1955; children—James II, Susan, Stephen, Scot. BSChemE, Purdue U., 1957. V.P., gen. mgr./gas products Linde div. Union Carbide Corp., Danbury, Conn., 1978-82; sr. v.p. compressed gases UGI Corp., Valley Forge, Pa., 1982-84, exec. v.p., COO, 1984-85, pres., COO, 1985-86, pres., CEO, 1986-88, chmn., pres., CEO, 1989-94; chmn., CEO UGI Corp., Valley Forge, 1994—; bd. dirs. Gilbert Assoc., Inc., Reading Pa., UGI Corp., Valley Forge; mem. Mellon PSFS Bd., Phila.; mem. bd. trustees Thomas Jefferson U. Chmn. United Way Chester/Montgomery Counties Region, 1991; bd. dirs., mem. exec. com. Reading is Fundamental, Washington. Lt. U.S. Army, 1958. Mem. Am. Gas Assn. (chmn. edn. com.), Greater Phila. C. of C. (bd. dirs., exec. com.), Pa. Bus: Roundtable (chmn. edn. subcom.), Pa. 2000 (bd. dirs., co-chair governance and opportuinity to learn com.), Phila. Country Club, Oyster Reef Country Club. Office: UGI Corp PO Box 858 Valley Forge PA 19482-0858

SUTTON, JOHN F., JR., law educator, university dean, lawyer; b. Alpine, Tex., Jan. 26, 1918; s. John F. and Pauline Irene (Elam) S.; m. Nancy Ewing, June 1, 1940; children: Joan Sutton Parr, John Ewing. J.D., U. Tex., 1941. Bar: Tex. 1941, U.S. Dist. Ct. (we. dist) Tex. 1947, U.S. Ct. Appeals (5th cir.) 1951, U.S. Supreme Ct. 1960. Assoc. Brooks, Napier, Brown & Matthews, San Antonio, 1941-42; spl. agt. FBI, Washington, 1942-45; assoc. Matthews, Nowlin, Macfarlane & Barrett, San Antonio, 1945-48; ptnr. Kerr, Gayer & Sutton, San Angelo, Tex., 1948-50, Sutton, Steib & Barr, San Angelo, 1951-57; prof. U. Tex.-Austin, 1957-65, William Stamps Farish prof., 1965-84, A.W. Walker centennial chair, 1984—, dean Sch. Law, 1979-84. Editor: (with McCormick and Wellborn) Materials on Evidence, 7th edit., 1992, (with Dzienkowski) Cases and Materials on Professional Responsibility of Lawyers, 1989, (with Schuwerk) Guideline to the Texas Disciplinary Rules of Professional Conduct, 1990; contbr. articles to profl. jours. Served to 1st lt. JAGC USAR, 1948-54. Fellow Am. Bar Found., Tex. Bar Found. (life); mem. ABA (com. on ethics 1970-76), State Bar Tex. (com. on rules of profl. conduct, com. adminstrn. rules of evidence), Inter-Am. Bar Assn., Fed. Bar Assn., Philos. Soc. Tex., Order of Coif, Phi Delta Phi, San Angelo Country Club, River Club of San Angelo, North Austin Rotary (pres. 1969). Presbyterian. Home: 3830 Sunset Dr San Angelo TX 76904-5956 Office: U Tex Sch Law 727 E 26th St Austin TX 78705-3224

SUTTON, JOHN PAUL, lawyer; b. Youngstown, Ohio, July 24, 1934; m. Jane Williamson, Aug. 20, 1958; children—Julia, Susan, Elizabeth. B.A., U. Va., 1956; J.D., George Washington U., 1963. Bar: Calif. 1965. Patent examiner U.S. Patent Office, Washington, 1956, 59-62; law clk. U.S. Ct. Customs and Patent Appeals, Washington, 1962-64; assoc. Flehr, Hohbach, Test, Albritton & Herbert, San Francisco, 1964-68; ptnr. Limbach, Limbach & Sutton, San Francisco, 1969-91; spl. counsel Keller, Ehrman, White & McAuliffe, San Francisco, 1992-95; of counsel Haverstock, Medlin & Carroll, San Francisco, 1995—; adj. instr. Practicing Law Inst., 1968-69; continuing edn. program Calif. State Bar, 1972, 75, U. Calif. Law Sch., Berkeley, 1975, 84. Contbr. articles to legal jours. Served with USNR, 1956-59. Mem. Calif. Patent Law Assn. (pres. 1975), San Francisco Patent Law Assn. (pres. 1976), State Bar Calif. (exec. com. patent sect. 1975-77), Am. Chem. Soc. Democrat. Episcopalian. Home: 2421 Pierce St San Francisco CA 94115-1131 Office: Haverstock Medlin & Carroll San Francisco CA 94104-2806

SUTTON, JONATHAN STONE, landscape architect; b. Columbus, Ohio, July 31, 1944; s. Charles Reuel and Theodora (Stone) S.; m. Karen Marie Johnson, May 21, 1970; children—Eva Marie, Theodore Stone. B.A., Amherst Coll., 1966; M.Arch., M.Landscape Architecture, U. Pa., 1970. Draftsman Pierre Zoelly (Architect), Zurich, Switzerland, 1966; designer Weissman/Spohn, Phila., 1967; research asst., regional planning br. Delaware River Port Authority, Phila., 1969; research asst. computer applications group Center Ecol. Research in Planning Design, U. Pa., Phila., 1970; instr. landscape architecture studio Center Ecol. Research in Planning Design, U. Pa. (Grad. Sch. Fine Arts), 1972-73, dir. urban design studio, 1973-79; partner Adaptive Design, Phila., 1970; architect, landscape architect Wallace, McHarg, Roberts & Todd, Phila., 1971—; asso. partner Wallace, McHarg, Roberts & Todd, 1973—; adj. asst. prof. Drexel U. Sch. Architecture, 1976—; affiliated Wallingford Community Arts Center.; prin. Hist. Devel. Corp., 1978—; Growth Properties, Renaissance Properties, 1990, Renaissance Assets, Inc., 1993. Contbr. articles to profl. jours. Mem. Citizens Council Delaware County, Pa. Mem. Am. Soc. Landscape Architects (Brad Williams medal 1974, 76, Merit award 1971), AIA, Am. Inst. Planners. Democrat. Presbyterian. Home: 355A Plush Mill Rd Media PA 19086-6022

SUTTON, JULIA SUMBERG, musicologist, dance historian; b. Toronto, Ont., Can., July 20, 1928; d. Samuel L. and Anne R. (Rubin) Sumberg. AB summa cum laude, Cornell U., 1949; MA, Colo. Coll., 1952; PhD, U. Rochester, 1962. Instr. music history New Sch. for Social Research, 1962-63; instr. music Queens Coll., CUNY, 1963-66; chmn. dept. music history and musicology New Eng. Conservatory Music, 1971-90, chmn. faculty senate, 1971-73; prof. emerita New England Conservatory Music, 1992; vis. asst. prof. George Peabody Coll. for Tchrs., 1966-67; instr. NYU, summers 1963, 64; pvt. tchr. piano, 1949-65; lectr., rsch. dir. in musicology, music as related to the dance; presenter numerous workshops and summer insts. on Renaissance dance. Dance dir. N.Y. Pro Musica prodn. An Entertainment for Elizabeth, Caramoor, N.Y., Saratoga, N.Y., U. Ariz., Stanford U., UCLA, 1969, nationwide tours, 1970, 71, 72, 73; dance dir. Descent of Rhythm and Harmony, Colorado Springs, Colo., 1970, Renaissance Revisited, Phila., 1972, An Evening of Renaissance Music and Dance, York U., Toronto, 1974; author: Jean Baptiste Besard's Novus Partus 1617, 1962; editor: Thoinot Arbeau: Orchesography 1588, 1967; translator, editor: Fabritio Caroso: Nobiltà di dame 1600, 1986; producer, co-dir. (tng. video) Il Ballarino, 1991; contbr. articles and book revs. to profl. jours. and encys. Mem. Am. Musicological Soc., Coun. of Rsch. in Dance, Soc. of Dance History Scholars, Phi Beta Kappa.

SUTTON, KELSO FURBUSH, publishing executive; b. Boston, Mar. 8, 1939. B.A. cum laude, Harvard U., 1961. With Time Inc., N.Y.C., 1961—; exec. v.p. Time, Inc., 1984-88, pres, chief exec. officer Mag. Group, 1985-86; pres., CEO Book div. Time Inc., 1986-93; exec. v.p. Times Inc., 1993-94. Office: Carnegie Hill Tower 40 East 94th St Ste 13E New York NY 10128

SUTTON, LYNN SORENSEN, librarian; b. Detroit, July 31, 1953; d. Leonard Arthur Edward and Dorothy Ann (Steele) Sorensen; m. Richard Dale Sutton, May 2, 1981 (div. Sept. 1992); children: Elizabeth, Alexander, Derek. AB, U. Mich., 1975, MLS, 1976. Dir. Med. Libr. South Chgo. Cmty. Hosp., 1976-77; corp. dirs. libr. Detroit-Macomb Hosp. Corp., Detroit, 1977-86; dir. librs. Harper Hosp., Detroit, 1987-88; dir. Sci. and Engring. Libr. Wayne State U., Detroit, 1988—; cons. Catherine McAuley Health Sys., Ann Arbor, Mich., 1993. Contbr. articles to profl. jours. Mem. ALA, Assn. Coll. and Rsch. Librs. (co-chair membership, sci. tech. sect., comparison sci. and tech. librs. 1990—), Mich. Health Scis. Librs. Assn. (pres. 1987-88), Met. Detroit Med. Libr. Group (pres. 1983-84), Phi Beta Kappa, Beta Phi Mu. Lutheran. Office: Wayne State U Sci & Engring Libr 5048 Gullen Mall Detroit MI 48202

SUTTON, NORMA J., lawyer, educator; b. Chgo., June 11, 1952; d. Harry and Beatrice (Ross) Sams; 1 son, Edward Michael. B.A., Loyola U., Chgo., 1974, J.D., 1980; M.A., Gov.'s State U., Park Forest, Ill., 1976. Bar: Ill. 1980, U.S. Dist. Ct. (no. dist.) 1980, U.S. Ct. Appeals (7th cir.) 1980. Tchr., Tri-County Head-Start, Benton Harbor, Mich., 1974; research assoc. CEMREL, Inc., Chgo., 1975-77; law clk. NACOLAH, Chgo., 1977-80; jud. clk. Ill. Jud. System, Chgo., 1980-82; corp. counsel Soft Sheen Products, Inc., Chgo., 1982-85; regional atty. Digital Equipment Corp., 1985; cen. area mng. atty., 1986—. Mem. Tuley Park Players Theater Group, Richard B. Harrison Little Theatre Group. Am. Polit. Sci. Assn. fellow, 1974-75; Fred Hampton Meml. scholar, 1977; Loyola U. Alumni scholar, 1977. Mem. ABA (mem. young lawyers div. computer law com. 1987-88), Ill. Bar Assn. (v.p. young lawyers div., community relations council 1987—), Chgo. Bar Assn., Pi Sigma Alpha. Roman Catholic. Home: 825 S Oakley Chicago IL 60612

Office: Digital Equipment Corp 100 NW Point Blvd Elk Grove Village IL 60007

SUTTON, PAT LIPSKY, artist, educator; b. N.Y.C., Sept. 21, 1941; d. Bernard G. and Bernice D. (Brown) S.; children: David Lipsky, Jonathan Lipsky. BFA, Cornell U., 1963; attended. Bklyn. Mus. Art Sch., 1960, 61; postgrad., Art Student's League, 1963; MA, Hunter Coll., 1968. Mem. faculty Fairleigh Dickinson U., 1968-69, Hunter Coll., 1972, San Francisco Art Inst., 1974; assoc. prof. U. Hartford, 1983—; guest lectr. Hirshhorn Mus., 1975, Va. Commonwealth U., Bennington Coll., 1977, U. Pitts., 1974, NYU, 1983, SACI, Florence, 1986, Springfield Mus., 1987, 88, Parsons Sch. Design, 1990, U. Miami, 1992; instr. SUNY, Purchase, 1980-81, Parsons Sch. Design, 1982-83, 90; mem. adv. coun. Cornell U. Coll. Art and Architecture, 1988—. One-woman shows include Andre Emmerich Gallery, N.Y.C., 1970, 72, 74, 75, Deitcher O'Reilly Gallery, 1976, Medici-Berenson Gallery, 1976, Everson Mus., 1970, Gloria Luria Gallery, Miami, Fla., 1988, Slater-Price Gallery, N.Y.C., 1989, Hartell Gallery Cornell U., 1989, Andre Zarre Gallery, 1991, Virginia Miller Gallery, Coral Gables, Fla., 1994; group exhbns. include Whitney Mus. Am. Art, 1971, Hirshhorn Mus. and Sculpture Garden, 1975, Promenade Gallery, Hartford, 1987, U. Mass. Art Gallery, Amherst, 1987, Gloria Luria Gallery, Miami, Fla., 1988, 92, Andre Zarre Gallery, 1990, Denise René Gallery, Paris, 1993; represented in permanent collections Herbert Johnson Mus., Ithaca, N.Y., Whitney Mus., Hirshhorn Mus., Walker Art Ctr., Hunter Coll., Fogg Art Mus., Harvard U., San Francisco Mus. Art, Bklyn. Mus., Wadsworth Atheneum, Hartford, Conn.; stage designer for play Custody, Westbeth Theatre, N.Y.C., 1991. Grantee N.Y. State Coun., 1972, N.Y. Found. for Arts, 1992, Winsor and Newton Paint Co. grantee, 1992; fellow Va. Ctr. for Creative Arts, 1986, 93. Home: 11 Riverside Dr New York NY 10023-2504

SUTTON, PETER ALFRED, archbishop; b. Chandler, Que., Can., Oct. 18, 1934. BA, U. Ottawa, 1960; MA in Religious Edn, Loyola U., Chgo., 1969. Ordained priest Roman Catholic Ch., 1960, bishop, 1974; oblate of Mary Immaculate; high sch. tchr. St. Patricks, Ottawa, Ont., 1961-63, London (Ont.) Cath. Cen. Sch., 1963-74; bishop of Labrador-Schefferville, Que., Can., 1974—; archbishop Missionary Diocese of Keewatin-Le Pas, Man., 1986, apptd. coadjutor archbishop, 1986—, archbishop, 1986—; mem. Can. Conf. Cath. Bishops, Western Cath. Conf. of No. Bishops, Man. Bishops; accompanying Bishop L'Arch Internat. (homes for mentally handicapped), 1983—. Contbr. religious articles to newspapers. Address: PO Box 270, 108 1st St W, The Pas, MB Canada R9A 1K4

SUTTON, RAYMOND L., JR., lawyer; b. Detroit, Oct. 4, 1951. BA, U. Mich., 1973; JD, U. Colo., 1976; LLM, U. Denver, 1979. Bar: Mich. 1976, Colo. 1978. Ptnr. Baker & Hostetler, Denver; adj. prof. law U. Denver, 1980-81, vis. asst. prof. law, 1981-82. Editor: Colo. Lawyer, 1984-86; contbr. articles to profl. jours. Fellow Am. Coll. Trust and Estate Coun.; mem. ABA, Colo. Bar Assn., State Bar Mich. Office: Baker & Hostetler 303 E 17th Ave Ste 1100 Denver CO 80203-1264

SUTTON, RICHARD LAUDER, lawyer; b. Dover, Del., July 4, 1935; s. Richard and Anna Kimber (Massey) S.; m. Violette Witwer, June 25, 1960; children: Jane Valentine, Richard Mohler. A.B. with distinction, U. Del., 1957; LL.B., Yale U., 1960. Bar: Del. 1961. Law clk. to Judge Edwin D. Steel, U.S. Dist. Ct., Wilmington, Del., 1960-61; assoc. firm Morris Nichols Arsht & Tunnell, Wilmington, 1961-65; ptnr. Morris Nichols Arsht & Tunnell, 1966—; v.p., sec. Prodair Corp.; mem. antitrust and trade regulation com. U.S. C. of C. 1976-80, mem. council on governance, 1980-82. Chmn. Del. Gov.'s Higher Edn. Commn., 1976; treas., bd. dirs., mem. exec. com. Greater Wilmington Devel. Coun., 1970-82; trustee Wilmington Pub. Libr.; bd. dirs. Grand Opera House, Inc., 1976-92, U. Del. Libr. Assocs.; chmn. William H. Heald Scholarship Fund. Mem. ABA, Am. Law Inst., Del. Bar Assn., Confrerie des Chevaliers du Tastevin, Soc. Colonial Wars, Wilmington Club, Wilmington Country Club, Pine Valley Golf Club, Vicmead Hunt Club, The Seminole, U.S. Srs. Golf Assn., Royal and Ancient Golf Club, Phi Beta Kappa, Phi Kappa Phi, Omicron Delta Kappa, Phi Delta Phi. Home: 10 Barley Mill Dr Wilmington DE 19807-2218 Office: PO Box 1347 Wilmington DE 19899-1347

SUTTON, ROBERT EDWARD, investment company executive; b. Burlington, Vt., July 3, 1943; s. Rollin Robert and Blanche Margaret (Deforge) S.; m. Julie Robin Levine, Feb. 1, 1975; children: Katherine Vanessa, David Robert. BA in Econs., St. Michaels Coll., 1962-66. V.p. Comprtic, Inc., Beverly Hills, Calif., 1967-70; brokerage cons. Conn. Gen. Life Ins. Co., Denver, 1970-74; pres. The Core Corp., Denver, 1975-80; mng. dir. Willshire Investments & Holding Co., Denver, 1981-91; pres., chmn. Gen. Capital, Inc., Denver, 1991-93; pres, CEO WK Capital Advisors, Inc., Denver, 1993—; dir. NAt. Assn. Indep. Contr., Denver. 1991—, Nat. Endowment Trust, Denver, 1990—, Tri Corp, Denver, 1980-89, Nat. Acceptance Corp., L.A., 1991—, Nat. Investment Holdings, L.A., 1990—. Mem. Nat. Rep. Eagles, Washington, 1986-90, Inner Circle, Washington, 1985-90, Denver Ctr. Performing Arts, 1976-86. Mem. Am. Cancer League, Glenmoor Country Club. Home: 57 Glenmoor Cir Cherry Hills Village CO 80110-7121 Office: WK Capital Advisors Inc Ste 650 3773 Cherry Creek Dr Denver CO 80209

SUTTON, ROGER, editor, writer, lecturer; b. Manchester, Conn., Oct. 26, 1956; s. Franklin Thomas and Mary Sheila (McNally) S. BA, Pitzer Coll., 1978; MA, U. Chgo., 1982. Libr. Zion (Ill.)-Benton Pub. Libr., 1981-83, Chgo. Pub. Libr., 1983-87; sr. editor Bulletin of ctr. children's books U. Chgo., 1988-92; exec. editor Bulletin of ctr. children's books U. Ill., Urbana, 1992-94; editor-in-chief Bulletin of the Ctr. fro Children's Books, 1994—; dir. Children's Lit. Inst., Columbia U., N.Y.C., 1987-91; lectr. Rosary Coll., River Forest, Ill., 1991—. Author: Hearing Us Out: Voices From the Gay and Lesbian Community, 1994; editor: The Best in Children's Books, 1992, Evaluating Children's Books, 1993; contbr. articles to jours. including N.Y. Times Bk. Rev. Recipient Disting. Achievement award EDPRESS, 1991, 92, 93. Mem. ALA (bd. dirs. young adult svcs. divsn. 1986-90), Friends of Dorothy, 1978—. Democrat. Roman Catholic. Office: U Ill Childrens Rsch Ctr 51 Gerty Dr Champaign IL 61820

SUTTON, RONNIE NEAL, lawyer, state legislator; b. Pembroke, N.C., June 17, 1941; s. Willie French and Vergie Mae (Oxendine) S.; m. Genny Chavis, June 19, 1967; children: Ronette, Fonda Lynn. BA, U. West Fla., 1970; MS, Naval War Coll., 1977; MA, Ctrl. Mich. U., 1979; JD, U. N.C., 1985. Commd. ensign USN, 1958, advanced through grades to comdr., ret., 1982; atty. Locknar, Jacobs, Sutton & Hunt, Pembroke, 1985-94; rep. N.C. Ho. of Reps., Raleigh, 1993—; bd. dirs. Lumber River Legal Svcs., Pembroke, N.C. Cancer Inst., Lumberton; bd. found. dir. Pembroke State U., 1992—. Chmn. Robeson County Dem. Party, Lumberton, 1991-92. Mem. Pembroke Kiwanis Club (pres. 1991-92, Kiwanian of Yr. 1992). Democrat. Home: Rt 1 Box 154 Pembroke NC 28372 Office: NC Ho of Reps Jones St Raleigh NC 27601

SUTTON, ROYAL KEITH, marketing professional; b. Tomah, Wis., Feb. 18, 1932; s. Rollin E. Sutton and Anna M. (Doebel) S.; m. Kathryn E. Bennett, April 7, 1957; children: Patricia Petite, Gregg Bennett, Margaret Mary. Student, Omaha U., 1958-59, Luzerne Community Coll. Lic. ins. salesperson, real estate salesperson. Photographer Rinehart-Marsden Studio, Omaha, 1957-72; salesperson N.Y. Life Ins. Co., Scranton, Pa., 1972-75, Educators Mut. Life Ins. Co., Scranton, 1975-83; mgr. time-share resort Ski Side Village, Tannersville, Pa., 1983-84; dir. mktg. Coachman's Beach Club, Cape May, N.J., 1984-86; owner Royal Mktg., Dallas, Pa., 1987—; mgmt. cons. Coachman's Motor Inn, Cape May. Author: Faces of Courage, 1972. Served with USAF, 1951-55. Republican. Methodist. Avocation: travel. Office: Royal Mktg 62 Dallas s/c #303 Dallas PA 18612

SUTTON, SAMUEL J., lawyer, educator; b. Chgo., July 21, 1941; s. Samuel J. and Elaine (Blossom) S.; m. Anne V. Sutton, Aug. 28, 1965; children: Paige, Jean, Leah, Jepson. BA in History and Philosophy, U. Ariz., 1964, BSEE, 1967; JD, George Washington U., 1969. Bar: Ariz. 1969, D.C. 1970, U.S. Ct. Appeals (fed. cir.) 1983. Patent atty. Gen. Electric Co., Washington, Phoenix, 1967-70; ptnr. Cahill, Sutton & Thomas, Phoenix, 1970—; prof. law Ariz. State U., Tempe, 1975—; expert witness Fed. Dist. Cts., 1983—; trial cons. to numerous lawyers, 1972—; v.p. engring. Shintech, Inc., 1991—; arbitrator Am. Arbitration Assn., Phoenix, 1971—. Author:

Patent Preparation, 1976, Intellectual Property, 1978, Commercial Torts, 1980, Art Law, 1988, Law, Science and Technology, 1991, Licensing Intangible Property, 1994. Chmn. air pollution hearing bd. City of Phoenix, 1970-85. Recipient Patent prize Patent Resources Group, 1979, Publ. award IEEE, 1967, Genematus award U. Ariz., 1964, Disting. Achievement award Ariz. State U., 1980, Construct Sculpture prize, 1989. Avocation: large scale steel sculpture. Office: Cahill Sutton & Thomas 2141 E Highland Ave Ste 155 Phoenix AZ 85016-4737

SUTTON, THOMAS C., insurance company executive; b. Atlanta, June 2, 1942; m. Marilyn Sutton; children: Stephen, Paul, Matthew, Meagan. BS in Math. and Physics, U. Toronto, 1965; postgrad., Harvard U., 1982. With Pacific Mut. Life Ins. Co., Newport Beach, Calif., 1963—, actuarial asst., 1966-69, successively asst. actuary, assoc. actuary, asst. v.p., 2d v.p., v.p. individual ins., 1969-80, successively v.p. individual fin., sr. v.p. corp. devel., exec. v.p. individual ins., 1980-87, pres., from 1987, now chmn. bd., chief exec. officer, also bd. dirs.; mem. affiliates adv. bd. U. Calif. Irvine Grad. Sch. Mgmt. Trustee South Coast Repertory; bd. dirs. Ind. Colls. So. Calif. Fellow Soc. of Actuaries (mem. numerous coms.); mem. Am. Acad. Actuaries (com. on dividend prins. and practices, 1978), Pacific States Actuarial Club, L.A. Actuarial Club (sec. 1974-75, pres. 1978-79). Office: Pacific Mut Life Ins Co 700 Newport Center Dr Newport Beach CA 92660-6307

SUTTON, WALTER, English educator; b. Milw., Jan. 25, 1916; s. Walter Evender and Maud (Farrington) S.; m. Vivian Irene Ryan, Dec. 22, 1941; 1 dau., Catherine S. Penner. B.A., Heidelberg Coll., 1937; M.A., Ohio State U., 1938, Ph.D., 1946. Instr. English U. Rochester, 1946-47; successively asst. prof., asso. prof., prof. English, dir. grad. studies, chmn. dept. English Syracuse (N.Y.) U., 1948—, now distinguished prof. humanities, 1971—; Vis. prof. U. Minn., summer 1960; vis. prof., sr. vis. fellow Council Humanities Princeton, 1960-61; vis. prof. U. Wash., summer 1966, Colgate U., 1967, U. Hawaii, summer 1968; Mem. com. examiners advanced lit. test Grad. Record Exam., 1962-72. Author: The Western Book Trade, 1961, Modern American Criticism, 1963, American Free Verse: The Modern Revolution in Poetry, 1973; Editor: Ezra Pound: A Collection of Critical Essays, 1963, (with Richard Foster) Modern Criticism: Theory and Practice, 1963, (with Vivian Sutton) Plato to Alexander Pope: Backgrounds of Modern Criticism, 1966, (with others) American Literature: Tradition and Innovation, 1969-74, Pound, Thayer, Watson and The Dial: A Story in Letters, 1994; editorial bd.: (with others) Am. Lit., 1973-76. Served with USCGR, 1942-45. Recipient Ohioana Book award, 1963; Howald fellow Ohio State U., 1947-48. Mem. AAUP, Am. Soc. Aesthetics, Am. Studies Assn., Modern Lang. Assn. Am. Office: Dept English 401 HL Syracuse U Syracuse NY 13244

SUTTON, WILLIAM WALLACE, JR., editor, newspaper executive; b. New Orleans, June 12, 1955; s. William Wallace and Leatrice (Hubbard) S.; m. Cheryl Franey, May 21, 1983. BA, Hampton Inst., 1977; postgrad., Harvard U., 1987-88. Mcpl. govt. reporter Courier-Post, Cherry Hill, N.J., 1977-80; reporter various govt., mcpl. and polit. assignments Phila. Inquirer, 1980-87, asst. editor Montgomery County Neighbors, 1988-89, editor Montgomery County Neighbors, 1989-90, asst. city editor, 1990, dep. city editor, 1990-91; mng. editor, mgr. newsroom Post-Tribune, Gary, Ind., 1991-93, editor, v.p., 1993—; mem. nat. adv. bd. Knight Ctr. for Specialized Journalism; judge William Randolph Hearst Found. Journalism Awards. Exec. bd. dirs. Calumet coun. Boy Scouts Am. Nieman fellow Harvard U., 1987-88. Mem. Am. Soc. Newspaper Editors, Nat. Assn. Black Journalists (past officer, bd. dirs.), Soc. Profl. Journalists, Nat. Assn. Hispanic Journalists, Asian Am. Journalists Assn., Nat. Lesbian and Gay Journalists Assn., Investigative Reporters and Editors, N.W. Ind. Assn. Black Journalists, Ind. Associated Press Mng. Editors, Chgo. Assn. Hispanic Journalists, Chgo. Assn. Black Journalists, Nat. Eagle Scout Assn., Kappa Tau Alpha (hon.), Omega Psi Phi (former local and dist. officer). Office: Post-Tribune 1065 Broadway Gary IN 46402-2998

SUTTON, WILLIS ANDERSON, JR., sociology educator; b. Atlanta, July 18, 1917; s. Willis Anderson and Louneal (Walton) S.; m. Dorothy Rebecca Drake, Dec. 22, 1941; children: Willis Anderson III, Franklin Drake, Sarah Sutton Haggard. Student, Young Harris Jr. Coll., 1934-36; B.A., U. N.C., 1939, M.A., 1941, Ph.D., 1952. Project dir. WPA, Ga., 1940-41; instr. Emory U., Atlanta, 1948-52; asst. prof. U. Ky., Lexington, 1952-58; asso. prof. U. Ky., 1959-68, prof. sociology, 1968-82, chmn. dept., 1976-82. Author: Village Level Workers and Their Work, 1960. Served to 2d lt. U.S. Army, 1941-45. Ford Found. fellow India, 1959-60. Mem. Am. Sociol. Assn., Soc. Study Social Problems, Soc. Study Symbolic Interaction, So. Sociol. Soc., North Central Sociol. Soc. Democrat. Presbyterian.

SUTTON-STRAUS, JOAN M., journalist; b. Mimico, Ont., Can., Nov. 30, 1932; d. Frederick Edward and Anna May (Taylor) Treble; m. Walter J. Sutton, Feb. 1955 (div. 1979); children: Walter John, Deborah Anne.; m. Oscar S. Straus, Mar. 1982. Student, U. Toronto, 1951-53. Fashion editor Toronto Telegram, 1972; lifestyle editor, daily columnist Sutton's Place, Toronto Sun, 1972-79; daily commentator Sta. CFRB, Toronto, 1974-77; columnist Toronto Star, 1979; agt. gen. to U.S. Ont., 1990-91; columnist Toronto, Calgary, Edmonton and Ottawa Sun. Fin. Post, 1992—; dir. Personal Ins. Co. Author: Lovers and Others, 1974, Once More with Love, 1975, Clothing and Culture, 1975, Lovelines, 1979, All Men are not Alike. Former mem. adv. bd. Peggy Guggenheim Mus.; former trustee Am. Acad. Dramatic Arts; nat. gov. The Shaw Festival; trustee Am. Friends of Can.; dir. Citizens Com. for N.Y.C., Soc. Meml. Sloan-Kettering Cancer Ctr. Recipient Judy award Garment Salesmen Ont., 1964, Canada medal, 1993; named Can. Woman of Yr., N.Y.C., 1990; honored with Freedom of City of London. Home: 812 Park Ave New York NY 10021-2759

SUUBERG, ERIC MICHAEL, chemical engineering educator; b. N.Y.C., Nov. 23, 1951; s. Michael and Aino (Berg) S.; m. Ina Inara Vatvars, Apr. 26, 1987; 1 child, Alessandra Anna. BSChemE, MIT, 1974, MSChemE, 1974, BS in Bus. Mgmt., 1974, MS in Bus. Mgmt., 1976, ScD in Chem. Engring., 1978. Asst. prof. chem. engring. Carnegie-Mellon U., Pitts., 1977-81; asst. prof. engring. Brown U., Providence, 1981-84, assoc. prof. engring., 1984-90, prof. engring., 1990—; rep. exec. com. fluids, thermal and chem. processes group, 1991—; vis. scientist Centre National de la Recherche Scientifique, Mulhouse, France, 1988; invited lectr. Ministry Edn., Monbusho, Japan, 1991, 93. Mem. internat. editorial bd. Fuel, 1988—; mem. editorial adv. bd. Energy and Fuels, 1990-93; contbr. over 75 articles to profl. jours. Elected mem. Estonian Am. Nat. Coun., N.Y.C. 1984—. Mem. Am. Inst. Chem. Engrs., Combustion Inst., Am. Chem. Soc. (chmn. div. fuel chemistry 1991). Office: Brown Univ Div Engring Box D Providence RI 02912

SUWYN, MARK A., paper company executive; b. Denver, Aug. 12, 1942. BS in Chemistry, Hope Coll., Holland, Mich., 1964; PhD in Inorganic Chemistry, Wash. State U., 1967. From R&D to gen. mgmt. positions DuPont Co., 1967-91, sr. v.p. imaging and med. products, 1989-91; exec. v.p. Internat. Paper, Purchase, N.Y., 1991—. Office: Internat Paper Co 2 Manhattanville Rd Purchase NY 10577

SUZIEDELIS, VYTAUTAS A., engineering corporation executive; b. Kaunas, Lithuania, June 22, 1930; s. Simas and Antanina S. B.S., Northeastern U., 1954; M.S., N.Y.U., 1955. With Stone & Webster Engring. Corp., Boston, 1956-90, chief power engr., 1972-74, v.p., 1974-76, sr. v.p., 1976-79, exec. v.p., 1979-87, dir., 1975-87, cons., 1987-90; pres. Vasair Corp., Brockton, Mass., 1977-91. Mem. ASME, Aircraft Owners and Pilots Assn., Pi Tau Sigma (hon.). Republican. Roman Catholic. Home: 6101 Pelican Bay Blvd Apt 1205 Naples FL 33963-7111

SUZUKI, BOB H., university president. Formerly v.p. acad. affairs Calif. State Univ., Northridge; pres. Calif. State Poly. Univ., Pomona, 1991—. Office: Calif State Polytech Univ Office of Pres 3801 W Temple Ave Pomona CA 91768-2557

SUZUKI, HIDETARO, violinist; b. Tokyo, June 1, 1937; came to U.S., 1956; s. Hidezo and Humi (Sakai) S.; m. Zeyda Ruga, May 16, 1962; children: Kenneth Hideo, Nantel Hiroshi, Elina Humi. Diploma, Toho Sch. Music, Tokyo, 1956, Curtis Inst. Music, 1963. Prof. violin Conservatory Province Que., Quebec, 1963-79, Laval U., Quebec, 1971-77, Butler U., Indpls., 1979—. Concertmaster Que. Symphony Orch., 1963-78, Indpls.

Symphony Orch., 1978—; performed as concert violinist Can., U.S., Ea. and Western Europe, Cuba, Japan, S.E. Asia, 1951—, formerly performed in USSR; guest condr. orchs. in numerous concerts, broadcasts, 1968—; mem. jury Mont. Internat. Competition, 1979, Violin Competition, 1979, Internat. Violin Competition of Indpls., 1982, 86, 90, 94; artistic dir. Suzuki and Friends chamber music series, 1980—; rec. artist. Office: Indpls Symphony Orch 45 Monument Cir Indianapolis IN 46204-2907

SUZUKI, HOWARD KAZURO, retired anatomist, educator; b. Ketchikan, Alaska, Apr. 3, 1927; s. Goerge K. and Tsuya S.; m. Tetsuko Fujita, Sept. 12, 1952; children: Georganne, Joan, James, Stanley. BS, Marquette U. 1949, MS, 1951; PhD, Tulane U., 1955. Instr. anatomy Yale U. Sch. Medicine, 1955-58; asst. prof. anatomy U. Ark. Med. Center, Little Rock, 1958-62; asso. prof. U. Ark. Med. Center, 1962-67, prof., 1967-70; prof. anatomy, asso. dean health related professions U. Fla., Gainesville, 1970-71; prof. anatomy U. Fla. (Coll. Medicine), 1970-71; dean U. Fla. (Coll. Health Related Professions), 1971-79; prof. anatomy U. Fla. (Coll. Medicine and Health Related Professions), 1979-90, ret., 1990; cons. NIH, VA, NASA; vis. research prof. U. Utah Sch. Medicine, 1962. Contbr. articles to profl. jours. Bd. dirs. Civitan Regional Blood Bank, 1977—; regional v.p. Fla. Retarded Citizens Assn., 1974-76; mem. Fla. Adv. Council on Vocat. Edn., 1978-86, chmn., 1981; active United Way. Fellow AAAS; mem. Soc. Exptl. Biol. Medicine, Am. Assn. Anatomists, Am. Soc. Allied Health Professions, Sigma Xi. Episcopalian. Home: 4331 NW 20th Pl Gainesville FL 32605-3436

SUZUKI, ISAMU, microbiology educator, researcher; b. Tokyo, Aug. 4, 1930; emigrated to Can., 1962; s. Jisaku and Michie (Baba) S.; m. Yumiko Kanehira, May 16, 1962; children: Kenji, Miyo, Kohji. B.Sc.Agr., U. Tokyo, 1953; Ph.D., Iowa State U., 1958. NIH postdoctoral fellow Western Res. U., 1958-60; instr. Inst. Applied Microbiology, U. Toyko, 1960-62; asst. prof. mcirobiology U. Man., Winnipeg, Can., 1964-66, assoc. prof., 1966-69, prof., 1969—, head. dept., 1972-85. Contbr. articles on chemoautotrophic bacteria, mechanism of inorganic oxidation to sci. jours. NRC of Can. postdoctoral fellow, 1962-64. Mem. AAAS, Can. Soc. Microbiologists, Can. Biochem. Soc., Am. Soc. Microbiology, Sigma Xi. Office: U Manitoba Dept Microbiology, Winnipeg, MB Canada R3T 2N2

SUZUKI, JON BYRON, dean, periodontist, educator; b. San Antonio, July 22, 1947; s. George K. and Ruby (Kanaya) S. BA in Biology, Ill. Wesleyan U., 1968; PhD magna cum laude in Microbiology, Ill. Inst. Tech., 1971; DDS magna cum laude, Loyola U., 1978. Med. technologist Ill. Masonic Hosp. and Med. Ctr., Chgo., 1966-67; instr. lab. in histology and parasitology Ill. Wesleyan U., Bloomington, 1967-68; med. technologist Augustana Hosp., Chgo., 1968-69; rsch. assoc., instr. microbiology Ill. Inst. Tech., Chgo., 1968-71; clin. rsch. assoc. U. Chgo. Hosps., 1970-71; clin. microbiologist St. Luke's Hosp. Ctr., Columbia Coll., Physicians and Surgeons, N.Y.C., 1971-73; assoc. med. dir. Paramed. Tng. and Registry, Vancouver, B.C., Can., 1973-74; dir. clin. labs. Registry of Hawaii, 1973-74; chmn. clin. labs. edn. Kapiolani Community Coll., U. Hawaii, Honolulu, 1974; lectr. periodontics, oral pathology Loyola U. Med. Ctr., Maywood, Ill., 1974-90; lectr. stomatology Northwestern U. Dental Sch., Chgo., 1982-90; NIH rsch. fellow depts. pathology and periodontics Ctr. for Rsch. in Oral Biology, U. Wash.-Seattle, 1978-80; prof. dept. periodontics and microbiology U. Md. Coll. Dental Surgery, Balt., 1980-90; assoc. prof. div. dentistry and oral and maxillofacial surgery The Johns Hopkins Med. Inst., Balt., 1982—; practice dentistry specializing in periodontics Balt., Pitts.; dean Sch. Dental Medicine, U. Pitts., 1989—; cons. Dentsply Internat., York, Pa., U.S. Army, Walter Reed Med. Ctr., Washington, USN, Nat. Naval Med. Command, Bethesda, The NutraSweet Co., Deerfield, Ill.; cons. Food and Drug Adminstrn., Rockville, Md.; mem. Oral Biology/medicine study sect. NIH, Bethesda, 1985-90; vis. scientist to Moscow State U., USSR, 1972, NASA, Houston, 1976—; lectr. Internat. Congress Allergology, Tokyo, 1973; lab. dir. Hawaii Dept. Health. Author: Clinical Laboratory Methods for the Medical Assistant, 1974; mem. editorial bd. Am. Health Mag.; contbr. articles on research in microbiology, immunology and dentistry to sci. jours. instr. water safety ARC, Honolulu, 1973—. Recipient Pres.'s medallion Loyola U., Chgo., 1977; named Alumnus of Yr., Wesleyan U., 1977. Fellow Acad. Dentistry Internat., Am. Coll. Dentists, Internat. Coll. Dentists, Am. Coll. Stomatognathic Surgeons; mem. AAAS, ADA (cons. coun. rsch.), AAUP, Am. Acad. Periodontology (diplomate), Am. Inst. Biol. Scis., Internat. Soc. Biophysics, Internat. Soc. Endocrinologists, Ill. Acad. Sci. , Am. Internat. Assn. Dental Rsch. (pres. Md. chpt.), Am. Acad. Microbiology (diplomate), Am. Acad. Microbiology (diplomate, examiner), N.Y. Acad. Scis. Sigma XI, Omicron Kappa Upsilon (nat. pres., past exec. sec.), Beta, Beta, Beta Hon. Soc. Home: 3501 Terrace St Pittsburgh PA 15213-2523 Office: U Pitts Sch Dental Medicine Dean's Office Pittsburgh PA 15261

SUZUKI, KUNIHIKO, biomedical educator, researcher; b. Tokyo, Japan, Feb. 5, 1932; came to U.S., 1960; s. Nobuo and Teiko (Suzuki) S.; m. Kinuko Ikeda, Dec. 20, 1960; 1 child, Jun. BA in History and Philosophy of Sci., Tokyo U., 1955, MD, 1959; MA (hon.), U. Pa., 1971. Diplomate Nat. Bd. Med. Licensure Japan. Rotating intern USAF Hosp. Tachikawa, Tokyo, Japan, 1959-60; asst. resident in neurology Bronx (N.Y.) Mcpl. Hosp. Ctr.-Albert Einstein Coll. Medicine, 1960-61, resident in neurology, 1961-62, clin. fellow in neurology, 1962-64; instr. in neurology Albert Einstein Coll. Medicine, Bronx, 1964, asst. prof., 1965-68; assoc. prof. U. Pa. Sch. Medicine, Phila. 1969-71, prof. neurology and pediatrics, 1971-72; prof. neurology Albert Einstein Coll. Medicine, 1972-86, prof. neurosci., 1974-86; prof. neurology and psychiatry, faculty curriculum in neurobiology U. N.C. Sch. Medicine, Chapel Hill, 1986—, dir. Brain and Devel. Rsch. Ctr., 1986—; staff dept. neuropsychiatry Tokyo U. Faculty Medicine, 1960, U. Pa. Inst. Neurol. Scis., 1969-72; attending physician Bronx Mcpl. Hosp. Ctr. 1976-86, Hosp. Albert Einstein Coll. Medicine, 1977-86; vis. prof. fellowship Japan Soc. for Promotion Sci., 1980, Yamada Sci. Found. 1981; mem. neurology B study sect. NIH, 1971-75, guest scientist, 1984-85, program com. mental retardation and devel. disabilities, 1989-92; mem. basic neurosci. task force Nat. Inst. Neurol. and Communicative Disorders and Stroke, 1978, adv. panel directions and opportunities for future research, 1983, bd. sci. counselors, NIH, 1980-84; mem. adv. com. on fellowships Nat. Multiple Sclerosis Soc., 1974-77; jury St. Vincent Internat. award for Med. Sci., 1979; mem. adv. com. Eunice Kennedy Shriver Ctr., Waltham, Mass., 1974-84; med. adv. bd. Children's Assn. for Research on Mucolipidosis Type IV, 1983—; mem. U.S. Nat. Com. for Internat. Brain Research Orgn., 1985-89. Editor: Ganglioside Structure and Function, 1984; chief editor Jour. Neurochemistry, 1977-82, dep. chief editor, 1975-77; mem. editorial bd. Jour. Neuropathology and Exptl. Neurology, 1981-83, Neurosci., 1975—; Molecular Chem. Neuropathology, 1983—, Neurochem. Research, 1985—, Metabolic Brain Disease, 1985-87, Molecular Brain Research, 1985—, Jour. Molecular Neurosci., 1987—, Developmental Neurosci., 1987—, Jour. Neurosci. Rsch., 1993—; contbr. articles to profl. jours. Mem. Nat. Adv. Commn. on Multiple Sclerosis, 1977-81; mem. med. adv. bd. United Leukodystrophy Found., 1982-86, Nat. Tay-Sachs and Allied Diseases Assn., 1971—, Canavan Found., 1992—. Recipient A. Weil award Am. Assn. Neuropathologists, 1970, M. Moore award Am. Assn. Neuropathologists, 1975, Jacob K. Javits Neurosci. Investigator award NIH, 1985, 92, Humboldt Sr. Rsch. award Humboldt Found., 1990, Eminent Scientist award Inst. Phys. Chem. Rsch., Japan, 1995. Mem. Am. Soc. for Neurochemistry (pres. 1985-87, coun. 1973-77, 87-91), Internat. Soc. for Neurochemistry (coun. 1987-89, treas. 1989-93, pres. 1993—), Soc. for Neurosci., Am. Soc. Biochemistry and Molecular Biology, Am. Acad. Neurology, NAS, AAAS, Japanese Med. Soc. Am. (Disting. Scientist award 1985), Japanese Neurochem. Soc., Internat. Brain Rsch. Orgn., Am. Soc. Human Genetics, Japan Soc. Inherited Metabolic Disease (hon.). Avocations: piano, photography, bird watching, skiing. Office: U NC Chapel Hill Brain & Devel Rsch Ctr Campus Box 7250 Chapel Hill NC 27599-7250

SUZUKI, MICHIO, mathematics educator; b. Chiba, Japan, Oct. 2, 1926; came to U.S., 1952; s. Kyosuke and Taka (Saito) M.; m. Naoko Akizuki, Nov. 11, 1952; 1 child, Kazuko. B.S., U. Tokyo, 1945-48, Ph.D. 1952; hon. degree, U. Kiel, Fed. Republic Germany, 1991. Asst. prof. math. U. Ill.-Urbana, 1955-57, assoc. prof., 1958, prof., 1959—, prof. Center Advanced Study, 1968—; research assoc. Harvard U., Univ. U. Chgo., 1960. Study, 1968—; research assoc. Harvard U., 1962, 68, 81. Recipient Acad. mem. Inst. Advanced Study, Princeton, N.J., 1962, 68, 81. Recipient Acad. prize Japan Acad., 1974; Guggenheim fellow, 1962. Mem. Am. Math. Soc. (council 1962-71), Math. Soc. Japan. Home: 2406 Melrose Dr Champaign

IL 61820-7607 Office: Dept Math U Ill 1409 W Green St Urbana IL 61801-2917

SUZUKI, MIKIO, machine manufacturing executive; b. Dairen, Japan, Apr. 15, 1938; s. Saburo and Taeko (Yuyama) S.; m. Sachiko Ohyagi, May 23, 1970; children: Yjka, Kiyoshi. BBA, Gonazga U., 1961; postgrad., Sophia U., Tokyo, 1963. Sales clk. New Orient Express, Tokyo, 1963; mem. staff export dept. Tokyo Juki Ind. Co., 1964-70; mem. staff liaison office Tokyo Juki Ind. Co., N.Y.C., 1970-74; v.p. Juki Am., Inc., N.Y.C., 1974-83; pres. Juki Am., Inc., Saddlebrook, N.J., 1983-89; exec. dir. export Juki Corp., Tokyo, 1989-91; pres., CEO Union Spl Corp., Huntley, Ill., 1991—. Office: Union Spl Corp i Union Spl Plaza Huntley IL 60142

SUZUKI, NOBUTAKA, chemistry educator; b. Nishio, Aichi, Japan, Nov. 8, 1942; s. Kihachiro and Masayo (Miwa) S.; m. Fumiko Sato, Mar. 21, 1971; children: Mina, Kumi. B of Chemistry, Nagoya U., Japan, 1966, D of Chemistry, 1972. Asst. prof. dept. chemistry Mie U., Tsu, Japan, 1971-88, assoc. prof., 1988; sr. rschr. Biophoton project JRDC, Sendai, Japan, 1988-90; assoc. prof. Shimonoseki (Japan) Nat. U. Fisheries, 1990-92, prof., 1993—. Author: Natural Products Chemistry, 1975, 2d rev. edit., 1983, Bioluminescence of Chemiluminescence, Current Status, 1991, Oxygen Radicals, 1992, Chemistry of Functional Dyes, vol. 2, 1993, Bioluminescence and Chemiluminescence, status report, 1993, Bioluminescence and Chemiluminescence: Fundamentals and Applied Aspects, 1994, Maillard Reactions in Chem., Food, and Health, 1994; editor (book) The Roles of Oxygen in Chemistry and Biochemistry, 1988, (book/tape) Scientific English in Fisheries, 1992, English for Science and Tech. Experiments, 1994, English for Pharmacy or Medical Science, 1995. Grantee Naito Meml. Found., 1977, Tokai Sci. Rsch. Found., 1986, Argl. Biological Chemistry Japan, 1990, Kiei-Kai Sci. Rsch. Found., 1991-95, Skylark Rsch. Found., 1992, The Sci. and Tech. Agy., Japan, 1994-95. Mem. Am. Chem Soc., Am. Soc. for Photobiology, Argl. Biological Soc. Japan, Chem. Soc. Japan, Japan Soc. Sci. Fish, Internat. Tech. Exch. Soc. (dir. 1995—). Office: Nat U Fisheries, Yoshimi, Shimonoseki Yamaguchi 75965, Japan

SUZUKI, RYOSUKE, securities firm executive; b. 1939. Grad., Aoyama-Gakuin U., Japan, 1962; student, Northwestern U., 1970-71. Joined Nikko Securities Co., Ltd., Japan, 1962, with internat. svcs. ops. divsn., 1971-72; chief rep. Zurich office Nikko Securities Co., Ltd., 1972-78, chief rep. Paris office, 1978-82, mng. dir., 1982-85, gen. mgr. internat. svcs. ops. divsn., 1985, gen. mgr. Niigata br., 1985, gen. mgr. internat. fin. divsn., 1986, 89, gen. mgr. internat. bonds divsn., 1987, gen. mgr. internat. bus. promotion and adminstrn. divsn., 1988, dep. COO Asia and Oceanic Group, 1991—, COO Am. Group, 1991—; CEO The Nikko Securities Co. Internat., Inc., 1991—; chmn. emeritus The Nikko Securities Co. Can. Inc. Office: Nikko Securities Co Internat Inc 200 Liberty St New York NY 10281

SUZUKI, TAKUYA, telecommunications executive; b. Hakodate, Hokkaido, Japan, Dec. 11, 1935; parents Yoshio and Kunie (Sato) S.; m. Ryoko Suzuki, Dec. 15, 1968; children: Naomi, Scott. BS, U. Calif., L.A. Loan officer Bank of Tokyo, 1960-68; v.p. Asahi Overseas Corp., Torrance, Calif., 1968-84; exec. v.p., chief fin. officer PhoneMate, Inc., Torrance, 1984—. Notary pub. Mem. UCLA Alumnus Club, Lion's Club. Avocation: golf. Home: 2520 S Angelcrest Dr La Puente CA 91745-4419 Office: Phonemate Inc 20665 Manhattan Pl Torrance CA 90501-1822

SVAASAND, LARS OTHAR, electronics researcher; b. Oslo, Feb. 3, 1938; married; 4 children. MSc, Norwegian Inst. Tech., Trondheim, 1961, PhD, 1976. Rsch. scientist div. radar and electronics Norwegian Def. Rsch. Establishment, Kjeller, 1961-65; rsch. scientist div. theoretical electronics U. Trondheim, 1966-69, asst. prof., 1971-74, assoc. prof. phys. electronics, 1974-81, head dept. elec. engrng. and computer sci., 1984-87; rsch. scientist Electronics Rsch. Labs., ELAB, Trondheim, 1969-71, head electro optics rsch. group, 1972-76; sci. advisor Continental Shelf and Petroleu1 Tech. Rsch. Inst., Iku, Norway, 1984—; prof. phys. electronics Norwegian Inst. Tech., U. Trondheim, 1982—; vis. and cons. prof. U. So. Calif. Sch. of Medicine, L.A., 1989—, U. Calif., Irvine, 1990—; bd. dirs. Norwegian Inst. Tech., 1990—, SINTEF Rsch. Group, Norway. Author books; co-editor: Lasers in Medical Science, 1985. Fellow Am. Soc. Laser Medicine and Surgery; mem. Am. Phys. Soc., Am. Soc. Photobiology, Internat. Soc. Optical Engring., Inst. Elec. Engrs., Norwegian Acad. Tech. Scis., N.Y. Acad. Scis., Royal Norwegian Soc. Scis. Office: U Trondheim Inst Tech, O S Bragstads plass 4, Trondheim N-7034, Norway

SVADLENAK, JEAN HAYDEN, museum administrator, consultant; b. Wilmington, Del., Mar. 4, 1955; d. Marion M. and Ida Jean (Calcagni) Hayden; m. Steven R. Svadlenak, May 26, 1979. BS in Textiles and Clothing, U. Del., 1977; MA in History Mus. Studies, SUNY, Oneonta, 1982; postgrad., U. Calif., Berkeley, 1982. Curatorial asst. The Hagley Mus., Wilmington, 1976-77; curator of costumes and textiles The Kansas City (Mo.) Mus., 1978-82, chief curator, 1982-84, assoc. exec. dir. for collection and exhibits mgmt., 1984-86, interim pres., 1986-87, pres., 1987-89; researcher, guest curator N.Y. State Hist. Assn., Cooperstown, 1980; grant reviewer Inst. for Mus. Svcs., 1985-89; ad hoc faculty U. Kans., 1991—, U. Mo., Kansas City, 1992—. Mem. Am. Assn. Museums (mus. assessment program surveyor 1985-89, accreditation vis. com. 1990—), Am. Assn. Stte and Local History, Costume Soc. Am., Heritage League of Kansas City (bd. dirs. 1987-89), Midwest Mus. Conf. (coun. 1992—), Mo. Mus. Assocs. (pres. 1992-94, com. on mus. profl. tng. 1993—). Avocations: music, sports, photography, cooking. Home: 624 Romany Rd Kansas City MO 64113-2037

SVAHN, JOHN ALFRED, government official; b. New London, Conn., May 13, 1943; s. Albert Russell and Esther Marilu (Caffero) S.; m. Jill Weber, July 12, 1977; children: Kirsten Marie, John Alfred III. B.A. in Polit. Sci., U. Wash., 1966; postgrad., U. Pacific, 1970-73, Georgetown U., 1973-74. Spl. asst. to dir. Calif. Dept. Public Works, 1968-70; chief dep. dir. Calif. Dept. Social Welfare, 1971-73, dir., 1973; acting commr. Community Services Adminstrn., HEW, Washington, 1973-74; commr. Assistance Payments Adminstrn., 1973-76; dep. administr. Social and Rehab. Service, 1974-75; adminstr. Social and Rehab. Svcs., 1975-76; mgr. Haskins and Sells, 1976-79; pres. John A. Svahn, Inc., Annapolis, Md., 1979-81; U.S. commr. social security Balt., 1981-83; undersec. HHS, Washington, 1983-84; assst. to Pres. for policy devel. Washington, 1984-86; chmn. Maximus Inc., Washington, 1988-94; U.S. commr. Commn. for Study of Alternatives for Panama Canal, 1987-92; exec. v.p. The Wexler Group, Washington, 1995—. Mem. Nat. Devel. Disability Adv. Council, 1975-76, Pres.'s Transition Team, 1980-81, Calif. Health Care Commn., 1972, pub. affairs com. United Way Am., 1987—; chmn. Govs. Commn. on Corrections Health Care, Md., 1990—; assoc. mem. Calif. Republican State Cen. Com., 1970-72; bd. dirs. Nat. Aquarium, Balt.; bd. dirs. Health Care Svcs. NAS Inst. Medicine, 1987-92; mem. Gov.'s Privatization Com., 1992—. Served to lt. USAF, 1966-68. Named Outstanding Young Man in HEW, 1974; recipient Sec.'s citation, 1975, Adminstr.'s spl. citation, 1975. Mem. Phi Delta Phi, Zeta Psi. Republican. Clubs: Annapolis Yacht, Sailing of the Chesapeake. Office: 1356 Beverly Rd Mc Lean VA 22101-3625

SVEC, HARRY JOHN, chemist, educator; b. Cleve., June 24, 1918; s. Ralph Joseph and Lillian Josephine (Pekarek) S.; m. Edna Mary Bruno, Oct. 27, 1943; children—Mary, Peter, Katherine, Jan, Thomas, Jean, Benjamin, Daniel, Lillian. BS, John Carroll U., 1941; PhD in Phys. Chemistry, Iowa State U., 1949. Asst. chemist Iowa State U., 1941-43; research asso. Inst. Atomic Research, 1946-50, asst. prof. chemistry, 1950-55, assoc. prof., 1955-60, prof., 1960-83, emeritus prof., 1983—, Disting. prof. in scis. and humanities, 1978—; assoc. chemist Ames Lab., 1950-55; chemist Ames Lab., Dept. Energy, 1955-60, sr. chemist, 1960-85, program dir., 1974-85, assoc. scientist, 1983—; jr. chemist Manhattan Project, 1943-46; cons., lectr. in field. Author lab. manual in phys. chemistry; contbr. numerous articles to profl. publs.; founding editor: Internat. Jour. Mass Spectrometry and Ion Processes, 1968-86. NSF grantee, 1972-82; EPA grantee, 1974-81; AEC grantee, 1950-74; ERDA grantee, 1974-77; Dept. Energy grantee, 1977-83; Am. Water Works Assn. grantee, 1977-79. Fellow AAAS, The Chem. Soc., Am. Chem. Soc.; mem. ASTM, Geochem. Soc., Am. Soc. Mass Spectroscopy (charter, v.p. 1972-74, pres. 1974-76), Sigma Xi, Alpha Sigma Nu, Phi Lambda Upsilon, Alpha Chi Sigma (cons. 1985—). Roman Catholic. Home: 2427 Hamilton Dr Ames IA 50014-8203 Office: 21 Gilman Hall Iowa

State U Ames IA 50011 *Success in anything we choose to do requires a commitment. The degree of one's success depends directly on the kind of commitment that is made.*

SVEDA, MICHAEL, management and research consultant; b. West Ashford, Conn., Feb. 3, 1912; s. Michael and Dorothy (Druppa) S.; m. Martha Augusta Gaeth, Aug. 23, 1936; children—Sally Anne, Michael Max. B.S., U. Toledo, 1934; Ph.D. (Eli Lilly research fellow), U. Ill., 1939. Tchr. chemistry U. Toledo, 1932-35, U. Ill., 1935-37; research, sales and product mgmt. positions E.I. du Pont de Nemours & Co., Inc., 1939-54; mgmt. counsel Wilmington, Del., 1955-59; dir. acad. sci. projects NSF, 1960-61; corp. assoc. dir. research FMC Corp., 1962-64; mgmt. and research counsel to academia, industry and govt., 1965—; lectr. univs., 1961—, fed. govt., groups, 1965—; mem. adv. com. on creativity in scientists and engrs. Rensselaer Poly. Inst., 1965—. Numerous appearances on pub. and comml. TV and radio. Named Outstanding Alumnus U. Toledo, 1954. Fellow AAAS (life); mem. Am. Chem. Soc., Sigma Xi, Phi Kappa Phi, Alpha Chi Sigma, Phi Lambda Upsilon. Patentee chems. and processes in polymers, pesticides, chem. intermediates; synthesizer, discoverer cyclamates, sweetening agts., 1937; deviser new concepts and patentee 3 dimensional models complex orgns., selection key personnel; new approach to diets, taking off human fat; new use Boolean algebra, theory of sets in people problems; active drive to have cyclamate sweeteners reinstated, 1973—. Home: Revonah Woods 228 West Ln Stamford CT 06905-3959 Office: PO Box 3086 Stamford CT 06905-0086 *Basic capacity for intelligence is given to us through inheritance. Knowledge—and stupidity—we acquire or develop. My objective has been to minimize my acquisition of, or contribution to, stupidity, while developing as much new knowledge as possible for mankind.*

SVEINSON, PAMELA J., human resources executive. BA in Sociology, Whitman Coll., 1974; M in Indsl. Rels., U. Minn., 1980. Social worker Mont. State Dept. Social & Rehab. Svcs., 1975-77; behavior therapist Spl. Tng. Exceptional People, Billings, Mont., 1977; asst. mgr. manpower planning Burlington Northern, St. Paul, 1978-80; sr. human resources planner Morrison-Knudsen Co., Inc., Boise, Idaho, 1980-83; asst. v.p. human resources 1st Bank System, 1983-84, v.p., 1984-88, sr. v.p., 1988-90; v.p. human resources Star Tribune and Cowles Media Co., Mpls., 1990—; program chair Human Resources Exec. Coun., 1994—. Mentor Minn. 100; mem. Mpls. Inst. Arts. Mem. Nat. Human Resources Planning Soc., Minn. Human Resources Planning Soc. (bd. dirs.), Horseman's Benevolent & Protective Assn., Park Ave. Meth. Ch. Avocations: thoroughbred horse racing, swimming, skiing, private pilot, racquetball. Home: 8537 Eagle Creek Blvd Shakopee MN 55379 Office: Cowles Media Co 329 Portland Ave Minneapolis MN 55415

SVENDSBYE, LLOYD AUGUST, college president, clergyman, educator; b. Hamlet, N.D., May 26, 1930; s. Anders A. and Gudrun J. (Birkelo) S.; m. Annelotte Frieda Erika Moertelmeyer, Dec. 20, 1958. BA, Concordia Coll., Moorhead, Minn., 1951, DD (hon.), 1983; BTh, Luther Theol.Sem., 1954; postgrad., U. Erlangen, Germany, 1954-55, Columbia U., 1959-60; ThD, Union Theol. Sem., 1966; LLD (hon.), Gettysburg Coll., 1977; LHD (hon.), Kilian C.C., 1992. Ordained to ministry, 1955; asst. pastor Our Saviours Luth. Ch., Mpls., 1955-56; adminstrv. asst. to dr. 3d Assembly Luth. World Fedn., 1956-57; asst. prof. religion Concordia Coll., 1957-59; asst. pastor Trinity Lutheran Ch., Bklyn., 1959-61; chmn. dept. religion Concordia Coll., 1962-66; editor in chief Augsburg Publ. House, Mpls., 1966-71; v.p., dean St. Olaf Coll., 1971-74; pres., prof. ch. history Luther Theol. Sem., St. Paul, 1974-82; pres. Northwestern Luth. Theol. Sem., 1976-82; pres. Luther Northwestern Theol. Sem., 1982-87; pres. Augustana Coll., Sioux Falls, S.D., 1987-92; v.p. Am. Luth. Ch., 1981-87; Mem. Am. Luth. Ch.-Luth. Ch. Am. coop. com., 1974-78; Luth. World Fedn. Com. on Info. Services, 1971-76; mem. Com. on Luth. Unity, 1978-82, Commn. To Form a New Luth. Ch., 1982-88. Chmn. senate dist. 49A, Democrat Farm Labor Com., 1970-71; bd. dirs. Luth. Brotherhood, 1970—; Lutheran Gen. and Health Care System, Park Ridge, Ill., 1981-87; trustee Luth. Deaconess Hosp., Mpls., 1970-71, Fairview-Southdale Hosp., 1975-87, Fairview Community Hosps., 1979-87. Recipient Alumni Achievement award Concordia Coll., 1974. Home: 2500 Quentin Ct Saint Louis Park MN 55416

SVENGALIS, KENDALL FRAYNE, law librarian; b. Gary, Ind., May 16, 1947; s. Frank Anthony and Alvida Linnea (Matheus) S.; m. Deborah Kay Andrews, May 23, 1970; children: Hillary Linnea, Andrew Kendall. BA, Purdue U., 1970, MA, 1973; MLS, U. R.I., 1975. Reference librarian Roger Williams Coll., Bristol, R.I., 1975, Providence (R.I.) Coll., 1975-77; asst. law librarian R.I. State Law Library, Providence, 1976-82, state law librarian, 1982—; adj. prof. libr. and info. studies U. R.I., 1987—. Editor: The Criv Sheet, 1988-94; contbr. articles to profl. jours. Chmn. jud. branch United Way Com. R.I., 1980. Mem. Am. Assn Law Librs. (state, ct. and county libr. spl. interest sect., recipient Connie E. Bolden significant publ. award 1993, bd. dirs. 1986-88), Law Librs. New Eng. (treas. 1983-85, v.p. 1985-86, pres. 1986-87), Com. on Rels. with Info. Vendors (editor 1988-94), New Eng. Law Libr. Consortium (v.p. 1990-92, pres. 1992-94). Republican. Lutheran. Home: 17 Mosher Dr Barrington RI 02806-1909 Office: RI State Law Libr Frank Licht Jud Complex 250 Benefit St Providence RI 02903-2719

SVENSON, CHARLES OSCAR, investment banker; b. Worcester, Mass., June 28, 1939; s. Sven Oscar and Edahjane (Castner) S.; m. Sara Ellen Simpson, Nov. 15, 1968; children: Alicia Lindall, Tait Oscar. A.B., Hamilton Coll., 1961; LL.B., Harvard U., 1964; LL.M., Bklyn. Law Sch., 1965. Bar: N.Y. 1965, U.S. Dist. Ct. (so. dist.) N.Y. 1965, U.S. Ct. Appeals (2d. cir.) 1965. Atty. Dewey, Ballantine, Bushby, Palmer & Wood, N.Y.C., 1964-68; v.p. Goldman Sachs & Co., N.Y.C., 1968-75; sr. v.p. Donaldson, Lufkin & Jenrette, N.Y.C, 1975-89; mng. dir., 1989—. Trustee Kirkland Coll., Clinton, N.Y., 1976-78; trustee Hamilton Coll., Clinton, 1979-83, 90—. Mem. ABA, N.Y. State Bar Assn., Assn. of Bar of City of N.Y. Clubs: Tuxedo (Tuxedo Park, N.Y.); Harvard (N.Y.C.). Home: 1185 Park Ave New York NY 10128 Office: Donaldson Lufkin & Jenrette Securities Corp 140 Broadway New York NY 10005-1101

SVETLOVA, MARINA, ballerina, choreographer, educator; b. Paris, May 3, 1922; came to U.S. from Australia, 1940; d. Max and Tamara (Andreieff) Hartman. Studies with Vera Trefilova, Paris, 1930-36, studies with I. Egorova and M. Kschessinska, 1936-39; studies with A. Vilzak, N.Y.C., 1940-57; D honoris causa, Fedn. Francaise de Danse, 1988. Ballet dir. So. Vt. Art Ctr., 1959-64; dir. Svetlova Dance Ctr., Dorset, Vt., 1965—; prof. ballet dept. Ind. U., Bloomington, 1969-92, prof. emeritus, 1992—, chmn. dept., 1969-78; choreographer Dallas Civic Opera, 1964-67, Ft. Worth Opera, 1967-83, San Antonio Opera, 1983, Seattle Opera, Houston Opera, Kansas City Performing Arts Found. Ballerina original Ballet Russe de Monte Carlo, 1939-41; guest ballerina Ballet Theatre, 1942, London's Festival Ballet, Teatro dell Opera, Rome, Nat. Opera, Stockholm, Sweden, Suomi Opera, Helsinki, Finland, Het Nederland Ballet, Holland, Cork Irish Ballet, Paris Opera Comique, London Palladium, Teatro Colon, Buenos Aires, others; prima ballerina Met. Opera, 1943-50, N.Y.C. Opera, 1950-52; choreographer: (ballet sequences) The Fairy Queen, 1966, L'Histoire du Soldat, 1968; tours in Far East, Middle East, Europe, S.Am., U.S.; performer various classical ballets Graduation Ball; contbr. articles to Debut, Paris Opera. Mem. Am. Guild Mus. Artists (bd. dirs.), Conf. on Ballet in Higher Edn., Nat. Soc. Arts and Letters (nat. dance chmn.). Office: 2100 E Maxwell Ln Bloomington IN 47401-6119 also: 25 W 54th St New York NY 10019-5411

SVINOS, JOHN GEORGIOS, software consulting firm executive; b. Kos, Greece, Aug. 3, 1957; came to U.S., 1975; s. Georgios I. and Maria (Kouyoumzoglou) S.; m. Allyson Mary Mazzarulli, Dec. 16, 1981; children: Geo, Alexandra. BSME, West Va. U., 1981, M in Mech. Engring., 1982. Engr. Gulf Oil Corp., Harmarville, Pa., 1981-83; rsch. engr. Gulf Oil Corp., Houston, 1983-85; sr. rsch. engr. Chevron Oil Field Rsc`. La Habra, Calif., 1985-89; pres., owner Theta Enterprises, Fullerton, Calif., 1989—; cons. Theta Enterprises, Fullerton, 1989-92, software devel., 1989-02. Author: (software) Rodstar, Roddiag, CBalance, 1991; contbr. tech. papers to publs. Mem. Soc. Petroleum Engrs. (chmn. 1991). Avocations: stamp collecting, fishing, bicycle riding. Home: 3906 N San Marcos Pl Fullerton CA 92635-1231 Office: Theta Enterprises 3906 N San Marcos Pl Fullerton CA 92635-1231

SWACKHAMER, GENE L., bank executive; b. Frankfort, Ind., 1938. BS, Purdue U., 1960; MS, Cornell U., 1963; PhD, Purdue U., 1966. Pres. Farm Credit Banks of Balt., Sparks, Md.; gov. KC Fed. Reserve Bank, 1966-69, U.S. Gov. FCA Dept., 1970-76. Lt. USN, 1962. Office: Farm Credit Banks of Baltimore 16429 Yeoho Rd Sparks Glencoe MD 21152-9553

SWADOS, ELIZABETH A., composer, director, writer; b. Buffalo, Feb. 5, 1951; d. Robert O. and Sylvia (Maisel) S. B.A., Bennington Coll., 1972. Composer, mus. dir. Peter Brook's Internat. Theatre Group, Paris, Africa, U.S., 1972-73; composer-in-residence La Mama Expl. Theater Club, N.Y.C., 1977—; mem. faculty Carnegie-Mellon U., 1974, Bard Coll., 1976-77, Sarah Lawrence Coll., 1976-77. Author: The Girl With the Incredible Feeling, 1976, Runaways, 1979, Lullaby, 1980, Sky Dance, 1980, Listening Out Loud: Becoming a Composer, 1988, The Four of Us, 1991, The Myth Man, 1994; composer theatrical scores: Medea, 1969 (Obie award 1972), Elektra, 1970, Fragments of Trilogy, 1974, The Trojan Women, 1974, The Good Women of Setzuan, 1975, The Cherry Orchard, 1977, As You Like It, 1979, The Sea Gull, 1980, Alice in Concert, 1980, (with Garry Trudeau) Doonesbury, 1983, Jacques and His Master, 1984, Don Juan of Seville, 1989, The Tower of Evil, 1990, The Mermaid Wakes, 1991; composer, dir., adapter, mem. cast: Nightclub Cantata, 1977 (Obie award 1977); composer, adapter (with Andrei Serban) Agamemnon, 1976, The Incredible Feeling Show, 1979, Lullaby and Goodnight, 1980; composer, dir., adapter: Wonderland in Concert, N.Y. Shakespeare Festival, 1978, Dispatches, 1979, Haggadah, 1980, The Beautiful Lady, 1984-86, Swing, 1987, Esther: A Vaudeville Megillah, 1988, The Red Sneaks, 1989, Jonah, 1990; author, composer, dir.: Runaways, 1978 (Tony award nominee for best musical, best musical score, best musical book 1978); adapter: Works of Yehuda Amichi, Book of Jeremiah; composer music for films: Step by Step, 1978, Sky Dance, 1979, Too Far to Go, 1979, OHMS, 1980, Four Friends, 1982, Seize the Day, 1986, A Year in the Life, 1986, Family Sins, 1987; composer music CBS Camera Three shows, 1973-74, PBS short stories, 1979, CBS-TV and NBC-TV spls.; composer: Rap Master Ronnie, 1986; composer, dir. Swing, Bklyn. Acad. Music, 1987; performer: Mark Taper Forum, Los Angeles, 1985, Jerusalem Oratorio, Rome, 1985. Recipient Outer Critics Circle award, 1977; Creative Artists Service Program grantee, 1976; N.Y. State Arts Council playwriting grantee, 1977—; Guggenheim fellow. Mem. Broadcast Music Inc., Actors Equity. Jewish. Home: 112 Waverly Pl New York NY 10011-9109 Office: care Sam Cohn Internat Creative Mgmt Co 40 W 57th St New York NY 10019-4001*

SWAFFORD, CYNTHIA WOLCOTT, nurse, educator; b. Warsaw, N.Y., Sept. 26, 1946; d. Vernon Raymond and Virginia (Manning) Wolcott; m. Donald Thomas Swafford, Aug. 17, 1971; children: J. Scott, Don T. BSN, SUNY, Buffalo, 1968; MSN, U. Mich., 1970; postgrad., U. Tenn. Instr. nursing U. Mich., Ann Arbor, Austin Peay State U., Clarksville, Tenn.; surp. helath occupations edn. Chattanooga Pub. Schs.; dir. nursing Chattanooga State Tech. Community Coll. Mem. ANA, Tenn. Nurses Assn., Sigma Theta Tau, Phi Kappa Phi. Home: 432 Valleybrook Rd Hixson TN 37343-3066

SWAGGART, JIMMY LEE, evangelist, gospel singer; b. Ferriday, La., Mar. 15, 1935; s. W. L. and Minnie Bell S.; married; 1 child. Began preaching on street corners Mangham, La., 1955; traveled throughout U.S. preaching at revival meetings, recording and marketing gospel songs, 1960's, preacher on TV and radio broadcasts; min., pastor Jimmy Swaggart Ministries, Baton Rouge. Gospel albums include This Is Just What Heaven Means To Me, 1971, There Is A River, 1972; author: (with Robert Paul Lamb) To Cross A River, 1977. Office: 8919 World Ministry Ave Baton Rouge LA 70810-9098

SWAILS, NORMAN E., church officer; b. St. Joseph, Mo.; m. Darleen Craven; children: Tom, Jan Shannon, John. AA, Graceland Coll., 1950; BA, Mo. Valley Coll., 1952. CFP. Exec. Boy Scouts Am., 1954-78, asst. chief scout exec., nat. dir. fin., 1978-85; mem. highest fin. coun. Reorganized Ch. of Jesus Christ of Latter Day Saints, 1985-88; presiding bishop, 1988—; reorganized Ch. of Jesus Christ of Latter Day Saints. Active Hope House. Mem. Rotary, Independence C. of C. Office: Reorganizrd Ch of Jesus Christ of Latter Day Saints PO Box 1059 Independence MO 64051

SWAIM, CHARLES HALL, lawyer; b. Delta, Colo., Dec. 31, 1939; s. H. Albert and Janet (Hall) S.; m. Patricia Fahey, Oct. 9., 1976; children: Caitlin Fahey, Bryan Hall. Grad. Geophys. Engr., Colo. Sch. Mines, 1961; JD, NYU, 1964. Asst. counsel Tex. Instruments Inc., Dallas, 1964-71; assoc. Hale & Dorr, Boston, 1971-74, ptnr., 1974—. Served to capt. U.S. Army, 1965-67, Vietnam. Mem. ABA, Mass. Bar Assn., Boston Bar Assn., Comml. Law League Am. Office: Hale & Dorr 60 State St Boston MA 02109-1816

SWAIM, DAVID DEE, diversified company financial executive; b. Ft. Wayne, Ind., Aug. 12, 1947; s. Carl Edwin and Pauline E. (Johnson) S.; m. Barbara Lynn Strock, June 21, 1969; children: Emily Anne, Benjamin Dee, Thomas Ryan. BS in Acctg., Ind. U., 1969. Sr. auditor Price Waterhouse & Co., Indpls., 1970-76; controller VideoInd., Inc., Indpls., 1976-77; treas., chief fin. officer Bindley Western Industries, Inc., Indpls., 1977-90, v.p., 1979-90, sr. v.p., 1986-90; v.p., treas. Bennett Mktg. Svcs., Indpls., 1990—, also bd. dirs.; bd. dirs., officer all subs. of Bindley Western Industries, Inc. Mem. Am. Inst. CPAs, Ind. CPA Soc., Fin. Execs. Inst. Republican. Methodist. Lodge: Masons. Office: Bennett Marketing Services PO Box 68824-0824 Indianapolis IN 46268

SWAIM, JOSEPH CARTER, JR., lawyer; b. S.I., N.Y., Jan. 15, 1934; s. J. Carter and Charlotte (Klein) S.; m. Elizabeth Lenora Owen, Aug. 2, 1958; children: Laura, Charles. BA, Oberlin Coll., 1955; JD, Columbia U., 1958. Bar: U.S. Dist. Ct. (we. dist.) Pa. 1960, Pa. 1961, U.S. Ct. Appeals (3rd cir.) 1964. Assoc. Kirkpatrick & Lockhart, Pitts., 1961-68, ptnr., 1968—. Bd. dirs. Davis and Elkins (W.Va.) Coll., 1976-82; bd. pensions Presbyn. Ch. in U.S.A., Phila., 1982-89; trustee, bd. sec. The Alban Inst., Inc., Bethesda, Md., 1991-94; trustee sec.-treas. Henry C. Frick Edn. Com., Pitts., 1976-94; bd. dirs., former pres. Family Resources, Pitts., 1975—; bd. dirs., sec. Desert Ministries, Inc., Ft. Lauderdale, Fla.; chmn. permanent jud. commn. Pitts Presbytery, 1991—; mem. Henry C. Frick Ednl. Fund Adv. Com. of Buhl Found., 1994—. With U.S. Army, 1959-61. Mem. ABA, Pa. Bar Assn., Allegheny County Bar Assn. Republican. Clubs: Duquesne, Allegheny (bd. dirs., sec. 1976—) (Pitts.). Avocations: tennis, reading. Home: 740 Scrubgrass Rd Pittsburgh PA 15243-1124 Office: Kirkpatrick & Lockhart 1500 Oliver Building Bldg Pittsburgh PA 15222-2312

SWAIM, RUTH CAROLYN, educator; b. Oklahoma City, May 3, 1940; d. G. Dale and Helen H. (Meister) Arbuckle; children: Stanley Kent, Sharon Gay. BS in Edn., U. Okla., 1963. Cert. secondary edn. tchr., Calif., Okla. Math. substitute tchr. USN Mil. Dependent, Sangley Pt., Philippines, 1961-63; math. tchr. Norman (Okla.) Pub. Schs., 1963, Bartlesville (Okla.) Pub. Schs., 1963-65, Dewey (Okla.) Pub. Schs., 1965-67; math. lab. instr. L.A. City Schs., 1975-83, math. tchr., 1984—; chair All Sch. Tutorial Program Taft High Sch. Instr. first Aid ARC, 1961-67; trustee Woodland Hills Community Ch., 1989—. Recipient Cert. Merit ARC, 1965, hon. svc. award PTA, 1980; named Outstanding Math. Tchr. Tandy, 1989-90. Mem. Nat. Coun. Tchrs. Math., NEA, Calif. Tchrs. Assn., Kappa Delta Pi. Home: 4555 San Feliciano Dr Woodland Hills CA 91364-5037 Office: Taft High Sch 5461 Winnetka Ave Woodland Hills CA 91364-2592

SWAIMAN, KENNETH FRED, pediatric neurologist, educator; b. St. Paul, Nov. 19, 1931; s. Lester J. and Shirley (Ryan) S.; m. Phyllis Kammerman Sher, Oct. 1985; children: Lisa, Jerrold, Barbara, Dana. B.A. magna cum laude, U. Minn., 1952, B.S., 1953, M.D., 1955; postgrad., 1956-58; postgrad. (fellow pediatric neurology), Nat. Inst. Neurologic Diseases and Blindness, 1960-63. Diplomate: Am. Bd. Psychiatry and Neurology, Am. Bd. Pediatrics. Intern Mpls. Gen. Hosp., 1955-56; resident pediatrics U. Minn., 1956-58, neurology, 1960-63; postgrad. fellow pediatric neurology Nat. Inst. Neurologic Diseases and Blindness, 1960-63; asst. prof. pediatrics, neurology U. Minn. Med. Sch., Mpls., 1963-66; assoc. prof. U. Minn. Med. Sch., 1969-94, exec. officer, dept. neurology, 1977—, interim head dept. neurology, 1994—, mem. internship adv. council exec. faculty, 1966-70; cons. pediatric neurology Hennepin County Gen. Hosp., Mpls.; St. Paul-Ramsey Hosp., St. Paul Children's Hosp., Mpls. Children's Hosp.; vis. prof. Beijing U. Med. Sch., 1989. Author: (with Francis S. Wright) Neuromuscular

Diseases in Infancy and Childhood, 1969, Pediatric Neuromuscular Diseases, 1979, (with Stephen Ashwal) Pediatric Neurology Case Studies, 1978, 2d edit., 1984, Pediatric Neurology: Practice and Principles, 1989; editor: (with John A. Anderson) Phenylketonuria and Allied Metabolic Diseases, 1966, (with Francis S. Wright) Practice Pediatric Neurology, 1975, 2d edit., 1982; mem. editorial bd.: Annals of Neurology, 1977-83, Neurology Update, 1977-82, Pediatric Update, 1977-85, Brain and Devel. (Jour. Japanese Soc. Child Neurology), 1980—, Neuropediatrics (Stuttgart), 1982-92; editor-in-chief: Pediatric Neurology, 1984—; contbr. articles to sci. jours. Chmn. Minn. Gov.'s Bd. for Handicapped, Exceptional and Gifted Children, 1972-76; mem. human devel. study sect. NIH, 1976-79, guest worker, 1978-81. Served to capt. M.C. U.S. Army, 1958-60. Fellow Am. Acad. Pediatrics, Am. Acad. Neurology (rep. to nat. council Nat. Soc. Med. Research); mem. Soc. Pediatric Research, Central Soc. Clin. Research, Central Soc. Neurol. Research, Internat. Soc. Neurochemistry, Am. Neurol. Assn., Minn. Neurol. Soc., AAAS, Midwest Pediatric Soc., Am. Soc. Neurochemistry, Child Neurology Soc. (1st pres. 1972-73, Hower award 1981, chmn. tech. affairs com., 1991—, mem. long range planning com. 1991—), Internat. Assn. Child Neurologists (exec. com. 1975-79), Profs. of Child Neurology (1st pres. 1978-80, mem. nominating com. 1986—), Japanese Child Neurology Soc. (Segawa award 1986, mem. nominating com. 1986—, chair internat. affairs com. 1991—, mem. long range planning com. 1991—), Soc. de Psiquiatria y Neurologia de la Infancia y Adolescencia, Phi Beta Kappa, Sigma Xi. Home: 420 Delaware St SE Minneapolis MN 55455-0374 Office: U Minn Med Sch Dept Pediatric Neurology Minneapolis MN 55455

SWAIN, DONALD CHRISTIE, university president, history educator; b. Des Moines, Oct. 14, 1931; s. G. Christie and Irene L. (Alsop) S.; m. Lavinia Kathryn Lesh, Mar. 5, 1955; children: Alan Christie, Cynthia Catherine. B.A., U. Dubuque, 1953; M.A. in History, U. Calif., Berkeley, 1958, Ph.D., 1961. Asst. research historian U. Calif., Berkeley, 1961-63; mem. faculty U. Calif., Davis, 1963-81, prof. history, 1970-81, acad. asst. to chancellor, 1967-68, asst. vice chancellor acad. affairs, 1971, vice chancellor acad. affairs, 1972-75; acad. v.p. U. Calif. System, Berkeley, 1975-81; pres. and prof. history U. Louisville, 1981—. Author: Federal Conservation Policy, 1921-33, 1963, Wilderness Defender: Horace M. Albright and Conservation, 1970; co-editor: The Politics of American Science 1939 to the Present, 1965. Bd. govs. J.B. Speed Art Mus., Coun. on Sci. and Tech.; bd. dirs. Louisville Orch., U. Louisville Found., Quality and Charity Care Trust, Ky. Econ. Devel. Corp., Greater Louisville Econ. Devel. Partnership; bd. dirs., chmn. U. Louisville Athletic Assn. Lt. (j.g.) USNR, 1953-56. Recipient Wm. B. Hesseltine award Wis. State Hist. Soc., 1967; Disting. Teaching award U. Calif., Davis, 1972. Mem. Am. Hist. Assn., Orgn. Am. Historians, Nat. Assn. State Univs. and Land Grant Colls. Democrat. Presbyterian. Home: 2515 Longest Ave Louisville KY 40204-2126 Office: U Louisville Office of Pres Louisville KY 40292

SWAIN, JUDITH LEA, cardiovascular physician, educator; b. Long Beach, Calif., Sept. 24, 1948; m. Edward W. Holmes. BS in Chemistry with deptl. honors, UCLA, 1970; MD, U. Calif., San Diego, 1974. Diplomate Am. Bd. Internal Medicine, cardiovasc. disease; lic. physician Calif., Pa., N.C. Intern in medicine Duke U. Med. Ctr., 1974-75, resident in medicine, 1975-76, fellow in cardiology, 1976-80, assoc. in medicine, 1979-81, from asst. prof. medicine to assoc. prof. medicine, 1981-91, asst. prof. physiology, 1981-88, assoc. prof. microbiology & immunology, 1988-91, Herbert C. Rorer prof. med. scis., prof. genetics, 1991—, mem. molecular biology grad. group, 1991—, chief cardiovasc. divsn., 1991—; vis. asst. prof. dept. genetics Harvard Med. Sch., Boston, 1985-86; mem. search com. for dir. Ctr. for Aging, Duke U. Med. Ctr., 1991—, mem. exec. com. deptl. awards selection, 1992—, chmn. combined degree dir. search com., 1993, mem. clin. rsch. ctr. adv. com., 1993-94, mem. grad. student admissions com., 1993, mem. search com. for chief cardiovasc. surgery, 1992, dept. medicine intern selection com., 1992—, mem. instnl. rev. com. Pa. Muscle Inst., 1993; cardiology adv. com. Nat. Heart, Lung, & Blood Inst., 1989-93; dir. USA-Russia Cardiovasc. Rsch. Program, 1992—; mem. NIH Task Force on Heart Failure, 1992-93; cons. Netherlands Rsch. Initiative in Molecular Cardiology, 1993; external adv. com. Ctr. for Prevention of Cardiovasc. Disease, Harvard Sch. Pub. Health, 1993—; lectr. in field. Exec. editor: Trends in Cardiovascular Medicine, 1990-93; mem. editl. bd. Circulation Rsch., 1991—, Circulation, 1991—, Jour. Clin. Investigation, 1992—; cons. editor: Circulation, 1993—; contbr. articles to med. jours. Mem. exec. com. Coun. on Basic Sci., Am. Heart Assn., 1986-93, chmn. Katz Prize Award Com., 1989-92, rsch. rev. com., 1990-93, fellowship rsch. com., 1992—, program com., 1992—, mem. Levine Young Investigator Awards Com., Coun. on Clin. Cardiology, 1994—, mem. Basic Sci. Coun.; bd. dirs. Southeastern Pa. Heart Assn., 1992—. Recipient Bristol-Myers Squibb Cardiovasc. Achievement award, 1992, also numerous rsch. grants. Fellow Am. Coll. Cardiology (internat. edn. com. 1994—), Coll. Physicians of Phila.; mem. Assn. Univ. Cardiologists, Assn. Am. Physicians, Assn. Prof. of Cardiology, Am. Soc. Cell Biology, Am. Fedn. Clin. Rsch., Am. Soc. Clin. Investigation (pres.-elect 1994—, councilor 1990—), Internat. Soc. Heart Rsch. (councilor 1988—), Interurban Clin. Club, Clin. and Climitol. Soc., John Morgan Soc. Office: Hosp of Univ of Pa Cardiovasc Divsn 3400 Spruce St Philadelphia PA 19104

SWAIN, ROBERT, artist; b. Austin, Tex., Dec. 7, 1940; s. Robert O. and Beth (Brower) S.; m. Annette Carol Leibel, Oct. 4, 1969. B.A., Am.U., 1964. Prof. fine arts Hunter Coll.; vis. artist to various schs., univs., including Bklyn. Mus. Art Sch., 1975, 77, 78; dept. architecture Harvard U. Grad. Sch. Design, 1977. One-man shows, Thenan Gallery, N.Y.C., 1965, Fischbach Gallery, N.Y.C., 1968-69, Everson Art Museum, N.Y.C., 1974, Susan Galdwell Gallery, N.Y.C., 1974, 75, 78, Tex. Gallery, Houston, 1975, Columbus (Ohio) Gallery Fine Arts, 1976, Nina Freundenhein Gallery, Buffalo, 1978, group shows include, Mus. Modern Art, N.Y.C., 1968, Grand Palais, Paris, 1968, Kunsthaus, Zurich, Switzerland, 1969, Tate Gallery, London, 1969, Corcoran Gallery Art, Washington, 1969, Whitney Mus. Am. Art, N.Y.C., 1971, Albright-Knox Gallery, Buffalo, 1971, Mus. Modern Art Internat. Circulating Exhbn.-Latin Am., 1974-75; represented in permanent collections, Corcoran Gallery Art, Walker Art Center, Mpls., Va. Mus. Fine Arts, Richmond, Everson Art Mus., Columbus Gallery Fine Arts, Detroit Inst. Art, Albright-Knox Mus., works include archtl. installations, Am. Republic Ins. Co., Des Moines, 1969, N.K. Winston Corp., N.Y.C., 1969, Schering Labs., Bloomfield, N.J., 1970, Skidmore, Owings and Merrill, N.Y.C., 1970, Kahn & Mallis Assos., N.Y.C., 1972, Harris Bank, Chgo., 1977, Powell/Kleinschmidt Chgo., 1977, Travenol Labs., Deerfield, Ill., 1977, Skidmore, Owings and Merrill, Chgo., 1977. John Simon Guggenheim Meml. Found. fellow, 1969; Nat Endowment for Arts grantee, 1976. Home and Office: 57 Leonard St 4th Fl New York NY 10013

SWAIN, WILLIAM GRANT, landscape architect; b. Covington, Ky., Sept. 5, 1923; s. George Wellington and Emma Grant (Holmes) S.; m. Sybil Yvonne Harris, Mar. 30, 1946 (div. 1954); 1 son, Grant Marc; m. Marjorie Page Reno, Dec. 21, 1957; children: Margaret Page, Jill Holmes. B.Arch., Carnegie-Mellon U., 1952. Registered landscape architect, Pa., Ohio, Mich., Ga. Prtnr. Griswold, Winters, Swain & Mullin, Pitts., 1957-75; pres. GWSM Inc., Pitts., 1975-83; chmn. bd. GWSM Inc., 1983—; chmn. Interproffl. Council on Environ. Design, Washington, 1974. Author: (with Ralph E. Griswold) Opportunities in Landscape Architecture, 1978. Mem. Mayor's Com. on Community Improvement, Monroeville, Pa., 1965; bd. dirs. W. Pa. Conservancy, Pitts., 1970—, Rachel Carson Homestead Assn., Springdale, Pa., 1976—; mem. Pa. State Art Commn., Harrisburg, 1977-84, chmn., 1981-84. Served as 1st lt. U.S. Army, 1943-46, ETO. Decorated Purple Heart; recipient Service award Carnegie-Mellon U. Alumni Fedn., 1963. Fellow Am. Soc. Landscape Architects (pres. 1973-74 recipient medals), Phi Kappa Phi. Republican. Episcopalian. Club: University (dir.) (1976-82). Home: 413 Harper Dr Monroeville PA 15146-1235 Office: GWSM Landscape Architects 1101 Greenfield Ave Pittsburgh PA 15217-2930 The central thread of my life is a sense of loyalty to those for whom I have worked or serve in professional capacities. I have been motivated to do my best for all who depend on me. It remains my belief that volunteer service to one's community is an obligation.

SWAISGOOD, HAROLD EVERETT, biochemist, educator; b. Ashland, Ohio, Jan. 19, 1936; s. Ray Weaver and Jennie (Morr) S.; m. Janet Cromwell, Sept. 15, 1956; children—Mark Harold, Ronald Ray. B.S., Ohio State U., 1958; Ph.D. in Chemistry (NIH fellow), Mich. State U., 1963. Reserach asst. Mich. State U., 1958-63; postdoctoral research asso. NIH, 1963-64; asst. prof. food sci. and biochemistry N.C. State U., 1964-67, asso.

prof., 1967-72, prof., 1972-84, William Neal Reynolds prof., 1984—; vis. prof. U. Lund, Sweden, 1974, chmn. biotech. program. Editor for Ams. Comments on Agr. and Food Chemistry; mem. editorial bd. Jour. Dairy Sci. 1975—, Jour. Food Sci, 1978—, Jour. Food Biochemistry, 1983—; contbr. articles, chpts. to profl. publs. USPHS fellow, 1963-64. Fellow Am. Chem. Soc. (agriculture food chem. divsn., award advancement of application of agrl. and food chemistry sponsored by IFF 1994); mem. Am. Inst. Nutrition, Am. Soc. Biochemists and Molecular Biologists, AAAS, Am. Dairy Sci. Assn. (Borden awardee 1987), Inst. Food Technologists, Sigma Xi, Phi Kappa Phi, Gamma Sigma Delta. Democrat. Methodist. Achievements include research in protein structure, interactions, and functionality; characteristics and applications of immobilized enzymes; patents in field. Office: Dept Food Sci NC State U Raleigh NC 27695

SWALES, THOMAS G., electronics executive; b. 1936. Grad., Swarthmore Coll., 1958; postgrad. degree, Rensselaer Polytech. Inst., 1961. With GE, Troy, N.Y., 1961, Schenectady, N.Y., 1968-72; with McDonnell Douglas, St. Louis, 1961-68, Fairchild Industries, Germantown, Md., 1972-78; with Swales & Assocs., Inc., Beltville, Md., 1978—, pres. Office: Swales & Assocs Inc 5050 Powder Mill Rd Beltsville MD 20705

SWALIN, RICHARD ARTHUR, scientist, company executive; b. Mpls., Mar. 18, 1929; s. Arthur and Mae (Hurley) S.; m. Helen Marguerite Van Wagenen, June 28, 1952; children: Karen, Kent, Kristin. B.S. with distinction, U. Minn., 1951, Ph.D., 1954. Rsch. assoc. GE, 1954-56; mem. faculty U. Minn., Mpls., 1956-77, prof. metall. Sch. Mineral and Metall Engring., 1962-68, assoc. dean Inst. Tech., 1968-71, dean Inst. Tech., 1971-77; acting dir. Space Sci. Center, 1965; v.p. tech. Eltra Corp., N.Y.C., 1977-80; v.p. R & D Allied-Signal Corp., Morristown, N.J., 1980-84; dean Coll. Engring. and Mines U. Ariz., Tucson, 1984-87, prof., 1984—; pres. Ariz. Tech. Devel. Corp., Tucson, 1987; prof. emeritus U. Ariz., Tucson, 1995—; guest scientist Max Planck Inst. für Phys. Chemie, Göttingen, Fed. Republic Germany, 1963, Lawrence Radiation Lab., Livermore, Calif., 1967; cons. to govt. and industry; bd. dirs. Medtronic Corp., BMC Industries; corp. adv. bd. AMP Inc., 1990-93. Author: Thermodynamics of Solids, 2d edit, 1972; Contbr. articles to profl. jours. Dir. div. indsl. coop. U. Ariz. Found., 1985-86; trustee Midwest Research Inst., 1975-78, Sci. Mus. Minn., 1973-77, Nat. Tech. U., 1983-90. Recipient Disting. Teaching award Inst. Tech., U. Minn., 1967, Leadership award U. Minn. Alumni, 1993; NATO sr. fellow in sci., 1971. Mem. Sigma Xi, Tau Beta Pi, Phi Delta Theta, Gamma Alpha. Home: 4705 N Via De La Granja Tucson AZ 85718-7404 Office: U Ariz Ariz Materials Lab 4715 E Fort Lowell Rd Tucson AZ 85712-1201

SWALM, THOMAS STERLING, aerospace executive, retired military officer; b. San Diego, Sept. 28, 1931; s. Calvin D. and Margaret A. (Rynning) S.; m. Charlene La Vern Garner, June 26, 1954; children: Edward Steven, Lori Ann. BS, U. Oreg., 1954; MS in Pub. Administrn., George Washington U., 1964; grad., Air Command and Staff Coll., 1964, Nat. War Coll., 1974. Commd. USAF, 1954, advanced through grades to maj. gen., 1982; instr. fighter-interceptor weapons sch. USAF, Tyndall AFB, Fla., 1956; pilot 434th Fighter-Day Squadron USAF, George AFB, Calif., 1957-58; engring. test pilot and flight examiner 50th Tactical Fighter Wing, 10th Tactical Fighter Squadron USAF, Toul-Rosieres AFB, France, and Hahn AFB, Fed. Republic Germany, 1958-61; hdqrs. 12th USAF, Waco, Tex., 1961-64; instr. pilot, flight examiner 4453d Combat Crew Tng. Wing USAF, Davis-Monthan AFB, Ariz., 1965-66; flight comdr. 12th Tactical Fighter Wing USAF, Cam Ranh Bay AFB, Republic Vietnam, 1966-67; comdr. air-to-air flight, instr. and chief R&D/OT&E sect. Fighter Weapons Sch., Nellis AFB, Nev., 1967-70; comdr., leader Thunderbirds USAF, 1970-73; chief fighter attack directorate USAF, Kirtland AFB, N.Mex., 1974-75, dep. dir. test and evaluation, 1975-76; from vice comdr. to comdr. 8th Tactical Fighter Wing USAF, Kunsan AFB, Republic of Korea, 1976-78; comdr. 3d Tactical Fighter Wing USAF, Clark AFB, Philippines, 1978-79; comdr. 57th Fighter Weapons Wing, comdr. fighter weapons sch. USAF, Nellis AFB, Nev., 1979-80; comdr. 833d air div. USAF, Holloman AFB, N.Mex., 1980-81; comdr. tactical air warfare ctr. USAF, Eglin AFB, Fla., 1981-86; ret. USAF, 1986; pres. T. Swalm and Assocs., Ft. Walton Beach, Fla., 1986-91; v.p. Melbourne Systems Div. Grumman Corp., 1991—; v.p. Applications Group Internat., Inc., Atlanta, 1986-89; scientific adv. bd. USAF, 1994—. Mem. editorial bd. Jour. Electronic Def., 1983-86; contbr. articles to profl. jours. Hon. chmn. Heart Assn., Las Vegas, Nev., 1972; exec. dir. Boy Scouts Am., Las Vegas and Alamogordo, N.Mex., 1970-81; chmn. AFA Scholarship Found., 1989-91; active Fla. Govs. Coun. for TQM, 1992-94; bd. dirs. Jr. Achievement, Ctrl. Fla., 1992-94; mem. USAF scientific adv. bd., 1994-98. Decorated D.S.M., Legion of Merit with two oak leaf clusters, DFC, Air medal with 14 oak leaf clusters, Vietnam Service medal with three service stars, Republic Vietnam Campaign medal; recipient R.V. Jones Trophy Electronic Security Command, 1984. Mem. Air Force Assn. (exec. advisor, Jerome Waterman award 1985, Jimmy Doolittle Fellow 1986), Thunderbirds Pilots Assn., Old Mission Beach Athletic Club (founder), Assn. Old Crows (editorial bd., R.V. Jones trophy 1984), Order of Daedalians (flight capt.), Melbourne C. of C. (trustee 1993—), Sigma Nu. Republican. Presbyterian. Avocations: golf, tennis, racquetball, sailing. Office: Grumman Melbourne Sys PO Box 9650 Melbourne FL 32902-9650

SWAN, BARBARA, artist; b. Newton, Mass., June 23, 1922; d. Carl Lilja and Clara May (Knowlton) S.; m. Alan D. Fink, June 28, 1952; children: Aaron, Joanna. B.A., Wellesley Coll., 1943; B.F.A., Boston Mus. Sch., 1948. Faculty mem. Wellesley Coll., 1947-48, Milton (Mass.) Acad., 1952-55, Boston U., 1961-64. Exhibited one-woman shows Boston Pub. Libr., 1994, Alpha Gallery, Boston, 1970, 73, 76, 80, 83, 87, 92, Addison Gallery Am. Art, Andover, Mass., 1973; group shows Inst. Contemporary Art, Boston, 1960, Boston Mus. Fine Arts, 1976, Nat. Inst. Arts and Letters, N.Y.C., 1976, Danforth Mus., Framingham, Mass., 1981; represented permanent collections Boston Mus. Fine Arts, Phila. Mus. Art, Worcester Mus., Nat Portrait Gallery. MacDowell Colony grantee Peterborough, N.H., 1947-48; Albert Whittin traveling fellow Boston Mus. Sch., Europe, 1949-51; Bunting fellow Radcliffe Coll., 1961-63. Democrat. Address: 808 Washington St Brookline MA 02146-2122

SWAN, GEORGE STEVEN, lawyer, educator; b. St. Louis. BA, Ohio State U., 1970; JD, U. Notre Dame, 1974; LLM, U. Toronto, 1976, SJD, 1983. Bar: Ohio 1974, U.S. Dist. Ct. (so. dist.) Ohio 1975, U.S. Supreme Ct. 1987, U.S. Ct. Appeals (6th and 11th cirs.) 1993, U.S. Ct. Appeals (10th cir.) 1994; registered investment advisor U.S. Securities and Exchange Commn., 1989, Sec. of State, N.C., 1990. Asst. atty. gen. state of Ohio, Columbus, 1974-75; jud. clk. Supreme Ct. Ohio, Columbus, 1976-78; asst. prof. Del. Law Sch., Wilmington, 1980-83, assoc. prof., 1983-84; prof. law St. Thomas U. Law Sch., Miami, Fla., 1988; jud. clk. U.S. Ct. Appeals 6th, 10th and 11th cirs., Chgo., 1988-89; assoc. prof. N.C. Agrl. & Tech. State U., Greensboro, 1989—. Contbr. articles to law jours. Mem. Ohio State Bar Assn., Internat. Assn. for Fin. Planning, Am. Polit. Sci. Assn. Republican. Office: NC Agrl & Tech State U Sch Bus 1601 E Market St Greensboro NC 27401-3209

SWAN, HENRY, retired surgeon; b. Denver, May 27, 1913; s. Henry and Carla (Denison) S.; m. Mary Fletcher Wardwell, June 25, 1937 (div. Jan. 25, 1964); children: Edith, Henry, Gretchen; m. Geraldine Morris Fairchild, Mar. 21, 1964. AB magna cum laude, Williams Coll., 1935; MD cum laude, Harvard Med. Sch., 1939; DSc (hon.), Williams Coll., 1958. Diplomate Nat. Bd. Med. Examiners, Am. Bd. Surgery. Pathology fellow Colo. Gen. Hosp., Denver, 1939-40; intern surgery Peter Bent Brigham Children's Hosp., Boston, 1940-42; pathology fellow Children's Hosp., Boston, 1942-43; asst. in surgery Harvard Med. Sch., Boston, 1942-43; from asst. to assoc. prof. surgery U. Colo. Med. Sch., 1946-50, prof. surgery, head dept. surgery, 1950-61, prof. surgery, rsch., 1963-82, prof. emeritus surgery, 1985—; Assoc. editor Jour. Cardiovascular Surgery, 1956-70; assoc. editor AMA Archives Surgery, 1956-66. Author: Thermoregulation and Bioenergetics, 1974; contbr. articles to profl. jours. Served in UAS, 1943-45, ETO. Mem. AMA (gold medal for original rsch. 1955), AAAS, Internat. Cardiovascular Soc., Internat. Soc. Surgery, Am. Surgical Assn., Am. Coll. Surgeons, Am. Assn. Thoracic Surgery, Soc. for Cryobiology, Soc. Univ. Surgeons, Soc. Vascular Surgery, Halsted Soc., Surgery Biology Club, Cen. Surgical Assn., Western Surgical Assn., Denver Acad. Surgery, Denver Clin. & Pathol. Soc., Assn. Surgery Costa Rica, Soc. Surgeons Chile, Soc. Cardiology Chile, Soc. Pediatrics Mex., Phi Beta Kappa, Alpha Omega Alpha. Republican. Epis-

copalian. Avocations: sailing, tennis, fly fishing, duck hunting, golf. Home: 6700 W Lakeridge Rd Lakewood CO 80227

SWAN, JAMES ROBERT DUNCAN, hotel executive. Vice-chmn. Holiday Inns, Inc., Memphis. Office: Holiday Inns Inc Ste 2000 3 Ravinia Dr Atlanta GA 30346*

SWAN, JUDITH, marine lawyer; b. June 8, 1944; d. William J. and Lee M. (Shannon) Lee; 1 child, Ward Swan. BA, McGill U., Montreal, 1966; LLB, U. Alta., Edmonton, 1970; LLM, U. London, 1971. Bar: Can. 1978. Lectr. law, assoc. dean U. Melbourne, Australia, 1971-75; vis. prof. law U. Toronto, Ont., Can., 1975-76; assoc. prof. law U. Ottawa, Ont., Can., 1976-80; internat. rels. officer Fisheries and Oceans Can., 1980-85; legal counsel South Pacific Forum Fisheries Agy., Honiara, Solomon Islands, 1985-90; exec. dir. Oceans Inst. of Can., Halifax, N.S., 1990-94; pres., CEO SwanSea Oceans Environment, Inc., Waverley, N.S., 1994—; cons. World Bank, 1993-95, UN Food and Agr. Orgn., Rome, 1994—, Fgn. Affairs and Internat. Trade Can., Ottawa, 1993—; Internat. Inst. for Sustainable Devel., Winnipeg, Man., 1995—, numerous other cons. positions; adj. prof. Dalhousie U.; sessional prof. dept. law Carleton U., 1975, 80, 81; rsch. dir. Ont. Commn. on Election Contbns. and Expenses, 1975; founder, Oceans Day. Contbr. articles to profl. jours., chpts. to books. Bd. dirs. Law of the Sea Inst., 1994—. Mem. Projet de Société, Cuisine Can., Law Soc. Upper Can. Avocations: metaphysics, ocean-related activities. Office: SwanSea Oceans Environment Inc, PO Box 188, Waverley, NS Canada B0N 2S0

SWAN, KENNETH CARL, physician, surgeon; b. Kansas City, Mo., Jan. 1, 1912; s. Carl E. and Blanche (Peters) S.; m. Virginia Grone, Feb. 5, 1938; children: Steven Carl, Kenneth, Susan. A.B., U. Oreg., 1933, M.D. 1936. Diplomate: Am. Bd. Ophthalmology (chmn. 1960-61). Intern U. Wis., 1936-37; resident in ophthalmology State U. Iowa, 1937-40; practice medicine specializing in ophthalmology Portland, Oreg., 1945—; staff Good Samaritan Hosp.; asst. prof. ophthalmology State U. Iowa, Iowa City, 1941-44; asso. prof. U. Oreg. Med. Sch., Portland, 1944-45, prof. and head dept. ophthalmology, 1945-78; Chmn. sensory diseases study sect. NIH; mem. adv. council Nat. Eye Inst.; also adv. council Nat. Inst. Neurol. Diseases and Blindness. Contbr. articles on ophthalmic subjects to med. publs. Recipient Proctor Rsch. medal, 1953; Disting. Svc. award U. Oreg., 1963; Meritorious Achievement award U. Oreg. Med. Sch., 1968; Howe Ophthalmology medal, 1977; Aubrey Watzek Pioneer award Lewis and Clark Coll., 1979, Disting. Alumnus award Oreg. Health Scis. U. Alumni Assn., 1988, Disting. Svc. award, 1988; named Oreg. Scientist of Yr. Oreg. Mus. Sci. and Industry, 1959. Mem. Assn. Research in Ophthalmology, Am. Acad. Ophthalmology (v.p. 1978, historian), Soc. Exptl. Biology and Medicine, AAAS, AMA, Am. Ophthal. Soc. (Howe medal for distinguished service 1977), Oreg. Med. Soc., Sigma Xi, Sigma Chi (Significant Sig award 1977). Home: 4645 SW Fairview Blvd Portland OR 97221-2624 Office: Oreg Health Scis U Portland OR 97201

SWAN, RICHARD ALAN, executive recruiter; b. Hollywood, Calif., May 5, 1944; s. Morris George and Mary Theresa (Fenusz) S.; m. Carol Ann Jacobs, Apr. 15, 1967; children: David Michael, Jennifer Marie, Matthew Richard. BS in Indsl. Mgmt., U. So. Calif., 1966; MS in Health Care Adminstrn., Trinity U., 1970. Adminstrv. resident Tucson (Ariz.) Med. Ctr., 1971; assoc. cons. A.T. Kearney and Co. Inc., Chgo., 1971-72; v.p. Tribrook Group Inc., Oakbrook, Ill., 1972-82; dir. program and spl. studies div. James A. Hamilton Assocs. Inc., Dallas, 1982-83; v.p. corp. devel. Vincentian Health Services, L.A., 1983-88; v.p., dir. healthcare group Boyden Internat., L.A., 1988-89; regional v.p. Kieffer Ford & Assocs., Ltd., Orange, Calif., 1989-92; ptnr. Witt/Kieffer, Ford, Hadelman & Lloyd, Irvine, Calif., 1992—. Contbr. articles to profl. jours. Served to capt. Med. Service Corps, U.S. Army, 1967-69. Fellow Am. Assn. Hosp. Cons., Am. Coll. Healthcare Execs.; mem. Soc. Hosp. Planning and Mktg., So. Calif. Soc. Hosp. Planners (charter), Health Care Execs. of So. Calif., Am. Hosp. Assn. Republican. Roman Catholic. Avocations: golfing, fishing. Office: Witt Kieffer Ford Hadelman & Lloyd 2030 Main St Ste 620 Irvine CA 92714-7235

SWAN, RICHARD GORDON, mathematics educator; b. N.Y.C., Dec. 21, 1933; s. A. Gordon and Rose (Nespor) S.; m. Erdmuthe J.D.B. Plesch-Ritz, Mar. 18, 1963; children—Adrian Alexander, Irit Alexandra. A.B., Princeton U., N.J., 1954, Ph.D. 1957. Instr. U. Chgo., 1958-60, asst. prof., 1960-62, assoc. prof., 1962-65, prof., 1965—, Louis Block prof., 1982—; Editor Am. Jour. Math., 1977-83, Jour. Algebra, 1981—. Author: Theory of Sheaves, 1964, Algebraic K-Theory, 1968, K-Theory of Finite Groups and Orders, 1970; also articles. Alfred P. Sloan fellow, 1961-65; recipient Cole prize in Algebra Am. Math. Soc., 1970. Fellow AAAS; mem. Nat. Acad. Scis., Am. Math. Soc., Math. Assn. Am., N.Y. Acad. Scis., Sigma Xi. Avocation: music. Home: 475 Oakdale Ave Glencoe IL 60022-2180 Office: U Chgo 5734 S University Ave Chicago IL 60637-1546

SWAN, WILLIAM, actor; b. Buffalo, N.Y., Feb. 6, 1932; s. Earl B. and Irene (Hall) S. Student, Geller Workshop, L.A. Appeared in films including Lady in a Cage, Hotel, The Parallax View, Bombers B-52; more than 200 TV guest appearances including Streets of San Francisco, Quincy, Perry Mason, Felony Squad, Twilight Zone, Have Gun Will Travel, Cannon, Barnaby Jones; appeared in off-Broadway plays including Anne of a Thousand Days, Night Fishing in Beverly Hills; appeared in regional theatres including A Delicate Balance, The Cocktail Hour, California Suite, The Middle Ages, Stained Glass, What the Butler Saw, and others; appeared in TV day-time drama, All My Children, 1982—. Trustee Berkshire Theatre Festival, Stockbridge, Mass., 1984—. Sgt. U.S. Army, 1948-49, ETO. Mem. Acad. TV Arts and Scis., The Players. Democrat. Avocation: tennis. Home: 141 E 55th St Apt 12B New York NY 10022-4036 Home: Barberry Close Monterey MA 01245

SWANBERG, EDMUND RAYMOND, investment counselor; b. Newton, Mass., Oct. 18, 1921; s. Raymond C. and Olga (Clement) S.; m. Ruth P. Mattson, May 24, 1943; children: Linda Ruth, Charles Howard, Peter Bush. BS, MIT, 1943; MBA, NYU, 1951. Chartered Investment Counselor. Assoc. Scudder, Stevens & Clark, Boston, 1946-48; assoc. Scudder, Stevens & Clark, N.Y.C., 1948-61, ptnr., sr. v.p., 1961-85, mng. dir., 1985-86, adv. mng. dir., 1987—; pres., dir. Scudder Devel. Fund 1970-86, Scudder Capital Growth, 1982-86, Scudder Internat. Fund, 1975-86. Capt. AUS 1943-46. Mem. Assn. for Investment Mgmt. and Rsch., N.Y. Soc. Security Analysts, Internat. Soc. Fin. Analysts, Racquet and Tennis Club (N.Y.C.), Somerset Club (Boston), Country Club of New Canaan (Conn.), Blind Brook Club (N.Y.), Mill Reef Club (Antigua), Wharf Rat Club (Nantucket), Union Club (N.Y.C.). Republican. Presbyterian.

SWANEY, THOMAS EDWARD, lawyer; b. Detroit, Apr. 25, 1942; s. Robert Ernest and Mary Alice (Slinger) S.; m. Patricia Louise Nash, Sept. 9, 1967; children: Julia Bay, Mary Elizabeth, David Paul. AB, U. Mich., 1963, JD, 1967; postdoctoral, London Sch. Econs., 1967-68. Bar: Ill. 1968. From assoc. to ptnr. Sidley & Austin, Chgo., 1968—; bd. dirs. Corey Steel Co., Cicero, Ill., Gertrude B. Nielsen Child Care & Learning Ctr., Northbrook, Ill., Ward C. Rogers Found., Chgo. Trustee H. Earl Hoover Found., Glencoe, Ill., 1986—, RF Found., Chgo., 1992—; officer, pres. bd. trustees 1st Presbyn. Ch., Evanston, Ill., 1984-89; bd. dirs. Lakeland Conservancy, Minocqua, Wis., 1987—. Mem. ABA, Ill. State Bar Assn., Chgo. Bar Assn., Legal Club Chgo. Office: Sidley & Austin 1 First Nat Plz Chicago IL 60603

SWANGER, STERLING ORVILLE, appliance manufacturing company executive; b. Battle Creek, Iowa, Jan. 5, 1922; s. Orville M. and Alma Louise (Messing) S.; m. Maxine O. Hindman, July 2, 1950; 1 son, Eric. B.S., Iowa State U., 1947; student U. Va., 1965. Registered profl. engr., Iowa. Indsl. engr. Maytag Co., Newton, Iowa, 1947-52, methods engr., 1952-54, asst. chief methods engr., 1954-57, chief methods engr., 1957-68, mgr. prodn. engring., 1968-71, mgr. engring., 1971-74, asst. v.p. mfg., 1974-75, v.p. mfg., 1975-86, sr. v.p. and chief mfg. officer, 1986-87, also dir., cons., 1987—. Mem., Newton Planning and Zoning Commn., 1966-70; trustee Newton Skiff Mem., 1970-85, chmn., 1982-85, Progress Industries, 1987-90; chmn. Progress Industries, 1991. Served with AUS 1943-46. Mem. Nat. Soc. Profl. Engrs., Iowa Engring. Soc., Nat. Mgmt. Assn., Am. Mgmt. Assn., Am. Ordnance Assn. Republican. Presbyterian. Clubs: Newton Country, Elks.

SWANGO, WILLIAM FRANKLIN, coal company executive; b. Logan, W.Va., Apr. 19, 1942; s. Arbery Beryl and Helen Rose (Frazier) S.; m. Laura Kathryn Seitter, Sept. 2, 1967; 1 child, Jamie Kathryn. AA, U. Cin., 1964, BA, 1965. Golf professional, 1965-70; sales rep. MacGregor Golf Equipment div. Brunswick Corp., Jacksonville, Fla., 1970-75; field and sales rep. Logan and Kanawha Coal Co., Cin., 1975-79, sales and traffic mgr., 1979-82, v.p. sales, 1982-84, pres., 1984—; bd. dirs. Eastern Coal Transp. Conf., Washington. Mem. Cin. Coun. on World Affairs. Recipient Spirit of Life award City of Hope Hosp., Cin., 1985. Mem. Cin. Coal Exchange (bd. dirs. 1983-87), N.C. Coal Inst., Pitts. Traffic Club, Detroit Coal and Rail Club, So. Coals Conf., Duquesne Club, Kenwood Country Club, Cin. Bankers Club, Innisbrook Country Club. Republican. Methodist. Avocations: golf, flying. Office: Logan & Kanawha Coal Co 3412 Carew Towers Cincinnati OH 45202

SWANI, PARVESH, transportation company executive; b. Peshawar, North-West Frontier, Pakistan, Sept. 12, 1937; s. Girdhari Lal and Krishna Kumari (Bagga) S.; m. Sushma Khanna, Aug. 28, 1965; children: Sanjay, Rahul. BS, Allahabad (india) U., 1956, MS in Math., 1958; MBA, U. Pitts. 1970. CPA, Fla., CMA. Traffic and operating exec. Indian Railways, various locations, India, 1961-69; traffic planning engr. Pa. Dept. Transp., Harrisburg, 1970-71; sr. cost analyst Seaboard Coastline R.R., Jacksonville, Fla., 1971-74, mgr. econ. analysis, 1974-77; dir. econs. Family Lines Rail System, Jacksonville, 1977-82; asst. v.p. strategic planning and analysis Seaboard System R.R., Jacksonville, 1982-85, v.p. corp. planning and analysis, 1985-86; v.p. joint planning Chessie System R.R., Balt., 1985-86; v.p. fin. and planning Distbn. Services Group CSX Transp., Inc., Balt., 1986—; bd. dirs. Total Distrn. Services, Inc., Balt. Pres. India Cultural Soc. Jacksonville, 1975-76; mem. Nat. Aquarium Balt., 1987—; nat. assoc. Smithsonian Instn., 1986—. Mem. Am Inst CPA's, Fla. Soc. CPA's, Am. Mgmt. Assn., Council Logistics Mgmt., Md. Acad. Scis., The Planning Forum, Center Club. Avocations: skiing, fishing, tennis, travel. Office: CSX Transp Inc 100 N Charles St Baltimore MD 21201-3802

SWANK, EMORY COBLENTZ, world affairs consultant, lecturer; b. Frederick, Md., Jan. 29, 1922; s. George Phillip and Mary Ruth (Coblentz) S.; m. Margaret Katherine Whiting, May 12, 1949. A.B., Franklin and Marshall Coll., 1942; A.M., Harvard, 1943. With U.S. Dept. State, 1946-75; vice consul U.S. Dept. State, Shanghai, China, 1946-48, Tsingtao, China, 1948-49; 2d sec. Am. Embassy, consul U.S. Dept. State, Djakarta, Indonesia, 1950-51, Moscow, U.S.S.R., 1953-55; polit. analyst, fgn. service officer U.S. Dept. State, Washington, 1956-57; conselor of legation U.S. Dept. State, Bucharest, 1958-60; spl. asst. to sec. of state U.S. Dept. State, 1961-63; assigned Nat. War Coll., Ft. L.J. McNair, Washington, 1963-64; counselor of embassy, dep. chief of mission Am. Embassy, Vientiane, Laos, 1964-67; minister Am. Embassy, Moscow, USSR, 1967-67; dep. asst. sec. state for European affairs Am. Embassy, 1969-70; ambassador to Cambodia, 1970-73; polit. adviser to CINC, Atlantic, and Supreme Allied Comdr., NATO Atlantic Forces, 1973-75; pres., chief exec. officer Cleve. Council on World Affairs, 1977-87, hon. trustee, 1987—. Served with AUS, 1943-46. Decorated Bronze Star medal; recipient Superior Honor award Dept. of State, 1973; Alumni Citation award Franklin and Marshall Coll., 1973. Mem. Phi Beta Kappa. Address: 2 Deerfield The Village Beachwood OH 44122

SWANK, ROY LAVER, physician, educator, inventor; b. Camas, Wash., Mar. 5, 1909; s. Wilmer and Hannah Jane (Laver) S.; m. Eulalia F. Shively, Sept. 14, 1936 (dec.); children: Robert L., Susan Jane (Mrs. Joel Keizer) Stephen (dec.); m. Betty Harris, May 23, 1987. Student, U. Wash., 1926-30; M.D., Northwestern U., 1935; Ph.D., 1935. House officer, resident Peter Bent Brigham Hosp., Boston, 1936-39; fellow pathology Harvard Med. Sch., 1938-39; mem. staff neurol. unit Boston City Hosp., 1948-57; asst. prof. neurology Montreal Neurol. Inst., McGill U., 1954-75; prof. neurology, head divsn. neurology Oreg. Med. Sch., 1954-74, prof. emeritus, 1974—, also former head div. neurology; pres. Pioneer Filters. Served to maj. M.C. AUS, 1942-46. Recipient Oreg. Gov.'s award for research in multiple sclerosis, 1966. Mem. Am. Physiol. Soc., Am. Neurol. Assn., European Microcirculation Soc., Sigma Xi. Achievements include invented micro embolic filter; research of phys. chem. changes in blood after fat meals and during surg. shock, platelet-leukocyte aggregation in stored blood and in hypotensive shock; low-fat diet in multiple sclerosis; research of phys. chem. changes in multiple sclerosis (plasma proteins); importance of plasma proteins in multiple sclerosis. Home: 789 SW Summit View Dr Portland OR 97225-6185

SWANKE, ALBERT HOMER, architect; b. Thomasville, Ga., Nov. 22, 1909; s. John Christian and Stella (Williams) S.; m. Margaret Anne Twaddell, Aug. 11, 1936 (dec. 1968); 1 son, Albert Homer; m. Dorothy Pratt Williams, Feb. 7, 1969. B.S., Ga. Inst. Tech., 1930; student, Beaux Arts Inst. Design, N.Y.C., 1931. Registered architect, N.Y., Conn., D.C., Fla., Ga., Ill., Ind., La., Md., Mass., Minn., Miss., Mo., N.H., N.J., N.C., Ohio, Pa., S.C., Va., Wis. registered profl. planner, N.J. Trainee Flagg, Embury and Ballard, N.Y.C., 1931-35; arch. N.Y. State Ins. Dept., 1936-42, Alfred Easton Poor, 1946; assoc. Walker & Poor, Archs., 1947-52; ptnr. Office of Alfred Easton Poor-Archs./Engrs., N.Y.C., 1952-71, Poor and Swanke & Ptnrs., N.Y.C., 1972-75; mng. prtnr. Poor, Swanke, Hayden & Connell, Archs., 1975-79; sr. ptnr. Swanke Hayden Connell & Ptnrs., 1979-81; cons. Swanke Hayden Connell Archs., 1981—; trustee, chmn. archtl. rev. bd. Historic Savannah Found.; mem. Village of Larchmont Archtl. Bd. Review, 1963-69, chmn., 1968-69; trustee Larchmont Manor Park Soc., 1962-69, Architects Emergency Com., 1956-76; mem. bd. design Extension of Capitol Project, Washington, 1956-79; alt. mem. consulting bd. Additional House Office Bldg. Project, Capitol Hill, 1955-60; alt. mem. archtl. adv. bd. Johns Hopkins U., 1961-70. Works include extension of East front of U.S. Capitol, James Madison Meml. Library of Congress Bldg; also restoration Supreme Ct. and Senate Chambers, Washington; Fed. Office Bldg. and Customs Ct., N.Y.C., Home Ins. Co, N.Y.C., Grumman Aircraft Engring. Plant and facilities, Calverton, L.I., N.Y., NATO Airbases at, Dreux and Evreux, France, Queens County (N.Y.) Courthouse and Prison, Hardened Communications Facilities, AT&T Long Lines; addition to, Chgo. Bd. of Trade Bldg.; Hdqrs. Office Bldg of Home Ins. Co., N.Y.C., Public Service Electric & Gas Co., Newark, NML Hdqrs, Milw., Continental Center, N.Y.C., Trump Tower, N.Y.C., 520 Madison Ave. Bldg., N.Y.C.; also numerous banking facilities in, U.S. and abroad; archtl. cons., French-Am. Com. for Restoration of Statue of Liberty. Trustee, mem. exec. com. N.Y. Med. Coll., Flower and 5th Ave. Hosps., 1963-79, Westchester Med. Center Devel. Bd., 1969-73; bd. mgrs. Am. Soc. Prevention Cruelty to Animals, 1976-79, dir. emeritus, 1980—; mem. Am. Arbitration Assn., 1971-80; mem. archtl. adv. bd. Archdiocese of N.Y., 1979—. Served as lt. comdr. USNR, 1943-45. Fellow AIA, Am. Soc. Registered Architects; mem. NAD (assoc.), N.Y. Soc. Architects, N.Y. Bldg Congress, Soc. Archtl. Historians, Navy League U.S., Soc. Cincinnati, Phi Sigma Kappa, Pi Delta Epsilon. Republican. Presbyn. Clubs: University (N.Y.C.); Met. (Washington); Boston (New Orleans). Home: 20 Richmond Pl New Orleans LA 70115-5020 Office: 4 Columbus Cir 58th St at 8th Ave New York NY 10023 also: 901 15th St NW Washington DC 20005

SWANKIN, DAVID ARNOLD, lawyer, consumer advocate; b. Boston, Jan. 18, 1934; s. Max and Anne (Rotefsky) S.; m. Jeanne Phyllis Herrick; 1 dau., Sheryl. A.B., Brandeis U., 1954; M.S., U. Wis., 1957; J.D., George Washington U., 1962. Mgmt. intern U.S. Dept. Labor, Washington, 1957-60; spl. asst. to asst. sec. labor U.S. Dept. Labor, 1961-63, dep. asst. sec. labor, 1967; dir. Bur. Labor Standards, 1967-68; exec. sec. Pres.'s Consumer Adv. Council, Washington, 1964; exec; dir. Pres's Com. on Consumer Interests, Washington, 1965-66; Washington rep. Consumer's Union, 1969-71; exec. dir. Consumer Interests Found., 1971-73; sr. partner Swankin & Turner, 1973—; pres. Regulatory Alternatives Devel. Corp., 1985—; pres. Citizen Advocacy Ctr. 1994—; cons. U.S. Dept. Labor; pres. Citizen Advocacy Ctr. 1994—. Mem. Pres.'s Council, Brandeis U., 1968-69. Served with AUS., 1954-56. Recipient Jump award U.S. Govt., 1969. Mem. Am. Bar Assn., Ombudsman Com. Home: 300 N Cherry St Falls Church VA 22046-3522 Office: 1424 16th St NW Washington DC 20036-2211

SWANN, BILL, judge; b. Boston, Sept. 30, 1942; married; 3 children. BA cum laude, Harvard U., 1964; PhD, Yale U., 1971; JD, U. Tenn., 1975. Bar: Tenn. 1975. Asst. prof. German Brown U., Providence, 1970-72; law clk. Tenn. Ct. Appeals, 1974-75; assoc. Kramer Johnson Rayson McVeigh &

Leake, Knoxville, Tenn., 1975-79, Hogin Guyton Swann & London, Knoxville, 1979-82; judge State of Tenn. Cir. Ct., Knoxville, 1982—; mem. faculty Law Edn. Inst. Inc., 1986—; faculty advisor Nat. Jud. Coll. 1978; tchr. in field. Contbr. articles to profl. jours. Mem. adv. bd. Sexual Assault Crises Ctr., Presch. Intervention Program; bd. dirs. Helen Ross McNabb Found., Child and Family Svcs. of Knox County; active Ch. St. United Meth. Ch. Named Man of Yr. Knoxville Area Social Workers, 1985; recipient svc. and membership awards Knoxville YMCA. Mem. ABA (family law and jud. adminstrn. sects.), Am. Judges Assn. (mem. editorial com.), Internat. Soc. Family Law, Knoxville Bar Assn., Tenn. Bar Assn. (gen. practice and family law sects., past del. to ho. of dels., Law through Liberty award 1987), Assn. Yale Alumni (past del.), Yale Club of Knoxville. Avocations: jogging, hiking, fishing. Office: M-44 City County Bldg Knoxville TN 37902

SWANN, BRIAN, writer, humanities educator; b. Wallsend, Northumberland, Eng., Aug. 13, 1940; came to U.S., 1963, naturalized, 1980; s. Stanley Frank and Lilyan Mary (Booth) S.; m. Roberta Metz. B.A., Queens' Coll., Cambridge U., 1962. M.A., 1965; Ph.D., Princeton U., 1970. Instr. Princeton U., 1964-65; lectr., 1968-70, asst. prof., 1970-72; instr. Rutgers U., 1965-66; asst. prof. humanities Cooper Union for Advancement Sci. and Art, N.Y.C., 1972-75, assoc. prof., 1975-80, prof., 1980—, acting dean, 1990-91; dir. Bennington Writing Workshops, 1988-91. Author: (poetry) The Middle of the Journey, 1982, Song of The Sky: Versions of Native American Song-Poems, 1993, also many other books of fiction, translations, children's books; The Plot of the Mice, 1984, A Basket Full of White Eggs, 1988; editor: Smoothing The Ground: Essays of Native American Oral Literature, 1983; (with Arnold Krupat) Recovering the Word, 1987, I Tell You Now: Autobiographical Essays by Native American Writers, 1987, Coming to Light: Contemporary Translations of the Native Literatures of North America, 1995; Essays on the Translation of Native American Literatures, 1992; editor The Smithsonian Series of Essays on Native American Literatures, 1990—. NEA fellow, 1981; Creative Arts in Pub. Service grantee, 1982. Office: Cooper Union Adv Sci & Art Faculty Humanities & Social Sci Cooper Sq New York NY 10003

SWANN, JERRE BAILEY, lawyer; b. Gadsden, Ala., May 12, 1939; s. Julius Seth and Alma Nell (McCartney) S.; m. Jane Goodwillie, June 26, 1965 (div. Jan. 1977); children: Jerre B. Jr., Eliza W.; m. Cynthia Pangia, Sept. 17, 1977. BA, Williams Coll., 1961; postgrad., U. St. Andrews, Scotland, 1961-62; LLB, Harvard U., 1965. Bar: N.Y., Ga., U.S. Dist. Ct. (no. and mid. dists.) Ga., U.S. Dist. Ct. (ea. dist.) Tex., U.S. Ct. Appeals (4th, 5th, 8th, 11th, fed. cirs.) Law clk. U.S. Dist. Ct. (so. dist.) N.Y., N.Y.C., 1965-67; assoc. Kilpatrick & Cody, Atlanta, 1967-72, ptnr., 1972—. Contbr. numerous articles to profl. jours. Mem. ABA, Ga. Bar Assn., Internat. Trademark Assn. (bd. dirs. 1989-91, editor-in-chief Trademark Reporter 1988-90), Cherokee Town and Country Club, Phi Beta Kappa. Democrat. Avocation: woodworking. Home: 9905 Huntcliff Trce Atlanta GA 30350-2715 Office: Kilpatrick & Cody 1100 Peachtree St Atlanta GA 30309

SWANN, LYNN CURTIS, sportscaster, former professional football player; b. Alcoa, Tenn., Mar. 7, 1952; s. Willie and Mildred (McGarity) S. B.A., U. So. Calif., 1974. Wide receiver Pitts. Steelers Profl. Football Team, 1974-83, leading receiver in team history, 1981; commentator ABC Sports, 1976—. Entertainment and media appearances as dancer with Twyla Tharp and Peter Martines Omnibus TV Spl., 1980, guest star Night of 100 Stars I, 1982, 100 Stars II, 1985; host and narrator Britten's Young Person's Guide to Orchestra, Wheeling Symphony Orch., 1982; host of 13 part art edn. spl. Arts Alive, PBS, 1984; major character in episodes Paper Chase, 1984, Hotel, 1984, Love American Style, 1985; other appearances on various TV shows including 20/20, Good Morning America, Merv Griffin, Hollywood Squares, others; intermittent host daily talk show Pittsburgh 2Day, 1985—. Spokesman for Big Bros./Big Sisters Assn.; trustee Pitts. Ballet Theatre, creator youth scholarship program; bd. dirs. Scott Newman Juvenile Drug and Alcohol Prevention Found.; bd. dirs. U. So. Calif. Sch. Journalism Alumni Assn. Named All Pro, 1976 77, 78, Most Valuable Player in Super Bowl X, 1976, Pitts. Multiple Sclerosis Athlete of Yr., 1980, NFL Man of Yr., 1981; holder 4 Super Bowl records, 2d in 2 categories; mem. Pitts. Steelers All-Time Team, 50th Anniv.; named to NFL Hall of Fame Team of Decade/1970's, AP, UPI, Kodak All Am. Teams, Pop Warner Hall of Fame; recipient Image award NAACP, 1979, Ebonics Soc. award, Outstanding Alumni award U. So. Calif., 1984, Oleg Cassini Competitors Fashion award, 1985. Mem. Screen Actors Guild, AFTRA. Office: Swann Inc 600 Grant St Fl 48 Pittsburgh PA 15219-2702*

SWANN, RANDE NORTOF, public relations executive; b. Louisville, July 14, 1952; d. Thomas Joseph and Garrith Louise (Hines) Nortof; m. William Donald Swann, Nov. 20, 1977; children: Nicole, Amy. BA, Hollins Coll. For Women, Roanoke, Va., 1974; MS, U. Louisville, 1980. Various positions Hollins Coll. For Women, Roanoke, 1971-74; exec. dir. USO-Louisville (Ky.) Svc. Club, Inc., 1974-81; asst. campaign dir. Metro United Way, Louisville, 1981-82; pub. affairs dir. Jefferson County Pub. Schs., Louisville, 1982-89; pub. rels. dir. Regional Airport Authority of Louisville & Jefferson County, 1989—; speaker, conductor seminars, workshops in field. Patron Actors Theatre Louisville, 1988; mem. pub. relations adv. com. Metro United Way, 1987-88; silent auction chair Actors Theatre, 1988; hon. life mem. 15th Dist. PTA. Recipient 2 Nat. Merit awards Advt. Club Am., 1984-88, 3 Louie awards Advt. Club Louisville, 1984-88, 2 Silver Certs., 2 Regional ADDYs, 1984-88. Mem. Internat. Assn. Bus. Communicators (Silver Quill award of Excellence, Award of Merit, Landmarks of Excellence award, 1984-88), Pub. Relations Soc. Am. (Dist. award of Excellence, Regional award, 1984-88), Nat. Sch. Pub. Relations Assn. (4 Golden Achievement awards, 2 Sch. Publs./Communications awards, Nat. Award of Honor, 1984-88), Am. Assn. Sch. Adminstrs., Rotary, Phi Beta Kappa. Democrat. Presbyterian. Avocations: reading, traveling. Office: Regional Airport Authority PO Box 9129 Louisville KY 40209-0129

SWANSEN, SAMUEL THEODORE, lawyer; b. Milw., June 6, 1937; s. Theodore Lawrence and Clarinda Dingwall (Crittenden) S.; m. Donna Rae Elizabeth Maloney, June 27, 1959; children: Jessica Swansen Bonelli, Theodor Arthur, Christopher Currie. AB, Dartmouth Coll., 1959; LLB, U. Wis., 1962. Bar: Wis. 1962, Pa. 1964, U.S. Supreme Ct. 1969. Law clk. to presiding justice Wis. Supreme Ct., Madison, 1962-63; assoc. Dechert, Price & Rhoads, Phila., 1963-68, 70-73, ptnr., 1973-93; asst. dist. atty. City of Phila. Dist. Atty.'s Office, 1968-70, chief frauds div., 1969; adj. prof. law Temple U., Phila., 1970-80; lectr. Pa. Bar Inst., Nat. Bus. Inst., Ctr. Profl. Edn., 1985—. Editor, author U. Wis. Law Rev., 1960-62. Violinist, trombonist North Penn Symphony Orch., 1977—; mem. Gwynedd Monthly Meeting of Friends, 1974—; bd. dirs. Friends Rehab. Program, Inc., Phila., 1966-73, 85—, Franklin Found., Phila., 1969—; v.p., sec. bd. dirs. Foulkeways at Gwynedd, 1979—, pres., 1986—; chmn. bd. dirs. Friends Life Care at Home, Inc., 1990—, bd. dirs., 1985—; bd. dirs. Friends Retirement Concepts, Inc., Gwynedd, Pa., sec. bd. dirs., 1985-92; hon. bd. dirs. Friends Neighborhood Guild, Greater Phila. Fedn. Settlements; corp. mem. Anna T. Jeanes Found., Fox Chase, Phila., 1985-93, Associated Svcs. for Blind, Phila., 1974-91, Bach Festival of Phila., 1989—, pres. 1993—; dir. sec. Energy Islands Internat., Inc., 1963—. Mem. ABA, Pa. Bar Assn., Phila. Bar Assn., Delta Upsilon, Phi Delta Phi., Dartmouth and Pyramid Club Phila. Republican. Mem. Soc. of Friends. Home: 221 Morris Rd Ambler PA 19002-5202 Office: 640 Sentry Pkwy Ste 104 Blue Bell PA 19422-2361

SWANSON, ARNOLD ARTHUR, retired biochemistry educator; b. Rawlins, Wyo., Mar. 11, 1923; s. Arnold David and Gladys Fern (Murphy) S.; m. Florence P. Swanson; children: Kathleen, Kristine, Annabeth. BA, Duke U., 1948; MA, Trinity U., 1959; PhD, Tex. A&M U., 1961. Asst. prof. The U. Tex. Southwestern, 1963-66; assoc. prof. Baylor U. Coll. Medicine, 1963-66; prof. Tex. Women's U., 1963-65, Baylor U., Waco, Tex., 1966-68, Med. U. S.C., Charleston, 1968-94; ret., 1994. Contbr. over 250 articles to profl. jours. Recipient Alexander von Humboldt-Stiftung, Fed. Republic Germany, 1974-75. Mem. Am. Chem. Soc., AAAS, Sigma Xi. Republican. Methodist. Home: 726 Wildwood Rd Charleston SC 29412 Office: Medical Univ South Carolina 171 Ashley Ave Charleston SC 29425-0001

SWANSON, AUGUST GEORGE, physician, retired association executive; b. Kearney, Nebr., Aug. 25, 1925; s. Oscar Valderman and Elnora Wilhelmina Emma (Block) S.; m. Ellyn Constance Weinel, June 28, 1947; children: Eric, Rebecca, Margaret, Emilie, Jennifer, August. BA, Westminster Coll., Fulton, Mo., 1951; MD, Harvard U., 1949; DSc (hon.), U. Nebr. 1979. Intern King County Hosp., Seattle, 1949-50; resident internal medicine U. Wash. Affiliated Hosp., 1953-55, neurology, 1955-57; resident neurology Boston City Hosp., 1958; dir. pediatric neurology, then dir. div. neurology U. Wash. Med. Sch., Seattle, 1958-67; assoc. dean acad. affairs U. Wash. Med. Sch., 1967-71; v.p. acad. affairs Assn. Am. Med. Colls., Washington, 1971-89, v.p. grad. med. edn., exec. dir. Nat. Resident Matching Program, 1989-91, ret., 1991; vis. fellow physiology Oxford (Eng.) U., 1963-64; cons. in field. Author articles brain function, physician edn., med. manpower. With USNR, 1943-46, 50-53. Markle scholar medicine, 1959-64; recipient Abraham Flexner awd. for Distinguished Service to Medical Education, Assn. of Am. Medical Coll., 1992. Mem. Inst. Medicine, Nat., Acad. Sci., Am. Neurol. Assn. Home: 3146 Portage Bay Pl E # H Seattle WA 98102-3878

SWANSON, BERNET STEVEN, consulting engineer, former educator; b. Chgo., Nov. 20, 1921; s. Bernet Stephanie and Emma (Conrad) S.; m. Lucile A. Clapham, June 12, 1948; children—Brian Bernet, David Herbert. BS, Armour Inst. Tech., 1942; MS, Ill. Inst. Tech., 1944, PhD, 1950. Mem. faculty Ill. Inst. Tech., Chgo., 1950-85; prof. chem. engring. Ill. Inst. Tech., 1960-85, head dept., 1967-85; cons. engr., 1944—. Author: Electronic Analog Computer, 1965. Mem. Am. Inst. Chem. Engrs., Instrument Soc. Am., Am. Soc. Engring. Edn., Sigma Xi, Alpha Chi Sigma, Phi Lambda Upsilon. Home: 2N151 Swift Rd Lombard IL 60148 Office: 3300 S Federal St Chicago IL 60616-3793

SWANSON, CHARLES ANDREW, mathematics educator; b. Bellingham, Wash., July 11, 1929; s. Clarence Otto and Esther (Hougen) S.; m. Carolyn Marie Dennis, Aug. 5, 1957; children:—Laird Randall, Denise Claire. BA, U. B.C., 1951, MA, 1953; PhD, Cal. Inst. Tech., 1957. Prof. U. B.C., Vancouver, 1957-94, prof. emeritus math., 1994—. Author: An Introduction to Differential Calculus, 1962, Comparison and Oscillation Theory of Linear Differential Equations, 1968; Contbr. articles to tech., profl. jours. Office: U British Columbia, Dept Math, Vancouver, BC Canada V6T 1Z2

SWANSON, DANE CRAIG, naval officer, pilot; b. Guam, Feb. 13, 1955; s. George Clair and Norma Francis (Brown) S. BS in Naval Architecture, U.S Naval Acad., 1977; MA, Webster U., 1980; grad., USAF Test Pilot Sch., 1985. Commd. ensign USN, 1977, advanced through grades to comdr., 1992; flight instr. USN, Kingsville, Tex., 1978-80; asst. ops. officer USS Eisenhower VF-142 USN, 1981-84; test pilot Air Test and Evaluation Air Test and Evaluation Squadron Four USN, Point Mugu, Calif., 1985-88; ops. officer USS Saratoga VF-103 USN, 1988-91; anti-air appraisal officer Naval Air System Command USN, Washington, 1991—. Decorated 4 Air medals. Mem. Soc. Exptl. Test Pilots, U.S. Naval Inst., Officers Christian Fellowship. Republican. Baptist. Avocations: backpacking, golf, fishing, hunting.

SWANSON, DAVID HEATH, agricultural company executive; b. Aurora, Ill., Nov. 3, 1942; s. Neil H. and Helen J. (McKendry) S.; children: Benjamin Heath, Matthew Banford. B.A., Harvard U., 1964; M.A., U. Chgo., 1969. Account exec. 1st Nat. Bank Chgo., 1967-69; dep. mgr. Brown Bros. Harriman & Co., N.Y.C., 1969-72; asst. treas. Borden, Inc., N.Y.C., 1972-75; v.p. treas. Continental Grain Co., N.Y.C., 1975-77, v.p chief fin. officer, 1977-79, gen. mgr. Financial div., 1979-81, exec. v.p. and gen. mgr. World Grain div., 1981-83, corp. v.p., chief fin. and adminstrv. officer, 1983-86, group pres., 1985-86; pres., chief exec. officer Cen. Soya, Ft. Wayne, Ind., 1986-93; chmn. Premiere Agri Techs., Inc., Ft. Wayne, 1994—; adv. bd. U.S. Export-Import Bank, 1985-86; mem. Gov.'s Agrl. Bd. Ind.; bd. dirs. Fiduciary Trust Internat. Bd. dirs. Internat. Policy Coun. on Agr. and Trade; mem. adv. bd. Purdue U. Agr. Sch.; mem. Gov.'s Econ. Devel. Bd.; bd. govs. Exec. Coun. on Fgn. Diplomats and U.S. Agr. Libr.; gov. Found. for U.S. Constn. Mem. Coun. Fgn. Rels. (bd. dirs.), Nat. Assn. Mfrs. (bd. dirs.), Ind. C. of C. (bd. dirs.), Ft. Wayne Hist. Soc. (bd. dirs.), Am. Alpine Club (bd. dirs.), Scottish Deerhound of Am. Club, Links Club, Racquet and Tennis Club, Explorers Club (bd. dirs., exec.). Republican. Congregationalist. Office: Premiere Agri Techs Inc 46 E 70th St New York NY 10021

SWANSON, DON RICHARD, university dean; b. Los Angeles, Oct. 10, 1924; s. Harry Windfield and Grace Clara (Sandstrom) S.; m. Patricia Elizabeth Klick, Aug. 22, 1976; children—Douglas Alan, Richard Brian, Judith Ann. B.S., Calif. Inst. Tech., 1945; M.A., Rice U., 1947; Ph.D., U. Calif., Berkeley, 1952. Physicist U. Calif. Radiation Lab., Berkeley, 1947-52, Hughes Research and devel. Labs., Culver City, Calif., 1952-55; research scientist TRW, Inc., Canoga Park, Calif., 1955-63; prof. Grad. Library Sch., U. Chgo., 1963—, dean, 1963-72, 77-79, 86—; mem. Sci. Info. Council, NSF, 1960-65; mem. toxicology info. panel Pres.'s Sci. Advisory Com., 1964-66; mem. library vis. com. Mass. Inst. Tech., 1966-71; mem. com. on sci. and tech. communication Nat. Acad. Scis., 1966-69. Editor: The Intellectual Founds. of Library Education, 1965, The Role of Libraries in the Growth of Knowledge, 1980; co-editor: Operations Research: Implications for Libraries, 1972, Management Education: Implications for Libraries and Library Schools, 1974; mem. editorial bd.: Library Quarterly, 1963—; Contbr.: chpt. to Ency. Brit., 1968—; sci. articles to profl. jours. Trustee Nat. Opinion Research Center, 1964-73; Research fellow Chgo. Inst. for Psychoanalysis, 1972-76. Served with USNR, 1943-46. Mem. Am. Soc. for Info. Sci. Home: 5825 S Dorchester Ave Apt 14E Chicago IL 60637-1701 Office: U Chgo Divsn Humanities 1010 E 59th St Chicago IL 60637-1596 *Problems I wish I could solve: how the universe got started, how volition arose in a heap of molecules, how to find information in a library, and how to sum up life in a sentence or two.*

SWANSON, DONALD ALAN, geologist; b. Tacoma, July 25, 1938; s. Leonard Walter and Edith Christine (Bowers) S.; m. Barbara Joan White, May 25, 1974. BS in Geology, Wash. State U., 1960; PhD in Geology, Johns Hopkins U., 1964. Geologist U.S. Geol. Survey, Menlo Park, Calif., 1965-68, 71-80, Hawaii National Park, 1968-71; sr. geologist Cascades Volcano Obs. U.S. Geol. Survey, Vancouver, Wash., 1980-90, rsch. scientist-in-charge, 1986-89; sr. geologist U.S. Geol. Survey, Seattle, 1990—; assoc. dir. Volcano Systems Ctr. U. Wash., 1993—; affiliate prof. U. Wash., 1992—; cons. U.S. Dept. Energy, Richland, Wash., 1979-83; volcanologist New Zealand Geol. Survey, Taupo, 1984; advisor Colombian Volcano Obs., Manizales, 1986. Assoc. editor Jour. Volcanology and Geothermal Rsch. 1976—, Jour. Geophys. Rsch., 1992-94; editor Bull. of Volcanology, 1985-90; contbr. numerous articles to profl. jours. Recipient Superior Service award U.S. Geol. Survey, 1980, Meritorious Service award U.S. Dept. Interior, 1985; postdoctoral fellow NATO, 1964-65. Fellow Geol. Soc. Am.; mem. AAAS, Am. Geophys. Union, Sigma Xi. Avocation: hiking. Home: 7537 34th Ave NE Seattle WA 98115-4802 Office: U Washington US Geol Survey Geol Scis Box 351310 Seattle WA 98195-1310

SWANSON, DONALD FREDERICK, retired food company executive; b. Mpls., Aug. 6, 1927; s. Clayton A. and Irma (Baiocchi) S.; m. Virginia Clare Hannah, Dec. 17, 1948; children—Donald Frederick, Cynthia Hannah Lindgren, Janet Clare Webster. B.A., U. Minn., 1948. With Gen. Mills, Inc., 1949-85, div. v.p., dir. marketing flour, dessert and baking mixes, 1964-65, v.p., gen. mgr. grocery products div., 1965-68, v.p., corporate adminstrn. officer consumer foods group, fashion div., transp. and purchasing depts., advt. and marketing services, 1969, exec. v.p. craft, game and toy group, fashion group, direct marketing group, travel group, dir., 1968-76, sr. exec. v.p. consumer non-foods, 1976-85, chief financial officer, 1977-79, sr. exec. v.p. restaurants and consumer non-foods, 1980-81, vice chmn. restaurants and consumer non-foods, 1981-85; ret. chmn. bd. Soo Line Corp.; bd. dirs. Costume Jewelry Group. Served with AUS, 1946-47. Mem. Lafayette Club, Mpls. Club, Wayzata Country Club, Audubon Country Club, Royal Poinciana Golf Club, Phi Kappa Psi. Home: 2171 Gulf Shore Blvd N Naples FL 33940-4625 Office: 641 Lake St E Wayzata MN 55391-1759

SWANSON, EMILY, state legislator; b. Oak Park, Ill., Jan. 12, 1947; m. Tim Swanson; 2 children. BA, Bennington Coll.; MA, U. Calif., Berkeley. Mem. Mont. Ho. of Reps. Office: Mont Ho of Reps State Capitol Helena MT 59620

SWANSON, GUY EDWIN, social scientist, educator; b. Warren, Pa., Oct. 6, 1922; s. Guy Edwin and Minnie Katherine (Haslett) S.; m. Eliane Marie Aerts, Aug. 19, 1977; children—Emily Gray, Elisabeth Huntley, Mary Alice, Sarah Catherine. A.B., U. Pitts., 1943, M.A., 1943; Ph.D., U. Chgo., 1948. Instr. Boston U., 1945-46, Ind. U., 1946-47, U. Chgo., 1947-48; mem. faculty U. Mich., 1948-69; fellow U. Mich. (Center Advanced Study Behavioral Scis.), 1957-58, prof., 1959-69, chmn. dept. sociology, 1961-64; prof. sociology U. Calif., Berkeley, 1969-84, prof. psychology, 1984—; dir. U. Calif. (Inst. Human Devel.), 1981-88; dir. Social Sci. Research Council, 1961-64. Author: (with Daniel R. Miller) The Changing American Parent, 1958, Inner Conflict and Defense, 1960, The Birth of the Gods, 1960, Religion and Regime, A Sociological Account of the Reformation, 1967, Rules of Descent, Studies in the Sociology of Parentage, 1969, Social Change, 1971, Emotional Disturbance and Juvenile Delinquency, 1980, Ego Defenses and the Legitimation of Behavior, 1988. Guggenheim fellow, 1964-65. Fellow Am. Sociol. Assn., Am. Psychol. Assn., AAAS (v.p. 1968-69). Home: 176 Ardmore Rd Kensington CA 94707-1311

SWANSON, LLOYD OSCAR, former savings and loan association executive; b. Mpls., June 26, 1913; s. Carl G. and Ellen (Peterson) S.; m. Eileen E. Hedlof, Mar. 29, 1958; children: Marcia L. (Mrs. Joseph Massee), Paul L., J. Bradley, Craig R. Student, U. Minn., 1930-31; B.A., Gustavus Adolphus Coll., 1935, L.H.D. (hon.), 1968. Dir. admissions and pub. relations Gustavus Adolphus Coll., 1935-37; spl. agt. John Hancock Life Ins. Co., Mpls., 1937-42; gen. agt. Nat. Life Ins. Co., Mpls., 1942-62; pres. First Fed. Savs. and Loan Assn., Mpls., 1962-77; chmn. bd. First Fed. Savs. and Loan Assn., 1967-84; chmn. bd. dirs. The Security Corp., 1967-84; dir. Soderberg Optical Co., St. Paul. Former trustee, chmn. bd. trustees Gustavus Adolphus Coll., St. Peter, Minn.; trustee Greater Gustavus Fund, 1952—; former chmn. bd. pensions Luth. Ch. in Am.; former chmn. bd. trustees Fairview Cmty. Hosps. Mem. Savs. League Minn. (dir., pres. 1970), Swedish Coun. Am. (mem. bd.), Athletic Club, Interlachen Country Club (past mem. bd. govs.), Royal Poinciana Golf Club (Naples, Fla.). Home: 2171 Gulf Shore Blvd N Naples FL 33940 Office: 4900 IDS Tower Minneapolis MN 55402

SWANSON, NORMA FRANCES, federal agency administrator; b. Blue Island, Ill., Oct. 24, 1923; d. Arnold Raymond and Bessie Oween (Bewley) Brown; m. George Clair Swanson, Mar. 18, 1948; 1 child, Dane Craig. AB, Asbury Coll., 1946; BS cum laude, Eastern Nazarene Coll., Wollaston, Mass., 1970; MA cum laude, Ind. Christian U., 1986. Confidential asst. dep. undersec. interagy. intergovt. affairs U.S. Dept. Edn., Washington, 1981—; pres. Window to the World, Inc., Schroon Lake, N.Y., 1985—; asst. dir. edn. Commn. Bicentennial U.S. Constn., Washington, 1987—; dir. Horizons Plus Values Program Hampton Roads Va. Detention Homes; dir. Project Fresh Start Washington D.C. Pub. Sch., 1993-94; cons. Conf. Industrialized Nations, Williamsburg, Va., 1982, Nellie Thomas Inst. Learning, Monterey, Calif., 1981-82. Author: Dear Teenager, A Teen's Guide to Correct Social Behavior, 1987, A Constitution Is Born, A Teacher's Guide to Resource Materials, 1987, Sunlights and More, Bright Beginnings, 1993, The Ones that Count and Other Stories with Values to Live By, 1994; editor: (anthology) Horizons Plus; developer ednl. materials; theorem artist Early Am. Life mag., 1974. Bd. regents Ind. Christian U., 1986—; program dir. Tidewater (Va.) Outreach, 1992; dir. project Fresh Start, Washington Pub. Sch., 1993-94; dir. youth outreach with values program U.S. Dept. Juvenile Justice, 1992-93. Recipient J.C. Penny award for volunteerism, 1993. Republican. Baptist. Avocation: theorem painting. Home: PO Box 308 Schroon Lake NY 12870

SWANSON, PATRICIA K., university official; b. St. Louis, May 8, 1940; d. Emil Louis and Patricia (McNair) Klick; 1 child, Ivan Clatanoff. BS in Edn., U. Mo., 1962; postgrad., Cornell U., 1963; MLS, Simmons Coll., 1967. Reference librarian Simmons Coll., Boston, 1967-68; reference librarian U. Chgo., 1970-79, sr. lectr. Grad. Library Sch., 1974-83, 86-88, head reference service, 1979-83, asst. dir. for sci. libraries, 1983-93, acting asst. dir. for tech. svcs., 1987-88, assoc. provost, 1993—; project dir. Office Mgmt. Svcs., Assn. Rsch. Librs., 1982-83; speaker in field; cons. on libr. mgmt., planning and space. Author: Great is the Gift that Bringeth Knowledge: Highlights from the History of the John Crerar Library, 1989; contbr. articles to profl. jours. Mem. Caxton Club. Office: U Chgo Office of the Provost 5801 S Ellis Ave Rm 501 Chicago IL 60637-1404

SWANSON, PAUL RUBERT, minister; b. Bakersfield, Calif., May 13, 1943; s. Roland Hilding and Myrtle Isabelle (Magnuson) S.; m. Mary Elizabeth Greene, June 18, 1967; children: Kristen Ann, Karlynn Marie, Jonathan Paul. BA, Pacific Luth. U., 1966; MDiv, Luth. Sch. Theology, 1970. Ordained minister, Luth. Ch. Pastor 1st Luth. Ch., Anaconda, Mont., 1970-76, King of Kings Luth. Ch., Milwaukie, Oreg., 1976-84; asst. to bishop Pacific N.W. Synod-Luth. Ch. in Am., Portland, Oreg., 1984-87; bishop Oreg. Synod-Evang. Luth. Ch. Am., Portland, 1987—; bd. dirs. Legacy Health System, Portland. Regent Pacific Luth. U., Tacoma, 1987—; bd. dirs. Emanuel Hosp., Portland, 1987; chmn. bd. dirs. Hearthstone, Inc., Anaconda, 1973-76; bd. dirs. Ecumenical Ministries Oreg., Portland, 1984—. Recipient Disting. Svc. award Pacific Luth. U., 1993. Avocation: golf.

SWANSON, PETER CARL, editor; b. Biloxi, Miss., Jan. 12, 1955; s. Robert Chester and Gloria Theresa (Carlson) S. BA in Journalism and English, U. Mass., 1978. Polit. reporter, columnist Westfield (Mass.) Evening News, 1977-78; reporter The Elmira (N.Y.) Star-Gazette, 1978-79; copy editor The Union Leader, Manchester, N.H., 1980-82; reporter, photographer N.H. Sunday News, Manchester, 1982-87; Sunday editor The Union Leader Corp., Manchester, 1987—. Harbor commr. Town of Salisbury, Mass., 1990-94. Recipient Merit award New Eng. Newspaper Assn., 1992, Page One Design award New Eng. News Execs. Assn., 1993. Mem. Soc. Profl. Journalists. Avocations: sailing, military and naval history, intelligence matters.

SWANSON, PHILLIP DEAN, neurologist; b. Seattle, Oct. 1, 1932; s. William Dean and Katharyn C. (Peterson) S.; m. Sheila N. Joardar, Apr. 17, 1957; children—Stephen, Jennifer, Kathryn, Rebecca, Sara. B.S., Yale U., 1954; student, U. Heidelberg, 1952-53; M.D., Johns Hopkins U., 1958; Ph.D. in Biochemistry, U. London, 1964. Intern Harvard med. svc. Boston City Hosp., 1958-59; resident in neurology Johns Hopkins Hosp., Balt. City Hosp., 1959-62; asst. prof. U. Wash. Sch. Medicine, Seattle, 1964-68; assoc. prof. U. Wash. Sch. Medicine, 1968-73, 1977—, head div. neurology, 1967—; mem. med. adv. bd. Puget Sound chpt. Nat. Multiple Sclerosis Soc., 1967—, chmn., 1970-74; mem. com. to combat Huntington's Disease Nat. Sci. Council, 1975-84. Author: (with others) Introduction to Clinical Neurology, 1976; editor: Signs and Symptoms in Neurology, 1984; contbr. articles to profl. jours. NIH spl. fellow, 1962-64; NIH grantee. Fellow Am. Acad. Neurology; mem. Am. Neurol. Assn., Assn. Univ. Profs. Neurology (pres. 1975-76), Am. Heart Assn., Am. Soc. Neurochemistry, Internat. Soc. Neurochemistry, Biochem. Soc. (London), Am. Soc. Clin. Investigation (emeritus). Home: 6537 29th Ave NE Seattle WA 98115-7234 Office: U Wash Sch Medicine Div Neurology Seattle WA 98195

SWANSON, RICHARD WILLIAM, statistician; b. Rockford, Ill., July 26, 1934; s. Richard and Erma Marie (Herman) S.; m. Laura Yoko Arai, Dec. 30, 1970. BS, Iowa State U., 1958, MS, 1964. Ops. analyst Stanford Rsch. Inst., Monterey, Calif., 1962-65; statistician ARINC Rsch. Corp., Washington, 1964-65; sr. scientist Booz-Allen Applied Rsch., Vietnam, 1965-67, L.A., 1967-68; sr. ops. analyst Control Data Corp., Honolulu, 1968-70; mgmt. cons., Honolulu, 1970-73; exec. v.p. SEQUEL Corp., Honolulu, 1973-75; bus. cons. Hawaii Dept. Planning and Econ. Devel., Honolulu, 1975-77, tax rsch. and planning officer Dept. Taxation, 1977-82; ops. rsch. analyst U.S. Govt., 1982-89; shipyard statisician U.S. Govt., 1989—. Served with

AUS, 1954-56. Mem. Hawaiian Acad. Sci., Sigma Xi. Home: 583 Kamoku St Apt 3505 Honolulu HI 96826-5240 Office: Pearl Harbor Naval Shipyard PO Box 400 Honolulu HI 96860-5350

SWANSON, ROBERT A., genetic engineering company executive; b. N.Y.C., Nov. 29, 1947; s. Arthur John and Arline (Baker) S.; m. Judy Church, Sept. 2, 1980. S.B. M.I.T., 1970, S.M. in Mgmt, 1970. Asst. treas. Citicorp Venture Capital Ltd., N.Y.C., 1970-74; partner Kleiner & Perkins Venture Capital Partnership, San Francisco, 1975; chief exec. Genentech, Inc., South San Francisco, Calif., from 1976, now chmn. bd. dirs. Mem. corp. MIT; bd. dirs. San Francisco Mus. Modern Art, San Francisco Ballet Assn., Tech. Ctr. Silicon Valley. Named Entrepreneur of Year Chgo. Research Dirs. Assn., 1981; Gold medal chief Exec. for Biotech. industry Wall Street Transcript, 1984. Mem. Am. Chem. Soc., Am. Soc. Microbiology, Royal Swedish Acad. Engring. Scis., AAAS. Office: Genentech Inc 460 Point San Bruno Blvd South San Francisco CA 94080-4990*

SWANSON, ROBERT DRAPER, college president; b. Sioux City, Iowa, Aug. 6, 1915; s. Alfred and Tida Ruth (Draper) S.; m. Roberta B. Clements, May 5, 1941 (dec. Oct. 1975); children: Sara Louise, Mark Robert; m. Dorothy B. Howe, Aug. 4, 1979. A.B., Park Coll., 1937; student, U. Iowa, 1937; B.D. McCormick Theol. Sem., 1941; D.D., James Millikin U., 1950; L.H.D., Tusculum Coll., 1966, Olivet Coll., 1971, Central Mich. U., 1979, Alma Coll., 1981; LL.D., Hillsdale Coll., 1968, Hope Coll., 1981. Dir. athletics, phys. edn. Park Coll., 1937-38; ordained to ministry Presbyn. Ch., 1941; pastor Second Presbyn. Ch., Tulsa, 1941-45; dean of students McCormick Sem., 1946-47, v.p., prof. preaching, 1948-56; pres. Alma Coll., 1956-80, pres. emeritus, 1980—; dir. Gen. Telephone Co. Mich. Served as lt. (j.g.), Chaplain's Corps USNR, 1945-46. Recipient Disting. Alumnus award McCormick Theol. Sem., 1981. Mem. Phi Beta Kappa. Club: Rotary (Alma). Home: 4105 Riverview Dr Alma MI 48801-9563

SWANSON, ROBERT KILLEN, management consultant; b. Deadwood, S.D., Aug. 11, 1932; s. Robert Claude and Marie Elizabeth (Kersten) S.; m. Nancy Anne Oyaas, July 19, 1958; children: Cathryn Lynn, Robert Stuart, Bart Killen. BA, U. S.D., 1954; postgrad., U. Melbourne, Australia, 1955. With Gen. Mills, Inc., Mpls., 1955-58, 71-79, v.p., 1971-73, group v.p., 1973-77, exec. v.p., 1977-79; with Marathon Oil Co., Findlay, Ohio, 1958-60; sr. v.p., dir. Needham, Harper & Steers, Inc., Chgo., 1961-69; joint mng. dir. S. H. Benson (Holdings) Ltd., Eng., 1969-71; pres., chief operating officer Greyhound Corp., Phoenix, 1980; chmn., chief exec. officer Del E. Webb Corp., Phoenix, 1981-87; chmn. RKS Inc., Phoenix, 1987—; bd. dirs. Grossman's Inc., The Thursley Group, Inc., Am. S.W. Concepts Inc., Ariz. Desert Saguaro, Internat. Imports Inc. Bd. dirs. Univ. S.D. Found. 2d lt. U.S. Army, 1955. Fulbright scholar, 1954-55; Woodrow Wilson scholar. Mem. U.S. Coun. Fgn. Rels., U.K. Dirs. Inst., U.S. Internat. Scholars Assn., English Speaking Union. Episcopalian. Home and Office: RKS Inc 5600 N Palo Christi Rd Paradise Valley AZ 85253

SWANSON, ROBERT LEE, lawyer; b. Fond du Lac, Wis., July 15, 1942; s. Walfred S. and Edna F. (Kamp) S.; m. Mary Ruth Francis, Aug. 19, 1967; children: Leigh Alexandra, Mitchell Pearson. BS, U. Wis., 1964; JD, Valparaiso U., 1970; LLM, Boston U., 1979. Bar: Wis. 1970, U.S. Dist. Ct. (ea. dist.) Wis. 1970, U.S. Dist. Ct. (we. dist.) Wis. 1974, U.S. Dist. Ct. (cen.) Ill. 1988, U.S. Tax Ct. 1981. Atty. Kasdorf, Dahl, Lewis & Swietlik, Milw., 1970-73; atty., ptnr. Wartman, Wartman & Swanson, Ashland, Wis., 1973-80; city atty. City of Ashland, Wis., 1976-80; atty., ptnr. DeMark, Kolbe & Brodek, Racine, Wis., 1980-95; ptnr. Hartig, Bjelajac, Swanson & Koenen, Racine, 1995—; lectr. civil rights and discrimination laws, 1980—. Columnist (legal) Burlington Std. Press, 1991—, Wis. Restaurant Assn. Mag., 1986. Vice compdr. USCG Aux. Bayfield (Wis.) Flotilla, 1975-81; v.p., bd. dirs. Meml. Med. Ctr., Ashland, 1975-80; chmn. Ashland County Rep. Party, 1976-79; vol. atty. ACLU Wis., 1975—. 1st lt. U.S. Army, 1964-66. Named one of Outstanding Young Men of Am., Jaycees, 1978; recipient Disting. Achievement in Art and Sci. of Advocacy award Internat. Acad. Trial Lawyers, 1970. Mem. Racine County Bar Assn. (bd. dirs. 1983), Wis. Acad. Trial Lawyers, Def. Rsch. Inst., Am. Hockey Assn. U.S. (coach, referee 1983—), Am. Legion, The Federalist Soc. Avocations: softball, volleyball, hockey. Home: 333 Hollow Creek Rd Racine WI 53402 Office: Hartig Bjelajac et al 601 Lake Ave Racine WI 53401-0038

SWANSON, ROBERT MCLEAN, retired business educator; b. Union City, Pa., Aug. 11, 1920; s. Peter Leonard and Mary Edna (McLean) S.; m. Marie Manda, May 25, 1946; children: Catherine, Robert Jr., Mary Ann, Christina. BS in Edn., Ind. U. of Pa., 1942; MA, Columbia U., 1949, EdD, 1953. Bus. tchr. Darlington (Pa.) Joint Schs., 1944-48; prof. bus. Thiel Coll., Greenville, Pa., 1948-52; vis. prof. Teachers Coll. Columbia U., N.Y.C., 1953; prof. bus. Ball State U., Muncie, Ind., 1954-85, head dept. bus. edn., 1961-67, prof. emeritus, 1985—. Author: (with others) Century 21 Accounting, 1967, 72, 77, 82, 87, 92, 95. Charter bd. dirs. Muncie Hosp. Hospitality House, 1983-86. Maj. U.S. Army, 1942-46, ETO. Mem. Nat. Bus. Edn. Assn., Ind. Bus. Edn. Assn., Delta Pi Epsilon. Roman Catholic. Avocations: home computer, traveling. Home: 1719 E Wexley Rd Bloomington IN 47401-4357

SWANSON, ROY ARTHUR, classicist, educator; b. St. Paul, Apr. 7, 1925; s. Roy Benjamin and Gertrude (Larson) S.; m. Vivian May Vitous, Mar. 30, 1946; children: Lynn Marie (Mrs. Gerald A. Snider), Robin Lillian, Robert Roy (dec.), Dyack Tyler, Dana Miriam (Mrs. Jon Butts). B.A., U. Minn., 1948, B.S., 1949, M.A., 1951; Ph.D., U. Ill., 1954. Prin. Maplewood Elementary Sch., St. Paul, 1949-51; instr. U. Ill., 1952-53, Ind. U., 1954-57; asst. prof. U. Minn., Mpls., 1957-61; assoc. prof. U. Minn., 1961-64, acting chmn. classics, 1963-64, prof. classics, chmn. comparative lit., 1964-65; prof. English Macalester Coll., St. Paul, 1965-67; coord. humanities program, 1966-67; prof. comparative lit. and classics U. Wis.-Milw., 1967—, prof. English, 1990—, chmn. classics dept., 1967-70, 86-89, chmn. comparative lit., 1970-73, 76-83, coord. Scandinavian studies program, 1982—; cons. St. Paul Tchrs. Sr. High Sch. English, 1964. Author: Odi et Amo: The Complete Poetry of Catullus, 1959, Heart of Reason: Introductory Essays in Modern-World Humanities, 1963, Pindar's Odes, 1974, Greek and Latin Word Elements, 1981, The Love Songs of the Carmina Burana, 1987, Pär Lagkrvist: Five Early Works, 1989; editor Minn. Rev., 1963-67; Classical Jour., 1966-72; contbr. articles to profl. jours. With AUS, 1944-46. Decorated Bronze Star; recipient Disting. Teaching award U. Minn., 1962, Disting. Teaching award U. Wis.-Milw., 1974, 91. Mem. Am. Philol. Assn., Am. Comparative Lit. Assn., Modern Lang. Assn., Soc. for Advancement Scandinavian Study, Phi Beta Kappa (pres. chpt. 1975-76). Home: 11618 N Bobolink Ln Mequon WI 53092-2804 Office: U Wis Dept English and Comparative Lit PO Box 413 Milwaukee WI 53201-0413

SWANSON, ROY JOEL, lawyer; b. Houston, Feb. 21, 1945; s. Roy J. and Daisy Lee (Speer) S.; m. Lynn Northway, Apr. 5, 1986; children: Emily Rebecca, Nell Cameron. BSChemE, U. Tex., 1967; MBA, Harvard U., 1972, JD, 1972. Bar: Tex. 1972. Assoc. Baker & Botts, Houston, 1972-80, ptnr., 1980—. Office: Baker & Botts 3000 One Shell Pla 910 Louisiana St Houston TX 77002

SWANSON, RUNE E., financial executive; b. Chgo., Aug. 9, 1919; s. John E. and Emma C. (Carlson) S.; m. Lenore Reed, Mar. 18, 1944; children: Deborah, Cynthia, Patricia. B.S. in Commerce (Univ. scholar), Northwestern U., 1943. Asst. contr. U.S. Gypsum Co., Chgo., 1946-56; contr. Internat. Minerals & Chem. Corp., Chgo., 1956-60, Mobil Chem. Co., N.Y.C., 1960-66; v.p. fin. Nat. Gypsum Co., Dallas, 1966-84; assoc. Swearingen Co., 1985-86; pres. Swanson Assocs., Dallas, 1986—; instr. Northwestern U. Served as lt. USNR, 1943-46, PTO. Mem. Fin. Execs. Inst., Northwood Country Club, Dallas Knife and Fork Club, Rotary, Masons, Scottish Rite, Shriners. Republican.

SWANSON, WALLACE MARTIN, lawyer; b. Fergus Falls, Minn., Aug. 22, 1941; s. Marvin Walter and Mary Louise (Lindsey) S.; m. Susan W. Swanson; children: Kristen Lindsey, Eric Munger. B.A. with honors, U. Minn., 1962; LL.B. with honors, So. Methodist U., 1965. Bar: Tex. 1965. Since practiced in Dallas; ptnr. firm Johnson & Swanson, Dallas, 1970-88; prin. Wallace M. Swanson, P.C., Dallas, 1988—; chmn., CEO Ace Cash Express Inc., Irving, Tex., 1987-88, State St. Capital Corp., 1990-94, Highland Park Caferias, Ltd., 1994—. Served with USNR, 1960-65. Mem. ABA,

Tex. Bar Found., State Bar Tex. (securities com. 1972-86, chmn. 1978-80, coun. bus. law sect. 1980-86), Dallas Bar Assn., Crescent Club. Methodist. Address: 3816 Miramar Ave Dallas TX 75205-3126

SWANSTROM, THOMAS EVAN, economist; b. Green Bay, Wis., May 17, 1939; s. Alfred Enoch and Elizabeth Nan (Thomas) S.; m. Nancy Anne Roche; children: Amy, Scott. Student, U. Notre Dame, 1957-59; B.A., U. Wis., 1962, M.A., 1963; postgrad., Am. U., 1963-66. Economist, U.S. Bur. Labor Statistics, Washington, 1963-66; dir. research Population Ref. Bur., Washington, 1966-68; economist Sears, Roebuck & Co., Chgo., 1968-70, market analyst, 1970-72, mgr. catalog research, 1972-75, asst. mgr. econ. research, 1974-80, chief economist, 1980-90; pres. Consumer Econs., Chgo., 1991—; mem. bus. research adv. council Bur. Labor Stats. Contbr. articles to industry publs. Mem. Nat. Assn. Bus. Economists, Conf. Bus. Economists.

SWANTON, SUSAN IRENE, library director; b. Rochester, N.Y., Nov. 29, 1941; d. Walter Frederick and Irene Wray S.; m. Wayne Holman, Apr. 12, 1969 (div. June 1973); 1 child, Michael; life ptnr. James Donald Lathrop; children: Kathryn, Kristin. AB, Harvard U., 1963; MLS, Columbia U., 1965. Libr. dir. Warsaw (N.Y.) Pub. Libr., 1963-64, Gates Pub. Libr., Rochester, N.Y., 1965—. Pres. Drug and Alcohol Coun., Rocheste,r 1985-91, mem. adv. coun., 1992-94; bd. dirs. Rochester Freenet, 1995—. Named Citizen of Yr., Gates-Chili Coun., 1995. Mem. Rochester Met. C. of C. (pres. Gates-Chili coun. 1982, sec. 1990-94, Citizen of the Yr. 1995), Harvard Club of Rochester (mem. adv. bd.). Avocations: hiking, camping. Office: Gates Pub Libr 1605 Buffalo Rd Rochester NY 14624

SWANTON, VIRGINIA LEE, author, publisher, bookseller; b. Oak Park, Ill., Feb. 6, 1933; d. Milton Wesley and Eleanor Louise (Linnell) S. BA, Lake Forest (Ill.) Coll., 1954; MA in English Lit., Northwestern U., 1955; cert. in acctg., Coll. of Lake County, Ill., 1984. Editorial asst. Publs. Office, Northwestern U., Evanston, Ill., 1955-58; reporter Lake Forester, Lake Forest, 1959; editor Scott, Foresman & Co., Glenview, Ill., 1959-84; copy editor, travel coord. McDougal Littell/Houghton Mifflin, Evanston, 1985-94; sr. bookseller B. Dalton Bookseller, Lake Forest, Ill., 1985—; author, pub. Gold Star Publ. Svcs., Lake Forest, 1994—. Contbr. articles to profl. jours. Mem. bd. deacons First Presbyn. Ch. of Lake Forest; mem., sec. bd. dirs., newsletter editor Career Resource Ctr., Inc., Lake Forest. Mem. Internat. Reading Assn., Deerpath Art League, Chgo. Women in Pub. Presbyterian. Avocation: gardening. Office: Gold Star Publ Svcs PO Box 125 Lake Forest IL 60045

SWANZEY, ROBERT JOSEPH, data processing executive; b. Bklyn., Feb. 4, 1935; s. Robert and Olivia (MacIntosh) S.; m. Marie Shannon, Nov. 23, 1957; children: Barbara Ann, Stephen. BA, Pace Coll., 1962. Teller Mfrs. Hanover Trust, N.Y.C., 1953-56; programmer N.Y. Cen. R.R., N.Y.C., 1956-64; systems analyst Schenley Industries, N.Y.C., 1964-70; v.p. systems and programming Raam Info. Services, Inc., N.Y.C., 1970-75; sr. v.p. ops. Century Bus. Credit Corp. (formerly Century Factors, Inc.), N.Y.C., 1975—. Treas. St. Patrick's Sports Programs, Bklyn., 1984-88; dir. basketball St. Patrick's Cath. Youth Orgnl. Program, Bklyn., 1976-84. Co-recipient Adult of Yr. award St. Patrick's Cath. Youth Orgn., 1983. Mem. Factors-Controllers Assn. (treas. 1983-84). Avocations: golf, music. Office: Century Bus Credit Corp 119 W 40th St New York NY 10018-2500

SWAP, WALTER CHARLES, academic dean, psychology educator; b. Seattle, Jan. 23, 1943; s. Clifford Lloyd and Edna Frances (Hastings) S.; m. Susan Webster McAllister, June 25, 1966; children: Clifford John, Alison Frances. BA, Harvard U., 1965; PhD, U. Mich., 1970. Prof. psychology Tufts U., Medford, Mass., 1971-94, chmn. psychology dept., 1983-89, dean undergrad. edn., 1990-94; dean colls., 1994—. Editor, author: Group Decision Making, 1984; contbr. articles to scholarly jours. Mem. Am. Psychol. Soc., Soc. for Exptl. Social Psychology. Democrat. Unitarian-Universalist. Avocations: competitive road running, musical performing, organic gardening. Home: 9 Harrison St Winchester MA 01890-2416 Office: Tufts U Ballou Hall Medford MA 02155

SWART, ROBERT H., lawyer; b. Grand Rapids, Mich., Nov. 12, 1946. AB, U. Mich., 1968, JD cum laude, 1970. Bar: Mich. 1970, D.C. 1971. Ptnr. Mayer, Brown & Platt, Washington. Mem. ABA (mem. taxation sect.), D.C. Bar. Office: Mayer Brown & Platt 2000 Pennsylvania Ave NW Washington DC 20006-1812

SWARTWOUT, JOSEPH RODOLPH, obstetrics and gynecology educator, university administrator; b. Pascagoula, Miss., June 17, 1925; s. Thomas Roswell and Marshall (Coleman) S.; m. Brandon C. Leftwich, Jan. 23, 1989. Student, Miss. Coll., 1943-44; MD, Tulane U., 1951. Intern Touro Infirmary, New Orleans, 1951-52; asst. in obstetrics and medicine Tulane U., 1952-53, instr., 1955-60; Nat. Found. fellow Harvard U., 1953-55; asst. in medicine Peter Bent Brigham Hosp., Boston, 1953-55; assoc. in obstetric medicine Boston Lying-In Hosp., 1953-55; asst. prof. U. Pitts., 1960-61; assoc. prof. Emory U., Atlanta, 1961-66; assoc. prof. ob-gyn. U. Chgo., 1967-80; chief ob-gyn. at Prime Health, also clin. assoc. prof. U. Kans. Sch. Medicine, 1978-80; prof. dept. ob-gyn. Mercer U. Sch. Medicine, Macon, Ga., 1980—, assoc. dean., 1982-92. Fellow Am. Coll. Obstetricians and Gynecologists, Am. Heart Assn. (coun. clin. cardiology), Am. Acad. Reproductive Medicine; mem. AAAS, AMA, APHA, Population Assn. Am., Med. Assn. Ga., Bibb County Med. Soc. Home: 1060 Old Mill Dr Watkinsville GA 30677-2919 Office: Mercer U Sch Medicine Macon GA 31207

SWARTZ, B(ENJAMIN) (KINSELL), JR., archaeologist, educator; b. L.A., June 23, 1931; s. Benjamin Kinsell and Maxine Marietta (Pearce) S.; m. Cyrilla Casillas, Oct. 23, 1966; children: Benjamin Kinsell III, Frank Casillas. AA summa cum laude, L.A. City Coll., 1952; BA, UCLA, 1954, MA, 1958; PhD, U. Ariz., 1964. Curator Klamath County Mus., Oreg., 1959-61, rsch. assoc., 1961-62; asst. prof. anthropology Ball State U., Muncie, Ind., 1964-68, assoc. prof., 1968-72, prof., 1972—; vis. sr. lectr. U. Ghana, 1970-71; exch. lectr. U. Yaounde, Cameroon, 1984-85; field rschr. N.Am. and West Africa; mem. exec. bd., pres. Am. Com. to Advanced Study of Petroglyphs and Pictographs and rep. to Internat. Fedn. Rock Art Orgns.; bd. dirs., sec.-treas. Coun. Conservation Ind. Archaeology; mem. adv. bd. Am. Com. for Preservation of Archaeol. Collections. Editor: Archaeological Reports; contbr. revs. and articles to profl. jours.; author books, monographs in field, including: West African Culture Dynamics, 1980, Indiana's Prehistoric Past, 1981, Rock Art and Posterity, 1991, Proceedings of 1st Internat. South African Rock Art Assn. Conf., 1991. Klamath County chmn. Oreg. Statehood Centennial, 1959. With USN, 1954-56. Fellow AAAS, Ind. Acad. Sci.; mem. Current Anthropology (assoc.), Soc. Am. Archaeology, Soc. African Archaeologists, Internat. Com. Rock Art, Ind. Fedn. Tchrs. (higher edn. trustee, exec. bd.), Sigma Xi, Lambda Alpha (nat. coun., exec. sec.). Home: 3600 W Brook Dr Muncie IN 47304-2923 Office: Ball State U Dept Anthropology Muncie IN 47306-0435

SWARTZ, DAVID H., ambassador; b. Chgo., Mar. 3, 1942; married; 2 children. BA, Southwestern Coll., 1964; MA, Fla. State U., 1966, Can. Def. Coll., Kingston, Ont., 1983. Joined Fgn. Svc.; consul gen. U.S. Consulate Gen., Zurich, Switzerland, 1980-82, Calgary, Can., 1983-84; dep. chief mission Am. Embassy, Warsaw, Poland, 1984-88; charge d'affaires Am. Embassy, Minsk, Belarus, 1992, U.S. amb. to Belarus, 1992—; staff dir. Nuclear Risk Reduction Ctr. Fgn. Svc. Inst., 1988-89, dean Sch. Lang. Studies, 1989-91; sr. inspector Office Inspector Gen. Dept. State, Washington, 1991-92. Office: Belarus, Starovilenskaya # 46, Minsk Belarus

SWARTZ, DONALD EVERETT, television executive; b. Mpls., Mar. 7, 1916; s. Albert L. and Sara (Shore) S.; m. Helen Gordon, Mar. 24, 1940; children: Stuart, Lawrence, Gary. Grad. high sch. Owner Ind. Film Distbrs., 1940-53, Tele-Film Assocs., 1953-57; pres., gen. mgr. KMSP-TV, Mpls., 1957-79; pres. United TV, Inc. (subs. 20th Century Fox Film Corp. until 1981); operating KMSP-TV, KTV4, Salt Lake City, KBHK-TV, San Francisco KMOL-TV, San Antonio; CEO United Television, Inc., Mpls., 1979-85; cons. KMOL-TV, 1985—; founder Tele-Video Assocs., 1985—, Tele-Video Entertainment, 1985—; owner/mgr. Donald Investment Co., 1989—. Vice pres. Twin City Broadcast Skills Bank (scholarship program), St. Paul Arts and Sci. Inst.; pres. U. Minn. Heart Hosp.; mem. Gov.'s

Commn. Bicentennial; bd. dirs. Mpls. United Jewish Fund and Council; Mem. Mpls. Inst. Arts, Mpls., St. Paul chambers commerce, Minn. Orch. Assn., Citizens League, U. Minn. Alumni Assn. Elected Minn. Pioneer Broadcaster of Yr., 1992. Mem. Press Club (Mpls.), Advt. Standard Club (Mpls.), Hillcrest Country Club (St. Paul), Variety Club, Mission Hills Country Club (Rancho Mirage, Calif.), Oak Ridge Country Club (Mpls.), B'nai B'rith. Jewish (pres. temple). Home: 2221 Youngman Ave Saint Paul MN 55116-3055 Office: 7101 York Ave S Minneapolis MN 55435-4450

SWARTZ, DONALD PERCY, physician; b. Preston, Ont., Can., Sept. 12, 1921; s. Simon Wingham and Lydia (Ethell) S.; m. Norma Mae Woolner, June 24, 1944 (dec. May 1980); children: Ian Donald, Rhonda Swartz Peterson; m. Isabelle Liz Dales, Apr. 21, 1984. B.A., U. Western Ont., 1951, M.D. cum laude, 1951, M.S. cum laude, 1953. Intern Victoria Hosp., London, Ont., 1951-52; asst. resident Westminster Hosp., London, 1953-54; resident Johns Hopkins U., Balt., 1954-58; asst. prof. ob-gyn. U. Western Ont., London, 1958-62; prof. Columbia U., N.Y.C., 1962-72; dir. ob-gyn. Harlem Hosp.; prof. dept. ob-gyn. Albany (N.Y.) Med. Coll., 1972—, chmn., 1972-79, chief sect. gen. gynecology, 1982-88, head. div. gen. gynecology, 1988—, acting chmn., 1992; vis. prof. dept. Ob-Gyn. U. Rochester, N.Y., 1981. Assoc. editor: Advances in Planned Parenthood. Vice pres., pres. Assn. Planned Parenthood Physicians, 1972-74. Served with RCAF, 1942-45. NRC Can. fellow, 1952-53; Am. Cancer Soc. fellow, 1956-57; Markle scholar, 1958-63. Fellow Royal Coll. Surgeons Can., Am. Coll. Obstetricians and Gynecologists, Am. Gynecologic Soc., Am. Gyn-Ob Soc., Am. Fertility Soc., Royal Soc. Health, Soc. Gynecologic Surgeons. Home: 24 Devon Rd Delmar NY 12054-3534 Office: Albany Med Coll 47 New Scotland Ave Albany NY 12208-3479 *It has been a privilege and a challenge to participate in the forefront of the revolutionary changes in the health care of women during the past four decades. Acceptance, initiation and implementation of positive change have been guidelines for gratifying action.*

SWARTZ, JACK, association executive; b. Dodge City, Kans., Nov. 24, 1932; s. John Ralph and Fern (Cave) S.; m. Nadine Ann Langlois, Aug. 4, 1956; children: Dana, Shawn, Tim, Jay. A.A., Dodge City Community Coll., 1953; student St. Mary of Plains Coll., 1953-55, 58; B.A. in Econs., Washburn U., 1974. B.B.A., 1973. Vice pres. D.C Terminal Elevator Co., Dodge City, Kans., 1957-65; exec. v.p. Kans. Jaycees, Hutchinson, 1965-68, Kans. C. of C. and Industry, Topeka, 1968-82; pres. Nebr. C of C. and Industry, Lincoln, 1982—. Past chmn., bd. regents U.S. C. of C. Inst. U Colo. Served with U.S. Army, 1955-57. Named Outstanding Local Pres. in State, Kans. Jaycees, 1961, Outstanding Young Man of Yr., Dodge City Jaycees, 1961; Outstanding State Vice Pres., U.S. Jaycees, 1962, Outstanding Nat. Dir., 1963. Mem. Am. Soc. Assn. Execs. (cert.), Am. Chamber Commerce Execs. (bd. dirs., cert.), Nebr. Chamber Commerce Execs. (sec.-treas.), Nebr. Soc. Assn. Execs. (past pres.), Nebr. Fedn. Bus. Assns. (pres. 1986-88), Washburn U. Alum. (bd. dirs.). Republican. Roman Catholic. Lodge: Rotary. Home: 2744 Laurel St Lincoln NE 68502-5142 Office: Nebr C of C and Industry 1320 Lincoln Mall PO Box 95128 Lincoln NE 68509

SWARTZ, JON DAVID, psychologist, educator; b. Houston, Dec. 28, 1934; s. Orville Elmo and Nina June (Baker) S.; m. Carol Joseph Hampton, Oct. 20, 1966; children: Eric Jason McFarland, Sally Katherine Baker, Edward Joseph Bryson. BA, U. Tex., Austin, 1956, MA, 1961, PhD, 1969, postgrad. (fellow), 1973-74. Research and teaching asst. dept. psychology U. Tex., 1956-62, asst. prof. dept. ednl. psychology, 1969-72; assoc. prof. psychology, chmn. U. Tex.-Permian Basin, 1974-78, chmn. anthropology and sociology, 1975-78, field dir., 1962-65; asst. dir. Austin Longitudinal Research project, 1965-69, co-dir., 1969-74; research scientist Hogg Found. for Mental Health, 1972-74; prof. edn. and psychology Southwestern U., Georgetown, Tex., 1978-90, vis. prof. psychology, 1991; dir. testing and guidance Southwestern U., 1978-81, holder Brown vis. chair, 1978-82, assoc. dean for libraries and learning resources, 1981-90; coord., adminstrv. head Killeen office Cen. Counties Ctr. for MHMR Svcs., Temple, Tex., 1990-91; chief psychol. svcs. Temple, Tex., 1991—; lectr. Nat. U., Mexico, 1962. Author: (with W.H. Holtzman) Inkblot Perception and Personality, 1961, (with C.C. Cleland) Mental Retardation: Approaches to Institutional Change, 1969, Administrative Issues in Institutions for the Mentally Retarded, 1972, Exceptionalities Through the Lifespan: An Introduction, 1982, Multihandicapped Mentally Retarded, 1973, (with W.H. Holtzman, R. Diaz-Guerrero) Personality Development in Two Cultures, 1975; editor: (with C.C. Cleland, L.W. Talkington) Profoundly Mentally Retarded, 1976, (with R.K. Eyman, C.C. Cleland) Research with the Profoundly Retarded, 1978, Holtzman Inkblot Technique: An Annotated Bibliography (supplement), 1988, (with R.C. Reinehr, W.H. Holtzman) Holtzman Inkblot Technique: An Annotated Bibliography 1956-1982, 1983, SW U. Bibliographic Series, 1986-90, (with R.C. Reinehr) Handbook of One-Time Radio, 1993; editorial assoc.: Current Anthropology, 1971-77; assoc. editor: Am. Corrective Therapy Jour. 1971-81, Exceptional Children, 1982-84; mem. editorial bd.: Texas Psychologist, 1979-83 , Phi Kappa Phi Jour./Nat. Forum, 1976-80; editorial cons.: Mental Retardation, 1972-77; book rev. editor: Jour. Biol. Psychology, 1972-80; book rev. editor for English lang. publs.: Revista Interamericana de Psicologia, 1983-89; cons. editor Jour. Personality Assessment, 1981-90; contbr. over 400 articles to profl. jours. Mem. Mayor's Drug Abuse Panel, Odessa, Tex., 1975-78; chmn. adv. bd. Human Potentials Center, Permian Basin Community Centers for Mental Health and Mental Retardation, Odessa and Midland, Tex., 1975-78; bd. govs. Mood-Heritage Mus., 1984-90. U.S. Office Edn. fellow, 1964-66; recipient Franklin Gilliam prize Humanities Research Center U. Tex., 1965; Spencer Research award Nat. Acad. Edn., 1972; Faculty Fellowship award Southwestern U., 1981. Fellow AAAS, Am. Psychol. Soc., Soc. Personality Assessment; mem. Western Rsch. Conf. on Mental Retardation, Am. Acad. Mental Retardation, Southwestern Psychol. Assn., Bell County Psychol. Assn., Sigma Xi, Psi Chi, Mu Alpha Nu, Delta Tau Kappa, Phi Kappa Phi, Phi Delta Kappa. Office: Cen Counties Ctr for MHMR Svcs 304 S 22rd St Temple TX 76503 *All my life I have had teachers, in school and out, who challenged me to do more than I thought I was capable of doing. Any success I have achieved, I owe to them and their efforts in my behalf.*

SWARTZ, MALCOLM GILBERT, retail executive, restaurateur; b. N.Y.C., Nov. 4, 1931; s. Morris Baer and Ethel (Gutstein) S.; m. Marjorie Diane Rose, Nov. 27, 1955; children: Lindsay Brian, James Michael, Donna Carrie, Andrea Gail. Grad., Cnt. Inst. of Chartered Accts., 1955. Ptnr. William Eisenberg and Co., Chartered Accts., Toronto, Ont., Can., 1962-69; exec. v.p. Shoppers Drug Mart, Toronto, 1969—, also bd. dirs.; pres. Papa Peachies Ristorante, Toronto, 1984—. Author: Basic Finance, 1975, Advanced Finance, 1979, Asset Productivity, 1983, Cash Flow and Financial Planning, 1986. Mem. Inst. Chartered Accts. Ont. Club: Toronto Thoroughbred Racing (past pres.). Avocation: tennis. Office: Shoppers Drug Mart, 225 Yorkland Blvd, Willowdale, ON Canada M2J 4Y7

SWARTZ, MORTON NORMAN, medical educator; b. Boston, Nov. 11, 1923; s. Jacob H. and Janet (Heller) W.; m. Cesia Rosenberg, Sept. 18, 1956; children: Mark David, Caroline Joan. BA, Harvard Coll., 1945; MD, Harvard U., 1947; MD (hon.), U. Geneva, Switzerland, 1988. Diplomate Am. Bd. Internal Medicine (subsplty. exam. com. 1971-76, bd. govs. 1979-85). Med. intern and resident Mass. Gen. Hosp., Boston, 1947-50, chief resident in medicine, 1953-54; USPHS postdoctoral rsch. fellow Johns Hopkins U., McCollum-Pratt Inst. Enzymology, Balt., 1954-56; chief infectious disease unit Mass. Gen. Hosp., Boston, 1956-90, chief James Jackson Firm, dept. medicine, 1990—; assoc. prof. medicine Harvard Med. Sch., Boston, 1967-73, prof., 1973—; vis. assoc. prof. biochemistry, Stanford Med. Sch., Palo Alto, Calif., 1969-70. Author: (with others) Osteomyelitis, 1971; editor: Current Clinical Topics in Infectious Diseases, 1980—; assoc. editor New Eng. Jour. Medicine, 1981—; contbr. articles to profl. jours. 1st lt. U.S. Army, 1950-52. Sir MacFarlane Burnett lectr. Australasian Soc. Infectious Disease, 1981. Fellow ACP (master 1988, Disting. Tchr. award 1989); mem. Am. Soc. Biochemistry and Molecular Biology, Am. Soc. for Clin. Investigation, Assn. Am. Physicians, Infectious Diseases Soc. Am. (Bristol award 1984, Feldman award 1989), Inst. Medicine, Nat. Inst. Child Health and Devel. (bd. sci. counselors 1992—). Jewish. Avocations: biology, bird watching. Home: 54 Shaw Rd Chestnut Hill MA 02167-3122 Office: Mass Gen Hosp 32 Fruit St Boston MA 02114-2620

SWARTZ, RENEE BECKER, civic volunteer; b. Newark, N.J., Feb. 25, 1935; d. Sidney David and Adeline (Kleinberg) Becker; m. Harry Mason

Swartz, Mar. 8, 1931; children: Stephen, Addi-Lyn, Sidney. Student, Rutgers U., 1950-52, Bryn Mawr Coll., 1952-53; BA, Barnard Coll.-Columbia U., 1955. mem. planning com. N.J. White Ho. Conf. on Librs. and Info. Sci., 1975-79, mem. del. selection com., mem. programs com., 1978-79; chairperson del. White Ho. Conf., 1979; re-elected permanent N.J. rep. Nat. Commn. Follow-up Activities White Ho. Conf. 1991, chairperson nat. awards com., 1984-86, chairperson fundraising com., 1989-90; chmn. N.J. Del. White Ho. Conf. of Librs. and Info. Svcs., 1991—. Pres. Friends of Monmouth County Libr. Assn., 1964-68; founding mem. N.J. Citizens for Better Librs., 1982; chairperson bldg. com. Dorothy L. Spiwak Meml. Libr., Rumson, N.J., 1971-73, trustee, 1971—; active N.J. Libr. Devel. Com., 1973-84; chairperson, bd. trustees Grad. Sch. of Comm., Info. and Libr. Studies, Rutgers U., 1980—, chairperson, 1983—; gov. appointee N.J. State Libr. Adv. Coun., 1975, chairperson, 1986—, Monmouth County Libr. Commn., 1965—, chair, 1976—; past trustee Barnard Coll. Recipient Hanna G. Solomon award Greater Red Bank sect. Nat. Coun. Jewish Women, 1979, Pres. medal Barnard Coll.-Columbia U., 1984, Columbia U. medal, 1985, Woman or Achievement award Monmouth County Adv. Com., 1987; named Nat. Trustee of Yr. ALA, 1991. Mem. Nat. Citizens Com. for Pub. Libraries (steering com. 1980-84), Am. Library Trustee Assn. (pres. com. 1983, nat. intellectual freedom com. 1984—), N.J. Library Assn. (centennial com. 1986-89, chairperson N.J Ednl. Inst. com. 1987-88, N.J. Trustee of the Yr. 1980), N.J. Library Trustee Assn. (exec. com. 1976-81, regional rep. 1983-86), Assn. N.J. Library Commrs. (pres. 1973-75), Lotus Club N.Y., Ocean Club of N.J. Avocations: tennis, sailing, walking. Home: 136 Rumson Rd Rumson NJ 07760-1238

SWARTZ, STEPHEN ARTHUR, banker, lawyer; b. Boston, Oct. 7, 1941; s. Norman and Frances S.; m. Karen M. McLoughlin, Aug. 18, 1992; children: Marti Anne, Nanci Beth, Lori Ellen, Stephen Arthur, Jr. BA in Polit. Sci., U. Mass., 1963; LLB, Boston U., 1966; postgrad. in fin. and mgmt, Boston Coll., 1968-70. Bar: Mass. 1967, N.Y. 1971. Asst. counsel Fed. Res. Bank Boston., 1968-70, Irving Trust Co., N.Y.C., 1970-74; counsel, asst. sec. Charter N.Y. Corp., N.Y.C., 1974-77; v.p., asst. dir. investor communications Charter N.Y. Corp., 1977-79; v.p., dir. investor communications Irving Bank Corp., N.Y.C., 1979-86; v.p. investor relations Seamen's Corp., N.Y.C., 1986-88, sr. v.p., corp. sec., 1990; sr. v.p. investor rels. H.F. Ahmanson & Co., L.A., 1990—. Served to capt. AUS, 1966-68, Vietnam. Decorated Bronze Star (2), Army Commendation medal (2), Air medal (2); Vietnamese Honor medal 1st class. Mem. ABA, Mass. Bar Assn., N.Y. State Bar Assn., Nat. Investor Rels. Inst. (former bd. dirs., treas. L.A. chpt.), Bank Investor Rels. Assn. (founder, former pres., bd. dirs., dir.), Bedford Riding Lns. Assn. Home: 2084 Liliano Dr Sierre Madre CA 91024 Office: HF Ahmanson & Co 4900 Rivergrade Rd Baldwin Park CA 91706-1438

SWARTZ, THOMAS R., economist, educator; b. Phila., Aug. 31, 1937; s. Henry Jr. and Elizabeth (Thomas) S.; m. Jeanne Marie Jourdan, Aug. 12, 1961; children: Mary Butler, Karen Miller, Jennifer, Anne, Rebecca. BA, LaSalle U., 1960; MA, Ohio U., 1962; PhD, Ind. U., 1965. Asst. prof. U. Notre Dame, Ind., 1965-70, assoc. prof. dept. 1968-70, assoc. prof., 1970-78, acting dir. grad. studies, 1977-78, prof. econs., 1978—; dir. program econ. policy, 1982-85; resident dir. U. Notre Dame London Program, 1990-91; vis. prof. U. Notre Dame London Program 1982, 85; fiscal cons. Ind. Commn. State Tax, Indpls., 1965-68; also spl. tax. cons., 1971-81, City of South Bend, Ind., 1972-75. Co-editor: The Supply Side, 1983, Changing Face of Fiscal Federalism, 1990, Urban Finance Under Siege, 1993, Taking Sides, 7th edit., 1995; contbr. articles to profl. jours. Bd. dirs. Forever Learning Inst., South Bend, Ind., 1988-93; mem. steering com, Mayor's Housing Forum, South Bend, 1989—; chair Com. Svcs. Block Grant, South Bend, 1985-90, Econ. Devel. Task Force, South Bend, 1985; mem. steering com. The Northeast Neighborhood Planning Project, 1992—. Recipient Teaching award Kanzajian Found., 1974, Madden Teaching award, 1983, Sheedy Teaching award, 1992, Danforth Assoc. award Danforth Found., 1972-86; rsch. fellow Nat. Ctr. Urban Ethnic Affairs, 1979-85, fellow Urban Inst. for Ednl. and Comty. Initiative, 1993—. Democrat. Roman Catholic. Avocation: racquetball. Home: 402 Marquette Ave South Bend IN 46617-1157 Office: U Notre Dame Dept Econs 414 Decio Hall Notre Dame IN 46556-5644

SWARTZ, WILLIAM JOHN, transportation resources company executive/retired; b. Hutchinson, Kans., Nov. 6, 1934; s. George Glen and Helen Mae (Prather) S.; m. Dorothy Jean Parshall, June 5, 1956; children: John Christopher, Jeffrey Michael. BSME, Duke U., 1956; JD, George Washington U., 1961; MS in Mgmt. (Alfred P. Sloan fellow), MIT, 1967. With AT & SF Ry., 1961-78, 79—, asst. v.p. exec. dept., 1973-77, v.p. adminstrn., 1977-78, exec. v.p., 1979-83; exec. v.p. Santa Fe Industries, Chgo., 1978-79, pres., 1983-90; vice chmn. Santa Fe So. Pacific, 1983-90; pres. AT & SF Ry., 1983-90. Past bd. dirs. Chgo. Mus. Sci. and Industry; mem. Dean's Coun. Duke U. Sch. Engring. With USMC, 1956-59. Mem. Assn. Am. R.R. (past bd. dirs.). Republican. Methodist. Home: 233 E Walton St Chicago IL 60611-1526

SWARTZBAUGH, MARC L., lawyer; b. Urbana, Ohio, Jan. 3, 1937; s. Merrill L. and Lillian K. (Hill) S.; m. Marjory Anne Emhardt, Aug. 16, 1958; children: Marc Charles, Kathleen Marie, Laura Kay. BA magna cum laude, Wittenberg Coll., 1958; LLB magna cum laude, U. Pa., 1961. Bar: Ohio 1961, U.S. Dist. Ct. (no. dist.) Ohio 1962, U.S. Claims Ct. 1991, U.S. Ct. Appeals (6th cir.) 1970, U.S. Ct. Appeals (3d cir.) 1985, U.S. Ct. Appeals (Fed. cir.) 1995, U.S. Supreme Ct. 1973. Law clk. to judge U.S. Ct. Appeals (3d cir.), Phila., 1961-62; assoc. Jones, Day, Reavis & Pogue, Cleve., 1962-69, ptnr., 1970—. Note editor U. Pa. Law Rev., 1960-61. Co-chmn. Suburban Citizens for Open Housing, Shaker Heights, Ohio, 1966; v.p. Lomond Assn., Shaker Heights, 1965-68; trustee The Dance Ctr., Clevel, 1980-83; Ambassador People to People Internat., 1986; chmn. legal div. United Negro Coll. Fund Cleve. campaign, 1989-95. Mem. ABA (litigation sect.), Fed. Bar Assn., Ohio Bar Assn., Cleve. Bar Assn., Order of Coif, Beta Theta Pi. Democrat. Club: 13th St Racquet (Cleve.). Avocations: poetry, painting, music, skiing, squash, photography. Office: Jones Day Reavis & Pogue N Point 901 Lakeside Ave E Cleveland OH 44114-1190

SWARTZENDRUBER, DALE, soil physicist, educator; b. Parnell, Iowa, July 6, 1925; s. Urie and Norma (Kinsinger) S.; m. Kathleen Jeanette Yoder, June 26, 1949; children: Karl Grant, Myra Mae, John Keith, David Mark. BS, Iowa State U., 1950, MS, 1952, PhD, 1954. Instr. sc. Goshen (Ind.) Coll., 1953-54; asst. soil scientist U. Calif., Los Angeles, 1955-56; assoc. prof. soil physics Purdue U., West Lafayette, Ind., 1956-63; prof. Purdue U., 1963-77; prof. soil physics U. Nebr., Lincoln, 1977—; vis. prof. Iowa State U., 1959, Ga. Inst. Tech., 1968, Hebrew U. Jerusalem at Rehovot, 1971, Griffith U., Brisbane, Australia, 1989-90, Centre for Environ. Mechanics, CSIRO, Canberra, Australia, 1990; vis. scholar Cambridge (Eng.) U., 1971. Contbr. articles on soil physics to profl. jours.; assoc. editor: Soil Sci. Soc. Am. Proc., 1965-70; mem. editorial bd. Geoderma (Amsterdam), 1975-93; cons. editor: Soil Sci., 1976—. Fellow Soil Sci. Soc. Am. (Soil Sci. award 1975, Editors' citation for excellence in manuscript rev. 1993), Am. Soc. Agronomy; mem. AAAS, Am. Geophys. Union, Internat. Soc. Soil Sci., Am. Sci. Affiliation, Sigma Xi. Mennonite. Achievements include research in water infiltration into soil, validity of Darcy's equation for water flow in soils, measurement of water and solid content in soils, mathematical solutions to problems of water flow in saturated and unsaturated soils. Home: 1400 N 37th St Lincoln NE 68503-2016 Office: U Nebr E Campus Dept Agronomy 133 Keim Hall Lincoln NE 68583 *Along with complete dedication and honesty in spirit and action, bring to each task a new thought, or ask the implications, should the customary or conventional wisdom not hold.*

SWARTZLANDER, EARL EUGENE, JR., engineering educator, former electronics company executive; b. San Antonio, Feb. 1, 1945; s. Earl Eugene and Jane (Nicholas) S.; m. Joan Vickery, June 9, 1968. BSEE, Purdue U., 1967; MSEE, U. Colo., 1969; PhD, U. So. Calif., 1972. Registered profl. engr., Ala., Calif., Colo., Tex. Devel. engr. Ball Bros. Rsch. Corp., Boulder, Colo., 1967-69; Hughes fellow, mem. tech. staff Hughes Aircraft Co., Culver City, Calif., 1969-73; mem. rsch. staff Tech. Vu. Co., Santa Monica, Calif., 1973-74; chief engr. Geophys. Systems Corp., Pasadena, Calif., 1974-75, staff engr. to sr. staff engr., 1975-79, project mgr., 1979-84, lab. mgr., 1985-87; dir. ind. R&D TRW Inc., Redondo Beach, Calif., 1987-90; Schlumberger Centennial prof. engring. dept. elec. and computer engring. U. Tex., Austin, 1990—; gen. chmn. Internat. Conf. Wafer Scale Integration, 1989, 11th

Internat. Symposium on Computer Arithmetic, 1992; gen. chmn. Internat. Conf. Application Specific Array Processors, 1990, co-gen. chmn., 1994; chmn. 3d Internat. Conf. Parallel and Distributed Sys., Taiwan, 1993. Author: VLSI Signal Processing Systems, 1986; editor: Computer Design Development, 1976, Systolic Signal Processing Systems, 1987, Wafer Scale Integration, 1989, Computer Arithmetic Vol. 1 and 2, 1990; editor-in-chief Jour. of VLSI Signal Processing, 1989-95, IEEE Transactions on Signal Processing, 1995—, IEEE Transactions on Computers, 1991-94, editor 1982-86, IEEE Transactions on Parallel and Distributed Systems, 1989-90; Hardware Area Editor ACM Computing Reviews, 1985—; assoc. editor: IEEE Jour. Solid-State Circuits, 1984-88; contbr. over 100 articles to profl. jours. and tech. conf. proc. Bd. dirs. Casiano Estates Homeowners Assn., Bel Air, Calif., 1976-78, pres. 1978-80; bd. dirs Benedict Hills Estates Homeowners Assn., Beverly Hills, Calif., 1984—, pres. 1990—. Recipient Disting. Engring. Alumnus award Purdue U., 1989, Outstanding Elec. Engr. award Purdue U., 1992,; knight Imperial Russian Order St. John of Jerusalem, Knights of Malta, 1993. Fellow IEEE; mem. IEEE Computer Soc. (bd. govs. 1987-91), IEEE Signal Proc. Soc. (bd. govs. 1992-94), IEEE Solid-State Cirs. Coun. (sec. 1992-93, treas. 1994—), Eta Kappa Nu, Sigma Tau, Omicron Delta Kappa. Office: U Tex Austin Dept Elec Computer Engring Austin TX 78712

SWARZ, SAHL, sculptor; b. N.Y.C., May 4, 1912; s. Samuel and Ida (Fass) S.; m. Naoco Kumasaka, May 1978. Student, Clay Club, N.Y.C., 1928-34, Art Students League, N.Y.C., 1930-31. Asso. Dir. Clay Club (and successor, Sculpture Center), 1938-54; creative sculpture in Italy, 1951-63; residence Am. Acad. in, Rome, 1955-57; lectr. sculpture Columbia U., N.Y.C., 1966-68, asst. prof., 1969-78; instr. Pratt Inst., Bklyn., 1964; instr. New Sch. for Social Rsch., 1965, 66; vis. lectr. art U. Wis., 1966; trustee Mus. Contemporary Sculpture, Tokyo. Author, illustrator: Blueprint for the Future of American Sculpture, 1943, also monograph.; one man exhbns. Sculpture Ctr., 1954, 57, 60, 62, 66, 71, 74, 78, Art Alliance, Phila., 1958, Fairweather-Hardin Gallery, Chgo., 1963, Brandeis U., Waltham, Mass., 1964, (retrospective exhbn.) Fair Lawn (N.J.) Pub. Library, 1977, Saikaya Gallery, Fujisawa, Japan, 1983, Mus. Contemporary Sculpture, Tokyo, 1985, Shonan Gallery, Fujisawa, Japan, 1985, 90, 93, (retrospective exhbn.) Toni de Rossi Gallery, Verona, Italy, 1983, 87, 91, Takashimaya Gallery, Yokohama, Japan, 1984, Atagoyama Gallery, Tokyo, 1988, 91, 94, 1st exhibition of painting Toni de Rossi Gallery, Verona, Italy, 1992, Move Gallery Chigasaki, Japan, 1993; group shows include Fairmont Park Internat., Phila., 1948, Whitney Mus. Am. Art, 1948, 58, 60, 62, 64, Pa. Acad., 1948, 52, 54, 57, 60, 62, 66, Bklyn Mus., 1935, Detroit Inst. Fine Arts, 1957, San Francisco Mus., 1955, U. Ill., 1960, 62, others; represented in permanent collections Norfolk (Va.) Mus., Whitney Mus. Am. Art, Ball State Tchrs. Coll., Williams Coll. Mus., Ford Found., Mpls. Inst. Fine Arts, Va. Mus. Fine Arts, Richmond, Newark Mus., N.J. State Mus. at Trenton, Vatican Mus. Collection Modern Religious Art, Rose Art Mus., Brandeis U., Stamford (Conn.) Mus., Columbia U., others; bronze group The Guardian at Brookgreen (S.C.), Gardens Mus.; terra cotta wall sculpture, Linden, (N.J.), Post Office, sculptural designs, Fed. Courthouse, Statesville, N.C.; equestrian monument Gen. Bidwell, Buffalo; fountain commn., Spruce Run State Park, N.J.; mall sculpture, Pittsfield, Mass.; monument to Demeter in stainless steel, Fujisawa, Japan; subject of biography: Fifty Years of Sculpture by Sahl Swarz. Chmn. sculpture panel N.J. Coun. on Arts. With AUS, 1941-45. Grantee Am. Acad. Arts and Letters, 1955; Guggenheim fellow, 1955, 58. Address: Kumasaka-Swarz, 11-9 2 Chome Ishigami, Kugenuma, Fujisawa, Kanagawa 251, Japan *The essence of creativity is in the searching after the form. Search leads to revelation, understanding, knowledge. Realization of one's ignorance is the first step to the attainment of wisdom. A wise man makes a work of art out of life itself.*

SWATEK, FRANK EDWARD, microbiology educator; b. Oklahoma City, June 4, 1929; s. Clarence Michael and Bessie (Doubek) S.; m. Mary Frances Over, Jan. 28, 1951; children: Frank Edward, Lorraine Beth Butcher, Martha Lynn Bradshaw, Susan Ann Denny, Cheryl Lee. B.S. in Zoology, San Diego State Coll., 1951; M.A. in Microbiology, UCLA, 1955, Ph.D., 1956. Mem. faculty Calif. State U. at Long Beach, 1956-92, prof. microbiology, 1962-92, chmn. dept., 1960-82; cons. to industry, 1953—; cons. dept. dermatology Long Beach VA Hosp., 1956—; lectr. postgrad. medicine U. So. Calif., 1958—; adj. prof. clin. med. U. Calif., Irvine, 1980—; mem. fuel sect. Coordinating Research Council, 1961—. Author: Textbook of Microbiology, 1967, Laboratory Manual and Workbook for General Microbiology, 1969; also articles. Fellow Royal Soc. Health, Am. Acad. Microbiology; mem. Am. Soc. Microbiology (chmn. bd. edn. and tng. 1980-85, Carski Found. Disting. Teaching award 1974), Internat. Platform Assn., Sigma Xi, Lambda Xi Alpha, Phi Kappa Phi. Club: Long Beach Aquatic (pres. 1963-65). Research on med. mycology. Home: 812 Stevely Ave Long Beach CA 90815-5022

SWATSKY, BEN, church administrator. Exec. dir. Evangelical Free Church Mission, Minneapolis, Minn. Office: The Evang Free Ch Am 901 E 78th St Minneapolis MN 55420-1334

SWATT, STEPHEN BENTON, communications executive, consultant; b. L.A., June 26, 1944; s. Maurice I. and Lucille E. (Sternberger) S.; m. Susan Ruth Edelstein, Sept. 7, 1968; 1 child, Jeffrey Michael. BSBA, U. Calif., 1966, M in Journalism, 1967. Writer San Francisco Examiner, 1967; reporter United Press Internat., L.A., 1968-69; producer news Sta. KCRA-TV, Sacramento, Calif., 1969-70, reporter news, 1970-79, chief polit. and capitol corres., 1979-92; exec. v.p. Nelson-Lucas Communications, Sacramento, 1992—; guest lectr. Calif. State U., Sacramento. Contbr. articles to profl. jours. With USCG, 1966. Recipient No. Calif. Emmy NATAS, 1976-77, Pub. Svc. award Calif. State Bar, 1977, Exceptional Achievement Coun. advancement and Support of Edn., 1976, Nat. Health Journalism award Am. Chiropractic Assn., 1978. Mem. Soc. Profl. Journalists (8 awards), Capitol Corres. Assn., U. Calif. Alumni Assn., Sacramento Press Club. Avocations: hiking, jogging, fishing. Office: Nelson-Lucas Communications 1029 J St # 400 Sacramento CA 95814

SWAYZE, PATRICK, actor, dancer; b. Houston, Aug. 18, 1954; s. Patsy Swayze. Student, Harkness Sch., Joffrey Ballet Sch. Dancer (Broadway) Goodtime Charley, Grease; film appearances include (debut) Skatetown, U.S.A., 1979, The Outsiders, 1983, Uncommon Valor, 1983, Red Dawn, 1984, Grandview U.S.A., 1984, Youngblood, 1986, Dirty Dancing, 1987, Steel Dawn, 1987, Tiger Warsaw, 1988, Road House, 1989, Next of Kin, 1989, Ghost, 1989, Point Break, 1991, City of Joy, 1992, Father Hood, 1993, Tall Tale, 1994, To Wong Foo, Thanks for Everything, Julie Newmar, 1995, Three Wishes, 1995. Recipient Golden Apple award. Office: care Annett Wolf Inc 1033 Gayley Ave Ste 208 Los Angeles CA 90024-3417

SWAZEY, JUDITH POUND, institute president, sociomedical science educator; b. Bronxville, N.Y., Apr. 21, 1939; d. Robert Earl and Louise Titus (Hanson) Pound; m. Peter Woodman Swazey, Nov. 28, 1964; children: Elizabeth, Peter. AB, Wellesley Coll., 1961; PhD, Harvard U., 1966. Rsch. assoc. Harvard U., 1966-71, 1969-71, rsch. fellow, 1971-72; cons. com. brain scis. NRC, 1971-73; staff scientist neurosci. rsch. program MIT, Cambridge, 1973-74; assoc. prof. dept. socio-med. scis. and community medicine Boston U., 1974-77, prof., 1977-80, adj. prof. Schs. Medicine and Pub. Health, 1980—; exec. dir. Medicine in the Pub. Interest, Inc., Boston and Washington, 1979-82, 89-93; pres. Coll. of the Atlantic, Bar Harbor, Maine, 1982-84, Acadia Inst., Bar Harbor, 1984—; mem. Army Sci. Bd., 1987-92. Author: Reflexes and Motor Integration, the Development of Sherrington's Integrative Action Concept, 1969, (with others) Human Aspects of Biomedical Innovation, 1971, (with R.C. Fox) The Courage to Fail, a Social View of Organ Transplants and Hemodialysis, 1975, rev. edit., 1978 (hon. mention Am. Med. Writers Assn., C. Wright Mills award Am. Sociol. Assn.), Chlorpromazine in Psychiatry, a Study of Therapeutic Innovation, 1974, (with K. Reeds) Today's Medicine, Tomorrow's Science, Essays on Paths of Discovery in the Biomedical Sciences, 1978; editor: (with C. Wong) Dilemmas of Dying, Policies and Procedures for Decisions Not to Treat, 1981, (with F. Worden and G. Adelman) The Neurosciences: Paths of Discovery, 1975, (with R.C. Fox) Spare Parts, Organ Replacement in American Society, 1992; assoc. editor IRB: A Jour. of Human Subjects Rsch., 1979—; contbr. articles to profl. jours. Mem. Maine Dept. Human Svcs. Bioethics Adv. Com. (chair 1991-94); bd. dirs. Maine Bioethics Network, 1994—. Wellesley Coll. scholar, 1961; Wellesley Coll. Alumnae fellow Harvard U.,

1966, NIH predoctoral fellow, 1966, Radcliffe Coll. Coll. grad. fellow, 1966. Mem. AAAS (sci. freedom and responsibility com. 1986-89), Inst. Medicine NAS (mem. health scis. policy bd. 1986-89), Grad. Record Exam. (bd. dirs. 1987-91), Sherrington Soc., Phi Beta Kappa, Sigma Xi. Office: Acadia Inst Bar Harbor ME 04609

SWEARER, DONALD KEENEY, Asian religions educator, writer; b. Wichita, Kans., Aug. 2, 1934; s. Edward Mays and Eloise Catherine (Keeney) S.; m. Nancy Chester; children: Susan Marie, Stephen Edward. AB cum laude, Princeton U., 1956, MA, 1965, PhD, 1967; BD, Yale U., 1962, STM, 1963. Instr. English dept. Bangkok Christian Coll., 1957-60; adminstrv. asst. Edward W. Hazen Found., New Haven, 1961-63; instr., then asst. prof. Oberlin (Ohio) Coll., 1965-70; assoc. prof. Swarthmore (Pa.) Coll., 1970-75, prof. Asian religions, 1975—, Eugene M. Lang Rsch. prof., 1987-92, Charles and Harriet Cox McDowell prof., 1993—, chair dept. religion, 1986-91; adj. prof. U. Pa., Phila., 1979—, Temple U., Phila., 1991—; film cons. ABC, 1972, WGBH, 1991—; lectr. Smithsonian Instn., 1982—, Asia Soc. N.Y., 1982—. Author: Buddhism in Transition, 1970, Toward the Truth, 1971, Secrets of the Lotus, 1971, Wat Haripunjaya, 1976, Dialogue. The Key to Understanding Other Religions, 1977, Buddhism and Society in Southeast Asia, 1981; co-author: For the Sake of the World. The Spirit of Buddhist and Christian Monasticism, 1989; co-editor: Ethics, Wealth and Salvation. A Study in Buddhist Social Ethics, 1989, Me-and-Mine. Selected Essays of Bhikkhu Buddhadasa, 1989, The Buddhist World of Southeast Asia, 1995; mem. editorial bd. Jour. Religious Ethics, 1978—, Jour. Ecumenical Studies, 1983—; book rev. editor S.E. Asia Religious Studies Rev., 1985—; contbr. articles various pubs. Chair adult edn. Swarthmore Presbyn. Ch., 1985-87, 92-93. Kent fellow, 1964-65, Asian religious study fellow Soc. Religion in Higher Edn., Sri Lanka, Thailand, Japan, 1967-68, NEH sr. fellow Thailand, 1972-83, Rockefeller Found. humanities fellow, Thailand, 1985-86, Guggenheim fellow, 1994; sr. rsch. scholar Fulbright Found., 1989-90; sr. rsch. scholar Fulbright Found., 1993-94; NEH Transl. grantee, 1990-91. Mem. AAUP, Assn. Asian Studies (bd. dirs. 1977-80), Am. Acad. Religion, Soc. mid-Atlantic region 1971-72), Am. Soc. Study of Religion, Soc. Buddhist-Christian Studies, Phi Beta Kappa. Democrat. Home: 109 Columbia Ave Swarthmore PA 19081-1615 Office: Swarthmore Coll Dept Religion 500 College Ave Swarthmore PA 19081-1390

SWEARINGEN, DAVID CLARKE, general practice physician, musician; b. Shreveport, La., Apr. 23, 1942; s. David C. and Alverne (Walker) S.; m. Marion Joan Adams; children: David, Joy. BS, Centenary Coll., 1963; MD, La. State U., 1967. Intern Confederate Meml. Med. Ctr., Shreveport, 1967-68, resident in ophthalmology, 1968-71; staff ophthalmologist U.S. Naval Hosp., Memphis, 1971-73; pvt. practice in ophthalmology Shreveport, 1973-78; jr. officer of deck USS Halsey CG23, 1979; comdr. med. corps, head dept. ophthalmology, chmn. utilization rev. com. ophthalmology, family practice resident instr. opthalmology U.S. Naval Hosp., Jacksonville, Fla., 1981-84; med. dir. Bio Blood Components, Shreveport, 1985-88; dir. phys. health support svcs. Ctrl. La. State Hosp., Pineville, La., 1991—, exec. hosp. and med. exec. com., chmn. infection control and pharmacy, therapeutics com.; chmn. infection control com., pharmacy and therapeutics com.; pres. Shreveport Eye and Ear Soc., 1973-74; med. cons. Cenla Chem. Dependency Coun., Pineville, 1989—; mem. Work Tng. Facility, Pineville, 1989—. Prin. bassoonist Cenla Symphonic Band, Pineville, 1988—; mem. Jacksonville Fla. Concert Choral, 1978-81; vestry mem. St. Michaels Ch., Pineville; active Am. Mus. Natural History Assocs. Mem. Internat. Platform Assn., So. Med. Assn., Nat. Parks and Conservation Assn., N.Y. Acad. Scis., La. Wildlife Fedn., Wilderness Soc., Nature Conservancy, Smithsonian Assocs., Cousteau Soc., Soc. Hist. Preservation, Environ. Def. Fund, Planetary Soc., Nat. Audubon Soc., Am. Legion, Alpha Epsilon Delta, Gamma Beta Gamma, Nu Sigma Nu. Republican. Episcopalian. Avocations: organ and bassoon music, collectibles, breeding exotic birds, shipmodel building. Home: 10 Azalea Rd Pineville LA 71360-8004 Office: Ctrl La State Hosp 242 W Shamrock Ave Pineville LA 71360-6439

SWEARINGEN, HAROLD LYNDON, oil company executive; b. Independence, Kans., Sept. 17, 1937; s. Lynn and Dorothy Grace (Swalley) S.; m. Charlene Faye Meyer, Oct. 17, 1959; children: Renee (Mrs. Michael Readinger), Lisa (Mrs. Dick Drumeller), Shari (Mrs. Dustin Garrett), Kurtis. AA, Independence Jr. Coll., 1957; BSEE, Kans. State U., 1960. Lic. gen. radio telephone operator, FCC. Microwave technician Sinclair Pipe Line Co., Indpendence, 1960-61, sr. telecomm. engr., 1961-67; admisntr. telecomm. ops. Sinclair Oil Corp., N.Y.C., 1967-69; sr. telcomm. system design engr. Trans Alaska Pipe Line Co., Houston, 1969-72; project mgr. telecomm. Atlantic Richfield Co., Tulsa, 1972-75; mgr. telecomm. ops. Arco Pipe Line Co., Indpendence, 1975-89, mgr. telecomm., 1989-92; ret., 1992; bd. dirs. First Fed. Savs. & Loan, Indpendence. Sch. bd. mem. Unified Sch. Dist. # 446, Indpendence, 1991-93. Sgt. U.S. Army, 1955-63. Mem. IEEE. Republican. Lutheran. Home: Rt 2 Box 240 Independence KS 67301

SWEDBACK, JAMES M., insurance company executive; b. 1935. With Pioneer Mut. Life Ins. Co., Fargo, N.D., 1962—, now pres., chief exec. officer, 1980—. Office: Pioneer Mut Life Ins Co 203 10th St N Fargo ND 58102-4645

SWEDBERG, ROBERT MITCHELL, opera company director; b. Glendale, Calif., Feb. 7, 1950; s. William Miller and Marion (Mitchell) S.; m. Melissa Ellen Libby, Aug. 4, 1954; children: Olivia Lauren, Erik Andrew. BA, BM, Calif. State U., Northridge, 1975. Dir. edn. and spl. projects, production stage mgr. Seattle Opera, 1978-82; mgr., artistic dir. N.C. Operas (now called Opera Carolina), Charlotte, 1982-87; gen. dir. Syracuse (N.Y.) Opera, 1987-90; dir. opera program Syracuse U., 1989-90; gen. dir. Orlando (Fla.) Opera, 1990—; stage dir. Anchorage Opera, 1979-81, San Francisco Opera, 1982, Greater Buffalo Opera, 1988; judge auditions Met. Opera, 1986—; cons. Nat. Endowment for Arts, 1991—. Host: Opera Hour Sta. WMFE, Orlando. Bd. dirs. arts svcs. coun. World Cup Spl. Events Com., Italian Cultural Soc., Downtown Orlando Partnership; mem. Leadership Orlando, 1995. Recipient Tiffany award Civic Morning Mus., 1989, Jaycees award, 1990. Avocations: camping, fishing. Home: 9437 Lake Douglas Pl Orlando FL 32817-2603 Office: Orlando Opera Co 1111 N Orange Ave Orlando FL 32804-6407

SWEEDEN, THOMAS RICHARD, hospital administrator; b. Abilene, Tex., June 16, 1947; married; BA, U. Houston, 1972; MA, Southwest Tex. State U., 1978. Asst. dir. mgmt. unit U. Tex. Med. Branch, Galveston, 1972-75; dir. unit mgmt. Scott and White Meml. Hosp., Temple, Tex., 1976-81, asst. administr. support svcs., 1981-86, administrat., 1988—; interim administr. Coryell Meml. Hosp., Gatesville, Tex., 1986-88. Office: Scott & White Meml Hosp 2401 S 31st St Temple TX 76508*

SWEEDLER, BARRY MARTIN, federal agency administrator; b. Bklyn., Mar. 11, 1937; s. Louis and Sadie (Bloch) S.; m. Kathryn Grace Stewart, June 26, 1988; children by previous marriage: Ian, Elizabeth. BME, CCNY, 1960; MBA, Baruch Sch., CUNY, 1966. Registered profl. engr., N.Y. Asst. and jr. engr. N.Y. State Pub. Svc. Commn., N.Y.C., 1960-66, sr. gas engr., 1966-69; chief pipeline safety div. Nat. Transp. Safety Bd., Washington, 1969-74, dep. dir. Bur. Surface Transp. Safety, 1974-76, dep. dir., acting dir. Bur. Plans and Programs, 1976-79, dep. dir. Bur. Tech., 1979-82, dir. Bur. Safety Programs, 1982-90; dir. Office of Safety Recommendations Nat. Transp. Safety Bd., 1990—; guest lectr. Inst. Gas Tech., 1973, U. Md., 1974, U. Calif., San Diego, 1986, 88-89, U. N.Mex., 1987, U. Calgary, 1988; participant Internat. Workshop on High Alcohol Consumers and Traffic, Paris, 1988; presented policy and tech. papers on alcohol and drug abuse in transp. at numerous internat. symposiums and congresses including 34th Internat. Congress on Alcoholism and Drug Dependencies, Calgary, Alta., Can., 1985, 10th Internat. Conf. on Alcohol, Drugs & Traffic Safety, Amsterdam, The Netherlands, 1986, and Internat. Symposium on Young Drivers Alcohol and Drug Impairment, Amsterdam, 1986; co-editor proc., chmn. alcohol, drugs and traffic safety program 35th Internat. Congress on Alcoholism and Drug Dependencies, Oslo, Norway, 1988, and 12th Internat. Conf. on Alcohol, Drugs and Traffic Safety, Cologne, 1992; 36th Internat. Inst. on Prevention and Treatment of Alcoholism, Stockholm, 1991; 12th World Congress of Internat. U.s. Med. Accident and Traffic Medicine, 1992. Author (with others) Gas Engineers Handbook, 1985; contbr. numerous articles on transp. safety to jours.; mem. editorial bd. Jour. Traffic Medicine,

1989—; numerous TV and print media interviews. Bd. dirs. Great Falls (Va.) Citizens Assn., 1980-85, Tysons Manor Home Owners Assn., Vienna, Va., 1975-77; mem. Fairfax County (Va.) oversight com. on drinking and driving, 1984—, chmn., 1986-88. Recipient Presdl. Rank of Meritorious Exec., 1987. Mem. ASME, Transp. Rsch. Bd. of NAS (chmn. com. on alcohol, other drugs and transp. 1991—, mem. com. on transp. of hazardous materials 1972-78, com. on highway/r.r. grade crossing safety 1977-86, com. on utilities 1972-79), Internat. Coun. on Alcohol and Addictions (vice chmn. sect. on traffic safety 1988—), Internat. Coun. Alcohol, Drugs and Traffic Safety (sec. 1992—, co-editor coun. newsletter ICADTS Reporter 1990—), Am. Acad. Forensic Scis. (adv. mem. drugs and driving com. 1988—), Operation Lifesaver (mem. program devel. coun. 1987—), Nat. Safety Coun. (mem. motor vehicle occupant protection com. 1983—), Am. Pub. Works Assn. (mem. exec. com. utility location and coordination coun. 1980-87, hon. life mem.),Internat. Transp. Safety Assn. (editor assn. newsletter ITSA Report 1994—). Jewish. Avocations: tennis, hiking, bicycling. Office: Nat Transp Safety Bd Office of Safety Recommendations 490 Lenfant Plz SW SW Washington DC 20594-0001

SWEENEY, ARTHUR HAMILTON, JR., metal manufacturing executive, retired army officer; b. Charleston, W.Va., Nov. 9, 1920; s. Arthur Hamilton and Neva Pauline (Davies) S.; m. Veronica Frances Donovan, Dec. 27, 1952. S.B., MIT, 1942; M.B.A., Harvard, 1947. Commd. officer U.S. Army, advanced through grades to maj. gen.; comdg. officer U.S. Army Springfield (Mass.) Armory, 1965-67, U.S. Army Watervliet (N.Y.) Arsenal, 1967-68; dep. comdg. gen. U.S. Army Weapons Command, Rock Island, Ill., 1968-70; comdg. gen. Quinhon Support Command, Vietnam, 1970, DaNang Support Command, Vietnam, 1970-72, White Sands Missile Range, N.Mex., 1972-74, U.S. Army Materiel Mgmt. Agy., Europe, 1974-76; dep. chief of staff for logistics U.S. Army Forces Command, 1976-78; ret., 1978; corporate dir., v.p. corp. devel. Reynolds Metals Internat., Richmond, Va., 1978-91; exec. cons. Bd. of Def. Enterprise Fund, 1994. Decorated D.S.M. with oak leaf cluster, Legion of Merit with oak leaf cluster, Joint Services Commendation medal, Army Commendation medal. Home: 2956 Hathaway Rd Richmond VA 23225-1728

SWEENEY, ASHER WILLIAM, state supreme court justice; b. Canfield, Ohio, Dec. 11, 1920; s. Walter William and Jessie Joan (Kidd) S.; m. Bertha M. Englert, May 21, 1945; children: Randall W., Ronald R., Garland A., Karen M. Student, Youngstown U., 1939-42; LL.B., Duke U., 1948. Bar: Ohio 1949. Practiced law Youngstown, Ohio, 1949-51; judge adv. gen. Dept. Def., Washington, 1951-65; chief Fed. Contracting Agy., Cin., 1965-68; corp. law, 1968-77; justice Ohio Supreme Ct., Columbus, 1977—. Democratic candidate for Sec. of State Ohio, 1958. Served with U.S. Army, 1942-46; col. Res. 1951-68. Decorated Legion of Merit, Bronze Star; named to Army Hall of Fame Ft. Benning, Ga., 1981. Mem. Ohio Bar Assn., Phi Delta Phi. Democrat. Home: 6690 Drake Rd Cincinnati OH 45243-2706 Office: Ohio Supreme Ct 30 E Broad St Fl 3D Columbus OH 43266

SWEENEY, CLAYTON ANTHONY, lawyer, business executive; b. Pitts., Oct. 20, 1931; s. Denis Regis and Grace Frances (Roche) S.; m. Sally Dimond, Oct. 4, 1958; children:Sharon, Lorrie, Maureen, Clayton Anthony, Tara, Megan. B.S., Duquesne U., 1957, LL.B., 1962. Bar: Pa. 1962, U.S. Supreme Ct. 1968. Supr. transp. claims H.J. Heinz Co., Pitts., 1955-57; mgr. market research Murray Corp. Am., Pitts., 1957-62; ptnr. Buchanan, Ingersoll, Rodewald, Kyle and Buerger, Pitts., 1962-78; sr. v.p. Allegheny Ludlum Industries, Inc., Pitts., 1978-81; exec. v.p., chief adminstrv. officer Allegheny Internat., Inc., Pitts., 1981-84, vice chmn., 1984-85; ptnr., mng. dir. Dickie, McCamey & Chilcote, Pitts., 1986—, also bd. dirs.; bd. dirs. Wilkinson Sword Group Ltd., U.K., Landmark Savs. and Loan Assn., Liquid Air N.Am., Halbouty Energy Co., Koppers Holding Corp., Koppers Industries, Inc.; co-founder, chmn. Schaefer Mfg., Inc., Schaefer Marine, Inc., Schaefer Equipment, Inc.; adj. prof. Duquesne U. Sch. Law; lectr. Pa. Bar Inst. Bd. dirs. Met. Pitts. Pub. Broadcasting, Inc., Diocesan Sch. Bd., Roman Cath. Diocese Pitts., Toner Inst., Christian Assocs. of Southwestern Pa., Wesley Inst., Inc., Jr. Achievement S.W. Pa., YMCA Western Pa.; chmn. Seton Hill Coll.; mem. St. Thomas More Sch. Bd., Bethel Park, Pa.; chmn. St. Francis Med. Ctr.; St. Francis Health System; chmn. bd. DePaul Inst. With U.S. Army, 1953-55. Named one of 100 Most Disting. Living Alumni Duquesne U. Century Club, 1978. Mem. Acad. Trial Lawyers Allegheny County, ABA, Pa. Bar Assn., St. Thomas More Soc. Home: 4972 Highland Ave Bethel Park PA 15102-2054 Office: Dickie McCamey & Chilcote Ste 400 2 PPG Pl Pittsburgh PA 15222-5402

SWEENEY, DANIEL THOMAS, cable television company executive; b. N.Y.C., Sept. 25, 1929; s. Daniel Thomas and Rose Marie (Delorenzo) S.; m. Anita Geraldine Madeo, Feb. 14, 1953; children: John, William, Robert, Ellen, Daniel, David. BS, N.Y. State Maritime Coll., 1952; LLB, Fordham U., 1957; LLM, NYU, 1962. Bar: N.Y. Assoc. Kirlin, Campbell and Keating, N.Y.C., 1957-62; dep. county atty. Nassau County, Garden City, N.Y., 1962-65, undersheriff, 1965-66, dep. county exec., 1966-69; chmn., chief exec. officer Mitchel Field Devel. Corp., Garden City, 1969-71; pres. Sweeney/Edman Enterprises Inc., Hempstead, N.Y., 1971-72; exec. v.p., chief oper. officer HBO, N.Y.C., 1972-73; dir. Cablevision Systems Corp., Woodbury, N.Y., 1973—; pres. Channel 21, Sta. WLIW-TV, Garden City, N.Y., 1970-74. Chmn. L.I. State Pk. and Recreation Com., Babylon, N.Y., 1976-83, Jones Beach State Pkwy. Authority, Babylon, N.Y., 1976-79. Lt. comdr. USN, 1952-54, Korea. Democrat. Roman Catholic. Home: 94 Glenlawn Ave Sea Cliff NY 11579-2038 Office: Cablevision Systems Corp 1 Media Crossways Woodbury NY 11797-2062

SWEENEY, DAVID BRIAN, lawyer; b. Seattle, June 23, 1941; s. Hubert Lee and Ann Louise (Harmon) S.; m. Janice Kay Goins, June 18, 1983; children: Stuart, Jennifer, Ann, Katharine. BA magna cum laude, Yale U., 1963; LL.B., Harvard U., 1967. Bar: Wash. 1968, U.S. Dist. Ct. (we. dist.) Wash., 1968, U.S. Ct. Appeals (9th cir.) 1968. Assoc. Roberts, Shefelman, Lawrence, Gay and Moch, Seattle, 1968-75; ptnr. Roberts, Shefelman, Lawrence, Gay & Moch, later Roberts & Shefelman, then Foster, Pepper and Shefelman, 1976—. Mem. Seattle-King County Bar Assn., Wash. State Bar Assn., ABA, Estate Planning Council of Seattle. Republican. Presbyterian. Clubs: College, Harbor, Columbia Tower (Seattle). Home: 2343 32nd Ave S Seattle WA 98144-5533 Office: Foster Pepper & Shefelman 1111 3rd Ave Fl 34 Seattle WA 98101-3207

SWEENEY, FRANCIS E., state supreme court justice; b. Jan. 26, 1934; married; 4 children. BSBA, Xavier U., 1956; JD, Cleve.-Marshall Law Sch., 1963. Profl. football player Ottawa Rough Riders, Ont., Can., 1956-58; mem. legal dept. Allstate Ins. Co., Cleve., 1958-63; asst. prosecuting atty. Cuyahoga County, Cleve., 1963-70; judge Cuyahoga County Ct. of Common Pleas, Cleve., 1970-88; judge (8th cir.) U.S. Ct. Appeals, Cleve., 1988-92; justice Ohio Supreme Ct., Columbus, 1992—. With U.S. Army, 1957-58. Recipient Legion of Honor award Xavier U., 1956, Outstanding Jud. Svc. award Ohio Supreme Ct., 1972-85, Alumnus of Yr. award Xavier U., 1977. Office: Ohio Supreme Ct 30 E Broad St Columbus OH 43266

SWEENEY, JAMES LEE, engineering and economic systems educator, cons.; b. Waterbury, Conn., Mar. 22, 1944; s. James Wallace and Aletha B. Sweeney; M. Susan L. Van Every, Aug. 21, 1971; children: Erin, Ryan, Regan. BSEE, M.I.T., 1966; PhD in Engring.-Econ. Systems, Stanford U., 1971. Dir. office energy systems, modeling and forecasting U.S. Fed. Energy Adminstrn. Washington, 1974-76; with Stanford U. 1967—, prof. engring.-econ. systems, 1971—, chmn. dept. engring.-econ. systems, 1991—; dir. Energy Modeling Forum, 1978-85, chmn. Inst. Energy Studies, 1981-84, cons. faculty Sch. of Law, 1980-82, mem. steering com. Ctr. Econ. policy Rsch., 1982—, dir. Ctr. Econ. Policy Rsch., 1984-86; cons. U.S. Dept. Energy, NRC, Exxon, Charles River Assocs. Recipient Disting. Service award Fed. Energy Adminstrn., 1975. Mem. Am. Econ. Assn., Internat. Assn. Energy Econs. (past v.p. for publs.), Eta Kappa Nu, Tau Beta Pi, Rotary (past pres.), Menlo Circus Club. Co-author: Macroeconomics Impacts of Energy Shocks, 1987, Fuels to Drive Our Future, 1990; editor: Handbook of Natural Resources and Energy Economics, 1985, 93; co-editor: (jour.) Resources and Energy; contbr. numerous publs. in field to profl. jours. Home: 445 El Escarpado Stanford CA 94305 Office: Stanford U Dept Engring-Econ Systems Terman Engring Ctr Rm 312 Stanford CA 94305-4025

SWEENEY, JAMES RAYMOND, lawyer; b. Chgo., Feb. 19, 1928; s. John Francis and Mae J. (McDonald) S.; m. Rhoda W. Davis, May 15, 1987; children from previous marriage: Margaret Elizabeth, John Francis, Thomas Edward. B.S., U. Notre Dame, 1950; J.D., Northwestern U., 1956. Bar: Ill. 1956. With firm Schroeder, Hofgren, Brady & Wegner, Chgo., 1956-61; ptnr. Hofgren, Wegner, Allen, Stellman & McCord, Chgo., 1962-71, Coffee, Wetzel, Sweeney, Chgo., 1971-72, Coffee & Sweeney, 1972-76, Mason, Kolehmainen, Rathburn & Wyss, Chgo., 1976-82, McWilliams, Mann, Zummer & Sweeney, 1983-86, Mann, McWilliams, Zummer, & Sweeney, 1986-89, Lee, Mann, Smith, McWilliams & Sweeney, 1989-91, Lee, Mann, Smith, McWilliams, Sweeney & Ohlson, 1991—; commr. for disbarment matters Ill. Supreme Ct., 1963-73; mem. hearing div. Atty. Registration and Discipline Commn., 1974-77, chmn. commn. 1983-90; dir. sec. Highland Park (Ill.) Hosp., 1972-79. Served as lt. (j.g.) USN, 1950-53; lt. comdr. Res. ret. Mem. ABA (coun. patent, trademark and copyright sect., sec. 1978-82), Ill. State Bar (assembly 1990—), Chgo. Bar Assn. (sec. 1977-79), Bar Assn. 7th Cir., Intellectual Property Law Assn. Chgo., Patent Law Assn. Chgo. (pres. 1974), The Law Club, Skokie (Ill.) Country Club, Union League. Home: 505 N Lake Shore Dr Chicago IL 60611-3427 Office: Lee Mann Smith McWilliams Sweeney & Ohlson 209 S LaSalle St # 410 Chicago IL 60604-1202

SWEENEY, JOHN W., III, newspaper executive; b. Jersey City, N.J., July 11, 1946; s. John William Jr. and Rita Constance (Dillon) S.; m. Jo Ellen Cooley, Nov. 7, 1970; children: John W. IV, Jessica Elizabeth. BA in English, King's Coll., Wilkes Barre, Pa., 1968. Dealer sales Humble Oil/Exxon, Washington, 1968-69; nat. automotive mgr. Washington Post, 1969-74; advt. dir. Trenton (N.J.) Times, 1974-78, Boston Herald, 1978-80; advt. dir. Houston Chronicle, 1980-83, sales & mktg. dir., 1983-86, v.p. sales & mktg., 1986-91, v.p., gen. mgr. 1991—. Chmn. mktg. com. United Way Tex. Gulf Coast, Houston, 1985-86, 90-91; bd. dirs. Jr. Achievement, Houston, 1991—, Better Bus. Bur., Houston, 1991—; mem. adv. bd. Houston Ballet, 1988-92. Mem. Newspaper Assn. Am. (bd. govs. 1993—, mem. mktg. ops. com. 1993—). Avocations: golf, coaching youth sports. Office: Houston Chronicle 801 Texas St Houston TX 77002-2996*

SWEENEY, JOSEPH MODESTE, lawyer, educator; b. Phila., Sept. 6, 1920; s. Joseph Patrick and Marie-Louise Sweeney; m. Barbara M. Cooper, June 27, 1948; children—Marly, Anne-Marie, Pamela, Jacqueline, Patrick. Baccalaureat. U. Grenoble, France, 1938, Licence en Droit, 1945; LL.B. Harvard U., 1948; Dr. honoris causa, U. Lyon, France, 1969. Bar: D.C. bar 1948, U.S. Supreme Ct. bar 1953. With Legal Adviser's Office, State Dept., 1948-56; from assoc. prof. to prof. law, dir. Inst. Comparative Law, N.Y.U. Law Sch., 1956-68; dean Tulane U. Law Sch., New Orleans, 1968-77, prof. law, 1977—. Author: (with Oliver and Leech) The International Legal System, Cases and Materials, 2d edit., 1981; papers in field. Served with AUS, 1942-45. Mem. Am. Law Inst., Am. Soc. Internat. Law. Home: 6028 Pitt St New Orleans LA 70118-6011 Office: Tulane U Law Sch New Orleans LA 70118

SWEENEY, JUDITH L., newspaper publishing executive. V.p., pres. Orange County edit. L.A. Times. Office: LA Times Times Mirror Sq Los Angeles CA 90012*

SWEENEY, SISTER MARGARET MARY, hospital administrator, nun; b. N.Y.C., Oct. 24, 1921; d. Jeremiah and Mary Jane (Dougherty) S. M.B.A., St. John's U., 1966; M.S. in Hosp. Adminstrn., Columbia U., 1970; DSc. (hon.), Iona Coll., 1987. Lic. nursing home adminstr., N.Y. joined Sisters of Charity, Roman Catholic Ch., 1946. Adminstrv. asst. St. Vincent's Hosp., N.Y.C., 1966-68, sr. v.p., 1970-80, pres., 1980—; adminstrv. resident Luth. Med. Ctr., Bklyn., 1969-70; trustee St. Joseph's Hosp., Yonkers, N.Y., 1977—, St. Vincent's Hosp., Harrison, N.Y., 1975—; assoc. prof. N.Y. Community Coll., 1973-77; preceptor hosp. adminstrn. Baruch U., George Washington U., N.Y.C., 1974-80; mem. bd. govs., trustee Greater N.Y. Hosp. Assn., 1983—, chmn.-elect, 1989—. Contbr. articles to profl. jours.; contbr. lecture series. Chmn. St. Joseph's Ch. Parish Council, Greenwich Village, N.Y., 1973; trusteeMedic Alert, vice chmn. bd. trustees, 1990—; trustee Coll. Mt. St. Vincent, Sisters of Charity Health Care System, Alliance for Cath. Health Care. Fellow Am. Coll. Hosp. Administrs.; mem. Hosp. Fin. Mgmt. Assn., N.Y.C. Pub. Health Assn., N.Y. State Hosp. Assn., Delta Mu Delta. Office: St Vincent's Hosp Office of Pres 153 W 11th St New York NY 10011-8397

SWEENEY, MARK OWEN, publisher; b. Cherryvale, Kans., Dec. 27, 1942; s. Paul Eldon and Clelia Eugenia (Bosette) S.; m. Janet Lynn Turner, July 24, 1964; children—Douglas, Jonathan. Grad., Moody Bible Inst., 1963; B.A., Pacific Coll., 1965; M.A., Wheaton Coll., Ill., 1967. Instr. history Cascade Coll., Portland, Oreg., 1967-70; editor Moody Bible Inst. (Radio div.), 1970-72; exec. producer Moody Corr. Sch., Moody Bible Inst. (Radio div.), 1972-74; dir. public relations Moody Bible Inst. (dir. Moody Lit. Ministries), 1974-77, mgr. publ. div., 1977-81; dir. Victor Books, Scripture Press Publs., 1981-83, v.p., 1983-90; pubr., COO Victor Books, Scripture Press Publs., Wheaton, Ill., 1990-94; corp. v.p., pub. Scripture Press Publs., Inc. and Victor Books, Wheaton, 1994—. Mem. Christian Booksellers Assn., Evang. Christian Pubs. Assn. (chmn. bd.), Nat. Assn. Evangelicals. Home: 1067 Wexford Ct Wheaton IL 60187-6169 Office: Victor Books 1825 College Ave Wheaton IL 60187-4480

SWEENEY, MICHAEL J., lawyer; b. Chgo., Feb. 17, 1953. BA with high honors, U. Ill., 1973; JD cum laude, U. Chgo., 1976. Bar: Ill. 1976, U.S. Dist. Ct. (no. dist.) Ill. 1976, U.S. Ct. Appeals (7th cir.) 1978, U.S. Ct. Appeals (3d cir.) 1986, U.S. Ct. Appeals (10th cir.) 1988. Ptnr. Sidley & Austin, Chgo.; part-time instr. DePaul U., Chgo., 1987, 89. Office: Sidley & Austin 1 First Nat Plz Chicago IL 60603

SWEENEY, RICHARD JAMES, economics educator; b. San Diego, Jan. 13, 1944; s. John Joseph and Catherine Scott (Spahr) S.; m. Joan Zita Long, June 19, 1965; children: Robin Scott, Erin Michaela. BA, UCLA, 1965; PhD, Princeton U., 1972. Acting asst. prof. econs. UCLA, 1968-71; asst. prof. Tex. A&M U., College Station, 1971-73; dep. dir. office of internat. monetary research U.S. Dept. Treasury, Washington, 1973-77; Charles M. Stone prof. econs. and fin. Claremont (Calif.) McKenna Coll., 1977-89, chmn. dept. econs., 1987-89; Sullivan/Dean prof. internat. fin. Georgetown U., Washington, 1989—; vis. assoc. prof. econs. U. Va., Charlottesville, 1975; vis. prof. bus. adminstrn. Dartmouth Coll., Hanover, N.H., 1979; vis. prof. fin. Gothenburg (Sweden) Sch. Econs., 1991, 92, 93, 94, 95. Author: A Macro Theory with Micro Foundations, 1974, Principles of Microeconomics, Macroeconomics, 1980, Wealth Effects and Monetary Theory, 1988, Profit-Making Speculation in Foreign Exchange Markets, 1992; author, editor: Exchange Rates, Trade and the U.S. Economy, 1985; contbr. articles to profl. jours. Fellow NSF 1966-68, Woodrow Wilson Found. 1965; grantee Gen. Electric Found., 1980, Mid.-Am. Found., 1987, Earhart Found., 1988. Mem. Western Econ. Assn. (editor Econ. Inquiry jour. 1984—), Am. Econ. Assn., Am. Fin. Assn., Western Fin. Assn., Phi Beta Kappa. Democrat. Avocations: writing, weightlifting, walking, aerobics. Office: Sch Bus Adminstrn Georgetown U Washington DC 20057

SWEENEY, THOMAS JOSEPH, JR., lawyer; b. N.Y.C., Oct. 29, 1923; s. Thomas Joseph and Johanna M. (Flynn) S.; m. Robin Virginia Thwaites, May 30, 1947; children: Thomas Joseph III, Deidre Ann. B.A., N.Y. U., 1947; J.D., Columbia U. 1949. Bar: N.Y. 1949. Assoc. in law Columbia U. Law Sch., 1949-50; assoc. Cravath, Swaine & Moore, N.Y.C., 1950-62; with Morgan Guaranty Trust Co. N.Y., 1962-89, v.p., 1965-76, sr. v.p., sr. trust officer, 1976-89, chmn. instl. trust and investment com., 1989—; of counsel Decker, Hubbard, Welden & Sweeney, N.Y.C., 1989—; bd. dirs. W.R. Kenan Fund. Trustee Pinkerton Found., Jean and Louis Dreyfus Found. Served to 2d lt. USAAF, 1943-45. Mem. N.Y. State Bar Assn. Democrat. Roman Catholic. Home: 525 Teaneck Rd Ridgefield Park NJ 07660-1127 Office: Decker Hubbard 30 Rockefeller Plz New York NY 10112-0001

SWEENEY, THOMAS LEONARD, chemical engineering educator, researcher; b. Cleve., Dec. 12, 1936; s. Patrick and Anne (Morrin) S.; m. Beverly Marie Starks, Dec. 30, 1961; children: Patrick E., Thomas J., Michael S., Kevin E. BS, Case Inst. Tech., 1958, MS, 1960, PhD, 1962; JD, Capital U., Columbus, Ohio, 1974. Bar: Ohio 1974, U.S. Supreme Ct. 1978.

Registered profl. engr., Ohio. Asst. prof. then assoc. prof. chem. engring. The Ohio State U., Columbus, 1963-73, prof., 1973-94, assoc. v.p. rsch., 1982-94, acting v.p. rsch. and grad., 1989-91, emeritus prof., assoc. v.p., 1995—; pres. The Ohio State U. Research Found., Columbus, 1989-91, exec. dir., 1988-94; Mem. Ohio Hazardous Waste Facility Bd., Columbus, 1984-93; asst. v.p., dir. office rsch., prof. chem. engring. U. Notre Dame, 1994—; mem. bd. dirs. Children's Hosp. Rsch. Found., Columbus, 1990-94; cons. numerous orgns. Editor: Hazardous Waste Management, 1982, Management of Hazardous and Toxic Waste, 1985; contbr. articles to profl. jours. Mem. Am. Inst. Chem. Engrs. (exec. com., cen. Ohio sect., 1970-72), Am. Chem. Soc., Am. Soc. for Engring. Edn. (chmn. environ. engring. div., 1973-74, mem. coun. govtl. rels. and public affairs, 1993—). Roman Catholic. Office: U Notre Dame Rsch Office 312 Main Bldg Notre Dame IN 46556

SWEENEY, TIMM RAYMOND PAUL, marketing research consultant; b. N.Y.C., Mar. 20, 1953; s. Francis James and Barbara Ann (Lynch) S.; m. Jeanne Elizabeth Wild, June 15, 1985. BA, CUNY, 1976. Sr. field supr. Home Testing Inst., L.I., N.Y., 1971-76; project dir. J. Walter Thompson, N.Y.C., 1976-78; sr. project dir. Marstellar Advt., N.Y.C., 1978-80; v.p. Tel. Rsch./TRIM, Westport, Conn., 1980-82, Perception Rsch., Englewood Cliffs, N.J., 1982-83; pres. Sweeney Internat. Ltd., Brookfield, Conn., 1983—; cons. Sami/Burke, Inc., 1988—, Burke Internat. Rsch., N.Y.C., 1983—; rsch. dir. Consumer Scis. Inc., Brookfield, 1987—. Patentee ski travel case, 1986. Mem. Am. Mktg. Assn., Qualitative Rsch. Cons. Assn., Am. Advt. Fedn., Advt. Club N.Y., Wings Club (N.Y.C.), Rock Ridge Club (Newtown, Conn.). Republican. Episcopalian. Avocations: skiing, golfing, sailing. Office: SIL/Group M Internat 221 Main St Danbury CT 06810-6606

SWEENY, MARY ELLEN, public relations and advertising executive; b. L.I., N.Y., July 18, 1951; d. Casper Joseph and Joan Mary (Sears) Lombardi; m. Thomas Paul Figlio, Dec. 12, 1970 (div. 1981); m. Michael Robert Sweeny, Apr. 25, 1981. BA, Glassboro State Coll., 1976. Cert. tchr. K-12, N.J. Editorial asst. Charles A. Slack Med. Pubs., Thorofare, N.J., 1977; assoc. editor N.Am. Pub. Co., Phila., 1977-80; copy writer, sales rep. Lee Assocs., Phila., 1980-85; mktg. comm. and pub. rels. assoc. Phila. Child Guidance Coun., Phila., 1986-88; account mgr. PRx, Inc., Phila., 1989—, account supr., 1990—, exec. v.p., 1992—. Creative dir. healthcare advt. series VMC Info Series, 1990-91 (Innovators award Calif. Assn. Pub. Hosps. 1991); contbr. articles to profl. jours. Co-founder, vol. dir. recruitment, sr. counselor Contact/Gloucester County, Glassboro, N.J., 1974-77; cons., profl. speaker Citizens Against Crime, Phila., 1986; dir. Phila. Kids. Day, City of Phila., 1986; dir. donor option campaign United Way, Phila., 1988. Recipient Best Newspaper Campaign in Silicon Valley award San Jose Bus. Jour., 1990, Bronze Newspaper Ad award San Jose Advt. Assn., 1990., First Place award Penninsula Press Club, 1992. Mem. NAFE, Pub. Rels. Soc. Am. Avocations: flower gardening, bridge, creative writing. Office: PRx Inc 97 S 2d St Ste 300 San Jose CA 95113-1205

SWEENY, STEPHEN JUDE, academic administrator; b. N.Y.C., Sept. 15, 1943; s. Herbert Vincent and Isabel Mary (Dolan) S.; m. Barbara Mary Stasz, Aug. 7, 1976. BA in Spanish, Cath. U., 1966; MA in Theology, Manhattan Coll., 1971, MA in Psychology, 1976; PhD, NYU, 1991. Prin. Incarnation Elem. and Jr. High Sch., N.Y.C., 1969-73; dir. campus ministry Manhattan Coll., N.Y.C., 1973-76; asst. to provost Coll. of New Rochelle, N.Y., 1976-78, mem. edn. dept., 1976—, exec. asst. to pres., 1978-80, v.p. for planning, 1980-81, sr. v.p., 1981—. Vice chair bd. dirs. The Home for the Aged, New Rochelle, 1988-92; chair, bd. trustees Convent of the Sacred Heart, Greenwich, Conn., 1990—; mem. com. on goals Soc. of the Sacred Heart, St. Louis, 1990—, chair 1995—; assoc. Sisters of Charity N.Y., 1984—. Mem. Nat. League Nurses (commn. on accreditation, appeals panel on accreditation actions). Roman Catholic. Office: Coll New Rochelle 29 Castle Pl New Rochelle NY 10805-2338

SWEET, CHARLES WHEELER, executive recruiter; b. Chgo., June 11, 1943; s. Charles Wheeler and Alice Nomi (Grush) S.; m. Joy Ann Weidenmiller, Mar. 23, 1968; children: Charles III, Kimberly Ann, Rebecca Townsend. AB, Hamilton Coll., Clinton, N.Y., 1965; MBA, U. Chgo., 1968. Salesman Procter & Gamble, Chgo., 1965-67; with pers. Ford, Dearborn, Mich., 1968-69, R.R. Donnelley, Chgo., 1969-72; executive recruiter A.T. Kearney Inc. Exec. Search, Chgo., 1972—; pres. A.T. Kearney Inc. Exec. Search, 1988—; bd. dirs. First Fed. Savs., Barrington, Ill. Trustee Village Barrington Hills, Ill., 1985—; chmn. bd., exec. advisor No. Ill. U, 1979-88; bd. dirs. Rehab. Inst. Chgo., 1987—, A.T. Kearney, Inc., 1985-89, Barrington Hills Country Club, 1993—. Mem. AESC. Avocations: tennis, bridge. Home: 92 Meadow Hill Rd Barrington IL 60010-9601 Office: A T Kearney Inc 222 W Adams St Chicago IL 60606-5235

SWEET, JUSTIN, legal educator, lawyer; b. 1929. B.A., 1951; LL.B., U. Wis., 1953. Bar: Wis. 1953, Calif. 1960. Atty. State Atty. Gen., Madison, Wis., 1953-54; atty., Milw., 1957-58; assoc. prof., 1958-63; prof. U. Calif. Law Sch.-Berkeley, 1963—; Fulbright lectr. U. Rome, 1965-66; vis. prof. Hebrew U., Jerusalem, 1970; vis. prof. U. Leuven (Belgium), 1973-74; vis. prof. Osgoode Hall, 1977; with U. Calif. Hastings Sch. Law, summers 1974-78; on leave at Hebrew U. and U. Tel Aviv, 1980-81. Served to 1st lt. JAGC, U.S. Army, 1954-57. Mem. Order of Coif, Phi Beta Kappa. Author: Role of the State Social Welfare Board in the Administration of ANC Program in California, 1961; Legal Aspects of Architecture, Engineering and the Construction Process, 1970, 77; former note editor Wis. Law Rev. Office: U Calif Sch Law 225 Boalt Hall Berkeley CA 94720

SWEET, PHILIP W. K., JR., former banker; b. Mt. Vernon, N.Y., Dec. 31, 1927; s. Philip W.K. and Katherine (Buhl) S.; m. Nancy Frederick, July 23, 1950; children—Sandra H., Philip W.K. III, David A.F. A.B., Harvard U., 1950; M.B.A., U. Chgo., 1957. Pres., dir. The No. Trust Co., Chgo., 1975-81; chmn., chief exec. officer No. Trust Corp., 1981-84. Alderman City of Lake Forest, Ill., 1972-74; adv. com. United Negro Coll. Fund; vis. com. U. Chgo. Grad. Sch. Bus.; trustee Chgo. Zool. Soc., past chmn., 1989-93; trustee Rush-Presbyn.-St. Luke's Med. Ctr.; vestryman Episc. Ch., 1971-74, 86-89. Mem. Soc. Colonial Wars (gov. Ill. chpt. 1978-80), Chgo. Sunday Evening Club (trustee, treas.), Econ. Club, Comml. Club, Commonwealth Club (past pres.), Old Elm Club (Highwood, Ill.), Onwentsia Club (gov.), Shoreacres Club (past pres. Lake Bluff).

SWEET, ROBERT WORKMAN, federal judge; b. Yonkers, N.Y., Oct. 15, 1922; s. James Allen and Delia (Workman) S.; m. Adele Hall, May 12, 1973; children by previous marriage—Robert, Deborah, Ames, Eliza. B.A., Yale U., 1944, LL.B., 1948. Bar: N.Y. 1949. Assoc. firm Simpson, Thacher & Bartlett, 1948-53; asst. U.S. atty. So. Dist. N.Y., 1953-55; assoc. firm Casey, Lane & Mittendorf, 1955-65, partner, 1957-65; counsel Interdepartmental Task Force on Youth and Juvenile Delinquency, 1958-78; dep. mayor City of N.Y., 1966-69; partner firm Skadden, Arps, Slate, Meagher & Flom, N.Y.C., 1970-77; mem. hearing office N.Y.C. Transit Authority, 1975-77; U.S. dist. judge So. Dist. N.Y., N.Y.C., 1978—; participant USIA Rule of Law Program in Albania, 1991; observer Albanian elections, 1992. Pres. Community Service Soc., 1961-78; trustee Sch. Mgmt. Urban Policy, 1970—, Taft Sch.; vestryman St. Georges Epis. Ch., 1958-63. Served to lt. (j.g.) USNR, 1943-46. Recipient Alumni citation of merit Taft Sch., 1985, various other awards, citations for service as dept mayor N.Y.C. Mem. ABA, Assn. of Bar of City of N.Y., N.Y. Law Inst., N.Y. County Lawyers Assn., State Bar Assn., Am. Legion (comdr. Willard Straight Post). Clubs: Quaker Hill Country, Century Assn., Merchants, Indian Harbor Yacht, Mid City Rep. Office: US Dist Ct US Courthouse 2202 Foley Sq New York NY 10007-1502

SWEETEN, GARY RAY, religious counseling educator; b. Ina, Ill., May 5, 1938; s. Thomas Jefferson and Leota Leone (Taylor) S.; m. Karen J. Sweeten, Nov. 21, 1961; children: Julia Rae, Timothy Andrew. AA, Rend Lake Coll., 1960; BS, So. Ill. U., 1965, MS, 1967; EdD, U. Cin., 1975. Tchr., coach pub. schs. Ina, Bellerive and Mt. Vernon, Ill., 1960-65; asst. dean U. Cin., 1967-69, asst. to univ. provost, 1969-73; minister of Christian edn. Coll. Hill Presbyn. Ch., Cin., 1973-76, minister of counseling and growth, 1973-89; chief exec. officer, pres. Lifeway Counseling Ctr., Cin., 1989—; founder, chairperson Equipping Mins. Internat., Cin., 1978—; cons., founder Sweeten Creative Cons., Cin., 1970—; founder, pres. Christian Info. Com., Cin., 1978—; pres. bd dirs Presbyn. Renewal Ministry, Oklahoma City, 1980-85. Author: Listening: For Heaven's Sake, 1993; author numerous articles,

monographs, tng. manuals. Bd. dirs. Citizens Against Substance Abuse. Named Outstanding Alumni Rend Lake Coll., Ina, 1986. Mem. Ohio Assn. Counselor Devel., Christian Assn. Psychol. Studies. Avocation: travel. Home: 11863 Tennyson Dr Cincinnati OH 45241-2195 Office: Lifeway Counseling Ctr 4015 Executive Park Dr Cincinnati OH 45241-4017

SWEETING, LINDA MARIE, chemist; b. Toronto, Ont., Can., Dec. 11, 1941; came to U.S., 1965, naturalized, 1979; d. Stanley H. and Mary (Robertson) S. BSc, U. Toronto, 1964, MA, 1965; PhD, UCLA, 1969. Asst. prof. chemistry Occidental Coll., L.A., 1969-70; asst. prof. chemistry Towson (Md.) State U., 1970-75, assoc. prof., 1975-85, prof., 1985—; guest worker NIH, 1976-77; program dir. chem. instrumentation NSF, 1981-82; vis. scholar Harvard U., 1984-85; contractor U.S. Army MRICD, 1991-93. Bd. dirs. Chamber Music Soc. Balt., 1985-91. Exec. com. Exptl. NMR. Conf. 1985-87, local arr. chair 1986. Mem. Md. Acad. Scis. (mem. sci. council 1975-83, 89-94), Assn. for Women in Sci. (treas. 1977-78, Woman of Yr. 1989), Am. Chem. Soc. (mem. women chemists Com. 1983-89), AAAS, Wilderness Soc., Nature Conservancy, Aircraft Owners and Pilots Assn., Sierra Club, Sigma Xi (sec. TSU Club 1979-81, Towson chpt. pres. 1987-88, 91-92, mid-Atlantic nominating com. 1987-90, regional dir. 1988-89, nat. nominating com. 1991-94). Office: Towson State U Dept Chemistry Baltimore MD 21204

SWEETLAND, LORAINE FERN, librarian, educator; b. Morristown Corners, Vt., Aug. 13, 1933; d. William Eric and Sylbil Bedina (Bailey) Bloomfield; m. Ronald David Sweetland, July 1, 1950; children: Kathy L. (dec.), Dale J. Bettis. BS in Elem. Edn., Columbia Union Coll., 1968; MS in Library Sci., Syracuse U., 1973. Tchr. 1st and 2d grade Beltsville (Md.) Seventh-Day Adventist Sch., 1960-67; asst. librarian, cataloger Vt. Tech. Coll., Randolph Vt., 1968-69; mid. sch. librarian Barre (Vt.) City Schs., 1970-74; teaching prin. Cen. Vt. Seventh-Day Adventist Sch., Barre, 1974-76, Brooklawn Seventh-Day Adventist Sch., Bridgeport, Conn., 1976-81; med. librarian Washington Adventist Hosp., Takoma Park, Md., 1981-85; dir. library services Seventh-Day Adventist World Hdqrs., Silver Spring, Md., 1985—; med. library cons., Balt., 1983-85; pres. Oasis, 1993-94; book reviewer, Libr. Jour., 1990—. Book reviewer Libr. Jour., 1990—. Trustee Randolph (Vt.) Pub. Library, 1970-71; sec. Nat. Area Hosp. Council, Washington, 1985. Mem. Assn. Seventh-Day Adventist Librarians, Laurel Rotary Club (bulletin editor 1990-94). Republican. Avocations: gardening, photography, knitting, sewing, crocheting. Home: 10182 High Ridge Rd Laurel MD 20723-1782 Office: Gen Conf Seventh Day Adventists 12501 Old Columbia Pike Silver Spring MD 20904-6601

SWEETMAN, BEVERLY YARROLL, physical therapist; b. Phila., Apr. 8, 1939; d. Albert Henry and Theresa (Payne) Yarroll; m. Denman John Sweetman, Apr. 1, 1961; children: Denman Eric, John Albert. BA in Biology, Hood Coll., 1961; cert. phys. therapist, Hahnemann U., 1983. Rsch. technician Mass. Gen. Hosp., Boston, 1961-62, Princeton (N.J.) U., 1965-66; phys. therapy aide Pain & Stress Control Ctr., Reading, Pa., 1979-80; part owner, phys. therapist Pain & Stress Control Ctr., Allentown, Pa., 1983-85; pvt. practice Body Ease Phys. Therapy Ctr., Grants Pass, Oreg., 1985; pvt. practice, pres. Body Ease Phys. Therapy Ctr., Staunton, Va., 1986—; co-presenter Total Body Concept Seminars; lectr. in field; pres. VMG Med., Staunton, 1988—; cons., co-presenter seminars Lossing Orthopedic, Mpls., 1985—. Fellow Am. Back Soc.; mem. Am. Phys. Therapy Assn. Office: Body Ease Phys Therapy Ctr 409 Walnut Hills Rd Staunton VA 24401-9467

SWEETMAN, BRIAN JACK, organic, analytical chemist, educator; b. Palmerston North, New Zealand, May 4, 1936; came to U.S., 1966; s. Walter Harold Jack and Elsie Marion (Holdaway) S.; m. Carolyn Juel Nepia, May 6, 1961; children: Peter Brian, Brendan Jack, Gareth Charles Kaira. BSc, U. Otago, Dunedin, New Zealand, 1958, MSc in Chemistry with honors, 1959, PhD in Chemistry, 1962. Rsch. chemist Commonwealth Sci. and Indsl. Rsch. Orgn. div. Protein Chemistry, Melbourne, Australia, 1963-66; rsch. assoc. dept. chemistry Vanderbilt U., Nashville, 1966-68, rsch. assoc. dept. pharmacology, 1969-89, rsch prof. dept. anesthesiology, 1989-91; sr. chemist Environ. Sci. Corp., Mt. Juliet, Tenn., 1992—; mem. human rels. coun. social life and cultural affairs subcom. Vanderbilt U., 1973-74, clin. rsch. ctr. adv. com., 1986-89; grant reviewer NSF div. internat. programs and div. regulatory biology and March of Dimes, 1972—; mem. ad hoc com. metallobiochemistry study sect. NIH, 1990-91. Manuscript reviewer Analytical Biochemistry, Jour. Andrology, Prostaglandins, Biomed. Mass. Spectrometry, Biomed. and Environ. Mass Spectrometry and Life Scis.; contbr. articles to profl. jours.; patentee in field. Rsch. Fund fellow, 1959-62, John Edmond fellow, 1959-62. Mem. Am. Soc. Mass Spectrometry. Home: 2928 Donna Hill Dr Nashville TN 37214-1512 Office: Environ Sci Corp 12065 Lebanon Rd Mount Juliet TN 37122-2508

SWEETS, HENRY HAYES, III, museum director; b. Lexington, Ky., May 8, 1949; s. Henry Hayes Jr. and Elizabeth (Keith) S.; m. Nancy Riley, Jan. 28, 1984; children: Amy Louisa, Henry Hayes IV. BS in Chemistry, U. Ill., 1971, MEd., 1973; MA in History, U. Del., 1978. Tchr. Scotch Plains (N.J.)-Fanwood High Sch., 1972-74, Byron (Ill.) High Sch., 1974-76; mus. dir. Mark Twain Mus., Hannibal, Mo., 1978—. Author: A Sesquicentennial History of the Hannibal, Missouri Presbyterian Church; editor The Fence Painter. Bd. dirs. Becky Thatcher coun. Girl Scouts U.S., 1984-88; mem. bd. edn. Hannibal, Mo. Pub. Schs., 1991—. Mem. Nat. Trust for Hist. Preservation. Methodist. Office: Mark Twain Home and Mus 208 Hill St Hannibal MO 63401-3316

SWEETSER, GENE GILLMAN, quality assurance professional, state legislator; b. Burlington, Vt., Apr. 24, 1948; s. Archelaus William and Stella Ruth (Brink) S.; m. Elizabeth Ann Hannett, Apr., 1967 (div. May 1972); 1 child, Analei; m. Susan Williams, Aug. 27, 1978 (div. Feb. 1995); 1 child, Virginia Lucretia. BA Polit. Sci. and Environ. Sci., Johnson State Coll., Vt., 1978; MS in Adminstrn., St. Michael's Coll., Vt., 1993. Maintenance machinist Avdel Internat., Inc., Parsippany, N.J., 1982-84; machine shop supr. Mitec Systems, Inc., Williston, Vt., 1984-84; maintenance supr. Fonda, Inc., Albans, Vt., 1985-88; asst. quality control mgr. Chatham Precision, Hinesburg, Vt., 1988-91; state representative Vt. State Ho. of Reps., 1990—; prodn. control IBM, Essex, Vt., 1992—; mem. Bd. Civil Authority, Essex, Vt., 1988—, Justice of the Peace, 1988—; mem. com. ways and means Vt. State Ho. of Reps., 1994—. Founder, bd. dirs. paper recycling program Worcester Vol. Fire Dept., 1978-82; founder, bd. dirs. Worcester Film Soc., 1978-82, Worcester Views Newsletter, 1978-82; vice chmn. Ctrl. Ct. Regional Planning Commn., 1980-82; vol. The Holiday Project, 1987-89; coach Essex Youth Soccer, 1988, 89; player agt. for minor league Essex Little League Assn., 1990; v.p. Survivors of Crime, Inc. With USMC, 1969-72, Vt. Army nat. Guard, 1978—. Address: 28 Foster Rd Essex Junction VT 05452

SWEETSER, RUTH EMILIE ZIEMANN, university administrator; b. Milw., July 26, 1945; d. Theodore William and Ottilia Loretta (Brandt) Ziemann; m. Steven Gary Sweetser, Aug. 22, 1970; children: Daniel Seth, Douglas William Alden. BA, Hope Coll., 1967; postgrad., Stanford U.; MA, U. Chgo., 1972; postgrad. seminar, Ill. State U., 1975. Tchr. Barrington (Ill.) Consolidated High Sch., 1968-75; asst. bus. mgr. Midwest Coll. Engring., Lombard, Ill., 1983-84, bus. and adminstrn. dir., 1984-86; facilities mgr. Ill. Inst. Tech., Glen Ellyn, 1986-89; assoc. dir. Ill. Inst. Tech., Wheaton, Ill., 1989—; mktg./communications chair III. R & D Corridor Coun., DuPage County, 1988-91, project dir. 1991-92; bd. dir. Corridor Group, Met. Econ. Devel. Alliance, Chgo./DuPage County, DuKane Valley Coun., 1993-95, DuPage Area Assn. of Bus. & Ind., 1994-96; achievement award judge Women in Mgmt., 1986. Dir. enrichment support group German for Kids YMCA, PALS, Lombard, 1980-86; chmn. DuPage Ares Engr.'s Week Program, DuPage County, 1985—; co-chair Glenbard Citizens for Quality Edn., DuPage County, 1989—; active Lombard Hist. Soc., 1986—, Am. Cancer Soc., Lombard, 1988-92, Friends of the Libr., Lombard, 1988—, Village of Lombard Plan Commn., 1990—, strategic plan com. Glenbard East High Sch., 1990—, Glenbard East Citizens Adv. Coun., mem. 1990—, pres., 1992-94, steering com. Sch. Dist. 44 Referendum Effort, Lombard, 1991—, traveling exhibit chair DuPage County Sesquicentennial Steering Coun., 1988-89, higher edn. symposium coun., 1989; past pres., mem. community EXPO steering com. Lombard Community Leaders; elder Community Presbyn. Ch., 1990-92, blood drive chair, 1984-92, accompanist, 1975—; founder ambassadors program Glenbard East Citizens Adv. Coun., 1992—. Fellow U. Chgo., 1967. Mem. AAUW (Ill. task force 1991—, nat.

membership com. 1989-93, membership v.p. Ill. div. 1986-90, Highest Membership Growth award 1988, chair nominating com., pres. local br., Named Gift Honoree 1983, Agent of Change award 1991, Ill. pres.1995—), Ill. Womens Agenda (pres. 1990-91), DuPage Area Assn. Bus. and Industry (nominating com. 1991, chair liaison com. 1992—). Avocations: professional piano accompanist, scuba diving, volleyball. Office: Ill Inst Tech 201 E Loop Rd Wheaton IL 60187-8488

SWEETSER, SUSAN W., state legislator, lawyer, advocate; b. Dec. 13, 1958; d. Robert Joseph and Lucretia Rose (Donnelly) Williams. BA in Polit. Sci./Environ. Adminstrn. with high honors, Johnson (Vt.) State Coll., 1982; JD magna cum laude, Vt. Law Sch., 1985. Bar: N.Y. 1986, Vt. 1986, U.S. Dist. Ct. Vt. 1989; CLU, ChFC. Confidential law clk. Appellate div. N.Y. Supreme Ct., Albany, 1985-86; assoc. Gravel & Shea, Burlington, Vt., 1986-90; atty. Nat. Life Ins. Co., Montpelier, Vt., 1990—; now mem. Vt. State Senate; victims rights adv. Essex Junction, Vt., 1980—; adj. prof. bus. law St. Michael's Coll., Winooski, Vt., 1991—; Johnson State Coll., 1995—; justice of peace Town of Essex, 1991-95; chair judiciary com.; former mem. Health and Welfare Com.; mem. Housing and Conservation Trust Fund Study Com., Civil Rights Study Com., Adoption Law Reform Study Com., Appropriations Com. Author articles on victims rights. Trustee Vt. State Colls., Waterbury, 1979-81, Univ. Health Ctr., 1992-94; mem. ethics com. Fanny Allen Hosp., Winooski, Vt., 1989-92; v.p. Lyric Theatre, Burlington, 1989—; mem. Vt. Rep. State Com., Montpelier, chmn. Rep. State Conv., 1988, 92; founder, pres. Survivors of Crime, Inc. Recipient Achievement award Vt. Law Enforcement Coordinating Com., 1990, Vt. Ctr. for Prevention and Treatment of Sexual Abuse and The Safer Soc. Program, 1991, Nat. recognition for victims rights work The Giraffe Project, 1991, award Nat. Found. for Improvement of Justice, 1993; named 754th Point of Light by former Pres. George Bush, 1992, Am. Heroine Ladies Home Jour., 1991. Fellow AAUW; mem. Vt. Bar Assn., N.Y. State Bar Assn., Internat. Assn. Fin. Planners (chmn. legis. affairs Greater Vt. chpt. 1988-91). Roman Catholic. Avocations: skiing, flower gardening, running, camping, horseback riding. Office: Survivors of Crimes Inc PO Box 8304 Essex Junction VT 05451-8304

SWEEZY, JOHN WILLIAM, political party official; b. Indpls., Nov. 14, 1932; s. William Charles and Zuma Frances (McNew) S.; BS in Mech. Engring., Purdue U., 1956; MBA, Ind. U., 1958; student Butler U., 1953-54, U. Ga., 1954-55, Ind. Cen. Coll., 1959; m. Carole Suzanne Harman, July 14, 1956; children—John William, Bradley E. Design, test engr. Allison div. GM, Indpls., 1953-57; power sales engr. Indpls. Power & Light Co., 1958-69; dir. pub. works City of Indpls., 1970-72; chmn. Marion County Rep. Cen. Com., 1972—; bd. dir. Lorco Engring., Indpls., Indpls. Industrial Products, Acme Screw & Mfg., Inc., Telnet, Inc., Landmarks Ltd.; ptnr. Arch. Products, Innovative Investment Co. Bd. dirs. Indpls. Humane Soc.; chmn. 11th Dist. Rep. Com., 1970, 73—; chmn. Nat. Assn. Urban Rep. County Chmn.; alt. del. Rep. Nat. Conv., 1968, del., 1972, 76, 80, 84, 88, 92, del., mem. credentials com., 1984, 88; mem. credentials com., 1980; mem. Rep. Nat. Com., 1984—, exec. com., 1984—; mem. Warren Schs. Citizens Screening Com., 1958-72; bd. dirs. Warren Devel. Com. With AUS, 1953-55. Mem. AMA, Mensa, Sigma Iota Epsilon. Home: 2089 S German Church Rd Indianapolis IN 46239-9620 Office: 12 N Delaware St Indianapolis IN 46204-3205

SWEEZY, PAUL MARLOR, editor, publisher; b. N.Y.C., Apr. 10, 1910; s. Everett Benjamin and Caroline (Wilson) S.; m. Zirel Dowd, June 17, 1961; children by previous marriage: Samuel Everett, Martha MacDougall, Martha Adams. BA, Harvard U., 1931, PhD, 1937; LittD (honoris causa), Jawaharlal Nehru U., 1983. With econs. dept. Harvard U., 1934-42; editor Monthly Rev., 1949—; vis. prof. Cornell U., Stanford U., New Sch. Social Research, U. Calif., Davis, Yale U., Hosei U., Tokyo, U. Manchester, Eng.; lectr. Cambridge (Eng.) U., 1971; pres. Monthly Rev. Found., Inc. Author or editor: Monopoly and Competion in the English Coal Trade, 1550-1850, 1938, The Theory of Capitalist Development, 1942, Socialism, 1949, The Present as History, 1953; co-author: (with Leo Huberman) Cuba: Anatomy of a Revolution, 1960, (with Paul Baran) Monopoly Capital, 1966, (with Leo Huberman) Socialism in Cuba, 1969, (with Charles Bettelheim) On the Transition to Socialism, 1971, (with Harry Magdoff) The Dynamics of U.S. Capitalism, 1972, Modern Capitalism and Other Essays, 1972, (with Harry Magdoff) The End of Prosperity, 1977, Post Revolutionary Society, 1981, (with Harry Magdoff) The Deepening Crisis of U.S. Capitalism, 1981, Four Lectures on Marxism, 1981, (with Harry Magdoff) Stagnation and Financial Explosion, 1987, (with Harry Magdoff) The Irreversible Crisis, 1988. Served with AUS, 1942-46. Decorated Bronze Star; recipient David A. Wells prize, 1938. Home: 2 Lindsley Dr Larchmont NY 10538-3808 Office: 122 W 27th St 10th Fl New York NY 10001-6227

SWENKA, ARTHUR JOHN, food products executive; b. Lone Tree, Iowa, Oct. 21, 1937; s. Samuel Joseph and Verdis Mary (Weed) S.; m. Elizabeth Simms, July 1956 (div. 1976); children: Lee Arthur, Timothy John; m. Dixie Jo Meade, Feb. 1982. Gen. equivalency diploma, U.S. Army, 1957. Truck driver U.S. Mail, Oelwein, Iowa, 1958-59, Stiles Supermarket, Oelwein, 1959-60; salesman Hoxie Inst. Wholesale Co., Waterloo, Iowa, 1960-68, slaes mgr., 1968-69, br. mgr., 1969-70; br. mgr. Hoxie Inst. Wholesale Co., Waterloo and Mason City, Iowa, 1970-72, Nobel Inc., Albuquerque, 1972-81; pres. Nobel/Sysco Food Svcs. Co., Albuquerque, 1981-84; sr. v.p. ops. Sysco Corp., Denver, 1995—; chmn. bd. dirs. Nobel/Sysco Food Svcs., Albuquerque, Sysco Food Svcs., Billings, Mont.; mem. Dirs. Coun., Houston, 1985—; bd. dirs. Mountain States Employee Coun., Sysco Corp. Treas., bd. dirs. Albuquerque Conv. and Visitors Bur., 1975-80; v.p., bd. dirs. Albuquerque Internat. Balloon Festival, 1975-82; bd. dirs. New Day Home for Runaway Children, Albuquerque, 1980-89; bd. dirs. Found. St. Joseph's Hosp., 1990—, pres. 1993—. Republican. Roman Catholic. Avocation: hot air ballooning. Home: 7112-32 Pan American Fwy Albuquerque NM 87109 Office: Nobel/Sysco Food Svcs Co 1101 W 48th Ave Denver CO 80217

SWENSEN, CLIFFORD HENRIK, JR., psychologist, educator; b. Welch, W.Va., Nov. 25, 1926; s. Clifford Henrik and Cora Edith (Clovis) S.; m. Doris Ann Gaines, June 6, 1948; children—Betsy, Susan, Lisa, Timothy, Barbara. B.S., U. Pitts., 1949, M.S., 1950, Ph.D., 1952. Diplomate Am. Bd. Profl. Psychology. Instr. U. Pitts., 1951-52; clin. psychologist VA, 1952-54; from asst. prof. to assoc. prof. U. Tenn., Knoxville, 1954-62; assoc. prof. psychology Purdue U., West Lafayette, Ind., 1962-65, prof., 1965—; dir. clin. tng. Purdue U., 1975-85; vice chair U. Senate, 1994-95; vis. prof. U. Fla., 1968-69, U. Bergen, Norway, 1976-77, 83-84; cons. VA, 1981 White House Conf. on Aging, others; Am. Psychol. Assn.-NSF Disting. Sci. lectr., 1968-69; Fulbright-Hays lectr., Norway, 1976-77. Author: An Approach to Case Conceptualization, 1968; Introduction to Interpersonal Relations, 1973; contbr. chpts. to books, articles to profl. jours. Served with USN, 1944-46. Recipient Gordon A. Barrows Meml. award for disting. contributions to psychology, 1990. Fellow APA (pres divsn. cons. psychology 1976-77), Am. Psychol. Soc., Soc. Personality Assessment, Am. Assn. Applied and Preventive Psychology, Acad. of Clin. Psychology; mem. Midwestern Psychol. Assn., Southeastern Psychol. Assn., Ind. Psychol. Assn., Gerontol. Soc., Sigma Xi, Psi Chi. Republican. Mem. Ch. of Christ. Home: 611 Hillcrest Rd West Lafayette IN 47906-2349 Office: Purdue U Dept Psychol Scis West Lafayette IN 47907

SWENSEN, LAIRD S., orthopedic surgeon; b. Provo, Utah, Oct. 5, 1944; s. Russel Brown and Beulah (Strickler) S.; m. Gloria Elaine Matoza, Sept. 23, 1973; children: Lara Ann, Christine, Russel, Tracy, Laird. BA in Chemistry, Brigham Young U., 1968; MD, George Washington U., 1972. Diplomate Am. Bd. Orthopedic Surgery; cert. added qualifications in surgery of hand, 1992. Intern San Francisco Gen. Hosp., 1972-73; resident in orthopedics U. Calif., San Francisco, 1973-77; pvt. practice orthopedic surgery Salt Lake City, 1978—; fellow in hand and microvascular surgery Jack Tupper, 1978; vice chmn. dept. surgery LDS Hosp.; chmn. div. orthopedics LDS Hosp., 1991-92; assoc. clin. prof. dept. orthopedic surgery U. Utah, 1979, asst. clin. prof., 1990—; vol. surgeon Orthopedics Overseas, Nepal, 1988, 90, Bhutan, 1992; med. project advisor Tibetan Resettlement Project, Salt Lake City. Fellow Am. Acad. Orthopedic Surgery; mem. Western Orthopedic Assn. (pres. Utah chpt. 1991), Am. Soc. Surgery of Hand, Utah State Med. Assn. Avocation: mountaineering. Office: 324 10th Ave Salt Lake City UT 84103-2853

SWENSEN, MARY JEAN HAMILTON, graphic artist; b. Laurens, S.C., June 25, 1910; d. Elvin A. and Della (Brown) Hamilton; m. Oliver Severn Swensen, Mar. 3, 1943 (dec.). BS, Columbia U., 1956, MA, 1960; Cert. Notable, U. Madrid, Spain; postgrad., Ariz. State U., 1974-80. mem. 1st USSA sr. internat. cross-country skiing team. One person shows at Colo. Fed. Savs. and Loan Assn., Denver, 1978, Panoras Gallery, N.Y.C., 1963; exhibited in group shows at Soc. Western Artist, M.H. de Young Mus., San Francisco, 1964, Nat. Art Roundup, Las Vegas, 1965, Fine Arts Bldg., Colo. State Fair, Pueblo, 1965, Duncan Gallery, Paris, 1974, Colo. Fed. Savs. & Loan Assn., Denver, 1978; graphics arts in pub. collections at Met. Mus. Art, N.Y.C., Nat. Graphic Arts Collection, Smithsonian Inst., Laurens (S.C.) Pub. Libr., N.Y.C. Pub. Libr. Recipient Duncan Gallery Prix de Paris, 1974, YWCA of U.S.A. Gold Medal as most admired athlete of the yr., 1979, USSA, Aspen and Vail collection of gold, silver and bronze medals in downhill, giant slalom, slalom and cross-country skiing. Mem. Am. Mensa, Delta Phi Delta.

SWENSON, COURTLAND SEVANDER, retired musician; b. Akron, Iowa, July 2, 1936; s. Clifford Sevander and Selma Lillian (Swanson) S.; m. Bonnie Jan Hull, Aug. 23, 1966; children: Callan Sevander, Corey McAllister. BFA, U. S.D., 1958, MusM, 1962; postgrad., U. Ill., 1968-69, U. Würzburg, Fed. Republic Germany, 1976. Tchr. music Sibley (Iowa) Public Schs., 1958-60; mem. faculty U. S.D., Vermillion, 1960-94; prof. music U. S.D., 1973-94; ret., 1994; instr., chmn. fine arts Ramey AFB, P.R., 1971-72; musical dir. Black Hills Playhouse, Custer Park, S.D., 1963-78; cons. music, Guatemala, 1977; prin. percussionist Sioux City (Iowa) Symphony, 1964-71; prin. timpanist Sioux Falls (S.D.) Symphony, 1973-76; bd. dirs. Arnie B. Larson Shrine to Nature of Antique Instruments, 1970-87. Mem. S.D. Arts Coun., 1987-90. Named Best Tchr. U. S.D., 1967, 83; recipient Burlington No. Found. award for excellence in teaching, 1987. Mem. AAUP, Nat. Endowment for Arts, Nat. Assn. Rudimental Drummers, Percussive Arts Soc., Lambda Chi. Address: 3386 Laurel Grove S Jacksonville FL 32223

SWENSON, DANIEL LEE, bishop; b. Oklahoma City, Feb. 2, 1928; s. Daniel and Lillian (Twedt) S.; m. Sally Mason, June 9, 1951; children: Martha Mason, Sara Swenson Shuford, Daniel Gerald. BA, U. Minn., 1950; DD (hon.), Seabury-Western Theol Sem., Evanston, Ill., 1987. Pvt. practice bus. mgmt. St. Martin's by the Lake, Alexandria, Minn., 1952-58; asst. min. St. Martin's By the Lake, Minnetonka Beach, Minn., 1959-62; vicar St. Edward's Mission, Wayzata, Minn., 1962-65; rector St. Paul's Ch., Virginia, Minn., 1965-75; dean Cathedral of Our Merciful Saviour, Faribault, Minn., 1975-78; rector St. John in the Wilderness, White Bear Lake, Minn., 1978-86; bishop Episc. Diocese Vt., Burlington, 1986—; dean Region II, Diocese of Minn., 1972-75; chmn., Diocesan Commn. on Ministry, Minn., 1976-83; examining chaplain Diocese of Minn., 1974-86; trustee Seabury-Western Theol. Sem., Evanston, Ill., 1978-89. Vice chmn. City Human Rights Commn., Virginia, Minn., 1972-75; dist. chmn. N.E. Minn. Boy Scouts Am., 1970-73; coun. mem. Indianhead and Green Mountain Boy Scouts Am., 1975-89. With U.S. Army, 1946-48. Office: Diocesan Ctr Rock Point Burlington VT 05401

SWENSON, EMILY BARRON, broadcast executive; b. Boston, Feb. 9, 1954; d. William Andros and Mary Douglas (Robertson) Barron; m. Peter F. Gerrity; m. 2d. Christopher B. Swenson, Oct. 7, 1984; children: Billy, Mike, Lisa. BA, Trinity Coll., 1975; M in Pub. and Pvt. Mgmt., Yale U., 1982. Mgr. bus. planning and interactive techs. Children's Television Workshop, N.Y.C., 1982-83, asst. to pres. for fin. and adminstrn., 1983, dir. of adminstrn., 1983-84, dir. fin. and adminstrn., 1984-85, asst. v.p. corp. affairs, 1985-87, v.p. corp. affairs, 1987, sr. v.p. corp. affairs, 1987-93, exec. v.p., COO, 1993—; trustee Trinity Coll., Conn.; bd. advisors KAPOW. Recipient Salute to Women Achievers award YWCA, 1994. Office: Childrens TV Workshop 1 Lincoln Plz 4th Fl New York NY 10023

SWENSON, ERIC PIERSON, publishing company executive; b. South Orange, N.J., Sept. 21, 1918; s. Svante Magnus and Dorothy Wharton (Mendelson) S.; m. Patricia Morgan, Sept. 14, 1945 (div. June 1965); children: Juliet Morgan Swenson Carter (dec.), Karen Rosamond Swenson McCollom, Dana Graham Swenson Seberg, Hilary Lloyd SwensonMoody; m. Ann Brooke Kirkland, Aug. 5, 1965; 1 child, Alexandra Brooke. Grad. magna cum laude, St. Paul's Sch., Concord, N.H., 1937; B.A. with high orations, Yale, 1941. Publicity asst., editor Pocket Books, Inc., N.Y.C., 1945-47; publicity, editor William Sloane Assos., N.Y.C., 1947-51; sr. editor, vice chmn., dir. W.W. Norton & Co., N.Y.C., 1951-91, editor emeritus, hon. bd. dirs., 1991—; bd. dirs. SMS Ranch Co., Stamford, Tex., Ctr. for Marine Conservation, Washington, Trafalger Sq. Pub. Co. Inc., North Pomfret, Vt. Author: The South Sea Shilling, 1952. With USN, 1941-45, PTO. Clubs: New York Yacht, Cruising of Am., Royal Yacht Squadron, Indian Harbor Yacht, Yale, Storm Trysail, Royal Ocean Racing, Coun. on Fgn. Rels. Home: 99 Eleven O'Clock Rd Weston CT 06883 Office: 500 Fifth Ave New York NY 10110-0002

SWENSON, GEORGE WARNER, JR., electronics engineer, radio astronomer, educator; b. Mpls., Sept. 22, 1922; s. George Warner and Vernie (Larson) S.; m. Virginia Laura Savard, June 26, 1943 (div. 1970); children: George Warner III, Vernie Laura, Julie Loretta, Donna Joan; m. Joy Janice Locke, July 2, 1971. B.S., Mich. Coll. Mining and Tech., 1944, E.E., 1950; M.S., Mass. Inst. Tech., 1948; Ph.D., U. Wis., 1951. Asso. prof. elec. engring. Washington U., St. Louis, 1952-53; prof. U. Alaska, 1953-54; asso. prof. Mich. State U., 1954-56; faculty U. Ill., Urbana, 1956—, prof. elec. engring. and astronomy, 1958-88, prof. emeritus, 1988—; acting head dept. astronomy U. Ill., 1970-72, head dept. elec. and computer engring., 1979-85; dir. Vermilion River Obs., 1968-81; vis. scientist Nat. Radio Astronomy Obs., 1964-68; cons. to govt. agys. and other sci. bodies; sr. rsch. assoc. U.S. Army Constrn. Engring. Rsch. Lab., 1988—. Author: Principles of Modern Acoustics, 1953, An Amateur Radio Telescope, 1980; co-author: Interferometry and Synthesis in Radio Astronomy, 1986; contbr. articles to profl. jours. Recipient citation for disting. service to engring. U. Wis., 1984; Guggenheim fellow, 1984-85. Fellow IEEE, AAAS; mem. NAE, Am. Astron. Soc., Internat. Sci. Radio Union (mem. U.S. nat. com. 1965-67, 80-82), Internat. Astron. Union, Sigma Xi, Eta Kappa Nu, Tau Beta Pi, Phi Kappa Phi. Achievements include chairing conceptual design group which produced the concept/proposal for the Very Large Array of National Radio Astronomy Observatory; designed and built two large innovative radio telescopes for the University of Illinois. Home: 1107 Kenwood Rd Champaign IL 61821-4718 Office: U Ill 328 CSRL 1308 W Main St Urbana IL 61801-2307

SWENSON, HAROLD FRANCIS, crisis management consultant; b. N.Y.C., Apr. 28, 1915; s. Charles Henry and Ethel Marie (Igoe) S.; A.B., Manhattan Coll., 1938; student Fordham U. Law Sch., 1938-41; m. Mildred Chandler, Dec. 31, 1943; 1 dau., Sally. Mem. law firm Root, Clark, Buckner & Ballantine, N.Y.C., 1938-41; spl. agt. FBI, 1941-47; indsl. relations exec. Gulf Oil, San Tome, Venezuela, 1947-52; employee relations and security exec. Sears, Roebuck & Co., Chgo., 1953-54; with State Dept., Washington, 1955-65, Def. Dept., Washington, 1965-68; pres., chief exec. officer, dir. Bishop's Service Inc., N.Y.C., 1969-73; v.p. surveys, mktg. and fgn. ops. Intertel Inc., Washington, 1974-78; with law dept., security exec. Chesebrough-Pond's Inc., Greenwich, Conn., 1978-86, crisis mgmt. cons. exec., 1986—. Polit. attache U.S. Embassy, Buenos Aires, Argentina, 1956-62. Served with USMC, 1944-46, PTO. Mem. Soc. Former FBI Agts., Internat. Assn. Chiefs of Police, Capital Marines, Mil. Order Carabao, U.S. Naval Inst., Mil. Order Fgn. Wars, Marine Corps Hist. Soc., Bad Ems Golf Alumni, Air Crew Assn. of London, Epsilon Sigma Pi, Beta Sigma. Clubs: Chantilly Golf and Country (Centerville, Va.); Army-Navy (Washington); Pathfinders (London); American (Buenos Aires). Home: 7337 Oak Moss Dr Sarasota FL 34241-6222 also: 7337 Oak Moss Dr Sarasota FL 34241-6222

SWENSON, JAMES REED, physician, educator; b. Utah, Nov. 18, 1933; s. Reed K. and Ruth (Freebairn) S.; m. Sharon Coray, Aug. 21, 1953; children—Richard, Karen, Leslie, David, Julie. Student, Weber Coll., 1952-54; M.D., U. Utah, 1959. Intern, then resident in phys. medicine and rehab.; mem. faculty div. phys. medicine and rehab. U. Utah Sch. Medicine, Salt Lake City; chmn. div. U. Utah Sch. Medicine, 1965—, asso. prof., 1970-85, prof., 1985—. Chmn. bd. trustees U. Utah Sch. Alcoholism and Other Drug Dependencies; founder Miss Wheelchair Utah Pageant. Served to capt. M.C. U.S. Army, 1960-62. Mem. AMA, Utah State Med. Assn., Am. Acad. Phys. Medicine and Rehab., Assn. Acad. Physiatrists, Am. Spinal Injury Assn.,

Utah Soc. Phys. Medicine & Rehab., Am. Med. Soc. Alcoholism. Office: U Utah Med Ctr 50 N Medical Dr Salt Lake City UT 84132-0002

SWENSON, KAREN, poet, journalist; b. N.Y.C., July 29, 1936; d. Howard William and Dorothy (Trautman) S.; m. Michael Shuter, 1958 (div. 1971); 1 son, Michael. B.A., Barnard Coll., 1959; M.A., NYU, 1971. Free lance journalist; preliminary judge CAPS grants, 1975; judge Walt Whitman Award, Acad. Am. Poets, 1976, 88. Author: An Attic of Ideals, 1974, East-West, 1980, A Sense of Direction, 1989, The Landlady in Bangkok, 1994. Runner up Arvon Poetry award, Ann Stanford Poetry award, 1988; winner Nat. Poetry Series, 1993; Yaddo fellow, 1987, 89, Albee Found fellow, 1990-91. Mem. Century Assn. Home: 430 State St Brooklyn NY 11217-1708

SWENSON, MARY ANN, bishop. Bishop Rocky Mountain Diocese, Denver. Office: Rocky Mountain Diocese 2200 S University Blvd Denver CO 80210

SWENSON, ORVAR, surgeon; b. Halsingborg, Sweden, Feb. 7, 1909; s. Carl Albert and Amanda (Johnson) S.; m. Melva Criley, Sept. 11, 1941; children: Melva, Elsa, Wenda. AB, William Jewell Coll., 1933, DSc (hon.), 1993; M.D., Harvard U., 1937; Dr hc, U. Aix, Marseilles, France, 1975. Diplomate Am. Bd. Surgery. Intern Peter Bent Brigham and Children's hosps., Boston, 1939-41; chief resident Peter Bent Brigham Hosp., 1944-45; Arthur Tracy Cabot fellow Harvard Med. Sch., 1941-44; surgeon Peter Bent Brigham Hosp., 1945-50, Children's Hosp., Boston, 1947-50; surgeon-in-chief Boston Floating Hosp. Infants and Children, 1952-60; asso. surgery Harvard Med. Sch., 1947-50; prof. pediatric surgery Tufts U. Med. Sch., 1957-60; surgeon-in-chief Children's Meml. Hosp., Chgo., 1960-73; prof. surgery Northwestern U. Med. Sch., 1960-73, U. Miami, Fla., 1973-78; chmn. sect. surgery Am. Acad. Pediatrics, 1954-57; lectr. Alex Simpson Smith Lecture Inst. of Child Health, U. London, 1954, Blackfan Lecture Harvard Med. Sch., Boston Children's Hosp., 1958; spl. guest lectr. 16th Gen. Assembly, Japan Med. Congress, 1963; Felton Bequest vis. prof. surgery Univs. Sidney and Melbourne, 1959; vis. prof. U. Bombay, 1980. Author: Pediatric Surgery, 1958; mem. editorial bd. Pediatrics, 1962-68. Recipient Mead Johnson award, 1952, Ladd award Surg. sect. Am. Acad. Pediatrics, 1969, Achievement award Modern Medicine mag., 1971, Frank Billings award AMA, 1949; Swenson Vis. Professorship established in his honor Tufts U. Sch. Medicine, 1987, Swenson Chair in Pediatric Surgery established in 1990. Hon. fellow Royal Coll. Surgeons (Dublin, Ireland), Royal Coll. Physicians and Surgeons Can., Brit. Assn. Pediatric Surgeons (hon., Denis Brown medal 1979); mem. A.C.S., Am. Surg. Assn., Soc. Univ. Surgeons, Am. Pediatric Surg. Assn. (pres. 1973). Discovered cause and cure of Hirschsprung's Disease, 1948. Home: PO Box 41 Rockport ME 04856 also: 172 Cabo de Lagos Fort Pierce FL 34951

SWENSSON, EARL SIMCOX, architect; b. Nashville, July 28, 1930; s. Earl Ebenezer and Viola Lazelle (Simcox) S.; m. Suzanne Dickenson, June 6, 1953; children: Krista, Lin, Kurt. BS in Bldg. Design, Va. Poly. Inst. and State U., 1952, MSArch, 1953; MSArch, U. Ill., 1955. Registered architect 28 states. Founder, prin. Earl Swensson Assocs., Inc., Nashville 1961—; adj. prof. Va. Poly. Inst., Blacksburg, 1971-72, Auburn U., 1976-83; lectr. in field. Contbr. articles to profl. jours. patentee systamodule for pharmacies. Author: (with Richard L. Miller and Earl S. Swensson) New Directions in Hospital and Healthcare Facility Design, 1995. Bd. dirs. Metro Arts Commn., 1979-86, Middle Tenn. Health Systems Aug. 1973-78, Leadership Nashville Alumni Groups, 1984—; mem. bd. advisers U. Tenn. Sch. Architecture, 1982, chmn., 1985-88; mem. architecture program adv. coun. Auburn U., 1990-94. Recipient Jefferson award Am. Inst. Public Service, Nashville chpt., 1985; named Outstanding Nashvillian of Yr. Downtown Kiwanis Club, 1992. Fellow AIA. Presbyterian. Office: Earl Swensson Assocs 2100 W End Ave Ste 1200 Nashville TN 37203-5239

SWERDLOFF, RONALD S., medical educator, researcher; b. Pomona, Calif., Feb. 18, 1938; s. Julius Lewis and Eva (Kelman) S.; m. Ramona Johana Rickinger, June 21, 1959 (div.); children: Jonathan Nicolai, Peter Loren. BS, U. Calif., 1959, MD, 1962. Diplomate Am. Bd. Internal Medicine, Am. Bd. Endocrinology. Intern U. Wash., Seattle, 1962-63, resident, 1963-64; rsch. assoc. NIH, Bethesda, Md., 1964-66; resident UCLA Sch. Medicine, 1966-67; rsch. fellow Harbor-UCLA Med. Ctr., Torrance, Calif., 1967-69, asst. prof. 1969-72, assoc. prof. divsn. Endocrinology, 1972-78, chief divsn. Endocrinology, 1973—, prof., 1978—; dir. UCLA Population Rsch. Ctr., Torrance, Calif., 1982-90; bd. dirs. WHO Collaborative Ctr. Reprodn., Torrance; cons. WHO, Geneva, 1982-90, NIH, Bethesda, 1981—, UN Fertility Planning Assn., Geneva, 1983—, Am. Bd. Internal Medicine, Phila., 1989—; inaugural lectr. Australian Soc. Reproductive Biology, Perth, 1990; mem. tech. adv. com. Contraceptive Rsch. and Devel. Agy. (CONRAD, AID), 1992—. Contbr. 50 chpts. to books, 250 articles to profl. jours. Fellow Am. Coll. Physicians; mem. Am. Soc. Andrology (pres. award 1986, pres. 1992-93), Am. Assn. Physicians, Am. Soc. Clin. Rsch. (pres. 1972-73), Pacific Coast Fertility (Squibb award, Outstanding rsch. award 1976, 84, Wyeth award 1984, pres. 1984), Endocrinology Soc., We. Soc. Clin. Rsch. (pres. 1983-84). Office: UCLA Sch Medicine/Harbor-UCLA Med Ctr Divsn Endocrinology 1000 W Carson St Torrance CA 90502-2004

SWERDLOW, MARTIN ABRAHAM, physician, pathologist; b. Chgo., July 7, 1923; s. Sol Hyman and Rose (Lasky) S.; m. Marion Levin, May 19, 1945; children—Steven Howard, Gary Bruce. Student, Herzl Jr. Coll., 1941-42; B.S., U. Ill., 1945; M.D., U. Ill., Chgo., 1947. Diplomate: Am. Bd. Pathology. Intern Michael Reese Hosp. and Med. Center, Chgo., 1947-48; resident Michael Reese Hosp. and Med. Center, 1948-50, 51-52, mem. staff, 1974—, chmn. dept. pathology, v.p. acad. affairs, 1974-90; pathologist Menorah Med. Ctr., Kansas City, Mo., 1954-57; asst. prof., pathologist U. Ill. Coll. Medicine, Chgo., 1957-59, assoc. prof., 1959-60, clin. assoc. prof., 1960-64, clin. prof., 1964-66, prof., pathologist, 1966-72, assoc. dean, prof. pathology, 1970-72; prof. pathology, chmn. U. Mo., Kansas City, 1972-74; prof. pathology U. Chgo., 1975-89, Geever prof., head pathology U. Ill. 1989-93, Geever prof., head pathology emeritus, 1993—; mem. com. standards Chgo. Health Systems Agy., 1976—. Served with M.C. U.S. Army, 1944-45, 50-54. Recipient Alumnus of Yr. award U. Ill. Coll. Medicine, 1973; Instructorship award U. Ill., 1960, 65, 68, 71, 72. Mem. Chgo. Pathology Soc. (pres. 1980—), Am. Soc. Clin. Pathologists, Coll. Am. Pathologists, Internat. Acad. Pathology, Am. Acad. Dermatology, Am. Soc. Dermatopathology, Inst. Medicine, AMA. Jewish. Office: Univ Ill Coll Medicine 1819 W Polk St Chicago IL 60612 *My credo these years has been to care about patients, students, colleagues, employees, my institution and the many publics I serve. Honesty and thoroughness has been a basic life style, irrespective of the cost. With all, competence is a necessity and ongoing. Continuous responsibility for my education and learning is my way of living.*

SWERDZEWSKI, JOSEPH, lawyer; b. Southampton, N.Y., Jan. 29, 1949; s. Frank and Rosella (Lapinski) S.; m. Natalie J. Conklin, Sept. 29, 1975 (div. Sept. 1991); children: Peter, Thomas, Matthew; m. Gayle Lela Swerdzewski, Feb. 26, 1994; stepchildren: Eric Soden, Jonathan Soden. BA, Coll. Holy Cross, Worcester, Mass., 1971; JD, Fordham U., 1974. Bar: N.Y. 1975, Colo. 1985. Law asst. Suffolk County, N.Y. County Execs. Office, Riverhead, N.Y., 1974-75; supervisory atty. Fed. Labor Rels. Authority, L.A., 1979-82; regional atty. Fed. Labor Rels. Authority, Denver, 1982-91, spl. coun. for gen. counsel, 1991-93; gen. counsel Fed. Labor Rels. Authority, Washington, 1993—; instr. Met. State Coll., Denver, 1985-93; cons. Griffith Assocs., Chgo., 1989-92. Apptd. by Pres. Clinton for a Senate Conformation. Capt. USAF, 1975-79. Democrat. Office: Fed Labor Rels Authority 607 14th St NW Ste 210 Washington DC 22404

SWERN, FREDERIC LEE, engineering educator; b. N.Y.C., Sept. 9, 1947; s. Reuben Swern and Anne Lillian Goldberg; m. Gayle Regina Unger, Dec. 25, 1969; children: Lauren, Michael. BEE, City Coll., N.Y.C., 1969; MSEE, Newark Coll. Engr., 1974; PhD Engr. Sci., N.J. Inst. Tech., 1981. Registered profl. engr., N.J. Engr. Navigation and Control divsn. Bendix, Teterboro, N.J., 1969-72, UNIVAC, divsn. Sperry Rand, Morris Plains, N.J., 1972-73; sr. systems analyst Chubb & Son Inc., Short Hills, N.J., 1973-78; sr. engr. Flight Systems divsn. Bendix, Teterboro, N.J., 1978-84; cons. Swerlin Assocs., 1981—; assoc. prof. engring Stevens Inst. Tech., Hoboken, N.J., 1984—; researcher, cons., Westinghouse Elevator, Morristown, N.J.,

1987, NASA Langley Rsch. Center, Hampton, Va., 1979-82, 1985-90, Hyatt Clark Industries, Clark, N.J., 1984-85, U.S. Army Armament Rsch. and Devel. Ctr., 1985-92, Gen. Motors Corp., Warren, Mich., 1983-84; reviewer Prentice-Hall, Englewood Cliffs, N.J.; cons. Gov. Commn. on Sci. and Tech., 1985-86. Contbr. to profl. jours. Mem. Inst. Elec. Electronic Engrs., Am. Soc. Mech. Engrs., Assn. Computing Machinery, Am. Inst. Aeronautics and Astronautics, Sigma Xi, Pi Tau Sigma. Achievements include Automatic Flight Control System Patent using instrument landing system information and including inertial filtering means for reduced ILS noise; Aircraft Control System Patent using inertial signals; Improved Flare Control Patent for transport aircraft. Home: 53 Village Rd Florham Park NJ 07932-2412 Office: Stevens Institute of Technology Mechanical Engring Lab Castle Point Hoboken NJ 07030

SWETMAN, GLENN ROBERT, English language educator, poet; b. Biloxi, Miss., May 20, 1936; s. Glenn Lyle and June (Read) S. BS, U. So. Miss., 1957, MA, 1959; PhD, Tulane U., 1966; m. Margarita Ortiz, Feb. 8, 1964 (div. 1979); children: Margarita June, Glenn Lyle Maximilian, Glenda Louise. Instr., U. So. Miss., 1957-58, asst. prof., 1964-66; instr. Ark. State U., 1958-59, McNeese U., 1959-61; instr. English, Univ. Coll. Tulane U., 1961-64, spl. asst. dept. elec. engring., 1961-64; assoc. prof. La. Inst. Tech., 1966-67; prof., head dept. langs. Nicholls State Coll., Thibodaux, La., 1967-69, head dept. English, 1969-71, prof., 1971-91, prof. emeritus, William Carey Coll., Gulfport, Miss., 1991—; writer in residence, prof. English William Carey Coll., Gulfport, Miss., 1991—. Ptnr., Breeland Pl., Biloxi, Miss., 1960—; stringer corr. Shreveport (La.) Times, 1966—; ptnr. Ormuba, Inc., 1975—; cons. tech. writing Union Carbide Corp., Am. Fedn. Tchrs. State v.p. Nat. Com. to Resist Attacks on Tenure, 1974—. Subdiv. coord. Rep. Party, Hattiesburg, Miss., 1964. With AUS, 1957. Recipient Poetry awards KQUE Haiku contest, 1964, Coll. Arts contest, L.A., 1966, Black Ship Festival, Yoqosuka, Japan, 1967; Green World Brief Forms award Green World Poetry Editors, 1965. Mem. MLA, S. Cen. MLA, So. Literary Festival Assn. (v.p. 1975-76, 82-83, pres. 1984-85), Coll. Writers Soc. La. (pres. 1971-72, exec. dir. 1983—), IEEE, Am. Assn. Engring. Edn., La. Poetry Soc. (pres. 1971-74, 1986—), Internat. Boswellian Inst., Nat. Fedn. State Poetry Socs. (2d v.p., nat. membership chmn. 1972-74, pres. 1976-77), Nat. Soc. Scholars and Educators (bd. dirs. 1982—, sec. exec. bd. 1986—, sec. bd. dirs. 1968—, sec. soc. 1989—), Am. Fedn. Tchrs. (chpt. pres. 1973-78), Nat. Fedn. State Poetry Socs. (1st v.p. 1975-76, exec. bd. 1972—), Phi Eta Sigma, Omicron Delta Kappa. Book reviewer Jackson (Miss.) State Times, 1961. Poems pub. in various publs. including Poet, Prairie Schooner, Trace, Ball State U. Forum, Film Quar., Poetry Australia, numerous others worldwide; (books of poems) Tunel de Amor, 1973, Deka #1, 1973, Deka #2, 1979, Shards, 1979, Concerning Carpenters, 1980, Son of Igor, 1980; A Range of Sonnets, 1981, Christmas, 1982, Poems of the Fantastic, 1990; contbr. articles (147) to encys.; cons. editor (poetry) Paon Press, 1974—, Scott-Foresman, 1975; editorial bd. Scholar and Educator, 1980—. Home: PO Box 146 Biloxi MS 39533-0146 Office: Nicholls State U Thibodaux LA 70310 also: William Carey Coll 01856 Beach Dr Gulfport MS 39507

SWETNAM, MONTE NEWTON, petroleum exploration executive; b. Alexandria, La., Oct. 9, 1936; s. Montreville Morris and Margaret Elizabeth (Cullison) S.; m. Elaine Adelia Taylor, Dec. 21, 1957; children: Scott David, Robert Troy. Student, Johns Hopkins, 1955-58; B.S. in Geology, U. Wyo., 1960, M.S. in Geology, 1961; M.B.A. in Bus. Adminstrn, Pepperdine U., 1978. Registered geologist, Calif. Exploration geologist Amerada Petroleum Corp., Durango, Colo., 1961-63; exploration geologist Tenneco Oil Co., Durango, 1963-65; dist. project geologist Tenneco Oil Co., Bakersfield, Calif., 1965-69; div. staff geologist Tenneco Oil Co., Bakersfield, 1969; partner Argonaut Oil & Gas Cons., Denver, 1969-71; internat. exploration mgr. Tesoro Petroleum Corp., San Antonio, 1971-73; v.p. internat. exploration Tesoro Petroleum Corp., 1973-74, sr. v.p. exploration, 1974-82; pres. Tesoro-Bolivia Petroleum Co., 1975-82, Tesoro-Algeria Petroleum Co., 1975-82; sr. v.p. exploration Natural Resource Mgmt. Corp./NRM, Dallas, 1983-86; sr. v.p. exploration and prodn. Harken Energy Corp., 1987-89, exec. v.p., 1991-93; pres. Harken Exploration Co., 1989-91, Harken Bahrain Oil Co., 1989-93; exec. v.p., chief oper. officer Giant Exploration and Prodn. Co., Farmington, N.Mex., 1994—; pres. Canyon Marinas, Inc., San Antonio. Contbr. articles to profl. jours. Mem. Am. Assn. Petroleum Geologists, Geol. Soc. Am., Sigma Xi. Republican. Clubs: Alamo Yacht, Lake Canyon Yacht. Home: 3500 Island Moorings Pky # 231 PO Box 154 Port Aransas TX 78373 Office: PO Box 2810 2200 Bloomfield Hwy Farmington NM 87401-8110

SWETS, JOHN ARTHUR, psychologist, scientist; b. Grand Rapids, Mich., June 19, 1928; s. John A. and Sara Henrietta (Heyns) S.; m. Maxine Ruth Crawford, July 16, 1949; children—Stephen Arthur, Joel Brian. B.A., U. Mich., Ann Arbor, 1950, M.A., 1953, Ph.D., 1954. Instr. psychology U. Mich., Ann Arbor, 1954-56; asst. prof. psychology M.I.T., Cambridge, 1956-60, assoc. prof. psychology, 1960-63; v.p. Bolt Beranek & Newman Inc., Cambridge, 1964-69, sr. v.p., 1969-74, gen. mgr. research, devel. and cons. dir., 1971-74; chief scientist BBN Labs., Cambridge, 1975—; lectr. dept. clin. epidemiology Harvard Med. Sch., 1985-88, prof. health care policy, 1988—; mem. corp. Edn. Devel. Ctr., Newton, Mass., 1971-75; vis. research fellow Philips Labs., Netherlands, 1958; Regents' prof. U. Calif., 1969; advisor vision com., com. on hearing and bioacoustics NAS-NRC, 1960—; mem. Commn. on Behavioral Social Scis. and Edn., NRC, 1988-92, vice chair, 1992-93, chmn., 1993—; advisor, cons., lectr. numerous govtl. and profl. orgns. in science. Co-author: (with D.M. Green) Signal Detection Theory and Psychophysics, 1966; (with R.M. Pickett) Evaluation of Diagnostic Systems: Methods From Signal Detection Theory, 1982; editor: Signal Detection and Recognition by Human Observers, 1964; (with L.L. Elliott) Psychology and the Handicapped Child, 1974; (with D. Druckman) Enhancing Human Performance, 1988; contbr. articles to profl. jours.; mem. editorial bd. Medical Decision Making, 1980-85, Psychological Science, 1989—. Past mem. numerous civic orgns.; mem. corp. Winchester Hosp., Mass., 1981-84. Fellow AAAS (coun. 1986-89), APA (Disting. Sci. Contbn. award 1990), Am. Acad. Arts and Scis., Acoustical. Soc. Am. (exec coun. 1968-71), Soc. Exptl. Psychologists (chmn. 1986, exec. com. 1986-89, Howard Crosby Warren medal 1985), Am. Psychol. Soc.; mem. NAS (Troland award com. 1991, chmn. 1992), Psychonomic Soc., Psychometric Soc., Soc. Math. Psychology, Evaluation Rsch. Soc., Sigma Xi, Sigma Alpha Epsilon, Winchester Country Club, Cosmos Club. Congregationalist (moderator). Office: Bolt Beranek & Newman Inc 10 Moulton St Cambridge MA 02138-1191

SWETT, ALBERT HERSEY, retired lawyer, business executive, consultant; b. Medina, N.Y., Feb. 18, 1923; s. Raymond Fuller and Marion (Hersey) S.; m. Mary Stewart, Oct. 10, 1944; children: Marion Hersey Swett Robinson, Margaret Stewart Swett Haskell, Albert Louis. Grad., The Hill Sch., 1941 B.Engring., Yale U., 1944; LL.B., Harvard U., 1949. Bar: N.Y. 1949. Assoc. Harris, Beach & Wilcox, Rochester, N.Y., 1949-56, ptnr., 1957-66; v.p., gen. counsel Xerox Corp., Stamford, Conn., 1966-75; v.p., gen. counsel Coca-Cola Co., Atlanta, 1975-78, v.p., counsel to chmn., 1978-80; ind. cons., 1980—. Trustee Practising Law Inst., 1977-83. Served with USNR, 1942-46. Mem. Assn. Gen. Counsel (emeritus), Tau Beta Pi. Republican. Methodist. Lodge: Masons. Home: PO Box 30319 River Ranch FL 33867

SWETT, DANIEL ROBERT, lawyer; b. Chgo., Sept. 17, 1936; s. Israel and Rose (Crocker) S.; m. Susan Kay Mann, Sept. 18, 1965; children—Karen Michelle, Brian Israel. A.B., Harvard U., 1958, LL.B., 1961. Bar: Ill. 1962. Assoc. Sonnenschein Carlin Nath & Rosenthal, Chgo., 1962-69; ptnr. Sonnenschein, Nath & Rosenthal, 1970—. Legal advisor Planned Parenthood Assn., Chgo., 1969—; asst. sec. Michael Reese Hosp. and Med. Ctr., Chgo., 1977-82, 87-91; sec. Michael Reese Health Plan Inc., 1972-91; bd. dirs. Jewish Fedn. Met. Chgo., 1979-85; gen. counsel Michael Reese Found., 1991—. Democrat. Jewish. Clubs: Standard (Chgo.); Lake Shore Country (Glencoe, Ill.). Home: 516 Sheridan Rd Glencoe IL 60022-1716 Office: Sonnenschein Nath Rosenthal 233 S Wacker Dr Ste 8000 Chicago IL 60606-6404

SWETT, STEPHEN FREDERICK, JR., principal, educator; b. Englewood, N.J., Sept. 14, 1935; s. Stephen Frederick and Frances (Gulotta) S.; B.A., Montclair State Coll., 1959, M.A., 1965; Ed.D. in Edn. Administrn., Rutgers U., 1976, graduate North Light Art School, 1969; m. Annette Palazzolo, Nov. 18, 1961; children—Susan, Kimberly Ann, Stephen Laurence. Tchr.,

Long Branch (N.J.) High Sch., 1961-62, Roselle Park (N.J.) High Sch., 1962-73; research asst. Rutgers U., New Brunswick, N.J., 1973-74; instructional supr. Elmwood Park (N.J.) Schs., 1974-76, Morris Hills Regional Schs., Denville, N.J., 1976-77; asst. prin. Lawrence High Sch., Lawrenceville, N.J., 1977-79; prin. Stafford Intermediate Sch., Manahawkin, N.J., 1979-94, recreation and art cons., 1994—. participant NSF Inst. in physics, chemistry and math. Seton Hall U., 1964, Newark Coll. Engring., 1965, Stevens Inst. Tech., summers 1966-68. Served with AUS, 1959-61. Mem. Roselle Park Edn. Assn. (pres. 1971-73). Nat. Soc. Study Edn., Am. Assn. Physics Tchrs., Am. Inst. Physics, N.J. assns. sch. administrs., Nat. Assn. Elementary and Middle Sch. Administrs., N.J. Assn. Elementary and Middle Sch. Adminstrs., Nat. Assn. Secondary Sch. Prins., Phi Delta Kappa (sec. Rutgers chpt. 1977-80, v.p. 1980-82, pres. 1983-84). Research on sch. fin. Home: 12 Louis St Old Bridge NJ 08857-2235

SWEZEY, CHARLES MASON, Christian ethics educator, administrator; b. Charlottesville, Va., May 16, 1935; s. Fenton Hendy and Catherine Jane (Mason) S.; m. Mary Evelyn Knight, June 16, 1960; children: Christopher Stephen, Margaret Fenton, Mary Mason. BA, Washington and Lee U., 1957; BD, Union Theol. Sem., 1961; STM, Yale U., 1962; MA, Phd, Vanderbilt U., 1974, 78. Ordained to ministry, Presbyterian Ch., 1962. Asst. minister Lexington (Va.) Presbyn. Ch., 1962-70; stated clk. Lexington Presbytery, 1967-68; vis. lectr. Mary Baldwin Coll., Staunton, Va., 1966-67, 68; asst. prof. Union Theol. Sem., Richmond, Va., 1974-80, assoc. prof., 1980-83, prof. Christian ethics, 1983—, dean of faculty, 1990—; mem. coop. com. on examination for candidates, Presbyn. Ch. U.S.A., 1978-88. Editorial bd. Interpretation, Richmond, 1981-92; co-editor: James Gustafson's Theocentric Ethics, 1988; contbr. articles to theol. publs. Bd. dirs. Richmond Met. Blood Svc., 1987—; mem. Human Fetal Tissue Transplantation panel NIH, Bethesda, Md., 1988. Grantee Danforth Found., 1968-69; Woodrow Wilson Found. fellow, 1970-71. Mem. Soc. Christian Ethics. Office: Union Theol Sem 3401 Brook Rd Richmond VA 23227-4514

SWHIER, CLAUDIA VERSFELT, lawyer; b. Mineola, N.Y., Jan. 15, 1950; d. William Holly and Ruth (Gerland) Versfelt; m. Robert Dewain Swhier Jr., June 5, 1974; children: James Robert, Jeffrey William. BA in Philosophy magna cum laude, Yale U., 1972; JD cum laude, Harvard U., 1975. Bar: Ind. 1975. Assoc. Barnes & Thornburg, Indpls., 1975-82, ptnr., 1982—. Mem. editorial bd. Harvard Law Rev., 1973-75; editor Thrift Law in Rev., Banking Law in Rev., 1989—. Mem. ABA, Ind. Bar Assn., Indpls. Bar Assn. Republican. Presbyterian. Avocations: skiing, swimming, aerobics. Office: Barnes & Thornburg 1313 Mchts Bank Bldg Indianapolis IN 46204

SWIBEL, STEVEN WARREN, lawyer; b. Chgo., July 18, 1946; s. Morris Howard and Gloria (Weindling) S.; m. Leslie Cohen; children: Deborah, Laura. SB, MIT, 1968; JD, Harvard U., 1971. Bar: Ill. 1971, U.S. Dist. Ct. (no. dist.) Ill. 1971, U.S. Tax Ct. 1973, U.S. Ct. Appeals (7th cir.) 1981. Assoc. Sonnenschein Carlin Nath & Rosenthal, Chgo., 1971-78, ptnr.; 1978-84; ptnr. Rudnick & Wolfe, 1984-93; ptnr. Schwartz, Cooper, Greenberger, Krauss Chartered, 1993—; adj. prof. taxation III. Inst. Tech. Kent Coll. Law, Chgo., 1989—; lectr. in field. Contbr. articles to profl. jours. Ednl. counselor MIT, 1979—; bd. dirs. MIT Alumni Fund, 1992—, Ragdale Found., 1987—, treas. 1987-92. Recipient Lobdell Disting. Svc. award MIT Alumni Assn., 1989. Mem. ABA (com. partnerships sect. taxation), Ill. Bar Assn., Chgo. Bar Assn. (fed. taxation com., exec. subcom. 1984—, chmn. subcom. on real estate, partnerships and tax sheltered investments 1986-87, vice chmn. 1988-89, chmn. 1989-90), Met. Club, MIT Club (dir. Chgo. chpt. 1980-91, sec. 1980-87, pres. 1987-89), Sigma Xi, Tau Beta Pi, Eta Kappa Nu. Office: Schwartz Cooper Greenberger & Krauss Chartered Ste 2700 180 N La Salle St Chicago IL 60601-1210

SWICHAR, EDWARD, lawyer; b. Phila., Apr. 18, 1940; s. Philip and Bella (Blonder) S.; m. Linda Terry Gordon, Oct. 31, 1970; children: Jonathan, Scott. BS in Pharmacy, Temple U., 1962, JD, 1968. Bar: Pa. 1968, D.C. 1971. Trial atty. civil div. U.S. Dept. Justice, Washington, 1968-72; ptnr. Wexler, Weisman, Forman & Shapiro, Phila., 1972-84; ptnr., co-chair litigation dept. Blank, Rome, Comisky & McCauley, Phila., 1984—. Mem. ABA, Pa. Bar Assn., Phila. Bar Assn. Office: Blank Rome Comisky McCauley 4 Penn Plz Philadelphia PA 19103

SWICK, HERBERT MORRIS, medical educator, neurologist; b. Baton Rouge, Nov. 22, 1941; s. Edgar Haight and Mary Ellen (Morris) S.; m. Mary Lynne McCluggage, June 29, 1963; children: Kristin Ann, Elizabeth May, Diane Marie. BA with honors, Johns Hopkins U., 1963, MD Sch. Medicine, 1966. Cert. Am. Bd. Psychiatry and Neurology, Am. Bd. Pediatrics. Resident in pediatrics Johns Hopkins U., Balt., 1966-69; resident in neurology U. Ky., Lexington 1971-74, asst. prof. neurology and pediatrics, 1974-75; asst. to assoc. prof. neurology and pediatrics Med. Coll. Wis., Milw., 1975-84, prof. pediats. and neurology, 1984-94, asst. dean med. edn., interm chmn. dept. neurology, 1987-88, asst. dean acad. affairs, 1988-91, sr. assoc. dean acad. affairs, 1991-93, sr. assoc. dean for acad. programs, 1993-94; prof. neurology, sr. assoc. dean acad. affairs U. Kans. Sch. Medicine, Kansas City, 1994—, acting chmn. dept. history and philosophy of medicine, 1995—; chief dept. neurology Children's Hosp. Wis., Milw., 1981-87, acting chmn. dept. neurology, 1987-88; vis. prof. neurol. edn. Mayo Clinic and Found., Rochester, Minn., 1985. Contbr. numerous articles to profl. jours. Bd. dirs. Milw. Chamber Music Soc., 1982-88, pres. 1986-88. Served to lt. commdr., USN, 1969-71. Fulbright sr. scholar, 1978. Fellow Am. Acad. Neurology (edn. com., undergrad. edn. subcom. 1985-89); mem. Am. Assn. History Medicine, Child Neurology Soc. (archives and history com. 1981-88, exec. com. 1982-86, sci. selection com. 1983, 84), Columbia History of Medicine Club, Internat. Child Neurology Assn., Milw. Acad. Medicine (coun. 1993-94), Profs. of Child Neurology (sec.-treas. 1981-82, pres.-elect 1982-84, pres. 1984-85), Assn. Univ. Profs. in Neurology (undergrad. edn. com. 1979-86).

SWID, STEPHEN CLAAR, business executive; b. N.Y.C., Oct. 26, 1940; s. David and Selma (Claar) S.; m. Nan Goldman, Mar. 1, 1963; children: Robin, Scott, Jill. BS, Ohio State U., 1962. Mgmt. trainee Alside Aluminum Co., Akron, Ohio, 1962-63; securities analyst Dreyfus Fund, N.Y.C., 1964-66; sr. investment officer Oppenheimer Fund, N.Y.C., 1966-67; gen. ptnr. City Assocs., 1967-69, Swid Investors, 1970-78; co-chmn. bd. Gen. Felt Industries Inc., Saddle Brook, N.J., 1974-86, Knoll Internat., 1977-86; chmn. bd., chief exec. officer SBK Entertainment World, Inc. N.Y.C., 1986-89; chmn., chief exec. officer SCS Communications, N.Y.C. 1989—; chmn. exec. com., dir. Inst. for East-West Studies. Trustee Solomon Guggenheim Mus.; mem. vis. com. 20th century art Met. Mus. Art; past trustee Horace Mann Sch., N.Y.C.; former exec. vp. bd. dirs. Lenox Sch. N.Y.; chmn. Mcpl. Art Soc. Office: SCS Communications 152 W 57th St New York NY 10019-3310

SWIDEN, LADELL RAY, travel company executive; b. Sioux Falls, S.D., June 17, 1938; s. Alick and Mildred Elizabeth (Larson) S.; m. Phyllis Lorriane Enga, Sept. 10, 1961; children: David, Daniel, Shari. BSEE, S.D. State U., 1961; MBA, S.D., 1982. Registered profl. engr., S.D., Minn. Instrument engr. Honeywell, Mpls., 1962-67; v.p. sales Swiden Appliance and Furniture, Sioux Falls, 1967-68; engring. mgr. Raven Industries, Inc., Sioux Falls, 1968-84; v.p. engring. Beta Raven Inc., St. Louis, 1984-85; pres. Delta Systems, Inc., St. Louis, 1985-86; acting dir. Engring. and Environ. Rsch. Ctr. S.D. State U., Brookings, 1986-94, dir. univ./industry tech. svc., 1986-94; v.p. Village Travel Inc., Brookings, 1994—; bd. dirs Brookings Econ. Devel. Ctr. Patentee in field. Chmn. Indsl. Devel. Com., Brookings 1989-90, vice-chair, 1988-89; chmn. bldg. com. Ascension Luth. Ch., 1988-90. Mem. NSPE, Nat. Assn. of Mgmt. and Tech. Assistance Ctrs. (bd. dirs.), Instrument Soc. Am., Aircraft Owners and Pilots Assn., Exptl. Aircraft Assn., Am. Bonanza Soc., S.D. Engring. Soc. (pres. N.E. chpt. 1991-92), Rotary, Elks. Avocations: flying, travel. Home: 105 Heather Ln Brookings SD 57006-4123 Office: Carlson Wagon Travel 1715 6th St Brookings SD 57006

SWIECICKI, MARTIN, neurosurgeon; b. Camden, N.J., June 29, 1934; s. Martin E. and Annetta Swiecicki; m. Gloria J. Whelpley; children: Diane, Annette, Karen, Sheryl, Martin C. BA, Colgate U., 1956; MD, Hahnemann Med. Sch., 1960. Diplomate Am. Bd. Neurol. Surgery. Intern West Jersey Hosp., Camden, 1960-61; resident in neurological surgery Jefferson U., Phila., 1961-65; mem. staff in neurol. surgery West Jersey Hosp., Camden,

Berlin, N.J., 1967—, chief Neurol. Surgery, 1967-89; clin. assoc prof. Neurol. Surgery Hahnemann Med. Coll., Phila., 1977—. Contbr. articles to profl. jours. Recipient N.J. Gov.'s award for Outstanding Svcs., 1970, 71, 72, 73, Award for Support and Svc. Boy Scouts Am., 1992. Fellow ACS; mem. AMA, Camden County Med. Soc. (v.p.1993, pres. 1995), West Jersey Med. Soc., N.J. State Med. Soc., N.J. Neurosurg. Soc.(sec.-treas. 978-79, pres. 1981, chmn. peer rev. com. 1983-89, mem. peer rev. com. 1977—), Camden County Med. Soc. (exec. com. 1977—, v.p. 1993, pres.- elect 1994, pres. 1995), Soc. Air Force Clin. Surgeons, Am. Assn. Neurol. Surgeons. Office: Neurosurg Assocs NJ 2301 Evesham Rd Ste 406 Voorhees NJ 08043

SWIFT, CALVIN THOMAS, electrical and computer engineering educator; b. Quantico, Va., Feb. 6, 1937; s. Thomas and Elsie (Hill) S.; m. Joanne Taylor, Sept. 5, 1959; children: Pamela, Janet. B.S., MIT, 1959; M.S., Va. Poly. Inst., 1965; Ph.D., William and Mary Coll., 1969. Research engr. N. Am. Aviation Co., Downey, Calif., 1959-62; aerospace technologist NASA, Hampton, Va., 1962-81; prof. elec. and computer engring. U. Mass., Amherst, 1981—; cons. engring., Amherst, 1981—. Editor: Transactions on Geoscience and Remote Sensing, 1980-84; assoc. editor: Jour. Oceanic Engring., 1980-84. F.L. Thompson fellow NASA, 1977. Fellow IEEE; mem. Internat. Union Radio Sci. (chmn. Commn. F 1988-91), Antennas and Propagation Soc. (adminstrv. com. 1974-77, 80-85), Geosci. and Remote Sensing Soc. (adminstrv. com. 1978-86, pres. 1985, Disting. Achievement award 1994). Office: U Mass Dept Elec & Computer Engring Amherst MA 01003

SWIFT, DAVID L., manufacturing company executive; b. Muncie, Ind., 1936. Grad., Ball State U., 1958, No. Ky. U., 1966. Former v.p., sec., gen. counsel Acme-Cleve. Corp., pres., CEO, chmn. bd. dirs., 1987—. Mem. ABA. Office: Acme-Cleve Corp 1242 E 49th St Cleveland OH 44114-3810

SWIFT, DOLORES MONICA MARCINKEVICH, public relations executive; b. Hazleton, Pa., Apr. 3, 1936; d. Adam Martin and Anna Frances (Lizbinski) Marcinkevich; student McCann Coll., 1954-56; m. Morden Leib Swift, Dec. 18, 1966. Pub. rels. coord. Internat. Coun. Shopping Ctrs., N.Y.C., 1957-59, Wendell P. Colton Advt. Agy., N.Y.C., 1959-61, Sydney S. Baron Pub. Rels. Corp., N.Y.C., 1961-65, Robert S. Taplinger Pub. Rels., N.Y.C., 1965-66; prin. Dolores M. Swift, Pub. Rels., Chgo., 1966—. Bd. dirs. Welfare Pub. Rels. Forum, 1971-79, treas., 1975-77; mem. pub. rels. adv. com. Mid-Am. chpt. A.R.C., 1973—; mem. women's com. Mark Twain Meml., 1968-69; pub. rels. dir. N.J. Symphony, Bergen County, 1969-70, mem. pub. rels. and promotion com.; mem. Wadsworth Atheneum, 1968-69; bd. dirs. Youth Guidance, 1972-75, Camp Fire, Met. Chgo. Coun., Inc., 1990-91; mem. NCCJ Labor, Mgmt. and Pub. Interest Conf., 1977-78; mem. pub. rels. com. United Way/Crusade of Mercy, 1979-80, 83, chmn. health svcs. com., 1984, direct mail com. 1985-86. Mem. Pub. Rels. Soc. Am. (accredited, coll. of fellows, Disting. Svc. award 1988, chmn. subcom. Nat. Ctr. for Vol. Action 1971-72, pub. svcs. com. Chgo. chpt. 1971-72, dir. 1975-82, chmn. counselors sect. 1976-77, assembly del. 1976, 79-81, 84-89, sec. 1977-78, v.p. 1978-79, pres.-elect 1979-80, pres. 1980-81, Midwest dist. chmn. 1984, nat. bd. dirs. 1985-89, sec. 1987-89, host chpt. chmn. 1981 conf., chmn. Midwest Dist. Conf. 1983, chmn. ethics awareness com. 1990-92, chmn. sr. forum com. 1993-94, mem. sr. forum com. 1995—, ednl. affairs com. 1990—), Women's Club (publs. chmn. Englewood, N.J., 1970-71), Publicity Club (chmn. pub. info. com. 1975-76). Mem. editorial bd. Public Relations Jour., 1978. Home and Office: 3800 N Lake Shore Dr Chicago IL 60613-3313

SWIFT, EDWARD FOSTER, III, investment banker; b. Chgo., Nov. 1, 1923; s. Theodore Philip I and Elizabeth (Hoyt) S.; m. Joan McKelvy, July 2, 1947; children: Theodore Philip II, Edward McKelvy, Lockhart McKelvy, Elizabeth Hoyt; m. Carol Coffey Whipple, June 21, 1968. Grad., Hotchkiss Sch., 1941; BA, Yale U., 1945. With Esmark, Inc. (formerly Swift & Co.), 1947-75, asst. to v.p. charge meat packing plants, 1958, asst. v.p. 1958-59, v.p. for provisions, fgn., casings and storage, 1959-64, exec. v.p., 1964-75; vice-chmn. Chgo. Corp., 1975-79; vice chmn. Bacon, Whipple & Co., Chgo., 1980-84; mng. dir. A.G. Becker Paribas Inc., Chgo., 1984-85; with E.F. Hutton and Co., Chgo., 1985-87; mng. dir. Shearson Lehman Hutton Inc. Chgo., 1987—; bd. dirs. Golden Cat Corp., South Bend, Ind., Santa Fe Pacific Corp., Santa Fe Pacific Pipelines, Inc. Chmn. So. Ind. chpt. United Negro Coll. Fund, 1956; trustee Northwestern U., Evanston, Ill.; bd. dirs. Northwestern Meml. Hosp., Chgo. Served to capt. U.S. Army, 1942-46. Mem. Chgo. Assn. Commerce and Industry (bd. dirs.), Scroll and Key, Chgo. Club, Racquet Club, Econ. Club, Valley Club, Country Club, Onwentsia Club, Old Elm ClubBirnam Wood Golf Club, Aurelian Honor Soc. Home: 1500 N Astor St Chicago IL 60610-1640 Office: 70 W Madison St Ste 1400 Chicago IL 60602-4270

SWIFT, EVANGELINE WILSON, lawyer; b. San Antonio, May 2, 1939; d. Raymond E. and Josephine (Woods) Wilson; 1 child, Justin Lee. Student So. Meth. U., 1956-59; LL.B., St. Mary's U., San Antonio, 1963. Bar: Tex. 1963, U.S. Ct. Appeals (5th cir.) 1972, D.C. 1976, U.S. Dist. Ct. D.C. 1976, U.S. Supreme Ct. 1980, U.S. Ct. Appeals (11th cir.) 1981, U.S. Ct. Appeals (10th cir.) 1982, U.S. Ct. Appeals (D.C. cir.) 1982, U.S. Ct. Appeals (fed. cir.) 1983. Atty.-adv. ICC, Washington, 1964-65; staff atty. Headstart Program, OEO, Washington, 1965; exec. legal asst. to chmn., spl. asst. to vice chmn. EEOC, Washington, 1965-71, chief decisions div., 1971-75, asst. gen. counsel, 1975-76; cons. to sec. Employment Standards Adminstrn., Dept. Labor, Washington, 1977-79; ptnr. Swift & Swift, P.C., Washington, 1977-79; gen. counsel Merit Systems Protection Bd., Washington, 1979-86, mng. dir., 1986-87, dir. policy and evaluation, 1987—; bd. govs. U.S. Ct. Appeals (fed. cir.) Bar Assn., 1984-93, treas., 1987-89, sec., 1989-90, pres. elect, 1990; Fed. Cir. Bar Assn. (pres. 1992); guest lectr. Drake U. U. Pa., MIT; mem. U.S. del. 23d Sessions UN Commn. on Status of Women, Geneva, 1970. Recipient Meritorious Service award Fed. Govt., 1967, Fed. Women's award, 1975, Performance award Merit Systems Protection Bd., 1981-86, 92, 93, 94, Gold award 1986, Presdl. CFC award, 1984, 86, 94, EEO award Merit Systems Protection Bd., 1985, 94, Theodore Roosevelt award, 1988, Elmer B. Staats award NCAC, 1994. Mem. Soc. Pub. Adminstrn., 1994. Methodist. Office: Merit System Protection Bd Office of Policy and Evaluation 1120 Vermont Ave NW Washington DC 20419-0002

SWIFT, FRANK MEADOR, lawyer; b. N.Y.C., Dec. 27, 1911; s. Frank Meador and Alberta (Rankin) S.; m. Harriet Elizabeth Simpson, May 30, 1944; children: Frank Meador, Thomas Lamar. Student, Emory U., 1930-32; LL.B., U. Ga., 1935. Bar: Ga. 1935. Partner Swift, Currie, McGhee & Hiers, Atlanta, 1965-82; of counsel Swift, Currie, McGhee & Hiers, 1982—. Served to comdr. USNR, 1942-46. Mem. Am., Ga. bar assns., Lawyers Club Atlanta, Am. Judicature Soc. Republican. Presbyn. Clubs: Piedmont Driving. Home: 3150 Palisades Ct Marietta GA 30067-5130 Office: Swift Currie McGhee & Hiers 1355 Peachtree St NE Atlanta GA 30309-3269

SWIFT, HUMPHREY HATHAWAY, manufacturing executive; b. Phila., Apr. 18, 1915; s. Robert Wesselhoeft and Edith (Steel) S.; m. Dorothea Banks, Apr. 8, 1943 (dec. 1951); children: Edith S., Alexandra Swift Bigelow; m. Pamela Ann Whitney, June 6, 1953; children: Pamela Swift Tarnower, Hope S. Baker, Alison Clarke. AB, U. N.C., 1939. Salesman Swift & Anderson Inc., 1946-50; mgr. sales Standard Thermometer Inc., Boston, 1951-55, pres., 1960-70; exec. v.p. Swift Instruments Inc., Boston, 1959-68, pres., 1968—; v.p. Swift Instruments Internat. S.A., Boston, 1959-68, pres., 1968—. Mem. Humphrey (Mass.) Adv. Com., 1965-66, Hingham Town Com., 1955-60. Lt. comdr. USNR, 1941-46, ETO. Mem. World Trade Ctr. Photog. Mktg., Nat. Sporting Good Assn., St. Anthony Club, New Bedford Yacht Club, Hingham Yacht Club, Corinthians. Republican. Episcopalian. Avocations: sailing, skiing. Office: Swift Instruments Inc 952 Dorchester Ave Boston MA 02125

SWIFT, ISABEL DAVIDSON, editorial director; b. Tokyo; d. Carleton Byron and Mary Howard (Davidson) S.; m. Steven C. Phillips. BA, Harvard U., 1976. Asst. editor Pocket Books, Simon & Schuster, N.Y.C., 1979-81; assoc. editor, editor, sr. editor, editorial mgr. Silhouette Books, N.Y.C., 1981-91, editorial dir., 1991—; internat. speaker on romance genre. Contbr. articles to profl. jours. Recipient RITA award Romance Writers Am., 1992, 94. Mem. N.Y. Women's Found. Office: Silhouette Books 300 E 42nd St New York NY 10017

SWIFT, JAMES WILLIAM, health care executive; b. Sheridan, Wyo., Nov. 21, 1945; s. Barney L. and Agnes S.; m. Elizabeth Ann Connors, Aug. 17, 1968; children—Courtney, Colleen, Molly, Jennifer, Michael, Matthew. B.A., St. Louis U., 1968, M.H.A., 1971, M.B.A., 1975; M.A., Central State U., Edmond, Okla., 1979. Asst. administr. St. John's Mercy Medical Center, St. Louis, 1971-75; exec. v.p. Mercy Health Center, Oklahoma City, 1975-78; exec. dir. Mercy Health Center, 1978-79; pres., dir. St. John's Regional Health Center, Springfield, Mo., 1979—; dir. Empire Bank; tchr. Maryville Coll., Florissant Valley Community Coll.; chmn. task force continuing edn. Bi-State Regional Med. Program, St. Louis, 1972. Exec. com. Breech Sch. Bus., Drury Coll.; devel. bd. Cath. Sch. System; bd. dirs. Adult Edn. Council of St. Louis, 1973; treas. Alumni Assn. St. Louis U. Program in Hosp. and Health Care Adminstrn., 1975-76; vice chmn. fin. com. St. Eugene Ch. and Sch., Oklahoma City, 1978. Fellow Am. Coll. Hosp. Adminstrs.; mem. Am. Hosp. Assn., Mo. Hosp. Assn., St. Louis U. Hosp. and Health Care Adminstrs. Alumni Assn. (dir. 1978—). Roman Catholic. Home: 1501 S Charing Rd Springfield MO 65809-2109 Office: St John's Regional Health Ctr 1235 E Cherokee St Springfield MO 65804-2203

SWIFT, JANE MARIA, state senator; b. North Adams, Mass., Feb. 24, 1965; d. John Maynard and Jean Mary (Kent) S.; m. Charles T. Hunt III, Feb. 19, 1994. BA in Am. Studies, Trinity Coll., Hartford, Conn., 1987. Exec. mgmt. trainee G. Fox. & Co., Hartford, 1987-88; adminstrv. aide Sen. Peter C. Webber, Boston, 1988-90; mem. Mass. State Senate, Boston, 1991—; 3d asst. minority leader, 1993—. Republican. Roman Catholic. Office: State Senate Rm 407 State House Boston MA 02133

SWIFT, JOHN FRANCIS, health care advertising company executive; b. N.Y.C., June 15, 1935; s. John F. and Mary Veronica (Kehoe) S.; m. Eleanor H. Cunniff, Oct. 10, 1964; children—John Francis, Sharon Ann. B.S. in Bus. Adminstrn, Seton Hall U., 1960, postgrad., 1960-61. Mktg. research mgr. Lederle Labs. div. Cyanamid Internat., 1960-63; account exec. Robert A. Becker Advt. Agy., N.Y.C., 1963-66; mgr. new products Chesebrough Ponds Co., N.Y.C., 1966-68; v.p. Frohlich Intercon Co., N.Y.C., 1968-72; pres., chief exec. officer Lavey/Wolff/Swift, Inc., N.Y.C., 1972-91, chmn., chief exec. officer, 1991-94; pres., chief exec. officer BBDO Health & Med. Communications Inc., 1977-91, chmn., chief exec. officer, 1991—; vice chmn. Lyons Lavey Nickel Swift, Inc., 1995—. Bd. govs. Stamford Healthcare Systems, 1991—; chmn. Cathedral Healthcare Found., 1994—. Served with USN, 1955-57. Mem. Pharm. Advt. Council (pres. 1979), Bio-Med. Mktg. Assn. Clubs: Canoe Brook (Summit, N.J.); Skytop (Pa.) Boca Raton (Fla.) Country, Boca West Country; N.Y. Athletic; Rodney Sq. (Del.). Home: 32 Peppermill Rd Chatham NJ 07928-1312 also: 19405 Cedar Glen Dr Boca Raton FL 33434-5132 also: 76 Bay Point Harbour Pt Pleasant NJ 08742-5509 Office: Lyons Lavey Nickel Swift Inc 488 Madison Ave New York NY 10022-5702

SWIFT, MICHAEL RONALD, physician, scientist, educator; b. N.Y.C., Feb. 5, 1935; s. Herbert Allen and Estelle (Clafter) S.; m. Ronnie Elaine Gorman, Nov. 27, 1971; children—Melissa, Amy, Laura. B.A., Swarthmore Coll., 1955; M.A., U. Calif.-Berkeley, 1958; M.D., NYU, 1962. Diplomate Am. Bd. Internal Medicine, Am. Bd. Med. Genetics. Instr., then asst. prof. NYU Sch. Medicine, N.Y.C., 1966-70; assoc. prof., then prof. U. N.C., Chapel Hill, 1972-92, also chief genetics div.; prof. pediatrics and dir. div. human molecular genetics N.Y. Med. Coll., N.Y.C., 1992—. Contbr. chpts. to books and articles to profl. jours. Mem. AAAS, Am. Soc. Human Genetics, Alpha Omega Alpha. Achievements include identification of human genes for breast cancer and for mental illness; devel. of new method for identifying specific genes that cause suchdiseases as cancer, diabetes mellitus, mental illness. Avocation: hiking, fishing, travel. Office: NY Med Coll 4 Skyline Dr Hawthorne NY 10532-2143

SWIFT, RICHARD (GENE), composer, educator; b. Middlepoint, Ohio, Sept. 24, 1927; s. Lisle Russell and Josephine (Ladd) S.; m. Dorothy Zackrisson, Feb. 10, 1951; children: Jeremy, John, Joel. MA, U. Chgo., 1956. Assoc. prof. music U. Calif., Davis, 1956-67, prof., 1967-91, prof. emeritus, 1991—, chmn. dept., 1963-71; vis. prof. Princeton U., 1977; faculty research lectr. U. Calif., 1983. Composer: A Coronal, 1954, String Quartet I, 1956, II, 1958, III, 1964, Sonata for Clarinet and Piano, 1957, Sonata for Solo Violin, 1958, Eve, 1959, Stravaganza III for Clarinet, Violin and Piano, 1960, Concerto for Piano and Chamber Ensemble, 1961, Extravaganza for Orchestra, 1962, Domains, I, II, III, 1963, Bucolics, 1964, Concerto for Violin and Chamber Ensemble, 1967, Music for A While, 1969, Thanatopsis, 1971, Prime, 1973, Quartet IV, 1973, Specimen Days, 1976, Mein blaues Klavier, 1979, Concerto II for piano and chamber ensemble, 1980, Quartet V, 1982, Things of August, 1985, Roses Only, 1991, In Arcadia, 1994; consulting editor: 19th Century Music. Served with AUS, 1950-52. Recipient award Rockefeller Found., 1956, 68; award Fromm Found.; Composers String Quartet award, 1973; award Nat. Endowment for Arts, 1976; Inst. award Am. Acad. and Inst. Arts and Letters, 1978; Disting. Teaching award U. Calif., 1980. Fellow Inst. Creative Arts; mem. Am. Music Ctr., ASCAP, Soc. for Music Theory. Home: 568 S Campus Way Davis CA 95616-3523

SWIFT, RICHARD J., engineering company executive; b. 1944. BS, U.S. Mil. Acad., 1966; MS, Purdue U., 1972; MBA, Fairleigh Dickinson U., 1972. With TVA, 1970-72; with Foster Wheeler Corp., Clinton, N.J., 1972-76, from various mgmt. positions to pres., COO, 1977-94, chmn. bd., pres., CEO, 1994—; with Union Carbide Corp., 1976-77. Served U.S. Army, 1966-70. Office: Foster Wheeler Corp Perryville Corp Pk Clinton NJ 08809*

SWIFT, ROBERT FREDERIC, music educator; b. Ilion, N.Y., July 7, 1940; s. Frederic Fay and Ruth Eleanor (Ainslie) S.; m. Margot Sue Werme, Nov. 24, 1962; children: Jeffrey Robert, Jennifer Sue. BS, Hartwick Coll., 1962, MA, 1968; PhD, Eastman Sch. Music, Rochester, N.Y., 1970. Music instr. West Winfield (N.Y.) Cen. Sch., 1962-67, N.Y. State Music Camp, Oneonta, 1962—, Brighton High Sch., Rochester, 1970-71; asst. prof. music Eastman Sch. Music, Rochester, 1971-76; assoc. prof. music Memphis State U., 1976-79; prof. music, dept. chmn. Plymouth State Coll. of U. N.H., Plymouth, 1979—; organist; choral condr. U.S., Can., Britain, Australia, New Zealand. Composer numerous musical compositions. Ch. musician Christian Sci., Presbyn., Bapt. chs. Bapt. chs. Nat. Def. Edn. Act Title IV fellow U. Rochester, 1967-70; recipient Disting. Teaching award Memphis State U., 1979, Disting. Teaching award Coll. for Lifelong Learning of U. System of N.H. 1987. Mem. N.H. Music Edn. Assn., Music Educators Nat. Conf., Am. Choral Dirs. Assn., Coll. Music Soc., Royal Sch. Ch. Music., Phi Mu Alpha Sinfonia, Kappa Delta Pi. Republican. Mem. Christian Science Ch. Home: PO Box 125 Plymouth NH 03264-0125 Office: Plymouth State Coll Dept Music And Theatre Plymouth NH 03264

SWIFT, STEPHEN JENSEN, federal judge; b. Salt Lake City, Sept. 7, 1943; s. Edward A. and Maurine (Jensen) S.; m. Lorraine Burnell Facer, Aug. 4, 1972; children: Carter, Stephanie, Spencer, Meredith, Hunter. BS, Brigham Young U., 1967; JD, George Washington U., 1970. Trial atty. U.S. Dept. Justice, Washington, D.C., 1970-74; asst. U.S. atty. U.S. Atty.'s Office, San Francisco, 1974-77; v.p., sr. tax counsel Bank Am. N.T. & S.A., San Francisco, 1977-83; judge U.S. Tax Ct., Washington, 1983—; adj. prof. Golden Gate U., San Francisco 1978-83, U. Balt., 1990—. Mem. ABA, Calif. Bar Assn., D.C. Bar Assn. Office: US Tax Ct 400 2nd St NW Washington DC 20217-0002

SWIFT, WILLIAM CHARLES, professional baseball player, olympic athlete; b. Portland, Maine, Oct. 27, 1961. Student, Maine. Mem. U.S. Olympic Baseball Team, 1984; with Seattle Mariners, 1984-91; pitcher San Francisco Giants, 1991-94, Colo. Rockies, 1994—. Nat. League Earned Run Average leader, 1992. Office: Colo Rockies 2850 W 20th Ave Denver CO 80211*

SWIGER, ELINOR PORTER, lawyer; b. Cleve., Aug. 1, 1927; d. Louie Charles and Mary Isabelle (Shank) Porter; m. Quentin Gilbert Swiger, Feb. 5, 1955; children: Andrew Porter, Clavin Gilbert, Charles Robinson. BA, Ohio State U., 1949, JD, 1951. Bar: Ohio 1951, Ill. 1979. Sr. assoc. Robbins, Schwartz, Nicholas, Lifton & Taylor, Ltd., Chgo., 1979—. Author: Mexico for Kids, 1971, Europe for Young Travelers, 1972, The Law and You, 1973 (Literary Guild award), Careers in the Legal Professions, 1978, Women Lawyers at Work, 1978, Law in Everday Life, 1977. Mem.

Northfield Twp. (Ill.) Bd. Edn., 1976-83; mem. Glenview (Ill.) Fire and Police Commn., 1976-86; chmn. Glenview Zoning Bd. Appeals, 1987—. Mem. ABA (chmn. pub. edn. com. urban, state and local govt. sect. 1982-85), Ill. Bar Assn. (chmn. local govt. sect. 1986-87, chmn. legal edn. sect. 1991-92), Ill. Coun. Sch. Attys. (chmn.), Women Bar Assn. Ill., Chgo. Bar Assn. (chmn. legis. exec. com. 1990-92), Soc. Midland Authors. Republican. Home: 1933 Burr Oak Dr Glenview IL 60025 Office: Robbins Schwartz Nicholas Lifton & Taylor 29 S La Salle St Ste 860 Chicago IL 60603-1505

SWIGER, ELIZABETH DAVIS, chemistry educator; b. Morgantown, W.Va., June 27, 1926; d. Hannibal Albert and Tyreeca Elizabeth (Stemple) Davis; m. William Eugene Swiger, June 2, 1948; children: Susan Elizabeth Swiger Knotts, Wayne William. BS in Chemistry, W.Va. U., 1948, MS in Chemistry, 1952, PhD in Chemistry, 1964. Instr. math. Fairmont (W.Va.) State Coll., 1948-49, instr. math. and phys. sci., 1956-57, instr. chemistry, 1957-60, asst. prof. chemistry, 1960-63, assoc. prof. chemistry, 1964-66, prof. chemistry, 1966—, head dept. chemistry, 1964-94, instr. chemistry and physics. sci., math, and health careers, 1991-92; NSF fellow rsch. W.Va. U., Morgantown, 1963-64; prof. emeritus, 1992; advisor Am. Chem. Soc. student affiliates, 1965-88. Author: Morton Family History, 1984-94, Davis-Winters Family History, 1994, Civil War Letters and Diary of Joshua Winters, 1991; contbr. articles to profl. jours. Bd. dirs. Prickett's Fort Meml. Found., Fairmont, 1988—, chmn. elect, 1990-92, chair., 1992—, Blacks Chapel Meml. Found., 1993—, rep. adv. coun. to Bd. Regents, Fairmont State Coll., Charleston, 1977-78, rep. instl. bd. advisors, Fairmont, 1990-92. NSF grantee, 1963; named Outstanding Prof. W.Va. Legislature, Charleston, 1990. Mem. Am. Chem. Soc. (sec. chmn. North W. Va. 1975, 83), W.Va. Acad. Sci. (pres. 1978-79, exec. com. edn. chmn. 1990-93), The Nature Conservancy (bd. dirs. W.Va. chpt. 1970-86, chmn. 1980-82), AAUW. Republican. Methodist. Avocations: local history, genealogy, gardening, computers. Home: 1599 Hillcrest Rd Fairmont WV 26554-4807 also: 382 Laird Dr Freeport FL 32439

SWIGERT, JAMES MACK, lawyer; b. Carthage, Ill., Sept. 25, 1907; s. James Ross and Pearl (Mack) S.; m. Alice Francis Titcomb Harrower, July 7, 1931 (dec. 1990); children: Oliver, David Ladd, Sally Harper (Mrs. Hamilton). Student, Grinnell Coll., 1925-27; SB, Harvard U., 1930, LLB, 1935. Bar: Ill. 1935, Ohio 1937. With Campbell, Clithero & Fischer, Chgo., 1935-36, Taft, Stettinius & Hollister, Cin., 1936—; ptnr. Taft, Stettinius & Hollister, 1948-79, sr. ptnr. and chmn. exec. com., 1979-85, of counsel, 1985—; dir., mem. exec. com. Union Cen. Life Ins. Co., 1963-79; dir., chmn. audit com. Philips Industries, 1975-82. Author articles on labor rels. and labor law. Bd. dirs. Cin. Symphony Orch., 1976-78; trustee, chmn. exec. com. Am. Music Scholarship Assn., 1987-92. Republican. Presbyterian. Clubs: Queen City (past dir.) Cincinnati Country (past v.p., dir.), Queen City Optimists (past pres.), Tennis (past pres.), Recess (past pres.), Harvard Law (past pres.) (Cin.). Home: 2121 Alpine Pl Cincinnati OH 45206-2690 Office: 1800 Star Bank Ctr Cincinnati OH 45202

SWIGGER, KEITH B., dean; b. Hutchinson, Kans., Feb. 3, 1943; s. Paul Clarke and Loneta (Miller) S.; children: Jessica, Nathaniel. BA, U. Chgo., 1965, MA, 1975; MA, Ind. U., 1967; PhD, U. Iowa, 1973. Teaching asst. Ind. U., Bloomington, 1967; teaching asst. U. Iowa, Iowa City, 1968-73, lectr., 1973-74, instr., 1976-77; asst. prof. East Tex. State U., Commerce, 1977-81; asst. prof. libr. scis. Tex. Woman's U., Denton, 1981-85, assoc. prof., 1985-89, prof., 1989—, interim dean Sch. Libr. Sci., 1991-92, dean Sch. Libr. and Info. Studies, 1992—. Contbr. numerous articles to profl. jours. Bd. dirs. ACLU, Denton, 1990-92. Postdoctoral fellow Coun. on Libr. Resources, U. Chgo., 1974-75; rsch. grantee OCLC, Inc., 1990-91, career tng. grantee U.S. Office Edn., 1990-95. Mem. ALA, Tex. Libr. Assn., Young Adult Libr. Svcs. Assn., Assn. Coll. Rsch. Librs., Tex. Faculty Assn., Assn. Libr. Info. Sci. Edn. Office: Tex Womans U Sch Libr & Info Studies PO Box 22905 Denton TX 76204-0905

SWIHART, FRED JACOB, lawyer; b. Park Rapids, Minn., Aug. 19, 1919; s. Fred and Elizabeth Pauline (Judnitsch) S.; m. Edna Lillian Jensen, Sept. 30, 1950; 1 child; Frederick Jay. BA, U. Nebr., 1949, JD, 1954; M in Russian Lang., Middlebury Coll., 1950; grad., U.S Army Command and Staff Coll., 1965. Bar: Nebr. 1954, U.S. Dist. Ct. Nebr. 1954, U.S. Ct. Appeals (8th cir.) 1977, U.S. Supreme Ct. 1972. Claims atty. Chgo. & Eastern Ill. R.R., 1954-56; atty. Nash Amer. R.R.s, Chgo., 1956-60; assoc. Wagener & Marx, Lincoln, Nebr., 1960-61; prosecutor City of Lincoln, 1961-68; sole practice Lincoln, 1968—. Editor Law for the Aviator, 1969-71. Served to lt. col. U.S. Army, 1943-46, ETO, Korea, ret. col., USAR, 1979. Fellow Nebr. State Bar Found.; mem. ABA, Nebr. Bar Assn., Fed. Bar Assn., Assn. Trial Lawyers Am., Am. Judicature Soc., Aircraft Owners and Pilots Assn. (legis. rep.), Nebr. Criminal Def. Attys. Assn., Nat. Assn. Criminal Def. Lawyers, Mercedes Benz Club Am., Nebr. Assn. Trial Attys., Nat. Assn. Uniformed Svcs., Res. Officers Assn., Nat. Assn. Legion of Honor, Internat. Footprint Assn., Am. Legion (adm. Nebr. Navy), Mason (knight comdr. of ct. of honor), Shriners, The Cabiri. Republican. Presbyterian. Avocations: collecting art, music, pistol competition. Home: 1610 Susan Cir Lincoln NE 68506-1854 Office: 4435 O St Ste 130 Lincoln NE 68510-1864

SWIHART, JAMES W., JR., diplomat; b. Washington, DC, July 25, 1946; s. James Wilbur and Ruth (Inge) S.; m. Ellen Jane Cendo Mar. 30, 1968; children: Jennifer Anne, Christopher John. BA, Columbia Coll., 1968. Vice consul Am. Embassy, Belize, Brit. Honduras, 1970-72; 2nd sec., polit. officer Am. Embassy, Belgrade, Yugoslavia, 1972-74; ops. officer ops. ctr. Dept. State, Washington, 1974-75, country officer for Italy and the Vatican, 1975-78; polit./mil. officer for U.S. Mission Berlin Dept. State, 1978-82; officer C.S.C.E. Bur. European Affairs Dept. State, Washington, 1982-83, officer for Fed. Republic of Germany, 1983-84; consul gen., prin. officer U.S. Consulate Gen., Zagreb, Yugoslavia, 1984-1988; mem. sr. seminar Dept. State, Washington, 1988-89; dir. Bur. for Ea. European and Yugoslavia Affairs, 1989-1991; min. counselor, deputy chief of mission Am. Embassy, Vienna, Austria, 1991-94, Chargé d'Affaires ad interim, 1993; amb. to Lithuania Am. Embassy, Vilnius, 1994—. Avocations: piano, harpsichord, jogging, classical music appreciation. Home and Office: American Embassy Vilnius Dept of State Washington DC 20521-4510 Office: Am Embassy Vilnius PSC 78 Box V APO AE 09723

SWIHART, JEAN OGDEN, psychoanalyst; b. Huntington, W.Va., May 10, 1945; d. Daniel Keller and Shirley (Stanard) Swihart; m. Theodore James Lehner, Dec. 3; children: Katherine Louise, Andrew Bruce, David Kaniel. BA, W.Va. U., 1968, MA, 1970, postgrad., 1975; MD, Med. Coll. Pa., Phila., 1978. Teaching/rsch. asst. W.Va. U., Morgantown, 1965-75; cytotechnologist W.Va. U., 1970-71, electron microscopist, 1971-75; intern U. Colo. Health Sci. Ctr., Denver, 1978-79; resident in psychiatry U. Colo. Health Sci. Ctr., 1979-81, Inst. of Pa. Hosp., Phila. 1981-83; psychiatric cons. Circle Lodge, Norristown, Pa., 1985-86, U. Pa. Student Health Svcs. Phila., 1986-89; med. dir. Life Ctrs., Inc., Phila., 1987-89; pvt. practice Phila. and Bala Cynwyd, Pa., 1989—. Author: The Fact Finding Freud, 1983, (poetry) The Full Ripened Grain, 1990. Mem. Am. Psychoanalytic Assn. Republican. Presbyterian. Avocations: writing, singing, skiing, basketball, tennis.

SWIHART, JOHN MARION, retired aircraft manufacturing company executive; b. New Winchester, Ohio, Dec. 27, 1923; s. Harry Miron and Fay I. (Cress) S.; m. Opal G. Carter, Nov. 8, 1966; children from previous marriages: Vicki Ann, John Richard, Thomas Marion, Mark Andrew, Karen Lee, Laurie Christine, Stacey Anne. BS in Physics, Bowling Green State U., 1947; BS in Aero. Engring., Ga. Inst. Tech., 1949, postgrad., 1951-53; postgrad., U. Va., 1951-53. Asst. group leader propulsion group NASA, 1956-

58, group leader spl. projects, 1958-59, head advanced configurations group aircraft, 1959-62, chief large supersonic tunnels br., 1962; with Boeing Co., 1962-89; dep. dir. internat. sales Boeing Co., Renton, Wash., 1974-75; v.p. Japan Boeing Internat. Corp. Boeing Co., Tokyo, 1973-74; program mgr. 7X7 Boeing Co., Kent, Wash., 1975-76; dir. new airplane product devel., sales, mktg. Boeing Co., Seattle, 1976-78; dir. product devel., sales mktg. Boeing Co., 1978-79, v.p. U.S., Can. sales, 1979-83, v.p. govt. tech. liaison, Boeing Co., Seattle, 1985-89; ret., 1989. Contbr. over 100 articles to profl. jours. 1st lt. USAAF, 1943-45. Decorated D.F.C., Air medal with 3 oak leaf clusters; recipient Wright Bros. Meml. Lectureship award, 1987, Maurice Roy medal for internat. cooperation Internat. Coun. Aeronautical Scie., 1992. Fellow AIAA (chmn. airdraft design com. Pacific N.W. sect. 1969-70, gen. chmn. aircraft sys. and design meeting 1977, pres. 1990-91), Royal Aero. Soc., Internat. Soc. for Air-Breathing Engines (pres. 1993—); mem. Japan-Am. Soc. (pres. 1978-79), Wash. State China Rels. Coun. (past pres.).

SWILLING, PAT, professional football player; b. Toccoa, Ga., Oct. 25, 1964. Student, Ga. Tech. U. With New Orleans Saints, 1986-92, Detroit Lions, 1993—. Named to Pro Bowl Team, 1990-93; named outside linebacker Sporting News NFL All-Pro Team, 1991, 92; led league in sacks, 1991. Office: Detroit Lions 1200 Featherstone Rd Pontiac MI 48342-1938*

SWIMMER, ROSS OWEN, federal agency administrator; b. Oklahoma City, Oct. 26, 1943; s. Robert Otis and Virginia Marie (Pounder) S.; m. Margaret Ann McConnell, June 30, 1965; children—Joseph Ross, Michael David. BA, U. Okla., 1965, JD, 1967. Bar: Okla. 1967. Partner firm Hanson, Peterson, Thompkins, Oklahoma City, 1967-72; counsel Cherokee Nation, Tahlequah, Okla., 1972-74; prin. chief Cherokee Nation, from 1976; exec. v.p. 1st Nat. Bank, Tahlequah, 1974; pres. 1st Nat. Bank, from 1975; asst. sec. Indian Affairs Dept. Interior, 1985—; dir. Five Civilized Tribes Found.; mem. Inter-tribal Council of Five Civilized Tribes. Mem. Okla. Indsl. Devel. Commn.; chmn. Tahlequah Planning and Zoning Commn.; mem. state com. on Indian work Episcopal Ch.; mem. exec. com. Eastern Okla. council Boy Scouts Am.; mem. Tahlequah Area Arts and Humanities Council; trustee Northeastern State U. Ednl. Found.; mem. Okla. Health Scis. Found. Mem. ABA, Okla. Bankers Assn., Okla. Bar Assn., Cherokee County Bar Assn., Cherokee Nat. Hist. Soc. (pres. 1979-80), Okla. Hist. Soc. Republican. Office: US Dept Interior C St Between 18th-19th St NW Washington DC 20240

SWINBURN, CHARLES, lawyer; b. Bowness on Windermere, Cumbria, Eng., Apr. 11, 1942; came to U.S., 1949; s. Joseph and Myra (Sullivan) S.; m. Carol Ann Ditzler, Dec. 16, 1972; children: Ann Elizabeth, Catherine Knowles. BA in Psychology, Princeton U., 1963; MBA, Harvard U., 1971; JD, U. Pa., 1993. Industry analyst U.S. Dept. Transp., Washington, 1971-73, chief Industry Analysis Div., 1973-76, dep. asst. sec., 1979-83; assoc. administr. fed. assistance Fed. R.R. Adminstrn., Washington, 1976-79; v.p. FS Rollins Environ. Svcs. Inc., Wilmington, Del., 1983-90; assoc. Morgan, Lewis & Bockius, Washington, 1993—; mem., bd. dirs RailAmerica, Inc. Capt. USMC, 1963-69; major USMCR, 1970-75. Decorated DFC (2), Air medal (35); recipient Presdl. Disting. Exec. award, 1980, Dept. Transp. Meritorious Achievement award, 1976, 78, 81. Home: 1713 Maple Hill Place Alexandria VA 22302

SWINBURNE, HERBERT HILLHOUSE, architect; b. Los Angeles, Dec. 6, 1912; s. George W. and Lucretia R. (Hillhouse) S.; m. Berenice A. Lawler, July 10, 1937; children: Herbert Hillhouse, Mary Jo, Stephen Richard, Lucretia Marie. Architect State of Nev., 1935-41; pvt. practice architecture Phila., 1947-49; ptnr. Nolen, Swinburne & Assocs., Phila., 1949-74; cons. in architecture and construction freelance, 1975—; vis. lectr. Princeton (N.J.) U., 1965-76. Prin. works include many colls. and univs., elem. and high schs., research and health scis. bldgs., office bldgs., country clubs; author: Design Cost Analysis for Architects and Engineers; contbr. articles to profl. jours. Mem. Bldg. Research Adv. Bd., 1966-73, exec. com., 1970; mem. Fed. Constrn. Council, 1966-78, chmn., 1971-73; mem. USN Design Revue Panel, 1966-68; adv. panel U.S. Bur. Standards, 1965-72; nat. adv. panel Gen. Services Adminstrn., 1967-69; bldgs. research com. Pa. State U.; trustee Illuminating Engring. Research Inst., 1972-76, Rosemont Coll. 1980-88, appointed lifetime trustee, 1988. Served with USNR, 1943-45. Recipient over 30 nat., state, and city awards for disting. design in architecture. Fellow AIA (chmn. research for architecture com., 1960-65, chmn. of two nat. conv. 1951, 71); mem. Am. Arbitration Assn. Home: 300 Cathedral Rd # L209 Philadelphia PA 19128

SWINDELL, ARCHIE CALHOUN, JR., research biochemist, statistician; b. Greenville, Tex., Sept. 26, 1936; s. Archie Calhoun and Louise Evelyn (Ellis) S.; m. Dolores Dyer Holland, Dec. 28, 1962; children: Randy Zidick, Matthew Earle. BS in Chemistry, So. Methodist U., 1958; M. Nutritional Sci., Cornell U., 1965, PhD in Biochemistry, 1968. NIH postdoctoral fellow Duke U. Med. Ctr., Durham, N.C., 1968-70; rsch. sci. positions in biochemistry, pharmacology, statis. Pfizer, Inc., Groton, Conn., 1970-95; statis. cons., 1995—. Contbr. articles on cholesterol metabolism, hormone action, cell culture, actions of drugs, data analysis, stats. to profl. jours., 1968-93. Patentee trimazosin, doxazosin as anti-atherosclerosis agt.; mem. Town Coun., Groton, Conn., 1991—. Served with U.S. Army, 1958-61. NIH fellow Cornell U., Ithaca, N.Y., 1967. Mem. AAAS, Am. Stat. Assn., Am. Heart Assn., Am. Assn. Artificial Intelligence, Sigma Xi. Club: Shennecossett Yacht (Groton). Avocations: astronomy, woodworking. Home: 192 Monument St Groton CT 06340-3915 Office: Pfizer Inc Cen Rsch Eastern Point Rd Groton CT 06340-4947

SWINDELLS, WILLIAM, JR., lumber and paper company executive; b. Oakland, CA, 1930; married. B.S., Stanford U., 1953. With Willamette Industries, Inc., Portland, Oreg., 1953—; v.p. prodn., mktg. bldg. materials Willamette Industries, Inc., until 1978, exec. v.p., 1978-80, pres. forest products div. 1980-82, pres., chief exec. officer, 1982—, also dir., chmn. 1984—; dir. Oreg. Bank, Portland. Office: Bohemia Inc 1300 S W 5th Ave Portland OR 97201*

SWINDLER, DARIS RAY, physical anthropologist, forensic anthropologist; b. Morgantown, W.Va., Aug. 13, 1925; s. George Raymond and Minnie Mildred (McElroy) S.; m. Kathryn Pardo, Nov. 10, 1977; children: Gary, Darece, Linda, Bruce, Geoffry, Jason. AB, W.Va. U., 1950; MA, U. Pa., 1952, PhD, 1959. Instr. Cornell Med. Sch., N.Y.C., 1956-57, W.Va. Med. Sch., Morgantown, 1957-59; asst. prof. Med. Coll. S.C., Charleston, 1959-64; assoc. prof. Mich. State U., East Lansing, 1964-68; prof. phys. anthropology, comparative primate anatomy, dental anthropology U. Wash., Seattle, 1968-91, prof. emeritus anthropology, 1991—; emeritus curator comparative primate anatomy Burke Mus., Seattle, 1991—; cons. King County Med. Examiner, Seattle, 1968—; vis. sr. scientist U. Frankfurt, Germany, 1982-83, Com. on Scholarly Comms. with Peoples Republic of China, 1987-88; vis. prof. U. Zurich, 1992; field participant Valley of Kings Expdn., Egypt., 1990-93; vis. prof. U. Padua, Italy, 1994. Author: A Racial Study of the West Nakani of New Britain, 1962, Dentition of Living Primates, 1976, Systematics, Evolution and Anatomy, Comparative Primate Biology; (with C.D. Wood) Atlas of Primate Gross Anatomy, 1973 (Gov's. award 1973), (with J. Sirianni) Growth and Development of Pigtailed Macaque, 1985. Served with USN, 1943-46. Recipient Alexander von Humboldt Sr. U.S. Scientist awrd, Germany, 1981. Fellow AAAS, Explorer's Club; mem. Am. Assn. Phys. Anthropologists (v.p. 1976-78), Dental Anthropology Assn. (pres. 1990-92), Internat. Primatology Soc., N.Y. Acad. Sci., Italian Primatol. Assn., Sigma Xi.

SWINERTON, WILLIAM ARTHUR, retired construction company executive; b. San Francisco, Dec. 12, 1917; s. Alfred Bingham and Jane Thomas (Hotaling) S.; m. Mary Nichols Clark, June 5, 1943; children: Leslie Engelbrecht, Susan McBaine, James B., Sarah Blake. B.S., Yale, 1939; postgrad., Stanford, 1940. With Swinerton & Walberg Co., San Francisco, 1940-88, ret. Served with USMCR, 1940-46. Decorated Bronze Star. Clubs: Pacific Union, Burlingame Country. Home: PO Box 620265 Redwood City CA 94062

SWING, JOHN TEMPLE, lawyer, association executive; b. London, Eng., June 7, 1929; s. Raymond Gram and Betty (Gram) S.; m. Devereux Loy Powell, June 19, 1976; children by previous marriage: Jennifer Anne, John Mead. A.B. cum laude, Harvard U., 1950; LL.B., Yale U., 1953. Bar: N.Y. 1955, Conn. 1956. Asso. firm Becket and Wagner, Lakeville, Conn., 1955-60; partner Becket and Wagner, 1960-61; partner firm Rorabeck and Swing, Canaan, Conn., 1961-63; dir. adminstrn. Council on Fgn. Relations, N.Y.C., 1963-67; assoc. exec. dir. Council on Fgn. Relations, 1967-72, v.p., sec., 1972-85, acting pres., 1985-86, exec. v.p., 1986-93; pres., CEO Fgn. Policy Assn., N.Y.C., 1993—; mem. adv. com. on law of the sea NSC, 1974-81; mem. U.S. del. to 3d UN Conf. on Law of the Sea, 1974-81, spl. adv. to del., 1977-78, alt. rep., 1978-81; expert cons. Dept. State, 1977-81; mem. adv. bd. Center for Oceans Law and Policy, U. Va. Sch. Law, 1975—; bd. dirs. Council on Ocean Law, 1980—; mem. adv. bd. Inst. for the Study of World Politics, 1971—. Contbr. articles to profl. jours. Selectman Town of Salisbury, Conn., 1959-61, 61-63; vice chmn. Salisbury Democratic Town Com., 1959-63; Dem. candidate State Senate, Conn., 1962; trustee Putney Sch. (Vt.), 1983-89, chmn., 1986-89; bd. advs. CUNY Grad. Sch. and Univ. Ctr., Grad. Study in Transl.; bd. dirs. Non-Profit Coordinating Com. of N.Y., 1984—, chmn. 1984-89, designated founding chmn., 1989. Mem. Coun. Fgn. Rels., Bar Assn. City of N.Y. (chmn. com. on lawyer's role in search for peace 1980-82, coun. on internal affairs, 1987—), Internat. Law Assn., Am. Soc. Internat. Law. Clubs: Century Assn. (sec. 1984-86); Fishers Island Yacht. Home: 61 E 86th St Apt 51 New York NY 10028-1037 Office: 470 Park Ave S 2d Floor New York NY 10016-6819

SWING, MARCE, producer, publisher; b. Wichita, Kans., Dec. 3, 1943; d. Eldon Derry and Ruth (Biddle) S. Bus. mgr. Old Westport Med. Assn., Kansas City, Mo., 1972-73; dept. chmn., instr. Ft. Bragg (N.C.) Nursery and Kindergarten, 1965-66, Luth. Schs., Tex. Dist., Irving, 1966-68, Kansas City (Kans.) Sch. Dist. 500, 1973-78, Extension Dept. U. Calif., Northridge, 1979-82, Pima Coll., Tucson, 1983-84, Kinder Care, Lake Buena Vista, Fla., 1989-90; TV/motion picture exec. producer, dir., writer Swing Prodns., Orlando, Fla., 1989—; owner, pres. Swing Enterprises/Swing Prodns., Orlando, 1978—, Living for Edn., Inc., Orlando, 1994—; exec. mgmt., acctg. andmktg. cons. to major internat. corps.; lectr., seminar instr., guest speaker, anchorperson, moderator, panelist. Exec. producer, dir., writer, featured talent on-air live and taped programming for networks, network affiliates and cable, feature motion picture, TV series, mini series, 30 celebrity profiles, 36 documentaries, 14 televents, 45 pub. svc. spots, 30 minute infomat, 12-hour entertinment Christmas Eve project; developer entertainment informational, ednl. and indsl. TV programs and videos; contbr. articles to profl. jours. Corp. adminstr., TV exec. producer, dir., fundraiser nat. hdqrs. March of Dimes, White Plains, N.Y., 1984-86, Arthritis Found., Atlanta, 1985; ofcl. hostess Seattle World's Fair; mem. Nat. Task Force for Child Care, Nat. Task Force for Youth Suicide, Nat. Task Force for Child Abuse; mem. Ariz. Commn. on Arts. Recipient local, regional and nat. art and craft awards. Mem. NEA, NAFE, AAUW, Am. Mgmt. Assn., Nat. Assn. Women Artists, Profl. Assn. Producers and Dirs., Nat. Printmaker's Assn., Nat. Thespian Soc., Thousand Oaks Art Assn., Show of Hands Gallery, Nat. Youth Camps. Lutheran. Avocations: reading, writing, photography, cooking, mural painting.

SWING, PETER GRAM, music educator; b. N.Y.C., July 15, 1922; s. Raymond and Betty (Gram) S.; m. Elizabeth Ann Sherman, May 27, 1948; children: Pamela Sherman, Bradford Scott. A.B., Harvard U., 1948, A.M., 1951; postgrad., U. Utrecht, Netherlands, 1951-52; Ph.D., U. Chgo., 1969. Instr., assoc. choirmaster Rollins Coll., 1952-53; instr. U. Chgo., 1953-55; mem. faculty Swarthmore Coll., 1955-89, assoc. prof., 1959-69, prof., 1969-89, dir. coll. chorus, 1955-89, chmn. dept. music, 1958-74; cond. faculty choir, assoc. Inst. Advanced Mus. Studies King's Coll., London, 1989-90; mem. faculty Berkshire Music Ctr., Lenox, Mass., 1962-86; mem. Nat. Humanities Faculty, 1969-70; vis. com. music U. Chgo., 1971-77. Served with USNR, 1942-46. Fulbright grantee Netherlands, 1951-52; Fulbright Sr. Research grantee Belgium, 1970-71. Mem. AAUP, Am. Musicol. Soc. (chmn. Phila. chpt. 1969-70), Coll. Music Soc., Vereniging voor Nederlandse Muziekgeschiedenis, Choral Arts Soc. Phila., Musical Fund Soc. Phila., Phi Beta Kappa (hon.). Research in early 16th century music. Home: 614 Hillborn Ave Swarthmore PA 19081-1122 *I have been incredibly lucky all my life to have had a "calling:" music—playing, teaching and conducting and thinking about it. Music is why I exist; it is in the center of what I can give to others. It helps me to love.*

SWING, WILLIAM EDWIN, bishop; b. Huntington, W.Va., Aug. 26, 1936; s. William Lee and Elsie Bell (Holliday) S.; M. Mary Willis Taylor, Oct. 7, 1961; children—Alice Marshall, William Edwin. B.A., Kenyon Coll., Ohio, 1954-58; D.Div. (hon.), Kenyon Coll., 1980; M.A., Va. Theol. Sem., 1958-61, D.Div., 1980. Ordained priest Episcopal Ch. Asst. St. Matthews Ch., Wheeling, W.Va., 1961-63; vicar St. Matthews Ch., Chester, W.Va., 1963-69, St. Thomas Ch., Weirton, W.Va., 1963-69; rector St. Columba's Episcopal Ch., Washington, 1969-79; bishop Episcopal Ch. Calif., San Francisco, 1980—; chmn. bd. Ch. Div. Sch. of the Pacific, 1983-84; founder, chmn. Episcopal Found. for Drama, 1976—. Republican. Home: 2006 Lyon St San Francisco CA 94115-1610 Office: Episcopal Ch Diocesan Office 1055 Taylor St San Francisco CA 94108-2209

SWING, WILLIAM LACY, ambassador; b. Lexington, N.C., Sept. 11, 1934; s. Baxter Dermot and Mary Frances (Barbee) S.; AB, Catawba Coll., 1956, LLD (hon.), 1980; BD, Yale U., 1960; postgrad. Oxford U., U. Tuebingen (Germany), 1961, Hofstra U.; LLD (hon.), 1994; m. Yuen Fong Cheong; children: Brian Curtis, Gabrielle. Vice consul Am. Consulate, Port Elizabeth, Republic of South Africa, 1963-66; internat. economist Bur. Econ. Affairs, Dept. State, 1966-68; consul, chief consular sect. Am. Consulate Gen., Hamburg, Germany, 1968-72; internat. rels. officer, desk officer for Federal Republic of Germany, Dept. State, Washington, 1972-74; dep. chief of mission, counselor Am. Embassy, Bangui, Central African Republic, 1974-76; fellow Center for Internat. Affairs, Harvard U., 1976-77; dep. dir. Office of Cen. African Affairs, 1977-79; ambassador to People's Republic of Congo, 1979-81; amb. to Republic of Liberia, Monrovia, 1981-85; amb. to South Africa, 1989-92; amb. to Fed. Republic of Nigeria, 1992-93; amb. to Haiti, 1993—; dir. Fgn. Svc. Career Devel. and Assignments, 1985, 87; sr. dep. asst. sec. state for pers., 1987-89. Recipient Meritorious Honor award USIA, 1971, Superior Honor award Dept. State, 1985, Presdl. Disting. Svc. award, 1985, Presdl. Meritorious Svc. award, 1987, 90, 94, Equal Employment Opportunity award Dept. State, 1988, Disting. Honor award, 1994, Valor award, 1995. Mem. Am. Fgn. Svc. Assn., Army and Navy Club (Washington), Yale Club (Washington and N.C.), Harvard Club (Washington), Internat. Club (Washington), Lions. Co-editor: Education for Decision, 1963. Office: Am Embassy Port-Au-Prince State Dept Washington DC 20521-3400

SWINGLE, HOMER DALE, horticulturist, educator; b. Hixson, Tenn., Nov. 5, 1916; s. Edward Everett and Sarah Elizabeth (Rogers) S.; m. Gladys F. Wells, Dec. 21, 1942 (dec. June 1961); 1 child, Janet Faye Swingle Scisci-oli; m. Ella Margaret Porterfield, Dec. 19, 1962. BS, U. Tenn., 1939; MS, Ohio State U., 1948; PhD, La. State U., 1966. Tchr. vocat. agr. Spring City (Tenn.) High Sch., 1939-46; hort. specialist U. Tenn., Crossville, 1946-47; from asst. prof. to prof. horticulture U. Tenn., Knoxville, 1948-79, prof. emeritus non-credit program, 1979—; cons. in plant and water rels. Oak Ridge (Tenn.) Nat. Lab., 1971-75; chmn. collaborators Vegetable Breeding Lab. USDA, Charleston, S.C., 1975. Cons. editor: Growing Vegetables and Herbs, 1984; contbr. 49 articles to sci. jours. Fellow Am. Soc. Hort. Sci. (chmn. so. sect. 1970-71); mem. Lions (life), Gamma Sigma Delta (pres. U. Tenn. chpt. 1977, teaching award of merit 1978-79). Republican. Methodist. Home: 3831 Maloney Rd Knoxville TN 37920-2823

SWINNEY, HARRY LEONARD, physics educator; b. Opelousas, La., Apr. 10, 1939; s. Leonard Robert and Ethel Ruth (Bertheaud) S.; m. Gloria Luyas, Oct. 21, 1967; 1 child, Brent Luyas. BS in Physics, Rhodes Coll., 1961; PhD in Physics, Johns Hopkins U., 1968. Vis. asst. prof. Johns Hopkins U., 1970-71; asst. prof. physics NYU, 1971-73; assoc. prof. CCNY, 1973-77, prof. physics U. Tex., Austin, 1978—, Trull Centennial prof., 1984-90, Sid Richardson Found. regents chair, 1990—, dir. Ctr. Nonlinear Dynamics, 1985—; Morris Loeb lectr. Harvard U., 1982. Editor: Hydrodynamic Instabilities and the Transition to Turbulence, 1985; contbr. articles to profl. jours. Regents chair Sid Richardson Found., 1990—. Grantee NSF, DOE, NASA, others; Guggenheim fellow, 1982-83. Fellow

Am. Phys. Soc. (exec. bd. 1992-94); mem. NAS, Am. Acad. Arts and Scis., Am. Assn. Physics Tchrs. Democrat. Methodist. Office: U Tex Dept Physics Ctr Nonlinear Dynamics Austin TX 78712

SWIRE, EDITH WYPLER, music educator, musician, violist, violinist; b. Boston, Feb. 16, 1943; d. Alfred R. Jr. and Frances Glenn (Emery) Wypler; m. James Bennett Swire, June 11, 1965; 1 child, Elizabeth Swire-Falker. BA, Wellesley (Mass.) Coll., 1965; MFA, Sarah Lawrence Coll., Bronxville, N.Y., 1983; postgrad., Coll. of New Rochelle, 1984-85. Tchr. instrumental music, viola, violin The Windsor Sch., Boston, 1965-66; tchr., dir. The Lenox Sch., N.Y.C., 1967-76; music curriculum devel. The Nightingale-Bamford Sch., N.Y.C., 1968-69; head of fine arts dept. The Lenox Sch., N.Y.C., 1976-78, head of instrumental music, 1978-80; founder, dir., tchr. of string sch. Serpentine String Sch., Larchmont, N.Y., 1981—; mem. founding com. Inter Sch. Orch., N.Y.C., 1972, trustee, 1976—; panelist Nat. Assn. Ind. Sch. Conf., N.Y.C., 1977. Mem. music and worship com., Larchmont Ave. Ch., 1978-82, 88. Mem. Westchester Musicians Guild, N.Y. State Music Tchrs. Assn., Music Tchrs. Nat. Assn., Music Tchrs. Coun. Westchester (program com.), Violin Soc. Am., Wellesley in Westchester. Avocations: study of Alexander technique, chamber music, encouraging music in schools. Home and Office: 11 Serpentine Trl Larchmont NY 10538-2618

SWIRSKY, JUDITH PERLMAN, arts administrator, consultant; b. Bklyn., Oct. 31, 1928; d. Samuel and Rose (Klein) Perlman; m. Leo Jerome Swirsky, June 26, 1949; 1 child, Marjorie Ann Swirsky Zelner. BA, NYU, 1947; postgrad., Columbia U., 1947-48. Rsch. asst. The Bklyn. Mus., 1947-49, vol. coord., 1983-89; exec. dir. Grand Cen. Art Galleries Edn. Assn., N.Y.C., 1988-90; freelance curator Genest Gallery, Lambertville, N.J., 1990—; dir. vol. resources, dir. spl. events Snug Harbor Cultural Ctr., S.I., 1992-95, dir. spl. events, 1994-95; dir. art sales and rental Gallery The Bklyn. Mus., 1974-77; del. Vol. Com. of Art Mus., Balt., 1973, panelist, 1979; mem., co-founder Vol. Program Adminstrs., N.Y.C., Cultural Inst., 1984—; ind. curator travelling exhbn. Relatively Speaking: Mothers and Daus. in Art, 1994-96. Co-author: On Exhibit, 1993, 94, 95: An Art Lover's Travel Guide to American Museums, 1993, 94. Pres. Community Com. for the Bklyn. Mus., 1969-70; bd. dirs. Greater N.Y. Girl Scouts U.S., 1965-71; founder Children's Sch. Time Program and Women's League, Bklyn. Acad. Music, 1961-64; chmn. Bklyn. Guild for Opera, 1966-77; bd. dirs. Arthritis Found. Greater N.Y., 1969-79; trustee Bklyn. Home for Children, 1961-70, Julia Bernstein League of the Free Nurses Inst., 1952-60. Mem. Am. Assn. Mus., Assn. Vol. Adminstrn. (cert., editor region II newsletter), Am. Assn. Mus. Vols., Civitas. Avocations: travel, cooking. Home and Office: 57 Montague St Brooklyn NY 11201-3374

SWISSLER, ROBERT, educational consultant; b. Camden, N.J., Apr. 4, 1938; widowed; children: Amy, Becky. BS in Literature Studies, St. Joseph's Coll., Phila., 1960; postgrad., L'Ecole Normale de Caen, France, 1965, U. Buffalo, 1968; MEd, Rutgers U., 1969, postgrad., 1977. English and French tchr., basketball and track coach Notre Dame H.S., Trenton, N.J., 1960-66; coord. pupil pers. svcs. Lawrence Twp. Pub. Schs., Lawrenceville, N.J., 1960-70; coord. curriculum and instrn. br., divsn. sch. programs N.J. State Dept. Edn., Trenton, 1970-75, dir. office planning & devel. divsn. ops., rsch./evaluation, 1975-80, dir. legis. svcs. office of commr., 1980-88, asst. commr. edn. divsn. fin., 1989-92, asst. commr. edn. divsn. adminstrn. and policy, 1992-93, Somerset County supt. of schs. divsn. urban and field svcs., 1993-95; edn. cons. Swissler Assocs., Titusville, N.J., 1995—; edn. cons. Random House Publs., N.Y., 1974-85. Bd. dirs. Somerset County Youth Svcs. Commn., Smerset and Hunterdon Bus. and Edn. Partnership, Somerset County Vocat.-Tech. Bd. Edn.; trustee Somerset County Edni. Svcs. Commn., Somerset County Alliance Steering Com.; mem. Somerset County Local Adv. Coun. on Alcoholism and Drug Abuse; mem. N.J. Edn./Law Enforcement Working Group; mem. Gov.'s Edn. Task Force, 1993-94; trustee, mem. facilities com. Raritan C.C.; mem. N.J. Commn. on Bus. Efficiency of Pub. Schs. Mem. Assn. C.C. Trustees, Am. Assn. Sch. Adminstrs., N.J. Assn. Sch. Adminstrs., Somerset County Governing Ofcls. Assn., Somerset County Sch. Bus. Ofcls., Phi Delta Kappa. Roman Catholic. Avocations: reading, current events, politics, sports, boating. Home and Office: St Dept of Edn 30 Maddock Rd Titusville NJ 08560

SWIT, LORETTA, actress; b. N.J., Nov. 4, 1939. Student, Am. Acad. Dramatic Arts, Gene Frankel Repertoire Theatre, N.Y.C. Broadway appearances include Same Time Next Year, Any Wednesday, Mame, The Mystery of Edwin Drood, Shirley Valentine, Chgo. (winner Sarah Siddons award 1990); films include Stand Up and Be Counted, 1972, Freebie and the Bean, 1974, Race with the Devil, 1975, S.O.B, 1980, Beer, 1985, Whoops, 1987, Apocalypse (U.K.), 1987; star TV series M*A*S*H, 1972-83 (Emmy awards for Outstanding Supporting Actress in a Comedy series 1979-81); TV movies include Shirts/Skins, 1973, The Last Day, 1975, Mirror, Mirror, 1979, Valentine, 1979, Friendships, Secrets and Lies, 1979, Cagney and Lacey, 1981, Games Mother Never Taught You, 1982, First Affair, 1983, The Execution, 1985, Dreams of Gold: The Mel Fisher Story, 1986, My Dad Can't Be Crazy, Can He?, Hell Hath No Fury, 1992, A Killer Among Friends, 1993; star on major dramatic shows and musical variety shows, including Bob Hope Christmas Special, Perry Como, The Muppets. Mem. AFTRA, Screen Actors Guild, Actors Equity. *

SWITZER, BARRY, professional football coach, former university athletic coach; b. Crossett, Ark., Oct. 5, 1937; s. Frank and Louise Switzer; m. Kay Switzer, 1963 (div. 1983); children: Greg, Kathy, Dove. BA, U. Ark., 1960. Asst. football coach U. Ark., 1960-65; asst. football coach U. Okla., 1966-72, head coach, 1973-89; head coach Dallas Cowboys, 1994—. author: Bootlegger's Boy, 1990. Served with U.S. Army. Named Coach of Year, 1973, AP/UPI Nat. Champions (shared with U. So. Calif.) 1974, consensus champions, 1975, 85. Coach winning Orange Bowl team, 1976, 79-81, 86-87. Office: Dallas Cowboys 1 Cowboys Pkwy Irving TX 75063-4945*

SWITZER, MAURICE HAROLD, publisher; b. Toronto, Ont., Can., Mar. 28, 1945; s. Harold Switzer and Ruby (Marsden) Hicks; m. Mary Helene Pavlik; children: Andrea Zimperi, Adin, Lisa Doracka. Student, Trent U., Peterborough, Ont., 1964-65. Journalist Belleville (Ont.) Intelligencer, 1965-67, sports editor, 1967-72, mng. editor, 1972-79; mng. editor Oshawa (Ont.) Times, 1979-81; pub. Timmins (Ont.) Daily Press, 1981-86, Sudbury (Ont.) Star, 1986-92, Winnipeg (Man.) Free Press, 1992-94; ret; owner Media Help Svcs., 1994—. Author: Bruno Cavallo a Conversation, 1991. Bd. dirs. Man. Art Gallery, Winnipeg, 1992-94, Man. Opera, Winnipeg, 1992-94, Health Sci. Ctr. Found., Winnipeg, 1992-94. Mem. Man. Club, St. Charles Country Club, Carlton Club.

SWITZER, PAUL, statistics educator; b. St. Boniface, Man., Can., Mar. 4, 1939. B.A. with honors, U. Man., 1961; A.M., Harvard U., 1963, Ph.D., 1965. Mem. faculty Stanford (Calif.) U., 1965—, now prof. stats. and earth scis., chmn. dept. stats., 1979-82. Fellow Internat. Statis. Inst., Am. Statis. Assn. (editor jour. 1986-88), Inst. Math. Stats. Office: Stanford U Dept Stats Sequoia Hall Stanford CA 94305-4065

SWITZER, RALPH JOSEPH, JR., diversified industry executive; b. New Rochelle, N.Y., July 1, 1930; s. Ralph Joseph and Kathleen Florence (Collins) S.; m. Gerd Hildegarde Wamnes, Feb. 7, 1954; children: Kurt Edmund, Gail Susan, Barbara Jean. BBA, Iona Coll., 1961; grad. advanced mgmt. program, Harvard U., 1976. With Abex Corp., N.Y.C., 1948-70; asst. treas. Whitman Corp. (formerly IC Industries), Chgo., 1970-73, dir. investments, 1973-81, asst. v.p., treas., 1981, v.p., treas., 1982-87, v.p. fin. ops., 1987-89, sr. v.p. fin. ops., 1989—. Mem. adv. bd. Ingalls Meml. Hosp. Devel. Found., Harvey, Ill., 1983—. With USN, 1951-55. Mem. Fin. Execs. Inst., Flossmoor Country Club, Plaza Club, Exec. Club.

SWITZER, ROBERT LEE, biochemistry educator; b. Clinton, Iowa, Aug. 26, 1940; s. Stephen and Elva Delila (Allison) S.; m. Bonnie George, June 13, 1965; children: Brian, Stephanie. BS, U. Ill., 1961; PhD, U. Calif., Berkeley, 1966. Research fellow Lab. Biochemistry, Nat. Heart Inst., Bethesda, Md., 1966-68; asst. prof. biochemistry U. Ill., Urbana, 1968-73; assoc. prof. U. Ill., 1973-78, prof. biochemistry and basic med. scis., 1978—, dept. head, 1988-93; mem. biochemistry study sect. NIH, 1985-89, chmn., 1987-89; guest prof. U. Copenhagen, 1995. Author: (with John M. Clark) Experimental Biochemistry, 1977; mem. bd. editors Jour. Bacteriology, 1977-82, 85—, Archives Biochemistry and Biophysics, 1977—, Jour. Biol. Chemistry, 1980-

85; contbr. articles to profl. jours. NSF predoctoral fellow, 1961-66; NIH postdoctoral fellow, 1966-68; Guggenheim fellow, 1975. Mem. Am. Soc. for Biochemistry and Molecular Biology, Am. Soc. Microbiology, Am. Chem. Soc., AAAS, Sigma Xi. Home: 404 W Michigan Ave Urbana IL 61801-4948 Office: U Ill Dept Biochemistry 600 S Mathews Ave Urbana IL 61801-3602

SWOAP, DAVID BRUCE, children's relief administrator; b. Kalamazoo, Aug. 12, 1937; s. Orlo Frederick and Aileen Esther (Hempy) S. B.A. in Govt. with honors, Denison U., 1959; M.A. in Govt, Claremont Grad. Sch., 1961; D.Sci. (hon.), U. Osteo. Medicine and Health Scis., Des Moines, 1981. Asst. sec. Calif. State Personnel Bd., Sacramento, 1972-73; chief dep. dir., acting dir. Calif. State Dept. Social Welfare, Sacramento, 1973; dir. Calif. State Dept. Social Welfare, 1973-74, Calif. State Dept. Benefit Payments, 1974-75; sr. research asso. Republican Study Com., U.S. Ho. of Reps., Washington, 1975-76; profl. staff mem. U.S. Senate Com. on Fin. Washington, 1976-79; legis. dir. U.S. Senator William L. Armstrong, Washington, 1979-81; dep. sec. HHS, Washington, 1981-83; sec. health and welfare State of Calif., Sacramento, 1983-85; ptnr. Franchetti & Swoap, San Francisco, 1985-90; vice chmn. Sacramento Advocates, 1991-93; owner David Bruce Gallery, La Jolla, Calif., Mana Olana Farms, Hakalau, Hawaii. Elder Presbyn. Ch.; bd. dirs. Friends of SOS Children's Villages, Inc., 1975-92, Covenant House, Calif.; bd. regents John F. Kennedy U., 1990-93; chmn. bd. dirs. Hope Unltd. Internat., 1991—. Rotary Club Found. fellow, 1961-62. Mem. Wycliffe Assocs., Phi Beta Kappa, Delta Upsilon. Republican. Office: Hope Unltd Ste 218 9888 Carroll Centre Rd San Diego CA 92126

SWOBODA, LARY JOSEPH, state legislator; b. Luxemburg, Wis., May 28, 1939; s. Joseph Francis and Catherine Magdalene (Daul) S.; m. Janice Marie Hendricks, Nov. 16, 1968. BS in Speech and Polit. Sci., U. Wis., Milw., 1963, M.S. in Polit. Sci., 1965, EdS, 1988; postgrad., U. Wis., Madison, 1988—. Cert. edni. specialist. Speech and English tchr. So. High Sch., Brussels, Wis., 1963-67; tchr. Luxemburg Schs., 1967-70; mem. Wis. State Legislature, Madison, 1970—; chair adminstrv. rules com. Wis. Ho. of Reps., Madison, 1993—; exec. dir. Wis. Nat. and Cmty. Svc. Bd., Madison. Active Dem. Cen. Com. Mem. K.C., Luxemburg C. of C., Lions, Phi Eta Sigma, Kappa Delta Pi, Phi Kappa Phi, Phi Delta Kappa. Roman Catholic. Avocations: reading, attending concerts, drama. Home: 1835 Broadway Dr Sun Prairie WI 53590 Office: Wis Nat and Cmty Svc Bd 101 E Wilson St Madison WI 53707

SWOBODA, RALPH SANDE, credit union official, lawyer; b. Neenah, Wis., Oct. 4, 1948. BA, U. Wis., 1970, JD, 1972. Bar: Wis. 1972. Law clk. to presiding justice Wis. Supreme Ct., Madison, 1972-73; assoc. Aberg, Bell, Blake & Metzner, Madison, 1973-75; v.p., gen. counsel ICU Svcs. Inc., Madison, 1975-83; exec. v.p., gen. counsel Credit Union Nat. Assn. and CUNA Svc. Group, Madison, 1983-86, exec. v.p., chief operating officer, 1983-87; pres., chief exec. officer Credit Union Nat. & Affiliates, Inc., Madison, 1987—. Mem. Wis. Bar Assn. Office: Credit Union Nat Assn 5710 Mineral Point Rd PO Box 431 Madison WI 53701

SWOFFORD, DONALD ANTHONY, architect; b. Houston, Apr. 14, 1947; s. Harry and Henrian (Engbrock) S.; m. Virginia M. Bauler, May 23, 1985; 1 child, James McShea. B.Arch., Tex. A&M U., 1969; M.Arch., U. Va., 1976. Registered architect, Va., Tex., D.C., Nat. Council Archtl. Registration Bds., lic. instrument pilot. Architect, urban designer City of Dallas, 1970-72; Office Milton L. Grigg, FAIA, Architects, 1972-78; prin., owner Wood, Swofford Assocs., Charlottesville, Va., 1978—; pres. Traditional Am. Concepts Ltd., 1983—. Author Dallas Hist. Landmark Program, 1972. Prin. works include Joseph Jarvis residence, 1978, Shrinemont Conf. Ctr., Episcopal Diocese of Va., Orkney Springs, 1981, United Coal/Martha Washington Inn, Bristol, Va., 1985, office and studio WVIR TV, 1985, restoration Farley, Culpeper, Va., 1987, renovation Holy Infant Cath. Ch., Elkton, Va., 1988, restoration St. Francis Assisi Cath. Ch., Stanton, Va., 1988, restoration and additions Goochland County (Va.) Courthouse, 1989, Saint Peter and Paul Cath. Ch., Palmyra, Va.; measured drawing and hist. investigation of Montpelier, home of James Madison, for Hist. Am. Bldg. Survey and Nat. Trust for Hist. Places, 1986, George M. McMath residence, Locustville, Va., 1991, restoration of Higlands, home of James Monro, Charlottesville, 1991, Holy Name of Mary, Bedford, Va., 1994, restoration of Clover Hill Tavern, Appomattox, Va., 1994, hist. rehab. of Danville Rail Passenger Sta., restoration of Gen. George C. Marshall Home, Leesburg, Va., 1994, Danville City Courthouse, Danville, Va., 1995. Bishop's archtl. rev. commn. Cath. Diocese of Richmond. Club Master, Pack 119, Stonewall Jachoon Coun. Recipient Tex.-AIA Design award, 1969-70, Loudon County award for Jarvis Residence, 1985; Jefferson fellow, 1972-83. Mem. AIA (mem. hist. resources com., mem. steering com., James River chpt. Design award for Farley 1991, Nat. Trust for Hist. Preservation Great Am. Homes award for Farley 1992), YSAIA (chair hist. resources com.), Albemarle County Hist. Soc., Nat. Trust Historic Preservation, Soc. Archtl. Historians, Assn. Preservation Tech. Office: Wood Swofford Assocs Archs 812 E High St Charlottesville VA 22902-5126

SWOFFORD, ROBERT LEE, newspaper editor, journalist; b. Berryville, Ark., Aug. 22, 1949; s. Andrew Madison and Verna Mae (England) S.; m. Karen King, Jan. 24, 1969 (div. 1977); children: Teri, Toby; m. Sandra Dunn, 1978 (div. 1979); m. B. Joanna Rongren, Feb. 14, 1981; 1 child, Tyler. AA, Coll. of the Sequoias, 1969; student, Calif. State U., 1969-71. Photographer, reporter, news editor The Advance-Register, Tulare, Calif., 1965-78; city editor The Record Searchlight, Redding, Calif., 1978-81; suburban editor, Neighbors editor The Sacramento Bee, 1981-86; assoc. metro. editor, community editor The Orange County Register, Santa Ana, Calif., 1986-89; exec. news editor The Press Democrat, Santa Rosa, Calif., 1989-90, mng. editor, 1990—. Mem. Assoc. Press Mng. Editors, Calif. Soc. of Newspaper Editors, Soc. of Newspaper Design. Office: The Press Democrat 427 Mendocino Ave Santa Rosa CA 95401-6313

SWOGGER, GLENN, JR., psychiatrist; b. Topeka, Kans., Aug. 28, 1935; s. Glenn and Isabel Zilla (Sutherin); m. Claire Schubert, Sept. 9, 1960. BA, U. Chgo., 1954; MD, Western Reserve U., 1960. Dir. day hosp. Roosevelt Hosp., N.Y.C., 1966-68; pvt. practice, N.Y.C., 1966-71; staff psychiatrist Menninger Clinic, Topeka, 1971-93, sr. psychiat. cons., 1987—; dir. Will Menninger Ctr., 1981-87; vice-chmn. Kaw Valley State Bank and Trust Co., 1981-89, chmn., 1989—. Producer films include A Man Named Ziegler, 1978; contbr. articles to profl. jours. Pres. Topeka Housing Info. Ctr., 1978-79. Fellow Am. Psychiat. Assn.; mem. Internat. Soc. Psychoanalytic Study of Orgns. (pres. 1993-95), Am. Coun.on Sci. and Health (bd. scientific advisors). Avocations: scuba diving, underwater photography. Office: Kaw Valley State Bank & Trust Co 4848 SW 21st St Topeka KS 66604

SWOPE, CHARLES EVANS, banker, lawyer; b. West Chester, Pa., June 16, 1930; s. Charles S. and Edna (McAllister) S.; m. Stephanie Swope; 1 son. Charles E. BS, Bucknell U., 1953; JD, Washington and Lee U., U. Va., 1959; MS, Ind. Coll., 1966; attended Naval War Coll. Judge Adv. Gen. Sch., 1957, Command and Staff Coll., 1969; D of Pub. Svc. (hon.), West Chester U., 1994. Assoc. firm Gawthrop & Greenwood, Attys., West Chester, Pa., 1960; pres., chmn. bd., sr. trust officer 1st Nat. Bank, West Chester, 1965—; also chmn. bd. dirs.; pres. Eachus Dairy Co. 1970-84; pres., bd. dirs. West Chester Corp.; bd. dirs. Madison Co., Penjerdel, Penn Mut. Fire Ins. Co.; 1st Nat. Bank West Chester; pres. Automobile Assn. Chester County; lectr. corp. law. Pres., West Chester Civic Assn., 1964; co-chmn. Chester County Heart Assn. Drive, West Chester Community Center Bldg. Drive, 1970-90, 175th Anniversary West Chester; mem. Nat. Football Found. and Hall of Fame; chair Chester County council Boy Scouts Am., 1961-72; bd. dirs. Chester County Service, Swope Found. Trust; bd. dirs., v.p. West Chester U. Found.; pres. West Chester Found.; mem. Marine Corps. Scholarship Found.; chmn. Bus. and Indsl. Council of Chester County, pres., 1981; chmn. Easter Seal Soc. Chester County; mem. Com. to Restore Tun Tavern; trustee, West Chester U., 1962-72, pres. bd. trustees, 1966-72; trustee Chester County Devel. Fund, Dr. Charles S. Swope Scholarship Fund, Hatfield Home; YMCA trustee West Chester Hosp. Corp. Served to maj. USMC, 1952-55, col. Res. Decorated Legion of Merit, Nat. Def. medal, Navy Commendation medal, Meritorious Svc. medal; recipient Coll. Football Centennial award, 1970; Congressional Medal of Merit, 1981; Disting. Eagle Scout award Boy Scouts Am., 1983. Mem. Pa. Bankers Assn. (chmn. Legis. com. 1965, 70), U.S. Naval Inst., Assn. Univ. Trustees Pa., Am. Soc. In-

ternat. Law, Chester County Bar Found. (v.p.), Greater West Chester C. of C. (pres. 1963), Marine Corps League Chester County (vice comdr. 1960-72), Freedoms Found., Am. Legion (life mem.), Chester County Hist. Soc., Marine Corps Res. Officer Assn. (nat. pres. 1982-83, vice chmn. bd. dirs.), Marine Corps Assn., Marine Corps League, Pa. C. of C., Navy League U.S., Washington and Lee Law Sch. Assn., Bucknell, West Chester U. alumni assns., Pa. Economy League, Brandywine Valley Assn., Maxwell Football Club, Phi Alpha Delta, Phi Kappa Psi. Republican. Methodist (ofcl. bd.). Clubs: West Chester (Pa.) Golf and Country; Union League (Phila.) Italian Social; Sky Top; Great Oaks Yacht and Country, Masons, Rotary (pres. West Chester, Pa., 1968-69, Paul Harris fellow), Elks. Home: 200 W Ashbridge St West Chester PA 19380-2371 Office: First Nat Bank 9 N High St West Chester PA 19380-3015

SWOPE, DONALD DOWNEY, retired banker; b. Martinsville, Ill., Feb. 26, 1926; s. Roy V. and Dorothy Irene (Downey) S.; m. Earla Long, Aug. 16, 1960. BS, Ind. State U., 1950. With Ill. Savs. and Loan Commn., Springfield, Ill., 1950-77, chief dept. commr., 1971-77; exec. v.p. Bank for Savs. & Loan Assn., Chgo., 1977-81, pres., 1981-90, dir. Dir., treas. Country Fair White Elephant, Green Valley, Ariz. With USNR, 1944-63. Mem. VFW (life), Nat. Assn. State Savs. and Loan Suprs. (pres. 1972-73), Am. Legion (life), Desert Hills Golf Club, Kiwanis (pres. Crete, Ill. 1977-78, treas. Green Valley, Ariz.), Elks (treas.).

SWOPE, JEFFREY PEYTON, lawyer; b. Evanston, Ill., June 11, 1945; s. Oliver P. and Elspeth E. (Cahill) S.; m. Linda Lee, Aug. 26, 1967; children: Matthew, Gregory, Timothy. AB, Harvard U., 1967, JD, 1970. Bar: Mass. 1970, U.S. Dist. Ct. Mass. 1971, U.S. Ct. Appeals (1st cir.) 1973, U.S. Ct. Claims 1974, U.S. Supreme Ct. 1979. Assoc. Palmer & Dodge, Boston, 1970-76, ptnr., 1977—; treas. Social Law Libr., Boston, 1984—. Treas. Ella Lyman Cabot Trust, Holliston, Mass., 1979—. Mem. Mass. Audubon Soc. (bd. dirs. 1985—). Home: 54 Hyde St Newton Highlands MA 02161 Office: Palmer & Dodge 1 Beacon St Boston MA 02108

SWOPE, JOHN FRANKLIN, retired insurance executive; b. Mt. Kisco, N.Y., June 21, 1938; s. Gerard and Marjorie (Park) S.; m. Marjory Mason, June 9, 1962; children: Kristin, Kevin, John. BA, Amherst Coll., 1960; LLB, Yale U., 1963. Bar: N.H. 1963; CLU. Atty. United Life and Accident Ins. Co., Concord, N.H., 1963-67; asst. counsel United Life and Accident Ins. Co., 1967-69, corp. sec., counsel, 1969-70, v.p., 1970-74, sr. v.p., 1974-77, pres., dir., 1977-91; pres. Chubb Life Ins. Co. Am., 1981—; pres., dir. Colonial Life Ins. Co. Am., N.J., 1981—, Chubb Am. Service Corp., N.H., 1982-94, Vol. State Life Ins. Co., Tenn., 1984-91; exec. v.p. Chubb Corp., N.Y.C., 1988-94; pres., dir. Chubb Sovereign Life Ins. Co., Calif., 1993-94; chmn. Chubb Securities Corp., 1988—; bd. dirs. Pub. Broadcasting System; mem. bd. govs. Sta. WNHP-TV, 1985—, pres., 1985-92; trustee N.E. Utilities, 1992—; mem. Loma Edn. Com., 1992—. Trustee N.H. Higher Edn. Assistance Found., 1969-80, Shaker Village, Inc., 1981-86, Currier Gallery Art, 1986—, Tabor Acad., 1987—; mem. nom. com. PBS, 1990-91, bd. dirs., 1994—; vice chmn. New Eng. Found. for Arts, 1988-94; mem. Concord Zoning Bd., 1973-82; bd. dirs. Concord Regional Devel. Corp., 1975-82, N.H. Bus. Com. for the Arts, chmn., 1986—; N.H. adv. com. to U.S. Commn. on Civil Rights, 1982-85, pres., bd. dirs., N.H. Pub. TV, 1988-92; incorporator N.H. Charitable Fund, 1984—, chmn. capital fund drive, 1985; mem. N.H. State Coun. on Arts, 1985-92; pres. Greater Concord C. of C., 1975-76. Mem. ABA, N.H. Bar Assn., Merrimack County Bar Assn., Assn. Life Ins. Counsel. Home: Long Pond Rd Concord NH 03301

SWORD, CHRISTOPHER PATRICK, microbiologist, university dean; b. San Fernando, Calif., Sept. 9, 1928; s. Christopher Patrick and Mary (Ross) S.; m. Mary Rose Gerhardt, June 18, 1959; children—Mary Anne, Carolyn, Jacqueline, Christopher. B.S. in Biology, Loyola U., Los Angeles, 1951; Ph.D. in Microbiology, UCLA, 1959. Research asso. in microbiology U. Kans., 1958-59, from asst. prof. to prof., 1959-70; research asso. Argonne (Ill.) Nat. Lab., 1961; prof. life scis., chmn. dept. Ind. State U., Terre Haute, 1970-76; prof. microbiology Center Med. Edn., 1971-76; prof. microbiology, dir. research, grad. dean S.D. State U., Brookings, 1976—; cons., evaluator for N. Cen. Assn. Colls. and Schs. Author numerous articles in field. Grantee USPHS, grantee Am. Heart Assn. Mem. Am. Soc. Microbiology, N.Y. Acad. Scis., AAAS, AAUP, Nat. Council U. Research Adminstrs., Council Grad. Schs., Midwestern Assn. Grad. Schs., Sigma Xi, Phi Kappa Phi. Home: 1500 Buffalo Trl Brookings SD 57006-3608 Office: SD State U Grad Sch Brookings SD 57007

SWORD, RUSS DONALD, hospital administrator; b. Dwale, Ky., Apr. 9, 1944; s. Hugh Edward and Verna (Moore) S.; m. Erma Foster, Nov. 6, 1966; children: Donna, Russ. BSBA, Berea Coll., 1966; M in Hosp. Adminstrn., Med. Coll. Va., 1973. Adminstrv. asst. Appalachian Regional Hosp., Man, W.Va., 1969-71; adminstrv. resident Charleston (W.Va.) Area Med. Ctr. Inc., 1972-73; asst. adminstr. Appalachian Regional Hosp., Hazard, Ky., 1973-75, adminstr., 1975—. Mem. Ky. Medicaid Adv. Com., Frankfort, Ky., 1986, Hazard Community Coll. Adv. Bd., 1986—; bd. dirs. Perry County Ambulance Authority, Hazard, 1981—. Served to 1st lt. U.S. Army, 1966-69. Mem. Am. Coll. Healthcare Execs., Am. Hosp. Assn., Ky. Hosp. Assn. (dist. v.p. 1983-84, chmn. 1983-86, speaker of house 1986—), Hazard-Perry County Jaycees (pres. 1976-77, Young Man of Yr. award 1976). Republican. Avocations: golf, high sch. football official. Office: Springdale Meml Hosp Assn 609 S Maple Dr Springdale AR 72764-5342

SWYGERT, H. PATRICK, law educator, university president; b. Phila., Mar. 17, 1943; s. LeRoy and Gustina (Rodgers) Huzzy; m. Sonja Branson, Aug. 22, 1969; children: Haywood Patrick, Michael Branson. AB in History, Howard U., 1965, JD cum laude, 1968. Bar: D.C. 1968, Pa. 1970, N.Y. 1970. Law clk. to chief judge U.S. Ct. Appeals (3d cir.), Phila., 1968-69; assoc. Debevoise, Plimpton, Lyons & Gates. N.Y.C., 1969-70; adminstrv. asst. to Congressman Charles B. Rangel, N.Y., 1971-72; spl. asst. dist. atty., Phila., 1973; from asst. prof. to prof. law Temple U., 1972-90, v.p. adminstrn., 1982-88, exec. v.p., 1988-90; pres. SUNY, Albany, 1990-95, pres. Howard U., Washington, D.C., 1995—. Bd. dirs. New Community Devel. Corp., HUD, 1980-82; gov.'s rep. Southeastern Pa. Transp. Authority, 1987-91, also bd. dirs. Vice-chmn. Phila. Pub. Service Com., 1974-77, Sta. WHYY-TV, 1987-90; bd. trustees Inst. Pub. Adminstrn., 1992—; mem. exec. com. Pub. Law Ctr. Phila., 1980-88, N.Y. State Coun. on Humanities, 1991—; bd. dirs. Albany area chpt. ARC, 1991—; chmn. N.Y. State Spl. Commn. on edni. structure, policies and practices, 1993—; co-chair joint task force grad. edni. Nat. Assn. State Univs. and Land Grant Colls., Am. Assn. State Colls. and Univs., 1993—. Mem. ABA, Amnivs. Coun. Edn. Commn. Women in Higher Edn., Middle States Assn Colls. and Schs. (commn. on higher edn. 1992—). Office: Howard U Office of Pres 2400 Sixth St NW Ste 402 Washington DC 20059

SWYMER, STEPHEN, principal. Prin. Gen. Wayne Mid. Sch., Malvern, Pa. Recipient Blue Ribbon award U.S. Dept. Edn., 1990-91. Office: Gen Wayne Mid Sch 20 Devon Rd Malvern PA 19355

SWYSTUN-RIVES, BOHDANA ALEXANDRA, dentist; b. Kopychynci, Ukraine, Jan. 31, 1925; came to U.S., 1951; d. Peter and Maria (Ottawa) Swystun; m. John Rives, June 20, 1952 (div. 1960); 1 child, Peter A. DMD, Ludwig Maximillians Universitat, Munich, 1951; DDS, NYU, 1960. Dentist Dr. Joseph Matriss, East Rutherford, N.J., 1960-61; gen. practice dentistry Clifton, N.J., 1961—. Vol. dentist Felician Sisters Orphanage, Lodi, N.J., 1982—; mem. Presdl. Task Force, Washington. Mem. ADA (award for commitment to professionalism and health), Ukrainian Med. Assn., Ukrainian Nat. Assn., Ukrainian Inst. Am., Clifton-Pasaic (N.J.) C. of C. Republican. Ukrainian Catholic. Avocations: reading, fgn. langs., walking, gold jewelry. Office: 1 Portland Ave Clifton NJ 07011-2347

SYKES, BRIAN DOUGLAS, biochemistry educator, researcher; b. Montreal, Que., Aug. 30, 1943; s. Douglas Lehman and Mary (Anber) S.; m. Nancy Lynne Sengelaub, May 25, 1968; children: David, Michael. B.Sc., U. Alta., 1965; Ph.D., Stanford U., 1969. Asst. prof. chemistry Harvard U., Cambridge, Mass., 1969-74; assoc. prof. Harvard U., 1974-75; assoc. prof. biochemistry U. Alta. (Can.), Edmonton, 1975-80, prof., 1980—, McCalla rsch. prof., 1994-95. Assoc. editor Biochemistry and Cell Biology, 1983-93; mem. editorial bd. Bull. Magnetic Resonance, 1983—, Magnetic Resonance in Chemistry, 1983—; assoc. editor Jour. Biomolecular NMR 1991—.

Recipient Steacie prize Nat. Sci. Engring. Rsch. Coun., 1982, Kaplan Rsch. award, 1992; Woodrow Wilson fellow, 1965, Alfred P. Sloan fellow, 1971. Fellow Royal Soc. of Can.; mem. Can. Biochem. Soc. (pres., Ayerst award 1982), Biophys. Soc. (councillor 1989-92), Am. Chem. Soc., Protein Soc. Home: 11312 37th Ave, Edmonton, AB Canada T6J 0H5

SYKES, GRESHAM M'CREADY, sociologist, educator, artist; b. Plainfield, N.J., May 26, 1922; s. M'Cready and Beatrice (Evans) S.; m. Carla Adelt, July 13, 1946. A.B. summa cum laude, Princeton U., 1950; Ph.D. (Woodrow Wilson fellow 1950-51, Univ. fellow 1951-52), Northwestern U., 1953; M.A. (hon.), Dartmouth Coll., 1961. Instr. sociology Princeton U., 1952-54, asst. prof., bicentennial preceptor, 1954-58; assoc. prof. Northwestern U., Evanston, Ill., 1958-60; prof. sociology Dartmouth Coll., Hanover, N.H., 1960-63; chmn. dept. Dartmouth Coll., 1961-63; exec. officer Am. Sociol. Assn., 1963-65; research prof. law and sociology, dir. adminstrn. of justice program U. Denver, 1965-72; chmn. dept. sociology U. Houston, 1973; prof. sociology U. Va., Charlottesville, 1974-88, chmn. dept., 1978-81, emeritus prof., 1988—; chmn. Salzburg (Austria) Seminar in Am. Studies, summer 1965; working as artist, with frequent group and one-man exhbns., 1988—. Author: Crime and Society, rev. edit., 1967, The Society of Captives, 1958, Law and the Lawless, 1969, Social Problems in America, 1971, Criminology, 1978, rev. edit., 1992, The Future of Crime, 1980; criminology editor Jour. Criminal Law, Criminology and Police Sci., 1959-64; assoc. editor Rev. Am. Sociol. Assn., 1960-62, Contemporary Sociology, 1977-80, Criminology, 1980-84; contbr. articles and revs. to Ency. Britannica, profl. jours. Served to capt., C.E. AUS, 1942-46, ETO. Recipient Edwin H. Sutherland award Am. Soc. Criminology, 1980. Home: 311-B 2nd St NW Charlottesville VA 22902

SYKES, LEONARD L., JR., newspaper editor; b. Chgo., Mar. 18, 1953; s. Leonard L. and Jean Kay (Richards) S. BJ, So. Ill. U., 1975. Asst. mng. editor Muhammad Speaks, Chgo., 1975-77; reporter Chgo. Defender, 1977-78; city hall reporter Waukegan (Ill.) News-Sun, 1978-86; city editor Milw. Jour. Sentinel, 1986—; assoc. editor Jet Mag., Chgo., 1980. Mem. Nat. Assn. Black Journalists. Home: 5706 N 27th St Glendale WI 53209 Office: Milw Jour Sentinel 333 W State St Milwaukee WI 53201

SYKES, LYNN RAY, geologist, educator; b. Pitts., Apr. 16, 1937; s. Lloyd Ascutney and Margaret (Woodburn) S. BS, MS, MIT, 1960; PhD in Geology, Columbia U., 1964. Phys. sci. aide geophys. lab. U.S. Geol. Survey, Silver Spring, Md., summer 1956; participant summer coop. program Geophys. Service Inc., Dallas, 1958; Summer Research fellow Woods Hole (Mass.) Oceanographic Inst., 1959; research asst. Lamont-Doherty Geol. Observatory Columbia U., 1961-64, research asso. in seismology, 1964-66, adj. asst. prof. geology, 1966-68, asst. prof., 1968-69, assoc. prof., 1969-73, prof., 1973-78, Higgins prof. geology, 1978—, mem. univ. com. on acad. priorities, 1977-79; research geophysicist earth scis. labs. U.S. Dept. Commerce, 1966-68; Mem. panel polar geophysics Nat. Acad. Scis., 1968; adv. com. to ESSA Research Labs., 1968-69; mem. subcom. geodesy and cartography applications steering com. NASA, 1968-70; mem. com. on world-wide standardized network Nat. Acad. Scis./NRC, 1969, com. seismology, 1972-73, panel earthquake prediction, 1973-75; organizing sec. Internat. Symposium Mech. Properties and Processes of Mantle of Internat. Upper Mantle Com., 1970; mem. panel on deep crustal drilling in marine areas JOIDES, 1970-71; advisor N.Y. State Geol. Survey and N.Y. State Environ. Protection Agy., 1970-80; mem. U.S. Geodynamics Panel on Mid-Atlantic Ridge, 1971-72; mem. working group U.S./USSR Joint Program for Earthquake Prediction, 1973-77; mem. U.S. Del. on Earthquake Prediction to USSR, fall, 1973; mem. adv. com. on proposals for earthquake prediction U.S. Geol. Survey, 1974, adv. panel earthquake hazards program, 1977-82; mem. U.S. Tech. Del. for talks on treaty on Threshold Limitations Underground Nuclear Explosions, Moscow, USSR, summer, 1974; mem. rev. panel earth scis. NSF, 1974-77; mem. study groups on plate interiors and Cocos and Caribbean plates U.S. Geodynamics Com.; mem. U.S. Seismology Group to People's Republic of China, fall, 1974; vis. prof. Earthquake Research Inst. of Tokyo (Japan) U., fall 1974; Fairchild vis. scholar Calif. Inst. Tech., 1981; vis. fellow Clare Hall, Cambridge U., 1982; chmn. nat. earthquake prediction evaluation council, U.S. Geol. Survey, 1984-88; mem. com. acad. priorities Columbia U., 1977-78, Columbia U. Arms Control Seminar, 1984—, mem. external rev. com. Nat. Earthquake Hazards Reduction Program, 1987-88; mem. com. on verification of nuclear testing, treaties, Office Tech. Assessment, U.S. Congress, 1986-87; participant Belmont (Md.) Conf. on Nuclear Test Ban Policy, 1988; U.S. com. for decade of natural hazards reduction NRC, 1989-90; participant on TV show NOVA. Contbg. author: History of the Earth's Crust, 1968, Geodynamics of Iceland and the North Atlantic Area, 1974, Encounter with the Earth, 1975; Assoc. editor: Jour. Geophys. Research, 1968-70; Contbr. numerous articles to profl. jours. Pres. Far West 77th St. Block Assn., N.Y.C., 1973-74. Recipient H. O. Wood award in seismology Carnegie Instn. of Washington, 1967-70, Edward John Noble Leadership award during first three years grad. study, Pub. Service award Fedn. Am. Scientists, 1986, John Wesley Powell award U.S. Geol. Survey, 1991; Sloan fellow, 1969-71; grantee NSF , AEC, Air Force Office Sci. Rsch., NASA, N.Y. State Sci. and Tech. Found., N.Y. State Atomic and Space Devel. Authority, U.S. Geol. Survey, Sloan Found., John D. and Catherine T. MacArthur Found., Carnegie Corp., 1988-89; Guggenheim fellow, 1988-89; Proctor & Gamble scholar. Fellow Am. Geophys. Union (Macelwave award to Outstanding Young Geophysicist for 1970, Walter H. Bucher medal for original contbns. to basic knowledge of Earth's crust 1975, pres. sect. tectonophysics 1972-74, pres. sect. on seismology 1982-84), Seismol. Soc. Am., Geol. Soc. Am., Geol. Soc. London; mem. Nat. Acad. Scis., Am. Acad. Arts. and Scis., Royal Astron. Soc., N.Y. Acad. Scis. (pres. geol. sect. 1970-71). Research includes maj. contbns. on plate tectonics, earthquake prediction and discrimination of underound nuclear explosions from earthquakes, arms control. Home: 100 Washington Springs Rd Palisades NY 10964-1624 Office: Columbia U Lamont-Doherty Earth Obs Palisades NY 10964

SYKES, MELVIN JULIUS, lawyer; b. Balt., Jan. 9, 1924; s. Philip Louis and Sara (Klein) S.; m. Judith Janet Konowitz, Sept.24, 1950; children: David K., Rachel A., Daniel E., Israel J. Grad., Balt. City Coll., 1940, Balt. Hebrew Coll., 1941; AB with honors, Johns Hopkins U., 1943; LLB magna cum laude, Harvard U., 1948. Bar. Md. 1949, U.S. Ct. Appeals (4th cir.) 1949, U.S. Dist. Ct. Md. 1950, U.S. Supreme Ct. 1955. Law clk. to Judge Morris A. Soper U.S. Ct. Appeals (4th cir.), 1948-49; pvt. practice Balt., 1949—; draftsman Md. Dept. Legis. Reference, 1949-50; rsch. cons. Md. Commn. Adminstrv. Orgn., 1951-52; reporter Md. commns. to study judiciary, 1953, to revise laws relating to pub. svc. commn., 1953-55; mem. standing com. on rules of practice, procedure Md. Ct. Appeals, 1954-72, 78—; mem. legis. coun. Commn. on Revision Condemnation Laws, 1961-63, Balt. Charter Revision Commn., 1962-63; pres. Bar Libr. of Balt., 1962-63; mem. Md. Constl. Conv. Commn., 1966-67; cons. Gov. Md. Commn. to Revise Testamentary Laws, 1967-69; mem. Gov. Md. commns. to study state aid to nonpub. edn., 1969-71, on annotated code Md., 1970-78. Co-author: West's Maryland Procedural Forms, 1964; co-translator Elon, Jewish Law—History, Principles, Sources, 1994. Mem. governing coun. Am. Assn. Jewish Edn., 1968-81; v.p. Balt. Jewish Coun., 1970-72; bd. dirs. Balt. chpt. Am. Jewish Com., Balt. Neighborhoods, Inc.; mem., former chmn. bd. trustees Balt. Hebrew Coll. With USAF, 1943-45. Fellow Am. Coll. Trial Lawyers, Am. Coll. Trust and Estate Counsel, Am. Bar Found., Md. Bar Found. (chmn. 1981-83); mem. ABA, Am. Law Inst., Md. Bar Assn., Balt. City Bar Assn. (lectr. continuing edn. programs), Am. Judicature Soc. (lectr. continuing edn. programs), Am. Jewish Congress, Zionist Orgn. Am., B'nai B'rith, Phi Beta Kappa Fellows. Democrat. Home: Maryland Bar Ctr Ste 310 520 W Fayette St Baltimore MD 21201-1781 Office: 520 W Fayette St Ste 310 Baltimore MD 21201-1770

SYKES, ROBERT REED, lawyer, former judge; b. Dallas, May 21, 1952; s. Bobby Reed and Patsy Ruth (West) S.; m. Lisa Jolley, Oct. 10, 1981; children: Reed, Nathan, Grant. BBA, Tex. A&M U., 1974; JD, So. Meth. U., 1977. Bar: Tex. 1977, U.S. Dist. Ct. (no. dist.) Tex. 1980, U.S. Dist. Ct. (we. dist.) Tex. 1986. Asst. county atty. Tom Green County Atty.'s Office, San Angelo, Tex., 1978-81; trust landman First Nat. Bank Midlan, Tex., 1981-83, RepublicBank First Nat., Midland, 1983-85; pvt. practice atty. Midland, 1985—; U.S. fed. magistrate judge U.S. Dist. Ct. (we. dist.) Tex., Midland, 1988-92. 1st lt. USAR, 1974-88. Mem. State Bar Tex., Midland County Bar Assn., Midland A&M Club. Baptist. Office: 203 W Wall St Ste 606 Midland TX 79701-4516

SYKES, RUTH L., special education educator; b. Fairfield, Tex., Dec. 19, 1941; d. F. W. and LaKatie (Jordan) McIlveen; m. Alexander Sykes, Sept. 15, 1963; children: Lajourka, Jennifer, Dorothy, Reneé. Student, Prairie View, 1960-62; BS, Bishop Coll., 1965; postgrad., Tex. State U., 1980. Cert. elem., special edn., Tex. Tchr. reading Fairfield (Tex.) Ind. Sch. Dist., 1965-66, parochial schs., Houston, 1968-70; substitute tchr. Houston Ind. Sch. Dist., 1972-75, tchr. special edn., 1975-87, tchr. 3d grade, 1987-88, tchr. 5th grade, 1988-89, coord., 1989-90, tchr. functional special edn., 1990-91, tchr. special edn. resource, 1991—; tchr. Career Ladder, Houston, 1987—; chair promotion/retention referral com., Highland Hgts. Sch., 1975-82, 89-90. Troop 336 leader Boy Scouts Am., Houston, 1975-80. Mem. Houston Tchrs. Assn., Charity Ch. (souvenir book 1992). Democrat. Baptist. Avocations: reading, travel, sports, church. Home: 6635 Brownie Campbell St Houston TX 77086-1904

SYKES, STEPHANIE LYNN, library director, archivist, museum director; b. Hamilton, Ont., Can., Sept. 14, 1948; d. Harold Joseph John and Ida Fern (Merritt) S. BA with honors, U. Western Ont., London, Ont., 1971; MA in History, U. Western Ont., 1978, MLS, 1984; cert. edn., Althouse Coll., Ont., 1972. Archival asst. D.B. Weldon Libr., London, Ont., Can., 1974-77; govt. pubs. libr. D.B. Weldon Libr., London, Ont., 1977-80; tech. svcs. libr. Bell Canada Hist. Svcs., Montréal, Québec, Can., 1980-81, sect. mgr. archives, 1981-83, dir. archives, libraries, and museum, 1983—. Editor: (catalogue) Regional Collection D.B. Weldon Library, 1977. Mem. Soc. Quebec Mus., Assn. Can. Archivists, Soc. Am. Archivists. Office: Bell Canada Hist Svcs, 1050 Beaver Hall Hill Rm 820, Montreal, PQ Canada H2Z 1S4

SYKORA, DONALD D., utility company excutive; b. Stamford, Tex., Aug. 23, 1930; s. John E. and Lillie A. S.; m. Beverly J. Dawson, Feb. 7, 1952; 1 child, Sandra Lynn. BBA, U. Houston, 1957; JD, South Tex. Coll. Law, 1969. Bar: Tex. 1969. With Houston Lighting & Power Co., 1956—, power cons. residential mktg., 1956-63, supr. residential devel., 1963-68, gen. supr. residential mktg., 1968-70, asst. mgr. comml. sales, 1970-72, mgr. comml. sales, 1972-74, mgr. orgnl. devel., 1974, gen. mktg. mgr., 1974-77, v.p. mktg., 1977-78, v.p. customer relations, 1978-80, v.p. customer and pub. relations, 1980-81, exec. v.p., 1981-93, pres., chief operating officer, 1993—, also bd. dirs.; also v.p., bd. dirs. parent co. Houston Industries Inc.; bd. dirs. Primary Fuels, Inc., Utility Fuels, Inc. Chmn. exec. adv. bd. customer service and mktg. com. Edison Electric Inst., Washington, 1974—; mem. exec. bd. Electrification Council, 1974—, Salvation Army, Houston, 1980—. Mem. Tex. Bar Assn., Houston C. of C. Club: Houston. Home: 9614 Briar Forest Dr Houston TX 77063-1007 Office: Houston Industries Inc 4400 Post Oak Pky Houston TX 77027

SYKORA, HAROLD JAMES, military officer; b. Tripp, S.D., Mar. 10, 1939; s. James J. and Mary (Tucek) S.; m. Patricia Ann Friedrich, Dec. 26, 1962; children: Montgomery James, Gina Marie. BS, U.S.D., 1961, MA in Math., 1965; postgrad., U. Wis., 1971-72, Indsl. Coll. Armed Forces, Ft. McNair, Washington, 1987-88. Math. tchr. Mitchell (S.D.) Sr. High Sch., 1961-64, 65-71, 72-74; commd. U.S. Army; advanced through grades to maj. gen.; with U.S. Army Command and Gen. Staff Coll., Ft. Leavenworth, Kans., 1974-75; exec. officer hdqs. 147th F.A.S.D N.G., Pierre, 1975-80; tng. officer hdqrs. S.D. N.G., Rapid City, 1980-83, chief of staff, 1983-87, adj. gen., 1988—. Mem. N.G. Assn. U.S., N.G. Assn. S.D. (pres. 1979-80), Am. Legion, Assn. U.S. Army, Adjutant's Gen. Assn. U.S. (sec. 1991—, Army res. forces policy com. 1992—), Kiwanis. Republican. Roman Catholic. Home: 5204 Pinedale Hts Rapid City SD 57702-2010 Office: SD NG 2823 W Main St Rapid City SD 57702-8186

SYLBERT, PAUL, production designer, art director; b. N.Y.C., Apr. 16, 1928. Art dir.: (films) The Wrong Man, 1956, (with Rolland M. Brooks and Howard Hollander) Teenage Millionaire, 1961; prodn. designer: (films) (with Richard Sylbert) Baby Doll, 1956, (with R. Sylbert) A Face in the Crowd, 1957, The Tiger Makes Out, 1967, The Drowning Pool, 1975, One Flew Over the Cuckoo's Nest, 1975, Mikey and Nicky, 1976, Hardcore, 1979, Kramer vs. Kramer, 1979, Wolfen, 1979, Resurrection, 1980, Blow Out, 1981, Gorky Park, 1983, Without a Trace, 1983, Firstborn, 1984, The Pope of Greenwich Village, 1984, The Journey of Natty Gann, 1985, Ishtar, 1987, Nadine, 1987, The Pick-Up Artist, 1987, Biloxi Blues, 1988, Fresh Horses, 1988, Career Opportunities, 1991, (with W. Steven Graham) The Prince of Tides, 1991 (Academy award nomination best art direction 1991), Rush, 1992, Sliver, 1993, Milk Money, 1994; prodn. designer, art dir.: (films) Riot, 1969, (with Edwin O'Donovan) Heaven Can Wait, 1978 (Academy award best art direction 1978); screenwriter: The Steagle, 1971, (with David Shaber) Night Hawks, 1981. Address: 52 E 64th St Ste 3 New York NY 10021-7356 Office: IATSE Local 816 11365 Ventura Blvd Ste 315 Studio City CA 91604*

SYLBERT, RICHARD, production designer, art director; b. N.Y.C., Apr. 16, 1928. V.p. prodn. Paramount Pictures, 1975-78. Art dir.: (films) Patterns, 1956, Wind Across the Everglades, 1958, The Fugitive Kind, 1960, Mad Dog Coll, 1961, Splendor in the Grass, 1961, Walk on the Wild Side, 1962, Lilith, 1964, The Pawnbroker, 1964, The Heartbreak Kid, 1972, (TV series) Inner Sanctum, 1951-53; prodn. designer: (films) Crowded Paradise, 1956, (with Paul Sylbert) Baby Doll, 1956, Edge of the City, 1957, (with P. Sylbert) A Face in the Crowd, 1957, Murder, Inc., 1960, The Young Doctors, 1961, The Connection, 1962, How to Murder Your Wife, 1965, Who's Afraid of Virginia Woolf?, 1966 (Academy award best art direction 1966), Grand Prix, 1966, The Graduate, 1967, Rosemary's Baby, 1968, The April Fools, 1969, Catch-22, 1970, Carnal Knowledge, 1971, Fat City, 1972, The Day of the Dolphin, 1973, Chinatown, 1974 (Academy award nomination best art direction 1974), The Fortune, 1975, Shampoo, 1975 (Academy award nomination best art direction 1975), Players, 1979, Reds, 1981 (Academy award nomination best art direction 1981), Frances, 1982, Partners, 1982, Breathless, 1983, The Cotton Club, 1984 (Academy award nomination best art direction 1984), Under the Cherry Moon, 1986, Shoot to Kill, 1988, Tequila Sunrise, 1988, Bonfire of the Vanities, 1990, Mobsters, 1991, Carlito's Way, 1993; prodn. designer, art dir.: (films) Long Day's Journey into Night, 1962, (with Phil Jeffries) The Manchurian Candidate, 1962, All the Way Home, 1963, Dick Tracy, 1990 (Academy award best art direction 1990), (TV movie) Last Hours Before Midnight, 1975; assoc. prodr.: (films) What's New Pussycat?, 1965; visual arts cons.: (films) The Illustrated Man, 1969; set designer: (theatre) The Prisoner of Second Avenue, 1971-74. Address: care Paul Sylbert 52 6th Ave Ste 3 New York NY 10013-2412*

SYLK, LEONARD ALLEN, housing company executive, real estate developer; b. Phila., Feb. 25, 1941; s. Harry S. and Gertrude (Bardy) S.; m. Barbara Ann Lovenduski, Dec. 1, 1975; children: Tristan, Tyler, Galen. BS in Econs., U. Pa., 1963; MBA, Columbia U., 1965. Cert. comml. property builder. Founder, chmn. bd., chief exec. officer Shelter Systems Corp., Hainesport, N.J., 1965—; bd. dirs. Hill Internat., Inc., Willingboro, N.J., Home Owners Warranty Corp., N.J., 1989—; bd. govs. Middle East Forum; trustee Nat. Bldg. Sys. Coun., 1986—; presdl. advisor on housing trade with Soviet Union, 1990. Contbr. articles to industry publs. Chmn. ann. giving Friends Cen. Sch., Phila., 1983-86; co-chmn. ann. fundraiser Pa. Hosp., Phila., 1987, Inst. for Contemporary Art, Phila., 1988; chmn. ann. awards dinner Jewish Nat. Fund, Phila., 1987, v.p., bd. dirs. Bd. dirs. Phila. Orch. Assn., 1990—, Pa. Ballet, 1994—; Resources for Childrens Health, 1993—, Acad. Music, Phila., 1990—; N.J. chmn. Builders for Bush, 1988; trustee Hahnemann U. and Hosp., 1991, St. Christophers Hosp. for Children, Phila., 1994. Named Man of Yr., 1988; recipient Tree of Life award presented by Rt. Hon. Margaret Thatcher, 1995. Mem. Nat. Assn. Homebuilders (com. chmn. nat. bd. dirs. 1984—, mem. exec. com. 1990—, fundraising chmn. 1991, Man of Yr. in Industrialized Housing 1990), Wood Truss Coun. Am. (bd. dirs. 1983—, pres. 1987, named to Hall of Fame 1990), Builders League South Jersey (v.p., bd. dirs. 1984—), N.J. Builders Assn. (bd. dirs. com. chmn., exec. com. 1990—), Le Club (N.Y.C.), Atlantic City Country Club, Vesper Club, Union League, Capitol Club (Washington), Masons. Republican. Home: 500 Delancey St Philadelphia PA 19106-4106 Office: Shelter Systems Corp Park Ave Hainesport NJ 08036

SYLVAIN, RICK, newspaper editor. Travel editor The Detroit Free Press, Mich. Office: Detroit Free Press Inc 321 W Lafayette Blvd Detroit MI 48226*

SYLVESTER, GEORGE HOWARD, retired air force officer; b. Riverside, N.J., Aug. 10, 1927; s. Ralph Davis and Dorothy Clarisse (Mealley) S.; m. Elaine Ruth Wenderling, June 7, 1949; children—Wendy, Susan, David. B.S., U.S. Mil. Acad., 1949; M.A., Georgetown U., 1956. Commd. 2d lt. U.S. Air Force, 1949, advanced through grades to lt. gen., 1976; pilot, 1949-54; asst. prof. social scis. U.S. Mil. Acad., 1956-60; long-range planner Hdqrs. U.S. Air Force, 1961-64; mil. asst. to sec. def., 1964-66; squadron comdr. F-4 squadron Vietnam, 1966; comdr. Danang Air Base, Vietnam, 1967; dir. test Eglin AFB, Fla., 1968-70; asst. dir. tactical systems test and evaluation Office Sec. Def., 1970-73; dep. for systems ASD, Wright-Patterson AFB, Ohio, 1973-74; vice comdr. ASD, 1974-76, comdr., 1976-79; vice comdr. AF Systems Command, Andrews AFB, Md., 1979-81; ret., 1981, ind. aerospace cons., 1981—. Decorated D.S.M. with 1 oak leaf cluster, Legion of Merit with 2 oak leaf clusters, D.F.C., Air medal with 7 oak leaf clusters, Air Force Commendation medal with 2 oak leaf clusters; Vietnamese Medal of Honor. Lutheran. Home: 4839 Coniceville Rd Mount Jackson VA 22842-9634

SYLVESTER, RONALD CHARLES, newspaper writer; b. Springfield, Mo., Feb. 10, 1959; s. Edgar Donald and Barbara Jean (Hedgecock) S.; 1 child, Christian Alexander. Sports writer Springfield (Mo.) News-Leader, 1976-88, entertainment writer, 1988—; mem. media panel Leadership Music, Nashville, 1993. Author: Branson: On Stage in the Ozarks, 1994; contbr. articles to New Country Music, Gannett News Svc., Colliers Ency. Bd. dirs. Entertainers Guild of Branson, Mo., 1993-94. Mem. Country Music Assn. Mem. Christian Ch. (Disciples of Christ). Avocations: music, reading, outdoor recreation. Office: Springfield News-Leader 651 Boonville Ave Springfield MO 65806

SYLVESTRE, JEAN GUY, former national librarian; b. Sorel, Que., Can., May 17, 1918; s. Maxime Arthur and Yvonne Marie (Lapierre) S.; m. Francoise Poitevin, Feb. 27, 1943; children: Marie, Jean, Paul. B.A., U. Ottawa, 1939, B.Ph., 1940, M.A., 1942, D.L.S. (hon.), 1969, D.Litt. (hon.), 1970, LL.D. (hon.), 1974, 75, 82. Translator Dept. Can. Sec. of State, 1942-44; editor Wartime Info. Bd., 1944-45; asst. pvt. sec. to minister of justice, 1945-47, pvt. sec. to sec. of state for external affairs, 1947-48, pvt. sec. to prime minister, 1948-50; adminstrv. officer Dept. Resources and Devel., 1950-53; asst. librarian Library of Parliament, Ottawa, Ont., 1953-56; asso. parliamentary librarian Library of Parliament, 1956-68, nat. librarian, 1968-83; pres., chmn. bd. Can. Inst. for Hist. Microprodns., 1983-86; chmn. Ottawa Valley Book Festival, 1988-92; hon. chmn., 1993—. Author: Louis Francoeur, journaliste, 1941, Situation de la poésie canadienne, 1941, Anthologie de la poésie canadienne-française, 1943, 58, 64, 66, 68, 74, Poétes catholiques de la France contemporaine, 1944, Sondages, 1945, Impressions de théâtre, 1950, Amours, délices et orgues, 1953, Panorama des lettres canadiennes-francaises, 1964, Canadian Writers, 1964, Literature in French Canada, 1967, A Century of Canadian Literature, 1967, The Future of the National Library of Canada, 1980, Guidelines for National Libraries, 1987 French, Spanish and Arabic edits., 1988; also articles in profl. jours., encys.; editor: A Canadian Errant (J.P. Manion), 1960; editor: Canadian Universities Today, 1961, Structures sociales du Canada francais, 1967. Chmn. Gov. Gen.'s Lit. Awards, 1960-62; organizer, chmn. World Poetry Conf., Expo 1967; chmn. Can. Council Com. on Aid-to-Publs., 1960-68; lectr. U. Ottawa Library Sch., 1954-71; v.p. Can. Library Week Council, 1965-67; Bd. dirs. Can. Writers Found., pres., 1960-61. Decorated comdr. Ordre International du Bien Public, officer Order of Can.; comdr. Order of Merit of Poland; recipient Centennial medal., Outstanding Pub. Service award, Internat. Fedn. Libr. Assn. medal. Fellow Royal Soc. Can.; mem. sec. 1959-62, pres. sect. I 1963-64, hon. libr. 1969-91, pres. 1973-74); mem. Soc. Ecrivains Canadiens, Can. Libr. Assn. (life), Ont. Libr. Assn. (hon. life), Can. Assn. Info. Sci. (pres. 1971-72), Assn. Scis. et Techniques (life) Home: 2286 Bowman Rd, Ottawa, ON Canada K1H 6V6

SYMANSKI, ROBERT ANTHONY, treasurer; b. Mineola, N.Y., June 17, 1946; s. Anthony John and Mary (Jozef) S.; m. Eileen Margaret Eardley; children: Susan, Robert, Patti. AAS, SUNY, Delhi, 1966; BBA, Pace U., 1972; MBA, Fairleigh Dickinson U., 1984. Sr. credit rep. Union Carbide Corp., N.Y.C., 1967-71; credit mgr. GAF Corp., N.Y.C., 1971-73; dir. cash mgmt. GAF Corp., Wayne, N.J., 1973-77; mgr. corp. cash Coca-Cola Bottling Co. N.Y., Hackensack, N.J., 1977-81; asst. treas. The BOC Group Inc., Montvale, N.J., 1981-86; treas. The BOC Group Inc., Murray Hill, N.J., 1986—. Sgt. USAF, 1967-69. Mem. Nat. Assn. Corp. Treas., Treasury Mgmt. Assn., Fin. Execs. Insts. Roman Catholic. Home: 16 Susan Dr Chatham NJ 07928-1049 Office: The BOC Group Inc 575 Mountain Ave New Providence NJ 07974-2002

SYMCHYCH, JANICE M., lawyer; b. St. Boniface, Man., Can., 1951. BA magna cum laude, U. Minn., 1973; JD magna cum laude, William Mitchell Coll. Law, 1977. Bar: Minn. 1977, U.S. Dist. Ct. (Minn. dist.) 1977, U.S. Ct. Appeals (8th cir.) 1981. Asst. atty. Hennepin County, Minn., 1977-80; asst. U.S. atty. U.S. Attys. Office, Minn., 1980-85; U.S. magistrate judge Dist. Minn., 1985-89; ptnr. Dorsey & Whitney, Mpls.; mem. task force on gender fairness in cts. Minn. Supreme Ct., 1987-90. Mem. Minn. State Bar Assn. (mem. task force on complex litigation 1991—, mem. civil litigation gov. coun. 1986—, chair Minn. CLE bd. dirs. 1990—). Office: Dorsey & Whitney 220 S 6th St Minneapolis MN 55402-4500

SYME, SHERMAN LEONARD, epidemiology educator; b. Dauphin, Man., Can., July 4, 1932; came to U.S., 1950; s. Robert and Rose (Bay) S.; m. Marilyn Elaine Egenes, July 28, 1932; children: Karen, David, Janet. BA, UCLA, 1953, MA, 1955; PhD, Yale U., 1957. Commd. USPHS, Washington, 1957-68; advanced through grades to chief Tng. Sta. USPHS, San Francisco, 1962-68; sociologist USPHS, Washington, 1957-60; exec. sec. NIH, Bethesda, Md., 1960-62; prof. epidemiology U. Calif., Berkeley, 1968—; chmn. Dept. Epidemiology, U. Calif., 1975-80; vis. prof. Teikyo U., Tokyo, 1977, York (Eng.) U., 1975, St. Thomas Sch. Medicine, London, 1980, U. London, 1989; expert adv. panels WHO, Geneva, 1975—. Co-editor Social Stress and Heart Disease, 1967, Social Support and Health, 1985; contbr. 115 articles to profl. jours. Fellow Am. Heart Assn., Soc. Epidemiol. Research; mem. Inst. Medicine, Am. Epidemiol. Soc. Office: U Calif Haviland Hall Berkeley CA 94720

SYMINGTON, J. FIFE, III, governor; b. N.Y.C., Aug. 12, 1945; s. John Fife Jr. and Martha (Frick) S.; m. Leslie Marion Barker, June 1, 1968 (div. Jan. 1973); childen: Fife IV, Scott; m. Ann Pritzlaff, Feb. 7, 1976; children: Whitney, Richard, Tom. Student, Harvard U., 1968. Ptnr. Lincoln Property Co., Phoenix, 1972-76; chmn. of the bd. The Symington Co., Phoenix, 1976-89; gov. State of Ariz., 1991—. Precinct committeeman Ariz.'s Legis. Dist. 24, Paradise Valley; fin. chmn. State Republican Party, Phoenix, 1982-84; campaign advisor Rep. John Rhodes, Sen. John McCain, Ariz.; chmn. Phoenix Citizens Police Protection Bond Com., 1988; v.p. bd. trustees Heard Mus.; mem. Men's Art Coun., Environ. Quality Commn., 1971-73, Ariz. Children's Found.; dep. sheriff Maricopa County Air Posse; exec. bd. Phoenix Community Alliance. Capt. USAF, 1968-71. Mem. Western Govs.' Assn. (chmn. 1992—). Episcopalian. Office: Govs Office 1700 W Washington Phoenix AZ 85007*

SYMMERS, WILLIAM GARTH, international maritime lawyer; b. Bronxville, N.Y., Nov. 30, 1910; s. James Keith and Agnes Louise (Shuey) S.; m. Marina Baruch, Apr. 25, 1936; children: Benjamin Keith, Ann St. Clair (Mrs. Edward L. Reed); m. Anne H. Ellis, Mar. 20, 1946; children: Barbara (Mrs. Thomas M. Bancroft, Jr.), Susan (Mrs. Peter Amory Bradford), Deborah. Grad. Lawrenceville (N.J.) Sch., 1929; AB, U. Va., 1933, JD, 1935. Bar: N.Y. 1937, U.S. Supreme Ct. 1940, D.C. 1953. Assoc. Bigham, Englar, Jones & Houston, N.Y.C., 1935-37; mem. Dow and Symmers, N.Y.C., 1940-56; founding ptnr. Symmers, Fish & Warner, N.Y.C. 1956-91; ret.; admiralty counsel U.S. Maritime Commn., 1937-41; spl. counsel to naval affairs com. U.S. Ho. of Reps.; active investigation loss of SS Normandie, 1942; spl. counsel War Shipping Adminstrn, 1942-45, admiralty and shipping litigation; U.S. del., v.p. Antwerp Conf., Comité Maritime Internat.; 1947; also del. Maritime Law Assn. U.S. to succeeding confs.; Amsterdam 1949, Brighton, 1952, Madrid 1955, Rijeka, 1966, Tokyo, 1968, Rio de Janeiro, 1977, Montreal, 1981; titular mem. Comité Maritime Internat., 1955—; mem. U.S. Supreme Ct. adv. com. on admiralty rules, 1960-72. Contbr. articles to maritime publs. Mem. ABA, Assn. Bar City of N.Y. (chmn. admiralty com. 1953-56), Am. Soc. Internat. Law,

Maritime Law Assn. U.S. (chmn. com. revision U.S. Supreme Ct. admiralty rules 1952-56, mem. exec. com. 1958-61, 1st v.p. 1964-66), Internat. Maritime Arbitration Orgn. (U.S. rep. 1978-81), Internat. C of C., St. Andrew's Soc. N.Y., English-Speaking Union U.S., Down Town Assn., N.Y. Yacht Club, Indian Harbor Yacht Club (Greenwich, Conn.), Phi Delta Phi, Phi Delta Theta. Address: 444 E 52d St New York NY 10022

SYMMONDS, RICHARD EARL, gynecologist; b. Greensburg, Mo., Mar. 19, 1922; s. Emmett E. S. A.B., Central Coll., Fayette, Mo., 1943; M.D., Duke U., 1946; M.S. in Ob-Gyn, U. Minn., 1953. Intern Los Angeles County Hosp., 1946, resident in Ob-Gyn, 1950-53, resident in gen. surgery, 1954-56; practice medicine specializing in gen. surgery Rochester, Minn., 1958—; mem. faculty Mayo Clinic, Rochester, 1953—; emeritus prof. gynecologic surgery Mayo Clinic, 1960—, chmn. dept., 1970-92, chmn. emeritus, 1992—. Contbr. articles to profl. jours. Served with USN, 1947-49. Fellow A.C.S.; mem. Am. Gynecol. Soc., Am. Assn. Obstetricians and Gynecologists, Soc. Pelvic Surgeons, Soc. Gynecologic Oncologists, Am. Coll. Obstetricians and Gynecologists. Office: 200 1st St SW Rochester MN 55905-0001

SYMON, LINDSAY, neurological surgery educator; b. Aberdeen, Scotland, Nov. 4, 1929; s. William Lindsay and Isabel (Shaw) S.; m. Pauline Barbara Rowland, Aug. 14, 1953; children: Lindsay Fraser, Barbara Rosemary, Fiona Margaret. MB, ChB with honors, Aberdeen U., Scotland, 1951; Diplomate, Royal Coll. Surgeons, 1957. Jr. specialist, house surgeon Royal Infirmary, Aberdeen, Scotland, 1952-3; surgical registrar Royal Infirmary, Aberdeen 1956-58; clin. rsch. fellow med. rsch. coun. neurosurgical registrar Middlesex & Maida Vale Hosp., London, 1958-61, sr. registrar in Neurosurgery, 1962-65; Rockefeller travelling fellow in medicine Wayne U., Detroit, 1961-62; cons. neurosurgeon Nat. Hosp. for Nervous Diseases, London, 1965-78; cons. St. Thomas Hosp., London, 1970-78; prof. Neurological Surgery Inst. Neurology, U. London Nat. Hosp. Queens Sq., London, 1978—; cons. (hon.) Hammersmith Hosp., London, Royal Ear, Nose and Throat Hosp., London; civilian advisor in Neurol. Surgery, The Royal Navy. Contbr. articles to profl. jours.; mem. many editorial bds. med. jours. Vol. med. advisor Mobile Neuorsurgical Unit, Territorial Army, Keogh Barracks, Mytchett, 1975-81. Maj. Royal Army Med. Corps, 1953-55. Decorated with Territorial decoration, The Queen, 1968, Comdr. of British Empire, Queen's Birthday, 1994. Fellow ACS (hon.), Royal Coll. Surgeons (Edinborough), Royal Coll. Surgeons (London), Royal Soc. Medicine; mem. Soc. Brit. Neurol. Surgeons, World Fedn. Neurosurg. Socs. (pres. 1989—), Caledonian Club, St. Andrews Royal and Ancient Golf Club, others. Mem. Conservative Party. Avocations: golf, medieval history. Home: "Cairngorm" 42 Granville Rd, EN5 4 DS Barnet Herts England Office: Inst Neurology, Queens Sq, WCIN 3BG London England

SYMONDS, PAUL SOUTHWORTH, mechanical engineering educator, researcher; b. Manila, Aug. 20, 1916; came to U.S., 1917; s. George R.B. and Claire Louise (Southworth) S.; m. Ilese Powell, Jan. 23, 1943; children: Alan Powell, Robin Peter. BS, Rensselaer Poly. Inst., 1938; MS, Cornell U., 1941, PhD, 1943; Docteur en Sciences Appliquées (hon.), Faculté Polytechnique de Mons, Belgium, 1988. Instr. mechanics Cornell U., Ithaca, N.Y., 1941-43; physicist Naval Research Lab., Washington, 1943-47; asst. prof. engring. Brown U., Providence, 1947-51, assoc. prof., 1951-54, prof., 1954-83, prof. engring. rsch. emeritus, 1983—, chmn. div. engring., 1959-62. Editor Quar. Applied Math., 1965—; mem. adv. bd. Internat. Jour. Mech. Sci., 1978—; mem. editorial adv. bd. Internat. Jour. Impact Engring., 1983—, Computer Methods in Applied Mechanics and Engring., 1983—; also numerous papers in tech. jours. Recipient Fulbright award 1949-50, 57-58; fellow Imperial Chem. Industries, Cambridge, U.K., 1950-51; Guggenheim fellow Swansea, Wales, 1957-58; NSF sr. postdoctoral fellow Oxford, Eng., 1964-65. Fellow ASME, ASCE, Am. Acad. Mechanics; mem. Internat. Assn. Bridge and Structual Engring. Home: 229 Medway St Apt 110 Providence RI 02906-5300 Office: Brown U Divsn Enging Providence RI 02912

SYMONS, EDWARD LEONARD, JR., lawyer, educator, investment advisor; b. Pitts., Dec. 21, 1941; s. Edward Leonard and Lillian Mae (Daniel) S.; m. Louise Quinn, July 18, 1970; children: Amy, Colin. B.A., Cornell U., 1963; J.D. summa cum laude, U. Pitts., 1969. Assoc., ptnr. Reding, Blackstone, Rea & Sell, Pitts., 1969-72; asst. atty. gen., chief counsel Pa. Dept. Banking, Harrisburg, 1972-74; prof. law U. Pitts. Sch. Law, 1974—; research dir. Pa. Tax Commn., 1979-81; pres. Dollins Symons Mgmt., Inc., 1983—. Co-author, Pennsylvania Professional Corporations, 1974, Banking Law Teaching Materials, 2d edit., 1984, 3d edit., 1991; contbr. articles to profl. jours. Commr. Mt. Lebanon, Pa., 1976-80; bd. dirs. Performing Arts for Children, Pitts., 1980-84, Mt. Lebanon Hosp. Authority, 1993—, St. Clair Hosp. Found., Pitts., 1994—. 1st lt. arty. AUS, 1964-66. Decorated Order of the Coif, 1969. Mem. ABA (banking law com., consumer fin. services com., devel. in investment svcs. com.). Office: U Pitts Sch Law 3900 Forbes Ave Pittsburgh PA 15213

SYMONS, J. KEITH, bishop; b. Champion, Mich., Oct. 14, 1932. Student, St. Thomas Sem., Bloomfield, Conn., St. Mary Sem., Balt. Ordained priest Roman Catholic Ch., 1958, consecrated bishop, 1981. Titular bishop of Siguritanum and aux. bishop of St. Petersburg Fla., 1981-83; bishop of Pensacola-Tallahassee, 1983-90, bishop of Palm Beach, 1990—. Office: 9995 N Military Trl Palm Beach Gardens FL 33410-5460*

SYMONS, JAMES MARTIN, environmental engineer, educator; b. Champaign, Ill., Nov. 24, 1931; s. George Edgar and Virginia (Thompson) S.; m. Joan Mildred Kinsman, June 29, 1958; children: Andrew James, Linda Joan, Julie Ann. BCE, Cornell U., 1954; SM in San. Engring., MIT, 1955, ScD in San. Engring., 1957. Registered engr., Tex.; diplomate Am. Acad. Environ. Engrs. Asst. prof. san. engring. MIT, 1957-62; research engr. USPHS, Cin., 1962-1970; supr. research engr. EPA, Cin., 1970-82; prof. civil engring. U Houston, 1982-95; Cullen Disting. prof. civil engring. U. Houston, 1995—. Contbr. articles to profl. jours. Fellow ASCE; mem. Am. Water Works Assn. (hon., life, chmn. water quality div. 1980-81), Water Environment Fedn., Nat. Acad. Engring. Methodist. Avocations: photography, golf. Office: U of Houston Dept Civil Environ Eng Houston TX 77204

SYMONS, JAMES MARTIN, theater and dance educator; b. Jacksonville, Ill., May 7, 1937; s. James and Pauline (Barton) S.; m. Judith White, Nov. 14, 1959; children: Tracy, Kelly, Carrie. BA, Ill. Coll., 1959; MA, So. Ill. U., 1964; PhD, Cornell U., 1970. Asst. prof. Yankton (S.D.) Coll., 1964-67; assoc. prof. Coll. St. Catherine, St. Paul, 1970-74, SUNY, Albany, 1974-77; prof., chair Trinity U., San Antonio, 1977-84; prof., chair theatre and dance dept. U. Colo., Boulder, 1984—; actor Off-Broadway, N.Y.C., 1959, Mo. Repertory Theatre, Kansas City, 1984; dir., actor Colo. Shakespeare Festival, Boulder, 1985—, producing artistic dir., 1994-95; leader People-to-People Del. of Theater Educators, USSR and Czechoslovakia, 1991. Author: Meyerhold's Theatre of the Grotesque, 1971 (Freedley Meml. award Theatre Libr. Assn. 1971); contbr. articles to scholarly jours. Lt. (j.g.) USN, 1960-63. Mem. Assn. for Theatre in Higher Edn. (pres. 1989-91), Assn. for Communication Adminstrn. (pres. 1990). Democrat. Methodist. Office: U of Colorado Dept Theatre And Dance Boulder CO 80309

SYMONS, ROBERT SPENCER, electronic engineer; b. San Francisco, July 3, 1925; s. Spencer W. and Avesia (Atkins) S.; m. Alice Faye Smith, Dec. 21, 1960; children: Julia Ann, Robert Spencer Jr. BS, Stanford U., 1946, MS, 1948. Engr. Eitel-McCullough, Inc., San Bruno, Calif., 1947, Heinz & Kaufman, South San Francisco, 1948, Pacific Electronics Co., Los Gatos, Calif., 1949; sr. engring. mgr. Varian Assocs., Palo Alto, Calif., 1950-83; tech. dir. Litton Industries, San Carlos, Calif., 1983—. Recipient Charles B. Thornton award for Advanced Technology Achievement, 1991. Patentee in field. Served to 1st lt. AUS 1950-53. Fellow IEEE (assoc. editor Transactions on Electron Devices jour. 1980-83); mem. Phi Beta Kappa, Tau Beta Pi. Club: Commonwealth of Calif. Home: 290 Surrey Pl Los Altos CA 94022-2146 Office: Litton Industries 960 Industrial Rd San Carlos CA 94070-4194

SYMONS, THOMAS H. B., historian, educator; b. Toronto, Ont., Can., May 30, 1929; s. Harry Lutz and Dorothy Sarah (Bull) S.; m. Mary Christine Ryerson, Aug. 17, 1963; children: Mary, Ryerson, Jeffrey. BA, U. Toronto,

1951, Oxford U., 1953; MA, Oxford U., 1955; postgrad. univs., Paris, Leyden, Rome, 1953, Harvard U., 1956; LLD (hon.), Wilfrid Laurier U., 1971, U. N.B., 1972, York U., 1973, Ottawa U., 1974, Trent U., 1975, Laurentian U., 1977, Mt. Allison U., 1979, Concordia U., 1981, U. P.E.I., 1983, Dalhousie U., 1983, Man. U., 1990; DLitt (hon.), U. Colombo, Sri Lanka, 1985. Dean men, tutor history Trinity Coll., U. Toronto, 1953-55; dean Devonshire House, 1955-63; founding pres., vice chancellor, prof. modern history Trent U., Peterborough, Ont., 1962-72; Vanier prof. Trent U., 1979—; vis. fellow Clare Hall, Cambridge U., 1984, Ctr. for Internat. Studies, Cambridge U., 1992—; mem. adv. com. on confedn. to prime minister, Ont., 1965-72; chmn. Ministerial Commn. on French Lang. Edn., 1971-72, Assn. Univs. Brit. Commonwealth, 1971-72, Internat. Bd. United World Colls., 1980-86, Nat. Commn. on Canadian Studies, 1972-84, Ont. Human Rights Commn., 1975-78, Nat. Stats. Council, 1986—, Hist. Sites and Monuments Bd. Can., 1986—, Nat. Library Bd., Can., 1987-90; chmn. nat. adv. com. on Nat. Atlas of Can., 1984—; pres. Canadian Assn. in Support Native Peoples, 1972-73; v.p. Social Scis. and Humanities Research Council Can., 1978-84; spl. adviser on higher edn. Sec. of State for Can., 1976-85; mem. Fed. Cultural Policy Rev., 1979-82; mem. adv. com. acad. relations Dept. External Affairs, Can., 1978—; mem. Commonwealth Standing Com. on Student Mobility, 1982-87; chmn. Can. Commonwealth Scholarship and Fellowship Com., 1983-87; chmn. Polar Rsch. Commn., Study, 1987-88. Author: (with others) Confederation Challenge, 2 vols., 1967, 70, One Country or Two, 1971, Life Together, A Report on Human Rights in Ontario, 1977, Report of the Commission on French Language Education, 1972, To Know Ourselves, Report of the Commission on Canadian Studies, 2 vols, 1976., The Canadian Confederation Forum, 1978, Issues in Higher Education, 1979, Britain and Canada, 1980, The Arctic and Canadian Culture, 1981, Public Policies in Canada and Australia, 1982, Report of the Federal Cultural Policy Review Committee, 1982, Archives, Libraries and the Canadian Heritage, 1983, Some Questions of Balance, 1984, Human Rights and Peace, 1985, Postsecondary Education: The Cultural Agenda, 1986, Canadian Polar Research, 1988, Canada and the Mediterranean World, 1989, Powerful Memories, Powerful Dreams: Report of the Confederation Birthplace Commission, 1991; also articles. Bd. dirs. Can. Council, 1976-79, Trinity Coll., 1963-74, Nat. Library, 1979-90, Lakefield (Ont.) Coll., 1964—, Sir Sandford Fleming Coll., Peterborough, 1964-69, Upper Can. Coll., Toronto, 1969-83, Simcoe Found., 1972-76, Ont. Arts Council, 1974-76, Ont. Med. Found., 1975-87, Pearson Coll. of the Pacific, 1976—, Robert and Mary Stanfield Found., 1976—, Celanese Can. Inc., 1980—; trustee Oriel Coll., Oxford U., 1975—; nat. adviser Can. Ency., 1980—. Decorated officer Order of Can., 1977; recipient Canadian Centennial medal, 1967, Civic award City of Peterborough, 1969; Queen's Silver Jubilee medal, 1977; Disting. Service to Edn. award Council for Advancement and Support of Edn., 1982; Massey fellow Oxford U., 1951; Rockefeller fellow Harvard, 1956. Fellow Royal Soc. Can., Royal Soc. Arts; mem. Brit.-N.Am. Com., Assn. Univs. and Colls. Can. (dir. 1969-72), Canadian Soc. Study Higher Edn. (founding dir. 1969—), World Univ. Service Can. (founding dir.), Canadian Hist. Assn., Canadian Polit. Sci. Assn., Inst. Pub. Adminstrn. Can., Assn. Canadian Studies in U.S. (council 1973—), Arctic Inst. N.Am. (dir. 1981-85). Clubs: Rideau (Ottawa); Univ. (Toronto); Athenaeum (London, Eng.). Office: Trent U, Peterborough, ON Canada K9J 7B8

SYMONS, TIMOTHY JAMES MCNEIL, physicist; b. Southborough, Kent, Eng., Aug. 4, 1951; came to U.S., 1977; s. Henry McNeil and Catherine Muriel (Rees) S.; m. Syndi Beth Master, Mar. 1, 1987; children: Henry Benjamin, Daniel Robert. BA, Oxford (Eng.) U., 1972, MA, DPhil, 1976. Rsch. fellow Sci. Rsch. Coun., Eng., 1976-77; postdoctoral fellow Lawrence Berkeley (Calif.) Lab., 1977-79, div. fellow, 1979-84, sr. physicist, 1984—, dir. nuclear sci. div., 1985—; vis. scientist Max-Planck Inst. Heidelberg, Germany, 1980-81; mem. U.S. nuclear physics del. to USSR, 1986; mem. program adv. coms. Gesellschaft fur schwerionen forschung, 1987-88, Continuous Electron Beam Accelerator Facility, 1989-92, Brookhaven Nat. Lab., 1991-92; mem. policy com. Relativistic Heavy Ion Collider, 1988—. Contbr. over 70 articles to sci. jours. Fellow Am. Phys. Soc. (chmn. Bonner prize com. 1994). Avocations: music, gardening, travel. Office: Lawrence Berkeley Lab Nuclear Sci Divsn 1 Cyclotron Rd 70A-3307 Berkeley CA 94720*

SYNAN, EDWARD ALOYSIUS, JR., clergyman, former institute president; b. Fall River, Mass., Apr. 13, 1918; s. Edward Aloysius and Mary F. (McDermott) S. AB, Seton Hall Coll., 1938; student, U. Louvain, Belgium, 1938-40, Immaculate Conception Sem., Darlington, N.J., 1940-41; STL, Cath. U. Am., 1942; LMS, Pontifical Inst. Mediaeval Studies, Toronto, 1951; MA, Pontifical U. Toronto, 1952. Ordained priest Roman Cath. Ch., 1942. Curate Immaculate Conception Ch., Montclair, N.J., 1942-44; prof. philosophy, chmn. dept. Seton Hall U., South Orange, N.J., 1952-59; prof. history of mediaeval philosophy Pontifical Inst. Mediaeval Studies, U. Toronto, 1959, pres., 1973-79, acting pres., 1989-90. Author: The Popes and The Jews in the Middle Ages, 1965, The Works of Richard of Campsall, Vol. I, 1968, Vol. II, 1982; assoc. editor, contbr.: The Bridge, Yearbook of Judaeo-Christian Studies, 1955-62; adv. bd.: Speculum, 1971-74; contbr. chpts. to books, articles and revs. to publs. Served as capt. (chaplain) USAF, 1944-48. Fellow Royal Soc. Can.; mem. Am. Cath. Philos. Assn. (Aquinas medal 1991), Mediaeval Acad. Am., Renaissance Soc. Am., Am. Soc. Polit. and Legal Philosophy. Address: 59 Queen's Park, Toronto, ON Canada M5S 2C4

SYNNOTT, MARCIA GRAHAM, history educator; b. Camden, N.J., July 4, 1939; d. Thomas Whitney and Beatrice Adelaide (Colby) S.; m. William Edwin Sharp, June 16, 1979; children: Willard William Sharp, Laurel Beth Sharp. AB, Radcliffe Coll., 1961; MA, Brown U., 1964; PhD, U. Mass., 1974. History instr. MacDuffie Sch., Springfield, Mass., 1963-68; instr. U. S.C., Columbia, 1972-74, asst. prof., 1974-79, assoc. prof. history, 1979—, dir. grad. studies history dept., 1990-92. Author: The Half-Opened Door, 1979; contbr. essays to books. Fulbright scholar, 1988; Am. Coun. Learned Socs. grantee, 1981. Mem. Am. Hist. Assn., So. Hist. Assn., Orgn. Am. Historians (membership com. 1990-93). Avocations: historic sites and museums, snow skiing, walking. Office: U SC Dept History Columbia SC 29208

SYNNOTT, WILLIAM RAYMOND, retired management consultant; b. Fall River, Mass., Dec. 29, 1929; s. William Joseph and Marie Aurore (Labrie) S.; m. Suzanne Pauline Moseley, Oct. 21, 1967; children—Dianne, Mark, Amy. Grad. cert., Rutgers U. Stonier Grad. Sch. Banking, 1958; B.S. summa cum laude, Boston U., 1973; grad. advanced mgmt. program, Harvard U., 1973. Sr. v.p. Bank of Boston, 1967-87; sr. dir. The Yankee Group, Boston, 1987-88; dir. Nolan Norton & Co., Lexington, Mass., 1988-91; pres. W.R. Synnott Assocs., Wellesley Hills, Mass., 1990-94; lectr., seminar leader on info. technology worldwide. Author: The Information Weapon, 1987; co-author: Information Resource Management, 1981. Served as sgt. AUS, 1951-53, Korea. Avocations: skiing; tennis; golf. Home: Green Hill Rd Jackson NH 03846

SYNODINOS, JOHN ANTHONY, academic administrator; b. Balt., Sept. 6, 1934; s. Anthony John and Jean (Asimakes) S.; m. Glenda J. Davis, Sept. 5, 1959; children: Jean Louise Ganias, Victoria Lynn Gertenbach. BS, Loyola Coll., Balt., 1959; EdM, Temple U., 1977. Control buyer Montgomery Ward, Balt., 1959-60; asst. dir. admissions Johns Hopkins U., Balt., 1960-63, dir. spl. events, 1963-65, assoc. dir. pub. rels., 1965-67, asst. dir. Ctr. for Study Social Orgn. Schs., 1960-68; assoc. dir. devel. Franklin & Marshall Coll., Lancaster, Pa., 1968-70, asst. to pres., 1970-71, v.p advancement, 1971-84; ptnr. John A. Synodinos & Assocs., Lancaster, 1984-88; pres. Lebanon Valley Coll., Annville, Pa., 1988—; bd. dirs. Econ. Devel. Corp. Lebanon County, Pa. Bd. dirs. United Way Lebanon County, 1989-93. Cpl. U.S. Army, 1952-55. Mem. Coun. Advancement & Support of Edn., Fortnightly Club (Lancaster) (pres. 1980). Democrat. Greek Orthodox. Avocation: acting. Home: RR 2 Box 990 Annville PA 17003-9202 Office: Lebanon Valley Coll Office of Pres Annville PA 17003-0501

SYPERT, GEORGE WALTER, neurosurgery educator, clinical neurosurgeon, research neurophysiologist; b. Marlin, Tex., Sept. 25, 1941; s. Claude Carl and Ruth Helen (Brown) S.; children: Kirsten Dianne, Shannon Ruth; m. Elaine Joy Arpin, Oct. 3, 1987. BA, U. Wash., 1963, MD with highest honors, 1967. Intern, Barnes Hosp., St. Louis, 1967-68; asst. resident

in neurol. surgery U. Wash. Sch. Medicine, Seattle, 1968, 1970-72, chief resident, 1973-74, instr., 1973-74; asst. prof. neurol. surgery and neurosci. grad. faculty U. Fla. Coll. Medicine, Gainesville, 1974-77, assoc. prof., 1977-80, prof., 1980-84; C.M. and K.E. Overstreet Family prof. and eminent scholar, 1984-89; mem. staff Shands Hosp. U. Fla., 1974-89, Southwest Fla. Med. Ctr, 1989—, Cape Coral Hosp., 1989—; neurobiology reviewer NSF, NIH, USPHS, 1979—; mem. merit rev. bd. neurobiology VA, 1979-82; examiner Am. Bd. Neurol. Surgery, 1984. Served to capt. U.S. Army, 1968-70. Fellow Internat. Coll. Surgeons; mem. Soc. Neurol. Surgeons, Am. Physiol. Soc., AAAS, Congress Neurol. Surgeons (exec. com. 1980-83), Am. Assn. Neurol. Surgeons (mem. exec. com. sect. spinal disorders 1982-85, pres. 1985-87), Soc. Neurosci., Am. Soc. Stereotactic and Functional Neurosurgery (pres. 1983-85; mem. exec. com. 1985-89), Internat. Congress Physiol. Sci., Brain Surgery Soc., Neurosurgery Forum, AMA, Alachua Inst. Union Physiol. Sci., Internat. Neurosurgery Forum (pres. 1984-85), S.W. Fla. Neurosurg. Assn., (pres. 1989—), S.W. Fla. Neurol. Inst. (chmn. 1989—), Fiddlesticks Country Club, Sigma Xi, Alpha Omega Alpha, Phi Sigma. Home: 15548 Fiddlesticks Blvd Fort Myers FL 33912-4037 Office: SW Fla Neuro Surgical Assocs 3677 Central Ave Ste A Fort Myers FL 33901-8226*

SYPHERD, PAUL STARR, microbiologist; b. Akron, Ohio, Nov. 16, 1936; s. Pearle Clinton and Mary Mildred (Flanick) S.; m. Linda J. Burden, Mar. 19, 1983; children: David Paul, Mary Denise, Gregory Dean, Cynthia Jean, Sean Michael Watkins, Scott Christopher Watkins. BS, Ariz. State U., 1959; MS, U. Ariz., 1960; PhD, Yale U., 1963. NIH postdoctoral fellow U. Calif., San Diego, 1962-64; asst. prof. U. Ill., Urbana, 1964-68, assoc. prof., 1968-70; assoc. prof. microbiology U. Calif. Coll. Medicine, Irvine, 1970-72, prof., 1972-93, chmn. dept., 1974-87, vice chancellor rsch., 1989-93, dean grad. studies, 1989-93; sr. v.p., provost U. Ariz, Tucson, 1993—; mem. NIH study sect., 1977-80, 87-91, chmn., 1990-91; mem. microbiology test com. Nat. Bd. Med. Examiners, 1980-84; mem. panel on basic biomed. scis. Nat. Rsch. Coun., 1981-86. Editor Jour. Bacteriology, 1979-83, mem. editorial bd., 1969-74; editor Molecular and Cellular Biology, 1980-87; contrib. articles to profl. jours. Sr. fellow NSF, 1970. Mem. AAAS, Am. Soc. Microbiology, Am. Soc. for Biochemistry and Molecular Biology, Am. Acad. for Microbiology. Office: U Ariz 512 Administration Tucson AZ 85721

SYPHERS, MARY FRANCES, music educator; b. Floresville, Tex., Sept. 26, 1912; d. Little Fleming and Lillian Frances (Herrington) Spruce; m. Ansel James Syphers, July 23, 1959 (dec. 1972). BA in English, U. Tex., 1938; MEd, So. Meth. U., Dallas, 1950; studied voice with Dr. Wilcox, 1947, studied composition with Roy Harris, 1947, studied Music Edn. with Augustus Zansig. Cert. high sch. music tchr., cert. elem. tchr., Tex. Tchr. music Ehlers Country Sch., Poth Tex., 1931-35, Poth Ind. Sch. Dist., 1936-40, Sinton (Tex.) Ind. Sch. Dist., 1941, Stephen J. Hay Sch., Dallas, 1942-50, Alamo Sch., Dallas, 1951—, Edwin J. Kiest Sch., Dallas, 1955—, Lakewood Elem., Dallas, 1976-81; voice, drama tchr. Poth Ind. Sch. dist., 1936-40. Contbg. author: New England To Texas, 1986. Choir dir. 1st Meth. Ch., Sinton, Tex., 1941-42; soloist, jr. choir dir. Oaklawn Meth. Ch., Dallas, 1942-43; soloist 1st Presbyn. Ch., Dallas, 1943-46, Highland Park Presbyn. Ch., Dallas, 1946-47; symphony chorus Dallas Music Staff, 1944-60; mem. choir St. Michael and All Angels Episocpal Ch., Dallas, 1949-91; organizer jr. female vols. USO, Dallas, 1960-70, coordinator jr. female vols. anniversary celebration, Dallas, 1966; mem. publicity com. So. Meml. Assn., Dallas, 1981; life mem. PTA; mem. Shakespeare Study Club. Recipient Citation as member of concert choir Am. Culture and Lang. Ctr., Salzburg, Austria, 1987. Mem. New Eng. Women (pres. Tex. chpt. 1985-87), Dallas Coun. World Affairs, Dallas Inst. Humanities (sponsor), Buckland Hist. Soc. (life), Nat. Soc. Colonial Dames (chmn. 1981-90), DAR (Jane Douglas chpt.), Standard Club Dallas (recreation sec. 1981-91), Delta Kappa Gamma (Epsilon chpt. pres. 1960-62). Republican. Episcopalian. Avocations: genealogy, book binding, picture taking, reading, family history. Home: 5106 Stanford Ave Dallas TX 75209-3322

SYRON, RICHARD FRANCIS, financial services executive, economist; b. Boston, Oct. 25, 1943; s. Dominick Richard and Elizabeth (McQuire) S.; m. Margaret Mary Garatoni, Oct. 21, 1972; children: Erin Elizabeth, Brendan Paul. BS in Econs.-Acctg. with high honors, Boston Coll., 1966; MA in Econs., Tufts U., 1969, PhD in Econs., 1971. Dep. dir. budget Commonwealth of Mass., 1973-74; v.p., economist Fed. Res. Bank of Boston, 1974-82; sr. v.p., econ. advisor, 1982-85; exec. asst. to sec. U.S. Treasury, Washington, 1979-80; dep. sec. for econ. policy U.S. Treasury, 1980-81; asst. to Chmn. Volcker Fed. Res. Bd., Washington, 1981-82; pres., prin. supervisory agt. Fed. Home Loan Bank of Boston, 1986-88; pres., chief exec. officer Fed. Res. Bank of Boston, 1989-94; chmn. Am. Stock Exch., N.Y.C., 1994—; vice chmn. Boston Coll.; past chmn. Boston Pvt. Industry Coun. Author: Urban Fire Insurance, 1972; contbr. articles to profl. jours. Teaching fellow Tufts U., 1966-69. Mem. Boston Econ. Club (past pres.), Comml. Club Boston, Clover Club (Boston), Wianno Yacht Club, N.Y. Athletic Club, N.Y. Athletic Club Yacht Club, Siwanoy Country Club. Office: Am Stock Exch 86 Trinity Pl New York NY 10006-1818

SYTSMA, FREDRIC ALAN, lawyer; b. Grand Rapids, Mich., Jan. 12, 1944; s. Fred A. and Josephine (Van Valkenberg) S.; m. Susan Lyn Simmons, Aug. 6, 1966; 1 child, Alan. BA, Mich. State U., 1964; JD, U. Mich., 1968. Bar: Mich., 1968. Ptnr. Landman, Luyendyk, Latimer, Clink & Robb, Muskegon, Mich., 1968-83, Varnum, Riddering, Schmidt & Howlett, Grand Rapids, Mich., 1983—. Fellow Am. Coll. of Trusts and Estates Counsel; mem. Mich. State Bar Assn. (chmn. coun. probate and estate planning sect. 1974—). Office: Varnum Riddering et al PO Box 352 Bridgewater Pl Grand Rapids MI 49501-0352

SYVERTSON, CLARENCE ALFRED, aerospace engineering consultant; b. Mpls., Jan. 12, 1926; s. Alfred and Esther Louise (Goertemiller) S.; m. Helen Hammond Gonnella, May 4, 1953 (dec. May 1981); 1 child, Marguerite Louise.; m. JoAnn Mary Caruso, May 8, 1982. B. Aero. Engring., U. Minn., 1946, M.S., 1948; postgrad., Stanford U., 1950-57; grad. Advanced Mgmt. Program, Harvard U., 1977. Research scientist Ames Aero. Lab., NACA, Moffett Field, Calif., 1948-58; exec. dir. Joint Dept. Transp./NASA Civil Aviation Research and Devel. Policy Study, 1970-71; with Ames Research Center, NASA, Moffett Field, 1958-84; dep. dir. Ames Research Center, NASA, 1969-78, dir., 1978-84; mem. adv. bd. Coll. Engring., U. Calif., Berkeley, 1980-85; cons. Stanford U., 1985-88. Served with U.S. Army, 1946-47. Recipient invention and contbn. award NASA, 1964, Exceptional Service medal, 1971, Disting. Service medal, 1984, Outstanding Achievement award U. Minn., 1982, Commanders award for civilian service U.S. Army, 1984. Fellow AIAA (Lawrence Sperry award 1957), Am. Astronautical Soc.; mem. Nat. Acad. Engring. Home: 15725 Apollo Heights Ct Saratoga CA 95070-6361

SZABAD, GEORGE MICHAEL, lawyer, former mayor; b. Nizhni Novgorod, Russia, Feb. 21, 1917; s. Michael and Nita (Szereszewski) S.; m. Shirley Meyers, Nov. 8, 1938; children: Peter James, Ellen Jo (Mrs. Ljung). B.S., Columbia U., 1937, LL.B., 1939. Bar: N.Y. 1940. Participated reorgn. Asso. Gas & Electric System, 1940-42; with Dept. Labor, 1942-47, chief appellate sect., 1944-47; with Dept. State, 1945-46; with firm Blum, Haimoff, Gersen, Lipson, Slavin & Szabad, N.Y.C., 1947—; partner Blum, Haimoff, Gersen, Lipson, Slavin & Szabad, 1949-80; former mayor Village of Scarsdale, N.Y.; v.p. Burndy Corp., 1956-76, sr. v.p., 1976-82. Served with USCG, 1943; Served with OSS, U.S. Army, 1945. Mem. Am. Arbitration Assn. (panel), Assn. Bar City N.Y., Am. Fed. bar assns. Club: Scarsdale Town. Home: 3300 Darby Rd Apt 2101 Haverford PA 19041-1068

SZABLYA, HELEN MARY, author, language professional, lecturer; b. Budapest, Hungary, Sept. 6, 1934; came to U.S., 1963; d. Louis and Helen (Bartha) Kovacs; m. John Francis Szablya, June 12, 1951; children: Helen, Janos, Louis, Stephen, Alexandra, Rita, Dominique-Mary. Diploma in Sales, Mktg., U.B.C., 1962; BA in Fgn. Lang., Lit., Wash. State U., 1976. Freelance writer, translator, 1976—; columnist Cath. News, Trinidad, W.I., 1980-91; adult educator TELOS Bellevue (Wash.) Community Coll., 1987-89; adult educator Pullman-Spokane (Wash.) Community Coll., 1976-80; faculty Christian Writers' Conf., Seattle, 1983-88, Pacific Northwest Writers' Conf., Seattle, Tacoma, 1987—; hon. consul for Wash., Oreg., Idaho Republic of Hungary, 1993—; lectr. Washington Commn. for Humanities, 1987-89. Author: (with others) Hungary Remembered, 1986 (Guardian of Liberty award 1986, George Washington Honor medal, Freedoms Found. award 1988), 56-os Cserészcsapat, 1986, numerous articles; pub., editor Hungary Internat. newsletter, 1990-93; columnist Hungarian Bus. Weekly, 1994—; translator: Emlékezünk, 1986, Mind Twisters, 1987. Recipient Nat. 1st place editorial Nat. Fedn. Press Women, 1987, Senator Tom Martin Meml. award Pacific N.W. Writers Conf., 1979; grantee Hungarian Am. Assn. Wash., 1986, Wash. Com. for Humanities, 1986; named Community Woman of Yr., Am. Bus. Women Assn., 1990. Mem. AAUW, Wash. Press Assn. (pres. 1987-88, 1st and 2d place awards, several editorial and profile awards 1983, 87, 89, 90, 91, 92, Communicator of Achievement award 1987), Nat. Fedn. Press Women (Affiliate Pres.' award 1988, bd. dirs. edn. fund northwest quadrant, mem. 21st century planning com.), Authors Guild, Am. Translators Assn., Arpad Acad. (Gold medal 1987), Nat. Writers Club, Internat. P.E.N. Club, Sigma Delta Chi (editorial award 1989). Avocations: children, reading, dancing, swimming, traveling. Home and Office: 4416 134th Pl SE Bellevue WA 98006-2104

SZABLYA, JOHN FRANCIS, electrical engineer, consultant; b. Budapest, Hungary, June 25, 1924; arrived in Can., 1957, naturalized, 1962; came to U.S., 1963, naturalized, 1979; s. John and Alexandra (Huszar) S.; m. Helen M. Bartha-Kovacs, June 12, 1951; children—Helen A., Janos L., Louis J., Stephen J.P., Alexandra H.R., Rita H.C., Dominique-Mary H. Diploma edn., Jozsef Nador U., Budapest, 1948, diploma engring., 1947, Dr. Econs., 1948. Registered profl. engr., Wash., Mont., Alaska, Wyo., Oreg., Colo., Idaho, B.C. and Ont., Can. Design engr. Ganz Elec. Works, Budapest, 1947-56; assoc. prof. Tech. U. Budapest, 1951-56; assoc. prof. U. B.C., Vancouver, 1957-63; prof. elec. engring. Wash. State U., 1963-82, now prof. emeritus; vis. prof. Technische Universitat Braunschweig, 1973-74, U. W.I., 1983—, U. Wash., 1985—, Seattle U., 1987; mgr. electrical, instrumentation and control engring. EBASCO Services Inc., 1981-90; ret., 1990; cons. engr., v.p. Szablya Cons., Inc., 1990—. Contbr. numerous articles to profl. jours., publ. over 150 articles. Recipient Zipernowszky medal Hungarian Inst. Elec. Engrs., 1954, Academia Gold medal ARPAD, 1991. Fellow IEEE, Instn. Elec. Engrs. (London); mem. Osterreichischer Verband der Elekrotechnik, European Register Higher Tech. Professions, Sigma Xi. Roman Catholic. Home: 4416 134th Pl SE Bellevue WA 98006-2104

SZABO, ALBERT, architect, educator; b. N.Y.C., Nov. 7, 1925; s. Benjamin and Jane (Margolies) S.; m. Brenda Dyer, Dec. 26, 1951; children: Ellen Szabo Laughlin, Stephen, Rebecca Szabo Salvadori, Jeannette. Student, Bklyn. Coll., 1942-47, Inst. Design, Chgo., 1947-48; MArch, Harvard U., 1952. Apprentice Marcel Breuer Architect, Harvard and M.I.T., Design, Chgo., 1951-53; prof. architecture Grad. Sch. Design Harvard U., Cambridge, Mass., 1954—, chmn. dept. archtl. scis., 1964-68, assoc. chmn., head tutor dept. visual and environ. studies, 1968-70, prof. visual and environ. studies, chmn. dept. visual and environ. studies, 1970-72, sec. faculty design, 1964-74, prof. visual and environ. studies, 1970-91; archtl. design practice with Brenda Dyer Szabo, Chgo. and Cambridge, 1953—; ptnr. Soltan/Szabo Assocs., Inc., Cambridge, 1967-71; vis. prof. Rensselaer Poly. Inst., 1967-68; Fulbright cons. to municipality of Tehran, Iran; Fulbright Hayes lectr. in architecture, Tehran, 1972, Kabul U., Afghanistan, 1974-76; cons. U.S. AID, Afghanistan, 1974-76, Govt. Afghanistan, 1974-76; acting curator Loeb Fellowship in advanced environ. studies, 1974, cons. King Faisal U. Coll. Architecture and Planning (Saudi Arabia), 1983; mem. edn. com. Boston Archtl. Ctr. Sch. Architecture, 1981-90; acting dir. Carpenter Ctr. For Visual Arts, Harvard U., 1990-92, Osgood Hooker prof. visual art Faculty of Arts and Scis., 1991—. Author: (with others) The Shape of Our Cities, 1957; editor: (with others) Housing generated by User Needs, 1972, (with B.D. Szabo) Preliminary Notes on Indigenous Architecture of Afghanistan, 1978, (with T.J. Barfield) Afghanistan: An Atlas of Indigenous Domestic Architecture, 1991 (Outstanding Acad. Book award ALA 1992). Served with USAAF, 1944-45. Recipient Alpha Rho Chi medal Harvard U., 1952; Wheelwright travelling fellow Harvard U., 1963, Nat. Endowment for Arts fellow, 1980; Tozier Fund rsch. grantee Harvard U., 1963, Milton Fund rsch. grantee, 1966, 72, 77, 84, 87, Faculty rsch. grantee, 1978, The Aga Khan Program Islamic Architecture grantee, 1988. Mem. Boston Soc. Architects (assoc.), AIA, Assn. Collegiate Schs. Architecture (N.E. regional dir. 1969-70), Mass. Assn. Architects. Office: Harvard U Carpenter Ctr 19 Prescott St Cambridge MA 02138-3999

SZABO, BARNA ALADAR, mechanical engineering educator, mining engineer; b. Martonvasar, Hungary, Sept. 21, 1935; came to U.S., 1967, naturalized, 1974; s. Jozsef and Gizella (Ivanyi) S.; m. Magdalin Gerstmayer, July 23, 1960; children: Mark, Nicholas. B.A.Sc., U. Toronto, Ont., Can., 1962; M.S., SUNY, Buffalo, 1966, Ph.D., 1969. Registered profl. engr., Mo. Mining engr. Internat. Nickel Co. Can., 1960-62; engr. Acres Cons. Services Ltd., Niagara Falls, Can., 1962-66; instr. SUNY, Buffalo, 1966-68; mem. faculty Washington U., St. Louis, 1968—, prof. mech. engring., 1974—, Albert P. and Blanche Y. Greensfelder prof., 1975—, dir. Ctr. Computational Mechanics, 1977-92; pres. engring. software Rsch. and Devel., Inc., St. Louis, 1989—. Author: (with Ivo Babuska) Finite Element Analysis, 1991; contbr. articles to profl. jours. Mem. ASME, Am. Acad. Mechanics, Soc. Engring. Sci., Internat. Assn. Computational Mechanics. Club: St. Louis Soaring Assn. Home: 48 Crestwood Dr Clayton MO 63105 Office: Washington U Campus Box 1129 Saint Louis MO 63130-4899

SZABO, DANIEL, government official; b. Budapest, Hungary, Mar. 23, 1933; came to U.S., 1950, naturalized, 1954; s. Alexander and Maria (Berger) S.; m. Corinne Holiber, July 3, 1955; children—Nancy Beth, Peter Stuart. B.A., CCNY, 1957; M.A., Johns Hopkins U., 1959. Internat. economist U.S. Tariff Commn., 1959-60; desk officer for Vietnam, Cambodia and Laos U.S. Dept. Commerce, 1960-63; spl. asst. to U.S. Senator Jacob K. Javits, 1963-69; dep. asst. sec. state for Inter-Am. Affairs, Washington, 1969-74; sr. adviser Inter-Am. Devel. Bank, Washington, 1974-95; cons Rockville, Md., 1995—; mem. nat. adv. coun. Am. Jewish Com. Mem. World Affairs Coun. of Washington. Served with U.S Army, 1954-56. Home: 11600 Danville Dr Rockville MD 20852-3716 *In approaching life I want my work to represent a service to our society. I am attracted to new ideas and new ways of solving old problems.*

SZABO, DENIS, criminologist, educator; b. Budapest, Hungary, June 4, 1929; s. Jenö and Catherine (Zsiga) S.; m. Sylvie Grotard; children—Catherine, Marianne. Doctorate in Social and Polit. Scis., U. Louvain, Belgium, 1956; diploma in criminology, Sorbonne U., Paris, 1958; hon. doctorate, U. Sienna, Italy, 1984, U. Budapest, Hungary, 1985, U. Aix-Marseille, 1992. Asst. in sociology U. Louvain, 1951-56; lectr. sociology Cath. Univs., Paris, Lyon, 1956-58; mem. research group Centre Nat. de la Recherche Scientifique, Paris, 1954-58; asst. prof. sociology U. Montreal, 1958, assoc. prof., 1959-66, founder, dir. dept. criminology, 1960-70, prof., 1966—; founder, dir. Internat. Center for Comparative Criminology, 1969-84; emeritus prof. law U. Ecuador, Quito, 1984. Author, editor: Canadian Criminal Justice System, 1977, Criminologie et Politique Criminelle, 1978, La Criminologie Empirique au Quebec, 1985, Science et Crime, 1986, De L'Anthropologie a la criminologie comparee, 1993, Le Traite de criminologie Empirique, 1993. Decorated officer Order Can.; recipient Beccaria award German Society Criminology, 1970; named prof. emeritus Law Faculty, Central U. Ecuador, Quito, 1984. Fellow Royal Soc. Can., Am. Sociol. Soc., Am. Soc. Criminology (exec. coun., Sutherland award 1968); mem. Internat. Soc. Criminology (pres. 1978-85, hon. pres.), Can. Soc. Criminology (v.p. 1962-64), Soc. de Criminology (v.p. 1962-64), Soc. de Criminologie du Que. (sec.-gen. 1960-70), Internat. Assn. Sociology, Nat. Order of Merit (comdr. Ivory coast 1987), Hungarian Acad. Scis. (elected). Roman Catholic. Home: PO Box 26, Georgeville, PQ Canada J0B 1T0 Office: 3150 Jean Brillant, Montreal, PQ Canada H3C 3J7

SZABO, ZOLTAN, medical science educator, medical institute administrator; b. Szeged, Hungary, Oct. 5, 1943; came to U.S., 1967; s. Imre and Maria (Szikora) S.; m. Wanda Toy, Dec. 5, 1983; children: Eva, Maria. Student, U. Med. Sch., Szeged, 1962-65; PhD, Columbia Pacific U., 1983. Tech. dir. microsurgery lab. R.K. Davies Med. Ctr., San Francisco, 1972-80; dir. Microsurg. Rsch. Inst., San Francisco, 1980—; assoc. dir. advanced laparoscopic surgery tng. ctr. Sch. Medicine U. Calif., San Francisco, 1992—; rsch. assoc. oral and maxillofacial surgery U. of Pacific, San Francisco, 1980-83, adj. asst. prof., 1983—. Author: Microsurgery Techniques, vol. 1 1974, vol. 2 1984 (1st Place award for excellence in med. writing 1982); contbr. chpt. books, articles to profl. jours. With U.S. Army, 1969-71. Recipient

Cert. of Merit, AMA, 1978, commendation Accreditation Coun. for Continuing Edn., 1984, 90, Spl. Recognition award Sch. Medicine Cen. U. Venezuela, 1988, Sci. Poste Sessions Hon. Mention award Am. Urol. Assn., 1992, 1st prize Roundtable for New Techs. and Innovations we. sect., 1992, James Barrett Brown award Am. Assn. Plastic Surgeons, 1993. Fellow Internat. Coll. Surgeons (Disting. Svc. award 1994); mem. Hungarian Gynecol. Soc. (hon.), Medico-Dental Study Guild Calif., Internat. Microsurg. Soc., Soc. Am. Gastrointestinal Endoscopic Surgeons (hon., 1st prize sci. exhibit 1977, 1st prize Residents and Fellows Rsch. and Sci. Presentation 1992, In-Utero Endoscopic Surgery award 1992), Am. Fertility Soc., Am. Soc. Reconstructive Microsurgery (assoc.), Soc. for Study of Impotence. Avocations: gardening, landscaping, oil painting, travel, competitive air pistol target shooting. Office: Microsurgery Operative Endoscopy Tng Inst 153 States St San Francisco CA 94114-1403

SZALA, SCOTT J., lawyer; b. Chgo., May 30, 1953. BA, Knox Coll., 1975; JD, Northwestern U., 1978. Bar: Ill. 1978, U.S. Dist. Ct. (no. dist.) Ill. 1978, U.S. Ct. Appeals (7th cir.) 1979. Law clk. to Hon. Dom J. Rizzi Ill. Appellate Ct., 1979-80; ptnr. Winston & Strawn, Chgo. Capt. USAR (JACG), 1985—. Mem. ABA (mem. litigation, jud. adminstrn. divsn., econs. of practice, antitrust and taxation sects., mem. young lawyers divsn., trial editor Barrister Mag. 1982-88, speaker conv. Sydney, Australia 1980), Ill. State Bar Assn., Chgo. Bar Assn. (mem. young lawyers sect., co-chmn. law explorers 1982-83, moot ct. 1983-84, chmn. bench/bar com. 1984-85, mem. exec. coun. 1982-85, mem. sr. bar tort litigation 1978-84), Assn. Trial Lawyers Am. Office: Winston & Strawn 35 W Wacker Dr Chicago IL 60601-1614

SZALKOWSKI, CHARLES CONRAD, lawyer; b. Amarillo, Tex., Apr. 14, 1948; s. Chester Casimer and Virginia Lee (Hess) S.; m. Jane Howe, Dec. 28, 1971; children: Jennifer Lee, Stephen Claude. BA, BS in Acctg., Rice U., 1971; MBA, JD, Harvard U., 1975. Bar: Tex. 1975. Assoc. Baker & Botts, L.L.P., Houston, 1975-82, ptnr., 1983—; speaker in field. Chmn. ann. fund campaign Rice U., Houston, 1991-93; chmn. adminstrv. bd. St. Luke's United Meth. Ch., Houston, 1994; co-chmn. profl. divsn. United Fund, Houston, 1985-86. Mem. ABA (fed. regulation of securities com.), Am. Law Inst., State Bar Tex. (chmn., vice chmn. bus. law sect. 1990-92), Houston Bar Assn. (chmn., vice chmn., corp. counsel sect. 1988-90), Harvard Law Sch. Assn. Tex. (pres. 1983-84), Tex. Bus. Law Found. (bd. dirs., exec. com. 1988—), Assn. Rice U. Alumni (chmn. various coms. 1981-86), Lincoln's Inn Soc., Houston Philos. Soc. Office: Baker & Botts LLP 1 Shell Plz 910 Louisiana St Houston TX 77002

SZALLER, JAMES FRANCIS, lawyer; b. Cleve., Jan. 22, 1945; s. Frank Paul and Ellen Grace (O'Malley) S.; m. Roberta Mae Curtin, Oct. 23, 1967 (div. Aug. 1975); m. Charlene Nancy Smith, Apr. 28, 1984. AA, Cuyahoga Community Coll., 1967; BA, Cleve. State U., 1970, JD cum laude, 1975. Bar: Ohio 1975, U.S. Dist. Ct. (no. dist.) Ohio 1975, U.S. Supreme Ct. 1982, U.S. Ct. Appeals (6th cir.) 1983, U.S. Ct. Appeals (4th cir.) 1986. Assoc. Metzenbaum, Gaines & Stern (now Gaines & Stern Co. L.P.A.), Cleve., 1975-79; sr. ptnr. Brown & Szaller Co., L.P.A., Cleve., 1979—; lectr. law Cleve. State U., 1978-81. Mem. editorial bd. Cleve. State U. Law Rev., 1973-75; contbr. articles to profl. jours. Mem. ABA, Fed. Bar Assn., Ohio State Bar Assn., Greater Cleve. Bar Assn., Cleve. Acad. Trial Lawyers, Ohio Acad. Trial Lawyers, Assn. Trial Lawyers Am., Am. Arbitration Assn. (panel arbitrators), Nat. Coll. Advocacy (advocate). Democrat. Roman Catholic. Avocations: gourmet cooking, automobile racing. Office: Brown & Szaller Co LPA 14222 Madison Ave Cleveland OH 44107-4510

SZAMEK, PIERRE ERVIN, research anthropologist; b. Budapest, Hungary; s. Eugene Jeno and Olga S. Grad., The Pingry Sch., Elizabeth, N.J.; B.A., Upsala Coll., 1942; M.A., Columbia U., 1944; A.M. fellow, Princeton U., 1946, Ph.D., 1947. Corr. Cen. European Press Service, 1939; etymol. asst. in linguistic anthropology to Dr. Harold H. Bender, etymol. editor The Webster Dictionary, 1947-48; vis. post-doctoral research fellow Princeton U., 1947-48; edn. broadcasting CBS, N.Y.C., 1948-65; research anthropologist Newark, 1950—; exec. dir. Internat. Ctr. Ednl. Advancement, 1984—, chancellor, 1989; vis. prof. anthropology Drew U., 1966-67, N.J. State Coll., 1968-71; Disting. vis. prof. Seton Hall U., 1980; lectr. New Sch. for Social Research, 1980; dir. Am. Sci. Research and Mktg.; mem. radio program Invitation to Learning, CBS Network, 1948-63; permanent chmn., moderator Invitation to Ideas, Nat. Pub. Broadcasting Series, 1981—; anthrop. cons. CBS-TV, 1950-65; chmn. bd. The Logos Scientific Corp., 1989; special anthrop. cons. Nat. Com. for Habitat in affiliation with UNCHS, sr. vice chmn. for Hungarian devel., the Hungarian Nat. Com. for Habitat. Author, contbg. critic: Invitation to Learning, 1966; contbr. numerous articles, broadcasts in Am. jours. and fgn. press; inventor multi-gyro ball-bearing, dual stage radio communications synthesizer; patentee. Served with USCGR, 1942-43. Decorated victory medal, knight Order of Star (Italy); knight officer Gold Cross of Royal Order of Phoenix (Greece); Order of St. Agatha (San Marino); chevalier de l'Ordre des Palmes Académiques, chevalier de la Legion d'Honneur (France); officer Order St. John (Eng.); NEH Match Fund grantee, 1947. Fellow N.J. Com. for Humanities fellow; NEH Match Fund grantee, 1947. Fellow Royal Anthrop. Inst. Gt. Britain and Ireland; mem. AAUP, Am. Oriental Soc., Am. Acad. Polit. Sci., N.J. Acad. Sci. Office: c/o Law Offices PO Box 255 Glen Ridge NJ 07028

SZAREK, STANISLAW JERZY, mathematics educator; b. Ladek Zdroj, Poland, Nov. 13, 1953; came to U.S., 1980; s. Mieczyslaw and Bronislawa (Brzezinska) S.; m. Malgorzata Chwascinska, June 22, 1980; children: Martina, Natalia; 1 stepchild, Olga. M in Math., Warsaw (Poland) U., 1976; PhD in Math. Scis., Polish Acad. Scis., Warsaw, 1979. Rsch. asst. Math. Inst. Polish Acad. Scis., Warsaw, 1976-79, rsch. fellow, 1979-83; asst. prof. Case Western Res. U., Cleve., 1983-87, prof., 1987—, chair math. dept., 1994—; vis. positions U. Ill., Urbana, 1980, Ohio State U., Columbus, 1981, U. Tex., Austin, 1981-83, Inst. des Hautes Etudes Scientifiques, Bures-Sur-Yvette, France, 1986-89, U. Paris, 1990, 92, 95. Contbr. articles to profl. jours. Recipient Prize of Sci. Sec., Polish Acad. Scis., 1979; rsch. grantee NSF, 1983—, U.S.-Israel Binat. Sci. Found., 1993—; Sloan fellow Alfred P. Sloan Found., 1986-88. Mem. Am. Math. Soc. Avocations: skiing, sailing, diving, bridge. Office: Case Western Res U Dept of Math Cleveland OH 44106

SZAREK, WALTER ANTHONY, chemist, educator; b. St. Catharines, Ont., Can., Apr. 19, 1938; s. Anthony and Sophia (Kania) S. B.Sc., McMaster U., 1960, M.Sc., 1962; Ph.D., Queen's U., 1964. Postdoctoral fellow in chemistry Ohio State U., Columbus, 1964-65; asst. prof. biochemistry Rutgers U., New Brunswick, N.J., 1965-67; asst. prof. chemistry Queen's U., Kingston, Ont., 1967-71, assoc. prof., 1971-76, prof., 1976—; dir. Carbohydrate Research Inst., 1976-85; cons. to govt. and industry; mem. Premier's Coun. Tech. Fund. Mem. editorial adv. bd. Carbohydrate Rsch. jour., 1973—, Jour. of Carbohydrate Chemistry, 1994—; contbr. articles on chemistry of carbohydrates to profl. jours. Recipient Teaching Excellence award Queen's U. Arts and Sci. Undergrad. Soc., 1988-89. Fellow Chem. Inst. Can.; mem. AAAS, Am. Chem. Soc. (chmn. div. carbohydrate chemistry 1982-83, Claude S. Hudson award in carbohydrate chemistry 1989, Melville L. Wolfrom award 1992), Inst. Theol. encounter with Sci. and Tech., Royal Soc. Chemistry, N.Y. Acad. Scis. Roman Catholic. Office: Queen's U, Dept Chemistry, Kingston, ON Canada K7L 3N6

SZARKA, LASLO JOSEPH, pharmaceutical company executive; b. Hungary, Sept. 6, 1935; came to U.S., 1974; s. Geza and Ilona (Woditsch) S.; m. Violet Varkonyi; children: Monica, Lawrence. MS, U. Budapest, Hungary, 1961, PhD, 1967. Rsch. assoc. Chinoin, Budapest, 1963-64; sect. head Drug Rsch. Inst., Budapest, 1966-74; rsch. investigator E.R. Squibb & Sons, New Brunswick, N.J., 1974-81; asst. dir. E.R. Squibb & Sons New Brunswick, 1981-86; dir. Bristol-Myers-Squibb, New Brunswick, 1986—. Patentee: 25 patents in Biotech.; contbr. articles to profl. jours. Com. mem. Sister Cities for New Brunswick, 1990—. Mem. AAAS, AIChE, N.Y. Acad. Sci., Am. Chem. Soc. Avocations: travel, tennis, hiking, music. Office: Bristol Myers Squibb PO Box 191 New Brunswick NJ 08903-0191

SZARWARK, ERNEST JOHN, lawyer; b. South Bend, Ind., May 11, 1951; s. Stanley I. and Genevieve (Zalejski) S.; m. Mary Priscity Smith, June 3, 1978; children: Mary Cresap, Catherine Case. BS with highest honors, U. Notre Dame, 1973, JD with highest honors, 1976. Bar: Ind. 1976, U.S.

Claims Ct. 1977, U.S. Tax Ct. 1977, U.S. Ct. Appeals (7th cir.) 1980, Fla. 1982, U.S. Ct. Appeals (6th cir.) 1986. Atty. advisor to Hon. Richard C. Wilbur U.S. Tax Ct., Washington, 1976-78; assoc. Barnes & Thornburg, South Bend, 1978-85, ptnr., 1985—. Bd. dirs. South Bend Art Ctr., 1985-88; mem. fin. com. Stanley Clark Sch. Fellow Ind. Bar Found.; mem. Ind. Bar Assn. (bd. dirs. taxation sect. 1985-93, chmn. taxation sect. 1992-93), Ind. Soc. of Chgo., Polish Nat. Alliance, Michiana Arts and Scis. Counsel, South Bend Country Club. Roman Catholic. Avocations: golf, cross country skiing, numismatics, reading. Home: 1140 E Woodside St South Bend IN 46614-1482 Office: Barnes & Thornburg 600 1st Source Ctr 100 N Michigan St South Bend IN 46601-1630

SZARY, RICHARD M., manufacturing company executive. Pres. powertrain products Fed. Mogul Corp., Detroit. Office: Fed-Mogul Corp PO Box 48235 Detroit MI 48235

SZASZ, THOMAS STEPHEN, psychiatrist, educator, writer; b. Budapest, Hungary, Apr. 15, 1920; came to U.S., 1938, naturalized, 1944; s. Julius and Lily (Wellisch) S.; m. Rosine Loshkajian, Oct. 19, 1951 (div. 1970); children: Margot Szasz Peters, Susan Marie. A.B., U. Cin., 1941, M.D., 1944; D.Sc. (hon.), Allegheny Coll., 1975, U. Francisco Marroquin, Guatemala, 1979. Diplomate: Nat. Bd. Med. Examiners, Am. Bd. Psychiatry and Neurology. Intern 4th Med. Service Harvard, Boston City Hosp., 1944-45; asst. resident medicine Cin. Gen. Hosp., 1945-46, asst. clinician internal medicine div. outpatient dispensary, 1946; asst. resident psychiatry U. Chgo. Clinics, 1946-47; tng. research fellow Inst. Psychoanalysis, Chgo., 1947-48; research asst. Inst. Psychoanalysis, 1949-50, staff mem., 1951-56; practice medicine, specializing in psychiatry, psychoanalysis Chgo., 1949-54, Bethesda, Md., 1954-56, Syracuse, N.Y., 1956—; prof. psychiatry SUNY Health Sci. Ctr., Syracuse, 1956-90, prof. psychiatry emeritus, 1990—; vis. prof. dept. psychiatry U. Wis., Madison, 1962, Marquette U. Sch. Medicine, Milw., 1968, U. N.Mex., 1981; holder numerous lectureships, including C.P. Snow lectr. Ithaca Coll., 1970; E.S. Meyer Meml. lectr. U. Queensland Med. Sch.; Lambie-Dew orator Sydney U., 1977; Mem. nat. adv. com. bd. Tort and Med. Yearbook; cons. com. mental hygiene N.Y. State Bar Assn.; mem. research adv. panel Inst. Study Drug Addiction; adv. bd. Corp. Econ. Edn., 1977—. Author: Pain and Pleasure, 1957, The Myth of Mental Illness, 1961, Law, Liberty and Psychiatry, 1963, Psychiatric Justice, 1965, The Ethics of Psychoanalysis, 1965, Ideology and Insanity, 1970, The Manufacture of Madness, 1970, The Second Sin, 1973, Ceremonial Chemistry, 1974, Heresies, 1976, Karl Kraus and the Soul-Doctors, 1976, Schizophrenia: The Sacred Symbol of Psychiatry, 1976, Psychiatric Slavery, 1977, The Theology of Medicine, 1977, The Myth of Psychotherapy, 1978, Sex by Prescription, 1980, The Therapeutic State, 1984, Insanity: The Idea and its Consequences, 1987, The Untamed Tongue: A Dissenting Dictionary, 1990, Our Right to Drugs: The Case for a Free Market, 1992, A Lexicon of Lunacy, 1993, Cruel Compassion, 1994; editor: The Age of Madness, 1973; cons. editor of psychiatry and psychology: Stedman's Medical Dictionary, 22d edit, 1973; contbg. editor: Reason, 1974—, Libertarian Rev., 1986—; mem. editorial bd. Psychoanalytic Rev, 1965—, Jour. Contemporary Psychotherapy, 1968—, Law and Human Behavior, 1977—, Jour. Libertarian Studies, 1977—, Children and Youth Services Rev, 1978—, Am. Jour. Forensic Psychiatry, 1980—, Free Inquiry, 1980—. Served to comdr., M.C. USNR, 1954-56. Recipient Stella Feiss Hofheimer award U. Cin., 1944, Holmes-Munsterberg award Internat. Acad. Forensic Psychology, 1969; Wisdom award honor, 1970; Acad. prize Institutum atque Academia Auctorum Internationalis, Andorra, 1972; Distinguished Service award Am. Inst. Pub. Service, 1974; Martin Buber award Midway Counseling Center, 1974, Thomas S. Szasz award Ctr. Ind. Thought , 1990, Alfred R. Lindesmith award for achievement in field of scholarship and writing Drug Policy Found., 1991; others; named Humanist of Year Am. Humanist Assn., 1973; Hon. fellow Postgrad. Center for Mental Health, 1961, Mencken award, 1981, Humanist Laureate, 1984, Statue of Liberty-Ellis Island Found. Archives Roster, 1986. Life fellow Am. Psychiat. Assn., Am. Psychoanalytic Assn., Internat. and Western N.Y. psychoanalytic socs. Home: 4739 Limberlost Ln Manlius NY 13104-1405 Office: 750 E Adams St Syracuse NY 13210-2306

SZCZARBA, ROBERT HENRY, mathematics educator, mathematician; b. Dearborn, Mich., Nov. 27, 1932; s. Michael and Julie (Hanas) S.; m. Arlene Lee Roschild, June 18, 1955; children: Garrett Lee, Cheryl Anne. B.S., U. Mich., 1955; M.A., U. Chgo., 1957, Ph.D., 1960. Instr. DePaul U., 1959-60; ONR research assoc. Yale U., 1960-61, asst. prof. math., 1961-65, assoc. prof., 1965-74, prof., 1974—, chmn. dept., 1980-83, dep. provost phys. scis. and engring., 1989-95; vis. mem. Inst. Advanced Study, Princeton, N.J., 1964-65, 72. Author: Calculus in Vector Spaces, 1979, Multivariable Calculus, 1982. Mem. Bethany Bd. Fin., Conn., 1971-77; treas. Bethany Democratic Com., 1980-83. NSF postdoctoral fellow, 1964-65. Mem. Am. Math. Soc. Office: Yale U Dept Math PO Box 208283 New Haven CT 06520-8283

SZCZEPANSKI, SLAWOMIR ZBIGNIEW STEVEN, lawyer; b. Lodz, Poland, Mar. 9, 1948; s. Wladyslaw and Janina Szczepanski; m. Cynthia Ellen Weagley, Sept. 30, 1972; children: Christine, Diana. BS in Chem. Engring., Rensselaer Poly. Inst., 1971; MS in Chem. Engring., Rensselaer Poly. Inst., 1972; JD, Union U., Albany, N.Y., 1975. Bar: N.Y. 1976, D.C. 1976, Ill. 1977, U.S. Dist. Ct. (no. dist.) Ill. 1977, U.S. Ct. Appeals (fed. cir.) 1988. Atty. Philips Petroleum Co., Washington, 1975-77; from assoc. to ptnr. Willian, Brinks, Hofer, Gilson & Lione, Chgo., 1977—. Author: Licensing in Foreign and Domestic Operations, 1985—; editor (legal periodical) Licensing Law and Business Report, 1986—; contbr. articles to profl. jours. Mem. ABA, Am. Intellectual Property Law Assn., Internat. Assn. Protection Indsl. Property, Assn. Trial Lawyers of Am., Nat. Advocates Soc., Licensing Execs. Soc., Intellectual Property Law Assn. of Chgo., Univ. Club. Avocations: tennis, sailing. Home: 641 W Willow St Apt 107 Chicago IL 60614-5176 Office: Willian Brinks 455 N Cityfront Plaza Dr Chicago IL 60611-5503

SZE, ANDY HOK-FAN, transportation executive; b. Hong Kong, Feb. 21, 1951; s. Wing-Cheung and Soo-Feng (Chan) S.; m. Lola Kong, Aug. 2, 1955; children: Stephanie Ping-Ping, Andrew Dunway. BS in Indsl. Engring., Ill. Inst. Tech., 1973; MS, Northwestern U., 1976; MBA, U. Chgo., 1982. Dir. research and devel. Clipper Exxpress Co., Chgo., 1976-78, asst. v.p. movement control, 1979-80, v.p. ops. 1980-82, exec. v.p. 1982-83, pres., chief exec. officer, 1983—; mem. bus. adv. com. Transp. Ctr. Northwestern U.; bd. dirs. Agile Freight System, Lemont, Ill., Agrl. Express Am., Lemont. Bus. adv. council Coll. Bus. Adminstrn. U. Ill., Chgo., 1984—; examiner Malcolm Baldridge Nat. Quality award, 1991, 92. Recipient Dwight D. Gardener award Am. Inst. Ind. Engrs., 1972; Murphy fellow Northwestern, 1973. Mem. Am. Soc. Transp. and Logistics. Clubs: Chgo. Yacht, Econ. Chgo. Avocation: fishing.

SZE, HELEN WANG YEE, lawyer; b. Shanghai, Republic of China, Sept. 21, 1953; d. Shiu Chuen and Fung Sin (Yu) S. BA, U. Hawaii, 1975; MBA, Cornell U., 1978, JD, 1979. Bar: N.Y. 1980, Calif. 1982. Assoc. Whitman & Ransom, N.Y.C., 1979-82; Graham & James, Singapore, Republic of China, 1982-83, Orrick, Herrington & Sutcliffe, San Francisco, 1984—. Office: Orrick Herrington & Sutcliffe 600 Montgomery St San Francisco CA 94111-2702

SZEBEHELY, VICTOR G., aeronautical engineer; b. Budapest, Hungary, Aug. 10, 1921; s. Victor and Vilma (Stockl) S.; m. Jo Betsy Lewallen, May 21, 1970; 1 dau., Julia. M.E., U. Budapest, 1943, Ph.D. in Engring, 1945; Dr. (hon.), Eotvos U. Budapest, 1991. Asst. prof. U. Budapest, 1945-47; research asso. State U. Pa., 1947-48; asso. prof. Va. Poly. Inst., 1948-53; research asso. Model Basin, U.S. Navy, 1953-57; research mgr. Gen. Electric Co., 1957-62; asso. prof. astronomy Yale U., 1962-68; prof. aerospace engring. U. Tex., Austin, 1968—; chmn. dept. U. Tex., 1977-81, R.B. Curran Centennial chair in engring., 1983—; cons. NASA-Johnson Space Center, U.S. Air Force Space Command, Lawrence Berkeley Lab., U. Calif. Author 18 books; contbr. over 200 articles on space research, celestial mechanics and ship dynamics to profl. jours. Knighted by Queen Juliana of Netherlands, 1956. Fellow AIAA, AAAS; mem. Am. Astron. Soc. (Brouwer award div. dynamical astronomy 1977), Internat. Astron. Union (pres. commn. on celestial mechanics), NAE, European Acad. Arts, Scis., Lit. Home: 2501 Jarratt Ave Austin TX 78703-2432 Office: U Tex Dept Aerospace Engring & Engring Mechs Austin TX 78712

SZEFLER, STANLEY JAMES, pediatrics and pharmacology educator; b. Buffalo, Aug. 24, 1948; s. Stanley and Bernice Laura (Platt) S.; m. Christine M. Drezek, Dec. 26, 1970; children: David, Paul. BS, SUNY, Buffalo, 1971, MD, 1975. Resident pediatrics Children's Hosp. Buffalo, 1975-77; postdoctoral fellow in clin. pharmacology and allergy immunology SUNY, Buffalo, 1977-79, asst. prof. pediatrics and pharmacology, 1979-82; assoc. prof. pediatrics and pharmacology U. Colo. Denver, 1982-90, prof. pediatrics, pharmacology, 1990—; dir. clin. pharmacology Children's Hosp. Buffalo, 1979-82, Nat. Jewish Ctr. for Immunology and Respiratory Medicine, Denver, 1982—. Contbr. articles to profl. jours. Mem. steering com. asthma camp for children Am. Lung Assn., Denver 1987—. Maj. USAR, 1979-88. NIH grantee, 1980-84, 90—; FDA grantee, Denver, 1988-91. Fellow Am. Acad. Allergy and Immunology (chmn. asthma, rhinitis and respiratory disease interest sect.), Am. Acad. Pediats. (liaison mem. com. drugs). Avocations: baseball, soccer. Office: Nat Jewish Ctr Dept Immunology/Respiratory Med 1400 Jackson St Denver CO 80206-2761

SZEGO, CLARA MARIAN, cell biologist, educator; b. Budapest, Hungary, Mar. 23, 1916; came to U.S., 1921, naturalized, 1927; d. Paul S. and Helen (Elek) S.; m. Sidney Roberts, Sept. 14, 1943. A.B., Hunter Coll., 1937; M.S. (Garvan fellow), U. Minn., 1939, Ph.D., 1942. Instr. physiology U. Minn., 1942-43; Minn. Cancer Research Inst. fellow, 1943-44; rsch. assoc. OSRD, Nat. Bur. Standards, 1944-45, Worcester Found. Exptl. Biology, 1945-47; rsch. instr. physiol. chemistry Yale U. Sch. Medicine, 1947-48; mem. faculty UCLA, 1948—, prof. biology, 1960—. Named Woman of Year in Sci. Los Angeles Times, 1957-58; Guggenheim fellow, 1956; named to Hunter Coll. Hall of Fame, 1987. Fellow AAAS; mem. Am. Physiol. Soc., Am. Soc. Cell Biology, Endocrine Soc. (CIBA award 1953), Soc. for Endocrinology (Gt. Britain), Biochem. Soc. (Gt. Britain), Internat. Soc. Rsch. Reprodn., Phi Beta Kappa (pres. UCLA chpt. 1973-74), Sigma Xi (pres. UCLA chpt. 1976-77). Achievements include rsch. and numerous pubs. on steroid protein interactions, mechanisms of hormone action and lysosome participation in normal cell function. Home: 1371 Marinette Rd Pacific Palisades CA 90272-2627 Office: U Calif Dept Biology Los Angeles CA 90024-1606

SZENBERG, MICHAEL, economics educator, editor, consultant; b. Sosnowiec, Poland, Apr. 8, 1934; came to U.S., 1961, naturalized, 1966; s. Henry and Sara (Rosensaft) S.; m. Miriam Silverstein, Sept. 2, 1962; children: Naomi, Avi. Student, Bar Ilan U., Israel, 1959-61; B.A. summa cum laude, L.I. U., 1963; Ph.D., City U. N.Y., 1970. Faculty L.I. U., Bklyn. Center, 1965—, prof. econs., 1974-83; prof. econs. Lubin Grad. Sch. Bus. Pace U., 1983—; adj. prof. Hunter Coll., 1970-76, Pace U., 1975-83; founder, dir. Lecture Bur. Econs., 1973; chmn. 1st Met. Grad. Conf. Econs., 1973; assoc. mem. Ctr. Tech. Assessment, Newark Coll. Engring., 1973; vis. prof. econs. NYU, summers 1977, 78, 79; cons. in field. Author: Economics of the Israeli Diamond Industry, 1973, The Welfare Effects of Trade Restrictions: A Case Study of the United States Footwear Industry, 1977, The Economics of the American Footwear Industry, 2d edit., 1984; editor: Essays in Economics, The John Commons Memorial Lectures, 1986, Eminent Economists: Their Life Philosophies, 1992; assoc. editor: Am. Economist, 1973-75, editor-in-chief, 1975—; econs. co-editor: Cambridge Univ. Press Encyclopedia; contbr. articles to profl. jours. Served with Israeli Air Force. 1956-59. Recipient Dean Hudson award L.I. U., 1962, Am. Coll. Abroad award, 1962, Dean Abelson award CUNY, 1963; fellow econs. CUNY, 1963; grantee Israel Diamond Inst., 1970; recipient Irving Fisher Monograph award, 1971; fellow Internat. Honor Soc. in Econs., 1972; grantee Dept. Labor, 1975; recipient Kenan award for teaching excellence Pace U., 1983, Schalkenbach Found. Research award, 1987, First Prize Recognition award for scholarly productivity, 1989, Tchr. of the Year Pace U., 1992, Teaching Excellence award Acad. Bus. Admin., 1993, Achievement award CUNY, 1993, Outstanding Publication award Pace U., 1993. Mem. Atlantic Econ. Soc., Internat. Trade and Fin. Assn., Internat. Fedn. Sci. Editors, Ea. Econ. Assn., Am. Econ. Assn., Assn. Cultural Econs., Internat. Honor Soc. Econs. (exec. bd. 1975—, regional dir. 1971-74), Optimates Soc. (pres. 1972-80). Home: 1442 E 9th St Brooklyn NY 11230-6405

SZENTIRMAI, GEORGE, electrical engineer, corporate executive; b. Budapest, Hungary, Oct. 8, 1928; came to U.S., 1959; s. Frederick Wilhelm and Magda (Dicker) Benis; m. Mariann Hartmann, Dec. 20, 1952 (div 1974); children: Andrea A., Susan E.; m. Irene A. Sharp, Sept. 6, 1992. Diploma in Elec. Engring., Tech. U., Budapest, 1951, Candidate tech. scis., 1955; PhDEE, Poly. U., 1963. Chartered elec. engr., Gt. Britain. Asst. prof. Tech. U., Budapest, 1955-56; engr. Standard Telephones & Cables, Woolwhich, Eng., 1957-58; mem. tech. staff Bell Labs., Murray Hill, Holmdel, N.J., 1959-68; prof. elec. engring. Cornell U. Ithaca, N.Y., 1968-74; staff scientist Rockwell Internat., Anaheim, Calif., 1975-80; dir. software div. Comsat Gen. Integrated System, Palo Alto, Calif., 1981-82; pres. DGS Assocs., Inc, Santa Clara, Calif., 1983—; lectr. Santa Clara U. Calif., 1981-88; adj. prof. UCLA, 1976-80; vis. prof. CUNY, 1974-75; cons. Bell Labs., Holmdel, 1968-75. Contbr. articles to profl. jours.; editor: Computer Aided Filter Des, 1973. Fellow IEEE; mem. IEEE Circuits and Systems Soc. (Meritorious Svc. award 1988), Instn. Elec. Engrs. of Gt. Britain. Avocations: tennis, music, philately, travel. Office: DGS Assocs Inc 125 Willow Rd Ste 205 Menlo Park CA 94025-2709

SZEP, PAUL MICHAEL, editorial cartoonist; b. Hamilton, Ont., Can., July 29, 1941; came to U.S., 1966; s. Paul Joseph and Helen (Langhorne) S.; m. Angela Diane Garton, Feb. 27, 1965 (div. 1976); children: Amy, Jason. A.O.C.A., Ont. Coll. Art, 1964; A.O.C.A. hon. degree, 1975, Framingham State Coll., 1975, Worcester State Coll., 1980, William Penn Coll., 1981. Sports cartoonist Hamilton Spectator, 1958-61; graphics designer Financial Post, Toronto, Ont., 1965-66; editorial cartoonist Boston Globe, 1966—; vis. fellow Harvard U., 1981; lectr. various univs. Author: In Search of Sacred Cows, 1967, Keep Your Left Hand High, 1969, At This Point in Time, 1973, The Harder They Fall, 1975, Unvote for a New America, 1976, Them Damned Pictures, 1977, Warts and All, 1979, To a Different Drummer, 1983, The Gang of Eight, 1985, The Next Szep Book, 1985, Often in Error, Never in Doubt, 1987, And Then Jack Said to Arnie, 1991, And Then Arnie Told Chi Chi And Then Chi Chi Said to Fuzzy, 1993; editl. cartoonist Sta. WNEV-TV, Boston; contbr. Golf Digest. Served with F.A. Royal Canadian Army, 1957-58. Recipient Pulitzer prize, 1974, 77, award Sigma Delta Chi, 1974, 77, Toyl award Boston Jaycees, 1976, Headliners award, 1977, Reuben award for best editorial cartoonist Nat. Cartoonist Soc., 1979, Thomas Nast award; Internat. Cartoonist award, Best Sports Cartoonist award Nat. Cartoonists Soc., 1988. Mem. Soc. Illustrators, Kittansett Club, Harvard Club, Weston Golf Club, Sterling Country Club. Home: 7 Stetson Rd Brookline MA 02146-3406 Office: Boston Globe Boston MA 02107

SZER, WLODZIMIERZ, biochemist, educator; b. Warsaw, Poland, June 3, 1924; came to U.S., 1968; s. Max and Chaia (Szapiro) S.; m. Felicja Kirsz, Oct. 1, 1946; children: Caroline, Ilona. M.S. in Chemistry, U. Lodz (Poland), 1950; Ph.D. in Biochemistry, Inst. Biochemistry and Biophysics, Polish Acad. Scis., 1959. Dozent Inst. Biochemistry and Biophysics, Warsaw, 1963-68; asst. prof., then assoc. prof. biochemistry Sch. Medicine, NYU, N.Y.C., 1968-73, prof., 1973—. Contbr. articles and revs. to profl. jours. Recipient Jacob K. Parnas Polish Biochem. Soc., 1964; recipient Faculty Am. Cancer Soc., 1973; USPHS grantee, 1971—. Mem. Am. Soc. Biol. Chemists, Harvey Soc. Office: NYU Sch Medicine Dept Biochemistry 550 1st Ave New York NY 10016-6481

SZERI, ANDRAS Z., engineering educator; b. Nagyvarad, Hungary, June 6, 1934; came to U.S., 1967; s. Andras F. and Julie (Farkas) S.; m. Mary J. Parkinson, Apr. 25, 1962; children: Andrew J., Elizabeth C., Maria J. B.S. with 1st class honors, U. Leeds, Eng., 1959, Ph.D., 1962. Research engr. English Electric Co., Stafford, Eng., 1962-64; prof. Universidad Santa Maria, Valparaiso, Chile, 1964-66; asst. prof. U. Pitts., 1967-70, assoc. prof., 1970-76, prof. math., 1977-93, prof. mech. engring., 1977-94, chmn. dept. mech. engring., 1984-87, William Kepler Whiteford prof. engring., 1990-94; prof. chmn. dept. mech. engring. U. Del., Newark, 1994—; cons. Westinghouse Electric Co., Pitts., 1967-82; external examiner W.I., 1989—. Editor: Tribology, 1980. Fellow ASME (assoc. editor Jour. Tribology 1978-87, tech. editor 1987-93); mem. Am. Acad. Mechanics, Soc. Indsl. and Applied Math., Soc. Engring. Sci., Soc. Natural Philosophy. Office: U Del Dept Mech Engring Newark DE 19176

SZEWCZYK, ALBIN ANTHONY, engineering educator; b. Chgo., Feb. 26, 1935; s. Andrew Aloysius and Jean Cecelia (Wojcik) S.; m. Barbara Valerie Gale, June 16, 1956; children: Karen Marie Knop, Lisa Anne, Andrea Jean Simpson, Terese Helen Sinka. BS, U. Notre Dame, 1956, MS, 1958; PhD, U. Md., 1961. Staff engr. Northrop Aircraft Corp., Hawthorne, Calif., 1956-57; grad. asst. U. Notre Dame, Ind., 1957-58, asst. prof. engring., 1962-65, assoc. prof., 1965-67, prof., 1967—, chmn. dept., 1978-88; research asst. U. Md., College Park, 1958-61, postdoctoral researcher, 1961-62; mem. tech. staff Aerospace Corp., El Segundo, Calif., 1962; cons. Argonne (Ill.) Nat. Lab., 1968-80, Miles Lab., Elkhart, Ind., 1983—, Chung Shan Inst. Sci. and Tech., Taiwan, Republic of China, 1987—; vis. prof. Imperial Coll., London, 1989, Kernforschungzentrum, Karlsruhe, Fed. Republic Germany, 1990. Editor: Development in Mechanics, 1971. Fellow AIAA (assoc.); mem. AAAS, ASME, Am. Phys. Soc., Am. Soc. Engring. Edn., N.Y. Acad. Sci., Sigma Xi, Pi Tau Sigma, Sigma Gamma Tau. Roman Catholic. Club: South Bend Country (bd. dirs. 1982-89, pres. 1986-88). Avocations: golfing, model railroading. Home: 17331 Willowbrook Dr South Bend IN 46635-1750 Office: Dept Aero & Mech Engring U Notre Dame Notre Dame IN 46556

SZILAGYI, DESIDERIUS) EMERICK, surgeon, researcher, educator; b. Nagykaroly, Hungary, June 20, 1910; came to U.S., naturalized, 1931; m. Martha Evelyn Fowlkes Harper (dec.); children: Martha, Christine; m. Sally Bolton, 1989. Diploma, Calvinist Coll., Klausenburg, Hungary, 1928; exam., U. Paris-Sorbonne; student, U. Debrecen; MD, U. Mich., 1935, MS, 1940; MD (hon.), Semmelweis Med. U., Budapest, Hungary, 1988. Diplomate Am. Bd. Surgery. Intern U. Mich. Hosp., Ann Arbor, 1935-36, asst. resident in surgery, 1936-37, instr. pathology, 1937-39; asst. resident in surgery Henry Ford Hosp., Detroit, 1939-42, chief resident, 1945, asst. surgeon, 1945-46, assoc. surgeon, 1946-49, chief div. II gen. surgery, 1949-66, chmn. dept. surgery, 1966-75, cons. vascular surgery, 1975—, chief of staff, 1968-71; emeritus clin. prof. surgery U. Mich. Med. Sch., Ann Arbor; dir. med. dept. Ford Rubber Plantations, Para, Brazil, 1942-45; Edwin A. Jarecki Meml. lectr. Albert Einstein Med. Ctr., Phila., 1964; David W. Yandell lectr. U. Louisville Med. Sch., 1973; William Mayo lectr. U. Mich., 1978; Matas Meml. lectr. XV Internat. Congress of Internat. Cardiovascular Soc., Athens, Greece, 1981. Editor Jour. Vascular Surgery, 1983—; contbr. articles to profl. jours. Mem. ACS, Am. Fedn. Clin. Research, AMA, Am. Surg. Assns., Am. Thyroid Assn., Central Surg. Assn. (past pres.), Internat. Soc. Cardiovascular Surgery (past chpt. pres.), Internat. Soc. Surgery, Midwestern Vascular Surg. Soc. (past pres.), Soc. Vascular Surgery (past pres.), Western Surg. Assn. (past v.p., pres.), Detroit Acad. Surgery, Detroit Surg. Assn., Mich. Med. Soc., Wayne County Med. Soc.; hon. mem. Sociedad Argentina de Angiologia, Sociedad Columbiana de Angiologia, Royal Australasian Coll. Surgeons, Deutsche Gesellschaft für Gefässchirurgie. Home: 1008 Stratford Pl Bloomfield Hills MI 48304-2934 Office: Henry Ford Hosp 2799 W Grand Blvd Detroit MI 48202-2689 *I regard it as an accidental stroke of good fortune that the beginning of my career as a surgeon coincided with the birth of a new branch of the surgical art: the surgery of the arterial system. Thus, I had the rare opportunity of making and publishing observations that were original and useful not because of their brilliance but because of their newness. The contribution for which I may perhaps take personal credit was a firm determination to describe my observations objectively and draw my conclusions honestly.*

SZILASSY, SANDOR, retired lawyer, library director, educator; b. Magyarbarnag, Hungary, Apr. 9, 1921; came to U.S., 1957; s. Sandor Sr. and Jolan (Fenyves) S.; m. Clara Ida Varkonyi, July 21, 1951; children: Peter S., Thomas S., Paul A. D. LLD, U. Budapest, Hungary, 1944, Lawyer-Judge Dipl., 1949; MA, Ind. U., 1959. Practicing atty. pvt. law firm Veszprém, Hungary, 1944-56; asst. libr. Anderson (Ind.) Coll. Libr., 1959-61; head div. sci. and tech. Auburn (Ala.) U. Libr., 1961-68; head libr., assoc. prof. Ind. State U., Evansville, 1968-69; dir. libr., prof. U. Tampa, Fla., 1969-72; dir. librs. Rowan Coll. of N.J., 1972-94; v.p. Ala. Acad. Sci., 1963-68; pres. Coun. N.J. Coll. and Univ. Librs., 1978-79, 89-90, Librs. Unltd., N.J., 1981-82, 88-89; cons. numerous orgns; radio commentator, Sta. WTEL, Phila., 1987-91. Author: Revolutionary Hungary, 1971 (Arpad Acad. Gold medal 1972), Ein Amerikanischer Diplomat uber Ungarn, 1974, Hungary's Road to Trianon, 1988, numerous others; author book chpts.; mem. editorial bd. Ency. Hungarica, 1989—; contbr. essays, studies, articles to profl. jours., newspapers, mags. Bd. elders Presbyn. Ch., Lakeland, Fla., 1970-72. Recipient Legion of Honor award Chapel of Three Chaplains, 1981. Mem. N.J. Acad. Libr. Network (exec. bd. 1988—), Tri-State Coll. Libr. Coop. (pres. 1975-76, 88-89, Johanniter Order Knights (Germany), Arpad Acad. (sect. pres. 1979—), Phi Alpha Theta. Mem. Reformed Ch. Avocations: research, writing, reading, swimming, hiking. Home: 133 N Pompano Beach Blvd # 103 Pompano Beach FL 33062

SZIRMAL, ENDRE ANREAS FRANZ, physician, writer; b. Budapest, Hungary, Aug. 21, 1922; s. Károly Péter and Erzsébet R. (Schwartz) S.; Dr.med., MD, Med. U. Szeged, Hungary, 1947; D in Sci. Medicine, PhD, Kobe U., Tokyo, 1961; Dr. med. lic. Innenministerium, Stuttgart, Germany, 1962; numerous hon. degrees from France, Hungary, Germany, Netherlands, Spain, U.S., Chile, Japan, Brazil, Ceylon, Mex., India, Italy, Can., Poland, Australia, USSR, New Zealand, Eng., others; m. Ilona Mikes, Feb. 13, 1945; children: Marta, Andrea. Specialist in lab. internal medicine, clin. pathology, biochemistry, nuclear and gen. hematology, ob-gyn, oncology, myology, hon. prof., 1954—; chmn. dept. nuclear hematology Inst. Nuclear Engring. and assoc. univs., London, 1960, Stuttgart, 1966—; prof. Univ. O.M.H. Sci , Des Moines, Iowa, 1965—, U. Louisville, 1975—, U. San Diego, 1985—, U.S. Internat. U.; dir. Inst. Stress Mgmt.; elected cons. Min. Sci. Zagreb, Croatia; founder Szirmai Archives; pres. bd. advisors Nobel Sci. Found., 1992. Proposed for Nobel Prize, 1969; recipient Letter of Appreciation Min. Sci. Croatia; Commemorative plaque Okayama U., Japan, others. Fellow Inst. Nuclear Engring. and Coll. Angiology of N.Y., Royal Soc. Medicine, Royal Soc. Chemists; mem. Internat. Nomenclature Com. (pres.), Germ. Ph. Acad. Sci., Hungarian Acad. Scis., Italian Acad. Scis., N.Y. Acad. Scis., Mex. Acad. Gerontology (hon.), also numerous med., nuclear, and lit. assns. Author books, poetry and novels transl. into 35 langs., numerous abstracts in 49 langs., publs. on med. atomic energy, linguistic arts; editorial bd. several jours.; research biochem. methods, drugs; developer myotonometer, angiomyograph, myograph, utero-embryo cardiotonograph, electrocoagulometer; developer theories in medicine, philosophy, music and art; established Rutherford Szirmai prize Szirmai Univ. Found.; Szirmai archives established librs. worldwide. Address: Adolf-Kroener Str 11, D-70184 Stuttgart Germany

SZKODY, PAULA, astronomy educator, researcher; b. Detroit, July 17, 1948; d. Julian and Pauline (Wolski) S.; m. Donald E. Brownlee, Mar. 19, 1976; children: Allison, Carson. BS in Astrophysics, Mich. State U., 1970; MS in Astronomy, U. Wash., 1972, PhD in Astronomy, 1975. Rsch. asst. Observatoire de Geneve, 1969, Kitt Peak Nat. Obs., 1970; rsch., teaching asst. U. Wash., Seattle, 1970-75, rsch. assoc., lectr., 1975-82; sr. rsch. assoc., 1982-83, rsch. assoc. prof., 1983-91, rsch. prof., 1991—; part-time mem. faculty Seattle U., 1974-75, 82, Bellevue Coll., 1975-77; vis. scientist Kitt Peak Nat. Obs., 1976, peer reviewer, 1983-85; vis. instr. UCLA, 1977, adj. asst. prof., 1980, 81; vis. asst. prof. U. Hawaii, 1978; vis. assoc. prof. Calif. Inst. Tech., 1978-79, 80; mem. users com. Internat. Ultraviolet Explorer, 1983-85, 93—; mem. A.J. Cannon adv. com. AAUW, 1986-91, chmn., 1988-90; mem. mgmt. ops. working group on Ultraviolet/Visual/Relativity, NASA, 1988-91. Contbr. more than 135 articles to profl. jours. Recipient Annie J. Cannon award, 1978. Mem. AAAS (mem. nominating com. 1990-93, chairperson 1993, mem.-at-large 1995—), Am. Assn. Variable Star Observers, Am. Astron. Soc., Internat. Astronomical Union (mem. commn. 42 organizing com. 1991—), Astron. Soc. Pacific (bd. dirs. 1988-92), Phi Beta Kappa. Office: U Wash Dept Astronomy Seattle WA 98195

SZMIT, FREDERICK ANDREW, paper manufacturing company executive; b. Lowell, Mass., May 26, 1938; s. Andrew and Jane (Dziekiewicz) S.; m. Frances Slavin, May 20, 1960; children: Kathleen Anne, Andrew Michael. BS, Lowell U., 1959; postgrad. program for mgmt. devel., Harvard U., 1981. Chemist Geigy Chem. Co., Ardsley, N.Y., 1960-61; mill mgr. Spaulding Fibre Co., North Rochester, N.H., 1961-71; mill mgr. Boise-Cascade Splty. Div., Brattleboro, Vt., 1971-78, mfg. mgr., 1978-83, gen. mgr., 1983-85; dir. Old Forge Pulp & Paper, Lyons Falls, N.Y., 1986—; pres., chief exec. officer, bd. dirs. Lyons Falls (N.Y.) Pulp & Paper, Inc., 1985—, Lyons Falls Hydroelectric, Inc., 1986—; bd. dirs. Am. Paper Inst., N.Y.C., 1976-85, Associated Industries of Vt., Montpelier, 1977-85, Bank of Vt. Adv. Bd., Brattleboro, 1980-85; del. Vt. Gov.'s Conf. Forest Industries, Montpelier, 1985. Pres. Southern Vt. Health Services Corp., Brattleboro, 1984-87; pres. Brattleboro Meml. Hosp., 1981-84; chmn. United Fund of Brattleboro, 1979. Mem. Am. Paper Inst. (bd. dirs.), Paper Industry Mgmt. Assn., Associated Industries of N.Y., Tech. Assn. Pulp and Paper. Home: PO Box 404 Walpole NH 03608-0404

SZOKA, EDMUND CASIMIR CARDINAL, cardinal; b. Grand Rapids, Mich., Sept. 14, 1927; s. Casimir and Mary (Wolgat) S. B.A., Sacred Heart Sem., 1950; J.C.B., Pontifical Lateran U., 1958, J.C.L., 1959. Ordained priest Roman Catholic Ch., 1954; asst. pastor St. Francis Parish, Manistique, Mich., 1954-55; sec. to bishop Marquette, Mich., 1955-57, 59-62; chaplain St. Mary's Hosp., Marquette, 1955-57; tribunal, notary, defender of bond Marquette, 1960-71; asst. chancellor Diocese of Marquette, 1962-69, chancellor, 1970-71; pastor St. Pius X Ch., Ishpeming, Mich., 1962-63, St. Christopher Ch., Marquette, 1963-71; bishop Diocese of Gaylord, Mich., 1971-81; archbishop of Detroit, 1981-90; elevated to cardinal, 1988; sec.-treas. Mich. Cath. Conf., Lansing, 1972-77; chmn. region VI Nat. Conf. Cath. Bishops, 1972-77; treas., mem. adminstrv. bd. and adminstrv. com., budget and fin. com. Nat. Conf. Cath. Bishops/U.S. Cath. Conf., 1981-84; trustee, mem. exec. com., chmn. com. for univ. relations Cath. U. Am., 1981-90; trustee Nat. Shrine of the Immaculate Conception, Washington, 1981-90; chmn. bd. trustees Cath. Telecommunications Network Am., 1984-90; pres. Prefecture for Econ. Affairs of the Holy See, 1990; mem. Secretariat of State, 2d sect. Coun. for Rels. with States. Mem. Congregation for Insts. Consecrated Life and Socs. Apostolic Life, Congregation for Causes of Saints, Congregation for Bishops, Congregation for Evangelization of Peoples, Congregation for Clergy. Address: Prefecture for Econ Affairs, 00120 Vatican City Vatican City

SZUCH, CLYDE ANDREW, lawyer; b. Bluefield, W.Va., Nov. 22, 1930; s. Nicholas and Aranka (Rubin) S.; m. Rosalie Hirschman Wulfson, Sept. 5, 1954; children: Peter Alan, Richard Clinton. BA, Rutgers, 1952; LLB, Harvard U., 1955. Bar: N.J. 1955, U.S. Dist. Ct. N.J. 1955, U.S. Ct. Appeals (3rd cir.) 1958, U.S. Supreme Ct. 1962. Law clk. to assoc. justice William J. Brennan Jr. U.S. Supreme Ct., Washington, 1956-57; asst. U.S. atty. U.S. Attys. Office, Newark, 1957-58; assoc. Pitney, Hardin & Kipp, Newark, 1958-62; ptnr. Pitney, Hardin, Kipp & Szuch, Morristown, N.J., 1962—; mem. panel Ctr. for Pub. Resources, N.J.; bd. dirs. Vt. Rwy. Inc., Clarendon & Pittsford R.R. Co., Burlington, Vt.; panelist AAA Large Complex Cases. Trustee Morris Mus., Morristown; chmn. State of N.J. Bicentennial Bill of Rights Project for the Nat. Conf. Christians and Jews, Princeton, N.J., 1990, gov. N.J. region. Fellow Am. Bar Found.; mem. ABA, Am. Law Inst., N.J State Bar Assn., Morris County Bar Assn., Essex County Bar Assn., Fed. Bar Assn., Ctr. for Pub. Resources Panel, Nat. Legal Defender Assn., Hist. Soc. of U.S. Ct. Appeals of 3d Cir., Park Ave. Club. Office: Pitney Hardin Kipp & Szuch PO Box 1945 Park Ave Morristown NJ 07962-1945

SZUCS, ZOLTAN DANIEL, religious organization executive, minister, psychologist, educator; b. Pastovce, Sloviakia, Oct. 29, 1935; came to U.S., 1958; m. Barbara Cecil Kizer; children: Ildiko, Aniko. Grad. summa cum laude, Reformed Kollegium, Papa, Hungary, 1954; postgrad., Reformed Theol. Seminary, Budapest, Hungary, 1955, U. Vienna, 1957-58, U. Del., 1959; grad., Princeton (N.J.) Theol. Seminary, 1962; MEd, Temple U.; PhD in Counseling Psychology, Tex. A&M U. Ordained to ministry Hungarian Reformed Ch. Am., 1960, Presbyn. Ch., 1963. With Brethren Svc. Commn., Linz; youth counselor World Coun. Chs., Steinbach Am Attersee; pastor St. George and Delaware City Presbyn. Chs., Del., 1963-73; dir. campus ministry Tex. A&M, College Station, 1973-78; pastor First Presbyn. Ch., Sealy, Tex., 1977-80, South Side Presbyn. Ch., Niles, Ohio, 1977-80; sr. pastor Hungarian Reform Ch., United Ch. Christ, Lorain, Ohio, 1980—; gen. sec. Calvin synod United Ch. Christ, 1989-93, bishop, 1993—, exec. coun., 1993—; chaplain Del. State Senate, 1965-66; adj. prof. psychology Wilmington Coll., New Castle, Del., 1970-73; instr. Tex. A&M Univ., College Station, 1973-77; del. Interdenominational Ch. Con. to Palestinians, Beirut, 1980; U.S. rep. Internat. Com. World Alliance of Reformed Chs. Soviet Union, 1989. Office: United Ch of Christ 3036 Globe Ave Lorain OH 44055

SZUHAJ, BERNARD FRANCIS, food research director; b. Lilly, Pa., Nov. 27, 1942; s. Theodore and Rose Dorothy (Karmen) S.; m. Carole Ann Brady, Dec. 26, 1964; children: Matthew, Timothy, Bernard. BS, Pa. State U., 1964, MS, 1966, PhD, 1969. Grad. asst. Pa. State U., Univ. Park, Pa., 1964-66; research asst. Pa. State U., Univ. Park, 1966-68; scientist Cen. Soya Co., Inc., Fort Wayne, Ind., 1968-73; research dir. Cen. Soya Co., Inc., Fort Wayne, 1973-84, dir. food research, 1984—; v.p. Am. Oil Chemists'Soc. Found., Ill., 1988—; bd. dirs. POS Pilot Plant Corp., Saskatoon, Canada, 1987—. Patentee in field; co-editor Lecithins, 1985; editor: (lecithins) Sources Manufacture & Uses, 1989. Mem. Am. Oil Chemists' Soc. (bd. dirs. 1989—), Am. Chem. Soc., Inst. Food Technologists, Inst. Shortening & Edible Oils, Sigma Xi. Democrat. Roman Catholic. Office: Cen Soya Co Inc PO Box 1400 Fort Wayne IN 46801-1400

SZUHY, LAWRENCE GREGORY, automotive company executive; b. Cleve., Aug. 10, 1942; s. Coleman Lawrence and Mary Margaret (Kemmeny) S.; m. Judith Mae Blair; children: Chris, Linda, Diana, Beth. BBA, Eastern Mich. U., 1965, MBA, 1969. Various mfg. mgmt. positions Ford Motor Co., 1964-72; from plant mgr. to v.p. mfg. ops. Arrow Automotive Industries Inc., Spartanburg, S.C., 1972-88; exec. v.p. Blue Chip Products, Inc., Fairless Hills, Pa., 1988—; instr. Schoolcraft Jr. Coll., Livonia, Mich., 1968-72, Rutledge Coll., 1973-74, U. S.C., Spartanburg, 1974-76. Bd. dirs. United Way, Spartanburg, 1987—, Spartanburg Devel. Assn., 1987—; chmn. Spartanburg Children's Shelter, 1987—. Mem. Automotive Parts Rebuilders Assn. (bd. dirs. 1979—, pres. 1986-87). Republican. Roman Catholic. Avocations: jogging, water skiing, golf, tennis. Office: Blue Chip Products Inc One Newbold Rd Fairless Hills PA 19030

SZULC, TAD, journalist, commentator; b. Warsaw, Poland, July 25, 1926; came to U.S., 1947, naturalized, 1954; s. Seweryn and Janina (Baruch) S.; m. Marianne Carr, July 8, 1948; children: Nicole, Anthony. Student, U. Brazil, 1943-45; LHD (hon.), Am. Coll. Switzerland, 1987. Reporter AP, Rio de Janeiro, 1945-46; corr. at UN for UPI, 1949-53; mem. staff N.Y. Times, after 1953; corr. N.Y. Times, Latin Am. 1955-61; with Washington bur. N.Y. Times, 1961-65, 69-72, corr. to Spain and Portugal, 1965-68, corr. to Eastern Europe, 1968-69, commentator fgn. policy, 1972—. Author: Twilight of the Tyrants, 1959, The Cuban Invasion, 1962, The Winds of Revolution, 1963, Dominican Diary, 1965, Latin America, 1966, Bombs of Palomares, 1967, United States and the Caribbean, 1971, Czechoslovakia since World War II, 1971, Portrait of Spain, 1972, Compulsive Spy: The Strnage Career of E. Howard Hunt, 1974, The Energy Crisis, 1974, Innocents at Home, 1974, The Illusion of Peace, 1978, Diplomatic Immunity, 1981, Fidel: A Critical Portrait, 1986, Then and Now: The World Since WW II, 1990, The Secret Alliance, 1991, Pope John Paul II: The Biography, 1995. Decorated Cross of Chevalier of Legion d'Honneur France, Order of Duarte, Sánchez, Meliá Dominican Republic; recipient Maria Moors Cabot gold medal Columbia U., Medal of Honor, World Bus. Coun., 1987. Mem. Overseas Press Club (award for best mag. interpretation fgn. affairs 1976, citations 1966, 74-75, 77-78, award for best book on fgn. affairs 1979, 86, 91), Cosmos Club. Address: 4515 29th St NW Washington DC 20008

SZURSZEWSKI, JOSEPH HENRY, physiologist; b. Pitts., May 25, 1940; s. Henry Joseph and Genevie (Rudzka) S.; m. Cecelia Johnson, Aug. 24, 1963; children: Joseph, Marie. B.S. in Zoology, Duquesne U., 1962; Ph.D. in Physiology, U. Ill., 1966; postgrad., Monash U., Clayton, Australia, 1969-70; B.Sc. in Pharmacology, Oxford (Eng.) U., 1971. Grad. teaching asst. U. Ill., 1963-65, NSF summer research fellow, 1963; asso. cons. in physiology Mayo Grad. Sch. Medicine, Rochester, Minn., 1971-73; cons. Mayo Grad. Sch. Medicine, 1973—; asst. prof. physiology Mayo Med. Sch., Rochester, 1971-75, asso. prof. physiology, 1975-77, prof. physiology, 1977—, asst. prof. pharmacology, 1971-77, asso. prof. pharmacology, 1977—, chmn. dept. physiology and biophysics, 1983, dir. for rsch. Mayo Group Practice; mem. coun. NIH, 1995—; NSF summer research fellow Duquesne U., 1961; Mayo Disting. Investigator, 1986. Served with ROTC. Recipient Merit award NIH; Univ. fellow Duquesne U., 1962-65, rsch. fellow NIH, 1966-68, Burn fellow Oxford (Eng.) U., 1971; Fulbright-Hays scholar, 1969-70. Mem.

AAAS, Am. Physiol. Soc. (rsch. prize gastrointestinal sect. 1990), Brit. Physiol. Soc., Am. Gastroent. Assn. (Disting. Achievement award, 1987), Soc. Neurosci., Sigma Xi. Research, numerous publs. in field. Office: 200 1st St SW Rochester MN 55905-0001

SZWARC, MICHAEL, polymer scientist; b. Poland, June 9, 1909; came to U.S., 1952; s. Maier and Regina (Prager) S.; m. Marja Frenkel, Aug. 6, 1933; children: Raphael, Myra, Rina. Ch.E., Warsaw Poly. Inst., Poland, 1932; PhD in Organic Chemistry, Hebrew U., Jerusalem, 1945; PhD in Phys. Chemistry, Manchester (Eng.) U., 1947, DSc (hon.), 1949; D (hon.), U. Leuven, Belgium, 1974; D.Sc. (hon.), Uppsala U., Sweden, 1975, Louis Pasteur U., Strasbourg, France, 1978. Researcher Hebrew U., Jerusalem, 1945-45; researcher Manchester U., Eng., 1946-52, univ. fellow, lectr. phys. chemistry, 1949-52; mem. faculty SUNY-Syracuse Coll. Environ. Scis., 1952-79; disting. prof. chemistry SUNY-Syracuse Coll. Forestry, 1964-80, dir. polymer ctr., 1966-80, prof. emeritus, 1980—. Author: Carbanions, Living Polymers and Electron Transfer Processes, 1968, Ionic Polymerization and Living Polymers, 1993; editor: Ions and Ion Pairs in Organic Chemistry, Vol. I, 1972, Vol. II, 1974. Recipient Polymer Chemistry award Am. Chem. Soc., 1970, Herman Mark award, 1989; Gold medal Internat. Soc. Plastics Engrs., 1972, Benjamin Franklin Soc., 1978, Kyoto prize for advanced tech., 1991. Fellow Royal Soc. (London); mem. Polish Acad. Scis. (fgn.), Soc. Polymer Sci. (Japan). Office: Univ So Calif Hydrocarbon Rsch Insti Los Angeles CA 90089

SZYBALSKI, WACLAW, molecular geneticist, educator; b. Lwów, Poland, Sept. 9, 1921; came to U.S., 1950, naturalized, 1957; s. Stefan and Michalina (Rakowska) S.; m. Elizabeth Hunter, Feb. 5, 1955; children: Barbara A. Sandor, Stefan H. BSChemE, Poly. Inst. Lwów, 1943; DSc, Poly Inst. Gdańsk, Poland, 1949; Ph.D. (hon.), U. Marie Curie, Lublin, Poland, 1980, U. Gdańsk, Poland, 1989. Asst. prof. Poly. Inst., Gdańsk, 1946-50; mem. staff Cold Spring Harbor (N.Y.) Biol. Labs., 1951-55; asst. prof. Inst. Microbiology, Rutgers U., New Brunswick, N.J., 1955-60; prof. oncology McArdle Lab., U. Wis.-Madison, 1960—; mem. recombinant DNA adv. com. (RAC) NIH, 1974-78; Wendel H. Griffith meml. lectr. St. Louis U., 1975. Author numerous papers, revs., abstracts and books in field; editor in chief: Gene; mem. editorial bd. other jours. Recipient Karl A. Forster lecture award U. Mainz, 1970, A. Jurzykowski Found. award in biology, 1977, Hilldale award in biology, 1994, Gold G.J. Mendel Hon. medal for merit in biol. scis. Acad. Scis. of Czech Republic, 1995; Cogene lectr. Int. Union Biochem., Nairobi, 1987, Cairo, 1988, Harare, Zimbabwe, 1989. Mem. AAAS, Am. Soc. Biochemists, Genetic Soc. Am., Am. Soc. Microbiologists (chmn. virology divsn. 1972-74, chmn. divsn. IV 1974-75), European Molecular Biology Orgns. (lectr. 1971, 76), Polish Soc. Microbiologists (hon.), Italian Soc. Exptl. Biology (hon.), Polish Med. Alliance (hon.), Polish Acad. Scis. (fgn. mem.). Home: 1124 Merrill Springs Rd Madison WI 53705-1317 Office: U Wis Mcardle Lab Madison WI 53706 *The profession should also be the hobby and a constant source of enjoyment and satisfaction.*

SZYMANSKI, JOYCE ANN, publicist; b. Oak Lawn, Ill., Aug. 25, 1964; d. Donald Daniel and Sylvia Ann (Grzyb) S. BA in Comm., Wash. State U., 1986. Reporter West Seattle Herald, Seattle, 1986; asst. cmty. rels. Seattle Mariners, 1980-86; intern pub. rels. Seattle Super Sonics, 1986-87; asst. media svcs. Chgo. Bulls, 1987-94; dir. pub. rels. Harlem Globetrotters, Alhambra, Calif., 1994—. Mem. Women Comm. Avocations: exercise, snow skiing, travel. Office: Harlem Globetrotters 1000 S Fremont Ave Alhambra CA 91803-1349

SZYMONIAK, ELAINE EISFELDER, state senator; b. Boscobel, Wis., May 24, 1920; d. Hugo Adolph and Pauline (Vig) Eisfelder; Casimir Donald Szymoniak, Dec. 7, 1943; children: Kathryn, Peter, John, Mary, Thomas. BS, U. Wis., 1941; MS, Iowa State U., 1977. Speech clinician Waukesha (Wis.) Pub. Sch., 1941-43, Rochester (N.Y.) Pub. Sch., 1943-44; rehab. aide U.S. Army, Chickasha, Okla., 1944-46; audiologist U. Wis., Madison, 1946-48; speech clinician Buffalo Pub. Sch., 1948-49, Sch. for Handicapped, Salina, Kans., 1951-52; speech pathologist, audiologist, counselor, resource mgr. Vocat. Rehab. State Iowa, Des Moines, 1956-85; mem. Iowa Senate, Des Moines, 1989—. Mem. Des Moines City Coun., 1978-88; bd. dirs. Nat. League Cities, Washington, 1982-84, Girl Scouts U.S., Civic Ctr., House of Mercy, Westminster House, Iowa Leadership Consortium, Coun. on Internat. Understanding, Iowa Commn. on Status of Women, Young Women's Christian Assn.; chairperson Greater Des Moines Coun. for Internat. Understanding, United Way, 1987-88, Urban Dreams. Named Woman of Achievement YWCA, 1982, Visionary Woman, Young Women's Resource Ctr. Mem. Am. Speech Lang. and Hearing Assn., Iowa Speech Lang. and Hearing Assn. (pres. 1977-78), Nat. Coun. State Legislators, Women's Polit. Caucus, Nexus (pres. 1981-82). Avocations: reading, traveling, swimming. Home: 2116 44th St Des Moines IA 50310-3011 Office: State Senate State Capitol Des Moines IA 50319

TA, TAI VAN, lawyer, researcher; b. Ninh Binh, Vietnam, Apr. 16, 1938; came to U.S., 1975; s. Duong Van and Loan thi (Pham) T.; m. Lien-Nhu Tran, Oct. 26, 1967; children: Becky, John, Khuong Virginia, Dora. LLB, U. Saigon, Vietnam, 1960; MA, U. Va., 1964, PhD, 1965; LLM, Harvard U., 1985. Bar: Mass. 1986, U.S. Dist. Ct. Mass. 1987. Prof. U. Saigon Law Sch., 1965-75, Nat. Sch. Adminstrn., 1965-75; ptnr. Tang thi Thanh Trai & Ta Van Tai, 1968-75; legal researcher Reed Smith Shaw & McClay, Pitts., 1975; rsch. assoc. Harvard U. Law Sch., Cambridge, Mass., 1975—; pvt. practice, Brookline, Mass., 1986—; rsch. scholar NYU Law Sch., N.Y.C., 1990-94; cons. Milbank Tweed Hadley & McCloy, N.Y.C., 1979, Shearman & Sterling, N.Y.C., 1979, Paul Weiss Rifkind Wharton and Garrison, N.Y.C., 1989, 90. Co-author: The Laws of Southeast Asia, 1986, The Le Code: Law in Traditional Vietnam, 1987, Investment Law in Vietnam, 1990; author: Vietnamese Tradition of Human Rights, 1988; contbr. articles to profl. jours. V.p. Vietnamese Refugees Assn., Mass., 1976-79; advisor to Vietnamese community, Mass., 1989—. Fulbright scholar 1960-62; grantee Asia Found., 1972, Ford Found., 1975-76, Aspen Inst. 1993. Avocations: piano, swimming, foreign languages. Home: 145 Naples Rd Brookline MA 02146-2548 Office: Harvard U Law Sch Pound 423 1563 Massachusetts Ave Cambridge MA 02138-2996

TAAFFE, EDWARD JAMES, geography educator; b. Chgo., Dec. 11, 1921; s. Edward James and Julia Loretta (Murphy) T.; m. Marialyce Dunne, Sept. 7, 1948; children: Maura Joan, Edward James Jr., Michael Robert, Julianne, Susan Deirdre, Brian Thomas, Karen Elizabeth, David Matthew. BS in Meteorology, NYU, 1944; BS in Journalism, U. Ill., 1945; SM in Geography, U. Chgo., 1949, PhD in Geography, 1952. Istr. U. Ill., Chgo., 1948-51; from instr. to asst. prof. econs. dept. Loyola U., Chgo., 1951-56; from asst. to assoc. prof. geography dept. Northwestern U., Evanston, Ill., 1956-63; prof. Geography dept. Ohio State U., Columbus, 1963—, chmn. geography dept., 1963-75; mem. editorial bd. cons. World Book Atlas, Chgo., 1963-69; cons. editor McGraw-Hill Pub. Co., 1969-79; adv. bd. geography coun. Ontario U., Toronto, Can., 1972-73. Author (books) Air Pass Hinterland of Chicago, 1952, The Peripheral Journey-To-Work, 1963, Geography of Transportation, 1973; editor (book) Geography, 1973. 1st lt. USAAF, 1943-46, West Europe. Mem. Assn. Am. Geographers (counselor 1966-69, v.p. 1970-71, pres. 1971-72, Honors award 1982, Edward Ullman award 1990), Nat. Coun. Geographic Edn. (master tchr. 1983), Soc. Sci. Rsch. Coun. (dir.-at-large 1970-74). Roman Catholic. Home: 4314 Olentangy Blvd Columbus OH 43214-3036 Office: Ohio State U Dept Geography 154 N Oval Mall Columbus OH 43210-1321

TAAFFE, JAMES GRIFFITH, university administrator, educator; b. Cin., Sept. 15, 1932; s. Griffith C. and Mary (Ropp) T.; m. Donna Click, June 8, 1955 (dec. 1986); children: Lauren Kathleen, Patrick Michael; m. Allison S. Blair, Nov. 7, 1987; 1 child, Michael Sean. AB, Columbia U., 1954; MA, Ind. U., 1956, PhD, 1960. Instr. English Williams Coll., Williamstown, Mass., 1959-62; asst. prof. English Vassar Coll., 1962-64; from asst. prof. to prof. English Case Western Res. U., Cleve., 1964—, chmn. advanced placement in English, 1968-73, chmn. dept.; 1969-72, asst. to pres., 1971-72, dean grad. studies, 1972-74, v.p. undergrad. and grad. studies, 1974-81, univ. v.p. acad. affairs, 1981-86, acting chair dept. theatre arts, 1989-90; v.p. for acad. affairs U. Ala., Tuscaloosa, 1990-91, provost, v.p. for acad. affairs, 1991—; mem. Joint Council, East Cleve. Sch. Dist., 1970. Co-author: A Milton Handbook, 1970; editor: Abraham Cowley, 1970; co-editor: Poems on

Poetry, 1965, Reading English Poetry, 1971. Newberry Libr. fellow; 1964; Am. Philos. Soc. fellow, 1967, 69; NEH fellow, 1971. Mem. MLA, Milton Soc., Dante Soc. Home: 9201 Enterprise Ave NE Tuscaloosa AL 35406-1005

TAAGEPERA, REIN, social science educator; b. Tartu, Estonia, Feb. 28, 1933; s. Karl and Elfriede Amalie (Erbak) T.; m. Mare Rünk, Oct. 14, 1961; children: Tiina-Kai, Salme, Jaan. B.A.Sc., U. Toronto, 1959, M.A., 1961; Ph.D. in Physics, U. Del., 1965, M.A. in Internat. Relations, 1969. Research physicist duPont Co., Wilmington, Del., 1964-70; mem. faculty U. Calif., Irvine, 1970-94; prof. social sci. U. Calif., 1978-94; dean Tartu U. Sch. of Soc. Scis., Estonia, 1992-94; prof. Tartu U. Sch. of Soc. Scis., Estonia, 1994—; mem. Estonian Constnl. Assembly, 1991-92, candidate for pres. Estonia, 1992. Co-author: (book) The Baltic States: Years of Dependence, 1940-90, 2d edit., 1993, Seats and Votes: The Effects and Determinants of Electoral Systems, 1989; author: Softening Without Liberalization in the Soviet Union: The Case of Jüri Kukk, 1984, Estonia: Return to Independence, 1993; co-editor: Problems of Mininations: Baltic Perspectives, 1973. Mem. Am. Polit. Sci. Assn., Assn. Advancement Baltic Studies (pres. 1986-88), Social Sci. History Soc., Constl. Assembly of Estonia. Home: 19 Mayapple Way Irvine CA 92715-2714 Office: U Calif Sch of Social Scis Irvine CA 92717

TAAM, RONALD EVERETT, physics and astronomy educator; b. N.Y.C., Apr. 24, 1948; s. Lawrence and Julia (Louie) T.; m. Rosa Wen Mei Yang, Oct. 19, 1974; children: Jonathan, Alexander. BS, Poly. Inst., N.Y.C., 1969; MA, Columbia U., 1971, PhD, 1973. Postdoctoral fellow U. Calif., Santa Cruz, 1973-76; vis. faculty U. Calif., Berkeley, 1976-78; asst. prof. Northwestern U., Evanston, Ill., 1978-83, assoc. prof., 1984-86, prof. physics and astronomy, 1986—. Fellow Am. Phys. Soc.; mem. Am. Astron. Soc., Royal Astron. Soc., Internat. Astron. Union. Office: Dept Physics and Astronomy Northwestern U 633 Clark St Evanston IL 60208

TABAK, RONALD JEROME, lawyer; b. Bklyn., July 23, 1949; s. Abraham S. and Frieda C. Tabak. BA, Yale U., 1971; JD, Harvard U., 1974. Bar: N.Y. 1975, U.S. Dist. Ct. (ea. and so. dists.) N.Y. 1975, U.S. Ct. Appeals (2d cir.) 1975, U.S. Dist. Ct. Appeals (11th cir.) 1983, U.S. Ct Appeals (5th cir.) 1984, U.S. Supreme Ct. 1984, U.S. Dist. Ct. (no. dist.) Calif. 1985, U.S. Ct. Appeals (9th cir.) 1985, Alaska 1988. Law clk. to hon. judge John F. Dooling Jr. U.S. Dist. Ct. (ea. dist.) N.Y., Bklyn., 1974-75; assoc. Hughes Hubbard & Reed, N.Y.C., 1975-83, spl. counsel, 1983-85; spl. counsel Skadden, Arps, Slate, Meagher & Flom, N.Y.C., 1985—; mem. exec. com. Lawyers for Legal Aid, N.Y.C., 1987—; v.p. Human Rights First, N.Y.C., 1989—. Contbr. articles to profl. jours. Chmn. N.Y. Lawyers Against the Death Penalty, N.Y.C., 1988—; vice chair Justice-PAC, N.Y.C., 1990—. Recipient Outstanding Vol. Svc. award Legal Aid Soc., 1984. Mem. ABA (chair death penalty com., sect. of individual rights and responsibilities 1988—), N.Y. State Bar Assn. (Pres.'s Pro Bono Svc. award 1985, Outstanding Contbn. to Def. Svcs. award 1990), Alaska Bar Assn., Coun. N.Y. Law Assocs. (bd. dirs. 1987-91). Avocations: jogging, baseball. Office: Skadden Arps Slate Meagher & Flom 919 3rd Ave New York NY 10022-3903

TABATZNIK, BERNARD, physician, educator; b. Mir, Poland, Jan. 8, 1927; came to U.S., 1959, naturalized, 1966; s. Max and Fay (Ginsberg) T.; m. Marjorie Turner, Jan. 8, 1956; children: Darron Mark, Keith Donald, Ilana Wendy; m. Charline Edwards Harmon, Aug. 7, 1992. B.Sc., U. Witwatersrand, South Africa, 1945; M.B., B.Ch., 1949. Intern Baragwanath Hosp., Johannesburg, South Africa, 1950-51, Hillingdon Hosp., Ashford Hosp., also research unit Canadian Red Cross Meml. Hosp., Taplow, Eng., 1951-54; med. registrar Ashford Hosp., 1954-56, Johannesburg Gen. Hosp., 1956-58; physician Baragwanath Hosp., 1958-59; fellow medicine Johns Hopkins Sch. Medicine, 1959-60, fellow cardiology, 1960-61, asst. prof. medicine, 1966—; head cardiopulmonary div. Sinai Hosp., Balt., 1961-72; asso. chief medicine Sinai Hosp., 1964-72; chief cardiology dept. North Charles Gen. Hosp., Balt., 1972; also dir. med. edn., dir. Postgrad. Inst., coordinator ambulatory services; med. dir. Nurse Practitioner-Physician Asst. Program, Ch. Hosp., Balt., 1987-90. Contbr. articles to profl. jours. Recipient Save-A-Heart Humanitarian award, 1977, Maimonides award, 1983, Shaarei Zion Humanitarian award, 1987. Fellow Royal Coll. Physicians (London); mem. South African Cardiac Soc., Am. Heart Assn., Md. Heart Assn. (chmn. health careers 1964-66), Laennec Cardiovascular Sound Group. Home: HC 3 Box 180 Monterey VA 24465 Office: 8417 Bellona Ln Baltimore MD 21208

TABELL, ANTHONY, financial analyst; b. Bklyn., Aug. 5, 1931; s. Edmund Weber and Margaret (Suydam) T.; m. Ellen Margaret Molwitz, May 23, 1953; children—Margaret Ellen, Roberta Jane, Sarah Elizabeth. Grad., St. Luke's Sch., New Canaan, Conn., 1948; A.B., Colgate U., 1952; student, N.Y. U., 1957-65. With Walston & Co. Inc., N.Y.C., 1954-70, v.p., 1961-65, sr. v.p., dir., 1965-70; assoc. Delafield, Harvey, Tabell div. Janney, Montgomery Scott, Inc., Princeton, N.J., 1970-83, v.p. parent co., 1971-83; mng. dir. Delafield, Harvey, Tabell Inc., Princeton, 1983-92; sr. v.p. U.S. Trust Co. of N.J., Princeton, 1992-93. Served with AUS, 1952-54. Mem. N.Y. Soc. Security Analysts, Market Technicians Assn. (pres. 1975-76), Nassau Club. Episcopalian. Home: 76 Crooked Tree Ln Princeton NJ 08540-2950

TABER, CAROL A., magazine publisher. AA, Green Mountain Coll., 1965. Network mgr. Media Networks, Inc., 1970-74; N.Y. advt. mgr. Ladies' Home Jour., 1974-79; assoc. pub., advt. dir. Working Woman, N.Y.C., 1979-83, pub., 1984-94; pub. Working Mother, N.Y.C., 1994—; exec. v.p., group pub. Working Woman and Working Mother mags., 1989. Office: Working Mother 230 Park Ave 7th fl New York NY 10169

TABER, EDWARD ALBERT, III, investment executive; b. Jacksonville, Fla., Aug. 25, 1943; s. Edward Albert, Jr. and Janet Gladys (Bickford) T.; m. Teresa Marie Scheidle, Nov. 13, 1982; children: Linley Marie, Laura Elizabeth, Lisa Kimberly. AB, Dartmouth Coll., 1965; MBA, Harvard Coll., 1971. V.p., treas. Fed. Home Loan Bank, Boston, 1971-73; v.p. T. Rowe Price Assocs., Inc., Balt., 1975-92, also bd. dirs.; exec. v.p. Legg Mason, Inc., 1992—. Capt. USMC, 1965-69, Vietnam. Decorated Silver Star, Purple Heart. Republican. Episcopalian.

TABER, MARGARET RUTH, electrical engineering technology educator; electrical engineer; b. St. Louis, Apr. 29, 1935; d. Wynn Orr and Margaret Ruth (Hellman) Gould Stevens; m. William James Taber, Sept. 6, 1958. B.Engring. Sci., Cleve. State U., 1958, B.E.E., 1958; M.S. in Engring., U. Akron, 1967; Ed.D, Nova U., 1976; postgrad., Western Res. U. 1959-64. Registered profl. engr., Ohio; cert. engring. technologist. Engring. trainee Ohio Crankshaft Co., Cleve., 1954-57, devel. engr., 1958-64, tng. dir. 1963-64; instr. elec.-electronic engring. tech. Cuyahoga Community Coll., Cleve., 1964-67, asst. prof., 1967-69, assoc. prof., 1969-72, prof., 1972-79, chmn. engring. tech., 1977-79; assoc. prof. elec. engring. tech. Purdue U., West Lafayette, Ind., 1979-83, prof., 1983—; lectr. Cleve. State U., 1963-64; mem. acad. adv. bd. Cleve. Inst. Electronics, 1981—, ednl. cons., author, 1979—. Author: (with Frank P. Tedeschi) Solid State Electronics, 1976, (with Eugene M. Silgalis) Electric Circuit Analysis, 1980, (with Jerry L. Casebeer) Registers, (with Kenneth Rosenow) Arithmetic Logic Units, Timing and Control, Memory Units, 1980, 6809 Architecture and Operation, 1984, Programming I: Straight Line, 1984; contbr. articles to profl. jours. Bd. dirs. West Blvd. Christian Ch., deaconess, 1974-77, elder, 1977-79; deacon Federated Ch. 1981-84, 86-89, Stephen Leader, 1988—; mem. Cancer Support Group; cochair svc. and rehab. com. Am. Cancer Soc., 1992—; vol. CanSurmount, 1993—; vol. Lafayette Reading Acad., 1992—; ednl. resource vol., vol. Sunburst Farm Rainbow Acres, Inc., Ariz., 1988—. Recipient Helen B. Schleman Gold Medallion award Purdue U. 1991, The Greater Lafayette Community Survivorship award, 1994, Outstanding Alumni award U. Akron Coll. Engring., 1994; Margaret R. Taber Microcomputer Lab. named in her honor Purdue U., 1991; NSF grantee, 1970-73, 78. Fellow Soc. Women Engrs. (counselor Purdue chpt. 1983—, Disting. Engring. Educator award 1987); mem. IEEE (sr.), Am. Bus. Women's Assn. (ednl. chmn. 1964-66), Am. Soc. Engring. Edn., Am. Tech. Edn. Assn., Tau Beta Pi (hon.), Phi Kappa Phi. Avocations: robotics; camping; housekeeping. Home: 3036 State Rd 26 W West Lafayette IN 47906-4743 Office: Purdue U Elec Engring Tech Dept Knoy Hall Tech West Lafayette IN 47907

TABER, ROBERT CLINTON, retired army officer; b. Ithaca, N.Y., Oct. 11, 1917; s. Laurence Sebring and Ethel (Lanning) T.; m. Jane Feeter, July 20, 1940 (dec. 1982); 1 child, John Robert; m. Lynn Parker, June 12, 1992. B.S., Cornell U., 1938; grad., Army War Coll., 1958. Commd. 2d lt. U.S. Army, 1940; advanced through grades to lt. gen.; comdg. gen. Joint U.S. Mil. Adv. Group Cambodia, 1963; asst. div. comdr. 82d Airborne Div., 1964-65; asst. comdt. U.S. Army Command and Gen. Staff Coll. Leavenworth, Kans., 1965-66; chief of staff U.S. Army Vietnam, 1967-68; dir. doctrine and systems Dept. Army, 1968-69; comdg. gen. 3d Inf. Div. Germany, 1970-71; prin. dep. asst. sec. def. manpower and res. affairs, 1971-74. Decorated DSM with 2 oak leaf clusters, Legion of Merit with 3 oak leaf clusters, Bronze Star, Purple Heart, Joint Commendation medal, Army Commendation medal with 2 oak leaf clusters, Air medal with 2 oak leaf clusters. Mem. U.S. Naval Acad. Sailing Sqdn. Clubs: Cruising of Am. Ocean Cruising, Internat. Aerobatic. Home: 1003 Justin Ln Apt 2042 Austin TX 78757

TABIN, JULIUS, patent lawyer, physicist; b. Chgo., Nov. 8, 1919; s. Sol and Lillian (Klingman) T.; m. Johanna Krout, Sept. 7, 1952; children: Clifford James, Geoffrey Craig. B.S., U. Chgo., 1940, Ph.D. in Physics, 1946; LL.B., Harvard U., 1949. Bar: Calif., D.C. 1949, Ill. 1950. Jr. physicist metall. lab. U. Chgo., 1943-44; physicist Los Alamos Sci. Lab. (U. Calif.), N.Mex., 1944-45, Argonne Nat. Lab., AEC, Chgo., 1946; staff mem., group supr. Inst. Nuclear Studies, Mass. Inst. Tech., 1946-49; patent examiner U.S. Patent Office, Washington, 1949-50; asso. firm Fitch, Even, Tabin & Flannery, Chgo., 1950-52; mem. firm Fich, Even, Tabin & Flannery, 1952—; lectr. U. Chgo., 1959. Mem. Am., D.C., Calif., Ill., Chgo. bar assns., Sigma Xi. Home: 162 Park Ave Glencoe IL 60022-1352 Office: 135 S La Salle St Chicago IL 60603-4105

TABLER, BRYAN G., lawyer; b. Louisville, Jan. 12, 1943; s. Norman Gardner and Sarah Marie (Grant) T.; m. Susan Y. Beidler, Dec. 28, 1968 (div. June 1987); children: Julie Elizabeth, Gillian Gardner; m. Karen Sue Strome, July 24, 1987. AB, Princeton U., 1969; JD, Yale U., 1972. Bar: Ind. 1972, U.S. Dist. Ct. (so. dist.) Ind. 1972, U.S. Dist. Ct. (no. dist.) Ind. 1976, U.S. Ct. Appeals (7th cir.) 1976, U.S. Supreme Ct. 1976. Assoc. Barnes & Thornburg, Indpls., 1972-79, ptnr., chmn. environ. law dept., 1979-94; v.p., gen. counsel, sec. IPALCO Enterprises, Inc., 1994—; sr. v.p., gen. coun., sec. Indpls. Power & Light Co., 1994—; mem. exec. com. Environ. Quality Control., Inc., Indpls., 1985—; bd. govs. Mid Am. Legal Found., Chgo., 1989—. Mem. Indpls. Mus. of Art, 1972—. 1st lt. U.S. Army, 1964-68, Vietnam. Mem. Ind. C. of C. (chmn. air com.), Indpls. C. of C. (govt. affairs coun. 1986—), ABA, Ind. Bar Assn., Bar Assn. of the 7th Cir., Indpls. Bar Assn. Avocations: trap and skeet shooting, reading. Home: 8932 Wickham Rd Indianapolis IN 46260 Office: Indpls Power & Light Co 25 Monument PO Box 1595 Indianapolis IN 46206

TABLER, NORMAN GARDNER, JR., lawyer; b. Louisville, Oct. 15, 1944; s. Norman Gardner and Marie (Grant) T.; m. Dawn Carla Martin, May 6, 1989; 1 child, Rachel Ann Ayres. BA, Princeton U., 1966; MA, Yale U., 1968; JD, Columbia U., 1971. Bar: Ind. 1971, U.S. Dist. Ct. (so. dist.) Ind. 1971. Assoc. Baker & Daniels, Indpls., 1971-77, ptnr., 1978—; adj. prof. Ind. U. Law Sch., Indpls., 1984-88; mem. antitrust task force Ind. Dept. Health, 1993-94; mem. adv. com. Ctr. for Law and Health, Ind. U., Indpls., 1987-91. Bd. dirs. Indpls. Repertory Theatre, Inc., Indpls., 1984—, Indpls. Art Ctr., 1988-93, Indpls. Pub. Broadcasting, 1992—, Indpls. 500 Festival, 1992—, Brickyard 400 Festival, 1993—, Found. of Indy Festivals, 1995—, Indy Festivals, 1995—; mem. Ind. Sec. of State's Com. on Revision of Ind. Nonprofit Corp. Act, 1989-92, Ind. Ednl. Fin. Authority, 1989-93, Ind. Recreational Devel. Commn., 1993—; mem. Medicaid task force Ind. Commn. Health Policy, 1990-92. Mem. ABA (health care com. of sect. antitrust law, forum health com., legal writing com. of sect. legal edn. and admissions to bar), Ind. Bar Assn., Indpls. Bar Assn., Am. Acad. Hosp. Attys. (com. on managed care and integrated delivery systems, com. on environ. law and OSHA, health care reform task force), Nat. Health Lawyers Assn., Princeton Alumni Assn. Ind. (pres. 1988—), Indpls. Athletic Club (bd. dirs. 1994—), Skyline Club (bd. govs. 1992—), Princeton Club N.Y., Indpls. Press Club. Avocations: reading biographies, squash. Office: Baker & Daniels 300 N Meridian St Ste 2700 Indianapolis IN 46204-1782

TABOR, BEVERLY ANN, elementary school educator; b. Dallas, Feb. 12, 1943; m. Charles W. Tabor, Aug. 22, 1964; children: Shawn, Josh. BS in Edn., U. N. Tex., 1964, MEd in Guidance, Counseling, 1970. Tchr. elem. art, guidance and counseling, supr., Tex. Elem. tchr. Ft. Davis (Tex.) Ind. Sch. Dist., 1964-65, Mesquite (Tex.) Ind. Sch. Dist., 1965-69, '71—; counselor Amarillo (Tex.) Ind. Sch. Dist., 1970-71; mem. ins. adv. com. Tchr. Retirement Sys. of Tex., Austin, 1986—; chmn. site based mgmt. com. Tosch Elem. Sch., Mesquite, 1992-94, mentor for new tchrs., student tchrs., H.S. students considering the tchg. profession. Life mem. Tosch Elem. PTA, 1985—. Named to Apple Corps, 1995. Mem. Tex. State Tchrs. Assn. (life), Mesquite Edn. Assn., Alpha Delta Kappa (past pres. Mesquite). Avocations: arts and crafts. Home: 5321 Meadowside Dr Garland TX 75043-2733 Office: Tosch Elem Sch 2424 Larchmont Dr Mesquite TX 75150-5233

TABOR, CURTIS HAROLD, JR., library director; b. Atlanta, July 3, 1936; s. Curtis Harold and Gertrude Olive (Casey) T.; m. Dorothy May Corbin, June 30, 1957; children: Timothy M., John M. AA, Fla. Coll., Temple Terrace, 1957; BA, Harding Coll., 1960; MA, Butler U., 1967; MDiv, Bapt. Missionary Assn. Theol. Sem., Jacksonville, Tex., 1974; MLS, Tex. Woman's U., 1977. Min. Ch. of Christ, Bowling Green, Ky., 1960-61, Hamilton, Ont., Can., 1961-64, Indpls., 1964-67, Nacogdoches, Tex., 1967-75, Dallas, 1976-77, Columbus, Miss., 1977-79, Tampa, Fla., 1993—; tchr. Gt. Lakes Christian Coll., Beamville, Ont., Can., 1961-64; bible chair Stephen F. Austin State U., Nacogdoches, 1967-75; prof., libr. Fla. Coll., Temple Terrace, 1979-85, libr. dir., 1985—; participated archaeol. excavations, Tell Gezer, Israel, 1969, Tell Lachish, Israel, 1980. Author: (with others) Resurrection, 1973, Biblical Authorship, 1974, The Lord of Glory, 1980. Cub master Cub Scouts Am., Nacogdoches, 1970-75; pres. Nacogdoches Baseball Assn., 1974-75. Recipient scouters key Cub Scouts Am., 1975. Mem. ALA, Fla. Libr. Assn., Tampa Bay Libr. Consortium (treas. 1986-89), Eta Beta Rho, Beta Phi Mu. Republican. Mem. Ch. of Christ. Avocation: Am. radio operator-KC4XS-Locksmith. Home: 12316 Kelly Ln Thonotosassa FL 33592-2754 Office: Fla Coll Libr 119 N Glen Arven Ave Tampa FL 33617-5578

TABOR, EDWARD, physician, researcher; b. Washington, Apr. 30, 1947; married; 4 children. BA, Harvard U., 1969; MD, Columbia U., 1973. Intern and resident Columbia-Presbyn. Med. Ctr., N.Y.C., 1973-75; rsch. investigator Bur. Biologics, Bethesda, Md., 1975-83; dir. divsn. anti-infective drug products FDA, Rockville, Md., 1983-88; assoc. dir. for biol. carcinogenesis Nat. Cancer Inst./NIH, Bethesda, 1988—. Contbr. articles to more than 200 publs. Capt. USPHS, 1975—. Achievements include research in hepatitis viruses, hepatocellular carcinoma. Office: NIH 9000 Rockville Pike Bethesda MD 20892

TABOR, HERBERT, biochemist; b. N.Y.C., Nov. 28, 1918; s. Edward and Henrietta (Tally) T.; m. Celia White, Apr. 8, 1946; children: Edward, Marilyn, Richard, Stanley. AB, Harvard U., 1937, MD, 1941. Intern Yale U. and New Haven Hosp., 1942; chief Lab. Biochem. Pharmacology Nat. Inst. Diabetes, Digestive and Kidney Disease, Bethesda, Md., 1943. Editor in chief Jour. Biol. Chemistry; contbr. articles to profl. jours. Mem. NAS, Am. Soc. Pharm. and Exptl. Therapeutics, Am. Chem. Soc., Am. Soc. for Biochemistry and Molecular Biology, Am. Acad. Arts and Scis. Office: NIH Rm 225 Bethesda MD 20892

TABOR, JOHN KAYE, retired lawyer; b. Uniontown, Pa., Apr. 19, 1921; s. Edward Otto and Marguerite B. (Kaye) T.; m. Kate Hill Williams, Dec 13, 1952; children: John Kaye, William H. BA, Yale U., 1943; BA (Henry fellow), Corpus Christi Coll., Cambridge, Eng., 1947, MA, 1950; LLB, Harvard U., 1950; DHL, Alliance Coll., 1974. Bar: N.Y. 1950, Pa. 1953, D.C. 1976. Assoc. Winthrop, Stimpson, Putnam & Roberts, N.Y.C., 1950-53; assoc. Kirkpatrick, Pomeroy, Lockhart & Johnson, Pitts., 1953-58, ptnr., 1958-63; ptnr. Kirkpatrick, Lockhart, Johnson & Hutchison, Pitts., 1970-73, Purcell & Nelson, Washington, 1976-80, Reavis & McGrath, Washington, 1980-85; adj. prof. law George Mason U., Arlington, Va., 1986-87; pvt. practice Washington, 1985-90; sec. commerce State of Pa., 1963-67, sec.

internal affairs, 1967-68, sec. labor and industry, 1968-69; chmn. Pa. Indsl. Devel. Authority, 1963-67; sec. Pa. Gen. State Authority, 1967-69; under sec. U.S. Dept. Commerce, Washington, 1973-75; chmn. housing task force and housing strike force Allegheny County Health and Welfare Assn., 1970-73. Trustee Masaryk Publs. Trust; bd. dirs. Citizens Assn. of Georgetown, 1985-89, 91; vestryman St. John's Ch., Georgetown. Lt. USNR, 1943-46, PTO. Mem. ABA (ad hoc criminal code and civil RICO coms.), Met. Club (Washington), Phi Beta Kappa. Home: 1616 34th St NW Washington DC 20007-2710

TABOR, THEODORE EMMETT, chemical company research manager; b. Great Falls, Mont., Dec. 28, 1940; s. John Edward and Alvira Lillian (Thorsen) T.; m. Jacqueline Lou Hart, Aug. 5, 1959; children: Lori, John, Lexi. BA, U. Mont., 1962; PhD, Kansas State U., 1967. Various research and devel. positions Dow Chem. Co., Midland, Mich., 1967-81, mgr. coop. research, 1981—; co. rep. to Coun. for Chem. Rsch., 1982—; co rep. Indsl. Rsch. Inst., Rsch. Dirs. Network, 1991—; Am. Chem. Soc., Co. Corp. Assocs., 1993—; program mgr. The Dow Chem. Co. Found., 1989-94. Mem. AAAS, Am. Chem. Soc., Soc. Rsch. Adminstrn., Nat. Coun. U. Rsch. Adminstrn. (assoc.), Tech. Transfer Soc. Mem. United Ch. Home: 2712 Mount Vernon Dr Midland MI 48642-6648 Office: Dow Chem Co 1801 Building Midland MI 48674

TABORN, JEANNETTE ANN, real estate investor; b. Cleve., June 9, 1926; d. Ralph Mason and Catherine MArie (Mitchell) Tyler; m. Albert Lorenzo Taborn, Oct. 4, 1947 (dec. 1994); children: Wesley Orren, Annette Loren, KAren Faye, Albert Lorenzo II, Thomas Tyler. Student, Ohio State U., 1944-47. Real estate agt. and investor Cleve., 1947-61; tech. proofreader Sass-Widder Tech Writers, Port Hueneme, Calif., 1961-66, Upjohn Co., Kalamazoo, Mich., 1966-84; mktg. rep. pvt. practice, Kalamazoo, Mich., 1984—; regional mgr. Primerica, 1994. Pres. Kalamazoo County Parent Tchr. Student Assn., 1975; active YWCA, 1981, NAACP, 1983; Kalamazoo Pub. Sch. bd., 1978; Greater Kalamazoo Arts Coun., 1979, Mich. sch. bd. vocat./Edn., Liberty uche C. of Com.; pres. Loy Norrix Trustee Fund, 1983; trustee Kalamazoo Intermediate Sch.; regional mgr. Al Williams. Recipient Cmty. Medal of Arts. Mem. So. West Mich. Alzheimer's Assn. (bd. mem.), Delta Sigma Theta (Mary McLeod Bethune award). Mem. Bahai Faith. Office: Taborn Realty 3872 Greenleaf Cir Kalamazoo MI 49008-2509

TACHA, ATHENA, sculptor, educator; b. Larissa, Greece, Apr. 23, 1936; came to U.S., 1963; MA, Nat. Acad. Fine aRts, Athens, Greece, 1959; MA in art History, Oberlin Coll., 1961; PhD, U. Paris, 1963. Curator modern art Allen Art Mus., Oberlin, Ohio, 1963-73; prof. art Oberlin Coll., 1973—. One-woman shows include Zabriskie Gallery, N.Y., 1979, 81, Max Hutchinson Gallery, N.Y., 1984, High Mus. Art, Atlanta, 1989, and many other exhibits throughout the world, 1966—; prin. pub. commns. include sculptures at Dept. Environ. Protection, Trenton, N.J., Case-Western Res. U., Cleve., U. South Fla., Ft. Myers, Low Water Dam Riverfront Pk., Tulsa; collections includes Mus. Fine Arts, Houston, Nat. Coll. Fine Arts, Washington, Cleve. Mus. Art, Allen Art Mus., Oberlin, U. Utah Art Gallery, Salt Lake City; contbr. articles to profl. jours. Recipient 1st prize May Show, Cleve. Mus. Art, 1968, 71, 79; NEA grantee, 1975. Home: 291 Forest St Oberlin OH 44074-1509

TACHA, DEANELL REECE, federal judge; b. Jan. 26, 1946. BA, U. Kans., 1968; JD, U. Mich., 1971. Spl. asst. to U.S. Sec. of Labor, Washington, 1971-72; assoc. Hogan & Hartson, Washington, 1973, Thomas J. Pitner, Concordia, Kans., 1973-74; dir. Douglas County Legal Aid Clinic, Lawrence, Kans., 1974-77; assoc. prof. law U. Kans., Lawrence, 1974-77, prof., 1977-85, assoc. dean, 1977-79, assoc. vice chancellor, 1979-81, vice chancellor, 1981-85; judge U.S. Ct. Appeals (10th cir.), Denver, 1985—. Office: US Ct Appeals 10th Cir 4830 W 15th St Ste 100 Lawrence KS 66049-3846

TACHMINDJI, ALEXANDER JOHN, systems engineering consultant; b. Athens, Greece, Feb. 16, 1928; came to U.S., 1950, naturalized, 1958; s. John and Athina (Andreades) T.; m. Diane E. Primeau, Dec. 4, 1965. B.Sc. with distinction, King's Coll., U. Durham, England, 1949; B.Sc. with honors, King's Coll., U. Durham, 1950; M.S., MIT, 1951; postgrad., U. Md., 1951-54. Head research and propeller br. David Taylor Model Basin, Washington, 1951-59; head tactical warfare group Inst. for Def. Analyses, Washington, 1959-64; asst. dir., dept. dir. sci. and tech. div. Inst. for Def. Analyses, 1964-69, dir. systems evaluation div., 1969-72; dir. tactical tech. office Def. Advanced Research Projects Agy., Washington, 1972-73; dep. dir. Def. Advanced Research Projects Agy., 1973-75; chief scientist The MITRE Corp., McLean, Va., 1975-76, v.p., 1976-79, v.p. and gen. mgr. Washington ops., 1979-84; sr. v.p. and gen. mgr. C3I divsn. The MITRE Corp., Bedford, Mass., 1984-85, sr. v.p., 1985-89; cons., 1989—. Editor: Jour. Def. Rsch., 1969-91; patentee in field. Recipient Meritorious Civilian Svc. award USN, 1956, Sec. of Def. Meritorious Civilian Svc. medal, 1975. Fellow AAAS, AIAA (pubs. com. 1990—), Royal Inst. Naval Architects; mem. Ops. Rsch. Soc. Am., N.E. Coast Inst. Engrs. and Shipbuilders, Soc. Naval Architects and Marine Engrs. (chmn. hydroelasticity panel, 1967-73, hydrodynamics com. 1967-86), Sigma Xi. Club: Cosmos (Washington).

TACKER, WILLIS ARNOLD, JR., academic administrator, medical educator, researcher; b. Tyler, Tex., May 24, 1942; s. Willis Arnold and Willie Mae (Massey) T.; m. Martha J. McClelland, Mar. 18, 1967; children: Sarah Mae, Betsy Jane, Katherine Ann. BS, Baylor U., 1964, MD, PhD, 1970. Lic. physician, Ind., Ohio, Alaska, Tex. Intern Mayo Grad. Sch. Medicine Mayo Clinic, Rochester, Minn., 1970-71; pvt. practice Prudhoe Bay, Alaska, 1971; instr. dept. physiology Baylor Coll. Medicine, Houston, 1971-73, asst. prof. dept. physiology, 1973-74; clin. prof. family medicine U. Ind. Sch. Medicine, West Lafayette, Ind., 1981—; vis. asst. prof. Biomed. Engring. Ctr., Purdue U., West Lafayette, 1974-76, assoc. dir. William A. Hillenbrand Biomed. Engring. Ctr., Purdue U., West Lafayette, 1980—, prof. Sch. Vet. Medicine, 1979—, acting dir., 1991-93; vis. rsch. fellow Sch. Aerospace Medicine, Brooks AFB, San Antonio, 1982; with Corp. Sci. and Tech., State of Ind., 1985-88; presentment, cons. in field. Author: Some Advice on Getting Grants, 1991; co-author: Electrical Defibrillation, 1980; author: (with others) Handbook of Engineering and Medicine and Biology, 1980, Implantable Sensors for Closed-Loop Prosthetic Systems, 1985, Encyclopedia of Medical Devices and Instrumentation, 1988; contbr. numerous articles to profl. jours. Chmn. bd. dirs. Assn. Advancement Med. Instrumentation Found., Arlington, Va., 1987—. Mem. Am. Heart Assn. (bd. dirs. Ind. affiliate 1975-81, med. edn. com. 1975-81, pub. health edn. com. 1975-81, chmn. ad hoc com. CPR tng. for physicians 1976-77, rsch. review com. 1988-90), Am. Physiol. Soc., Ind. State Med. Assn., Tippecanoe County Med. Soc., Assn. Advancement Med. Instrumentation (chmn. various coms., bd. dirs. 1981-84, pres. 1985-86), Am. Men and Women Sci., Alpha Epsilon Delta, Beta Beta Beta, Soc. Sigma Xi. Achievements include research in biomedical engineering, cardiovascular physiology, medical education, emergency cardiovascular care, motor evoked potentials, skeletal muscle ventricle; patents for an apparatus and method for measurement and control of blood pressure, electrode system and method for implantable defibrillators, pressure mapping system with capacitive measuring pad. Office: Purdue U 1293 A A Potter Bldg 204 West Lafayette IN 47907

TACKETT, STEPHEN DOUGLAS, education services specialist; b. Waverly, Ohio, Apr. 27, 1939; s. James Elbert and Zelma Iola (Manahan) T.; m. Magdalena Schneider, Jan. 4, 1958; children: Doris, Jenna, Jerry, Suzanne. AA, El Paso C.C., 1974; BS, SUNY, Albany, 1976; MA, Ball State U., 1979. Nat. cert. counselor; lic. profl. clin. counselor. Enlisted U.S. Army, 1955, advanced through grades to Command Sgt. Maj., 1973, retired, 1982; instr. Mt. Wachusett C.C., Gardner, Mass., 1979-81; asst. dir. Evaluation U.S. Army Sgts. Maj. Acad., Ft. Bliss, Tex., 1981-82; dir. substance abuse treatment Sun Valley Hosp., El Paso, Tex., 1982-84; from guidance counselor to ednl. svcs. officer U.S. Army Europe, Germany, 1984-86, 88-90; edn. advisor U.S. Army Sgts. Maj. Acad., Fort Bliss, 1990-92; edn. svcs. specialist Mil. Entrance Processing Sta., El Paso, 1992—; mem. adv. bd. for Counselor Edn. U. Tex., El Paso. 1983. Cubmaster Boy Scouts Am., Ft. Leonard Wood, Mo., 1970-71, com. member, Frankfurt, Germany, 1972-73, asst. scoutmaster, Kaiserslautern, Germany, 1976-79. Mem. ACA, DAV, Am. Vocat. Assn., Nat. Assn. Secondary Sch. Prins., N.Mex. sch. Counselors Assn., Tex. Assn.

Secondary Sch. Prins., Tex. Counseling Assn., Internat. Platform Assn. Office: Mil Entrance Processing Sta 700 E San Antonio Ave Fl 5 El Paso TX 79901-7020

TACKMAN, ARTHUR LESTER, newspaper publisher, management consultant; b. Chgo., July 28, 1916; s. Arthur Lester and Lucy Louise (Gutekunst) T.; m. Mary Lillian Connor, Mar. 31, 1939; children: Arthur Lester III, Laurence Connor, Alan Rhead. BA, Ohio State U., 1938, MPA, 1939. With various depts. U.S. Govt., Washington, 1938-49; staff asst. mem. pers. policy bd. Dept. Def., Washington, 1949; asst. mgr. Savannah river plant AEC, Aiken, S.C., 1950-55; asst. dir. inspection AEC, Washington, 1955-59, dir. pers., 1959-65; dir. pers. HUD, Washington, 1965-70; mgmt. cons. Glenwood, N.Mex., 1970-78; owner, operator Deep Creek Ranch, Inc., Glenwood, 1972—; publisher Catron Co. Pub. Co., Inc., Reserve, N.Mex., 1986-91. Pres. Gila Nat. Forest Permittees, Reserve, 1978-86; mem., treas. N.Mex. Pub. Lands Coun., Albuquerque, 1967-87; coun. mem. Boy Scouts Am., S.C., Washington, 1950-65. Lt. USN, 1943-46. Recipient Man Yr. Award Aiken County C. of C., 1953, Citation for Meritorious Svc. United Def. Fund, 1957. Mem. N.Mex. Press Assn. Democrat. Unitarian. Home: Deep Creek Rnch Glenwood NM 88039

TADDEI, EDWARD P., school system administrator; b. Jenkintown, Pa., Dec. 19, 1930; s. Vincent J. and Josephine (Ronciglione) T.; m. Joan Marie Heffernan, Aug. 25, 1956; children: Joanne, Edward Jr., Barbara Joan, Gerard. BS in Secondary Edn., Temple U., 1952, MEd, 1956. Math. tchr. Upper Dublin Jr./Sr. High Sch., Ft. Washington, Pa., 1954-64, chmn. math. dept., 1957-64; asst. prin. Upper Dublin Jr. High Sch., Ft. Washington, 1964-67; dir. mid. sch. Upper Dublin Sch. Dist., Ft. Washington, 1976-78, pers. asst. to supt., 1978-89, asst. supt., 1989-93, ret.; 1993; varsity basketball coach Upper Dublin High Sch., 1960-67; adj. prof. math. Montgomery County C.C., Blue Bell, Pa., 1984—. Bd. dirs. Turning Point drug and alcohol prevention program, Ambler, Pa., 1989—, We Can Say No, Jenkintown, Pa., 1989—; basketball official Pa. Interscholastic Athletic Assn., 1948-78. Cpl. U.S. Army, 1952-54. Decorated Legion of Honor. Mem. St. Alphonsus Men's Club, Oak Terr. Country Club, Rotary. Republican. Roman Catholic. Avocations: golf, travel, coaching basketball. Home: 1530 Temple Dr Maple Glen PA 19002-3318

TADDEI, GIUSEPPE, baritone; b. Genova, Italy. Appeared as Figaro in The Marriage of Figaro, Salzburg, 1948; N.Y. Met. debut as Falstaff in Falstaff, 1985; performances include Vienna Staatsoper, 1946—; numerous recs. including La Bohème, Ernani, Un Ballo in Maschera, Guillaume Tell, Rigoletto, Falstaff, Don Giovanni, Cosi Fan Tutte, others. Office: care Met Opera Lincoln Ctr New York NY 10023 Also: c/o Stattstheater Stuttgart, Oberer Schlossgarten 6, D-7000 Stuttgart 1, Germany*

TADE, GEORGE THOMAS, university dean; b. Casey, Ill., Dec. 17, 1923; s. Thomas Clement and Lena (Myers) T.; m. Wilma Jean Daily, July 7, 1946; children—Mitzi Jean Tade Mills, Terry Nan Tade Helmick. B.S., Ind. State U., 1945, M.S., 1946; Ph.D., U. Ill., 1955. Ordained to ministry Disciples of Christ Ch., 1944. Asst. prof., then assoc. prof. speech Greenville (Ill.) Coll., 1946-53, dean coll., prof. speech, 1953-59; dean coll. Chapman (Calif.) Coll., 1959-62; prof. speech, chmn. dept., chmn. div. humanities Tex. Christian U., Ft. Worth, 1962-72, acting dean Sch. Fine Arts, 1972-73, dean Sch. Fine Arts, 1973-87, dean Coll. Fine Arts and Communication, 1987-89, emeritus dean, 1989—; interim headmaster Ft. Worth Acad., 1989-90; cons. communication to pvt. and govt. agy.; coord. liberal arts study N. Central Assn. Colls., 1959. Contbr. numerous articles to profl. jours. Councilman-at-large, Greenville, Ill., 1956-59; bd. dirs. Ft. Worth Acad., Van Cliburn Internat. Piano Competition; mem. exec. bd. Arts Council, Ft. Worth and Tarrant County. Mem. Speech Communication Assn., So. Speech Assn. (exec. council 1972-75), Western Coll. Deans Assn. (sec. 1960-62), Internat. Council Fine Arts Deans, Nat. Conf. Acad. Deans (vice chmn. 1984, chmn. 1985), Tex. Council on Arts in Edn. (v.p. 1975-77, pres. 1978-80), Tex. Speech Communication Assn. (pres. 1973-74), Pi Kappa Delta, Gamma Theta Upsilon, Sigma Alpha Eta. Mem. Univ. Christian Ch. (mem. bd., trustee 1973-75). Home: 3705 Arborlawn Dr Fort Worth TX 76109-3304

TADLOCK, R. JERRY, manufacturing and logistics consultant; b. Quanah, Tex., Sept. 27, 1942; s. Warren Bates and Mary Louise (Wynn) T.; children: Jodie Elaine, Valerie Rene, Tracy Lynn. Student, Rockford (Ill.) Coll. 1960-61, Rock Valley Coll., Rockford, 1966-68, North Ctrl. Coll., Naperville, Ill., 1991—. Prodn. control mgr. Barber-Colman Co., Rockford, 1962-73, Bohn Heat Transfer, G&W, Jackson, Mich., 1973-76, G.A.T.X., Houston, 1976-77; pres., gen. mgr. Metalforms, Inc., Beaumont, Tex., 1977-79; plant mgr. Richmond Tank Car Co., Houston, 1979-82; task force mgr. The Austin Co., Santa Ana, Calif., 1982-88; v.p. ops. Austin Cons., Rosemont, Ill., 1988-92; ind. cons. Ops. Turnaround Specialty, Rolling Meadows, Ill., 1992—. Contbr. articles to mags. Advisor Jr. Achievement, Danville, Ill., 1975. Mem. Inst. Indsl. Engrs., Soc. Am. Mil. Engrs., Inst. Mgmt. Cons., Ill. State C. of C., (coms.), Rosemont (Ill.) C. of C. (coms.). Republican. Avocations: archery, sailing, bicycling, golf, reading. Home and Office: 4925 Alta Vista Ave Saint Augustine FL 32084

TAEUBER, CONRAD, demography educator, former government statistician; b. Hosmer, S.D., June 15, 1906; s. Richard Ernst and Emmy (Mussgang) T.; m. Irene Barnes, July 26, 1929 (dec. Feb. 24, 1974); children: Richard Conrad, Karl Ernst; m. Dorothy Harris, Sept. 10, 1979. A.B., U. Minn., 1927, M.A., 1929, Ph.D., 1931; student, U. Heidelberg (1929-30), Germany, U. Wis., 1930-31. Instr. U. Wis., 1930-31; asst. prof. Mt. Holyoke Coll., 1931-33; assoc. econ. analyst Fed. Emergency Relief Adminstrn., 1934-35; agrl. economist Bur. Agrl. Econ., Dept. Agr., 1935-40, sr. social scientist 1940-42, prin. social sci., acting head div. of farm population and rural welfare, 1942-43; head agrl. economist Bur. Agrl. Econ., 1943-46; statistician Food and Agrl. Orgn. of UN, 1946-51; asst. dir. Bur of Census, 1951-68, assoc. dir., 1968-73; Joseph F. Kennedy Sr. prof. demography Kennedy Inst., Georgetown U., Washington, 1973-85. Contbr. articles to social science jours.; Author: (with C.E. Lively) Rural Migration in the United States, 1939, (with Irene B. Taeuber) The Changing Population of the United States, 1958, People of the United States in the 20th Century, 1972. Recipient U. Minn. award, 1951, Exceptional Service award Dept. Commerce, 1963. Fellow Am. Statis. Assn., AAAS, Am. Sociol. Assn. (Disting. Career award for Practice of Sociology 1986); mem. Population Assn. Am. (former pres.), Inter-Am. Statis Inst. (past pres.), Rural Sociol. Soc., Internat. Statis. Inst., Sociol. Research Assn. Club: Cosmos (Washington). Home: 10 Allds St Nashua NH 03060-4716

TAFEL, EDGAR, architect; b. N.Y.C., Mar. 4, 1912; s. Samuel and Rose (Chary) T. Student, NYU, 1930-32. Sr. fellow Frank Lloyd Wright's Taliesin Fellowship, Spring Green, Wis., 1932-41; practice architecture N.Y.C., 1946—; lectr. architecture 1946—; lectr. USIS, Eng., Israel, India, Netherlands, 1972-73, New Sch. for Social Research, N.Y.C., 1974; faculty Smithsonian Instn., 1978. Author: Years with Frank Lloyd Wright, About Wright, 1993; contbr. articles to profl. jours.; Prin. works include: Protestant Chapel at Kennedy Airport, 1964, First Presbyn. Ch. Addition, 1959, De Witt Ch., all N.Y.C., Fine Arts Bldg., State U. N.Y. at Geneseo, 1967, Fulton-Montgomery Community Coll., Johnstown, N.Y., 1969, Grace Ch, White Plains, 1970, Allentown (Pa.) Art Mus. addition, 1975, Columbia-Greene Community Coll, Hudson, N.Y., 1974, Salvation Army Corps Community Centers; master plans for: State Coll. at Geneseo, York Coll., N.Y.C., Cadet Corps Hdqrs., Bronx, N.Y.; designed over 100 residences. Bd. dirs. N.Y.C. Mission Soc. Served with AUS, World War II, CBI. Recipient award of merit for Presbyn. Ch. Fifth Ave. Assn., N.Y.C., service citation State U. N.Y. Coll. at Geneseo, 1970. Fellow AIA; mem. Nat. Acad. Arts (assoc.), Taliesin Fellowship (coun.), Fallingwater (adv. com.). Home and Office: 14 E 11th St New York NY 10003-4402

TAFLOVE, ALLEN, electrical engineer, educator, researcher, consultant; b. Chgo., June 14, 1949; s. Harry and Leah (Natovich) T.; m. Sylvia Hinda Friedman, Nov. 6, 1977; children: Michael Lee, Nathan Brent. BS with highest distinction, Northwestern U., 1971, MS, 1972, PhD, 1975. Assoc. engr. IIT Rsch. Inst., Chgo., 1975-78, rsch. engr., 1978-81, sr. engr., 1981-84; assoc. prof. Northwestern U., Evanston, Ill., 1984-88, prof., 1988—; originator 6-yr. BS/PhD degree program in engring. Northwestern U., 1988—; cons. Electric Power Rsch. Inst., Palo Alto, Calif., 1985-86,

Lawrence Livermore Nat. Lab., 1985-87, Lockheed Missiles & Space Co., Sunnyvale, Calif., 1985-88, MRJ, Inc., Oakton, Va., 1987-90, U.S. Naval Rsch. Lab., Washington, 1988—, Cray Rsch., Inc., Eagan, Minn., 1991—, Village of Wilmette, Ill., 1991—, City of Wheaton, Ill., 1991-92, B.C. Hydro, Vancouver, Can., 1991-92, Commonwealth Edison, Chgo., 1992—, MIT Lincoln Lab., 1992-93. Co-author: Computational Electrodynamics: Integral Equation Approach, 1993; author: Computational Electrodynamics: The Finite-Difference Time-Domain Method, 1995; contbr. over 60 articles to profl. jours.; holder 10 patents; pioneer of finite-difference time-domain method in computational electromagnetics. Keynote speaker Salishan Conf. on High Performance Computing, 1994, IEEE ICAP '95, 1995. Recipient Adviser of Yr. award Northwestern U., 1991; Cabell fellow, 1975; rsch. grantee USAF, Electric Power Rsch. Inst., Lawrence Livermore Nat. Lab., NSF, OFfice Naval Rsch., Gen. Dynamics Corp., Northrop Corp., Lockheed Corp., Sci. Applications, Inc., Cray Rsch., Inc., Northwestern Meml. Hosp., NASA Ames Ctr., NASA Lewis Ctr., 1977—. Fellow IEEE (Best Paper award 1983), mem. AAAS, IEEE Antennas and Propagation Soc. (Disting. nat. lectr. 1990-91, chmn. tech. program com. Internat. Symposium 1992), Electromagnetics Acad., Internat. Union Radio Sci. (commn. B, D and K), N.Y. Acad. Scis., Sigma Xi, Eta Kappa Nu, Tau Beta Pi. Avocation: amateur radio. Office: Northwestern U Dept Elec Engring & Computer Sci 2145 Sheridan Rd Evanston IL 60208-0834

TAFOYA, ARTHUR N., bishop; b. Alameda, N.Mex., Mar. 2, 1933; s. Nicholas and Rosita Tafoya. Ed., St. Thomas Sem., Denver, Conception (Mo.) Sem. Ordained priest Roman Cath. Ch., 1962. Asst. pastor Holy Rosary Parish, Albuquerque, 1962-65; pastor Northern N.Mex., from 1965, San Jose Parish, Albuquerque; rector Immaculate Heart of Mary Sem., Santa Fe; ordained bishop of Pueblo Colo., 1980—. Office: 1001 N Grand Ave Pueblo CO 81003-2915*

TAFT, BOB, state official; b. Jan. 8, 1942; m. Hope Taft; 1 child, Anna. BA, Yale U., 1963; MA, Princeton U., 1967; JD, U. Cin., 1976. Pvt. practice; rep. Ohio Ho. Reps., 1976-80; commr. Hamilton County, Ohio, 1981-90; sec. of state Ohio, 1990—. Office: 30 E Broad St 14th Fl Columbus OH 43266-0418

TAFT, DAVID DAKIN, chemical executive; b. Cleve., Mar. 27, 1938; s. Kingsley A. and Louise D. T.; m. Sararose Leonard, July 8, 1961; children: Amy Rose, Kingsley Leonard, Elisabeth Kirkland. AB, Kenyon Coll., 1960; PhD in Chemistry, Mich. State U. 1963. Sr. rsch. chemist Archer-Daniels Midland, 1964-67; mgr. polymer rsch. Ashland Chem., 1967-72; dir. comml. devel. Gen. Mills Chems., 1972-74; v.p., dir. R&D, Henkel Corp., 1973-78, group v.p. consumer and splty. products, 1978-81, exec. v.p. chem. products div., 1981-82, also dir.; gen. mgr. materials div. Raychem Corp., Menlo Park, Calif., 1983-84; gen. mgr. Telecom group, 1983-86; v.p. Raychem Corp., 1984-93, v.p. manufacturing, 1986-93; COO Landec Corp., Menlo Park, Calif., 1993—. Author: Fundamentals of Powder Coatings; bd. editors Research Mgmt. Jour. Trustee Mpls. Soc. Fine Arts, 1981-83, Kenyon Coll., 1990—. Mem. Comml. Devel. Assn., Indsl. Research Inst., Am. Chem. Soc., Kenyon Alumni Assn. (pres. 1978). Republican. Presbyterian. 24 patents in field. Office: Landec Corp 3603 Haven Ave Menlo Park CA 94025

TAFT, EARL JAY, mathematics educator; b. N.Y.C., Aug. 27, 1931; s. David and Terry (Gordon) T.; m. Hessy Levinsons, Jan. 18, 1959; children: Nina, Alexander. BA, Amherst Coll., 1952; MA, Yale U., 1953, PhD, 1956. Instr. Columbia U., N.Y.C., 1956-59; asst. prof. Rutgers U., New Brunswick, N.J., 1959-62, assoc. prof., 1962-66, prof. math., 1966—. Exec. editor: Communications in Algebra, 1974—, math. series Marcel Dekker Inc., 1974—; contbr. numerous articles to profl. jours. NSF grantee. Mem. Am. Math. Soc., Math. Assn. Am., Phi Beta Kappa, Sigma Xi. Home: 48 Robert Rd Princeton NJ 08540-5333 Office: Rutgers U Dept Math New Brunswick NJ 08903

TAFT, ROBERT ANTHONY, government official, educator; b. N.Y.C., Apr. 13, 1946; s. Robert Davis and Margaret (Neracher) T.; m. Pamela Heller; children: Kristine, Mary Shea. BA in English, St. Michael's Coll. 1968; cert. in mgmt., U. Va., 1973; MBA, U. Conn., 1975. Vol. Peace Corps, The Philippines, 1968-70; policy analyst Dept. Commerce, Washington, 1976-80, mgr. export promotion servs., 1980-86; comml. min. Dept. Commerce, Australia, 1986-90, Venezuela, 1990-92; dir. western hemisphere Dept. Commerce, Washington, 1993-94, dep. asst. sec., 1994—. Internat. Bus. fellow Dept. Commerce, 1974. Office: Dept Commerce 14th & Constitution Ave NW Washington DC 20230

TAFT, SETH CHASE, retired lawyer; b. Cin., Dec. 31, 1922; s. Charles Phelps and Eleanor K. (Chase) T.; m. Frances Prindle, June 19, 1943; children: Frederick, Thomas, Cynthia, Tucker. B.A., Yale U., 1943, LL.B., 1948. Bar: Ohio 1948. Assoc. Jones, Day, Reavis & Pogue, Cleve., 1948-59, ptnr., 1959-88. Mem. Cuyahoga County (Ohio) Bd. Commrs., 1971-78, pres., 1977-78; mem. Cuyahoga County Charter Commn., 1958-59; Rep. candidate for mayor of Cleve., 1967, for gov. of Ohio, 1982; pres. Fedn. for Community Planning, Cleve., 1986-89, Cleve. Internat. Program, 1990-94; chmn. Substance Abuse Initiative Greater Cleve., 1989—. With USNR, 1943-46. Home: 6 Pepper Ridge Rd Cleveland OH 44124-4904 Office: Jones Day Reavis & Pogue 901 Lakeside Ave E Cleveland OH 44114-1190

TAFT, SHELDON ASHLEY, lawyer; b. Cleve., Mar. 2, 1937; s. Kingsley Arter and Louise Parsons (Dakin) T.; m. Rebecca Sue Rinehart, Dec. 26, 1962; children: Mariner R., Ashley A., Curtis N. BA, Amherst Coll., 1959; LLB, Harvard U., 1962. Bar: Ohio 1962. Assoc. Vorys, Sater, Seymour & Pease, Columbus, Ohio, 1965-69, 71-73, ptnr., 1974—; chief legal counsel Pub. Utilities Commn. Ohio, Columbus, 1969-71; Ohio bd. advisors Chgo. Title Ins. Co., 1967—. Rep. candidate for justice Ohio Supreme Ct., 1974; bd. advisors Coun. on Econ. Regulation, 1986—; trustee Opera Columbus 1989—, pres, 1991-93. 1st lt. USAF, 1963-65. Mem. ABA (mem. pub. utilities sect.), Ohio Bar Assn. (pres. pub. utilities com. 1984-87), Columbus Bar Assn., Ohio Camera Collectors Soc. (pres. 1985-87), Rocky Fork Hunt and Country Club, Univ. Club (Columbus), Capital Club, 41 Club. Congregationalist. Avocations: camera collecting, sailing. Home: 317 Stanbery Ave Columbus OH 43209-1468 Office: Vorys Sater Seymour & Pease PO Box 1008 52 E Gay St Columbus OH 43216-1008

TAFT, WILLIAM HOWARD, journalism educator; b. Mexico, Mo., Oct. 24, 1915; s. Raymond E. and Ferrie (Dains) T.; m. Maryle Marie Adams, Jan. 18, 1941; children: Marie, William Howard, Alice. AB, Westminster Coll., 1937; B in Journalism, U. Mo., 1938, MA, 1939; PhD, Western Res. U., 1951. Dir. pub. rels. Hiram (Ohio) Coll., 1939-40, 47-48; asst. prof. journalism Youngstown (Ohio) Coll., 1946-48; prof. Defiance (Ohio) Coll., 1948-50; assoc. prof. Memphis State Coll., 1950-56; prof. U. Mo., Columbia, 1956-81, assoc. dean grad. programs, 1980-81; yearbook cons., 1957—. Author: Let's Publish That Top-Rated Yearbook, 1961, (with others) Modern Journalism, 1962, Missouri Newspapers, 1964, Missouri Newspapers, When and Where, 1808-1962, 1964, American Journalism History, 1968, rev. edit., 1977, Newspapers as Tools for Historians, 1970, (with others) Mass Media and the National Experience, 1971, Donrey Media: A Low Profile Group, 1976, Magazines for the Eighties, 1981, Encyclopedia of 20th Century Journalists, 1986, Missouri Newspapers and the Missouri Press Association, 125 Years of Service, 1867-92, 1992; contbr. articles to profl. jours., encys. With USAAF, 1941-45. Recipient Faculty-Alumni citation U. Mo., 1979, Alumni Achievement award Westminster Coll., 1987; rsch. fellow Washington Journalism Ctr., 1967. Mem. Assn. Edn. Journalism and Mass Comm. (Presdl. award 1991), Boone County Hist. Soc. (past pres.), Kiwanis (past pres., Churchman of Yr. 1987, Kiwanian of Yr. 1993), Delta Tau Delta, Pi Delta Epsilon, Kappa Tau Alpha (nat. treas., exec. dir. 1962-91). Republican. Methodist. Home: 107 Sondra Ave Columbia MO 65202-1416

TAGATZ, GEORGE ELMO, obstetrician, gynecologist, educator; b. Milw., Sept. 21, 1935; s. George Herman and Beth Elinore (Blain) T.; m. Susan Trunnell, Oct. 28, 1967; children: Jennifer Lynn, Kirsten Susan, Kathryn Elizabeth. A.B., Oberlin Coll., 1957; M.D., U. Chgo., 1961. Diplomate Am. Bd. Obstetricians and Gynecologists, Am. Bd. Reproductive Endocrinology (examiner, bd. reproductive endocrinology 1976-79). Rotating intern Univ. Hosps. of Cleve., 1961-62, resident in internal medicine, 1962-63; resident in ob-gyn U. Iowa, 1965-68; sr. research fellow in endocrinology U. Wash. dept. obstetrics and gynecology, 1968-70; asst. prof. ob-gyn U. Minn.

Med. Sch., 1970-73, asso. prof., 1973-76, prof., 1976—, asst. prof. internal medicine, 1970-73, dir. div. reproductive endocrinology, 1974-92; mem. fertility and maternal health adv. com. FDA, USPHS, HHS, 1982-86; cons. in field, 1986-87. Ad hoc editor: Am. Jour. Ob-Gyn, Fertility and Sterility; contbr. articles to profl. publs. Served with M.C. U.S. Army, 1963-65. Mem. AMA, Minn. Hennepin County med. socs., Minn. Obstet. and Gynecol. Soc., Am. Coll. Ob-Gyn (subcom. on reproductive endocrinology 1979-82), Endocrine Soc., Am. Fertility Soc., Central Assn. Obstetricians and Gynecologists, U. Iowa Ob-Gyn Alumni Soc. Home: 5828 Long Brake Trl Minneapolis MN 55439-2622 Office: U Minn Hosps & Clinic PO Box 395 Minneapolis MN 55458

TAGER, JACK, historian, educator; b. Bklyn., Oct. 18, 1936; s. Alexander and Mildred T.; children: David, Miriam. B.A., Bklyn. Coll., 1958; M.A., U. Calif.-Berkeley, 1959; Ph.D., U. Rochester, N.Y., 1965. Asst. prof. Ohio State U., Columbus, 1964-67; prof. history U. Mass., Amherst, 1967—; dir. univ. honors program U. Mass., 1978-82. Author: The Intellectual as Urban Reformer: Brand Whitlock and the Progressive Movement, 1968, The Historical Atlas of Massachusetts, 1991, also articles; editor: Urban Vision, 1970, Massachusetts in the Gilded Age, 1985. Served with U.S. Army, 1959, 61-62. Mem. Orgn. Am. Historians, Am. Hist. Assn. Home: 6 Eaton Ct Amherst MA 01002-2828 Office: U Mass History Dept Amherst MA 01003

TAGGART, G. BRUCE, professional society administrator; b. Phila., Apr. 8, 1942; s. Robert Henry Taggart and Rachael Elizabeth Burtt. BS in Physics, Coll. William and Mary, 1964; postgrad. in engineering mechanics, U. Pa., 1964-65; PhD in Physics, Temple U., 1971. Instr. dept. physics Drexel U., Phila., 1970; asst. prof. dept. physics Va. Commonwealth U., Richmond, 1971-77, assoc. prof., 1977-82, prof., 1982-83; from mgr. materials sci. tech. to prin. staff mem., phys. scis. tech. divsn. BDM Internat., McLean, Va., 1983-90; program dir. materials theory, divsn. materials rsch. NSF, Washington, 1990—; vis. asst. prof. dept. physics Temple U., Phila., 1970-71; rsch. assoc. with theory group Oak Ridge (Tenn.) Nat. Lab., 1974; vis. prof. dept. theoretical physics Oxford (Eng.) U., 1978, Fed. U. Pernambuco, Recife, Brazil, 1980; vis. assoc. prof. dept. physics U. Ill. Urbana, 1978-79; guest worker with statis. physics group thermophysics divsn. Nat. Inst. Standards and Tech., Gaithersburg, Md., 1978-88; lectr. dept. physics and astronomy U. Md., College Park, 1989-90; vis. scientist divsn. materials rsch. on leave from BDM Internat., NSF, 1989-90; presenter in field. Referee: Phys. Rev., Physics Letters, Jour. of the Physics and Chemistry of Solids, Acad. Press, DARPA, NSF; contbr. numerous articles to profl. jours. Scholar Coll. William and Mary, 1964; Ford fellow U. Pa., 1964-65; NSF summer fellow and Univ. fellow Temple U., 1971. Mem. AAAS, Am. Phys. Soc. (condensed matter physics divsn., materials physics divsn., high polymer physics divsn.), Materials Rsch. Soc., Sigma Pi Sigma. Achievements include research in condensed matter physics, materials science and statistical mechanics. Office: Nat Sci Found Divn Materials Rsch Rm 1065 4201 Wilson Blvd Arlington VA 22230

TAGGART, GANSON POWERS, management consultant; b. Albany, N.Y., Aug. 16, 1918; s. Ralph Cone and Ruth Harriett (Townsend) T.; m. Paulett Long, June 30, 1945; children: H.Tee, Paulett Long, Cornelia V.C. B.S. in Chem. Engring., U. Mich., 1940, M.S. in Chem. Engring., 1941; postgrad., Northeastern Sch. Advanced Mgmt., 1964. Registered engr., Mass. Mng. dir. Badger N.V., The Hague, Netherlands, 1965-70; v.p. world sales Badger Co., Cambridge, Mass., 1970-71; sr. v.p., dir. Badger Co. Inc., Cambridge, 1978-82; mgmt. cons. Devel. Scis. Inc., Sandwich, Mass., 1972-77; chmn. bd. Serapis Energy Inc., Boston, 1982-85, dir.; pres. Mgmt. Systems Inc., 1984—. Contbr. articles to mags. Oil mem. Energy Facilities Siting Coun. Mass., Boston, 1979-82; mem. Planning Bd., Winchester, Mass., 1972-77, Town Meeting, 1960-64; mem. exec. com. Internat. Sch. of the Hague, 1965-70; trustee USS Constn. Mus., 1989—, treas., 1991-92; moderator Winchester Unitarian Soc., 1983-93; active Mus. Sci., Boston, Found. Global Community. Lt. (j.g.) USNR, 1944-48. Mem. AICE (chmn. Boston sect. 1956, Order of Xiphias), Soc. Chem. Industry (London), Am. Chem. Soc., World Bus. Acad., Inst. of Noetic Scis. Unitarian. Clubs: Chemists (N.Y.C.) Annisquam Yacht (Gloucester, Mass.); Downtown (Boston). Office: PO Box 516 7 Church St Winchester MA 01890-0716 *Hard work and flexibility in doing and thinking pays big dividends, as long as you are honest with yourself and others. I have always tried to see things from the other person's point of view, to give them the benefit of the doubt. I strive always to do the best I can and I do not spend a lot of time analyzing or criticizing what is wrong with others. And most important is a wonderful wife who accepts constructively life as it is dealt to you.*

TAGGART, JAMES KNOX, electric utility executive; b. Tampa, Fla., Feb. 3, 1937; s. James Warren and Marguerite (Knox) T.; 1 child, Mark Wilson. B.S.B.A. in Acctg., U. Fla. Ptnr. Bogue Compton & Vass, C.P.A.s, Tampa, Fla., 1959-66; v.p. fin. Tampa Electric Co., Tampa, Fla., 1974-80, sr. v.p. fin., 1980—; dir. Paradyne Corp., Largo, Fla., Barnett Bank of Tampa, Fla., Smalley Transp., Tampa. Mem. Ye Mystic Krewe of Gasparilla, Tampa. Republican. Methodist. Club: Tampa Yacht and Country, University, Tampa (pres. 1985-86), Merrymakers (pres. 1962-63). Lodge: Kiwanis. Home: 5510 N Himes Ave Apt 1603 Tampa FL 33614-5776 Office: TECO Energy Inc 723 Seddon Cove Way Tampa FL 33602-5702

TAGGART, THOMAS MICHAEL, lawyer; b. Sioux City, Iowa, Feb. 22, 1937; s. Palmer Robert and Lois Allette (Sedgwick) T.; m. Dolores Cecilia Baroway Renfro, Jan. 4, 1963; children: Thomas Michael Jr., Theodore Christopher; m. Mary Ann Gribben, Feb. 7, 1976. BA, Dartmouth Coll. 1959; JD, Harvard U., 1965. Bar: Ohio 1965, U.S. Dist. Ct. (so. dist.) Ohio 1967, U.S. Dist. Ct. (no. dist.) Ohio 1981. Ptnr. Vorys, Sater, Seymour & Pease, Columbus, Ohio, 1965—; lectr. Ohio Legal Ctr. Inst., Ohio Mfrs. Assn., Capital U. Ctr. for Spl. and Continuing Legal Edn. Served to capt. USMC, 1959-63. Mem. ABA, Ohio State Bar Assn. (bd. govs.), Columbus Bar Assn. (bd. govs., pres. 1989-90), Ohio Assn. Civil Trial Attys., Am. Arbitration Assn., Columbus Area C. of C., Univ. Columbus Club. Methodist. Home: 145 Stanbery Ave Columbus OH 43209-1465 Office: Vorys Sater Seymour & Pease 52 E Gay St Columbus OH 43216-1008

TAGIURI, CONSUELO KELLER, child psychiatrist, educator; b. San Francisco; d. Cornelius H. and Adela (Rios) Keller; m. Renato Tagiuri; children: Robert, Peter, John. BA, U. Calif.-Berkeley; MD, U. Calif.-San Francisco. Diplomate Am. Bd. Psychiatry and Neurology. Resident psychiatry Mass. Gen. Hosp., Boston; staff psychiatrist Children's Hosp., Boston, 1951-59; med. dir. Gifford Sch., Weston, Mass., 1965-85; chief psychiatrist Cambridge (Mass.) Guidance Ctr., 1961-84; mem. faculty dept. psychiatry Harvard Med. Sch., Cambridge, 1965—; cons. early childhood program Children's Hosp., 1985—. Contbr. articles in field to books. Fellow Am. Orth. psychiat. Assn., Mass. Med. Soc., New Eng. Council Child Psychiatry.

TAGLIABUE, PAUL JOHN, national football league commissioner; b. Jersey City, Nov. 24, 1940; s. Charles and Mary T.; m. Chandler M. Minter, Aug. 28, 1965; children: Drew, Emily. BA, Georgetown U., 1962; JD, NYU, 1965. Bar: NJ 1965, D.C. 1969. Atty. to sec. def. Dept. Def., Washington, 1966-69; assoc. Covington & Burling, Washington, 1969-74, ptnr., 1969-89; commissioner NFL, N.Y.C., 1989—. Contbr. articles to profl. jours. Mem. ABA (chmn. sports and entertainment industry com. antitrust sect. 1986), D.C. Bar Assn. Office: NFL Commr's Office 410 Park Ave New York NY 10022-4407

TAGLIAFERRI, LEE GENE, investment banker; b. Mahanoy City, Pa., Aug. 14, 1931; s. Charles and Adele (Cirilli) T.; B.S., U. Pa., 1957; M.B.A., U. Chgo., 1958; m. Maryellen Stanton, Apr. 29, 1962; children—Mark, John, Maryann. Div. comptroller Campbell Soup Co., Camden, N.J., 1958-60; securities analyst Merrill, Lynch, Pierce, Fenner & Smith, Inc., N.Y.C., 1960-62; asst. v.p. U.S. Trust Co. of N.Y., 1962-71; v.p. corporate finance div. Laidlaw & Co., Inc., N.Y.C., 1972-73; pres. Everest Corp., N.Y.C., 1973—; dir. Fairfield Communities Inc., UEC, Inc., LRA, Inc., Industrialized Bldg. Systems, Inc. Past pres. West Windsor Community Assn. Trustee Schuyler Hall, Columbia, Madison Sq. Boys Club. Served with AUS, 1953-55. K.C. Clubs: University of Pa., Princeton (N.Y.C.). Home: 77 Lillie St Princeton Junction NJ 08550-1307 Office: 1 Penn Plz New York NY 10119-0001

TAGLIAFERRO, JOHN ANTHONY, broadcasting company executive; b. Pittsfield, Mass., Apr. 26, 1944; s. James Felix and Janet Dean (Thorndike)

T.; m. Jill Mary Lanfair, June 24, 1967 (wid. Dec. 1994); children: John David, Amanda Paige. BA, Yale U., 1967. Mgr., network transmission facilities CBS, Inc., N.Y.C., 1967-75; dir. broadcast services Western Union, Upper Saddle River, N.J., 1975-77; sr. v.p. Madison Square Garden Network, N.Y.C., 1977-86; pres. Hughes TV Network, N.Y.C., 1977-87, pres., chief operating officer, 1987—; pres. IDB Broadcast Group, 1991—. Mem. NATAS, Nat. Assn. Broadcasters, Soc. Satellite Profls. (sec., bd. dirs. 1984—), Nat. Cable TV Assn. Club: Yale Golf Assn. (sec. 1983—), N.Y. Roadrunners. Office: IDB Broadcast Group 380 Madison Ave New York NY 10017-2513

TAGLIARINO, SCOTT ALAN, public relations executive; b. Albuquerque, Apr. 18, 1953; s. John Joseph and Jayne (Darnaby) T.; m. Donna Korte, Apr. 13, 1985; children: Nicholas, Leah. BA of Journalism, U. Tex., 1976; MBA, Pepperdine U., 1986. Editor UPI, Dallas, 1976-77; info. coord. Tex. Electric Svc., Ft. Worth, 1977-81; mgr. pub. affairs Valero Energy Corp., San Antonio, 1981-82; v.p. Ogilvy and Mather, Houston, 1982-84, Burson-Marsteller, L.A., 1984-85; sr. v.p. Fleishmann-Hillard, L.A., 1985-91; exec. v.p. Dewe Rogerson, N.Y.C., 1991; pres. corp. and fin. Edelman Fin. Worldwide, N.Y.C., 1991—. Mem. NIRI (pres. so. Calif. chpt. 1989-90). Avocations: reading, tennis. Office: Edelman Fin Worldwide 1500 Broadway New York NY 10036-9999

TAGLIATTINI, MAURIZIO, construction executive, historian, writer; b. Messina, Italy, June 2, 1933; came to U.S., 1959, naturalized, 1970; s. Giovanni and Vittoria (Federighi) T.; m. Marsha Croce, Nov. 4, 1973 (div. 1979). Diploma of Geometra, Inst. Tech. per Geometri, Modena, Italy. Founder, past pres. Tagliattini Marble Co., N.Y.C. Author: The Discovery of North America by European Navigators (with a critical study on the origin of Christopher Columbus), 1992. With NATO Air Force, 1957-58. Roman Catholic.

TAGUCHI, AILEEN TAKAYO, special education educator; b. Lahaina, Hawaii, Apr. 16, 1943; d. Robert Tamotsu and Asako (Michikami) Tanaka; m. Donald Earl Taguchi, Aug. 21, 1965; children: Wendy Takae, Kara Keiko, Kristie Kiyoko. BS, Ind. U., 1965; MA, Calif. Luth. U., 1989. Spl. edn. tchr., elem. tchr., coord. early childhood edn. Bandini St. Sch., L.A., 1965-77; tchr. learning disabled group L.A. Unified Sch. Dist., 1977-79, itinerant tchr. of physically handicapped, 1979-80; resource specialist tchr. 156th St. Sch., L.A., 1980-85; program specialist L.A. Unified Sch. Dist. 1985-89, coordinating specialist spl. edn., 1989-94, specialist, div. of spl. edn., 1994—. Home: 16903 Betty Ave Artesia CA 90701-3437

TAGUCHI, TADAO, electronics company executive. Pres., dir. Toshiba America, Inc., Wayne, N.J. Office: Toshiba Am Inc 1251 6th Ave # 4100 New York NY 10020-1104

TAGUCHI, YOSHITAKA, architect; b. Urawa, Japan, Feb. 12, 1933; s. Washio and Masa Taguchi; m. Yukiko Misuda, Apr. 21, 1968; children: Naeko, Morihiko. B in Architecture, Tokyo Inst. Tech., 1955. Dir. design div. Ministry Posts and Telecom., Tokyo, 1979-84; dir. gen. bldg. dept. Ministry Post and Telecommunication, Tokyo, 1984-87; prin. Taguchi Yoshitaka Architect Office, Tokyo, 1987-89; pres. Marunouchi Architects & Engrs., Tokyo, 1989—. Prin. works include Mielbarque Matsuyama, Casa de Kampo Urayasu, Fukuoka Ctrl. Post Office, Nagoya Sorting Office, Sapparo Ctrl. Post Office, Miyazaki Ctrl. Post Office. Mem. Japan Inst. Architects. Home: Naruse 5092-3-803, Machidashi, Tokyo 194, Japan Office: Yurakucho 1-8-1-419, Chiyodaku, Tokyo 100, Japan

TAGUE, BARRY ELWERT, securities trader; b. Phila., June 17, 1938; s. Edward James, Jr. and Eleanor May (Elwert) T.; m. Dorothy Elizabeth Beausang, May 14, 1960; children: Kimberly, Nancy, Barry Elwert, Edward James. Student, Bucknell U., 1956-59. Ptnr. E.J. Tague & Co., Phila., 1959-68, Barry E. Tague & Co., Phila., 1968—; exec. v.p., vice chmn. Raymond, James & Assocs., Inc., Phila., 1968-76; pres.; dir. Tague Securities Corp., Phila., 1976—; chmn. bd. The Bryn Mawr Corp., 1977-88; pres., dir. The Bryn Mawr Group, 1977-88, BancAm. Options, Inc., 1983-88; mem. investment partnerships and industry coms.; bd. govs. Phila Stock Exch., 1967-77, 90-92, vice-chmn. bd., 1963-74, chmn. bd., 1974-76, 90-92, trustee, 1973-92; bd. dirs. Options Clearing Corp., Chgo., 1987-94. Active Little League Baseball, 1961-65, 76-88, pres., 1978-86; pres. Ithan Sch. PTA, 1971-72, Radnor Twp. Sch. Authority, 1980—; bd. trustees Bucknell U., 1994—. With USMCR, 1959-65. Mem. Kappa Sigma. Republican. Episcopalian. Clubs: Waynesborough Country (Paoli, Pa.). Office: Tague Securities Corp 1900 Market St Ste 510 Philadelphia PA 19103-3512

TAGUE, CHARLES FRANCIS, retired engineering, construction and real estate development company executive; b. N.Y.C., Aug. 16, 1924; s. Charles and Isabelle (Carey) T.; m. Alicia Patricia Murtha, Aug. 6, 1949; children: Patrick, Charles, Thomas, Mary Alicia Haberman, James, Beth Anne Giuliano. B.S., Fordham U., 1952. Auditor Scovell, Wellington & Co., N.Y.C. 1951-57; comptroller Chesm. Constrn. Corp., N.Y.C., 1957-75; controller Burns and Roe, Inc., Oradell, N.J., 1975-81; fin. dir. Alfred Sanzari Enterprises, Hasbrouck Heights, N.J., 1981-84; v.p. fin. Alexander Summer Co., 1984-93; ret., 1993; domestic and fgn. tax cons. Mem. Colts Neck (N.J.) Sports Found.; active Boy Scouts Am.; pres. parish council Ch. of Presentation. Served with USNR, 1943-46, PTO, ETO, NATOUSA. Mem. Controllers Inst., Nat. Contract Mgmt. Assn., Assn. Govt. Accountants. Democrat. Roman Catholic. Address: PO Box 401 Lake Ariel PA 18436-0401

TAGUE, KARL RAYMOND, health care executive; b. Russell, Kans., Oct. 23, 1946; s. Raymond Joseph Tague and Esther (Laubhan) White; m. Linda Jean Hearn, Dec. 15, 1989; children from previous marriage: Brian, Andrea. BA in Bus. Adminstrn., Wichita State U., 1968; MA in Health Care Adminstrn., George Washington U., 1972. Adminstrn. resident St. Clair Meml. Hosp., Pitts., 1971-72; asst. hosp. dir. Kent Community Hosp., Grand Rapids, Mich., 1972-75; asst. dir. hosp. ops. Miami Valley Hosp., Dayton, Ohio, 1975-79, assoc. dir. hosp. ops., 1979-80, v.p., 1980-81, sr. v.p., 1981-82, chief operating officer, 1982-85, pres., chief exec. officer, 1985-88, bd. trustees; chief exec. officer Manatee Meml. Hosp., Bradenton, Fla., 1988—. Mem. Southwestern Ohio Health Execs. Forum, Dayton, 1975; mem. campaign cabinet United Way Dayton Area, 1986-87; bd. dirs. Manatee County United Way, 1988—, Fla. Westcoast Symphony. With AUS, 1968-70. Fellow Am. Coll. Healthcare Execs.; mem. Am. Hosp. Assn. (alternate del. serving on AMA commn. on Emergency Med. Services 1984-87), Fla. Hosp. Assn., Greater Dayton Area Hosp. Assn. (bd. dirs. 1985-88). Republican. Lutheran. Lodge: Kiwanis. Avocations: tennis, gardening, racquetball, skiing. Office: Manatee Meml Hosp 206 2nd St E Bradenton FL 34208

TAGUE, PETER WINSTON, law educator; b. Columbus, Ga., Mar. 31, 1943; s. Robert Gordon and Betty (Wade) T. AB, Harvard Coll., 1965; JD, Mich. Law Sch., 1969. Clerk Judge Walter Mansfield, N.Y.C., 1969-70; lawyer Howard Prim, San Francisco, 1970-72; pub. defender Alameda City Pub. Defenders, Oakland, Calif., 1972-76; prof. law Georgetown U. Law Ctr., Washington, 1976—. Contbr.: (book) Georgetown U Law Ctr 1507 Isherwood St NE # 1 Washington DC 20002-5564

TAI, CHEN-TO, electrical engineering educator; b. Soochow, China, Dec. 30, 1915; came to U.S., 1943; m. Chia Ming Shen, Apr. 28, 1941; children: Arthur, Bing, Julie, David, James. BSc, Tsing Hua U., Beijing, 1937; DSc, Harvard U., 1947. Rsch. fellow Harvard U., Cambridge, Mass., 1947-49; rsch. scientist Stanford Rsch. Inst., Palo Alto, Calif., 1949-54; assoc. prof. Ohio State U., Columbus, 1954-56, prof., 1960-64; prof. Tech. Inst. Electronics, Brazil, 1956-60; prof. U. Mich., Ann Arbor, 1964-86, prof. emeritus, 1986—. Author: Dyadic Green's Functions, 1971, 2d edit., 1994, Generalized Vector and Dyadic Analysis, 1991; contbr. numerous articles to profl. jours. Fellow IEEE (life, Centennial award 1985); mem. U.S. Nat. Acad. Engring. Home: 1155 Arlington Blvd Ann Arbor MI 48104-4023 Office: Univ of Mich Dept EECS Ann Arbor MI 48109

TAI, JULIA CHOW, chemistry educator; b. Shanghai, China, Dec. 15, 1935; came to U.S., 1957; d. Fei-chen and Jean-tson (Liao) Chow; m. Hung-Chao Tai, Aug. 14, 1960; children: Eve, Helen, Michael. BS in Chemistry, Nat. Taiwan U., 1957; MS in Chemistry, U. Okla., 1959; PhD in Chemistry,

U. Ill., 1963. Rsch. assoc. Wayne State U., Detroit, 1963-66, 67-68; vis. assoc. prof. Nat. Taiwan U., Taipei, Republic of China, 1968-69; asst. prof. U. Mich., Dearborn, 1969-73, assoc. prof., 1973-79, prof. chemistry, 1979—. Contbr. articles to sci. jours. Mem. Am. Chem. Soc., Quantum Chemistry Program Exch., Mich. Coll. Chemistry Tchrs. Assn. Avocations: music, reading. Office: Univ Mich Dearborn 4901 Evergreen Rd Dearborn MI 48128-1491

TAICHMAN, NORTON STANLEY, pathology educator; b. Toronto, Ont., Can., May 27, 1936; s. Louis and Frances (Kline) T.; m. Louise Sheffer, June 1, 1958; children: Russell, Susan, Darren, Leslie, Audrey. DDS, U. Toronto, 1961; Diploma in Periodontics, Harvard U., 1964; PhD, U. Toronto, 1967; MSc (hon.), U. Pa., 1972. Asst. prof. U. Toronto, 1967-69, assoc. prof., 1969-72; prof., chmn. pathology dept. sch. dental medicine U. Pa., Phila., 1972—; assoc. dean acad. affairs, 1990—. Recipient Birnberg award Columbia U., 1987, Disting. Alumnus award Harvard U., 1988. Mem. Internat. Assn. Dental Rsch. (Rsch. Basic Sci. award 1985), Am. Soc. Microbiology, Soc. for Leukocyte Biology. Office: U Pa Dept Dental Pathology 4010 Locust St Philadelphia PA 19104-6002

TAIGANIDES, E. PAUL, agricultural-environmental engineer, consultant; b. Polymylos, Macedonia, Greece, Oct. 6, 1934; s. Pavlos Theodorou and Sophia ((Elezidou) T.; m. Maro Taiganides, Dec. 25, 1961; children: Paul Anthony, Tasos E., Katerina. BS in Agri. Engring., U. Maine, 1957; MS in Soil and Water Engring., Iowa State U., 1961, D of Environ. Engring., 1963. Cert. engr., Iowa, Colo. Rsch. assoc., asst. prof. Iowa State U., Ames, 1957-65; prof. Ohio State U., Columbus, 1965-75; mgr., chief tech. adviser UN, FAO, Singapore, Singapore, 1975-84, mgr., chief engr., 1984-85; mgr., chief tech. adviser UN, FAO, Kuala Lumpur, Malaysia, 1985-87; mgr., owner EPT Cons., Columbus, 1987—; cons. EPD/Hong Kong, 1988-92, WHO, UN, Denmark, Poland, Czechoslovakia, 1972-75, Internat. Devel. Rsch. Ctr., Can., China, Asian, 1984-89, NAE, Thailand, 1990, FAO, Malaysia, Foxley & Co., Nu-Tek Foods; environ. advisor to Bertam Devel. Corp., Kuala Lumpur, Malaysia, 1992—; waste cons. to U.S. Feed Grains Coun., Taiwan, Malaysia, 1992, Venezuela, 1993; pres. Fan Engring., (US) Inc., 1991—, Red Hill Farms, Ohio, 1992—. Author: (video) Waste Resources Recycle, 1985, Pig Waste Treatment and Recycle, 1992; editor: Animal Wastes, 1977; coeditor Agricultural Wastes/ Biological Wastes, 1979; contbr. articles to profl. jours. Bd. govs., v.p. Singapore Am. Sch., Singapore, 1978-83; clergy-leity congress Greek Orthodox Ch., Houston, 1974. Recipient rsch. awards EPA, 1971-75, Water Resources Inst., 1968-73; rsch. grantee UNDP, FAO, IDRC, GTZ, Asean, 1975-88. Fellow Am. Soc. Agrl. Engrs. (chmn. deptr., A.W. Farral award 1974), Am. Assn. Environ. Engrs. (diplomate); mem. Am. Soc. Engring. Edn. (div. chmn.), Singapore Lawn Tennis Assn. (v.p. 1980-84), Am. Club (mgmt. com. 1980-85), Sigma Xi. Greek Orthodox. Avocations: tennis, classical music, folk dancing. Home and Office: 1800 Willow Forge Dr Columbus OH 43220-4414

TAISHOFF, LAWRENCE BRUCE, publishing company executive; b. Washington, Aug. 30, 1933; s. Sol Joseph and Betty (Tash) T.; m. Nancy Lee Stuckey, Sept. 17, 1962 (div. 1979); children: Robert Paul, Randall Lawrence, Jonathan Bradford. AB, Duke U., 1955. Asst. dir. Sta. WTOP-TV, Washington, 1955-56; with Broadcasting Publs., Inc., Washington, 1958—, pres., pub., 1971-91, chmn., 1991—, also dir.; adviser Cahners Consumer/Entertainment Pub. div. Cahners Pub. Co., 1991—; v.p. Jolar Corp., Washington, 1952-72, dir., 1958-72; gen. ptnr. Jolar Assocs., Washington, 1972—; chmn. bd., pres. Graphictype, Inc., 1976-86, also dir.; chmn., pres. Solar Corp., 1982-86; chmn. Broadcasting-Taishoff Found., 1982—; chmn., CEO Chuckie Broadcasting, Ardmore, Okla., 1993—, Trustco, Washington, 1988—; trustee Washington Journalism Ctr., 1982-93, Nat. Press Found., 1993—, mem. adv. bd., 1993—; bd. dirs. Nat. Press Found., 1982—, mem. exec. com., 1990-94; mem. journalism and communications exec. com. Capital Campaign for Arts and Sci., Duke U., 1984—; bd. advisors Am. Journalism Ctr., Budapest, 1991-95; bd. dir. Ardissone, Naples, Fla., 1994—; mem. White House Press Corps, 1983—; mem. Met. Washington Bd. Trade, 1970—. Co-author radio and TV segment Britannica Book of the Year, 1983—. Team capt. pubs. div. United Givers Fund drive, 1965; mem. admissions adv. com. Duke Alumni Assn., 1968-70; mem. U.S. Senate and Ho. of Reps. Periodical Press Gallery, 1958—; trustee Broadcast Pioneers Ednl. Fund Inc., 1985; judge VFW Voice of Democracy contest, 1978—; mem. bd. judges Peabody awards, 1985-91; mem. Am. U. Sch. Communications Disting. Adv. Commn., 1985—; mem. Founders Soc. Duke U., 1985—. The Mus. of TV and Radio Roundtable, 1988-89; bd. dirs. Ardissone, Naples, Fla., 1994—. With AUS, 1956-58. Mem. IEEE (sr.). Internat. Radio & TV Soc., Broadcast Pioneers (life, bd. dirs., exec. com. Broadcast Pioneers Library), Am. Sportscasters Assn. (exec. com. 1990—), White House Corrs. Assn., Nat. Press Club, Woodmont Country Club (Rockville, Md.), Bryce Resort Club (Basye, Va.), Cosmos Club (Washington), Sigma Delta Chi, Zeta Beta Tau. Jewish. Office: 1705 Desales St NW Washington DC 20036-4405

TAIT, ELAINE, restaurant critic. Restaurant critic The Phila. Inquirer, Phila., Pa. Office: The Philadelphia Inquirer 400 N Broad St Philadelphia PA 19103

TAIT, JOHN CHARLES, Canadian government official; b. Montreal, Que., Can., Dec. 4, 1945; s. John Watterson and Eleanor (Raymond) T.; m. Sonia Plourde. BA, Princeton U., 1967, U. of Oxford, Eng., 1969; BCL, McGill U., Montreal, 1972. Bar: Que. 1974. Asst. sec. Cabinet Privy Coun. Office, Can., 1978-81; asst. dep. minister Can. Dept. Indian Affairs, 1981-83; asst. dep. minister Can. Dept. Justice, 1983-86, dep. solicitor gen., 1986-88; dep. minister of justice Can. Dept. Justice, Ottawa, Que., Can., 1988-94; sr. advisor Privy Coun. Office, Ottawa, 1994-95; Shelton-Clark fellow Queen's U. Sr. fellow Can. Ctr. for Mgmt. Devel.; Rhodes scholar, Eng., 1967. Mem. Can. Bar Assn. Avocation: sports. Office: Privy Council Office, 80 Wellington St, Ottawa, ON Canada K1A 0A3

TAIT, JOHN EDWIN, insurance company executive; b. Moline, Ill., July 8, 1932; s. Edwin Marshall and Hazel Marie (Dodson) T.; m. Erlane Dorothy Dauffenbauch, July 20, 1953; children: Michael, Robert, Kathryn. LL.B., U. Ill., 1961. V.p. mortgages Penn Mut. Life Ins. Co., Phila., 1975-79, v.p. investments, 1979-80, fin v.p., 1980-81, exec. v.p., 1981-82, pres., chief operating officer, 1982-86, pres., chief exec. officer, 1987-88, chmn., chief exec. officer, 1988-95, chmn., pres., chief exec. officer, 1991-94; bd. dirs. Janney, Montgomery, Scott, Inc., Phila., Penn Mut. Life Ins. Co., Phila., Mut. Life Ins. Tax Conf., Phila.; bd. dirs. Indepro Group, Phila. Airport Adv. Com., 1988-93; mem. task force Phila. Police, 1987, tax com. Mut. Life Ins., 1988—. Bd. dirs. Drama Guild, 1982-90, Phila. Ranger Corps, Phila. Orch., 1991—, PENJERDEL, 1991—, Women's Way, 1991—; elder Bryn Mawr (Pa.) Presbyn. Ch., 1978, trustee, 1986; bd. visitors U. Ill. Coll. Law, 1979-88; trustee Penn Mut. Charitable Trust, 1982—; active Mayor's Mgmt. and Productivity Task Force, 1992—; vice chmn. Mayor's Mgmt. Implementation Partnership, 1993—. With USAF, 1952, Korea; major ANG. Mem. Am. Coun. Life Ins. (bd. dirs.), Ins. Fedn. Pa., Greater Phila. C. of C. (bd. dirs.), Greater Phila. First (bd. dirs.), Phila. Country Club, Union League Phila. Republican. Avocations: flying, tennis, golf, boating, scuba diving. Office: Penn Mut Life Ins Co Independence Sq Philadelphia PA 19106

TAIT, ROBERT ED, lawyer; b. Lima, Ohio, Sept. 3, 1946; s. Robert and Helen (Smith) T.; m. Donna G. Dome, June 22, 1968; children: Heather, Jennifer, Robert. BA, Kenyon Coll., 1968; JD, U. Mich., 1973. Bar: Ohio 1973, U.S. Dist. Ct. (so. dist.) Ohio. 1976, U.S. Dist. Ct. (no. dist.) Ohio 1976, U.S. Dist. Ct. Md. 1980, U.S. Ct. Appeals (6th cir.) 1981, U.S. Supreme Ct. 1982. Ptnr. Vorys, Sater, Seymour & Pease, Columbus, Ohio, 1973—. Staff counsel Govs. Select Com. on Prevention Indsl. Accidents, Columbus, 1977-78. Seved with U.S. Army 1969-70. Fellow Columbus Bar Found.; mem. ABA (litigation sect., products liability com.), Ohio Bar Assn. (worker's compensation com.), Columbus Bar Assn. (workers compensation professionalism coms.), Def. Rsch. Inst. (workers compensation com.), Columbus Def. Assn., Assn. Def. Trial Attys. (exec. com.). Clubs: Capital, Columbus Country. Home: 2045 Wickford Rd Columbus OH 43221-4223 Office: Vorys Sater Seymour & Pease PO Box 1008 52 E Gay St Columbus OH 43215-3161

TAJON, ENCARNACION FONTECHA (CONNIE TAJON), retired educator, association executive; b. San Narciso, Zambales, Philippines, Mar. 25,

1920; came to U.S., 1948; d. Espiridion Maggay and Gregoria (Labrador) Fontecha; m. Felix B. Tajon, Nov. 17, 1948; children: Ruth F., Edward F. Teacher's cert., Philippine Normal Coll., 1941; BEd, Far Eastern U., Manila, 1947; MEd, Seattle Pacific U., 1976. Cert. tchr., Philippines. Tchr. pub. schs. San Narciso and Manila, 1941-47; coll. educator Union Coll. Manila, 1947-48; tchr. Auburn (Wash.) Sch. Dist., 1956-58, Renton (Wash.) Sch. Dist., 1958-78; owner, operator Manila-Zambales Internat. Grill, Seattle, 1980-81, Connie's Lumpia House Internat. Restaurant, Seattle, 1981-84; founder, pres. Tajon-Fontecha, Inc., Renton, 1980—, United Friends of Filipinos in Am. Found., Renton, 1985—; founder Labrador Fontecha and Baldovi-Tajon Permanent Scholarship Fund of The Philippine Normal U., 1990; bd. mem. World Div. of the Gen. Bd. of Global Ministries of the United Meth. Ch., 1982-84, Ch. Women United Seattle Chapt.; mem. advisory bd Univ. Wash. Burke Mus., 1991—; mem. King TV Asian Am. Adv. Forum, 1993. Editor bull. Renton 1st United Meth. Ch., 1994. Bd. dirs. women's divsn. Gen. Bd. Global Ministries United Meth. Ch., 1982-84, Renton Area Youth Svcs., 1980-85, Girls' Club of Puget Sound, Ethnic Heritage Coun. of Pacific N.W., 1989—; mem. Mcpl. Arts Commn., Renton, 1980—; chair fundraising steering com. Washington State Women's Polit. Caucus, 1985-89; governing mem. nat. steering com. Nat. Women's Polit. Caucus Wash. State Coun., 1990—, mem. vol. action, 1990 Goodwill Games, Seattle, vol. worker Native Am. Urban Ministries, 1990—; adv. bd. Renton Comty. Housing Devel.; comty. adv. bd. U. Wash. Thomas Burke Meml. Mus., 1990—; mem. program com. UN, 1992—, Asian Pacific Task Force of Ch. Coun. Greater Seattle, 1993—; ch. women coord. United Ecumenical World Comty. Day Celebration, 1994; coord. of estabishment and devel. United Filipino-Am. Coll. Fund, Seattle-Renton area, 1995. Recipient spl. cert. of award Project Hope, 1976, U.S. Bicentennial Commn., 1976, UNICEF, 1977, Spirit of Liberty award Ethnic Heritage Coun. Pacific Northwest, 1991; named Parent of Yr. Filipino Community of Seattle, Inc., 1984, One of 500 Seattle Pacific U. Centennial "Alumni of a Growing Vision", 1991. Mem. NEA, Wash. State Edn. Assn. (bd. dirs. 1990-92), Am. Assn. Ret. Persons, Nat. Ret. Tchrs. Assn., Renton Ret. Tchrs. Assn., U. Wash. Alumni Assn. (life), U. Wash. Filipino Alumni Assn. (pres. Wash. state chpt. 1985-87), Renton Hist. Mus. (life), Internat. Platform Assn., United Meth. Women, Pres.'s Forum, Alpha Sigma, Delta Kappa Gamma. Democrat. Avocations: reading, bowling, crocheting, cooking, walking. Home and Office: 2033 Harrington Pl NE Renton WA 98056-2303

TAKAHASHI, JOSEPH S., neuroscientist; b. Tokyo, Dec. 16, 1951; s. Shigeharu and Hiroko (Hara) T.; m. Barbara Pillsbury Snook, June 28, 1985; children: Erika S., Matthew N. BA, Swarthmore (Pa.) Coll., 1974; PhD, U. Oreg., 1981. Pharmacology rsch. assoc. NIMH, NIGMS, Bethesda, Md., 1981-83; asst. prof. Neurobiology and Physiology Northwestern U., Evanston, Ill., 1983-87, assoc. chmn., 1988—, assoc. prof., 1987-91, prof., 1991—; acting assoc. dir. Inst. for Neuroscience Northwestern U., Evanston, 1988—; active NIMH Psychobiology and Behavior Rev. Com., 1988-92. Assoc. editor Neuron; mem. adv. bd. Jour. Rhythms, 1984—; contbr. over 80 articles to profl. jours. Grantee Britol-Myers Squibb, 1995—; recipient Alfred P. Sloan award A.P. Sloan Found., 1983-85, Searle Scholars award Chgo. Community Trust, 1985-88, Merit award NIMH, 1987, Honma Prize in Biol. Rhythms Honma Found., 1986, Presdl. Young Investigator award NSF, 1985-90. Mem. AAAS, Soc. Neurosci., Assn. for Rsch. in Vision and Ophthalmology, Soc. for Rsch. on Biol. Rhythms (mem. adv. bd. 1986—), Mammalian Genome Soc. Achievements include discovery of the expression of circadian oscillations in cells from vertebrates; and isolation of first circadian clock mutant in mice. Office: Northwestern U Neurobiology 2153 North Campus Dr Evanston IL 60208-3520

TAKAHASHI, KEIICHI, zoology educator; b. Yokkaichi, Japan, May 31, 1931; s. Shozo and Toshi (Imamura) T.; m. Mihoko Terada, Sept. 26, 1957; children: Michiko, Yoshiki. BSc, U. Tokyo, 1953, MSc, 1955, PhD, 1960. Instr. U. Tokyo, 1956-68, assoc. prof., 1968-73, prof., 1973-92, emeritus prof., 1992—; prof. Internat. Christian U., Tokyo, 1992—; rsch. fellow Bedford Coll., U. London, 1960-62; dir. Misaki Marine Biol. Sta., U. Tokyo, 1988-92. Contbr. numerous articles to profl. jours. Mem. Japanese Soc. for Comparative Physiology and Biochemistry (pres. 1990-93), Japan Soc. for Biol. Scis. in Space (v.p. 1987-92), Japan Soc. for Biol. Scis. Edn. (v.p. 1984-95), Japan Soc. for Cell Biology (councillor 1983), Zool. Soc. Japan (councillor), Japan Soc. for Ichthyology (bd. dirs.), Inst. of Biology of U.K., Sci. Coun. of Japan. Mem. Christian Ch. Avocations: music, arts. Home: 14-31 Yochomachi, Shinjuku-Ku, Tokyo 162, Japan Office: Internat Christian U Dept Biology, 3-10-2 Osawa, Mitaka, Tokyo 181, Japan

TAKAL, PETER, artist; b. Bucharest, Romania, Dec. 8, 1905; emigrated to U.S., 1939, naturalized, 1944; s. Gustave and Renee (Vassal) T.; m. Charlotte Tournerie, 1933; 1 dau., Anne; m. Susy Laytha, 1951; 1 son, Kim; m. Jean Mali Noyes, Aug. 8, 1956; 1 son, Pierre. Student schs. of Paris, France, also Berlin, Germany. One-man shows include Gallery Gurlitt, Berlin, 1932, Gallery Zak, Paris, 1933, Gallery Jeanne Castel, 1935, 37, Santa Barbara Mus. Art, 1941, Gallery Charpentier, 1939, Palazzo Strozzi, Florence, Italy, 1960, Gallery Benador, Geneva, 1977, Smithsonian Instn., 1959-60, Kestner Mus. Hanover, throughout West Germany, 1961-62, others; group exhbn. White House, 1966, 70, Whitney Mus. Art, 1955-74, Bklyn. Mus., 1954-64, Libr. Congress, 1955-62, Mus. Modern Art Print Coun. Am.; retrospective exhbns. Geneva, 1970, 90, Kresge Art Mus., 1986, Pfalzgalerie Kaiserslautern, Germany, 1993 (illus. catalogue); works in over 100 permanent collections in Berlin, Bremen, Kassel, Zurich, Geneva, Florence, Montreal, Hamburg, Copenhagen, Stockholm, Hanover, Stuttgart, Darmstadt, USIS, Cleveland Mus. Art, Hunt Bot. Libr., Pitts., Art Inst., Chgo., San Francisco Mus. Art, L.A. County Mus., Met. Mus. Art, N.Y., Pa. Acad. Fine Arts, Nat. Gallery, Washington, Libr. Congress, Victoria and Albert Mus., London, Whitney Mus. Am. Art, Mus. Modern Art, Bklyn. Mus., Phila. Mus. Art, E.B. Crocker Art Gallery, Sacramento, Dallas Mus. Fine Art, Balt. Mus. Art, John Herron Art Inst., Indpls., Musee de l'Art Moderne, Paris, others; author: portfolio drawings and poems Takal, 1945, About The Invisible Art, Theodore Lyman Wright Art Ctr., Beloit, 1965, Takal Dessins, 1930-90, Danses (portfolio drawings), 1992, others; contbr. illustrations to mags., U.S., Paris, Stockholm; catalogue raisonne of prints by Peter Takal published by Kresge Art Mus., 1986. Ford Found. grantee to Tamarind Worshop, 1963; Ford Found. grant artist-in-residence in museums Beloit (Wis.) Coll., 1965; recipient award for drawing biennnialexhbn. Bklyn. Mus., 1954, 8th ann. Knickerbocker art exhbn. Riverside Mus., N.Y., 1955, Print Club award Ball State Tchrs. Coll., 1958, drawing prize Providence Print Club, 1963.

TAKANO, MASAHARU, physical chemist; b. Tainan, Taiwan, Jan. 20, 1935; s. Shuzo and Misao (Rengakuji) T.; m. Hiroko Takenoshita, Aug. 28, 1965; children: Kentaro, Jojiro, Miwako. B.S., Hokkaido U., 1957; M.S., U. Tokyo, 1959, D.Sc., 1963. Postdoctoral fellow McGill U, Montreal, 1963-67; with Monsanto Co. St. Louis, 1967-90; pres. Takano Internat., St. Louis, 1991—; cons. on bus., travel, tech. Sr. contbr. articles on phys. chemistry to profl. jours. Fellow Am. Inst. Chemists; mem. AAAS, Am. Chem. Soc., Am. Phys. Sic., Japan Am. Soc., Japanese Am. Citizens League, Japan Soc., World Affairs Coun., Japan Soc., Mo. Sheriff Assn. (hon.). Buddhist. Home: 13146 Roundstone Ct Saint Louis MO 63146-3642 Office: 425 N New Ballas Rd Ste 280 Saint Louis MO 63141-6848 *This country has everything which other countries envy: a vast land, rich environment, natural resources and opportunities. We can work for all human beings if we want, and there are a million things to do.*

TAKASAKI, ETSUJI, urology educator; b. Tokyo, Apr. 24, 1929; s. Kuranosuke and Fumi Takasaki; m. Sachiko Shinkai, Nov. 1, 1960; children: Satoshi, Masumi, Hiromi. MD, U. Tokyo, 1955, D. Med. Sci., 1960. Instr. urology U. Tokyo, 1960-62, asst. prof., 1962-67; chief. urol. svc. Musashino Red Cross Hosp., Tokyo, 1967-69, Komagome Met. Hosp., Tokyo, 1969-74; prof. urology Dokkyo U. Sch. Medicine, Tochigi, Japan, 1974-95; lectr. U. Tokyo, 1969-74. Author: Urolithiasis, 1978; contbr. articles to Japanese Jour. Urology, 1960, Jour. Urology, 1986, Urologia Internat., 1989. Mem. Japanese Urol. Assn. (bd. dirs. 1963—), Japanese Soc. Andrology (bd. dirs. 1982—), Japanese Soc. Endourology and ESWL (bd. dirs. 1988—), Internat. Soc. Urology (Paris). Avocation: Kendo (Japanese fencing). Office: Dokkyo U Sch Med Shimotsuga gun, Mibu machi 880, Tochigi Japan 321 02

TAKASUGI, NAO, state official, business developer; b. Oxnard, Calif., Apr. 5, 1922; s. Shingoro and Yasuye (Hayashi) T.; m. Judith Shigeko Mayeda,

Mar. 23, 1952; children—Scott, Russell, Ronald, Tricia, Lea. B.S., Temple U., 1945; M.B.A., U. Pa. Wharton Sch., 1946. Mem. city council City of Oxnard, Calif., 1976-82, mayor, 1982-92; mem. Calif. State Assembly, 1992—; bus. developer, cons. Mem. Oxnard Planning Commn., 1974-76; pres. World Trade Ctr. Assn., Oxnard; apptd. (by Calif. gov.) chmn. UN Anniversary; assemblyman Calif. State Assembly 37th Dist. Decorated Order of Sacred Treasure with Gold Rayette medal Japanese Gov., 1992. Mem. Ventura County Japanese Am. Citizens League, World Trade Ctr. Assn. (pres. Oxnard chpt.), U.S. Conf. Mayors (mem. nat. adv. bd.), Nat. League of Cities (nat. bd. dirs.), Ventura County Transp. Com., League Calif. Cities (bd. dirs.), South Coast Area Bd. Dirs. (chmn. transp. com.), Assn. Ventura County Cities, Oxnard Housing Authority (chmn.), Oxnard Redevel. Agy. (chmn.), Optimists Club (Oxnard). Republican. Methodist. Home: 1221 El Portal Way Oxnard CA 93035-2511 Office: Rm 5158 State Capitol Sacramento CA 95814 also: 221 Daily Dr Ste 7 Camarillo CA 93010-5833

TAKASUGI, ROBERT MITSUHIRO, federal judge; b. Tacoma, Sept. 12, 1930; s. Hidesaburo and Kayo (Otsuki) T.; m. Dorothy O. Takasugi; children: Jon Robert, Lesli Mari. BS, UCLA, Los Angeles, 1953; LLB, JD, U. So. Calif., 1959. Bar: Calif. bar 1960. Practiced law Los Angeles, 1960-73; judge East Los Angeles Municipal Ct., 1973-75, adminstrv. judge, 1974, presiding judge, 1975; judge Superior Ct., County of Los Angeles, 1975-76; U.S. dist. judge U.S. Dist. Ct. (cen. dist.) Calif., 1976—; nat. legal counsel Japanese Am. Citizens League; guest lectr. law seminars Harvard U. Law Sch. Careers Symposium; commencement spkr.; mem. Legion Lex U. So. Calif. Law Ctr.; chmn. Pub. Defs. Indigent Def. & Psychiat. Panel Com.; mem. Affirmative Action Com., Habeas Corpus-Death Penalty Com., Exec. Com., Jury Com., Settlement Rule Com., Adv. Com. on Codes of Conduct of the Jud. Conf. of the U.S., 1988-92, Code of Conduct of Judges. Mem. editorial bd. U. So. Calif. Law Rev., 1959; contbr. articles to profl. jours. Mem. Calif. adv. com. Western Regional Office, U.S. Commn. on Civil Rights; chmn. blue ribbon com. for selection of chancellor L.A. C.C. With U.S. Army, 1953-55. Recipient U.S. Mil. Man of Yr. award for Far East Theater U.S. Army, 1954, Jud. Excellence award Criminal Cts. Bar Assn., cert. of merit Japanese-Am. Bar Assn., Disting. Svc. award Asian Pacific Ctr. and Pacific Clinics, 1994, others; named Judge of Yr. Century City Bar Assn.; Harry J. Bauer scholar, 1959. Mem. U. So. Calif. Law Alumni (dir.). Office: US Dist Ct 312 N Spring St Los Angeles CA 90012-4701

TAKAYAMA, AKIRA, economics educator; b. Yokohama, Japan; came to U.S., 1957; s. Tsunaki and Shoko (Takeuchi) T.; m. Machiko Onabe, Jan. 31, 1970. B.A., Internat. Christian U., Tokyo, 1957; M.A., U. Rochester, 1960, Ph.D., 1962; Ph.D., Hitotsubashi U., Tokyo, 1964. Instr., then asst. prof. econs. Internat. Christian U., Tokyo, Japan, 1962-64; fellow in econ. stats. U. Manchester, Eng., 1964-65; vis. assoc. prof. econs. U. Minn.-Mpls., 1965-66; assoc. prof. econs. Purdue U.-West Lafayette, 1967-68, prof. econs., 1968-80; prof. econs. Tex. A&M U., College Station, 1978-82, Kyoto U., Japan, 1982-85; Vandeveer prof. econs. So. Ill. U., Carbondale, 1983—; vis. prof. econs. U. Rochester, 1969-70, Australian Nat. U., 1968, 77, U. Hawaii, 1971-72, U. Tokyo, 1974-75, Doshisha U., Japan, 1989, Tulane U., New Orleans, 1991, Internat. Christian U., Japan, 1993, 94; J. Fish Smith profl. Brigham Young U., Provo, Utah, 1976. Author: Mathematical Economics, 1974, 2d edit. 1985, International Trade, 1972, Analytical Methods in Economics, 1993; co-editor: Economic Development in East and Southeast Asia, 1990, Trade, Policy, and International Adjustments, 1991; contbr. articles to profl. jours. Mem. Am. Econs. Assn., Econometric Soc., Japan Econ. Research Ctr., Japan Assn. Econs. and Econometrics. Office: So Ill Univ Dept Econs Carbondale IL 62901

TAKEI, TOSHIHISA, otolaryngologist; b. L.A., Apr. 19, 1931; s. Taketomi and Mitsue (Hagihara) T.; m. Emiko Kubota, Jan. 25, 1955; children: H. Thomas, T. Robert. BA, UCLA, 1954; MD, Boston U., 1962. Diplomate, Am. Bd. Otolaryngology. Intern L.A. County Harbor Gen. Hosp., 1962-63; resident in otolaryngology L.A. County/U. So. Calif. Med. Ctr., 1963-67; staff physician Covina (Calif.) Ear, Nose & Throat Med. Group, 1968—; asst. prof. Sch. Medicine, U. So. Calif., L.A., 1968—. 1st lt. U.S. Army, 1955-56, Korea. Fellow Am. Acad. Otolaryngology, Royal Soc. Medicine. Republican. Buddhist. Office: Covina ENT Med Group Inc 236 W College St Covina CA 91723-1902

TAKEMOTO, KIICHI, chemistry educator; b. Osaka, Japan, Feb. 14, 1930; s. Kenzo and Hatsue (Asakura) T.; m. Etsuko Tamaki, Apr. 26, 1959; children: Tatsuo, Mariko. B of Engring., Osaka U., Japan, 1953, DEng, 1962. Asst. fellow Osaka City U., Japan, 1953-59, lectr., 1959-64, assoc. prof., 1964-69; prof. Osaka U., Japan, 1969-93, Ryukoku U., 1993—. Author: Functional Polymers, 1987. Recipient Award for Chem. Soc., 1989, Award for Polymer Sci. Achievements, 1991. Mem. Am. Chem. Soc., Chem. Soc. Japan, Soc. Polymer Sci. Japan. Avocations: travel, railways, stamp collections. Home: Sakae 4-10-26, Takatsuki Osaka 569, Japan Office: Rykoku U, Sci Technol Faculty, Seta Otsu Shiga 520-21, Japan

TAKEUCHI, HIROSHI, investment company executive, consultant; b. Okayama, Japan, Apr. 23, 1938; s. Shoichi and Shigeko (Ueda) T.; m. Nobuko Hayashi, May 10, 1967; 1 child, Tsuruichi. Degree in lit., Osaka U., 1962, degree in lang., 1962. Chief exports Mitsui Engr. & Shipbuilding Co., Tokyo, 1965-69, mgr. off-shore bus. devel., 1973-81; spl. rep. Mitsui Engring. & Shipbuilding Co., London, 1969-73; gen. mgr., exec. v.p. Mitsui Zosen (U.S.A.), Inc., Houston, 1981-90; exec. v.p. dir. Global Tech. Inc., Houston, 1990-93, Arlington, Va., 1993—; mktg. cons. Iben, Albuquerque, N.M., 1993—, Takt Internat., N.J., 1993—. Avocations: swimming, tennis, reading, diving. Office: Global Tech Inc 4301 N Fairfax Dr Ste 850 Arlington VA 22203

TAKUMI, ROY MITSUO, state representative; b. Honolulu, Oct. 13, 1952; m. Wanda A. Kutaka; children: Aisha, Jaron. BA, Friends World Coll., 1991; MPA, U. Hawaii, 1993. Cmty. organizer Osaka, Japan, 1977-83; program dir. Am. Friends Svc. Com., Honolulu, 1984-90; polit. coord. Hawaii State AFL-CIO, Honolulu, 1990-92; rep. Ho. of Reps., Honolulu, 1992—. Office: State Ho of Reps State Capitol Honolulu HI 96813

TALALAY, PAUL, pharmacologist, physician; b. Berlin, Mar. 31, 1923; came to U.S., 1940, naturalized, 1946; s. Joseph Anton and Sophie (Brosterman) T.; m. Pamela Judith Samuels, Jan. 11, 1953; children—Antony, Susan, Rachel, Sarah. S.B., Mass. Inst. Tech., 1944; student, U. Chgo. Sch. Medicine, 1944-46; M.D., Yale U., 1948; D.Sc. (hon.), Acadia U., 1974. House officer, asst. resident surg. services Mass. Gen. Hosp., Boston, 1948-50; asst. prof. surgery U. Chgo., 1950-51, asst. prof. biochemistry, 1955-57, asso. prof., then prof., 1957-63; asst. prof. Ben May Lab. Cancer Research, 1951-57, asso. prof., then prof., 1957-63; John Jacob Abel prof., dir. dept., pharmacology and exptl. therapeutics Johns Hopkins Sch. Medicine, 1963-75, John Jacob Abel Distinguished Service prof., 1975—; Am. Cancer Soc. prof., 1958-63, 77—; sr. asst. surgeon USPHS, 1951-53; vis. prof. Guy's Hosp. Med. Sch., London, 1970, 74-76; nat. adv. cancer council USPHS, 1967-71; vis. com. dept. biology Mass. Inst. Tech., 1964-67; bd. sci. advisers Jane Coffin Childs Meml. Fund for Cancer Research, 1971-81; bd. sci. consultants Sloan-Kettering Inst. Cancer Research, 1971-81. Hon. editorial adv. bd.: Biochem. Pharmacology, 1963-68; editorial bd.: Jour. Biol. Chemistry, 1961-66, Molecular Pharmacology, 1965-68, 71-80; editor-in-chief, 1968-71. Recipient Premio Internationale La Madonnina Milan, 1978; Med. Alumni Disting. Service award U. Chgo., 1978; Am. Cancer Soc. scholar, 1954-58; Guggenheim Meml. fellow, 1973-74. Fellow Am. Acad. Arts and Scis.; mem. AAAS (Theobald Smith award med. scis. 1957), Nat. Acad. Scis., Am. Philosophical Soc., Am. Soc. Biol. Chemists, Am. Soc. Clin. Investigation, Biochem. Soc., Am. Chem. Soc., Am. Soc. Pharm. and Exptl. Therapeutics, Phi Beta Kappa, Sigma Xi, Alpha Omega Alpha. Home: 5512 Boxhill Ln Baltimore MD 21210-2039 Office: Johns Hopkins U Sch Medicine Baltimore MD 21205

TALBERT, BOB, newspaper columnist. Columnist Detroit Free Press. Office: Detroit Free Press Inc 321 W Lafayette Blvd Detroit MI 48226

TALBERT, JAMES LEWIS, pediatric surgeon, educator; b. Cassville, Mo., Sept. 26, 1931; s. William David and Frances (Lewis) T.; m. Alice Quintavell, July 25, 1958; children: William David, Alison Whitney. B.A., Vanderbilt U., 1953, M.D., 1956. Diplomate: Am. Bd. Surgery (with cert. of

spl. competence in pediatric surgery), Am. Bd. Thoracic Surgery. Intern, then resident in surgery Johns Hopkins Hosp., 1956-64, resident in thoracic surgery, 1964-65, Harvey Cushing fellow, 1958-59; instr. surgery, Garrett scholar pediatric surgery Johns Hopkins U. Med. Sch., 1965-66, asst. prof., 1966-67; mem. faculty U. Fla. Med. Sch., Gainesville, 1967—; prof. pediatric surgery, chmn. div., chief children's surgery U. Fla. Med. Sch., 1970—; mem. affiliated faculty VA Hosp., Gainesville; med. dir. Fla. Regional Med. Program for Diagnosis and Treatment Cancer in Children, 1970-73, N. Referral Center Children's Med. Service Program Fla., 1970-80; chmn. Alachua County Emergency Med. Advisory Svc. Council, 1973-75; chmn. emergency med. services com. N. Central Fla. Health Planning Council, 1972-73; mem. Fla. Emergency Med. Services Adv. Council, 1973-75, 76-79. Author numerous articles in field; contbr. 16 chpts. to books. Served with USPHS, 1960-62. Recipient Founders medal, Roche award Vanderbilt U. Med. Sch., 1956. Fellow ACS (chmn. Fla. trauma com. 1969-77, gov.-at-large 1979-85, sec. bd. govs. 1982-85, rep. to Coun. of Med. Spl. Socs. 1988-89), Am. Acad. Pediatrics (exec. com. sect. oncology and hematology 1978-85); mem. Am. Pediatric Surg. Assn. (founding mem., chmn. trauma com. 1976-79), Pediatric Oncology Group (chmn. group retreat 1980), Am. Fedn. Clin. Research, Assn. Acad. Surgery, Soc. U. Surgeons, Univ. Assn., Soc. Pediatric Research, Am. Coll. Emergency Physicians, Am. Surg. Assn., Halsted Soc., Am. Assn. Surgery Trauma, Am. Burn Assn., Am. Pediatric Soc., Brit. Assn. Pediatric Surgeons, Soc. Internat. Chirurgie, So. Surg. Assn., Fla. Med. Assn., Fla. Heart Assn. (chmn. cardio-pulmonary resuscitation com. 1972-76), Fla. Assn. Pediatric Surgeons (pres. 1976-78), Fla. Assn. Pediatric Tumor Programs (pres. 1973—), Alachua County Med. Soc. (chmn. emergency med. services adv. com. 1973-75), Phi Beta Kappa, Alpha Omega Alpha, Phi Eta Sigma. Office: J Hillis Miller Health Ctr PO Box 100286 Gainesville FL 32610-0286

TALBERT, LUTHER MARCUS, physician; b. Abington, Va., Dec. 30, 1926; s. Marcus Aurelius and Mary Elizabeth (Thompson) T.; m. Annie Brown Edmondson, Dec. 24, 1949; children: John T., Luther E., Martha C. B.A., Emory and Henry Coll., 1949, D.Sc. (hon.), 1980; M.D., U. Va., 1953. Med. intern U. Va., 1953-54, resident in Ob-Gyn, 1954-58, fellow in reproductive physiology, 1956-57; mem. faculty U. N.C. Med. Sch., Chapel Hill, 1958-92; prof. Ob-Gyn. U. N.C. Med. Sch., 1975-92, dir. div. reproductive endocrinology, 1975-84; dir. clin. svcs. N.C. Ctr. for Reproductive Medicine, Cary, N.C. Served with USN, 1944-46. Mem. Assn. Profs. Ob-Gyn (pres. 1979-80), Soc. Gynecologic Investigation, Am. Gynecol. and Obstet. Soc., AAAS. Republican. Baptist. Home: 101 Stoneridge Dr Chapel Hill NC 27514-9733 Office: NC Ctr for Reproductive Medicine 204/60 Asheville Dr Cary NC 27514-4216

TALBERT, MELVIN GEORGE, bishop; b. Clinton, La., June 14, 1934; s. Nettles and Florence (George) T.; m. Ethlelou Douglas, June 3, 1961; 1 child, Evangeline. BA, So. U., 1959; MDiv, Interdenominational Theol. Ctr., Gammon Theol. Sem., Atlanta, 1962; DD hon., Huston Tillotson Coll., Austin, 1972; LLD (hon.), U. Puget Sound, Tacoma, 1987. Ordained deacon, Meth. Ch., 1960, elder, 1962, elected to episcopacy, United Meth. Ch., 1980. Pastor Boyd Chapel, Jefferson City, Tenn., 1960-61, Rising Sun, Sunrise, Tenn., 1960-61, St. John's Ch., L.A., 1961-62, Wesley Ch., L.A., 1962-64, Hamilton Ch., L.A., 1964-67; mem. staff So. Calif.-Ariz. Conf. United Meth. Ch., L.A., 1967-68; dist. supr. Long Beach dist. So. Calif.-Ariz. Conf. United Meth. Ch., 1968-73; gen. sec. Gen. Bd. Discipleship, Nashville, 1973-80; resident bishop Seattle area Pacific N.W. conf. United Meth. Ch., 1980-88, resident bishop San Francisco area Calif.-Nev. Conf., 1988—; sec. coun. bishops, 1988—; mem. exec. com. World Meth. Coun., 1976-81, 84—; mem. governing bd. Nat. Coun. Chs., 1980—; v.p., chmn. funding com. Gen. Commn. on Religion and Race, 1980-84, pres., 1984-88; chmn. Missional Priority Coordinating com. Gen. Coun. Ministries, 1980-84; mem. Gen. Commn. on Christian Unity and Interreligious Concerns, 1984—; African Ch. Growth and Devel. Com., 1981-84. mem. steering com. Student Non-Violent Coordinating com. Atlanta U. Ctr., 1960-61; trustee Gammon Theol. Sem., Atlanta, 1976—, U. Puget Sound, Tacoma, 1980-88 ; Sch. Theology at Claremont, Calif., 1981-88, Pacific Sch. Religion, 1988—; bd. dirs. Glide Found., 1988—. Recipient award of merit for outstanding svc. in Christian edn. Gen. Bd. Edn., 1971; recipient Spl. achievement award Nat. Assn. Black Bus. Women, 1971; Nat. Meth. scholar, 1960; Crusade scholar, 1961. Mem. Theta Phi. Democrat. Home: 13816 Campus Dr Oakland CA 94605-3830

TALBERT, ROY, JR., history educator; b. Cheraw, S.C., Aug. 1, 1943; s. Roy and Betty Jean (Harper) T.; BA (Furman Scholar), Furman U., 1965; MA (NDEA fellow), Vanderbilt U., 1967, PhD, 1971; grad. Inst. Ednl. Mgmt., Harvard U., 1981; grad. Computer Literacy Inst., Pepperdine U., 1983; Jane Boyd Holbert, Oct. 24, 1986; children: Matthew, Rebecca Anne, Drew, Elizabeth. Sr. teaching fellow Vanderbilt U., Nashville, 1967-70; asst. prof. history Ferrum (Va.) Coll., 1974-76, dir. curriculum and programs, 1976-79; vice chancellor for acad. affairs Coastal Carolina U., Conway, 1979-84, assoc. prof. history, 1979-89, prof., chmn. 1991—; producer, host The Public Eye, TV Show, 1978-79; host Waccamaw Mag., TV show, 1983; project dir. numerous film, TV and pub. programming projects for community and civic groups, 1975-79. Served to capt. U.S. Army, 1970-72. Mem. So. Hist. Assn., Orgn. Am. Historians. Methodist. Author: FDR's Utopian: Arthur Morgan of the TVA, 1987, Negative Intelligence: The Army and the American Left, 1917-41, 1991, No Greater Legacy: The Centennial History of Willcox, McLeod, Buyck and Williams, 1995. Home: 106 Wofford Ln Conway SC 29526-8823 Office: Coastal Carolina Univ Conway SC 29526

TALBOT, ARDITH ANN, editor; b. Superior, Nebr., Mar. 11, 1933; d. Charles Howard and Dollie Eunice (Ryan) Snell; m. Richard Charles Talbot, Oct. 17, 1954; children: Richard Daryl, Robert Charles. BA in Edn., U. Nebr., 1956. Recorded Friends min., 1993. Tchr. high sch. Pub. Schs. Juniata, Nebr., 1957-59, Hudson, Iowa, 1962-68, New Providence, Iowa, 1968-71; owner Retail Bookstore, Sutherland, Iowa, 1971-72, Marshalltown, Iowa, 1972-74, Mason City, Iowa, 1974-89; mgr. book store Friends United Mktg., Richmond, Ind., 1986-89; mgr., editor Friends United Press, Richmond, Ind., 1989—. Republican. Avocations: antiques, public speaking. Home: PO Box 343 Lynn IN 47355-0343 Office: Friends United Meeting 101 Quaker Hill Dr Richmond IN 47374-1926

TALBOT, BERNARD, government medical research facility official, physician; b. N.Y.C., Oct. 6, 1937; s. Harry and Gertrude (Salkin) T.; m. Ane Katrine Larsen, June 2, 1963; children: Akia, Kamilla. B.A., Columbia U., 1958, M.D., 1962; Ph.D, MIT, 1967. NIH postdoctoral fellow MIT, 1962-69; NSF postdoctoral fellow U. Rome, 1969-70; commd. USPHS, 1975—, advanced through grades to med. dir.; med. officer Nat. Cancer Inst., Bethesda, Md., 1971-75; spl. asst. intramural affairs NIH, Bethesda, 1975-78; spl. asst. to dir. NIH, 1978-81; dep. dir. Nat. Inst. Allergy and Infectious Diseases, Bethesda, 1981-87, med. officer nat. ctr. for rsch. resources 1987—. Contbr. articles on protein chemistry to profl. jours., chpts. on recombinant DNA guidelines to books. Recipient Commendation medal USPHS, 1977, Meritorious Service medal, 1984. Mem. Phi Beta Kappa. Office: NIH 9000 Rockville Pike Bethesda MD 20892-7965

TALBOT, DONALD ROY, consulting services executive; b. Bridgeport, Conn., Jan. 15, 1953; s. Grant Edward and Elvera (Gilbert) T.; m. Beverly Rinebold, Aug. 15, 1953; children: Donna, Randall, Theodore, Timothy, Thomas. B in Marine Engineering., N.Y. State Maritime Coll. Project engr. atomic power equipment div. GE, San Jose, Calif., 1952-58; mgr. nuclear labs., nuclear div. Martin Marietta Corp., Balt., 1958-62, project dir. nuclear div., 1962-67; dir. spl. studies Martin Marietta Corp., Friendship, Md., 1967-71; project dir. environ. programs Martin Marietta Corp., Balt., 1971-74; dir. environ. tech. ctr. Martin Marietta Corp., Relay, Md., 1974-83; gen. mgr. environ. systems div. Martin Marietta Corp., Columbia, Md., 1984-87; corp. v.p. Versar, Inc., Springfield, Va., 1987-89; pres. R.E. Mgmt. Svc., Inc, Towson, Md., 1989—. Recipient Antarctica Svc. medal Civil Engrs. Corps USN, 1965, Cert. of Appreciation Sec. Dept. Commerce, 1975. Avocation: outdoor activities. Home: 712 Hickory Lot Rd Baltimore MD 21286-1427 Office: R E Mgmt Svcs Inc PO Box 10614 Baltimore MD 21285-0614

TALBOT, EARL ARMOUR, lawyer; b. Chgo., Jan. 23, 1939; s. George A. and Ollie (Tadd) T.; m. Lydia A. Hildreth, June 20, 1964; children: Elizabeth, Earl A. Jr. AB, Wabash Coll., 1961; JD, U. Ill., 1964. Bar: Ill. 1964. Title examiner, trust adminstr. Chgo. Title & Trust Cofd., 1964-67; ptnr. Kirkland & Ellis, Chgo., 1967-85, Hoogendoorn, Talbot, Davids, Godfrey & Milligan, Chgo., 1985—. Contbr. to legal jours. Pres. Ill. conf. United Ch. of Christ, 1991-92. Mem. ABA, Ill. Bar Assn., Chgo. Bar Assn., Am. Coll. Real Estate Lawyers, Univ. Club, Plaza Club, Lambda Alpha. Mem. United Ch. of Christ. Office: Hoogendoorn Talbot Davids Godfrey & Milligan 122 S Michigan Ave Chicago IL 60603-6107

TALBOT, EMILE JOSEPH, French language educator; b. Brunswick, Maine, Apr. 12, 1941; s. Joseph Emile and Flora (Schinck) T.; m. Elizabeth Mullen, Aug. 6, 1966; children: Marc, Paul. BA, St. Francis Coll., Biddeford, Maine, 1963; MA, Brown U., 1965, PhD, 1968. Instr. French U. Ill., Urbana, 1967-68, asst. prof., 1968-73, assoc. prof., 1973-86, prof., 1986—, head dept. French, 1988-94. Author: Stendhal and Romantic Esthetics, 1985, Stendhal Revisited, 1993; editor: La Critique stendhalienne, 1979; assoc. editor: Quebec Studies, 1993—; rev. editor: The French Review, 1979-82, Quebec Studies, 1988-93; mem. editorial bd.: Nineteenth-Century French Studies, 1986—, La Revue Francophone, 1990—. Fellow Ctr. for Advanced Study U. Ill., 1973, assoc., 1988; NEH fellow, 1973-74; Camargo Found. fellow, France, 1976. Mem. MLA, Am. Comparative Lit. Assn., Am. Assn. Tchrs. French, Assn. for Can. Studies in U.S., Am. Coun. for Québec Studies. Roman Catholic. Office: U Ill Dept French 707 S Mathews Ave Urbana IL 61801-3625

TALBOT, FREDERICK HILBORN, bishop, former Guyanese diplomat; b. Mahaicony, East Coast Demerara, Guyana, Oct. 13, 1927; m. Sylvia Ross. Student, Allen U., Yale U., Pacific Sch. Religion. Pastor St. Peter's A.M.E. Ch., Georgetown, 1961-71; permanent rep. UN, 1971-73; Guyanese ambassador to U.S., 1973-75, high commr. to Can., 1973-74, high commr. to Jamaica, 1975-82; bishop, formerly pres. bd. 6th Dist. A.M.E. Ch., Atlanta, 1987—. Address: PO Box 684 Frederiksted Saint Croix VI 00840-0684

TALBOT, HOWARD CHASE, JR., retired museum administrator; b. New Berlin, N.Y., Oct. 6, 1925; s. Howard Chase and Gladys (Jacobs) T.; m. Alice Caroline Losee, Sept. 11, 1948; children—Julia Anna, Judith Ann, James Clayton. Student, Utica (N.Y.) Sch. Commerce, 1946-47. Acct. Leatherstocking Corp., Cooperstown, N.Y., 1947-51; asst. dir., then asst. treas. Nat. Baseball Hall of Fame and Mus., Cooperstown, 1951-78; dir. Nat. Baseball Hall of Fame and Mus., 1978-93; ret., 1993; dir. N.Y. Central Mut. Fire Ins. Co., Edmeston. Trustee Village of Cooperstown, 1957-62, mayor, 1962-63; bd. dirs. Little League Mus., Williamsport, Pa. Served with AUS, 1942-46. Mem. Am. Legion. Republican. Clubs: Cooperstown Rotary (past pres.), Masons.

TALBOT, KATHLEEN MARY, elementary education educator; b. Lansdown, Pa., Apr. 11, 1944; d. Bernard Lawrence and Kathleen T. (Fleck) T. BS, Chestnut Hill Coll., 1971; MEd, Kutztown U., 1980. Cert. elem. tchr., Pa., Del. Tchr. elem. schs. Archdiocese of Phila., 1965-83, 1986—, Diocese of Wilmington (Del.), 1965-83, Garnet Valley Sch. Dist., Concordville, Pa., 1986—; co-chairperson mid. states evaluation, Drexel Hill, Pa., 1979-81; adj. prof. Chestnut Hill Coll., Phila., 1980-91; coord. math. curriculum Garnet Valley Sch. Dist., Corcordville, 1991—; mem. strategic planning steering com., 1994-95. Grantee Impact Ptnrs. in Edn., 1989, Garnet Valley Sch. Dist., 1992; recipient Gift of Time award, 1994. Mem. NEA, ASCD, Nat. Coun. Tchrs. Math., Pa. Edn. Assn., Chester County Reading Assn., Garnet Valley Edn. Assn. (mem. negotiating team 1992-93). Democrat. Roman Catholic. Avocations: gardening, walking, golf, tennis, skiing.

TALBOT, LEE MERRIAM, ecologist, environmental specialist, consultant; b. New Bedford, Mass., Aug. 2, 1930; s. Murrell Williams and Zenaida (Merriam) T.; m. Martha Walcott Hayne, May 16, 1959; children: Lawrence Hayne, Russell Merriam. B.A., U. Calif., Berkeley, 1953, M.A., 1963, Ph.D., 1963. Biologist Arctic Research Lab., Point Barrow, Alaska, 1951; staff ecologist Internat. Union for Conservation, Brussels, 1954-56; ecologist, dir. East African ecol. research project Nat. Acad. Scis., Govts. of Kenya and Tanzania, 1959-63; wildlife advisor UN Spl. Fund, Africa, 1963-64; dir. S.E. Asia project Internat. Union for Conservation, 1964-65; resident ecologist, field rep. for internat. affairs Smithsonian Instn., Washington, 1966-70; sr. scientist, dir. internat. activities Pres.'s Council on Environ. Quality, Washington, 1970-78; sr. sci. advisor Internat. Council Sci. Unions, Paris, 1978-83; dir. conservation, spl. sci. advisor World Wildlife Fund Internat., Switzerland, 1978-80; dir. gen. Internat. Union for Conservation of Nature and Natural Resources, Gland, Switzerland, 1980-83; research fellow Environ. and Policy Inst., East West Ctr., 1983-87; vis. fellow World Resources Inst., Washington, 1984-89; sr. environ. advisor World Bank, 1984—; pres. Lee Talbot Assocs. Internat., 1991—; sr. prof. environ. scis. & internat. affairs George Mason U., Va., 1994—; cons. UNESCO, World Bank, Asian Devel. Bank, Nat. Geog. Soc., Inter-Am. Devel. Bank, The Nature Conservancy, U.S. Govt., U. Calif., UN Spl. Fund, WHO, UN Environment Program. Author: New Principles for the Conservation of Wild Living Resources, 1978, The Ecology of Sustainable Agricultural Development, 1987, Dams and the Environment, 1989, Crisis and Opportunity: Environment and Development in Africa, 1992; contbr. articles to profl. jours. Active Boy Scouts Am., Geneva, 1980-82, Washington, 1987—; pres. Cornwell Homeowners Assn., 1974-78. Served with USMC, 1953-54. Decorated officer Order of Lion (Senegal); recipient Fgn. Field Rsch. award Nat. Acad. Scis., 1959, CINE Golden Eagle award, 1969, Albert Schweitzer medal, 1975, Regents Lectureship award U. Calif.-Santa Barbara, 1986, Pierre Chaleur prize for lit. French Acad. Scis., 1993. Fellow Royal Geog. Soc., Royal Soc. Arts, AAAS, N.Y. Zool. Soc.; mem. Am. Inst. Biol. Scis. (Disting. Service award 1979), Acad. Medicine, Am. Assn. for Club of Rome, Am. Soc. Mammalogists, Ecol. Soc., Wildlife Soc. (Outstanding Publ. award 1963), Internat. Union for Conservation of Nature and Natural Resources (mem. of honor 1988), Sigma Xi, Phi Kappa Sigma. Clubs: Boone and Crockett (N.Y.C.), Explorers (N.Y.C.); Cosmos (Washington). Achievements include incorporation of ecological principles in international development; development of new principles for management of wild resources; biodiversity conservation; definition of ecosystem dynamics of tropical savannahs including role of fire, feeding habits and migrations of wild herbivores; development and negotiation of international agreements for environmental protection. Home: 6656 Chilton Ct Mc Lean VA 22101-4422 *My career is based on two premises: first, that our most important challenges are environmental issues which determine the earth's carrying capacity for human life and, equally important, the quality of that life; and second, that it is important to obtain direct experience in as much of the world as possible (over 120 countries so far) to understand the human ecological setting as a basis for action to improve it.*

TALBOT, MATTHEW J., oil company executive, rancher; b. Sept. 4, 1937; s. Matthew J. and Margaret A. (Green) T.; m. Maureen Donlan, June 3, 1958; children: Maureen A., Matthew J., Kathleen M. BBA in Acctg., Iona Coll., 1963. Acct. S.D. Leidesdorf (now Ernst & Young), N.Y.C., 1961-67; sr. analyst Gen. Foods Corp., White Plains, N.Y., 1967-68; asst. to comptroller Tosco Corp., Los Angeles, 1968-70, comptroller, 1970-83, v.p., 1972-76, sr. v.p., 1976-78, exec. v.p., 1978-83; pres. Tosco Corp., Santa Monica, Calif., 1983-87, Talbot Ranch, 1987—. Treas., bd. dirs. Ctr. Theatre Group, Los Angeles; trustee Craft and Folk Art Mus., Los Angeles. Mem. Am. Inst. CPA's, Fin. Execs. Inst., Sunkist Growers. Roman Catholic. Office: Edward White & Co 21700 Oxnard St Woodland Hills CA 91367-3642

TALBOT, PAMELA, public relations executive; b. Chgo., Aug. 10, 1946. BA in English, Vassar Coll., 1968. Reporter Worcester, Mass. Telegram and Gazette, 1970-72; account exec. Daniel J. Edelman, Inc., Chgo., 1972-74, account supr., 1974-76, v.p., 1976-78, sr. v.p., 1978-84, exec. v.p., gen. mgr., 1984-90; pres. Edelman West, Chgo., 1990—. Office: Edelman Pub Rels 211 E Ontario St Chicago IL 60611-3219*

TALBOT, PHILLIPS, Asian affairs specialist; b. Pitts., June 7, 1915; s. Kenneth Hammet and Gertrude (Phillips) T.; m. Mildred Aleen Fisher, Aug. 18, 1943; children: Susan Talbot Jacox, Nancy, Bruce Kenneth. BA, U. Ill. 1936, BS in Journalism, 1936; student, London Sch. Oriental Studies, 1938-39, Aligarh Muslim U., India, 1939-40; Ph.D., U. Chgo., 1954; LL.D. (hon.), Mills Coll., 1963. Reporter, Chgo. Daily News, 1936-38; corr. Chgo. Daily News, India and Pakistan, 1946-48, 49-50; assoc. Inst. Current World Affairs, Eng. and India, 1938-41; part-time Inst. Current World Affairs, 1946-51; instr. U. Chgo., 1948-50; instr. Columbia U., N.Y.C., 1951; exec. dir. Am. Univs. Field Staff, 1951-61; asst. sec. Near Eastern and S. Asian affairs

Dept. State, 1961-65; U.S. ambassador to Greece, 1965-69; pres. Asia Soc., N.Y.C., 1970-81; emeritus Asia Soc., 1981—; Phi Beta Kappa vis. scholar, 1973-74. Author: (with S.L. Poplai) India and America, 1958, India in the 1980s, 1983; editor: South Asia in the World Today, 1950. Trustee emeritus U.S.-Japan Found.; counselor United Bd. for Christian Higher Edn. in Asia; elder Presbyn. Ch. 2d lt. cav. Officers Res. Corps, 1936; 1st lt. N.G., 1937-38; lt. comdr. USNR, 1941-46. Mem. Am. Acad. Diplomacy, Assn. Asian Studies, Coun. Fgn. Relations, Century Assn., Cosmos Club. Address: 200 E 66th St New York NY 10021-6728

TALBOT, PRUE, biology educator. BA, Wilson Coll., 1966; MA, Wellesley Coll., 1968; PhD, U. Houston, 1972. Postdoctoral fellow U. Houston; from asst. prof. to assoc. prof. U. Calif., Riverside, 1977-85, prof., 1986—. Assoc. editor several profl. jours.; contbr. articles to profl. jours. Mem. Am. Soc. Cell Biology, AAAS, Crustacean Soc., Sigma Xi. Office: U Calif Riverside Dept Biology Riverside CA 92521

TALBOT, RICHARD JOSEPH, library administrator; b. Lynn, Mass., Dec. 18, 1932; s. Joseph Anthony and Mary Kathleen (Connolly) T.; m. Joanne Frances Hines, Sept. 2, 1961; children: Mary Frances, Jean Ann. A.B., Manhattan Coll., 1954; M.S. in Library Sci., Simmons Coll., 1961; M.B.A., Syracuse U., 1980. Reference librarian N.Y. Pub. Library, N.Y.C., 1961-62; cataloger, acquisitions librarian, library systems analyst NASA, Cambridge, Mass., Dept. Air Force, Bedford, Mass., 1962-70; assoc. dir. U. Mass. Library, Amherst, 1970-73; dir. libraries U. Mass. Library, 1973—; bd. dirs. Nelinet. Contbr. articles to profl. jours. Served to 1st lt. USAF, 1954-57. Mem. ALA, Assn. Coll. and Research Libraries (dir., exec. com., chmn. fin. com. 1980-83), Assn. Research Libraries (dir. 1982-86, pres. 1984-85). Roman Catholic. Home: 40 High Point Dr Amherst MA 01002-1224 Office: U Mass U Libr Amherst MA 01003

TALBOTT, BEN JOHNSON, JR., lawyer; b. Louisville, May 2, 1940; s. Ben Johnson and Elizabeth (Farnsley) T.; m. Sandra Riehl, Oct. 19, 1963; children: Elizabeth, Betty, John, Ben, Sandra. AB magna cum laude, Xavier U., Cin., 1961; LLB, Harvard U., 1964. Bar: Ky. 1965, U.S. Ct. Appeals (6th cir.) 1967. Law clk. to presiding justice U.S. Dist. Ct. Ky., Louisville, 1964-65; assoc. Middleton, Reutlinger & Baird, Louisville, 1965-68, ptnr., 1968-80; ptnr. Westfall, Talbott & Woods, Louisville, 1980—; atty. Stitzel-Weller Distillery, 1970-72, Louisville Gen. Hosp., 1974-83, Louisville and Jefferson County Bd. Health, 1974-80, U. Louisville, Louisville, 1980—. Mem. adv. bd. Louisville 15, Sta. WKPC-TV, bd. dirs., 1972-74, pres., 1974; past bd. dirs. U. Louisville Found., U. Louisville Med. Sch. Fund Orgn., Def. Enterprise Fund, 1994—; bd. dirs. Louisville Theatrical Assn., 1971—, pres., 1975-76, chmn., 1977-78; bd. dirs. Macauley Theatre, 1975, TARC Adv. Com., 1971, Jefferson County Capital Constrn. Com., 1971, Louisville Orch., 1976-86, pres., 1979-81; bd. trustees, trustee U. Louisville, 1970-79, sec., 1974, vice chmn., 1975, chmn. fin. com., 1976; bd. dirs. Ky. Ctr. for the Arts, 1983—, Louisville Lung Assn., 1974-75, treas., 1975; bd. dirs. Historic Homes Found., 1972-78, v.p., 1978, advisor, atty. 1978—. Named Outstanding Young Man of Louisville, Louisville Jaycees, 1976. Mem. ABA, Ky. Bar Assn. (chmn. 1989, Gen. Practice Session of the CLE), Louisville Bar Assn. (past mem. exec. com.), Nat. Assn. Coll. and Univ. Attys., The Def. Rsch. and Trial Lawyers Assn., Am. Ins. Attys., Harvard Law Sch. Assn. of Ky. (sec. 1965, pres. 1989—), Phi Kappa Phi. Avocations: golf, tennis, skiing. Home: 566 Blankenbaker Ln Louisville KY 40207-1167 Office: Westfall Talbott & Woods 501 S 2nd St Louisville KY 40202-1864

TALBOTT, FRANK, III, lawyer; b. Danville, Va., Mar. 26, 1929; s. Frank and Margaret (Jordan) T.; m. Mary Beverley Chewning, July 11, 1952; children: Beverley, Frank IV. BA, U. Va., 1951, LLB, 1953. Bar: Va. 1952. Gen. practice law Danville, 1956-66; with Dan River Inc., 1966-76, v.p., gen. counsel, 1968-76; partner firm Clement, Wheatley, Winston, Talbott & Majors, Danville, 1977-78; individual practice law Danville, 1979-92; gen. counsel Va. Mfrs. Assn. Inc., 1983-92; of counsel Woods, Rogers & Hazlegrove, Danville, Va., 1992—; chmn. adv. bd. NationsBank, Danville, 1984-94. Vice-chmn. Danville Sch. Bd., 1964-70; trustee Va. Student Aid Found., 1963-68; bd. dirs. United Fund Danville, 1953-62, Meml. Hosp., Danville, 1977-90. Served with AUS, 1953-56. Decorated Commendation medal. Fellow Am. Bar Found. (life); mem. Va. Bar Assn. (v.p. 1965-66, exec. com. 1967-70), Danville Bar Assn. (pres. 1965-66), Am. Judicature Soc., Newcomen Soc., U. Va. Alumni Assn. (bd. mgrs.), Danville Golf Club, German Club, Farmington Country Club, Country Club Va., Delta Psi, Phi Alpha Delta. Methodist. Home: 420 Maple Ln Danville VA 24541-3532 Office: PO Box 560 Danville VA 24543-0560

TALBOTT, STROBE, journalist; b. Dayton, Ohio, Apr. 25, 1946; s. Nelson S. and Josephine (Large) T.; m. Brooke Lloyd Shearer, Nov. 14, 1971; children: Devin Lloyd, Adrian Nelson. BA, Yale U., 1968, MA (hon.), 1976; MLitt, Oxford U., Eng., 1971. East european corr. Time Mag., 1971-73, U.S. state dept. corr., 1973-75, white house corr., 1975-77, diplomatic corr., 1977-84, chief Washington bur., 1984-89; editor at large, 1989—; editor, translator: Khrushchev Remembers, 1970, Khrushchev Remembers: Last Testament, 1974; author: Endgame: Inside Story of SALT II, 1979, Deadly Gambits: Reagan Administration & Arms Controls, 1984, The Russians and Reagan, 1984, Reagan and Gorbachev, 1987, Master of the Game, 1988. Trustee Yale U. 1976-82, Hotchkiss Sch., 1982-87; bd. dirs. Carnegie Endowment Internat. Peace; Council on Fgn. Relations. Recipient Edward Weintal Prize for Disting. Diplomatic Reporting Georgetown U., Overseas Press Club award, Stanley Hillman award. Office: Time Magazine 1050 Connecticut Ave NW Washington DC 20036-5303

TALENT, JAMES M., congressman, lawyer; b. St. Louis, Mo., Oct. 18, 1956; m. Brenda Lyons, 1984; children: Michael, Kathleen Marie. BA in Polit. Sci., Washington U., 1978; JD, U. Chgo. Law Sch., 1981. Law clk. 7th Ct. Appeals, 1981-82; adj. prof. law, 1982-84; mem. Mo. State Ho. Reps., 1984-93; minority leader, 1989-93; mem. 103rd-104th Congresses from 2nd Mo. Dist., 1993—, mem. econ. & devel. opportunity com., nat. security com., chmn. small bus. subcom. on regulation and paperwork. Legislative Achievement award Mo. Hosp. Assn., 1989. Mem. Mo. Bar Assn. (Award for significant contbns. to adminstrv. justice 1989), Mo. C. of C. (Spirit of Enterprise award 1990), Order of the Coif. Republican. Office: US Ho Reps 1022 Longworth Office House Members Washington DC 20515-2502*

TALESE, GAY, writer; b. Ocean City, N.J., Feb. 7, 1932; s. Joseph Francis and Catherine (DiPaola) T.; m. Nan Ahearn, June 10, 1959; children—Pamela, Catherine. B.A. in Journalism, U. Ala., 1953. Staff writer N.Y. Times, N.Y.C., 1955-65; writer Esquire mag., N.Y.C. 1960. Author: New York - A Serendipiter's Journey, 1961, The Bridge, 1964, The Overreachers, 1965, The Kingdom and the Power, 1969, Fame and Obscurity, 1970, Honor Thy Father, 1971, Thy Neighbor's Wife, 1980, Unto the Sons, 1992; co-author: (with Barbara Lounsberry) The Literature of Reality, 1995; contbr. articles to Esquire mag., others. Served to 1st lt. AUS, 1954-56. Mem. P.E.N. (v.p. 1984-87, bd. dirs. 1980—), Phi Sigma Kappa. Home: 109 E 61st St New York NY 10021-8101 also: 154 E Atlantic Blvd Ocean City NJ 08226-4511

TALESE, NAN AHEARN, publishing company executive; b. N.Y.C., Dec. 19, 1933; d. Thomas James and Suzanne Sherman (Russell) Ahearn; m. Gay Talese, June 10, 1959; children: Pamela Frances, Catherine Gay. B.A., Manhattanville Coll. of Sacred Heart, 1955. Fgn. exchange student 1st Nat. City Bank, London and Paris, 1956; editorial asst. Am. Eugenics Soc., N.Y.C., 1957-58, Vogue mag., N.Y.C., 1958-59; copy editor Random House Pub., N.Y.C., 1959-64; assoc. editor Random House Pub., 1964-67, sr. editor, 1967-73; sr. editor Simon & Schuster Pubs., N.Y.C., 1974-81; v.p. Simon & Schuster Pubs., 1979-81; exec. editor v.p. Houghton Mifflin Co., N.Y.C., 1981-83, v.p., v.p.-editor-in-chief, 1984-86, v.p., pub., editor-in-chief, 1986-88; sr. v.p. Doubleday & Co., N.Y.C., 1988-90; pres., pub. editorial dir. Nan A. Talese Books, 1990—. Home: 109 E 61st St New York NY 10021-8101

TALINGDAN, ARSENIO PREZA, health science administrator; b. Dolores, Abra, The Philippines, Mar. 30, 1930; came to U.S., 1973; s. Mariano T. and Candida (Tordil) Preza; m. Josefa Fernandez Biason. Apr. 21, 1954; children: Melda, Arsenio Jr., Jocelyn Almerick, Mario, Abe. AA, U. Philippines, 1951, AB, MPA, 1955; MAPA, The Am. U., 1956; BS, La Salle Extention U., Chgo., 1977; MBA, Century U., 1983, PhD, 1985. Cert.

nursing home adminstr., life, health and securities underwriter. Job analyst, orgn. analyst, budget examiner Kroeger & Assocs. Project, Philippine Budget Commn., Manila, 1954-55; scholar, tech. asst., participant USA-ICA-NEC Program, 1955-56; supr. mgmt. analyst Philippine Budget Commn., Manila, 1957-59; asst. budget dir., IBM coordinator U. Philippines, Quezon City, 1959-65, mgmt. specialist, chief of studies 1969-70; asst. v.p. for budget and mgmt. Sarmiento Enterprises, Inc., Makati, Rizal, Philippines, 1965-69; adminstr. Philippine Gen. Hosp., Manila, 1970-73; budget and facilities mgr. Hunter Coll., CUNY, N.Y.C., 1973-76; acctg. systems editor J.C. Penney Co., N.Y.C., 1977; regional med. care adminstr. N.Y. State Dept. Health, Office Health Systems Mgmt., N.Y.C., 1977-78; assoc. med. care adminstr., Medicaid mgmt. info. systems Dept. Health State of N.Y., N.Y.C., 1978—; with dental Medicaid program Dept. Health State of N.Y., 1978-82, with med. ops. br., 1982-84, with dental ops. br., 1984-91, with patient care investigations, long term care program, 1991—; asst. prof., chmn. social scis. dept. U.P. Coll., Manila, 1969-73; 1st Philippine tech. assistance fellow on orgn. and mgmt. U.S. Agy. for Internat. Devel., Washington, 1955-56; professorial lectr. U. Philippines, Manila, 1960-69. Co-author: Accounting, Auditing and Internal Auditing, 1964; author: Public Administration and Management, 1966, Management and Supervision, 1966, Work Simlfication Handbook, 1957 and others; contbr. articles to profl. jours. Pres. Abra Varsitarians, Quezon City, 1949-53; founder, Dolores Young Men and Women's Assn., Manila, Abra, 1949-71; founder, pres. Philippine Execs. and Profls. Golf Assn., Quezon City, 1965-69, others. Maj. Res. Officer, Philippine Army, 1960-73. Recipient Hall of Nations award Am. U., 1956, Pub. Health Sci. award Del. Valley Assn. Philippines, 1980, Profl. award in Pub. Adminstrn. U. Philippines Alumni Assn. Am., 1991. Mem. Pub. Employees Fedn., U. of the Philippines Alumni Assn. in N.J. (founder, 1st pres. 1979-83), U. of the Philippines Alumni Assn. in Am. (founder, 1st pres. 1980-83), Filipino Am. Soc. of Teaneck (pres. 1983-84). Republican. Avocation: writing.

TALKE, FRANK EBERHARD, education educator; b. Dresden, Germany, Sept. 16, 1939; came to U.S., 1965; s. Artur and Louise T.; m. Kathryn Ann Talke; children: Stefan, Kristen, Kurt. Diploma Enginng., U. Stuttgart, Germany, 1965; MS, U. Calif., Berkeley, 1966, PhD, 1968. Staff mem. IBM, San Jose, Calif., 1969-86; prof. U. Calif. San Diego, 1986—, chair AMES dept., 1993—; vis. prof. U. Calif. Berkeley, 1984. Author numerous tech. papers; patentee in field. Mem. ASME, IEEE (chair local sect. 1990-92). Office: Univ Calif San Diego 9500 Gilman Dr La Jolla CA 92093

TALKINGTON, ROBERT VAN, state senator; b. near Patrick, Tex., Aug. 23, 1929; s. William Henry and Nannie J. (Patrick) T.; m. Donna Jill Schmaus, Mar. 25, 1951; children—Jill Talkington McCaskill, Jacki Talkington Chase, James, Thomas, Lisa. A.A., Tyler Jr. Coll., 1949; B.S., U. Kans., 1951, LL.B., 1954, J.D., 1971. Bar: Kans. 1954. County atty. Allen County, Kans., 1957-63; city atty. Moran, Kans., 1968—; mem. Kans. Ho. of Reps. from 10th Dist., 1969-73; mem. Kans. Senate from 12th Dist., 1973-89, v.p., 1977-81; majority leader, 1981-85, pres., 1985-89; chmn. Republican Party, Allen County, 1964-68, state treas., 1964-66. Trustee Iola Pub. Library, 1962-70; mem. advisory bd. Greater U. Fund, U. Kans., 1967-72. Served with CIC AUS, 1954-56. Mem. Am. Legion, Sigma Alpha Epsilon, Phi Delta Phi. Clubs: Masons, Shriners, Elks. Home: 20 W Buchanan St Iola KS 66749-1823 Office: 20 N Washington St Iola KS 66749-2836

TALKINGTON, WILLIAM ALE, publishing company executive; b. Seymour, Ind., Apr. 14, 1948; s. Robert James and Margaret (Ale) T.; m. Marilyn Kay Huffman, Aug. 30, 1969; children—Matthew A., Bradley. A.B. in English, Ind. U., 1970. Mktg. mgr. McGraw-Hill, N.Y.C., 1974-75, dist. mgr., 1975-78, editor, 1978-80, regional mgr., 1980-82, editorial dir., 1982-84, dir. mktg. services, 1984-92; v.p. sales and mktg. Merrill Pub., 1984-92; pres. Holt, Rinehart & Winston, Austin, 1992—. Mem. Am. Mgmt. Assn., Assn. Am. Pubs. Home: 24 Franklin Dr Plainsboro NJ 08536-2303

TALL, FRANKLIN DAVID, mathematician, neurolinguistic programming master practitioner; b. N.Y.C., Apr. 21, 1944; s. Martin and Faye T. AB, Harvard U., 1964; PhD, U. Wis., 1969. Asst. prof U. Toronto, Ont., Can., 1969-74; assoc. prof. U. Toronto, 1974-80, prof. math., 1980—. Author: (monograph) Set Theoretic Consistency Results and Topological Theorems Concerning the Normal Moore Space Conjecture and Related Problems, 1977, The Work of Mary Ellen Rudin, 1993. Nat. Scis. and Engring. Research Council Can. grantee, 1973—. Mem. Am. Math. Soc. (mem. editorial bd. Proc.), Can. Math. Soc., Assn. Symbolic Logic, Japan-Can. Soc., N.Am. Assn. Neurolinguistic Programming. Office: U Toronto, Dept Math, Toronto, ON Canada M5S 1A1

TALL, JOANN, ecologist. Recipient Goldman Environ. prize Goldman Environ. Found., 1993. Office: BIA Highway #27 PO Box 47 Porcupine SD 57772*

TALLACKSON, HARVEY D., real estate and insurance salesman; b. Grafton, N.D., May 15, 1925; s. Arthur J. and Mabel R. (McDougald) T.; m. Glenna M. Walstad, Aug. 4, 1946; children: Lynda, Thomas, Debra, Amy, Laura. Grad. high sch., Park River, N.D. Grain and potato farmer Grafton, 1946-68; ins. agt. Tallackson Ins., Grafton, 1968—; state senator Grafton, 1976—; real estate salesman Johnson Real Estate, Grafton, 1982—; chmn. state senate appropriation com., Bismarck, 1987—. Bd. dirs. Nodak Rural Electric Co-op, Grand Forks, N.D., 1965—, Minnkota Power Co-op, Grand Forks, 1979—, pres. bd. dirs., 1990—. Recipient Pub. Svc. award N.D. Lignite Coun., 1989; named Outstanding Young Farmer by Area Chamber of Walsh & Pembina Counties, 1951-52. Mem. Nat. Coun. Ins. Legislatures (mem. exec. com. 1985—, vice pres. 1994—), Lions (pres. 1977-79), Masons. Democrat. Lutheran. Avocations: golf, curling, travel, reading. Office: Tallackson Ins & Real Estate 53 W 5th St Grafton ND 58237-1468

TALLACKSON, JEFFREY STEPHEN, lawyer; b. Washington, May 10, 1943; s. John Robert and Betty Marcelle (Crockett) T.; m. Christine Ann Johnson, Aug. 10, 1974. BA, Yale U., 1965; LLB, Columbia U., 1968. Bar: N.Y. 1968. Law clk. to judge U.S. Dist. Ct. (so. dist.) N.Y., N.Y.C., 1968-70; assoc. Milbank, Tweed, Hadley & McCloy, N.Y.C., 1970-78, ptnr., 1979-87; exec. v.p., gen. counsel, sec. Am. Savs. Bank, White Plains, N.Y., 1987-92; ptnr. Lowy & Tallackson, N.Y.C., 1993—; mem. exec. com. N.Y. Law Inst., N.Y.C., 1980-87; bd. dirs., exec. v.p., gen. counsel, sec. Riverhead Savs. Assn. Bar City N.Y. Democrat. Mem. ABA, N.Y. State Bar Assn., Assn. Bar City N.Y. Democrat. Home: 301 E 52nd St # 2B New York NY 10022-6319 Office: Lowy & Tallackson Olympic Tower 645 Fifth Ave 18th flr New York NY 10022-2585

TALLAL, PAULA, cognitive neuroscientist; b. Austin, Tex., May 12, 1947; d. Joseph P. and Ruth Lois (Epstein) Tallal; m. Ian Nigel Creese, July 22, 1972. BA, NYU, 1969; PhD, Cambridge U., Eng., 1973. Cert. clin. psychologist, Calif. Asst. prof. psychology Johns Hopkins U., Balt., 1976-79; dir. rsch. Children's Hosp. and Health Ctr., San Diego, 1979-85; asst. prof. psychiatry U. Calif., San Diego, 1979-80, assoc. prof. psychiatry, 1980-86, prof. psychiatry, 1986-88; adj. prof. dept. neurosci. U. Medicine and Dentistry N.J./N.J. Med. Sch., Newark, 1989—; prof. II, co-dir. Neurosci. Ctr. Rutgers U., Newark, 1988—; Lectr. Soc. for Neurosci., 1992, U.S. Congress, 1992, Nat. Inst. Deafness, 1993. Co-editor: New York Academy of Science, 1993; co-author: Language, Speech and Reading Disorders in Children, 1988; contbr. articles to profl. jours. Mem. sci. exec. bd. March of Dimes. Recipient Disting. Young Scientist Creativity in Sci. Pres.'s award, Notre Dame Coll., Md. 1977. Mem. Soc. Neurosci., N.Y. Acad. Sci., Am. Psychol. Soc., Internat. Neuropsychology Soc., Acad. of Aphasia, Am. Speech-Lang.-Hearing Assn. (Cert. of Appreciation 1982). Office: Rutgers U Neurosci Ctr 197 University Ave Newark NJ 07102-1814

TALLAL, SCOTT VICTOR, television research consultant; b. Dallas, Dec. 27, 1954; s. Joseph J. Sr. and Ruth Lois (Epstein) T.; m. Jimy Dee Spotts, Apr. 26, 1986. BA, U. North Tex., 1976. News dir. Sta. KDNT-AM-FM, Denton, Tex., 1973-74; news anchorman Sta. KNUS-FM, Dallas, 1974-76; asst. news dir. Stas. KTSA/KTFM-FM, San Antonio, 1976-78; news dir. Sta. KDWB-AM-FM, Mpls., 1978-79; news producer Sta. KMSP-TV, Mpls., 1979-80; producer, dir. Diamond Group, Inc., Dallas, 1980-84; researcher, cons. Audience Research and Devel., Dallas, 1981—. Home: 5827 Saint Marks Cir Dallas TX 75230-4076 Office: Media & Marketing Inc 22548 Pacific Coast Hwy Ste 303 Malibu CA 90265

TALLANT, DAVID, JR., lawyer; b. Oak Park, Ill., Mar. 16, 1931; s. David and Mary E. (Hosick) T.; m. Beryle Schwabe: children: David III, Elizabeth Tallant Dickey, Cathrine Tallant VanDemerkt. AB, Claremont Men's Coll., 1953; JD, Duke U., 1956. Bar: Ill. 1956. Ptnr. Chapman & Cutler, Chgo. Mem. Am. Bar Assn., Chgo. Athletic Assn., Skokie Country Club, Country Club of Fla. Home: 21 Country Rd S Vlg Of Golf FL 33436-5604 Office: Chapman & Cutler 111 W Monroe St Chicago IL 60603

TALLCHIEF, MARIA, ballerina; b. Fairfax, Okla., Jan. 24, 1925; d. Alexander Joseph and Ruth Mary (Porter) T.; m. Henry Paschen, Jr., June 3, 1956; 1 child, Elise. DFA (hon.), Lake Forest (Ill.) Coll., Colby Coll., Waterville, Maine, 1968, Ripon Coll., 1973, Boston Coll., Smith Coll., 1981, Northwestern U., Evanston, Ill., 1982, Yale U., 1984, St. Mary-of-the-Woods (Ind.) Coll., 1984, Dartmouth Coll., 1985, St. Xaviar Coll., 1989. Ballerina Ballet Russe de Monte Carlo, 1942-47; with N.Y.C. Ballet Co., 1947-65, prima ballerina, 1947-60; founder Chgo. City Ballet, 1979; now artistic dir. Lyric Opera Ballet; prima ballerina Am. Ballet Theatre, 1960; founder Sch. Chgo. Ballet. Guest star, Paris Opera, 1947, Royal Danish Ballet, 1961; created roles in Danses Concertantes, 1944, Night Shadow, 1946, Four Temperaments, 1946, Orpheus, 1948, The Firebird, 1949, Bourée Fantastique, 1949, Capriccio Brillante, 1951, À la Française, 1951, Swan Lake, 1951, Caracole, 1952, Scotch Symphony, 1952, The Nutcracker, 1954, Allegro Brillante, 1956, The Gounod Symphony, 1958; appeared in films Presenting Lily Mais, 1943, Million Dollar Mermaid, 1953. Named Hon. Princess Osage Indian Tribe, 1953; recipient Disting. Service award U. Okla., 1972, award Dance mag., 1960, Jane Addams Humanitarian award Rockford Coll., 1973, Bravo award Rosary Coll., 1983, award Dance Educators Am., 1956, Achievement award Women's Nat. Press Club, 1953, Capezio award, 1965, Leadership for Freedom award Roosevelt U. Scholarship Assn., 1986. Mem. Nat. Soc. Arts and Letters. *

TALLENT, STEPHEN EDISON, lawyer; b. Columbus, Nebr., Aug. 10, 1937; s. William E. and Helen T.; m. Martha Sutcliffe, Apr. 6, 1971; 1 child, Jennifer Diane. BA, Stanford U.; JD, U. Chgo., LLD (hon.), Lincoln U. Bar: Calif. 1963, U.S. Dist. Ct. (so. and cen. dists.) Calif. 1965, U.S. Dist. Ct. (so. and ea. dists.) N.Y., 1989, U.S. Ct. Appeals (D.C. cir.) 1981, U.S. Ct. Appeals (2d cir.) 1987, U.S. Ct. Appeals (3d cir.) 1980, U.S. Ct. Appeals (4th cir.) 1982, U.S. Ct. Appeals (6th cir.) 1986, U.S. Ct. Appeals (9th cir.) 1968, U.S. Ct. Mil. Appeals 1965, U.S. Supreme Ct. 1973. Ptnr. Gibson, Dunn & Crutcher, L.A., 1962—; former adj. prof. Loyola Law Sch., L.A.; mem. vis. com. U. Chgo. Law Sch. Former mem. Calif. Atty. Gen.'s adv. com. for Evaluation of Anti-Organized Crime Programs; mem. L.A. Town Hall, L.A. World Affairs Council; mem. bd. vis. Stanford Law Sch.; founding dir. Am. EMployment Law Coun., 1993—. Mem. ABA (coun. of labor and employment law sect.), Calif. Bar Assn., D.C. Bar Assn., N.Y. Bar, L.A. County Bar Assn., Indsl. Rels. Rsch. Assn. Home: 7020 Glenbrook Rd Bethesda MD 20814-1223 Office: Gibson Dunn & Crutcher 1050 Connecticut Ave NW Ste 900 Washington DC 20036-5303 also: 333 S Grand Ave Los Angeles CA 90071-1504

TALLENT, WILLIAM HUGH, chemist, research administrator; b. Akron, Ohio, May 28, 1928; s. Charles Othar and Agnes Annette (Johnson) T.; m. Joy Anne Redfield, Aug.23, 1952; children: Elizabeth Ann, Cinda Marie, Raymond Charles. BS, U. Tenn., 1949, MS, 1950; PhD, U. Ill., 1953. Chemist Nat. Heart Inst., Bethesda, Md., 1953-57, G.D. Searle & Co., Skokie, Ill., 1957-64; head new crops evaluation investigations Agr. Rsch. Svc., USDA, Peoria, Ill., 1964-69, chief indsl. crops lab., 1969-74, asst. dir., 1974-75, ctr. dir. No. Regional Rsch. Ctr., 1975-83, regional adminstr. N.E. region, 1983-84; asst. adminstr. Agr. Rsch. Svc., USDA, Washington, 1984-94; tech. transfer advisor Agr. Rsch. Svc., USDA, Beltsville, Md., 1994—. Recipient Merit award Gamma Sigma Delta, 1979, Presdl. Rank award for Sr. Execs., 1988. Mem. AAAS, Am. Chem. Soc. Econ. Botany. Home: 6100 Westchester Park Dr Apt 4L College Park MD 20740-2852 Office: USDA Agr Rsch Svc Bldg 005 BARC-W Beltsville MD 20705-2350

TALLETT, ELIZABETH EDITH, biopharmaceutical company executive; b. London, Apr. 2, 1949; d. Edward and Edith May (Vickers) Symons; m. Martin Richard Tallett, Oct. 3, 1970 (div.); children: James Edward, Alexander Martin; m. James Edward Wavle, Jr.; 1 child, Christopher Andrew Wavle. BS with honors, U. Nottingham (Eng.) 1970. Ops. rsch. analyst So. Gas Bd., 1970-73; mgmt. svcs. mgr. Warner-Lamber (UK), Eastleigh, Eng., 1973-77, strategic planning mgr., 1977-81; internat. dir. strategic planning Warner-Lambert, Morris Plains, N.J., 1981-82, corp. dir. strategic planning, 1982-84; dir. mktg. ops. Parke-Davis, Morris Plains, 1984-87; exec. v.p. therapeutic products Centocor, Malvern, Pa., 1987-89, pres. pharms. div., 1989-92; pres., CEO Transcell Techs., Inc., Monmouth Junction, N.J., 1992—; bd. dirs. Prin. Mut. Life Ins. Co., Biotech. Coun. N.J. Contbr. articles to profl. jours. Mem. Ch. of Eng. Avocations: acting, badminton, travel, skiing.

TALLEY, CAROL LEE, newspaper editor; b. Bklyn., Sept. 10, 1937; d. George Joseph and Viola (Kovash) T.; children—Sherry, Jill, Scott. Student, U. Ky., 1955-57, Ohio U., 1957-58. Reporter Easton (Pa.) Daily Express, 1958-60; reporter N.J. Herald, 1962-64, edn. editor, 1964-66; reporter Daily Advance, Dover, N.J., 1966-68, polit. editor, investigative reporter, from 1969, mng. editor, 1974-81; editor Evening Sentinel, Carlisle, Pa., 1982—; Mem. A.P. Task Force N.J., 1970, Pa. Associated Press Mng. Editor's Bd. Dirs. Past bd. dirs. Helen Stevens Cmty. Mental Health Ctr. (chair), Carlisle; past pres. bd. dirs. Stevens Mental Health Ctr., Carlisle. Recipient pub. service awards Nat. Headliners, 1971, Sigma Delta Chi, 1971, George Polk Meml. award for local reporting, 1974, Dew Meml. award Pa. Newspaper Pub.'s Assn., 1985. Mem. Pa. Newspaper Editors Soc., Kiwanis Club. Office: 457 E North St Carlisle PA 17013-2620

TALLEY, CHARLES RICHMOND, commercial banking executive; b. Richmond, Va., Dec. 23, 1925; s. Charles Edward and Marie (Throckmorton) T.; m. Anne Marie Smith, June 4, 1948; children: Laurie Anne, Charles Richmond. B.A. in Econs, U. Richmond, 1949; postgrad., Sch. Banking Rutgers U., 1959-61, Sch. Fin. Pub. Relations, Northwestern U., 1954-55; grad. exec. program, U. Va., 1974. Asst. cashier 1st & Mchts. Nat. Bank, Richmond, 1955-57; asst. v.p. 1st & Mchts. Nat. Bank, 1957-63, v.p., 1963-69, sr. v.p., 1969-73, exec. v.p., 1973-84; corp. exec. officer Sovran Bank N.A., 1984-86, ret., 1986; ret., 1986; bd. dirs. Security Atlantic Life Ins. Co., Richmond; v.p., bd. dirs. Security Atlantic Ins. Agy., Richmond; bd. dirs. Sovran Properties, Inc.; vice chmn. bd. dirs. Va. Edn. Loan Authority, 1983-87, chmn., 1988-91. Pres. Richmond Jr. C of C., 1960-61; pres. Budget Extension Bd. Va., 1973-75, bd. dirs., 1985-95; treas. Richmond chpt. Nat. Found., 1956—; v.p., mem. exec. com. Richmond Eye and Ear Hosp., pres. 1988-91; bd. dirs. Commonwealth Eye and Ear Inst., 1986-89; bd. dirs. Richmond Symphony Orch., Richmond Better Bus. Bur. With USNR, 1944-46. Mem. Richmond Met. C. of C. (bd. dirs. 1979-89), Richmond Clearing House Assn. (pres. 1977), Willow Oaks Country Club (pres. 1971), Build and Bear Club, Farmington Country Club, Rotary (bd. dirs. Richmond 1981-83). Home: 4301 Stratford Rd Richmond VA 23225-1060

TALLEY, DARRYL VICTOR, professional football player; b. Cleveland, July 10, 1960. Degree in Physical Edn., U. W.Va., 1983. Linebacker Buffalo Bills, 1983—. Named linebacker The Sporting News Coll. All-Am. Team, 1982, outside linebacker The Sporting News NFL All-Pro Team, 1990, 93. Played in Pro Bowl, 1990, 91. Office: Buffalo Bills 1 Bills Dr Orchard Park NY 14127-2237*

TALLEY, ROBERT MORRELL, aerospace company executive; b. Erwin, Tenn., Mar. 13, 1924; s. Robert Taylor and Anna Laura (Morrell) T.; m. Mary Sue Williams, June 5, 1948; children: David, Carol. Student, East Tenn. State Coll., 1942-43, U. Va., 1943-44; B.S. U. S.C., 1945; M.S., U. Tenn., 1948, Ph.D., 1950. Chief infrared br., chief solid state div. U.S. Naval Ordnance Lab., White Oak, Md., 1951-58; mgr. lab. Santa Barbara Rsch. Ctr. subs. Hughes Aircraft, Calif., 1958-69, v.p., 1969-76, pres., 1976-89, ret.; mem. adv. bd. dept. elec. and computer engring. U. Calif.-Santa Barbara. Contbr. articles to profl. jours.; patentee in field. Trustee U. Calif.-Santa Barbara Found.; bd. dirs. Industry Edn. Coun., Santa Barbara; commr. econ.

devel. Santa Barbara County. With USN, 1943-46. Fellow Am. Phys. Soc.; mem. Optical Soc. Am., LaCumbre Club, Sigma Xi.

TALLEY, TRUMAN MACDONALD, publisher; b. N.Y.C., Feb. 3, 1925; s. Truman Hughes and Helen Nicholson (Macdonald) T.; m. Madelon DeVoe, Oct. 17, 1953; children: Melanie, Macdonald, Marina. Student, Buckley Sch., Deerfield Acad., Sorbonne, 1945-46; grad. cum laude, Princeton U., 1949. Assoc. editor New Am. Library of World Lit., N.Y.C., 1949-59; editorial v.p. New Am. Library of World Lit., 1959-64; press., editorial dir. Weybright & Talley, N.Y.C., 1966-78; pub. Truman Talley Books with Times Books, 1978-82; with E.P. Dutton, 1983—; mem. grad. bd. Princeton Tiger, 1950—. Trustee Clinton Hall Assn. Mercantile Library, N.Y.C. Served with AUS, 1943-46, ETO. Decorated Purple Heart. Mem. P.E.N. Clubs: Anglers, Brook, Maidstone, Southampton Beach. Home: 876 Park Ave New York NY 10021-1832 Office: Dutton/Signet Penguin USA 375 Hudson St New York NY 10014-3658

TALLEY, WILLIAM GILES, JR., container manufacturing company executive; b. Adel, Ga., Sept. 25, 1939; s. William Giles and Mary (McGlamry) T.; BSBA, U. S.C., 1961; m. Jacqueline Vickery, Apr. 14, 1962; children: William Giles, Bronwyn Ashley. Mgmt. trainee Talley Veneer & Crate Co., Inc., Adel, 1961-62, plant mgr., salesman, Waynesboro, Ga., 1965-67; with Talley's Box Co., Leesburg, Fla., 1962-69, plant mgr., partner, 1967-69; gen. mgr. Growers Container Coop., Inc., Leesburg, 1969—; pres. Talley Acres, Inc., 1979—, pres. Talley Classic Woods, Inc., 1992—; bd. dirs. Sun Bank N.A., Orlando, Fla. Past chmn. and bd. dirs. Leesburg Hosp. Assn. Served with USAAF, 1961. Mem. Leesburg C. of C. (dir.), Fla. Forestry Assn. (dir. 1977—), Elks, Kiwanis, Sigma Alpha Epsilon. Democrat. Methodist. Home: 2206 Talley Court Rd Leesburg FL 34748-3177 Office: PO Box 490817 Leesburg FL 34749-0817

TALLICHET, LEON EDGAR, retired publishing executive, financial administrator; b. Tupelo, Miss., Jan. 10, 1925; s. Leon Edgar and Irene Elizabeth (Reid) T.; m. Betty Jean Baumann, May 31, 1947; children: Judie Elizabeth, Kathryn Louise. B.M.E., U. Louisville, 1946; M.B.A., Harvard U., 1949. Office mgr. Brown-Forman Distillers Corp., Louisville, 1949-58; from asst. sec. and asst. treas. to sr. v.p. and treas. Courier-Jour. and Louisville Times Co., Standard Gravure Corp., WHAS Inc., Louisville, 1958-86; dir. Courier-Jour. and Louisville Times Co., Standard Gravure Corp., WHAS Inc., 1975-86; fin. adminstr. Barry Bingham, Sr., Louisville, 1987-88, Mary C. Bingham, 1987—; pres. chpt. Fin. Exec. Inst., 1969-70. Bd. dirs. Met. United Way Louisville, 1972-74; chmn. investment com. Ky. Ctr. for Arts Endowment Fund, 1991—; mem. fin. com. Louisville Community Found., 1988—; commr., treas. City of Ten Broeck, Ky., 1988—. With USNR, 1943-46, lt. USNR, 1950-52. Office: Mary C Bingham 2320 Meidinger Towers Louisville KY 40202

TALLMAN, CLIFFORD WAYNE, school system administrator, consultant; b. Columbus, Ohio, June 13, 1932; s. Frank Albert and Ella Louse (Ott) T.; m. Ruth Anne Fletcher, Apr. 6, 1958; children: Martin, David, Kathy Haines. BS in Edn., Capital U., 1954; MA, Ohio State U., 1960; EdS, Bowling Green U., 1965. Cert. supt., Ohio, Ill., Mich., Ky., Pa., N.Y. Tchr. Southwestern City Schs., Grove City, Ohio, 1954-60; supt. Republic (Ohio) Local Schs., 1960-63, Columbus Grove Schs., Grove City, 1963-65, Jackson Local Schs., Massillon, Ohio, 1965-73, Brecksville (Ohio) City Schs., 1973-78, Kent County Schs. Independence, Ky., 1978-80, Otsego Local Schs., Tontogany, Ohio, 1980-86; prof. Bowling Green (Ohio) U., 1980-86; supt. Coloma (Mich.) Community Schs., 1986-93; ednl. cons. AMA, Chgo., 1963; commr. Right to Read, Washington, 1973. Contbr. articles to profl. jours. Active Berrien County Hist. Assn., Coloma, Selective Svc. Bd., Washington; newsletter editor Rotary Club, Coloma, 1986-90. With USNR, 1951-54, USA, 1954-56. IDEA scholar, 1969; FEE scholar, 1971; named to Honorable Order of Ky. Colonels. Mem. Ohio Edn. Assn., Mich. Assn. Sch. Bds., Berrien Assn. Sch. Adminstrs., Am. Assn. Sch. Adminstrs., Mich. Assn. Sch. Adminstrs., Buchey Assn. Sch. Adminstrs., Coloma C. of C., Bowling Green U. Alumni Assn., Phi Delta Kappa. Lutheran. Avocations: gardening, computers, organ music, chess, traveling. Home: 5540 Red Arrow Coloma MI 49038 Office: Box 550 Coloma MI 49038

TALLMAN, RICHARD C., lawyer; b. Oakland, Calif., Mar. 3, 1953; s. Kenneth A. and Jean M. (Kemppe) T.; m. Cynthia Ostolaza, Nov. 14, 1981. BSC, U. Santa Clara, 1975; JD, Northwestern U., 1978. Bar: Calif. 1978, Wash. 1979, U.S. Dist. Ct. (no. dist.) Calif. 1979, U.S. Dist. Ct. (we. dist.) Wash. 1979, U.S. Ct. Appeals (9th cir.) 1979, U.S. Dist. Ct. Hawaii 1986. Law clk to Hon. Morrell E. Sharp U.S. Dist. Ct. (we. dist.) Wash., Seattle, 1978-79; trial atty. U.S. Dept. Justice, Washington, 1979-80; asst. U.S. atty. U.S. Dist. Ct. (we. dist.) Wash., Seattle, 1980-83; ptnr. Schweppe, Krug & Tausend, PS, Seattle, 1983-89, Bogle & Gates, Seattle, 1990—. Instr. Nat. Park Svc. Seasonal Ranger Acad., Everett and Mt. Vernon, Wash., 1983-93; chmn. Edmonds C.C. Found., Lynnwood, Wash., 1990-92; gen. counsel Seattle-King County Crime Stoppers, 1991—. Mem. ABA, FBA (trustee 1992-93, v.p. 1994, pres. 1995), Seattle-King County Bar Assn., Rainier Club, Wash. Athletic Club. Avocations: hunting, hiking, model railroads. Office: Bogle & Gates Two Union Sq 601 Union St Seattle WA 98101-2322

TALLMAN, ROBERT HALL, investment company executive; b. Creston, Iowa, Aug. 10, 1915; s. Ralph H. and Hazel Verne (Hall) T.; m. Elizabeth Childs, Sept. 19, 1938; children: Susan, Mary, Timothy. BS, U. Nebr., 1937. Trainee to dist. mgr. Firestone Tire & Rubber Co., Akron, Ohio, 1937-50; pres. Tallman Oil Co., Fargo, N.D., 1950-80; chmn. bd. State Bank of Hawley, Minn., 1966-70, 1st Nat. Bank of Barnesville, Minn., 1965-88; pres. Tallman Investment Ent., Fargo, 1980—; pres. dir. Dak Tech. Inc.; dir. Bell Farms. Past pres. Fargo Bd. Edn., N.D. Petroleum Coun.; past pres. St. Lukes Hosp. Assn.; past chmn. trustees 1st Congl. Ch. of Fargo. Mem. Fargo C. of C. (past pres.), Am. Assn. Ret. Persons, Nat. Rifle Assn., N.D. State U. Teammakers Club (past pres.), Fargo Country Club, Kiwanis (past pres.), Masons, Shriners, Elks. Republican. Congregationalist. Avocations: golf, hunting, fishing, travel, photography. Home: 3201 16th Ave S Fargo ND 58103 Office: Box 9723 2108 S University Dr Fargo ND 58103-5348

TALLMER, MARGOT SALLOP, psychologist, psychoanalyst, gerontologist; b. N.Y.C., Sept. 8, 1925; d. Harry and Mildred (Schifrin) Sallop; m. Jonathan Tallmer, Apr. 12, 1949 (dec.); children—Mary, Megan, Jill, Andrew. M.S., N.Y. U., 1948; M.A., Yeshiva U., 1962, Ph.D, 1967. Mem. faculty dept. ednl. founds. Hunter Coll., N.Y.C., 1969—; assoc. prof. Hunter Coll., 1976-79, prof., 1979—; staff psychologist Mt. Sinai Hosp., 1967-68; postgrad. Center for Mental Health, 1968-69; pvt. practice psychoanalysis N.Y.C., 1967—; faculty, trustee, bd. dirs. Nat. Psychol. Assn. for Psychoanalysis; faculty N.Y. Ctr. for Psychoanalytic Tng. Editor: Sex and Life Threatening Illness, HIV Testing Positive, The Child and Death, also books on aging and loss; editorial bd. Current Issues in Psychoanalysis, Psychoanalytic Rev.; contbr. chpts. to textbooks, articles to profl jours. Mem. APA, Boston Soc. Gerontologic Psychiatry, N.Y. State Psychol. Assn. (pres. divsn. adult devel. and aging). Address: 26 E 81st St New York NY 10028

TALLY, LURA SELF, state legislator; b. Statesville, N.C., Dec. 9, 1921; d. Robert Ottis and Sara (Cowles) Self; A.B., Duke U., 1942; M.A., N.C. State U., Raleigh, 1970; m. J.O. Tally, Jr., Jan. 30, 1943 (div. 1970); children: Robert Taylor, John Cowles. Tchr., former guidance counselor Fayetteville (N.C.) city schs.; mem. N.C. Ho. of Reps. from 20th Dist., 1971-83, chmn. com. higher edn., from 1975, also 1980-83, vice chmn. com. appropriations for edn., 1973-86; state senator from 12th Dist. N.C., 1983-94; chmn. N.C. Senate Com. of Natural Resources, Community Devel. and Wildlife, 1987, Environment and Natural Resources, 1989-94. Past pres. Cumberland County Mental Health Assn., N.C. Historic Preservation Soc.; trustee Fayetteville Tech. Inst., 1981-94; mem. Legis. Research com. Mem. Am. Personnel and Guidance Assn., Fayetteville Bus. and Profl. Women's Club, Kappa Delta, Delta Kappa Gamma. Methodist. Club: Fayetteville Woman's (past pres.). Office: W Jones St Raleigh NC 27601

TALLY, TED, screenwriter; b. Winston-Salem, N.C., Apr. 9, 1952; s. David K. and Dorothy E. (Spears) T.; m. Melinda Kahn, Dec. 11, 1977. BA, Yale U., 1974, MFA, 1977. Scripts include (plays) Terra Nova, 1977 (Kazan award Yale U. 1977, Theron Rockwell Field prize Yale U. 1977, Obie award

1984), Hooters, 1978, Coming Attractions, 1980 (John Gassner Playwriting award N.Y. Outer Critics Cir. 1981), Silver Linings, 1983, Little Footsteps, 1986, (with other) Urban Blight, 1988, The Gettysburg Sound Bite, 1989, (screenplays) White Palace, 1990, The Silence of the Lambs, 1991 (Academy award best adapted screenplay 1991), (TV) Hooters, 1983, Terra Nova, 1984, The Father Clements Story, 1987 (Christopher award 1988). Columbia Broadcasting Sys. Found. Playwriting fellow Yale U., 1977, Guggenheim fellow, 1985-86; N.Y. State Creative Artists Pub. Svc. grantee, 1980, NEA Playwriting grantee, 1983-84. Office: ICM 8899 Beverly Blvd Los Angeles CA 90048*

TALMADGE, JOHN BARNES, science foundation administrator; b. Needham, Mass., Mar. 30, 1936; s. Nelson Alcorn and Mildred Francis (Barnes) T.; m. Elinor Beth Dunsmore, Nov. 27, 1965 (div. Nov. 1976); children: Leslie Jean, Alison Elinor; m. Patricia Russell, Apr. 24, 1993. BA, Williams Coll., 1958. Pub. info. officer NASA Ames Rsch. Ctr., Moffett Field, Calif., 1962-64; adminstrv. asst. to pres. Reed Coll., Portland, Oreg., 1964-66; adminstrv. asst. to Congressman John Dellenback, U.S. Ho. of Reps., Washington, 1967; fed. rels. assoc. Assn. Am. Colls., Washington, 1968-70; various positions NSF, Washington, 1970, now head Polar coordination, 1986—. Staff asst. Lodge for Senate, Mass., 1962, McCall for Sec. State, Oreg., 1964; campaign mgr. Dellenback for Congress, Eugene, Oreg., 1966. Capt. USMCR, 1958-61. Episcopalian. Avocations: hiking, canoeing, ecotourism. Home: 4433 Westover Pl NW Washington DC 20016 Office: Geosciences 4201 Wilson Blvd Arlington VA 22203-1803

TALMADGE, MARY CHRISTINE, nursing educator; b. Monticello, Ga., Nov. 6, 1940; d. Herbert Pope and Margaret (Allen) T.; m. Larry Benson, Aug. 10, 1962 (div. 1975). Diploma, Crawford W. Long Hosp. Sch. of Nursing, Atlanta, 1961; BSN, U. Dayton, 1966; MPH, U. Hawaii, 1971, PhD, 1989. RN; cert. Family Life Edn. Staff charge nurse Crawford W. Long Hosp., Atlanta, 1961-62; instr. LPN program Dayton (Ohio) Bd. Edn., 1963-66; instr. Miami Valley Hosp. Sch. of Nursing, Dayton, 1967-69; clin. nurse specialist Hawaii State Hosp., Kaneohe, 1970-77, dir. nursing, 1978-80; adminstrv. asst. to dir. health Hawaii State Dept. of Health, Honolulu, 1977-78; clin. nurse specialist Windward Community Counseling Ctr., Kaneohe, 1980-83; asst. prof. U. Hawaii, 1983-85; assoc. prof. Hawaii Loa Coll., Kaneohe, 1987-89; assoc. prof., acting dept. head Ga. So. U., Statesboro, 1990-93; prof., chair dept. nursing Calif. State U., Long Beach, 1993—; cons. Tokyo Women's Med. Coll. Sch. of Nursing, 1988-90; local and internat. healthcare orgns. Sec., mem. Gov.'s Commn. on Mental Health and Criminal Justice, Honolulu, 1978-80; mem., chmn. Windward Oahu Svc. Area Bd. on Mental Health and Substance Abuse, Honolulu, 1985-86; candidate Neighborhood Bd. Kaneohe, 1988; bd. dirs. New Beginnings for Children; chair nursing task force, health com. Statesboro C. of C. Recipient Cmty. Svc. award African-Am. Caucus, Ga. So. U., 1993. Mem. NLN, Sigma Theta Tau, Phi Kappa Phi. Democrat. Methodist. Avocation: breeder and handler of miniature Schnauzers. Home: 105 Lancaster Pt Statesboro GA 30458-6238 Office: Calif State Univ Long Beach CA 90802

TALMAGE, DAVID WILSON, microbiology and medical educator, physician, former university administrator; b. Kwangju, Korea, Sept. 15, 1919; s. John Van Neste and Eliza (Emerson) T.; m. LaVeryn Marie Hunicke, June 23, 1944; children: Janet, Marilyn, David, Mark, Carol. Student, Maryville (Tenn.) Coll., 1937-38; B.S., Davidson (N.C.) Coll., 1941; M.D., Washington U., St. Louis, 1944. Intern Ga. Baptist Hosp., 1944-45; resident medicine Barnes Hosp., St. Louis, 1948-50; fellow medicine Barnes Hosp., 1950-51; asst. prof. pathology U. Pitts., 1951-52; asst. prof., then assoc. prof. medicine U. Chgo., 1952-59; prof. medicine U. Colo., 1959—, prof. microbiology, 1960-86, disting. prof., 1986—, chmn. dept., 1963-65, assoc. dean, 1966-68, dean, 1969-71; dir. Webb-Waring Lung Inst., 1973-83, assoc. dean for research, 1983-86; mem. nat. council Nat. Inst. Allergy and Infectious Diseases, NIH, 1963-66, 73-77. Author: (with John Cann) Chemistry of Immunity in Health and Disease; editor: Jour. Allergy, 1963-67, (with M. Samter) Immunological Diseases. Served with M.C. AUS, 1945-48. Markle scholar, 1955-60. Mem. NAS, Inst. Medicine, Am. Acad. Allergy (pres.), Am. Assn. Immunologists (pres.), Phi Beta Kappa, Alpha Omega Alpha. Office: U Colo Box C321 Sch Medicine Denver CO 80262

TALMAGE, JOHN H., food company executive. With Agway, Inc., Syracuse, N.Y. Office: Agway Inc 500 Rutherford Ave Charlestown MA 02129-1621

TALMI, YOAV, conductor, composer; b. Kibbutz Merhavia, Israel, Apr. 28, 1943; diploma Rubin Acad. Music, Tel Aviv; postgrad. diploma Juilliard Sch. Music; m. Erella Gottesmann; 2 children. Assoc. condr. Louisville Orch., 1968-70; co-condr. Israel Chamber Orch., 1970-72; artistic dir., condr. Gelders Symphony Orch., Arnhem, 1974-80; prin. guest condr. Munich Philharm. Orch., 1979-80; artistic dir., condr. Israel Chamber Orch., 1984-88; music dir. New Israeli Opera, 1985-89, San Diego Symphony Orch., 1990—, Waterloo Festival, N.J. 1994-95; guest condr. Berlin Philharm., Munich Philharm., London Philharm., Philharmonia, Concertgebouw, Rotterdam Philharm., Israel Philharm., Tokyo Symphony, New Japan Philarm., Vienna Symphony, St. Petersburg Philharm., Detroit Symphony, St. Louis Symphony, Houston Symphony, Dallas Symphony, N.Y. Chamber Symphony, L.A. Chamber Orch., Oslo Philharm., Tonhalle Orch. Zurich, others. Composer: Dreams for choir a capella, Music for Flute and Strings; Overture on Mexican Themes (recorded), 3 Monologues for Flute Solo (pub.), Inauguration Fanfare; recs. include: Bruckner 9th Symphony (Oslo Philharm.), Gliére 3rd Symphony, Brahms Sextet/4 Serious Songs, Rochmaninov's Isle of the Dead, Berlioz Overtures (San Diego Symphony), Tchaikowsky/Scoenberg, Bloch/Barber/Grieg/Puccini (Israel Chamber Orch.); (with Erella Talmi) works for flute and piano. Recipient Boskovitch prize for composition, Israel, 1965; Koussevitzky Meml. Conducting prize, Tanglewood, 1969; award Ruppert Found. Donor competition, London, 1973. Home: PO Box 1384, Kfar Saba 44113, Israel Office: ICM Artists 40 W 57th St New York NY 10019 also: San Diego Symphony Orch 1245 7th Ave San Diego CA 92101-4302

TALTON, CHESTER LOVELLE, bishop; b. El Dorado, Ark., Sept. 22, 1941; s. Chester Talton and Mae Ola (Shells) Henry; m. Karen Louise Warren, Aug. 25, 1963; children: Kathy Louise, Linda Karen, Frederick Douglass, Benjamin Albert. BS, Calif. State U. Hayward, 1967; MDiv, Ch. Divinity Sch. of Pacific, 1970. Ordained to ministry Episcopal Ch., as deacon, 1970, as priest, 1971, as bishop, 1991. Vicar Good Shepherd Episc. Ch., Berkeley, Calif., 1970-71, St. Mathias Mission, Seaside, Calif., 1971-73, Ch. of the Holy Cross, Chgo., 1973-76; curate All Sts. Episc. Ch., Carmel, Calif., 1971-73; rector St. Philips Episc. Ch., St. Paul, 1976-81, St. Philips Ch., N.Y.C., 1985-90; mission officer Parish of Trinity Ch., N.Y.C., 1981-85; suffragan bishop Diocese of L.A., Episc. Ch., 1990—. Pres. Community Svc. Coun. Greater Harlem, N.Y.C., 1985-90, Upper Manhattan Child Devel. Ctr., N.Y.C., 1985-90, Peter Williams Jr. Housing Corp., N.Y.C., 1988-90. Mem. Union of Black Episcopalians. Office: Episc Diocese LA PO Box 2164 1220 W 4th St Los Angeles CA 90017-1412

TALUCCI, SAMUEL JAMES, retired chemical company executive; b. Newark, Del., Feb. 13, 1929; s. Anthony and Josephine (Valocchi) T.; m. Charlotte Sisofo, Sept. 22, 1951 (dec. Oct. 1985); children: Samuel J., Charlene, Anthony, Catherine, Christina, Louisa; m. Louise Coulter, Oct. 1987. BS, U. Del., 1951. Resident mgr. Italian Subs. Rohm & Haas Co., Milan, 1956-58; gen. mgr. Italian Subs. Rohm & Haas Co., 1958-66; mng. dir. Brit. Subs. Rohm & Haas Co., London, 1966-68; dir. European ops. Rohm & Haas Co., Phila., 1968; asst. gen. mgr. Internat. div. Rohm & Haas Co., 1971, v.p. gen. mgr. Plastics div., 1974, v.p. corporate bus., group dir. agrl. and indsl. chems. Plastics div., 1975-83, regional dir. N.Am. region, 1983-89, ret. 1989. Bd. dirs. Rosemont Coll. Mem. Nat. Agrl. Chems. Assn. (bd. dirs.), Pa. Chamber Bus. & Industry (bd. dirs.), Middle States Assn. Colls. and Secondary Schs. (mem. commn. on secondary schs.). Address: 140 Golf House Rd Haverford PA 19041

TALVI, ILKKA ILARI, violinist; b. Kuusankoski, Finland, Oct. 22, 1948; came to U.S., 1977; s. Veikko Tuomo and Irja Margareta (Saajos) T.; m. Judith Frances Aller, Sept. 4, 1969 (div. Aug. 1982); children: Silja Joanna, Sonja Louisa; m. Marjorie Jill Kransberg, Aug. 29, 1984; children: Anna Mirjam, Sarah Lilian. Diploma in violin, Sibelius Acad., Helsinki, Finland, 1966; student Heifetz master class, U. So. Calif., 1967-68; student, Curtis

Inst., Phila., 1968-69; pvt. studies, Bouillon, Odnoposoff, Paris, Vienna, 1965-67. Lectr. Sibelius Acad., Helsinki, 1969-75, Porin Musiikkiopisto, Pori, Finland, 1970-76; concertmaster Malmö (Sweden) Symphony, 1976-77; prin. Los Angeles Chamber Orch., Pasadena, Calif., 1979-85; concertmaster Seattle Symphony, 1985—, Seattle Opera, 1985—, Waterloo Festival, N.J., 1988—; guest concertmaster Seattle Symphony, 1983-85; freelance violinist, film, TV, and recording industries, Los Angeles, 1977-85. Performed as soloist and in recital in Europe, U.S., 1965—; appeared in Finland, U.S., 1972—; played Klami Violin Concerto, Albert "In Concordian," Diamond 2, violin concerto and numerous other recordings. Recipient Kuusankoski (Finland) award, 1967, numerous grants, Finland, 1965-75. Lutheran. Avocations: dogs, computers, science. Home: 3456 10th Ave W Seattle WA 98119-1413 Office: Seattle Symphony Seattle Center House 305 Harrison St 4th Fl Seattle WA 98109-4645

TALWANI, MANIK, geophysicist, educator; b. Patiala, India, Aug. 22, 1933; came to U.S., 1954; s. Bir Sain and Saraswati (Khosla) T.; m. Anni Fittler, Apr. 3, 1958; children: Rajeev Manik, Indira, Sanjay. BSc with honors, Delhi U., India, 1951, MSc, 1953; PhD, Columbia U., 1959; PhD (hon.), Oslo U., 1981. From rsch. scientist to assoc. prof. Lamont-Doherty Geol. Obs., Columbia U., N.Y.C., 1959-70, dir. obs., 1972-81; prof. Columbia U., N.Y.C., 1970-82; dir. Ctr. for Crustal Studies Gulf R & D Co., Pitts., 1981-83; chief scientist exploration div. Gulf R & D Co., Houston, 1983-85; Schlumberger prof. geophysics Rice U., Houston, 1985—; cons. Govt. of Iceland, 1982—; dir. Geotech. Rsch. Inst., Houston Advanced Rsch. Ctr., Woodlands, 1985—; co-chmn. exec. com. Energy Rsch. Clearning House; Sackler disting. lectr. U. Tel Aviv, 1987; mem. adv. coun. Indian Oil and Gas Corp. Co-author: Geophysical Atlas of the Norwegian Sea; editor 5 books on earth sci.; Maurice Ewing Mmel. Symposium; co-editor: Geophysical Atlases of Indian, Atlantic and Pacific Oceans; contbr. over 100 papers to profl. jours. Recipient Krishnan award Indian Geophys. Union, 1964, Exceptional Sci. Achievement award NASA, 1973, Guggenheim award, 1974, Alfred Wegener medal European Union Geoscis., 1993; Fulbright-Hays fellow, 1974. Fellow AAAS, Am. Geophys. Union (James B. Macelwane award 1964, Maurice Ewing award 1981), Geol. Soc. Am. (George P. Woollard award 1984); mem. Soc. Exptl. Geophysicists, Am. Assn. Petroleum Geologists, Norwegian Acad. Scis., Petroleum Club, Acad. Nat. Scis. Russian Fedn., Houston Geophys. Soc. (hon. mem. 1993), Houston Philos. Soc, Sigma Xi. Home: 1111 Hermann Dr 10-D Houston TX 77004 Office: Rice U PO Box 1892 Houston TX 77251-1892

TAM, FRANCIS MAN KEI, physics educator; b. Macao, Asia, Dec. 7, 1938; came to U.S., 1960; naturalized, 1974; s. Anthony Wai Chiu and Agatha (Yeung) Tam; m. Margaret McGann, Oct. 28, 1978; children: Mary Christina, Peter Anthony, Matthew Philip. Gen. cert. edn., U. London, 1959; cert. of matriculation, U. Hong Kong, 1959; BA, U. Calif., Berkeley, 1963; MS, U. Minn., 1967. Reader U. Calif., Berkeley, 1962-63; teaching asst. U. Minn., Mpls., 1963-65, rsch. asst., 1965-67; asst. prof. physics Frostburg (Md.) State U., 1967—; cons. sci. fair projects Regional Edn. Svc. of Appalachia, Cumberland, Md., 1989—. Author: Thunderstorm Electrification, 1972; reviewer textbooks in field; contbr. articles to profl. publs. Pastoral leader Mary, Servant of the Lord Prayer Community, St. Peter and Paul's Cath. Ch., Cumberland, 1977-80; advisor Dem. Club, Frostburg State Coll., 1969-70. Westinghouse Corp. grantee, 1990; recipient Outstanding Alumnus award Yuet Wah Coll., 1970. Mem. Am. Geophys. Union, Am. Meteorol. Soc., Am. Assn. Physics Tchrs. (Disting. Svc. award Appalachian sect. 1991, sect. rep. 1991—, sec.-treas. 1981-91, pres. 1978-79, chmn. com. on minorities in physics edn. 1989-91, mem. com. on profl. concerns 1991-94, membership and benefits com., 1994). Roman Catholic. Avocations: collecting Chinese antiques, table tennis, tai chi. Home: 33 Teaberry Ln Frostburg MD 21532-2301 Office: Frostburg State U Physics Dept Frostburg MD 21532

TAM, WILLIAM, secondary school principal. Prin. Kalaheo High Sch., Kailua, Hawaii. Recipient Blue Ribbon award U.S. Dept. Edn., 1990-91. Office: Kalaheo High Sch 730 Iliaina St Kailua HI 96734

TAMAGAWA, TSUNEO, mathematics educator. Prof. math. Yale Univ., dept. chmn. Office: Yale U Dept Math New Haven CT 06520

TAMARELLI, ALAN WAYNE, chemical company executive; b. Wilkinsburg, Pa., Aug. 13, 1941; s. John Adam Tammarelli and Florence Eleanor (Heacock) T.; m. Carol Ann Crawford, Aug. 3, 1963; children: Robin Carol, Alan Wayne. BS, Carnegie Mellon U., 1963, MS, 1965, PhD, 1966; MBA, NYU, 1972. Engr. Exxon Corp., Linden, N.J., 1966, project leader, 1968-70; corp. planner Engelhard Minerals & Chem. Corp., Newark, 1970-71, asst. to exec. v.p., 1971-74, gen. mgr., 1974-77, v.p., 1977-79, group v.p., 1979-81; sr. v.p. Engelhard Corp., Iselin, N.J., 1981-83; chmn., chief exec. officer Dock Resins Corp, Linden, NJ, 1983—. Mem. exec. com. nat. adv. coun. for environ. policy and tech. U.S. Dept. Environment Protection, Gov's. Econ. Task Force, N.J.; mem. exec. com. Alliance for Union County. Capt. U.S. Army, 1966-68. NSF fellow, 1963-66. Mem. Synthetic Organic Chems. Mfrs. Assn. (vice chmn., bd. govs.), Am. Chem. Soc., N.Y. Paint and Coatings Assn. (pres., v.p., sec., treas., bd. dirs.), Chem. Industry Coun. (chmn., bd. dirs., exec. com.), N.J. Energy Rsch. Inst. (founding trustee), Am. Mgmt. Assn., N.Y. Acad. Scis., Scabbard and Blade, Rotary (pres., v.p., sec. Linden Club), Linden Indsl. Assn. (pres.), Sigma Xi, Tau Beta Pi, Phi Kappa Phi, Omicron Delta Kappa. Home: 49 Wexford Way Basking Ridge NJ 07920-2432 Office: Dock Resins Corp 1512 W Elizabeth Ave Linden NJ 07036-6323

TAMBIAH, STANLEY JEYARAJAH, anthropologist; b. Sri Lanka, Jan. 16, 1929; came to U.S., 1973; s. Charles Rajakone and Eliza Chellamma (Moothathamby) T.; m. Mary Wynne Huber, Mar. 15, 1969; children: Jonathan Anand, Matthew Arjun. BA, U. Ceylon, Peradeniya, 1951; PhD, Cornell U., 1954; DLitt (hon.), Jaffna U., Sri Lanka, 1981; LHD (hon.), U. Chgo., 1991; LittD (hon.), U. Peradeniya, Sri Lanka, 1991. Lectr. U. Ceylon, 1955-60; UNESCO tech. assistance expert Thailand, 1960-63; Smuts fellow U. Cambridge (Eng.) and Commonwealth fellow St. John's Coll., U. Cambridge, 1963-64; lectr. U. Cambridge, 1964-72; fellow Clare Hall, 1965-70; fellow, tutor grad. students, dir. studies in social anthropology King's Coll., 1970-72; fellow Center for Advanced Study in Behavioral Scis., Palo Alto, Calif., 1968-69; prof. anthropology U. Chgo., 1973-76; curator South Asian ethnology Peabody Museum, Harvard U., 1976—; chmn. dept. anthrop. Harvard U., 1984-87; Malinowski meml. lectr. London Sch. Econs., 1968; Radcliffe-Brown meml. lectr. Brit. Acad., 1979; Radhakrishnan meml. lectr. Oxford U., 1982; Kingsley Martin meml. lectr. Cambridge U., 1982; Lewis Henry Morgan meml. lectr., Rochester U., 1984, Am. Ethnol. Soc. disting. lectr., 1988, Daryll Forde meml. lectr. U. Coll., London, 1991. Author: Buddhism and the Spirit Cults in Northeast Thailand, 1970, (with Jack Goody) Bridewealth and Dowry, 1973, World Conqueror and World Renouncer, A Study of Religion and Polity in Thailand against a Historical Background, 1976, The Buddhist Saints of the Forest and the Cult of Amulets, 1984, Culture, Thought and Social Action, 1986, Magic, Science, Religion, and the Scope of Rationality, 1990, Buddhism Betrayed? Religion, Politics and Violence in Sri Lanka, 1992. Social Sci. Research Council Gt. Brit. grantee, 1971; NSF grantee, 1978; Guggenheim fellow, 1982; vis. scholar Phi Beta Kappa, 1990-91. Fellow Am. Acad. Arts and Scis., Royal Anthrop. Inst. (Curl Bequest prize 1964, Rivers Meml. medal 1973), Am. Anthrop. Assn.; mem. Assn. Asian Studies (pres. 1989-90, presdl. address 1990), Nat. Acad. of Scis. of U.S. Office: Harvard U Dept Anthropology Cambridge MA 02138

TAMBOR, JEFFREY, actor, theatre director, educator; b. San Francisco, July 8, 1944. BA, San Francisco State; MFA, Wayne State U. acting tchr. Milton Katselas' Acting Workshops, Beverly Hills, Calif. Appearances include (theatre) Sly Fox, 1976 (Broadway and L.A.), Measure for Measure, The Hands of the Enemy, Flea in Her Ear, American Mosaic, (films) ...And Justice For All, 1979, Saturday the 14th, 1981, The Man Who Wasn't There, 1983, Mr. Mom, 1983, No Small Affair, 1984, Desert Hearts, 1985, Three O'Clock High, 1987, Lisa, 1990, City Slickers, 1991, Life Stinks, 1991, Pasttime, 1991, Article 99, 1992, Brenda Star, 1992, Crossing the Bridge, 1992, Radioland Murders, 1994, Heavyweights, 1994, (TV series) The Ropers, 1979-80, Hill Street, 1981-87, 9 to 5, 1982, Mr. Sunshine, 1986, Max Headroom, 1987-88, Studio 5B, 1989, American Dreamer, 1990, The Larry

Sanders Show, 1992— (Emmy award nominee 1993), (TV episodes) M*A*S*H, Barney Miller, L.A. Law, The Golden Girls, Empty Nest, Who's The Boss, Doogie Houser, M.D., Equal Justice, Murder She Wrote, Tales From The Crypt (Dead Right), (TV movies) Eddie and Herbert, 1977, Alcatraz: The Whole Shocking Story, 1980, A Gun in the House, 1981, The Star Maker, 1981, Take Your Best Shot, 1982, The Zertigo Diamond Caper, 1982, The Awakening of Candra, 1983, Cocaine: One Man's Seduction, 1983, Sadat, 1983, The Three Wishes of Billy Grier, 1984, Robert Kennedy and His Times, 1985, Wildfire, 1986, The Burden of Proof, 1992, (TV spls.) Living and Working in Space: The Countdown Has Begun; dir. for numerous theatre companies including Seattle Repertory Theatre, Actors Theatre of Louisville, Milw. Repertory Theatre, Acad. Festival Theatre, Chgo., San Diego Shakespeare Festival, South Coast Repertory Theatre, Loeb Drama Ctr., Cambridge, Mass., Sky Light Theatre, L.A. Office: Care The Gersh Agency 232 N Caron Dr Beverly Hills CA 90210*

TAMBORLANE, WILLIAM V., JR., physician, biomedical researcher, pediatrics educator; b. N.Y.C., Aug. 25, 1946; s. William and Eleanor (Bernabo) T.; m. Kathleen Mary Blinn, Dec. 27, 1969; children: Melissa, Amy, James. BS, Georgetown U., 1968, MD, 1972. Diplomate Am. Bd. Pediatrics, Am. Bd. Pediatric Endocrinology. Attending physician Yale New Haven Hosp., 1977—; asst. prof. pediatrics Yale U., New Haven, 1977-81, dir. Children's Diabetes Ctr., 1977—; assoc. prof. pediatrics Sch. Medicine, New Haven, 1981-86; acting chief Pediatric Endocrinology, New Haven, 1982-83; chief pediatric endocrinology and diabetes Yale Sch. Medicine, 1985—, prof. prdiatrics, 1986—; program dir. Yale Children's Clin. Rsch. Ctr., N.H., Conn., 1986—; imm. Lawson Wilkens Diabetes Com., 1988-89. Recipient Jonathan May award, Charles Best award Am. Diabetes Assn., 1979, Clin. Investigator award NIH, 1979-82. Mem. Am. Fedn. Clin. Rsch., Am. Soc. Clin. Investigation, Endocrine Soc., Soc. Pediatric Rsch., Phi Beta Kappa. Office: Yale U Sch Med Children's Clin Rsch Ctr 333 Cedar St New Haven CT 06510-3206

TAMBS, LEWIS ARTHUR, diplomat, historian, educator; b. San Diego, July 7, 1927; s. Fred B. and Marguerite Johanna (Tambs) Jones; m. Phyllis Ann Greer, 1982; children: Kari, Kristin, Jeanifer, Heidi, Greer, Michael, Alexa. B.S., U. Calif.-Berkeley, Berkeley, 1953; M.A., U. Calif.-Santa Barbara, 1962, Ph.D., 1967. Plant engr. Standard Brands, San Francisco, 1953-54; pipeline engr. Creole Petroleum Co., Caracas, Maracaibo, Venezuela, 1954-57; gen. mgr. Cacyp, Maracaibo, 1957-59; instr. Creighton U., 1965-67, asst. prof., 1967-69; prof. history Ariz. State U., Tempe, 1969-82, 87—, dir. Center Latin Am. Studies, 1972-76; cons. Nat. Security Council, 1982-83; US ambassador to Colombia, 1983-85, U.S. ambassador to Costa Rica, 1985-87. Author: East European and Soviet Economic Affairs, 1975, Historiography, Method and History Teaching, 1975, (with others) Hitler's Spanish Legion, 1979; editor: United States Policy Toward Latin America, 1976, Inter-American Policy for the 80's; co-author periodical guides; contbr. articles to profl. jours. Bd. dirs. Ariz.-Mex. Commn., 1974-82, Coun. Inter-Am. Security, 1979-90. With U.S. Army, 1945-47, 50-51. Faculty grantee Ariz. State U., 1970, 71, 74, 78, 79. Roman Catholic. Office: Ariz State U Dept History Tempe AZ 85287-2501

TAMEN, HARRIET, lawyer; b. Yonkers, N.Y., May 17, 1947; d. Saul and Lily (Balglau) T. A.B., Bryn Mawr Coll., 1969; J.D., George Washington U., Washington, 1973. Bar: N.Y. 1974, U.S. Dist. Ct. (so. dist.) N.Y. 1975. Atty. W.T. Grant, N.Y.C., 1974-76; atty. City of N.Y. Office Econ. Devel., Div. Real Property, N.Y.C., 1977-81; atty. Credit Lyonnais Bank, N.Y.C., 1981-86, Chase Manhattan Bank, 1986-89; v.p., counsel internat. corp. fin. Citibank, 1989-92, partner, Claugus Tamen & Orenstein, 1992-93; pvt. practice, N.Y.C., 1994—. Bd. dirs. Dromenon Theatre, N.Y., 1980-86, Nat. Dance Inst., N.Y., 1982, chmn. bd. dirs., 1984-87; chmn. bd. dirs. Theatre & Dance Alliance, 1989-90; del. exch. program Women in Law, South Am., 1987—; mem. campaign staff Ed Koch for Mayor, N.Y.C., 1977, steering com. Soviet Am. Banking Law Working Group, 1991—; guest lectr. Moscow Conf. on Banking, 1992, Ulaan Baatar, Mongolia, 1993-94, Harriman Inst. of Columbia U., 1994. Mem. ABA, Bar of Assn. of City of N.Y.

TAMHANE, AJIT C., statistician, engineer, educator; b. Bhiwandi, India, Nov. 12, 1946; came to U.S., 1970; s. Chintaman M. and Sarla C. (Durve) T.; m. Meenal A. Dikshit, June 18, 1975; children: Shalaka, Salil. B Tech. in Mech. Engring., Indian Inst. Tech., Bombay, 1968; MS, Cornell U., 1973, PhD, 1975. Design engr. Larsen & Toubro Ltd., Bombay, 1968-70; prof. Northwestern U., 1975—; cons. in field. Co-authored: Multiple Comparison Procedures, 1987. W-J-Youden award Chem. Proceedings Divns. Am. Soc. Quality Controll, 1985. Fellow Am. Stats. Assn. (pres. N.E. Ill. chpt. 1993). Office: Northwestern U 2006 Sheridan Rd Evanston IL 60208

TAMIR, THEODOR, electrophysics researcher, educator; b. Bucharest, Roumania, Sept. 17, 1927; came to U.S., 1958, naturalized, 1968; s. Martin and Helena (Hart) Berman; m. Hadassah Cohen, Oct. 5, 1949; children: Jonathan, Yael. B.S. Technion, Israel Inst. Tech., 1953, Dipl. Ingenieur, 1954, M.S., 1958; Ph.D., Poly. Inst. Bklyn., 1962. Instr. Technion Israel Inst. Tech., Haifa, 1956-58; mem. rsch. staff Poly. Inst., Bklyn., 1958-62; mem. faculty Poly. Univ., Bklyn., N.Y., 1962—; prof. electrophysics Poly. Inst. N.Y., 1969-92, Univ. prof., 1992—, head dept. elec. engring., 1974-79; sci. and engring. cons. to indsl. and govtl. labs. Editor, author: Integrated Optics, 1975 (transl. into Russian and Chinese), Guided Wave Optoelectronics, 1988 (transl. into Russian); co-editor: Springer Series in Optical Sciences, 1979—; contbr. chpts. to books, articles to profl. jours. Served with Israeli Army, 1947-49. Awarded Instn. Premium, 1964, Electronics Premium, 1967, Instn. Elec. Engrs., London; citation for disting. research Polytechnic chpt. Sigma Xi, 1978. Fellow IEEE, Instn. Elec. Engrs. (London), Optical Soc. Am.; mem. Internat. Union Radio Sci., Sigma Xi. Home: 981 E Lawn Dr Teaneck NJ 07666-6604 Office: 100 Tech Pl Brooklyn NY 11201

TAMKE, GEORGE WILLIAM, electronics and electrical equipment executive; b. Beacon, N.Y., May 16, 1947; s. George William and Josephine Edna (Carbone) T.; m. Christine Barbara MacLeod, June 28, 1969; children: Kara Lee, Shannon. BSchemE, Vanderbilt U., 1969; MS in Mgmt. Sci., Stanford U., 1979. With IBM, N.Y., Fla., Calif., Ga., Minn., 1969-86; dir. orgn. planning and sec. to corp. mgmt. com. IBM, White Plains, N.Y., 1981-82, v.p. mfg. Communication Products div., 1982-83, v.p. display products Communication Products div., 1983-84, asst. group exec. Info Systems, Products Group, 1984-86; pres. Cullinet Software, Inc., Westwood, Mass., 1986-87, chief ops. officer, 1987; pres., v.p. Emerson Electric Co., St Louis, 1989—; CEO Astec (BSR) Plc, Hong Kong, 1989—. Contbr. articles to profl. jours. Avocations: tennis, golf. Home: 9915 Litzsinger Rd Saint Louis MO 63124-1129 Office: Emerson Electric Co 8000 W Florissant Ave Saint Louis MO 63136-1414

TAMKIN, S. JEROME, business executive, consultant; b. L.A., Apr. 19, 1926; s. William W. and Thelma (Brandel) T.; m. Judith Deborah, Mar. 23, 1963; children: Wendy Lynn, Gary William, Sherry Dawn. B.S., U. So. Calif., 1950; M.A., Fremont Coll., 1951, Ph.D., 1952; LL.D., St. Andrews U., London, 1954. Mem. rsch. staff chemistry dept. U. Calif. at Los Angeles, 1943; rsch. chemist, analyst supr. synthetic rubber div. U.S. Rubber Co., 1943-44; pres., gen. mgr. Majicolor, Inc., Los Angeles, 1947-49; rsch. engr. Coil. Engring., U. So. Calif., 1946-48; gen. mgr. Pan Pacific Oil Co., Long Beach, Calif., 1948-55; plant mgr. indsl. sales and mfg., 1953-55; v.p., sales mgr. Wilco Co., Los Angeles, 1948-55; v.p charge indsl. sales and mfg. Wilco Co., 1953-55; v.p., sales mgr. Unit Chem. Corp., Los Angeles, 1955-56; pres. Phillips Mfg. Co. (merger Instl. Food Equipment Corp.), Los Angeles, 1957-62, Waste King Corp. (subs. Instl. Food Equipment Corp.), 1962-67; also dir., v.p., dir. Dyna Mfg. Co., Los Angeles, 1962-68; pres., dir. Profl. Rsch. Inc., Los Angeles, 1965-73; exec. v.p. Am. Med. Internat., Inc., Beverly Hills, Calif., 1966-71; dir. Am. Med. Internat., Inc., 1966-89; sec., dir. Rodger Young, Inc., L.A., 1971-77; pres., chmn. bd. TGT Petroleum Corp., Wichita, 1972—; pres., dir. Tamkin Cons. Corp., 1978—; owner, operator Tamkin Securities Co., 1979-86; vice chair dir., dir. Integrated Voice Solutions Inc., Chattanooga, 1991—; bd. dirs. CAPP Care Inc., Newport Beach, Calif., 1991—; tech. cons. Daylin Inc., Beverly Hills, 1973-75; founder First Beverly Bank, Beverly Hills. Contbr. articles to profl. jours. Cmty. warden W. Adams-Baldwin Hills Cmty. CD, 1950-52; bd. govs. We. Los Angeles County coun. Boy Scouts Am.; dep. sheriff Los Angeles County, 1949; bd. dirs. Sunair Home Asthmatic Children; city commr. L.A. Bd.

Environ. Quality, 1972-73; bd. dirs. Recovery Found., Fund for Higher Edn.; mem. exec. com. adv. coun. crime prevention L.A. Police, 1985—; U. Calif. at Irvine trustee Calif. Coll. Medicine, 1989-94; bd. visitors UCLA Sch. Medicine, 1990—; trustee Morehouse Sch. Medicine, 1995—. Served as officer USNR, 1944-46. Mem. AIM, Am. Mgmt. Assn., Inst. Aero. Scis. Am. Soc. Naval Engrs., Soc. Am. Mil. Engrs., Am. Chem. Soc., IEEE, Soc. Motion Picture and TV Engrs., Am. Inst. Chem. Engrs., Soc. Advancement Mgmt., U.S. Naval Inst., Calif. Scholarship Fedn. (life). Nat. Eagle Scout Assn., Sunrise Country Club, The Springs Country Club, Malibu Riding and Tennis Club, Alpha Eta Rho. Patentee electronic gas detector, circuits for automatic control hazardous vapors. Home: Pacific Palisades CA Office: 2100 Sawtelle Blvd Ste 201 Los Angeles CA 90025

TAMMEUS, WILLIAM DAVID, journalist, columnist; b. Woodstock, Ill., Jan. 18, 1945; s. W. H. and Bertha H. (Helander) T.; m. Marcia A. Bloom, Sept. 21, 1968; children: Lisen, Kate. BJ, U. Mo., Columbia, 1967; postgrad., U. Rochester, 1967-69. Reporter Rochester (N.Y.) Times-Union, 1967-70; reporter Kansas City (Mo.) Star, 1970-77, Starbeams columnist, 1977—; syndicated columnist N.Y. Times News Svc., 1989—. Editor-at-large Presbyn. Outlook, 1993; contbg. editor Mo. Life mag., 1980-81; commentator Sta. KCPT-TV, 1979-90. Co-recipient Pulitzer prize for gen. local reporting of Hyatt Regency Hotel disaster, 1982; recipient 1st pl. opinion-editorial divsn. Heart of Am. award Kansas City Press Club, 1991, 1st pl. opinion-analysis divsn. Heart of Am. award Kansas City Press Club, 1993. Mem. Nat. Soc. Newspaper Columnists (v.p. 1990-92, pres. 1992-94, 1st pl. items divsn. Writing award 1992), Soc. Profl. Journalists. Presbyterian. Office: 1729 Grand Blvd Kansas City MO 64108-1413

TAMRAT, BEFECADU, aeronautical engineer; b. Addis Ababa, Ethiopia, July 12, 1947; came to U.S., 1976; s. Tamrat Aberra and Yirgedu Reta; m. Assefash Kidane, July 5, 1980. BS, U. Ariz., 1969, MS, 1970. Sr. engr. sounding rocket project Space Vector Corp., Northridge, Calif., 1977-80; project engring. specialist Northrop Corp., Hawthorne, Calif., 1980-88; lead aeronautical engr. Rockwell Internat. NAAO, El Segundo, Calif., 1988—. Contbr. articles on fighter aircraft agility and performance to profl. publs. Mem. AIAA. Democrat. Achievements include introduction of new method of assessing fighter aircraft agility and performance. Home: 22334 Harbor Ridge Ln # 3 Torrance CA 90502 Office: Rockwell Internat 201 N Douglas St El Segundo CA 90009

TAMRES, MILTON, chemistry educator; b. Warsaw, Poland, Mar. 12, 1922; s. Morris and Lillian (Solberg) T.; m. Francoise Raymonde Lucot, Aug. 16, 1960; children—Louise R., Marc P. B.A. in Sci., Bklyn. Coll. 1943; Ph.D., Northwestern U., 1949. Control chemist Celanese Corp., Cumberland, Md., 1943-44; research and teaching fellow Northwestern U., Evanston, Ill., 1944-48; instr. chemistry U. Ill., Champaign-Urbana, 1948-51, asst. prof., 1951-53; asst. prof. chemistry U. Mich., Ann Arbor, 1953-57, assoc. prof., 1957-63, prof., 1963-87, prof. emeritus, 1987—; vis. scholar U. Tokyo, 1974. Contbr. articles to profl. jours. Guggenheim fellow, 1959-60; Am. Chem. Soc.-Petroleum Research Fund Internat. fellow, 1966-67. Fellow AAAS, Am. Inst. Chemists; mem. Am. Chem. Soc., Sigma Xi, Phi Lambda Upsilon (past nat. pres.), Alpha Chi Sigma. Home: 1307 Brooks St Ann Arbor MI 48103-3171 Office: Univ Mich 3533 Chemistry Ann Arbor MI 48109

TAMURA, CARY KAORU, fundraiser; b. Honolulu, Jan. 9, 1944; s. Akira and Harue (Otake) T.; m. Denise Jeanne Mitts, Oct. 17, 1987; children from previous marriage: Jennifer Joy, Matthew D. Student, U. Hawaii, 1961-63; BA in Philosophy, Nyack Coll., 1966; MA in Theology, Fuller Sem., 1986. Cert. fund-raising exec. Dir. svc. tng. ops. Fin. Adv. Clinic of Hawaii, Honolulu, 1972-76; dir. planned giving The Salvation Army, Honolulu, 1976-78; planned giving cons. InterVarsity Christian Fellowship, Portland, Oreg., 1978-80; account exec. Am. Income Life, Portland, Oreg., 1980-81; dir. planned giving The Salvation Army, Portland, Oreg., 1981-84, L.A., 1984-85; dir. devel. planned giving U. So. Calif., 1985-90; dir. gift planning UniHealth America, Burbank, Calif., 1990-94; pvt. gift planning cons. Brea, Calif., 1995—; bd. dirs. Nat. Com. on Planned Giving, Indpls., 1991-93, sec. exec. com., 1993; mem. adv. com., adj. faculty UCLA Extension; lectr. in field. Bd. dirs. Japanese Evang. Missionary Soc., 1990—, v.p., 1993; bd. deacons Evang. Free Ch., 1992-95. With U.S. Army, 1969-72. Named Outstanding Nominee in profl. category Nat. Philanthropy Day, 1992. Mem. Planned Giving Round Table So. Calif. (pres. 1989-91, Pres.'s award 1992), Nat. Soc. Fund Raising Execs. (Greater L.A. chpt. bd. dirs. 1990—, v.p. 1993, 95, chair FR Day 1994), So. Calif. Assn. Hosp. Developers, Assn. for Healthcare Philanthropy. Republican. Avocations: photography, golf, travel. Home and Office: 1413 N Robert Ct Brea CA 92621-2165

TAN, AMY RUTH, writer; b. Oakland, Calif., Feb. 19, 1952; d. John Yuehhan and Daisy Ching (Tu) T.; m. Louis M. DeMattei, Apr. 6, 1974. BA in Linguistics and English, San Jose (Calif.) State U., 1973, MA in Linguistics, 1974; LHD (hon.), Dominican Coll. San Rafael, 1991. Specialist lang. devel. Alameda County Assn. for Mentally Retarded, Oakland, 1976-80; project dir. M.O.R.E. Project, San Francisco, 1980-81; free-lance writer, 1981-88. Author: The Joy Luck Club, 1989 (Nat. Book Critics Circle award for best novel nomination 1989, L.A. Times Book award nomination 1989, Gold award for fiction Commonwealth Club 1990, Bay Area Book Reviewers award for best fiction 1990), The Kitchen God's Wife, 1991, The Moon Lady, 1992, The Chinese Siamese Cat, 1994; also numerous short stories and essays; screenwriter, prodr.: (film) The Joy Luck Club, 1993. Recipient Best Am. Essays award, 1991. *

TAN, ENG MENG, biomedical scientist; b. Seremban, Malaysia, Aug. 26, 1926; came to U.S., 1950; s. Ming Kee and Chooi Eng (Ang) T.; m. Liselotte Filippi, June 30, 1962; children: Philip, Peter. B.A.. Johns Hopkins U., 1952, M.D., 1956. Rsch. assoc. Rockefeller U., N.Y.C., 1962-65; assoc. prof. Washington U. Sch. Medicine, St. Louis, 1965-67; assoc. mem. Scripps Rsch. Inst., LaJolla, Calif., 1967-70, mem., 1970-77, dir. Autoimmune Disease Ctr., 1982—; prof. U. Colo. Sch. Medicine, Denver, 1977-82; chmn. allergy and immunology rsch. com. NIH, Bethesda, Md., 1982-84; mem. nat. arthritis adv. bd. HHS, Washington, 1981-85. Contbr. chpts. to books, articles to profl. jours. Named to Nat. Lupus Hall Fame, 1984; recepient U.S. Sr. Scientist award Humboldt Found., Fed. Republic Germany, 1986, award Ciba-Geigy-Internat. League Against Rheumatism, 1989, Carol Nachman award Wiesbaden, Fed. Republic Germany, 1989, Paul Klemperer award and medal N.Y. Acad. Medicine, 1993. Fellow AAAS; mem. Arthritis Found. (Lee Howley Sr. award 1989), Am. Coll. Rheumatology (pres. 1984-85, Disting. Investigator award 1991), Assn. Am. Physicians, Am. Soc. Clin. Investigation, Western Assn. Physicians (v.p. 1980-81), Am. Assn. Immunologists, Brazilian Soc. Rheumatology (hon.), Australian Rheumatism Assn. (hon.), Brit. Soc. Rheumatology (hon.). Rsch. on characterization of autoantibodies in autoimmune diseases, systemic lupus erythematosus, scleroderma, Sjogren's syndrome, myositis and mixed connective tissue disease; relationship of autoantibodies to pathogenesis. Home: 8303 Sugarman Dr La Jolla CA 92037-2224 Office: Scripps Rsch Inst 10666 N Torrey Pines Rd La Jolla CA 92037-1027

TAN, VERONICA Y., psychiatrist; b. Manila, The Philippines, Oct. 8, 1944; came to U.S., 1970; children: Terrence, Kristine. MD, U. St. Thomas, Manila, 1969. Intern U. Ill. Hosp., Chgo., 1970-71; resident Lafayette Clinic & Children's Hosp., Detroit; child, adolescent psychiatrist Bon Secours Hosp., Grosse Pointe, Mich., 1993—. Author: The Gifted Child, 1970.

TAN, WILLIAM LEW, lawyer; b. West Hollywood, Calif., July 25, 1949; s. James Tan Lew and Choon Guey Louie; m. Shelly Mieko Ushio. BA, U. Pa., 1971; JD, U. Calif. Hastings Coll. Law, San Francisco, 1974. Bar: Calif. 1975, U.S. Dist. Ct. (cen. dist.) Calif. 1975, U.S. Ct. Appeals (9th cir.) 1975, U.S. Supreme Ct. 1979. Assoc. Hiram W. Kwan, Los Angeles, 1974-79; sole practice Los Angeles, 1979-80; sole practice Los Angeles, 1980-81; ptnr. Mock & Tan, Los Angeles 1981-87, Tan & Sakiyama, Los Angeles, 1987—; bd. dirs. Am. Bus. Network, L.A.; pres., bd. dirs. Asian Rsch. Cons., L.A.; mem. adv. bd. Cathay Bank. Co-founder Asian Pacific Am. Roundtable, Los Angeles, 1981; chmn. bd. dirs. Leadrhip Edn. for Asian-Pacifics, Los Angeles, 1984-87; alt. del. Dem. Nat. Conv., San Francisco, 1984; mem. Calif. State Bd. Pharmacy, Sacramento, 1984-92, v.p. 1988-91, pres., 1991-92; mem. Los Angeles City and County Crime Crisis Task Force, Los Angeles, 1981, Los Angeles Asian Pacific Heritage Week

Com., 1980-85, Asian Pacific Women's Network, Los Angeles, 1981, Los Angeles City Atty.'s Blue Ribbon Con. of Advisors, 1981, community adv. bd. to Mayor of Los Angeles, 1984, allocations vol. liaison team health and therapy div. United Way, Los Angeles, 1986, mem. nominating com. bd. dirs., 1994—; bd. dirs. Chinatown Service Ctr., Los Angeles, 1983; conf. advisor U.S.-Asia, Los Angeles, 1981-83; atty. Los Angeles City Housing Adv. Com.; mem. Pacific Bell Consumer Product Adv. Panel; vice chair community adv. bd. Sta. KCET-TV, PBS, 1993-94; mem. adv. commn. State of Calif. Com. on State Procurement Practices, 1989-90; mem. L.A. City Attys. Citizens' Task Force on Pvt. Club Discrimination, 1989-90; mem. Calif. Med. Summit, 1993; mem. Mayor's Commn. Children, Youth and Families, 1993—; mem. pub. access subcom. Mayor's Spl. Adv. Com. on Tech. Implementation, 1994—. Named one of Outstanding Young Men of Am., 1979. Mem. ABA (mem. numerous coms.), Calif. State Bar Assn. (vice chmn. com. ethnic minority relations 1983-85, chmn. pub. affairs com. 1981-82, mem. others), Los Angeles County Bar Assn. (vice chmn. 1980-82, mem. numerous coms.), So. Calif. Chinese Lawyers Assn. (pres. 1980-81, chmn., 1987-88, mem. various coms.), Minority Bar Assn. (chmn. 1981-82, sec. 1980-81, chmn. adv. bd. 1982-83), Asian Pacific Bar of Calif., Nat. Asian Pacific Am. Bar, Japanese Am. Bar Assn., Assn. Trial Lawyers Am., Bench and Bar Media Council, Calif. Trial Lawyers Assn., Soc. Intercultural Edn. (conf. coordinator, advisor panelist tng. and research com. 1983),. Avocations: gourmet cooking, bicycling, swimming, tennis, water color painting. Office: 300 S Grand Ave Ste 2750 Los Angeles CA 90071-3137

TANABE, BARBARA JEAN, communications company executive; b. Tokyo, Jan. 12, 1949; came to U.S., 1955; d. Frank Shinichiro and Setsuko (Onishi) T.; m. Roy H. Kawaguchi, June 18, 1971; children: Bucikas G., Jawagycgu. BA in Comm., U. Washh., 1971; MBA, U. Hawaii, 1983. Anchor, reporter, writer Sta. KOMO-TV, ABC, Seattle, 1970-74; news dir., anchor, prodr. Sta. KHON-TV, NBC, Honolulu, 1974-87; pres., CEO, Hill and Knowlton Hawaii, Inc., Honolulu, 1987—; bd. dirs. Bank of Hawaii, Honolulu; participant oral history project Nat. Press Club, Washington. Prodr., writer documentary The Fence at Minidoka, 1971 (Emmy award 1972). Bd. dirs. Hawaii Visitors Bur., Honolulu, 1991—, chmn. bd., 1994-95; bd. dirs. Conv. Ctr. Authority, Honolulu, 1994-96. Named One of State's Outstanding Women, YWCA, Honolulu, 1987. Mem. Honolulu Japanese C. of C. (bd. dirs. 1989—), Japan-Am. Soc. Hawaii (bd. dirs.). Office: Hill & Knowlton Hawaii Inc 820 Mililani St Ste 400 Honolulu HI 96813

TANAKA, FLOYD HIDEO, consulting firm executive; b. Colusa, Calif., Mar. 5, 1924; s. Tsunetaro and Tsuyo (Saito) T.; m. Rose Hanawa, June 12, 1949; children: Daniel, Susan, Paul, Ken. BArch, U. Denver, 1951. Planning dir. City of Colorado Springs, 1951-54; city planner Harmon O'Donnell & Henninger, Denver, 1954-56; tech. dir. Denver Urban Renewal Authority, 1956-65; assoc. Harmon O'Donnell & Henninger, Denver, 1965-67; prin. Tanaka & Assocs., Denver, 1967-69; pres. THK Assocs., Inc., Denver, 1969—; cons. firm exec. Commr. Colo. Land Use Commn., Denver, 1970-71. With U.S. Army, 1944-46. Mem. Am. Inst. Planners, Am. Planning Assn., Nat. Assn. Housing and Redevel. Ofcls., Deans Coun. Sch. Architecture and Planning U. Colo. at Denver, Met. Club. Democrat. Unitarian. Home: 204 Madison St Denver CO 80206-5407 Office: THK Assocs Inc Ste 200 5325 S Valentia Way Englewood CO 80111-3115

TANAKA, KAY, genetics educator; b. Osaka, Japan, Mar. 2, 1929; came to U.S., 1969; d. Kumaji and Fusa (Nakamae) T.; m. Tomoko Hasegawa, Nov. 5, 1954; children: Atau, Elly Margaret. MD, U. Tokyo, 1956, Dr. Med. Sci., 1961; MA (hon.) Yale U., 1983. Asst. prof. medicine Harvard Med. Sch., Boston, 1969-73; sr. research scientist Yale U., New Haven, Conn., 1973-82, prof. genetics, 1983-94, prof. emeritus, 1995—; mem. biochemistry study sect. NIH, Bethesda, Md., 1983-84. Contbr. numerous articles to sci. jours., chpts. to books. Grantee NIH, 1971-95, March of Dimes, 1974-92. Mem. Am. Soc. Biol. Chemistry, Am. Soc. Human Genetics, Soc. Inborn Metabolic Disorders. Office: Yale U Dept Genetics 333 Cedar St New Haven CT 06510-3206

TANAKA, KOUICHI ROBERT, physician, educator; b. Fresno, Calif., Dec. 15, 1926; s. Kenjiro and Teru (Arai) T.; m. Grace Mutsuko Sakaguchi, Oct. 23, 1965; children—Anne M., Nancy K., David K. B.S., Wayne State U., 1949, M.D., 1952. Intern Los Angeles County Gen. Hosp., 1952-53; resident, fellow Detroit Receiving Hosp., 1953-57; instr. Sch. Medicine, UCLA, 1957-59, asst. prof. medicine, 1959-61, asso. prof. medicine, 1961-68, prof., 1968—; asso. chmn., chief hematology, dept. medicine Harbor-UCLA Med. Center, Torrance, Calif., 1961—. Served with AUS, 1946-48. Fellow ACP (gov. so. Calif. region I 1993—); mem. Am. Fedn. Clin. Rsch., Western Soc. Clin. Investigation, L.A. Soc. Internal Medicine (pres. 1971), Am. Soc. Hematology, Internat. Soc. Hematology, Western Assn. Physicians, Am. Soc. Clin. Investigation, Assn. Am. Physicians, Sigma Xi, Alpha Omega Alpha. Research red cell metabolism. Home: 4 Cayuse Ln Rancho Palos Verdes CA 90275 Office: Harbor UCLA Med Ctr PO Box 2910 Torrance CA 90509-2910

TANAKA, RICHARD I., computer products company executive; b. Sacramento, Dec. 17, 1928; s. G. and Kei Tanaka; m. Edith M. Arita, Aug. 18, 1951; children: Steven Richard, Jean Elizabeth, John Richard, Anne Mariko. B.S. with highest honors, U. Calif., Berkeley, 1950, M.S., 1951; Ph.D., Calif. Inst. Tech., 1958. Sr. research engr. N.Am. Aviation, Inc., 1951-54; mem. tech. staff Hughes Aircraft Co., 1954-57; dept. mgr., sr. mem. computer research Lockheed Missiles & Space Co., Palo Alto, Calif., 1957-65; sr. v.p. Cal Comp (Calif. Computer Products, Inc.), Anaheim, Calif., 1966-77; pres. Internat. Tech. Resources Co., Tustin, Calif., 1977-80; pres., chief exec. officer Systonetics, Inc., Fullerton, Calif., 1980-86; pres. Lundy Electronics & Systems, Inc., Glen Head, N.Y., 1986-89; chmn., chief exec. officer, pres. Scan-Optics, Inc., East Hartford, Conn., 1989—; vis. prof. U. Calif., Berkeley, 1962. Author: Residue Arithmetic and Its Applications to Computer Technology, 1967. Hughes fellow Calif. Inst. Tech., 1955-57. Fellow IEEE (nat. chmn. computer soc. 1965-66, centennial medal); mem. Internat. Fedn. Info. Processing (pres. 1974-77, hon. life mem., U.S. del.), Am. Fedn. Info. Processing Socs. (pres. 1969-71, disting. service award 1983), Phi Beta Kappa, Tau Beta Pi, Eta Kappa Nu. Home: 19 Stratford Park Bloomfield CT 06002-2143 Office: Scan-Optics Inc 22 Prestige Park Cir East Hartford CT 06108-1917

TANAKA, RICHARD KOICHI, JR., architect, planner; b. San Jose, Calif., Oct. 16, 1931; s. Richard Inoru and Mae Yoshiko (Koga) T.; m. Barbara Hisako Kumagai, Oct. 7, 1961; children: Craig, Todd, Sandra, Trent. BArch, U. Mich., 1954; M in Urban Planning, Calif. State U., San Jose, 1978. Exec. v.p. Steinberg Group, San Jose, L.A., 1954—. Author: American on Trial, 1988. Dir. Human Rels. Com., San Jose, 1969-73; dir., pres. Bicentennial Com., San Jose, 1974-77; bd. dirs. Santa Clara County Sch. Bd. Assn., 1980—; pres. Internment of Local Japanese Ams., San Jose, 1984—; past pres., trustee East Side H.S. Dist., San Jose, 1971-72, Japanese Am. Citizens League, San Jose; mem. bd. govs. Boy Scouts Am., San Jose, 1978—, NCCJ, San Jose, 1978—; past pres. Tapestry and Talent, 1976-80; trustee San Jose/Evergreen C.C., 1992—, pres., 1993-94. Mem. AIA (pres. 1993-94), Am. Planning Inst., Constrn. Specification Inst., Rotary. Avocations: golf, painting. Home: 14811 Whipple Ct San Jose CA 95127-2570 Office: 60 Pierce Ave San Jose CA 95110-2819

TANAKA, TED TOKIO, architect, educator; b. Tokyo, Nov. 27, 1942; came to U.S., 1958, naturalized, 1963. B.Arch., Ariz. State U., 1969. Registered architect, Calif. Designer Gruen Assocs., Los Angeles, 1969-70; ptnr. Environ. Communications, Los Angeles, 1969-76; project designer Flood & Assocs., Los Angeles, 1970-71; dir. design Jenkins Architects, Beverly Hills, Calif., 1971-75; prin. Ted T. Tanaka Architect, Venice, Calif., 1975—; instr. Santa Monica (Calif.) Coll., 1976-78; prin. works include: Hubert Humphrey Comprehensive Health Ctr., Los Angeles, Martin Luther King Service and Supply Bldg., Los Angeles, Hansui Restaurant, Santa Monica, Gilberg Psychiat. Bldg., Sunlight Picture offce bldg., Hollywood, Calif., St. Louis Convention Ctr. Contbr. articles to profl. jours. Varney Sexton Seydnor scholar Ariz. State U., 1963. Mem. AIA, Mus. Contemporary Art Los Angeles. Office: Ted Tokio Tanaka Arch AIA 4223 Glencoe Ave # B107 Marina Del Rey CA 90292

TANAKA, TOYOICHI, science educator; b. Nagaoka, Niigata, Japan, Jan. 4, 1946; came to the U.S., 1972; s. Toyosuke and Shizu (Homma) T.; m. Tomoko Tahira, Apr. 26, 1970; children: Kazunori, Ayako. BS, U. Tokyo, 1968, MS, 1970, PhD, 1973. Rsch. assoc. MIT, Cambridge, Mass., 1972-75, asst. prof., 1975-79, assoc. prof., 1979-82, prof., 1982—; vis. prof. Univ. Louis Pasteur, Strasbourg, France, 1980-81; Rashmer lectr. U. Wash., 1987. Editor-in-chief Polymer Gels and Networks, London, 1992; contbr. articles to profl. jours. Recipient Vinci d'Excellence Moet Hennessy Louis Vuitton, Paris, 1993, Inoue Scis. prize, 1994. Fellow Am. Phys. Soc.; mem. Chem. Soc. Japan, Physical Soc. Japan (Nishina Meml. prize 1985), Polymer Soc. Japan (award 1986). Avocations: tennis, swimming, Japanese dishes. Home: 22 Lowell Rd Wellesley MA 02181-2754 Office: MIT 77 Massachusetts Ave Cambridge MA 02139-3594

TANCREDI, LAURENCE RICHARD, law and psychiatry educator, administrator; b. Hershey, Pa., Oct. 15, 1940; s. Samuel N. and Alvesta (Pera) T. A.B. in English, Franklin and Marshall Coll.; 1962; M.D., U. Pa., 1966; J.D., Yale U., 1972. Diplomate Am. Bd. Neurology and Psychiatry. Bar: N.Y. 1982. Sr. profl. assoc. Inst. of Medicine, Nat. Acad. Scis., Washington, 1972-74; fellow dept. psychiatry Columbia U. Coll. Physicians and Surgeons, N.Y.C., 1974-75; postdoctoral fellow in psychiatry Yale Med. Sch., New Haven, 1975-77; assoc. prof. psychiatry and law NYU Med. Sch., 1977-84, adj. prof. law Sch. of Law, 1977-84; Kraft Eidman prof. medicine and law U. Tex. Health Sci. Ctr., Houston, 1984-92, dir. Health Law Program, U. Tex. Health Sci. Ctr., Houston, 1984-92; prof. clin. psychiatry med. sch., NYU, 1992—; med. dir. The Regent Hosp., N.Y.C., 1992-93; clin. prof. healthcare scis. U. Calif., San Diego Med. Sch., 1993—. v.p. Internat. Acad. of Law and Mental Health, 1981—; pvt. practice, N.Y.C.; nat. advisory bd. NIMH Ctr. for the Study of Pub. Mental Health N.Y. State Office Mental Health, 1994—. mem. bd. tech. dirs. Milbank Meml. Fund, N.Y.C., 1981-84; mem. adv. com. on heart transplantations Health Care Fin. Adminstrn., Dept. HHS, 1981-84, other coms.; cons. Commn. on Med. Profl. Liability, co-prin. investigator study ABA, 1978-80; cons. in field. Coauthor 7 books. Editor and contbg. author 4 books. Contbr. articles to profl. jours. Mem. editorial bd. Ann. Bibliography on Bioethics, Kennedy Inst. Bioethics, 1979—. Mem. Am. Psychiat. Assn. (chmn. council on govt. policy and the law 1979-81), Am. Soc. Law and Medicine, Soc. Med. Jurisprudence (trustee 1983-85), Am. Coll. Psychiat., Group for the Advancement of Psychiatry.

TANDLER, BERNARD, cell biology educator; b. Bklyn., Feb. 18, 1933; s. Arthur and Pauline (Solomon) T.; m. Helen Weisman, Dec. 25, 1955 (dec. Aug. 14, 1986); children: Janice Dena, Evan Charles. B.S. Bklyn. Coll., 1955; A.M., Columbia U., 1957; Ph.D., Cornell U., 1961. Instr. anatomy NYU, N.Y.C., 1962-63; assoc. Sloan Kettering Inst., 1963-67; asst. prof. cell biology Cornell U., N.Y.C., 1965-67; assoc. prof. Case Western Res. U., Cleve., 1967-72, prof. oral biology, 1972-91, acting chmn. dept. oral biology, 1987-89; affiliate prof. oral biology U. Wash., Seattle, 1993—; vis. prof. U. Copenhagen, 1973, U. Cagliari, 1983, Kyushu Dental Coll., 1994—; cons. NIH, NSF, VA. Author: (with C.L. Hoppel) Mitochondria, 1972; assoc. editor: Anatomical Record, 1974—; guest editor: Microscopy Rsch. and Technique, 1993-94; contbr. chpts. to books, articles to profl. jours. Recipient Disting. Alumnus award Bklyn. Coll., 1981, Robert E. Kennedy award for Acad. Freedom, Ohio chpt. AAUP, 1992; USPHS fellow, 1957-62. Mem. Am. Assn. Anatomists, Am. Soc. Cell Biology, Electron Microscopy Soc. Am., Japanese Soc. Oral Biology, Japanese Assn. Anatomists, Internat. Assn. Dental Research, Am. Soc. Mammalogists, Italian Soc. Anatomy (hon.), Sigma Xi.

TANDON, RAJIV, psychiatrist, educator; b. Kanpur, India, Aug. 3, 1956; came to U.S., 1984; s. Bhagwan Sarup and Usha (Mehrotra) T.; m. Chanchal Nammi Vohra; children: Neeraj, Anisha. Student, St. Xavier's Coll., Bombay, India, 1974; BS, All India Inst., New Delhi, 1980; MD, Nat. Inst. of MH, India, 1983. Sr. resident Mental Health and Neuro-Scis., India, 1983-84; resident U. Mich. Hosps., Ann Arbor, 1984-87, attending psychiatrist, 1987—; dir. schizophrenia program U. Mich., Ann Arbor, 1987—; assoc. prof., 1993—; cons. Lenawee County Community Mental Health, Adrian, Mich., 1985—. Author: Biochemical Parameters of Mixed Affective States; Negative Schizophrenic Symptoms: Pathophysiology and Clinical Implications; contbr. more than 120 articles to profl. jours. Recipient Young Scientist's award Biennial Winter Workshop on Schizophrenia, 1990, 92, Travel award Am. Coll. Neuropsychopharmacology/Mead, 1990, Rsch. Excellence award Am. Assn. Psychiatrists from India, 1993, Sci. award, Gerald Klerman award for outstanding rsch. NARSAD Young Investigator, 1995. Mem. Am. Psychiat. Assn. (Wisniewski Young Psychiatrist Rschr. award 1993), World Fedn. Mental Health, Soc. for Neurosci., N.Y. Acad. Scis., Soc. Biol. Psychiatry, Mich. Psychiat. Soc. Democrat. Hindu. Office: U Mich Med Ctr Dept Psychiatry 1500 E Medical Center Dr # 8D Ann Arbor MI 48109-0116

TANEN, NED STONE, motion picture company executive; b. Los Angeles, 1931. Grad., UCLA, 1954. With MCA Inc. (and subsidiaries); v.p. MCATTV, 1964-67; founder UNI Records, later MCA Records, 1967; exec. v.p. Universal City Records, Calif., 1967-69; v.p. MCA Inc., Universal City, 1967—; pres. Universal Theatrical Motion Pictures div., 1976; pres. Universal Picture div., 1979-82, also dir.; pres. motion picture group Paramount Pictures, 1984—; ind. producer, 1982—. Served with USAF, 1950-52. Office: Paramount Pictures Motion Picture Group 5555 Melrose Ave Los Angeles CA 90038-3197

TANENBAUM, BASIL SAMUEL, engineering educator; b. Providence, R.I., Dec. 1, 1934; s. Harry Milton and Rena Ada (Herr) T.; m. Carol Binder, Aug. 26, 1956; children: Laurie, Stephen, David. B.S. summa cum laude, Brown U., 1956; M.S. (NSF fellow, 1956-60), Yale U., 1957, Ph.D. in Physics, 1960. Staff physicist Raytheon Co., Waltham, Mass., 1960-63; prof. engring. Case Western Res. U., Cleve., 1963-75; dean of faculty Harvey Mudd Coll., Claremont, Calif., 1975-93, prof. engring., 1975—; vis. scientist Cornell U., Arecibo (P.R.) Obs., 1968-69; vis. assoc. prof. Northwestern U., Evanston, Ill., 1970; vis. scholar U.C. Irvine Beckman Laser Inst., 1993-94; sci. adv. com. Nat. Astronomy and Ionosphere Center, 1972-77, Calif. Poly. Inst., Pomona, 1976-87; engring. and sci. adv. com. Calif. State U., Fullerton, 1976-87; mem. nat. adv. com. Rowan Coll., Glassboro, N.J., 1993—; Eisenhower adv. com. Cal. Postsec. Edn. Com., 1993—; bd. dirs. University Circle, Inc., 1973-75; dir. Minority Engrs. Indsl. Opportunity Program, 1973-75; dir. summer sci. program Thacher Sch., Ojai, Calif., 1977-82; cons. various corps., univ. labs., govt. agencies. Author: Plasma Physics, 1967. Woods Hole Oceanog. Inst. fellow, 1959; sr. Sterling fellow, 1959; recipient Wittke teaching award, 1974. Mem. AAAS, Am. Phys. Soc., Am. Soc. for Engring. Edn., IEEE, AAUP, Sigma Xi (research award 1969). Home: 611 W Delaware Dr Claremont CA 91711-3458 Office: Harvey Mudd Coll 301 E 12th St Claremont CA 91711-5994

TANENBAUM, BERNARD JEROME, JR., corporate executive; b. Little Rock, Nov. 26, 1934; s. Bernard Jerome and Naomi (Dante) T.; m. Patricia Wise, June 9, 1955; children: Bernard Jerome III, Albert Wise. B.B.A., Tulane U., 1956; D.Pub. Service, Ark. Bapt. Coll., 1974. Salesman Dantan Co., Dumas, Ark., 1955; buyer Dantes Stores, Dumas, 1956-61; exec. v.p. Dante and Tanenbaum, Dumas, 1961; pres. UDS Inc. (formerly United Dollar Stores, Inc.), Dumas, 1967—; pres. Pudata Inc.; chmn. JAT II, Inc., vice chmn. Ark. Tax Revision Commn. County chmn. ARC, 1957-60; v.p., dir. Desota coun. Boy Scouts Am.; pres. Henry S. Jacobs Camp, S.W. region Union Am. Hebrew Congregations, also vice chmn. bd. trustees, mem. exec. com., mem. nat. com. camps and insts., rep. S.W. region to long-range planning com.; chmn. N.Am. bd. World Union Progressive Judaism, 1995, mem. exec. governing body, 1989; bd. dirs. Dante & Tanenbaum Found., Ark. dept. NCCJ, Ark. chpt. Arthritis Found.; pres., dir. Camp Assn. So. Temples; mem. bd. govs. Hebrew Union Coll.-Jewish Inst. of Religion; trustee adv. bd. Tulane U.; trustee Leo N. Levi Hosp., 1994; bd. dirs. Hot Spring Documentary Film Festival, 1994. Recipient Ark. Ten Outstanding Young Men award, 1971, Outstanding Service award Sickle Cell Anemia Found., 1973, Distinguished Arkansan award, 1974. Mem. Ark. Retail Mchts. Assn. (dir.), Dumas Mchts. Assn. (past chmn.), Dumas Jr. C. of C. (past pres.), Ark. Jr. C. of C. (past internat. dir.), Dumas C. of C, Zeta Beta Tau; mem. B'nai B'rith (past dir.). Jewish religion (past pres., trustee temple). Club: Mason (32). Home: 130 S Lakeland Point Hot Springs

National Park AR 71913-7608 Office: 1401 Malvern Ave Ste 160 Hot Springs National Park AR 71901

TANENBAUM, GERALD STEPHEN, lawyer; b. Phila., Dec. 12, 1945; s. Harold Jack and Matilda (Fleischman) T.; m. Gretchen Jonas; children: Jennifer, Rebecca. AB, U. N.C., 1967; JD, U. Ga., 1970. Bar: Ga. 1970, N.Y. 1971, U.S. Dist. Ct. (so. dist.) N.Y. 1974, U.S. Ct. Appeals (2d cir.) 1974. Assoc. Cahill Gordon & Reindel, N.Y.C., 1970-78, ptnr., 1978—. Office: Cahill Gordon & Reindel 80 Pine St New York NY 10005-1702

TANENBAUM, STUART WILLIAM, biotechnologist, educator; b. N.Y.C., July 15, 1924; s. Julius and Anna (Saphirstein) T.; m. Hannah Mehler, Feb. 18, 1962; children: Jonas, Stefanie. BS, CCNY, 1944; PhD, Columbia U., 1951. Rsch. assoc. Stanford U., 1951-53; prof. microbiology Columbia Univ., Coll. of Physicians and Surgeons, N.Y.C., 1953-73; dean, Sch. Biology, Chemistry and Ecology SUNY-Coll. of Environ. Sci. & Forestry, Syracuse, 1973-85; assoc. mem. Polymer Rsch. Inst.; biotechnology prof. SUNY-Coll. of Environ. Sci. & Forestry, Syracuse, 1985-93, prof. emeritus, 1993—; adj. prof. microbiology SUNY Health Sci. Ctr., Syracuse, 1973—; vis. prof. Istituto Superiore di Sanità, Rome, 1963-64; program dir. biochemistry NSF, Washington, 1970-71; bd. dirs. Coll. Forestry Found., Syracuse, 1974-91; biotechnology cons., 1993—; chmn. ASI mtg. NATO, Sitges, Spain, 1990. Editor: Cytochalasins, 1978; contbr. over 150 articles to profl. jours.; patentee in field. Vis. scientist Fedn. Am. Socs. for Exptl. Biology Minorities Instns. Program, 1989. With U.S. Army, 1944-46; ETO. Decorated Combat Infantry award, U.S. Army, 1944; recipient Sigma Xi Faculty Rsch. award 1986, SUNY's Best Teaching award 1990, United Univ. Professions Excellence award, 1991. Mem. Am. Chem. Soc., Am. Soc. Biol. Chemists, Soc. for Indsl. Microbiology, Soc. Am. Microbiologists, Sigma Xi. Home: 7472 Armstrong Rd Manlius NY 13104-1418 Office: Coll Environ Sci & Forestry 310 Baker Labs Syracuse NY 13210

TANEY, J. CHARLES, advertising agency executive. Formerly sr. exec. v.p. FCB/Leber Katz Ptnrs., N.Y.C., now pres., chief operating officer. Office: FCB/Leber Katz Ptnrs GM Bldg 767 Fifth Ave New York NY 10153-0001

TANG, ESTHER DON, development consultant, retired social worker; b. Tucson, Mar. 5, 1917; d. Don Wah and Yut (Gnan) Fok; m. David W. Tang, June 14, 1942; children: Patricia Karen Tang Crowley, Diana Cherly Tang Simones, David. Jr., Elizabeth Carol. Student, Draughn's Bus. Sch., San Antonio, 1936, U. Ariz., 1938-41; DHL (hon.), U. Ariz., 1992, LHD (hon.), 1992. Owner, operator supermarket, Tucson, 1944-66; exec. dir. Pio Decinio Ctr. Cath. Diocese, Tucson, 1966-85; cons., ptnr., vice chmn. bd. Netwest Devel. Corp., Tucson, 1985—. Mem. Tucson Airport Authority, 1975—; chmn. Tucson-Taichung Sister Cities, 1979-91; chmn. Tucson Sister Cities Steering Com., 1984—, Sister Cities Assn. Tucson, 1990, Ariz. Pers. Bd.; chmn. bd. dirs. Pima Community Coll., 1975-85; pres. bd. dirs. Pima Coun. on Aging, 1986-90; coord. U.S. Bicentennial, Tucson; mem. adv. bd. Ariz. Dept. Econ. Security. Named Woman of Yr., City of Tucson, 1955, Woman of Yr. in Adminstrn., 1968, Lady Comdr. the Holy Sepluchre Jerusalem; recipient Disting. Friend of the Humanities award Nat. Adv. Bd., 1989, Jefferson award Ariz. Daily Star, 1987, Svc. award Pima Coun. on Aging, 1987-89, Disting. Svc. award U. Pima C.C. Found., 1988, Roots and Wings Comty. award, 1988, Rosie award So. Ariz. Ctr. Against Sexual Assault, 1990, Lifetime Achievement award YWCA, 1992, 93. Mem. Soroptimist (hon.). Roman Catholic. Avocations: travel, cooking, golf. Home: 701 E Camino De Los Padres Tucson AZ 85718-1921 Office: Netwest Devel Corp 2221 E Broadway Blvd Ste 211 Tucson AZ 85719-6032

TANG, PAUL CHI LUNG, philosophy educator; b. Vancouver, B.C., Can., Jan. 23, 1944; came to U.S., 1971; s. Pei-Sung and Violet (Wong) T. BSc with high distinction, U. B.C., 1966; MA in Edn., Simon Fraser U., Vancouver, 1971; MA, Washington U., St. Louis, 1975, PhD, 1982; cert. Inst. Ethics, Georgetown U., 1983; diploma in piano, U. Toronto, 1962. Teaching asst. philosophy of edn. Simon Fraser U., 1969-71; instr. philosophy St. Louis C.C. at Meramec, Kirkwood, Mo., 1975-82; instr.; lectr. philosophy Washington U., 1972-76; adj. asst. prof. Harris-Stowe State Coll., St. Louis, 1980-82; asst. prof. philosophy Grinnell (Iowa) Coll., 1982-85; asst. prof. to assoc. prof. to prof. dept. philosophy Calif. State U., Long Beach, 1985—, chmn. dept. philosophy, 1988-94. Contbr. numerous articles and revs. to profl. publs.; editor Philosophy of Sci. Assn. Newsletter, 1985-90; asst. editor Philosophy of Sci. acad. jour., 1972-75. Senator Internat. Parliament for Safety and Peace, Palermo, Italy. Washington U. fellow, 1971, Summer Rsch. fellow Calif. State U., Long Beach, 1988, NEH fellow Harvard U., 1988, NEH Summer Seminar fellow, 1988; Internat. scholar Phi Beta Delta, Interdisciplinary scholar Phi Kappa Phi, 1993; grantee Vis. Philosophers Program, Coun. for Philos. Studies, 1987, 91, 92, Disting. Vis. Scholars and Artists Fund, Calif. State U., Long Beach, 1988, 89; recipient Cert. of Merit, Student Philosophy Assn., 1988, 89, 90, 93, 94; named Faculty Mem. of Yr., 1991; recipient Meritorious Performance award, 1986, 88, 90, Associated Students' Faculty Advisor of Yr. award, 1987, 90, 91, award for internationalizing the curriculum Calif. State Univ., Long Beach, 1993, Univ. Disting. Faculty Tchg. award, 1994-95, Disting. Grad. Prof. award, 1995, Coll. Liberal Arts Most Favorite Prof. award, 1995. Mem. Am. Philos. Assn., Philosophy of Sci. Assn., History of Sci. Soc., Kennedy Inst. Ethics, Hastings Ctr., Iowa Philos. Soc. (pres. 1985-86), Internat. Platform Assn., Internat. Order of Merit, World Literary Academy (fellow), Brit. Soc. Philosophy of Sci., Soc. Philosophy and Psychology, Templar Order of Jerusalem (knight), Order of the Holy Cross of Jerusalem (knight), Lofsenic Ursinius Order (knight commdr.), Chevalier Grand Croix de la Milice du Saint Sepulcre, Maison Internat. des Intellectuels de L'Académie Française, numerous others. Avocations: hiking, tennis, chess, music, travel. Home: 5050 E Garford St Apt 228 Long Beach CA 90815-2859 Office: Calif State U Dept Philosophy 1250 N Bellflower Blvd Long Beach CA 90840-0004

TANG, THOMAS, federal judge; b. Phoenix, Jan. 11, 1922. B.S., U. Santa Clara, 1947, law student, 1948-50; LL.B. with distinction, U. Ariz., 1950. Bar: Ariz. 1950, Calif. 1951. Dep. county atty. Maricopa County, Ariz., 1953-57; asst. atty. gen. State of Ariz., 1957-58; judge Ariz. Superior Ct., 1963-70; mem. firm Sullivan, Mahoney & Tang, Phoenix, 1971-77; councilman City of Phoenix, 1960-62, vice mayor, 1962; judge U.S. Ct. of Appeals 9th Circuit, Phoenix, 1977-93, sr. status judge, 1993—. Mem. State Bar Ariz. (bd. govs. 1971-77, pres. 1977), State Bar Calif. Office: US Ct Appeals 9th Cir 6412 Courthouse & Fed Bldg 230 N 1st Ave Phoenix AZ 85025-0230

TANG, WILSON HON-CHUNG, engineering educator; b. Hong Kong, Aug. 16, 1943; came to U.S., 1962, naturalized, 1979; s. Shu-Chun and Shui-Kuen Chan T.; m. Bernadette Tim, July 29, 1969; children: Tze-John, Joyce Wing-Yi. BS, MIT, 1966, MS, 1967; CE, PhD, Stanford U., 1969. Asst. prof. civil engring. U. Ill., Urbana-Champaign, 1969-74, assoc. prof., 1974-79, prof., 1979—, assoc. head dept. civil engring., 1989-91; Guggenheim fellow Norwegian Geotech. Inst., Oslo, Imperial Coll., London, 1976-77; vis. prof. Nat. U. Singapore, U. Hong Kong, 1983, Hong U. Sch. and Tech., 1995; prin. Wilson Tang and Assocs., 1986—; cons. to indsl. firms and govtl. agys. on reliability evaluation of structure and geotech. performances; mem. rev. panel Fulbright awards. Author: (with A. H-S. Ang.) Probability Concepts in Engineering Planning and Design, Vol. I, 1975, Vol. II, 1984; mem. editorial bd. Internat. Jour. Structural Safety, 1989—. Guggenheim fellow, 1976; NSF research grantee, 1972—; recipient Campus teaching award, 1991. Fellow ASCE (scholar 1965, Outstanding Tchr. award 1980, chmn. com. on reliability of offshore structures 1984-87, State of the Art Paper award 1990, co-chmn. com. on geotechnical safety and reliability, 1993—); mem. Geotech. Bd. of Nat. Rsch. Coun. (chmn. com. on workshop on Reliability Methods for Risk Mitigation in Geotech. Engring.), Am. Soc. Engring. Edn. Internat. Geostatis. Assn., Internat. Assn. for Structural Safety and Reliability, Internat. Assn. for Civil Engring. Reliability and Risk Analysis, Internat. Soc. Soil Mechanics and Found. Engring., Chinese-Am. Asssn. Natural Disaster Mitigation Rsch. (bd. dirs. 1989-91). Home: 310 E Willard St Urbana IL 61801-6653 Office: 205 N Mathews Ave Urbana IL 61801-2350

TANGNEY, JOSEPH G., insurance executive; b. Boston, Dec. 7, 1944; m. Virginia Tangney (div.); children: Christopher, Patrick, Nicole; m. Janice L. Mackin; 1 child, Leah. AB in Econs., Providence Coll., 1966; JD, Boston

Coll., 1969; cert. in advanced mgmt., Harvard U., 1982. Atty. Liberty Mut. Ins. Co., Boston, 1969-72, asst. counsel, 1972-78, counsel, 1978-80, v.p., asst. gen. counsel, 1980-83, v.p., mgr. gen. claims, 1983—. Mem. ABA, Arbitration Forums Inc., Ins. Crime Prevention Inst., Mass. and N.J. Guaranty Funds, Mass. Bar Assn., Boston Bar Assn.

TANGUAY, NORBERT ARTHUR, municipal police training officer; b. Winchendon, Mass., May 22, 1933; s. Arthur T. and Yvonne (Brunette) T.; (div.); children: MIchael N., Theresa Y., Mark T.; m. Sherrie Ann Miller, Aug. 17, 1983; 1 child, William Arthur. Comml. pilot cert., East Coast Aero Tech., Lexington, Mass., 1957; AS, Manchester (Conn.) C.C., 1974. Lic. comml. pilot. Ins. cons. Met. Life Ins. Co., Manchester, Conn., 1966-70; lt. U. Conn. Police Dept., Storrs, 1970-75; tng. officer Mcpl. Police Tng. Acad., Meriden, Conn., 1975—; rangemaster Mcpl. Police Tng. Acad., 1977—; lectr. on child abuse, Conn., 1977—. Author: Dispatcher's Guide to Crimes/ Incidents in Progress, 1988, Police Officers Response Guide to Crimes/ Incidents in Progress, 1991; inventor: handgun muscle trainer, 1993. With U.S. Navy, 1951-55, Korea. Mem. NRA, VFW, Narcotic Enforcement Officers Assn., Nat. Assn. Fed. Lic. Firearms Dealers, Internat. Assn. Law Enforcement Firearms Instrs. Democrat. Roman Catholic. Avocations: golf, gardening, swimming, chess. Office: Tanguay Pubs PO Box 290266 Wethersfield CT 06129-0266

TANGUAY, PETER EUGENE, child and adolescent psychiatry educator; b. Quebec City, Que., Can., Nov. 6, 1935; came to U.S., 1960, naturalized, 1971; s. Oscar E. and Marion L. (Grady) T.; m. Margaret Fife, Dec. 22, 1960; children: Heather Louise, Gretchen Marie. BA, U. Ottawa, Ont., Can., 1956, MD, 1960. Diplomate Am. Bd. Psychiatry and Neurology (com. for cert. in child and adolescent psychiatry 1981-87, written exam. com. for child and adolescent psychiatry 1981-87, chmn. 1985-87, dir. 1990—). Intern Harper Hosp., Detroit, 1960-61; resident in psychiatry UCLA Med. Ctr.-Harbor Gen. Hosp., 1961-64; registrar in psychiatry Kingsway Hosp., Derby, Eng., 1966-68; fellow in child psychiatry UCLA Ctr. for Health Scis., 1968-70, from asst. prof. to assoc. prof., 1970-8076, prof., 1980-94, dir. child psychiatry clin. rsch. ctr., 1977-87, assoc. chief div., 1984-91, acting chief, 1992-94; Ackerly prof. child psychiatry U. Louisville Sch. Medicine, 1994—; tech. advisor Rainman, 1988; vis. prof. U. Tours, France, 1982, U. Hawaii, 1987, 90; Roy Grinker vis. prof. Michael Reese Hosp., Chgo., 1984; mem. gen. assembly Am. Bd. Med. Specialists, 1990—, rep. to Accreditation Coun. on Continuing Med. Edn., 1993—; mem. exec. com., 1994-96; bd. advisors Rieger Found., Santa Barbara, Calif., 1992—; mem. psychol. scis. rev. com. NIMH, 1976-80; lectr., presenter in field; editl. cons. EEG and Clin. Neurophysiology, 1979-85; numerous others. Author: (with Margaret Tanguay) Travel Adventure in Europe with Tent, Van or Motorhome, 1970; contbr. over 60 articles, abstracts and book revs. to sci. jours., over 20 chpts. to books. Mem. Clinton-Gore Nat. Leadership Coun., 1991-93. Recipient career sci. devel. award NIMH, 1970-75; grantee USPHS, 1977-87, 84-89, NIMH, 1980-95, MacArthur Found., 1983-88. Fellow Am. Psychiat. Assn. (coun. on rsch. 1980-95, vice chmn. 1981-94, mem. com. on chronically ill-emotionally handicapped child 1990-94), Am. Acad. Child and Adolescent Psychiatry (assoc. editor Jour. 1988—, co-chmn. task force on universal access to health care 1991—), Am. Coll. Psychiatry; mem. AMA, AAAS, Group for Advancement Psychiatry (chmn. child com. 1988—), Soc. for Rsch. in Child and Adolescent Psychopathology, Royal Coll. Psychiatry (Gt. Britain, affiliate). Democrat. Avocations: microcomputers, vegetable gardening, travel. Home: 1129 Cardinal Dr Louisville KY 40213 Office: U Louisville Bingham Child Guidance Ctr 200 E Chestnut St Louisville KY 40202

TANGUY, CHARLES REED, foundation administrator, consultant, former foreign service officer; b. Phila., Dec. 24, 1921; s. Edward Earley and Dorothy (Reed) T.; m. Irene Jane McDaniel, Sept. 4, 1943; children: Charles Reed, Sarah Beauchamp, Peter Sackville. Student (scholar), Swarthmore Coll., 1939-41; A.B., Pa. State Coll., 1947; postgrad., George Washington U., summer 1946, Johns Hopkins U., 1947. Joined U.S. Fgn. Service, 1947; 3d sec. Athens, Greece, 1947-49; vice consul Rabat, Morocco, 1949-52; assigned State Dept., 1952; 2d sec. Rome, 1953-54, Bern, Switzerland, 1954-55; consul, prin. officer Penang, Malaya, 1955-56; assigned State Dept., 1957, internat. relations officer, 1957-59, officer charge Malayan affairs, 1959-61; 2d sec., later 1st sec., dep. chief polit. sect. Ankara, Turkey, 1961-65; 1st sec. dep. chief polit. sect. Paris, 1965-68; country dir. France and Benelux, Dept. State, 1968-72; minister-counselor Am. embassy, The Hague, Netherlands, 1972-75; mem., pres. 18th sr. seminar in fgn. policy Dept. State, Washington, 1975-76; sr. fgn. service insp., 1976-78; dep. dir. Office of Equal Employment Opportunity, 1978-80; ret., 1980; exec. dir. Netherlands-Am. Amity Trust, Inc., Washington, 1980—; program dir. Com. for a Community of Democracies-U.S.A., Washington, 1984-90. Mem. original bldg. com., warden St. Nicolas Anglican Episc. Ch., Ankara, 1962; mem. Companions in World Mission. Served to 1st lt. AUS, 1942-46. Decorated officer Order of Orange Nassau (The Netherlands); recipient John Jacob Rogers award Dept. State. Mem. Sigma Alpha Epsilon. Home: 2235 Q St NW Washington DC 20008-2825 Office: 1725 Desales St NW Ste 300 Washington DC 20036-4406

TANHAM, GEORGE KILPATRICK, retired research company executive; b. Englewood, N.J., Feb. 23, 1922; s. Francis Thomas and Irene (Kilpatrick) T.; m. Mary Finch, 1958 (div. 1962); m. Barbara Hunt, May 27, 1966 (div. 1989); children: George K., Gerald Francis, Helen Tanham Woods, Barbara Tanham Stampora, Maedi Carney, Ruth Tanham Marshall, Ramsey; m. Kathleen Van Wyck, Oct. 27, 1989. BA, Princeton U., 1943; MA, Stanford U., 1947, PhD, 1951. Assoc. prof., master student houses Calif. Inst. Tech., Pasadena, 1947-55; research staff Rand Corp., Santa Monica, Calif., 1955-58; dep. to v.p. Rand Corp., Washington, 1958-64, 65-68, v.p., trustee, 1971-82, sr. researcher, 1982-87, cons., 1987—; assoc. dir. AID, Saigon, Vietnam, 1964-65; minister counsellor U.S. Embassy, Bangkok, Thailand, 1968-70; cons. ESL, Sunnyvale, Calif.; lectr. in field. Author: Communist Revolutionary Warfare: The Vietminh in Indochina, 1961, 67, 85, War Without Guns: American Civilians in Rural Vietnam, 1966, Contribution a l'Histoire de la Resistance Belge, 1971, Trial in Thailand, 1974; co-author: (with Douglas S. Blaufarb) Who Will Win a Key: An Answer to the Puzzle of Revolutionary War, 1989; contbr. chpts. to books, articles to profl. jours. Bd. visitors Patterson Sch. of Diplomacy and Internat. Commerce, U. Ky., 1985—, U. Pitts., 1982-92; bd. dirs. Ethics and Pub. Policy Ctr., 1988—; adv. trustee Rand Corp., 1988—. Served with U.S. Army, World War II. Decorated Purple Heart, Silver Star with oak leaf cluster, Air medal; Croix de Guerre avec etoile d'argent (Republic of France); Most Exalted Order of White Elephant (Thailand); Belgian-Am. Edn. Found. grantee, 1950; Ford Found. fellow, 1952-53; Social Scis. Research Council grantee, 1955-57; grantee U.S. Inst. Peace and Rockefeller Found., 1989-91; Rajiv Gandhi Found. vis. fellow, New Delhi, 1995. Mem. Coun. Fgn. Rels., Internat. Inst. Strategic Studies, Cosmos Club, Spl. Forces Club (London), India Internat. Ctr. (New Delhi). Avocations: music, travel, gardening, sports. Home: PO Box 373 Strasburg VA 22657-0373 Office: Rand 2100 M St NW Ste 800 Washington DC 20037-1270

TANIGUCHI, TOKUSO, surgeon; b. Eleele, Kauai, Hawaii, June 26, 1915; s. Tokuichi and Sana (Omaye) T.; BA, U. Hawaii, 1941; MD, Tulane U., 1946; 1 son, Jan Tokuichi. Intern Knoxville (Tenn.) Gen. Hosp., 1946-47; resident in surgery St. Joseph Hosp., also Marquette Med. Sch., Milw., 1947-52; practice medicine, specializing in surgery, Hilo, Hawaii, 1955—; chief surgery Hilo Hosp.; teaching fellow Marquette Med. Sch., 1947-49; v.p., dir. Hawaii Hardware Co., Ltd. Capt. M.C., AUS, 1952-55. Diplomate Am. Bd. Surgery. Fellow Internat., Am. colls. surgeons; mem. Am. Hawaii med. assns., Hawaii County Med. Soc., Pan-Pacific Surg. Assn., Phi Kappa Phi. Contbr. articles in field to profl. jours. Patentee automated catheter. Home: 277 Kaiulani St Hilo HI 96720-2530

TANIMOTO, GEORGE, agricultural executive, farmer; b. Gridley, Calif., Feb. 10, 1926; s. Hikoichi and Rewa Tanimoto; m. Hanami Yamasaki, Dec. 19, 1946; 1 child, Patricia. Grad., Coyne Electric Sch., Chgo., 1950. Elec. technician, 1951, owner peach and prune orchards, 1952; founder Kiwifruit Nursery, Calif., 1965; pres. Tanimoto Bros., Gridley, Calif., 1977—, Tanimoto Enterprises, Inc., Gridley, 1979—; bd. dirs. Blue Anchor, Inc., Sacramento; chmn. Calif. Fruit Exchange, Inc.; U.S. rep. Internat. Kiwifruit Orgn., Lake Tahoe, Calif., 1985, Rome, 1986, Biarritz, France, 1987, Hong Kong, 1988, chmn. Orgn.,Rome, 1986; dir. Butte County Agrl. Adv. Commn., Oroville, Calif.; founder, chmn. Calif. Kiwifruit Commn., 1980-84,

1988-89, vice chmn. 1985-87. Pres. South Shore Assn., Bucks Lake, Calif. 1989. Mem. Kiwifruit Growers Calif. (founder, bd. dirs., pres. 1973-80), Kiwifruit Mktg. Assn. Calif. (founder, chmn. 1989-95), Gridley Sportsman Club (founder, pres. 1975-78). Republican. Buddhist. Avocations: fishing, boating, photography. Pioneered the first comml. planting and devel. of cultural practice for kiwifruit in Calif. Home: 948 River Ave Gridley CA 95948-9774

TANIO, TONY, electrical engineer, hotel executive; b. Waipahu, Hawaii, Mar. 26, 1938; s. Aguido Higas and Eleoteria (Basalo) T.; m. Rosemarie Echter, Jan. 26, 1960 (div. July, 1987); childen: Stephen Anthony, Melanie Elizabeth, Nadine Anne, Brian A-J. AA in Mgmt., Wright Jr. Coll., Chgo., 1975; AAS, C.C. of Air Force, Montgomery AFB, Ala., 1975; BS in Profl. Aeronautics, Embry Riddle Aero. U., Daytona Beach, Fla., 1976; MS in Mgmt., Troy State U., 1979. Enlisted USAF, 1957; maintenance supt. USAF, various locations, 1957-79; supr. test engring. Hughes Aircraft Co., El Segundo, Calif., 1980-87; chief engr. Kaiser Permanente Hosp., Honolulu, 1988-89, St. Francis Med. Ctr., Ewa, Hawaii, 1989-90; Hawaiian Waikiki Beach Hotel, 1990—. Charter mem. Rep. Presidential Task Force, 1986—; bd. dirs. Inst. for Affordable Homes, Honolulu, 1988-91; singer Honolulu Chorale, 1989—. Roman Catholic. Avocations: coin collecting, singing, camping. Home: 2152 Apio Ln Honolulu HI 96817 Office: Hawaiian Waikiki Beach Hotel 2570 Kalakaua Ave Honolulu HI 96815

TANIS, JAMES ROBERT, library director, history educator, clergyman; b. Phillipsburg, N.J., June 26, 1928; s. John Christian and Bertha Marie (Tobiasson) T.; m. Florence Borgmann, June 26, 1963; children—Marjorie Martha, James Tobiasson. B.A., Yale, 1951; B.D., Union Theol. Sem., N.Y.C., 1954; Dr. Theol., U. Utrecht, Netherlands, 1957; LittD (hon.), Dickinson Coll., Carlisle, Pa., 1994. Ordained to ministry Presbyn. Ch., 1954. Co-pastor Greystone Presbyn. Ch., Elizabeth, N.J., 1954-55; librarian, mem. faculty Harvard Div. Sch., 1956-69; univ. librarian Yale U., 1965-68; mem. faculty Yale Div. Sch., 1968-69; dir. libraries, prof. history Bryn Mawr (Pa.) Coll., 1969—. Author: Calvinistic Pietism in the Middle Colonies, 1967; co-author: Bookbinding in America, 1983, Images of Discord/De Tweedracht Verbeeld, 1993. Knighted as Officer in Order of Orange-Nassau, The Netherlands, 1993. Home: 111 Deep Dene Rd Villanova PA 19085-1317 Office: Bryn Mawr Coll Canaday Libr 101 N Merion Ave Bryn Mawr PA 19010-2899

TANIS, JOHN JACOB, manufacturing company executive; b. Prospect Park, N.J., Aug. 25, 1926; s. John and Jennie (Ver Voorn) T.; m. Janice Helen Eggleston, Apr. 1, 1950 (dec. Oct. 1971); children: Carrie, John, David; m. Nancy Jane Young, Oct. 7, 1972. BCE, Case Inst. Tech., 1949; cert. advanced mgmt. program, Harvard U., 1970. Regional mgr. E. F. Hauserman Co., Cleve., 1952-66; pres. Figgie Internat., Cleve., 1966-73; pres., chief exec. officer United Screw and Bolt Corp., North Olmsted, Ohio, 1973—; bd. dirs. Bank One, Cleve., NA. Bd. trustees Health Cleve. With USN, 1944-45. Mem. Union Club, Westwood Country Club (pres. Rocky River 1984-85), Quail Creek Country Club, Naples Bath and Tennis Club, Masons. Republican. Avocations: golf, tennis, fishing. Home: 1082 Lake Point Dr Cleveland OH 44107-1033 Office: United Screw & Bolt Corp 24950 Great No Corp Ctr 11 North Olmsted OH 44070-5333

TANIS, NORMAN EARL, retired university dean, library expert; b. Grand Rapids, Mich., Aug. 15, 1929; s. Aaron Orrie and Gertrude (Medendorp) T.; m. Terese R. Tiernan; children: Kathryn, Laura. AB, Calvin Coll., 1951; AM in Libr. Sci., U. Mich., 1952, MA in History, 1956, MA in Edn., 1961; DHL (hon.), U. San Fernando, 1973; LLD (hon.), Mid-Valley Coll. Law, 1976. Cataloger Strauss Meml. Libr., U. Mich., 1951-52; statis. clk. polio vaccine evaluation ctr. U. Mich., Ann Arbor, 1955; libr. Henry Ford Community Coll., Dearborn, Mich., 1956-63, head libr., 1963-66; dir. libr. Kans. State U., Pittsburg, 1966-69; dean librs. Calif. State U. Northridge, 1969-91, ret., 1991, prof. emeritus; team mgr./planner robotically controlled book storage unit Leviathan II, Calif. State U., 1986-91, chmn. editorial adv. bd. for univ. history, 1988-91; trustee San Fernando Valley Coll. Law, 1977-79; mem. adv. coun. Libr. Sch., UCLA, 1970-77; mem. adv. com. Libr. Sch., U. So. Calif., 1971-74; disting. alumnus-in-residence Sch. Info. and Libr. Svc., U. Mich., 1989; part-time libr. Our Lady Queen of the Angels Sem., 1993-94. Co-author: Three Hundred Million Books, 1974, Problems in Developing Academic Library Collections, 1974, Native Americans of North America, 1975, Lynton R. Kistler: Printer-Lithographer, 1976, Cost Analysis of Library Functions: A Total System Approach, 1978, China in Books, 1979, India and its People, A Bibliography, 1980, The Twilight of Orthodoxy in New England, 1987; contbr. articles to profl. publs.; editor: Northridge Facsimile Series, 1974-91; exec. editor Santa Susana Press, 1975-91. Mem., lectr., extraordinary eucharistic min. and catechist for prison ministries St. John Eudes Roman Cath. Ch., Chatsworth, Calif.; postulant Oblates of Monastery of Risen Christ, San Luis Obispo, Calif., 1991—. With USMCR, 1948-50; with U.S. Army, 1952-54. Named knight comdr. Supreme Order and Mil. of Temple of Jerusalem, 1990—, knight of Order of St. Constantine, 1991—, mil. and hospitaller knight of Order of St. Lazarus of Jerusalem, 1992—. Mem. ALA, Nat. Librs. Assn. (pres. 1980), Bibliog. Soc. Calif. State U.-Northridge, Hist. Soc. So. Calif., Calif. Acad. and Rsch. Librs., Cath. Libr. Assn., Order of St. Lawrence-Malta (duke). Marine Meml. Club (San Francisco), Rounce and Coffin Club, Phi Beta Phi, Phi Beta Mu. Home: 10009 Jovita Ave Chatsworth CA 91311-3938 Office: Calif State U Libr Rm 202 1811 Nordhoff St Northridge CA 91324

TANIUCHI, KIYOSHI, retired mechanical engineering educator; b. Kahoku-choo, Kami-gun, Kôchi-ken, Japan, Aug. 8, 1920; s. Takeshi and Toshi (Yoshimoto) T.; m. Teiko Wakamatsu, Jan. 7, 1960; 1 child, Satoshi. Student, Kanto Gakuin Tech. Coll., Yokohama, Japan, 1946; BEng, Meiji U., Tokyo, 1952, DEng (hon.), 1980. Asst. Meiji U. Sch. Sci. and Tech., Kawasaki-shi, Japan, 1957-81, lectr. mech. engring., 1981-91, assoc. prof., 1991-95; ret., 1995; instr. engring. Shibaura Inst. Tech., Ohmiya-shi, Saitama-ken, Japan, 1974-90. Co-author 3 books on mech. engring.; also articles. Mem. ASTM, Soc. Exptl. Mechanics, Japanese Soc. Mech. Engrs. Avocations: photography, art appreciation. Home: 5-10-12 Wakamatsu, Sagamihara 229, Japan Office: Meiji U Sch Sci and Tech, 1-1-1 Higashimita, Tama-ku, Kawasaki 214, Japan

TANKIN, RICHARD SAMUEL, fluid dynamics engineer, educator; b. Balt., July 14, 1924; s. Harry Jacob and Bertha (Haberer) T.; m. Anne Raudelunas, Dec. 2, 1956; children: Roberta, David, John. B.A., Johns Hopkins U., 1948, B.S., 1950; M.S., Mass. Inst. Tech., 1954; Ph.D., Harvard U., 1960. Asst. prof. U. Del., 1960-61; mem. faculty Northwestern U., 1961—, prof. fluid dynamics, 1968—, chmn. dept. mech. engring. and astronautical scis., 1973-78. Served with AUS, 1943-44; Served with USNR, 1944-45. Mem. ASME, Am. Inst. Aeros. and Astronautics, Am. Geophys. Union, Tau Beta Pi. Home: 820 Ridge Ter Evanston IL 60201-2430

TANLER, RONALD F., retail executive. Pres. Lord and Taylor div. May Dept. Stores Co., N.Y.C. Office: Lord & Taylor 424 Fifth Ave New York NY 10018-2703

TANNEHILL, JOHN C., aerospace engineer, educator; b. Salem, Ill., Oct. 14, 1943; s. John Bell and Pearl Hanna (Trulin) T.; m. Marcia Kay George, Jan. 28, 1967; children: Michelle, Johnny. BS, Iowa State U., 1965, MS, 1967, PhD, 1969. Aerospace engr. NASA Flight Rsch. Ctr., Edwards, Calif., 1965; mem. tech. staff Aerospace Cor., El Segundo, Calif., 1967; NASA-ASEE fellow NASA Ames Rsch. Ctr., Moffett Field, Calif., 1970-71; asst. prof. aerospace engring. Iowa State U., Ames, 1969-74, assoc. prof., 1974-79, prof., 1979—, mgr. Computational Fluid Dynamics Ctr., 1984—; chmn. bd. Engring. Analysis, Inc., Ames, 1994—. Co-author: Computational Fluid Mechanics and Heat Transfer, 1984, Handbook of Numerical Heat Transfer, 1988; contbr. articles to profl. jours. NSF trainee, 1965-68; Iowa State U. Rsch. Found. fellow, 1968-69; NASA fellow, 1970-71. Fellow AIAA (chmn. Iowa sect. 1989-91); mem. Am. Soc. Engring. Edn., Sigma Xi, Sigma Gamma Tau, Tau Beta Pi. Home: 3214 Greenwood Cir Ames IA 50014-4570 Office: Iowa State U Dept Aerospace & Mechs Engring Ames IA 50011

TANNEN, DEBORAH FRANCES, writer, linguist; b. Bklyn., June 7, 1945; d. Eli S. and Dorothy (Rosen) T. BA, SUNY, Binghamton, 1966; MA, Wayne State U., 1970, U. Calif., Berkeley, 1976; PhD, U. Calif., 1979. Instr.

Greek-Am. Cultural Inst., Herakleion, Greece, 1966-67; instr. in English as fgn. lang. Hellenic Am. Union, Athens, Greece, 1967-68; English instr. Detroit Inst. Tech., 1969, Mercer County C.C., Trenton, N.J., 1970-71; lectr. in acad. skills CUNY, Bronx, N.Y., 1971-74; asst. prof. Georgetown U., Washington, 1979-85, assoc. prof. linguistics, 1985-90; univ. prof., 1991—; McGraw disting. lectr. in writing Coun. for Humanities and dept. anthropology Princeton U., fall 1991; visitor Inst. for Advanced Study, Princeton, spring 1992; fellow Ctr. for Advanced Study in Behavioral Scis., Stanford (Calif.) U., 1992-93. Author: Lilika Nakos, 1983, Conversational Style: Analyzing Talk Among Friends, 1984, That's Not What I Meant!: How Conversational Style Makes or Breaks Your Relations With Others, 1984, Talking Voices: Repetition, Dialogue and Imagery in Conversational Discourse, 1989, You Just Don't Understand: Women and Men in Conversation, 1990, Gender and Discourse, 1994, Talking From 9 to 5: How Women's and Men's Conversational Styles Affect Who Gets Heard, Who Gets Credit, and What Gets Done at Work, 1994; editor: Analyzing Discourse: Text and Talk, 1982, Spoken and Written Language: Exploring Orality and Literacy, 1982, Coherence in Spoken and Written Discourse, 1984, Perspectives on Silence, 1985, Linguistics in Context, 1986, Gender and Conversational Interaction, 1993, Framing In Discourse, 1993; editor: Linguistics in Context: Connecting Observation and Understanding, 1988. Rockefeller Humanities fellow, 1982-83, Ctr. Advanced Study Behavioral Scis. fellow, Stanford, Calif., 1992-93; grantee NEH, 1980, 85, 86; recipient Elizabeth Mills Crothers prize U. Calif., 1976, Dorothy Rosenberg Meml. prize U. Calif., 1977, Joan Lee Yang Meml. Poetry prize U. Calif., 1977, Shrout Short Story prize, 1978, Emily Chamberlain Cook prize, 1978. Office: Georgetown U Linguistics Dept Washington DC 20057

TANNENBAUM, BERNICE SALPETER, association executive; b. N.Y.C.; d. Isidore and May Franklin; B.A., Bklyn. Coll.; 1 child, Richard Salpeter. chmn. Commn. on the Status of Women of the World Jewish Congress; mem. exec. bd. Am. sect. World Jewish Congress, chmn. internat. affairs com.; mem. Zionist Gen. Council; active Exec. World Zionist Orgn.; bd. govs., mem. gen. assembly Jewish Agy.; bd. dirs., v.p. United Israel Appeal; mem. exec. com. Am. Zionist Mvmt.; mem. Conf. of Pres. of Maj. Jewish Orgns.; nat. pres. Hadassah, N.Y.C., 1976-80; nat. chmn. Hadassah Internat., 1984—; v.p. Jewish Telegraphic Agy.; bd. govs. Hebrew U. Office: Hadassah 50 W 58th St New York NY 10019

TANNENBAUM, PERCY H., psychology educator; b. Montreal, Que., Can., May 31, 1927; s. Charles and Ronya (Tannenbaum) T.; m. Brocha Kaplan, Sept. 16, 1948; children: Brian Dov, Nili. B.Sc., McGill U., 1948; M.S., U. Ill., 1951, Ph.D. 1953. Reporter, staff writer Montreal Herald, 1947-50; asst. prof. Mich. State U., 1953-54; research asst. prof. U. Ill., 1954-59; prof. psychology and journalism, dir. Mass Communication Research Center, U. Wis., 1959-67; prof. communication and psychology U. Pa., 1967-70; prof. public policy emeritus, rsch. psychologist U. Calif., Berkeley, 1970—; Cons. panel social psychology NSF, NIMH, Nat. Acad. Scis., govt. and industry; fellow Center Advanced Study Behavioral Scis., 1965-66; fellow Inst. Advanced Studies, Berlin, Fed. Republic Germany, 1984-85. Author: Turned-On TV/Turned-Off Voters, 1983; Author: (with others) The Measurement of Meaning, 1957; Co-editor: (with others) Theories of Cognitive Consistency: A Sourcebook; editor: (with others) Entertainment Functions of Television. Fellow Am. Psychol. Assn., AAAS; mem. AAUP, Am. Assn. Public Opinion Research, Internat. Assn. Mass. Communications Research. Home: 962 Cragmont Ave Berkeley CA 94708-1432

TANNENBAUM, STEVEN ROBERT, toxicologist, chemist; b. N.Y.C., Feb. 23, 1937; m. Carol Eigen, Sept. 6, 1959; children: Lisa, Mark. B.S. in Food Tech., MIT, 1958, Ph.D. in Food Sci. and Tech, 1962. Asst. prof. MIT, Cambridge, Mass., 1964-69; assoc. prof. MIT, 1969-74, prof. food chemistry, 1974-81, prof. chemistry and toxicology, registration and admissions officer: 1981—; vis. prof. Hebrew U. of Jerusalem, 1973-74; BASF vis. prof. U. Kaiserdoutern, 1994; mem. com. on food stds. and fortification policy NAS-NRC, 1970-73; mem. adv. com. on biochemistry and chem. carcinogenesis Am. Cancer Soc., 1977-81; bd. scientific advisors divsn. cancer etiology Federick Cancer Rsch. Facility, Nat. Cancer Inst., 1995; mem. cancer spl. program adv. com., 1979-82; mem. peer rev. com. Nat. Toxicology Program, 1983-85; founder, bd. dirs. Vicam, Ltd., Partnership; mem. scientific adv. bd. Xenometrix, Inc., Free Radical Scis., Inc. Editor: (with D.I.C. Wang) Single-Cell Protein II, 1975, (with others) The Economics, Marketing and Technology of Fish Protein Concentrate, 1974, (with J.R. Whitaker) Goof Proteins, 1977, Nutritional Safety Aspects of Food Processing, 1979, (with others) Gastrointestinal Cancer: Endogenous Factors, 1981, (with R.A. Scanlan) N-Nitroso Compounds, 1981; contbr. over 300 articles to profl. jours.; mem. editorial bd. Japanese Jour. Cancer Rsch., 1986—, Chem. Rsch. Toxicology, 1988-91, 95—, Cancer Epidemiology, Prevention and Biomarkers, 1990—, Cancer Rsch., 1993—. Mem. AAAS, Am. Chem. Soc., Inst. Food Technologists (sect. councillor N.E. chpt. 1966-69, Samuel Cate Prescott Rsch. award 1970, Babcock Hart award 1980), editorial bd. sci. jour. 1970-73, Am. Inst. Nutrition, Am. Assn. Cancer Rsch., Sigma Xi. Achievements include 7 U.S. patents. Office: MIT Dept Chemistry Toxicology Bldg 16 Rm 822a 77 Massachusetts Ave Cambridge MA 02139 *Motto: Crisis equals danger plus opportunity.*

TANNENBERG, DIETER E. A., manufacturing company executive; b. Chevy Chase, Md., Nov. 24, 1932; s. E.A. Wilhelm and Margarete Elizabeth (Mundhenk) T.; m. Ruth Hansen, Feb. 6, 1956; 1 child, Diana Tannenberg Collingsworth Cann Marlinski. BSME, Northwestern U., 1959. Registered profl. engr. N.Y., Conn., Ohio, Ill., Ind., Wis., N.J. Supervising engr. Flexonics div. Calumet & Hecla, Inc., Chgo., 1959-61, chief engr., 1961-63, program mgr. advanced space systems, 1963-65, dir. mfg. services, 1965-67; dir. mfg. engring. SCM Corp., Cortland, N.Y., 1967-69; tech. dir. internat. Singer Co., N.Y.C., 1969-71; v.p. ops. internat. div. Addressograph-Multigraph Corp., Cleve., 1971-74; mng. dir. Addressograph Multigraph GmbH, Frankfurt/Main, W. Ger., 1974-78; v.p., gen. mgr. Europe, Middle East, Africa AM Internat. Inc., Chgo., 1978-79; pres. AM Bruning div., 1979-82, AM Multigraphics Div., Mt. Prospect, Ill., 1982-86; corp. v.p. AM Internat., Inc., 1981-83, corp. sr. v.p., 1983-86; chmn. bd. dirs., pres. chief exec. officer Sargent-Welch Sci. Co., Skokie, Ill., 1986-89; pres., chief exec. officer ExhibitGroup, Inc., Elk Grove Village, Ill., 1990-91, Bell & Howell Document Mgmt. Products Co., Chgo., 1991-94; Bell and Howell DocuMail sys. Co., Chgo., 1994—; corp. v.p. Bell & Howell Co., Skokie, Ill., 1991—; chmn. AM Internat. GmbH, Frankfurt, 1977-86; bd. dirs. Gerard Daniel & Co., GDC Internat., Inc. Contbr. chpts. to handbooks, articles to tech.; trade mags.; patentee in machinery field. Served with M.I., U.S. Army, 1953-56. Named Man of Yr. Quick Print Mag., 1985. Mem. NSPE, ASME, ASCE, Assn. Reprodn. Materials Mfrs. (bd. dirs. 1979-82, v.p. 1980-82), Nat. Assn. Quick Printers (bd. dirs. 1982-84), Nat. Printing Equipment and Supplies Mfg. Assn. (bd. dirs. 1983-86, chmn. govt. affairs com. 1985-86), Computer and Bus. Equipment Mfg. Assn. (bd. dirs. 1983-86, 91-93), Soc. Am. Value Engrs. (hon. v.p. 1985-), Value Found. (trustee 1985—), Chgo. Coun. Fgn. Rels., German-Am. C. of C. (Chgo.), Barrington Hills Country Club, Execs. Club of Chgo., Econ. Club, Pi Tau Sigma. Office: Bell & Howell Co 6802 N McCormick Blvd Chicago IL 60645-2785

TANNENWALD, LESLIE KEITER, educational administrator; b. Boston, May 5, 1949; d. Irving Jules and Barbara June (Caplan) Keiter; m. Robert Tannenwald. BA, Brandeis U., 1971, MA, 1976; MAT in Social Studies, Simmons Coll., Boston, 1972. Cert. Social Worker, Tchr., Mass. Sr. assoc. Combined Jewish Philanthropies of Greater Boston, 1977-84; interim dir., asst. dir. Cambridge (Mass.) Community Svcs., 1984-85; ednl. cons. Bur. Jewish Edn., Boston, 1985-87; ednl. dir. Congregation Shalom Emeth, Burlington, Mass., 1987-92, Congregation Temple Aliyah, Needham, Mass., 1992-93; religious sch. dir. Falmouth (Mass.) Jewish Congregation, 1993—; cons. Selected Ednl. Orgns. Boston 1972. Author: Curriculum, Male and Female, 1979 (Honors award 1971), Understanding the Holocaust, 1990. Officer, bd. dirs. Combined Jewish Philanthropies of Greater Boston 1972—; mem. Am. Jewish Congress, Boston 1976—. Recipient Leadership award Inst. Leadership Devel. and Fund Raising. Mem. Nat. Alliance Profl. & Exec. Women, Alumni Assn. Benjamin S. Hornstein Program of Jewish Communal Svc., Assn. Jewish Community Personnel. Democrat. Avocations: swimming, watercolor painting, music. Home: 6 Clifton Rd Newton MA 02159-3147

TANNENWALD, PETER, lawyer; b. Washington, Apr. 8, 1943; s. Judge Theodore and Selma (Peterfreund) T.; m. Carol B. Baum, May 25, 1969; 1 child, Jonathan Mark. AB, Brown U., 1964; LLB, Harvard Coll., 1967. Bar: U.S. Dist. Ct. D.C. 1968, U.S. Ct. Appeals (D.C. cir.) 1968, U.S. Supreme Ct. 1972. Assoc. Arent, Fox, Kintner, Plotkin & Kahn, Washington, 1967-74, ptnr., 1975-94; ptnr. Irwin, Campbell & Tannenwald, P.C., Washington, 1994—. Columnist The LPTV Report, 1988-92. Mem. community coun. Sta. WAMU-FM, Washington, 1986-93; dir. Brown Broadcasting Svc., Ind., Providence, 1970—; chmn. maj. law firms divsn. Nat. Capital Area affiliate United Way, 1977-79. Mem. Harvard Law Sch. Assn. D.C. (pres. 1979-80), Harvard Law Sch. Assn. (sec. 1982-84). Avocations: electronics, photography. Office: Irwin Campbell Tannenwald 1320 18th St NW Ste 400 Washington DC 20036-1800

TANNENWALD, THEODORE, JR., federal judge; b. Valatie, N.Y., July 28, 1916; s. Theodore and Myra (Barnet) T.; m. Selma Peterfreund, Aug. 3, 1940; children: Peter, Robert. A.B. summa cum laude, Brown U., 1936; LL.B. magna cum laude, Harvard U., 1939; D.L.L., U. Cin., 1976; D.H.L., Hebrew Union Coll., 1976. Bar: N.Y. 1939, D.C. 1946. Assoc. Weil, Gotshal & Manges, N.Y.C., 1939-42; ptnr. Weil, Gotshal & Manges, 1947-65; judge U.S. Tax Ct., Washington, 1965-81; chief judge U.S. Tax Ct., 1981-83, sr. judge, 1983—; prin. legal cons. Lend Lease Adminstrn., 1942; acting asst. chief, fgn. funds control div. Dept. State, 1942-43; spl. cons. sec. war, 1943-45, cons. sec. def., 1947-49, counsel to spl. asst. to pres., 1950-51; asst. dir., chief of staff to dir. for mut. security Exec. Office Pres., 1951-53; spl. counsel to Moreland Commn., 1955-58; N.Y. mem. Tri-State Tax Commn., 1958-59; mem. Pres.'s Task Force on Fgn. Aid, spl. asst. to sec. state, 1961; professorial lectr. George Washington U. Sch. Law, 1968-76; lectr. Sch. Law U. Miami, 1976-85; disting. adj. prof. Sch. Law U. San Diego, 1985-90. Hon. chmn., hon. mem. bd. govs. Hebrew Union Coll.-Jewish Inst. Religion; mem. nat. exec. coun. Am. Jewish Com. Mem. ABA, Fed. Bar Assn., D.C. Bar Assn., Am. Law Inst., Coun. Fgn. Rels., Cosmos Club (D.C.), Phi Beta Kappa. Office: US Tax Ct 400 2nd St NW Washington DC 20217

TANNER, DANIEL, curriculum theory educator; b. N.Y.C., Sept. 22, 1926; s. Jack and Lillian (Jupiter) T.; m. Laurel Nan Jacobson, July 11, 1948 (div. 1988). B.S. with honors, Mich. State U., 1949, M.S., 1952; Ph.D. (Univ. Scholar), Ohio State U., 1955. Asst. prof. edn. San Francisco State Coll., 1955-60; asso. prof. edn., coordinator Midwest program on airborne TV instrn. Purdue U., 1960-62; asso. prof. edn., asso. dir. internat. program for edn. leaders Northwestern U., 1962-64; asso. prof. research div. tchr. edn. City U. N.Y., 1964-66; prof. edn., dir. Center for Urban Edn., U. Wis-Milw. Sch. Edn., 1966-67; prof. edn., dir. grad. programs in curriculum theory and devel. Grad. Sch. Edn., Rutgers U., New Brunswick, N.J., 1967—; chmn. dept. curriculum and instrn. Grad. Sch. Edn., Rutgers U., 1969-71, faculty research fellow, 1974-75, 88-89; vis. lectr. U. Kansas City, summer 1956, Tchrs. Coll. Columbia, summer 1966; vis. prof. Emory U., summer 1968, SUNY, Binghamton, winter 1968, U. London, 1975, King Abdulaziz U., Saudi Arabia, winter 1992; disting. lectr. ASCD, 1985, 86, Dewey Meml. lectr., 1984, Raths Meml. lectr., SUNY, 1984; Leadership Inst. lectr. U. Del., summer 1990; vis. scholar U. London Inst. Edn., 1974-75; mem. rev. bd. coll. work-study program U.S. Office Edn., 1965; mem. symposium on comparative curriculum history Inst. Sci. Edn. Kiel U., Fed. Republic Germany, 1989; cons. U. Tex. Med. Center, 1961-62, Chgo. Sch. Survey, 1964-65, Center Urban Edn., N.Y.C., 1964-65, West Chicago (Ill.) Sch. Survey, 1963-64, Nat. Ednl. TV Center, N.Y.C., 1963, Campbell County (Va.) Sch. Survey, 1970, Memphis Schs., 1977-78, ASCD Commn. on Gen. Edn., 1980-81, West Orange, N.J., Curriculum Study, 1984, ASCD Commn. on Secondary Sch. Practices, 1985, ASCD Ednl. Policy Task Force, 1985, NASSP Curric Coun., 1985—; SUNY Buffalo External Evaluation, 1988; dir. Nat. Curriculum Inst., 1987; delivered founder's day address Delaware Valley Coll., 1985. Author: Schools for Youth: Change and Challenge in Secondary Education, 1965, Secondary Curriculum: Theory and Development, 1971, Secondary Education: Perspectives and Prospects, 1972, Using Behavioral Objectives in the Classroom, 1972, Curriculum Development: Theory into Practice, 3d edit., 1995, Supervision in Education, 1987, History of the School Curriculum, 1990, Crusade for Democracy: Progressive Education at the Crossroads, 1991; contbg. author: Curriculum Issues, 87th Yearbook NSSE, 1988, Ency. of Ednl. Research, 5th edit., 1982, Readings in Educational Psychology, 1965, Yearbook of the Association for Student Teaching, 1962, The Great Debate, Our Schools in Crisis, 1959, Educational Issues in a Changing Society, 1964, Programs, Teachers and Machines, 1964, Views on American Schooling, 1964, The Training of America's Teachers, 1975, Curriculum and Instruction, 1981; co-editor: Teen Talk: Curriculum Materials in Communications, 1971; co-editor: Improving the School Curriculum, 1988, Restructuring for an Interdisciplinary Curriculum, 1992, Curriculum Issues and the New Century, 1995; contbg. editor: Ednl. Leadership, 1969-74; mem. editorial bd.: Tex. Tech. Jour. Edn., 1984-89, Teaching Edn., 1986-90, Jour. Curriculum Supervision; editorial cons.: Ency. of Ednl. Research, 5th edit., Jour. Ednl. Psychology; contbr. Atlantic Monthly, Bull. of Atomic Scientists and other nat. mags., ednl. jours. Trustee Delaware Valley Coll., Doylestown, Pa., 1981—; bd. dirs. Ohio State Alumni Assn. N.J., 1990—. Recipient award for excellence Edn. Press Am., 1989. Fellow AAAS, John Dewey Soc. (bd. dirs. 1985-88, archivist 1989—); mem. AAUP, Am. Ednl. Rsch. Assn., N.Y. Acad. Sci., Am. Polit. Sci. Assn., Am. Ednl. Studies Assn., Nat. Soc. Study Edn., Phi Kappa Phi, Phi Delta Kappa (Svc. award 1957). Home: Highwood Rd Somerset NJ 08873 Office: Grad Sch Edn Rutgers U New Brunswick NJ 08903 *The essential quality of education and life is growth. Hence problems must be seen as opportunities and not as limitations if solutions are to be found and progress is to be made.*

TANNER, DEE BOSHARD, lawyer; b. Provo, Utah, Jan. 16, 1913; s. Myron Clark and Marie (Boshard) T.; m. Jane Barwick, Dec. 26, 1936 (div. Aug. 1962); children: Barry, Diane McDowell; m. Reeta Walker, Dec. 6, 1981. BA, U. Utah, 1935; LLB, Pacific Coast U., 1940; postgrad., Harvard U., 1936, Loyola U., L.A., 1937. Bar: Calif. 1943, U.S. Dist. Ct. (so. dist.) Calif. 1944, U.S. Ct. Appeals (9th cir.) 1947, ICC 1964, U.S. Dist. Ct. (ea. dist.) Calif. 1969, U.S. Supreme Ct. 1971. Assoc. Spray, Davis & Gould, L.A., 1943-44; pvt. practice L.A., 1944; assoc. Tanner and Sievers, L.A., 1944-47, Tanner and Thornton, L.A., 1947-54, Tanner, Hanson, Meyers, L.A., 1954-64; ptnr. Tanner and Van Dyke, L.A., 1964-65, Gallagher and Tanner, L.A., 1965-70; pvt. practice Pasadena, Calif., 1970—. Mem. L.A. Bar Assn., World Affairs Assn., Harvard Law Sch. Assn., Lawyers' Club L.A. Home and Office: 1720 Lombardy Rd Pasadena CA 91106-4127

TANNER, DOUGLAS ALAN, lawyer; b. Palo Alto, Calif., Aug. 30, 1953; s. Bernard R. and Caroline (Orris) T.; m. Carol Scilacci, May 28, 1977; children: Lauren Elizabeth, Wynn Ann, Leigh Caroline. AB in History, Stanford U., 1974, MBA, 1978, JD, 1978. Bar: Calif. 1978, U.S. Dist. Ct. (no. dist.) Calif. 1978, U.S. Ct. Appeals (9th cir.) 1979, N.Y. 1987. Law clk. to judge U.S. Ct. Appeals (9th cir.), San Francisco, 1978-79; assoc. Orrick, Herrington & Sutcliffe, San Francisco, 1979-83; ptnr. Orrick, Herrington & Sutcliffe, San Jose, Calif., 1984-86, N.Y.C., 1986-89; ptnr. Milbank, Tweed, Hadley & McCloy, L.A., 1989-92, Hong Kong, 1992—. Mem. San Francisco Barristers (chmn. corps. com. 1981-82), Order of Coif, Phi Beta Kappa. Republican. Episcopalian. Home: Grenville House Apt G5, 1 Magazine Gap Rd, Hong Kong Hong Kong Office: Milbank Tweed Hadley & McCloy, 3007 Alexandra Hs/16 Chater Rd, Ctrl Hong Kong Hong Kong

TANNER, GLORIA GERALDINE, state legislator; b. Atlanta, July 16, 1935; d. Marcellus and Blanche Arnold Travis; m. Theodore Ralph Tanner, 1955 (dec.); children: Terrance Ralph, Tanvis Renee, Tracey Lynne. BA, Met. State Coll., 1974; MUA, U. Colo., 1976. Office mgr. Great Western Mfg. Co., Denver, 1965-67; writer Rage mag., 1969-70; reporter, feature writer Denver Weekly News, 1970-75; dir. East Denver Cmty. Office, 1974—; also real estate agt.; mem. Colo. Ho. of Reps., 1985—; minority caucus chairwoman; mem. appropriations, bus. affairs, labor coms. Dist. capt. Denver Dem. Com., Colo., 1973-75; chairwoman Senatorial Dist. 3 Dem. Com., 1974-82; adminstrv. aide Colo. State Senator Regis Groff, Denver, 1974-82; alt. del. Dem. Nat. Conv., 1976, del., 1980; commr. Colo. Status of Women, 1977—; chairwoman Colo. Black Women for Polit. Action, 1977—; exec. coun. to Lt. Gov., 1978-79; mem. adv. bd. United Negro Coll. Fund, Colo. State Treas. Served USAF, 1952-55. Recipient Outstanding Svc. Leadership award Scott's Meth. Ch., 1974, Tribute to Black Women award, 1980; named Woman of Yr., Colo. Black Women Caucus, 1974. Mem. Colo. Black Media Assn. (pub. dir. 1972—), Reginas' Civic Club (founder, first pres. 1959—, Outstanding Woman of Yr. 1975), Nat.

Assn. Real Estate Brokers. Roman Catholic. Democrat. Home: 2150 Monaco Pky Denver CO 80207-3951 Office: Colo Ho of Reps State Capital Denver CO 80203

TANNER, HAROLD, investment banker; b. N.Y.C., May 7, 1932; s. Irving and Pauline (Steinlauf) T.; m. Estelle Newman, Aug. 6, 1957; children: David, James, Karen. B.S., Cornell U., 1952; M.B.A., Harvard U., 1956. V.p., dir. Blyth & Co. Inc., N.Y.C., 1956-69; exec. v.p. New Court Securities Corp., N.Y.C., 1969-76, Blyth Eastman Dillon & Co., Inc., N.Y.C., 1977-80; ptnr. Salomon Bros. Inc., 1980-81, mng. dir., 1981-87; pres. Tanner & Co., Inc., N.Y.C., 1987—; co-founder Vol. Urban Cons. Group; dir. TIG Holdings, Inc., Grossman's, Inc. Trustee Cornell U., Russell Sage Found. Lt. (j.g.) USNR, 1952-54. Mem. Coun. on Fgn. Rels., Century Country Club, Harmonie Club. Home: 18 Kensington Rd Scarsdale NY 10583-2217 Office: 650 Madison Ave New York NY 10022-1004

TANNER, HELEN HORNBECK, historian; b. Northfield, Minn., July 5, 1916; d. John Wesley and Frances Cornelia (Wolfe) Hornbeck; m. Wilson P. Tanner, Jr., Nov. 22, 1940 (dec. 1977); children—Frances, Margaret Tanner Tewson, Wilson P., Robert (dec. 1983). A.B. with honors, Swarthmore Coll., 1937; M.A., U. Fla., 1949; Ph.D., U. Mich., 1961. Asst. to dir. pub. rels. Kalamazoo Pub. Schs., 1937-39; with sales dept. Am. Airlines Inc., N.Y.C., 1940-43; teaching fellow, then teaching asst. U. Mich., Ann Arbor, 1949-53, 57-60, lectr. extension svc., 1961-74, asst. dir. Ctr. Continuing Edn. for Women, 1964-68; project dir. Newberry Libr., Chgo., 1976-81, rsch. assoc., 1981—; dir. D'Arcy McNickle Ctr. for Indian History, 1984-85; cons., expert witness Indian treaties; mem. Mich. Commn. Indian Affairs, 1966-70. Author: Zespedes in East Florida 1784-1790, 1963, 89, General Green Visits St. Augustine, 1964, The Greeneville Treaty, 1974, The Territory of the Caddo Tribe of Oklahoma, 1974, The Ojibwas, 1992; editor: Atlas of Great Lakes Indian History, 1987. NEH grantee, 1976, fellow, 1989; ACLS grantee, 1990. Mem. Am. Soc. Ethnohistory (pres. 1982-83), Am. Hist. Assn., Conf. Latin Am. History, Soc. History Discoveries, Orgn. Am. Historians, Ojibway Mah Soc., Fla. Hist. Soc. Home: 5178 Crystal Dr Beulah MI 49617-9618 Office: The Newberry Libr 60 W Walton St Chicago IL 60610-3305

TANNER, JIMMIE EUGENE, college dean; b. Hartford, Ark., Sept. 27, 1933; s. Alford C. and Hazel Ame (Anthony) T.; m. Carole Joy Yant, Aug. 28, 1958; children—Leslie Allison, Kevin Don. BA, Okla. Baptist U., 1955; MA, U. Okla., 1957, PhD, 1964. Assoc. prof. English, Franklin Coll., Ind., 1964-65; prof. English, Okla. Bapt. U., Shawnee, 1958-64, 65-72; v.p. acad. affairs Hardin-Simmons U., Abilene, Tex., 1972-78, La. Coll., Pineville, 1978-80; dean William Jewell Coll., Liberty, Mo., 1980—, interim pres., 1993-94. Contbr.: The Annotated Bibliography of D.H. Lawrence, Vol. 1, 1982, Vol. 2, 1985. Mem. Shawnee Sch. Bd., 1966-72; mem. edn. commn. So. Bapt. Conv., 1967-72. So. Fellowships Fund fellow, 1960-61; Danforth fellow, 1962-63. Mem. AAUP, Am. Assn. for Higher Edn. Democrat. Baptist. Avocations: tennis; photography. Home: 609 Lancelot Dr Liberty MO 64068-1023 Office: William Jewell Coll Office Provost Liberty MO 64068

TANNER, JOHN S., congressman, lawyer; b. Dyersburg, Tenn., Sept. 22, 1944; s. E.B. and Edith (Summers) T.; m. Betty Ann Portis, Sept. 2, 1967; children: Elizabeth Tanner Atkins, John Portis. BS, U. Tenn., 1966, JD, 1968. Bar: Tenn., 1968. Mem. Tenn. Ho. of Reps., 1976-88, 101st-104th Congresses from 8th Tenn. dist., Washington, D.C., 1988—; mem. Nat. Security Comm., mem. Sci. Comm. Active Obion County Cancer Soc.; former chmn. bd. visitors U.S. Mil. Acad. Lt. USN, 1968-72; col. Tenn. Army N.G., 1974—. Mem. Obion County C. of C., Obion County Bar Assn., Rotary. Democrat. Disciples of Christ. Avocations: golf, hunting. Office: US Ho of Reps 1127 Longworth House Washington DC 20515

TANNER, LAUREL NAN, education educator; b. Detroit, Feb. 16, 1929; d. Howard Nicholas and Celia (Solvich) Jacobson; m. Daniel Tanner, July 11, 1948; m. Kenneth J. Rehage, Nov. 25, 1989. BS in Social Sci, Mich. State U., 1949, MA in Edn., 1953; EdD, Columbia U., 1967. Pub. sch. tchr., 1950-64; instr. tchr. edn. Hunter Coll., 1964-66, asst. prof., 1967-69; supr. Milw. Pub. Schs., 1966-67; mem. faculty Temple U., Phila., 1969—; prof. edn. Temple U., 1974-89, U. Houston, 1989—; vis. professorial scholar U. London Inst. Edn., 1974-75; vis. scholar Stanford U., 1984-85, U. Chgo., 1988-89; curriculum cons., 1969—; disting. vis. prof. San Francisco State U. 1987. Author: Classroom Discipline for Effective Teaching and Learning, 1978, La Disciplina en la enseñanza y el Aprendizaje, 1980; co-author: Classroom Teaching and Learning, 1971, Curriculum Development: Theory into Practice, 1975, 3d edit., 1995, Supervision in Education: Problems and Practices, 1987, (with Daniel Tanner) History of the School Curriculum, 1990; editor Nat. Soc. Study Edn. Critical Issues in Curriculum, 87th yearbook, part 1, 1988. Faculty rsch. fellow Temple U., 1970, 80, 81; recipient John Dewey Rsch. award, 1981-82, Rsch. Excellence award U. Houston, 1992; Spencer Found. rsch. grantee, 1992. Mem. ASCD (dir. 1982-84), Soc. Study Curriculum History (founder, 1st pres. 1978-79), Am. Edn. Rsch. Assn. (com. on role and status of women in ednl. R & D 1994—), Profs. Curriculum Assn. (Facotum 1983-84, chair membership com. 1994-95), Am. Ednl. Studies Assn., John Dewey Soc. (bd. dirs. 1989-91), Alumni Coun. Tchrs. Coll. Columbia U. *In my view, America has progressed over the years, and the best days are still to come. We have the single necessary resource to solve our most urgent problems and achieve our deepest moral values —human intelligence.*

TANNER, LAURENCE ARAM, hospital administrator; b. Chelsea, Mass., June 27, 1946; s. Sylvan and Doris (Liss) T.; m. Janis A. Piazza, Aug. 23, 1969; children: Rebecca, David, Sarah. BS in Mgmt., U. R.I., 1970; MPH, Yale U., 1972; postgrad., U. Indiana, 1974, Yale U., 1979. Resident in adminstrn. The Waterbury (Conn.) Hosp., 1972, asst. adminstr., 1972-76, assoc. adminstr., 1976-80; pres., chief exec. officer Bristol (Conn.) Hosp., 1980-87; pres. Greater Bristol Health Svcs. Corp., 1984-87, BHV, Inc., 1984-87, BMOB Corp., 1984-87, Bristol Hosp. Devel. Found., 1984-87; pres., chief exec. officer New Britain (Conn.) Gen. Hosp., 1987—; Preceptor dept. epidemiology and pub. health Yale U., 1974—; health care mgmt. U. Conn., 1978—; lectr. hosp. adminstrn. Yale U., 1980—; lectr. biostatistics The Hartford Grad. Ctr., 1977-78; bd. dirs. Burritt Internat. Fin. BanCorp, South Cen. Conn. Health Care Coalition, mem. Capital area health consortium mgmt. council, 1980—. Contbr. articles to profl. jours. Mem. health systems mgmt. adv. com. U. Conn., 1981—, adv. council U. Conn. Health Ctr., 1987—; bd. dirs. United Community Svcs., Inc., 1987—, Burritt Interfinancial Bancorp, 1990—; mem. adv. bd. United Bank and Trust Co., 1980-90, com. long range facilities Burlington Bd. Edn., 1986—; mem. adv. coun. to grad. program in health adminstrn. Western Conn. State U. Lt. USAF, 1967-70. James scholar, 1964. Mem. Am. Coll. Hosp. Adminstrs., Conn. Hosp. Assn., New Eng. Hosp. Assembly, Am. Hosp. Assn., Assn. for Advancement of Med. Instrumentation (v.p. health industry bd. dirs., mem. exec. com. 1983—), Yale U. Alumni Assn. in Mass. (pres.), Omicron Delta Epsilon, Phi Delta Phi. Home: 11 Two Buck Ring Burlington CT 06013-1407 Office: New Britain Gen Hosp 100 Grand St New Britain CT 06052-2016

TANNER, R. MARSHALL, lawyer; b. Santa Monica, Calif., Dec. 4, 1946; s. Stanley Robert and Kathryn (Lau) Tanner; m. Colleen Bonner, Sept. 3, 1969; children: David, Brent, Julie, Glenn, Scott, Holly. BA, Brigham Young U., 1970; JD, UCLA, 1977. Ptnr. Lawler, Felix & Hall, L.A., 1977-86, Pettit & Martin, Newport Beach, Calif., 1986—. Lt. USNR, 1970-74. Mem. ABA (region 9 chair, disaster legal assistance program), Calif. State Bar Assn., Orange County Bar Assn. Mem. LDS Ch. Office: Pettit & Martin 4695 Macarthur Ct Ste 1200 Newport Beach CA 92660-8805

TANNER, ROBERT HUGH, engineer, consultant; b. London, July 22, 1915; s. George John and Evelyn (Stratton) T.; m. Joan Margaret Garnham, July 6, 1940; children: Christopher John, Rosemary June, Peter Pinckney, David Stephen. BS in Engring., U. London, 1936, MS in Engring., 1962; LLD, Concordia U., 1989. Registered profl. engr., Eng., Can., Fla. From TV to rsch. engr. BBC, London, 1936-47; from engr. to dir. info. No. Electric Co., Ltd., Ottawa, Can., Ont., 1947-70; dir. info. Bell-No. Rsch., Ottawa, Can., Ont., 1970-72; pres. IEEE, N.Y.C., 1972; dir. indsl. rsch. Can. Dept. Comm., Ottawa, 1973-75; pvt. practice cons. engr. Naples, Fla., 1975—; cons. in field. Inventor various patents. Maj. Brit. Army, 1939-45, ETO. Fellow IEEE (pres. 1972, McNaughton Gold medal 1974, Pratt

award 1981, Award for Engring Professionalism, 1993), Acoustical Soc. Am., Engring. Inst. Can., Instn. of Elec. Engrs.; mem. Nat. Coun. Acoustical Cons. (bd. dirs. 1982-88). Episcopalian. Office: PO Box 655 Naples FL 33939-0655

TANNER, TRAVIS, travel company executive; b. 1951. With So. Airlines, Inc., Ft. Lauderdale, Fla., 1972-79, Republic Airlines Inc., Mpls., 1984-90, Walt Disney Travel Co. Inc., Orlando, Fla.; various positions, now CEO, chmn. Carlson Travel Group, Inc., Mpls., 1990—. Office: Carlson Travel Group Inc Carlson Pkwy 701 Tower Minneapolis MN 55459

TANNER, W(ALTER) RHETT, lawyer; b. Athens, Ga., May 16, 1938; s. John Bryson and Walterette (Arwood) T.; m. Carolyn Laverne Watson, Nov. 11, 1967; 1 child, Walter Rhett (dec. 1989). A.B. cum laude, U. Ga., 1960, J.D. cum laude, 1962. Bar: Ga. 1961. Assoc. firm Hansell, Post, Bandon & Dorsey, Atlanta, 1963-66; ptnr. Hansell, Post, Bandon & Dorsey, 1966-89; ptnr. Jones, Day, Reavis & Pogue, Atlanta, 1989-95, of counsel, 1995—. Bd. dirs. Atlanta Symphony Orch., 1975—, mem. exec. com., 1977-86, v.p., 1978, chmn. maj. gifts campaign, 1980; mem. Leadership Atlanta, 1980, Leadership Ga., 1982; bd. visitors Grady Meml. Hosp., 1983—; bd. dirs. Econ. Opportunity Atlanta, 1986-87; trustee Ga. Legal History Found., 1986—. Lt. comdr. USNR, 1964-72. Mem. ABA, Atlanta Bar Assn. (bd. dirs. 1982-87, exec. com. 1983-87), State Bar Ga. (vice chmn. bar and media com. 1979-82), Atlanta Bar Found. (trustee 1985-91), U. Ga. Alumni (pres. chpt. 1973-74, chmn. Atlanta/Met. coun. 1975, mem. state bd. mgrs., v.p. 1976-78), Atlanta Lawyers Club, Gridiron, Phi Beta Kappa, Omicron Delta Kappa, Phi Kappa Phi, Phi Delta Phi, Delta Tau Delta. Club: Capital City. Office: Jones Day Reavis & Pogue 3500 One Peachtree Ctr 303 Peachtree St NE Atlanta GA 30308

TANNIAN, FRANCIS XAVIER, economist, educator; b. Boston, Dec. 5, 1933; s. John Joseph and Marie (Killian) T.; m. Beatrix Laube, May 19, 1962; children—Monica, Margaret Joyce, Mark, Michele. B.A., Boston Coll., 1955, M.A., 1959; Ph.D., U. Va., 1965. Bus trainee Gen. Electric Co., Schenectady, 1955-56; asst. prof. econs. Duquesne U., Pitts., 1962-66; assoc. prof. econs. U. Del., Newark, 1967-72, prof. urban econs., 1972—, assoc. dean, 1978-79; vis. prof. U. Stuttgart, Fed. Republic Germany, 1972-73, U. Karlsruhe, Fed. Republic Germany, 1982, San Diego State U., 1989, U. Nitra, Czechoslovakia, 1990; cons. Fed. Water Pollution and Control Adminstrn., 1965-68, Deutsche Gesellschaft, Frankfurt, Fed. Republic Germany, 1982-83; lectr. urban studies U.S. Dept. State, Budapest, Bucharest, Belgrade, 1975; guest lectr. Czechoslovakian Acad. Scis., 1975. Editor: Externalities, 1972; contbr. articles to profl. jours. Mem. Del. Gov.'s Econ. Adv. Council, 1969-72; bd. dirs. Del. OIC, Wilmington, 1970-78; bd. dirs. Parity Econ. Devel. Corp., Wilmington, 1978-84; mem. Wilmington Mayor's Econ. Devel. Com., 1976-82. Served with U.S. Army, 1957-58. Mem. Am. Econ. Assn., So. Econs. Assn., Am. Real Estate and Urban Econs. Assn. Democrat. Roman Catholic. Home: 910 Baylor Dr Newark DE 19711-3128 Office: U Del Coll Urban Affairs Newark DE 19711

TANOUS, MICHAEL ALLAN, consulting company executive; b. Hettinger, N.D., Dec. 11, 1939; s. Alfred George and Wilma Verna (Potter) T.; m. Jean Marie Maercklein, Aug. 22, 1960; (div. Dec. 1974); children: Stephen, David, Carl, Jennifer, Elizabeth; m. Valerie Ann Pokoyski, June 6, 1986. B in Philosophy, U. N.D., 1961; postgrad., U. Calif., L.A., 1970-72. Mathematician System Devel. Corp., Grand Forks, N.D., 1961-63; systems analyst System Devel. Corp., Santa Monica, Calif., 1963-68; group mgr. System Devel. Corp., Santa Monica, 1968-75; program mgr. Gen. Electric Co., Valley Forge, Pa., 1976-77; v.p. Sci. Applications Internat. Corp., Colorado Springs, Colo., 1978-86; v.p., ptnr. Booz, Allen & Hamilton, Inc., Colorado Springs, 1986-89; pres. The Matrix Group, Colorado Springs, 1990-92; v.p. Nat. Systems & Rsch. Co., Colorado Springs, 1992—; Contbr. articles to profl. jours. Mem. engring. adv. com. U. Colo., 1987—; bd. dirs. Multiple Sclerosis Soc., Colorado Springs, 1986—. Mem. IEEE, AIAA, Tau Kappa Epsilon. Republican. Avocations: photography, fishing, hunting. Office: Nat Systems & Rsch Co 5475 Mark Dabling Blvd Colorado Springs CO 80918

TANPHAICHITR, KONGSAK, rheumatologist, allergist, immunologist, internist; b. Bangkok, Feb. 22, 1946; came to U.S., 1971; s. Boonchoo and Hong (Nayakovit) T.; m. Sirirat Tareesung, June 17, 1973; children: Saksiri Marc, Marisa. Student, Mahidol U., Bangkok, Thailand, 1964-66, MD cum laude, 1970. Diplomate Am. Bd. Internal Medicine, Am. Bd. Rheumatology, Am. Bd. Allergy and Immunology; cert. Rheumatologist Royal Coll. Physicians Can. Straight med. intern Detroit Gen. Hosp.-Wayne State U., 1971-72; resident Barnes Hosp.-Washington U., St. Louis, 1972-74, fellow in rheumatology and immunology, 1974-76; instr. in medicine Washington U., St. Louis, 1976-77, asst. prof. medicine, 1977—; attending physician Barnes Hosp., St. Louis, 1976—, Jewish Hosp. of St. Louis, 1981—; dir. Allergy, Rheumatology & Immunology Specialists, St. Louis; cons. rheumatology Washington U., St. Louis, 1976—. Author: Amyloid Fibrils in Joint Fluid, 1976, Studies of Tolerance in NZB/NZW Mice, 1977, Vasculitis and Multiple Sclerosis, 1980, Buddhism: Answers to Common Questions, 1990, Buddhism Answers Life, 1995. Dharma tchr., bd. dirs., sec. Wat Phrasrirataram Buddhist Temple, St. Louis, 1983—; co-dir. Buddhist Coun. St. Louis, 1985-90. Fellow ACP, Am. Acad. Allergy and Immunology, Am. Coll. Rheumatology, Royal Coll. Physicians Can.; mem. Thai Physicians Assn. Am. (treas. Midwest chpt. 1994), Thai Assn. Greater St. Louis (pres.), Thai Temple Karate Shorinryu Club (Black Belt). Avocations: karate, insight meditation, swimming, karaoke. Home: 12413 Ladue Rd Saint Louis MO 63141-8100 Office: Allergy Rheumatology & Immunology Specialists 11115 New Halls Ferry Rd Florissant MO 63033-7613

TANSELLE, GEORGE THOMAS, English language educator, foundation executive; b. Lebanon, Ind., Jan. 29, 1934; s. K. Edwin and Madge R. (Miller) T. BA magna cum laude, Yale U., 1955; MA, Northwestern U., 1956, PhD, 1959. Instr. Chgo. City Jr. Coll., 1958-60; instr. U. Wis., Madison, 1960-61, asst. prof., 1961-63, assoc. prof., 1963-68, prof. English, 1968-78; v.p. John Simon Guggenheim Meml. Found., 1978—; adj. prof. English and comparative lit. Columbia U., 1980—; mem. Planning Inst. Commn. on English, 1961; mem. exec. com. Ctr. for Edits. Am. Authors, 1970-73; mem. adv. com. for drama for bicentennial Kennedy Ctr., 1974-76; mem. Soviet-Am. symposium on editing Ind. U., 1976; mem. adv. com. Howells Meml., Kittery Point, 1976-78; exec. com. Ctr. for Scholarly Edits., 1976-81; mem. nat. adv. bd. Ctr. for Book, Libr. of Congress, 1978—; mem. adv. bd. Burton's Anatomy of Melancholy, 1978—, Pub. and Printing History, A Guide to Manuscript Resources in the U.S., 1980—; bd. dirs. Lit. Classics of U.S., Inc., 1979—, chmn. editl. standards com., 1979—, corp. sec., 1989—; mem. adv. com. N.Am. imprints program, 1980-92; Hanes lectr. U. N.C., 1981; mem. adv. coun. Rosenbach Mus. and Libr., 1980—; mem. adv. coun. Ind. U. Inst. Adv. Study, 1983—; mem. faculty Summer Rare Book Sch., Columbia U., 1984—; mem. adv. bd. Ctr. for Am. Culture Studies, Columbia U., 1985-94; mem. adv. coun. Am. Trust for the Brit. Libr., 1987—; Rosenbach lectr. U. Pa., 1987; mem. adv. coun. Am. Literary Manuscripts project, 1988—; bd. dirs. 18th Century Short-Title Catalogue/N.Am., Inc., 1988—, chmn., 1994—, Mark Twain Edition Project, 1991—; mem. vis. com. Lilly Libr., 1988-92; mem. adv. bd. Ctr. for Renaissance and Baroque Studies, U. Md., 1990—; mem. adv. com. Writings of J.F. Cooper, 1990—. Author: Royall Tyler, 1967, Guide to the Study of United States Imprints, 1971, A Checklist of Editions of Moby-Dick, 1976, Selected Studies in Bibliography, 1979, The History of Books as a Field of Study, 1981, Textual Criticism since Greg, 1987, A Rationale of Textual Criticism, 1989, Parkman Dexter Howe Library, Hawthorne and Melville, 1989, Textual Criticism and Scholarly Editing, 1990, Libraries, Museums, and Reading, 1991, A Description of Descriptive Bibliography, 1992, The Life and Work of Fredson Bowers, 1993; co-editor: The Writings of Herman Melville, 1968—, Samuel Johnson's Translation of Sallust, 1993; editor: Library of Am. Melville, 1982-83, Books as a Way of Life: Essays by Gordon N. Ray, 1988; mem. editorial bd. Contemporary Literature, 1962-91, Abstracts of English Studies, 1964-78, Papers of Bibliog. Soc. Am, 1968-80, Resources for American Literary Study, 1971—, Analytical and Enumerative Bibliography, 1977—, Review, 1978—, Am. Literature, 1979-82, Literary Research, 1986-90, Common Knowledge, 1991—; contbr. articles to books and profl. jours. Mem. coun. Friends of Columbia U. Librs., 1990-94; bd. dirs. Friends of Lilly Libr., 1990-92. Recipient Kiekhofer Teaching award U. Wis., 1963, Jenkins award for bibliography, 1973; Guggenheim fellow, 1969-

70; Am. Council Learned Socs. fellow, 1973-74; Nat. Endowment for the Humanities fellow, 1977-78, Laureate award Am. Printing History Assn., 1987. Mem. MLA (mem. exec. com. bibliog. evidence group 1974-75, methods of lit. rsch. div. 1979-83, chmn. 1982, mem. Hubbell award Com. Am. lit. sect. 1978-82, chmn. 1982, mem. com. on prize for lit. scholars 1983-87, chmn. 1985-87, chmn. ad hoc com. on future of print record 1993—), Modern Humanities Rsch. Assn., Bibliog. Soc. London (pres. Am. Friends 1992—), Bibliog. Soc. Australia, Bibliog. Soc. Am. (com. council 1970-94, vice chmn. publs. com. 1974-76, chmn. 1981-84, sec. 1976-78, chmn. com. on regional groups, 1978-80, 2d v.p. 1978-80, 1st v.p. 1980-82, pres. 1984-88), Bibliog. Soc. U. Va. (pres. 1992—), Oxford, Cambridge, Edinburgh, Birmingham, No. Ill., Can. biblog. socs., Soc. for Bibliography of Natural History, Printing Hist. Soc. (Am. corr. 1970-84), Am. Priee N.Y. chpt. 1979-85). Pvt. Librs. Assn., Ind. Research Libraries Assn. (com. on standards for rare book cataloging in machine-readable form 1978-79), Fellows Morgan Libr., Manuscript Soc. (bd. dirs. 1974-79), Am. Pub. Libr. Film Project (bd. advisors 1993—), Am. Antiquarian Soc. (mem. publs. com. 1972-81, chmn. com. 1978-81, mem. council 1974-92, hon. councillor, 1992—, del. to Am. Coun. Learned Socs. 1978-93, exec. com. dels., 1987-89, chmn. exec. com. program on book in Am. culture 1983-89, com. on edn., 1982-85, chmn., 1983-85, chmn. com. on libr. 1988-91), Soc. Textual Scholarship (adv. bd. 1979—, pres. 1981-83), The Johnsonians (chmn. 1993), Melville Soc. (pres. 1982), Book Club Calif., Typophiles, Guild Book Workers, Wis. Acad. Scis., Arts and Letters, Renaissance Soc. Am., Am. Soc. 18th-Century Studies, Renaissance English Text Soc., Assn. Documentary Editing (chmn. Julian Boyd award com. 1986, Boydston award com. 1994—), Soc. Scholarly Pub., Assn. internationale de bibliophilie, Soc. History of Authorship, Reading and Publishing (bd. dirs. 1993—), Phi Beta Kappa. Clubs: Century, Yale, Caxton, Grolier (publs. com. 1979-82, 83-87, council 1980—, small exhbns. com. 1979-87, chmn. 1980-82, sec. 1982-86, chmn. library com. 1985-86, 1986-90), Odd Volumes. Office: John Simon Guggenheim Meml Found 90 Park Ave New York NY 10016-1302

TANSILL, FREDERICK JOSEPH, lawyer; b. Washington, Feb. 27, 1948; s. Frederick Riker and Mary Eileen (Loftus) T.; m. Joan Louise Trefsgar, July 10, 1971; children: Brendan Frederick, Brooke Charlotte, Charlotte Trefsgar. BA with honors, Brown U., 1970; JD, Georgetown U., 1974, LLM in Taxation, 1982. Bar: D.C. 1974, U.S. Tax Ct. 1976, Va. 1983. Assoc. Cross, Murphy & Smith, Washington, 1974-77; ptnr. Bird & Tansill, Washington, 1977-79; assoc. Ober, Grimes & Shriver, Washington 1979-81; ptnr. Lewis, Mitchell & Moore, Vienna, Va., 1981-86; counsel Boothe, Prichard & Dudley, McLean, Va., 1986-87; ptnr. McGuire, Woods, Battle & Boothe, McLean, 1987-90; ptnr. Verner, Liipfert, Bernhard, McPherson & Hand, Chartered, McLean, 1990—; bd. dirs. Atlantic Trust Co. Mem. trusts and estates sect. Va. State Bar, 1983—, bd. govs., 1988—, chmn. bd. govs. 1991-92, co-chmn. spl. task force on lawyers as fiduciaries, 1993. Fellow Am. Coll. Trust and Estate Counsel; mem. ABA, Va. Bar Assn. (coun. taxation sect. 1989-92, coun. and legis. com. will sect. 1993—), Fairfax County Bar Assn. (chmn. will sect. 1986, chmn. tax sect. 1987-88, CLE com. 1988-89), No. Va. Estate Planning Coun. (exec. com. 1987-92, pres. 1990-91), Tower Club (bd. dirs. 1988—). Office: Verner Liipfert Bernhard McPherson & Hand 8280 Greensboro Dr Fl 6 Mc Lean VA 22102-3807

TANSILL, FREDERICK RIKER, retired judge; b. Washington, July 12, 1914; s. Frederick Guida and Elizabeth Estele (Riker) T.; m. Mary Eileen Loftus, Dec. 31, 1940; children: Claire Tansill Hermann, Constance Tansill Gelfuso, Fred, Celine Tansill Kramer, Eileen Tansill Suddath. BSS, Georgetown U., 1936, JD, 1941; postgrad., Benjamin Franklin U., 1951-53. Bar: D.C. 1940. Credit reporter Dun & Bradstreet, Washington, 1938; instr. R.O.T.C., Georgetown U., 1940-42; spl. atty. IRS, N.Y.C., 1945-48; ptnr. Goodwin, Rosenbaum & Meacham, Washington, 1948-68, Cox, Langford & Brown, Washington, 1968-69, McInnis, Wilson, Munson & Woods, Washington, 1969-72, Bird & Tansill, Washington, 1972-79, Ober, Grimes & Shriver, Balt. and Washington, 1979-80; spl. trial judge U.S. Tax Ct., 1980-86; sole practice Washington, 1986—; instr. tax Ben Franklin U., 1956-57, instr. econs., 1967; appointed hearing examiner of two cases Legal Svcs. Corp., 1987, 89. Acting gen. counsel Children to Children, Inc., Washington, 1975-79; bd. dirs. Woodley Park Community Assn., Washington, 1968-76, v.p., 1975-76; pres. parish council Roman Cath. ch., 1973-76, 78-79. Served with AUS, 1940-45. Mem. ABA, Fed. Bar Assn., D.C. Bar Assn., Bar Assn. D.C., Delta Theta Phi. Republican. Home: 3001 Veazey Ter NW Apt 516 Washington DC 20008-5401

TANSOR, ROBERT HENRY, investor; b. Chgo., Apr. 1, 1935; s. John S. and Leora Caroline (Buhmann) T.; m. Stephanie Trainor, Sept. 10, 1977; children: John Frederick, Adam Robert. BS, Northwestern U., 1957. CPA, Ill., N.J. Sr. acct. Arthur Young & Co., Chgo., 1961-65; mem. corp. staff Litton Industries, 1965-67; v.p. fin., controller Royal Typewriter Co., Conn., 1968-72, Sweda Internat. div. Litton Industries, Pinebrook, N.J., 1973-75; v.p. fin., adminstrn. Paramount Pictures Corp., N.Y.C., 1975-77, Otis Elevator Corp., Farmington, Conn., 1977-83; v.p. fin., chief fin. officer Gulton Industries Inc., Princeton, N.J., 1983-86; sr. v.p., treas., chief fin. officer The Polymer Corp., Reading, Pa., 1986-89; pvt. investor, 1989—. Served to lt. (j.g.) USN, 1957-61; ret. comdr. USNR, 1980. Mem. AICPA, Ill. CPA Soc., Fin. Execs. Inst., Navy League U.S. Republican. Roman Catholic. Avocations: golf, swimming, theater, music.

TANTLEFF, IRWIN, food products executive; b. Bklyn., Apr. 19, 1935; s. Julius and Henrietta (Bass) T.; m. Judith Zimmer, July 6, 1956; children: Jack Zimmer, Debra Termine. BS in Econs., U. Pa., 1956; MBA, NYU, 1991. Founder, chief exec. officer FoodTown Supermarkets IUT Ltd., Oyster Bay, N.Y., 1965-86; dir., corp. sr. v.p. First Nat. Supermarkets Inc., Maple Heights, Ohio, 1986-89; mng. ptnr. Four T Assocs., Laurel Hollow, N.Y., 1986—; chmn. N.Y. State Food Merchants, Albany, 1975—; officer and exec. com. mem. Twin County Grocers Inc.-FoodTown, Edison, N.J., 1976-86; bd. dirs. Health Info. Techs., Princeton, N.J. Dir. Oyster Bay C. of C., 1969-86, pres., 1971; trustee Community Found., Oyster Bay, 1977-79, Oyster Bay Jewish Ctr., 1970-82, v.p., 1987. Lt. U.S. Army, 1957-61. Recipient cert. appreciation Double Day Babcock Sr. Ctr., 1979, #1 award Police Boys Club, 1981, Humanitarian Appreciation award WA-Fedn., 1990; named Couple of Yr., State of N.Y., 1989. Mem. U.S. Power Squadron, Masons. Office: Four T Assocs 1486 Laurel Hollow Rd Laurel Hollow NY 11791

TANUR, JUDITH MARK, sociologist, educator; b. Jersey City, Aug. 12, 1935; d. Edward Mark and Libbie (Berman) Mark; m. Michael Isaac Tanur, June 2, 1957; children: Rachel Dorothy, Marcia Valerie. BS, Columbia U., 1957, MA, 1963; PhD, SUNY, Stony Brook, 1972. Analyst Biometrics Rsch., N.Y.C., 1955-67; lectr. SUNY, Stony Brook, 1967-71, from asst. prof. to prof. sociology, 1971-94, disting. teaching prof., 1994—; cons. NBC, N.Y.C., 1976-89, Lang. of Data Project, Los Altos, Calif., 1980-89; mem. Com. on Nat. Stats. of Nat. Acad. of Scis., 1980-87; trustee NORC, U. Chgo., 1987—. Editor: Statistics: A Guide to the Unknown, 1972, Internat. Encyclopedia of Statistics, 1978, Cognitive Aspects of Survey Methodology, 1984, Questions About Questions, 1991; editor Internat. Ency. of Social Scis., N.Y.C., 1963-67; contbr. articles to sci., statis. and social sci. jours. Bd. dirs. Vis. Nurse Svc., Great Neck, N.Y., 1970—; bd. govs. Gen. Soc. Survey, Chgo., 1989-92. Sr. rsch. fellow, Am. Statis. Assn./NSF/Bur. Labor Statistics, 1988-89. Fellow, AAAS, Am. Statis. Assn.; mem. Internat. Statis. Inst., Phi Beta Kappa. Home: 17 Longview Pl Great Neck NY 11021-2508 Office: SUNY Dept Sociology Stony Brook NY 11794

TANZER, LESTER, editor; b. N.Y.C., Aug. 3, 1929; s. Charles and Clara (Ente) T.; m. Marlene June Luckton, June 29, 1949; children—Stephen Drew, Jeffrey Marc, Andrew Wayne, M. David. A.B., Columbia U., 1951, M.S., Sch. Journalism, 1952. Reporter, Washington bur. Wall St. Jour., 1952-59; assoc. editor Changing Times mag., Washington, 1959-64; assoc. editor U.S. News & World Report, Washington, 1964-76, mng. editor, 1976-85; editor Cosmos Jour., 1990-93. Author: (with Stefan Ilok) Brotherhood of Silence, 1962; editor: The Kennedy Circle, 1961. Mem. Nat. Symphony Assn. Club: Cosmos. Home: 4859 30th St N Arlington VA 22207-2715

TANZMANN, VIRGINIA WARD, architect; b. Tuxedo, N.Y., July 6, 1945; d. John A. Ward and Helen Pound. BA in Architecture, Syracuse U., 1968, BArch, 1969. Registered architect, Calif., Nev., NCARB. Intern architect Burke Kober Nicolais Archuleta, Los Angeles, 1969-72; project architect

Daniel L. Dworsky & Assocs., Los Angeles, 1972-74, SUA, Inc., Los Angeles, 1974-75; staff architect So. Calif. Rapid Transit Dist., L.A., 1975-78; prin. The Tanzmann Assocs., L.A., 1978—. Prin. works, clients, include transp. facilities, retail stores, comml. and office facilities 8 railroad stations, L.A. MTA Red and Blue Lines, L.A. Metro North Hollywood Sta., Conv. Ctr. Expansion Team, Renovation of Hollywood Bowl, Petroleum Lab. Chevron USA, Inc., El Segundo, Calif., Hyperion Treatment Plant, UCLA Med. Ctr., L.A. Unified Sch. Dist., L.A. Mission, So. Calif. Gas Co. Valencia, Gas Co. Computer Ctr., L.A. Dept. Water and Power, Oxnard Housing Authority, L.A. Housing Authority. Work exhibited: Monterey Design Conf., Calif., 1981, 87, 100/100 Exhibit, PDC, 1995. Pres. YWCA of L.A., 1984-87. founder, Kay Bixby Libr. on Volunteerism, 1992; mem. exec. com. United Way of L.A., 1992-93, bd. dirs. 1992-93; pres. Vol. Ctr. L.A., 1990-91, mem., 1973-94; exec. com. Dorland Mountain Arts Colony, 1990-91; mem. Mus. Contemporary Art, L.A. Conservancy; founder Women's Transp. Coalition, 1993, pres. 1993, 94, 95; bd. dirs. Info Line, 1995. Recipient Vesta award, 1991, Architect of Yr. award Women Construction Owners and Execs., 1994. Fellow AIA (CCAIA bd.), 1989-91, 92-94, L.A. pres. 1994); mem. Assn. Women in Architecture (pres. 1977-78, 87-88), Archtl. Guild (treas. 1987-88, v.p 1988-89, pres. 1990), Calif. Women in Environ. Design (founder), Architects Designers and Planners for Social Responsibility, L'Union Internationale des Femmes Architectes. Office: The Tanzmann Assocs 820 E 3rd St Los Angeles CA 90013-1820

TAO, RONGJIA, physicist, educator; b. Shanghai, China, Jan. 28, 1947; came to U.S., 1979; s. Yun Tao and Xiao-Mei Zou; m. Weiying Duanmu, Dec. 22, 1976; children: Han, Jing. MA, Columbia U., 1980, PhD, 1982. Rsch. assoc. U. Wash., Seattle, 1982-84; rsch. fellow U. Cambridge, Eng., 1984; rsch. asst. prof. U. So. Calif., L.A., 1984-85; asst. prof. physics Northeastern U., Boston, 1985-89; asst. prof. physics So. Ill. U., Carbondale, 1989-91, assoc. prof. physics, 1991-92, prof. physics, 1993—; cons. UN Developing Program, N.Y. and China, 1992—; chair Internat. Conf. on Electrorheological Fluids, Carbondale, 1991, Feldkirch, Austria, 1993. Editor, author: Electrorheological Fluids, 1992, Electrorheological Fluids, Mechanism, Properties, Materials and Applications, 1994; contbr. articles to profl. publs. Office of Naval Rsch. grantee, 1990, 92; recipient award Omni mag., 1987. Mem. Am. Phys. Soc. Achievements include discovery that electric-field induced solidification is the physical mechanism of electrorheological fluids; the crystalline structure of electrorheological fluids is a body-centered tetragonal lattice. Office: So Ill U Dept Physics Carbondale IL 62901

TAPE, GERALD FREDERICK, former association executive; b. Ann Arbor, Mich., May 29, 1915; s. Henry A. and Flora (Simmons) T.; m. Josephine Waffen, June 18, 1939; children: Walter Richard, James William, Thomas Gerald. A.B., Eastern Mich. U., 1935, Sc.D. (hon.), 1964; M.S., U. Mich., 1936, Ph.D., 1940. Asst. physics Eastern Mich. U., 1933-35, U. Mich., 1936-39; instr. physics Cornell U., 1939-42; staff mem. radiation lab. Mass. Inst. Tech., 1942-46; asst., then assoc. prof. physics U. Ill., 1946-50; asst. to dir., then dep. dir. Brookhaven Nat. Lab., 1950-62; v.p., then pres. Associated Univs., Inc., 1962-63, pres., 1969-80, spl. asst. to pres., 1980-82; commr. AEC, 1963-69; U.S. rep. to IAEA with rank of amb., 1973-77; former pres., cons. Associated Univs., Inc.; dir. Sci. Service Inc., 1971—; Atomic Indsl. Forum, 1970-73; mem. Pres.'s Sci. Adv. Com., 1969-73, Def. Sci. Bd., 1970-73, chmn., 1970-72; mem. sci. adv. com. IAEA, 1972-73; mem. gen. adv. com. ERDA, 1975-77; mem. adv. council Electric Power Research Inst., 1978-85; mem. U. Chgo. bd. govs. for Argonne Nat. Lab., 1982-85. Author: (with L.J. Haworth) Relay Radar Chapter of MIT Radiation Laboratory Technical Series, 1947; also papers, reports. Recipient Army-Navy Certificate of Appreciation, 1947, Meritorious Civilian Service medal Sec. Def., 1969, Dept. State Tribute Appreciation, 1969, Dept. Def. medal for pub. service, 1973; Henry DeWolf Smyth Nuclear Statesman award Atomic Indsl. Forum/Am. Nuclear Soc., 1978; Disting. Pub. Service award NSF, 1980; Disting. Assoc. award Dept. Energy, 1980; Enrico Fermi award U.S. Energy Dept., 1987; decorated comdr. Order Leopold II, Belgium. Fellow Am. Phys. Soc., Am. Nuclear Soc., AAAS; mem. Nat. Acad. Engring., Am. Astron. Soc., Phi Beta Kappa, Sigma Xi, Phi Kappa Phi, Kappa Delta Pi. Home: 4970 Sentinel Dr Apt 502 Bethesda MD 20816-3569 Office: Associated Univs Inc 1400 16th St NW Ste 730 Washington DC 20036-2217

TAPELLA, GARY LOUIS, manufacturing company executive; b. Antioch, Calif., Sept. 1, 1943; s. Anthony M. and Mary (Lopez) T.; m. Karen Kent, June 24, 1967; children: Robert, Michael. BA in Internat. Rels., San Francisco State U., 1969. Staff asst. Rheem Mfg. Co., N.Y.C., 1969-71; plant mgr. Rheem Can., Vancouver, 1971-73; mktg. mgr. Rheem Can., Toronto, 1973-79; regional sales mgr. Rheem Mfg. Co., New Orleans, 1979-80; mng. dir. Rheem Far East, Singapore, 1980-85; gen. mgr. Rheem Can., Toronto, 1985-89; corp. v.p. internat. Rheem Mfg. Co., N.Y.C., 1989-90, chief oper. officer, 1990-91, pres., chief exec. officer, 1991—; dir. various Rheem Cos. With USN, 1961-63. Avocation: scuba diving. Office: Rheem Mfg Co 405 Lexington Ave New York NY 10174-0002

TAPIA, RICHARD ALFRED, mathematics educator; b. Santa Monica, Calif., Mar. 25, 1939; s. Amado and Magda Tapia; m. Jean Rodriguez, July 25, 1959; children: Circee (dec.), Richard, Rebecca. BA, UCLA, 1961, MA, 1966, PhD, 1967. Asst. prof. math. rsch. ctr. U. Wis., Madison, 1968-70; asst. prof. math. scis. U. Houston, 1970-72, assoc. prof. 1972-76, prof. math. scis., 1976—; chair dept. math. scis., 1978-83, assoc. dir. minority affairs Office Grad. Studies, 1989—; vis. assoc. prof. ops. rsch. Stanford (Calif.) U., 1976-77. Author: Nonparametric Density Estimation; contbr. articles to profl. publs. Named to 20 Most Influential in Minority Math. Edn., NSF, 1990; recipient Nat. Achievement award for Edn. Hispanic Engring. Mag., 1990. Mem. NAE, Am. Math. Soc. (mem. com. on edn.), Soc. for Indsl. and Applied Math. (trustee, lectr. 1988), Math. Assn. Am., Math. Programming Soc., Soc. for Advancement of Chicanos and Native Ams. in Sci. Home: 5723 Portal Dr Houston TX 77096-6010 Office: Rice U Dept Math Scis PO Box 1892 Houston TX 77251-1892

TAPLETT, LLOYD MELVIN, human resources management consultant; b. Tyndall, S.D., July 25, 1924; s. Herman Leopold and Emiley (Nedvidek) T.; B.A., Augustana Coll. 1949; M.A., U. Nebr., 1958; postgrad. S.D. State U., U. S.D., U. Iowa, Colo. State U.; m. Patricia Ann Sweeney, Aug. 21, 1958; children: Virginia Ann, Sharon Lorraine, Carla Jo, Carolyn Patricia, Catherine Marie, Colleen Elizabeth. Accredited pers. mgr. Profl. Human Resources. Tchr., Sioux Falls (S.D.) public schs., 1952-69; with All-Am. Transport Co., Sioux Falls, 1969-78, Am. Freight System, Inc., Overland Park, Kans., 1978-79; dir. human resources and public relations, corp. affirmative action compliance ofcl. Chippewa Motor Freight Inc., Sioux Falls, 1979-80; human resource and mgmt. cons., 1980-81; mgr. Sioux Falls Job Svcs. 1981-85, Pioneer Enterprises, Inc., 1985-86; ops. mgr. ATE Environ., Inc., 1986-88, cons. Royal River Casino, 1988-90; acad. dean Huron U., Sioux Falls, 1990-92, instr. econs Coll. Bus., 1992—; chmn. Chippewa Credit Union; mem. adv. bd. dirs. Nelson Labs., Sioux Falls 1981-82; evening mgmt. instr Nat. Coll., Sioux Falls, 1981-90, chmn. adv. com., 1984—, Huron U., 1990—, S.F. Washington High Sch. Sports Heritage 1899-1989. Past bd. dirs. Jr. Achievement, United Way, Sioux Vocat. Sch. for Handicapped; past mem. Gov.'s Adv. Bd. for Community Adult Manpower Planning; chmn. bus. edn. adv. com. Sioux Falls Public Schs., 1982-85; chmn. adv. com. South East Area Vocat. Sch., 1982-85 ; mem. alumnae bd. Augustana Coll., 1985-88. Capt. USMC, 1943-46, 50-52, Korea. Recipient V.F.W. Commendation award, 1990, Liberty Bell award S.D. Bar Assn., 1967; Sch. Bd. award NEA/Thom McAn Shoe Corp., 1966, S.D. Unsung Heroes Edn. Recognition award 1992; named Boss of Yr., Sioux Falls, 1977; cert. tchr. and counselor, S.D. Mem. Am. Soc. for Personnel Adminstrn. (accredited personnel mgr. life, S.D. dist. dir. 1980-84), Am. Trucking Assn. (mem. pub. rels. coun.), NEA (life mem., Pacemaker award), S.D. Edn. Assn. (life), Sioux Falls Personnel Assn. (past pres.), Sales and Mktg. Club Sioux Falls, Sioux Falls Traffic Club, VFW (life, Nat. Polit. Action Recognition award 1990), Am. Legion. Republican. Roman Catholic. Clubs: Toastmasters (past gov. dist. 41, Disting. Toastmaster award, Outstanding Toastmaster award dist. 41, Hall of Fame 1977), Elks. Contbr. articles to nat. mags. Office: Huron U PO Box 90003 Sioux Falls SD 57105-9060

TAPLEY, BYRON DEAN, aerospace engineer, educator; b. Charleston, Miss., Jan. 16, 1933; s. Ebbie Byron and Myrtle (Myers) T.; m. Sophia

Philen, Aug. 28, 1959; children: Mark Byron, Craig Philen. B.S., U. Tex., 1956, M.S., 1958, Ph.D., 1960. Registered profl. engr., Tex. Engr. Structural Mechanics Research Lab. U. Tex., Austin, 1954-58, instr. mech. engring., 1958, prof. aerospace engring. and engring. mechanics, 1960—, chmn. dept. aerospace engring. and engring. mechanics, 1966-77, Woolrich prof. engring., 1974-80, dir. Ctr. Space Research, 1983—, Clare Cockrell Williams chair in aerospace engring., 1984—; mem. adv. com. on guidance control and nav. NASA, 1966-67, com. on space rsch., panel I, 1974-76, chmn. region IV, engring. coun. on profl. devel., 1974-76; chmn. geodesy com. NRC, 1981-84, mem. acros. and space engring. bd., 1984-86, mem. space sci. bd., chmn. com. on earth studies, 1988-91; bd. dirs. Tex. Space Grant Consortium. Editor: Celestial Mech. Jour, 1976-79; assoc. editor: Jour. Guidance and Control, 1978-79; assoc. editor: Geophys. Revs, 1979-81. Dir. Tex. Space Grant Consortium, 1990—. Recipient NASA Exceptional Sci. Achievement medal, 1983, NASA Pub. Svc. medal, 1994. Fellow AAAS (pres. engring. sect.), AIAA (chmn. com. on astrodynamics 1976-78, Mech. and Control of Flight award 1989, Mechanics of Flight medal 1987), Am. Geophys. Union (pres. geodesy sect. 1984-86); mem. ASME, IEEE, NAE, Am. Acad. Mechanics, Am. Astronautics Soc. (pres. div. dynamic astronomy 1988-89), Soc. Engring. Sci., Am. Astron. Soc., Internat. Astron. Union, Sigma Xi, Pi Tau Sigma, Sigma Gamma Tau, Phi Kappa Phi, Tau Beta Pi. Home: 3100 Perry Ln Austin TX 78731-5327

TAPLEY, DONALD FRASER, university official, physician, educator; b. Woodstock, N.B., Can., May 19, 1927; s. Roy Donald and Velma (Fraser) T.; m. Caroline Southall, Sept. 14, 1957; children—Katherine, Elizabeth, Sarah Tapley Bangs. B.S., Acadia U., 1948; M.D., U. Chgo., 1952. Intern Presbyn. Hosp., N.Y.C., 1952-53; asst. resident, 1953-54, asst. attending physician, 1957-64, assoc. attending physician, 1964-72, attending physician, 1972—; Life Ins. Research fund fellow dept. chemistry Johns Hopkins U., Balt., 1954-56; Jane Coffin Childs fellow dept. physiol. chemistry Oxford U., Eng., 1956-57; asst. prof. medicine Columbia U., 1956-64, assoc. prof., 1964-72, prof., 1972—, assoc. dean for faculty affairs Coll. Physicians and Surgeons, 1970-73, acting dean, 1973-74, dean, 1974-84, alumni prof., sr. dep. v.p., 1984—. Trustee Morris Jumel Mansion, The Riverkeeper. Contbr. numerous articles to profl. publs. Assoc. editor Endocrinology Mag., 1963-68. Mem. Am. Soc. Clin. Investigation, Endocrine Soc., Am. Thyroid Assn., Harvey Soc., N.Y. Med. and Surg. Soc. Office: Columbia U Coll Physicians & Surgeons 630 W 168th St New York NY 10032-3702

TAPLEY, JAMES LEROY, retired lawyer, railway corporation executive; b. Greenville, Miss., July 10, 1923; s. Lester Leroy and Lillian (Clark) T.; m. Priscilla Moore, Sept. 9, 1950; children: Lane, Taylor, Cameron, James Clark, Meredith. AB, U. N.C., 1947, JD, 1950. Bar: N.C. 1951, D.C. 1962. With So. Ry. Co., Washington, 1953-83; gen. solicitor So. Ry. Co., 1967-74, asst. v.p. law, 1974-75, v.p. law, 1975-83; v.p. Washington counsel Norfolk So. Corp., Washington, 1983-87. Mem. Phi Beta Kappa, Kappa Sigma. Clubs: Chevy Chase, Univ.

TAPLEY, PHILIP ALLEN, English language and literature educator; b. Blackwell, Okla., June 11, 1938; s. Robert G. Sr. and Valena M. (Simmons) T.; m. Mary Stringer, Aug. 10, 1974; children: Mary Margaret, Laura Katherine. BA, U. North Tex., 1960, MA, 1962; PhD, La. State U., 1974. Cert. secondary tchr., Tex. Teaching asst. U. North Tex., Denton, 1960-61; teaching asst. La. State U., Baton Rouge, 1961-65, 68-69, instr., 1965-68; asst. prof. La. Coll., Pineville, 1969-74, assoc. prof., 1974-80, prof., 1980—; maj. scholar, presenter La. Endowment for the Humanities, Alexandria, 1977—; vis. cons. Ctrl. La. Electric Co., Pineville, 1989—. Author: A History of First United Methodist, 1976, 2d edit., 1989, (with others) Procs. of the Red River Symposium, 1987, 2d edit., 1991; contbr. articles to profl. jours. Pres., Friends of Rapides Libr., Alexandria, 1985-86. Mellon Found. fellow, 1982, 88, Ford Found. fellow, 1989. Mem. AAUP, South Ctrl. MLA (program chair so. lit. 1979), La. Folklore Soc. (pres. 1978-79), Hist. Assn. Ctrl. La. (pres. 1978-80, bd. dirs. 1978—), Phi Kappa Phi, Alpha Chi, Sigma Tau Delta, Omicron Delta Kappa. Democrat. Episcopalian. Avocations: reading, music, historic preservation, folklore collecting. Home: 1721 Polk St Alexandria LA 71301-6334 Office: La Coll English Dept 1140 College Blvd Pineville LA 71359

TAPLIN, FRANK E., JR., trustee education and arts institutions and associations; b. Cleve., June 22, 1915; s. Frank Elijah and Edith R. (Smith) T.; m. Ngaio I. Thornton, Sept. 3, 1943 (div. Mar. 1951); children: Caroline I. Taplin Ruschell, Jennifer Taplin Jerome, David F.; m. Margaret A. Eaton, Apr. 27, 1953; stepchildren: Jennifer A. Sichel Dickerman, Martha E. Sichel Kelly, Susan Sichel Panella. BA in History, Princeton U., 1937; MA in Jurisprudence (Rhodes scholar), Oxford U., 1939; JD, Yale U., 1941; MusD (hon.), Cleve. Inst. Music, 1981; DHL (hon.), Fordham U., 1984; Dr. Mus. Arts (hon.), Manhattan Sch. Music, 1984; LLD (hon.), Rider Coll., 1988. Bar: Ohio 1946. With firm Jones, Day Cockley & Reavis, Cleve., 1946-50; asst. to Sen. Taft in Ohio senatorial campaign, 1950; pvt. bus. investments Cleve., 1951-57; asst. to pres. Princeton U., 1957-59; chmn. bd. Scurry-Rainbow Oil, Ltd., 1954-74; trustee Inst. for Advanced Study, Princeton U., 1972-88, trustee emeritus, 1988—; dir. NACCO Industries, Inc., trustee Environ. Def. Fund., 1990—; pres. Cleve. Inst. Music, 1952-56; trustee Cleve. Orch., 1946-57, pres., 1955-57; pres. Nat. Council Met. Opera, 1961-64; dir. Met. Opera Assn., 1961-91, hon. dir. 1991—, pres., chief exec. officer, 1977-84; hon. trustee Bradford (Mass.) Coll.; trustee Princeton (N.J.) Day Sch., 1966-72, Princeton Area United Community Fund, 1963-76; mem. Princeton U. Music Dept. Adv. Council, 1960-85, hon. mem., 1987—, chmn., 1965-71; trustee Sarah Lawrence Coll., 1969-77, chmn., 1973-77, hon. trustee, 1977—; trustee Lincoln Center for Performing Arts, 1972-88, trustee emeritus, 1988—, vice chmn., 1981-84; trustee, founding pres. Lincoln Center Chamber Music Soc., 1969-73; fellow Morgan Library; mem. council Friends Princeton Library; chmn. bd. Marlboro Sch. Music, 1964-70; now trustee; trustee Woodrow Wilson Nat. Fellowship Found., 1972—, Am. Schs. Oriental Research, 1970-75, Western Res. Hist. Soc., Cleve.; internat. bd. dirs. United World Colls., London, 1973-76; also chmn. United World Colls. (U.S. com.), 1973-75; bd. dirs. Am. Friends of Covent Garden and Royal Ballet, Friends of Aldeburgh Festival.; mem. vestry Trinity Ch., Princeton, 1984-87. Vice chmn. council of fellows Morgan Library, 1987-90. Served from ensign to lt. comdr. USNR, 1941-46. Decorated hon. mem. (mil. div.) Order Brit. Empire; recipient Gold Medal award Nat. Inst. Social Scis. Disting. Service award Third St. Music Sch. Settlement, 1983. Mem. ABA, Assn. Am. Rhodes Scholars, Am. Philos. Soc., Am.-Scandinavian Found. (exec. trustee), Univ. Club (N.Y.C.), Century Club (N.Y.C.), bd. mgmt. 1981-84), Springdale Golf Club, Nassau Club (Princeton), Pretty Brook Club (Princeton), Tavern Club (Cleve.).

TAPLIN, WINN LOWELL, historian, retired senior intelligence operations officer; b. Saint Albans, Vt., Oct. 3, 1925; s. Winn Lowell and Elinor (Cunningham) T.; m. Ellajean Allard, Aug. 14, 1949; children: Leslie Taplin Baumann, Mark Allard. BSCE, U. Mich, 1946, AB, 1948, AM, 1950, PhD, 1956. Oper. officer CIA, Washington, 1955-81; cons. Stowe, Vt., 1981-94, Sarasota, Fla., 1994—. Author: Secret New England: Spies of the American Revolution, 1991, We Vermonters, 1992. Pres. Vt. Hist. Soc., 1989-93, trustee; pres. Mansfield View Water Corp., Stowe, 1989-92. 1st lt. USMC, 1943-46, U.S., 1950-52, Korea. Decorated Bronze Star, Intelligence Medal of Merit. Mem. Central Intelligence Retirees Assn., Assn. Former Intelligence Officers (dir. New England chpt.), First Day Cover Soc., Am. Philatelic Assn., Am. Legion, Disabled Am. Vets. Avocations: historical research, genealogy, classical music, stamp collecting. Home (summer): 903 Worcester Loop Stowe VT 05672-4326 Home: 7641 Sandalwood Way Sarasota FL 34231-5333

TAPP, JOHN CECIL, physician, educator, futures trader; b. Horse Cave, Ky., Dec. 1, 1940; s. Ernest and Lottie Belle (Gill) T.; divorced; children: John Randolph, Gregory Patrick. Student David Lipscomb Coll., 1958-59, Western Ky. U., 1959-61; postgrad. Sch. Pharmacy, U. Ky., 1961-62; MD, U. Louisville, 1966. Diplomate Am. Bd. Family Practice, Nat. Bd. Med. Examiners, Am. Bd. Chelation Therapy; cert. practitioner, master practitioner neurolinguistic programming. Intern U. Louisville, 1966-67, resident in internal medicine, 1969-70; pvt. practice medicine, Bowling Green, Ky., 1971—; mem. staff Greenview Hosp., Med. Ctr. Hosp. Bowling Green (Ky.), U. Louisville, Vanderbilt U.; assoc. clin. prof. vol. faculty Coll. Allied Health Professions, U. Ky., Lexington, asst. prof. Coll. Medicine; clin. instr. vol.

faculty Travecca-Nazarene Coll., Nashville, U. Louisville, Vanderbilt U.; tng. cons. div. regional med. programs Nat. Inst. Health, 1967-69; fiberoptic endoscopist laser surgeon. Maj. USPHS, 1967-69. Named to Hon. Order Ky. Cols. Fellow Am. Acad. Family Physicians; mem. Am. Acad. Bariatric Physicians, Am. Coll. for Advancement of Medicine, Ky. Acad. Family Physicians, Bowling Green. Med. Soc., Bowling Green-Warren County C. of C., Internat. Bio-Oxidative Medicine, Alpha Omega Alpha, Alpha Kappa Kappa, Kappa Psi. Avocations: raquetball, tae kwon do, tai chi, Zen. Office: 414 Old Morgantown Rd Bowling Green KY 42101-2899

TAPPÉ, ALBERT ANTHONY, architect; b. Pitts., Aug. 12, 1928; s. Albert Anthony and Martha Ann (McKee) T.; m. Jean Bates, June 27, 1963; children: Eliza Bruce, Albert Anthony III. Student, William and Mary Coll., 1947-48, Fontainebleau Fine Art and Music Sch., 1951; B.S., U. Va., 1952; M.Arch., MIT, 1958, M.City Planning. Designer, McLeod & Ferrara (Architects), Washington, 1954-55; planner Boston City Planning Bd., 1957-58; architect and planner Architects Collaborative, Cambridge, Mass., 1958-61; partner Huygens & Tappé, Inc. (architects and planners), Boston, 1962-80; pres. A. Anthony Tappé & Assocs., Inc., Boston, 1980—; instr. dept. city planning MIT, 1959-60; cons. architect Mass. Bur. Library Extension, 1965-76; chmn. bldg. commn., Brookline, Mass., 1977, mem. bd. examiners, Brookline; v.p. Guild Religious Architecture; mem. Back Bay Archtl. Commn.; bd. dirs. Boston Archtl. Center, 1980. Author: Guide to Planning a Library Building, 1967; important works include: Longy Concert Hall, Cambridge, Mass., Campus N.H. Coll., Franklin Park Zoo, Boston, Lynn Inst. for Savs., Interfaith Religious Ctr., Columbia, Md., student housing W.Va. Wesleyan Coll., Hotel, Costa Smeralda, Sardinia, Newton Pub. Libr., Beverly Pub. Libr., Am. Coll., Athens, Greece; also residences in U.S., France, Switzerland, housing projects in New Eng. Served with AUS, 1946-47, 52-54. Recipient Progressive Architecture Design award, 1966, 1st place single family category Plywood Design Awards Program, 1973, award of Merit, 1974. Fellow AIA (mem. nat. urban planning and design com. 1975, citation, hon. mentions 1969, 1st honor award 1970, honor award New Eng. Regional Council 1976); mem. Mass. Assn. Architects (exec. com.), Boston Soc. Architects (dir., v.p. 1981-82, pres. 1982-83), Am. Inst. Planners, Am. Planning Assn., Am. Inst. Cons. Planners. Clubs: Union Boat (Boston); Eastern Point Yacht (Gloucester, Mass.). Home: 58 Euston St Brookline MA 02146-4045 Office: 132 Lincoln St Boston MA 02111-2522

TAPPER, JOAN JUDITH, magazine editor; b. Chgo., June 12, 1947; d. Samuel Jack and Anna (Swoiskin) T.; m. Steven Richard Siegel, Oct. 15, 1971. BA, U. Chgo., 1968; MA, Harvard U., 1969. Editor manuscripts Chelsea House, N.Y.C., 1969-71, Scribners, N.Y.C., 1971; editor books Nat. Acad. Scis., Washington, 1972-73; assoc. editor Praeger Pubs., Washington, 1973-74; editor New Rep. Books, Washington, 1974-79; mng. editor spl. pubs. Nat. Geog. Soc., Washington, 1979-83; editor Nat. Geog. Traveler, Washington, 1984-88; editor-in-chief Islands (internat. mag.), Santa Barbara, Calif., 1989—. Named Journalist Yr. Pacific Asia Travel Assn., 1995. Mem. Am. Soc. Mag. Editors, Soc. Am. Travel Writers (editors' coun.), Channel City Club. Democrat. Jewish. Avocations: travel, reading, tennis. Home: 603 Island View Dr Santa Barbara CA 93109-1508 Office: Islands Mag 3886 State St Santa Barbara CA 93105-3112

TAQQU, MURAD SALMAN, mathematics educator; b. Mar. 21, 1942. Diploma in physics, Inst. Tech., Lausanne, Switzerland, 1965; licence in math., U. Lausanne, 1966; MA, Columbia U., 1969, PhD, 1972. Lectr. math. Hebrew U., Jerusalem, 1972-73; postdoctorate rsch. fellow Weizmann Inst., Rehovot, Israel, 1973-74; asst. prof. Cornell U., Ithaca, N.Y., 1974-81, assoc. prof., 1981-85, prof., 1985-86; prof. Boston U., 1985—; vis. assoc. prof. Stanford (Calif.) U., 1981-82; vis. rsch. scientist Courant Inst., NYU, N.Y.C., 1985; vis. scholar Harvard Coll., Cambridge, Mass., 1987-88; organizer profl. confs.; cons. sci. reviewer. Author: Stable Non-Gaussian Random Processes: Stochastic Models with Infinite Variance, 1994; editor: Dependence in Probability and Statistics, 1986; assoc. editor Stochastic Processes and their Applications, 1989—; contbr. articles to profl. publs. John Simon Guggenheim fellow, 1987. Fellow Inst. Math. Stats., Am. Math. Soc., Internat. Statis. Inst., Ops. Rsch. Soc. Am., Bernoulli Soc. Office: Boston U Dept Math 111 Cummington St Boston MA 02215-2411

TAQUEY, CHARLES HENRI, writer, consultant; b. Paris; came to U.S., 1942, naturalized, 1942; s. Henri and Marguerite (Normand) T.; m. Ruth McVitty, Feb. 1, 1947 (dec. May 1994); children: Antony, Chantal Sanders. B.S. U. Paris, 1929; Lauréat, Ecole Libre des Sciences Politiques, 1933; Licencié and Lauréat, D.E.S. Paris Law Sch., 1934. French Treasury rep. Paris, London, Berlin, N.Y.C., 1934-39; local currencies mgr. ECA, 1948-51; staff officer Exec. Office of Pres., 1952-57; fgn. service econ. officer Am. embassies Phnom-Penh, Cambodia, Tunis, Tunisia, Kingston, Jamaica; also detailed to Dept. Commerce as dep. dir. fgn. activities mgmt., 1957-70; mgmt. cons., ecol. economist (internat. trade and resources recovery), 1970—; expert witness Internat. Trade Commn., Ways and Means Com. U.S. Ho. of Reps., GAO, fgn. govts. Author: German Financial Crisis, 1931, Richard Cobden, 1938, Trusts and Patents, 1946, Obstacles to Development in Indonesia, 1952, Fisheries in Cambodia, 1959, Against Full Employment, 1973, Democracy and Socialism, 1976, Transnational Corporations and the State, 1979, Beyond Free Trade, 1983, Free Trade, Morality of Nations, 1987. Served as lt., arty. French Army, 1940; lt., arty. AUS, 1942-46; capt. 1952. Mem. Consumers for World Trade. Address: 1681 31st St NW Washington DC 20007-2968 also: Les Quatre Vents, 84580 Oppède France

TARALLO, ANGELO NICHOLAS, industrial gas and health care company executive, lawyer; b. Bklyn., May 3, 1940; s. Nicola and Josephine (Guariglia) T.; m. Patricia Klubnik, Nov. 21, 1964; 4 children. BA, Columbia U., 1961, JD, 1964; LLM, NYU, 1970. Bar: N.Y., N.J. Assoc. gen. counsel, mng. atty. The BOC Group, Inc., Murray Hill, N.J., 1977, asst. v.p., 1978-80, v.p. corp. activities, 1980-83, v.p. fin. and adminstrn., 1983-84, sr. v.p. fin. and adminstrn., gen. counsel, 1984-92; chief exec. legal affairs, strategy and policy com. The BOC Group plc, Windlesham, Surrey, Eng., 1992—; adj. prof. Ramapo Coll. N.J., Mahwah. Bd. dirs. United Way Bergen County, Paramus, N.J., 1984-89. Mem. ABA, N.Y. State Bar Assn., N.J. State Bar Assn., Fin. Execs. Inst. Roman Catholic. Office: The BOC Group plc, Chertsey Rd, Windlesham Surrey GU20 6HJ, England

TARAN, LEONARDO, classicist, educator; b. Galarza, Argentina, Feb. 22, 1933; came to U.S., 1958, naturalized, 1976; s. Miguel and Liuba (Etlis) T.; m. Judit Sofia Lida, Dec. 10, 1971; 1 child, Gabriel Andrew. Legal degree, U. Buenos Aires, 1958; Ph.D. in Classics, Princeton U., 1962. Jr. fellow Inst. Research in Humanities, U. Wis., 1962-63, Center Hellenic Studies, Washington, 1963-64; asst. prof. classics U. Calif., Los Angeles, 1964-67; mem. faculty Columbia U., 1967—, prof. Greek and Latin, 1971—, Jay prof. Greek and Latin, 1987—, chmn. dept., 1976-79; mem. Inst. Advanced Study, Princeton, N.J., 1966-67, 78-79; trustee Assn. Mems. Inst. Advanced Study, 1974-79; mem. mng. com. Am. Sch. Classical Studies, 1976—. Author: Parmenides, 1965, Asclepius of Tralles, Commentary to Nicomachus' Introduction to Arithmetic, 1969, Plato, Philip of Opus and the Pseudo-Platonic Epinomis, 1975, Anonymous Commentary on Aristotle's De Interpretatione, 1978, Speusippus of Athens, 1981; co-author: Eraclito: Testimonianze e imitazioni, 1972; Editorial bd.: Columbia Studies in the Classical Tradition, 1976-80. Am. Coun. Learned Socs. fellow, 1966-67, 71-72, Guggenheim Found. fellow, 1975, NEH fellow, 1986-87; grantee Am. Philos. Soc., 1963, 71, 75, Am. Coun. Learned Socs., 1968, 72, NEH, 1985-87, 88-89. Mem. Am. Philol. Assn., Classical Assn. Atlantic States, Soc. Ancient Greek Philosophy, Assn. Guillaume Bude. Home: 39 Claremont Ave New York NY 10027-6824 Office: Columbia U 615 Hamilton Hall New York NY 10027

TARANIK, JAMES VLADIMIR, geologist, educator; b. Los Angeles, Apr. 23, 1940; s. Vladimir James and Jeanette Downing (Smith) T.; m. Colleen Sue Glessner, Dec. 4, 1971; children: Debra Lynn, Danny Lee. B.Sc. in Geology, Stanford U., 1964; Ph.D., Colo. Sch. Mines, 1974. Chief remote sensing Iowa Geol. Survey, Iowa City, 1971-74; prin. remote sensing scientist Earth Resources Observation Systems Data Ctr., U.S. Geol. Survey, Sioux Falls, S.D., 1975-79; chief non-renewable resources br., resource observation div. Office of Space and Terrestrial Applications, NASA Hdqrs., Washington, 1979-82; dean mines Mackay Sch. Mines U. Nev., Reno, 1982-87, prof. of geology and geophysics, 1982—; pres. Desert Research Inst., Univ.

and Community Coll. System Nev., 1987—; adj. prof. geology U. Iowa, 1971-79; vis. prof. civil engring. Iowa State U., 1972-74; adj. prof. earth sci. U. S.D., 1976-79; program scientist for space shuttle large format camera expt. for heat capacity mapping mission, liaison Geol. Scis. Bd., Nat. Acad. Scis., 1981-82; dir. NOAA Coop. Inst. Aerospace Sci. & Terrestrial Applications, 1986-94; program dir. NASA Space Grant consortium Univ. and Community Coll. System Nev., Reno, 1991—; team mem. Shuttle Imaging Radar-B Sci. Team NASA, 1983-88, mem. space applications adv. com. 1986-88; chmn. remote sensing subcom. SAAC, 1986-88; chmn. working group on civil space commercialization U.S. Dept. Commerce, 1982-84, mem. civil operational remote sensing satellite com., 1983-84; bd. dirs. Newmont Gold Co.; mem. NASA Space Sci. and Applications adv. com., 1988—, Nat. Def. Exec. Res., 1986—; AF Studies Bd., Com. on Strategic Relocatable Targets, 1989-91; mem. NASA Pre-Launch Rev. Bd., Space Radar Lab., 1993-94; mem. NASA Fed. Lab. Rev. Task Force, 1994—; prin. investigator Japanese Earth Resources Satellite, 1991—; mem. eviron. task force, MEDEA Mitre Corp., McLean Va., 1993—; cons. Jet Propulsion Lab. Calif. Tech. Inst., Hughes Aircraft Corp., Lockheed-Marietta Corp., Mitre Corp., TRW; developer remote sensing program and remote sensing lab. for State of Iowa, ednl. program in remote sensing for Iowa univs. and U. Nev., Reno; Office Space and Terrestrial Applications program scientist for 2d space shuttle flight; terrestrial geol. applications program NASA, 1981—. Contbr. to profl. jours. Served with C.E. U.S. Army, 1965-67; mil. intelligence officer Res. Decorated Bronze Star medal; recipient Spl. Achievement award U.S. Geol. Survey, 1978, Exceptional Sci. Achievement medal NASA, 1982, NASA Group Achievement award Shuttle imaging radar, 1990, NASA Johnson Space Ctr. Group Achievement award for large format camera, 1985; NASA prin. investigator, 1973, 83-88, prin. investigator French Spot-1 Program to Evaluate Spot 1986-88; NDEA fellow, 1968-71. Fellow AAAS, Explorers Club, Geol. Soc. Am.; mem. Am. Assn. Petroleum Geologists (charter, mem. energy minerals divsn., divsn. environ. geoscis.), Soc. Mining Engrs., Am. Inst. Profl. Geologists (certified, pres. Nev. sect. 1985-87), AIAA (sr. mem.), Am. Astronautical Soc. (sr. mem., mem. engring. scis. sect. 1994—), Internat. Acad. Astronautics (corr. mem. 1986-94), Soc. Exploration Geophysicists, Geosci. and Remote Sensing Soc. of IEEE (bd. dirs., geosat com. 1983-94), Am. Soc. Photogrammetry and Remote Sensing (dep. dir. for remote sensing cert., conf. chmn. annual meeting Reno 1994, Merit award 1994), Internat. Soc. Photogrammetry and Remote Sensing (pres. working group II/4 1976-80, working group VII-5 non-renewable resources 1980-88, working group VII-4 geology and mineral resources applications 1992—, U.S. corr. commn. VII, 1994—), Nev. Quality and Productivity Inst. (chmn. bd. 1989-94), Nev. Industry Sci., Engring., and Tech. Task Force, Grand Canyon Visibility Commn. (pub. adv. com. 1992—), Bohemian Club, Sigma Xi, Phi Kappa Phi (life). Home: PO Box 7175 Reno NV 89510-7175 also: 2108 Calle De Espana Las Vegas NV 89102-4013 Office: Univ and Community Coll Sys Nev Desert Rsch Inst Pres Reno I have always been in awe of the universe in which we live and the little time we have on earth to perceive and understand it.

TARANTINO, DOMINIC A., accounting firm executive; b. San Francisco, Aug. 1, 1932; m. Leona Lazzareschi, July 24, 1954; children: John Robert, Stephen, Leanne. BS, U. San Francisco, 1954. With Price Waterhouse, 1957—, mem. policy bd. and mgmt. com., 1979-93, vice chmn. tax svcs., 1982-88, co-chmn. bd., mng. ptnr., 1988-93; chmn. Price Waterhouse World Firm, 1995—; mem. IRS Commr.'s Adv. Group, 1978. Mem. AICPA (mem. bd. dirs. 1988-95, vice chair 1992-3, chmn. 1993-94, Dixon Meml. award 1990). Office: Price Waterhouse 1251 Ave Of The Americas New York NY 10020-1104

TARANTINO, QUENTIN, film director, screenwriter; b. Knoxville, Tenn., 1963; s. Tony and Connie T. Screenwriter, dir., actor: Reservoir Dogs, 1992, Pulp Fiction, 1994 (Palme d'Or,Cannes Internat. Film Festival, 1994, Academy award best original screenplay 1994); screenwriter: True Romance, 1993; story: Natural Born Killers, 1994; producer: Killing Zoe, 1994; film appearances include Sleep With Me, 1994, Destiny Turns On the Radio, 1995; TV appearances include The Golden Girls, All-American Girl. Office: A Band Apart Production Capra Bldg 112 10202 Washington Blvd Culver City CA 90232-3119 also: 6201 Sunset Blvd Ste 35 Los Angeles CA 90028*

TARAS, PAUL, physicist, educator; b. Tunis, Tunisia, May 12, 1941; emigrated to Can., 1957, naturalized, 1962; s. Wladimir and Benita (Koort) T.; m. Marja-Leena Malinen, Aug. 3, 1963; children—Lisa Helene, Michele Anne. B.A.Sc., U. Toronto, 1962, M.A., 1963, Ph.D., 1965. Asst. prof. physics U. Montreal, Que., Can., 1965-70; assoc. prof. U. Montreal, 1970-76, prof., 1976—; spokesman U. Montreal in rsch. projects. Helios, SDC, Pep-II. Rsch. on nuclear and particle physics; co-managed conception and constrn. of 8pi Spectrometer, Chalk River Nuclear Labs, 1984-86; contbr. articles to profl. jours.; presenter papers to profl. confs. U. Toronto, Province of Ont., U.K. Atomic Energy Authority fellowships; France-Que., NRC, Natural Scis. and Engring. Research Council Can. grantee. Mem. Am. Phys. Soc., Can. Assn. Physicists. Home: 1639 Norway Rd, Montreal, PQ Canada H4P 1Y3 Office: Univ de Montreal, Lab Physique Nucleaire, Montreal, PQ Canada H3C 3J7

TARBELL, DEAN STANLEY, chemistry educator; b. Hancock, N.H., Oct. 19, 1913; s. Sanford and Ethel (Millikan) T.; m. Ann Hoar Tracy, Aug. 15, 1942; children: William Sanford, Linda Tracy, Theodore Dean. A.B., Harvard U., 1934, M.A., 1935, Ph.D., 1937. Postdoctoral fellow U. Ill. 1937; mem. faculty U. Rochester, 1938—, successively instr., asst. prof., asso. prof., 1938-48, prof. chemistry, 1948-62, Charles Frederick Houghton prof. chemistry, 1960—, chmn. dept., 1964—; Disting. prof. chemistry Vanderbilt U., 1967—, Branscom disting. prof., 1975-76, disting. prof. emeritus, 1976—; Guggenheim fellow and vis. lectr. chemistry Stanford U., 1961-62; Fuson lectr., 1972; cons. USPHS, Army Q.M.C.; mem. various sci. adv. bds. to govt. agencies. Author: (with Ann T. Tarbell) Roger Adams, Scientist and Statesman, 1981, Essays on the History of Organic Chemistry in the United States, 1875-1955, 1986 , also papers on history of chemistry. Recipient Herty award Ga. Sect. Am. Chem. Soc., 1973 Dexter award Div. History of Chemistry Am. Chem. Soc., 1989; Guggenheim fellow, 1946-47. Mem. Nat. Acad. Sci., Am. Chem. Soc. (chmn. div. history of chemistry 1980-81), Chem. Soc. London, Am. Acad. Arts and Scis., History of Sci. Soc. Home: 6033 Sherwood Dr Nashville TN 37215-5734

TARBOX, DICK, communications engineering executive. Exec. dir., engring. rsch. ctr. Am. Tel. and Telegraph Co., Princeton, N. J. Office: Am Tel & Telegraph Co Engring Rsch Ctr PO Box 900 Princeton NJ 08542-0900*

TARBOX, FRANK KOLBE, retired insurance company executive; b. Mineola, N.Y., Feb. 27, 1923; s. John Preston and Mary (Kolbe) T.; m. Eleanor Borden, May 1, 1948; children: John Borden, Kathryn Ann. Student, Swarthmore Coll., 1940-42; A.B., U. Pa., 1947, LL.B., 1950. Pvt. practice law, 1950-53, 55-60; asst. U.S. atty. Eastern Dist. Pa., 1953-55; v.p. adminstrn. Penn Mut. Life Ins. Co., Phila., 1960-71; pres. Penn Mut. Life Ins. Co., 1971-78, chief exec. officer, 1973-86, chmn. bd. dirs., 1979-87; ret., 1995; bd. dirs. Penn Mut. Life Ins. Co. With USNR, 1942-46. Office: Penn Mut Life Ins Co Independence Sq Philadelphia PA 19172

TARBOX, GURDON LUCIUS, JR., retired museum executive; b. Plainfield, N.J., Dec. 25, 1927; s. Gurdon Lucius and Lillie (Hodgson) T.; B.S., Mich. State U., 1952; M.S., Purdue U., 1954, D Pub. Svc. U. S.C., 1993; m. Milver Ann Johnson, Sept. 25, 1952; children—Janet Ellen LeGrand, Joyce Elaine Schumacher, Paul Edward, Lucia Ann. Asst. dir. Brookgreen Gardens, Murrells Inlet, S.C., 1954-59, trustee, 1959—, dir. 1963-94, pres., 1990—. Chmn. Georgetown County Mental Health Commn., 1964-66; mem. exec. council Confedn. S.C. Local Hist. Socs., 1976—; trustee S.C. Hall Fame, 1976—, S.C. Heritage Trust, 1981-86, S.C. Mansion Commn., 1986—. Served with AUS, 1946-48. Mem. Am. Foresters, Am. Assn. Bot. Gardens and Arboreta (dir. 1971-74, sec.-treas. 1982, v.p. 1983, pres. 1985-86), Georgetown County Hist. Soc. (pres. 1970-74), Am., Royal hort. socs., Am. Assn. Mus. (council 1983), Southeastern Mus. Conf. (dir. 1977-80), S.C. Fedn. Museums (pres. 1974-76), Am. Assn. State and Local History, S.C. Confedn. Local Hist. Socs. Episcopalian. Lodge: Rotary (pres. 1979-80). Home: 641 Crooked Oak Dr Pawleys Island SC 29585

TARBOX, KATHARINE RIGGS, investor relations executive; b. N.Y.C., Feb. 8, 1948; d. Henry Fisk and Mary (Powell) T.; m. Jeremy M.F. Warner,

Sept. 25, 1975 (div. Nov. 1982); m. Donald O. McLeod, May 25, 1983. BA in Econs., Wellesley Coll., 1970. Cash mgr., specialist Citibank, N.A., N.Y.C., 1970-75, sr. account officer, 1975-77; cash mgr. Chesebrough-Ponds, Inc., Greenwich, Conn., 1977-79, mgr. investor relations, 1979-82; dir. investor relations Chesebrough Ponds, Inc., Westport, Conn., 1982-86; v.p. investor relations Colgate-Palmolive Co., N.Y.C., 1987—. Mem. alumnae bd. govs. Westover Sch., Middlebury, Conn., 1987-91. Mem. Nat. Investor Relations Inst. (dir. N.Y.C. chpt. 1981-82). Office: Colgate-Palmolive Co 300 Park Ave New York NY 10022-7402

TARBUTTON, LLOYD TILGHMAN, motel executive, franchise consultant; b. Easton, Md., Jan. 3, 1932; s. William Lloyd and Ethel Ford T.; m. Virginia Rachael Johnson, Nov. 1, 1952 (div. 1977); children: Gregory Alan, Kenton Lyle.; m. Layne E. Johnson, Apr. 15, 1981; 1 stepchild, C. Todd Woolston. Dr Comml. Sci. in Mktg., Pacific Western U., 1993. Grad. Realtors Inst.; cert. franchise exec., cert. hotel adminstr. Div. sales mgr. Reuben H. Donnelley Corp. (advt. agy.), Norfolk, Va., 1953-58; owner, operator Tie Centre Stores, Norfolk, 1958-60; gen. mgr. Hembree Realty Co., Norfolk, 1960-62; chmn. bd., dir. Tarbutton Assocs., Inc., comml. real estate, real estate tax assessment Contesting, hotel-motel mgmt., and franchise cons., Norfolk, 1962—; co-founder, dir., pres., chmn. bd. Econo Lodges of Am. (formerly Econ-Travel Motor Hotel Corp.), Norfolk and Virginia Bch., 1967-83; chmn. bd. emeritus Econo Lodges of Am. (formerly Econ-Travel Motor Hotel Corp.), Norfolk, 1983—; co-founder, chief judge Franchising Hall of Fame, Washington, 1979-82; co-founder, chmn. Coun. Franchise Suppliers, Washington, 1986-88. Author: Franchising--The How To Book, 1986. Trustee Edn. Found. Old Dominion U., 1979-86, chmn. bd. trustees Ctr. Econ. Edn., Old Dominion U., 1983-84. Hon. editor Hotel and Motel Mgmt. Mag., 1974-83; hon. mem. Motel Day's Com. Internat. Hotel and Motel Ednl. Exposition, 1974-83; recipient Hon. Tchr. award Maury High Sch., Norfolk, 1959. Mem. Internat. Franchise Assn. (hon. life, chmn. bd. dirs., chmn. 1st Asian Symposium on Franchising, Tokyo 1978, 1st European Symposium on Franchising, Amsterdam 1978, 1st Indonesian Symposium on Franchising, Jakarta 1991), Internat. Council Hotel/Motel Mgmt., Va. Hotel and Motel Assn., Realtor's Inst. Norfolk (chmn. 1965), Nat. Assn. Realtors, Nat. Assn. Real Estate Brokers, Norfolk Bd. Realtors (dir., v.p.), Internat. Sales Execs. Club (dir., v.p., Distinguished Sales award 1957), Norfolk C. of C., Internat. Platform Assn., Airplane Owners and Pilots Assn. Presbyterian. Clubs: Cove Point Yacht (commodore), Cavalier Golf and Yacht, Town Point, Cape Henry Racquet, Registry Resort Tennis. Lodges: Masons, Shriners. Office: Birdneck Pla Bldg 1072 Laskin Rd Ste 202 Virginia Beach VA 23451-6364 I believe the greatest assist to my progress in business and personal life came when I became more aware of the "value of self" and thus others.

TARDE, GERARD, magazine editor. Editor Golf Digest, Trumbull, Conn. Office: Golf Digest 5520 Park Ave Trumbull CT 06611

TARDIO, THOMAS A., public relations executive; b. Pa., Jan. 26, 1952. V.p. strategic planning and other positions Columbia Pictures Industries, 1979-88; CFO, v.p. adminstrn. Rogers & Cowan, Inc., L.A., 1988-89, exec. v.p. entertainment sect., 1989-91, pres., CEO, 1991—. Mem. Pub. Rels. Soc. Am., Nat. Acad. Recording Arts and Scis., Acad. Motion Picture Arts and Scis. Offcie: Rogers & Cowan Inc Ste 400 10000 Santa Monica Blvd Los Angeles CA 90067

TARDY, MEDNEY EUGENE, JR., otolaryngologist; b. Scottsburg, Ind., Dec. 3, 1934. MD, Ind. U., 1960. Diplomate Am. Bd. Otolaryngology (v.p. 1993, pres. 1994). Intern Tampa Gen. Hosp., 1960-61; resident in otolaryngology U. Ill. Hosp., 1963-67, fellow head, neck and plastic surgery, 1967-68; otolaryngologist St. Joseph Hosp., Chgo.; prof. clin. otolaryngology U. Ill.; pvt. practice Chgo. Mem. Am. Acad. Facial Plastic and Reconstructive Surgery, Am. Acad. Otolaryngology, Am. Coll. Surgeons, Am. Otological Soc. Office: 2913 N Commonwealth Ave Ste 430 Chicago IL 60657-6224*

TAREN, JAMES ARTHUR, neurosurgeon, educator; b. Toledo, Nov. 10, 1924; s. Joseph Clarence and Mary Frances (Walker) T. BS, U. Toledo, 1948; MD, U. Mich., 1952. Diplomate Am. Bd. Neurosurgery. Intern U. Mich. Hosp., Ann Arbor, 1952-53, resident in surgery, 1953-54, resident neurosurgery, 1955-57; clin. instr. U. Mich. Med. Sch., Ann Arbor, 1955-57, instr. neurosurgery, 1957-58, asst. prof., 1958-63, assoc. prof., 1963-67, prof. neurosurgery, 1967—, dir. neurobehavioral sci. program, 1975-78, assoc. dean acad. programs, 1978-87, dir. Brain Tumor Lab., 1985-88; dir. Integrated Acad. Info. Mgmt., 1988-89; dir. neuromodulation program U. Mich. Med. Sch., Ann Arbor, 1994—; neurosurgeon Wayne County Gen. Hosp., Eloise, Mich., 1957-71, VA Hosp., Ann Arbor, 1957-73, U.S.S. Hope (Project Hope), Peru, 1962, Ecuador, 1963, Guinea, 1965; vis. prof. Hosp. Foch, Paris, 1966-67, St. Anne Hosp., Paris, 1981, Karolinski Inst., Stockholm, 1981, Haukland Sykehus, Bergen, Norway, 1984, Gumma U., Japan, 1989, Nihon U. Sch. Medicine, Tokyo, 1990. Author, co-editor: Correlative Neurosurgery, 1969, 3rd edit., 1982; contbr. articles to profl. jours. Dep. med. examiner Washtenaw County Dept. Health, Ann Arbor, 1962—. Served with USMC, 1943-46, PTO. Fellow NIH, 1953; rsch. fellow in neurosurgery Boston Children's Hosp., Peter Bent Brigham Hosp., Boston, 1955. Fellow ACS; mem. AMA, Congress of Neurol. Surgeons, Am. Assn. Neuro. Surgery, Am. Assn. Med. Colls., Am. Soc. for Stereotactic and Functional Neurosurgery, Am. Neuromodulation Soc. (treas. 1994), Royal Soc. Medicine (affiliate), Brit. Med. Soc., Internat. Assn. Study of Pain, Ferrari Club Am. Office: U Mich Hosps Sect Neurosurgery Box 0338 2124 Taubman Ann Arbor MI 48109

TARGAN, DAVID, science administrator; b. Morristown, N.J., Dec. 14, 1955; s. Albert and Anita (Dinnerstein) T. ScB, Brown U., 1979; MA, UCLA, 1981; PhD, U. Minn., 1988. Asst. prof. physics Brown U., Providence, R.I., 1988-90, dir. Ladd Observatory, 1989—, asst. dean of coll., 1990—. Mem. Am. Astronomical Soc. Office: Brown Univ PO Box 1843 Providence RI 02912-1843

TARGOFF, MICHAEL BART, defense corporation executive, lawyer; b. N.Y.C., July 20, 1944; s. Jerome H. and Tillie R. T.; m. Cheri Kamen, June 11, 1966; children: Ramie, Joshua, Jason, Hannah. AB, Brown U., 1966; JD cum laude, Columbia U., 1969. Bar: N.Y. 1969. Law clk. to presiding justice U.S. Dist. Ct. Mass., 1969-70; assoc. Willkie, Farr & Gallagher, N.Y.C., 1970-76; ptnr. Willkie, Fair & Gallagher, N.Y.C., 1976-80; gen. counsel, v.p. Savin Corp., Valhalla, N.Y., 1980-81; gen. counsel, sr. v.p., sec. Loral Corp., N.Y.C., 1981-92; sr. v.p., 1992—; also sec. Harlan Fiske Stone scholar, 1968-69. Mem. ABA, N.Y. State Bar Assn., chmn. of Bar of City of N.Y. Office: Loral Corp 600 Third Ave New York NY 10016*

TARJAN, ROBERT ENDRE, computer scientist, educator; b. Pomona, Calif., Apr. 30, 1948; s. George and Helen Emma (Blome) T.; m. Gail Maria Zawacki, Apr. 22, 1978 (div. June 1992); children: Alice Marisha, Zosia Emma Zawacki, Lily Maxine. BS, Calif. Inst. Tech., 1969; MS, Stanford U., 1971, PhD, 1972. Asst. prof. Cornell U., Ithaca, N.Y., 1972-73; Miller fellow U. Calif., Berkeley, 1973-75; asst. prof. Stanford U., Palo Alto, Calif., 1975-77; assoc. prof. Stanford U., Palo Alto, 1977-80; mem. tech. staff AT&T Bell Labs., Murray Hill, N.J., 1980-90; adj. prof. NYU, 1981-85; James S. McDonnell Disting. U. prof. Princeton (N.J.) U., 1985—; co-dir. DIMACS Princeton U. and Rutgers U., 1989—; adj. fellow NEC Rsch. Inst., Princeton, 1989—. Author: Data Structures and Network Algorithms, 1983; (with G. Polya and D. Woods) Notes on Introductory Combinatorics, 1983. Recipient Nevanlinna prize Internat. Meth. Union, 1983; Guggenheim fellow, 1978. Fellow AAAS, Am. Acad. Arts and Scis.; mem. NAS, NAE, Am. Philos. Soc., Assn. Computing Machinery (A.M. Turing award 1986), Soc. Indsl. and Applied Math. Office: Princeton U Dept Computer Sci Princeton NJ 08544

TARJAN, ROBERT WEGG, information services executive; b. Evanston, Ill., July 28, 1943; s. Robert David and Constance Rita (Wegg) T.; m. Elizabeth Linder; children: Robert J., Anne Marie, Katie, Michael, Eileen. BS in Math., Loyola U., Chgo., 1965. Programmer Kemper Nat. Ins. Cos., Long Grove, Ill., 1965-67, supr., 1967-79, teleprocessing mgr., 1969-78, tech. systems mgr., 1978-81, ops. and system support mgr., 1981-85, asst. mgr. info. svcs., 1985-86, v.p. info. svcs., 1986—; bd. dirs. Acord,

Pearl River, N.Y. Roman Catholic. Avocation: golf. Office: Kemper Nat Ins Cos 1 Kemper Dr Long Grove IL 60049

TARKENTON, FRANCIS ASBURY, computer comany executive, sports commentator, management consultant, former professional football player; b. Richmond, Va., Feb. 3, 1940; 3 children. Grad., U. Ga., 1961. Quarterback Minn. Vikings Nat. Football League team, 1961-67, 72-79, N.Y. Giants, 1967-72; former football commentator ABC Sports; pres., founder Tarkenton Productivity Group, Atlanta, 1984-86; chmn., CEO KnowledgeWare, Atlanta, 1986—; founder, chmn. bd. Tarkenton & Co., 1969—; host ABC's That's Incredible, 1980-83; mem. Nat. Football Conf. championship team, 1973. Author: Broken Patterns: The Education of a Quarterback, Playing to Win, Fran Tarkenton's Strategies to Business Success, How to Motivate People, 1986; co-author: Tarkenton, 1976. Active Diabetes Found., Mpls., Viking Children's Fund; chmn. major gift campaign Henrietta Egleston Children's Hosp., Atlanta; mem. nat. bd. advisors Fiscal Policy Council, Inc.; chmn. nat. steering com. bicentennial fund capital campaign U. Ga. Named Most Valuable Player in NFL, 1975; inducted Nat. Football of Fame, 1986, Coll. Football Hall of Fame, 1987. Mem. Fellowship Christian Athletes. Methodist. Address: KnowledgeWare Inc 3340 Peachtree Rd NE Ste 1100 Atlanta GA 30326 *I've come to really believe that the people who make it in the world aren't the most talented ones or the smartest or the luckiest or necessarily the bravest. The ones who make it are the dogged ones. Just plain tenacity.*

TARKOFF, MICHAEL HARRIS, lawyer; b. Phila., Oct. 3, 1946. BA, U. Miami, 1968, JD, 1971. Bar: Fla. 1973, U.S. Supreme Ct. 1976, N.Y. 1983, U.S. Tax Ct. 1984. Asst. pub. defender Miami Pub. Defender's Office, Fla., 1973-77; guest lectr. U. Miami Sch. Law, 1977; ptnr. Flynn, Rubio & Tarkoff, Miami, 1977-83; ptnr. Flynn and Tarkoff, Miami, 1983-90; pvt. practice, 1990—; mem. substantial asst. in trafficking cases com. criminal law sect. Fla. Bar. Mem. Dade County Dem. Exec. Com., 1970-72, Tiger Bay; legal counsel Dade County Dem. Com., 1978. Sponsor, South Fla. coun. Boy Scouts Am.; USTA sectional umpire; active FTA Jr. Tournament Com., FTA Dist. Dir. Officials. Mem. ABA, Fla. Bar Assn. (narcotics practice, legis. com. criminal law sect., crim. law sect., fed. practice com., criminal procedure rules subcom. 1989-), Nat. Inst. Trial Advocacy (mem. faculty), Nat. Assn. Criminal Def. Lawyers (membership com., NORML legal com.), Fla. Criminal Def. Lawyers Assn. Office: 2601 S Bayshore Dr Ste 1400 Miami FL 33133-5413

TARLETON, LARRY WILSON, newspaper editor; b. Wadesboro, N.C., July 19, 1943; s. Harold Wilson and Martha (Roberson) T.; m. Judith Elaine Huntley, Sept. 8, 1963; children: Laurie Leigh, Larry Huntley. BA in Journalism, U.N.C., 1965. Reporter The Charlotte (N.C.) Observer, 1965-73; sporte writer The Miami (Fla.) Herold, 1973-74; sports editor The Charlotte Observer, 1974-76; exec. sports editor, mng. editor, exec. editor The Dallas Times Herald, 1976-88; exec. editor The Post and Courier, Charleston, S.C., 1988—. Mem. Am. Soc. Newspaper Editors, S.C. Press Assn., Dallas Press Club (pres. 1988). AP Mng. editors, AP Sports Editors. Avocations: golf, travel. Home: 27 New St Charleston SC 29401 Office: The Post and Courier 134 Columbus St Charleston SC 29403*

TARLOV, ALVIN RICHARD, former philanthropic foundation administrator, physician, educator, researcher; b. Norwalk, Conn., July 11, 1929; s. Charles and Mae (Shelinsky) T.; m. Joan Hylton, June 12, 1956 (div. 1976); children: Richard, Elizabeth, Jane, Suzanne, David. BA, Dartmouth Coll., 1951; MD, U. Chgo., 1956. Intern Phila. Gen. Hosp., 1956-57; resident in medicine U. Chgo. Hosps., 1957-58, 62-63, research assoc., 1958-61; asst. prof. medicine U. Chgo., 1963-68, assoc. prof., 1968-70, prof., 1970-84, chmn. dept. medicine, 1969-81; chmn. grad. med. edn. nat. adv. com. HHS, Washington, 1980; pres. Henry J. Kaiser Family Found., Menlo Park, Calif., 1984-90; sr. scientist New Eng. Med. Ctr., Boston, 1990—, exec. dir. The Health Inst., 1995—; prof. of Pub. Health Harvard U., Boston, 1990—; prof. of medicine Tufts U., 1990—. Pres. Med. Outcomes Trust, Inc., 1993—; chmn. bd., pres. Mass. Health Data Consortium, 1994—. Served to capt. U.S. Army, 1958-61. Recipient Research Career Devel. award NIH, 1962-67; John and Mary Markle Found. scholar, 1966-71. Mem. ACP (master), Inst. Medicine of Nat. Acad. Scis. Office: The Health Inst New Eng Med Ctr 750 Washington St # 345 Boston MA 02111-1526

TARN, NATHANIEL, poet, translator, educator; b. Paris, June 30, 1928; s. Marcel and Yvonne (Suchar) T.; children : Andrea, Marc. BA with honors, Cambridge (Eng.) U., 1948, MA, 1952; postgrad., U. Sorbonne, U. Paris, 1949-51; M.A. U. Chgo., 1952, PhD, 1957; postgrad., London Sch. Econs. 1953-58. Anthropologist Guatemala, Burma, Alaska, and other locations, 1952—; prof. comparative lit. Rutgers U., 1970-85; vis. prof. SUNY, Buffalo and Princeton, 1969-70. Author: Old Savage/Young City, 1964, Where Babylon Ends, 1968, The Beautiful Contradictions, 1969, October, 1969, A Nowhere for Vallejo, 1971, Lyrics for the Bride of God: Section: The Artemision, 1972, The Persephones, 1974, Lyrics for the Bride of God, 1975, The House of Leaves, 1976, Birdscapes, with Seaside, 1978, The Desert Mothers, 1985, At the Western Gates, 1985, Palenque, 1986, Seeing America First, 1989, Flying the Body, 1993, Views from the Weaving Mountain: Selected Essays in Poetics and Anthropology, 1991; co-author: (with Janet Rodney) The Forest, 1978, Atitlan/Alaskha, 1979, The Ground of Our Great Admiration of Nature, 1978; contbg. author: Penguin Modern Poets No. Seven: Richard Murphy, Jon Silkin, Nathaniel Tarn, 1965, A.P.E.N. Anthology of Contemporary Poetry, 1966, The Penguin Book of Modern Verse Translation, 1966, Poems Addressed to Hugh MacDiarmid, 1967, Music and Sweet Poetry: A Verse Anthology, 1968, Frontier of Going: Anthology of Space Poetry, 1969, Shaking the Pumpkin, 1972, America: A Prophecy, 1973, Open Poetry, 1973, Active Anthology, 1974, Symposium of the Whole, 1983, Random House Book of Twentieth Century French Poetry, 1983, Beneath a Single Moon: Buddhism in American Poetry, 1991, American Poetry since 1950: Innovators and Outsiders, 1993; translator: The Heights of Macchu Picchu (Pablo Neruda), 1966, Stelae (Victor Segalen), 1969, Zapotec Struggles, 1993; editor, co-translator: Con Cuba: An Anthology of Cuban Poetry of the Last Sixty Years, 1969, Selected Poems (Pablo Neruda), 1970; editor Cape Edits. and founder-dir. Cape Goliard Press, J. Cape Ltd., 1967-69. Recipient Guinness prize for poetry, 1963. Office: PO Box 8187 Santa Fe NM 87504-8187

TARNOFF, PETER, governmental official; b. N.Y.C., Apr. 19, 1937; s. Norman Tarnoff and Henrietta (Goldfarb) Laing; m. Mathea Oudinot, Jan. 13, 1962 (div. Oct. 1981); children: Nicholas, Alexander; m. Mathea Falco, Dec. 24, 1981; 1 child, Benjamin. Student, U. Paris, 1956-57, postgrad. 60-61; BA, Colgate U., 1958; postgrad., U. Chgo., 1958-60. Joined Fgn. Svc., Dept. State, 1961; spl. asst. to amb. Am. Embassy, Bonn, Fed. Republic Germany, 1969; trainee Nat. Sch. Adminstrn., Paris, 1970; prin. officer Am. Consulate Gen., Lyon, France, 1971-73; dep. chief of mission Am. Embassy, Luxembourg, 1973-75; dir. Office Rsch. and Analysis for Western Europe Dept. State, Washington, 1975-76, exec. sec. Dept. State, 1977-81; fgn. affairs fellow Dept. State, San Francisco 1981-82; exec. dir. World Affairs Coun. No. Calif., San Francisco, 1983-86; pres., dir. Coun. on Fgn. Rels., N.Y.C., 1986-93; under sec. state for polit. affairs Dept. State, Washington, 1993—. Office: Dept State 2201 C St NW Washington DC 20520-0001

TARNOPOL, MICHAEL L., bank executive; b. 1936; s. Irving and Charlotte (Weber) T.; m. Lynne Lichtenstein, June 29, 1958; children: Lisa, Lori Moore. Gen. ptrn., sr. mng. dir., also bd. dirs. Lehman Bros. Inc., 1959-75; with Bear Stearns Cos. Inc., 1975—, exec. v.p., dir.; mem. exec. com., chmn. investment banking divsn./bd. dirs. Bear Stearns Internat.; bd. dirs. Leslie Fay Cos., U.S. Equestrian Team; trustee T.A. bd. overseers The Wharton Sch., U. Pa.; chmn. bd. divs. Bear Stearns Internat., Ltd., Robert Steel Found., Inc. Mem. Palm Beach Polo Club, Harmonie Club, East Hampton Tennis Club, Greenwich Polo Club (bd. dirs.). Office: 245 Park Ave New York NY 10167-0001

TARNOW, ROBERT L., manufacturing corporation executive; b. Rochester, N.Y., 1924. A.B. in Physics, Oberlin Coll., 1949. With sales dept. Goulds Pumps Inc., Seneca Falls, N.Y., 1951-66, v.p. adminstrn., 1966-69, v.p. mfg., 1969-71, pres., 1971-78, chmn. bd., chief exec. officer, dir., 1978-83, chmn. bd., dirs., 1983—; bd. dirs. Raymond Corp., Utica Mut. Ins. Co., Bausch & Lomb, Norstar Bancorp. Office: Goulds Pumps Inc 240 Fall St Seneca Falls NY 13148-1590*

TARONJI, JAIME, JR., lawyer; b. N.Y.C., Nov. 20, 1944; s. Jaime and Ruth (Vazquez) T.; m. Mary Pineda, May 16, 1970; children: Ian A., Mark N., Nicole V. BA, George Washington U., 1972; JD, Georgetown U., 1976. Bar: Va. 1977, U.S. Ct. Appeals (4th and D.C. cirs.) 1977, D.C. 1978, U.S. Dist. Ct. D.C. 1978. Congl. intern U.S. Ho. of Reps., Washington, 1971; asst. to dep. staff dir. U.S. Commn. on Civil Rights, Washington, 1972-76; trial atty. FTC, Washington, 1976-79; antitrust counsel Westinghouse Electric Corp., Pitts., 1979-81; group legal counsel Dana Corp., Toledo, 1982-88; v.p., gen. counsel, asst. sec. Packaging Corp. Am. subs. Tenneco, Evanston, Ill., 1988—. Author: The 1970 Census Undercount of Spanish Speaking Persons; 1974. Editor: Puerto Ricans in the U.S., 1976. Bd. dirs. Puerto Rican Legal Def. and Edn. Fund. Served to capt. M.I., U.S. Army, 1965-70, Vietnam. Recipient spl. achievement award U.S. Commn. on Civil Rights, 1976; award for meritorious service FTC, 1979. Mem. ABA (antitrust and litigation sects.), Am. Corp. Counsel Assn., Fibre Box Assn. (chmn. legal adv. com.), Am. Forest and Paper Assn. (paper industry gen. counsel group). Democrat. Roman Catholic. Home: 1146 Furlong Dr Libertyville IL 60048-3701 Office: Packaging Corp of America 1603 Orrington Ave Evanston IL 60201-3853

TARPLEY, BRENDA MAE See LEE, BRENDA

TARPLEY, JAMES MERRELL, utility company executive; b. Leonard, Tex., Aug. 23, 1934; s. Claude Alvin and Willa (Mae) T.; m. Suzanne Wright, June 30, 1956; children: Jimmy Claude, Sheri Broadway. BSEE with honors, So. Meth. U., 1963. Registered profl. engr., Tex., N.Mex. Elec. engr. Community Pub. Service Co. (now named Tex.-N.Mex. Power Co.), Pecos, Tex., 1963-65; supt. elec. div. N.Mex. Power Co., Clifton, Tex., 1965-70; supt. of dist. N.Mex. Power Co., Ft. Worth, 1970-74, mgr. contracts and regulations, 1974-86, v.p. contracts and regulations, 1986-87, pres., chief exec. officer, 1987—, also bd. dirs.; bd. dirs. Bayport Cogeneration, TNP Operating Co., TNPE, Ft. Worth; engring. cons. various firms throughout Tex. Contbr. articles to mags. Chmn. Heart of Tex. drive Boy Scouts Am., Clifton, 1972-74; mem. bd. dirs. Meth. Ch. Clifton, 1971-74; bd. dirs. Lake Whitney (Tex.) Assn., 1973, Agri-Bus. program Tex. A&M U., College Station, 1976-78. Served with USN, 1952-54. Mem. NSPE, IEEE, Tex. Soc. Profl. Engrs., Sigma Tau, Eta Kappa Nu, Jaycees (pres. Clifton chpt. 1971-74). Republican. Clubs: Ridglea, Ft. Worth, Petroleum. Avocations: flying, hunting, fishing. Office: Tex-New Mex Power Co PO Box 2943 4100 International Plz Fort Worth TX 76109-4817

TARPY, THOMAS MICHAEL, lawyer; b. Columbus, Ohio, Jan. 4, 1945; s. Thomas Michael and Catherine G. (Sharshal) T.; m. Mary Patricia Canna, Sept. 9, 1967; children: Joshua Michael, Megan Patricia, Thomas Canna, John Patrick. A.B., John Carroll U., 1966; J.D., Ohio State U., 1972. Bar: Ohio 1969, U.S. Dist. Ct. (so. dist.) Ohio 1972, U.S. Dist. Ct. (no. dist.) Ohio 1974, U.S. Ct. Appeals (6th cir.) 1982. Assoc. Vorys, Sater, Seymour & Pease, Columbus, 1969-74, ptnr., 1977-85; v.p., chief adminstrv. officer Liebert Corp, Columbus, 1985-87; ptnr. Vorys, Sater, Seymour & Pease, Columbus, 1987—. Chmn. Columbus Graphics Commn., 1980; mem. Columbus Area Leadership Program, 1975. Served with U.S. Army, 1969-75. Mem. ABA, Ohio State Bar Assn., Columbus Bar Assn. Office: Vorys Sater Seymour & Pease PO Box 1008 52 E Gay St Columbus OH 43215-3161

TARR, CHARLES EDWIN, physicist, educator; b. Johnstown, Pa., Jan. 14, 1940; s. Charles Larned and Mary Katherine (Wright) T.; m. Bex Suzanne Harrell, Sept. 4, 1964 (div. Feb. 1977); m. Gudrun Kiefer, Nov. 18, 1977. B.S. in Physics (Morehead scholar 1957-61), U. N.C., Chapel Hill, 1961, Ph.D, 1966. Research assoc. U. N.C., Chapel Hill, 1966, U. Pitts., 1966-68; mem. faculty U. Maine, Orono, 1968—; assoc. prof. physics U. Maine, 1973-78, prof., 1978—, chmn. dept., 1977-79, assoc. dean Coll. Arts and Scis., 1979-81, acting dean Grad. Sch., 1981-87, acting v.p. research, 1984-87, dean Grad. Sch., 1987—; past docent U. Groningen, Netherlands, 1975-76; dir. Maine Toxicology Inst., 1992—, co-chair, 1993, chair, 1994; mem. exec. com. Coun. Rsch. Policy and Grad. Edn. of Nat. Assn. State Colls. and Land Grant Univs., 1993—; cons. in field. Contbr. articles to profl. jours. NASA grantee, 1970-72; NSF grantee, 1972—. Mem. IEEE, Am. Phys. Soc. Assn. Computing Machinery, Northeastern Assn. Grad. Schs. (mem. at large 1988—, pres. elect 1990-91, pres. 1991—), Sigma Xi. Quaker. Home: 519 College Ave Orono ME 04473-1211 Office: Univ Maine Grad Sch Orono ME 04469

TARR, CURTIS W., business executive; b. Stockton, Calif., Sept. 18, 1924; s. F.W. and Esther (Reed) T.; m. Elizabeth May Myers, 1955 (div. 1978); children: Pamela Elizabeth, Cynthia Leigh; m. Marilyn Van Stralen, 1979 (div. 1991); m. Mary Katherine Stegmiller, 1992. B.A., Stanford U., 1948, Ph.D., 1962; M.B.A., Harvard U., 1950; L.H.D., Ripon Coll., 1965, Grinnell Coll., 1969, Lincoln Coll., 1980; LL.D., Lawrence U., 1974, Ill. Wesleyan U., 1980. Rsch. asst., instr. Harvard U., 1950-52; v.p. Sierra Tractor & Equipment Co., Chico, Calif., 1952-58; staff mem. 2d Hoover Commn., 1954-55; asst. dir. summer session Stanford U., 1961-62, dir., 1962-63, asst. dean humanities and scis., 1962-63; lectr. bus. sch., 1962-63; pres. Lawrence U., Appleton, Wis., 1963-69; asst. sec. for manpower and res. affairs Air Force, 1969-70; dir. SSS, Washington, 1970-72; under sec. state for security assistance, 1972-73, acting dep. under sec. state for mgmt., 1973; v.p. overseas devel. Deere & Co., Moline, Ill., 1973; v.p. parts distbn. and materials mgmt. Deere & Co., 1973-81, v.p. mgmt. devel., 1981-83; dean and prof. Johnson Sch. Mgmt., Cornell U., 1984-89, prof. mgmt., 1989-90, dean emeritus, 1990—; vice chmn. Intermet Corp., 1992—; trustee Inst. Paper Chemistry, 1963-69; bd. dirs. Banta Corp., Menasha, Wis., Intermet Corp., Atlanta, State Farm Mut. Ins. Co., Bloomington, Ill., Phyton Corp., Ithaca, N.Y., State Farm Inst. Cos.; mem. internat. Rsch. Coun. Ctr. for Strategic and Internat. Studies, Washington, 1989-92; adj. prof. mgmt. Emory U., 1991-93. Author: Private Soldier, 1976, By the Numbers, 1981, Youth, 1994. Chmn. Task Force on Govt. Orgn., Fin. and Tax Distbn. for State Wis., 1967-69; chmn. Def. Manpower Commn., 1974-76, Ill. State Scholarship Commn., 1978-79, Quad Cities Grad. Study Ctr., 1982-84, Rep. candidate for Congress 2d Dist., Calif., 1958; trustee Am. Coll., Bryn Mawr, Pa., 1989-92. Served with AUS, 1943-46, ETO. Recipient Exceptional Civilian Service medal Air Force Dept., 1970; Distinguished Service award SSS, 1975. Mem. University Club (Chgo., N.Y.C.), Cosmos (Washington). Methodist.

TARR, DAVID WILLIAM, political scientist, educator; b. Melrose, Mass., July 25, 1931; s. Charles Howard and Pauline (Bryant) T.; children: Susan, Bryant. B.A., U. Mass., 1953; M.A., U. Chgo., 1956, Ph.D., 1961. Instr. Amherst and Mt. Holyoke colls., 1958-59; nat. def. analyst Legis. Reference Service, Library of Congress, 1959-62; research asso. Washington Center Fgn. Policy, 1962-63; mem. faculty U. Wis.-Madison, 1963—, prof. polit. sci., 1969—, dir. nat. security studies group, 1966-69, chmn. dept., 1972-75, fellow Inter-univ. Seminar on armed Forces and Soc., 1975—, dir. Ctr. for Internat. Cooperation and Security Studies, 1988—. Author: American Strategy in the Nuclear Age, 1966, Nuclear Deterrence and International Security: Alternative Nuclear Regimes, 1991; co-editor: Modules in Security Studies, 1974; contbr. articles to profl. jours. Chmn. U. Wis. Athletic Bd., 1979-86. Served to 1st lt. AUS, 1953-55. Rockefeller grantee, 1962-63; fellow, 1977. Mem. Internat. Studies Assn., Am. Polit. Sci. Assn. Unitarian.

TARR, JOEL ARTHUR, history and public policy educator; b. Jersey City, May 8, 1934; s. Max Alfred and Florence (Levine) Tartalsky; m. Arlene Green, Sept. 2, 1956 (dec. June 1969); children: Michael Jay, Joanna Sue; m. Tova Brafman, Aug. 11, 1978; children: Maya Leah, Ilana Ariel. BS, Rutgers U., 1956, MA, 1957; PhD, Northwestern U., 1963. Asst. prof. Calif. State U., Long Beach, 1961-66; vis. prof. U. Calif., Santa Barbara, 1966-67; asst. prof. Carnegie Mellon U., Pitts., 1967-70, assoc. prof., 1969-72, prof. history and pub. policy, 1973-90, Richard S. Caliguiri prof. urban and environ. history and policy, 1990—, dir. program in tech. and soc., 1975-87, co-dir. program in applied history and social sci., 1978-86, acting dean Sch. Urban and Pub. Affairs, 1986, assoc. dean Coll. Humanities and Social Sci., 1988-91, acting dean Coll. Humanities and Social Sci., 1991-92, acting head dept. history, 1992-93. Author: A Study in Boss Politics, 1971; editor: Patterns of City Growth, 1974, Retrospective Technology Assessment, 1977, Transportation Innovation and Spatial Change in Pittsburgh, 1850-1934, 1978, Pittsburgh-Sheffield: Sister Cities, 1986, Technology and the Rise of the Networked City in Europe and America, 1988. Bd. dirs. Action Housing, Pitts., 1983; trustee Hist. Soc. Western Pa., 1993—. NEH fellow,

1969-70; grantee NSF, 1975-79, 78-80, 83-85, NOAA, 1982-84; recipient Robert Doherty Prize for contbns. to excellence in edn., 1992. Mem. AAAS, Pub. Works Hist. Soc. (pres. 1982-83, Abel Wolman prize 1989), Orgn. Am. Historians, Pub. History Assn. (nat. council), Am. Soc. Environ. History, Soc. for the History of Tech. Democrat. Jewish. Home: 5418 Normlee Pl Pittsburgh PA 15217-1116 Office: Carnegie-Mellon U Schenley Pk Pittsburgh PA 15213

TARR, PAUL CRESSON, III, insurance company executive; b. Upper Darby, Pa., Feb. 27, 1933; married; children: Elizabeth A., Kathryn D., Deborah P., Paul C. IV. AB in Econs., Dickinson Coll., 1954. Ins. agt. INA Life, Phila., 1956-73; sr. v.p. Horace Mann Life Ins. Co., Springfield, Ill., 1973-80, exec. v.p., 1980-85; exec. v.p. Horace Mann Educators Corp., Springfield, 1986—; sr. v.p. Allegiance Life Ins. Co., Springfield, 1974-77, securities com., 1977, pres. 1977-85, exec. com., 1977-93, exec. v.p., 1985—; pres. Assn. & Consumer Mktg. Svc. Corp., Springfield, 1979—; exec. com. Educators Life Ins. Co. Am., Springfield, 1987-93, exec. v.p., 1987—; exec. com. Horace Mann Growth Fund, Inc., Springfield, 1980—, nominating com., 1981—, pres., CEO, 1981—; pres., CEO, exec. com., nominating com., Horace Mann Balanced Fund, Inc., Springfield, 1983—, also bd. dirs.; pres., CEO, exec. com., nominating com. Horace Mann Income Fund, Inc., Springfield, 1983—, also bd. dirs.; pres., CEO, exec. com., nominating com., Horace Mann Short-Term Investment Fund, Inc., Springfield, 1983—, also bd. dirs.; exec. com. Horace Mann Ins. Co., Springfield, 1982-93, Tchrs. Ins. Co., Springfield, 1981-93; exec. v.p. Horace Mann Svc. Corp., 1990—; pres. Well-Care, Inc., Springfield, 1980-87; asst. sec. Life Ins. N.Am., Phila., 1963-67, sec., 1967-69, v.p., 1969-73. Bd. dirs. United Way, Springfield, 1983-89, United Way Found., 1989—. Cpl. U.S. Army, 1954-56. Mem. Am. Soc. Chartered Life Underwriters. Lutheran. Office: The Horace Mann Cos 1 Horace Mann Pl Springfield IL 62715

TARR, RALPH WILLIAM, lawyer, former federal government official; b. Bakersfield, Calif., Sept. 29, 1948. BA, Dartmouth Coll., 1970; MPA, Calif. State U., 1973; JD, U. Calif., Hastings, 1976. Extern to assoc. justice Calif. Supreme Ct., 1976; rsch. atty. to presiding justice Ct. Appeal (5th dist.) Calif., 1976-77; assoc. Baker, Manock & Jensen, Fresno, Calif., 1977-81, dir., mem. exec. com., 1981-82; mem. adminstrv. com. Fed. Register, Washington, 1982-85; dep. asst. atty. gen. U.S. Dept. Justice, Washington, 1982-84, acting asst. atty. gen., 1984-85; solicitor U.S. Dept. Interior, Washington, 1985-89, counselor to the solicitor, 1989-90; pvt. practice L.A., 1990—. Home: 24011 Alder Pl Calabasas CA 91302-2394 Office: Andrews & Kurth LLP 601 S Figueroa St Fl 4200 Los Angeles CA 90017-5747

TARR, ROBERT JOSEPH, JR., publishing executive, retail executive; b. Freeport, N.Y., Dec. 7, 1943; s. Robert Joseph and Janet Christman (Laughton) T.; m. Molly Worthington Upton, Feb. 28, 1970; children: William Upton, Robert Joseph, III, David Worthington. BS, U.S. Naval Acad., 1966; MBA, Harvard U., 1973; MA, Fletcher Sch. Law & Diplomacy, 1976. Asst. v.p. corp. fin. Paine Webber Jackson Curtis, Boston, 1973-75; dir. corp. planning, then v.p., treas. Gen. Cinema Corp., Chestnut Hill, Mass., 1976-78, sr. v.p., 1978-83, exec. v.p., COO, 1983-85, pres., COO, 1985-91; pres., CEO, COO Harcourt Gen., Inc. (Gen. Cinema Corp., 1993), Chestnut Hill, Mass., 1991—; pres., COO The Neiman Marcus Group, Inc., 1987-91, pres., bd. dirs, CEO, COO, 1991—; bd. dirs. Nat. Retail Fedn. Bd. trustees Tufts U.; chmn. bd. visitors Fletcher Sch. Law and Diplomacy; trustee Tenacre Country Day Sch., Belmont Hill Sch. Lt. USN, 1966-71. Mem. Univ. Club (Boston), Comml. Club Boston, Quissett Yacht Club, Brae Burn Country Club. Home: 40 White Oak Rd Wellesley MA 02181-1435 Office: Harcourt Gen Inc 27 Boylston St Chestnut Hill MA 02167-1719

TARRANCE, VERNON LANCE, JR., behavior research executive; b. Harlingen, Tex., Dec. 4, 1940; s. Vernon Lance Sr. and Mary Gilmore (Rea) T.; m. Eugenia Aline McCuiston, July 2, 1966; children: Vernon Lance III, Haloway McCuistion, Kyle Rea. BA, Washington & Lee U., 1962; postgrad., U. Mich., 1971; MA, Am. U., 1973; postgrad., Harvard U., 1973-74. Dir. research Tex. Rep. Party, Austin, 1964-67, Rep. Nat. Com., Washington, 1969-70; spl. asst. to dir. U.S. Census Bur., Washington, 1970-73; v.p. Decision Making Info. Inc., Santa Ana, Calif., 1974-77; pres., founder Tarrance, Hill, Newport & Ryan, Houston, 1977-92; bd. dirs. Gallup Orgn.; pres., mng. dir. Gallup China Ltd., Beijing, 1993-95; co-chmn. adv. adjustment panel U.S. Census. Co-author: The Ticket Splitter, A New Force in American Politics, 1972; editor: Texas Precinct Votes '66, '68, '70, 1971. Fellow John F. Kennedy Inst. Politics Harvard U., 1973-74; named one of 150 People Who Influence Fed. Govt. Nat. Jour. Mag., 1986. Mem. Asia Soc., Houston World Affairs Coun., Coun. on Fgn. Rels. (Houston com.), Kappa Sigma. Avocations: mountain trekking, golf, aviculture, travel. Office: The Tarrance Group 14450 Walter Rd Ste 200 Houston TX 77014-1320

TARRANT, R(ICHARD) J(OHN), classicist, educator; b. Brooklyn, N.Y., Apr. 4, 1945; s. John Joseph and Bertha (Slaney) T.; m. Jacqueline Brown, Sept. 14, 1968. B.A., Fordham U., 1966; D.Phil., Oxford U., 1972; A.M. hon., Harvard U., 1982. P.S. Allen jr. research fellow Corpus Christi Coll., Oxford, Eng., 1968-70; lectr. Univ. Coll., Toronto, Ont., Can., 1970-71, asst. prof., 1971-74, assoc. prof., 1974-79; prof. U. Toronto, 1979-82; prof. Greek and Latin Harvard U., Cambridge, Mass., 1982-87, Carl A. Pescosolido prof. Roman civilization, 1987-93, Pope prof. Latin language and Literature, 1993—, chmn. dept., 1988-94; acting dean grad. sch. arts & scis., 1995—; bd. dirs. Scholars Press; vis. Mellon prof. Inst. for Advanced Study, Princeton, 1991-92; vis. fellow Corpus Christi Coll. U. Oxford, Eng., 1992. Author: Greek and Latin Lyric Poetry in Translation: A Bibliographical Survey, 1972, Seneca, Agamemnon, 1976, (with others) Texts and Transmission: A Survey of the Latin Classics, 1983, Seneca's Thyestes, 1985; editor Phoenix: Jour. Classical Assn. Can., 1978-82, Harvard Studies in Classical Philology, 1985-88, 93-94; editorial bd. Toronto Medieval Latin Texts, 1977—, Cambridge Classical Texts and Commentaries, 1992—; advisory bd. Text: Transactions of the Soc. for Textual Scholarship, 1994—; contbr. articles to profl. jours. Cabot fellow, 1993-94; Marshall scholar, 1966-69. Mem. Am. Philol. Assn. (bd. dirs. 1987-89, v.p. publs. 1992-95), Cambridge Philol. Assn., Classical Assn. Can., Classical Assn. New Eng., Phi Beta Kappa. Office: Harvard U Dept. Classics 319 Boylston Hall Cambridge MA 02138

TARRANT, ROBERT FRANK, soil science educator, researcher; b. Portland, Oreg., Mar. 11, 1918; s. Frank A. and Vera Leona (Tibbits) T.; m. Jean Inez Horton, Sept. 20, 1941; children: Christopher R., Susan J., Brian H., Stephanie A. Tarrant Martin. BS, Oreg. State U., 1941. Soil scientist USDA Pacific N.W. Forest Research Sta., Portland, 1946-71, asst. dir., 1971-74, dep. dir., 1975, dir., 1975-79; prof. forest scis. Oreg. State U., Corvallis, 1979—. Co-editor: The Biology of Alder, 1968, From the Forest to the Sea, 1988, Biology and Management of Red Alder, 1994; contbr. articles, reports to profl. jours. Bd. dirs. Oreg. Easter Seal Soc., Portland, 1969-75, pres., 1971-73. Served to lt. comdr. USN, 1942-45, ETO, PTO, also 1950-52. Recipient Superior Svc. award USDA, Washington, 1971, fellowship Tarrant Rsch. Oreg. State U., 1993—. Mem. N.W. Sci. Assn. (hon. life), Oreg. Hardwoods Commn., Sigma Xi Rsch. Soc. Episcopalian. Home: 2660 SW Fairmont Dr Corvallis OR 97333-1424

TARRANTS, WILLIAM EUGENE, government official; b. Liberty, Mo., Dec. 9, 1927; s. Joseph Eugene and Mildred Jane (Wright) T.; m. Mary Jo Edman, Jan. 19, 1952 (div. 1981); children: James Timothy, Jennifer Lynn; m. Lorna D. Lundberg, Sept. 24, 1988; stepchildren: David Murphy, Christine Walls, Janelle McCrea. B.Indsl. Engring., Ohio State U., 1951; M.S. in Indsl. Engring, 1959; Ph.D., N.Y. U., 1963. Registered profl. engr., Calif., Ohio, N.Mex. Instr. indsl. engring. Ohio State U., Columbus, 1958-59; asst. prof., research asso. N.Y. U., 1959-64; chief accident research div. Bur. Labor Stats., Dept. Labor, Washington, 1964-67; dir. manpower devel. div. Nat. Hwy. Traffic Safety Adminstrn., Dept. Transp., 1967-80; chief scientist Office of Program and Demonstration Evaluation, 1980-84; program analyst Office of Occupant Protection, 1984-87, program analyst evaluation staff, 1987—, also chmn. sci. and tech. info. adv. bd.; instr. Johns Hopkins U., 1984—, U. Md., 1991-02; mem. planning and adminstrn. transp. safety Transp. Rsch. Bd., NAS; cons. on safety program evaluation Indsl. Commn. Ohio, 1959. Contbr.: chpt. to Selected Readings in Safety, 1973, Readings in Industrial Accident Prevention, 1980; Author: chpt. to A Selected Bibliography of Reference Materials in Safety Engineering and Related Fields, 1967, Dictionary of Terms Used in the Safety Profession, 1971, Measurement of Safety Performance, 1980, Handbook of Occupational Safety and Health,

1987, also manuals and articles in field; mem. editorial bd.: Jour. Safety Research, Accident Analysis and Prevention, An Internat. Jour.; editor-in-chief: Traffic Safety Evaluation Research Rev. Trustee, ch. chmn. Evang. Covent Ch., 1976-80, 84-88, region 8 rep. to bd. trustees East Coast Conf., 1986-92. Capt. USAF, 1951-57. Recipient Founder's Day award NYU, 1963, 1st pl. Nat. Tech. Paper awards, 1961, 63, 67, cert. for outstanding performance Nat. Hwy. Traffic Safety Adminstrn., 1973, 86, Disting. Svc. to Safety award Nat. Safety Coun., 1989, Disting. Career Svc. award U.S. Dept. Transp., 1990; inducted into Safety and Health Hall of Fame Internat., 1990. Fellow Am. Soc. Safety Engrs. (dir., v.p. rsch. and tech. devel., pres. 1977-78, chmn. acad. accreditation coun. 1978—, mem. fellow rev. bd. 1980—); mem. Am. Soc. Safety Rsch. (trustee), Am. Inst. Indsl. Engrs., Human Factors Soc., System Safety Soc., Evaluation Rsch. Soc., Vets. of Safety, Am. Nat. Standards Inst. (standards com.), Soc. for Risk Analysis, AAAS, Nat. Safety Coun. (chmn. rsch. projects com. 1973-78, mem. exec. com. indsl. conf. 1977-78, Disting. Svc. award 1989), Alpha Pi Mu, Kappa Delta Pi. Mem. Evangelical Covent Ch. (trustee, ch. chmn. 1976-80, 84-88). Home: 606 Woodsmans Way Crownsville MD 21032-2317 Office: 400 7th St SW Washington DC 20590-0002 *We often look with awe at the successful person, much as we admire a well designed structure or a beautiful painting. Behind the finished product usually lies exhaustive effort, frustration, disappointment, and even failure which is obscured by the glow of accomplishment. Success is achieved by some ability, lots of hard work, perserverance, courage of convictions, help and support from others, a desire to reach a goal, self-discipline, and considerable personal sacrifice as we make choices concerning the use of our limited resources. The ability to bounce back from adversity is crucial. Most important of all is the strength and insight gained through prayer and the willingness to permit your life to be guided by Christian faith.*

TARRO, GIULIO, virologist; b. Messina, Italy, July 9, 1938; s. Emanuele and Emanuela (Iannello) T. MD, U. Naples, 1962, postgrad. in nervous diseases, 1968, PhD in Virology, 1971; postgrad. in med. and biol. scis., Roman Acad., 1979; hon. degree, U. Pro Deo, Albany, N.Y., 1989, St. Theodora Acad., N.Y., 1991. Asst. in med. pathology Naples U., Italy, 1964-66; rsch. assoc. div. virology and cancer rsch. Children's Hosp., Cin., 1965-68; asst. prof. rsch. pediatrics U. Cin. Coll. Medicine, 1968-69; rsch. fellow Nat. Rsch. Coun., Naples, 1966-74, rsch. chief, 1974; prof. oncologic virology U. Naples Coll. Medicine, 1971-85; prof. microbiology and immunology Sch. Specialization, U. Naples, 1972—; div. chief virology D. Cotugno Hosp. for Infectious Diseases, Naples, 1973—; dean faculty natural and phys. scis. Nobile Accademia di Santa Teodora Imperatrice, Capua, Italy, 1993—; sr. scientist Nat. Cancer Inst. Frederick (Md.) Ctr., 1973; project dir. Nat. Cancer Inst., Bethesda, Md., 1971-75; edn. min. rep. Zool. Sta., Naples, 1975-79; cons. Italian Pharmacotherapic Inst., Rome, 1980—; pres. De Beaumont Bonelli Found. for Cancer Rsch., Naples, 1978—; mem. Nat. Com. on Bioethics, 1995—. Author: Virologia Oncologica, 1979 (award 1985), Patologia dell'AIDS, 1991, Conil Cancro si Può vivere, 1992, AIDS cosa possiamo fare cosa dobbiamo sapere, 1994; contbr. over 300 sci. papers in field; patentee in field. Pres. Sci. Cultural Com., Torre Annunziata, Italy, 1984, Tumor Prevention Assn., Rome, 1984; mem. acad. senate Constantinian U., Providence, 1990, U. Pro Deo, N.Y., 1994. Maj. Italian Navy, 1982-84, lt. col., 1993. Decorated Comdr. Nat. Order of Merit, 1991; recipient Internat. Lenghi award Lincei Acad., 1969, Gold Microscope award Italian Health Min., 1973, Knights of Humanity award Internat. Register of Chivalry, Malta, 1978, Gold medal of Culture, Pres. of Italian Republic, 1975, Decorated Star of Europe, 1980, Culture award, 1985, 1st prize biomed. rsch. Italian Acad. Arts and Scis., 1987, Castello di Pietrarossa award, Italy, 1991, Gold Cesare award Padua, 1991, Internat. Man of Yr. in Biomed. Rsch. Internat. Biog. Centre Cambridge, Eng., 1992; named Knight of Grand Cross Sovereign Constantinian Order St. George, 1993, 20th Century award in Medicine, 1994. Fellow AAAS; mem. Am. Soc. Microbiology, N.Y. Acad. Scis., Internat. Assn. for Leukemias, Internat. League Doctors for Abolition of Vivisection (pres. 1992—), Italian Soc. Immuno-Oncology (v.p. 1975—, pres. 1990—), Assn. Rsch. Prevention of Cancer (sci. com. Turin 1995), Lions (pres. Pompei chpt. 1987-89, vice govt. dist. 108y 1991-92, prse. to fight cancer 1992-94, pres. com. sci. and life 1994-95, Melvin Jones fellow 1993). Roman Catholic. Achievements include discovery of RSV virus in infant deaths in Naples. Home: 286 Posillipo, 80123 Naples Italy Office: D Cotugno Hosp USL 41, 54 Quagliariello, 80131 Naples Italy

TARR-WHELAN, LINDA JANE, political organization administrator; b. Springfield, Mass., May 24, 1940; d. Albert and Jane Zack; m. Keith Tarr-Whelan; children: Scott, Melinda. BSN, Johns Hopkins U., 1963; MS, U. Md., 1967. Program dir. AFSCME AFL-CIO, Washington, 1968-74, union area dir., 1974-76; adminstrn. dir. N.Y. State Labor Dept., Albany, N.Y., 1976-79; dep. asst. to pres. Carter White House, Washington, 1979-80; dir. govt. rels. NEA, Washington, 1980-86; CEO, pres. Ctr. for Policy Alternatives, Washington, 1986—. Bd. dirs. Benton Found., Advocacy Inst., Voters for Choice, State Issues Forum, Nat. Consumers League, Ctr. for Policy Alternatives, Washington, 1985—. Named Japan Leadership Fellow Japan Soc., 1987-88, Disting. Grad. Johns Hopkins U., 1981. Democrat. Avocations: walking, travel. Home: 3466 Roberts Ln N Arlington VA 22207 Office: Ctr for Policy Alternatives 1875 Connecticut Ave NW Washington DC 20009-5728

TARSKY, EUGENE STANLEY, accountant, management and systems consultant; b. Meriden, Conn., Mar. 10, 1935; s. Joseph and Fannie (Apkin) T.; m. Irene M. Goldstein, Sept. 22, 1957; children: Julie B., Jeffrey A. Grad., U. Mass., 1957; M of Sci. in Taxation, Bentley Coll., 1978. CPA, Mass. Salesman, mgr. Margene Supply Co., Springfield, Mass., 1951-57; entry level acct. Coopers & Lybrand, Boston, 1957-58, auditor, system designer, 1961-64; CPA Martin Braver & Co., Chestnut Hill, Mass., 1964-65; pvt. practice Boston, 1965-70; ptnr. Orlando C. Moyer & Co. CPAs, Boston, 1970-72; pvt. practice Newton, Mass., 1972-82; pres. Eugene S. Tarsky CPA, Inc., Needham, Mass., 1982—; guest lectr. Continuing Edn. Program, Northeastern U., Boston, 1980, Boston U., 1982. Bd. dirs., asst. treas. Hospice of the Good Shepherd, Newton, 1982-85; bd. dirs., treas. Newton Boys and Girls Club, 1988—. With USAF, 1958-61. Recipient Benefactor of Youth award West Suburban YMCA, 1986, 89. Mem. AICPA, Mass. Soc. CPA's (speaker's bur. 1976—, discussion leader continuing edn. program 1983-90, mgmt. of acctg. practice com. 1984-89, Disting. Speaker award 1985), Route 128 Practitioners Forum (guest lectr. 1990, 93), Newton-Needham C. of C. (bd. dirs. 1975-76, 81-90, treas. 1986-87, pres. 1987-88, Outstanding Leadership award 1989, 10-Yr. Loyal Svc. award 1990), Kiwanis (bd. dirs. Newton 1989-94). Avocations: swimming, golf, bridge, travel, family. Home: 75 Haynes Rd Newton MA 02159 Office: 56 Pickering St Needham MA 02192-3124

TARSON, HERBERT HARVEY, university administrator emeritus; b. N.Y.C., Aug. 28, 1910; s. Harry and Elizabeth (Miller) T.; m. Lynne Barnett, June 27, 1941; 1 son, Stephen. Grad., Army Command Gen. Staff Coll., 1942, Armed Forces Staff Coll., 1951, Adavnced Mgmt. Sch. Sr. Air Force Comdrs., George Washington U., 1954; B.A., U. Calif., Los Angeles, 1949; Ph.D., U.S. Internat. U., 1972. Entered U.S. Army as pvt., 1933, advanced through grades to maj., 1942; transfered to U.S. Air Force, 1947, advanced through grades to lt. col., 1949; adj. exec. officer Ft. Snelling, Minn., 1940-42; asst. adj. gen. 91st Inf. Div., 1942-43; chief of personnel, advance sec. Comd. Zone, ETO, 1944-45; dir. personnel services 8th Air Force, 1946-47; dep. dir. dept. info. and edn. Armed Forces Info. Sch., 1949-51; dir. personnel services Japan Air Def. Force, 1951-53, Continental Air Command, 1953-62; dir. adminstrv. services, spl. asst. to Comdr. 6th Air Force Res. Region, 1962-64; ret., 1964; asst. to chancellor L.I. U., Brookville, 1964-69; dean admissions Tex. State Tech. Inst., San Diego Indsl. Center, 1970-72; v.p. acad. affairs Nat. U., San Diego, 1972-75, sr. v.p., 1975-88, founding sr. v.p. emeritus, 1988—. Decorated Bronze Star medal with oak leaf cluster, Air Force Commendation medal with 2 oak leaf clusters. Fellow Bio-Med Research Inst.; mem. Doctoral Soc. U.S. Internat. U. Am. Soc. Tng., Devel., World Affairs Council, Air Force Assn., Navy League U.S., Pres.'s Assos. of Nat. U. *(presidential visit)* Home: 4611 Denwood Rd La Mesa CA 91941-4803 *The greatest motivating force in my life is to explore the challenging frontiers of the future. Nothing can be compared to it.*

TART, JERRY GORDON, federal judge; b. Newton Grove, N.C., Apr. 15, 1934; s. Gordon G. and Ellen (Warren) T.; m. Zilphia Britt, June 2, 1956; children: Laura Tart Rhodes, Rachel E. BA, Wake Forest U., 1955, JD,

1957. Bar: N.C. 1957, U.S. Dist. Ct. (mid. dist.) N.C. 1970, U.S. Ct. Appeals (4th cir.) 1974. Ptnr. Hoyle, Boone, Dees and Johnson, Greensboro, N.C., 1962-69, Dees, Johnson, Tart, Giles and Tedder, Greensboro, 1969-85, Johnson and Tart, Greensboro, 1985-86; judge U.S. Bankruptcy Ct., Greensboro, 1986—. Capt. USAF, 1958-62. Mem. Nat. Assn. Chpt. 13 Trustees, Nat. Conf. Bankruptcy Judges, N.C. Bar Assn., Greensboro Bar Assn., 18th Dist. Jud. Bar Assn. (charter mem. bankruptcy and law office mgmt. sect. 1978-80), Bankruptcy Coun., N.C. Coll. Advocacy, Masons (master 1970, lodge treas. 1976-88, grand master 90, grand treas. 1991—), York Rite, Scottish Rite. Republican. Methodist. Avocations: beekeeping, fishing, water sports. Office: US Bankruptcy Ct PO Box 3603 202 S Elm St Greensboro NC 27401-2605

TARTER, CURTIS BRUCE, physicist, science administrator; b. Louisville, Sept. 26, 1939; s. Curtis B. and Marian Turner (Cundiff) T.; m. Jill Cornell, June 6, 1964 (div. 1975); 1 child, Shana Lee; m. Marcia Cyrog Linn, Sept. 6, 1987. BS, MIT, 1961; PhD, Cornell U., 1967. Teaching asst. Cornell U., Ithaca, N.Y., 1961-63, rsch. asst., 1964-67; physicist Lawrence Radiation Lab., Livermore, Calif., summers 1962, 63; staff mem. Theoretical Physics div. U. Calif., Lawrence Livermore Nat. Lab., 1967-69, group leader macroscopic properties of matter, 1969-71, assoc. div. leader, 1971-74, group leader opacities, 1972-78, div. leader, 1974-84; dep. assoc. dir. for physics Lawrence Livermore Nat. Lab., 1984-88, assoc. dir. for physics, 1988-94, dep. dir., 1994; dir., 1994—; sr. scientist Applied Rsch. Labs. Aeronutronic Div. Philco-Ford Corp., 1967; lectr., grad. student advisor dept. applied sci., U. Calif., Davis/Livermore, 1970—; cons. Hertz Found., 1970—, field com. study on astronomy in the 80's, NRC, 1980; mem. Army Sci. Bd., Washington, 1989—. Contbr. numerous articles to profl. jours. Mem. Am. Phys. Soc., Am. Astron. Soc., Internat. Astron. Union. Republican. Avocations: golf, squash, bridge. Home: 676 Old Jonas Hill Rd Lafayette CA 94549-5214 Office: Lawrence Livermore Nat Lab PO Box 808 Livermore CA 94551-0808

TARTER, FRED BARRY, advertising executive; b. Bklyn., Aug. 16, 1943; s. Irving and Edna (Kupferberg) T.; m. Barbara Jane Smith, Apr. 12, 1969; children: Scott Andrew, Heather, Megan. BS, CCNY, 1966. Pres. Jamie Publs. Hootenanny Enterprises, Inc., 1962-65; mdse. dir. Longines Symphonette Soc., 1965-67; with Universal Communications, Inc., N.Y.C., 1967—, pres., chief exec. officer, 1969-74; exec. v.p. Deerfield Communications, Inc., N.Y.C., 1974-87, pres., chief exec. officer, 1977-88; pres. Deerfield Books, Inc., N.Y.C., 1988-89; pub. S.E.W. mag., N.Y., 1977-88; pres. The Rainbow Group Ltd., N.Y.C., 1988—; bd. dirs. Deerfield Internat. News Corp., Screenvision, Inc., Lakeside Group, Inc., Boardwalk Entertainment, Ltd.; chmn. Pharmacy Fund, Inc.; exec. prodr. Joanne Carson's VIP's, Miss Am. Teenager Pageant, 1972-73; pres. The Programme Exch., U.K. Ltd.; prodr. Spenser Judas Goat, Ceremony Wounded Heart, 1994, Marriage Counselor, 1994. Mem. Friars Club, The Reform Club (London). Home: 9 Davis Dr Armonk NY 10504-3006 Office: The Pharmacy Fund Inc 210 E 39th St New York NY 10016-0911 *An integral part of success is the capacity for failure. Persistence, combined with responsibility, has proven to be the winning combination time and again.*

TARTER, MICHAEL ERNEST, biostatistician, educator; b. Bronx, N.Y., Dec. 20, 1938; s. William Tarter and Frieda Browdy; m. Orna Benzenburg, Aug. 30, 1975; children: Douglas, Robin. BA in Math., UCLA, 1959, MA in Math., 1961, PhD in Biostats., 1963. Asst. prof. U. Mich., Ann Arbor, 1964-66, assoc. prof., 1967; assoc. prof. U. Calif., Irvine, 1968-70; assoc. prof. U. Calif., Berkeley, 1970-76, prof., 1977—. Author books and articles; editor: Jour. Am. Statis. Assn. (screening editor for applications 1971-80). Fellow Am. Statis. Assn. (chmn. com. resources biometrics sect. 1981—, editorial bds. computational stats. and data analysis 1983-86, biometrics 1976-84, communications in stats. 1977—). Office: U Calif Sch Pub Health Dept Biomed Environ Health Scis 779 University Hall Berkeley CA 94720

TARTIKOFF, BRANDON, broadcast executive; b. L.I., N.Y., Jan. 13, 1949; m. Lilly Samuels, 1982; children: Calla Lianne, Elizabeth Justine. B.A. with honors, Yale U., 1970. With promotion dept. ABC TV, New Haven, Conn., 1971-73; program exec. dramatic programming Sta. WLS-TV (ABC), Chgo., 1973-76; mgr. dramatic devel. ABC TV, N.Y.C., 1976-77; writer, producer Graffiti; dir. comedy programs NBC Entertainment, Burbank, Calif., 1977-78, v.p. programs, 1978-80, pres., 1980-90; chmn. NBC Entertainment Group, 1989-91, Paramount Pictures, 1991-92, New World Entertainment, Ltd., 1994—. Co-author: The Last Great Ride, 1992. Named 1 of 10 Outstanding Young Men Am. U.S Jaycees, 1981; recipient Tree of Life award Jewish Nat. Found., 1986. Office: New World Entertainment Ltd 1440 S Sepulveda Blvd Los Angeles CA 90025

TARULLO, DANIEL K., federal official; b. Boston, Nov. 3. AB summa cum laude, Georgetown U., 1973; MA, Duke U., 1974; JD summa cum laude, U. Mich., 1977. Bar: D.C. 1978. Assoc. Arnold & Porter, 1977-78; atty. antitrust divsn. Dept. Justice, 1978-79; spl. asst. Office of Sec. Dept. Commerce, 1980-81; asst. prof. law Harvard U., Cambridge, Mass., 1981-87; chief employment counsel Senate Com. on Labor and Human Resources, 1987-89; internat. counsel Shearman & Sterling, Washington, 1989-93; asst. sec. econ. and bus. affairs Dept. State, Washington, 1993—; econ. advisor Clinton-Gore Transition Team, 1992. Articles editor Law Rev.; contbr. articles to profl. jours. Mem. Order of Coif, Phi Beta Kappa. Office: Econ & Bus Affairs Bur Dept State 2201 C St NW Washington DC 20520*

TARUN, ROBERT WALTER, lawyer; b. Lake Forest, Ill., Sept. 1, 1949; s. Donald Walter and Bonnie Jean (Cruickshank) T.; m. Helen J. McSweeney, May 1, 1987; children: Abigail Ech, Tyler Vincent, Parker Donald, Aimée Dakota. AB, Stanford U., 1971; JD, DePaul U., 1974; MBA, U. Chgo., 1982. Bar: Ill. 1974, Calif. 1975, U.S. Dist. Ct. (no. dist.) Ill. 1974, U.S. Dist. Ct. (so. dist.) Ind. 1995, U.S. Dist. Ct. (we. dist.) Ark. 1986, U.S. Ct. Appeals (5th cir.) 1992, U.S. Ct. Appeals (3d cir.) 1993, U.S. Ct. Appeals (7th cir.) 1975, U.S. Supreme Ct. 1978. Asst. atty. gen. State of Ill., Chgo., 1974-76; asst. U.S. atty. U.S. Dept. Justice, Chgo., 1976-79, dep. chief criminal div., 1979-82, exec. asst. U.S. atty. no. dist. Ill., 1982-85; ptnr. Reuben & Proctor, Chgo., 1985-86, Isham, Lincoln & Beale, Chgo., 1986-88, Winston & Strawn, Chgo., 1988—; lectr. criminal law practice Northwestern U. Sch. Law, 1986; instr. Atty. Gen.'s Advocacy Inst., Washington, 1980-85, Nat. Inst. Trial Adv., 1990. Co-author: (with Dan K. Webb and Steven F. Molo) Corporate Internal Investigations, 1993. Bd. dirs. Chgo. Ctrl. Area Com., 1994—. Fellow Am. Coll. Trial Lawyers (mem. fed. criminal procedure com. 1993—); mem. ABA, Bar Assn. San Francisco, Chgo. Bar Assn., Nat. Assn. Criminal Def. Lawyers, U. Chgo. Grad. Sch. Bus. Alumni Assn. (bd. dirs. 1986), Racquet Club, Wong Sun Soc. (San Francisco), Kenilworth Club, Chgo. Stanford Assn. Presbyterian. Avocations: hockey, architecture, 20th Century Louisiana politics, forensic science. Office: Winston & Strawn 35 W Wacker Dr Ste 4700 Chicago IL 60601

TARVER, JACKSON WILLIAMS, newspaper executive; b. Savannah, Ga., Mar. 2, 1917; s. Otis Merritt and DeLuth (Williams) T.; m. Margaret Birch Taylor, Mar. 24, 1940; children: Jack Williams, Margaret (Mrs. Peter Jason). Student, U. Ga., 1936; A.B., Mercer U., 1938, LL.D., 1965. Reporter Vidalia (Ga.) Advance, 1938; editor Toombs County (Ga.) Democrat, 1939-40, Macon (Ga.) News, 1940-43; asso. editor Atlanta Constn., 1943-49; asst. to pres. Atlanta Newspapers, Inc. (pub. Atlanta Jour., Atlanta Constn.), 1950-53, gen. mgr., 1953-58, v.p., 1956-58, pub., 1958—; also dir.; chmn. Fed. Res. Bank of Atlanta, 1962-68; chmn., dir. Theaters Service Co.; vice chmn. Cox Enterprises, Inc.; dir. So. Bell Telephone Co., Am. Motors Corp., Maccabees Mut. Ins. Co.; chmn. A.P., 1977-82. Mem. Ga. Bd. Edn., 1942-43; trustee Mercer U. Reid Found. fellow to S.A. 1949; recipient Humanitarian of Yr. award Inst. Human Relations, 1979. Mem. Am. Newspaper Pubs. Assn. (chmn. bur. advt. 1962-64), So. Newspaper Pubs. Assn. (pres. 1976-77), Am. Soc. Newspaper Editors, Sigma Delta Chi, Sigma Alpha Epsilon. Clubs: Capital City (Atlanta), Piedmont Driving (Atlanta), Commerce (Atlanta), Stadium (Atlanta). Office: 72 Marietta St NW Atlanta GA 30303-2804

TARVER, MICHAEL KEITH, lawyer; b. Monroe, La., Oct. 12, 1941; s. Mike Davis and Bernadine (Kilcrease) T. Student, U. Paris Inst. Polit. Studies, 1962; BA, Tulane U., 1963, LLB, 1966; LLM, NYU, 1967. Bar: La. 1966, N.Y. 1987. Assoc. Jones, Walker, Waechter, Poitevent, Carrere & Denegre, New Orleans, 1967-72, ptnr., 1972—. Asst. editor Tulane Law

Rev., 1961-63. Mem. Am. Coll. Real Estate Lawyers, Phi Beta Kappa. Roman Catholic. Home: 828 Burgundy St New Orleans LA 70116-3062 Office: Jones Walker Waechter Poitevent Carrere & Denegre 201 St Charles Ave Fl 50 New Orleans LA 70170-0001

TASA, KENDALL SHERWOOD, chemistry educator; b. Greenville, Tex., Apr. 29, 1947; s. Kenneth A. and Juanita (Holley) T.; m. Patricia Ann Langford, Mar. 28, 1969; children: Laura Ann, Heather Denise. BS, East Tex. State U., 1967, MS, 1969, EdD, 1973. Tchr. Lone Oak (Tex.) High Sch., 1969-72; prof. chemistry Brazosport Coll., Lake Jackson, Tex., 1973—, pres. faculty assembly, 1990-91, chmn. div. Math. and Sci., 1991—. Contbr. articles to sci. jours. Chmn. adminstrv. bd. 1st United Meth. Ch., Angleton, Tex., 1991-93. Mem. Tex. Jr. Coll. Tchrs. Assn. (campus rep., resolutions com. 1993-94). Republican. Avocations: golf, upland bird hunting, astronomy, tennis. Office: Brazosport Coll 500 College Dr Lake Jackson TX 77566-3199

TASCHETTI, VINCENT S., advertising executive; b. Bklyn., Jan. 29, 1945; s. Anthony Thomas and Rosalie (Laudisi) T.; children: Jill, Melisa, Jamie; m. Mary Theodore, May 1993. Student, St. Johns U., N.Y.C., Sch. Visual Arts, N.Y.C. Art dir. P.J. Pearlman, N.Y.C., 1967-69; art dir., designer Revlon, N.Y.C., 1969-70, NBC, N.Y.C., 1970-73; sr. v.p., assoc. creative dir. Batten, Barton, Durstine & Osborn, Inc., N.Y.C., 1973—. Photographer: Art Photography Diversified, 1988; one man showing BBDO Gallery, N.Y.C. Recipient Clio award, 1982, Bronze award Effie 1986, Art Dir. award 1987, Silver award Houston Internat. Film Festival 1987, Finalist award London Internat. Advt. award 1987, Freeport Arts Coun. award, N.Y.C. Avocation: photography. Office: BBDO NY 1285 Ave of the Americas New York NY 10019-6095

TASCO, FRANK JOHN, insurance brokering company executive; b. N.Y.C., Aug. 18, 1927; s. Frank and Jean (Pisapia) T.; m. Edwardine Dordoni, Oct. 30, 1954; children—Jill, Lisbeth, Diana. B.A., NYU, 1949. Vice pres. Guy Carpenter & Co., N.Y.C., 1962-76; dir. Guy Carpenter & Co., 1971—, pres., chief exec. officer, 1976-84; pres., chief operating officer Marsh & McLennan Cos., N.Y.C., 1984-85, chmn., chief exec. officer, 1986-92, also bd. dirs.; chmn. bd. dirs. Borden, Inc.; bd. dirs. Faugere & Jutheau, Paris, Terra Nova Ins. Co., London, N.Y. Telephone Co.; mem. industries adv. com. Advt. Coun., publishers' adv. panel Fortune mag.; chmn. Listed Cos. adv. com. to N.Y. Stock Exch. Mem. Pres.'s Drug Adv. Coun.; Corp. Fund Leadership com. Lincoln Ctr., N.Y.C.; bd. Inner-City scholarship fund; bd. dirs., chmn. St. Francis Hosp., Roslyn, N.Y., 1981, Phoenix Ho. Found. Inc., N.Y.C. Partnership; bd. dirs. Nat. Multple Sclerosis Soc.; trustee Nat. Commn. Against Drunk Driving; patron Project 100 for Mentally Handicapped of Bermuda; bd. govs. Met. N.Y. U.S. Olympic Com. With USN, 1945-46. Mem. Fgn. Policy Assn., Bus. Coun. of UN, Life Saving Benevolent Assn., City Midday Drug and Chem. (bd. dirs. 1972-77), Econ. Club, Links (N.Y.C.), Meadow Brook Club (Jericho, N.Y.). Clubs: Economic, Links (N.Y.C.); Meadow Brook (Jericho, N.Y.).

TASH, MARTIN ELIAS, publishing company executive; b. N.Y.C., Jan. 24, 1941; s. David and Esther (Milch) T.; m. Arlene Sue Klein, June 23, 1962; children: Nathan, Faye, Jill. B.B.A., Baruch Sch. City Coll. N.Y., 1962. C.P.A. Staff accountant S.D. Leidesdorf & Co. (C.P.A.'s), N.Y.C., 1962-66; v.p. fin., dir. LMC Data Inc., N.Y.C., 1966-71; with Plenum Pub. Corp., N.Y.C., 1971—, chmn. bd., pres., 1977—; chmn. bd. Gradco Systems, Inc., 1990—. Office: Plenum Pub Corp 233 Spring St New York NY 10013-1522

TASH, PAUL C., editor-in-chief; b. South Bend, Ind., July 17, 1954; s. Robert N. and Barbara R. (Eller) T.; m. Karyn E. Krayer, Aug. 19, 1983; children: Kaley Marie, Kendyl Barbara. BA, Ind. U., 1976; LLB, Edinburgh (Scotland) U., 1978. Reporter Times Pub. Co., 1978-83, city editor, 1983-86, metro editor, 1986-90, editor, pub. Fla. Trend Mag., 1990-91, Washington Bur. chief, 1991-92; exec. editor, v.p. St. Petersburg Times, 1992—; Bd. dirs. Times Pub. Co., Fla. Trend Mag. Bd. dirs. Leadership Fla., Tallahassee, 1994. Scholar Marshall Aid Commemoration Commn., 1976-78. Mem. Phi Beta Kappa. Home: 111 Bay Point Dr NE Saint Petersburg FL 33704-3805 Office: St Petersburg Times 490 1st Ave S Saint Petersburg FL 33701-4204

TASHIMA, ATSUSHI WALLACE, federal judge; b. Santa Maria, Calif., June 24, 1934; s. Yasutaro and Aya (Sasaki) T.; m. Nora Kiyo Inadomi, Jan. 27, 1957; children: Catherine Y., Christopher I., Jonathan I. A.B. in Polit. Sci., UCLA, 1958; LL.B., Harvard U., 1961. Bar: Calif. 1962. Dep. atty. gen. State of Calif., 1962-67; atty. Spreckels Sugar div. Amstar Corp., 1968-72, v.p., gen. atty., 1972-77; partner Morrison & Foerster, Los Angeles, 1977-80; judge U.S. Dist. Ct. Central Dist. Calif., Los Angeles, 1980—; mem. Calif. Com. Bar Examiners, 1978-80. Served with USMC, 1953-55. Mem. ABA, State Bar Calif., Los Angeles County Bar Assn. Democrat. Office: US Dist Ct 312 N Spring St Los Angeles CA 90012-4701

TASHJEAN, CATHERINE RICHARDSON, librarian; b. St. Paul; d. James A. and Katherine D. (Connolly) Richardson; m. John Tashjean, June 2, 1962. BS in Library Sci., Coll. St. Catherine, St. Paul, 1949. Asst. cataloguer Loyola U., Chgo., 1949-50; jr. libr. sch. engring. U. Minn., Mpls., 1950-51, cataloguer law sch., 1951-53, libr. sch. journalism, 1953-62; reference libr. FHA, Washington, 1966; acquisitions libr. Canisius Coll., Buffalo, 1966-71; staff libr. Manhattanville Coll., Purchase, N.Y., 1972-73, acting dir., 1974-75, dir., 1975-78; libr. U.S. Office Personnel Mgmt., Washington, 1978-84, dir. libr., 1984-94.

TASHKIN, DONALD P., physician; s. Reuben and Betty (Klevans) T.; m. Elaine Susan Rachman, Jan. 23, 1966; children: Jonathan Scott, Kimberly Irene. BA in Chemistry, U. Pa., 1957, MD, 1961. Diplomate in Internal Medicine, Am. Bd. Pulmonary Diseases. Rotating intern Albert Einstein Med. Ctr., 1961-62; resident in internal medicine VA Hosp., Phila., 1962-65; PHS acad. fellowship in chest disease/pulmonary physiology UCLA Sch. of Medicine, 1967-69; rsch. and edn. assoc. VA Ctr., L.A., 1969-71; asst. prof. medicine, divsn. pulmonary medicine UCLA Sch. of Medicine, 1969-76; attending physician Wadsworth VA Hosp., L.A., 1971-80, Sepulveda VA Hosp., L.A., 1971—; co-dir. UCLA Asthma and Cough Ctr., 1993—; unit med. dir., pulmonary function UCLA Med. Plaza, 1990—; dir. pulmonary function lab. UCLA Med. Ctr., 1971—; assoc. prof. medicine divsn. pulmonary disease Dept. Medicine, UCLA Sch. Medicine, 1971-81, prof. divsn. pulmonary and critical care medicine, 1981—; cons. drug abuse rsch. rev. com. Nat. Inst. on Drug Abuse, 1979, Tobacco Rsch. Coun. of Am., Inc., 1980, AMA Coun. on Continuing Physician Edn., 1980, Behavioral Medicine Study sect. NIH, 1980, Inst. of Medicine, Nat. Acad. of Scis., 1981, The Med. Letter, 1981, Rand Corp., 1982, 85, So. Calif. Edison, 1983, Pharmacotherapy, The Jour. of Human Pharmacology and Drug Therapy, 1983—, Am. Lung Assn. Com. on Drug Edn., 1983—, Western Oil and Gas Assn., 1984, NHLBI Interagency Tech. Com., 1987, Am. Lung Assn. of L.A. County, 1988, L.A. Unified Sch. Dist., Drug Abuse Resistance Edn. Program, 1989—, NIDA for organizing nat. conf. on cardiopulmonary effects of crack cocaine. Guest editor numerous jours. including Jour. of Pharmacoloy and Exptl. Therapeutics, 1994, pediatric Pulmonology, 1994, Jour. of Applied Physiology, AIDS, 1992, Jour. of the Am. Geriatrics Soc., 1993, Exptl. Lung Rsch., 1992, Annlas of Allergy, 1992, Bone Marrow Transplantation, 1991—, Western Jour. of Medicine, 1991—, Obstets. and Gyn., 1990; contbr. over 200 articles to profl. publs. Lt. comdr. USPHS, 1965-67. Fellow ACP, Am. Coll. of Chest Physicians; mem. Am. Thoracic Soc., Calif. Thoracic Soc., Am. Fedn. for Clin. Rsch., Western Soc. for Clin. Investigation, Western Assn. of Physicians, Internat. Cannabis Rsch. Soc., Internat. Drug Strategy Inst., Soc. for Rsch. on Nicotine and Tobacco, Trudeau Soc. of LA (chest disease sect. L.A. Med. Assn., program chmn. 1972-74, sec. 1974-76, pres.-elect 1976-77, pres. 1977-78), Phi Delta Epsilon, Phi Beta Kappa, Phi Lambda Upsilon. Achievements include leading expert on effects of smoked marijuana and crack cocaine on the lung; rsch. in the field of effects of air pollution on the lung, prevention of chronic obstructive lung disease, phamacotherapy of asthma. Office: Dept Medicine UCLA Sch Medicine 10833 Le Conte Ave Los Angeles CA 90095-1690

TASHMAN, MYLES RICHARD, lawyer; b. N.Y.C., Nov. 8, 1942; s. Solomon and Mildred (Schwartz) T.; m. Diana Saenz, May 21, 1977. BA, U. Vt., 1964; JD, Bklyn. Law Sch., 1967. Bar: N.Y. 1968, Pa. 1993, U.S. Supreme Ct. 1984. Asst. counsel N.Y.C. Econ. Devel. Adminstrn., 1967-69;

sr. advanced underwriting cons. Mut. Life Ins. Co. N.Y., N.Y.C., 1969-70; asst. counsel, asst. sec. Std. Security Life Ins. Co. N.Y., N.Y.C., 1970-75; sr. v.p., gen. counsel, corp. sec. Savs. Banks Life Ins. Fund, N.Y.C., 1975-86, United Pacific Life Ins. Co., Phila., 1986-93; chmn. Del. LIfe & Health Ins. Guaranty Assn., Wilmington, 1993; bd. dirs. Wash. Life & Health Ins. Guaranty Assn., Seattle, Mont. Life & Health Ins. Guaranty Assn., Bozeman. Mem. ABA, Am. Corp. Counsel Assn., N.Y. State Bar Assn., Soc. Fin. Examiners. Home: 298 Pennington Titusville Rd Pennington NJ 08534-4106 Office: United Pacific Life 14 Fl 1 Penn Center Plz Fl 14 Philadelphia PA 19103-1821

TASKER, JOHN BAKER, veterinary medical educator, college dean; b. Concord, N.H., Aug. 28, 1933; s. John Baker and Catherine Mabel (Baker) T.; m. Grace Ellen Elliott, June 17, 1961; children—Sybil Alice, Sarah Catherine, Sophia Ethel. D.V.M., Cornell U., 1957, Ph.D., 1963. Instr. Cornell U., Ithaca, N.Y., 1960-61; from assoc. prof. to prof. Cornell U., 1967-78; from asst. prof. to assoc. prof. Colo. State U., Fort Collins, 1963-67; prof. vet. clinical pathology, assoc. dean La. State U., 1978-84; prof. vet. pathology Coll. Vet. Medicine, Mich. State U., East Lansing, 1984—, dean, 1984-94; cons. Ralston-Purina Co., St. Louis, 1978, Universidad Nacional P. Urena, Dominican Republic, 1980, U. Nebr., Lincoln, 1982-83. Editor: Veterinary Clinics of North America, 1976. Served to 1st lt. U.S. Army, 1958-60. Recipient Outstanding Instr. award Colo. State U. Vet. Coll., 1967; Norden Teaching award Cornell U. Vet. Coll., 1977. Mem. AVMA, Mich. Vet. Med. Assn., Am. Coll. Vet. Pathologists (diplomate; examiner 1972-74), Am. Soc. Vet. Clin. Pathology (pres. 1971-72), Assn. Am. Vet. Med. Colls. (exec. com. 1986-91, pres. 1989-90). Avocations: reading; traveling. Home: 513 Brentwood Ct Severna Park MD 21146 Office: Mich State U Coll Vet Medicine G-100 Vet Med Ctr East Lansing MI 48824

TASKER, STEVEN JAY, professional football player; b. Leoti, Kans., May 19, 1962. Student, Dodge City C.C.; B in Communication Studies, Northwestern, 1985. With Houston Oilers, 1985-86; wide receiver Buffalo Bills, 1986—. Played in Pro Bowl 1987, 90-93. Office: Buffalo Bills 1 Bills Dr Orchard Park NY 14127-2237*

TASMAN, WILLIAM SAMUEL, ophthalmologist, medical association executive; b. Phila., 1929. MD, Temple U., 1955. Intern Phila. Gen. Hosp., 1955-56; resident in ophthalmology Wills Eye Hosp., Phila., 1959-61; fellow Mass. Eye and Ear Infirmary, Boston, 1961-62; prof., chmn. dept. ophthalmology Jefferson Med. Coll., Phila., 1985—; attending surgeon Wills Eye Hosp., Phila., 1974—, ophthalmologist-in-chief, 1985—. Mem. AMA, Am. Acad. Ophthalmologists (sec. ann. meeting 1992), Pa. Acad. Ophthalmologists, Am. Ophthal. Soc. Office: Wills Eye Hosp 900 Walnut St Philadelphia PA 19107-5598

TASSANI, SALLY MARIE, communications executive, marketing consultant; b. Teaneck, N.J., Dec. 30, 1948; d. Peter R. and Marie Irene (Sorbello) T. BA, Am. U., 1970. Elem. sch. tchr., Washington, 1970-73; asst. prodn. and promotion mgr. First Nat. Bank of Chgo., 1973-74; exec. dir. Jack O'Grady Graphics, Inc., Chgo., 1974-76; creative dir. Dimensional Mktg., Inc., Chgo., 1976-78; CEO, founder Tassani & Paglia, Inc. (formerly Tassani Comm., Nexus, Inc.), Chgo., 1978—; mem. adv. bd. Heizer Entrepreneurship Rsch. Ctr. Northwestern U. J.L. Kellogg Grad. Sch. Mgmt., U.III. Urbana-Champaign Coll. Commerce and Bus. Administrn. Elected to Com. of 200; hon. bd. dirs. Girl Scouts Chgo. Named one of Ad Age's Best and Brightest Women in Advt., Top Women Entrepreneur Crain's Chgo. Bus., Top Entrepreneurs poll USA Today, Who's Who in Chgo. Bus. 1990-93, Top Woman-Owned Firms 1990-92, Entrepreneur of Yr. women's category INC, 1990; named to Nat. Women's Hall Fame. Mem. Alliance, The Art Inst. Chgo., Chgo. Coun. on Fgn. Rels. (Chgo. com.), Old Town Triangle Assn, Entrepreneur of Yr. Inst., Internat. Assn. of Bus. Communicators (Spectra award 1987, guest speaker 1988), Women's Advt. Club of Chgo. (hon., bd. dirs., Advt. Woman of Yr. 1994), Young Pres.' Orgn., Econ. Club, Chgo. Advt. Fedn., The Chgo. Network, The Execs. Club Chgo. Avocations: power walking, sailing, photography, American crafts, graphic design. Home: 173 N Orleans St Chicago IL 60614-5719 Office: Tassani & Paglia Inc 515 N State St Chicago IL 60610-4320

TASSÉ, ROGER, lawyer, former Canadian government official; b. Montreal, Que., Can., 1931. BA, Coll. St. Marie, Montreal, 1952; Lic. in Law, U. Montreal, 1955; diploma d'Etudes Superieures, U. Ottawa, Ont., Can., 1957. Bar: Que. 1956, Ont. 1986; called to Queens Counsel 1971. Joined Dept. Justice, 1956, law counsel for Can. govt., from 1957, supt. bankruptcy, 1965-68, asst. dep. min. consumer and corp. affairs, 1968-72; dep. min. Dept. of Solicitor Gen., 1972-77; dep. min. of justice, atty. gen. of Can., 1977-85; ptnr. Land Michener Lash Johnston, Toronto and Ottawa, Noel Décary Aubry & Associates, Hull, Que., 1985-88; exec. v.p. legal and environ. affairs Bell Can., 1988-91; of counsel Fraser & Beatty, Toronto, 1992—; pvt. practice law Ottawa, 1991—; prin. constl. advisor to Spl. Joint Com. of the Senate and the House of Commons on a Renewed Can., 1991-92. Mem. Citizens' Forum on Canada's Future, 1990; co-chair task force Can. Mags., 1993; mem. DTH Panel, 1995. Decorated officer Order of Can. Avocations: skiing, tennis. Office: 1200-180 Elgin St, Ottawa, ON Canada K2P 2K7

TASSELL, JON VAN, optical engineer. Optical engr. Polaroid Corp., Cambridge, Mass. Recipient Engring. Excellence award Optical Soc. Am., 1994. Office: Polaroid Corp 730 Main St 1st Fl Cambridge MA 02139*

TASSIA, MARIE C., health facility administrator; b. York, Pa., Sept. 25, 1939; d. Peter A. and Chritine R. (Ganse) T. Diploma, Fitzgerald Mercy Hosp., 1960; BS in Nursing, U. Md., Balt., 1973, MS, 1977. RN, Pa.; cert. nurse adminstr. Asst. supr. Mt. Sinai Med. Ctr., N.Y.C.; staff nurse York (Pa.) Hosp., coord. insvc. edn., asst. dir., dir. nursing, dir. nursing. Mem. Am. Orgn. Nurse Execs., Nat. League for Nursing, Pa. League Nurses (bd. dirs. 1978-81), Pa. Orgn. Nurse Execs., South Cen. Orgn. Nurse Execs. (chair program com. 1990, legis. com. 1991-92, pres. elect 1993-95), Sigma Theta Tau.

TASSINARI, MELISSA SHERMAN, toxicologist; b. Lawrence, Mass., Sept. 26, 1953; m. R. Peter Tassinari; children: Michael, Emily, Sara. AB, Mt. Holyoke Coll., 1975; postgrad., U. St. Andrews, Scotland, 1973-74; PhD, Med. Coll. Wis., 1979. Rsch. asst. in orthopedic surgery., Lab. Human Biochemistry Children's Hosp. Med. Ctr., Boston, 1981-83; tech. affiliate in toxicology Toxicology Dept. Forsyth Dental Ctr., Boston, 1983-86, staff assoc., 1986-89; asst. prof. cell biology U. Mass. Med. Ctr., Worcester, 1989-91; mgr. reproductive toxicology Pfizer Ctrl. Rsch., Groton, Conn., 1991—; rsch. fellow oral biology Harvard Sch. Dental Medicine, Boston, 1978-81, instr. oral biology and pathophysiology, 1981-83; asst. prof. biol. scis. Wellesley Coll., Mass., 1983-86, cons. teratology Arthur D. Little, Inc., Cambridge, Mass., 1985-91; asst. prof. biology Simmons Coll., Boston, 1986-87. Contbr. abstracts, articles to profl. jours. Mem. Teratology Soc., Neurobehavioral Teratology Soc., Mid Atlantic Soc. Toxicology, Mid Atlantic Reproduction and Teratology Assn. (steering com. 1994), Sigma Xi. Office: Pfizer Central Research Eastern Point Rd Groton CT 06340

TASSINARY, LOUIS GEORGE, psychology educator; director laboratory; b. Bridgeport, Conn., Dec. 27, 1954; s. Louis Evangelist and June Theresa (Davis) T.; m. Melanie Marie Ihrig, July 15, 1990; children: Damien David, Alexas Marie. BA in Psychology, Eckerd Coll., 1976; PhD in Psychology, Dartmouth Coll., 1985. Rsch. asst. U. Conn. Mental Health Ctr., Farmington, 1976-77; grad. rsch. asst. Dartmouth Coll., Hanover, N.H., 1978-84; postdoctoral fellow U. Iowa, Iowa City, 1985-86, asst. rsch. scientist, 1986-89, vis. asst. prof., 1989-90; asst. prof., dir. psychophysiology lab. Tex. A&M U., College Station, 1990—. Co-editor: Principles of Psychophysiology: Physical, Social and Inferential Elemtns, 1990; contbr. articles to profl. jours. USDA Forest Svc. Rsch. grantee, 1991-94, U.S. Golf Assn. grantee, 1991-94; Presidl. Faculty fellow, 1993-98. Mem. APA, N.Y. Acad. Scis., Internat. Soc. Ecol. Psychology, Soc. for Psychophysiol. Rsch., Sci. Rsch. Assn., Sigma Xi. Democrat. Achievements include discovery that electrocortical potentials can signify whether a facial action is spontaneous or intended; documentation of important boundary conditions on the sensitivity & specificity of facial electromyography as a tool. Home: 304 W Dexter Dr College Station TX 77840-2921 Office: Tex A&M U Environ Psychophysiol Lab Coll Architecture College Station TX 77843-3137

TASSONE, GELSOMINA (GESSIE TASSONE), metal processing executive; b. N.Y.C., July 8, 1944; d. Enrico and A. Cira (Petriccione) Gargiulo; children: Ann Marie, Margaret, Theresa, Christine; m. Armando Tassone, Mar. 20, 1978. Student, Orange County Community Coll., 1975-79, Iona Coll., 1980—. Head bookkeeper Gargiulo Bros. Builders, N.Y.C., 1968-72; pres., owner A&T Iron Works, Inc., New Rochelle, N.Y., 1973—. Recipient Profl. Image award Contractors Coun. Greater N.Y.C., 1986; named Businesswoman of Yr., Contractors Coun. Greater N.Y.C., 1985, N.Y. State Small Bus. Person of Yr., 1988, Entrepreneur of Yr. Inc. mag., 1990; company named a Successful Small Bus. Co. Westchester County C. of C./ BSBA, 1986-88. Mem. Nat. Ornamental and Miscellaneous Metal Assn., Builders Inst. Westchester and Putnam County, Westchester Assn. Women Bus. Owners, Profl. Women in Constrn., Westchester C. of C. Office: A&T Iron Works Inc 25 Cliff St New Rochelle NY 10801-6803

TASWELL, HOWARD FILMORE, pathologist, blood bank specialist, educator; b. Paterson, N.J., July 21, 1928; s. Herman Albert and Pauline Ruth (Abels) T.; children: Amy, Carl, Eric, Steven, Laura, Ruth; m. Beryl Byman, May 7, 1989. A.B., Harvard U., 1949; M.D., NYU, 1953; M.S. in Pathology, U. Minn. Mayo Grad. Sch. Medicine, 1961. Diplomate Am. Bd. Pathology; subcert. in clin. and anatomic pathology, blood banking/transfusion medicine. Intern St. Albans Naval Hosp., N.Y., 1953-54; resident in internal medicine Mayo Clinic, Rochester, Minn., 1956-57; resident in anatomical and clin. pathology Mayo Clinic, 1957-61; assoc. pathologist Harrisburg Hosp., Pa.; asst. prof. pathology Hahneman Coll. Medicine, Phila., 1961-63; head sect. blood bank and transfusion services Mayo Clinic; prof. lab. medicine Mayo Med. Sch., Rochester, Minn., 1963-88, Vernon F. and Earlene D. Dale prof. lab. medicine, 1985-93, prof. emeritus, 1993—; fellow Bush Found. of Minn., dept. psychiatry U. Chgo. Hosps., 1993—; cons. Nat. Heart, Lung, Blood Inst., FDA Bur. Biologics. Contbr. over 200 articles to med. jours. and textbooks. Served to lt. comdr. USNR, 1953-56. Mem. AMA, Minn. Med. Assn., Ill. State Med. Soc., Am. Assn. Blood Banks (pres. 1978-79), Minn. Assn. Blood Banks (pres. 1969-70), Minn. Soc. Clin. Pathologists (pres. 1972-73), Am. Soc. Clin. Pathology, Am. Soc. Hematology, Coll. Am. Pathologists, Internat. Soc. Blood Transfusion, Am. Family Therapy Acad., Sigma Xi. Home: 2500 N Lakeview Ave # 3204 Chicago IL 60614

TATARIAN, HRACH ROGER, journalist; b. Fresno, Calif., Dec. 25, 1916; s. Edward Y. and Rose (Yeghishan) T.; m. Eunice E. Krauchi, Aug. 1, 1939; 1 son, Allan Roger. B.A., Fresno State Coll., 1938; Litt.D. (hon.), Windham Coll., 1967; LL.D. (hon.), Colby Coll., 1980. With UPI, 1938-72; assigned Fresno, San Francisco and Phoenix, 1938-43; overnight news editor Washington, 1943-48; mgr. London, 1949-51; mgr. for Italy, 1951-53; gen. European news mgr., London, 1953-59; mng. editor N.Y.C., 1959-62; exec. editor, 1963-65, v.p., 1963, editor, 1965-72; prof. journalism Calif. State U., Fresno, 1972-87; dir. McClatchy Newspapers, 1984—; cons. UNESCO, Paris, 1978, U.S. Nat. Commn. for UNESCO, 1978-81; mem. adv. bd. Ctr. Fgn. Journalists. Recipient Distinguished Journalism award Ohio U., 1968; named Outstanding Journalism Prof. Calif. Newspaper Pubs. Assn., 1979; mem. 20th Century Task Force on Internat. News Flow, 1978; Recipient Elijah Parish Lovejoy award for achievement in journalism, 1980. Fellow Sigma Delta chi (Hall of Fame N.Y. chpt.). Home: 5302 N Colonial Ave Apt 101 Fresno CA 93704-2305 Office: Fresno Bee 1626 E St Fresno CA 93786-0001

TATARSKII, VALERIAN IL'ICH, physics researcher; b. Kharkov, USSR, Oct. 13, 1929; s. Il'ya A. and Elizabeth A. (Lapis) T.; m. Maia S. Granovskaia, Dec. 22, 1955; 1 child, Viatcheslav V. MS, Moscow State U., 1952; PhD, Acoustical Inst. Acad. Scis., 1957; DSc, Gorky State U., 1962. Scientific rschr. Geophys. Inst. Acad. Sci. USSR, Moscow, 1953-56; scientific rschr. Inst. Atmospheric Physics, Acad. Sci. USSR, Moscow, 1956-59, sr. scientific rschr., 1959-78, head lab., 1978-90; head dept. Lebedev. Phys. Inst. Acad. Sci., Moscow, 1990-91; sr. rsch. assoc. U.S. Colo. Coop. Inst. for Rsch. in Environ. Sci., Boulder, 1991—, NOAA/ERL/Wave Propagation Lab., Boulder. Author: Wave Propagation in a Turbulent Medium, 1961, 67, The Effect of the Turbulent Atmosphere on Wave Propagation, 1971, Principles of Statistical Radiophysics, 1989; contbr. articles to profl. jours. Recipient of Max Born Awd., 1994, Optical Soc. of Am. Fellow Optical Soc. Am. (Max Born award 1994); mem. Russian Acad. Sci., U.S.A. Nat. Acad. Engring. (fgn. assoc.), N.Y. Acad. Sci. Avocations: classical music, kayaking. Office: NOAA/ERL/ETL 325 Broadway St Boulder CO 80303-3328

TATE, CURTIS E., management educator; b. Trezvant, Tenn., July 5, 1920; s. Curtis E. and Mary Kathryn (Haskins) T.; m. Evelyn Ruth Mann, Apr. 12, 1945 (div. May, 1969); m. Mary Jim Combs, Aug. 28, 1977; children: Curtis Emory, Milton Oglesby. Student, N. Ga. Coll., 1943-44, U. Ga., 1945-46; AB, Bethel Coll., 1946; MS, U. Tenn., 1952. Clk. Family Gen. Grocery, Trezvant, Tenn., 1938-42; clk. purchasing dept. P&G Defense Corp., Milan, Tenn., 1942; plant mgr. Keathley Pie Co., Memphis, 1946-50; instr. Furman U., Greenville, S.C., 1952-53; bus. mgr. Lander Coll., Greenwood, S.C., 1953-56; from asst. to assoc. prof. Coll. of Bus. Adminstrn. U. Ga., Athens, 1956-74; prof. emeritus Terry Coll. of Bus. U. Ga., Athens, 1991—; bd. dirs. Flexible Products, Inc., Marietta, Ga., 1984-76, asst. Dean Fund Raising, 1991—. Co-author: Successful Small Business Management, 1975, latest rev. edition, 1985, Complete Guide to Your Own Business, 1977, Dow-Jones-Irwin Business Papers, 1977, Bus. Policy: Administrative, Strategic and Constituency Issues, 1983, '92, Managing for Profits, 1984, Small Business Management and Entrepreneurship, 1992. With U.S. Army, 1942-45, ETO. Fellow N. Am. Case Rsch. Assn. (sec., v.p., bd. dirs., pres. so. casewriters, Outstanding Case Contbr. 1992), Acad. Mgmt., Kiwanis, Sigma Iota Epsilon, Beta Gamma Sigma. Home and Office: 1640 Broadlands Dr Watkinsville GA 30677-2148

TATE, DANIEL CLYDE, JR., federal agency administrator; b. Athens, Ga., Dec. 14, 1966; s. Danny Clyde and Ruth (McGaughey) T. BA, Amherst Coll., 1988. With spl. events CNN, Washington, 1989; legis. dir. Congressman W.J. Tanzin, Washington, 1989-93; dep. asst. sec. for House liaison U.S. Dept. Energy, Washington, 1993—. Field worker Mondale for Pres., Maine, 1984; issues aide Robb for Senate, Fairfax, Va., 1988; vol. Clinton-Gore Campaign, Washington and Pa., 1992. Avocations: lacrosse, golf, skiing. Home: 1276 N Wayne St # 1225 Arlington VA 22201 Office: Congl & Intergovt Affairs 1000 Independence Ave SW Washington DC 20585

TATE, FREDERICK WAYNE, federal agency administrator; b. N.Y.C., Jan. 26, 1946; s. Frederick R. and Ruth C. (Henze) T.; m. Rita Beth Sayles, Dec. 11, 1971; children: James B., David L. BA in History, Adelphi U., 1967; MPA in Pub. Policy, Harvard U., 1980; diploma in strategic studies, Nat. War Coll., Washington, 1993. Contract negotiator strategic systems project office Dept. Def., 1968-71; contract negotiator U.S. Agy. for Internat. Devel., 1971-74; program analyst office devel. programs Bur. Latin Am., 1974-76; dep. chief program divsn. office devel. planning Bur. Africa, 1976-79, officer-in-charge Sahel devel. program, 1979, asst. dir. for planning office So. African affairs, 1980-82; econ. advisor to U.S. exec. dir. Asian Devel. Bank, Manila, Philippines, 1982-85; dep. dir. program office USAID Mission to Pakistan, U.S. Embassy, Islamabad, 1985-89; dir. office devel. programs USAID Mission to Bolivia, U.S. Embassy, La Paz, 1989-92; dep. dir. office devel. planning and programs Bur. Latin Am. and Caribbean, 1993; dir. office South Am. and Mexican affairs AID, Washington, 1993—. Mem. Trout Unlimited, Harvard Club Washington. Episcopalian. Avocations: fly fishing, hunting, coins, history.

TATE, HAROLD SIMMONS, JR., lawyer; b. Taylors, S.C., Sept. 19, 1930; s. Harold Simmons and Cleone (Clayton) T.; m. Elizabeth Anne Coker, Dec. 22, 1952; children—Mary Elizabeth Anne, Martha Coker, Virginia Clayton. A.B. cum laude, Harvard U., 1951, J.D., 1956, postgrad., 1954. Bar: S.C. 1956. Ptnr. firm Sinkler and Boyd, P.A. (formerly Boyd, Knowlton, Tate & Finlay), Columbia, S.C., 1962—; chmn. U.S. Dist. Ct. (S.C.) Adv. Com., 1984—; lectr. Am. Law Inst.-ABA seminars; mem. adv. com. on rules and procedures U.S. Ct. Appeals (4th cir.), 1990—. Co-author: South Carolina Appellate Practice, 1985; bd. editors Federal Litigation Guide Reporter, 1985—; contbr. articles and book revs. to profl. jours. Chmn. Richland County Mental Health Center, 1965-66; co-chmn. Columbia Hearing and Speech Center, 1962-64; mem. admission and scholarship com. Harvard U., 1961—; chmn. subcom. on legislation, legislation

and fin. study commn. Gov.'s Adv. Group on Mental Health Planning, 1963-65; chmn. Columbia Bd. Supervisory of Registration, 1961-70; pres. Columbia Philharmonic Orch., 1966-67, Town Theatre, 1967-70; trustee Richland County Pub. Library, 1973-78, Hist. Columbia Found., 1971-75, Caroliniana Soc., 1978—, Bostick Charitable Trust, 1968—; bd. mgrs. S.C. Hist. Soc., 1993—. Served to capt. U.S. Army, 1951-53. Mem. ABA, Am. Law Inst., Am. Judicature Soc., S.C. Bar Assn., S.C. Hist. Soc. (bd. mgrs. 1993—), Richland County Bar Assn., Harvard Law Sch. Assn. S.C. (sec.-treas. 1968-70, pres. 1988—). Episcopalian. Clubs: Tarantella, Forest Lake Country, Columbia Drama, (pres. 1963-64), Palmetto (sec. 1963-70, pres. 1973-76), The Forum, Harvard (N.Y.C.); Harvard of S.C. Home: 15 Gibbes Ct Columbia SC 29201-3923 Office: Sinkler & Boyd 1426 Main St Columbia SC 29201-2834

TATE, JAMES VINCENT, poet, English educator; b. Kansas City, Mo., Dec. 8, 1943; s. Samuel Vincent Appleby and Betty Jean Whitsitt. BA, Kans. State Coll., 1965; MFA, U. Iowa, 1967. Instr. U. Iowa, Iowa City, 1966-67; vis. lectr. U. Calif., Berkeley, 1967-68; asst. prof. English Columbia U., N.Y.C., 1969-71; assoc. prof., now prof. English U. Mass., Amherst, 1971—; poet-in-residence Emerson Coll., 1970-71; cons. Coord. Coun. Literary Mags., 1971-74, Ky. Arts Commn., 1979; mem. Bollingen Prize Com., 1974-75; poetry editor Dickinson Rev., 1967-76; trustee, assoc. editor Pym-Randall Pr., 1968-80; assoc. editor Barn Dream Pr. Author: (poems) Cages, 1966, The Destination, 1967, The Lost Pilot, 1967 (Yale Younger Poets award 1966), Notes of Woe, 1968, Camping in the Valley, 1968, Mystics in Chicago, 1968, The Torches, 1968, Row with Your Hair, 1969, Is There Anything?, 1969, Shepherds of the Mist, 1969, Amnesia People, 1970, Are You Ready Mary Baker Eddy, 1970, Deaf Girl Playing, 1970, The Oblivion Ha-Ha, 1970, Wrong Songs, 1970, Hints to Pilgrims, 1971, Nobody Goes to Visit the Insane Anymore, 1971, Absences, 1972, Apology for Eating Geoffrey Movius' Hyacinth, 1972, A Dime Found in the Snow, 1973, Hottentot Ossuary, 1974, Marfa, 1974, Suffering Bastards, 1975, Who Gets the Bitterroot?, 1976, Viper Jazz, 1976, Riven Doggeries, 1979, The Rustling of Foliage, the Memory of Caresses, 1979, If It Would All Please Hurray, 1980, Land of Little Sticks, 1981, Constant Defender, 1983, Just Shades, 1985, Reckoner, 1986, Distance from Loved Ones, 1990, Selected Poems, 1991 (Pulitzer Prize for poetry 1992), Worshipful Company of Fletchers, 1993 (Nat. Book Award for Poetry 1994); (novel) Lucky Darryl, 1977. Named Poet of Yr. by Phi Beta Kappa, 1972; recipient Nat. Inst. Arts and Letters award for poetry, 1974; Mass. Arts and Humanities fellow, 1975, Guggenheim fellow, 1976, Nat. Endowment for the Arts fellow, 1980. Office: U Mass Dept English Amherst MA 01003*

TATE, JEFFREY L., biology institute administrator; b. Mpls., Dec. 18, 1957; s. Ronald L. and Betty M. (Nilson) T.; m. Tracey J. Benson, Sept. 9, 1989. BSc in Botany, U. Minn., 1980, PhD in Plant Physiology, 1985, postgrad., 1992—. Staff scientist Biol. Process Tech. Inst. U. Minn., St. Paul, 1985-87; rsch. assoc. Balt. Co. U. Md., 1987-89; spl. asst. to dir. Biol. Process Tech. Inst. U. Minn., 1989—. Dist. dir. Dem. Farmer Labor Party, Roseville, Minn., 1992—. Mem. Minn. Biotech. Assn. (sec./treas. 1991-93), Coun. Biotech. Ctrs. (chmn. 1993-). Lutheran. Avocation: gardening. Home: 2511 Lexington Ave N Saint Paul MN 55113 Office: U Minn Biol Process Tech Inst 1479 Gortner Ave Ste 240 Saint Paul MN 55108

TATE, MANFORD BEN, guided missile scientist, investor; b. Okolona, Ark., Aug. 3, 1916; s. Ernest and Mabel (Burley) T.; m. Marjorie Belle Stone, Sept. 9, 1942; children: Howard Ernest, Virginia Louise (Gina), Tate Smythe, Barbara Anne. Student, Cen. Coll. Liberal Arts, 1935-37; BSCE, U. Mo., 1940, MSCE, 1942; PhD in Theoretical and Applied Mechanics, Iowa State U., 1949. Grad. fellow, instr., asst. prof., assoc. prof. U. Mo., Columbia, 1940-51; lectr. engring. mechanics U. Va., Hampton, 1944-45; grad. fellow, instr. Iowa State U., Ames, 1946-47; engr. U.S. Naval Ordnance Lab., White Oak, Md., 1950-56; lectr., advisor U. Md., White Oak, 1950-56; guided missile rsch. scientist Johns Hopkins U. Applied Physics Lab., Laurel, Md., 1956-78, prof. missile structures, 1958-64; pres., gen. ptnr. Tate Ptnrs., Silver Spring, Md., 1968—; concrete inspector Mo. Hwy. Dept., 1940; vis. prof. Cath. U. Am., Washington, 1956-58; aeronautical rsch. Nat. Adv. Com. Aeronautics, Langley Field, Va., 1944-45; cons. in field. Bridge designer Bur. of Bridges, 1941; Crane designer Dravo Corp. Pitts.; co-inventor Tomahawk Cruise Missile (patentee 1971); derived theoretical solution for shock strength of the Fat Man Atom Bomb; author: (with others) Selected Problems in Materials Testing, 1943; contbr. more than 400 articles to profl. jours./publs. Cub scouts chmn., cubmaster Boy Scouts Am., 1956-61, chmn. rev. bd., 1962-65; civil def. chmn. PTA, 1961-63; hon. mem. coun. Lakota Sioux Indian tribe, Chamberlain, S.C., Ogalala Sioux Indian tribe, Rapid City, S.D. Recipient medal for disting. svc. in engring. U. Mo., Columbia, 1995. Mem. ASCE, ASTM, ASME, Am. Soc. Engring Edn., Am. Soc. Ordnance Engrs., Soc. Exptl. Stress Analysis, Sigma Xi, Phi Kappa Phi, Chi Epsilon. Democrat. Methodist. Achievements include patents on the Tomahawk Cruise Missile; first investigator in world to derive theoretical solution for air oscillations in ducted missiles/derived theoretical solution for shock strength of the Fat Man atom bomb.

TATE, RANDALL J. (RANDY), congressman; b. Puyallup, Wash., Nov. 23, 1965; m. Julie; 1 child. AA, Tacoma C. C., Wash.; BA in Econs. and Polit. Sci., We. Wash. U. Mem. Wash. Ho. of Reps., 1988-94, 104th Congress from 9th Wash. dist., 1994—; mem. Com. Rules, Com. Fin. Instns. and Ins., JudiciaryCom. Wash. Ho. Reps. Home: 13011 Meridian E #301 Puyallup WA 98373 Office: US House Reps 1535 Longworth House Office Bldg Washington DC 20515-4709*

TATE, SHEILA BURKE, public relations executive; b. Washington, Mar. 3, 1942; d. Eugene L. and Mary J. (Doherty) Burke; m. William J. Tate, May 2, 1981; children: Hager Burke Patton, Courtney Paige Patton. BA in Journalism, Duquesne U., 1964; postgrad. in mass communications, U. Denver, 1975-76. former chairperson bd. dirs. Corp. for Pub. Broadcasting. Rsch. asst. Westinghouse Air Brake Co.; asst. account exec. Falhgren and Assos.; copywriter Ketchum, MacLeod and Grove, 1964-66; account exec. Burson-Marsteller Assocs., Pitts., 1967; sr. v.p. Burson-Marsteller Assocs., Washington, 1985-87; public rels. mgr. Colo. Nat. Bank, Denver, 1967-71; account exec. Hill and Knowlton, Inc., Houston, 1977-78; v.p. Hill and Knowlton, Inc., Washington, 1978-81; dep. to the chmn. Hill and Knowlton Inc., Washington, 1987-88; press sec. to First Lady White House, Washington, 1981-85; press sec. George Bush for Pres. Campaign, 1988; press sec. to Pres.-elect George Bush, 1988-89; vice chmn. Cassidy and Assocs. Pub. Affairs, Washington, 1989-91; pres. Powell Tate, Washington, 1991—; bd. dirs. Corp. for Pub. Broadcasting, chmn., 1991-94. Mem. civilian pub. affairs adv. bd. U.S. Mil. Acad.; mem. adv. bd. Ronald Reagan Inst. Emergency Medicine, George Washington U. Hosp., Washington. Mem. Nat. Press Club, Nat. Press Found. (bd. dirs.). Republican. Clubs: Duquesne U. Century, F Street, Washington Golf and Country. Office: Powell Tate 700 13th St NW # 1000 Washington DC 20005

TATE, STONEWALL SHEPHERD, lawyer; b. Memphis, Dec. 19, 1917; m. Janet Graf; children: Adele Shepherd, Shepherd Davis, Janet Reid Walker. BA, Southwestern at Memphis (now Rhodes Coll.), 1939; JD, U. Va., 1942; LLD (hon.), Samford U., 1979, Suffolk U., 1982, Capital U., 1989, Rhodes Coll., 1993. Bar: Va. 1941, Tenn. 1942. Mem. Martin, Tate, Morrow & Marston, P.C. (and predecessor firms), Memphis, 1947—. Sec. bd. trustees Rhodes Coll., 1968-77, 1979-84; pres. Episcopal Churchmen of Tenn., 1961-62; sec. standing com. Episcopal Diocese of Tenn., 1969-71; pres. Chickasaw Coun. Boy Scouts Am., 1967-78. With USNR, 1942-46; comdr. USNR; ret. Decorated Order of Cloud Banner (China); recipient Silver Beaver award Boy Scouts Am., 1963, Disting. Eagle Scout award, 1980, Disting. Svc. medal Rhodes Coll., 1978, Disting. Alumni award, 1991, Lawyers' Lawyer award Memphis Bar Assn., 1990; Memphis Rotary Club Civic Recognition award, 1983; Paul Harris fellow, 1985. Fellow Am. Bar Found., Tenn. Bar Found., Memphis and Shelby County Bar Found., Am. Coll. Trust and Estate Counsel, Internat. Acad. Estate and Trust Law, Coll. Law Practice Mgmt. (hon.); mem. ABA (chmn. standing com. on profl. discipline 1973-76, chmn. standing com. on scope and correlation of work 1977, chmn. task force on lawyer advt. 1977, pres. 1978-79, chmn. standing com. on lawyer competence 1986-92), Am. Judicature Soc. (past bd. dirs.), Tenn. Bar Assn. (pres. 1963-64), Memphis and Shelby County Bar Assn. (pres. 1959-60), Nat. Conf. Bar Assn. (pres. 1972-73), Am. Law Inst., Am. Arbitration Assn. (large complex case panel 1993—), Lawyer-Pilots Bar

Assn., U. Va. Law Sch. Alumni Assn. (mem. exec. coun. 1974-77), Order of Coif, Raven Soc., Rotary (pres. 1982-83, bd. dirs. 1974, 80-84, 89-90), Phi Beta Kappa, Omicron Delta Kappa, Phi Delta Phi, Sigma Alpha Epsilon (highest effort award N.Y.C. Alumni Assn. 1979). Office: Martin Tate Morrow & Marston PC Falls Bldg 22 N Front St Ste 1100 Memphis TN 38103-1182

TATE, THADDEUS W(ILBUR), JR. (THAD TATE), history educator, historical institute executive, historian; b. Winston-Salem, N.C., May 27, 1924; s. Thaddeus Wilbur and Elizabeth Kent (Llewellyn) T.; m. G. V. U.N.C., 1947, M.A., 1948; Ph.D., Brown U., 1960. Historian U.S. Nat. Park Service, 1948-54; research assoc. Colonial Williamsburg Found., (Va.), 1954-57, asst. dir. research, 1957-61; book rev. editor William and Mary Quar., Williamsburg, 1961-66, editor, 1966-72; asst. prof. history Coll. William and Mary, 1961-64, assoc. prof., 1964-69; prof. Coll. William and Mary, 1969-90; Murden prof. humanities Coll. William and Mary, 1990-92, emeritus, 1992—; dir. Inst. Early Am. History and Culture, Williamsburg, 1972-89, Commonwealth Ctr. for Study of Am. Culture, Williamsburg, 1988-92. Author: Negro in Eighteenth-Century Williamsburg, 1966; co-author: Colonial Virginia: A History, 1986, The College of William and Mary: A History, 1993; co-editor, contbg. author: Chesapeake in the Seventeenth Century, 1979; co-editor: Saints and Revolutionaries, 1984, An Uncivil War: The Southern Backcountry in the American Revolution, 1985; mem. adv. bd.: Environ. Rev., 1976-85; chair editorial adv. bd.: Papers of John Marshall. Mem. Williamsburg Wetlands Bd., 1980—; chair bd. dirs. Va. Found. for Humanities and Pub. Policy; mem. tercentary commn. Coll. William and Mary. With USNR, 1943-46. Recipient Grad. Alumni citation Brown U., 1985; Thomas Jefferson award Coll. William and Mary, 1986; Brown U. fellow, 1949-51; NEH fellow, 1982-83; fellow Am. Council Learned Socs., 1970-71. Mem. Orgn. Am. Historians, Am. Hist. Assn., So. Hist. Assn., Va. Hist. Soc. (hon.), Am. Soc. Legal History, Mass. Hist. Soc., Am. Soc. Environ. History, Assocs. John Carter Brown Library, Am. Antiquarian Soc., Library Co. Phila., Phi Beta Kappa, Phi Alpha Theta. Democrat. Episcopalian. Home: 313 1/2 Burns Ln Williamsburg VA 23185-3908

TATEL, DAVID STEPHEN, federal judge; b. Washington, Mar. 16, 1942; s. Howard Edwin and Molly (Abramowitz) T.; m. Edith Sara Bassichis, Aug. 29, 1965; children: Rebecca, Stephanie, Joshua, Emily. BA, U. Mich., 1963; JD, U. Chgo., 1966. Bar: Ill. 1966, U.S. Dist. Ct. (no. dist.) Ill. 1966, U.S. Dist. Ct. D.C. 1970, U.S. Ct. Appeals (7th and D.C. cirs.) 1970, U.S. Supreme Ct. 1971, U.S. Ct. Appeals (5th cir.) 1976, U.S. Ct. Appeals (11th and 4th cirs.) 1986. Instr. U. Mich., Ann Arbor, 1966-67; assoc. Sidley & Austin, Chgo. and Washington, 1967-69, 70-72; dir. Chgo. Lawyer's Com., 1969-70, Nat. Lawyers Commn. for Civil Rights Under Law, Washington, 1972-74; dir. Office for Civil Rights HEW, Washington, 1977-79; ptnr. Hogan & Hartson, Washington, 1979-94; circuit judge D.C. Circuit, Washington, D.C., 1994—; lectr. Stanford U. Law Sch., 1991-92; co-chmn. Nat. Lawyers Com. for Civil Rights Under Law, Washington, 1989-91; bd. dirs. Washington Lawyers Com. for Civil Rights Under Law; chmn., bd. dirs. Spencer Found., Chgo., 1990—. Mem. editorial adv. com. West's Edn. Law Reporter, Mpls., 1983-89; mem. vis. com. to law sch. U. Chgo., 1986-89; spl. master U.S. Dist. Ct. D.C., Washington, 1988-89; mem. Montgomery County Bd. Edn. Com. on Excellence in Teaching, Rockville, Md., 1985-87; mem. adv. com. on the governance of edn. Carnegie Found. for Advancement in Teaching, Princeton, N.J., 1980-82; gen. counsel Legal Svcs. Corp., Washington, 1975-76; bd. dirs. Refugee Policy Group, Washington, 1985-90, Mental Health Law Project; active Pew Forum on Edn. Reform, 1992—. Mem. D.C. Bar Assn. (bd. govs. Washington chpt. 1980-81), Chgo. Coun. Lawyers (bd. govs. Chgo. chpt. 1969-70). Office: 333 Constitution Ave Washington DC 20001*

TATGENHORST, (CHARLES) ROBERT, lawyer; b. Cin., Apr. 21, 1918; s. Charles and Clara (Strebel) T.; m. Louise Thompson, Sept. 6, 1951; children: David, John, James, Richard. A.B., Dartmouth Coll., 1940; LL.B., U. Cin., 1947. Bar: Ohio 1947. Asst. atty. gen. State of Ohio, 1947-49; assoc. firm Taft, Stettinius & Hollister, Cin., 1951-58; ptnr. firm Tatgenhorst & Tatgenhorst, Cin., 1958-61; prin. firm Robert Tatgenhorst & Assos., Cin., 1961-85; ptnr. Tatgenhorst & Bruestle, Cin., 1986—; adj. prof. law Chase Coll. Law, No. Ky. U., 1962-86. Pres. Westwood Civic Assn., Cin., 1959, Meth. Union, 1960; chmn. dist. Boy Scouts Am., 1970; trustee Twin Towers Retirement Ctr., 1968-93, Westwood United Meth. Ch., bd. trustees 1985-88, pres., 1990-92, trustee, 1992. With CIC U.S. Army, 1942-46. Mem. Ohio State Bar Assn., Cin. Bar Assn. (sec. 1973-75), Ryland Lakes Country Club, Optimists (pres. Cin. club 1962), Dartmouth of Cin. Club (pres. 1965), Masons (33 deg.), Sigma Alpha Epsilon, Phi Alpha Delta (pres. 1946). Republican. Office: Tatgenhorst & Bruestle 432 Walnut St Cincinnati OH 45202-3909

TATHAM, DAVID FREDERIC, art historian, educator; b. Wellesley, Mass., Nov. 29, 1932; s. Richard Merton and Florence Elizabeth (Mallette) T.; m. Cleota Reed, Dec. 12, 1979. A.B., U. Mass., 1955; M.A., Syracuse U., 1960, Ph.D., 1970. Dean students Syracuse (N.Y.) U., 1966-71; assoc. prof. fine arts, 1972-78, prof., 1978—; chmn. dept. fine arts, 1980-86. Author: (books) The Lure of the Striped Pig, 1973, Prints and Printmakers of New York State, 1986, Winslow Homer and the Art of the Book, 1990, Winslow Homer and the Illustrated Book, 1992, Winslow Homer in the Adirondacks, (exhbn. catalogs) Winslow Homer Drawings, 1979, Art, Artists and Museums, 1980, Bolton Brown, 1981, Abraham Tuthill, 1983; contbr. articles to profl. jours. Served with U.S. Army, 1956. Daniels research fellow, 1974; Am. Philos. Soc. grantee, 1980, 86; Am. Art Jour. award for outstanding scholarship, 1984; NEH grantee, 1987-88. Mem. Am. Antiquarian Soc. (rec. sec. 1988-93), Coll. Art Assn., Fellow Athenaeum of Phila. Home: 329 Westcott St Syracuse NY 13210-2107 Office: Syracuse U Dept Fine Arts Bowne Hall Syracuse NY 13244

TATIBOUET, ANDRÉ STEPHAN, condominium and resort management firm executive; b. Honolulu, Mar. 10, 1941; s. Joseph J. F. and Annalie (Knaack) T.; m. Jane Inez Barrows, Apr. 19, 1968; children: Cartier, Cecily. BA in Russian and Am. History, U. Hawaii, 1964. Cert. Hotel Adminstr. Owner, developer Pacific Beach Hotel, Honolulu, 1968-69; founder, pres. Aston Hotels & Resorts (formerly Hotel Corp. of Pacific), Honolulu, 1969—. Life mem. founders circle Punahou Sch., 1981—; mem. Honolulu chpt. Am. Friends of Hebrew U., 1982—; emeritus mem. U. Hawaii Pres. Club, 1983—; state chmn. U.S. Commn. on Civil Rights, 1985—; 2d v.p. Waikiki Improvement Assn., 1985—; mem. travel industry mgmt. adv. com. U. Hawaii, 1986—; mem. Honolulu Symphony Soc., 1986—, vice chmn. bd. dirs., 1988-89; mem. travel industry mgmt. adv. coun. Hawaii Pacific Coll., 1988—; mem. Hawaii Tourism Coun. Econ. Edn., 1988—; trustee Honolulu Chamber Music Soc., 1975-85, Jewish Fedn. Hawaii, 1982-86; bd. dirs. Hawaii Performing Arts Co., 1982-87; regent Chaminade U., 1986—. Recipient Gov.'s award for svc. as mem. of Commn. on Yr. 2000, 1978, Man of Yr. award Temple Emanu-El, 1986, Beautification award Hawaii Outdoor Circle, 1987, Judah L. Magnes Gold Medal award Am. Friends Hebrew U., 1988, Exec. of Yr. award Hawaii chpt. Profl. Secs. Internat., 1988. Mem. Hawaii Execs. Coun., Hawaii Hotel Assn. (pres. 1987-88, treas. polit. action com. 1985—), Am. Hotel and Motel Assn. (nat. bd. dirs. 1985-87), Waikiki Beach Operators Assn. (founding charter mem., exec. dir. 1984—), Soc. of Family Hoteliers of Am. Hotel and Motel Assn., Hawaii ParkConv. Coun. (founding dir., sustaining mem.), Young Pres.' Orgn., Skal Club Hawaii, Plaza Club, Beverly Hills Country Club, Honolulu Club, Oahu Country Club, Outrigger Canoe Club. Congregationalist. Avocations: tennis, music, history, literature. Office: Aston Hotels & Resorts 2255 Kuhio Ave Ste 1800 Honolulu HI 96815-2684

TATLOCK, ANNE M., trust company executive; b. White Plains, N.Y., July 1, 1939; d. John and Kathleen (McGrath) McNiff; m. William Tatlock, Apr. 29, 1967; children: Julina, Kerry, Christopher. BA, Vassar Coll., 1961; MA in Econs., NYU, 1968. 1st v.p. Smith Barney Harris Upham, N.Y.C., 1962-84; exec. v.p. Fiduciary Trust Internat., N.Y.C., 1984-94, pres., 1994, 1994—; bd. dirs. Franklin United Life Ins. Co., Garden City, N.Y., Americare Gen. Corp., Houston, PHH Corp., Hunt Valley, Md. Treas., bd. dirs. West Side Day Nursery, N.Y.C., Stanley Isaacs Neighborhood Ctr., N.Y.C., 1988-90; chair fin. com. Am. Ballet Theatre, N.Y.C., trustee Vassar Coll., 1994—, Am. Ballet Theatre, N.Y.C., The Teagle Found., Inc., N.Y.C., 1995, Cultural Instns. Retirement Sys., N.Y.C., 1989—. Elected to Acad. Women Achievers, YWCA, N.Y.C., 1983.

TATNALL, GEORGE JACOB, aeronautical engineer; b. Cin., Aug. 9, 1923; s. George Henry and Ida Mae (Hazelbaker) T.; m. G. Virginia Morgan, Feb. 5, 1949; children: Robert, William, Jeffrey, Thomas, Jane. BSME in Aeronautics, U. Pitts., 1949. Devel. engr. Naval Air Devel. Ctr., Warminster, Pa., 1949-57; supr. electro-mech. design br., supr. radome antenna sect. Naval Air Devel. Ctr., Warminster, 1957-62, 63-78; engring. group leader Corning (N.Y.) Glass Works, 1962-63; cons. Semcor, Inc., Warminster, 1979-81; cons. pvt. practice Warminster, 1982-84; cons. Rome Rsch. Corp., New Hartford, N.Y., 1993—; Tech. advisor Seventh Fleet USN, S.E. Asia, during Vietnam War, 1971. Contbr. to sci. papers presented at confs. (many also pub. in proceedings); author: (with others) chpt. in book Environmental Simulation and Test Data; author: manuals and documentation aircraft equipment. With US Army AF, 1943-45, China. Mem. AIAA (pres. U. Pitts. chpt. 1948), VFW, Flying Tiger U.S. 14th Air Force Assn. Achievements include patents for Speed Brake Retarding Mechanism for an Air Dropped Store, Air Dropped Minature Sonobuoy, Rotatable and Tiltable Radome with ind. scan and tilt antenna; developed low noise coupling through laminar boundary layer for acoustic homing missile, test facilities for supersonic rain erosion of aircraft materials. Home: 551 Walter Rd Warminster PA 18974-5553

TATOOLES, CONSTANTINE JOHN, cardiovascular and thoracic surgeon; b. Chgo., May 7, 1936; m. Betty Ann, Jan. 30, 1960; children: Julie Denise, Anton John, Jon William. BS, Albion (Mich.) Coll., 1958; MS in Physiology, Loyola U., Chgo., 1961, MD, 1961. Research asst. Loyola U., 1958-59, research assoc., 1959-60; intern U. Chgo. Hosps., 1961-62, resident in surgery, 1962-68, instr. in surgery, 1966-68; clin. assoc. surgery Nat. Heart Inst., 1964-66; sr. registrar in surgery Gt. Ormond St. Hosp. for Children, London, 1968-69; practice medicine specializing in cardiovascular and thoracic surgery, Chgo., 1969—; asst. prof. surgery and physiology, Loyola U., 1969-78, attending surgeon, 1969-73; assoc. attending surgeon thoracic and cardiovascular surgery Cook County Hosp., Chgo., 1969-78, chmn. dept. cardio-thoracic surgery, 1969-78, attending surgeon, 1970, lectr. in cardiac surgery, 1970; chief cardiovascular and thoracic surgery Abraham Lincoln Sch. Medicine, U. Ill., Chgo., 1973-77, assoc. prof. surgery, 1973-76, prof. surgery, 1976-83; attending surgeon U. Ill., 1973-77, chief dept. surgery, 1989-91; chmn. dept. cardiothoracic surgery St. Francis Hosp., Evanston, Ill., 1977-78, St. Mary's of Nazareth Hosp., Chgo., 1981-88; chief cardiothoracic surgery U. Ill., 1989-91, Mt. Sinai Hosp. Med. Ctr., Chgo., 1992—; attending surgeon VA Hosp., Chgo., 1989-91, N.W. Comm., Arlington Heights, 1991-; chmn. Chgo. Inst. for Heart and Lung, 1972; chmn. bd. Penda Corp., Portgage, Wis., 1981-85; mem. Chgo. Bd. Trade. Contbr. to films in field, articles to profl. publs. Fellow A.C.S., Am. Coll. Cardiology, Am. Coll. Chest Physicians (chmn. motion picture div., 1975-76); mem. Am. Coll. Angiography, Am. Assn. Thoracic Surgery, Am. Heart Assn. (council on cardiovascular surgery), AMA, Am. Thoracic Soc., Assn. for Acad. Surgery, Chgo. Heart Assn. (council on cardiovascular surgery), Chgo. Med. Soc., Chgo. Surg. Soc., Ill. State Med. Soc., Inst. of Medicine Chgo., Royal Soc. Medicine London (Eng.), Soc. Thoracic Surgeons, Chgo. Thoracic Soc. (pres. 1981), A.G. Morrow Soc. (exec. dir.), Warren J. Cole Soc., Ill. Vascular Inst. (founder 1990). Office: Mt Sinai Hosp Med Ctr Calif Ave At 15th St Rm F944 Chicago IL 60608

TATUM, JOAN GLENNALYN JOHN, secondary school educator; b. Scottsbluff, Nebr., Jan. 5, 1934; d. Glenn Edwin and Blanche Constance (Dundon) John; m. William Earl Tatum, Apr. 6, 1954 (div. Apr. 1988); children: Cherie Elizabeth Tatum Love, Michele Tatum Brackett, John William, Amy Denise Tatum Stanton. AA, U. Fla., 1954; BA, U. South Fla., 1969, MA, 1971. Cert. tchr., Fla. Substitute tchr. Pub. Sch. Dist., Sarasota, Fla., 1966-67; bus., vocat. edn. tchr. Riverview High Sch., Sarasota, 1969—; curriculum coord. bus. and vocat. edn., 1990—; bus., vocat. edn. tchr. Sarasota Tech. Inst., 1969—; curriculum coord. bus./vocat. edn. dept. Riverview High Sch., 1990—; adj. prof. St. Francis Coll., Joliet, Ill., 1988, 91, 93, 94; state and dist. textbook evaluation teams Fla. Dept. Edn., Sarasota, sch. to dist. tech. rep., 1985—; chmn., tech. coord. Riverview Tech. Com., 1987—; assoc. master tchr. State Fla. Bd. Edn., 1984-87; coun. chair Dist. Sch. Based Mgmt., Sarasota, 1991-93; chmn. Riverview Sch. Based Mgmt., 1991-93; project coord. Riverview Sr. Acad. Integrated Studies, 1991—; dance tchr. various studios, Sarasota, 1949-67; sec. and office staff various govtl., community and dance studios, Sarasota, 1951-59. Supervisory com. Sarasota Coastal Credit Union, 1985—. Senate Edn. scholar Sarasota High/Fla. Legislature, 1951; named Tchr. of Yr. Riverview High Sch., 1991-92. Mem. Internat. Soc. Bus. Educators, Nat. Bus. Edn. Assn., Am. Vocat. Assn., So. Bus. Edn. Assn., Fla. Bus. Edn. Assn., Fla. Vocat. Assn., Sarasota County Vocat. Adult Assn. (pres. 1989-90), Order of Rainbow (mem. adv. bd. 1977—, Grand Cross Color award 1949), Order Ea. Star, Kappa Delta Pi, Delta Pi Epsilon, Alpha Delta Kappa (chpt. treas. 1982-86, chpt. pres. 1986-88, chmn. state ad hoc com. 1989-90, chmn. state candidate qualifications com. 1994-96, dist. treas. 1987-92, dist. 1992-94, State Honoris Causa award 1992). Presbyterian. Avocations: theatre, choreography, dance, family, walking. Home: 4561 Ashton Rd Sarasota FL 34233-3405 Office: Riverview HS One Ram Way Sarasota FL 34231

TATUM, RITA, communications executive; b. Elkhart, Ind., Nov. 30, 1948; d. Edward Anthony and Edith Ann (Chomer) Osowski; m. Michael Ray Tatum, May 22, 1971 (div. 1977). BA in English, St. Mary of the Woods, 1971, BA in Journalism, 1971; postgrad., Loyola U., Chgo., 1977-78. Reporter Stas. WTHI and WTHI-TV, Terre Haute, Ind., 1970-71; assoc. editor Bldg. Design and Constrn., Chgo., 1972-76; editor-in-chief Gorman Pub., Chgo., 1976-79; prin. Tatum Communications, Elkhart, Ind., 1979—; editorial cons. ABA, Aspen Pubs., Bonus Books, Dearborn Fin. Pub., Duquesne Univ. Press, Edison Electric Inst., FASA Corp., Precept Press, Teach 'Em, S/H Publs., Ltd., Trade Press Pub., others. Author, collaborator: The Alternative House, 1978, Sourcebook of Food and Nutrition, 1980, 2nd edit. 1982, Yearbook of Special Education, 1980, Standard Education Almanac, 1984, 4 edits., Financial Planner's Seminar Kit, 1985, CPA's Guide to Financial Planning, 1985, The Financial Planner: A New Professional, 1986, University Hospital Consortium Recruitment/Orientation Manual, 1989, Ellis Island, 1990; contbr. articles to profl. jours., chpts. to books. Recipient Jesse Neal award Am. Bus. Press, 1976, 2d Place award Soc. Nat. Assn. Publs., 1987, 3d Place award Writer's Digest Writing Competition, 1989. Mem. AAAS, Soc. Profl. Journalists, Nature Conservancy. Office: Tatum Communications 55714 Merle St Elkhart IN 46514-9591

TATUM, RONALD WINSTON, physician, endocrinologist; b. Joplin, Mo., Apr. 29, 1931; s. Dorothy Elizabeth (Messick) T.; m. Phyllis Wainman, June 25 (div. May 1974); children: Jeffrey, Stacey; m. Ruby Germaine Trujillo, Aug. 21, 1983 (div. Sept. 1993); children: Tracea, Susan; m. Yvonne Marie Laug, Oct. 8, 1994. AB, Harvard U., 1957; MD, U. Rochester, 1961. Intern Strong Meml. Hosp., Rochester, N.Y., 1961-62; resident U. Rochester, 1962-64, fellow, 1966-66; clin. endocrinologist in pvt. practice Albuquerque, 1966—; active staff Presbyn. Hosp. and St. Joseph Hosp., Albuquerque, 1966—; med. dir. Cottonwood Treatment Ctr., Albuquerque, 1985-90, N.Mex. Monitored Treatment Program, Albuquerque, 1990—; clin. endocrine cons. Charter Hosp. and Heights Psychiat. Hosp., Albuquerque, 1985—. Contbr. articles to profl. jours. Mem. med. adv. com. Hospice Home Health Care, Albuquerque, 1991—. Mem. Am. Assn. Clin. Endocrinologists (charter), Am. Assn. Internal Medicine, Am. Diabetes Assn. (pres. N.Mex. chpt. 1970, 74), Am. Soc. Addiction Medicine, Assn. for Med. Rsch. in Substance Abuse. Avocations: photography, computer investing. Home: 842 Southeast Cir NW Albuquerque NM 87104 Office: 8008 Constitution Pl NE Albuquerque NM 87110

TATYREK, ALFRED FRANK, consultant, materials/environmental engineer, analytical and research chemist; b. Hillside, N.J., Jan. 23, 1930; s. Frank Peter and Frances (Luxa) T. BS, Seton Hall U., 1954; postgrad., Rutgers U., 1956-57. Rsch. chemist Bakelite div. Union Carbide, Bloomfield, N.J., 1953-58, U.S. Radium Corp., Morristown, N.J., 1959-62; analytical chemist insp. Chem. Procurement Dist. U.S. Army, N.Y.C., 1962-64; rsch. chemist Picatinny Arsenal U.S. Army, Dover, N.J., 1964-73; chem. materials engr. U.S. Army Armament Rsch., Devel. and Engring. Ctr., N.J., 1973-95; cons. polymer materials, environ. chemistry. Patentee pyrotechnic compositions, chemiluminescent compositions and processes, crank case oil vacuum purification sys. for internal combustion engines; lectr., contbr. articles on mountaineering expdns. and adventures in the great mountain ranges of N.Am., S.Am., Europe and Africa to mags.; contbr. more than 50 sci. and tech. reports. 1st aid instr. ARC, Essex County, N.J., 1969-82; chief 1st aid Maplewood (N.J.) CD, 1971-91; patrol dir. Nat. Ski Patrol, Phoenicia, N.Y., 1978-84, sr. lifetime Nat. Ski patroller So. N.Y. region, 1979—. Climbed Mt. Blanc, highest mountain peak in Europe; climbed to highest summit of 19, 730 feet on Mt. Kilimanjaro, highest mountain peak in Africa, 1972; leader of climb on Matterhorn and Monte Rosa, Switzerland's highest peak; participant in numerous mountain expdns. in U.S. and Can., including 2 first ascents in No. Cascades of Wash. (S.E. ridge of Mt. Goode, Aug. 1963, Peak 7732 via the Snow Chute, Aug. 1964, East ridge of Bear Mountain, Aug. 1964). Mem. Nat. Soc. Inventors, Nat. Assn. Underwater Instrs. (cert. advanced diver and underwater photographer 1971—), Sigma Xi Sci. Rsch. Soc. (pres. Picatinny chpt. 1974-75, 79-80, 85-86), Magician's Round Table, Alpine Club of Can., Appalachian Mountain Club, Sierra Club. Roman Catholic. Achievements include six patents in field.

TATZ, PAUL H., real estate executive; b. Des Moines, June 24, 1935; s. Simon M. Tatz and Esther (Schumaker) Steele; m. Rochelle Sue Krantman, Feb. 26, 1981; children: John P., Jennifer A., Stephen C., Suzanne E. Student, U. Iowa, 1953, Drake U., 1956-59; LLB, Drake U., 1962. Bar: Iowa 1962, Ill. 1969, Mich. 1970, Calif. 1973. Sole pratice Des Moines, 1962-68; asst. atty. gen. State of Iowa, Des Moines, 1968; atty. Inland Steel Co., Chgo., 1968-70; sr. v.p. Wickes Corp., Mich., Ill. and Calif., 1970-76; sole practice Calif. and Iowa, 1976-82; asst. gen. counsel Del E. Webb Co., Phoenix, 1982-83; exec. v.p. Del E. Webb Devel. Co., Sun City West, Ariz., 1983-84, pres., chief oper. officer, 1984-85; pres., chief exec. officer Del. E. Webb Communities, Sun City West, 1985-89. Mem. Ariz. Acad.-Ariz. Town Halls, Phoenix, 1985—, nat. bd. advisors U. Ariz., Tucson, 1987; assoc. mem. Urban Land Inst., Washington, 1985—; bd. dirs., vice chmn. Sun Health Corp., Sun City, 1986—. Served with AUS, 1954-56, Korea. Mem. Calif. Bar Assn., Ill. Bar Assn., Iowa Bar Assn., Mich. Bar Assn., Phoenix C. of C. (bd. dirs. 1987—), Econs. Club (dean's coun. 100, 1986—), Arrowhead Country Club (Glendale, Ariz.). Republican. Office: Del Webb Corp 2231 E Camelback Rd Phoenix AZ 85016-3453

TAUB, HENRY, retired computer services company executive; b. Paterson, N.J., Sept. 20, 1927; s. Morris and Sylvia (Sievitz) T.; m. Marilyn Adler, Sept. 13, 1958; children: Judith, Steven, Ira. B.S., N.Y. U., 1947. Pres. Automatic Data Processing, Inc., Roseland, N.J., 1949-69; chmn. bd. Automatic Data Processing, Inc., 1970-77, 82-86, chmn. exec. com., 1977—, hon. chmn. bd., 1986—; dir. Leumi Bank & Trust Co., N.Y.C., Rite Aid Corp., Hasbro, Inc.; past pres., hon. chmn. Joint Distbn. Com. Chmn., hon. pres. N.Y. chpt. Hemophilia Found., 1970-76; past vice chmn. Nat. Hemophilia Found.; bd. dirs. Am. Friends Hebrew U., Interfaith Hunger Appeal, 1979—, N.Y. Shakespeare Festival, 1981—, Ch. United Israel Appeal, 1986-90; trustee NYU, Avi Chai Found.; mem. bd. govs. Jewish Agy., 1981-90; pres. Jewish Community Ctr. of Palisades, 1980-84; chmn. Bus. Employment Found., Inc., 1980-90. Mem. Am. Technion Soc. (chmn. internat. bd. govs. 1990—), Paterson Alumni Assn. (chmn. 1987-94). Office: ADP Inc 1 A D P Blvd Roseland NJ 07068-1728 also: NJ Nets Meadowlands Arena East Rutherford NJ 07073

TAUB, JESSE J., electrical engineering researcher; b. N.Y.C., Apr. 27, 1927; s. Julius and Ida (Orlansky) T.; m. Eva Pollack, Dec. 24, 1955 (dec. Nov. 1973); children: Richard Lawrence, Jocelyn Cara, Suzanne Mara; m. Naomi Etta Trachtenberg, June 30, 1974. BEE, CCNY, 1948; MEE, Poly. U., 1949. Group leader microwave electronics, Material Lab. USN, Bklyn., 1949-55; engr. Airborne Instruments Lab., Mineola, N.Y., 1955-58, sect. leader, 1958-61, engring cons., 1961-75; chief scientist AIL Systems Inc., Melville, N.Y., 1975-93; cons., 1993—. Author: (with others) Microwave Measurements, 1963; contbr. numerous papers to profl. publs.; patentee microwave techniques. With USN, 1945-46. Fellow IEEE (Centennial medal 1984, C.A. Fowler award 1993, adminstrv. com. 1972-74, program chmn. microwave symposium, steering com.); mem. Archaeology Inst. Am. Democrat. Jewish. Avocations: classical musician, contract bridge, archaeology. Home: 115 Northgate Cir Melville NY 11747-3045 Office: AIL Systems Inc Commack Rd Deer Park NY 11729

TAUB, RICHARD PAUL, social sciences educator; b. Bklyn., Apr. 16, 1937; s. Martin Glynn and Frances (Israel) T.; m. Doris Susan Leventhal, Aug. 14, 1961; children: Neela Robin, Zachariah Jacob. BA, U. Mich., 1959; MA, Harvard U., 1962, PhD in Social Relations, 1966. Asst. prof. sociology Brown U., Providence, 1965-69; from asst. prof. to Paul Klapper prof. of social scis. U. Chgo., 1969—, assoc. dean Coll. of Univ., 1982-86; chair adv. bd. Nat. Cmty. Devel. Initiative, 1991—; dir. South Ark. Rural Devel. Study, 1988—. Author: Community Capitalism, Bureaucrats Under Stress, (with D. Garth Taylor and Jan Dunham) Paths of Neighborhood Change, (with Doris L. Taub) Entrepreneurship in India's Small Scale Industries; editor: (with Doris L. Taub) American Society in Tocqueville's Time and Today; co-editor Studies of Urban Soc., 1978—; contbr. articles to profl. jours. Chmn. bd. St. Thomas the Apostle Sch., 1983-86; bd. dirs. Hyde Park Kenwood Cmty. Conf., Chgo., 1972-75; adv. bd. Neighborhood Preservation Initiative, 1993—. Angell scholar U. Mich., 1956; Woodrow Wilson fellow Harvard U., 1959-60; grantee Am. Inst. Indian Studies, Ford Found., MacArthur Found., NSF, Wiebold Found., Nat. Inst. Justice. Mem. Am. Sociol. Assn., Midwest Sociol. Soc., Assn. for Asian Studies. Avocations: bicycling, squash, music. Office: Univ Chgo 5845 S Ellis Ave Rm 223 Chicago IL 60637-1404

TAUB, ROBERT ALLAN, lawyer; b. Denver, Nov. 25, 1923; s. Clarence Arthur and Mary Frances (Jones) T.; m. Doris Irene Schroeder, Dec. 22, 1945; children: Amanda, Jonathan, Barbara. BA, U. Chgo., 1944, JD, 1947. Bar: Ill. 1947. Legal staff Marshall Field & Co., Chgo., 1947-50; mgr. exec. compensation Ford Motor Co., Dearborn, Mich., 1950-63; asst. sect. Ford Motor Co., Dearborn, 1963-74, dir. corp. affairs planning, 1974—. Pres. Dearborn Community Arts Council, 1971-72; trustee Internat. Mus. Photography, George Eastman House, Rochester, N.Y., 1976—, chmn., 1979-82; mem. adv. bd. U. Mich. Dearborn, 1980—, Met. Mus. Art, N.Y.C., 1987—; trustee Henry Ford Hosp., Detroit, 1983—; chmn. Dearborn Pub. Libr., 1986—; bd. dirs., mem. exec. com., chmn. fin. com., Health Alliance Plan, 1992—. mem. ABA, Ill. Bar Assn. Presbyterian. Home: 1824 Hawthorne St Dearborn MI 48128-1448 Office: Ford Motor Co The American Rd Rm 950 Dearborn MI 48126

TAUB, THEODORE CALVIN, lawyer; b. Springfield, Mass., Jan. 1, 1935; s. Samuel and Sara Lee (Daum) T.; m. Roberta Mae Ginsburg, Aug. 23, 1959; children: Tracy, Andrew, Adam. AB, Duke U., 1956; JD, U. Fla., 1960. Bar: Fla., 1960, U.S. Supreme Ct. Atty. Broad and Cassel, Tampa; asst. city atty. City of Tampa, 1963-67; city atty. City of Temple Terrace, Fla., 1974—; panelist in field. Contbr. articles to profl. jours. Chmn. Tampa-Hillsborough (Fla.) County Expy. Authority, 1974-84; mem. Hillsborough County Charter Commn., 1966-69, Local Govt. Mgmt. Efficiency Com., 1979, State of Fla. Environ. Efficiency Study Commn., 1986-88; founder Tampa Bay Performing Arts Ctr. Fellow: Am. Bar Found; mem. ABA (chmn. real property litigation com. 1981-86, chmn. com. on housing and urban environ. 1989-91), Am. Coll. Real Estate Lawyers (bd. govs.), Am. Land Title Assn. (lenders' counsel group), Fla. Bar Assn. (bd. cert. real estate lawyer), Fla. Jaycees (pres.), Tau Epsilon Phi. Democrat. Jewish. Home: 4937 Lyford Cay Rd Tampa FL 33629-4828 Office: 100 N Tampa Ste 3500 Tampa FL 33602

TAUBE, HENRY, chemistry educator; b. Sask., Can., Nov. 30, 1915; came to U.S., 1937, naturalized, 1942; s. Samuel and Albertina (Tiledetski) T.; m. Mary Alice Wesche, Nov. 27, 1952; children: Linda, Marianna, Heinrich, Karl. BS, U. Sask., 1935, MS, 1937, LLD, 1973; PhD, U. Calif., 1940; PhD (hon.), Hebrew U. of Jerusalem, 1979; DSc (hon.), U. Chgo., 1983, Poly. Inst., N.Y., 1984, SUNY, 1985, U. Guelph, 1987; DSc honoris causa, Seton Hall U., 1988; Lajos Kossuth U. of Debrecen, Hungary, 1988; DSc, Northwestern U., 1990, Northwestern U., 1991; hon. degree, U. Athens, 1993. Instr. U. Calif., 1940-41; instr. & asst. prof. Cornell U., 1941-46; faculty U. Chgo., 1946-62, prof., 1952-62, chmn. dept. chemistry, 1955-59; prof. chemistry Stanford U., 1962—, Marguerite Blake Wilbur prof., 1976, chmn. dept., 1971-74; Baker lectr. Cornell U., 1965. Hon. mem. Hungarian Acad. Scis., 1988. Guggenheim fellow, 1949, 55; recipient Harrison Howe award, 1961, Chandler medal Columbia U., 1964, F. P. Dwyer medal U. NSW, Australia, 1973, Nat. medal of Sci., 1976, 77, Allied Chem. award for Excellence in Grad. Tchg. and Innovative Sci., 1979, Nobel prize in Chemistry, 1983, Bailar medal U. Ill., 1983, Robert A. Welch Found. award in

Chemistry, 1983, Disting. Achievement award Internat. Precious Metals Inst., 1986, Brazilian Order of Sci. Merit award, 1994. Fellow Royal Soc. Chemistry (hon.), Indian Chem. Soc. (hon.); mem. NAS (award in chem. scis. 1983), Am. Acad. Arts and Scis., Am. Chem. Soc. (Kirkwood award New Haven sect. 1965, award for nuclear applications in chemistry 1955, Nichols medal N.Y. sect. 1971, Willard Gibbs medal Chgo. sect. 1971, Disting. Svc. in Advancement Inorganic Chemistry award 1967, T.W. Richards medal NE sect. 1980, Monsanto Co. award in inorganic chemistry 1981, Linus Pauling award Puget Sound sect. 1981, Priestley medal 1985, Oesper award Cin. sect. 1986, G.M. Kosolapoff award Auburn sect. 1990), Royal Physiographical Soc. of Lund (fgn. mem.), Am. Philos. Soc., Finnish Acad. Sci. and Letters, Royal Danish Acad. Scis. and Letters, Coll. Chemists of Catalonia and Beleares (hon.), Can. Soc. Chemistry (hon.), Hungarian Acad. Scis. (hon. mem.), Royal Soc. (fgn. mem.), Brazilian Acad. Scis. (corr.), Engring. Acad. Japan (fgn. assoc.), Australian Acad. Scis. (corr.), Chem. Soc. Japan (hon. mem. 1993), Phi Beta Kappa, Sigma Xi, Phi Lambda Upsilon (hon.). Office: Stanford U Dept Chemistry Stanford CA 94305

TAUBER, ALFRED IMRE, hematologist, immunologist, philosopher of science; b. Washington, June 24, 1947; s. Laszlo Nandor Tauber and Lilly Katherine (Manovill) Endrei; m. Susan Alice Swerdlow, Dec. 22, 1966; children: Joel, Dylan, Benjamin, Hannah. BS, Tufts U., 1969, MD, 1973. Intern, resident in internal medicine U. Wash., Seattle, 1973-75; clin. and research fellow in hematology Tufts-N.Eng. Med. Ctr., Boston, 1975-77; instr. in medicine Harvard Med. Sch., Boston, 1978-80; jr. assoc. in medicine Brigham and Women's Hosp., Boston, 1979-82; research assoc. Robert B. Brigham Hosp., Boston, 1979-82; asst. prof. medicine Harvard Med. Sch., Boston, 1980-82; assoc. prof. medicine, assoc. rsch. prof. biochemistry Boston U. Sch. Medicine, 1982-86, prof. medicine, 1986—, assoc. prof. pathology, 1985-87, prof. pathology, 1987—; prof. philosophy Boston U., 1992—, dir. Ctr. for Philosophy and History of Sci., 1993—; assoc. vis. physician Boston City Hosp., 1982-87, vis. physician, 1988—, chief hematology and oncology, 1982-91. Author: The Immune Self: Theory or Metaphor, 1994; co-author: Metchnikoff and the Origins of Immunology, 1991; editor: Organism and the Origins of Self, 1991, The Elusive Synthesis: Aesthetics and Science, 1995; contbr. over 145 articles on neutrophil biochemistry and history/philosophy of biology to profl. jours. Fellow Brandeis U. Waltham, Mass., 1978. Fellow ACP; mem. Am. Soc. Hematology, Reticuloendothelial Soc., Am. Assn. Immunology, Am. Soc. Cell Biology, Am. Assn. Biol. Chemistry and Molecular Biology, Am. Soc. Clin. Investigation, Assn. Am. Physicians, History of Sci. Soc., Am. Assn. History of Medicine, Am. Philos. Assn., Philosophy of Sci. Assn. Jewish. Office: Boston Univ 745 Commonwealth Ave Boston MA 02215

TAUBER, JOEL DAVID, manufacturing company executive; b. Detroit, June 28, 1935; s. Benjamin and Anne (Merliss) T.; m. Shelley Tauber; children: Julie, Ellen, Benjamin Brian, Melissa, Juliana. B.B.A., U. Mich., 1956, J.D., 1959, M.B.A., 1963. Bar: Mich. 1959. Pres. Key Internat. Mfg. Inc., Southfield, Mich., 1969-86; pres. Tauber Enterprises, 1986—; trustee Nat. Indsl. Group Pension Plan, 1980; bd. dirs. Fed. Home Loan Bank, 1986-91, Reid Plastics Inc., 1989-93; chmn. bd. Key Mfg. Group Inc., Key Plastics Inc., Keywell Corp., 1986—. Pres. Jewish Welfare Fedn., Detroit, 1983-86, Jewish Community Ctr., 1978-80; nat. chmn. United Jewish Appeal, 1992-94, pres., 1994—; bd. dirs. United Found., 1980—, v.p. 1986—; co-chmn. Detroit Round Table-Nat. Coun. Christians, Jews and Muslims, 1989-91; trustee Sinai Hosp., Detroit, 1980-91; mem. Fed. Judges Selection Panel Ea. Dist. Mich., 1978; mem. U. Mich. Devel. Adv. Bd., 1986—; trustee Growth Fund, 1988—. Recipient Frank A. Wetsman Meml. Leadership award Jewish Welfare Fedn., 1970, Butzel award, 1990; named Entrepreneur of Yr., 1990. Mem. Mich. Bar Assn., World Bus. Council, Franklin Hills Country Club, Detroit Athletic Club, U. Mich. Alumni Club, U. Mich. Victors Club, Masons. Office: Tauber Enterprises 27777 Franklin Rd Ste 1850 Southfield MI 48034

TAUBER, MARK J., lawyer; b. Detroit, Mar. 25, 1949; s. Max M. and Beatrice R. (Roth) T.; m. Anita L. Tilben, June 23, 1970; children: Melissa A., Benjamin M., Allison B. BA, U. Mich., 1970; JD, George Washington U., 1973. Bar: D.C. 1973, Md. 1974, U.S. Supreme Ct. 1980. Assoc. Pierson, Ball & Dowd, Washington, 1973-79, ptnr., 1980-82; ptnr. Piper & Marbury, Washington, 1982—. Home: 11515 Big Piney Way Potomac MD 20854 Office: Piper & Marbury 1200 19th St NW Washington DC 20036

TAUBER, ORNER J., SR., petrochemical company executive; b. 1914; married. Grad., Tex. Christian U. With MKT R.R., 1932-35, So. Steamship Line, 1937-39; asst. to pres. Eastern States Petroleum Co., Inc., 1942-50; with Gabriel Oil Co., 1950-53; with Tauber Oil Co., Houston, 1953—, chmn., 1977—, also bd. dirs. Office: Tauber Oil Co 55 Waugh Dr Ste 700 Houston TX 77007-5837

TAUBER, RONALD STEVEN, investment banker; b. N.Y.C., Jan. 24, 1944; s. William and Lillian (Slanger) T.; m. Adele Sharon Lieberman, June 21, 1966; children: Daniel, Miriam, Michael, Elizabeth. BA, Bklyn. Coll., 1965; LLB, Harvard U., 1968. Bar: N.Y. 1969. Law clk. presiding justice U.S. Dist. Ct., Bklyn, 1968-70; assoc. Stroock & Stroock & Lavan, N.Y.C., 1970-76, ptnr., 1976-79; sr. v.p. J. Aron & Co., N.Y.C., 1979-81; gen. ptnr. Goldman, Sachs & Co., N.Y.C., 1981-86, limited ptnr., 1987-88; mng. officer Brook Street Assocs. L.P., N.Y.C., 1987-88; pres., chief exec. officer Rayner & Stonington, L.P., 1988-91; pres. Tricon Fin. Svcs., Co., N.Y.C., 1991-93, Blenheim Investments, Inc., Somerset, N.J., 1993—. Trustee Maimonides Hosp., Bklyn., 1978-88. Mem. Comex Clearing Assn. (gov. 1984-87), Futures Industry Assn. (bd. dirs. 1985-87), Nat. Futures Assn. Home: 885 Park Ave New York NY 10021-0325 Office: Blenheim Investments Inc C/O R&S Mgmt Group 126 E 56th St Ste 1500 New York NY 10022-3213

TAUBERT, FREDERICK WAYNE, oil company executive; b. Worcester, Mass., Feb. 15, 1933; s. Fredrick Otto and Florence (Ploch) T.; m. Sandra J. Taubert, Nov. 1, 1954 (div. 1972); m. Maureen A. Taubert, June 9, 1978; children: Martyn W., Debra L. BA, Worcester Jr. Coll., 1968; BS, Clark U., 1970. Service mgr. Central Oil Co., Worcester, 1958-60, sales 1960-62; sales mgr. Union Oil Co., Boston, 1963-73, v.p. sales, 1973-79; sr. v.p. gen. mgr. New Eng., Inc., Boston, 1980; pres. The Belcher Co. of N.Y., Inc. and Belcher of New Eng., Inc., 1984—; now pres. Belcher New Eng., Inc.; dir. Better Home Heat Council, Boston, 1971-72, New Eng. Fuel Inst., 1976-83. Served with U.S. Army, 1954-56. Office: Belcher New England Inc 222 Lee Burbank Hwy Revere MA 02151-4096

TAUBES, CLIFFORD H., mathematician, educator. Prof. math. Harvard U., Cambridge, Mass. Recipient Oswald Veblen Geometry prize Am. Math. Soc., 1991. Office: Harvard U Dept Of Math Cambridge MA 02138

TAUBES, GARY, scientific writer. Recipient Forum award Am. Phys. Soc., 1994. Office: 337 W 87th St New York NY 10024-2602*

TAUBIN, ROBIN LIVINGSTON, lawyer; b. N.Y., June 20, 1952; d. Edgar Alan and Arlene (Caro) L.; m. Michael Jay Taubin, Aug. 8, 1976; children: (Ian Lloyd, Lance Harris. BA in History, Russel Sage Coll., 1974; JD, Hofstra U. Law Sch., 1977. Nat. underwriting atty. Chgo. Title Ins. Co., N.Y., 1977-80; sr. counsel Paramount Comm., Inc., N.Y., 1981-94; v.p., counsel real estate Viacom Inc., N.Y., 1994—; pro-bono counsel N.Y. Landmarks Conservancy, N.Y., 1984—. Mem. N.Y. State Bar Assn. Comml. Real Estate Women (v.p. 1994-95). Office: Viacom Inc 1515 Broadway New York NY 10036

TAUBITZ, FREDRICKA, financial executive; b. Los Angeles, Feb. 25, 1944; d. Ferdinand C. and Marie L. (Stewart) T. AA, Pasadena City Coll., 1963; BSBA, U. Calif., Berkeley, 1965; MSBA, UCLA, 1967; grad. advanced mgmt. program, Harvard U., 1980-81. CPA, Calif. Acct. Coopers & Lybrand, Los Angeles, 1965-75, ptnr., 1976-85; exec. v.p. chief fin. officer Zenith Nat. Ins. Corp., Woodland Hills, Calif., 1985—; founding dir. Women's Bank Calif., Los Angeles, 1974-76. Bd. dirs. Soroptimist Found. Los Angeles, 1978-79; bd. dirs. Girls' Club, Pasadena, Calif., 1973-84, pres., 1981-83; mem. Calif. Mus. Found. Adv. Bd., 1978-81. Recipient Outstanding Young Bus. Leader award Los Angeles Jr. C. of C., 1978, Internat.

Achievement award Soroptimist Internat., 1977. Mem. AICPA (ins. coms. com. 1990-93), Calif. Soc. CPAs, L.A. C. of C. (bd. dirs. women's coun. 1978-81), Fin. Execs. Inst., Phi Beta Kappa. Office: Zenith Nat Ins Corp 21255 Califa St Woodland Hills CA 91367-5005

TAUBMAN, A. ALFRED, real estate developer; b. Pontiac, Mich., Jan. 31, 1925; s. Philip and Fannie Ester (Blustin) T.; m. Reva Kolodney, Dec. 1, 1949 (div. July 1977); children: Gayle Kalisman, Robert S., William S.; m. Judith Mazor, June 17, 1982. Student, U. Mich., 1945-48, LLD (hon.), 1991; student, Lawrence Inst. Tech., 1948-49, DArch (hon.), 1985; D in Bus. (hon.), Eastern Mich. U., 1984; D in Edn. (hon.), Mich. State U., 1993; HHD (hon.), No. Mich. U., 1995. Chmn. The Taubman Co., Bloomfield Hills, Mich., 1950—, The Taubman Ctrs., Inc., Bloomfield Hills, Mich., 1992—; chmn. Sotheby's Holdings, Inc., N.Y.C., 1983—; bd. dirs. Live Entertainment of Can., Inc. Trustee Ctr. for Creative Studies, Detroit, Harper-Grace Hosps., Detroit; chmn. emeritus Archives Am. Art Smithsonian Inst., Washington, U. Pa. Wharton Real Estate Ctr., Phila.; pres. Arts Commn. of Detroit; mem. nat. bd. Smithsonian Assocs.; established Taubman Ctr. for State and Local Govt. Harvard U., Cambridge, Mass., chmn. Mich. Partnership for New Edn., Program in Am. Instns., U. Mich., Brown U.'s Pub. Policy and Am. Instns. Program; prin. benefactor A. Alfred Taubman Health Care Ctr. and A. Alfred Taubman Med. Libr., U. Mich.; bd. dirs. Detroit Renaissance, Inc., Friends of Art and Preservation in Embassies, Washington; active State of Mich. Gaming Commn. Recipient Bus. Statesman award Harvard Bus. Sch. Club of Detroit, 1983, Sportsman of Yr. award United Found. Detroit, SE Mich. Chpt. March of Dimes Birth Defects, 1983; named Michiganian of Yr. The Detroit News, 1983. Mem. Urban Land Inst. (trustee), Nat. Realty Com. (bd. dirs.).

TAUBMAN, JANE ANDELMAN, Russian literature educator; b. Boston, Oct. 23, 1942; d. Hyman M. and Esther (Rosenthal) Andelman; m. William Chase Taubman; children: Alexander, Phoebe. BA, Radcliffe Coll., 1964; MA, Yale U., 1968, PhD, 1972. Instr. Russian Smith Coll., Northampton, Mass., 1968-72; asst. prof. Russian Amherst (Mass.) Coll., 1973-83, assoc. prof. Russian, 1983-89, prof. Russian, 1989—. Author: A Life Through Poetry: Marina Tsvetaeva's Lyric Diary, 1989; co-author: Moscow Spring, 1989; co-editor: Marina Tsvetaeva: One Hundred Years, 1994; contbr. articles to profl. jours. Woodrow Wilson Found. fellow, 1964—, Am. Coun. Learned Socs.-SSRC, 1974, trustee-faculty fellow Amherst Coll., 1978, fellow Nat. Def. Title VI, 1965-68; grantee Am. Philos. Soc., 1975, Amherst Coll., 1991, 94, IREX grantee USSR, 1988. Mem. AAUP, Modern Langs. Assn., Am. Assn. Tchrs. Slavic and East European Langs., Am. Assn. Slavic Studies, Am. Coun. Tchrs. of Russian, Am. Assn. Tchrs. of Slavic and East European Langs. Office: Amherst Coll Dept Russian Amherst MA 01002

TAUBMAN, MARTIN ARNOLD, immunologist; b. N.Y.C., July 10, 1940; s. Herman and Betty (Berger) T.; m. Joan Petra Mikelbank, May 30, 1965; children: Benjamin Abby, Joel David. B.S., Bklyn. Coll., 1961; D.D.S., Columbia U., 1965; Ph.D., SUNY, Buffalo, 1970. Asst. mem. staff Forsyth Dental Center, Boston, 1970—; head immunology dept. Forsyth Dental Center, 1972—; assoc. mem. staff, 1974-80, sr. staff mem., 1980—; asst. clin. prof. oral biology and pathophysiology Harvard U. Sch. Dental Medicine, 1976-79, assoc. clin. prof., 1979—; mem. oral biology and medicine study sect. NIH, 1980-84. Editor: (with J. Siots) Contemporary Microbiology and Immunology; contbr. articles to profl. jours, chpts. to books. Recipient Rsch. Career Devel. award, 1971-76, Fred Birnberg Alumni award for dist-ing. dental rsch. Columbia U. Assn. Dental Alumni, Disting. Faculty award Harvard Sch. Dental Medicine, 1990, MERIT award NIH, 1991; USPHS fellow, 1962-63; postdoctoral fellow, 1966-70. Mem. Am. Soc. Microbiology, , Soc. Mucosal Immunology, Internat. Assn. Dental Research (Oral Biology award 1991), Am. Assn. Immunologists, Am. Assn. Dental Research (v.p. 1987—, pres. elect 1988, pres. 1989). Office: Forsyth Dental Ctr 140 Fenway Boston MA 02115-3799*

TAUBMAN, PAUL JAMES, economics educator; b. Fall River, Mass., Dec. 24, 1939; s. Abraham and Lena (Rubin) T.; m. Joan Greenburg, Aug. 19, 1962; children: Geoffry, Rena. BS, U. Pa., 1961, PhD, 1964. Asst. prof. Harvard U. Cambridge, Mass., 1964-65; mem. staff Coun. Econ. Advisers, 1965-66; assoc. prof. dept. econs. U. Pa., Phila., 1966-72, prof., 1972—; rsch. assoc. Nat. Bur. Econ. Rsch., 1977—, head econs. of drugs program, 1988-91. Author: Sources of Inequality of Earnings, 1975, Kinometrics: Determinants of Socioeconomic Success Within and Between Families, 1977. Fellow AAAS (sect. K), Econometric Soc., Internat. Soc. for Twin Studies; mem. Am. Econ. Assn. Office: U Pa Dept of Economics Philadelphia PA 19174

TAUBMAN, WILLIAM CHASE, political science educator; b. N.Y.C., Nov. 13, 1941; s. Howard and Nora (Stern) T.; m. Jane Dea Andelman, May 18, 1969; children—Alexander, Phoebe. A.B., Harvard U., 1962; M.A., Columbia U., 1965, cert. of Russian Inst., 1965, Ph.D., 1969; M.A. (hon.), Amherst Coll., 1978. Instr. Amherst Coll., Mass., 1967-69; asst. prof. Amherst Coll., 1969-73, assoc. prof., 1973-78, prof. polit. sci., 1978-83, Bertrand Snell prof., 1983—; mem. planning staff U.S. Dept. State, Washington, 1970-71; mem. bd. Internat. Rsch. and Exch. Bd., N.Y.C., 1971-74, mem. selection com., 1984-85; vis. assoc. prof. Yale U., New Haven, spring 1975; chmn. adv. com. Cold War Internat. History Project, Woodrow Wilson Ctr., Washington, 1993—; mem. Internat. Acad. Adv. Group, Russian Fgn. Ministry Archives, 1992—. Author: The View from Lenin Hills, 1967; Governing Soviet Cities, 1973; Stalin's American Policy, 1982; co-author: (with Jane Taubman) Moscow Spring, 1989; editor, translator: Khrushchev on Khrushchev (Sergei N. Khrushchev), 1990; editor: Globalism and Its Critics, 1973. Woodrow Wilson Nat. Found. fellow, 1962; Ford Found. fellow, 1963-67; Council Fgn. Relations fellow, 1970-71; Rockefeller Found. fellow, 1983; Columbia U. Harriman Inst. sr. fellow, 1987; grantee Nat. Council Soviet and East European Research, 1984; Fulbright-Hays Faculty Rsch. fellow, 1988, NEH fellow, 1992. Fellow Russian Research Ctr. Harvard U.; mem. Council Fgn. Relations, Authors Guild. Home: 43 Hitchcock Rd Amherst MA 01002-2500 Office: Amherst Coll Dept Polit Sci Box 2259 Amherst MA 01002-5000

TAUC, JAN, physics educator; b. Pardubice, Czechoslovakia, Apr. 15, 1922; came to U.S., 1969, naturalized, 1978; s. Jan and Josefa (Semonska) T.; m. Vera Koubelova, Oct. 18, 1947; children: Elena (Mrs. Milan Kokta), Jan. Ing.Dr. in Elec. Engring., Tech. U. Prague, 1949; RNDr., Charles U., 1956; Dr.Sc. in Physics, Czechoslovak Acad. Scis., 1956. Scientist microwave research Sci. and Tech. Research Inst., Tanvald and Prague, 1949-52; head semiconductor dept. Inst. Solid State Physics, Czechoslovak Acad. Scis., 1953-69; prof. expll. physics Charles U., 1964-69, dir. Inst. Physics, 1968-69; mem. tech. staff Bell Telephone Labs., Murray Hill, N.J., 1969-70; prof. engring. and physics Brown U., 1970-83, L. Herbert Ballou prof. engring. and physics, 1983-92, L. Herbert Ballou prof. emeritus, 1992—, dir. material research lab., 1983-88; dir. E. Fermi Summer Sch., Varenna, Italy, 1965; vis. prof. U. Paris, 1969, Stanford U., 1977, Max Planck Inst. Solid State Research, Stuttgart, Germany, 1982; UNESCO fellow, Harvard, 1961-62. Author: Photo and Thermoelectric Effects in Semiconductors, 1962, also numerous articles; editor: The Optical Properties of Solids, 1966, Amorphous and Liquid Semiconductors, 1974; co-editor: Solid State Communications, 1963-92. Recipient Nat. prize Czechoslovak Govt., 1955, 69; Sr. U.S. Scientist award Humboldt Found., 1981, Silver medal Union of Czechoslovak Mathematicians and Physicists, 1992. Fellow AAAS, Am. Phys. Soc. (Frank Isakson prize 1982, David Adler award 1988); mem. NAS, European Phys. Soc. (founding), Czechoslovak Acad. Scis. (corr. 1963-71, 90-91, fgn. 1991-92, Hlavka medal 1992). Office: Brown U Divsn Engring Providence RI 02912

TAUCHERT, THEODORE RICHMOND, mechanical engineer, educator; s. Elwyn Harding and Eleanor (Eckmann) T.; m. Ann Dudley Bradlee, May 10, 1958; children: Amy T., Sarah T. Rushing, Rebecca T. McGowan, Macy G. B.S.E., Princeton U., 1957; M.Eng., Yale U., 1960, D.Eng., 1964. Structural engr. Sikorsky Aircraft, Stratford, Conn., 161-61; research assoc., lectr. Princeton U., N.J., 1964-65, asst. prof., 1965-70; assoc. prof. U. Ky., Lexington, 1970-76, prof. engring. mechanics, 1976—; chmn. dept., 1980-84, 88-94. Editorial bd.: Acta Mechanica, 1976—, Jour. Thermal Stresses, 1981—; author: Energy Principles in Structural Mechanics, 1974; contbr. articles to profl. jours. Served to 2d lt. U.S. Army, 1957-58. Mem. ASCE,

ASME, Am. Soc. Engring. Edn., Soc. Engring. Sci., Sigma Xi. Home: 1620 Richmond Rd Lexington KY 40502-1620

TAUREL, SIDNEY, pharmaceutical executive; b. Casablanca, Morocco, Feb. 9, 1949; came to U.S., 1986; s. Jose and Marjorie (Afriat) T.; m. Kathryn H. Fleischmann, Mar. 22, 1977; children: Alexis, Patrick, Olivi-a. BSBA, Ecole des Hautes Etudes Commerciales, Paris, 1969; MBA, Columbia U., 1971. With Eli Lilly Internat. Corp., Indpls., 1971-72; mktg. planning mgr. Eli Lilly Do Brasil Limitada, Sao Paulo, Brazil, 1972-75, gen. mgr., 1982-83; mgr. pharm. ops. Eastern Europe Eli Lilly und Elanco Gesmbh, Vienna, Austria, 1976; sales mgr. pharm. Eli Lilly France SA, Paris, 1977-79, mktg. dir. pharm., 1980-81; v.p. Europe Lilly European ops., London, 1984-85; exec. v.p. Eli Lilly Internat. Corp., Indpls., 1986, pres., 1986-91, exec. v.p. pharm. divsn., 1991-93; exec. v.p. Eli Lilly and Co., 1993—, pres. pharm. divsn., 1993—, bd. dirs., 1993—; bd. overseers Columbia Bus. Sch. Mem. Indpls. Symphony Orch.; bd. dirs. RCA Tennis Championships. Mem. Pharm. Rsch. and Mfrs. Assn. (chmn. internat. com. 1994—, chmn. membership com. 1994—, bd. dirs., treas. 1995—), Indpls. Racquet Club. Avocations: tennis, music. Home: 6160 Sunset Ln Indianapolis IN 46208-1456 Office: Eli Lilly and Co Lilly Corporate Center Indianapolis IN 46285

TAURO, JOSEPH LOUIS, federal judge; b. Winchester, Mass., Sept. 26, 1931; s. G. Joseph and Helen Maria (Petrossi) T.; m. Elizabeth Mary Quinlan, Feb. 7, 1959 (dec. 1978); children—Joseph L., Elizabeth H., Christopher M.; m. Ann Lefavour Jones, July 12, 1980. AB, Brown U., 1953; LLB, Cornell U., 1956; JD (hon.), U. Mass., 1985, Suffolk U., 1986, Northeastern U., 1990, New Eng. Sch. Law, 1992. Bar: Mass. 1956, D.C. 1960. Assoc. Tauro & Tauro, Lynn, Mass., 1958-59; asst. U.S. atty. Dept. Justice, Boston, 1959-60; ptnr. Jaffee & Tauro, Boston and Lynn, Mass., 1960-71; chief legal counsel Gov. of Mass., Boston, 1965-68; U.S. atty. Dept. Justice, Boston, 1972; judge U.S. Dist. Ct., Boston, 1972—; chief judge U.S. Dist. Ct., Mass., 1992—; mem. exec. com. Cornell Law Assn., Ithaca, N.Y., 1968-71; mem. adv. coun. Cornell Law Sch., Ithaca, 1975-80; adj. prof. law Boston U. Law Sch., 1977—; mem. Jud. Conf. U.S., 1994—, mem. com. on operation of jury sys., 1979-86, mem. adv. com. on codes of conduct, 1988-94. Trustee Brown U., 1978—, Mass. Gen. Hosp., Boston, 1968-72, Children's Hosp. Med. Ctr., Boston, 1979-94. 1st lt. U.S. Army, 1956-58. Recipient Disting. Alumnus award Cornell U. Law Sch., 1992, Brown Bear award Brown U., 1993; named one of 10 Outstanding Young Men, Greater Boston Jaycees, 1966. Fellow Am. Bar Found.; mem. ABA, Mass. Bar Assn., Boston Bar Assn. (coun. 1968-71), D.C. Bar Assn., Boston Yacht Club (Marblehead, Mass.). Republican. Roman Catholic. Avocations: sports; reading; music; films; theater. Office: US Dist Ct Mccormack PO Courthouse Rm 1 Boston MA 02109

TAUSCH, WILLIAM JOSEPH, advertising agency executive; b. Chgo., Sept. 22, 1930; s. Benjamin Joseph and Marian Bridget (Rowland) T.; m. Marianne Merritt, Sept. 1, 1953; children—Benjamin Joseph, William Joseph. B.Sc., DePaul U., 1959. Copywriter Marsteller, Inc., Chgo., 1966-68; copywriter Campbell-Ewald Co., Detroit, 1968-79, account supr., 1969-73, dir. retail service div., 1975-79; exec. v.p., account dir. Campbell-Ewald Co., Warren, Mich., 1979—; account supr. McCann-Erickson, Detroit, 1973-75. Served to sgt. U.S. Army, 1951-53. Republican. Clubs: Adcraft, The Recess (Detroit); Birmingham Country (Mich.). Home: 281 Nantucket Dr Bloomfield Hills MI 48304-3346 Office: Campbell-Ewald Co 30400 Van Dyke Ave Warren MI 48093-2316

TAUSCHER, JOHN WALTER, retired pediatrician, emeritus educator; b. LaSalle, Ill., Feb. 3, 1929; s. John Robert and Ella (Danz) T.; m. Mary Claire Cline, June 19, 1954 (dec. 1989); children—Michael, John, Claire, Mark, Matthew. B.S., U. Ill., 1952, M.D., 1954. Diplomate Am. Bd. Pediatrics. Intern Cook County Hosp., Chgo., 1954-55; resident in pediatrics Hurley Hosp., Flint, Mich., 1958-60; practice medicine specializing in pediatrics Flint, 1960-75; assoc. prof. human devel. Coll. Human Medicine, Mich. State U., East Lansing, 1975-80, prof. emeritus, 1994; ret., 1994; v.p. After Hours Pediatric Care, P.C., Flint, 1972-87; chmn. pediatrics Hurley Med. Ctr., 1980-90, dir. pediatric edn., dir. primary care pediatrics, 1991-94; dir. clin. svcs. Mott Children's Health Ctr., 1981-85, v.p. health affairs, 1985-91. Served with USAF, 1955-58. Recipient Outstanding Teaching award Coll. Human Medicine, Mich. State U., 1977, 84, 85, Clin. Instr. of Yr. award St. Joseph Hosp., 1977, Disting. Community Faculty award Mich. State U., 1989. Mem. AMA, Genesee County Med. Soc. (pres. 1990), Mich. State Med. Soc., Northeastern Mich. Pediatric Soc., Am. Acad. Pediatrics. Roman Catholic. Home: 1069 S Parkwood Davison MI 48423 Office: Dept Pediatric Edn One Hurley Plaza Flint MI 48503-5905

TAUSCHER, WILLIAM YOUNG, pharmaceutical and cosmetic products executive; b. Hyattsville, Md., 1950; s. Gilbert Young and Dorcas (Jones) T.; m. Janet Mariani, Oct. 25, 1975; children: Lauren M., Joseph William. B.S., Yale U., 1972. With mktg. dept. IBM Co., Chgo., 1972-75; computer exec. MST Co., Chgo., 1975-78; pres. Western Textile Co., Chgo., 1978-79; pres. Foxmeyer Corp., Denver, 1979-85, chmn., from 1979; chmn. Computerland Corp., Pleasanton, Calif., 1987—, pres., 1988—; dir. Far Western, San Jose, Calif., Nat. Wholesale Druggists Assn., Washington. Office: Computerland Corp PO Box 9012 5964 W Las Positas Blvd Pleasanton CA 94588

TAUSSIG, JOSEPH KNEFLER, JR., retired government official, lawyer; b. Newport, R.I., May 28, 1920; s. Joseph Knefler and Lulie Augusta (Johnston) T.; m. Betty Carney, Dec. 2, 1943; children: Joseph Knefler III, Susan Taussig Graves (dec.). B.S., U.S. Naval Acad., 1941; J.D. with honors, George Washington U., 1949. Bar: U.S. Supreme Ct., 1975. Commd. U.S. Navy, 1937, advanced through grades to capt., 1954, ret., 1954; exec. sec. U.S. Naval Inst., Annapolis, Md., 1954-56; also pub. books, mags. U.S. Naval Inst., 1952-56; in various positions Westinghouse, Joy Mfg., Raytheon, Washington, 1956-62; pres. Taussig-Tomb & Assocs., Washington, 1962-81, 93—; dep. asst. sec. Dept. Navy, Washington, 1981-85; asst. dep. undersec. for safety and survivability Dept. Navy, Arlington, Va., 1985-93. Contbr. numerous articles to various publs., 1942—. Candidate for U.S. Congress from Md., 1956; pres. Md. Easter Seal Soc., 1968-74; pres. Internat. Assn. Pollution Control, Washington, 1970-74. Decorated Navy Cross, 2 Navy Disting. Pub. Svc. medals; recipient commendation U.s. Atty. Gen., 1994, Pres.'s award Ret. Officers Assn., 1966, 68. Mem. Naval Hist. Found. (trustee 1980—), U.S. Naval Inst. (sec.-treas. 1952-56), U.S. Naval Acad. Alumni Assn. (trustee 1956-60), Navy League (local bd. dirs. 1962-64). Republican. Episcopalian. Club: Army-Navy (treas. 1974-80) (Washington). Lodge: Rotary (bd. dirs. local club 1954-58). Avocations: philately; boating; piano playing. Home: 400 Ridgely Ave Annapolis MD 21401-1306

TAUZIN, W. J. BILLY, II (WILBERT J. TAUZIN), congressman; b. Chackbay, LA, June 14, 1943; s. Wilbert Joseph and Enola (Martinez) T.; m. Cecile Bergeron, May 29, 1993; children: Kristie René, Wilbert J. III, John Ashton, Thomas Nicholas, Michael James. BA, Nicholls State U., 1964; JD, La. State U., 1967. Bar: La. 1967. Practice Houma and Thibodaux, La., 1967-80; mem. firm Marcel Fanguy & Tauzin, 1967-72, Tauzin-Sonnier, 1972-80; mem. La. Ho. of Reps., 1971-80, house floor leader, 1974-79, chmn. Teche Clearinghouse Rev. Bd., 1975-78, chmn. house natural resources com., 1975-80; mem. 96th-104th Congresses from 3d La. Dist., 1980—; mem. energy, commerce, merchant marine, fisheries coms., subcoms. energy, power, telecom., coast guard, navigation, wildlife conservation, environment. Mem. Thibodaux Playhouse, 1967-75; mem. Criminal Justice Inst. Recipient Thibodaux Outstanding Young Man award, 1971. Mem. ABA, La. State Bar Assn., Lafourche Parish Bar Assn. (past pres.), Chackbay-Choupic Jr. C. of C. (past pres.), Nicholls Alumni Council (v.p.). Lodges: Kiwanis; K.C. Home: Rienzi B-5 813 Hwy 20 Thibodaux LA 70301 Office: 2330 Rayburn US Ho Reps Washington DC 20515-1803

TAVEGGIA, THOMAS CHARLES, management educator, management consultant; b. Oak Lawn, Ill., June 15, 1943; s. Thomas Angelo and Eunice Louise (Harriss) T.; m. Brigitte I. Adams, Jan. 23, 1965; children—Michaela, Francesca. BS, Ill. Inst. Tech., 1965; MA, U. Oreg., 1968, PhD, 1971. Prof., U. Oreg. Eugene, 1970, U. B.C. (Can.), Vancouver, 1970-73, U. Calif.-Irvine, 1973-74, Ill. Inst. Tech., Chgo., 1974-77; mgmt. cons. Towers, Perrin, Forster & Crosby, Chgo., 1977-80; ptnr. Manplan Cons., Chgo., 1980-81; ptnr. Coopers & Lybrand, San Francisco, 1981-86; ptnr. Touche Ross, San

Francisco, 1986-88; prof. Calif. Sch. Profl. Psychology, Berkeley, 1988—. NDEA Title IV fellow, 1967-71; U. B.C. faculty research grantee, 1970, 71, 73. Faculty Rsch. grantee Calif. Sch. Profl. Psychology, 1993-94. Mem. Acad. Mgmt. Soc., Am. Sociol. Assn., Nat. Bur. Profl. Mgmt. Cons., Human Resource Mgmt. Soc., Inst. Mgmt. Cons. Presbyterian. Author: (with R. Dubin and R. Arends) From Family and School To Work, 1967; (with Dubin) The Teaching-Learning Paradox: A Comparative Analysis of College Teaching Methods, 1968; (with Dubin and R.A. Hedley) The Medium May Be Related to the Message: College Instruction by TV, 1969; contbr. numerous articles to books and profl. jours. Home: 2188 Lariat Ln Walnut Creek CA 94596-6515 Office: Calif Sch Profl Psychology 1005 Atlantic Ave Alameda CA 94501-1148

TAVEL, MARK KIVEY, money management company executive, economist; b. Cambridge, Mass., May 9, 1945; s. Bernard Benjamin and Elizabeth (Rogers) T.; m. Susana Sara Doño, Dec. 14, 1980; children: Sarah Emily, Rachel Florence, Amanda Victoria, Nathaniel Benjamin, Roberto Aaron Doño. BA cum laude, Harvard U., 1967; MBA, Columbia U., 1968. Pres. Rothschild Asset Mgmt., Inc., N.Y.C.; also bd. dirs. Rothschild N.Am., N.Y.C.; bd. dirs. N. M. Rothschild Internat. Asset Mgmt., London. Trustee The Day Sch. of the Ch. of the Heavenly Rest, N.Y.C. Mem. Harvard Club (N.Y.C.), Women's Nat. Rep. Club. Home: 110 Riverside Dr New York NY 10024 Office: Rothschild Inc 1251 Ave of the Americas New York NY 10020-2001

TAVEL, MORTON ALLEN, physics educator, researcher; b. Bklyn., June 14, 1939; s. Irving and Sylvia (Cutler) T.; m. Judith Carol Fibkins, June 29, 1969; 1 child, Phillip Alden. B.S., CCNY, 1960; M.S., Stevens Inst., 1962; Ph.D., Yeshiva U., 1964. Asst. scientist Brookhaven Nat. Lab., Upton, N.Y., 1964-67; asst. prof. Vassar Coll., Poughkeepsie, 1967-69, assoc. prof., 1970-75, prof. physics, 1975—; vis. prof. Va. Poly., Blacksburg, Va., 1971-72, SUNY-Stony Brook, 1976-77; mem. summer faculty IBM, Poughkeepsie, N.Y., 1978-80, engring. cons., 1980—. Author: Introduction to Electricity and Magnetism I and II, 1971, Information Theory, 1989. NSF fellow, 1962-64. Mem. IEEE (sr.), Am. Phys. Soc., Soc. Wine Educators, Sigma Xi. Avocation: oenology. Home and Office: Vassar Coll PO Box 471 Poughkeepsie NY 12602-0471

TAVENAS, FRANÇOIS, civil engineer, educator; b. Bourg de Péage, Drôme, France, Sept. 12, 1942; arrived in Can., 1966; s. Adrien and Marie Thérèse (Bazin) T.; m. Gundula Schlichting, Apr. 27, 1963; children: Anne Catherine, Philippe, Sophie. BCE, Inst. Nat. des Scis. Appliquées, Lyon, France, 1963; PhD, U. Grenoble, France, 1965. Registered profl. engr., Que. Engr. Piette & Assocs., Que., Can., 1966-70; asst. prof. civil engring. Laval U., Que., 1970-73, assoc. prof., 1973-79, prof., 1979-85, dean, 1985-89; vice prin. planning and resources McGill U., Montreal, Que., 1989—; cons. Golder & Assocs., Toronto, Ont. Can., 1973-75, Terratech, Montreal, 1975-85, Soc. d'Energie de la Baie James, Montreal, 1980-84; mem. coun. Natural Scis. and Engring. Rsch. Coun. Can., 1989—. Author: (with others) Embankments On Soft Soils, 1985; contbr. articles to profl. jours. Mem. ASCE, Can. Geotech. Soc. (v.p. 1982-85, pres.-elect 1990, pres. 1991-92), Internat. Soc. Soil Mechanics and Found. Engring. Avocations: tennis, travel. Office: McGill U, 845 Sherbrooke St W # 536, Montreal, PQ Canada H3A 2T5

TAVERAS, JUAN MANUEL, physician, educator; b. Dominican Republic, Sept. 27, 1919; came to U.S., 1944, naturalized, 1950; s. Marcos M. and Ana L. (Rodriguez) T.; m. Bernice Helen McGonigle, June 12, 1947 (dec. 1990); children: Angela Taveras Summers, Louisa Helen Taveras Koranda, Jeffrey Lawrence; m. Mariana Margarita Bucher, Mar. 18, 1991. BS, Normal Sch. Santiago, Dominican Republic, 1937; MD, U. Santo Domingo, Dominican Republic, 1943, U. Pa., 1949; MS honoris causa, Harvard Med. Sch., 1971; Dr. honoris causa, Univ. Nacional Pedro Henriquez Ureña, Dominican Republic, 1987; Doctor Honoris Causa, U. Catolica Madre Y Maestra, Santiago, Dominican Republic, 1992. Diplomate: Am. Bd. Radiology. Instr. anatomy U. Santo Domingo, 1943-44; fellow radiology Grad. Hosp. U. Pa., 1945-48; rotating intern Misericordia Hosp., Phila.,1949-50; asst. radiologist Presbyn. Hosp., N.Y.C., 1950-52; asst. attending radiologist Presbyn. Hosp., 1953-56, assoc. attending radiologist, 1956-60, attending radiologist, 1960-65; dir. radiology Neurol. Inst., N.Y.C., 1952-65; cons. USPHS Hosp., S.I., N.Y., 1952-65, Morristown (N.J.) Meml. Hosp., 1957-65, St. Barnabas Hosp., N.Y.C., 1959-65, VA Hosp., Bronx, N.Y., 1960-65; asst. instr. radiology U. Pa. Sch. Medicine, 1947-48; faculty Columbia Coll. Phys. and Surg., 1950-65, prof. radiology, 1959-65; prof. radiology, chmn. dept., dir. Mallinckrodt Inst. Radiology, Washington U. Sch. Medicine, St. Louis, 1965-71; radiologist-in-chief Barnes and Allied Hosps., St. Louis, 1965-71; cons. neuroradiology service Unit 1 St. Louis City Hosp., 1966-71; cons. radiology Jewish Hosp., St. Louis, 1966-71; prof. radiology Harvard Med. Sch., 1971-89, prof. radiology emeritus, 1989—; radiologist-in-chief Mass. Gen. Hosp., Boston, 1971-88; pres. VII Symposium Neuroradiologieum, 1964. Author: (with Ross Golden) Roentgenology of the Abdomen, 1961, (with Ernest H. Wood) Diagnostic Neuroradiology, 1964, 2d edit., 1976, (with Norman Leeds) Dynamic Factors in Diagnosis of Supratentorial Brain Tumors by Cerebral Angiography, 1969, (with F. Morello) Normal Neuroradiology, 1979, (with James Provenzale) Clinical Cases in Neuroradiology, 1994, (with Laszlo Szlary) Noncoronary Angioplasty, 1994; editor: (with others) Recent Advances in the Study of Cerebral Circulation, 1970, Cysticercosis of the Central Nervous System, 1983, Radiology: Diagnosis, Imaging, Intervention, 1986; chief editor: Am. Jour. Neuroradiology, 1980-89; contbr. numerous articles to profl. jours. Bd. dirs. Edward Mallinckrodt, Jr. Found., 1980—. Decorated knight Order of Duarte Sanchez y Mella (Dominican Republic) 1972; Juan M. Taveras professorship established in his honor Harvard Med. Sch., 1988. Fellow Am. Coll. Radiology (gold medal 1985); mem. AMA, Am. Neurol. Assn., Am. Roentgen Ray Soc. (gold medal 1988), Radiol. Soc. N.Am. (gold medal 1981), Mass. Med. Soc., Inter-Am. Coll. Radiology, World Fedn. Neurology, Am. Soc. Neuroradiology (pres. 1962-64, gold medal, 1995), N.Y. Acad. Scis., Am. Assn. Neurol. Surgeons (assoc.), Assn. U. Radiologists (gold medal 1985), Mass. Radiol. Soc., New Eng. Roentgen Ray Soc.; pres. Iberrian Latin Am. Soc. of Neurol. 1988-91, pres. IV Congress of Iberian Latin Am. Soc. of Neurol. 1992, hon. mem. Phila. Roentgen Ray Soc., Radiol. Soc. Venezuela, Rocky Mountain Radiol. Soc., Tex. Radiol. Soc., Radiol. Assn. Ctrl. Am. and Panama, Hungarian Radiologic Soc., European Soc. Neuroradiology (hon.), Alpha Omega Alpha. Republican. Home: 22 Glen Rd Wellesley MA 02181-1551 Office: Mass Gen Hosp Boston MA 02114

TAVIS, LEE A., business educator. BS, U. Notre Dame, 1953; MBA, Stanford U., 1960; DBA, Ind. U., 1969. With U. Notre Dame, Ind., 1976—now C.R. Smith prof. bus. adminstrn. Office: U Notre Dame Sch Bus Adminstrn Ctr Rsch in Bus Notre Dame IN 46556

TAVLIN, MICHAEL JOHN, telecommunications company executive; b. Lincoln, Nebr., Dec. 16, 1946. BEd, Oklahoma City U., 1970; JD, U. Nebr., 1973; LLM in Taxation, Washington U., St. Louis, 1977. Bar: Nebr. 1973, Mo. 1974. Ptnr. Nelson & Harding, Lincoln, 1973-77; sr. tax. mgr. Touche Ross & Co., Lincoln and Tulsa, 1979-84, Coopers & Lybrand, Tulsa, 1984-86; v.p., treas., sec. Lincoln Tececomms. Co. and subs., 1986—. Office: Lincoln Telecommunications Co 1440 M St Lincoln NE 68508-2513

TAVON, MARY E., public relations, marketing and communications executive; b. Montreal, Apr. 4, 1958. Student, Marianopolis Coll. Lit. and Langs., 1977; BA in English, Theatre and Film, McGill U. 1980. Mktg. analyst Korea Trade Promotion Assn., 1980-82; advt., pub. rels. asst. Ann Taylor, 1983-84; acct. exec. Michael Klepper Assocs., N.Y.C., 1984-86; acct. supr. Michael Klepper Assocs., N.Y.C., 1986-88; v.p. Michael Klepper Assocs., N.Y.C., 1988-89, exec. prodr., 1989. Recipient cert. merit Chgo. Internat. Film Festival, 1990. Office: Michael Klepper Assoc Inc 805 3d Ave New York NY 10022

TAVOULARIS, DEAN, motion picture production designer; b. Lowell, Mass., May 18, 1932; s. Nicholas John and Pota (Georges) T.; m. Barbara Joan Wiess; children: Alison, Gina; m. Aurore Clement, Sept. 7, 1980. Student, Otis Art Inst., L.A., El Camino City Coll., L.A., L.A. City Coll. Prodn. designer various films, 1968—. Prodn. designs include Bonnie and Clyde, 1968, The Conversation, 1974, The Godfather, 1972, Godfather II, 1974, Godfather III, 1990, The Brink's Job, 1978, Apocalypse Now, 1979,

Zabriskie Point, 1970, Little Big Man, 1970, One From the Heart, 1981, Hammett, 1982, Peggy Sue Got Married, 1986, Final Analysis, 1992, Rising Sun, 1993, I Love Trouble, 1994, others. Recipient Acad. award Acad. Motion Picture Arts and Scis., 1974, nominations, 1978, 79, 88, 90; Brit. Acad. award Brit. Acad. Film and TV Arts, 1988. Office: care Art Directors Guild 11365 Ventura Blvd #315 Studio City CA 91604

TAW, DUDLEY JOSEPH, sales executive; b. Cleve., Mar. 11, 1916; s. William C. and Ella (Gedeon) T.; m. Louise E. Forshey, Sept. 10, 1938; children: Judith (Mrs. William W. Beck, Jr.), Dudley Joseph. Student, Hiram Coll., 1938. With McKesson & Robbins, Inc. (pharm. co.), after 1937; sales mgr. McKesson & Robbins, Inc. (pharm. co.), Boston, 1947; v.p. sales McKesson & Robbins, Inc. (pharm. co.), N.Y.C., 1953-60; v.p. Revlon, Inc., N.Y.C., 1960-64; v.p. mktg. East Ohio Gas Co., Cleve., 1964-74, pres., 1975-81, chmn., 1981-82; chmn. Middtaw, Ltd., Inc., 1982; bd. dirs. No. New England Gas Corp., First Union Mgmt. Co., Biskind Devel. Co., Vt. Gas Systems Inc. Mem. Better Bus. Bur., Cleve., 1975-91; trustee Lakewood Hosp.; treas. Salvation Army, Cleve. With USNR, 1946-47. Named Sales Exec. of Year Sales and Mktg. Execs. Cleve., 1966, Man of Year, 1977. Mem. Sales and Mktg. Execs. Cleve. (pres. 1969-70), Westwood Country Club, Union Club, Pepper Pike Club, Rotary (pres. Cleve. 1972-73). Methodist. Home (summer): 20975 Avalon Dr Cleveland OH 44116-1303 Home (winter): Apt 220 Bldg 3 6050 Bahia Del Mar Cir Saint Petersburg FL 33715 Office: 806 Statler Office Tower Cleveland OH 44115

TAY, GRACE SO, biomedical engineer, researcher; b. Davao City, Philippines, Aug. 2, 1968; came to U.S., 1985; d. Joseph Liong Kian and Victoria (So) T. BS in Engring., Marquette U., 1988, PhD in Biomed. Engring., 1992. Tchg. asst. Marquette U., Milw., 1988-89, instr., 1989; rsch. asst. VA Med. Ctr., Milw., 1989-90; rsch. asst. Med. Coll. Wis., Wauwatosa, 1990-92, asst. prof., 1992—; adj. asst. prof. Marquette U., Milw., 1992—. Contbr. articles to profl. jours. Recipient New Investigator award Am. Found. Urologic Diseases, 1994. Mem. IEEE, Soc. Urology and Engring., Am. Inst Ultrasound in Medicine, Alliance in Engring., Medicine and Biology, Tau Beta Pi. Avocations: photography, guitar music, reading. Office: Med Coll Wis 9200 W Wisconsin Milwaukee WI 53226

TAYLER, EDWARD WILLIAM, English language educator; b. Berlin, Germany, Mar. 13, 1931; came to U.S.; s. William Robert and Violetta Jesse (Klavin-Zeiden) T.; m. Irene B. Smith, June 3, 1961; m. 2d Christina Lee Moustakis, Mar. 3, 1978; children: William E., David S., Letta M., Edward W., Jesse W. B.A., Amherst Coll., 1954; Ph.D., Stanford U., 1960. Prof. English Columbia U., N.Y.C., 1960—. Author: Nature and Art in the Renaissance, 1964, Milton's Poetry, 1979; editor: anthology Literary Criticism of 17th Century England, 1967. Office: Columbia Univ 116th St and Broadway New York NY 10027

TAYLER, IRENE, English educator; b. Abilene, Tex., July 13, 1934; d. B. Brown and Madeline (Bowron); m. Edward W. Tayler, June 3, 1961 (div. 1971); children: Edward Jr., Jesse; m. Saul Touster, Jan. 14, 1978. BA in Philosophy, Stanford U., 1956, MA in Am. Lit., 1961, PhD in English Lit., 1968. Tchr. Breadloaf Sch. of Eng., Middlebury, Vt., 1970, 71, 75, 76; teaching asst. Stanford U., Calif., 1958-60; lectr. Columbia U., N.Y., 1961-71; asst. prof. CUNY, 1971-73, assoc. prof., 1973-76; assoc. prof. MIT, Cambridge, 1976-82; prof. MIT, 1982—; sec. of the faculty MIT, 1993—; chair governing com. The English Inst., 1981. Author: (book) Blake's Illustrations to the Poems of Gray, 1971, Holy Ghosts: The Male Muses of Emily and Charlotte Bronte, 1990; contbr. numerous articles to profl. jours. Faculty Rsch. Found. grantee CUNY, 1972-73, Study grantee ACLS, 1968-69; Mac Vicar Faculty fellow MIT, 1991—, Sr. Scholar fellow NEH, 1980, Wilson fellow Stanford U., 1961-62, Internat. Inst. fellow U. Munich, 1957-58. Office: M I T 14 N 412 Cambridge MA 02139

TAYLOR, ALFRED HENDRICKS, JR., former foundation executive; b. Evanston, Ill., May 16, 1930; s. Alfred Hendricks and Joy (Scheidenhelm) T.; m. Elizabeth Ann Turner, Sept. 29, 1953; children: John, Elizabeth, Jeffrey. Ann. BA, Williams Coll., 1952; LLD (hon.), Albion Coll., 1986, Monmouth Coll., 1991, Western New England Coll., 1994; LHD (hon.), Ill. Coll. 1988. Group v.p. Harris Bank, Chgo., 1955-69; asst. dir. OEO, Washington, 1970-72; chmn. Kresge Found., Troy, Mich., 1972-94, trustee, 1972—; bd. dirs. Comerica Bank, Detroit. Chmn., trustee Am. Farmland Trust, 1989—; trustee emeritus Nat. Trust for Hist. Preservation, 1990—; bd. dirs. The Conservation Fund, Washington, 1990—. Lt. USNR, 1952-55. Recipient g. Mennen Williams humanitarian award, 1988, Michiganian of Yr. award, 1991, award for exemplary leadership in philanthropy Nat. Soc. Fund Raising Execs., 1993. Mem. Williams Coll. Alumni Assn. (pres. Chgo. chpt. 1969-70, chmn. 25th Reunion Class '52, class agt. 1992—). Home: 1165 Main St Williamstown MA 01267-2621 office: The Kresge Foundation PO Box 3151 3215 W Big Beaver Road Troy MI 48007

TAYLOR, ALLAN BERT, lawyer; b. Cin., June 28, 1948; s. H. Ralph and Henrietta Irene (Medalia) T.; m. Sally Ann Silverstein, June 6, 1971; children: Rachel Elizabeth, Karen Ruth. AB, Harvard U., 1970, M in Pub. Policy, 1975, JD, 1975. Bar: Conn. 1975, U.S.C. Appeals (D.C. cir.) 1977, U.S. Dist. Ct. Conn. 1978, U.S. Dist. Ct. (so. dist.) N.Y. 1979, U.S. Ct. Appeals (2d cir.) 1979, U.S. Supreme Ct. 1979, U.S. Ct. Appeals (1st and 10th cirs.) 1991. Law clk. to J. Skelly Wright D.C. Cir., Washington, 1975-76; law clk. to Thurgood Marshall U.S. Supreme Ct., Washington, 1976-77; assoc. Day, Berry & Howard, Hartford, Conn., 1977-83, ptnr., 1983—; overseer Bushnell Meml. Hall Corp., Hartford, 1992—. Elected mem. Hartford City Coun., 1981-87, Hartford Bd. Edn., 1989-93, v.p., 1991-93, pres., 1992-93; mem. Conn. State Bd. Edn., 1994—; bd. dirs. Conn. Assn. Bds. Edn., Hartford, 1989-93, Hartford Infant Action Project, 1990—. Mem. ABA, Conn. Bar Assn., Hartford County Bar Assn., Phi Beta Kappa. Democrat. Jewish. Avocations: astronomy, reading. Home: 238 Whitney St Hartford CT 06105-2270 Office: Day Berry & Howard City Place Hartford CT 06103

TAYLOR, ALLAN RICHARD, retired banker; b. Prince Albert, Sask., Can., Sept. 14, 1932; s. Norman and Anna Lydia (Norbeck) T.; m. Shirley Irene Ruston, Oct. 5, 1957; children: Rodney Allan, Leslie Ann. LLD (hon.), U. Regina, Sask., 1987, Concordia U., Montreal, Can., 1988; DBA (hon.), Laval U., Quebec City, Can., 1990; LLD (hon.), Queen's U., Kingston, Ont., 1991; Doctorate of Univ. (hon.), U. Ottawa, 1992. With Royal Bank of Can., Toronto, Ont., Can., 1949—, mgr. main br., 1971-74; dep. gen. mgr. internat. div. Royal Bank of Can., Montreal, 1974-77, sr. v.p. internat. div., 1977-78, exec. v.p., 1978-83; pres., COO, dir. Royal Bank of Can., Toronto, 1983-86, chmn., CEO, dir., 1986-94, chmn., 1994-95, ret., 1995; d. dirs Royal Bank of Can., TransCan. Pipelines Ltd., Toronto, Can.-Pacific Ltd., GM Can. Ltd., Oshawa, Ont.; mem. adv. coun. Can. Exec. Svc. Overseas; former chmn. Can. Bankers Assn.; past pres. Internat. Monetary Conf. Mem. adv. com. Sch. Bus. Adminstrn., U. We. Ont. London; founding dir., hon. mem. Corp.-Higher Edn. Forum; trustee Queen's U., Kingston, Ont.; mem. Coun. Patrons, Can. Outward Bound Wilderness Sch.; past chmn., bd. dirs. Jr. Achievement Can.; bd. govs. Olympic Trust, Can.; mem. bd. advisors Internat. Assn. Students in Econs. and Commerce Can.; mem. nat. adv. coun., former chmn. corp. program IMAGINE; mem. adv. bd. Can. Found. AIDS Rsch. Decorated officer Order of Can. Address: 200 Bay St 18th Fl North Tower, Toronto, ON Canada M5J 2J5

TAYLOR, ALLAN ROSS, linguist, educator; b. Palisade, Colo., Dec. 24, 1931; s. Athel Ross and Marjorie Verle (Walters) T.; m. Mary Callas, Sept. 8, 1958; children: Artemisia, Anthony, Peter, Anna, Yoana. AB, U. Colo., Boulder, 1953; PhD (Woodrow Wilson fellow, Fulbright fellow, NDEA fellow), U. Calif., Berkeley, 1969. Teaching asst., lectr. U. Calif., Berkeley, 1958-63; instr. U. Colo., 1964-65, asst. prof., 1965-70, assoc. prof., 1970-77, prof., 1977-93, prof. emeritus, 1993—, also past chmn. dept. linguistics, dept. French and Italian; cons. bilingual edn. for Native Ams. Active Dem. Party and in environ. issues. With U.S. Army, 1954-57. NEH grantee, 1972-76, 80-82, 87-90, 89-93. Mem. Linguistic Soc. Am., Am. Anthrop. Assn. Home: 787 17th St Boulder CO 80302-7601 Office: U Colo Dept Linguistics PO Box 295 Boulder CO 80309-0295 *Reading in physical anthropology and genetics, and many years of an advocacy role in environmental issues, have convinced me that man's highest calling is custodial: to protect, preserve, and pass on inviolate the world and all of its inhabitants, even when it may appear to be against our own short-term interest to do this. For the grand*

plan, if there is any, is to allow diversity to make the choices which prove ultimately to be the only viable ones.

TAYLOR, ALLEN JOHN, U.S. Coast Guard officer; b. N.Y.C., Jan. 28, 1939; s. John Joseph and Florence (Marion) T.; m. Eve Claire Horodyski, Jan. 22, 1961; children—Lynn Claire, Allen John, Jr., Steven Fitzgerald. B.S. with honors, Coast Guard Acad.; B.C., Rensselaer Polytech. Inst., M.S. in Environ. Engring.; M.B.A. with distinction, Pace U.; D.B.A., George Washington U. Registered profl. engr., N.Y., Va. Commd. ensign U.S. Coast Guard, 1960, advanced through grades to capt.; assoc. chief FACENG Coast Guard Base, N.Y.C., 1966-69; mem. nat. nav. planning staff, 1969-70, with Office of Operatives hdqrs., 1971-74, with marine environ. protection div. hdqrs., 1971-74, chief FAC engring. div. Coast Guard Base, Kodiak, Alaska, 1974-76; chief marine environ. PLG branch Coast Guard Headquarters, Washington, 1970-74; chief civil engring. branch 5th Coast Guard Dist., Norfolk, Va., 1976-80; chief civil engring. div. Coast Guard Hdqrs., Washington, 1980-85, 3rd Coast Guard dist., N.Y.C., 1985-86, comdg. officer Coast Guard Support Ctr., Governors Island, N.Y., 1986-88, dep. comdr. maintenance and logistics command, Atlantic, 1988—. Chmn. Bicentennial Com., Kodiak, 1976. Named Outstanding Young Man Am. Jr. C. of C., 1968. Fellow Soc. Am. Mil. Engrs. (dir. 1982-85); mem. Am. Soc. Engring. Mgmt. (pres. 1984-85, v.p. 1984). Republican. Roman Catholic.

TAYLOR, ALTON LEE, education educator; b. Kannapolis, N.C., Aug. 8, 1936; s. Robert Lee and Elizabeth Rose (Pitts) T.; m. Ann Paige Gill, July 31, 1964; children: Shannon Leigh, Hunter Page (dec.). BA, Pfeiffer Coll., 1958; MEd, U. Va., 1962, EdD, 1965. Tchr. Morehead City (N.C.) High Sch., 1958-60, Newport News (Va.) High Sch., 1960-61; rsch. supr. Dept. Edn., Richmond, Va., 1965-67; prof., adminstr. U. Va., Charlottesville, 1967—. Editor: Individual Privacy, 1977; co-author several books; contbr. articles to profl. jours. Mem. sch. bd. Albemarle County, Va., Charlottesville, 1972-75; bd. dirs. Appalachian Regional Lab., Charleston, W.Va., 1966-67. Fellow AAAS; mem. Assn. Instnl. Rsch. (treas. 1974-77, Outstanding Svc. award 1990), Assn. Univ. Summer Session (pres. 1985-86), Assn. Study Higher Edn., Kappa Delta Pi, Omicron Delta Kappa, Phi Delta Kappa, Raven Soc. Presbyterian. Home: 2601 Bennington Rd Charlottesville VA 22901-2210 Office: U Va Summer Session 209 Garrett Hall Charlottesville VA 22903

TAYLOR, ANN LOUISE, marketing executive; b. Fairmont, Minn., Aug. 8, 1937; d. Eugene and Celia Ethel (Fulton) Lundahl; m. James Harold Taylor, May 23, 1959; children: Kimberly Taylor Locey, Jayme K. BA in Edn., U. Minn., 1959; postgrad., Am. Inst. Banking, 1985-87. Tchr. Nokomis Jr. High Sch., Mpls., 1959-61, Helen Keller Mid. Sch., Easton, Conn., 1973-75; photojournalist Suburban & Wayne Times, Berwyn, Pa., 1975-80; cons. pub. relations Fla. Internat. Bank, Miami, Fla., 1981-84; v.p. Fla. Internat. Bank, Miami, 1984-94; employee rels. mgr. Am. Bankers Ins. Group, Miami, 1994—. Contbr. articles to profl. jours. Mem. women's adv. coun. Bapt. Hosp. of Miami, 1991—. Mem. Women in Comms. (pres. Greater Miami chpt. 1987-88, v.p. so. region 1989-92, v.p. Fin. 1993-94, nat. pres. elect 1994-95), Greater South Dade-South Miami C. of C. (bd. dirs. 1987—, pres.-elect 1989—, chmn. 1991-92), Founders of South Dade (pres. 1987-88). Republican. Presbyterian. Avocations: tennis, boating, music, dancing. Office: Am Bankers Ins Group 11222 Quail Roost Dr Miami FL 33157

TAYLOR, ANNA DIGGS, federal judge; b. Washington, Dec. 9, 1932; d. Virginius Douglass and Hazel (Bramlete) Johnston; m. S. Martin Taylor, May 22, 1976; children: Douglass Johnston Diggs, Carla Cecile Diggs. BA, Barnard Coll., 1954; LLB, Yale U., 1957. Bar: D.C. 1957, Mich. 1961. Atty. Office Solicitor, Dept. Labor, W, 1957-60; asst. prosecutor Wayne County, Mich., 1961-62; asst. U.S. atty. Eastern Dist. of Mich., 1966; ptnr. Zwerdling, Maurer, Diggs & Papp, Detroit, 1970-75; asst. corp. counsel City of Detroit, 1975-79; U.S. dist. judge Eastern Dist. Mich. Detroit, 1979—. Trustee Detroit Symphony, United Found., Cmty. Found., SE Mich. Found. Soc., Detroit Inst. Arts, Greater Detroit Health Coun., Eastern Region Henry Ford Health Sys.; co-chair, v.p. Leadership Coun. for SE Mich. Mem. Fed. Bar Assn., State Bar Mich., Wolverine Bar Assn. (v.p.), Yale Law Assn. Episcopalian. Office: US Dist Ct 740 US Courthouse 231 W Lafayette Blvd Detroit MI 48226-2719

TAYLOR, ARTHUR ROBERT, college president, business executive; b. Elizabeth, N.J., July 6, 1935; s. Arthur Earl and Marion Hilda (Scott) T.; m. Kathryn Pelgrift; 3 daus. by previous marriage. B.A. magna cum laude, Brown U., 1957, M.A. in Am. Econ. History, 1961; H.H.D. (hon.), Bucknell U., 1975, Allentown Coll. of St. Francis de Sales; L.H.D. (hon.), Rensselaer Poly. Inst., 1975, Simmons Coll., 1975; LL.D. (hon.), Mt. Scenario Coll., 1975. Asst. dir. admissions Brown U., Providence, 1957-61; with First Boston Corp., N.Y.C., 1961-70, asst. v.p., 1964-66, v.p., 1966-70, also dir.; v.p. fin. Internat. Paper Co., N.Y.C., 1970-71, exec. v.p., dir., 1971-72; pres. CBS Inc., N.Y.C., 1972-76, also dir.; pres. Muhlenberg Coll., Allentown, Pa., 1992—; chmn. Arthur Taylor & Co., Inc., 1977—; chmn. The Entertainment Channel, 1980-83; dean faculty of bus. Fordham U., 1985-89; bd. dirs. Nomura Pacific Basin Fund, Pitney Bowes, La. Land & Exploration Co., Jakarta Growth Fund, Japan OTC Equity Fund; mem. adv. com. Toshiba Internat. Mem. Population Resource Ctr.; trustee Brown U. Mem. Coun. Fgn. Rels., Trilateral Commn., Phi Beta Kappa. Congregationalist. Clubs: Brook, Century (N.Y.C.); Met. (Washington); California (Los Angeles). Office: Muhlenberg Coll Office of Pres 2400 Chew St Allentown PA 18104

TAYLOR, BARBARA JO ANNE HARRIS, government official, librarian, educator, civic and political worker; b. Providence, Sept. 9, 1936; d. Ross Cameron and Anita (Coia) Harris; m. Richard Powell Taylor, Dec. 19, 1959; 1 child, Douglas Howard. Student, Tex. Christian U., 1952, Salve Regina Coll., 1952-53; Student, Our Lady of the Lake Coll. and Convent, 1953-54, St. Mary's U., 1954, Incarnate Word Coll., 1954-55, Georgetown U., 1956-59, 62-63; BS cum laude, Georgetown U., 1963. Adminstrv. asst. profl. devel. and welfare NEA, Washington, 1956-59; asst. to dir. Georgetown U., Washington, 1960; spl. assts. asst. mil. affairs to chmn. mil. R & D subcom. U.S. Senate Armed Svcs. Com., 1971-72; U.S. nat. commr. UNESCO, 1982—, mem. exec. com. U.S. nat. commn., 1983—, sr. advisor 22d gen. conf., 1983. Del. numerous internat. confs.; U.S. commr. Nat. Commn. Libns. and Info. Sci., 1985—, mem. various coms.; gen. chmn. George Bush for Pres. Md. State Steering Com., 1987-88; co-chmn. Md. del. Rep. Nat. Conv., 1988, 92; dep. chmn. Md. Victory '88, Bush-Quayle Campaign; mem. Nat. Fin. Com. Reagan for Pres. 1980, Reagan-Bush, 1984; state fin. chmn. Md. Rep. Party, 1980; mem. Nat. Rep. Club; mem. exec. bd. Salvation Army Aux., Washington, 1967-75, chmn. membership com., 1969-70, chmn. fund-raising com., 1968-69, mem. exec. com. of exec. bd., 1970-75, treas., mem. fin. com., 1970-71, v. 1971-72, historian, 1972-73, editor newsletter, 1968-69, chmn. nominating com., 1974-75, spl. awards. for exceptional vol. svc., 1969, 72; mem. exec. bd. Welcome to Washington Internat., 1969-74, bd. advisers, 1969-74, dir. workshop, 1969-74; exec. bd. Am. Opera Sch. Soc., Washington, 1970—, v.p. Assoc. Ch. Home for Aged Women's Aux., 1970-75, Episc. Ctr. for Emotionally Disturbed Children Women's Aux., 1970-75; exec. bd. St. David's Episc. Ch. Aux., 1970-72, 73-74; bd. dirs., treas. Spanish-Portuguese Study Group, 1970-72; mem. exec. bd. League Rep. Women Clubs N.Y.C., 1964-67, 75-77, treas., 1964-67; mem. nat. coun. Women's Nat. Rep. Club, N.Y.C., 1969—, chmn. Washington-Md.-Va. legis. com., 1973-74; mem. nat. Fedn. Rep. Women, 1964—; mem. nat. fin. com. Reagan for Pres., 1979-80; mem. governing bd. Capital Speakers Club, 1973-75, chmn. by-laws com., 1973-74; mem. exec. bd. Nat. Vols. in Action, 1975-77; mem. adv. com. Rock Creek Found. Mental Health, 1982-87; mem. 50th anniversary com. Save the Children; mem. fund-raising com. Washington Choral Arts Soc., 1982-84; state fin. chmn. Reagan-Bush campaign Md. Rep. Com., 1980; Md. coord. Nat. Inaugural Com., 1981, 85; trustee Crossnore Sch., Inc., N.C., 1983—, vice chmn. bd; trustee Kate Duncan Smith DAR Sch., Grant, Ala., 1983-86, Tamassee (S.C.) DAR Sch., 1983-86; adviser Bacone Am. Indian Coll., Inc., Muscogee, Okla., 1983-88. Mem. ALA, Spl. Librs. Assn., Coun. on Libr. Resources (commn. on preservation and access), Am. Libr. Trustees Assn., Libr. Adminstrn. and Mgmt. Assn., Assn. Coll. and Rsch. Librs., Am. Antiquarian Soc., Internat. Platform Assn., Spanish-Portuguese Study Group, Nat. Lawyers' Wives, Nat. Capital Law League, DAR (chmn. nat. resolutions com. 1980-83, chmn. nat. DAR sch. com. 1983-86; state historian 1978-80, mem state bd. mgmt., 1973—; libr. gen., mem. exec. com. 1986-89, chmn. nat. commemorative events com. 1992—, numerous other offices), Nat. Soc. Children Am. Revolution (sr. nat. asst. registrar 1978-80, mem. sr. nat. bd. mgmt. 1978-80, sr. nat. exec. com. 1978-80), Nat. Assn. Parliamentarians, World Affairs Council, League of Rep. Women, Md. Fedn. Rep. Women, WNRC, Nat. Fed. Rep. Women, Commn. on Preservation and Access, Lit. Vols. Am. (Washington Met. area affiliate), Exec. Women in Govt., Am. News Women's Club, Internat. Club, Capitol Hill Club, Washington Club, Congl. Country Club (Potomac, Md.).

TAYLOR, BARRY NORMAN, physicist; b. Phila., Mar. 27, 1936; s. Morris and Sarah (Weiss) T.; m. Sheila Anne Cohen, Dec. 28, 1958; children: Deborah Susan, David Joel, Denise Beth. AB, Temple U., Phila., 1957; MS, U. Pa., 1960, PhD, 1963. Instr., then asst. prof. physics U. Pa., 1963-66; mem. tech. staff RCA Rsch. Labs., 1966-70; chief absolute elec. measurements sect. Nat. Bur. Standards (name changed to Nat. Inst. of Standards and Tech. 1988), Gaithersburg, Md., 1970-74, adminstr. NIST Precision Measurement Grants Program, 1974—, chief electricity divsn., 1974-89; mgr. Fundamental Cons. Data Ctr., 1989—; instr. Rider Coll., Trenton, N.J., 1969-70; mem., chairperson nat. and internat. tech. coms. Co-author: Fundamental Constants and Quantum Electrodynamics, 1969; co-editor: Precision Measurement and Fundamental Constants, 1971; co-editor: Precision Measurement and Fundamental Constants II, 1984; contbr. articles to sci. jours. Recipient Silver medal U.S. Dept. Commerce, 1975, Gold medal, 1989, John Price Wetherill medal Franklin Inst., 1975. Fellow IEEE, Am. Phys. Soc. (chair topical group on fundamental constants and precise tests of phys. laws 1990-92), Washington Acad. Scis.; mem. Sigma Xi. Office: Nat Inst of Stds and Tech Bldg 245 Rm C229 Gaithersburg MD 20899-0001

TAYLOR, BENJAMIN B., newspaper publishing executive; b. 1947; s. John I. T.; m. Katherine Taylor; children: Abigail, Samuel, William. Grad., Harvard U. Various positions including asst. mng. editor/local news, consumer affairs reporter, polit. reporter Boston Globe, 1972-88, exec. editor, 1988; v.p. Globe Newspaper Co., 1991, exec. v.p., 1992, pres., 1993—, COO, 1994—. Trustee Radcliffe Coll., Park Sch., Brookline, Mass. Office: Globe Newspapers Co 135 Morrissey Blvd Boston MA 02107*

TAYLOR, BERNARD J., II, banker; b. Phila., Nov. 10, 1925; s. Bernard and Marie (Pearce) T.; m. Barbara Silverstein; children: Dorothy Taylor Tomlinson, Lawrence Dean, David Stewart. B.S. U. Pa., 1949. Asst. mgr. McCrory Stores Corp., Phila., 1949-51; fin. analyst Fidelity Bank, Phila. 1951-57; asst. to v.p. investments Fidelity Bank, 1957-59, asst. to pres., 1959-60, corp. sec., 1960-63, v.p., sec., 1963-66, sr. v.p. in charge adminstrn. dept., 1966-72, exec. v.p., 1972-74; v.p. Fidelcor, Inc. (parent co. Fidelity Bank), 1969-72, exec. v.p., 1973-76; sr. exec. v.p., 1976-79; pres., dir. Fidelity Bldg. Corp., 1970-79; pres., CEO Wilmington (Del.) Trust Co., Del., 1979-92; dir. Wilmington (Del.) Trust Co., 1979—, chmn., 1980-92; ptnr. Golf Ptnrs. (Hartefield Nat. Golf Course), 1993—. Pres. Savoy Opera Co., Phila., 1961-63, prodn. mgr., dir. 1975-70; pres., bd. dirs. Pa. Opera Theatre, 1975-80, treas., bd. dirs., 1980-93; mem. adv. bd. mgrs. Inglis House Phila. 1967-70; mem. Del. Round Table, 1980-92; bd. dirs. Greater Wilmington Devel. Coun., 1980-84, Sta. WHYY, PBS-TV, Phila., 1980-92; bd. dirs., 1986-91; bd. dirs. Del. Theatre Co., 1987-91. With AUS, 1944-46, PTO. Clubs: Orpheus (Phila); Wilmington Country. Home: 6 Hillspur Rd Kennett Square PA 19348

TAYLOR, BILLIE WESLEY, secondary education educator; b. Charleston, W.Va, Aug. 14, 1940; s. Billie W and Effie (Adams) T.; m. Elisabeth Julia Coler, Jan. 27, 1960; 1 child, Rose Letitia Taylor Allen. BA, Wilmington Coll., 1961; MA, Ohio State U., 1963; PhD, Columbia Pacific U., 1993. Cert. secondary tchr., prin., Ohio. Tchr. Columbus Pub. Schs., Ohio, 1961-64; records, forms, mgnt. officer VI U.S Army Corps, Battle Creek, Mich., 1964-65; production planner Hoover Ball & Bearing Co., Ann Arbor, Mich., 1965-66; dist. exec. Boy Scouts of Am., Detroit, 1966-72; sales tng. Standard Register Co., Dayton, Ohio, 1972-74; tchr. Dayton Pub. Schs., Dayton, Ohio, 1974—, curriculum specialist for computer tech., 1989-93. Author: History of the D-MC Park District, 1988, Classroom Discipline, 1987. Pres. Johnson Sch. Parent Tchrs. Assoc., Taylor, Mich., 1966-67; dist. chmn., Boy Scouts of Am., Dayton, 1974-79; bd. mem., Southeast Dayton Priority Bd., Dayton, 1976-77. Recipient Pres. trophy Boy's Souts of Am., 1970; Jenning's scholar Martha Holden Jennings Found., 1980-81. Mem. Am. Assn. Individual Investors (life), Nat. Geographic Soc. (elected life mem.), Nat. Audubon Soc., Smithsonian Nat. Assocs. (charter mem.), Libr. of Congress Assocs. (charter mem.), Nat. Mus. of the Am. Indian (charter mem.), Western Ohio Edn. Assn. (del.), Am. Birding Assn., The Nature Conservancy (life), Masons, Dayton Racquet Club, Good Sam Club (life). Avocations: birding, motorhoming, foreign travel, reading, chess. Home: 131 Snow Hill Ave Kettering OH 45429

TAYLOR, BILLY (WILLIAM EDWARD TAYLOR), jazz musician; b. Greenville, N.C., July 24, 1921; s. William Edward and Antoinette (Bacon) T.; m. Theodora Castion, June 22, 1946; children: Duane, Kim. B.S. in Music, Va., State Coll., 1942; D. Mus. Edn., U. Mass.; L.H.D., Fairfield U.; D. Mus., Va. State Coll.; Ph.D, Clark Coll.; Mus.D. (hon.), Berklee Coll. Mus., 1981. lectr. Music Educators Nat. Conf., 1957, New Eng. Music Tchrs. Assn., 1958, New Jazz Soc., Phila., 1967; owner Sta. WSOK, Savannah, Ga., Sta. WLIB, also WBLS-FM, N.Y.C.; pres. Billy Taylor Productions, Duane Music Co., both N.Y.C.; spl. cons. to chmn. Nat. Endowment Arts; chmn. bd. Creative Arts Public Service. Jazz pianist, 1937—; producer, staff: weekly jazz TV program Billy Taylor Show, 1965; performer, narrator: TV prodns. The Pop Explosion, 1966, Dial M for Music, 1965; pres., founder: TV prodns. Jazz Mobile, 1967; host, narrator, performer: TV prodns. Black, White and Blue, 1966; music dir., cons., leader orch. TV prodn. The Subject was Jazz, 1957; program dir. WLIB-FM, 1965-69; mus. dir. David Frost Show, N.Y.C., from 1969; mus. cons. TV prodns. 1964—; host: Jazz Alive, Nat. Public Radio; guest soloist numerous symphonies; composer music ballet Your Arms Too Short to Box with God; Suite for Jazz Piano and Orch., Make a Joyful Noise, Peaceful Warrior, For Rachel; numerous other works; mus. dir. PBS variety show. Black Jour. Tonight; recs. include: Jazz Alive, 1977, Where've You Been, 1980, Dr. T, 1993, Custom Taylored, 1994, It's A Matter of Pride, 1994; author: Jazz Piano. Bd. dirs. Harlem Cultural Council; trustee Rockefeller Found., 1978—; mem. Nat. Council Arts, 1972-78. Recipient Mayor's award for arts and culture, 1981; Edward E. Elson Disting. Service award Nat. Public Radio, 1981; named to Nat. Assn. Jazz Educators Hall of Fame, 1979; George Foster Peabody award, 1981; Emmy award; Lifetime Achievement award Down Beat mag., 1984. Mem. Arts and Bus. Council N.Y. (pres.), Nat. Acad. Rec. Arts and Scis. (v.p. 1964—), ASCAP (dir. 1976-78), Acad. TV Arts and Scis. *

TAYLOR, BILLY D., principal. Prin. Dyersburg (Tenn.) High Sch. Recipient Blue Ribbon award U.S. Dept. Edn., 1990-91. Office: Dyersburg High Sch 125 Us Highway 51 Byp N Dyersburg TN 38024-3660

TAYLOR, CARL ERNEST, physician, educator; b. Landour, Mussoorie, India, July 26, 1916; s. John C. and Elizabeth (Siehl) T.; m. Mary Daniels, Feb. 14, 1943; children—Daniel, Elizabeth, Henry. B.S., Muskingum Coll., 1937, D.Sc., 1962; M.D., Harvard, 1941, M.P.H., 1951, D.P.H., 1953; L.H.D. (hon.), Towson U., 1974. Diplomate: Am. Bd. Preventive Medicine. Intern, resident pathology, surg. staff, tropical disease research Gorgas Hosp., Panama C.Z., 1941-44; charge med. service Marine Hosp., Pitts., 1944-46; supt. Meml. Hosp., Fategarh, India, 1947-50; research assoc. Harvard Sch. Pub. Health, Boston, 1950-52; asst. prof. epidemiology Harvard Sch. Pub. Health, 1957-59, assoc. prof., 1959-61; prof. preventive and social medicine Christian Med. Coll., Ludhiana, Punjab, India, 1953-56; prof. internat. health Johns Hopkins Sch. Hygiene and Pub. Health, Balt., 1961-83; prof. emeritus Johns Hopkins Sch. Hygiene and Pub. Health, 1984—, chmn. dept. internat. health, 1961-83; Cons. AID, 1959—; UNICEF country rep. in China, 1984-87; mem. expert com. WHO, 1963, 66, 67, 70, 71, 72, 73, 75; mem. Inst. Medicine, Nat. Acad. Medicine, Nat. Adv. Commmn. Health Manpower; chmn. Nat. Council for Internat. Health. Contbr. numerous articles to proff. jours. Fellow Royal Coll. Physicians (Can.), Royal Soc. Tropical Medicine and Hygiene, Am. Pub. Health Assn.; mem. Assn. Tchrs. Preventive Medicine, Am. Soc. Tropical Medicine and Hygiene, Indian Assn. for Advancement Med. Edn. Research on rural health, population dynamics, nutrition, epidemiology of leprosy. Home: Bittersweet Acres 1201 Hollins Ln Baltimore MD 21209-2209 *The growing*

complexity of human relationships around this increasingly crowded world presents new challenges to concerned scientists. Solutions to our problems must come from new collaborative styles of work bridging the usual boundaries between people, since the problems we face are mutual.

TAYLOR, CARL LARSEN, lawyer; b. Honolulu, Apr. 9, 1937; s. William Henry and Dorothy (Gray) T.; m. Linda Ann Farrell, Aug. 3, 1963. AB, Harvard U., 1958, LLB, 1961. Bar: U.S. Ct. Appeals (D.C. cir.) 1965, U.S. Ct. Appeals (9th cir.) 1975, U.S. Ct. Appeals (2d cir., 4th cir.) 1977, U.S. Ct. Appeals (3d cir.) 1981, U.S. Ct. Appeals (7th cir.) 1982, U.S. Ct. Appeals (5th cir.) 1986, U.S. Ct. Appeals (10th cir.) 1987, U.S. Ct. Appeals (11th cir.) 1990; others.*. Assoc. Hogan & Hartson, Washington, 1966-69, ptnr., 1978-80; gen. counsel Retail Clerks Internat. Assn., Washington, 1969-76; assoc. gen. counsel NLRB, Washington, 1976-78; ptnr. Kirkland & Ellis, Washington, 1980-87, Johnson & Gibbs, Washington, 1987—. Served to lt. (j.g.) USN, 1961-65. Mem. Barristers. Club: Belle Haven (Alexandria, Va.). Office: Johnson & Gibbs 1001 Pennsylvania Ave NW Washington DC 20004-2505

TAYLOR, CAROLYN L., principal. Prin. James Madison High Sch., Madison, Wis. Recipient Blue Ribbon award U.S. Dept. Edn., 1990-91. Office: James Madison Meml High Sch 201 S Gammon Rd Madison WI 53717

TAYLOR, CARSON WILLIAM, electrical engineer; b. Superior, Wis., May 24, 1942; s. William Stanley and Elizabeth Marie (Christophersen) T.; m. Gudrun Renate Leistner, Dec. 28, 1966; 1 child, Natasha Marie. BSEE, U. Wis., 1965; M in Engring., Rensselaer Poly. Inst., 1969. Elec. engr. U.S Bur. Reclamation, Billings, Mont., 1967-68; elec. engr. Bonneville Power Adminstrn., Portland, Oreg., 1969-89, prin. engr., 1989—; prin. Carson Taylor Seminars, Portland, 1986—. Author: Power System Voltage Stability, 1994; contbr. papers to profl. publs.; patentee in field. Lt. U.S. Army, 1965-67. U.S. Army, 1965-67. Fellow IEEE (chmn. working group 1982—); mem. Conférence Internationale des Grands Réseaux Electrigues a Haute Tension (CIGRE), Eta Kappa Nu. Lutheran. Avocations: fishing, hunting, woodworking, reading, computers. Office: Bonneville Power Adminstrn PO Box 3621 Portland OR 97208-3621

TAYLOR, CECIL PERCIVAL, pianist, composer, educator; b. N.Y.C., Mar. 15, 1933; s. Percy Clinton and Almeida (Maitie) Ragland. Studied music privately; studied music, N.Y. Coll. Music, New Eng. Conservatory. Music intructor U. of WI, 1970-71, Antioch Coll., Yellow Springs, OH, 1972-74, Glassboro State College; instr. U. Wis., 1970-72, Antioch Coll., 1972-74, Glassboro State Coll. Played with Hot Lips Page, Lawrence Brown; formed own quartet in late 1950's; performed as solo pianist and with quartet including Jimmy Lyons, 1961; recorded and performed as solo pianist and with quartet including Jimmy Lyons, Andrew Cycille, Sam Rivers; compositions include Indent; albums include: Jazz Advance, 1956, Nefertiti, the Beautiful One Has Come, 1962, Unit Structures, 1966, Conquistador!, 1966, Silent Tongues, 1974, Air Above Mountains, 1976, Cicil Taylor, 1978, 3 Phasis, 1978, One Too Many Salty Swift and Not Goodbye, 1986, For Olim, 1986, Garden, 1986, The Eight, 1987, Cecil Taylor in Berlin '88, 1988, Looking, 1989, In Florescence, 1990, Dark to Themselves, 1990, Looking Ahead, 1990. Recipient Record of Year Downbeat Critics Poll, 1975; winner Down Beat Critics Poll for best acoustic piano, 1984; recipient Piano Player of Year award, 1972, 79; named to Downbeat Hall of Fame, 1975; Guggenheim fellow, 1973. *

TAYLOR, CELIANNA I., information systems specialist; b. Youngstown, Ohio; d. Paul Thornton and Florence (Jacobs) Isley; m. (div.); children: Polly, Jerry, Jim. Bachelors degree, Denison U., 1939; MLS, Western Res. U., 1942. Worked in several pub. librs. and u. librs., 1939-50; head Libr. Cataloging Dept. Battelle Mem. Inst., Columbus, Ohio, 1951-53; head Personnel Office and assoc. prof. of Libr. Adminstrn. Ohio State U. Librs., Columbus, Ohio, 1954-65; coord. Info. Svcs. and Assoc. Prof. of Libr. Adminstrn. Nat. Ctr. for Research in Vocat. Edn., Ohio State U., Columbus, 1966-70; sr. research assoc., adminstrv. assoc., assoc. prof. libr. adminstrn. Dept. of Computer and Info. Sci. Ohio State U., Columbus, 1970-86, retired assoc. prof. emeritus Univ. Librs., 1986—; mem. Task Force on a Spl. Collections Database, Ohio State U. Librs., Columbus, 1988-89, comm. systems and recs. coord. Ohio State U. Retirees Assn., Columbus, 1992-93; cons. for several profl. orgns. including Ernst & Ernst CPA's and Oreg. State Systems of Higher Edn., 1961-82. Author: (with J. Magisos) book, Guide for State Voc-Tech Edn. Dissemination Systems 1971, (with A.E. Petrarca, and R.S. Kohn) book, Info. Interaction 1982; several articles for profl. jours.; designer: info. systems, CALL System, 1977-82, Channel 2000 Proj. Home Info. Svc., 1980-81, Continuing Education CE Info., 1989-90, Human Resources (HUR) System, 1976-77,1979-82, DECOS, 1975-86, Computer-asst. libr. System, Optical Scan System, 1972-73, ERIC Clearinghouse for vocat. edn., 1966-70. Bd. dirs. Columbus Reg. Info. Svc., 1974-78, Cmty. Info. Referral Svc., Inc., 1975-81; chmn. subcom. on design, info. and ref. com. Columbus United Cmty. Coun., 1972-73; dir. Computer Utility for Pub. Info. Columbus, 1975-81; account coord. Greater Columbus Free-net, 1994—. Mem. ALA, Assn. Computing Machinery-Ctrl. Ohio Chpt., Am. Soc. for Info. Sci., Assn. Faculty and Profl. Women Ohio State U., Columbus Metro Club, Coun. for Ethics in Econs., Olympic Indoor Tennis Club. Avocations: bicycling, bird watching, folk dancing, gourmet cooking, tennis. Home: 3471 Greenbank Ct Columbus OH 43221-4724

TAYLOR, CHARLES H., congressman; b. Brevard, N.C., Jan. 3, 1941; m. Elizabeth Owen; 3 children. BA, Wake Forest U., 1963, JD, 1966. Mem. N.C. Ho. of Reps., Raleigh, 1967-73, minority leader, 1969-73; mem. N.C. Senate, Raleigh, 1973-75, minority leader, 1973-75; mem. 102nd-104th Congresses from 11th N.C. dist., Washington, 1991—; mem. appropriations subcoms. commerce, justice, state jud. and related agys.; legis. com.; tree farmer N.C.; mem. Rep. rsch. com., com. on mcht. marine and fisheries, subcom. on environ. and natural resources. Baptist. Office: US Ho of Reps 516 Cannon HOB Washington DC 20515 also: 22 S Pack Sq Ste 330 Asheville NC 28801*

TAYLOR, CHARLES HENRY, psychoanalyst, educator; b. Boston, Oct. 2, 1928; s. Charles Henry and Rosamond (Stewardson) T.; m. Diana Burgess, 1950; children: Stephen, Diana Beth, Charles S., Eleanor; m. Patricia Finley, 1988. B.A., Yale U., 1950, M.A., 1952, Ph.D., 1955; postgrad., Cambridge (Eng.) U., 1950-51. Instr., then asst. prof. English Ind. U., 1955-61; asst. dean, then asso. dean, also asso. prof. English Yale U., 1961-63, acting provost, 1963-64, provost, prof. English, 1964-72, pres. rep., 1972-76; grad. C.G. Jung Inst., N.Y., 1979; pvt. practice psychoanalysis, 1976—; bd. dirs. Globe Newspaper Co. Inc., Meridian Audio, Ltd. Author: The Early Collected Editions of Shelley's Poems, 1958; editor: Essays on the Odyssey, 1963; contbr. articles to profl. jours. Mem. com. on libr. Yale U. Coun., 1990-95; trustee Hampshire Coll., 1988-93. Mem. Internat. Assn. Analytical Psychology Archive for Rsch. in Archetypal Symbolism (pres. 1987-93, treas. 1993—), N.Y. Assn. Analytical Psychology, Nat. Assn. for Advancement Psychoanalysis, Phi Beta Kappa. Home: 40 Rogers Ave Milford CT 06460-6435

TAYLOR, C(HARLES) RICHARD, biological sciences educator; b. Phoenix, Ariz., Sept. 8, 1939; s. Norman W. and Rosiland E. (Gregory) T.; m. Ann Boyd, June 7, 1969; children: Greg, Caitlin. BA, Occidental Coll., 1960; AM, Harvard U., 1962, PhD, 1963; MD (hon.), U. Bern, Switzerland, 1993. Rsch. fellow U. Coll., Nairobi, Kenya, 1964-68; rsch. assoc. dept. zoology Duke U., Durham, N.C., 1968-70; assoc. prof. Harvard U., Cambridge, 1970-73, Alexander Agassiz prof. zoology, 1973-91, prof. biology, 1973-91, Charles P. Lyman prof. biology 1991—; dir. Concord Field Sta., 1970—; scientist East African Rsch. Orgnn., hon. lectr. zoology, 1960's; vis. prof. dept. animal physiology U. Nairobi, 1977; vis. prof. U. Bern, 1987—; chmn. Interunion Commn. Comparative Physiology, 1981—. Mem. editorial bd. Am. Jour. Physiology, 1982—. John Simon Guggenheim Meml. Found. fellow, 1977. Mem. NAS, Am. Physiol. Soc., Am. Soc. Zoologists, Phi Beta Kappa, Sigma Xi. Home: 329 Silver Hill Rd Concord MA 01742-5307 Office: Harvard U Concord Field Sta Old Causeway Rd Bedford MA 01730

TAYLOR, CHRISTOPHER ANDREW, securities industry regulation executive; b. West Chester, Pa., Jan. 13, 1947; s. William Downham and Christine (Robinson) T.; m. Dahrl Louise Hill, Aug. 22, 1970; children:

Lucius, Nora, C. Jared. BA, Swarthmore Coll., 1969; MA, Princeton U., 1971, PhD, 1974. Economist Capital Markets Sect. Bd. of Govs. of the Fed. Res. System, 1973-78; dir. Office of Fin. Office of N.Y. Fin., U.S. Dept. Treasury, Washington, 1978; pres. Mcpl. Securities Rulemaking Bd., Washington, 1978—. Mem. Am. Econ. Assn., Am. Fin. Assn., Inst. CFAs, Belle Haven Country Club, George Town Club. Mem. Soc. of Friends. Avocations: tennis, golf, hiking, reading. Home: 6120 Vernon Ter Alexandria VA 22307-1151 Office: Mcpl Securities Rulemaking Bd Ste 400 1150 18th St NW Washington DC 20036

TAYLOR, CLAUDE I., airlines executive; b. Salisbury, N.B., Can., May 20, 1925; s. Martin Luther and Essie (Troope) T.; m. Frances Bernice Watters, Nov. 4, 1947; children: Karen, Peter. Student, Robinson Bus. Coll., 1942; R.I.A., McGill U. Extension, 1953; D.C.L. (hon.), U. N.B.; LL.D. (hon.), McMaster U. With Air Can., Montreal, Canada, 1949—, various sr. positions including gen. mgr. mktg., v.p. strategic devel., v.p. govt. and industry affairs, v.p. pub. affairs, pres., chief exec. officer, 1962-84, chmn. bd., 1984-90, chmn., pres., chief exec. officer, 1990-92, chmn. emeritus, 1992—; chmn. exec. com. and coun. Gov. Gen.'s Can. Study Conf. 1987. Hon. dir. Aviation Hall of Fame, Can. Nat. Exhbn. Assn.; past pres. Boy Scouts Can.; life gov. Douglas Hosp. Corp. Decorated comdr. Order St. John, officer Order Can.; recipient Gordon R. McGregor Meml. Trophy Royal Can. Air Force Assn., 1980, Excellence in Communications Leadership award Internat. Assn. Bus. Communicators, Merit award B'nai Brith Can., McGill Mgmt. Achievement award, Human Relations award Can. Council Christians and Jews, Gold Medal award Adminstrv. Mgmt. Soc., Tony Jannus award, 1988, C. D. Howe award, 1989; named Nat. Transp. Person, 1987; inducted Can. Aviation Hall of Fame. Fellow Soc. Mgmt. Accts. Can., Inst. Transport; mem. Profl. Corp. Indsl. Accts. Que., Order of Can. (officer), Beaver Club (Montreal). Baptist. Clubs: Beaver, Mt. Royal, Forest and Stream (Montreal). Office: Air Canada, Air Canada Ctr 270, PO Box 14000, Montreal, PQ Canada H4Y 1H4

TAYLOR, CLAUDE J., sales executive, consultant; b. Winston-Salem, N.C., Apr. 29, 1943; s. Claude V. and Jessie K. T.; m. Frances T. Denty, Dec. 22, 1962; children: Joseph Vinston, Jeffrey Alan, Marc David, Michael Edward. Student, U.S. Army Schs., 1961-62; AS in Aircraft Comms., Nat. Inst., 1966-68, AS in Indsl. Electronics, 1968-71; student, Palm Beach Jr. Coll., 1971-73. Inside salesman and office ops. Graybar Electric Co., West Palm Beach, Fla., 1964-66; mgr. Lewisville (N.C.) Shell Svc., 1966-67; salesman Joyce Foods, Inc., Lewisville, 1967-69; instrument tech. Pratt-Whitney Aircraft, West Palm Beach, 1969-73; tech. resp., instr., tech. mgr. Siemens Med. Systems, Iselin, N.J., 1973-87; salesman, mfr. rep. Ohmeda div. BOC, Littleton, Colo., 1987-88; dist. sales mgr. Planmeca, Inc. and Planmed, Wood Dale, 1988-93; owner, pres. dental and medical sales Tech. Splty. Mktg., Jupiter, Fla., 1993—; cons. Instrumentarium Imaging, Inc., Milw., 1993—. With U.S. Army, 1961-64. Home: PO Box 1443 Jupiter FL 33468-1443 Office: Tech Splty 16220 128th Trail N Jupiter FL 33478

TAYLOR, CLAYBORNE DUDLEY, engineering educator; b. Kokomo, Miss., July 15, 1938; s. Dudley Clayborne and Winnie Lee (Holmes) T.; m. Mary Jean Blue, June 23, 1963; children: Clayborne Dudley Jr., David Edward, Rebecca Lynn Taylor Burg. BS in Physics, Miss. State U., 1961; MS in Physics, N.Mex. State U., 1964, PhD in Physics, 1965. Registered profl. engr., Miss. Tech. staff mem. Sandia Labs., Albuquerque, 1965-67; assoc. prof. Miss. State U., Starkville, 1967-69, 1969-71, prof. elec. engring., 1972-86, 88-91, assoc. dean. engring., 1991—; prof. elec. engring. U. Miss. Oxford, 1971-72; vis. Stocker prof. Ohio U., Athens, 1986-88; cons. Phillips Lab., Albuquerque, 1972—. Author: High-Power Microwave Systems and Effects, 1994; contbr. articles to tech. jours. Recipient Cert. of Recognition, NASA, 1986; Electromagnetic Pulse Tech. fellow Summa Found., 1988. Mem. IEEE (sr.), Internat. Union of Radio Scientists, Am. Soc. Engring. Edn. Presbyterian. Home: 214 Hiwassee Dr Starkville MS 39759 Office: Miss State U Coll Engring 106 McCain Bldg Mississippi State MS 39762

TAYLOR, CLAYTON CHARLES, management and political legislative consultant; b. Douglas, Ariz., Feb. 9, 1952; s. Clay Arvle and Nellie Josephine (Swaggart) T.; m. Marian Jane Brehmer, July 18, 1981; children: Clayton Charles Jr., Gardner Clark. BSBA, Oklahoma State U., 1974. Lyndon Baines Johnson intern U.S. Ho. Reps., Washington, 1972; asst. to Congressman Clem McSpadden, 1972; asst. to Congressman Gillis Long U.S. Ho. of Reps., Washington, 1975, legis. dir. to Congressman Risenhoover, 1976, adminstrv. asst. to Congressman Hubbard, 1976-77; dir. fed. govt. rels. McDonald's Corp., Chgo., 1978-81; dir. govt. rels. Phillips Petroleum Co., Okla. City, 1982-85; western states dir. govt. rels. Phillips Petroleum Co., Denver, 1986-87; dir. govt. rels. and pub. affairs Phillips Petroleum Co., Oklahoma City, 1988-91; v.p. corp. affairs Coastal Aruba, San Nicolas, Aruba, Dutch West Indies, 1991-93; v.p. govt. affairs Coastal Corp., Houston, 1993-94; pres. The Taylor Consulting Group, Okla. City, 1994—, The Taylor Group. Campaign dir. 2d Dist. Congl. Campaign, Muskogee, Okla., 1976, Congressman Brewster, 3d Congl. Dist., 1994; agrl. cons. U.S.-Egyptian pvt. venture, Cairo and Washington, 1977; pres. alumni assn., bd. dirs. Leadership Okla., pres., 1991-92; founding chmn. Okla. Leadership Congress, 1989; v.p. Ballet Okla., 1989; bd. dirs. Better Bus. Bur., Okla. Energy Found., Internat. Sch. Aruba, chmn. internat. staff recruitement; mem. alumni bd. dirs. Okla. State U. Coll. Bus. Adminstrn.; found. bd. dirs., nat. program adv. com. South/West Energy Coun.; bd. dirs., state pres. coun. Okla. 4-H Club Found.; bd. dirs. Okla. City Met. Libr. Commn.; mem. nat. meeting adv. com. Nat. Conf. State Legislatures; nat. co-chmn., states coun. Consumers for Competitive Fuels. Recipient Nat. Leadership Excellence award Nat. Assn. Cmty. Leadership; named Outstanding Cmty. Leader Aruba, 1992-93. Fellow Amundsen Inst. for U.S.-Mex.; mem. Aruba Industry and Trade Assn. (mem. exec. bd. 1993-94), Okla. Mid-Continent Oil and Gas Assn. (exec. com. 1991), Okla. State U. Bus. Coll. Alumni Assn. (bd. dirs. 1987-89), Petroleum Club Oklahoma City, Houston City Club. Home: 3212 N Aarvey Pkwy Oklahoma City OK 73118 Office: Bar 7 Ranch RR 1 Box 1785 Oktaha OK 74450-9768

TAYLOR, CLYDE CALVIN, JR., literary agent; b. Anderson, S.C., July 27, 1936; s. Clyde Calvin and Ellen Letitia (Hamilton) T.; children—Catherine Ellen, Emily Taylor Bradley, Andrew Hamilton. A.B., Wofford Coll., 1958. Tchr. Westminster Schs., Atlanta, 1958; advt. copywriter Harper and Row, 1960, Macmillan & Co., 1961; advt. mgr. Collier-Macmillan Library Div., 1962; asst. bus. mgr. book div. AM. Heritage Pub. Co., 1963-65; dir. subs. rights G.P. Putnam's Sons, 1965-69; v.p. World Pub. Co., 1970; v.p., gen. mgr. G.P. Putnam's Sons, N.Y.C., 1972-74; v.p., pub. G.P. Putnam's Sons, 1974-77, exec. v.p., pub. 1977; pres. Clyde Taylor Lit. Agcy., Inc., 1978-79; v.p. Curtis Brown Ltd., 1980-94; lit. agt. affiliated with Knox Burger Assocs., Ltd. 1994—. Home: 216 E 6th St New York NY 10003-8212

TAYLOR, SIR CYRIL (JULIAN HEBDEN), education association administrator, consultant; b. Leeds, Yorkshire, Eng. May 14, 1935; s. Cyril Eustace and Margaret Victoria (Hebden) T.; m. Judith Taylor, June 5, 1965; 1 child, Kirsten. MA, U. Cambridge, Eng., 1961; MBA, Harvard U., 1961; D in Law (hon.), New Eng. Coll., 1991. Brand mgr. Proctor & Gamble, Cin., 1961-64; founder, chmn. Am. Inst. for Fgn. Study, London, 1964—; advisor to Brit. Sec. of State for Edn., London, 1987—; chmn. City Tech. Coll. Trust, 1987—. Author: No More Tick, 1974, The Elected Member's Guide to Reducing Public Expenditure, 1980, A Realistic Plan for London Transport, 1982, Reforming London's Government, 1984, Qualgoes Just Grow, 1985, London Preserv'd, 1985, Bringing Accountability Back to Local Government, 1985, Employment Examined: The Right Approach to More Jobs, 1986, (with others) The Guide to Study Abroad, Raising Educational STandards, 1990. Dep. leader, mem. The Conservative Group, 1977-86; pres. Ruislip/Northwood Conservative Assn. parliamentary candidate Keighley, 1974, Huddersfield East, 1974; chmn. Lexham Gardens Resident's Assn., 1986—; active Coun. Westfield Coll., 1983-89, coun. Royal Coll. Music, 1988—; bd. govs. Holland Park Comprehensive Sch. 1971-74. Served with inf. Brit. Army, 1954-56. Decorated knight Order of Brit. Empire; Charles Bell scholar London C. of C., 1961. Mem. Ctr. for Policy Studies (bd. dirs. 1984—), Harvard Bus. Sch. Club (pres. Londonchpt. 1990-93, v.p. alumni coun.), Racquet Club of N.Y., Harvard Club of N.Y. Anglican. Clubs: Carlton, Chelsea Arts, Hurlingham (London). Office: Am Inst Foreign Study 102 Greenwich Ave Greenwich CT 06830-5504

TAYLOR, D(ARL) CODER, architect, engineer; b. Ft. Wayne, Ind., July 18, 1913; s. Frank A. and Edith (Zook) T.; m. Audrey Helen Larkin, June 5, 1944; children: Barbara Helen Taylor Reddy, Thomas Coder, Julie Marie Taylor Hitchins; m. Harriett Pribble Sinding, July 27, 1985. BArch, Carnegie Inst. Tech., 1935; spl. student, U. Wash., 1933. Draftsman Chgo., 1935; partner Zook & Taylor, architects, Chgo., 1939-42, Holsman, Holsman, Klekamp & Taylor, architects, Chgo., 1948-52, Yost & Taylor, architects and engrs., Kenilworth, Ill., 1952-60; chmn. Coder Taylor Assos., Inc., architects-engrs.-planners, Kenilworth, 1960-78; chmn. bd. Coder Taylor Assos., Inc., 1978-81, spl. cons., 1981—; cons. in field, 1935—. Prin. works include Mcpl. Bldg., St. Charles, Ill., 1940, listed Nat. Register Hist. Places, 1990, Prize Home No. 1, 1946 (Chgo. Tribune prize home competition), Sherman Garden Apts., 1951 (Chgo. chpt. AIA honor award), Kincheloe AFB, Mich., 1962 (Best Family Housing Project No. Area), Chanute AFB, Ill., 1959 (Best Family Housing Project Cen. Area), U.S. Naval Tng. Ctr., Great Lakes, Ill., 1964 (Merit award FHA), Swimming Pool House, Northfield, Ill., 1967 (Chgo. chpt. AIA-Chgo. Assn. Commerce and Industry Disting. Bldg. award), 510 Green Bay Rd. Bldg., Kenilworth, Ill. (AIA-Chgo. Assn. Commerce and Industry award 1967), Roberts Residence, Lake Forest, Ill., 1968 (AIA-Chgo. Assn. Commerce and Industry Disting. Bldg. award), Glenview Pub. Libr., 1970 (Chgo. chpt. AIA-Chgo. Assn. Commerce and Industry Disting. Bldg. award), Kroch's & Brentano's stores, Chgo., 1961-77, Des Plaines Pub. Libr., 1974 (Des Plaines C. of C. Outstanding Achievement award), Wilmette (Ill.) Park Dist. Recreation Ctr., 1974, Wilmette Village Adminstrn. Bldg., 1975, Glenview Cen. Fire Sta., 1976 (Glenview Appearance Commn. Outstanding Bldg. and Landscape award), Internat. Hdqrs. Alpha Phi Frat., Evanston, Ill., 1975, Barrington Area Pub. Libr., 1977; represented in spl. exhbns. and permanent collections Art Inst. Chgo., Chgo. Hist. Soc., Wilmette Hist. Soc., Evanston Hist. Soc., Graham Found.; author: Oral History of D. Coder Taylor, 1989; contbr. articles to profl. jours. Mem. Glenview (Ill.) Planning Commn., 1962-65; chmn. Glenview Appearance Commn., 1968-72, Picasso Day Com., Chgo., 1967; mem. fine arts com. Ill. Sesquicentennial Commn., 1967-68; exec. com., treas. Fedn. Open Lakefront, 1966-68; mem. tech. studies adv. com. NAS-NRC, 1962—; mem. tech. panel, adv. com. HUD, NAS, NAE, 1969; nat. panel arbitrators Am. Arbitrators Assn., 1952—. Lt. comdr. Civil Engr. Corps USNR, 1942-45. Recipient merit award for archtl. accomplishments Carnegie-Mellon U. Alumni Assn., 1982. Fellow AIA (dir. Chgo. chpt. 1965-66, pres. 1967, v.p. Ill. council 1968); mem. Ill. Assn. Professions (dir. 1968), Mich. Soc. Architects, Nat. Assn. Redevel. Ofcls., Tau Sigma Delta (pres. 1934- 35), Sigma Phi Epsilon (pres. 1934-35), Scarab (1934-35). Methodist. Club: North Shore Country (Glenview, Ill.). Home and Office: 727 Redwood Ln Glenview IL 60025-4460 *" Early in my professional career, I decided that quality of work created was more important than quantity. To have the largest practice was not to be the goal, but rather to have personal involvement in the work produced, which would result in less work, but work of high class and character.".*

TAYLOR, DAVID, clergy member, religious administrator. Dir. World Witness Dept. of the Pentecostal Free Will Baptist Ch., Dunn, N.C. Office: The Pentecostal Baptist Ch PO Box 1568 Dunn NC 28335-1568

TAYLOR, DAVID BROOKE, lawyer, banker; b. Salt Lake City, Oct. 14, 1942; s. Lee Neff and June (Bitner) T.; m. Carolyn Kaufholz, May 29, 1965; children: Stewart, Allison. BA, U. Utah, 1966; JD, Columbia U., 1967. Bar: N.Y. 1967, N.C. 1995. Ptnr. Wickes, Riddell, Bloomer, Jacobi & McGuire, N.Y.C., 1967-79, Morgan, Lewis & Bockius, N.Y.C., 1979-89; banker, lawyer Chase Manhattan Bank, N.A., N.Y.C., 1989-92; pres. Geoenertec Corp., N.Y.C., 1992-93; ptnr. Fennebresque, Clark, Swindall & Hay, Charlotte, N.C., 1994—. Mem. ABA, N.Y. State Bar Assn., Internat. Bar Assn. Home: 225 Loring Ave Pelham NY 10803-2254 Office: Fennebresque Clark Swindall & Hay NationsBank Corporate Ctr 100 N Tryon St Ste 2900 Charlotte NC 28202-4011

TAYLOR, DAVID GEORGE, retired banker; b. Charlevoix, Mich., July 29, 1929; s. Frank Flagg and Bessie (Strayer) T.; m. Robyne T. McCarthy, July 28, 1990; children from previous marriage: David, Amy, Jeanine. BS, Denison U., 1951; MBA, Northwestern U., 1953. With Continental Ill. Nat. Bank and Trust Co. Chicago, 1958-86, asst. cashier, 1961-64, 2d v.p., 1964-66, v.p., 1966-72, sr. v.p., 1972-74, exec. v.p., 1974-80, exec. v.p., treas., 1980-83, vice chmn., 1983-84, chmn., chief exec. officer, 1984; vice chmn. Irving Trust Co. N.Y.C., 1986-89; group exec. Chem. Bank, N.Y.C., 1989-94, ret., 1994. Mem. Dealer Bank Assn. Com. on Glass-Steagall Reform, 1985-86. Bd. dirs. Evanston Hosp., Glenbrook Hosp.; trustee Art Inst. Chgo., 1981-86; advisor J.L. Kellogg Grad. Sch. Mgmt., Northwestern U., 1984—. Served to lt. USN, 1953-56. Mem. Pub. Securities Assn. (bd. dirs. 1977-78, chmn. 1977, treas. 1978), Govt. and Fed. Agys. Securities Com. (chmn. bd. dirs 1982-83), Assn. Res. City Bankers (asset/liability com/govt. relations com. 1983—). Republican. Presbyterian.

TAYLOR, DAVID KERR, international business educator, consultant; b. Oxford, N.C., Oct. 11, 1928; s. David Kerr and Myrtle Norman (Shamburger) T.; m. Isabel de Sousa Botelho de Albuquerque, Apr. 23, 1960; children: Anne de Albuquerque Taylor Grave, Katherine Rowena Taylor. BA, Duke U., 1947, JD, 1949. Bar: N.Y., N.C. Atty. Ins. Co. N.Am., N.Y.C., 1949-51, Milbank, Tweed, Hadley & McCloy, N.Y.C., 1954-55; internat. exec. Mobil Corp., N.Y.C., Washington, Can., Portugal, Nigeria, France, others, 1955-86; rsch. prof. internat. affairs, sr. fellow intrnat. bus. Georgetown U. Sch. Fgn Svc., Washington, 1987—; pres. Luso-Am. Bus. Coun., 1987-89; bd. visitors Duke U. Law Sch. 1st lt. U.S. Army, 1951-54, Germany. 1st lt. U.S. Army, 1951-54, Germany. Mem. Am. Portuguese Soc. (bd. dirs., pres. 1968-70, 76-80), Washington Export Coun., Textile Mus. Adv. Coun., Washington Internat. Bus. Coun., Washington Inst. Fgn. Affairs, Cosmos Club, Phi Beta Kappa. Avocations: piano playing, singing. Home: 2737 Devonshire Pl NW Washington DC 20008 Office: Georgetown U Sch Fgn Svc Washington DC 20057

TAYLOR, DAVID WYATT AIKEN, retired clergyman; b. Tsingkiangpu, Kiangsu, China, Dec. 13, 1925; s. Hugh Kerr and Fanny Bland (Graham) T.; m. Lillian Ross McCulloch, Aug. 25, 1951; children: Frances Bland, David Wyatt. B.A., Vanderbilt U., 1949; B.D. cum laude, Union Theol. Sem. Va., 1952; Th.M., Princeton Theol. Sem., 1953; D.D. (hon.), King Coll., Bristol, Tenn., 1959. Ordained to ministry Presbyn. Ch. U.S., 1952. Pastor chs. Elkton, Va., 1953-55, Bristol, Va., 1955-62; ednl. sec. bd. world missions Presbyn. Ch. U.S., 1962-68, program dir. dir., 1968-73; ecumenical officer gen. assembly mission bd. Presbyn. Ch. U.S., Atlanta, 1973-82; pastor Orange Park Presbyn. Ch., Orange Park, Fla., 1982-86; gen. sec. for strategy and interpretation Consultation on Ch. Union, Princeton, N.J., 1986-88, gen. sec., 1988-93; ret., 1993; instr. Bible Presbyn. Jr. Coll., Maxton, N.C., 1951; mem. program bd., div. Christian edn. Nat. Council Chs., 1965-69, bd. mgrs., dept. edn. for mission, 1962-68, mem. program bd., div. overseas ministries, 1968-78, mem. governing bd., 1976-80, chmn. governing bd. credentials com., 1978; chmn. Church World Service, Inc., 1973-75; mem. adminstrn. and fin. com. Nat. Council Chs., 1973-75, mem. commn. on faith and order, 1978-93; mem. commn. on interchurch aid World Council Chs., 1973-75; mem. 5th Assembly, 1975; rep. Presbyn. Ch. U.S. to World Alliance Ref. Chs., 1976-82; bd. dirs. Presbyn. Survey mag., 1963-68; mem. Consultation on Ch. Union, 1974-93; chmn. Nat. Ecumenical Officers Assn. 1978-81. Bd. dirs. Abingdon Presbytery's Children's Home, Wytheville, Va., 1958-62. Served with AUS, 1944-46, PTO. Mem. Sigma Chi. Home: PO Box 1909 Elizabethtown NC 28337

TAYLOR, DERMOT BROWNRIGG, pharmacology researcher; b. Ireland, Mar. 30, 1915; came to U.S., 1950, naturalized, 1955; s. Roland L. and Sarah J. (White) T.; m. Charlotte C. Taylor, 1965; 1 child, Tina. B.A., Trinity Coll. Dublin, 1937, M.B., B.Ch., 1938, M.A., M.D. Asst. to prof. physiology Trinity Coll., 1938-39; lectr. physiology King's Coll., U. London, 1939-45, lectr. pharmacology, 1945-50; assoc. prof. pharmacology U. Calif., San Francisco, 1950-53; prof. pharmacology UCLA, 1953-85, chmn. dept., 1953-68; prof., biomed. researcher U. Calif., Santa Barbara, 1985—. Contbr. to: Essentials of Pharmacology, 1968, A Guide to Molecular Pharmacology-Toxicology, 1973; co-author: Green Medicine. Travelling fellow U. London, 1948; fellow Yale, 1948. Mem. Faraday Soc., Biochem. Soc., Physiol. Soc., Brit. Pharmacol. Soc., Soc. Pharmacology and Exptl. Therapeutics, Soc. Exptl. Biology and Medicine. Home: 4325 Via Presada Santa Barbara CA 93110-2225 Office: U Calif Dept Pharmacology Santa Barbara CA 93106

TAYLOR, DONALD, retired manufacturing company executive; b. Worcester, Mass., June 2, 1927; s. John A. B. and Alice M. (Weaver) T.; m. Ruth L. Partridge, June 24, 1950; children: Linda Taylor Robertson, Donald, Mark, John. BSME, Worcester Poly. Inst., 1949; grad., Northeastern U. Mgmt. Devel. Program, 1962, Harvard Bus. Sch. Advanced Mgmt. Program, 1979. Registered profl. engr., Mass. With George J. Meyer Mfg. Co., Milw., 1954-69; pres. mfg. div. A-T-O, Inc., 1969; exec. v.p. Nordberg div. Rex Chainbelt, Inc., Milw., 1969-73; v.p. ops. Rexnord Inc., Brookfield, Wis., pres., chief operating officer, 1978-85, chief exec. officer, from 1985, chmn., 1985-88; pres. Nordberg Machinery Group, Milw., 1973-78; dir. Harnischfeger Corp., Johnson Controls, Inc., Banc One Wis. Inc., Banta Corp. Bd. dirs. Blood Ctr. Southeastern Wis., Greater Milw. Com., Met. Milw. YMCA; bd. dirs. Milw. Symphony Orch. Served with USNR, 1951-54. Mem. ASME. Clubs: Milw. Country, Milw. Athletic, Town, Univ., Masons. Office: 7850 N Club Cir Milwaukee WI 53217-2939

TAYLOR, DONALD ARTHUR, marketing educator; b. Windsor, Ont., Can., Sept. 27, 1923; came to U.S., 1947, naturalized, 1955; s. David Cameron and Eva (Perry) T.; m. Shirley Marion Jenner, 1949; children: John Cameron, Stephen Bruce, Michael James. B.A., U. Western Ont., 1947; M.B.A., U. Mich., 1949, Ph.D. (Horace H. Rackham fellow), 1955. Asst. prof. marketing Mich. State U. at, East Lansing, 1955-58; asso. prof. Mich. State U. at, 1958-62, prof., 1962—, chmn. dept. marketing and transportation adminstrn., 1969-81, prof., 1981-84, chmn. dept. mktg. and transp. adminstrn., 1984-86, chmn., prof. emeritus, 1986—; adviser, chief of party to mission at various univs., Brazil, 1956-58, 62-64; dir. Latin Am. Studies Center, 1968-69; also co-dir. Latin-Am. Market Planning Center, sr. cons. food distbn. studies, N.E. Brazil, Colombia; cons. Geigy Agrl. Chems., Johnson & Johnson Domestic Operating Co., Ford Motor Co., Westinghouse Electric Corp., Whirlpool Corp., Burroughs Corp.; dir. Clark-Graveley Corp., 1972-77. Author: (with D.J. Luck, D.A. Taylor, H. Wales, R. Rubin) Marketing Research, 6th edit, 1982, (with T.A. Staudt, D.A. Taylor and D.J. Bowersox) A Managerial Introduction to Marketing, 3d edit, 1976, (with D.A. Taylor) Institution Building in Business Administration: The Brazilian Experience, 1968, (with Bowersox, Cooper, Lambert and Taylor) Management in Marketing Channels, 1980. Mem. bd. edn. Holt Sch. Dist., 1960-62. Recipient Homenagen Especial award 1st graduating class Escola de Administracao de Empresas, Sao Paulo, Brazil, 1958; named hon. prof., 1964. Mem. Am. Marketing Assn. (bd. dirs. 1969). Home: 3724 Harolds Rd Traverse City MI 49686

TAYLOR, DONNA LYNNE, adult education coordinator; b. Balt., July 1, 1944; d. Noel Leroy and Dorothy Anna (Henry) Welsh; 1 child, Tom A., Jr. BS, Okla. State U., 1965, EdD, 1992; MS, Phillips U., 1984. Cert. vocat. bus. and trade and indsl. edn. tchr., prin., supt., vocat. adminstr., Okla. Retail sales Tulsa, 1961-62; secretary Okla. State U. Coop. Extension Svc., Stillwater, 1965-67; secondary instr. social studies Waller Jr. High, Enid, Okla., 1967-69; substitute instr. Autry Tech. Ctr., Enid, 1971-78, instr. vocat. bus. part-time, 1978-84, instr. vocat. bus. full time, 1984-94; small bus. owner Lynne's Country Crafts, Enid, 1975-85; adult educator Sch. Continuing Edn., Enid, 1981-85; mem. strategic planning com. and policy and procedures com. Staff Devel. Affirmative Action, Enid, 1989—; presenter ann. confs. and meetings Okla. State Dept. Vocat. Tech., Stillwater, 1991-92; coord., chair Articulation Agreement Com., Enid, 1991—; advisor FBLA/Phi Beta Lambda, Enid, 1990-94; mem. North Ctrl. Accreditation Steering Com., 1992-93, staff devel. chair, 1993-94. Bd. Sch. Continuing Edn., Enid, 1975-85; mem. vol. YWCA, March of Dimes, Am. Heart Assn., MS Soc., Am. Diabetes Assn., Enid Art Assn., 1985—; deacon Christian Ch., Enid, 1986-88, elder, 1988-92, 95—; active Leadership Greater Enid. Recipient Women of Achievement award March of Dimes, 1992; named Okla. Bus. Tchr. of Yr., 1994. Mem. ASCD, Am. Vocat. Assn., Okla Vocat. Assn., Mountain Plains Bus. Edn. Assn., Okla. Bus. Edn. Assn., Nat. Bus. Edn. Assn., Nat. Assn. Classroom Bus. Educators, Vocat. Bus. and Office Edn., Enid C. of C. (edn. com. 1991-92), Phi Delta Kappa (sec. 1992—), PEO. Republican. Avocations: art, volunteering, reading. Home: 2110 Appomattox Enid OK 73703 Office: Autry Tech Ctr 1201 W Willow Enid OK 73703

TAYLOR, EDNA JANE, employment program counselor; b. Flint, Mich., May 16, 1934; d. Leonard Lee and Wynona Ruth (Davis) Harvey; children: Wynona Jane MacDonald, Cynthia Lee Zellmer. BS, No. Ariz. U., 1963; MEd, U. Ariz., 1967. Tchr. high sch. Sunnyside Sch. Dist., Tucson, 1963-68; employment program counselor employment devel. dept. State of Calif., Canoga Park, 1968—. Mem. adv. coun. Van Nuys Cmty. Adult Sch., Calif., 1983—, steering coun., 1989-91, leadership coun., 1991-92; mem. adv. coun. Pierce C.C., Woodland Hills, Calif., 1979-81; first aid instr., recreational leader ARC. Mem. NAFE, Internat. Assn. of Pers. in Employment Security, Calif. Employment Counselors Assn. (state treas. 1978-79, state sec. 1980), Delta Psi Kappa (life). Avocations: writing, tennis, health and fitness. Office: State of Calif Employment Devel Dept 21010 Vanowen St Canoga Park CA 91303-2804

TAYLOR, EDWARD CURTIS, chemistry educator; b. Springfield, Mass., Aug. 3, 1923; s. Edward Curtis and Margaret Louise (Anderson) T.; m. Virginia Dion Crouse, June 29, 1946; children: Edward Newton, Susan Raines. Student, Hamilton Coll., 1942-44, DSc (hon.), 1969; AB, Cornell U., 1946, PhD, 1949. Postdoctoral fellow Nat. Acad. Scis., Zurich, Switzerland, 1949-50; DuPont postdoctoral fellow chemistry U. Ill., 1950-51, faculty, 1951-54, asst. prof. organic chemistry, 1952-54; faculty Princeton U., 1954—, prof. chemistry, 1964—, A. Barton Hepburn prof. organic chemistry, 1966—, chmn. dept. chemistry, 1974-79; vis. prof. Technische Hochschule, Stuttgart, Fed. Republic Germany, 1960, U. East Anglia, 1969, 71; Disting. vis. prof. U. Buffalo, 1968, U. Wyo., 1977; Backer lectr. U. Groningen, Holland, 1969; mem. chemistry adv. com. Office Sci. Research, USAF, 1962-73, Cancer Chemotherapy Nat. Service Ctr., 1958-62; mem. internat. adv. bd. Ctr. Medicinal Chemistry, Bar-Ilan U., Israel, 1994—; cons. rsch. divs. Procter & Gamble, 1953-80, Eastman Kodak Co., 1965-83, Tenn. Eastman Co., 1968-83, Eli Lilly & Co., 1970—, Burroughs Wellcome Co., 1983—, E.I. duPont de Nemours & Co., 1986-90, Polaroid Corp., 1986—, Dow Elanco Co., 1989—, DuPont Merck Pharm. Co., 1990—. Author: (with McKillop) Chemistry of Cyclic Enaminonitriles and o-Aminonitriles, 1970, Principles Chemistry; film and audio courses, 1974; editor: (with Raphael Wynberg) Advances in Organic Chemistry, vols I-V, 1960-65, (with Wynberg) vol. VI, 1969, vols. VII-IX, 1970-79, (with W. Pfleiderer) Pteridine Chemistry, 1964, The Chemistry of Heterocyclic Compounds, 1968—, General Hetrocyclic Chemistry, 1968—; organic chemistry editorial adviser, John Wiley & Sons, Inc., 1968—; mem. editorial adv. bd. Jour. Medicinal Chemistry, 1962-66, Jour. Organic Chemistry, 1971-75, Synthetic Communications, 1971—, Heterocycles, 1973—, Chem. Substructure Index, 1971—, Advances in Heterocyclic Chemistry, 1983—, Pteridines, 1994—. Recipient rsch. awards SmithKline and French Found., 1955, Hoffmann-LaRoche Foun., 1964-65, Ciba Found., 1971, Disting. Hamilton award, 1977, U.S. Sr. Scientist prize Alexander von Humboldt Found., 1983, Disting. Alumni medal Hamilton Coll., 1990, F. Gowland Hopkins medal, 1993; sr. faculty fellow Harvard U., 1969, Guggenheim fellow, 1979-80. Fellow N.Y. Acad. Scis., Am. Inst. Chemists; mem. Am. Chem. Soc. (award for creative work in synthetic organic chemistry, 1974, chmn. organic chemistry div. 1976-77, Cope scholar award 1994), German Chem. Soc., Chem. Soc. London, Internat. Soc. Heterocyclic Chemistry (5th Internat. award 1989), Phi Beta Kappa, Sigma Xi, Phi Kappa Phi. Home: 288 Western Way Princeton NJ 08540-5337

TAYLOR, EDWARD STEWART, physician, educator; b. Hecla, S.D., Aug. 20, 1911; s. Robert Stewart and Sylvia Frances (Dewey) T.; m. Ruth Fatherson, June 15, 1940; children: Edward Stewart, Elizabeth Dewey Taylor Bryant, Catherine Wells Taylor Lynn. B.A., U. Iowa, 1933, M.D., 1936. Diplomate Am. Bd. Ob-Gyn (dir. 1962-69). Intern, Hurley Hosp., Flint, Mich., 1936-37; splty. tng. ob-gyn LL Coll. Hosp., 1937-41; prof. ob-gyn, chmn. dept. Sch. Medicine, U. Colo., 1947-76, clin. prof., 1976-81, prof., chmn. emeritus, 1981—; cons. ob-gyn Fitzsimons Gen. Hosp.; attending obstetrican and gynecologist St. Joseph's Hosp., Rose Hosp. Med. Center, both Denver; nat. cons. ob-gyn to surg. gen. USAF, 1958-62. Author: Manual of Gynecology, 1952, Essentials of Gynecology, 4th edit.; editor: Beck's Obstetrical Practice, 10th edit.; editor-in-chief for obstetrics: Obstetrical and Gynecol. Survey, 1967-92. Trustee Denver Symphony Orch., 1979-85. Served to lt. col. AUS, 1942-45; surgeon 107th Evacuation Hosp., ETO. Fellow ACS, Am. Coll. Obstetricians and Gynecologists (Disting. Svc. award 1984); mem. AMA, Am. Gynecol. Soc. (v.p. 1974-75), Am. Assn.

Obstetricians and Gynecologists (pres. 1970-71), Ctrl. Assn. Obstetricians and Gynecologists, S.W. Obstet. and Gynecol. Soc. (hon.), Am. Gynecol. and Obstet. Soc., Assn. Profs. Ob-Gyn (pres. 1974-75), Western Surg. Soc., Finnish Gynecol. Soc. (hon.), University Club (Denver), Alpha Omega Alpha. Congregationalist. Club: University (Denver). Home: 80 S Dexter St Denver CO 80222-1051

TAYLOR, ELDON DONIVAN, government official; b. Holdenville, Okla., July 29, 1929; s. Rome B. and Alma (Collins) T.; m. Hypatia Ethel Roberts, Feb. 7, 1953; 1 child, Teresa Lynn. Student, Murry State A. and M. Coll., 1948-49, George Washington U., 1949-50; B.S. cum laude, Am. U., 1959, M.A., 1966, postgrad., 1966-68. Research budget analyst, budgetary adminstrn. Office Naval Research, Navy Dept., Washington, 1949-51, 55-56; chief research and devel. budget sect., research and devel. planning adminstrn. Bur. Ordnance, 1956-60; dir. program rev. and resources, mgmt. div. research, devel. planning and adminstrn. Office Space Scis., NASA, Washington, 1960-70; dep. asst. adminstr. for resources mgmt. EPA, 1970-73; asst. dir. adminstrn. NSF, 1973-79; insp. gen. NASA, 1979-80; dir. adminstrn. Va. Ctr. Innovative Tech., 1984-85; v.p. Assn. Univs. for Research in Astronomy, 1985-86; pres. Taylor Mgmt. Assistance Inc., 1987—. Served with USAF, 1951-55. Recipient Commendation award for outstanding performance Dept. Navy, 1958; William A. Jump Meritorious award for achievement in pub. adminstrn., 1964; Exceptional Service award NASA, 1969; Disting. Service award NSF, 1978. Mem. Am. Soc. Pub. Adminstrn. (past sec. com. research pub. adminstrn.), Assn. Univs. for Research in Astronomy, Pi Sigma Alpha, Phi Theta Kappa. Home and Office: 7931 Wolf Run Hills Rd Fairfax Station VA 22039

TAYLOR, ELIZABETH ROSEMOND, actress; b. London, Feb. 27, 1932; d. Francis and Sara (Sothern) T. Student, Byron House, Hawthorne Sch., Metro-Goldwyn-Mayer Sch. Motion pictures include There's One Born Every Minute, 1942, Lassie Come Home, 1943, The White Cliffs of Dover, 1944, Jane Eyre, 1944, National Velvet, 1944, Courage of Lassie, 1946, Cynthia, 1947, Life with Father, 1947, A Date with Judy, 1948, Julia Misbehaves, 1948, Little Women, 1950, Conspirator, 1950, The Big Hangover, 1950, Father of the Bride, 1950, Father's Little Dividend, 1951, A Place in the Sun, 1951, Callaway Went Thataway, 1951, Love Is Better Than Ever, 1952, Ivanhoe, 1952, The Girl Who Had Everything, 1953, Elephant Walk, 1954, Rhapsody, 1954, Beau Brummel, 1954, The Last Time I Saw Paris, 1954, Giant, 1956, Raintree County, 1957, Cat on a Hot Tin Roof, 1958, Suddenly Last Summer, 1959, Scent of Mystery, 1960, Butterfield 8, 1960 (Acad. award best actress), Cleopatra, 1963, The V.I.P.'s, 1963, The Sandpiper, 1965, Who's Afraid of Virginia Woolf?, 1966 (Acad. award best actress), The Taming of the Shrew, 1967, The Comedians, 1967, Reflections in a Golden Eye, 1967, Dr. Faustus, 1967, Boom!, 1968, Secret Ceremony, 1968, The Only Game in Town, 1970, Under Milkwood, 1971, X, Y and Zee, 1972, Hammersmith Is Out, 1972, Night Watch, 1973, Ash Wednesday, 1973, That's Entertainment, 1974 (guest star), The Driver's Seat, 1974, Blue Bird, 1975, Winter Kills, 1977, A Little Night Music, 1977, The Mirror Crack'd, 1980, Young Toscanini, 1988, The Flintstones, 1994; TV appearances include Divorce His/Divorce Hers, 1973, Victory at Entebbe, 1977, Return Engagement, 1979, Between Friends, 1982, Hotel (series), 1984, Malice in Wonderland, 1986, North and South (miniseries), 1986, There Must Be a Pony, 1986, Poker Alice, 1987, Sweet Bird of Youth, 1989; theatre appearances in The Little Foxes, 1981 (Broadway debut), Private Lives, 1983; narrator film documentary Genocide, 1981; author: (with Richard Burton) World Enough and Time, poetry reading, 1964, Elizabeth Taylor, 1965, Elizabeth Taylor Takes Off: On Weight Gain, Weight Loss, Self Esteem and Self Image, 1988; lics. (fragrances) Elizabeth Taylor's Passion, Passion for Men, White Diamonds/Elizabeth Taylor, Elizabeth Taylor's Diamonds & Emeralds, Diamonds & Rubies, Diamonds & Sapphires, (jewelry) The Elizabeth Taylor Fashion Jewelry Collection for Avon. Active philanthropic, relief, charitable causes internationally, including Israeli War Victims Fund for the Chaim Sheba Hosp., 1976, UNICEF, Variety Children's Hosps., med. clinics in Botswana; initiated Ben Gurion U.-Elizabeth Taylor Fund for Children of the Negev, 1982; supporter AIDS Project L.A., 1985; founder, nat. chmn. Am. Found. for AIDS Rsch. (AmFAR), 1985—, internat. fund, 1985—; founder Elizabeth Taylor AIDS Found., 1991—. Named Comdr. Arts Letters (France), 1985; recipient Legion of Honor (France), 1987 (for work with AmFAR), Aristotle S. Onassis Found. award, 1988, Jean Hersholt Humanitarian Academy award, 1993 (for work as AIDS advocate), Life Achievement award Am. Film Inst., 1993; honored with dedication of Elizabeth Taylor Med. Ctr. Whitman-Walker Clinic, Washington, 1993. Address: care Chen Sam & Assocs Inc 506 E 74th St ste 3E New York NY 10021-3486

TAYLOR, ESTELLE WORMLEY, English educator, college dean; b. Washington, Jan. 12, 1924; d. Luther Charles and Wilhelmina Wormley; m. Ivan Earle Taylor, Dec. 26, 1953. BS magna cum laude, Miner Tchrs. Coll., 1945; MA, Howard U., 1947; PhD, Cath. U. Am., 1969. Instr. English Howard U., 1947-52; instr. Langley Jr. High Sch., Washington, 1952-55, Eastern Sr. High Sch., Washington, 1955-63; instr. D.C. Tchrs. Coll., 1963-66, asst. prof., 1966-69, assoc. prof., 1969-71, prof., 1971-91, prof. English emerita, 1991—, acad. dean, 1975-76; assoc. provost Fed. City Coll., Washington, 1974-75; prof. Howard U., 1976-91, chmn. dept. English, 1976-85, assoc. dean Coll. Liberal Arts, 1985-86; dir. expository writing program Grad. Sch. Arts and Scis., 1988-91; mem., sec. Edn. Licensure Commn. of D.C., 1993—; mem. Commn. on Higher Edn., Mid. States Assn. Colls. and Schs., 1984-87, 88-90, co-chair steering com. to revise Characteristics of Excellence, 1992-93; mem. ctrl. exec. com. Folger Inst. Renaissance and 18th Century Studies, 1982-91. 2d v.p. order daus. of king Episc. Ch. Diocese Washington D.C., 1994—; commr. Edn. Licensure Com. D.C., 1993—; also sec.; trustee U. D.C., 1979-83, vice chmn. 1983; mem. D.C. Cmty. Humanities Coun., 1990-91; co-chair planning com. Centennial Celebration of Andrew Rankin Chapel Howard U., 1994. Commr. Edn. Licensure Com. of D.C., 1993—, also sec., vice chmn. 1995—; trustee U. D.C., 1979-83, vice chmn., 1983; mem. D.C. Cmty. Humanities Coun., 1990-91; co-chmn. planning com. Centennial Celebration of the Andrew Rankin Chapel, Howard U., 1994. Named Disting. Alumni, Howard U., 1995; So. fellow, 1968-69; Rockefeller/Aspen Inst. fellow, 1978-79. Mem. MLA (del. assembly 1994—), Nat. Assn. for Equal Opportunity in Higher Edn., Coll. Lang. Assn., Shakespeare Assn. Am., Pub. Mem. Assn. Fgn. Svc. Dept. of State, Links (v.p. Capital City chpt. 1979-81, corr. sec. 1989, rec. sec. 1991-93, 95—). Democrat. Home: 3221 20th St NE Washington DC 20018-2421 *Throughout my career I have been climbing a giant ladder, invisible to all but me. The challenging but humbling feature of this ladder is that whenever I get the feeling that I have almost reached the top, several additional rungs attach themselves to my Jacob's Ladder. Thus, that thing called success is for me forever a goal to be reached. As long as I continue to feel a restlessness and a yearning to climb another rung, I shall know that I am alive.*

TAYLOR, FOSTER JAY, retired university president; b. Gibsland, La., Aug. 9, 1923; s. Lawrence Foster and Marcia Aline (Jay) T.; m. Lou Kavanaugh; 1 son, Terry Jay. Student, La. Poly. Inst., 1940-42; BA, U. Calif., Santa Barbara, 1948; MA, Claremont (Calif.) Grad. Sch., 1949; PhD, Tulane U., 1952. Assoc. prof. history, dean men. La. Coll., Pineville, 1952-56; prof. La. Coll., 1956-62, dean coll., 1962-87, pres. emeritus, 1987—; past chmn. La. Labor Mediation Bd.; arbitrator Am. Arbitration Assn., Fed. Mediation and Conciliation Svc.; former mem. La. Adv. Coun. on Vocat.-Tech. Edn.; mem. Air Force ROTC Adv. Coun.; bd. dirs. Michael's Stores, Pizza Inn, Inc., Ill. Ctrl. R.R. Author: The United States and the Spanish Civil War, 1936-39, 1956, Reluctant Rebel, The Secret Diary of Robert Patrick, 1861-1865, 1959. Bd. dirs. Ruston Civic Symphony; trustee Falcon Found. Served to lt. comdr., aviator USNR, 1942-46. Mem. Am. Hist. Assn., Miss. Valley Hist. Assn., So. Hist. Assn., Nat. Acad. Arbitrators., Phi Alpha Theta. Club: Rotary. Home: 2502 Tanglewood Dr Ruston LA 71270-2244

TAYLOR, FRED M., school system administrator. Supt. Gadsden (Ala.) City Schs. State finalist Nat. Supt. Yr. award, 1993. Office: Gadsden City Schs 1026 Chestnut St Gadsden AL 35901-3918

TAYLOR, FREDERICK WILLIAM, JR., lawyer; b. Cleve., Oct. 21, 1933; s. Frederick William Sr. and Marguerite Elizabeth (Kistler) T.; m Mary Phyllis Osborne, June 1, 1985. BA in History, U. Fla., 1957; MA in Near East Studies, U. Mich., 1959; JD cum laude, NYU, 1967. Bar: N.Y. 1968,

Calif. 1969, U.S. Dist. Ct. (cen. dist.) Calif. 1969. Govt. rels. rep. Arabian Am. Oil Co., Dhahran, Saudi Arabia, 1959-63; oil supply coord. Arabian Am. Oil Co., N.Y.C., 1963-68; sr. counsel Arabian Am. Oil Co., Dhahran, 1969-71, gen. mgr. govt. rels. orgn., 1971-74, v.p indsl. rels., 1974-78; assoc. O'Melveny & Myers, L.A., 1968-69; ptnr. Burt & Taylor, Marblehead, Mass., 1978-80; pres., chief exec. officer nat. med. enterprises Internat. Group, L.A., 1980-82; counsel Chadbourne, Parke & Afridi, United Arab Emirates, 1982-84; ptnr. Sidley & Austin, Cairo, 1984-87, Singapore, 1987-93; spl. counsel Heller Erhman White & McAuliffe, L.A. and Singapore, 1993-94; svc. counsel law divsn. AT&T Internat., Riyadh, Saudi Arabia, 1994—. Contbr. articles to profl. jours. Mem. ABA, Calif. Bar Assn. Order of Coif, Singapore Cricket Club, Tanglin Club, Chanqi Sailing Club, American Club. Home: Box 6942 Taos NM 87571 Office: AT&T Internat, PO Box 4945 al Mutlaq Bldg Sitteen St. Riyadh 11412, Saudi Arabia

TAYLOR, GARY L., federal judge; b. 1938. AB, UCLA, 1960, JD, 1963. Assoc. Wenke, Taylor, Evans & Ikola, 1965-86; judge Orange County Superior Ct., 1986-90, U.S. Dist. Ct. (ctrl. dist.) Calif., Santa Ana, 1990—. With U.S. Army, 1964-66. Mem. Am. Coll. Trial Lawyers, State Bar Calif., Orange County Bar Assn. (bd. dirs 1980-82, founder, chmn. bus. litigation com., Disting. Svc. award 1983).

TAYLOR, GARY LEE, marketing executive; b. Akron, Ohio, Mar. 28, 1953; s. Robert Eugene and Betty Jayne (Mayles) T.; m. Karen Sue Bates, Oct. 7, 1978; children: Lindsay Rose, Craig Scott. BBA in Mktg., U. Akron, 1975, MBA in Mktg., 1977. Media coordinator Rex Humbard Found., Akron, 1977-79, gen. mgr. advt., 1979-80, dir. mktg., 1980-82; pres., chief exec. officer InfoCision Mgmt. Corp., Akron, 1982—. Editor newsletter Telephone Fundraising News, 1986; contbr. articles to Religious Broadcasting mag., Fundrasing Mgmt. mag. Speaker, lectr. Nat. Religious Broadcasters Conv., 1982-89; chmn. bd. Profl. Transp. Services, Inc., 1988—; bd. dirs. M.W. Region Athletes and Entertainers for Kids. Republican. Methodist. Avocations: golf, fishing, racquetball. Office: InfoCision Mgmt Corp 325 Springside Dr Akron OH 44333-4505

TAYLOR, GENE, congressman; b. New Orleans, La., Sept. 17, 1953; m. Margaret Gordon; children: Sarah, Emily. Ba, Tulane U.; grad., U. So. Miss. Sales rep. Stone Container Corp.; U.S. senator from Miss., dist. 46, 1984-89; mem. 101st-104th Congresses from 5th Miss. dist., 1989—; mem. govt. reform & oversight com., ranking minority mem. merchant marine. With USCGR. Mem. Lions, Rotary, Kappa Sigma. Roman Catholic. Office: US Ho of Reps 2447 Rayburn Washington DC 20002-1025*

TAYLOR, GEORGE ALLEN, advertising agency executive; b. Lake City, Iowa, Oct. 26, 1906; s. Bertrand Franklin and Mabel (Minard) T.; m. Regina Helen Wickland, July 3, 1938 (div. 1956). PhB in Fine Arts, Northwestern U., 1947, MEd, 1951, postgrad., 1951-54; art edn. diploma, U. No. Iowa, 1926. Art supr. pub. schs. Indianola, Iowa, 1926-29; instr. art Simpson Coll., Indianola, 1926-29; designer Modern Art Studios, Chgo., 1929-30; display designer W.J. Rankin Corp., Chgo., 1930-35; creative dir. Arthur Meyerhoff Assocs., Inc., Milw., 1935-38; br. mgr. Arthur Meyerhoff Assocs., Inc., L.A., 1938-42; account exec. Arthur Meyerhoff Assocs., Inc., Chgo., 1942-59, account supr., 1959-61, v.p. adminstrn., 1961-65, vice chmn., 1965-80; pres. GATA Ltd.; lectr. semantics Ill. Inst. Tech., Chgo., 1947-50, Northwestern U. Sch. Commerce, 1948. Lyricist popular songs. Reader Recs. for Blind, Inc., 1956—, CRIS Radio, 1981-85; mem. Chgo. Architecture Found., Landmarks Preservation Coun. Ill. Recipient 1st place awards in copy and layout L.A. Advt. Club, 1940. Mem. Lions, Clubs, Friends of Downtown, Art Inst. Chgo. Home (summer): 1212 N Lake Shore Dr Apt 29a-s Chicago IL 60610-2375 Home (winter): 4767 Ocean Blvd # 201 San Diego CA 92109-2475

TAYLOR, GEORGE FREDERICK, newspaper publisher, editor; b. Portland, Oreg., Feb. 28, 1928; s. George Noble and Ida Louise (Dixon) T.; m. Georga Bray, Oct. 6, 1951; children—Amelia Ruth, Ross Noble. B.S., U. Oreg., 1950. Reporter Astoria (Oreg.) Budget, 1950-52, Portland Oregonian, 1952-54; copy reader Wall St. Jour., 1955-57, reporter, 1957-59, Detroit Bur. chief, 1959-64, Washington corr., 1964-68; asst. mng. editor Wall St. Jour., San Francisco, 1968-69; mng. editor Wall St. Jour., N.Y.C., 1970-77, exec. editor, 1977-86; pub. North Bend (Oreg.) News, 1986—, Prime Time, 1987—, Coquille Valley Sentinel, 1989—. Served to lt. USAF, 1955-57. Office: 1 Bartons Aly Coquille OR 97423-1270

TAYLOR, GEORGE KIMBROUGH, JR., lawyer; b. Atlanta, Aug. 28, 1939; s. George Kimbrough and Helen Whiteside (Shepard) T.; m. Carol Ann McKinney, July 1, 1961 (div. 1976); children: George Kimbrough III, Thomas Haynes; m. Triska Ashley Drake, Oct. 2, 1981. BA, Emory U., 1961; LLB, U. Va., 1964. Bar: Ga. 1964, U.S. Dist. Ct. (no. dist.) Ga. 1964, U.S. Ct. Appeals (11th cir.) 1964. Assoc. Kilpatrick & Cody, Atlanta, 1964-70, ptnr., 1970—; bd. dirs. Ont. Reins. Co. Ltd., Cayman Islands; pres., bd. dirs. Rugby Holdings, Inc., Atlanta, 1984-94, Norcros U.S.A., Inc., Atlanta, U.S. Properties, Inc., Atlanta, 1983-92. Chmn. bd. dirs. Spl. Audiences, Inc. Atlanta, 1985-87; bd. dirs. Atlanta Symphony Orch., 1986—, Atlanta Opera, 1995—, Ga. Humanities Coun., Atlanta, 1986-93, Ga. Coun. Internat. Visitors, Atlanta, 1987—, pres., 1993, Brit.-Am. Bus. Group, 1989—, pres., 1994, Ga. Conservancy, 1979-85; bd. visitors Emory U., Atlanta, 1993—; mem. exec. com. Brit.-Am. Bus. Coun., 1995—; mem. alumni coun. U. Va. Law Sch.; active Leadership Atlanta. Woodrow Wilson fellow, 1961. Mem. ABA, Internat. Bar Assn., Atlanta Bar Assn., Order of Coif, Soc. Internat. Bus. Fellows, Phi Beta Kappa, Omicron Delta Kappa. Democrat. Clubs: Capital City, World Trade (Atlanta). Avocations: sailing, skiing. Office: Kilpatrick & Cody 1100 Peachtree St Ste 2800 Atlanta GA 30309

TAYLOR, GERALD H., communications comapny executive; b. 1941; married. BS in Physics, San Francisco State U. With MCI Telecom. Corp., 1969—, past pres. Mid-Atlantic and West divsns., MCI Airsignal, MCI Consumer Markets, now pres., COO; also pres., COO MCI Comm. Corp., 1994—, also bd. dirs. Office: MCI Telecommunications Corp 1133 19th St NW Washington DC 20036-3604 also: MCI Comm Corp 1801 Pennsylvania Ave NW Washington DC 20006

TAYLOR, GLENHALL E., banker; b. 1925; married. B.S., U. Calif., 1949. With Wells Fargo Bank N.A., San Francisco, 1949-82, asst. v.p., 1963-65, v.p. consumer loans, 1965-66, v.p. credit cards, 1966-70, v.p. consumer loans, 1970-74, sr. v.p. comml. loans, 1974-77, sr. v.p., sr. credit officer internat., 1977-80, exec. v.p. credit policy, 1980-82; vice chmn. Seafirst Corp., Seattle, 1983-85; dir. Seafirst Corp., 1985-95; vice chmn. bd. BankAmerica Corp., San Francisco, 1985-90; ret., 1990. Office: BankAmerica Corp 555 California St San Francisco CA 94104-1502

TAYLOR, GRACE ELIZABETH WOODALL (BETTY TAYLOR), lawyer, educator, law library administrator; b. Butler, N.J., June 14, 1926; d. Frank E. and Grace (Carlyon) Woodall; m. Edwin S. Taylor, Feb. 4, 1951 (dec.); children: Carol Lynn Taylor Crespo, Nancy Ann Filer. AB, Fla. State U., 1949, MA, 1950; JD, U. Fla., 1962. Instr. asst. librarian U. Fla. 1950-56; asst. law librarian Univ. Libraries, U. Fla., 1956-62; dir. Legal Info. Ctr., 1962—, prof. law, 1976—; Clarence J. TeSelle prof. of law U. Fla., 1994—; trustee Nat. Ctr.for Automated Rsch., N.Y.C., 1978—; past chmn. joint com. on LAWNET, Am. Assn. Law Librs., Am. Assn. Law Schs. and ABA, 1978-86; cons. to law librs., 1975—; mem. adv. com. N.E. Regional Data Ctr., U. Fla.1990—. Co-author: American Law Publications, 1986, 21st Century: Technology's Impact, 1988, also articles. Recipient 1st Disting. Aluni award Fla. State U. Sch. Libr. Sch., 1983; Lewis Scholar Fla. Legislature, 1949-50; Grantee NEH,1981-82, Coun. Libr. Resources, 1984-86. Mem. ABA (Law Libr. Congress facilities com. 1991—), Am. Assn. Law Librs. (exec. bd. 1981-84), Am. Assn. Law Schs. (accreditation com. 1978-81), OCLC Users Coun. (pres. 1983-86), Phi Beta Kappa (v.p. U. Fla. chpt. 1994-95), Beta Phi Mu. Democrat. Methodist. Avocations: computers, genealogy, crafts, gardening, grandchildren. Office: U Fla Legal Info Ctr Gainesville FL 32611

TAYLOR, GUY WATSON, symphonic conductor; b. Anniston, Ala., Dec. 25, 1919; s. Stokely Brackston and Ola Mae (Shaw) T.; m. Renee Lifton, Oct. 19, 1947; children: Eric Anthony, Ellen Jane. Diploma, Birmingham Conservatory of Music, 1941, Juilliard Sch. Music, 1948; pvt. studies and

workshops with, Dimitri Mitropoulos, 1941-42, L'Ecole Monteux, 1949, Eugene Ormandy, 1953, George Szell, 1956. Conductor Springfield (Ohio) Symphony Orch., 1948-51, Nashville Symphony Orch., 1951-59, Phoenix Symphony Orch., 1959-69, Fresno Philharmonic Orch., 1969-84; guest conductor, U.S., Gt. Britain, Philippines, P.R., Can. and Mexico City; musical commentator Springfield News & Sun, 1948-51, Ariz. Republic, 1959-61, Fresno Bee, 1970-76. Has appeared on, BBC Radio, CBS-TV. Served with AUS, 1942-45. Recipient Conductor Recognition award Am. Symphony Orch. League, 1960, Alice M. Ditson Orch. award, 1961, citation for adventuresome programming of contemporary music ASCAP, 1977. Mem. Am. Symphony Orch. League, Phi Mu Alpha Sinfonia.

TAYLOR, HAL WINSLOW, lawyer; b. Memphis, Nov. 3, 1940; s. Charles Sidney and Frances (Yarbrough) T.; m. Patricia Diane Martin, Dec. 27, 1969 (div. Jan. 1986). BS, U. Tenn., 1962; JD, U. Va., 1966; LLM, Georgetown U., 1972. Bar: Tenn. 1966, Calif. 1971, N.Y. 1986, Mass. 1989. Asst. counsel Dept. Labor, Washington, 1971-75; assoc. Heller, Ehrman, White & McAuliffe, San Francisco, 1976-78; tax counsel INA Corp., Phila., 1979-80; v.p., sr. counsel Chem. Bank, N.Y.C., 1981-86; ptnr. Gaston & Snow, Boston, 1986—. Lt. USN, 1966-69. Mem. University Club (N.Y.C.), Union Club (Boston). Democrat. Presbyterian. Office: Gaston & Snow 1 Federal St Boston MA 02110-2003

TAYLOR, HAROLD ALLEN, JR., federal agency administrator; b. San Jose, Calif., June 27, 1936; s. Harold Allen and Marie Anna (Briody) T.; B.A., Brown U., 1958; M.A., U. Minn., 1968; m. Theresa Josephine Kustritz, Aug. 29, 1963; children: Harold A., III, Ruth F. Cook, Jonathan L.E. Project leader office Mineral Supply, U.S. Bur. Mines, Mpls., 1968-70, commodity specialist div. ferrous metals, Washington, 1970-74; commodity analyst U.S. Internat. Trade Commn., Washington, 1974-80; sr. commodity specialist br. indsl. minerals U.S. Bur. Mines, Washington, 1980—. Pres. Arlington (Va.) Interfaith Coun., 1994, 95. Mem. AIME (sec 1983-84, first vice chmn. 1984-85, chmn. 1985-86, exec. adv. bd. mineral econs. subsect. 1981-83, 87-91), Am. Soc. Testing and Materials (chair subcom. nomenclature of com. on dimension stone 1987—, sec. com. dimension stone 1990—), Soc. Govt. Economists (chmn. materials policy panels 1979-84), Toastmasters (pres. 1978, 81, 87, 91, asst. area gov. 1978-79, area gov. 1979-80, dep. div. lt. gov. 1989-90), Capitol Metals Forum (steering com. 1979-85), Sigma Gamma Epsilon. Contbr. articles to profl. jours. and encys. Home: 6321 11th Rd N Arlington VA 22205-1717 Office: US Bur Mines 810 7th St NW Washington DC 20241-0001

TAYLOR, HARRY WILLIAM, physics educator; b. nr. Sturgeon Valley, Sask., Can., Sept. 28, 1925; s. William and Gladys (Evans) T.; m. Wanda Jason, June 18, 1949; children: Allison Leslie, Karen Elizabeth. B.Sc., U. Man., 1951, M.Sc., 1952, Ph.D., 1954. Lectr. U. Man., Winnipeg, 1952-53; fellow NRC, Ottawa, Ont., Can., 1954-55; mem. faculty Queen's U., Kingston, Ont., 1955-61; asst. prof. Queen's U., 1957-61; asso. prof. U. Alta., Edmonton, 1961-65; prof. physics U. Toronto, 1965-91, prof. emeritus physics, 1991—. Mem. Am. Phys. Soc., Inst. Physics, Inst. Nuclear Engrs., AAAS. Research and publs. in nuclear structure through gamma-ray spectroscopy; observation of angular correlations of cascade gamma rays; heavy ion nuclear spectroscopy; nuclear fallout on arctic plants. Home: 3525 Grand Forks Rd, Mississauga, ON Canada Office: U Toronto, Physics Dept, Toronto, ON Canada 5

TAYLOR, HELEN LAVON HOLLINGSHED, association executive, early childhood consultant; b. Fort Valley, Ga., July 27, 1942; d. Earl Herman Hollingshed and Helen (Flowers) Southall; m. Robert Joseph Taylor, Sept. 11, 1965. BA, Howard U., 1964; MA, Cath. U., 1973; cert. mgmt., Tex. Tech. U., 1985, UCLA, 1991. Grad. asst. Howard U., Washington, 1964-65; social worker Nat. Child Day Care Assn., Washington, 1966-68, head start program dir., 1968-70, preschool project dir., 1971-78, exec. dir., chief exec. officer, 1979—; early childhhod cons. various orgns., 1970—; founder, bd. dirs. Washington (D.C.) Child Devel. Coun., 1975—; child care adv. com. Nat. Black Child Devel. Inst., Washington, 1988—. Chairperson D.C. Coun. Adv. Com. on Child Care Facilities, Washington, 1974-78, Mayor's Adv. Com. for Early Childhood Devel., Washington, 1986—; chair pers. com. Bright Beginnings, Inc., Washington, 1991-92. Recipient Svc. award Adminstrn. for Children, Youth and Families, Washington, 1986, Svc. award Nat. Head Start Assn., Alexandria, Va., 1988, Community Svc. award D.C. Dept. Consumer and Regulatory Affairs, Washington, 1990. Mem. Nat. Assn. for Edn. Young Children (conf. chairperson 1982, bd. mem. 1991—), Assn. for Childhood Edn. Internat. (publ. com. 1983-85), Washington (D.C.) Assn. for Edn. Young Children (co-chairperson 1978-80, Svc. award 1991), Delta Sigma Theta, Inc. (chair arts and letters com. 1984-86), Coalition of 100 Black Women). African Methodist Episcopal. Office: Nat Child Day Care Assn 1501 Benning Rd NE Washington DC 20002

TAYLOR, HENRY ROTH, marketing executive; b. Phila., Sept. 25, 1940; s. Henry and Helen Jacquelyn (Roth) T.; B.S., Millersville State Coll., 1962; postgrad., Pa. State U., 1963-65; MS, Temple U., 1966; postgrad., Queens Coll., Oxford U., summer 1973; m. Cynthia Mary DeMarco, Aug. 17, 1968; children: Christopher, Peter, Brett, Melissa. Mng. editor Montgomery Newspapers, Ft. Washington, Pa., 1962-66; news bur. dir. Drexel U., Phila. 1966-68, ann. fund dir., 1971-72; dir. pub. relations Ursinus Coll., Collegeville, Pa., 1968-71, Widener U., Chester, Pa., 1972-74; asst. v.p., dir. athletics Spring Garden Coll., Phila., 1974-87, lectr. mass media, 1979-87; exec. dir. Phila. sect. Profl. Golfers Assn., 1987-89; dir. Athletics, chmn. physical edn. Phila. Coll. Textiles and Sci., 1989-92; dir. sports, hobby rels. Fleer Corp., Mt. Laurel, N.J., 1992—; mem. exec. com. Eastern Pa. Athletic Conf., 1982-86; pres. Eastern States Athletic Conf., 1985-87; part-time sportscaster, talk show host, announcer Sta. WIFI, Phila., 1965-70; with Ted Taylor Assocs., Abington, Pa., part-time 1965-74; part-time sportscaster and announcer WIBF Radio, Jenkintown, Pa., 1970-74, Sta. WNPV, Lansdale, Pa., 1983-88; host collectibles syndicated radio show, Sports By-Line USA, 1992—. Founding pres. Glenside Boys Athletic Club, 1958-63; commr. Keystone State Football Conf., 1959-62; dir. Pop Warner Found., 1963-65; pres. Warminster Youth 963-65; pres. Warminster Youth Activities Orgn., 1965-71; mem. Abington Twp. Spl. Police, 1974-81, sec., 1977-78; exec. com. Highland Sch. PTA, 1974-81; mem. Abington Twp. Police Rev. Bd., 1977-81; co-chmn. Phila. Baseball Card and Sports Memorabilia Shows, 1975-82, Ocean City (N.J.) Shows, 1981-84, North Penn. Shows, 1991-92. Named Man of Yr., Hatboro Jr. C. of C., 1962, Suburban Bucks Jr. C. of C., 1967, Citizen of Yr., Southampton Kiwanis, 1972, One of 100 Outstanding Grads. in 100 Yrs., Cheltenham (Pa.) High Sch., 1984; recipient Ursinus Coll. Varsity Club award, 1970; Piece of the Walk civic award Ocean City, N.J., 1981. Mem. Council for Advancement and Support of Edn., Pa. Assn. Colls. and Univs., Phila. Pub. Relations Assn., Pub. Relations Soc. Am., Suburban Pub. Relations Club, Phila. Sportswriters Assn., Coll. Sports Info. Dirs. Am., Eastern Pa. Sports Collectors Club (pres. 1978-82). Republican. Presbyterian. Lodge: Rotary. Author: (with Robert E. Schmierer) Phillies Checklist Book, 1979, World Series Baseball Cards, 1987, The Rookie Book, 1988, 300 All-Time Baseball Stars, 1988, Encyclopedia of Baseball Cards, 1988, Sports Card Explosion, 1993; assoc. editor Sports Collectors Bible, 1978; columnist Sports Collectors Digest, 1980-92, Phila. Daily News, 1991—; contbr. articles to profl. jours. Home: 1527 Edgehill Rd Abington PA 19001-2609 Office: Fleer Corp Exec Plz 1120 Route 73 Mount Laurel NJ 08054-5113

TAYLOR, HENRY SPLAWN, literature educator, poet, writer; b. Loudoun County, Va., June 21, 1942; s. Thomas Edward and Mary Marshall (Splawn) T.; m. Sarah Spencer Bean, June 12, 1965 (div. 1967); m. Frances Ferguson Carney, June 29, 1968 (div. 1995); children: Thomas Edward, Richard Carney; m. Sarah Spencer, June 11, 1995. BA, U. Va., 1965; MA, Hollins (Va.) Coll., 1966. Instr. English Roanoke (Va.) Coll., 1966-68; asst. prof. U. Utah, 1966-71; mem. faculty Am. U., Washington, 1971—, prof. lit., 1976—, co-dir. M.F.A. program in creative writing, 1982—, dir. Am. studies program, 1983-84; dir. U. Utah Writers' Conf., 1970-72; writer-in-residence Hollins Coll., spring 1978; poet-in-residence Wichita State U., 1994. Author: (poems) The Horse Show at Midnight, 1966, Breakings, 1971, An Afternoon of Pocket Billiards, 1975, Desperado, 1979, The Flying Change, 1985 (Pulitzer prize 1986), (essays) Compulsory Figures: Essays on Recent American Poets, 1992, (textbooks) Poetry: Points of Departure, 1974, The Water of Light: A Miscellany in Honor of Brewster Ghiselin, 1976, (cassette album) Landscape with Tractor, 1985, co-translator: The Children of Herakles, 1981; contbg. editor Hollins Critic, 1971-78; editorial cons.: Magill's Literary Ann.,

1972-90; cons. editor: Poet Lore, 1977-84. Fellow creative writing Nat. Endowment Arts, 1978, 86; grantee Nat. Endowment Humanities, 1980-81. Mem. Agrl. History Soc., Am. Lit. Translators Assn. Democrat. Quaker. Club: Cosmos (Washington). Home: PO Box 23 Lincoln VA 22078-0023 Office: Am U Dept Lit Washington DC 20016

TAYLOR, HUGH PETTINGILL, JR., geologist, educator; b. Holbrook, Ariz., Dec. 27, 1932; s. Hugh Pettingill and Genevieve (Fillerup) T.; m. Candis E. Hoffman, 1982. B.S., Calif. Inst. Tech., 1954; A.M., Harvard U., 1955; Ph.D., Calif. Inst. Tech., 1959. Asst. prof. geochemistry Pa. State U., 1960-62; mem. faculty div. geol. and planetary scis. Calif. Inst. Tech., 1962—, now prof. geology, Robert P. Sharp prof., 1981; Crosby vis. prof. M.I.T., 1978; vis. prof. Stanford U., 1981; William Smith lectr. Geol. Soc. London, 1976; Hofmann lectr. Harvard U., 1980; Cloos lectr. Johns Hopkins U., 1986; with U.S. Geol. Survey, Saudi Arabia, 1980-81. Author: The Oxygen Isotope Geochemistry of Igneous Rocks, 1968, Stable Isotopes in High Temperature Geological Processes, 1986, Stable Isotope Geochemistry, 1991; assoc. editor Bull. Geol. Soc. Am, 1969-71, Geochimica Cosmochimica Acta, 1971-76; editor Chem. Geology, 1985-91. Recipient Day medal Geol. Soc. Am., 1993, Urey medal European Assn. Geochemistry, 1995. Fellow NAS, Soc. Econ. Geol., Geol. Soc. Am., Am. Geophys. Union, Mineral. Soc. Am. (councillor); Am. Acad. Arts and Scis.; mem. Geochem. Soc. (councillor). Republican.

TAYLOR, HUMPHREY JOHN FAUSITT, information services executive; b. Meshed, Iran, Sept. 6, 1934; came to U.S., 1976; s. Geoffrey Fausitt and Frances Margaret (Kenyon) T.; m. Penelope Helen Taylor, Dec. 19, 1970; children: Zanthe, Helena. BA with honors, Cambridge (Eng.) U., 1958. Dist. officer Govt. of Tanganyika, 1959-62; mktg. and opinion researcher Nat. Opinion Poll, Eng., 1963-66; mng. dir. Opinion Rsch. Ctr., Eng., 1966-76; with Louis Harris and Assocs., N.Y.C., 1976-81; pres. Harris and Assocs., N.Y.C., 1981—; CEO, 1992—. Trustee U.S. com. UNICEF, N.Y.C., 1981-87, Overseas Devel. Coun., Washington, 1987—, Am. Health Found., 1988-91, chmn.; trustee Royal Soc. Medicine Found., 1992—. 2d lt. Brit. Army, 1953-55. Avocations: history, biographies, skiing, tennis, traveling. Office: Louis Harris & Assoc 630 5th Ave 11th FL New York NY 10111-0001

TAYLOR, JACK C., automobile company executive; b. 1922. With Lindburg Cadillac, St. Louis, 1944-50, Forrest Cadillac, St. Louis, 1951-56; chmn. bd. Enterprise Rent-A-Car, St. Louis, 1980—. With USN, ret. Office: Enterprise Rent-A-Car 8850 Ladue Rd Saint Louis MO 63124*

TAYLOR, JACK G., JR., art director. Art dir.: (films) Nine to Five, 1980, Looker, 1981, Uncommon Valor, 1983, Nightmares, 1983, Star 80, 1983, Real Genius, 1985, Gung Ho, 1986, Cape Fear, 1992, A Perfect World, 1993; prodn. designer: (films) Million Dollar Mystery, 1987. Office: care Art Directors Guild 11365 Ventura Blvd #315 Studio City CA 91604*

TAYLOR, JACQUELINE SELF, state legislator; b. Thomas, Okla., Feb. 16, 1935; d. MArtin Richard and Bertha Inez (Murray) Self; m. Nelson Edwin Taylor, May 17, 1952; children: Lucinda Susan Shannon, Robin Melinda. BA in Social Work, Boise State U., 1971. Lic. social worker Idaho. Dir. vol. svcs. Idaho Dept. of Health & Welfare, Caldwell, 1971-77; dir. Clatsop County Assn. REtarded Citizens, Astoria, Oreg., 1980-81; ptnr., owner Johnson Drug Store, Warrenton, Oreg., 1984-92; state rep. Legis. Assembly State of Oreg., 1991-93. Bd. dirs. Pioneer House, Warrenton, 1992, Astoria C. of C., 1988-91, treas., 1988-91; civil svc. com. City of Astoria, 1988-91; mem. North Coast Women's Polit. Caucus, 1988 (named Outstanding Woman 1988), Oreg. Women's Polit. Caucus. Democrat. Avocations: gardening, history, tribal work. Home: 1324 Miller Ln Astoria OR 97080 Office: Oreg State Legis State Capitol Salem OR 97310

TAYLOR, JAMES, JR., lawyer; b. Florence, S.C., Dec. 6, 1942; s. James and Thelma (Baker) T.; m. Jayne S.C. Bridge, May 19, 1974; children: James Robson, Ashley Baker. BA cum laude, U. of the South, 1965; JD, Georgetown U., 1973. Bar: D.C. 1973, U.S. Ct. Internat. Trade 1977, U.S. Ct. Appeals (fed. cir.) 1982, U.S. Supreme Ct. 1978. Assoc. Busby Rivkin Sherman Levy and Rehm, Washington, 1973-76, Busby and Rehm, Washington, 1977-78; ptnr. Busby Rehm and Leonard, Washington, 1979-87, Dorsey & Whitney, Washington, 1988-92, Stroock & Stroock & Lavan, Washington, 1992—. Lt. USN, 1967-70; Vietnam. Mem. ABA, D.C. Bar Assn., Club Interallié (Paris). Episcopalian. Avocations: skiing, fishing, languages. Home: 3319 Cleveland Ave NW Washington DC 20008-3456 Office: Stroock & Stroock & Lavan 1150 17th St NW Ste 600 Washington DC 20036-4652

TAYLOR, JAMES B., securities trader, financial planner; b. Kenosha, Wis., June 23, 1944; s. George R. and Virginia Dare (Scenters) T.; m. Rebecca Matthew, Feb. 14, 1983; children: Joseph F., Jennifer R., Jessica J. Cert., Ky. Bus. Coll., Lexington, 1969; student, U. Wis., 1970-72. Lic. NASD Securities Broker, Tex. Securities Exchange Commn. Lab. technician Allen-Bradley Co., Inc., Milw., 1962-65; mktg. Jaeger Ols, Inc., Milw., 1965-68; mktg., retail mgmt. G.W. Taylor Co., Inc., Williamson, W.Va., 1968-69; acct. RTE Corp., Waukesha, Wis., 1969-72; mktg. new product introduction Victor Comptometer, Milw., Chgo., 1972-76; account exec., personal fin. mgmt. Merrill Lynch Pierce Fenner & Smith, Houston, 1977-80, Rotan Mosle Inc. (merger with Paine Webber Corp.), Houston, 1980-84, Paine Webber Corp./Rotan Mosle Inc., Houston, 1984—; instr. investing and personal fin. mgmt., Merrill Lynch, Houston. 1976-80, Paine Webber, Houston, 1980—; internat. stockbroker. Author articles on personal investing and fin. mgmt. for bus. mags., profl. newsletters, and internat. newspapers; prin. works exhibited in numerous galleries including Art Cetera, Houston, Harris County Coll. Gallery, Houston, Wimberly (Tex.) Galleries; photographs represented in pvt. collections in Europe and the U.S.; contbr. photos to local newspapers. Parrish coun. Catholic Ch., Livingston, Tex., 1979, 80, 81; dir. Hispanic Arts Group, Houston, 1990-91; active election campaign Ronald Reagan, Jack Fields. Mem. Stockbroker Soc. Am., Visual Arts Alliance. Avocations: art, photography, travel. Office: Paine Webber/Rotan Mosle Inc 16945 Norhchase Ste 100 Houston TX 77060

TAYLOR, JAMES BLACKSTONE, aviation company executive; b. N.Y.C., Dec. 14, 1921; s. James Blackstone Taylor, Jr. and Aileen (Sedgwick) Taylor Lippincott; m. Margaret Krout, May 3, 1947; children—James Blackstone IV, Ray K., Jane A., W. Thorne. Grad., Taft sch., Watertown, Conn. Pres. Upressitmetal Cap Corp., N.Y.C., 1948-59; v.p. Am. Flange, N.Y.C., 1959-62, Pan Am. World Airways, N.Y.C., 1962-69, Cessna Aircraft, Wichita, Kans., 1969-76, pres., chmn. bd. Canadair, Inc., Westport, Conn., 1976-85; pres., chief exec. officer, dir. Gates Learjet Corp., Tucson, 1985-88; vice chmn., advisor Flight Svcs. Group, Fairfield, Conn., 1988—; pres. James B. Taylor Assoc., Westport, Conn., 1988—. Served to lt. USNR, 1942-46. Recipient Runner Up award World Skeet Shooting Championship, 1962. Mem. Gathering of Eagles (Aviation Man of Yr. 1984), Nat. Aviation Club, Wing's Club (v.p., bd. dirs. 1965-67, 83-87), Country Club of Fairfield, Weston Gun Club, Clove Valley Rod and Gun Club (LaGrangeville, N.Y.) (bd. dirs. 1983-87). Republican. Episcopalian. Home: 32 Regents Park Westport CT 06880-5533 Office: Flight Svcs Group 111 Beach Rd Fairfield CT 06430-6668

TAYLOR, JAMES DAVID, health care executive; b. Pitts., Oct. 3, 1947; s. Howard Alvin and Florence Elizabeth (Dale) T.; m. Helen Blair, Apr. 14, 1973; children: Megan, Brian. BA, Westminster Coll., 1969; MBA, Duquesne U., 1972; MPH, U. Pitts., 1974. Fin. trainee Gen. Electric Co., Erie, Pa., 1969-70; adminstrv. trainee Presbyn. U. Hosp., Pitts., 1972; adminstrv. resident Montefiore Hosp., Pitts., 1973-74; mgr. Geisinger Med. Ctr., Danville, Pa., 1974-76, adminstrv. officer, 1976-78; asst. adminstr. Scott & White, Temple, Tex., 1978-81; dir. Scott & White co., Temple, Tex., 1982-91; prin. Inova, Temple, Tex., 1991-93; exec. dir. Christie Clinic Assn. Champaign, Ill., 1993—; chmn. of bd. Personal Care Health Mgmt. Inc. 1993—; fellowship preceptor Scott & White, Temple, Tex., 1985—; chmn. Joint Am. Coll. of Health Care Execs. and Med. Group Mgmt. Nat. Com. Chgo. and Denver, 1986-87; bd. dirs. Personal Care HMO and Covenant Med. Ctr. Contbr. articles to profl. jours. Bd. dirs. Columbia-Montour Home Health, Bloomburg, Pa., 1976-78; chmn. Grace Sch., Temple 1980-86; elder Grace Presbyn. Ch., Temple 1985-87. Recipient Third Place Nat. award Health Industry Mfg. Assn., 1975. Fellow Am. Coll. Healthcare

Execs.; Am. Coll. Med. Group Adminstrs.; mem. Am. Mktg. Assn., Issues Mgmt. Assn., Med. Group Mgmt. Assn. (chmn. Joint Am. Coll. Health Care Execs. and Med. Group Mgmt. Nat. Com. 1986-87), Beta Gamma Sigma, Omicron Delta Epsilon. Republican. Avocations: running, swimming, coin collecting. Home: 2003 O Donnell Dr Champaign IL 61821-6466 Office: Christie Clinic Assos 101 W University Ave Champaign IL 61820

TAYLOR, JAMES E., lawyer. BS, U. Mo., 1964, JD, 1966. Bar: Mo. 1966. Pvt. practice St. Joseph, Mo., 1966-70; atty. Southwestern Bell Telephone Co., St. Louis, 1970-75; gen. atty. Southwestern Bell Telephone Co., Kansas City, Mo., 1975-81; gen. atty.-Mo. Southwestern Bell Telephone Co., 1981, gen. solicitor-Mo., 1983; v.p., gen. counsel Southwestern Bell Telephone Co., Tex., 1986-88; v.p., gen. counsel, sec. Southwestern Bell Telephone Co., St. Louis, 1988-92; v.p., gen. counsel Southwestern Bell Telephone Co., 1992—

TAYLOR, JAMES F., JR., computer graphics company executive; b. 1944. BS, U. Montevallo, 1966. With IBM Fed. Systems, Huntsville, Ala., 1966-69; with Intergraph Corp., 1969—, formerly v.p. graphics software, now exec. v.p., also bd. dirs. Office: Intergraph Corp 1 Madison Industrial Park Huntsville AL 35894-0001

TAYLOR, J(AMES) HERBERT, cell biology educator; b. Corsicana, Tex., Jan. 14, 1916; s. Charles Aaron and Delia May (McCain) T.; m. Shirley Catherine Hoover, May 1, 1946; children: Lynne Sue, Lucy Delia, Michael Wesley. B.S., So. Okla. State U., 1939; M.S., U. Okla., 1941; Ph.D., U. Va., 1944. Asst. prof. bacteriology and botany U. Okla., Norman, 1946-47; assoc. prof. botany U. Tenn., Knoxville, 1948-51; asst. prof. botany Columbia U., N.Y.C., 1951-54; assoc. prof. Columbia U., 1954-58, prof. cell biology, 1958-64; prof. biol. sci. Fla. State U., Tallahassee, 1964-83, Robert O. Lawton disting. prof. biol. sci., 1983-90, prof. emeritus, 1990—; assoc. dir. Inst. Molecular Biophysics, Fla. State U., 1970-79; dir. Inst. Molecular Biophysics, 1980-85; cons. Oak Ridge Nat. Lab., 1949-51; research collaborator Brookhaven Nat. Lab., 1951-58; nat. lectr. Sigma Xi Research Soc. Author: Molecular Genetics, Vol. 1, 1963, Vol. 2, 1965, Vol. 3, 1979; DNA Methylation and Cellular Differentiation, 1983; also papers on molecular genetics; contbr. over 100 articles in field to profl. jours. Pres. Unitarian Ch. Tallahassee, 1968-70. Served with M.C. U.S. Army, 1944-46, PTO. Recipient Meritorious Research award Mich. State U., 1960; Guggenheim fellow Calif. Inst. Tech., 1958-59. Mem. Nat. Acad. Scis., AAAS, Am. Inst. Biol. Sci., Am. Soc. Cell Biologists (pres. 1969-70), Biophysics Soc., Genetics Soc. Am. Democrat. Office: Fla State U Inst Molecular Biophysics Tallahassee FL 32306

TAYLOR, JAMES JOHN, academic adminstrator; b. Mpls., July 26, 1940; s. James John and Mary Elizabeth (Mason) T.; m. Margaret Claire Zacha, Dec. 28, 1976; children: Jerry William, John Allen. BA, Oblate Coll. of S.W., 1966; MEd, St. Louis U., 1969, MBA in Fin., 1972; cert. of advanced studies, Harvard U., 1977. Dept. head, tchr. Althoff High Sch., Belleville, Ill., 1966-71; asst. to controller U. of South Fla., Tampa, 1972-79; project mgr. W.Va. Bd. of Regents, Morgantown, 1979-83; prin., project dir. Am. Mgmt. Systems, Arlington, Va., 1983-90; mng. cons. Taylor Mgmt. Group, Arlington, 1990-91; v.p. bus. and finance Guam Community Coll., 1991—; founder, treas. Guam Ednl. Radio Found., KPRG-FM. Member adv. com. on spl. edn. Arlington Sch. Bd., 1981-83; founder, producer St. Louis High Sch. Film Makers Festival, 1968-72; contbr. articles to profl. jours. Founding mem. Harvard Club at Nat. Press Club; mem. Phi Delta Kappa. Avocations: photography, duplicate bridge, scuba diving. Home: # 29 Cruz Heights Talofofo GU 96930

TAYLOR, JAMES MARION, II, automotive wholesale executive; b. Andalusia, Ala., Jan. 20, 1926; s. Marion Doby and Catherine (Hill) T.; m. Abbie Chapman Henderson, Mar. 22, 1947; children: Cathy, James III, Merrily, Abbie, John. Student, U.S. Merchant Marine Acad., 1944-46, Auburn U., 1946-47. Salesman Taylor Parts, Inc., Andalusia, 1947-49, salesman, dir., 1950, v.p., sales mgr., 1950-61, v.p., gen. mgr., 1961-62, pres., 1962-88, chmn., chief exec. officer, 1988-92; bd. dirs. Covington County Bank, Andalusia, chmn. Southern Nat., Andalusia, 1986—; mem. adv. bd. Shatterproof Glass Co., Detroit, 1968, AC-Delco, Detroit, 1966-67, Walker (Tenneco), Racine, Wis., 1985. Bd. dirs. Ala. Wildlife Fedn., Montgomery, Ala., 1974-77, pres., 1977-78; bd. dirs. Lurleen B. Wallace Jr. Coll. Found., Andalusia, 1986-89, Covington County Bd. Edn., Andalusia, 1960-74, City of Andalusia Downtown Devel. Authority, 1989-92, City of Andalusia Indsl. Devel. Bd., 1969-71. Mem. Nat. Assn. Wholesalers (bd. dirs. and 1st vice chmn. 1988-90, chmn.-elect 1991, chmn. 1992, treas. 1993-94), Automotive Hall of Fame (Midland, Mich. bd. dirs. 1986-94), Automotive Info. Coun. (bd. dirs. 1987-92), Andalusia C. of C. (bd. dirs. 1960-62, 89-92), Auburn Alumni Assn. (life), Kiwanis (pres. Andalusia club 1969-70), Am. Legion. Republican. Baptist. Avocations: hunting, fishing, gun collecting. Home: 104 S Ridge Rd Andalusia AL 36420-4214 Office: Taylor Parts Inc PO Box 4008 Montgomery AL 36103-4008

TAYLOR, JAMES MARSHALL, food products executive; b. MorganField, Ky., Dec. 13, 1929; s. James Mansfield and Hester Louise (Marshall) T.; m. Pauline Elizabeth Kasper, Feb. 1, 1959; children: Christopher David, Timothy Michael. BSC, U. Louisville, 1958, MBA, 1963. Asst. treas. Savannah (Ga.) Foods and Indys., 1968-72, asst. v.p. corp. devel., 1972-75, v.p. corp. devel., 1975-88, sr. v.p. administrn., 1988—. Served to cpl. U.S. Army, 1951-53. Republican. Clubs: Chatham, Savannah. Avocations: golf, lepidopterist. Home: 4 Tangletree Ln Savannah GA 31411-2604 Office: Foods & Industries Inc PO Box 339 Savannah GA 31402-0339

TAYLOR, JAMES VERNON, musician; b. Boston, Mar. 12, 1948; s. Isaac M. and Gertrude (Woodard) T.; children: Sarah Maria, Benjamin Simon. Student, Milton Acad., Mass., 1962-66, Arlington Sch., Belmont, Mass., 1966-67. Recorded for Apple Records, 1968, Warner Bros. Records, 1970-77, CBS Records, 1977; numerous concert appearances; composer, performer: (albums) Sweet Baby James, 1970, Mud Slide Slim and The Blue Horizon, 1971, One Man Dog, 1972, Walking Man, 1974, Gorilla, 1975, In the Pocket, 1976, James Taylor's Greatest Hits, 1977, J.T., 1977, Flag, 1979, Dad Loves His Work, 1981, That's Why I'm Here, 1985, Never Die Young, 1986, New Moon Shine, 1991, James Taylor (Live), 1993. Recipient 13 Gold Album awards, 4 Platinum Album awards, 3 Gold Single awards, Grammay award; named Best Pop Vocal Male, 1971, 77. Office: care Peter Asher Mgmt 644 N Doheny Dr West Hollywood CA 90069-5596

TAYLOR, JAMES WALTER, marketing educator; b. St. Cloud, Minn., Feb. 15, 1933; s. James T. and Nina C. Taylor; m. Joanne Syktte, Feb. 3, 1956; children: Theodore James, Samuel Bennett, Christopher John. BBA, U. Minn., 1957; MBA, NYU, 1960; DBA, U. So. Calif., 1975. Mgr. research div. Atlantic Refining, Phila., 1960-65; dir. new product devel. Hunt-Wesson Foods, Fullerton, Calif., 1965-72; prof. mktg. Calif. State U., Fullerton, 1972—; cons. Smithkline Beecham Corp., Tokyo, Govt. of Portugal, Lisbon, Sealand Svcs., Seattle, KF Fackhandel, Stockholm. Author: Profitable New Product Strategies, 1984, How To Create A Winning Business Plan, 1986, Competitive Marketing Strategies, 1986, The 101 Best Performing Companies In America, 1987, How to Write A Successful Advertising Plan, 1988, The Complete Manual for Developing Winning Strategic Plans, 1988, Every Manager's Survival Guide, 1989, Developing Winning Strategic Plans, 1992, How to Develop Successful Advertising Plans, 1993. Fulbright scholar Ministry of Industry, Lisbon, Portugal, 1986-87, U. We. Sydney, Australia, 1989-90; recipient Merit award Calif. State U., 1986-90. Mem. The Planning Forum, Am. Mktg. Assn., Strategic Mgmt. Assn., Assn. for Consumer Rsch., Acad. Mktg. Sci. Home: 3190 Mountain View Dr Laguna Beach CA 92651-2056 Office: Calif State U Dept of Mktg Nutwood at State College Fullerton CA 92634

TAYLOR, JANELLE DIANE WILLIAMS, writer; b. Athens, Ga., June 28, 1944; d. Alton L. and Frances (Davis) Williams; m. Michael H. Taylor, Apr. 8, 1965; children: Angela Michelle, Alisha Melanie. Student, Augusta Coll., 1980-81. Orthodontic nurse Dr. W.H. Williams, Athens, 1962-65, Dr. James Metts, Augusta, Ga., 1969-72, Dr. Jack Carter, Augusta, 1973; med. research technologist Med. Coll. Ga., Augusta, 1975-77; writer Ga., 1977—; bd. dirs. So Beth Williams Romance Screenplay Award; lectr. writing Augusta Coll., other schs. and workshops, 1982—. Author: Savage Ecstasy, 1981, Valley of Fire, 1984, First Love, Wild Love, 1984 (Maggie awd. 1984),

Golden Torment, 1984 (Reviewer's Choic awd. Romantic Times 1984), Savage Conquest, 1985, Stolen Ecstasy, 1985, Moondust and Madness, 1986, Sweet, Savage Heart, 1986 (Golden Pen cert. 1986), Destiny's Temptress, Defiant Ecstasy, 1982, Forbidden Ecstasy, 1982, Brazen Ecstasy, 1983, Tender Ecstasy, 1983, Love Me With Fury, 1983, Bittersweet Ecstasy, 1987, Wild Is My Love, 1987, Fortune's Flames, 1988, Passions Wild and Free, 1988, Wild Sweet Promise, 1989, Kiss of the Night Wind, 1989, Whispered Kisses, 1990, Follow the Wind, 1990 (Romantic Times Reviewers Choice award 1990-91), Forever Ecstasy, 1991, Promise Me Forever, 1991, Christmas Rendezvous, 1991, Sharing Christmas, 1991, Stardust and Shadows, 1992, Midnight Secrets, 1992, Taking Chances, 1993, Janelle Taylor Three Complete Novels, 1993, The Last Viking Queen, 1994, Chase The Wind, 1994, Starlight And Splendor, 1994, The New Janelle Taylor Three Novel Collection, 1994, Destiny Mine, 1995, Anything for Love, 1995, Moonbeams and Magic, 1995; contbr. How to Write a Romance and Get It Published, 1983, 2d edit., 1984, Candlelight, Romance and You, 1983, My First Real Romance, 1985, Booksellers' Cookbook, 1988. Recipient trophy award for Indian series Romantic Times, 1985, Sioux Sacred Medicine Wheel and Cheyenne Red-tail Hawk Feather Coup hon. Gray Eagle Siouc Indian series, 1983-84; cert. Vocat. Indsl. Clubs Am., 1986, cert. of merit AAUW, 1986, Bronze Pen award, 1988, Silver Pen award, 1989; named to Writers' Hall of Fame, Romantic Times, 1988, Cowboy Hall of Fame; named hon. flying col. Delta Airlines, 1987. Mem. Romance Writers Am., Novelists Inc., Western Writers Am., Ga. Romance Writers Am., Aughors League/ Authors Guild, Ga. Writers Coalition for Literacy, Augusta Author's Club. Republican. Baptist. Avocations: collecting spoons and coins, swimming, fishing, genealogy, English, Indian and American history. Office: PO Box 211646 Augusta GA 30917-1646 Office: PO Box 211646 Augusta GA 30917-1646

TAYLOR, JEFF, reporter. Reporter Kansas City Star. Recipient Pulitzer Prize for nat. reporting, 1992, Sigma Delta Chi award. Office: Kans City Star 1729 Grand Ave Kansas City MO 64108*

TAYLOR, JERRY LYNN, microbiologist, educator; b. Warrenton, Mo., Jan. 12, 1947; d. Albert Marcus and Naomi Azalee (Greer) Hafner; m. William Carl Taylor, June 12, 1971. BA in Microbiology, U. Mo. Columbia, 1969, MA in Botany, 1971; PhD in Microbiology, So. Ill. U. 1976. Asst. prof. microbiology Calif. State U., Long Beach, 1976-77; postdoctoral fellow Med. Coll. Wis., Milw., 1977-79, instr., 1979-80, asst. prof. microbiology, 1980-81, asst. prof. microbiology, ophthalmology, 1981-84, assoc. prof. microbiology and ophthalmology, 1984-90, prof., 1990—, vice-chmn. microbiology, 1988—. Contbr. sci. papers to jours. Mem. AAAS, Am. Soc. Microbiology, Am. Soc. Virology, Internat. Assn. Antiviral Rsch., Internat. Assn. Interferon and Cytokine Rsch., Assn. Rsch. in Vision and Ophthalmology, Phi Beta Kappa, Sigma Xi. Office: Med Coll Wis Dept Microbiology 8701 W Watertown Plank Rd Milwaukee WI 53226-3548

TAYLOR, JIMMIE WILKES, naval officer; b. Nashville, Apr. 16, 1934; s. James Wilkie and Mary Elizabeth (Steagall) T.; m. Annette Lee, June 20, 1958; children: Jimmie W. II, Todd L. (dec.), Tracey E. Taylor Mitchell. Student, U. Tenn., 1952-54, Mid. Tenn. State U., 1954-56; BA in Geography, San Diego State U., 1979. Commd. ensign USNR, 1958; augmented in USN, 1965, advanced through grades to rear adm., 1987, various assignments, 1958-65; air launch missile officer USS Constellation, 1965-67; asst. ops. officer Fighter Squadron 124, 1967-68; ops. officer Fighter Squadron 51, 1968-70; squadron ops. officer Fighter Squadron 124, 1970-74; exec. officer Fighter Squadron 2, 1974-75, comdg. officer, 1975-76; officer in charge, comdr. Navy Blue Force Air Test and Evaluation Squadron 4, 1976-77; detailed to Naval Adminstrv. Command, Naval Tng. Ctr., San Diego, 1977-79; ops. officer USS Coral Sea, 1979-81; chief of staff Comdr. Fighter Airborne Early Warning Wing, Pacific, 1981-82; comdr. Tng. Air Wing 2, 1982-84; head aviation plans and program div. Office of Chief of Naval Ops., 1984-85; vice chief naval edn. and tng., 1985-88, chief naval air tng., 1988-91; v.p. armed svcs. Pensacola (Fla.) Area C. of C. Contbr. articles to profl. jours. Bd. dirs. USO, Corpus Christi, Tex., 1988-91; pres. Tex. aux. Navy-Marine Corps Relief Soc., Corpus Christi, 1988-91; bd. dirs. Nimitz Mus. Found. (life), Navy Tailhook Assn. (life), Corpus Christi C. of C. (bd. dirs. 1989-91), Corpus Christi Yacht Club, Kappa Sigma, Pensacola Sports Assn. Decorated Legion of Merit with two gold star, Meritorious Svc. Medal, Air medal with7, Navy Expeditionary Medal, Nat. Def. Svc. Medal, Armed Forces Expeditionary Medal, Vietnam Svc. Medal with Silver Star; Gallantry Cross Color (Republic of Vietnam); recipient Topcat award USN/Grumman Aerospace Corp., 1973. Mem. Assn. Naval Aviation Inc. (life), Naval Aviation Mus. Avocations: racquetball, golf, skiing, hunting, fishing. Home: 6064 Forest Green Rd Pensacola FL 32505 Office: Burdeshaw Assocs Ltd 4701 Sangamore Rd Bethesda MD 20816-2508 also: 117 W Garden St PO Box 550 Pensacola FL 32505

TAYLOR, J(OCELYN) MARY, museum administrator, zoologist, educator; b. Portland, Oreg., May 30, 1931; d. Arnold Llewellyn and Kathleen Mary (Yorke) T.; m. Joseph William Kamp, Mar. 18, 1972 (dec.). B.A., Smith Coll., 1952; M.A., U. Calif., Berkeley, 1953, Ph.D., 1959. Instr. zoology Wellesley Coll., 1959-61, asst. prof. zoology, 1961-65; assoc. prof. zoology U. B.C., 1965-74; dir. Cowan Vertebrate Mus., 1965-82, prof. dept. zoology, 1974-82; collaborative scientist Oreg. Regional Primate Research Ctr., 1983-87; prof. (courtesy) dept. fisheries and wildlife Oreg. State U., 1984—; dir. Cleve. Mus. Nat. History, 1987—; adj. prof. dept. biology Case Western Res. U., 1987—. Assoc. editor Jour. Mammalogy, 1981-82. Contbr. numerous articles to sci. jours. Trustee Benjamin Rose Inst., 1988-93, Western Res. Acad., 1989-94, U. Circle, Inc., 1987—, The Cleve. Aquarium, 1990-93, Cleve. Access to the Arts, 1992—; corp. bd. Holden Arboretum, 1988—. Fulbright scholar, 1954-55; Lalor Found. grantee, 1962-63; NSF grantee, 1963-71; NRC Can. grantee, 1966-84; Killam Sr. Research fellow, 1978-79. Mem. Soc. Woman Geographer's, Am. Soc. Mammalogists (1st v.p. 1978-82, pres. 1982-84, Hartley T. Jackson award 1993) Australian Mammal Soc., Cooper Ornithol., Assn. Sci. Mus. Dirs. (v.p. 1990-93), Rodent Specialist Group of Species Survival Commn. (chmn. 1989-93), Sigma Xi. Episcopalian. Office: Cleve Mus Natural History 1 Wade Oval Dr Cleveland OH 44106-1701

TAYLOR, JOE CLINTON, judge; b. Durant, Okla., Mar. 28, 1942; s. Luther Clinton and Virena (Parker) T.; m. Margaret Pearl Byers, June 8, 1963; children: Marna Joanne, Leah Alison, Jocelyn Camille. Student, Southeastern State Coll., 1960-62; BA, Okla. State U., 1965; J.D., U. Okla., 1968. Bar: Okla. 1968. Practice law Norman, Okla., 1968-69; apptd. spl. dist. judge Durant, 1969-72; asso. dist. judge Bryan County, Okla., 1972-76; dist. judge, chief judge 19th Dist. Ct., 1976-93; presiding judge Southeastern Okla. Jud. Adminstrv. Dist., 1984-92, Choctaw Tribal Ct., 1979-83; pres. Okla. Jud. Conf., 1987-88; chmn. Assembly Presiding Judges, 1989-90; presiding judge trial div. Okla. Ct. on the Judiciary, 1991-93; Okla. Ct. of Tax Rev., 1992-93; judge Okla. Ct. of Appeals, Tulsa, 1993—. Chmn. bd. dirs. Durant Youth Svcs., 1976-93; bd. dirs. Bryan County Youth Svcs., Inc., 1971-93. Mem. Phi Sigma Epsilon, Delta Theta Phi. Mem. Ch. of Christ. Club: Lion. Home: PO Box 329 Durant OK 74702-0329 Office: Ct Appeals 601 State Bldg 440 S Houston Ave Tulsa OK 74127-8919

TAYLOR, JOEL SANFORD, lawyer; b. Hazleton, Pa., Oct. 8, 1942; s. Robert Joseph and Alice Josephine (Sanford) T.; m. Donna Rae Caron, Mar. 26, 1967; children: Jason, Adam, Jeremy. BA, Swarthmore Coll., 1965; LLB, Columbia U., 1968. Bar: N.Y. 1969, U.S. Dist. Ct. (so. and ea. dists.) N.Y. 1970, U.S. Ct. Appeals (2d cir.) 1970, Ohio 1973, U.S. Dist. Ct. (no. dist.) Ohio 1974, U.S. Supreme Ct. 1974, U.S. Dist. Ct. (so. dist.) Ohio 1975, U.S. Ct. Appeals (6th cir.) 1975, U.S. Dist. Ct. (ea. dist.) Ky. 1979. Law clk. hon. Constance B. Motley U.S. Dist. Ct., N.Y.C., 1968-69; assoc. Paul, Weiss, Rifkind, Wharton & Garrison, N.Y.C., 1969-72; exec. asst. Ohio Office of Budget & Mgmt., Columbus, Ohio, 1972-74; asst. atty. gen. Ohio Atty. Gen., Columbus, 1974-83, chief counsel, 1983-91; ptnr. Dinsmore & Shohl, Columbus, 1991—; pres. Ohio Sundry Claims Bd., Columbus, 1972-74, Ohio State Controlling Bd., Columbus, 1973-74; mem., bd. trustees Ohio State Tchrs. Retirement System, Columbus, 1986-91. Mem. ABA, Ohio State Bar Assn., Columbus Bar Assn., Environ. Law Inst., Columbia Law Alumni Assn., Ohio Sierra Club. Office: Dinsmore & Shohl 175 S 3rd St Ste 330 Columbus OH 43215-5134

TAYLOR, JOHN BRIAN, economist, educator; b. Yonkers, N.Y., Dec. 8, 1946; s. John Joseph and Lorraine (Crowley) T.; m. Raye Allyn Price, Dec. 30, 1972; children: Jennifer Lynn, John Andrew. AB in Econs. summa cum laude, Princeton U., 1968; PhD, Stanford U., 1973. Asst. prof. econs. Columbia U., N.Y.C., 1973-77, assoc. prof., 1977-79, prof., 1979-80; prof. econs. and pub. affairs Princeton U., 1980-84; prof. econs. Stanford U., 1984—, dir. ctr. for Econ. Policy Rsch., 1994—; vis. prof. econs. Yale U., 1980; sr. staff economist Pres.'s Coun. Econ. Advisers, 1976-77, mem. 1989-91; econometric cons. Townsend-Greenspan and Co., N.Y., 1978-81; research advisor Fed. Res. Bank Phila., 1981-84; research assoc. Nat. Bur. Econ. Research, 1980—; exec. com. Am. Econ. Assn., 1991-94; rsch. economist Bank Of Japan, Tokyo, 1987; hon. adviser, 1994—. Author: Macroeconomics, 1986; Macroeconomic Policy in the World Economy, 1993, Economics, 1995; co-editor Am. Econ. Rev., 1985-89; assoc. editor Econometrica, 1981-85, Jour. Econ. Dynamics and Control, 1978-85, Jour. Monetary Econs., 1978-83; contbr. articles to profl. jours. NSF grantee, 1979-81, 81-83, 83-86, 86-89, 92-95; Guggenheim Found. fellow, 1983-84. Fellow Econometric Soc., Am. Acad. of Arts and Sci. Office: Stanford U Dept Econs Stanford CA 94305

TAYLOR, JOHN CHESTNUT, III, lawyer; b. N.Y.C., Jan. 7, 1928; s. John Chestnut and Jean Elizabeth (Willis) T.; m. Dolores Yvonne Sunstrom, Nov. 17, 1950; children: Jane Willis Taylor Salem, John Sunstrom, Anne Holliday Taylor Bambino. B.A., Princeton U., 1947; LL.B., Yale U., 1950. Bar: N.Y. 1950, D.C. 1972. Assoc. Paul, Weiss, Rifkind, Wharton & Garrison, N.Y.C., 1950, 52-60, ptnr., 1961-85, 87-91, of counsel, 1986-87, 92—; exec. v.p. AEA Investors Inc., N.Y.C., 1985-86, pres., 1986-87. Bd. dirs. AFS Intercultural Programs, Inc., N.Y.C., 1972-80, trustee, 1973-79, chmn., 1975-79; trustee Carnegie Corp. N.Y., N.Y.C., 1975-84, chmn., 1979-84; bd. dirs. Vocat. Tng. Ctr., Inc., 1986-88, N.Am. Tng. Svcs. Inc., 1988-92; trustee, mem. exec. com. Devereux Found., 1992—, vice chmn., 1994—. Served to capt. JAGC, AUS, 1950-52. Mem. Assn. of Bar of City of N.Y., Order of Coif, Phi Beta Kappa, Phi Delta Phi. Democrat. Home: 1 Hammock View Ln Savannah GA 31411-1611 Office: Paul Weiss Rifkind Wharton & Garrison 1285 Ave of the Americas New York NY 10019-6064

TAYLOR, JOHN JACKSON (JAY), writer, international consultant, retired foreign service officer; b. Little Rock, Dec. 4, 1931; s. Alfred Wesley and Annie Laurie (Cain) T.; m. Elizabeth Rose, July 9, 1954; children: John Jr., Laurie, Amy, Cynthia. BA, Vanderbilt U., 1952; MA, U. Mich., 1968. 3d sec. U.S. Fgn. Service, Accra, Ghana, 1957-59; 2d sec. U.S. Fgn. Service, Taichung and Taipei, Republic of China, 1960-65; Chinese affairs analyst Dept. State, Washington, 1966-67; staff assoc. Ctr. for Chinese Studies, U. Mich., Ann Arbor, 1967-68; U.S. consul Kuching, Malaysia, 1968-70; chief external reporting U.S. Consulate Gen., Hong Kong, 1970-74; officer-in-charge Chinese affairs Dept. State, Washington, 1974-75; staff mem. Asian affairs Nat. Security Council, Washington, 1975-77; polit. counselor U.S. Embassy, Pretoria/Capetown, 1977-80; polit. cons. U.S. Embassy, Peking, 1980-82; research fellow Fairbanks Ctr. for Chinese Studies, Harvard U., Cambridge, Mass., 1982-83; dir. East Asian analysis Dept. State, Washington, 1983-85; dep. asst. sec. state Bur. Intelligence and Research, Dept. State, Washington, 1986-87; chief of mission U.S. Interests Sect., Havana, Cuba, 1987-90; diplomat in residence Carter Presdl. Ctr., Emory U., 1990-92; sr. mem. State Task Force 2000, 1992-93; vice pres. Global Bus. Access. Author: China and Southeast Asia, 1974, 76, The Dragon and the Wild Goose, 1987, 90, The Rise and Fall of Totalitarianism, 1993; contbr.: China and National Security, 1985. Served as Naval Aviator with USMC, 1953-57. Mem. Fgn. Svc. Assn., Asian Soc., Royal Asian Soc., Acad. of Polit. Sci. Unitarian.

TAYLOR, JOHN JOSEPH, nuclear engineer; b. Hackensack, N.J., Feb. 27, 1922; s. John J.D. and Johanna F. (Thibideau) T.; m. Lorraine Crowley, Feb. 5, 1943; children: John B., Nancy M., Susan M. BA, St. John's U., Jamaica, N.Y., 1942, DSc (hon.), 1975; MS, U. Notre Dame, 1947. Mathematician Bendix Aviation Corp., Teterburo, N.J., 1946-47; engr. Kellex Corp., N.Y.C., 1947-50; v.p. water reactor div. Westinghouse Electric Corp., Pitts., 1950-81; v.p. nuclear power Electric Power Research Inst., Palo Alto, Calif., 1981-83; mem. adv. com. Oak Ridge (Tenn.) Nat. Lab., 1973-83, Brookhaven Nat. Lab., Upton, N.Y., 1986-92, Inst. for Nuclear Power Ops., 1988-95; mem. adv. com. Argonne (Chgo.) Nat. Lab., 1980-86, bd. dirs.; cons. Office of Tech. Assessment, Washington, 1975-93; mem. internat. adv. group Internat. Atomic Energy Agy., Vienna, Austria, 1992—. Co-author Reactor Shielding Manual, 1953, Naval Reactor Physics Manual; contbr. articles to profl. jours. Bd. regents St. Mary's Coll., Moraga, Calif. Lt. (j.g.) USN, 1942-45. Recipient Order of Merit, Westinghouse Electric Corp., 1957, George Westinghouse Gold medal ASME, 1990. Fellow AAAS (bd. dirs.), NAE, Am. Nuclear Soc. (bd. dirs., Walter Zinn award 1993); mem. Am. Phys. Soc., Cosmos Club (Washington). Republican. Roman Catholic. Home: 15 Oliver Ct Menlo Park CA 94025-6685 Office: Electric Power Research Inst PO Box 10412 3412 Hillview Ave Palo Alto CA 94304-1395

TAYLOR, JOHN L., communications executive; b. 1951. BS, U. N.C., Charlotte, 1976. With Deloitte Haskins & Sells, Charlotte, 1976-84, Video Vision, Inc., Charlotte, 1986; various positions, now pres., CEO Ingram Entertainment Inc., La Vergne, Tenn. Office: Ingram Entertainment Inc 1123 Heil Quaker Blvd La Vergne TN 37086-3610

TAYLOR, JOHN LOCKHART, city official; b. N.Y.C., Nov. 4, 1927; s. Floyd and Marian (Lockhart) T.; m. Barbara Becker, July 19, 1952; children: Catherine, Robert, William, Susan. A.B., Middlebury Coll., 1952; M.Govtl. Adminstrn., U. Pa., 1956. Reporter Providence Jour.-Bull., 1952-54; adminstrv. intern City of Xenia, Ohio, 1955-56; mcpl. mgr. Borough of Narberth, Pa., 1956-60, Twp. of Lakewood, N.J., 1960-64; asst. city mgr. Fresno, Calif., 1964-65; city mgr., 1965-68, Kansas City, Mo., 1968-74, Berkeley, Calif., 1974-76; lectr. U. Pa., 1957-58, Golden Gate U., 1977; sr. urban mgmt. specialist Stanford Research Inst., 1977-80; dir. Internat. Devel. Center, 1980-82; clk. of bd. suprs. City of San Francisco, 1982—; pres. Calif. Clks. Bd. Suprs. Assn., 1988-89. Served with USN, 1945-48. Mem. Internat. City Mgrs. Assn., Am. Soc. Pub. Adminstrn., Mcpl. Execs. Assn. (pres. 1991-93). Home: 2133 Stockton St San Francisco CA 94133-2067 Office: City Hall 401 Van Ness Ave San Francisco CA 94102

TAYLOR, JOHN WILKINSON, education educator; b. Covington, Ky., Sept. 26, 1906; s. John Wesley and Ethel (Wilkinson) T.; m. Katherine Willis Wright; 1 child, Walter Bradford; m. Helen Hutchinson Greene (dec. Jan. 1966); stepdau. Patricia (Mrs. H.E. Thornber, Jr.); m. June Cornell Fairbank (dec. Oct. 1986); step-children: Margaret, Mrs. Terrill K. Jory) (dec. Aug. 1985), Laura (Mrs. Louis C. Sudler, Jr.), Kellogg III, Susan (Mrs. Walter B. Taylor), Elizabeth (Mrs. John W. Cameron), David. A.B., Columbia, 1929, A.M., 1930, Ph.D., 1936; H.D., St. Joseph Coll., 1970. Asst. curriculum research Tchrs. Coll., Columbia, 1927; asst. elementary edn. Tchrs. Coll., 1928, asst. curriculum, 1929, asst. secondary edn., 1929-30, instr. comparative edn., 1930; tchr. English Kaiser Friederich Realgymnasium, Berlin-Neukoeln, Germany, 1930-31; adml. adviser to pres. John Day Co., 1932-33; asso. in edn., dir. fgn. study Columbia, 1934-35; also asst. to chmn. Columbia (New Coll.), 1935-37; chmn. admissions, scholarship, loan, curriculum and personnel guidance coms., 1937-38; assoc. prof. comparative edn. and sec. instnl. survey com., adminstrv. asst. to pres. La. State U., 1938-40, dir. bur. ednl. research, 1941-43; pres. U. Louisville, 1947-50; dep. dir.-gen. UNESCO, 1951-54, acting dir.-gen., 1952-53; exec. dir. Chgo. Ednl. TV Assn., 1954-71, bd. mem., 1969-73; acting pres. Learning Resources Inst., N.Y.C., 1960-63; pres. Learning Resources Inst., Chgo., 1963-70; dir. Midwestern Ednl. Television Network, Inc., 1966-70; bd. dirs. Fed. Res. bank Louisville, 1948-50; spl. cons. on ednl. TV N.Y. U., 1958; Dir. Adult Edn. Council Greater Chgo., 1956-62, vice chmn., 1959-60; mem. Chgo. Council on Fgn. Relations, 1954-72, bd. mem., 1970-72; citizens bd. U. Chgo., 1956-80; adv. com. Midwest Office Inst. Internat. Edn., 1954-58; S.E. Chgo. Commn., 1955-63; mem. Midwest Council on Airborne TV Instrn., 1959-62; Exec. sec. to Am. Council on Edn. Commn., survey U. Ill. 1942; on leave from La. State U.; mem. Round Table Meeting on Peace UNESCO, Paris, 1966; Bd. dirs. Chgo. Area Sch. TV, 1964-70, Sight Systems Inst., 1974-78; mem. Mass. Edn. Study, 1963-64; Mem. bus. adv. council Chgo. City Jr., 1964-66; chmn. bd. Chgo. City Coll., 1966-84; bd. dirs. North River Commn., 1967-70; Bd. dirs. Internat. Inst. Adminstrv. Scis., 1951-55; council advisors U.S. Commr. Edn., 1950-52; adv. panel Comptroller Army, 1950-53. Author: Youth Welfare in Germany, 1936, also survey reports.; contbr.

articles to edn. profl. jours. Mem. Supts. Roundtable No. Ill., 1954-71, Tricounty Ednl. TV Coun., 1955-63, Citizens Com. U. Ill., 1959-73, Chgo. Civic Com. World Refugees, 1960-69. Commd. capt. O.R.C. AUS; div. mil govt. occupied countries, 1943; maj., 1944; lt. col., 1945, promoted to brig. gen. (assimilated rank), 1946, NATOUSA; North Africa asst. dir., then dir. studies Mil. Govt. Sch. and Holding Ctr., 1943-44; chief edn. and religious affairs br. U.S. Mil. Govt. for Germany (planning unit in Eng., 1944-45, operational unit in Berlin, 1945-47); U.S. rep. on Quadripartite Edn. Com. for Germany 1945-47, Berlin. Decorated Legion of Merit; chevalier French Legion of Honor; officer French Legion of Honor; named Man of Year Louisville, 1950, Chicagoan of Yr. in Edn. Jr. C. of C., 1962; recipient Chgo. medal for merit, 1972, Disting. Alumnus award Peabody Demonstration Sch.-Univ. Sch. Nashville, 1990. Mem. NEA, Am. Acad. Polit. and Social Sci., Am. Legion, Chgo. Assn. Commerce and Industry (chmn. edn. com. 1959-69), Internat. Platform Assn., Acad. TV Arts and Scis. (gov. Chgo. 1958-71), Omicron Delta Kappa, Phi Delta Kappa, Kappa Delta Pi, Phi Kappa Phi. Presbyn. Clubs: Executives (Louisville), Filson (Louisville), Arts (Louisville), Rotary (Louisville), Salmagundi (Louisville), Pendennis (Louisville); Allied Circle (London); Union League (Chgo.), Wayfarers (Chgo.), Casino (Chgo.), Commercial. (Chgo.) Home and Office: 2960 N Lake Shore Dr Apt 2706 Chicago IL 60657-5600

TAYLOR, JONATHAN FRANCIS, agribusiness executive; b. Kampala, Uganda, Aug. 12, 1935; came to U.S., 1980; s. Reginald William and Ruth (Tyson) T.; m. Anthea Gail Proctor, May 1965; children: Luke Augustus James, Matthew Justinian Robert, James Maximillian Rex. B.A., Oxford U. (Eng.), 1957, M.A., 1959. Adminstrv. sec. Booker Agribusiness Ltd., London, 1960-64; mgr. projects Booker Agribusiness Ltd., Nigeria, Kenya, Indonesia & others, 1964-76; chmn. Booker Agribusiness Ltd., 1976-84; chief exec. Booker PLC, London, 1984-93, chmn., 1993—; bd. dirs. Arbor Acres Farm Inc., Glastonbury, Conn., Tate & Lyle PLC, London, MEPC PLC, London; chmn. Ellis & Everard PLC, Bradford, Equitable Life Assurance Soc. Chmn. Bodleian Libr. campaign; gov. Sch. Oriental and African Studies London U; chmn. Found. Devel. of Polish Agriculture; dir. Internat. Agribus. Mgmt. Assn., Winrock Internat. Inst. Agrl. Devel. Clubs: Knickerbocker (N.Y.C.); Travellers (London). Office: Booker PLC, Portland Ho / Stag Pl, London SW1E 5AY, England

TAYLOR, JOSEPH HOOTON, JR., radio astronomer, physicist; b. Phila., Mar. 29, 1941; s. Joseph Hooton and Sylvia Hathaway (Evans) T.; m. Marietta Bisson, Jan. 3, 1976; children: Jeffrey, Rebecca, Anne-Marie. BA in Physics, Haverford Coll., 1963; PhD in Astronomy, Harvard U., 1968; DSc (hon.), U. Chgo., 1985, U. Mass., 1994. Research fellow, lectr. Harvard U., 1968-69; asst. prof. astronomy U. Mass., Amherst, 1969-72; assoc. prof. U. Mass., 1973-77, prof., 1977-81; profl. physics Princeton U., 1980—, James McDonnell Disting. prof. physics, 1986—. Author: Pulsars, 1977. Recipient Dannie Heineman prize in astrophysics Am. Inst. Physics/Am. Astron. Soc., 1980, Tomalla Found. prize in gravitation and cosmology, 1985, Magellanic Premium award Am. Philos. Soc., 1990, Einstein prize laureate Albert Einstein Soc., 1991, Wolf Prize in Physics, Wolf Found., 1992, Nobel Prize in Physics, Nobel Foundation, 1993; MacArthur fellow, 1981. Fellow Am. Acad. Arts and Scis., Am. Phys. Soc.; mem. NAS (Henry Draper medal 1985, John J. Carty medal Advancement Sci. 1991), Am. Philos. Soc., Am. Astron. Soc., Internat. Sci. Radio Union, Internat. Astron. Union. Mem. Soc. of Friends. Home: 272 Hartley Ave Princeton NJ 08540-5656 Office: Princeton U PO Box 708 Dept Physics Princeton NJ 08544*

TAYLOR, JOYCE, religious organization executive. Pres. Youth Dept. of Ch. of God in Christ Internat. Office: 137-17 135th Ave S Ozone Park NY 11420

TAYLOR, JUDITH ANN, sales executive; b. Sheridan, Wyo., July 9, 1944; d. Milo G. and Eleanor M. (Wood) Rinker; m. George I. Taylor, Sept. 15, 1962; children: Monte G., Bret A. Fashion dept. mgr. Montgomery Ward, Sheridan, 1968-73; pers. mgr., asst. mgr. Dan's Ranchwear, Sheridan, 1973-80; sales/prodn. coord. KWYO Radio, Sheridan, 1981-83; sales mgr., promotions coord. KROE Radio, Sheridan, 1984—; mng. editor BOUNTY Publ., 1993—; notary pub. State of Wyo., 1985—; lectr., instr. BSA Merit U.; lectr. acad. achievement LVA Adv. Bd., 1993—, instr. TRMS Academic Enrichment Program, 1994-95. mng. editor BOUNTY Publ., 1993—. Sec.-treas. Sheridan County Centennial Com., 1986-89; local sec.-treas. Wyo. Centennial Com., Sheridan, 1986-90; exec. dir. Sheridan-Wyo. Rodeo Bd., 1983—; bd. dirs. Sheridan County Fair Bd., 1991—, treas., 1995—; bd. dirs. "Christmas in April" Sheridan County, 1992—; mem. WJTP Coun., Cheyenne, 1990-92; mem. adv. coun. Tutor-Literacy Vols. of Am., 1993—; Mrs. Santa Claus for local groups; vol. coord. AIDS Quilt. Mem. Wyo. Assn. Broadcasters, S.C.C. of C. (bd. 1988—, pres. 1989-91), UMWA Aux. (pres. 1982-89), Kiwanis (v.p. 1992—, pres.-elect 1993, pres. 1994). Democrat. Christian Ch. Home: 98 Decker Rd Sheridan WY 82801 Office: KROE AM PO Box 5086 Sheridan WY 82801-1386

TAYLOR, JUDITH MUNDLAK, neurologist; b. London, July 26, 1934; came to U.S., 1959; d. Max and Fanny (Shapiro) Mundlak; m. Irvin S. Taylor, 1961; children: David, Hugh. BA, U. Oxford, Eng., 1956; BM, BCh, MA, U. Oxford, 1959. Intern Bklyn. Hosp., 1959-60; resident in ophthalmology Kings County Hosp., Bklyn., 1960-61; resident in neurology Albert Einstein Coll. Medicine/Jacobi Hosp., Bronx, N.Y., 1961-65; asst. prof. neurology, then assoc. clin. prof. neurology Albert Einstein Coll. Medicine/Jacobi Hosp., 1965-78; attending neurologist affiliated hosps. Albert Einstein Coll. Medicine, various locations, 1965-78; with HCFA/ HEW, Washington, 1978-79; acting dir. med. affairs N.Y.C. Health and Hosp. Corp., 1979-80; pres. Med. Assoc. Woodhull P.C., Woodhull Med. & Mental Health Ctr, Bklyn., 1980-83; med. dir. Mobile Health Svc., Pelham, N.Y., 1983-86; dir. med. adminstrn. Travelers Health Network, N.Y.C., 1986—. Contbr. numerous articles on neurology and on history of medicine to various profl. pubs. Fellow N.Y. Acad. Medicine; mem. Med. Adminstrs. Conf. (pres. 1988-89). Office: Travelers Health Network NY 701 Westchester Ave # 310E White Plains NY 10604

TAYLOR, JULIA W., bank executive; b. 1936. Student, N.C. Cen. U., Stonier Graduate Sch. of Banking. With Mechanics and Farmers Bank, Raleigh, 1955-60, asst. cashier, 1966-77, v.p., mgr., 1967-78, sr. v.p., city exec. officer, 1978-83, pres., chief exec. officer, 1983-87, chmn., pres. and chief exec. officer, 1987—; With Bank of Am., L.A., 1960, Broadway Fed. Savs. and Loan Assn., L.A., 1961-63; bd. dirs., exec. com. Mechanics and Farmers Bank, Durham; bd. dirs. Am. Inst. of Banking, Triangle Better Bus. Bur., Downtown Raleigh Devel. Corp., Wheeler Flying Svc., Inc.; mem. N.C. Assembly on Women and Economy; bd. trustees U.N.C. Wilmington. Trustee Bd. St. Joseph's African Meth. Episcopal Ch., Durham; vice chmn. N.C. State Ednl. Assistance Authority; bd. dirs. Jr. Achievement of Raleigh and Wake Co., N.C. Bus. Adv. Bd. Fuqua Sch. of Bus. Duke U., N.C. 4-H Devel. Fund, Inc.; mem. Raleigh Civic Ctr. Authority; bd. assocs. N.C. Child Advocacy Inst. Named Women of Achievement award Silver Medallion in Bus. and Industry YWCA, 1985, The Tarheel of the Week News and Observer, 1986, Atlanta Regional Minority Bus. Advocate of Yr. award U.S. Dept. of Commerce Minority Bus. Devel. Agy., 1987, Nat. Minority Bus. Advocate of Yr. award U.S. Dept. Commerce, 1987; recipient Citizen award Ind. Weekly 1988, 1989. Mem. N.C. Cen. U. Sch. Law (bd. vis.), N.C. Citizens for Bus. & Industry, Conf. State Bank Suprs. (regional rep.), Forest at Duke (bd. dirs.), Africa News (bd. dirs.), N.C. Bankers Assn. (bd. dirs.). Office: Mechanics & Farmers Bank PO Box 1932 Durham NC 27702-1932

TAYLOR, JULIAN HOWARD, metals company executive; b. Emporia, Kans., July 17, 1943; s. Robert Milton and LuVine Ella (Ballard) T. Student, Earlham Coll., Richmond, Ind., 1961-62; B.A., Emporia State U., (Kans.), 1965; Ph.D., Iowa State U., 1969. Economist Bank of Am., San Francisco, 1969-73; v.p., sr. economist Bank of Am., Los Angeles, 1973-75; chief economist Reynolds Metals Co., Richmond, Va., 1975-80, v.p., treas., 1980—. Mem. Internat. Sector Adv. Com., Washington, 1976-80; mem. adv. bd. econs. Gov. Va., 1977-82; bd. dirs. Goodwill of Richmond, 1980-84; chmn. econ. devel. Gov.'s Commn. on Future of Va., 1983. Mem. Nat. Assn. Corp. Treas. (founding dir. 1982—). Office: Reynolds Metals Co 6601 W Broad St Richmond VA 23230-1701

TAYLOR, JULIUS WILLARD, director student health services, physician; b. Holtville, Calif., Dec. 12, 1922; s. Henry Walter and Nancy (Strawn) T.;

m. Lois Ann Derby, June 25, 1949; children: Scott Derby, Sandra Lee. BA, U. Louisville, 1944, MD, 1946. Chief surgeon Aramco, Dhahran, Saudi Arabia, 1956-66, dir. med. dept., 1966-79; dir. student health svcs. Boston U., 1979—; bd. dirs. Butler Bank, Lowell, Mass. Author: Cancer in Saudi Arabia, 1975. Dir. health edn. Boston U., 1980-90; chmn. Charles River Health Svcs., Boston, 1988-90. Capt. USAF, 1946-48. Mem. ACP, Mass. Med. Soc., New Eng. Tennis Assn., Weston Golf Club, Waltham Tennis Club. Republican. Presbyterian. Avocation: fitness. Office: Boston U Student Health Svc 881 Commonwealth Ave Boston MA 02215-1303

TAYLOR, KENARD LYLE, JR., senior manager training; b. Syracuse, N.Y., Dec. 22, 1943; s. Kenard Lyle and Nina T.; m. Sharon Lee Stookey, Dec. 31, 1965; children: Kimberly, Kenard III. BSCE, Ind. Tech. U., 1968; postgrad., Purdue U., 1970-72. Process engr. ARCO, East Chicago, Ind., 1968-71; plant engr. Kiel Chem., Hammond, Ind., 1971-72; mgr. ops. tng. ARCO, 1972-76; sr. mgr. Mfg. Tech., St. Louis, 1976—; chmn. bd. dirs. Mfg. Tech. Author 150 plant tng. workbooks and articles, 1976-95. City coun. mem. City of Valparaiso (Ind.), 1978-83; campaign mgr. Rep. Candidates Porter County, Ind., 1976-95; Center Twp. Rep. chmn., Porter County, Ind., 1993-95; v.p. Ind. JCI Senate, 1978, Ind. Jaycees, 1976; pres. Valparaiso Jaycees, 1974. Mem. Great Lakes API Com. Tng. (assoc.). Republican. Avocations: golf, fishing. Office: Mfg Tech 306 Napoleon St Valparaiso IN 46383-4744

TAYLOR, KENNETH BYRON, JR., librarian, minister, religion educator; b. Russellville, Ala., Dec. 25, 1953; s. Kenneth Byron Sr. and Willene Martha (Sudduth) T.; m. Sheila Carol Mashburn, May 24, 1975; children: Justin, Jonathan, Jordan, Jessica. BS, U. North Ala., 1975; JD, U. Ala., 1978; MDiv, New Orleans Bapt. Theol. Sem., 1986, PhD, 1993; MLIS, La. State U., 1994. Bar: Ala. 1979; ordained to ministry Bapt. Ch., 1987. Staff atty. Legal Svcs. Corp. Ala., Florence, 1979-83; assoc. pastor Elysian Fields Ave. Bapt. Ch., New Orleans, 1984-87, pastor, 1987—; dir. libr. New Orleans (La.) Bapt. Theol. Sem., John T. Christian Libr., 1991—, asst. prof. Evangelism, 1993—. Avocations: hiking, gardening. Office: New Orleans Bapt Theol Sem John T Christian Libr 4110 Seminary Pl New Orleans LA 70126-4619

TAYLOR, KENNETH GRANT, chemistry educator; b. Paterson, N.J., May 12, 1936; s. Ulysses Grant and Susan (De Haan) T.; m. Carla May Rydell, June 17, 1961; children: Koren Lynn, Kevin Grant, Kaylyn Jo. BA, Calvin Coll., 1957; PhD, Wayne State U., 1963. Rsch. assoc. MIT, Cambridge, 1963-64; sr. rsch. assoc. Wayne State U., Detroit, 1964-66; from asst. to assoc. prof. chemistry U. Louisville, 1966-73, prof., 1974—, acting chmn., 1973-74, vice chmn., 1976-78, chmn., 1978-87, assoc. dean. Rsch. Arts and Scis., 1991—; prof. associé Univ. de Nancy I, Nancy Cedex, France, 1974-75, 82-83; vis. prof. U. Lund, Sweden, 1991. Contbr. numerous articles to profl. jours.; co-author, presentor numerous papers at sci. meetings. Rsch. and teaching grantee NIH, NSF, Am. Cancer Soc., Am. Chem. Soc., Dept. Interior, U. Louisville, 1966—. Fellow AAAS; mem. Am. Chem. Soc., Ky. Acad. Sci. Democrat. Presbyterian. Home: 1838 Yale Dr Louisville KY 40205-2031 Office: U Louisville Dept Chemistry Louisville KY 40292

TAYLOR, KENNETH JOHN W., physician of diagnostic imagery; b. Essex, Eng., Mar. 9, 1939; came to U.S., 1975; s. William and Florence (Soulsby) T.; m. Caroline Rix, May 17, 1975; 1 child, Andrew Ian; 1 child by previous marriage, Sally-Anne. B.Sc., U. London, 1961, M.B., B.S., 1964, Ph.D., 1973, M.D., 1975; M.A., Yale U., 1979. Tng. in surgery Royal Surrey Hosp.; tng. in neurosurgery Guys Hosp., London, 1963-66; asst. lectr., then lectr. Guys Hosp., 1967-72; research fellow Royal Marsden Hosp., London, 1973-75; mem. faculty Yale U. Med. Sch., 1975—, prof. diagnostic imaging, 1978—, dir. diagnostic ultrasound, 1975—. Author: Atlas of Grey Scale Ultrasound, 1977, 2d edit., 1985; editor: Diagnostic Ultrasound in Gastrointestinal Disease, 1979; co-author: Manual of Diagnostic Ultrasound, 1981, Medical Imaging Techniques, 1979, Diagnostic Ultrasound in Emergency Medicine, 1981, Doppler in Diagnostic Imaging, 1987, Clinical Applications of Doppler Ultrasound, 1988, 2d edit., 1995, Duplex Doppler Ultrasound, 26, 1990; chief editor: Clinics in Diagnostic Ultrasound, 1978—; internat. editl. bd. Ultrasonics, 1989, Jour. Ultrasound in Medicine, 1980, Jour. U.S. Medicine and Biology, 1982; assoc. editor Jour. Cardiovascular Tech., 1990—, Italian Jour. Gastroenterology, 1985, Radiology, 1990. Grantee Am. Cancer Soc., 1978-80, 86-88, NIH, 1989-92. Fellow ACP, Am. Inst. Ultrasound in Medicine; mem. Radiol. Soc. N.Am., Royal Coll. Surgeons. Home: 1611 Great Hill Rd Guilford CT 06437-3647 Office: TE2 Yale Univ Med Sch 333 Cedar St New Haven CT 06510-3206

TAYLOR, KENNETH NATHANIEL, publishing executive, author; b. Portland, Oreg., May 8, 1917; s. George Nathaniel and Charlotte Bodwell (Huff) T.; m. Margaret Louise West, Sept. 13, 1940; children: Becky, John, Martha, Peter, Janet, Mark, Cynthia, Gretchen, Mary Lee, Alison. BA, Wheaton Coll., 1938, DLitt (hon.), 1965; student, Dallas Theol. Sem., 1940-43; ThM, No. Bapt. Theol. Sem., 1944; DLitt (hon.), Trinity Evang. Div. Sch., 1972; LHD (hon.), Huntington Coll., 1974, Taylor U., 1989. With Moody Press (pub. protestant religious lit.), Chgo., 1947-63; dir. Moody Press (pub. protestant religious lit.), 1948-62, Moody Lit. Mission (prodn. and distbn. lit.), 1948-62; pres. Tyndale House Publishers, 1963-84, chmn. bd., 1984—; chmn. bd. Coverdale House Pubs., London, Eng., 1969-79; pres. Tyndale House Found., 1964-79, bd. dirs., 1964—; dir. Inter-Varsity Christian Fellowship, 1956-59, Evang. Lit. Overseas, 1951-70, Short Terms Abroad, 1963-77; pres. Living Bibles Internat., Wheaton, Ill., 1968-77, internat. pres., 1977-90, internat. chmn. emeritus, 1990-92; chmn. Unilit., Inc., Portland, 1972-73. Author: Is Christianity Credible, 1946, Living Letters: The Paraphrased Epistles, 1962; juveniles Stories for the Children's Hour, 1953, Devotions for the Children's Hour, 1954, I See, 1958 (reprinted as Small Talks about God, 1995), Bible in Pictures for Little Eyes, 1956, Lost on the Trail, 1959, Romans for the Children's Hour, 1959; Living Prophecies - The Minor Prophets Paraphrased, 1965, Living Gospels, 1966, Living Psalms and Proverbs With the Major Prophets Paraphrased, 1967, The Living New Testament, 1967, Living Lessons of Life and Love, 1968, Living Books of Moses, 1969, Living History of Israel, 1970, The Living Bible, 1971, Taylor's Bible Story Book, 1970; juveniles What High School Students Should Know about Creation, 1983, What High School Students Should Know About Evolution, 1983, Big Thoughts for Little People, 1983, Giant Steps for Little People, 1985, Wise Words for Little People, 1987, Next Steps for New Christians (originally How To Grow), 1989, My First Bible in Pictures, 1989 (ann. Angel award 1990, Platinum Book award 1990), The Good Samaritan, 1989, Jesus Feeds A Crowd, 1989, The Lost Sheep, 1989, The Prodigal Son, 1989; Good News for Little People, 1991 (ann. Angel award 1992), My Life, A Guided Tour, 1991, Daniel and the Lions' Den, 1992, Noah's Ark, 1992, Family-Time Bible in Pictures, 1992, A Boy Helps Jesus, 1994, The Good Neighbor, 1994, Noah Builds a Boat, 1994, A Very Special Baby, 1994, The Story of Noah's Ark, 1994; co-editor: The Bible for Children, 1990 (ann. Angel award 1991); pub. The Christian Reader, 1964-92, Have a Good Day, 68—. Bd. dirs. Christian Libr. Svc., 1972-75, Inter-Skrift forlage Aktiebolag, Sweden, Internat. Bible Soc., 1992-94; trustee Living Bible Found., Fuller Theol. Sem.; mem. adv. bd. Internat. Bible Reading Assn. Recipient citation Layman's Nat. Bible Com.; 1971; award Religious Heritage Am., 1972; disting. svc. citation Internat. Soc. Christian Endeavor, 1973; Nelson Bible award, 1973; Better World award VFW Aux., 1974; disting. pub. svc. award 1974; Recognition award Urban Ministries, Inc., 1977; Svc. award Wheaton Coll. Alumni Assn., 1977; Crusader award Wheaton Coll., 1979; Gutenberg award Chgo. Bible Soc., 1981; Internat. Christian Edn. Assn. award, 1983; named Man of Yr. Com. Internat. Goodwill, 1983; recipient 1st Ann. Lit. award Evang. Lit. Overseas, 1983; Svc. award YFC/USA, 1984; Gold Medallion Achievement award Evang. Pubs. Assn., 1984; named to Christian Booksellers Hall of Fame, 1989; recipient Ann. James DeForest Murch award Nat. Assn. Evangelicals, 1995. Mem. Wheaton Coll. Scholastic Honor Soc. Home: 1515 E Forest Ave Wheaton IL 60187-4469 Office: 351 Executive Dr Carol Stream IL 60188-2420 *Who but God could make an unending universe, staged by billions of light years? And who could dream of knowing such a God personally? I am one who believes this, and have based my life on the Bible as God's message to mankind, and to you and me. But how to manage Bible reading when it is in such an ancient language? How to crack the shell of the coconut and find the milk and meat? That is why I spent 16 years translating the Bible into living English, with 37 million copies now in print.*

TAYLOR, KRISTIN CLARK, media specialist; b. Detroit, Mar. 26, 1959; d. James W. and Mary Elizabeth (Moore) Clark; m. Lonnie Paul Taylor; children: Lonnie Paul II, Mary Elizabeth. BA in Classical Lit., Mich. State U., 1982. Editor, writer USA Today, Washington, 1982-86; corp. writer Gannett Co., Inc., Washington, 1986; bus. corr. Gannett News Svc., Washington, 1987; asst. press sec. to Vice President Bush White House, Washington, 1987-88, spl. asst. to Vice President Bush for press rels., 1988-89; dir. White House media rels., 1989-90; dir. comm. BellSouth Corp., Washington, 1990-94; v.p. external affairs Student Loan Mktg. Assn. (Sallie Mae), Washington, 1994—. Author: The First To Speak, A Woman of Color Inside the White House, 1993. Republican.

TAYLOR, LANCE JEROME, economics educator; b. Montpelier, Idaho, May 25, 1940; s. Walter Jerome and Ruth (Robinson) T.; m. Yvonne S.M. Johnsson. May 31, 1963; children: Ian Lance, Signe Marguerite. BS with honors, Calif. Inst. Tech., 1962; PhD, Harvard U., 1968. Instr. econs. Harvard U., Cambridge, Mass., 1967-68; asst. prof., assoc. prof. Harvard U., 1970-74; research assoc. MIT, Cambridge, 1968-70; prof. econs. MIT, 1974-93, New Sch. for Social Rsch., N.Y.C., 1993—; vis. prof. U. Brasilia, 1974, Pontifical Cath. U. Rio de Janeiro, 1981, U. Delhi, 1987-88, Stockholm Sch. Econs., 1990; Marshall lectr. Cambridge U., 1986-87; cons. World Bank, UN, various fgn. govts. Author: Macro Models for Developing Countries, 1979, Models of Growth and Distribution for Brazil, 1980, Structuralist Macroeconomics, 1983, Varieties of Stabilization Experience, 1988, Income Distribution, Inflation, and Growth, 1991, The Market Meets its Match: Restructuring the Economies of Eastern Europe, 1994. Fulbright fellow, 1962-63. Mem. Am. Econ. Assn., Royal Econ. Soc. Home: PO Box 378 Washington ME 04574-0378 Office: New School for Social Rsch Grad Faculty 65 Fifth Ave New York NY 10003

TAYLOR, LAWRENCE, sports commentator, former professional football player; b. Williamsburg, Va., Feb. 4, 1959; s. Clarence and Iris Taylor; m. Linda Taylor; children: T.J., Tanisha, Paula. Student, U. N.C. With N.Y. Giants, 1981-93; sports commentator The Stadium Show TNT, 1994—; owner All-Pro Products, 1993—; mem. Superbowl Championship Team, 1986, 90. Author: Living on the Edge, 1987. Recipient Bert Bell award, Humanitarian award Nat. Black United Fund; NFL Rookie of the Year, 1981, named Most Valuable Player NFL, 1986, NFL Player of Yr. AP, Def. Player of Yr. AP, Player of Yr. Sporting News mag., Schick Co., Washington Touchdown Club, Seagrams Corp., Gillette Co., Tums Co.; named to All-NFL team, All-NFC team, All-Star game NFL Pro Bowl, 1981-90; elected Top Linebacker NFL Players' Assn. Led NFL in sacks, 1986. Office: NY Giants Stadium East Rutherford NJ 07073

TAYLOR, LAWRENCE PALMER, diplomat; b. Cleve., Apr. 18, 1940; s. Sheldon A. and Juanita (Springer) T.; m. Lynda Ellen Gorham; children: Lori, Tracey, Scott. AB, Ohio U., 1963; MA, Am. U., 1969; MPA, Harvard U., 1977. Consular officer Zagreb, Yugoslavia, 1972-73; econ. officer U.S. Embassy, Belgrade, Yugoslavia, 1973-76; petroleum attache U.S. Embassy, Jakarta, Indonesia, 1976-79; energy officer U.S. Embassy, Ottawa, Can., 1980-84; econ. minister U.S. Embassy, Ottawa, Ont., Can., 1989-92; econ. counselor U.S. Embassy, London, 1985-89; dir. Fgn. Svc. Inst., Washington, 1992—. Avocation: collecting polit., military ephemera, maps. Home: 2025 Mummasburg Rd Gettysburg PA 17325-7421 Office: Nat Fgn Affairs Tng Ctr 4000 Arlington Blvd Arlington VA 22204-1500

TAYLOR, LEIGH HERBERT, college dean; b. Chgo., Oct. 23, 1941; s. Herbert and Leona Taylor; m. Nancy E. Young; children: Jennifer, Jeremiah. BA, U. Tulsa, 1964, JD, 1966; LLM, NYU, 1969. Bar: Okla. 1966, Ill. 1976. Trial atty. Civil Rights div. Dept. Justice, Washington, 1966-68; prof. DePaul U. Coll. Law, Chgo., 1969-77; assoc. dean, 1973-77; dean Coll. Law, Ohio No. U., Ada, 1977-78, Sch. Law Southwestern U., L.A., 1978—; mem. adv. bd. 1st Woman's Bank of L.A., 1981-85; dir. Law Sch. Admissions Svcs., Inc., 1982-86; chmn. audit com. Law Sch. Admissions Coun., 1989-91, trustee, 1991—, chair-elect, 1994-95, chair, 1995—; mem. bd. trustees Coun. on Legal Edn. Opportunity, 1993—. Editor-in-chief Tulsa Law Jour., 1966; author: Strategies for Law-Focused Education, 1977; (with others) Law in a New Land, 1972; mem. editorial bd. Family Law Quarterly, 1977-78. Bd. dirs. Criminal Def. Consortium Cook County (Ill.), Inc., 1975-77, L.A. Press Club Found. With AUS, 1959. Fellow Am. Bar Found.; mem. ABA (accreditation com. 1991—), Law in Am. Soc. Found., Ill. Bar Assn., Chgo. Bar Assn. (rec. sec.), L.A. County Bar Assn., Okla. Bar Assn. Office: Southwestern U Sch Law Office of Dean 675 S Westmoreland Ave Los Angeles CA 90005-3992

TAYLOR, LEONARD STUART, engineering educator, consultant; b. N.Y.C., Dec. 28, 1928; m. Lillian Rachel Schlang, Apr. 12, 1954; children: Robin Jolie, Allyn Lise. AB, Harvard Coll., 1951; MSc, N.Mex. State U., 1955, PhD, 1960. Microwave engr. Raytheon Mfg. Co., Bedford, Mass., 1950-55; research physicist Gen. Electric Co., Phila., 1960-63; assoc. prof. Case Western Res. U., Cleve., 1964-67; prof. U. Md., Coll. Park, Md., 1967—; cons. USN, Silver Spring, Md., 1967—. Contbr. articles to profl. jours; inventor Microwave Scalpel, Implantable Microwave Hyperthermia Applicator and numerous others. Recipient Disting. Alumni N.Mex. State U. 1975. Fellow IEEE (life), Am. Soc. for Laser Medicine and Surgery; mem. Am. Phys. Soc., Optical Soc. of Am., Bioelectromagnetics Soc. Avocations: tennis, music. Office: U Md EE Dept College Park MD 20742

TAYLOR, LYLE DEWEY, economic development company executive; b. Traer, Iowa, Sept. 26, 1934; s. John Dewey and Lorriane (Burrows) T.; m. Margaret Conn, Dec. 29, 1955; children: Lylette, Robin, Carla, Pennie. Student, LaJunta Jr. Coll., 1951-52. Plant worker Rath Packing co., Waterloo, Iowa, 1952-61; rec. sec. local 46 United Food & Comml. Workers Union, 1961-69, pres. local 46, 1969-82, exec. v.p., 1982-83; pres., chief exec. officer Rath Packing Co., 1983-85; v.p. Blackhawk Holding Co., Waterloo, 1985-88; pres. Black Hawk Econ. Devel. Co., Waterloo, 1988—; pres. Ray Price Cherokee Farms, 1986-89; dir. Am. Meat Inst., Washington, 1983. Sec. Cedar Valley Partnership, 1989—; past mem. Guv.'s Adv. Com. on OSHA, Iowa U. Alumni Adv. Bd., Ames; past bd. dirs. Goodwill, Inc., Waterloo, Adult's Care, Exceptional Persons. Served with USAR, 1956-64. Democrat. Baptist. Home: 826 Skyview Rd Waterloo IA 50703 Office: Black Hawk Econ Devel Co 606 Fairview PO Box 330 Waterloo IA 50704-0330

TAYLOR, MARIA CENTOFANTI, marketing professional; b. Youngstown, Ohio, Sept. 5, 1963; d. Louis Frances and Elaine Marie (Haus) Centofanti; m. Steven Scott Taylor, Oct. 8, 1988. ABJ, U. Ga., 1985. Spl. events dir. Cystic Fibrosis Found., Atlanta, 1985-86, Stone Mountain Pk., Atlanta, 1986-87; account exec. A. Brown-Olmstead Assocs., Atlanta, 1987-88; mktg. mgr. Sta. WSB, Atlanta, 1988-94, ABC Sch. Supply, Duluth, Ga., 1994—. Mem. pub. rels. com. Boys Club of Atlanta, 1988—, Nat. Kidney Found. of Ga., Atlanta, 1988; mem. assoc. bd. Cystic Fibrosis Found., Atlanta, 1987—. Recipient Am. Women in Radio and TV-TARA award, 1989. Mem. Pub. Rels. Soc. Am. (chmn. banquet com. Atlanta chpt. 1987, chmn. hosp. com. 1989—, Pres.'s award, 1986, 87, 88, 89). Office: ABC Sch Supply 3312 North Berkeley Lake Rd Duluth GA 30136

TAYLOR, MARK DOUGLAS, publishing executive; b. Geneva, Ill., Jan. 16, 1951; s. Kenneth Nathaniel and Margaret Louise (West) T.; m. Carol E. Rogers, May 28, 1973; children: Jeremy Peter, Kristen Elizabeth, Margaret Louise, Rebecca Cynthia, Stephen Rogers. BA, Duke U., 1973. Exec. dir. Tyndale House Found., Wheaton, Ill., 1973-78; v.p. Tyndale House Pubs., Wheaton, Ill., 1978-84; pres., chief exec. officer Tyndale House Pubs., 1984—; dir. Living Bibles Internat. U.S., Naperville, Ill., 1972-92. Author The Complete Book of Bible Literacy, 1992. Mem. Wheaton Liquor Control Commn., 1986—, chmn., 1994—; chmn. bd. dirs. Outreach Cmty. Ctr., 1986-93. Mem. Internat. Bible Soc. (bd. dirs. 1993—). Office: Tyndale House Publishers Inc 351 Executive Dr Box 80 Wheaton IL 60189 *What we accomplish in life is soon forgotten. Our best legacy is to pass on to our children and grandchildren our positive values.*

TAYLOR, MELDRICK, professional boxer, Olympic athlete. Jr. welterweight champion Internat. Boxing Fedn., 1988-90; welterweight champion World Boxing Assn., 1991-92. Recipient Gold medal boxing featherweight divsn. Olympics, 1984. Office: World Boxing Assn 1 S Calvert St Baltimore MD 21202*

TAYLOR, MERRILY ELLEN, university librarian; b. Winchester, Mass., May 24, 1945; d. Philip Forbes and Ruth Ellen (Piper) T. A.A., St. Petersburg Jr. Coll., 1965; B.A., U. South Fla., 1967, M.A., 1973; M.S. in L.S., Fla. State U., 1968. Reference librarian U. South Fla. Library, Tampa, 1968-69, head circulation dept., 1969-74, head collection devel., 1974-77; asst. to univ. librarian Yale U. Library, New Haven, 1977-78; dir. services group Columbia U. Libraries, N.Y.C., 1978-82; univ. librarian Brown U., Providence, 1982—; pres. Consortium R.I. Acad. and Research Libraries, 1985-87. Author: The Yale University Library 1901-1978, 1978; author, editor: Remembering P.D. Ouspensky (exhbn. catalog), 1978; contbr. articles to profl. jours. Mem. R.I. State Commn. on the Pricing Libr. Svcs., 1987-88; mem. adv. com. R.I. Libr. Study, 1987-88, Libr. Bd. of R.I., 1992, chair planning and budget com., 1992—; mem. R.I. Coun. on the Preservation Rsch. Resources, 1989-93. Acad. Library Mgmt. intern Council on Library Resources Washington, 1976. Mem. ALA, R.I. Libr. Assn. (chmn. pub. rels. com. 1985), Rsch. Libs. Group (bd. govs. 1982-91, chmn. bd. govs. system comm. 1989-90, chmn. pub. svcs. com. 1984-86), Assn. Rsch. Librs. (com. on libr. edn., chmn. com. on info. policies 1989-92, adv. com. pub. svcs. self study program 1982-84, bd. mem. 1986-89), Nat. Trust for Hist. Preservation Soc. Democrat. Methodist. Home: 110 Charlesfield St Providence RI 02906-2044 Office: Brown U Libr Box A Rockefeller Libr Providence RI 02912

TAYLOR, MESHACH, actor; b. Boston, Apr. 11; m. Bianca Taylor; 4 children. Student, Fla. A&M U. With Organic Theatre Group, Chgo. Leading role in the touring co. of Hair, Chgo., (play) Sizwe Banzi is Dead (Joseph Jefferson award) Goodman Theatre, Chgo., 1976, Huckleberry Finn (Emmy award) PBS Prodn., Chgo.; actor: (film) Damien - Omen II, Buffalo Bill, (motion picture for TV) How to Murder a Millionaire; co-star: Mannequin, House of Games.; guest star (TV series) Barney Miller, Lou Grant, The White Shadow, M*A*S*H; host: (TV show) WMAQ-TV Black Life; with TV series Designing Women, 1986-93, Dave's World, 1993—. Avocations: travel, studying fgn. langs. Office: care Paradigm Talent Agy 10100 Santa Monica Blvd Los Angeles CA 90067

TAYLOR, MICHAEL ALAN, psychiatrist; b. N.Y.C., Mar. 6, 1940; s. Edward D. and Clara D. T.; m. Ellen Schoenfield, June 28, 1963; children—Christopher, Andrew. B.A., Cornell U., 1961; M.D., N.Y. Med. Coll., 1965. Intern Lenox Hill Hosp., N.Y.C., 1965-66; resident N.Y. Med. Coll., 1966-69, asst. prof. psychiatry, 1971-73; asso. prof. SUNY Med. Sch., Stony Brook, 1973-76; prof. psychiatry Univ. Health Scis., Chgo. Med. Sch., 1976—, dept., 1976-94. Author: The Neuropsychiatric Mental Status Examination, 1981; sr. author: General Hospital Psychiatry, 1985, The Neuropsychiatric Guide to Modern Everyday Psychiatry, 1993; editor-in-chief Neuropsychiat., Neuropsychology and Behavioral Neurology Jour.; also numerous articles. Served to lt. comdr. M.C. USNR, 1969-71. Grantee NIMH, 1971-73; Grantee Ill. Dept. Mental Health, 1976-81; VA grantee, 1985-93. Fellow Am. Psychiat. Assn.; mem. Am. Psychopath. Assn., Soc. Biol. Psychiatry, AAAS, Assn. Acad. Psychiatry, Ill. Psychiat. Assn. Office: UHS Chgo Med Sch 3333 Green Bay Rd North Chicago IL 60064-3037

TAYLOR, MICHAEL R., federal agency administrator, lawyer. BA in Political Science, Davidson (N.C.) Coll.; JD, U. Va. Atty. Office of the Gen. Counsel FDA, 1976-80, exec. asst. to commr., 1980-81; assoc. King & Spalding, Washington, 1981-84, ptnr., 1984-91; dep. commr. for policy FDA; undersecretary for food safety U.S. Dept. Agr., 1994—; mem. Nat. Acad. Scis. Com. on Scientific and Regulatory Issues Underlying Pesticide Use Patterns and Agrl. Innovation. mem. editl. bd. Food Drug Cosmetic Law Jour., 1988-91. With U.S. Army, 1971-73. Office: Dept of Agriculture Food Safety & Inspection Service 5600 Fishers Ln Rockville MD 20857-0001*

TAYLOR, MILLARD BENJAMIN, concertmaster, educator; b. Crete, Nebr., Aug. 9, 1913; s. Joseph Elbert and Anna Blodgett (Bennett) T.; m. Marie Jeanne Capasso, Jan. 2, 1939; children: Virginia Ann (Mrs. James Edward Smith), Jeanne Taylor Hernandez. MusB, Eastman Sch. Music, 1935; MusD, Doane Coll., 1967; DLitt, Nebr. Wesleyan U., 1975. Prof. violin Eastman Sch. Music, Rochester, N.Y., 1944-79; prof. emeritus Eastman Sch. Music, 1979—, chmn. string dept., 1950-76; Edward F. Arnold vis. prof. music Whitman Coll., 1979-80; head string dept. Chautauqua Summer Music Schs. Concertmaster Nat. Symphony Orch., 1938-44, Rochester Philharm. Orch., 1944-67, Pro-Musica Chamber Orch. of Columbus, 1980-89, Naples (Fla.) Philharm., 1983-92; concertmaster Chatauqua Symphony Orch., 1965-89, mus. dir., 1985-86; guest concertmaster Dallas Symphony Orch., N.J. Symphony Orch.; violinist Eastman Piano Quartet, 1967-79, Eastman String Trio, New England Piano Quartet, 1992—; 1st violinist, leader Chautauqua String Quartet; contbr. articles to Instrumentalist mag. Bd. dirs. Rochester Civic Music Assn., 1969-72. Named Musician of Year Rochester chpt. Mu Phi Epsilon, 1966. Mem. Pi Kappa Lambda, Phi Mu Alpha Sinfonia.

TAYLOR, MILLICENT RUTH, middle school educator; b. Kingston, Jamaica, Nov. 18, 1944; came to U.S., 1981; m. Henry Taylor; children: T'ousant, Howard, Annette, Kerry-Ann. BE, U. West Indies, 1981; MS, U. Miami, 1991. Cert. elem. edn. tchr., secondary social sci. tchr., Fla. Chairperson dept. history Mays Middle Sch., Miami, Fla., 1987—, peer tchr., 1987-90, seminar presenter, 1987-88; leader, trainer Global Edn., Miami, Fla. 1989, sponsor History Bee, Miami, 1988-90, Geography Bee, 1988-90. Recipient State award for teaching economics Dade County Sch., 1992, Nat. award for teaching economics Joint Coun. Economic Edn., 1991. Mem. Ednl. Leadership, Fla. Coun. Social Studies, Dade County Coun. Social Studies, Assn. Supervision and Curriculum Devel. Seventh Day Adventist. Avocations: reading, travel, sewing, photography. Home: 19834 SW 118th Ave Miami FL 33177 Office: Mays Middle Sch Goulds FL 33170

TAYLOR, NICOLE RENÉE, model; b. Miami, Fla.; d. Ken and Barbara T. With Irene Marie, Miami, 1989; contracts with L'Oreal, 1990-92, Cover Girl Makeup; appeared in Seventeen (cover girl) 1989, Vogue, Elle, Mademoiselle, Harper's Bazaar; modeled for Yves Saint Laurent, Karl Lagerfeld. Office: IMG Models 170 Fifth Ave 10th Fl New York NY 10010

TAYLOR, NORMAN FLOYD, computer educator, administrator; b. Dover, Ohio, Oct. 29, 1932; s. James Benton and Lela Augusta (Sinden) T.; m. Peggy Ann Cox, Sept. 7, 1952; children: Norman Dudley, Steven Dexter, Gregory Dennis. BS, U. Houston, 1954; MEd, Kent State U., 1963, EdS, 1977. Band dir. Ashtabula (Ohio) Area City Schs., 1958-70, prin., 1970-74; prin. Shaker Heights (Ohio) City Schs., 1974-81, Perry (Ohio) Local Schs., 1981-85; treas. Jos. Badger Local Schs., Kinsman, Ohio, 1987-89; supr. computer instrn. support svcs. Ashtabula (Ohio) Area City Schs., 1989-93, computer instr., 1993—; asst. prof. Computer Sci. Kent State U., Burton, Ohio, 1982-86, Ashtabula, 1987-88. Contbr. articles to profl. jours. Dir. Ashtabula Ch. Choir, 1958-78; mem. Ludlow Community Assn., Shaker Heights, 1974-81. Mem. Ohio Edn. Assn., Shaker Heights Elem. Prins. Assn. (pres. 1980-81), Ashtabula Mid. Mgmt. Assn. (pres. 1973-74), Kiwanis Club, Phi Delta Kappa. Presbyterian. Avocations: music, golf, skiing. Home: 2501 Southwood Dr Painesville OH 44077-4956 Office: Ashtabula Area City Schs 401 W 44th St Ashtabula OH 44004-6807

TAYLOR, NORMAN WILLIAM, economics educator; b. Wigan, Eng., Jan. 9, 1923; s. Albert and Jessie (Slonker) T.; m. Eleanor Dorothy Harper, July 18, 1953; children—David Gordon, Laurie Elizabeth. B.Sc., U. London, 1950; M.A., Yale, 1954, Ph.D., 1958; LLD (hon.), Tohoku Gakuin U., Japan, 1988. Clk. London, Midland & Scottish Ry. Co., Preston, Eng., 1939-40; clk. City Treas. Office, Wigan, 1940-42, 47-48; exec. officer War Office, U.K., 1948-49; asst. instr. econs. Yale, 1955-57, instr. econs., 1957-59; asst. prof. econs. Lawrence U., 1959-62; vis. asst. prof. econs. U. Wis., 1961-62; assoc. prof. econs. Franklin and Marshall Coll., Lancaster, Pa., 1962-69; prof. econs. Franklin and Marshall Coll., 1969-80, Charles A. Dana prof. econs., 1980-88, emeritus, 1988—, chmn. dept., 1964-79, 81-84; vis. prof. Tunghai U., Taiwan, 1967-68. Contbr. articles profl. jours. Served to capt. Brit. Army, 1942-47. Recipient Lindback award for disting. teaching, 1981. Mem. Am. Econ. Assn., Econ. History Assn., Econ. History Soc., Am. Anthrop. Assn., Am. Assn. Chinese Studies (dir., v.p., treas.), AAUP. Home: 1716 Linwood Ave Lancaster PA 17603-4508

TAYLOR, PATRICIA, theater company managing director. BA in English and Econs., Vassar Coll.; MFA in Theater Mgmt., Columbia U. With

mgmt. svcs. dept. Theatre Comms. Group; gen. mgr. Williamstown Theatre Festival; mng. dir. Classic Stage Co., N.Y.C., 1990—; mgmt. assoc. for Broadway prodrs. and gen. mgrs. McCann and Nugent for prodns. including Crimes of the Heart, Amadeus, Mass Appeal, Good, Pacific Overtures; various theater mgmt. positions Manhattan Theatre Club, Shubert Orgn., The Lucille Lortel Theatre, Vivian Beaumont Theatre. Contbr. articles on mgmt. issues Am. Theatre, Mgr.'s Bull., Trustee Newsletter. Office: Classic Stage Co 136 E 13th St New York NY 10003-5306

TAYLOR, PAUL, choreographer; b. Allegheny County, Pa., July 29, 1930; s. Paul B. and Elizabeth (Rust) T. Student, Syracuse U., 1949-52, Juilliard Sch. Music, 1952-53; hon. doctoral degrees include, Duke U., 1983, Conn. Coll., 1983, Syracuse U., Juilliard, SUNY at Purchase. Artistic dir. Paul Taylor Dance Co., 1957—; dancer Merce Cunningham Co., 1954, Martha Graham, 1955-60. Paul Taylor Dance Co. has performed in over 300 U.S. cities and made 34 overseas tours; participated numerous arts festivals in 36 nations; PBS TV appearances include Dance in America, Live From the American Dance Festival, Two Landmark Dances, Three Modern Classics, The Taylor Company: Recent Dances; choreographer over 100 works including Aureole, 1962, Private Domain, 1969, Esplanade, 1975, Cloven Kingdom, 1976, Airs, 1978, Le Sacre du Printemps (the Rehearsal), 1980, Arden Court, 1981, Mercuric Tidings, 1982, Sunset, 1983, Roses, 1985, Last Look, 1985, Musical Offering, 1986, Ab Ovo Usque ad Mala, 1986, Syzygy, 1987, Kith and Kin, 1987, Minikin Fair, 1989, Speaking in Tongues, 1989, Company B, 1991, Spindri Ft., 1993, A Field of Grass, 1993, Oz, 1993, Moonbine, 1994, Aureole, 1994; author: (autobiography) Private Domain, 1987 (Nat. Book Critics Circle award for biography 1987). Recipient Internat. Circle of Criticism for Artistic Research and Cultural Exchange award Festival Nations, Paris, 1962; named Dancer of Year London's Dance and Dancers, 1965; decorated chevalier des Arts et Lettres France, elevated to officier, 1984; prize for best fgn. attraction by Critics of Chile, 1966; Guggenheim fellow, 1961, 66, 83, MacArthur Found. fellow, 1985; recipient Capezio Dance award, 1967, Creative Arts award gold medal Brandeis U., 1978, Dance Mag. award, 1980, Samuel H. Scripps Am. Dance Festival award, 1983; Arts award state of N.Y., 1987, Lions of Performing Arts award N.Y. Pub. Libr., 1989, Emmy award Speaking in Tongues, 1992, Kennedy Ctr. Honors, 1992, Am. Soc. Graphic Artists award, 1992, Nat. Medal of Arts, 1993. Office: Paul Taylor Dance Co 552 Broadway New York NY 10012-3922*

TAYLOR, PAUL ALBERT, banker; b. St. John, N.B., Can., June 17, 1943; s. Albert and Mary Kathleen (McCullough) T.; children—Beth E., Brian P., Stephen C. B.A. in Econs., U. Western Ont., 1966; M.B.A. in Fin., U. Windsor, 1971. Area exec. Orion Bank Ltd., London, 1974-76, exec. dir. 1977-78; sr. mgr. Global fin. Royal Bank of Can., Montreal, Que., 1978-80, asst. gen. mgr. Global Fin., 1980; asst. gen. mgr. national accts. Royal Bank of Can., Toronto, Ont., 1980-82, sr. v.p. national accts., 1982-83, sr. v.p. world corp. banking, 1983-86; sr. v.p. investment banking, internat. and dep. chmn. Orion Royal Bank, London, 1986-88; exec. v.p. investment banking head office Royal Bank Can., Toronto, Ont., 1988-90, exec. v.p. treasury and investment banking head office, 1990-95, exec. v.p. trading head office, 1995—; bd. dirs. Royal Bank Investment Mgmt. Inc., RBC Dominion Securities Ltd.; co-chmn. fin. sector Can. Japan Bus. Com. Mem. Halton Prog. Conservative Assn., Founders Club, Zeta Psi. Roman Catholic. Office: Royal Bank of Can, 200 Bay St Royal Bank Plaza, Toronto, ON Canada M5J 2J5

TAYLOR, PAUL B., dancer. Attended, Syracuse U. soloist Martha Graham Dance Co., 1955-62; guest artist George Balanchine's Episodes N.Y.C. Ballet, 1959; author: (autobiography) Private Domain, 1987. elected to knighthood as "Chevalier de l'Ordre des Arts et des Lettres" French Gov't., 1969, officier, 1984, commdr., 1990. Recipient more than forty awards including 3 Guggenheim fellowships and six hon. Doctor of Fine Arts degrees, and lifetime achievement awards; Emmy award for outstanding individual achievement in choreography Speaking in Tongues, 1991; Nat. Medal of Arts award by Pres. Clinton The White House and numerous others. Office: Paul Taylor Dance Co 552 Broadway New York NY 10012-3922

TAYLOR, PAUL BRADFORD, judge; b. Charlotte, N.C., Nov. 4, 1955. BA in English Lit. and History, U. N.C., 1978; JD, Cath. U. Am., Washington, 1981. Bar: N.C., U.S. Dist. Ct. (ea., mid. and we. dist.) N.C. 1981, U.S. Ct. Appeals (4th cir.) 1986, U.S. Supreme Ct. 1986. Asst. to fed. prosecutors felony trial divsn. Office of U.S. Atty., Washington, 1981; law clk. U.S. Dist. Ct. (we. dist.) N.C., 1981-83; assoc. Blakeney, Alexander & Machen, Charlotte, N.C., 1983-88; U.S. magistrate judge U.S. Dist. Ct. (we. dist.) N.C., 1988—. Mem. ABA (criminal law working group Ctrl. and Ea. Europe Law initiative). Home: 2000 Harris Rd Charlotte NC 28211-2152 Office: US Courthouse 401 W Trade St Charlotte NC 28202-1619

TAYLOR, PAUL DANIEL, ambassador; b. Lockport, N.Y., May 16, 1939; s. Charles Erwin and Anita (Schweigert) T.; m. Dorcas Ann Billings, Aug. 9, 1962; Jonathan, Katherine, Matthew. AB magna cum laude, Princeton U., 1960; M in Pub. Adminstrn., Harvard U., 1967. Assoc. dir. Peace Corps, Quito, Ecuador, 1965-66; various fgn. service assignments Bangkok, Sao Paulo and Washington, 1967-76; chief food policy div. Dept. State, Washington, 1976-77; econ. comml. counselor U.S. Embassy, Madrid, 1978-81; dep. chief of mission U.S. Embassy, Guatemala, 1981-84; dep. asst. sec. of state for inter-am. affairs, 1985-88; U.S. ambassador to the Domican Republic U.S. Embassy, Santo Domingo, 1988—. Served to lt. (j.g.) USN, 1960-63. Recipient Meritorious Honor award U.S. Dept. State, 1972, Presdl. Meritorious Svc. award, 1989; decorated Order of Merit of Duarte, Sanchez and Mella (Dominican Repubic), 1992. Home and Office: Am Embassy Santo Domingo APO AA 34041-0008

TAYLOR, PEYTON TROY, JR., gynecologic oncologist, educator; b. Tuscaloosa, Ala., July 21, 1941; s. Peyton Troy Sr. and Frances (Sutter) T.; m. Helena Strom, Sept. 23, 1967; children: Annika, Karin, Sarah. BS, U. Ala., 1963; MD, Med. Coll. Ala., 1968. Intern U. Va. Hosp., Charlottesville, 1968-69, resident, 1969-70, 72-75; asst. prof. ob-gyn U. Va., 1976-79; assoc. prof., dir. ob-gyn div. U. Va., Charlottesville, 1981-87; Richard N. and Louise R. Crockett prof. U. Va., 1987—; prof. ob-gyn, assoc. dir. Cancer Ctr., dir. div. ob-gyn. U. Va. Health Scis. Ctr., Charlottesville, 1987—; assoc. dir. U. Va. Cancer Ctr., 1995—; clin. assoc. surgery Nat. Cancer Inst., Bethesda, Md., 1970-72; assoc. prof. U. Ala., Birmingham, 1979-81. Contbr. articles to profl. jours. Served with USPHS, 1970-72. Fellow ACS, Am. Coll. Obstetricians and Gynecologists; mem. Am. Acad. Surgeons, Soc. Gynecol. Oncologists, Soc. Surg. Oncology, Am. Soc. of Clin. Oncology, Am. Assn. for Cancer Rsch., Internat. Gynecol. Cancer Soc. Episcopalian. Office: U Va PO Box 387 Charlottesville VA 22908-0001

TAYLOR, PHILIP BATES, III, diplomat; b. Berkeley, Calif., Jan. 9, 1945; s. Philip Bates Jr. and Dorris Jane (Whisler) T.; m. Anna Maria Pannunzio, May 28, 1979. BA, Williams Coll., Williamstown, Mass., 1967; ND, Nat. War Coll., 1986. Vol. Peace Corps, Washington, 1967-71; fgn. svc. officer Dept. of State, Washington, 1972—; dep. chief of mission Am. Embassy Guatemala, 1989-92; Am. consul gen. Sao Paulo, Brazil, 1992—. Hon. pres. Am. Soc., Sao Paulo, 1992—. Mem. Am. C. of C. (hon. pres. Sao Paulo 1992-95), Army and Navy Club, Am. Fgn. Svc. Assn. Office: Brazil PO Box 8063 APO AA 34030 Office: Am Consulate Gen Unit 3502 APO NY 34030

TAYLOR, PHILIP LIDDON, physics educator; b. London, Oct. 17, 1937; came to U.S., 1962; s. Arthur and Alice Florence (Ivison) T.; m. Sarah Louisa Butler, July 16, 1966; children: Camilla Bronwen, Imogen Ruth. BSc, Kings Coll., London, 1959; PhD, Cambridge U., 1962. Rsch. assoc. Case Western Res. U., Cleve., 1962-64, from asst. prof. to prof. physics, 1964-87, Perkins prof. physics, 1987—; cons. in field, 1964—. Author (book) A Quantum Approach to the Solid State. Fellow Am. Phys. Soc., AAAS. Democrat. Home: 2894 Meadowbrook Blvd Cleveland OH 44118-2872 Office: Case Western Res U Dept Physics Cleveland OH 44106-7079*

TAYLOR, RALPH ARTHUR, JR., lawyer; b. Washington, Jan. 19, 1948; s. Ralph Arthur Sr. and Mary Florence (Aylor) T.; m. Joanna Lamba Moorhead, Jan. 30, 1988; children: Alison M., John Duncan. BS in Engring. with honors, Princeton, 1970; JD, U. Va., 1975. Bar: Va. 1975, D.C. 1976, Md.

1989, U.S. Dist. Ct. D.C. 1977, U.S. Dist. Cts. (ea. and we. dists.) Va. 1986, U.S. Dist. Ct. Md. 1988, U.S. Ct. Appeals (4th cir.) 1991, U.S. Ct. Appeals (D.C. cir.) 1977, U.S. Ct. Appeals (6th cir.) 1991, U.S. Ct. Claims 1985, U.S. Supreme Ct. 1980. Program advisor U.S. EPA, Boston, 1970-72; assoc. Steptoe & Johnson, Washington, 1975-84; assoc. Shaw, Pittman, Potts, & Trowbridge, Washington, 1984-86, ptnr., 1986—. Assoc. editor Litigation News, 1985—; notes editor Va. Law Rev., 1974-75; contbg. author: International Technology Transfers, 1995. Pres. Cloisters West Homeowners Assn., Washington, 1989, 90; pres. 1625 Q St. Condominium Assn., Washington, 1982-86. Lt. USPHS, 1970-72. Mem. Order of the Coif, Met. Club (Washington), Kenwood Golf and Country Club, Barristers, Princeton Club (Washington). Protestant. Avocations: sailing, skiing, tennis, squash, amateur radio. Office: Shaw Pittman Potts & Trowbridge 2300 N St NW Washington DC 20037-1122

TAYLOR, RAMONA GARRETT, executive assistant; b. Dallas, 1930. Student So. Meth. U. Sec. to pres. Universal Fin. Co., Dallas, 1957-61; corp. sec., exec. asst. to chmn. bd. dirs., CEO Lomas Fin. Corp., Dallas, 1965-90, sr. v.p., sec., 1990—. Office: Lomas Fin Corp PO Box 655644 Dallas TX 75265-5644

TAYLOR, RAY, state senator; b. Steamboat Rock, Iowa, June 4, 1923; s. Leonard Allen and Mary Delilah (Huffman) T.; student U. No. Iowa, 1940-41, Baylor U., 1948-49; m. Mary Allen, Aug. 29, 1924; children—Gordon, Laura Rae Taylor Hansmann, Karol Ann Taylor Rogers, Jean Lorraine Taylor Mahl. Farmer, Steamboat Rock, Iowa, 1943—; mem. Iowa Senate, 1973-95; bd. dirs., sec. Am. Legis. Exchange Council, 1979—. Sec., Hardin County Farm Bur., 1970-72; mem. Iowa div. bds. Am. Cancer Soc.; chmn. Am. Revolution Bicentennial Com. Mem. Steamboat Rock Community Sch. Bd., 1955-70; coordinator Republican youth, 1968-72. Chmn. bd. Faith Bapt. Bible Coll.; pres. Am. Council Christian Chs.; chmn. Iowans for Responsible Govt. Named Guardian of Small Bus., NFIB/Iowa, 1989-90, for outstanding support for good govt. and accessible, affordable health care in Iowa, Iowa Physician Assistant Soc., 1991, Ind. Bapt. fellow of the Midwest, Christian Patriots, 1994, Hon. alumnus Faith Bapt. Bible Coll. & Theol. Sem., 1995; recipient Contenders award Am. Coun. Christian Chs., 1991, Legislator of Yr. award Iowa Soc. of Friends, 1991-92. Mem. Wildlife Club. Baptist. Home: 31363 185th St Steamboat Rock IA 50672

TAYLOR, RAYMOND ELLORY, mechanical engineering researcher; b. Ames, Iowa, Oct. 19, 1929; s. Alva A. and Maude Marguerite (Crowe) T.; m. Elfa M. Shaffer, Apr. 22, 1952; children, Wayne, David. BS in Chem. Tech., Iowa State U., 1951; MS in Phys. Chemistry, U. Idaho, 1956; PhD in Solid State Tech., Pa. State U., 1967. Chemist, supr. GE, Richland, Wash., 1951-56; sr. rsch. engr. Atomics Internat., Canoga Park, Calif., 1957-64; assoc. sr. rschr. Thermophysical Properties Rsch. Lab/Purdue U., West Lafayette, Ind., 1967-75, dir., 1975-95; cons. Ordinance Enrging. Assocs., GE, Sandia Nat. Labs., Lockheed Missle and Space Co., Atomic Energy Commn. Can., Bendix Brake Divsn., Theta Industries, Technometrics, Air Force Materials Lab., Combustion Engring. Co., Supertemp Co., Argonne Nat. Lab., GM, Office Naval Rsch., Pennwalt Corp., Vesuvius Crucible Co., Gibson Electric Co., Proctor and Gamble, ALCOA, Corning Glass Co., Dept. Energy, Naval Surface Weapons Ctr., Bethlehem Steel, Cohart Refractories Co., Corp., Roll Mfrs. Inst., Carborundum Co., Areospace Corp., Sandvik Corp., Cummings Engine Corp., Travenol Labs., Sloan Kettering, Dana Perfect Circle, Teledyne Energy Systems, Pfizer Inc., Hughes Aircraft, Allegheny Ludlum Steel Co., CMW Inc., We. Electric Co., Reliance Universal Inc., AMP Inc., Kock Rsch. and Tech. Ctr., Ctrl. Inst. Indsl. Rsch., Semi-Alloys, Gen. Scis. Inc., Carpenter Techs., Hercules Aerospace Co., Bush-Wellman, Brunswick Corp., North Am. Refractories, Zicar Corp., Hayes Internat., E. I. DuPont, Ferro Corp., Storgae Techs., CTS, IBM Inc., Sci. Applications, Outboard Marine Corp.; presenter in field. Editor Review Sci. Instruments; contbr. numerous articles and reports to sci. jours.; co-inventor direct heating flash diffusivity apparatus, device and techniques to measure thermal diffusivity/conductivity of thin films; research in transport properties at high tempuratures, diffusivity of composite materials, transport propreites, multiproperty measurements, thermophotovoltaic energy conservation work, computer applications in the laboratory, high tempurature thermal conductivity reference standards, sonic measurements of insulations; inventor automatic non-destructive aircraft brake discs. Mem. ASTM (governing bd.), North Am. Thermal Analysis Soc., Internat. Thermal Conductivity Conf. (governing bd.), Thermal Expansion Symposium, (governing bd., by-laws com.), Sigma Xi, Phi Lambda Upsilon, Phi Eta Sigma Phi Beta Kappa. Home: 618 Essex St Lafayette IN 47906 Office: Purdue U Thermophysical Properties Rsch Lab 2595 Yaeger Rd West Lafayette IN 47906

TAYLOR, REESE HALE, JR., lawyer, former government administrator; b. Los Angeles, May 6, 1928; s. Reese Hale and Kathryn (Emery) T.; m. Lucille Langdon, Dec. 29, 1948 (div. 1959); children: Reese Hale (dec.), Stuart Langdon, Anne Kathryn, Lucille Emery; m. Jolene Yerby, June 30, 1972. B.A. with distinction, Stanford U., 1949; LL.B., Cornell U., 1952. Bar: Calif. 1954, Nev. 1966. Assoc. Gibson, Dunn & Crutcher, Los Angeles, 1952-58; pvt. practice Los Angeles, 1958-65; assoc. Wiener, Goldwater & Galatz, Las Vegas, Nev., 1966-67; chmn. Nev. Pub. Service Commn., Carson City, 1967-71; ptnr. Laxalt, Berry & Allison, Carson City, 1971-78, Allison, Brunetti, MacKenzie & Taylor, Carson City, 1978-81; chmn. ICC, Washington, 1981-85; ptnr. Heron, Burchette, Ruckert & Rothwell, Washington, 1986-90, Taylor & Morell, Washington and Long Beach, Calif., 1990-92, Taylor, Morell & Gitomer, Washington and Long Beach, 1992-94; of counsel Keesal, Young & Logan, Long Beach, 1994—; vice chmn. Nev. Tax Commn., Carson City, 1967-69; mem. Nev. Gov.'s Cabinet, Carson City, 1967-70, Carson City Bd. Equalization, 1970-71, chmn., 1979-80; bd. dirs. U.S. Rail Assn., Washington, 1981-85. Del. Republican Nat. Conv., Kansas City, Mo., 1976, mem. platform com., 1976, alt. del., Detroit, 1980; mem. Rep. Nat. Com. 1980-81. Mem. ABA, Am. Judicature Soc., Capitol Hill Club, Internat. Club, Cornell Club (N.Y.), Order of Coif, Phi Gamma Delta, Phi Delta Phi. Episcopalian. Office: 310 Golden Shore Ste 230 Long Beach CA 90802

TAYLOR, REGINA, actress; b. Dallas; d. Nell Taylor. Student, So. Meth. U. TV appearances include (movies) Crisis at Central High, 1989, Howard Beach: Making the Case for Murder, 1989, (mini-series) Children of the Dust, 1995, (series) I'll Fly Away, 1991-93 (Emmy award nominee best actress in a drama 1993, Golden Glove award), Law and Order, 1990, 94; films include Lean on Me, 1989, Losing Isaiah, 1995, Clockers, 1995; stage appearances include Romeo and Juliet, 1986, King Lear, 1987, The Tempest, 1988, one-woman show Escape From Paradise, 1994. Office: c/o William Morris Agency 1350 Ave of the Americas New York NY 10019

TAYLOR, RICHARD, philosopher, educator; b. Charlotte, Mich., Nov. 5, 1919; s. Floyd Clyde and Marie Louise (Milbourn) T.; m. Thelma Maxine Elworthy, Jan. 14, 1944 (div. 1961); children: Christopher, Randall; m. Hylda Carpenter Higginson, Dec. 26, 1961 (div. 1985); 1 step dau., Molly; m. Kim Fontana, Oct. 8, 1985; children: Aristotle, Xeno. A.B., U. Ill., 1941; A.M., Oberlin Coll., 1947; Ph.D., Brown U., 1951. Faculty Brown U., 1951-52, 53-63, prof. philosophy, 1958-63, chmn. dept., 1959-60, William Herbert Perry Faunce prof. philosophy, 1959-63; prof. philosophy grad. faculty Columbia, 1963-66; prof. philosophy U. Rochester, N.Y., 1966—; chmn. dept. U. Rochester, 1966-69; Faculty Swarthmore Coll., 1953, Ohio State U., summer 1959, Cornell U., summer 1961; vis. prof. philosophy Columbia, 1962, Ohio State U., 1963; vis. Robert D. Campbell prof. philosophy Wells Coll., 1967-68; vis. Robert H. Truax prof. philosophy Hamilton Coll., 1971-73; vis. Melvin Hill prof. humanities Hobart-William Smith Colls., 1974; Leavitt-Spencer adj. prof. philosophy Union Coll., 1981-89; Disting. resident philosopher Hartwick Coll., 1989—. Author: Metaphysics (Spanish, Dutch, Japanese, Portugese, Korean transl.), 1963, rev. edit., 1974, 83, 91, Action and Purpose, 1965, Good and Evil, 1970, Freedom, Anarchy and the Law, 1973, With Heart and Mind, 1973, Having Love Affairs, 1982, 2d edit., 1990, Ethics, Faith and Reason, 1985; editor: Theism (J.S. Mill), 1957, Selected Essays (Schopenhauer), 1963; assoc. editor: Am. Philos. Quar, 1972-81; Contbr. articles to pubs., U.S., Eng. Australia. Served to lt. USNR, 1943-47. Mem. Am. Philos. Assn., Phi Beta Kappa. Home: 9374 State Route 89 Trumansburg NY 14886-9227

TAYLOR, RICHARD EDWARD, physicist, educator; b. Medicine Hat, Alta., Can., Nov. 2, 1929; came to U.S., 1952; s. Clarence Richard and Delia Alena (Brunsdale) T.; m. Rita Jean Bonneau, Aug. 25, 1951; 1 child, Norman Edward. B.S., U. Alta., 1950, M.S., 1952; Ph.D., Stanford U., 1962; Docteur honoris causa, U. Paris-Sud, 1980; DSc, U. Alta., 1991; LLD (hon.), U. Calgary, Alta., 1993; DSc (hon.), U. Lethbridge, Alta., 1993, U. Victoria, B.C., Can., 1994. Boursier Lab. de l'Accelerateur Lineaire, Orsay, France, 1958-61; physicist Lawrence Berkeley Lab., Berkeley, Calif., 1961-62; staff mem. Stanford (Calif.) Linear Accelerator Ctr., 1962-68, assoc. dir., 1982-86, prof., 1968—. Fellow Guggenheim Found., 1971-72, von Humboldt Found., 1982; recipient Nobel prize in physics, 1990. Fellow AAAS, Am. Acad. Arts and Scis., Am. Phys. Soc. (W.K.H. Panofsky prize div. particles and fields 1989), Royal Soc. Can.; mem. Can. Assn. Physicists, Nat. Acad. Scis. (fgn. assoc.). Office: Stanford Linear Accelerator Ctr PO Box 4349, M/S 96 Stanford CA 94309

TAYLOR, RICHARD FRED, JR., lawyer; b. Salt Lake City, Feb. 28, 1933; s. Richard Fred and Edna Amanda (Olsen) T.; m. Charlaine LeSueur, June 8, 1956 (div. 1972); children—Richard, Michael, Merrianne, Susan, Wendy; m. Yoly Barrio, Aug. 16, 1975; 1 child, Jaime. B.S. in Polit. Sci., U. Utah, 1955; J.D., Georgetown U., 1962. Bar: Utah 1962, D.C. 1990, N.Y. 1991. Contracting officer U. S. Dept. Navy, Washington, 1960-62; sr. asst. counsel Pratt & Whitney Aircraft div. United Techs., East Hartford, Conn., 1962-72; v.p., gen. mgr. Hamilton Test Systems, Inc., Windsor Locks, Conn., 1978-81; v.p., counsel Hamilton Standard div. United Techs. Corp, Windsor Locks, Conn., 1972-78, 81-82; v.p., gen. counsel Carrier Corp., Syracuse, N.Y., 1982-90, sec., dir., 1982-90; pvt. practice, Syracuse, 1991—; exec. v.p., sec., dir. Testcom Inc., N.Y., 1992—; v.p., gen. counsel, sec., dir. N.Y. Testcom Inc., Albany, 1993—; Albany. Bd. dirs., gem. exec. com. Ctrl. N.Y. Health Systems Agy., Syracuse, 1984-87; trustee Upstate N.Y. Multiple Sclerosis Soc., Syracuse, 1983—, chmn., 1986-90, 92—; mem. exec. com., bd. dirs. Vol. Ctr., Inc., Syracuse, 1984-90; bd. dirs. Syracuse Opera Co., 1984—, pres., 1991-93, chmn., 1993—; trustee Crouse Irving Meml. Found., Syracuse, 1989-92. Served to lt. USAF, 1956-58. Mem. ABA, Am. Corporate Counsel Assn., N.Y. State Bar Assn., Greater Syracuse C. of C., Onondaga County Bar Assn. Republican. Clubs: Century (Syracuse); Onondaga Golf & Country (Fayetteville, N.Y.), Cazenovia (N.Y.) Golf. Avocation: boating. Home: West Lake Rd Cazenovia NY 13035 Office: 1 Lincoln Ctr Syracuse NY 13202-1324

TAYLOR, RICHARD POWELL, lawyer; b. Phila., Sept. 13, 1928; s. Earl Howard and Helen Moore (Martin) T.; m. Barbara Jo Anne Harris, Dec. 19, 1959; 1 child, Douglas Howard. BA, U. Va., 1950, JD, 1952. Bar: Va. 1952, D.C. 1956. Law clk. U.S Ct. Appeals for 4th Circuit, 1951-52; assoc. Steptoe & Johnson, Washington, 1956-61, ptnr., 1962—, chmn. transp. dept., 1978—; sec., corp. counsel Slick Corp., 1963-69, asst. sec., 1969-72, also bd. dirs., 1965-68; sec., corp. counsel Slick Indsl. Co., 1963-72; sec., bd. dirs. Slick Indsl. Co. Can. Ltd, 1966-72; bd. dirs. Intercontinental Forwarders, Inc., 1969-72. Mem. Save the Children 50th Anniversary Com., 1982; gen. counsel Am. Opera Scholarship Soc., 1974—; mem. lawyer's com. Washington Performing Arts Soc., 1982—; mem. adv. com. Rock Creek Found. Mental Health, 1982—; mem. nat. adv. bd. DAR, 1980-83, chmn., 1983—; mem. men's com. Project Hope Ball, 1980—; nat. vice chmn. for fin. Reagan for Pres., 1979-80; mem. exec. fin. com. 1981 Presdl. Inauguration; mem. President's Adv. Com. for Arts, 1982—; Rep. Nat. Com., 1983—; Md. fin. chmn. Reagan-Bush '84, Bush-Quayle '88. Served to lt (j.g.), Air Intelligence USNR, 1952-56. Mem. ABA (co-chmn. aviation com. 1976-84, chmn. 1976-77), Fed. Bar Assn., D.C. Bar Assn., Va. Bar Assn., Fed. Energy Bar Assn., Am. Judicature Soc., Assn. Transp. Practitioners, Internat. Platform Assn., Raven Soc., Order of Coif. Episcopalian. Clubs: International, Capitol Hill, Nat. Aviation, Aero, Congl. Country (Washington); Potomac (Md.) Hunt. Home: 14908 Spring Meadows Dr Germantown MD 20874-3444 Office: Steptoe & Johnson 1330 Connecticut Ave NW Washington DC 20036-1704 *Everyone should devote a portion of his or her life to efforts which help ensure that our country remains free and strong and that its concept of government under law is maintained and expanded throughout the world.*

TAYLOR, RICHARD TRELORE, retired lawyer; b. Kewanee, Ill., Aug. 5, 1917; s. Earl G. and Lucile (Cully) T.; m. Maureen Hoey, Feb. 9, 1946. B.S., U. Ill., 1939, J.D., 1946; LL.M., Columbia U., 1947. Bar: Ill. 1946, N.Y. 1947. Assoc. Cadwalader, Wickersham & Taft, N.Y.C., 1947-57, ptnr., 1957-87, presiding ptnr., 1977-87, of counsel, 1988-91; vis. prof. Hebrew U. of Jerusalem, 1973-74; BASF vis. prof. U. Kaiserdoutern, 1994; mem. com. on food stds. and fortification policy NAS-NRC, 1970-73; mem. adv. com. on biochemistry and chem. carcinogenesis Am. Cancer Soc., 1977-81; bd. scientific advisors divsn. cancer etiology Federick Cancer Rsch. Facility, Nat. Cancer Inst., 1995; mem. cancer spl. program adv. com., 1979-82; mem. peer rev. com. Nat. Toxicology Program, 1983-85; founder, bd. dirs. Vicam, Ltd., Partnership; mem. scientific adv. bd. Xenometrix, Inc. Free Radical Scis., Inc. Editor: (with D.I.C. Wang) Single-Cell Protein II, 1975, (with others) The Economics, Marketing and Technology of Fish Protein Concentrate, 1974, (with J.R. Whitaker) Goof Proteins, 1977, Nutritional Safety Aspects of Food Processing, 1979, (with others) Gastrointestinal Cancer: Endogenous Factors, 1981, (with R.A. Scanlan) N-Nitroso Compounds, 1981; contbr. over 300 articles to profl. jours.; mem. editorial bd. Japanese Jour. Cancer Rsch., 1986—, Chem. Rsch. Toxicology, 1988-91, 95—, Cancer Epidemiology, Prevention and Biomarkers, 1990—, Cancer Rsch., 1993—. Trustee Marlboro Coll., Vt. Served with U.S. Army, 1941-45. Decorated Bronze Star. Mem. ABA. Clubs: University (N.Y.C.), The Pilgrims (N.Y.C.). Home: 870 Un Plz New York NY 10017

TAYLOR, RICHARD WILLIAM, investment banker, securities broker; b. Toledo, Sept. 16, 1926; s. Everett Ellsworth and Hazel (Broer) T.; m. Lyn Westerlund, Sept. 11, 1954; children: Julie Everett, Richard William, Alison Nichols, Jennifer Broer, Liane Westerlund. BS, US. Naval Acad., 1949; postgrad., U. Calif., 1952. Mem. Ohio Ho. of Reps. (100th gen. assembly from 9th Dist.); asst. mgr. Navy sales Martin Aircraft, Balt., 1953-56; with McKinsey & Co. (mgmt. cons.), N.Y.C., 1956-60; asst. to v.p. Cerro Corp., N.Y.C., 1960-62, spl. asst. to pres., 1965; pres. Cerro Aluminum Co., N.Y.C., 1962-65; successively v.p., exec. v.p., pres. and CEO Carter, Walker & Co., Inc., 1967-69; pres., CEO Burton, Dana, Westerlund, Inc., N.Y.C., 1969—; v.p. Sterling, Grace & Co., Inc., 1971-74, sr. v.p. corp. fin., 1980-81; v.p. corp. fin. Moseley, Hallgarten, Estabrook & Weeden Inc., 1975-80; v.p. Kidder, Peabody & Co. Inc., 1981-93, Oppenheimer & Co., Inc., 1993—. Bd. trustees, sec.-treas. Am. Econ. Found., Inc.; bd. dirs., v.p YWCA Retirement Fund, Inc. With USN, 1944-52. Decorated Air medal, Navy Commendation medal. Mem. U.S. Naval Acad. Alumni Assn. (bd. govs.), Downtown Athletic Club. Home: Elmwood Orange VA 22960 Office: Oppenheimer & Co Inc Oppenheimer Tower World Financial Ctr New York NY 10281

TAYLOR, RICHARD WIRTH, political science educator; b. Cleve., Jan. 15, 1923; s. Robert and Irmgard (Wirth) T.; m. Sadie White, Sept. 19, 1946; children: Peter, Karla, Mark, Stephen. B.A., U. Ill., 1947, M.A., 1948, Ph.D., 1950. Instr. polit. sci. U. Minn., Mpls., 1950-52; asst. prof. polit. sci. Lehigh U., Bethlehem, Pa., 1952-55, Wis. State U., Stevens Point, 1955-56; vis. asst. prof. Northwestern U., Evanston, Ill., 1956-57; assoc. prof. Coe Coll., Cedar Rapids, Iowa, 1957-60, chmn., prof., 1960-67; prof. polit. sci. Kent State U., Ohio, 1967-92, prof. emeritus, 1992—, chmn., 1974-82; vis. prof. Karl-Marx-Universität, Leipzig, Fed. Republic Germany, 1990. Co-exec. editor Peace and Change, 1986—. Mem. policy com. Friends Com. Nat. Legis., Washington, 1964-85, exec. com., 1986-87; mem. acad. adv. com., ombudsman com. Internat. Bar Assn., Edmonton Alta., Can., 1980—

TAYLOR, ROBERT BROWN, medical educator; b. Elmira, N.Y., May 31, 1936; s. Olaf C. Taylor and Elizabeth (Place) Brown; m. Anita Dopico; children: Diana Marie, Sharon Jean. Student, Bucknell U., 1954-57; MD, Temple U., 1961. Diplomate Am. Bd. Family Practice. Gen. practice medicine New Paltz, N.Y., 1964-78; faculty physician Bowman Gray Sch. Medicine Wake Forest U., Winston-Salem, N.C., 1978-84; prof., chmn. dept. family medicine Oreg. Health Scis. U. Sch. Medicine, Portland, 1984—; mem. comprehensive part II com. Nat. Bd. Med. Examiners, Phila., 1986-91. Author: Common Problems in Office Practice, 1972, The Practical Art of Medicine, 1974; editor: Family Medicine: Principles and Practice, 1978, 4th edit., 1994, Health Promotion: Principles and Clinical Applications, 1982, Difficult Diagnosis, 1985, Difficult Medical Management, 1991, Difficult

Diagnosis II, 1992; contbg. editor Physicians Mgmt. Mag., 1972—; editorial bd. The Family Practice Rsch. Jour., 1980-90, The Female Patient, 1984—, Frontiers of Primary Medicine, 1983—. Am. Family Physician, 1990—, Jour. of Family Practice, 1990-93, Med. Tribune, 1993-93, Med. Tribune, 1993—. Served as surgeon USPHS, 1961-64. Fellow Am. Acad. Family Physicians (sci. program com.), Am. Coll. Preventive Medicine; mem. Soc. Tchrs. Family Medicine (bd. dirs. cert. of excellence), Assn. Am. Med. Colls., Am. Assn. for Study Headache, City Club, Multnomah Athletic Club, Phi Beta Kappa, Alpha Omega Alpha.. Home: 680 SW Regency Ter Portland OR 97225-6070 Office: Oreg Health Scis U Sch Medicine Mail Code FP 3181 Sam Jackson Pk Rd Portland OR 97201

TAYLOR, ROBERT HOMER, quality assurance professional, pilot; b. Rochester, N.Y., Mar. 18, 1922; s. C. Gilbert and Josephine Mary (Woodward) T.; m. Mignon Jane Beight, Aug. 1945; children: Robert Jr., Douglas Beight, Scott Woodward, Sondra Lee. BSME, Case Western Res. U., 1947. Commd. 2d lt. USAF, 1944, advanced through grades to lt. col., 1975; v.p., gen. mgr. Taylor Corp., 1947-53; mgr. quality assurance Spectra Physics Laserplane, Dayton, Ohio, 1976-89; pres., gen. mgr. CON-AV Corp., Tipp City, Ohio, 1989—; quality assurance staff on NASA Mercury Booster USAF, Cape Canaveral, Fla., 1961-63. Advisor Aero Scis. Alternatives, Tipp City, 1990—. Lt. col. CAP. Decorated Air medal with three oak leaf clusters, DFC; named to Aviation Hall of Fame, 1986. Mem. Exptl. Aircraft Assn., Flying Angels, Inc. (pres. 1991), Masons, Beta Theta Pi (Case chpt. pres. 1942), Theta Tau, Early Birds. Episcopalian. Avocations: boating, flying, fishing, refurbishing antique aircraft. Home: 5855 State Rt 40 Tipp City OH 45371 Office: CON-AV Corp 5855 State Rt 40 Tipp City OH 45371

TAYLOR, ROBERT LEE, financial services and sales executive, information systems account executive, educator; b. Adrian, Mich., Jan. 9, 1944; s. Jack Raleigh and Virginia Dixon (Oakes) T.; m. Janice Grace George, Dec. 9, 1961; children—Robin, Lynne, David. A.A., Siena Heights Coll., 1974, B.A., 1976. With computer operation Gen. Parts div. Ford Motor Co. Rawsonville, Mich., 1965-66, prodn. monitoring supr., Saline Plant, Mich., 1966-75, methods and systems analyst, Ypsilanti Plant, Mich., 1975-77, data processing supr. Milan Plant, Mich., 1977-82, sr. systems analyst, Plastics, Paint and Vinyl div., Wixom, Mich., 1982-85; systems engr. Electronic Data Systems, Warren, Mich., 1985-86, systems engr. mgr. Romulus (Mich.) Parts Distbn. Ctr. Plant, 1986-87, customer service mgr., Toledo, 1987-88; project mgr. Computer Task Group, Southfield, Mich., 1988-89; tech. svcs. mgr., 1989-92, spl. agent Prudential, Tecumseh, Mich., 1992-94; ret. plan specialist Variable Annuity Life Ins. Co., Tecumseh, Mich., 1994—; instr. data processing Siena Heights Coll., Adrian, 1985-86; bd. dirs. Lenawee Area Life Underwriters, 1993—, pub. chmn., 1993, nat. committeeman, 1994—. Commr. Tecumseh Planning Commn., Mich., 1976-80, vice-chmn., 1981-82; trustee Tecumseh Bd. Edn., 1981-82, sec., 1983-84, chmn. citizens adv. com., 1983, chmn. computer adv. com., 1984, chmn. policy com., 1983-84; chmn. Tecumseh Area Laymen's Assn., 1983; mem. exec. com. Lenawee County Republican party, 1982-88, precinct del., 1982-88, chmn. computer com., 1984-86; state del. State of Mich., 1983-85, 87; founding advisor Evang. Free Ch. Adrian-Tecumseh, 1984-85, elder, 1986-88, 90-92, 94—, Sunday Sch. supt., 1984-87, 89-90, chmn. Christian edn., 1986-89, 90-91, chmn. planning-bldg. com., 1987-93; asst. Sunday Sch. supt. Berean Baptist Ch., Adrian, 1980-83; tchr. mentally impaired, 1977-83; deacon, Sunday Sch. supt., Grace Bible Ch., Tecumseh, 1973-76; chmn. bd. deacons First Bapt. Ch., Tecumseh, 1970-71, youth advisor, 1968-71, Layman of Yr., 1970; vice chmn. Tecumseh Area Crusade for Christ, 1973, facilities chmn. Lenawee County Crusade for Christ, 1986; chmn. Life Action Crusade, 1987. Served with USAF, 1961-65. Mem. Computer & Automated Systems Assn. (sr.) Mfg. Automation Protocol, Lenawee Assn. Life Underwriter, Nat. Assn. Life Underwriters, Mich. Assn. Life Underwriters, Soc. Mfg. Engrs. Avocations: golf, genealogy. Home: 603 Outer Dr Tecumseh MI 49286-1446 Office: VALIC 603 Outer Dr Tecumseh MI 49286

TAYLOR, ROBERT LEWIS, academic administrator; b. Pitts., Dec. 10, 1939; s. Robert William and Elinor (Miller) T.; m. Linda Taylor Shapiro, Oct. 28, 1988; 1 child, Kara; children by previous marriage: Rob, Mike. AB in Am. Studies, cum laude, Allegheny Coll., 1961; MBA, Ohio State U., 1966; D in Bus. Adminstrn., Mgmt., Ind. U., 1972. Asst. prof., dir. rsch. USAF Acad., Colorado Springs, Colo., 1971-77, assoc. prof., dir. instrn. dept. econ., geography, mgmt., 1977-79, prof. mgmt., head dept. Econ., Geology, Mgmt., 1980-81; assoc. dean Coll. Letters and Sci., head div. Bus. and Econs., Carl N. Jacobs Prof. of Bus. U. Wis., Stevens Point, 1981-84; dean Coll. Bus. Pub. Adminstrn. U. Louisville, 1984—; chmn. bd. dirs. Ky. Wood Floors, Louisville; bd. dirs. Japan-Am. Soc. of Ky., Pvt. Industry Coun., Louisville, Bane One Ky. Corp., Louisville; cons., advisor Kellogg Nat. Fellowship Program, Kellogg Found., Battle Creek, Mich., 1985-89. Co-author, editor: Contemporary Issues in Leadership, 1984, 3d edit., 1993, Military Leadership: In Pursuit of Excellence, 1984, 2d edit., 1992, Leadership Challenges for Today's Manager, 1988; contbr. articles to profl. jours. chmn. Mayor's Strategic Planning Group, Louisville, 1986—; mem. Gov.'s Econ. Devel. Com., Frankfort, Ky., 1987-89, exec. com. Bus. Advs., 1988-92, task force on econ. devel. Ky. Legis. Rsch. Coun., 1991, Leadership Louisville, 1986, Leadership Ky., 1987. Mem. Acad. Mgmt. (proceedings editor 1976-77, newsletter editor 1983-86), Louisville C. of C. (bd. dirs., exec. com 1990—), Sigma Xi, Beta Gamma Sigma, Pi Gamma Mu. Mem. Eastern Orthodox Ch. Avocations: travel, walking, stamp collecting, reading. Home: 1516 Sylvan Way Louisville KY 40205-2408 Office: U Lousiville Coll Bus & Pub Adminstrn Louisville KY 40292

TAYLOR, ROBERT MORGAN, electronics executive; b. Orange, N.J., May 13, 1941; s. Morgan H. M. Taylor and Grace Anna (Bonynge) Loding; m. Sandra Ruth Cox, Sept. 11, 1965; children; Scott Joseph, Karen Lynne. BA in Chemistry, Williams Coll., 1963; PhD in Chemistry, Pa. State U., 1968; MBA, Drexel U., 1973. Scientist Leeds & Northrup Co., North Wales, Pa., 1968-70, sr. scientist, 1970-72, prin. scientist, 1972-84, corp. scientist, 1984-85, dir. R&D, 1985-92, dir. analytical mktg., 1990—. Contbr. articles to profl. jours.; 3 patents in dissolved oxygen sensing. Chmn. indsl. com. Montgomery County (Pa.) Sci. Rsch. Competition, 1987—. Mem. IEEE, Electrochem. Soc. (fin. com. 1971-73, controlling mems. com. 1977), Am. Chem. Soc., Instrument Soc. Am. (sr. mem.), Indsl. Rsch. Inst. (rep.). Republican. Presbyterian. Office: Leeds & Northrup Co Sumneytown Pike PO Box 2000 North Wales PA 19454

TAYLOR, ROBERT P., lawyer; b. Douglas, Ariz., May 6, 1939; s. Paul Burton and Mary Ruth (Hart) T.; m. Sybil Ann Cappelletti, May 30, 1963 (div. Apr. 1974); children: David Scott, Nicole; m. Anne Dale Kaiser, Sept. 21, 1991. BSEE, U. Ariz., 1961; JD, Georgetown U., 1969. Bar: U.S. Ct. Appeals (9th circ.) 1969, U.S. Ct. Appeals (1st, 2d, 3d, 6th, and Fed. circs.), U.S. Supreme Ct., 1975. Elec. engr. Motorola Corp., Phoenix, 1961, Bell & Howell, Pasadena, Calif., 1964-65; examiner U.S. Patent Office, Washington, 1966-69; atty. Pillsbury Madison & Sutro, San Francisco 1969—; mem. adv. commn. Patent Law Reform, Washington, 1990-92; mem. adv. bd. Litigation Risk Analysis, Palo Alto, Calif., 1985—. Contbr. articles to profl. jours. Dir. Ind. Colls. of No. Calif., San Francisco, 1982-88, officer, 1984-94. Fellow Am. Coll. Trial Lawyers; mem. ABA (chair secat. antitrust 1991-92), Am. Law Inst. Avocations: Bicycling, cooking, hiking. Office: Pillsbury Madison & Sutro 225 Bush St Rm 574 San Francisco CA 94104-4207

TAYLOR, ROBERT SUNDLING, English educator, art critic; b. Newton, Mass., Jan. 19, 1925; s. Frank Millikan and Elsie (Sundling) T.; m. Brenda K. Slattery, June 20, 1964; children: Gillian, Douglas. A.B., Colgate U., 1947; postgrad., Brown U. Art, music, film and theatre critic Boston Herald, 1948-67; editor publs. Inst. Contemporary Art, Boston, 1967; art critic Boston Globe, 1967-90, arts editor, 1973-76, book columnist, 1978—; prof. English Wheaton Coll. Norton, Mass., 1961—; fiction 'coordinator Eastern States Writers Conf., Salem (Mass.) State Coll., 1979-80. Author: (novel) In Red Weather, 1961, Saranac: America's Magic Mountain, 1986, Fred Allen: His Life and Wit, 1989, New England: The Home Front, WWII, 1991; co-author: Treasures of New England, 1976. Trustee, Abbot Public Library, Marblehead, Mass., 1980-83. Served with USAF, 1943-46. Mem. Mass. Hist. Soc. Club: St. Botolph (Boston). Home: 1 Thomas Cir Marblehead MA 01945-1203 Office: Wheaton Coll Norton MA 02766

TAYLOR, ROBERT WILLIAM, research director; b. Dallas, Feb. 10, 1932; s. Raymond Autie and Audrey (Burke) T.; m. Joanne L. Honnold, Sept. 1, 1955 (div. Dec. 1983); children: Kurt, Derek, Erik. Student, So. Meth. U., 1948-51; BA, U. Tex., 1957, MA, 1959. Rsch. scientist psychoacoustics lab. Def. Rsch. Lab, U. Tex., 1955-59; math. instr. Howey (Fla.) Acad., 1959-60; sr. systems engr., Pershing systems Martin Co., Orlando, Fla., 1960-61; sr. rsch. engr. electronics div. ACF Industries, Riverdale, Md., 1961-62; program mgr. manned flight control and display sect. Office of Advanced Rsch. and Tech. NASA, Washington, 1962-65; dir. info. processing techniques Def. Advanced Rsch. Projects Agy. Office Sec. of Def., Washington, 1965-69; dir. info. rsch. lab. U. Utah, 1969-70; mgr. computer sci. lab. Xerox Palo Alto (Calif.) Rsch. Ctr., 1970-83; dir. systems rsch. ctr. Digital Equipment Corp., Palo Alto, 1983—; mem. adv. com. on computing and computer sci. Stanford U., Palo Alto, 1971-81, chmn. com., 1977-78; mem. adv. com. for computer sci. NSF, Washington, 1979-81. With USNR, 1952-54. Fellow Assn. for Computing Machinery (Software System award 1984); mem. NAE, IEEE (editor spl. issue IEEE Transactions of Electronics Jour. 1967). Avocations: tennis, gardening, music, reading. Home: 1 Stadler Dr Woodside CA 94062-4810 Office: Digital Equipment Corp Systems Rsch Ctr 130 Lytton Ave Palo Alto CA 94301-1044

TAYLOR, ROBERT WILLIAM, association executive; b. Brownsville, Tenn., July 28, 1929; s. Charles William and Annie Laura (Taliaferro) T.; m. Jeanette Henshaw, Jan. 4, 1953; children: Robert William, Teresa, Mark Thomas. B.S. in Chemistry, Murray (Ky.) State U., 1949; M.S. in Journalism, Ohio U., 1950. Asst. editor Jour. Petroleum Tech., 1953, editor, 1954-63; exec. dir., sec. AIME, 1963-68; exec. v.p., gen. mgr. Soc. Mfg. Engrs., 1968-81; publishing dir. Mfg. Engring., 1968-81; pres. Am. Soc. Assn. Execs., Washington, 1981—, ASAE Found., Washington, 1981—, ASAE Service Corps., Washington, 1981—, ASAE Ins. Co., 1993—; bd. dirs. Inst. Orgn. Mgmt. Assoc. editor: Petroleum Prodn. Handbook, 1961. Past bd. dirs. One to One Found., Mfg. Engring. Edn. Found.; hon. co-chmn. Clinton/Gore Inaugural. Served to 2d lt. USAF, 1951-53. Fellow Soc. Mfg. Engrs., Jr. Engring. Tech. Soc. (past dir.), Am. Soc. Engring. Edn. (past dir.), Council Engring. and Sci. Soc. Execs (past pres.), Am. Assn. Engring. Socs. (past dir.). Club: City of Washington (dir.). Home: 1401 N Oak St Apt 605 Arlington VA 22209-3648 Office: Am Soc of Assoc Executives 1575 I St NW Washington DC 20005-1105

TAYLOR, ROGER CONANT, writer; b. Newport, R.I., Nov. 18, 1931; s. Conant and Marjorie Perry (Buffum) T.; m. Priscilla Greene, June 12, 1953; children: Roger Conant, John Dean, Rebecca Buffum, Stephen Greene; m. 2d, Kathleen Elizabeth Carney, Aug. 17, 1991. AB, Harvard U., 1953; MS, Boston U., 1966. Commd. ensign U.S. Navy, 1953, advanced through grades to comdr. Res., 1967, ret., 1975; served in destroyers and submarines; editorial dir. U.S. Naval Inst., Annapolis, Md., 1960-69; pres. Internat. Marine Pub. Co., Camden, Maine, 1969-86. Author: Good Boats, 1977, More Good Boats, 1979, Still More Good Boats, 1981, The Elements of Seamanship, 1982, The Fourth Book of Good Boats, 1984, Knowing the Ropes, 1989, Thirty Classic Boat Designs, 1992. Mem. U.S. Naval Inst. (life). Home: 218 S Main St Apt 4 Rockland ME 04841-3360

TAYLOR, ROGER LEE, lawyer; b. Canton, Ill., Apr. 6, 1941; s. Ivan and Pauline Helen (Mahr) T.; m. E. Anne Zweifel, June 13, 1964. BA, Knox Coll., 1963; JD cum laude, Northwestern U., 1971. Bar: Ill. 1971, U.S. Dist. Ct. (no. dist.) Ill. 1971, U.S. Dist. Ct. (no. dist.) Tex. 1975, U.S. Dist. Ct. (no. dist.) Ill. 1982, U.S. Ct. Appeals (7th cir.) 1972, U.S. Ct. Appeals (5th and 11th cirs.) 1981, U.S. Supreme Ct. 1975. Assoc. Kirkland & Ellis, Chgo., 1971-78, ptnr., 1978—. Trustee Knox Coll. Lt. USNR, 1964-68. Mem. ABA, Chgo. Council Lawyers, Ill. Bar Assn., Order of Coif, Univ. Club, Mid-Am. Club Chgo. Office: Kirkland & Ellis 200 E Randolph Dr Chicago IL 60601

TAYLOR, RONALD LEE, school administrator; b. Urbana, Ill., Nov. 11, 1943; s. Lee R. and Katherine L. (Becker) T.; m. Patricia D. Fitzsimmons, Mar. 10, 1973; children: Jamie, Lara, Meredith, Dana. AB, Harvard U., 1966; MBA, Stanford U., 1971. Asst. contr. Bell & Howell, Chgo., 1971-73; pres. DeVry Inc./Keller Grad. Sch., Chgo., 1973—; bd. dirs. Precision Plastic, Columbia City, Ind., L. Karp & Sons, Elk Grove Village, Ill. Pres. Hindsdale (Ill.) Sch. Bd., 1983-91; com. chmn. Ill. Bd. Higher Edn., Springfield, 1985—. 1st lt. U.S. Army, 1966-69. Mem. Ill. State C. of C. (mem. edn. com. 1987—). Office: DeVry Inc 1 Tower Ln Villa Park IL 60181

TAYLOR, ROWAN SHAW, music educator, composer, conductor; b. Ogden, Utah, June 1, 1927; s. Hugh Taylor and Lucille (Olsen) Gaenger; m. Dorothy Foulger, June 26, 1946 (div. 1953); children: Kathleen, Scott; m. Priscilla Pulliam, Aug. 29, 1957; children: Mark, Dianne, Paul, Eric, Brent, Charlotte. BA, Brigham Young U., 1952, MA, 1957. Tchr. San Juan Sch. Dist., Blanding, Utah, 1948-50; with C.F. Braun Engring. Firm, 1950-58; tchr. L.A. Unified Dist., 1958-64; from instr. to prof. L.A. Community Coll., Woodland Hills, Calif., 1964—. Conductor, composer 142 symphonies and numerous musical works, 1994—. With U.S. Army, 1955-56, Korea. Republican. Mem. Ch. Jesus Christ of LDS. Avocation: collecting cologne bottles. Home: 22544 Tiara St Woodland Hills CA 91367-3335

TAYLOR, ROY LEWIS, botanist, educator; b. Olds, Alta., Can., Apr. 12, 1932; s. Martin Gilbert and Crystal (Thomas) T. B.Sc., Sir George Williams U., Montreal, Que., Can., 1957; Ph.D., U. Calif. at Berkeley, 1962. Pub. sch. tchr. Olds Sch. Div., 1949-52; jr. high sch. tchr. Calgary Sch. Bd., Alta., 1953-55; chief taxonomy sect., research br. Can. Agrl. Dept., Ottawa, Ont., 1962-68; dir. Bot. Garden, prof. botany, prof. plant scis. U. B.C., Vancouver, 1968-85; pres., CEO Chgo. Horticultural Socs., 1985-94; dir. Chgo. Bot. Garden, Glencoe, Ill., 1985-94; exec. dir. Rancho Santa Ana Bot. Garden, Claremont, Calif., 1994—; prof. botany, chmn. botany program Claremont Grad. Sch.; pres. Western Bot. Svcs. Ltd. Author: The Evolution of Canada's Flora, 1966, Flora of the Queen Charlotte Islands, Vols. I and II, 1968, Vascular Plants of British Columbia: A Descriptive Resource Inventory, 1977; The Rare Plants of British Columbia, 1985. Mem. State of Ill. Bd. Natural Resources and Conservation, 1987-94; trustee Nature Ill. Found., 1990-94. Fellow Linnean Soc. London; mem. Can. Bot. Assn. (pres. 1967-68, Biol. Coun. Can. (pres. 1973-74), Am. Assn. Mus. (accreditation com. 1980-85, chmn. 1985-91, chmn. ethics commn. 1991-93), Am. Assn. Bot. Gardens and Arboreta (pres. 1976, 77, Award of Merit 1987), Ottawa Valley Curling Assn. (pres. 1968-69), B.C. Soc. Landscape Architects (hon.), B.C. Bot. garden (hon.), Chgo. Hort. Soc. (life, medal 1994), Gov.'Gen.'s Curling Club of can. (life). Fellow Linnean Soc. London; mem. Can. Bot. Assn. (pres. 1967-68), Biol. Coun. Can. (pres. 1973-74), Am. Assn. Mus. (accreditation com. 1980-85, chmn. 1985-91, chmn. ethics commn. 1991-93), Am. Assn. Bot. Gardens and Arboreta (pres. 1976, 77, Award of Merit 1987), Ottawa Valley Curling Assn. (pres. 1968-69), B.C. Soc. Landscape Architects (hon.), B.C. Bot. Garden (hon.), Gov.-Gen.'s Curling Club of Can. (life), Univ. Club. Office: Rancho Santa Ana Bot Garden Claremont CA 91711-3157

TAYLOR, SAMUEL ALBERT, playwright; b. San Francisco, June 13, 1912; m. Suzanne Combes, June 4, 1940; children: Ellinor, Michael, David. Student, U. Calif., Berkeley. Ind. playwright, 1950—; chmn. emeritus Dramatists Play Svc., Inc., N.Y.C. playwright: The Happy Time, 1950, Sabrina Fair, 1953, The Pleasure of His Company, 1958, First Love, 1961, No Strings (mus. with Richard Rodgers), 1962, Beekman Place, 1964, Avanti!, 1968, A Touch of Spring, 1975, Legend, 1976, Perfect Pitch, 1978, Flying Colours, 1985, Three by Three, 1988. Mem. Dramatists Guild, Authors Guild, Writers Guild Am., Acad. Motion Picture Arts and Scis. Club: Century Assn. (N.Y.C.). Home: Meadow Rue East Blue Hill ME 04629

TAYLOR, SAMUEL JAMES, mathematics educator; b. Carrickfergus, Northern Ireland, Dec. 13, 1929; came to U.S., 1984; s. Robert James and Janie (Catherwood) T.; married; children—Richard, Charles, Jonathan, Helen. B.Sc., Queen's U., Belfast, No. Ireland, 1950; Ph.D., Cambridge U., 1954. Bye fellow Peterhouse, Cambridge U., Eng., 1953-55; lectr. Birmingham U., Eng., 1955-62; prof. London U., 1962-75, Liverpool U., Eng., 1975-83; vis. prof. U. B.C., Vancouver, Can., 1983-84; Whyburn prof. math. U. Va., Charlottesville, 1984—, chmn. dept., 1986-89. Author: Introduction to Measure and Probability, 1966, Exploring Mathematical Thought, 1970, Introduction to Measure and Integration, 1973; editor:

Decomposition of Probability Distributions, 1964. Procter vis. fellow Princeton U., N.J. 1952. Fellow Cambridge Philos. Soc., Inst. Math. Stats.; mem. London Math. Soc. (sec. 1962-65, 68-71, editor 1980-83), Am. Math. Soc. Presbyterian. Office: U Va Dept Math Kirchoff Hall Charlottesville VA 22903-3145

TAYLOR, SHERRIL WIGHTMAN, broadcasting company executive; b. Salt Lake City, Jan. 4, 1924; s. Kenneth E. and Florence May (Wightman) T.; m. Josephine Vermillion, May 2, 1970; 1 child by previous marriage, Sarah. Student, U. Utah, 1943-46; BJ, U. Mo., 1947; postgrad., Yale U. Promotion mgr. KSL Radio, Salt Lake City, 1947-51; sales promotion mgr. CBS, Hollywood, Calif., 1951-53; CBS radio sales CBS, N.Y.C., 1953-56; dir. sales promotion and advt. CBS Radio, N.Y.C.; also v.p. Radio Advt. Bur., N.Y.C., 1956-58; sr. group head J. Walter Thompson, Chgo., 1958-61; ind. TV producer Kukla, Fran, and Ollie Show, N.Y.C., 1961-64; v.p. Nat. Assn. Broadcasters, Washington, 1964-67; dir. Nat. Assn. Broadcasters, 1969-78; v.p. affiliate relations CBS, 1967-79; cons. Bonneville Internat. Corp., 1979-85; pres. Taylor Co., 1985-91; vice chmn. Coltrin & Assoc., 1991—; pvt. sector coordinator USIA, Washington, 1982, cons., 1982—; chmn. adv. com. Voice of Am., Washington, 1989—; vis. lectr. Brigham Young U., Provo, Utah, 1980—; Emerson Coll., Boston, Mich. Central U., Southern Vt. Coll.; adv. faculty-industry seminar, 1980, 81; bd. dirs. Am. Communications Inc., Utica-Rome TV Svcs. Inc., 1988—. Author: Radio Programming in Action, 1967. Mem. Carnegie Hall com. for Utah Symphony, Park Avenue Preservation Com.; chmn. Freedom of Info. Fund, U. Mo.; past trustee The Helene Toolen Inst. Med. Rsch., Bennington, Vt., 1985—; mem. futures com. Bennington Mus., 1985—; bd. dirs. Nautical Ventures Inc., N.Y.C., 1987—. Mem. So. Calif. Broadcasters Assn. (dir.), Internat. Radio and TV Soc. (v.p., bd. dirs., pres., chmn., bd. dirs. found.), Broadcasters' Found. (dir.), Food and Wine Soc. (N.Y. chpt.), Am. Values Inc. (officer, bd. dirs.), Belleair (Fla.) Country Club, Sigma Chi. Episcopalian. Home: 430 E 86th St New York NY 10028-6476

TAYLOR, STEPHEN DEWITT, savings and loan association executive; b. Provo, Utah, Aug. 12, 1945; s. Weldon J. and Gayle (Dewitt) T.; m. Margaret Dickerson, May 16, 1969; children: Phoebe, Jacob. BA, Brigham Young U., 1969; MBA, Harvard U., 1971. Mgr. Citibank, Calcutta, India, 1974; gen. mgr. Citicorp Australia, Sydney, 1974-79; pres., chief exec. officer Investors Fin. Corp., Manila, Philippines, 1979-82; Citicorp Credit, Tokyo, 1982-85; exec. v.p. Citicorp, Mid-Atlantic, Washington, 1985-86; pres., chief exec. officer Citicorp Savs., Miami, Fla., 1986-88; with Citicorp, New York, 1988-91; pres., chief exec. officer Am. Savs. of Fla. FSB, Miami, 1991—. Office: Am Savs of Fla 17801 NW 2d Ave Miami FL 33169-5029

TAYLOR, STEPHEN EMLYN, publishing executive; b. Cambridge, Eng., Apr. 28, 1951; s. Charles Henry and Diana (Burgess) T.; m. M. E. Malone, May 24, 1987; children: Maxwell, Conrad. BA in Psychology, Yale U., 1973. U.S. sales mgr., tech. advisor Snapir Ltd., Boston, 1973-74; mgr., sail designer North Sails, Boston, 1974-80; mgmt. trainee Boston Globe, 1980-82, asst. to bus. mgr., 1980-82, dir. info. svcs., 1982-86, asst. bus. mgr., 1986-88, bus. mgr., 1988-91, v.p., 1991-93, exec. v.p., 1993—. Bd. dirs. Greater Boston Food Bank, 1991—; mem. corp. Woods Hole (Mass.) Oceanographic Inst., 1993—; mem. U.S. Olympic Yachting Com., 1980-84. Mem. New Eng. Newspaper Assn. (bd. dirs.), Yale Sailing Assocs. (treas., trustee), Cruising Club Am., N.Y. Yacht Club, New Bedford Yacht Club. Home: 18 Webster Rd Milton MA 02186-5318 Office: Globe Newspaper Co PO Box 2378 Boston MA 02107-2378

TAYLOR, STEPHEN LLOYD, food toxicology educator; b. Portland, Oreg., July 19, 1946; s. Lloyd Emerson and Frances Hattie (Hanson) T.; m. Susan Annette Kerns, June 23, 1973; children: Amanda, Andrew. BS in Food Sci. Tech., Oreg. State U., 1968, MS in Food Sci. Tech., 1969; PhD in Biochemistry, U. Calif., Davis, 1973. Research assoc. U. Calif., Davis, 1973-74, research fellow, 1974-75; chief food toxicology Letterman Army Inst., San Francisco, 1975-78; asst. prof. food toxicology U. Wis., Madison, 1978-83, assoc. prof., 1983-87; head dept. food sci. technology, dir. Food Processing Ctr. U. Nebr., Lincoln, 1987—; cons. in field, 1978—. Contbr. articles to profl. jours. Fellow Nat. Inst. Environ. Health Sci., Nat. Acad. Scis. (chair food chems. codex com., bd. food and nutrition), Inst. Food Technologists (dir. chmn. 1981-82, sect. chmn. 1984-85, exec. com. 1988-91); mem. Am. Acad. Allergy, Am. Chem. Soc. Democrat. Presbyterian. Home: 941 Evergreen Dr Lincoln NE 68510-4131 Office: U Nebr Dept Food Sci Tech Lincoln NE 68583-0919

TAYLOR, STEVE HENRY, zoologist; b. Inglewood, Calif., Mar. 18, 1947; s. Raymond Marten and Ardath (Metz) T.; 1 child, Michael Travis; m. Sarah Margaret Young, May 14, 1993. BA in Biology, U. Calif-Irvine, 1969. Animal keeper Los Angeles Zoo, 1972-75, assoc. curator, 1975-76; children's zoo mgr. San Francisco Zoo, 1976-81; zoo dir. Sacramento Zoo, 1981-88; dir. Cleve. Met. Zoo, 1989—. Bd. dirs. Sacramento Soc. Prevention Cruelty to Animals, 1983-87, Sacramento Red Cross, 1988-89, Conv. and Visitor Bur. of Greater Cleve., 1995—. Fellow Am. Assn. Zool. Parks and Aquariums (infant care diet advisor 1979, 85, bd. dirs. 1987-93, pres. 1991-92, chmn. pub. edn. com. 1987-89, bd. regents, mgmt. sch., Outstanding Svc. award); mem. Captive Breeding Specialist Group, Internat. Union of Dirs. Zool. Gardens, The Wilds (bd. dirs. Ohio club), Sierra Club, Audubon Soc. Democrat. Home: 1265 Elmwood Rd Rocky River OH 44107-3616 Office: Cleveland Metroparks Zoo 3900 Brookside Dr Cleveland OH 44109-3187

TAYLOR, STEVEN BRUCE, agriculture company executive; b. Salinas, Calif., Dec. 29, 1954; s. Edward Horton and Joanne (Church) T.; m. Kathryn Hagler, Dec. 17, 1978; children: Meghan Jean, Kyle Hagler, Christian Steven. BA, U. Calif., Berkeley, 1978; MBA, Harvard U., 1985. Pres. Fresh Concepts, San Marino, Calif., 1985-87; mktg. staff Bruce Church, Inc., Salinas, Calif., 1987-91; pres. Fresh Express Retail Mktg., Salinas, 1991—, Fresh Internat., Salinas, 1991—; v.p. Salinas Valley Lettuce Co-op, Salinas, 1990—; bd. dirs. Produce for Better Health, Del., 1991—. Bd. Elders First Presbyn. Ch., Salinas, 1989-92, personnel com. 1989-94, bldg. com. 1990—; founding mem. Lincoln Club of Monterey County, Salinas, 1990. Avocations: basketball, skiing, soccer coach, bible study, board games. Home: 515 Santa Paula Dr Salinas CA 93901 Office: Fresh Internat 1020 Merrill St Salinas CA 93912

TAYLOR, STRATTON, state senator, lawyer; b. Sallisaw, Okla., Jan. 25, 1956; s. Owen and Velma T. AA, Claremore (Okla.) Jr. Coll., 1976; BSE with hons., U. Tulsa, 1978, JD, 1983. Bar: Okla. 1983. State rep. State of Okla., 1978-82, state senator, 1982—; ptnr. Carle, Higgins, Mosier & Taylor, Claremore, 1985—; commr. Uniform Commrs. on State Laws, 1985—; pres. pro tempore of Okla.Sen., 1994—. Chmn. Okla. Senate judiciary com., 1985-88, chmn. appropriations com., 1988—; bd. dir. Oklahomans for Energy & Jobs, Oklahoma City, 1988—; Acypl tour of Japan; bd. dirs. Claremore Reg. Med. Ctr. Mem. Okla. Bar Assn., Okla. Trial Lawyers Assn. Democrat. Baptist. Home: PO Box 1267 Claremore OK 74018-1267 Office: Oklahoma State Senate 522 State Capital Bldg Oklahoma City OK 73105

TAYLOR, TELFORD, lawyer, educator; b. Schenectady, Feb. 24, 1908; s. John Bellamy and Marcia Estabrook (Jones) T.; m. Mary Eleanor Walker, July 2, 1937 (dec.); children: Joan, Ellen, John Bellamy II, Ursula Taylor Rechnegal; m. Toby Barbara Golick, Aug. 9, 1974; children: Benjamin Waite, Samuel Bourne. AB, Williams Coll., 1928, AM, 1932, LLD, 1949; LLB, Harvard U., 1932; LHD (hon.), Yeshiva U., 1987; D in Civil Law (hon.), Union U., 1987; LLD (hon.), Brandeis U., 1988. Instr. history and polit. sci. Williams Coll., 1928-29; law clk. to U.S. circuit judge N.Y.C., 1932-33; asst. solicitor U.S. Dept. Interior, Washington, 1933-34; sr. atty. A.A.A., 1933-34; assoc. counsel U.S. Senate com. on inter-state commerce, 1935-39; spl. asst. to atty. gen. U.S., 1939-40; gen. counsel FCC, 1940-42; practiced with Taylor, Scoll, Ferencz & Simon; vis. lectr. Yale U. Law Sch., 1957-76; vis. lectr. Columbia U. Law Sch., 1958-63, prof. law, 1963-74, Nash prof., 1974-76, emeritus, 1976—; prof. Cardozo Law Sch., 1976-77, 78—; vis. prof. Harvard U. Law Sch., 1977-78; Fed. Spl. master U.S. Dist. Ct. for So. Dist. N.Y., 1977-82; Administr. Small Def. Plants Adminstrn., 1951-52; counsel Joint Council for Edn. TV, 1951-61; chmn. N.Y.C. Adv. Bd. Pub. Welfare, 1960-63, mem., 1963-66. Author: Sword and Swastika, 1952, Grand Inquest, 1954, The March of Conquest, 1958, The Breaking Wave, 1967, Two Studies in Constitutional Interpretation, 1969, Nuremberg and Vietnam, 1970, Courts of Terror, 1976, Munich: The Price of Peace, 1979,

The Anatomy of the Nuremberg Trials; also articles on polit., legal, mil. subjects. Commd. maj. M.I. service U.S. Army, 1942; lt. col. Gen. Staff Corps, 1943; col. (assigned as mil. intelligence officer ETO, 1943-45) assoc. counsel, U.S. rep. for prosecution of war criminals, brig. gen. 1946; U.S. chief of counsel for war crimes Office Mil. Govt., 1946-49, U.S. Decorated DSM; Order Brit. Empire; French Legion of Honor; Polonia Restituta Poland; comdr. Order of Orange-Nassau, Netherlands, 1950; Lateran Cross, 3d class Vatican); recipient Nat. critics prize for non-fiction, 1979; Overseas fellow Churchill Coll., Cambridge, 1969. Fellow Am. Acad. Arts and Scis.; mem. Assn. of Bar of City of N.Y., Am. Law Inst., ASCAP, Res. Officer's Assn., Author's Guild, Mil. Order World Wars, Theta Delta Chi. Democrat. Club: Harvard. Home: 54 Morningside Dr New York NY 10025-1740

TAYLOR, THEODORE BREWSTER, physicist, business executive; b. Mexico City, July 11, 1925; s. Walter Clyde and Barbara (Howl) T.; m. Caro Dwight Arnim, June 13, 1948; children: Clare E. Taylor Hastings, Katherine W. Taylor Robertson, Christopher H., Robert P., Jeffrey J. B.S., Calif. Inst. Tech., 1945; Ph.D., Cornell U., 1954. Theoretical physicist U. Calif. Radiation Lab., Berkeley, 1946-49, Los Alamos Sci. Lab., 1949-56; sr. research adviser Gen. Atomic div. Gen. Dynamics Corp., San Diego, 1956-64; dep. dir. (sci.) Def. Atomic Support Agy., Dept. Def., 1964-67; chmn. bd. Internat. Research & Tech. Corp., 1967-76; vis. lectr. Princeton U., 1976-80; pres. Appropriate Solar Tech. Inst., 1980-87, Nova, Inc., 1980—; also bd. dirs.; pres. So. Tier Environ. Protection Soc., 1990—; mem. Pres.'s Commn. on Accident at Three-Mile Island, 1979; cons. Los Alamos Sci. Lab., 1956-64, Aerospace Corp., 1960-61, Air Force Sci. Adv. Bd., 1955-58, AEC, 1966-70, Def. Atomic Support Agy., 1966-69, U.S. Army Sci. Adv. Panel, 1967-71, Office of Tech. Assessment, 1976—; Rockefeller Found., 1977-80, Princeton U., 1980—; Fedn. Am. Scientists, 1986—; chmn. Los Alamos Study Group, Air Force Space Study Com., 1961; mem. panel outer space ACDA, 1961; mem. adv. bd. Solar Energy Research Inst., 1980-81. Served to ensign USNR, 1942-46. Recipient Ernest Orlando Lawrence award, 1965. Mem. Am. Phys. Soc. Home and Office: PO Box 662 Wellsville NY 14895-0662

TAYLOR, THEODORE LANGHANS, author; b. Statesville, N.C., June 23, 1921; s. Edward Riley and Elnora Alma (Langhans) T.; m. Gweneth Ann Goodwin, Oct. 25, 1946; children: Mark, Wendy, Michael; m. Flora Gray Schoenleber, Apr. 18, 1981. Student, Fork Union Mil. Acad., 1939-40, U.S. Mcht. Marine Acad., 1942-44. Reporter Portsmouth (Va.) Star, 1941-42; Bluefield (W.Va.) News, 1946-47; sportswriter NBC-Radio, N.Y.C., 1942; asst. dir. pub. relations N.Y.U., 1947-48; dir. pub. relations YMCA Schs. and Colls., N.Y.C., 1948-50; publicist Paramount Pictures, Hollywood, Calif., 1955-56; assoc. producer Perlberg-Seaton Prodns., Hollywood, 1956-61. Free-lance writer, 1961—; author: The Magnificent Mitscher, 1954, Fire on the Beaches, 1957, People Who Make Movies, 1968, The Cay, 1969 (Jane Addam's Children's Book award 1970), The Children's War, 1971, Air Raid: Pearl Harbor, 1971, The Maldonado Miracle, 1973, Rebellion Town, 1973, Showdown, 1973, Teetoncey, 1974, Teetoncey and Ben O'Neal, 1975, Battle in the Arctic Seas, 1976, The Odyssey of Ben O'Neal, 1977, A Shepherd Watches, A Shepherd Sings, 1977, Jule, 1979, Battle of Midway Island, 1981, The Trouble with Tuck, 1981, HMS Hood vs Bismarck, 1982, Battle in the English Channel, 1983, Sweet Friday Island, 1984, The Cats of Shambala, Rocket Island, 1985, Walking up a Rainbow, 1986, The Stalker, 1987, The Hostage, 1988, Monocolo, 1989, Sniper, 1989, Tuck Triumphant, 1991, The Weirdo, 1991, Maria, 1992. To Kill the Leopard, 1993, Timothy of the Cay, 1993, The Bomb, 1995. Served with USNR, 1945-46, 50-55. Recipient Lewis Carroll Shelf award, 1970, Silver medal Commonwealth Club, 1970, Best Book award So. Calif. Coun. on Children's Lit., 1970, Best Book award U. Calif. at Irvine, 1970, 74, Best Non-fiction award Western Writers Am., 1977, Young Reader's medal Calif. Reading Assn., 1984, 92, Edgar Allan Poe award, 1992, Utah Young Adult Book award, 1993, Md. Children's Book award, 1994. Mem. Calif. Writers Guild, Acad. Motion Picture Arts and Scis., Screen Writers Guild. Republican. Lutheran. Address: 1856 Catalina Laguna Beach CA 92651-3340

TAYLOR, THOMAS ALEXANDER, III, retired newspaper editor; b. Mobile, Ala., Apr. 9, 1930; s. Thomas Alexander and Mary Helen (McKee) T.; m. Nadine Cecelia Lose, Dec. 5, 1956 (div.); children—Sean Edwin, Julia Marie Taylor Lolley, Stephen Alexander; m. Sandra Joy Johnson McCarter, Jan. 17, 1976; 1 child, Thomas Alexander IV; stepchildren—Steven, Samantha Baxley. B.A., U. Ala.-Tuscaloosa, 1952. Reporter Biloxi Daily Herald, Miss., 1949-50, 52; reporter Columbus Dispatch, Ohio, 1956-57; reporter Mobile Press Register, Ala., 1954-56, 57-60, asst. news editor, then news editor, 1960-83, exec. editor, 1983-94. Served to 1st lt. USAF, 1952-54, col. Res., 1954-79. Mem. Soc. Profl. Journalists (pres. Mobile chpt. 1963), Ala. AP Assn. (pres. 1973-74, treas. 1979-85), Mobile United (treas. 1991-94), Press Club of Mobile (pres. 1981, 93, Career Achievement award 1980). Episcopalian. Home: Rt 1 Box 135 Cohassett AL 36474

TAYLOR, T(HOMAS) ROGER, educational consultant, educator; b. Urbana, Ill., May 31, 1945; s. Thomas and Ora Wilma T.; m. Beverly Milam, Dec. 19, 1981; 1 child, Whitney Brinson. BS, U. Ill., 1967; MA, So. Ill. U., 1972, PhD, 1980. Tchr., Mt. Vernon (Ill.) Schs., 1967-71; cons. Ill. Dept. State, 1971-74; dir. Area Svc. Ctr. for Gifted Children, South Cook County, Ill., 1975-79; prof. urban edn. Govs. State U., 1975-79; cons. Ednl. Cons. Assocs., Denver, 1977-82, also dir.; pres. Curriculum Design for Excellence, Oak Brook, Ill.; former sr. ptnr. T & H Investments, Hinsdale, Ill. Vice-pres. Mt. Vernon Community Coll. Orch. Named K.y. Col., 1979. Recipient Outstanding Young Men of Am. award, 1980; named Best of the Best, IDEA Fellows Program, 1992, 93. Mem. U. Ill. Alumni Assn. (dir. 1967-71), NEA, Ill. Edn. Assn. (bd. dirs.), Nat. Assn. Gifted Children, World Council for Gifted, Assn. Childhood Edn. Internat., Profl. Assn. Diving Instrs., Nat. Rifle Assn., Phi Delta Kappa. Clubs: Demolay. Contbr. in field. Home: 1907 Midwest Club Pky Oak Brook IL 60521-2525 Office: PO Box 4505 Hinsdale IL 60522-4545

TAYLOR, THOMAS WILLIAM, lawyer; b. Columbus, Ind., Feb. 11, 1943; s. Virgil W. and Margaret Emma (Voiles) T.; m. Linda Kay Followell, Jan. 1, 1964; children: Pamela Kay, William Lansing. AB with honors, Ind. U., 1965; LLB cum laude, Harvard U., 1968. Bar: Mass. 1968, U.S. Dist. Ct. Mass. 1969. Assoc. Ropes & Gray, Boston, 1968-78, ptnr., 1978—; lectr. Pres.'s urban policy program seminars U.S. Coun. of Mayors, 1982; chmn. tax panel nat. workshop Coun. of Infrastructure Financing Authorities, 1993. Mem. Nat. Assn. Bond Lawyers (opinions com., chmn. securities law panel Washington workshop 1992, lectr. atty.'s workshop Chgo. chpt. 1993—). Avocations: rock climbing, snowboarding, orienteering, trumpet playing. Office: Ropes & Gray 1 International Pl Boston MA 02110

TAYLOR, TONY S., research scientist. Head stability physics group Gen. Atomics, San Diego. Recipient award for Excellence in Plasma Physics Rsch. Am. Physical Soc., 1994. Office: General Atomics PO Box 85608 San Diego CA 92186-9784*

TAYLOR, VIRGINIA S., lawyer; b. Quitman, Ga.; d. Allen Candler and Anne (Sanderson) Smith; divorced; children: Anne Taylor Hendry, Thomas Fielding. AB, Smith Coll., 1961; JD with distinction, Emory U., 1977. Bar: Ga. 1977, U.S. Dist. Ct. (no. dist.) Ga. 1977, U.S. Dist. Ct. (mid. dist.) Ga. 1979, U.S. Dist. Ct. (ea. dist.) Miss. 1988, U.S. Ct. Appeals (5th and 11th cirs.) 1981, U.S. Ct. Appeals (fed. cir.) 1982, U.S. Supreme Ct. 1981. Assoc. Kilpatrick & Cody, Atlanta, 1977-83, ptnr., 1983—. V.p Olmstead Parks Soc., Atlanta, 1985-93; bd. dirs. Piedmont Park Conservancy, Atlanta, 1991—, YWCA Metro. Atlanta, 1989-92, Leadership Atlanta, 1990. Mem. Ga. State Bar (chair patent, trademark and copyright sect. 1985-86), Order of Coif, Lawyer's Club Atlanta, Internat. Trademark Assn. (chair internat. forums subcom. 1992—, bd. dirs. 1991-93, chair pub. com. 1988-90). Democrat. Methodist. Avocations: gardening, traveling, reading. Office: Kilpatrick & Cody 1100 Peachtree St Ste 2800 Atlanta GA 30309

TAYLOR, VOLNEY, marketing company executive; b. Portsmouth, Ohio, Dec. 6, 1939; s. Lafayette and Martha Louise (Frederick) T.; m. Kathleen Ann MacMahon, May 17, 1969; children—Lafayette, Lloyd MacMahon, Kerry Erin, Frederick Daly. B.S. in Indsl. Engring. Ohio State U., 1962; M.B.A., Harvard U., 1964. Mem. mem McKinsey & Co., Inc. (mgmt. cons.), N.Y.C., 1966-72; exec. v.p., dir. Funk & Wagnalls, Inc., N.Y.C., 1972-74; v.p. fin. Reuben H. Donnelley Co., N.Y.C., 1974-76; dir. corp.

planning Dun & Bradstreet Corp., N.Y.C., 1976-77, v.p. corp. planning, 1977-78, corp. v.p., 1979-80, sr. v.p., 1980-82, exec. v.p., 1982—, also bd. dirs.; gen. mgr. Official Airline Guides, Oak Brook, Ill., 1978-79, also bd. dirs.; chmn. bd. dirs. Dun & Bradstreet Info. Svcs., Murray Hill, N.J., 1991—; bd. dirs Dun & Bradstreet, Inc., Dun & Bradstreet Europe, Dun & Bradstreet Internat., Dun's Mktg. Svcs., Inc., Moody's Investors Svc.; pres. The Reuben H. Donnelley Corp., 1988-90. Served to lt. (j.g.) USNR, 1962-64. Mem. Harvard Bus. Sch. (N.Y.C.) Club, Beta Theta Pi. Office: Dun & Bradstreet Info Svcs 1 Diamond Hill Rd Murray Hill NJ 07974-0027*

TAYLOR, WAYNE FLETCHER, lawyer; b. Evansville, Ind., Jan. 23, 1943; s. Fletcher S. and Dortha Mae (Schnute) T.; m. Mary Sue Stephens, June 13, 1965; children: Wayne F. Jr., Deborah G. BBA, Vanderbilt U., 1965, JD, 1968. Bar: Tenn. 1968, Ohio 1970. Assoc. Dearborn Berry and Warner, Nashville, 1968-69; asst. corp. counsel The Midland Co., Cin., 1969-74, Emery Industries Inc., Cin., 1974-78; sec., corp. counsel Cin. Milacron Inc., 1978-90, v.p., gen. counsel, sec., 1990—. Republican. Avocations: photography, sports, woodworking, fishing, gardening. Office: Cin Milacron Inc 4701 Marburg Ave Cincinnati OH 45209-1025

TAYLOR, WELFORD DUNAWAY, English language educator; b. Caroline County, Va., Jan. 3, 1938; s. George Welford and Minnie (Durrette) T.; m. Carole Virginia Wickham, Jan. 19, 1942; 1 child, Virginia Welford. BA, U. Richmond, 1959, MA, 1961; PhD, U. Md., 1966. Tchr. Randolph-Macon Acad., Front Royal, Va., 1959-60, St. Christopher's Sch., Richmond, Va., 1960-61; instr. English Va. Commonwealth U., Richmond, 1961-63; prof. English U. Richmond (Va.), 1964—; chmn. English dept. U. Richmond, 1978-86, James H. Bostwick chair English, 1991—; book reviewer Richmond News Times-Dispatch, 1986—. Author: Amélie Rives (Princess Troubetzkoy), 1973, Sherwood Anderson, 1977; editor: The Buck Fever Papers, 1971, The Newsprint Mask, 1990, Our American Cousin/The Play Changed History, 1990, The Woodcut Art of J.J. Lankes, 1995. Mem. Poe Found. (1st v.p-sec. 1994), Sherwood Anderson Soc. (founder 1976), Va. Writers Club, English-Speaking Union, Country Club Va. (Richmond). Republican. Episcopalian. Avocations: book collecting, art collecting. Home: 5 Calycanthus Rd Richmond VA 23221-3101 Office: U Richmond Dept English Richmond VA 23173

TAYLOR, WESLEY BAYARD, JR., army officer; b. Covington, Ky., June 5, 1944; s. Wesley B. Sr. and Varina Martha (Morgan) T.; m. Linda L. Taylor, June 2, 1967; children: Kathleen C., Clint C. BS, U.S. Mil. Acad., 1965; MA in Internat. Rels., U. Calif., Santa Barbara, 1973; student, U.S. Army War Coll., 1985-86. Commd. 2d lt. U.S. Army, 1965, advanced through grades to brig. gen., 1990; staff officer Dept. of Army, Washington, 1980-81; bn. comdr. 3rd Bn., 5th Inf. U.S. Army, Republic of Panama, 1981-83; bn. comdr. 1st Ranger Bn. U.S. Army, Hunter Army Airfield, Ga., 1983-85; chief staff, strategic fellow U.S. Army War Coll., Carlisle Barracks, Pa., 1986-87; regimental comdr. 75th Ranger Regiment U.S. Army War Coll., Ft. Benning, Ga., 1987-89; asst. divsn. comdr. 1st Armored Divsn. U.S. Army War Coll., Germany, 1989-91; dep. dir. ops, readiness and mobilization Dept. of Army, Washington, 1991-92; dep. asst. sec. of def. for policy and missions Office Sec. of Def. for Spl. Ops. and Low Intensity Conflict, Washington, 1992—; asst. bn. advisor, sr. bn. advisor Airborne Divsn. Adv. Detachment, U.S. Mil. Assistance Command, Vietnam, 1967-68; dep. asst. sec. of def. for policy and missions Office of Asst. Sec. of Def. for Spl. Ops. and Low Intensity Conflict, Washington, 1992—. Dist. commr. Boy Scouts Am., Germany, 1984-91; treas. Home Owners Assn., Fairfax Station, Va., 1992-94. Decorated Silver Star, Legion of Merit with oak leaf cluster, Def. Meritorious Svc. medal, Bronze Star medal with oak leaf cluster, Air medals. Mem. Assn. U.S. Army, U.S. Army Ranger Assn., 75th Ranger Regiment Assn., Soc. Vietnamese Airborne Advisors, Soc. 173rd Airborne Brigade. Methodist. Avocations: fishing, hunting. Office: Dept Def The Pentagon Rm 2B535 Washington DC 20301-2500

TAYLOR, WILLIAM AL, church administrator; b. Danville, Va., Sept. 26, 1938; s. Preston Floyd and Helen Elizabeth (Doss) T.; m. Brenda Flo Owen, June 4, 1961; children: Fawnia Rae Ricks, Albert Todd, Athena Dawn Jarman. AA, Lee Coll., 1957; postgrad., U. Calif., Santa Barbara, 1980. Br. mgr. Ency. Britannica, Greensboro, N.C., 1960-62; divsn. trainer Ency. Britannica, Mpls., 1963; dist. mgr. Ency. Britannica, Omaha, 1964-72; adminstrv. asst. Forward in Faith Internat. Broadcast, Cleveland, Tenn., 1972-80; gen. mgr. Sta. WQNE-FM, Cleveland, 1980—; dir. stewardship Ch. of God Internat. Offices, Cleveland, 1980—; pres. Pathway Credit Union, Cleveland, 1985—; Vision Found., Cleveland, 1985—, exec. dir., 1979-80; chmn. Internat. Commn. on Prayer, Cleveland, 1986—. Author: Proving God, 1991, Days of Heaven on Earth, 1993, Stewardship Masterplanning, 1993. Pres. Clean Water Soc., Gastonia, N.C., 1974-75; speaker Citizens Against Legalized Liquor, Bradley County, Tenn., 1973, 75; advisor Mothers on March, Cleveland, 1976; active Nat. Conf. on Drug Abuse, Washington, 1978; master of ceremonies Nat. Religious Leaders Conf. on Alcohol and Drug Abuse, Indpls., 1979. Recipient Mass Communications award Ch. of God Media Ministries, 1980, Stephen award Ch. of God Lay Ministries, 1990. Mem. Nat. Assn. Evangelicals (bd. adminstrs. 1985—, chmn. stewardship commn. 1985-89), Christian Stewardship Assn. (bd. dirs. 1990-94). Avocations: flying, travel, racquetball. Office: Ch of God Dept Stewardship 2490 Keith St NW Cleveland TN 37311-1309 *We are all spending the precious gift of life, and we have been given the privilege to decide upon what we shall spend it. I have found the most worthy and fulfilling investment of life is God's stated purpose, "that we be conformed to the image of His son Jesus Christ."*

TAYLOR, WILLIAM B., history educator; b. L.A., Mar. 23, 1943; s. James Chapman and Alma (Berley) T.; m. Barbara E. Tresch, June 17, 1964; children: Karin Elise, Jill Linda. BA, Occidental Coll., L.A., 1964; MA, U. of Ams., Mexico City, 1965; PhD, U. Mich., 1969. Asst. prof. history U. Colo., Denver/Boulder, 1969-72; assoc. prof. history U. Colo., Boulder, 1972-77; prof. history U. Colo., 1977-82; Edward F. Arnold Disting. prof. Whitman Coll., Walla Walla, Wash., 1980; vis. prof. history Harvard U., Cambridge, Mass., 1981; prof. history U. Va., Charlottesville, 1982—; mem. nat. adv. coun. John Carter Brown Libr., Providence, 1986-89; mem. internat. adv. bd. The Mesopotaian Archive, U. Colo., 1989—; cons./expert witness Cochiti Queblo, 1979-85, U.S. Dept. Justice, 1974-82. Author: Drinking, Homicide and Rebellion..., 1979, Landlord and Peasant in Colonial Oaxca, 1975. Nat. Humanities Ctr. fellow, 1990—, Inst. for Advanced Study fellow, 1987, Guggenheim fellow, 1979-80, NEH fellow, 1974-75, U. Colo. teaching awardee, 1974. Mem. Am. Hist. Assn., Conf. on Latin Am. History, Phi Beta Kappa. Office: University of Virginia Charlottesville VA 22903

TAYLOR, WILLIAM BROOKS, II, retired dermatologist; b. Bethany, W.Va., Aug. 25, 1910; s. William B. and Amanda Jean (Eales) T.; m. Helen Motz, 1979; 1 son, Michael B. M.D., U. Mich., 1935. Diplomate: Am. Bd. Dermatology. Intern Miami Valley Hosp., 1935-36; practice family medicine Jackson, Ohio, 1936-50; resident in dermatology U. Mich., Ann Arbor, 1950-53; mem. faculty U. Mich., 1953—, asso. prof. dermatology, 1963-75, prof., 1975-81, prof. emeritus, 1981—. Mem. Am. Acad. Dermatology, Am. Dermatological Assn. Home: 1200 Earhart Rd Ann Arbor MI 48105-2768

TAYLOR, WILLIAM JAMES (ZAK TAYLOR), lawyer; b. Milw., Jan. 26, 1948; s. William Elmer and Elizabeth Emily (Lupinski) T.; m. Marlou Belyea, Sept. 20, 1975; children: Danielle Belyea, James Zachary Belyea. BA in Econs., Yale U., 1970; JD, Harvard U., 1976. Bar: Calif. 1976, U.S. Dist. Ct. (cen. dist.) Calif. 1976, U.S. Dist. Ct. (no. dist.) Calif. 1977, U.S. Ct. Appeals (9th cir.) 1977, U.S. Dist. Ct. (ea. dist.) Calif. 1980, U.S. Supreme Ct. 1980, U.S. Tax Ct. 1988. Law clk. to presiding judge U.S. Ct. Appeals (9th cir.), L.A., 1976-77; assoc. Broebeck, Phleger & Harrison, San Francisco, 1977-83; ptnr. Broebeck, Phleger and Harrison, San Francisco, 1983—; bd. dirs Berkeley (Calif.) Law Found., 1988-91, Legal Svcs. for Children (recipient Jean Waldman Child Advocacy award) San Francisco 1988), 1983-89; co-chmn. Attys. Task Force for Children, San Francisco 1983-89. Editor-in-chief Havard Civil Rights, Civil Liberties Law Review 1976; bd. editors No. Dist. of Calif. Digest, 1978-83; co-author California Antitrust Law, 1991. With U.S. Army, 1970-73. Mem. ABA, Bar Assn. San Francisco (bd. dirs. 1986-87, chair antitrust sect. 1987, chair fed. cts. sect. 1995—), Am. Bus. Trial Lawyers Assn., Barristers of San Francisco (bd.

dirs. 1980-82, v.p. 1982-83). Democrat. Office: Brobeck Phleger & Harrison Spear St Tower 1 Market Plz San Francisco CA 94105-1019

TAYLOR, WILLIAM JAMES, III, federal official; b. Petersburg, Va., Feb. 12, 1954; s. William James Jr. and Erma Glenn (Brown) T.; m. Elneita Sylvia Hutchins, Dec. 11, 1982; children: Royce Alan, Christian Alexander, Kellye Audrey. BA in Mass Comm., Howard U., 1977; JD, U. Tex. Sch. Law, 1981. Bar: Tex., 1981. Adminstrv. asst. Office Hon. William P. Hobby, Lt. Gov., Tex., 1980-81; staff atty. II Tex. Edn. Agy., 1981-82; campaign coord. Bill Hobby Campaign, 1982; exec. asst. county atty. Office Harris County Atty. Mike Driscoll, 1983; coun. coord. Office former Houston Councilman Rodney Ellis, 1984; divsn. chief Office Harris County Atty. Mike Driscoll, 1983; adminstrv. asst., legal coun. Office late congressman Mickey Leland, 1985-88; atty. Hutcheson & Grundy L.L.P., 1989-93; asst. sec. congl. and intergovernmental affairs Dept. Energy, Washington, 1993—. mem. bd, regents East Tex. State U., 1991-93; v.p. Houston Housing Fin. Corp., 1992-93; pres. Tex. Black Leadership Congress, 1988-93; mem. bd. dirs. Juvenile Ct. Vols. Harris County, 1989-92, Tex. Lyceum Assn., Inc., 1989, NAACP, 1991-93, Ctr. for the Retarded, 1991-93, Houston Prep. Acad., 1991-93; com. cons., chmn. legis. com. Houston Mus. Fine Arts, 1989-93; lectr. CLE programs U. Houston Law Ctr., 1990-91; mem. citizens adv. com. Tex. Lottery Startup, 1991; mem. adv. bd. The Chinquapin Sch., 1992-93. Mem. Thurgood Marshall Legal Soc. (pres. 1980). Avocations: basketball, skiing. Office: Congl & Intergovt Affairs 1000 Independence Ave SW Washington DC 20585-0001

TAYLOR, WILLIAM JAPE, physician; b. Booneville, Miss., Sept. 5, 1924; s. William Melton and Cora Leona (Smith) T.; m. Audrey Y. Dennison, Jan. 31, 1948; children—J. Holley, Andrew D., Richard M., D. Lee. B.S., Yale U., 1944; M.D., Harvard U. 1947. Intern in internal medicine Boston City Hosp., 1947-48; resident in internal medicine Duke U. Hosp., 1948-50, fellow in cardiology, 1950-52, 54-55; instr. Duke U. Med. Sch., 1954-55, U. Pitts. Med. Sch., 1955-58; mem. facul'v U. Fla. Coll. Medicine, Gainesville, 1958—; prof. medicine U. Fla. Coll. Medicine, 1964—, chief cardiology, 1958-74, disting. service prof. medicine, 1974—; vis. prof. U. Ife (Nigeria) Med. Sch., 1974-75; bd. dirs. PSRO, Fla. Area II, 1977-81. Author papers in field, chpts. in books. Mem. human rights advocacy com. mentally retarded Fla. Dist. III, 1977-81; bd. dirs. Gainesville-Natagalpa Sister City, 1988—. Fellow ACP (research fellow 1950-51), Am. Coll. Cardiology; mem. Assn. U. Cardiologists, Am. Heart Assn. (fellow council clin. cardiology), Am. Fedn. Clin. Research. So. Soc. Clin. Investigation (pres. 1972-73), Fla. Heart Assn. (Disting. Service award 1975), Physicians for Social Responsibility (ho. of dels. 1980-86). Democrat. Home: 500 NW 80th Blvd Gainesville FL 32607-1531 Office: U Fla Med Sch Dept Medicine Gainesville FL 32610

TAYLOR, WILLIAM JESSE, JR., international studies educator, research center executive; b. Florence, S.C., Dec. 28, 1933; s. William J. and Dorothy (Byrd) T.; m. Louise Inger Haegerstrom, Apr. 9, 1977; 1 child, Nicolaus; children by previous marriage: Juliana C., William J. III, L. Scott, Christopher B., Helen B. B.S., U. Md., 1962; M.A., Am. U., 1964, Ph.D, 1967. Enlisted U.S. Army, commd. 2d lt., 1955, advanced through grades to col., 1976; prof. U.S. Mil. Acad., West Point, N.Y., 1970-81; vis. prof. U.S. Nat. War Coll., 1975-76; ret. U.S. Army, 1981; dir. polit. mil. studies Ctr. for Strategic and Internat. Studies Georgetown U., Washington, 1980-83; exec. dir., chief operating officer Ctr. for Strategic and Internat. Studies, 1983-87, v.p. internat. security programs, 1987-92; pres. Taylor Assocs. Inc., 1984—; sr. v.p. Internat. Security Affairs, 1992—; internat. lectr., debater, T.V. mil. analyst, 1970—. Author: Future of Conflict: U.S. Interests, 1982, Future of Conflict into the 21st Century, 1987; co-author: American National Security: Policy and Process, 1981, 83, 89, 93; co-editor: Defense Manpower Planning, 1980, The Future of Conflict in the 1980's, 1982, Strategic Requirements for the Army to the Year 2000, 1983, Strategic Responses to Conflict in the 1980's, 1984, Nordic Defense: Comparative Decisionmaking, 1985, Strategic Dimensions of Military Manpower, 1987, The Future of U.S.-Republic of Korea Security Ties, 1989, The Korean Peninsula: Prospects for Arms Control, 1990, Korea 1991: The Road to Peace, 1991, Elvis in The Army, 1995. Mem. Presiding Bishop's Nat. Episc. Roundtable, 1983-86. Decorated Bronze Star with oak leaf cluster, Legion of Merit (2), Air Medal (3), Air medal for valor, Vietnam Cross of Gallantry, Combat Infantry Badge; recipient Pitman Potter Medal Am. U., 1964; named to Infantry Officer Hall of Fame, 1976; named Disting. Alumnus, Episcopal Acad., 1995. Mem. Council on Fgn. Relations, Internat. Inst. Strategic Studies, St. Anthony Club, Internat. Club of Washington. Republican. Episcopalian. Office: Ctr for Strategic & Intl Studies 1800 K St NW Washington DC 20006-2200

TAYLOR, WILLIAM OSGOOD, newspaper executive; b. Boston, July 19, 1932; s. William Davis and Mary (Hammond) T.; m. Sally Coxe, June 20, 1959; children: William Davis II, Edmund C., Augustus R. BA, Harvard U., 1954. With Globe Newspaper Co., Boston, 1956—, treas., 1963—, bus. mgr., 1965-69, gen. mgr., 1969—; now chmn. bd., pub. Boston Globe. Trustee Boston Pub. Libr.; bd. dirs. United Way New Eng., Boston Adult Literacy Fund; trustee Mus. of Fine Arts. With U.S. Army, 1954-56. Mem. Newspaper Assn. Am. (bd. dirs.). Office: Globe Newspaper Co 135 Morrissey Blvd Dorchester MA 02125-3338

TAYLOR, WILSON H., diversified financial company executive. Grad., Trinity Coll. With Conn. Gen., 1954-82, sr. v.p., chief fin. officer, 1980-82; v.p. Aetna Ins. Co., 1975; exec. v.p. Cigna Corp., Phila., 1982-88, pres. property casualty group, 1983-88, corp. vice-chmn., chief operating officer, from 1988, chief operating officer, 1988, pres., chief exec. officer, 1988—, then chmn., pres., chief exec. officer, now chmn., chief exec. officer. Phi Beta Kappa. Office: Cigna Corp 1 Liberty Plz Philadelphia PA 19192-2078*

TAYLOR, W.O. (BILL), state legislator, business consultant; b. Zanesville, Ohio, July 29, 1932; s. Henry Ray and Lorena Louise (Winkler) T.; m. Shirley Ann Jacobs, Mar. 11, 1951; children: Bill, Larry, Sallie, Charles, Richard, Julie. AA in Bus. Adminstrn., Jacksonville (Fla.) U., 1957; B of Sci. Edn. Midwestern State U., Wichita Falls, Tex., 1968, MEd, 1972. Advanced secondary cert., Idaho. Acct. Swift & Co., Jacksonville, 1955-58; v.p. Taylor Bros. Inc., Baton Rouge, 1958-60; pres. Carter Paint Co., Inc., Wichita Falls, 1960-68; tchr. econs. Wichita Falls Pub. Sch., 1968-78; pres. Taylor Enterprises, Inc., Nampa, Idaho, 1978—; mem. Ho. of Reps, State of Idaho, Boise, 1986—, chmn. bus. com., 1994. Bishop Ch. of Jesus Christ of Latterday Saints, Wichita Falls, 1964-69. Served to sgt. USMC, 1950-53, Korea. Named Republican of Yr., Canyon County Rep. Ctrl. Com., 1987. Mem. DAV, Sertoma (life, pres. 1965, Sertoman of Yr. award 1964). Republican. Avocations: history, geneaology. Home: 8367 Track Rd Nampa ID 83686-9424 Office: Idaho Ho of Reps State Capitol Boise ID 83720

TAYLOR-LITTLE, CAROL J(OYCE), state legislator, real estate agent; b. Berkeley, Calif., Aug. 13, 1941; d. Harold Robert and Marjorie Evelyn (Strawn) Hochmuth; m. Nicholas G. Kappas, Aug. 29, 1959 (div. Sept. 1980); children: Anthony N., Katherine M.; m. Donald L. Little, June 19, 1982. Student in real estate Red Rocks Community Coll., 1978; cert. degree adminstrn. non-profit agts. Met. State Coll., Denver, 1981, postgrad. in urban studies and polit. sci., 1981—. Lic. in real estate, Colo. Recreation instr. North Jefferson Recreational Dist. (Colo.), 1970-82; real estate sales agt. Crown Realty/Better Homes & Gardens, Arvada, Colo., 1979-88, Realty Ptnrs. Referral Network, Lakewood, Colo., 1989—; mem. Colo. Ho. of Reps., 1982-84, 84-86, 86-88, 88-90, House majority whip, 1984-86; chmn. House Majority caucus, 1988-90. Chairperson Med. Malpractice Task Force; vice chmn. Victims' Assistance Adv. Council; mem. Met. Air Quality Council. Named Legislator of Yr. Colo. Univ. Alumni Assn., 1988; Spl. Recognition Colo. Spl. Olympics, 1988, Colo. Bankers Assn., 1988; recipient Cert. Appreciation United Veterans Com., 1988, 90. Mem. Nat. Fedn. Ind. Bus., Colo. Adv. Small Bus., Nat. Conf. State Legislators's, Nat. Fedn. Rep. Women, Colo. Hist. Soc., Arvada C of C. (bd. dirs.), Arvada Ctr. for Arts and Humanities. Office: State Capitol Ho of Reps Denver CO 80203

TCHAIKOVSKY, LESLIE J., judge; b. 1943. BA, Calif. State Univ., Hayward, 1967; JD, Univ. of Calif. Berkeley, 1976. Law clk. to Hon. John Mowbray Nev. Supreme Ct., 1976-77; with Dinkelspiel, Steefel, Leavitt & Weiss, 1977-80, Gordon, Peitzman & Lopez 1981, Dinkelspiel, Donovan & Reder, 1981-88; bankruptcy judge U.S. Bankruptcy Ct. (Calif. no. dist.), 9th

circuit, Oakland, 1988—. Office: US Courthouse 1300 Clay St Oakland CA 94604-2070

TCHERKASSKY, MARIANNA ALEXSAVENA, ballerina; b. Glen Cove, N.Y., Oct. 28, 1952; d. Alexis and Lillian (Oka) T.; m. Terrence S. Orr. Student, Washington Sch. Ballet (scholar), 1965-67, Sch. Am. Ballet and Profl. Children's Sch., 1967-70; pupil of Edward Caton. Appeared with Bolshoi Ballet in Ballet Sch., 1961, 62, N.Y.C. Ballet in A Midsummer Night's Dream, 1963; profl. debut with Andre Eglevsky Ballet Co., 1968; mem., Am. Ballet Theatre, 1970—, soloist, 1972-76, prin. dancer, 1976—, guest appearances throughout U.S. and in Europe, also on TV; roles include The Nutcracker, La Bayadere, Bruch Violin Concerto No. 1, Coppelia, Giselle, Etudes, Les Liaisons Dangereuses, Romeo and Juliet, The Sleeping Beauty, La Sylphide, Les Sylphides, The Leaves are Fading. Winner Nat. Soc. Arts and Letters competition, 1967; Ford Found. scholar, 1967-70. Office: care Am Ballet Theatre 890 Broadway New York NY 10003-1211*

TCHOBANOGLOUS, GEORGE, civil engineering educator; b. Patterson, Calif., May 24, 1935; s. Christo and Penelope (Megdani) T.; m. Rosemary Ash, June 16, 1957; children—Kathryn, Lynn, Julianne. B.C.E., U. Pacific, 1958; M.C.E., U. Calif., Berkley, 1960; Ph.D., Stanford U., 1969. Registered profl. engr., Calif., Mont. Research engr. U. Calif.-Berkeley, 1960-62; cons. Metcalf & Eddy Engrs., Palo Alto, Calif., 1963-81, Nolte & Assocs., Sacramento, 1981—, Calif. Water Resources Control Bd., 1972-80; assoc. prof. U. Calif.-Davis, 1970-76, prof. engring., 1976—. Prin. author: Wastewater Engineering: Collection, Treatment, Disposal, 1972; author: (with R. Smith and R. Crites) Wastewater Management: A Guide to Information Sources, 1976, (with H. Theisen and R. Eliassen) Solid Wastes: Engineering Principles and Management Issues, 1977, (with Schroeder) Water Quality: Characteristics, Modeling, Modification, 1985, (with Peavy and Rowe) Environmental Engineering, 1985, (with H. Theisen, S.A. Vigil) Integrated Solid Waste Management: Engineering Principles and Management Issues, 1993; co-author: Wastewater Engineering: Treatment, Disposal, Reuse, 1991; author, editor: Wastewater Engineering: Collection and Pumping of Wastewater, 1981; co-editor: Pumping Station Design, 1989; contbr. numerous articles to profl. jours. Mem. bd. Calif. Integrated Waste Mgmt.; lectr. T.R. Camp, 1990. Mem. AAAS, ASCE, Assn. Environ. Engring. Profs. (bd. dirs., past pres.), Am. Acad. Environ. Engrs., Water Environ. Fedn. (Gordon Masken Fair medal 1985), Am. Water Works Assn. (Thomas R. Camp lectr. 1991), World Mariculture Soc., Sigma Xi. Home: 662 Diego Pl Davis CA 95616-0123

TEACHOUT, NOREEN RUTH, writer; b. Oak Park, Ill., July 12, 1939; d. Anselm Uriel and R. Lydia (Bagne) Asp; m. Willem Heyneker, Nov. 20, 1958 (dec. 1964); children: Carolyn Heyneker Fors, Diana Heyneker Olds; m. Richard Kenneth Teachout, Jan. 21, 1966 (div. 1982); children: Jill, Janelle. BS, U. Minn., 1965. Tchr. Bloomington (Minn.) Pub. Schs., 1965-85; writer, pubr., CEO The Peace Curriculum, Mpls., 1986—; educator Stockton & Franks Chiropractors, Burnsville, Minn., 1986-92; edn. svcs. dept. coord. Dame Comms., Plymouth, Minn., 1990—; cons., workshop leader Dame Comms.; writer U. Calif., Berkeley, 1967, Environ. Sci. Ctr., Mpls., 1968-69; educator, presenter Women's World Peace Conf., Dallas, 1988, Word Peace Conf., San Jose, Costa Rica, 1989, 92; sponsor Therapeutic Humor Inst. Minn. Author curriculum programs, health and revitalization programs. Avocations: ballroom dancing, reading, gardening. Home: 1014 20th Ave SE Minneapolis MN 55414-2512

TEAGAN, JOHN GERARD, newspaper executive; b. Detroit, Sept. 23, 1947; s. Stanley John and Margaret Suzanne (Sullivan) T.; m. Carla Kay Eurich, Sept. 13, 1975; 1 child, Elizabeth Margaret. B.B.A., U. Notre Dame, 1969. C.P.A., Mich. Audit supr. Ernst & Whinney (C.P.A.s), Detroit, 1969-73; acctg. mgr. Detroit Free Press, 1973-77, treas., controller 1977-83, v.p. fin., treas. 1983-89, v.p., bus. mgr., 1989—. Adv. bd. Providence Hosp., Southfield, Mich., 1984—, sec., 1989, vice chmn. 1990, chmn., 1991. Mem. AICPA, Inst. Newspaper Controllers and Fin. Officers, Mich. Assn. CPSa, Detroit Club Notre Dame Club (Detroit dir. 1970-76, 92—, treas. 1993-94, sec. 1994-95). Roman Catholic. Office: Detroit Free Press Inc 321 W Lafayette Blvd Detroit MI 48226

TEAGUE, BARRY ELVIN, lawyer; b. Dayton, Ohio, Mar. 10, 1944; s. Arthur Leo and Mary Catherine (Pendley) T.; m. Dianne Duke, Dec. 30, 1966; children: Matthew Patrick, William Clay. B.A., Asbury Coll., 1966; J.D., Jones Law Sch., 1971. Bar: Ala. 1972. Tchr., coach Montgomery County (Ala.) Sch. System, 1966-68, tchr., 1968-71; dep. clk. U.S. Dist. Ct., Middle Dist., Ala., 1971-73; atty. gen. Ala., 1973-74; chief dep. dist. atty. 15th Jud. Circuit Ala., 1974-77; U.S. atty. for Middle Dist. Ala., 1977-81; mem. Ala. senate, 1983; spl. asst. atty. gen. State of Ala., 1983-87; pvt. practice Montgomery, Ala., 1981—. Mem. Fed. Bar Assn. Ala. Bar Assn., Montgomery County Bar Assn. (dir. young lawyers sect.), Montgomery Fed. Bar Assn. (pres. 1980-81), Ala. Jr. C. of C. (state govt. affairs chmn.), Montgomery Jr. C. of C. (dir. legal counsel). Presbyterian. Office: 644 S Perry St Montgomery AL 36104-5820

TEAGUE, EDWARD B., III, insurance and investment broker; b. Lowell, Mass., Nov. 25, 1946; s. Edward B. Jr. and Margaret (McCartin) T.; m. Kathleen J. Hogan, Apr. 8, 1972; children: Edward, Matthew, Kate, Christian. BA in Polit. Sci., St. Anselm Coll., 1971; MBA, Pepperdine U., 1974. CLU. Agt. Conn. Mut. Life, Boston, 1975-79; account exec. Compensation Planning Group, Wellesley, Mass., 1979-82, asst. dir. brokerage, 1982-84; dir. brokerage Commonwealth Fin. Group, Waltham, Mass., 1984—. Mem. Old King's Hwy. Hist. Dist. Commn., Yarmouth, Mass., 1985-86; treas. Village of Yarmouth Improvement Soc., 1982-86; chmn. Yarmouth Heart Fund Dr., 1978; selectman Town of Yarmouth, 1986-89, state rep., 1988—, Rep. floor leader, 1995; bd. dirs. Seton Acad., Hyannis, Mass., 1984-85; corporator Cape Cod Hosp., Hyannis, 1986—. Served with U.S. Army, 1971-75, maj. USNG, 1977—. Mem. Nat. Assn. Life Underwriters, Boston Assn. Life Underwriters, Mass. Assn. Life Underwriters, Am. Assn. Individual Investors, Army N.G. Assn. Republican. Roman Catholic. Avocations: jogging, reading, sailing. Home: 115 Main St Yarmouth Port MA 02675-1709 Office: Commonwealth Fin Group PO Box 244 Yarmouth Port MA 02675-0244

TEAGUE, HYMAN FARIS, former publishing company executive; b. San Angelo, Jan. 14, 1916; s. John Henry and Minnie Adele (Gauldin) T.; m. Sophia Golda Harvey, Dec. 26, 1944; children: Carl Robin, Alan Cole. B.A., McMurry Coll., 1935, postgrad.; 1940; postgrad, Hardin Simmons U., 1935-36. Tchr., public schs. Tex., 1935-43; prodn. mgr. Steck Vaughn Co. (and predecessor co.), Austin, 1946-57; editor in chief Steck Vaughn Co. (and predecessor co.), 1957-65, v.p., 1964-65, pres., 1965-80, chmn., 1981-82, dir., 1965-82 v.p. Intext Inc., Scranton, Pa., 1975-80. Served with USNR, 1943-46. Democrat. Baptist. Clubs: Austin, Rotary. Home: 4906 Rollingwood Dr Austin TX 78746-5527

TEAGUE, LARRY GENE, editor; b. Victoria, Tex., May 13, 1954; s. Edward Marvin and Nettie Naomi (Welch) T. BJ, U. Houston, 1980. Outdoor correspondent Houston Post, 1977-80; editor Gulf Tide mag. Gulf Coast Conservation Assn., Houston, 1980-85; editor Southern Outdoors mag. Bass Anglers Sportsmans Soc., Montgomery, Ala., 1985—; cons. editor So. Outdoor Saltwater mag., 1986-87. Served with U.S. Army, 1972-75. Recipient writing, photography awards. Avocations: fishing, hunting, gardening, photography. Home: 5832 Red Barn Rd Montgomery AL 36116-1034 Office: Southern Outdoors 5845 Carmichael Rd Montgomery AL 36117-2329

TEAGUE, PEYTON CLARK, chemist, educator; b. Montgomery, Ala., June 26, 1915; s. Robert S. and Sara McGehee (Clark) T.; m. Patricia Cussons Lamb, June 12, 1937; 1 dau., Norah Teague Grimball. Student, Huntingdon Coll., 1932-35; B.S. Auburn U., 1936; M.S., Pa. State U., 1937; Ph.D., U. Tex., 1942. Research chemist Am. Agrl. Chem. Co., Newark, 1937-39; instr. dept. chemistry Auburn U., Ala., 1941-42, asst. prof., 1943-45; research chemist U.S. Naval Research Lab, 1942-45; asst. prof. U. Ga., Athens, 1945-48, U. Ky., Lexington, 1948-50; assoc. prof. dept. chemistry U. S.C., Columbia, 1950-56, prof., 1956-82, disting. prof. emeritus, 1982—, assoc. dean grad. schs., 1966-68, chmn. grad. council, 1980-81, dept. dir. grad. studies, 1971-82; sec. grad. admission com. U. S.C., 1982—; vis. prof. chemistry U. Coll., Dublin, Ireland, 1963-64, 77; dir. Teague Hardware Co., Montgomery,

Ala., 1955-74. Contbr. articles to sci. jours. Vestryman Trinity Episcopal Cathedral, 1968-71, lay reader, 1963—; bd. dirs. S.C. chpt. Arthritis Found., 1983-86; bd. dirs. Columbia Town Theatre, 1984-91. Recipient Outstanding Tchr. award U.S.C., 1976. Mem. Am. Chem. Soc. (chmn. S.C. sect. 1958-59), Phytochem. Soc. N.Am. (pres. 1969-70), S.C. Acad. Sci., Blue Key, Sigma Xi (pres. U.S.C. chpt. 1962-63), Phi Kappa Phi, Phi Lambda Upsilon, Phi Delta Theta. Club: Forest Lake Country. Lodge: Kiwanis. Home: 1550 Adger Rd Columbia SC 29205-1408 Office: U SC Dept Chemistry Columbia SC 29208

TEAGUE, RANDAL CORNELL, SR., lawyer; b. Durham, N.C., May 19, 1944; s. Roy M. Sr. and Lottie (Rhew) T.; m. Jessica Townsend, Oct. 29, 1977; children: R. Cornell, R. Townsend, Mary Robb Durham, James K.B. BA, Am. U., 1967; JD, George Washington U., 1971, LLM with highest honors, 1972; LLD (hon.), Allen U., 1973. Bar: Fla. 1972, D.C. 1972, U.S. Dist. Ct. D.C. 1972, U.S. Tax Ct. 1972, U.S. Ct. Mil. Appeals 1972, U.S. Ct. Appeals (D.C. and fed. cirs.) 1972, U.S. Ct. Appeals (5th cir.) 1973, U.S. Supreme Ct. 1975, Mass. 1979, U.S. Ct. Appeals (1st cir.) 1979, U.S. Dist. Ct. Mass. 1979, U.S. Ct. Internat. Trade. Coordinator policy devel. OEO, Washington, 1971-73; adminstrv. asst., legis. counsel to Rep. Jack F. Kemp Ho. of Reps., Washington, 1973-79; div. counsel Cabot Corp., 1979-81; counsel Vorys, Sater, Seymour & Pease, Washington, 1981-83, ptnr., 1984—. Pres. Internat. Exch. Coun., 1984—, Am. Coun. Young Polit. Leaders, Washington, 1982-83; trustee Fund Am. Studies, Washington, 1976—, Air Force Acad. Found., Colorado Springs, Colo., 1983—; chmn. adv. com. voluntary fgn. aid U.S. Agy. Internat. Devel., 1987-91; trustee Agrl. Coll. Humid Tropics, Costa Rica, 1987—, councillor Atlantic Coun. of U.S., 1990—. Named one of Outstanding Young Men Am., 1973; recipient George Washington medal Freedoms Found., 1978. Mem. ABA, Fed. Bar Assn., Fla. Bar Assn. Republican. Episcopalian. Club: University (Washington). Office: Vorys Sater Seymour & Pease 1828 L St NW 11th Fl Washington DC 20036-5104

TEAGUE, SAM FULLER, association executive, educator.; b. Birmingham, Ala., Aug. 2, 1918; s. Sam Fuller and Virginia (White) T.; m. Frances Middleton, July 2, 1939; children: John Russell, Melanie Olivia. B.S., Auburn U., 1939. Chemist Sloss-Sheffield Steel & Iron Co., Birmingham, 1939-40; asst. dir. sales Monsanto Chem. Co., St. Louis, 1945-60; gen. mgr. sales ITT Rayonier, Inc., N.Y.C., 1960-67; v.p. planning and devel. ITT Rayonier, Inc., 1967-68, sr. v.p., 1968-72, v.p., product mgr., paper and splty. pulp sales, 1972-78, v.p., dir. pulp sales, 1978-80, v.p. prodn./mktg. devel., 1981-83, ret., 1983, also dir.; exec. dir. Rayon/Acetate Council, Inc., Auburn, Ala., 1983-93; adj. prof. textile engring. Auburn U., 1983—; dir., mem. exec. com. Rayonier Can. Pres. Auburn Heritage Assn., 1983-86; v.p. Auburn Beautification Council, 1985-86; councilman, mayor pro tem City of Auburn, 1986—; vestryman and sr. warden Holy Trinity Episcopal Ch., 1985-86. Served to lt. col. AUS, 1940-45. Decorated Bronze Star with oak leaf cluster. Mem. Am. Chem. Soc., Salesmen's Assn. Am. Chem. Industry (past dir.). Auburn C. of C. (treas. and bd. dirs. 1986, pres. 1989, bd. dirs. 1994). Clubs: Town (Newcastle) (past sec., dir.); Whippoorwill (Armonk, N.Y.) (pres. 1968-69, gov.); Chemists (N.Y.C) (trustee 1970, pres. 1976-77). Home: 1349 Burke Ln Auburn AL 36830 Office: Auburn U Textile Bldg Auburn AL 36849 My career is based on honesty, fairness, consideration for my fellow man, trust in God, and always trying to follow the principles set forth by Jesus Christ. I've always felt that people are the most important element of any organization. Whereas bricks and mortar can be bought, people must be considered as individuals.

TEAGUE, WAYNE, state education official; b. Cullman, Ala., Nov. 19, 1927; s. Levi Wade and Floy Irene (McKelvey) T.; m. Eleanor Josephine Jones, June 5, 1949; children—Karen Jo, Dewey Wayne. B.S., Auburn U., 1950, M.S., 1953, Ed.D., 1962; LL.D., Troy State U., 1978. Tchr., coach, asst. prin. Heard High Sch., Franklin, Ga., 1950-55; prin. Marion County Elem. and High Sch., Buena Vista, Ga., 1955-56, Jonesboro (Ga.) Sr. High Sch., 1956-58, S.W. DeKalb High Sch., Decatur, Ga., 1958-63; coordinator field services Sch. Edn., dir. correspondence study, asso. prof. ednl. adminstrn. Auburn (Ala.) U., 1963-69; supt. Auburn City Schs., 1969-75; state supt. edn. Ala. Dept. Edn., 1975-95; ret. Served with USAAC, 1946. Methodist. Club: Masons.

TEARE, IWAN DALE, research scientist; b. Moscow, Idaho, July 24, 1931; s. Mylrea Henry and Crystal Ann (Atkinson) T.; m. Claudia Joy Patterson, Sept. 14, 1952; children: Steven, Bradley, Curtis, Kelly. BS in Agronomy, U. Idaho, 1953; MS in Agronomy, Wash. State U., 1959; PhD, Purdue U., 1963. Instr. agronomy Purdue U., West Lafayette, Ind., 1961-63; asst. prof. agronomy Wash. State U., Pullman, 1963-69; prof. agronomy Kans. State U., Manhattan, 1969-79; dir. Agrl. Rsch. and Edn. Ctr., U. Fla., Quincy, 1979-82; rsch. scientist U. Fla., Quincy, 1982— Active Boy Scouts Am. Served to 1st lt. U.S. Army, 1954-56. Recipient Disting. Grad. Faculty award Kans. State U., 1974; U. Fla. scholar. Fellow Am. Soc. Agronomy; mem. Am. Soc. Crop Sci., Sigma Xi, Phi Kappa Phi, Gamma Sigma Delta. Mem. Ch. Jesus Christ of Latter-Day Saints. Assoc. editor Agronomy Jour., 1979-85, tech. editor, 1986-92; co-editor: Crop-Water Relations, 1983; editor symposium, conf. proceedings; contbr. numerous articles to profl. jours. Home: 420 Maxwell Dr Cairo GA 31728 Office: N Fla Rsch & Edn Ctr Univ of Fla RR 3 Box 4370 Quincy FL 32351-9500

TEARE, RICHARD WALLACE, ambassador; b. Cleve., Feb. 21, 1937; m. Jeanie Walter; 3 children. BA, Harvard U., 1958; student, Naval War Coll., 1977-78. Joined Fgn. Svc., 1959; vice consul U.S. Consulate, Bridgetown, Barbados, 1960-62; consular officer U.S. Embassy, Manila, The Philippines, 1962-64; polit. officer U.S. Embassy, Saigon, Vietnam, 1965-67, Mexico City, 1971-74; counselor for polit. affairs U.S. Embassy, Vientiane, Laos, 1974-77; dep. chief mission U.S. Embassy, Wellington, New Zealand, 1983-86, Canberra, Australia, 1986-89; dep. and acting prin. officer U.S. Consulate Gen., Nha Trang, Vietnam, 1973; intelligence and rsch. specialist Vietnam Working Group Dept. State, 1967-69, desk officer, 1969-71, spl. asst. to asst. sec. for East Asian and Pacific Affairs, 1976-77, dep. dir. Office Philippine Affairs, 1978-80, dep. and acting U.S. rep. for Micronesian Status Negotiations, 1980-83, dir. Office of Indonesia, Malaysia, Brunei and Singapore Affairs, 1989-92, spl. projects officer Office of Dir. Gen., 1992-93, U.S. amb. to Papua New Guinea, Solomon Islands and Vanuatu, 1993—. Mem. Am. Fgn. Assn., Sr. Fgn. Svc. Assn., Asia Soc., Malaysia-Am. Soc., Indonesian-Am. Soc., Nat. Trust Hist. Preservation. Office: Port Moresby Dept of State Washington DC 20521-4240

TEASDALE, KENNETH FULBRIGHT, lawyer; b. St. Louis, Nov. 8, 1934; s. Kenneth and Ann (Fulbright) T.; m. Elizabeth Driscol Langdon, June 13, 1964; children: Caroline, Doug, Cindy. AB, Amherst Coll., 1956; LLB, Washington U., St. Louis, 1961. Bar: Mo. 1961. Atty. antitrust div. U.S. Dept. Justice, Washington, 1961-62; asst. counsel Dem. Policy Com. U.S. Senate, Washington, 1962-63, gen. counsel Dem. Policy Com., asst. to majority leader, 1963-64; assoc. Armstrong, Teasdale, Kramer & Vaughan, St. Louis, 1964-67, ptnr., 1967-86; mng. ptnr. Armstrong, Teasdale, Schlafly & Davis, St. Louis, 1986-93, chmn. of firm, 1993—; bd. dirs. Magna Bank Mo., St. Loouis, GTE S.W. Corp.; trustee United Way Greater St. Louis, St. Louis; trustee, chmn., bd. regents St. Louis U. Mem. nat. coun. Washington U. Law Sch., 1988—. Mem. ABA, Bar Assn. Mo., Bar Assn. St. Louis, Racquet Club, Noonday Club, Old Warson Country Club. Presbyterian. Office: Armstrong Teasdale Schlafly & Davis Metropolitan Sq Saint Louis MO 63106

TEASDALE, THOMAS HENNINGS, architect; b. St. Louis, Mar. 3, 1933; s. David Guernsey and Ruth Celeste (Hennings) T.; m. June Maune, July 26, 1958; children: Laura Lynne, Thomas Hennings, Marjorie Sara. B.Arch., Washington U., St. Louis, 1956. Architect Kenneth E. Wischmeyer, St. Louis, 1959-65; ptnr. Wischmeyer Architects, St. Louis, 1965-89, mng. ptnr., 1989-92, pres., 1993—; v.p. dir. PSAE Corp., 1978. Prin. works include Florissant Valley Campus, St. Louis Jr. Coll, 1968, C.V. Mosby corp. office bldgs, 1968-78, Mo. State Sch. for Handicapped, St. Louis, 1977. Active Laclede Groves Retirement Community, 1992. Served with USAF, 1956-59. Fellow AIA (bd. dirs. 1977-79, v.p. 1980, George I. Barnett award 1980, treas. Coll. Fellows, vice-chancellor Coll. Fellows 1993, chancellor 1994), Mo. Coun. Architects, St. Louis Landmarks Assn., Execs. Assn. St. Louis (pres. 1973, 81). Presbyterian. Home: 1732 W Adams Ave Saint Louis MO 63122-3727 Office: 1221 Locust St Saint Louis MO 63103-2364

TEASE, JAMES EDWARD, judge; b. Sheffield, Ala., Dec. 28, 1939; s. James Albert and Hattie Wayne (Counts) T.; m. Anne Elizabeth Gilley, Sept. 2, 1972. B.S., Florence State U., 1961; LL.B., U. Ala., 1964; grad., Nat. Coll. State Judiciary, 1971. Bar: Ala. 1964. Gen. practice law Florence, 1965-67, city prosecutor, 1966-67; dep. dist. atty. Lauderdale County, Ala., 1967-71; circuit judge 11th Jud. Cir. Ala., Florence, 1971-89; extra judge Ala. Ct. Civil Appeals, 1989; U.S. adminstrv. law judge Social Security Adminstrn., Office Hearings & Appeals, Florence, Ala., 1989—; Mem. Ala. Constl. Commn.; chmn. Ala. Citizens Adv. Com. on Election Reform; mem. Ala. Ct. of Judiciary, 1981-89. Bd. dirs. Regional Library System. Served with AUS, 1964-65. Named Florence Outstanding Young Man Jaycees, 1974, Alumnus of Year U. N. Ala., 1975. Mem. Am. Judicature Soc., Nat. Conf. State Trial Judges, Ala. Assn. Circuit Judges (pres. 1986), Lauderdale County Bar Assn.; Am. Legion, Sigma Delta Kappa. Baptist. Home: 1926 Monticello Rd Florence AL 35630-2740 Office: Walnut St Exec Ctr 205 S Walnut St Ste D Florence AL 35630-5721

TEATER, DOROTHY SEATH, county official; b. Manhattan, Kans., Feb. 11, 1931; d. Dwight Moody and Martha (Stahnke) Seath; m. Robert Woodson Teater, May 24, 1952; children: David Dwight, James Stanley, Donald Robert, Andrew Scott. B.S. U. Ky., 1951; MS, Ohio State U., 1954. Home econs. tchr. Georgetown (Ky.) City Schs., 1951-53; extension specialist Ohio Coop. Extension, Columbus, 1967-73; consumer affairs adminstr. City of Columbus, 1974-79, Bank One Columbus NA, 1980-85; councilmember Columbus City Coun., 1980-85; commr. Franklin County, Columbus, Ohio, 1985—; active Ohio Cmty. Corrections Adv. Bd., Columbus, Columbus Met. Area Cmty. Action Orgn., Land Policy & Boom Bust Real Estate Markets, 1994, Lincoln Inst. Land Policy. Bd. dirs. BBB; mem. hon. adv. bd. Girl Scouts. Recipient Outstanding Alumnus award U. Ky., 1989, Women of Achievement award YWCA, 1995; named Disting. Alumni, Ohio State U. 1977. Mem. County Commrs. Assn. Ohio (pres. 1994), Columbus Met. Club. Republican. Methodist. Avocations: gardening, sewing. Office: Franklin County Commrs 373 S High St Columbus OH 43215

TEATES, CHARLES DAVID, radiologist, educator; b. Luray, Va., July 1, 1936; s. Gilbert Grove and Mae Frankie (Pierce) T.; m. Mary Bruce Bucher, June 6, 1958; children—Elizabeth Susan, David Bruce, Mary Catherine. B.S., Lebanon Valley Coll., Annville, Pa., 1958; M.S., U. Va., Charlottesville, 1963, M.D., 1963. Diplomate Am. Bd. Radiology, Am. Bd. Nuclear Medicine. Intern U. Kans. Med. Ctr., 1963-64; resident in radiology U. Va. Med. Ctr., 1964-67; asst. prof. radiology U. Va., Charlottesville, 1969-73, assoc. prof., 1973-79, prof., 1979—. Contbg. author books on radiology and nuclear medicine. Served to maj. M.C., U.S. Army, 1967-69, Vietnam. Mem. Am. Coll. Radiology (pres. Va. chpt. 1984-85), Soc. Nuclear Medicine (pres. Mid-Eastern chpt. 1984-86), AMA, Alpha Omega Alpha. Home: Box 259A 4635 Watts Passage Charlottesville VA 22901 Office: U Va Med Ctr PO Box 486 Charlottesville VA 22908-0001

TEBALDI, RENATA, opera singer; b. Pesaro, Italy, Feb. 1, 1922; d. Teobaldo and Giuseppina (Barbieri) T. Student, Arrigo Boito Conservatory, Parma, Gioacchino Rossini Conservatory, Pesaro; Pupil, Carmen Melis, Giuseppe Pais. Lyric soprano, profl. debut in Mefistofele, Rovigo, 1944; debut at LaScala, 1946; singer opera houses of Naples, Rome, Venice, Bologna, Florence, Modena, Cesana, Turin, Venice, Pompeii; Am. debut in Aida, San Francisco Opera Co., 1950; debut in Otello, Met. Opera House, N.Y.C., 1955; singer operatic roles in La Boheme, Madama Butterfly, Tosca, Die Meistersinger. Toured U.S.S.R., 1975, 76; ret. 1976. Named Commander for Arts and Letters, France, 1987. Roman Catholic. Office: care SA Gorlinsky Ltd, 33 Dover St, London England W1X 4NJ*

TEBAY, JAMES ELWOOD, retired foundation executive; b. Spring Valley, Minn., Oct. 28, 1930; s. Clarence M. and Esther I. (Nagel) T.; m. Lavonne E. Rosel, Aug. 30, 1952 (div. June 1980); children: Jamie E., Jacquelyn E. Rhodes, Jeffrey E.; m. Jean Park McIlwraith, May 16, 1981. B.S, U. Colo., 1956; MBA, U. So. Calif., 1962. V.p. mktg. Hewlett-Packard, Avondale, Pa., 1965-70; pres. Tebay Mgmt. Resources, Kennett Sq., Pa., 1970-75, Valmont Irrigation, Omaha, 1975-80; v.p. Planning Dynamics, Pitts., 1980-82; pres. Rexnord Automation, Timonium, Md., 1982-90, Found. for Mfg. Excellence, Catonsville, Md., 1991-93; ret., 1993. Served to sgt. USAF, 1948-52. Republican. Home: 5 Yearling Way Lutherville MD 21093-4590

TEBBEL, JOHN, writer, educator; b. Boyne City, Mich., Nov. 16, 1912; s. William and Edna (Johnston) T.; m. Kathryn Carl, Apr. 29, 1939; 1 child, Judith. A.B., Central Mich Coll. Edn., 1935; M.S., Columbia U., 1937. City editor Isabella Co. Times-News, Mt. Pleasant, Mich., 1935-36; writer Newsweek mag., 1937; reporter Detroit Free Press, 1937-39; feature writer, roto news editor Providence Jour., 1939-41; mng. editor Am Mercury, 1941-43; Sunday staff writer N.Y. Times, 1943; assoc. editor E.P. Dutton & Co., 1943-47; asst. in journalism Sch. Journalism Columbia U., 1943-45; chmn. dept. journalism N.Y. U., 1954-65, prof. journalism, 1965—; Cons. Ford Found., 1966—. Author: An American Dynasty, 1947, The Marshall Fields, 1947, George Horace Lorimer and the Saturday Evening Post, 1948, Battle for North America, 1948, Your Body, 1951, The Conqueror, 1951, Touched With Fire, 1952, The Life and Good Times of William Randolph Hearst, 1952, George Washington's America, 1954, A Voice in the Street, 1954, The Magic of Balanced Living, 1956, The American Indian Wars, 1960, The Inheritors, 1962, The Epicure's Companion, 1962, David Sarnoff, 1963, Compact History of the American Newspaper, 1964, From Rags to Riches, 1964, Open Letter to Newspaper Readers, 1968, Compact History of American Magazines, 1969, A History of Book Publishing in the United States, 4 vols, 1972, 75, 78, 81, The Battle of Fallen Timbers, 1972, The Media in America, 1975, The Press and the Presidency, 1985, Between Covers, 1987, A Certain Club, 1989, The Magazine in America, 1991, Turning the World Upside Down, 1993; contbr. to Sat. Rev., other mags. Named to Pub. Hall of Fame. Home: 4033 The Forest at Duke 2701 Pickett Rd Durham NC 27705-5654 *From the time my writing career began, at 14, I have tried to write as well and clearly and accurately as I can, so that I could best inform the people who read my books and articles about the world they live in. To me it is the obligation of every writer to recognize the responsibility his talent imposes on him, and understand that he is one of the transmitters of knowledge upon whom the world depends for advancement and the betterment of human society.*

TEC, LEON, psychiatrist; b. Baranovicze, Poland, June 1, 1919; came to U.S., 1952; s. Boris and Sarah (Limon) T.; m. Nechama Bawnik, May 15, 1931; children: Leora, Roland Boris. MD, St. Joseph U., Beirut, Lebanon, 1944. Diplomate Am. Bd. Psychiatry and Neurology, Am. Bd. Child Psychiatry. Intern Hadassah Hosp., Tel Aviv, Israel, 1943-44; resident psychiatry Bellevue Hosp., N.Y.C., 1952-55; fellow in child psychiatry Jewish Bd. Guardians, N.Y.C., 1955-57; faculty mem. Bellevue Coll. Medicine, NYU, N.Y.C., 1955-60, N.Y. Coll. Medicine, N.Y. Downstate U., N.Y.C., 1957-62; med. dir. Mid-Fairfield Child Guidance Ctr., Norwalk, Conn., 1959-86; pvt. practice psychiatry and child psychiatry Westport, Conn., 1959—; cons. staff mem. Norwalk Hosp., 1965—; radio host Sta. WEZN, Bridgeport, 1972-79; adv. bd. mem. Channel 5 TV Network, N.Y.C., 1987—. Author: The Fear of Success, 1976, Targets: How to Set Goals and Reach Them, 1980; contbr. articles to profl. jours. and The New York Times. Fellow Am. Orthopsychiat. Assn. (life), Am. Acad. Child Psychiatry (life), Royal Soc. Medicine (London, life), Am. Acad. Psychosomatic Medicine (life), Am. Group Psychotherapy Assn. (life), Am. Psychiat. Assn. (life, pres. Fairfield-Litchfield, Conn. chpt.); mem. Conn. Assn. Psychiat. Clinics for Children (v.p.), Conn. Group Psychotherapy Assn. (pres.), Internat. Coun. on Alcohol And Addictions (bd. dirs.), Internat. Assn. Child Psychiatry, World Mental Health Orgn., South Shore Music Club. Jewish. Avocations: tennis, swimming, bicycling, walking. Home and Office: 11 Rockyfield Rd Westport CT 06880-2202

TECCO, ROMUALD GILBERT LOUIS JOSEPH, violinist, concertmaster; b. Toulon, Var, France, May 1, 1941; came to U.S., 1960; s. Raymond Charles and Angele (Cornille) T. Student, Paris Conservatoire, 1954-60; diploma, postgrad. diploma, Juilliard Sch. Music, 1967-68. Mem. N.Y. String Quartet, 1969-72; concertmaster Juilliard Ensemble, N.Y.C., 1969-72, St. Paul Chamber Orch., 1972—; soloist Chgo. Symphony, Bavarian Radio Orch., Orch. of Mex., Orchestre Colonne, Paris, Rotterdam Philharm.; performer numerous festivals, Sweden, Finland, France, Italy, U.S. Recs. with Aaron Copland and Lou Harrison Chamber Music. Served with

French Navy, 1964-65, NATO hdqrs. Recipient first prize in violin Conservatoire Paris; recipient first prize chamber music Conservatoire Paris. Mem. St. Paul Univ. Club. Office: St Paul Chamber Orch 75 W 5th St Saint Paul MN 55102-1431

TECKLENBURG, HARRY, pharmaceutical products executive; b. Seattle, Nov. 3, 1927; s. Harry and Frieda (Rasche) T.; m. Mary Louise Beaty, Sept. 1, 1951; children: Don, Bruce. B.S. in Chem. Engring., MIT, 1950; M.S. in Chem. Engring., U. Wash., 1952. With Procter & Gamble Co., Cin., 1952—; chem. engr., group leader, sect. leader. dir., mgr. research and devel. dept., v.p. research and devel. Procter & Gamble Co., 1952-76; sr. v.p., 1976—; gen. mgr. Norwich Div. N.Y., 1984—; rep. to Indsl. Research Inst., 1973-76. Mem. corp. devel. com. MIT, 1977-82; trustee Ohio Valley Goodwill Industries Rehab. Center, 1969-84, pres., 1974-82; bd. dirs. Goodwill Industries Am., 1978-84, vice chmn. bd., 1980-82, chmn. bd., 1982-84, dir. emeritus, 1984-87; mem. vis. com. dept. chem. engring. U. Wash., 1983; chmn. Goodwill Industries Internat. Fund, 1986. Served with AUS, 1946-48. Mem. Engring. Soc. Cin., Am. Inst. Chem. Engrs., Am. Chem. Soc., Pharms. Mfrs. Assn. (dir. 1984—), TAPPI, AAAS. Office: Norwich Eaton Pharms Inc Norwich NY 13815

TECLAFF, LUDWIK ANDRZEJ, law educator, consultant, author, lawyer; b. Czestochowa, Poland, Nov. 14, 1918; came to U.S., 1952, naturalized, 1958; s. Emil and Helena (Tarnowska) T.; m. Eileen Johnson, May 30, 1952. Mag Iuris, Oxford (Eng.) U., 1944; MS, Columbia U., 1955; LLM, NYU, 1961, JSD, 1965. Attaché Polish Fgn. Ministry, London, 1943-46; consul in Ireland, Polish Govt. in London, 1946-52; student libr. Columbia U. Sch. Libr. Sci., 1953-54; libr. Bklyn. Pub. Libr., 1954-59; rsch. librar. Fordham U. Sch. Law, 1959-62, asst. prof. law, 1962-65, assoc. prof. law, 1965-68, prof. 1968-89, prof. emeritus, 1989—, bd. dirs. law libr., 1962-86; cons. in field. Trustee Pilsudski Inst., N.Y.C. With Polish Army, 1940-43, France, Eng. Recipient Clyde Eagleton award in internat. law NYU, 1965. Mem. Am. Soc. Internat. Law, Internat. Law Assn., Am. Law Librs. Assn., Internat. Coun. Environ. Law, Internat. Water Law Assn. Roman Catholic. Author: The River Basin in History and Law, 1967; Abstraction and Use of Water, 1972; Legal and Institutional Responses to Growing Water Demand, 1978; Economic Roots of Oppression, 1984, Water Law in Historical Perspective, 1985; editor: (with Albert E Utton) International Environmental Law, 1974, Water in a Developing World, 1978, International Groundwater Law, 1981, Transboundary Resources Law, 1987; contbr. articles on water law, law of the sea and environ. law to law jours. Office: Fordham U Sch Law 140 W 62nd St New York NY 10023-7407

TEDESCHI, ERNEST FRANCIS, JR., naval officer; b. New Britain, Conn., Mar. 28, 1942; s. Ernest and Rose (Malucci) T.; m. Christine Ann Dieleuterio, Apr. 15, 1972; children: Gina, Ernest. BS in Marine Engring., U.S. Naval Acad., 1965; MS in Mgmt., Salve Regina U., 1987. Commd. ensign USN, advanced through grades to rear adm., 1992; weapons officer USS Gridley (CG 21), San Diego, 1974-76; operational test & evaluation force Pacific USS John Paul Jones (DDG 32), 1978-81; commdg. officer USS Duncan (FFG 10), Long Beach, Calif., 1982-85; instr. Surface Warfare Officers Sch., Newport, R.I., 1985-87; sponsor, chief of naval ops. Aegis Program, Washington, 1987-89; commdg. officer USS Valley Forge (CG 50), San Diego, 1990-91; dir. plans and policy Supreme Allied Commdr. Atlantic NATO, Norfolk, Va., 1991-93; commdr. naval base, combat logistics group 1 USN, San Francisco, 1993—; weapons officer USS Brownson (DD 868), Newport, R.I., 1970-72; exec. com. Fed. Exec. Bd., Oakland, Calif., 1993-94. Bd. dirs. ARC, San Francisco, 1993-94; regional chmn. Navy/Marine Corps Relief Soc., No. Calif., 1993-94. Decorated Meritorious Svc. medal with gold star, Bronze Star with combat "V", Legion of Merit with gold star, Def. Superior Svc. medal. Mem. Ret. Officer's Assn., Surface Navy Assn., San Francisco C. of C. (exec. bd. 1993-94). Roman Catholic. Avocations: tennis, basketball, jogging, baseball. Home: 1 Whiting Way San Francisco CA 94130 Office: Commdr NAval Base SF Treasure Island 410 Palm Ave San Francisco CA 94130

TEDESCHI, JAMES THEODORE, JR., psychologist educator; b. Coatesville, Pa., Oct. 4, 1928; s. James Theodore and Mable Belle (Reynolds) T.; m. Leatha Peddicord, June 19, 1955 (div.); children: J. Bradley, Linda Ann, Jamie Sue, Nancy, J. Anthony; m. Valentina Melburg, Jan. 10, 1985; 1 child, Alexander. AB, U. Miami, 1956, MS, 1958; PhD, U. Mich., 1960. Asst. prof. Utah State U., Logan, 1959-61; assoc. prof. U. Miami, Coral Gables, Fla., 1961-69; prof. U.S. Internat. U., San Diego, 1969-70, U. Albany, N.Y., 1970—. Author: Impression Management, 1981; co-author: Conflict Power and Games, 1974, Social Psychology, 1985, Aggression and Violence, 1993, Voilence, Aggression, and Coercive Actions, 1994; contbr. articles to profl. publs. Served to capt. U.S. Army, 1951-52. Nat. Sci. Fedn. grantee, 1970-71, Nat. Inst. Health grantee, 1974. Fellow Am. Psychol. Assn.; mem. Soc. Exptl. Social Psychologists, European Assn. Exptl. Social Psychology. Avocations: tennis, opera, ballet, spectator sports, reading. Home: RR 3 Amsterdam NY 12010-9803 Office: SUNY 1400 Washington Ave Albany NY 12222-0001

TEDESCHI, JOHN ALFRED, historian, librarian; b. Modena, Italy, July 17, 1931; came to U.S., 1939, naturalized, 1944; s. Caesar George and Piera (Forti) T.; m. Anne Wood Christian, Sept. 8, 1956; children: Martha, Philip, Sara. BA, Harvard U., 1954, MA, 1960, PhD, 1966. Bibliographer European history and lit. Newberry Library, Chgo., 1965-84, curator rare books and manuscripts, head dept. spl. collections, 1970-82, dir. Ctr. Renaissance Studies, 1979-84; curator rare books and spl. collections Meml. Library U. Wis.-Madison, 1984—; lectr. history U. Chgo., 1969-71; vis. prof. U. Ill.-Chgo., 1972-73, adj. prof., 1979-84. Co-editor: (series) Corpus Reformatorum Italicorum, 1968—; editor-in-chief: Bibliographie Internat. de L'Humanisme et de la Renaissance, 1977-82; editor: Italian Reformation Studies in Honor of Laelius Socinus, 1965, (with Anthony Molho) Renaissance Studies in Honor of Hans Baron, 1971, (with Gustav Henningsen) The Inquisition in Early Modern Europe: Studies on Sources and Methods, 1986, The Prosecution of Heresy: Collected Studies on the Inquisition in Early Modern Italy, 1991, Tommaso Sassetti, Il Massacro di San Bartolomeo, 1995; translator: (with Anne Tedeschi) The Cheese and the Worms. The Cosmos of a Sixteenth-Century Miller (Carlo Ginzburg), 1980 (named an Outstanding Acad. Book by Choice mag.), The Night Battles. Witchcraft and Agrarian Cults in the Sixteenth and Seventeenth Centuries (Carlo Ginzburg), 1983, Clues, Myths, and the Historical Method (Carlo Ginzburg), 1989; mem. editl. com.: Index des Livres Interdits (Sherbrooke), Collected Works of Erasmus (Toronto); mem. editl. bd.: Studi e Testi per la Storia Religiosa Italiana del '500 (Florence); contbr. articles to profl. jours. Served with U.S. Army, 1954-56. Grantee Am. Philos. Soc., 1961; grantee NEH, 1967; Old Dominion fellow Harvard U. Ctr. Renaissance Studies, Florence, Italy, 1967-68; fellow Inst. Research in Humanities, U. Wis.-Madison, 1976-77; Huntington Library fellow, 1984. Mem. Am. Soc. Reformation Research (pres. 1972), Renaissance Soc. Am. (exec. bd. 1971—), 16th Century Studies Conf. (pres. 1987), Am. Hist. Assn. Home: 202 N Spooner St Madison WI 53705-4035 Office: U Wis-Madison Meml Libr Dept Spl Collection 728 State St Madison WI 53706-1418

TEDESCO, FRANCIS JOSEPH, health sciences university president; b. Derby, Conn., Mar. 8, 1944; s. Lena (Tufano) Tedesco; m. Luann Lee Ekern, Aug. 1, 1970; 1 child, Jennifer Nicole. BS cum laude, Fairfield U., 1965; MD cum laude, St. Louis U., 1969. Asst. instr. Hosp. of U. Pa., Phila., 1971-72; asst. prof. Washington U. Sch. Medicine, St. Louis, 1974-75; asst. prof. U. Miami (Fla.) Sch. Medicine, 1975-77, co-dir. clin. research, 1976-78, assoc. prof., 1977-78; assoc. prof. Med. Coll. Ga., Augusta, 1978-81, chief of gastroenterology dept., 1978-88, prof., 1981—, acting v.p. clin. activities, 1984, v.p. for clin. activities, 1984-88, interim dean U.S. Medicine, 1986-88, pres., 1988—; cons. Med.-Letter/AMA div. drugs, Dwight D. Eisenhower Army Med. Ctr., Ft. Gordon, Ga., VA Med. Ctr., Augusta, Walter Reed Army Med. Ctr., Washington; mem. gastroenterology spl. study sect. NIH, Washington, 1982—, mem. nat digestive disease adv. bd., 1985-88, vice chmn., 1986-87, chmn., 1987-88. Contbr. numerous articles to profl. jours. Bd. dirs. Augusta Country Day Sch., 1981-83; bd. dirs. Am. Cancer Soc., Augusta, 1985—, v.p. 1986—; chmn. Gov.'s Health Strategies Coun., 1992—. Capt. N.G., 1970-72. Recipient Eddie Palmer award for gastrointestinal endoscopy, 1983, cert. of appreciation Am. Cancer Soc., 1986, Outstanding Faculty award Med. Coll. Ga. Sch. Medicine, 1988, Profl. Achievement award Fairfield U., 1993; Avalon Found. scholar St. Louis U.,

1968-69, Paul Harris fellow Rotary, 1990. Fellow ACP, Am. Fedn. Clin. Investigation, Am. Gastroent. Assn., Am. Soc. Gastrointestinal Endoscopy (treas., Rudolph Schindler award 1993). Roman Catholic. Avocations: reading, swimming. Home: 920 Milledge Rd Augusta GA 30904-4455 Office: Med Coll Ga Office Pres 1120 15th St Augusta GA 30912-7600

TEDLOCK, DENNIS, anthropology and literature educator; b. St. Joseph, Mo., June 19, 1939. BA, U. N.Mex., 1961; PhD in Anthropology, Tulane U., 1968. Asst. prof. anthropology Iowa State U., 1966-67; asst. prof. rhetoric U. Calif., Berkeley, 1967-69; research assoc. Sch. Am. Research, 1969-70; asst. prof. anthropology Bklyn. Coll., 1970-71; asst. prof. Yale U., 1972-73; assoc. Univ. prof., anthropology and religion Boston U., 1973-82, Univ. prof., anthropology and religion, 1982-87; James H. McNulty prof. dept. English SUNY, Buffalo, 1987—, rsch. prof. dept. anthropology, 1987—; vis. asst. prof. Wesleyan U., 1971-72; adj. prof. U. N.Mex., 1980-81; mem. Inst. for Advanced Study, 1986-87. Author: Finding the Center: Narrative Poetry of the Zuni Indians, 1972, The Spoken Word and the Work of Interpretation, 1983, Days from a Dream Almanac, 1990 (Victor Turner prize 1991), Breath on the Mirror: Mythic Voices and Visions of the Living Maya, 1993; co-editor: Teachings from the American Earth, 1975, Am. Anthropologist, 1974—; contbr. articles to profl. jours. Dumbarton Oaks fellow in pre-Columbian Studies, 1993-94, Guggenheim fellow, 1986; recipient PEN transl. prize for Popol Vuh: The Mayan Book of the Dawn of Life, 1986. Office: SUNY Buffalo Dept English Buffalo NY 14260

TEDROS, THEODORE ZAKI, educator, real estate broker, appraiser; b. Cairo, June 25, 1910; Naturalized, 1966; s. Zaki and Faika (Lotfi) T.; married 1962; 1 child, Samuel N. BA in Math., Tex. Christian U., 1957, MEd with honors, 1958; postgrad., Fla. State U., 1961. Tchr. pub. schs., Addis Ababa, Ethiopia, 1947-56, The American Inst., Addis Ababa, Ethiopia, 1952-56; instr. math. Fla. State U., Tallahassee, 1958-59; tchr. math. Fla. Mil. Sch. and Coll., Deland, Fla., 1961-64; tchr. Volusia County Bd. Instrn., Deland, 1964-75; real estate broker, appraiser Daytona Beach, Fla., 1978-92; prof. ednl. sociology U. Man., Winnipeg, Can., summers 1962-64. Sunday sch. tchr., Fla.; mem. Nat. Coun. Math. Tchrs., 1959-75, Phi Delta Kappa, 1960-80. Mem. Nat. Assn. Master Appraisers (v.p. 1985-86), Fla. Assn. Realtors, Daytona Beach Area Bd. Realtors, Nat. Assn. Realtors (cert. 1978—). Democrat. Home: 227 E Kensington Ave Deland FL 32724

TEDROW, JOHN CHARLES FREMONT, soils educator; b. Rockwood, Pa., Apr. 21, 1917; s. John Wesley and Emma Grace (Younkin) T.; m. Mary Jane Lough, Mar. 20, 1943 (dec. Mar. 1991); children: John Charles Fremont, Thomas Lough. BS, Pa. State U., 1939; MS, Mich. State U., 1940; PhD, Rutgers U., 1950. Jr. soil technologist Dept. Agr., 1941-42, soil scientist, 1946-47; instr. Rutgers U., New Brunswick, N.J., 1947-50, asst. prof., 1950-53, assoc. prof., 1953-57, prof. soils, 1957-84, prof. emeritus, 1984—; cons. N.S. Research Found., 1949—; sr. pedologist Boston U., 1953—; prin. investigator Arctic Inst. N.Am., Washington, 1955-68, NSF, 1961-62, Atomic Energy Commn., Washington, 1961-63; cons. to govt. and industry. Author: (with R.C. Murray) Forensic Geology: Earth Sciences and Criminal Investigation, 1974, Soils of the Polar Landscapes, 1977, (with K.A. Linell) Soil and Permafrost Surveys in the Arctic, 1981, Soils of New Jersey, 1986, (with R.C. Murray) Forensic Geology, 1991; editor in chief Soil Science, 1968-79; editor: Antarctic Soils and Soil Forming Processes, 1966. Served to lt. USNR, 1942-46. Recipient Lindback Research award Rutgers U., 1978, Antarctic Service medal. Fellow Am. Soc. Agronomy, Soil Sci. Soc. Am., Arctic Inst. N.Am.; mem. Internat. Soc. Soil Sci., Am. Geophys. Union, Am. Arbitration Assn., Sigma Xi, Alpha Zeta (hon.), Phi Mu Delta. Investigator polar soils in Alaska, Can., Greenland, Scandinavia, Siberia and Antarctica. Home: 5 Bluebird Ct Edison NJ 08820-3677 Office: Rutgers U Environ Resources PO Box 231 New Brunswick NJ 08903-0231

TEECE, DAVID JOHN, economics and management educator; b. Marlborough, New Zealand, Sept. 2, 1948; came to U.S., 1971; s. Allan Teece. BA, U. Canterbury, Christchurch, N.Z., 1970, MA in Commerce, 1971; MA in Econs., U. Pa., 1973, PhD, 1975. Asst. prof. Stanford U., 1975-78, assoc. prof., 1978-82; prof. U. Calif., Berkeley, 1982—, dir. Ctr. Rsch. in Mgmt., 1983—. Author: Profiting from Innovation, 1986, and numerous other articles and books. Mem. Am. Econ. Assn. Office: U Calif 554 Barrows Hall Berkeley CA 94720

TEEGARDEN, KENNETH LEROY, clergyman; b. Cushing, Okla., Dec. 22, 1921; s. Roy Albert and Eva B. (Swiggart) T.; m. Wanda Jean Strong, May 28, 1944; children: David Kent, Marshall Kirk. Student, Okla. State U., 1938-40; A.B., Phillips U., 1942, M.A., 1945, D.D., 1963; B.D., Tex. Christian U., 1949, D.D., 1976; D.D., Bethany Coll., 1974; LL.D., Lynchburg Coll., 1975; L.H.D., Culver-Stockton Coll., 1975. Ordained to ministry Christian Ch. (Disciples of Christ), 1940; pastor in Chandler, Okla., 1944-47, Texas City, Tex., 1947-48, Healdton, Okla., 1948-49, Vernon, Tex., 1949-55, Fort Smith, Ark., 1955-58; exec. minister Christian Ch. in, Ark., 1958-65; asst. to pres. Christian Ch. in U.S. and Can., Indpls., 1965-69; exec. minister Christian Ch. in Tex., 1969-73; gen. minister, pres. Christian Ch. in U.S. and Can., 1973-85; faculty Brite Div. Sch., Tex. Christian U., 1985-89; mem. governing bd. Nat. Council Chs., 1973-85; del. 5th Assembly of World Council Chs., Nairobi, Kenya, 1975, 6th Assembly, Vancouver, B.C., Can, 1983; rep. Nat. Council Chs. in Exchange of Ch. Leadership with Soviet Union, 1974. Author: We Call Ourselves Disciples, 1975. Named Disting. Alumnus Tex. Christian U., 1973, Phillips U., 1975; Outstanding Citizen Vernon, Tex., 1954. Home: 7013 Serrano Dr Fort Worth TX 76126-2317

TEEGUARDEN, DENNIS EARL, forest economist; b. Gary, Ind., Aug. 21, 1931; s. Gary Leon and Mary Dessa (Pursifull) T.; m. Sally Annette Gleason, Dec. 23, 1954; children—Jason Earl, Julie Annette, Justin Gary. B.S. in Forestry with honors, Mich. Tech. U., Houghton, 1953; M.Forestry, U. Calif., Berkeley, 1958, Ph.D. in Agrl. Econs. (Bidwell research fellow 1962-63), 1964. Rsch. aid U.S. Forest Service, 1957; asst. rsch. specialist U. Calif., Berkeley, 1958-64, mem. faculty, 1964-91, prof. forestry econs. Sch. Forestry, 1964-91, S.J. Hall prof. forest econs., 1989-91, prof. emeritus, 1991—, chmn. dept. forestry and resource mgmt., 1978-86, acting dir. forest products lab., 1987-88, assoc. dean for acad. affairs, 1990-92, assoc. dean rsch. and extension, 1992-93; mem. Calif. Commn. on Agr. and Higher Edn., 1993-95; mem. com. scientists Dept. Agr., 1977-80; cons. in field; mem. adv. bd. U. Calid. Forest Products Lab. 1994—. Co-author: Forest Resource Management: Decision-Making Principles and Cases, 1979; contbr. articles to profl. jours. Trustee Mich. Tech. Fund, Mich. Tech. U., Houghton, 1994—. Lt. USNR, 1953-57, Korea. Recipient Outstanding Alumnus award Mich. Tech. U., 1993, Berkeley citation U. Calif., Berkeley, 1994; grantee U.s. Forest Svc., Bur. Land Mgmt. 010HomeSoc. Am. Foresters; mem. Western Forest Economists, Nat. Audubon Soc., Calif. Water Fowl Assn. Home: 4732 Westwood Ct Richmond CA 94803-2441 Office: U Calif Coll Natural Resources Berkeley CA 94720

TEEL, JAMES E., supermarket and drug store retail executive; b. 1930. Co-chmn. dir. Raley's, West Sacramento, 1950—. Office: Raleys 500 W Capitol Ave West Sacramento CA 95691*

TEEL, JOYCE, supermarket and drugstore retail executive; b. 1930. Co-chmn. bd., sec., dir. Raley's, West Sacramento. Office: Raley's 500 W Capitol Ave West Sacramento CA 95691*

TEELE, THURSTON FERDINAND, economist; b. New Rochelle, N.Y., Mar. 27, 1934; s. Stanley Ferdinand and Dorothy Thurston (Newman) T.; m. Shari May Barton, June 15, 1957 (div. 1965); children: Edward B., Stacia L.; m. Dorothy Locy, Aug. 1967 (div. 1980); children: Kristy, Allen F.; m. Barbara Carmichael Mangrum, Feb. 7, 1982. BA, Amherst Coll., 1956; MA, Tufts U., 1962; PhD, Georgetown U., 1964. Fgn. svc. officer U.S. Dept. State, Washington and Athens, Greece, 1956-64; cons. economist, chief party Checchi. Co., Washington and overseas, 1964-75; pres., CEO Chemonics Internat., Washington, 1975—; vice chmn. Profl. Svc. Coun. AID Task Force, Washington, 1992. With U.S. Army, 1957-58. Democrat. Mem. United Ch. of Christ. Avocations: travel, reading, working out. Home: 2231 Q St NW Washington DC 20008-2825 Office: Chemonics Internat 2000 M St NW Washington DC 20036-3307

TEEM, JOHN MCCORKLE, retired association executive, consultant; b. Springfield, Mo., July 23, 1925; s. Lon Vester and Judith (McCorkle) T.; m. Sylvia Victoria Konvicka; children—Judith Majka Teem Donald, Paul Norman. A.B., Harvard U., 1949, M.A., 1951, Ph.D., 1954. Sr. research fellow Calif. Inst. Tech., Pasadena, 1954-60; v.p., chief scientist Electro Optical Systems, Pasadena, 1960-67; dir. tech. staff, research and devel. Xerox Corp., Stamford, Conn., 1967-72; asst. gen. mgr., dir. phys. research AEC, Washington, 1973-75; asst. administr. ERDA, Washington, 1975-76; pres. Assn. Univs. for Research in Astronomy, Washington, 1977-86. Served with U.S. Army, 1943-46. Recipient Disting. Service medal AEC, 1975; named Fairchild Disting. scholar Calif. Inst. Tech., 1976-77. Fellow AAAS; mem. Am. Astron. Soc. Democrat. Roman Catholic. Home: Apt 1710 3800 Fairfax Dr Arlington VA 22203

TEEM, PAUL LLOYD, JR., savings and loan executive; b. Gastonia, N.C., Mar. 10, 1948; s. Paul Lloyd Sr. and Ruth Elaine (Bennett) T. BA, U. N.C., 1970; Cert., Inst. Fin. Edn., Chgo., 1984, Diploma, 1985, Degree of Distinction, 1989. Cert. tchr. N.C.; consumer credit exec.; licensed real estate broker. Exec. v.p., sec. Gaston Fed. Savs. and Loan Assn., Gastonia, N.C., 1983—; exec. v.p., sec., bd. dirs Gaston Fin. Svcs., Inc., Gastonia, 1988—. Bd. dirs. Gastonia Mchts. Assn., Inc., 1981-83; lay reader Episcopal Ch. Decorated Order Purple Cross, Legion of Honor; named Ky. Col., 1995. Fellow Soc. Cert. Credit Execs.; mem. SAR, SCV, Mil. ORder of Stars and Bars, Masons (32d degree, bd. dirs. 1981—, Disting. Svc. award 1987, Gold Honor award 1989, Active Legion of Honor 1989, Order of the Purple Cross of York 1990), Shriners, KT, Royal Order of Scotland, Hon. Order Key. Cols., Phi Alpha Theta. Democrat. Avocation: genealogy. Home: 1208 Poston Cir Gastonia NC 28054-4634 Office: Gaston Fed Savs and Loan Assn 245 W Main Ave PO Box 2249 Gastonia NC 28053-2249

TEEPEN, THOMAS HENRY, newspaper editor, journalist; b. Nashville, Jan. 19, 1935; s. Albert George and Elizabeth Blanche (Winfree) T.; m. Nancy Irene Roux, Feb. 2, 1957 (div. 1974); children—Kristina Lynn, Jeremy Roux; m. Sandra Jean Richards, May 14, 1975; 1 stepchild, Jennifer Koerlin. B.S. in Journalism, Ohio U., 1957. Reporter Urbana (Ohio) Daily Citizen, 1957-58; asst. editor Kettering-Oakwood Times, Dayton, Ohio, 1958-59; from reporter to editorial writer Dayton Daily News, 1959-68, editorial page editor, 1968-82; editorial page editor Atlanta Constitution, 1982-92; nat. corr. Cox Newspapers, Atlanta, 1992—. Former pres. Joel Chandler Harris Assn., Atlanta; mem. Atlanta Opera, 1985—, Joint Internat. Observer Group, Ethiopian Elections, 1992; mem. internat. adv. com. The African-Am. Inst., N.Y.C., 1985—; trustee Ga. Coun. Internat. Visitors; mem. Capitol Area Mosaic. Profl. journalism fellow Stanford Univ., 1967. Home: 900 Charles Allen Dr NE Atlanta GA 30308-1722 Office: Cox Newspapers care The Atlanta Constn Box 4689 Atlanta GA 30302

TEEPLE, FIONA DIANE, librarian, lawyer; b. St. Thomas, Ont., Can., Jan. 9, 1943; d. William Lloyd and Grace (Hathaway) T. BA, U. Western Ont., London, 1964; BLS, U. B.C., Vancouver, 1965; MLS, U. Toronto, Ont., 1976; LLB, York U., Toronto, 1980. Bar: Ont., 1985. Asst. law librarian U. Western Ont., London, 1965-70; reference librarian York U. Law Library, Toronto, 1971-77; administrv. asst. Ont. Legis. Library, Toronto, 1980, exec. asst., 1981-83; chief librarian Supreme Ct. of Can., Ottawa, 1983-90, dir. libr., 1990—. Editor: Practitioner's Desk Book, 1976-80; mng. editor CALL Newsletter, 1973-75; contbr. articles, revs., book chpts. in field. Mem. Can. Assn. Law Librs., Law Soc. Upper Can. Mem. United Ch. Can.

TEEPLE, RICHARD DUANE, lawyer; b. Portland, Ind., Oct. 31, 1942; s. Joseph Carlise and Sylvia Ann (Bailey) T.; m. Julie Favorite, June 5, 1965; children: Laura, Darin. BA, Purdue U., 1964; JD, U. Cin., 1967. Bar: Ohio 1967. Assoc. Wilke & Company, Cin., 1967-72; atty. Gen. Motors Corp., Dayton, Ohio, 1972-77; v.p., gen. counsel Cooper Tire & Rubber Co., Findlay, Ohio, 1977—. Mem. advisory bd. Salvation Army, Findlay, 1982—. Mem. ABA, Ohio Bar Assn. (bd. govs. corp. counsel sect. 1984—), Findlay/Hancock Bar Assn., Am. Corp. Counsel Assn. Office: Cooper Tire & Rubber Co Lima & Western Aves Findlay OH 45840

TEER, JAMES G., foundation administrator. Dir. Welder Wildlife Found., Sinton, Tex. Recipient Aldo Leopold Meml. award Wildlife Soc., 1994. Office: Welder Wildlife Found PO Box 1400 Sinton TX 78387*

TEER, KAY STOLTZ, museum director; b. Southern Pines, N.C., July 30, 1947; d. John Wesley and Ellen (Kathrine (Wheeless) Stoltz; m. William Stewart Teer, June 2, 1968; children: John Stewart, Marguerite Kathrine. BS, East Carolina U., 1969; postgrad., U. S.C., 1971-89, U. N.C., 1983. Tchr. English Sch. Dist. 17, Sumter, S.C., 1969-73; exec. dir. Sumter Gallery of Art, 1982-88; grants writer S.C. Arts Commn., Columbia, 1988-89; advocacy coord. S.C. Arts Alliance, Columbia, 1988-89; exec. dir. Sumter County Mus., 1989—. Bd. dirs. Sumter Sch. Dist. 17, 1978-94, S.C. Arts Alliance, 1985-88, Fine Arts Coun., Sumter, 1986-93. Mem. Am. Assn. Mus., S.C. Fedn. Mus. (sec. 1994—), Southeastern Mus. Conf., Sumter C. of C. (bd. dirs. 1979-81, 90-92). Methodist. Avocations: reading, travel, family, singing. Home: 11 Snowden St Sumter SC 29150-3224 Office: Sumter County Mus PO Box 1456 Sumter SC 29151-1456

TEERLINK, RICHARD FRANCIS, motor company executive; b. Chgo., Oct. 12, 1936; s. James and Martha (Vogel) T.; m. Ann L. Hofing, Apr. 23, 1960; children—John Robert, Leslie Ann, Victoria Lynn. B.S., Bradley U., 1961; M.B.A., U. Chgo., 1976. Sr. v.p. adminstrn. Union Special Corp., Chgo., 1971-78; v.p. fin. RTE Corp., Waukesha, Wis., 1978-80; sr. v.p., chief fin. officer Herman Miller, Inc., Zeeland, Mich., 1980-81; v.p., chief fin. officer Harley Davidson Motor Co., Inc., Milw., 1981-88, also bd. dirs.; pres., CEO Harley Davidson, Inc., Milw., 1987—, CEO, dir. Served with U.S. Army, 1955-58. Home: 1765 Wedgewood Dr W Elm Grove WI 53122-1056 Office: Harley-Davidson Inc Box 653 3700 W Juneau Ave Milwaukee WI 53208-2818

TEES, RICHARD CHISHOLM, psychology educator, researcher; b. Montreal, Que., Can., Oct. 31, 1940; s. Ralph Charles and Helen Winnifred (Chisholm) T.; m. Kathleen F. Coleman, Sept. 1, 1962; children: Susan M., Carolyn V. BA., McGill U., 1961; Ph.D., U. Chgo., 1965. Asst. prof. U. B.C., Vancouver, 1965-67, assoc. prof., 1969-75, prof. psychology, 1975—; head dept. psychology U. B.C., 1984-94; rsch. prof. U. Sussex, Brighton, Eng., 1972-73, 77-78; grants panelist Nat. Scis. and Engring. Rsch. Coun. Can., Ottawa, 1993—, B.C. Health Care Rsch. Found., Vancouver, 1984-87; chmn. studentship com. Med. Rsch. Coun., Ottawa, 1985-92. Author: (with Kolb) Cerebral Cortex of the Rat, 1990; mem. editorial bd. Can. Jour. Exptl. Psychology, 1975-84, 87—; contbr. articles to profl. jours., chpts. to books. Research fellow Killam Found., 1972-73, 77-78; research fellow Can. Council, 1972-73. Fellow APA, Am. Psychol. Soc., Can. Psychol. Assn.; mem. Soc. for Neurosci., Psychonomic Soc., U. B.C. Senate, Faculty Club. Home: 1856 Acadia Rd, Vancouver, BC Canada V6T 1R3 Office: U BC, Dept Psychology, Vancouver, BC Canada V6T 1Z4

TEETER, DWIGHT LELAND, JR., journalism educator; b. L.A., Jan. 6, 1935; s. Dwight Leland and Ruth Elizabeth (Sauer) T.; m. Letitia Ruth Thoreson, July 7, 1956; children: Susan Letitia, John Thoreson, William Weston. A.B. in Journalism, U. Calif.-Berkeley, 1956, M.J., 1959; Ph.D. in Mass Communications, U. Wis., 1966. Reporter Waterloo Daily Courier, Iowa, 1957-60; asst. prof. Iowa State U., Ames, 1964-66; asst. to assoc. prof. U. Wis., Madison, 1966-72; assoc.prof. to prof. U. Ky., Lexington, 1972-77, dir. journalism dept., 1975-77; prof. journalism, chmn. dept. journalism U. Tex., Austin, 1977-84, William P. Hobby Centennial prof. communication, 1983-87; prof., dept. mass communications U. Wis., Milw., 1987-91; dean, prof. Coll. Communications U. Tenn., Knoxville, 1991—; vis. assoc. prof. U. Wash., Seattle, 1969-70; treas. Journalism Council, Inc., N.Y.C., 1972-81. Author: (with Don R. Le Duc) Law of Mass Communications, 8th edit., 1995, (with Jean L. Folkerts) Voices of a Nation: A History of Media in the United States, 2d edit., 1994; contbr. articles to legal, hist., comm. jours. Chair Headliners Club of Tex. Media Contest, 1979-83; judge Tex. Bar Assn. Media Contest, 1981-85; mem. pub. affairs com. Tex. State Bar, 1985-87. Recipient Tex. Excellence in Teaching award Tex. Ex-Students' Assn., 1983, Harold L. Nelson award U. Wis., 1985. Mem. Assn. for Edn. in Journalism and Mass Communication (chmn. prof. freedom and responsibility com. 1971-73, pres. 1985-86), Soc. Profl. Journalists (Disting. Prof. award 1991),

Phi Kappa Phi, Kappa Tau Alpha. Office: U Tenn Coll Comm Knoxville TN 37996

TEETER, KARL VAN DUYN, retired linguistic scientist, educator; b. Berkeley, Calif., Mar. 2, 1929; s. Charles Edwin and Lura May (Shaffner) T.; m. Anita Maria Bonacorsi, Aug. 25, 1951; children—Katharine Emilie, Judith Ann, Teresa Maria, Martha Elisabeth. AB in Oriental Langs. with highest honors, U. Calif., Berkeley, 1959, PhD Linguistics, 1962; AM (hon.), Harvard U., 1966. From instr. to prof. linguistics Harvard U., 1962-89, prof. emeritus, 1989—, chmn. dept. linguistics, 1966-69, 70-71, 77-78; assoc. Kirkland Ho., Harvard U., 1977-82, fellow, 1983-89, hon. assoc., 1989—; guest rsch. fellow Rsch. Inst. Logopedics and Phoniatrics, Faculty of Medicine, Tokyo U., 1969-70; mem. summer faculty U. Mich., 1962, UCLA, 1966, U. N.C., 1972. Author: Maliseet Texts, 1963, The Wiyot Language, 1964, Wiyot Handbook, I and II, 1993; editor: In Memoriam Peter Lewis Paul, 1902-89, 1993. Bd. dirs. Mass. Found. for Humanities and Pub. Policy, 1984-90, exec. com., 1985-89; bd. dirs. New Eng. Found. for Humanities, 1986-93; active New Eng. Native Am. Inst., 1992—. Served with AUS, 1946, 51-54. Fulbright rsch. fellow Japan, 1969-70; NSF grantee, 1990—. Mem. Linguistic Soc. Am. (life, long range planning com. 1969-73, lang. rev. com. 1980-82), Soc. Study Indigenous Langs. of the Ams., Phi Beta Kappa, Sigma Xi. Home: 14 1/2 Woodbridge St Cambridge MA .02140 Office: Harvard Univ Widener T Cambridge MA 02138

TEETERS, NANCY HAYS, economist; b. Marion, Ind., July 29, 1930; d. S. Edgar and Mabel (Drake) Hays; m. Robert Duane Teeters, June 7, 1952; children: Ann, James, John. A.B. in Econs., Oberlin Coll., 1952, LL.D. (hon.), 1979; M.A. in Econs., U. Mich., 1954, postgrad., 1956-57, LL.D. (hon.) 1983; LL.D. (hon.), Bates Coll., 1981, Mt. Holyoke Coll., 1983. Teaching fellow U. Mich., 1954-55, instr., 1956-57; instr. U. Md. Overseas, Germany, 1955-56; staff economist govt. fin. sect. Bd. Govs. of FRS, Washington, 1957-66; mem. bd. Bd. Govs. of FRS, 1978-84; economist (on loan) Coun. Econ. Advs., 1962-63; economist Bur. Budget, 1966-70; sr. fellow Brookings Instn., 1970-73; v.p., specialist Congl. Rsch. Svc., Library of Congress, Washington, 1973-74; asst. dir., chief economist Ho. of Reps. Com. on the Budget, 1974-78; v.p., chief economist IBM, Armonk, N.Y., 1984-90; bd. dirs., trustee Prudential Mut. Funds, 1985—; bd. dirs. Inland Steel Industries; mem. Coun. on Fgn. Rels., Forum for World Affairs, Women in Mgmt. Author: (with others) Setting National Priorities: The 1972 Budget, 1971, Setting National Priorities: The 1973 Budget, 1972, Setting National Priorities: The 1974 Budget, 1973; contbr. articles to profl. publs. Recipient Comfort Starr award in econs. Oberlin Coll., 1952; Disting. Alumnus award U. Mich., 1980. Mem. Nat. Economists Club (v.p. 1973-74, pres. 1974-75, chmn. bd. 1975-76, gov. 1976-79), Am. Econ. Assn. (com. on status of women 1975-78), Am. Fin. Assn. (dir. 1969-71). Democrat. Home: 243 Willowbrook Ave Stamford CT 06902-7020

TEETS, JOHN WILLIAM, diversifed company executive; b. Elgin, Ill., Sept. 15, 1933; s. John William and Maudie T.; m. Nancy Kerchenfaut, June 25, 1965; children: Jerri, Valerie Sue, Heide Jane, Suzanne. Student, U. Ill.; LLD (hon.), Trinity Coll., 1982; DBA in Foodsvc. Mgmt. (hon.), Johnson and Wales U., 1991; D in Comml. Sci. (hon.), Western Internat. U., 1992. Pres., ptnr. Winter Garden Restaurant, Inc., Carpentersville, Ill., 1957-63; v.p. Greyhound Food Mgmt. Co.; pres. Post Houses, Inc., and Horne's Enterprises, Chgo., 1964-68; pres., chief operating officer John R. Thompson Co., Chgo., 1968-71; pres., corp. v.p. pub. restaurant divsn. Canteen Corp., Chgo., 1971-75; divsn. pres. Jacques Restaurant Group, 1975; exec. v.p., CEO Bonanza Internat. Co., Dallas, 1975; group v.p. food svcs., pres. Greyhound Food Mgmt., Inc. (now named Restaura), Phoenix, 1975; vice chmn. The Greyhound Corp., Phoenix, 1980; chmn., CEO Greyhound Corp. (now The Dial Corp), Phoenix, 1981—; now chmn., pres., CEO The Dial Corp, Phoenix; vice chmn. Pres.' Conf. on Foodservice Industry. Recipient Silver Plate award, Golden Plate award Internat. Foodservice Mgrs. Assn., 1980, Order of the Crown Kingdom of Belgium, 1990, Bus. Leadership award Harvard Bus. Sch. Club Ariz., 1985; named Top Bus. Speaker of Yr. Forbes Mag., 1990, Capt. of Achievement Acad. of Achievement, 1992, CEO of Yr. Leaders Mag., 1986. Mem. Nat. Inst. Foodsvc. Industry (trustee), Am. Mgmt. Assn., Christian Businessmen's Assn. (chmn. steering com. 1977). Office: The Dial Corp 1850 N Central Ave Phoenix AZ 85077-0001

TEETS, PETER B., aerospace executive; b. 1942. BS, U. Colo., MS, 1978. V.p. Denver Aerospace subs. Martin Marietta Corp., Colo., 1980-85, corp. v.p., pres., 1985-87, sr. v.p., 1987—; sr. v.p., group pres., Martin Marietta Corp. Office: Martin Marietta Astronautics PO Box 179 Denver CO 80201-0179 Office: Martin Marietta Corp 6801 Rockledge Dr Bethesda MD 20817-1877

TEEVAN, RICHARD COLLIER, psychology educator; b. Shelton, Conn., June 12, 1919; s. Daniel Joseph and Elizabeth (Halliwell) T.; m. Virginia Agnes Stehle, July 28, 1945; children—Jan Elizabeth, Kim Ellen, Clay Collier, Allison Tracy. B.A., Wesleyan U., Middletown, Conn., 1951; M.A., U. Mich., 1952, Ph.D., 1955. Rubber buffer Sponge Rubber Product Co., Derby, Conn., 1939-41; with U. Mich., 1951-57, teaching fellow, 1951-53, instr., 1953-57; asst. prof. Smith Coll., 1957-60; assoc. prof. Bucknell U., 1960-64, prof., 1964-69; chmn. psychology, prof. SUNY-Albany, 1969—; pres. Teevan Assocs., Cons., 1991—; cons. on coll. teaching, 1989—. Author: Reinforcement, 1961, Instinct, 1961, Color Vision, 1961, Measuring Human Motivation, 1962, Theories of Motivation in Learning, 1964, Theories of Motivation in Personality and Social Psychology, 1964, Motivation, 1967, Fear of Failure, 1969, Readings in Elementary Psychology, 1973; contbr. articles to sci. jours. Served to capt. AUS, 1941-47; prisoner of war 1943-45, Ger. Office Naval Research grantee, 1956-72; recipient Lindbach award Bucknell U., 1966. Mem. AAAS, AAUP, Am. Psychol. Assn. (Disting. visitor 1981-85), Eastern Psychol. Assn., Phi Beta Kappa, Sigma Xi. Home: 45 Pine St Delmar NY 12054-3413 Office: SUNY Dept Psychology 1400 Washington Ave Albany NY 12222-0001

TEGTMEYER, RENE DESLOGE, lawyer; b. St. Louis, Jan. 5, 1934; s. Adolph Henry and Elise (Desloge) T.; m. Joan Lynch, Aug. 2, 1969; children: Stephen W., Jean M. BSME, Wash. U., 1956; JD, George Washington U., 1963. Bar: Va., D.C., U.S. Ct. Appeals (Fed. cir.). Patent examiner U.S. Patent and Trademark Office, Washington, 1959-64; specialist legis. and internat. affairs U.S. Patent and Trademark Office, 1964, dir. legis. and internat. affairs, 1964-71, asst. commr. for appeals legis. and trademarks, 1971-73, asst. commr. for trademarks, 1973-75, asst. commr. for patents, 1975-89; ptnr. Fish & Richardson, Washington, 1989—. Contbr. articles to profl. jours. Lt. USAF, 1956-59; with Res. 1960-68. Congl. fellowship Am. Polit. Sci. Assn., 1967-68. Mem. ABA, Am. Intellectual Property Law Assn., Fed. Bar Assn., N.J. Patent Law Assn. (Jefferson medal 1985), Pi Tau Sigma, Tau Beta Pi. Republican. Roman Catholic. Avocations: reading, skiing. Home: 1332 Timberly Ln Mc Lean VA 22102-2504 Office: Fish & Richardson 601 13th St NW Washington DC 20005-3807

TEHAN, JOHN BASHIR, lawyer; b. Utica, N.Y., May 13, 1948; s. Louis Bashir and Frances Mary (Argenzia) T.; m. Regina Anne Callahan, Aug. 1, 1970; children—Aaron J., Lauren R., Eileen L. B.A., LeMoyne Coll., 1970; J.D., Catholic U., Washington, 1973. Bar: N.Y. 1974, U.S. Dist. Ct. (so. and ea. dists.) N.Y. 1975, U.S. Ct. Appeals (2d cir.) 1975. Assoc. Sullivan & Cromwell, N.Y.C., 1973-81; ptnr. Simpson Thacher & Bartlett, N.Y.C., 1981—. Roman Catholic. Home: 10 Warwick Rd Rockville Centre NY 11570-1337 Office: Simpson Thacher & Bartlett 425 Lexington Ave New York NY 10017-3954

TEICH, MALVIN CARL, electrical engineering educator; b. N.Y.C., May 4, 1939; s. Sidney R. and Loretta K. Teich. S.B. in Physics, MIT, 1961; M.S.E.E., Stanford U., 1962; Ph.D. in Quantum Electronics, Cornell U., 1966. Research scientist MIT Lincoln Lab., Lexington, Mass., 1966-67; prof. engring. sci. Columbia U., N.Y.C., 1967—; chmn. dept. elec. engring., 1978-80, mem. Columbia Radiation Lab./faculty applied physics dept.; mem. Columbia Radiation Lab.; mem. sci. bd. Inst. Physics, Czech Acad. Scis., Prague. Author: (with B.E.A. Saleh) Fundamentals of Photonics, 1991; dep. editor Quantum Optics, 1988-92; bd. editors Jour. Visual Comm. and Image Representation, 1989-92, Jemná Mechanika a Optika, 1994—; contbr. articles to profl. jours.; patentee in field. Recipient Citation Classic award Inst. for Sci. Info., 1981, Meml. Gold medal of Palacky U., Czech Republic, 1992; Guggenheim Meml. Found. fellow, 1973. Fellow AAAS, IEEE

(Browder J. Thompson Meml. prize 1969), Optical Soc. Am. (editl. adv. panel Optics Letters 1977-79), Am. Phys. Soc., Acoustical Soc. Am.; mem. Assn. Rsch. in Otolaryngology, N.Y. Acad. Scis., Sigma Xi, Tau Beta Pi. Office: Columbia U Dept Elec Engring New York NY 10027

TEICHER, MORTON IRVING, social worker, educator; b. N.Y.C., Mar. 10, 1920; s. Sam and Celia (Roth) T.; m. Mildred Adler, Oct. 4, 1941; children: Phyllis Margaret, Oren Jonathan. B.S. in Social Sci., CCNY, 1940; M.S.W., U. Pa., 1942; Ph.D., U. Toronto, 1956. Chief social worker in New Eng. VA, 1946-48; asst. prof., clin. tchr. U. Toronto, 1948-56; cons. Oppenheimer Coll., No. Rhodesia (Zambia), 1962-63; dean Sch. Social Work, Yeshiva U., 1956-72, prof., 1956-72; prof. Sch. Social Work, U. N.C., Chapel Hill, 1972-81, 83-85; dean Sch. Social Work, U. N.C., 1972-81, dean emeritus, 1985—; prof. sociology and psychiatry, dir. Center on Aging, U. Miami, Coral Gables, 1981-83; instr. Elders Inst. Fla. Internat. U., 1987-88; faculty advisor Walden U., 1993—; seminar assoc. creativity in sci. NYU, 1959-73; cons. Bar Ilan U., Israel, 1965-69, VA, 1965-69; cons., vis. prof. Henrietta Szold Inst., Jerusalem, 1975; preceptor Ctrl. Inst. Mgmt., Sr. Civil Svc., Israel, 1975; external examiner U. Zambia, 1968-69; cons. in field, 1950—; cons. U. W.I., 1982; chmn. U.S. com. Internat. Coun. Social Welfare, 1978-79; mem. adminstrv. bd. Sch. Pub. Health, U. N.C., 1974-79. Author: Windigo Psychosis, 1960, Looking Homeward: A Thomas Wolfe Photo Album, 1993; co-author Distant Partners, 1990; sr. editor Inside Books, 1988-89; co-editor: Reaching the Aged, Data-Based Planning in the Field of Aging, 1982; book rev. editor: Jour. Jewish Communal Service, 1961-68, Jewish Floridian, 1982-86; mem. editorial bd. Human Orgn., 1963-66, Jour. Am. Soc. Cybernetics, 1970-72, Ednl. Gerontology, 1978-84; book reviewer South Fla. Jewish Jour., Phila. Jewish Exponent, Metrowest Jewish News, Jerusalem Post; also contbr. numerous articles to profl. jours., books. Research chmn. Westchester Democratic Com., 1958-62; bd. dirs. Lake Success Capital Corp., 1967-71; trustee Wurzweiler Found., 1966-90, Coler Found., 1970-72; participant Fla. Gov.'s Challenge Program, 1981; exec. sec. Nat. Conf. Jewish Communal Service, 1968-70; mem. exec. com. Miami chpt. Am. Jewish Com., 1981-83; bd. dirs. N.Y. Social Work Recruiting Center, 1960-70; mem. policy bd. Carolina Population Center, 1973-77; bd. dirs. Internat. Conf. Jewish Communal Service, 1965-85, Hillel, U. Miami, 1981-83, Beth David Synagogue, Miami, 1991—; pres. Durham-Chapel Hill Jewish Fedn., 1980; mem. planning and budgeting com. Project Renewal Commn., Miami Jewish Fedn., 1981—; adv. coun. Sch. Social Work Barry U., 1986—. Served to 1st lt. AUS, 1942-46, CBI. Recipient Disting. Alumnus cert. U. Pa., 1979. Mem. AAUP, Am. Assn. Retired Persons (v.p. South Miami Beach chpt. 1992), Acad. Cert. Social Workers, Nat. Assn. Social Workers (chmn. Westchester chpt. 1960-62, mem. commn. ethics 1964-67, mem. exec. com. Eastern N.C. chpt. 1972-74, chmn. profl. advancement travel com. 1980-83), Thomas Wolfe Soc. (dir. 1981—, v.p. 1985-87, pres. 1987-91). Anthrop. field work among the Eskimo and Iroquois; tour leader to internat. social welfare confs. in Athens, Helsinki, Nairobi, The Hague, San Juan, Jerusalem, Hong Kong, and Brighton, Eng. Home: 4275 Nautilus Dr Miami FL 33140-2821

TEICHERT, CURT, geologist, educator; b. Koenigsberg, Germany, May 8, 1905; came to U.S., 1952, naturalized, 1959; s. Richard and Luise (Zander) T.; m. Gertrud Margarete Kaufmann, Dec. 28, 1928. Student, U. Munich, Germany, 1923-25, U. Freiburg, Germany, 1925, U. Koenigsberg, 1925-28; Ph.D., Albertus U., 1928; D.Sc., U. Western Australia, Perth, 1944. Rockefeller fellow U.S., 1930; privatdozent Tech. U., Berlin, 1931-35; research paleontologist U. Copenhagen, Denmark, 1933-37; research lectr. U. Western Australia, 1937-45; asst. chief govt. geologist Dept. Mines, Melbourne, Australia, 1946-47; sr. lectr. U. Melbourne, 1947-53; Fulbright scholar U. Kans., Lawrence, 1951-52; prof. geology N.Mex. Sch. Mines, 1953-54; geologist U.S. Geol. Survey, 1954-90; chief Petroleum Geology Lab., 1954-58, research geologist, 1958-61; AID adviser Geol. Survey, Pakistan, 1961-64; Regents Distinguished prof. geology, dir. Paleontol. Inst. U. Kans., Lawrence, 1964-75; prof. emeritus U. Kans., 1975—; adj. prof. geol. scis. U. Rochester, N.Y., 1977—; geologist Danish N.E. Greenland Expdn., 1931-32; guest prof. U. Bonn, Germany, U. Goettingen, U. Freiburg, 1958, U. Tex., 1960, Free U. Berlin, 1974; U.S. coordinator AID-CENTO Stratigraphic Working Group, 1965-76; Cons. to oil cos., 1940-53, Australian Bur. Mineral Resources, 1948-52. Author: Ordovician and Silurian Faunas from Arctic Canada, 1937, (with Clarke, Prider) Elements of Geology, 1944, 4th ed., 1967, Elementary Practical Geology, 1946, 4th edit., 1968, (with others) Treatise on Invertebrate Paleontology, Part K, 1964; several book size monographs.; Editor: (with others) Treatise on Invertebrate Paleontology, 1964-80; also miscellaneous symposia; contbr. articles to profl. jours. Recipient David Syme Prize sci. research U. Melbourne, 1950, R.C. Moore medal for excellence in paleontology Soc. Econ. Paleontologists and Mineralogists, 1982. Fellow Geol. Soc. Am., Geol. Soc. London (hon.), AAAS; mem. Internat. Geol. Congress (past sec. internat. com. Gondwana system), Soc. Geol. France (fgn. assoc.), Paleontol. Soc. (past corr., pres. 1971-72, medal 1984), Paleont. Gesellschaft (hon.), Soc. Geol. Belgique (hon.), Royal Soc. Western Australia (hon.), Paleontol. Soc. India (fgn. corr.), Geol. Soc. Australia (hon.), Senckenberg. Naturforsch. Gesellschaft (corr. mem., Curt Teichert Festschrift 1989), Internat. Paleontol. Union (1st v.p. 1968-72), Internat. Paleontol. Assn. (pres. 1976-80). Office: 5505 N 10th St Arlington VA 22205

TEICHNER, LESTER, management consulting executive; b. Chgo., Apr. 21, 1944; s. Ben Bernard and Eva Bertha (Weinberg) T.; m. Barbara Rae Bush, Jan. 30, 1966 (div. Aug. 1969); m. Doris Jean Ayres, Jan. 31, 1980; children: Lauren Ayres, Caroline Ayres. BSEE, U. Ill., 1965; MBA in Mktg. and Fin., U. Chgo., 1969. Sales engr. Westinghouse Electric Corp., Chgo., 1965-69; v.p. ops. Intec Inc., Chgo., 1969-74; pres., CEO The Chgo. Group Inc., 1974—, also bd. dirs.; bd. dirs. Strategic Processing Inc., N.Y.C., Dees Communications Ltd., Vancouver, B.C., Maxcor Mfg. Co., Colorado Springs; CEO, bd. dirs. Axxess Worldwide Ltd., Coal Gasification, Inc., Chgo.; guest lectr. U. Chgo. Grad. Sch. Bus., 1982-92. Co-inventor U.S. patent electronic marketplace; contbr. articles to profl. publs. Mem. The Chgo. Forum, 1976—; bd. dirs. Am. Israeli C. of C. Mem. Am. Mgmt. Assn., Am. Mktg. Assn., Midwest Planning Assn. (bd. dirs. 1981). Republican. Jewish. Avocations: comml. renovation, astronomy, skiing, venture capital investment. Home: 2230 N Seminary Ave Chicago IL 60614-3507 Office: Chgo Group Inc 744 N Wells St Chicago IL 60610-3521

TEICHOLZ, PAUL M., civil engineering educator, administrator; b. N.Y.C., May 24, 1937; s. David and Rose (Frankel) T.; m. Susan Swire, June 28, 1959; children: Marc, Nina, Leslie. BCE, Cornell U., 1959; MCE, Stanford U., 1960, PhD, 1963. Registered profl. civil. engr., Calif. Cons., ptnr. Jacobs Assocs., San Francisco, 1963-68; dir. mgmt. info. systems and strategic planning Guy F. Atkinson Co., South San Francisco, 1968-88; prof. civil. engring., dir. Ctr. for Integrated Facility Engring. Stanford (Calif.) U., 1988—; dir. devel. Coll. Prep. Sch., Oakland, Calif., 1985-90. Contbr. articles to profl. jours. Mem. ASCE (Constrn. Mgmt. Man of Yr. 1985), Optical Rsch. Soc. Am. Democrat. Jewish. Office: Stanford U Ctr Integrated Facility Engring Terman Engring Ctr Stanford CA 94305

TEICHROB, CAROL, Canadian provincial official; b. Sask., Can., Aug. 27, 1939; d. J. Delbert and Elizabeth (Spenst) Sproxton; m. Donald P. Teichrob, Mar. 1, 1958; children: Lori, Sharon, James. Sr. matriculation, Notre Dame Convent, Morinville, Alta., Can. Cert. profl. ct. reporter, exec. mem. Can. and Saskatchewan Fedns. Agriculture, 1976-81; chmn. Can. Turkey Mktg. Agy., 1980-81, Plains Poultry Wynyard, Sask., 1981-88; founding ptnr. Primrose Books, Saskatoon, Sask., 1988—; Reeve, Rural Municipality of Corman Park, Saskatoon, Sask., 1981-91; active U. Sask. Senate, 1981-86; mem. legis. assembly N.D.P. Caucus. Recipient Golden WHeel award Sask. Rotary, 1990; named Woman of Yr. in Bus., Saskatoon YWCA, 1981. Mem. Saskatoon C. of C. Office: MLA Saskatoon River Heights, Legis Bldg Rm 105, Regina, SK Canada S4S OB3

TEICHROEW, DANIEL, information science educator; b. Manitoba, Can., Jan. 5, 1925; came to U.S., 1949, naturalized, 1956; s. Henry and Catharine (Rosenfeld) T.; m. Edith Lillian McKnight, Mar. 17, 1950; 1 child, Dana Elaine. BA, U. Toronto, Ont., Can., 1948, MA, 1949; PhD, U. N.C., 1953. Rsch. assoc. Inst. Numerical Analysis UCLA, 1951-54; analyst Nat. Cash Register Co., Hawthorne, Calif., 1954-57; assoc. prof. Sch. Bus. Stanford Calif., 1957-62, prof. mgmt., 1962-64; prof., head div. organizational scis. Case Inst. Tech., 1964-68; chmn. dept. indsl. engring. U. Mich.,

Ann Arbor, 1968-73, prof., 1973—; trustee, chmn. Meta Systems, Ltd., Ann Arbor, 1983—; bd. dir. Info. Systems Engring., Ann Arbor. Author: (with J. Howell) Mathematical Analysis for Business Decisions, 1963, Introduction to Management Science, 1964, (with others) Optimal Control of Dynamic Operations Research Models, 1967. Editor: Business Applications, Communications of Association Computing Machinery, 1962. With RCAF, 1942-45. Mem. IEEE, Soc. Mgmt. Info Systems (pres. 1978-79).

TEIGER, DAVID, management consultant; b. Newark, June 13, 1929; s. Samuel and Fannie (Ginsburg) T.; children: Lauren, Douglas, Matthew, Kristen, Justin, Robert. B.S., Cornell U., 1951. Ptnr. Samuel Teiger & Co., Newark, 1953-59, Ira Haupt & Co., N.Y.C., 1959-64, Bache & Co., N.Y.C., 1964-65; exec. v.p. Shearson, Hammill & Co., Inc., N.Y.C., 1965-73; chmn., chief exec. officer United Rsch. Co., Morristown, N.J., 1973-90; chmn. Gemini Consulting, Morristown, N.J., 1990—. Served to lt. U.S. Army, 1951-53. Clubs: Meadowood; Mountain Ridge. Office: Gemini Consulting 25 Airport Rd Morristown NJ 07960-4655

TEIMAN, RICHARD B., lawyer; b. Bklyn., May 19, 1938. AB, Princeton U., 1959; LLB, Harvard U., 1962. Bar: N.Y. 1963. Ptnr. Winston & Strawn (and predecessor Cole & Deitz), N.Y.C., 1968—. Trustee Citizens Budget Commn., 1993—. Mem. Assn. Bar City N.Y. (com. Admiralty 1975-78, 87, chair 1988-91), Maritime Law Assn. (com. Maritime Financing 1980—, chmn. subcom. Recodification U.S. Ship Mortgage Act 1986-91, chmn. subcom. U.S. Coastguard, Citizenship and Related Matters 1988-94), Phi Beta Kappa. Home: 5 Pryer Ln Larchmont NY 10538-4012 Office: Winston & Strawn 175 Water St New York NY 10038-4918

TEITEL, SIMON, economist; b. Buenos Aires, Dec. 5, 1928; came to U.S., 1961; s. Gregorio and Regina (Tarnorudzka) T.; m. Raquel Schenkolewski, June 20, 1954; children: Rut Gabriela, Ariel Dan. BS in Indsl. Engring., U. Buenos Aires, 1956, MS in Indsl. Engring., 1963; PhD in Econs., Columbia U., 1969. Econ. affairs officer Ctr. for Indsl. Devel., UN, N.Y.C., 1963-67; sr. indsl. devel. officer policies and programming div. UN Indsl. Devel. Orgn., Vienna, Austria, 1967-68; sr. cons. Office Program Advisor to Pres., Inter-Am. Devel. Bank, Washington, 1968-76, sr. econ. advisor econ. and social devel. dept., 1976-89; sr. rsch. adv., 1989-92; rsch. cons. World Bank, Washington, 1992-94; econ. cons. UN, 1994—; adj. assoc. prof. econs. Cath. U. Am., Washington, 1971-77, adj. prof., 1977-81, prof., 1981-88; adj. prof. Am. U., 1992; lectr. Georgetown U., Washington, 1976; vis. lectr. internat. econs. Yale U., New Haven, 1977-78; lectr. to numerous profl. assns. and univs.; occasional referee Econ. Devel. and Cultural Change, Jour. Devel. Econs., World Devel., Latin Am. Rsch. Rev.; mem. spl. internat. panel on appropriate techs. for developing countries Bd. on Sci. and Tech. for Internat. Devel., NAS-Nat. Acad. Engring., 1974-77. Author: Política Económica en Centro y Periferia, 1976, Integracion Economica, 1977, Trade, Stability, Technology and Equity in Latin Am., 1982, Symposium on Technological Change and Industrial Development, 1984, Growth, Reform and Adjustment: Latin America's Trade and Macroeconomic Policies in the 1970s and 1980s, 1986, Handbook of Latin Am. Studies, Libr. of Congress, Economics: Argentina, 1989, Towards a New Development Strategy for Latin America, 1992, Industrial and Technological Development, 1993, Technology and Enterprise Development, 1994; contbr. articles to profl. jours. Mem. Am. Econ. Assn. Jewish. Home: 5610 Wisconsin Ave # 606 Chevy Chase MD 20815

TEITELBAUM, HARRY, English educator; b. Leipzig, Germany, Sept. 23, 1930; came to U.S., 1939; s. Simon and Rencia (Spindel) T.; m. Marilyn L. Nober, Nov. 7, 1953; children: Mark, David, Deborah. BA, Bkyn. Coll., 1952, MA, 1953; ABD, NYU, 1968. Cert. tchr. English, math., supr. secondary edn., N.Y.; cmty. coll. instr. liberal arts, Calif. Teaching fellow Bklyn. Coll., 1953; instr. U.S. Armed Forces Inst., Germany, 1954-55; substitute tchr. N.Y.C. High Schs., Bklyn., 1955; tchr. English Elmont (N.Y.) Meml. High Sch., 1955-60; tutor SAT Plainview, N.Y., 1964-86; English tchr. Plainview-Old Bethpage Sch. Dist., 1960-85; dept. chmn. John F. Kennedy High Sch., Plainview, 1966-70; adj. prof. Hofstra U., Hempstead, N.Y., 1958-74, Suffolk County Coll., Selden, N.Y., 1974-87, Saddleback Coll., Mission Viejo, Calif., 1988—; judge various writing and speaking contests, L.I., N.Y., 1964-85; scholar-lectr. Orange County Calif. Librs., 1989. Author: How to Write Themes, 1964, 75, 94, How to Write Book Reports, 1975, 89, 95; co-author: How to Write Themes and Essays, rev. edit. 1994; contbr. articles to profl. jours. and newspapers. Cpl. U.S. Army, 1953-55. Recipient Disting. Tchr. award Alpha Sigma Lambda Hofstra U., 1969, John F. Kennedy High Sch., 1979. Avocations: skiing, tennis, woodworking, jogging. Home: 29562 Avante Laguna Niguel CA 92677-7949 Office: Saddleback C C 28000 Marguerite Pky Mission Viejo CA 92692-3635

TEITELBAUM, IRVING, retail executive; b. Montreal, Que., Apr. 12, 1939; s. Nathan and Esther T.; m. Maida Shier, June 19, 1960; children: Carole, Joel. B of Commerce, Concordia U., Montreal, 1960. V.p., gen. mgr. Shier Ltee, Que., 1960-66, also bd. dirs., 1960—; chmn. Suzy Shier Ltd. and Suzy Shier Inc., Montreal, 1966—; bd. dirs. Tanurb Devels., Toronto, St. Regis Real Estate Montreal; chmn. Wet Seal Inc., Irvine, Calif., 1984—, La Senza Lingerie Inc., La Senza PLC, London, 1994—; pres. 1st Can. Mgmt. Cons. Ltd., Montreal, 1976—. Avocations: tennis, cycling, mountain hiking.

TEITELBAUM, PHILIP, psychologist; b. Bklyn., Oct. 9, 1928; s. Bernard and Betty (Schechter) T.; m. Osnat Boné; children: Benjamin, Daniel, David, Jonathan, Gideon. BS., CCNY, 1950; M.A., Johns Hopkins U., 1952, Ph.D., 1954. Instr., asst. prof. physiol. psychology Harvard U., 1954-59; assoc. prof. psychology U Pa., Phila., 1959-63; prof. U. Pa., 1963-73; prof. psychology U. Ill.-Urbana-Champaign, 1973-85, emeritus prof., 1985—, Disting. prof. Ctr. Advanced Studies, 1980-85; grad. research prof. U. Fla., Gainesville, 1984—. Author: Fundamental Principles of Physiological Psychology, 1967; editor: (with E. Satinoff) Motivation: Handbook Behavioral Neurobiology, 1983. Contbr. chpts. to books, articles to profl. jours. Fellow Ctr. for Advanced Study in Behavorial Scis., Stanford U., 1975-76, Fulbright fellow Tel Aviv U., 1978-79, Guggenheim fellow, 1984-85, Carnegie Found. fellow Inst. Neurol. Scis., U. Pa. Med. Sch., 1958-59. Fellow APA (pres. div. physiol. psychology, disting. sci. contbn. award 1978), Am. Psychol. Soc. (William James fellow); mem. NAS, AAAS, Am. Physiol. Soc., Soc. for Neurosci., Soc. Exptl. Psychology. Home: 2239 NW 17th Ave Gainesville FL 32605-3909 Office: U Fla Dept Psychology Gainesville FL 32611

TEITELBAUM, STEVEN LAZARUS, pathology educator; b. Bklyn., June 29, 1938; s. Hyman and Rose Leah (Harnick) T.; m. Marilyn Ruth Schaffner; children: Caren Beth, Aaron Michael, Rebecca Lee. BA, Columbia U., 1960; MD, Washington U., St. Louis, 1964. Intern Washington U. Sch. Medicine, St. Louis, 1964-65, 3d. yr. asst. resident, ACS clin. fellow, 1967-68; intern NYU, 1965-66, 2d yr. resident, 1966-67; assoc. pathologist Jewish Hosp. at Washington U. Med. Ctr., St. Louis, 1969-89, pathologist-in-chief, 1987—; asst. pathologist Barnes Hosp., St. Louis, 1986—; pathologist St. Louis Shriners Hosp. for Crippled Children, 1986—; Wilma and Roswell Messing prof. pathology Washington U. Sch. Medicine, St. Louis, 1987—; mem. Othopedics and Musculoskeletal Study Sect. NIH, 1983-87. Author 210 published sci. articles in med. jours., 1965—, 12 chpts. in med. books and texts, 1976—; mem. editorial bd. Calcified Tissue Internat., 1980-85, 89-91, Human Pathology; mem. bd. assoc. editors Jour. Orthopaedic Rsch., Jour. Cellular Biochemistry. Mem. Am. Soc. Clin. Investigation, Am. Assn. Physicians, Am. Acad. Orthopaedic Surgeons (Ann Doner Vaughan Kappa Delta award 1988), Paget's Disease Found. (adv. panel), Am. Soc. for Bone and Mineral Rsch. (pres.). Office: Washington U Med Ctr Jewish Hosp 216 S Kingshighway Blvd Saint Louis MO 63110-1092

TEITELL, CONRAD LAURENCE, lawyer, author; b. N.Y.C., Nov. 8, 1932; s. Benson and Belle (Altman) T.; m. Adele Mary Crummins, May 26, 1957; children: Beth Mary, Mark Lewis. A.B., U. Mich., 1954; LL.B., Columbia U., 1957; LL.M., N.Y. U., 1968. Bar: N.Y. 1958, D.C, 1968. Mem. Prerau & Teitell, White Plains, N.Y., 1964—; of counsel Perkins Coie, Seattle, 1991—; dir. Philanthropy Tax Inst., Old Greenwich, Conn., 1964—. Author: Philanthropy and Taxation, 5 vols., 1983-95; editor, pub. Taxwise Giving, 1964—; contbr. articles to legal jours. Served with U.S. Army, 1957. Recipient Disting. Svc. to Higher Edn. award Am. Coll. Pub. Relations

Assn., 1970, Disting. Svc. award Nat. Com. on Planned Giving, 1990, Harrison Tweed Spl. Merit award Am. Law Inst./ABA, 1992. Fellow Am. Coll. Trust and Estate Counsel; mem. ABA (former co-chmn. com. charitable giving, trusts, founds.), Assn. of Bar of City of N.Y., Nat. Assn. Coll. Univ. Attys., Am. Soc. Hosp. Attys. Home: 16 Marlow Ct Riverside CT 06878 Office: Prerau & Teitell 50 Main St White Plains NY 10606-1920 also: 13 Arcadia Rd Old Greenwich CT 06870

TEIXEIRA, ARTHUR ALVES, food engineer, consultant; b. Fall River, Mass., Jan. 30, 1944; s. Arthur Araujo and Emelia (Alves) T.; m. Jean E. Lamb, Dec. 26, 1966 (dec. Dec. 1983); children: A. Allan, Scott C.; m. Marjorie St. John, June 28, 1986; 1 stepchild, Craig St. John. PhD, U. Mass., 1971. Profl. engr., Fla., Mass. Rsch. engr. Ross Labs., Columbus, Ohio, 1971-73, R&D group leader, 1973-77; sr. cons. Arthur D. Little, Inc., Cambridge, Mass., 1977-82; assoc. prof. U. Fla., Gainesville, 1982-89, prof., 1989—; sci. adv. Escola Superior de Biotechnologia, Porto, Portugal, 1991—; FMC Corp., Santa Clara, Calif., 1989-92; internat. cons. Brazil, Cuba, Hungary, Poland, Portugal, Romania and Bulgaria. Author: Computerized Food Processing Operations, 1989; contbr. 8 chpts. to books, 30 articles to profl. jours. Judge Internat. Sci. Fair., Orlando, Fla., 1991; reviewer U.S. Dept. Agriculture, Washington, 1991, 92, 93. Sr. Guest fellow NATO, 1988, 89; Fulbright grantee U.S. Info. Agy., 1990-91. Fellow Am. Soc. Agrl. Engrs. (dir. 1988-90, Paper awards 1988-89, assoc. editor Transactions of ASAE 1985—); mem. AICE, Inst. Food Technologists (mem. editl. bd. 1980-83), Am. Soc. Engring. Edn., Inst. Thermal Process Specialists, Coun. on Agrl. Sci. and Tech., R & D Assocs. Republican. Roman Catholic. Achievements include design of on-line process control system to assure safety of sterilized canned foods; tech. and econ. feasiblty for radiation sterilization of disposable feeding devices; research in computer optimization and control of food sterilization processes. Office: U Fla Rogers Hall Gainesville FL 32611-0570

TEIXEIRA, JOSEPH, advertising executive; b. Azores, Portugal, Aug. 11, 1949; came to U.S., 1961, naturalized, 1968; s. Fernando J. and Luisa M. (Mendonca) T.; m. Angelica Maria Cabral, Oct. 12, 1974; children: Christine, Debora. B.S. Bently Coll., 1975. Vice pres. Arnold & Co., Boston, 1978-80, sr. v.p., 1980-82, exec. v.p., 1982-95, exec. v.p., CFO, 1995—. Served with U.S. Army, 1969-71. Roman Catholic. Office: Arnold & Co Inc 101 Arch St Boston MA 02110-1103

TEJA, AMYN SADRUDIN, chemical engineering educator, consultant; b. Zanzibar, Tanzania, May 11, 1946; came to U.S., 1980; s. Sadrudin N. and Amina (Dharsi) T.; m. Carole Rosina Thurlow, July 3, 1971; children: Kerima Amy, Adam Riaz. BSc in Engring., U. London, London, 1968; PhD, U. London, 1972. Intern Warren Springs Lab., Stevenage, Eng., summer 1966, Brit. Gas Corp., London, summer 1968; rsch. fellow in chem. engring. Loughborough (U.K.) U. Tech., 1971-74; chem. engring. lectr. Loughborough (Eng.) U. Tech., 1974-80; assoc. prof. chem. engring. Ga. Inst. Tech., Atlanta, 1980-83, prof., 1984-90, regents prof. Woodruff Sch. Mech. Engring., 1991—, regents prof. Sch. Chem. Engring., 1990—, dir. Fluid Properties Rsch. Inst., 1985—, co-dir. Specialty Separations Ctr., 1992—, assoc. dir. grad. studies, 1994—; vis. assoc. prof. chem. engring. U. Del., Newark, 1978-79, Ohio State U., 1980; cons. Laporte Chems., Eng., 1971, Mobil Rsch. and Devel. Co., N.J., 1979, Conoco Ltd., Humberside Refinery, Eng., 1980, Milliken Chem. Co., Spartanburg, S.C., 1981-83, Hoechst Celanese Corp., Corpus Christi, Tex., 1984, Charlotte, 1992. Philip Morris U.S.A., Richmond, Va., 1984-87, DuPont Co., 1988, Union Carbide Corp., South Charleston, W.Va., 1989—, Shell Oil Co., 1989-93; presenter in field, reviewer various jours. Editor: Chemical Engineering and the Environment, 1981; mem. editl. bd. Reports on the Progress of Applied Chemistry, 1972-76, Critical Reports on Applied Chemistry, 1976-80, Jour. Chem. and Engring. Data, 1991—, Chem. Engring. Rsch. Compendium, 1990—, Jour. Supercritical Fluids, 1990—; assoc. editor The Chem. Engring. Jour., 1973—; contbr. more than 170 articles to profl. jours. Recipient Hinchley medal Instn. Chem. Engrs., 1968, IBM Rsch. scholarship, 1968-71, Gas Coun. Rsch. scholarship, 1968-71, Brit. Coun. Younger Rsch. Workers award, 1977, Outstanding Tchr. award Omega Chi Epsilon, 1990. Mem. AIChE (pub. com. 1992—, jour. rev.), Am. Soc. Engring. Edn., Am. Chem. Soc., Sigma Xi (v.p. Ga. Tech. chpt. 1991-92, pres. 1992-93, Supr. Outstanding MS Thesis in Engring. 1984, 90, Supr. Outstanding PhD Thesis 1993, Sustained Rsch. award 1987). Avocations: tennis, science fiction. Home: 1953 Huntington Hall Ct Atlanta GA 30338-5712 Office: Ga Inst Tech Chem Engring Atlanta GA 30332

TEJADA, FRANCISCO, physician, educator; b. Moyobamba, San Martin, Peru, July 25, 1942; s. Francisco Tejada and Semiramis Reatequi; m. Barbara Ann Kotowski, Feb. 1, 1970; children: Anamaria, Semiramis, Barbara Lee, Francisco, James. BS, U. Nacional Mayor de San Marcos, Lima, Peru, 1961; MD, U. Peruana Cayetano Heredia, Lima, 1967. Diplomate Am. Bd. Internal Medicine, Am. Bd. Oncology. Resident in medicine Johns Hopkins U., Balt., 1970-72; sr. cancer researcher Nat. Cancer Inst., NIH, Bethesda, Md., 1972-75; asst. clin. dir. Comprehensive Cancer Ctr. Fla., Miami, Fla., 1975-80; asst. prof. U. Miami, 1975-79, assoc. prof., 1979-85, prof., 1985—; sr. ptnr. Oncology Assocs., Miami, 1980-85; chief cancer control Papanicolaou Cancer Ctr., Miami, 1984-86; assoc. dir. AMC Cancer Rsch. Ctr., Denver, 1986-87; pres. Am. Oncology Ctrs., Miami, 1985—; prof. U. San Agustin, Arequipa, Peru, 1992—, U. Peruana Cayetano Heredia, Lima, Peru, 1994—; oncology expert Pan Am. Health Orgn., Washington, 1975-85; oncological expert Nat. Cancer Inst., Bethesda, 1984-86; dir. Miami Cancer Inst., 1980—, Peruvian-Am. Endowment Inc., 1993—. Editor Miami Med. Letter, 1986—; inventor cancer risk assessment. Mem. Beacon Coun., Miami, 1984, Latin Am. Cancer Info., Washington, 1976, Hispanic Cancer Rsch. Network, Washington, 1990; chpt. pres. Peruvian Am. Med. Soc., Miami, 1986. Lt. Peruvian Army, 1966-67. Recipient Gold Medal Merit award Ministry of Edn., Lima, 1959, Hipolito Unanue award Hipolito Unanue Inst., Lima, 1968. Fellow ACP, Johns Hopkins U., Nat. Cancer Inst.; mem. Colegio Medico del Perú, Am. Assn. Cancer Rsch., Am. Soc. Clin. Oncology, Am. Soc. Hematology, Bolivian Cancer Soc. (hon. mem.), Peruvian Cancer Soc. (hon. mem.), Chilean Soc. Cancer (hon. mem.), Argentinian Soc. Head and Neck Pathology (hon. mem.). Roman Catholic. Avocations: hiking, photography, reading. Office: 1321 NW 14th St Ste 401 Miami FL 33125-1653

TEJEDA, FRANK, congressman; b. San Antonio, Tex., Oct. 2, 1945; 3 children. BA in Government, St. Mary's U., 1970; JD, U. Calif., Berkeley, 1974; MPA, Harvard U., 1980; LLM, Yale U., 1989. Lawyer; mem. Tex. Ho. of Reps., 1977-87, Tex. State Senate from Dist. 19, 1987-93; mem. house armed svcs. com., mem. house vets. affairs com. 103rd-104th Congress from 28th Tex. dist., Washington, D.C., 1993—; mem. house judicial affairs Tex. Ho. Reps., 1983; chmn. sub-com. Urban Affairs Tex. Senate, 1991; mem. senate fin com. Tex. Senate, 1991; mem. nat. security com., vets affairs com.; chmn. intergovernmental com. urban affairs Tex. Senate, 1991. Maj. UMMCR, Vietnam. Decorated Bronze Star, Purple Heart. Mem. Cath. War Vets., Marine Corps. League. Democrat. Roman Catholic. Office: US Ho of Reps 323 Cannon Washington DC 20515-4328*

TE KANAWA, KIRI, opera and concert singer; b. Gisborne, N.Z., Mar. 6, 1944; d. Thomas and Elanor Te Kanawa; m. Desmond Park, Aug. 30, 1967; children—Antonia Aroha, Thomas Desmond. Student, St. Mary's Coll., Auckland, N.Z., 1957-60, London Opera Centre, 1966-69; DMus (hon.), Oxford U., 1983; DLitt (hon.), U. Warwick, Coventry, England, 1989. Joined Royal Opera House, London, 1971; appeared in role of Countess in Le Nozze di Figaro, 1973; U.S. debut in Santa Fe Festival, 1971; Met. Opera debut as Desdemona in Otello, 1974; appears regularly with all major European and Am. opera houses, including Australian opera cos., Royal Opera House, Covent Garden, London, Paris Opera, Houston Opera, Munich Opera, La Scala, others; opera appearences include Boris Gudonov, Carmen, Don Giovanni, the Magic Flute, Eugene Onegin, La Boheme, Manon Lescant, many others; appeared in film Don Giovanni as Elvira, 1979; recs. include Blue Skies, 1986, Kiri Sings Gershwin, 1987, Kiri Te Kanawa: Italian Opera Arias, 1991, Kiri Her Greatest Hits, Ave Maria (Sacred and Devotional Music By Handel, Gounod, et. al., Kiri on Broadway, The Kiri Selection, Kiri Side Tracks, My Fair Lady (with Jeremy Irons, Warren Mitchell, John Gielgud, et. al.; PBS appearance: Great Performances: West Side Story, 1985; author: Land of the Long White Cloud, 1989. Decorated comdr. Order Brit. Empire, 1973, Dame Comdr.

Brit. Empire, 1983. Office: Jack Mastroianni Cami 165 W 57th St New York NY 10019-2201 also: Jiles Haefliger Impresario, Postfach 4113, CH-6002 Lucerne Switzerland also: London Records/Philips c/o PGD World Wide Plz 825 8th Ave New York NY 10019 also: c/o IMG Artists (N Am) 22 E 71st St New York NY 10021*

TELANG, NITIN T., cancer biologist, educator; b. Bombay, India, July 3, 1943; came to U.S., 1976; s. Trimbak Pandharinath and Madhumalati (Kanitkar) T. BSc, U. Poona, India, 1963, MSc, 1966, PhD, 1974. Assoc. rsch. scientist Tata Meml. Hosp. Cancer Rsch., Bombay, 1974-76; rsch. assoc. U. Nebr., Lincoln, 1976-78; staff fellow Am. Health Found., Valhalla, N.Y., 1978-81; rsch. assoc. Sloan-Kettering Inst., N.Y.C., 1981-85; asst. attending biochemist Meml. Sloan-Ketering Cancer Ctr., N.Y.C., 1985-91; assoc. prof. Cornell U. Med. Coll., N.Y.C., 1991—; dir. divsn. carcinogenesis & prevention Strang-Cornell Cancer Rsch. Lab., N.Y.C., 1991—, dir. carcinogenesis and nutrition core lab., 1991—; vis. investigator The Rockefeller U., N.Y.C., 1985-89. Contbr. numerous articles to profl. jours. Mem. Am. Assn. Cancer Rsch., Am. Soc. Cell Biology, Am. Inst. Nutrition, European Assn. Cancer Rsch. Office: Strang-Cornell Cancer Rsch Lab 510 E 73rd St New York NY 10021-4004

TELESCA, FRANCIS EUGENE, architect; b. Dunmore, Pa., Oct. 22, 1921; s. Joseph J. and Bernetta (Bocchiccio) T.; children: Celeste Ann Sullivan, Anthony, Francis Eugene II (Gino), Tina Le; m. Alyce G. Wuenstel, July 28, 1992. B.Arch. summa cum laude, Catholic U. Am., 1953. Designer-draftsman, architect various archtl. and engring. firms Washington and Miami, Fla., 1951-59; pvt. practice architecture Miami, 1959-63; pres. Greenleaf/Telesca, engrs., planners and architects, Miami, 1964-85; exec. v.p. Genesis III, Miami Lakes, Fla., 1985-87; chief programming Miami Internat. Airport, 1987—; dir. Greenleaf Enterprises, Inc., Bonefish Towers, Inc.; mem. Nat. Com. Architecture for Commerce and Industry, 1965-66, Fla. Planning and Zoning Assn., 1960—, Met. Dade County Uniform Code Enforcement Com., 1963-64; bd. dirs. South Fla. Inter-Profl. Council, 1965; planning com. U. Miami Inst. Urban Affairs, 1965; adv. com. City Miami Coconut Grove Zoning, 1965; adv. com. dept. architecture and bldg. constrn. Miami Dade Jr. Coll., 1966. (award of merit Fla. chpt. AIA for Miami Lakes Sr. High Sch., award of excellence for 20th St. Transfer Sta., Dade County 1980, Archtl. award of excellence for Hangar 2, Miami Internat. Airport, Am. Inst. Steel Constrn. 1974, also Grand Conceptor award Am. Cons. Engrs. Council 1974, award of excellence for Primera Casa, Fla. Internat. U., Fla. Concrete and Products Assn. 1973, award for outstanding concrete structure for Acad. One Bldg., Fla. Internat. U. 1980). Past pres., dir. Coconut Grove Assn. (arts festival), Grove House (sch. and marketplace for Fla. craftsmen). Served with AUS, 1940-45, 50-51. Decorated Bronze Star; recipient Grand Nat. award Nat. Community Fallout Shelter competition (shopping center), 1964. Mem. AIA (pres. Fla. South chpt. 1965, dir. Fla. 1966-69), Coconut Grove C. of C. (past pres., dir.), Greater Miami C. of C. (mem. aviation com.), Phi Eta Sigma. Roman Catholic. Home: 3509 Estepona Ave Miami FL 33178 Office: Miami Internat Airport Aviation Dept PO Box 592075 Miami FL 33159

TELESCA, MICHAEL ANTHONY, federal judge; b. Rochester, N.Y., Nov. 25, 1929; s. Michael Angelo and Agatha (Locurcio) T.; m. Ethel E. Hibbard, June 5, 1953; children: Michele, Stephen. A.B., U. Rochester, 1952; J.D., U. Buffalo, 1955. Bar: N.Y. 1957, U.S. Dist. Ct. (we. dist.) N.Y. 1958, U.S. Ct. Appeals (2d cir.) 1960, U.S. Supreme Ct. 1967. Ptnr. Lamb, Webster, Walz, Telesca, Rochester, N.Y., 1957-73; surrogate ct. judge Monroe County, N.Y., 1973-82; judge U.S. Dist. Ct. (we. dist.) N.Y., Rochester, 1982—, chief judge, 1989—; bd. dirs. Fed. Jud. Ctr. Bd. govs. Genesee Hosp., Rochester; mem. adv. bd. Assn. for Retarded Citizens, Al Sigl Ctr., Rochester. Served to 1st lt. USMC, 1955-57. Recipient Civic medal Rochester C. of C., 1983, Hutchinson medal U. Rochester, 1990. Mem. ABA, Am. Judicature Soc., Am. Inns. of Ct. (founder, pres. Rochester chpt.), Justinian Soc. Jurists, N.Y. State Bar Assn., Monroe County Bar Assn. Republican. Roman Catholic. Office: US Dist Ct 272 US Courthouse 100 State St Rochester NY 14614-1387

TELESETSKY, WALTER, government official; b. Boston, Jan. 22, 1938; s. Keril and Nellie (Krelka) T.; m. Sharron-Dawn Lamp, July 15, 1961; children: Stephanie Ann, Anastasia Marie. BS in Mech. Engring., Northeastern U., 1960; MBA, U. Chgo., 1961; postgrad., Harvard U., 1977. Engr. trainee Chrysler Corp., Detroit, 1956-59; rsch. asst. Microtech Rsch. Co., Cambridge, Mass., 1959-60; engr. Allis Chalmers Mfg. Co., Milw., 1960-61; mem. tech. staff The Mitre Corp., Bedford, Mass., 1962-68; sr. mem. tech. staff Data Dynamics, Inc., Washington, 1969; phys. scientist NOAA, Rockville, Md., 1970-71, U.S. Gate Project coord., 1972-74, dir. U.S. Global Weather Experiment Project Office, 1974, dir. Program Integration Office, 1975-77, dir. Programs and Tech. Devel. Office, 1977-79, dir. Programs and Internat. Activities Office, 1979-81; dep. assoc. dir. for tech. svcs., chief AFOS ops. div. Nat. Weather Svc., Silver Spring, Md., 1981-86, dir. Office of Systems Ops., 1986—; liaison to NAS coms. on atmospheric scis., geophysics studies and internat. environ. programs, 1975-81; U.S. coord. U.S./Japan Coop. Program in Natural Resources, 1980-88; chmn. U.S.-Japan Marine Resources and Engring. Coordination Com., 1980-88; U.S. del. governing coun. UN Environ. Program and World Meteorol. Orgn.; mem. commn. for Basic Systems World Meteorol. Orgn., 1988—; speaker in field. Contbr. articles to profl. publs. Recipient Silver medal Dept. Commerce, 1975. Mem. AAAS, Am. Geophys. Union, Am. Meteorol. Soc., Am. Soc. Mech. Engrs., Marine Tech. Soc. Home: 16 Eton Overlook Rockville MD 20850-3003 Office: 1325 E West Hwy Silver Spring MD 20910-3280

TELFORD, IRA ROCKWOOD, anatomist, educator; b. Lincoln, Idaho, May 6, 1907; s. John Witt and Martha Starr (Rockwood) T.; m. Thelma Challis Shrives, June 13, 1933; children—Ira Ralph, John Larry, Kent Matthews, Martha Ann. Student, Ricks Coll., 1924-26; A.B., U. Utah, 1931, A.M., 1933; student, U. Calif. at Berkeley, 1937-40; Ph.D., George Washington U., 1942. High sch. adminstr., 1933-37; instr., asst. prof. anatomy George Washington U., 1940-47, prof., exec. officer dept. anatomy, 1946-47, prof., chmn. dept., 1953-72; prof. anatomy dept. anatomy U. Tex. Dental Br., 1947-53; cons. anatomy (Univ. Hosp.), 1953-72; prof. anatomy Georgetown U., Washington, 1972-78; vis. prof. anatomy Uniformed Services U., Bethesda, Md., 1978-93. Contbr. articles to biol. med. jours. Fulbright scholar Gt. Britain, 1960. Fellow AAAS (council 1958-60); mem. Am. Assn. Anatomists, Soc. Exptl. Biology and Medicine, Am. Acad. Neurology, Tex. Acads. Sci., Internat. Soc. Dental Research, AMA (assoc.), Sigma Xi (chpt. pres. 1958-59), Phi Sigma (chpt. pres. 1932-33). Mem. Ch. of Jesus Christ of Latter-day Saints. Home: 3424 Garrison St NW Washington DC 20008-2037

TELL, A. CHARLES, lawyer; b. Chgo., May 9, 1937; s. William K and Virginia S (Snook) T.; m. Wendy Thomsen, June 16, 1962; children—Tracey, Melissa, A. Charles, Jr. A.B., Dartmouth Coll., 1961; J.D., Ohio State U. 1963. Ptnr. George, Greek, King & McMahon, Columbus, Ohio, 1964-78, Baker & Hostetler, Columbus, 1978—; dir. Kaplan Trucking Co., Cleve.; trustee Ohio Trucking Assn., 1989—. Editor Your Letter of the Law, 1984. Contbr. articles to profl. jours. Served with U.S. Army, 1958-60. Mem. ABA, Am. Judicature Soc., Ohio State Bar Assn., Columbus Bar Assn., Transp. Lawyers Assn. (pres. 1986-87). Republican. Presbyterian. Clubs: City (pres. 1985), Columbus Country (pres. 1989-90), University. Office: Baker & Hostetler 65 E State St Columbus OH 43215-4213

TELL, WILLIAM KIRN, JR., oil company executive, lawyer; b. Evanston, Ill., Feb. 27, 1934; s. William Kirn and Virginia (Snook) T.; m. Karen Nelson, July 16, 1960; children—Catherine, Caroline, William F. B.A. in Govt., Dartmouth Coll., 1956; J.D., U. Mich., 1959. Bar: Ohio, 1960, D.C., 1979. Atty. Texaco Inc., N.Y.C., 1968-70, asst. to v.p. gen. counsel, 1970, assoc. gen. counsel, 1970-73, asst. to chmn., 1973; v.p. Texaco Inc., Washington and N.Y.C., 1973-79, sr. v.p., 1979—; pres. Texaco Corp. Communications Div., 1989—. Editor Your Letter of the Law, 1984. Mem. adv. bd. dirs. Met. Opera, N.Y.C., 1983—. Mem. Am. Petroleum Inst. (bd. dirs. 1980—), Greenwich Country Club, Congressional Club, Metropolitan Club, Everglades Club. Home: 320 Old Church Rd Greenwich CT 06830-4824 Office: Texaco Inc 2000 Westchester Ave White Plains NY 10650

TELLEEN, JOHN MARTIN, retired judge; b. Cambridge, Ill., Dec. 16, 1922; s. Leonard E. and Vina (Elm) T.; m. Nell Joanne Larson, June 17,

1950 (dec. 1987); children—Jane, Mary, John D., Thomas; m. Kari Arentzen Larson, May 29, 1988. A.B., Augustana Coll., 1947; LL.B., U. Ill., 1950. Bar: Ill. 1950. Practice in Moline, 1950-53, Rock Island, 1953-81; partner firm Katz, McAndrews, Durkee & Telleen, Rock Island, 1953-81; judge 14th Judicial Circuit, 1981-94; ret., 1994; mem. exec. com. Ill. Jud. Conf., 1986-92; former counsel Luth. Hosp., Moline. Bd. dirs. Augustana Coll., Rock Island, 1968-76, sec., 1968-70, vice chmn., 1970, chmn., 1971-76; bd. dirs. Luth. Hosp., 1957-68. Served with USNR, 1943-46. Mem. ABA, Ill. Bar Assn., Rock Island County Bar Assn. (pres. 1970). Home: 4 Windy Pt Rock Island IL 61201-9219

TELLEFSEN, GERALD, management consultant; b. Jersey City, Sept. 19, 1938; s. James and Anna (Freudenberg) T.; children: Eric, Jill, Lynn. BA, Columbia U., 1960. Programmer System Devel. Corp., Paramus, N.J., 1961-63; analyst Internat. Electric Co., Paramus, 1963-64, IBM, Poughkeepsie, N.Y., 1964-65; mgr. Western Union, Mahwah, N.J., 1965-67; sr. scientist Control Data Corp., N.Y.C., 1967-68; sr. v.p. Booz Allen & Hamilton, N.Y.C., 1968-84, Tellefsen Cons. Group, N.Y.C., 1984—; bd. dirs. Nat. Consumer Products Co., Atlanta, Delphi Ptnrs., Atlanta. Contbr. articles to profl. jours. Mem. Futures Industry Assn. Avocations: golf, fishing. Office: Tellefsen Cons Group 19 Rector St Ste 1708 New York NY 10006-2302

TELLEM, SUSAN MARY, public relations executive; b. N.Y.C., May 23, 1945; d. John F. and Rita C. (Lietz) Cain; m. Marshall R.B. Thompson; children: Tori, John, Daniel. BS, Mt. St. Mary's Coll., L.A., 1967. Cert. pub. health nurse; RN. Pres. Tellem Pub. Rels. Agy., Marina del Rey, Calif., 1977-80, Rowland Grody Tellem, L.A., 1980-90; chmn. The Rowland Co., L.A., 1990—; pres., CEO Tellem, Inc., L.A., 1992-93; instr. UCLA Extension, 1983—; speaker numerous seminars and confs. on pub. rels. Editor: Sports Medicine for the '80's, Sports Medicine Digest, 1982-84. Bd. dirs. Marymount High Sch., 1984-87, pres., 1984-86; bd. dirs. L.A. Police Dept. Booster Assn., 1984-87; mem. Cath. Press Coun.; mem. pres.'s coun. Mus. Sci. and Industry. Mem. Am. Soc. Hosp. Mktg. and Pub. Rels., Healthcare Mktg. and Pub. Rels. Assn., Pub. Rels. Soc. Am. (bd. dirs. 1994—), L.A. Counselors, PETA, Am. Lung Assn. (chair comm. com. L.A. chpt.) Soc. for Prevention of Cruelty to Animals (chair PetSet), Sports Club (L.A.). Roman Catholic. Avocations: reading, tennis, aerobic dance. Office: Tellem Inc Museum Sq 5757 Wilshire Blvd Ste 655 Los Angeles CA 90036

TELLEP, DANIEL MICHAEL, aerospace executive, mechanical engineer; b. Forest City, Pa., Nov. 20, 1931; m. Pat. Tellep; 6 children. B.S in Mech. Engring. with highest honors, U. Calif., Berkeley, 1954, M.S., 1955; grad. Advanced Mgmt. Program, Harvard U., 1971. Prin. scientist Lockheed Missiles & Space Co., 1955-69, chief engr. missile systems div., 1969-75, v.p., asst. gen. mgr. advanced systems div., 1975-83, exec. v.p., 1983-84, pres., 1984—; pres. Lockheed Missiles & Space Systems Group, 1986—; chmn., chief exec. officer Lockheed Corp., 1989-95; chmn. bd., CEO Lockheed Martin Corp., Bethesda, Md., 1995—; cons. in field; bd. dirs. 1st Interstate Bancorp., SCECorp. Contbr. article to profl. jours. Bd. govs. Music Ctr. Los Angeles County, 1991—; mem. adv. bd. U. Calif. Berkeley Sch. Engring.; mem. Calif. Bus. Roundtable, 1992—; nat. chmn. vol. com. U.S. Savs. Bond Campaign, 1993. Recipient Tower award San Jose State U., 1985, Aeronautics and Propulsion Laureis award Aviation Week and Space Tech., 1993, John R. Alison award AFA, 1993, Indsl. Leadership award AAS, 1992; named Exec. of Yr., NMA, 1993. Fellow AIAA (Lawrence Sperry award 1964, Missile Systems award 1986, Hon. Fellow 1995), Am. Astronautical Soc. (Indsl. Leadership award 1992); mem. NAE, Nat. Aero. Assn., Soc. Mfg. Engrs., Sigma Xi, Pi Tau Sigma, Tau Beta Pi. Office: Lockheed Martin Corp 6801 Rockledge Dr Bethesda MD 20817

TELLER, ALVIN NORMAN, music industry executive; b. N.Y.C., Sept. 3, 1944; s. Sheldon and Selma (Gofsaof) T.; m. Jennifer Rodsjo, Aug. 26, 1979; 1 child, Alexis. B.S. in Electronics Engring., Columbia U., 1965, M.S. in Ops. Research, 1967; M.B.A., Harvard U., 1969. Asst. to pres. CBS Records, CBS, Inc., N.Y.C., 1969-70, v.p. merchandising, 1971-74; dir. corp. devel. Playboy Enterprises, Chgo., 1970-71; pres. United Artists Records, Los Angeles 1974-76; mgmt. cons. Alvin N. Teller & Assocs., Los Angeles, 1976-79; pres. Windsong Records Los Angeles, 1979-81; sr. v.p., gen. mgr. Columbia Records CBS, Inc., N.Y.C., 1981-85, pres. CBS Records div., 1985-88; pres., chief oper. officer MCA Records, Inc., 1988-89; chmn. MCA Music Entertainment Group, 1989—, Hollywood, Calif., 1989—. Bd. dirs. Rock and Rock Hall of Fame Found., 1985—; hon. dir. T.J. Martell Found. for Cancer Research, N.Y.C., 1981—. Recipient Humanitarian of Yr. award T.J. Martell Found. for Cancer Rsch., 1988, Unsung Hero award Betty Clooney Found., 1990, Spirit of Life award City of Hope, 1991. Mem. Rec. Industry Assn. Am. (bd. dirs. 1985—), Nat. Acad. Rec. Arts and Scis. (pres.'s adv. council), Internat. Fedn. Phongram and Videogram Producers (bd. dirs.), Nat. Info. Infracture Adv. Coun. Office: MCA Music Enterntainment 70 Universal City Plz Universal City CA 91608

TELLER, DAVID NORTON, neurochemist; b. Bklyn., Oct. 1, 1936; s. Frank and Ruth (Goldberg) T.; m. Sonia Ruth Safir, Jan. 18, 1959. B.S. Bklyn. Coll., 1957; M.S., N.Y. U., 1960, Ph.D., 1964. Biologist Fine Organics, Inc., N.Y.C., 1956-57; research asst. pediatric hematology and nutrition Flower-Fifth Ave. Hosp., N.Y.C., 1957-59; sr. research scientist N.Y. State Dept. Mental Hygiene, Wards Island, N.Y.C., 1959-65; asso. research scientist N.Y. State Dept. Mental Hygiene, 1965-76; asso. prof. psychiatry U. Louisville Med. Sch., 1976-79, prof., 1979—; lectr. grad. sch. Fairleigh Dickinson U., 1970-73. Contbr. articles to profl. jours. Mem. AAAS, Am. Chem. Soc. (sect. chmn 1977), ASTM (subcom. chmn. 1968-85), Am. Soc. Neurochemistry, Coll. Internat. Neuropsychopharmacology, Am. Soc. Pharm. Exptl. Therapeutics, N.Y. Acad. Scis., Sigma Xi. Home: 8013 Deronia Ave Louisville KY 40222-4847 Office: U Louisville Med School Dept of Psych & Behavioral Scis Louisville KY 40292

TELLER, DAVIDA YOUNG, psychology, physiology and biophysics educator; b. Yonkers, N.Y., July 25, 1938; d. David Aidan and Jean Marvin (Sturges) Young; m. David Chambers Teller, June 18, 1960 (div. May 1986); children: Stephen, Sara; m. Anthony William Young, July 28, 1990. BA, Swarthmore Coll., 1960; PhD, U. Calif., Berkeley, 1965. Lectr., research prof. U. Wash., Seattle, 1965-69, asst. prof. psychology, physiology and biophysics, 1969-71, assoc. prof., 1971-74, prof., 1973—; researcher visual sci. and devel.; rsch. affiliate Regional Primate Rsch. Ctr., Child Devel. & Mental Retardation Ctr.; mem. com. on vision Nat. Acad. Scis.-Nat. Rsch. Coun., 1971-80, vision rsch. program com. Nat. Eye Inst. and NIH, 1973-76, visual scis. B study sect. NIH, 1981-85, chmn. 1983-85; U. Wash. appointments include chmn. Univ. Com. on Vision, 1971; mem. Univ. Coun. Women, 1971-76, Faculty Senate Spl. Com. Faculty Women, 1972-75, ad hoc com. Evaluation Dir. Black Studies Program, 1976, faculty adv. bd. Women Studies, 1980-82, ad hoc com. to search for Chmn. Psychology, 1981, standing com. Women Studies, 1982—, faculty senate coun. Grants & Contract Rsch., 1985-86, Univ. Acad. Coun., 1986—; dept. psychology appoints include Exec. Com., 1973-75, 77-79; chmn. Budget and Facilities Com., 1979-81; mem. ad hoc com. Staff Employment, 1982-83; honors advisor and dir. Honors Program, 1982—; mem. planning com. 1984-87, 90—. Mem. editorial bd. Infant Behavior and Development, 1981-85, Behavioral Brain Research, 1984-87, Vision Research, 1985—, Clinical Vision Sciences, 1986-87; contbr. numerous articles to profl. jours.; patentee in field. Recipient Sabbatical award James McKeen Cattell Fund, 1981-82. Fellow AAAS, Optical Soc. Am. (program com. vision 1986-88, vice chmn. vision tech. group 1986-87, chmn. 1988-89, tech. coun. 1988-89, Tillyer award 1987—); mem. Assn. Rsch. Vision & Ophthalmology, Assn. Women Scis., Am. Acad. Ophthalmology (Glenn Fry award 1982). Office: U Wash Dept Psychology Ni # 25 Seattle WA 98195

TELLER, EDWARD, physicist; b. Budapest, Hungary, Jan. 15, 1908; naturalized, 1941; s. Max and Ilona (Deutch) T.; m. Augusta Harkanyi, Feb. 26, 1934; children: Paul, Susan Wendy. Student, Inst. Tech., Karlsruhe, Germany, 1926-28, U. Munich, 1928; Ph.D., U. Leipzig, Germany, 1930; D.Sc. (hon.), Yale U., 1954, U. Alaska, 1959, Fordham U., 1960, George Washington U., 1960, U. So. Calif., 1960, St. Louis U., 1960, Rochester Inst. Tech., 1962, PMC Colls., 1963, U. Detroit, 1964, Clemson U., 1966, Clarkson Coll., 1969; LL.D., Boston Coll., 1961, Seattle U., 1961, U. Cin., 1962, U. Pitts., 1963, Pepperdine U., 1974, U. Md. at Heidelberg, 1977; D.Sc., L.H.D., Mt. Mary Coll., 1964; Ph.D., Tel Aviv U., 1972; D.Natural Sci., DeLaSalle U., Manila, 1981; D. Med. Sci. (n.c.), Med. U. S.C.,

1983. Research assoc. Leipzig, 1929-31, Goettingen, Germany, 1931-33; Rockefeller fellow Copenhagen, 1934; lectr. U. London, 1934-35; prof. physics George Washington U., Washington, 1935-41, Columbia, 1941-42; physicist U. Chgo., 1942-43, Manhattan Engr. Dist., 1942-46, Los Alamos Sci. Lab., 1943-46; prof. physics U. Chgo., 1946-52; prof. physics U. Calif., 1953-60, prof. physics-at-large, 1960-70, Univ. prof., 1970-75; Univ. prof. emeritus, chmn. dept. applied sci. U. Calif., Davis and Livermore, 1963-66; asst. dir. Los Alamos Sci. Lab., 1949-52; cons. Livermore br. U. Calif. Radiation Lab., 1952-53; asso. dir. Lawrence Livermore Lab., U. Calif., 1954-58, 60-75; dir. Lawrence Livermore Radiation Lab., U. Calif., 1958-60; now dir. emeritus, cons. Lawrence Radiation Nat. Lab., U. Calif. Manhattan Dist. of Columbia, 1942-46; also Metall. and Lab. of Argonne Nat. Lab., U. Chgo., 1942-43, 46-52, and Los Alamos, N.Mex., 1943-46; also Radiation Lab., Livermore, Calif., 1952-75; sr. research fellow Hoover Instn. War, Revolution and Peace, Stanford U., 1975—; mem. sci. adv. bd. USAF; bd. dirs. Assn. to the Unite the Democracies; past mem. gen. adv. com. AEC; former mem. Pres.'s Fgn. Intelligence Adv. Nat. Space Coun. Bd. Author: (with Francis Owen Rice) The Structure of Matter, 1949, (with A.L. Latter) Our Nuclear Future, 1958, (with Allen Brown) The Legacy of Hiroshima, 1962, The Reluctant Revolutionary, 1964, (with G.W. Johnson, W.K. Talley, G.H. Higgins) The Constructive Uses of Nuclear Explosives, 1968, (with Segre, Kaplan and Schiff) Great Men of Physics, 1969, The Miracle of Freedom, 1972, Energy: A Plan for Action, 1975, Nuclear Energy in the Developing World, 1977, Energy from Heaven and The Earth, 1979, The Pursuit of Simplicity, 1980, Better a Shield than a Sword, 1987, Conversations on the Dark Secrets of Physics, 1991. Past bd. dirs. Def. Intelligence Sch.; Naval War Coll.; bd. dirs. Fed. Union, Hertz Found., Am. Friends of Tel Aviv U.; sponsor Atlantic Union, Atlantic Council U.S., Univ. Ctrs. for Rational Alternatives; mem. Com. to Unite Am., Inc.; bd. govs. Am. Acad. Achievement. Recipient Joseph Priestley Meml. award Dickinson Coll., 1957, Harrison medal Am. Ordnance Assn., 1955; Albert Einstein award, 1958; Gen. Donovan Meml. award, 1959; Midwest Research Inst. award, 1960; Research Inst. Am. Living History award, 1960; Golden Plate award Am. Acad. Achievement, 1961; Gold medal Am. Acad. Achievement, 1982; Thomas E. White and Enrico Fermi awards, 1962; Robins award of Am., 1963; Leslie R. Groves Gold medal, 1974; Harvey prize in sci. and tech. Technion Inst., 1975; Semmelweiss medal, 1977; Albert Einstein award Technion Inst., 1977; Henry T. Heald award Ill. Inst. Tech., 1978; Gold medal Am. Coll. Nuclear Medicine, 1980; A.C. Eringen award, 1980; named ARCS Man of Yr., 1980, Disting. Scientist, Nat. Sci. Devel. Bd., 1981; Paul Harris award Rotary Found., 1980; Disting. Scientist Phil-Am. Acad. Sci. and Engring., 1981; Lloyd Freeman Hunt Citizenship award, 1982; Nat. medal of Sci., 1983; Joseph Handleman prize, 1983, Sylvanus Thayer Medal, 1986; Shelby Cullom Davis award Ethics & Pub. Policy Assn., 1988; Presdl. Citizen medal Pres. Reagan, 1989; Ettore Majorana Erice Scienza Per La Pace award, 1990; Order of Banner with Rubies of the Republic of Hungary, 1990. Fellow Am. Nuclear Soc., Am. Phys. Soc., Am. Acad. Arts and Scis., Hungarian Acad. Scis. (hon.); mem. Nat. Acad. Scis., Am. Geophys. Union, Soc. Engring. Scis., Internat. Platform Assn. Research on chem., molecular and nuclear physics, quantum mechanics, thermonuclear reactions, applications of nuclear energy, astrophysics, spectroscopy of polyatomic molecules, theory of atomic nuclei. Office: Hoover Inst Stanford CA 94305 also: PO Box 808 Livermore CA 94551-0808[*]

TELLER, RICHARD E., lawyer; b. Cleve., July 7, 1949; s. Aaron Joseph and Sherry (April) T. BA, Tulane U., 1971; JD, Duke U., 1974. Assoc. Seder & Chandler, Worcester, Mass., 1974-77; ptnr. Rackemann, Sawyer & Brewster, Boston, 1977-90, Burns & Levinson, Boston, 1990—. Trustee Boston Chamber Music Soc.; dir. Corp. Design Found., Boston; mem. New Eng. com. Archives of Am. Art, Boston. Mem. ABA, Mass. Bar Assn., Boston Bar Assn., The Boston Athanaeum. Avocation: sailing. Office: Burns & Levinson 125 Summer St Boston MA 02110-1624

TELLES, MARTIN JACK, marketing executive; b. Bklyn., May 7, 1948; s. Sam and Rose (Broitman) T.; m. Ina Schrank, May 30, 1982; 1 child, Selene; stepchildren: Jennifer Spielvogel, Randi Spielvogel. AAS, N.Y. City C.C., Bklyn., 1968; BBA, Pace U., 1973. V.p. sales and mktg. Citicorp Indsl. Credit, Inc., N.Y.C., 1969-85; unit head-bus. mgr. Xerox Credit Corp., Stamford, Conn., 1985-87; nat. mktg. mgr. Integrated Resources, Inc., N.Y.C., 1987-90; dir. mktg. Royal Alliance Assocs., N.Y.C., 1990-92; exec. v.p., chief mktg. officer Equico Securities, Inc., N.Y.C., 1992—. With USAR, 1969-74. Avocations: cycling, walking. Office: Equico Securities Inc 1755 Broadway New York NY 10019-3743

TELLIER, HENRI, retired Canadian military officer; b. Montreal, Que., Can., Sept. 1, 1918; s. Henry Joseph and Jeanne (St. Cyr) T.; m. Virginia Wright, July 23, 1945; children: Pierre, Michele, Suzanne, John, Nicole. Student, U. Montreal, 1935-40, U. Ottawa, 1946-47, Canadian Army Staff Coll., 1942-43, Imperial Def. Coll., London, Eng., 1966, Dept. Def. Computer Inst., Washington, 1968. With Robert Howard & Co. (ins. brokers), Montreal, 1937-40; commd. 2d lt. Canadian Army, 1940, advanced through grades to lt. gen., 1973; asst. sec. to minister (Nat. Def.), 1945-48; comdg. officer (Royal 22d Regt.), 1948-51; instr. (Canadian Army Staff Coll.), 1951-54; army mem. (Joint Intelligence Staff), 1954-57; mil. adviser Vietnam, 1957-58; chief of staff (Que. Mil. Dist.), 1958-60; mil attache Rome, Italy, 1960- 63; dir. mil. ops. and plans Army, 1960-64, dir. internat. plans, 1964-65; comdr. (Canadian Contingent) Cyprus, 1965-66; dir. gen. plans (Forces Hdqrs.), Ottawa, Ont., 1967-70; dep. chief plans (Forces Hdqrs.), 1970-71; Canadian mil. rep. to mil. com. (NATO Hdqrs.), Brussels, Belgium, 1971-73; ret., 1973; assoc. nat. commr. Canadian Red Cross Soc., Toronto, Ont., 1973-75, nat. commr., 1975, sec.-gen., 1981-83, hon. v.p.; ret. mem. Refugee Status Adversary Com., 1984-89; chmn. Canadian sect. Mil. Coop. Com. Can.-U.S., Joint Permanent Bd. Def. Can.-U.S.; commr. Commn. for Strategic and Internat. Studies; mem. adv. council Can. Exec. Services Orgn. Decorated Disting. Service Order (Canada); Queens medal Netherlands; comdr. Order of Merit (Italy), officer Order of Red Cross; named to Order of Can. Mem. Canadian Inst. Internat. Affairs., Can. Exec. Svc. Orgn., Inst. Assn. Execs., The Empire Club of Can., Royal 22 Regiment Assn., UN Assn. Office: 19 Bay Hill Ridge, Stittsville, ON Canada K2S 1B9

TELLIER, PAUL M., Canadian railway transportation executive; b. Joliette, Que., Can., May 8, 1939; s. Maurice J. and Eva M. (Bouvier) T.; m. Andree Poirier, June 6, 1959; children: Claude, Marc. B.A., U. Ottawa, 1959, LLL, 1962; B.Litt., Oxford U., 1966. Bar: Que. bar 1963. Asst. prof. U. Montreal, 1966-67; exec. asst. minister energy, 1967-68; with Privy Council Office, Ottawa, Ont., Can., 1968-70; dep. clk. to Cabinet, exec. council Govt. of Que., 1970-72; dir.-gen. urban policy Ministry of State for Urban Affairs, 1972-73; joined Public Service Commn., 1974-75, exec. dir., 1975-76; asst. dep. minister fisheries and environ. Govt. of Can., 1976-77; dep. sec. to cabinet Fed.-Provincial Relations Office, 1977-79; dep. minister Indian affairs and no. devel., 1979-82, dep. minister energy, mines and resources, 1982-85; chmn. governing bd. Internat. Energy Agy., 1985-92; clk. of Privy Council and sec. to Cabinet Govt. of Can., Ottawa, 1985-92; dir. Petro Can., 1985-92; pres., CEO Canadian Nat. Railways, 1992—; also CEO Grand Trunk, Detroit; dir. Manulife Fin., Toronto, Grand Trunk Corp., Grand Trunk Western Railroad Co., Ctrl. Vt. Railway, Inc., Duluth, Winnipeg & Pacific Railway Co., Detroit, Dome Consortium Investments, Inc., Toronto. Recipient Companion of Order of Canada Gov. Gen. Canada, 1992, Pub. Svc. Outstanding Achievement award Gov. Gen., 1989, Pub. Policy Forum Achievement award Gov. Gen., 1989; named Queen's Privy Coun. Her Majesty Queen Elizabeth, 1992, Queen's Counsel Fed. Justice Minister, 1981. Mem. Quebec Bar, Railway Assn. Can. (dir.), Assn. Am. Railroads. Roman Catholic. Office: CN North America, 935 De La Gauchetiere St West, Montreal, PQ Canada H3B 2M9 also: PO Box 8100, Montreal, PQ Canada H3C 3N4

TELLIER, RICHARD DAVIS, management educator; b. Darby, Pa., Feb. 18, 1942; s. Joseph Campbell and Jane Grace (Davis) T.; m. Susan Gammon, June 10, 1974; children: John-Jo, Tiekka (twins). BSEE, Drexel U., 1967; MBA, Fla. State U., 1971, DBA, 1973. Elec. engr. Philco-Ford Corp., Phila., 1967-70; aerospace systems engr. Gen. Elec. Co., Cape Canaveral, Fla., 1967-70; lectr. Fla. State U., Tallahassee, 1970-73; prof. mgmt. Calif. State U., Fresno, 1973—; chmn. dept. mgmt. and mktg. Calif. State U., 1979-84, assoc. dean Sch. Bus., 1984-85, asst. dean, 1990-92; cons. ops. mgmt., market research organizational behavior. Author: Operations Management: Fundamental Concepts and Methods, 1978, Production and Operations Management Test Bank, 1990 ; contbr. articles to profl. jours.

Grantee 1975; recipient Meritorious Performance award, 1987, 88, 90. Mem. Ops. Research Soc. Am., Phi Kappa Phi. Home: 8294 N Academy Ave Clovis CA 93611-9454 Office: Calif State U Fresno CA 93740-0007

TELLING, EDWARD RIGGS, former retail, insurance, real estate and financial services executive; b. Danville, Ill., Apr. 1, 1919; s. Edward Riggs and Margaret Katherine (Matthews) T.; m. Nancy Hawkins, Dec. 29, 1942; children: Edward R. III, Pamela Telling Grimes, Kathryn Telling Bentley, Nancy Telling O'Shaughnessy, Thomas Cole. Ph.B., Ill. Wesleyan U., 1942, LL.D., 1978; LL.D., St. Norbert Coll., 1985. With Sears, Roebuck & Co., 1946-85, store mgr., 1954-59, zone mgr., 1960-64, mgr. met. N.Y.C. area ops., 1965-67; adminstrv. asst. to v.p. Eastern ter. Sears, Roebuck & Co., Phila., 1968; v.p. Eastern ter. Sears, Roebuck & Co., 1969-74; exec. v.p. Midwestern ter. Sears, Roebuck & Co., Chgo., 1974-75, sr. exec. v.p. field, 1976-77; chmn., chief exec. officer Sears, Roebuck & Co., 1978-85. Lt. USNR, 1941-45. Mem. Bus. Coun., Chgo. Club, Old Elm Club, Seminole Club, Lost Tree Club (Fla.). Office: Sears Tower Chicago IL 60684

TELMER, FREDERICK HAROLD, steel products manufacturing executive; b. Edmonton, Alta., Can., Dec. 28, 1937; Ingar and Gertrude Bernice (Floen) T.; m. Margaret Goddard Hutchings, Oct. 30, 1959; children: Christopher, Kevin, Colin. BA in Econs., U. Alberta, 1961, MA in Econs., 1964. With Stelco, Inc., Hamilton, Ont., Can., 1963—, gen. mgr. corp. affairs and strategic planning, 1984-85, v.p. corp. affairs and strategic planning, 1985-87, pres. Stelco Steel, 1988-90, dir., 1989, chmn., chief exec. officer, 1991—; dir. Inco Ltd., CT Fin. Svcs., Inc., Internat. Iron and Steel Inst., Am. Iron and Steel Inst., chmn. N.Am. steel coun.; dir., chmn. Can. Steel Prodrs. Assn.; founding dir. Japan Soc.; vice chmn. Inst. for Work & Health, Can.-Japan Bus. Com.; mem. bd. govs. Chamber of Maritime Commerce. Mem. Toronto Club, Hamilton Club, Burlington Golf and Country Club, Hamilton Golf and Country Club, Delta Kappa Epsilon. Avocations: golf, woodworking, tennis, skiing, piano. Office: Stelco Inc, PO Box 2030, Hamilton, ON Canada L8N 3T1

TELNACK, JOHN J., automobile designer; b. 1937. Student, Art Ctr. Coll. Design, 1960-62. With Ford Motor Co., Dearborn, Mich., 1958—; stylist A-Ford Studio, 1962, head stylist Mercury Prodn. Styling, 1964, head stylist Lincoln and Mercury Prodn., 1965; chief designer Ford Motor Co., Australia, 1967; design exec. Falcon and Mustang Ford Motor Co., Dearborn, 1969, design exec. Mustang and Pinto, 1971, design exec. Mustang Maverick and Pinto, 1972, chief designer Eng., 1973; v.p. design Europe Ford Motor Co., 1974; dir. internat. spl. vehicles concepts Ford Motor Co., Dearborn, 1976, exec. dir. N.Am. light car and truck design, 1976, exec. dir. N.Am. mid-size car and interior design, 1978, exec. dir. N.Am. mid-size and luxury car design and engring., chief design exec. N.Am. design, 1980, v.p. design, 1987—. Office: Ford Design Center The American Rd Dearborn MI 48121

TEMA-LYN, LAURIE, management consultant; b. Bklyn., Mar. 25, 1951; d. Morton and Jeanne (Lite) Carlin. BA, Bklyn. Coll., 1972. Mgmt. supr. Rapp & Collins, Inc., N.Y.C., 1972-78, v.p., 1978-80; assoc. Synectics, Cambridge, Mass., 1980-83; founder, gen. ptnr. IdeaScope Assocs., Cambridge, 1983—; presenter European Conf. on Innovation and Creativity, 1987, 94. Contbr. articles to bus. publs. Bd. dirs Arica Inst., N.Y.C., 1979-80. Mem. Creative Problem Solving Inst. (presenter, leader), Am. Mktg. Assn., Direct Mktg. Assn. (presenter at industry meetings), Product Devel. Mgmt. Assn., New Eng. Bus. Assn. for Social Responsibility, Mgmt. Roundtable, Sharing a New Song. Office: IdeaScope Assocs 25 Mt Auburn St Cambridge MA 02138-6028

TEMAM, ROGER M., mathematician; b. Tunis, Tunisia, May 19, 1940; s. Ange M. and Elise (Ganem) T.; m. Claudette Cukorja, Aug. 21, 1962; children: David, Olivier, Emmanuel. M in Math., U. Paris, 1962, DSc, 1967. Asst. prof. math. U. Paris, 1960-67, prof., 1967—; prof. Ecole Polytechnique, Paris, 1968-85. Author: Numerical Analysis, 1969, Navier-Stokes Equations, 1977, Mathematical Problems in Plasticity, 1983, Infinite Dimensional Dynamical Systems in Mechanics and Physics, 1988; contbr. 200 articles to sci. jours.; editor Math. Model. and Num. Analysis, Physica D, assoc. editor other profl. jours. Recipient Grand Prix Joannidès, Acad. Sci. Paris, 1993. Mem. AAAS, Am. Math. Soc., N.Y. Acad. Scis., Soc. Indsl. and Applied Math., Soc. Math. Applications of Industry (founding pres. 1983-87).

TEMANE, BAHITIK, government employee; b. Maun, Botswana, Mar. 3, 1934; m. Dorcas G. Mompati, June 19, 1944; 4 children. MBIM, British Inst. Mgmt., London, 1975; MCIT, Chartered Inst. Transport, London, 1976; MSc, U. Wisconsin, Madison, Wis., 1981. Gen. mgr. Ctrl. Transport Orgn., Gaborone, Botswana, 1973-75; dist. commr. Dist. Adminstrn., Molepolole, Botswana, 1976; dep. permanent sec. Local Govt., Gaborone, Botswana, 1977-78, permanent sec., 1979-81; clerk Parliament, Nat. Assembly, Gaborone, Botswana, 1981-83; dir., fin. and adminstrn. Cirdafrica, Arusha, Tanzania, 1983-86; cons. Botswana Tech. Ctr., Gaborone, Botswana, 1987-88; mem. Parliament, Nat. Assembly, Gaborone, Botswana, 1989—; minister of health Botswana Govt., Gaborone, Botswana, 1992—; chmn. World Health Orgn., Africa, 1993-94; pres. World Health Assembly, 1994—. Mem. Pub. Accounts. Com., Gaborone, 1989-92. Mem. Commonwealth Parliament Assn. Office: Ministry Health, P/Bag 0038, Gaborone Botswana Office: Embassy of Botswana 3400 International Dr NW Ste 7 Washington DC 20008-3006

TEMERLIN, LIENER, advertising agency executive; b. Ardmore, Okla., Mar. 27, 1928; s. Pincus and Julie (Kahn) T.; m. Karla Samuelsohn, July 23, 1950; children: Dana Temerlin Crawford, Lisa Temerlin Gottesman, Hayden Crawford, Sandy Gottesman. BFA, U. Okla., 1950. Assoc. editor Sponsor Mag., N.Y.C., 1950-51; copywriter Glenn Advt. Inc., Dallas, 1952-54, creative dir., 1954-70, chief oper. officer, 1970-74; pres. Glenn, Bozell & Jacobs, Inc., 1974-79; chmn. bd. dirs. Bozell & Jacobs Inc., 1979-86, Bozell, Jacobs, Kenyon & Eckhardt, Dallas, 1986-89; chmn. Bozell, 1989-92, Temerlin McClain, 1992—. Chmn. Winston Churchill Found. award dinner, 1986; chmn. Dallas Symphony Assn., 1986-88, pres., 1984-86, mem. bd. govs., 1982-84, pres. coun. 1989—; mem. Blair House Restoration Com., 1987-88; vice chmn. Am. Film Inst., 1992-93, bd. trustees 1992—; bd. dirs. United Way of Met. Dallas Exec. Com. 1986-89, Dallas Bus. Com. for Arts, 1989, Dallas Citizen's Coun., 1984-86, 92; trustee Southwestern Med. Found., 1988—, bd. trustees, 1992—, So. Meth. U., trustee com. Univ. devel., 1988, exec. bd. 1990-91; trustee and chmn. of devel. com. Dallas Mus. Art, 1990-94; mem. steering com. Susan G. Komen Found., 1989-91, art acquisition com. Meyerson Symphony Ctr., 1989-92, exec. coun. Daytop/Dallas, 1989—; chmn. grand opening fortnight Morton H. Meyerson Symphony Ctr., 1989; mem. Madison Coun. Libr. Congress, Washington, 1991—. Recipient Bill D. Kerss award Dallas Advt. League, 1983, Brotherhood award NCCJ, 1984, Susan G. Komen Found. for Breast Cancer Rsch. Community award, 1989, James K. Wilson Silver Cup award, 1990, Linz award 1990, Silver Medal award Dallas Advt. League, 1991, Vol. Fundraiser of Yr. award Nat. Soc. Fundraising Execs., 1991, Best Man in Advt. award McCall's Mag., 1992; named Dallas Father of Yr., 1991. Office: 201 E Carpenter Fwy Irving TX 75062

TEMES, GABOR CHARLES, electrical engineering educator; b. Budapest, Hungary, Oct. 14, 1929; s. Erno and Rozsa (Angyal) Wohl-Temes; m. Ibi Kutasi-Temes, Feb. 6, 1954; children: Roy Thomas, Carla Andrea. Dipl.Ing., Tech. U. Budapest, 1952, DSc (hon.), 1991; Dipl. Phys., Eotvos U., Budapest, 1954; Ph.D., U. Ottawa, Ont., Can., 1961. Asst. prof. Tech. U. Budapest, 1952-56; project engr. Measurement Engring. Ltd., 1956-59; dept. head No. Electric Co. Ltd., 1959-64; group leader Stanford Linear Accelerator Center, 1964-66; corp. cons. Ampex Corp., 1966-69; prof. elec. engring. UCLA, 1969-90, chmn. dept., 1975-80; dept. head Oreg. State U., Corvallis, 1990—; cons. Xerox Corp., ANT GmbH. Author: (with others) Introduction to Circuit Synthesis and Design, 1977, Analog MOS Integrated Circuits for Signal Processing, 1986; assoc. editor: (with others) Jour. Franklin Inst, 1971-82; co-editor, contbg. author: (with others) Modern Filter Theory and Design, 1973, Oversampling Delta-Sigma Data Converters, 1991. Recipient Western Electric Fund award Am. Soc. Engring. Edn., 1982, Humboldt Sr. Rsch. award, 1991; NSF grantee, 1970—. Fellow IEEE (editor Transactions on Circuit Theory 1969-71 Best Paper award 1969, 81, 85, Centennial medal 1984, Edn. award 1987, Tech. Achievement award

1989). Home: 7100 NW Grandview Dr Corvallis OR 97330-2708 Office: Oreg State U Corvallis OR 97330

TEMIN, MICHAEL LEHMAN, lawyer; b. Phila., July 18, 1933; s. Henry and Annette (Lehman) T.; divorced; children—Aaron Lehman, Seth Lehman. B.A. magna cum laude, Yale U., 1954; LL.B. cum laude, U. Pa. 1957. Bar: Pa. 1958, U.S. Ct. Appeals (3d cir.) 1958, U.S. Supreme Ct. 1969, U.S. Ct. Appeals (2d cir.) 1986, U.S. Ct. Appeals (9th cir.) 1992. Asst. U.S. atty. U.S. Atty's Office, Phila., 1958-59; assoc. Wolf, Block, Schorr and Solis-Cohen, LLC, Phila., 1959-66; ptnr. Wolf, Block, Schorr and Solis-Cohen, Phila., 1966—; lectr. Law Sch., U. Pa., Phila., 1982-90, adj. prof., 1990-93, 94—; Thomas A. O'Boyle vis. disting. practitioner, 1985, I. Grant Irey lectr., 1988. Editor U. Pa. Law Rev., 1955-57. Vice chmn. Ednl. Nominating Panel, Phila., 1981-83; bd. dirs. Citizens Com. in Pub. Edn., Phila., 1970—, pres. 1980-82. Fellow Am. Coll. Bankruptcy; mem. Phila. Bar Assn. (chmn. bankruptcy com., sect. corp., banking and bus. law 1979-86, chmn. profl. guidance com. 1985, sec. sect. corp. banking and bus. law 1985, treas. sect. corp. banking and bus. law 1986, vice chmn. sect. corp. banking and bus. law 1987, chmn. sect. corp. banking and bus. law 1988), Pa. Bar Assn. (ho. of dels. 1985-89, 90—), ABA (bus. bankruptcy com. of sect. corp. banking and bus. law chmn. rules subcom., 1985-92, vice chmn. chpt. 11 subcom. 1992—, vice chmn. ea. dist. Pa. bankruptcy conf. 1994-95, chmn. ea. dist. Pa. bankruptcy conf., 1995-96), Order of Coif. Jewish. Office: Wolf Block Schorr & Solis-Cohen 12th Fl Packard Bldg Philadelphia PA 19102

TEMIN, PETER, economics educator; b. Phila., Dec. 17, 1937; s. Henry and Annette T.; m. Charlotte Brucar Fox, Aug. 21, 1966; children: Elizabeth Sara, Melanie Wynn. B.A., Swarthmore (Pa.) Coll., 1959; Ph.D., Mass. Inst. Tech., 1964. Mem. faculty MIT, 1965—, prof. econs., 1970—. Author: Iron and Steel in Nineteenth Century America, 1964, The Jacksonian Economy, 1969, Causal Factors in American Economic Growth in the 19th Century, 1975, Did Monetary Forces Cause the Great Depression?, 1976, Taking Your Medicine: Drug Regulation in the United States, 1980, The Fall of the Bell System, 1987, Lessons from the Great Depression, 1989. Mem. Am. Econ. Assn., Econ. History Assn., Econ. History Soc., Phi Beta Kappa. Home: 15 Channing St Cambridge MA 02138-4713 Office: MIT Dept Econs Cambridge MA 02139

TEMKIN, HARVEY L., lawyer; b. Madison, Wis., Jan. 1, 1952; s. Joe L. and Sylvia (Libanoff) T.; m. Barbara Jean Myers, June 13, 1976; children: James, Daniel, Eli. BA, U. Wis., 1974; JD, U. Ill., 1978. Bar: Wis. 1978. Assoc. Foley & Lardner, Madison, 1978-83; prof. Tulane Law Sch., New Orleans, 1983-87; ptnr. Foley & Lardner, Madison, 1987—; lectr. U. Wis. Law Sch.; mem. U.S. Senator Feingold's Bus. Adv. Group. 1st v.p. Hillel Found., Madison, 1982-83, bd. dirs., 1987—; chmn. edn. com. Beth Israel Synagogue, Madison, 1980-82; chmn. Downtown Madison, Inc., 1989-91; chmn. Jewish edn. panel Madison Jewish Community Coun., 1993—. Fellow Am. Coll. Real Estate Lawyers; mem. ABA (real property probate and trust sect., reporter significant legis. panel 1983-85, significant lit. panel 1985-87). Home: 6609 Inner Dr Madison WI 53705-4218 Office: Foley & Lardner PO Box 1497 150 E. Gilman St Madison WI 53701-1497

TEMKIN, LARRY SCOTT, philosopher, educator; b. Milw., May 29, 1954; s. Blair Huntly and Leah Dahlia (Sigman) T.; m. Margaret Ellen Grimm, May 26, 1975; children: Daniel Eric, Andrea Beth, Rebecca Leigh. BA-Honors degree in Philosophy, U. Wis., 1975; student, Oxford U., Eng., 1978-79; PhD, Princeton U., 1983. Instr. philosophy Rice U., Houston, 1980-83, asst. prof., 1983-89, assoc. prof., 1989-95, prof., 1995—; vis. appointment U Pitts., 1986; speaker in field. Author: Inequality; contbr. articles to profl. jours. Danforth fellow, Nat. Humanities Ctr. fellow, Weiner fellow, Harvard fellow for Program in Ethics and the Professions. Mem. Am. Philos. Assn., Phi Beta Kappa (Outstanding Tchr. award, George R. Brown awards for superior teaching, George R. Brown awards for excellence in teaching). Avocations: camping, sports. Home: 4924 Valerie St Bellaire TX 77401-5708 Office: Rice U Dept Philosophy 6100 S Main Houston TX 77005-1892

TEMKIN, ROBERT HARVEY, accountant; b. Boston, Oct. 21, 1943; s. Max and Lillian (Giller) T.; m. Ellen Phyllis Band, Sept. 25, 1966; children: Aron, Rachel, Joshua. BBA, U. Mass., 1964. CPA, Mass., N.Y. With Ernst & Young, 1964-72, 73—, ptnr., 1976—; nat. dir. auditing standards Arthur Young & Co., CPAs, 1980-88; assoc. prof. NYU, 1982. Bd. dirs. Jewish Home for Elderly of Fairfield County, 1979-94, pres., 1985-87; mem. Bd. Edn., Weston, Conn., 1983-87; dir. United Synagogue Am.; mem. bus. adv. coun. U. Mass.; bd. dirs. Jewish Cmty. Ctrs. of Greater Boston, Combined Jewish Philanthropies of Greater Boston; mem. exec. bd. N.E. region Anti-Defamation League; treas. Synagogue Coun. Mass., 1988-93; asst. treas. Temple Reyim, Newton, Mass. Recipient Acctg. Alumni award U. Mass., 1978, Alumnus Award Sch. Mgmt. U. Mass., 1986. Mem. AICPA (staff dir. commn. on auditors responsibilities 1976-78, mem. task force on auditor's report 1978-81, peer rev. com. 1982-84, auditing standards bd. 1984-88, chmn. internat. auditing task force 1988-90), Mass. Soc. CPAs (Silver medal 1964), N.Y. State Soc. CPAs, Conn. Soc. CPAs, Mass. Bd. Pub. Accountancy, Greater Boston C. of C. (bd. dirs.), N.E.-Israel C. of C. (bd. dirs.), Bostonian Club (adv. bd.), Belmont Country Club. Home: 1611 Commonwealth Ave Newton MA 02165-2800 Office: Ernst & Young 200 Clarendon St Boston MA 02116-5021

TEMKO, ALLAN BERNARD, writer; b. N.Y.C., Feb. 4, 1924; s. Emanuel and Betty (Alderman) T.; m. Elizabeth Ostroff, July 1, 1950; children: Susannah, Alexander. AB, Columbia U., 1947; postgrad, U. Calif., Berkeley, 1949-51, Sorbonne, 1948-49, 51-52. Lectr. Sorbonne, 1953-54, Ecole des Arts et Metiers, Paris, 1954-55; asst. prof. journalism U. Calif., Berkeley, 1956-62, lectr. in city planning and social scis., 1966-70, lectr. Grad. Sch. Journalism, 1991; prof. art Calif. State U., Hayward, 1971-80; lectr. art Stanford U., 1981, 82; architecture critic San Francisco Chronicle, 1961-93, art editor, 1979-82; archtl. planning cons.; chmn. Yosemite Falls Design Workshop, 1992; Pulitzer Prize juror, 1991-92. Author: Notre Dame of Paris, 1955, Eero Saarinen, 1962, No Way To Build a Ballpark and Other Irreverent Essays on Architecture, 1993; contbr. articles to U.S. and fgn. mags. and newspapers; West Coast editor, Archtl. Forum, 1959-62. Served with USNR, 1943-46. Recipient Gold medal Commonwealth Club Calif., 1956, Silver medal, 1994, Journalism award AIA, 1961, Silver Spur award San Francisco Planning and Urban Renewal Assn., 1985, AIA Inst. Honor award, 1991, Nathaniel A. Owings award AIA Calif. Coun., 1995, 1st prize in archtl. criticism Mfrs. Hanover/Art World, 1986, Critic's award Mfrs. Hanover/Art World, 1987, Profl. Achievement award Soc. Profl. Journalists, 1988, Pulitzer Prize for criticism, 1990; grantee Rockefeller Found., 1962-63, 20th Century Fund, 1963-66, NEA, 1988, Graham Found., 1990; Guggenheim fellow, 1956-57. Home: 1015 Fresno Ave Berkeley CA 94707-2517 *My chief intellectual and professional goal has always been to create excellence in a democratic America and, where possible, in the world at large. This Jeffersonian aim, which came to me directly from Lewis Mumford, naturally includes architecture, environmental planning, the fine arts, and literature. Through education, in which history, criticism, and serious journalism play important roles, I think it is still possible to attain such excellence despite the complex problems of technological civilization.*

TEMKO, STANLEY LEONARD, lawyer; b. N.Y.C., Jan. 4, 1920; s. Emanuel and Betty (Alderman) T.; m. Francine Marie Salzman, Mar. 4, 1944; children—Richard J., Edward J., William D. A.B., Columbia U., 1940, LL.B., 1943. Bar: N.Y. bar 1943, D.C. bar 1951. Practice in N.Y.C., 1943, 46-47; law clk. Mr. Justice Wiley Rutledge, U.S. Supreme Ct., Washington, 1947-48; assoc. firm Covington & Burling, Washington, 1949-55; ptnr. Covington & Burling, 1955-90, sr. counsel, 1990—. Editor-in-chief: Columbia Law Rev, 1942-43. Trustee Beauvoir Sch., 1963-69, Columbia U., 1980-91, trustee emeritus, 1991—; bd. govs. St. Albans Sch., 1967-73, chmn., 1971-73; bd. visitors Columbia U. Sch. Law, 1961—. Served to 2d lt. U.S. Army, 1943-46. Decorated Bronze Star; recipient Columbia U. medal for conspicuous alumni service, 1979. Fellow Am. Bar Found. (chmn. research com. 1970-72); mem. Am. Bar Assn., D.C. Bar Assn., Am. Law Inst., Columbia U. Sch. Law Alumni Assn. (pres. 1982-84), Phi Beta Kappa. Clubs: Metropolitan, City Tavern, Nat. Press. Home: 4811 Dexter Ter NW Washington DC 20007-1020 Office: Covington & Burling 1201 Pennsylvania Ave NW PO Box 7566 Washington DC 20044

TEMMER, GEORGES MAXIME, physicist; b. Vienna, Austria, Apr. 10, 1922; came to U.S., 1939; s. Frederic M. and Margaret D. (Jeiteles) T.; m. Odette Fluchere (div., 1978); m. Sylvia Bjornberg, Feb. 25, 1979. BS in Physics, Queens Coll., 1943; MA in Physics, U. Calif., Berkeley, 1944, PhD in Physics, 1949; ScD (hons.), Queens Coll., 1994. Rsch. assoc. U. Rochester, N.Y., 1949-51; physicist Nat. Bur. Standards, Washington, 1951-53; staff mem. Carnegie Instn. of Washington, 1953-63; prof., dir. Nuclear Physics Lab., Fla. State U., Tallahassee, Fla., 1960-63; dir. Nuclear Physics Lab., Rutgers U., New Brunswick, N.J., 1963-85; prof. of physics Rutgers U., New Brunswick, N.J., 1985-91, prof. emeritus, 1991—; mem. adv. bd. Nat. SANE/freeze campaign for global security, 1990—, physics panel NSF; vis. prof., scholar, Denmark, France, Switzerland, Germany, Austria, China, Mexico, Italy. Translator (from Italian) Fundamentals of Atomic Mech., E. Persico; (from French) Quantum Mechanics, AML Messiah, 1960, Atomic Rivals, B. Goldschmidt, 1990; editor Chinese Physics Am. Inst. of Physics, 1985-92; contbr. more than 100 articles on nuclear and atomic physics to profl. jours. Vice chmn. Coalition for Nuclear Disarmament, Princeton, N.J., 1988—; With U.S. Navy, 1944-46. Recipient John S. Guggenheim Meml. fellowship, 1956-57, Lindback award Rutgers Univ., 1975, Alexander von Humboldt prize, Humboldt Found., Bonn, Germany, 1984; named Sr. Exchange Fellow, Nat. Acad. of Sci., People's Republic of China, 1980. Fellow Am. Physical Soc.; mem. Cosmos Club. Achievements include discoveries in basic experimental nuclear physics. Home: 42 Skillman Rd Skillman NJ 08558-0020 Office: Rutgers U Dept Physics New Brunswick NJ 08903

TEMPEL, JEAN C., bank executive. Former sr. v.p. Conn. Bank & Trust, Hartford; now exec. v.p. Boston Safe Deposit & Trust Co. Office: Boston Safe Deposit & Trust Co 1 Boston Pl Boston MA 02108-4459

TEMPEL, JEAN CURTIN, venture capitalist; b. Hartford, Conn., Mar. 23, 1943; d. John J. and Sally (Miller) Curtin Jr.; m. Louis J. Tempel, Nov. 23, 1968 (div. 1978); m. Peter A. Wilson, May 10, 1980. BA, Conn. Coll., 1965; MS, Rensselaer Poly. Inst., 1972; advanced mgmt. program cert., Harvard U., 1979. Sr. v.p., mgr. of custody The Boston Co., 1983, pres. Boston Safe Clearing Corp., 1984-90, exec. v.p., chief ops., info. officer, 1985, exec. v.p., COO, 1988-90; prin. Tempel Ptnrs. Inc., Boston, 1991; pres., COO Safeguard Scientifics Inc., Wayne, 1992-93, mem. bd. dirs.; gen. ptnr. Technology Leaders LP, Boston, 1994—; bd. dirs. Cambridge (Mass.) Tech. Ptnrs., Dallas, Centrocol, Malvern, Pa.; trustee Scudder Funds, Boston; overseer Northeastern U., Conn.Coll. Mem. Internat. Women's Forum (dir.). Avocations: skiing, bicycling, sailing. Office: Safeguard Scientifics Inc Ste 1325 10 Post Office Sq Boston MA 02109

TEMPEL, THOMAS ROBERT, army officer, periodontist; b. Denver, Mar. 12, 1939; s. Carl W. and Ruth (Rochow) T.; m. Elaine Gardner, 1963; children: T. Robert, Carl G., Kimberly Lynn. AA, Kemper Mil. Coll., 1959; DDS, U. Pa., 1963; MS in Edn., U. Kans., 1976. Diplomate Am. Bd. Periodontology. Commd. 2d lt. U.S. Army, 1959, advanced through grades to maj. gen., 1990; dental intern Madigan Army Med. Ctr., Ft. Lewis, Wash., 1963-64; with 8th Med. Bn., 8th Inf. Div., 1964-66; clinic chief Coleman Army Dental Clinic, 768th Med. Detachment, Mannheim, Fed. Republic Germany, 1966-67; guest scientist Nat. Inst. Dental Rsch., NIH, Washington, 1968-70; periodontal resident Walter Reed Army Med. Ctr., Washington, 1970-71; chief periodontist Letterman Army Inst. Rsch., San Francisco, 1971-74; student Command and Gen. Staff Coll., Ft. Leavenworth, Kans., 1974-75; dep. comdr. U.S. Army Inst. Dental Rsch., Walter Reed Army Med. Ctr., Washington, 1976-77; chief periodontics Hosp. Dental Clinic, then chief of clinic and chief periodontics svc., Walter Reed Army Med. Ctr. Washington, 1977-79; dir. grad. dental edn. Army Edn. and Tng. Div., USAMEDDPERSA, Washington, 1979-81; student Army War Coll., Carlisle, Pa., 1981-82; comdr. U.S. Army Dental and 123d Med. Det., Wuerzburg, Fed. Republic Germany, 1982-83; dep. to chief Army Dental Corps, Washington, 1983-87; dep. comdr. 7th Med. Command, Heidelberg, Fed. Republic Germany, 1987-90; asst. surgeon gen., chief Army Dental Corps; dir. med. info. mgmt. systems Office of Army Surgeon Gen., Falls Church, Va., 1990—. Cons. Jour. Periodontology, 1984-85; contbr. articles to profl. jours. Pres. Am.-German Friendship Club, Heidelberg, 1987-90, Girl Scout Fund Coun., Heidelberg, 1987-90; chmn. Boy Scout Activities, Hdqrs. U.S. Army Europe, Heidelberg, 1987-90. Decorated D.S.M., Legion of Merit, Meritorious Svc. medal; recipient 'A' Designator in Periodontics award Army Surgeon Gen., 1981, German Army sports badge in gold, 1990. Mem. ADA, Am. Acad. Periodontology, Am. Assn. Dental Schs., Assn. Mil. Surgeons, Am. Coll. Dentists, Pierre Fouchard Acad., Omicron Kappa Upsilon. Republican. Lutheran. Avocations: swimming, wood carving, fishing, cycling. Home: 16B Jackson Ave Fort Myer VA 22211 Office: Office Army Surgeon Gen 5109 Leesburg Pike Falls Church VA 22041-3258

TEMPELIS, CONSTANTINE HARRY, immunologist, educator; b. Superior, Wis., Aug. 27, 1927; s. Harry and Thelma Marie (Hoff) T.; m. Nancy Louise Foster, Aug. 27, 1955; children: William H., Daniel S. BS, U. Wis.-Superior, 1950; MS, U. Wis.-Madison, 1953, PhD, 1955. Project assoc. immunology U. Wis., Madison, 1955-57; instr. immunology U. W.Va., Morgantown, 1957-58; asst. rsch. immunologist U. Calif., Berkeley, 1958-66, assoc. prof. immunology, 1966-72, prof., 1972—; vis. scientist Wellcome Rsch. Labs., Beckenham, Kent, Eng., 1977-78, U. Innsbruck, Austria, 1985, 90, 91; cons. in field. Contbr. articles to profl. jours. Served with USNR, 1945-46. Recipient Rsch. Career Devel. award, 1965-70; Fogarty sr. internat. fellow NIH, 1977-78. Mem. AAAS, N.Y. Acad. Scis., Am. Assn. Immunologists, Fedn. Am. Soc. Exptl. Biology, Sigma Xi. Office: U Calif Sch Pub Health Berkeley CA 94720

TEMPERO, KENNETH FLOYD, pharmaceutical company executive, physician, clinical pharmacologist; b. Morrisville, Vt., Sept. 30, 1939; s. Howard Everett and Lucile Lois (Lalouette) T.; m. Jeanne Marie Smith, Jan. 12, 1980; children: Suzelle Jeanne, Gavin Kenneth. BSc, U. Nebr., 1961; MSc, Northwestern U., 1964, PhD, 1966, MD, 1967; MBA, Fairleigh Dickenson U., 1981. Straight med. intern Cin. Gen. Hosp., 1967-68; resident in internal medicine U. Minn. Hosps., Mpls., 1968-69, 71-72; dir. clin. pharmacology Merck/MSDRL, Rahway, N.J., 1973-75, sr. dir. clin. pharmacology, 1975-78, exec. dir. clin. research, 1978-83; sr. v.p. clin. research and med. affairs G.D. Searle & Co., Skokie, Ill., 1983-87; chmn., chief exec. officer MGI PHARMA, Inc. (formerly Molecular Genetics, Inc.), Mpls., 1987—; instr. U. Minn., Mpls., 1972-73; vis. physician Rockefeller U., N.Y.C., 1974-85; assoc. prof. Drew Postgrad. Med. Sch., Los Angeles, 1985-87. Contbr. numerous articles to sci. jours. Treas., Villa Turicum Assn., Lake Forest, Ill., 1985. Served to maj. U.S. Army, 1969-71, Vietnam. Trainee NIH, Northwestern U., 1963-66; NIH spl. research fellow U. Minn., 1972-73. Mem. ACP, Am. Soc. Clin. Pharmacology and Therapeutics, Drug Info. Assn. Methodist. Avocations: canoeing; woodworking; swimming. Office: MGI PHARMA Inc 9900 Bren Rd E Ste 300E Hopkins MN 55343-9608

TEMPEST, HARRISON F., bank executive. Pres. LaSalle Nat. Bank, Chgo.; dir. LaSalle Bank, Lakeview; chmn., pres. European Am. Bank, Uniondale, N.Y., 1990—. Office: European Am Bank 1 EAB Plz Uniondale NY 11553

TEMPEST, RICHARD BLACKETT, state senator, general contractor; b. Salt Lake City, Oct. 4, 1935; s. John Henry and Kathryn (Blackett) T.; m. Ruth Ottosen, Sept. 8, 1958; childrn: Robert, Lynne Anne, Michael, Mathew, David. BS, U. Utah, 1959. Sec.-treas. The Tempest Co., Murray, Utah, 1960—; senator Utah State Senate, Salt Lake City, 1987—; bd. dirs. Sta. KUED, Salt Lake City. With U.S. Army, 1958-59. Mem. Associated Gen. Contractors (past sec.-treas.). Republican. Mormon. Avocations: shooting, hunting, gun collecting. Home: 4671 S 300 W Murray UT 84107 Office: The Tempest Co 4681 S 300 W Salt Lake City UT 84107-3737

TEMPLE, DONALD, allergist, dermatologist; b. Chgo., May 31, 1933; s. Samuel Leonard and Matilda Eve (Riff) T.; m. Sarah Rachel Katz, Sept. 29, 1957; children: Michael A., Matthew D., Madeline B. AB in Biology cum laude, Harvard U., 1954; MD, U. Chgo., 1958. Am. Bd. Allergy and Immunology, Am. Bd. Dermatology, Nat. Bd. Med. Examiners; lic. Intern Michael Reese Hosp., Chgo., 1958-59; resident in dermatology U. Chgo. Hosps., 1959-62; clin. asst., dept. dermatology Boston U. Sch. Medicine,

1963-64; clin. instr. dermatology Stanford U. Sch. Medicine, 1965; preceptee in allergy Offices of Leon Unger, M.D., and Donald Unger, M.D. Chgo., 1965-69; practice medicine specializing in allergy and dermatology Des Plaines, Ill., 1969-76; mem. allergy dept. Glen Ellyn (Ill.) Clinic, 1972—; mem. dermatology and allergy staff, Louis A. Weiss Hosp., Chgo., 1965-73, allergy sect. Loyola U. Med. Ctr., Maywood, Ill., 1977-80, exec. and contract medicine coms. Glen Ellyn; clin. asst. prof. dermatology Abraham Lincoln Sch. Medicine, U. Ill., 1972-75; clin. asst. prof. medicine sect. allergy and dermatology, Loyola U., 1977-85; mem. staff Cen. DuPage Hosp., Winfield, Ill., 1973—, Glen Oaks Med. Ctr., Glendale Heights, Ill., Glendale Heights Community Hosp., 1980-92. Contbr. articles to profl. jours. Bd. dirs. Am. Lung Assn., DuPage, McHenry counties, 1980—; chmn. Contract Medicine, HMO Com., Glen Ellyn Clinic, 1985, mem. exec. com., 1988-92. Fellow Am. Coll. Chest Physicians, Am. Assn. Cert. Allergists, Am. Coll. Allergists, Am. Acad. Allergy, Am. Acad. Dermatology, Ill. Soc. Allergy and Clin. Immunology, Chgo. Dermatol. Soc.; mem. AMA, Ill. State Med. Soc., DuPage County Med. Soc., Chgo. Med. Soc. Jewish. Avocations: sailing, investing. Home: 110 E Delaware Pl Apt 2004 Chicago IL 60611-1440 Office: Glen Ellyn Clinic 454 Pennsylvania Ave Glen Ellyn IL 60137-4496

TEMPLE, JOSEPH GEORGE, JR., pharmaceutical company executive; b. Bklyn., Aug. 29, 1929; s. Joseph George and Helen Frances (Beney) T.; m. Ann Elizabeth McFerran, June 21, 1952; children: Linda Jo, James, John. BSChemE, Purdue U., 1951, DEng (hon.), 1988. With Dow Chem. Co., Midland, Mich., 1951-89, v.p. mktg., 1976-78, dir., 1979-94; pres. Dow Chem. Latin Am., Coral Gables, Fla., 1978-80; group v.p. human health Dow Chem. Co., Cin., 1980-83; chief exec. officer, pres. Merrell Dow Pharms. Inc., Cin., 1983-87; exec. v.p. Dow Chem. Co., 1983-89; chief exec. officer, chmn. bd. dirs. Merrell Dow Pharms. Inc., Cin., 1988-89; chmn., chief exec. officer Marion Merrell Dow, Inc., Kansas City, Mo., 1989-92, also bd. dirs.; chmn. Marion Merrell Dow Pharms. Inc., 1992-94; vice chmn., 1994—; former trustee Com. for Economic Devel. Mem. pres.'s coun. Purdue U., 1978—; bd. fellows Saginaw Valley State U., 1987-89. Recipient Disting. Engr. Alumni award Purdue U., 1978, Outstanding Chem. Engr. award, 1993. Mem. Am. Inst. Chem. Engrs., Soc. Plastics Industry (bd. dirs. 1980-82), Pharm. Mfrs. Assn. (bd. dirs. 1981-83), Mgmt. Assn. (Silver Knight award 1976, Gold Knight award 1982). Episcopalian. Office: Marion Merrell Dow Inc 9300 Ward Pky Kansas City MO 64114-3321

TEMPLE, LARRY EUGENE, lawyer; b. Plainview, Tex., Dec. 26, 1935; s. Herman Edward and Grace Eileen (Ivey) T.; m. Laura Louann Atkins, Feb. 23, 1963; children: Laura Allison, John Lawrence. BBA, U. Tex., 1957, LLB with honors, 1959; LLD (hon.), Lamar U., 1985. Bar: Tex., U.S. Dist. Ct. (we. dist.) Tex., U.S. Ct. Appeals (5th cir.), U.S. Supreme Ct. Law clk. to justice Tom Clark U.S. Supreme Ct., Washington, 1959-60; assoc. Powell, Rauhut, McGinnis, Reavley & Lochridge, Austin, Tex., 1960-63; legal adminstrn. asst., exec. asst. Tex. Gov. John B. Connally, Austin, 1963-67; spl. counsel to pres. Lyndon Baines Johnson, Washington, 1967-69; pvt. practice Austin, 1969—; bd. dirs. Temple-Inland, Inc., Guaranty Fed. Bank, CRSS, Inc. Mem. U. Tex. Cancer Found., Houston, 1978-84, U. Tex. Devel. Bd., Austin, 1980-85, 90—, chmn., 1993—; mem. Tex. Higher Edn. Coordinating Bd., Austin, 1983-89, chmn., 1983-87; chmn. Select Com. for Higher Edn., Austin, 1985-87; bd. dirs. Lyndon B. Johnson Found., 1986—, vice chmn., 1989—; trustee U. Tex. Law Sch. Found., 1989—. Recipient Faculty award U. Tex. Law Sch., 1987, Humanitarian award Austin region NCCJ, 1988, Santa Rita award U. Tex. System, 1989, Disting. Alumnus award U. Tex., Austin, 1990. Fellow Tex. Bar Found.; mem. ABA, Tex. Bar Assn. (chmn. legis. com. 1980, 83-86), Tex. Jr. Bar Assn. (chmn. bd. dirs. 1967), Austin Jr. Bar Assn. (pres. 1962-63). Democrat. Episcopalian. Home: 2606 Escondido Cv Austin TX 78703-1610 Office: 400 W 15th St Ste 1510 Austin TX 78701-1648

TEMPLE, RILEY KEENE, lawyer; b. Richmond, Va., July 9, 1949; s. David L. Sr. and Helen B. (Jones) T. AB, Lafayette Coll., 1971; JD, Georgetown U., 1974. Bar: Va. 1975, D.C. 1978. Asst. gen. coun. Corp. Pub. Broadcasting, Washington, 1974-77; legis. asst. U.S. Senator Charles Mathias, Washington, 1977-78; sr. counsel RCA Global Comms., N.Y.C., 1978-80; comm. counsel U.S. Senate Com. on Commerce, Sci. & Transp., Washington, 1980-83; asst. v.p. comm. policy Bell Comm. Rsch., Inc., Livingston, N.J., 1983-85; ptnr. Halprin, Temple & Goodman, Washington, 1993—; Oliver Cromwell Cox lectr. Harvard U., Cambridge, Mass., 1983. Pres. bd. dirs. Arena Stage, Washington AIDS Action Found.; v.p. D.C. Hotline; pres.-emeritus, Whitman-Walker Clinic, Washington; past bd. dirs. Human Rights Campaign Fund; mem. community bd. The John F. Kennedy Ctr. for Performing Arts, The Ellington Fund of Duke Ellington Sch. Performing Arts; bd. trustees Lafayette Coll., Easton, Pa.; vice chmn. Frederick B. Abramson Meml. Found. Mem. Fed. Comm. Bar Assn. Republican. Episcopalian. Office: Halprin Temple & Goodman 1100 New York Ave NW Ste 650 E Washington DC 20005-3934 also: Arena Stage 6th & Maine Ave SW Washington DC 20024

TEMPLE, WAYNE CALHOUN, historian; b. nr. Richwood, Ohio, Feb. 5, 1924; s. Howard M. and Ruby March (Calhoun) T.; m. Lois Marjorie Bridges, Sept. 22, 1956 (dec. Apr. 1978); m. Sunderine Wilson, Apr. 9, 1979; 2 stepsons, James C. Mohn, Randy E. Mohn. A.B. cum laude, U. Ill., 1949 A.M., 1951, Ph.D., 1956; Lincoln Diploma Honor, Lincoln Meml. U., Harrogate, Tenn., 1963. Rsch. asst. history U. Ill., 1949-53, teaching asst., 1953-54; curator ethnohistory Ill. State Mus., 1954-58; editor-in-chief Lincoln Herald, Lincoln Meml. U., 1958-73, assoc. editor, 1973—, also dir. dept. Lincolniana, dir. univ. press, John Wingate Weeks prof. history, 1958-64; with Ill. State Archives, 1964—, now chief dep. dir.; lectr. U.S. Mil. Acad. 1975; Sec.-treas. Nat. Lincoln-Civil War Council, 1958-64; mem. bibliography com. Lincoln Lore, 1958—; hon. mem. Lincoln Sesquicentennial Commn., 1959-60; advisory council U.S. Civil War Centennial Commn., 1960-66; maj. Civil War Press Corps, 1962—. Author: Indian Villages of the Illinois Country: Historic Tribes, 1958, rev. edits., 1966, 77, 87, Lincoln the Railsplitter, 1961, Abraham Lincoln and Others at the St. Nicholas, 1968, Alexander Williamson-Tutor to the Lincoln Boys, 1971, (with others) First Steps to Victory: Grant's March to Naples, 1977, Lincoln and Grant: Illinois Militiamen, 1981, Stephen A. Douglas: Freemason, 1982, Lincoln as a Lecturer, 1982, By Square and Compasses: The Building of Lincoln's Home and Its Saga, 1984, Lincoln's Connections with the Illinois and Michigan Canal, 1986, Dr. Anson G. Henry: Personal Physician to the Lincolns, 1988, Abraham Lincoln: From Skeptic to Prophet, 1995; co-author: Illinois's Fifth Capitol: The House that Lincoln Built, 1988; contbg. author: Capitol Centennial Papers, 1988; editor: Campaigning with Grant, 1961, 72, The Civil War Letters of Henry C. Bear, 1961; 71 radio scripts A. Lincoln 1809-1959, Indian Villages of the Illinois Country: Atlas Supplement, 1975; editorial advisory bd. Am. Biog. Inst., 1971—, Ency. Indians of Ams., 1973—; contbr. to profl. jours., encys. Sponsor Abraham Lincoln Bay, Washington Nat. Cathedral; mem. Ill. State Flag Commn., 1969—; bd. dirs. Vachel Lindsay House; trustee, regent Lincoln Acad. Ill., 1970-82; bd. govs. St. Louis unit Shriners Hosps. for Crippled Children, 1975-81; mem. commissioning com., hon. crew mem. and plank owner USS Springfield submarine, 1990—; hon. crew mem. USS Abraham Lincoln aircraft carrier, 1989—. With U.S. Army, 1943-46, gen. Res. (ret.). Decorated Bronze Star Medal, Silver Citizenship medal SAR, 1993, Literary Merit Gold medal Ill. Lodge of Rsch., 1993; recipient Order of Arrow Boy Scouts Am., 1957, Scouters award, 1960, Scouter's Key, also medallion, 1967, Lincoln medallion Lincoln Sesquicentennial Commn., 1960, award of Achievement U.S. Civil War Centennial Commn., 1965, Algernon Sydney Sullivan medallion, 1969, Distinguished Service award, 1971, legion of honor Internat. Supreme Council, Order of De Molay, 1972, Disting. Service award Civil War Round Table of Chgo., 1983, 91, Cert. Excellence Ill. State Hist. Soc., 1985; named Hon. Ky. Col., Marshall of Okla. Territory. Fellow Royal Soc. Arts (life); mem. Lincoln Group D.C. (hon.), U. Ill. Alumni Assn., Ill. State Hist. Soc., Ill. Profl. Land Surveyors Assn., Ill. State Dental Soc. (citation plaque 1966), Res. Officers Assn., Lincoln Fellowship of Wis., NRA (life), Iron Brigade Assn. (hon. life), Mil. Order Loyal Legion U.S. (hon. companion), Masons (33 degree, meritorious svc. award, Red Cross of Constantine, grand rep. to Grand Lodge of Colo.), Shriners, K.T., Kappa Delta Pi, Phi Alpha, Phi Alpha Theta (Scholarship Key award), Chi Gamma Iota, Tau Kappa Alpha, Alpha Psi Omega, Sigma Pi Beta (Headmaster), Sigma Tau Delta (Gold Honor Key award for editorial writing). Presbyterian (elder). Home: 1121 S 4th Street Ct Springfield IL 62703-2200 Office: Ill State Archives Springfield IL 62756 *Only in America could a poor farm boy from Ohio work his way* *through a great university, like the University of Illinois, and receive a doctor's degree. Life has been kind to me, and I have tried hard and worked hard. I am proud to be an American.*

TEMPLE, WICK, journalist; b. Little Rock, Oct. 24, 1937; s. Robert Wickliffe and Lorene (Bullard) T.; m. Margaret A. McCay, May 27, 1989; children by previous marriage: Wick III, Ellen Wallace, Carol Halter, Shawn Temple. A.A., Texarkana Coll., 1957; postgrad., U. Tex., 1958-59. Reporter, sports editor Texarkana (Tex.) Gazette-News, 1954-58; reporter Austin (Tex.) American-Statesman, 1958-59; reporter, news editor AP, Little Rock, 1959-65; corr. AP, St. Louis, 1965-66; bur. chief AP, Helena, Mont., 1966-68, Seattle, 1968-73; sports editor AP, N.Y.C., 1973-80, mng. editor, 1980-85, dir. human resources, 1985-88, v.p., 1988, dir. newspaper membership, 1988—. Home: 10 Berkeley Rd Millburn NJ 07041-2012 Office: AP 50 Rockefeller Pla New York NY 10020

TEMPLE, WILLIAM NORMAN, foundry executive; b. Texarkana, Tex., Dec. 21, 1932; s. Herbert William and Kathleen May (Twyman) T.; m. Nancy Caroline Pennington, May 29, 1955; children: Nancy Carol, William Norman Jr., Alan Moore. BBA in Acctg., U. Miss., 1955. Cost analyst U.S. Steel Corp., Fairfield, Ala., 1957-61, internal auditor, 1961-65; acctg. supr. positions U.S. Pipe and Foundry Co., Birmingham, Ala., 1965-69, controller, 1969-71, pres. Southeastern Bolt and Screw div., 1971-72, pres. Fastener and Spl. Products div., 1973-74, v.p., 1973-74, v.p., group exec. Walter Industries, Inc., Tampa, Fla., 1974-91; sr. v.p. group exec. Walter Industries, Inc., 1991—; pres., COO United Land Corp., Birmingham, 1990—, U.S. Pipe and Foundry Co., Birmingham, 1993—. Served to 1st lt. USMCR, 1955-57. Mem. Wildcat Cliffs Country Club, Old Overton Club. Republican. Avocations: golf, hunting, tennis, reading. Office: US Pipe & Foundry Co 3300 1st Ave N Birmingham AL 35222

TEMPLETON, ALAN ROBERT, biology educator; b. Litchfield, Ill., Feb. 28, 1947; s. John Smith and Lois Arlene (McCormick) T.; m. Bonnie A. Altman, Dec. 20, 1969; children: Jeremy Alan, Jeffrey Alan. BA, Washington U., 1969; MS in Stats., U. Mich., 1972, PhD in Genetics, 1972. Jr. fellow Mich. Soc. Fellows, Ann Arbor, 1972-74; asst. prof. U. Tex., Austin, 1974-77; assoc. prof. Washington U., St. Louis, 1977-81, prof., 1981—; cons. St. Louis Zool. Park, 1979—; founding mem., dir. Soc. for Conservation Biology, 1985—. Editor: Theoretical Population Biology, 1981-91; mem. editorial bd. Molecular Phylogenetics & Evolution, 1991—, Brazilian Jour. of Genetics, 1991—; contbr. numerous article to profl. jours. Grantee NSF, 1974-80, 90—, NIH, 1980—, Nixon Griffis Fund for Zool. Rsch., 1986-87. Mem. Soc. for Study Evolution (v.p. 1982, pres.-elect 1995), Genetics Soc. Am., Soc. Conservation Biology (bd. dirs. 1985-88), Nature Conservancy (bd. trustees Mo. chpt. 1988-94). Avocations: hiking, caving, music, ethnomusicology, scuba diving. Office: Washington U Dept Biology Saint Louis MO 63130-4899

TEMPLETON, CARSON HOWARD, engineer, policy analyst; b. Wainwright, Alta., Can., Sept. 9, 1917; s. Samuel Howard and Ellen Florence T.; m. Laurie Jean MacLachlan, May 29, 1948; children—Colleen, Neil. B.S., U. Alta., 1943. L.L.D. (hon.), U. Man., 1982; D.E.S. (hon.), U. Waterloo, 1983. Registered profl. engr., B.C., Alta., Man. Chief engr. Greater Winnipeg Dyking Bd., Can., 1948-50; sr. ptnr. Templeton Engring. Co., Winnipeg, 1955-81; pres. Templeton Facilities Ltd., Winnipeg, 1958—; v.p. Teshmont Cons., Inc., Winnipeg, 1970-81; cons. Pub. Utilities Bd. Man., 1962-70. Bd. dirs. Childrens Hosp. Winnipeg, 1958-70; vice chmn. bd. govs. U. Man. Recipient Gzowski medal Engring. Inst. Can., 1951, fellow, 1978; named Officer of the Order of Can. Gov. Gen. of Can., 1978. Mem. Assn. Profl. Engrs. Man. (recipient merit award, named for outstanding service), Assn. Cons. Engrs. Can. (pres. 1968-69)

TEMPLETON, IAN MALCOLM, retired physicist; b. Rugby, Eng., July 31, 1929; emigrated to Can., 1957, naturalized, 1967; s. William and Eleanor Clayton (Butcher) T.; m. Elsa Wood, Aug. 11, 1956; children—Nicola Jean, Jennifer Jane. M.A., Univ. Coll., Oxford, Eng., 1950, D.Phil., 1953. Fellow NRC Can., Ottawa, Ont., 1953-54; asst. rsch. officer NRC Can., 1957-60, assoc. rsch. officer, 1960-64, sr. rsch. officer, 1964-71, prin. rsch. officer, 1971-94, joint head metal physics group, 1969-76, head electronic structure and calorimetry group, 1976-87; mem. staff rsch. lab. Associated Elec. Industries, Rugby, Eng., 1955-57. Contbr. articles to profl. jours. Fellow Inst. Physics, Royal Soc. Can. Home: 17 Dunvegan Rd, Ottawa, ON Canada K1K 3E8

TEMPLETON, JOHN ALEXANDER, II, coal company executive; b. Chgo., Mar. 31, 1927; s. Philip Henry and Florence (Moore) T.; B.S., Ind. U., 1950; m. Norma Frazier, Aug. 10, 1949; children—Lori, Linda, Leslie, Sally. Agt., Conn. Mut. Life Ins. Co., Terre Haute, Ind., 1949-51; ptnr. Miller, Templeton, Scott Ins. Agy., Terre Haute, 1951-64; pres. v.p. Templeton Coal Co., Inc., Terre Haute, 1964-72, pres., 1972-94, elected chmn. 1994, also dir.; pres. Sherwood Templeton Coal Co., Inc, Indpls., 1968—, also dir.; chmn. bd., dir. Plumb Supply Co., Des Moines, 1965—, Dicksons, Inc., Seymour, Ind., 1986—; dir. Mchts. Nat. Bank of Terre Haute. Chmn., Vigo County Goldwater for Pres. Com., 1964; trustee Union Hosp., 1968—, v.p., 1975—, chmn. bd. dirs., 1986—; bd. dirs. Ind. State U. Found., 1970—; trustee U. Evansville, 1974-77; bd. of assocs. Rose-Hulman Inst. Tech., 1977; v.p., trustee Ind. Asbury Towers, Greencastle, Ind., 1980-83. Served with U.S. Army, 1946-48. Mem. Nat. Assn. Ins. Agts. (pres. 1959-60), Ind. Coal Assn. (dir.), Lynch Coal Ops. Reciprocal Assn., Interstate Coal Conf., Ind. State C. of C. (bd. dirs. 1981—), Ind. U. Alumni Assn. (exec. council 1983-86). Republican. Methodist. Clubs: Masons, Elks, Scottish Rite.

TEMPLETON, JOHN MARKS, investment counsel, financial analyst; b. Winchester, Tenn., Nov. 29, 1912; s. Harvey Maxwell and Vella (Handly) T.; m. Judith Dudley Folk, Apr. 7, 1937 (dec. Feb. 1951); children: John Marks, Anne Dudley, Christopher Winston; m. Irene Reynolds Butler, Dec. 31, 1958 (dec. Nov. 1993). A.B., Yale U., 1934; M.A. (law) (Rhodes scholar), Balliol Coll., Oxford, Eng. 1936; LLD (hon.), Beaver Coll., 1968, Marquette U., 1980, Jamestown Coll., 1983, Maryville Coll., 1984, Manhattan Coll., 1990, Babson Coll., 1992, Rhodes Coll, 1992, U. Rochester, 1992, La. Coll., 1993, Moravian Coll., 1994; D.Litt. (hon.), Wilson Coll., 1974; D.D. (hon.), Buena Vista Coll., 1979; D.C.L. (hon.), U. of South, 1984; LHD, U. Dubuque, 1992, Fla. Southern Coll., 1992; DLitt (hon.), Campbell U., 1993; LLD, Moravian Coll., 1994. Chartered fin. analyst. Sec.-treas., v.p, dir. Nat. Geophys. Co., Dallas and N.Y.C., 1937-41; pres., dir. Templeton, Dobbrow & Vance, Inc., N.Y.C., 1941-65; chmn. Templeton Damroth Corp., 1959-62; v.p., dir. First Trust Bank Ltd., Bahamas, 1963—; pres., dir. Templeton Funds Inc., 1977-86, Templeton Global Funds Inc., 1981-86, Templeton Growth Fund Can., Ltd., Toronto, 1954-85; chmn Templeton Galbraith & Hansberger Ltd, 1986-92. Author: The Humble Approach, 1981; co-author: The Templeton Touch, 1985, The Templeton Plan, 1987, Global Investing, 1988, The God Who Would Be Known, 1989, Riches for the Mind and Spirit, 1990, Looking Forward, 1993, Discovering the Laws of Life, 1994, Is God the Only Reality?, 1994, Evidence of Purpose, 1994; contbr. articles to fin. publs. Past pres. Lyford Cay (Bahamas) Property Owners Assn.; Chmn. YMCA Bergen County, 1952-54; dir., campaign chmn. Englewood Community Chest, 1953-54; trustee Englewood Hosp., 1953-56, Soc. for Promoting Christian Knowledge, 1984-87, Balliol Coll. Endowments (Oxford), Templeton Project Trust (Eng.); chmn. bd. trustees Princeton Theol. Sem., 1973-73, 79-85, trustee for restoration of Westminster Abbey, 1991—; trustee Wilson Coll., 1941-73, Buena Vista Coll., 1981—, Templeton Found. Inc., 1952—, John Templeton Found. Inc., 1987—, council on theol. sems. United Presbyn. Ch. U.S.A., 1946-83; mem. Ctr. Theol. Inquiry, 1979-92, Commn. on Ecumenical Mission, 1961-70; bd. corporators Presbyn. Ministers Fund, Inc., 1960-93; bd. visitors Harvard Div. Sch., 1981-88; adv. bd. Harvard Ctr. for the study of World Religions, 1975-89; bd. mgrs. Am. Bible Soc., 1972-92; mgmt. Council Templeton Coll. (Oxford); pres. Templeton Theol. Sem., Bahamas, 1984-88; hon. rector Dubuque U., 1982-92. Chancellor Fla. Southern Coll., 1992. Decorated knight Order of Brit. Empire; recipient Churchman of Yr. award Religious Heritage Am., 1979, Internat. Churchman of Yr. award, 1981, Ecumenical Patriarch's Hon. Order of Mt. Athos, Free Enterprise award Palm Beach Atlantic Coll., 1984, Centennial medal N.Y. Mayflower Soc., 1987, award USA Today, 1991, award for excellence in investment mgmt., 1991, Benjamin Franklin award Royal Soc. Arts, 1994; named to Wall Street Week Hall of Fame, 1990. Mem. Soc. Security Analysts, World Pres. Orgn. (pres. Chief Execs. Orgn. (pres.

1968-69), Bahamas C. of C. (bd. dirs. 1976-79), Internat. Acad. Religious Scis., Mt. Pelerin Soc., Elihu Club, Elizabethan Club (New Haven), Yale Club, University Club (N.Y.C.), Lyford Cay Club of Bahamas (dep. chmn. 1980-86), Lansdowne Club, Royal Overseas League, Athenaeum (Eng.), United Oxford and Cambridge Univs. Club (Eng.), White's Club (Eng.), Rotary (Bahamas), Phi Beta Kappa., Zeta Psi. Office: Box N7776, Nassau Bahamas

TEMPLETON, ROBERT EARL, engineering and construction company executive; b. Pitts., June 21, 1931; s. Robert James and Alice Wilma (Scheppele) T.; m. Barbara Ann McDonald, June 9, 1956; children: Shirley Anne (dec.), Susan Elaine, Sally Irene. BSCE, Carnegie Mellon U., 1953, MSCE, 1954; MBA in Mgmt., NYU, 1960. Registered profl. engr., N.Y. With M.W. Kellogg Co., Houston, 1954-93, project engr., 1963-66, mgr. contract status, 1966-68, mgr. sales forecasting, 1968-72, mgr. market forecasting, 1972-73; mgr. Venture Analysis, Houston, 1973-74, mgr. analysis and methods div., 1974-76, mgr. Project Cost Services div., 1976-81, mgr. Cost Mgmt. Services div., 1981-85, project control mgr., 1985-93; pres. Templeton Enterprises, Houston, 1993—; cons. project mgmt. profl. total cost mgmt., work process improvement reengring., benchmarking, electronic data interchange ISO 9000 Stds., Houston, 1993—. Editorial bd. Engring. and Process Econs., 1976-85. Area chmn. United Campaign, Summit, N.J., 1969-70; pres. Jefferson Sch. PTA, Summit, N.J., 1967-69, v.p., 1965-67; security chmn. Fonn Villas Civic Assn., Houston, 1973, chmn. archtl. standards com., 1974, v.p., 1975, pres., 1976; mem. exec. com., bd. dirs. Houston Advocates for Mentally Ill Children; active: Can Care of Houston Inc., For-By-To Cancer Survivors (church ministry), Income Tax Assistance (VITA), Tax Couseling for the Elderly (TCE), AARP, Houston. J. Waldo Smith Hydraulic fellow ASCE, 1953-54. Fellow Am. Assn. Cost Engrs. (award of merit 1977, award of recognition 1980, cert. cost engr.; nat. pres. 1971-72, nat. adminstrv. v.p. 1970-71, nat. adv. staff 1973—, spl. projects chmn. 1974-75, cert. bd. chmn. 1976-79, chmn. assn. standards and recommended practices com. 1985-89, chmn. quality mgmt. com. 1988—); mem. N.Am. Soc. Corporate Planners (program dir. 1974, chmn. ad hoc cert. com. 1986—), Am. Assn. Engring. Socs., Project Mgmt. Inst. (cert. project mgmt. profl., v.p. certification Houston chpt. 1993-94, v.p. edn. 1985-86, 87-88, 91-92, pres. 1988-89, chmn. advisor 1989-90), Sigma XI (Sec. M.W. Kellogg Sc. 1973-74), Sigma Xi (2d v.p. 1976-77, 84-85, 1st v.p. 1985-86), Houston Comml. Bridge League (v.p. 1973-75), Houston C. of C. (life mem., dir. engring. and constrn. internat. bus. network exec. com.), Am. Mktg. Assn., Acad. for Health Services Mktg. (profl. mem.), Health Services Mktg. Soc. (bd. dirs.), Tau Beta Pi, Beta Theta Pi. Republican. Presbyterian (deacon 1956-59, elder 1980-82). Club: M.W. Kellogg Quarter Century (pres. 1986-87). Home: 12718 Old Oaks Dr Houston TX 77024-4016

TEMPLIN, JOHN LEON, JR., healthcare consulting executive; b. New Brunswick, N.Y., Aug. 5, 1940; s. John Leon and Theresa Veronica (Revolinski) T.; m. Barbara Maria Ribley, Sept. 12, 1970; children: John, Joseph, Kevin, Nan, Danielle, Christopher. BS in Mgmt. Engring., Rensselaer Poly. Inst., 1962, MS in Mgmt., 1969. Mgr. customer svc. Norton Abrasives, Troy, N.Y., 1968-70; cons., sr. cons. Hosp. Assn. N.Y. State, Albany, 1970-79, dir. mgmt. svcs., 1979-80, sr. dir. mgmt. svc., 1981-83; dir. productivity improvement Applied Leadership Technologies, Inc., Greenfield Center, N.Y., 1983-84, v.p., productivity improvement div., 1984-85, pres., 1985-86; pres. Templin Mgmt. Assocs., Inc., Greenfield Center, 1987—, The Neny Cons. Alliance, Greenfield Center, 1995—; pres. The Northeastern N.Y. Cons. Alliance, 1995—. Editor quar. jour. Healthcare Supr., 1983—; mem. editorial com. ann. Manual for Workload Recording, 1978-91. Mem. budget com. Greater Saratoga Sch. Dist., Saratoga Springs, N.Y., 1978-79; mem. energy com. Blue Cross Assn., Chgo., 1978-81; mem. Gov.'s Task Force on Nursing, Albany, 1980; mem. parish com. St. Joseph's Ch., Greenfield Center, 1981-87. Capt. U.S. Army, 1962-64. Fellow Am. Coll. Healthcare Execs., Healthcare Info. and Mgmt. Systems Soc. (liaison Coll. Am. Pathologists 1978-91); mem. Am. Hosp. Assn. (seminar speaker 1980-93), Healthcare Fin. Mgmt. Assn., Clin. Lab. Mgmt. Aasn. (bd. dirs. 1980-84), K.C. Republican. Roman Catholic. Avocations: karate, golf, computers, gardening, fishing. Home and Office: Templin Mgmt Assocs Inc 265 Locust Grove Rd Greenfield Center NY 12833-1501

TEMPLIN, KENNETH ELWOOD, paper company executive; b. Mason City, Nebr., Jan. 26, 1927; s. Otto Rudolph and Marianna (Graf) T.; m. Harriet Elaine Ressel, Aug. 24, 1951; children: Steven, David, Daniel, Benjamin, Elizabeth. B.S. in Bus. Adminstrn., U. Nebr., 1950; M.B.A., Wayne State U., 1961. Fin. analyst Ford Motor Co., 1950-54; fin. analyst, corp. staff Chrysler Corp., 1955-60, div. controller marine engine div., 1961-63, gen. sales mgr., 1964-65; v.p. Marsh and Templin, N.Y.C., 1966-69; v.p., gen. mgr. operating group Saxon Industries, N.Y.C., 1970-79; group v.p. Saxon Industries, 1979-82, sr. v.p., 1982-85; v.p.-converting Paper Corp. Am., Wayne, Pa., 1985-86; exec. v.p. Quality Park Products Inc., St. Paul, 1986-88, 1986-88, pres., 1988—; mem. exec. com. Single Service Inst., 1971-79. Regional chmn. Minn. devel. com. Nat. Multiple Sclerosis Soc., 1970-71; co-pres. Home and Sch. Assn., Bernardsville, N.J., 1975-76. Served with U.S. Army, 1945-47, 50-51. Mem. Envelope Mfrs. Assn. Am. (postal affairs com 1989—, fin. com. chmn. 1994—, bd. dirs. 1990-91, 93—). Presbyterian. Home: 3993 Country Rd 42 NE Alexandria MN 56308

TENAGLIA, JOHN FRANC, broadcasting executive; b. Clairton, Pa., Jan. 17, 1935; s. Fileno Albert and Gina (Zucconi) T.; m. Judith Ann Droder, June 30, 1962; children: Christine Mary, Lisa Ann. BBA, U. Pitts., 1958. Gen. mgr. local affiliate ABC, Pitts., 1959-69; exec. v.p. GCC Communications Inc., Boston, 1970-80; prin. owner, pres., chief exec. officer TK Communications Inc., Bala Cynwyd, Pa., 1980—; bd. dirs. WK Cable, Junction City, Kans. Served with U.S. Army, 1954-56. Mem. Nat. Assn. Broadcasters. Republican. Roman Catholic. Avocations: skiing, golf, boating. Office: Sta WSRF-AM 3000 SW 60th Ave Fort Lauderdale FL 33314

TEN CATE, ARNOLD RICHARD, dentistry educator; b. Accrington, Lancashire, Eng., Oct. 21, 1933; s. Gys Johan and Lien (Dalenoord) Ten C.; m. Alice Mitchell, Apr. 7, 1956 (dec.); children: Pauline Ann, Jill Elaine, Ian Richard. B.Sc., U. London, 1955, Ph.D. in Anatomy, 1957, B.D.S., 1960; DSc (hon.), McGill U., 1989, U. Western Ont., 1989. Leverhulme fellow in dental sci. Royal Coll. Surgeons, Eng., 1961-63; sr. lectr. in anatomy in relation to dentistry Guy's Hosp. Med. Sch., U. London, 1963-68; prof. dentistry Faculty Dentistry, U. Toronto, Ont., Can., 1968-77; chmn. div. biol. scis. Faculty Dentistry, U. Toronto, 1971-77, dean, 1977-89, vice provost health scis., 1989-94. Author: Advanced Dental Histology, 4th edit., 1983, Oral Histology, Development, Structure and Function, 1980, 4th edit., 1994; others, also articles. Recipient Colyer prize Royal Soc. Medicine, 1962; Mil. Hellman award Am. Assn. Orthodontists, 1975. Mem. Internat. Assn. Dental Research (pres. 1984, Isaac Schour Meml. award 1978). Conservative. Mem. Christian Ch. Home: 50 Squire Baker's Ln, Markham, ON Canada L3P 3G9 Office: Faculty of Dentistry, 123 Edward St, Toronto Canad M5G 1G6

TENDLER, DAVID, international trade company executive; b. N.Y.C., Jan. 15, 1938; s. Philip and Pearl (German) T.; m. Beatrice Weisberg, Oct. 11, 1958; children: Pearl, Karen. BBA in Internat. Econs., CCNY, 1959. With Philipp Bros. Co., 1960—, mgr. Far Eastern ops., 1968-75; pres. Philipp Bros. Co., N.Y.C., 1975—; dir. parent corp. Engelhard Minerals & Chems. Corp. (name changed to Phibro Corp. 1981), N.Y.C., 1975-85; vice chmn. bd. Engelhard Minerals & Chems. Corp. (name changed to Phibro Corp. 1981), 1979-81, chmn. bd., chief exec. officer, 1981—; co-chmn., co-chief exec. officer Phibro-Salomon Inc., 1983-84; founder Tendler Beretz Assocs. Ltd., 1985—; chmn. subcom. trade U.S-German Dem. Rep. Trade and Econ. Coun., 1978-84; bd. dirs., mem. exec. com. U.S./USSR Trade and Econ. Coun., 1979-85, U.S.-China Bus. Coun., 1983-94; bd. dirs. Ryan, Beck & Co., West Orange, N.J., Biotech. Gen. Corp., Iselin, N.J. Mem. bd. overseers NYU Grad. Sch. Bus., 1981-85; trustee Lenox Hill Hosp., 1981-94; mem. exec. com. N.Y. Blood Ctr., 1987—; bd. dirs., mem. exec. com. Fgn. Policy Assn., 1983—. Recipient Torch of Liberty award metals and metal products div. Anti-Defamation League, 1976, Edith and Herbert Lehman award Henry St. Settlement, 1982; named Man of Yr., Fgn. Trade Soc., Baruch Coll., CUNY, 1985. Office: Tendler Beretz Assocs 101 E 52nd St New York NY 10022-6018

TENDLER, PAUL MARC, lawyer; b. N.Y.C., Oct. 22, 1943; s. Leonard and Gladys (Steisel) T.; m. Elaine Lynn Isaacson, Mar. 28, 1971; children: Jamie Meredith, Seth Evan. B.A., Queens Coll., N.Y.C., 1965; M.S., So. Ill. U., Carbondale, 1966; J.D., Howard U., 1969; postgrad. U. Pitts., 1969-70. Bar: D.C. 1980. Press asst to Congressman Begich, Washington, 1971; legis. asst. to Congressman Halpern, Washington, 1972, Congressman Rinaldo, 1973; dir. legis. rsch. Cost of Living Council, Washington, 1973-74; asst. dir. govt. affairs Am. Nurses Assn., Washington, 1974-75; pres. Paul Tendler Assocs., Washington, 1975—; mng. ptnr. Tendler & Biggins, 1982-89; ptnr. Tendler, Goldberg, Biggins & Geltzer, 1989—; adj. prof. Georgetown U., 1980-83, asst. prof., 1975-80; dir. bus. program Trinity Coll., Washington, 1983-86. Author: The Federal Government at Work, 1976; An LPNs Guide to the Federal Government, 1978, 84. Ford Found. scholar, 1967-69. Mem. D.C. Bar Assn., Am. Arbitration Assn., ABA, Assn. Trial Lawyers Am., Delta Sigma Rho, Tau Kappa Alpha. Democrat. Jewish. Home and Office: 1090 Vermont Ave NW Washington DC 20005-4905

TENENBAUM, JEFFREY MARK, academic librarian; b. Phila., Apr. 10, 1945; s. Paul and Hansi (Barber) T. BA, Pa. State U., 1966; MLS, McGill U., 1968. Documents librarian, then reference librarian U. Toronto (Ont., Can.) Library, 1968-72; reference librarian U. Mass. Library, Amherst, 1973—; mem. Info. Access Co. Acad. Libr. Product Adv. Bd., Foster City, Calif., 1992-94. Mem. Amherst Pub. Art Commn., 1994—. Mem. ALA, Assn. Can. Studies in U.S., Am. Coun. Que. Studies, Mid-Atlantic and New Eng. Conf. for Can. Studies (sec. 1992—), Pioneer Valley Assn. Acad. Librs. (pres. 1989-90), Assn. Coll. and Rsch. Librs., Beta Phi Mu, Phi Alpha Theta, Pi Gamma Mu. Jewish. Home: 48 Riverside Park Amherst MA 01002-4011 Office: U Mass Univ Libr Amherst MA 01003-4710

TENENBAUM, MICHAEL, steel company executive; b. St. Paul, July 23, 1913; s. Harry and Ida Vivian (Kolohoski) T.; m. Helen Zlatovski, Aug. 16, 1941 (div. 1981); children: Susan Rose Tenenbaum Uyama, Anne Louise Benjamin; m. Martha Smith Berner, July 30, 1982. Met.E., U. Minn., 1936, M.S., 1937, Ph.D., 1940; D.Sc. hon., Northwestern U., 1976. Metallurgist Inland Steel Co., East Chicago, Ind., 1940-50, mgr., 1950-65; v.p. Inland Steel Co., Chgo., 1965-71, pres., 1971-78, dir., 1971-84; cons., 1984—. Fellow AIME (hon., Hunt and Raymond award 1949), Am. Soc. Metals (disting. mem.); mem. The Metall. Soc. (pres.), Western Soc. Engrs. (Washington award 1976), Brit. Metals Soc. (Bessemer Gold medal 1980), Assn. Iron and Steel Engrs., Am. Iron and Steel Inst., Nat. Acad. Engring. Home: 4049 220th Pl SE Issaquah WA 98027-7212

TENGI, FRANK R., lawyer, insurance company executive; b. Garfield, N.J., Aug. 11, 1920; s. John and Mary (Fedush) T.; m. Shirley H. Mitchell, May 17, 1952; children: Christopher, Nancy. BS, Georgetown U., 1946; LLD, Fordham U., 1951. CPA, N.Y. Bar: N.Y. 1955, U.S. Supreme Ct. 1967, U.S. Ct. Claims 1967, U.S. Dist. Ct. (so. dist.) N.Y. 1967, U.S. Dist. Ct. (ea. dist.) N.Y., 1967, U.S. Tax Ct. 1968. Asst. sec. Am. Internat. Aviation Agy., Inc., N.Y.C., 1961-69; assoc. Lee Mulderig & Celentano, N.Y.C., 1965-70; asst. sec. Am. Internat. Underwriting Corp., N.Y.C., 1965—; Am. Internat. Underwriters Assn., 1965—, Starr Tech. Risks Agy., Inc., 1967-78; asst. comptroller taxation A.I.G. Inc., N.Y.C., 1971-75; asst. sec. C.V. Starr & Co., Inc., N.Y.C., 1965—; pres. Estate Maintenance Co., Inc., N.Y.C., 1969-71; mgr. reinsurance security World-wide, Am. Internat. Group, Inc., N.Y.C., 1978—. Mem. Mayor's Budget Adv. Com. (Millburn N.J.). Treas., Starr Found., 1970—. Served with U.S. Army, 1941-46; ETO. Mem. N.Y. State Bar Assn., Tax Execs. Inst. Home: 17 Madison Ave Apt 58 Madison NJ 07940-1466 Office: 70 Pine St New York NY 10270-0001

TENHOEVE, THOMAS, academic administrator; b. Bklyn., Oct. 1, 1935; s. Thomas and Adeline Ruth (Vander Hill) T.; m. Suzanne Underwood, June 7, 1957; children: Thomas III, Carol, Timothy. AB, Hope Coll., 1956; MA, U. Mich., 1957; PhD, U. Toledo, 1965; postgrad., U. Western Mich. Biology tchr. South Haven. Mich. Pub. Schs., 1957-58; biology instr. Northwestern Coll., Orange City, Iowa, 1958-63; supr. biology students U. Toledo, Ohio, 1963-65; acad. dean, acting pres. Northwestern Coll., Orange City, 1965-70; pres. Butler (Pa.) County Community Coll., 1970-84, Oakton Community Coll., Des Plaines, Ill., 1984—. Bd. dirs. Sister Cities, 1986—; trustee Northwestern Coll., 1988—; mem. Ill. C.C. State Found. Bd., 1993—, Ill. Math. and Sci. Academy Selection Bd., 1986, 87, Cook County Sheriff's Scholarship Panel; exec. com. Golden Corridor, 1986-92. Recipient Pacesetter award Nat. Coun. for Community Rels., 1986, Orchard Village award. Mem. Am. Coun. on Internat. Intercultural Edn. (chmn. 1992-93), Coun. North Ctrl. Two Yr. Colls. (state rep. 1988-92, exec. bd. 1989—, 2d v.p. 1990-91, 1st v.p. 1991-92, pres. 1992-93). Office: Oakton Community College Office of the President 1600 E Golf Rd Des Plaines IL 60016

TENNANT, GERALDINE B., judge; b. Clarendon, Tex., Aug. 31, 1922; d. James D. and Josephine (Chamberlain) Browder; m. James P. Tennant, Dec. 28, 1952 (dec. 1962); children: James B., Lucile B., Josephine A. BA, Tex. Christian U., 1943; postgrad., So. Methodist U., 1946; JD, U. Tex.-Austin, 1949. Bar: Tex. 1949, U.S. Dist. Ct. (so. dist.) Tex. 1970, U.S. Ct. Appeals (5th cir.) 1970. Pvt. practice Ft. Worth, Houston, 1949-67; probate asst. to county judge Harris County, Houston, 1967-73, referee for juvenile cts., 1973-80; pvt. practice Houston, 1980-83; dist. judge State of Tex., Houston, 1983-95, sr. dist. judge, 1995—. Contbr. to book: Desk Book for Juvenile Courts, 1980. Bd. dirs. YWCA, Houston, 1970, Mental Health Assn. Tex., Austin, 1980, LWV, Houston, 1967. Mem. ABA, Assn. Women Attys., Nat. Assn. Judges, State Bar Tex., Houston Bar Assn., Tex. State Bar Coll., Rotary. Democrat. Roman Catholic. Home: PO Box 130289 Houston TX 77219-0289

TENNANT, JOHN RANDALL, management advisory company executive; b. North Bend, Wash., Aug. 23, 1940; s. Maurice Andrew and Jane Downing (Vinnedge) T.; m. Nikki Mae Priem, July 17, 1965 (div.); children: Ann Elizabeth, Randall Warren; m. Deborah Ann Francis, Oct. 25, 1986 (div.); 1 child, Alyssa Jane. B.S. in Indsl. Engring., Stanford U., 1962; M.B.A., U. Wash., 1966. Registered profl. engr., Wash. Sr. research engr. Boeing Co., Seattle, 1962-68; mgr. Price Waterhouse, Seattle, 1968-73; ptnr. Price Waterhouse, Tokyo, 1973-79, Los Angeles, 1979-89; founder, chief exec. officer Manex, Inc., Newport Beach, Calif., 1989—; dir. subs. Price Waterhouse Assocs., Pacific region, 1975-79. Mem. John Tracy Clinic Men's Com., Santa Catalina Island Conservancy, pres., 1985-87. Mem. NSPE, Japan Computer Assn. (founder, pres. 1976-77), Japan Modapts Assn. (founder) Japan Am. Soc., Inst. Mgmt. Cons., Am. Inst. Indsl. Engrs. (pres. Seattle chpt. 1970-71), Data Processing Mgmt. Assn., Tokyo Lawn and Tennis Club, L.A. Country Club, Jonathan Club, Empty Saddle Club, Los Rancheros Visitadores Club, Los Caballeros Club. Home: 13928 Tahiti Way # 111 Marina Del Rey CA 90292

TENNANT, SAMUEL MCKIBBEN, aerospace systems company executive; b. Feb. 1, 1928; s. Richard Grenville and Margaret Louise (McKibben) T.; m. June Ann Fleischer, June 20, 1953; children: Samuel McKibben Jr., Ann Tennant Boehler, Catherine Tennant Jacobi. BME, MIT, 1950; MME, Purdue U., 1951. Vibration engr. Change Vought Aircraft Corp., Dallas, 1951-52; group engr. dynamics and computations Temco Aircraft Corp., Dallas, 1952-58; sr. staff engr. Titan Space Tech. Labs., Redondo Beach, Calif., 1958-61; assoc. group dir. advanced planning Aerospace Corp., El Segundo, Calif., 1961-66, group dir. engring. manned orbiting lab., 1966-69, v.p., gen. mgr. advanced orbital systems div., 1969-84, group v.p. programs, 1984-87, exec. officer, 1987—; cons. Los Alamos (N.Mex.) Nat. Lab. Patentee total knee prosthesis. Mem. sci. adv. bd. USAF, 1984-88; mem. sci. adv. group Air Force Logistics Ctr.; mem,. Def. Sci. Bd., 1988—. Mem. AIAA. Office: Aerospace Corp 2350 E El Segundo Blvd El Segundo CA 90245-4609

TENNANT, THOMAS MICHAEL, lawyer; b. Anniston, Ala., July 23, 1948; s. Thomas Edward and Mary Eugenia (Warren) T.; m. Sharon Leigh Ebert, Mar. 21, 1970; children: Sharon Michelle, Michael Ebert. BS, Auburn U., 1970; JD, Walter F. George Sch. Law, 1973. Assoc. Webb, Fowler & Tanner, Lawrenceville, Ga., 1973-76, ptnr., 1976-77; mng. ptnr. Tennant, Andersen & Davidson, P.C., Lawrenceville, 1977-81, Tennant, Andersen, Davidson & Edmondson, P.C., Lawrenceville, 1982-85, Tennant, Davidson & Edmondson, P.C., Lawrenceville, 1985-86, Tennant, Davidson & Thompson, P.C., Lawrenceville, 1986-87, Tennant, Davidson, Thompson & Sweeny, Lawrenceville, 1987-89, Tennant, Thompson & Sweeny, 1990,

Alston & Bird, Atlanta, 1991—; judge Recorder's Ct., Lawrenceville, 1979-80; mem. State Disciplinary Bd., 1988-91. Bd. dirs. Gwinnett Found., Inc., Lawrenceville, 1984—. Served to 1st lt. U.S. Army, 1970-78. Mem. State Bar Ga. (chmn. lawyer ethics com. young lawyers sect. 1979-80, bd. govs. 1986-92), Gwinnett County Bar Assn. (pres. 1978), Ga. Trial Lawyers Assn., Atlanta Lawyers Club, Gwinnett County C. of C. (pres. 1986). Presbyterian. Home: 4069 Nobleman Pt Duluth GA 30136 Office: Alston & Bird One Atlantic Ctr 1201 W Peachtree St Atlanta GA 30309-3424

TENNENBAUM, MICHAEL ERNEST, investment banker; b. St. Petersburg, Fla., Sept. 17, 1935; s. Reubin and Frieda (Miller) T.; m. Suzanne Stockfisch; children by previous marriage—Mark Stephen, Andrew Richard. B.S., Ga. Inst. Tech., 1958; M.B.A. with honors, Harvard U., 1962. Assoc. Burnham & Co., N.Y.C., 1962-64; assoc. Bear, Stearns & Co., N.Y.C., 1964-69, sr. mng. dir., 1969—, vice chmn. investment banking div., 1988-93; chmn. bd. dirs. Tech. Park, Atlanta, 1978-81, Ariz. City Devel. Co. 1978—. Bd. dirs. Challengers Boys and Girls Club; nat. bd. trustees Boys and Girls Clubs Am.; mem. nat. adv. bd. Ga. Inst. Tech., 1971-77; mem. vis. com. Harvard U. Sch. Bus., Cambridge, Mass., 1986-92, bd. assocs., 1992—; bd. trustees Ga. Inst. Tech. Found., Inc., Atlanta, 1988—; bd. dirs. Joffrey Ballet, 1990-92, chmn. exec. com., 1991-92; bd. dirs. Music Ctr. L.A. County Unified Fund Cabinet, 1990-91; chmn. L.A. Mayor's Spl. Adv. Com. on Fiscal Adminstrn., 1993-94; commr. Calif. Intercity HighSpeed Ground Transp. Commn. Mem. Malibu Racquet Club. Home: 118 Malibu Colony Rd Malibu CA 90265-4642 Office: 32d Fl 1999 Avenue Of The Stars Los Angeles CA 90067-4607

TENNENT, MICHAEL D., park ranger administrator; b. Augusta, Ga., Aug. 24, 1948; s. William Edward and Bette (Sanford) T.; m. Toni Lane Dorsett, June 13, 1970; children: Kelli, Patrick. BA in History, U. So. Fla., 1971. Historian Manassas (Va.) Nat. Battlefield, 1972-76; chief ranger George Washington Carver Nat. Monument, Diamond, Mo., 1976-78, Statue of Liberty Nat. Monument, N.Y.C., 1978-81, Castillo de San Marcos Nat. Monument, St. Augustine, Fla., 1981-90; supt. Ft. Frederica Nat. Monument, St. Simons Island, Ga., 1990—. Author computer software. Coach St. Johns County Soccer Club, St. Augustine, 1988-90, Golden Isles Soccer, St. Simons Island, 1991. Mem. Fla. Inst. Park Pers. (dir. fin., 1990—, Member of Yr. 1991), Golden Isles Track Club (sec., editor). Democrat. Avocations: triathlons, computers, model railroads, soccer. Office: Ft Frederica Nat Monument RR 9 Box 286-c Saint Simons Island GA 31522-9710

TENNENT, VALENTINE LESLIE, accountant; b. Apia, Western Samoa, Apr. 5, 1919; came to U.S., 1922; s. Hugh Cowper and Madge Grace (Cook) T.; m. Jeanne Marie Elder, Dec. 10, 1941; children: Madeline Jeanne Walls, Hugh Cowper II, Michael Waller, Val Leslie, Paul Anthony. Student, U. Calif., Berkeley, 1938-40. CPA, Hawaii, La. Mgr. Tennent & Greaney, CPAs, Hilo, Hawaii, 1945-50; ptnr. Cameron, Tennent & Dunn, CPAs, Honolulu, 1950-56; ptnr. KPMG Peat Marwick LLP, Honolulu, 1956-79, cons., 1979-84; indl. rschr., pud. fin. and banking, politico-econ. sci., San Diego, 1984—. Co-founder, pres., treas. Tennent Art Found., Honolulu, 1955-77; trustee, treas. Watumull Found., Honolulu, 1963-90 (G.J. Watumull award for disting. achievement 1982); bd. dirs. Iolani Sch., Inst. for Human Svcs., Honolulu, Lyman Mus., Hilo. Capt. USAF, 1941-45. Recipient Bishop's Cross for Disting. Svc. Protestant Episcopal Ch., Dist. of Hawaii, 1965. Mem. AICPA (governing coun. 1961-64), Hawaii Soc. CPAs (pres. 1960), Univ. Club (San Diego). Episcopalian. Avocations: swimming, fine arts, music, literature. Home and Office: 700 Front St No 1607 San Diego CA 92101

TENNEY, DARREL R., materials science administrator. Chief Langley Research Ctr. Structures Directorate Materials Division, Hampton, Va. Office: Langley Rsch Ctr Mail Stop 188M Hampton VA 23665

TENNEY, DUDLEY BRADSTREET, lawyer; b. N.Y.C., July 13, 1918; s. Parker Gillespie and Josephine (Keeler) T.; m. Margaret Carter, June 13, 1941 (div. Oct. 1977); children: Ann, Janet Greene; m. Dorothy Walsh, Jan. 7, 1978 (dec. Sept. 1982); m. Joyce McPherson, Jan. 4, 1986. A.B. summa cum laude, Oberlin Coll., 1939; J.D. magna cum laude, Harvard U., 1942. Bar: N.Y. 1948. Assoc. firm Cahill, Gordon & Reindel, N.Y.C., 1946-54, ptnr., 1955-86. Pres.: Harvard U. Law Rev., 1941-42. Served to maj. AUS, 1942-46, CBI. Mem. ABA, Assn. Bar City of N.Y., World Trade Ctr. Club (N.Y.C.), Manhasset Bay Yacht Club (Port Washington, N.Y.). Home: Wood Rd Harbor Acr Port Washington NY 11050 Office: Cahill Gordon & Reindel 80 Pine St New York NY 10005-1701

TENNEY, STEPHEN MARSH, physiologist, educator; b. Bloomington, Ill., Oct. 22, 1922; s. Harry Houser and Caroline (Marsh) T.; m. Carolyn Cartwright, Oct. 18, 1947; children: Joyce B., Karen M., Stephen M. AB, Dartmouth; MD, Cornell U.; ScD (hon.), U. Rochester. From instr. to assoc. prof. of medicine and physiology U. Rochester Sch. Medicine, 1951-56; prof. physiology Dartmouth Med. Sch., Hanover, N.H., 1956-74; dean Dartmouth Med. Sch., 1960-62, acting dean, 1966, 73, dir. med. scis., 1957-59, chmn. dept. physiology, 1956-77, Nathan Smith prof. physiology, 1974-88, Nathan Smith prof. emeritus, 1988—; med. dir. Parker B. Francis Found., 1975-83, exec. v.p., 1984-89; Chmn. physiology study sect. NIH, 1962-65; mem. Nat. Heart Inst., 1968-71; mem. exec. com. NRC; mem. physiology panel NIH study Office Sci. and Tech.; mem. regulatory biology panel NSF, 1971-75; chmn. bd. sci. counselors Nat. Heart and Lung Inst., 1974-78; chmn. Commn. Respiratory Physiology Internat. Union Physiol. Scis. Asso. editor Jour. Applied Physiology, 1976—, Handbook of Physiology; notes editor: News in Physiol. Sci., 1989—; editorial bd.: Am. Jour. Physiology, Circulation Research, Physiol. Revs; Contbr. articles to sci. jours. Served with USNR, 1947-49; sr. med. officer Shanghai. Markle scholar in med. sci., 1954-59. Fellow Am. Acad. Arts and Scis., AAAS; mem. Inst. Medicine of Nat. Acad. Scis., Am. Physiol. Soc., Am. Soc. Clin. Investigation, N.Y. Acad. Scis., Gerontol. Soc., Am. Heart Assn., Assn. Am. Med. Colls., Alpha Omega Alpha, Sigma Xi.

TENNEY, WILLIAM FRANK, pediatrician; b. Shreveport, La., June 5, 1946; s. William Bonds and Pat (Patton) T.; m. Elizabeth Carter Steadman, Oct. 4, 1973; children: Amy Karen, William Allen. BA, Vanderbilt U., 1968; MD, La. State U., New Orleans, 1972. Diplomate Am. Bd. Pediatrics, sub-Bd. Pediatric Nephrology. Intern Grady Meml. Hosp., Atlanta, 1972-73; resident in pediatrics Emory U. Affiliated Hosps., Atlanta, 1973-74, fellow in pediatric nephrology and inorganic metabolism, 1974-76; practice medicine specializing in pediatric nephrology St. Helens, Oreg., 1976-79, Shreveport, 1979-85, Seattle, 1985—; mem. staff Children's Orthopedic Hosp. and Med. Ctr., Seattle; chief dept. pediatrics Swedish Hosp. Med. Ctr., Seattle 1987-90, 95—; clin. assoc. prof. pediatrics La. State U. Sch. Medicine, 1979-85, U. Wash. Sch. Medicine, Seattle, 1985—; chmn. Renal com. Schumpert Med. Ctr., Shreveport, 1982, co-chmn. 1979-81, mem. 1983-84, co-dir. Renal Dialysis Unit, 1979-84, mem. renal transplantation com., 1984; cons. pediatric nephrology Shriner's Hosp. Crippled Children, Shreveport, 1979-84, Shreveport Regional Dialysis Ctr., 1979-84, Bossier Dialysis Ctr., Bossier City, La., 1983-84, Natchitoches (La.) Dialysis Facility, 1984. Author: (with others) Pediatric Case Studies, 1985; contbr. articles to profl. jours. Mem. Union Concerned Scientists, Cambridge, Mass., 1986—, Internat. Physicians for Prevention of Nuclear War, Boston, 1986—, Fellow Am. Acad. Pediatrics; mem. Am. Soc. Pediatric Nephrology, North Pacific Pediatric Soc., AMA, Wash. State Med. Assn., Internat. Soc. Peritoneal Dialysis, Empirical Soc. Emory U., King County Med. Soc., AAAS, Northwest Renal Soc., Southwest Pediatric Nephrology (mem. study group 1981-84). Avocations: oil painting, rockhounding, camping, jogging. Home: 23915 SE 42d Ct Issaquah WA 98027 Office: 1221 Madison St Seattle WA 98104-1360

TENNIES, ROBERT HUNTER, headmaster; b. Bogotá, Colombia, Aug. 19, 1952; s. Leo C. and Ruth (Winston) T.; m. Ruth Ellen Fischer, June 14, 1975; children: Debbie, Julie. BS, Wheaton (Ill.) Coll., 1973; MA, U. South Fla., 1975; EdS, Fla. Atlantic U., 1978, EdD, 1982. Sch. tchr. Cypress Lake Middle Sch., Ft. Myers, Fla., 1973-77; sci. tchr. Boca Raton (Fla.) Christian Sch., 1977-78, asst. adminstr., 1978-84, headmaster, 1984—, min. of children, 1984-90; interim. min. of edn., 1991-93. Recipient Excellence in Edn. award Nat. Assn. Elem. Prins., 1990. Mem. Nat. Sci. Tchrs. Assn., Assn. of Christian Schs. Internat. (accreditation commn.), Nat. Assn. Elem. Sch.

Prins. Avocation: camping. Home: 2415 NW 30th Rd Boca Raton FL 33431-6214 Office: Boca Raton Christian Sch 600 NW 4th Ave Boca Raton FL 33432-3670

TENNIS, CALVIN CABELL, bishop. Bishop Episcopal Ch., Wilmington, Del., 1986—. Office: Diocesan Office 2020 N Tatnall St Wilmington DE 19802-4821

TENNSTEDT, KLAUS, conductor; b. Merseburg, Germany, June 6, 1926. Formerly gen. music dir. Dresden Opera, and dir., State Orch. and Theatre in Schwerin, Ger.; gen. music dir. and resident condr. Buehnen der Landeshauptstadt Kiel, Ger.; N.Am. debut, Toronto Symphony, U.S. debut, Boston Symphony, 1974; named prin. guest condr. Minn. Orch., 1978, has since conducted all major orchs. of world including Cleve. Symphony, Phila. Orch., N.Y. Philharm., Chgo. Symphony, Berlin Philharm., Israel Philharm., Swedish Radio Orchestra, Metropolitan Opera; prin. guest condr. The London Philharm., music dir. 1983-87, condr. laureate, 1987—; chief condr. Norddeutscher Rundfunk Orchestra, 1979; recordings include Complete Symphonies of Mahler. Home: Roesoll 13, Heikerdorf 2305 Kiel Germany Office: The London Philharm, 35 Doughty St, London WC1N 2AA, England*

TENNYSON, G(EORG) B(ERNHARD), English educator; b. Washington, July 13, 1930; s. Georg B. and Emily (Zimmerli) T.; m. Elizabeth Caroline Johnstone, July 13, 1953; children: Cameron, Holly. BA, George Wash. U., 1953, MA, 1959; MA, Princeton U., 1959, PhD, 1963. Instr. English U. N.C., Chapel Hill, 1962-64; asst. prof. to prof. English UCLA, 1964—. Author: Sartor Called Resartus, 1965, An Introduction to Drama, 1969, Victorian Devotional Poetry, 1981, Owen Barfield on C.S. Lewis, 1990, Literary Language, 1991, A Carlyle Reader, 1984, Nature and the Victorian Imagination, 1977, An Index to Nineteenth-Century Fiction, 1977, Religion and Modern Literature, 1975, Victorian Literature: Prose and Poetry (2 vols.), 1976; author, prodr. video film Owen Barfield: Man and Meaning, 1995; contbr. articles to profl. jours.; editor: Nineteenth Century Fiction, 1971-73, Nineteenth Century Literature, 1983—. With U.S. Army, 1954-56. Fullbright fellow, Freiburg, Germany, 1953-54, Guggenheim fellow, Guggenheim Found., London, 1970-71. Mem. MLA (chmn. Victorian sect. 1973), Philological Assn. of Pacific Coast (chmn. English 2 1969), Carlyle Soc. (Edinburgh). Republican. Anglican. Office: UCLA Dept of English Los Angeles CA 90095-1530

TENNYSON, PETER JOSEPH, lawyer; b. Winona, Minn., Mar. 18, 1946; s. Richard Harvey and Sylvia Josephine (Jadrich) T.; m. Mary Eileen Fay, Jan. 3, 1970; children: Mark Christian, Rachel Christine, Matthew Patrick, Erica Ruth/. BA, Purdue U., 1968; JD, U. Va., 1975. Bar: Calif. Assoc. atty. O'Melveny & Myers, L.A., 1975-82; v.p., gen. counsel Cannon Mills Co., Kannapolis, N.C., 1982-84; ptnr. Stradling, Yocca, Newport Beach, Calif., 1984-89, Jones, Day, Reavis & Pogue, Irvine, Calif., 1990-95; mem. Calif. Commn. on Future of Legal Profession and State Bar, 1994; lectr. in field. Mem. St. Joseph Hosp. Benefit, Orange, Calif., 1987-93; bd. dirs. Lincoln Club Orange County, 1991-93, South Coast Symphony, 1989-92. Capt. U.S. Army, 1968-72. Mem. Orange County Bar Assn., Performing Arts Fraternity. Roman Catholic. Avocations: down hill skiing, swimming. Home: 2621 Circle Dr Newport Beach CA 92663-5616 Office: Jones Day Reavis & Pogue 2603 Main St Ste 900 Irvine CA 92663

TENNYSON, RODERICK C., aerospace scientist; b. Toronto, Ont., Can., June 7, 1937; m. Judith Grace Williams, June 17, 1961; children: Shân, Marc, Kristin. BA. U. Toronto, Ont., 1960, MA, 1961, PhD, 1965. Prof. inst. aerospace studies U. Toronto, 1974—, dir., 1985—, chmn. dept. engring. sci., 1982-85; selected as Can. experimienter on space shuttle flights; dir. ctr. excellence for Inst. Space & Terrestrial Sci.; chmn. Can. Found. for Internat. Space U.; cons. in field. Contbr. numerous articles to profl. jours., chpts. to books. Fellow Can. Aeronautic and Space Inst. Avocations: sailing, writing, recreations. Home: 104 McClure Dr, King City, ON Canada M3H 5T6 Office: Inst Aerospace Studies, 4925 Dufferin St, Downsview, ON Canada M3H 5T6

TENUTA, JEAN LOUISE, sports reporter, medical technologist; b. Kenosha, Wis., Apr. 12, 1958; d. Fred and Lucy Ann (Taylor) Tenuta; m. Robert Louis Bennett, Nov. 22, 1989. BS in Biology, U.Wis., 1979; BA in Journalism, Marquette U., 1983; MS in Print Journalism, Northwestern U., 1989. Sports reporter Kenosha News, 1978-84, Washington Post, 1984-86, Jour. Messenger, Manassas, Va., 1986, Jour. Times, Racine, Wis., 1988-89; med. technologist St. Therese Med. Ctr., Waukegan, Ill., 1980-83, 86-87, Suburban Hosp., Bethesda, Md., 1985-86, Group Health Assn., Washington, 1985-86, St. Francis Hosp., Milw., 1988-89; sports reporter Jour.-Gazette, Ft. Wayne, Ind., 1989-90; med. technologist Columbia Hosp., Milw., 1991; tech. assoc. Coll. Am. Pathologists, 1991—. Recipient 1st place in sports writing Capital Press Women, 1986, 87, Women's Press Club of Ind., 1990, 91, Nat. Fedn. Press Women, 1986, 91. Mem. Assn. Women in Sports Media (Midwest region coord 1990—), Nat. Fedn. Press Women (treas. Capital area 1985-87, 1st pl. in sports writing 1986, 91), Soc. Profl. Journalists, Women in Comms. (v.p., sec. Milw. chpt.), Nat. Writers Club, Midwest Assn. for Toxicology & Therapeutic Drug Monitoring (sec., treas. 1995—). Democrat. Avocations: bicycling, running, reading, baseball. Home: 9110 32d Ave Kenosha WI 53142 Office: Coll Am Pathologists 325 Waukegan Rd Northfield IL 60093-2719

TEPEDINO, FRANCIS JOSEPH, business management company executive; b. Bklyn., Mar. 3, 1937; s. Frank and Maria (Panza) T.; children: Scott, Robert, Michael. BS in Marine Engring., Maine Maritime Acad., 1958; BS in Indsl. Mgmt., Fairleigh Dickinson U., 1963; MBA, Pacific Luth. U., 1968; JD, U. San Diego, 1974. Bar: Calif. 1975, Oreg. 1978, U.S. Supreme Ct. 1980; lic. marine engr. Naval officer USN, USS DeSoto County, 1958-60; design engr. Worthington Corp., Harrison, N.J., 1960-63; indsl. engr. Gen. Dynamics Corp., New London, Conn., 1963-66; mgr. fin. analysis Boeing Corp., Seattle, 1966-68; mgr. contracts Nat. Steel & Shipbuilding Co., San Diego, 1968-71; mgr. purchasing Gen. Atomic Corp., San Diego, 1971-75; corp. atty. FMC Corp., Portland, Oreg., 1975-77; corp. mgr. contracts Pacific Power & Light, Portland, 1977-82; pres., CEO The Condor Group, San Diego, 1982—. Author: Contract Claims and Litigation Avoidance, 1988. Pres. Planning Commn., Tigard, Oreg., 1977-83; atty., referee Calif. State Bar Atty./Client Dispute Panel, San Diego, 1991—. Lt. USN, 1958-60. Mem. State Bar Calif., State Bar of Oreg., U.S. Supreme Ct. Bar, Am. Arbitration Assn. (arbitrator 1991—), Nat. Assn. Contract Mgmt., Nat. Mgmt. Cons. Orgns. Avocations: model A club, H.O. train model club, col. in confederate airforce. Office: The Condor Group 3638 Camino del Rio N Ste 100 San Diego CA 92108

TEPHLY, THOMAS ROBERT, pharmacologist, toxicologist, educator; b. Norwich, Conn., Feb. 1, 1936; s. Samuel M. and Anna (Pieniadz) T.; m. Joan Bernice Clifcorn, Dec. 17, 1960; children: Susan Lynn, Linda Ann, Annette Michele. B.S., U. Conn., 1957; Ph.D., U. Wis., 1962; M.D., U. Minn., 1965. Research asst. U. Wis., Madison, 1957-62, instr., 1962; asst. prof. U. Mich., Ann Arbor, 1965-69, assoc. prof., 1969-71; prof. pharmacology U. Iowa, Iowa City, 1971—. Contbr. articles to profl. jours. Rsch. scholar Am. Cancer Soc., 1962-65; recipient John Jacob Abel award, 1971, Samuel P. Dubois award, 1992; Fogarty sr. internat. fellow NIH, 1978; rsch. grantee NIH, 1966. Mem. Am. Soc. Pharmacology and Exptl. Therapeutics, Soc. Toxicology, AAAS, Am. Soc. Biol. Chemists, Research Soc. on Alcoholism. Home: 6 Lakeview Dr NE Iowa City IA 52240 Office: U Iowa Dept Pharmacology Iowa City IA 52242

TEPLOW, THEODORE HERZL, valve company executive; b. Brockton, Mass., Apr. 14, 1928; s. Edward Abraham and Evelyn (Stone) T.; m. Charlotte Leah Savitz, June 14, 1953; children: Rachel P., David I., Deborah R., Evan S., Jonathan P. B.S. U.S. Mcht. Marine Acd., 1950; M.B.A. Harvard U., 1953. Mgmt. trainee to pres. Crosby Valve & Gage Co., (a Moorco Co.), Wrentham, Mass., 1953-82, cons., 1982—; dir. Emerson Investment Mgmt., Inc., Boston, 1985—; cons. Firesafe Products Corp., N.Y.C., 1982—. Trustee Internat. Catacomb Soc., Boston, 1982—, pres. Beth El-Atereth Israel, Newton Center, Mass., 1975-85, Beth El Community Hebrew Sch., Newton Center, 1965-85, USMMA Found., Kings Point, N.Y., 1988—; trustee Am. Mcht. Marine Mus. Found., Kings Point, 1988—; asst.

treas. and dir. Am. Com. for Weizmann Inst. Sci., N.Y.; gov. Weizmann Inst. Sci., Rehovoth, Israel, 1991—; bd. dirs. Wilstein Inst. Jewish Policy Studies, L.A., 1993—; bd. trustees Rofeh Internat., Boston, 1990—, Stone Charitable Found., 1982—. Lt. USN, 1953-55; comdr. USNR. Recipient Outstanding Prof. Achievement award Alumni Assn. U.S. Mcht. Marine Acad., 1970, Meritorious Alumni Svc. award, 1990. Democrat. Office: Crosby Valve & Gage Co 43 Kendrick St Wrentham MA 02093-1544

TEPPER, LLOYD BARTON, physician; b. L.A., Dec. 21, 1931; m. Lamonte Leverage; children: Jeffrey Hamilton, Evan Clothier. AB, Dartmouth Coll., 1954; MD, Harvard U., 1957, MIH, 1960, ScD in Hygiene, 1962. Diplomate in occupational medicine Am. Bd. Preventive Medicine. Rsch. fellow Harvard Med. Sch., Boston, 1958-59; clin. fellow Mass. Gen. Hosp., Boston, 1958-60; rsch. assoc. MIT, Cambridge, 1959-62; physician U.S. AEC, Washington, 1962-65; prof. environ. health U. Cin., 1965-72; assoc. dir. Kettering Lab., Cin., 1965-72; assoc. commr. U.S. FDA, Washington, 1972-76; corp. med. dir. Air Products and Chems., Inc., Allentown, Pa., 1976—; dir. Chem. Industry Inst. Toxicology, Research Triangle Park, N.C., 1982-89; trustee Am. Bd. Preventive Medicine, vice chair, 1986-94. Editor Jour. Occupational Medicine, 1979-91. Fellow Am. Coll. Occupational and Environ. Medicine, Am. Acad. Occupational Medicine (pres. 1980-81). Office: Air Products and Chems Inc 7201 Hamilton Blvd Allentown PA 18195-1501

TEPPER, LYNN MARSHA, gerontology educator; b. N.Y.C., Mar. 16, 1946; d. Jack Mortimer and Ida (Golembe) Drukatz; m. William Chester Tepper, Aug. 27, 1967; children: Sharon Joy, Michelle Dawn. BS, SUNY, Buffalo, 1967; MA, Wayne State U., 1971; MS, Columbia U., 1977, EdM, 1978, EdD, 1980. Instr. John F. Kennedy Sch., Berlin, 1967-68, ednl. counselor, 1968-69; ednl. coordinator Army Edn. Ctr., Berlin, 1969-71; psychologist U.S. Dept. Def., Berlin, 1971-73; prof. Gerontology L.I. U., Dobbs Ferry, N.Y., 1979—, Columbia U., N.Y.C., 1982—; cons. NATO, Belgium, Naples, Italy, 1969-71, numerous nursing homes, N.Y.C., 1978—, Found. for Long Term Care, 1992—; prof. gerontology Mercy Coll., Dobbs Ferry, 1979—; dir. Gerontology Resource Ctr., Ctr. for Geriatrics and Gerontology, Columbia U., N.Y.C., 1980-85, dir. divsn. behavioral sci., 1982—; del. White House Conf. on Aging, 1980. Author: (textbooks) Long Term Care, 1993, Respite Care, 1993; contbr. articles to profl. jours. and textbooks. Advisor Office on Aging, State of N.Y., Albany, 1980—; dir. Mercy Coll., Inst. Gerontology, 1990—; trustee St. Cabrini Nursing Home, 1991—. Brookdale Inst. on Aging fellow, 1983. Fellow Gerontol. Soc. Am.; mem. Northeastern Gerontol. Soc., N.Y. Assn. Gerontol. Edn., Am. Psychol. Assn. Avocations: physical fitness. Home: 50 Burnside Dr Hastings Hdsn NY 10706-3013 Office: Columbia U Med Campus Box 20 630 W 168th St New York NY 10032

TEPPER, MICHAEL HOWARD, publishing company executive; b. Balt., Sept. 4, 1941; s. Jack and Betty Lee (Chodak) T.; m. Veronica Ann Schofield, Nov. 15, 1972; children: Alex, Megan, Sarah. B.A., U. Md., 1963; M.A., NYU, 1965, Ph.D., 1970. Pres., mng. editor Geneal. Pub. Co., Inc., Balt., 1971—. Author: American Passenger Arrival Records, 1988; editor: The Famine Immigrants (7 vols.), 1983-86, Passenger Arrivals at the Port of Philadelphia 1800-1819, 1986, Passenger Arrivals at the Port of Baltimore 1820-1834, 1982, New World Immigrants (2 vols.), 1979, Immigrants to the Middle Colonies, 1978, Passengers to America, 1977, Emigrants to Pennsylvania, 1975. Recipient Founders' Day award NYU, 1970. Office: Geneal Pub Co Inc 1001 N Calvert St Baltimore MD 21202-3809

TERAN, TIMOTHY ERIC ALBA, marketing professional; b. N.Y.C., Apr. 11, 1956; s. Eric Henry Alba and Patricia (Wheel) T. BA in Market Psychology, Oberlin Coll., 1978. Rsch. intern Needham Harper & Steers, Chgo., 1977; rsch. exec. Grey Advt., N.Y.C., 1979-80, sr. rsch. exec., 1981, asst. rsch. dir., 1982-83, assoc. rsch. dir., 1984, v.p. assoc. rsch. dir., 1985-88, v.p. sr. assoc. dir. strategic svcs., 1989-92, sr. v.p., deputy dir. strategic svcs., 1992—. Home: 13 Gramercy Park S New York NY 10003-1755 Office: Grey Advt 777 3rd Ave New York NY 10017

TERAO, TOSHIO, physician, educator; b. Shimizu, Japan, Jan. 18, 1930; s. Eiji and Mitsuko (Katagiri) T.; m. Setsuko Nishigaki, Nov. 13, 1961; children: Toshiya, Yasuo, Yoshio. Diploma U. Tokyo, 1953, M.D., 1960. Intern, Tokyo U. Hosp., 1953-54; sr. scientist Nat. Inst. Radiol. Sci., Chiba, Japan, 1963-67; research assoc. Mayo Clinic, Rochester, Minn., 1970-72; asst. U. Tokyo, 1972-77, lectr. in medicine 1977-79; prof. medicine Teikyo U., 1980-91, prof. neurology, 1991—; pres. Teikyo U. Med. Hosp., 1987-93, dean, 1993—. Author, editor in field. Mem. Am. Acad. Neurology, Japanese Soc. Internal Medicine, Japanese Soc. Neurology, Japanese Soc. Neuropathology, Japanese Soc. EEG and Electromyography, Japanese Soc. Psychiatry and Neurology, Japanese Soc. Cerebrovascular Disease, Sigma Xi. Office: Teikyo U, 2-11-1 Kaga Itabashiku, Tokyo 173, Japan

TERASMAE, JAAN, geology educator; b. Estonia, May 28, 1926; s. Enn and Virge (Lepik) T.; m. Vaike Jurima, July 31, 1954. Phil. Cand., U. Uppsala, Swden, 1951; Ph.D., McMaster U., Can., 1955. Head palynology lab. Geol. Survey of Can., 1955-67, head paleoecology and geochronology sect., 1968; prof. dept. geology Brock U., St. Catharines, Ont., Can., 1968-91; prof. emeritus Brock U., St. Catharines, Ont., 1991—; chmn. dept. geology Brock U., St. Catharines, Ont., Can., 1969-73, 75-76. Contbr. numerous articles to profl. jours. Fellow Geol. Assn. Can., Geol. Soc. Am., Royal Soc. Can.; mem. Am. Assn. Stratigraphic Palynologists, Am. Quaternary Assn., Arctic Inst. N.Am., Can. Assn. Palynologists (pres. 1984-85), Can. Quaternary Assn. (William A. Johnston medal 1990), Internat. Assn. Gt. Lakes Rsch., Internat. Glaciological Soc., Internat. Limnological Soc., Internat. Orgn. Palaeobotany, Internat. Peat Soc., Tree-Ring Soc., Royal Can. Geog. Soc. Lutheran. Avocation: photography. Home: 196 Woodside Dr, Saint Catharines, ON Canada L2T 1X6 Office: Brock U, Dept Geol Sciences, Saint Catharines, ON Canada L2S 3A1

TERBORGH, BERT, dancer; b. Bennebroek, Netherlands, Mar. 8, 1945; came to U.S., 1975; s. Cornelius Franciscus and Petronella Maria (Berbee) Zwetsloot. Grad., Gymnasium, Haarlem, Netherlands, 1964. Dancer with Scapino Ballet, Australian Dance Theatre and Rotterdam Dance Theater, 1967-72; prin. dancer Bat Dor Dance Co., Israel, 1973-74, Paul Sanasordo and Australian Dance Theater, N.Y.C. and, Australia, 1975; prin. dancer Martha Graham Dance Co., N.Y.C., 1976-82, rehearsal dir., tchr., 1982-87; mem. dance faculty SUNY, Purchase, 1987—; mem. faculty Martha Graham Ctr., N.Y.C., Neighborhood Playhouse, N.Y.C.; tchr. dance univs., schs., cos., U.S., Europe and Australia. Mem. Am. Guild Mus. Artists. Home: 484 W 43rd St Apt 23T New York NY 10036-6341

TERBORG-PENN, ROSALYN MARIAN, historian, educator; b. Bklyn., Oct. 22, 1941; d. Jacques Arnold Sr. and Jeanne (Van Horn) Terborg; 1 dau., Jeanna Carolyn Terborg Penn. B.A. in History, Queens Coll., CUNY, 1963; M.A. in History, George Washington U., 1967; Ph.D. in Afro-Am. History, Howard U., 1978. Day care tchr. Friendship House Assn., Washington, 1964-66; program dir. Southwest House Assn., Washington, 1966-69; adj. prof. U. Md.-Balt. County, Catonsville, 1977-78, Howard Community Coll., Columbia, Md., 1970-74; prof. history Morgan State U., Balt., 1969—, project dir. oral history project, 1978-79, coord. grad. programs in history, 1986—; project dir. Assn. Black Women Hist. Research Conf., Washington, 1982-83. Author: (with Thomas Holt and Cassandra Smith-Parker) A Special Mission: the Story of Freedmen's Hospital, 1862-1962, 1975. Editor (with Sharon Harley) The Afro-American Woman: Struggles and Images, 1978, 81; (with Sharon Harley and Andrea Benton Rushing) Women in Africa and The African Diaspora, 1987. History editor Feminist Studies, 1984-89; mem. editorial bd. Md. Hist. Mag., 1988—. Founding mem. Howard County Commn. for Women. Ford Found. fellow, 1980-81, Smithsonian Instn. fellow, 1982; Howard U. grad. fellow in history, 1973-74, recipient Rayford W. Logan Grad. Essay award Howard U., 1973. Mem. Assn. Black Women Historians (co-founder, 1st nat. dir. 1980-82, nat. treas. 1984-85, cert. outstanding achievement 1981), Am. Hist. Assn. (mem. com. on women historians 1978-81, Joan Kelly Prize com. 1984-86, chair com. on women historians 1991—), Orgn. Am. Historians (mem. black women's history project adv. com. 1980-81), Alpha Kappa Alpha. Office: Morgan State U Baltimore MD 21239

TERENZIO, JOSEPH VINCENT, hospital administrator; b. New Haven, Feb. 4, 1918; s. Vincent and Marianna (Piantino) T.; m. Marie Louise Cozzolino, Feb. 3, 1945; children: Mary Louise (Mrs. Jeffrey Shafer), Joanne (Mrs. J. Haywood Blakemore, IV), John Joseph. BA, Yale U., 1939; JD, Fordham U., 1947; MS, Columbia U., 1954. Bar: Conn. bar 1947. Mem. firm Curran, DiSesa and Vining, New Haven, 1947-50; asst. administr. Knickerbocker Hosp., N.Y.C., 1951-52, Western Pa. Hosp., Pitts., 1952-56; exec. dir. Knickerbocker Hosp., N.Y.C., 1956-60; dir. Brooklyn Hosp., 1960-64, exec. v.p., 1964-66; commnr. hosps. City N.Y., 1966-70; pres. Evanston (Ill.) Hosp., 1970-72; exec. v.p. United Hosp. Fund of N.Y., 1972-74, pres., 1974-83; chmn. bd. dirs. Meta Health Tech., Inc., N.Y.C., 1983—; lectr. hosp. law U. Pitts., 1952-56; lectr. hosp. law U. Mich. Sch. Bus. Adminstrn., 1955—, Cornell U. 1958—; lectr. hosp. adminstrn. Columbia, 1958-72, spl. adviser to pres., 1972-80, adj. prof. pub. health, 1972—; mem. Nat. Acad. Scis., Inst. of Medicine, 1981, N.Y. State Hosp. Rev. and Planning Council, 1976-78; chmn. N.Y.C. Adv. Com. on Office of Chief Med. Examiner, 1976-77; asst. chief. Publ. Pharmacy, 1963-66; trustee Emigrant Savs. Bank N.Y.C., 1976-90, Nat. Health Council, 1978-80, pres., 1979-80; mem. tech. adv. bd. Nat. Exec. Service Corps. Sec. Yale U. Class of 1939, 1975-88; bd. mgrs. New Haven Boys Club, 1948-50; bd. dirs. Tb Inst. Chgo., 1970-72, Harlem Neighborhoods Assn., Health Manpower Devel. Corp., Washington, 1970-77; dir. Med. and Health Research Assn., N.Y.C., 1972-77; treas. Health and Hosp. Planning Council So. N.Y., 1972-78; trustee Coll. Mt. St. Vincent, Riverdale, N.Y.; chmn. bd. trustees Milton Helpern Library of Legal Medicine, 1981-90; vice chmn. Bellevue Assn., 1983-90; bd. dirs., exec. com. N.Y. Blood Ctr. Served to lt. comdr. USNR, 1941-46. Fellow Am. Coll. Hosp. Adminstrs., Am. Pub. Health Assn.; mem. Hosp. Assn. N.Y. State, Am., N.Y.C. pub. health assns., Am. Hosp. Assn. (chmn. com. on health care for disadvantaged 1971-74, mem. nat. adv. com. on health 1970-72), Greater N.Y. Hosp. Assn., Hosp. Assn. Pa., Am. Bar Assn. Clubs: University (N.Y.C.), Rembrandt (N.Y.C.), Yale (N.Y.C.); Faculty House (Columbia); Pequot Ycht Club (Southport, Conn.). Home: One Grove Isle Dr #308 Coconut Grove FL 33133 Office: Meta Health Tech Inc 363 7th Ave New York NY 10001-3904

TERENZIO, PETER BERNARD, hospital administrator; b. N.Y.C., Mar. 6, 1916; s. Vincent and Marianna (Piantino) T.; m. Eileen Alma Mosher, May 29, 1941; children—Mary Ellen Alecci, Vincent, Nancy Britton, Peter Bernard. Student, Yale U., 1934-37; J.D., U. Conn., 1940; M. Hosp. Adminstrn., Northwestern U., 1950. Bar: Conn. bar 1941. Practice in New Haven, 1945-48; with standardization div. A.C.S., Chgo., 1948-49; adminstrv. resident Evanston (Ill.) Hosp., 1949-50; asst. dir. Roosevelt Hosp., N.Y.C., 1950-52; exec. v.p., dir. Roosevelt Hosp., 1953-76, cons., 1976-81; pres. Hosp. Bur. Inc., Pleasantville, N.Y., 1977-81; dir. Greenville (S.C.) Gen. Hosp., 1952-53; cons. to surgeon gen. USPHS, 1960-65, 66-69; to commnr. Dept. Hosps., N.Y.C., 1961-68; prof. clin. dentistry community Sch. Dental and Oral Surgery, Columbia U., 1963-84; univ. lectr. pub. health and adminstrv. medicine; adj. prof. Pace U., 1978-82, New Sch. Social Research 1977-85; Mem. facilities planning com. Hosp. Rev. and Planning Council of So. N.Y., 1963-69; mem. vol. adv. staff N.Y. State Health and Mental Retardation, 1966-69. Adv. editorial bd., Hosp. and Health Services Adminstrn. Bd. dirs., exec. com. Asso. Hosp. Service N.Y., 1970-74, N.Y. Coll. Podiatry, 1971-73; bd. dirs. Blue Cross-Blue Shield Greater N.Y., 1974-78, Abacus, 1965-86, Dominican Sisters Home Health Agy., 1977-82, Health Services Improvement Fund, 1978-85; mem. exec. adv. bd. Hosp. Home Care Santa Ana, Calif., 1984-86; vol., assoc., Sr. Friendship Health Ctr., Naples, Fla., 1986—, mem. adv. bd., 1992—. Capt., Med. Adminstrn. Corps AUS, 1941-45. Fellow Am. Coll. Hosp. Execs. (gov. 1964-65, regent 2d dist. 1960-64, pres. 1966-67, chmn. bd. dirs.), Am. Pub. Health Assn.; mem. Am. Hosp. Assn. (ho. of dels. 1969-76, rep. Am. Blood Commn., trustee liaison com. podiatry), Hosp. Research and Devel. Inst., N.Y. Acad. Medicine, Pub. Health Assn. N.Y.C. (dir., v.p. 1973-74, pres. 1976-77), Roosevelt Hosp. Alumni Assn. (asso.), Hosp. Assn. N.Y. (pres. 1970-71), Middle Atlantic Hosp. Assembly (bd. govs.), Hosp. Adminstrs. Study Soc., Am. Bar Assn., Greater N.Y. Hosp. Assn. (pres. 1960), Hosp. Adminstrs. Club (pres. 1959), Hosp. Soc. (pres. 1965), Coquina Club of Naples, Inc. (sec., treas. 1984-86, pres. 1987-90). Roman Catholic. Home and Office: Apt G608 127 Moorings Park Dr Naples FL 33942 Home (summer): 85 Hartford Ave Madison CT 06443

TERESI, JOSEPH, publishing executive; b. Mpls., Mar. 13, 1941; s. Cliff I.A. and Helen Ione (Leslie) T.; divorced; 1 child, Nicholas. Chief exec. officer Jammer Cycle Products Inc., Burbank, Calif., 1968-80, Paisano Pubs. Inc., Agoura Hills, Calif., 1970—. Pub. (mags.) Easyriders, 1971—, In the Wind, 1974—, Biker Lifestyle, 1986—, Tatoo, 1986—, Am. Rodder, 1987, Womens Enterprise, 1987-89, Eagles Eye, 1989—, Tattoo Flash, 1993—, Tattoo Savage, 1993—, VQ, 1994—, Earlyriders, 1994—, Quick Throttle 1995—, Roadware, 1995—. Holds world speed record for motorcycles set at 322 miles per hour, 1990. Avocations: motorcycles, race cars, boats, marlin fishing, skiing. Office: Paisano Pubs Inc PO Box 3000 Agoura Hills CA 91376-3000

TERET, STEPHEN PAUL, health law educator; b. N.Y.C., Mar. 28, 1945; s. Jules and Betty (Paul) T.; m. Marilyn Anne Cavanaugh, Oct. 23, 1986; children: Michael D., Elizabeth, Christopher P., Walker D. BA, St. Lawrence U., 1966; JD, Bklyn. Law Sch., 1969; MPH, Johns Hopkins U., 1979. Bar: N.Y. 1969, Md. 1979, U.S. Dist. Ct. N.Y. 1974, U.S. Ct. Appeals (2d cir.) 1975, U.S. Ct. Appeals (11th cir.) 1984. Staff atty. Harlem Assertion Rights, N.Y.C., 1969-70; assoc. Brandt and Laughlin, P.C., Westfield, N.Y., 1970-78; asst. prof. Sch. Pub. Health, Johns Hopkins U., Balt., 1979-82, assoc. prof., 1982-88, prof. and dir., 1988—; adj. prof. law Georgetown U. Law Ctr., Washington, 1987—; cons. HHS, Washington, 1979—, Dept. Transp., Washington, 1979—, U.S. Congress, 1979—, WHO, Geneva, 1983. Recipient Golden Apple Teaching award Johns Hopkins U., 1984 and 1989. Mem. Am. Pub. Health Assn., Assn. Trial Lawyers Am., North Chautauqua Bar Assn. (pres. 1978), Delta Omega. Avocation: classical music. Office: Johns Hopkins Sch Pub Health 624 N Broadway Baltimore MD 21205-1901

TERHAR, LOUIS F., waste management administrator; b. 1949. BS in Enging., U.S. Naval Acad., 1972; MBA, Syracuse U., 1978; degree in Liberal Arts, Harvard U., 1982. With W.R. Grace & Co., N.Y., 1978-83, Emhart Corp., Balt., 1983-89; with SHV N.Am. Corp., Cin., 1989—, now pres., COO. With USN, 1972-78. Office: SHV North Am Corp 300 Pike St Cincinnati OH 45202-4222

TERHORST, CHERYL ANN, journalist; b. Buffalo, Aug. 3, 1960; d. Paul Bernard and Mary Jean (McNab) terH.; m. Burt W. Constable, Mar. 26, 1988. BS in Journalism, U. Ill., 1982. Editorial asst. Woman's Day mag., N.Y.C., 1982-84; city reporter Daily Herald, Arlington Heights, Ill., 1984-85, edn. reporter, 1985-86, feature writer, 1987—. Vol. Community Response, Oak Park, Ill., 1992-94. Recipient Peter Lisagor award Soc. Profl. Journalists, 1991, 94. Avocations: flying, travel. Office: Daily Herald 217 W Campbell St Arlington Heights IL 60005

TERHORST, JERALD FRANKLIN, public affairs counsel; b. Grand Rapids, Mich., July 11, 1922; s. John Henry and Maude (Van Strien) ter H.; m. Louise Jeffers Roth, Jan. 20, 1945; children: Karen Bayens Morris, Margaret Fulton Robinson, Peter Roth, Martha Morgan Lubin. Student, Mich. State U., 1941-42; A.B., U. Mich., 1947. Reporter Grand Rapids Press 1946-51; mem. staff Detroit News, 1953-74, city and state polit. writer, 1953-57, Washington corr., 1958-60; chief Detroit News (Washington bur.), 1961-74; White House press sec. to Pres., 1974; columnist Detroit News/Universal Press Syndicate, 1974-81; nat. dir. public affairs Ford Motor Co. 1981-91; fgn. assignments include Berlin crisis Geneva Fgn. Ministers Conf., Yugoslavia, 1959, 70, Israel, 1960, Eng., Ireland, Germany, Italy and France, 1963, 69, Vietnam, India and Pakistan, 1966, 70, China, 1972, Moscow, 1974, Africa, 1978; writer N.Am. Newspaper Alliance, 1958-74. Author: Gerald Ford and Future of the Presidency, 1974, The Flying White House: The Story of Air Force One, 1979; contbr. to mags. and TV documentaries. Bd. dirs. Nat. Press Found., Gridiron Found., Grad. Sch. Polit. Mgmt., George Washington U., Washington, Handgun Control, Inc. Officer USMCR, 1943-46, 51-52. Mem. Pub. Rels. Soc. Am., Soc. Profl. Journalists, Psi Upsilon. Presbyterian (elder). Clubs: Gridiron, Nat. Press. Overseas Writers.

TERHUNE, ROBERT WILLIAM, optics scientist; b. Detroit, Feb. 8, 1926; married; 2 children. BS, U. Mich., 1947, PhD in Physics, 1957; MA, Dartmouth Coll., 1948. Supr. digital computation and logic design sect. Willow Run Labs. U. Mich., 1951-54, rsch. physicist, 1954-59, mgr. Solid State Physics Lab., 1959-60; rsch. physicist Sci. Lab. Ford Motor Co. Dearborn, Mich., 1960-65, mgr. physics electronics dept., 1965-75, sr. staff scientist engring. and rsch. staff, 1976-87; sr. mem. tech. staff JPL Calif. Tech., 1988—; vis. scholar Stanford U., 1975-76. Editor Optics Let. Jour., 1977-83. Recipient Sci. and Engring. award Drexel Inst. Tech., 1964, Frederic Ives Medal, 1992, Optical Soc. Am. Mem. IEEE, Optical Soc. Am. (editor jour. 1984-87, Frederic Ives medal 1992), Am. Phys. Soc. Achievements include research in quantum electronics, nonlinear optics, optical properties of solids and surfaces, molecular spectroscopy, advanced instrumentation. Office: 1460 Pegfair Estates Dr Pasadena CA 91103-1929

TERILLI, SAMUEL A., JR., newspaper publishing executive. Gen. Coun. The Miami Herald, Fla. Office: The Miami Herald 1 Herald Plz Miami FL 33132-1693*

TERKEL, STUDS (LOUIS TERKEL), author, interviewer; b. N.Y.C., May 16, 1912; s. Samuel and Anna (Finkel) T.; m. Ida Goldberg, July 2, 1939; 1 son, Paul. PhB, U. Chgo., 1932, JD, 1934. Stage appearances include Detective Story, 1950, A View From the Bridge, 1958, Light Up the Sky, 1959, The Cave Dwellers, 1960; moderator: (TV program) Studs Place, 1950-53, (radio programs) Wax Museum, 1945— (Ohio State Univ. award 1959, UNESCO Prix Italia award 1962), Studs Terkel Almanac, 1952—, Studs Terkel Show, Sta. WFMT-FM, Chgo.; master of ceremonies Newport Folk Festival, 1959, 60, Ravinia Music Festival, 1959, U. Chgo. Folk Festival, 1961, others; panel moderator, lectr., narrator films; author: (books) Giants of Jazz, 1957, Division Street: America, 1967, Hard Times: An Oral History of the Great Depression, 1970, Working: People Talk about What They Do All Day and How They Feel about What They Do, 1974 (Nat. Book award nomination 1975), Talking to Myself: A Memoir of My Times, 1977, American Dreams: Lost and Found, 1980, The Good War: An Oral History of World War II (Pulitzer prize in nonfiction 1985), Chicago, 1986, The Great Divide: Second Thoughts On The American Dream, 1988, Race: How Blacks and Whites Think and Feel About the American Obsession, 1992, Coming of Age, 1995; (play) Amazing Grace, 1959; also short stories. Named Communicator of Yr. U. Chgo. Alumni Assn., 1969. Office: 303 E Wacker Dr Chicago IL 60601-5212*

TERKEL, SUSAN NEIBURG, author; b. Lansdale, Pa., Apr. 7, 1948; d. Sidney Aaron and Deborah (Burstein) Neiburg; m. Lawrence Arthur Terkel, Oct. 25, 1970; children: Ari Garth, Marni Anne, David Samuel. BS, Cornell U., 1970. Freelance writer, 1978—. Author: Abortion: Facing the Issue, 1988, Should Drugs Be Legalized?, 1990, Understanding Child Custody, 1991, Ethics, 1992, other books. Co-founder, bd. dirs. Spiritual Life Soc., Hudson, Ohio, 1978—, Ohio State Freeze Campaign, Columbus, 1987, Soviet-Am. Youth Ambs., 1988. Charles Rieley Armington Found. grantee Case Western Res. U., 1988. Mem. P.E.N., Author's Guild, Soc. Children's Writers. Democrat. Jewish. Avocations: sewing, needlework, traveling.

TER KEURS, HENK E. D. J., cardiologist, educator; b. Delft, The Netherlands, Aug. 27, 1942; married; 3 children. Degree. Huygens Lyceum, Voorburg, The Netherlands, 1960; MD, State Univ. Leiden, The Netherlands, 1966, PhD cum laude, 1970, Splty. Cert. Med. Physiology, 1980, Splty. Cert. Cardiology, 1983. Cert. cardiology specialist, Can., 1988. Rsch. asst. dept. physiology State Univ. Leiden, 1966-66, docent dept. physiology, 1966-73, sr. rsch. assoc dept. cardiology, 1973-84; med. scientist Alta. (Can.) Heritage Found., 1984—; prof. medicine and med. physiology U. Calgary, Alta., 1984—; Merck Frosst prof. in cardiovascular rsch. U. Calgary, Alta., 1994—; established investigator dept. cardiology Netherlands Heart Found., State U. Leiden, 1976-81; rsch. fellow Midhurst Med. Rsch. Inst., U.K., 1979-85; chmn. sci. rev. com. Heart and Stroke Found. Can., 1992—; mem. cardiovascular A com. Med. Rsch. Coun. Can., 1990—; mem. cardiovascular study sect. NIH, 1991—; vis. scholar dept. anesthesiology U. Wash., 1976-77; guest lectr. dept. physiology U. Surinam, 1972-75. Assoc. editor: Can. Jour. Physiology and Pharmacology, 1989—, editorial referee, 1984—, editorial referee Pflugers Archive Jour. Gen. Physiology, 1977—, Jour. Gen. Physiology, 1977—, Jour. Cellular Molecular Cardiology, 1984—, Jour. Neurosci. Methodology, 1984—, Biophys. Jour., 1985—, Circulatory Rsch. 1989—; contbr. articles, abstracts to Cardiovascular Rsch., Brain Rsch. Jour. Physiology, Circulation, Biophysics Jour., others. Sec./treas. Einthoven Found., 1983-84, adv. coun., 1989—; fellow Coun. Circulation Am. Heart Assn., 1986. Recipient AKZO Medicine prize Dutch Sci. Soc., 1980. Fellow Royal Coll. Physicians and Surgeons Can.; mem. Am. Biophys. Soc., Dutch Fedn. Physiology, Can. Cardiovascular Soc., Physiolog. Soc. U.K. (fgn.). Office: U Calgary-Cardiovascular Rsch, 3330 Hospital Dr NW, Calgary, AB Canada T2N 4N1

TERKHORN, HENRY K., food company executive; b. Brownstown, Ind., July 10, 1930; s. Henry K. and Louise M. (Wolka) T.; m. Imogene Grant, May 23, 1952; children—Deborah, Pamela. BS, Ind. U., 1957. C.P.A., Tex. Div. controller, internat. controller Cummins Engine Co., Dallas, London, Eng., 1966-69; v.p. finance Streater Industries div. Litton Industries, Albert Lea, Minn., 1969-70; asst. controller Oscar Mayer & Co., Madison, Wis., 1970-74; corporate controller Oscar Mayer & Co., 1974-v.p., 1976—. Bd. dirs. Family Service, 1972—; treas., 1973-74. Served with USN, 1950-54. Mem. Am. Inst. C.P.A.'s, Nat. Assn. Accountants, Financial Execs. Inst. Club: Elk. Office: 751 Coventry Dr Seymour IN 47274-1489

TERKLA, LOUIS GABRIEL, retired university dean; b. Anaconda, Mont., Mar. 24, 1925; s. George G. and Blanche (Wareham) T.; m. Phyllis Jean Cohn, Aug. 21, 1949; children—Darryl G., Linda J. Student, U. Mont., 1946-48; D.M.D., U. Oreg., 1952. Mem. faculty U. Oreg. Dental Sch., 1952—, prof., asst. to dean acad. affairs, 1961-67, dean, 1967-84, rsch. prof. and dean emeritus, 1984—. Author: (with others) Partial Dentures, 3d edit, 1963; also articles, chpts. in books. Served with inf. AUS, World War II. Fellow AAAS, Am. Coll. Dentists (pres. 1973-74), Acad. Gen. Dentistry (hon.); mem. Am. Dental Assn., Oreg. Dental Assn., Am. Assn. Dental Schs. (pres. 1975-76), Western Conf. Dental Examiners and Dental Sch. Deans (pres. 1975-76), Omicron Kappa Upsilon. Home: 1215 SW Kari Ln Portland OR 97219-6446 *Much of my success as a school of dentistry adminstrator can be attributed to a willingness to listen patiently to the problems borne by faculty, students and staff and to make a sincere effort toward their resolution. This requires an absolutely open-door administrative style, integrity and dedication to being a service agent to the people who make the school live.*

TERKUHLE, ABBY, graphic designer; b. 1954. With MTV Networks, N.Y.C., 1986—, now sr. v.p. creative and animation dept. Office: MTV Networks 1515 Broadway New York NY 10036*

TERMAN, LEWIS MADISON, electrical engineer, researcher; b. San Francisco, Aug. 26, 1935; s. Frederick Emmons and Sibyl (Walcott) T.; m. Barbara Chertok, Aug. 28, 1958. BS in Physics, Stanford U., 1956, MSEE, 1958, PhD, 1961. Mem. tech. staff T.J. Watson Rsch. Ctr., IBM, Yorktown Heights, N.Y., 1961-89, sr. mgr., 1989-91, sr. mem. tech. planning staff, 1991-93; mgr. VLSI processor design IBM, Yorktown Heights, N.Y., 1993-94; program mgr., 1994—; co-chmn. Symposium on Very Large Scale Integrated Technology, Systems and Application, Taiwan, 1989, 91, 93, 95, tech. program co-chmn., 1985, 87; tech. program chmn. Internat. Solid State Cirs. Conf., N.Y.C., 1983; chmn. Symposium on Very Large-Scale Integrated Tech., Kobe, Japan, 1985, San Diego, 1986, Symposium on Very Large-Scale Integrated Cirs., Karuizawa, Japan, 1988, Kyoto, Japan, 1989, Symposium on Low Power Electronics, San Diego, 1994. Contbr. articles to profl. jours.; holder 24 patents. Pres. Twin Lakes Water Works Corp., S. Salem, N.Y., 1980—. Recipient IEEE Solid-State Cirs. Tech. Field award, 1995. Fellow IEEE (tech. activities bd. 1990-94), AAAS; mem. IBM Acad. Tech. (chair components and processes com.), Electron Devices Soc. of IEEE (v.p. 1988-89, pres. 1990-91), Solid State Circuits Coun. of IEEE (treas. 1988-89, editor jour. 1974-77), IEEE Tech. Activities Bd. (chmn. tech. meetings coun. 1993-94), Circuits and Sys. Soc. of IEEE (adminstrv. com. 1981-83). Avocations: music, theatre, opera, hiking. Home: 61 Twin Lakes Rd South Salem NY 10590-1012 Office: IBM TJ Watson Rsch Ctr PO Box 218 Yorktown Heights NY 10598-0218

TERMEER, HENRICUS ADRIANUS, biotechnology company executive; b. Tilburg, Holland, Feb. 28, 1946; s. Jacques and Mary (Van Gorp) T.; came to U.S., 1971. Student, Ekonomisch Hogeschool, Rotterdam, Netherlands, 1969; M.B.A., U. Va., 1973. Mgr. mgmt. services Norvic Co., Norwich, England, 1969-71; mgr. internat. product planning Baxter Travenol, Inc., Deerfield, Ill., 1973-74, internat. mktg. mgr., 1975-76; gen. mgr. Travenol GMBH, Munich, W.Ger., 1976-79, v.p. Hyland Therapeutics div. Baxter Travenol, Glendale, Calif., 1979-81, exec. v.p., 1981-83; pres. Genzyme Corp., Inc., Boston, 1983—, chief ops. officer, 1983-85, chief exec. officer, 1986—, chmn., 1988—; dir. Lotus Devel. Corp., Autoimmune Corp., Abiomed, Xenova Ltd., Mass. Cystic Fibrosis Found., Neozyme Corp., IG Labs., Inc., Genzyme Transgenetics Corp.; vice chmn. Biotech. Industry Orgn.; treas. Mass. High Tech. Coun. Trustee Hambrecht & Quist Healthcare Investors Fund, Mus. of Sci., Boston. Served to 1st lt. Netherlands Royal Air Force, 1966-67. Office: Neozyme Corp 1 Kendall Sq Cambridge MA 02139

TERMINI, DEANNE LANOIX, research company executive; b. New Orleans, May 2, 1943; d. Albert Oliver and Freida (Fisher) Lanoix; m. Raymond Joseph Termini, Sept. 4, 1965; 1 dau., Andrea. BA, Tulane U., 1964; MA, U. Tex., Austin, 1968. Research analyst Belden Assocs., Dallas, 1968-70, research assoc., 1970-75, v.p., 1975-79, sr. v.p., 1979-87, exec. v.p., 1987-89, pres., 1989—; discussion leader Am. Press Inst., Reston, Va., 1983—. Author research reports. Speaker European and Latin confs., 1986—. Mem. Am. Mktg. Assn., Newspaper Assn. Am., Internat. Newspaper Mktg. Assn., Coun. Am. Survey Rsch. Orgns. Home: 13641 Far Hills Ln Dallas TX 75240-5533 Office: Belden Assocs 3102 Oak Lawn Ave Ste 500 Dallas TX 75219-4295

TERMINI, ROSEANN BRIDGET, lawyer; b. Phila., Feb. 2, 1953; d. Vincent James and Bridget (Marano) T. BS magna cum laude, Drexel U., 1975; MEd, Temple U., 1979, JD, 1985. Bar: Pa. 1985, U.S. Dist. Ct. (ea. dist.) Pa. 1985, D.C. 1986. Jud. clk. Superior Ct. of Pa., Allentown, 1985-86; atty. Pa. Power & Light Co., Allentown, 1986-87; corp. counsel food and drug law Lemmon Co., Sellersville, Pa., 1987-88; sr. dep. atty. bur. consumer protection plain lang. law Office of Atty. Gen., Harrisburg, Pa., 1988—; Contbr. articles to profl. jours., law revs.; spkr. continuing legal edn.-plain lang. laws, environ. conf. Contbr. articles to profl. jours, law revs.; speaker environ. conf. Active in Sr. Citizens Project Outreach, Hospice, 1986—; mem. St. Thomas More Law Bd. Named Outstanding Young Women of Yr., Dauphin County Bar Assn., 1987; Edn. fellow Temple U., 1978-79. Mem. ABA (various coms.), Bar Assn. D.C., Pa. Bar Assn. (ethics, exceptional children and environ. sects.), Temple U. Law Alumni Assn., Drexel U. Alumni Assn., Omicron Nu, Phi Alpha Delta. Avocations: tap dancing, hiking, cross-country skiing. Home: 5511 Blakeslee Dr Harrisburg PA 17111 Office: Office Atty Gen Harrisburg PA 17120 *Notable cases include: Waste Conversion case, 1990, violation of Pa. Solid Waste Mgmt. Act.*

TERNBERG, JESSIE LAMOIN, pediatric surgeon; b. Corning, Calif., May 28, 1924; d. Eric G. and Alta M. (Jones) T. A.B., Grinnell Coll., 1946, Sc.D. (hon.), 1972; Ph.D., U. Tex., 1950; M.D., Washington U., St. Louis, 1953; Sc.D. (hon.), U. Mo., St. Louis, 1981. Diplomate: Am. Bd. Surgery. Intern Boston City Hosp., 1953-54; asst. resident in surgery Barnes Hosp., St. Louis, 1954-57; resident in surgery Barnes Hosp., 1958-59; research fellow Washington U. (Sch. Medicine), 1957-58; practice medicine specializing in pediatric surgery St. Louis, 1966—; instr., trainee in surgery Washington U., 1959-62, asst. prof. surgery, 1962-65, assoc. prof., 1965-71, prof. surgery in pediatrics, 1975—, prof. surgery, 1971—, chief div. pediatric surgery, 1972-90; mem. staff Barnes Hosp., 1974-90, pediatric surgeon in chief, 1974-90, mem. operating room com., 1971—, mem. med. adv. com., 1975—; mem. staff Children's Hosp., dir. pediatric surgery, 1972-90. Contbr. numerous articles on pediatric surgery to profl. jours. Trustee Grinnell Coll., 1984—. Recipient Alumni award Grinnell Coll., 1966, Faculty/Alumni award Washington U. Sch. Medicine, 1991, 1st Aphrodite Jannopaulo Hofsommer award, 1993. Fellow ACS; mem. AAAS, SIOP, Am. Pediatric Surg. Assn., Western Surg. Assn. (2d v.p. 1984-85), St. Louis Med. Soc., Soc. Surgery of the Alimentary Tract, Am. Acad. Pediatrics, Soc. Pelvic Surgeons (v.p. 1991-92), Brit. Assn. Paediatric Surgeons, Mo. State Surg. Soc., St. Louis Surg. Soc. (pres. 1980-81), St. Louis Pediatric Soc., Soc. Surg. Oncology, Pediatric Oncology Group (chmn. surg. discipline 1983—), St. Louis Childrens Hosp. Soc. (pres. 1979-80), Barnes Hosp. Soc., Phi Beta Kappa, Sigma Xi, Iota Sigma Pi, Alpha Omega Alpha. Office: St Louis Childrens Hosp 1 Childrens Pl Saint Louis MO 63110

TERP, DANA GEORGE, architect; b. Chgo., Nov. 5, 1953; s. George and June (Hansen) T.; m. Lynn Meyers, May 17, 1975; children: Sophia, Rachel. BA in Architecture, Washington U., St. Louis, 1974; postgrad., Yale U., 1975-76; MArch, Washington U., 1977. Registered architect, Ill., Calif., Fla. Architect Skidmore Owings & Merrill, Chgo., 1976, 1978-84, Terp Meyers Architects, Chgo., 1984—; prin. Arquitectonica Chgo. Inc., 1986—. Exhibited in group shows at Morning Gallery, Chgo., 1980, Printers Row Exhibit, 1980, Frumkin Struve Gallery, Chgo., 1981, Chgo. Art Inst., 1983; pub. in profl jours. including Progressive Architecture, Los Angeles Architect; work featured in various archtl books; exhibited 150 Yrs. of Chgo. Architecture. Bd. dirs. Architecture Soc. Art Inst. Chgo. Recipient hon. mention Chgo. Townhouse Competition, 1978, award Progressive Architecture mag., 1980, Archtl. Record Houses, 1989, Global Architecture Ga. Houses/26, 1989, Casa Vogue, 1989, 2d place award Burnham Prize Competition, 1991. Office: Terp Meyers Architects 919 N Michigan Ave Ste 2402 Chicago IL 60611-1601

TERP, THOMAS THOMSEN, lawyer; b. Fountain Hill, Pa., Aug. 12, 1947; s. Norman T. and Josephine (Uhran) T.; m. Pamela Robinson; children: Stephanie, Brian, Adam; step-children: Taylor Mefford, Grace Mefford. BA, Albion (Mich.) Coll., 1969; JD, Coll. of William and Mary, 1973. Bar: Ohio 1973, U.S. Dist. Ct. (so. dist.) Ohio 1973, U.S. Ct. Appeals (6th cir.) 1973, U.S. Supreme Ct. 1979. Assoc. Taft, Stettinius & Hollister, Cin., 1973-80, ptnr., 1981—; bd. dirs. Starflo Corp., Orangeburg, S.C., Attorney's Liability Assurance Soc., Ltd., Hamilton, Bermuda, 1995—, ALAS, Inc., Chgo., 1995—. Editor-in-chief Coll. of William & Mary Law Rev., 1972-73; mem. bd. editors Jour. of Environ. Hazards, 1988—, Environ. Law Jour. of Ohio, 1989—. Mem. Cin. Athletic Club, Coldstream Country Club, Epworth Assembly (Ludington, Mich.), Lincoln Hills Golf Club (Ludington). Avocations: tennis, golf, racquetball, travel. Office: Taft Stettinius & Hollister 1800 Star Bank Ctr 425 Walnut St Cincinnati OH 45202-3912

TERPSTRA, VERN, marketing educator; b. Wayland, Mich., Aug. 20, 1927; s. Benjamin and Lucy (Jonker) T.; m. Bonnie Lou Fuller; children: Benjamin Mark, Kathryn Ann, James Richard. BA, U. Mich., 1950, MBA, 1951, PhD, 1965. Dir. normal sch. Grace Mission, Zaire, 1952-61; rsch. asst., assoc. prof. mktg. Wharton Sch. U. Penn., Phila., 1964-66; prof. Sch. Bus. U. Mich., Ann Arbor, 1967-92, prof. emeritus, 1992—; cons. govt., bus. and acad. orgns., 1972—. Author: The Cultural Environment of International Business, 1978, 3d edit., 1991, International Marketing, 1972, 6th edit., 1994. Fellow Ford Found., Mktg. Sci. Inst.; mem. Am. Mktg. Assn., Acad. Internat. Bus. Presbyterian. Avocations: tennis, theatre, reading. Office: U Mich Bus Sch Ann Arbor MI 48109-1234

TERR, LENORE CAGEN, psychiatrist, writer; b. N.Y.C., Mar. 27, 1936; d. Samuel Lawrence Cagen and Esther (Hirsh) Cagen Rainen; m. Abba I. Terr; children: David, Julia. AB magna cum laude, Case Western Res. U., 1957; MD with honors, U. Mich., 1961. Diplomate: Am. Bd. Psychiatry and Neurology. Intern Med. Ctr. U. Mich., Ann Arbor, 1961-62, resident Neuropsychiat. Inst. 1962-64, fellow Children's Psychiat. Hosp., 1964-66; from instr. to asst. prof. Med. Sch. Case Western Res. U., Cleve., 1966-71; pvt. practice Terr Med. Corp., San Francisco, 1971—; from asst. clin. prof. to clin. prof. psychiatry Sch. Medicine U. Calif., San Francisco, 1971—; lectr. law, psychiatry U. Calif., Berkeley, 1971—, U. Calif., Davis, 1974—; bd. dirs. Am. Bd. Psychiatry and Neurology, Deerfield, Ill., 1988—. Author: Too Scared to Cry, 1990, Unchained Memories, 1994; contbr. articles to profl. jours. Rockefeller Found. scholar-in-residence, Italy, 1981, 88; project grantee Rosenberg Found., 1977, 80-81, William T. Grant Found., 1986-87; recipient Career Tchr. award NIMH, 1967-69, Child Advocacy award APA, 1994. Fellow Am. Psychiat. Assn. (Child Psychiatry Rsch. award 1984, Clin. Rsch. award 1987), Am. Coll. Psychiatrists (program chair 1991-92),

Am. Acad. Child and Adolescent Psychiatry (coun. 1984-87); mem. Group for Advancement Psychiatry (bd. dirs. 1986-88), Phi Beta Kappa, Alpha Omega Alpha. Avocations: piano, walking, travel. Office: Terr Med Corp 450 Sutter St Rm 2534 San Francisco CA 94108-4204

TERRA, DANIEL JAMES, chemical company executive; b. Phila., June 8, 1911; s. Louis J. and Mary (DeLuca) T.; m. Adeline Evans Richards, Aug. 7, 1937 (dec. 1982); children: Penny Jane (dec.), James D.; m. Judith Anne Farabee, June 27, 1986. BS, Pa. State U., 1931; LLD, MacMurray Coll., 1972; DFA (hon.), Nat. Coll., 1980, U. Ill., 1984. Founder Lawter Internat. Inc., Chgo., 1940; chmn. bd. dirs., CEO Lawter Internat. Inc., 1964—; amb.-at-large for cultural affairs U.S. Dept. State, 1981-89; chmn. Mercury Fin. Corp., 1989—; bd . dirs. Lawter Internat. Inc., Mercury Fin. Corp. Founder, chmn., bd. dirs. Terra Mus. Am. Art, Chgo. and Evanston, Ill., Musée Américain Giverny, France; chmn. Terr Found. for Arts; past v.p., mem. exec. com. United Republican Fund Ill., pres., 1973-79; past chmn. Everett Dirksen 500 Club.; nat. fin. chmn. Ronald Reagan for Pres. of U.S. campaign, 1979-80; co-chmn. Pres.'s Task Force for the Arts and Humanities, 1981-82; mem. Pres.'s Com. for Arts and Humanities, 1982-89; bd. dirs. Chgo. Lyric Opera; ex officio trustee Nat. Gallery Art, Washington . Decorated Order of Leopold II (Belgium), comdr. Order Arts and Letters (France; recipient Winthrop Sears medal Chem. Industry Assn., 1972; Distinguished Alumni medal Pa. State U., 1976, Lincoln Acad. medal, Springfield, Ill., 1982. Clubs: Westmoreland Country (Wilmette, Ill.); Chicago (Chgo.), Commercial (Chgo.), Chicago Mid-America (Chgo.), Casino (Chgo.); Indian Hill (Winnetka, Ill.); Nat. Arts (N.Y.C.), Links (N.Y.C.). Home: 2430 Lake View Ave Chicago IL 60614 also: 3263 N St NW Washington DC 20007 also: 62 Ave de Ardeche, 27620 Vernon France Office: Lawter International Inc 990 Skokie Blvd Northbrook IL 60062-4096

TERRACCIANO, ANTHONY PATRICK, banker; b. Bayonne, N.J., Oct. 27, 1938; s. Patrick and Grace Terracciano; m. Rita Cuddy, Apr. 20, 1963; children: Laura, Karen, Kenneth. BS in Econs. St. Peter's Coll., Jersey City, N.J., 1960; MA in Philosophy, Fordham U., 1962. with Chase Manhattan Bank, N.Y.C., 1964—, exec. v.p. internat., 1974-76, 84-85, exec. v.p., treas., 1976-80, exec. v.p. ops. trusts and systems dept., 1980-83, exec. v.p., chief fin. officer, 1983-84, vice chmn. global banking, 1985-87, pres., chief operating officer, Mellon Bank Corp., Pitts., 1987-90, chmn., pres., chief exec. officer, First Fidelity Bancorp., Newark, N.J., 1990—; dir. N.J. Bell Tel. Co., Pitcairn Co.. Dir. N.J. Performing Arts Ctr. Copr, N.Y. Philharm., Metro Newark C. of C.; mem. exec. coun. Better Bus. Bur., Newark; trustee Renaissance Newark, Inc.; mem. Coun. on Fgn. Rels. 1st lt. U.S. Army, 1962-64. Mem. N.J. Banker's Assn. (exec. com.). Avocations: music, reading. Office: First Fidelity Bancorp PO Box 6980 Lawrenceville NJ 08648*

TERRACE, HERBERT S(YDNEY), psychologist, educator; b. Bklyn., Nov. 29, 1936; s. Morris Abraham and Esther (Marsh) T.; m. Kathleen A. Frederick, July 26, 1986; 1 child, Gillian Frederick. A.B., Cornell U., 1957, M.A., 1958; Ph.D., Harvard U., 1961. Instr. psychology Columbia U., 1961-63, asst. prof. psychology, 1963-66, assoc. prof., 1966-68, prof., 1968—; vis. prof. Harvard U., 1972-73. Author: Introduction to Statistics, 1971, (with Scott Parker) Individual Learning Systems, 1971, Nim, 1979; editor: (with T.G. Bever) Human Behavior: Prediction and Control in Modern Society, 1973, (with H.L. Roitblat and T.G. Bever) Animal Cognition, 1983, (with C. Locurto and J. Gibbon) Autoshaping and Conditioning Theory, 1981, (with P. Marler) Biology of Learning, 1984; editor Jour. Exptl. Analysis Behavior, 1966-74; assoc. editor Animal Learning and Behavior, 1971-75, 83-86, Learning and Motivation, 1970-72, Behaviorism, 1972-84, Jour. Exptl. Psychology: Animal Learning Processes, 1986—. John Simon Guggenheim fellow, 1969-70; Harry Frank Guggenheim fellow, 1976-77; NIMH grantee, 1962—; NSF grantee, 1963-81; Fulbright sr. research scholar, 1983-84; W.T. Grant Found. grantee, 1975-76; fellow All Souls Coll., Oxford U., 1983-84; Whitehall Found. grantee, 1986—. Fellow Am. Psychol. Assn., AAAS, Soc. Exptl. Analysis Behavior (pres. 1972-73), Soc. Exptl. Psychologists; mem. Eastern Psychol. Assn. (bd. dirs. 1986—). Home: 460 Riverside Dr Apt 91 New York NY 10027-6820 Office: 418 Schermerhorn Hall Columbia U New York NY 10027

TERRACINA, ROY DAVID, food executive; b. Chgo., Aug. 24, 1946; s. Angelo R. and Josephine T.; m. Dana Wheeler, July 6, 1984; children: Joseph, Vincent, Angela, Peter, Paul. B.S. in Fin., Marquette U., 1968, M.B.A., 1972. Officer First Wis. Nat. Bank, Milw., 1968-71; account exec. Robert W. Baird Co., Milw., 1971-74; v.p. mktg. Midwest Retail Group, Milw., 1974-76; mgmt. cons. Anderson-Roethle, Milw., 1976-77; v.p., treas. Farm House Foods Corp., Milw.. 1977-84; pres. Sterling Foods, Inc., San Antonio, 1984-93, pvt. investor, 1994—; instr. personal fin. Marquette U.; instr. fin. Trinity U.; bd. dirs. Tex. Commerce Bank, Security Trust; entrepreneur in residence St. Mary's U. Bd. dirs. YMCA, San Antonio; chmn. Tex. Spl. Olympics. Mem. Young Pres.'s Orgn., Marquette U. Alumni Assn. (pres. 1977-78), Lions Internat. (pres. 1975-76). Roman Catholic. Office: 311 3d St San Antonio TX 78205

TERRAGNO, PAUL JAMES, information industry executive; b. Ogden, Utah, May 17, 1938; s. Charles L. and Florence E. (Gabardi) T.; m. Nancy Robinson, Aug. 26, 1961; children—Thomas C., Paul A., Teresa A. B.A. U. Utah, 1960; M.S., U. Wyo., 1962. Vice pres. Westat, Inc., Rockville, Md., 1962-70; vice pres. Remac Information, Gaithersburg, Md., 1970-76; dir. U.S. Patent Office, Washington, 1976-80; v.p. Pergamon Internat., McLean, Va., 1980-84; pres. Pergamon InfoLine, McLean, Va., 1984-87, Pergamon ORBIT InfoLine, McLean, 1987-89, Maxwell Online, Inc., 1989-92; pres. Pergamon Orbit InfoLine, Ltd., London, 1984-89, Pergabase, Inc., Gainesville, Fla., 1985-92, pres. Topate Information Svcs. Inc., 1992—. Contbr. articles to various publs. Mem. Am. Soc. Info. Sci. Roman Catholic. Home: 10607 Vantage Ct Rockville MD 20854-4244 Office: Topate Info Svcs 10607 Vantage Ct Potomac MD 20854

TERRANOVA, PAUL, former corporate executive; b. N.Y.C., Oct. 27, 1919; s. Joseph and Rachel (Falantano) T.; m. Marion Horvath, Sept. 18, 1943; 1 child,Victor Paul. BSEE, Bklyn. Poly. Inst., 1955. Project engr. ITT, Nutley, N.J., 1944-61; founder, chmn. and CEO Merrimac Industries, Inc., West Caldwell, N.J., 1961-94; ret., 1994. Office: Merrimac Industries Inc 41 Fairfield Pl West Caldwell NJ 07007

TERRAS, AUDREY ANNE, mathematics educator; b. Washington, Sept. 10, 1942; d. Stephen Decatur and Maude Mae (Murphy) Bowdoin. BS with high honors in Math., U. Md., 1964; MA, Yale U, 1966, PhD, 1970. Instr. U. Ill., Urbana, 1968-70; asst. prof. U. P.R., Mayaguez, 1970-71; asst. prof. Bklyn. Coll., CUNY, 1971-72; asst. prof. math. U. Calif.-San Diego, La Jolla, 1972-76, assoc. prof., 1976-83, prof., 1983—, vis. positions MIT, fall 1977, 83, U. Bonn (W.Ger.), spring 1977, Inst. Mittag-Leffler, Stockholm, winter, 1978, Inst. Advanced Study, spring 1984, Math. Scis. Rsch. Inst., Berkeley, Calif., winter 1992, spring 1995; dir. West Coast Number Theory Conf., U. Calif.-San Diego, 1976, AMS joint summer rsch. conf., 1984; lectr. in field. Author: Harmonic Analysis on Symmetric Spaces and Applications, Vol. 1, 1985, Vol. II, 1988. Contbr. articles and chpts. to profl. publs. Woodrow Wilson fellow, 1964; NSF fellow, 1964-68; NSF grantee Summer Inst. in Number Theory, Ann Arbor, Mich., 1973; prin. investigator NSF, 1974-88. Fellow AAAS; AAAS (nominating com. math. sect. project 2061), Am. Math. Soc. (com. employment and ednl. policy com. on coms., council, transactions editor, com. for the yr. 2000), Math. Assn. Am. (program com. for nat. meeting 1980-90, chair joint com. mem. Am. Math. Soc. and Math. Assn. Am. 1991), Soc. Indsl. and Applied Math., Assn. for Women in Math., Assn. for Women in Sci. Research in harmonic analysis on symmetric spaces and number theory. Office: U Calif San Diego Dept Math La Jolla CA 92093-0112

TERRAS, VICTOR, Slavic languages and comparative literature educator; b. Poltsamaa, Estonia, Jan. 21, 1921; came to U.S., 1952, naturalized, 1956; s. Evald and Elena (Rosenberger) T.; m. Rita Schubert, 1951; 1 child, Alexander. Mag. Phil., U. Tartu, Estonia, 1942; Ph.D., U. Chgo., 1963. Lectr. U. Tartu, 1943-44; instr. to assoc.prof. U. Ill., Urbana, 1959-64, prof. Slavic langs., 1965-66; prof. U. Wis., Madison, 1966-70; prof. Slavic langs. and comparative lit. Brown U., Providence, 1970-88, prof. emeritus, 1988—. Author: The Young Dostoevsky: A Critical Study, 1969, Belinskij and Russian Literary Criticism, 1974, A Karamazov Companion, 1981, Vladimir Mayakovsky, 1983; editor: Handbook of Russian Literature, 1984, The Idiot:

An Interpretation, 1990, A History of Russian Literature, 1991. Mem. Am. Assn. Advancement Slavic and East European Studies, Am. Assn. Tchrs. Slavic and East European Langs. (pres. 1981-82), Internat. Dostoevsky Soc. (v.p. 1983—). Home: 128 Maple Ave Little Compton RI 02837-1714 Office: Brown U Box E Providence RI 02912

TERREAULT, R. CHARLES, engineer, management educator, researcher; b. Montreal, Que., Can., Mar. 21, 1935; s. Charles Terreault and Antonia Clark; m. Marie Rolland, Sept. 10, 1960; children: Geneviève, François, Patrick, Olivier-Hugues. B.A. Coll. Stanislas, Montreal, 1954; BA in Sci., Ecole Poly., Montreal, 1959; hon. doctorate, U. Que., 1986. Engr. Bell Can., Montreal, 1959-65, staff engr., 1967-69, chief engr., 1971-73, asst. v.p. rsch., 1978-91; researcher Bell Telephone Labs., Holmdel, N.J., 1965-67; dir. planning Bell No. Rsch., Ottawa, Ont., Can., 1969-71; v.p. systems engring. Bell No. Rsch., Montreal, 1973-78; Jvr Cyr prof. mgmt. tech. Ecole Poly., Montreal, 1991—; bd. dirs. Natural Scis. and Engring. Rsch. Coun. Can., Ottawa, 1989—. Contbr. articles to profl. jours. Fellow IEEE (Armstrong award 1984); mem. Canadian Acad. Engring., Ordre Ingénieurs de Que., Inst. Mgmt. Sci., Que. Assn. Indsl. Rsch. (Annual award 1992). Avocations: computers, classical music, skiing. Home: 1665 Victoria # 804, Saint Lambert, PQ Canada J4R 2T6 Office: Ecole Polytechnique, PO Box 6079 Br Centre-ville, Montreal, PQ Canada H3C 3A7

TERREL, RONALD LEE, civil engineer, business executive, educator; b. Klamath Falls, Oreg., Sept. 2, 1936; s. Theodore Thomas and Ruth Margaret (Fausset) T.; m. Susan Laura Harrower, Feb. 28, 1959 (div. July 1981); children: Douglas Scott, Nancy Dawn, Janet Lynn; m. 2d Alice Marie Blanchard, July 23, 1981. B.S.C.E., Purdue U., 1960, M.S., 1961; Ph.D., U. Calif.-Berkeley, 1967. Estimator J.H. Pomeroy & Co., San Francisco, 1955; lab. asst. Purdue U., 1956-60; asst. field geologist Bear Creek Mining Co., Mpls., 1957-58; materials engr. U.S. Bur. Reclamation, Denver, 1960-64; project engr. J.H. Pomeroy & Co., Antigua, B.W.I. and Calif., 1964-65; research asst. U. Calif.-Berkeley, 1965-67; asst. prof. civil engr. U. Wash., Seattle, 1967-70, assoc. prof., 1970-75, prof., 1975-85, prof. emeritus, 1985—, head Transp. Constrn. and Geometronics divsn., 1976-79; prof., sr. researcher Oreg. State U., 1989-94; pres. Pavement Systems Inc., 1970-82; exec. v.p. Seattle Engring. Internat., Inc., 1979-81; pres. Terrel Assocs., Inc., 1981-85; owner Terrel Research, 1986—; v.p. Pavement Technologies Inc., 1985-86; bd. dirs. Hydrogenesis, Inc.; cons. in field. Patentee in field. Co-founder, dir. Wash. State Transp. Ctr., 1981-84. Nominated Constrn. Man of Yr. Engring. News-Record, 1972; Purdue Alumni scholar, 1959-60; Ford fellow, 1965-67. Mem. ASTM, ASCE, Transp. Research Bd., Assn. Asphalt Paving Technologists (bd. dirs. 1979-83, W.J. Emmons 1983, award of merit 1990), Triaxial Inst. (chmn. 1971-73), Can. Tech. Asphalt Assn., Internat. Soc. for Asphalt Pavements (founding mem. 1987), Sigma Xi, Tau Beta Pi, Chi Epsilon, Sigma Gamma Epsilon. Office: 9703 241st Pl SW Edmonds WA 98020-6512

TERRELL, G. IRVIN, lawyer; b. Houston, Sept. 28, 1946; s. George I. and Adella (Weichert) T.; m. Karen Steenberg, Jan. 8, 1984; 1 child, Katharine. BA, U. Tex., 1968, JD, 1972. Bar: Tex., U.S. Supreme Ct., U.S. Ct. Appeals (5th cir.), U.S. Dist. Ct. (so. dist.) Tex. Assoc. Baker & Botts, Houston, 1972-79; ptnr. Baker & Botts, 1980—. Mem. ABA, Houston Bar Assn., Internat. Soc. Barristers. Office: Baker & Botts 3000 One Shell Pla 910 Louisiana St Houston TX 77002

TERRELL, J. ANTHONY, lawyer; b. N.Y.C., Sept. 20, 1943; s. Claude M. and Kathleen L. (Prevost) T.; m. Karen E. Terrell, Aug. 8, 1969; 1 child, Elizabeth S. BA, NYU, 1965, LLM in Taxation, 1975; JD, Villanova U., 1968. Bar: N.Y. With Frueauff, Farrell, Sullivan & Bryan, N.Y.C., 1970-74, ptnr., 1974; assoc. Reid & Priest, N.Y.C., 1974-76, ptnr., 1977—. Mem. ABA (sect. bus. law, sect. taxation, sect. pub. utility, comm. and transp. law, vice chmn. corp. finance com., vice chmn. taxation and acctg. com.), Nat. Assn. Bond Lawyers, Belle Haven Club, Met. Club, Coral Beach and Tennis Club. Home: Indian Harbor Greenwich CT 06830 Office: Reid & Priest 40 W 57th St New York NY 10019-4001

TERRELL, (NELSON) JAMES, physicist; b. Houston, Aug. 15, 1923; s. Nelson James Sr. and Gladys Delphine (Stevens) T.; m. Elizabeth Anne Pearson, June 9, 1945; children—Anne (dec.), Barbara, Jean. B.A., Rice U., 1944, M.A., 1947, Ph.D., 1950. Research asst. Rice U., Houston, 1950; asst. prof. physics Western Res. U., Cleve., 1950-51; mem. staff Los Alamos Nat. Lab., U. Calif., 1951-89, assoc., 1989-94; affiliate, 1994—. Producer (computer generated movie) The X-Ray Sky, 1969-76; contbr. articles to profl. jours. and encys. Served to 1st lt. AUS, 1944-46. Graham Baker scholar, 1943-44; fellow Rice U., 1946-48, AEC, 1948-50. Fellow Am. Phys. Soc., AAAS; mem. Am. Astron. Soc., Internat. Astron. Union, Phi Beta Kappa, Sigma Xi. Clubs: Los Alamos Ski, Los Alamos Choral Soc. Research in relativity, quasars, x-ray and gamma ray astronomy, nuclear physics, lasers. Home: 85 Obsidian Loop Los Alamos NM 87544-2528 Office: Los Alamos Nat Lab Mail Stop D436 Los Alamos NM 87545

TERRELL, JOSEPH ALCASAR, interior designer; b. San Angelo, Tex., July 16, 1946; s. Lorene Miller; m. Renée Shub, Jan. 20, 1971 (div. Mar. 1977); m. Jackie Howard, Oct. 22, 1984 (div. 1995); children: Heather Fufumoto, Miró Alcasar. Student, U. Frankfurt, Germany, 1967-68; BA in Art History, UCLA, 1969, MA in Art History and Design, 1971, postgrad., 1973-75. Curator musicology Craft and Folk Art Mus., L.A., 1975-76; assoc. and exhbn. dir. Fotofest/Internat. Universal Studios, Century City, Calif., 1977-78; artistic dir. City of L.A. and L.A. St. Scene Festival City of L.A., Office of the Mayor and Dept. Gen. Svcs., 1978-82; prin. Alcasar Terrell, Inc., L.A., 1982—; cons., designer, founder, coord. Exhibitionists Inc./Art, L.A., 1976-82; design cons. Craft and Folk Art Mus., L.A., 1989—; mem. arts adv. coun. Cedars-Sinai Med. Ctr., L.A., 1993—; mem. adv. coun. Calif. Mus. Sci. and Industry, L.A., 1994—. Exhbns. include Bridge Gallery, L.A., Landau/Alexander Gallery, Craft and Folk Art Mus., L.A. (1st Pl. L.A. Interior Design Awards Am. Soc. Interior Designers 1990), Joslyn Ctr. Arts, Torrance, Children's Mus. La Habra, Orange County, Calif., Gallery K, L.A., Main St. Gallery, L.A., City Hall, L.A., Alexander Gallery, L.A.; prin. works include Del Rey Colony, Venice, Calif. (Project of Yr. Builder's Mag. 1987), Harold Lloyd Estate, Beverly Hills, Calif. (Designer of Yr. Am. Soc. Interior Designers 1988). Com. mem. L.A. Archtl. Found., 1993—; pres. bd. trustees Millicent Rogers Mus. Taos, N.Mex., 1993-95. Honoree L.A. Archtl. Found., 1993. Mem. Am. Soc. Interior Designers, Mcpl. Arts Gallery Assn. (pres. bd. dirs. 1990—). Office: Alcasar Terrell Design Group 119 1/2 N Larchmont Blvd Los Angeles CA 90004

TERRELL, W(ILLIAM) GLENN, university president emeritus; b. Tallahassee, May 24, 1920; s. William Glenn and Esther (Collins) T.; m. Gail Strandberg Terrell; children by previous marriage: Francine Elizabeth, William Glenn III. BA, Davidson Coll., 1942, LLD (hon.), 1969; MS, Fla. State U., 1948; PhD, State U. Iowa, 1952; LLD (hon.), Gonzaga U., 1984, Seattle U., 1985. Instr., then asst. prof. Fla. State U., Tallahassee, 1948-55; asst. prof., then assoc. prof., chmn. dept. psychology U. Colo., Boulder, 1955-59, assoc., acting dean Coll Arts and Scis., 1959-63; prof. psychology, dean Coll. Liberal Arts and Scis., U. Ill. at Chgo. Circle, 1963-65, dean faculties, 1965-67; pres. Wash. State U., Pullman, 1967-85, pres. emeritus, 1985—; Pres. Nat. Assn. State Univs. and Land-Grant Colls., 1977-78; cons. The Pacific Inst., Seattle, 1987—. Contbr. articles to profl. jours. Served to capt. inf. U.S. Army, 1942-46, ETO. Recipient Disting. Alumnus award U. Iowa, 1985. Fellow APA, Soc. Rsch. in Child Devel.; mem. AAAS, Sigma Xi, Phi Kappa Phi. Avocations: golf, reading, traveling. Home: 2438 36th Ave W Seattle WA 98199-3704 Office: The Pacific Inst 1011 Western Ave Seattle WA 98104-1040

TERRILL, CLAIR ELMAN, animal scientist, geneticist, consultant; b. Rippey, Iowa, Apr. 27, 1910; s. Otis Wallace and Mary Irene (Grow) T.; m. Zola Mae Alexander, June 9, 1932; children: Ronald Lee (dec.), Richard Eugene. BS, Iowa State U., 1932; PhD, U. Mo., 1936. Rsch. asst. U. Mo., 1932-36; asst. animal husbandman Ga. Expt. Sta. USDA, 1936; animal husbandman Agrl. Rsch. Svc. USDA, Dubois, Idaho, 1936-53, dir. U.S. Sheep Expt. Sta., 1953-55; chief sheep and fur animal rsch. br. USDA, Beltsville, Md., 1955-72, staff scientist nat. program staff Agrl. Rsch. Svc., 1972-81, collaborator nat. program staff, 1981—; Mem. sub-panel Pres.'s Sci. Adv. Com. World Food Supply, 1966; adj. prof. Utah State U., Logan, 1986-87;

cons. FAO, 1984. Contbr. chpts. to several books. Recipient Silver Ram award Am. Sheep Industry, 1975, Saddle and Sirloin Portrait award, 1989; inductee Internat. Stockmen's Hall of Fame, 1987, Agrl. Rsch. Svc. Hall of Fame, 1993; Fulbright grantee U NSW, Kensington, Australia, 1969. Fellow AAAS, Am. Soc. Animal Sci. (pres. Western sect. 1951, chmn. com. rsch. 1950-52, com. monographs 1955-60, editorial bd. 1954-57, sec.-treas. 1960-62, v.p. 1963, pres. 1964, bd. dirs.); mem. World Assn. Animal Prodn. (coun. 1965-68), Am. Forage and Grasslands Coun. (bd. dirs. 1963-63), Am. Registry Profl. Animal Scientists, Internat. Goat Assn. (bd. dirs.), Genetic Soc. Am., Am. Genetic Assn. (coun. 1965-68, v.p., pres. 1970), Am. Meat Sci. Assn., Am. Assn. Anatomists, Am. Inst. Biol. Scis., Soc. Study Reprodn., Sigma Xi, Alpha Zeta, Gamma Sigma Delta. Home: 318 Apple Grove Rd Silver Spring MD 20904-2745 Office: USDA Nat Program Staff Agrl Rsch Svc Barc W # 005 Beltsville MD 20705

TERRILL, ROBERT CARL, hospital administrator; b. Oklahoma City, Dec. 10, 1927; s. D. Willard and Velma (Mitchell) T.; m. Jessica Doe, Dec. 14, 1957; children—Thane Bennett, Sarah Haven. B.A., U. Okla., 1948, M.A. in History, 1961; M.A. in Hosp. Adminstrn. State U. Iowa, 1954; Ed.D. in Ednl. Adminstrn, Ind. U., 1978. Adminstrv. resident Mary Fletcher Hosp., Burlington, Vt., 1953-55; asst. adminstr., personnel dir. Mary Fletcher Hosp., 1955-61, assoc. adminstr., 1961-65; adminstr. Hosps. of U. Okla., Oklahoma City, 1965-72; dir. Ind. Univ. Hosps., Indpls., 1972-76; instr. health adminstrn. Ind. U., 1976-77; assoc. prof. Coll. Mgmt. U. Mass., Boston, 1977-87; preceptor in hosp. adminstrn. Washington U., St. Louis, Trinity U., San Antonio; asst. prof. U. Okla. Health Scis. Center; pub. edn. planning svcs. corp. 1987—. Fellow Am. Coll. Hosp. Adminstrs.; mem. Mass. Hosp. Assn., Am. Hosp. Assn., Assn. Programs in Hosp. Adminstrn., Pub. Health Assn., New Eng. Hosp. Assembly, Nat. League for Nursing, State U. Iowa. Alumni Assn., Ind. U. Alumni Assn. Club: Rotarian. Home: 26 Grove St Sandwich MA 02563-2125 Office: 93 Old Kings Hwy Sandwich MA 02563

TERRILL, ROSS GLADWIN, author, educator; b. Melbourne, Australia; Came to U.S., 1965, naturalized, 1979; s. Frank and Miriel (Lloyd) T. B.A. with 1st class honors, U. Melbourne; Ph.D., Harvard U., 1970. Tutor in polit. sci. U. Melbourne, 1962-63; staff sec. Australian Student Christian Movement, 1964-65; teaching fellow Harvard, 1968-70, lectr. govt., 1970-73, asso. prof., 1974-78, research fellow East Asian studies, 1970—; dir. programs Harvard (Center Internat. Affairs), 1974-78; contbg. editor Atlantic Monthly, 1970-84; research fellow Asia Soc., 1977-79. Author: China Profile, 1969, China and Ourselves, 1971, 800,000,000: The Real China, 1972, R.H. Tawney and His Times, 1973, Flowers on an Iron Tree, 1975, The Future of China, 1978, The China Difference, 1979, Mao: A Biography, 1980, revised 1993, White-Boned Demon, 1984, The Australians, 1987, Madam Mao, 1992, China in Our Time, 1992; contbr. numerous articles to profl. jours. Recipient Nat. Mag. award, 1972; George Polk Meml. award outstanding mag. reporting, 1972; Sumner prize, 1970. Mem. Authors Guild, PEN. Club: Harvard of N.Y.C. Home: 200 Saint Botolph St Boston MA 02115-4911

TERRIS, ALBERT, metal sculptor; b. N.Y.C., Nov. 10, 1916; s. Aaron and Fania (Rosenthal) Terraspulsky; children: Susan, Abby, David, Enoch. BSS, CCNY, 1939; postgrad., NYU Inst. Fine Arts, 1939-42. lectr. Met. Mus. Art, 1941-42; tchr. fine arts N.Y.C. High Sch. System, 1947-54; prof. emeritus Bklyn. Coll., 1947-86. Steel sculptures include Non-Fixed Relationship, 1948, Anti-Gravity, 1950, Giraffes, 1953, Short Art, 1953, Pro-Gravity Chains, 1956, Tools, 1956, Crushed Sculpture, 1956, Words, 1957, Discursive-Illegible-Boustrophedon, 1975, Plates of Charlemagne, 1975, Fireharps, 1975, Cycle of Life, 1977; one-man shows: Saidenberg, 1955, Duveen-Graham, 1958, Carnagie Internats., 1958, 62, Bklyn.. Mus. Biennale (awarded first prize), 1960, Allan Stone, 1962, Critics Choice, 1972, Artists Space, 1975, Gloria Cortella, 1977, (retrospective) Artists in the Civil Svc., Bklyn. Coll. Gallery, 1985; exhibited in group shows at Tanager Gallery, 1953-61, Stable anns., 1953-60, Mus. Modern Art, N.Y.C., 1962, and others; represented in permanent collections: Stephen Paine, Boston, Arnold Maremont, Evanston, G. David Thompson Estate, NBC-TV, others. Served with 1st Allied Airborne, 1942-45. Home: 280 S Ocean Ave Freeport NY 11520-4939

TERRIS, MILTON, physician, educator; b. N.Y.C., Apr. 22, 1915; s. Harry and Gussie (Dokshitski) T.; m. Rema Lapouse, Nov. 23, 1941 (dec. Aug. 1970); children—Andrew David, Eugene Charles (dec.); m. Lillian Long, Feb. 6, 1971. A.B., Columbia, 1935; M.D., N.Y.U., 1939; M.P.H., Johns Hopkins, 1944. Intern Harlem Hosp., N.Y.C., 1939-41; resident Bellevue Hosp., N.Y.C., 1941-42; practice medicine specializing in preventive medicine Buffalo, 1951-58, N.Y.C., 1960-80, South Burlington, Vt., 1980—; asst. dean post-grad. edn. Sch. Medicine, U. Buffalo, 1951-58, assoc., 1952-54, asst. prof., 1954-55, assoc. prof. preventive medicine, 1955-58; prof. epidemiology Sch. Medicine, Tulane U., 1958-60; head chronic disease unit dept. epidemiology Pub. Health Research Inst., N.Y.C., 1960-64; prof. preventive medicine N.Y. Med. Coll., 1964-80, chmn. dept. community and preventive medicine, 1968-80; vis. prof. U. Toronto, 1984-93, U. Montreal, 1985—. Author: Goldberger on Pellagra, 1964, La Revolución Epidemiológica y la Medicina Social, 1980; Editor: Jour. Public Health Policy, 1980—. Recipient Abraham M. Lilienfeld award Am. Coll. Epidemiology. Fellow N.Y. Acad. Medicine, Am. Pub. Health Assn. (past pres.; Sedgwick Meml. award 1984); mem. Assn. Tchrs. Preventive Medicine (Duncan Clark award 1984; past pres.), Soc. Epidemiologic Research (past pres.), Nat. Assn. Pub. Health Policy (past pres.), Phi Beta Kappa, Alpha Omega Alpha, Delta Omega. Home and Office: 208 Meadowood Dr South Burlington VT 05403-7401

TERRIS, SUSAN, physician, cardiologist; b. Morristown, N.J., Sept. 5, 1944; d. Albert and Virginia (Rinaldy) T. BA in History, U. Chgo., 1967, PhD in Biochemistry, 1975, MD, 1976. Diplomate Am. Bd. Internal Medicine, Am. Bd. Endocrinology and Metabolism, Am. Bd. Cardiovascular Disease. Resident in internal medicine Washington U., Barnes Hosp., St. Louis, 1976-78; fellow in endocrinology and metabolism U. Chgo., 1978-80, fellow cardiology, 1980-83; fellow cardiology U. Mich., Ann Arbor, 1983-85, instr. cardiology, 1985-86; head cardiac catheterization lab., head cardiology Westland (Mich.) Med. Ctr., 1985. Contbr. articles to Jour. Biol. Chemistry, Am. Jour. Physiology, Am. Jour. Cardiology, Jour. Clin. Investigation, other profl. publs. Grantee Juvenile Diabetes Found., 1978-80, NIH, 1978-79. Mem. AAAS, Am. Heart Assn., N.Y. Acad. Sci., Am. Women in Sci. Achievements include rsch. demonstrating dependence of intracellular degradation of insulin upon its prior receptor-mediated uptake by liver; studies of effects of various drugs on human circulatory system.

TERRIS, WILLIAM, publishing executive; b. Chgo., Sept. 24, 1937; s. William and Evelyn M. (Dykstra) T.; m. Shirley Ann Gellinger, Sept. 8, 1958; 1 child, Bruce Robert. BS in Indsl. Scis., Purdue U., 1959; MS in Psychology, Ill. Inst. Technology, 1962, PhD in Psychology, 1964. Registered psychologist, Ill. Asst. prof. U. Okla., Norman, 1964-67; assoc. prof. DePaul U., Chgo., 1967-86; instr. bd. London House, Inc., Park Ridge, Ill., 1975-92; pres., CEO PSB Corp., Mundelein, Ill., 1993—; cons. Assoc. Consulting Psychologists, St. Louis 1975-78. Author: (psychological test) Personnel Selection Inventory, 1979, Employee Theft, 1985. Mem. APA, Am. Soc. for Indsl. Security, Soc. for Human Resource Mgmt., Chgo. Crime Commn. Republican. Baptist. Avocation: reading. Home and Office: PSB Co 21851 W Riviera Ct Mundelein IL 60060-5328

TERRY, CLARK, musician; b. St. Louis, Dec. 14, 1920; m. Pauline Reddon; 2 children. Privately educated. Pres. Etoile Music Prodns., 1955—, Pastel Music, 1958—; v.p. Creative Jazz Composers, Inc., 1972—; itinerant jazz clinician and educator; exec. dir. Internat. of Jazz. Leader, Clark Terry Big Bad Band, 1966—; albums include: The World of Duke Ellington, Vol. 2, Duke Ellington Such Sweet Thunder, The Terry-Brookmeyer Quintet, Cruisin', Cool Blues, Oscar Peterson Trio with Clark Terry, Clark Terry's Big Bad Band Live on 57th Street, The Happy Horns of Clark Terry, Yes, The Blues, 1981, Paris 1960, 1985, Live at the Village Gate, 1991, (with Red Mitchell) Jive at Five, 1993. Author: Let's Talk Trumpet, 1973, Interpretation of the Jazz Language, 1976, Circular Breathing, 1977. Served with USN, 1942-45. Recipient numerous awards, including Grammy nominations, Pote Distinguished Jazz Artist, Phil., 1989. Office: care Pablo Records 451 N Canon Dr Beverly Hills CA 90210-4819*

TERRY, CLIFFORD LEWIS, journalist; b. Highland Park, Ill., Jan. 19, 1937; s. Clifford Lewis and Isabelle (Marlow) T.; m. Patricia West Dickelman, Sept. 1, 1966; children: Christopher West, Scott Marlow. Student, Carleton Coll., Northfield, Minn., 1954-55; BA, Trinity Coll., Hartford, Conn., 1958; postgrad., Columbia U., 1962-63. Tchr., English and history Mt. Hermon (Mass.) Sch., 1958-59; police reporter City News Bur. Chgo., 1959-60; mem. staff Chgo. Tribune, 1960—, movie critic, 1965-70; assoc. editor Chgo. Tribune (Sunday mag.), 1970-82, feature writer, 1982—, TV critic, 1985—, arts feature writer, 1989-94; ind. writer, 1994—. Served with AUS, 1960. Nieman fellow Harvard U., 1969-70. Mem. Phi Beta Kappa.

TERRY, ELIZABETH BENNETT, chef, restaurant owner; b. Ohio, Oct. 9, 1942; m. Michael Holtslander Terry; children: Alexis, Celeste. BS in Psychology, Lake Erie Coll. for Women, 1966. Chef, owner Thyme for You, Atlanta, 1979-80, Elizabeth on 37th, Savannah, Ga., 1981—. Bd. dirs. Small Bus. Assistance Corp., Savannah, 1994. Recipient Rising Star award James Beard Found., 1987, Gt. Regional Chef award James Beard Found., 1991, award DiRona, 1992, 93, 94, Top 25 Restaurants in Am. award Food and Wine mag., 1992-93; name to Fine Dining Hall of Fame, Nations Restaurants News, 1993; profiled in numerous nat. mags. Mem. Savannah C. of C. (mem. tourism bd. 1994). Office: Elizabeth on 37th 105 E 37th St Savannah GA 31401

TERRY, F. DAVIS, JR., investment company executive; b. Atlanta, Apr. 30, 1954; s. Frederick Davis and Jane Frances (Hargrave) T.; m. Tai Chang, June 23, 1979. BA, Yale U., 1976; MBA, U. Pa., 1979. Assoc. Dillon, Read & Co. Inc., N.Y.C., 1979-82, v.p., 1983-85, sr. v.p., 1986-89, mng. dir., 1989—. Office: Dillon Read & Co Inc 535 Madison Ave New York NY 10024

TERRY, FRANK JEFFREY, bishop. Bishop Diocese of Spokane, Wash., 1991—. Office: Diocese of Spokane 245 E 13th Ave Spokane WA 99202-1114

TERRY, FREDERICK ARTHUR, JR., lawyer; b. Buffalo, May 24, 1932; s. Frederick Arthur and Agnes Elizabeth (Tranter) T. BA, Williams Coll., 1953; LLB, Columbia U., 1956. Bar: N.Y. 1957, U.S. Dist. Ct. (so. and ea. dists.) N.Y. 1958, U.S. Ct. Appeals (2d cir.) 1958, U.S. Supreme Ct. 1971, U.S. Tax Ct. Law clk. U.S. Ct. Appeals (2nd cir.), 1956-57; assoc. Sullivan & Cromwell, N.Y.C., 1957-65, ptnr., 1965—. Bd. dirs. Eisenhower Exch. Fellowships, Grand Ctrl. Partnership, Inc., Natural Resources Def. Coun., Am. Fedn. for Aging Rsch., Inc., Weinman Found.; sec., mem. bd. McIntosh Found.; trustee, chmn. com. on trust and estate gift plans Rockefeller U.; trustee Harold K. Hochschild Found., Guild Hall, East Hampton; chmn. Flagler Found. Mem. ABA, N.Y. State Bar Assn., Assn. Bar City NY., Maidstone Club (East Hampton, N.Y.), Century Club, River Club, Union Club (N.Y.C.). Office: Sullivan & Cromwell 125 Broad St New York NY 10004

TERRY, GARY A., lawyer, former trade association executive; b. Ogden, Utah, Apr. 2, 1935; s. Hyrum Aceal and Viola (Sorenson) T.; m. Carole Ann Eitel, June 23, 1962; children—Stephanie Ann, Brendan Gary. B.A. in Polit. Sci., UCLA, 1964; J.D., George Washington U., 1968. Bars: Va. 1969 D.C. 1969. Mem. staff U.S. Ho. of Reps., Washington, 1964-65; Washington staff Bethlehem Steel Corp., 1965-69; atty. HUD, Washington, 1969; exec. v.p. Am. Land Devel. Assn. (now Am. Resort Devel. Assn.), Washington, 1969-82, pres., 1982-91; also dir. Am. Land Devel. Assn. (now Am. Resort Devel. Assn.); with Jones, Waldo, Holbrook & McDonough, Washington, 1991—; dir. Internat. Found. for Timeshare, Washington, 1981-91, mem. consultative council Nat. Inst. Bldg. Scis., Washington, 1982-85; U.S. rep. land use and town planning com. Internat. Real Estate Fedn., Brussels, 1984-91; mem. Found. for Internat. Meetings, Washington, 1984—; del. Lincoln Inst. Land Policy, Harvard U., 1984, 85. Contbr. articles to profl. jours. Asst. to exec. dir. 1969 Presidential Inaugural Com., 1969-70; mem. adv. bd. NOAA, Washington, 1972; bd. dirs. Zacchaeus Free Med. and Legal Clinics, Washington, 1991—, co-chair lawyers com., 1992—; mem. Fairfax County Republican Orgn., Va., 1978—. Served with U.S. Navy, 1953-58. Decorated Am. Spirit of Honor medal. Mem. Va. Bar Assn., D.C. Bar Assn., Am. Soc. Assn. Execs. Mem. LDS Ch. Avocations: music; literature; architectural design; art; travel. Home: 1001 Wilhelm Dr Great Falls VA 22066-2524 Office: Jones Waldo Holbrook & McDonough 2300 M St NW Ste 900 Washington DC 20037-1434

TERRY, GEORGE MARSHALL, vocational studies educator; b. Aulander, N.C., Jan. 19, 1944; s. Godfrey Jackson and Virginia Elizabeth (Burden) T.; m. Judith Elaine Bland, June 12, 1964; children: Randy, Jeffrey, Michelle, Cynthia. AS, Mt. Olive Coll., 1982. Cert. tchr., N.C. Vocat. tchr. Bertie Jr. H.S., Windsor, N.C., 1970-72; home builder various locations, 1967—; tchr. carpentry Lakewood H.S., Roseboro, N.C., 1984-93; vocat. testing coord. Sampson County Schs., 1993—; curriculum carpentry team leader N.C. Trade and Indsl. Dept. Edn., Raleigh, 1989-93; trade and industry adv. bd. N.C. Dept. Pub. Edn., Raleigh, 1989-93. Pastor Weldon (N.C.) Pentecostal Holiness Ch., Mt. Olive, N.C., 1979-82, Sharon Pentecostal Holiness Ch., Clinton, N.C., 1982-94. Mem. NEA, ASCD, Am. Vocat. Assn., Nat. Assn. Trade and Indsl. Educators, N.C. Vocat. Assn., Associated Gen. Contractors Am. (cert. master residential carpenter), Millenium/Aulander Lions Club (pres. 1970-71). Republican. Home: PO Box 603 Salemburg NC 28385 Office: Sampson County Schs PO Box 439 Clinton NC 28328

TERRY, JAMES JOSEPH, JR., lawyer; b. Yonkers, N.Y., July 2, 1952; s. James Joseph Sr. and Marie Catherine (O'Boyle) T.; m. Marguerite Mary O'Connor, Sept. 29, 1985; 1 child, James Daniel. BA, NYU, 1974; JD, Columbia U., 1977. Bar: N.Y. 1978, U.S. Dist. Ct. (so. and ea. dists.) N.Y. 1978, U.S. Ct. Appeals (2d cir.) 1981, U.S. Ct. Appeals (3d cir.) 1989. Assoc. Cole & Deitz, N.Y.C., 1977-86; ptnr. Winston & Strawn (formerly Cole & Deitz), N.Y.C., 1986—. Mem. ABA, N.Y. State Bar Assn., Def. Rsch. Inst., Maritime Law Assn. U.S., N.Y. County Lawyers Assn. Democrat. Roman Catholic. Avocations: fishing, reading. Home: 190 Kneeland Ave Yonkers NY 10705-2713 Office: Winston & Strawn 175 Water St New York NY 10038-4918

TERRY, JANNIE LEE, elementary education educator; b. Kinston, N.C., July 7, 1937; d. German and Anna Lee (Baker) Bennett; m. Joseph Terry, Aug. 4, 1963; 1 child, Charlene J. BS in Home Econs. Edn., Del. State U., Dover, 1963. Cert. vocat. and occupational edn. adminstr., home econs. educator, secondary prin., Mass. Tchr. Boston Pub. Schs., 1970-93. Mem. NAFE, Boston Tchrs. Union (vocat. edn. com.). Democrat. Home: 1902 Washington St Stoughton MA 02072-3351 Office: Boston Pub Schs Boston MA 02108

TERRY, JOHN ALFRED, judge; b. Utica, N.Y., May 6, 1933; s. Robert Samuel and Julia Berenice (Collins) T. B.A. magna cum laude, Yale U., 1954; J.D., Georgetown U., 1960. Bar: D.C. 1960. Asst. U.S. atty. for D.C., 1962-67; staff atty. Nat. Commn. Reform of Fed. Criminal Laws, Washington, 1967-68; pvt. practice law Washington, 1968-69; chief appellate div. U.S. Atty.'s Office for D.C., 1969-82; judge D.C. Ct. Appeals, 1982—. Mem. D.C. Bar (bd. govs. 1977-82), ABA, Phi Beta Kappa. Office: DC Ct Appeals 500 Indiana Ave NW Washington DC 20001-2138

TERRY, JOHN HART, lawyer, former utility company executive, former congressman; b. Syracuse, N.Y., Nov. 14, 1924; s. Frank and Saydee (Hart) T.; m. Catherine Jean Taylor Phelan, Apr. 15, 1950; children: Catherine Jean (Mrs. Richard Thompson), Lynn Marie (Mrs. Robert Tacher), Susan Louise (Mrs. Stanley Germain), Mary Carole (Mrs. Stephen Brady). B.A., U. Notre Dame, 1945; J.D., Syracuse U., 1948. Bar: N.Y. 1950, D.C. bar 1972. Asst. to partner Smith & Sovik, 1948-59; asst. sec. to Gov. State of N.Y., 1959-61; sr. partner firm Smith, Sovik, Terry, Kendrick, McAuliffe & Schwarzer, 1961-73; sr. v.p., gen. counsel, sec. Niagara Mohawk Power Corp., Syracuse, 1973-87; counsel Hiscock & Barclay, Syracuse, 1987-94; mem. N.Y. State Assembly, 1962-70, 92d Congress from 34th N.Y. Dist., 1971-73; presdl. elector, 1972. State chmn. United Services Orgn., 1964-73; past pres. John Timothy Smith Found.; Founder, dir. Bishop Foery Found., Inc.; dir. St. Joseph's Hosp. Council; past pres. Lourdes Camp; bd. dirs. N.Y. State Traffic Council; past nat. bd. dirs. Am. Cancer Soc.; mem. adv. council Syracuse Art Mgmt.; past pres. Cath. Youth Orgn.; bd. dirs.

TERRY, JOHN JOSEPH, transportation investor; b. Chgo., July 29, 1937; s. Michael Parnell and Honore (Ryan) T.; m. Terese Rose Mulkern, Dec. 31, 1960; children—Michael P., Gregory, Deirdre. B.S., Loyola U., Chgo., 1959; postgrad., U. So. Fla., 1967. C.P.A., Ill. With Touche, Ross & Co., 1959-65; v.p. Nat. City Lines, Denver, 1965-71; v.p. fin. Pepsico Transp., Inc., Tulsa, 1971-74; v.p. U.S. Rwy. Assn., Washington, 1974-76; chmn. P.I.E. Transport Europe, 1976-79; exec. v.p. IU Internat. Corp., Wilmington, Del., 1976-85; pres. Transp. Mgmt. Investment Group, Inc., Phila., 1985—; v.p.-at-large Am. Trucking Assn., Washington, 1984-85, chmn. internat. competitiveness task force, 1991, tax policy com. 1987—; bd. dirs. Transp. Ctr. MIT, Boston; chmn. bd. dirs. Caldwell Freight Lines, Lenoir, N.C., Basin Western Inc., Roosevelt, Utah; cons. freight transp. World Bank and European Bank for Reconstn. and Devel., 1986—. Served with U.S. Army, 1960-63. Recipient Best Motor Carrier Rsch. award Transp. Rsch. Forum, 1991. Office: Transp Mgmt Investment Group Inc 103 Eton Rd Yardley PA 19067

TERRY, JOHN TIMOTHY, insurance company executive; b. Los Angeles, Nov. 23, 1933; s. Victor Taylor and Geraldine (Swiler) T.; m. Sally Beeman, June 23, 1956 (div. June 1966); children: Victoria Botsford, Michael Timothy, Carolyn Ann Larkin; m. Myonne Walsh, Aug. 1, 1966 (div. Dec. 1993), children: Jennifer Louise, Suzanne Lenore. AB in History, Stanford U., 1955. Pres. Sovereign Life Ins. Co., Santa Barbara, Calif., 1975-93; also bd. dirs., 1964-93; exec. v.p. Chubb Life Am., Concord, N.H., 1987-93, also bd. dirs., 1987-93; bd. dirs. Colonial Life Ins. Co., Parsippany, N.J., 1987-93, Vol. State Life Ins. Co., Chattanooga, 1987-93, United Life Ins. Co. Concord, 1987-93. Chmn. Regional Coastal Commn., Santa Barbara, 1973-79, Local Agy. Formation Com., Santa Barbara, 1975-79; bd. dirs. Montecito (Calif.) Water Bd., 1975-80. Served to capt. USNR, 1962-92. Awarded Israeli Parachute Wings, 1988. Mem. Reserve Officers Assn. (Navy v.p. 1980-81), Naval War Coll. Found., Navy League (chpt. pres. 1971), Navy Inst. Republican. Clubs: Calif. (Los Angeles), Birnam Wood (Montecito). Avocations: travel, swimming, history, military and naval affairs, student of Winston Churchill. Home: 131 Por La Mar Circle Santa Barbara CA 93103 Office: Sovereign Life Ins Co 30 W Sola St Santa Barbara CA 93101-2526

TERRY, LEON CASS, neurologist, educator; b. Northville, Mich., Dec. 22, 1940; s. Leon Herbert and Zella Irene (Boyd) T.; m. Suzanne Martinson, June 27, 1964; children: Kristin, Sean. Pharm. D., U. Mich., 1964; M.D., Marquette U., 1969; Ph.D., McGill U., 1982, MBA, U. S Fla., 1994. Dipolmate Am. Bd. Psychiatry and Neurology. Intern U. Rochester, N.Y., 1969-70; staff assoc. NIH, 1970-72; resident in neurology McGill U., Montreal, Que., Can., 1972-75, MRC fellow, 1975-78; assoc. prof. U. Tenn., Memphis, 1978-81; prof. neurology U. Mich., Ann Arbor, 1981-89, assoc prof. physiology, 1982-89; asst. chief neurology VA Med. Ctr., Ann Arbor, 1982-89; prof. neurology and physiology, chmn. dept. neurology Med. Coll of Wis., Milw., 1989—; dir. clin. neurosci. ctr. and multiple sclerosis clinic, Med. Coll. Wis.; vice chief of staff Froedtert Hosp., 1994—. Contbr. articles to profl. jours., chpts. to books. Served to lt. comdr. USPHS, 1970-72. NIH grantee, 1981-92; VA grantee, 1980-92; VA Clin. Investigator award, 1980-81. Mem. AMA, Am. Soc. Clin. Investigation, Cen. Soc. Clin. Investigation, So. Soc. Clin. Investigation, Am. Neurol. Assn., Am. Coll. Physician Execs. (vice chmn. academic health ctr. soc. 1994-95, chair, 1995—), Am. Coll. Healthcare Execs., Endocrine Soc., Am. Acad. Neurology, Internat. Soc. Neuroendocrinology, Internat. Soc. Psychoneuroendocrinology, Soc. Neurosci, Soc. Rsch. Biol. Rhythms, Milw. Acad. Physicians, Wis. Neurol. Assn., Wis. State Med. Soc., Med. Soc. Milw. County, Milw. Neuropsychiatric Soc. (pres.-elect). Avocations: pilot, skiing, scuba diving, computers. Office: Med Coll Wis Dept Neurology Froedtert Hosp 9200 W Watertown Plank Rd Milwaukee WI 53226-3557

TERRY, MARGARET SMOOT, special education educator; b. Elkin, N.C., July 5, 1945; d. Claude Dennis and Eula (Powell) Smoot; div.; 1 child, Susan Leigh. BEd, Fla. Atlantic U., 1966, MEd, 1969; Edn. Specialist, U. South Fla., 1985. Cert. tchr., Fla. Tchr. Wynnebrook Elem. Sch., West Palm Beach, Fla., 1967-73; tchr. spl. edn. Boca Raton (Fla.) Elem. Sch., 1973-75, J.C. Mitchell Elem. Sch., Boca Raton, 1975-83, Loggers Run Mid. Sch., Boca Raton, 1983-84; computer specialist Palm Beach County Schs., West Palm Beach, 1984-89; coord. exceptional student edn. Addison Mizner Elem. Sch., Boca Raton, 1989-92, Del Prado Elem. Sch., Boca Raton 1992—; adj. prof. Fla. Atlantic U., Boca Raton, 1987-89; computer trainer Palm Beach County Schs., 1984-89, tech. trainer, 1991-92; cons. Weiss Sch. for Gifted, West Palm Beach, 1988-89; presenter program at computer conf., Palvia, Bulgaria, 1984. Mem. Fla. Assn. Sci. Tchrs., Fla. Assn. Gifted, Phi Beta Kappa, Delta Kappa Gamma (pres. Alpha Omega chpt. 1988-90). Democrat. Home: 735 Heron Dr Delray Beach FL 33444-1923 Office: Del Prado Elem Sch Del Prado Cir Delray Beach FL 33483

TERRY, MARSHALL NORTHWAY, JR., English language educator, author; b. Cleve., Feb. 9, 1931; s. Marshall Northway and Margaret Louise (Carpenter) T.; m. Antoinette Barksdale, Sept. 5, 1953; children: Antoinette, Terry Bryant, Mary Marshall. Student, Amherst Coll., 1949-50, Kenyon Coll., 1950-51; B.A., So. Meth. U., 1953, M.A., 1954. Teaching fellow English So. Meth. U., Dallas, 1954; dir. pub. relations, lectr. English So. Meth. U., 1957-64, instr. English, 1956, 65-67, asst. dir., 1968, assoc. prof., 1969-71, prof. English, 1972—, prof. English, 1971-75, 79-82, dir. creative writing program; book critic Dallas News, 1970-75; pres. faculty senate So. Meth. U., 1993-94, assoc. provost, 1994—. Author: OLd Liberty, 1961, Tom Northway 1968, Dallas Stories, 1986, Ringer, 1987, My Father's Hands, 1993, New Creations, 1994; contbr. short stories to various jours. and mags.; editor Prize Stories, 1986. Past trustee Incarnate Word Coll., San Antonio; sec. bd. trustees Fort Burgwin Research Ctr., Ranchos de Taos, N.Mex. Recipient Jesse H. Jones fiction award Tex. Inst. Letters, 1968, Best Short Story award S.W. Rev., 1973, S.W. Writer of Yr. award, 1988, Willis M. Tate award So. Meth. U., 1990, 94, Lon Tinkle award for continuing excellence in Letters, Tex. Inst. Letters, 1991. Mem. AAUP (chpt. pres. 1971), Coll. Conf. Tchrs. English, South Central MLA, Tex. Inst. Letters (pres. 1977-79, councilor 1980—). Democrat. Methodist. Home: 2717 Lovers Ln Dallas TX 75225-7905 Office: So Meth Univ Dept English Dallas TX 75275

TERRY, MEGAN, playwright, performer , photographer; b. Seattle, July 22, 1932; d. Harold Joseph and Marguerite Cecelia (Henry) Duffy. Student, Banff Sch. Fine Arts, summers, 1950-52, 56, U. Alta., Edmondton, Can., 1952-53; B.Ed., U. Wash., 1956. Founding mem. Open Theater, N.Y.C., 1963; ABC fellow Yale U., 1966-67; founding mem., v.p. N.Y. Theatre Strategy, 1971; adj. prof. theatre U. Nebr., Omaha, until 1977; Hill prof. fine arts U. Minn-Duluth, spring 1983; Bingham prof. humanities U. Louisville, 1981; mem. theatre panel, mem. overview panel Nat. Endowment Arts, 1976-86, mem. opera/music theatre panel, 1985, mem. advancement panel, 1987; mem. theatre panel Rockefeller Found., 1977-85; mem. performing arts panel Nebr. State Council for Arts, 1977; mem. Nebr. Com. for Humanities, 1983-86; mem. Gov.'s Com. on Film and Telecommunications, 1985-86; founding mem. N.Y. Open Theatre, 1963-73; judge playwriting competition Mass., Wis., Ohio, Oreg. states, So. Playwrights Competition; Nat. Endowment Arts vis. artist in residence Iowa, 1992. Dir. Cornish Players, Cornish Sch. Allied Arts, Seattle, 1954-56, founding dir. playwrights workshop, Open Theatre, N.Y.C., 1963-68, playwright-in-residence, literary mgr. Omaha Magic Theatre, 1974—; author plays including: Kegger, Comings and Goings, The Magic Realists, Sanibel & Captiva, The People vs. Ranchman, Kepp Tightly Closed in a Cool Dry Place, The Gloaming Oh My Darling, Approaching Simone, Viet Rock, Massachusetts Trust, The Tommy Allen Show, Calm Down Mother, Sleazing Toward Athens, Babes in the Big House, Ex Miss Copper Queen, Mollie Bailey's Traveling Family Circus, Goona-Goona, Retro, Hothouse, Dinner's in the Blender, Objective Love, Katmandu, Fifteen Million Fifteen Year Olds, Fireworks, The Trees

Blew Down, Choose a Spot on the Floor, Future Soap, Brazil Fado, Pro Game., Amtrak, Headlights, Breakfast Serial, Do You See What I'm Saying?, The Snow Queen, India Plays, I Forgot How Much I Like You; editor, writer: plays including Sea of Forms, Nightwalk, 1001 Horror Stories of The Plains, Running Gag, Couplings and Groupings, Walking Through Walls, Babes Unchained, Cancel That Last Thought; or See The 270 Foot Woman in Spandex, X-Raydiate: E-Motion in Action, Body Leaks, Sound Fields, Belches on Couches, Star Path Moonstop; photographer/editor: Right Brain Vacation Photos: Production Photographs of Omaha Magic Theatre Productions, 1972-92; mem. performance ensemble Omaha Magic Theatre nat. and internat. performance tours Body Leaks, 1991, Body Leaks, 1992, Sound Fields, 1993, 94, Belches on Couches, 1993, 94; contbr. articles in field to profl. jours. Mem. Nebr. Artist-in-the-Schs., 1987—. Recipient Stanley Drama award, 1965, Office of Advanced Drama Rsch. award, 1965, Obie award, 1970, Disting. Contbrn. To and Svc. in Am Theatre Silver medal Amoco Oil Co., 1977; Dramatists Guild Com. of Women Ann. award, 1983, Nebr. Artist of Yr. 1992; Gov. award Nebr., 1992; Rockefeller grantee, 1968, 87; NEA Lit. fellow, 1973; Guggenheim fellow, 1978; NEA playwriting fellow, 1989, Lifetime Am. Theatre fellow, 1994. Mem. NEA (reporter and panelist for theatre program, 1975-85), Women's Theatre Coun. (founding 1971), Women's Forum (charter); Am. Theatre Assn. (co-chmn. playwriting program 1977, chmn. playwrights project com. 1978-79, C. Crawford playwriting judge of 1987); Theatre Comm. Group (bd. dirs. 1988-92), New Dramatists (alumni, judge nat. playwriting competition 1987-88), ASSISTEJ-USA (bd. dirs. 1986-91). Home: 2309 Hanscom Blvd Omaha NE 68105-3143 Office: E Marton Agy Rm 612 One Union Sq New York NY 10003-3303

TERRY, MORTON, academic administrator, physician; b. Utica, N.Y., Mar. 23, 1921; s. Isadore and Fanny (Brooks) T.; m. Geraldine Marie Rafferty, Oct. 31, 1948; children: Matthew, Jeffrey, Sheryl, Pamela. BA, Bklyn. Coll., 1942; DO, Phila. Coll. Osteo. Medicine, 1945, MS, 1950; postgrad., Am. Coll. Osteo. Internists, 1961. Diplomate Am. Osteo. Bd. Internal Medicine, Am. Osteo. Bd. Nuclear Medicine. Intern Osteo. Hosp. Phila., 1945-46, resident in internal medicine, 1946-48; internist, chmn. dept. internal medicine, exec. com. staff Biscayne (Fla.) Osteo. Hosp., 1953-60, chief staff, 1956-57; internist, chmn. dept. internal medicine Osteo. Gen. Hosp., 1960-75, chief staff, 1962-76; pres., founder Coll. Ostheopathic Medicine Southeastern U. Health Scis., North Miami Beach, Fla., 1979—; cons. internal medicine, 1949—; bd. dirs. County Nat. Bank. Chmn. osteo. div. United Way Dade County, 1966-75; bd. dirs. Am. Heart Assn. Greater Miami, 1971—, del. state of Fla., 1975-77; bd. dirs. Comprehensive Health Planning Coun. Dade County, 1969-73, Health Systems Agy. South Fla., 1976-79, Dade County unit Am. Cancer Soc., 1974-76, Am. Osteo. Bd. Internal Medicine, 1971-73, South Fla. Scholarship and Awards Found, 1973-81, Boys Town Fla., 1958-71, Biscayne Osteo. Found., 1979-82, Southeastern Coll. Osteo. Medicine, 1979—. Recipient Recognition and Appreciation cert. City North Miami Beach, 1973, Outstanding Svc. award, Osteo. Profession and Community, 1973, Recognition and Appreciation cert. State of Fla., 1982, Leadership award Fla. chpt. Bklyn. Coll. Pharmacy, 1989, O. J. Snyder medal Disting. Alumnus Phila. Coll. Osteo. Medicine, 1990. Mem. Am. Coll. Osteo. Internists (bd. dirs. 1975—, Disting. Svc. award 1981), Am. Assn. Colls. Osteo. Medicine (bd. dirs. 1979—), Am. Osteo. Assn. (life), Fla. Osteo. Med. Assn. (pres. 1961-62, hon. life), Dade County Osteo. Med. Assn. (pres. 1952-53), Sigma Sigma Phi (hon.). Office: Southeastern U Health Sci 1750 NE 168th St North Miami Beach FL 33162-3017

TERRY, PETER ANTHONY, lawyer; b. Sterling, Colo., Nov. 3, 1952; s. Fred Ward and Marian (Conroy) T. BA, U. Ariz., 1975, JD, 1978. Bar: Ariz. 1978, U.S. Dist. Ct. Ariz. 1978, Calif. 1979. Assoc. B. Wells O'Brien, Scottsdale, Ariz., 1978-79; ptnr. Fannin, Terry, & Lemberg, P.A.(formerly Fannin, Terry, Hay & Lemberg, PA, Phoenix, Ariz., 1979-88, Quarles & Brady, Phoenix, 1988—. Mem. Fed. Bar Assn., Ariz. Bar Assn., Calif. Bar Assn. Office: Quarles & Brady 1 E Camelback Rd Ste 400 Phoenix AZ 85012-1649

TERRY, RICHARD ALLAN, consulting psychologist, former college president; b. Lincoln, Nebr., June 4, 1920; s. Lester C. and Dorothy (Weeden) T.; m. Z. Inci Incikaya, June 3, 1959; 1 child, Deniz. A.B., U. Notre Dame, 1944; M.S., Catholic U. Am., 1950, Ph.D., 1954. Instr., asst. prof., chmn. psychol. dept. U. Portland, Oreg., 1953-59; prin. scientist, chief advanced research, life scis. North Am. Aviation, Downey, Calif., 1959-63; assoc. prof. indsl. engring., dir. systems research center U. Okla., Norman, 1963-69; prof., head dept. psychology U. Tulsa, 1970-73; prof. psychology SUNY Coll. at Oswego, 1973-75, dean grad. studies and research, 1973-75, acting v.p. acad. affairs, 1973-74; v.p. for instrn. and curriculum SUNY Coll. at Brockport, 1975-78; pres. Quinnipiac Coll., Hamden, Conn., 1978-86; sr. ptnr. Richard Allan Terry Assocs., Cons., Hamden, 1986-91; vis. prof. Hacettepe U., Ankara, Turkey, 1969-70; v.p. Found. for Study of Behavioral Scis., Downey, 1965-68; assoc. fellow Timothy Dwight Coll., Yale U., 1982—; v.p. Conn. Council Higher Edn., 1983-84, pres., 1984-85. Trustee Chamber Orch. of New Eng., 1979-82, chmn. bd., 1982-83; vice chmn. Mgmt. Study Group, Town of Hamden, 1982-83; bd. dirs. Urban League Greater New Haven, 1983-90, sec. 1988-90; chmn. oversight com. Study of Police-Media Rels., 1983-84; mem. steering com. New Haven Initiative for Excellence in Edn. 1986-90, steering com. Town of Hamden Plan for the Future, 1988-91, adv. bd. Conn. Small Bus. Devel. Ctr., 1989-91; mem. Town of Hamden Planning and Zoning Commn., 1991-93. Mem. Am. Psychol. Assn., Conn. Conf. Ind. Colls. (sec.-treas. 1983-86), Greater New Haven C. of C. (bd. dirs. 1982-86, chmn. jobs compact planning com., 1984-85, steering com. 1985-86) Sigma Xi. Democrat. Roman Catholic. Home: 24 Talon Dr Schenectady NY 12309-1839

TERRY, RICHARD EDWARD, public utility holding company executive; b. Green Bay, Wis., July 7, 1937; s. Joseph Edward and Arleen (Agamet) T.; m. Catherine Lombardo, Nov. 19, 1966; children—Angela, Edward. BA, St. Norbert's Coll., West DePere, Wis., 1959; LLB, U. Wis., 1964; postgrad., Harvard U., 1986. Assoc. Ross & Hardies, Chgo., 1964-72; atty. Peoples Energy Corp., Chgo., 1972-79, asst. gen. counsel, 1979-81, v.p., gen. counsel, 1981-84; exec. v.p. People's Energy Corp., Peoples Gas Light & Coke Co. and North Shore Gas Co., 1984-87, pres., COO, 1987—; chair, CEO People's Energy Corp., Peoples Gas Light & Coke Co. and North Shore Gas Co., Chgo., 1990—; bd. dirs. Peoples Energy Corp., Peoples Gas Light, North Shore Gas Co., Harris Bancorp, Harris Trust & Savs., Amsted Industries. Bd. dirs. Mus. Sci. & Ind., 1991—, Inst. Gas Tech., 1987—, Ill. Coun. on Econ. Edn., 1987—, Big Shoulders, 1991—; mem. Chgo. Area Ctrl. Com., 1991—; mem. bus. adv. coun. Chgo. Urban League, 1991—; prin. Chgo. United, 1991—; trustee St. Xavier U., 1989—, St. Norbert Coll., 1982—, DePaul U., 1992—. 1st lt. U.S. Army, 1959-61. Mem. Am. Gas Assn. (bd. dirs. 1991—), Nat. Petroleum Coun., Chgo. C. of C. (bd. dirs. 1988—), Univ. Club, Mid-Am. Club, Chgo. Club, Econ. Club, Comml. Club Chgo. (mem. civic com. 1991—). Avocations: golf, fishing, reading. Office: Peoples Energy Corp 130 E Randolph Dr Chicago IL 60601-6207

TERRY, RICHMOND BOHLER, textiles executive; b. Langdale, Ala., Feb. 7, 1934; s. George Thomas and Allyne Elizabeth (Bohler) T.; m. Shirley Anne Robinson, Dec. 26, 1954; children: Tana Lynn Terry Johnson, Richmond Bohler Jr., Christopher John. BS in Textile Mgmt., Auburn U., 1959. V.p. mfg. svcs. J.P. Stevens & Co., Inc., Greenville, S.C., 1988-89; dir. prodn. planning Shawmut (Ala.) Indsl. Plant, West Point-Pepperell, Inc., 1965-69, asst. plant mgr., 1969-73, plant mgr., 1973-76, plant mgr. Landale (Ala.) Plant., 1976-77; v.p. mfg. indsl. fabrics div. West Point-Pepperell, Inc., West Point, Ga., 1977-80, v.p. ops., 1980-88, v.p. mfg. svcs., 1989, sr. v.p. mfg. svcs., 1989—. Trustee, bd. dirs. Chattahoochee Valley Hosp. Soc., Valley, Ala., 1976-91; asst. treas. Ala. Textile Edn. Found., Auburn, 1984—; mem. Chattahoochee Valley Healthcare Found., Valley, 1991—. Named Outstanding Alumni Textile Engring. Dept., Auburn U. Coll. Engring., 1989. Mem. Am. Textile Mfrs. Assn. (bd. dirs., pres. 1982-86), Phi Kappa Phi, Phi Psi (pres. 1977-78). Methodist. Office: WestPont Stevens Inc 507 W 10th St West Point GA 31833-1232

TERRY, ROBERT DAVIS, neuropathologist, educator; b. Hartford, Conn., Jan. 13, 1924; m. Patricia Ann Blech, June 27, 1952; 1 son, Nicolas Saul. AB, Williams Coll., 1946, DSc (hon.), 1991; MD, Albany (N.Y.) Med. Coll., 1950. Diplomate: Am. Bd. Pathology, Am. Bd. Neuropathology.

Postdoctoral tng. St. Francis Hosp., Hartford, 1950, Bellevue Hosp., N.Y.C., 1951, Montefiore Hosp., N.Y.C., 1952-53, 54-55, Inst. Recherches sur le Cancer, Paris, France, 1953-54; sr. postdoctoral fellow Inst. Recherches sur le Cancer, 1955-66; asst. pathologist Montefiore Hosp., 1955-59; assoc. prof. dept. pathology Einstein Coll. Medicine, Bronx, N.Y., 1959-64; prof. Einstein Coll. Medicine, 1964-84, acting chmn. dept. pathology, 1969-70, chmn., 1970-84; prof. depts. neuroscis. and pathology U. Calif.-San Diego, 1984-94, prof. emeritus, 1994—; mem. study sect. pathology NIH, 1964-68; study sects. Nat. Multiple Sclerosis Soc., 1964-72, 74-78; mem. bd. sci. counselors Nat. Inst. Neurol. and Communicative Disorders and Stroke, NIH, 1976-80, chmn., 1977-80; mem. nat. sci. coun. Huntington's Disease Assn., 1978-81; mem. med. and sci. adv. bd. Alzheimer Assn., 1978-88; mem. sci. adv. bd. Max Planck Inst., Martinsried, 1990—. Mem. editorial adv. bd. Jour. Neuropathology and Exptl. Neurology, 1963-83, 85-88, Lab. Investigation, 1967-77, Revue Neurologique, 1977-87, Annals of Neurology, 1978-82, Ultrastructural Pathology, 1978-86, Am. Jour. Pathology, 1985-89. Served with AUS, 1943-46. Recipient Potamkin prize for Alzheimer Rsch., 1988, Met. Life Found. award, 1991. Fellow AAAS; mem. Am. Assn. Neuropathologists (pres. 1969-70, Meritorious Contbn. award 1989), N.Y. Path. Soc. (v.p. 1969-70, pres. 1971-73), Am. Assn. Pathologists, Am. Neurol. Assn., Am. Acad. Neurologists. Research, publs. on Alzheimer's disease and Tay Sachs disease. Office: U Calif San Diego Dept Neuroscis La Jolla CA 92093

TERRY, ROBERT MEREDITH, French language educator; b. Danville, Va., Dec. 16, 1939; s. Willard Terry and Martha Willeford; m. Anne Reynolds Beggarly, Jan. 30, 1965; children: Michael Reynolds, Christopher Robert, Meredith Anne. BA in French, Randolph-Macon Coll., Ashland, Va., 1962; PhD in Romance Langs., Duke U., Durham. N.C., 1966. Asst. prof. French U. Fla., Gainesville, Fla., 1966-68; assoc. prof. French U. Richmond, Richmond, Va., 1968-83, prof. French, 1983—; pres. Am. Coun. on Teaching of Fgn. Langs., 1994; editor, Dimension, Southern Conf. on Lang. Teaching, 1991—. Co-author: Accent: Conversational French I, 1980, Vous Y Etes!, 1990, Intersections, 1991; contbr. articles to profl. jours. Recipient Stephen A. Freeman award, Northeast Conf. on the Teaching of Fgn. Lang., 1990. Mem. Am. Coun. on Teaching Fgn. Langs., Fgn. Lang. Assn. Va., Am. Assn. Tchrs. French, So. Conf. on Lang. Teaching. Home: 1504 Cloister Dr Richmond VA 23233 Office: Univ Richmond PO Box 25 28 Westhampton Way University Of Richmond VA 23173

TERRY, RONALD ANDERSON, bank holding company executive; b. Memphis, Dec. 5, 1930; s. John Burnett and Vernon (Lucas) T.; m. Wynoka W. Evans, May 21, 1989; children by previous marriage: Natalie Carol, Cynthia Leigh. B.S., Memphis State U., 1952; postgrad., So. Meth. U., 1961, Harvard U., 1970. Mgmt. trainee First Tenn. Bank, Memphis, 1957; pres. First Tenn. Nat. Corp., Memphis, 1971, chmn., chief exec. officer, 1973—; chmn., chief exec. officer First Tenn. Bank N.A., Memphis, 1979—, also bd. dirs.; bd. dirs. BellSouth Corp., Promus Cos., Inc. Past pres. Boys Clubs Memphis, Future Memphis; past chmn. Memphis Jobs Conf.; bd. dirs. St. Jude Hosp.; chmn. adv. coun. Baptist Meml. Hosp.; trustee U. Tenn.; past Tenn. State chmn. com. for econ. devel.; adv. bd. Memphis Arts Coun. Lt. USN, 1953-57. Mem. Am. Bankers Assn. (treasury adv. com., bd. dirs., past chmn. govt. relations council), Assn. Res. City Bankers (dir., past chmn. govt. relations com. and pub. affairs com.), Assn. Bank Holding Cos. (legis. policy com., past pres. fed. adv. council), Econ. Club of Memphis (past pres.). Office: 1st Tenn Nat Corp PO Box 84 Memphis TN 38101

TERRY, THOMAS EDWARD, investment company executive, lawyer; b. Milw., Nov. 6, 1937; s. Eugene John and Mary Josephine (Boullioun) T.; m. Jan Beare, Dec. 11, 1971; 1 child, Hathaway. BS, U. Wis., 1961, JD, 1964. Bar: Wis. 1964. V.p., sec., treas. Am. Express Investment Mgmt. Co., San Francisco, 1964-75, Capital Rsch. and Mgmt. Co., L.A., 1975-94; pres. Endowments, Inc., Bond Portfolio for Endowments, Inc., 1985; chmn. Am. Variable Ins. Series, 1988; sr. v.p. Am. Balanced Fund, Inc., 1987-94, Growth Fund of Am., Inc., 1987-94, Income Fund of Am., 1987-94; v.p. The Bond Fund Am., Inc., 1981-94, AMCAP Fund, Inc., 1984, Capital World Bond Fund, Inc., 1987-94, Tax-Exempt Fund Calif., 1986-94, others. Past chmn., mem. Bascum Hill Soc., U. Wis., 1986-89; bd. dirs. Ketchum L.A. YMCA, 1991-94, Citizens Scholarship Found., Wis. chpt. Nat. Football Found.; mem. exec. com. Bascum Hill Soc., U. Wis. Found.; dir. ICI Mutual Ins. Co. Mem. ABA, Wis. Bar Assn. (non-resident dir. 1982-86). Republican. Roman Catholic. Home: 6034 S Highlands Ave Madison WI 53705 Office: Capital Rsch and Mgmt Co 51st Fl 333 S Hope St Los Angeles CA 90071

TERRY, WARD EDGAR, JR., lawyer; b. Denver, Aug. 1, 1943; s. Ward E. and Peggy Helen Louise (Smith) T.; m. Juliann Dire, Apr. 8, 1967; children: Seth S., Nicole E. BA, U. Colo., 1965, JD, 1968; LLM in Taxation, U. Denver, 1976. Bar: Colo. 1968, U.S. Dist. Ct. Colo. 1968, U.S. Tax Ct. 1980. Assoc. McMartin & Burk, Englewood, Colo., 1968-70, Modesitt & Shaw, Denver, 1970-71, Gorsuch, Kirgis, Campbell, Walker & Grover, Denver, 1971-72, Hopper and Kanouff, Denver, 1976-78; sec., dir. Ward Terry and Co., Denver, 1972-76; ptnr. Hopper, Kanouff, Smith, Peryam & Terry, Denver, 1979-91; shareholder Hopper and Kanouff, P.C., Denver, 1991—, also bd. dirs.; gen. ptnr. PSW Investments Ltd., Denver, 1984—. Trustee Denver Country Day Sch., Englewood, 1969-70; campaign chair Roseanne Ball Election Com., Denver, 1974. Mem. ABA (bus. law sect., real estate and probate sect., taxation sect., antitrust sect.), Colo. Bar Assn. (bus. law and taxation sect.), Denver Bar Assn., Denver Gyro Club (pres. 1994-95, v.p. 1993-94, membership chmn. 1991-92), Phi Alpha Delta. Republican. Presbyterian. Avocations: long-distance running, golf, skiing, bicycling. Office: Hopper and Kanouff PC 1610 Wynkoop St Ste 200 Denver CO 80202-1196

TERRY, WAYNE GILBERT, healthcare executive, hospital administrator; b. Plymouth, Mass., Feb. 10, 1932; s. Lawrence Arthur Terry and Betty Frances (Bouteman) McClellan; m. Barbara Bromwell, Sept. 20, 1980; children: Karleton Wayne, Dale Duane, Kendrick Shane, Kristen Alayne, Tammye Van Clief, Wade Bromwell Delk. AA, Allan Hancock Jr. Coll., Santa Maria, Calif., 1960; BBA, U. Hawaii, 1966; M. Hosp. Adminstrn., Med. Coll. Va., 1973. Commd. USAF, advanced through grades to maj.; asst. administr. for registrar activities USAF Hosp., Orlando AFB, Fla., 1966-67; assoc. administr. aeromed. evacuation activities USAF, Hickam AFB, Hawaii, 1967-71; adminstrv. resident USAF Regional Hosp., Langley AFB, Va., 1972-73; CEO USAF Hosp., Columbus AFB, Miss., 1973-75; nat. health edn. and tng. program advisor Office of Surgeon Gen., Dept. of Air Force, Washington, 1975-78; dir. health professions pers. planning and policy divsn. Office of Asst. Sec. Def. for Health Affairs, The Pentagon, Washington, 1978-80; dep. project mgr./adminstrv. dir. King Faisal U. Teaching Hosp., Al-Khobar, Saudi Arabia, 1980-82; dep. project mgr., hosp. dir. North Yemen Healthcare Project, As-Salem Hosp., Sadah, Yemen Arab Republic, 1982-83; hosp. dir., CEO Armed Forces Hosps., Khamis Mushayt, Saudi Arabia, 1983-84; chief adminstr./commissioning team chief Orbit Summit Health, Ltd., Riyadh, Saudi Arabia, 1984-85; hosp. dir., adminstrv. dir. Truk State Dept. Health Svcs., Moen, 1985-87; assoc. administr. support svcs. King Fahad Hosp., Saudi Arabian N.G., Riyadh, 1987-90; project mgr., CEO N.W. Armed Forces Hosps. Program, Tabuk, Saudi Arabia, 1990—; lectr. in field; cons. in field; mem. supervisory bd. Royal Coll. Surgeons in Ireland/Witikar Saudi Arabia Ltd., 1990-94; active various symposium organizing coms. Contbr. articles to profl. jours. Warden to Am. Cmty., N.W. Region of Saudi Arabia to Am. Embassy in Riyadh, 1990-94; mem. Internat. Sch. Sys. Coord. Com., Tabuk, 1990-94; waren to Am. Cmty. N.W. Region of Yemen ARab Republic to Am. Embassy in Sanaa, 1982-83; bd. dirs. Taif Sch. Dist. Sys., Saudi Arabia, 1981-82. Decorated Air Force Commendation medal with 2 oak leaf clusters, Air medal with 2 oak leaf clusters, Meritorious Svc. medal with 3 oak leaf clusters; recipient Citation of Appreciation, Nat. Coun. Social Welfare, Seoul, Korea, 1963, Suchan Province Gov., Choong Nam, Korea, 1963, Outstanding Rsch. award Med. Coll. Va., 1973, Men of Achievement award, Cambridge, Eng., 1982, Citation of Appreciation, Govt. Truk State, 1987, Citation of Merit Internat. Red Cross Commn., 1991, N.W. Armed Forces Hosps., Ministry of Def. and Aviation, Tabuk, Saudi Arabia, 1991, Citation of Appreciation, Presidency of Gen. Staff Hdqrs., Ministry of Def. and Aviation, Tabuk, Saudi Arabia, 1992, 93. Fellow Am. Coll. Healthcare Execs., Royal Soc. Health; mem. Am. Hosp. Assn., Am. Mgmt. Assn., Air Force Med. Svc. Corps Assn., Air Force Assn., Assn. Mil. Surgeons of U.S. Republican. Baptist. Avocations:

tennis, numismatics, travel. Office: NW Armed Forces Hosp Program, USMTM Unit 62007, AE 09810-2007 APO Saudi Arabia

TERRY, WILLIAM E., rear admiral; b. Borger, Tex., Jan. 9, 1940; s. Ralph Thompson and Elva Lee (Petty) T.; m. Johanna Elizabeth Madden, May 9, 1964; children: Shannon Elizabeth, Michael Eric. BA, U.S. Naval Postgrad. Sch., 1973, MS, 1974. Ensign USN, 1964; pilot helicopter anti-sub. squadron four (HS-4) USN, San Diego, 1963, instr. helicopter anti-sub. squadron ten (HS-10), 1964-66, detachment helicopter anti-sub. squadron ten (HS-10), 1966-69, officer-in-charge helicopter combat support squadron (HC-1), 1969-71, maintenance officer helicopter anti-sub. squadron six (HS-6), 1975-76, exec. officer helicopter anti-sub. squadron ten (HS-10), 1976, comdg. officer helicopter anti-sub. squadron eight (HS-8), 1976-79; exec. officer USS Okinawa, USN, San Diego, 1979-81; comdg. officer helicopter anti-sub. squadron ten (HS-10) USN, San Diego, 1981-83; branch head Office of the Chief of Naval Ops., USN, Washington, 1983-84; comdg. officer USS Okinawa, USN, San Diego, 1985-86; chief of staff, comdr. cruiser destroyer group one USN, San Diego, 1986-87, commodore, comdr. amphibious squadron seven, USN, Washington, 1989-90; asst., commander, chief of staff for logistics Allied Forces So. Europe, USN, Naples, Italy, 1990-92; commander combat logistics group two USN, Norfolk, Va., 1992—. Republican. Episcopalian. Home: 216 Dale Ave Norfolk VA 23511 Office: Logistics Comdr Navy Dept 9730 Maury Ave Norfolk VA 09506-5310

TERSIGNI, ANTHONY, health science facility administrator; b. Det., July 25, 1949; s. Andrea and Benedetta (D'Annunzio) T.; m. Flora Pelino Tersigni, June 12, 1977; children: Maria Teresa, John, Andrea. BA, U. Mich., 1971; MPA, Oakland U., Mich. 1983; EDD, We. Mich. U., 1988. Sr. v.p. St. Joseph Hosp., Mich., 1978-84; dir. ops. Det. Med. Ctr., Mich., 1984-85; pres., chief exec. officer Huron Valley Hosl.- DMC, Mich., 1985-86, Oakland Gen. Health Systems, Mich.; dir. SE Mich. Hosp. Assn.-Fin. Plng. Com. Southfield 1986; vice chmn. Mich. Hosp. Assn., Service Corp. Lansing 1985. Dir. Orch. Hall Det., 1985. Nat. Guard 1969-75 Det. Mem. Am. Coll. Hosp. Administrs., Am. Pub. Health Assn., Am. Coll. Healthcare Execs. Roman Catholic. Avocations: golfing, tennis, racquetball. Home: 11258 Olive St Warren MI 48093 Office: Oakland Gen Health Systems 27351 Dequindre Madison Heights MI 48071

TERTZAKIAN, HOVHANNES, bishop; b. Aleppo, Syria, Jan. 3, 1924. Philosophy & Theology, Pontifical Gregorian U., Rome, Italy, 1949. ordained priest Sept. 8, 1948. Teacher, then Dean Mekhitarist Sch., Alexandria, Egypt, 1949-56; dean of studies & admin. Mekhitarist Sch., Aleppo, Syria, 1956-60; headmaster Mekhitarist Sch., Aleppo, 1960-70; rector Moorat-Raphael Coll., Venice, Italy, 1970-79, Samuel-Moorat Coll., Sevres, France, 1980-82, St. Anne's Armenian Catholic Cathedral, New York, N.Y., 1986-89; Pro Exarch, 1989-90, Exarchate Chancellor, 1990-95; Apostolic Exarch for Armenian Catholics 1995—; mem. Mekhitarist Order of Venice (superior 1960-70, gen. council mem. 1970-76, gen. admin. 1976-79, provincial supr. 1979-80, Abbot Gen. 1982-84). Office: Chancery Office 110 E 12th New York NY 10003*

TERWILLIGER, GEORGE JAMES, III, lawyer; b. New Brunswick, N.J., June 5, 1950; s. George James Jr. and Ruth Nancy (Mellilo) T.; m. Carol Anne Hitchings, Dec. 18, 1976; children: Sarah Katherine, George Zachary Grant, Virginia. BA in Communications, Seton Hall U., 1973; JD, Antioch Law Sch., 1978. Bar: D.C. 1978, U.S. Dist. Ct. D.C., 1979, U.S. Ct. Appeals (D.C. cir.) 1979, U.S. Dist. Ct. (so. dist.) Fla. 1980, U.S. Dist. Ct. Vt. 1981, U.S. Ct. Appeals (2d cir.) 1982, Vt. 1983, U.S. Supreme Ct. 1992, U.S. Ct. Appeals (4th cir.) 1993. Asst. U.S. atty. Office of U.S. Atty., Washington, 1978-81; asst. U.S. atty. Dist. of Vt., Burlington, 1981-86, U.S. atty., 1986-91; dep. atty. gen. Washington, 1992-93; partner McGuire, Woods, Battle & Boothe, Washington, 1993—. Mem. ABA, Vt. Bar Assn., D.C. Bar Assn., Rep. Nat. Lawyers Assn. (pres. 1994-95). Republican. Congregationalist. Avocations: skiing, tennis, fishing. Office: McGuire, Woods, Battle & Boothe Army and Navy Club Building 1627 I St NW Washington DC 20006-4007

TERZIAN, PHILIP HENRY, journalist; b. Kensington, Md., July 5, 1950; s. L.A. and Louise (Anderson) T.; m. Grace Barrett Paine, Oct. 20, 1979; children: William Thomas Hillman, Grace Benedict Paine. BA, Villanova U., 1973; DTS, Oxford U., Episcopal Theol. Seminary, Va., 1995. Desk editor Reuters, Washington, 1973, U.S. News & World Report, Washington, 1973-74; asst. editor The New Republic, Washington, 1974-78; mem. policy planning staff Dept. State, Washington, 1978-79; asst. editor Anniston (Ala.) Star, 1979-80; assoc. editor Lexington (Ky.) Herald, 1980-82; asst. editor of editorial pages L.A. Times, 1982-86; editor of editorial pages Providence Jour., 1986-92, assoc. editor, columnist, 1992—; panelist Washington Week in Review, etc.; mem. bd. of advisors, Inst. of Am. Values, Nichols Coll. Contbr. articles to newspapers and jours. Exec. dir. Providence Com. Fgn. Rels., 1989-92. Recipient Edn. Writers award Ida Lee Willis Assn., 1981, Ida Lee Willis Svc. to Preservation award Ida Lee Willis Found., 1982; named finalist Pulitzer prize Disting. Commentary, 1991, Pulitzer Prize juror, 1994-95. Mem. Am. Coun. on Germany, Va. Hist. Soc., St. Andrew's Soc. Washington, Theodore Roosevelt Assn., Hon. Order Ky. Cols., Soc. King Charles the Martyr, Va. Foxhound Club, Nat. Press Club, Hope Club. Republican. Episcopalian. Avocations: reading, book collecting, riding, music. Home: 10505 Adel Rd Oakton VA 22124 Office: Providence Jour 400 N Capitol St NW Washington DC 20001

TERZIAN, YERVANT, astronomy and astrophysics educator; b. Alexandria, Egypt, Feb. 9, 1939; came to U.S., 1960, naturalized, 1971; s. Bedros and Maria (Kiriakaki) T.; m. Araxy M. Hovsepian, Apr. 16, 1966; children: Sevan, Tamar. BS, Am. U., Cairo, 1960; MS, Ind. U., 1963, PhD, 1965, DSc (hon.), 1989; DSc (hon.) Yerevan State U., 1994. Rsch. assoc. Arecibo Obs., P.R., 1965-67; asst. prof. astronomy and astrophysics Cornell U., Ithaca, N.Y., 1967-72, assoc. prof., 1972-77, prof., 1977—, chmn. dept. astronomy, 1979—, dir. Program in Sci. Edn., 1988—, James A. Weeks prof. in phys. scis., 1990. Editor: Interstellar Ionized Hydrogen, 1968; Planetary Nebulae, 1978; co-editor: Cosmology and Astrophysics, 1982; assoc. editor The Astrophysical Jour., 1989—; contbr. over 170 articles to tech. jours. Recipient Clark Disting. Teaching award Cornell U., 1984. Mem. Internat. Astron. Union, Soc. Sci. Exploration, Internat. Sci. Radio Union, Am. Astron. Soc., Armenian Acad. Sci. (fgn. mem.). Home: 109 Brandywine Dr Ithaca NY 14850-1747 Office: Cornell U Astronomy Dept Space Scis Bldg Ithaca NY 14853

TESAR, DELBERT, machine systems and robotics educator, researcher, manufacturing consultant; b. Beaver Crossing, Nebr., Sept. 2, 1935; s. Louis and Clara (Capek) T.; m. Rogene Kresak, Feb. 1, 1957; children: Vim Lee, Aleta Anne, Landon Grady, Allison Jeanne. B.Sc. in Mech. Engring., U. Nebr., 1958, M.Sc., 1959; Ph.D., Ga. Tech. U., 1964. Assoc. prof. U. Fla., Gainesville, 1965-71, prof., 1972-83, grad. research prof., 1983-84, dir., founder Ctr. Intelligent Machines and Robotics, 1978-84; Curran chair in engring. U. Tex., Austin, 1985—; lectr. in field.; mem. rev. panel Nat. Bur. Standards, Gaithersburg, Md., 1982-88; mem. sci. adv. bd. to Air Force, 1982-86, numerous others; interactor with Russian Acad. Sci. on sci. and tech. Author: (with others) Cam System Design, 1975. Patentee in field; contbr. articles to profl. jours.; assoc. editor 3 computer and mfg. jours. Expert witness house sci. and tech. com. U.S. Ho. of Reps., 1978-84. Mem. Fla. Engring. Soc. (Outstanding Tech. Achievement award 1982), ASME (machine design award 1987). Avocations: antiques, art, travel. Home: 8005 Two Cove Dr Austin TX 78730-3125 Office: U Tex Dept Mechanical Engineering Austin TX 78712-1063*

TESAR, MILO BENJAMIN, agricultural researcher and educator; b. Tobias, Nebr., Apr. 7, 1920; s. Frank and Frances (Cihal) T.; m. Marian Olive Hunt, Sept. 3, 1944; children: Robert, Ann, Joyce, Janet. BS with distinction, U. Nebr., 1941; MS, U. Wis., 1947, PhD, 1949; DSc (hon.), U. Nebr., 1989. Asst. prof. crop-soil sci. Mich. State U., East Lansing 1949-53, assoc. prof., 1953-58, prof., 1958-88, prof. emeritus, 1988—, acting chmn. dept. crop and soil sci., 1964-66; agrl. advisor China, Australia, New Zealand, Scotland, USSR, Japan, Eng., Brazil, Somalia, Egypt, Finland. Author: Forage Management, 1982, 2nd edit., 1984, 3rd edit., 1986; editor: Physiological Basis of Crop Growth and Development, 1988; author (with others), assoc. editor: Alfalfa Science and Technology, 1972, Alfalfa and

Alfalfa Improvement, 1988. Chmn. bd. elders People's Ch., East Lansing, 1966; mem. East Lansing Sch. Bd., 1966-70. Maj. U.S. Army, 1942-46, PTO, Hiroshima, Japan. Decorated Silver Star, Bronze Star; named NATO fellow NSF, Hurley, Eng., 1959-60; recipient King Charles Educator award Nebr Czechs, 1987, Disting. Rsch. award Mich. State U. Coll. Agr., 1985, hon. extension svc. award, 1984, Alumni Achievement award U. Nebr., 1991. Fellow AAAS, Crop Sci. Soc. Am. (DeKalb-Prizer Disting. Crop Sci. Career award 1988), Am. Soc. Agronomy (cert. agronomist, crop scientist, Agronomic Achievement award 1984); mem. Mich. State U. President's Club, Sigma Xi. Republican. Home: 2379 Emerald Forest Cir East Lansing MI 48823-7214 Office: Mich State U Dept Crop Soil Sci East Lansing MI 48824

TESCHNER, DOUGLASS PAUL, state legislator; b. Cambridge, Mass., Oct. 29, 1949; s. Douglass P. Teschner and Mary Elizabeth (Bernt) Teschner Zeller; m. Martha Weaver, Sept. 26, 1981. BS in Forestry, U. Mass., 1971, EdD in Adminstrn., 1985; MS in Botany, U. Vt., 1978. Land surveyor Lincoln Engring. and Burnell Land Surveying, 1974, 78; tchr. White Mountain Sch., 1976; dir. Inst. Exptl. Studies, various locations, 1981-84, 86-88; fin. officer Becket Acad., East Haddam, Conn., 1984-86; devel. dir. Central N.H. Community Mental Health Svcs., Concord, 1987—; state rep. N.H. Ho. Reps., Concord, 1988—. Co-editor: Wilderness Challenge: Outdoor Education Alternatives for Youth in Need, 1984; contbr. articles to profl. jours. Mem. Haverhill Hist. Soc.; vol. Peace Corps, 1971-73; mem. Oliverian Watershed Coun. Mem. Congregational Ch. Avocations: mountaineering, hiking, rock and ice climbing, skiing. Home: RR 2 Box 173 Pike NH 03780-9706 Office: Ctrl NH Cmty Mental Health Svc PO Box 2032 Concord NH 03302-2032

TESCHNER, RICHARD REWA, retired lawyer; b. Milw., Feb. 5, 1908; s. Bruno A. and Thekla (Rewa) T.; m. D. Joy Griesbach, Sept. 24, 1932; 1 son, Richard Vincent. B.A., U. Wis., 1931, LL.B., 1934; L.H.D. (hon.), Carroll Coll., 1976. Bar: Wis. 1934, U.S. Supreme Ct. 1944. Tax counsel Wis. Dept. Taxation, 1938-45; ptnr. Quarles & Brady, 1945-87. Mem. Milwaukee County War Meml. Devel. Com., chmn., 1960-70; mem. Greater Milw. Com.; past mem. Wis. Arts Bd.; chmn. Milw. Performing Arts Center, 1969-74; co-chmn. United Performing Arts Fund drive, 1977; pres. Will Ross Meml. Found.; chmn. Milw. Found., 1978-79; bd. dirs. Second Harvesters of Wis., Inc., 1980-91, Ice Age Park and Trail of Wis. Found., 1989-90. Mem. ABA, Wis. Bar Assn., Milw. Bar Assn. (pres. 1964-65), Pi Kappa Alpha, Phi Delta Phi. Presbyterian. Lodge: Rotary. Home: 1840 N Prospect Ave Milwaukee WI 53202-1960

TESH, JOHN, television talk show host; b. Garden City, N.Y., 1953; s. John and Mildred Tesh; m. Connie Sellecca, Apr. 4, 1992; children: Gib, Prima. Co-host Entertainment Tonight, 1986—; host One-On-One with John Tesh, 1991; co-host John and Leeza from Hollywood, 1993. Television appearances include: The U.S. Open Tennis Championship, 1985, Macy's Thanksgiving Day Parade, 1987, Wimbledon, 1991; film appearances include Shocker, 1989, Soapdish, 1991; albums include Tour de France, 1988, The Early Years, 1990, Ironman, 1992, The Games, 1992, Monterey Nights, 1993, A Romantic Christmas, 1993; composers theme music Bobby's World, 1990, The Knife and Gun Club, 1990, One on One, 1991, NFL Live. Recipient 4 Emmy awards for composing, 2 Emmy awards for reporting. Office: Paramount TV 5555 Melrose Ave Los Angeles CA 90038-3149

TESICH, STEVE, author; b. Titovo Utice, Yugoslavia, Sept. 29, 1942; came to U.S., 1955, naturalized, 1961; s. Radisa and Gospava (Bulaich) T.; m. Rebecca Fletcher, May 24, 1971. BA, Ind. U., 1965; MA, Columbia U., 1967. Freelance writer, 1968—; author: (plays) The Carpenters, 1970, Lake of the Woods, 1971, Baba Goya, 1972 (Drama Desk award 1973), Gorky, 1975, Passing Game, 1977, Touching Bottom, 1978, Division Street, 1980, Speed of Darkness, 1989, Square One, 1990, On The Open Road, 1992; (novel) Summer Crossing, 1982; (film) Breaking Away, 1979 (Academy award, 1979, N.Y. Film Critics Circle award 1980, Nat. Soc. Film Critics award 1980, Critics Circle Film Sect. award 1980), Eyewitness, 1981, Four Friends, 1981, The World According to Garp, 1982 (Exceptional Film award, Nat. Bd. Rev. 1983), American Flyers, 1985, Eleni, 1985. NDEA fellow, Rockefeller fellow, 1972. Mem. Acad. Motion Picture Arts and Scis. (award 1980), Writers Guild (award 1980), Dramatists Guild, Phi Beta Kappa. Democrat. Office: 40 W 57th St New York NY 10019-4001

TESKE, RICHARD HENRY, veterinarian; b. Christiansburg, Va., July 22, 1939; s. August Frank and Peggy Marie (Macomber) T.; m. Mary Helen Webb, June 11, 1961; children: Helen Desiree, Mary Michele. BS, Va. Tech. U., 1962; DVM, U. Ga., 1965; MS, U. Fla., 1966. Diplomate Am. Bd. Vet. Toxicology. Asst. prof. U. Fla., Gainesville, 1967; dir. toxicology Hill Top Rsch., Inc., Miamiville, Ohio, 1967-70; chief pharmacology/toxicology br. Ctr. for Vet. Medicine FDA, Beltsville, Md., 1971-77, dep. dir. div. med. rsch. Ctr. for Vet. Medicine, 1977-78, dir. div. vet. med. rsch. Ctr. for Vet. Medicine, 1978-82; assoc. dir. for sci. Ctr. for Vet. Medicine FDA, Rockville, Md., 1982-85, dep. dir. Ctr. for Vet. Medicine, 1985—; mem. vet. med. adv. bd. panel U.S. Pharmacopeial Conv., Rockville, 1984—. Fellow Am. Acad. Vet. Pharms. and Therapeutics, Am. Acad. Vet. and Comparative Toxicology. Office: FDA Ctr for Vet Medicine 7500 Standish Pl Rockville MD 20855-2773

TESLER, LAWRENCE GORDON, computer company executive; b. N.Y.C., Apr. 24, 1945; s. Isidore and Muriel (Krechmer) T.; m. Shelagh Elisabeth Leuterio, Oct 4, 1964 (div. 1970); 1 child, Lisa Traci; m. Colleen Ann Barton, Feb. 17, 1987. BS in Math., Stanford U., 1965. Pres. Info. Processing Corp., Palo Alto, Calif., 1963-68; rsch. asst. Stanford U. Artificial Intelligence Lab., 1968-73; mem. rsch. staff Xerox Corp., Palo Alto, 1973-80; sect. mgr. Lisa div. Apple Computer, Inc., Cupertino, Calif., 1980-82, cons. engr., 1983-86, v.p. advanced tech., 1986-90, v.p. advanced products, 1990-92, v.p. engring., 1992-93, chief scientist, 1993—; bd. dirs. Advanced RISC Machines Ltd.; mem. Computer Sci. and Telecom. Bd., 1991-94. Contbr. articles to profl. jours., various computer software. Bd. dirs. Peninsula Sch., Menlo Park, Calif., 1974-78. Mem. Assn. Computing Machinery (conf. cochmn. 1987-88). Office: Apple Computer Inc 1 Infinite Loop Cupertino CA 95014-6201

TESLOW, PAUL ANDRE, retired health executive; b. Chgo., May 12, 1934; s. Reuben Clayton and Eva Valborg (Oefstedal) T.; m. Marilyn Renée Lund, Aug. 28, 1955; children: Lori, Linda Teslow Gerlach, Sandra Teslow Wagner. BA, Concordia Coll., 1956; MHA, U. Minn., 1959. Adminstrv. staff asst. Immanuel Hosp., Mankato, Minn., 1956-57; adminstrv. resident San Jose (Calif.) Hosp., 1958-59; administr. Good Samaritan Hosp., Puyallup, Wash., 1959-70; pres., CEO Northridge (Calif.) Hosp., 1970-79, HealthWest Found., Chatsworth, Calif., 1979-88; pres., CEO UniHealth Am., Burbank, Calif., 1988-92, pres. emeritus, bd. dirs., 1993—. Mem. editl. bd. Managed Care Quar. Mem. adv. bd. health svcs. adminstrn. U. So. Calif.; mem. cabinet L.A. Music Ctr. Campaign, 1992; bd. dirs. PacifiCare NASDAQ, 1988-93, Nat. Fund for Med. Edn. Recipient VICA award for corporate excellence, 1987. Fellow Am. Coll. Healthcare Execs.; mem. Am. Hosp. Assn., Am. Healthcare Syss. (bd. dirs., exec. com.), Calif. Assn. Hosps. and Health Sys. (trustee, Walker fellow 1986), Hosp. Coun. So. Calif. (bd. dirs. 1973-75, mem. exec. com. 1975-82, chmn. 1982-83), Indian Wells Country Club. Home: 615 Bayside Dr Newport Beach CA 92660

TESORO, GIULIANA CAVAGLIERI, chemistry research educator, consultant; b. Venice, Italy, June 1, 1921; came to U.S., 1939; d. Gino and Margherita (Maroni) Cavaglieri; m. Victor Tesoro, Apr. 17, 1943; children: Claudia, Andrew. PhD, Yale U., 1943. Rsch. chemist Am. Cyanamid Co., Bloundbrook, N.J., 1943-44; asst. dir. rsch. Onyx Chem. Co., Jersey City, 1944-58, J. P. Stevens & Co., Inc., Garfield, N.J., 1958-68; dir. chem. rsch. Burlington Industries, Greenboro, N.C., 1968-72; sr. scientist, adj. prof. MIT, Cambridge, 1973-82; rsch. prof. Poly. U., Bklyn., 1982—; Mem. nat. materials adv. bd. NRC, Washington, 1979-82. Contbr. numerous articles to profl. publs.; patentee in field. Recipient Am. Dyestuff Reporter award, 1959, Achievement award Soc. Women Engrs., 1978. Fellow Textile Inst. Gt. Britain; mem. AAAS (co-chmn. polymer combustion and fire retardance conf. 1977), Am. Assn. Textile Chemists and Colorists (Olney medal 1963), Am. Chem. Soc., Am. Inst. Chemists, Info. Coun. Fabric flammability, N.Y. Acad. Sci., Textile Rsch. Inst. (editorial bd.jours.), Fiber Soc. (pres. 1974-75). Democrat. Home: 278 Clinton Ave Dobbs Ferry NY 10522-3007 Office: Poly U 333 Jay St Brooklyn NY 11201-2907

TESSER, ABRAHAM, social psychologist; b. N.Y.C., May 24, 1941; s. Louis and Ruth (Buchholz) T.; m. Marsha Richman Rosenthal, June 4, 1967 (div. Feb. 22, 1983); children: Louis J., Rachel A.; m. Carmen Chaves, Dec. 15, 1990. BA, L.I.U., 1962; MS, Purdue U., 1965, PhD, 1967. Rsch. assoc. Inst. for Behavioral Rsch., U. Ga., 1971-78, assoc. dir., 1978-84, acting dir. Ctr. for Rsch. on Deviance, 1984-86, dir., 1984-94; from asst. prof. to assoc. prof. social psychology U. Ga., 1967-74, prof., 1974-89, rsch. prof. psychology, 1989—; vis. fellow Yale U., 1976-77; Princeton U., spring 1983; fellow Ctr. for Advanced Studies in the Behavioral Scis., Stanford, Calif., 1992-93. Editor Jour. Personality and Social Cognition, 1991-94; contbr. numerous articles to profl. jours. Mem. AAUP, APA, Am. Psychol. Soc., Soc. for Personality and Social Psychology, Soc. Exptl. Social Psychology, Soc. Psychophysiol. Rsch., Soc. for Social Psychology. Office: Univ Ga Dept Psychology Athens GA 30602

TESSLER, ALLAN R., trucking company executive; b. 1936. AB, Cornell U., 1958, LLB, 1963. Bar: N.Y. 1963. Atty., mem. exec. com. Shea & Gould, 1976-88; chmn. bd. dirs. Internat. Controls Corp., Kalamazoo, Mich., 1989—; chmn. bd. dirs. Internat. Fin. Group, Inc., N.Y.C., Enhance Fin. Svcs., Americsribe Corp. Lt. USN, 1958-61. Office: Internat Controls Corp 2016 N Pitcher St Kalamazoo MI 49007-1869

TESSLER, ALLAN ROGER, lawyer; b. Phila., Sept. 29, 1936; s. Irving and Rhoda T.; m. Frances Goudsmit, June 17, 1958; children: Andrea, Christopher, Karla. BA, Cornell U., 1958, LLB. 1963. Bar: N.Y. 1963, U.S. Dist. Ct. (so. dist.) N.Y. 1963. Assoc. Cleary Gotlieb, Steen and Hamilton, N.Y.C., 1963-67; arbitrageur Loeb, Rhoades, N.Y.C., 1967-68; mng. ptnr. Devon Securities, N.Y.C., 1969-72; exec. v.p. Landenburg, Thalman, N.Y.C., 1972; pres., chmn. Fifth Ave. Coach Lines, N.Y.C., 1972-73; pres. Slater Walker of Am., N.Y.C., 1973-75; of counsel Spengler, Carlson et al, N.Y.C. 1975-76; sr. ptnr. Shea & Gould, N.Y.C., 1976-88, of counsel, 1989-92; chmn., pres. Internat. Fin. Group, Inc., Jackson, Wyo. and N.Y.C.; co-CEO, chmn. Data Broadcasting Corp., N.Y.C. Wyo.; chmn., CEO Americsribe Corp. , N.Y.C.; chmn. bd. dirs. Enhance Fin. Services, N.Y.C., Internat. Controls Corp., Mich.; bd. dirs. Jackpot Enterprises, Inc., Las Vegas, The Ltd., Inc., Columbus, Ohio, Allis-Chalmers Corp. Wis. Nat. chmn. Cornell LaW Sch. Fund, 1983-85; mem. adv. council Cornell Law Sch., 1987—; co-chmn. Cornell Law Sch. Capital Campaign, 1991-93; trustee Cornell U., Hudson Inst., Ind., Jackson Hole Land Trust, Wyo. Served to lt. (j.g.) USN, 1958-61. Mem. Phi Beta Kappa. Clubs: Harmonie, Sky (N.Y.C.).

TESTA, MICHAEL HAROLD, lawyer; b. N.Y.C., Sept. 4, 1939; m. Carol Waldenberg, June 16, 1962; 2 children. BS summa cum laude, NYU, 1958, LLB cum laude, 1961, LLM in Taxation, 1967. Bar: N.Y. 1961. Assoc. White & Case, N.Y.C., 1962-71; assoc. Skadden, Arps, Slate, Meagher & Flom, N.Y.C., 1971-72, ptnr., 1972-91; spl. counsel Living Oceans Program, Nat. Audubon Soc., 1993—; advisor U.S. Delegation to UN Conf. on Straddling Fish Stocks and Highly Migratory Fish Stocks, 1994-95; adj. assoc. prof. law NYU Law Sch., 1986; lectr. in field. Assoc. editor; contbr. NYU Law Rev., 1960-61; contbr. articles to legal jours. Mem. planning bd. Town of Tuxedo (N.Y.), 1971-76. Served to capt. USAFR, 1961-72. Root-Tilden scholar, 1958-61. Mem. ABA, N.Y. State Bar Assn., N.Y. State Bar Assn. com. tax sect. 1978-82), Assn. Bar of City of N.Y. (mem. environ. law com. 1993—), Order of Coif. Home: 32 Wildwood Dr Great Neck NY 11024-1246 Office: 919 3rd Ave New York NY 10022

TESTER, JOHN ROBERT, biologist, educator; b. New Ulm, Minn., Nov. 18, 1929; s. Roland Otto and Evelyn Anna (Monson) T.; m. Joyce Jeanette Lund, Sept. 12, 1959; children: Hans, Peter. B.S., U. Minn., 1951, Ph.D. 1960; M.S., Colo. State U., 1953. Research biologist Minn. Dept. Natural Resources, St. Paul, 1954-56; ecologist Minn. Mus. Natural History, Mpls., 1956-61; lectr. to prof., head dept. ecology and behavioral biology, dir. Cedar Creek Natural History Area U. Minn., Mpls., 1961—; v.p. State Bank Gibbon, Minn., 1966-83, pres., 1983—; also dir. State Bank Gibbon; mem. behavioral scis. tng. com. NIH, 1968-73. Contbr. articles to sci. publs. Fellow AAAS, Aberdeen U. (Scotland) (hon.); mem. Ecol. Soc. Am., Am. Inst. Biol. Sci., Wildlife Soc., Am. Soc. Mammalogists, N.Y. Acad. Scis., Minn. Acad. Sci., Explorers Club, Sigma Xi. Republican. Lutheran. Research in ecology and resource mgmt. Home: 10 Eagle Ridge Rd Saint Paul MN 55127-6410

TETELMAN, ALICE FRAN, city government official; b. N.Y.C., Apr. 15, 1941; d. Harry and Leah (Markovitz) T.; m. Martin A. Wenick, Dec. 7, 1980. BA, Mt. Holyoke Coll., South Hadley, Mass., 1962. Rsch. and info. asst. Edn. and World Affairs, N.Y.C., 1963-67; legis. asst. U.S. Sen. Charles Goodell, Washington, 1968-70; land use and energy specialist Citizens Adv. Com. on Environ. Quality, Washington, 1973-74; sr. assoc. prog. mgr. Linton & Co., Washington, 1971-73, 75-76; pub policy cons. Washington, 1977-78; adminstrv. asst. U.S. Congressman Bill Green (N.Y.), Washington, 1978-81; cons. The Precious Legacy Project, Prague, Czechoslovakia, 1982-83; Rep. staff dir. Select Com. on Hunger, U.S. Ho. of Reps., Washington, 1984-85; dir. State of N.J. Washington Office, 1986-90; exec. dir. Coun. of Gov.'s Policy Advisors, Washington, 1991-94; dir. Washington Office The City of N.Y., 1994—. Bd. mem. Republican Women's Task Force, Nat. Women's Polit. Caucus, 1976-80. European Community grantee, 1975. Mem. Ripon Soc. (nat. exec. com. 1971-73). Republican. Office: City of NY Washington Office 555 New Jersey Ave NW Washington DC 20001

TETER, GORDON F., fast food chain company executive. Past exec. v.p. Wendy's Internat. Inc., Dublin, Ohio, pres., CEO, COO. Office: Wendy's Internat Inc 4288 W Dublin Granville Rd Dublin OH 43017-2093*

TETHER, ANTHONY JOHN, aerospace executive; b. Middletown, N.Y., Nov. 28, 1941; s. John Arthur and Antoinette Rose (Gesualdo) T.; m. Nancy Engle Pierson, Dec. 27, 1963 (div. July 1971); 1 child, Jennifer; m. Carol Suzanne Dunbar, Mar. 3, 1973; 1 child, Michael. AAS, Orange County C.C., N.Y., 1961; BS, Rensselaer Poly Inst., 1964; MSEE, Stanford (Calif.) U., 1965, PhD, 1969. V.p., gen. mgr. Sys. Control Inc., Palo Alto, Calif., 1968-78; dir. nat. intelligence Office Sec. of Def., Washington, 1978-82; dir. strategic tech. DARPA, Washington, 1982-86; corp. v.p. Ford Aerospace, Newport Beach, Calif., 1986-90, LORAL, Newport Beach, 1990-92; corp. v.p., gen. mgr. Sci. Application Internat., Inc., San Diego, 1992-94; CEO Dynamics Tech. Inc., Torrance, Calif., 1994—; chmn., bd. dirs. Condyne Tech., Inc., Orlando, Fla., 1990-92; dir. Orincon, La Jolla, Calif. Contbr. articles to profl. jours. Recipient Nat. Intelligence medal DCI, 1986, Civilian Meritorious medal U.S. Sec. Def., 1986. Mem. IEEE, Cosmos Club, Sigma Xi, Eta Kappa Nu, Tau Beta Pi. Avocations: ham radio, skiing. Home: 4518 Roxbury Rd Corona Del Mar CA 92625-3125

TETLEY, GLEN, choreographer; b. Cleve., Feb. 3, 1926; s. Glenford and Eleanor (Byrne) T. Student, Franklin and Marshall Coll., 1944-46; BS, NYU, 1948; student contemporary dance with, Hanya Holm, Martha Graham, 1946; student classical ballet with, Margaret Craske, Anthony Tudor at Met. Opera Ballet Sch., 1949. guest instr. Yale Dramatic Workshop, 1947-48, Colo. Coll., 1946-49, Hanya Holm Sch. Contemporary Dance, 1946-52, Ballet Rambert, 1966-68, Netherlands Dance Theatre, 1962-65, B. De Rothschild Found., Israel, 1965-67. Featured dancer in Broadway musical Kiss Me Kate, 1949, Out of This World, 1950, Juno, 1958; premiered in Broadway musical Menotti's Amahl and the Night Visitors, NBC Opera, 1951; soloist with Broadway musical, N.Y.C. Opera, 1951-54, John Butler's Am. Dance Theatre, 1951-55, Robert Joffrey Ballet, 1955-56, Martha Graham Dance Co., 1957-59, Am. Ballet Theatre, 1959-61, Jerome Robbins: Ballets USA, 1961-62, Netherlands Dance Theater, 1962-65, own co., 1962-69; made govt.-sponsored tour of Europe, 1969, appearances at Spoleto Festival, all maj. Am. dance festivals; guest choreographer, Netherlands Dance Theatre; artistic dir.: Netherlands Dance Theatre, 1969; guest choreographer, Am. Ballet Theatre, Ballet Rambert, Batsheva Co. Israel, Robert Joffrey Ballet, Alvin Alley Co., U. Utah Repertory Dance Theatre, Vancouver Festival, Royal Danish Ballet, 1969, Royal Ballet Covent Garden, Royal Swedish Ballet, Den Norske Opera, Hamburg State Opera, Stuttgart Ballet; former artistic dir.: Stuttgart Ballet Co.; artistic assoc., Nat. Ballet of Canada, Toronto, 1987-89; ballets include Pierrot Lunaire, 1962, Birds of Sorrow, 1962, The Anatomy Lesson, 1964, Sargasso, 1964, Field Mass, 1965, Mythical Hunters, 1965, Ricercare, 1966, Chronochromie, 1966, Tehilim, 1966, Freefall, 1967, The Seven Deadly Sins, 1967, Dithyramb, 1967, Ziggurat, 1967, Circles, 1968, Embrace Tiger and Return to Mountain, 1968,

Arena, 1968, Imaginary Film, 1970, Mutations, 1970, Field Figures, 1971, Rag Dances, 1971, Small Parades, 1972, Threshold, 1972, Laborintus, 1972, Strophe-Antistrophe, 1972, The Moveable Garden, 1973, Gemini, 1973, Voluntaries, 1973, Sacre du Printemps, 1974, Tristan, 1974, Strender, 1974, Daphnis and Chloe, 1975, Greening, 1975, Alegrias, 1975, Poeme Nocturne, 1977, Sphinx, 1978, Praeludium, 1979, The Tempest, 1979, Contredances, 1979, Summer's End, 1980, Dances of Albion-Dark Night: Glad Day, 1980, Firebird, 1981, Murderer Hope of Women, 1983, Revelation and Fall, 1984, Pulcinella, 1984, Dream Walk of the Shaman, 1985, Alice, 1986, Orpheus, 1987, La Ronde, 1987, Tagore, 1989, Dialogues, 1991, Oracle, 1994; off-Broadway choreographer-dir. ballets including Fortuna, 1961, Ballet Ballads, 1961. Patron Benesh Inst. Choreology; bd. dirs. Tag Found., N.Y.C. Served with USNR, 1944-46. Recipient German critics award for Die Feder; Queen Elizabeth II Coronation award Royal Acad. Dancing, 1981; recipient Prix Italia Rai prize, 1982, Tennant Caledonia award Edinburgh Festival, 1983, Ohioana Career Medal, 1986, achievement award N.Y.U., 1988. Address: 15 W 9th St New York NY 10011

TETLIE, HAROLD, priest; b. Madison, Minn., Aug. 24, 1926; s. H. Ben and Anna (Mauland) T. BA cum laude, St. Olaf Coll., Northfield, Minn., 1951; MBA, U. Denver, 1956; postgrad., Cornell U., 1959-60; BST, Luther Theol. Sem., St. Paul, 1965. Ordained to ministry Am. Luth. Ch., 1965. Pastor Christ the King Chs. (Evang. Cath. Ch.), Alice, Tex., 1965—, congregation supr., 1969—; cir. parish priest, Nuevo Leon, Tamaulipas, Hidalgo, San Luis Potosi, Mex. Coord. Joint Action in Cmty. Svc., Inc., Alice, 1970—. Sgt. U.S. Army, 1945-46, PTO. Recipient Svc. to Mankind award Sertoma Club, Corpus Christi, Regional Vol. of Yr. award Joint Action in Cmty. Svc., 1991; commd. Ky. Col., 1992. Mem. NEA (life), VFW, Am. Legion, 40 et 8, Family Motor Coach Assn., Sons of Norway, Order of Ky. Col., Internat. Platform Assn., Thousand Trails. Home and Office: Christ the King Chs PO Box 1607 Alice TX 78333-1607 *It is by the Power of Jesus Christ: He tells us in John 13:34: "Love one another, even as I loved you."*

TETLOW, EDWIN, author; b. Altrincham, Eng., May 19, 1905; s. William Chadwick and Mary (Entwistle) T.; m. Kathleen Whitworth Brown, Sept. 14, 1932; children: Susan Edwina, Timothy Chadwick. Student, Manchester (Eng.) U., 1924. Trainee journalist Daily Dispatch, Manchester, 1924-30; mem. staff Eve. News. London, 1930-33, Daily Mail, London, 1933-45; naval war corr. Daily Mail, 1940-42, army War corr., 1942-45; Berlin corr. Daily Telegraph, 1945-50, N.Y., 1950-65; freelance author Esopus, N.Y., 1965—. Author: Eye on Cuba, 1966, The United Nations, 1971, The Enigma of Hastings, 1974, 2d edit., 1993, As It Happened, 1990; book reviewer: Christian Sci. Monitor; contbr.: Economist newspaper, Director Mag., London, Telegraph Sunday Mag., London, N.Y. Times, New Republic. Life mem. Fgn. Press Assn. (pres. 1964-65, mem. exec. bd. 1965—). Home: Druids' Dell PO Box 140 Esopus NY 12429-0140

TETTLEBAUM, HARVEY M., lawyer; m. Ann Safier; children: Marianne, Benjamin. AB, Dartmouth Coll., 1964; JD, Washington U. Sch. Law, 1968, AM in History, 1968. Asst. dean Washington U. Sch. Law, 1969-77; asst. atty. gne., chief counsel Consumer Protection and Anti-Trust Div., 1970-77; pvt. practice Jefferson City, Mo., 1977-90; ptnr., chmn. health care, adminstrv. and govtl. law dept. Husch & Eppenberger, Jefferson City, Mo., 1990—; vice-chmn. Nat. Health Lawyers Long Term Care and the Law Programs, mem., bd. dirs., 1993—; legal subcom. Am. Health Care Assn., 1994—. Contbr. articles to profl. jours. Treas. Mo. Rep. Party, 1976—; v.p. Moniteau County R-1 Sch. Dist. Bd., 1991—; mem. Calif. R-1 Sch. Bd., 1990—, v.p., 1993-95, pres., 1995—. Mem. Nat. Health Lawyers Assn. (bd. dirs.), Mo. Bar Assn. (health and hosp. law com., chmn. adminstrv. law com.), Am. Health Care Assn. (legal subcom. 1994—). Home: Rte # 2 Box 2726 California MO 65018 Office: Husch & Eppenberger Monroe House Ste 300 235 E High St Jefferson City MO 65101-3236

TETZELI, FREDERICK EDWARD, banker; b. Chomutove, Czech Rep., Sept. 12, 1930; came to U.S., 1951; s. Louis and Sophie (Deym) T.; m. Margaret Lee Weld, Sept. 6, 1958; chilren: Frederick John, William George, Christopher Weld. BS, Georgetown U., 1952. Assoc. Merrill Lynch, Havana, Cuba, 1952-54; treas. Cuban Trading Co., Havana, 1954-61; exec. adminstr. Waterman S.S. Corp., Mobile, Ala., 1962-64; mng. dir. J.P. Morgan, N.Y.C., 1964—; Bd. dirs., chmn. investment com. Luso Am. Bus. Council. Chmn., mem. exec. com. Am. Portuguese Soc., 1980—; bd. dirs. past chmn. Spain-U.S. C of C, 1979—, past pres., bd. dirs. Belgian-Am. C of C., 1973—; councillor French C. of C., 1973—; bd. dirs., past pres. Am.-Italy Soc., 1973—; bd. dirs. U.S.-Netherlands C. of C., 1980—; bd. dirs., mem. exec. com. France Am. Soc. Decorated grand officer Order of Italian Republic, knight Order of Royal House for Civilian Merit, Spain; mem. Legion of Comdrs. (Italy). Mem. U.S.-Italy C. of C. (bd. dirs.), Am. C. of C. Cuba (bd. dirs., vice chmn.), Bankers Assn. for Fgn. Trade (vice chmn. membership com.). Republican. Roman Catholic. Clubs: Downtown Assn., Met. (N.Y.C.); Sloane (London). Home: 336 Rosedale Rd Princeton NJ 08540-6708 Office: JP Morgan 60 Wall St New York NY 10260-0001

TETZLAFF, THEODORE R., lawyer; b. Saukville, Wis., Feb. 27, 1944. AB magna cum laude, Princeton U., 1966; LLB, Yale U., 1969. Bar: Ind. 1969, D.C. 1969, Ill. 1974. Legis. asst. to Congressman John Brademas, 1970; exec. dir. Nat. Conf. Police Community Rels., 1970-71; acting dir. U.S. Office Legal Svcs., Office Econ. Opportunity, Washington, 1972-73; counsel, Com. Judiciary U.S. Ho. of Reps., Washington, 1974; v.p., legal and external affairs Cummins Engine Co., 1980-82; gen. coun. Tenneco, Inc., Houston, 1992—; ptnr. Jenner & Block, Chgo., 1976-80, 80—. Pres. Chgo. area Found. Legal Svcs., 1983—; commr. Pub. Bldg. Commn. Chgo., 1990—. Reginald Heber Smith fellow, 1969-70. Mem. ABA (chair sect. litigation 1991-92), Ill. State Bar Assn., Ind. State Bar Assn., D.C. Bar. Office: Tenneco Inc PO Box 2511 1010 Milam Houston TX 77252-2511 also: Jenner & Block 1 IBM Plz Ste 4200 Chicago IL 60611

TEUBNER, FERDINAND CARY, JR., retired publishing company executive; b. Phila., Sept. 22, 1921; s. Ferdinand Cary Teubner and Esther Roslyn (Test) Alperstein; m. Ruth May Hazen, Nov. 1, 1953; 1 child, Janell Caron Teubner Crispyn. Student, U. Pa., 1940-41; grad., Charles Morris Price Sch. Advt. and Journalism, 1949. Rep. W.H. Hoedt Studios, Inc., Phila., 1945-52; account exec. Patterson Prochs., Inc., Phila., 1955-56, v.p., 1956-57; staff exec. Am. Assn. Advt. Agys., N.Y.C., 1957-59; rep. W.H. Martin & Co., Inc., N.Y.C. 1959-62; advt. salesman Editor & Pub. Co., Inc., N.Y.C., 1962-65, advt. mgr., 1965-76, gen. mgr., treas., 1976-78, treas., pub., 1978-95, dir., 1969-95; sec.-treas., dir. E & P Research, Inc., N.Y.C., 1985-95, ret., 1995. Served with USAAF, 1942-45, ETO; served to maj. U.S. Army, 1952-55, Korea. Decorated Purple Heart; recipient Silver Shovel award Internat. Newspaper Mktg. Assn., 1993. Mem. Sales Execs. Club N.Y.C., Res. Officer Assn. Episcopalian. Clubs: Union League, Lake Valhalla Country. Home: 18 Lenape Dr Montville NJ 07045-9795

TEUSCHER, GEORGE WILLIAM, dental educator; b. Chgo., Jan. 11, 1908; s. Albert Christian and Elizabeth (Klesch) T.; m. Eleanor C. Oeler, Sept. 29, 1934 (div.); children: Carol Ann, John William; m. Eleanor E. Wilson, May, 1968. D.D.S., Northwestern U., 1929, M.S.D., 1936, A.M., 1940, Ph.D., 1942; Sc.D. (hon.), N.Y. U., 1965. Charter mem. Am. Acad. Pedodontics (pres. 1960-61), Am. Bd. Pedodontics. Engaged in gen. practice of dentistry, 1929-34, in pedodontics, 1934-69; instr. pedodontics Northwestern U., 1933-38, asst. prof., 1938-41, asso. prof., 1941; lectr. surgery Northwestern U. Med. Sch., 1945—, prof. pedodontics, 1946—; dean Northwestern U. Med. Sch. (Dental Sch.), 1953-71; mem. staff Wesley Meml. Hosp., 1946-69, chief dental sect. dept. otolaryngology, 1946-69; mem. adv. com. dentistry Smithsonian Instn., 1967—; lectr. on pedodontics and edn. in, U.S. and Can.; cons. Naval Dental Research Inst., Gt. Lakes. Editor: Dental Progress, 1959-63, Jour. Dentistry for Children, 1967—, Jour. Dental Edn, 1970-73; contbr. articles to dental jours. Bd. dirs. Tb Inst. Chgo. and Cook County, 1964-70; regent Nat. Library Medicine, 1968-72; bd. govs. Chgo. Heart Assn., 1964-74; Pres. Gen. Alumni Assn., Northwestern U., 1948-51. Served with Res. Officers Corps, 1929-42. Fellow Am. Coll. Dentists, Inst. Medicine Chgo.; mem. Internat. Assn. Dental Research, Am. Assn. Dental Schs. (pres. 1962-63), Am. Dental Assn. (council dental edn. 1964-70), Ill. Dental Soc., Chgo. Dental Soc. (pres. 1958-59), Odontographic Soc. (pres. 1952-53), Am. Soc. Dentistry for Children (pres. 1952-53, exec. officer 1982—), Am. Dental Soc. Europe (hon.), Xi Psi Phi, Omicron Kappa

Upsilon. Clubs: Tavern (Chgo.), Chicago Literary (Chgo.). Home: 730 Blaney Dr Dyer IN 46311-2306

TEUTSCH, CHAMPION KURT, psycho-geneticist; b. Leipzig, Germany, Feb. 10, 1921; came to U.S., 1939; s. Friedrich Wilhelm and Elizabeth (Babette) T.; m. Joel Marie Noel, Apr. 24, 1954 (dec. Mar. 1992); 1 child, Lee Brooks. BCE with high honors, U. Fla., 1942; degree, U. So. Calif., L.A., 1948-49, 57; postgrad., Harvard U., 1947-48; MS in Psychology, Calif. Coast U., Santa Ana, 1975, PhD in Psychology, 1978. Sr. engr., tech. writer, editor various aerospace firms, Columbus, San Francisco, L.A., 1946-60; cons., gene-physicist, psycho-geneticist L.A., 1960—; pres. Acad. Teutsch Ideal Method, L.A., 1981—; chmn. bd. dirs. Internat. Human Rsch. Ctr. "Sunray" Moscow State U., 1993—; cons. med. clinics, law firms, real estate, computer, electronics, ins. firms, automobile agys., entertainment orgns., So. and No. Calif., La., Kans., Nev., 1964—; guest nat. and local TV programs, 1968—; cons. Bush Presidential campaign, L.A., 1988; lectr. Moscow State U., 1993—, U. St. Petersburg, 1993, U. Zaparoche, Ukraine, 1994, med. coll. U. Fla., 1994, Sunray, Moscow, 1994—. Co-author: Understand and Raise Your Consciousness--From Here to Happiness, 1961,66,72, Understand and Raise Your Consciousness--From Here to Greater Happiness or How to Change Your Life For Good, 1975, 88, Victimology: An Effect of Consciousness, Interpersonal Dynamics and Human Physics, 1973, Stress, Genetics and Interpersonal Relationships:The Type D Complex, 1979, From Human Bondage to Liberty: an Introduction to Genephysics, 1993, Joel's Revelations: The Bible As Text for Joyous and Effective Living, 1994, A Nonmedical Answer to Cancer and Other Diseases, 1994, Winning the War on Cancer, 1995; developer (with J.M. Noel Teutsch) genogram and B.I.D. (basic inner direction or desire). Served to 1st lt. USAF, 1942-52. Mem. Friar's Club, Vikings Club, Optimist Internat. (pres. 1982). Avocation: tennis, skiing. Home: 2131 Century Park Ln Unit 401 Los Angeles CA 90067-3811 Office: Acad Teutsch Ideal Method 2049 Century Park E Ste # 2730 Los Angeles CA 90067-3202

TEVRIZIAN, DICKRAN M., JR., federal judge; b. Los Angeles, Aug. 4, 1940; s. Dickran and Rose Tevrizian; m. Geraldine Tevrizian, Aug. 22, 1964; children: Allyson Tracy, Leslie Sara. BS, U. So. Calif., 1962, JD, 1965. Tax acct. Arthur Andersen and Co., Los Angeles, 1965-66; atty., ptnr. Kirtland and Packard, Los Angeles, 1966-72; judge Los Angeles Mcpl. Ct., Los Angeles, 1972-78, State of Calif. Superior Ct., Los Angeles, 1978-82; ptnr. Manatt, Phelps, Rothenberg & Tunney, Los Angeles, 1982-85, Lewis, D'Amato, Brisbois & Bisgaard, Los Angeles, 1985-86; judge U.S. Dist. Ct., Los Angeles, 1986—. Office: US Dist Ct Royal Federal Bldg 255 E Temple St Los Angeles CA 90012-3334

TEW, JEFFREY ALLEN, lawyer; b. Miami, Fla., Mar. 8, 1944; s. Cornelius Thomas and Mamie Ophelia (Clements) T.; m. Maureen Mary Magill, Oct. 15, 1950; children:--David, Spencer. BA, Dartmouth Coll., 1966; JD cum laude, U. Miami, 1969. Bar: Fla. 1969, U.S. Supreme Ct. 1973. Ptnr. Tew & Tew, Miami, Fla., 1969-77, Tew Spittler Berger & Bluestein, Coral Gables, Fla., now mem. Kirkpatrick & Lockhart, Miami. Office: Kirkpatrick & Lockhart 2000 Miami Ctr 201 S. Biscayne Blvd Miami FL 33131

TEWELL, JOSEPH ROBERT, JR., electrical engineer; b. Albany, N.Y., May 19, 1934; s. Joseph Robert and Florence Edna (MacKinnon) T.; m. Barbara Ann Johnson, Nov. 20, 1960; children:--Patricia Ann, Donna Lynn, Joseph Robert, III. B.E.E., Rensselaer Poly. Inst., 1955, M.E.E. 1958. Research engr. N.Am. Aviation, Inc., Downey, Calif., 1955; asso. research engr. Lockheed Aircraft Corp., Burbank, Calif., 1956; instr. Rensselaer Poly. Inst., 1957-64; sr. research scientist Martin Marietta Corp., Denver, 1964-79; mgr. advanced programs Martin Marietta Corp., Michoud, La., 1979-87, mgr. shuttle-C project, 1988-90, mgr. computer-aided productivity, 1991—; founding sponsor Challenger Ctr.; cons. Redford Corp., Scotia, N.Y., 1961. Contbr. articles to profl. jours.; inventor dual action single drive actuator, spacecraft docking and retrieval mechanism. Founding sponsor Challenger Ctr. Served with Army Security Agy., 1957. Recipient NASA Manned Awareness citation, 1970, NASA Skylab Achievement award, 1974, NASA New Tech. award, 1976, Tech. Achievement award Martin Marietta Corp., 1977, Sustained Performance award Martin Marietta Corp., 1981, NASA cert. of recognition, 1977, Author of Yr. award, 1986, also 38 publ. awards, 1965—. Fellow Explorers Club; mem. AIAA, Smithsonian Assocs., Air and Space Mus., Unmanned Vehicle Sys. Nat. Audubon Soc., Sigma Xi, Eta Kappa Nu, Tau Beta Pi, Theta Chi. Home: 619 Legendre Dr Slidell LA 70460-9546 Office: Mail No 4220 PO Box 29304 New Orleans LA 70189

TEWI, THEA, sculptor; b. Berlin, Germany; came to U.S., 1938, naturalized, 1943; d. Jules and Claire (Kochmann) Wittner; m. Charles K. Schlachet; 1 son, Peter. Grad., Nat. Acad. Fine Arts, Berlin; student New Sch., Art Students League, N.Y.C., 1956-57. Pres. League of Present Day Artists, 1964-70; pres. Sculptors League, 1970-88. Exhibited in one-man shows at, Village Art Center, N.Y.C., 1961, La Boetie Gallery, N.Y.C., 1966, 68, 70, Sala Michelangelo, Carrara, Italy, 1969, Lehigh U., Bethlehem, Pa., 1970, U. Notre Dame, 1970, Hallway Gallery, Washington, 1976, 80, Randall Gallery, N.Y.C., 1977, 79, 81, 83, Vorpal Gallery, N.Y.C., 1985, 87, Bklyn. Bot. Garden, 1989, N.Y. Acad. Scis., 1992, 93, others; exhibited in numerous group shows; represented in permanent collections at, Smithsonian Instn., Washington, Cin. Art Mus., Norfolk (Va.) Mus. Arts and Scis., U. Notre Dame, Norton Simon Collection, Citicorp, N.Y., Fort Worth Nat. Bank, Parks Dept. City of N.Y., N.Y. Acad. Scis., Govt. Ecuador; also represented in pvt. collections U.S., France, Italy, Spain, Switzerland, Japan. Recipient numerous awards and purchase awards, including 1st prize Am. Soc. Contemporary Artists, 1971, 75, 76, 78, medal of merit Nat. Arts Club, 1974, Nawa Peabody award Nat. Acad., 1975, medal of merit Knickerbocker Artists, 1975. Nat. mem. Assn. Women Artists (1st prize, medal of honor 1969), Am. Soc. Contemporary Artists, Sculptors League (founder, pres. 1971-88). Home: 10030 67th Dr Forest Hills NY 11375

TEWKSBURY, JOAN F., film director, writer; b. Redlands, Calif., Apr. 8, 1936; d. Walter S. and Frances M. (Stevenson) T.; m. Robert F. Maguire, III, Nov. 30, 1960 (div.); children: Robin Tewkesbury, Peter Harlan. Student, Am. Sch. Dance, 1947-54, Mt. San Antonio Jr. Coll., Walnut, Calif., 1956-58; drama scholar, U. So. Calif., 1958-60. Dancer in: film Unfinished Dance, 1946; dancer, flying understudy Peter Pan, LosAngeles and N.Y.C., 1954-55; choreographer film, Los Angeles, 1958-70, tchr. dance and drama, U. So. Calif., 1966-69, Immaculate Heart Coll., Los Angeles, 1960-63, Am. Sch. Dance, Los Angeles, 1959-69; tchr. film writing UCLA, 1986; choreographer, dir., actress, U. So. Calif. Repertory Co., 1965-68, London and Edinburgh (Scotland) Festival, 1965-68; scriptgirl: film McCabe and Mrs. Miller, 1970; author: screenplays Thieves Like Us, 1974, Nashville, 1975 (Los Angeles Critics Best Screenplay award), A Night in Heaven, 1983; playwright, dir. Cowboy Jack Street, 1978; dir. film Old Boyfriends, 1979; film writer, dir. TV 10th Month, 1979, The Acorn People, 1981; dir. film documentary Anna Freud, 1976; writer, dir. (TV show) Alfred Hitchcock Presents, from 1986, (TV movie for TNT) Cold Sassy Tree, 1989; screenwriter, dir., scriptwriter, co-exec. producer TV pilot Elysian Fields, 1988; dir. (Time-Life cable TV film) Sudie and Simpson; scriptwriter, dir.(TV) Shannon's Deal; dir. (TV movie) Wild Texas Wind, 1991, The Stranger (HBO), 1992; dir. (TV episodes) Northern Exposure, 1992, Picket Fences, 1992, Doogie Hauser, 1992; dir.(theater) Chippy, 1993; dir. (TV movie Disney Cable) On Promised Land, 1993. Mem. Literacy Vols. Am. Mem. Writers Guild Am., Dirs. Guild Am., ACLU, Nat. Abortion Rights Action League, Calif. Abortion Rights Action League. Office: care Jane Sindell Creative Artists Agy 1888 Century Park E Ste 1400 Los Angeles CA 90067-1718*

TEWKSBURY, CHARLES G., textiles technology executive. Pres. Inst. of Textile Tech., Charlottesville, Va. Office: Inst Textile Tech PO Box 391 2551 Ivy Rd Charlottesville VA 22903-4614

TEWKSBURY, ROBERT ALAN, professional baseball player; b. Concord, N.H., Nov. 30, 1960. Student, Rutgers U., St. Leo Coll. With N.Y. Yankees, 1981-87, Chgo. Cubs, 1987-88; pitcher St. Louis Cardinals, 1989-94, Tex. Rangers, 1994—; player Nat. League All-Star Game, 1992. Ranked 2d in Nat. League for earned run average, 1992, 3d in Nat. League for wins. Office: Tex Rangers 1000 Ballpark Way Arlington TX 76011*

TEWSLEY, ROBERT WILLIAM, dancer; b. Leicester, Eng., Apr. 13, 1972; came to Can., 1990; s. Eric William and June (Sainsbury) T. Grad., Royal Ballet Sch., London, 1990. Soloist Nat. Ballet Can., Toronto, 1992-93, 1st soloist, 1993-94, prin., 1994—. Appeared in The Nutcracker, 1991, Swan Lake, 1994, Giselle, 1992, Onegin, 1994, The Sleeping Beauty, 1994, La Sylphide, Romeo and Juliet, The Merry Widow, Divertimento No. 15, The Four Temperaments, The Taming of the Shrew, The Actress, Frames of Mind, Interrogating Slam, Now and Then, The Rite of Spring, Voluntaries, numerous others. Avocations: hiking, camping, playing piano. Office: Nat Ballet of Can, 157 King St E, Toronto, ON Canada M5C 1G9

TEXTOR, ROBERT BAYARD, cultural anthropology writer, consultant, educator; b. Cloquet, Minn., Mar. 13, 1923; s. Clinton Kenney and Lillian (Nickles) T.; divorced; children: Alexander Robertson, Marisa Elizabeth. Student, Lafayette Coll., 1940-41, Antioch Coll., 1941-43; B.A. in Asian Studies, U. Mich., 1945; Ph.D. in Cultural Anthropology, Cornell U., 1960. Civil info. and edn. officer Mil. Govt., Kyoto-Wakayama, Japan, 1946-48; rsch. fellow anthropology and S.E. Asia studies Yale U., 1959-60, assoc., 1960-61; rsch. fellow in stats. Harvard U., 1962-64; assoc. prof. edn. and anthropology Stanford U., 1964-68, prof. edn. and anthropology, 1968-86, prof. anthropology, 1986-90, prof. anthropology emeritus, 1990—; vis. prof. U. Saar, Saarbrücken, Germany, 1984-85; cons. Motorola U., 1991—; mem. S.E. Asia Coun., 1974-77; cons. cultural anthropology to govt. agys., 1957-58, 61-62. Author: (most recent) Roster of the Gods: An Ethnography of The Supernatural in a Thai Village, 6 vols., 1973, Austria 2005: Projected Sociocultural Effects of the Microelectronic Revolution, 1983, Anticipatory Anthropology, 1985, (with Sippanondha Ketudat) The Middle Path for the Future of Thailand, 1990; assoc. editor Jour. Conflict Resolution, 1965-70; mem. editorial bd. Human organ., 1964-71, Jour. Cultural Futures, 1979-87; adv. editor Behavior Sci. Rsch., 1974-86. Bd. dirs. Vols. in Asia, Stanford, Calif., 1968-73; mem. Metro Portland Future Vision Commn., 1993-95. Served with U.S. Army, 1943-46. Fellow Rockefeller Found., 1951-52, fgn. area tng. fellow Ford Found., Thailand 1955-58, Carnegie fellow, 1958-59, Fulbright West Europe rsch. fellow, 1984-85, East-West Ctr. fellow, 1988-90; NSF grantee, Thailand, U.S., 1969-73, Volkswagen Found. grantee, Thailand and Germany, 1984. Fellow Am. Anthrop. Assn. (life mem.); mem. Siam Soc. (life mem.), Assn. Asian Studies (life mem.), Council on Anthropology and Edn. (pres. 1974-75), AAUP (pres. Stanford chpt. 1975-76), Phi Kappa Phi.

THACHER, CARTER POMEROY, diversified manufacturing company executive; b. 1926. With Wilbur-Ellis Co., San Francisco, 1960—, v.p., 1963-67, pres., from 1967, chmn. bd., 1989—, also bd. dirs. Office: Wilbur-Ellis Co 320 California St San Francisco CA 94104-1403

THACKER, CHARLES P., computer engineer, engineering executive. BA, U. Calif., 1967. Engr. U. Calif., Berkeley, 1967-68; project leader Berkeley Computer Corp., 1969-71; mem. rsch. staff Xerox Palo Alto (Calif.) Rsch. Ctr., 1971-75, mgr. processor architecture sys. devel. divsn., 1975-77, mgr. digital processor develop. electronics divsn., 1977-79, prin. engr., 1979-80, rsch. fellow, 1980-82, sr. rsch. fellow, 1982-83; sr. cons. engr. Digital Equipment Corp. Sys. Rsch. Ctr., Palo Alto, 1983-89, corp. cons. engr., 1989—. Mem. NAE, IEEE, Assn. Computer Mach. Achievements include research in digital computer development. Office: Digital Equipment Corp 130 Lytton Ave Palo Alto CA 94301*

THACKERAY, JONATHAN E., lawyer; b. Athens, Ohio, July 30, 1936; s. Joseph Eugene and Betty Rutherford (Boright) T.; m. Sandra Ann McMahon, 1979; children: Jennifer, Sara, Amy, Jonathan. A.B. cum laude, Harvard U., 1958, J.D., 1961. Bar: Ohio 1961, U.S. Dist. Ct. (no. dist.) Ohio 1961, U.S. Supreme Ct. 1972, U.S. Ct. Appeals (6th cir.) 1973, U.S. Ct. Appeals (9th cir.) 1982, N.Y. 1993. Assoc. Vorys, Sater, Seymour & Pease, Columbus, Ohio, 1961; assoc. Baker & Hostetler, Cleve., 1965-72, ptnr., 1973-93; v.p., gen. counsel The Hearst Corp., N.Y.C., 1993—. Served to lt. USNR, 1961-65. Mem. ABA, Ohio Bar Assn., Cleve. Bar Assn., Am. Law Inst. Office: The Hearst Corp 959 8th Ave New York NY 10019-3737 Notable cases include: administrative proceedings leading to approval of joint newspaper operating agreements in Cincinnati, Seattle and Las Vegas; litigation of newspaper antitrust cases in Cin., Seattle, Memphis, Trenton and Dallas.

THACKRAY, ARNOLD WILFRID, historian, foundation executive; b. Eng., July 30, 1939; came to U.S., 1967, naturalized, 1982; s. Wilfrid Cecil and Mary (Clarke) T.; m. Diana Schuelles; children: Helen Mary, Gillian Winifred, Timothy Arnold. B.Sc., Bristol (Eng.) U., 1960; M.A., Cambridge (Eng.) U., 1965, Ph.D., 1966. Research chemist Robert Dempster and Co., Yorkshire, Eng., 1960-61; research fellow Churchill Coll., Cambridge U., 1965-68; prof. history and sociology of sci. U. Pa., Phila., 1968-86, Joseph Priestley prof. history and sociology of sci., 1987—, chmn. dept., 1970-77, dir. Beckman Ctr. for History of Chemistry, 1982—; prof. history, prof. chemistry, dean grad. studies and research U. Md., 1985-86; exec. dir. Chem. Heritage Found., 1987—; vis. lectr. Harvard U., 1967-68; vis. fellow All Souls Coll., Oxford, Eng., 1977-78; mem. Inst. Advanced Study, 1980. Editor: Isis, an Internat. Rev. of History of Science and its Cultural Influences, 1978-85, Osiris, 1985-94, Science After '40, 1992, Constructing Knowledge in the History of Science, 1995, (with others) Science and Values, 1974, Toward a Metric of Science, 1978; author: Atoms and Powers, 1970, John Dalton, 1972, (with others) Gentlemen of Science, 1981-82, Chemistry in America, 1985; mem. editorial bd. Minerva, Victorian Studies, History of Science, The Scientist; contbr. articles to profl. jours. Recipient Gladstone Essay prize, also pub. speaking prize Churchill Coll., Cambridge U.; Guggenheim fellow, 1971-72, 85-86; Ctr. for Advanced Study in Behavioral Scis. fellow, 1973-74, 83-84. Fellow Am. Acad. Arts and Scis., Royal Hist. Soc., Royal Chem. Soc.; mem. Am. Chem. Soc. (Dexter award 1983), Am. Hist. Assn., Manchester Lit. and Philos. Soc. (corr.), History of Sci. Soc., Am. Coun. Learned Socs. (bd. dirs., treas. 1985—), Soc. for Social Studies of Sci. (pres. 1981-83) Am. Coun. on Edn. (bd. dirs. 1987), Chemists Club (N.Y.C.), Cosmos Club (Washington). Episcopalian.

THACKRAY, RICHARD IRVING, psychologist; b. Wausau, Wis., Jan. 27, 1927; s. Irving Brownsell and Virginia (Weaver) T.; m. Marilyn Ann Patterson, June 20, 1953; children: Rick, Susette. B.A., Lawrence U., 1950; M.A., U. Mo., 1952; Ph.D., Purdue U., 1956. Instr. psychology U. Wis. 1952-54; asst. prof. psychology Allegheny Coll., Meadville, Pa., 1956-59; research psychologist Wright-Patterson AFB, Dayton, Ohio, 1959-65; psychophysiologist Inst. Pa. Hosp., 1965-67; instr. U. Pa. Med. Sch.; supr. stress behavior research Civil Aeromed. Inst., FAA, Oklahoma City, 1967-90; pvt. cons. in aviation human factors, 1991—; prin. scientist Galaxy Sci. Corp., 1993—. Contbr. articles to profl. jours. Fellow Am. Psychol. Assn., Aerospace Med. Assn. (Raymond F. Longacre award 1988); mem. Human Factors Soc., Sigma Xi, Psi Chi.

THACKSTON, EDWARD LEE, engineer, educator; b. Nashville, Apr. 29, 1937; s. Guy Carleton and Sydney Virginia (Adams) T.; m. Betty Tucker, Mar. 19, 1961; children: Carol Elizabeth Thackston Nixon, Leah Virginia Thackston Hawkins. BE summa cum laude, Vanderbilt U., 1961; MS, U. Ill., 1963; PhD, Vanderbilt U., 1966. Registered profl. engr., Tenn. City engr. City of Lebanon, Tenn., 1959; design engr. City of Nashville, 1961-62; instr. Vanderbilt U., Nashville, 1965-66, asst. prof., 1966-69, assoc. prof., 1969-75, prof. engring., 1975—, chmn. dept. civil and environ. engring., 1980—; asst. to gov. for environ. affairs, State of Tenn., 1972-74; cons. in field. Author book, tech. reports; contbr. to profl. publs. Bd. dirs. Tenn. Environ. Coun., Nashville, 1971-76; bd. dirs. Tenn. Conservation League, Nashville, 1974—, v.p. 1977, pres., 1978-80; trustee Cumberland Mus., Nashville, 1986-92. Named Tenn. Conservationist of Yr., 1974. Fellow ASCE; mem. Am. Water Works Assn., Water Environ. Fedn., Assn. Environ. Engring. Profs., Tenn. Hist. Soc., Tau Beta Pi, Chi Epsilon. Republican. Episcopalian. Avocations: genealogy, history, hiking, photography, basketball. Office: Vanderbilt U PO Box 133 Nashville TN 37235-0133

THADDEUS, PATRICK, physicist, educator; b. Wilmington, Del., June 6, 1932; s. Victor and Elizabeth (Ross) T.; m. Janice Petherbridge Farrar, Apr. 6, 1963; children: Eva, Michael. B.Sc., U. Del., 1953; M.A., Oxford (Eng.) U., 1955; Ph.D., Columbia U., 1960. Research assoc. Columbia Radiation Lab., 1960-61; research assoc. Goddard Inst. Space Studies, N.Y.C., 1961-63; mem. sci. staff Goddard Inst. Space Studies, 1963-86; mem. faculty Columbia U., 1965-86, adj. prof. physics, 1971-86; prof. astronomy and applied physics Harvard U., 1986—; mem. sci. staff Smithsonian Astrophys. Obs., 1986—; vis. com. Nat. Radio Astronomy Obs., 1973-76, 91—; mem. Astronomy Survey Com., 1978-80, 89-90; Fairchild disting. scholar Calif. Inst. Tech., 1994; Russell Marker lectr. Pa. State U., 1989; vis. fellow Inst. Astronomy, Cambridge, Eng., 1983. Author papers on microwave spectroscopy, optical and radio astronomy. Recipient Exceptional Sci. Achievement medal NASA, 1970, 85; John C. Lindsay Meml. award Goddard Space Flight Center, 1976; Alexander von Humboldt award, 1983; Fulbright fellow, 1953-55. Fellow Am. Phys. Soc.; mem. Am. Astron. Soc., Am. Acad. Arts and Scis., Nat. Acad. Scis., Internat. Astronomical Union, Sigma Xi. Address: 58 Garfield St Cambridge MA 02138

THADEN, EDWARD CARL, history educator; b. Seattle, Apr. 24, 1922; s. Edward Carl and Astrid (Engvik) T.; m. Marianna Theresia Forster, Aug. 7, 1952. B.A., U. Wash., 1944; student, U. Zurich, Switzerland, 1948; Ph.D., U. Paris, 1950. Instr. Russian history Pa. State U., 1952-55, asst. prof., 1955-58, assoc. prof., 1958-64, prof., 1964-68; vis. prof. Ind. U., 1957, U. Marburg, 1965, U. Ill., 1964, Urbana, 1980, U. Halle, German Dem. Republic, 1988, U. Helsinki, Finland, 1990; prof. U. Ill., Chgo., 1968—, chmn. dept. history, 1971-73; editorial cons. Can. Rev. Studies in Nationalism, 1973-78; vis. rsch. scholar USSR Acad. Scis., 1975, 88, 90; Ford Found. project prin. researcher, 1975-78; U.S. rep. to Internat. Congress of Hist. Scis., 1980; project dir. NEH grant, 1980-82. Author: Conservation Nationalism in Nineteenth-Century Russia, 1964, Russia and the Balken Alliance of 1912, 1965, Russia Since 1801: The Making of a New Society, 1971, Russia's Western Borderlands, 1710-1870, 1984, Interpreting History: collected Essays on Russia's Relations with Europe, 1990, Essays in Russian and East European History: Festschrift in Honor of Edward C. Thaden, 1995; co-author, editor: Russification in the Baltic Provinces and Finland, 1955-1914, 1981; co-author, co-editor: Finland and the Baltic Provinces in the Russian Empire, 1984; mem. editorial bd. Jour. Baltic Studies, 1984—, assoc. editor, 1987—. Served to lt. (j.g.) USNR, 1943-46. Carnegie Inter-Univ. Com. travel grantee to USSR, 1956; Fulbright research grantee Finland, 1957-58; Fulbright research grantee Germany, 1965; Fulbright research grantee Poland and Finland, 1968; Soc. Sci. Research Council grantee, 1957; Am. Council Learned Socs. grantee, 1963, 65-66; fellow Woodrow Wilson Internat. Center for Scholars, 1980. Mem. Am. Assn. for Advancement Slavic Studies (pres. Midwest br. 1975-76, exec. sec. 1980-82), Chgo. Consortium for Slavic and Eastern European Studies (pres. 1982-84), Commn. Internat. des Etudes Historiques Slaves (v.p. 1985—), Baltische Historische Kommission, Göttingen (corr. mem. 1985—). Office: U Ill Dept History 723 SEO (M/C 198) 851 S Morgan St Chicago IL 60607-7049

THAGARD, NORMAN E., astronaut, physician, engineer; b. Marianna, Fla., July 3, 1943; s. James E. Thagard and Mary F. Nicholson; m. Rex Kirby Johnson; children: Norman Gordon, James Robert, Daniel Cary. BS, Florida State U., 1965, MS, 1966; M.D., U. Texas Southwest Med. Sch., 1977. Intern, internal medicine Medical U. South Carolina, 1977-78; astronaut NASA, 1978—; mission specialist NASA Space Shuttle Challenger Flight STS-7, deployed satellites (ANIK C-2, PALAPA B-1), operated Remote Manipulator Sys., conducted experiments, 1983, NASA Spacelab-3 Mission STS-51 B, 1985, NASA Space Shuttle Atlantis Flight STS-30, deployed Magellan Venus exploration spacecraft, 1989; payload commander NASA Space Shuttle Discovery Flight STS-42, International Microgravity Lab.-1 module experiments, 1992; crew mem. Space Station MIR-18, 1995. Contbr. articles to profl. jours. With USMC, 1966-70, Capt. 1967-70, in Vietnam flew 163 combat missions. Decorated 11 Air medals, Navy Commednation medal with Combat V, Marine Corps E award, Vietnam Svc. medal, Vietnamese Cross of Gallantry with Palm. Mem. AIAA, Phi Kappa Phi. Avocations: classical music, electronic design. Office: Lyndon B Johnson Space Ctr NASA 2101 Nasa Rd mail code CB Houston TX 77058-0123

THAKKER, ASHOK, aerospace engineering company executive; b. Bombay, Aug. 9, 1947; came to U.S., 1970; s. Bhagwandas P. and Champa (Lakhpatla) T.; m. Sarla A. Bhate, Dec. 30, 1975; 1 child, Amish. B of Engring., U. Bombay, 1970; MS, S.D. Tech. Inst., 1971; PhD, Va. Polytech. Inst. & State U., 1974; MBA, Fla. Inst. Tech., 1980. Registered profl. engr., Va., Fla.; cert. mfg. engr. Instr. Va. Poly. Inst., Blacksburg, 1972-74; engr. Alcoa Tech. Ctr., Alcoa Ctr., Pa., 1974-76; sr. engr., 1976-78; group leader Pratt and Whitney Aircraft, West Palm Beach, Fla., 1978-83; project mgr. U.S. govt. programs Rolls-Royce, Inc., Atlanta, 1983-85, mgr. materials rsch., 1985-86, sr. project mgr., 1986-88, sr. mgr. engring., 1988-94, dir. materiels, 1994—. Contbr. numerous articles to profl. jours. and tech. reports to coms. Chmn. Internat. Student Assn., Blacksburg, 1972-73; advisor Jr. Achievement Program, Palm Beach, Fla., 1982-83. R & D Sethna Scholarship award, 1970; recipient Best Paper award AIAA-Atlanta Symposium, 1987. Mem. ASTM (reviewer tech. papers, composites, fatigue and fracture coms.), Am. Soc. Materials (chpt. program chmn. 1982, internat. chpt. membership com. 1989, vice chmn., then chmn. Atlanta chpt. 1989, 90, nat. devel. coun. 1990-91, nat. govt. and pub. affairs com. 1992-94, advisor, profl. as resource for instruction in sci. and math. student outreach program 1992—, tech. awareness adv. com., edit. bd. Materials & Process Jour. 1993—), Soc. Exptl. Mechanics (chpt. chmn. 1978, 81-82, chmn. fatigue com. 1984), Soc. Advancement Material and Process Engring., Soc. Mfg. Engrs. (com. mem., 1st vice chmn. Atlanta chpt. 1991-92, chmn. 1992-93, sr. internat. dir. 1992-93), Materials Rsch. Soc., Am. Ceramics Soc. (exec. com.), NASA Space Consortium (exec. com. 1992-93), Toastmasters, Lions, Sigma Xi, Vinings Club. Clubs: Toastmasters, Lions, Sigma Xi, Vinings (social com. 1992-93). Avocations: music, reading, traveling, golf, tennis. Home: 2690 Spencer Trl Marietta GA 30062 Office: Rolls-Royce Inc 2849 Paces Ferry Rd NW Atlanta GA 30339-3769

THAKOR, HAREN BHASKERRAO, manufacturing company executive; b. Ahmedabad, Gujarat, India, Dec. 12, 1938; came to U.S., 1960; s. Bhaskerrao Balvantrai and Kumud T.; m. Barbara Ann Martin, July 26, 1969; children: Manisha Ann, Sunil Haren. B.Civil Engring., Gujarat U., 1960; M.S. in Structural Engring., U. Ill., 1961; M.B.A., U. Calif.-Berkeley, 1965. Acct. Friden, Inc., San Leandro, Calif., 1965-67; sr. acct. bus. product group Xerox, Rochester, N.Y., 1967-69; mgr. budget and planning Xerox, Chgo., 1969-70; sr. policy analyst Xerox, Stamford, Conn., 1970-72, mgr. intercompany pricing, 1972-74; dir. bus. planning, automotive div. Arvin Industries, Inc., Columbus, Ind., 1974-77, v.p. fin. automotive div., 1977-81, treas., 1981-82, chief fin. officer, dir., 1982-90, pvt. investor, cons. Mem. AICPA, N.Y. Assn. CPAs. Club: Chapel Hill Country. Home and Office: The Oaks 1023 Cleland Dr Chapel Hill NC 27514-5619

THAL, HERBERT LUDWIG, JR., electrical engineer, engineering consultant; b. Mt. Vernon, N.Y., Feb. 15, 1932; s. Herbert Ludwig and Mildred (Martinson) T.; m. Joan Madeline Ragsdale, Jan. 30, 1954; children: Herbert Ludwig III, Wayne, Carolyn, David, Eric. BEE, Rensselaer Poly. Inst., 1953, MEE, 1955, PhDEE, 1962. Rsch. assoc. Rensselaer Poly. Inst., Troy, N.Y., 1953-56; project engr. GE, Schenectady, 1956-67; staff engr. GE, King of Prussia, Pa., 1967-77, mgr. electromagnetics, 1977-89; v.p. Microlab/FXR, Livingston, N.J., 1989-92; adj. prof. Drexel U., Phila., 1983-90; adj. assoc. prof. U. Pa., Phila., 1986-87. 2d lt. U.S. Army, 1957. Fellow IEEE, Sigma Xi, Tau Beta Pi, Eta Kappa Nu. Presbyterian.

THALACKER, ARBIE ROBERT, lawyer; b. Marquette, Mich., Apr. 17, 1935; s. Arbie Otto and Jeanne (Emmett) T.; m. Rita Annette Skaaren, Sept. 11, 1956 (div. July 1992); children: Marc Emmett, Christopher Paul, Robert Skaaren. AB, Princeton U., 1957; JD, U. Mich., 1960. Bar: N.Y. 1961, U.S. Ct. Appeals (2d cir.) 1962. Assoc. Shearman & Sterling, N.Y.C., 1960-68, ptnr., 1968—; bd. dirs. Detrex Corp., Detroit, 1981—, chmn., 1993—. Leader Rep. Dist. Com., 1966-68; v.p., trustee Greenwich Village Soc. for Hist. Preservation. Mem. ABA, N.Y. Bar Assn., Assn. Bar City N.Y. (securities regulatory commn. 1975-78), Wine and Food Soc. (bd. dirs. 1976-78, 85-93, 94—), Chevaliers du Tastevin, Commanderie de Bordeaux, Siwanoy Country Club (bd. govs. 1976-79), Derby Club, Links Club, Verbank Hunting and Fishing Club. Home: 17 Commerce St New York NY 10014-3763 Office: Shearman & Sterling 599 Lexington Ave at 53rd St New York NY 10022

THALDEN, BARRY R., architect; b. Chgo., July 5, 1942; s. Joseph and Sibyl (Goodwin) Hechtenthal; m. Irene L. Mittleman, June 23, 1966 (div. 1989); 1 child, Stacy Elizabeth. BArch, U. Ill., 1965; M in Land Architecture, U. Mich., 1969. Landscape architect Hellmuth, Obata, Kassebaum, St. Louis, 1969-70; dir. landscape architect PGAV Architects, St. Louis, 1970-71; pres. Thalden Corp (formerly Saunders-Thalden & Assocs. Inc.), St. Louis, 1971—. Prin. works include Rock Hill Park, 1975 (AIA award 1977), Wilson Residence, 1983 (AIA award), Nat. Bowling Hall of Fame, 1983 (St. Louis RCGA award 1984), Village Bogey Hills (Home Builders award 1985, St. L. ASLA award 1994), St. Louis U. Campus Mall (St. L. ASLA award 1989), Horizon Casino Resort, Lake Tahoe, Nev., St. Louis Airport's Radisson Hotel, Lady Luck, Treasure Bay, Palace Casinos, Bioloxi, Miss., Boomtown Casino, New Orleans, Pres. Casino on the Admiral, St. Louis. Bd. dirs. St. Louis Open Space Council, 1973-83; trustee United Hebrew Temple, St. Louis, 1984-88; apptd. Mo. Lands Architect Coun., 1990. Named Architect of Yr. Builder Architect mag., 1986. Fellow Am. Soc. Landscape Architects (nat. v.p. 1979-81, pres. St. Louis chpt. 1975, trustee 1976-79, nat. conv. chair 1991); mem. AIA, World Future Soc. (pres. St. Louis chpt. 1984-94). Avocations: painting, fishing, tennis, guitar. Home: 8 Edgewater Is Saint Louis MO 63105 Office: Thalden Corp 7777 Bonhomme Ave Ste 2200 Saint Louis MO 63105-1911

THALER, NANCY REGINA, state agency administrator; b. Kingston, Pa., Apr. 2, 1949; d. Walter Raymond and Dolores Bernadette (Gitautis) Kuzma; m. Karl Williams, Dec. 26, 1970; 1 child, Aaron Richards. BA in Music, Coll. Misericordia, Dallas, Pa., 1971; MA in Human Sci., Villanova U., 1989. Special edn. tchr. Lacawanna Intermediate, Scranton, Pa., 1971-72; childcare aid Ken Crest Svcs., Plymouth Meeting, Pa., 1972-74, houseparent in group home, 1974-78, dir. residential scvs., 1978-87; dir. bur. community programs Dept. Pub. Welfare, Commonwealth of Pa., Harrisburg, Pa., 1987-92; dep. sec. Office of Mental Retardation, Dept. Pub. Welfare, Commonwealth of Pa., Harrisburg, Pa., 1992—. Recipient Positive Approaches award Assn. Persons with Severe Handicaps, San Francisco, 1993. Office: Office Mental Retardation Health Welfare Bldg Rm 512 Harrisburg PA 17105-2675

THALER, RICHARD H., economics educator; b. East Orange, N.J., Sept. 12, 1945; s. Alan M. and Roslyn (Melnikoff) T.; children: Gregory Scott, Maggie Rose, Jessica Lynn. BA, Case Western Res. U., 1967; MA, U. Rochester, 1970, PhD, 1974. Asst. prof. U. Rochester (N.Y.), 1974-78; assoc. prof. Cornell U., Ithaca, N.Y., 1978-86, prof., 1986—; H.J. Louis prof., 1988—; vis. scholar Nat. Bur. Econ. Rsch., Stanford, Calif., 1977-78, Russell Sage Found., N.Y.C., 1991-92; vis. prof. U. B.C., Vancouver, 1984-85. Author: The Winner's Curse, 1992; contbr. articles on psychology and econs. Mem. Am. Econs. Assn. Office: Cornell U Johnson Grad Sch Mgmt Ithaca NY 14853

THALHEIMER, LOUIS B., diversified corporation executive; b. 1944. Grad., Amherst Coll., 1966; postgrad., NYU, 1969. With Cable McDaniel Bowie and Bond, 1970-80; With Am. Trading and Prodn. Corp., Balt., 1980—, previously pres., now CEO, chmn. bd. dirs. Office: Am Trading & Prodn Corp Blaustein Bldg PO Box 238 Baltimore MD 21203-0238

THALL, BURNETT MURRAY, newspaper executive; b. Toronto, Ont., Can., Sept. 27, 1922; s. Henry and Selina (Harris) Rosenthal; m. Eleanor Langbord, Sept. 23, 1945; children: Nelson Spencer, Martin Evan. B.A.Sc., U. Toronto, 1945, M.A.Sc., 1947, Ph.D., 1949. Registered profl. engr., Ont. Spl. lectr. applied sci. and engring. U. Toronto, 1947; cons. engr., then prodn. engr. Toronto Star, 1947-50, v.p., 1958-68, sr. v.p., 1968—, also dir.; chmn. Toronto Star Newspapers Ltd. Author articles in field. Trustee Atkinson Charitable Found.; bd. govs., hon. treas. Women's Coll. Hosp., 1963—; bd. dirs. Princess Margaret Hosp., Ont. Cancer Treatment and Research Found.; bd. govs. U. Toronto. Urgent Care Centre named in his honour Women's Coll. Hosp., 1989; named to Hall of Distinction Engring. Alumni U. Toronto, 1990. Mem. Am. Newspaper Pubs. Assn., Assn. Profl. Engrs. Ont. (Citizenship medal 1991), Can. Daily Newspaper Pubs. Assn. Home: 15 Rosemary Ln, Toronto, ON Canada M5P 3E7 Office: The Toronto Star, 1 Yonge St Toronto, ON Canada M5E 1E6

THALL, RICHARD VINCENT, education program director; b. San Francisco, Sept. 12, 1940; s. Albert Vincent and Alice Stella (O'Brien) T.; m. Ellyn Marie Wisherop, June 15, 1963; children: Kristen Ellyn, Richard Vincent Jr. AA, City Coll. San Francisco, 1961; BA, San Francisco State Coll., 1964; MA, San Francisco State U., 1971. Cert. elem. tchr. Calif.; cert. secondary tchr., Calif.; cert. community coll. tchr., Calif. Tchr. biology San Francisco Unified Sch. Dist., 1965-66; tchr. biology Mt. Diablo Unified Sch. Dist., Concord, Calif., 1966-79, coord. water environ. studies program, 1979—; ranger/naturalist State of Calif., Brannan Island, 1973-78; naturalist Adventure Internat., Oakland, Calif., 1979-81; lectr. Princess Cruise Lines, 1982-84, Sea Goddess, 1986—, Sun Lines, 1987, Sitmar Lines, 1989, RCCL, 1991-94; spkr. commencements U. Calif., Berkeley, 1989. Author: Ecological Sampling of the Sacramento-San Joaquin Delta, 1976; Water Environment Studies Program, 1986; co-author: Project MER Laboratory Manual, 1982. Mem. Contra Costa County (Calif.) Natural Resources Commn., 1975-78, vice-chmn., 1977-78; active Save Mt. Diablo, Concord, 1969-76, v.p., 1974-75; mem. citizens com. Assn. Bay Area Govt. Water Quality, 1979-82, vice-chmn., 1980-82; active John Marsh Home Restoration Com., Martinez, Calif., 1977-78; mem. nat. adv. com. Marine World/Africa USAd, Vallejo, Calif., 1988—; troop com. chmn. Boy Scouts Am., Concord, 1984-86, asst. scoutmaster, 1985-87. Recipient Recognition and Excellence cert. Assn. Calif. Sch. Adminstrs., 1984, Wood Badge award Boy Scouts Am., 1986; grantee State Calif., 1982, 84, San Francisco Estuary Project, 1992, EPA, 1992, Shell Oil Co., 1993. Mem. AAAS, Nat. Assn. Biology Tchrs., Nat., Audubon Soc., Am. Mus. Natural Hist., Nat. Geog. Soc., Smithsonian Instn. (assoc.). Republican. Roman Catholic. Avocations: skiing, jogging, reading, hiking, photography. Home: 1712 Lindenwood Dr Concord CA 94521-1109 Office: Mt Diablo Unified Sch Dist 1936 Carlotta Dr Concord CA 94519-1358

THAPA, KHAGENDRA, survey engineering educator; b. Murtidhunga, Dhankuta, Nepal, Oct. 16, 1950; came to U.S., 1982; s. Ranadhoj and Krishna (Basnet) T.; m. Rajani Basnet, July 7, 1981; children: Samrat, Birat, Charisma. BSc, Tribhuran J., Kathmandu, Nepal, 1973, U. East London, 1978; MSCE, U. N.B., Fredericton, Can., 1980; MS, Ohio State U., 1985, PhD, 1987. Rsch. asst. U. N.B., Fredericton, 1978-80; researcher Geodetic Survey Can., Ottawa, 1980; lectr. Engring. Inst. Tribhuvan U., Kathmandu, 1980-82; teaching/rsch. assoc. Ohio State U., Columbus, 1982-87; assoc. prof. Ferris State U., Big Rapids, Mich., 1987-91, prof. Coll. Tech., 1991—; rschr. Ctr. for Mapping, Columbus, Ohio, 1990; cons. Techs., Archs. and Engrs. Consultancy, Kathmandu, 1980-82; chairperson Engring. Topographic Mapping Com. Am. Soc. Photogrammetry and Remote Sensing, Washington, 1991—; evaluator accreditation bd. for engring. and tech. Engring. Accreditation Commn. Grantee NSF, Washington, 1989, 91. Mem. Royal Instn. Chartered Surveyors (rsch. grant 1988-89), Am. Congress on Surveying and Mapping, Am. Soc. Photogrammetry, Inst. Navigation, Geodetic Sci. Club (v.p. 1985-86). Achievements include devising a new technique to find inconsistent observations and constraints in horizontal networks, using linear programming in optimal design of leveling networks, devising a new method of line generalization in computer cartography and digital mapping; worked on critical points detection and data compression using zero-crossings; analysed the accuracy of spatial data used in geographic information system. Home: 20796 Edewood Dr Big Rapids MI 49307 Office: Ferris State U Coll Tech Surveying Engring Program 915 Campus Dr Rm 312 Big Rapids MI 49307-2291

THAR, FERDINAND AUGUST (BUD THAR), trade company executive; b. Paw Paw, Mich., Oct. 26, 1940; s. James Ferdinand and Louise Olga (Schmidt) T.; m. Siri Ashelman, Jan. 28, 1967; children: Jonathan Justin, Christina Sheri, Amanda Hope. BA, Mich. State U., 1964; postgrad., Boston U., 1964-65, Am. U., 1968-72, U. Ga. Sch. Internat. Law, 1978. Program officer Govtl. Affairs Inst., Washington, 1964-73; led trade mission to Taiwan, 1979; exec. dir. Ctr. Internat. Transp. for Nat. Govs.' Assn., East Lansing, Mich., 1980-82; assoc. dir. Battle Creek (Mich.) Unltd., 1982-84; mem. mfg. trade mission to France, 1983; pres. Eagle Trade, Battle Creek, 1983—; exec. dir. Great Lakes World Trade Ctr., Detroit, 1986; instr. MBA Internat.

Trade Ednl. Svcs. Exch. with Peoples Republic of China, 1987-88, with Hungary, 1992; U.S. del. 1st World Agrl. Fair, New Delhi, 1959-60, Internat. Farm Youth Exch., Israel, 1962; mem. White House Conf. on Internat. Cooperation, Washington, 1972, White House Conf. on Balanced Growth, Washington, 1978; mem. NAS, Washington, 1979—; mem. intergovtl. rels. com. Transp. Rsch. Bd., 1985—; guest govts. of France, Jamaica, Taiwan, Yugoslavia, Germany, Brit Rail, Eng.; cons. in field; author devel. proposal agribus. project, 1982; cons. Gt. Lake Regional Commn., Ann Arbor, Mich., 1984-85. Author: Influence of International Travel on Teens Vocational Choice, 1963, Rural Youth in Michigan, 1964. Leader youth vol. group, Costa Rica, 1963; chief elder Battle Creek Bible Ch., 1991-92. Mem. Gideons Internat. Office: Eagle Trade 615 Jennings Lndg Battle Creek MI 49015-3528

THARNEY, LEONARD JOHN, education educator, consultant; b. New Haven, Nov. 6, 1929; s. Lillian A. Batey; m. Denise A. Gauvin, June 20, 1981; children: Karen L., Linda L. BS, Trenton (N.J.) State Coll., 1954; MEd, Rutgers U., 1959; postgrad., Lehigh U., Bethlehem, Pa., Columbia U. Cert. secondary math. and sci. tchr., elem. tchr. Tchr. (elem. demonstration) Trenton State Coll., 1954-60; tchr. (Jr. High demonstration) Ewing Twp. (N.J.) Schs., 1960-63; cons., evaluator Am. Coun. on Edn. and Mid. States Assn., Washington, 1963—; prof. Trenton (N.J.) State Coll., 1963-92, prof. emeritus, 1993—, dept. chmn., 1988-92; cons. to internat. schs. for curriculum or sci. edn. Monrovia, Accra, Athens, Mogadishu, Cairo, Alexandria, Aleppo, Damascus, 1975—; tchr. grad. courses in curriculum and edn. rsch. at overseas sites, Spain, Cyprus, Saudi Arabia, Syria, 1981—; exch. prof. Worcester Coll. Higher Edn., Eng., 1984-85; presenter sci. edn. workshops AISA Internat. Conf., Nairobi, 1987; rep. from Coll. to Prins. Tng. Ctr., London, 1994; bd. dirs. People to People Internat., Trenton. Co-author 7 manuals for uniform constrn. codes. Col. AUS, 1947-81. Recipient ACE Award of Outstanding Svc. in Mil. Evaluations, 1987, Meritorious Svc. medal U.S. Army, 1981, Cert. of Appreciation, Presdl. Citation, 1989, Spl. Plaque award, others. Mem. ASCD, Assn. Tchr. Educators, Assn. for Edn. Tchrs. in Sci, Nat. Coun. Social Studies. Home: 20 Lawrenceville Pennington Rd Lawrenceville NJ 08648

THARP, BENJAMIN CARROLL, JR., architect; b. Austin, Tex., Sept. 3, 1919; s. Benjamin Carroll Tharp and Norris (Ophelia) Wallis; m. Mae Sibley; children: Ronald Emery, Carolyn Jeanine Tharp Love. BArch, U. Tex., 1943. Registered architect, Tex. Draftsman Wurdeman & Beckett, L.A., 1944, Richard Neutra, L.A., 1945, Merrill Baird, L.A., 1946, Golemon & Rolfe, Houston, 1947, Milton Foy Martin, Houston, 1948; prin. Koetter & Tharp, Houston, 1949-64, Koetter, Tharp & Cowell, Houston, 1964-78; architect Koetter, Tharp, Cowell and Lockwood, Andrews, Newman, Houston, 1978-81; ret. Lockwood, Andrews, Newman, 1981. Bd. dirs. Harris County Soil and Water Conservation Dist., Houston, 1972-82; pres. Constrn. Industry Coun., Houston, 1970. Recipient 1st Restoration award Red Cedar Shingle and Handsplit Shake Bur./AIA, Seattle, 1975. Fellow AIA, Tex. Soc. Architects (chmn. hist. resources com. 1986); mem. Montgomery (Tex.) Hist. Soc., Optimist Club (pres. Houston chpt. 1970). Republican. Baptist. Home: RR 3 Box 51A Montgomery TX 77356-2323

THARP, ROLAND GEORGE, psychology, education educator; b. Galveston, Tex., June 6, 1930; s. Oswald Roland and Berma Lucille (Keefer) T.; m. Stephanie Dalton; children: Donald Martin, Thomas Roland, David Michael, Julie. Student, Middlebury Coll., 1956, 60; BA cum laude, U. Houston, 1957; MA, U. Mich., 1958, PhD, 1961. Cert. Adm. Bd. Examiners in Profl. Psychology. Reporter Tex. City Sun, 1946-47; mgr. Tharp Lumber Co., LaMarque, Tex., 1949-54; intern VA Hosp., Menlo Park, Calif., 1960; asst. prof. U. Ariz., Tucson, 1961-65, assoc. prof., 1965-68; prof., dir. clin. studies, dir. multicultural ctr. for higher edn. U. Hawaii, Honolulu, 1968-87; provost and v.p. for acad. affairs U.S. Internat. U., San Diego, 1987-89; prof. edn., psychology U. Calif., Santa Cruz, 1990—; dir. Nat. Rsch. Ctr. for Diversity, 1995—; prin. investigator Kamehameha Early Edn. Program, Honolulu, 1969-89; field selection officer Peace Corps, Washington, 1965-67. Author: (poetry) Highland Station, 1978; co-author: (book) Behavior Modification in the Natural Environment, 1969, Self-Directed Behavior, 1980, Rousing Minds to Life, 1988; writer, producer, dir. film Scenes from the Life, 1981 (Purchase prize The Contemporary Mus. 1981). Mem. Bd. Psychologist Examiners, Ariz., 1964-67; pres. Hawaii Literary Arts Coun., Honolulu, 1982. Robert Frost fellow Middlebury Coll., 1960; recipient Am. Film Mag. award for filmmaking Hawaii Internat. Film Festival, 1990, Grawemeyer award edn., 1993. Mem. Am. Ednl. Rsch. Assn., Am. Anthropol. Assn. Episcopalian. Avocation: tennis. Office: University of California Crown College Santa Cruz CA 95064

THARP, TWYLA, dancer, choreographer; b. Portland, Ind., July 1, 1941; m. Peter Young (div.); m. Robert Huot (div.); 1 child, Jesse. Student, Pomona Coll.; BA in Art History, Barnard Coll., 1963; D of Performing Arts (hon.), Calif. Inst. Arts, 1978, Brown U., 1981, Bard Coll., 1981; LHD, Ind. U., 1987; DFA, Pomona Coll., 1987; studied with Richard Thomas, Merce Cunningham, Igor Schwezoff, Louis Mattox, Paul Taylor, Margaret Craske, Erick Hawkins. Dancer Paul Taylor Dance Co., 1963-65; freelance choreographer with own modern dance troupe and various other cos. including Joffrey Ballet and Am. Ballet Theatre, 1965-87; founder, choreographer Twyla Tharp Dance Found., N.Y.C., 1965-87; artistic assoc., resident choreographer Am. Ballet Theatre, N.Y.C., 1987-91; teaching residencies various colls. and univs. including U. Mass., Oberlin Coll., Walker Art Ctr., Boston U.; choreographer White Oak Dance Project. Choreographer: Tank Dive, 1965, Re-Moves, 1966, One Two Three, 1966, Forevermore, 1967, Generation, 1968, Medley, 1969, After Suite, 1969, Dancing in the Streets of London and Paris, 1969, The One Hundreds, 1970, The Fugue, 1970, The Big Pieces, 1971, Eight Jelly Rolls, 1971, The Raggedy Dances, 1972, Deuce Coupe, 1973, As Time Goes By, 1974, Sue's Leg, 1975, Ocean's Motion, 1975, Push Comes to Shove, 1976, Once More Frank, 1976, Mud, 1977, Baker's Dozen, 1979, When We Were Very Young, 1980, Nine Sinatra Songs, 1982, The Catherine Wheel, 1982, Bach Partita, 1984, The Little Ballet, 1984, (with Jerome Robbins) Brahms/Handel, 1984, At the Supermarket, 1984, In the Upper Room, 1987, Ballare, 1987, Stations of the Crossed, 1988, Everlast, 1989, Quartet, 1989, Bum's Rush, 1989, The Rules of the Game, 1990, Brief Fling, 1990, Grand Pas: Rhythm of the Saints, 1991, Deuce Coupe II, 1992, The Men's Piece, 1992, (with Mikhail Baryshnikov) Cutting Up, 1992-93, Demeter and Persephone, 1993, Waterbaby Bagatelles, 1994, Demeter and Persephone, 1994, Red, White & Blues, 1995, How Near Heaven, 1995; (film) Hair, 1979, Ragtime, 1981, Amadeus, 1984, White Nights, 1985, Valmont, 1989, I'll Do Anything, 1994; (video splis.) Making Television Dance, 1977, CBS Cable Confessions of a Corner Maker, 1980; (Broadway shows) Sorrow Floats, 1985, Singin' In The Rain, 1985; (TV) Baryshnikov by Tharp (Emmy award Outstanding Choreography 1985, Emmy award Outstanding Writing of Classical Music/Dance Programming 1985, Emmy award Outstanding Directing of Classical Music/Dance Programming 1985), The Catherine Wheel, 1982 (Emmy award nom. Outstanding Choreography 1982); author (autobiography): When Push Comes to Shove, 1992. MacArthur Found. Chgo. fellow, 1992; recipient Creative Arts award Brandeis U., 1972, Dance mag. award, 1981, Univ. Excellence medal Columbia U., 1987, Lions of the Performing Arts award N.Y. Pub. Libr., 1989, Samuel M. Scripps award Am. Dance Festival, 1990. Office: Tharp Productions 336 Central Park West No 17B New York NY 10025*

THARPE, FRAZIER EUGENE, journalist; b. Panama City, Fla., Jan. 10, 1941; s. Henry Clayton and Margaret Jane (Jenkins) T.; m. Barbara Ann Hembree, Oct. 30, 1971. B.A. in Polit. Sci. and History, Vanderbilt U., Nashville, 1963. Reporter Miami (Fla.) News, 1963; reporter U.P.I., Atlanta and Columbia, S.C., 1964; pub. relations exec. Atlanta, 1965-69; fin. editor Atlanta Constn., 1969-73. Editorial assoc., columnist, 1974-83, columnist Helpline, 1983—. Free-lance writer. Office: 72 Marietta St NW Atlanta GA 30303-2804

THATCHER, GEORGE ROBERT, banker; b. Austin, Pa., Sept. 18, 1922; S. Walter Robert and Roberta Estelle (Bernard) T.; widowed; children: Georgia Anne Thatcher Faneca, Janie Estelle Thatcher Holmes, Walter Wimberly. BA in English, U. Miss., 1948; grad. diploma in bus., Ind. U., 1973; degree of distinction, Inst. Fin. Edn., Chgo. Enlisted U.S. Army, 1942, advanced through grades to maj.; 1948, stationed in Pacific, Korea, ret., 1952; ptnr. Rand-Thatcher Advt. Agy., Gulfport, Miss., 1948-69; COO

Coast Fed. Savings, Gulfport, 1969-81; pres. coast divsn. Magnolia Fed. Bank, Gulfport, 1981-92; also bd. dirs Magnolia Fed. Bank, Hattiesburg, Miss.; councilman City of Gulfport, 1989; bd. dirs. Miss. Econ. Coun., Jackson, 1991-94. Author: Misrepresentation in Mississippi, 1954. Commr. Miss. Arts Commn., Jackson, 1991—; past chmn. United Way, Harrison County, Gulfport Carnegie Libr., Harrison County Libr.; past trustee Gulfport Meml. Hosp. Found.; past pres. Episcopal Laymen of Miss.; past sr. warden, layreader St. Peter's Episcopal Ch., Gulfport; mem., co-chmn. planned giving com. Episcopal Diocese Miss.; past dir. Miss. Hist. Assn. Decorated Bronze Star; named Outstanding Citizen, Gulfport Jaycees. Mem. Gulfport Rotary Club (pres. 1995—, named Citizen of Yr. 1993, Paul Harris fellow), Century Club (pres.), Gulfport Yacht Club (chmn. Olympic Sailing Commn.), Bayou Bluff Tennis Club, Great So. Club., Newcomen Soc. of U.S., Miss. Gulf Coast C. of C. Republican. Avocations: tennis, chess, reading, classical music. Home: 1302 Second St Gulfport MS 39501 Office: Magnolia Fed Bank 2200 14th St Gulfport MS 39501

THATCHER, KRISTINE MARIE, actress, writer; b. Lansing, Mich., June 22, 1950; d. Joseph and Marjorie Suzanne (McKeone) Schneider; m. David Darlow, May 11, 1990; 1 child, Kerry Miriam. Grad. high sch., Lansing. Appeared numerous theatre prodns. including Hunting Cockroaches, The Taming of the Shrew, The Real Thing, The Life and Adventures of Nicholas Nickleby, You Never Can Tell, Boy Meets Girl, Custer, A Doll's House, As You Like It, Merton of the Movies, The Nerd, Translations, Arms and the Man, Cat on a Hot Tin Roof, Macbeth, The Threepenny Opera; TV appearances include Trial of the Moke, Hyde and Seeke, Another World, Search for Tomorrow; playwright: The Adventures of Captain Karma, 1976, Michigan Bio (The Rustic Village), 1983, Niedecker, 1985, (with Larry Shue) Waiting for Tina Meyer, 1989, Under Glass, 1991; dir. Eleemosynary, A Christmas Carol, Road to Mecca, Niedecker, Tartuffe, Sidekick, Fiddler on the Roof. Mem. Actors' Fund Am., N.Y.C., 1985—, Dem. Nat. Com., Washington, 1988—; vol. Greenpeace, Chgo. and Washington, 1987-88. Nominated for Plays in Process Theatre Communications Group, 1987, Joseph Kesselring award Nat. Arts Club, 1987, Joseph Jefferson award, 1985, Susan Smith Blackburn award, 1985, 91; finalist Nat. One-Act Play Contest, 1990. Mem. AFTRA, Actors Equity Assn., Dramatists' Guild, Soc. Stage Dirs. and Choreographers, Inc. Roman Catholic. Avocations: gardening, reading, dialects. Home and Office: 6722 N Bosworth Ave Chicago IL 60626-4221

THATCHER, REX HOWARD, newspaper publisher; b. Williamston, Mich., Feb. 22, 1932; s. Howard Alden and Emma (Rappuhn) T.; m. Yvonne Lee Taft, Mar. 22, 1954; children: Thomas D., Richard M., Karen L., Dana L. BJ, Mich. State U., 1954. Advt. salesman The Jackson (Mich.) Citizen Patriot, 1964-69, promotion mgr., 1970, mktg. dir., 1971, asst. gen. mgr., 1972; pub. The Saginaw News, 1990—. Bd. dirs Bay Medical Ctr., 1983—; mem., officer Bay Area C. of C., 1974-83, Bay Area Community Found., 1982-88. Mem. Mich. Press Assn., Inland Daily Press Assn., Am. Newspaper Pubs. Assn., Rotary. Presbyterian. Avocations: fly fishing, hunting, competitive and postal chess. Office: The Saginaw News 203 S Washington Ave Saginaw MI 48607-1283*

THATCHER, SANFORD GRAY, publishing executive; b. Washington, Aug. 4, 1943; s. Harold Wesley and Genevieve (Harnett) T.; m. Barbara Boal, June 1966 (div.); m. Catherine Dammeyer, May 27, 1980; children: Corinne, Christopher. BA summa cum laude, Princeton U., 1965, postgrad., 1966-67; postgrad., Columbia U., 1965-66. Editor manuscript div. Princeton (N.J.) U. Press, 1967-69, editor social sci. divsn., 1969-78, asst. dir., 1978-85, editor in chief, 1985-89; dir. Pa. State U. Press, University Park, 1989—. Author: AAUP Guide to 1976 Copyright Law, 1977; contbr. articles to profl. jours. Mem. Ch. and Soc. Commn., St. Paul's United Meth. Ch., 1990-92; bd. dirs. The Daily Collegian newspaper, Pa. State U., 1991—. Mem. Am. Philos. Assn., L.Am. Studies Assn., Assn. Am. Pubs. (copyright com. 1972—, freedom to read com. 1982-86), Assn. Am. Univ. Presses (chair copyright com. 1972-93, bd. dirs. 1995—), Assn. for Copyright Enforcement (bd. dirs. 1988-93), Copyright Clearance Ctr. (bd. dirs. 1992—). Democrat. Methodist. Avocations: swimming, sailing, tennis, rare book collecting, music. Home: 2239 Concord Dr State College PA 16801 Office: Pa State U Press 820 N University Dr University Park PA 16802

THAU, WILLIAM ALBERT, JR., lawyer; b. St. Louis, June 22, 1940; s. William Albert and Irene Elizabeth (Mundy) T.; m. Jane Hancock, Sept. 7, 1961; children: William Albert, Caroline Jane, Jennifer Elizabeth. BS in Indsl. Mgmt., Georgia Inst. Tech., 1962; JD, U. Tex., 1965. Bar: Tex. 1965. Ptnr., head of real estate sect. Jenkens & Gilchrist, Dallas, 1965—; chmn. real estate developer/builder symposium S.W. Legal Found., 1975-79; bd. dirs. Southwestern Film Archives, So. Meth. U.; lectr. Practicing Law Inst. Bd. dirs. St. Philips Sch., Tex., Dallas, 1988, So. Meth. U.; trustee Dallas Can. Acad., 1987-88. Mem. ABA, Tex. State Bar Assn. (chmn real estate, probate, trust law sect.), Am. Coll. Real Estate Lawyers, Brook Hollow Golf Club. Republican. Episcopalian. Author: Negotiating the Purchase and Sale of Real Estate, 1975; editor Tex. State Bar Assn. Newsletter on Real Estate, Probate & Trust Law, 1978-81, Best Lawyers in Am., 1983—; contbr. articles to Real Estate Rev., 1983—. Office: Jenkens & Gilchrist 1445 Ross Ave Ste 3200 Dallas TX 75202-2799

THAXTER, PHYLLIS ST. FELIX, actress; b. Portland, Maine, Nov. 20, 1919; d. Sidney St. Felix and Phyllis (Schuyler) T.; m. James T. Aubrey Jr., Nov. 16, 1944 (div. May 1961); children: Susan Schuyler, James Watson; m. Gilbert Lea, Oct. 27, 1962. Student, St. Genviève Coll., Montreal, Que., Can., 1938; DFA, Nasson Coll., Maine, 1979. Ind. actress 1938—. Actress in numerous films including Thirty Seconds Over Tokyo, 1944, Bewitched, Weekend At the Waldorf, Living In a Big Way, Sea of Grass, Act of Violence, Tenth Avenue Angel, Sign of the Ram, Blood on the Moon, Breaking Point, Jim Thorpe-All American, Fort Worth, Operation Secrets, Come Fill the Cup, Working Her Way Through College, Springfield Rifle, (as Ma Kent) Superman I, numerous live TV appearances including Armstrong Circle Theater, Playhouse 90, General Electric Theater, Philco Playhouse, (TV series) The Loretta Young Show, Alfred Hitchcock Presents, Wagon Train, Rawhide, Marcus Welby M.D., numerous stage prodns. including What a Life, 1938-39, There Shall Be No Night, 1940-41, Claudia, Take Her, She's Mine with Art Carney, 1961, In the Gin Game with Larry Gates, 1980, Three Soverigns for Sarah (Am. Playhouse), 1985, Murder She Wrote, 1992. Mem. Colonial Dames, Maine chpt., 1968—. Mem. Actors Equity Assn., Screen Actors Guild, Acad. Motion Picture Arts and Scis., Nat. Acad. TV Arts and Scis., AFTRA. Republican. Episcopalian. Clubs: Portland Country; Riomar Country (Vero Beach, Fla.). Avocations: painting, needlepoint, golf.

THAXTON, MARVIN DELL, lawyer, farmer; b. Electra, Tex., June 1, 1925; s. Montgomery Dell and Ida (Scheurer) T.; m. Carolyn Moore Alexander, Aug. 30, 1949; children: Rebecca Thaxton Henderson, Gail Thaxton Fogleman, Marvin D. Jr. JD, U. Ark., 1949. Bar: Ark. 1949, U.S. Dist. Ct. (ea. dist.) Ark. 1952, U.S. Dist. Ct. (we. dist.) Ark. 1978, U.S. Dist. Ct. (we. dist.) Okla., U.S. Supreme Ct. 1987. Prin. Thaxton Furniture Co., Newport, Ark., 1949-50; ptnr. Thaxton, Hout & Howard, Attys., Newport, 1950—; spl. assoc. justice Ark. Supreme Ct., 1978, 84; examiner Ark. State Bd. Law Examiners, 1968-73, chmn. 1973. Pres. Newport C. of C., 1956, Newport Sch. Dist. Bd. Edn., 1964; past pres. Ea. Ark. Young Men's Clubs; adult leader Newport area Boy Scouts Am., 1949—. Officer U.S. Mcht. Marine, 1945-46, PTO. Fellow Ark. Bar Found.; mem. Ark. Bar Assn. (honor cert. 1973), Ark. Trial Lawyers Assn., Newport Rotary Club (past pres., Paul Harris fellow 1990), Sigma Chi. Democrat. Methodist. Avocations: hunting, fishing, boating. Home: 12 Lakeside Ln Newport AR 72112-3914 Office: Thaxton Hout & Howard 600 3rd St Newport AR 72112-3218

THAYER, CHARLES J., investment banker; b. Abilene, Kans., Feb. 28, 1944; s. Bruce V. and Neoma (Obermeyer) T.; 1 child, Travis J. Grad., U. Kans., 1967. Exec. v.p.; CFO Citizens Fidelity Bank, Louisville, 1977-87; exec. v.p. fin. PNC Bank Corp., Pitts., 1987-89; chmn., mng. dir. Chartwell Capital Ltd., Ft. Lauderdale, Fla., 1989—; interim chmn. Sunbeam-Oster, Providence, 1993; bd. dirs Sunbeam-Oster, Providence, 1993; bd. dirs. Sunbeam-Oster Co., Ft. Lauderdale, 1990—; adv. dir. Keefe Mgrs. Inc., N.Y.C., 1990—. Trustee Cystic Fibrosis Found., Washington, 1980—; chmn. Cystic Fibrosis Svcs., Washington, 1994—. Avocation: sailing. Office: Chartwell Capital Ltd 56 Fiesta Way Fort Lauderdale FL 33301

THAYER, EDWIN CABOT, musician; b. Weymouth, Mass., May 16, 1935; s. Elliot Pierce and Barbara (Senior) T.; m. Joan Peregoy, June 24, 1961; children: Bruce, Laura, Richard, William. MusB cum laude, U. Ill., 1957, MusM with performing honors, 1958. Instr. horn Brevard (N.C.) Music Center, summers 1957, 58, 62; grad. asst. U. Ill., 1957-58; prin. horn Washington Brass Choir, 1958-61, Norfolk (Va.) Symphony, 1961-65, Richmond (Va.) Symphony, 1960-72; assoc. prof. music Va. Commonwealth U. (formerly Richmond Profl. Inst.), Richmond, 1963-72; head piano dept. Va. Commonwealth U., 1965-69, head brass and winds dept., 1969-72, music librarian, 1965-72; prin. horn Washington Nat. Symphony, 1972—; hornist Nat. Symphony Wind Soloists, 1978—, Euterpe Chamber Players, 1981-89, Chamber Soloists Washington, 1986—, Tanglewood (Mass.) Berkshire Music Festival Orch., summers 1955-56; hornist Brass Prins. and Woodwind Prins. Quintets Nat. Symphony Orch., 1988—; solo recitalist, chamber ensemble recitalist, horn soloist; guest artist Internat. Horn Workshops, Hartford, Ct., 1977, Potsdam, N.Y., 1981, Towson, Md., 1985; mem. World Philharm. Orch., Rio de Janeiro, 1986. Served with AUS, 1958-61. Mem. Internat. Horn Soc., Musicians Union, Pi Kappa Lambda, Phi Mu Alpha Sinfonia. Home: 11902 Triple Crown Rd Reston VA 22091-3016 Office: Nat Symphony Orch Kennedy Ctr Performing Washington DC 20566

THAYER, GERALD CAMPBELL, beer company executive; b. Rockville Centre, N.Y., July 19, 1943; s. Gerald Earl and Celia Storrs (Campbell) T.; m. Candace Wheatley, June 29, 1968; children—Jonathan, Matthew. B.A., Middlebury Coll., 1965; M.B.A., Columbia U., 1970. Sr. planning analyst Anheuser-Busch Co., St. Louis, 1970-73, asst. to v.p. fin., 1973-75, asst. treas., 1975-81, treas., 1981-85; v.p., treas. Anheuser-Busch Co., 1985-93, v.p., contr., 1994—. Served to capt. U.S. Army, 1966-68, Vietnam. Home: 12749 Topping Acres Saint Louis MO 63131-1435 Office: Anheuser-Busch Cos Inc 1 Busch Pl Saint Louis MO 63118-1849

THAYER, JANE See WOOLLEY, CATHERINE

THAYER, KEITH B., engineering company executive; b. 1927. BSME, Kans. State U., 1950. With Phillips Petroleum Co., Barlesville, Okla., 1950-51, Foster-Wheeler, Houston, 1951-53, Raymond Jenkins, Houston, 1953-54; with Overbeck Stubbs & Assocs., Houston, 1954—, now pres., CEO. Office: Overbeck Stubbs & Assocs 12727 Featherwood Dr Houston TX 77034-4414*

THAYER, LEE, educator, author, consultant; b. Grenola, Kans., Dec. 18, 1927; s. Garrett Osborne and Ruth (Ray) T.; m. Suzanne Katherine Schwan, Apr. 27, 1986: children: Joshua Lee, Jessica Sam. B.A. cum laude, U. Wichita, 1953, M.A., 1956; Ph.D., U. Okla., 1963. Instr. U. Okla., 1956-58; with Pratt & Whitney Co., Inc., 1958-59; assoc. prof. adminstrn. and psychology U. Wichita, 1959-64; prof., dir. Center Advanced Study Communication, U. Mo. at Kansas City, 1964-68; George H. Gallup prof. communication research U. Iowa, Iowa City, 1968-73; prof. communication studies Simon Fraser U., Burnaby, B.C., Can., 1973-76; vis. prof. U. Mass., 1976-77; Fulbright prof. U. Helsinki, Finland, 1977; Disting. vis. prof. U. Houston, 1978-80; prof. and past chmn. communication U. Wis.-Parkside, 1978-93, founding dir. Parkside Honors Program, 1983-87; Disting. vis. prof. Kuring-gai Coll. Advanced Edn., Sydney, Australia, 1986; cons. to govt. and industry, 1956—. Author: Administrative Communication, 1961, Communication and Communication Systems, 1968, On Communication: Essays in Understanding, 1988, Pieces: Toward a Revisioning of Communication/ Life, 1995; editor: Communication: Theory and Research, 1967, Communication: Concepts and Perspectives, 1967, Communication: General Semantics Perspectives, 1969, Communication: Ethical and Moral Issues, 1974, Ethics, Morality, and the Media, 1980, Organization-Communication: Emerging Perspectives I, 1985, Organization-Communication: Emerging Perspectives II, 1987, vol. III, 1995, vol. IV, 1994; editor book series: The Human Context, 1985—; founding editor: Communication, 1970-80. Served to lt. USNR, 1953-55. Danforth Found. fellow, 1961-63; Found. Econ. Edn. fellow, 1963-64; Ford Found. fellow, 1963-64, 65, Fulbright fellow U. Helsinki, 1977-78. Home: 908 Melrose Avenue Ext Tryon NC 28782-3223

THAYER, RUSSELL, III, airlines executive; b. Phila., Dec. 5, 1922; s. Russell and Shelby Wentworth (Johnson) T.; m. Elizabeth Wright Mifflin, June 12, 1947; children: Elizabeth, Dixon, Shelby, Samuel, David. Student, St. George's Sch., 1937-42; A.B., Princeton U., 1949. Mgmt. trainee Eastern Air Lines, 1949-52; mgr. cargo sales and service Am. Airlines, Los Angeles, 1952-63; v.p. mktg. Seaboard World Airlines, N.Y.C., 1963-70; sr. v.p. Braniff Airways, Inc., Dallas 1970-72; exec. v.p. Braniff Airways, Inc., 1972-77, pres., chief oper. officer, 1977-80, vice chmn., 1981-82; dir. (Braniff Airways, Inc.) 1971-82; v.p. Pan Am. World Airways, Inc., N.Y.C. 1982-84; sr. v.p., 1984-88; sr. v.p. Airline Econs., Inc., Washington, 1989—, also bd. dirs., 1988—; dir. Ft. Worth Nat. Bank, 1977-82; vice chmn. Airline Capital Assn; bd. dirs. Kiwi Internat. Airlines, Inc., World Aux. Power Corp. Mem. Trinity Ch. Ushers Guild, Princeton, N.J., 1968—; Trustee Aviation Hall of Fame N.J. Served with USAAF, 1942-45, ETO. Decorated D.F.C., Air medal with 11 oak leaf clusters. Mem. Am. Aviation Hist. Assn., Air Force Assn., Exptl. Aircraft Assn., Nat. Aeros. Assn., Ivy Club (Princeton), Pretty Brook Tennis Club (Princeton), Bay Head (N.J.) Yacht Club, Nassau Club (Princeton), Wings, Princeton Club (N.Y.C.), Philadelphia Club, Delta Psi. Clubs: Ivy (Princeton), Pretty Brook Tennis (Princeton); Bay Head (N.J.) Yacht; Wings, Princeton (N.Y.C.); Philadelphia. Home: 21 Lilac Ln Princeton NJ 08540-3021 Office: Airline Econs Inc 1130 Connecticut Ave NW # 675 Washington DC 20036-3904

THAYER, W(ALTER) STEPHEN, III, state supreme court justice; b. N.Y.C., Jan. 13, 1946; s. Walter S. and Dorothy (Pflum) T.; m. Judith O. O'Brien, Dec. 27, 1982. B.A. in Polit. Sci., Belmont Abbey Coll., 1968; J.D., John Marshall Law Sch., Chgo., 1974. Bar: N.H. 1975, U.S. Dist. Ct. N.H. 1975, U.S. Ct. Appeals (1st cir.) 1981. Sole practice Law Offices W. Stephen Thayer, III, Manchester, N.H., 1975-81; U.S. atty. Dist. N.H., Concord, 1981-84; assoc. justice N.H. Superior Ct., 1984-86, N.H. Supreme Ct., 1986—; legal counsel N.H. State Senate, 1978-80, N.H. Rep. State Com., 1977-80; cons. GSA, Washington, 1981. Alt. del. Rep. nat. conv., 1980; presdl. elector electoral coll., 1980. Served to 1st lt. U.S. Army, 1968-71. Decorated Bronze Star. Mem. N.H. Bar Assn., N.H. Trial Lawyers Assn. Roman Catholic. Home: 1943 Elm St Manchester NH 03104-2528 Office: NH Supreme Ct Noble Dr Concord NH 03301

THÊ, HOANG-DINH, middle school educator; b. Thua-Thien, Vietnam, Mar. 12, 1943. BS, Lincoln U., 1966, MA, 1973; cert. in edn., U. San Francisco, 1979; MA, San Diego State U., 1980; D Naturopathy, Internat. U., 1993. Cert. tchr., Calif. Instr. Def. Lang. Inst., Monterey, Calif., 1966-71; social worker Internat. Inst. of San Francisco, 1975-78; spl. asst. to the dean Lincoln U., San Francisco, 1971-73; tchr. social studies, math. and scis. Francisco Mid. Sch., San Francisco, 1980—; cons. Ctr. for Internat. Communication and Devel., Long Beach, Calif., 1988—. Mem. Nat. Geographic Soc., Internat. Phonetic Assn., Internat. Soc. of Naturopathy. Avocations: reading, writing, stamp collector, Tai-Chi. Home: PO Box 42-5386 San Francisco CA 94142-5386

THEALL, DONALD FRANCIS, retired university president; b. Mt. Vernon, N.Y., Oct. 13, 1928; s. Harold A. and Helen (Donaldson) T.; m. Joan Ada Benedict, June 14, 1950; children: Thomas, Margaret, John, Harold, Lawrence, Michael. B.A. with honors, Yale U., 1950; M.A. with 1st class honors, U. Toronto, Ont., Can., 1951, Ph.D. with 1st class honors, 1954. Teaching fellow U. Toronto, 1950-52, mem. faculty, 1952-65, prof. English, chmn. joint depts. English, 1964-65; dir. communication studies York U., also prof. English and communications, 1965-66; dir. English Atkinson Coll., 1965-66; mem. faculty McGill U., Montreal, Que., Can., 1966-79; prof. English McGill U., 1966-79, chmn. depty., Isma 74, Molson prof., 1972-79, dir. grad. program in communications, 1976-79; adj. prof. grad. comm. McGill U., Montreal, Que., Can., 1989-91; pres., vice chancellor, prof. English and cultural studies Trent U., Peterborough, Ont., 1980-87, univ. prof., 1987-94, univ. prof. emeritus, 1994—; cultural exch. prof. Govt. of Can. and China, 1974; mem. adv. bd. Semiotic Inquiry, 1982—; cons. in field. Author: (with Robinson and Wevers) Let's Speak English, 4 vols., 1960-61, The Medium Is the Rear View Mirror: Understanding McLuhan, 1971, (with G.J. Robinson) Studies in Canadian Communications, 1975; Beyond the Word: Reconstructing Sense in the Joyce Era of Technology, Culture, and Communication, 1995; mem. editl. bd. Sci.

Fiction Studies, 1976—, Can. Jour. Comm., 1979—, Jour. Can. Studies, 1980-87. Mem. Greater Peterborough Econ. Council, 1982-87; mem. fed. adv. council to minister employment and immigration for Peterborough area, 1986-87. Recipient awards Social Sci. and Humanities Rsch. Coun., 1991-94, 94—, Can. Fedn. Humanities-Aid to Scholarly Publs., 1994; grantee Humanities Rsch. Coun. Can., 1954-56, 73-76, Ont. Dept. Edn., 1956-59, 91, Atkinson Found., 1960, CBC, 1961, Can. Coun., 1966-68, 73-76, Eastman Kodak Corp., Nat. Film Bd. Can., Can. Dept. Industry, Can. Dept. Trade adn Commerce, Can. Ctrl. Mortgage and Housing, 1967-69, Que. Ministry Communications, 1977; sr. leave fellow Can. Coun., 1975. Corr. fellow Acad. Medicine (Toronto); mem. Internat. Communications Assn. (dir. 1978-81), Can. Communications Assn. (chmn. com. to investigate formation 1978, pres. 1979-80), MLA, Philol. Soc. Gt. Britain, Can. Assn. Chmn. English (founding chmn. 1971-74), Assn. Can. Univ. Tchrs. English, Internat. Inst. Communications, Soc. Arts Publs. (v.p. 1967-68), Sci. Fiction Research Assn., University Club of Toronto, Yale Club (Toronto), McGill Faculty Club, Elizabethan Club (Yale). Office: Trent Univ, Peterborough, ON Canada K9J 7B8

THEE, CHRISTIAN, artist, designer; b. Long Branch, N.J., Sept. 27, 1934; s. Walter Christian and Edith Draper (Steinmetz) T. Degree in arch. and design, U. S.C., 1964; degree in stage/lighting/costume design, Columbia U., 1966; student, Lester Polakov Forum Stage Des, 1968-71; design asst. to Joe Mielziner, Ben Edwards and Howard Bay. Illustrator: Behind the Curtain, 1994; commissions include portrait of Prince Andrew of Eng., 1981, mural for Taj Mahal Casino Hotel, Atlantic City, lobby decor of Empire Hotel, N.Y.C., sky ceiling for lobby of LINPRO Corp., Wilmington, Del., Lincoln Post-Hotel, Houston, St. Paul Hotel, New Belvue Stratford, Phila., Clarion Hotel, New Orleans, Belk Dept. Store, Columbia, S.C., Willard Hotel, Washington, Stouffer's Riverview Plaza Hotel, Mobile, Ala.; designed numerous theatrical prodns. including Rashmon, The Robber Bridegroom, Irma La Douce, Pal Joey, Brigadoon, View from a Bridge, Dracula, The Countess Dracula, You Can't Take It With You, Sweet Bird of Youth, The Prime of Miss Jean Brodie, Monique, The Last of the Red Hot Lovers, Finian's Rainbow, Pajama Game, Old Herbaceous, Cabaret, The Importance of Being Earnest, The Ballad of the Sad Cafe, Richard III, The Miraculous Mandarin, Charlie's Aunt, The Physicists, Androcles and the Lion, Drat, Flight into Egypt, Carnival, Under the Yum Yum Tree, American Buffalo, Something's Afoot, A Christmas Carol, The Marriage Go-Around, The Vinegar Tree, Cat on a Hot Tin Roof, The Time of the Coo-Coo, The Visit, and numerous others; theatrical designs for regional and stock cos. including Am. Place Theatre, N.Y.C., Olney (Md.) Theatre, Avondale Playhouse, Indpls., Cafe La Mama, N.Y.C., Equity Libr. Theatre, N.Y.C., Spoleto Festival, Charlestown, S.C., Scott Repertory Theatre, Ft. Worth, and many others; works featured in many books and mags. Avocation: performing magic. Office: Christian Thee & Assoc 6196 East Shore Rd Columbia SC 29206-4310

THEEN, ROLF HEINZ-WILHELM, political science educator; b. Stadthagen, Germany, Feb. 20, 1937; came to U.S., 1956, naturalized, 1962; s. Walter and Gertrud (Tysper) T.; m. Norma Lee Plunkett, June 14, 1959; children: Tanya Sue, Terrell René. B.A. magna cum laude, Manchester Coll., 1959; M.A., Ind. U., 1962, cert. with high distinction Russian and East European inst., 1962, Ph.D., 1964. Asst. prof. Iowa State U., 1964-67, assoc. prof., 1968-70; assoc. prof. polit. sci. Purdue U., West Lafayette, Ind., 1971-73, prof., 1974—; dir. Purdue U.-Ind. U. study program U. Hamburg, 1980-81; translator, editor U.S. Joint Publs. Research Service. Author: Lenin: Genesis and Development of a Revolutionary, 1973, 74, 79; co-author: Comparative Politics: An Introduction to Six Countries, 1986, Comparative Politics: An Introduction to Seven Countries, 1992; editor, translator: The Early Years of Lenin (N. Valentinov), 1969; editor: The USSR First Congress of People's Deputies: Complete Documents and Records, 4 vols., 1991; contbr. articles to profl. jours., chpts. to books. Recipient Wilton Park award Iowa State U., 1971; Fgn. Area Tng. fellow Russian and East European Inst., 1962-64; grantee Am. Philos. Soc., Inter Univ. Com., Joint Com. Slavic Studies, Fulbright grantee, 1995; NEH sr. fellow, 1974-75, rsch. fellow Kennan Inst. Advanced Russian Studies, Woodrow Wilson Internat. Ctr. for Scholars, 1976, Ctr. Humanistic Studies fellow Purdue U., 1982, 88, 91. Mem. Am. Polit. Sci. Assn., Am. Assn. Advancement Slavic Studies, Am. Acad. Social and Polit. Sci. Mem. Ch. of Brethren. Home: 717 Orchard Dr Lafayette IN 47905-4435 Office: Purdue U Dept Polit Sci Liberal Arts/Edn Bldg 2221 West Lafayette IN 47907-1363

THEEUWES, FELIX, physical chemist; b. Duffel, Belgium, May 25, 1937. Licentiaat physics, Cath. U. Louvain, 1961, DSc in Physics, 1966. Tchr. St. Vincent Sch., Westerlo, Belgium, 1961-64; rsch. assoc. chemistry U. Kans., 1966-68, asst. prof., 1968-70; rsch. scientist pharm. chemistry Alza Corp., Palo Alto, Calif., 1970-74, prin. scientist, 1974—, v.p. prodn., rsch. and devel., 1980—; Louis Busse lectr. dept. pharmacology U. Wis., 1981. Mem. Am. Chem. Soc., Acad. Pharm. Sci., N.Y. Acad. Sci. Achievements include research in osmosis, diffusion, solid state physics, cryogenics, high pressure, thermodynamics, pharmacology, pharmacokinetics, calorimetry. Office: Alza Corp PO Box 10950 950 Page Mill Rd Palo Alto CA 94303-0802*

THEIL, HENRI, economist, educator; b. Amsterdam, Netherlands, Oct. 31, 1924; s. Hendrik and Hermina (Siegmann) T.; m. Eleonore A.I. Goldschmidt, June 15, 1951. Ph.D. in Econs, U. Amsterdam, 1951; LL.D. (hon.), U. Chgo., 1964; D. honoris causa, Free U., Brussels, 1974, Erasmus U., Rotterdam, 1983; LL.D. (hon.) Hope Coll. 1985. Mem. staff Central Planning Bur. (The Hague), 1952-55; prof. econometrics Netherlands Sch. Econs., Rotterdam, 1953-66; vis. prof. econs. U. Chgo., 1955-56, 64, Stanford U., 1956, 59, Harvard U., 1960, U. So. Calif., 1979, 80, 81, U. Western Australia, 1982; dir. Econometric Inst. (Netherlands Sch. Econs.), 1956-66; prof. U. Chgo., 1965-81, dir. Center Math. Studies in Bus. and Econs., 1965-81; McKethan-Matherly prof. econometrics and decision scis. U. Fla., 1981—. Author: Linear Aggregation of Economic Relations, 1954, Economic Forecasts and Policy, 2d edit., 1961, Optimal Decision Rules for Government and Industry, 1964, Operations Research and Quantitative Economics, 1965, Applied Economic Forecasting, 1977, Economics and Information Theory, 1967, Principles of Econometrics, 1971, Statistical Decomposition Analysis with Applications in the Social and Administrative Sciences, 1972, Theory and Measurement of Consumer Demand, Vol. 1 1975, Vol. 2 1976, Introduction to Econometrics, 1978, The System-Wide Approach to Microeconomics, 1980, System-Wide Explorations in International Economics, Input-Output Analysis, and Marketing Research, 1980, International Consumption Comparisons, 1981, Exploiting Continuity, 1984, Applied Demand Analysis, 1987, International Evidence on Consumption Patterns, 1989, Contributions to Consumer Demand and Econometrics: Essays in Honour of Henri Theil, 1992, Henri Theil's Contributions to Economics and Econometrics, 1992, Studies in Global Econometrics, 1995; editor Mathematical and Managerial Economics, 1964—; co-editor Series on Econometrics and Management Sciences, 1984—. Fellow Am. Acad. Arts and Scis., Royal Netherlands Acad. Scis., Am. Statis. Assn.; mem. Internat. Statis. Inst., Am. Econ. Assn., Ops. Research Soc. Am., Econometric Soc. (pres. 1961), Inst. Mgmt. Scis. (council 1961-64). Home: PO Box 518 Saint Augustine FL 32084

THEILEN, GORDON HENRY, veterinary surgery educator; b. Montevideo, Minn., May 29, 1928; s. Lou Ernst and Ema Kathryn (Schaller) T.; m. Carolyn June Simon, Mar. 6, 1953; children—Kyle, John, Ann. B.S., U. Calif.-Davis, 1953, D.V.M., 1955. Pvt. practice, Tillamook, Oreg., 1955-56; specialist, instr. U. Calif.-Davis, 1956-57, instr., 1957-58, asst. prof. 1958-64, assoc. prof., 1964-70, prof., chief clin. oncology, 1970—. Co-author: Veterinary Cancer Medicine, 1979, 2nd edit., 1987; co-discoverer Feline sarcoma virus and simian sarcoma virus, 1968, 70; patentee Bovine leukemia virus, 1980; feline leukemia virus vaccine, 1977; contbr. articles to profl. jours. Served with U.S. Army, 1946-48. NIH fellow, 1964-66; N.Y. Cancer Immunology fellow, 1972-73; Alexander von Humboldt Sr. Scientist award, 1979-80; Fleishmann Found. award, 1980-85; Ralston Purina award in Small Animal Medicine, 1982, Alumni Achievement award U. Calif.-Davis, 1987. Mem. AVMA, Am. Coll. Vet. Internal Medicine, Assn. Vet. Clinicians, Am. Assn. Cancer Rsch., Vet. Cancer Soc., Internat. Assn. for Comparative Rsch. on Leukemia and Related Diseases (mem. world com.), Am. Brittany Club (bd. dirs. 1992—), Phi Zeta, Sigma Xi. Democrat. Lutheran. Office: U Calif Dept Veterinary Surgery Davis CA 95616

THEIS, FRANCIS WILLIAM, business executive; b. Joliet, Ill., July 10, 1920. Student, Joliet Jr. Coll., 1937-39; B.S., Purdue U., 1941. Dir. devel. PPG Industries, Barberton, Ohio, 1951-56; mgr. planning chem. div. PPG Industries, Pitts., 1956-60; pres., chief exec. officer PPG Internat., Pitts., 1960-63, v.p. internat., 1963-65; pres., chief exec. officer Devoe & Raynaolds Co., Louisville, 1965-67; pres. Celanese Chem. Co., N.Y.C., 1967-71; group v.p. Celanese Corp., N.Y.C., 1971-72; exec. v.p. Internat. Paper Corp., N.Y.C., 1972-73; pres., chief exec. officer Hooker Chem. Corp., Stamford, Conn., 1973; dir. Occidental Petroleum Corp., Stamford, 1973; pres., chief exec. officer, dir. Am. Ship Bldg. Co., Cleve., 1975-79; dir., pres., chief operating officer GATX Corp., Chgo., 1979-86. Named Disting. Alumnus Purdue U., 1965. Mem. Shipbuilders Council Am. (dir.), Nat. Maritime Council (bd. govs.). Clubs: Cleve. Athletic (Cleve.), Union (Cleve.); Shaker Heights (Ohio) Country); Clifton (Lakewood, Ohio); Landmark (Stamford); Sky (N.Y.C.); Chicago. Office: 9 Middleton Rd Savannah GA 31411-1420

THEIS, FRANK GORDON, federal judge; b. Yale, Kans., June 26, 1911; s. Peter F. and Maude (Cook) T.; m. Marjorie Riddle, Feb. 1, 1939 (dec. 1970); children: Franklin, Roger. A.B. cum laude, U. Kans., 1933; J.D., U. Mich., 1936. Bar: Kans. 1937. Since practiced in Arkansas City; sr. mem. firm Frank G. Theis, 1939—; atty. Kans. Tax Commn., 1937-39; chief counsel OPS for Kans., 1951-52; U.S. dist. judge Dist. Kans., 1967—; chief judge, 1977-81, active sr. status, 1981—; Pres. Young Democrats Kans., 1942-46, Kans. Dem. Club, 1944-46; chmn. Kans. Dem. Com., 1955-60; mem. nat. adv. com. polit. orgn. Dem. Nat. Com., 1956-58, nat. committeeman from Kans., 1957-67; chmn. Dem. Midwest Conf., 1959-60; Dem. nominee for Kans., Supreme Ct., 1950, U.S. Senate, 1960. Mem. ABA, Kans. Bar Assn., Kans. Jr. Bar Conf. (pres. 1942), Phi Beta Kappa., Phi Delta Phi, Sachem. Presbyterian. Club: Mason. Office: US Dist Ct 414 US Courthouse 401 N Market St Wichita KS 67202-2011

THEISEN, EDWIN MATHEW, utility company executive; b. 1930. BA, St. Johns U., 1952. With No. States Power Co., Mpls., 1954—, v.p., 1970-80, pres., chief oper. officer, from 1980; also dir. 1st. lt. USMC, 1952-54. Office: Northern States Power Co-Minn 414 Nicollet Mall Minneapolis MN 55401*

THEISMANN, JOSEPH ROBERT, former professional football player, announcer; b. New Brunswick, N.J., Sept. 9, 1949; s. Joseph James and Olga (Tobias) T.; m. Chery Lynn Brown, Dec. 5, 1970 (div.); children: Joseph Winton, Amy Lynn, Patrick James. B.A. in Sociology, U. Notre Dame, 1971. With Toronto Argonauts, CFL, 1971-74; with Washington Redskins, 1974-86, punt returner, 1974-79, starting quarterback, 1979-86; analyst CBS Nat. Football League broadcasts, 1987-88, ESPN Nat. Football League broadcasts, 1988—; tchr. Offense-Def. Football Camp; Superstar participant, 1979-80, played in Pro-Bowl, 1983-84; mem. Pres.'s Athletic Adv. Com., 1975; active Pres. Nat. Svc. Adv. Com., 1993. Author: Quarter Backing. Mem. corp. bd. Children's Hosp. Nat. Med. Center, Washington; participant benefits for Multiple Sclerosis children's hosps., Armed Forces Christmas benefits. High sch. All-Am. Football, 1967; All-Am. Coll., 1971; Acad.-All-Am.; All-Pro UPI; recipient Brian Piccolo award; played in Pro Bowl, 1982, 83; mem. Super Bowl XVII Championship Team, 1982; cable Ace award, Best Sports Commentator-Analyst, 1994. Mem. Nat. Football Players Assn. Republican. Methodist. Office: JRT Assocs 5912 Leesburg Pike Falls Church VA 22041*

THELEN, BRUCE CYRIL, lawyer; b. St. Johns, Mich., Nov. 24, 1951. BA, Mich. State U., 1973; JD, U. Mich., 1977. Bar: N.Y. 1978, U.S. Dist. Ct. (so. dist.) N.Y. 1978, Mich. 1980, U.S. Dist. Ct. (ea. dist.) Mich. 1980, Ill. 1992. Assoc. Dewey, Ballantine, Bushby, Palmer & Wood, N.Y.C., 1977-80; assoc. Dickinson, Wright, Moon, Van Dusen & Freeman, Detroit, 1981-83, ptnr., 1984—. Contbr. articles to profl. publs. Mem. allocation panel, mem. speakers bur. United Way of Detroit, 1987—; mem. State of Mich. Task Force on Internat. Trade, Lansing, 1990; mem. Detroit Com. on Fgn. Rels., Greater Detroit-Windsor Japan Am. Soc. Mem. N.Y. Bar Assn. (mem. internat. law sect.), Mich. Bar Assn., State Bar Mich. (chmn. internat. law sect. 1990-91), Internat. Bar Assn., Am. Soc. Internat. Law, Ill. Bar Assn. (internat. law sect.), Internat. Law Assn., French-Am. C. of C. of Detroit, German Am. C. of C. of Midwest (bd. dirs. 1992—), pres. Mich. chpt. 1994—), Greater Detroit C. of C. (chmn. European mission com. 1991-92, 95, export com. 1992—, Leadership Detroit VIII program 1986-87), World Trade Club (exec. com. 1992—). Office: Dickinson Wright Moon Van Dusen & Freeman One Detroit Center 500 Woodward Ave Ste 4000 Detroit MI 48226-3524

THELEN, GIL, newspaper editor; b. Chgo.; s. Gilbert Carl and Violet (Okonn) T.; m. Carol Abernathy, July 1966 (div. Apr. 1978); children: Deborah Brooke, Todd Foster; m. Cynthia Jane Struby, Sept. 2, 1979; children: Matthew David, Jonathan Whitfield. BA, Duke U., 1960. Reporter Milw. Jour., 1960-61, AP, Washington, 1965-72; writer Consumer Reports, Mt. Vernon, N.Y., 1972-77; reporter Chgo. Daily News, 1977-78; asst. met. editor Charlotte (N.C.) Observer, 1978-82, met. editor, 1982-83, asst. mng. editor, 1983-87; editor The Sun News, Myrtle Beach, S.C., 1987-90; exec. editor The State, 1990—; adj. prof. U. S.C. Aiken, 1989—. Pres. Montgomery County Big Brothers, Bethesda, Md., 1967-69; co-founder Alpha Group, Myrtle Beach, S.C., 1989. Mem. Am. Soc. Newspaper Editors, S.C. Press Assn., Columbia Rotary Club, Leadership S.C., Leadership Columbia, Phi Beta Kappa, Omicron Delta Kappa. Methodist. Avocations: golf, tennis, reading, classical music. Home: 128 Alexander Cir Columbia SC 29206-4956 Office: The State newspaper 1401 Shop Rd Columbia SC 29201-4843

THELEN, MAX, JR., foundation executive, lawyer; b. Berkeley, Calif., Aug. 18, 1919; s. Max and Ora Emily (Muir) T.; m. Phyllis J. Barnhill, Mar. 8, 1952; children—Nancy B. Thelen Rehkopf, Jane M. Thelen Greene, Max, III, William B. A.B. with highest honors, U. Calif., Berkeley, 1940; J.D. cum laude, Harvard U., 1946. Bar: Calif. 1946. Ptnr. Thelen, Marrin, Johnson & Bridges, San Francisco, 1946-87; v.p., dir. S.H. Cowell Found., 1970—. Trustee World Affairs Council. Served to lt. USNR, 1942-46. Mem. State Bar Calif., Am. Coll. Trial Lawyers, Com. Fgn. Rels., Commonwealth Club, World Trade Club, Marines Meml. Club. Home: 199 Mountain View Ave San Rafael CA 94901-1347 Office: 2 Embarcadero Ctr Ste 2100 San Francisco CA 94111

THELIAN, LORRAINE, public relations executive; b. N.Y.C., Jan. 13, 1948; d. Anthony G. and Inez (Gelfo) Bufano. BA, Molloy Coll., 1969. Account coordinator Basford Pub. Rels., N.Y.C., 1969-71; from asst. account exec. through v.p. Paluszek & Leslie Assoc., N.Y.C., 1971-74; asst. v.p., assoc. dir. Ketchum Pub. Rels., Washington, 1985-91, exec. v.p., dir., 1991—, mem. pub. affairs coun., 1990—; bd. dirs. Ketchum Comm., Inc., Washington, 1994—; bd. dirs. Ketchum Comm., Inc., Washington; mem. Pub. Affairs Coun., 1990—; mem. Washington Bd. Trade, 1987—. Mem. Pub. Rels. Soc. Am. (accredited, chmn. accreditation com. Washington chpt. 1987), Washington Comms. Assn., Women in Pub. Rels. (adv. panel 1994, honoree Pub. Rels. Woman of Yr. 1993). Roman Catholic. Avocations: oil painting, swimming, tennis. Office: Ketchum Pub Rels 1201 Connecticut Ave NW # 300 Washington DC 20036-2605

THELIN, JOHN ROBERT, academic administrator, education educator, historian; b. West Newton, Mass., Oct. 15, 1947; s. George Willard and Rozalija Katherine (Komarec) T.; m. Anna Sharon Blackburn, June 24, 1978. AB, Brown U., 1969; MA, U. Calif., Berkeley, 1972, PhD, 1973. Rsch. asst. Brown U. Providence, 1968-69; researcher, lectr. U. Calif., Berkeley, 1972-74; asst. prof. U. Ky., Lexington, 1974-77; asst. dean Pomona Coll., Claremont, Calif., 1977-79; from asst. dir. to rsch. dir. Assn. Ind. Calif. Colls. and Univs., Santa Ana, 1979-81; chancellor prof. Coll. William and Mary, Williamsburg, Va., 1981-93, pres. faculty assembly, 1990-91; prof. higher edn. & philanthropy Ind. U., Bloomington, 1993—; vis. prof. grad. sch. Claremont U., 1978-81; curator Marquandia Soc., 1971-91; essay rev. editor Rev. of Higher Edn., 1979-91; rsch. com. NSF, Washington, 1991. Author: Higher Education and Its Useful Past, 1982, The Cultivation of Ivy, 1976, (with others) The Old College Try, 1989, Higher Education and Public Policy, 1991, Games Colleges Play, 1994; assoc. editor: (jour.) Higher Eduation: Theory and Research, 1983-91. Pres., bd. dirs. United Way, Williamsburg, 1987-89; pres. Friends of Williamsburg Libr., 1989. Rsch. grantee Spencer Found., 1989-91; Regents fellow U. Calif., 1972. Mem. Assn. for

Study of Higher Edn. (bd. dirs. 1988-90, keynote speaker 1994), History of Edn. Soc. (mem. editl. bd. 1988-91), Phi Beta Kappa. Avocations: long-distance running, history of Los Angeles and California, sports history. Home: 5125 N Pennsylvania St Indianapolis IN 46205 Office: Indiana Univ Sch of Edn Bloomington IN 47401

THEMELIS, NICKOLAS JOHN, metallurgical and chemical engineering educator; b. Athens, Greece. B in Engring., McGill U., Montreal, Que., Can., 1956, PhD, 1961. Registered profl. engr., Conn. Mgr. engring. divsn. Noranda Tech. Ctr., Pointe Claire, Que., 1962-72; v.p. tech. Kennecott Corp., N.Y.C., 1972-80; Stanley-Thompson prof. chem. metallurgy Columbia U., N.Y.C., 1980—. Author 4 books; contbr. articles to profl. jours. Fellow Minerals, Metals and Materials Soc.; mem. NAE, Metallurgical Soc. AIME (3 gold medals). Democrat. Mem. Christian Orthodox Ch. Avocations: sailing, music. Office: Columbia Univ Henry Krumb Sch Mines New York NY 10027

THENO, DANIEL O'CONNELL, former state legislator; b. Ashland, Wis., May 8, 1947; s. Maurice William and Janet Nova (Humphrey) T.; B.S., U. Wis., Madison, 1969; student, Brazil, 1969; m. Sue Burnham, June 16, 1973; children—Scott Patrick, Tad William. Tchr. agr. public schs., Oregon, Wis., 1969-72; mem. Wis. State Senate, 1972-87; mayor, Ashland, 1986—; mem. Wis. Bldg. Commn. Named Superior Hon. Alumni, U. Wis., 1977; recipient Vet. Recognition award, 1978. Mem. Coll. Agr. Alumni Assn., U. Wis. Alumni Assn., Iron Cross Honor Soc., Ashland County Club (Wis.) Elks, K.C. Republican.

THEOBALD, EDWARD ROBERT, lawyer; b. Chgo., Feb. 10, 1947; s. Edward Robert Theobald Jr. and Marie (Turner) Logan; m. Bonnie J. Singer, July 18, 1970; children: Debra Marie, Kimberly Ann. BA, So. Ill. U., 1969; JD, Ill. Inst. Tech., 1974. Bar: Ill. 1974, U.S. Dist. Ct. (no. dist.) Ill. 1974. Asst. state's atty. Cook County, Chgo., 1974-79, supr. felony trial div., 1980-81; assoc. Conklin, Leahy & Eisenberg, Chgo., 1977; ptnr. Boharic & Theobald, Chgo., 1981-83, owner, ptnr., 1983—; legal adv. Sheriff of Cook County, Ill., 1986-89; spl. state's atty. U.S. Dist. Ct. no. dist. Ill., 1989-91; apptd. spl. corp. counsel City of Chgo., 1994. Mem. Parent adv. bd. Downers Grove (Ill.) South H.S., 1992-94. Named Number One Trial Atty. in Felony Trial Div. of Office of Cook County State's Atty., Felony Trial Div. Suprs., 1979. Mem. ABA (sect. on tort and ins. law, sect. on labor and employment law, chmn. com. on sentencing alternatives young lawyers sect. 1982-83, tort and ins. practice sect., labor and employment law sect.), Chgo. Bar Assn. (bd. mgrs. 1985-87, labor and employment law com. 1983—, com. on coms. 1990-94, membership com. 1990—), Ill. Bar Assn., Assn. Trial Lawyers Am., Christian Legal Soc. (bd. dirs. Ill. chpt. 1993—), Civil War Roundtable (Chgo. chpt.). Roman Catholic. Home: 7104 Grand Ave Downers Grove IL 60516-3915 Office: 135 S La Salle St Ste 1246 Chicago IL 60603-4204

THEOBALD, H. RUPERT, retired political scientist; b. Berlin, Mar. 12, 1930; came to U.S., 1950; s. Hans Herman and Marlene (Rackow) T.; m. Elizabeth Joanna Frisella, Nov. 3, 1951; children: H. Michael, Marlies J., Peter J. MA, U. Wis., 1960, PhD, 1971. Rschr. Wis. Legis. Reference Bur., Madison, 1957-60, coord., 1960-63, acting chief, 1963-64, chief, 1964-94; ret., 1994; lay mem. bd. govs. State Bar Wis., 1994—. Editor: Laws of Wisconsin, 1991-94; contbr. articles to profl. jours. Mem. Coun of State Governments, 1963-94 (Charles McCarthy award 1986), Com. on Suggested State Legis., 1964-94.

THEOBALD, THOMAS CHARLES, banker; b. Cin., May 5, 1937; m. Gigi Mahon, Jan. 1987. AB in Econs., Coll. Holy Cross, 1958; MBA in Fin. with high distinction, Harvard U., 1960. With Citibank, N.A. div. Citicorp, 1960-87; vice-chmn. Citicorp, N.Y.C., 1982-87; CEO, chmn. Continental Bank Corp., Chgo. 1987-94; chmn. bd. dirs. Continental Bank N.A., Chgo., 1987-94; ptnr. Blair Capital Mgmt, Chgo., 1994—; bd. dirs. Xerox Corp., Enron Global Power and Pipelines. Trustee Nat. Lekotek Ctr., Mut. of N.Y., Northwestern U.; bd. dirs. Assocs. of Harvard Bus. Sch., Chgo. Coun. on Fgn. Rels.; mem. com. on arch. Art Inst. of Chgo. Mem. Ill. Bus. Roundtable, Comml. Club (civic com.), Chgo. United Inc., Econ. Club (Chgo.). Office: 222 W Adams St Ste 3300 Chicago IL 60606

THEODORE, EUSTACE D., alumni association executive, management consultant; b. Marietta, Ohio, Aug. 4, 1941; s. Demetrios E. and Nicoletta D. T.; m. Carol Nagy, June 13, 1964; children: Kyle James, Graham Clark. B.A., Yale U., 1963; M.A., Cornell U., 1965, Ph.D. 1967. Mem. faculty Hollins Coll., Roanoke, Va., 1967-71, Mt. Holyoke Coll., South Hadley, Mass., 1971-72; dean Calhoun Coll., Yale U., New Haven, 1972-81; exec. dir. Assn. Yale Alumni, 1981—; mgmt. cons., 1965—. Contbr. articles to jours. Recipient NSF-COSIP award, 1966. Mem. Coun. Alumni Assn. Execs. (bd. dirs. 1991—), Coun. for Advancement and Support Edn. (trustee 1992—). Office: Yale U Alumni Assn PO Box 209010 New Haven CT 06520-9010

THEODORE, NICK ANDREW, lieutenant governor; b. Greenville, S.C., Sept. 16, 1928; s. Andrew John and Lula (Meros) T.; m. Emilie Demosthenes, Apr. 25, 1955; children: Drew, Angela, Stephanie. BA, Furman U., 1952. Mem. S.C. Ho. of Reps., Columbia, 1963-66, 69-78, chmn. house edn. and pub. works commn., 1977-78; mem. S.C. Senate, Columbia, 1967-68, 81-86, co-chmn. S.C. edn. fin. act. task force com., chmn. joint legis. study com. on alcohol and drugs, chmn. state employees com., mem. textile commn.; lt. gov. State of S.C., Columbia, 1986-90, 90-94. Past co-dir. ARC; past co-chmn. March of Dimes Campaign; sec. St. George Greek Orthodox Ch., 1955-57; chmn. Commn. on the Future of S.C., 1987-89, Hazardous Waste Task Force, 1987-88. Named Outstanding Young Man Greenville County, 1962, Outstanding Young Man S.C., 1962, Outstanding Rep., S.C. Sch. Bd. Assn., 1976-77, Outstanding Legislator, S.C. Alcohol and Drug Abuse Assn., 1978, Citizen of Yr. S.C. Hosp. Assn.; recipient Friend of Edn. award Phi Kappa Delta, 1987. Mem. Greenville Jaycees (pres. 1957-58). Office: PO Box 1827 Greenville SC 29602-1827

THEODORESCU, RADU AMZA SERBAN, mathematician, educator; b. Bucharest, Romania, Apr. 12, 1933; emigrated to Can., 1968, naturalized, 1975; s. Dan and Ortensia Maria (Butoianu) T.; children: Dan, Paul, Anne. BSc, U. Bucharest, 1954, DSc, 1967; PhD, Acad. Romania, 1958. Asst. prof. Inst. Math. of Acad., Romania, Bucharest, 1954-57, sr. asst. prof. Inst. Math. of Acad., 1957-60, assoc. prof., sci. sec., 1960-64; prof. head dept. Center Math. Statistics, 1964-68; prof. U. Bucharest, 1968-69, Laval U., Quebec, Que., Can., 1969—; guest prof., lectr. univs. in Europe, N.Am. and Australia. Author: (with G. Ciucu) Processes with Complete Connections, 1960, (with S. Guiasu) Mathematical Information Theory, 1968, Uncertainty and Information, 1971, (with M. Iosifescu) Random Processes and Learning, 1969, (with W. Hengartner) Concentration Functions, 1973, 2d edit., 1980, Monte-Carlo Methods, 1978; mem. editorial bd. Annales des Sciences Mathématiques du Québec, Optimization, Statistics and Decisions; contbr. articles to profl. jours. Mem. bd. European Orgn. Quality Control, 1966-69. Recipient prize Acad. Romania, 1960. Fellow Inst. Math. Stats., Am. Soc. Quality Control; mem. Can. Math. Soc., Am. Math. Soc., Internat. Statis. Inst. Home: 9 Jardins Mérici Apt 1603, Quebec, PQ Canada G1S 4S8 Office: Laval U, Dept Math and Stats, Quebec, PQ Canada G1K 7P4

THEODORIDIS, GEORGE CONSTANTIN, biomedical engineering educator, researcher; b. Braila, Romania, Dec. 3, 1935; came to U.S., 1959; s. Constantin George and Anastasia (Haritopoulos) T.; m. Lilly Kate Hyman, Sept. 20, 1975; 1 child, Alexander. BS in Mechanical and Elec. Engring., Nat. Tech. U. Athens, 1959; DSc, MIT, Cambridge, Mass., 1964. Rsch. assoc. MIT, Cambridge, Mass., 1964; sr. scientist Am. Sci. Engring., Cambridge, Mass., 1964-68; assoc. prof. in residence U. Calif., Berkeley, 1968-70; biomedical engring. U. Va., Charlottesville, 1970—; prof. elec. engring. U. Patras, Greece, 1976-83; cons. Food and Drug Adminstrn., Washington, 1975-76, Applied Physics Lab, Columbia, Md., 1978-79. Author: Applied Math, 1983; contbr. articles to profl. jours. Den leader Boy Scouts Am., Charlottesville, Va., 1984-85. Fulbright fellow U.S. Govt., MIT, 1959-60; Nato fellow NATO, MIT, 1961-64; Spl. fellow NIH, U. Calif., 1968-70; recipient teaching award GE, MIT, 1963. Mem. Inst. Elec. and Electronics Engrs., Sigma Xi. Greek Orthodox. Avocations: history, travel. Home:

1817 Fendall Ave Charlottesville VA 22903-1613 Office: U Va Dept Biomed Engring Box 377 Medical Ctr Charlottesville VA 22908

THEODOSIUS, HIS BEATITUDE METROPOLITAN See LAZOR, THEODOSIUS

THEON, JOHN SPERIDON, meteorologist; b. Washington, Dec. 12, 1934; s. Lewis and Merope (Xydias) T.; m. Joanne Edens, July 31, 1965; children—Christopher James, Catherine. B.S. in Aero. Engring, U. Md., 1957; B.S. in Meteorology, Pa. State U., 1959, M.S. 1962; Ph.D. in Engring. Sci. and Mechanics, U. Tenn., 1985. Aero. engr. Douglas Aircraft Co., Santa Monica, Calif., 1957-58; engr. U.S. Naval Ordnance Lab., White Oak, Md., 1962; rsch. meterologist, 1962-74; head meterology br. NASA Goddard Space Flight Center, Greenbelt, Md., 1974-77; asst. chief Lab. for Atmospheric Scis., 1977-78, Nimbus project scientist, 1972-78, Landsat discipline leader meteorol. investigations, 1974-78; mgr. global weather research program NASA Hdqrs., Washington, 1978-82, chief Atmospheric Dynamics and Radiation br., 1982-89; Spacelab 3 program scientist NASA Hdqrs., 1979-86, chmn. space shuttle weather adv. panel, 1985-87; chief atmospheric, dynamics, radiation and hydrol. processes, 1989-93, chief phys. climate br., 1993-94, divsn. program scientist, 1994-95, exec. sec. task force on observations and data mgmt., 1994-95, ret., 1995; exec. sec. task force on observation and data mgmt., 1994—. Contbr. articles to profl. jours. Served with USAF, 1958-60. Recipient Nimbus F Instrument Team award NASA-Goddard, 1976, Goddard Exceptional Performance award, 1978, NASA Exceptional Performance award, 1986, Radio Wave award Ministry of Posts & Telecomm. of Japan, 1995; name Disting. Alumnus U. Tenn. 1989. Fellow Am. Meteorol. Soc., AIAA (assoc. fellow, chmn. atmospheric environment tech. com. 1986-89, Losey Atmos. Sci. award 1986); mem. Am. Geophys. Union, Sigma Xi. Presbyterian. Home: 6801 Lupine Ln Mc Lean VA 22101-1518 Office: 300 E St NW Washington DC 20546-0001

THERMENOS, NICHOLAS, engineering company executive; b. Honolulu, Dec. 30, 1939; s. Nicholas and Helen Mae (Rhine) T.; m. Panagiota Economou, Oct. 14, 1967 (dec. Aug. 1985); children: Nicholas John, Jennifer Lee; m. Gloria Gravel, June 14, 1987. Student, Lafayette Coll., 1963-66; AS in Mech. Engring., Waterbury (Conn.) State Tech. Coll., 1982. Cert. mfg. engr., engring. tech. Sr. designer Harris Intertype Corp., Easton, Pa., 1966-68; design engr. Packer Industries, Meriden, Conn., 1968-71; project engr. Ridson Mfg. Co., Naugatuck, Conn., 1971-75, Cushman Industris, Inc., Hartford, Conn., 1976-79; mgr. spl. products Cushman Industries, Inc., Hartford, Conn., 1986-87; mgr. sales and engring. Powerhold, Inc., Middlefield, Conn., 1979-85; mgr. engring. svcs. Huron Machine Products, Inc., Ft. Lauderdale, 1987-90; pres. ASW Techs., Inc. Middlefield, 1991—; speaker, cons. Workholding Tech., 1981-88, author treatise, 1982. Mem. Boy Scouts Am., Cheshire, Conn., 1974; coun. mem Holy Trinity Greek Orthodox Ch., Waterbury, Conn., 1980-84. Mem. Nat. Inst. for Certification in Engring. Techs., Soc. Mfg. Engrs. (charter, sr., program chmn. Hartford chpt. #7, 1974-76), Computer and Automated Systems Assn. Republican. Avocation: running, remodeling, tennis, skiing, photography. Home: 273 Greenwood Dr Chesire CT 06410-4113 Office: ASW Techs Inc 6 Way Rd Middlefield CT 06455-1003

THERNSTROM, STEPHAN ALBERT, historian, educator; b. Port Huron, Mich., Nov. 5, 1934; s. Albert George and Bernadene (Robbins) T.; m. Abigail Mann, Jan. 3, 1959; children—Melanie Rachel, Samuel Altgeld. B.S., Northwestern U., 1956; A.M., Harvard, 1958, Ph.D. 1962. Instr. history Harvard U., Cambridge, Mass., 1962-66, asst. prof., 1966-67, prof., 1973-81, Winthrop prof., 1981—, chmn. com. on higher degrees in history of Am. civilization, 1985-92; prof. Brandeis U., 1967-69, UCLA, 1969-73; Pitt. prof. Am. history and instns. Cambridge U., 1978-79; dir. Charles Warren Ctr. for Research in Am. History, 1980-83. Author: Poverty and Progress, 1964, Poverty, Planning and Politics in the New Boston, 1969, The Other Bostonians, 1973, History of the American People, 1984, 88; editor: Harvard Ency. Am. Ethnic Groups; co-editor: Harvard Studies in Urban History; Cambridge Interdisciplinary Perspectives on Modern History Series. Recipient Bancroft prize, R.R. Hawkins award, Faculty prize Harvard U. Press, Waldo G. Leland prize; Guggenheim fellow; John M. Olin fellow; ACLS fellow. Office: Harvard U Robinson Hall Cambridge MA 02138

THEROUX, EUGENE, lawyer; b. Medford, Mass., Apr. 29, 1938; s. Albert and Anne (Dittami) T.; m. Phyllis Grissim, Feb. 13, 1963 (div. 1978); children: Christian, Elizabeth, Justin; m. Colleen Marie Pankratz, Feb. 27, 1982; children: Jean-Paul, Alexandra, Sebastien. Student, Harvard U., 1959, 60; BID, Pratt Inst., 1961, LittD, 1982; JD, Georgetown U., 1968. Bar: D.C. 1969, Mass. 1982, Va. 1985. Ptnr. Baker & McKenzie, Washington, 1969—, mem. policy com., 1974-94; spl. counsel joint econ. com. U.S. Congress, Washington, 1972; adv. prof. Fudan U., Shanghai, People's Republic China, 1986—; adv. bd. Fletcher Sch. Law and Diplomacy, 1987—; trustee Monterey Inst. Internat. Studies. Author: (book) Joint Ventures In USSR, 1989, Business Guide To Moscow. 1990. Trustee Am. Leprosy Found., Washington, 1987—; v.p. U.S.-China Bus. Coun., Washington, 1973-75, dir., vice chair of bd., 1991—. 1st lt. inf., U.S. Army, 1962-64, MAC/V So. Vietnam, 1968. Mem. ABA (chair Soviet law com. 1989-91), Army and Navy Club, Univ. Club. Roman Catholic. Avocations: drawings, painting, running. Home: Short Hill Mountain Farm Lovettsville VA 22080 Office: Baker & McKenzie 815 Connecticut Ave NW Washington DC 20006-4004

THEROUX, PAUL EDWARD, author; b. Medford, Mass., Apr. 10, 1941; s. Albert Eugene and Anne (Dittami) T.; m. Anne Castle, Dec. 4, 1967 (div. 1993); children: Marcel, Louis. BA, U. Mass., Amherst, DLitt. 1988; DLitt, Trinity Coll., Washington, 1980, Tufts U., 1980. Lectr. U. Urbino, Italy, 1963, Soche Hill Coll., Malawi, 1963-65; mem. faculty English dept. Makerere U., Uganda, 1965-68, U. Singapore, 1968-71; vis. lectr. U. Va., 1972-73. Author: (fiction) Waldo, 1967, Fong and the Indians, 1968, Girls at Play, Murder in Mt. Holly, 1969, Jungle Lovers, 1971, Sinning with Annie, 1972, Saint Jack, 1973, The Black House, 1974, The Family Arsenal, 1976, The Consul's File, 1977, Picture Palace, 1978 (Whitbread prize for fiction), A Christmas Card, 1978, London Snow, 1980, World's End, 1980, The Mosquito Coast, 1981, The London Embassy, 1982, Half Moon Street, 1984, O-Zone, 1986, My Secret History, 1988, Chicago Loop, 1990, Millroy the Magician, 1993, (nonfiction) V.S. Naipaul, 1973, The Great Railway Bazaar, 1975, The Old Patagonian Express, 1979, The Kingdom by the Sea, 1983, Sailing Through China, 1983, Sunrise with Sea Monsters, 1985, The White Man's Burden, 1987, Riding the Iron Rooster, 1988, The Happy Isles of Oceania, 1992, The Pillars of Hercules, 1995, (film script) Saint Jack, 1979. Recipient Editorial award Playboy mag., 1972, 76, 77, 79, Lit. award AAAL, 1977, James Tait Black award, 1982, Yorkshire Post Best Novel award, 1982, Thomas Cook Travel Book prize, 1989. Fellow Royal Soc. Lit., Royal Geog. Soc.; mem. AAAS.

THESEN, ARNE, industrial engineering educator; b. Oslo, May 6, 1943; came to U.S., 1963; s. Gudbrand and Astrid (Siggerud) T.; m. Maria Tan, Jan. 25, 1969 (div. Dec. 1987); children: Anita Mei-Ling, Britt Wei-Ling; m. Sharon W. Foster, June 21, 1991 (div. Mar. 1994). Student, Schous Tekniske Inst., Oslo, 1961-63; B.S., U. Ill., 1965, M.S., 1968, Ph.D., 1972. Systems analyst Bell Telephone Labs., Piscataway, N.J., 1970-72; prof. dept. indsl. engring. U. Wis.-Madison, 1972—; chmn. dept. indsl. engring., 1978-81, 91—, prof. dept. computer sci., 1981-93; ptnr. Troll Assocs., Madison, 1976-84; prin. Troll Software, Madison, 1984—. Author: Computer Methods in O.R., 1976; co-author: Systems Tools for Planning, 1976, Simulation for Decision Making, 1992; contbr. articles to profl. jours. With Royal Norwegian Air Force, 1965-66. Mem. Ops. Research Soc. Am., Inst. Mgmt. Scis., Assn. Computer Machinery. Home: 4310 Fawn Ct Cross Plains WI 53528-9780 Office: Univ Wis Dept Indsl Engring 1513 University Ave Madison WI 53706-1572

THESING, JAMES J., arts organization executive; b. Cin., Nov. 21, 1941. BA, U. Dayton, 1963; MA, Ohio State U., 1966. Writer Merv Griffin Prodns., N.Y.C., 1972-75, various TV prodn. cos., L.A., N.Y.C., 1975-79; adminstrv. dir. Paper Mill Playhouse, Millburn, N.J., 1979-87; exec. dir. Nat. Alliance Mus. Theatre, N.Y.C., 1987—. Producer (play) A Song for the First of May, 1971; dir. various regional theatre prodns., 1968-78. Emmy award nominee Acad. TV Arts and Scis., 1975. Office: Nat Alliance Mus Theatre Prodrs 330 W 45th St Apt Lb New York NY 10036-3854

THEUNER, DOUGLAS EDWIN, bishop; b. N.Y.C., Nov. 15, 1938; s. Alfred Edwin Kipp and Grace Elizabeth (MacKean) T.; m. Jane Lois Szuhany, May 16, 1959; children: Elizabeth Susan, Nicholas Frederick Kipp. BA, Coll. of Wooster, 1960; BD, Kenyon Coll., 1962; MA, U. Conn., 1968. Ordained to ministry Episcopal Ch. as deacon, then priest, 1962. Curate St. Peter's Episcopal Ch., Ashtabula, Ohio, 1962-65; vicar St. George's Episcopal Ch., Bolton, Conn., 1965-68; rector St. Paul's Episcopal Ch., Wllimantic, Conn., 1968-74, St. John's Episcopal Ch., Stamford, Conn., 1974-86; bishop Diocese of N.H., Concord, 1986—. Chmn. Community Housing Coalition, Stamford, Conn., 1975-86, Instituto Pastoral Hispano, N.Y.C., 1979-86; pres. Holderness (N.H.) Sch., 1987—, White Mountain Sch., Littleton, N.H., 1987—. Mem. N.H. Coun. Chs. (v.p.). Avocations: photography, cooking, hiking, skiing. Office: Concord Diocese Diocesan Office 63 Green St Concord NH 03301-4243

THIBADEAU, EUGENE FRANCIS, educator, consultant; b. N.Y.C., May 18, 1933; s. Eugene Servanis and Lillian (Archer) T.; m. Christine; m. Patricia M. Batchelder, March 16, 1993. BA, NYU, 1959, MA, 1967; MA, NYU, 1968, PhD, 1973. Instr. NYU, N.Y.C., 1968; lectr. in philosophy Dowling Coll., Oakdale, N.Y., 1968-70; prof. edn. Indiana U. of Pa., Indiana, Pa., 1970—; vis. assoc. prof. Adelphi U., Garden City, N.Y., 1974-75; vis. scholar NYU, N.Y.C., 1984-85; vis. prof. Hofstra U., Hempstead, N.Y., 1974, 75, 84, 86; cons. Central Bur. of Ednl. Visits, London, 1980-81, Commonwealth Speakers Bur., Harrisburg, Pa., 1983-85, U.S. Dept. Edn., Washington, 1983-85, Pa. Dept. Edn., Harrisburg, 1988—. Author: Opening Up Education-In Theory and Practice, 1976, Curriculum Theory, 1988, Existentialism in the Classroom, 1994; rev. editor: Focus on Learning, 1973-77, editor, 1977-84; contbg. editor: International Encyclopedia of Education, 2d edit.; contbr. articles to profl. jours. Active in United Way, Indiana, Pa., 1980—, NAACP, Indiana, 1985—, Red Cross, Indiana, 1985—. Fulbright sr. lectr. Thames Polytechnic, London, 1978-79, Janus Pannonius U., Peces, Hungary, 1990-91; foreign expert Educational U. (China) Tchrs. U., 1988; designated faculty rsch. assoc. Inst. for Applied Rsch. and Pub. Policy, Indiana U. of Pa., 1989; named Commonwealth Teaching fellow, Pa. State Colls. and Univ. Disting. Faculty Awards Com., 1976; recipient Founder's Day award, NYU, 1973. Fellow Am. Philosophy Edn. Soc.; mem. Am. Ednl. Studies Assn., AAUP, The S.W. Philosophy Edn. Soc., ASCD. Avocations: traveling, skiing, tennis, reading, chess. Home: RR 1 Box 103 Penn Run PA 15765-9733 Office: Indiana Univ of Pa 133 Stouffer Hall Indiana PA 15701

THIBAUDEAUX, MARY FRANCES, cultural organization administrator; b. Anaconda, Mont., Dec. 6, 1943; d. Frank Albert and Mary (May) T.; m. Alex W. Wells, Jr.; 1 child, Christopher. BA magna cum laude, U. Washington, Seattle, 1969. Therapist, counselor Thibaudeaux and Assocs., Atlanta, 1976-88; chmn. Vietnam Reconciliation Bus. Group, Atlanta, 1988—; cons. Ga. Vets. Leadership Program, Atlanta, 1994. Exec. producer (documentary) Vietnam: The Final Healing, 1991; co-author, editor (screenplay) Perfume River, 1995. Exchange dir. Friendship Force Internat., Atlanta, 1993-94. Named Ga. Outstanding Citizen, Ga. Sec. State, 1994. Mem. Atlanta Vets. Assn. (hon.). Avocations: travel, reading, languages, hiking, photography. Home: 185 Softwood Cir Roswell GA 30076

THIBAULT, J(OSEPH) LAURENT, service company executive; b. Sturgeon Falls, Ont., Can., Dec. 31, 1944; s. J. Rene and Leone (Doucet) T.; m. Paulette Patricia Lalonde, June 4, 1966; children—Alain, Andre. B.A. in Econs., Laurentian U., Sudbury, 1966; M.A. in Econs., U. Toronto, Ont. 1968. Cons. Kates, Peat & Marwick Co., Toronto, 1968-72; dir. econs. and communications Can. Mfrs. Assn., Toronto, 1972-76; v.p. Can. Mfrs. Assn., 1976-81, sr. exec. v.p., 1981-84, pres., exec. dir., 1985-91; co-chair Can. Labour Force Devel. Bd., Ottawa, Ont., Can., 1991—. Club: National. Home: 24 Cindebarke Terr, Georgetown, ON Canada L7G 4S5 Office: Can Labour Force Devel Bd, 66 Slater St, Ottawa, ON Canada K1P 5H1

THIBEDEAU, RICHARD HERBERT, environmental planner, administrator; b. Needham, Mass., Apr. 2, 1942; s. Richard and Mary (Neenan) T.; m. Susan McAllister Richardson, Nov. 8, 1986; children: Susan, Richard, Catherine, Julie, Billy. BSFS, Georgetown U., 1964; M of Internat. Rels., U. Pa., 1967; M of Regional Planning, Harvard U., 1974. Field rep. CARE, Sri Lanka, 1967-70; asst. county dir. CARE, Korea, 1971-72; chief pvt. land planning Adirondack Park Agy., Ray Brook, N.Y., 1974-78; dep. dir. Mass. Coastal Zone Mgmt., Boston, 1978-80; chief planner Mass. Divsn. Water Resources, Boston, 1981-87, dir., 1987-90; dir. Bur. Resource Protection Dept. Environ. Mgmt., Boston, 1990—; Reservist Fed. Emergency Mgmt. Agy., 1992—; chmn. Conn. River Flood Control Commn., Vt., N.H., Mass. and Conn., 1993-94. Clk. 45 Trowbridge Condominium Assn., Cambridge, 1991—. 1st lt. U.S. Army, 1964-66, Korea. Recipient Mass. Citation for Outstanding Performance, 1988, Mass. Cert. Performance, State Gov., 1990. Mem. Am. Planning Assn. (Disting. Leadership award N.E. chpt. 1989), Am. Inst. Cert. Planners (cert.), Am. Water Assn., Appalachian Mountain Club (com. chmn. 1986—). Avocations: hiking, sailing, skiing. Home: 15 Village St Marblehead MA 01945-2212 Office: Mass Dept Environ Mgmt 100 Cambridge St Boston MA 02202-0001

THIBERT, ROGER JOSEPH, clinical chemist, educator; b. Tecumseh, Ont., Can., Aug. 29, 1929; s. Charles and Violet (Hebert) T.; m. Audrey M. Wissler, July 10, 1954; children: Mark Roger, Robert Francis. BA, U. Western Ont., 1951; MS, U. Detroit, 1954; PhD, Wayne State U., 1958. Diplomate: Am. Bd. Clin. Chemistry, also past bd. dirs. Mem. faculty U. Windsor, Ont., Can., 1953—; prof. chemistry U. Windsor, 1967-94, dir. clin. chemistry, 1972-94, prof. emeritus, 1994—; prof. pathology Med. Sch. Wayne State U., Detroit, 1972-94; assoc. dir. head, clin. chemistry Detroit Receiving Hosp., Univ. Health Center, 1972-94; mem. med. staff Detroit Receiving Hosp.-Univ. Health Center, 1973—. Contbr. articles on chemistry, biochemistry, analytical chemistry, clin. chemistry to profl. jours. Recipient Smith Kline award Am. Assn. Clin. Chemistry, 1980, Alumni Teaching award U. Windsor, 1988, Alumni Award of Merit, 1994, Teaching award Ont. Confedn. U. Faculty Assns., 1990, Beckman Edn. Excellence award Canadian Soc. Clin. Chemists, 1992; Chem. Inst. Can. fellow, 1968—; Nat. Acad. Clin. Biochemistry fellow, 1978—; recipient grants Natural Scis. and Engring. Rsch. Coun., Can., award Union Carbide, Chem. Inst., Can., 1978. Fellow AAAS, Can. Acad. Clin. Biochemistry; mem. Am. Chem. Soc., Chem. Inst. Can., Assn. Chem. Profession Ont. Am. Assn. Clin. Chemistry, Nat. Acad. Clin. Biochemistry, Can. Soc. Clin. Chemists (Ames award 1988), Ont. Soc. Clin. Chemists, Am. Soc. for Biochemistry and Molecular Biology, Fedn. Am. Socs. Exptl. Biology, Can. Biochem. Soc., Can. Fedn. Biol. Scis., Can. Assn. Univ. Tchrs., Can. Soc. for Chemistry, Sigma Xi. Roman Catholic. Home: 4612 Dali Ct, Windsor, ON Canada N9G 2M8 Office: U Windsor, Dept Chemistry/Biochemistry, Windsor, ON Canada N9B 3P4

THIBODEAU, GARY A., university administrator; b. Sioux City, Iowa, Sept. 26, 1938; m. Emogene J. McCarville, Aug. 1, 1964; children: Douglas James, Beth Ann. BS, Creighton U., 1962; MS, S.D. State U., 1967, S.D. State U., 1970; PhD, S.D. State U., 1971. Profl. service rep. Baxter Lab., Inc., Deerfield, Ill., 1963-65; tchr., researcher dept. biology S.D. State U., Brookings, 1965-76, asst. to v.p. for acad. affairs, 1976-80, v.p. for adminstrn., 1980-85; chancellor U. Wis., River Falls, 1985—; mem. investment com. U. Wis., River Falls Found.; trustee W. Cen. Wis. Consortium U. Wis. System; bd. dirs. U. Wis. at River Falls Found.; mem. Phi Kappa Phi nat. budget rev. and adv. comm., Phi Kappa Phi Found. investment comm., comm. on Agrl. and Rural Devel., steering commn. Coun. of Rural Colls. and Univs., Joint Coun. on Food and Agrl. Scis., USDA. Author: Textbook of Anatomy and Physiology, 1993, Basic Concepts in Anatomy and Physiology, 1983, Athletic Injury Assessment, 1989, Structure and Function of the Body, 1992, The Human Body in Health and Disease, 1992. Mem. AAAS, Sigma Xi, Phi Epsilon Phi, Gamma Sigma Delta, Gamma Alpha. Office: U Wis 116 N Hall River Falls WI 54022

THIEBAUD, WAYNE, artist; b. Mesa, Ariz., Nov. 15, 1920; s. Morton J. and Alice Eugenia (LeBaron) T.; m. Betty Jean Carr, Dec. 11, 1959; children: Twinka, Mallary Ann, Paul LeBaron. B.A.. Sacramento State Coll., 1951, M.A., 1952; D.F.A. (hon.), Calif. Coll. Arts and Crafts, 1975. Art dir. N.Y.C.; also Hollywood, 1946-49; chmn. art dept. Sacramento City Coll., 1951; design cons. Calif. State Fair and Expn.; guest instr. San Francisco Art Inst., 1958; assoc. prof. art U. Calif. at Davis, now prof., Emeritus lectr. from 1973; vis. artist Cornell U., U. Hawaii, U. Wis., U. Utah, U. Ill.,

Yale, U. Va., Bradley U. One man shows include, Crocker Art Gallery, Sacramento, 1952, Artists Coop. Gallery, Sacramento, 1954, DeYoung Mus., San Francisco, 1962, Allan Stone Gallery, N.Y.C., 1962-70, Stanford, 1965, Galleria Schwarz, Milan, Italy, 1963, San Francisco Mus., 1967, Whitney Mus., 1972, Walker Art Ctr., Mpls., 1981, Ft. Worth Art Mus., 1981, Mus. Fine Arts, St. Petersburg, Fla., 1981, exhibited museums, U.S., Toronto, Can., Hague, Holland, Vienna, Berlin, Hong Kong, S.Am., traveling exhibit, Pasadena Mus. Art, 1967-68; one-man traveling exhibit Survey of Works, Oakland Mus., Phoenix Mus., U. So. Calif., Des Moines Mus., Boston Inst. Contemporary Art, 1976; U.S. rep. one-man traveling exhibit, Sao Paulo Biennale, 1966, Indocumenta, 1972; group exhbns. include, Santa Barbara Mus. Art, 1980, Bklyn. Mus., 1980, 81, Whitney Mus. Am. Art, 1981, San Antonio Mus. Art, 1981, Indpls. Mus. Art, 1981, Inst. Contemporary Art, U. Pa., 1981, Carnegie Inst., Pitts., 1981, Allan Stone Gallery, N.Y.C., 1982; represented permanent collections museums and galleries, Europe, U.S., including, Mus. Modern Art, Whitney Mus., Albright Knox Mus., Wadsworth Athenaeum, Library Congress, Woodward Found., Rose Art Mus., Brandeis U., Stanford, also numerous pvt. collections, commd. fountain mobile sculpture, Calif. State Fair, 1952, Sacramento Municipal Utility Dist. Bldg., 1959; producer, dir. 12 ednl. motion pictures. (Recipient 1st prize Art Film Festival 1956, Golden Reel Film Festival award for Space, Calif. State Fair 1956, named Univ. Art Studio Tchr. of Yr., Coll. Art Assn. Am. 1981, Faculty Research medal U. Calif.-Davis, 1984, Award of Distinction, Nat. Art Schs. Assn., 1984, Spl. Citation, Nat. Assn. Schs. Art and Design, 1984); commd. to do paintings of Wimbledon Tennis Tournament, 1968, of Yosemite Ridge Line for Bicentennial Exhbn., 1976; sent to Kyoto, Japan to do woodblock prints by Crown Point Press, 1987; 42 works on paper at Arts Club Chgo., 1987. Author: etchings Delights, 1965, Prints, 1970-71, Seven Still Lifes and a Rabbit. Recipient Cyril Magnin award, San Francisco, 1987, Golden Plate award Am. Acad. Achievement, 1987, Nat. Medal of the Arts, 1994. Mem. Am. Acad. and Inst. Arts and Letters, Nat. Acad. Design (academician). "Wayne Thiebaud" exhbn. organized by San Francisco Mus. Modern Art for 50th anniversary, 1985, scheduled to travel to Newport Harbor, R.I., Milw., Columbus, Ohio and Kansas City. Office: Care Allan Stone Galle New York NY 10028

THIEL, ARTHUR WARREN, journalist; b. Hot Springs, Mont., Nov. 27, 1952; s. Robert Harry and Mary (Previs) T.; m. Julia Claire Akoury, July 16, 1988. BA, Pacific Luth. U., 1975. Reporter News Tribune, Tacoma, 1972-76; reporter, asst. sports editor Jour. Am., Bellevue, Wash., 1976-80; reporter, columnist Post-Intelligencer, Seattle, 1980—; commentator, analyst Sta. KIRO, Seattle, 1989—; commentator Sta. KZOK-FM, Seattle, 1991—. Bd. dirs. Alzheimers Assn. Western and Ctrl Wash., Seattle, 1990—. Named State Sportswriter of Yr., Nat. Sportswriter & Sportscasters Assn., 1990, 92, Disting. Alumnus, Pacific Luth. U., 1991. Avocations: sea kayaking, gardening, adventure travel. Office: Seattle Post-Intelligencer 101 Elliott Ave W Seattle WA 98119

THIEL, PHILIP, design educator; b. Bklyn., Dec. 20, 1920; s. Philip and Alma Theone (Meyer) T.; m. Midori Kono, 1955; children: Philip Kenji, Nancy Tamiko, Susan Akiko, Peter Akira (dec.). BSc, Webb Inst. Naval Architecture, 1943; MSc, U. Mich., 1948; BArch, MIT, 1952. Instr. design MIT, Cambridge, 1949-50; instr. U. Calif., Berkeley, 1954-56, asst. prof., 1956-60; assoc. prof. U. Wash., Seattle, 1961-66; prof. visual design and experiential notation U. Wash., 1966-91; guest prof. Tokyo Inst. Tech., 1976-78; prof. Sapporo (Japan) Sch. of Arts, 1992—; lectr., U.S., Can. Japan, Norway, Denmark, Sweden, Eng., Austria, Switzerland, Peru, Bolivia; cons. FAO, Rome, 1952; co-founder Environment and Behavior, 1969; founder Ctr. for Experiential Notation, Seattle, 1981; patentee in field. Soc. Naval Architects and Marine Engrs. scholar, 1947; Rehmann scholar AIA, 1960; NIMH grantee, 1967; Nat. Endowment for Arts grantee, 1969.

THIEL, THELMA KING, foundation executive; b. East Orange, N.J., Feb. 12, 1926; d. Thaddeus and Elizabeth Clara (Fickert) King; m. Charles T. Thiel, Mar. 25, 1954 (div. 1976); children: Mark Douglas, Donna Kalani, Dean Alan (dec.). B.A in Health Edn. and Sch. Nursing, Jersey City State Coll., 1973. Cert. health educator, N.J. Exec. dir. Am. Council for Healthful Living, East Orange, 1973-79; commr. Nat. Com. of Digestive Diseases, Bethesda, Md., 1977-79; founder, chair Dean Thiel Found., Cedar Grove, N.J., 1971—; vice chmn. exec. dir. Am. Liver Found., Cedar Grove, N.J., 1979-84, pres., COO, 1984-94; founder, chair, CEO Hepatitis Found. Internat., 1994—. active Nat. Digestive Diseases Adv. Bd.; advisor Nat. Digestive Diseases Edn. and Info. Clearinghouse; charter mem. Rutgers U. Sch. Communication, Info. and Library Studies Bd. of Adv. Assocs. Author: Foundation for Decision Making, 1978. Mem. AAUW, Digestive Diseases Nat. Coalition (chmn. 1985-90, chmn. Nat. Health Coun., nom. com. 1989-91), Am. Nursing Assn., Soroptimist Internat., Am. Assn. Occupational Health Nurses, Nat. Soc. Fund Raising Execs. Presbyterian (elder). Office: 30 Sunrise Terr Cedar Grove NJ 07009-1423

THIELE, HOWARD NELLIS, JR., lawyer; b. Dayton, Ohio, June 22, 1930; s. Howard Nellis and Irma Laura (Schiebe) T.; m. Joan Elizabeth Smith, Dec. 28, 1950; children: Leslie, Howard III, Craig. AB, Miami U., Oxford, Ohio, 1952; JD with distinction, U. Mich., 1955. Bar: Ohio 1955. Assoc., ptnr. Smith & Schnacke, LPA, Dayton, Ohio, 1955-89; ptnr. Thompson, Hine & Flory, Dayton, 1989—. Pres. Dayton Art Inst., 1981-85; v.p., gen. counsel Jr. Achievement; bd. dirs. Dayton Area chpt. ARC, 1983—, 1st vice chmn., 1990-91, chmn., 1992-94. Capt. USAF, 1955-57. Mem. ABA, Ohio State Bar Assn., Dayton Bar Assn., Order of the Coif, Dayton Racquet Club, Engineers Club, Phi Beta Kappa. Republican. Episcopalian.

THIELE, PAUL FREDERICK, mining company executive; b. Appleton, Wis., Aug. 5, 1914; s. William Frederick and Villa (Crawford) T.; m. Bernice Hoppe, Aug. 21, 1936 (dec.); 1 child, Lessie Elaine. BSEE, U. Wis., 1936. Test engr. GE, 1936-38; with dept. sales quotations GE, Schenectady, N.Y., 1938; elec. engr. Combined Locks (Wis.) Paper Co., 1938-41; engr. Inst. Paper Chemistry, Appleton, 1946; mgr., treas.-sec. Thiele Kaolin Co., Sandersville, Ga., 1947-60, CEO, pres., chmn. bd., 1960-87, CEO, chmn. bd., 1987—. Mem. adv. coun. Office State Supt. Schs., Atlanta, 1978-79; exec. bd. Cen. Ga. coun. Boy Scouts Am.; Macon; chmn. Hosp. Authority Washington County, Sandersville; bd. dirs., mem. Community Concert Assn., Sandersville. With USNR, 1942-45. Recipient Silver Beaver award Boy Scouts Am., Hon. Alumni award Brewton-Parker Coll., 1991. Mem. Am. Mgmt. Assn., Tech. Assn. Pulp and Paper Industry, Ga. Mining Assn. (past pres., bd. dirs.), China Clay Producers Assn., Clay Minerals Soc., Ga. Bus. and Industry Assn. (v.p. bd. dirs., Entrepreneur of Yr. award 1979), Ga. Found. for Ind. Colls. (chmn., bd. dirs. 1979-81), Washington County Hist. Soc. (chmn. fin. com. 1979-80). Office: Thiele Kaolin Co PO Box 1056 Sandersville GA 31082-1056

THIELSCH, HELMUT JOHN, engineering company executive; b. Berlin, Nov. 16, 1922; came to U.S., 1939, naturalized, 1944; s. Kurt and Anna-Sibylle T.; m. Margaret E. McKenna, Aug. 16, 1952; children: Barbara Anne, Donald Kurt, Deborah Lee, Helmut John. BS, Auburn U., 1943; postgrad., U. Mich., 1943-45, Lehigh U., 1948. Registered profl. engr., R.I., Mass., Maine, N.J., Ga., Calif. Research engr. Allis Chalmers Co., Milw., 1945-46; metall. engr. Black, Sivalls & Bryson, Inc., Kansas City, Mo., 1946-47; research engr. Lukens Steel Co., Coatsville, Pa., 1948-49; engr. Welding Research Council, N.Y.C., 1949-52; dir. research Eutectic Welding Alloys Co., N.Y.C., 1952-53; v.p., dir. research, devel. and engring. ITT Grinnell Corp., Providence, 1954-84; pres. Thielsch Engring., Inc., Providence, 1984—; pres. HiTech Realty Assocs. Inc.; cons. on failure analysis to industry, public utilities, equipment builders, 1954—; lectr. at confs. on failures and failure prevention; mem. component tech. com. Argonne (Ill.) Nat. Lab.; bd. dirs. Ind. Energy, Inc. Author: Defects and Failures in Pressure Vessels and Piping, 1965; contbr. numerous articles to profl. publs.; patentee in field. Recipient Nat. Safety award Nat. Bd. Boiler and Pressure Vessel Insps., 1990. Fellow ASME, Am. Soc. Metals, Am. Soc. Nondestructive Testing, Am. Welding Soc. (Adams Lecture award 1982); mem. TAPPI, Am. Soc. Quality Control, Am. Nuclear Soc., Nat. Assn. Corrosion Engrs., Am. Chem. Soc., Am. Mgmt. Assn., Am. Soc. Profl. Engrs. (Freeman award 1985). Office: 195 Frances Ave Cranston RI 02910-2211

THIEMANN, CHARLES LEE, banker; b. Louisville, Nov. 21, 1937; s. Paul and Helen (Kern) T.; m. Donna Timperman, June 18, 1960; children: Laura Gerette, Charles Lee, Rodney Gerard, Jeffrey Michael, Matthew Joseph. BA in Chemistry, Bellarmine Coll., 1959; MBA, Ind. U., 1961, DBA, 1963. Mem. faculty Grad. Sch. Bus. and Grad. Sch. Savs. and Loan, Ind. U., Bloomington, 1959-61; mgmt. cons., 1961-63; mem. rsch. dept. Fed. Res. Bank, St. Louis, 1963-64; with Fed. Home Loan Bank, Cin., 1964—, sr. v.p., then exec. v.p., 1974, pres., 1975—; adj. prof. Grad. Sch. Bus., Xavier U., Cin., bus. adv. coun. univ. Coll. Bus. Adminstrn.; faculty Sch. Mortgage Banking, Northwestern U.; trustee Fin. Instns. Retirement Fund, Leadership Group Social Compact, First Step Home; chmn. Resolution Funding Corp. Directorate. Past mem. Mayor of Cin. Housing Com.; past chmn. real estate exec. adv. coun. U. Cin. Mem. Cin. C. of C., Queen City Club, Rotary. Roman Catholic. Office: Fed Home Loan Bank 221 E 4th St Cincinnati OH 45202-4124

THIEMANN, RONALD FRANK, dean, religion educator; b. St. Louis, Oct. 4, 1946; s. Frank Joseph and Marie Magdalene (Graeser) T.; m. Beth Arlene Barkow, June 15, 1968; children: Sarah Elizabeth, Laura Kristen. B.A. magna cum laude, Concordia Sr. Coll., Fort Wayne, Ind., 1968; M.Div., Concordia Sem., St. Louis, 1972; M.A., Yale U., 1973, M.Philosophy, 1974, Ph.D., 1976; postgrad., Eberhard-Karls Universitat, Tubingen, W.Ger., 1974-75. Asst. prof. dept. religion Haverford Coll., Pa., 1976-82, assoc. prof. dept. religion, 1982-85, prof. dept. religion, 1985-86, acting provost, 1985, acting pres., 1986; dean Div. Sch. Harvard U., Cambridge, Mass., 1986—; John Lord O'Brian prof. divinity Harvard U., Cambridge, 1986—; vis. prof. honors program Villanova U., 1981; vis. asst. prof. Luth. Theol. Sem., Phila., 1977; mem. Ctr. Theol. Inquiry, Princeton, N.J., 1982-83; mem. consultation on Christianity and Marxism, U.S.A. nat. com. Luth. World Fedn., 1979-83, mem. consultation on civil religion, 1983-86, mem. consultation on problem of common good, 1985-88; bd. dirs. Trinity Press Internat.; mem. exec. com. Assn. Theol. Schs., 1994—. Author: Revelation and Theology, 1985, Constructing a Public Theology: The Church in a Pluralistic Culture, 1991, Religion in American Public Life: A Dilemma for Democracy, 1995; editor: The Legacy of H. Richard Niebuhr, 1991; mem. editl. bd. Dialog, 1987—; contbr. numerous articles to profl. jours. Mem. bd. trustees Buckingham Browne & Nichols Schs., 1988-90; mem. task force on theol. education, Evang. Luth. Ch. in Am., 1989-91, task force on Luth.-Reformed Conversations, Evang. Luth. Ch. Am., 1988-92. Recipient Disting. Teaching award Lindback Found., 1982; Mellon Found. fellow, 1982-83; Deutscher Akademischer Austauschdienst fellow, 1974-75. Mem. Am. Acad. Religion, (chmn. narrative interpretation and theology group 1982-86). Avocations: tennis; squash; piano. Home: 44 Francis Ave Cambridge MA 02138-1912 Office: Harvard Div Sch 45 Francis Ave Cambridge MA 02138-1994

THIER, SAMUEL OSIAH, physician, educator; b. Bklyn., June 23, 1937; s. Sidney and May Henrietta (Kanner) T.; m. Paula Dell Finkelstein, June 28, 1958; children: Audrey Lauren, Stephanie Ellen, Sara Leslie. Student, Cornell U., 1953-56; MD, SUNY, Syracuse, 1960, DSc (hon.), 1987; DSc (hon.), Tufts U., 1988, Mt. Sinai Sch. Medicine, CUNY, 1988, George Washington U., 1989, Hahnemann U., 1989, U. Pa., 1994; LHD (hon.), Rush U., 1988, Va. Commonwealth U., 1992, Med. Coll. Pa., 1992, Brandeis U., 1994. Diplomate: Am. Bd. Internal Medicine (dir. 1977-85, exec. com. 1981-85, chmn. 1984-85). Intern Mass. Gen. Hosp., Boston, 1960-61; asst. resident Mass. Gen. Hosp., 1961-62, sr. resident, 1964-65, clin. and research fellow, 1965, chief resident, 1966; clin. assoc. Nat. Inst. Arthritis and Metabolic Diseases, 1962-64; from instr. to asst. prof. medicine Harvard U. Med. Sch., 1967-69; prof. medicine, health care policy Harvard Med. Sch., 1994—; asst. in medicine, chief renal unit Mass. Gen. Hosp., Boston, 1967-69; asso. prof., then prof. medicine U. Pa. Med. Sch., 1969-74, vice chmn. dept., 1971-74; assoc. dir. med. svcs. Hosp. U. Pa., 1969-71; David Paige Smith prof. medicine Yale U. Sch. Medicine, 1978-81, Sterling prof. medicine, 1981-85, chmn. dept., 1975-85; pres. Inst. Medicine NAS, Washington, 1985-91; Univ. prof. Brandeis U., Waltham, Mass., 1991-94; pres. Mass. Gen. Hosp., Boston, 1994—, Ptnrs. HealthCare Sys., Inc., Boston, 1994—; prof. medicine, prof. health care policy Harvard Medical Sch., 1994—; chief medicine Yale-New Haven Hosp., 1975-85, trustee, 1978-85; bd. dirs. Conn. Hospice, Inc., 1976-82. Mem. editorial bd.: New Eng. Jour. Medicine, 1978-81; Contbr. articles to med. jours. Mem. adv. com. to the dir. NIH, 1980-85. Served with USPHS, 1962-64. Recipient Christian R. and Mary F. Lindback Found. Distinguished Teaching award, 1971. Fellow ACP (bd. regents 1982-85); mem. Assn. Am. Med. Colls. (adminstrv. bd. council acad. socs.), John Morgan Soc., Am. Fedn. Clin. Research (pres. 1976-77), Am. Soc. Nephrology, Am. Physiol. Soc., Inst. Medicine, Nat. Acad. Scis., Internat. Soc. Nephrology, Assn. Profs. Medicine, Assn. Am. Physicians, Interurban Clin. Club; Alpha Omega Alpha. Home: 99-20 Florence St # 4B Chestnut Hill MA 02167

THIERRY, JOHN ADAMS, heavy machinery manufacturing company executive, lawyer; b. Watertown, Mass., May 8, 1913; s. Louis Sidney and Adelaide (Hamlin) T.; m. Mary Mills Hatch, June 6, 1953 (div.); 1 child, Charles Adams; m. Silvie Marie Frère, Dec. 1977. A.B. summa cum laude, Harvard U., 1935, A.M., 1936, J.D., 1940; postgrad. (Sheldon traveling fellow Harvard), U. Cambridge, Eng., 1936-37. Bar: Mass. 1941. With Bucyrus-Erie Co., South Milwaukee, Wis., 1940-82; sec. Bucyrus-Erie Co., 1958-77, gen. atty., 1958-76, v.p., 1960-77, sr. v.p., 1977-78, dir., 1961-79, mem. exec. com., 1967-78; v.p. dir. Bucyrus Erie Co. Can., Ltd., 1959-78; dir. Ruston-Bucyrus Ltd., Lincoln, Eng., 1964-79, Komatsu-Bucyrus K.K., Japan, 1971-81; former dir. Bucyrus (Australia) Pty. Ltd., Bucyrus Internat., Inc., Brad Foot Gear Works, Inc., Pitts. Gear Co., South Milw. Marine Bank, Atlas Chain & Precision. Dir. Wis. Pub. Expenditure Survey, 1954-78; v.p., bd. dirs. Bucyrus-Erie Found., 1963-78; bd. dirs. Pub. Expenditure Research Found., 1964-78, YMCA, Milw., 1973-78, Milw. Symphony Orch., 1974-78; trustee Wis. Conservatory Music, 1969-78, S.E. Asia Art Found., 1977—; pres. United Performing Arts Fund, Milw., 1969; mem. adv. council Coll. Engrng. U. Wis.-Milw., 1975-78, mem. adv. council Sch. Bus., 1975-78; mem. council Med. Coll. Wis., 1975-78; pres. Milw. Patent Law Assn. 1961-62. Served to capt., C.E. AUS, 1942-46. Recipient Granite State award U. N.H., 1986. Mem. Mass. Wis. patent office bars, Cambridge Union Soc., Phi Beta Kappa. Episcopalian. Club: Harvard (Boston and N.Y.C.). Home: Murray Hill Rd Hill NH 03243-9711

THIERS, HARRY DELBERT, biology educator, research mycologist; b. Ft. McKavett, Tex.; married, 1953; 1 child. AB, Schreiner Inst., 1938; BA, U. Tex., 1941, MA, 1947; PhD, U. Mich., 1955. Asst. U. Tex., 1945-47; instr. botany and mycology Tex. A&M U., 1947-50, asst. biology, 1950-55, assoc. prof., 1955-59; assoc. prof., 1959-63; prof. biology San Francisco State U., 1963—; assoc. plant pathologist USDA, 1948. Mem. Botany Soc. Am., Mycology Soc. Am. (disting. mycologist award 1990), Am. Bryol. & Lichenological Soc. Research in taxonomy of fleshy fungi of California and West Coast of North America. Office: San Francisco State U Dept of Biology 1600 Holloway Ave San Francisco CA 94132*

THIES, AUSTIN COLE, retired utility company executive; b. Charlotte, N.C., July 18, 1921; s. Oscar Julius and Blanche (Austin) T.; m. Marilyn Joy Walker, June 26, 1945 (dec. Dec. 1992); children: Austin Cole, Robert Melvin, Marilyn Leone; m. Fay Best Britt, May 7, 1993; stepchildren: Jeff Britt, Mike Britt. BSME, Ga. Inst. Tech., 1943. With Duke Power Co., Charlotte, 1946-86; mgr. steam prodn. Duke Power Co., 1963-65, asst. v.p., 1965-67, v.p. prodn. and operation, 1967-71, sr. v.p., 1971-82, exec. v.p., 1982-86, also dir.; past chmn. prodn. com., engrng. and operating div. Southeastern Electric Exchange; chmn. tech. advisory com. Carolinas Va. Nuclear Power Assos.; chmn. N.C. Air Control Advisory Council. Mem. nat. adv. bd. Ga. Inst. Tech.; pres. Arts and Scis. Council; chmn. bd. dirs. Mercy Hosp.; trustee Alexander Childrens Center; bd. visitors Boy's Town.; 1st v.p. Sci. Museums of Charlotte; bd. dirs. Sci. Mus. Served with USNR, 1943-46. Decorated Purple Heart; named to Ga. Tech. Hall of Fame, 1994. Mem. Edison Electric Inst. (past chmn. engrng. and operating div. exec. com.), IEEE, Charlotte C. of C., ASME (past chmn. Piedmont Carolina sect.), Am. Nuclear Soc., Air Pollution Control Assn., N.C. Soc. Engrs. (past pres., Engr. of Yr. 1985), Charlotte Engrs. Club (Disting. Service award 1984), Nat. Rifle Assn. (life), Kappa Sigma. Presbyterian (elder). Clubs: Rotary (past pres., dir. N. Charlotte), Cowans Ford Country (bd. dirs.), Quail Hollow Country (bd. dirs.), Charlotte City (bd. dirs.), Charlotte Ga. Inst. Tech. (past pres.), Charlotte Rifle and Pistol (past pres.). Home: 2429

Red Fox Trl Charlotte NC 28211-3766 Office: 422 S Church St Charlotte NC 28242-0001

THIES, RICHARD BRIAN, lawyer; b. Chgo., Dec. 14, 1943; s. Fred W. and Loraine C. (Mannix) T.; m. Anita Marie Rees, Aug. 5, 1972; children: Emily Marie, Richard Clarke. BA, Miami U., 1966; JD, Loyola U., 1974. Bar: Ill. 1974, U.S. Tax Ct. 1989. Assoc. Wilson & McIlvaine, Chgo., 1974-78; assoc.-ptnr. Isham, Lincoln & Beale, Chgo., 1978-88; ptnr. Wildman, Harrold, Allen & Dixon, Chgo., 1988—. Bd. govs. Chgo. HEart Assn., 1980-87, exec. com., 1982-87; bd. dirs. Juvenile Protective Assn., Chgo., 1984—; v.p. Samaritan Counseling Ctr., Evanston, 1989-94, pres., 1994. Mem. ABA, Chgo. Bar Assn., Chgo. Estate Planning Coun. Avocations: coaching children's sports, photography, music. Home: 305 Driftwood Ln Wilmette IL 60091-3441 Office: Wildman Harrold Allen & Dixon 225 W Wacker Dr Chicago IL 60606-1224

THIESEN, GREGORY ALAN, accountant; b. Denver, Apr. 24, 1958; s. Gene Duane and Virginia Ruth (Haas) T.; m. Karen Elise McGrew, Aug. 17, 1984; children: Jeffrey Richard, Jeremy Eugene. BS in Bus., U. Colo., 1980. CPA, Colo. Sr. mgr. Ernst & Whinney, Denver, 1980-89; chief fin. officer, chief info. officer Monfort, Inc., Greeley, 1989-95, CFO, CIO ConAgra Refrigerated Products, 1995—. Mem. student adv. coun. U. No. Colo.; mem. exec. com. Pvt. Industry Coun. Weld County; active Weld County Retirement Bd. Mem. MIT Enterprise Forum Colo. (mem. exec. com. 1987-89), Greeley Country Club, No. Colo. Acctg. Club. Office: MonFort Inc PO Box G Greeley CO 80632-0350

THIESENHUSEN, WILLIAM CHARLES, agricultural economist; b. Waukesha, Wis., Feb. 12, 1936; s. Arthur Henry and Myrtle O. (Honeyager) T.; children—James Waring, Kathryn Hague, Gail Ann. BS, U. Wis., 1958, MS, 1960, PhD, 1965; M.P.A. (Danforth Found. fellow), Harvard U., 1962, postgrad., 1968-69. Instr. agrl. extension U. Wis., Madison, 1959-61; exec. asst. Land Tenure Center and Instituto de Economia Universidad de Chile research team in Santiago, 1963-65; asst. prof. agrl. econs. Land Tenure Center and Instituto de Economia Universidad de Chile research team in, 1965-68, asso. prof. agrl. econs., 1971-72, asso. prof. agrl. journalism, 1968-72, prof. agrl. journalism and agrl. econs., 1972—; dir. Land Tenure Ctr., 1971-75, 94—; asst. prof. econs. U. Wis., Milw., 1966-67; prof. agrl. econs. Escuela Nacional de Agricultura, Chapingo, Mex.; under AID contract, summer 1965; vis. prof. Universidad Autonoma de Madrid, Fulbright Program, 1977; cons., condr. seminars in field; Fulbright-Hays lectr., 1965, 72. Author: Chile's Experiments in Agrarian Reform, 1966, Reforma Agraria en Chile: Experimentos en Cuatro Fundos de la Iglesia, 1968, Broken Promises: Agrarian Reform and the Latin American Campesino, 1995; editor: Searching for Agrarian Reform in Latin America, 1989; mem. editl. bd. Latin Am. Rsch. Rev., Pakistan Devel. Rev.; contbr. articles to profl. jours. Served with USAR, 1960. Recipient award for best article Am. Jour. Agrl. Econs., 1969; Alpha Zeta nat. fellow, 1957; U. Wis. fellow, 1956; Harvard U. Adminstrn. fellow, 1962. Mem. Am. Agrl. Econs. Assn., Am. Econ. Assn., Latin Am. Studies Assn., Council Internat. Exchange Scholars (chmn. com. econs. selection 1979-80), Inter-Am. Found. (selection bd.), Wis. Acad. Scis., Arts and Letters, Phi Kappa Phi, Alpha Zeta, Sigma Delta Chi. Unitarian. Office: U Wis Land Tenure Ctr 1300 University Ave Madison WI 53715

THIESSEN, DELBERT DUANE, psychologist; b. Julesberg, Colo., Aug. 13, 1932; s. David and Eva Peters (Wetherby) T.; children—Trevor, Theron, Kendell Courtney. B.A. in Psychology with great distinction, San Jose (Calif.) State Coll., 1958; Ph.D., U. Calif., Berkeley, 1963. Extension instr. U. Calif., La Jolla, fall 1964; asst. sect. med. psychology, div. psychiatry and neurology Scripps Clinic and Research Found., La Jolla, 1962-65; mem. faculty U. Tex., Austin, 1965—; prof. psychology U. Tex., 1971—; research cons. NIMH. Author: Gene Organization and Behavior, 1972, The Evolution and Biochemistry of Aggression, 1976, Bitter-Sweet Destiny: The Stormy Evolution of Human Behavior, 1995; contbr. articles and chpts. to books. Served with AUS, 1952-54, Korea. Fellow USPHS, 1960-61; recipient Career Devel. award NIMH, 1967-72, grantee, 1967-78; grantee Russel Sage Found.; grantee NSF; grantee U. Tex. Research Inst. Mem. AAAS, Alumni Assn. Roscoe B. Jackson Meml. Lab., Am. Psychol. Assn., Am. Genetic Assn., Psychonomic Soc., Animal Behavior Soc., Southwestern Psychol. Assn., Behavior Genetics Assn., Sigma Xi, Phi Kappa Phi, Psi Chi. Home: 7300 Barcelona Dr Austin TX 78752-2003 Office: Univ Tex Dept Psychology Mezes 330 Austin TX 78712

THIESSEN, GORDON GEORGE, banker; b. South Porcupine, Ont., Canada, Aug. 14, 1938; m. Annette Margaret Hillyar, Oct. 3, 1964; 2 children. BA with honours, U. Sask., 1960, MA, 1961; PhD in Econs., London Sch. Econs., 1972. Lectr. U. Sask., Saskatoon, Can., 1961-62; Economist Bank of Can., Ottawa, Ont., 1963-73; chief monetary and fin. analysis dept. Bank of Can., Ottawa, 1975-79, adviser, 1979-84, dep. gov., 1984-87, sr. dep. gov., 1987-94; gov. Bank of Can., Ottawa, Ont., 1994—; also chmn. bd. dirs. Bank of Can., Ottawa; vis. economist Res. Bank Australia, Sydney, 1973-75. Avocations: sailing; skiing.

THIGPEN, ALTON HILL, motor transportation company executive; b. Kinston, N.C., Feb. 3, 1927; s. Kirby Alton and Alice (Hill) T.; m. Rebecca Ann Braswell, May 16, 1953; children: David Alton, Jennifer Ann, Steven Roy. B.S. in Indsl. Engring., N.C. State U., 1950. With Asso. Transport, Inc., Burlington, N.C., 1950-71; engr. Asso. Transport, Inc., 1950-57; asst. terminal mgr. Asso. Transport, Inc., Phila., 1957-58; terminal mgr. Asso. Transport, Inc., Knoxville, Tenn., 1959; regional mgr. Asso. Transport, Inc., Valley region, 1960-62, South region, 1962-68; v.p.-dir. So. div. Asso. Transport, Inc., 1968-71; v.p. R.S. Braswell Inc. Co., Kannapolis, 1971-80; pres. R.S. Braswell Co. Inc., 1980—, Hartford Motor Inn Inc., North Myrtle Beach, S.C., 1982—, A.T. Developers, Inc., North Myrtle Beach, S.C., 1983—; pres. Cherokee 2 Inc., Shelby, N.C., 1986—, bd. dirs.; bd. dirs. First Union Nat. Bank, Earl Ownsby Studios Inc., Shelby. Bd. regents Berkshire Christian Coll., Lenox, Mass., 1975—; mem. adv. bd. Salvation Army. Served with USNR, 1945-46. Mem. Motor Carriers Va. (pres. 1967-68), N.C. Motor Carriers Assn. (dir. 1968—), Sigma Chi, Tau Beta Pi. Mem. Advent Christian Ch. Club: Mason (32 deg.), Lions. Home: 5395 Mooresville Rd Kannapolis NC 28081-8726 Office: PO Box 1197 Kannapolis NC 28082-1197

THIGPEN, RICHARD ELTON, JR., lawyer; b. Washington, Dec. 29, 1930; s. Richard Elton and Dorathy (Dotger) T.; m. Nancy H. Shand, Dec. 15, 1951; children: Susan B., Richard M. AB, Duke U., 1951; LLB, U. N.C., 1956. Bar: N.C. 1956, U.S. Ct. Appeals (4th cir.) 1960, U.S. Ct. Appeals (5th cir.) 1960, U.S. Ct. Appeals (10th cir.) 1974, U.S. Tax Ct. 1958, U.S. Ct. Claims 1978. Lawyer FTC, Washington, 1956-58, Thigpen & Hines, Charlotte, N.C., 1958-84, Moore & Van Allen, Charlotte, N.C., 1984-88; ptnr. Poyner & Spruill, Charlotte, N.C., 1988-93; gen. counsel Richardson Sports, 1994—. Dir. Charlotte-Mecklenburg YMCA, 1964-88, Heineman Med. Rsch. Ctr., Charlotte, 1970—, Charlotte C. of C., 1982-85. Lt. USNR, 1951-53. Fellow Am. Bar Found., Am. Coll. Tax Counsel (regent 1989—, vice chmn. 1992, chmn. 1993-94); mem. ABA, N.C. State Bar, N.C. Bar Assn. (pres. 1988-89, chmn. tax sect. 1976-80). Avocation: golf, travel. Home: 2518 Forest Dr Charlotte NC 28211-2110 Office: Richardson Sports 227 W Trade St Ste 1650 Charlotte NC 28202-1675

THIMANN, KENNETH VIVIAN, biology educator; b. Ashford, Eng., Aug. 5, 1904; came to U.S., 1930, naturalized Am. citizen; s. Israel Phoebus and Muriel Kate (Harding) T.; m. Ann Mary Bateman, Mar. 20, 1929; children—Vivianne Thimann Nachmias, Karen Thimann Romer, Linda Thimann Dewing. Student, Caterham Sch., Eng., 1915-21; B.Sc., Imperial Coll. Sci and Tech. London Royal Coll. Sci., 1924, A.R.C.S., 1924, Ph.D., 1928; A.M. (hon.), Harvard U., 1938; Ph.D. (hon.), U. Basel, Switzerland, 1960, U. Clermont-Ferrand, France, 1961; DSc (hon.), Brown U., 1989. Demonstrator bacteriology Kings Coll., London, 1927-29; instr. biochemistry and bacteriology Calif. Inst. Tech., Pasadena, 1930-35; lectr. botany Harvard U., 1935-36, asst. prof. plant physiology, 1936-39, assoc. prof., 1939-46, prof., 1946-62, Higgins prof. biology, 1962-65, prof. emeritus, 1965—; dir. Biol. Labs., Harvard U., 1946-50, tutor in biology Eliot House, 1936-52, assoc., 1952-65; master East House, Radcliffe Coll., 1962-65; exch. prof. U. Paris, 1954-55; prof. biology U. Calif., Santa Cruz, 1954-84, prof. emeritus, 1984—; provost Crown Coll., 1965-72; vis. prof. U. Mass., 1974,

U. Tex., 1976; pres. XI Internat. Bot. Congress, 1969; pres. 2d Nat. Biol. Congress, Miami, 1970, Internat. Plant Growth Substance Assn. Triennial Meeting, Tokyo, 1973. Author: (with F. W. Went) Phytohormones, 1937, L'Origine et les Fonctions des Auxines, 1956, The Life of Bacteria, 2d edit., 1963, The Natural Plant Hormones, 1972, Hormones in the Whole Life of Plants, 1977, (with J.H. Langenheim) Botany: Plants and Human Affairs, 1982; author (with others) and editor Senescence in Plants, 1981; editor (with R.S. Harris) Vitamins and Hormones (ann.) Vol. 1, 1943, to Vol. 20, 1962, (with G. Pincus) The Hormones, 5 vols., 1948, 55, 63; mem. editorial bd. Archives of Biochemistry and Biophysics, 1949-70, Canadian Jour. Botany, 1966-73, Plant Physiology, 1974-85; contbr.over 300 articles to tech. jours. Bd. dirs. Found. Microbiology, Biol. Scis. Info. Services. Served as civilian scientist, USN, 1942-45. Recipient Stephen Hales prize research Am. Soc. Plant Physiologists, 1936; Guggenheim fellow, Eng., 1950-51, Italy, 1958; medallist Internat. Plant Growth Substance Assn., 1976, Balzan prize, 1982. Fgn. mem. Royal Soc. (London), Soc. Nazionale dei Lincei (Rome), Akad. Leopoldina (Halle), Acad. Nat. de Roumanie (Bucharest), Acad. des Sci. (Paris), Acad. d' Agr. de France, Bot. Soc. Netherlands, Bot. Soc. Japan, Indian Soc. Plant Physiology; mem. Am. Soc. Biol. Chemists, Am. Philos. Soc. (council 1973-76), Am. Acad. Arts and Scis., Nat. Acad. Scis. (chmn. botany sect. 1962-65, mem. council 1967-71, exec. com. assembly life scis. 1972-76), Bot. Soc. Am. (pres. 1960), AAAS (dir. 1968-72), Am. Soc. Plant Physiologists (pres. 1950-51), Soc. Gen. Physiologists (pres. 1949-50), Biochem. Soc., Am. Soc. Naturalists (pres. 1954-55), Am. Inst. Biol. Scis. (pres. 1965), Soc. Study Devel. and Growth (pres. 1955-56). Home: 3300 Darby Rd Apt 3314 Haverford PA 19041-1070

THIMOTHEOSE, KADAKAMPALLIL GEORGE, psychologist; b. Karipuza, India, Feb. 11, 1938; came to the U.S., 1976; s. K.G. and Mariamma Varghese; m. Mariamma Thimotheose, May 20, 1968 (div.); children: Geebee, Sonia. MA in Psychology, Kerala U., India, 1967, B in Edn., 1960, MA in Sociology, 1969; MA in History, Kerala U., 1975, PhD in Psychology, 1975. Lic. psychologist, marriage and family therapist, Mich.; diplomate Am. Bd. Med. Psychotherapists, Am. Bd. Psychotherapy, Am. Bd. Sexology. Lectr., head dept. ednl. psychology S.N. Tchrs. Coll., Trivandrum, India; clin./adminstrv. dir. Alexandrine House, Inc., Detroit, 1976-81; chief exec. officer Cen. Therapeutic Svcs., Inc., Southfield, Mich., 1981—; adv. bd. Trivandrum Med. Coll. Hosps., 1969-75; edn. faculty mem. U. Calicut, Kerala, India, 1969-75; v.p. forum ednl. rsch. and studies Kerala U., 1969-73. Author: Educational Psychology for B.Ed. Students, 1970; editor: Kerala University Journal of Education, 1969-73. Fellow Am. Bd. Med. Psychotherapists, Am. Acad. Clin. Sexologists; mem. Am. Psychol. Assn., Am. Coll. Sexologists (sexologist), Am. Bd. Sexology (clin. supr.), World U. Round Table (hon. cultural doctorate in therapeutic philolsophy). Republican. Avocations: photography, travel, reading, sightseeing. Home: 3048 Brewster Ct West Bloomfield MI 48322-2421 Office: Cen Therapeutic Svcs Inc 17600 W 8 Mile Rd Ste 7 Southfield MI 48075-4316

THIND, TEJ PAL, international management consultant; b. Nairobi, Kenya, July 8, 1934; arrived in Can., 1966; s. Ran jit Singh and Basant Kaur (Gill) T.; m. Arlene Highcazony, Feb. 12, 1958 (div.); 1 child, Tanya; m. Liliane Therese Maglia, Mar. 10, 1964; children: Naveena, Amrita. Student, Guildford Sch. of Art, Surrey, Eng., 1958. Registered trust and estate practitioner, U.K. Account exec. IOS Can. Ltd., Montreal, 1968-70; pres. Indo Can. Foods Ltd., Montreal, 1970-72; v.p. Maginn Mktg. Inc., Montreal, 1972-75; mng. dir. Akal Corp., St. Hubert, 1975-83; pres. Paragon Internat., Montreal, 1983-86; v.p. Can-Am Trust Ltd., Plymouth, Montserrat, 1988—; CEO, pres. IFM-Internat. Fin. Mktg., Inc., Montreal, 1986—; dir. Can-Am Trust Ltd., Plymouth, Can-Am Mgmt. (IOM) Ltd., Douglas, Isle of Man, Alpine Trust Go. Geneva S.A., Nova Trustees and Fiuciaries (UK) Ltd., London; pres. Royalton Healthcare Corp. Author: A Foreign Trust - Your Last Fortress, 1991; mng. editor The Offshore Hotline, 1991. Vice pres. Que. Assn. of Integration of Ugandan Asians, Montreal, 1972-73. Fellow Inst. Bus. Adminstrn.; mem. Nat. Assn. Canadians of Origins in India (nat. sec. 1987-88), Bank Mktg. Assn., Inst. Corp. Dirs., Montreal Badminton and Squash Club, Internat. Assn. of Offshore Banks (exec. dir. 1988-91), Masons. Avocations: reading, golf, racquet games, fitness. Home: 2700 Berlioz, Brossard, PQ Canada J4Z 2R6 Office: IFM Internat Fin Mktg Inc, 2050 Mansfield Ste 600, Montreal, PQ Canada H3A 1Y9

THIOUNN, PRASITH, foreign service official; b. Phnom Penh, Cambodia, Feb. 3, 1930. Economist Engr., U. Paris, 1954. Minister in charge coordination in Royal Govt., Nat. Union Cambodia, 1970-74; sec. polit. bur. Nat. United Front Cambodia, 1970-75; dir. internat. relations Ministry Fgn. Affairs of Democratic Cambodia, 1975-79; mem. Gen. Assembly of UN, Ministerial and Summit Confs. Non-Aligned Countries, 1975—; permanent rep. Cambodia to UN, 1979. Office: UN Permanent Mission Cambodia 820 2nd Ave Fl 15 New York NY 10017-4504

THISSELL, JAMES DENNIS, physicist; b. Lincoln County, S.D., June 1, 1935; s. Oscar H. and Bernice G.J. (Olbertson) T. BA cum laude, Augustana Coll., 1957; MS, U. Iowa, 1963. Rsch. physicist U. Iowa, Iowa City, 1958-64; engr. McDonnell Douglas, St. Louis, 1965-66; scientist E.G. & G., Inc., Las Vegas, Nev., 1967-68; engr. Bendix Field Engring. Corp. Ames Rsch. Ctr., Moffett Field, Calif., 1970-77, Lockheed Missiles & Space Co., Sunnyvale, Calif., 1978-95, Lockheed Martin Tech. Ops., Sunnyvale, 1995—. Mem. AIAA, IEEE, Am. Phys. Soc., Am. Geophys. Soc., Sigma Xi. Republican. Lutheran. Home: 38475 Jacaranda Dr Newark CA 94560-4727 Office: Lockheed Corp 0/23-20 B-100 FAC 1 PO Box 61687 Sunnyvale CA 94088-1687

THISTLETHWAITE, DAVID RICHARD, architect; b. Burlington, Iowa, Aug. 24, 1947; s. Robert and Nona (Binder) T.; m. Carol Anne Armstrong, Aug. 22, 1970. BArch, Iowa State U., 1971. Registered arch., Calif., Minn.; registered Nat. Coun. Archtl. Registration Bds. Designer Morrison Architects, St. Paul, 1971-73, Times Architects, Mpls., 1973-74; project architect Bentz/Thompson Assocs., Mpls., 1974-77; project mgr. Setter Leach Lindstrom, Mpls., 1977-78; project architect Wurster Bernardi Emmons, San Francisco, 1978-79, Strotz & Assocs., Tiburon, Calif., 1979-81, Hood Miller Assoc., San Francisco, 1981-84; prin., ptnr. R S T Architects, San Francisco, 1984-88; prin. Thistlethwaite Archtl. Group, San Francisco, 1988—. Contbr. articles to profl. jours. Mem. AIA (nat. profl. devel. com. 1983-86, treas. San Francisco chpt. 1985-86, chmn. Calif. coun. health facilities com. 1994—, chmn. design com. Acad. Architecture for Health 1994—), Am. Soc. Hosp. Engrs. Office: 250 Sutter St San Francisco CA 94108

THODE, EDWARD FREDERICK, chemical engineer, educator; b. N.Y.C., May 31, 1921; s. E. Frederick and Kathleen V. (McGowan) T.; m. Isobel Zoeller, May 27, 1944; children: Karen (Mrs. Paul M. O'Neil), Stephen Frederick, Jonathan Edward. S.B., M.I.T., 1942, S.M., 1943, Sc.D., 1947. Registered profl. engr., Maine, N.Mex. Chem. engr. Boston Woven Hose & Rubber Co., Cambridge, Mass.; asst. prof. chem. engring. U. Maine, Orono, 1947-49; asso. prof. U. Maine, 1949-54; sr. research engr. 3M Co., St. Paul, 1954-55; research assos., faculty mem. Inst. Paper Chemistry, Appleton, Wis., 1955-63; mgr. dept. engring. computer and computer ctr. Inst. Paper Chemistry, 1959-63; prof. chem. engring. N.Mex. State U., Las Cruces, 1963-74; head dept. chem. engring. N.Mex. State U., 1963-74, prof. mgmt., 1974-86, prof. emeritus chem. engring. and mgmt., 1986—; cons. Am. Cyanamid Co., IBM, Gen. Elec. Co., Bell Telephone Labs.; affiliate staff mem. Los Alamos Sci. Lab, 1965-90; propr. EIT Cons., 1972-91. Contbr. numerous articles to profl. jours. Mem. exec. bd. Yucca council Boy Scouts Am., 1968-72; dir. Mesilla Park Heritage Assn., 1988-93, sec., 1988-89, v.p., 1990, pres. 1991; treas. Mesilla Valley Conf. Cms, 1989; vestryman, lay reader, lay eucharistic minister, warden, 1970, 71, 87, 93, 94. Recipient Disting. faculty award N. Mex. State U, 1981, 83. Mem. Am. Soc. Chem. Engrs. (chmn. Rio Grande sect. 1990), Am. Soc. Engring. Edn., Sigma Xi, Tau Beta Pi, Beta Gamma Sigma, Phi Kappa Phi. Republican. Episcopalian. Home: 905 Conway # 45 Las Cruces NM 88005 *To discover God's will for our lives is difficult; the search is worth the effort.*

THOM, DOUGLAS ANDREW, paper company executive; b. San Mateo, Calif., Nov. 1, 1939; s. Andrew Phillip and Mary Agnes (Bailey) T.; m. Lisbeth Jane Steinhauer, Mar. 17, 1962; children: Cathryn, Mark, Kristen. BS in Graphic Communications, Calif. Poly. State U., 1962. Supr. Container Corp. Am., Oakland, Calif., 1962-68; supr. Ga. Pacific, San

Francisco, 1968-70, plant mgr., 1970-73; gen. mgr. Ga. Pacific, Sheboygan, Wis., 1973-79, regional mgr., 1979-85; regional mgr. Ga. Pacific, Atlanta, 1985, v.p. package div., 1985-88; v.p. Containerboard Mfg., Atlanta, 1989-90, v.p. packaging div., 1990—. Bd. dirs. YMCA, Sheboygan, 1979-85. Mem. Fiber Box Assn. (chmn. 1988-89, bd. dirs.), Internat. Corrugated Packaging Found. (bd. dirs.), Internat. Corrugated Case Assn. (bd. dirs.), Pine Hills Country Club (pres. 1983-84), Cherokee Town and Country Club. Republican. Roman Catholic. Avocation: golf.

THOM, JOSEPH M., librarian; b. Bronx, N.Y., Oct. 22, 1919; s. Harry and Jennie T.; m. Lillian Rosenstein, Sept. 1, 1945; children—Janice Eleanor, Eric Frederick. B.A., N.Y.U., 1948, M.A., 1949; M.S. in L.S, Columbia, 1950; postgrad., Washington U., 1951-53, instr. librarianship, 1950-54; Library asst. N.Y.U., 1940-42, 46-49; library fellow Bklyn. Coll., 1949-50; chief reference dept. Washington U., 1955-60, instr. librarianship, 1950-54; dir. Research Information Service of St. Louis, 1954-55; supr. records and dir. Research Information Service of St. Louis, 1954-55; supr. records and library Goodyear Atomic Corp., 1955-60; dir. libraries Yeshiva U., 1960; librarian Port Jefferson (N.Y.) Schs.; library and multi-media cons. on design and services. Editor: Reference Sources in Education, 1953, Personnel Notes and News; Compiler: Reference Sources in Political Science, 1953; Contbr. articles to profl. jours. Served with AUS, 1942-45. Home: PO Box 2514 East Setauket NY 11733-0755

THOM, RICHARD DAVID, aerospace executive; b. St. Louis, Oct. 4, 1944; s. Reginald James and Vlasta (Koukl) T.; m. Linda Marie Hunt, Sept. 9, 1967; children: Elizabeth Marie, Robert James. BS in Physics, U. Mo., Rolla, 1967; MSEE, UCLA, 1971. Co-op engr. McDonnell Aircraft Corp., St. Louis, 1962-67; head advanced tech. group IR systems dept., aerospace group Hughes Aircraft Co., Culver City, Calif., 1967-72; mem. tech. staff Santa Barbara Rsch. Ctr., Hughes Aircraft Co., Goleta, Calif., 1972-76, asst. mgr. R&D Lab., 1976-80, mgr. advanced applications, 1980-83, chief engr., 1984-86, chief scientist, 1986-90, dir. tech., 1990—. Contbr. articles to profl. jours.; patentee in field. Recipient Hughes Group Patent award for pioneering contbns. in infrared detector tech., 1990. Mem. IEEE, Tau Beta Pi, Sigma Pi Sigma, Delta Sigma Phi. Republican. Avocation: freelance travel writing and photography, specializing in railway travel around the world. Home: 1236 Camino Palomera Santa Barbara CA 93111-1013 Office: Santa Barbara Rsch Ctr 75 Coromar Dr Goleta CA 93117

THOMAJAN, ROBERT, lawyer, management and financial consultant; b. N.Y.C., May 4, 1941; s. Leon and Fay T. BS, NYU, 1962; JD, St. John's U., 1965. Bar: N.Y. 1965, U.S. Ct. Appeals (2nd cir.) 1966, U.S. Dist. Ct. (ea. and so. dists.) N.Y. 1967, U.S. Ct. Internat. Trade 1975, U.S. Supreme Ct. 1975, U.S. Ct. Appeals (9th cir.) 1976, U.S. Dist. Ct. (we. dist.) Tex. 1979, Tex. 1987. Atty. Nixon, Mudge, Rose, Guthrie, Alexander & Mitchell, N.Y.C., 1964-68; ptnr. Milgrim, Thomajan & Lee, N.Y.C., 1968-91; pres. Eterna Benefits, Austin, Tex., 1995—. Arbitrator Civil Ct., N.Y., 1981-86; mem. adv. bd. Ronald McDonald House, 1988-90; bd. dirs., counsel Big Bros./Big Sisters, 1988-90; mem. World Econ. Forum, 1990-93. Mem. Am. Soc. Internat. Law, Asia-Pacific Layers Assn., Internat. Law Assn. Office: 3674 Ranch Creek Dr Austin TX 78730

THOMAN, G. RICHARD, computer company executive; b. Tuscaloosa, Ala., June 25, 1944; s. Richard S. and Evelyn (Zumwalt) T.; m. Wenke Helina Brier, Aug. 25, 1966 (div. Dec. 1987); children: Camille, Alexis; m. Lynn Susan Bendheim, Sept. 24, 1989; children: Arielle, Max. BA with honors, McGill U., 1966; diploma, Grad. Inst. Internat. Studies, Geneva, 1968; MA in Internat. Econs., Tufts U., 1971, PhD Fletcher Sch. Law & Diplomacy, 1971. Exec. trainee Citicorp, N.Y.C., 1968-69; sr. fin. analyst Exxon Corp., N.Y.C., 1968-72; sr. assoc. McKinsey and Co., N.Y.C. and Paris, 1972-79; exec. v.p., CFO Am. Express Travel Related Svcs., N.Y.C., 1979-85, pres., Travel Related Svcs. Internat., 1985-89, chmn., CEO, 1989-92; pres., CEO Nabisco Internat. RJR Nabisco, Inc., N.Y.C., 1992-94; sr. v.p., group exec. IBM Corp., Somers, N.Y., 1994—; bd. dirs. Union Banque Prive, Geneva, Club Med, Paris. Author: Foreign Investment and Regional Development, 1972. Bd. dirs. Ams. Soc., N.Y.C., 1990—; bd. advisors Fletcher Sch. of Law and Diplomacy, Tufts U., Medford, Mass., 1990—. Recipient Legion of Honors, Govt. of France, 1992. Mem. Coun. on Fgn. Rels. Avocations: tennis, reading, jogging, travel. Office: IBM Corp RR 1 Somers NY 10589

THOMAN, HENRY NIXON, food industry executive; b. Cin., May 5, 1957; s. Richard B. and Barbara (Lutz) T.; m. Kathleen Brewer Thoman, Aug. 14, 1982; children: Victoria E., Nicholas B. BA, Duke U., 1979; JD, U. Chgo., 1982. Bar: Ohio 1982, U.S. Dist. Ct. (so. dist.) Ohio, 1982. With Taft, Stettinius & Hollister, Cin., 1982-88; sr. atty. John Morrell & Co., Cin. 1988-90; sr. counsel Chiquita Brands Internat. Inc., Cin., 1990-91, corp. planner, 1991-92; sr. dir. CTP ops. Chiquita Brands, Inc., Cin., 1993-94, chief adminstrv. officer Armuelles divsn., 1994—. Mem. counselors com. U.S. Swimming, Colo., 1983-89; bd. dirs. Friends of Cin. Parks, 1990-93, Mariemont Aquatic Club, v.p. 1992-93; pres. Club Atletico Y Socialde Chiriqui, 1994—. Mem. Ohio State Bar, Cin. Bar Assn. Office: Chiriqui Land Co Armuelles Divsn, Apartado 6-2637, Estafeta El Dorado Panama Panama

THOMAN, JOHN EVERETT, architect, mediator; b. Dixon, Ill., Aug. 6, 1925; s. George Dewey and Agnes Katherine (Fane) T.; m. Paula Ann Finnegan, Oct. 31, 1953; children: Shawn Michael, Brian Gerard, Kevin Charles, Trace Marie, Patricia Ann, Ronan Patrick, Caron Lynn. AA, UCLA, 1948; BArch cum laude, U. So. Calif., 1955. Registered architect and gen. contractor, Calif. Project dir. A. Quincy Jones & Frederick E. Emmons, L.A., 1956-57, assoc., 1958, dir. constrn., 1958-73; dir. specifications A. Quincy Jones, FAIA & Assocs., L.A., 1973-77; dir. specifications Albert C. Martin and Assocs., L.A., 1977-79, dir. constrn. and industry rels., 1979—, assoc., 1979-90, sr. assoc., 1990—, prin. 1991—; gen. contractor Martin of Calif., L.A., 1984—, v.p., 1985—; guest lectr. U. So. Calif. Lusk Sch. Real Estate, UCLA Grad. Sch., also various student, trade and tech. groups. Mem., vice chmn. Culver City (Calif.) Planning Commn., 1959; mem. Calif. Gov.'s Housing Commn., L.A., 1960, Community Redevel. Agy., Culver City, 1992—. With U.S. Army, 1943-45, USAF, 1950-51. Mem. AIA (chmn. design awards com. L.A. 1960), Constrn. Specifications Inst. (bd. dirs. 1977-80, guest lectr.), Phi Eta Sigma, Tau Sigma Delta. Avocations: fishing, military history. Office: Albert C Martin and Assocs 811 W 7th St Los Angeles CA 90017-3408

THOMAN, MARK, lawyer; b. Cin., Apr. 28, 1935; s. Henry Augustus and Valeska (Wurlitzer) T.; child by previous marriage, George; m. Nancy Flaun Karlins, Oct. 1, 1981. B.A., Yale U., 1956; LL.B., Harvard U., 1959. Bar: N.Y. 1960. Assoc. Lord Day & Lord, Barrett Smith and predecessor firm, N.Y.C., 1960-66, ptnr, 1966-94; ptnr. McDermott, Will & Emery, N.Y.C., 1994—. Mem. N.Y. Athletic Club. Home: 100 Ridgewood Ave Glen Ridge NJ 07028-1016 Office: McDermott Will & Emery 1211 6th Ave New York NY 10036

THOMAN, MARK EDWARD, pediatrician; b. Chgo., Feb. 15, 1936; s. John Charles and Tasula Mark (Petrakis) T.; AA, Graceland Coll., 1956; BA, U. Mo., 1958, MD, 1962; m. Theresa Thompson, 1984; children: Marlisa Rae, Susan Kay, Edward Kim, Nancy Lynn, Janet Lea, David Mark. Intern, U. Mo. at Columbia, 1962-63; resident in pediatrics Blank Meml. Children's Hosp., Des Moines, 1963-65, chief resident, 1964-65; cons. in toxicology, 1966-67; chief dept. pediatrics Shiprock (N.Mex.) Navajo Indian Hosp., dir. N.D. Poison Info. Center, also practice medicine, specializing in pediatrics Quain & Ramstad Clinic, Bismarck, N.D., 1967-69; dir. Iowa Poison Info. Center, Des Moines, 1969—; pvt. solo practice pediatrics, Des Moines, 1969—; sr. aviation med. examiner, accident investigator FAA, 1976—; faculty Iowa State U., U. Iowa, U. Osteo. Sci. and Health; dir. Cystic Fibrosis Clinic, 1973-82; dir. Mid-Iowa Drug Abuse Program, 1972-76; mem. med. adv. bd. La Leche League Internat., 1965—; pres. Medic-Air Ltd., 1976—; aviation seminars lectr. Editor-in-chief AACTION, 1975-90. Bd. dirs. Polk County Pub. Health Nurses assn., 1969-77, Des Moines Speech and Hearing Center, 1974-79, Ecumenical Coun. of Iowa, 1990—; pres.-elect bd. govs. Mo. U. Sch. Medicine Alumni, 1988—. Served with USMCR, 1954-59; lt. comdr. USPHS, 1965-66; capt. USNR, 1993—. Recipient N.D. Gov.'s award of merit, 1969; Cystic Fibrosis Rsch. Found. award, 1975, Am. Psychiat. Assn. Thesis award, Diplomate Am. Bd. Pediatrics, Am. Bd. Med. Toxicology (examiner) 1962. Mem. AMA (del. 1970—),

NRA (life), Assn. Am. Physicians & Surgeons, Polk County Med. Soc., Iowa State Med. Assn., Aerospace Med. Assn., Res. Officers Assn., Civil Aviation Med. Assn., Am. Public Health Assn., 1986—, Soc. Adolescent Medicine, Inst. Clin. Toxicology, Internat. Soc. Pediatrics, Am. Acad. Pediatrics (chmn. accident prevention com. Iowa chpt. 1975—), Cystic Fibrosis Club, Am. Acad. Clin. Toxicology (trustee 1969-90, pres. 1982-84), Am. Assn. Poison Control Centers, U.S. Naval Inst. Republican. Elder mem. Reorganized Latter-Day Saints Ch. Clubs: Flying Physicians, Aircraft Owners and Pilots Assn., Nat. Pilots Assn. (Safe Pilot award), Hyperion Field and Country. Editor in chief AACTION, 1976-90. Home: 6896 NW Trail Ridge Johnston IA 50131-1322 Office: 1426 Woodland Ave Des Moines IA 50309-3287

THOMAS, ABDELNOUR SIMON, software company executive; b. Kfarhoune, Lebanon, Oct. 25, 1913; came to U.S., 1920; s. Simon Thomas and Mary Sawaya-Thomas; m. Eva Maria Balling, Mar. 26, 1951; children: Robert F., David C., Paul J., Simon P., Mary E., Joan T. BS, Holy Cross Coll., 1937; MEd, Boston U., 1939, PhD, 1950. Registered profl. engr., Mass. Prof. math. and math. stats. Boston Coll., 1941-51; founder, dir. rsch. activities A. S. Thomas, Inc., 1955—; vis. prof. MIT. Contbr. Ency. Britanica, numerous. sci. publs. Mem. Nat. Rep. Com., Right to Life. Lt. sgt. USNR, 1942-46, PTO. Recipient Forty-One for Freedom award Sec. USN, 1967. Mem. IEEE (life, sr.), SME, N.C. Soc. Roman Catholic. Achievements include development of theory of graded and hybrid absorber materials, theory of modulated surface wave antennas, re-entry vehicle antennas; characterizabtion of radar cross section of metallic, coated metallic and non-metallic bodies. Office: A S Thomas Inc 355 Providence Hwy Westwood MA 02090-1997

THOMAS, ADRIAN WESLEY, laboratory director; b. Edgefield, S.C., June 23, 1939; s. Hasting Adrian and Nancy Azalena (Bridges) T.; m. Martha Elizabeth McAllister, July 12, 1964; children: Wesley Adrian, Andrea Elizabeth. BS in Agrl. Engring., Clemson U., 1962, MS in Agrl. Engring., 1965; PhD, Colo. State U., 1972. Rsch. scientist USDA-Agrl. Rsch. Svc., Tifton, Ga., 1965-69, Fort Collins, Colo., 1969-72; rsch. leader USDA-Agrl. Rsch. Svc., Walkinsville, Ga., 1972-89; lab. dir. USDA-Agrl. Rsch. Svc., Tifton, 1989—; mem. acad. faculty Colo. State U. Ft. Collins, 1969-72; acad. faculty U. Ga., Athens, 1973—; grad. faculty, 1988—. Contbr. agrl. rsch. articles to profl. jours. With U.S. Army, 1962-63. Mem. Am. Soc. Agrl. Engrs., Am. Soc. Agronomy, Soil and Water Conservation Soc. Am., Soil Sci. Soc. Am., Sigma Xi, Alpha Epsilon, Gamma Sigma Delta, Phi Kappa Phi. Lutheran. Avocations: reading, gardening, yard care, remodeling home, sports. Office: USDA Agrl Rsch Svc PO Box 946 Tifton GA 31793-0946

THOMAS, ALAN RICHARD, natural resources products executive; b. Toronto, Ont., Can., Dec. 14, 1942; s. Ronald H. Thomas and Edna M. Green; m. Jill H.E. Parkinson; children: Kimberley Anne, Michael. B in Commerce, U. Toronto, 1964. Chartered acct., Ont. Ptnr. Ernst & Young, Toronto, 1964-87; CFO, treas. Noranda Inc., Toronto, 1987—. Recipient Bronze medal Can. Inst. Chartered Accts., 1967. Mem. Ont. Inst. Chartered Accts., Donalda Club, Toronto Cricket Club, Cambridge Club, Royal Ottawa Golf Club. Mem. United Ch. Can. Office: Noranda Inc, 181 Bay St Ste 4100 PO Box 755, Toronto, ON Canada M5J 2T3

THOMAS, ALLEN LLOYD, lawyer, private investor; b. Orange, N.J., Sept. 15, 1939; s. Richard Lloyd and Dorothy (Carr) T.; m. Virginia Dehnert, June 24, 1961 (div. 1974); children: Sarah Ann, Anne Marjorie; m. Barbara Singer, Mar. 12, 1978; 1 child, Allen Lloyd Jr. BA, Wesleyan U., 1961; LLB, Yale U., 1964. Bar: N.Y. 1965, U.S. Ct. Appeals (D.C. cir.) 1981. Ptnr. Paul Weiss Rifkind Wharton & Garrison, N.Y.C., 1964-92; resident ptnr. Hong Kong, 1983-87; dir., gen. counsel Gerard Atkins & Co. Ltd., 1992-94; gen. counsel Gen. Atlantic Group Ltd, 1992-94; bd. dirs. Mitsubishi Bank Trust Co. N.Y., N.Y.C., 1987-92. Chmn. Urban Bus. Assis. Corp., N.Y.C., 1971-82; chmn. Hong Kong Ballet, 1985-87; co-chmn. Internat. Com., N.Y.C. Ballet, 1986-91; pres. Internat. Salzburg Assn. Am., 1987-92; dir., mem. exec. com., gen. counsel Child Care Action Campaign, 1990-92. Fellow Am. Coll. Investment Counsel, Hartford, Conn. Mem. River Club, N.Y. Met. Club of Washington, Hong Kong Club, Royal Hong Kong Jockey Club, Coral Beach and Tennis Club, Lenox Club, Queens Club, Buck's Club. Home: 3 Chester St, London England

THOMAS, ANN VAN WYNEN, lawyer, educator; b. The Netherlands, May 27, 1919; came to U.S., 1921, naturalized, 1926; d. Cornelius and Cora Jacoba (Daansen) Van Wynen; m. A.J. Thomas, Jr., Sept. 10, 1948. A.B. with distinction, U. Rochester, 1940; J.D., U. Tex., 1943; post doctoral degree, So. Meth. U., 1952. U.S. Ign. service officer Johannesburg, London, The Hague, 1943-47; research atty. Southwestern Legal Found., So. Meth. U. Sch. Law, Dallas, 1952-67; asst. prof. publ. sci. So. Meth. U. Sch. Law, 1968-73, assoc. prof., 1973-76, prof., 1976-85, prof. emeritus, 1985—. Author: Communism versus International Law, 1953, Non-Intervention—The Law and its Import in the Americas, 1956, OAS: The Organization of American States, 1962, International Legal Aspects of Civil War in Spain, 1936-1939, 1967, Legal Limitations on Chemical and Biological Weapons, 1970, The Concept of Aggression, 1972, Presidential War Making Power: Constitutional and International Law Aspects, 1981, An International Rule of Law—Problems and Prospects, 1974. Chmn. time capsule com. Grayson County Commn. on Tex. Sesquicentennial, 1986-88; co-chmn. Grayson County Sesquicentennial, 1994—. Recipient Am. medal Nat. DAR Soc., 1992. Mem. Tex. Bar Assn., Am. Soc. Internat. Law, Grayson County Bar Assn. Home: Spaniel Hall Pottsboro TX 75076

THOMAS, BETH EILEEN WOOD (MRS. RAYMOND O. THOMAS), editor; b. North Vernon, Ind., May 12, 1916; d. Fayette J. and Emma J. (Ream) Wood; m. Raymond O. Thomas, Feb. 28, 1941; 1 son, Stephen W. Comml. diploma, Bedford High Sch., 1934; student, Lockyear Bus. Coll., 1936. Sec. WPA, Vincennes, Ind., 1935-36, Evansville, Ind., 1937-38, Indpls., 1939-41; sec. to adj. AAF Storage Depot, Indpls., 1941-44; sec. Coll. Life Ins., Indpls., 1957-58, Indpls. Sch. Bd., 1958-59; classified office mgr. North Side Topics Newspaper, Indpls., 1960-67. Editor: Child Life mag., 1967-71, Brownie Reader, 1971-73, Children's Playmate mag., 1968-91; editorial assoc. Saturday Evening Post, 1971; exec. editorial dir. Jack and Jill mag., 1971-91, Young World mag., 1971-79, Child Life mag., 1971-91, Design mag., 1977-80, Turtle mag. for Presch. Kids, 1979-91, Humpty Dumpty's mag., 1980-91, Children's Digest, 1980-91; editor emeritus juvenile mags., Children's Better Health Inst., 1991—. Mem. Women in Communications, Indpls. Press Club, Soc. Children's Book Writers. Club: Thetis. Home: 3831 Rue Voltaire Indianapolis IN 46220-1541 Office: Children's Better Health Inst Box 567 1100 Waterway Blvd Indianapolis IN 46202-2156

THOMAS, BETTY, actress; b. St. Louis. BFA, Ohio U. Former sch. tchr.; co-star M.I.T. Blues, from 1981; Joined Second City Workshop, Chgo.; appeared on Second City TV, 1984; appeared in after sch. spl. The Gift of Love, 1985, Prison of Children, 1986. Appeared in The Fun Factory game show, 1976; film: Troop Beverly Hills, 1989; in TV film Outside Chance, 1978, Nashville Grab, 1981, When Your Lover Leaves, 1983; star TV series Hill Street Blues, 1981-87 (Emmy nominations 1981, 82, 83); dir.: (TV) Dream On: "For Peter's Sake" (Emmy award, Outstanding Individual Achievement in Directing in a Comedy Series, 1993), 1993, (film) The Brady Bunch Movie, 1995. Emmy Best Supporting Actress, 1985. Office: care ICM 8942 Wilshire Blvd Beverly Hills CA 90211*

THOMAS, BILLY MARSHALL, retired army officer; b. Crystal City, Tex., Aug. 14, 1940; s. Harold Dennis and Ivy Marie (Moore) T.; m. Judith Kathryn McConnell, Jan. 31, 1981; children: Jonathon Scott, Kimberly Michelle, Jeanette Kirsten. David Eldon. BS, Tex. Christian U., 1962; MS, George Washington U., 1974; postgrad., Army War Coll., Carlisle, Pa., 1980, Harvard U., 1986. Commd. 2d lt. U.S. Army, 1962, advanced through grades to lt. gen., 1990; co. comdr. U.S. Army, Vietnam, 1968; pers. staff officer U.S. Army Mil. Pers. Ctr., Alexandria, Va., 1974-77; bn. comdr. 5th Sig. Bn., 5th Div., Ft. Polk, La., 1977-79; brigade comdr. 93d brigade signal VII U.S. Corps, Stuttgart, Germany, 1981-83; dep. comdg. gen. U.S. Army Signal Ctr. and Sch., Ft. Gordon, Ga., 1983-85; mem. staff for rsch., devel. and acquisition Dept. Army, Washington, 1985-87; comdg. gen. Communi-

cations and Electronics Command, Ft. Monmouth, N.J., 1987-90; dep. comdg. gen. for rsch., devel. and acquisition Army Materiel Command, Alexandria, 1990-92; founder, chmn. Engring. and Mgmt. Execs. Inc., Alexandria, Va., 1992—; spkr. regional and nat. forums on quality mgmt., 1988-92. Contbr. articles to mil. publs. Pres. PTA, Springfield, Va., 1974-75; host, chmn. Ft. Monmouth Mayor's Roundtable, 1987-90; host Chief Exec. Officers Round Table, Ft. Monmouth, 1987-90. Decorated Legion of Merit with two oak leaf clusters, Bronze Star medal with oak leaf cluster, D.S.M. with oak leaf cluster; named Vol. of Yr., Big Bros. and Big Sisters, N.J., 1990. Mem. Armed Forces Communications and Electronics Assn. (internat. bd. dirs. 1986-92, chmn. scholarship com. Edn. Found. 1986-90), Am. Def. Preparedness Assn., Assn. U.S. Army, Nat. Mil. Family Assn., DAV. Methodist. Avocations: golf, skiing, reading, jazz. Home: 8249 Clifton Farm Ct Alexandria VA 22306-3268

THOMAS, BOB, public relations executive; b. San Diego. Sports editor, automotive writer, columnist L.A. Times; pres. Bob Thomas & Assocs., 1972-92, chmn. Office: Bob Thomas & Assos Inc Pub Rels 340 Main St Venice CA 90291

THOMAS, BRENDA C., county official; b. Russell, Ky., Mar. 16, 1948; d. Charles X. and Jeannette Frances (Thompson) Calia; m. Evan Thomas, July 11, 1972; children: Alexandra Logan, Jessica Theon, Erin Elizabeth. Dir. Am. Lang. Ctr., Fez, Morocco, 1968-70; proprietor The Bookshop, St. Paul, 1981-90. Commr. human rights Roseville, Minn., 1979-88, chmn., 1986-88; mem. Roseville City Coun., 1990-92; commr. Ramsey County, 1993—. Office: Office Bd County Commrs Courthouse RM 220 15 W Kellogg Blvd Saint Paul MN 55102

THOMAS, BRIAN CHESTER, state legislator, engineer; b. Tacoma, Wash., May 19, 1939; s. Ralph R. and Katheryne (Chester) T.; m. Judith Lynn Adams, Feb. 20, 1965; children: Jeffrey, Kyle, Cheryl. BS in Indsl. Engring., Oreg. State U., 1961; postgrad., U. Wash., 1968-70; MBA, Pacific Luth. U., 1979. Civil engr. U.S. Coast Guard, Seattle, 1962-63; ops. officer U.S. Coast Guard, Astoria, Oreg., 1964-65; sr. sales engr. Puget Sound Power & Light Co., Bellevue, Wash., 1965-70, mgr. market rsch., 1971-80, rsch. adminstr., 1981-89, prin. engr., 1989—; mem. Wash. Ho. of Reps., Olympia, 1993—, chmn. joint select com. on edn. restructuring, 1991—, chmn. fin., edn. natural resources coms., 1991—; chair EEI Rsch. Mgmt. Com., Washington, 1988-89, EPRI Renewable Com., Palo Alto, Calif., 1989-90; adv. bd. Nat. Renewable Energy Lab., Golden, Colo., 1990-92; mem. adv. bd. sch. elec. engring. Oreg. State U., Corvallis, 1991-93; dep. dir. region 10 U.S. Dept. Transp. Emergency Orgn., Seattle, 1989-93. Bd. dirs. Issaquah (Wash.), Sch. Dist., 1989-93. Capt. USCGR, 1961-84. Mem. Issaquah Rotary (pres. 1982-83), Rainier Club. Republican. Avocation: restoring Studebakers. Home: 14715 182nd Pl SE Renton WA 98059 Office: Wash Ho Reps PO Box 40610 Olympia WA 98504-0610 Office: Puget Sound Power & Light PO Box 97034 Bellevue WA 98009-9734

THOMAS, BROOKS, publishing company executive; b. Phila., Nov. 28, 1931; s. Walter Horstman and Ruth Sterling (Boomer) T.; m. Galen Pinckard Clark, Apr. 15, 1969 (div. 1973). B.A., Yale U., 1953, LL.B., 1956; grad., Advanced Mgmt. Program, Harvard, 1973. Bar: Pa. 1957, N.Y. 1960. With law firm Winthrop, Stimson, Putnam & Roberts, N.Y.C., 1960-68; sec., gen. counsel Harper & Row, Pubs., Inc., N.Y.C., 1968-69; v.p., gen. counsel Harper & Row, Pubs., Inc., 1969-73, exec. v.p., 1973-79, chief operating officer, 1977-81, pres., 1979-87, chief exec. officer, 1981-87, chmn. bd., 1986-87; chmn. bd. Harper & Row, Ltd., London, 1973-87; dir. Harper & Row, Pty. Ltd., Australia, Harla S.A. de C.V., Mex., Harper & Row Pubs. Asia, Pte. Ltd., Singapore. Pres., bd. dirs. Butterfield House, 1968-72, 90-93; trustee, dir. RADG, Inc., 1987-89; dir. Thompson Island Outward Bound Edn. Ctr., 1987—, Colo. Outward Bound Sch., 1990—; bd. dirs. Young Audiences, Inc., 1977—, chmn., 1985—; trustee Outward Bound USA, 1980—, vice chmn., 1983-84, chmn., 1984-87; chmn. Am. Book Awards, 1984-85, dir., 1985-87; mem. devel. bd. Yale U., 1985-89; adv. bd. Yale Sch. Orgn. and Mgmt., 1987—; chmn. Vail Valley Inst., 1989—. Lt. (j.g.) USNR, 1956-59. Mem. Am. Bar Assn., Assn. Bar City of N.Y., Assn. Am. Pubs. (bd. dirs. 1980-85, chmn. 1983-85), Council Fgn. Relations, Yale U. Alumni Assn. (law sch. rep. 1980-83). Clubs: Merion Cricket (Phila.); Century (N.Y.C.), Yale (N.Y.C.), University (N.Y.C.), N.Y. Yacht (N.Y.C.); Essex Yacht (Conn.). Home: 37 W 12th St New York NY 10011-8502 also: 141 Saybrook Rd Essex CT 06426 also: 63 Willow Pl Vail CO 81657

THOMAS, CALVERT, lawyer; b. Balt., Nov. 1, 1916; s. William Douglas Nelson and Elizabeth Steuart (Calvert) T.; m. Margaret Somervell Berry, Sept. 1, 1943; children:—Calvert Bowie, Carolyn Brooke Dold. Douglas Mackubin. B.S., Washington and Lee U., 1938; LL.B., U. Md., 1940. Bar: Md. bar 1940, D.C. bar 1972, Mich. bar 1947, N.Y. State bar 1974, Conn. bar 1979. Asso. atty. Legal Aid Bur., Balt., 1940-41; atty. Lehmeyer & Moser, Balt., 1941-42, Solicitor's Office, Dept. Labor, Washington, 1942-43, Tax Ct. of U.S., Washington, 1943-44, Chief Counsel's Office, Bur. Internal Revenue, Washington, 1944-46; atty. legal staff Gen. Motors Corp., Detroit, 1946-72; asst. gen. counsel Gen. Motors Corp., 1972-78; sec., asst. gen. counsel in charge N.Y. legal staff, N.Y.C., 1973-78; chmn. Thomas Cadillac, Inc., 1978—. Councilman, Franklin Village, Mich., 1958-60, pres., 1960-64; Bd. dirs. Franklin Community Assn., 1956-58; vice chmn. Kingswood Sch., Cranbrook, 1968-69, chmn., 1969-71; trustee Cranbrook Schs., 1971-73, Washington and Lee U., 1975—; chmn. Old Guard West Hartford, 1992-93. Mem. Am., Fed., Detroit, Md., D.C., N.Y. bar assns., State Bar Mich. (chmn. tax sect. 1971-72), Am. Soc. Corp. Secs., So. Md. Soc., Soc. Colonial Wars, Lords of Md. Manors, Descendants of the Signers of the Declaration of Independence, Sons of the Am. Revolution, Soc. of the Ark and Dove, Soc. of Founders and Patriots of Am., Beta Theta Pi, Phi Delta Phi, Omicron Delta Kappa. Republican. Episcopalian. Clubs: Orchard Lake (Mich.) Country; Recess (Detroit); Princeton (N.Y.C.); Country of Farmington (Conn.); Hartford, Hartford Golf. Home: 138 Stoner Dr West Hartford CT 06107-1306 Office: 1530 Albany Ave Hartford CT 06112-2114

THOMAS, CAROL TAYLOR, general services coordinator; b. Southern Pines, N.C., Jan. 13, 1952; d. Elbert Watson and Lela Frances (Reynolds) Taylor; m. Michael Conley Thomas, Sept. 8, 1973; children: Kelli R. Thomas, Melvin Conley Thomas. Student, Sandhills Community Coll., 1970-72. Asst. purchasing officer County of Moore, Carthage, N.C., 1978-83, purchasing officer, 1983—, purchasing officer, airport mgr., 1988—. Mem. Moore County Airport Adv. Com., N.C. Airport Assn., Nat. Purchasing Mgmt. Assn., Purchasing Mgmt. Assn. of Carolinas-Va. Inc. (triangle chpt. 1988—). Presbyterian. Avocations: gardening, exercising, bicycling, go kart racing, family. Office: Moore County Airport Moore County Courthouse PO Box 905 Carthage NC 28327

THOMAS, CAROLE DOLORES, gerontologist; b. Huntington, Ind., Dec. 20, 1937; d. James Robert and Gladys Agnes (Walraven) Williams; m. Norman Day Thomas, Sept. 1, 1962 (separated); children: Diane Thomas Laucirica, Mark Alexander. BA in Polit. Sci., U. Ill., 1960; MA in Gerontology, U. South Fla., 1982. Human servs. analyst Dept. Health and Rehab. Svcs., Tampa, Fla., 1983-94; adult protective investigator 1994—; mem. Adult Protection Team, Tampa, 1990—, Bradenton, Fla., 1990—; Long Term Care Ombudsman Coun., Tampa, 1989—. Mem. Fla. Orch. Guild, Tampa, 1985—; guardian ad litem 13th Jud. Cir., Tampa, 1991—; vol. Performing Arts Ctr., Tampa, 1992—. Avocations: personal computing, reading, games. Home: 14314 Oludinar Dr Tampa FL 33613-3107 Office: Dept Health & Rehab Svcs 4000 W Martin Luther King Dr Tampa FL 33614

THOMAS, CHARLES ALLEN, JR., molecular biologist, educator; b. Dayton, Ohio, July 7, 1927; s. Charles Allen and Margaret Stoddard (Talbott) T.; m. Margaret M. Gay, July 7, 1951; children: Linda Carrick, Stephen Gay. AB, Princeton (N.J.) U., 1950; PhD, Harvard U., 1954. Rsch. scientist Eli Lilly Co., Indpls., 1954-55; NCR fellow U. Mich., Ann Arbor, 1955-56, prof. biophysics, 1956-57; prof. biophysics Johns Hopkins U., Balt., 1957-67; prof. biol. chemistry Med. Sch. Harvard U., Boston, 1967-78; chmn. dept. cellular biology Scripps Clinic & Rsch. Found., La Jolla, Calif., 1978-81; pres., dir. Helicon Found., San Diego, 1981—; founder, CEO The Syntro Corp., San Diego, 1981-82; pres., CEO, dir. of R&D Pantox Corp., San Diego, 1989—; mem. genetics study sect. NIH, 1968-72; mem. rsch. grants com. Am. Cancer Soc., 1972-76, 79-85. Mem. editorial bd. Virology, 1967-73, Jour. Molecular Biology, 1968-72, BioPhysics Jour., 1965-68, Chromosoma, 1969-79, Analytic Biochemistry, 1970-79, Biochim Biophys. ACTA, 1973-79, Plasmid, 1977—. With USNR, 1945-46. NRC fellow, 1965-66. Mem. AAAS, Am. Acad. Arts and Scis., Am. Fedn. Biol. Chemists, Genetics Soc. Am., Am. Chem. Soc. Achievements include rsch. in genetic and structural orgn. of chromosomes and devel. of a practical assessment of ind. antioxidant def. system by analytical biochemistry. Home: 1640 El Paso Real La Jolla CA 92037-6304 Office: Helicon Foundation 4622 Santa Fe St San Diego CA 92109-1601

THOMAS, CHARLES HOWARD, II, federal official; b. Buffalo, June 23, 1934; s. John Charles Thomas and Helen (Wright) Cogswell; m. Lourana Swift, Dec. 28, 1956; children: John, Stuart, Jennifer Thomas McGrath, Andrew. AB, Harvard U., 1956; student, Nat. War Coll., 1977-78. Fgn. service officer U.S. Consulate, Cuidad Juarez, Mex., 1960-62, U.S. Embassy, La Paz, Bolivia, 1962-64, Dept. State, Washington, 1964-66; dep. dir. Peace Corps, Tegucigalpa, Honduras, 1966-67; dir. Peace Corps, Montevideo, Uruguay, 1967-69; polit. counselor U.S. Embassy, Lisbon, Potugal, 1974-77; dep. chief of mission U.S. Embassy, Brussels, 1982-85; dir. ops. center Dept. State, Washington, 1970-74, dir. NATO affairs, 1978-82, dep. asst. sec. of state for European and Can. Affairs, 1985-89; amb. to Hungary Dept. State, Budapest, 1990-94; spl. envoy for Burdensharing, Bur. Politico-Mil. Affairs Dept. State, Washington, 1994—. Served to lt., USN, 1956-59. Recipient Heroism award, Dept. State, 1965. Mem. Am. Fgn. Service Assn. Episcopalian. Avocation: skiing. Office: Bur Politico-Mil Affairs Dept State 2201 C St NW Rm 2422 Washington DC 20520

THOMAS, CHRISTOPHER ROBERT, food products company executive; b. San Diego, Dec. 5, 1948; m. Christina Q. Thomas, Apr. 16, 1979. BSBA, U. So. Calif., 1977. CPA, Calif. Auditor Arthur Andersen & Co., Calif., 1977-84; v.p. fin., chief fin. officer Collins Foods Internat. Inc., L.A., 1984—. Sgt. USMC, 1967-70. Mem. AICPA, Calif. Soc. CPA's, Fin. Acctg. Found., Fin. Execs. Inst. Office: Collins Foods Internat Inc 12665 W Jefferson Blvd Los Angeles CA 90066-7008

THOMAS, CHRISTOPHER YANCEY, III, surgeon, educator; b. Kansas City, Mo., Oct. 27, 1923; s. Christopher Yancey and Dorothea Louise (Engel) T.; m. Barbara Ann Barcroft, June 27, 1946; children—Christopher, Gregg, Jeffrey, Anne. Student, U. Colo., 1942-44; M.D., U. Kans., 1948. Diplomate Am. Bd. Surgery. Intern U. Utah Hosp., Salt Lake City, 1948-49; resident in surgery Cleve. Clinic Found., 1949-52; pvt. practice specializing in surgery Kansas City, Mo., 1954-89; mem. staff St. Luke's Hosp., chief surgery, 1969-70; mem. staff Children's Mercy Hosp.; prof. surgery U. Mo., Kansas City Med. Sch.; adv. dir. Bank IV; pres. St. Luke's Hosp. Edn. Found., 1977-83, Med. Plaza Corp., 1977-79; pres. Midwest Organ Bank, 1977-82. Editor IMTRAC investment adv. letter, 1978—. Served to capt. M.C., U.S. Army, 1952-54. Fellow ACS; mem. AMA, Southwestern Surg. Congress, Central Surg. Assn., Mo. State Med. Soc., Kansas City Surg. Soc. (pres. 1968), Jackson County Med. Soc. (pres. 1971). Republican. Methodist. Clubs: Kansas City Country, Homestead Country. Home: 5830 Mission Dr Shawnee Mission KS 66208-1139 Office: Ste 100 4210 Shawnee Mission Pky Mission KS 66205

THOMAS, CLARA MCCANDLESS, retired English language educator, biographer; b. Strathroy, Ont., Can., May 22, 1919; d. Basil and Mabel (Sullivan) McCandless; m. Morley Keith Thomas, May 23, 1942; children: Stephen, John. B.A., U. Western Ont., London, 1941, M.A., 1944; Ph.D., U. Toronto, 1962; DLitt (hon.), York U., 1986, Trent U., 1991; LLD (hon.), Brock U., 1992. Instr. English U. Western Ont., London, 1947-61, U. Toronto, 1958-61; asst. prof. English York U., Toronto, 1961-68; prof. York U., 1969-84, prof. emeritus, 1984—; acad. adv. panel Social Scis. and Humanities Research Council, 1981-84; mem. Killam Awards Selection Bd., 1978-81. Author biography of Anna Jameson, 1967, of Egerton Ryerson, 1969, of Margaret Laurence, 1969, 75, of William Arthur Deacon, 1982; Literary criticism (Can.), 1946, 72; 94; mem. editl. bd. Literary History of Can., 1980—; Collected Works of Northrop Frye, 1993—. Recipient Internat. Coun. of Can. Studies prize No. Telecom, 1989; grantee Can. Coun., 1967, 73, Social Sci. and Humanities Rsch. Coun. Can., 1978-80. Fellow Royal Soc. Can.; mem. Assn. Can. Univs., Tchrs. English (pres. 1971-72), Assn. Can. and Que. Lit., Bus. and Profl. Women's Club. For Can. Studies. New Democratic. Office: York U 305 Scott Libr, 4700 Keele St, Downsview, ON Canada M3J 1P3

THOMAS, CLARENCE, U.S. supreme court justice; b. Savannah, Ga., June 23, 1948. BA, Holy Cross Coll. 1971; JD, Yale U., 1974. Bar: Mo. Asst. atty. gen. State of Mo., Jefferson City, 1974-77; atty. Monsanto Co., St. Louis, 1977-79; legis. asst. to Sen. John C. Danforth, Washington, 1979-81; asst. sec. for civil rights Dept. Edn., Washington, 1981-82; chmn. U.S. EEOC, Washington, 1982-90; judge U.S. Ct. Appeals, Washington, 1990-91; assoc. justice U.S. Supreme Ct., Washington, 1991—. Office: US Supreme Court Supreme Ct Bldg 1 First St NE Washington DC 20543

THOMAS, CLAUDEWELL SIDNEY, psychiatry educator; b. N.Y.C., Oct. 5, 1932; s. Humphrey Sidney and Frances Elizabeth (Collins) T.; m. Carolyn Pauline Rozansky, Sept. 6, 1958; children: Jeffrey Evan, Julie-Anne Elizabeth, Jessica Edith. BA, Columbia U., 1952; MD, SUNY, Downstate Med. Ctr., 1956; MPH, Yale U., 1964. Diplomate Nat. Bd. Med. Examiners, Am. Bd. Psychiatry. From instr. to assoc. prof. Yale U., New Haven, 1963-68, dir. Yale tng. program in social community psychiatry, 1967-70; dir. div. mental health service programs NIMH, Washington, 1970-73; chmn. dept. psychiatry U.M.D.N.J., Newark, 1973-83; prof. dept. psychiatry Drew Med. Sch., 1983—, chmn. dept. psychiatry, 1983-93; prof. dept. psychiatry UCLA, 1983-94, vice chmn. dept. psychiatry, 1983-93, prof. emeritus dept. psychiatry, 1994—; cons. A.K. Rice Inst., Washington, 1978-80, SAMSA/PHS Cons., 1991—; mem. L.A. County Superior Ct. Psych. Panel, 1991—. Author: (with B. Bergen) Issues and Problems in Contemporary Society, 1966; editor (with R. Bryce LaPorte) Alienation in Contemporary Society, 1976, (with J. Lindenthal) Psychiatry and Mental Health Science Handbook; mem. editorial bd. Internat. Jour. Mental Health, Adminstrn. In Mental Health. Served to capt. USAF, 1959-61. Fellow Am. Psychoanalytic Assn., Am. Psychiat. Assn. (hon. life), Am. Pub. Health Assn., Royal Soc. Health, N.Y. Acad. Sci., N.Y. Acad. Medicine; mem. Am. Sociol. Assn. Avocations: tennis, racquetball, violin, piano. Home and Office: 30676 Palos Verdes Dr E Palos Verdes Peninsula CA 90274-6354 Personal philosophy: Integrity sooner or later calls upon courage. If courage is not home integrity goes away.

THOMAS, COLIN GORDON, JR., surgeon, medical educator; b. Iowa City, July 25, 1918; s. Colin Gordon and Eloise Kinzer (Brainerd) T.; m. Shirley Forbes, Sept. 14, 1946; children: Karen, Barbara, James G., John F. B.S., U. Chgo., 1940, M.D., 1943. Diplomate Am. Bd. Surgery. Intern U. Iowa Hosp., 1943-44, resident surgery, 1944-45, 47-50; assoc. in surgery U. Iowa Med. Sch., 1950-51, asst. prof., 1951-52; mem. faculty U. N.C. Med. Sch., Chapel Hill, 1952—, prof. surgery, 1961—, Byah Thomason Doxey-Sanford Doxey prof. surgery, 1982—, chmn. dept., 1966-84, chief div. gen. surg., 1984-89, part-time prof., 1991—. Mem. editorial bd. Current Surgery; contbr. surg. texts, numerous articles to med. jours. Served to capt., M.C. AUS, 1945-47. Recipient Prof. award U. N.C. Sch. Medicine, 1964, Disting. Svc. award U. Chgo., 1982, Med. Alumni Disting. faculty award U. N.C., 1984; Berryhill lectr. U. N.C., 1989. Mem. AMA, ACS (Disting. Leadership award N.C. chpt. 1990), AAUP, Am. Thyroid Assn., Am. Assn. Cancer Research, Am. Assn. Endocrine Surgeons (pres. 1989-90), Soc. Univ. Surgeons, So. Surg. Assn. (v.p. 1989-90), N.Y. Acad. Scis., Halsted Soc., Ga. Surg. Soc., Soc. Exptl. Biology and Medicine, Am. Surg. Assn., Womack Surg. Soc. (pres. 1981-83), Soc. Internationale de Chirurgie, Soc. Surgery Alimentary Tract, N.C. Surg. Assn., Internat. Assn. Endocrine Surgeons, Alpha Omega Alpha. Episcopalian (warden 1961-62). Home: 408 Morgan Creek Rd Chapel Hill NC 27514-4934

THOMAS, CRAIG, senator; b. Cody, Wyo. Feb. 17, 1933; s. Craig E. and Marge Oweta (Lynn) T.; m. Susan Roberts; children: Peter, Paul, Patrick, Alexis. BS, U. Wyo., 1955. Exec. v.p. Wyo. Farm Bur., Laramie, 1960-66; asst. legis. dir. Am. Farm Bur., Wash., 1966-71; dir. nat. resource Am. Farm Bur., Chgo., 1971-75; gen. mgr. Wyo. Rural Elec. Assn., 1975-89; mem. Wyo. Ho. of Reps., 1985-1989, 101st-103rd Congresses from Wyo., Washington, D.C., 1989-95; senator State Wyo., Washington, 1995—. Former

---

chmn. Natrona County (Wyo.) Rep. Com.; state rep. Natrona County Dist.; del. Rep. Nat. Conv., 1980. Capt. USMC. Mem. Am. Soc. Trade Execs., Masons. Methodist. Office: US Senate Washington DC 20510

THOMAS, DALE E., lawyer; b. New Rochelle, N.Y., Jan. 25, 1947. AB summa cum laude, Princeton U., 1969; MDiv, Yale Divinity Sch., 1973; JD, Yale U., 1974. Bar: Ill. 1975. Law clerk U.S. Ct. Appeals 2d cir., 1974-75; ptnr. Sidley & Austin, Chgo. Mem. ABA, Ill. State Bar Assn., Chgo. Bar Assn., Phi Beta Kappa. Office: Sidley & Austin 1 First Nat Plz Chicago IL 60603

THOMAS, DANIEL FOLEY, telecommunications company executive; b. Washington, Aug. 24, 1950; s. Richard Kenneth and Margaret (Foley) T.; m. Barbara Jane Clark, June 30, 1973; 1 child, Alison Clark. BS in Acctg., Mt. St. Mary's Coll., 1972. CPA, Va. Auditor Deloitte, Haskins and Sells, Washington, 1972-74; various fin. positions Communications Satellite Corp., Washington, 1974-78, asst. treas., 1984-85, treas., 1986-87, controller, 1987-89; controller Comsat Telesystems, Washington, 1978-79; mgr. acctg. and taxes Satellite Bus. Systems, McLean, Va., 1979-81, treas., 1981-84; v.p. fin. Comsat Tech. Products, Inc., Washington, 1985-86, Comsat Video Enterprises, Inc., Washington, 1989-90; v.p. Leasetec Corp., Boulder, Colo., 1990—. Named One of Outstanding Young Men Am., 1981. Mem. AICPA, Va. Jaycees (life), Great Falls Jaycees (pres. 1978). Roman Catholic. Avocations: running, raquetball. Home: 1299 S Teal Ct Boulder CO 80303-1480 Office: Leasetec Corp 1401 Pearl St Boulder CO 80302-5319

THOMAS, DANIEL HOLCOMBE, federal judge; b. Prattville, Ala., Aug. 25, 1906; s. Columbus Eugene and Augusta (Pratt) T.; m. Dorothy Quina, Sept. 26, 1936 (dec. 1977); children: Daniel H., Jr., Merrill Pratt; m. Catharine J. Miller, Oct. 25, 1979. LL.B., U. Ala., 1928. Bar: bar. Pvt. practice Mobile, Ala., 1929; asst. solicitor Mobile County; mem. firm Lyons, Chamberlain & Courtney, Mobile County, 1932-37, Lyons & Thomas, Mobile County, 1937-43, Lyons, Thomas & Pipes, Mobile County, 1946-51; judge U.S. Dist. Ct., Mobile, 1951—, now sr. judge. Mem. exec. bd. Mobile Area council Boy Scouts Am., 1963—, v.p., 1967-69, pres., 1973—; mem. nat. council, 1973—, Trustee dept. archieves and history, State of Ala. Served with USNR, 1943-45. Recipient Silver Beaver award Boy Scouts Am., 1970, Silver Antelope award, 1975. Methodist. Club: Mobile Country. Home: 13 Dogwood Cir Mobile AL 36608-2308 Office: US Dist Ct PO Box 137 Mobile AL 36601-0137

THOMAS, DARRELL DENMAN, lawyer; b. Lake Cormorant, Miss., Sept. 10, 1931; s. Darrell Dane and Maggie Adele (McKay) T.; m. Dora Ann Bailey, Feb. 12, 1957 (div. 1988). BS, Memphis State U., 1957; JD, U. Denver, 1960. Bar: Colo. 1960, U.S. Dist. Ct. Colo. 1960, U.S. Supreme Ct. 1967, U.S. Ct. Appeals (10th cir.) 1971. Law clk. to presiding justice U.S. Dist. Ct., Colo., 1960-61; ptnr. Mills & Thomas, Colorado Springs, Colo., 1961-65; pvt. practice Colorado Springs, 1965—; U.S. commr. U.S. Dist. Ct., 1961-71, U.S. magistrate, 1971-91. Pres. Colorado Springs Symphony, 1979-82; v.p. Colorado Springs Symphony Orch. Found. With U.S. Army, 1952-54. Mem. ABA, Colo. Bar Assn., El Paso County Bar Assn., El Paso Club (dir. 1985-88), Broadmoor Golf Club, Garden of the Gods Club, Masons, Shriner. Republican. Avocations: golf, fishing, hunting, cooking. Office: 115 E Vermijo Ave Colorado Springs CO 80903-2004

THOMAS, DARWIN LAMAR, sociology educator; b. Genola, Utah, Dec. 3, 1933; s. David Bynon and Grace (Hartvigsen) T.; m. Beverly Morrison, Sept. 14, 1959; children: Kim, Suanne, Rebecca, Kristi, Sara, David. BS with honors, Brigham Young U., 1962, MA, 1964; PhD, U. Minn., 1968. Instr. Clara Elizabeth Fund, Flint, Mich., 1962-63; instr. Child Devel. and Family Relations dept. Brigham Young U., Provo, Utah, 1964-65, assoc. prof. sociology, 1972-77, prof., 1977—, dir. Family Research Inst., 1973-77, editor Family Perspective mag., 1983-91; asst. prof. sociology Wash. State U., Pullman, 1968-72. Author: Family Socialization and the Adolescent, 1974, Social Psychology, 1980; editor Population Resources and Future, 1972, Religion and Family Connection, 1988; contbr articles to profl. jours. Served with U.S. Army, 1956-58. NIMH fellow, 1965-68; named Outstanding Social Scientist, Western Behavioral Sci. Inst., La Jolla, Calif. 1973. Mem. Am. Sociol. Assn., Nat. Council Family Relations (pres. family theory com. 1972-73). Mormon. Avocations: horsemanship, ranching. Office: Brigham Young U Dept Sociology # 844 Swkt Provo UT 84602

THOMAS, DAVID ALBERT, law educator; b. L.A., Feb. 4, 1944; s. Albert Rees and Betty Lou (Adams) T.; m. Paula Rasmussen, Aug. 7, 1967; children: Rebecca, David R., John H., Matthew A., Susannah, Amanda, Christina, Erin. BA, Brigham Young U., 1967; JD, Duke U., 1972; MLS, Brigham Young U., 1977. Jud. clk. U.S. Dist. Ct. Utah, Salt Lake City, 1972-73; pvt. practice Salt Lake City, 1973-74; asst. prof. Law Sch. Brigham Young U., Provo, Utah, 1974-76; assoc. prof. Law Sch. Brigham Young U., Provo, 1976-79, prof. Law Sch., 1979—, dir. law libr. Law Sch., 1974-90; accreditation site insp. ABA, Chgo., 1979—. Author: Utah Civil Procedure, 1980, (with others) A Practical Guide to Disputes Between Adjoining Landowners, 1989, Utah Civil Practice, 1992; editor-in-chief, prin. author: (15 volumes) Thompson on Real Property, Thomas Edit. With U.S. Army, 1969-71, Vietnam. Home: 188 E 1864 S Orem UT 84058-7864 Office: Law Sch Brigham Young U Provo UT 84602

THOMAS, DAVID ANSELL, retired university dean; b. Holliday, Tex., July 5, 1917; s. John Calvin Mitchell and Alice (Willet) T.; m. Mary Elizabeth Smith, May 18, 1946; 1 dau., Ann Elizabeth. B.A., Tex. Tech. Coll., 1937; M.B.A., Tex. Christian U., 1948; Ph.D., U. Mich., 1956. C.P.A., Tex. Accountant Texaco, Inc., 1937-42; assoc. prof. Tex. Christian U., 1946-49; lectr. U. Mich., 1949-53; prof. accounting Cornell U., Ithaca, N.Y., 1953-84; assoc. dean Cornell U. Grad. Sch. Mgmt., 1962-79; acting dean Cornell U. Grad. Sch. Bus. and Pub. Adminstrn., 1979-81; dean Samuel Curtis Johnson Grad. Sch. Mgmt. Cornell U., 1981-84. Author: Accelerated Amortization of Defense Facilities, 1958, Accounting for Home Builders, 1952; Contbr. numerous articles to publs.; Editor: Fed. Accountant, 1956-58. Pres. Exec. Investors, Inc.; exec. dir. Charles E. Merrill Family Found., 1954-57, Robert A. Magowan Found., 1957-60; administr. Charles E. Merrill Trust, 1957-81, Ithaca Growth Fund.; Bd. dirs. Ithaca Opera Assn., Cornell Student Agys. Served to capt. USAAF, 1942-46, PTO. Mem. Tex. Soc. C.P.A.'s, Nat. Assn. Accountants, Am. Accounting Assn., Phi Beta Kappa, Beta Alpha Psi. Clubs: Cornell of N.Y, University, Statler (pres., dir.). Home: Devenshire Park 1560 Jasper Ct Venice FL 34292-4336

THOMAS, DAVID HURST, archaeologist; b. Oakland, Calif., May 27, 1945; s. David Hurst and Barbara (Longwell) T.; m. Lorann S.A. Pendleton, Aug. 25, 1985; 1 child, David Hurst III. BA, U. Calif., Davis, 1967, MA, 1968, PhD in Anthropology, 1971. Asst. prof. anthropology CCNY, 1971-72; asst. curator Am. Mus. Natural History, 1972-77, assoc. curator, 1977-82, curator, 1982—, chmn. dept. anthropology, 1976-84; adj. curator Fla. State Mus.; overseers com. to visit the Peabody Mus. Harvard U., 1983-89; founding trustee Nat. Mus. of the Am. Indian, 1990—, vice chmn., 1992—; panelist in behavioral sci. NSF, 1988-91; exec. com. Soc. Am. Archeology, 1986-88. Author: Predicting the Past, 1974, Figuring Anthropology, 1976, Archaeology, 1979, 89, Refiguring Anthropology, 1986, St. Catherines: An Island in Time, 1988, The Native Americans, 1993, Exploring Ancient Native America, 1994; gen. editor: The North American Indian, 1986, Columbian Consequences: vol. 1, 1989, vol. 2, 1990, vol. 3, 1991, The Archaeology of the Spanish Borderlands (25 vol.), 1991; editor American Anthropologist, 1990—, Illustrated History of Humankind, 5 vols., 1993, Native Am. 1995; mem. editorial bd. Geoarcheology; adv. bd. N.Am. Archaeologist, Advances in Archaeol. Method and Theory, Jour. Quantative Anthropology, New Directions in Archaeology. Recipient Presidential recognition award Am. Archeology, 1991, Franciscan Inst. medal, 1992; NSF grantee, 1977-78; Edward John Noble Found. grantee, 1974—; Nat. Geographic Soc. grantee, 1975-76, 81. Mem. NAS, Soc. Am. Archaeology (exec. com. 1986-88), Am. Anthrop. Assn. (arch. section editor), Internat. Union Pre-and Proto-Sci., Writers Guild of Am. Research on Desert West and Am. S.E. Home: 200 Piermont Ave South Nyack NY 10960-4507 Office: Am Mus Natural History Dept of Anthropology New York NY 10024

THOMAS, DAVID PHILLIP, forestry educator, college administrator; b. Wasco, Oreg., July 7, 1918; s. William Phillip and Mabel Josephine (Hulery)

T.; m. Geraldine Alaire Culross, Oct. 15, 1943; children: Larry K., Jeffrey A., Glenn R. B.S., U. Wash., 1941, M.F., 1947; postgrad., N.Y. State Coll. Forestry, Syracuse U., 1947-50. Research asso. Engring. Expt. Sta., U. Wash., Seattle, 1946-47; instr. wood tech. N.Y. State Coll. Forestry, 1947-50; mem. faculty U. Wash., Seattle, 1950—; prof. forest resources U. Wash., 1966-84, prof. emeritus, 1984—; spl. asst. to v.p. acad. affairs, 1964-72, dir. Inst. Forest Products, 1966-72, asso. dean Coll. Forest Resources, 1973-75; chmn. mgmt. and social scis. div. U. Wash. (Coll. Forest Resources), 1975-80; Instl. rep. Assn. Naval ROTC Colls., 1966-72; curriculum cons. U.S. Army ROTC program, 1969; program dir. Peace Corps, U. Wash., 1968-72; mem. Chile Forestry Vol. Tech. Support Program, 1968-72; del. Internat. Union Forestry Research Orgns., 1967, 76, World Forestry Congress, 1978. Trustee Nellie Martin Carmen Coll. Scholarship, 1992—; mem. King County Environ. Devel. Commn., Seattle, 1972-79; mem. exec. bd., chief Seattle coun. Boy Scouts Am., 1957-80, coun. commr., 1965-67; mem. Wash. State Forest Practices Adv. Com., 1974-79, Wash. State Forest Practices Appeals Bd., 1981-85; trustee Keep Wash. Green Assn., 1975-86, adv. com., 1986-90, Wash. State Forestry Conf., 1985-90; bd. dirs. U. Lions Found., 1986—, chmn., 1991—. Lt. comdr. USNR, 1941-45. Recipient Silver Beaver award Boy Scouts Am., 1961; Outstanding Service award Wash. State Forestry Conf., 1984; Stewart H. Holbrook Disting. Service award for wild fire prevention Keep Wash. Green Assn., 1987. Fellow Soc. Am. Foresters (chmn. S. Puget Sound chpt. 1977-78, chmn.-elect state soc. 1979-80, chmn. 1980-81 Forester of Yr. award Wash. Soc. 1982); mem. Forest Products Rsch. Soc., Forest History Soc., Soc. Wood Sci. and Tech., Western Forestry and Conservation Assn., U. Wash. Foresters Alumni Assn. (pres. 1978-79, Honored Alumnus award 1985), Am. Forestry Assn. (life), Lions Internat. Svcs. Club, Sigma Xi, Xi Sigma Pi, Phi Sigma. Mem. United Ch. of Christ. Home: 3607 NE 100th St Seattle WA 98125-7818

THOMAS, (CHARLES) DAVIS, editor; b. Detroit, Dec. 20, 1928; s. Charles Richard and Nellie Clare (Davis) T.; m. Karin Ronnefeldt, Apr. 21, 1956; 1 child, Cord Alexander. B.A., U. Mich., 1950. Reporter Detroit News, 1950; reporter Life Mag., N.Y.C., 1954-57; staff corr. Life Mag., Los Angeles, 1957-60; photography editor Saturday Evening Post, Phila., 1961; asst. mng. editor Saturday Evening Post, 1962, mng. editor, 1962-63; editor in chief Ladies' Home Jour., N.Y.C., 1964-65; pub. cons. N.Y.C., Toronto, Geneva, Switzerland, 1965-70; exec. editor Holiday Mag., N.Y.C., 1970, Travel & Leisure Mag., N.Y.C., 1971-75; editor in chief Down East Mag., Camden, Maine, 1976-93, v.p., assoc. pub., 1984-93; editor at large Down East Mag., 1994—. Editor: Moon, Man's Greatest Adventure, 1970 (Annual award Aviation Space Writers' Assn. 1971), (with Karin Ronnefeldt) People of the First Man: Life Among the Plains Indians in their Final Days of Glory, 1976. Served with AUS, 1951-54. Home and Office: 57 Megunticook St Camden ME 04843-1643

THOMAS, DEBI (DEBRA J. THOMAS), ice skater; b. Poughkeepsie, N.Y., Mar. 25, 1967; d. McKinley and Janice T.; m. Brian Vanden Hogen. Student, Stanford U. Competitive figure skater, 1976-88. Winner U.S. figure Skating Championship, 1986, 88, Women's World Figure Skating Championship, 1986, World Profl. Figure Skating Championship, 1988, 89. Recipient Am. Black Achievement Award, Ebony mag., named Women Athlete of Yr., 1986; winner Bronze medal Olympic Games, 1988. Address: care IMG 22 E 71st St New York NY 10021-4911*

THOMAS, DEBORAH ALLEN, English educator; b. Biddeford, Maine, Sept. 1, 1943; d. Donald Paine and Marjorie (Thompson) Allen; m. Gordon Albert Thomas, Sept. 10, 1966; 1 child, Allen Mansfield. AB magna cum laude, Brown U., 1965; MA, Duke U., 1966; PhD, U. Rochester, 1972. Assoc. in humanities Eastman Sch. Music U. Rochester, N.Y., 1969-72; adj. asst. prof. English Fairleigh Dickinson U., Madison, N.J., 1973-76; co-adj. asst. prof. English Rutgers U., New Brunswick and Newark, N.J., 1976-80; asst. prof. English Villanova (Pa.) U., 1980-84, assoc. prof. English, 1984-91, prof. English, 1991—; visiting scholar Harvard U., Cambridge, Mass., 1985-86. Author: Dickens and the Short Story, 1982, Thackeray and Slavery, 1993; editor: Dickens, Selected Short Fiction, 1976; contbr. articles to profl. jours. Scholar Duke U., 1965-66; fellow U. Rochester, 1966-67, NEH fellow, 1985-86; faculty rsch. grantee Villanova U., summer 1984, 87, 92. Mem. MLA, N.E. Victorian Studies Assn., Dickens Soc. (sec., treas. 1979-81), Phi Beta Kappa. Avocations: swimming, hiking, aerobics. Office: Villanova U English Dept Villanova PA 19085

THOMAS, DONALD CHARLES, microbiology educator, former university dean and administrator; b. Cin., Sept. 26, 1935; s. Howard G. and Elsie M. (Sack) T.; m. Barbara J. Kindt, Sept. 2, 1957; children: Mark D., Matthew K., Michael J. B.S., Xavier U., Cin., 1957; M.S., U. Cin., 1959; Ph.D., St. Louis U., 1968. Instr. Villa Madonna Coll., Covington, KY., 1961-63; asst. prof. Ohio State U., Columbus, 1968-72; assoc. dir. Ohio State U. Research Found., Columbus, 1972-77; assoc. prof. pathology, microbiology and immunology Wright State U., Dayton, Ohio, 1977-94; dean , prof. emeritus Wright State U., 1977-83, dean, vice provost, 1983-86, assoc. v.p. for research, 1986-90; mem. rsch. adv. com. Children's Hosp. Rsch. Found., Columbus, Ohio, 1968-77, cancer com. Ohio State U. Hosp., 1971-72, Com. on Biomed. Ethics, 1973-77, human subjects rev. com. Children's Hosp., Columbus, 1975-77, com. on rsch. devel. VA Ctr., Dayton, Ohio, 1977-80, steering com. Consortium for Cancer Control in Ohio, 1978—, evaluation com., 1980—, pilot rsch. com. Am Cancer Soc., Ohio Div., Inc., 1979-82, regents adv. com. for grad. studies Ohio Bd. Regents, 1980-90, Gov.'s Tech. Task Force, Ohio Dept. Econ. and Community Devel., 1982-82, chmn. bd., 1989-92; adminstrv. adviser Nat. Reyes Syndrome Found., Bryan, Ohio, 1975-81; lab cons. VA Med. Ctr., Dayton, 1978-81. Treas. bd. dirs. Hospice of Dayton, Inc., 1981—; staff participant Young Pastors Seminar, United Presbyn. Ch., N.Y.C., 1977-79; v.p. bd. dirs. St. Leonard Ctr., Dayton, 1983-89; bd. dirs. Miami Valley Bus. Incubator, 1985-90; trustee St. Elizabeth Med. Ctr. Found., 1985-89, bd. dirs. Applied Info. Tech. Ctr. Inc., 1986-88, bd. dirs. Miami Valley Regional Small Bus. Inc., 1985-90. NIH predoctoral trainee, 1963-68; grantee NIH, 1968-72, Dept. Edn., 1978-88. Mem. Am. Soc. Microbiology, AAAS, Licensing Execs. Soc., Fedn. Am. Scientists, Am. Soc. for Virology, Union of Concerned Scientists. Clubs: Woodhaven Swim, Dayton Exec. (Dayton). Office: Wright State U 3640 Colonel Glenn Hwy Dayton OH 45435-0001

THOMAS, DOROTHY WORTHY, English educator; b. Charlotte, N.C., Dec. 13, 1940; d. Utah Worthy and Myrtle Lee (Harvey) Kirkpatrick; m. Leon R. Thomas, Dec. 15, 1963; children: Tonya Monique, Tracy Michele, Tecla Mionne, Tasha Monette. BA in English, Bennett Coll., 1963; MA in French, Hampton U., 1973; Cert. in Advanced Studies in Ednl. Adminstrn., Coll. of William and Mary, 1982; postgrad., Ind. U. of Pa., 1993—. Cert. tchr., Va. French and English tchr. Irwin Ave. Jr. High Sch., Charlotte, 1963-65, Huntington High Sch., Newport News, Va., 1966-71, Warwick High Sch. Newport News, 1971-88; English tchr. Booker T. Washington High Sch., Reidsville, N.C., 1965-66; staff devel. specialist Newport News Pub. Schs., 1988-91; asst. prof. English Hampton (Va.) U., 1991—; cons. Newport News Pub. Schs., 1988-91. Author brochure Program for Effective Teaching, 1990. Fellow ASCD, Va. Assn. Tchrs. of English, Nat. Coun. Tchrs. of English, Jack & Jill of Am., Inc., Kappa Delta Pi, Alpha Kappa Alpha (Epistoleus 1992—). Democrat. Presbyterian. Avocations: aerobics, reading, travel, bowling. Home: 1232 Patrick Ln Newport News VA 23602-2428

THOMAS, DUDLEY BRECKINRIDGE, newspaper pubisher; b. Caldwell, N.J., Oct. 29, 1933; s. Calvin Lewis and Margaret M. (Mosier) T.; m. Elisabeth Platt, Jan. 27, 1957; children: Gregory Calvin, Thomas Laurence. BA in History, Washington and Lee U., 1955; LLB, George Washington U., 1960. Advt. sales, mgmt. Washington Post, 1958-70; bus. mgr. Star-Exponent, Culpeper, Va., 1970; editor, bus. mgr. Daily Record, Long Branch, N.J., 1971-74; pub. Lake County News-Herald, Willoughby, Ohio, 1974-88; Bridgeport (Conn.) Post and Bridgeport Telegram, 1988-92, Conn. Post, Bridgeport, 1992—. With USMC, 1956-58. Republican. Episcopalian. Avocations: walking, boating, Civil War History. Office: Conn Post 410 State St Bridgeport CT 06604-4501

THOMAS, DUKE WINSTON, lawyer; b. Scuddy, Ky., Jan. 25, 1937; s. William E. and Grace T.; m. Jill Staples, Oct. 24, 1964; children: Deborah L., William E. II, Judith A. BSBA, Ohio State U., 1959, JD, 1964. Bar: Ohio 1964, U.S. Dist. Ct. Ohio 1966, U.S. Ct. Appeals (3d cir.) 1971, U.S.

Ct. Appeals (6th cir.) 1972, U.S. Supreme Ct. 1973, U.S. Ct. Appeals (7th cir.) 1979. Ptnr. Vorys, Sater, Seymour and Pease, Columbus, Ohio, 1964—; bd. dirs. Clinton Gas System, Columbus, Ohio Bar Liability Ins. Co., Columbus, Symix Inc., Columbus. Fellow Am. Coll. Trial Lawyers (chmn. Ohio ho. and senate joint select com. on jud. compensation 1987), Am. Bar Found., Ohio Bar Found., Columbus Bar Found.; mem. ABA (ho. of dels. 1985—, state del. 1989—), Ohio Bar Assn. (pres. 1985), Columbus Bar Assn. (pres. 1978), Pres.'s Club Ohio State U., Golf Club, Worthington Hills Country Club, Columbus Athletic Club. Home: 2090 Sheringham Rd Columbus OH 43220-4358 Office: Vorys Sater Seymour & Pease PO Box 1008 52 E Gay St Columbus OH 43216-1008

THOMAS, DWIGHT REMBERT, writer; b. Savannah, Ga., Dec. 8, 1944; s. Huguenin and Alma (Sanders) T. BA in English with honors, Emory U., 1967; PhD in Am. Lit., U. Pa., 1978. Fellow English dept. U. Pa., Phila., 1971-78; writer Savannah, 1979—; cons. Film Odyssey, Washington, 1988-89. Author: The Poe Log: A Documentary Life of Edgar Allan Poe, 1987. Dir. Edgar Allan Poe Mus., Richmond, Va., 1988—. With U.S. Army, 1969-71. Mem. MLA, Am. Med. Writers Assn., Mensa (treas. Savannah area 1985-88, local sec. 1989-90), Phi Beta Kappa. Roman Catholic. Avocations: German lang., current cinema, bicycling. Home: 7 E Gordon St Savannah GA 31401-4925

THOMAS, EDWARD DONNALL, physician, researcher; b. Mart, Tex., Mar. 15, 1920; married; 3 children. AB, U. Tex., 1941, MA, 1943; MD, Harvard U., 1946; MD (hon.), U. Cagliari, Sardinia, 1981, U. Verona, Italy, 1991, U. Parma, Italy, 1992, U. Barcelona, Spain, 1994. Lic. physician Mass., N.Y., Wash.; diplomate Am. Bd. Internal Medicine. Intern in medicine Peter Bent Brigham Hosp., Boston, 1946-47, rsch. fellow hematology, 1947-48; NRC postdoctoral fellow in medicine dept. biology MIT, Cambridge, 1950-51; chief med. resident, sr. asst. resident Peter Bent Brigham Hosp., 1951-53, hematologist, 1953-55; instr. medicine Harvard Med. Sch., Boston, 1953-55; rsch. assoc. Cancer Rsch. Found. Children's Med. Ctr., Boston, 1953-55; physician-in-chief Mary Imogene Bassett Hosp., Cooperstown, N.Y., 1955-63; assoc. clin. prof. medicine Coll. Physicians and Surgeons Columbia U., N.Y.C., 1955-63; attending physician U. Wash. Hosp., Seattle, 1963-90; prof. medicine Sch. Medicine U. Wash., Seattle, 1963-90, head divsn. oncology Sch. Medicine, 1963-85, prof. emeritus medicine Sch. Medicine, 1990—; dir. med. oncology Fred Hutchinson Cancer Rsch. Ctr., Seattle, 1974-89, assoc. dir. clin. rsch. programs, 1982-89, mem., 1974—; mem. hematology study sect. NIH, 1965-69; mem. bd. trustees and med. sci. adv. com. Leukemia Soc. Am., Inc., 1969-73; mem. clin. cancer investigation review com. Nat. Cancer Inst., 1970-74; 1st ann. Eugene C. Eppinger lectr. Peter Bent Brigham Hosp. and Harvard Med. Sch., 1974; Lilly lectr. Royal Coll. Physicians, London, 1977; Stratton lectr. Internation Soc. Hematology, 1982; Paul Aggeler lectr. U. Calif., San Francisco, 1982; 65th Mellon lectr. U. Pitts. Sch. Medicine, 1984; Stanley Wright Meml. lectr. Western Soc. Pediatric Rsch., 1985; Adolfo Ferrata lectr. Italian Soc. Hematology, Verona, Italy, 1991. Mem. editl. bd. Blood, 1962-75, 77-82, Transplantation, 1970-76, Proc. of Soc. for Exptl. Biology and Medicine, 1974-81, Leukemia Rsch., 1977-87, Hematological Oncology, 1982-87, Jour. Clin. Immunology, 1982-87, Am. Jour. Hematology, 1985—, Bone Marrow Transplantation, 1986—. With U.S. Army, 1948-50. Recipient A. Ross McIntyre award U. Nebr. Med. Ctr., 1975, Philip Levine award Am. Soc. Clin. Pathologists, 1979, Disting. Svc. in Basic Rsch. award Am. Cancer Soc., 1980, Kettering prize Gen. Motors Cancer Rsch. Found., 1981, Spl. Keynote Address award Am. Soc. Therapeutic Radiologists, 1981, Robert Roesler de Villiers award Leukemia Soc. Am., 1983, Karl Landsteiner Meml. award Am. Assn. Blood Banks, 1987, Terry Fox award Can., 1990, Internat. award Gairdner Found., 1990, N.Am. Med. Assn. Hong Kong prize, 1990, Nobel prize in medicine, 1990, Presdl. medal of sci. NSF, 1990. Mem. NAS, Am. Assn. Cancer Rsch., Am. Assn. Physicians (Kober medal 1992), Am. Fedn. Clin. Rsch., Am. Soc. Clin. Oncology (David A. Karnoksky Meml. lectr. 1983), Am. Soc. Clin. Investigation, Am. Soc. Hematology (pres. 1987-88, Henry M. Stratton lectr. 1975), Internat. Soc. Exptl. Hematology, Internat. Soc. Hematology, Academie Royale de Medicine de Belgique (corresponding mem.), Swedish Soc. Hematology (hon.), Swiss Soc. Hematology, Royal Coll. Physicians and Surgeons Can. (hon.), Western Assn. Physicians, Soc. Exptl. Biology and Medicine, Transplantation Soc., Nat. Acad. Medicine (hon.). Office: Fred Hutchinson Cancer Ctr 1124 Columbia St Seattle WA 98104-2092

THOMAS, EDWARD ST. CLAIR, hospital administrator; b. Montgomery, Ala., Nov. 11, 1934; married. BS, Xavier U., 1956; MHA, U. Mich., 1970. Adminstrv. resident Harper Hosp., Detroit, 1968-69, adminstrv. asst., 1969-70, asst. administr., 1970-77, assoc. administr., 1977-79; dir. corp. adminstrn. Harper-Grace Hosps., Detroit, 1979-81, v.p. corp. adminstrv. affairs, 1981; pres, CEO Detroit Receiving Hosp., 1991—. Mem. Mich. Hosp. Assn. (mem. various coms.). Office: Detroit Receiving Hosp 4201 Saint Antoine Blvd Detroit MI 48201-2194

THOMAS, EDWIN L., materials engineering educator. Prof., materials science MIT, Cambridge, Mass. Recipient High-Polymer Physics prize Am. Phys. Soc., 1991. Office: MIT Dept Materials Sci 13-5094 77 Massachusetts Ave Cambridge MA 02139

THOMAS, ELLEN LOUISE, private school administrator; b. Doylestown, Pa., Nov. 30, 1940; d. Edward Martin and Evelyn Graham (Axenroth) Happ; m. Eugene Greene Leffever, June 30, 1963 (dec. Nov. 1978); children: Eugene Greene II, Jeanette Ellen Dellaripa; m. William Dewey Thomas, Sept. 15, 1981; 1 child, Jeremiah David. BA in Edn., Immaculata (Pa.) Coll., 1962; postgrad., Pa. State U., 1962-67. Pvt. practice tutor Doylestown, 1958-65; tchr. Cen. Bucks Sch. System, Doylestown, 1962-65; adminstr. The Curiosity Shoppe, Doylestown, 1965—, The Toddler Ctr., Doylestown, 1979—; exec. dir. Camp Curiosity, Doylestown, 1984—; Thomas Lea Equestrian Ctr., Doylestown, 1988—; tchr. trainer Confortunity of Christian Doctrine, Doylestown, 1965-78; cons. early childhood Am. Sch. in Hong Kong, 1981-84; lectr. in early childhood Bucks County Community Ctr., Newtown, Pa., 1978-90; workshop facilitator Head Start, Phila., 1990; cons. day care Cen. Bucks C. of C., Doylestown, 1989-90; ednl. coord. Forest Grove Presbyn. Ch., 1984-90. Mem. U.S.C. of C., Washington, Bucks County C. of C., Doylestown, Nat. Fedn. of Ind. Bus., Washington. Mem ASCD, Assn. for Childhood Edn. Internat., United Pvt. Acad. Schs. Assn., Bucks County Assn. Edn. Young Children (pres. 1974-78). Home: 4425 Landisville Rd Doylestown PA 18901-1134 Office: The Curiosity Shoppe 4425 Landisville Rd Doylestown PA 18901-1134

THOMAS, ELLIOTT G., bishop; b. Pittsburgh, PA, July 15, 1926. ordained priest June 6, 1964. Bishop Diocese of St. Thomas in the Virgin Islands, 1993—. Office: Bishop's Residence PO Box 1825 68 Kronprind Gade Charlotte Amalie VI 00803*

THOMAS, ELWOOD LAUREN, state supreme court justice; b. Council Bluffs, Iowa, July 24, 1930; s. Lauren D. and Atla M. (Fight) T.; m. Susanne Faye Higdon, June 5, 1955; children: Mark, Sandra, Steven. BA, Simpson Coll., 1954; JD, Drake U., 1957. Bar: Iowa 1957, U.S. Dist. Ct. (no. dist.) Iowa 1957, U.S. Dist. Ct. (so. dist.) Iowa 1962, Mo. 1976, U.S. Dist. Ct. (we. dist.) Mo. 1978, U.S. Tax Ct. 1980, U.S. Ct. Appeals (8th cir.) 1982, U.S. Supreme Ct. 1982. Ptnr. Karr, Karr & Thomas, Webster City, Iowa, 1957-61, Qualley & Thomas, Sioux City, Iowa, 1961-65, Shook, Hardy & Bacon, Kansas City, Mo., 1978-91; prof. law U. Mo., Columbia, 1965-78; justice Supreme Ct. Mo., Jefferson City, 1991—; faculty mem. Mo. Jud. Coll., 1973-92, Nat. Jud. Coll., Reno, 1975-87, Nat. Inst. Trial Advocacy, 1982-83; reporter com. civil jury instrns. Mo. Supreme Ct., 1978-81, chmn., 1981-91; speaker Citizens Forums Mo. Jud. Sys., 1992. Author: (with others) Missouri Evidence Restated, 1984, Missouri Damages Deskbook, 1987, II Missouri Tort Law, 2d edit., 1990; co-author: Missouri Practice Series-Litigation Guide, 1991. Trustee sch. law U. Mo.-Columbia, 1979-91. Recipient Faculty Alumni award U. Mo.-Columbia, 1971, Disting. Non-Alumni award sch. law U. Mo.-Columbia, 1989, Outstanding Alumni award law sch. Drake U., 1992, Alumni Achievement award Simpson Coll., 1993. Fellow Am. Bar Found.; mem. ABA, Am. Law Inst., Order of Coif, Law Soc. U. Mo. Sch. Law (charter). Methodist. Avocation: sailing. Office: Supreme Court Mo PO Box 150 Jefferson City MO 65102-0150

THOMAS, EVERETTE EARL, federal judge; b. Knoxville, Tenn., Nov. 13, 1935; s. Vaughn Lewis and Anna (Marsee) T.; m. Joy Valante, Aug. 29, 1964. BS, U. Tenn., 1958, JD, 1968. Bar: Tenn. 1968, Va. 1972, D.C. 1972, U.S. Ct. Appeals (D.C. cir.) 1972. Trial atty. Fed. Trade Commn., Washington, 1968-73, regional dir., 1973-77; adminstrv. law judge U.S. Dept. Labor, Washington, 1977-80, dep. chief judge, 1980-87; chief judge U.S. Dept. Labor, Ft. Lauderdale, Fla., 1987—. Author: (monograph) Administrative Law Judges, The Corps Issue, 1987; contbr. articles to profl. jours. Pres. Lake Bancroft Commn. Assn., Falls Church, Va., 1982. Lt. USN, 1959-64. Recipient scholarship NSF, 1957. Mem. ABA (exec. com. Nat. Conf. Adminstrv. Law Judges 1982-90, chmn. 1990-91). Avocations: scuba diving, boating, sport fishing. Home: 2009 SE 21st Ave Fort Lauderdale FL 33316-3629 Office: Office Adminstrv Law Judges 101 NE 3rd Ave Ste 500 Fort Lauderdale FL 33301-1100

THOMAS, FRANCIS THORNTON, surgeon, immunologist, consultant; b. Hibbing, Minn., June 24, 1939; s. Gerald M. and Patricia E. (Thornton) T.; m. Judith M. Jannino, June 20, 1968; children: Francis Scott, David Randolph, Jason Hunter. BS, U. Minn., 1960, MS, 1962, MD, 1964. Diplomate Am. Bd. Surgery, Am. Bd. Thoracic Surgery. Intern, resident, chief resident surgery N.Y.U.-Bellevue Med. Ctr., 1964-69; fellow cardiothoracic surgery Case-Western Res. U., 1969-71; instr. to assoc. prof. Med. Coll. of Va., Richmond, 1971-79; prof. surgery East Carolina Sch. Medicine, Greenville, N.C., 1979—, dir. surg. rsch., 1990; attending surgeon Univ. Med. Ctr. Served to capt. U.S. Army, 1965-69. Office: East Carolina U Dept Surgery Greenville NC 27834

THOMAS, FRANK EDWARD, professional baseball player; b. Columbus, Ga., May 27, 1968. Student, Auburn U. With Chgo. White Sox, 1990—. Named to Sporting News All-Star Coll. All Am. team, 1989; Sporting News All-Star team, 1991, 93-94; recipient Silver Slugger award, 1991, 93, 94; mem. Am. League All-Star Team, 1993, 94; recipient Am. League MVP award, 1993, 94; named Major League Player of Yr., Sporting News, 1993. Office: Chgo White Sox Comiskey Park 333 W 35th St Chicago IL 60616-3621*

THOMAS, FRANK M., JR., lawyer; b. Feb. 20, 1947. BA, Amherst Coll., 1969; M in City Planning, Harvard U., 1973; JD, U. Pa., 1977. Bar: Pa. 1977, U.S. Supreme Ct. 1983. Ptnr. Morgan, Lewis & Bockius, Phila. Office: Morgan Lewis & Bockius 2000 One Logan Sq Philadelphia PA 19103

THOMAS, FRANKLIN AUGUSTINE, foundation executive; b. Bklyn., May 27, 1934; s. James and Viola (Atherley) T.; divorced; children: Keith, Hillary, Kerrie, Kyle. B.A., Columbia U., 1956, LL.B., 1963; LL.D. (hon.), Yale U., 1970, Fordham U., 1972, Pratt Inst., 1974, Pace U., 1977, Columbia U., 1979. Bar: N.Y. 1964. Atty. Fed. Housing and Home Finance Agy.-N.Y.C., 1963-64; asst. U.S. atty. for So. Dist. N.Y., 1964-65; dep. police commr. charge legal matters N.Y.C., 1965-67; pres., chief exec. officer Bedford Stuyvesant Restoration Corp., Bklyn., 1967-77; pres. The Ford Found., 1979—; bd. dirs. Citicorp/Citibank, CBS, Inc., ALCOA, Cummins Engine Co., AT&T. Trustee Ford Found., Columbia U., 1969-75. Served with USAF, 1956-60. Recipient LBJ Found. award for contbn. to betterment of urban life, 1974, medal of excellence Columbia U., 1976, Alexander Hamilton award Columbia U., 1983.

THOMAS, FRED, police chief; b. Cherryville, N.C., Feb. 11, 1944; s. Jordan and Helen Martha (Surrat) T.; m. Gigi Josephine Gorée; children: Page Frederick, Tiffany-Dian. BS in administration of Justice, Am. U., 1973, MS in Justice, 1981. Dep. chief police Met. Police Dept., Washington, 1965-85, chief police, 1985—; exec. v.p. Met. Police Boys and Girls Clubs, Washington, 1985-92. Bd. dirs. NCCJ, Washington, Met. Police Boys & Girls Club, Washington. Recipient Lodestar award for Disting. Alumni Am. U., 1993. Avocations: collecting antiques, refinishing old furniture. Office: Metropolitan Police Department 300 Indiana Ave NW Rm 5080 Washington DC 20001-2106

THOMAS, FREDERICK BRADLEY, lawyer; b. Evanston, Ill., Aug. 13, 1949; s. Frederick Bradley and Katherine Kidder (Bingham) T.; m. Elizabeth Maxwell, Oct. 25, 1975; children: Bradley Bingham, Stephens Maxwell, Rosa Macaulay. AB, Dartmouth Coll., 1971; JD, U. Chgo., 1974. Bar: Ill. 1974. Law clk. to hon. judge John C. Godbold U.S. Ct. Appeals (5th cir.), Montgomery, Ala., 1974-75; assoc. Mayer, Brown & Platt, Chgo., 1975-80, ptnr., 1981—. Bd. dirs. St. Gregory Episcopal Sch., 1989—; bd. trustees La Rabida Children's Hosp., 1990—. Mem. ABA, Chgo. Council Lawyers. Republican. Episcopalian. Office: Mayer Brown & Platt 190 S La Salle St Chicago IL 60603-3410

THOMAS, GARETH, metallurgy educator; b. Maesteg, U.K., Aug. 9, 1932; came to U.S., 1960, naturalized, 1977; s. David Bassett and Edith May (Gregory) T.; 1 child, Julian Guy David. B.Sc., U. Wales, 1952; Ph.D., Cambridge U., 1955, Sc.D., 1969. I.C.I. fellow Cambridge U., 1956-59; asst. prof. U. Calif., Berkeley, 1960-63; assoc. prof. U. Calif., 1963-67, prof. metallurgy, 1967—; assoc. dean grad. div., 1968-69, asst. chancellor, acting vice chancellor for acad. affairs, 1969-72; founder, sci. dir. Nat. Ctr. Electron Microscopy, 1982-93; cons. to industry. Author: Transmission Electron Microscopy of Metals, 1962, Electron Micoscopy and Strength of Crystals, 1963, (with O. Johari) Stereographic Projection and Applications, 1969, Transmission Electron Microscopy of Materials, 1980; contbr. articles to profl. jours. Recipient Curtis McGraw Rsch. award Am. Soc. Engring. Edn., 1966, E.O. Lawrence award Dept. Energy, 1978, I-R 100 award R & D mag., 1987, Henry Clifton Sorby award Internat. Metallographic Soc., 1987, Albert Sauveur Achievement award, 1991; Guggenheim fellow, 1972. Fellow Am. Soc. Metals (Bradley Stoughton Young Tchrs. award 1965, Grossman Publ. award 1966), Am. Inst. Mining, Metall. and Petroleum Engrs.; mem. Electron Microscopy Soc. Am. (prize 1965, pres. 1976), Am. Phys. Soc., Nat. Acad. Scis., Nat. Acad. Engring., Brit. Inst. Metals (Rosenheim medal 1977), Internat. Fedn. Electron Microscopy Socs. (pres. 1986-90), Brit. Iron and Steel Inst. Club: Marylebone Cricket (Eng.). Patentee in field. Office: U Calif Dept Material Sci & Engring 561 Evans Hall Berkeley CA 94720-1760

THOMAS, GARTH JOHNSON, psychology educator emeritus; b. Pittsburg, Kans., Sept. 8, 1916; s. Leslie Homer and Lou Opal (Johnson) T.; m. Mary Mona Gee, Sept. 21, 1945; children: Gregory Allen, Barbara Elizabeth. A.B., Kans. State Tchrs. Coll. at Pittsburg, 1938; M.A., U. Kans., 1941, Harvard, 1943; Ph.D., Harvard, 1948. Instr., asst. prof. U. Chgo., 1948-54; asso. prof. U. Ill. Med. Sch., 1954-57; research prof. physiology and elec. engring. U. Ill., Urbana, 1957-66; prof. U. Rochester, N.Y., 1966-82, dir. Ctr. for Brain Rsch., 1970-77, prof. emeritus, 1982—; mem. rev. com. Exptl. Psychology Fellowship panel NIMH, 1965-70, chmn., 1970; mem. psychobiology panel NSF; cons. editor Sinauer Press, Inc. Cons. editor: Jour. Comparative and Physiol. Psychology, 1969-75, 82-91, editor, 1975-81; cons. editor: McGraw Hill Ency. of Sci. and Tech.; contbr. articles to profl. jours. Served to 1st lt. AUS, 1944-47. Recipient research grants NSF, research grants NIMH, research grants U.S. Army, 1951—; Alumni Meritorious Achievement award Kans. State Coll. at Pittsburg, 1976. Mem. Am. Psychol. Assn., Animal Behavior Soc., AAAS, Psychonomic Soc., Soc. Exptl. Psychology, Soc. for Neurosci. Home: 186 Buckland Ave Rochester NY 14618-2139

THOMAS, GARY EDWARD, educator, researcher; b. Lookout, W.V., Oct. 25, 1934; s. Garland Eugene Thomas and Dorothy Mae (Fish) Johnson; m. Susan Jade Cherup, Jan. 20, 1963; children: Curtis Andrew, Jennifer Ann. BS, New Mex. State U., 1957; PhD, U. Pitts., 1963. Rsch. assoc. Svc. d'Aeronomie du CNRS, Paris, France, 1962-63; staff scientist Aerospace Corp., El Segundo, Calif., 1965-67; prof. U. Colo., Boulder, 1967—; sec. Internat. Comm. on Meteorology of the Upper Atmosphere, 1988-95. Assoc. editor Jour. Geophysical Research, 1992—; contbr. articles to profl. jours. 1st lt. Signal Corps U.S. Army, 1963-65. Recipient Award Rsch. Excellence U. Colo., 1994; fellowship U. Colo., 1974-75. Mem. Am. Geophysical Union (assoc. editor 1992). Office: U Colo CB 392 Boulder CO 80309-0392

THOMAS, GARY L., academic administrator; b. Willows, Calif., May 12, 1937; s. Leonel Richard and Myrtle Blanch (Moncur) T.; m. Margaret

Anderson, Aug. 11, 1960 (div. 1975); children: Katelin, Elizabeth Ann, Derek Alan. AA, Modesto Jr. Coll., 1958; BS in Elec. Engring., U. Calif., Berkeley, 1960, MA in Physics, 1962, PhD in Elec. and Computer Engring., 1967. Acting asst. prof. U. Calif., Berkeley, 1967; asst. prof. elec. engring. SUNY, Stony Brook, 1967-70, assoc. prof. elec. engring., 1970-73, assoc. dean grad. sch., 1973-74, chairperson, prof. elec. engring., 1975-79; congl. fellow A.A.A.S., Washington, 1974-75; provost, vp.p acad. affairs N.J. Inst. Tech., Newark, 1980—; student asst. bd. Dept. Higher Edn., N.J., 1980—; chairperson rsch. adv. bd. PSE & G, Newark, 1986-90, Regional Transp. Rsch. Bd., N.Y. and N.J., 1987-90; mem. Kessler Inst. for Rehab., West Orange, N.J., 1988—. Author, editor: Fundamentals of Electrical and Computer Engineering, 1983. State of Calif. scholar, 1960, Schumberger scholar, 1961; NSF grantee, 1973-79. Home: 209 Gregory Ave West Orange NJ 07052-4529 Office: NJ Inst Tech University Heights Newark NJ 07102

THOMAS, GARY LYNN, financial executive; b. Port Vue, Pa., May 15, 1942; s. Willis L. and Luella M. (Rorabaugh) T.; m. Sharen A. Gibbons, May 13, 1967; children—Gregory Scott, Tara Elizabeth. B.S. in Bus. Adminstrn, Pa. State U., 1964; grad., Sch. Bank Adminstrn., U. Wis., 1973. CPA, Pa. Sr. auditor Arthur Andersen & Co., Los Angeles and Pitts., 1964-69; v.p. and dep. comptroller Pitts. Nat. Bank, 1969-77; v.p. and treas. Md. Nat. Corp., Balt., 1977-80; v.p., mgr. corp. fin. div Md. Nat. Bank, Balt.; exec. v.p. adminstrn. Peterson, Howell & Heather, Hunt Valley, Md., 1980-82; v.p. fin. Am. TeleServices, Inc, a Metromedia co., Balt., 1983-85; chief fin. officer First Cellular Group, Inc., Balt., 1985-88, Schelle, Warner, Murray & Thomas, Inc., Balt., 1988—; mng. dir. Schelle Cellular Group, Inc., 1989—; pres. Ruxton Capital Group, Inc., 1989—; chief fin. officer Am. Personal Communications, Inc., Balt. and D.C., 1990—; adj. instr. Sch. Bank Adminstrn., U. Wis., 1975-80; speaker 14th ann. Bank Tax Inst., 1978. Mem. adv. bd., fin. com. St. Joseph Hosp., Balt.; bd. dirs. industry luncheon club Towson State U. Served with USAR, 1968. Inducted into McKeesport H.S. Hall of Fame, 1994. Mem. AICPA, Pa. Inst. CPAs, Md. Assn. CPAs (prior chmn. mems. in industry com.). Republican. Methodist. Home: 2211 Spring Lake Dr Lutherville Timonium MD 21093-3352 Office: 2212 Old Court Rd Baltimore MD 21208-3432

THOMAS, GEOFFREY C., finance company executive. Chief exec. officer GMAC Mortgage, Phila.; v.p. GMAC, Detroit. Office: GMAC Mortgage 8360 Old York Rd Elkins Park PA 19117

THOMAS, GLADYS ROBERTS, foundation executive. BA, Bryn Mawr Coll. Pub. relations mgr. Am. Internat. Group, N.Y., 1978-80, dir. corp. communications, 1980-90; v.p. The Starr Found., N.Y.C., 1990—. Mem. India House. Republican. Office: Starr Found 70 Pine St New York NY 10270-0001

THOMAS, HAROLD ALLEN, JR., civil engineer, educator; b. Terre Haute, Ind., Aug. 14, 1913; s. Harold A. and Katherine (Sass) T.; m. Gertrude A. Grim, July 2, 1935; children—Harold Allen III, Stephen C., Calvin R. B.S. in Civil Engring, Carnegie Inst. Tech., 1935; S.D., Harvard, 1938. Faculty mem. Harvard, 1939—, successively instr., asst. prof., asso. prof., 1939-56, Gordon McKay prof. civil and san. engring., 1956-84, prof. emeritus, 1984—; profl. cons. HEW, 1949—; div. med. scis. NRC-Nat. Acad. Scis., 1943-63, also Dept. Def., AEC; cons. Exec. Office Pres., also Dept. Interior, 1961—; Mem. sci. bd. for Middle East and Southeast Asia, Nat. Acad. Scis., 1964-66, exec. com. social consequences of population changes, 1968—. Co-author: Design Water Resource Systems, 1961, Models for Managing Regional Water Quality, 1973. Fellow Am. Acad. of Arts and Scis.; mem. Am. Geophys. Union (RE Horton medal 1978), ASCE, Nat. Acad. Engring., Boston Soc. C.E. Home: 61 Cotuit Rd Sandwich MA 02563-2654 Office: Harvard U Cambridge MA 02138

THOMAS, HAROLD WILLIAM, avionics systems engineer, flight instructor; b. Cle Elum, Wash., Sept. 29, 1941; s. Albert John and Margaret Jenny (Micheletto) T.; children: Gregg Wallace, Lisa Michele. BS, U. Wash., 1964; M of Engring., U. Fla., 1968. Sci. programmer Aerojet Gen. Corp., Sacramento, Calif., 1964-65; systems analyst GE Co., Daytona Beach, Fla., 1965-69; systems engr. GE Co., Phoenix, 1969-70; sr. software engr. Sperry Flight Systems, Phoenix, 1970-77; sr. systems engr. Honeywell, Inc., Phoenix, 1977-80; engr. section head Sperry Flight Systems, Phoenix, 1980-87; free lance flight instr., 1981—; staff engr. Honeywell, Inc., Phoenix, 1987—; designated engring. rep. Fed. Aviation Adminstrn., Long Beach, 1987—. Mem. AIAA, SAE Internat. Internat. Soc. Air Safety Investigators, Am. Mensa Ltd. Achievements include patent for rotating round dial aircraft engine instruments, patent for dynamic approach display format with plan and profile views. Home: 2514 W Pershing Ave Phoenix AZ 85029-1445 Office: Honeywell INc 21111 N 19th Ave Phoenix AZ 85027-2708

THOMAS, HELEN A. (MRS. DOUGLAS B. CORNELL), newspaper bureau executive; b. Winchester, Ky., Aug. 4, 1920; d. George and Mary (Thomas) T.; m. Douglas B. Cornell. BA, Wayne U., 1942; LLD, Eastern Mich. State U., 1972, Ferris State Coll., 1978, Brown U., 1986; LHD, Wayne State U., 1974, U. Detroit, 1979; LLD, St. Bonaventure U., 1988, Franklin Marshall U., 1989, No. Michigan U., 1989, Skidmore Coll., 1992; Susquehanna U., 1993, Sage Coll., 1994, U. Mo., 1994. With UPI, 1943—; wire svc. reporter UPI, Washington, 1943-74; White House bur. chief UPI, 1974—. Author: Dateline White House. Recipient Woman of Yr. in Comm. award Ladies Home Jour., 1975, 4th Estate award Nat. press Club, 1984; Journalism award U. Mo., Dean of Sch. Journalism award, Al Newharth award, 1990, Ralph McGill award, 1995. Mem. Women's Nat. Press Club (pres. 1959-60, William Allen White Journalism award), Am. Newspaper Women's Club (past v.p.), White House Corrs. Assn. (pres. 1976), Gridiron Club (pres. 1993), Sigma Delta Chi (fellow, Hall of Fame), Delta Sigma Phi (hon.). Home: 2501 Calvert St NW Washington DC 20008-2620 Office: UPI World Hdqrs 1400 I St NW Washington DC 20005-2208

THOMAS, HENRY LEE, JR., professional football player; b. Houston, Jan. 12, 1965. Student, La. State U. Defensive tackle Minnesota Vikings, 1987—. Played in Pro Bowl, 1991, 94, 92. Office: Minnesota Vikings 9520 Viking Dr Eden Prairie MN 55344-3898*

THOMAS, HERMAN L., school system administrator. Asst. supt. Arkadelphia (Ark.) Sch. Dist. Recipient Blue Ribbon Sch. Award, 1990-91. Office: Arkadelphia Sch Dist 235N 11th St Arkadelphia AR 71923

THOMAS, HOWARD PAUL, civil engineer, consultant; b. Cambridge, Mass., Aug. 20, 1942; s. Charles Calvin and Helen Elizabeth (Hook) T.; m. Ingrid Nybo, Jan. 4, 1969; children: Kent Michael, Lisa Karen, Karina Michelle. BS in Engring., U. Mich., 1965, MS in Engring., 1966. Registered profl. engr., Alaska, Calif. Engr. Ove Arup & Ptnrs., London, 1966-67; project engr. Woodward-Clyde Cons., San Francisco, 1967-73; assoc. Woodward-Clyde Cons., Anchorage, 1975-89; spl. cons. Cowiconsult Cons., Copenhagen, 1973-75; prin. engr. Harding-Lawson Assocs., Anchorage, 1989-90; v.p., chief engr. EMCON Alaska, Inc., Anchorage, 1991-94; gen. mgr. Internat. Tech. Corp., Anchorage, 1994—; chmn. Nat. Tech. Coun. Cold Regions Engring., 1982-84; chmn. 4th Internat. Conf. Cold Regions Engring., Anchorage, 1986; iiaison Nat. Acad. Sci./Nat. Rsch. Coun. Polar Commn., 1989-93. Contbr. articles to profl. jours. Named Alaskan Engr. Yr., 1986. Fellow ASCE (pres. Anchorage chpt. 1985-86, mem. mgmt. group A. 1994—); mem. Internat. Soc. Coil Mechs. and Found. Engring., Soc. Am. Mil. Engrs., Cons. Engrs. Coun. Alaska (pres. 1989-90), Am. Cons. Engrs. Coun. (nat. dir. 1990-91), Project Mgmt. Inst. (v.p. Alaska chpt. 1991-95), Toastmasters (pres. Anchorage club 1984), Sons of Norway. Lutheran. Avocations: music, travel, skiing, sailing. Home: 2611 Brittany Dr Anchorage AK 99504-3332

THOMAS, IAN LESLIE MAURICE, publisher; b. Bearsden, Scotland, May 10, 1937; came to U.S., 1989; s. Maurice and Fanny Olive (White) T.; m. Margaret June Thomas, Aug. 13, 1960; children: Fiona, Diana, Ian. BSc with honours, U. Glasgow, Scotland, 1960; ARCST with honors, U. Strathclyde, Scotland, 1960. Chartered engr., U.K. Indentured apprentice Brit. Polar Engines, Scotland, 1955-60; installation engr. Free Piston Engine Co., Singapore, 1961-62; prodn. mgr. Imperial Chem. Industries, Eng., 1963-72; gen. mgr. wall coverings Reed Internat., 1973-78; mng. dir. Odhams (Watford) Ltd., 1979-82; CEO Reed Travel Group, Eng., 1983-92, Reed

Telepublishing, Secaucus, N.J., 1983—; bd. dirs. Reed Internat. PLC, Reed Elsevier PLC. Mem. Instn. Mech. Engrs. Avocations: sailing, rugby. Office: Reed Travel Group 500 Plaza Dr Secaucus NJ 07094-3602

THOMAS, ISIAH LORD, III, former professional basketball player, basketball team executive; b. Chgo., Apr. 30, 1961. Grad. in Criminal Justice, Ind. U., 1987. With Detroit Pistons, 1981-94; v.p. Toronto Raptors, 1994—, now v.p.; mem. U.S. Olympic Basketball Team, 1980, NBA Championship Teams, 1989-90. Named to All-Star team, 1982-93, All NBA First Team, 1984, 85, 86; recipient All-Star team MVP award, 1984, 86, NBA Playoff MVP award, 1990, NBA Finals MVP, 1990. Named to NBA All-Rookie team 1982. Office: Toronto Raptors, 150 York St Ste 1100, Toronto, ON Canada M5H 3S5*

THOMAS, ISSAC DAVID ELLIS, clergy member; b. Llandovery, Wales, U.K., Apr. 30, 1921; came to U.S. 1972; s. David and Blodwen T.; m. Mildred Stevenson, Feb. 14, 1972. BA, U. Wales, 1943, BD, 1946; PhD, Calif. Grad. Sch. Theology, 1971, DLitt, 1989. Ordained to ministry Baptist Ch., 1946. Pastor Bapt. Ch., Glanaman, Wales, 1946-52, Caernarvon, Wales, 1952-58; pastor Zion Ch., Llanelli, Wales, 1958-62; free-lance evangelist, 1962-72; pastor First Bapt. Ch., Maywood, Calif., 1973—; commentator B.B.C., 1973—; prof. Calif. Grad. Sch. Theology, 1972-89, internat. pres., 1989-90, pres., 1991-92; provost St. Charles U., La., 1993—. Author: Golden Treasury of Puritan Quotations, 1975, A Word from the Wise, 1978, The Omega Conspiracy, 1984, Puritan Power, 1990. Named Citizen of the Yr. City of Maywood, 1981; recipient Cert. Freedom Found. of Valley Forge, 1973. Mem. Lions (pres. 1976). Avocations: reading, travel. Home: 2170 Century Park E Apt 1002 Century City CA 90067-2221

THOMAS, J. EARL, physicist; b. Seattle, Sept. 7, 1918; s. Jacob Earl and Ursula May (Johnson) T.; m. Margaret Louise Johnston, June 15, 1977; children—Richard Bruce, Jacob Earl, John Calvin, James Hayden, Denise May, Stillman Jefferson. A.B., Johns Hopkins U., 1939; Ph.D., Calif. Inst. Tech., 1943. Group leader rocket devel. Calif. Inst. Tech., Pasadena, 1942-45; group leader Manhattan Project, U. Calif., Los Alamos, 1945-46; asst. prof. elec. engring. M.I.T., Cambridge, 1946-51; mem. tech. staff Bell Telephone Labs., Murray Hill, N.J., 1951-52; group leader M.I.T. Lincoln Labs., Lexington, 1952-55; prof., chmn. dept. physics Wayne State U., Detroit, 1955-59; dir. research Sylvania Electric, Woburn, Mass., 1959-62; mgr. solid state devel. IBM, Poughkeepsie, N.Y., 1962-64; mgr. new product devel. Gen. Instrument Co., Newark, 1964-67; v.p. Carman Sapphire Co., Reseda, Calif., 1967-70; cons. Warnecke Electron Tubes, Des Plaines, Ill., 1970-71; dir. components research Victor Comptometer Co., Des Plaines, 1971-75; mgr. advanced devel. NCR Corp., Ithaca, N.Y., 1975-84; cons. pvt. cos. and govt. agys. Contbr. articles to sci. jours. Active S.E. Asian refugee resettlement program. Recipient Service award U.S. Office Sci. Research and Devel., 1946. Fellow IEEE, Am. Phys. Soc.; mem. Sigma Xi, Phi Beta Kappa, Tau Beta Pi. Democrat. Presbyterian. Patentee in field. Home: 101 Park Ln Ithaca NY 14850-6309

THOMAS, JACK E., utility company executive. Exec. v.p., chief operating officer San Diego Gas & Electric Co. Office: San Diego Gas & Electric Co 101 Ash St San Diego CA 92101-3096

THOMAS, JACK WARD, wildlife biologist; b. Ft. Worth, Sept. 7, 1934; s. Scranton Boulware and Lillian Louise (List) T.; m. Farrar Margaret Schindler, June 29, 1957 (dec. Feb. 1944); children: Britt Ward, Scranton Gregory. BS, Tex. A&M U., 1957; MS, W.Va. U., 1969; PhD, U. Mass., 1972. Biologist Tex. Game & Fish Commn., Sonora, 1957-60; rsch. biologist Tex. Parks & Wildlife Dept., Plano, 1962-67; wildlife rsch. biologist, forestry sci. lab., Northeastern Forest Exptl. Sta. U.S. Forest Svc., Morgantown, W.Va., 1967-71; project dir. environ. forestry rsch. Pinchot Inst. Environ. Forestry, 1971-73; project leader range & wildlife habitat rsch. Pacific Northwest Forest Exptl. Sta. U.S. Forest Svc., LaGrande, Oreg., 1973-93; chief U.S. Dept. Agr.- Forest Svc., Washington, 1993—. Author, editor: Wildlife Habitats in Managed Forests, 1979 (award The Wildlife Soc. 1980), Elk of North America, 1984 (award The Wildlife Soc. 1985); contbr. numerous articles to profl. jours. Served to lt. USAF, 1957. Recipient Conservation award Gulf Oil Corp., 1983, Earle A. Childs award Childs Found., 1984, Disting. Svc. award USDA, Disting. Citizen's award, E. Oreg. State Coll., Nat Wildlife Fedn. award for Sci., 1990, Disting. Achievement award Soc. for Cons. Biology, 1990, Giraffe award The Giraffe Project, 1990, Scientist of Yr. award Oreg. Acad. Sci., 1990, Disting. Svc. award Soc. Conservation Biology, 1991, Sci. Conservation award Nat. Wildlife Fedn., 1991, Chuck Yeager award Nat. Fish and Wildlife Found., 1992, Conservationist of Yr. award Oreg. Rivers Coun., 1992, Chief's Tech. Transfer award USDA, 1992, Tech. Transfer award Fed. Lab. Consortium, 1993. Fellow Soc. Am. Foresters; mem. The Wildlife Soc. (cert., hon., pres. 1977-78, Oreg. chpt. award 1980, Arthur Einarsen award 1981, Spl. Svcs. award 1984, Aldo Leopold Meml. medal 1991, Group Achievement award 1990), Am. Ornithol. Union, Am. Soc. Mammalogists, Lions, Elks. Avocations: hunting, fishing, white-water rafting. Office: US Forest Svc 14th & Independence PO Box 96090 Washington DC 20090*

THOMAS, JACQUELINE MARIE, journalist, editor; b. Nashville, Aug. 31, 1952; d. John James and Dorothy Jacqueline (Phillips) T. B.A., Briarcliff Coll., 1972; M.Internat. Affairs, Columbia U., 1974. Reporter Chgo Sun-Times, 1974-85; assoc. editor Courier-Jour. and Louisville Times, 1985-86, Detroit Free Press, 1986-93; deputy bureau chief, news editor Detroit News, Washington Bureau, 1993-94, bureau chief, 1994—; instr. Roosevelt U., Chgo., 1983. Nieman fellow Harvard U., 1983. Mem. Chgo. Assn. Black Journalists (Print Journalist of Yr. 1982), Nat. Assn. Black Journalists, Am. Soc. Newspaper Editors. Office: Detroit News Washington Bur 1148 National Press Bldg Washington DC 20045

THOMAS, JACQUELYN MAY, librarian; b. Mechanicsburg, Pa., Jan. 26, 1932; d. William John and Gladys Elizabeth (Warren) Harvey; m. David Edward Thomas, Aug. 28, 1954; children: Lesley J., Courtenay J., Hilary A. BA summa cum laude, Gettysburg Coll., 1954; student U. N.C., 1969. MEd, U. N.H., 1971. Libr., Phillips Exeter Acad., Exeter, N.H., 1971-77, acad. libr., 1977—, chair governing bd. Child Care Ctr., 1987-91; chair Com. to Enhance Status of Women, Exeter, 1981-84; chair Loewenstein Com., Exeter, 1982—; pres. Cum Laude Soc., Exeter, 1984-86; James H. Ottaway Jr. prof., 1990—. Editor: The Design of the Libr.: A Guide to Sources of Information, 1981, Rarities of Our Time: The Special Collections of the Phillips Exeter Academy Libr. Trustee, treas. Exeter Day Sch., 1965-69; mem. bd. Exeter Hosp. Vols., 1954-59; mem. Exeter Hosp. Corp., 1978—; mem. bldg. com. Exeter Pub. Libr., 1986-88; chair No. New Eng., Coun. for Women in Ind. Schs., 1985-87; chmn. Lamont Poetry Program, Exeter, 1984-86; dir. Greater Portsmouth Community Found., 1990—. N.H. Coun. for Humanities grantee, 1981-82; NEH grantee, 1982; recipient Lillian Radford Trust award, 1989. Mem. ALA, New Eng. Libr. Assn., N.H. Ednl. Media Assn., New Eng. Assn. Ind. Sch. Librs., Am. Assn. Sch. Librs. (chmn. non-pub. sch. sect., program com. 1985—), Phi Beta Kappa. Home: 16 Elm St Exeter NH 03833 Office: Acad Libr Phillips Exeter Acad 20 Main St Exeter NH 03833-2460

THOMAS, JAMES BERT, JR., government official; b. Tallahassee, Mar. 16, 1935; s. James Bert and Stella E. (Lewis) T.; m. Sharon Mae Kelly, June 16, 1962; children: James Bert III, Mary Elizabeth, John Christopher. B.S., Fla. State U., 1957. C.P.A., Fla. Spl. auditor Office State Comptroller, Jacksonville, Fla., 1958; jr. auditor J.D.A. Holley & Co., C.P.A.'s, Tallahassee, 1959; sr. auditor Office of the State Auditor, Tallahassee, 1959-60; trainee, audit dir. HUD audit div., Washington, 1960-71; asst. dir. Bur. Accounts ICC, Washington, 1972-75, dir. Bur. Accounts, 1977-80; inspector gen. U.S. Dept. HUD, Washington, 1975-77, U.S. Dept. Edn. Washington, 1980—; mem. Pres.'s Coun. Integrity and Efficiency, chmn. audit standards subcom., 1984—, chmn. audit com., 1989-90. mem. Pres.'s Coun. Integrity and Efficiency, chmn. audit standards subcom., 1984—, chmn. audit com., 1989-94. Mem. AICPA (strategic planning com. 1987-90, chmn. govt. auditing standards adv. coun. 1991—), Inst. Internal Auditors (trustee Rsch. Found. 1991-92), Assn. Govt. Accts. (chmn. fin. mgmt. standards bd. 1985-86), Accts. Roundtable. Roman Catholic. Home: Unit 601 8340 Greensboro Dr McLean VA 22102 Office: US Dept Edn Inspector General 330 C Street SW Washington DC 20202-1510

THOMAS, JANEY SUE, elementary school principal; b. Clarksville, Tenn., Feb. 10, 1949; d. James Ernest and Ethel Mae (Evans) Kirkland; m. Tony Lee Thomas, Oct. 9, 1965; children: Jeff, Kelli. BS in Elem. Edn., Austin Peay State U., 1979, MA in Elem. Edn. Adminstrn., 1982, postgrad., 1987-89. Tchr. Charlotte (Tenn.) Jr. High Sch., 1979-86; prin. Vanleer (Tenn.) Elem. Sch., 1986-91, Oakmont Elem. Sch., Dickson, Tenn., 1991—. Ednl. rep. Concerned Citizens for Edn., Dickson County, 1988; mem. com. United Way Med. Tenn., Dickson County, 1990-91, bd. dirs., 1992-93. Recipient Nat. Sch. of Recognition award U.S. Dept. Edn., 1990. Mem. NAESP (Excellence in Edn. award 1989-90), Tenn. Assn. Elem. Sch. Prins. (Nat. Exemplary Sch. award 1989-90), Dickson County Edn. Assn. (pres. 1989-90). Baptist. Avocations: reading, traveling, shopping. Home: 226 Druid Hills Dr Dickson TN 37055 Office: Oakmont Elem Sch 630 Hwy 46 S Dickson TN 37055

THOMAS, JAY, actor; b. New Orleans; s. Harry and Kathy Thomas; m. Sally Michelson, Dec. 1986. Morning disk jockey KPWR, L.A., 1986—. Performances include: (TV) Mork and Mindy, 1979-81, Cheers, 1987-90, Married People, 1990, Murphy Brown, 1990-92, Love and War, 1992-95 (Emmy award nominee for lead actor in comedy series 1994); (films) C.H.U.D., 1984, The Gig, 1992, Straight Talk, 1992. Office: Don Buchwald and Assocs 9229 Sunset Blvd Ste 710 Los Angeles CA 90069*

THOMAS, JEAN-JACQUES ROBERT, Romance languages educator; b. Mirecourt, Vosges, France, Jan. 20, 1948; s. Jean-Robert and Yvonne Marie-Rose (Ladner) T.; m. Mary Lorene Hammial, Aug. 21, 1976; children: Dominick, Robert. Lic., U. Lille, France, 1968, M, 1969; diplome in lang. Orientales, U. Paris, France, 1972, PhD, 1972. Teaching asst. U. Paris, 1969-71, asst. researcher, 1971-72; lectr. U. Mich., 1972-75; asst. prof. Columbia U., N.Y.C., 1975-81; assoc. prof. Duke U., Durham, N.C., 1981-87, prof., 1989—, chmn. romance studies, 1989-94; pres. Educo, Paris, 1988-89; dir. Institute French Studies U. Calif., Santa Barbara, 1991—; bd. dirs. Studies in Twenty-Century Lit., Lincoln, Nebr., Palmes Académiques, 1994. Author: Lire Leiris, 1972, La Langue la Poésie, 1987, La Langue Volée, 1988; co-author: Poétique Générative, 1978, Poética Generativa, 1983, 89; translator: Sémiotique de la Poésie, 1983; assoc. editor: Sub-Stance, 1975—, Poetics Today, 1980—. Grantee Rackham Found., 1973, IBM, 1984, Sloan Found., 1985. Mem. Semiotic Soc. Am., NEMLA (chmn. sect. 1982-83), MLA (chmn. divsn. 1980-81, 86-87, 1993-95, adv. com. 1994). Home: 26 Porchlight Ct Durham NC 27707-2442 Office: Duke U Dept Romance Studies Durham NC 27706

THOMAS, JEFFREY NOEL, aviation consulting company executive, management consultant; b. Pitts., June 29, 1942; s. William L. and Elizabeth (Noel) T.; m. Lynda A. Cooper, Aug. 9, 1960; 1 son, Barry N. B.B.A., U. Cin., 1967. Cons. Landrum & Brown, Cin., 1967-70, pres., chmn. bd., 1980—; project mgr. Booz Allen & Hamilton, Cin., 1970-75, v.p., 1975-80; pres., chmn. bd. Thomas & Holder Inc., Cin., 1983—; tech. adviser, mem. O'Hare Daley Task Force, Chgo., 1975-76; mem. FAA/Airport Operators Council Internat. Task Force on Airport Capacity, Washington, 1982—. Office: Landrum & Brown Inc 11279 Cornell Park Dr Cincinnati OH 45242

THOMAS, JERRY, pharmacist; b. Milan, Ga., Oct. 2, 1942; s. Robert Guy and Myrtice (Hinson) T.; m. Marianne Norris, Nov. 14, 1964; children: Angela, Tammy, Melanie, Jamey, Jason. BS in Pharmacy, Auburn (Ala.) U., 1966. Lic. pharmacist, Ala. Pharmacist Harco Drug Inc., Tuscaloosa, 1966-75, v.p., 1975-79, exec. v.p., 1979-93, pres., 1993—. Bd. dirs. West Ala. Easter Seal Rehab., 1994-95, Salvation Army, 1993-95, fin. chmn. Mem. Am. Pharm. Assn. (legis. affairs com.), Ala. Pharm. Assn. (A.A. Ribbon Bowl of Hygiene 1989), Lions (pres. 1987). Baptist. Avocations: jogging, reading. Home: 4929 Emerald Bay Dr Northport AL 35476 Office: Harco Drug Inc 3925 Rice Mine Rd NE Tuscaloosa AL 35406

THOMAS, JIM, professional basketball team executive. Mng. gen. ptnr. Sacramento Kings. Office: Sacramento Kings 1 Sports Pky Sacramento CA 95834*

THOMAS, JIMMY LYNN, financial executive; b. Mayfield, Ky., Aug. 3, 1941; s. Alben Stanley and Emma Laura (Alexander) T.; m. Kristin H. Kent, Oct. 1986; children: James Nelson, Carter Danforth. BS, U. Ky., 1963; MBA, Columbia U., 1964. Fin. analyst Ford Motor Co., Detroit, 1964-66; asst. treas. Joel Dean Assocs., N.Y.C., 1966-67; asst. contr. Trans World Airlines, N.Y.C., 1967-73; sr. v.p. fin. svcs., treas. Gannett Co., Inc., Arlington, Va., 1973—; bd. dirs. Marine Midland Bank, Rochester, Arkwright Boston Mut. Ins. Co-Atlantic Region, Tremont Ptnrs., Brown Devel. Co., Newspaper Printing Corp., Pacific Media, Inc., Guam Publs., Gannett Supply Corp., Gannett Fla. Corp., Gannett Pacific Corp. With U.S. Army, 1966-72. Ashland Oil Co. scholar, 1959-63, McKinsey scholar 1964; Samuel Bronfman fellow, 1963-64. Mem. U. Ky. Alumni Assn., Columbia U. Alumni Assn., Fin. Execs. Inst., Inst. Newspaper Contrs. and Fin. Officers, Country Club of Rochester, Genessee Valley Club, Georgetown Club, Washington Golf and Country Club, Beta Gamma Sigma, Omicron Delta Kappa, Sigma Alpha Epsilon. Democrat. Mem. Christian Ch. (Disciples of Christ). Home: 100 Gibbon St Alexandria VA 22314-3836 Office: Gannett Co Inc 1100 Wilson Blvd Arlington VA 22234

THOMAS, JOAB LANGSTON, academic administrator, biology educator; b. Holt, Ala., Feb. 14, 1933; s. Ralph Cage and Chamintney Elizabeth (Stovall) T.; m. Marly A. Dukes, Dec. 22, 1954; children: Catherine, David, Jennifer, Frances. AB, Harvard U., 1955, MA, 1957, PhD, 1959; DSc (hon.), U. Ala., 1981; LLD (hon.), Stillman Coll., 1987; LHD (hon.), Tri-State U., 1994. Cytotaxonomist Arnold Aboretum, Harvard, 1959-61; faculty U. Ala., University, 1961-76, prof. biology, 1966-76, 88-91, asst. dean Coll. Arts and Scis., 1964-65, 69, dean for student devel. Coll., 1969-74, v.p., 1974-76, dir. Herbarium, 1961-76, dir. Arboretum, 1964-65, 66-69; pres. U. Ala., Tuscaloosa, 1981-88; chancellor N.C. State U., Raleigh, 1976-81; pres. Pa. State U., University Park, 1990—; bd. dirs. Blount, Inc., First Ala. Bank, Tuscaloosa, Lukens, Inc., Mellon Corp.; intern acad. adminstrn. Am. Coun. on Edn., 1971. Author: A Monographic Study of the Cyrillaceae, 1960, Wildflowers of Alabama and Adjoining States, 1973, The Rising South, 1976, Poisonous Plants and Venomous Animals of Alabama and Adjoining States, 1990. Bd. dirs. Internat. Potato Ctr., 1977-83, chmn. 1982-83; bd. dirs. Internat. Svc. for Nat. Agrl. Rsch., 1985-91. Named Outstanding Prof. U. Ala., 1964-65, Ala. Acad. Honor, 1983, Citizen of Yr., Tuscaloosa, 1987. Mem. Golden Key, Phi Beta Kappa, Sigma Xi, Omicron Delta Kappa, Phi Kappa Phi. Office: Pa State U 201 Old Main University Park PA 16802-1589

THOMAS, JOE CARROLL, human resources director; b. Belmont, N.C., Nov. 2, 1931; m. Ruth Stone, June 17, 1951; children: Joe, Jerry, Angela. BA, Belmont Abbey Coll., 1954; MS, Cornell U., 1961. Mgr. terr. sales Gen. Foods Corp., San Antonio, 1954-62; asst. dir. personnel textiles divsn. Kendall Co., Charlotte, N.C., 1962-64; dir. personnel S.E. region Gifford Hill & Co., Charlotte, 1964-71; dir. mgmt. svcs. Ervin Industries, Charlotte, 1971-75; v.p. indsl. rels. Crompton & Knowles, Charlotte, 1975-76; exec. v.p., dir. human resources Barclays Group Inc. (USA), Charlotte, 1976—; mem. adv. coun. Sch. Bus., Western Carolina U., Cullowhee, N.C., 1980-84. Vice chmn. bd. trustees Belmont Abbey Coll., 1982-88; chmn. fundraising campaign Charlotte chpt. Am. Heart Assn., 1984; mem. bd. visitors Mercy Hosp., Charlotte, 1984-87; bd. dirs. Mercy Health Svcs., Charlotte, 1988—; bd. dirs. Jr. Achievement Charlotte, 1985-88; mem. bd. visitors Johnson C. Smith Univ., 1989-92. Mem. Soc. for Human Resource Mgmt., The Employers Assn. (bd. dirs. 1993—, exec. com. 1995), Charlotte Athletic Club (pres. 1982-83), Charlotte Rotary, Tower Club, Charlotte C. of C. (bd. advisors 1992—). Democrat. Methodist. Avocations: golf, reading. Office: Barclays Group Inc (USA) 201 S Tryon St Charlotte NC 28202

THOMAS, JOHN BOWMAN, educator, electrical engineer; b. New Kensington, Pa., July 14, 1925; s. John Bowman and Lenna Iva (Sturms) T.; m. Eleanor W. Graefe, June 3, 1944; children—Sharon Lenore (Mrs. Guy G. Miller), Bronwyn Lee (Mrs. Robert Knight), John Andrew, Gwendolyn Elizabeth, Randall Stuart, Gailyn Brooke. A.B., Gettysburg Coll., 1944; B.S., Johns Hopkins, 1952; M.S., Stanford, 1953, Ph.D., 1955. Elec. engr., then asst. chief engr. Koppers Co., Inc., 1946-52; faculty Princeton, 1955—; prof. elec. engring., 1962—; Indsl. cons., 1955—. Author tech. papers,

books. Served with AUS, 1944-46. NSF sr. postdoctoral fellow Berkeley, Stanford, 1967-68. Fellow I.E.E.E. (exec. com. Princeton sect. 1955-63), IEEE (officer 1960-63); mem. Sigma Xi, Tau Beta Pi. Home: 3651 Las Pilitas Rd Santa Margarita CA 93453-9637

THOMAS, JOHN CHARLES, lawyer, former state supreme court justice; b. Norfolk, Va., Sept. 18, 1950; s. John and Floretta V. (Sears) T.; m. Pearl Walden, Oct. 9, 1982; children: John Charles Jr., Ruby Virginia, Lewis LeGrant. B.A. in Am. Govt. with distinction, U. Va., 1972, J.D., 1975. Bar: Va. 1975, U.S. Dist. Ct. (ea. and we. dists.) 1976, U.S. Ct. Appeals (4th cir.) 1976, U.S. Supreme Ct. 1979, U.S. Ct. Appeals (D.C. cir.) 1980, U.S. Ct. Appeals (10th cir.) 1991, U.S. Ct. Appeals (11th cir.) 1992. Assoc. Hunton & Williams, Richmond, Va., 1975-82, ptnr., 1982-83, 89—; justice Supreme Ct. of Va., Richmond, 1983-89; mem. adv. con. on appellate rules U.S. Jud. Conf. Bd. dirs. U. Va. Law Sch. Found., Thomas Jefferson Meml. Foun. Master John Marshall Inn of Ct. (exec. com.); fellow Am. Bar Found., Va. Bar Found.; mem. Am. Arbitration Assn. (bd. dirs., exec. com.), Va. State Bar, Va. Bar Assn., Bar Assn. City of Richmond, Old Dominion Bar Assn., Va. State C. of C. (bd. dirs.), Omega Psi Phi. Office: Hunton & Williams Riverfront Plz East Tower 951 E Byrd St Richmond VA 23219-4040

THOMAS, JOHN COX, JR., publisher; b. Port Chester, N.Y., July 27, 1927; s. John Cox and Henrietta Edna (Cook) T.; widowed; children: Mark Gregory, Pamela Cook, Suzanne Elizabeth. BA, Columbia U., 1948, MBA, 1950. Advt. salesman McCall's mag., N.Y.C., 1955-58; advt. salesman Time mag., N.Y.C., 1959-62; mgr. Los Angeles, 1962-67, dir. N.Y. sales, 1967-71, U.S. sales dir., 1971-73; pub. N.Y. mag., N.Y.C., 1973-76, New West mag., Los Angeles, 1975-76; pres. A/S/M Communications, N.Y.C., 1978-89, chmn., 1989—. Sr. Warden St. John's of Lattingtown, Locust Valley, N.Y., 1986. Mem. Mag. Pubs. Assn. Clubs: The Creek (Locust Valley), The Links (N.Y.C.). Avocations: golf, travel. Home: 305 Bayville Rd Locust Valley NY 11560-1401 Office: ADWSSK Mags 1515 Broadway New York NY 10036-5702

THOMAS, JOHN EDWIN, retired university administrator; b. Fort Worth, Tex., Apr. 23, 1931; s. John L. and Dorothy F. T.; m. Janice Paula Winzinek, Jan. 29, 1967; children—John L., Christa T., Scott A., Brandon F. BSEE, U. Kans., 1953; JD, U. Mo., Kansas City, 1961; MS, Fla. State U., 1965, DBA, 1970. With Wagner Electric Corp., St. Louis, 1955-63; mgr. elec. apparatus div. Wagner Electric Corp., Atlanta, 1961-63; with NASA, Cape Kennedy, Fla., 1963-70; chief requirements and resources office, dir. tech. support NASA, 1966-70; prof., head gen. bus. dept. East Tex. State U., 1970-72; dean (Coll. Scis. and Tech.), 1972-74; vice chancellor for acad. affairs Appalachian State U., Boone, N.C., 1974-79; chancellor Appalachian State U., 1979-93; ret. N.C. Utilities Commn., Raleigh, 1993; spl. advisor for sci., tech. & higher edn. Gov. State of N.C., Raleigh, 1994, ret., 1994; chair utilities commn., 1993-94; spl. advisor to Gov. of the State of N.C. on sci./ tech. and higher edn. Mem. N.C. Agy. for Pub. Telecommunications. Served with USN, 1949-50, USMC, 1953-55. NDEA fellow, 1968. Mem. Fed. Bar Assn., Soc. Advancement Mgmt., So. Mgmt. Assn., Phi Delta Kappa, Pi Sigma Epsilon, Delta Gamma Sigma., Phi Kappa Phi. Methodist. Club: Kiwanis. Home: 109 Pelham Rd Oak Ridge TN 37830

THOMAS, JOHN HOWARD, astrophysicist, engineer, educator; b. Chgo., Apr. 9, 1941; s. William Whitney and Dorothy Loretta (Derris) T.; m. Lois Ruth Moffit, Aug. 11, 1962; children: Jeffrey, Laura. B.S. in Engring. Sci., Purdue U., 1962, M.S. in Engring. Sci., 1964, Ph.D. in Engring. Sci., 1966. Registered profl. engr., N.Y. State. NATO postdoctoral fellow U. Cambridge, Eng., 1966-67; asst. prof. mech. and aerospace sci. U. Rochester, 1967-73, assoc. prof., 1973-81, prof., 1981—, prof. astronomy, 1986—, assoc. dean for grad. studies Coll. Engring. and Applied Sci., 1981-83, univ. dean grad. studies, 1983-91; vis. astronomer Nat. Solar Obs., Sunspot, N.Mex.; vis. scientist Max-Planck Inst. for Physics and Astrophysics, Munich, 1973-74, High Altitude Obs., Boulder, Colo., 1985; vis. fellow Worcester Coll, vis. prof. dept. theoretical physics Oxford (Eng.) U., 1987-88; affiliate scientist Nat. Ctr. for Atmospheric Rsch., Boulder, 1989—; vis. prof. Rsch. Ctr. for Theoretical Astrophysics, U. Sydney, Australia, 1991, Sch. Math. and Stats., 1993; prin. investigator NASA, NSF, USAF, Office Naval Rsch. Editor: The Physics of Sunspots, 1981, Sunspots: Theory and Observations, 1992; assoc. editor Astrophysical Jour., 1993—; author articles on astrophysics, solar physics and fluid dynamics. NSF fellow, 1963-66; Guggenheim fellow, 1993-94. Mem. AAAS, Am. Astron. Soc., Internat. Astron. Union, Am. Phys. Soc., Am. Geophys. Union, Sigma Xi, Tau Beta Pi, Sigma Delta Chi. Office: U Rochester 223 Hopeman Bldg Rochester NY 14627

THOMAS, JOHN KERRY, chemistry educator; b. Llanelli, Wales, May 16, 1934; came to U.S., 1960; s. Ronald W. and Rebecca (Johns) T.; m. June M. Critchley, Feb. 28, 1959; children: Delia, Roland, Roger. BS, U. Manchester, Eng., 1954, PhD, 1957, DSc, 1969. Rsch. assoc. Nat. Rsch. Coun. Can., Ottawa, 1957-58; sci. officer Atomic Energy. U.K., Harwell, Eng., 1958-60; rsch. assoc. Argonne (Ill.) Nat. Lab., 1960-70; prof. chemistry U. Notre Dame, Ind., 1970-82, Nieuwland prof. chemistry, 1982—. Author: Chemistry of Excitation at Interfaces, 1984; mem. editorial bd. Macromolecules Langmuir, Jour. of Colloid and Interface Sci. Recipient of Rsch. Awd., 1994, Radiation Rsch. Fellow Royal Soc. Chemistry; mem. Am. Chem. Soc. (award in colloids and surface 1994), Radiation Rsch. Soc. (editorial bd. jours., rsch. award 1972, 1994), Photochem. Soc. Home: 17704 Waxwing Ln South Bend IN 46635-1327 Office: Univ Notre Dame Dept Chemistry Notre Dame IN 46556*

THOMAS, JOHN LOVELL, history educator; b. Portland, Maine, Oct. 28, 1926; d. John White and Ruth Arlene (Lovell) T.; m. Patricia Ann Blake, Sept. 30, 1951; children: John Blake, Jayn. B.A., Bowdoin Coll., 1947; M.A., Columbia U., 1950; Ph.D., Brown U., 1960. Instr. Barnard Coll., N.Y.C., 1950-53; instr. Brown U., Providence, 1955-59, asst. prof. history, 1959-60, assoc. prof., assoc. prof. history, 1964—; George L. Littlefield Prof. Am. History; asst. prof. history Harvard U., Cambridge, Mass., 1960-64. Author: The Liberator, 1963 (recipient Bancroft prize 1963), Alternative America, 1983; editor: Slavery Attacked, 1966, John C. Calhoun, 1965. Recipient Allan Nevins prize Soc. Am. Historians, 1960; fellow Guggenheim Found., 1970; Charles Warren fellow Harvard U., 1967; fellow Woodrow Wilson Found., 1982. Mem. Am. Hist. Assn. Office: Brown U Dept History 142 Angell St Providence RI 02912-9040

THOMAS, JOHN MELVIN, surgeon; b. Carmarthen, U.K., Apr. 26, 1933; came to U.S., 1958; s. Morgan and Margaret (Morgan) T.; m. Betty Ann Mayo, Nov. 3, 1958; children: James, Hugh, Pamela. MB, BChir, U. Coll. Wales, U. Edinburgh, 1958. Intern Robert Packer Hosp., Sayre, Pa., 1958-59, chief surg. resident, 1963, med. staff, 1968; assoc. surgeon Guthrie Clinic Ltd., Sayre, 1963-69, chmn. dept. surgery, 1969-91; pres. bd. dirs. Guthrie Clinic Ltd., 1972-89; trustee Robert Packer Hosp.; chmn. exec. com. Guthrie Healthcare Sys., 1990-92, dir. 1994—; guest examiner Am. Bd. Surgery, 1979, 81, 85; bd. dirs. Measurement Innovations Corp., Citizen Fin. Bank, Mansfield, Pa. Bd. dirs. Donald Guthrie Found. for Rsch., pres. 1983—; bd. dirs. Pa. Trauma System Found., 1984-90, pres. 1988, 89; chmn. licensure and accountability Gov.'s Conf., 1974; bd. dirs. Pa. Hosps. Am., 1993—; trustee Mansfield (Pa.) U. Found., 1991—. Mem. ACS (gov. 1985-91), AMA, Am. Group Practice Assn., Am. Soc. Parental and Enteral Nutrition, Pa. Med. Soc., Bradford County Med. Soc., Cen. N.Y. Surg. Soc., Internat. Soc. Surgery, Soc. Surgery Alimentary Tract, Ea. Vascular Soc., Shepard Hills Country Club, Moselem Springs Golf Club. Presbyterian. Home: 383 Lansing Station Rd Lansing NY 14882-8606 Office: Guthrie Clinic Ltd Sayre PA 18840

THOMAS, JOHN RICHARD, chemist; b. Anchorage, Ky., Aug. 26, 1921; s. John R. and Mildred (Woods) T.; m. Beatrice Ann Davidson, Dec. 7, 1944; children: Jonnie Sue Jacobs, Randy G. B.S., U. Calif., Berkeley, 1943, Ph.D., 1947. With U.S. AEC, 1949-51; rsch. chemist Chevron Rsch. Co., Richmond, Calif., 1948-49; sr. rsch. chemist Chevron Rsch. Co., 1951-60, sr. rsch. scientist, 1961-67, pres., also bd. dirs., 1970-86, v.p. petroleum rsch., 1984-86, ret. 1986; mgr. R&D Ortho div. Chevron Chem. Co., Richmond, 1967-68; asst. sec. Standard Oil Co., Calif., 1968-70. Contbr. articles to profl. jours. Mem. Am. Chem. Soc. Democrat. Republican. Patentee in field. Home: 847 McEllen Way Lafayette CA 94549-5134 Office: Chevron Research Co 576 Standard Ave Richmond CA 94801-2016

THOMAS, JOHN THIEME, management consultant; b. Detroit, Aug. 21, 1935; s. John Shepherd and Florence Leona (Thieme) T.; m. Ellen Linden Taylor, June 27, 1959; children: Johnson Taylor, Evan Thurston. BBA, U. Mich., 1957, MBA, 1958. Mfg. dept. mgr. Procter & Gamble Co., Cin., 1958-60, brand mgr., 1960-63; sr. cons. Glendinning Cos. Inc., Westport, Conn., 1964-66; v.p. Glendinning Cos. Inc., London, 1967-69; exec. v.p. Glendinning Cos. Inc., Westport, 1970-74; also bd. dirs.; exec. v.p., chief operating officer Ero Industries, Chgo., 1974-76; v.p. Lamalie Assocs. Inc., Chgo., 1977-81; pres. Wilkins & Thomas Inc., Chgo., 1981-87; ptnr. Ward Howell Internat., Chgo., 1987—; also bd. dirs.; exec. dir. Procter & Gamble Alumni Assn., Chgo., 1981—; bd. dir. Ward Howell Internat., N.Y. Pub. Proctor & Gamble Mfg. Alumni directory, 1981—; author articles in profl. jours. Chmn. bd. dirs. Winnetka (Ill.) Youth Orgn., 1986—; selector Winnetka Town Coun., 1978, 80, 84. Mem. Nat. Assn. Corp. & Profl. Recruiters, Assn. Exec. Search Cons., Am. Soc. Personnel Adminstrn. Club: Fairfield (Conn.) Hunt (treas. 1971-74). Avocations: gardening, music, playing tuba. Home: 525 Ash St Winnetka IL 60093-2601 Office: Ward Howell Internat 300 W Wacker Dr Chicago IL 60606

THOMAS, JOSEPH ALLAN, lawyer; b. L.A., Aug. 12, 1929; s. Joseph Smith and Blanche Aileen (Henry) T.; m. Jacquelynne Beverly Jones, June 13, 1954; children: Douglas, Scott, Kevin, Matthew. B.S., U. So. Calif., 1954, J.D., 1957. Bar: Calif. 1958, U.S. Supreme Ct. 1990. Pvt. practice law Downey, Calif., 1958-60; with law dept. Pacific Mut. Life Ins. Co., Newport Beach, Calif., 1960-92; sr. v.p., gen counsel Pacific Mut. Life Ins. Co., 1978-92; of counsel Barger and Wolen, Irvine, Calif., 1992—; treas. Assn. for Calif. Tort Reform, 1981-92. Mem. bd. advisors Fairview State Hosp., 1985-93. Fellow Life Office Mgmt. Inst.; mem. Calif. Bar Assn., Assn. Life Ins. Counsel (bd. govs. 1990-94), Inst. Corp. Counsel (bd. govs. 1985-92). Office: Barger & Wolen 19800 Macarthur Blvd Ste 800 Irvine CA 92715-2437

THOMAS, JOSEPH ERUMAPPETTICAL, psychologist; b. Piravom, Kerala, India, Feb. 11, 1937; came to U.S., 1971; s. Iype Erumappettiyil and Kunjamma M. (Padiyil) T.; m. Chinnamma Kavatt, Nov. 23, 1964; children: Joseph Jr., Kurian, Elizabeth. BA, Kerala U., India, 1957, MA, 1960, PhD, 1969. Diplomate Internat. Acad. Behavioral Medicine, Counseling, and Psychotherapy; lic. psychologist. Lectr. psychology U. Kerala, Trivandrum, India, 1967-70; postdoctoral fellow in psychology Northwestern U. Med. Sch., Chgo., 1971-72; psychologist U. Chgo., 1972-74; instr. psychiatry Northwestern U. Med. Sch., Chgo., 1972-76, asst. prof. dept. psychiatry, 1977—; psychologist Northwestern Meml. Hosp., Chgo., 1974-80; pvt. practice psychology Chgo., 1980—; cons. Michael Reese Hosp., Chgo., 1980-86; founding mem. Inst. Psychiatry, Northwestern U., Chgo. Contbr. articles to profl. jours. Mem. Dupage County Health Planning Com., Wheaton, Ill., 1984; founding mem., trustee St. Thomas Ch. Chgo., St. Gregorios Orthodox Ch., Oak Park, Ill. Commonwealth fellow Govt. U.K., U. Glasgow, 1970. Mem. Am. Psychological Assn., Mental Health Assn. DuPage County (bd. dirs. 1982-84), Biofeedback Soc. Ill. (pres. 1984-85). Home: 16 W 731 89th Pl Hinsdale IL 60521 Office: 10 W Martin Ave Ste 227 Naperville IL 60540-4205

THOMAS, JOSEPH FLESHMAN, architect; b. Oak Hill, W.Va., Mar. 23, 1915; s. Robert Russel and Effie (Fleshman) T.; m. Margaret Ruth Lively, Feb. 28, 1939 (dec.); children: Anita Carol, Joseph Stephen; m. Dorothy Francene Root, Apr. 29, 1967 (div.); m. Bonnie Abbott Buckley, June 15, 1991. Student, Duke, 1931-32; B.Arch., Carnegie-Mellon U., 1938. Practice architecture various firms W. Va., Va., Tenn., Calif., 1938-49; staff architect Calif. Div. Architecture, Los Angeles, 1949-52; prin. Joseph F. Thomas, architect, Pasadena, Calif., 1952-53; mem. Neptune & Thomas (architects-engrs.), Pasadena and San Diego, 1953-78; Mem. Pasadena Planning Commn., 1956-64, chmn., 1963-64; pres. Citizens Coun. for Planning, Pasadena, 1966-67; mem. steering com. Pasadena NOW, 1970-74; mem. Pasadena Design Com., 1979-86; mem. adv. bd. Calif. Office Architecture and Constrn., 1970-72; mem. archtl. adv. com. Calif. State U. System, 1981-84; mem. adv. coun. Sch. Environ. Design Calif. Poly. Inst., 1983—; mem. outreach for architecture com. Carnegie Mellon U., 1989—, pres.'s devel. com., 1991—. Prin. works include Meth. Hosp, Arcadia, Calif., Foothill Presbyn. Hosp, Glendora, Calif., master plans and bldgs., Citrus Coll., Azusa, Calif., Riverside (Calif.) Coll., Westmont Coll., Monticeto, Calif., Northrop Inst. Tech., Inglewood, Calif., Indian Valley Coll., Marin County, Calif.; other coll. bldgs. Pacific Telephone Co, Pasadena, Los Angeles County Superior Ct. Bldg, U.S. Naval Hosp, San Diego. Trustee Almansor Edn. Ctr., 1986-92; bd. dirs., co-founder Syncor Internat., 1973-83; founding dir. Bank of Pasadena, 1962-65. Lt. (j.g.) USNR, 1943-46. Recipient Service award City of Pasadena, 1964; Disting. Service award Calif. Dept. Gen. Services, 1972; Gold Crown award Pasadena Arts Council, 1981. Fellow AIA (4 awards honor, 13 awards merit 1957-78, dir. Calif. coun. 1966-68, exec. com. 1974-77, pres. Pasadena chpt. 1967, chmn. Calif. sch. facilities com. 1970-72, mem. nat. jud. bd. 1973-74, nat. dir. 1974-77, treas. 1977-79, exec. com., planning com., chmn. finance com.); mem. Breakfast Forum (chmn. 1983), Annandale Golf Club, Pi Kappa Alpha. Republican. Methodist. Home: 330 San Miguel Rd Pasadena CA 91105-3030

THOMAS, JOSEPH R., retail chain stores executive; b. 1935. With K Mart Corp., 1952—, store mgr., 1961-65, dist. mgr., 1965-74, mdse mgr. so. region, 1974-79, asst. regional mgr. so. region, 1976-79, asst. to exec. v.p. for store mgmt., 1979-82, v.p., 1982-84, exec. v.p., chief adminstrv. officer, 1984—. Served with U.S. Army, 1954-56. Office: K Mart Corp 3100 W Big Beaver Rd Troy MI 48084-3163

THOMAS, JULIA DESSERY, planner; b. Riverside, Calif., Dec. 4, 1938; d. Floyd Gordon and Myrtle (Thomas) Dessery; m. David B. Thomas, Nov. 30, 1963 (div.); 1 child, Leslie; m. Michael Lawrence Bobrow, Mar. 24, 1980; stepchildren—Elizabeth, Erica, David. B.A., Calif. State U-San Francisco, 1963; M.A., Sch. Architecture and Urban Planning, UCLA, 1974. Dir. communications William L. Pereira Assocs., Los Angeles, 1972-73; sr. assoc. Bobrow/Thomas and Assocs., Los Angeles, 1973-78, pres., 1978-84, chmn. bd., chief exec. officer, 1984-92, pres., CEO, 1992—; guest lectr. U. So. Calif., Los Angeles, UCLA, Scripps Coll., Claremont, Calif., Calif. Poly. U., Pomona; mem. exec. com., dean's council UCLA Sch. Architecture and Urban Planning, 1982—; mem. design award jury Progressive Architecture, Stamford, Conn., 1983; adv. dir., mem. pub. policy com. Blue Cross Calif. Prin. works include: Merle Norman Pavilion, Shriners Hosps. for Crippled Children, Los Angeles, Shreveport, Santa Monica Hosp. Med. Ctr., UCLA Arroyo Bridge, Mus. Cultural History; restoration of adminstrn. bldg. Calif. Inst. Tech., Pasadena; Motion Picture and TV Hosp. and Country Home, Woodland Hills, Calif.; Kings Road Housing for Elderly, Hollywood, Calif. (Los Angeles chpt. AIA award 1981), Natividad Med. Ctr., U. Ariz. Cancer Ctr., Cook County Hosp. Replacement Plan, Stanford Psychiatry/Behavioral Scis. Acsd. Clinic, San Bernardino City Replacement Hosp., St. Luke's Med. Ctr. Milw., City of Hope, VA Outpatient Clinic, L.A./Hong Kong Hosp. Authority. Contbr. articles to profl. publs. Recipient Los Angeles Conservancy award, 1984, Alumni award for Excellence Profl. Achievement UCLA, 1988, AIA, NAVFAC award of merit, Spl. award for Energy Conservation for Med. Clinic, Kaneohe, Hawaii. Fellow UCLA Found., 1985—; bd. vis. UCLA Grad. Sch. Mgmt., 1985—; past vice chmn. Calif. Council for Humanities, San Francisco, 1980-83; mem. Nat. Women's Forum, Urban Land Inst. Task Force; co-conferrer Bobrow-Thomas fellowship, UCLA; past pres. Com. of 200, 1984-85; bd. regents Mt. St. Mary's Coll. Leadership award Calif. Chpt. Am. Planning Assn., 1986, Design Excellence award U.S. Dept. Def. for Naval Med. Clinic, Mem. L.A. Area C. of C., Am. Inst. Cert. Planners, Am. Inst. Planners, Tech. Corridor Assn., Regency (Los Angeles). Office: Bobrow/Thomas and Assoc Ste 1600 15301 Valley Vista Blvd Sherman Oaks CA 91403-3932

THOMAS, KAREN P., composer, conductor; b. Seattle, Sept. 17, 1957. BA in Composition, Cornish Inst., 1979; MusM in Composition, Conducting, U. Wash., 1985. Condr. The Contemporary Group, 1981-85; condr., music dir. Wash. Composers Forum, 1984-86; artistic dir., condr. Seattle Pro Musica, 1987—. Conducting debut Seattle, 1987; composer: Four Delineations of Curtmantle for trombone or cello, 1982, Metamorphoses on a Machaut Kyrie for strong orch. or quartet, 1983, Cowboy Songs for voice and piano, 1985, There Must Be a Lone Range for soprano and chamber ensemble, 1987, Brass Quintet, 1987, Four Lewis Carroll Songs for choir, 1989, (music/dance/theater) Boxiana, 1990, Elementi for clarinet and percussion, 1991, (one-act children's opera) Coyote's Trail, 1991, Clarion

Dances for brass ensemble, 1993, Roundup for sax quartet, 1993, Three Medieval Lyrics for choir, 1992, Sopravvento for wind quartet and percussion, 1994, Whne Night Came for Clarinet and chamber orch. or clarinet and piano, 1994, also numerous others. Recipient Composers Forum award N.W. Chamber Orch., 1984, King County Arts Commn., 1987, 90, Artist Trust, 1988, 93, Seattle Arts Commn., 1988, 91, 93, New Langton Arts, 1988, Delius Festival, 1993; fellow Wash. State Arts Commn., 1991; Charles E. Ives scholar AAAL. Mem. Broadcast Music, Am. Music Ctr., Internat. Alliance for Women in Music, Soc. Composers, Chorus Am.

THOMAS, KATHERINE JANE, newspaper business columnist; b. Bryan, Tex., Mar. 22, 1942; d. William Holt Jr. and Mary Anne (McCasland) Oliver; m. Robert Wayne Thomas, June 1, 1968; children: Jennifer Ann, Michael Frederick. BA, U. Tex., 1964. News reporter Abilene Reporter, Tex., 1964-67; with Ralston Purina Co., 1967-68; journalist The Eagle, Bryan, Tex., 1969-72, Wall St. Jour., Houston Bus. Jour., 1976-80; bus. columnist Houston Post, 1980-95; English instr. Walton Jr. Coll., 1968-69. Judge Houston Women on the Move Sect. Com., 1989-90, 91; judge Houston Area Inc. Mag. Entrepreneur of Yr., 1995; vol. judge out-of-state journalism competitions. Recipient Writing awards Tex. Press Assn., 1978-79, AP, 1966, 88, 91, Dallas Press Club Katie Finalist, 1990, 94, Matrix, 1989-90, Press Club of Houston, 1987, 89, 90, 91, 95, Sierra Club of Houston, 1989, St. Louis United Fund, 1968, Abilene C. of C., 1965. Mem. Press Club of Houston (bd. dirs., sec. 1991), Press Club of Houston Ednl. Found. (treas. 1991, bd. dirs.). Episcopalian. Avocations: sailing, entertaining, walking, reading. Office: The Houston Post PO Box 4747 Houston TX 77210

THOMAS, KENNETH EASTMAN, cardiothoracic surgeon; b. Evanston, Ill., Mar. 3, 1934; s. Kenneth Henry and Eloise (Eastman) T.; m. Sara Anne Stephens, Aug. 14, 1971; children: Diana, Allison, Michael. BA, Dartmouth Coll., 1956; MD, Stanford U., 1959. Med. diplomate, Ga. Med. intern dept. medicine U. Minn. Hosp., Mpls., 1959-60; med. resident dept. medicine U. Minn. Med. Sch., Mpls., 1960-61; surg. resident dept. surgery W.Va. U. Sch. Medicine, Morgantown, 1961-66, cancer rsch. fellow dept. surgery, 1966; clin. instr. thoracic surgery Med. Coll. Va., Richmond, 1969-71, fellow thoracic and cardiovascular surgery, 1969-71; ptnr., officer Peachtree Cardiovascular and Thoracic Surgeons, Atlanta, 1972—; bd. trustees St. Joseph's Hosp., Atlanta, 1990—, chmn. and dir. cardiothoracic surgery 1992-94; active staff St. Joseph's Hosp., Piedmont Hosp., Ga. Bapt. Hosp; courtesy hosp. staff Northside Hosp., Dunwoody Med. Ctr. Contbr. articles to profl. jours. Participant Talented and Gifted Program of Fulton County Schs., Atlanta, 1985—; mem. adv. bd. Atlanta (Ga.) Heart Ball, 1993—. Capt. USAF-Med. Corp., 1966-69, Vietnam. Decorated Bronze star USAF, Vietnam, 1969. Mem. ACS, AMA, Med. Assn. Ga., Med. Assn. Atlanta, Am. Heart Assn., Ga. Heart Assn., Soc. Thoracic Surgeons, Ga. Thoracic Soc., Am. Coll. Cardiology, So. Thoracic Surg. Assn., Am. Coll. Chest Physicians, N.Am. Soc. of Pacing and Electrophysiology. Republican. Episcopalian. Avocations: golf, travel, investments. Office: Peachtree Cardiovascular 5669 Peachtree Dunwoody Rd Atlanta GA 30342

THOMAS, KENNETH GLYNDWR, mining executive; b. Llanelli, Wales, June 25, 1944; arrived in Can., 1980; m. Elizabeth June Hickman, Sept. 25, 1976; children: Louise June, Kelly Jane. BSc in Metallurgy, U. Wales, Cardiff, 1970; MSc in Mgmt. Sci., U. London, 1971; PhD in Tech. Sci., U. of Delft, The Netherlands, 1994. Chartered engr., U.K.; registered profl. engr., Ont., Can. Metallurgist Brit. Steel Corp., Wales, 1959-67, Anglo Am. Corp. Kitwe, Zambia, 1971-75; plant supt. Anglo Am. Corp., Klerksdorp, South Africa, 1975-80; design metallurgist Kilborn Engring., Toronto, Ont., 1980-85; mill supt. Giant Yellowknife (Can.) Mines Ltd., N.W.T., 1985-87; sr. v.p. metallurgy and constrn. Barrick Gold Corp., Toronto, 1987—. Contbr. articles to tech. jours.; co-patentee in field. Mem. Inst. Materials (U.K.), Can. Inst. Mining, Metallurgy and Petroleum (Mill Man of Yr. award 1990). Office: Barrick Gold Corp, Royal Bank Pla S Twr 200 Bay St, Toronto, ON Canada MSJ 2J3 :

THOMAS, LAVON BULLOCK, interior designer; b. San Angelo, Tex., Oct. 6, 1929; d. J. T. and Ina (Malone) Bullock; m. W. Grant Thomas, June 9, 1956; children: Lorin Gwen Thomas Tavel, Lance Kevin. BS, Sam Houston State U., 1950; MEd, U. Houston, 1961. Tchr. Houston Ind. Sch., 1950-58; youth dir. St. Paul's Meth. Ch., Houston, 1958-60; designer Grant Thomas, Inc., Houston, 1960—, builder, 1994—; real estate broker Houston, 1975—. Unit pres. LWV, Houston, 1990, 91; v.p. Houston Assembly Delphian Chpts., Houston, 1992-93; bd. dirs. Panhellenic, Houston, 1993-94; active Houston UN Assn., 1994; Harris County Forest Landowners Assn. Recipient Cachet award for community svc. Women Helping Women, 1993. Mem. Nat. Assn. Realtors, Tex. Assn. Interior Designers, Tex. Assn. Realtors, Tex. Forestry Assn., Houston Assn. Realtors, Alpha Chi Omega (pres. Beta Zeta Beta chpt. 1994-95). Democrat. Methodist. Avocations: art, music, drama. Home: 15422 Mauna Loa Ln Houston TX 77040-1345

THOMAS, LAWRASON DALE, oil company executive; b. Saginaw, Mich., Apr. 21, 1934; s. Dale Edward and Ellen Ida (Johnson) T.; m. Barbara Marie Barter, Sept. 1, 1956; children: Robert B., Kimberly M., Edward D. B.S.C.E., U. Mich., 1956, M.B.A., 1957. Salesman Amoco Chems. Corp., Chgo., 1958-69; adminstrv. mgr. Amoco Oil Co., Atlanta region, 1969-71; dist mgr. Amoco Oil Co., Chgo. region, 1971-73, dir. mktg., 1971-73; dir. mktg. Amoco Oil Co., Kansas City region, 1973-75; v.p. ops., planning and transp. Amoco Oil Co., Chgo., 1976-79, exec. v.p., 1979-81, pres., 1981-90; mng. dir. Australia Amoco Internat. Co., 1975-76; bd. dirs. Boulevard Bank. Trustee nat. 4-H Coun., 1982-90. Mem. NAM (bd. dirs. 1986—), Ill. Mfrs. Assn. (bd. dirs. 1981-90), Chgo. Assn. Commerce and Industry (bd. dirs. 1982-89). Office: Amoco Corp PO Box 87703 200 E Randolph Dr Chicago IL 60601-6401

THOMAS, LAWRENCE ELDON, mathematics educator; b. Columbus, Ohio, Mar. 15, 1942; s. Bertram D. and Glorian (Butler) T.; m. Rebecca Nolan, June 13, 1970; children: David Nolan, Kathleen Rebecca. BS, U. Mich., 1964; PhD, Yale U., 1970. Rsch. asst. math. dept. Swiss Fed. Inst. Tech., Zurich, 1970-72; rsch. asst. physics dept. U. Geneva, 1972-74; asst. prof. math. U. Va., Charlottesville, 1974-76, assoc. prof., 1976-82, prof., 1982—, chmn. dept., 1989-93. Contbr. articles on theory of Schrodinger operators, statis. mechanics and stochastic processes to profl. jours. Mem. Am. Math. Soc., Am. Physics Soc., Internat. Nat. Math. Physics, Phi Beta Kappa. Avocations: sailing, tennis. Home: 2308 Glenn Ct Charlottesville VA 22901-2913 Office: U Va Dept Math Cabell Dr Charlottesville VA 22903

THOMAS, LEELAMMA KOSHY, women's health care nurse; b. Kerala, Kozhencherry, India, Feb. 10, 1936; naturalized Am. citizen, 1977; d. V.T. and Kunjamma (Koruth) Koshy; m. C.A. Thomas, Oct. 26, 1967; children: Linda Thomas, Lucie Thomas. BS in Nursing with honors, Coll. Nursing, Delhi, 1960; MA, Karnatak U., Dharwar Karnataka, Mysore, 1968. Cert. RN, Punjab, India 1960, Tex., 1972, AWHONN, 1993; reg. nurse midwife, Punjab, India 1960; reg. pub. health nurse, Punjab, India 1960; cert. inpatient obstet. PHN operational rsch. Nat. Tuberculosis Inst., Banglore, Mysore State, India, 1960-67; lectr. nursing Armed Forces Med. Coll., Maharstra State, India, 1961—; nurse labor and delivery U. Tex. Med. Br., nurse infant spl. care unit, nursing care coord. ob-gyn; head nurse U. Tex. Med. Br., Galveston, 1980-92, nurse clinician IV women and infants, 1993—; clin. instr. U. Tex. Sch. Nursing, Galveston, 1982—; presenter in field. Contbr. articles to profl. jours. Sunday sch. tchr. First Bapt. Ch., Galveston, Tex., 1982—. Recipient U. Tex. Med. Br. Maternal Health Coun. award, 1984; Am. Women's scholar. Mem. AWHONN, Sigma Theta Tau. Avocation: born-again Christian/ch. activities. Home: 16 San Jacinto Dr Galveston TX 77550-5714 Office: U Tex Med Br Ob-Gyn Nursing Svc Galveston TX 77550 also: U Tex Sch Nursing Galveston TX 77550

THOMAS, LEO J., imaging company executive; b. Grand Rapids, Minn., Oct. 30, 1936; s. Leo John and Christal (Dietrich) T.; m. Joanne Juliani, Dec. 27, 1958; children: Christopher, Gregory, Cynthia, Jeffrey. Student, Coll. St. Thomas, 1954-56; BS, U. Minn., 1958; MS, U. Ill., 1960, PhD, 1961. Rsch. chemist Eastman Kodak Co., Rochester, N.Y., 1961-67, lab. head, 1967-70, asst. div. head color photography div., 1970-72, tech. asst. to dir., 1972-75, asst. dir., 1975-77, v.p., dir., 1977-78, sr. v.p., dir., 1978-84; sr. v.p., gen. mgr. Life Scis., Rochester, N.Y., 1985-88; vice-chmn., chmn. Sterling Drug Inc., N.Y.C., 1988-89; group v.p., gen. mgr. Health Eastman Kodak Co.,

Rochester, 1989-91, group v.p., pres. imaging, 1991-94, exec. v.p., 1994—; bd. dirs. Frontier Corp., John Wiley and Sons Inc., N.Y.C., Eastman Kodak Co. Mem. AIChE, AAAS, NAE, Am. Acad. Arts and Scis., Am. Inst. Med. and Bioengring., Rochester C. of C. Office: Eastman Kodak Co 343 State St Rochester NY 14650-0234

THOMAS, LEROY, newspaper executive editor; b. Detroit, Dec. 17, 1936; s. Leroy and Victoria (Shelton) T.; divorced; children: Sheldon L., Stephen M. AA, Wilson Jr. Coll., Chgo., 1962; student, Roosevelt U., 1962-63, Northwestern U., 1982-83. Asst. mng. editor Chgo. Defender, 1970-76, exec. editor, 1985—; pub. relations rep. midwest region Ford Motor Co., Chgo., 1976-80; sr. editor Blue Cross and Blue Shield of Ill., Chgo., 1981-82; asst. press sec. Office of Mayor, Chgo., 1982-85; adj. instr. journalism Columbia Coll., Chgo., 1973-85; lectr. and cons. various Black orgns. and civic groups. Democrat. Baptist. Club: Jackson Park Yacht (Chgo.). Avocations: sailboating, traveling, collecting antiques, creative writing. Office: Chicago Defender Robert S Abbott Pub Co 2400 S Michigan Ave Chicago IL 60616

THOMAS, LEWIS JONES, JR., anesthesiology educator, biomedical researcher; b. Phila., Dec. 13, 1930; s. Lewis Jones and Margaretta Eleanore (Schmid) T.; m. Jane E. Priem, June 18, 1955; children: Lewis Jones III., Sarah Jane Thomas Snell. BS in Biology, Haverford Coll., 1953; MD cum laude, Washington U., St. Louis, 1957. Diplomate Am. Bd. Anesthesiology. Assoc. dir. Biomed. Computer Lab., Washington U. Sch. Med., St. Louis, 1972-75, dir., 1975—, assoc. prof. physiology and biophysics, 1974-85, assoc. prof. elec. engring., 1978—, assoc. prof. anesthesiology, biomed. engring., 1974—, assoc. prof. physiology, dept. cell biology and physiology, 1985—; assoc. prof. Inst. Biomed. Computing, Washington U., 1984-89, prof., 1989—, assoc. dir. Inst. for Biomed. Computing, 1984-91, 92—, acting dir., 1991-92; cons. Health Resources Admin., Rockville, Md., 1974-75, Nat. Ctr. Health Svc. Rsch., Washington, 1978-82; mem. biomed. rsch. tech. rev. com., div. rsch. resources NIH, 1988-92; cons. Diagnostic Radiology Coordinating Com. NIH Planning Subcom., 1990; Nat. Task Force NIH Stategic Plan, 1992; NIH Reviewers Reserve NCRR, 1992—. Contbr. articles to profl. jours. and books. Bd. dirs. Bd. Edn., University City, Mo., 1970, 72-73; v.p. Symphony Orch., University City, 1984-86, pres., 1988-89, treas. 1990-91. Sr. asst. surg. USPHS, 1962-64. Recipient USPHS Rsch. Career Devel. award, 1966. Mem. Am. Physiol. Soc., AAAS, N.Y. Acad. Scis. Avocations: music performance, recreational computing. Office: Washington U Biomed Computer Lab 700 S Euclid Ave Saint Louis MO 63110-1085

THOMAS, LLOYD BREWSTER, economics educator; b. Columbia, Mo., Oct. 22, 1941; s. Lloyd B. and Marianne (Moon) T.; m. Sally Leach, Aug. 11, 1963; 1 child, Elizabeth. AB, U. Mo., 1963, AM, 1964; PhD, Northwestern U., 1970. Instr. Northwestern U., Evanston, Ill., 1966-68; asst. prof. econs. Kan. State U., Manhattan, 1968-72; assoc. prof., 1974-81, prof., 1983—; asst. prof. Fla. State U., Tallahassee, 1973-74; vis. prof. U. Calif., Berkeley, 1981-82, U. Del., 1993. Author: Money, Banking and Economic Activity, 3d edit., 1986, Principles of Economics, 2d edit., 1993, Principles of Macroeconomics, 2d edit., 1993, Principles of Microeconomics, 2d edit., 1993; contbr. articles to profl. jours. Mem. Am. Econs. Assn., Midwest Econs. Assn., So. Econs. Assn., Western Econs. Assn., Phi Kappa Phi. Avocations: tennis, classical music. Home: 1501 N 10th Ct Manhattan KS 66502

THOMAS, LOWELL, JR., author, lecturer, former lieutenant governor Alaska, former state senator; b. London, Oct. 6, 1923; s. Lowell Jackson and Frances (Ryan) T.; m. Mary Taylor Pryor, May 20, 1950; children: Anne Frazier, David Lowell. Student, Taft Sch., 1942; B.A., Dartmouth Coll., 1948; postgrad., Princeton Sch. Pub. and Internat. Affairs, 1952. Asst. cameraman Fox Movietone News, S.Am., 1939, Bradford Washburn Alaskan mountaineering expdn., 1940; illustrated lecturer, 1946—; asst. economist, photographer with Max Weston Thornburg, Turkey, 1947, Iran, 1948; film prodn. Iran, 1949; Tibet expdn. with Lowell Thomas, Sr., 1949; field work Cinerama, S.Am., Africa, Asia, 1951-52; travels by small airplane with wife, writing and filming Europe, Africa, Middle East, 1954-55; mem. Rockwell Polar Flight, first flight around the world over both poles, Nov., 1965; mem. Alaska State Senate, 1967-74; lt. gov. State of Alaska, 1974-79; owner Talkeetna Air Taxi, Inc., air contract carrier, Anchorage, Alaska, 1980-94. Producer series of films Flight to Adventure, NBC-TV, 1956; producer, writer TV series High Adventure, 1957-59; producer documentary film Adaq, King of Alaskan Seas, 1960; producer two films on Alaska, 1962, 63, film on U. Alaska, 1964, South Pacific travel documentary, 1965, film on Arctic oil exploration, Atlantic-Richfield Co., 1969. Author: Out of this World, A Journey to Tibet, 1950, (with Mrs. Lowell Thomas, Jr.) Our Flight to Adventure, 1956, The Silent War in Tibet, 1959, The Dalai Lama, 1961, The Trail of Ninety-Eight, 1962, (with Lowell Thomas Sr.) More Great True Adventures, 1963, Famous First Flights that Changed History, 1968. Past pres. Western Alaska council Boy Scouts Am.; bd. dirs. Anchorage unit Salvation Army, Alaska Conservation Fund. Served 1st lt. USAAF, 1943-45. Mem. Nat. Parks and Conservation Assn. (bd. dirs.), Alaska C. of C., Aircraft Owners and Pilots Assn. Clubs: Explorers, Marco Polo, Dutch Treat (N.Y.C.), Rotary, (Anchorage), Press (Anchorage); Dartmouth Outing; American Alpine. Address: 10800 Hideaway Lake Dr Anchorage AK 99516-1145

THOMAS, LYDIA WATERS, research and development executive; b. Norfolk, Va., Oct. 13, 1944; d. William Emerson and Lillie Ruth (Roberts) Waters; m. James Carter Thomas (div. 1970); 1 child, Denee Marrielle. BS in Zoology, Howard U., 1965, PhD in Cytology, 1973; MS in Microbiology, Am. U., 1971. Sr. v.p. gen. mgr. The MITRE Corp., McLean, Va., 1973-94, 1994—; affiliate Ctr. Sci. and Internat. Affairs, Harvard U., Cambridge, Mass., 1990—; bd. dirs. Cabot Corp.; mem. Draper Labs., Inc. Author: Automation Impacts on Industry, 1983. Mem. Invention. Adv. Bd., U.S. C.E., 1980-82; expert witness, Senate, U.S. govt. pub. hearings, Washington, 1985; mem. adv. bd. INFORM, N.Y.C, George Wash. U. Va. Campus; mem. Supt.'s Bus./Industry Adv. Coun. Fairfax County Pub. Schs. Recipient Tribute to Women in Internat. Industry YMCA, 1986, EBONE Image award Coalition of 100 Black Women, 1990, Dean's award Black Engineer of the Year, 1991. Mem. AAAS, AIAA, Am. Def. Preparedness Assn., Am. Mgmt. Assn., Am. Soc. Toxicology, Am. Astronautical Soc., Nat. Energy Resources Orgn., Nat. Security Indsl. Assn., Soc. Macro-Engring., Teratology Soc., U.S. Energy Assn., African Sci. Inst., Women in Aerospace, Nat. Space Club, Sigma Xi (steering com.), Alpha Kappa Alpha. Office: The MITRE Corporation 7525 Colshire Dr Mc Lean VA 22102

THOMAS, MABLE, communications company executive, former state legislator; b. Atlanta, Nov. 8, 1957; d. Bernard and Madie Thomas. BS in Pub. Adminstrn., Ga. State U., 1982, postgrad., 1983—. With acctg. dept. Trust Co. Bank, Atlanta, 1977; recreation supr. Sutton Community Sch., Atlanta, 1977-78; data transcriber Ga. Dept. Natural Resources, Atlanta, 1978-79; clk. U.S. Census Bur., Atlanta, 1980; laborer City of Atlanta Parks and Recreation, 1980-81; student asst. Ga. State U., Atlanta, 1981-82; state rep. Ga. House Reps., Atlanta, 1984-94; pres. Master Comms. Inc. Atlanta, 1994—; mem. exec. com. Ga. Legis. Black Census, Atlanta, 1985—. Mem. adv. youth council Salvation Army Bellwood Club, 1975; founder Vine City Community Improvement Assn., Atlanta, 1985; mem. Neighborhood Planning Unit, Ga. State U. Adv. Bd. of Comprehensive Youth Services, 1988—, Nat. Black Women's Health Project, Ga. Housing Coalition; actively involved in Say No to Drugs Program; bd. dirs. Am. Cancer Soc., 1988—. Recipient Bronze Jubilee award City of Atlanta Cultural Affairs, 1984, Disting. Service award Grady Hosp., 1985, Human Service award for community and political leadership for disadvantaged, 1986, Exceptional Service award Young Community Leaders, 1986, Citizenship award Salvation Army Club; named Outstanding Freshman Legislator, 1986, one of Outstanding Young People of Atlanta, 1987. Mem. Ga. Assn. Black Elected Officials (mem. housing and econ. devel. com.), Conf. Minority Pub. Adminstrn. (Outstanding Service award), Nat. Polit. Congress Black Women (bd. dirs.). Democrat. Methodist. Home: PO Box 573 Atlanta GA 30301-0573

THOMAS, MARGARET JEAN, clergywoman, religious research consultant; b. Detroit, Dec. 24, 1943; d. Robert Elcana and Purcella Margaret (Hartness) T. BS, Mich. State U., 1964; MDiv, Union Theol. Sem., Va., 1971; DMin, San Francisco Theol. Sem., 1991. Ordained to ministry United Presbyn. Ch., 1971. Dir. rsch. bd. Christian edn. Presbyn. Ch. U.S., Richmond, Va., 1965-71; dir. rsch. gen. coun. Presbyn. Ch. U.S., Atlanta,

1972-73; mng. dir. rsch. div. support agy. United Presbyn. Ch. U.S.A., N.Y.C., 1974-76; dep. exec. dir. gen. assembly mission coun. United Presbyn. Ch. U.S.A., 1977-83; dir. N.Y. coordination Presbyn. Ch. (U.S.A.), 1983-85; exec. dir. Minn. Coun. Chs., Mpls., 1985-95; synod exec. Synod of Lakes and Prairies Presbyn. Ch. (U.S.A.), Bloomington, Minn., 1995—; mem. Permant Jud. Commn., Presbyn. Ch. (U.S.A.), 1985-91, moderator, 1989-91, mem. adv. com. on constn., 1992—; sec. com. on ministry Twin Cities Area Presbytery, Mpls., 1985-91, vice moderator, 1991-92, moderator, 1992-93; mem. joint religious legis. coalition, 1985-95; mem. Commn. on Regional and Local Ecumenism Nat. Coun. Chs., 1988-91, officer Ecumenical Networks, 1992—, mem. Unity and Rels. unit, 1992-93; mem. nat. planning com. Nat. Workshop on Christian Unity, 1992—; bd. dirs. Franklin Nat. Bank, Mpls., 1987—. Contbr. articles to profl. jours. Mem. adv. panel crime victims svcs. Hennepin County Atty.'s Office, 1985-86, Police and Cmty. Rels. Task Force, St. Paul, 1986; mem. adv. panel Hennepin County Crime Victim Coun., 1990-93, chmn., 1990-93; bd. dirs. Minn. Foodshare, 1985-95, Minn. Coalition on Health, 1989-92, Minn. Black-on-Black Crime Task Force, 1988, Twin Cities Coalition Affordable Health Care, 1986-87, Presbyn. Homes of Minn., 1995—, Clearwater Forest, Deerwood, Minn., 1995—; co-chmn. Minn. Interreligious Com., 1988-95; bd. dirs. Abbott Northwestern Pastoral Counseling Ctr., 1988-91, chmn., 1990-91. Recipient Human Rels. award Jewish Community Rels. Coun./Anti-Defamation League, 1989, Gov.'s Cert. of Commendation for Women's Leadership, 1993. Mem. Nat. Assn. Ecumenical Staff, N.Am. Acad. Ecumenists, Religious Edn. Assn. (sec. 1974-76), NOW (Outstanding Woman of Minn. 1986), Amnesty Internat. Mem. Democrat-Farm-Labor Party. Office: Synod of Lakes and Prairies Presbyn Ch USA 8012 Cedar Ave S Bloomington MN 55425

THOMAS, MARILYN JANE, insurance company executive; b. Fremont, Ohio, Dec. 11, 1944; d. Myron Elwood and Elvira Evelyn (Plagman) Magsig; m. William E. Thomas, Jr., Nov. 7, 1992; stepchildren: Dana Lauren Thomas, Keira Anne Schwartz. BS in Edn., Capital U., Columbus, 1966; postgrad., U. Calif., Irvine, Fullerton, 1969-70. Tchr. pub. schs., Ohio, Calif., La., 1966-71; underwriter Tenn. Life Ins. Co., Houston, Tex., 1971-73; supr., mgr. contracts adminstrn. Phila. Life Ins. Co. (merger Tenn. Life Ins. Co.), Houston, 1973-80; systems analyst Phila. Life Ins. Co., Houston, 1980-84; dir. market research/product devel. Phila. Am. Life Ins. Co. (merger Phila. Life Ins. Co.), Houston, 1984-87; 2d v.p. mktg. Phila. Am. Life Ins., Houston, 1987—. Vol. Spl. Olympics, Houston; tchr. Project Business, 1981. Recipient Outstanding Woman award, Houston YWCA, 1984. Mem. Am. Bus. Women's Assn. (chmn. edn. com. 1987-88), Soc. Group Contract Analysts (chmn. com. 1977-80), Houston Assn. Health Underwriters. Republican. Lutheran. Avocation: cooking. Office: Phila Am Life Ins 3121 Buffalo Speedway Houston TX 77098-1805

THOMAS, MARLIN ULUESS, industrial engineering educator; b. Middlesboro, Ky., June 28, 1942; s. Elmer Vernon and Hellen Lavada (Banks) T.; m. Susan Kay Stoner, Jan. 18, 1963; children: Pamela Claire Thomas Davis, Martin Phillip. BSE, U. Mich., Dearborn, 1967; MSE, U. Mich., Ann Arbor, 1968, PhD, 1971. Registered profl. engr., Mich. Asst. and assoc. prof. dept. ops. rsch. Naval Postgrad. Sch., Monterey, Calif., 1971-75; assoc. prof. systems design dept. U. Wis., Milw., 1976-78; mgr. tech. planning and analysis vehicle quality-reliability Chrysler Corp., Detroit, 1978-79; prof. dept. indsl. engring. U. Mo., Columbia, 1979-82; prof. indsl. engring., chmn. dept. Cleve State U., 1982-88, acting dir. Advanced Mfg. Ctr., 1984-85; prof., chmn. indsl. engring. Lehigh U., Bethlehem, Pa., 1988-93, chmn. dept., 1988—; prof., head Sch. Indsl. Engring. Purdue U., West Lafayette, Ind., 1993—; program dir. NSF, Washington, 1987-88. Contbr. numerous articles on indsl. engring. and ops. rsch. to profl. jours. With USN, 1958-62. Named Outstanding Tchr., U. Mo. Coll. Engring., 1980, Coll. Man of Yr, Cleve. State U. Coll. Engring., 1985. Fellow Inst. Indsl. Engrs; mem. Ops. Rsch. Soc. Am., Am. Soc. for Engring. Edn., Am. Soc. Quality Control, Am. Statis. Assn., Soc. Am. Mil. Engrs., VFW. Office: Purdue U Sch Indsl Engring 1287 Grissom Hall West Lafayette IN 47907-1287

THOMAS, MARLO (MARGARET JULIA THOMAS), actress; b. Detroit, Nov. 21, 1943; d. Danny and Rose Marie (Cassanti) T.; m. Phil Donahue, May 21, 1980. Ed., U. So. Calif. Theatrical appearances in Thieves, Broadway, 1974, Barefoot in the Park, London, Social Security, Broadway, 1986, The Shadow Box, Broadway, 1994; star: TV series That Girl, 1966-71 (Golden Globe award Best TV actress, 1967); appeared in TV films: The Body Human: Facts for Girls (Emmy award Best Performer Children's Program), 1981, The Last Honor of Kathryn Beck, 1984 (also exec. prodr.), Consenting Adults, 1985, Nobody's Child, 1986 (Emmy Best Dramatic Actress), Held Hostage: The Sis and Jerry Levin Story, 1991, Ultimate Betrayal, 1994, Reunion, 1994; conceived book and record, starred in TV spl. Free to Be. . . You and Me, 1974 (Emmy for best children's show); films include Thieves, 1977, In the Spirit, 1991, Jenny, 1963; conceived book, record and TV spl. Free to Be A Family (Emmy Best Children's Show). Recipient 4 Emmys, Golden Globe award, George Foster Peabody award, Tom Paine award Nat. Emergency Civil Liberties Com. Mem. Ms. Found., Nat. Women's Polit. Caucus. Office: CAA 9830 Wilshire Blvd Beverly Hills CA 90210*

THOMAS, MARTHA WETTERHALL, advertising agency executive; b. Ann Arbor, Mich., Aug. 23, 1949; d. Roy Christner and Doreen (Armstrong) Wetterhall; m. James William Thomas, May 22, 1982. BA cum laude, U. Mich., 1971. Copywriter McCaffrey & McCall, N.Y.C., 1972-76, Cunningham & Walsh, N.Y.C., 1976-78; sr. copywriter Grey/2 Advt., N.Y.C., 1978-79; Symon, Thomas & Hilliard, N.Y.C., 1979-82; pres. Thomas & Thomas Advt., N.Y.C., 1983—. Writer, producer 1st paid TV advt. campaign for art mus., 1985. Recipient Encore award N.Y. Arts and Bus. Council, 1985, Effie award Am. Mktg. Assn., 1987, Telly award for local and regional TV commls., 1988. Mem. Advt. Women of N.Y., Am. Women's Econ. Devel. Corp., Ad Net (2d v.p.).

THOMAS, MARTIN LEWIS H., marine ecologist, educator; b. London, Feb. 9, 1935; s. John Breton H. and Evelyn Jessie Thomas; m. Mary Lou Harley, June 15, 1976; children: Calluna, Tiana. BSc, U. Dunelm, Newcastle, U.K., 1956; MSA, U. Toronto, Ont., 1963; PhD, Dalhousie U., Halifax, N.S. 1970. Ont. diploma in horticulture. Rsch. biologist Fisheries Rsch. Bd. Can., London, Ont., 1956-62; rsch. scientist Fisheries Rsch. Bd. Can., Ellerswe, P.E.I., 1962-70; asst. prof. U. New Brunswick, Saint John, 1971-74, assoc. prof., 1974-77, prof., 1977—; bd. dirs. Marine Rsch. Group U. New Brunswick, Saint John, 1970—. Author: Introducing the Sea, 1973, A Guide to the Ecology of Shoreline and Shallow-Water Marine Communities of Bermuda, 1992; editor: Marine and Coastal Systems, 1985. Sgt. U.K. mil., 1954-56. Hon. rsch. assoc. Bermuda Aquarium, Flatts, 1992. Mem. Marine Biology Assn. U.K., Brit. Biol. Soc., N.Y. Acad. Sci. (hon. life mem.). Office: U New Brunswick, PO Box 5050, Saint John's, NF Canada E2L 4L5

THOMAS, MELISSA ANN, lawyer; b. San Diego, Aug. 11, 1955; d. Frank H. and Ann (Beyerle) T.; m. John W. Spiegel, Sept. 19, 1987. AB, U. Calif., Davis, 1975; JD, Harvard U., 1978. Bar: Va. 1978, D.C. 1984, Calif. 1988. Assoc. McGuire, Woods & Battle, Richmond, Va., 1978-83; ptnr. Miller & Chevalier, Washington, 1984-87, Pillsbury, Madison & Sutro, L.A., 1987—; legis. atty. U.S. Joint Com. on Taxation, Washington, 1979-80; mem. Tax Coalition, Washington, 1984—. Counsel, bd. dirs. Va. Women's Cultural Project, Inc., Richmond, 1982-87. Office: Pillsbury Madison & Sutro 515 S Flower St Ste 3300 Los Angeles CA 90071

THOMAS, NATHANIEL CHARLES, clergyman; b. Jonesboro, Ark., June 24, 1929; s. Willie James and Linnie (Elias) T.; B.A., Miss. Indsl. Coll., Holly Springs, 1951; B.D., Lincoln U., 1954, M.Div., 1974; student Lancaster (Pa.) Theol. Sem., 1952-53; D.Div., Tex. Coll., Tyler, 1981; m. Juanita Fanny Jefferson, May 20, 1961 (dec. 1970); children—Gina Charlise, Nathaniel Charles, Keith Antony; m. 2d, Mary Elizabeth Partee, June 8, 1971. Ordained to ministry Christian Meth. Episcopal Ch., 1954; dir. Christian edn. 8th dist. Christian Meth. Episc. Ch., 1954-58; pastor in Waterford, Miss., 1949-51, Wrightville, Ark., 1955-57, Hot Springs, Ark., 1957-60, Little Rock, 1960-62, Mt. Pisgah Christian Meth. Episc. Ch., Memphis, 1966-67, Greenwood Christian Meth. Episc. Ch., Memphis, 1980-81; dir. Christian edn., adminstrv. asst. to Bishop B. Julian Smith, Christian Meth. Episc. Ch., Memphis, 1954-74, presiding elder South Memphis dist., 1971-74, sec. gen. conf. of ch., 1970-82, gen. sec. gen. bd. personnel services, 1978—, also mem.

gen. connectional bd., program adminstr. ministerial salary supplement program, 1974-90, asst. to sec. gen. Gen. Bd. Pensions, 1974-78; program dir. CME Ch. Group Fire & Casualty Ins. Plan, 1978—, Annual CME Convocation and CME Reader Resource Series, 1990—; sec. Ministerial Assn. Little Rock, 1960-62; v.p. youth work sect., div. Christian edn. Nat. Council Chs., del. World Council Chs. Conf., Upsalla Sweden, 1968. Dir. Haygood-Neal Garden Apts., Inc., Eldorado, Ark., 1969—, Smith-Keys Village Apts., Inc., Texarkana, Ark., 1968—, East Gate Village Apts., Inc., Union City, Tenn., 1971—; trustee Collins Chapel Health Care Center, Memphis, 1974—, Tex. Coll., 1981—; bd. dirs. Family Service Memphis, 1972-73, Newsday Coop., Inc., exec. trustee; chmn. bd. dirs. Memphis Opportunities Indsl. Ctr., 1976-78. Mem. NAACP, Urban League, Community on Move for Equality, Memphis Interdenomminational Ministers Alliance, Memphis Ministers Assn., Tenn. Assn. Chs., Ark. Council Chs., Ark. Council Human Relations, Tenn. Council Human Relations, Family Service Memphis, A.B. Hill PTA. Author: Christian Youth Fellow Guide, 8th Episcopal District, 1959; Living Up to My Obligations to the Christian Methodist Episcopal Church, 1956; Steps Toward Developing an Effective Program of Christian Education, 1972; co-author: Worship in the Local Church, 1966; co-author, editor: Coming to Grips with the Teaching Work of the Church, 1966, Discipleship: Creation, Covenant, Community, 1994—. Co-editor: Developing Black Families, 1975; compiling editor: Dedicated . . . Committed-Autobiography of Bishop B. Julian Smith, 1978—. Home: PO Box 9 Memphis TN 38101-0009 Office: PO Box 74 Memphis TN 38101-0074

THOMAS, ORVILLE C., physician; b. Haynesville, La., Aug. 23, 1915; children—David, Diane, Cody. Pre-med. Student, Marian Mil. Inst., 1932-33, Tulane U., 1933; M.D., Tulane U., 1939. Diplomate Am. Bd. Pediatrics. Diplomate Am. Bd. Allergy and Immunology. Intern Shreveport Charity Hosp., La., 1939-40; asst. resident in pediatrics Children's Meml. Hosp., Chgo., 1946-47, resident in pediatrics, 1947, chief resident in pediatrics, 1948; active staff Tex. Children's Hosp., Houston, 1962—, fellow pediatric allergy, 1963-65, chief allergy sect., 1973-78; fellow in pediatric allergy Baylor Coll. Medicine, Houston, 1963-65; chief pediatrics Schumpert Meml. Hosp., Shreveport, La, 1958-61, chief of staff, 1958; sr. staff pediatrics Confederate Meml. Hosp., Shreveport, La, 1948-61; active staff Highland Hosp., Shreveport, La, 1948-61, North La. Hosp., Shreveport, La, 1948-61, Physicians and Surgeons Hosp., Shreveport, La, 1948-61, Ben Taub Gen. Hosp., Houston, 1962—, Hermann Hosp., Houston, 1966-69; hon. staff St. Luke's Hosp., Houston, 1962—; conss. staff Meth. Hosp., Houston, 1962—, St. Joseph Hosp., Houston, 1966—, Bellaire (Tex.) Gen. Hosp., 1966-86, Rosewood Gen. Hosp., Houston, 1967—, Meml. Bapt. Hosp., Houston, 1968—, Pasadena Bayshore Hosp., Pasadena, Tex., 1970—; instr. pediatrics Northwestern U. Sch. Medicine, Chgo., 1948; assoc. prof. pediatrics La. State U. Postgrad. Sch. Medicine, 1956-61; clin. instr. pediatrics Baylor Coll. Medicine, Houston, 1961-66, asst. clin. prof. pediatrics, 1966-76, assoc. clin. prof. pediatrics, 1977—; assoc. clin. prof. allergy and immunology U. Tex. Grad. Sch. Biomed. Scis., Houston, 1970—. Book reviewer: Venom Diseases; Aspects of Allergy and Applied Immunology. Contbr. articles to profl. jours. Served to maj. USMC AUS, 1942-46. Fellow Am. Coll. Allergy and Immunology (pediatrics com. 1964—, pres. 1978), Am. Acad. Allergy and Immunology, Am. Assn. Cert. Allergists (bd. govs. 1974, pres. 1979); mem. AMA, Am. Acad. Pediatrics, So. Med. Assn. (chmn. allergy sect. 1970-71), Tex. Allergy Research Found. Houston(research and edn. com. 1966-86, chmn. sci. adv. council 1973—), Tex. Pediatric Soc., Harris County Med. Soc., Tex. Med. Assn. (chmn. allergy sect. 1976-77), Am. Assn. for Inhalation Therapy (awards com. 1969-72, spl. edn. com. 1969-72), Greater Houston Allergy Soc. (pres. 1977), Joint Council of Allergy and Immunology, Internat. Assn. of Allergology and Clin. Immunology (U.S. rep. 1981-85). Home: 1111 Bering Dr Apt 704 Houston TX 77057-2320 Office: 6969 Brompton St Houston TX 77025-1611

THOMAS, OWEN CLARK, clergyman, educator; b. N.Y.C., Oct. 11, 1922; s. Harrison Cook and Frances (Arnold) T.; m. Margaret Ruth Miles, June 6, 1981; children: Aaron Beecher, Addison Lippitt, Owen Clark Jr. A.B., Hamilton Coll., 1944, D.D., 1970; grad. student physics, Cornell U., 1943-44; B.D., Episcopal Theol. Sch., Cambridge, Mass., 1949; Ph.D., Columbia U., 1956. Ordained to ministry Episcopal Ch., 1949. Dir. coll. work Episcopal Diocese, N.Y., 1951-52; chaplain to Episcopal students Sarah Lawrence Coll., 1950-52; mem. faculty Episcopal Div. Sch. (formerly Episcopal Theol. Sch.), Cambridge, Mass., 1952—, prof. theology, 1965-93, prof. emeritus, 1993—; chmn. dept. coll. work Episcopal Diocese Mass., 1956-59; vis. prof. Pontifical Gregorian U., 1973-74, N. Am. Coll., Rome, 1982-83. Author: William Temple's Philosophy of Religion, 1961, Science Challenges Faith, 1967, Attitudes Toward Other Religions, 1969, rev. edit., 1986, Introduction To Theology, 1973, rev. edit., 1983, God's Activity in the World, 1983, Theological Questions: Analysis and Argument, 1983; contbr. chpts. to books. Mem. Episcopal Democratic City Com., 1966-80, 88—. Served to ensign USNR, 1944-45. Elihu Root fellow Hamilton Coll., 1943; Univ. fellow Columbia U., 1949-50; scholar in residence Rockefeller Found. Study and Conf. Ctr., Bellagio, Italy, 1991. Fellow Soc. Values in Higher Edn.; mem. Am. Theol. Soc., Phi Beta Kappa. Home: 243 Concord Ave Apt 12 Cambridge MA 02138-1362

THOMAS, PATRICIA ANNE, retired law librarian; b. Cleve., Aug. 21, 1927; d. Richard Joseph and Marietta Bernadette (Teevans) T.; BA, Case Western Res. U., 1949, JD, 1951. Admitted to Ohio bar, 1951, U.S. Supreme Ct. bar, 1980; libr. Arter & Hadden, Cleve., 1951-62; asst. libr., then libr. IRS, Washington, 1962-78; libr. dir. Adminstrv. Office, U.S. Cts., 1978-93; ret. 1993. Mem. Am. Assn. Law Libraries, Law Librs. Soc. D.C. (pres. 1967-69), Soc. Benchers.

THOMAS, PATRICK HERBERT, information services company executive; b. Atlanta, Aug. 29, 1942; s. Joseph Murray and Ruby Lois (Davis) T.; m. Nell McLaurin, Aug. 28, 1965; children—Laurin Nicole, William Patrick. B.S., Ga. State U., 1971. Ops. officer First Nat. Bank, Atlanta, 1968-71; treas. First Fin. Mgmt., Atlanta, 1971-72, exec. v.p., 1972-74, chmn. bd., pres., chief exec. officer, 1974—; v.p. First Ga. Bank, Atlanta, 1973-75; sr. v.p. First R.R. and Banking, Augusta, Ga., 1977—; dir. First Fin. Mgmt. T.A. Communications, Atlanta, Ga. Interchange Network, Atlanta. Served to 1st lt. U.S. Army, 1962-66. Republican. Methodist. Clubs: Atlanta Athletic, Sporting (Atlanta). Home: 7485 Brigham Dr Atlanta GA 30350-5613 Office: 1st Fin Mgmt Corp 3 Corporate Sq NE Atlanta GA 30329-2008*

THOMAS, PAUL EMERY, mathematics educator; b. Phoenix, Feb. 15, 1927; m. Chi-Yuen Chan, 1958; children: Jenny, Valerie. BA, Oberlin Coll., 1950, Oxford U., Eng., 1952; PhD in Math, Princeton U., 1955. Rsch. instr. Columbia U., 1955-56; asst. prof. math. U. Calif., Berkeley, 1956-60, assoc. prof., 1960-63, prof., 1963-91, prof. emeritus, 1991—; prof. Miller Inst. Basic Research in Sci., 1966-67, mem. exec. com., 1983-89; exec. dir. Miller Inst. Basic Research in Sci., 1987-89; dep. dir. Math. Scis. Rsch. Inst., 1987-90; vis. prof. Princeton U., fall 1971, mem. adv. coun. dept. math., 1987—. Served with USNR, 1945-46. NSF fellow Princeton U., 1955, U. Calif., 1958-59; Guggenheim Meml. Found. fellow, 1961; Rhodes scholar Oxford U., 1950-53. Mem. Am. Math. Soc. (trustee 1980-84, chmn. bd. trustees 1983). Office: Evans Hall Mathematics Dept U Calif Berkeley CA 94720

THOMAS, PAUL S., principal. Prin. Passel-Cokato (Minn.) Sr. High Sch. Recipient Blue Ribbon award U.S. Dept. Edn., 1990-91. Office: Dassel-Cokato Sr High Sch Hwy # 12 and Wright County Rd # 100 Cokato MN 55321

THOMAS, PAYNE EDWARD LLOYD, publisher; b. Balt., May 11, 1919; s. Charles C. and Nanette (Payne) T.; m. Sally Claire Gunther; children: John Fuller, Michael Payne, Peter Charles, LeAnne Marie, Jennifer Nanette. Founder, dir. Thomas Found. and its memorials: Edward Waldron Payne Library, Harvey Cushing Hall, Chapel of Margaret and Charles Crankshaw; exec. v.p. Charles C Thomas, Pub., Springfield, Ill., 1942-48; editor- in-chief sci., tech., med. depts. Charles C Thomas, Pub., 1948-55, pres., 1955—. Mem. Tavern Club (Chgo.), Island Bay Yacht Club (Springfield), Coral Reef Yacht Club (Miami, Fla.), Riviera Country Club (Miami). Presbyterian. Home: 2600 S 1st St Springfield IL 62704-4730 Office: Charles C Thomas Pub 2600 S 1st St Springfield IL 62704-4730

THOMAS, PETER M., real estate developer; b. Las Vegas, Nev., Feb. 6, 1950; s. E. Parry and Peggy (Chatterton) T.; m. Nancy Paxman, June 12, 1972; children: David P., Megan, Lindsey, Adam. BS, U. Utah, 1972. V.p. Valley Bank of Nev., Las Vegas, 1977-79, exec. v.p., 1979-82, pres., 1982-92; pres. Bank of Am., Nev., 1992-95, pres., coo, 1992-95; bldg. dir. Thomas and Mack Co., 1995—. Mem. long range planning com. United Way, 1982-84; bd. dirs. Friends of Channel 10, 1982-85; mem. Las Vegas Conv. and Visitor's Authority, 1984-88, sec./treas., 1985-86, treas./v.p., 1987-88; chmn. Las Vegas Met. Police Dept. Com. Fiscal Affairs, 1994—, Citizen's Adv. Com. on Downtown Redevel., 1986—, Nev. Bankers Legislative Com., Nev. Devel. Authority, (mem. exec. com. 1986—, trustee 1986-90, chmn.-elect 1992—); mem. Downtown Progresss assn., 1986-90, Nev. Nuclear Projects Commn., 1993—, Am. Bankers Assn. Govt. Rels. and Adminstrv. Coms., Las Vegas Mayor's Multi-jurisdictional Cmty. Empowerment Commn.; mem. vision project exec. coun. U. Nev., 1988-90, Pres's Assn., 1988—; bd. trustees U. Nev. Las Vegas Found., 1994—. Mem. Nev. Bar Assn., Utah Bar Assn., D.C. Bar Assn., Las Vegas C of C., Nev. Bankers Assn. (pres. 1987-89, chmn. legis. com. 1988—), Am. Bankers Assn. (govt. rels. coun. mgmt. com. 1988—), Young Pres.'s Orgn. Office: Thomas and Mack Co 2300 W Sahara Box 1 Las Vegas NV 89102

THOMAS, PHILIP STANLEY, economics educator; b. Hinsdale, Ill., Oct. 23, 1928; s. Roy Kehl and Pauline (Grafton) T.; m. Carol Morris, Dec. 27, 1950; children: Lindsey Carol, Daniel Kyle, Lauren Louise, Gay Richardson. B.A., Oberlin Coll., 1950; M.A., U. Mich., 1951, Ph.D., 1961; postgrad., Delhi U., 1953-54. Instr. U. Mich., 1956-57; asst. prof. Grinnell (Ia.) Coll., 1957-63, assoc. prof., 1963-65; assoc. prof. econs. Kalamazoo Coll., 1965-68, prof. econs., 1968-94; econ. advisor Pakistan Inst. Devel. Econs., 1963-64, USAID, 1965, 66, 67, 68, 71, Planning Commn., Pakistan, 1969-70, Ctrl. Bank of Swaziland, 1974-75, Ministry of Planning, Kenya, 1980-81, 83, 84, 85, 86-88, Ministry of Fin., Swaziland, 1990, Kenya, 1991, 92. Contbr. articles to profl. jours. Mem. alumni coun. Oberlin Coll., 1961-63, 74-76, 83-86, 95—. Served with AUS, 1954-56. Fulbright scholar; Ford Found. overseas fellow India, 1953-54. Mem. Am. Econs. Assn., Midwest Econs. Assn., Phi Beta Kappa. Home: 313A S Shabwasung St Northport MI 49670-9604 Office: Kalamazoo Coll Kalamazoo MI 49006

THOMAS, R. DAVID, food services company executive; b. Atlantic City, July 2, 1932; s. R. and Olivia (Sinclair) T.; m. I. Lorraine Buskirk, May 21, 1954; 5 children. Student pub. schs. Past owner, mgr. Ky. Fried Chicken Franchise; founder, chmn. bd. Wendy's Internat., Inc. (parent co. Wendy's Old Fashioned Hamburgers restaurants), Columbus, Ohio, from 1969, also Dublin, Ohio.; now sr. chmn. bd. Wendy's Internat., Inc. (parent co. Wendy's Old Fashioned Hamburgers restaurants), also Dublin, 1981—. Bd. dirs. Children's Hosp., Columbus, Ohio, St. Jude Children's Research Hosp., Memphis. Served with U.S. Army. Recipient Horatio Alger award, 1979. Mem. Ohio Restaurant Assn., Nat. Restaurant Assn. (dir.). Club: Ohio Commodores. Office: Wendy's Internat Inc PO Box 256 4288 W Dublin Granville Rd Dublin OH 43017-2093

THOMAS, RALPH CHARLES, III, federal official; b. Roanoke, Va., Apr. 10, 1949; s. Ralph C. Jr. and Dorothy (Easley) T. BA, U. Calif., Berkeley, 1975; JD, Harvard U., 1978. Assoc. Bergson, Borkland, Margolis & Adler, Washington, 1978-80; sr. ptnr. Thomas, John & Everett, Washington, 1980-85; clin. instr. in Law Sch. George Washington U., Washington, 1982-83; exec. dir. Nat. Assn. Minority Contractors, Washington, 1985-92; assoc. adminstr. for small/disadvantaged bus. utilization NASA, Washington, 1992—; mem. Chancellor's Adv. Com. on Constrn. Mgmt., Princess Anne, Md., 1986-92; adj. instr. U. Va., Charlottesville, 1989-91; mem. Small Bus. Procurement Adv. Com., 1994—; co-chmn. Fed. Small Bus. Dirs. Interagy. Coun., 1994—. Contbr. articles to profl. jours. General counsel D.C. Statehood Constnl. Conv., Washington, 1982. Staff sgt. USAF, 1967-71, Vietnam. Recipient Fed. Adv. award, 1994, Adv.-of-the-Yr. award, 1994. Office: NASA Small & Disadvantaged Business Utilization 300 E Street SW Washington DC 20546

THOMAS, REGINALD HARRY, SR., minister; b. Wilkes-Barre, Pa., Aug. 1, 1954; s. Warren Leroy and Nancy Carol (Roche) T.; m. Linda Lee Fine, May 31, 1975; children: Reginald H., Jamie Lynn. BA, Messiah Coll., Grantham, Pa., 1976. Ordained to ministry Primitive Meth. Ch. in the USA, 1981. Minister Boone (Iowa) Primitive Meth. Ch., 1976-77, Shamokin (Pa.) Primitive Meth. Ch., 1977-78, 2nd Primitive Meth. Ch., Pitts., 1978-80, Maitland Meml. Primitive Meth. Ch., New Castle, Pa., 1980-82, Messiah Primitive Meth. Ch., Wilkes-Barre, Pa., 1982—; sec. bd. trustees Primitive Meth. Ch. Conf., 1982-89, pres., 1992-94, conf. gen. sec., 1989—; mem. world relief commn. Nat. Assn. Evangelicals. Track and Field ofcl. Pa. Interscholastic Athletic Assn.; bd. dirs. Wyo. Valley Stridon Running Assn. Republican. Home: 110 Pittston Blvd Wilkes Barre PA 18702-9607 Office: Messiah Primitive Meth Ch 100 Pittston Blvd Wilkes Barre PA 18702-9607

THOMAS, RHONDA CHURCHILL, lawyer; b. 1947; m. J. Regan Thomas; children: Ryan, Aaron, Evan. BA, Drury Coll., 1969; JD, U. Mo., 1972, Yale U., 1973. Bar: Mo. 1973. Newswoman Sta. KFRU Radio, Columbia, Mo., 1969-70; law clk. to Hon. Robert E. Seiler Supreme Ct. of Mo., Jefferson City, 1973-74; asst. city counselor City of Columbia, 1974-76, city counselor, chief legal advisor to city coun., dept. heads, 1976-79; assoc. prof. law U. Mo., 1979-82; ptnr. Thompson & Mitchell, St. Louis, 1985—; past chmn. franchise com. Nat. Inst. Mcpl. Law Officers. Contbr. articles to profl. jours. Past chmn. Boone County Home Rule Charter Commn.; past pres. Boone County Indsl. Devel. Authority. Mem. ABA (local govt. law sect., taxation sect.), Mo. Bar Assn. (mem. edn. law com., mem. local govt. law com., mem. med.-legal rels. com., past mem. spl. com. on quality and methods of practice), St. Louis Bar Assn., Nat. Assn. Bond Lawyers, Mo. Mcpl. Attys. Assn. (past pres.). Office: Thompson & Mitchell 1 Mercantile Ctr Ste 3400 Saint Louis MO 63101-1623

THOMAS, RICHARD, civilian military employee; b. Boise, Idaho, May 29, 1941; s. Ormond and Mary Lacey T.; m. Linda Hill, Oct. 5, 1963; children: Lauren, Sharon, Steven. BS Aeronautical Engring., Rensselaer Polytech. Inst., 1963; MS Ops. Rsch., George Washington U., 1973; postgrad. program for sr. execs., MIT, 1986. Rschr. David Taylor Rsch. Ctr., Carderock, Md., 1963-68; head support forces, logistic sect. Office Naval Ops., 1969-75; mgr. Am. Mgmt. Systems Inc., 1976-77; dir. Office Policy and Plans Maritime Adminstrn. (U.S. Dept. Commerce, now U.S. Dept. Transp.), Washington, 1978-82; dir. resources and policy evaluation Office Asst. Sec. Navy U.S. Dept. Navy, 1983-90, dep. asst. sec. Shore Resources, 1991—. Office: Shore Resources Installations & Environment 1000 Navy Pentagon Washington DC 20350-1000

THOMAS, RICHARD, actor; b. N.Y.C., June 13, 1951; s. Richard and Barbara (Fallis) T.; m. Alma Gonzalez, Feb. 14, 1975 (div.); children: Richard F., Barbara, Gwyneth and Pilar (triplets); m. Georgiana Bischoff, Nov. 20, 1995; children: Brooke, Kendra. Student, Columbia U. Owner, prin. Melpomene Prodns. Made Broadway debut at age 7 in Sunrise at Campobello, 1958; regular on children's series One, Two, Three - Go!, 1961-62, regular on TV series The Waltons, 1972-77 (Emmy award 1973); films include Winning, 1969, Last Summer, 1969, You Can't Have Everything, 1970, Red Sky at Morning, 1971, The Todd Killings, 1971, Cactus in the Snow, 1971, You'll Like My Mother, 1972, 9/30/55, 1977, Battle Beyond the Stars, 1980; stage appearances include Sunrise at Campobello, 1958, Whose Life Is It Anyway?, 1980, The Fifth of July, 1981, The Sea Gull, 1984, The Count of Monte Cristo, 1985, Citizen Tom Paine, 1986, The Front Page, 1986, Hamlet, 1987, Peer Gynt, 1989, Love Letters, 1989-90, Square One, 1990, Lisbon Traviata, 1990, Danton's Death, 1992, Richard II, 1993, Richard III, 1994; author: Poems by Richard Thomas, Vols. I and 2, 1974; TV dramatic spl. and movies The Homecoming— A Christmas Story, 1971, The Red Badge of Courage, 1974, The Silence, 1975, All Quiet on the Western Front, 1979, The Hank Williams Jr. Story, 1983, Hobson's Choice, 1984, The Master of Ballantrae, 1984, Glory!, Glory!, 1990, Andre's Mother, 1990, It, 1990, Mission of the Shark, 1991, Yes Virginia, There Really Is a Santa Claus, 1991, I Can Make You Love Me: The Stalking of Laura Black, 1993, A Walton's Thanksgiving Reunion, 1993, Death in Small Doses, 1993, Linda, 1993, A Walton Wedding, 1995; host children's spl. H.M.S. Pinafore, 1973. Nat. chmn. Better Hearing Inst., 1987—. Office: care Springer Assoc 1501 Broadway Ste 1314 A New York NY 10036

THOMAS, RICHARD D., newspaper editor; b. Hogansville, Ga., Oct. 8, 1949; s. Benjamin J. Thomas and Marie (Phillips) Cook; m. Martha Yates, June 25, 1971; children: Richard J., Elizabeth L. BA, Mercer U., 1975. Pub. affairs coord. WMAZ-TV-Radio, Macon, Ga., 1971-72; reporter The Macon (Ga.) Telegraph, 1973, city editor, 1973-76, asst. mng. editor, 1976-77; mng. editor Boca Raton (Fla.) News, 1977-81, editor, 1981-83; v.p., editor The Macon (Ga.) Telegraph, 1983—. Pres. Goodwill Industries, Macon, 1988-89, Macon (Ga.) Arts Alliance, 1994-95; chmn. Kids Voting/Ga., Macon, 1992-94. Profl. Journalism fellow Stanford (Calif.) U., 1979-80. Mem. Am. Soc. Newspaper Editors, Ga. Press Assn. (bd. dirs. 1991-93). Roman Catholic. Home: 1132 St Andrews Dr Macon GA 31210 Office: The Macon Telegraph 120 Broadway Macon GA 31201

THOMAS, RICHARD LEE, banker; b. Marion, Ohio, Jan. 11, 1931; s. Marvin C. and Irene (Harruff) T.; m. Helen Moore, June 17, 1953; children: Richard L., David Paul, Laura Sue. BA, Kenyon Coll., 1953; postgrad. (Fulbright scholar), U. Copenhagen, Denmark, 1954; MBA (George F. Baker scholar), Harvard U., 1958. With First Nat. Bank Chgo., 1958—, asst. v.p., 1962-63, v.p., 1963-65; v.p., gen. mgr. First Nat. Bank Chgo. (London (Eng.) br.), 1965-66; v.p. term loan divsn. First Nat. Bank, Chgo., 1968; sr. v.p., gen. mgr. First Chgo. Corp., 1969-72, exec. v.p., 1972-73, vice chmn. bd., 1973-75, pres., 1975-92, chmn., pres., CEO, 1992-94; chmn., CEO First Chgo., Chgo., 1994—; also dir. First Chgo. Corp., 1973-74; dir. CNA Fin. Corp., Sara Lee Corp. Trustee, past chmn. bd. trustees Kenyon Coll.; Orchestral Assn.; trustee Rush-Presbyn.-St. Luke's Med. Ctr.; trustee Northwestern U. With AUS, 1954-56. mem. chgo. Coun. Fgn. Rels., Sunningdale Golf Club (London), Econ. Club (past pres.), Comml. Club, Chgo. Club, Casino Club, Mid-Am. Club, Indian Hill Club (Winnetka, Ill.), Old Elm Club (Highland Park, Ill.), Phi Beta Kappa, Beta Theta Pi. Office: First Nat Bank of Chgo 1 First Nat Plz Chicago IL 60670

THOMAS, RICHARD LYNN, geologist, researcher, educator, director university geecology center; b. Aberystwyth, Wales, U.K., Sept. 14, 1934; arrived in Can., 1967, naturalized, 1984; s. Ivor and Mary Dorothy (Richards) T.; m. Barbara Jean Ruthven, May 15, 1961; children: Sarah Caroline, Julian Richard. BSc with honors, Univ. Coll., Swansea, Wales, 1959, PhD, 1966, DSc, 1989. Geophysicist Robert H. Ray Geophysics, Inc., Libya, North Africa, 1959-60; mine geologist Sierra Leone (W. Africa) Selection Trust Ltd., 1961-64; post-doctoral fellow U.K. Inst. Geological Scis., 1966-67; from rsch. sci. 1 to rsch. sci. 2 limnogeology sect. Can. Ctr. Inland Waters, Burlington, Ont., 1967-73; head geolimnology unit Can. Ctr. Inland Waters, Burlington, 1973-74, rsch. mgr., head sedimentary and chem. processes sect., 1974-75, sr. rsch. sci. Biological Processes Rsch. Divsn., 1975-76, dir. Great Lakes Biolimnology Lab., 1976-84, sr. rsch. sci. Nat. Water Rsch. Inst., 1987-90; dir. Great Lakes Regional Office Internat. Joint Commn., Windsor, Ont., Can., 1984-87; prof. dept. geology, dir. Great Lakes Inst. U. Windsor, 1990-92; dir. Waterloo (Ont.) Ctr. for Groundwater Rsch. U. Waterloo, 1992—; vis. prof. U. Geneva, 1982, prof. associe dept. earth scis., 1984—; adj. prof. dept. geology U. Waterloo; invited rschr. U. Geneva, 1972; mem. assoc. com. sci. criteria environ. quality objective Can. Nat. Rsch. Coun., 1987-91; mem. Dept. Environ. Com. for Rsch. Scis., 1987-90, chmn. com. devel. strategic plan for mgmt. of Great Lakes Basin, 1983-84; mem. Sci. Adv. Bd., Internat. Joint Commn., 1982-84, Can. co-chmn., 1983-84; mem. DFO Acid Rain Policy Com., 1982-84, past mem. sci. com. nat. program, long range transport of atmospheric pollutants, past mem. Can./U.S. bilateral com. long range transport of atmospheric pollutants, 1982; mem. pollution from land use activities ref. group Internat. Joint Commn., 1971-80; organizer, chmn., keynote lectr., participant, invited spkr., convenor, paper presenter symposia, meetings, workshops, confs. in field worldwide. contbr. chpts. to books, articles to profl. jours. Mem. Tech. Com. of Prosperity 2000 Strategic Planning for City of Windsor, 1990-92. With RAF, 1952-54. Mem. Internat. Assn. Sediment Water Sci. (founding pres. 1982-84, past pres. 1991—), Internat. Assn. Great Lakes Rsch. (bd. dirs. 1978-82, v.p. 1979-80, pres. 1980-81, past pres. 1981-82). Office: U Waterloo Waterloo Ctr Groundwater Rsch, 200 Univ Ave W, Waterloo, ON Canada N2L 3G1

THOMAS, RICHARD VAN, state supreme court justice; b. Superior, Wyo., Oct. 11, 1932; s. John W. and Gertrude (McCloskey) T.; m. Lesley Arlene Ekman, June 23, 1956; children: Tara Lynn, Richard Ross, Laura Lee, Sidney Marie. B.S. in Bus. Adminstrn. with honors, U. Wyo., 1954, LL.B. with honors, 1956; LL.M., NYU, 1961. Bar: Wyo. 1956, U.S. Ct. Appeals (10th cir.) 1960, U.S. Ct. Mil. Appeals 1960, U.S. Supreme Ct. 1960. Law clk. to judge U.S. Ct. Appeals (10th Circuit), Cheyenne, 1960-63; assoc. firm Hirst & Applegate, Cheyenne, 1963-64; partner firm Hirst, Applegate & Thomas, Cheyenne, 1964-69; U.S. atty. Dist. Wyo., Cheyenne, 1969-74; justice Wyo. Supreme Ct., Cheyenne, 1974—, chief justice, 1985-86. Pres. Laramie County United Way, 1972, trustee, 1973-74, chmn. admissions and allocations com., 1968-69, chmn. exec. com., 1973, chmn. combined fed. campaign, 1974; bd. dirs. Goodwill Industries Wyo., Inc., 1974-77; exec. com. Cheyenne Crusade for Christ, 1974; v.p., exec. com. Wyo. Billy Graham Crusade, 1987; bd. dirs. Cheyenne Youth for Christ, 1978-81; chancellor Episcopal Diocese of Wyo., 1972—; lay dep. gen. conv., 1973—; chmn. search evaluation nomination com., 1976-77, lay reader, 1969—; bd. dirs. Community Action of Laramie County, 1977-82; chmn. Cheyenne dist. Boy Scouts Am., 1977-78, mem. nat. council, 1982-84, mem. Longs Peak council, 1977—, v.p. dist. ops., v.p. membership relationships, 1979-81, pres., 1981-83; mem. North Cen. Region Exec. Bd., 1986—, pres. Old West Trails Area, 1988—; chmn. Laramie County Health Planning Com., 1980-84. Served with JAGC USAF, 1957-60. Named Boss of Year, Indian Paintbrush chpt. Nat. Secs. Assn., 1974; Civil Servant of Year, Cheyenne Assn. Govt. Employees, 1973; Vol. of Yr., Cheyenne Office, Youth Alternatives, 1979; recipient St. George Episcopal award, 1982, Silver Beaver award Boy Scouts Am., 1985. Mem. Am., Laramie County bar assns., Wyo. State Bar, Phi Kappa Phi, Phi Alpha Delta, Omicron Delta Kappa, Sigma Nu. Clubs: Kiwanis (Cheyenne) (program com. 1969-70, dir. 1970-72, chmn. key club com. 1973-76, disting. pres. 1980-81), Masons (Cheyenne) (33 deg., past master); Shriners; Nat. Sojourners (Cheyenne). Office: Wyo Supreme Ct Supreme Ct Bldg Cheyenne WY 82002

THOMAS, RITCHIE TUCKER, lawyer; b. Cleve., Aug. 12, 1936; ž; s. Myron F. and Marjorie (Ritchie) T.; m. Elizabeth Blackwell Haynes Main, Jan. 1, 1994. BA, Cornell U., 1959; JD, Case-Western Res. U., 1964. Bar: Ohio 1964, U.S. Dist. Ct. (no. dist.) Ohio 1964, U.S. Ct. Appeals (D.C. 1971, U.S. Ct. Appeals (fed. cir.) 1973, U.S. Ct. Internat. Trade 1976, U.S. Ct. Appeals (9th cir.) 1985. Assoc. office of gen. counsel U.S. Tariff Commn., Washington, 1964-67; assoc. Squire, Sanders & Dempsey, Cleve., 1967-69, Cox, Langford & Brown, Washington, 1969-74; ptnr. Squire, Sanders & Dempsey, Washington, 1974—; mem. exec. com. Meridian House Internat., Washington, 1977—; Washington rep. Am. C. of C. in Germany, 1984—; v.p. bd. dirs. Belgian Am. Assn., 1989—. Assoc. editor Western Res. U. Law Rev., 1964; contbr. articles to profl. jours. Recipient various book award West Pub. Co., 1964. Mem. Fed. Bar Assn., Ohio Bar Assn., D.C. Bar Assn., Order of Coif. Home: 6700 Bradley Blvd Bethesda MD 20817-3045 Office: Squire Sanders & Dempsey 1201 Pennsylvania Ave NW PO Box 407 Washington DC 20044

THOMAS, ROBERT ALLEN, environmental policy administrator, educator; b. Luling, Tex., Apr. 10, 1946; s. Julian H. and Katie (Schneider) T.; m. Paulette M. Jung, Aug. 17, 1968; children: Jennifer Leigh, Aimee Kathryn, Patrick Julian. BS, U. Southwest La., 1970; MS, Tex. A&M U., 1974, PhD, 1976. Lectr. Tex. A&M U., College Station, 1976-77; instr. La. State U. Med. Ctr., New Orleans, 1977-78; exec. dir. La. Nature and Sci. Ctr., New Orleans, 1978-94; v.p. environ. policy The Audubon Inst., 1994; adj. prof. biol. sci. U. New Orleans, 1979—; cons. for environ. issues, New Orleans. Contbr. articles to profl. jours.; columnist. Recipient Elsie Naumburg award Nat. Soc. for Youth Found., 1983; Margaret Stone medal The Garden Club Am., 1994. Mem. Soc. for Study of Amphibians and Reptiles, Herpetologists League, Am. Soc. Ichthyologists and Herpetologists, La. Assn. Mus. (pres. 1986-88), Am. Assn. Mus. (accreditation commn.), Southwestern Assn. Naturalists (bd. govs. 1982-85), East New Orleans C. of C. (exec. com.). Roman Catholic. Lodge: Rotary (pres. 1984-85, 94—). Avocations: tennis; writing. Office: The Audubon Inst PO Box 4327 New Orleans LA 70178-4327

THOMAS, ROBERT DEAN, publisher; b. Elkhart, Ind., Mar. 28, 1933; s. Floyd D. and Ottie (Silvers) T.; m. Beverly I. Neuhaus, Apr. 21, 1956; children: Mary Beth, Matthew, Susanna. Grad., Bradley U., 1956. Staff asst. to gen. mgr. Reuben H. Donnelley Co., 1958; dist. mgr., Western mgr. Conde Nast, 1964; account mgr. Mademoiselle Mag.; Western mgr. Ladies Home Jour., N.Y.C., 1966; account mgr., pub. Ladies Home Jour.; pub. Bon Appetit mag., 1990-91. Served with U.S. Army, 1956-58. Mem. Silver Spring Country Club (Ridgefield, Conn.). Home: 223 Mariomi Rd New Canaan CT 06840-3315

THOMAS, ROBERT EGGLESTON, former corporate executive; b. Cuyahoga Falls, Ohio, July 28, 1914; s. Talbott E. and Jane S. (Eggleston) T.; children: Robert Eggleston, Barbara Ann. B.S. in Econs, U. Pa., 1936. Asst. to gen. mgr., sec., mgr. r.r. investments Keystone Custodian Funds, Boston, 1936-53; v.p. Pennroad Corp., N.Y.C., 1953-59; chmn. exec. com., dir. M.K.- T. R.R., 1956-65; mem. exec. com. MAPCO Inc., 1960-80, dir. chief exec. officer, 1960-80, pres., 1960-76, chmn. bd., 1973-84; adv. bd. BancOkla. Corp. Mem. Am. Petroleum Inst. (hon. dir.), Nat. Coal Assn. (hon. dir.), Newcomen Soc., Chicago Club, So. Hills Country Club (Tulsa), San Diego Yacht Club, Desert Horizons Country Club (Indian Wells, Calif.), Wianno (Mass.) Club, Teton Pines Country Club (Jackson Hole, Wyo.). Episcopalian. Office: MAPCO Inc PO Box 645 Tulsa OK 74101-0645

THOMAS, ROBERT JOSEPH, columnist, author; b. San Diego, Jan. 26, 1922; s. George H. and Marguerite (Creelman) T.; m. Patricia Thompson, Sept. 6, 1947; children: Nancy Katherine, Janet Elizabeth, Caroline Brooke. Student, UCLA, 1943. With AP, 1943—, Hollywood columnist, 1944—; radio, TV, lecture appearances; editor Action Mag., 1968-74. Author: The Art of Animation, 1958; (novel) Flesh Merchants, 1959; The Massie Case, 1966, King Cohn, 1967, Walt Disney: Magician of the Movies, 1967, Will Penny, Star, 1968, Thalberg, 1969, Selznick, 1970, The Heart of Hollywood, The Secret Boss of California, Winchell, 1971; (novel) Weekend '33, 1972; Marlon, 1974, Walt Disney, An American Original, 1976, Bud and Lou, The Abbott and Costello Story, 1977, The Road to Hollywood (with Bob Hope), 1977, The One and Only Bing, 1977, Joan Crawford, 1978, Golden Boy, the Untold Story of William Holden, 1983, Astaire, 1984, I Got Rhythm, The Ethel Merman Story, 1985; also numerous mag. articles. Mem. Beta Theta Pi. Office: Associated Press 221 S Figueroa St Ste 300 Los Angeles CA 90012

THOMAS, ROBERT LEE, financial services company executive, consultant; b. San Antonio, Dec. 29, 1938; s. Lawrence Grant and Mabel Louise (Carlson) T.; m. Terry Eileen Morgan, Dec. 14, 1972; 1 child, Evan Grant. Cert., Am. Coll., 1984, 85, cert. in fin. planning, 1990, cert. in health underwriting, 1991; postgrad., Northeastern U., 1991—. Cert. fin. planner, investment specialist; designated registered employee benefit cons. Various middle mgmt. positions Gen. Fin. Corp., Dallas, 1962-65; full charge mgmt. positions TransAm. Fin. Corp., Dallas, 1965-74; sr. agt. Am. Security Life, San Antonio, 1974-81; chmn., pres. Thomas Fin. Svcs., Inc., Dallas, 1981—; bd. dirs. Cherokee Children's Home; mem. adv. bd. Am. Security Life, 1977—; frequent guest on internat. and nat. radio and TV talk shows; host radio program, 1986—; tchr. high sch. fin. planning course, 1993—. Mem. fin. profl. adv. panel Digest of Financial Planning Ideas mag., 1984; designer, creator Mortgage Pre-Payment System, 1990, Mortgage Management Software, 1990; author: Cost Cutter Mortgage Management Manual, 1990, creator Commercial Debt Expense Reduction System and Debt Cash Flow Analysis Software, 1991; columnist Jour. Shepherding group leader Meadowview Ch. Christ, Mesquite, Tex., 1983—; Bible class tchr., 1978—, deacon, 1987—; regular spokesman pub. svc. and promotional messages various civic orgns.; chmn. charity telethon Million Dollar Round Table; leader internat. missions ministry, New Guinea, 1989, S.E. Asia, 1990; team mem. for tribal contact, New Guinea, 1991; dir. Senior Information Svcs. of Ameritech, 1994—; bd. dirs. Cherokee Home for Children, 1994—. Recipient Lone Star Leader award Tex. Assn. Life Underwriters, 1982—, Nat. Sales Achievement award, Nat. Quality award Nat. Assn. Life Underwriters, 1976—. Fellow Life Underwriting Tng. Council; mem. Dallas Estate Planning Council, Dallas Assn. Life Underwriters (chmn. health com. 1979-80, president's cabinet 1989—, pub. rels. com. 1992—), Internat. Assn. Registered Fin. Planners, Internat. Assn. Fin. Planning, Am. Soc. CLUs, Am. Inst. Cert. Fin. Planners, Am. Assn. Fin. Profls., Am. Health Ins. Assn., Investment Rsch. Inst., Million Dollar Round Table (life), Dallas Assn. Life Underwriters (mem. steering com. 1992—), Tex. Assn. Life Underwriters (life, lone star leader award, 1982—), Nat. Assn. Life Underwriters (nat. sales achievement award, 1976—, nat. quality award, 1976—), Am. Arbitration Assn. (nat. arbitration panel, securities arbitrator 1989-90), Better Bus. Bur. (sr. arbitrator nat. panel), Gen. Agts. and Mgmt. Assn. (yearling achievement, 1975), Internat. Platform Assn., Internat. Assn. Registered Fin. Planners, Tex. Investment Mgmt. Coun., Aircraft Owners and Pilots Assn. Avocations: sailing, diving, travel. Office: Thomas Fin Svcs Inc 9330 Lyndon B Johnson Fwy Ste 900 Dallas TX 75243-3470

THOMAS, ROBERT LEIGHTON, physicist, researcher; b. Dover-Foxcroft, Maine, Oct. 10, 1938; s. Tillson Davis and Ruth (Leighton) T.; m. Sandra Evenson, June 23, 1962; 1 child, Stephen Leighton. AB, Bowdoin Coll., 1960; PhD, Brown U., 1965. Rsch. assoc. Wayne State U., Detroit, 1965-66, from asst. to assoc. prof. physics, 1966-76, prof. physics, 1976—, dir. Inst. for Mfg. Rsch., 1986—; mem. organizing com. 5th Internat. Meeting on Photoacousies, Heidelberg, Fed. Republic Germany, 1987; chmn. Gordon Rsch. Conf. in Nondestructive Evaluation, 1991-92. Assoc. editor Rsch. in Nondestructive Evaluation; contbr. over 100 articles to sci. jours. Fellow Am. Phys. Soc.; mem. Mich. Tech. Coun. (bd. dirs. S.E. div. 1988—), Acad. Scholars, Sigma Xi (chpt. pres. 1990-91). Achievements include patents for Thermal Wave Imaging Apparatus, for Vector Lock-In Imaging System, and for Single Beam Interferometer. Office: Wayne State U Inst for Mfg Rsch Detroit MI 48202

THOMAS, ROBERT MORTON, JR., lawyer; b. Kansas City, Kans., Jan. 1, 1941; s. Robert Morton Sr. and Arlowyne Edith (Arganbright) T.; m. Rebecca Ann Myers, Aug. 21, 1965; children: Brooke J., Austin B. BA, U. Kans., 1962; LLB, Harvard U., 1966. Bar: N.Y., U.S. Dist. Ct. (so. dist.) N.Y., U.S. Ct. Appeals (2nd cir.). Local govt. advisor Republic of Botswana, Gaborone, 1966; dist. officer Republic of Botswana, Serowe, 1967; dist. commr. Republic of Botswana, Maun, 1968; assoc. Sullivan & Cromwell, N.Y.C., 1969-75, ptnr., 1975—; ptnr.-in-charge Sullivan & Cromwell, London, 1979-82; mng. ptnr. gen. practice group Sullivan & Cromwell, N.Y.C., 1986-91. Mem. ABA, N.Y. State Bar Assn., Assn. of Bar of City of New York, Internat. Bar Assn., India House, Buck's Club, Harvard Club, Mill Reef Club. Republican. Presbyterian. Office: Sullivan & Cromwell 125 Broad St New York NY 10004-2498

THOMAS, ROBERT MURRAY, educational psychology educator; b. Cheyenne, Wyo., July 28, 1921; s. Robert MacDonald and Elizabeth (Carson) T.; m. Shirley Louise Moore, July 3, 1948; children: Robert Gilmour, Kathryn Elizabeth. A.B., Colo. State Coll., 1943, M.A., 1944; Ph.D., Stanford U., 1950. Tchr. Kamehameha Schs., Honolulu, 1944-45; Tchr. Mid-Pacific Inst., Honolulu, 1945-47; instr. San Francisco State Coll., 1949-50; prof. State U. Coll., Brockport, N.Y., 1950-58, Padjadjaran (Indonesia) U., 1958-61, 64-65; prof. edul. psychology U. Calif. at Santa Barbara, 1961-64, 69-91, prof. emeritus edul. psychology, 1992—; dean U. Calif. at Santa Barbara (Grad. Sch.), 1965-69. Author: Judging Student Progress, 2d edit, 1960, Ways of Teaching, 1955, Integrated Teaching Materials, 2d edit, 1963, Individual Differences in the Classroom, 1965, Social Differences in the Classroom, 1965, Aiding the Maladjusted Pupil, 1967, A Chronicle of Indonesian Higher Education, 1973, Comparing Theories of Child Development, 1979, 4th edit., 1995, Japanese edit., 1985, Education in American Samoa-1700 to 1980, 1987, The Puzzle of Learning Difficulties-Applying a Diagnostic and Treatment Model, 1989, Counseling and Life-span Development, 1990, Classifying Reactions to Wrongdoing, 1995; editor: Strategies for Curriculum Change: Cases from 13 Nations, 1968, Politics and Education: Cases from 11 Nations, 1983, Ency. of Human Development and Education, 1990, International Comparative Education, 1990, Education's Role in National Development Plans, 1992; co-author: Decisions in Teaching Elementary Social Studies, 1971, Curriculum Patterns in Elementary Social Studies, 1971, Penggunaan Statistik Dalam Ilmu Pengetahuan Sosial, 1971, Teaching Elementary Social Studies: Readings, 1972, Indonesian Education: An Annotated Bibliography, 1973, Social Strata in Indonesia, 1975, Political Style and Education Law in Indonesia, 1980, Schooling in the ASEAN Region, 1980, Schooling in East Asia, 1983, Schooling in the Pacific Islands, 1984, Die Entwicklung des Kindes, 1986, Educational Technology, 1987, Oriental Theories of Human Development, 1988, What Wrongdoers Deserve, 1993, Etude Comparee des Théories du Dévelopment de l'Enfant, 1994, Prevent, Repent, Reform, Revenge, 1995. Home: 1436 Las Encinas Dr Los Osos CA 93402-4520

THOMAS, ROBERT WILBURN, broadcasting and advertising executive; b. Athens, Ga., Nov. 20, 1937; s. Ernest Wilburn and Bobbie (Morton) T.; m. Betsey Ruth Thorne, Sept. 6, 1958; children: Richard Gregory, Coleen Suzanne. BS in Speech, Northwestern U., 1960, MA, 1961. Producer radio, TV broadcasts Northwestern U., Evanston, Ill., 1961-68, instr., 1967-68; exec. producer Sta. WCNY-TV, Syracuse, N.Y., 1968-70; gen. mgr., v.p. Sta. WEKT-FM, Hammondsport, N.Y., 1970-71; gen. mgr. Sta. KWMU-FM, St. Louis, 1971-76; dir. broadcasting Sta. KWIT, Sioux City, Iowa, 1976-79; sta. expansion mgr. Corp. for Pub. Broadcasting, Washington, 1979-82; exec. dir. Cable Comm. Prince Georges County (Md.), 1982-83; cable adminstr. City of Raleigh (N.C.), 1983-86; pres. B&B Media, Inc. (advt. and pub. rels. agy.), 1986—; co-owner, gen. mgr. Sta. WBLB, Pulaski, Va., 1986-89; co-innkeeper Claytor Lake Homestead Inn, Draper, Va., 1990-91; news, pub. affair dir. Sta. WRAD-WRIQ, Radford, Va., 1993-94; bd. dirs. S.W. Devel. Financing, Inc.; mem. Emmy awards com. Chgo. chpt. Nat. Acad. TV Arts and Scis., 1962-65; mem. radio adv. com. Ill. Telecommunications Commn., 1968; chmn. radio divsn. Midwest Telecommunications Conf., Nat. Assn. Ednl. Broadcasters, 1972; mem. Va. News Network adv. bd., 1987—; co-founder, bd. dirs. Pulaski County HOSTS, pres. 1991; bd. dirs. New River Valley HOSTS tourism project, 1992-93. Mem. pack com. Cub Scouts Am., Florissant, Mo., 1971-72; chmn. Mo. Jr. Miss Pagent, 1971-72, co-chmn., 1972-73, exec. dir., 1973-76; past bd. dirs. Sioux City Youth Orch. Assn., Siouxland Arts Coun., Sioux City Chamber Music Assn.; founding mem. Pub. Radio in Mid. Am.; Program chmn., 1976-77; bd. dirs. Pulaski County United Way, 1987-92, pub. rels. chmn., 1987-89; bd. dirs. Salvation Army, 1987-90, pub. rels. chmn., 1987, v.p., 1988; bd. dirs. Count Pulaskifest 1987-90; prodr., dir. Ms. Va. Sr. Citizen Pageant, 1993—; bd. dirs. Pulaski County Emergency Needs Task Force, 1989-92, Radford Heritage Found.; bd. dirs., pub. rels. chmn., 1993—. Recipient award Freedoms Found., 1963, 65, Outstanding Program award Ill. Med. Soc., 1965; named Outstanding State chmn. in Nation America's Jr. Miss Pageant, 1974. Mem. Mo. Pub. Radio Assn. (pres. 1975-76), Nat. Assn. Telecom. Officers and Advisors (bd. dirs. 1982-86, secc. 1983-85, v.p. 1985-86), Pulaski County C. of C. (bd. dirs. 1987-89), Pulaski Mchts. Assn. (chmn. promotions com. 1986-89, bd. dirs. 1987-89, 4th of July com. 1987, 91, town hist. com. 1987-89), Pulaski Main St. (chmn. corp. rels. com. 1988-89), Rotary (v.p. Radford 1993-94, pres.-elect 1994-95, pres. 1995-96, Paul Harris fellow 1990). Home and Office: 1006 3rd St Radford VA 24141-1306 Without belief in and enthusiasm for the undertakings of life, achievement is slowed, if not actually blocked.

THOMAS, ROGER MERIWETHER, lawyer; b. Hartford, Conn., Feb. 28, 1930; s. Frederick Metcalf and Helen Meriwether (Lewis) T.; m. Mary Dorothea Wyman, Dec. 4, 1965; children—Donald Wyman, Helen Dorothea. A.B., Princeton U., 1952; LL.B., Va. U., 1957; LL.M., Boston U., 1964. Bar: N.Y. 1958, Mass. 1960, U.S. Dist. Ct. (Mass) 1965, U.S. Tax Ct. 1965, U.S. Supreme Ct. 1967. Assoc. Angulo, Cooney, Marsh & Ouchterloney, N.Y.C., 1957-60; assoc., then ptnr. Gaston & Snow, Boston, 1960-91; counsel Condit & Assocs., P.C., Boston, 1992-94; outline author and lectr. Mass. Continuing Legal Edn., Inc., Boston; past panelist New Eng. Law Inst. Estate Planning Forums, Boston. Trustee Buckingham Browne & Nichols Sch., Cambridge, Mass., 1967-69. Served to 1st lt. U.S. Army, 1952-54, Korea. Mem. Am. Coll. Trust and Estate Counsel, Boston Bar Assn., Mass. Bar Assn. Avocations: reading; sports; old movies. Home: 40 Byron Rd Weston MA 02193-2229

THOMAS, ROGER WARREN, lawyer; b. South Weymouth, Mass., Sept. 17, 1937; s. Clement Rogers and Beatrice (Merritt) T.; m. Maria Sava Brenner, July 5, 1968; children: Caroline, Andrew, Phillip. BA, U. N.H., 1959; postgrad. (Rotary Internat. fellow), Free U. Berlin, 1960; LLB (Root-Tilden scholar), NYU, 1963, LLM (Ford Found. grantee), 1965; postgrad., U. Chile, Santiago, 1965. Bar: N.Y. 1964. Assoc. Cleary, Gottlieb, Steen and Hamilton, N.Y.C., 1965-66, 69-74; partner Cleary, Gottlieb, Steen and Hamilton, 1974—; mem. Harvard-Chile Tax Reform Project, 1966-68, head project in Chile, 1968-69; cons. to UN, Santiago, 1969; adj. prof. taxation NYU, 1974—. Co-author: El Impuesto a la Renta, 1969. Bd. dirs. Spanish Repertory Theatre. Mem. ABA, Am. Fgn. Lawyers Assn. (dir.), N.Y. State Bar Assn., N.Am.-Chilean C. of C. (pres. 1984—), Am. Soc., Coun. of Am., Down Town Assn. N.Y.C. Home: 1165 Fifth Ave New York NY 10029-6931 Office: 1 Liberty Plz New York NY 10006-1401

THOMAS, ROSS ELMORE, author; b. Oklahoma City, Feb. 19, 1926; s. J. Edwin and Laura (Dean) T. B.A., U. Okla., 1949. Reporter Daily Oklahoman, Oklahoma City, 1943-44; pub. relations dir. Nat. Farmers Union, 1952-56; pres. Stapp, Thomas & Wade, Inc., Denver, 1956-57; reporter Bonn, Germany, 1958-59; rep. Patrick Dolan & Assos., Ltd., Ibadan, Nigeria, 1959-61; cons. U.S. Govt., 1964-66. Author: The Cold War Swap, 1966, The Seersucker Whipsaw, 1967, Cast a Yellow Shadow, 1967, The Singapore Wink, 1969, (pseudoname Oliver Bleeck) The Brass Go-Between, 1969, The Fools in Town are on Our Side, 1970, The Back-Up Men, 1971, Protocol for Kidnapping, 1971, The Procane Chronicle, 1972, The Porkchoppers, 1972, If You Can't Be Good, 1973, The Highbinders, 1974, The Money Harvest, 1975, Yellow-Dog Contract, 1977, Chinaman's Chance, 1978, The Eighth Dwarf, 1979, The Mordida Man, 1981, Missionary Stew, 1983, Briarpatch, 1984, Out on the Rim, 1987, The Fourth Durango, 1989, Twilight at Mac's Place, 1990, Voodoo Ltd., 1992, Ah, Treachery, 1994. Served with inf. AUS, 1944-46. Recipient Mystery Writers Am. award for best 1st mystery, 1966, Edgar award, 1967, 85.

THOMAS, ROY LEE, minister; b. Greeley, Colo., Sept. 14, 1930; s. Rue and Mary (Malone) T.; m. Patricia A. King, July 19, 1954; children: Patsy Lee, Mark Randall. BA, Free Will Bapt. Bible Coll., 1960; MDiv, Luther Rice Sem., 1978; postgrad., Calif. Ch. Coll., 1970; DD, Bethany Bible Coll. & Sem., 1989. Farmer Castleford, Idaho, 1948-49; pastor 1st Free Will Bapt. Ch., Artesia, N.Mex., 1954-56, Springfield, Tenn., 1956-57; pastor Shady Grove Free Will Ch., Clarksville, Tenn., 1957-60; missionary 1st Free Will Bapt. Ch., Denver, 1960-70; assoc. dir. Home Missions Dept., Nashville, 1970-78, dir., 1978—. Author: Planting & Growing A Fundamental Church, 1978, Studies on the Church Covenant, 1993; editor: Benjamin Randall Journal, 1993. With USAF, 1951-55. Office: Free Will Baptists Nat Assn PO Box 5002 Antioch TN 37011-5002

THOMAS, RUSSELL ALVIN, hardware company executive; b. Butler, Pa., Aug. 7, 1939; s. Lawrence Rosco and Helen (Hemphill) T.; m. Joan Macefe, Feb. 18, 1961; children: Mark Russell, Jo Alison, Lara, Joclyn. BA, Grove City Coll., 1961; postgrad., George Washington U., 1965-66, St. Francis U., Loretto, Pa., 1975-79. Contract negotiator Spang & Co., Butler, 1969-70; dir. indsl. relations Wolverine Toy Co., Booneville, Ark., 1971-74; mgr. employee relations Am. Hardware Supply Co., Butler, 1974-78, asst. v.p. personnel, 1978-80, v.p. personnel, 1980-91, sr. v.p. human rels., 1991—; pers. cons. Speer Hardware Co., Ft. Smith, Ark., 1976—; bd. dirs. 1991; v.p. pers. Advocate Svcs., Inc., Butler, 1982—; Tech Expn. Concepts, Inc., Harrisburg, Pa., 1985—; bd. dirs. C. of C. Svc. Corp., 1993—. Author: People Part of Retail, 1988, The People Part of Rental, 1990, The Services of Servistar, 1992. Bd. dirs. Easter Seal Soc., Butler, 1982-85; mem. adv. bd. Slippery Rock (Pa.) Coll., Butler, 1987—. Served from ensign to lt. USN, 1961-69. Named Outstanding Bus. Leader Booneville Bus. and Profl. Women, 1973. Mem. VFW, Am. Soc. Personnel Adminstrs., Butler County Human Relations Assn. (bd. dirs. 1984—, pres. 1986-87), Butler Personnel Assn., Pitts. Personnel Assn., C. of C. Svc. Corp. (bd. dirs. 1994—). Lodge: Elks. Avocations: boating, swimming, fishing, flying. Home: 5 Oakhurst Dr Butler PA 16001 Office: Servistar Corp PO Box 1510 Marie St Butler PA 16003-1510

THOMAS, S. BERNARD, history educator; b. N.Y.C., Oct. 17, 1921; s. Hyman and Rose (Samilow) T.; m. Evelyn Green Hechtlinger, Dec. 28, 1955; 1 child, Ruth Thomas; stepchildren: Ira, John. BS in Social Sci., CCNY, 1942; MA, Columbia U., 1947, cert. East Asian Inst., 1951, PhD, 1964. Rsch. assoc. internat. secretariat Inst. Pacific Rels., 1950-55; chmn. social studies

Colby Acad., N.Y.C., 1955-58; tchr. social studies Forest Hills (N.Y.) High Sch., 1958-65; asst. prof. history Oakland U., Rochester, Mich., 1965-67, assoc. prof., 1967-71, prof., 1971-89, prof. emeritus 1989—, chmn. area studies programs, 1967-71, chmn. dept. history, 1984-87. Author: Government and Administration in Communist China, 1953, reprinted, 1972, Labor and the Chinese Revolution, 1983; contbr. numerous articles and revs. to acad. jours. With Signal Corps, AUS, 1942-46. East Asian Inst. fellow, 1962, Fulbright fellow, 1969-70. Mem. Assn. Asian Studies, Fulbright Assn. Home: 926 Norwich Rd Troy MI 48084-2671 Office: Oakland U Dept History Rochester MI 48309-4401

THOMAS, SCOTT E., federal government executive, lawyer; b. Buffalo, Wyo., Mar. 5, 1953; s. Ralph E. and Bonnie E. (Kaan) T.; m. Elena W. King, Apr. 28, 1984. BA, Stanford U., 1974; JD, Georgetown U., 1977. Bar: D.C., U.S. Ct. Appeals (9th cir.) 1980, U.S. Supreme Ct. 1981. Atty. Office of Gen. Counsel, Fed. Election Commn., Washington, 1977-80, asst. gen. counsel, 1980-83; exec. asst. to commr. Fed. Election Commn., Washington, 1983-86, commr., 1986—. Mem. D.C. Bar Assn. Office: Fed Election Commn 999 E St NW Washington DC 20463-0002

THOMAS, SHIRLEY, author, educator, business executive; b. Glendale, Calif.; d. Oscar Miller and Ruby (Thomas) Annis; m. W. White, Feb. 22, 1949 (div. June 1952); m. William C. Perkins, Oct. 24, 1969. BA in Modern Lit., U. Sussex, Eng., 1960, PhD in Comm., 1967; diploma, Russian Fedn. Cosmonautics, 1995. Actress, writer, producer, dir. numerous radio and TV stas., 1942-46; v.p. Commodore Prodns., Hollywood, Calif., 1946-52; pres. Annis & Thomas, Inc., Hollywood, 1952—; hand technical writing U. So. Calif., L.A., 1975—; Hollywood corr. NBC, 1952-56; editor motion pictures CBS, Hollywood, 1956-58; corr. Voice of Am., 1958-59; now free lance writer; cons. biol. scis. communication project George Washington U., 1965-66; cons Stanford Rsch. Inst., 1967-68, Jet Propulsion Lab., 1969-70. Author: Men of Space vols. 1-8, 1960-68, Spanish trans., 1961, Italian, 1962; Space Tracking Facilities, 1963, Computers: Their History, Present Applications and Future, 1965; The Book of Diets, 1974. Organizer, chmn. City of L.A. Space Adv. Com., 1964-73, Women's Space Symposia, 1962-73; foudner, chmn. aerospace hist. com. Calif. Mus. Sci. and Industry; chmn. Theodore von Karman Postage Stamp Com., 1965—, stamp issued 1992. Recipient Aerospace Excellence award Calif. Mus. Found. 1991, Nat. Medal Honor DAR, 1992, Yuri Gagarin Medal Honor, 1995. Fellow Brit. Interplanetary Soc.; mem. AIAA, AAAS, Internat. Soc. Aviation Writers, Air Force Assn. (Airpower Arts and Letters award 1961), Internat. Acad. Astronautics, Nat. Aero. Assn., Nat. Assn. Sci. Writers, Soc. for Tech. Communications, Am. Astronautical Soc., Nat. Geog. Soc., Am. Soc. Pub. Adminstrn. (sci. and tech. in govt. com.), Achievement Awards for Coll. Scientists, Muses of Calif., Theta Sigma Phi, Phi Beta. Home: 8027 Hollywood Blvd Los Angeles CA 90046-2510 Office: U So Calif Profl Writing Program University Park Waite-Phillips Hall 404 Los Angeles CA 90089-4034

THOMAS, SIDNEY, fine arts educator, researcher; b. N.Y.C., Dec. 21, 1915; s. Hyman and Rose (Samilowitz) T.; m. Rae Dinkowitz, May 26, 1940; children: David Phillip, Deborah Rose. B.A., CCNY, 1935; M.A., Columbia U., 1938, Ph.D., 1943. Tutor in English CCNY, N.Y.C., 1939-43; instr. English Queens Coll., N.Y.C., 1946-54; self-employed as editor, 1954-58; asst. editor Merriam-Webster, Springfield, Mass., 1958-61; assoc. prof. fine arts Syracuse U. (N.Y.), 1961-66, prof., 1966-85, prof. emeritus, 1985—, dir. humanities doctoral program, 1964-72, chmn. dept. fine arts, 1969-73; bibliographer Shakespeare Assn., N.Y.C., 1949-54. Author: The Antic Hamlet, 1943; co-editor: The Nature of Art, 1964; editor: Images of Man, 1972. Served to sgt., inf. U.S. Army, 1943-45, ETO. Research fellow Folger Shakespeare Library, Washington, 1947-48. Fellow Royal Soc. Arts (London); mem. MLA (life), Shakespeare Assn. Am., Internat. Shakespeare Assn., AAUP (pres. Syracuse U. chpt. 1974), ACLU, Phi Beta Kappa. Office: Syracuse U Dept Fine Arts Syracuse NY 13210

THOMAS, STEPHEN CLAIR, software publisher, writer, editor, consultant; b. Paulding, Ohio, Sept. 18, 1952; s. Isaac Rily and Mabel Marie (Essex) T.; m. Marsha Elaine Nichols, Nov. 10, 1978 (div. May, 1992); children: Seth Thomas, Sondra Pfuhl; m. Janet Marie Middleton Pfuhl, Feb. 20, 1993. BSCBchemE, U. Dayton, Ohio, 1977; BS in Math., Defiance Coll., 1991. Editor The Observer, Paulding, 1970-72; photographer McJon, inc., Ft. Wayne, Ind., 1972-73, Chromalloy Photographic, Janesville (Wis.) and Indpls., 1973-74; researcher processing engring. Drackett Co. div. Bristol-Myers, Cin., 1977-79; researcher fats and oils Cen. Soya, Ft. Wayne, 1979-81; mng. editor APRAWS, Inc., Ft. Wayne 1981-88; freelance writer Ft. Wayne, 1988-90; dir. of devel. SETHware, Paulding, Ohio, 1991—; cons. New Haven (Ind.) Star-Times, 1981-82, New Ft. Wayne mag., 1983-84; columnist Ft. Wayne News-Sentinel, 1985-89; editor Waynedale News, Ft. Wayne, 1986; programmer, analyst CompuServe, Columbus, Ohio, 1992—. Author: Computer-Based Estimating, 1983, BYOB-Be Your Own Boss!, 1987, Aerobic Gardening, 1987, Tax Scrooge, 1989. Mem. Ft. Wayne Writers Guild (bd. dirs. 1985-90), Assn. Shareware Profls., Shareware Trade Assn. & Resources, Explorer Post (leader). Methodist. Home: 1398 Crown Point Ct Beavercreek OH 45434-6913 Office: 4719 Reed Rd Ste 232 Columbus OH 43220-3051

THOMAS, STEPHEN PAUL, lawyer; b. Bloomington, Ill., July 30, 1938; s. Owen Wilson and Mary Katherine (Paulsen) T.; m. Marieanne Sauer, Dec. 7, 1963 (dec. June 1984); 1 child, Catherine Marie; m. Marcia Aldrich Toomey, May 28, 1988; 1 child, Ellen Antonia. BA, U. Ill., 1959; LLB, Harvard U., 1962. Bar: Ill. 1962. Vol. Peace Corps, Malawi, Africa, 1963-65; assoc Sidley & Austin and predecessor firms, Chgo., 1965-70, ptnr., 1970—; lectr. on law Malawi Inst. Pub. Adminstrv., 1963-65. Pres. Hyde Park-Kenwood Community Conf., Chgo., 1988-90; trustee Chgo. Acad. for Arts, 1991—, chmn., 1992—. Recipient Paul Cornell award Hyde Park Hist. Soc., 1981. Mem. ABA, Chgo. Bar Assn., Chgo. Fedn. of Musicians, Legal Club Chgo., Union League Club Chgo. Democrat. Roman Catholic. Avocation: jazz piano playing. Home: 5740 S Harper Ave Chicago IL 60637-1841 Office: Sidley & Austin 1 First National Plz Chicago IL 60603

THOMAS, TED, SR., minister; b. Raeford, N.C., Oct. 19, 1935; s. Simuel and Nancy Anna (McPhatter) T.; m. Charletta Virginia Clifton, May 30, 1957; children: Ted, Christopher, Marc, Charles, Jonathan, Reuben. BS, Norfolk State Coll., 1959; MA in Math., Edn. and Secondary Edn., Hampton Inst., 1972. Ordained to ministry Ch. of God in Christ Inc., 1957. Pastor New Community Ch. of God in Christ, Churchland, Portsmouth, Va., 1967—; State project dir. Chs. of God in Christ, Va. Jurisdiction 1, 1965—; supt. cen. dist. Chs. of God in Christ, Va., 1964—; asst. prin. Ruffner Jr. High Sch., Norfolk, Va., 1983-84; past pres. young people Willing Works, 1962-66; Sunday sch. supt., 1970-73; asst. bishop 1st jurisdiction Chs. of God in Christ Inc. of Va., 1977-84, State Bishop, 1984—. Mem. NEA, Va. Edn. Assn., Edn. Assn. Norfolk. Home: 4145 Sunkist Rd Chesapeake VA 23321-3131 Office: Ch of God in Christ 3615 Tyre Neck Rd Portsmouth VA 23703-3125

THOMAS, THOMAS A., lawyer; b. Geneva, N.Y., May 16, 1919; s. Abraham and Mary (Norman) T.; m. Margaret Jane Ajay, Mar. 30, 1947; children: Frank Thomas II, Thomas A., Mary Frances, Julie Ann. BA, Syracuse U., 1942; LLB, Vanderbilt U., 1948; LLM, Harvard U., 1949. Bar: Fla. 1953. Pvt. practice law Hollywood, Fla., 1953—; prof. law U. Miami, Fla., 1949-74, assoc. dean Law Sch., 1969-72; pvt. practice Thomas & Thomas, 1973—; city atty. Hollywood, 1965-69; chmn. bd. Am. Bank, Hollywood, 1972-75. Author: Florida Estates Practice Guide, 2 vols., 1964. With U.S. Army, 1942-46. Van Allen scholar, 1940. Mem. Fla. Bar Assn., South Broward County Bar Assn., Hollywood C. of C., Iron Arrow, Order of Coif, Omega Delta Kappa. Episcopalian. Home: 2519 Madison St Hollywood FL 33020-5328 Office: 1917 Harrison St Hollywood FL 33020-5017

THOMAS, THOMAS DARRAH, chemistry educator; b. Glen Ridge, N.J., Apr. 8, 1932; s. Woodlief and Jean (Darrah) T.; m. Barbara Joan Rassweiler, Sept. 8, 1956; children: David, Steven, Kathleen, Susan. BS, Haverford Coll., 1954; PhD, U. Calif., Berkeley, 1958. Instr. chemistry U. Calif., Berkeley, 1957-58, asst. prof., 1958-59; research assoc. Brookhaven Nat. Lab., Upton, N.Y., 1959-61; asst. prof. Princeton (N.J.) U., 1961-66, assoc. prof., 1966-71; prof. Oreg. State U., Corvallis, 1971-89, disting. prof.,

1989—, chmn. dept. chemistry, 1981-84, dir. Ctr. Advanced Materials Research, 1986-91; cons. Los Alamos (N.Mex.) Sci. Lab., 1965. Contbr. articles to profl. jours. Fellow Alfred P. Sloan Found., 1966-68, Guggenheim Found., 1969, U. Liverpool, Eng., 1984-85. Fellow AAAS, Am. Phys. Soc.; mem. Am. Chem. Soc., Sigma Xi, Phi Beta Kappa. Home: 1470 NW Greenwood Pl Corvallis OR 97330-1827 Office: Oreg State U Dept Chemistry Gilbert Hall 153 Corvallis OR 97331-4003

THOMAS, THOMAS STANTON, health system executive; b. Louisiana, Mo., Nov. 3, 1944; s. Glenn Stanton and Hilda Ruth (Gamm) T.; m. Nancy Lee Waller, June 7, 1967; 1 child, David Stanton. BA, Westminster Coll., Fulton, Mo., 1966; MEd, U. Mo., 1968, BHSM, 1982, MPA, 1985. Asst. dir. office of planning Mo. Regional Med. Program, 1972-73; chief planing specialist Mo. Div. Health Cancer Control Program, 1973; asst. dir. cmty. cancer control Mo. Div. Health Cancer Control Program, Columbia, 1973-76, adminstrv. dir., 1976-79; dir. planning and shared svcs. Boone County Hosp., Columbia, 1979-82; asst. to pres., dir. instnl. devel. and affil. svcs. Boone Hosp. Ctr., Columbia, 1982-85, v.p. planning and mktg., exec. dir. hosp. found., 1985-88; corp. dir. govtl. and regulatory affairs Christian Health Svcs. Devel. Corp., Columbia, 1988-93, v.p. govtl. and regulatory affairs, 1993-94; dir. state and fed. rels. BJC Health System, St. Louis, 1994-95; exec. dir. health policy coun. St. Louis (Mo.) Health Care Network, 1995—; corp. exec. pub. policy SSM Health Care Sys., St. Louis, 1995—; mem. Mo. State Bd. Health, 1987-91, chmn., 1989-91; former mem. Am. Healthcare Sys. Health Reform ad hoc Adv. Group. Co-chair cmty. svcs. div. United Way of Columbia, 1980; pres. Boone County div. Am. Heart Assn., 1983-84; trustee Westminster Coll., 1988—, mem. exec. com., 1991—, vice chmn., bd. trustees; policy com., Wis. Catholic Hosp., 1995—. Fellow Am. Coll. Healthcare Execs. (regents adv. coun.); mem. Mo. Health and Ednl. Facilities Authority (v. chair 1991—), Mo. Hosp. Assn. (Medicaid com.), Mo. Pub. Health Assn., Am. Assn. Lobbyists, Ill. Hosp. Assn. (legis. coun. 1994-95), Columbia C. of C. (bd. dirs. 1991-93, co-chair town and gown com. 1992-93), Rotary Internat. (charter pres. Columbia South 1989-90), Elks, Phi Delta Kappa, Phi Gamma Delta. Presbyterian. Office: SSM Health Care Sys 1701 E Broadway Columbia MO 65201

THOMAS, THURMAN, professional football player; b. Houston, May 16, 1966. Student, Okla. State U. With Buffalo Bills, 1988—. Named to Pro-Bowl team, 1989-93, Sporting News All-Pro team, 1990, 91; named MVP, NFL, 1991, Player of Yr., Sporting News, 1991. Office: care Buffalo Bills 1 Bills Dr Orchard Park NY 14127-2237*

THOMAS, TOM, retired plastics company executive; b. Malang, Java, Indonesia, Feb. 15, 1932; arrived in Can., 1954; s. Ferdinand and Elfrieda Emma (Macht) T.; m. Jannie Chine Sneep, Jan. 19, 1956; children: Gregory John, Renée Sonja Elfrieda, Michael Grant, Thomas. Grad. high sch., The Hague, Holland. Jr. mgr. Lever Bros. Ltd., Toronto, Ont., Can., 1954-60; sr. mgr. Impac & Somerville Plastics, Toronto, Ont., Can., 1960-64; founder, C.E.O. Can. Cup Inc., Toronto, Ont., Can., 1964—, also bd. dirs., 1964-93, ret., 1993; Inventor in field. Trustee Frazer Inst., Vancouver, B.C., Can., 1977-93; gov. Massey and Roy Thomson Hall, Toronto, 1991-92; bd. dirs. Toronto Symphony, 1986-92, mem. Maestro's Club, 1984, mem. pres.'s coun. Can. Opera Co., 1980, adv. coun. Toronto Symphony, 1995, pres. Coun. Can. Opera, 1980-95. Avocations: sailing, history, classical music, chess.

THOMAS, VIOLETA DE LOS ANGELES, real estate broker; b. Buenos Aires, Dec. 21, 1941; came to U.S., 1962; d. Angel and Lola (Andino) de Rios; m. Jess Thomas, Dec. 23, 1974; 1 child, Victor Justin. Student, Harvard U. and U. Buenos Aires, 1967-73. Mgr. book div. Time-Life, N.Y.C., 1967-73; real estate broker First Marin Realty, Inc., Mill Valley, Calif., 1985—. Bd. dirs. City of Tiburon, Calif., 1987-93, Art and Heritage Commn., Tiburon, Alliannuse Francaise, St. Louis. Named Woman of Yr., City of Buenos Aires, 1977, Agt. of Yr., Marin County and San Francisco 1987-92. Home: PO Box 6608 Town & Country MO 63006

THOMAS, W. DENNIS, paper company executive, former government official; b. Balt., Dec. 8, 1943; s. George Crosby and Justa Mae (Witherspoon) T.; m. Dawn Frances Haines, 1965; 1 son, William David. BS, Frostburg State Coll., 1965; M.S.W., U. Md., 1967. Asst. to Hon. J. Glenn Beall, Jr., Washington, 1969-71, spl. asst., 1971-73, adminstrv. asst., 1973-77; adminstrv. asst. to Hon. William V. Roth, Jr., Washington, 1977-81; asst. sec. legis. affairs Dept. Treasury, Washington, 1981-83; dep. asst. to Pres. legis. affairs White House, 1983-85; ptnr. Touche Ross and Co., Inc., 1985; asst. to Pres., The White House, 1985-87; v.p. govt. rels. Internat. Paper Co., Washington, 1987—. Republican. Office: Internat Paper Ste 200 1101 Pennsylvania Ave NW Washington DC 20004

THOMAS, WALTER DILL, JR., forest pathologist, consultant; b. St. Louis, July 3, 1918; s. Walter D. and Helen (Gardner) T.; m. Dolores B. Thomas, Dec. 31, 1939 (div. May 1984); children: Sandra Thomas Bosworth, Arthur D; m. Nancy McCarthy, Feb. 15, 1985. BS, Colo. State U., 1939; MS, U. Minn., 1943, PhD, 1947. Prof. plant pathology Colo. State U., Ft. Collins, 1947-55; supr. biol. research Chevron Chem. Co., Richmond, Calif., 1955-70; v.p. research Nat. Resources Mgmt., Eureka, Calif., 1970-72; pres. Forest Ag Corp., Lafayette, Calif., 1972-86; coord. bd. Forest Stewardship Calif. Dept. of Forestry and Fire Control, 1990-94; cons. in field, 1986-95, ret. 1995. Author: Field Manual of Forest and Shade Tree Diseases, 1947, Not Long Apart, 1965, Mauget Field Manual: Insects and Diseases of Shade Trees, 1995. commmr. Park and Recreation Com., Ft. Collins, 1949-54, Concord, Calif., 1959-65; city forester, Ft. Collins, 1950-55. Comdr. USNR, 1944-80. Fellow AAAS (life); mem. Am. Phytopathol. Soc., Soc. Am. Foresters, Foresters Assn (calif. lic.), Pesticide Applicators Professional Assn., Internat. Soc. of Arboriculture, Nat. Forensic Soc., Bd. Forensics Examiners, Soc. of Tech. Comm. (sr.), Assn. Cons. Foresters, Am. Soc. Cons. Arborists, Soc. Tech. Comms. (sr. mem.), VFW, Elks, Lions. Republican. Lodges: Elks, Lions. Avocations: music, swimming, writing. Home and Office: 2435 Heatherleaf Ln Martinez CA 94553-4337

THOMAS, WAYNE LEE, lawyer; b. Tampa, Sept. 22, 1945; s. Willard McSwain and June Frances (Jones) T.; m. Patricia H., Mar. 16, 1968; children: Brigitte Elisabeth, Kate Adelaide. BA, U. Fla., 1967, JD cum laude 1971. Bar: Fla., 1971, U.S. Supreme Ct., 1975, U.S. Ct. Appeals (5th cir.), 1975, U.S. Ct. Appeals (11th cir.), 1981, U.S. Ct. Claims 1976, U.S. Dist. Ct. (mid. dist.) Fla., 1973, U.S. Dist. Ct. (so. dist. trial bar) Fla., 1975. Law clk. U.S. Dist. Ct. (mid. dist.) Fla., 1971-73; assoc. Trenam, Simmons, Kemker, Scharf, Barkin, Frye & O'Neill, P.A., Tampa, 1973-77, ptnr., 1978-81; founder, pres. McKay & Thomas, P.A., Tampa, 1981-89; ptnr. Carlton, Fields, Ward, Emmanuel, Smith & Cutler, P.A., 1989—. Mem. Fla. Bar (chmn. sect. gen. practice, 1981-83, mem. ethics com., vice chmn. unauthorized practice law com. 1994—, vice chmn. fed. practice com. 1995—, mem. bd. bar examiners 1986-91, chmn. 1990-91), ABA, Hillsborough County Bar Assn. (chmn. grievance com. 1985-86), Order of Coif, Fla. Blue Key, Phi Kappa Phi, Omicron Delta Kappa. Democrat. Office: Carlton Fields Ward Emmanuel Smith & Cutler PA 1 Harbor Pl 777 S Harbour Island Blvd Tampa FL 33602-5729

THOMAS, W(ILLIAM) BRUCE, retired steel, oil, gas company executive; b. Ripley, Mich., Oct. 25, 1926; s. William and Ethel (Collins) T.; m. Phyllis Smith, June 25, 1950; 1 son, Robert William. BA magna cum laude, Western Mich. U., 1950; JD with distinction, U. Mich., 1952; postgrad., Law Sch., NYU, 1953. Bar: Mich. 1952. With USX Corp. (formerly U.S. Steel) and subs., various locations, 1952-91; tax atty. Oliver Iron Mining Div., Duluth, Minn., 1952-53; tax atty., tax supr., comptroller Orinoco Mining Co., N.Y.C. and Venezuela, 1953-64; dir. v.p. taxes, 1967-70, v.p., asst. treas., 1970-71, v.p. treas., 1971-75; exec. v.p., CFO, dir. USX Corp., Pitts., 1975-82, vice chmn., CFO, dir., 1982-91; dir. Chem. Banking and Chem. Bank. Bd. dirs. Duquesne U., Allegheny Gen. Hosp.; trustee Kenyon Coll. With USAAF, 1943-45. Mem. ABA, Mich. Bar Assn., Fin. Execs. Inst., Order of Coif, Duquesne Club, Pitts. Club, Laurel Valley Golf Club, Rolling Rock Club, Allegheny Country Club, Sky Club, Links, Bellair Country Club, Phi Alpha Delta. Methodist. Home: Blackburn Rd Sewickley PA 15143 Office: USX Corp 600 Grant St Ste 6200 Pittsburgh PA 15219

THOMAS, WILLIAM GERAINT, museum administrator; b. Columbo, Sri Lanka, June 27, 1931; came to U.S., 1941; s. Cecil James and Iris Katharine (Evans) T.; m. Maria Alcalde, Jan. 2, 1976; 1 child, Laura. BA, U. Calif.,

Berkeley, 1952. Reporter, editor San Francisco Chronicle, 1952-64; asst. to mayor City of San Francisco, 1964-66; chief cons. majority caucus Calif. State Assembly, Sacramento, 1966-68; adminstrv. asst. U.S. Congressman Phillip Burson, Washington, 1968-70; cons. interior com. U.S. Ho. of Reps. Washington, 1972-78; ptnr. Thomas & Iovino, San Francisco, 1972-78; asst. regional dir. Nat. Park Svc., San Francisco, 1978-89; supt. San Francisco Maritime NHP, 1989—. Mem. Nat. Dem. Club; bd. dirs. Nat. Liberty Ship Meml., 1978-80. Sgt. U.S. Army, 1952-54, Korea. Mem. Nat. Maritime Mus. Assn., Nat. Maritime Hist. Soc., Press Club of San Francisco (pres. 1973-74, Best News Story 1963). Episcopalian. Avocation: sailing. Office: San Francisco Maritime Bldg 201 Ft Mason San Francisco CA 94123

THOMAS, WILLIAM GRIFFITH, lawyer; b. Washington, Nov. 1, 1939; s. Henry Phineas and Margaret Wilson (Carr) T.; m. Suzanne Campbell Foster, June 7, 1960. Student Williams Coll., 1957-59, Richmond Coll., 1960; J.D., U. Richmond, 1963. Bar: Va. 1963. Mem., pres. Hazel & Thomas, P.C., Alexandria, Va., 1987—; Va. Electric and Power Co., Richmond. Sec., Va. Dem. Com., 1968-70, chmn., 1970-72. Mem. ABA, Va. State Bar Assn., Alexandria Bar Assn., Am. Law Inst., Am. Coll. Real Estate Lawyers. Home: 200 S Fairfax St # 14 Alexandria VA 22314-3331 Office: Hazel & Thomas 510 King St Ste 200 Alexandria VA 22314-3132

THOMAS, WILLIAM LEROY, geography educator, cruise lecturer; b. Long Beach, Calif., Mar. 18, 1920; s. William LeRoy and Margaret Lucile (Young) T.; m. Mildred Phyllis Smith, Apr. 10, 1942 (div.); children: Barbara Jean, Lawrence Charles, Virginia Jane, Margaret Joan, Pamela June; m. Loida Ayson Aquino, Aug. 29, 1964 (dec.); children: William John Aquino, Lloyd Aquino; m. Rosalinda Zuñiga Valencia, July 4, 1986; 1 adopted child, Don Valencia. A.B., UCLA, 1941, M.A., 1948; Ph.D., Yale U., 1955. Instr. geography Rutgers U., 1947-50; research asst. S.E. Asia studies Yale U., 1949-50; asst. dir. research Wenner-Gren Found. Anthrop. Research, N.Y.C., 1950-57; asst. to assoc. prof. geography U. Calif., Riverside, 1957-63; prof. anthropology and geography Calif. State U., Hayward, 1963-71, chmn. dept. anthropology and geography, 1963-66, prof. geography and Southeast Asian studies, 1971-91, prof. emeritus, 1983—, chmn. dept. geography, 1971-74; assoc. dir. Ctr. for Filipino Studies Calif. State U., 1990-91; v.p. rsch. and devel. Heritage Tours, Ltd., Oakland, Calif. 1981-83; v.p. rsch. and devel., chmn. bd. Geo-Expdns. Internat., Inc., 1981-83; pres. Thomas Opportunity Program Services, 1983-90; vis. prof. La. State U., spring 1966, U. Hawaii, summer 1966, U. Wis., fall 1966, U. Toronto, Canada, fall 1968, 69, Georgetown U., 1992; vis. research assoc. Inst. Philippine Culture, Ateneo de Manila U., Quezon City, 1970, 76-77; Fulbright lectr. Centre for Asian Studies, U. Western Australia, Nedlands, 1974; Fulbright sr. research scholar Mariano Marcos State U., Batac, Ilocos Norte, Philippines, 1984-85; organizer internat. symposium Man's Role in Changing the Face of the Earth, Princeton, N.J., 1955; cons. Nat. Acad. Scis.-NRC, in orgn. of sect. 6th Nat. Conf. UNESCO, 1957; mem. tech. cons. group Calif. Pub. Outdoor Recreation Plan Com., 1958-62; geog. cons. Pacific Missile Range, Pt. Mugu, Calif., 1958-60; organizer geography sect. 10th Pacific Sci. Congress, 1961; foreign field research, Philippines, 1961-62, Philippines, Thailand, Burma, 1970, Australia, Indonesia, 1974, Philippines, 1976-77, 84-85, 86, French Polynesia, 1992, 93, Thailand, Malaysia, Indonesia, Singapore, 1993, Indonesia, 1994, 95 Northern Australia, 1995; mem. ad hoc com. on geography Nat. Acad. Scis.-NRC, 1963-65, cons. effects of herbicides in, Vietnam, 1972-74; chmn. Asian studies council Calif. State Colls., 1971-72; mem. com. internat. symposium earth as transformed by human action Clark U., Worcester, Mass., 1987; invited speaker V.I. Vernadsky anniversary symposium USSR Acad. Scis., Leningrad, Kiev, Moscow, 1988; guest lectr. Cunard Line 'Vistafjord' cruise, Feb. 1992, Royal Viking Line 'Sun' Cruise, 1992, Paquet Cruise Company 'Ocean Pearl' cruise, 1993, Cunard Line 'Sagafjord' cruise, 1993, Seven Seas Cruise Line 'Song of Flower' cruise, 1993-94, Cunard Line 'Vistafjord' Cruise, 1994, Crystal Cruises 'Crystal Harmony' Cruise, 1994, Regency Cruises 'Regent Sea' Cruise, 1994, Orient Line 'Marco Polo' Cruise, 1994, Holland-Am. Line 'Rotterdam' Grand World Voyage Cruise, 1995, Orient Line 'Marco Polo' Cruise, 1995. Author: (with J. F. Embree) Ethnic Groups of Northern Southeast Asia, 1950, Land, Man and Culture in Mainland Southeast Asia, 1957, (with J.E. Spencer) Cultural Geography, 1969, Asia, East by South, 2d edit, 1971, Introducing Cultural Geography, 1973, 2d edit., 1978; Editor: (with Anna M. Pikells) International Directory of Anthropological Institutions, 1953, Yearbook of Anthropology, 1955, Current Anthropology, 1956, Man's Role in Changing the Face of the Earth, 1956, Am. Anthrop. Assn. Bull, 1958-60, Man, Time, and Space in Southern California, 1959;paperback series Man-Environment System in The Late 20th Century, 1969-75. Moderator United Ch. Hayward, 1988-90. 1st lt. C.E., AUS, 1942-45. Mem. Assn. Asian Studies, Asian Studies on Pacific Coast (chmn. standing com. 1979-80, conf. chmn. 1980), Pacific Sci. Assn. (U.S. mem. sci. com. on geography), Assn. Am. Geographers (Pacific Coast regional councilor 1971-74, citation for meritorious contbn. to geography 1961), Assn. Pacific Coast Geographers (v.p. 1976-77, pres. 1977-78, Disting. Svc. award 1988), Calif. Geog. Soc. (pres. 1967-68, Outstanding Educator award 1986). Democrat. Address: 307 Shalako Dr Oakdale CA 95361

THOMAS, WILLIAM MARSHALL, congressman; b. Wallace, Idaho, Dec. 6, 1941; s. Virgil and Gertrude Thomas; m. Sharon Lynn Hamilton, Jan. 1968; children: Christopher, Amelia. B.A. San Francisco State U., 1963, M.A., 1965. Mem. faculty dept. Am. govt. Bakersfield (Calif.) Coll., 1965-74, prof., 1965-74; mem. Calif. State Assembly, 1974-78, 96th-104th Congress from 18th, now 21st Calif. Dist., 1979—; vice chmn. of House Task Force on Campaign Fin. Reform; mem. Ho of Reps. Ways and Means Com.; chmn. Com. on House Oversight, Ways & Means Health Subcom.; mem. Ways & Means subcom on Trade; mem. del. to Soviet Union, by Am. Council Young Polit. Leaders, 1977; chmn. Kern County Republican Central Com., 1972-74; mem. Calif. Rep. Com., 1972-80; del. Republican Party Nat. Conv., 1980, 84, 88; mem. Rep. Leader's Task Force on Health Care Reform. Office: Ho of Reps 2208 Rayburn Ho Office Bldg Washington DC 20515

THOMAS, WILLIAM SCOTT, lawyer; b. Joliet, Ill., Aug. 16, 1949; s. William Edward and Audrey Ann (Johnson) T.; m. Carolyn Smith Cotter, Aug. 10, 1974; children: Derek Cotter, Kimberley Cotter. AB, Stanford U., 1971; JD, U. Calif., Hastings, 1974; LLM in Taxation, Golden Gate U., 1981. Bar: Calif. 1975, U.S. Dist. Ct. (no. dist.) Calif. 1975, U.S. Tax Ct. 1982. Tax editor Internat. Bur. Fiscal Documentation, Amsterdam, Holland, 1974-75; tax atty. Chevron Corp., San Francisco, 1975-77; from assoc. to ptnr. Brobeck, Phleger & Harrison, San Francisco, 1978—; bd. dirs. Value Line Inc., N.Y.C. Mem. ABA (taxation sect.), Calif. Bar Assn. (exec. com. taxation sect. 1984-89, chmn. 1987-88). Office: Brobeck Phleger & Harrison 1 Market Plz San Francisco CA 94105-1019

THOMAS, WYNN P., art director, production designer. Art dir.: (films) Beat Street, 1984, She's Gotta Have It, 1986; prodn. designer: (films) Eddie Murphy Raw, 1987, School Daze, 1988, Do the Right Thing, 1989, Mo' Better Blues, 1990, The Five Heartbeats, 1991, Jungle Fever, 1991, Malcolm X, 1992, A Bronx Tale, 1993, Crooklyn, 1994. Office: care Art Directors Guild 11365 Ventura Blvd #315 Studio City CA 91604*

THOMASCH, ROGER PAUL, lawyer; b. N.Y.C., Nov. 7, 1942; s. Gordon J. and Margaret (Molloy) T.; children: Laura Leigh, Paul Butler. BA, Coll. William and Mary, 1964; LLB, Duke U., 1967. Bar: Conn. 1967, Colo. 1974. Assoc. atty. Cummings & Lockwood, Stamford, Conn., 1967-70; trial atty. U.S. Dept. Justice, Washington, 1970-73; ptnr. Roath & Brega, Denver, 1975-87; mng. ptnr. Ballard, Spahr, Andrews & Ingersoll, Denver, 1987—; vis. assoc. prof. of law Drake U. Sch. Law, Des Moines, 1973-74; frequent lectr. in field, U.S. and Can.; co-dean commit. litigation program of Nat. Advanced Coll. of Advocacy, 1982-86; adj. faculty mem. U. Denver Coll. Law, 1976-80. Recipient Leland Forrest Outstanding Prof. award, Drake U. Sch. Law, 1973. Mem. ABA, Colo. Bar Assn., Denver Country Club, Univ. Club, Denver Athletic Club. Office: Ballard Spahr Andrews & Ingersoll 1225 17th St Denver CO 80202-5534

THOMASON, FRANK W., superintendent. Supt. Dalton City Schs., Dalton, Ga. Recipient State Finalist for Nat. Supt. of Yr. award, 1993. Office: Dalton City Schs PO Box 1408 100 S Hamilton St Dalton GA 30720-4216

THOMAS-ORR, BETTY JO, retired public relations specialist; b. Chgo., Sept. 28, 1937; d. William H. and Elizabeth (Brown) Shannon; m. Wilbur E. Thomas, June 28, 1958 (div. 1979); m. Vernon A. Orr, June 2, 1980 (dec. 1985); children: Pamela F., Kenneth E., Neil A. BBA, Nat. U., 1988, MBA, 1989. Campaign and project dir., 1978-79; customer svc. rep. Mainliner Reservations United Airlines, Chgo., 1983; customer svc. rep. United Airlines, Las Vegas, Nev., 1983-92; ret., 1992; asst. dir. pub. rels. Am. Lung Assn., Las Vegas, 1989-92; mem. Bd. Vet. Med. Examiners, Reno, Nev., 1990-93. Named 4-H Leader of Yr., State of Ill., 1978. Mem. Am. Bus. Women Assn., Nat. Univ. Student Alumni Assn. (treas. 1990), Las Vegas Drifters (past pres., sec., treas.), The Links, Alpha Kappa Alpha. Democrat. Roman Catholic. Avocations: arts, crafts, ceramics. Home: 5155 Myrtlewood Ave Las Vegas NV 89122-6835

THOMASSON, PATSY, federal official. BA, Henderson State U.; MA, U. Mo. Staff asst. to congressman Wilbur D. Mills U.S. House Reps., Washington, Ark., 1969-71, 72-74; exec. dir. Dem. Party Ark.; assoc. adminstr. Doctors Hosp., Little Rock; pres. So. Mgmt. Assn.; exec. v.p., pres. Phoenix Group; spl. asst. to pres., dir. Office adminstrn. Mgmt. and Adminstrn., Washington, 1993—. Overseer Coord. Campaign Ark. Mem. Am. Assn. State Highway and Transp. Officials. Office: The White House Statutory Offices 1600 Pennsylvania Ave NW Washington DC 20500-0001

THOMINET, MAURICE J., architect; b. Chgo., May 18, 1928; s. Maurice J. and Josephine Ann (Baffetti) T.; m. Rosemarie Ann Voruda, July 9, 1949; children: Rene Thominet Noyes and John. Student, Wright Jr. Coll., Bucknell U., U. Ill., Chgo., Art Inst. Chgo. Registered architect, Ill., Mo. Archtl. designer Chgo. Pk. Dist., 1952-67, architect, 1967-74, asst. engr. design, 1974-77, design engr., 1977-80, asst. chief engr., 1981-82, chief engr., 1982-86; pres. M.O.S.T. Constrn. Co., Hollister, Mo., 1987-88; pvt. practice Hazel Crest, Ill., 1955-67, Libertyville, Ill., 1988-94, Hollister, Mo., 1995—; bd. dirs. Bags-Up Corp., Ill.; mem. bldg. commn., vice chmn. zoning bd. appeals, Hazel Crest, 1964-74, village architect, 1965-74. Inventor automobile accessory. Pres. Boy's Baseball Assn., Hazel Crest, 1967. With U.S. Navy, 1945-46. Recipient Meritous Svc. award Village of Hazel Crest, 1974, Profl. Svc. Cup award Grant Pk. Symphony Orch., 1978, citation Lincoln Pk. Zoo Soc., 1985, citation State of Ill., Dept. Interior Nat. Pk. Svc., 1985. Fellow AIA (honor award 1986). Roman Catholic. Avocations: architecture, landscape architecture, art, travel, museums. Home and Office: 134 Sleepy Hollow Rd Hollister MO 65672

THOMLINSON, RALPH, demographer, educator; b. St. Louis, Feb. 12, 1925; s. Ralph and Ora Lee (Barr) T.; m. Margaret Mary Willits, Dec. 21, 1946; children: Elizabeth Barr, William Lockwood. BA, Oberlin Coll., 1949; postgrad., U. Pitts., 1943-44, Harvard U., 1948; MA, Yale U., 1949; PhD, Columbia U., 1960. Asst. town planner Montclair, N.J., 1949-50; asst. city planner Paterson, N.J., 1950; research asst. Bur. Applied Social Research, N.Y.C., 1952; med. statistics asst. actuarial dept. Met. Life Ins. Co., N.Y.C., 1952-53; instr. statistics and population U. Wis., 1953-56; instr. sociology and anthropology Denison U., Granville, Ohio, 1956-59; asst. prof. sociology Calif. State U., L.A., 1959-62; assoc. prof. Calif. State U., 1962-65, prof., 1965-88, prof. emeritus, 1988—, chmn. dept. sociology, 1967-69; vis. prof. sociology U. Alta., Can., 1966; vis. prof. biostatistics U.N.C., Chapel Hill, 1972-73; demographic adviser Inst. Population Studies, Chulalongkorn U., Bangkok, Thailand, 1969-71; cons. Nat. Family Planning Program, Thailand, Census of Thailand, 1970-71, Population/Food Fund, 1977-79, also various research centers abroad, 1969-73; cons. to fourteen book pubs., 1965—; field assoc. Population Coun., N.Y.C., 1969-71; rsch. adviser Ctr. for Rsch. and Demographic Studies, Rabat, Morocco, 1972-73; acad. visitor Population Investigation Com., London Sch. Econs., 1973; vis. scholar Nat. Inst. Demographic Studies, Paris, 1973-74. Author: A Mathematical Model for Migration, 1960, Population Dynamics, 2d edit, 1976, Sociological Concepts and Research, 1965, Demographic Problems, 2d edit, 1976, Urban Structure, 1969, Thailand's Population, 1971, (with others) The Methodology of the Longitudinal Study of Social, Economic and Demographic Change, 1971; editor: (with Visid Prachuabmoh) The Potharam Study, 1971; adv. editor: Sociol. Abstracts, 1963-67, Sociology Quar, 1978-84; cons. editor: Assoukan, 1972-73; assoc. editor: Pacific Sociol. Rev, 1976-83; Sociol. Perspective, 1983-85; chmn. editorial bd. Calif. Sociologist, 1981-84; cons.: Dictionary of Modern Sociology, 1969; contbr. to: Dictionary of Demography, 5 vols., 1985-86; books, profl. jours. Served with AUS, 1943-45, ETO. Mem. Population Assn. Am., Internat. Union for Sci. Study Population, Am. Sociol. Assn., Internat. Assn. Survey Statisticians, Assn. Asian Studies. Home: 712 Coronado Ln Foster City CA 94404-2925

THOMLISON, RAY J., university dean, educator; b. Edmonton, Alta., Can., Jan. 22, 1943; s. Herbert MacLeod and Margaret Patricia (Hagen) T.; m. Barbara Buckler, Aug. 22, 1964; children: Lynn, Breanne. BSc, U. Alta., 1963; B in Social Work, U. BC, 1964, MSW, 1965; PhD, U. Toronto, 1972. Social worker Dept. Pub. Welfare, Edmonton, 1964-65; psychiat. social worker Mental Health Ctr., Burnaby, B.C., Can., 1965-67; mental health cons. Lower Mainland & North B.C., 1967-68; assoc. prof. Wilfrid Laurier U., Waterloo, Ont., Can., 1971-73; prof. U. Toronto, Ont., 1973-83; prof., dean U. Calgary, Alta., 1983—; vis. prof. U. B.C., Vancouver, 1980-81, U. Regina, Sask., Can., 1977; sessional faculty Atkinson Coll., York U., Downsview, Ont., 1978-83, Wilfrid Laurier U., 1974-83; mem. adv. com., chair Com. Native Social Work Edn., Alta, 1986-90; mem. adv. com. Profl. Exam. Bd. Social Work, Alta., 1983-87; mem. bd. accreditation Can. Assn. Schs. Social Work, 1978; mem. Univ. Coord. Coun., Alta., 1984-86; content advisor Nat. Film Bd.; employee assistance cons. Esso Can., Bank of Montreal. Editor: Perspectives on Industrial Social Work Practice, 1983, (with J.S. Ismael) Perspectives on Social Services and Social Issues, 1987, (with C.R. Bagley) Child Sexual Abuse: Critical Perspectives on Prevention, Intervention, and Treatment, 1991, (with J. Hudson and J. Mayne) Action-Oriented Evaluation in Organizations: Canadian Practices, 1992; contbr. articles to profl. jours., book chpts., reports, and papers to confs. U. Toronto Faculty teaching fellow, 1974. Mem. Coun. Social Work. Edn., Assn. Advancement Behaviour Therapy, Assn. Behavioral Social Work, Rsch. Inst. Social Work (People's Rep. of China), Assn. Social Workers of Russia, Alberta Assn. Social Workers, Met. Toronto Children's Aid (bd. dirs. 1979-83), Family Service Assn. Met. Toronto Employee Assistance Program (adv. bd. 1977-83). Home: 1139 Varsity Estates Dr NW, Calgary, AB Canada T3B 3B5 Office: U of Calgary Faculty Soc Work, 2500 Univ Dr NW, Calgary, AB Canada T2N 1N4

THOMOPULOS, GREGS G., consulting engineering company executive; b. Benin City, Nigeria, May 16, 1942; s. Aristoteles and Christiana E. (Ogiamien) T.; m. Patricia Walker, Sept. 4, 1966 (div. 1974); 1 child, Lisa; m. Mettie L. Williams, May 28, 1976; children: Nicole, Euphemia. BSCE with highest distinction, U. Kans., 1965; MS in Structural Engring., U. Calif., Berkeley, 1966. Sr. v.p. internat. div. Stanley Cons., Inc., Muscatine, Iowa, 1978-84; sr. v.p. project div. Stanley Consultants, Inc., Muscatine, Iowa, 1984-87, pres.; 1987—; exec. v.p. SC Co., Inc., Muscatine, 1992—; also bd. dirs.; chmn., CEO Stanley Cons. Environ., Inc., Chgo., 1991—, also bd. dirs.; chmn., CEO SC Power Devel., Inc., 1992—; bd. dirs. Stanley Cons., Inc., Muscatine. Bd. dirs. Goodwill Industries Ea. Iowa, 1987—, pres., 1992-94; mem. adv. bd. U. Iowa Coll. Engring., Ctrl. State U. Water Resources Ctr. Fellow ASCE, Am. Cons. Engring. Coun.; mem. NSPE, 33 Club (pres. 1987), Rotary. Presbyterian. Avocations: tennis, computers, music. Home: 1002 Estron St Iowa City IA 52246-4602 Office: Stanley Cons Inc 225 Iowa Ave Muscatine IA 52761-3730

THOMPSON, ALDEN LLOYD, biblical studies educator, author; b. Loma Linda, Calif., Sept. 9, 1943; s. George Alden and Lola Elizabeth (Lukens) T.; m. Wanda Diane Hoffman, June 8, 1965; children: Karin, Krista. BA, Walla Walla Coll., 1965; MA, Andrews U., 1966, BD, 1967; PhD, U. Edinburgh, Scotland, 1975. Ordained to ministry, Seventh-day Adventist Ch., 1971. Assoc. pastor local ch. Redlands, Calif., 1967-68; pastor local ch. Fontana, Calif., 1969-70; mem. staff Sch. Theology Walla Walla (Wash.) Coll., 1970—, prof. bibl. studies, 1990—, provost, 1986-90; exch. tchr. Marienhoehe Sem., Darmstadt, Germany, 1980-81. Author: Responsibility for Evil in the Theodicy of IV Ezra, 1977, Who's Afraid of the Old Testament God?, 1988, Inspiration: Hard Questions, Honest Answers, 1991; columnist: Signs of the Times, 1985-94, Gleaner, 1987-90, 92—. Office: Walla Walla Coll 204 S College Ave College Place WA 99324-1198

THOMPSON, ALMOSE ALPHONSE, lawyer, educator; b. Shawnee, Okla., Mar. 12, 1942; s. Almose Alphonse and Lucille (Marshall) T.; m. Delma Jean Jackson, Aug. 28, 1968; children: Gennie Markete, Almose Alphonse III. BS in History and Phys. Edn., UCLA, 1965, EdD, 1972; MS in Curriculum and Instrn., Calif. State U., Long Beach, 1970; JD, Vanderbilt U., 1988. Bar: Tenn; cert. tchr., Calif. Head edn. div., v.p. Curatron Systems, Inc., Inglewood, Calif.; ednl. specialist, cons. Martin L. King Hosp.-Charles Drew Med. Sch., L.A., 1976-78; dir. exptl. edn. program Calif. State U. Dominquez Hills, Carson, 1975-76; asst. prof. edn. Moorhead (Minn.) State U.; head Black studies dept. Portland (Oreg.) State U., 1972-75; assoc. dean students U. Calif., Santa Barbara, 1971-72; dir. Project Upward Bound Calif. State U., Long Beach, 1968-80; instr., tchr. L.A. City Sch. Dist., 1965-68; prof. adminstrn. Tenn. State U., Nashville, 1979—; ptnr. Thompson and Assocs., Nashville, 1989—; cons. Black Caucus of Tenn. Gen. Assembly, 1979—, Tenn. Office Minority Affairs, Nashville, 1979-88, Black Econ. Alliance Leaders, Nashville, 1990, Tenn. Black Leadership Roundtable, Nashville, 1989. Author: The Black Discovery of America Before Columbus, 1975, Black Leadership in Nashville, 1982, Student's Guide to Better Grades, 1983; syndicated columnist for Black newspapers; pub., mng. editor nat. jour. N.W. Jour. African and Black Am. Studies; contbr. articles to profl. jours. Candidate for Bd. Edn., Nashville, 1982; cons. Black Caucus of Tenn. Black Elected Ofcls., 1979—; polit. cons. to numerous candidates for pub. office. With USN, 1963-65. So. Edn. Found. fellow, 1982-84; Charles Stewart Mott Found. fellow, 1982-84. Mem. ABA, Tenn. Bar Assn., Nashville Bar Assn., Nat. Assn. Social and Behavioral Scientists, Nat. Curriculum and Instrn. Assn., Tenn. Polit. Sci. Assn., Phi Delta Kappa. Democrat. Baptist. Avocations: writing, spectator sports. Home: 3313 Calais Cir Antioch TN 37013-5513 Office: 3313 Calais Cir Nashville TN 37209-1500

THOMPSON, ANNA BLANCHE, educator; b. Ft. Worth, Oct. 8, 1914; d. George Lewis and Gula Gertrude (Cook) Turnbow; m. Jess Lee, May 27, 1939; children: Jess Lee II, Mary Ann Thompson Archbold. BA in Edn., Ariz. State U., Tempe, 1935; postgrad., U. Ariz., 1940, U. Hawaii, 1964, Pepperdine U., 1967. Tchr. Parke (Ariz.) Elem. Sch., 1935-40; tchr. music Parker High Sch., 1940-42; tchr. Scottsdale (Ariz.) Elem. Sch., 1948-71; tchr. U. Hawaii, Laie, 1971-72; tchr. U. Hawaii, 1972-79, ret., 1979. Mem. edn. bd. Phoenix Women's Club, 1983-84; pres. Ariz. Res. Officers Ladies, Phoenix, 1982-84, state pres., 1986-87; pres. Ladies of the Ribbon, Phoenix, 1987-90, Tempe Garden Club, 1987-88. Recipient Mus. plaque Phoenix Symphony Symphonette, 1982-83, Cert. of Appreciation, St. Luke's Hosp. Aux., 1985, Cert. of Appreciation, Mil. Order of World Wars, 1989. Mem. Ariz. Res. Officers Ladies (state sec. 1990—), Tri-City Angels of Ariz. (pres. 1984—), Collectors Club Am. (nat. pres. 1987—), Ikebana Internat., AAUW (historian Tempe chpt. 1987-90), Delta Kappa Gamma (pres. Phoenix chpt. 1974-76, 88-90, parliamentarian 1990—). Avocations: needlepoint, travel. Home: 533 E Fairmont Dr Tempe AZ 85282-3722

THOMPSON, ANNE ELISE, federal judge; b. Phila., July 8, 1934; d. Leroy Henry and Mary Elise (Jackson) Jenkins; m. William H. Thompson, June 19, 1965; children: William H., Sharon A. BA, Howard U., 1955, LLB, 1964; MA, Temple U., 1957. Bar: D.C. bar 1964, N.J. bar 1966. Staff atty. Office of Solicitor, Dept. Labor, Chgo., 1964-65; asst. dep. public defender Trenton, N.J., 1967-70; mcpl. prosecutor Lawrence Twp., Lawrenceville, N.J., 1970-72; mcpl. ct. judge Trenton, 1972-75; prosecutor Mercer County, Mercer County, Trenton, 1975-79; judge U.S. Dist. Ct. N.J., Trenton, 1979—, now chief judge; vice chmn. Mercer County Criminal Justice Planning Com., 1972; mem. com. criminal practice N.J. Supreme Ct., 1975-79, mem. com. mcpl. cts., 1972-75; v.p. N.J. County Prosecutors Assn., 1978-79; chmn. juvenile justice com. Nat. Dist. Attys. Assn., 1978-79. Del. Democratic Nat. Conv., 1972. Recipient Assn. Black Women Lawyers award, 1976, Disting. Service award Nat. Dist. Attys. Assn., 1979, Gene Carte Meml. award Am. Criminal Justice Assn., 1980, Outstanding Leadership award N.J. County Prosecutors Assn., 1980, John Mercer Langston Outstanding Alumnus award Howard U. Law Sch., 1981; also various service awards; certs. of appreciation. Mem. Am. Bar Assn., Fed. Bar Assn., N.J. Bar Assn., Mercer County Bar Assn. Democrat. Office: US District Court 343 US Courthouse 402 E State St Trenton NJ 08608-1507

THOMPSON, ANNE MARIE, newspaper publisher; b. Des Moines, Feb. 7, 1920; d. George Horace and Esther Mayer Sheely; m. J. Ross Thompson, July 31, 1949; children: Annette McCracken, James Ross. BA, U. Iowa, 1940; postgrad. U. Colo., 1971. Co-pub. Baca County Banner, Springfield, Colo., 1951-54, Rocky Ford (Colo.) Daily Gazette, 1954-82, pub., 1982—. Editor Toastmasters, 1983-94. Mem. Otero Jr. Coll. Coun., 1987-93, Colo. Ho. of Reps., 1957-61; Colo. presdl. elector, 1972; chmn. Colo. adv. com. SBA, 1979-81. Recipient Community Service award Rocky Ford C. of C., 1975; named Colo. Woman of Achievement in Journalism, 1959, Colo. Bus. Person of Yr., Future Bus. Leaders of Am., 1981; elected to Colo. Community Journalism Hall of Fame, 1981. Mem. Nat. Fedn. Press Women (dir. 1971-81), Nat. Newspaper Assn. (Emma C. McKinney award 1984), Colo. Press Assn. (dir. 1981-83, Golden Make-Up award 1991) , Colo. Press Women, PEO, Bus. and Profl. Women's Club. Republican. Methodist.

THOMPSON, ANNIE FIGUEROA, academic director, educator; b. Río Piedras, P.R., June 7, 1941; d. Antonio Figueroa-Colón and Ana Isabel Laugier; m. Donald P. Thompson, Jan. 23, 1972; 1 child, John Anthony. BA, Baylor U., 1962; MSLS, U. So. Calif., 1965; AMD, Fla. State U., 1978, PhD, 1980. Educator Mayan Sch., Guatemala City, Guatemala, 1962-63; cataloger libr. system U. P.R., Río Piedras, 1965-67, head music libr., 1967-81, assoc. prof. librarianship, 1981-85; dir. grad. sch. libr. info. sci. U. P.R., Río Piedras, 1986-93; prof. U. P.R., Río Piedras, 1986—. Author: An Annotated Bibliography About Music in Puerto Rico, 1975; co-author: Music and Dance in Puerto Rico from the Age of Columbus to Modern Times, An Annotated Bibliography, 1991; contbr. articles to profl. jours.; performed song recitals Inst. of P.R. Culture and U. P.R. Artist Series, 1974-78; soloist with P.R. Symphony Orch., San Juan, 1978; performed in opera, on radio and TV, San Juan, 1968-81;. con. P.R. Symphony Orch. League, San Juan, 1982-84; mem. pub. libr. adv. com. Adminstrn. for Devel. of Arts and Culture, P.R., 1982-84, Pub. Libr. Adv. Bd., 1989—. Recipient Lauro a la Instrucción Bibliotecaria Sociedad de Bibliotecarios de P.R., 1985, Lauro a la Bibliografía Puertorriqueña, 1993. Mem. AIA Minn. Episcopalian. Home: N-64 Acadia St Park Gardens Rio Piedras San Juan PR 00926 Office: Grad Sch Library & Info Sci U of PR PO Box 21906 Rio Piedras San Juan PR 00931-1906

THOMPSON, ANNIE LAURA, foreign language educator; b. Henderson, Tenn., July 8, 1937; d. Wesley Sylvester and Letha Irene (Jones) T.; m. Edward L. Patterson, June 7, 1980. BA, U. Ala., 1959; MA, Duke U., 1961; PhD, Tulane U., 1973. Instr. Spanish lang. U. Miss., Oxford, 1960-64; instr. Auburn (Ala.) U., 1964-66; teaching asst. Tulane U., New Orleans, 1966-70; prof. Spanish lang. Delgado C.C., New Orleans, 1970—; instr. Spanish for Physicians and Med. Persons Tulane U., La. State U. Med. Eye Ctr., Ochsner Clinic and Hosp. Author: Religious Elements in the Quijote, 1960, The Attempt of Spanish Intellectuals to Create a New Spain, 1930-36, 1973, The Generation of 1898: Intellectual Politicians; asst. editor The Crusader, 1961-64. Rep. candidate for gov. State of La., 1991, 95, for 1st Dist. U.S. Congress, 1992; alt. mem. La. Coastal Commn., 1984—; del. Women's State Rep. Conv., 1987, La. State Rep. Conv., 1990, 93; active Women for Better Edn., 1984-89, La. Coastal Adv. Coun., 1988, Pan Am. Commn., 1992-95; v.p. pub. rels. Alliance for Good Govt., 1990. Recipient Outstanding Tchr. award Delgado Coll. Student Govt. Assn., 1974; Woodoow Wilson fellow, 1959-60; NDEA fellow, 1968-69. Mem. AAUP, MLA (South Cen. and South Atlantic), Pachyderm Club, Women's Rep. Club, Phi Beta Kappa, Phi Alpha Theta, Sigma Delta Pi. Republican. Mem. Ch. of Christ. Home: PO Box 24399 New Orleans LA 70184-4399 Office: Delgado Coll Isaac Delgado Hall 113W-1 615 City Park Ave New Orleans LA 70119

THOMPSON, A(NSEL) FREDERICK, JR., environmental engineering and consulting company executive; b. Birmingham, Ala., Oct. 19, 1941; s. Ansel Frederick Sr. and Irene (Turner) T.; m. Susan Elizabeth Weston, Dec. 28, 1963; children: Ansel Frederick III, Jennifer Katherine, Melissa Susan. BSE, Pa. State U., 1963; MSCE, Calif. Inst. Tech., 1965, PhDCE, 1968; postgrad., U. Pa., 1989. Lic. profl. engr. Pa., 1970. Project engr. Roy F. Weston, Inc., West Chester, Pa., 1967-70, prin. engr., 1970-73, dept. mgr., 1973-75, v.p. engring. design, 1975-79, v.p. design and constrn. mgmt., 1979-80, v.p.

quality assurance and fin., 1980-87, exec. v.p., 1987-90, vice-chmn. 1990-91, chmn., 1991—; bd. dirs. PSG, Inc. Bd. dirs. S.E. chpt. ARC, 1994, University City Sci. Ctr.; bd. govs. Pa. Econ. League, Phila.; mem. Pa. State Great Valley Adv. Bd., 1992. Mem. ASCE (mem. corp. adv. bd. Civil Engring. Rsch. Found. 1989—), Newcomer Soc., Am. Acad. Environ. Engrs. (diplomate), Water Environ. Fedn., Am. Water Works Assn., Profl. Svcs. Mgmt. Assn., Sigma Xi. Avocations: tennis, photography, music, travel, reading. Office: Roy F Weston Inc Weston Way West Chester PA 19380

THOMPSON, ANTHONY RICHARD, electrical engineer, astronomer; b. Hull, Humberside, Eng., Apr. 7, 1931; came to U.S., 1957; s. George and Ada Mary (Laybourn) T.; m. Sheila Margaret Press, Oct. 12, 1963; 1 child, Sarah Louise. BSc in Physics with honors, U. Manchester, Eng., 1952, PhD, 1955. Engr. E.M.I. Electronics Ltd., Feltham, Eng., 1956-57; rsch. fellow Coll. Obs. Harvard U., Cambridge, Mass., 1957-62; sr. rsch. assoc. Radio Astronomy Inst. Stanford (Calif.) U., 1962-72; head electronics divsn., VLA and VLBA projects Nat. Radio Astronomy Obs., Charlottesville, Va., 1973-92, dep. head Ctrl. Electronics Lab., 1993—; vis. sr. rsch. fellow Owens Valley Radio Obs., Calif. Inst. Tech., Pasadena, 1966-72; mem. Com. on Radio Frequencies NAS, Washington, 1980-91; sec. Interunion Commn. on Frequency Allocations for Radio Astronomy and Space Sci., 1982-88, mem., 1991—; guest lectr. in radio astronomy Ukrainian Acad. Sci., 1988. Prin. author: (monograph) Interferometry and Synthesis in Radio Astronomy, 1986; contbr. articles to Astrophys. Jour., Astron. Jour., Proceedings of IEEE, Sci., Radiosci. Fellow IEEE; mem. Internat. Telecom. Union (radiocommunication sector, chmn. working group on radio astronomy U.S. Study group 7 1978—), Am. Astron. Soc., Internat. Astron. Union. Achievements include research in astronomy and contributions to system design of the VLA and VLB array; design of instruments: frequency coordination for radio astronomy. Office: Nat Radio Astronomy Obs 520 Edgemont Rd Charlottesville VA 22903

THOMPSON, ANTHONY WAYNE, metallurgist, educator, consultant; b. Burbank, Calif., Mar. 6, 1940; s. William Lyman and Mary Adelaide (Nisbet) T.; m. Mary Ruth Cummings, Aug. 24, 1963; children: Campbell Lyman, Michael Anthony. BS, Stanford U., 1962; MS, U. Wash., 1965; PhD, MIT, 1970. Research engr. Jet Propulsion Lab., Pasadena, Calif., 1962-63; mem. tech. staff Sandia Labs., Livermore, Calif., 1970-73, Rockwell Sci. Ctr., Thousand Oaks, Calif., 1973-77; assoc. prof. Carnegie Mellon U., Pitts., 1977-79, prof. 1980-94, dept. head, 1987-90; staff scientist Lawrence Berkeley Lab., Berkeley, Calif., 1994—; vis. scientist U. Cambridge, Eng., 1983, Risø, Denmark, 1987, U. Calif., 1991; cons. Sandia Labs., 1977—, GE, 1988—. Editor: Work Hardening, 1976, Metall. Transactions, 1983-88; co-editor: Hydrogen in Metals, 1974, Hydrogen Conf. Proc., 1976, 81, 89, 94; mem. editl. bd. Internat. Metals Revs., 1980-88; contbr. articles to profl. jours. Overseas fellow Churchill Coll. Cambridge U., 1982. Fellow Am. Soc. Metals; mem. AAAS, AIME, Sigma Xi. Democrat. Clubs: Sierra, Nat. Model R.R. Assn. Home: 2942 Linden Ave Berkeley CA 94705 Office: Lawrence Berkeley Lab Material Sci Divsn Berkeley CA 94720

THOMPSON, ARLENE RITA, nursing educator; b. Yakima, Wash., May 17, 1933; d. Paul James and Esther Margaret (Danroth) T. BS in Nursing, U. Wash., 1966, Masters in Nursing, 1970, postgrad., 1982—. Staff nurse Univ. Teaching Hosp., Seattle, 1966-69; mem. nursing faculty U. Wash. Sch. Nurses, Seattle, 1971-73; critical care nurse Virginia Mason Hosp., Seattle, 1973—; educator Seattle Pacific U. Sch. Nursing, 1981—; nurse legal cons. nursing edn., critical care nurse. Contbr. articles to profl. jours. USPHS grantee, 1969; nursing scholar Virginia Mason Hosp., 1965. Mem. Am. Assn. Critical Care Nurses (cert.), Am. Nurses Assn., Am. Heart Assn., Nat. League Nursing, Sigma Theta Tau, Alpha Tau Omega. Republican. Presbyterian. Avocations: sewing, swimming, jogging, bicycle riding, hiking. Home: 2320 W Newton St Seattle WA 98199-4115 Office: Seattle Pacific U 3307 3rd Ave W Seattle WA 98119-1997

THOMPSON, BARBARA STORCK, state official; b. McFarland, Wis., Oct. 15, 1924; d. John Casper and Marie Ann (Kassabaum) Storck; m. Glenn T. Thompson, July 1, 1944; children:—David C., James T. B.S., Wis. State U., 1956; M.S., U. Wis., 1959, Ph.D, 1969; L.H.D. (hon.), Carroll Coll., 1974. Tchr. pub. schs. West Dane County, Mt. Horeb, Wis., 1944-56; instr. Green County Tchrs. Coll., Monroe, Wis., 1956-57; coordinator curriculum Monroe Pub. Schs., 1957-60; instr. U. Wis., Platteville, 1960; supr. schs. Waukesha County Schs., Wis., 1960-63; supt. schs. Waukesha County Schs., 1963-65; prin. Fairview Elem. Schs., Brookfield, Wis., 1962-64; adminstrv. cons. Wis. Dept. Pub. Instrn., Madison, 1964-72; state coordinator Wis. Dept. Pub. Instrn., 1971-72; instr. U. Wis., Madison and Green Bay, 1972; supt. pub. instrn. Madison State of Wis., 1973-81; mem. Wis. State Bd. Vocat. Edn., 1973-81, Wis. Edn. Comm. Bd. 1973-81. Author: A Candid Discussion of Critical Issues, 1975; Mem. editorial bd.: The Education Digest, 1975—; Contbr. articles to profl. jours. Mem. White House Conf. Children, 1970, Gov.'s Com. State Conf. Children and Youth, 1969-70, Manpower Council, 1973-81; bd. dirs. Vocational, Tech. and Adult Edn., 1973-81, Ednl. Communications, 1973-81, Higher Edn. Aids, 1973-81, Agy. Instructional TV, 1975-81; mem. nat. panel on SAT score decline; bd. regents U. Wis., 1973-81. Recipient State Conservation award Madison Lions Club, 1996; Waukesha Freeman award, 1961. Mem. Nat. Council Administrv. Women in Edn. (named Woman of Year 1974), Nat. Council State Cons. in Elementary Edn. (pres. 1974-75), Wis. Assn. Sch. Dist. Adminstrs., Assn. Supervision and Curriculum Devel., Wis. Assn. Supervision and Curriculum Devel., Southwestern Wis. Assn. Supervision and Curriculum Devel., Southeastern Wis. Assn. Supervision and Curriculum Devel. (mem. exec. council 1972-73), Dept. Elementary Sch. Prins., Wis. Elementary Sch. Prins. Assn., NEA, Wis. Edn. Assn. (pres. local chpt. 1970-71); life mem. So. Wis. Edn. Assn., Wis. Ednl. Research Assn., Dept. Elementary-Kindergarten-Nursery Edn., Assn. Childhood Edn. Internat., Assn. Childhood Edn., Council Chief State Sch. Officers, Edn. Commn. of States, Nat. Council State Cons. in Elementary Edn. (pres. 1974-75), Am. Assn. Sch. Dist. Adminstrs. (chmn. policy com. 1963-81), Delta Kappa Gamma. Office: 204 3rd St W Bradenton FL 34205-8850

THOMPSON, BASIL F., ballet master; b. Newcastle-on-Tyne, Eng., 1937; came to U.S., 1958; Grad., Royal Acad. Dance; studies with, David Lichine, Tania Riabouchinska; student, Sch. Classical. Ballet, 1958-60. Dancer Covent Garden Opera Co., Sadler Wells Opera Co., London, 1954-55, Royal Ballet Eng., London, 1955-58; instr. ballet and character Eugene Loring Sch. Ballet, L.A., 1958-60, Al Gilber Sch. Ballet, L.A., 1958-60; instr. ballet Michael Panaieff Sch. Ballet, L.A., 1958-60; soloist Am. Ballet Theatre, N.Y.C., 1960-67; ballet master Joffrey Ballet Co., N.Y.C., 1967-79; ballet master, choreographer N.J. Ballet Co., West Orange, 1979-80; mem. faculty ballet and character N.J. Ballet Sch., Morristown/West Orange, 1979-80; ballet master Milw. Ballet, 1981-86, also artistic head; currently ballet master Pa. and Milw. Ballet; guest ballet instr. Internat. Ballet Inst., Aix-en-Provence, France, 1980; guest instr. character Am. Ballet Co. Sch., 1981. Roles include (prin.) Billy the Kid, Sleeping Beauty, Graduation Ball, La Sylphide, Moon Reindeer, Peter and The Wolf, Three Cornered Hat, others, (soloist) Rodeo, Fall River Legend, Fire Bird, Coppelia, Swan Lake, Cinderella, La Boutique Fantastic, Undertow, others (opera) Aida; guest appearances include for Dame Margo Fontayne Royal Acad. Gala, Pres. John F. Kennedy, Pres. Lyndon B. Johnson, L.A. Civic Light Opera, Michael Panaieff Ballet Theatre; TV appearances include Bell Telephone Hour Spectacular prodn. Graduation Ball, NBC prodn. Sleeping Beauty and Cinderella, Broadway prodns. On a Clear Day You Can See Forever, Tavarich, Happiest Girl in the World; choreographer La Traviata. Office: Milw Ballet 504 W National Ave Milwaukee WI 53204-1746

THOMPSON, BENNIE, professional football player. Student, Grambling State. Safety Kansas City Chiefs, Mo., 1989-94; with Cleveland Browns, 1994—. Played in Pro Bowl, 1991. Office: Cleveland Browns 80 First Ave Berea OH 44017-0679*

THOMPSON, BENNIE G., congressman; b. Bolton, Miss. BA Polit. Sci., Tougaloo Coll.; MS Ednl. Adminstrn., Jackson State U., Miss.; grad., U. So. Miss. Alderman Bolton, Miss., 1970-74, mayor, 1979-80; supr. dist. 2 Hinds County Bd., Miss., 1980-93; mem. 103d-104th U.S. Congress from 2d dist. Miss., 1993—; mem. agr. com., 1993—; mem. Small Bus. Com. Presdl. appointee Nat. Coun. Health Planning and Devel. Bd. trustees Tougaloo Coll.; bd. dirs. So. Regional Coun., Housing Assistance Coun. Mem. Miss.

WHO'S WHO IN AMERICA 4163 THOMPSON

Assn. Black Mayors (founder), Miss. Assn. Black Suprs. Democrat. Original plaintiff in 1975 Ayers case. Office: 1408 Longworth House Office Bl Washington DC 20515*

THOMPSON, BERT ALLEN, retired librarian; b. Bloomington, Ind., Dec. 13, 1930; s. James Albert and Dorothy Fern (Myers) T.; m. Martha Ellen Palmer; children—John Carter II, Anne Palmer, Paul Julian. B.S., Ball State Tchrs. Coll., 1953; A.M., Ind. U., 1960; certificate in archival adm., U. Denver, 1967. Tchr., librarian Ind. pub. schs., 1953-55; reference asst. Indpls. Pub. Library, 1956-59; head reference service Mankato (Minn.) State Coll., 1959-61; instr. Grad. Library Sch., No. Ill. U., Dekalb, 1961-63; dir. libraries, asst. prof. ednl. media Kearney (Nebr.) State Coll., 1963-69; dir. library service Ill. Benedictine Coll. Lisle, Ill., 1969-90, spl. collections librarian, 1990-92. Mem. exec. bd. Ill. regional Library Council, 1976-79. Recipient 1st Melvin R. George LIBRAS award for Outstanding Svc. to Libr. Cooperation, 1993. Mem. Ill. (de Lafayette Reid Research scholar 1976), Catholic Library Assn. (treas. Ill. chpt. 1973-75, nat. sec.-treas. coll./univ. sect. 1981-85, nat. bd. dirs. 1987-93), Nebr. Library Assn, chmn. coll. and univ. sect. 1963-64). Episcopalian. Home: 1011 N Cross St Wheaton IL 60187-3587

THOMPSON, BERTHA BOYA, retired educator; b. New Castle, Pa., Jan. 31, 1917; d. Frank L. and Kathryn Belle (Park) Boya; m. John L. Thompson, Mar. 27, 1942; children: Kay Lynn Thompson Koolage, Scott McClain. BS in Elem. & Secondary Edn., Slippery Rock State Coll., 1940; MA in Geography and History, Miami U., 1954; EdD, Ind. U. 1961. Cert. elem. and secondary edn. tchr. Elem. tchr., reading specialist New Castle (Pa.) Sch. System, 1940-45; tchr., chmn. social studies Talawanda Sch. System, Oxford, Ohio, 1954-63; assoc. prof. psychology and geography, chair edn. dept. Western Coll. for Women, Oxford, 1963-74; assoc. prof. edn., reading clinic Miami U., Oxford, 1974-78, prof. emeritus, 1978—; pvt. antique dealer, appraiser Oxford, 1978—. Contbr. articles to profl. jours. Mem. folk art com. Miami U. Art Mus., Oxford, 1974-76; mem. adv. com. Smith libr., Oxford Pub. Libr., 1978-81. Mem. AAUP, Nat. Coun. Geographic Edn. (exec. bd. dirs. 1966-69), Nat. Soc. for Study Edn., Assn. Am. Geographers, Soc. Women Geographers, Nat. Coun. for the Social Studies, Pi Lambda Theta, Zeta Tau Alpha, Pi Gamma Mu, Gamma Theta Upsilon, Kappa Delta Pi. Avocations: antique collecting, reading, travel, tennis. Home: 6073 Contreras Rd Oxford OH 45056-9708

THOMPSON, BJORN J., food products company executive, mechanical engineer; b. Madison, Wis., June 9, 1934; s. Frederick and Marie (Olsen) T.; m. Gail Michele Olwell, July 27, 1957; children—Kai, Kristin, Kirk. B.S. in Mech. Engring., U. Wis., 1957; A.M.P., Harvard U., 1983. Registered profl. engr., Wis. Plant layout and materials handling supr. Madison plant OM Foods Corp., Wis., 1960-66; supr. Davenport plant Oscar Mayer Foods Corp., Iowa, 1966-67; corp. methods and planning coordinator Oscar Mayer Foods Corp., Madison, 1967-71; corp. facilities planning mgr., 1971-74, gen. mgr. facilities planning mgr., 1974-78, v.p. engring. devel., 1978-84; v.p. fresh meat ops. Oscar Mayer Foods Corp., 1984—, group v.p. tech. services, 1985—, sr. v.p. tech. services, 1987—, sr. v.p. strategic planning and bus. devel., 1988—, sr. v.p. ops., 1990-91, exec. v.p., 1991—. Trustee bd. Village of Maple Bluff, Wis., 1979-83. Served to 1st C.E., U.S. Army, 1957-59. Recipient Disting. Service citation U. Wis. Madison, 1984. Mem. Am. Material Handling Soc. (pres. 1964-65, bd. dirs. 1965-66), Inst. Indsl. Engrs. Clubs: Maple Bluff Country (bd. dirs. 1981-83, v.p. 1983—, pres. 1984), Madison. Office: Oscar Mayer Foods Corp PO Box 7188 Madison WI 53707-7188

THOMPSON, BONNIE RANSA, secondary educator, chemistry educator; b. Charleroi, Pa., Oct. 12, 1940; d. William Edward and Edith Lorraine Ransa; m. Joel E. Thompson, June 15, 1963 (div. Dec. 1980). BA, Seton Hill Coll., Greensburg, Pa., 1963; MEd, Ariz. State U., 1979, postgrad. Cert. in secondary chemistry, anthropology, and gifted edn., Ariz. Tchr. chemistry Scotch Plains (N.J.)-Fanwood High Sch., 1963-74; tchr. chemistry and anthropology Tolleson (Ariz.) Union High Sch., 1974-93; tchr. chemistry Westview High Sch., Phoenix, 1992—; instr. anthropology and archaeology Rio Salado C.C., Sun City, Ariz., 1981-88; instr. chemistry Glendale (Ariz.) C.C., 1988—; pres. Brite Ednl. Programs, Ltd., Phoenix, 1988-91; mem. Ariz. Reagent and Task Force on Lab. Sci., Tempe, 1987; tchr., cons. Pitts. SuperComputer Project, Tolleson, 1992—; amb. People to People Sci. Exchange, Russia, Australia, New Zealand, summer 1989-92; rsch partnership High Sch./Coll. Flinn Found. Rsch. Corp., 1988-91. Editor: Starting at Ground Zero, 1988, others; editor: Energy Education Kits, 1985; contbr. articles to mags. V.p Villa Casitas Townhouse Assn., Phoenix, 1991-92, pres., 1993—; vol. Perot Org. for Pres., Phoenix, 1992. Woodrow Wilson fellow, 1983; recipient Golden Bell award Ariz. Sch. Bd. Assn., 1985, 88; recipient Growth Incentives for Tchrs. award GTE Corp., 1987, Tech. Scholar award Tandy Corp., 1990; named Outstanding High Sch. Sci. Tchr. Ariz. Coun. for Engring. and Scientific Assocs., 1993. Mem. NEA, Ariz. Edn. Assn., Tolleson Edn. Assn. (pres. 1981-83), Nat. Sci. Tchrs. Assn., Ariz. Sci. Tchrs. Assn., Ariz. Alliance for Math., Sci. and Tech., S.W. Archeol. Team. Avocations: reading, touring motorcycles. Office: Tolleson Union HS Dist 9419 W Van Buren St Tolleson AZ 85353-2804

THOMPSON, BRIAN JOHN, university administrator, optics educator; b. Glossop, Eng., June 10, 1932; came to U.S., 1962; s. Alexander William and Edna May (Gould) T.; m. Joyce Emily Cheshire, Mar. 31, 1956; children: Karen Joyce, Andrew Derrick. B of Sci. Tech., U. Manchester, Eng., 1955, PhD, 1959. Demonstrator in physics Dept. Tech., U. Manchester, 1955-56, asst. lectr., 1957-59; lectr. physics U. Leeds, Eng., 1959-62; sr. physicist Tech. Optics, Inc., Burlington, Mass., 1963-65, dir. dept. optics, 1966-67, mgr. tech. ops., Western tech. dir. Beckman & Whitley div., 1967-68; prof. Inst. Optics U. Rochester, N.Y., 1968—, dir. Inst. Optics, 1968-75, dean Coll. Engring. and Applied Scis., 1975-84, Wm. F. May prof. engring., 1982-85, provost, 1984-94, provost emeritus, disting. univ. prof., 1994—, Disting. univ. prof., 1994—. Internat. editor: Optics and Laser Tech., 1969—; assoc. editor: Optical Engineering, 1972-76, Optics Comm., 1978-86; Am. editor: Optica Acta, 1981-85; editor: Optical Engineering Series, vol. 1-42, 1980—; mem. editl. adv. bd. Laser Focus, 1970—, Particle Characterization, 1984—; Optics and Lasers in Engring., 1985, Milestone Service of Selection Papers Vols. 1-108, 1984—, Optical Engring., 1991—; chmn. adv. bd. Marquis Who's Who Directory Optical Scientists and Engrs., 1983-86; contbr. articles to profl. jours. Served with Brit. Army, 1950-52. Fellow Optical Soc. Am. (bd. dirs. 1969-72, exec. com. 1970-73, assoc. editor jour. 1966-77), Inst. Physics and Phys. Soc. (Gt. Britain 1955), Soc. Photo-Optical Instrumentation Engrs. (pres. 1974, 75-76, gen. editor series of selected papers 1983—, editor Optical Engring. jour. 1991—, Pres.'s award 1961, Pezzuto award 1978, Kingslake medal 1978, Gold medal 1986); mem. Am. Phys. Soc., AAAS. Home and Office: 692 Mt Hope Ave Rochester NY 14620

THOMPSON, BRUCE EDWARD, JR., brokerage house executive, former government official; b. Cleve., June 5, 1949; s. Bruce Edward and Mary Ruth (Miller) T.; m. Kathleen Ann Vaughn, May 27, 1972; children: Lesley, Bret. B.S.B.A. in Fin., Georgetown U., 1971. Sr. analyst Govt. Research Corp., Washington, 1971-74; legis. asst. U.S. Sen. William V. Roth Jr., 1974-81; dep. asst. sec. legis. affairs U.S Treasury Dept., 1981-83, asst. sec. bus. and consumer affairs, 1983-84, asst. sec. legis. affairs, 1984-86; v.p. dir. govt. rels. Merrill Lynch & Co., Inc., 1986—. Staff dir. fiscal and monetary affairs subcom. Republican Platform Com., 1980; adviser Pres. Reagan's Tax Policy Task Force; asst. Pres. Reagan's Transition Hqrs., 1980. Recipient Alexander Hamilton award, 1986. Roman Catholic. Office: Merrill Lynch & Co Inc 3000 K St NW Ste 620 Washington DC 20007-5109

THOMPSON, CAROL LEWIS, editor; b. N.Y.C., Dec. 26, 1918; d. Jasper Robert and Freda (Rafalsky) Lewis; m. Elbert Paul Thompson, July 4, 1942; children: Timothy Lewis, Ellen, John, Abigail. A.B. Wellesley Coll., 1940; M.A., Mt. Holyoke Coll., 1942. Asst. editor Current History, 1943, asso. editor, 1943-55, editor, 1955-91, editorial cons., 1991—; editor Ency. of Developing Nations; asso. editor Forum mag., 1945-49; contbr. to Ency. Brit., World Book Ency. Mem. Am. Hist. Assn., Nat. Council Social Studies, Phi Beta Kappa. Mem. Soc. of Friends. Home and Office: Apt J112 Pennswood Village Newtown PA 18940

THOMPSON, CAROLINE WARNER, film director, screenwriter; b. Washington, Apr. 23, 1956; d. Thomas Carlton Jr. and Bettie Marshall (Warner) T.; m. Alfred Henry Bromell, Aug. 28, 1982 (div. 1985). BA summa cum laude, Amherst Coll., 1978. Author: First Born, 1983; screenwriter: (films) Edward Scissorhands, 1990, The Addams Family, 1991, Homeward Bound: The Incredible Journey, 1993, The Secret Garden, 1993, Tim Burton's The Nightmare Before Christmas, 1993; screenwriter, dir.: Black Beauty, 1994. Mem. Phi Beta Kappa. Avocation: horseback riding. Office: William Morris Agency Inc 151 S El Camino Dr Beverly Hills CA 90212-2775*

THOMPSON, CARSON R., retail, manufacturing company executive; b. Wilson, Okla., Feb. 10, 1939; s. Silas and Della (Woods) T.; m. Charlotte Arwine, Dec. 26, 1959; children—Shelley Elaine, Susan Denise. B.S., Tex. Wesleyan U., 1962, D Bus. and Fin. (hon.). Leather buyer, mdse. mgr. Tandy Leather Co., Ft. Worth, 1970-74, 74-77; pres. Tex Tan Welhausen Co., Yoakum, Tex., 1978; v.p. Tandy Brands Corp., Fort Worth, 1981—, chmn., CEO, 1982—; chmn. bd. Bombay Co., Inc. (formerly Tandy Brands, Inc.); chmn. bd., pres., CEO CRT Group, Inc., 1991—. Home: 1801 Sanguinet Fort Worth TX 76107 Office: 2501 Avenue J Ste 110 Arlington TX 76006-6182

THOMPSON, CHARLES EDWARD, electronics company executive; b. Seattle, July 30, 1929; s. Edward Oliver and Mae (Green) T.; m. Jean Thompson (div. 1974); children: Lynn, David; m. Wanda Laverne Wallace, Nov. 15, 1974; children: Richard, Russell, Steven. BS in Math., U. Wash., 1951. With software devel. dept. Hanford div. GE, Richland, Wash., 1951-61; product planning mgr. computer div. Hanford div. GE, Phoenix, 1961-64, div. mktg. mgr., 1965-69; dir. mgmt. info. systems Motorola Semicondr. Prodn. Sector, Phoenix, 1969-75, dir. mktg., 1975-79, v.p., dir. worldwide mktg., 1980—. Bd. dirs. Mesa (Ariz.) Luth. Hosp., 1979-81. Mem. Phoenix C. of C., Phi Beta Kappa, Mesa Country Club, White Mountain Country Club (Pinetop, Ariz.). Home: 3750 E Minton Pl Mesa AZ 85215-1700 Office: Motorola Semicondr 56th St Thomas Ave Phoenix AZ 85008

THOMPSON, CHARLES EDWIN, import consultant and manufacturer; b. Chgo., July 1, 1938; s. J. Edwin and H. Loraine (Jirasek) T. BS in Bus., Loyola U. Chgo., 1960, postgrad., 1968; postgrad., Northwestern U., 1961-62. Sales agt. J. Hudson & Co., Birmingham, Eng., 1968—; pres. Thompson Corp., Oak Park, Ill., 1977—; N.A. sales agt. Hiatt & Co., Birmingham, Eng., 1986—; pres. Hiatt-Thompson Corp., Bedford Park, Ill., 1988—; v.p. Refast Systems Corp., Palatine, Ill., 1988—; bd. dirs. Mktg. Matters Inc., Elk Grove Village, Ill.; pres. PowerTalon Ltd., Oak Park, Ill.; chmn., pres. SP&B Corp. Inventor type of handcuffs, handcuff key, handcuff cover. 1st lt. U.S. Army, 1961-63. Mem. Fraternal Order Police (hon.). Avocations: home renovations, boating. Office: 945 Garfield St Oak Park IL 60304-1848

THOMPSON, CHARLES KERRY, company executive; b. Chgo., Sept. 11, 1943; s. Charles Edward and Rose Elizabeth (Peacock) T.; children: Charles Edward, Tiffany Shaffer, Rebecca Lynn. Student, Parsons Coll., 1961-62. Dept. mgr. Montgomery Ward, Chgo., 1962-65; gen. mgr. Jackie's Smartwear, Inc., Niles, Ill., 1965-76; pres. Am. Woman, Inc., Richardson, Tex., 1976-79; zone mgr. The Southland Corp., Dallas, 1979-86; pres. Printelligence Inc. (formerly Graphic Telesis, Inc.), Dallas, 1986—; pres. Charles K. Thompson Mktg. and Promotional Cons., NeoMail, Inc. Contbr. articles to profl. jours. Chmn. Muscular Dystrophy, Southland, N. Tex., 1982-86, March of Dimes, 1982-86. Mem. Intertel, Mensa, Jaguar Club (pres. 1972-74). Republican. Avocations: photography, cooking, hunting, cabinetry, furniture refinishing. Home and Office: 4067 Beltway 126 Dallas TX 75244

THOMPSON, CHARLES KEVIN, architect, lighting designer; b. Cleborne, Tex., Feb. 15, 1958; s. Royce Elwood and Mary Nette (Farrington) T.; m. Marie Annette Weaver, July 2, 1976 (div. Sept. 1985); 1 child, Jennifer Marie. BArch, U. Tex., Austin, 1981. Registered architect, Tex.; lic. real estate broker, Tex. Engr., designer Colwell & Nichols, Austin, 1977-80; prin. EM, Inc., Austin, 1980-85; prin., owner CKTA/Lights, Austin, 1985—; lectr. U. Tex., Austin, 1987, Austin Women in Architecture, 1987. Recipient Cert. of Merit, Henry Adams Fund, U. Tex., Austin, 1981. Mem. AIA (chmn. code com. Austin chpt. 1986), Tex. Soc. Architects, AUstin Women in Architecture (hon.). Republican. Baptist. Avocations: photography, camping.

THOMPSON, CHARLES MURRAY, lawyer; b. Childress, Tex., Oct. 13, 1942; s. Walter Lee and Lois S. (Sheehan) T.; m. Charlotte Ann McKay, June 13, 1970; children: Murray McKay, McLean Ann. BS with honors, Colo. State U., 1965; JD cum laude, U. S.D., 1969. Bar: S.D. 1969, U.S. Dist. Ct. S.D. 1969, U.S. Ct. Claims 1989, U.S. Ct. Appeals (8th cir.) 1972, U.S. Supreme Ct. 1973. Prtnr. May, Adam, Gerdes & Thompson, Pierre, S.D., 1969—; speaker at trial lawyer and state bar seminars; bd. dirs. Bank West, Pierre, S.D. Editor S.D. Law Rev., 1969. Pres. S.D. Council Sch. Attys., 1984-86. Fellow Am. Bar Found. (chmn. 1991-92, bd. dirs. 1989-92), Internat. Acad. Trial Lawyers, Am. Coll. Trial Lawyers; mem. ABA (ho. of dels. 1978—, bd. govs. 1983-86), State Bar S.D. (pres. young lawyers sect. 1974-75, pres. 1986-87), S.D. Bar Found. (pres. 1991), Assn. Trial Lawyers Am., Am. Bd. Trial Advs., Am. Counsel Assn., S.D. Trial Lawyers Assn. (pres. 1980-81), Jackrabbit Bar Assn. (chancellor 1981-82), Am. Judicature Soc. (bd. dirs. 1981-85), Nat. Conf. of Bar Pres.'s (exec. coun. 1986-94, pres. 1992-93), Am. Bar Endowment (bd. dirs. 1991—), Kiwanis (pres. local club 1977). Democrat. Avocations: flying, sailing, ranching. Home and Office: PO Box 160 Pierre SD 57501-0160

THOMPSON, CHESTER FRANKLIN, graphic arts and advertising executive; b. Washington, June 2, 1931; m. Ann L. Butler, Feb. 3, 1955; children—Stephen, Glenn. Pres. C.F. Thompson Group, Inc., Windsor, Conn., 1955—; pres. Thompson Assocs., Inc., Frank Thompson Assocs., Inc., both graphic arts cos.

THOMPSON, CLAUDE M., finance officer, pharmacy consultant; b. Maysville, Ga., Apr. 19, 1921; s. William Berry and Mary L. Indiana (Buffington) T.; m. Reba Watkins, May 5, 1946; children: Claudia, Cathy, David, Billy, Dickie. Student in bus. adminstrn., U. Houston, 1942; BS in Pharmacy, U. Ga., 1948. Registered pharmacist; cert. real estate broker, finance officer. Clin. coord. Hoffman-LaRoche, Inc., Atlanta, 1951-59; pres., owner Thompson's Pharmacy, Inc., Fayetteville and Peachtree, Ga., 1959-67; sales mgr. The Realty Group, Inc., Atlanta, 1970-71; v.p. The Howell-Thompson Inc, Atlanta, 1971-87; pres. First Madison Fin., Inc., Peachtree City, Ga., 1988—; cons. pharmacist Pharmacies, Inc., Atlanta, 1988-93; active United Mortgage Investment Corp. With USN, 1942-46, Korea. Mem. Internat. Alliance of Fin. Counselors, Ga. Pharm. Assn., Ga. Bd. Realtors, Elks, Flat Creek Country Club. Republican. Presbyterian. Avocations: golf, reading, writing. Office: First Madison Fin Inc 306 Willow Rd Ste 2306 Peachtree City GA 30269-1639

THOMPSON, CLEON F., JR., university administrator. BS in Biology, N.C. Cen. U., 1956, MS in Biology, 1958; PhD in Edn. Adminstrn., Duke U., 1977. Vice-pres. student services and spl. programs U. N.C., to 1985; chancellor Winston-Salem State U., N.C., 1985—. Office: Winston Salem State U Office of Chancellor Winston Salem NC 27110

THOMPSON, CLIFF F., lawyer, educator; b. Kansas City, Mo., Aug. 15, 1934; s. James Frederick and Grace Caroline (Wiese) T.; m. Judith Anne Phillips, June 23, 1957; children: James Frederick, Laura Marie, John Phillips, Hannah Caroline. AB magna cum laude, Harvard U., 1956, JD, 1960; MA (Rhodes scholar), Oxford (Eng.) U., 1962. Bar: Kans. 1960, U.S. Dist. Ct. (we. dist.) Wis. 1984. Asst. program officer Near East and Africa program Ford Found., N.Y.C., 1960-61; law lectr. dir. Sudan Law Project, U. Khartoum, Sudan, 1961-65; assoc. dir., co-founder Africa Law Ctr., Columbia U., 1965-66; co-founder, sr. lectr. law U. Zambia, 1966-68; dean, prof. law Haile Selassie I U., Ethiopia, 1969-73; prof. law So. Meth. U., Dallas, 1973-77; prof. law, dean Law Sch., U. Hawaii, 1977-78, Coll. Law, U. Idaho, 1978-83; dean U. Wis. Law Sch., Madison, 1983-90, prof. law, 1983—; dir. African studies program U. Wis., 1992-93; legal edn. adv. Govt. of Indonesia, 1993—; cons. legal edn. Ethiopia, Sudan, Uganda, Tanzania, Kenya, Zambia, Zimbabwe. Author: Land Law of the Sudan, 3 vols., 2d edit, 1979; founder Zambia Law Reports, 1969, African Law Digest, 1965; contbr. articles to law jours. Bd. dirs. Hawaii Legal Aid, 1977-78, Idaho

Law Found., 1978-83, Four Lakes Coun. Boy Scouts Am., 1984-93; chmn. screening com. Fulbright Law Award, Washington, 1988-90, 92. Fulbright Disting.Prof. award to Africa, 1983; hon. vis. scholar Inst. Advanced Legal Studies and Sch. Oriental and African Studies, U. London, 1990-91. Fellow, Explorers Club; mem. ABA, Rotary, Signet Soc., Phi Beta Kappa, Phi Kappa Phi. Democrat. Methodist. Avocations: reading, tennis, walking. Home: 4133 Nakoma Rd Madison WI 53711-3018 Office: U Wis Law Sch 975 Bascom Mall Madison WI 53706-1399

THOMPSON, CLIFTON C., chemistry educator, university administrator; b. Franklin, Tenn., Aug. 16, 1939; s. Clifton C. and Ruby M. (Moore) T.; m. Sarah Ellen Gaunt, Dec. 1, 1978; children: Brenda Kay, Victoria Lea. B.S., Middle Tenn. State U., 1961; Ph.D., U. Miss., 1964. Asst. prof. Rutgers U., New Brunswick, N.J., 1965, Marshall U., Huntington, W.Va., 1965-66; assoc. prof. Middle Tenn. State U., Murfreesboro, 1966-68, Memphis State U., 1968-74; prof. chemistry, dept. head, dean Coll. Sci. and Math., dir. Ctr. for Sci. Rsch., assoc. v.p. for grad. studies and rsch. S.W. Mo. State U., Springfield, 1974—; research assoc. U. Tex., Austin, 1964-65; research Oak Ridge Nat. Lab., 1968; cons. Mid-South Research Assocs., Memphis, 1969-71; mem. med. tech. rev. com. Nat. Accrediting Agy. for Clin. Lab. Sci., Chgo., 1974-80. Author: Ultraviolet-Visible Absorption Spectroscopy, 1974. Mem. health care com. Springfield C. of C., 1978-79, mem. econ. devel. com., 1983-89; bd. dirs. United Hebrew Congregation, Springfield, 1983-86, United Hebrew Found., Inc., 1994—. NSF fellow, 1961-64; Sigma Xi grantee-in-aide, 1970; NSF sr. fgn. scientist grantee, 1971; NSF coop-coll. sch. sci. grantee, 1972; Higher Edn. Applied Projects grantee, 1987-90. Mem. Am. Chem. Soc., Royal Soc. Chemistry, AAAS, Sigma Xi, Phi Kappa Phi. Jewish. Office: SW Mo State U 901 S National Ave Springfield MO 65804-0027

THOMPSON, CRAIG SNOVER, corporate communications executive; b. Bklyn., May 24, 1932; s. Craig F. and Edith (Williams) T.; m. Masae Sugizaki, Feb. 21, 1957; children: Lee Anne, Jane Laura. Grad., Valley Forge Mil. Acad., 1951; B.A., Johns Hopkins U., 1954. Newspaper and radio reporter Easton (Pa.) Express, 1954-55, 57-59, Wall St. Jour., 1959-60; account exec. Moore, Meldrum & Assocs., 1960; mgr. pub. relations Cen. Nat. Bank of Cleve., 1961-62; account exec. Edward Howard & Co., Cleve., 1962-67; v.p Edward Howard & Co., 1967-69, sr. v.p., 1969-71; dir. pub. relations White Motor Corp., Cleve., 1971-76; v.p. pub. relations No. Telecom Inc., Nashville, 1976-77, White Motor Corp., Farmington Hills, Mich., 1977-80; v.p. corp. communications White Motor Corp., 1980-81; dir. exec. communications Rockwell Internat. Corp., Pitts., 1981-86, El Segundo, Calif., 1986-91, Seal Beach, Calif., 1992—. Bd. dirs. Shaker Lakes Regional Nature Center, 1970-73. Served to 1st lt, inf. U.S. Army, 1955-57. Mem. Pub. Rels. Soc. Am. (accredited), Alumni Assn. Valley Forge Mil. Acad. (bd. dirs. 1988-94). Office: Rockwell Internat Corp 2201 Seal Beach Blvd Seal Beach CA 90740-5603

THOMPSON, CURTIS BROOKS, manufacturing company executive; b. Conway, Ark., Feb. 8, 1930; s. Curtis Barnabus and Clara Brooks (Terry) T.; m. Sally Talbert, Apr. 12, 1952; children—Cheryl, Nan, Gary. B.S.E.E., Purdue U., 1951, M.S.E.E., 1952. With Honeywell Inc., Mpls., 1952—; v.p.-ops. process control div. Honeywell Inc., Fort Washington, Pa., 1968-72; v.p. and gen. mgr. test instruments div. Honeywell Inc., Denver, 1972-76; v.p. corp. devel. Honeywell Inc., Mpls., 1976-79; v.p. indsl. products group Honeywell Inc., 1979-82, sr. corp. v.p., 1983-85, group v.p. components, 1986-88, sr. v.p. indsl., 1989—. Recipient Disting. Engring. Alumnus award Purdue U., 1981. Mem. IEEE, Instrument Soc. Am. Home: 10085 Edgecombe Pl NE Bainbridge Is WA 98110-4333 Office: Honeywell Inc 4800 E Dry Creek Rd # 223 Littleton CO 80122-3701

THOMPSON, DALE WILLARD, JR., career officer; b. Oklahoma City, Feb. 2, 1938; s. Dale William and Virginia Lee (Crosby) T.; m. Cheryl Lea Stokes, June 8, 1960; children: Dale Willard III, Stacey Ann Grosvenor. BS, USAF Acad., 1960; MPA, Auburn U., 1976. Commd. 2d lt. USAF, 1960, advanced through grades to maj. gen., 1989; F-11 pilot 29th Tactical Fighter Wing, Upper Heyford Air Base, Eng., 1971-75; dep. comdr. ops. 20th Tactical Fighter Wing, Upper Heyford Air Base, Eng., 1979-80, comdr., vice comdr., 1981-86; student Air War Coll., Maxwell AFB, Ala., 1975-76; chief support div. J-3, Joint Chiefs of Staff, Pentagon, Washington, 1976-79; dir. fighter ops. Hdqrs. U.S. Air Forces in Europe, Ramstein Air Base, Fed. Republic Germany, 1980-81; vice comdr. Ogden Air Logistics Ctr., Hill AFB, Utah, 1986-87, comdr., 1990—; chief of staff Hdqrs. Air Force Logistics Command, Wright-Patterson AFB, Ohio, 1987-90. Decorated D.S.M., Legion of Merit, D.F.C with three oak leaf clusters, Def. D.S.M. Mem. Air Force Assn., Rotary (Ogden club). Avocations: skiing, golf. Home: 419 Johnson Dr Dayton OH 45433-1128 Office: USAF Ogden Aflc Hill Air Force UT 84056

THOMPSON, DAVID ALFRED, industrial engineer; b. Chgo., Sept. 9, 1929; s. Clifford James and Christobel Eliza (Sawin) T.; children: Nancy, Brooke, Lynda, Diane, Kristy. B.M.E., U. Va., 1951; B.S. in Indsl. Engring. U. Fla., 1955, M.S. in Engring. 1956; Ph.D., Stanford U., 1961. Registered profl. engr., Calif; cert. profl. ergonomist. Research asst. U. Fla. Engring. and Industries Instl. Sta., Gainesville, 1955-56; instr. indsl. engring. Stanford U., 1956-58, acting asst. prof., 1958-61, asst. prof., 1961-64, asso. prof., 1964-72, prof., 1972-83, prof. emeritus, 1983—; mem. clin. faculty occupational medicine U. Calif. Med. Sch., San Francisco, 1985—; pres. chief scientist Portola Assocs., Palo Alto, Calif., 1969—; prin. investigator NASA Ames Research Center, Moffatt Field, Calif., 1974-77; cons. Dept. State, Fed. EEO Commn., maj. U.S. and fgn. cos.; cons. emergency communications ctr. design Santa Clara County Criminal Justice Bd., 1974, Bay Area Rapid Transit Control Ctr., 1977, Govt. of Mex., 1978, Amadahl Corp., 1978-79, Kerr-McGee Corp., 1979, Chase Manhattan Bank, 1980, St. Regis Paper Co., 1980-82, Pacific Gas & Electric, 1983-85, Pacific Bell, 1984-86, 89-93, IBM, 1988-91, Hewlett-Packard, 1990-91, Reuter's News Svc., 1990-92, Safeway Corp., 1992—, mem. com. for office computers Calif. OSHA. Dir.: producer: documentary film Rapid Answers for Rapid Transit, Dept. Transp., 1974; mem. editorial adv. bd. Computers and Graphics, 1970-85; reviewer Indsl. Engring. and IEEE Transactions, 1972-86; contbr. articles to profl. jours. Served to lt. USNR, 1951-54. HEW grantee, 1967-70. Mem. Am. Inst. Indsl. Engrs., Human Factors Soc., IEEE, Am. Soc. Safety Engrs., World Safety Orgn., Internat. Assn. Indsl. Ergonomics and Safety Rsch. Home: 121 Peter Coutts Cir Stanford CA 94305-2519 Office: Portola Assocs 2600 El Camino Real Ste 414 Palo Alto CA 94306

THOMPSON, DAVID ALLEN, health care company executive; b. Milbank, S.D., Dec. 4, 1941; s. Lester George and Henrietta Josephine (Gannon) T.; m. Marilyn Marie Selgeby, June 27, 1964; children: Dawn, Virginia, Brian. B.S. in Dairy Sci., S.D. State U., 1964. With Abbott Labs., 1964—, dir. mfg. and engring., Columbus, Ohio, 1972-75, v.p. mfg. and engring., 1975-76, v.p. ops., 1976-81, v.p. corp. materials mgmt., North Chicago, Ill., 1981-82, v.p. personnel, 1982-83, pres. Abbott diagnostics div., 1983—, sr. v.p. diagnostic ops., pres. Abbott diagnostic div., 1990—; bd. dirs. Dainabot Co., Ltd., Tokyo, Clara Abbott Found. Mem. Governing Coun. Good Shepherd Hosp., Barrington, Ill. Mem. Health Industry Mfg. Assn. (assn. mem.), N.Am. Biologicals (bd. dirs.), Wynstone Golf Club (Barrington, Ill., bd.dirs). Republican. Roman Catholic. Office: Abbott Labs Abbott Park IL 60064

THOMPSON, DAVID B., bishop. Ordained priest, 1950; consecrated bishop, 1989. Coadjutor bishop Diocese of Charleston, 1989-90, bishop, 1990—. Office: Bishop of Charleston 119 Broad St Charleston SC 29401*

THOMPSON, DAVID DUVALL, physician; b. Ithaca, N.Y., June 1, 1922; s. Homer C. and Clara (Smith) T.; m. Lynn Poucher, Dec. 22, 1945; children: David D., Richard M., Catherine R., Peter L. B.A., Cornell U., 1943, M.D., 1946. Diplomate Nat. Bd. Med. Examiners (treas. 1984-86, mem. spl. com. to space 1989-92). Intern, resident N.Y. Hosp., N.Y.C., 1946-50; head div. metabolism N.Y. Hosp., 1957-65, acting physician in chief, 1965-66, dir., 1967-87, cons., 1987—; vis. prof. hosp. adminstrn. Cornell U., 1974—; coordinator clin. edn. Cornell U. Med. Coll., 1987—; trustee Mut. Life Ins. of N.Y. Mem. State Hosp. Rev. and Planning Coun., 1982-90; trustee Mary

Imogene Bassett Hosp., Cooperstown, N.Y., chmn. bd. trustees, 1986-94; bd. overseers Mt. Desert Island Biol. Lab., 1988—, trustee, 1990—. Recipient Lederle Med. Faculty award, 1955-57; Otty award, N.Y.C., 1982; Man of Yr., East Mid-Manhattan C. of C., 1983; Spl. Tribute award Greater N.Y. Hosp. Assn., 1987; Recognition award Ctr. Alumni Council, 1988. Fellow ACP; mem AMA, Am. Physiol. Soc., Harvey Soc., Am. Soc. Clin. Investigation, Assn. Am. Med. Colls., Am. Fedn. Clin. Research, Soc. Med. Adminstrs. (pres. 1977-78), Greater N.Y. Hosp. Assn. (chmn. 1979), Hosp. Assn. N.Y. State (chmn. 1980), Am. Skin Assn., Inc. (bd. dirs. 1988—), Sigma Xi. Home: 11 Creston Ave Tenafly NJ 07670-2905 Office: 525 E 68th St New York NY 10021-4873

THOMPSON, DAVID JEROME, chemical company executive, biochemist, nutritionist; b. Sand Creek, Wis., July 21, 1937; s. Marshall and Bernice (Severson) T.; m. Virginia Ruth Williams, Aug. 11, 1962; children—Keith D., Craig M. B.S., U. Wis., 1960, M.S., 1961, Ph.D., 1963; M.B.A., U. Chgo., 1975. Research biochemist Internat. Minerals and Chem. Corp., Libertyville, Ill., 1964-68, supr. animal research, 1968-69, dir. tech. service, Mundelein, Ill., 1969-79, sales mgr., 1979-81, v.p. sci. and tech., Northbrook, Ill., 1981-84, 85-87, v.p. and gen. mgr. Sterwin div., 1984-85; v.p. planning and devel., Pitman-Moore, Inc., Mundelein, Ill., 1987-92; ret., 1992; cons. Am. Assn. Feed Control Ofcls., 1974-85; com. mem. Nat. Research Council, Nat. Acad. Scis., 1976-80. Co-author: Mineral Tolerance of Domestic Animals, 1980; contbr. articles to profl. jours. Mem. Am. Inst. Nutrition, AAAS, Poultry Sci. Assn., Am. Dairy Sci. Assn., Am. Soc. Animal Sci., Am. Chem. Soc., N.Y. Acad. Scis., Am. Feed Mfrs. Assn. (chmn. nutrition council 1980), Sigma Xi, Gamma Alpha, Phi Lambda Upsilon, Theta Delta Chi. Club: Liberty Road and Track. Avocations: competitive running, jazz and classical music, art, landscape gardening. Home: 826 Fair Way Libertyville IL 60048-1402

THOMPSON, DAVID RENWICK, federal judge. BS in Bus., U. So. Calif., 1952, LLB, 1955. Pvt. practice law with Thompson & Thompson (and predecessor firms), 1957-85; judge U.S. Ct. Appeals (9th cir.), 1985—. Served with USN, 1955-57. Mem. ABA, San Diego County Bar Assn., Am. Bd. Trial Lawyers (sec. San Diego chpt. 1983, v.p. 1984, pres. 1985). Office: US Ct Appeals 940 Front St San Diego CA 92101-8994*

THOMPSON, DAVID RUSSELL, agricultural engineering educator, academic dean; b. Cleve., Apr. 4, 1944; s. Dwight L. and Ella Caroline (Wolff) T.; m. Janet Ann Schall, Aug. 27, 1966; children: Devin Mathew, Colleen Michelle, Darin Michael. BS in Agrl. Engring., Purdue U., 1966, MS in Agrl. Engring., 1967; PhD in Agrl. Engring., Mich. State U., 1970. Asst. prof. agrl. engring., food sci. and nutrition depts. U. Minn., St. Paul, 1970-75, assoc. prof., 1975-81, prof., 1981-85; prof. agrl. engring., head dept. Okla. State U., Stillwater, 1985-91, assoc. dean Coll. Engring., Architecture and Tech., 1991—; engr. ops. dept. Green Giant Co., La Sueur, Minn., 1978-79; reviewer Colo. State U., CRS, USDA, Ft. Collins, 1989, foods, feeds and prodn. cluster U. Mo., Columbia, 1989, 93, dept. agrl. engring. Pa. State U., University Park, 1990, Tex. A&M U., College Station, 1992, Utah State U., Logan, 1993, others; reviewer USDA, 1983; vis. scholar Va. Poly. Inst. and State U., Blacksburg. Author: The Influence of Materials Properties on the Freezing of Sweet Corn, 1984, Mathematical Model for Predicting Lysine and Methionine Losses During Thermal Processing of Fortified Foods; contbr. over 50 articles to sci. jours., including Jour. Food Sci. Fellow Am. Soc. Agrl. Engrs. (div. chmn. 1976-77, bd. dirs. 1981-84, 87-89, v.p. 1994—, FIEI Young Rschr. award 1983, Pres.'s citation 1989); mem. ASHRAE, NSPE (chair Okla. mid-north sect. 1994—), Inst. Food Technologists (program com. 1982-85, state officer 1987-89), Am. Soc. Engring. Edn. (chair Midwest sect. 1994-95), Sigma Xi Phi Kappa Phi, Tau Beta Pi, Alpha Epsilon, Phi Eta Sigma, Gamma Sigma Delta. Office: Okla State U Coll Engring Arch & Tech 111 Engineering N Stillwater OK 74078-0522

THOMPSON, DAVID WALKER, astronautics company executive; b. Phila., Mar. 21, 1954; s. Robert H. and Nancy S. (Walker) T.; m. Catherine K. Ahulii, April 16, 1983. BS in Aeronautics and Astronautics, MIT, 1976; MS, Calif. Inst. Tech., 1977; MBA, Harvard U., 1981. Project engr. Jet Propulsion Lab., Pasadena, Calif., 1976; aerospace engr. NASA, Houston, 1977; project mgr. NASA, Huntsville, Ala., 1977-79; spl. asst. to pres. Hughes Aircraft Co., Los Angeles, 1981-82; pres., chief exec. officer Orbital Scis. Corp., Dulles, Va., 1982—; cons. Rockwell Internat., Thousand Oaks, Calif., 1980-81, Rand Corp., Santa Monica, Calif., 1982. Recipient Nat. award Space Found., Houston, 1981, Nat. Medal Tech. U.S Dept. Commerce Tech. Adminstrn., 1991; Nat. Air and Space Mus. Trophy, 1990; fellow Hertz Found., 1976, NSF fellow, 1976, Rockwell Internat. fellow, Harvard U. fellow, 1979; named Va. Industrial of Yr., 1991, Satellite Exec. of Yr., 1990. Fellow AIAA (assoc., Young Engr./Scientist Yr. award 1984, George M. Low Space Trans. award 1994), mem. Nat. Space Club. Office: Orbital Sciences Corp 21700 Atlantic Blvd Dulles VA 20166

THOMPSON, DAVID WILLIAM, business educator; b. Ft. Wayne, Ind., Sept. 3, 1914; s. William Byron and Georgia Louise (Davis) T.; m. M. Miriam Vollmer, Dec. 21, 1956 (dec.). B.S., Ind. U., 1938, M.S., 1940. C.P.A., N.Y., Ill., Ind., Va., N.C., N. Mex., La. Prof. Samford U., Birmingham, Butler U., Indpls., 1941-42, Ind. U., Bloomington, 1942-54; cons. Gen. Electric Co., N.Y.C., 1954-56; ptnr. Peat, Marwick, Mitchell & Co., N.Y.C., 1956-76; Frank S. Kaulback Jr. prof. commerce McIntire Sch. Commerce U. Va., Charlottesville, 1976—; chmn. State Bd. Examiners C.P.A.s, N.Y.C., 1966-70, State Bd. Pub. Accountancy, N.Y.C., 1974-76. Dir. Univ. of the Ams., Mexico City, U. of the Ams. Found., San Antonio. Mem. AICPA, Ind. U. Acad. Alumni Fellows, Indpls. Athletic Club, India House Club N.Y.C., Univ. Club N.Y.C., Farmington Country Club Charlottesville Va. Home: Ednam Forest 425 Wellington Dr Charlottesville VA 22903-4746 Office: U Va Monroe Hall McIntire Sch Commerce Charlottesville VA 22903

THOMPSON, DENNIS FRANK, political science and ethics educator, consultant; b. Hamilton, Ohio, May 12, 1940; s. Frank and Florence (Downs) T.; m. Carol Thompson, June 22, 1963; children: Eric, David. BA, Coll. of William and Mary, 1962, Oxford U., 1964; MA, Oxford U., 1968; PhD, Harvard U., 1968; LHD (hon.), Coll. of William and Mary, 1990. Instr. govt. Harvard U., Cambridge, Mass., 1967-68; Alfred North Whitehead prof. Harvard U., 1986—, dir. univ. program in ethics and professions, 1986—; asst. prof. politics Princeton U., N.J., 1968-72, assoc. prof., 1972-75, dept. chmn., 1972-73, 76-79, 82-83, prof., 1975-86; cons. to spl. counsel U.S. Senate Select Com. on Ethics, 1990-91, U.S. Dept. HHS, 1980—. Author: The Democratic Citizen, 1970, John Stuart Mill and Representative Government, 1976, Political Ethics and Public Office, 1987, Ethics in Congress, 1995; mem. editorial bd. Polit. Theory, 1974—, Philosophy and Pub. Affairs, 1971—, Am. Polit. Sci. Rev., 1985-88. Trustee Smith Coll., 1994—. Fellow Am. Acad. Arts and Scis.; mem. Soc. Legal and Polit. Philosophy (v.p. 1977-80, pres. 1986-89). Home: 9 Shady Hill Sq Cambridge MA 02138-2035 Office: Harvard U 406 Taubman 79 JFK St Cambridge MA 02138

THOMPSON, DENNIS PETERS, plastic surgeon; b. Chgo., Mar. 18, 1937; s. David John and Ruth Dorothy (Peters) T.; m. Virginia Louise Williams, June 17, 1961; children: Laura Faye, Victoria Ruth, Elizabeth Jan. BS, U. Ill., 1957, BS in Medicine, 1959, MS in Physiology, MD, 1961. Diplomate Am. Bd. Surgery, Am. Bd. Plastic Surgery. Intern Presbyn.-St. Lukes Hosp., Chgo., 1961-62; resident in gen. surgery Mayo Clinic, Rochester, Minn., 1964-66, fellow in gen. surgery, 1964-66; resident in gen. surgery Harbor Gen. Hosp., Los Angeles, 1968-70; resident in plastic surgery UCLA, 1971-73, clin. instr. plastic surgery, 1975-82, asst. clin. prof. surgery, 1982—; practice medicine specializing in plastic and reconstructive surgery, Los Angeles, 1974-78, Santa Monica, Calif., 1978—; chmn. plastic surgery sect. St. John's Hosp., 1986-91; mem. staff Santa Monica Hosp., UCLA Ctr. Health Scis., Brotman Med. Ctr.; chmn. dept. surgery Beverly Glen Hosp., 1978-79; pres. Coop. of Am. Physicians Credit Union, 1978-80, bd. dirs., 1980—, chmn. promotion com., 1983—, treas., 1985—. Contbr. articles to med. jours. Moderator Congl. Ch. of Northridge (Calif.), 1975-76, chmn. bd. trustees, 1973-74, 80-82; bd. dirs. L.A. Bus. Coun., 1987-90. Am. Tobacco Inst. research grantee, 1967-90. Fellow ACS; mem. AMA (Physicians Recognition award 1971, 74, 77, 81, 84, 87, 90, 93), Calif. Med. Assn., Los Angeles County Med. Assn. (chmn. bylaws com. 1979-80, chmn. ethics com. 1980-81, sec.-treas. dist. 5 1982-83, program chmn. 1983-84,

pres. 1985-86, councilor 1988—), Pan-Pacific Surgical Assn., Am. Soc. Plastic and Reconstructive Surgeons, Calif. Soc. Plastic Surgeons (chmn. bylaws com. 1982-83, chmn. liability com. 1983-85, councilor 1988-91, sec. 1993-95, v.p. 1995—), Los Angeles Soc. Plastic Surgeons (sec. 1980-82, pres. 1982—), Lipoplasty Soc. N.Am., UCLA Plastic Surgery Soc. (treas. 1983-84), Am. Soc. Aesthetic Plastic Surgery, Western Los Angeles Regional C. of C. (bd. dirs. 1981-84, 86-89, chmn. legis. action com. 1978-80), Phi Beta Kappa, Alpha Omega Alpha, Nu Sigma Nu, Phi Kappa Phi, Delta Sigma Delta, Omega Beta Pi, Phi Eta Sigma. Republican. Office: 2001 Santa Monica Blvd Santa Monica CA 90404-2102

THOMPSON, DONALD CHARLES, electronics company executive, former coast guard officer; b. Hollis, N.Y., Nov. 9, 1930; s. Arthur I. and Gertrude M. (Hauck) T.; m. Jeannie Germaine Kline, Oct. 4, 1952; children: Dennis C., Mitchell L., Sandra J., Janice M., Theresa A., Patrick J. B.S., U.S. Coast Guard Acad., 1952; M.S. (Krannert scholar), Krannert Grad. Sch., Purdue U., 1966. Commd. ensign USCG, 1952, advanced through grades to vice adm., 1986; shipboard navigator and engr., 1952-54, naval flight tng., 1954-55; search and rescue aviator and aircraft maintenance officer Calif., Ill., Alaska and Fla., 1955-65; chief computer-based mgmt. info. div. Elizabeth City, N.C., 1966-70; chief aero. engring. div. USCG Hdqrs., 1970-74; capt. of the port, group comdr., air sta. comdr. San Diego, 1974-76; chief ops. 11th USCG Dist., Long Beach, Calif., 1976-78; chief of staff 11th USCG Dist., 1979; chief office of engring. USCG Hdqrs., Washington, 1979-81; chief office of ops. USCG Hdqrs., 1981-82, chief staff, 1984-86, comdr. Atlantic area, 1986-88; comdr. 7th Coast Guard Dist., Miami, Fla., 1982-84; math. instr. Coll. Albermarle, N.C., 1967-70, Nat. U., San Diego, 1975-76; chmn. Interagy. Com. Search and Rescue, 1981-82; ret. USCG, 1988; v.p. strategic devel. R&E Electronics, Inc., Wilmington, N.C., 1990-93; pres. consulting firm, 1994—; v.p.'s coordinator for S.E. region Nat. Narcotics Border Interdiction System, 1983-84. Contbr. articles to profl. jours. Coordinator White House South Fla. Task Force on Crime, 1983-84. Decorated DSM with two gold stars, Coast Guard Meritorious Service medal, Def. Superior Service medal, Commendation medal with three gold stars, Legion of Merit with gold star. Mem. Soc. Am. Mil. Engrs. (dir. 1979-81), Am. Soc. Naval Engrs., Am. Helicopter Soc. (dir. 1981-82), Air Force Assn., Naval Inst. Roman Catholic. Clubs: Propeller, Nat. Aviation. Home: 1903 Market St Wilmington NC 28403-1015

THOMPSON, DONALD EDWARD, engineering company executive; b. Decatur, Ill., Sept. 21, 1930; s. William Homer and Margaret (Casey) T.; m. Doris Joan Schwendeman, Nov. 8, 1958; children: Patricia, James, Diane, Judith, Daniel, Andrew. BSCE, U. Ill., 1953. Registered profl. engr., Ill. Engr. Crawford, Murphy & Tilly, Inc., Springfield, Ill., 1955-69, chief engr., 1969-80, pres., 1980—, chmn. bd., 1985—. Fellow ASCE (pres. Ill. 1966-67, spl. recognition award 1967), Am. Cons. Engrs. Coun. (pres. 1973-74); mem. NSPE, Am. Pub. Works Assn., Soc. Am. Mil. Engrs., Cons. Engrs. Coun. Ill. (pres. 1973-74), Ill. C. of C. (bd. dirs. 1988-90). Roman Catholic. Home: 2113 Briarcliff Dr Springfield IL 62704-4127 Office: Crawford Murphy & Tilly Inc 2750 W Washington St Springfield IL 62702-3497

THOMPSON, DOROTHY BARNARD, elementary school educator; b. Flushing, N.Y., Aug. 14, 1933; d. Henry Clay and Cecelia Minnie Theresa (La Pardo) Barnard; m. Norman Earl Thompson, Aug. 12, 1956; children: Greg, Scot, Henry, Marc, Matthew. BSEd, SUNY, New Paltz, 1953; MS, Hofstra U., 1984. Cert. elem. tchr. K-6th grades, reading specialist K-12th grades, N.Y. Adjunct prof. Suffolk Community Coll., Brentwood, N.Y., 1987—, Nassau Community Coll., Uniondale, N.Y., 1986—; adjunct prof., instr. Ctr. for Acad. Achievement Long Island U., Greenvale, N.Y., 1984-92; tchr. reading, K-5th grades Long Beach (N.Y.) Pub. Schs., 1988—; mem. founding group Parent/Tchr., The Learning Tree, Garden City, N.Y., 1971; founder parent coop. Happy Day Nursery Sch., Bellmore, N.Y., 1975; parent-tchr. Commonwealth Sch., Bay Shore, Oakdale, 1976-82. Mem. NEA, Nassau Reading Coun., N.Y. State Tchrs. Assn., Assn. for Supervision and Curriculum Devel. Home: 2385 Warren Ave Bellmore NY 11710-2545 Office: 456 Neptune Blvd Long Beach NY 11561-2425

THOMPSON, DOUGLAS A., aerospace engineer. BS Indsl. Tech. in Mfg., North Tex. State U., 1984. Resident asst. housing dept. North Tex. Stat U., Denton, 1984; sr. engr. engring. models Lockheed Ft. Worth Co., 1984—. With USAF, 1978-81. Mem. Nat. Mgmt. Assn. Avocations: furniture design and fabrication, swimming. Office: Lockheed Ft Worth Co 7901 Clear Brook Cir Fort Worth TX 76123

THOMPSON, EARL ALBERT, economics educator; b. Los Angeles, Oct. 15, 1938; s. Hyman Harry and Sue (Field) T.; m. Velma Montoya, June 9, 1961; 1 son, Bret. B.A., UCLA, 1959; M.A. (fellow), Harvard U., 1961, Ph.D., 1961. Asst. prof. econs. Stanford (Calif.) U., 1962-65; asst. prof. econs. UCLA, 1965-68, assoc. prof., 1968-70, prof., 1970—. Grantee NSF; Grantee Lily Found.; Grantee Found. Research Econs. and Edn. Mem. Am. Econ. Assn. Home: 6970 Los Tilos Rd Los Angeles CA 90068-3107

THOMPSON, EARLENE, civic volunteer; b. Pelzer, S.C., Nov. 12, 1942; d. Tobie and Sallie (Moss) Tate; m. Willie J. Thompson, Apr. 19, 1958; children: Quenton, Quentena, Quenleasa, Quendrida. CEO Neighbor in the Hood Resource Ctr. Foster parent Ventura County DPSS, Simi Valley, Calif., 1969-73, L.A. County, 1983-87; exec. dir. Wilene's Re-Growth Ctr., San Dimas, Calif., 1986—; CEO Wilene's Children of the Village Foster Family Agy. Recipient Woman of Achievement award YWCA, 1991. Mem. Soroptimist (photographer 1988-89). Democrat. Office: Neighbor in the Hood Resource Ctr 637 N Park Ave Pomona CA 91768

THOMPSON, EDWARD FRANCIS, corporate executive; b. Waukegan, Ill., June 23, 1938; s. Francis Edward and Elsie (Birtic) T.; m. Gail Jean Walulis, Dec. 26, 1964; children—Michele Lisa, Melinda Joy, Holly Beth. B.S. in Aerospace Engring., U. Ill., 1961; M.B.A. in Fin., Santa Clara U., 1968. Assoc. engr. Lockheed Missiles, Sunnyvale, Calif., 1963-65; mgr. mktg. IBM, Palo Alto, Calif., 1965-68; dist. mgr. Computer Scis. Corp., Los Altos, Calif., 1968-72; v.p. equity devel. U.S. Leasing Internat., San Francisco, 1972-76; v.p. fin. Amdahl Corp., Sunnyvale, Calif., 1976—, also dir.; dir. Digital Network Engring. SPA, Rome, Amdahl Corp., Sunnyvale; chmn. Amdahl Ireland Ltd., Dublin. Bd. dirs. Jr. Achievement, 1981-85; deacon Presbyn. Ch. Mem. Fin. Execs. Inst., Data Gamma Sigma. Republican. Avocations: golf; tennis; skiing. Home: 1517 Edgewood Dr Palo Alto CA 94303-2818 Office: Amdahl Corp 1250 E Arques Ave Sunnyvale CA 94086-4730*

THOMPSON, EDWARD IVINS BRAD, biological chemistry and genetics educator, molecular endocrinologist, department chairman; b. Burlington, Iowa, Dec. 20, 1933; s. Edward Bills and Lois Elizabeth (Bradbridge) T.; m. Lynn Taylor Parsons; children: Elizabeth Lynn, Edward Ernest Bradbridge. BA with distinction, Rice U., 1955; postgrad., Cambridge U., 1957-58; MD, Harvard U., 1960. Intern The Presbyn. Hosp., N.Y.C., 1960-61, asst. resident internal medicine, 1961-62; rsch. assoc. Nat. Inst. Mental Health, NIH, Bethesda, Md., 1962-64; rsch. scientist Nat. Inst. Arthritis and Metabolic Diseases, NIH, Bethesda, Md., 1964-68; rsch. scientist Lab of Biochemistry, Nat. Cancer Inst., NIH, Bethesda, Md., 1968-73, sect. chief, 1973-84; I.H. Kempner prof. U. Tex. Med. Br., Galveston, 1984, prof. chmn. dept. human biol. chemistry and genetics, 1984—, prof. internal medicine, 1984—; attending physician Nat. Naval Med. Ctr., Bethesda, 1978-80; chmn. hormones and cancer task force NIH, Bethesda, 1978-80; co-chmn. Gordon Research Conf., 1980; mem. adv. com. on Biochem. & Chem. Carcinogenesis, Am. Cancer Soc., 1982-86; mem. revision com. Endocrinology adv. panel U.S. Pharmacopoeial Conv., Inc., 1980-85; mem. council for clin. investigation and research awds., Am. Cancer Soc., 1989-93; bd. scientific overseers Pennington Nutrition Rsch. Ctr. La. State U., 1991—; Fulbright prof., Marburg, Germany, 1992-93. Co-editor Gene Expression and Carcinogenesis in Cultured Liver, 1975, Steroid Receptors and the Management of Cancer, 1979, DNA: Protein Interactions and Gene Regulation, other vols. in field; assoc. editor Cancer Rsch. jour., 1976-86; corr. editor Jour. Steroid Biochemistry, 1977-85; founding editor-in-chief Molecular Endocrinology Jour., 1985-92; contbr. 200 sci. articles to profl. jours. Mem. troop com. Girl Scouts U.S. Rockville, Md., 1970-76; mem. PTA, Rockville, 1967-71; Wilderness Soc., Washington, 1964-75; initiator sci. edn. liaison program Galveston Pub. Schs., 1991; mem. pres.'s cabinet U. Tex. Med. Br. Served as med. dir. USPHS, 1962-84. Grantee NIH, Walls

Rsch., Nat. Inst. Diabetes and Digestive and Kidney Diseases, Nat. Cancer Inst.; Am. Cancer Soc. scholar, 1992-93; Fulbright scholar. Mem. Am. Soc. Cell Biology, Am. Assn. Cancer Rsch., Am. Soc. Biol. Chemists, Endocrine Soc., Am. Soc. Microbiology, Am. Coll. Med. Genetics (affiliate), Tissue Culture Assn., S.W. Environ. Mutagen Soc., Rotary Internat., The Yacht Club, Galveston Yacht Club, Racquet Club, Harvard Club, Pres.'s Club of Rice U., Phi Beta Kappa, Alpha Omega Alpha. Achievemetns include patent on anti-tumor activity of a modified frament of the glucocorticoid receptors. Avocations: sailing, gardening, tennis, jogging, music. Office: U Tex Med Br Dept Human Biol Gene Galveston TX 77555

THOMPSON, EDWARD KRAMER, editor, publisher; b. Mpls., Sept. 17, 1907; s. Edward T. and Bertha E. (Kramer) T.; m. Marguerite M. Maxam, May 14, 1927 (div.); children—Edward T. Colin R.; m. Lee Eitingon, Apr. 1, 1963. A.B. U. N.D., 1927, H.H.D. 1958. Editor Foster County Independent, Carrington, N.D., 1927; city editor Fargo (N.D.) Morning Forum, 1927; picture editor, asst. news editor Milw. Jour., 1927-37; asso. editor Life, 1937-42, asst. mng. editor, 1945-49, mng. editor, 1949, editor, 1961-68; spl. asst. to sec. state, 1968; editor, pub. Smithsonian mag., 1969-81, cons. to sec., 1981-83, cons. to editor, pub., 1983—. Served to lt. col. USAAF, 1942-45. Decorated Legion of Merit Order Brit. Empire; named to N.D. Hall of Fame, 1968; named Editor of Year Nat. Press Photographers Assn., 1968; recipient Joseph Henry medal Smithsonian Instn., 1973; Lifetime Achievement award Internat. Inst. Photography, 1986, Sioux Achievement award U. N.D., 1987, Dumke award for achievement in visual communication Wis. News Photographers Assn., 1988; named to Pub. Hall of Fame, 1987, U. N.D. Mil. Hall of Fame, 1988. Mem. Phi Beta Kappa, Sigma Delta Chi, Phi Delta Theta. Office: Smithsonian Instn Washington DC 20560

THOMPSON, EDWARD THORWALD, magazine editor; b. Milw., Feb. 13, 1928; s. Edward Kramer and Marguerite Minerva (Maxam) T.; m. Margaret Kessler, 1949; children: Edward T. III, Anne B., Evan K., David S.; m. Nancy Cale, May 28, 1966; 1 child, Julie.; m. Susan L. Jacobson, Nov. 28, 1981. Grad., Lawrenceville Sch., 1945; SB, MIT, 1949. Engr. Mobil Oil Co., Beaumont, Tex., 1949-52; assoc. editor Chem. Engr. mag., N.Y.C., 1952-55; mng. editor Chem. Week mag., N.Y.C., 1955-56; assoc. editor Fortune mag., 1956-60; with Reader's Digest., Pleasantville, N.Y., 1960-84; asst. mng. editor, then mng. editor Reader's Digest., 1973-76, editor-in-chief, mem. exec. com., 1976-84; cons. in pub. Waccabuc, N.Y., 1984—; pres. Thompson Assocs.; bd. dirs. The Quarton Group. Recipient Golden Plate award Am. Acad. Achievement, 1977. Mem. Am. Soc. Mag. Editors, Waccabuc Country Club. Home: 3 Hunt Farm Rd Waccabuc NY 10597-1100

THOMPSON, ELIZABETH JANE, small business owner; b. Ithaca, N.Y., Jan. 11, 1927; d. Merle Godley and Nellie Gray (Trowbridge) T. AB, Syracuse U., 1948, MA, 1962, PhD, 1971. Writer, editor Cornell U., Ithaca, N.Y., 1950-53; dir. pub. rels. Taylor Ward Advt., Ithaca, 1953-54; account exec. Doug Johnson Assocs., Syracuse, N.Y., 1954-58; assoc. in community rels., Youth Devel. Ctr. Syracuse U., 1958-66, grad. asst., 1967-68; from asst. prof. to prof. sociology Shippensburg (Pa.) U., 1968-90, dir. Fashion Archives, 1980-90; owner Timelines & Hemlines Cons. Svc., Shippensburg, 1991—; lectr. on costume, fashion and sociology of dress to numerous civic and ednl. groups. Co-editor: Among the People: Studies of the Urban Poor, 1968; contbr. articles on sociology of dress to numerous publs. Mem. Costume Soc. Am., Am. Sociol. Soc. Dutch Reform. Avocations: vintage clothing, photography, travel, historical architecture. Home and Office: 19 S Prince St Shippensburg PA 17257-1919

THOMPSON, EMMA, actress; b. London, Apr. 15, 1959; d. Eric Thompson and Phyllida Law; m. Kenneth Branaugh, Aug. 1989. Student of English, Cambridge U., Eng. Performances include: (films) Henry V, 1989, The Tall Guy, 1989, Dead Again, 1991, Impromptu, 1991, Howard's End, 1992 (Acad. award for best actress), Peter's Friends, 1992, Much Ado About Nothing, 1993, The Remains of the Day, 1993 (Acad. award nominee for best actress 1993), In the Name of the Father, 1993 (Acad. award nominee for best supporting actress 1993), My Father, the Hero, 1994, Junior, 1994, Carrington, 1995; (TV in Eng.) Al Fresco, Up For Grabs (a.k.a. Sexually Transmitted), Tutti Frutti, (miniseries) Fortunes of War, Thompson; (TV in Am.) Fortunes of War, Cheers, 1991; (London stage) Me and My Girl, Look Back in Anger. Active in Footlights Theatrical Group, Cambridge, Eng. Office: William Morris Agy 151 El Camino Beverly Hills CA 90212*

THOMPSON, EWA M., foreign language educator; b. Kaunas, Lithuania; came to U.S., 1963; d. Jozef and Maria (Adamowicz) Majewski; m. James R. Thompson. BA in English and Russian, U. Warsaw, Poland, 1963; MFA in Piano, Sopot Conservatory Music, 1963; MA in English, Ohio U., 1964; PhD in Comparative Lit., Vamderbilt U., 1967. Instr. Vanderbilt U., Nashville, Tenn., 1964-67; asst. prof. Ind. State U., Terre Haute, 1967-68, Ind. U., 1968-70; assoc. prof. Rice U., Houston, 1970-74, assoc. prof., 1974-79, prof., 1979—, chair, 1987-90; assoc. prof. U. Va., Charlottesville, 1973-74; cons. NEH, 1973—, The John D. and Catherine T. MacArthur Found., The John Simon Guggenheim Found., U.S. Dept. Edn.; vis. cons. Tex. A&M U.; seminar dir. NEH Summer Inst., Southeastern La. U., 1990; chair Russian lit. conf. Rice U., 1989; lectr. various colls. and univs. Author: Russian Formalism and Anglo-American New Criticism: A Comparative Study, 1971, Witold Gombrowicz, 1979, Understanding Russia: The Holy Fool in Russian Culture, 1987, The Search for Self-Definition in Russian Literature, 1991; contbr. articles to profl. jours., chpts. to books. Mellon grant, 1990, Rice U. grant 1990, Internat. Rsch. and Excahnges Sr. Scholar grant, 1991; Hoover Inst. fellow, 1988; scholar Vanderbilt U., 1964-67; recipient Silver Thistle award Houston's Scottish Heritage Found., 1988. Roman Catholic. Office: Rice University PO Box 1892 6100 South Main Houston TX 77251

THOMPSON, FRANCIS NEAL, financial services consultant; b. Yonkers, N.Y., Oct. 21, 1940; s. Maury Weldon and Mary Temple (Meacham) T.; m. Patricia Jennings Turner, June 12, 1962 (div. 1980); children: Melissa Temple Thompson, Turner Jennings Thompson; m. Sharon Griffin, May 8, 1982. BA in Econs., Lynchburg Coll., 1962; MBA, U. Richmond, 1966. Chartered life underwriter; ChFC; CFP. Stockbroker Mason & Lee (now Legg, Mason & Co.), Lynchburg and Richmond, Va., 1960-63; pension analyst Southwestern Life Ins. Co., Dallas, 1963-68; v.p. mktg. dir. Fidelity Bankers Life Ins. Co., Richmond, 1968-75; v.p., dir., chmn. exec. com. Wheat Ins. Svcs. Inc. (now Wheat 1st, Butcher Singer Inc.), Richmond, 1975-78; chmn., CEO Corp. Cons. Inc., Richmond, 1978-84; exec. v.p., dir. Fin. Mgmt. Group, Richmond, 1984-88; v.p. mktg. dir. Ind. Fin. Mktg. Group, White Plains, N.Y., 1988-89; spl. projects mgr. The Acacia Group, Washington, 1990-91; ins. cons. Blue Cross/Blue Shield of Va., Richmond, 1992-93; regional sales mgr. Allmerica Fin., State Mut. Life and Provident Mut., 1993—; founder Fin. Svcs. Consultants, Inc., Richmond, 1994—; cons. Signet Ins., Richmond, 1984-88, Funds of Am., Portland, 1990-91. Author: Assessing Individual Managerial Performing, 1967. Bd. dirs. Emergency Shelter Inc., Richmond, 1991—; Boy Scouts Am.-Robert E. Lee Coun., Richmond, 1984—. With USN, 1955-58. Recipient Disting. Prof. Svc. award Coll. for Fin. Planning, 1987. Fellow Life Underwriters Tng. Coun.; mem. Ctrl. Va. Soc. CFP's (bd. dirs. 1991—, edn. chmn. 1991-92), Richmond Life Underwriters Assn. (bd. dirs. 1994—). Presbyterian. Avocations: sailing, tennis, racketball. Home: 10006 Bellona Ct Richmond VA 23233-2044 Office: 2008 Libbie Ave Richmond VA 23226

THOMPSON, FRANK JOSEPH, political science educator; b. New Ulm, Minn., Mar. 21, 1944; s. Joseph Mariem and Alice Louise (Lindquist) T.; m. Benna Miriam, June 15, 1944; children: Samuel, Aliza, Elizabeth. BA in Polit. Sci., U. Chgo., 1966; MA in Polit. Sci., U. Calif., Berkeley, 1967, PhD Polit. Sci., U. Chgo., 1966; MA in Polit. Sci., 1973. Asst. prof. polit. sci. Calif. State U., Long Beach, 1971-72; asst. prof. U. Ga., Athens, 1972-78, assoc. prof., 1978-83, prof., 1983-88, head dept. 1982-87; prof. pub. adminstrn., policy, polit. sci. and pub. health SUNY, Albany, 1987—, acting dean Grad. Sch. of Pub. Affairs, 1988, dean, 1988—, acting provost Rockefeller Coll., 1989, assoc. provost, 1990—; analyst HEW, Washington, fond, part-time with City Govt. Oakland, Calif., 1968-71; cons. USPHS, 1976-79, 82, U.S. Pres.'s Commn. for Nat. Agenda for 80's, 1980, Am. Pub. Welfare Assn., 1981-83; publ. cons. U.S. Adv. Commn. on Intergovtl. Rels., 1983; mem. task force on exec. and mgmt. devel. U.S. Office Pers. Mgmt., 1990; exec. dir. Nat. Commn. on the State and Local Pub. Svc., 1991—. Author: Personnel Policy in the City, 1975, Health Policy and the Bureaucracy, 1981, Public Administration: Challenges,

Choices, Consequences, 1990; editor: Classics of Public Personnel Policy, 1979, 2d edit., 1991, Revitalizing State and Local Public Service, 1993; contbr. articles to profl. jours. Mem. Ga. PTA, Athens, 1980-86, N.Y. PTA, 1989—; bd. dirs. Upper Hudson Planned Parenthood, 1990—. Pub. adminstrn. fellow U.S. Pub. Health Service, 1975-76, NSF fellow, 1970-71; recipient Simon award Internat. Jour. Pub. Adminstrn., 1981. Fellow Nat. Acad. Pub. Adminstrn.; mem. Am. Pub. Health Assn., Assn. for Pub. Policy Analysis and Mgmt., Am. Soc. for Pub. Adminstrn. (publs. com. 1982-84, William E. Mosher award 1983), Am. Polit. Sci. Assn. (chmn. departmental services com. 1987-89, chair com. sect. pub. adminstrn. 1985-87, 89—, chair sect. pub. adminstrn. 1990-91, chair Gaus award com. 1991-92), Nat. Assn. Schs. Pub. Affairs and Adminstrn. (peer rev. com. 1984-86, 1st chmn. commn. on peer rev. and accreditation 1986-87, chmn. task force on revitalizing the pub. svc., v.p. 1990-91, pres. 1991-92), N.Y. State Acad. Pub. Adminstrn. (bd. dirs. 1994—). Home: 9 Harvard Ave Albany NY 12208-2019 Office: SUNY Grad Sch Pub Affairs Albany NY 12222

THOMPSON, FRED CLAYTON, engineering executive, consultant; b. Snow Shoe, Pa., Feb. 26, 1928; s. Clayton Alfred and Edna (Pearl) T.; m. M. Joanne Bender; children: Marjorie Ann, Richard Clayton, Scott David, Carol Ann. BSEE, Pa. State U., 1950, MSEE, 1958. Electronics engr. Martin Corp., Balt., 1965-54; tech. dir. HRB System S, State Coll., Pa., 1954-68; v.p. engring. Locus, Inc., State Coll., 1958-78, pres., chmn., 1978-88, cons., 1989—. Patentee in microwave circuitry. Past pres. and dir. Private Industry Coun. With U.S. Army, 1950-52. Named Hon. Alumni Pa. State U., 1987, Disting. Toastmaster, Toastmaster Internat., 1976. Avocation: barbershop quartet singing. Office: care Locus Inc PO Box 740 State College PA 16804-0740

THOMPSON, FRED DALTON, senator; b. Sheffield, Ala., Aug. 19, 1942. BA, Memphis State U., 1964; JD, Vanderbilt U., 1967. Asst. U.S. atty. Mid. Tenn., 1969-72; min. counsel Senate Watergate Com., 1973; pvt. practice, 1975-94, film actor, 1979—; spl. counsel U.S. Intelligence and Fgn. Rels. Coms., 1982; atty. Arent, Fox, Kintner, Plotkin & Kahn, 1991-94; U.S. senator from Tenn., 1995—. Appeared in films The Hunt for Red October, Born Yesterday, In the Line of Fire, Cape Fear. Office: US Senate 523 Dirksen Senate Bldg Washington DC 20510-4203

THOMPSON, GARY W., public relations executive; b. Berkeley, Calif., July 15, 1947. BA, Northwestern U., England, 1969—. Acct. exec. Allen & Doward Advt., 1971-74; acct. exec. Hoefer-Amedei Assocs., 1978-81, acct. supr., 1978, v.p., 1978-81; v.p., assoc. dir. Ketchum, 1981-82, sr. v.p., dir., 1982-84, exec. v.p., 1984-87, exec. v.p., dir. we. region, 1987-89, exec. v.p., dir. U.S.A., 1989-90; pres., CEO Hi-Tech Comm., 1990—. Mem. Pub. Rels. Soc. Am. (counselors acad., membership chmn. San Francisco chpt. 1983, placement, newsletter chmn. 1985), Internat. Assn. Bus. Communicators. Office: Hi-Tech Comm 101 Howard St San Francisco CA 94107-1616

THOMPSON, GEORGE ALBERT, geophysics educator; b. Swissvale, Pa., June 5, 1919; s. George Albert Sr. and Maude Alice (Harkness) T.; m. Anita Kimmell, July 20, 1944; children: Albert J., Dan A., David C. BS, Pa. State U., 1941; MS, MIT, 1942; PhD, Stanford U., 1949. Geologist, geophysicist U.S. Geol. Survey, Menlo Park, Calif., 1942-76; asst. prof. Stanford (Calif.) U., 1949-55, assoc. prof., 1955-60, prof. geophysics, 1960—, chmn. geophysics dept., 1967-86, chmn. geology dept., 1979-82, Otto N. Miller prof. earth scis., 1980-89, dean sch. earth scis., 1987-89; cons. adv. com. on reactor safeguards Nuclear Regulation Commn., Washington, 1974-94; mem. bd. earth sci. NAS/NRC, 1986-88, vice chmn. Yucca Mountain Hydrotectonics panel NAS/NRC, 1990-92; mem. exec. com. Inc. Rsch. Inst. for Seismology, Washington, 1990-92; mem. sr. external events rev. com. Lawrence Livermore Nat. Lab., 1989-93; mem. Coun. on Continental Sci. Drilling, 1990-94; cons. Los Alamos Nat. Lab., 1993—; cons. to S.W. Rsch. Inst., 1993; chair com. to rev. scientific issues, Ward Valley, Calif., NAS/NRC, 1994-95; panel on probabalistic volcanic hazard analysis, Yucca Mountain, Nev., Geomatrix Consultants Inc., 1995—. Author over 100 research papers. With USNR, 1944-46. Recipient G.K. Gilbert award in seismic geology, 1996; NSF postdoctoral fellow, 1956-57; Guggenheim Found. fellow, 1963-64. Fellow AAAS, Geol. Soc. Am. (coun. mem. 1983-86, George P. Woollard award 1983), Am. Geophys. Union: mem. NAS, Seismol. Soc. Am., Soc. Exploration Geophysicists. Avocation: forestry. Home: 421 Adobe Pl Palo Alto CA 94306-4501 Office: Stanford U Geophysics Dept Stanford CA 94305

THOMPSON, GEORGE HOWARD, livestock transportation company executive; b. Prophetstown, Ill., Oct. 18, 1930; s. George Warren and Gladys (Bayles) T.; m. Shirley Rae VanDamme, Mar. 4, 1950; children: George Mark, Rebecca. Student, Augustana Coll., Rock Island, Ill., 1947-48. U. N.Mex., Taos, 1948. Pres. Geo. Thompson & Son, Inc., Prophetstown, 1948-94; chmn. bd. Prophetstown Mfg., Inc., 1984-93. Pres. Ill. Assn. Sch. Bds., 1975-77; mem. Ill. State Bd. Edn., Springfield, 1978-93; mem. local bds. of edn. Prophetstown/Lyndon, 1959-78; moderator Ill. conf. United Ch. of Christ No. Assn., 1991-92; chmn. Whiteside County Reps. Recipient awards Ill. Coun. for the Gifted, Chgo., 1982, Ill. Alliance for Arts Edn., 1984, Ill. Assn. Regional Supts. of Schs., 1991, Humanitarian award Sterling/Rock Falls NAACP, 1983; honored by Ill. Ho. of Reps. resolution #1213, 1993. Mem. Ind. Livestock Mktg. Assn. (nat. pres. 1970s), Livestock Conservation Inc. (exec. com. 1970s). Congregationalist. Avocations: painting and all fine arts, good music, travel. Home: 102 Market St Prophetstown IL 61277-1232

THOMPSON, GEORGE LEE, manufacturing company executive; b. Denver, June 12, 1933; s. George H. and Frances M. (Murphy) T.; m. Patricia M. MacKenzie, Sept. 25, 1993; children: Shannon, Tracy, Bradley. BS in Bus., U. Colo., 1957; postgrad. in advanced mgmt., NYU, 1969. With GTE Sylvania, Denvers, Mass., 1957-65, nat. sales mgr., 1965-67, mktg. mgr., 1967-68; v.p. sales entertainment products Batavia, N.Y., 1968-73; dir. corp. mktg. Stamford, Conn., 1973-74; v.p. mktg. Servomation Corp., N.Y.C., 1974-76, exec. v.p., 1976-78; exec. v.p. Singer Co., Edison, N.J., 1978-81, pres., 1981-83; pres. consumer products SCM Corp., N.Y.C., 1983-86; pres., CEO Smith-Corona Corp., New Canaan, Conn., 1986-89, chmn., chief executive officer, 1989—; bd. dirs. Smith Corona, Ltd., U.K., France, Singapore, Germany, Can., Histacount Corp., OSI. Bd. dirs. Internat. Tennis Hall of Fame, Am. Jr. Golf Found., United Way of New Canaan, 1989-93; chmn. EC-92 Standards Com. U.S. Dept. Commerce; mem. bus. alumni adv. coun. U. Colo., 1989-94; mem. bd. overseers Sch. Bus. U. Conn.; mem. Pres.'s Export Coun., 1991-93; mem. bd. advisors Jr. league. Recipient Disting. Bus. Alumni award U. Colo., 1990. Mem. Computer and Bus. Equipment Mfg. Assn. (bd. dirs. 1992-94), Sales and Mktg. Execs. Internat. (trustee), Am. Mgmt. Assn. (bd. trustees, exec. com. chmn., gen. mgmt. coun.), St. John Assn. (bd. dirs. pres. 1983-93), New Canaan Field Club, Woodway Country Club, Club at Seabrook Island, Wilton Riding Club (bd. govs 1980-83), Navesink Country Club (bd. govs. 1981-83), Harbour Ridge Yacht and Country Club, Chi Psi. Episcopalian. Home: 27 Bank St New Canaan CT 06840-5721 Office: Smith Corona Corp 65 Locust Ave New Canaan CT 06840-4725

THOMPSON, GEORGE RALPH, church denomination administrator; b. Barbados, Mar. 20, 1929; s. George Gilbert and Edna (Griffith) T.; m. Imogene Clotilde Barker, July 19, 1959; children: Carol Jean, Linda Mae, Gerald Randolph. BA, Atlantic Union Coll., 1956; MA, Andrews U., 1958, BD, 1962, DD (hon.), 1983. Ordained to ministry Seventh-day Adventists, 1959. Evangelist South Caribbean conf. Seventh-day Adventists, Trinidad and Tobago, 1950-53; tchr., ch. pastor, chmn. dept. theology Caribbean Union Coll., Trinidad and Tobago, 1953-54, 59-64; pres. East Caribbean conf. Seventh-day Adventists, Barbados, 1964-70; pres. Caribbean Union conf. Seventh-day Adventists, Trinidad and Tobago, 1970-75; v.p. Gen. Conf. Seventh-day Adventists, Washington, 1975-80; sec. Gen. Conf. Seventh-day Adventists, Silver Spring, Md., 1980—; host radio shows, Barbados. Office: Gen Conf Seventh-day Adventist Ch 12501 Old Columbia Pike Silver Spring MD 20904-6600

THOMPSON, GERALD E., historian, educator; b. Oakland, Calif., Nov. 27, 1947; s. Norman J. and Margaret L. (Daniels) T.; m. Margaret H. Hood, June 6, 1970. BA, U. Ariz., 1969, MA, 1972, PhD, 1978. Editorial asst. Ariz. and the West, Tucson, 1975-77; asst. editor Ariz. and the West, 1977-78; asst. prof. history U. Toledo, 1978-83, assoc. prof., 1983-88, prof.,

1988—; editor The Historian, Toledo, 1983-90; hist. cons. Mescalero Apache Tribe, various pubs.; humanities lectr. U. Toledo, 1993-94; vis. assoc. prof. dept. history U. Ariz., summer 1984; instr. Pima Coll., fall 1977. Author: Army and the Navajo, 1976, Edward F. Beale and the American West, 1983; compiler: A Guide to History-Related Microform Holdings, 1986; contbr. articles to profl. jours., chpts. to books. Counselor Ariz. Dept. Corrections, 1970-71. Served with Ariz. N.G., 1969-75. Recipient Ariz. Hist. Found. award, Exceptional Faculty Mem. award U. Toledo, 1985, 91; Edwin Turville fellow U. Ariz., 1975. Mem. Am. Hist. Assn., Western Hist. Assn., Nat. Assn. Scholars, Soc. Calif. Pioneers, Orgn. Am. Historians, Ariz. Hist. Soc., Ohio Acad. History (publs. awards com. 1982-83), Phi Beta Kappa, Phi Kappa Phi, Phi Alpha Theta (historian 1983-90, merit achievement award 1989). Office: U Toledo Dept History 2801 W Bancroft St Toledo OH 43606-3390

THOMPSON, GERALD JORDAN, management consultant; b. Shreveport, La., Apr. 1, 1930; s. Raymon Hudgins and Helen Ashford (Robinson) T.; m. Ann Zuehl, Oct. 25, 1954; children: Daniel Jordan, Amy Denman Mangum, Raymon Hudgins. BS, U.S. Naval Acad., 1952; MBA, Stanford U., 1960. Commd. ensign USN, 1952, advanced through grades to rear adm., 1977; comdg. officer naval supply ctr. USN, Bremerton, Wash., 1974-76; dir. contracts div. Naval Sea Systems Command, Arlington, Va., 1977-79; dep. dir. Def. Logistics Agy., Alexandria, Va., 1979-81; ret. USN, 1981; ptnr. Coopers & Lybrand, Washington, 1982—. Decorated Legion of Merit. Fellow Nat. Contract Mgmt. Assn.; mem. U.S.C. of C. (coun. chmn. 1985-87), Navy League, Profl. Services Council. Republican. Methodist. Office: Coopers & Lybrand 1525 Wilson Blvd 8th Floor Arlington VA 22209 Also: Coopers & Lybrand 1800 M St NW Washington DC 20036-5873

THOMPSON, GERALD LUTHER, operations research and applied mathematics educator; b. Rolfe, Iowa, Nov. 25, 1923; s. Luther and Sylva Carlotta (Larson) T.; m. Dorothea Vivian Mosley, Aug. 25, 1954; children: Allison M., Emily A., Abigail E. B.S. in Elec. Engring, Iowa State U., 1944; M.S. in Math, Mass. Inst. Tech.; 1948; Ph.D., U. Mich., 1953. Instr. math. Princeton, 1951-53; asst. prof. math. Dartmouth, 1953-58; prof. math. Ohio Wesleyan U., Delaware, 1958-59; assoc. prof. applied math. and indsl. adminstrn. Carnegie-Mellon U., Pitts., 1959-63; prof. Carnegie-Mellon U., 1963—, IBM prof. systems and operations research, 1980—; E.D. Walker Centennial fellow IC2 Inst. U. Tex., 1985—; cons. Econometric Research Program, Princeton, IBM, Bethlehem Steel Co., Port Authority of Allegheny County, McKinsey & Co., Applied Devices Corp., PPG Industries, Westinghouse Electric Corp., Timken Co., J & L Steel, GM; prin. investigator Mgmt. Scis. Research Group, Carnegie-Mellon U. Co-author, author: Introduction to Finite Mathematics, 1957, Finite Mathematical Structures, 1959, Finite Mathematics with Business Applications, 1962, Industrial Scheduling, 1963, Programming and Probability Models in Operations Research, 1973, Mathematical Theory of Expanding and Contracting Economies, 1976, Optimal Control Theory: Management Science Applications, 1981, Computational Economics: Economic Modeling with Optimization Software, 1992; assoc. editor: Inst. Mgmt. Scis. Jour. 1966-69; Contbr. articles to profl. jours. Rep. of Inst. Mgmt. Scis. to NRC. Served with USNR, 1943-46. Ford Found. research fellow, 1963-64. Mem. AAAS, Math. Assn. Am., Inst. Mgmt. Scis., Operations Research Soc. Am., Phi Beta Kappa, Phi Kappa Phi, Tau Beta Phi, Eta Kappa Nu, Phi Mu Alpha. Home: 15 Wedgewood Ln Pittsburgh PA 15215-1560

THOMPSON, GLENN JUDEAN, library science educator; b. Sioux Falls, S.D., Oct. 16, 1936; s. Carl Melvin and Emma Bertina (Johnson) T.; m. Agnes Myrleen Nord, Aug. 23, 1958; children—Christine Faye, Nathan Glenn. B.S., Augustana Coll., Sioux Falls, S.D., 1958; M.A., U. Minn., 1966; Ed.D., U. S.D., 1969. Cert. music tchr., English tchr., librarian, audiovisual dir., Minn. Music tchr. Wayzata Pub. Schs. (Minn.), 1958-63; librarian, audiovisual dir. Perham Pub. Schs. (Minn.), 1963-66; mem. faculty St. Cloud State Coll. (Minn.), 1966-70; mem. faculty U. Wis.-Eau Claire, 1970—, chmn. dept. library sci. and media edn., 1972-90, prof., 1988—. Mem. ALA, Wis. Library Assn., Wis. Ednl. Media Assn., NEA. Home: N7191 540th St Menomonie WI 54751 Office: U Wis Eau Claire Found & Libr Sci Dept Garfield Ave Eau Claire WI 54702-4004

THOMPSON, GORDON, JR., federal judge; b. San Diego, Dec. 28, 1929; s. Gordon and Garnet (Meese) T.; m. Jean Peters, Mar. 17, 1951; children—John M., Peter Renwick, Gordon III. Grad., U. So. Calif., 1951, Southwestern U. Sch. Law, Los Angeles, 1956. Bar: Calif. 1956. With Dist. Atty.'s Office, County of San Diego, 1957-60; partner firm Thompson & Thompson, San Diego, 1960-70; U.S. dist. judge So. Dist. Calif., San Diego, 1970—, chief judge, 1984-91, sr. judge, 1994—. Bd. dirs. Sharp Meml. Hosp. Mem. Am. Bd. Trial Advocates, ABA, San Diego County Bar Assn. (v.p. 1970), Delta Chi. Club: San Diego Yacht. Office: US Dist Ct 940 Front St San Diego CA 92101-8994

THOMPSON, GORDON WILLIAM, dentist, educator; b. Vancouver, B.C., Can., Dec. 22, 1940; s. Clarence and Emma Jean T.; m. Marilyn Jean Lust, May 23, 1964; children: Janice Lynne, Phillip Glen, Andrew James. Student, U. B.C., Vancouver, 1958-61; D.D.S., U. Alta., Edmonton, Can., 1965; M.Sc.D., U. Toronto, Ont., Can., 1967, Ph.D., 1971. Practice dentistry Wetaskiwin, Alta., 1965; asst. prof. dentistry U. Toronto, 1969-72, asso. prof., 1972-77, prof., 1977-78; prof., dean Faculty of Dentistry, U. Alta., 1978-89, chmn. dept. dental health care, 1989-94; exec. dir. Alta. Dental Assn., Edmonton, 1994—; condr. rsch. programs in Scotland, Portugal, Ecuador. Editor Ont. Dental Assn. Jour., 1977-78; contbr. over 100 articles and 60 abstracts to profl. jours. Fellow Royal Coll. Dentists (Can.), Internat. Coll. Dentists, Acad. Internat. Dental Studies, Acad. Dentistry Internat.; mem. Alta. Dental Assn., Can. Dental Assn., Internat. Assn. Dental Rsch., Assn. Can. Faculties of Dentistry (pres. 1982-84), Can. Fund for Dental Edn. (chmn. 1991-93), Dentistry Can. Fund (chmn. 1993-95). Conservative. Mem. United Ch. Canada. Home: 12429 28th Ave, Edmonton, AB Canada T6J 4G4 Office: Alta Dental Assn, 8230 105th St, Edmonton, AB Canada T6E 5H9

THOMPSON, GUY BRYAN, investment company executive; b. N.Y.C., Mar. 10, 1940; s. Frederick Roeck and Carolyn Laura (Bryan) T.; m. Sallie Ann Mullins, Apr. 22, 1972 (div. Feb. 1982); 1 child, Kathryn Clarke. BA, U. Tex., 1962; postgrad., Baylor Law Sch., 1962-63; MBA, Columbia U., 1970. Adminstrv. asst. Alaska Barge & Transport, Inc., Southeast Asia, 1967; asst. mgr. corp. trading First Boston Corp.,, N.Y.C., 1970-72; sr. assoc. corp. fin. dept. Reynolds Securities, Inc., N.Y.C., 1972-73; portfolio mgr./fin. analyst Continental Ins. Cos., N.Y.C., 1973-74; asst. v.p. domestic banking 1st City Nat. Bank, Houston, 1974-77; dir. corp. relations, v.p. Credit Suisse, Houston, 1977-82; sr. v.p., prin. fin. officer Seneca Oil Co., Okla. City, 1982-83; chief fin. ops. exec. Seneca Exploration Co., Okla. City, 1982-83; pres., sec., dir. Seneca Fin. Svcs., Inc., Oklahoma City, 1983; exec. v.p. MPetroleum Corp, Dallas, 1984-86; pres. Austin Investment Co., 1987—; mng. dir. Houston Investment Co., 1989—; pres., CEO Thompson Oil Co., Houston, 1990—; sr. ptnr. Nagel-Thompson Enterprises, Austin, Tex., 1960—, gen. ptnr. Gibraltar Ltd., Houston, 1976-89, San Jacinto Investment Co., Houston, 1979-92. Mem. principal's ctr. St. Francis Episcopal Day Sch., Houston, 1983; patron Houston Ballet, 1981—; Stephen F. Austin Coll., 1983, Kinkaid Sch., Houston, 1987; mem. Cultural Arts Council Houston, 1984; charter mem. Rep. Presdl. Task Force, Washington, 1984; sponsor Rep. Presdl. Fund Nat. Com., 1980—, mem. Associated Reps. Tex., Austin, 1990—; patron Houston Lyric Theater Found., 1985; benefactor Worthan Ctr., Houston, 1983; mem. Mus. Fine Arts, Houston. Capt. USNR, 1963—; Vietnam. Recipient medal of merit Pres. of U.S., 1988, Rep. Presdl. Legion of Merit, 1992; named hon. adm. Tex. Navy, 1975, commd. adm., 1992; also various mil. decorations, commendations and svc. awards from U.S. and fgn. govt.; mem. SAR, SCV, Houston C. of C. (ports and waterways com. 1978-83), Dallas C. of C. (natural resources com. 1984-86, internat. com. 1985), Dallas Geol. Soc. (assoc. 1985-86), English Speaking Union U.S., Naval Order U.S., Navy League U.S. Naval Res. Assn., Res. Officers Assn. U.S., Heritage Soc., Mil. Order Stars and Bars, Sons Republic Tex., Tex. Corinthian Yacht Club, Houston Club, Camp Fire Am. Club, Houstonians Club, Cadre Club (chmn. bd., pres. 1993-94, bd. dirs. 1989-90), Forum Club. Avocations: tennis, sailing, hunting, golf, antique collecting. Home: 5828 Valley Forge Dr Houston TX 77057-2241

THOMPSON, GUY THOMAS, safety engineer; b. Chattanooga, Dec. 29, 1942; s. Thomas Nelson and Dorothy Leona (Dobbs) T.; m. Joy Ann Gray, July 22, 1966 (div. 1978); children: Jeffrey Leighton, Lydia Ann; m. Vicki Lynn Brogdon, Dec. 6, 1979; 1 child, Laura Lynn. BA in Engring. Electronic, Park Coll., Parkville, Mo., 1976; MS in Indsl. Safety, Middle Tenn. State U., 1989. Factory rep. Modern Maid Appliances, Chattanooga, 1966-68; biomed. tech. USAF, 1968-77, commd. 2d. lt., 1977, advanced through grades to capt., 1981, ret., 1987; tng. and safety coord. Murfreesboro (Tenn.) Area Vocat. Tech. Sch., 1987—; cons. Tenn. Elec. Coop. Assn., Nashville, 1987—, Tenn. Mcpl. Elec. Power Assn., Brentwood, 1987-92; dir. safety and loss control Okla. Assn. Electric Coops., 1992—. Author: Tech/Logistic Development Plans, 1978, Comprehensive Safety, 1988; copyright: Root Causes of Electric Contact Accidents and Electric Utility Safety Policy; inventor hyperbaric breathing apparatus. Coach Little League, Charleston, S.C., 1962-64, Girl's Softball League, Warner Robins, Ga., 1978-80, Girl's Softball, Tullahoma, Tenn., 1984-86. Mem. Am. Soc. Safety Engrs., Nat. Utility Tng. and Safety Edn. Assn. (coord. conf. 1989), Nat. Safety Coun., Tenn. Safety Congress (exec. com.), Am. Tech. Edn. Assn., Tri-County Bowling Assn. (pres. 1982-88), Arnold Engring. & Devel. Ctr. Golf Club (coun. 1984-88), Am. Legion, Phi Kappa Phi. Republican. Methodist. Avocations: golf, boating, Indian artifacts, bowling. Home: 15089 N Oak Dr Choctaw OK 73020-7009 Office: Okla Assn Electric Coops PO Box 54309 Oklahoma City OK 73154-1309

THOMPSON, HENRY NAINOA, hospital administrator; b. Honolulu, July 15, 1921; s. Henry Nainoa Sr. and Irmgard Luukia (Harbottle) T.; m. Pearl Elvina Mary Barbel, Nov. 16, 1946; children: Scott Henry Nainoa, Noni Nora Glynnis Bridget Skeffington Thompson, Kirk Leopold Kumulani. Student, U. Wash., 1940-42, Columbia U., 1942-44; BA in Phys. Therapy, Columbia U., 1946, MA in Corrective Phys. Edn. & Rehab., 1950; cert. poliomyelitis, U. So. Calif., L.A., 1950; cert. adminstr. phys. therapy, Stanford U., 1950; cert. adminstrn. rehab., Inst. Phys. Medicine & Rehab., 1953; cert. adminstrn. pers., U. Hawaii, 1956; cert. job sampling testing, Ins. for Crippled and Disabled, 1958; cert. analysis fin. statements, U. Hawaii, 1960. Phys. therapist VA Regional Office, N.Y.C., 1946; chief phys. therapy Nat. Soc. for Crippled Children and Adults, Honolulu, 1948-49, Kauikeolani Children's Hosp., Honolulu, 1950-53; asst. dir. Rehab. Ctr. Hawaii, Honolulu, 1953-68; adminstr. Wahiawa (Hawaii) Gen. Hosp., 1968-71; hosp. adminstr. The Queen's Med. Ctr., Honolulu, 1971-74; dir. arthritis ctr. U. Hawaii Sch. Medicine, Honolulu, 1974-75; dep. dir. county state hosps. Dept. of Health, State of Hawaii, Honolulu, 1975-82; adminstr. Hawaii State Health Planning and Devel. Agy, State of Hawaii, Honolulu, 1982—; past dir. Family Medicine, Inc. Honolulu. Past pres. Hawaii Kai Contry. Assn.; past pres., dir. Abilities Unltd. With AUS, 1946-48. Named one of 12 Nat. Phys. Fitness Leaders of Am., Pres.'s Johnson's Program for Phys. Fitness, 1965. Fellow Am. Coll. Hosp. Adminstrs.; mem. APHA, Am. Health Planning Assn., Hosp. Assn. Hawaii (assoc.), Am. Hosp. Assn. (assoc.), Koko Head Athletic Club (past pres.), Hawaii State Health Coun. (past pres.), Nat. Rehab. Assn. (past dir. Hawaii chpt.), Am. Assn. Phys. Therapy (past pres. Hawaii chpt.), Elks. Home and Office: 6815 Niumalu Loop Honolulu HI 96825

THOMPSON, HERBERT, JR., bishop; b. N.Y.C.; m. Ruselle Cross, 1968; children: Herbert, Owen, Kyrie. Grad. cum laude, Lincoln U., 1962; MDiv, Gen. Theol. Sem., N.Y.C., 1965; postgrad., Stony Brook U., Ch. Divinity Sch. of Pacific; D of Ministry, United Theol. Sem., Dayton, Ohio, 1992. Ordained to ministry Episcopal Ch. as deacon, 1965, then as priest. Chaplain Chester County, Pa.; vicar St. Gabriel's Ch., Bklyn.; rector Christ Ch., Bellport, N.Y., 1971-77, Grace Ch., Jamaica, 1977-88; bishop coadjutor Diocese of So. Ohio, 1988-91, bishop, 1992—; exec. dir. Interfaith Svcs., Bklyn.; colloquium moderator Gen. Theol. Sem.; instr., lectr. Mercer Sch. Theology; bd. dirs. Jamaica Devel. Corp. Reader Gen. Ordination Exams.; mem. Presiding Bishop's Commn. on Black Ministries, Coalition for Human Needs; mem. joint standing com. on planning for Gen. Conv., coun. of advice to pres. of Ho. of Deps.; bd. dirs. Cen. Queens YMCA, Queens Fedn. Chs., St. Christopher-Ottilie Home; chmn. Mayor's Commn. on Children, Cin. Served with USAF. Named Hon. Canon Cathedral of the Incarnation Diocese of Long Island, 1985. Mem. Jamaica C. of C. (bd. dirs.) Address: 412 Sycamore St Cincinnati OH 45202-4166

THOMPSON, HERBERT STANLEY, neuro-ophthalmologist; b. Shansi, China, June 12, 1932; came to U.S., 1949, naturalized, 1955; s. Robert Ernest and Ellen (Mulligan) T.; m. Delores Lucille Johnson, June 27, 1953; children: Geoffrey, Peter, Kenneth, Philip, Susan. Student, Methodist Coll., Belfast, No. Ireland, 1947-49; B.A., U. Minn., 1953, M.D., 1961; M.S., U. Iowa, 1966. Diplomate Am. Bd. Ophthalmology (assoc. examiner 1972-84, bd. dirs. 1989—). Intern U. Iowa, Iowa City, 1961-62; resident in ophthalmology U. Iowa, 1962-66; fellow in pupillography Columbia Coll. Physicians and Surgeons, 1962; fellow in clin. neuro-ophthalmology U. Calif., San Francisco, 1966-67; prof. ophthalmology U. Iowa, Iowa City, 1976—; dir. neuro-ophthalmology unit U. Iowa, 1967—; practice medicine specializing in neuro-ophthalmology Iowa City, 1967—. Editor: Topics in Neuro-ophthalmology, 1979; assoc. editor: Am. Jour. Ophthalmology, 1981-84, book rev. editor, 1984-91. Served with AUS, 1954-55. NIH spl. fellow, 1966-67; research career devel. awardee, 1968-72. Fellow Am. Acad. Ophthalmology, N.Am. Neuro-ophthalmol. Soc.; mem. Am. Ophthalmol. Soc. Primary research interest: movements of the pupil of human eye. Office: U Iowa Dept Ophthalmology Iowa City IA 52242

THOMPSON, HOWARD ELLIOTT, business educator; b. West Allis, Wis., July 30, 1934; s. Leonard Adolph and Hulda Axelina (Granstrom) T.; m. Judith M. Gram, June 30, 1956; children: Linda Kay, Karen Marie, James Howard, John Leonard, Ann Elizabeth. BS, U. Wis., 1956, MS, 1958, PhD, 1964. Mathematician, ops. rsch. analyst A.O. Smith Corp., Milw., 1957-61; asst. prof. Sch. Bus. U. Wis., Madison, 1964-67, assoc. prof., 1967-69, prof., 1969—, Mary Rennebohm prof., 1975-85, Kuechenmeister-Bascom prof., 1985—; vis. prof. Ohio State U., 1970-71; cons. various utilities and utility commns., 1968—; cons. World Bank, 1981-83; Wis. atty. gen., 1973-74; cons. U.S. Energy Info. Adminstrn., 1990—. Author: Applications of Calculus in Business and Economics, 1973, A Brief Calculus with Applications to Business and Economics, 1976, Management Science, 1981, Regulatory Finance, 1991; contbr. articles to profl. jours. Mem. Am. Fin. Assn., Am. Econs. Assn., Ops. Rsch. Soc., Am. Inst. Mgmt. Scis., Am. Inst. Decision Scis., Math. Assn. Am., Pi Mu Epsilon, Beta Gamma Sigma, Alpha Iota Delta, Phi Kappa Phi. Home: 7529 Fox Point Cir Madison WI 53717-1058 Office: Univ Wis Sch Business Grainger Hall 975 University Ave Madison WI 53706-1323

THOMPSON, HUGH LEE, university president; b. Martinsburg, W.Va., Mar. 25, 1934; s. Frank Leslie and Althea T.; m. Patricia Smith; children: Cheri, Linda, Tempe, Vicki. B.S., B.A. in English and Secondary Edn, Shepherd Coll., Shepherdstown, W.Va., 1956; MS, Pa. State U., 1958; Ph.D. in Higher Edn. Adminstrn, Case Western Res. U., 1969. Mem. faculty Pa. State U., 1957-60, Akron (Ohio) U., 1960-62; mem. faculty Baldwin-Wallace Coll., Berea, Ohio, 1962-70, asst. to pres., 1966-69, dir. instl. planning, asst. to pres., 1969-70; coordinator Associated Colls., Cleve., 1970-71; pres. Siena Heights Coll., Adrian, Mich., 1971-77, District Inst. Tech., 1977-80; chancellor Ind. U., Kokomo, 1980-90; pres. Washburn U., Topeka, 1990—; mem. president's adv. coun. Assn. Governing Bds. Univs. and Colls. Mem. Am. Assn. State Colls. and Univs. (coun. of state reps., steering com. urban and met. univs. coun.), North Ctrl. Assn. (evaluator, cons.). Home: 3130 SW Shadow Ln Topeka KS 66604-2541 Office: Washburn U Office of Pres Topeka KS 66621 *I have found that to be successful in any field of endeavor an individual must work very diligently at finding solutions to problems, be highly goal oriented, honest and forthright, and adhere to the teachings of Christ.*

THOMPSON, HUNTER STOCKTON, author, political analyst, journalist; b. Louisville, July 18, 1937; s. Jack R. and Virginia (Ray) T.; 1 child, Juan. Carribean corr. Time mag., 1959, N.Y. Herald Tribune, 1959-60; South Am. corr. Nat. Observer, 1961-63; West Coast corr. The Nation, 1964-66; columnist Ramparts, 1967-68, Scanlan's, 1969-70; nat. affairs editor Rolling Stone, 1970—; global affairs corr. High Times, 1977-82; political columnist San Francisco Examiner, 1985—; editor at large Smart, 1988—; polit. analyst European mags. London Observer, Tempo, Time Out, Das Magazine, Nieuwe Revu, Die Woche, 1988—; judge Nat. Book Awards,

1975. Author: Prince Jellyfish, 1960, Hell's Angels, 1966, The Rum Diary, 1967, Fear and Loathing in Las Vegas, 1972, Fear and Loathing On the Campaign Trail '72, 1973, The Great Shark Hunt, 1979, (with Ralph Steadman) The Curse of Lono, 1983, Generation of Swine, 1988, Songs of the Doomed, 1990, Screwjack, 1991, Better Than Sex, 1993; creator Gonzo journalism. Mem. Pitkin County (Colo.) Sheriff's Adv. Com., 1976-81; mem. president's task force ACLU; mem. nat. adv. bd. NORML, 1976; founder 4th Amendment Found. Mem. NRA (exec. dir.), U.S. Naval Inst. (exec. dir.), Air Force Assn. (exec. dir.), Hong Kong Fgn. Corrs., Kona Coast Marlin Fisherman's Assn., Vincent Black Shadow Soc., Woody Creek Rod and Gun Club (exec. dir.), Overseas Press Club (exec. dir.), Nat. Press Club. Clubs: Key West Mako, Nat. Press, Hong Kong Fgn. Corrs. Office: Janklow & Nesbit 598 Madison Ave New York NY 10022-1614*

THOMPSON, J. ANDY, bank executive; b. Ft. Worth, Sept. 21, 1943; s. Fredrick Dickson and Mary Alice (Rhea) T.; m. Nancy Sealy, Jan. 15, 1966; children: J. Andrew Jr., Christopher Sealy. BBA, U. Tex., 1965. Exec. v.p. Internat. Svc. Ins. Co., Ft. Worth, 1968-83; exec. v.p Tex. Security Bancshares, Ft. Worth, 1984-86, pres., 1986-88, chmn, chief exec. officer, 1988—; chmn., chief exec. officer Cen. Bank & Trust, Ft. Worth, 1988—, North Ft. Worth Bank, 1988—; adv. bd. Policy Mgmt. Systems, Columbia, S.C., 1975-83; bd. dirs. Ft. Worth C. of C., 1989—. Mem. administrv. bd. First Meth. Ch.; trustee, chmn. Harris Meth. Hosp., Ft. Worth; vice chmn., trustee Harris Meth. Health System; mem. exec. com., bd. dirs. Lena Pope Home for Children: bd. dirs. James L. West Presbyn. Spl. Care Ctr. Capt. U.S. Army, 1966-68, Vietnam. Mem. Tex. Banker's Assn., Am. Banker's Assn., Ft. Worth Club (pres. 1993—, mem. bd. govs.), Rotary Internat. Republican. Methodist. Avocations: tennis, sailing, golf.

THOMPSON, J. KEN, gas, oil industry executive. Mgr., v.p. Arco Exploration Prodn. Tech., Plano, Tex. Office: Atlantic Richfield Co ARCO Exploration Prodn Tech 2300 W Plano Pky Plano TX 75075

THOMPSON, JACK EDWARD, mining company executive; b. Central City, Nebr., Nov. 17, 1924; s. Ray Elbert and Bessie Fay (Davis) T.; m. Maria del Carmen Larrea, May 8, 1948; children: Jack Edward, Ray Anthony, Robert Davis. Student, Northwestern U., 1942-43, Colo. Sch. Mines, 1943-45; D of Engring. (hon.), Colo. Sch. Mines, 1993. V.p. Cía. Química Comercial de Cuba S.A., 1946-60, Cía. de Fomento Químico S.A., 1946-60; with Newmont Mining Corp., N.Y.C., 1960-86; asst. to pres. Newmont Mining Corp., 1964-67, v.p., 1967-71, dir., 1969-86, exec. v.p., 1971-74, pres., 1974-85, vice chmn., 1985-86, cons., 1986-90. Chmn. bd. trustees Minerals Industry Ednl. Found.; mem. Pres.'s Coun. Colo. Sch. Mines. Recipient Distinguished Achievement medal Colo. Sch. Mines, 1974. Mem. AIME, Mining and Metall. Soc. Am., Mining Found. of S.W. (pres., bd. govs.), Tucson Country Club.

THOMPSON, JAMES BRUCE, national park administrator; b. Toledo, Iowa, Dec. 27, 1937; s. Irvin Warren and Ruth Marian (Elston) T.; m. Janice Ruth Huizinga, Aug. 24, 1957; children: Samantha Ruth, Ian Bruce. Student, U. Iowa, 1955-56; BS, U. Wyo., 1959; postgrad., George Washington U., 1966-67. Park ranger Rocky Mountain Nat. Park, Estes Park, Colo., 1960-65, supt., 1984—; park mgr. Jewel Cave Nat. Monument, Custer, S.D., 1965-66; program analyst Nat. Park Service, Washington, 1966-69; assoc. regional dir. Pacific NW region Nat. Park Service, Seattle, 1976-78; dep. regional dir. Rocky Mountain region Nat. Park Service, Denver, 1978-84; supt. Theodore Roosevelt Nat. Park, Medora, N.D., 1969-72, Death Valley (Calif.) Nat. Monument, 1972-76; mem. numerous task forces on info. mgmt. and mgmt. systems. Author: Geology of Jewel Cave, 1967. Trustee Estes Park Music Festival Found., 1987—; v.p. Longs Peak Highland Festival, Estes Park, 1985-91. Named One of Outstanding Young Men of Am., 1971; recipient Meritorious Service award Dept. of Interior, 1980, Disting. Svc. award, 1990. Lodge: Rotary. Office: Rocky Mountain Nat Pk Office of Supt Highway 35 Estes Park Estes Park CO 80517

THOMPSON, JAMES BURLEIGH, JR., geologist, educator; b. Calais, Maine, Nov. 20, 1921; s. James Burleigh and Edith (Peabody) T.; m. Eleanora Mairs, Aug. 3, 1957; 1 son, Michael A. A.B., Dartmouth, 1942, D.Sc. (hon.), 1975; Ph.D., Mass. Inst. Tech., 1950. Instr. geology Dartmouth, 1942; research asst. Mass. Inst. Tech., 1946-47, instr., 1947-49; instr. petrology Harvard, 1949-50, asst. prof., 1950-55, assoc. prof. mineralogy, 1955-60, prof., 1960-77, Sturgis Hooper prof. geology, 1977-92, Sturgis Hooper prof. geology emeritus, 1992—; guest prof. Swiss Fed. Inst. Tech., 1977-78; adj. prof. geology Dartmouth Coll., 1992—. Served to 1st lt. USAAF, 1942-46. Guggenheim fellow, 1963; Sherman Fairchild distinguished scholar Calif. Inst. Tech., 1976. Fellow Mineral. Soc. Am. (pres. 1967-68, recipient Roebling medal 1978), Geol. Soc. Am. (A.L. Day medal 1964), Am. Acad. Arts and Scis.; mem. NAS, AAAS, Am. Geophys. Union, Geochem. Soc. (pres. 1968-69, Goldschmidt medal 1985), Mineral. Soc. of Gt. Britain and Ireland (hon.), Sigma Xi. Office: Harvard U Cambridge MA 02138

THOMPSON, JAMES CLARK, utilities executive; b. St. Louis, Sept. 24, 1939; s. Leonard Andrew and Virginia Evelyn (Clark) T.; m. Gerry Marie Rush, Oct. 2, 1965; children: Ren James, David James. BSBA, Washington U., St. Louis, 1968. Various positions then corp. sec. Union Electric Co., St. Louis, 1982—; sec. Union Electric Devel. Corp., 1982—, also dir. Trustee Laumeier Sculpture Park. Petty officer 2d class USN, 1957-60. Mem. Am. Soc. Corp. Secs. (pres. St. Louis chpt. 1989-90), U.S. Naval Cryptologic Vets. Assn., 1904 World's Fair Soc. (sec. 1987—). Republican. Avocation: collecting 1904 World's Fair memorabilia. Office: Union Electric Co PO Box 149 Saint Louis MO 63166-0149

THOMPSON, JAMES DAVID, financial services company executive, lawyer; b. Gulfport, Miss., Oct. 22, 1945; s. James David and Dorothy (O'Dom) T.; m. Carol Vail, Aug. 23, 1969; children: Meredith, Adrienne, James. BA in Econs., Millsaps Coll., Jackson, Miss., 1967; JD, U. Miss., 1970. Bar: Miss. 1970, U.S. Dist. Ct. (no. dist.) Miss. 1970, U.S. Ct. Mil. Appeals 1971. Asst. gen. counsel ITT Fin. Corp., St. Louis, 1974-77, sr. v.p., gen. counsel, 1977-90, exec. v.p., 1990-93, dir. ins. ops., 1981-93, also bd. dirs.; pres., CEO ITT Diversified Fin. Corp., St. Louis, 1990-93; chmn., pres., CEO Lyndon Ins. Group, 1984-93; exec. v.p., CFO ING Am. Life, Atlanta, 1993—; bd. dirs. ITT Fin. Corp., ITT Diversified Fin. Corp., ITT Lyndon Ins. Group, ITT Fin. Securities, Inc., ITT Real Estate Loan Corp., ITT Fed. Bank, f.s.b., Newport Beach, Calif., chmn. Served to capt. USAF, 1970-74. Mem. ABA, Miss. Bar Assn., Bar Assn. Met. St. Louis, Ga. Life and Health Ins. Guarantee Assn. (bd. dirs.). Methodist. Office: ING Am Life 5780 Powers Ferry Rd NW Atlanta GA 30327

THOMPSON, JAMES HAROLD, judge; b. Chgo., Aug. 15, 1927; s. Robert Bruce and Jimmie Lee (Walls) T.; m. Jean Fay Ruttenbur, Sept. 21, 1953; 1 child, Irene Lee. BS in Pub. Adminstrn., The Am. Univ., 1958, LLB, 1961. Bar: D.C. 1962, Nev. 1963. State court Nev. Dept. Hwys., 1965-70; atty. gen. State of Nev., 1971-78, spl. dep. atty. gen., 1979-81, judge 2d jud. dist., 1981-83, judge Reno Justice Ct., 1983—; rep. State of Nev. to U.S. Supreme Ct. in Calif. vs. Nev. boundary litigation, 1979-81. Past mem. editorial bd. Better Roads mag., 1968-69; contbr. articles to profl. jours. With U.S. Army, 1946-47, 51-53. Recipient Am. Jurisprudence prize for Excellence in Trusts. Mem. Washoe County Bar Assn., First Jud. Dist. Bar Assn. (v.p. 1967-68), Am. Arbitration Assn. (nat. constrn. panel), Delta Theta Phi. Democrat. Methodist. Home: 136 Greenridge Dr Reno NV 89509-3927

THOMPSON, JAMES HOWARD, historian, library administrator; b. Memphis, Aug. 20, 1934; s. Curtis Barnabas and Clara (Terry) T.; m. Margareta Ortenblad, Nov. 24, 1961; children—Ralph, Anna, Howard. B.A. in History, Rhodes Coll., Memphis, 1955; M.A., U. N.C., Chapel Hill, 1957, Ph.D. in History, 1961; M.S. in Library Sci, U. Ill., 1963. Teaching fellow U. N.C., Chapel Hill, 1955-56; departmental asst. U. N.C., 1956-57, reference asst., 1959-61, dir. undergrad. library, lectr. in history, 1968-70; circulation asst. U. Ill., 1961-63; asst. Center for Russian Area and Lang. Studies, 1962-63; cataloger Duke U., 1963-65; asst. prof. history U. S.W. La., 1965-66; asst. prof. U. Colo., 1966-68; dir. libraries, prof. history U. N.C., Greensboro, 1970-94; ret., 1994; bd. dirs. Southeastern Library Network, 1979-82, treas., 1981-82. Contbr. articles, revs. to profl. jours. Ford Found. research fellow, 1957-58; U. Colo. grantee, 1967; U. N.C. at Greensboro grantee, 1977-78, 89. Mem. Phi Beta Kappa (chpt. pres. 1979-80), Beta Phi Mu, Phi

Alpha Theta, Chi Beta Phi. Episcopalian. Home: 3006 New Hanover Dr Greensboro NC 27408-6710

THOMPSON, JAMES KIRK, transportation executive; b. Little Rock, 1953. Grad., U. Ark., 1978. Pres., CEO, dir. J.B. Hunt Transport Svcs., Inc., Lowell, Ark. Office: J B Hunt Transport Svcs Inc 615 Jb Hunt Dr Lowell AR 72745

THOMPSON, JAMES ROBERT, JR., lawyer, former governor; b. Chgo., May 8, 1936; s. James Robert and Agnes Josephine (Swanson) T.; m. Jayne Carr, 1976; 1 dau., Samantha Jayne. Student, U. Ill., Chgo., 1953-55, Washington U., St. Louis, 1955-56; J.D., Northwestern U., 1959. Bar: Ill. 1959, U.S. Supreme Ct. 1964. Asst. state's atty. Cook County, Ill., 1959-64; assoc. prof. law Northwestern U. Law Sch., 1964-69; asst. atty. gen. State of Ill., 1969-70; chief criminal div., 1969, chief dept. law enforcement and pub. protection, 1969-70; 1st asst. U.S. atty. No. Dist. Ill., 1970-71, U.S. atty., 1971-75; counsel firm Winston & Strawn, Chgo., 1975-77, ptnr., chmn. exec. com., 1991—; gov. Ill., 1977-91; mem. joint com. to revise Ill. criminal code, mem. drafting subcom. Chgo.-Ill. bar assns., 1959-63, chmn. joint com. to draft indigent def. legis., 1966-68; mem. com. to draft handbooks for petit jurors in civil and criminal cases and for grand jurors Jud. Conf. Ill., 1959; mem. com. to draft uniform instrn. in criminal cases Ill. Supreme Ct.; co-dir. criminal law course for Chgo. Police and Indsl. Security Personnel, 1962-64; mem. Chgo. Mayor's Com. to Draft Legis. to Combat Organized Crime, 1964-67; adviser Pres.'s Commn. Law Enforcement and Adminstrn. Justice, 1966; mem. Pres.'s Task Force on Crime, 1967; lectr. Northwestern U. Law Sch., U. Calif.-Davis, Mich. State U., Nat., Ill., Ohio, U.D. Va., N.J., Ala., Md. and Ga. prosecutors' assns.; former bd. dirs. Chgo. Crime Commn.; v.p. Americans for Effective Law Enforcement, 1967-69; chmn. Pres.'s Intelligence Oversight Bd., 1990—, adv. bd. Fed. Emergency Mgmt. Agy., 1991—; Ill. Acad. Fine Arts; bd. govs. Chgo. Bd. of Trade;trustee FMC Corp., Nat. Trust for Historic Preservation, Chgo. Mus. Contemporary Art. Co-author: Cases and Comments on Criminal Justice, 2 vols, 1968, 74, Criminal Law and Its Adminstration, 1970, 74; asst. editor-in-chief: Jour. Criminal Law, Criminology and Police Sci., 1965-69; bd. editors: Criminal Law Bull. Pres. Ill. Math. and Sci. Acad. Found.; co-chmn. U.S. Atty. Gen's. Task Force on Violent Crime, 1981; chmn. Rep. Gov's. Assn., 1982, Coun. Gt. Lakes Gov's., 1985, NGA Task Force on Teen Pregnancy, 1987, NGA Task Force on Transp. Infrastructure, 1988, NGA Task Force on Global Climate Change, 1989; mem. Nat. Commn. to Prevent Infant Mortality, 1986. Mem. ABA, Ill. Bar Assn. (past chmn. criminal law sect.), Fed. Bar Assn., Chgo. Bar Assn., Nat. Gov's. Assn. (chmn. 1983). Republican. Office: Winston & Strawn 35 W Wacker Dr Chicago IL 60601-1614

THOMPSON, JAMES WILBER, symphony performer; b. Frankfurt, Germany, May 12, 1949; came to U.S., 1951; s. James Wilbur and Bertie Lee (Perry) T.; m. Ann King Millsop, May 17, 1973; children: Caitlin, Joseph, Lesley. BMus, New Eng. Conservatory, Boston. Prin. trumpet Phoenix Symphony Orch., 1969-73, Orch. of State of Mex., Tomca, 1973-76; solo trumpet Montreal Symphony Orch., 1976-80; prin. trumpet Atlanta Symphony Orch., 1990—; prof. trumpet No. Ariz. U., Flagstaff, 1969-73, McGill U., Montreal, 1976-90; instr. trumpet Ga. State U., Atlanta, 1994—; tchr. trumpet Nat. Conservatory of Music, Mexico City. Over 50 recordings with Montreal Symphony; 2 concertos for solo trumpet written for him; recordings include Shostakovich Piano Concerto, Malcolm Forsyth's Concerto for trumpet, 1992; performer Que. premier of Jacques Hetu's Trumpet Concerto, 1990, Glenn Buhr's Concerto for Trumpet, 1992. Recipient 3d prize, Maurice Andre Internat. Trumpet Competition, Paris, 1979. Mem. Am. Fedn. Musicians. Avocations: computers, skiing, tennis, billiards. Home: 100 Foal Dr Roswell GA 30076 Office: Atlanta Symphony Orchestra 1293 Peachtree St NE Atlanta GA 30309

THOMPSON, JAMES WILLIAM, banker; b. Dunn, N.C., June 18, 1939; s. William J. and Lucy (Pope) T.; m. Meredith Cromartie, June 10, 1961; children—Ann, Lucy, Bill. BSBA, U. N.C. 1961. Credit analyst NCNB Corp., Charlotte, N.C., 1963-68; v.p., bond dept. mgr. NCNB Corp., 1968-71, investment portfolio mgr., 1971-74, sr. v.p., funds mgmt. exec., 1974-77, exec. v.p., 1977-83, corp. exec. v.p., 1983-85, vice chmn. bd., 1985—; chmn. Southeastern Banking, Charlotte, 1988-91; chmn. NCNB Nat. Bank N.C., 1990, NationsBank East, 1992—, NationsBank N.C., 1992—, NationsBank Md., 1992—, NationsBank Va., 1992—, NationsBank Washington, 1992—NationsBank S.C., 1993—; vice chmn. NationsBank Corp., 1993—. Past pres. Mint Mus. of Charlotte; mem. bd. visitors U. N.C.; bd. dirs. Found. of U. N.C., Charlotte, Univ. Rsch. Pk., N.C. Performing Arts Ctr., pres. 1993—; trustee U. N.C., Charlotte; mem. Gov.'s Bus. Coun. of Arts and Humanities; past pres. N.C. Edn. Coun. Mem. Bankers Roundtable, Charlotte City Club (past pres.). Democrat. Methodist. Home: 459 Hempstead Pl Charlotte NC 28207-2315 Office: NationsBank Corp NC1007-5802 NationsBank Corp Ctr Charlotte NC 28255

THOMPSON, JAMES WILLIAM, lawyer; b. Dallas, Oct. 22, 1936; s. John Charles and Frances (Van Slyke) T.; BS, U. Mont., 1958, JD, 1962; m. Marie Hertz, June 26, 1965 (dec. 1995); children: Elizabeth, Margaret, John. Acct., Arthur Young & Co., N.Y.C., summer 1959; instr. bus. adminstrn. Eastern Mont. Coll., Billings, 1959-60, U. Mont., Missoula, 1960-61; admitted to Mont. bar, 1962; assoc. Cooke, Moulton, Bellingham & Longo, Billings, 1962-64, James R. Felt, Billings, 1964-65; asst. atty. City of Billings 1963-64, atty., 1964-66; ptnr. Felt, Speare & Thompson, Billings, 1966-72, McNamer, Thompson & Cashmore, 1973-86, McNamer & Thompson Law Firm PC, 1986-89, McNamer, Thompson, Werner & Stanley, P.C., 1990-93, McNamer Thompson Law Firm PC, 1993—; bd. dirs. Associated Employers of Mont., Inc., 1989—. Mem. Billings Zoning Commn., 1966-69; v.p. Billings Community Action Program (now Dist. 7 Human Resources Devel. Council), 1968-70, pres., 1970-75, trustee, 1975—; mem. Yellowstone County Legal Services Bd., 1969-70; City-County Air Pollution Control Bd., 1969-70; pres. Billings Symphony Soc., 1970-71; bd. dirs. Billings Studio Theatre, 1967-73, Mont. Inst. of Arts Found., 1986-89, Downtown Billings Assn., 1986-90, Billings Area Bus. Incubator, Inc., 1991-94, Found. of Mont. State U., Billings, 1992—; mem. Diocesan exec. council, 1972-75; mem. Billings Transit Commn., 1971-73, chmn. City Devel. Agy., 1972-73; bd. dirs. United Way, Billings, 1973-81. CPA, Mont. Mem. ABA, Am. Acad. Estate Planning Attys., Nat. Acad. Elder Law Attys., State Bar Mont., Yellowstone County Bar Assn. (bd. dirs. 1983-87, pres. 1985-86), C. of C., Elks, Kiwanis (pres. Yellowstone chpt. 1974-75), Sigma Chi (pres. Billings alumni assn. 1963-65). Episcopalian. Home: 123 Lewis Ave Billings MT 59101-6034 Office: 300 First Bank Bldg Billings MT 59101

THOMPSON, JEAN TANNER, retired librarian; b. San Luis Obispo, Calif., June 15, 1929; d. Chester Corey and Mildred (Orr) T.; 1 child, Anne Marie Miller. Student, Whitworth Coll., Spokane, Wash., 1946-49; A.B., Boston U., 1951; postgrad., U. Wis., Eau Claire, 1964-67; M.S.L.S., Columbia U., 1973; Ed.M., U. Va., Charlottesville, 1978. Asst. social sci. librarian Univ. Libraries Va. Polytechnic Inst. and State U., Blacksburg, 1973-77, head social sci. dept. Univ. Libraries, 1977-83; head reference dept. Meml. Library U. Wis., Madison, 1983-86, asst. dir. reference and info. svcs., 1986-91, ret. Contbg. editor: ALA Guide to Information Access, 1994; mem. editorial bd. RQ, 1984-89. Mem. ALA Assn. Coll. and Research Libraries (edn. and behavioral sci. sect. vice chmn. 1985-86, chmn. 1986-87), Wis. Library Assn., Wis. Assn. of Acad. Librarians. Methodist. Home: 103 S Hunter Ln Troy AL 36081-8206

THOMPSON, JERE WILLIAM, retail food company executive; b. Dallas, Jan. 18, 1932; s. Joe C. and Margaret (Philp) T.; m. Peggy Dunlap, June 5, 1954; children: Michael, Jere W., Patrick, Deborah, Kimberly, Christopher, David. Grad. high sch., 1950; B.B.A. U. Tex., 1954. With Southland Corp., Dallas, 1954—; v.p. stores Southland Corp. (merged with Thompson Co. 1988), Dallas, 1962-73, exec. v.p., 1973-74, pres., 1974-91, dir., 1962—; chief exec. officer, 1986-91, co-vice chmn., 1991—. MCorp. Bd. dirs. St. Paul Hosp. Found. Served to lt. (j.g.) USNR, 1954-56. Office: Philip Corp 300 Crescent Ct Ste 900 Dallas TX 75201

THOMPSON, JESSE ELDON, vascular surgeon; b. Laredo, Tex., Apr. 7, 1919; s. Jesse Eathel and Sara Gail (Bolton) T.; m. Madeleine Jane Curtis, Sept. 18, 1944; children: Sally C., Jesse E., Janet E., Diane B. BA, U. Tex. 1939; MD, Harvard U., 1943; Rhodes scholar, Oxford U., 1949-50. Intern Mass. Gen. Hosp., Boston, 1943; resident in surgery Mass. Gen. Hosp.,

1944-48; practice medicine specializing in surgery, tchr. surgery Boston U., 1949-54; practice medicine specializing in surgery, tchr. vascular surgery Baylor Hosp., Dallas, 1954—; chief vascular surgery Baylor Hosp., 1980-86; clin. prof. surgery U. Tex. Southwestern Med. Sch., Dallas; attending surgeon Baylor Hosp., 1954—; chief surgery Baylor Hosp., Dallas, 1982-86; Mem Tex. and Dist. Rhodes Scholar Selection Coms. Author: Surgery for Cerebrovascular Insufficiency, 1968; editorial bd.: Surgery, 1975-89, Jour. Cardiovascular Surgery, 1975—; sr. editor Jour. Vascular Surgery, 1984-86; contbr. numerous articles to profl. jours. Served to capt. M.C AUS, 1945-47. Fulbright sr. fellow, 1949-50. Fellow ACS (treas.); mem. Am. Surg. Assn., So. Surg. Assn., Tex. Surg. Soc., Soc. Vascular Surgery, Internat. Cardiovascular Soc., Internat. Soc. Surgery, So. Assn. for Vascular Surgery, Dallas Petroleum Club, Dallas Country Club, Masons. Methodist. Home: 3705 Stanford Ave Dallas TX 75225-7204 Office: 712 N Washington Ave Ste 509 Dallas TX 75246-1635

THOMPSON, JOAN KATHRYN, university official; b. Portsmouth, Va., Jan. 24, 1956; d. Alfred Colbein and Ruby (Skiee) Lee; div.; children: Chad David, Allison Rae. BS in Bus. Edn., Drake U., 1977. Tchr. Des Moines Pub. Schs., 1978-80; commodity broker R.G. Dickinson, Des Moines, 1980-82; investment officer 1st Interstate Bank, Des Moines, 1982-87, v.p., sales mgr., 1987-88; treas. Iowa State U., Ames, 1988—. Treas. Iowa 4-H Found., Ames, 1988—. Mem. Nat. Treasury Mgmt. Assn., Iowa Treasury Mgmt. Assn., Ea. Iowa Cash Mgmt. Assn. Republican. Lutheran. Avocations: swimming, tennis, golf. Office: Iowa State U 122 Beardshear Hall Ames IA 50011

THOMPSON, JOE FLOYD, aerospace engineer, research director; b. Grenada, Miss., Apr. 13, 1939; s. Joe Floyd and Bernice Thompson; m. Emilie Kay Wilson, June 1, 1974; children: Mardi, Douglass. BS, Miss. State U., 1961, MS, 1963; PhD, Ga. Tech., 1971. Aerospace engr. NASA Marshall, Huntsville, Ala., 1963-64; prof. Miss. State U., Starkville, 1964-90, dir., 1990—; mem. tech. rev. bd. Army Rsch. Lab., Adelphi, Md., 1993—; dir. computer code Nat. Grid Project, 1993; dir. NSF Engring. Rsch. Ctr. for Computational Field Simulation. Author: Numerical Grid Generation, 1985, (computer code) Eagle Grid System, 1987; sr. assoc. editor Applied Math. and Computation, 1985-94; assoc. editor Numerical Heat Transfer, 1989—; mem. edit. bd. Computational Fluid Dynamics Jour., 1993—, Jour. Computational Physics, 1995—. Recipient Commdr.'s award Army Waterways Exp. Sta., Vicksburg, Miss., 1992. Mem. IEEE, IEEE Computer Soc., AIAA (Aerodynamics award 1992), SIAM. Presbyterian. Achievements include establishment of NSF Engineering Research Center; pioneering work in field of numerical grid generation. Home: Miss State U Box 255 Mississippi State MS 39762 Office: Miss State U Box 6176 Mississippi State MS 39762

THOMPSON, JOHN, college basketball coach; b. Washington, Sept. 2, 1941. Student, Providence Coll., 1960-64; M in Counseling and Guidance, U. D.C., 1971; LHD (hon.), St. Peter's Coll., 1982; H.H.D., Wheeling Coll., 1982. Player Boston Celtics, Nat. Basketball Assn., 1964-66; basketball coach St. Anthony High Sch., Washington, 1966-72; basketball coach Georgetown U., Washington, 1972—; presdl. asst. on urban affairs, 1977; founder Summer Basketball Sch. Georgetown U.; mem. Nat. Invitation Tournament Championship Team, 1963, Nat. Basketball Assn. Championship Team, 1965, 66; won NCAA championship, 1984, 2nd place NCAA championship, 1982, 85. Inducted Providence Coll. Hall of Fame, 1974; U.S. asst. coach Olympic Games Montreal, Que., Can., 1976; recipient Pres.'s award, Patrick Healy award Georgetown U., 1982; named U.S. Basketball Writers Assn. Coach of Yr., 1982; recipient other awards; named Coach of Yr., United Press Internat., 1987; Coach U.S. Olympic Games, Seoul, Korea, 1988; recipient bronze medal Olympic Games, 1988. Mem. Nat. Assn. Basketball Coaches (bd. dirs. 1976—, chmn. selection com. for east team, NABC Coach of Yr. 1984-85). Office: Georgetown U Basketball Office Washington DC 20057*

THOMPSON, JOHN DOUGLAS, financier; b. Montreal, Que., Can., Sept. 28, 1934; s. William Douglas and Anne F. (Whebby) T.; children: Jacqueline, Catherine, Peter, Anne Marie, Francois. B.Eng., McGill U. 1957; M.B.A., U. Western Ont., 1960. Dep. chmn. bd. Montreal Trustco Inc.; past chmn. bd. Trust Cos. Assn. of Can., vice-chmn. Domtar Inc.; bd. dirs. Société Générale de financement du Que., J.S. Redpath Holdings, Inc., BCE Mobile, Montrusco Assocs. Inc., Boréal Assurances Inc., Sedgwick Air Transat, Manitex, Inc. Bd. dirs. MacDonald Stewart Found., Salvation Army, chmn. Montreal adv. bd.; chmn. Montreal YMCA Found.; mem. audit com. McGill U.; past dirs. St. Mary's Hosp. Found.; gov., past pres. St. Mary's Hosp. Ctr. Mem. Assn. Profl. Engrs., Que. and Ont., Mt. Royal Club (Montreal), Royal Montreal Golf Club, Montreal Amateur Athletic Club, Mt. Bruno Country Club Inc., The Forest and Stream Club. Roman Catholic. Office: 1800 McGill College Ave 17th Fl, Montreal, PQ Canada H3A 3K9

THOMPSON, JOHN E., principal. Prin. Ardmore (Okla.) Middle Sch. Recipient Blue Ribbon Sch. award U.S. Dept. Edn., 1990-91. Office: Ardmore Mid Sch PO Box 1709 Ardmore OK 73402

THOMPSON, JOHN HENRY, consulting executive; b. Ute, Iowa, May 15, 1933; s. Frederick Stephen and Georgia (Wilkins) T.; m. Beverly Diane Price, Aug. 25, 1956; 1 child, Jennifer. BA in Psychology, Calif. State U., Fresno, 1960; PhD in Psychology, U. Ill., 1964. Lic. psychologist, Ill., Wash., Calif. Asst. prof. psychology Gonzaga U., Spokane, Wash., 1964-65, chmn. psychology dept., 1965-67; staff psychologist Rohrer, Hibler & Replogle, Portland, Oreg., 1967-69; mng. ptnr. Rohrer, Hibler & Replogle, Seattle, 1969-72; mgr. Rohrer, Hibler & Replogle, L.A., 1972-75; v.p. Rohrer, Hibler & Replogle, 1975-83; exec. v.p. Rohrer, Hibler & Replogle, 1984-85; pres., COO Rohrer, Hibler & Replogle, Chgo., 1985-87; pres., CEO RHR Internat. Co., Wood Dale, Ill., 1987—, chmn., CEO, 1991; bd. dirs. Target Sales, Fresno, Calif., 1978-84. Contbr. articles to profl. jours. and chpts. to books. Mem. State Bd. Med. Quality Assurance, Calif., 1974-77. Sgt. USMC, 1952-55, Korea. Roman Catholic. Avocations: hunting, fishing, target shooting, hiking, music. Office: RHR Internat Co 220 Gerry Dr Wood Dale IL 60191-1147

THOMPSON, JOHN MORE, managment consultant; b. Leicester, Eng., Nov. 26, 1938; came to U.S., 1963; s. John Kenneth and Jenny (More) T.; m. Carol Jane Valpy, Sept. 28, 1963; children: Rupert, Juliet, Jessica. BA, Cambridge U., Eng., 1962, MA, 1962. Tech. specialist Shell Chem., 1962-63; mktg. mgr. Celanese Corp., 1963-68; v.p. Interactive Data Corp., Waltham, Mass., 1968-73; vice chmn. Index Group, Cambridge, Mass., 1973-89; chmn., CEO CSC Europe, London, 1989-93. Chmn. bd. trustees Charles River Sch., Dover, Mass., 1974-78; pres. Ind. Schs. Chairmens Assn., N.Y.C., 1978. Lt. Royal Signals, Brit. Army, 1957-59. Mem. Oxford and Cambridge Club (London), Royal Overseas Club (London). Office: CSC Europe, 20 Savile Row, London W1X 1AE, England

THOMPSON, JOHN WILLIAM, international management consultant; b. Hurricane, Utah, Oct. 14, 1945; s. Thomas Thurman and Lula (Brinkerhoff) T.; m. Pamela Ruth Williams, Sept. 14, 1991. BSEE, Utah State U., 1969, MBA, 1972; PhD, U. Oreg., 1978. Rsch. asst. Utah State U., Logan, Utah, 1967-69, tching. asst., 1971-72; elec. engr. Collins Radio, Newport Beach, Calif., 1969-72; tching. fellow U. Oreg., Eugene, 1972-78; tng. dir. Lifespring Inc., San Rafael, Calif. 1978-80; pres., CEO Human Factors Inc., San Rafael, Calif., 1980—; chmn. bd. Acumen Internat., San Rafael, Calif., 1985—. Author: The Human Factor: An Inquiry into Communication and Consciousness, 1983, Leadership in the 21st Century in New Traditions in Business, 1992, The Renaissance of Learning in Learning Organizations: Developing Cultures for Tomorrow's Workplace, 1994; author of software based management assessment programs, system theory based management development courses, 1980-92. Rockefeller Found. grantee, 1971. Avocations: sailing, raising koi, gardening, bicycling. Office: Human Factors Inc 4000 Civic Center Dr Ste 500 San Rafael CA 94903

THOMPSON, JOYCE ELIZABETH, retired state education official; b. Pearson, Okla., Nov. 22, 1929; d. Walter Samuel and Clara Gertrude (Davis) T.; m. Gordon Pybas, May 22, 1989. BS, Okla. State U., 1951; M in Home Econs., Okla. U., 1974. Cert. vocat. and gen. home econs., Okla. Home econs. tchr. Wister (Okla.) High Sch., 1951-55, Tishomingo (Okla.) High

Sch., 1955-56, Wilson (Okla.) High Sch., 1956-67, Konawa (Okla.) High Sch., 1967-71; dist. supr. State Dept. of Vo-Tech., Oklahoma City, 1971-80; state supr. State Dept. of Vo-Tech., Stillwater, Okla., 1980-88; ret., 1988; mem. adv. com. Future Homemakers Am., Oklahoma City, 1961-68; treas. Nat. Assn. State Suprs., Washington, 1983-87; advisor Nat. Assn. Vocat. Home Econs. Tchrs., Washington, 1986-87. Chairperson Okla. Home Econs. Legis. Network, Stillwater, 1984; mem. fin. com. Wes Watkins for Gov., Stillwater, 1988-90. Named Tchr. of Yr. Ancient Free and Accepted Masons, Wilson, 1960, 65; recipient Grand Cross of Colors, Internat. Order of Rainbow, Wilson, 1964, Hon. membership Future Homemakers of Am., Oklahoma City, 1976, Young Homemakers of Okla., Oklahoma City, 1977, Spl. award of merit Nat. Assn. Vocat. Home Econs. Tchrs., Washington, 1986. Mem. Am. Vocat. Assn. (life mem., membership chair 1981-84), Okla. Vocat. Assn. (life mem., v.p. 1965), Am. Legion Aux., Order Ea. Star. Democrat. Mem. Church of Christ. Avocations: reading, sewing, vol. work, cooking, water skiing. Home: RR 2 Box 113 Wanette OK 74878-9725

THOMPSON, JOYCE ELIZABETH, arts management educator; b. Pasadena, Tex., Aug. 15, 1951; d. James Little and Ruth Lake (Skinner) Wilkison; divorced; children: Christine Joy, Cassidy Jane. BA in Psychology, David Lipscomb Coll., 1974; MA in Speech, Theater, Murray State U., 1976; postgrad., U. Tex., 1978; MA in Arts Adminstrn., Ind. U., 1981. Asst. prof. speech Vincennes (Ind.) U., 1976-79; asst. dir. mktg. Hartford (Conn.) Ballet, 1981-82; touring dir. Hartford Ballet/Conn. Opera, 1982-84; exec. dir. Wis. Arts Coun., Cheyenne, 1984-91, South Snohomish County Arts Coun., Lynwood, Wash., 1991-92; asst. prof. arts mgmt. Sangamon State U., Springfield, Ill., 1992—; adj. instr., Manchester (Conn.) Community Coll., 1982-84, Chapman Coll., 1990—, Edmonds Community Coll., 1992—; mem. selection com. Coca-Cola Scholars Found., 1989, 90, 91. Mem. adv. bd. Cheyenne Little Theatre Players, 1986, Cheyenne Civic Ctr., 1987-88. Mem. Assn. Arts Adminstrn. Educators (sec.), Assn. Performing Arts Producers, Speech Communication Assn., Western States Arts Fedn. (bd. dirs. 1984-91, chair performing arts com. 1985-87). Democrat. Avocations: singing, theater, reading. Home: 854 S Glenwood Springfield IL 62704 Office: Sangamon State Univ PAC 370 Springfield IL 62794-9243

THOMPSON, JULIA ANN, physicist, educator; b. Little Rock, Mar. 13, 1943; d. Erwin Arthur and Ruth Evelyn (Johnston) T.; m. Patrick A. Thompson, Mar. 22, 1964 (div. 1974); 1 child, Diane E.; m. David E. Kraus, Jr., June 22, 1976; children: Vincent Szewczyk, Larry Lynch. B.A., Cornell Coll., Mt. Vernon, Iowa, 1964; M.A., Yale U., 1966, Ph.D., 1969. Research assoc. Brookhaven Lab., Upton, N.Y., 1969-71; research assoc./assoc. instr. U. Utah, Salt Lake City, 1971-72; asst. prof. physics U. Pitts., 1972-78, assoc. prof., 1978-85, prof., 1986—; mem. users coms. Brookhaven Nat. Lab., 1983-86; condr. expts. Inst. Nuclear Physics, Novosibirsk, USSR, Ctr. Europeene Recherche Nucleaire, Switzerland, Brookhaven Natl. Lab., L.I.; spokesperson hyperon decay expt BNL, 1972-80. Contbr. articles to profl. jours. Bd. dirs. 1st Unitarian Ch., Pitts., 1980-83; zone councillor Soc. Physics Students, 1986-88; with Nat. Acad. Sci. Exch. to USSR, 1989-90. Woodrow Wilson fellow, 1964-65. Mem. Am. Phys. Soc. (com. on status of women in physics 1983-86, exec. com. forum on physics and soc. 1990—). Democrat. Unitarian. Avocations: promoting effective science education, hiking, reading, music. Achievements include research with W.E. Cleland and D.E. Kraus in optical triggering; with the collaboration with AFS and HELIOS expt. in direct photon and lepton production, leading to modified understanding of the gluon function, and limits on anomalous electron production; studies of rare and semi-rare kaon decays.

THOMPSON, KENNETH W(INFRED), educational director, author, editor, administrator, social science educator; b. Des Moines, Aug. 29, 1921; s. Thor Carlyle and Agnes (Rorbeck) T.; m. Beverly Bourret; children: Kenneth Caryle, Paul Andrew, James David, Carolyn A. A.B., Augustana Coll., 1943, L.H.D. (hon.), 1986, LLD, 1986; M.A., U. Chgo., 1948, Ph.D., 1950; LL.D., U. Notre Dame, 1964, Bowdoin Coll., 1972, St. Michael's Coll., 1973, St. Olaf Coll., 1974, U. Denver, 1983; L.H.D., W.Va. Wesleyan U., 1970, Nebr. Wesleyan Coll., 1971. Lectr. social scis. U. Chgo., 1948, asst. prof. polit. sci., 1951-53; asst. prof. polit. sci. Northwestern U., 1949-55, chmn. internat. relations coms., 1951-55; cons. internat. relations Rockefeller Found., 1953-55, asst. dir. social scis., 1955-57, assoc. dir. social scis., 1957-60, dir. social scis., 1960-61, v.p., 1961-73; dir. higher edn. for devel. Internat. Council for Ednl. Devel., 1974-76; Commonwealth prof. govt. and fgn. affairs U. Va., 1975-78, White Burkett Miller prof. govt. and fgn. affairs, 1979-86; J. Wilson Newman prof. govt. and fgn. affairs, 1986—, dir. White Burkett Miller Ctr. of Public Affairs, 1978—; Riverside Meml. lectr. Riverside Ch., N.Y.C., 1958; Lilly lectr. Duke, 1959; James Stokes lectr. N.Y.U., 1962; Rockwell lectr. Rice U., 1965; Ernest Griffith lectr. Am. U.; Andrew Cecil lectr. U. Tex., 1983; Stuber lectr. U. Rochester, 1984; Morgenthau Meml. lectr., N.Y.C., Mike Mansfield Ctr. lectr., U. Mont.; dir. Inst. Study World Politics, N.Y.C., 1975—. Author, editor: Principles and Problems of International Politics, 1951, 82, Man and Modern Society, 1953, Christian Ethics and the Dilemmas of Foreign Policy, 1959, 81, Conflict and Cooperation Among Nations, 1960, Political Realism and the Crisis of World Politics, 1960, 82, American Diplomacy and Emergent Patterns, 1962, 82, Foreign Policies in a World of Change, 1964, The Moral Issue in Statecraft, 1966, Reconstituting the Human Community, 1972, Foreign Assistance: A View From Private Sector, 1972, 82, Higher Education for National Development, 1972, Understanding World Politics, 1975, Higher Edn. and Social Change, 1976, World Politics, 1976, Truth and Tragedy, 1977, Ethics and Foreign Policy, 1978, Interpreters and Critics of the Cold War, 1978, Foreign Policy and the Democratic Process, 1978, Ethics, Functionalism and Power, 1979, Morality and Foreign Policy, 1980, Masters of International Thought, 1980, The Virginia Papers, vols. 1-28, 1979-94, The President and the Public Philosophy, 1981, Cold War Theories: World Polarization, 1944-53, Vol. I, 1981,91. Winston S. Churchill's World View, 1983, 89, Toynbees's World Politics and History, 1985, Moralism and Morality, 1985, Theory and Practice of International Relations, 1987, Arms Control and Foreign Policy, 1990, Traditions and Values in Politics and Diplomacy, 1992, Fathers of International Thought, 1994; editor: Am. Values Series, Vols. I-XX, Presdl. Nominating Process, Vols. I-IV, Portraits of American Presidents, Vols. I-XI, Herbert Butterfield: The Ethics of History; The American Presidency, Vols. I-III, 1982-83, Ethics and International Relations, 1985, Moral Dimensions of American Foreign Policy, 1985, 94, The Credibility of Leadership and Institutions, Vols. I-XX, 1988-93, Rhetoric and Political Discourse, Vols.I-XX, Governance, Vols. I-V, 1990-94, Constitutionalism, Vols. I-VII, 1989-91, Presidency and Science Advising, Vols. I-VIII, 1986-90, Political Transitions and Foreign Policy, Vols. I-IX, 1985-91; bd. editors Va. Quar. Rev., Society, Ethics and International Affairs, Interpretation, The Rev. of Politics; contbr. articles to profl. jours. Pres. Dist. of Scarsdale and Mamaroneck (N.Y.) Bd. Edn., 1965-68; trustee Union Theol. Sem., 1967-71, Dillard U., 1975—; Social Sci. Found., U. Denver, 1974-94, Compton Found., 1975. 1st ll. AUS, 1943-46. Named Va. laureate, 1981; recipient Phi Beta Kappa and Va. Coll. Stores prizes, Va. Social Sci. Assn. ann. award, English Speaking Union award, medal U. Chgo., 1968. Fellow Soc. Religion Higher Edn., Am. Acad. Arts and Scis.; mem. Century Club, Scarsdale Town Club, Raven Soc. (ann. award U. Va.), Phi Beta Kappa (pres.), Omicron Delta Phi. Office: Univ Va Miller Ctr PO Box 5106 Charlottesville VA 22905-5106

THOMPSON, LARRY A., principal. Prin. Lake Region Mid. Sch., Bridgton, Maine. Recipient Elem. Sch. Recognition award U.S. Dept. Edn., 1989-90. Office: Lake Region Middle Sch Kansas Rd Bridgton ME 04009

THOMPSON, LARRY ANGELO, lawyer, producer, personal manager; b. Clarksdale, Miss., Aug. 1, 1944; s. Angelo and Anne (Tuminello) T.; BBA, U. Miss., 1966, JD, 1968. Bar: Miss. 1968, Calif. 1970. In-house counsel Capitol Records, Hollywood, Calif., 1969-71; sr. ptnr. in entertainment law Thompson, Shankman and Bond, Beverly Hills, Calif., 1971-77; pres. Larry A. Thompson Orgn., Inc., 1977—; co-owner New World Pictures, 1983-85; lectr. entertainment bus. UCLA, U. So. Calif., Southwestern U. Law Sch. Co-chmn. Rep. Nat. Entertainment Com.; apptd. by Gov. of Calif. to Calif. Entertainment Commn. Recipient Show Bus. Atty. of Yr. award Capitol Records, 1971. Mem. Inauguration of Thompson Ctr. for Fine Arts in Clarksdale, Miss., 1986. Served with JAGC, U.S. Army, 1966-72. Mem. ABA, Miss. Bar Assn., Calif. Bar Assn., Inter-Am. Bar Assn., Hon. Order Ky. Colonels, Am. Film Inst., Nat. Acad. Recording Arts and Scis., Acad. TV Arts and Scis. Republican. Roman Catholic. Author: How to Make a Record Deal & Have Your Songs Recorded, 1975, Prime Time Crime, 1982;

producer: (TV) Jim Nabors Show, 1977 (Emmy nominee), Mickey Spillane's Margin for Murder, 1981, Bring 'Em Back Alive, 1982, Mickey Spillane's Murder Me, Murder You, 1982, The Other Lover, 1985, Convicted, 1986, Intimate Encounters, 1986, The Woman He Loved, 1988, Original Sin, 1989, Class Cruise, 1989, Little White Lies, 1989, Lucy and Desi: Before The Laughter, 1990, Broken Promises, 1993, Separated By Murder, 1994; (motion pictures) Crimes of Passion, 1984, Quiet Cool, 1987, My Demon Lover, 1987, Breaking the Rules, 1992. Recipient Vision award, 1993. Home: 9451 Hidden Valley Pl Beverly Hills CA 90210-1310 Office: Larry A Thompson Orgn 335 N Maple Dr Ste 361 Beverly Hills CA 90210-3854

THOMPSON, LARRY DEAN, lawyer; b. Hannibal, Mo., Nov. 15, 1945; s. Ezra W. and Ruth L. (Robinson) T.; m. Brenda Anne Taggart, June 26, 1970; children: Larry Dean, Gary E. B.A. cum laude, Culver-Stockton Coll., Canton, Mo., 1967; M.A., Mich. State U., 1969; J.D., U. Mich., 1974. Bar: Mo. 1974, Ga. 1978. Indsl. relations rep. Ford Motor Co., Birmingham, Mich., 1969-71; atty. Monsanto Co., St. Louis, 1974-77, King & Spalding, Atlanta, 1977-82; U.S. atty. U.S. Dist. Ct. (no. dist.) Ga., 1982-86; ptnr. King & Spalding, Atlanta, 1986—; mem. lawyer's adv. com. U.S. Ct. Appeals (11th cir.); assoc. ind. counsel HUD investigation; mem. Ga. Bd. Bar Examiners. Editor: Jury Instructions in Criminal Antitrust Cases 1976-80, 1982. Mem. bd. dirs. Ga. Rep. Found.; chmn. Atlanta Urban League. Recipient Outstanding Achievement award FBA, 1992. Mem. ABA, Nat. Bar Assn. Presbyterian. Home: 2015 Wallace Rd SW Atlanta GA 30331-7756 Office: King & Spalding 191 Peachtree St NE Atlanta GA 30303-1740

THOMPSON, LARRY FLACK, semiconductor equipment company executive; b. Union City, Tenn., Aug. 31, 1944; s. Rufus Russell and Polly (Flack) T.; m. Joan Benquad, Aug. 30, 1964; children: Anthony Scott, Russell Allen. BS, Tenn. Tech. U., Cookeville, 1966; MS, Tenn. Tech. U., 1968; PhD, U. Mo., Rolla, 1970. Mem. tech. staff Bell Labs., Murray Hill, N.J., 1971-80; dept. head AT&T Bell Labs., Murray Hill, N.J., 1981-94; v.p. product devel. Integrated Solutions, Inc., Tewksbury, Mass., 1994—. Author: Introduction to Microlithography, 1993; patentee in field. Mem. NAE, Am. Chem. Soc. (bd. dirs. 1993—, Indsl. Chemistry award 1993, Roy W. Tess award 1993), Am. Inst. Chem. Engring. Avocations: gardening, hunting. Home: 1511 Long Hill Rd Millington NJ 07946-1813 Office: Integrated Solutions Inc PO Box 279 Millington NJ 07946

THOMPSON, LAWRENCE HYDE, federal agency official; b. Hamilton, Ohio, Oct. 6, 1943; s. William Hayton and Evelyn (Covault) T.; m. Catherine Crosby, Feb. 3, 1973; children: Bradford Stephen, Sarah Catherine. BS, Iowa State U., 1966; MBA, U. Pa., 1966; PhD, U. Mich., 1971. Economist Office Sec. Health, Edn. and Welfare, Washington, 1974-77, dir. Soc. Security Planning, 1977-79; assoc. commr. Social Security Adminstrn., Washington, 1979-81, dir. rsch., 1981-83; chief economist Gen. Acctg. Office, Washington, 1983-89, asst. comptroller gen., 1989-93; prin. dep. commr. Social Security Adminstrn., 1993—. Contbr. articles to pubs., books. Mem. Am. Economic Assn., Nat. Acad. Social Ins. (bd. dirs. 1985-93). Avocations: racquetball, choral singing. Office: Social Security Adminstrn 960 Altmeyer 6401 Security Blvd Baltimore MD 21235

THOMPSON, LAWRENCE LEONARD, federal agency administrator; b. St. Paul, Jan. 11, 1937; s. Theodore Spencer and Louise Catherine (Leonard) T.; m. Gretchen Converse Laun, June 25, 1960 (div. June 1980); children: Heidi Louise, Erik Converse, Mark Laun, Holly Anne; m. Anna Sophia Zaremba, Oct. 23, 1982. BA, Harvard Coll., 1958; MPA, Princeton U., 1963. Microwave tube engr. Raytheon Co., Burlington, Mass., 1958-61; budget examiner U.S. Office Mgmt. and Budget, Washington, 1963-67; sr. rsch. assoc. Rep. Nat. Com., Washington, 1967-69; spl. asst. to under sec. U.S. Dept. Housing and Urban Devel., Washington, 1969-70; area dir. U.S. Dept. Housing and Urban Devel., Hartford, Conn., 1970-78; assoc. prof. pub. adminstrn. U Hartford, West Hartford, 1979-82; exec. dir. Hartford (Conn.) Redevel. Agy., 1982-89; exec. asst. to asst. sec. U.S. Dept. Housing and Urban Devl., Washington, 1989-91, gen. dep. asst. sec. for policy devel. and rsch., 1991—. Mem. ASPA, Harvard Club Washington, Capitol Hill Choral Soc. Republican. Roman Catholic. Avocations: choral music, baseball, history, travel. Home: 1018 E Capitol St NE Washington DC 20003 Office: US Dept Housing Urban Devel 451 7th St SW Washington DC 20410

THOMPSON, LEONARD ALLEN, insurance sales and marketing specialist, consultant; b. Freeport, Ill., Apr. 1, 1927; s. Allen Marvin and Anna (Baughman) T.; m. Esther Gertrude Johnson, Nov. 4, 1949; children: Daniel J., David C., Deborah D. BTh, No. Bapt. Sem., Chgo., 1949; postgrad., U. Iowa, 1950-53. Salesman Bankers Trust Life, Phoenix, Ariz., 1957-64; nat. sales mgr. Sons of Norway, Mpls., 1964-80, salesman, 1980-87, CEO, 1987-89; cons., 1990—. Mem. Nat. Assn. Life Underwriters, Chartered Life Underwriters, Million Dollar Round Table (life), Fraternal Field Mgrs. Assn. (bd. dirs., pres. 1965-71), Nat. Assn. Fraternal Ins. Counselors (bd. dirs. 1984—, pres. 1994—). Republican. Home: 5565 Zachary Ln N Minneapolis MN 55442-3903

THOMPSON, LEROY, JR., radio engineer, military reserve officer; b. Tulsa, July 7, 1913; s. LeRoy and Mary (McMurrain) T.; BS. in Elec. Engring., Ala. Poly Inst., 1936; m. Ola Dell Tedder, Dec. 31, 1941; 1 son, Bartow McMurrain. Commd. 2d lt. U.S. Amy Res., 1935, advanced through grades to col., 1963; signal officer CCC, 1936-40; radio engr. Officer Hdqrs. 4th C A., 1941; with signal sect. Hdqrs. Western Def. command and 4th Army, San Francisco, 1942, comdg. officer 234th Signal Ops. Co., 1942; asst. chief, chief signal corps ROTC U. Calif., Berkeley, 1942-43; radio engring. officer O.C. SigO War Dept., Washington, 1943; radio engring officer Hdqrs. 3105th Signal Service Co. Hdqrs. CBI, New Delhi, 1944; signal officer Hdqrs. Northern Combat Area Command, Burma, 1944; signal officer Hdqrs. OSS Det 101, Burma, 1945; signal officer Hdqrs. OSS, China, 1945, radio engr., tech. liaison officer, Central Intelligence Group, CIA, 1945-50; chief radio br. Hdqrs. FEC, Tokyo, 1950-53, chief radio engring br. Signal C Plant Engring. Agy., 1953-55; radio cons. to asst. def. research and engring. communications, 1960-62; ret., 1973; pvt. research and devel. on communication and related problems, 1963—; owner Thompson Research Exptl. Devel. Lab. Lic. profl. radio engr., Ga. Mem. IEEE (life sr.), NRA, Vet. Wireless Operators Assn., Am. Radio Relay League, Mil. Order World Wars, Res. Officers Assn., Am. Motorcycle Assn., Nat. Wildlife Fedn. Baptist. Home: 6450 Overlook Dr Alexandria VA 22312-1327

THOMPSON, LESLIE MELVIN, college dean, educator; b. Trinidad, Colo., May 19, 1936; s. J. Roy Thompson and E. Irene (Lance) Campbell; m. Margaret Sue Coward, June 14, 1959; children: Stephen Gregory, Michael Christopher. BA, Wayland Bapt. U., 1959; MA, Tex. Tech U., 1963, PhD, 1965. Cert. health edn. specialist. Instr. Tex. Tech U., Lubbock, 1965; asst. prof., dir. grad. studies in English So. Ill. U., Edwardsville, 1965-68; prof., dir. grad. studies in English Stephen F. Austin State U., Nacogdoches, Tex., 1968-79; dean grad. sch., dir. rsch. Ga. So. Coll., Statesboro, 1979-84; assoc. v.p. for rsch., dean grad. sch. Tex. Woman's U., Denton, 1984—. Mem. editorial bd. Papers on Lang. and Lit., 1967-71, Loss Grief and Care (jour.), 1986—; assoc. editor essays Illness, Crises and Loss; contbr. articles to profl. jours., chpts. to books. Cons. Ga. Endowment for Humanities, 1982-84; mem. budget com. United Way, Nacogdoches, 1975-76; mem. Ptnrs. of Ams., Statesboro, 1981-84; bd. dirs. Home Bound Services, Statesboro, 1982-84. Served with U.S. Army, 1959-61. Named Danforth Assoc. Stephen F. Austin State U., 1969-79; Nat. Def. Edn. Act fellow Office Edn., 1961-65. Mem. Coun. Soc. Grad. Schs. (pres. 1985-86), Coun. Grad. Schs. (bd. dirs.), Humanities and Tech. Assn. (v.p. 1984-87), Tex. Folklore Soc., Conf. Christianity and Lit., Hastings Ctr., Denton C. of C., Assn. for Advancement of Health Edn., Phi Kappa Phi (pres. Statesboro chpt. 1981-83, chmn. nat. investment com. 1983-89). Democrat. Presbyterian. Avocations: numismatics, antiques. Office: Tex Woman's U Grad Sch PO Box 22479 Denton TX 76204-0479

THOMPSON, LOHREN MATTHEW, oil company executive; b. Sutherland, Nebr., Jan. 21, 1926; s. John M. and Anna (Ecklund) T.; children: Terence M., Sheila M., Clark M. Ed., U. Denver. Spl. rep. Standard Oil Co., Omaha, 1948-56; sales mgr. Frontier REF. Co., 1956-67, v.p. mktg., 1967-68; mgr. mktg. U.S. region Husky Oil Co., Denver, 1968-72; v.p. Westar Stas., Inc., Denver, 1967-70; chmn. bd. Colo. Petroleum, Denver, 1971—. Served with USAAF, 1944-46. Mem. Colo. Petroleum Council,

Am. Petroleum Inst., Am. Legion. Lutheran. Clubs: Denver Petroleum, Denver Oilman's, Lodge: Lions. Home: 2410 Spruce Ave Estes Park CO 80517-7146 Office: Colo Petroleum 4080 Globeville Rd Denver CO 80216-4906

THOMPSON, LOIS JEAN HEIDKE ORE, industrial psychologist; b. Chgo., Feb. 22, 1933; d. Harold William and Ethel Rose (Neumann) Heidke; m. Henry Thomas Ore, Aug. 28, 1954 (div. May 1972); children: Christopher, Douglas; m. Joseph Lippard Thompson, Aug. 3, 1972; children: Scott, Les, Melanie. BA, Cornell Coll., Mt. Vernon, Iowa, 1955; MA, Idaho State U., 1964, EdD, 1981. Lic. psychologist, N.Mex. Tchr. pub. schs. various locations, 1956-67; tchr., instr. Idaho State U., Pocatello, 1967-72; employee/orgn. devel. specialist Los Alamos (N.Mex.) Nat. Lab., 1981-84, tng. specialist, 1984-89, sect. leader, 1989-93; pvt. practice Los Alamos, 1988—; sec. Cornell Coll. Alumni Office, 1954-55, also other orgns.; bd. dirs. Parent Edn. Ctr., Idaho State U., 1980; counselor, Los Alamos, 1981-88. Editor newsletter LWV, Laramie, Wyo., 1957; contbr. articles to profl. jours. Pres. Newcomers Club, Pocatello, 1967, Faculty Womens Club, Pocatello, 1968; chmn. edn. com. AAUW, Pocatello, 1969. Mem. APA, ACA, N.Mex. Psychol. Assn. (bd. dirs. div. II, 1990, sec. 1988-90, chmn. 1990), N.Am. Soc. Adlerian Psychology, N.Mex. Soc. Adlerian Psychology (pres. 1990, treas. 1991-94), Soc. Indsl. and Orgnl. Psychology, Nat. Career Counseling Assn. Mem. LDS Ch. Avocations: racewalking, backpacking, skiing, tennis, biking. Home: 340 Aragon Ave Los Alamos NM 87544-3505 Office: Thompson Counseling & Cons 340 Aragon Ave Los Alamos NM 87544-3505

THOMPSON, LORING MOORE, retired college administrator, writer; b. Newton, Mass., Feb. 17, 1918; s. Henry E. and Ella (Gould) T.; m. Pearl E. Judiesch, Dec. 30, 1949; children—Bruce C., Douglas P. (dec.). B.S. in Indsl. Engring. Northeastern U., 1940; M.S., U. R.I., 1947; Ph.D., U. Chgo., 1956. Instr. U. R.I., 1946; asst. to pres. Assn. Colls. Upper N.Y., 1947-49; assoc. prof. U. Toledo, 1952-59, asst. dean acad. adminstrn., 1958-59; dir. univ. planning Northeastern U., Boston, 1959-63; dean adult programs Northeastern U., 1964-66, v.p. planning, 1967-80, emeritus, 1980—; faculty assoc. continuing edn. Ariz. State U., 1982-84; cons. in field. Author: (with others) Business Communication, 1949; contbr. (with others) articles to profl. publs. Bd. dirs. Back Bay Assn., Boston, 1961-63, v.p., 1963; trustee Huntington Gen. Hosp., Boston, 1970-80; mem. Fenway Project Area Com., 1973-76; mem. Mass. conf. ch. and edn. com. United Ch. of Christ, 1972-78, chairperson, 1973-74; mem. task force on ch. growth, 1978-80; mem. Chandler Area Coun., 1988-89; sec. Sun Lakes Interfaith Coun., 1993—. Lt. USNR, 1942-45. Mem. Spiritual Frontiers Fellowship, Tau Beta Pi. Home: 25408 S Sedona Dr Sun Lakes AZ 85248-6636

THOMPSON, LOUIS A., company executive; b. Ketchikan, Alaska, July 21, 1936; s. Louis and Agnes Rose (Young) T. Grad. high sch., Sitka, Alaska. Pres., chmn., CEO, Kavilco Inc., Kasaan, Alaska, 1972—. Councilman, vice mayor City of Kasaan, 1975-87. With U.S. Army, 1958-60. Home: 5th and Main Sts Kasaan AK 99950-0340 Office: Kavilco Inc One Copper Crescent Dr Kasaan AK 99950-0340

THOMPSON, LOUIS MILTON, agronomy educator, scientist; b. Throckmorton, Tex., May 15, 1914; s. Aubrey Lafayette and Lola Terry (Frazier) T.; m. Margaret Stromberg, July 10, 1937 (dec. Nov. 1972); children: Louis Milton, Margaret Ann, Glenda Ray (dec.), Carolyn Terry, Jerome Lafayette; m. Ruth Hiatt Phipps, July 7, 1990. B.S., Tex. A. and M. U., 1935; M.S., Iowa State U., 1947, Ph.D., 1950. Soil surveyor Tex., 1935-36, 39-40; instr. Tex. A. and M. U., 1936-39, 40-42; asst. prof. soils Iowa State U., Ames, 1947-50; prof. soils, head farm operation curriculum Iowa State U., 1950-58, assoc. dean agr. charge resident instrn., 1958-83, emeritus prof. agronomy, 1983—, assoc. dean emeritus, 1984—. Author: Soils and Soil Fertility, rev. edit., 1957, co-author rev. edit., 1978, 83, 93, Russian edit., 1983; contbr. articles on weather-crop yield models and climate change to profl. jours. Elder Presbyn. Ch. With AUS, 1942-46; col. Res. (ret.). Recipient Henry A. Wallace award disting. svc. to agr., 1982, faculty citation Iowa State U. Alumni Assn., 1990, Disting. Iowa Scientist award Iowa Acad. Sci., 1991, Agr. Innovator award Iowa State U. Agr. Alumni Soc., 1992, Friends of Agrl. award Iowa Dept. Agriculture and Nat. Agrl. Mktg. Assn., 1993, Disting. Achievement citation Iowa State U. Alumni Assn., 1993. Fellow AAAS, Am. Soc. Agronomy, Soil Sci. Soc. Am., Soil and Water Conservation Soc. (pres.'s citation); mem. Am. Meterol. Soc., Farm House (hon.), Rotary (past local pres., Paul Harris fellow), Sigma Xi, Alpha Zeta (Tall Corn award 1957), Gamma Sigma Delta (nat. pres. 1956-58), Phi Kappa Phi (chpt. pres. 1961). Home: 414 Lynn Ave Ames IA 50014-7318

THOMPSON, MACK EUGENE, history educator; b. Burley, Idaho, Feb. 24, 1921; s. Eugene and Nora (McFate) T.; m. Helen Goldhamer, Oct. 30, 1945. A.B., Queen's Coll., CUNY, 1948; M.A., Brown U., 1951, Ph.D., 1955. Instr. history Brown U., 1954-55; asst. prof. Calif. Inst. Tech., 1955-56; asst. prof. U. Calif. at Riverside, 1956-62, assoc. prof., 1962-66, prof., 1966-77; emeritus prof., 1977—; chmn. div. humanities U. Calif. at Riverside, 1961-63, assoc. univ. dean acad. planning, 1965-66, dean, div. undergrad. studies, 1971-74; exec dir. Am. Hist. Assn., Washington, 1974-81; Chmn. editorial bd. Experiment and Innovation: New Directions in Edn., U. Calif., 1966-68. Author: The Ward-Hopkins Controversy and the American Revolution in Rhode Island: An Interpretation, 1959, Moses Brown, Reluctant Reformer, 1962, Causes and Circumstances of the Du Pont Family's Emigration, 1969. Bd. dirs. Harry S. Truman Libr. Inst., 1974-81. With AUS, 1942-45. Home: 150 James Ct Oldsmar FL 34677

THOMPSON, MARGARET M., physical education educator; b. nr. Falls Church, Va., Aug. 1, 1921; d. Lesley L. and Madeline (Shawen) T. B.S., Mary Washington Coll., 1941; M.A., George Washington U., 1947; Ph.D., U. Iowa, 1961. Tchr., supr. phys. edn. Staunton (Va.) City Schs., 1941-44; tchr. jr. high sch. phys. edn. Arlington County, Va., 1944-47; instr. women's phys. edn. Fla. State U., Tallahassee, 1947-51; instr., assoc. prof. phys. edn. Purdue U., Lafayette, Ind., 1951-65; dir. gross motor therapy lab. Purdue U., 1963-65; assoc. prof. phys. edn. U. Mo., Columbia, 1965-68; prof. U. Mo., 1968-71, dir. Cinematography and Motor Learning Lab. Dept. Health and Phys. Edn., 1965-71; prof. phys. edn. U. Ill., Champaign-Urbana, 1971-87, prof. emeritus, 1987—. Author: (with Barbara B. Godfrey) Movement Pattern Checklists, 1966, (with Chappelle Arnett) Perceptual Motor and Motor Test Battery for Children, 1968, (with Barbara Mann) An Holistic Approach to Physical Education Curriculum: Objectives Classification System for Elementary Schools, 1977, Gross Motor Inventory, 1976, revised edit., 1980, Developing the Curriculum, 1980, Setting the Learning Environment, 1980, Sex Stereotyping and Human Development, 1980; also film strips, articles. Mem. AAHPER, Ill. Assn. Health, Phys. Edn. and Recreation, Internat. Assn. Phys. Edn. and Sports for Coll. Girls and Women. Home: 1311 Wildwood Ln Mahomet IL 61853-9770 Office: U Ill Freer Gymnasium Dept Kinesiology 906 S Goodwin Ave Urbana IL 61801-3816

THOMPSON, MARGUERITE MYRTLE GRAMING (MRS. RALPH B. THOMPSON), librarian; b. Orangeburg, S.C., Apr. 23, 1912; d. Thomas Laurie and Rosa Lee (Stroman) Graming; m. Ralph B. Thompson, Sept. 17, 1949 (dec. Oct. 1960). BA in English cum laude, U. S.C., 1932, postgrad., 1937; BLS, Emory U., 1943. Tchr. English pub. high schs., S.C., 1932-43; libr. Rockingham (N.C.) High Sch., 1943-45, Randolph County (N.C.) Libr., Asheboro, 1945-48, Colleton County (S.C.) Libr., Walterboro, 1948-61; dir. Florence (S.C.) County Libr., 1961-78. Sect. com. community facilities, svcs. and instns. Florence County Resources Devel. Com., 1964-67; vice chmn. Florence County Coun. on Aging, 1968-70, exec. bd. 1968-82, bd. treas., 1973-75, bd. sec., 1976-77, bd. v.p., 1979; mem. Florence County Bicentennial Planning Com., 1975-76; mem. rels. and allocations com. United Way, 1979-80. Named Boss of Yr. Nat. Secs. Assn., 1971. Mem. ALA (coun. 1964-72), Southeastern Libr. Assn., S.C. Libr. Assn. (pres. 1960, chmn. assn. handbook revision com. 1967-69, 80, sect. co-chmn. com. standards for S.C. pub. libs. 1966-75, felt. rels. coord. 1972-73, planning com. 1976-78), Greater Florence C. of C. (women's div. chmn. 1969-70, bd. dirs. 1975-77), S.E. Regional Conf. Women in C. of C. (bd. dir. 1970-71), Florence Bus. and Profl. Women's Club (2d v.p. 1975-76, Career Woman of Yr. 1974, parliamentarian 1980-81, chmn. scholarship com. 1981-82), Delta Kappa Gamma (county chpt. charter pres. 1963-65, treas. 1966-70, chmn. com. on expansion 1977-80, 82-84, state chpt. chmn. state scholarship com. 1967-73, state 2d v.p. 1971-73, state 1st v.p. 1973-75, state pres. 1975-77, chmn. policy manual 1977-81, chmn. adv. coun. 1978-85, chmn. fin. com. 1981-83, parliamentarian 1987-91, adminstrv. bd. 1987—, chmn. nominations com. 1989-91, dir. S.E. Region 1978-80, coord. S.E. Regional Golden Anniversary Conf. 1979, internat. scholarship com. 1970-74, internat. exec. bd. 1975-77, 78-80, internat. adminstrv. bd. 1978-80, internat. constn. com. 1980-82, internat. achievement award com., 1986-88), Florence Literary Club (sec. 1964-66, 79-82, pres. 1970-72). Methodist (chmn. ch. libr. com. 1965-71, chmn. com. ch. history, 1968-69, sec. adminstrv. bd. 1979-82). Home: 1000 Live Oaks Dr SW # 8B Orangeburg SC 29115-9600

THOMPSON, MARTIN CHRISTIAN, news service executive; b. Council Bluffs, Iowa, Oct. 25, 1938; s. Ross Kenneth and Mary Ellen (Pierce) T.; m. Janet Ann Morrow, Aug. 4, 1962; children: Chris Michael, Sean Martin. B.A. in Communications, U. Wash., 1960. Newsman Sta. KEDO, Longview, Wash., 1960-61; news dir. Sta. KREW, Sunnyside, Wash., 1961-66; newsman AP, Seattle, 1966-68; corr. AP, Reno, Nev., 1968-70; newsman AP, San Francisco, 1970-72; news editor AP, 1972-75; chief of bur. AP, San Francisco, 1975-86, Los Angeles, 1986—, mng. editor AP, N.Y.C., 1989-92, dir. state news, 1992—. Mem. Beta Rho Tau, Sigma Delta Chi. Methodist. Office: 50 Rockefeller Plz New York NY 10020-1605

THOMPSON, MARY EILEEN, chemistry educator; b. Mpls., Dec. 21, 1928; d. Albert C. and Blanche (McAvoy) T. B.A., Coll. St. Catherine, 1953; M.S., U. Minn., 1958; Ph.D., U. Calif.-Berkeley, 1964. Math. and sci. tchr. Derham Hall High Sch., St. Paul, 1953-58; faculty Coll. St. Catherine, St. Paul, 1964—, prof., chmn. dept. chemistry, 1969-90; project dir. Women in Chemistry, 1984—. Contbr. articles to profl. jours. Mem. Am. Chem. Soc. (chair women chemists com. 1992-94), Coun. Undergrad. Rsch. (councilor 1991—), N.Y. Acad. Sci., Chem. Soc. London, AAAS, Sigma Xi, Phi Beta Kappa. Democrat. Roman Catholic. Achievements include research interests in Cr(III) hydrolytic polymers, kinetics of inorganic complexes, Co(III) peroxo/superoxo complexes. Office: Coll St Catherine 2004 Randolph Ave Saint Paul MN 55105-1789

THOMPSON, MARY KOLETA, sculptor, non-profit organization director; b. Portsmouth, Va., Dec. 27, 1938; m. James Burton Thompson, May 5, 1957; children: Burt, Suzan, Kate, Jon. BFA, U. Tex., 1982; postgrad., Boston U. Cert. fund raising exec. Pres. The Planning Resource People, Austin, Tex., 1990—; Tex. fin. devel. specialist ARC Tex., 1994—; devel. dir. Very Spl. Arts Tex., 1991-92; dir. devel. ARC, Austin, 1992-94; dir. Tex. Children's Mus., Fredericksburg, 1987-88, Internat. Hdqrs. SHAPE Command Arts and Crafts Ctr., 1985-86; com. chmn. Symposium for Encouragement Women in Math. and Natural Sci., U. Tex., Austin, 1990. Sculptor portrait busts. Bd. dirs. Teenage Parent Coun., Austin, 1990-92. Named U.S. Vol. of Yr., Belgium, 1986; grantee NEA, 1988. Mem. AAUW (life, pres. 1990-92), Women in Comm. (co-chmn. S.W. regional conf.), U. Tex. Ex-Student Assn. (life), Tex. Hist. Found. (life), Leadership Tex. (life), Leadership Tex. Alumnae Assn. (bd. dirs.), Raleigh Tavern Soc. (founder), Austin Antiques Forum (founder 1990). Avocations: writing, lecturing, meeting and strategic planning. Office: San Antonio Area Chpt ARC 3642 E Houston St San Antonio TX 78219-3830

THOMPSON, MICHAEL F., food service executive; b. 1948. Grad., John Carroll U., 1970. Ski instr. N.Y., Calif., 1970-75; ops. control mgr. racetrack divsn. Del. North Cos. Inc., 1975-78; pvt. cons., 1978-80; with Sportservice Corp., Buffalo, 1980—, pres., 1984—. Office: Sportservice Corp 438 Main St Buffalo NY 14202

THOMPSON, MORLEY PUNSHON, textile company executive; b. San Francisco, Jan. 2, 1927; s. Morley Punshon and Ruth (Wetmore) T.; m. Patricia Ann Smith, Jan. 31, 1953; children: Page Elizabeth Tredennick, Morley Punshon. A.B., Stanford U., 1948; M.B.A., Harvard U., 1950; J.D., Chase Law Sch., 1969; LL.D., Xavier U., 1981. CPA, Ohio. Chmn. Stearns Tech. Textiles Co., Cin., 1985—, Stearns Can., Inc., Cin., 1985—, M. Mortgage West Co., 1989—; bd. dirs. Hilltop Basic Resources, Inc. Bd. dirs. Cin. Inst. Fine Arts. Lt. Supply Corps USNR, 1952-54. Mem. ABA (life). Office: Stearns Tech Textiles Co 100 Williams St Cincinnati OH 45215-4683

THOMPSON, M(ORRIS) LEE, lawyer; b. Hutchinson, Kans., Nov. 29, 1946; s. Morris J. and Ruth W. (Smith) T.; m. M. Susan Morgan, May 26, 1974; children: Deborah, Erin, Andrew, Christopher. BA, Wichita State U., 1968; MA, Emporia State U., 1970; JD, George Washington U., 1974. Bar: Kans., 1974, U.S. Dist. Ct. Kans., 1974, U.S. Ct. Appeals (10th cir.) 1976, U.S. Supreme Ct., 1978. Instr., lectr. Emporia (Kans.) State U., 1969-70; lctr. in speech George Washington U., Washington, 1970-71; asst. to Senator James Pearson Washington, 1971-75; assoc. Martin, Pringle, et al., Wichita, Kans., 1976-78, ptnr., 1979-89; U.S. atty. for dist. of Kans., Dept. Justice, Wichita, 1990-93; mng. ptnr. Triplett, Woolf & Garretson, Wichita, 1993—. Treas. Kansans for Kassebaum, Wichita, 1978-88; mem. Kans. State Rep. Cen. Com., Topeka, 1978-79, 88-90; candidate U.S. Ho. of Reps., Kans., 1988; chmn. civil issues subcom. Atty. Gen.'s Adv. Com. of U.S. Attys., 1992-93. Mem. Kans. Bar Assn. (pres. criminal law sect. 1994-95). Methodist. Office: Triplett Woolf & Garretson 151 N Main St Ste 800 Wichita KS 67202-1489

THOMPSON, MOZELLE WILLMONT, lawyer, federal agency administrator; b. Pitts., Dec. 11, 1954; s. Charles and Eiko (Suzaki) T. AB, Columbia U., 1976; M in Pub. Affairs, Princeton U., 1980; JD, Columbia U., 1981. Bar: N.Y. 1984, D.C. 1984, U.S. Dist. Ct. (ea. dist.) Mich. 1984, U.S. Dist. Ct. (so. and ea. dists.) N.Y. 1985, U.S. Ct. Appeals (11th cir.) 1986. Clk. to presiding judge US Dist. Ct. (so. dist.) Fla., Miami, 1981-82; assoc. Skadden, Arps, Slate, Meagher & Flom, N.Y.C., 1982-90; spl. counsel to supr. Town of Babylon, N.Y., 1988-90; counsel and sec. N.Y. State Housing Fin. Agy., N.Y.C.; counsel, sec. N.Y. State Med. Care Facilities Fin. Agy., N.Y. State Affordable Housing Corp., N.Y. State Mcpl. Bond Bank Agy., N.Y. State Project Fin. Agy., N.Y.C., 1990-93; sr. v.p. gen. coun. N.Y. State Mortgage Agy., N.Y.C., 1993; dep. asst. sec. for govt. fin. policy Dept. of Treasury, Washington, 1993—; gen. counsel North Amityville Cmty. Econ. Coun., Inc., 1989-90; pres. Greenwich Corp., 1987-93; adj. assoc. prof. Bklyn. Law Sch., 1986-91, Fordham U. Law Sch., 1992—; mem. adv. bd. Udall Ctr., U. Ariz., Tucson, 1994—. Mem. exec. bd. Practicing Attys. for Law Students, N.Y.C., 1986-93. Mem. ABA (coms. litigation, tort and ins. practice 1984—), Nat. Coun. State Housing Agys. (co-chair legal affairs com., disclosure task force, 1991-93), Nat. Coun. Health Care Facilities Fin. Authorities (co-chair advocacy and strategic planning coms., 1991-93) N.Y. State Bar Assn., N.Y. County Lawyers Assn. (com. on fed. cts. 1984-86), D.C. Bar Assn., Assn. of Bar of N.Y., Assn. Princeton Grad. Alumni, Assn. Black Princeton Alumni, Columbia Law Sch. Alumni Assn., Columbia Coll. Alumni Assn., Columbia Black and Latino Alumni Assn., Columbia Coll. Class 1976 (pres. 1986—). Avocations: music, theater arts, architecture. Home: 155 11th St NE Washington DC 20002 Office: Dept of Treasury Rm 2334 1500 Pennsylvania Ave NW Washington DC 20220

THOMPSON, MYRON H., federal judge. BA, Yale U., 1969, JD, 1972. Asst. atty. gen. State of Ala., 1972-74; sole practice Montgomery, Ala., 1974-79; ptnr. Thompson & Faulk, Montgomery, 1979-80; judge U.S. Dist. Ct. (mid. dist.) Ala., Montgomery, 1980—, chief judge, 1991—. Mem. ABA, Ala. Bar Assn., Nat. Bar Assn., Ala. Lawyers Assn. Office: US Dist Ct PO Box 235 Montgomery AL 36101-0235

THOMPSON, NEAL PHILIP, food science and nutrition educator; b. Bklyn., July 18, 1936; s. Thomas I. and Ellenor (Backie) T.; m. Beverly Ethel Godshall, Oct. 4, 1958; children: Erick, Victor, Clifford, Karen, Stuart. BS, Wheaton Coll., 1957; MA, Miami U., 1962; PhD, Princeton U., 1965. From asst. to assoc. prof. U. Fla., Gainesville, 1965-76, prof., 1976, asst. dean, 1980-86, assoc. dean, 1986-93. Capt. USNR, ret. Home: 727 SW 27th St Gainesville FL 32607 Office: U Fla Inst Food & Agrl Scis Food & Environ Toxicology Gainesville FL 32611-0720

THOMPSON, N(ORMAN) DAVID, insurance company executive; b. Rockville Centre, N.Y., July 30, 1934; s. Norman J. and Laurel H. (Johnson) T.; m. Joyce L. Angeletti, June 7, 1958; children: John L., Jennifer L., Sarah S. BA with distinction, Wesleyan U., 1956; LLB, Columbia U., 1959; postgrad., Harvard U., 1973. Bar: N.Y. Pvt. practice law N.Y.C., 1961-62;

corp. sec. Gen. Reins. Corp., N.Y.C., 1964-69; v.p. Gen. Reins. Corp., Greenwich, Conn., 1969; v.p., gen. counsel sec. Gen. Reins. Corp., 1976-77; exec. v.p. N.Am. Reins. Corp., N.Y.C., 1977-78; pres. N.Am. Reins. Corp., 1978-92; chmn., CEO N.Am. Reins Corp., 1992—, SwissRe Holding, 1992—; chmn. SwissRe Group Cos. (U.S.), 1992—. Dir. Nat. Legal Ctr. for Pub. Interest, chmn., 1992—; trustee Coll. Ins., 1992. With U.S. Army, 1959-60. Mem. Reins Assn. Am. (chmn. 1982-83), Nat. Assn. Casualty and Surety Execs. (pres. 1986-87), Am. Arbitration Assn. (bd. dirs., chmn. fin. com. 1992-93), Am. Inst. Property and Casualty Underwriters (trustee), Univ. Club (N.Y.C.), Saugatuck Harbor Yacht Club (Westport, Conn.). Home: 47 Kettle Creek Rd Weston CT 06883-2208

THOMPSON, NORMAN WINSLOW, surgeon, educator; b. Boston, July 12, 1932; s. Herman Chandler and Evelyn Millicent (Palmer) T.; m. Marcia Ann Veldman, June 12, 1956; children: Robert, Karen, Susan, Jennifer. BA, Hope Coll., 1953; MD, U. Mich., 1957. Diplomate Am. Bd. Surgery. Intern U. Mich., Ann Arbor, 1957-58, resident in surgery, 1959-62, instr., 1962-64, asst. prof., 1964-66, assoc. prof., 1966-71, prof. surgery, 1971-79, Henry King Ranson prof. surgery, 1979—, chief endocrine surg. svc., 1979—. Contbr. articles to profl. jours. Trustee Hope Coll., Holland, Mich., 1973-88. Mem. ACS, (gov. 1979-85), Cen. Surg. Assn., Western Surg. Assn. (1st v.p. 1992-93), F.A. Coller Surg. Soc. (pres. 1986), Am. Surg. Assn., Am. Thyroid Assn., Soc. Surg. Alimentary Tract, Internat. Cardiovascular Soc., Internat. Assn. Endocrine Surgeons (pres. 1989-91), Am. Assn. Endocrine Surgeons (pres. 1980-81, 81-82), Royal Soc. Medicine, British Assn. Endocrine Surgeons, Assn. French Endocrine Surgeons, Scandanavian Surg. Soc., Alpha Omega Alpha. Home: 465 Hillspur Rd Ann Arbor MI 48105-1048 Office: U Mich Med Ctr 2920 Taubman Bldg Ann Arbor MI 48109

THOMPSON, OTIS NATHANIEL, JR., executive; b. Balt., Aug. 28, 1923; s. Otis Nathaniel and Mary Willie (Holman) T.; m. Lorraine Cornelia Jones, Mar. 14, 1959; children: Bruce Campbell, Kimberly Ann. B of Journalism, Lincoln U., 1950. Asst. city editor St. Louis Argus Newspaper, 1950-55; pub. rels. assoc. Moss H. Kendrix Orgn., Washington, 1955-61; reporter Assoc. Corr. News Svc., Washington, 1961-63; info. specialist USDA, Washington, 1963-74, chief, 1974-87; exec. dir. Orgn. Profl. Employment USDA, Washington, 1989—. Pres. D.C. chpt. Lincoln U. Alumni Assn., Washington. 1989-92, Whitfield Civic Assn., Lanham, Md., 1966-72. Sgt. U.S. Army Corps Engrs., 1943-46. Methodist. Avocation: collecting historical data on African Am. achievements. Office: OPEDA PO Box 381 Washington DC 20044

THOMPSON, PAUL HAROLD, university president; b. Ogden, Utah, Nov. 28, 1938; s. Harold Merwin and Elda (Skeen) T.; m. Carolyn Lee Nelson, Mar. 9, 1961; children: Loralyn, Kristyn, Shannyn, Robbyn, Daylyn, Nathan. BS, U. Utah, 1964; MBA, Harvard U., 1966, D Bus. Adminstrn., 1969. Rsch. assoc. Harvard U., Cambridge, Mass., 1966-69; asst. prof. Harvard U., Cambridge, 1969-73; assoc. prof. bus. Brigham Young U., Provo, Utah, 1973-78, prof., 1978-84, asst. dean, 1978-81, dean, 1984-89, v.p., 1989-90; pres. Weber State U., Ogden, Utah, 1990—; cons. Goodyear, Hughes Aircraft, Portland GE, Esso Resources Ltd., GE. Coauthor: Organization and People: Readings, Cases, and Exercises in Organizational Behavior, 1976, Novations: Strategies for Career Management, 1986; also articles. Named Outstanding Prof. of Yr., Brigham Young U., 1981; Baker scholar Harvard U., 1966. Mem. Am. Assn. State Colls. and Univs. (com. 1991—), Ogden C. of C. (exec. com. 1990—), Rotary (program com. 1989—), Harris fellow 1992—), Phi Beta Kappa. Office: Weber State U 3750 Harrison Blvd Ogden UT 84408-0001

THOMPSON, PAUL MICHAEL, lawyer; b. Dubuque, Iowa, Aug. 30, 1935; s. Frank W. and Genevieve (Cassutt) T.; m. Mary Jacqueline McManus, Jan. 30, 1960; children—Anne, Tricia, Paul, Tim, Jim. BA magna cum laude, Loras Coll., 1957; LL.B., Georgetown U., 1959. Bar: Iowa 1959, D.C. 1959, Va. 1966. Atty. appellate ct. br. NLRB, Washington, 1962-66; assoc. Hunton & Williams, Richmond, Va., 1966-71, ptnr., 1971—; adj. prof. The T.C. Williams Sch. Law, U. Richmond. Served with JAGC, USAF, 1960-62. Mem. ABA, Va. State Bar, Va. Bar Assn., Internat. Bar Assn. Roman Catholic. Club: Downtown (Richmond). Office: Hunton & Williams 951 E Byrd St Riverfront Plza E Tower Richmond VA 23219-4074

THOMPSON, PETER L. H., golf course architect; b. Modesto, Calif., Apr. 26, 1939. BS in East Asian Studies, U. Oreg., 1962, B in Landscape Architecture, 1971, M in Urban Planning, 1971; postgrad., U. Calif., Berkeley, 1975, Nat. U. Registered landscape arch., Calif., Oreg., Wash., Nev. With Oreg. Planning Commn., Lane County, 1965-70; commr. Oreg. Planning Commn., Eugene, 1981-83; sr. assoc. Ruff, Cameron, Lacoss, Eugene, Oreg., 1971-75; prin. Peter L. H. Thompson & Assocs., Eugene, 1975-82, John H. Midby & Assocs., Las Vegas, 1982-86, Thompson-Wihlborg, Ltd., Corte Madera, Calif., 1982-89, Thompson Planning Group, Ltd., San Raphael, Calif., 1989—; with Oreg. Planning Commn., commr., 1981-83, Novato, Calif. Planning Commn., commr. 1989-93, pres. 1989-93; spkr. Oreg. Home Builders Conf., 1980, Pacific Coast Builders Conf., 1984, Tacoma Country Club Pro-Pres. Tournament, 1991, Madrona Links Men's Golf Club, 1991, Twin Lakes Country Club Pro-Pres. Tournament, 1992, Golf Expo, Palm Springs, Calif., 1993, 95, Golf Expo, Nashville, 1993, Golf Expo, Monterey, Calif., 1994, others. Contbr. articles to mags. Mem. citizen's adv. bd. City of Eugene, Oreg., City of Las Vegas. Mem. USGA, Am. Soc. Landscape Archs., Am. Assn. Planners, Nat. Golf Found., Urban Land Inst., Rotary Internat. Office: Thompson Planning Gp Ltd 2175 E Francisco Blvd Ste A San Rafael CA 94901

THOMPSON, PHILIP MASON, museum director; b. N.Y.C., June 9, 1942; s. William R. and Marie J. (Buckovecky) T.; m. Vilja Maria Horner, Sept. 4, 1966; children: Philip Jr., Tyra. BA in Mktg. and Polit. Sci., Ariz. State U., 1969, MA in Anthropology, 1986; postgrad., 1986. Asst. dir. Phoenix Art Mus., 1971-73; asst. dir. devel. Phila. Mus. Art, 1973-78; dir. devel. and cmty. affairs Phoenix Meml. Hosp., 1978-81; dir. devel. St. Joseph's Hosp., Phoenix, 1981-83; dir., CEO Mus. No. Ariz., Flagstaff, 1983-93; chmn., CEO Wooster Constrn. and Devel., Phoenix, 1992-93; pres., CEO Eiteljorg Mus. Am. Indians and Western Art, Indpls., 1993—; nat. adv. bd. practitioners No. Ariz. U., Flagstaff, 1986; bd. dirs. Western Mus. Conf. Ariz. Mus. Assn. Mem., vice chmn. Ariz. Hist. Gov.'s Adv. Commn., Phoenix, 1984—; mem. steering com. BLOC Grant Program, 1980-83. Served with U.S. Army, 1963-66. Mem. Am. Assn. Mus., Am. Anthropol. Assn., Coun. Mus. Anthroplogy, Assn. Sci. Mus. Dirs. (membership com. 1986-90, nominating com. 1990—), Sigma Xi. Republican. Presbyterian. Club: Continental Country (Flagstaff). Avocations: fly fishing, skiing, golf. Home: RR 4 Box 718 Flagstaff AZ 86001-9301 Office: Mus No Ariz RR 4 Box 720 Flagstaff AZ 86001-9302

THOMPSON, RALPH GORDON, federal judge; b. Oklahoma City, Dec. 15, 1934; s. Lee Bennett and Elaine (Bizzell) T.; m. Barbara Irene Hencke, Sept. 5, 1964; children: Lisa, Elaine, Maria. B.B.A., U. Okla., 1956, J.D. 1961. Bar: Okla. 1961. Ptnr. Thompson, Thompson, Harbour & Selph (and predecessors), Oklahoma City, 1961-75; judge U.S. Dist. Ct. for Western Dist. Okla., Oklahoma City, 1975—; chief judge U.S. Dist. Ct. (we. dist.) Okla., 1986-93; mem. Okla. Ho. of Reps., 1967-75, asst. minority floor leader, 1969-70; spl. justice Supreme Ct. Okla., 1970-71; tchr. Harvard Law Sch. Trial Advocacy Workshop, 1981—; apptd. by chief justice of U.S. to U.S. Fgn. Intelligence Surveillance Ct., 1990—. Rep. nominee for lt. gov., Okla., 1970; chmn. bd. ARC, Oklahoma City, 1970-72; chmn., pres. Okla. Young Lawyers Conf., 1965; mem. bd. visitors U. Okla., 1975-78; pres. bd. dirs. St. John's Episcopal Sch., Oklahoma City. Lt. USAF, 1957-60, col. Res., ret. Decorated Legion of Merit; named Oklahoma City's Outstanding Young Man, Oklahoma City Jaycees, 1967, Outstanding Young Oklahoman, Okla. Jaycees, 1968, Outstanding Fed. Trial Judge, Okla. Trial Lawyers Assn., 1980, inductee Okla. Hall of Fame, 1995; recipient Regents Alumni award U. Okla., 1990, Disting. Svc. award U. Okla., 1993. Fellow Am. Bar Found.; mem. ABA, FBA, Okla. Bar Assn. (chmn. sect. internat. law and gen. practice 1974-75), Oklahoma county Bar Assn. (Jud. Svc. award 1988), Nat. Conf. Fed. Trial Judges, Jud. Conf. U.S. (com. on ct. adminstrm. 1981-89, com. on fed.-state jurisdiction 1988-91), U.S. Dist. Judges Assn. 10th Cir. (pres. 1992-94), Rotary (hon.), Order of Coif, Phi Beta Kappa (pres. Oklahoma City chpt. 1985-86, Phi Beta Kappa of Yr. 1991), Beta Theta Pi, Phi Alpha Delta. Episcopalian. Office: US Dist Ct 200 NW 4th St Oklahoma City OK 73102-3003

THOMPSON, RALPH NEWELL, former chemical corporation executive; b. Boston, Mar. 4, 1918; s. Ralph and Lillian May (Davenport) T.; m. Virginia Kenniston, Jan. 31, 1942; children: Pamela, Nicholas, Diana. B.S., MIT, 1940. Research engr. Middlesex Products Co., Cambridge, Mass., 1940-42; tech. dir. Falulah Paper Co., Fitchburg, Mass., 1945-48; staff engr. to v.p., div. gen. mgr. Calgon Corp., Pitts., 1948-70; v.p. mktg., corp. devel. Pa. Indsl. Chem. Corp., Clairton, 1970-74; gen. mgr. chem. div. Thiokol Corp., Trenton, N.J., 1974-76; group v.p.-chem. Thiokol Corp., Newtown, Pa., 1976-82; marine artist, specializing in lighthouses and historic sailing vessels, 1982—; dir. Mulford Co. Inc., Mass., 1956-82, Thiokol Can. Ltd., 1975-82, Thiokol Chems., Ltd., Eng., 1976-82, Toray Thiokol Co. Ltd., Japan, 1976-82, Nisso-Ventron K.K., Japan, 1977-82, S.W. Chem. Services Inc., Tex., 1978-82, S.W. Plastics Europe (S.A.), Belgium, 1978-82, Dynachem. Corp., Calif., 1979-82, Carstab Corp., Ohio, 1980-82. Patentee in field. Mem. Mt. Lebanon (Pa.) Civic League, 1950-74. Served with USNR, 1942-45. Recipient Goodreau Meml. Fund medal in chemistry, 1936. Fellow Am. Inst. Chemists; mem. TAPPI (contributor monograph series 1950-65), N.Y. Acad. Scis., Soc. Chem. Industry, Nat. Maritime Soc., Am. Soc. Marine Artists, Mil. Order World Wars, Pa. Soc., Soc. Descs. Colonial Clergy. Republican. Presbyterian.

THOMPSON, RAYMOND HARRIS, anthropologist, educator; b. Portland, Me., May 10, 1924; s. Raymond and Eloise (MacIntyre) T.; m. Molly Kendall, Sept. 9, 1948; children: Margaret Kelsey, Luchetta, Mary Frances. B.S., Tufts U., 1947; A.M., Harvard U., 1950, Ph.D, 1955. Fellow div. hist. research Carnegie Instn., Washington, 1950-52; asst. prof. anthropology, curator Mus. Anthropology, U. Ky., 1952-56; faculty U. Ariz., 1956—, prof. anthropology, 1964—, Riecker Disting. prof., 1980—, head dept., 1964-80; dir. Ariz. State Mus., from 1964; mem. adv. panel program in anthropology NSF, 1963-64, mem. mus. collections program, 1983-85; mem. NSF grad. fellowship panel Nat. Acad. Scis.-NRC, 1964-66; mem. research in nursing in patient care rev. com. USPHS, 1967-69; com. on social sci. commn. edn. in agr. and natural resources Nat. Acad. Scis., 1968-69; mem. anthropology com. examiners Grad. Record Exam., 1967-70, chmn., 1969-70; mem. com. recovery archaeol. remains, 1972-77, chmn., 1973-77; collaborator Nat. Park Service, 1972-76; mem. Ariz. Hist. Adv. Commn., 1966—, chmn., 1971-74, chmn. hist. sites rev. com., 1971-83; chmn. Ariz. Humanities Council, 1973-77, mem., 1979-85; adv. bd. Ariz. Hist. Recors, 1976-84; mem. research review panel for archaeology NEH, 1976-77, mem. rev. panel for museums, 1978, Ariz. Archaeology Adv. Commn., 1985—; cons. task force on archaeology Adv. Council on Historic Preservation, 1978. Author: Modern Yucatecan Maya Pottery Making, 1958; editor: Migrations in New World Culture History, 1958; editorial bd.: Science, 1972-77. Trustee Mus. No. Ariz., 1969—; bd. dirs. Tucson Mus. Art, 1974-77. Served with USNR, 1944-45, PTO. Fellow AAAS (chmn. sect. H 1977-78), Tree-Ring Soc., Am. Anthrop. Assn. (Disting. Service award 1980); mem. Soc. Am. Archaeology (editor 1958-62, mem. exec. com. 1963-64, pres. 1976-77); mem. Soc. Conservation Archaeology (Conservation award 1980), Seminario de Cultura Maya, Am. Assn. Museums, Internat. Council Museums (asso.), Council Museum Anthropology (dir. 1978-79, pres. 1980-83), Assn. Sci. Mus. Dirs. (sec.-treas. 1978—), Ariz. Acad. Sci., Ariz. Archaeol. and Hist. Soc., Ariz. Mus. Assn. (pres. 1983, 84), Phi Beta Kappa, Sigma Xi. Office: Univ Ariz Ariz State Museum Tucson AZ 85721*

THOMPSON, RENOLD DURANT, mining and shipping executive; b. Cleve., July 28, 1926; s. James Renold and Gertrude Goldie (Meyers) T.; m. Shirley Ann Sprague, June 24, 1949; children: Renold Durant, Jr., Bradley Sprague, Patricia Sprague Hickey. B.A., Dartmouth Coll., 1946; B.S., Case Inst. Tech., 1948. Metallurgist, U.S. Steel Corp., Cleve. and Duluth, Minn., 1948-52; with Oglebay Norton Co., Cleve., 1952—; sr. v.p. Oglebay Norton Co., 1972-73, exec. v.p. ops., 1973-81, exec. v.p., 1981-82, pres., chief exec. officer, 1982-92, vice chmn., 1992—, also dir.; bd. dirs. Lubrizol Corp., 1st Union Mgmt., Inc.; chmn., CEO Work in Northeast Ohio Coun. Mem. Pepper Pike Club, Chagrin Valley Hunt Club, Union Club. Office: Oglebay Norton Co 1100 Superior Ave E Ste 2000 Cleveland OH 44114-2518

THOMPSON, RICHARD C., magazine executive. Pub. U.S. News and World Report, Washington. Office: US News & World Report 2400 N St NW Washington DC 20037-1153

THOMPSON, RICHARD FREDERICK, psychologist, neuroscientist, educator; b. Portland, Oreg., 1930; s. Frederick Albert and Margaret St. Clair (Marr) T.; m. Judith K. Pedersen, May 22, 1960; children: Kathryn M., Elizabeth K., Virginia St. C. B.A., Reed Coll., 1952; M.S., U. Wis., 1953, Ph.D., 1956. Asst. prof. med. psychology Med. Sch. U. Oreg., Portland, 1959-63, assoc. prof., 1963-65, prof., 1965-67; prof. psychobiology U. Calif., Irvine, 1967-73, 75-80; prof. psychology Harvard U., Cambridge, Mass., 1973-74; Lashley chair prof. Harvard U., Cambridge, 1973; prof. psychology, Bing prof. human biology Stanford U., Palo Alto, Calif., 1980-87; Keck prof. psychology and biol. scis. U. So. Calif., L.A., 1987—; dir. neuroscience program, 1989—. Author: Foundations of Physiological Psychology, 1967, (with others) Psychology, 1971, Introduction to Physiological Psychology, 1975; Psychology editor (with others), W.H. Freeman & Co. publs., chief editor, Behavioral Neurosci., 1983—; editor: Jour. Comparative and Physiol. Psychology, 1981-83; regional editor: (with others) Physiology and Behavior; contbr. (with others) articles to profl. jours. Fellow AAAS, APA (Disting. Sci. Contbn. award 1974, governing coun. 1974—), Soc. Neurosci. (councilor 1972-76); mem. NAS, Internat. Brain Rsch. Orgn., Psychonomic Soc. (gov. 1972-77, chmn. 1976), Am. Psychol. Soc. (pres. 1994-96), Western Psychol. Assn. (pres. 1994-95), Soc. Exptl. Psychology (Warren medal). Office: Univ of So Calif Neuroscis Program HNB 122 Univ Park Los Angeles CA 90007

THOMPSON, RICHARD LEON, pharmaceutical company executive, lawyer; b. Rochester, N.Y., Dec. 5, 1944; s. Leslie L. and Marion (Cosad) T.; m. Catherine Jean Terry, July 6, 1974; children: Kristin Anne, Catherine Elizabeth. AB cum laude, SUNY, Albany, 1966; MA, Syracuse U., 1967; JD, Cath. U., 1975. Staff dir., counsel U.S. Ho. of Reps., Washington, 1973-78; dir. Abbott Labs., Washington, 1978-83; v.p. Squibb Corp., Washington, 1983-89, Bristol-Myers Squibb Corp., Washington, 1989—, chmn. legis. adv. com. Proprietary Assn., Washington, 1984; bd. dirs. Bus. Govt. Rels. Coun. Mem. com. on changing enrollments Fairfax (Va.) County Pub. Sch., 1983-84, Supts. adv. com., 1984-85, mem., 1988—; mem. Fed. City Coun., 1992; chmn. legis com. P.R.-U.S.A. Found., 1985—; co-chair edn. in 2010; bd. dirs. D.C. Hospice, Bryce Harlow Found., 1990—. 1st lt. U.S. Army, 1968-69, Vietnam. Named one of Outstanding Young Men of Am., Jaycees, 1976. Mem. ABA, D.C. Bar Assn., Pharm. Mfrs. Assn. (chmn. Washington reps. com. 1988), Congl. Country Club, Georgetown Club, City Club. Home: 1005 Woburn Ct Mc Lean VA 22102-2133 Office: Bristol-Myers Squibb Corp 655 15th St NW Ste 410 Washington DC 20005-5714

THOMPSON, RICHARD STEPHEN, management consultant; b. Des Moines, Oct. 14, 1931; s. Richard Stephen and Mary Ellen (Dailey) T.; m. Nancy Ann Jensen, Apr. 17, 1954; children—Traci Nan, Gregory Christian, Jonathan Richard. B.S.C. State U. Iowa, 1953; M.B.A., Ind. U., 1960. Regional dir. Bristol Meyers Co., N.Y.C., 1969-75; regional dir. Warner Lambert Co., Morris Plains, N.J., 1975-78; exec. v.p. Milton Bradley Co., Milton Bradley Internat., Inc., Springfield, Mass., 1979-83, pres., 1983-84; sr. v.p. internat., dir. Hasbro, Inc., Pawtucket, R.I., 1984-89; pres. Richard Thompson Assocs., London, 1989—. Served to 1st lt. USAF, 1954-55. Republican. Clubs: Chatham Beach Tennis (Mass.); Pilgrims (London and N.Y.); American (London); Roehampton (London). Avocations: tennis; skiing; hiking; reading.

THOMPSON, ROBERT CHARLES, lawyer; b. Council, Idaho, Apr. 20, 1942; s. Ernest Lavelle and Evangeline Montgomery (Carlson) T.; m. Marilyn Ann Wilcox, Jan. 17, 1960 (dec. Mar. 1962); m. Patricia Joan Price, June 1, 1963 (div. 1969); m. Jan Nesbitt, June 29, 1973; 1 child, Tanya. AB, Harvard U., 1963, LLB, 1967. Bar: Mass. 1967, Calif. 1983, U.S. Dist. Ct. (ea. dist.) Mass. 1975, U.S. Ct. Appeals (1st cir.) 1976, U.S. Ct. Appeals (9th cir.) 1984, U.S. Dist. Ct. (no. dist.) Calif. 1983. Assoc. Choate, Hall & Stewart, Boston, 1967-73; assoc. regional counsel EPA, Boston, 1973-75, regional counsel, 1975-82, assoc. gen. counsel, 1979-82; regional counsel EPA, San Francisco, 1982-84; ptnr. Graham & James, San Francisco, 1984-91, LeBoeuf, Lamb, Greene & MacRae, San Francisco, 1992—. Contbr. articles to profl. jours. Bd. dirs. Peninsula Indsl. and Bus. Assn., Palo Alto, Calif.,

1986—; chmn. Cambridge (Mass.) Conservation Commn., 1972-74; co-chmn. The Clift Confs. on Environ. Law, 1983-94. John Russell Shaw traveling fellow Harvard Coll., 1963-64; recipient Regional Administs. Bronze medal EPA, 1976, 84. Mem. ABA (natural resources sect., com. on native Am. natural resources law, spl. com. on mktg.), Natural Resources Def. Coun., Sierra Club, Commonwealth Club. Democrat. Episcopalian. Avocations: personal computers, yoga, antiques, wines, cooking. Office: LeBoeuf Lamb Greene & MacRae One Embarcadero Ctr San Francisco CA 94111

THOMPSON, ROBERT ELLIOTT, columnist, writer; b. Los Angeles, June 28, 1921; s. Robert W. and Sadie (Berry) T.; m. Mary C. Mattern, Feb. 27, 1954; children: Robert Elliott, Monica Louise. A.B., Ind. U., 1949. Reporter Ft. Wayne (Ind.) Jour.-Gazette, 1949-51, INS, 1951-58; press sec. John F. Kennedy's re-election campaign in, Mass., 1958; reporter N.Y. Daily News, 1959-62; White House corr. Los Angeles Times, 1962-66; chief Washington bur. Hearst Newspapers, 1966-68, nat. editor, 1968-74, columnist, 1978—; pub. Seattle Post-Intelligencer, 1974-78, chief Washington bur., 1978-89. Author: (with Hortense Myers) Robert Kennedy: the Brother Within, 1962. Mem. standing com. Corrs. House and Senate, 1960-62, chmn., 1961. Served with USNR, 1942-45. Mem. White House Corr. Assn. (pres. 1966-67), Seattle C. of C. (past trustee). Episcopalian. Clubs: Nat. Press, Cosmos, Gridiron (Washington).

THOMPSON, ROBERT EUGENE, employment agency executive; b. Pitts., Dec. 4, 1942; s. John Thomas and Mary (Bell) T.; m. Julie Anne Wollerman; children: Amy, Robby, Regina. BS in Acctg., Ind. U., 1970. Divisional controller Montgomery Ward Inc., Chgo., 1971-81; v.p. Kelly Services Inc., Troy, Mich., 1982-88, sr. v.p., group exec., 1989—; bd. dirs. J. Thompson & Assocs., Huntington Beach, Calif., 1980—. Home: 71 S Berkshire Rd Bloomfield Hills MI 48302-0409 Office: Kelly Svcs Inc 999 W Big Beaver Rd Troy MI 48084-4716

THOMPSON, ROBERT L., JR., lawyer; b. St. Paul, Aug. 9, 1944; s. Robert L. and Dorothy R. (Bergstrom) T.; m. Carolyn H. Foss, Aug. 4, 1973; children: Sarah, Kathryn, Jill. BA, Macalester Coll., St. Paul, 1967; JD, U. Oreg., 1973; LLM, NYU, 1988. Bar: Minn. 1973, U.S. Dist. Ct. Minn. 1978, N.Y. 1984. Corp. counsel Northrup King Co., Mpls., 1974-84; assoc. gen. counsel Sandoz Corp., N.Y.C., 1984-88, v.p., gen. counsel, sec., 1989—; mem. adv. bd. Allendale Ins. Co., N.Y.C., 1990—; dir. Orgn. for Internat. Investment, Washington, 1993—. Trustee Sandoz Found., 1993—. 1st lt. U.S. Army, 1968-70. Mem. ABA, Am. Corp. Counsel Assn., European-Am. Gen. Counsels Assn., Assn. Bar City N.Y. Republican. Congregationalist. Office: Sandoz Corp 608 Fifth Ave New York NY 10020-2303

THOMPSON, ROBERT LEE, agricultural economist, nonprofit executive; b. Canton, N.Y., Apr. 25, 1945; s. Robert M. and Esther Louise (Weatherup) T.; m. Karen Hansen, Aug. 9, 1968; children—Kristina Marie, Eric Robert. B.S., Cornell U., Ithaca, N.Y., 1967; M.S., Purdue U., West Lafayette, Ind., 1969, Ph.D., 1974. Vol. agriculturalist Internat. Vol. Service, Pakse and Vientiane, Laos, 1968-70; vis. prof. Fed. Univ. Vicosa, Brazil, 1972-73; prof. Purdue U., West Lafayette, Ind., 1974-93, dean of agriculture, 1987-93; rsch. scholar Internat. Inst. for Applied Systems Analysis, Laxenburg, Austria, 1983; sr. staff economist Council Econ. Advisers, Washington, 1983-85; asst. sec. econs. U.S. Dept. Agr., Washington, 1985-87; pres., CEO Winrock Internat. Inst. Agrl. Devel., 1993—; vis. prof. Econ. Rsch. Svc., USDA, 1979-80; bd. dirs. Vigoro Corp., Nat. Coop. Bank, Washington, Commodity Credit Corp., Washington, 1985-87, PSI Resources and P.S.I. Energy, 1987-94; chmn. adv. coun. Nat. Ctr. for Food and Agrl. Policy, Washington, 1987-92; mem. Ind. Commn. on Agr. and Rural Devel., 1989-93, Nat. Commn. on Agrl. Trade and Export Policy, 1985-86; bd. advisors NRC, 1987-92, Internat. Policy Coun. on Agr. and Trade, USDA Joint Coun. on Food and Agrl. Scis.; cons. USAID, Agr. Can., Ford Found., Brazilian Agr. Ministry, FAO, World Bank, Internat. Food Policy Rsch. Inst., Internat. Maize and Wheat Improvement Ctr., U.S. Feed Grains Coun., Nat. Planning Assn., USIA, Centre for Internat. Econs., Canberra, Club d'Experts en Economie Agricole Internat., Paris, Danish Coun. Rsch. Policy, FAO, Rome. Contbr. numerous articles to profl. publs. Author monographs, book chpts. Bd. dirs. Ind. 4-H Found., Ind. Inst. Agr. Food and Nutrition, 1987-93, Inst. for Sci. in Soc., 1991-93, USDA Grad. Sch., Washington, 1985-87; mem. nat. adv. coun. Minorities in Agr., Natural Resources and Related Sci.; bd. dirs. Farm Found., 1987-92, chmn. 1991-92. Recipient Agrl. Rsch. award Purdue U., 1983, Outstanding Alumni award Cornell U., 1988, Superior Svc. award USDA, 1989, Nat. 4-H Alumni award, 1992, Chgo. Farmers Agriculturalist of Yr. award, 1992. Fellow AAAS, Am. Agrl. Econs. Assn. (editl. coun. 1983-85, quality com. award 1979, 91, 93); mem. Internat. Agribus Mgmt. Assn. (bd. dirs.), Am. Econ. Assn., Internat. Assn. Agrl. Economists (pres.), Coun. on Fgn. Rels., Royal Swedish Acad. Agr. and Forestry (fgn.), Ukrainian Acad. Agrl. Scis., Cosmos Club (Washington), Sigma Xi, Alpha Gamma Rho, Alpha Zeta, Gamma Sigma Delta. Republican. Avocation: foreign language study. Office: Winrock Internat Inst Agr Devel Rte 3 Petit Jean Mtn Morrilton AR 72110-9537

THOMPSON, ROBERT MCBROOM, publishing executive; b. Evanston, Ill., Nov. 15, 1928; s. William M. and Ethel L. (McBroom) T.; m. Barbara J. Roepke, June 8, 1957; children: Janet, Sandra, Steven, Michael, Linda. BS, U. Ill., 1950. CPA, Ill. Sr. acct. Walton, Joplin, Langer & Co., Chgo., 1952-57; contr. Huntington Mosp. Pub. Co., Chgo., 1957-64; asst. contr. McGraw-Hill, Inc., N.Y.C., 1964-65, contr., 1966-93, v.p., 1969-93; retired, 1993. With U.S. Army, 1950-52, Korea. Mem. AICPA, Fin. Execs. Inst. Home: 21 Gulf Rd East Brunswick NJ 08816-1362

THOMPSON, ROBERT RANDALL (ROBBY THOMPSON), professional baseball player; b. West Palm Beach, Fla., May 10, 1962. Student, Palm Beach Jr. Coll., Fla. State U. With San Francisco Giants, 1983—; mem. Nat. League All-Star Team, 1988, 93. Named Sporting News Rookie Player of Yr., 1986, Nat. League Leader in Triples, 1989, Nat. League Gold Glove 1993, Silver Slugger Team 1993; named to Sporting News All-Star Team, 1988, 93. Office: San Francisco Giants Candlestick Park San Francisco CA 94124*

THOMPSON, ROBERT THOMAS, lawyer; b. Pontiac, Ill., Feb. 15, 1930; s. McDuffie and Ivy (Slaughter) T.; m. Elaine Elmers, Oct. 1, 1950; children: Robert Thomas, Randall C., David L. A.B., Emory U., 1950, J.D. with honors, 1952. Bar: Ga. 1951, S.C. 1964, D.C. 1973. Assoc., ptnr. Wilson, Branch, Barwick & Vandiver, Atlanta, 1952-64; sr. ptnr. Thompson & Hutson, Greenville, S.C., 1964—, Washington, S.C., 1970—; lectr. Law Sch. Emory U.; mgmt. adv. U.S. Del. to Internat. Labor Orgn., 1970; mem., chmn. task force NLRB, 1974-77; mem. pub. Administrv. conf. U.S. Bd. vistors Emory U.; chmn. bd. advisors Furman U.; past trustee Buncombe St. United Meth. Ch. Contbr. articles to profl. jours. Bd. dirs., v.p. Greenville Symphony Assn. Recipient medal Emory U., 1989. Fellow Am. Bar Found. (life); mem. State Bar Ga. (past pres. young lawyers sect., past bd. govs.), S.C. Bar Assn., Atlanta Bar Assn. (past sec.-treas.), U.S. C. of C. (past chmn. bd. dirs., past chmn. labor rels. and bylaws coms.), S.C. C. of C. (spl. counsel labor rels., adv. com. on labor rels.), Poinsett Club, Commerce Club, Met. Club (Washington and N.Y.C.). Office: Thompson & Hutson Nations Bank Plz Greenville SC 29601 also: 1317 F St NW Ste 900 Washington DC 20004-1105

THOMPSON, ROBERT W., surgeon; b. Grand Rapids, Mich., Aug. 12, 1957. MD, U. Mich., 1983. Diplomate Am. Bd. Surgery, Am. Bd. Gen. Vascular Surgery. Intern Brigham & Women's Hosp., Boston, 1983-84, resident in gen. surgery, 1984-91; fellow in gen. vascular surgery U. Calif. San Francisco, 1991-92; vascular surgeon Barnes Hosp., St. Louis, 1992—; asst. prof. Washington U., St. Louis, 1992—. Faculty fellow ACS, 1994. Office: Queeny Tower Suite 5103 1 Barnes Hosp Plz Saint Louis MO 63110*

THOMPSON, ROBERT W., theoretical physicist; b. Mpls., 1919. BS with highest distinction, U. Minn., 1941; PhD, MIT, 1948. With Los Alamos, 1943-45; asst. prof. Indiana U., 1948-53; prof. physics U. Chgo., 1953. Contbr. to profl. jours. Achievements include discovery of the Neutral Kaons, the Isotope PU 240, and execution of the P it assembly for the Nagasaki Bomb; patents include the Multiwire Proportional Counter. Home: 50 S La Salle St Chicago IL 60603-1003

THOMPSON, RONALD EDWARD, lawyer; b. Bremerton, Wash., May 24, 1931; s. Melville Herbert and Clara Mildred (Griggs) T.; m. Marilyn Christine Woods, Dec. 15, 1956; children—Donald Jeffery, Karen, Susan, Nancy, Sally, Claire. B.A., U. Wash., 1953, J.D., 1958. Bar: Wash. 1959. Asst. city atty. City of Tacoma, 1960-61; pres. firm Thompson, Krilich, LaPorte, Tucci & West, P.S., Tacoma, 1961—; judge pro tem Mcpl. Ct., City of Tacoma, Pierce County Dist., 1972—, Pierce County Superior Ct., 1972—. Chmn. housing and social welfare com. City of Tacoma, 1965-69; mem. Tacoma Bd. Adjustment, 1967-71, chmn., 1968; mem. Tacoma Com. Future Devel., 1961-64, Tacoma Planning Commn., 1971-72; bd. dirs., pres. Mcpl. League Tacoma; bd. dirs. Pres. Tacoma Rescue Mission, Tacoma Pierce County Cancer Soc., Tacoma-Pierce County Heart Assn., Tacoma-Pierce County Council for Arts, Econ. Devel. Council Puget Sound, Tacoma Youth Symphony, Kleiner Group Home, Tacoma Community Coll. Found., Pierce County Econ. Devel. Corp., Wash. Transp. Policy Inst.; Coalition to Keep Wash. Moving, precinct committeeman Republican party, 1969-73. Served with AUS, 1953-55; col. Res. Recipient Internat. Community Service award Optimist Club, 1970, Patriotism award Am. Fedn. Police, 1974, citation for community service HUD, 1974, Disting. Citizen award Mcpl. League Tacoma-Pierce County, 1985; named Lawyer of the Yr. Pierce County Legal Secs. Assn., 1992. Mem. Am. Arbitration Assn. (panel of arbitrators), ABA, Wash. State Bar Assn., Tacoma-Pierce County Bar Assn. (sec. 1964, pres. 1979, mem. cts. and judiciary com. 1981-82), Assn. Trial Lawyers Am., Wash. State Trial Lawyers Assn., Tacoma-Pierce County C. of C. (bd. dirs., exec. com., v.p., chmn.), Downtown Tacoma Assn. (com. chmn., bd. dirs. exec. com., chmn.), Phi Delta Phi, Sigma Nu. Roman Catholic. Clubs: Variety (Seattle); Lawn Tennis, Tacoma, Optimist (Tacoma, Internat. Pres. 1973-74). Home: 3101 East Bay Dr NW Gig Harbor WA 98335 Office: 524 Tacoma Ave S Tacoma WA 98402-5416

THOMPSON, RONALD MACKINNON, family physician, artist, writer; b. N.Y.C., Oct. 19, 1916; s. George Harold and Pearl Anita (Hatfield) T.; m. Ethel Joyce Chastant, June 30, 1950; children: Phyllis Anita, Walter MacKinnon, Charles Chastant, Richard Douglas. BS, U. Chgo., 1947, MS, 1948, MD, 1949. Diplomate Am. Bd. Family Practice. Intern U. Mich., Ann Arbor, 1950-51; resident in psychiatry U. Tex., Galveston, 1951-52; pvt. practice, family and internal medicine South Dixie Med. Ctr., West Palm Beach, Fla., 1952-85; instr. Anatomy, U. Chgo., 1946-47, Pharmacology, 1948-49. Contbr. articles to profl. jours.; exhibited in 7 one-man shows (over 30 awards for painting in regional and nat. shows); represented in permanent collections at 5 mus. Mem. Civitan Club W. Palm Beach, Fla., 1951; former bd. dirs. Norton Gallery Mus. of Art West Palm Beach. Mem. Fla. Nat. Guard, 1936-40; cadet Army Air Force, 1943-44. Over thirty awards for painting in juried regional and nat. shows. Fellow Am. Acad. Family Physicians; mem. AMA, Fla. Med. Assn., Fla. Acad. of Family Physicians, Palm Beach County Med. Soc., Nat. Watercolor Soc., Ariz. Watercolor Soc. Republican. Episcopalian. Avocations: chess, tennis, writing, square and round dancing. Home: 308 Leisure World Mesa AZ 85206

THOMPSON, RONELLE KAY HILDEBRANDT, library director; b. Brookings, S.D., Apr. 21, 1954; d. Earl E. and Maxine R. (Taplin) Hildebrandt; m. Harry Floyd Thompson II, Dec. 24, 1976; children: Clarissa, Harry III. BA in Humanities magna cum laude, Houghton Coll., 1976; MLS, Syracuse U., 1976; postgrad., U. Rochester, 1980, 81; cert., Miami U., 1990. Libr. asst. Norwalk (Conn.) Pub. Libr., 1977; elem. libr. Moriah Cen. Schs., Port Henry, N.Y., 1977-78; div. coord. pediatric gastroenterology and nutrition U. Rochester (N.Y.) Med. Ctr., 1978-81, cons., mem. pediatric housestaff libr. com., 1980-81; dir. Medford Libr. U.S.C. Lancaster, 1981-83; dir. Mikkelsen Libr., libr. assocs., Ctr. for Western Studies, mem. acad. computing com., libr. com. Augustana Coll., Sioux Falls, S.D., 1983—, mem. administrv. pers. coun., 1989-94; presenter in field. Contbr. articles to profl. jours. Mem. adv. com. S.D. Libr. Network, 1986—, chair, 1989-91, 94—; mem. Sioux Falls Community Playhouse, S.D. Symphony, Sioux Falls Civic Fine Arts Assn.; advisor Minnehaha County Libr., pers. dept. City of Sioux Falls. Named one of Outstanding Young Women Am., 1983; Syracuse U. Gaylord Co. scholar, 1976; recipient YWCA leader award, 1991. Mem. ALA, AAUW, Assn. Coll. and Rsch. Librs. (nat. adv. coun. coll. librs. sect. 1987—), Mountain Plains Libr. Assn. (chair acad. sect., nominating com. 1988, pres. 1993-94), S.D. Libr. Assn. (chair interlibr. coop. task force 1986-87, pres. 1987-88, chair recommended munumum salary task force 1988, chair local arrangements com. 1989-90), S.D. Libr. Network (adv. coun. 1986—, exec. com. 1992—, chair adv. coun. 1994—). Office: Augustana Coll Mikkelsen Libr 29th & Summit Sioux Falls SD 57197

THOMPSON, RUFUS E., lawyer; b. Lubbock, Tex., Aug. 15, 1943; s. Glenn Wesley and Naomi Elvina T.; m. Sandra Jean Lemons, Aug. 8, 1965; children—Michael Glenn, Mark Gregory, Matthew Wesley. B.B.A., U. Tex., Austin, 1965, J.D., 1968. Bar: Tex. bar 1968, N.Mex. bar 1969. Assoc. firm Atwood & Malone, Roswell, N.Mex., 1968-71; ptnr. firm Atwood, Malone, Mann & Cooter, Roswell, 1971-78; U.S. Atty. Dist. N.Mex., Albuquerque, 1978-81; now ptnr. firm Modrall, Sperling, Roehl, Harris & Sisk, Albuquerque, 1981—. mem. Nat. Conf. Commrs. on Uniform State Laws, 1975-79; chmn. N.Mex. Supreme Ct. Com. on Rules of Evidence, 1972-94; U.S. Atty. for N.Mex. Com., 1978-82; mem. U.S. Atty. Gen.'s Adv. Com., 1980—, chmn., 1981. Mem. N.Mex. Democratic Party Central Com., 1972-78; mem. N.Mex. State Senate, 1973-78; mem. Gov.'s Commn. on Prevention of Organized Crime, 1985-89. Mem. Am. Bar Assn. (exec. council young lawyers sect. 1972), N.Mex. Bar Assn. (chmn. young lawyers sect. 1970). Baptist. Office: PO Box 607 Albuquerque NM 87103-0607

THOMPSON, SALLY ENGSTROM, state official; b. Spokane, Wash., Feb. 17, 1940; d. Logan C. and Ava Leigh (Phillips) Engstrom; m. Donald Edward Colcun, 1981; children: Lauri Thompson, Tom Thompson, Tami Thompson, Sheri Colcun Trumpfheller. BS magna cum laude, U. Colo., 1975. CPA, Colo. 1976, Kans. 1986. Audit mgr. and mgmt. cons. Touche Ross & Co., Denver, 1975-82; v.p., mgr. planning and fin. analysis United Bank, Denver, 1982-85; pres., chief oper. officer Shawnee Fed. Svgs., Topeka, 1985-90; treas. State of Kans., 1990—. Past editorial advisor New Accountant mag. Bd. dirs. Everywoman's Resource Ctr., Topeka, 1988-92, Community Svc. Found. Kans., Kids Voting Kans. (hon.); v.p., bd. dirs. Downtown Topeka Inc., YWCA, Topeka, 1986-93, Woman of Achievement award, 1984; mem. fin. com. Girl Scouts U.S.A., Kaw Valley, various coms., United Way of Greater Topeka; chmn. art auction com. KTWU-TV, summer concert, Topeka Civic Theatre. Recipient Disting. Community Leadership award Topeka Pub. Schs., 1989, Disting. Leadership award Nat. Assn. Community Leadership, 1991, 1991 Class Leadership Kans. Mem. AICPAs, Am. Soc. Women Accts., Kans. Soc. CPAs, Kansas C. of C. and Industry, Greater Topeka C. of C. (bd. dirs. 1989-92), Emporia State U. Bus. Sch. Adv. Bd., Nat. Assn. State Auditors, Controllers and Treas., Nat. Assn. State Treas. (v.p., Midwest regional chair), Women Execs. in Govt., Beta Alpha Psi. Democrat. Offices: Office State Treasurer Landon State Office Bldg 900 SW Jackson St Ste 201N Topeka KS 66612-1220*

THOMPSON, SHAWNA MARGARET, lawyer; b. Glen Cove, N.Y., Sept. 4, 1961; d. Vincent John and Margaret Catherine (Kelly) Haley; m. John Arthur Thompson, April 30, 1994. BA in Bus., U. Ariz., 1981; JD cum laude, U. San Diego, 1986. Assoc. Lee & Holbrook, Redondo Beach, Calif., 1987-89; sr. staff CSL Litigation Northrop Grumman Corp., L.A., 1989—; arbitrator Superior Ct., L.A., 1993-94; mem. Sr. Women in Aerospace, L.A., 1994. Mem. ABA, Calif. Bar Assn., L.A. Bar Assn., Century City Bar Assn. Avocations: violin, running, gardening, cooking. Office: Northrop Grumman Corp 1840 Century Park E Los Angeles CA 90067-2199

THOMPSON, SHELDON LEE, refining company executive; b. Mpls., Oct. 7, 1938; s. Wallace E. and Madeline A. (King) T.; m. Karen Beatrice Gallison, Aug. 25, 1962; children: Jeffrey, Paul, Daniel. BS, U. Minn., 1960, MS, 1962; grad. advanced mgmt. program, Harvard U., 1983. Registered profl. chem. engr., Pa. Rsch. engr. Sun Refining & Mktg. Co., Marcus Hook, Pa., 1962-69, assoc. engr., 1969-70, chief engring. rsch., 1970-72, rsch. program mgr. corp. R & D, 1972-74, mgr. venture engring., 1974-77, mgr. R & D chems., 1977-80, dir. R & D, 1980-88; v.p. chems., lubricants and tech. Sun Refining & Mktg. Co., Phila., 1988-91; sr. v.p., chief administrv. officer Sun Co., Inc., Phila., 1992—. Inventor 11 patents chems., fuels and lubes processing. Mem. exec. edu. adv. bd. Wharton sch. Bus., U. Pa.; bd. trustees Acad. Nat. Scis., Phila. Orch. Mem. AICE, Am. Petroleum Inst., Greater Phila. C. of C. (mem. exec. com.). Republican. Presbyterian. Avocation:

music. Office: Sun Co Inc 1801 Market St 10 Penn Ctr Philadelphia PA 19103-1699

THOMPSON, STANLEY B., church administrator. Pres., CEO, dir. The Free Meth. Found., Spring Arbor, Mich. Office: The Free Meth Found Box 580 Spring Arbor MI 49283

THOMPSON, STEPHEN ARTHUR, publishing executive; b. Englewood, N.J., Jan. 24, 1934; s. Stephen Gerard and Doris Lillian (Evans) T.; m. Joan Frances O'Connor, May 12, 1955 (div. 1978); children: Stephen Andrew, Craig Allen, David John; m. Sandra Rene Fingernut, May 27, 1979. BS, Ohio State U., 1961. Physicist Rocketdyne div. North Am. Aviation, Canoga Park, Calif., 1961-62, Marquardt Corp., Van Nuys, Calif., 1962-63; mem. tech. staff Hughes Rsch. Labs., Malibu, Calif., 1963-69; editor, with advt. sales dept. Chilton Co., L.A., 1969-77; sr. v.p. mfg. group pub. Cahners Pub. Co., Newton, Mass., 1977—; founder Design News Engring. Edn. Foundn., Newton, 1991—; pub. Design News Mag. Author: Basketball for Boys, 1970; contbr. articles to Jour. Spacecraft/Rockets, 1966. Club leader YMCA, Canoga Park, 1963-78; active PTA, Canoga Park, 1961-80; bd. dirs. Chatsworth (Calif.) High Booster Club, 1972-80. 1st lt., jet fighter pilot USAF, 1952-58. Mem. Bus. Profl. Advt. Assn. (Golden Spike award 1980, 81, 82, 83), L.A. Mag. Reps. Assn. (life), Nat. Fluid Power Assn. Achievements include patents for ion source, system and method for ion implantation of semiconductors. Office: Cahners Pub Co 275 Washington St Newton MA 02158

THOMPSON, STEVE ALLAN, writer; b. Mpls., Sept. 10, 1951; s. John Thomas and Charlotte Joan (Ellis) T.; m. Michele Rae Jones, July 16, 1983; 1 child, Kent Lloyd. Student, U. Minn., 1969-73. Dept. supr. Hennpin County Libr., Edina, Minn., 1973-87; writer, 1987—; cons. Okefenokee Glee & Perloo Inc., Manassa, Va., 1988—. Author: Walt Kelly Collector's Guide; co-author: Pogo Files for Phophiles, 1992; editor The Fort Mudge Most 1988—; contbr. articles to profl. jours. Mem. Walt Kelly Soc. (pres. 1987—), Lewis Carroll Soc., Bakr Street Irregulars. Achievements include international recognized on life and career of Walt Kelly. Home: 6908 Wentworth Ave S Richfield MN 55423

THOMPSON, THEODORE ROBERT, pediatric educator; b. Dayton, Ohio, July 18, 1943; s. Theodore Roosevelt and Helen (Casey) J.;m. Lynette Joanne Shenk; 1 child, S. Beth. BS, Wittenberg U., 1965; MD, U. Pa., 1969. Diplomate Am. Bd. Pediatrics (Neonatal, Perinatal Medicine). Resident in pediatrics U. Minn. Hosp., Mpls., 1969-72, chief resident in pediatrics, 1971-72, fellow neonatal, perinatal, 1974-75, asst. prof., 1975-80, dir. of neonatology and newborn intensive care unit, 1977-80, assoc. prof., 1980-85, prof., 1985—, co-dir. Med. Outreach, 1988-91, dir. med. outreach, 1991—, assoc. chief of pediatrics, 1988—; med. dir. U. Minn. Clin. Assocs., 1992—. Editor: Newborn Intensive Care: A Practical Manual, 1983. Bd. dirs. Life Link III, St. Paul, 1987—; cons. Maternal and Child Health, Minn. Bd. Health, 1975—. With USPHS. 1972-74. Fellow Am. Acad. Pediatrics (chmn. perinatal newborn com. Minn. chpt. 1985-92); Gt. Plains Orgn. for Perinatal Health Care (Sioux Falls, S.D., Kunshe award 1989). Lutheran. Avocations: swimming, football. Office: U Minn Hosp and Clinic 420 Delaware St SE Box 39 Minneapolis MN 55455-0374

THOMPSON, THOMAS EDWARD, educator, administrator, researcher; b. El Paso, Tex., Nov. 29, 1950; s. William Edward and Gloria Mae (Berryhill) T.; m. Tedi Maureen Swenson, May 20, 1982 (div. June 1985); 1 stepchild, Jon. BA in English Lit., Met. State Coll., Denver, 1972, BA in Elem. Edn., 1974; MEd in Ednl. Adminstrn., Colo. State U., Greeley, 1979; PhD in Ednl. Adminstrn., Denver U., 1985. Cert. ednl. administr. elem. and secondary. Instr., asst. Littleton (Colo.) Pub. Schs., 1973-75; elem. tchr. Bear Creek Elem., Lakewood, Colo., 1975-80; tchr. social studies O'Connell Jr. High, Lakewood, 1980-84; tchr. computers Deer Creek Jr. High, Littleton, Colo., 1984-89; coord. Acad. of Choice, Littleton, 1990-93, tchr. English, 1993-95; tchr. Am. lit. Bay House Sch., Gosport, Hants, Eng., 1995-96; lectr. Denver U., 1985-89; cons. computers Park County Schs., Cripple Creek, Colo., 1985-86; mem. planning com. Jefferson County Edn. Specifications, Lakewood, Colo., 1989-90; dir. grad. seminars, Littleton, 1985-90. Author: IBM in Remediation, 1985. Mem. Rocky Mountain Study Coun., Littleton, 1985—; coach Colo.-Columbine Football, Littleton, 1986—; dir. Colo. Mentor Project, Littleton, 1990. Fulbright fellow, 1995-96. Mem. Colo. Assn. Sch. Execs., Colo. Assn. Middle Level Edn., Rocky Mountain Study Group, Jr. High Improvement Project, Phi Kappa Phi, Phi Kappa Delta. Avocations: black belt/Tae Kwon Do, weightlifting. Home: 6223 E Phillips Pl Englewood CO 80112-3034 Office: Bay House Sch, Gomer Ln Alverstoke, Gosport Hants, England

THOMPSON, THOMAS HENRY, philosophy educator; b. Sioux City, Iowa, Jan. 10, 1924; s. Elmer Edwin and Ruth Alma (Baker) T.; m. Diane Sargent, Nov. 23, 1955; children: Brenda, Alicia, Mark, Rosemary. B.A., U. Iowa, 1948, M.A., 1950, Ph.D., 1952. Asst. instr. U. Iowa, Iowa City, 1948-52; mem. faculty U. No. Iowa, Cedar Falls, 1952—; prof. philosophy U. No. Iowa, 1969—, head dept., 1969-81, acting dean Coll. Humanities and Fine Arts, 1981-82, dean Coll. Humanities and Fine Arts, 1982-90; prof. emeritus, 1994—. Sigmund Freud Gesellschaft (Vienna), Am. Philosophy Assn. Home: 2122 California St Cedar Falls IA 50613-4721 Office: U No Iowa Comm Arts Ctr Baker 35 1222 W 27th St Cedar Falls IA 50613-4800

THOMPSON, THOMAS MARTIN, lawyer; b. Albion, Pa., Jan. 7, 1943; s. Donald C. and Mabel Louise (Martin) T.; m. Judith E. Daucher; children: Reid, Chad, Matthew, Molly. AB, Grove City Coll., 1965; JD cum laude, Harvard U., 1968. Bar: Pa. 1968. Ptnr. Buchanan Ingersoll, Pitts., 1968—, chair corp. fin. group; adj. prof. law U. Pitts.; dir., past chairperson Pa. Lawyer Trust Acct. Bd. Past pres. Neighborhood Legal Svcs. Assn.; bd. dirs., past pres. Pitts. chpt. Assn. for Corp. Growth; bd. dirs. Pitts. Pub. Theater. Mem. ABA, Pa. Bar Assn. (Pro Bono award 1989, mem. corp., bus. and banking coun.), Allegheny County Bar Assn. (past chairperson pub. svc. com., chair corp., banking and bus. coun.). Democrat. Home: 1142 Dartmouth Rd Pittsburgh PA 15205-1705 Office: Buchanan Ingersoll 600 Grant St Ste 58 Pittsburgh PA 15219

THOMPSON, THOMAS SANFORD, former college president; b. Lewistown, Mont., Apr. 9, 1916; s. Thomas Swing and Sadie (Mixer) T.; m. Margaret Ann Wiese, June 1, 1941; children—Roger John, Thomas Warren, Pamela Ann, Mary Ann. B.S., Pacific U., 1938, L.H.D., 1966; postgrad., U. Wash., 1939, U. Oreg., 1941; M.Ed., Oreg. State U., 1949. Tchr.-coach Siuslaw Union High Sch., Florence, Oreg., 1938; prin. Siuslaw Union High Sch., 1939-42; coordinator tng. within industry War Manpower Commn., Portland, Oreg., 1942-43; employee utilization dir. North Pacific div. U.S. Army C.E., 1946-47; acting prin. Portland Apprentice Sch., 1947-48; partner Davis Sales Cons., Portland, 1948-51; dir. devel. Lewis and Clark Coll., Portland, 1952-57; dir. sustaining assocs. program Washington U., St. Louis, 1957-60; dir. devel. Knox Coll., Galesburg, Ill., 1960-63; v.p. for devel. U. Pacific, Stockton, Calif., 1963-69; pres. Morningside Coll., Sioux City, Iowa, 1969-78; lectr. coll.-univ. devel. adminstrn. Cons. Council on Christian Philanthropy, 1970, Council for Financial Aid to Edn., 1963. Bd. dirs. United Fund, Sioux City, 1969-78, Pacific Med. Center, San Francisco, 1966-68, Marian Health Center, Sioux City, 1977-78, St. Joseph's Hosp., Stockton, 1979-85. Served to lt. col USAAF, 1943-46; Served to lt. col USAF, 1951-52. Mem. Greater Stockton C. of C. (dir. 1967-69), Galesburg C. of C. (dir. 1961-63), Sioux City (dir. 1971-78), Oreg. Mental Health Assn. (pres. 1956-57), Assn. Am. Colls., Am. Colls. Pub. Relations Assn., Royal Rosarians, Phi Delta Kappa. Democrat. Roman Catholic. Club: Rotary (Sioux City) (past pres.). Home: 6879 Atlanta Cir Stockton CA 95219-3233

THOMPSON, TINA LEWIS CHRYAR, publisher; b. Houston, Dec. 31, 1929; d. Joshua and Mary Christine (Brown) Thompson; m. Joseph Chryar, May 25, 1943; 1 child, Joseph Jr. Cosmetologist, Franklin Coll., Houston, 1950; student, Crenshaw Coll., L.A., 1961. Pubr., composer adminstr. Member ABMI., N.Y.C., 1964-74; pubr. ASCAP, N.Y.C., 1974-86, The Fox Agy., N.Y.C., 1986—, Tech. World, L.A., 1990—; v.p. music Asset Records, L.A., 1978—; music dir., v.p. Roach Records, L.A., 1968; music dir. Rendezvous Records, Hollywood, 1950; v.p. assoc. Internat., L.A., 1973; bd. govs. ABI, Inc., 1994; pres. Cling Music Pub., Soprano Music; pub. processor music catalogs Broadcast Music Inc. Author: Soprano Poems, 1985; creator/designer Baby

Napin brand form-fitting, no-leak, no pins baby diaper, 1967, Saver Belt, 1993; patentee/pub. Letter's Tech in Word, used by TV stas. to advertise, 1972. Recipient recognition award IBC, Cambridge, Eng., 1991, cert. of proclamation Internat. Woman of Yr., 1991-92, Merit award Pres. Ronald Reagan, 1986; named Most Admired Woman of Decade, ABI, 1993. Mem. AAUW, NARAS, NOW, ABI (bd. govs. 1994), Am. Soc. Authors and Composers, Nat. Mus. Pubs. Assn., Songwriters Guild Am. (Cert. of Ranks of Composers and Lyracists 1991), Am. Fedn. Label Co. Unions, Am. Theatre Assn. Broadcast Music Inc. (pres. Soprano Music Publ. 1968), Rec. Acad. Country Music Acad., Internat. Platform Assn., L.A. Women in Music. Home: PO Box 7731 Beverly Hills CA 90212-7731

THOMPSON, TOMMY GEORGE, governor; b. Elroy, Wis., Nov. 19, 1941; s. Allan and Julia (Dutton) T.; m. Sue Ann Mashak, 1969; children: Kelli Sue, Tommi, Jason. BS in Polit. Sci. and History, U. Wis., 1963, JD, 1966. Polit. intern U.S. Rep. Thomson, 1963; legis. messenger Wis. State Senate, 1964-66; sole practice Elroy and Mauston, Wis., 1966-87; mem. Dist. 87 Wis. State Assembly, 1966-87, asst. minority leader, 1972-81, floor leader, 1981-87; self-employed real estate broker Mauston, 1970—; gov. State of Wis., 1987—; alt. del. Rep. Nat. Conv., 1976; chmn. Intergovtl. Policy Adv. Commn. to U.S. Trade Rep.; mem. nat. govs. assn. exec. com.; bd. dirs. AMTRAK. Served with USAR. Recipient meal. award for Legis. Wis. Acad. Gen. Practice, Thomas Jefferson Freedon award Am. Legis. Exchange Coun., 1991, Most Valuable Pub. Official award City and State Mag., 1991, Governance award Free Congress Found., 1992. Mem. ABA, Wis. Bar Assn., Rep. Govs. Assn., Phi Delta Phi. Roman Catholic. Office: Office of Gov 115 East Ave Madison WI 53702*

THOMPSON, TRAVIS, psychology educator, administrator, researcher; b. Mpls., July 20, 1937; s. William Raymond and Loretta (Travis) T.; m. Anna Leyens, June 12, 1970; children: Rebecca Lynn, Jennifer Eva, Andrea Laura, Peter Erich. BA, U. Minn., 1958, MA, PhD, 1961. Lic. psychologist. NSF postdoctoral fellow U. Md., College Park, 1961-63; asst. prof. U. Minn., Mpls., 1963-66, assoc. prof., 1966-69, prof., 1969-91, dir. inst. disabilities studies, 1987-91; prof., dir. John F. Kennedy Ctr. Vanderbilt U., Nashville, 1991—; vis. fellow Cambridge (U.K.) U., 1968-69; vis. scientist Nat. Inst. Drug Abuse, Rockville, Md., 1979-80; mem. rsch. review com. Nat. Inst. Child Health, Bethesda, Md. Hastings Ctr., Rights of Retarded, Hastings-on-Hudson, 1977-78; mem. instl. review bd. Minn. Dept. Human Svcs., 1986-89; mem. exec. com. 1990 planning com. Gatlinburg Conf. on Rsch. in Mental Retardation, 1988—, exec. com., 1992; mem. Human Devel. 3 Rsch. Review com. NIH, 1988-91; mem. adv. com. Inst. on Community Intergration, U. Minn., 1988-91, Rehab. Rsch. and Tng. Ctr in Adolescent Health, 1989-91; mem. local adv. com. Geriatric Rsch., Edn. and Clin. Ctr., VA Med. Ctr., Mpls., 1989-91; cons. in field, including North Star Rsch. and Devel. Inst., Mpls., 1963-65, Honeywell, Inc., Mpls., 1964-67, Faribault (Minn.) State Hosp., 1968-75, 87—, Cambridge (Minn.) State Hosp., 1972-74, Ctr. for Behavioral Therapy, Mpls., 1973-80, Clara Doerr Residence, Inc., Mpls., 1975-77, Ill. Sci. Adv. Com. on Mental Health and Devel. Disabilities, 1975-77, Minn. Dept. Pub. Welfare, 1978-80, Psychol. and Behavioral Cons., St. Paul., 1981-85, People, Inc., Mpls., 1985., NIH, 1986, Emerson Sch., 1986-87, U. Tex. Mental Scis. Inst., 1991—, Livonia (Mich.) Pub. Schs., 1992; invited speaker in field including Oxford (U.K.) U., 1968, Mario Negri Inst., Milan, Italy, 1969, York U., Toronto, Can., 1971, Uppsala U., Sweden, 1972, U. Auckland, New Zealand, 1974, European Behaviour Therapy Assn. Meeting, Uppsala, 1977, Bermuda Coll., 1983, Maudsley Hosp., U. London, 1985, European Behavioral Pharmacology Soc. Meeting, Antwerp, Belgium, 1986, Amsterdam, The Netherlands, 1990, Rehab. Inst., Dalhouise U., Halifax, Nova Scotia, Can., 1989, U. Otago, New Zealand, 1992. Author: (with C. R. Schwster) Behavioral Pharmacology, 1968, (with J.P. Grabowski) Reinforcement Schedules and Multi-operant Analysis, 1972; editor: Behavioral Modification of Mental Retardation, 1972, 2nd edit., 1977, (with S. C. Hupp) Saving Children at Risk, 1992, (with Peter B. Dews and James Barrett) Advances in Behavioral Pharmacology, numerous others; regional editor Pharmacology Biochemistry & Behavior, 1974-88; mem. editorial bd. Psychopharmacologia, 1967-78, Applied Rsch. in Mental Retardation, 1978-89, Mental Retardation, 1978-88, Analysis and Intervention in Devel. Disabilities, 1981-88, Jour. for Analysis and Modification of Behavior (Italy), 1982-87, The Behavior Analyst, 1984-90, Jour. Spl. Edn., 1992—, Exptl. and Clin. Psychopharmacology, 1992—; guest reviewer Jour. Exptl. Analysis of Behavior, 1965—, Jour. Applied Behavioral Analysis, 1968—, Behavior Therapy, 1972-80, Jour. Pharmacology and Exptl. Therapeutics, 1966-80, Psychopharmacology, 1978-88; author ednl. films. Predoctoral fellow USPHS, 1959-61. Fellow APA (divsns. exptl. analysis behavior, history psychology, pres. divsn. psychopharmacology 1974, divsn. mental retardation, 1990, com. ethics in protection of human participants in rsch. bd. sci. affairs 1988-91, congl. testifier 1988, 89, 90, 92, Don Hake award 1990), Coll. on Problems Drug Abuse (charter); mem. Am. Acad. Mental Retardation (state chpt. award 1981), Am. Assn. Univ. Affilited Programs (exec. bd. 1989—), Assn. for Advancement Behavior Therapy (mem.-at-large 1971-72, pres. Minn. chpt. 1972-73, chair profl. affairs ethics com. 1973-81), Am. Coll. Neuropsychopharmacology (sci. assoc. 1979-81), Am. Assn. for Behavioral Analysis (sustaining, program chair for behavioral pharmacology and to1984, 85, editorial adv. com. 1986-90), Am. Acad. Pediatrics (com. on DSM IV PC), Nat. Assn. for Dual Diagnosis, Behavioral Pharmacology Soc. (pres. 1972-73), European Behavioral Pharmacology Soc., Twin Cities Soc. for Children and Adults with Autism (hon., bd. profl. advisors 1982-91). Achievements include co-discovery of technique for screening abuse liability of new drugs. Office: Vanderbilt U John F Kennedy Ctr Box 40 GPC Nashville TN 37203

THOMPSON, TYLER, minister, philosophy educator; b. Corona, Calif., Oct. 18, 1915; s. Francis Forbes and Sadie Cassandra (Tyler) T.; m. Phyllis Elizabeth Oechsli, June 19, 1937 (dec. July, 1991); children: Francia, Wendy, Heidi, Becky, Peter; m. Patricia Ann Smith, Aug. 1, 1992. B.S., Calif. Inst. Tech., 1936; S.T.B., Boston U., 1939, Ph.D., 1950. Ordained to ministry Meth. Ch., 1938. Exec. sec. Calif. Inst. Tech. YMCA, 1935-36; asst. pastor Epworth Meth. Ch., Cambridge, Mass., 1936-37; pastor Barre (Mass.) Meth. Ch., 1937-39; Meth. missionary Singapore, 1939-46; pastor Weston (Mass.) Meth. Ch., 1946-49; asst. prof. religion and philosophy Allegheny Coll., 1949-51, chaplain, 1950-51; assoc. prof. philosophy of religion Garrett-Evangelical Theol. Sem., 1951-56, prof., 1956-78, dir. summer sessions, 1959-72; Vis. prof. philosophy Northwestern U., 1952-58; vis. prof. philosophy of religion McCormick Theol. Sem., 1963-65; adj. prof. Fuller Theol. Sem., 1981-84. Author: Freedom in Internment: Under Japanese Rule in Singapore, 1942-45, 1990. Pres. Evanston (Ill.) Human Relations Council, 1952-54, Evanston Democratic Club, 1956-58; Dem. nominee for Congress 13th Dist. in Ill., 1960; mem. Cook County (Ill.) Central Com. Dem. Party, 1966-68; pres. Dem. Party Evanston, 1970-72; Bd. dirs. Ill. div. ACLU, 1953-68, pres., 1959-64. Am. Assn. Theol. Schs. Faculty fellow, 1965. Mem. Am. Theol. Soc. (pres. midwest 1965-66), Am. Philos. Assn., AAUP, Am. Acad. Religion, Tau Beta Pi. Home: 363 W Walnut St Pasadena CA 91103-3501 Office: Garrett-Evangelical Theol Sem Evanston IL 60201 *Useful life depends on hope, but every object of hope is subject to some uncertainty. The more important the object, the less possibility of proof. Risk is needed: we live by faith. To reflect and act on what it means to love one's enemies is to probe the deepest dimensions of faith.

THOMPSON, VERDINE MAE, financial planner, tax preparer; b. Kilgore, Tex., Dec. 3, 1941; d. John Wesley and Verdine Mae (Brookes) Ford; m. James William Thompson, Jan. 25, 1963; 1 child, Susan Marie. Student, So. Meth. U., 1960-62; BA, Stephen F. Austin State U., 1964; MA, U. Tenn., 1975; grad. in credit union fin. counseling, Fla. Credit Union League, Tallahassee, 1987. CFP, Coll. for Fin. Planning, 1990. Tchr. Channelview (Tex.) Ind. Sch. Dist., 1968-69, Goose Creek Consol. Sch. Dist., Baytown, Tex., 1969-71, McMinn County Sch. Dist., Athens, Tenn., 1972-77; tax preparer H&R Block, Sweetwater, Tenn., 1978-86; mgr. APCO Employees Credit Union, Athens, 1978-92; fin. and tax planner, preparer Athens, 1986-91; fin. planner, tax preparer Verdine's Fin. Planning and Tax Svc., 1991—; developing support groups in East Tenn. for Tenn. Mental Health Consumers Assn., 1992-94. Organizer, leader Pendulum Depression Support Group, Athens, 1987—; pres. bd. dirs. Dakoda Place, a consumer-run drop-in ctr. for adults with mental illness, 1994-95; chm. sch. sec. Trinity United Meth. Ch., Athens, 1985—, mem. handbell choir, 1983-92; mem. United Meth. Women, 1963—; mem., pres., treas. Contact Teleministries Bd. McMinn, Tenn., 1975-81. Mem. IBCFP, ICFP, IAFP. Home and Office: 1110 Sioux St Athens TN 37303-3335

THOMPSON, VICTOR ALEXANDER, political science educator; b. Hannah, N.D., Sept. 23, 1912; s. Alexander Wood and Amelia (Gagstad) T.; m. Elnora Haynie, June 18, 1947; children: Victoria Wood, Alexander Wood. B.A., U. Wash., 1939; Ph.D., Columbia U., 1949. Prof., chmn. dept. polit. and social sci. Ill. Inst. Tech., Chgo., 1950-62; prof. Syracuse U., 1962-66, U. Ill., Urbana, 1966-71; head dept. polit. sci. U. Ill., 1966-68; grad. research prof. polit. sci. U. Fla., Gainesville, 1971-81; emeritus U. Fla., 1981—, chmn., 1975-77; vis. prof. Makerere Coll., Uganda, 1960-61; asst. dir. fuel and automotive rationing OPA, 1944-45; cons. NSRB, 1948-51, Econ. Stblzn. Agy., 1951; spl. asst. to dir. econ. stablzn., 1952-53; tng. contractor IRS, 1956, 64. Author: The Regulatory Process in OPA Rationing, 1950, (with Herbert A. Simon and Donald W. Smithburg) Public Administration, 1950, Modern Organization, 1961, Bureaucracy and Innovation, 1969, Without Sympathy or Enthusiasm: The Problem of Administrative Compassion, 1975, Bureaucracy and the Modern World, 1976. Mem. Nat. Adv. Health Manpower Council, 1967-69. Mem. Phi Beta Kappa, Sigma Iota Epsilon. Home: 2255 NW 4th Pl Gainesville FL 32603-1407

THOMPSON, WADE FRANCIS BRUCE, manufacturing company executive; b. Wellington, New Zealand, July 23, 1940; came to U.S., 1961, naturalized, 1990.; m. Angela Ellen Barry, Jan. 20, 1967; children: Amanda and Charles (twins). B in Commerce, Cert. Acctg., Victoria U., Wellington, 1961; MSc, NYU, 1963. Dir. diversification Sperry & Hutchinson, N.Y.C., 1967-72; v.p. Texstar Corp., N.Y.C., 1972-77; chmn. Hi-Lo Trailer Co., Butler, Ohio, 1977—; chmn., pres., chief exec. officer Thor Industries Inc., Jackson Center, Ohio, 1980—. Trustee Mystic Seaport Mus., Conn., 1984—; trustee Wade F.B. Thompson Charitable Found. Inc., 1985—, N.Y. Studio Sch., 1993—, Munic. Art Soc., N.Y.C., 1993—. Mem. Union Club, N.Y. Yacht Club (N.Y.C.). Avocations: tennis, collecting contemporary art. Office: Thor Industries Inc 419 W Pike St Jackson Center OH 45334-9728

THOMPSON, WARREN A., mental health services educator, director; b. Bristow, Okla., June 27, 1927; married; 3 children. BS in Acctg., U. Okla., 1950; MBA, Okla. State U., 1962; PhD in Mgmt., U. Mo., 1966. Auditor Traders & Gen. Ins. Co., Dallas, 1950-51; acct., roughneck Unit Drilling Co., Bristow, 1951-53; self-employed gasoline and oil products wholesaler Woodward, Okla., 1954-58; bus. administr. Western State Hosp., Ft. Supply, Okla., 1958-61; instr. bus. mgmt. Coll. Bus. & Pub. Adminstrn. U. Mo., Columbia, 1963-65; exec. dir. Psychiat. Rsch. Found. Mo., St. Louis, 1966-75; prof. grad. program health adminstrn. and planning Sch. Medicine Washington U., St. Louis, 1975-80; adminstrv. dir. Mo. Inst. Psychiatry, St. Louis, 1965-80; prof. dept. psychiat. Sch. Medicine U. Mo., Columbia, 1965-80; prof. Health Svcs. Mgmt. Sch. Medicine U. Mo., 1980—, dir. grad. studies Health Svcs. Mgmt., 1993—; chair psychiat. adv. com. hosp. adminstrv. svcs. Am. Hosp. Assn., Chgo., 1966-69; mem. adv. com. Community Mental Health Ctrs., Fin. Adminstrn. and Mental Health Svcs., NIMH, 1968, Am. Hosp. Assn., 1968-69; mem. program com. Am. Psychiat. Assn., 1974; cons., evaluator, project dir. Farmington (Mo.) State Hosp., 1970; mem. adv. com., conf. participant to establish nat. commn. adminstrv. standards in mental health; expert witness, participant Commn. Edn. for Health Adminstrn., 1974; commr. Accrediting Commn. Edn. on Health Svcs. Adminstrn., 1976-79; many other coms. in field; lectr. Sch. Nursing, St. Louis U., 1980. Numerous civic, ch. activities 1954-61. Recipient Appreciation award Mental Health Assn. St. Louis; NIMH grantee. Fellow Assn. Mental Health Adminstrs. (pres. 1973-74, gov. at large 1974-75, exec. com. 1972-75, chair adminstrv. rsch. and practices com. 1968-72, credentials com. 1984-87, cert. merit 1978, cert. appreciation 1975, Harold C. Piepenbrink award 1984, founder & editor Jour. Mental Health Adminstrn. 1972-78); mem. AAUP, Assn. Human Resource Mgmt. and Orgnl. Behavior, Orgnl. Behavior Teaching Soc., Mo. Assn. Mental Health Adminstrs. (founder, meeting coord.), Mental Health Assn. Mo. (pres. 1977-78, v.p. 1973-76, bd. dirs., exec. com., Appreciation award 1980, cons. 1983-87), Alpha Kappa Psi (life). Office: Univ of Mo 324 Clark Hall Columbia MO 65211

THOMPSON, WARREN S., forestry educator, university dean; b. Utica, Miss., Aug. 19, 1929; s. John Edwin Thompson and Collise (Kitchens) Gibson; m. Marilyn Burney, July 18, 1953; children: Ruth, Lydia, John, Dee. BS, Auburn U., 1951, MS, 1955; PhD, N.C. State U., 1960. Asst. forester Miss. Agr. Experiment Sta., Mississippi State, 1953-54, assoc. dir., 1983—; grad. asst. Auburn (Ala.) U., 1954-55, N.C. State U., Raleigh, 1955-57; wood technologist Masonite Corp., 1957-59; asst. prof. La. State U., Baton Rouge, 1959-63, assoc. prof., 1963-64; dir., prof. Forest Products Lab., Miss. State U. Sch. Forest Resources, Mississippi State, 1964—; dean Miss. State U., Mississippi State, 1983—; mem. USDA Coop. Forestry Rsch. Coun., McIntire Stennis Coun. Contbr. articles to profl. jours. 1st lt. U.S. Army, 1951-53, Korea. Mem. Am. Wood Preservers Assn. (chmn. rsch. com.), Nat. Assn. Profl. Forestry Schs. and Colls. (chmn. nat. com., pres.), Miss. Forest Assn. (Meritorious Svc. award), Forest Products Rsch. Soc. (Disting. Svc. award mid-south region, co-chmn. Nat. Planning Group, regional bd. dirs.), Soc. Wood Sci. and Tech. (chmn. accreditation com., pres.), Nat. Assn. State Univs. and Land Grant Colls. (chmn. commn. on forestry), N.C. State U. Alumni Assn. (Disting. alumnus award). Republican. Avocations: reading, gardening, fishing. Office: Miss State U Sch Forest Resources Bldg PO Box 9680 Mississippi State MS 39762

THOMPSON, WAYNE PAUL, healthcare executive; b. Balt., Sept. 2, 1941; s. Charles Panet and Flora Christina (Ludloff) T.; m. Carol Ann Rockett, May 16, 1964 (div. May 1987); children: Wayne Paul Jr., Amy M. BS in Acctg., Loyola Coll., Balt., 1963. CPA, Md. Staff acct. Main La Frentz & Co., CPA, Balt., 1963-64; sr. acct. Peat, Marwick, Mitchell & Co., CPAs, Balt., 1966-70; controller Union Meml. Hosp., Balt., 1970-72; sr. v.p., chief fin. officer Franklin Square Hosp. Ctr., Balt., 1972-87; v.p., chief fin. officer Helix Health System, Balt., 1987—; bd. dirs. Greater Atlantic Savs. Bank, Balt., Surg. Specialties Inc., Cofton, Md. Co-author: Guide to Rate Review in Maryland, 1978. 1st lt. U.S. Army, 1964-66. Fellow Healthcare Fin. Mgmt. Assn. (officer, dir. 1973-80); mem. Md. Assn. CPAs. Avocations: golf, reading, woodworking, gardening. Office: Helix Health System Inc 2330 W Joppa Rd Ste 301 Lutherville Timonium MD 21093-4635

THOMPSON, WESLEY DUNCAN, grain merchant; b. Blenheim, Ont., Can., Oct. 18, 1926; s. Wesley Gairdner and Anna Corneil (McCallum) T.; m. Patricia Florence Coatsworth, June 6, 1957; children—Wesley, Jennifer, Frank. B.A., U. Western Ont., London, Can., 1950. Pres., chmn. bd. dirs. W.G. Thompson & Sons Ltd, Blenheim, Can., 1950—; v.p. Hyland Farms Ltd., Ridgetown, Ont. Office: W G Thompson & Sons Ltd, 122 George St, Blenheim, ON Canada N0P 1A0

THOMPSON, WILLIAM, JR., engineering educator; b. Hyannis, Mass., Dec. 4, 1936; s. William and Dinella Helen (Szeliga) T.; m. Martha Marion Cate, July 4, 1959; children: Melanie A., Sharon E., Jennifer L., Keith W. SB, MIT, 1958; MS, Northeastern U., 1963; PhD, Pa. State U., 1971. Staff engr. Raytheon Co., Wayland, Mass., 1958-60; sr. engr. Cambridge (Mass.) Acoustical Assocs., 1960-66; research asst. Applied Research Lab., State College, Pa., 1966-72; asst. prof. engring. sci. Pa. State U., University Park, 1972-78, assoc. prof., 1978-85, prof., 1985—; head transducer group Applied Rsch. Lab., State College, 1971-80; sabbatic leave Naval Rsch. Lab., Orlando, Fla., 1988-89. Contbr. articles to profl. jours.; patentee in field. Bd. dirs., treas., past pres. Nittany Mountain chpt. Am. Diabetes Assn., State College, 1979-92; bd. dirs., asst. treas., treas. Mid-Pa. affiliate, Bethlehem, Pa., 1980-90. Recipient Disting. Svc. citation Mid-Pa. Affiliate Am. Diabetes Assn., 1981, and Affiliate Svc. award, 1988. Fellow Acoustical Soc. Am. (patent reviewer of assoc. jour. 1990—); mem. IEEE (sr.), Soc. Engring. Sci., Lions (pres. State College 1981-82, 89-90, sec.-treas. 1984-88, 90-92, treas. 1992—, dist. diabetes chmn. 1983-88, 91—, chmn. Ct. Lions Foresight Commn. 1992—, Melvin Jones fellow 1991). Republican. Avocations: sports, reading, photography. Home: 601 Glenn Rd State College PA 16803-3475 Office: Pa State U Dept of Engring Sci and Mechanics 230B Hammond Bldg University Park PA 16802

THOMPSON, WILLIAM ANCKER, intramural-recreational sports director, educator; b. Syracuse, N.Y., Apr. 26, 1931; s. Frederick Howe Thompson and Ellen (Ensten) Ancker; m. Sally Whitmer; children: Cary, Paige. BS, Springfield (Mass.) Coll., 1953; MA, Calif. State U., Long Beach, 1960; postgrad., U. So. Calif., L.A., 1961-62. Phys. dir. Wendell P. Clark Meml., Winchendon, Mass., 1956-57; dir. intramural/recreational sports

Long Beach City Coll., 1958—; with promotion and sales div. Calif. Sports, Inc. (L.A. Lakers, Kings), L.A. and Inglewood, 1960-76; v.p. sales Calif. Sports, Inc. (L.A. Lakers, Kings), L.A. and Englewood, 1970-71. Co-author: Modern Sports Officiating, 1974, 5th rev. edit., 1993, 6th rev. edit., 1995. 1st lt. USMC, 1954-56, Korea. Mem. Nat. Intramural-Recreational Sports Assn. (v.p. 1974-76, pres. 1976-77, Honor award 1980), Old Ranch Country Club. Avocations: swimming, golf, writing, reading, avocado grower. Office: Long Beach City Coll 4901 E Carson St Long Beach CA 90808-1780

THOMPSON, WILLIAM BENBOW, JR., obstetrician/gynecologist, educator; b. Detroit, July 26, 1923; s. William Benbow and Ruth Wood (Locke) T.; m. Constance Carter, July 30, 1947 (div. Feb. 1958); 1 child, William Benbow IV; m. Jane Gilliland, Mar. 12, 1958; children: Reese Ellison, Belinda Day. AB, U. So. Calif., 1947, MD, 1951. Diplomate Am. Bd. Ob-Gyn. Resident Gallinger Mun. Hosp., Washington, 1952-53; resident George Washington U. Hosp., Washington, 1953-55; asst. ob-gyn. La. State U., 1955-56; asst. clinical prof. UCLA, 1957-64; assoc. prof. U. Calif.-Irvine Sch. Med., Orange, Calif., 1964-92; dir. gynecology U. Calif.-Irvine Sch. Med., 1977-92; prof. emeritus U. Calif.-Irvine Sch. Med., Orange, 1993—; vice chmn. ob-gyn. U. Calif.-Irvine Sch. Med., 1978-89; assoc. dean U. Calif.-Irvine Coll. Med., Irvine, 1969-73. Inventor: Thompson Retractor, 1976; Thompson Manipulator, 1977. Bd. dirs. Monarch Bay Assn. Laguna Niguel, Calif. 1969-77, Monarch Summitt II A ssn. 1981-83. With U.S. Army, 1942-44, PTO. Fellow ACS, Am. Coll. Ob-Gyn. (life), L.A. Ob-Gyn. Soc. (life); mem. Orange County Gynecology and Obstetrics Soc. (hon.), Am. Soc. Law and Medicine, Capistrano Bay Yacht Club (commodore 1975), Internat. Order Blue Gavel. Avocation: boating. Office: UCI Med Ctr OB/GYN 101 City Blvd W Orange CA 92668-2901

THOMPSON, WILLIAM CANNON, JR., advertising agency executive; b. Phila., Aug. 21, 1938; s. William Cannon and Mary Bertha (Harris) T.; A.B., U. N.C., 1959; m. Linda Krutchkoff, Nov. 6, 1965; children—William Cannon III, James Stuart, Kevin Harris. Media planner Doyle Dane Bernbach Adv't., N.Y.C., 1960-63; account supr. Batten Barton Durstine & Osborn, N.Y.C., 1963-65; account mgmt. J. Walter Thompson Co., N.Y.C., 1965-82, sr. v.p. in charge account mgmt., 1974-75, sr. v.p., group account dir., 1976-79, exec. v.p., 1979-82, also bd. dirs.; bd. dirs. J. Walter Thompson Worldwide; vice-chmn. Client Ops., 1988—. Republican. Presbyterian. Clubs: Wykagyl Country (pres.), Jonathan Landing Club, Genessee Valley. Home: 112 Bon Air Ave New Rochelle NY 10804-3105 Office: J Walter Thompson Co 466 Lexington Ave New York NY 10017-3140

THOMPSON, WILLIAM DAVID, investment banking executive; b. Pitts., Nov. 30, 1921; s. Ross Ephraim and Blanche (Watson) T.; m. Mimi Wainwright Coleman, June 12, 1992; B.S., Yale U., 1944. Asst. advt. mgr. Scovill Mfg. Co., Waterbury, Conn., 1945-48; acctg. supr. James Thomas Chirurg, N.Y.C., 1948-52; mgr. mktg. dept. McCann-Erickson, N.Y.C., 1951-52; exec. v.p. Young & Rubicam, N.Y.C., 1952-89; chmn. Ctr. Devel. Investments, Inc., Greenwich, Conn., 1990, Union League (N.Y.C.), Wee Burn Country Club, John's Island Club. Lt. U.S. Army, 1943-44. Republican. Presbyterian. Avocations: golf, tennis. Home and Office: John's Island Ste 345 650 Beach Rd Vero Beach FL 32963-3394

THOMPSON, WILLIAM DAVID, minister, homiletics educator; b. Chgo., Jan. 11, 1929; s. Robert Ayre and Mary Elizabeth (McDowell) T.; m. Linda Brady Stevenson, Nov. 2, 1968; children—Tammy, Kirk, Lisa, Rebecca, Gwyneth. A.B., Wheaton Coll., Ill., 1950; B.D., No. Baptist Sem., 1954; M.A., Northwestern U., 1955, Ph.D., 1960. Ordained to ministry Am. Baptist Ch., 1954. Instr. speech Wheaton Coll., 1952-55; pastor Raymond Baptist Ch., Chgo., 1956-58; assoc. prof. homiletics No. Bapt. Sem., Chgo., 1958-62; mem. faculty Eastern Bapt. Sem., Phila., 1962-87, prof. preaching 1969-87; minister 1st Bapt. Ch., Phila., 1983-90. Author: A Listener's Guide to Preaching, 1966, Recent Homiletical Thought, 1967, Dialogue Preaching, 1969, Preaching Biblically, 1981, Listening on Sunday for Sharing on Monday, 1983, Philadelphia's First Baptists, 1989. Mem. Phila. Hist. Commn., 1984-92. Vis. fellow Cambridge U., 1968-69. Mem. Nat. Speakers Assn., Acad. Homiletics (pres. 1973), Religious Speech Communication Assn. (v.p 1983, pres. 1984), Union League Club. Republican. Home: 765 Ormond Ave Drexel Hill PA 19026-2417

THOMPSON, WILLIAM GRANT, management executive; b. Westville, N.S., Can., June 27, 1925; s. Harvey Alden and Jessie (MacGregor) T.; m. Margaret Jean Mackenzie, Sept. 24, 1952; children: Heather, Anne, Andrew, Carole. Degree in bus. edns., Maritime Bus. Coll., Halifax, N.S., 1943. Chartered acct., N.S. Treas. Maritime Steel and Foundries, Ltd., New Glasgow, N.S., 1951-58; v.p, gen. mgr. EMI Elecs. Can., Ltd., Halifax, 1958-69; ptnr. Price Waterhouse, Ltd., Halifax, 1970-87; v.p., 1977-87; pres. Revenue Mgmt., Ltd., Halifax, 1987—; pres. MacCulloch & Co., Ltd., Halifax, 1983-87, Oakwood Investments, Halifax, 1983-87. Mem. Commn. Food Prices Rev. Bd., Ottawa, Ont., 1974-77; chmn. fin. com. Waterfront Devel. Corp., Halifax, 1977-81; chmn. Pine Hill Div. Hall, Halifax, 1974-79, Atlantic Sch. Theology, Halifax, 1982-85, Maritime Bd. Trustees, Sackville, N.B., 1982-88; treas., chmn. investment com. Fin. Svcs. Maritime Conf., 1988—; chmn. Windsor Elms Srs. Home, Windsor, N.S., 1983-87. Fellow Inst. Chartered Accts. N.S., Inst. Chartered Secs. and Adminstrs.; mem. Soc. Mgmt. Accts. N.S., Inst. Mgmt. Cons. Atlantic Can., Can. Litigation Acctg. and Valuation Inst., Saraguay Club. Liberal. Mem. United Ch. Can. Home: 2184 Connaught Ave, Halifax, NS Canada B3L2Z3

THOMPSON, WILLIAM IRWIN, humanities educator, author; b. Chgo., July 16, 1938; s. Chester Andrew and Lillian Margaret (Fahey) T.; m. Gail Joan Gordon, Feb. 3, 1960 (div. Jan. 1979); children: Evan Timothy, Hilary Joan, Andrew Rhys; m. Beatrice Madeleine Rudin, Mar. 1, 1979. B.A. with honors in Philosophy, Pomona Coll., 1962; M.A. (Woodrow Wilson fellow), Cornell U., 1964, Ph.D. (Woodrow Wilson dissertation fellow), 1966. Instr. humanities MIT, Cambridge, 1965-66; asst. prof. MIT, 1966-67, Old Dominion fellow, 1967, assoc. prof. humanities, 1968; assoc. prof. humanities York U., Toronto, Ont. Can., 1968-72; prof. York U., 1973; vis. prof. religion Syracuse (N.Y.) U., 1973; vis. scholar in polit. sci. U. Hawaii, 1981, vis. prof., 1985; vis. prof. Celtic studies U. Toronto, 1984; founding dir. Lindisfarne Assocs., 1972—. Author: Imagination of an Insurrection: Dublin, Easter 1916, 1967, At the Edge of History, 1971, Passages about Earth, 1974, Evil and World Order, 1976, Darkness and Scattered Light, 1978, The Time Falling Bodies Take to Light, 1981, From Nation to Emanation, 1981, Blue Jade from the Morning Star, 1983, Islands Out of Time, 1985, Pacific Shift, 1986, GAIA: A Way of Knowing, 1987, Imaginary Landscape, 1989, Selected Poems 1959-89; GAIA TWO: Emergence, the New Science of Becoming, 1991, Reimagination of the World, 1991, The American Replacement of Nature, 1991. Hon. colleague and Lindis Farne Scholar of the Cathedral of St. John the Divine, N.Y.C. Recipient Obstfelder prize Oslo Internat. Poetry Festival, 1986; Rockefeller scholar Calif. Inst. Integral Studies, 1993; Laurance S. Rockefeller fellow, 1992-95. Address: Calif. Inst. of Integral Studies 765 Ashbury St San Francisco CA 94117

THOMPSON, WILLIAM MOREAU, radiologist, educator; b. Phila., Oct. 20, 1943; s. Charles Moreau and Aileen (Haddon) T.; m. Judy Ann Seel, July 1965; children—Christopher Moreau, Thayer Haddon. B.A., Colgate U., 1965; M.D., U. Pa., 1969. Diplomate Am. Bd. Radiology. Intern, Case Western Res. U., Cleve., 1969-70; resident in radiology Duke U., Durham, N.C., 1975-77, asst. prof. Duke U. Med. Center, 1976-77, assoc. prof., 1977-82, prof. radiology, 1982-86; prof., chmn. dept. radiology, Vilhelmina and Eugene Gedgared chair in Radiology, U. Minn. Hosp. and Clinic, Mpls., 1986—. Served with USPHS, 1970-72. Recipient James Picker Found. Scholar in Acad. Medicine award, 1975-79; research and devel. grantee VA, 1977-86. Fellow Am. Coll. Radiology; mem. AMA, Radiology Soc. N.Am. (program chmn. 1994—), Minn. Med. Soc., Am. Roentgen Ray Soc., Assn. Univ. Radiologists (pres. 1989-90), Soc. Gastrointestinal Radiology (pres. 1995), Sigma Xi. Republican. Presbyterian. Contbr. chpts. to books, articles to profl. jours. Home: 18700 Woolman Dr Minnetonka MN 55345-3164 Office: U Minn Med Sch UMHC Box 292 Harvard Street Rd Minneapolis MN 55455-0361

THOMPSON, WILLIAM REID, public utility executive, lawyer; b. Durham, N.C., Aug. 13, 1924; s. William Reid and Myrtle (Siler) T.; m. Mary Louise Milliken, Aug. 16, 1952; children: Mary Elizabeth, William

Reid III, John Milliken, Susan Siler. BS, U. N.C., 1945; LLB, Harvard U., 1949. Bar: N.C. 1949. Ptnr. Barber and Thompson, Pittsboro, N.C., 1949-58; judge Superior Cts. N.C., 1958-60; assoc. gen. counsel Carolina Power & Light Co., 1960-63, v.p., gen. counsel, 1963-67, exec. v.p., 1967-71; chmn. bd., chief exec. officer Potomac Electric Power Co., Washington, 1971-89, chmn. bd., 1989-92; bd. dirs. Potomac Elec. Power Co., Geico Corp. Bd. dirs. Nat. Symphony Orch. Assn.; mem. Fed. City Coun., N.C. Gen. Assembly from Chatham County, 1955-57. Served to lt. (j.g.) USNR, 1943-45, PTO. Mem. ABA, Edison Electric Inst. (bd. dirs., past chmn.), Southeastern Electric Exchange (past pres.), Assn. Edison Illuminating Cos. (past pres.), Bus. Council, Bus. Roundtable, Phi Beta Kappa, Delta Kappa Epsilon. Democrat. Methodist. Clubs: Met., Burning Tree, Chevy Chase, 1925 F St (Washington). Lodge: Rotary. Office: Potomac Electric Power Co 1900 Pennsylvania Ave NW Washington DC 20068-0002

THOMPSON, WILLIAM SCOTT, lawyer; b. Grand Rapids, Mich., Feb. 6, 1930; s. William Scott Thompson and Mary Louise (Chatel) Kruse; m. Margaret Jane Favier, June 16, 1951; children: William, Michelle, Marta, Rebecca. BSME, U. Mich., 1952; JD, U. Notre Dame, 1959. Bar: Ind. 1959, U.S. Dist. Ct. (so. dist.) Ind. 1959, U.S.Ct. Appeals (Fed. cir.) 1963. Engr. Bendix Corp., South Bend, Ind., 1954-57, patent agt., 1957-59, patent atty., 1959-64, regional patent counsel, Utica, N.Y. and Detroit, 1964-74; patent dept. mgr. Caterpillar Inc., Peoria, Ill., 1974-94; with Internat. Intellectual Property Cons., Ft. Myers, Fla., 1994—. 1st lt. USAF, 1952-54. Mem. Am. Intellectual Property Law Assn. (past pres.), Internat. Patent and Trademark Assn. (v.p.), Assn. Corp. Patent Counsel, ABA (internat. activities coord.). Office: Internat Intellectual Property Cons 4327 W Tara Cir Peoria IL 61615-2437

THOMPSON, W(ILMER) LEIGH, pharmaceutical company executive; physician, pharmacologist; b. Shreveport, La., June 25, 1938; s. Wilmer Leigh and Mary Bissell (McIver) T.; m. Maurice Eugenie Horne, Mar. 29, 1957; 1 child, Mary Linton Bounetheau. BS, Coll. Charleston, 1958; MS in Pharmacology, Med. U. S.C., 1960, PhD, 1963; MD, John Hopkins U., 1965; ScD (hon.) Med. U. S.C., 1994. Diplomate Am. Bd. Internal Medicine. Intern, Johns Hopkins Hosp., 1965-66, resident, 1966-67, 1969-70; staff assoc. NIH, Bethesda, Md., 1967-69; asst. prof. medicine and pharmacology Johns Hopkins U., Balt., 1970-74, dir. critical care medicine and emergency medicine, 1970-74; prof. medicine, assoc. prof. pharmacology Case Western Res. U., Cleve., 1974-82, head critical care and clin. pharmacology, 1974-82; prof. medicine Ind. U., 1985—; dir. Lilly Rsch. Labs., Eli Lilly & Co., Indpls., 1982, exec. v.p., 1982-86, v.p., 1986-88, group v.p., 1988-91, exec. v.p., 1992-93, chief sci. officer, 1993-94; chmn., CEO Profound Quality Resources Consulting, Charleston, 1995—. Editor: Textbook of Critical Care Medicine, 1984, 89, State of the Art: Critical Care, 1980-83. Served to surgeon USPHS, 1967-69. Burroughs Wellcome Fund scholar 1975-80; recipient Faculty Devel. award Pharm. Mfrs. Assn. Found. Fellow ACP, Am. Coll. Critical Care Medicine; mem. Soc. Critical Care Medicine (pres. 1981-82, hon. life mem. 1987), Cen. Soc. Clin. Rsch., Am. Soc. Pharmacology and Exptl. Therapeutics. Episcopalian and Huguenot. Office: Profound Quality Resources Consulting 54 King St Charleston SC 29401-2731

THOMPSON, WINFRED LEE, university president, lawyer; b. Little Rock, July 28, 1945; s. Vester Lee and Willow Mae (Mills) T.; m. Carmen Angeles Tiongson; children: Emily, Michael. BA, U. Ark., 1967; MA, U. Chgo., 1970, PhD, 1987; JD, George Washington U., 1978. Congl. aide U.S. Ho. of Reps., Washington, 1973-77; exec. asst. to asst. sec. labor U.S. Dept. Labor, Washington, 1977-78; atty. Hatfield and Thompson, Searcy, Ark., 1978-81; dir. devel. Ark. State U., Jonesboro, 1981-82, v.p. for planning and devel., 1982-84; v.p. for fin. and adminstrn. U. Ark. System, Fayetteville, 1984-85; vice chancellor for fin. and adminstrn. U. Ark, Fayetteville, 1985-87; pres. U. Cen. Ark., Conway, 1988—; bd. dirs. Ark. Sci. and Tech. Authority, Little Rock, 1984-89. Bd. dirs. Ark. Symphony Orch., 1991-94. 2d lt. USAR. Woodrow Wilson fellow U. Chgo., 1969-70. Mem. Phi Beta Kappa. Home: 140 Donaghey Ave Conway AR 72032-6252 Office: U Ctrl Ark Office of President Conway AR 72035

THOMPSON, WYNELLE DOGGETT, chemistry educator; b. Birmingham, Ala., May 25, 1914; d. William Edward and Dollie Odessa (Ferguson) Doggett; m. Davis Hunt Thompson, Sept. 17, 1938; children: Carolyn Wynelle, Helen Hunt, Cynthia Carle, Davis Hunt, Jr. BS summa cum laude, Birmingham Southern, 1934, MS, 1935; MS, U. Ala., 1956, PhD, 1960. From grad. lab. asst. to instr. chemistry Birmingham (Ala.) Southern Coll., 1934-36,39-44; tchr. Bd. Edn., Sheffield, Ala., 1936-37; jr. chemist Bur. Home Econs. USDA, Washington, 1937-38; instr. chemistry U. Ala. extension ctr., Birmingham, 1950-54; grad. asst. biochemistry U. Ala. Med. Coll., Birmingham, 1954-55; from asst. prof. chemistry to prof. emerita Birmingham (Ala.) Southern Coll., 1955-76; rsch. assoc. U. Ala. Dept. Biochemistry, Birmingham, 1965, 1968, 1969, Dept. Biophysics, 1976-78; adj. prof. chemistry New Coll. Tuscaloosa, Ala., 1980—. Contbr. articles to profl. jours. Bd. dirs. Cahaba Coun. Girl Scouts U.S. (vol. chmn. troop orgn., camping.). Grantee NSF, Appleton, Wis., Emory U., Atlanta; recipient disting. alumna award Birmingham So. Coll., 1976, medal of svc. award, 1994. Fellow Am. Inst. Chemists; mem. AAUW (bd. dirs., treas.), Am. Chem. Soc. (sec. 1942-44, 72-73, chmn.-elect 1966-67, chmn. 1967-68, 50-Yr. Mem. award 1992), Ala. Acad. Sci. (chmn. edn. sect. 1960-62), Phi Beta Kappa, Sigma Xi (sec. 1970-72), Theta Chi Delta, Delta Phi Alpha, Theta Sigma Lambda, Kappa Delta Epsilon, Delta Kappa Gamma, Kappa Mu Epsilon. Republican. Methodist. Avocations: music, camping, travel, needlework. Home: 1237 Berwick Rd Hoover AL 35242-7124

THOMSEN, CHARLES BURTON, engineering design company executive; b. Springfield, Mo., Sept. 25, 1932; s. Fred Charles and Sunbeam (Burton) T.; m. Lois Ann Leivestad, June 8, 1956; children: Melissa Ann, Charles Jeffrey. Student, U. Minn.; BArch, U. Okla., 1957; MArch, MIT, 1963. Cert. Nat. Coun. Archtl. Registration. Mem. faculty Sch. Architecture Rice U., Houston, 1962-65; assoc. Caudill Rowlett Scott Inc., Houston, 1965-69; chmn. bd., pres. CM Inc., Houston, 1971-79, chmn. bd., CEO, 1979-82; pres., chief oper. officer 3D-Internat., Houston, 1982-92; pres., CEO 3D/International, Houston, 1992—. Fellow AIA. Office: 3D/International 1900 W Loop S Ste 600 Houston TX 77027

THOMSEN, DONALD LAURENCE, JR., institute executive, mathematician; b. Stamford, Conn., Apr. 21, 1921; s. Donald Laurence and Linda (Comstock) T.; m. Linda Rollins Leach, June 14, 1958; children: Melinda Rollins, Katherine Thomsen Love, Donald Laurence III. Grad. Phillips Exeter Acad., 1938; BA in Math. magna cum laude, Amherst Coll., 1942; PhD, MIT, 1947. Tchg. fellow MIT, 1942, instr., 1943-47; instr., then asst. prof. Haverford (Pa.) Coll., 1947-50; rsch. fellow, then rsch. engr. Jet Propulsion Lab., Calif. Inst. Tech., 1950-52; asst. prof. Pa. State U., 1952-54; with IBM Corp., 1954-72, spl. asst. to dir. edn., 1961-62, dir. profl. activities, 1963-66, corp. dir. engring. edn., 1967-72; pres. Societal Inst. of Math. Scis., New Canaan, Conn., 1973—, also bd. dirs.; mem. vis. com. Coll. Sci., Drexel Inst. Tech., 1969-71; mem. adv. com. for individualized sci. instructional sys. Coll. Edn., Fla. State U., 1973-75; prin. investigator rsch. studies in environ. pollution and human exposure; AIDS rschr. Author: Higher Transcendental Functions, 3 vols; contbr. articles to profl. jours. Recipient Spl. cert. Milw. Sch. Engring., 1969. Mem. AAAS, AAUW, Am. Math. Soc., Am. Statis. Assn., Math. Assn. Am. (chmn. com insts.), Soc. Indsl. and Applied Math. (pres. 1959, chmn. trustees 1960-72, Merit cert. Inst. Math. and Soc. 1972), Am. Fedn. Info. Processing Socs. (chmn. edn. com. 1965-66, chmn. U.S. com. IFIP Congress 1968, 66-69, bd. dirs. 1969-77, exec. com 1975-77), Assn. Computing Machinery, Am. Ordnance Assn. (chmn. research div.), Internat. Fedn. Info. Processing (chmn. exhibits com. N.Y.C. Congress 1965), Conf. Bd. Math. Scis. (chmn. budget and fin com.), Internat. AIDS Soc., Internat. Soc. Exposure Analysis, Conn. Acad. Arts and Scis., Phi Beta Kappa, Sigma Xi, Delta Tau Delta. Presbyn. Clubs: Cosmos (Washington); The Princeton (N.Y.C.); Woodway Country (Darien, Conn.). Home and Office: Societal Inst Math Scis 97 Parish Rd S New Canaan CT 06840

THOMSEN, MARCIA ROZEN, marketing executive; b. St. Louis, Sept. 23, 1958; d. Saul and Ruth (Burstein) Rozen; m. Timothy Lars Thomsen, Sept. 3, 1984; 1 child, David Rozen. B in Journalism, U. Mo., 1980. Media planner, buyer Leo Burnett Co., Chgo., 1980-82, asst. acct. exec., 1982-83; acct. exec. D'Arcy Masius, Benton & Bowles, St. Louis, 1983-85, acct. supr.,

1985-86, v.p., 1986-89; dir. mktg. Pizza Hut, Inc. subs. PepsiCo Inc., St. Louis, 1989-90; dir. of delivery mktg. Pizza Hut, Inc. subs. PepsiCo Inc., Wichita, Kans., 1990-91, sr. dir. nat. segment mktg., 1991-92, v.p. nat. mtkg., 1992—; chmn. com. DMB&B Account Mgmt., St. Louis, 1988—. Mem. Chgo. Advt. Club. Office: Pizza Hut Inc 9111 E Douglas Ave Wichita KS 67207-1296

THOMSEN, MARK WILLIAM, religious organization administrator; b. Owatonna, Minn., Feb. 24, 1931; s. Jens Harry and Helena Rogna (Hansen) T.; m. Mary Lou Kafer, Nov. 29, 1952; children: Mark Lawrence, Derek James, Sandra Kay, Sheryl Louise. BA, Dana Coll., 1953; BDiv, Trinity Theol. Sem., 1956; ThM, Princeton Theol. Sem., 1957; PhD, Northwestern U., 1971; DD, Dana Coll., 1982. Vice prin. acad. affairs, mem. faculty Theol. Coll. No. Nigeria, Bukuru, 1957-66; Luth. campus pastor U. No. Iowa, Cedar Falls, 1966-67; assoc. prof. philosophy and religion Dana Coll., Blair, 1967-72; pastor St. Peter Luth. Ch., Dubuque, 1972-80; assoc. prof. mission and world religions Luth. Northwestern Theol. Sem., St. Paul, 1980-81; dir. Divsns. for World Mission and Interch. Coop. Am. Luth. Ch., Mpls., 1981-87; exec. dir. Divsn. for Global Mission Evang. Luth. Ch. in Am., Chgo., 1987—; guest lectr. mgmt. of ministry Wartburg Theol. Sem., Dubuque, 1979; bd. dirs. Luth. World Relief, N.Y.C.; project com. Dept. for Mission and Devel., Luth. World Fedn., Geneva, 1990—; mem. gen. bd. Nat. Coun. of the Chs. of Christ in USA, N.Y.C., 1988—; advisor Ch. Coun., Evang. Luth. Ch. in Am., Chgo., 1988—. Author: Introducing New Testament Theology, 1964, The Word and the Way of the Cross: Christian Witness Among Muslim and Buddhist People, 1993, (booklet) Together in Witness: A Study of the Acts of the Apostles, 1983. Recipient Disting. Alumnus award Dana Coll., 1988. Mem. Am. Soc. Missiology. Lutheran. Avocations: jogging, golf. Office: Evang Luth Ch in Am Divsn Global Mission 8765 W Higgins Rd Chicago IL 60631

THOMSEN, THOMAS RICHARD, communications company executive; b. Avoca, Iowa, July 29, 1935; s. Howard August and Edna Mary (Walker) T.; m. Raylene Alice Tomes, Sept. 1, 1956; children: Jeffrey, Cathy. BSME, U. Nebr., 1958; MS, MIT, 1973. Engr. Western Electric Co., Omaha, 1957-64; mgr. Western Electric Co., Columbus, Ohio, 1964-72; v.p. Bell Sales West Western Electric Co., Morristown, N.J., 1979-80; asst. v.p. ops. staff AT&T, Basking Ridge, N.J., 1980-81; exec. v.p. Western Electric Corp., N.Y.C., 1981-82; pres. AT&T Tech. Systems, Berkeley Heights, N.J., 1982-90, ret., 1990; bd. dirs. AT&T Credit Corp., Sandia Corp., Albuquerque, Olivetti Corp., Western Electric Corp. Trustee Rensselaer Poly. Inst. Mem. Telephone Pioneers Am. (former pres.), Pi Tau Sigma, Sigma Tau. Republican. Presbyterian. Avocations: golf, tennis. Home: 26 Bellinghamshire Pl New Hope PA 18938-1040 Office: care AT&T Tech Systems 1 Oak Way Berkeley Heights NJ 07922-2727

THOMSON, ALEX, cinematographer. Cinematographer: (films) Fear Is the Key, 1973, The Cat and the Canary, 1978, The Class of Miss MacMichael, 1978, Excalibur, 1981 (Academy award nomination best cinematography 1981), The Keep, 1983, Blueshot, 1983, Eureka, 1984, Electric Dreams, 1984, Labyrinth, 1985, Year of the Dragon, 1985, Legend, 1986, Raw Deal, 1986, The Sicilian, 1987, Date with an Angel, 1987, Duet for One, 1987, High Spirits, 1988, Track 29, 1988, Leviathan, 1989, The Rachel Papers, 1989, Mr. Destiny, 1990, Alien 3, 1992, Cliffhanger, 1993, Demolition Man, 1993, Black Beauty, 1994. Office: care Am Soc of Cinematographers PO Box 2230 Los Angeles CA 90078*

THOMSON, BASIL HENRY, JR., lawyer, corporate; b. Amarillo, Tex., Jan. 17, 1945; m. Margaret Shepard, May 4, 1985; children: Christopher, Matthew, Robert. BBA, Baylor U., 1968, JD, 1973. Bar: Tex. 1974, U.S. Ct. Mil. Appeals 1974, U.S. Supreme Ct. 1977, U.S. Dist. Ct. (we. dist.) Tex. 1988, U.S. Ct. Appeals (fed. cir.) 1990. Oil title analyst Hunt Oil Co., Dallas, 1971-73; atty. advisor Regulations and Adminstrv. Law div. Office of Chief Counsel USCG, Washington, 1973-77; dir. estate planning devel. dept. Baylor U., Waco, Tex., 1977-80, gen. counsel, 1980—; adj. prof. law Baylor U.; lobbyist legis. Ind. Higher Edn., 71st Session of Tex. Legislature; mem. legis. com. Gov.'s Task Force on Drug Abuse; dir. govtl. relations Baylor U.; speaker at meetings of coll. and univ. adminstrs.; assisted in drafting legis. for Texan's War on Drugs Tex. Legislature. Active Heart O'Tex coun. Boy Scouts Am., Heart of Tex. Coun. on Alcoholism and Drug Abuse, bd. dirs., 1987-91. Recipient President's award Ind. Colls. and Univs. Tex., 1994, dist. award of merit, Boy Scouts Am. Fellow Coll. State Bar Tex.; mem. ABA, Fed. Bar Assn., Nat. Assn. Coll. and Univ. Attys. (fin., nominations and elections coms., 1994-95, bd. dirs. 1988-91), Tex. Bar Assn., Coll. State Bar Tex., Waco Bar Assn., McLennan County Bar Assn., Sierra Club (congl. dist. coord.). Baptist. Avocations: tennis, running, environ. concerns. Home: 100 Sugar Creek Pl Waco TX 76712-3410 Office: Baylor U PO Box 97034 Waco TX 76798-7034

THOMSON, GEORGE RONALD, lawyer, educator; b. Wadsworth, Ohio, Aug. 25, 1959; s. John Alan and Elizabeth (Galbraith) T. BA summa cum laude, Miami U., Oxford, Ohio, 1982, MA summa cum laude, 1983; JD with honors, Ohio State U., 1986. Bar: Ill. 1986, U.S. Dist. Ct. (no. dist.) Ill. 1986. Teaching fellow Miami U., 1982-83; dir. speech activities Ohio State U., Columbus, 1983-86; assoc. Peterson, Ross, Schloerb & Seidel, Chgo., 1986-87, Lord, Bissell & Brook, Chgo., 1987-94; asst. corp. counsel City of Chgo., 1994—; adj. prof. dept. comm. DePaul U., Chgo., 1988-93; presenter in field. Contbr. articles to profl. jours. Fundraiser Chgo. Hist. Soc., Steppenwolf Theater Co., AIDS Legal Counsel Chgo., 1989—, Smithsonian Instn., Washington, 1988—, U.S. Tennis Assn., 1990—; bd. dirs. Metro Sports Assn., 1992-94, Gerber-Hart Libr. and Archives, 1993-95, Gay and Lesbian Tennis Alliance Am., 1991—; Team Chicago, 1994—; mem. coord. coun. Nat. Gay and Lesbian History Month; mem. Lawyer's Com. for Ill. Human Rights. Recipient Spl. Commendation Ohio Ho. of Reps., 1984, 85, Nat. Forensics Assn. award, 1982. Mem. ABA, Chgo. Bar Assn., Lesbian and Gay Bar Assn., Speech Comm. Assn. Am., Mortar Bd., Phi Beta Kappa, Phi Kappa Phi, Omicron Delta Kappa, Delta Sigma Rho-Tau Kappa Alpha, Phi Alpha Delta. Democrat. Presbyterian. Avocations: tennis, flute performance, antique collecting, reading, travel. Home: 2835 N Pine Grove Ave Unit 2S Chicago IL 60657-6109 Office: Lord Bissell & Brook 115 S La Salle St Ste 3300 Chicago IL 60603-3903

THOMSON, H. BAILEY, editor; b. Aliceville, Ala., Feb. 4, 1949; s. William Joshua and Attie (Kimbrell) T.; m. Reba Kristi Garrison, Nov. 19, 1977; 1 child, Sarah Rachel. BA, U. Ala., 1972, MA, 1974, PhD, 1995. Copy editor Huntsville (Ala.) Times, 1971-72, staff writer, 1975-77; reporter, copy editor Tuscaloosa (Ala.) News, 1972-75; editorial page editor Shreveport (La.) Jour., 1977-86; chief editorial writer Orlando (Fla.) Sentinel, 1986-92; assoc. editor Mobile (Ala.) Press Register, 1992—. Author: Shreveport, 1986. vice chmn. La. Endowment Humanities, 1984-85. Profl. journalism fellow Stanford U., 1981-82. Mem. Nat. Conf. Editorial Writers (bd. dirs. 1991-92), Capstone Alumni Soc. (bd. dirs. 1994). Methodist. Avocations: historical writing, jogging, reading, gardening, Spanish. Home: 706 Oak Bluff Dr Daphne AL 36526-4038 Office: The Mobile Press Register Inc PO Box 2488 304 Government St Mobile AL 36630-0001

THOMSON, JAMES ALAN, research company executive; b. Boston, Jan. 21, 1945; s. James Alan and Mary Elizabeth (Pluff) T.; m. Darlene Thomson; children: Kristen Ann, David Alan. BS, U. N.H., 1967; MS, Purdue U., 1970, PhD, 1972. Research fellow U. Wis., Madison, 1972-74; systems analyst Office Sec. Def., U.S. Dept. Def., Washington, 1974-77; staff mem. Nat. Security Council, White House, Washington, 1977-81; v.p. RAND, Santa Monica, Calif., 1981-89, pres., chief exec. officer, 1989—. Contbr. articles to profl. jours. and chpts. to books. Mem. Internat. Inst. for Strategic Studies (council 1985—), Coun. Fgn. Rels. Office: Rand 1700 Main St Santa Monica CA 90407-2138

THOMSON, JOHN ANSEL ARMSTRONG, biochemist; b. Detroit, Nov. 23, 1911; s. John Russell and Florence (Antisdel) T.; m. June Anna Mae Hummel, June 24, 1938; children: Sheryll Linn, Patrisha Diane, Robert Royce. AA, Pasadena (Calif.) City Coll., 1935; AB cum laude, U. So. Calif., 1957; BGS (hon.). Calif. Poly. State U., 1961; MA, PhD, Columbia Pacific U., 1978, 79; DA, Internat. Inst. Advanced Studies, Clayton, Mo., 1979. Cert. secondary tchr., Calif. Chemist J.A. Thomson Bio-Organic Chemist, L.A., 1938, Vitamin Inst. (formerly J.A. Thomson Bio-Organic Chemist), L.A. and North Hollywood, Calif., 1939—; vocat. edn. instr. U.S.

War Manpower Commn., 1943-44; chmn. activities coun. World Coun. of Youth, L.A., 1932; pres. Coun. of Young Men's Divs. Athletic Commns., YMCA Pasadena area, 1931, chmn. exec. coun., 1932; dist. officer Boy Scouts Am., San Fernando Valley coun., 1954-64, del. to nat. conf., 1959, and others. Author: (booklets) Whose Are the Myths?, 1949, Open Eyes, Illegalize Agency Abuses, 1968, Non-toxic Vitamins-hormones Answers to Environmental, Public Problems, 1972, Lobby Interest Goals to Sequester Nutrients Among Those Rarely Educated in Them, 1973, Support of Pressures to Homeostasis, Normality, 1990, Minimization of Toxics in Agriculture, 1991; contbr. articles to jours. Prog. leader United Meth. Men Quadrennial Conf., Lafayette, Ind., 1982, instr. United Methodist Ch. nat. seminar for profls., Nashville, Tenn., 1983, pres. United Meth. Men, 1979-80, mem. adminstv. bd., 1952—, chmn. commn. ch. and soc., 1986—; First United Meth. Ch., North Hollywood; mem. Rep. county ctrl. Com. L.A. County, 1941-50, chmn. 63d assembly dist., 1948-50, Rep. state ctrl. com., Calif. 1948-50. Recipient Sci. and Industry award San Francisco Internat. Expn., 1940, various scouting leadership awards Boy Scouts Am., Civic Svc. award State of Calif., 1949, others. Mem. AAAS (life), Am. Inst. Biol. Scis., Soc. Nutrition Edn., N.Y. Acad. Scis., Am. Horticultural Soc., Am. Chem. Soc. (So. Calif. sect.), Internat. Acad. Nutrition and Preventive Medicine, Western Gerontol. Assn., Am. Forestry Assn., Am. Assn. Nurserymen, Garden Writers Assn. Am., Profl. Grounds Mgmt. Soc., Soc. Am. Florists and Ornamental Horticulturists, Internat. Soc. Hort. Sci., Nat. Coun. Improved Health, Nat. Recreation and Parks Assn., Nat. Landscape Assn., Nat. Nutritional Foods Assn. (Pioneer Svc. award 1970), Nat. Health Fedn. (life), Nat. Assn. Mfrs., Nat. Resources Def. Coun., Nat. Lawn and Garden Distbrs. Assn., Universal City-North Hollywood C. of C., Sierra Club, Soc. Colonial Wars (life), Kiwanis (projects panelist internat. confs. 1987, 91), Friends of the Earth, Negative Population Growth, Amnesty Internat. Republican. Achievements include origination of a high proportion of known uses for horticultural hormones, with first products, many of them via solely-invented and produced Horms 4, 1 and 2, Superthrive, Cutstart and Seedyield, multiple vitamins-hormones, distributed worldwide; development of highest known efficacies in plant activating, reviving, transplanting, growing, perfecting, rooting and seed invigoration; creation of water-miscible multiple vitamins powder Auzon, for humans creation of more than 100 other formula products. Office: Vitamin Inst PO Box 230 5411 Satsuma Ave North Hollywood CA 91601-2838

THOMSON, KEITH STEWART, science museum administrator, writer; b. Heanor, Eng., July 29, 1938; s. Ronald William and Marian Adelaide (Coster) T.; m. Linda Gailbreath Price, Sept. 27, 1963; children: Jessica Adelaide, Elizabeth Rose. B.Sc. with honors, U. Birmingham, Eng., 1960; A.M., Harvard U., 1961, Ph.D. (NATO fellow), 1963. NATO postdoctoral fellow Univ. Coll., London U., 1963-65; asst. prof. to prof. biology Yale U., 1965-87, dean Grad. Sch., 1979-87; dir. Peabody Mus. Natural History, 1976-79; pres. Acad. Natural Scis., Phila., 1987—; dir. Sears Found. Marine Rsch. and Oceanographic History; hon. rsch. fellow Australian Nat. U., 1967; trustee, mem. corp. Woods Hole Oceanographic Inst.; bd. dirs. Wistar Inst. Ctrl. Phila. Devel. Corp., Wetlands Inst., Phila. Cultural Alliance; rschr. in vertebrate evolution. Mem. editl. bd. Paleobiology, Jour. Morphology, 1988, Aspects of Lower Vertebrate Evolution, 1968, Origin of Terrestrial Vertebrates, 1968, Saltwater Fishes of Conn., 1971, 88, Priorities and Needs in Systematic Biology, 1981, Morphogenesis and Evolution, 1988, Living Fossil, 1991, The Common But Less Frequent Loon and Other Essays, 1993, HMS Beagle, 1995. Fellow Linnean Soc. London, Zool. Soc. London; mem. Soc. Vertebrate Palaeontology, Sigma Xi. Office: Acad Natural Scis 1900 Benjamin Franklin Pky Philadelphia PA 19103-1101

THOMSON, KENNETH R. (LORD THOMSON OF FLEET), publishing executive; b. Toronto, Ont., Can., Sept. 1, 1923; s. Lord Thomson of Fleet; m. Nora Marilyn Lavis, June 1956; children: David Kenneth Roy, Peter John, Lesley Lynne. Student, Upper Can. Coll., Toronto; BA, MA, U. Cambridge, Eng., 1947. With editorial dept. Timmins Daily Press, Eng., 1947; with advt. dept. Cambridge (Galt) Reporter, 1948-50, gen. mgr., 1950-53; owner Thomson Newspapers, Toronto, 1953—; chmn., bd. dirs. Thomson Corp., Thomson Corp. Plc, Thomson U.S. Inc., The Woodbridge Co. Ltd.; pres., bd. dirs. Thomson Works of Art Ltd.; bd. dirs. Hudson's Bay Co., Markborough Properties Inc. With RCAF, World War II. Mem. Granite Club, Hunt Club, National Club, Toronto Club, York Club, York Downs Club. Baptist. Avocations: collecting paintings and works of art, walking. Home: 8 Castle Frank Rd, Toronto, ON Canada M4W 2Z4 Office: Thomson Corp, 65 Queen St W Ste 2500, Toronto, ON Canada M5H 2M8

THOMSON, MAYNARD F., lawyer; b. Cin., Dec. 3, 1944. BA, Boston U., 1967; MA, U. Sussex, Eng., 1968; JD, Case Western Res. U., 1971; MPA, Harvard U., 1974. Bar: Ohio 1971. Mem. legal staff Ohio Atty. Gen. Office, Cleve., 1971-73, Bur. Competition, FTC, 1974-77; ptnr. Jones, Day, Reavis & Pogue, Cleve. Office: Jones Day Reavis & Pogue North Point 901 Lakeside Ave E Cleveland OH 44114-1190

THOMSON, PAUL VAN KUYKENDALL, priest, educator; b. Weehawken, N.J., Dec. 14, 1916; s. Walter Scott and Mary Ann (van Kuykendall) T.; m. Mildred Marie Cole, Dec. 27, 1945; children: Thomas, Catherine, Monica, Jane, Ann, Madeleine, Peter. AB, Columbia U., 1937; STB, Berkeley Div. Sch., New Haven, 1940; STM, Gen. Theol. Sem., N.Y.C., 1943; MA, Brown U., 1952, PhD, 1956; DHL (hon.), Salve Regina Coll., 1966. Ordained to ministry Episc. Ch., 1941; ordained priest Roman Cath. Ch., 1983. Rector St. Stephen's Episcopal Ch., Providence, 1946-49; mem. faculty English dept. Providence Coll., 1959-83, acad. v.p., 1965-82, prof. emeritus, 1983—; cons. USOE Project English, Washington, 1960, Carnegie Project, R.I. Coll., 1966-67; mem. wage bds. U.S. Dept. Labor, San Juan, P.R., 1961-64. Author: Why I Am a Catholic, 1959, Francis Thompson, 1960, Plus Sign on the Roof, 1990. Trustee Butler Hosp., Providence, 1965-66, Providence Pub. Libr., 1980—; v.p. N.E. Cath. Coll. Assn., Boston, 1968-69, pres. 1969-70. Chaplain USN, 1943-46, PTO. Recipient Disting. Grad. Alumni award Brown U., 1983, Univ. fellow, 1955. Mem. Eighteen Nineties Soc. London (v.p. 1970—). Home: PO Box 814 Wakefield RI 02880-0898 Office: Providence Coll Dept English Providence RI 02918

THOMSON, RICHARD MURRAY, banker; b. Winnipeg, Man., Can., Aug. 14, 1933; s. H.W. and Mary T. BASC in Engring., U. Toronto, 1955; MBA, Harvard U., 1957; fellow course in banking, Queen's U., 1958. With Toronto Dominion Bank, Ont., Can., 1957—; asst. to pres. head office, 1963-68, chief gen. mgr. 1968-71, v.p., chief gen. mgr., dir., 1971-72, pres., 1972-77, pres. and CEO, 1977-78, chmn., CEO, 1978—; also bd. dirs. Toronto Dominion Bank; bd. dirs. C.G.C. Inc., Eatons of Can., S.C. Johnson & Son Inc., The Prudential Ins. Co. Am., The Thomson Corp., Inco Ltd., The Hosp. for Sick Children Found. Office: Toronto-Dominion Bank, 55 King St PO Box 1, Toronto, ON Canada M5K 1A2

THOMSON, ROBERT HENNESSEY, manufacturing executive; b. Amesbury, Mass., July 28, 1933; s. Robert H. and Mary Catherine (Hennessey) T.; m. Suzanne Louise Locher, Aug. 26, 1957; children: Robert H. Jr., Karen Cantor, David L., Peter J., Christine. BSBA, Seton Hall U., 1957. Salesman Constrn. Specialties Inc., Cranford, N.J., 1957-59, product mgr. 1959-61, v.p., gen. mgr., Toronto office, 1961-68, v.p., gen. mgr., 1969-73, exec. v.p., 1973-75, chief exec. officer, 1975—, also bd. dirs. Served with USMC, 1953-55, Korea. Mem. Pres. Assn. of Am. Mgmt. Assn., Baltusrol Golf Club. Republican. Roman Catholic. Avocations: golf, tennis, swimming. Home: 112 Colchester Rd New Providence NJ 07974-1620 Office: Constrn Specialties Inc 55 Winans Ave Cranford NJ 07016-3144

THOMSON, ROBERT JAMES, natural gas distribution company executive; b. Detroit, Dec. 16, 1927; s. Harold E.J. and Irene L. (Silsbee) T.; m. Doris L. Mullen, Sept. 19, 1953; children—Gregory R., Susan C., Jeffrey S., Arthur J. A.B., Mich. State U., 1951, M.B.A., 1967. C.P.A., Mich. Mgr. Arthur Andersen & Co., Detroit, 1951-58; v.p. Southeastern Mich. Gas Co., Port Huron, 1961-71, pres., 1971-84, pres., chief exec. officer, 1984-86; pres., CEO Southeastern Mich. Gas Enterprise, Inc., Pt. Huron, 1977-93; chmn. Southeastern Mich. Gas Enterprise, Inc., Port Huron 1987-95; bd. dirs. Mich. Nat. Bank-Port Huron. Trustee Community Found. St. Clair County, 1972—, pres. 1981-83; bd. dirs. Indsl. Devel. Corp., Port Huron 1972-86, pres., 1976-78; trustee Port Huron Hosp., 1981-90, vice chmn. 1985-90; bd. dirs. Blue Water Health Svcs. Corp., 1981—, vice chmn., 1981-93, chmn., 1993—; trustee Marwood Manor Nursing Home, 1987—; vestryman Grace

Episcopal Ch., Port Huron, 1990-93. With USN, 1946-47. Mem. Mich. C. of C. (bd. dirs. 1982-88), Mich. Utilities Assn. (bd. dirs., treas. 1983-85), Renaissance Club, Port Huron Golf Club, Port Huron Yacht Club, Mich. State U. Advanced Mgmt. Program Club. Home: 3355 Lomar Dr Fort Gratiot MI 48059 Office: Mich Nat Bank Bldg 800 Military St Ste 302 Port Huron MI 48060

THOMSON, SHIRLEY LAVINIA, museum director; b. Wakerville, Ont., Can., Feb. 19, 1930; d. Walter T. and Edith May (MacKenzie) Cull. BA in History with honors, U. Western Ont., 1952; MA in Art History, U. Md., 1974; PhD in Art History, McGill U., 1981; PhD (hon.), Ottawa U., 1988; Doctorat honoris causa, McGill U., 1989, Mt. Allison U., 1990, U. Western Ont., 1990. Officer, conf. NATO, Paris, 1956-60; asst. sec. gen. World Univs. Svc. Can., Toronto, Ont., 1960-63; asst. sec. gen. Can. Commn. for UNESCO, Ottawa, 1964-67, sec. gen. dir., 1985-87; dir., dep. commn. UNESCO Pavilion at Man and His World, Montreal, 1978-80; rsch. coord., writer Memoirs of Sen. Thérèse Casgrain, 1968-70; spl. coord. Largillière Exhbn., Mus. Fine Arts, Montreal, 1981; dir. McCord Mus., Montreal, 1982-85, Nat. Gallery Can., Ottawa, 1987—. Decorated Chevalier des Arts et Lettres (France), officer Order of Can.; fellow Can. Coun., 1977-78, doctoral awardee, 1978-79. Mem. Can. Soc. Decorative Arts (coun.), Can. Mus. Assn. (dir.). Office: Nat Gallery, 380 Sussex Dr, Ottawa, ON Canada K1N 9N4

THOMSON, THYRA GODFREY, former state official; b. Florence, Colo., July 30, 1916; d. John and Rosalie (Altman) Godfrey; m. Keith Thomson, Aug. 6, 1939 (dec. Dec. 1960); children—William John, Bruce Godfrey, Keith Coffey. B.A. cum laude, U. Wyo., 1939. With dept. agronomy and agrl. econs. U. Wyo., 1938-39; writer weekly column Watching Washington pub. in 14 papers, Wyo., 1955-60; planning commn. Nat. Fedn. Republican Women, Washington, 1961; sec. state Wyo. Cheyenne, 1962-86; mem. Marshall Scholarships Com. for Pacific region, 1964-68; del. 72d Wilton Park Conf., Eng., 1965; mem. youth commn. UNESCO, 1970-71, Allied Health Professions Council HEW, 1971-72; del. U.S.-Republic of China Trade Conf., Taipei, Taiwan, 1983; mem. lt. gov.'s trade and fact-finding mission to Saudi Arabia, Jordan, and Egypt, 1985. Bd. dirs. Buffalo Bill Mus., Cody, Wyo., 1987—; adv. bd. Coll. Arts and Scis., U. Wyo., 1989, Cheyenne Symphony Orch. Found., 1990—. Recipient Disting. Alumni award U. Wyo., 1969, Disting. U. Wyo. Arts and Scis. Alumna award, 1987; named Internat. Woman of Distinction, Alpha Delta Kappa; recipient citation Omicron Delta Epsilon, 1965, citation Beta Gamma Sigma, 1968, citation Delta Kappa Gamma, 1973, citation Wyo. Commn. Women, 1986. Mem. N.Am. Securities Adminstrs. (pres. 1973-74), Nat. Assn. Secs. of State, Council State Govts. (chmn. natural resources com. Western states 1966-68), Nat. Conf. Lt. Govs. (exec. com. 1976-79). Home: 3102 Sunrise Rd Cheyenne WY 82001-6136

THOMSON, WILLIAM BARRY, retail company executive; b. Morristown, N.J., Dec. 3, 1952; s. James Bruce and Ruth Janet (Hill) T. BA, Drew U., 1974. Dir. spl. projects F.W. Woolworth Co., N.Y.C., 1979-82, asst. sec., 1982-86, sec., 1986-90; v.p. pub. affairs Woolworth Corp. (formerly F.W. Woolworth Co.), N.Y.C., 1990-91, sr. v.p. adminstrn., 1991-93; sr. v.p., chief adminstrv. officer Woolworth Corp., N.Y.C., 1993—. Office: Woolworth Corp Woolworth Bldg 233 Broadway New York NY 10279-0001

THON, WILLIAM, artist; b. N.Y.C., Aug. 8, 1906; s. Felix Leo and Jane (Upham) T.; m. Helen Elizabeth Walters, June 3, 1929. Student, Art Students League, 1924-25; A.F.D., Bates Coll., 1957. Represented in nat. art exhibits at Corcoran Gallery Art, Washington, Art Inst. Chgo., Pa. Acad., Va. Mus., Toldeo Mus., Met. Mus., Nat. Acad., Carnegie Inst.; one-man show Farnsworth Mus., Rockland, Me.; included in permanent collections Swope Art Gallery, Terre Haute, Ind.; Farnsworth Mus., Bloomington Art Assn., Ency. Brit., Toledo Mus., Am. Acad. Arts and Letters, Mus. of Ann Arbor, Mich., Met. Mus. Art, N.Y.C., Portland Mus. Art, U. Hawaii, Honolulu, Johnson's Wax Collection, Bklyn. Mus., Whitney Mus., Portland Mus., Oquenquet Mus., others.; artist-in-residence Am. Acad., Rome, 1956. Served with USNR, 1942-46. Recipient prize Salmagundi Club, 1941, Dana Watercolor medal Pa. Acad., 1950, 2d Altman prize for landscape NAD, 1951, 1st Altman prize NAD, 1954, 67, Palmer Meml. prize NAD, 1944, Bklyn. Mus. prize, 1945, prix de Rome, 1947, Samuel F.B. Morse medal NAD, 1956, Silver medal Am. Watercolor Soc., 1957, 67, Altman prize for landscape NAD, 1961, Gordon Grant Maml. award Am. Watercolor Soc., 1963, Gold medal of Honor Am. Watercolor Soc., 1970, Adolph and Clara Obrig prize NAD, 1965, Maine State award, 1970, Lena Newcastle Meml. award Am. Watercolor Soc., 1976, Ranger Fund Purchase award NAD, 1976, Silver medal Audubon Artists, 1986, Ogden Pliessner Meml. prize Nat. Acad., 1988, William A. Patton prize Nat. Acad. Design, 1991, Adolph and Clara Obrig award NAD, 1992, Lillian Judith Newman award Audubon Artists, 1992, Florence and H. Samuel Slater Meml. award Adirondacks Nat. Exhibit Arts Guild of Old Forge, Inc., 1992, Pulsifer award Arts Guild of Old Forge, Inc., 1993; Nat. Inst. Arts and Letters grantee, 1951. Mem. Nat. Inst. Arts and Letters, N.A.D., Am. Watercolor Soc. (Gold Medal of Honor 1979, Caroline Stern award 1986), Audubon Artists, Friendship Sloop Soc. Home: Port Clyde ME 04855

THONG, TRAN, biomedical company executive; b. Saigon, Vietnam, Dec. 8, 1951; came to U.S., 1969, naturalized, 1980; s. Vy and Vinh-Thi (Nguyen) T.; m. Thuy Thi-Bich Nguyen, Jan. 12, 1978. BSEE, Ill. Inst. Tech., 1972; MS in Engring., Princeton U., 1974, MA, 1974, PhD, 1975. Rsch. scientist Western Geophys. Houston, 1975-76; computer devel. engr. GE Co., Syracuse, N.Y., 1976-79; dir. electronic system lab. Tektronix, Inc., Beaverton, Oreg., 1980-90, v.p. engring., and digital signal processing gen. mgr., Tektronix Fed. Systems Inc., Beaverton, Oreg., 1990-93; v.p. systems design and devel. Micro Systems Engring., Inc., Lake Oswego, Oreg., 1993—; adj. asst. prof. Syracuse U., 1979-81, Oreg. State U., Corvallis, 1980-83, U. Portland, Oreg., 1981-83; adj. assoc. prof. Oreg. Grad. Ctr., Beaverton, 1984—; founding mem. Pacific Advanced Comm. Consortium, Eugene, Oreg. Founding mem., chmn. Vietnamese Assn. for Computing, Engring. Tech. and Sci., 1994-95, past pres., 1995—. Author numerous sci. papers and U.S. patents. Princeton U. fellow, 1974. Fellow IEEE (com. chmn. 1982-88, assoc. editor transaction 1979-81, gen. chmn. 1989, exec. v.p. circuits and sys. 1989); mem. Eta Kappa Nu, Tau Beta Pi, Sigma Xi. Republican. Office: Micro Sys Engring 6024 SW Jean Rd Lake Oswego OR 97035

THOR, LINDA MARIA, college president; b. L.A., Feb. 21, 1950; d. Karl Gustav and Mildred Dorrine (Hofius) T.; m. Robert Paul Huntsinger, Nov. 22, 1974; children: Erik, Marie. BA, Pepperdine U., 1971, EdD, 1986; MPA, Calif. State U., Los Angeles, 1980. Dir. pub. info. Pepperdine U., Los Angeles, 1971-73; pub. info officer L.A. C.C. Dist., 1974-75, dir. comm., 1975-81, dir. edn. svcs., 1981-82, dir. high tech., 1982-83, sr. dir. occupl. and tech. edn., 1983-86; pres. West Los Angeles Coll., Culver City, Calif., 1986-90, Rio Salado C.C., Phoenix, 1990—; bd. dirs. Coun. for Adult and Experiential Learning, 1990—; Tech. Exch. Ctr., 1986—; Greater Phoenix Econ. Coun., 1994—. Editor: Curriculum Design and Development for Effective Learning, 1973; author: (with others) Effective Media Relations, 1982, Performance Contracting, 1987; contbr. articles to profl. jours. Active Am. Assn. Cmty. Coll. Commn. Urban Cmty. Coll., 1992-95, Publs./Pub. Rels. Commn., 1993—, Continuous Quality Improvement Network for Cmty. Coll., 1991—; mem. Ariz. Gov.'s Adv. Coun. on Quality, 1992; pres. Ariz. Cmty. Coll. Pres.'s Coun., 1995—. Recipient Delores award Pepperdine U., 1986, Alumni Medal of Honor, 1987, Outstanding Achievement award Women's Bus. Network, 1989; named Woman of the Yr., Culver City Bus. and Profl. Women, 1988. Office: 640 N First Ave Phoenix AZ 85003

THOR, PETER K., marketing executive; b. July 17, 1954. BS, U. Calif. Davis, 1976, MS, 1977, PhD, 1980. Asst. to pres. Tri Valley Growers, San Francisco, 1979-82, v.p. strategic planning, 1982-83, v.p. mktg. and planning, 1983-87, exec. v.p. mktg. and planning, 1987—; prof. U. Santa Clara, Calif. Named Young Alumnus of Yr., U. Calif., 1988. Office: Tri Valley Growers Inc PO Box 7114 San Francisco CA 94120-7114

THORARENSEN, ODDUR C.S., pharmacist; b. Reykjavik, Iceland, Apr. 26, 1925; s. Stefan and Ragnheidur (Hafstein) T.; m. Asta Baldvinsdottir, Oct. 24, 1948; (div. Aug. 1956); children: Stefan, Baldvin Hafsteinn; m. Unnur Arny Long Thorarensen, Nov. 27, 1958; children: Ragnheidur Katrin,

---

Sigridur Elin, Unnur Alma. Grad. diploma, Reyjavik Latin Sch., Iceland, 1945; examinatus Pharmaciae, U. Iceland, 1948; candidatus Pharmaciae, Royal Danish Coll. Pharmacy, Copenhagen, Denmark, 1949, 53, 54; student, P.C.P. & S., Phila., 1950. Proprietary Pharmacist, 1963. Asst. pharmacist Laugavegs Apotek, Reykjavik, Iceland, 1950-51, chief pharmacist, 1954-57, owner, mgr., 1963—; gen. mgr. Efnagerd Reykjavikur Ltd., Reykjavik, Iceland, 1957-69. Chmn. and diverse other positions, Independence Party, Local Orgn., Gardabaer, Reykjavik, Iceland, 1980-90; mem. Diverse Comnx., Min. Health, Reykjavik, Iceland, 1970—; Parish Bd. Gardar Ch., Gardabaer, Reykjavik, Iceland, 1972-84. Mem. Iceland C. of C. (bd. electors 1974-91), Gimli Lodge, Masonic Nat. Grand Lodge Iceland, Iceland Pharmacist Union (sec. 1955-56, chmn. 1956-57), Iceland Proprietary Pharmacist Assn. (sec. 1973-74, 77-80), Reykjavik Proprietary Pharmacist Assn. (chmn. 1974-77, sec. 1977-78). Lutheran. Avocations: reading, jazz music, freemasonry, science fiction, space exploration, computers. Office: Laugavegs Apotek, 16 Laugavegi PO Box 477, 121 Reykjavik Iceland

THORBECKE, ERIK, economics educator; b. Berlin, Feb. 17, 1929; s. William and Madeleine (Salisbury) T.; m. Charla J. Westerberg, Oct. 17, 1954; children: Erik Charles, Willem, Jon. Student, Netherlands Sch. Econs., Rotterdam, 1948-51; Ph.D., U. Calif., 1957; hon. doctorate, U. Ghent, 1981. Asst. prof. econs. Iowa State U., 1957-60, assoc. prof., 1960-63, prof., 1963-73; prof. Cornell U., 1974—, chmn. dept. econs., 1975-78, H.E. Babcock prof. econs. and food econs., 1978—; econ. adviser Nat. Planning Inst., Lima, Peru, 1963-64; asso. asst. adminstr. for program policy AID, Washington, 1966-68, mem. research advisory com., 1976-81; sr. economist world employment program Internat. Labor Office, Geneva, 1972-73; vis. prof. Erasmus U., Rotterdam, 1980-81; mem. com. on internat. nutritional programs NRC-NAS, 1979-81; dir. program on comparative econ. devel., Cornell U., 1988—; sr. rsch. fellow USAID Inst. Policy Reform, 1990—. Author: The Tendency Towards Regionalization in International Trade, 1960, (with Irma Adelman) Theory and Design of Economic Development, 1966, (with K. Fox, J. Sengupta) Theory of Quantitative Economic Policy, 1968, Role of Agriculture in Economic Development, 1968, (with G. Pyatt) Planning Techniques for a Better Future, 1976; (with J. Defourny) Structural Path Analysis and Multiplier Decomposition within a Social Matrix, 1984, (with J. Lecaillon, C. Morrisson) Economic Policies and Agricultural Performance of Low Income Countries, 1987, Planning Techniques for Social Justice In: The Balance between Industry and Agriculture in Economic Development, vol. 4, 1989, (with I. Adelman) The Role of Institutions in Economic Development, Special Issue of World Development, 1989, (with others) Adjustment and Equity in Indonesia, 1992, (with T. van der Pluijm) Rural Indonesia: Socio-economic Development in a Changing Environment, 1993. Mem. Am. Econ. Assn., Am. Agrl. Econs. (Nat. award for best pub. research 1970). Home: 108 N Sunset Dr Ithaca NY 14850-1460 Office: Cornell U Dept Econs Ithaca NY 14853

THORBURN, DAVID, literature educator; b. N.Y.C., Aug. 14, 1940; s. Frank and Claire (Feller) T.; m. Barbara Ellen Levitan, June 30, 1963; children: Daniel, Adam, Rachel. AB, Princeton U., 1962; MA, Stanford U., 1966, PhD, 1968. With dept. English Yale U., New Haven, 1966-76, successively instr., asst. prof., then assoc. prof.; prof. lit., dir. film and media studies, cultural studies project MIT, Cambridge, 1976—; vis. appointments include U. Calif., Santa Barbara, U. Ill. Author: Conrad's Romanticism, 1974; contbr. articles to profl. jours.; editor scholarly collections; gen. editor Media and Popular Culture, 1986—. Fulbright fellow, Morse fellow, Woodrow Wilson fellow and Rockefeller fellow, 1966-77. Mem. MLA, Popular Culture Assn., Am. Studies Assn., Soc. for Cinema Studies. Democrat. Avocation: basketball. Office: MIT Lit Faculty 14N-335 Cambridge MA 02139

THORBURN, JAMES ALEXANDER, humanities educator; b. Martins Ferry, Ohio, Aug. 24, 1923; s. Charles David and Mary Edna (Ruble) T.; m. Lois McElroy, July 3, 1954; children: Alexander Maurice, Melissa Rachel; m. 2d, June Yingling O'Leary, Apr. 18, 1981. BA, Ohio State U., 1949, MA, 1951; postgrad., U. Mo., 1954-55; PhD, La. State U., 1977. Head English dept. high sch., Sheridan, Mich., 1951-52; instr. English, U. Mo., Columbia, 1952-55, Monmouth (Ill.) Coll., 1955-56, U. Tex., El Paso, 1956-60, U. Mo., St. Louis, 1960-61, La. State U., Baton Rouge, 1961-70; prof. Southeastern La. U., Hammond, 1970-89, ret., named prof. emeritus English and linguistics; testing and cert. examiner English Lang. Inst., U. Mich., 1969—; participant Southeastern Conf. on Linguistics; mem. Conf. Christianity and Lit. Contbg. author: Exercises in English, 1955, also poetry, short stories; book rev. editor: Experiment, 1958-87; editor: Innisfree, 1984-89. With F.A., AUS, 1943-46. Mem. MLA, Linguistic Assn. S.W., Avalon World Arts Acad., Linguistic Soc. Am., Am. Dialect Soc., La. Assn. for Coll. Composition, La. Retired Tchrs. Assn., Internat. Poetry Soc., Internat. Acad. Poets, Sociedad Nacional Hispánica, Sigma Delta Pi, Phi Kappa Phi (named emeritus life), Phi Mu Alpha Sinfonia. Republican. Presbyterian. Home: 602 Susan Dr Hammond LA 70403-3444 Office: Southeastern La U # 739 Hammond LA 70402 *I have always felt that no experience is wasted, if it is not selfish or vicious. Every such experience adds something, I believe, to that inner fund on which one draws, consciously or unconsciously, throughout one's life.*

THORFINNSON, A. RODNEY, hospital administrator; b. Kandahar, Sask., Can., Nov. 30, 1934; married. BA, U. Sask., Can., 1958; MA, U. Toronto, 1960. Adminstrv. resident Humber Meml. Hosp., Toronto, 1959-60; cons. Dept. Pub. Health, Regina, Sask., 1960-61; asst. dir. Sask. Hosp. Assn., Regina, 1961-62, exec. dir., 1962-64; asst. dir. Univ. Hosp., Saskatoon, Sask., 1964-65; adminstr. Victoria Hosp., London, Ont., 1966-69; v.p. Comtron Systems, Inc., London, Ont., 1969-70; exec. dir. Victoria Hosp. Corp., London, Ont., 1970-78, pres., 1978-85; pres. Health Scis. Ctr., Winnipeg, Man., 1985—. Office: Health Scis Ctr, 820 Sherbrook St Rm GB127B, Winnipeg, MB Canada R3A 1R9

THORGEIRSSON, SNORRI SVEINN, physician, pharmacologist; b. Iceland, Dec. 1, 1941; came to U.S., 1972, naturalized, 1980; d. Thorgeir Jonsson and Sigurlina Sigujonsdottir; M.D., U. Iceland, 1968; Ph.D., U. London, 1971; m. Unnur Thorgeirsson, Sept. 5, 1969; children—Sif, Christian. Intern, Univ. Hosp., Reykjavik, Iceland, 1968-69; registrar, research fellow dept. clin. pharmacology Royal Postgrad. Med. Sch., London, 1969-71; vis. fellow Lab. Chem. Pharmacology, Nat. Heart and Lung Inst., NIH, Bethesda, Md., 1972-73, vis. scientist sect. devel. pharmacology, Neonatal and Pediatric Medicine br. Nat. Inst. Child Health and Human Devel., 1974-75, chief sect. on molecular toxicology devel. pharmacology br., 1975-76; head biochem. pharmacology sect. Lab. Chem. Pharmacology, Nat. Cancer Inst., 1976-81, chief Lab. Carcinogen Metabolism, 1981—; mem. Chem. Selection Working Group, 1978—; mem. Com. on Occupational Carcinogenesis, 1979; mem. com. on amines Nat. Acad. Scis., 1979-80; co-chmn. Internat. Conf. on Carcinogenic and Mutagenic N-Substituted Aryl Compounds, NIH, Bethesda, 1979; preceptor Pharmacology Research Assoc. Program, Nat. Inst. Gen. Med. Scis., 1977—; mem. biol. response modifiers decision network com. Nat. Cancer Inst., 1980; lectr. in field. Mem. Am. Assn. Cancer Research, AAAS, Am. Soc. Exptl. Pharmacology and Exptl. Therapeutics, Am. Chem. Soc., N.Y. Acad. Scis., Environ. Mutagen Soc., Soc. Toxicology, European Assn. Cancer Research. Contbr. numerous articles, chpts. to profl. publs.; research in mechanisms of chem. carcinogenesis, control of differentiation in neo-plastic cells. Office: National Cancer Institute Cancer Etiology 9000 Rockville Pike Bldg 31 Bethesda MD 20892-0001

THORIN, DONALD E., cinematographer. Cinematographer: (films) Thief, 1981, An Officer and a Gentleman, 1982, (with Bruce Surtees) Bad Boys, 1983, Against All Odds, 1984, Purple Rain, 1984, Mischief, 1985, Wildcats, 1986, The Golden Child, 1986, American Anthem, 1986, Midnight Run, 1988, Collision Course, 1988, The Couch Trip, 1988, Tango & Cash, 1989, Troop Beverly Hills, 1989, Lock Up, 1989, The Marrying Man, 1991, Out On a Limb, 1992, Scent of a Woman, 1992, Cloak and Diaper, 1992, Undercover Blues, 1993, Little Big League, 1994, Boys on the Side, 1995. Office: Broder Kurland Webb Uffner Agy 9242 Beverly Blvd Ste 200 Beverly Hills CA 90210*

THORINGTON, JOHN M., JR., computer graphics company executive; b. 1943. BS, Auburn U., 1963, MS, 1967, PhD, 1971. With Bell Telephone Labs., N.J., 1971-77; with Intergraph Corp., Huntsville, Ala., 1977—; exec. v.p. for graphics engring.; pres. Dazix Intergraph Corp., Sunnyvale, Calif.

THORN, ARLINE ROUSH, English language educator; b. New Haven, Nov. 22, 1946; d. Jack and Joy (Yonker) Roush; m. Eric Paul Thorn, June 10, 1968 (div. 1991); 1 child, Paul Arthur. BA, Marshall U., 1967; MA, U. Ill., 1968, PhD, 1971. Prof. W.Va. State Coll., Institute, 1971—, chair dept. English, 1986-94, adj. prof. W.Va. Coll. Grad. Studies, 1989—; pub. Trillium Press Appalachian Writers, 1992—; cons. W.Va. Humanities Found., Charleston, 1987—; chair adv. coun. faculty State Coll. System, 1992-94, bd. dirs., 1994—. Author: Mining the Seam, 1992, Fire and Ice, 1993; editor: Origins: Texts for an Inquiry, 1988. Woodrow Wilson Found. fellow, 1970; grantee Fund for Improvement of Postsecondary Edn., 1986-89; named Outstanding Prof., W.Va. State Legis., 1989; Fulbright Seminar, Brazil, 1993. Mem. MLA, W.Va. Assn. Coll. English Thrs. (pres. 1988), Audubon Soc. (editor newsletter Huntington tri state chpt. 1987-94). Avocations: birding, writing poetry. Home: 620 Edgehill Dr Saint Albans WV 25177-3741 Office: WVa State Coll Institute WV 25112

THORN, GEORGE WIDMER, physician, educator; b. Buffalo, Jan. 15, 1906; s. George W. and Fanny R. (Widmer) T.; m. Doris Weston, June 30, 1931 (dec. Jan. 1984); 1 son, Weston Widmer; m. Claire Steinert, Dec. 28, 1985 (dec. Mar. 1990). Student, Coll. of Wooster, 1923-25; MD, U. Buffalo, 1929; MA (hon.), Harvard U., 1942, DSc (hon.), 1987; DSc (hon.), Temple U., 1951, Suffolk U., 1961, Coll. Wooster, 1963, N.Y. Med. Coll., 1972, Boston U., 1983; LLD (hon.), Dalhousie U., 1950; LLD, Queen's U., Can., 1954; DMed, Cath. U., Louvain, 1960; MD (hon.), U. Geneva, 1965; DSc (hon.), Med. Coll. of Ohio, Toledo, Rockefeller U., 1993. Diplomate Am. Bd. Internal Medicine. House officer Millard Fillmore Hosp., Buffalo, 1929-30; researcher dept. physiology U. Buffalo, 1930-31, asst. researcher dept. physiology and medicine, 1931-34; asst. prof. physiology Ohio State U., Columbus, 1935-36; asst. physician Johns Hopkins Hosp., Balt., 1937-39, assoc. prof. medicine, 1938-42, assoc. physician, 1939-42; mem. med. adv. bd. Howard Hughes Med. Inst., 1955-85, dir., res., 1956-78, chmn. med. adv. bd., 1975-85, mem. exec. com., 1977-84, pres., 1981-84, chmn. bd. trustees, 1984-90; physician-in-chief Peter Bent Brigham Hosp., Boston, 1942-72, physician-in-chief emeritus, 1972—; Samuel A. Levine prof. medicine Harvard U., Cambridge, 1967-72, Samuel A. Levine prof. emeritus, 1972—; Hersey prof. theory and practice physic emeritus, 1972—; Hugh J. Morgan vis. prof. Vanderbilt U., 1967; vis. prof. medicine Columbia Coll. Physicians and Surgeons, 1968, Cornell U. Med. Sch. and N.Y. Hosp., 1970; Wingate Johnson vis. prof. Bowman Gray Sch. Medicine Wake Forest U., 1972; cons. internist Boston Psychopathic Hosp., 1943—; mem. research and devel. adv. bd. Smith, Kline and French Labs., 1953-69; cons. Children's Med. Ctr., USPHA, U.S. Army Med. Services Grad. Sch.; mem. com. stress NRC; mem. Nat. Com. on Radiation, 1958—; mem. drug research bd. NRC-Nat. Acad. Scis., 1972; lectr.U. London, 1957; Jacobaeus lectr., Oslo, 1957; Maurice C. Pincoff lectr. U. Md. Sch. Medicine, 1958; Mellon lectr. U. Pitts., 1959; Banting Meml. lectr. Am. Diabetes Assn., 1959; 1st Lilly lectr. Royal Coll. Physicians, 1966, Soc. Mexicana de Nutricion y Endocrologia, Mexico, 1969; Thayer lectr. Johns Hopkins U., 1967; Billings lectr. AMA, 1968; John C. Leonard Med. lectr. Hartford Med. Soc., 1969; mem. corp. MIT, 1965—, Mus. Sci., 1979—; v.p. Whitaker Health Scis. Fund, Inc., 1974-92; bd. visitors Boston u. Sch. Medicine, 1979—; chmn. sci. adv. bd. Whitaker Found., 1979-93. Editor-in-chief Principles of Internal Medicine, 8th edit., 1974. Pres. Howard Hughes Med. Inst., Boston, 1981-84, chmn. bd. dirs. and trustee, 1984—. Rockefeller fellow in medicine, Harvard U., 1936-37, Johns Hopkins U. Sch. Medicine, 1938, Read Ellsworth fellow in medicine John Hopkins U. Sch. Medicine, 1938; recipient Chancellor's medal U. Buffalo, 1943, Osler oration Can. Med. Assn., 1949, U.S. Pharm. Mfrs. Assn. award 1950, Alvarenga award, 1951, Dr. Charles V. Chapin Meml. award 1956, Ann. Meml. award Buffalo Urol. Soc., 1958, Modern Medicine award, 1961, Oscar B. Hunter Meml. award Am. Therapeutic Soc., 1967, Robert H. Williams award Assn. Profs. of Medicine, 1972, George M. Kober medal Assn. Am. Physicians, 1976, Medical Times Physician of Excellence award, 1980, Hubert H. Humphrey Research Ctr. award Boston U., 1980, Gold medal Phi Lambda Kappa, 1981. Fellow Royal Coll. Physicians (London), ACP (master, John Phillips Meml. award 1955); mem. Am. Soc. Clin. Investigation (emeritus), AMA (gold medalist 1932, 39, George Minot award 1963), Assn. Am. Physicians (pres. 1970), Am. Physiol. Soc., Royal Soc. of Medicine (hon. mem. endocronology sect.), Endocrine Soc. (pres. 1962), Am. Clin. and Climatol. Assn. (pres.), Am. Acad. Arts and Scis., Royal Soc. Medicine (hon.), Royal Acad. of Medicine of Belgium, Interurban Clin. Club, John Hopkins Soc. Scholars, Aesculapian Club, Order of Hipolito ofmdr. 1960), Sigma Xi, Nu Sigma Nu, Alpha Omega Alpha. Clubs: Harvard, Harvard Faculty; Country (Brookline); Essex County, St. Botolph, Tavern, Badminton & Tennis, Singing Beach (Manchester). Office: Howard Hughes Med Inst 320 Longwood Ave Enders 661 Boston MA 02115

THORN, ROSEMARY KOST, librarian; b. N.Y.C., Dec. 15, 1954; d. Stephen John and Henrietta (Rosso) K.; m. Michael Thorn; children: Russell, Stephen. BA in Anthropology, Rutgers U., 1977; MLS, U. N.C., 1980. Head libr. U.S. EPA, Research Triangle Park, N.C., 1980—; EPA. Avocations: running, gardening, travel. Office: EPA Libr Svcs Mail Drop 35 Durham NC 27711

THORN, TERENCE HASTINGS, gas industry executive; b. Takoma, Md., July 6, 1946; s. John Hastings and Norine R. (Freytag) T.; m. Judith Carol Bailey, Aug. 15, 1970; children: Kristin Lynn, Matthew Hastings. BA, U. Md., 1969, MA, 1973. Dir. congl. rels. Am. Gas Assn., Arlington, Va., 1975-79; dir. govt. rels. J. Walter Thompson Co., Washington 1979-81; v.p. govt. rels. Houston Natural Gas Co., Washington, 1981-85; exec. v.p. Mojave Pipeline Co., Houston, 1986-89; pres., CEO Transwestern Pipeline Co., Houston, 1993—; sr. v.p., exec. mgmt. com. bd. Enon Corp., 1993—; chmn. bd. Mojave Pipeline Oper. Co., Houston, 1989-93; chmn. Pacific Coast Gas Assn., 1994—. Bd. dirs. Houston Pops, 1989-90, Pin Oak Charities, Houston, 1991—; city alderman, 1992-93; mem. Hermann Soc., 1993—, Energy Industry Sector Adv. Com. U.S. Dept. Commerce; prin. liason Pres.'s Coun. Sustainable Devel. Democrat. Avocation: tennis. Office: Transwestern Pipeline Co PO Box 1188 Houston TX 77251

THORNBERRY, TERENCE PATRICK, criminologist, educator; b. N.Y.C., Jan. 28, 1945; s. Patrick and Rose (Small) T.; m. Eileen Delores O'Connor, Aug. 27, 1966; children: Donna Ann, Patrick. BA, Fordham U., 1966; MA, U. Pa., 1971, PhD, 1971. Asst. dir. Ctr. for Studies in Criminology and Criminal Law, U. Pa., Phila., 1971-79; dir. Research Ctr. in Crime and Delinquency, U. Ga., Athens, 1979-84; dean Sch. Criminal Justice, SUNY, Albany, 1984-89; prof. 1984—; dir. Rochester Youth Devel. Study, 1986—; cons. Commn. on Obscenity and Pornography, 1970, Nat. Commn. on Marijuana and Drug Abuse, 1973, Commn. on Rev. of Nat. Policy Toward Gambling, 1975-76; chmn. criminal and violent behavior rev. com. NIMH, 1988-90. Author: Evaluating Criminology, 1978, The Criminology Index, 1978, The Criminally Insane: A Community Followup of Mentally Ill Offenders, 1979 (ABA Gavel award, cert of merit 1980), From Boy to Man: From Delinquency to Crime, 1987; editor: Images of Crime: Offenders and Victims, 1974, Crime and Delinquency: Dimensions of Deviance, 1974; mem. editorial bd.: Jour. Criminal Law and Criminology, Social Forces, Jour. Quantitative Criminology, Criminology: An Interdisciplinary Jour.; contbr. articles to profl. jours. Recipient Appreciation certificate Nat. Inst. Mental Health, 1990. Mem. Am. Soc. Criminology (v.p. 1974-75, exec. counsellor 1974-77, 82, 85—, Presdl. Citation 1975), Am. Sociol. Assn. Home: 39 Gladwish Rd Delmar NY 12054-4421 Office: SUNY Sch Criminal Justice 135 Western Ave Albany NY 12203-1011

THORNBERRY, WILLIAM HOMER, federal judge; b. Jan. 9, 1909; s. William Moore and Mary Lillian (Jones) T.; m. Eloise Engle, Feb. 24, 1945 (dec. Apr. 27, 1989); children: Molly, David, Kate; m. Marian Harris, Feb. 24, 1990. BBA, U. Tex., 1932, LLB, 1936; LLD, Gallaudet U., 1954. Bar: Tex. Assoc. Powell, Wirtz, Rauhut & Gideon, Austin, Tex. 1936; mem. Tex. Ho. of Reps., 1937-40; dist. atty. 53d jud. dist. Travis County, Tex., 1941-42; ptnr. Jones & Thornberry, Austin, 1946-48; mayor pro tem City of Austin, 1947-48; mem. Ho. of Reps. from 10th Tex. dist., 1949-63; judge U.S. Dist. Ct. (we. dist.) Tex., 1963-65, U.S.Ct. Appeals (5th cir.) Tex., 1965—; now senior judge; mem. com. to implement criminal justice act Jud. Conf., 1964-79, com. on criminal justice act 5th Jud. Coun., 1967. Mem. city coun. City of Austin, 1946-48. Lt. comdr. USN, 1942-46. Recipient Disting. Alumnus award Tex. U., 1965, Silver Beaver award Boy Scouts Am. Mem. ABA, Tex. State Bar Assn., Travis County Bar Assn., Masons (32d degree), Shriners, Kiwanis, Order of Coif. Office: US Ct Appeals for 5th Cir

Homer Thornberry Jud Ctr 903 San Jacinto Blvd Ste 310 Austin TX 78701-2450

THORNBERRY, WILLIAM M. (MAC THORNBERRY), congressman; b. Clarendon, Tex., July 15, 1958; m. Sally Thornberry; 2 children. BA in History summa cum laude, Tex. Tech U., 1980; JD, U. Tex., 1983. Legis. coun. Rep. Tom Loeffler, 1983-85; chief of staff Rep. Larry Combest, 1985-88; dep. asst. sec. legis. affairs U.S. State Dept., 1988-89; def. atty. Peterson, Farris, Doores & Jones, Amarillo, Tex., 1989—; mem. 104th Congress from 13th Tex. dist., 1995—; family rancher. Mem. Tex. and Southwestern Cattle Raisers Assn. Republican. Office: US House Reps 1535 Longworth House Office Bldg Washington DC 20515-4313

THORNBURG, FREDERICK FLETCHER, diversified business executive, lawyer; b. South Bend, Ind., Feb. 10, 1940; s. James F. and Margaret R. (Major) T.; children: James Brian, Charles Kevin, Christian Sean, Christopher Herndon; m. Patricia J. Malloy, Oct. 4, 1981. AB, DePauw U., 1963; postgrad., U. Notre Dame, 1965; JD magna cum laude, Ind. U., 1968. Bar: Ind. 1968, U.S. Tax Ct. 1970, U.S. Ct. Appeals (7th cir.) 1970, U.S. Supreme Ct. 1971. Tchr., coach U.S. Peace Corps, Colombia, 1963-65; law clk. to chief judge U.S. Ct. Appeals (7th cir.), 1968-69; assoc. Thornburg, McGill, Deahl, Harman, Carey & Murray, South Bend, 1969-75, ptnr., 1975-80; v.p. systems and svcs. group The Wackenhut Corp., Coral Gables, Fla., 1981-82, sr. v.p. adminstrn., 1982-86, exec. v.p. 1986-88, also bd. dirs.; pres. Wackenhut Internat. Corp. and Wackenhut Svcs., Inc.; v.p. and legal counsel St. Thomas U., 1988-90, adj. prof. law, 1989-90; pres., CEO PropServ, Inc., 1991-94; cons. Ideas N Motion, Inc., Musselman Steel Corp., Private Freezer Corp., Am. Tel Corp.; legal & mgmt. cons., mem. bd. advisors, Publix Supermarkets, Inc., St. Thomas U.; bd. dirs. Doral Oaks Inc. Assocs.; trustee U. Community Hosp. Found., 1991-94; adj. prof. bus. St. Mary's Coll., 1975-78; vis. prof. CTA, 1985—; vice-chmn., pvt. sec. adv. coun. Fla. Sec. of State, 1985-90. Assoc. editor in chief: New Law Jour., 1967-68; contbr. articles to legal and bus. jours. Bd. dirs. YMCA, Channel 34, Symphony Orch. Assn. Fulbright selectee, Halleck scholar. Mem. ABA, Ind. Bar Assn., greater Miami C. of C. (former corp. rep. trustee), City Club of Miami, Carrollwood Country Club, Doral Park Country Club, Rotary, Order of Coif, Phi Delta Phi, Alpha Delta Sigma.

THORNBURG, LACY HERMAN, judge; b. Charlotte, N.C., Dec. 20, 1929; s. Jesse Lafayette and Sarah Ann (Ziegler) T.; m. Dorothy Todd, Sept. 6, 1953; children—Sara Thornburg Evans, Lacy Eugene, Jesse Todd, Alan Ziegler. A.A., Mars Hill Coll., 1950; B.A., U. N.C., 1951, J.D., 1954. Bar: U.S. Dist. Ct. (we. dist.) N.C. Practiced law Webster, N.C., 1954-67; superior ct. judge State of N.C., 1967-83; atty. gen State of N.C., Raleigh, 1985-92; emergency judge N.C. Superior Ct., Webster, N.C., 1993-94; mem. Nat. Indian Gaming Commn., 1994-95; judge N.C. western dist. U.S. Dist. Ct., 1995—; mem. staff Congressman Taylor, Sylva, N.C., 1960, Congressman David Hall, Sylva, 1959-60; mem. N.C. Ho. of Reps., 1961-65; mem. N.C. Cts. Commn., N.C. Criminal Code Commn., Capital Planning Commn., Raleigh; chmn. Law Enforcement Coordinating Com., Raleigh, 1985—. Chmn. Jackson County Bd. of Health, Sylva, 1965-84; commr. Tryon Palace, New Bern, N.C. Served with U.S. Army, 1947-48. Mem. Lions, Masons, Shriners. Democrat. Avocations: fly fishing, skeet shooting.

THORNBURGH, DICK (RICHARD L. THORNBURGH), lawyer, former United Nations official, former U.S. attorney general, former governor; b. Pitts., July 16, 1932; s. Charles Garland and Alice (Sanborn) T.; m. Virginia Walton Judson, Oct. 12, 1963; children: John, David, Peter, William. B in Engring., Yale, 1954; LLB, U. Pitts., 1957; hon. degrees, from 30 colls. and univs. Bar: Pa. 1958, U.S. Supreme Ct. 1965. Atty. Kirkpatrick & Lockhart, Pitts., 1959-69, 77-79, 87-88, 91-92, 94—; U.S. atty. for Western Pa. Pitts., 1969-75; asst. atty. gen. criminal divsn. Dept. Justice, Washington, 1975-77; gov. State of Pa., Harrisburg, 1979-87; dir. Inst. Politics, John F. Kennedy Sch. Govt., Harvard U., 1987-88; U.S. atty. gen. Washington, 1988-91; under-sec.-gen. for adminstrn. and mgmt. UN, N.Y.C., 1992-93; del. Pa. Constl. Conv., 1967-68. Mem. Coun. on Fgn. Rels. Fellow Am. Bar Found.; mem. Am. Judicature Soc., Nat. Acad. Pub. Adminstrn. Republican. Office: Kirkpatrick & Lockhart South Lobby 9th Fl 1800 M St NW Washington DC 20036-5891

THORNBURY, JOHN ROUSSEAU, radiologist, physician; b. Cleve., Mar. 16, 1929; s. Purla Lee and Gertrude (Glidden) T.; m. Julia Lee McGregor, Mar. 20, 1955; children: Lee Allison, John McGregor. A.B. cum laude, Miami U., Oxford, Ohio, 1950; M.D., Ohio State U., 1955. Diplomate: Am. Bd. Radiology. Intern Hurley Hosp., Flint, Mich., 1955-56; resident U. Iowa Hosps., Iowa City, 1958-61; intern, asst. prof. radiology U. Colo. Med. Center, Denver, 1962-63; practice medicine specializing in radiology Denver, 1962-63, Iowa City, 1963-66, Seattle, 1966-68, Ann Arbor, Mich., 1968-79, Albuquerque, 1979-84, Rochester, N.Y., 1984-89, Madison, Wis., 1989-94; mem. staff U. Wisconsin Hosp., Madison, prof. radiology, chief sect. of body imaging, Med. Sch., 1989-94, prof. emeritus, 1994—; asst. prof. radiology U. Iowa Hosps., 1963-66, U. Wash. Hosp., Seattle, 1966-68; assoc. prof. radiology U. Mich. Med. Ctr., 1968-71, prof. radiology, 1971-79; prof. radiology, chief divsn. diagnostic radiology dept. radiology Sch. Medicine, U. N.Mex., 1979-84; prof. radiology U. Rochester Sch. Medicine, 1984-89, acting chmn., 1985-87; chmn. sci. com. on efficacy studies Nat. Coun. on Radiation Protection, 1980-95; rapporteur/mem. sci. group on indications/limitations of x-ray diagnostic procedures WHO, 1983; cons. com. on efficacy of magnetic resonance nat. health tech. adv. panel Australian Inst. Health, 1986; invited U.S. cons. MRI program, Nijmegen, The Netherlands, 1992; lectr. in field; cons. tech. assessment and outcome rsch., 1994—; cons. to Am. Soc. of Neuroradiology, 1995-97. Co-author/cons. Clin. Efficacy Assessment Project, Am. Coll. Physicians, 1986-89; assoc. editor: Yearbook of Radiology, 1971-82; editorial bd.: Contemporary Diagnostic Radiology, 1977-84, Urologic Radiology, 1977-84. Served to capt., M.C. USAF, 1956-58. Grantee Agy. Health Care Policy and Rsch., 1986-91, U. Rochester, 1986-89, U. Wis., Madison, 1989-91. Fellow Am. Coll. Radiology; mem. Soc. Uroradiology (pres. 1976-79, dir. 1977-79), Assn. Univ. Radiologists (pres. 1980-81), Radiol. Soc. N.Am., Am. Roentgen Ray Soc. (Caldwell medal 1993), Wis. Radiol. Soc., Phi Beta Kappa, Delta Tau Delta, Omicron Delta Kappa, Phi Chi. Republican. Presbyterian. Address: 185 Morgan Pl Castle Rock CO 80104 Home: Castle Pines Village 185 Morgan Pl Castle Rock CO 80104

THORNDIKE, EDWARD HARMON, physicist; b. Pasadena, Calif., Aug. 2, 1934; s. Edward Moulton and Louise (Harmon) T.; m. Elizabeth H. Wenger, Sept. 8, 1955; children—Susan Lee, Patricia Lynn, Edward Harmon Jr. A.B., Wesleyan U., Middletown, Conn., 1956; M.S., Stanford U., 1957; Ph.D., Harvard U., 1960. Research fellow Harvard U., Cambridge, Mass., 1960-61; mem. faculty U. Rochester, N.Y., 1961—; assoc. prof. physics U. Rochester, 1965-72, prof., 1972—; dir. 130" Cyclotron Lab., 1965-69; vis. prof. U. Geneva, 1969-70; vis. scientist CERN, Geneva, 1970; mem. adv. coun. Ctr. Environ. Info. Rochester, 1974-93; mem. adv. com. Stanford Linear Accelerator Ctr. Exptl. Program, 1987-89; mem. Univs. Rsch. Assn. Inc.; mem. vis. com. for Fermilab, 1993-95. Author: Energy and Environment, a Primer for Scientists and Engineers, 1976; contbr. articles to profl. jours. NSF fellow, 1970, Guggenheim fellow, 1987-88. Fellow Am. Phys. Soc. Office: U Rochester Dept Physics/Astronomy Rochester NY 14627

THORNDIKE, JOHN LOWELL, investment executive; b. Boston, Oct. 17, 1926; s. Augustus and Olivia (Lowell) T.; m. Dorothy Wood Dudley, Sept. 16, 1950; 1 child, John Amory. BS, Harvard U., 1949. Registered rep Tucker Anthony & Co., Boston, 1950-57; v.p. Putnam Mgmt. Co., Boston, 1957-62; asst. to treas. Harvard U., Cambridge, Mass., 1962-66; v.p. Fiduciary Trust Co., Boston, 1966-92, also bd. dirs.; dir. Fiduciary Co. Inc., 1984—; trustee Provident Instn. for Savs., Boston, 1965-85; trustee, ptnr. Eaton Vance Mut. Funds, Boston, 1987-97. Trustee Boston Symphony Orch., 1960-80, treas., 1965-77 v.p., 1977-80; trustee Brigham and Women's Hosp., 1982-87, Cotting Sch., treas., 1982—; mem. warrant com. Town of Dover, Mass., 1966-69, chmn., 1968-69, town moderator, 1971-75; mem. Mass. Health and Ednl. Facilities Authority, Boston, 1970-88, sec., 1972-84, chmn., 1984-87; mem. cemetery commn. Town of Dover, 1992—; bd. dirs. Mass. Audubon Soc., 1971-89, chmn., 1984-89. With Army Air Corps, 1945. Recipient 1st prize Assn. Town Fin. Coms., 1969. Mem. Boston Security Analyst Soc., Boston Econ. Club, Union Club of Boston (pres. 1978-79), Harvard Club of Boston (pres. 1980-83), Harvard Mus. Assn.

(pres. 1988-91). Republican. Episcopalian. Avocations: tennis, bird watching. Home: 10 Main St Dover MA 02030-2022 Office: Fiduciary Trust Co 175 Federal St Boston MA 02110-2222

THORNDIKE, JOSEPH JACOBS, JR., editor; b. Peabody, Mass., July 29, 1913; s. Joseph Jacobs and Susan Ellison (Farnham) T.; m. Virginia Lemont, Sept. 7, 1940; children—John, Alan; m. Margery Darrell, Oct. 3, 1963; 1 son, Joseph Jacobs III. A.B., Harvard, 1934. Asst. editor Time Mag., 1934-36; assoc. editor Life Mag., 1936-46; mng. editor Life, 1946-49; pres. Thorndike, Jensen & Parton, Inc.; co-founder, contbg. editor Am. Heritage Pub. Co. Author: The Very Rich, 1976, The Magnificent Builders, 1978, The Coast, 1993; editor: Seafaring America, 1974, Mysteries of the Past, 1977, Discovery of Lost Worlds, 1979, Mysteries of the Deep, 1980, Three Centuries of American Architects, 1981. Unitarian. Club: Harvard (N.Y.C.). Home: 34 Oak St Harwich MA 02645-2703

THORNDIKE, RICHARD KING, former brokerage company executive; b. Millis, Mass., 1913; s. Richard King and Florence A. (Macy) T.; m. Lucy Saltonstall Rantoul, Sept. 21, 1935 (dec. May 1958); children: Richard III, Rose, Sylvia; m. Mercy Bours Archibald, Oct. 1, 1960. Grad., Harvard, 1935. With F.S. Moseley & Co., Boston, 1935—; asst. analyst F.S. Moseley & Co., 1937-46, partner, 1947-73; v.p. Moseley, Hallgarten, Estabrook & Weeden Inc., 1973-83. Republican. Episcopalian. Clubs: Myopia (Hamilton, Mass.); Ponte Ve dra Inn and Club; Phoenix-SK (Harvard), Lenox (Lenox, Mass.). Home: Apt F-206 1000 Vicars Landing Way Ponte Vedra Beach FL 32082-3118

THORNDYKE, LLOYD MILTON, computer company executive; b. Edgerton, Minn., May 28, 1927; s. W. Keith and Grace A. Thorndyke; m. Jo Ann M. Thompson, July 23, 1949; children: Lloyd, Keith. BS in Physics, Hamline U., St. Paul, 1950. Engr. AB McMahon Co., St. Paul, 1950-54; engr., mgr. Sperry Univac Co., St. Paul, 1954-60; mgr., v.p., chief engr. peripheral equipment MPI, 1960-75; sr. v.p. computer sys. Control Data Corp., 1975-77, sr. v.p. rsch. and supercomputers, 1977-83; chmn., pres., CEO ETA Sys. Inc., 1983-88, chmn., 1988-89; chmn., CEO DataMax Inc., 1989-94; sr. technologist Recyclights, Bloomington, Minn., 1994—. Trustee Hamline U. With USNR, 1945-46. Mem. IEEE, Am. Assn. Engring. Socs. (Chmn. award 1988), Air Force Assn., Am. Legion. Methodist. Office: 401 E 86th St Bloomington MN 55420

THORNE, BARBARA LOCKWOOD, guidance counselor, secondary education educator; b. Rochester, N.Y., Nov. 12, 1938; d. Harvey J. and Clara (Lee) Lockwood; m. Marc E. Thorne, July 21, 1962; children: John, Andrew. BA, Westminster Coll., 1960; MEd, Cornell U., 1961; MS, U. Bridgeport, 1987, 6th Yr. Cert., 1991. Cert. tchr., N.Y., counselor, Conn. Tchr. social studies Greece Olympia High Sch., Rochester, N.Y., 1961-63, East High Sch., Rochester, 1963-64; tchr. recreation Fairfield (Conn.) YMCA, 1965-70; tutor, substitute tchr. Needham (Mass.) Alternate High Sch., 1970-78; tchr. social studies Alternate Learning Program Darien (Conn.) High Sch., 1978-88, team leader, 1982-88, guidance counselor, 1988—, coord. student assistance team, 1991—; locat advisor A Better Chance, Darien, 1989—. Chmn. Youth Commn., Darien, 1982-85, Park and Recreation Commn., Darien, 1985—, chmn., 1991-95; vol. soup kitchen Salvation Army, Stamford, Conn., 1988-90. Recipient Vol. Svc. award Community Coun. Darien, 1977. Mem. ASCD, NEA, LWV (pres., bd. dirs. 1975-85, Sears Found. award 1963, Vol. in Govt. award 1993), Assn. Secondary Sch. Adminstrn., Am. Assn. Counseling and Devel., Nat. Coun. Social Studies, Jr. League Stamford/Norwalk. Democrat. Congregationalist. Avocations: reading, tennis, cross-country skiing.

THORNE, FRANCIS, composer; b. Bay Shore, N.Y., June 23, 1922; s. Francis Burritt and Hildegarde (Kobbé) T.; m. Ann Cobb, Dec. 9, 1942; children: Ann Boughton (Mrs. William F. Niles), Wendy Oakleigh (Mrs. William H. Forsyth, Jr.), Candace Kobbé (Mrs. Anthony M. Canton). B.A. in Music Theory, Yale, 1942. Founder, pres. Thorne Music Fund, Inc., 1965-75; pub. Edward B. Marks Music Corp., 1963—, Gen. Music Pub. Co., 1971—, G. Schirmer/AMP, 1985—, Theodore Presser Co., 1989—; exec. dir. Lenox Arts Center, 1972-76, Am. Composers Alliance, 1975-85; co-founder, pres. Am. Composers Orch., 1976—. Composer: Elegy for Orch., 1964, Burlesque Overture, 1966, Lyric Variations for Orch., 1967, Symphony No. 1, 1963, No. II, 1966, No. III, 1970, No. IV, 1977, Fortuna, 1961-62, Liebesrock, 1969, Sonar Plexus, 1969, Six Set-Pieces, 1969, Contra Band Music, 1970, Antiphonies, 1970, Simultaneities, 1971, Quartessence, 1971, Fanfare, Fugue and Funk, 1972, Lyric Variations II, 1972, Piano Sonata, 1972, Lyric Variations III, 1973, Cantata Sauce, 1973, Evensongs, 1973, Cello Concerto, 1974, Piano Concerto, 1974, Violin Concerto, 1975, String Quartet 1, 1960, 2, 1967, 3, 1976, 4, 1983, Spoon River Overture, 1976, Grand Duo, 1976, Five Set Pieces, 1976, Love's Variations, 1976, Pop Partita, 1978, The Eternal Light for Soprano and Orchestra, 1979, Divertimento for Flute, Strings and Percussion, 1979, Lyric Variations IV for Solo Violin, 1980, Divertimento 2 for Bassoon and Stringed Instruments, 1980, Eine Kleine Meyermusik, 1980, Gems From Spoon River, 1980, Lyric Variations No. 6 for solo clarinet, 1981, Divertimento No. 3, 1982, Praise and Thanksgiving, 1983, Lyric Variations No. 5 for Orch., 1980-81, Symphony No. 5, 1984, Concerto Concertante, 1985, Rhapsodic Variations, No. 2, 1985, Humoresque for Orch., 1985, Rhapsodic Variations No. 3 for Oboe and Strings, 1986, The Affirming Flame for Soprano and Chamber Ensemble, 1987; seven simple syncopations for Piano solo, 1987, Rhapsodic Variations No. 4 for Viol Solo, 1987, Rhapsodic Variations No. 5 for Violins and Piano, 1988, Money Matters for Tenor and Chamber Ensemble, 1988, Piano Concerto No. 3, 1989, Remembering Dizzy for Brass Quintet, 1990, Pop Partita No. 2 for woodwinds and strings, 1991, Mario and The Magician, opera after Thomas Mann, in Prologue and 1 Act, 1991, Symphony No. 6 for Strings, 1992, Symphony No. 7 Along the Hudson for chorus and orch., 1994; recs. on Composers' Recs., Inc., Serenus, Owl, Louisville Opus One and New World; founder, pres. Am. Composers Orch., 1976. Trustee Am. Symphony Orchestra League, Manhattan Sch. Music, Am. Music Center, MacDowell Colony, Walter W. Naumburg Found., Contemporary Music Soc., Theater Devel. Fund, Group for Contemporary Music., Am. Brass Quintet. Served to lt. USNR, 1942-45. Nat. Endowment Arts grantee, 1966, 73; fellow, 1976, 79; Nat. Inst. Arts and Letters grantee, 1968; N.Y. State Arts Council ballet commn., 1973. Mem. Contemporary Music Soc. (dir.) Broadcast Music, Inc., Am. Composers Alliance, League of Composers, Am. Acad. Inst. Arts and Letters. Club: Century Assn. (N.Y.C.). Home: 116 E 66th St New York NY 10021-6547 *Having spent ten years as a businessman, I have been privileged to serve my composer colleagues as an administrator for musical organizations. The practical experience has also served me well as a creative artist in having instilled the virtues of discipline. Serving music as composer and administrator gives the highest sense of satisfaction, from participating in this life-giving world in a total comprehensive way.*

THORNE, JOHN REINECKE, business educator, venture capitalist; b. Pitts., Mar. 25, 1926; s. John Mueller and Louise (Reinecke) T.; m. Barbara Siebert, Aug. 31, 1951 (dec. Feb. 1995); children: John S., Barbara L., Richard W. BS, Brown U., 1947; MSEE, U. Pitts., 1949; MS in Indsl. Adminstrn., Carnegie Mellon U., 1952. Devel. engr. Westinghouse Elec. Corp., Pitts., 1947-50; mgr. fin. analysis Hughes Aircraft Co., L.A., 1952-54; dir. computer systems lab. Litton Industries, L.A., 1954-61; chmn., pres. The Scionics Corp., L.A., 1961-69; cons., L.A., 1969-72; prof. bus. Carnegie-Mellon U., Pitts., 1972—, Morgenthaler prof. entrepreneurship, 1987—, dir. Donald H. Jones Ctr. for Entrepreneurship, 1990—; founder, chmn. Enterprise Corp. Pitts., 1983—; gen. ptnr. Pitts. Seed Fund, 1985—; bd. dirs. Orion Capital Corp., Medrad, Inc., other pvt. corps. Contbr. numerous articles on entrepreneurship to profl. jours. Named Fin. Svcs. Adv. of Yr. by SBA, 1988. Mem. Duquesne Club, Rolling Rock Club, University Club. Unitarian. Home: Furnace Run Laughlintown PA 15655 Office: Carnegie-Mellon U Schenley Park Pittsburgh PA 15213

THORNE, JOHN WATSON, III, advertising and marketing executive; b. Washington, Jan. 16, 1934; s. John Watson, Jr. and Mary Washington (Tucker) T.; m. Joan Kramer Vail, Mar. 2, 1957; children: Vail Tucker, Tracy Tucker, John Watson, IV. BA in Polit. Sci., George Washington U., 1955; MA in Sociology, New Sch. Social Research, 1957. Asst. account exec. Young & Rubicam, Inc., N.Y.C., 1957-59; advt. mgr. Gen. Electric Co., Decatur, Ill., 1959-63; dir. advt. promotion Brand Names Found.,

N.Y.C., 1963-66; account exec. Tatham-Laird & Kudner (advt.), N.Y.C., 1966-67; v.p., mgmt. supr. Wells, Rich, Greene, Inc., N.Y.C., 1973-76; v.p., account supr. Batten, Barton, Durstine & Osborn, Inc., N.Y.C., 1967-73, sr. v.p., mgmt. supr., 1976-81, exec. v.p., 1981-87, also dir.; mem. operating com.; chmn., CEO Thorne & Assocs., N.Y.C., 1987—; pres. Telerx Mktg., Spring House, Pa., 1991-95; mem. bus. program com. Proprietary Assn. Washington, 1984-85; adj. prof. advt. Syracuse (N.Y.) U. Pres. Hastings-on-Hudson (N.Y.) Bd. Edn.; bd. dirs. Young Concert Artists, N.Y.C.; mem. communications coms. Nat. Urban League, Carnegie Hall. Served as 1st lt. USMCR, 1955-57. Mem. Buckingham Racquet Club. Republican. Roman Catholic. Home: 100 Stoney Brook Rd Newtown PA 18940 Office: Thorne & Assocs 336 E 50th St New York NY 10022

THORNE, JOYE HOLLEY, special education administrator; b. Shreveport, La., Jan. 4, 1933; d. Lockett Beecher and A. Irene (McWilliams) Holley; m. Michael S. Thorne, July 24, 1953; 1 child, Michael S. Jr. BS, Centenary Coll., 1954; MEd, U. Houston, 1969, EdD, 1974. Cert. tchr., Tex. Tchr. Aldine Ind. Sch. Dist., Houston, 1959-66, curriculum cons., 1966-69, dir. spl. edn., 1969—; adj. prof. U. Houston, Clear Lake, Tex., 1974-83; spl. edn. specialist Dept. Def. Dependent Schs., Washington, 1983-84. Recipient Pres.'s award Gulf Coast chpt. Coun. Exceptional Children, Austin, Tex., 1980. Mem. Coun. Exceptional Children (pres. Gulf Coast chpt. 1976-77, pres. Tex. fedn. 1982-83, Pres.'s award 1980), Tex. Coun. Adminstrs. Spl. Edn. (pres. 1985-86, Dir. of Yr. award 1993). Republican. Methodist. Avocations: needlework, quilting, travel. Office: Aldine Ind Sch Dist 1617 Lauder Rd Houston TX 77039-3096

THORNE, KIP STEPHEN, physicist, educator; b. Logan, Utah, June 1, 1940; s. David Wynne and Alison (Comish) T.; m. Linda Jeanne Peterson, Sept. 12, 1960 (div. 1977); children: Kares Anne, Bret Carter; m. Carolee Joyce Winstein, July 7, 1984. B.S. in Physics, Calif. Inst. Tech., 1962; A.M. in Physics (Woodrow Wilson fellow, Danforth Found. fellow), Princeton U., 1963, Ph.D. in Physics (Danforth Found. fellow, NSF fellow), 1965, postgrad. (NSF postdoctoral fellow), 1965-66; D.Sc. (hon.), Ill. Coll., 1979; Dr.h.c., Moscow U., 1981. Research fellow Calif. Inst. Tech., 1966-67, assoc. prof. theoretical physics, 1967-70, prof., 1970—, William R. Kenan, Jr. prof., 1981-91, Feynman prof. theoretical physics, 1991—; Fulbright lectr., France, 1966; vis. assoc. prof. U. Chgo. 1968; vis. prof. Moscow U., 1969, 75, 78, 82, 83, 86, 88, 90; vis. sr. rsch. assoc. Cornell U., 1977, A.D. White prof.-at-large, 1986-87; adj. prof. U. Utah, 1971; mem. Internat. Com. on Gen. Relativity and Gravitation, 1971-80, 92—, Com. on U.S.-USSR Coop. in Physics, 1978-79, Space Sci. Bd., NASA, 1980-83. Co-author: Gravitation Theory and Gravitational Collapse, 1965, Gravitation, 1973, Black Holes: The Membrane Paradigm, 1986, Black Holes and Time Warps: Einstein's Outrageous Legacy, 1994. Alfred P. Sloan Found. Rsch. fellow, 1966-68; John Simon Guggenheim fellow, 1967; recipient Sci. Writing award in physics and astronomy Am. Inst. Physics, 1969, 94. Mem. Nat. Acad. Scis., Am. Acad. Arts and Scis., Am. Astron. Soc., Am. Phys. Soc., Internat. Astron. Union, AAAS, Sigma Xi, Tau Beta Pi. *

THORNE, OAKLEIGH BLAKEMAN, publishing company executive; b. Santa Barbara, Calif., 1932. BA, Harvard U., 1954. With First Nat. City Bank N.Y., 1954-62; chmn., dir. Ct Corp. Systems; with Commerce Clearing House, Inc., Deerfield, Ill., 1959—; chmn., pres. legal info. Commerce Clearing House, Inc., Deerfield, 1975—. Office: Commerce Clearing House Inc 2700 Lake Cook Rd Deerfield IL 60015-3888 Office: CCH Computax Inc 21250 Hawthorne Blvd Torrance CA 90503*

THORNE, RICHARD MANSERGH, physicist; b. Birmingham, Eng., July 25, 1942; s. Robert George and Dorothy Lena (Goodchild) T.; children: Peter Baring, Michael Thomas. B.Sc., Birmingham U., 1963; Ph.D., M.I.T., 1968. Grad. asst. M.I.T., 1963-68; asst. prof. dept. atmospheric scis. UCLA, 1968-71, asso. prof., 1971-75, prof., 1975—, chmn. dept., 1976-79; vis. fellow St. Edmunds Coll., Cambridge (Eng.) U., 1986-87, 92; cons. Jet Propulsion Lab., Aerospace Corp. Contbr. articles to profl. jours. Recipient numerous grants NSF, NASA, NATO, Jet Propulsion Lab. Mem. Am. Geophys. Union. Home: 10390 Caribou Ln Los Angeles CA 90077-2809 Office: UCLA Dept Atmospheric Scis Los Angeles CA 90024

THORNELL, JACK RANDOLPH, photographer; b. Vicksburg, Miss., Aug. 29, 1939; s. Benjamin O. and Myrtice (Jones) T.; divorced; children—Candice, Jay Randolph. Ed. pub. schs. Photographer Jackson (Miss.) Daily News, 1960-64; with A.P., 1964—; assigned A.P., Dominican Republic, 1965, Selma, Ala., 1965; assigned Democratic Nat. Conv., 1968. Served with AUS, 1958-60. Recipient Pulitzer prize for news photography of shooting of James Meredith, 1967; Headliners Photography award, 1967. Home: 5236 Utica St Metairie LA 70006-6446 Office: 3800 Howard Ave New Orleans LA 70140-1097

THORNER, MICHAEL OLIVER, medical educator, research center administrator; b. Beaconsfield, Eng., Jan. 14, 1945; came to U.S. 1977; s. Hans and Ilse T.; m. Prudence Maria Ross, July 7, 1966; children—Benjamin Bruno, Anna Rosa. M.B.B.S., Middlesex Hosp., U. London, 1970. Intern, resident Middlesex Hosp., St. Bartholomew Hosp., London; lectr. in chem. pathology St. Bartholomews Hosp., London, 1974, research fellow, 1974-75, lectr. in medicine, 1977; assoc. prof. medicine U. Va., Charlottesville, 1977-82, prof. medicine, 1982—, head div. endocrinology and metabolism, 1986—, dir. Clin. Research Ctr., 1984—, assoc. dir. CRC, 1981-84, Kenneth R. Crispell prof. in internal medicine, 1990—; mem. FDA Endocrinologic and metabolic drugs adv. com., 1984-88, NIH biochem. endocrinology study sect., 1985-89. Contbr. articles to profl. jours. Recipient Albion O. Bernstein award, 1984; Virginia Scientist of Yr. award, 1985, Gen. Clin. Rsch. Ctrs. program award, 1995. Fellow Royal Coll. Physicians, ACP; mem. Soc. Endocrinology, Endocrine Soc. (Edwin B. Astwood award 1992), Assn. Am. Physicians, Am. Soc. Clin. Investigations. Home: Mount Ammonett RR 1 Box 487 North Garden VA 22959-9639 Office: U Va Hosps Dept Internal Medicine PO Box 511-66 Charlottesville VA 22908-0001

THORNER, PETER, retail executive; b. Bklyn., Oct. 7, 1943; s. Alice Cecily (Blei) Horelick; children: Brian Reid, Sarah Jill. BS in Econs., CUNY, Bklyn., 1965. Ptnr. Deloitte, Haskins & Sells, N.Y.C., 1978-82; sr. v.p., chief fin. officer Ogden Corp., N.Y.C., 1982-85; CFO, exec. v.p. Rapid-Am. Corp., N.Y.C., 1985-87, also bd. dirs.; mng. dir. Wheelabrator Techs., Inc., Hampton, N.H., 1987-90; CFO, exec. v.p. Ames Dept. Stores, Rocky Hill, Conn., 1990-92; pres. New Eng. Strategies, Weston, Conn., 1994—. Mem. AICPA, Internat. Mass Retailers Assn. (bd. dirs.), N.Y. State Soc. CPAs, N.Y. Econs. Club, Fin. Execs. Inst., Fairfield County Fish and Game Protecting Assn., Bristol Gun Club. Office: 8 Messex Ln Weston CT 06883-1932

THORNE-THOMSEN, THOMAS, lawyer; b. El Dorado, Kans., Oct. 22, 1949; s. Fletcher and Barbara (Macoubrey) T.-T. BA, Vanderbilt U., 1972; JD, U. Colo., 1976; LLM in Taxation, NYU, 1983. Bar: Colo. 1976, Ga. 1977, Ill. 1983. Law clk. to Chief Judge Alfred A. Arraj U.S. Dist. Ct. Colo., Boulder, 1976-77; assoc. Alston & Bird, Atlanta, 1977-82, Keck, Mahin & Cate, Chgo., 1983-95; ptnr. Schiff, Harden & Waite, Chgo., 1995—. Bd. dirs. Century Place Devel. Corp., Chgo., 1989—, Sutherland Neighborhood Devel. Corp., Chgo., 1989—, South Shore Neighborhood Devel. Corp., Chgo., 1990—, Argyle Neighborhood Devel. Corp., Chgo., 1991—, Howard Brown Health Ctr., Chgo., 1991-94; com. mem. Chgo's Comprehensive Housing Affordability Strategy, Chgo., 1992—; mem. bond leverage trust fund task force Ill. Housing Authority, 1993. Mem. ABA, Colo. State Bar Assn., Ill. State Bar Assn., Ga. State Bar Assn. Avocations: jogging, biking, swimming, boating. Home: 680 N Lake Shore Dr Apt 1110 Chicago IL 60611-4407 Office: Schiff Harden & Waite 7200 Sears Tower Chicago IL 60606-6473

THORNHILL, ARTHUR HORACE, JR., retired book publisher; b. Boston, Jan. 1, 1924; s. Arthur Horace and Mary Josephine (Pretersary) T.; m. Dorothy M. Matheis, Oct. 28, 1944; children: Sandra Susanne Thornhill Brushart, Arthur Horace. A.B. magna cum laude, Princeton U., 1948. With Little, Brown & Co., Inc., Boston, 1948-88; v.p. Little, Brown & Co., Inc., 1955-58, gen. mgr., 1960-87, chief exec. officer, pres., 1962-87, chmn. bd., 1970-87; chmn., pres. dir. Little, Brown & Co. (Can.), Ltd., 1955-84; v.p. Time, Inc., 1968-87; dir. Conrac Corp. 1971-87; mem. adv. council history dept. Princeton U., 1964-85; trustee, treas. Princeton U. Press, 1972-85; dir. Am. Textbook Pubs. Inst., 1965-68, Grosett & Dunlop, 1965-67, Bantam Books, Inc., 1965-67. Trustee Bennington Coll., 1969-76; fellow emeritus Ctr. for Creative Photography U. Ariz.; bd. dirs. Am. Book Pubs. Council, 1964-67. Served to 1st lt. USAAF, World War II. Decorated Air medal; recipient Princeton U. Press medal, 1985. Mem. Assn. Am. Pubs. (dir. 1978-81), Edgartown Yacht Club, Edgartown Reading Room (pres. 1990-92), Union Club (N.Y.C.), Princeton Club (N.Y.C.), Century Club (N.Y.C.), Publs. Lunch Club (N.Y.C.), PEN, Union Club (Boston), St. Botolph (Boston). Home: 50 S School St Portsmouth NH 03801-5258

THORNHILL, GABRIEL FELDER, III, securities company executive; b. N.Y.C., Mar. 14, 1928; s. Gabriel Felder Jr. and Weta Acker (Ingram) T.; m. Mary Elizabeth Vick, Feb. 26, 1960; children: Gabriel Felder IV, Elizabeth, Mary Ann. BBA, U. Tex., 1948; postgrad. in banking, U. Pa., 1962. Ptnr. Dewar Robertson & Pancoast, Austin, Tex., 1953-68; exec. v.p. Hornblower & Weeks, Austin, 1968-74, Rotan Mosle, Austin, 1974-80, Fin. Svcs. Austin, 1980-88; pres. Thornhill Securities, Austin, 1988—; exec. v.p. FSA Inc., Austin, 1980-89; pres. FSA Capital, Austin, 1982-84; bd. dirs. Austin Trust Co. Vestryman Good Shepherd Episcopal Ch., Austin, 1967-69, mem. endowment fund com., 1988—; treas. Laguna Gloria Art Mus., Austin, 1963, bd. dirs. 1962-64; treas. Child and Family Svc., Austin, 1965, v.p. 1966; chmn. pacesetter div. United Way, Austin, 1967; bd. dirs. Child Guidance Ctr., Austin, 1973-75; mem. Austin Urban Renewal Bd., 1978-82; bd. dirs. Austin History Ctr., 1987-93, v.p., 1989; trustee Westminster Manor, Austin, 1985—, vice chmn., 1989, chmn., 1994. Sgt. U.S. Army, 1950-52, Korea. Mem. Investment Bankers Am. (fin. com. 1954-57), Austin Investment Assn. (founder, bd. dirs. 1963-69, v.p. 1963, pres. 1964), Allegro Club, Headliners Club, Westwood Country Club, Adms. Club (chmn. 1975), Coronet Club (pres. 1969), Tarry House (bd. dirs., v.p. 1989, pres. 1990-92). Avocations: swimming, tennis, hunting, skiing. Home: 3233 Tarryhollow Dr Austin TX 78703-1638 Office: 100 Congress Ave Ste 790 Austin TX 78701-4042

THORNLEY, SHIRLEY BLUMBERG, architect; b. Cape Town, South Africa, Feb. 4, 1952; d. Alec and Anne (Minkowitz) Katz; m. Scott; 1 child, Charles R. Attended, U. Cape Town; BArch (with honors), U. Toronto, 1976. Assoc. Barton Myers Assoc., 1977-87; architect Kuwabara Payne McKenna Blumberg Architects; selected projects incl. Hazelton Townhouses Toronto, 1983, Unionville Library Markham, 1984, Hasbro Corp. H.Q. Phase One R.I., 1986; selected projects with present firm include Hasbro Corp. H.Q. Phase Two R.I., 1994, King James Place Toronto, 1991, The Desogn Exchange Toronto, 1994, Stauffer Library Interiors Queen's U., 1994, Min. Culture, Tourism & Recreation Niagara Falls, 1995. adj. asst. prof. U. Toronto, 1987, 90; guest critic Carleton U., U. Waterloo; mem. bd. dirs. Royal Arch. Inst. Can., 1990-93, mem. bd. trustees Ont. Sci. Ctr., 1988-91. Recipient Toronto Arts award for Architecture & Design, 1993, Gov. Gen's. award of Merit King James Place, 1992, Gov. Gen's. award for Architecture Royal Archtl. Inst. Can., 1992. Mem. Ont. Assn. Architects, Royal Arch. Inst. Can. Office: Kuwarbara Payne McKenna Blumberg, 322 King St W 3rd Fl, Toronto, ON Canada M5V 1J2

THORNTON, CHARLES VICTOR, metals executive; b. Salt Lake City, Feb. 8, 1915; s. Charles Victor and Winnie May (Fitts) T.; m. Margaret Louise Wiggins, Apr. 17, 1937; children: Charles Victor III, Carolyn Louise (Mrs. John J. Moorhouse), David Frank. BS in Civil Engring., U. Utah, 1935; HHD, Ind. Inst. Tech., 1972. Registered profl. engr., Ohio, Tex. Engr. Truscon Steel Co., Youngstown, Ohio, 1935-37; dist. engr. Truscon Steel Co., Washington, 1937-40; chief engr. So. Iron Works, Inc., Alexandria, Va., 1940-45; pres. Thornton Industries, Inc., Ft. Worth, 1945-75; chmn. bd. Thornton Industries, Inc., 1975-88; ptnr. TRANSOL Transp. Cons., 1993—; bd. dirs. Bank Commerce and Comml. Fin. Corp. Author: American Association of Private Railroad Car Owners Roster of Private R.R. Cars, 1991, Autobiography, 1993, Charlie, 1994, Winnie, 1994. Chmn. bd. Southview Corp., 1980—, chmn. emeritus Shriners Hosps. for Crippled Children; mem. nat. adv. coun. U. Utah, 1985—; chmn. investment com. Longhorn coun. Boy Scouts Am., 1985-88; v.p. campaign chmn. Ft. Worth Arts United, 1989; v.p. Tarrant County Arts Coun., 1989; pres. Tarrant County Water Bd., 1984-88; mem. policy com. Dallas-Ft. Worth Railtran, 1991—; pres. Ft. Worth chpt. Internat. Good Neighbor Coun., 1991-92. Recipient Salesman of Yr. award Ft. Worth Sales and Mktg. Execs., 1984, Good Neighbor of Yr. award Internat. Good Neighbor Coun., 1984, Merit of Honor award U. Utah, 1986; holder airplane speed record Dallas to Wichita, Kans., 1969. Mem. ASCE (life) (Tex. sect. Svc. to People award 1995), Tex. Assn. Bus. (life), Ft. Forth C. of C. (pres. 1960), Am. Assn. Pvt. R.R. Car Owners (pres. 1982-83), Fort Worth Club, City Club, Exch. Club of Fort Worth (past pres.), La Cima Club, Oxford Club, Grand Coun. (Fort Worth chpt. Confrerie Saint Etienne), Masons (33 degree s.w.r.), Shriners (past imperial potentate), Kiwanis (past pres.), Elks, Tau Beta Pi. Office: PO Box 136397 Fort Worth TX 76136-0397

THORNTON, CLARENCE GOULD, electronics engineering executive; b. Detroit, Aug. 3, 1925; s. Lorenzo C. and Violet (Gould) T.; m. Gloria Fuchs, June 18, 1949; children: Susan Carol, Richard Scott. BS, U. Mich., 1949, MS, 1950, PhD, 1952. Project engr. Sylvania Electric Co., Woburn, Mass., 1951-52; sect. head to dir. Semiconductor div. Philco Corp., Lansdale, Pa., 1952-60; dir. R&D Philco Corp., Blue Bell, Pa., 1960-72; dir. Electronics Technology and Devices Lab., U.S. Army, Fort Monmouth, N.J., 1972-92; directorate exec. Army Rsch. Lab., 1992-95; mem. Common. on Engring. and Tech. Systems Bd. on Army Sci. and Tech., Nat. Rsch. Coun., 1995—. Contbr. articles to profl. jours. Mem. Colts Neck Bd. Health, 1974-79. Served with USN, 1944-46. Recipient Local Svc. award Boy Scouts Am., 1963, Sci. Conf. award Dept. Army, 1976, Rsch. and Devel. Achievement award, 1976, Lab. of Yr. award, 1980, 83, 88, Lab. Excellence award, 1981, 85, 86, Sr. Exec. award, 1980-93, Gold medal Armed Forces Comms. and Electronics Assn., 1983, Handicapped Adv. Coun. award of achievement, 1985, Exceptional Civilian Svc. medal Dept. Army, 1985, Presdl. Rank award of Meritorious Svc., 1986, Presdl. Rank award of Disting. Sr. Exec., 1987, Crozier award, 1990, Superior Civilian Svc. medal, 1995, Exceptional Civilian Svc. medal, 1995. Fellow IEEE (Centennial medal 1994, Engring. Leadership Recognition award 1994, Joint Logistics Comdrs. award 1994); mem. AAAS, Electrochemical Soc., Am. Chem. Soc., Armed Forces Electronics Assn., Sr. Execs. Assn. (Exec. Achievement award 1994), Am. Defense Preparedness Assn., Alpha Chi Sigma, Phi Kappa Phi, Phi Lambda Upsilon. Mem. Reformed Ch. Patentee in field of electronics. Home: 28 Glenwood Rd Colts Neck NJ 07722-1015 Office: AMSRL-EP Fort Monmouth NJ 07703

THORNTON, D. WHITNEY, II, lawyer; b. Miami, Fla., Oct. 17, 1946; s. Dade Whitney and Hilda (Bryan) T.; m. Jane Collis, Nov. 27, 1971; children: Bryan Whitney, Elizabeth Jane, Virginia Anne. B.A., Washington and Lee U., 1968, J.D. 1970. Bar: Va. 1970, D.C. 1976, Calif. 1987, U.S. Ct. Appeals (4th cir.) 1978, U.S. Ct. Appeals (9th cir.) 1987, U.S. Sup. Ct. 1980, Calif. 1987, U.S. Ct. Appeals (9th cir.) 1987. Atty., Naval Air Systems Command, Dept. Navy, Washington, 1970-73; asst. counsel to comptroller Dept. Navy, 1973-74, asst. to gen. counsel, 1974-76; assoc. Sullivan & Beauregard, Washington, 1976-77; ptnr. 1977-81; ptnr. Bowman, Conner, Touhey & Thornton, Washington, 1981-83; pres. Continental Maritime Industries, Inc., San Francisco, 1983-87; ptnr. Dempsey, Bastianelli, Brown & Touhey, San Francisco, 1987-91; ptnr. Seyfarth, Shaw, Fairweather & Geraldson, San Francisco, 1992—. Mem. ABA (public contract law sect., chmn. suspension and debarment com. 1977), Fed. Bar Assn. (vice chmn. govt. contracts council; Disting. Service award 1981). Republican. Methodist. Club: Washington Golf and Country (Arlington, Va.). Contbr. articles to profl. jours. Office: Seyfarth Shaw Fairweather 101 California St Ste 2900 San Francisco CA 94111

THORNTON, DEAN DICKSON, retired airplane company executive; b. Yakima, Wash., Jan. 5, 1929; s. Dean Stoker and Elva Maud (Dickson) T.; m. Joan Madison, Aug. 25, 1956 (div. Apr. 1978); children—Steven, Jane Thornton; m. Mary Shultz, Nov. 25, 1981; children—Volney, Scott, Peter, Todd Richmond. B.S. in Bus., U. Idaho, 1952. C.P.A., Wash. Acct. Touche, Ross & Co., Seattle, 1954-63; treas., controller Boeing Co., Seattle, 1963-70; various exec. positions Boeing Co., 1974-85; pres. Boeing Comml. Airplane Co., 1985-94, retired, 1994; sr. v.p. Wyly Co., Dallas, 1970-74; bd. dirs. Seafirst Corp., Prin. Fin. Group, Flow Internat. Bd. dirs. YMCA, Seattle, 1966-68, Dir. Achievement, Seattle, 1966-68; chmn. Wash. Council on

Internat. Trade, Seattle, 1984-87. Served to 1st lt. USAF, 1952-54. Named to U. Idaho Alumni Hall of Fame. Mem. Phi Gamma Delta. Republican. Presbyterian. Clubs: Rainier, Seattle Tennis, Seattle Yacht, Conquistadores de Cielo. Avocations: skiing; sailing; fishing. Home: 1602 34th Ct W Seattle WA 98199-3906 Office: Boeing Co 7755 E Marginal Way PO Box 3707 Seattle WA 98124-2207

THORNTON, DOROTHY HABERLACH, artist, photographer; b. Tillamook, Oreg., May 20, 1913; d. Carl Emil and Amanda (Tinnerstet) Haberlach; m. Robert Y. Thornton, Mar. 13, 1937; 1 child, Thomas Wells. BA, U. Oreg., 1934; postgrad., George Washington U., 1936-37, Willamette U., 1940-60, U. Mich., 1943. Draftsman USN, Tillamook, 1942-43; pvt. practice Salem, Oreg., 1952—. Editor Jour. Watermark, 1988-91; photographer (books) Images of Oreg. Women, 1983, N.W. Originals, 1987 photographer for 5 TV documentaries on Japan; rsch. photographer Preventing Crime in America & Japan: A Comparative Study, 1992; exhibited in group show Oreg. Women Artists, 1993. Docent, bd. dirs. Fortland Art Mus., 1987—, mentor, 1991—; campaign chmn. Robert Thornton for State Atty. Gen., Oreg., 1952-67, Robert Thornton for Ct. Appeals Judge, Oreg., 1968-80; founder, mem. Mid Valley Art Commn., Salem Art Assn. Guides, Salem Assistance League; active Oreg. Commn. for Humanities; pres. Friends of Libr. Willamett U. Named Art Citizen of Yr., Oreg. Art Commn., 1991. Mem. AAUW (state pres., nat. bd. dirs., v.p. North Pacific Region States, nat. arts com. chmn. 1970-80, Nat. Endowment Rsch. grantee (hon.)), Photog. Soc. Am. (nat. chmn., pub. rels. com. 1985, hon. Assoc. Photo. Soc. of Am. degree), Arts Oreg. Coun. (bd. dirs., past state chmn.), Watercolor Soc. Oreg. (bd. dirs. 1991—), Oreg. UN Assn. (bd. dirs. 1980—, past state pres.), Ikebana Internat., Alpha Phi. Democrat. Episcopalian. Avocations: civic activities, art consulting, tour docent, photography, artist. Home: 2895 Alvarado Ter S Salem OR 97302-5433

THORNTON, GEORGE WHITELEY, investment company executive; b. York, Pa., Aug. 11, 1936; s. Henry Moser and Virginia (Whiteley) T.; m. Dianne Fay George, Sept. 9, 1961; children: Sandra Whiteley, William Foster. B.A., U. Va., 1958. Asst. to pres. mfg. Dentsply Internat., York, Pa., 1963-69, v.p. mfg., 1969-79, sr. v.p., 1979-85; pres., bd. dirs. Thornton Group Ltd., 1985—; chmn., chief exec. officer Thornton-White Inc., Charleston, S.C., 1986-92; bd. dirs. Dentsply Internat., York, Commonwealth Nat. Bank (York region). Bd. dirs. United Way, York County, 1974-76; exec. com. Nat. Alliance Businessman, York, 1972-73, chmn., York metro, 1974-75; bd. dirs. Pennsylvanians for Right to Work, 1979-81; bd. trustees Right to Work Def. and Edn. Found., 1979-81. Recipient Dirksen Meml. award Pennsylvanians for Right to work, 1979, Employer of Yr. award. Mem. Country Club of York (Pa.), Delta Phi. Republican. Presbyterian. Home: 1040 Box Hill Ln York PA 17403-4436

THORNTON, J. EDWARD, lawyer; b. Starkville, Miss., Nov. 25, 1907; s. Marmaduke Kimbrough and Annie (Knox) T.; m. Mary Belle Quinn. A.B., Miss. Coll., 1928; LL.B., Harvard, U., 1933. Bar: Ala. bar 1934, Mass. bar 1936. Asst. prosecutor Jefferson County, 1936-39; asst. gen. counsel Ala. Dept. Revenue, 1939-42; mem. firm Thornton & McGowin, Mobile, Mem. Spl. Supreme Ct. Ala., 1967-68, Ala. Ct. of Judiciary, 1984, 87, Jud. Conf. 5th Cir. U.S., 1951-78; mem. adv. com. on proposed new appellate rules Ala. Supreme Ct., 1972-74, mem. standing com. on appellate rules, 1974-80; chmn. sect. on practice and procedure Ala. State Bar, 1969-72, 73-75. Contbr. articles to prof. publs. Pres. Mobile Chamber Music Soc., 1972-73; adv. coun. home health svcs. Mobile County Bd. Health, 1969-74; Mem. Ala. Democratic Conv., 1950-54. Lt. comdr. USNR, 1942-45. Fellow Am. Bar Found.; mem. ABA (ho. dels., state del. for Ala. 1958-59), Ala. Bar Assn. (chmn. com. on jurisprudence and law reform 1951-63, pres. 1963-64), Mobile Bar Assn. (pres. 1955, founder, editor Mobile Bar Bull. 1966-91), Selden Soc., Am. Law Inst., Ala. Law Inst., Mobile Arts Coun. (pres. 1956), English Speaking Union (pres. Mobile 1960-61), Mobile Opera Guild (pres. 1963-65), Mobile C. of C., Scribes. Baptist. Clubs: Athelstan, Bienville (dir.), International Trade. Address: PO Box 23 Mobile AL 36601-0023

THORNTON, J. RONALD, university administrator; b. Fayetteville, Tenn., Aug. 19, 1939; s. James Alanda and Thelma White (McGee) T.; m. Mary Beth Packard, June 14, 1964 (div. Apr. 1975); 1 child, Nancy Carole; m. Martha Klemann, Jan. 23, 1976 (div. Apr. 1982); 1 child, Trey; m. Bernice McKinney, Feb. 14, 1986; 1 child, Paul Leon. BS in Physics & Math., Berry Coll., 1961; MA in Physics, Wake Forest Coll., 1964; postgrad., U. Ala., 1965-66, Rollins Coll., 1970. Research physicist Brown Engring. Co., Huntsville, Ala., 1963-66; sr. staff engr. Martin Marietta Corp., Orlando, Fla., 1966-75; dep. dir. NASA, Washington, 1976-77; exec. asst. Congressman Louis Frey, Jr., Orlando, 1978; pres. Tens Tec, Inc., Orlando, 1978-79; dir. So. Tech. Applications Ctr. U. Fla., Gainesville, 1979—; treas. bd. dirs. North Fla. Technology Innovation Corp., 1995—; mem. light wave tech. com. Fla. High Tech. and Indsl. Coun., Tallahassee, 1986-93, NASA Tech. Transfer Exec. Com., Washington, 1987—, Javits Fellowship Bd., Washington, 1986-91, Gov.'s New Product Award Com., Tallahassee, 1988—, Fla. K-12 Math., Sci. and Computer Sci. Edn. Quality Improvement Adv. Coun., 1989-92, Fla. Sci. Edn. Improvement Adv. Com., 1991-92; treas., bd. dirs. North Florida Tech. Innovation Corp., 1995. Pres. Orange County Young Rep. Club, Orlando, 1970-71; treas. Fla. Fedn. Young Reps., Orlando, 1971-72; chmn. Fla. Fedn. Young Reps., Orlando, 1972-74; pres. Gainesville Area Innovation Network, 1988-89. Named Engr. Exhibiting Tech. Excellence and Accomplishment cen. Fla. chpt. Fla. Engring. Soc., 1975, Achievement award NASA, 1977. Mem. IEEE, SME, Tech. Transfer Soc., Nat. Assn. Mgmt. and Tech. Assistance Ctrs. (bd. dirs. 1988, pres. 1992), Gainesville Area C. of C. Republican. Avocations: music, travel, reading. Home: 17829 NW 20th Ave Newberry FL 32669-9627 Office: U Fla So Tech Applications Ctr 1 Progress Blvd Box 24 Alachua FL 32615

THORNTON, JOHN IRVIN, forensic scientist, educator; b. Sacramento, Jan. 11, 1941; s. Lewis T. and Zilpha G. (Bowman) T.; m. Kim Stanchfield Wildman, May 22, 1976; children: Edward Lewis, Christian John, Chad Wildman, Reed Wildman. BS in Criminology, U. Calif., Berkeley, 1962; MS in Criminology, U. Calif., 1968, D of Criminology, 1974. Criminalist Contra Costa County (Calif.) Sheriff's Dept., Martinez, 1963-72, supervising criminalist, 1970-72, lab. dir., 1969-70; prof. forensic sci. U. Calif., Berkeley, 1982—; cons. Law Enforcement Assistance Administrn. U.S. Dept. Justice, 1974, 75, 78, Calif. Coun. on Criminal Justice, 1970-71, Am. Coun. on Edn., 1978, Internal Rev. Bur. Dept. Transp. and Pub. Facilities, State of Alaska, 1978; various police agys., pub. defender's offices and attys., 1972—; mem. project adv. com. Nationwide Crime Lab. Proficiency Testing Project, Forensic Sci. Found., 1979. Contr. numerous articles to jours. in forensic sci. Mem. Am. Acad. Forensic Scis. (chmn. criminalistics sect. 1979, mem. coun. 1979-80, Criminalistics Sect. award 1979), Am. Chem. Soc., Calif. Assn. Criminalists (pres. 1974-75, editorial sec. 1967-70, Disting. Mem. award 1989), Forensic Sci. Soc. Gt. Britain, Forensic Sci. Soc. India, Soc. of Friends, Sigma Xi. Home: 1093 Lokoya Rd Napa CA 94558-9714 Office: U Calif Dept Biomed Environ He Berkeley CA 94720

THORNTON, JOHN S., IV, bishop. Bishop Diocese of Idaho, Boise, 1990—. Office: Diocese of Idaho Box 936 510 W Washington St Boise ID 83702-5953

THORNTON, JOHN T., corporate financial executive; b. N.Y.C., Oct. 22, 1937; s. John T. and Catherine (Burke) T.; m. Patricia C. Robertson; children: Kevin, Brian, Vincent, Elizabeth, Monica. BBA, St. John's U., 1959, JD, 1972. Bar: N.Y.; CPA. Auditor Peat, Marwick, Mitchell & Co., N.Y.C., 1961-67; asst. controller Texasgulf Inc., Stamford, Conn., 1967-81, v.p., controller, 1981-84; sr. v.p., controller Norwest Corp., Mpls., 1984-87, exec. v.p., chief fin. officer, 1987—; bd. dirs. Exel., Ltd., Stock Exch. Listed Co. Office: Norwest Ctr 6th & Marquette Minneapolis MN 55479-1052

THORNTON, JOHN VINCENT, lawyer, educator; b. N.Y.C., Jan. 13, 1924; s. Thomas Francis and Elizabeth Rose (McCullough) T.; m. Edna Grace Lawson, June 28, 1952; children: John, Nancy, Sarah, Amy, Laura. BS, St. John's U., 1944; JD, Yale U., 1948; LLD (hon.), N.Y. Law Sch., 1969. Bar: N.Y. 1948. Assoc. in law Columbia U., 1948-49; assoc. Skadden Arps, 1949; law clk. to assoc. judge N.Y. Ct. of Appeals, 1950-52; ptnr. Whitman & Ransom, N.Y. Inc., 1952-69, of counsel, 1989-93; asst. gen. counsel Consol. Edison Co. N.Y. Inc., 1969, v.p., 1970-73, v.p., treas., 1973-76, sr. v.p. fin., 1976-79, exec. v.p. fin., 1979-80, sr. exec. v.p., 1980-84, vice

chmn., 1984-89; exec. v.p. Columbia U., N.Y.C., 1989-92; of counsel Whitman & Ransom, N.Y.C. 1989-93, Whitman, Breed, Abbott & Morgan, N.Y.C., 1993—; mem. bd. mgrs. Arden Conf. Ctr., 1989-92; treas. Empire State Electric Energy Research Corp., 1975-78; bd. dirs. Reid Hall, 1989-92; adj. prof. law NYU Sch. Law, 1949-66; Lubin lectr. Pace U., 1982; adj. prof. law, assoc. dean N.Y. Law Sch., 1964-69, v.p., 1969-73, chmn., 1973-85, hon. chmn., 1985—; asst. in econs. Yale U., 1946-48; instr. econs. Albertus Magnus Coll., 1946-48; assoc. dir. USPHS Study on Heart Disease and the Law, 1958-61; counsel judiciary com. N.Y. State Constl. Conv., 1967; mem. Bd. Edn., Bronxville, N.Y., 1970-76, pres. bd., 1972-74. Contbg. editor: Ann. Survey of Am. Law, 1950-60, Ann. Survey of N.Y. Law, 1950-60, Jour. Occupational Medicine, 1964-67, Pub. Utilities Fortnightly, 1969-89. Bd. dirs., sec. Hall of Sci. N.Y.C., 1968-76; trustee Pace U., N.Y. Bot. Garden; vice chmn. Lawrence Hosp., 1990-93, trustee, 1990—; Arden Conf. Ctr., 1989-92, N.Y.C. Citizen's Budget Commn., 1980-89, com. and fund for modern cts., 1983-88; bd. visitors City Coll. of CUNY, 1976-82; mem. bd. advisers Dickinson Coll., chmn., 1979-81, trustee, 1979-89; mem. pres.'s adv. coun. NYU Sch. Social Work, 1969-75; mem. Can.-Am. 1980-85. Lt. (j.g.) USNR, 1944-46, PTO. Mem. Order of Coif, Phi Delta Phi. Home: 55 Prescott Ave Bronxville NY 10708-1717 Office: Whitman Breed Abbott & Morgan 200 Park Ave New York NY 10166

THORNTON, JOSEPH SCOTT, research institute executive, materials scientist; b. Sewickley, Pa., Feb. 6, 1936; s. Joseph Scott and Evelyn (Miller) T.; divorced; children: Joseph Scott III, Chris P. BSME, U. Tex., 1957, PhD, 1969; MSMetE, Carnegie Mellon U., 1962. Engr. Walworth Valve Co., Boston, 1958; metall. engr. Westinghouse Astronuclear Lab., Large, Pa., 1962-64; instr., teaching assoc. U. Tex., Austin, 1964-67; group leader Tracor Inc., Austin, 1967-69, dept. dir., 1973-75; dept. mgr. Horizons Rsch., Inc., Cleve., 1969-73; chmn., chief exec. officer Tex. Rsch. Internat., Inc. (formerly Tex. Rsch. Inst., Inc.), Austin, 1975—. Contbr. numerous tech. papers to profl. publs.; editor: WANL Materials Manual, 2 vols., 1964; patentee in field. Fellow Alcoa, Austin, 1964, RC Baker Found., 1967. Mem. ASME, ASTM, Am. Soc. Metals Internat. (exec. com. 1965-66), Adhesion Soc. Office: Tex Rsch Internat Inc 9063 Bee Caves Rd Austin TX 78733-6201

THORNTON, JUDITH ANN, economist; b. Kansas City, Mo., Oct. 17, 1935; s. Tom and Helene (Burnson) G.; m. Gerald E. Gettel, May 6, 1978. B.A., Vassar Coll., 1956; M.A., Radcliffe Coll., 1958, Ph.D., 1960. Mem. faculty U. Wash., Seattle, 1961—; prof. econs. U. Wash., 1972—. Author: Economic Analysis of the Soviet-Type System, 1976, (with M. Cave A. McAuley) New Trends in Soviet Economics, 1981. Recipient grants Ford Found., 1975-77, grants Am. Council Learned Socs., 1976, grants NSF, 1977-79, grants Nat. Council Soviet and East European Reserach, 1980-81. Mem. Am. Econ. Assn., Am. Assn. Advancement Slavic Studies, Econometric Soc. Home: 3338 43d Ave NE Seattle WA 98105 Office: Dept Econs U Wash Seattle WA 98105

THORNTON, LARRY LEE, psychotherapist, author, educator; b. Lake, Miss., Nov. 9, 1937; s. Harvey L. and Onzell (Goodson) T.; children: Matt Alan, Leigh Ann. BA, Miss. Coll., 1959; MDiv, New Orleans Bapt. Theol. Sem., 1963, MRE, 1964; MS, U. So. Miss., 1966, PhD, 1969; postgrad., Harvard U., 1985. Dir. admissions Miss. Coll., Clinton, 1961; sr. prof. psychology Delta State U., Cleveland, Miss., 1968—; founder, dir. Lic. Profl. Counseling, Assocs., Cleveland, 1988—; chmn. Miss. Bd. Lic. Profl. Counselors, 1992-93. Author: Insights into Human Development, 1978. Charter mem. Internat. Devel. Coun., Bapt. Theol. Sem., Rüschlikon, Zurich, Switzerland, 1992. Recipient Panhellenic Outstanding Faculty award, 1995, S.E. Rossman Outstanding Tchr. award, 1991. Mem. APA, ACA. Avocations: golf, tennis, jogging. Home: PO Box 11 104 S 4th Ave Cleveland MS 38732

THORNTON, MAURICE, university administrator; b. Birmingham, Ala., Dec. 31, 1930; s. William Cullen and Alberta (Jones) T.; m. Elizabeth Ann McDonald, Apr. 15, 1961; children: Karen, Susan, Christopher. BS, Ala. State U., 1952; MEd, Cleve. State U., 1973; EdD, Nova U., 1981. Investigative caseworker, supr. title V Cuyahoga County Welfare Dept., Cleve., 1958-67, coord. neighborhood youth corps, asst. dir. pers. dept., 1958-67; equal employment officer, minority recruiter Cuyahoga C.C., Cleve., 1967-82, dir. equal opportunity, 1967-82; dir. affirmative action compliance SUNY, Albany, 1982—; dir. affirmative action program SUNY-Central, Albany, 1982—; sec. Capital Dist. Human Rights Adv. Com., Albany; N.Y. mid-Hudson coord. Am. Assn. Affirmative Action Officers, Albany; univ. coord. Capital Dist. Black and Puerto Rican Caucus, Albany; participant Leadership Devel. Program, Cleve. and Albany. Contbr. articles to profl. jours. Active NAACP; fundraiser United Negro Coll. Fund., Albany and Cleve., loaned exec. program United Way, Albany and Cleve.; exec. adv. bd. Boy Scouts Am. Scholar State of Ala., State of Ohio. Mem. VA 369th 100 Black Men (charter), Omega Psi Phi, Sigma Pi Phi (charter). Avocations: walking, reading, golf, traveling, history buff. Home: 7 Keith Rd Delmar NY 12054-4006 Office: SUNY State University Plz Albany NY 12246

THORNTON, RAY, congressman; b. Conway, AR, July 16, 1928; s. R.H. and Wilma (Stephens) T.; m. Betty Jo Mann, Jan. 27, 1956; children: Nancy, Mary Jo, Stephanie. B.A., Yale, 1950; J.D., U. Ark., 1956. Bar: Ark. 1956, U.S. Supreme Ct 1956. Pvt. practice in Sheridan and Little Rock, 1956-70; atty. gen. Ark., 1971-73; mem. 93d-95th Congresses from 4th Ark. dist.; exec. dir. Quachita Bapt. U./Henderson State U. Joint Ednl. Consortium, Arkadelphia, Ark., 1979-80; pres. Ark State U., Jonesboro and Beebe, 1980-84, U. Ark. System, Fayetteville, Little Rock, Pine Bluff, Monticello, 1984-89; mem. 102nd-103rd Congresses from 2d Ark. dist., 1991—; chmn. Ark. Bd. Law Examiners, 1967-70; Del. 7th Ark. Constl. Conv., 1969-70. Chmn. pres.'s devel. council Harding Coll., Searcy, Ark., 1971-73. Served with USN, 1951-54, Korea. Mem. AAAS (chmn. com. on sci. engring. and public policy 1980). Office: US Ho of Reps 1214 Longworth House Office Bldg Washington DC 20515

THORNTON, ROBERT ALAN, JR., state legislator, lawyer; b. Dover, Del., July 13, 1948; s. Robert Alan and Harriet Miriam (Lapham) T.; m. Carol Anne Vincent, Jan. 22, 1972; children: Erin Brynn, Blair Allyn. BS, U. Md., 1971; JD, U. Balt., 1975. Bar: Md. 1976, U.S. Ct. Appeals (2d cir.) 1976. Revenue officer IRS, Easton, Md., 1971-75; pvt. practice, Denton, Md., 1985—; ptnr. Kent, Ogletree and Thornton, 1976-85; del. Md. Gen. Assembly, Annapolis, 1991—; adj. faculty Chesapeake Coll., 1978-83. Pres. Caroline County Dem. State Ctrl. Com., Denton, 1986-90; pres., v.p. Caroline County Bd. Edn., Denton, 1983-89. Mem. Assn. Trial Lawyers Am., Choptank Ruritan Club (past pres.), Denton Lions (past pres.), Caroline County C. of C. Avocations: reading, traveling, auto restoration/repair, golf. Home: 24720 Pealiquor Rd Denton MD 21629 Office: 118 Market St Denton MD 21629-1035

THORNTON, SANDI TOKOA, elementary education educator; b. Albany, Ga., Aug. 1, 1953; d. Charlie and Beauty (Miller) Bush; 1 child, Allen. BS, Barry U., Miami, 1983; MS, Nova U., 1987. Cert. tchr., Fla. Counselor Health and Rehab. Services, Miami, 1979-86; tchr. Dade County (Fla.) Pub. Schs., Miami, 1986—; educator, tutor Ind. Children's Group, Miami, 1987—; co-chmn. hall of fame Dade County Sch. Bd., 1986—, world of difference 1987—. Contbr. articles to profl. jurs.; author: World of Poetry Anthology "The Sun", 1991. Mem. Faith Deliverance Cathedral, 1988— Mem. Smithsonian Assocs. (recognition award 1988), Nova U. Alumni Assn. (recruitment com. 1987-88, recognition award 1988), Nova U. Assocs. assoc. mem. The Am. Mus. of Natural History, Am. Mus. Natural History. Avocations: reading, classical music, walking, jogging, tennis. Office: Sch Bd PO Box 421382 Miami FL 33242-1382

THORNTON, SPENCER P., ophthalmologist, educator; b. West Palm Beach, Fla., Sept. 16, 1929; s. Ray Spencer and Mae (Phillips) T.; m. Annie Glenn Cooper, Oct. 6, 1956; children: Steven Pitts, David Spencer, Ray Cooper, Beth Ellen. BS, Wake Forest Coll. 1951, MD, 1954. Diplomate: Am. Bd. Ophthalmology. Intern Ga. Bapt. Hosp., Atlanta, 1954-55; resident surgery U. Ala. Med. Center, 1955-56; resident ophthalmology gen. surgery U. Ala. Med. Center, 1960-63, clin. instr. eye surgery, 1963-66; practice medicine specializing in ophthalmic surgery Nashville, 1960—; dir. cataract and corneal service Bapt. Hosp. Outpatient Surgery Ctr., Nashville, 1983—; mem. staff Bapt. Hosp., chief ophthalmology service 1982-87; guest prof. & vis. lectr. U. Toronto 1990, 91, 92, U. Paris 1989, Rothchilds Inst.,

Paris, 1992, 94, U. Pretoria, 1991, 93, others; instr. Moscow Inst. Eye Microsurgery 1981; instr. ophthalmic surgery Am. Acad. Ophthalmology Ann. Courses; lectr. lens implant symposiums Eng., Spain, Australia, Switzerland, Canada, Sweden, Greece, Germany, France, Republic of South Africa, Japan; internat. adv. com. European Implantlens Council, 1987-92; Berzelius lectr. U. Lund, Sweden, 1992; P.J. Hay Gold medal lectr., North of Eng. Ophthal. Soc., Scarborough, 1992. King Features syndicated newspaper columnist, 1959-60, feature writer, NBC radio and TV, 1958-60; author and co-author textbooks on cataract and refractive surgery; mem. editorial bd. Jour. Refractive and Corneal Surgery, Jour. Cataract and Refractive Surgery, Video Jour. Ophthalmology, Ocular Surgery News, Ophthalmic Practice (Can.); contbr. articles to profl. jours.; inventor instruments and devices for refractive and lens implant surgery. Capt. M.C. AUS, 1956-58. Named among Outstanding Young Men of Yr., U.S. Jaycees, 1965; recipient Honor award Can. Implant Assn., 1993. Fellow ACS, Internat. Coll. Surgeons, Am. Acad. Ophthalmology; mem. Am. Intra-Ocular Implant Soc. (founder), Am. Soc. Cataract and Refractive Surgery (exec. com. 1991—, pres.-elect 1995, chmn. internat. com. standards and quality control for ophthalmic instruments and devices), Internat. Soc. Refractive Keratoplasty (sci. adv. bd.), AMA (Physician's Recognition award), Am. Med. Soc. Vienna (life), South African Intraocular Implant Soc. (life), Can. Implant Soc. (life), Tenn. Soc. Medicine, Nashville Acad. Medicine, Spencer Thornton Profl. Assn. (chmn. bd. dirs. 1972—), Internat. Refractive Surgery Club (v.p. 1994), Phi Rho Sigma, Delta Kappa Alpha. Baptist. Home: 5070 Villa Crest Dr Nashville TN 37220-1425 Office: 2010 Church St Nashville TN 37203-2012

THORNTON, THEODORE KEAN, investment advisor; b. St. Louis, June 4, 1949; s. Leonard Frene and Maxine Belle (McKinley) T.; m. Colleen Bridget Purdy, June 23, 1974; children: Theodore McKinley, Alastair Griffin. BA, MBA, Harvard U. asst. treas. Chase Manhattan Bank, N.Y.C., 1975-79; asst. treas. Colgate-Palmolive Co., N.Y.C., 1979-84, Sperry Corp., N.Y.C., 1984-85; v.p., treas. Household Internat., Prospect Heights, Ill., 1985-87, v.p. investments, 1987-91, pres., 1991—; pres. Marble Corp., 1991-94; 1st v.p. Carr Asset Mgmt., Chgo., 1884—. Mem. Am. Fin. Assn. Clubs: Harvard (N.Y.C.). Home: 465 Maplewood Rd Lake Forest IL 60045-2415 Office: Ste 1650 225 W Washington St Chicago IL 60606

THORNTON, THOMAS NOEL, publishing executive; b. Marceline, Mo., Apr. 23, 1950; s. Bernard F. and Helen F. (Kelley) T.; m. Cynthia L. Murray, Nov. 26, 1971; children: T. Zachary, Timothy. B.J., U. Mo., 1972. Asst. to editor Universal Press Syndicate, Kansas City, Mo., 1972; v.p. Universal Press Syndicate, 1974, dir. mktg., 1976; v.p., dir. mktg. Universal Press Syndicate and Andrews & McMeel, Kansas City, 1976-87; pres. Andrews & McMeel, 1987—. Office: Universal Press Syndicate 4900 Main St Kansas City MO 64112-2644

THORNTON, WILLIAM E., mayor, oral surgeon; b. Abilene, Tex., 1945; m. Carolyn Cleveland Giles; children: Kate, Ted. BS in Biology, Trinity U., 1966; DDS, Baylor Coll. Dentistry, 1969; MSD, Baylor U., 1972. Diplomate Am. Bd. Oral and Maxillofacial Surgeons. Clin. prof. U. Tex. Health Sci. Ctr.; chmn. Bexar County Hosp. Dist., 1981-91; chmn. bd. dirs. Greater San Antonio C. of C., 1989. Active San Antonio Symphony Soc., Trinity Baptist Ch., Am. Red Cross, United Way, Am. Cancer Soc., Nat. Conf. Christians and Jews. Office: Office of the Mayor PO Box 839966 San Antonio TX 78283*

THORNTON, WILLIAM JAMES, JR., composer, music educator; b. Birmingham, Ala., July 31, 1919; s. William James and Ada Beaune (Gray) T.; m. Vivian Quine Dyer, Nov. 11, 1939 (dec. 1981); m. Alice Marilyn Dutcher, Mar. 3, 1984 (dec. 1993); m. Katherine Cornell, Nov. 26, 1993. B.Mus., La. State U., 1941, Mus.M., 1948; B.A., Birmingham-So. Coll., 1949; Ph.D., U. So. Calif., 1953. Instr. music U. Minn., 1955-56; prof., chmn. div. fine arts Parsons Coll., Fairfield, Iowa, 1956-60; prof., chmn. music dept. Trinity U., San Antonio, 1960-80, prof. music theory and composition, 1988-88, prof. emeritus, 1988—; tchr. music Pointe Coupee Parish, La., 1939-40; tchr. music St. James Parish, La., 1942, San Juan Capistrano, Calif., 1952-54, Pleasanton, Calif., 1954-55; prof. emeritus Trinity U. San Antonio, 1988; lectr. music composition U. Tex., San Antonio, 1991-93. Performer double bass, 1939-54; composer: major mus. works including String Quartet 1, 1949, Sonata for Cello and Piano, 1950, Serenade for Winds, 1950, Symphony 1, 1953, Sonata for Piano, 1955, Festive Music for Orchestra, 1962, Ceremony of Psalms for Soloists, Choir, Percussion, Organ, 1969, Sinfonia Bejar, Bicentennial commn. San Antonio Symphony, 1976, Sonata for piano, 4 hands, 1982, Solomon Songs, 1983, Sonata for Saxophone and Piano, 1985, Sonata for Harp, 1986, Spirit Divine for chorus and organ, 1986, Fanfare for brass, 1986, Homage for Chamber Orch. commd. Tex. Fedn. Music Clubs Manuscript Archives Com., 1987, Fanfare for Band commd. Trinity U. Wind Symphony and Tex. Composers Forum, 1987, The Grasshopper for chorus, 1987, Psalm No. 1 for mezzo-soprano, harp and flute, 1988, Then in Thy Mercy for mezzo-soprano and organ, 1988, Elegy for Trumpet and Piano, 1989, Woodwind Quintet commd. The King William Winds, 1991, Elegy for Trumpet and Strings to the Memory of Halsey Stevens, 1992, Jambalaya for Four Guitars, 1992, Te Deum Laudamus for organ, 1993, also others. Served with USAAF, 1942-46, PTO. Recipient composition commns. from San Antonio Symphony, Parsons Coll., La. State U., Trinity U., Manuscript Archives Commn.; stipends Trinity U., summers 1979, 81. Mem. Phi Mu Alpha Sinfonia, Phi Kappa Phi, Phi Sigma Iota, Sigma Nu. Home: 15927 Alsace San Antonio TX 78232-2791

THORNTON, WINFRED LAMOTTE, railroad executive; b. Winston-Salem, N.C., July 9, 1923; s. Winfred Lewis and Mildred (Cain) T.; m. Mary Ann Hege, Aug. 18, 1951; children: Winfred LaMotte, Mary Ann. B.S., Va. Mil. Inst., 1950. With So. Ry. System, 1950-59; chief operating officer Fla. East Coast Ry. Co. (now Fla. East Coast Industries Inc.), St. Augustine, 1960, v.p., chief operating officer, 1961-64, pres., CEO, 1964—, also chmn., dir., 1983—; pres., chief operating officer St. Joe Paper Co., Jacksonville, Fla.; pres., dir. Fla. Sugar Refinery, Inc., Talisman Sugar Corp.; dir. Charter Co., Fruit Growers Express Co.; pres. St. Joe Industries Inc.; pres., chief exec. officer Atlantic East Coast Terminal, Dade County Land Holding Co.; chmn., chief exec. officer Gran Cen. Corp. Bd. dirs. U.S. Indsl. Council; bd. dirs. Nat. Right to Work Com.; v.p., bd. dirs. Nemours Children's Hosp., Inc.; bd. dirs. Nemours Health Clinic, Inc.; mem. Fla. Council 100; cotrustee Alfred I. duPont Estate. Mem. Am. Ry. Engring. Assn., Am. Assn. R.R. Supts. Baptist (deacon). Office: St Joe Paper Co 1650 Prudential Dr Jacksonville FL 32207-8135 also: Fla E Coast Industries Inc 1 Malaga St Saint Augustine FL 32084

THORP, BENJAMIN A., III, paper manufacturing company executive; b. Albany, N.Y., May 31, 1938; s. Benjamin A. Jr. and Anna C. (Head) T.; m. Barbara Sue Telloch, Aug. 1, 1964 (div. Mar. 1986); 1 child, Benjamin A. IV; m. Laurie Diane Murdock, Oct. 25, 1987. Student in elec. engring., Rensselaer Poly. Inst., 1956-61, postgrad. in mgmt., 1967-68; BS in Physics, U. Md., 1964; postgrad. in engring., U. Bridgeport, 1966; postgrad. in mktg., U. Tenn., 1970. Product devel. mgr. Huyck Formex div. Huyck, Greenville, Tenn., 1969-71, mktg. mgr., 1971-73, v.p. gen. mgr., 1973-75; v.p., gen. mgr. Huytech Systems div., Wake Forest, N.C., 1975-78; v.p. dir. research Huyck Corp., Rensselaer, N.Y., 1978-80; pres. Benjamin A. Thorp Inc., Albany, 1980-82, POYRY-BEK Inc., Raleigh, N.C., 1982-84; v.p. engring. BE&K Inc., Birmingham, Ala., 1984-85; v.p. engring. James River Corp., Richmond, Va., 1984-95, v.p. process tech. consumer products bus., 1995—; bd. dirs. Naheola Cogeneration Ltd. Partnership; mem. exec. com. Pulp and Paper Found. Bd., Ga. Inst. Tech., 1991—, pres., 1993-95. Tech. editor Paper Machine Operations, Vol. 7, 3d edit., 1991; contbr. over 50 articles to profl. jours.; patentee in field. Bd. dirs. Richmond Math. and Sci. Ctr., 1987-93, Sic. Mus. of Va. Found., 1989—; chmn. papermaking project adv. com: Inst. Paper Sci. and Tech., 1990-94. Fellow TAPPI (chmn. apermakers com. 1984-86, vice chmn. paper and bd. div. 1988-90, chmn. 1990-92, bd. dirs. Leadership award 1994); mem. Paper Industry Mgmt. Assn. (2nd v.p.), Exptl. Aircraft Assn. Presbyterian. Office: James River Corp PO Box 2218 Richmond VA 23217-2218

THORP, JAMES HARRISON, III, aquatic ecologist; b. Kansas City, Mo., July 23, 1948; s. James Harrison Jr. and Delores Ray (Robinson) T.; m. Margaret Ellen Svoboda, Jan. 21, 1970; children: Sara Elizabeth, Zachary

Ward. BA, U. Kans., 1970; MS, N.C. State U., 1973, PhD, 1975. Rsch. assoc. Savannah River Ecology Lab., Aiken, S.C., 1975-82; vis. assoc. prof. Cornell U., Ithaca, N.Y., 1982-85; dir. Calder Conservation and Ecology Ctr. Fordham U., Bronx, N.Y., 1985-88, assoc. prof. biology, 1985-88; dir. water resources lab., prof. biology U. Louisville, 1988—; environ. cons., 1982—; team mem. Regional Urban Design Assistance Team, Fargo, N.C., Moorhead, Minn., 1989. Editor: Ecology and Classification of North America Freshwater Invertebrates, 1991, Energy and Environmental Stress in Aquatic Systems, 1978; assoc. editor Freshwater Invertebrate Biology; contbr. articles to Oikos, Ecology. Mem. Mayor's Aquarium Study com., Louisville, 1989—. Mem. AAAS, Ecol. Soc. Am., N.Am. Bethological Soc., Soc. Internat. Limnology. Office: Biology Dept U Louisville Louisville KY 40292

THORP, JAMES SHELBY, electrical engineering educator; b. Kansas City, Mo., Feb. 7, 1937; s. Joseph Chester and Ruth Veffe (McNamara) T.; m. Barbara Anne Curit, June 27, 1959 (div. July 1976); children: Jeffrey Barton, Elizabeth Anne; m. Christine Annette Moore, Aug. 10, 1980; children: Gregory, William. BEE, Cornell U., 1959, MS, 1961, PhD, 1962. Asst. prof. Cornell U., Ithaca, N.Y., 1962-66, assoc. prof., 1966-75, prof., 1975—, assoc. dir. Sch. Elec. Engring., 1991-94, dir. Sch. Elec. Engring., 1994—; faculty intern Am. Electric Power Svc. Corp., N.Y.C., 1976-77; Charles H. Mellowes prof. engring., 1994—; fellow Churchill Coll., U. Cambridge, Eng., 1988—; cons. Am. Electric Power Svc. Corp., 1977-83, Dowty Control Techs., Boonton, N.J., 1988—. Author: Computer Relaying for Power Systems, 1988; contbr. chpts. to books, articles to profl. jours. Fellow IEEE. Avocation: golf. Office: Cornell Univ Phillips Hall Ithaca NY 14853

THORPE, JAMES, humanities scholar; b. Aiken, S.C., Aug. 17, 1915; s. J. Ernest and Ruby (Holloway) T.; m. Elizabeth McLean Daniells, July 19, 1941; children: John D., Sally Jans-Thorpe. A.B., The Citadel, 1936, LL.D. 1971; M.A., Princeton U., 1937; Ph.D., Harvard U., 1941; Litt.D., Occidental Coll., 1968; L.H.D., Claremont Grad. Sch., 1968; H.H.D., U. Toledo, 1977. Instr. to prof. English Princeton, 1946-66; dir. Huntington Libr., Art Gallery and Bot. Gardens, San Marino, Calif., 1966-83; sr. research assoc. Huntington Libr., San Marino, Calif., 1966—. Author: Bibliography of the Writings of George Lyman Kittredge, 1948, Milton Criticism, 1950, Rochester's Poems on Several Occasions, 1950, Poems of Sir George Etherege, 1963, Aims and Methods of Scholarship, 1963, 70, Literary Scholarship, 1964, Relations of Literary Study, 1967, Bunyan's Grace Abounding and Pilgrim's Progress, 1969, Principles of Textual Criticism, 1972, 2d edit., 1979, Use of Manuscripts in Literary Research, 1974, 2d edit., 1979, Gifts of Genius, 1980, A Word to the Wise, 1982, John Milton: The Inner Life, 1983, The Sense of Style: Reading English Prose, 1987, Henry Edwards Huntington: A Biography, 1994. Served to col. USAAF, 1941-46. Decorated Bronze Star medal.; Guggenheim fellow, 1949-50, 65-66. Fellow Am. Acad. Arts and Scis., Am. Philos. Soc.; mem. MLA, Am. Antiquarian Soc., Soc. for Textual Scholarship. Democrat. Episcopalian. Clubs: Zamorano, Twilight. Home: 1199 Arden Rd Pasadena CA 91106-4143 Office: Huntington Libr San Marino CA 91108

THORPE, JAMES ALFRED, retired utilities executive; b. Fall River, Mass., Apr. 19, 1929; s. James and Charlotte Ann (Brearley) T.; m. Maxine Elva Thompson, Mar. 4, 1950; children: James Alfred, Peter R., David T., Carol L., Mark W. B.S., Northeastern U., 1951. Asst. supt. prodn. Fall River Gas Co., 1951-55; chief engr. Lake Shore Gas Co., Ashtabula, Ohio, 1955-57; cons. Stone & Webster Mgmt. Corp., 1958-67; pres. Wash. Natural Gas Co., Seattle, 1972; chmn., chief exec. officer Wash. Natural Gas Co., 1980-94; also chmn., chief exec. officer, dir. Wash. Energy Co.; dir. Sea First Corp. Bd. dirs. Salvation Army. Mem. Am. Gas Assn., Pacific Coast Gas Assn. (pres. 1977-78), Rainier Club (Seattle). Methodist. Home: 11160 SE 59th St Bellevue WA 98006-2606

THORPE, NORMAN RALPH, lawyer, automobile company executive, retired air force officer; b. Carlinville, Ill., Oct. 17, 1934; s. Edwin Everett and Imogene Midas (Hayes) T.; m. Elaine Frances Pritzman, Nov. 1, 1968; children: Sarah Elizabeth, Carrie Rebecca. AB in Econs., U. Ill., 1956, JD, 1958; LLM in Pub. Internat. Law, George Washington U., 1967. Bar: Ill. 1958, Mich. 1988, U.S. Supreme. Ct. 1969. Commd. 2d lt. USAF, 1956, advanced through grades to brig. gen., 1983; legal advisor U.S. Embassy, Manila, 1969-72; chief internat. law hdqrs. USAF, Washington, 1972-77; staff judge adv. 21st Air Force, McGuire AFB, N.J., 1977-80, USAF Europe, Ramstein AB, Fed. Republic Germany, 1980-84; comdr. Air Force Contract Law Ctr., Wright-Patterson AFB, Ohio, 1984-88, ret., 1988; mem. legal staff, group counsel GM Def. and Power Products Gen. Motors Corp., Detroit, 1988—; adj. prof. U. Dayton Sch. Law, 1986-87; partnership counsel U.S. Advanced Battery Consortium, 1990—; legal adv. U.S. Automotive Rsch., 1990—. Contbr. articles to profl. jours. Staff mem. Commn. on Police Policies and Procedures, Dayton, 1986; trustee Dayton Philharm. Orch., 1987-88. Mem. ABA (chmn. com. internat. law sect. 1977-80, coun. mem. pub. contract law sect. 1986-88, chmn. com. pub. contract law sect. 1988—), Air Force Assn., Dayton Coun. on World Affairs, Army/Navy Club, Detroit Econ. Club. Republican. Avocations: music, piano, gardening. Home: 498 Abbey Rd Birmingham MI 48009-5618 Office: Gen Motors Corp Legal Staff 3031 W Grand Blvd Detroit MI 48232-5122

THORPE, OTIS HENRY, professional basketball player; b. Boynton Beach, Fla., Aug. 5, 1962. Student, U. Providence. Basketball player Kansas City Kings, 1984-85, Sacramento Kings (formerly Kansas City), 1985-88, Houston Rockets, 1988-94, Portland Trail Blazers, 1994—. Mem. NBA championship team 1994. NBA All-Star, 1992. Office: Portland Trail Blazers Port of Portland Bldg 700 NE Multnomah St Ste 600 Portland OR 97232*

THORSEN, NANCY DAIN, real estate broker; b. Edwardsville, Ill., June 23, 1944; d. Clifford Earl and Suzanne Eleanor (Kribs) Dain; m. David Massie, 1968 (div. 1975); 1 child, Suzanne Dain Massie; m. James Hugh Thorsen, May 30, 1980. BSc in Mktg., So. Ill. U., 1968, MSc in Bus. Edn., 1975; grad. Realtor Inst., Idaho, 1983. Cert. resdl. and investment specialist, fin. instr.; Designated Real Estate Instr. State of Idaho; accredited buyer rep. Personnel officer J.H. Little & Co. Ltd., London, 1969-72; instr. in bus. edn. Spl. Sch. Dist. St. Louis, 1974-77; mgr. mktg./ops. Isis Foods, Inc., St. Louis, 1978-80; asst. mgr. store Stix, Baer & Fuller, St. Louis, 1980; assoc. broker Century 21 Sayer Realty, Inc., Idaho Falls, Idaho, 1981-88, RE/MAX Homestead Realty, 1989—; speaker RE/MAX Internat. Conv., 1990, 94, RE/MAX Stars Cruise, 1993, RE/MAX Pacific N.W. Conv., 1994; real estate fin. instr. State of Idaho Real Estate Commn., 1994. Bd. dirs. Idaho Vol., Boise, 1981-84, Idaho Falls Symphony, 1982; pres. Friends of Idaho Falls Library, 1981-83; chmn. Idaho Falls Mayor's Com. for Vol. Coordination, 1981-84; power leader Power Program, 1995. Recipient Idaho Gov.'s award, 1982, cert. appreciation City of Idaho Falls/Mayor Campbell, 1982, 87, Civitan Disting. Pres. award, 1990; named to Two Million Dollar Club, Three Million Dollar Club, 1987, 88, Four Million Dollar Club, 1989, 90, Top Investment Sales Person for Eastern Idaho, 1985, Realtor of Yr. Idaho Falls Bd. Realtors, 1990, Outstanding Realtors Active in Politics, Mem. of Yr. Idaho Assn. Realtors, 1991, Women of Yr. Am. Biog. Inst., 1991, Profiles of Top Professionals award Real Estate Edn. Assn.; named Western Region Power Leader, Darryl Davis Seminars. Mem. Nat. Spkrs. Assn., Idaho Falls Bd. Realtors (chmn. orientation 1982-83, chmn. edn. 1983, chmn. legis. com. 1989, chmn. program com. 1990, 91), Idaho Assn. Realtors (pres. Million Dollar Club 1988—, edn. 1989-90-93), So. Ill. U. Alumni Assn., Idaho Falls C. of C., Newcomers Club, Civitan (pres. Idaho Falls chpt. 1988-89, Civitan of Yr. 1986, 87, outstanding pres. award 1990), Real Estate Educators Assn. Office: RE/MAX Homestead Inc 1301 E 17th St Ste 1 Idaho Falls ID 83404-6273

THORSLAND, EDGAR, JR., health facility administrator; b. Ithaca, N.Y., Mar. 4, 1942; m. Sylvia Thorsland; 2 children. BA in Govt., Cornell U. Mgmt. intern ctrl. office VA, Washington, 1971-73; mem. survey staff DM&S VA, 1973-74, team capt. systematic external review program, health care review svc., 1974-76; adminstr. trainee med. ctr. VA, Richmond, Va., 1976-78; asst. dir. med. ctr. VA, Lake City, Fla., 1978-79; assoc. dir. med. ctr. VA, Tuscaloosa, Fla., 1979-83, Bronx, N.Y., 1983-88; dir. outpatient clinic VA, El Paso, Tex., 1988-91; dir. med. ctr. VA, Dayton, Ohio, 1991—.

Capt. USAF, 1965-71, Vietnam. Office: VA Med Ctr 4100 W 3rd St Dayton OH 45428-1000

THORSON, CONNIE CAPERS, library educator; b. Dallas, July 25, 1940; d. Ewing Ashby and Constance (Romberg) Capers; m. James Llewellyn, June 6, 1970. BA, U. Ark., 1962, MA, 1964; PhD, U. N.Mex., 1970; MS in Library Sci., U. Ill., 1977. Instr. English S.E. Mo. State U., Cape Girardeau, 1963-67; with U. N.Mex., Albuquerque, 1970-71, 79—, acquistions libr., 1980—, assoc. prof. libr., 1984-90, prof., 1990—, pres. faculty senate, 1991-92. Editor: A Million Stars, 1981, Pocket Companion for Oxford, 1989. Mem. South Cen. Soc. for 18th Century Studies (pres. elect 1988-89, pres. 1989-90), Modern Lang. Assn., Am. Soc. for 18th Century Studies, ALA. Avocations: traveling, reading, walking. Office: U N Mex Libr Albuquerque NM 87131

THORSON, JAMES LLEWELLYN, English language educator; b. Yankton, S.D., Jan. 7, 1934; s. James Albert and Doris Reece (Burgi) T.; m. Barbara Gay Jelgerhuis, Sept. 6, 1957 (div. 1970); m. Connie Capers, June 6, 1970. BS in Edn., U. Nebr., 1956, MA, 1961; PhD, Cornell U., 1966; MA (hon.), Oxford (Eng.) U., 1976. Instr. English U. Nebr., Lincoln, 1961-62; asst. prof. U. N.Mex., Albuquerque, 1965-70; assoc. prof. U. N.Mex., 1970-84; vis. prof. U. Kiril i Metodij, Skopje, Yugoslavia, 1971-72, U. Wurzburg, Wurzburg, Fed. Republic of Germany, 1983; prof. English U. N.Mex., Albuquerque, 1984—; vis. prof. U. Munster, Munster, Fed. Republic of Germany, 1985-86, 92-93; lectr. USIA, Yugoslavia, Switzerland, Denmark, Czechoslovakia, Fed. Republic of Germany, Eng., Belgium, 1971, 85, 93, 95. Editor: Yugoslav Perspectives on American Literature, 1980, Humphry Clinker, 1983, Thomas D'Urfey, Butler's Ghost, 1984, (with Connie Thorson) A Pocket Companion for Oxford, 1988. Lt. USN, 1956-59. Fulbright professorship Skopje, 1971-72, Munster, 1985-86. Mem. Modern Lang. Assn., AAUP (pres. U. N.Mex. chpt. 1968-70), Old Mems. Jesus College Oxford, Am. Soc. for Eighteenth-Century Studies (patron), Wig and Pen Club (London). Democrat. Avocations: travel, skiing. Home: Apt 412 1331 Park Ave SW Albuquerque NM 87102 Office: U New Mexico Dept English Univ Of New Mexico NM 87131

THORSON, JOHN MARTIN, JR., electrical engineer, consultant; b. Armstrong, Iowa, Dec. 16, 1929; s. John Martin and Hazel Marguerite (Martin) T.; m. Geraldine Carol Moran, Apr. 21, 1956 (dec. 1975); children—John Robert, James Michael; m. Lee Houk, Sept. 24, 1977. B.S.E.E., Iowa State U., 1951. Transmission engr. No. States Power Co., Mpls., 1953-58, system operation relay engr., 1962-74; telephone engr. No. States Power Co., Minot, N.D., 1958-62; utility industry mktg. mgr. Control Data Corp., Mpls., 1974-77, product/program mgr. utilities, 1977-84, sr. cons. energy mgmt. systems, 1984-90; pres. Thorson Engrs., Inc., Chanhassen, Minn., 1991—; inductive coordination cons. SNC Corp., Oshkosh, Wis., 1985—, Ill. Inst. Tech. Rsch. Inst., Chgo., 1980-83, Electric Power Rsch. Inst., Palo Alto, Calif., 1981-83; U.S. rep. Internat. Electrotech. Commn., Geneva, 1985—; tech. cons. Power Technologies, Inc., Schenectady, N.Y., 1991—, Control Corp., Osseo, Minn., 1992—, Control Data, Plymouth, Minn., 1991—, Hathaway, Denver, 1992—, Scottish Hydro-Electric, plc, Perth, Scotland, 1992—, NRG Energy Inc., Mpls., 1993—. Contbr. tech. papers to profl. jours. Dist. commr. Boy Scouts Am., Minn., 1954-58, 64-65, coun. commr. N.D., Mont., 1959-62; mem. coun. St. Philip Luth. Ch., Wayzata, Minn., 1968-69; county del. Rep. Com., Chanhassen, Minn., 1980-82. 1st lt. USAF, 1951-53. Recipient Alumni Service award Iowa State U. 1972. Fellow IEEE (life mem., bd. dirs. 1981-82, dir. region 4, 1981-82, mem. U.S. activities bd. 1981-82, regional activities bd. 1981-82, Centennial medal 1984); mem. Internat. Conf. on Large High Voltage Electric Sys., Iowa State U. Alumni Assn. (v.p., pres. 1963-66). Republican. Avocations: canoeing; back packing; mountain climbing. Home and Office: 7320 Longview Cir Chanhassen MN 55317-9797

THORSON, LEE A., lawyer; b. Seattle, Nov. 10, 1949; s. Theodore Arthur and Irene Mary (Dakers) T.; m. Elizabeth Clayton Hay, June 7, 1975; children: Kirk Hunter, Alex Peter. BA, U. Wash., 1971; JD, U. Pacific, Sacramento, 1975; LLM Taxation, Boston U., 1976. Atty. Dahlgren & Dauenhauer P.S. Seattle, 1975-79, Lane Powell Spears Lubersky, Seattle, 1980-93; shareholder Birmingham Thorson & Barnett, P.C., 1993—; lectr. U. Wash. Grad. Program in Taxation, 1995—. Mem. ABA (health law forum), Internat. Found. Employee Benefits, Employee Benefits and Health Law coms., Wash. State Bar Assn. Avocations: bicycling, skiing. Office: Birmingham Thorson Barnett 601 Union St Ste 3315 Seattle WA 98101-2317

THORSON, MARCELYN MARIE, applied art educator; b. Houston, Dec. 18, 1927; d. Oliver Herbert and Helene Marie (Brown) Fritts; m. Edward L. Thorson, June 16, 1956. BS, Pratt Inst., N.Y.C., 1950. Cert. home economist, tech. tchr. Apparel designer Dallas Sportswear Co., 1954-64, Srader Sportswear Co., Dallas, 1964-65; instr., coordinator apparel design program and pattern design program El Centro Coll., Dallas, 1966-88; cons. computer research Camsco, Inc., Richardson, Tex., summer 1976-77; project devel. coordinator state grant Fashion Design Series, North Tex. State U., summer 1978-79; instr. Indsl. Tng. Lab., summer 1978. Instr. Adult Christian Edn. Found., Bethel Bible Series, Luth. Ch., 1965-80. Mem. Costume Soc. Am., Am. Home Econs. Assn., Cert. Home Economist, Dallas Met. Home Economists in Home and Community, The FAshion Group (edn. com. 1975-90, scholarsip chmn. 1975-85, bd. dirs. fashion mus. 1963-65, Silver Tray award 1965). Republican. Avocations: antique clothing, embroidery, sewing, researching costumes, attending Hist. Soc. and art exhibits. Home: 11229 Lanewood Cir Dallas TX 75218-1908

THORSON, OSWALD HAGEN, architect; b. Forest City, Iowa, Dec. 19, 1912; s. Thorwald and Josephine (Hagen) T.; m. Maxine Rustad, Dec. 27, 1941; children: Sigrin, Thorwald. BArch, U. Minn., 1937. Registered architect, Iowa. Ptnr. Thorson & Thorson, Forest City, 1939-52, Thorson & Brom, Forest City, 1952-65, Thorson Brom Broshar Snyder, Waterloo, Iowa, 1965-79, ret. Fellow AIA (nat. sec. 1965-67, Lifetime Achievemnt award Iowa chpt. 1982). Democrat. Home: 919 N Barfield Dr Marco Island FL 33937-2348

THORSON, STUART J., political science educator; b. Vallejo, Calif., Dec. 1, 1946; s. Stuart Verne and Dorothy May (Timberg) T.; m. Esther Lynn Whiteside, Aug. 24, 1968 (div. 1977); 1 child, Kjerstin Sonja; m. Kristi Jean Andersen, Apr. 9, 1979; children: Emily Andersen, Daniel Andersen. B.A., Macalaster Coll., St. Paul, 1968; Ph.D., U. Minn., Mpls., 1972. Mem. faculty polit. sci. Ohio State U., Columbus, 1971-84; mem. faculty polit. sci. Syracuse U., N.Y., 1984—, chmn. dept., 1989-93; dir. Global Affairs Inst., 1993—. Contbr. articles to profl. jours. Mem. Am. Polit. Sci. Assn., AAAS, ACM, Peace Sci. Soc. (treas. 1973-74). Office: Syracuse U Global Affairs Inst Maxwell Sch Syracuse NY 13244

THORSON, THOMAS BERTEL, zoologist, educator; b. Rowe, Ill., Jan. 12, 1917; s. Thomas B. and Hertha (Fylpaa) T.; m. Margaret L. Overgaard, Dec. 31, 1941; children—Sharon M., Joel T. Student, Waldorf Coll., 1934-36; B.A., St. Olaf Coll., 1939; M.S., U. Wash., 1941, Ph.D., 1952. Faculty Yakima (Wash.) Coll., 1946-48, Calif. State U.-San Francisco, 1952-54, S.D. State U., 1954-56; faculty U. Nebr., Lincoln, 1940-58, 56—; prof. zoology U. Nebr., 1961-82, prof. emeritus, 1982—, chmn. dept., 1967-71, vice dir. Sch. Biol. Scis., 1975-77. Editor: Investigations of the Ichthyofauna of Nicaraguan Lakes, 1976. Served to capt. USAAF, 1942-46. Fellow AAAS, Explorers Club, Am. Elasmobranch Soc. (disting.); mem. Am. Inst. Biol. Scis., Am. Soc. Zoologists, Am. Ichthyologists and Herpetologists, Am. Fisheries Soc., Sigma Xi (pres. Nebr. chpt. 1972-74), Phi Sigma. Research, publs. on water economy of amphibians, patterns of body water partitioning in cold-blooded vertebrates, biology of freshwater sharks and sawfish of Lake Nicaragua, Amazon River freshwater stingrays S. Am., Africa. Address: 21233 SW Martinazzi Ave Tualatin OR 97062-9324 Office: U Nebr-Lincoln Sch Biol Sci Lincoln NE 68588

THORSTAD, DALE J., manufacturing company executive; b. St. Paul, Oct. 30, 1950; s. Joseph H. and Ardell C. (Johnson) T.; m. Andrea L. Peterson, June 22, 1971; children: Jeffrey A., Janelle L., Jocelyn M., Jolana J. Student, Mpls. Vocat. Tech. Sch., 1970. Quality control mgr. Starkey Labs., Inc., Mpls., 1971-75, service mgr., 1975-79, service mgr., quality control mgr., 1978-79, plant mgr., 1979-81, v.p. ops., 1981—. Mem. Internat. Soc. Hybrid Microelectronics. Jehovah's Witness. Home: 2941 Hampshire Ave N Minneapolis MN 55427-3031 Office: Starkey Labs Inc 6700 Washington Ave S Eden Prairie MN 55344-3476

THORSTEINSSON, RAYMOND, geology research scientist; b. Wynyard, Sask., Can., Jan. 21, 1921; m. Jean Kristjansson, Dec. 23, 1944; children: Eirikur, Anna Ingrid. BA, U. Sask., 1944; MA, U. Toronto, Can., 1950; PhD, U. Kans., 1955. Rsch. scientist Geol. Survey of Can., Calgary, 1952-92, emeritus rsch. sci., 1992—. Contbr. articles, bulletins and papers to various jours. Decorated Officer Order of Can., 1989; recipient Founders medal Royal Geog. Soc., London, 1968, Outstanding Achievement in Sci. award Govt. Province of Alta., 1973, Massey medal Royal Can. Geog. Soc., 1992, Commemorative medal 125th Anniversary Can. Confedn., 1992, Massey medal, 1981, presented by Gov. Gen. Can., 1981, R.J.W. Douglas medal Can. Soc. Petroleum Geologists, 1982, Gold medal Sci. Profl. Inst. Pub. Svc. Can., 1987. Fellow Arctic Inst. N.Am., The Royal Soc. Can. (Willet G. Miller medal 1973), Geol. Assn. Can. (Logan medal 1979). Office: Geol Survey Can, 3303 33 St NW, Calgary, AB Canada T2L 2A7

THORSTENBERG, (JOHN) LAURENCE, oboe and English horn player; b. Salt Lake City, Dec. 6, 1925; s. Laurence Nathaniel and Alys Josephine (Blomquist) T. MusB, Curtis Inst. Music, Phila., 1951. Instrumental tchr., 1975—, New Eng. Conservatory, Boston U., 1980—; mem. Symphony Orch. Balt., 1951-52, Dallas Symphony Orch., 1952-54, Chgo. Symphony Orch., 1954-63, Boston Symphony Orch., 1964-93; appeared summers, Marlboro (Vt.) Music Festival, 1952-54. Served with U.S. Army, 1944-46, ETO. Mem. Am. Fedn. Musicians, Internat. Conf. Symphony and Opera Musicians.

THOULESS, DAVID JAMES, physicist, educator; b. Bearsden, Scotland, Sept. 21, 1934; came to U.S. 1979; U.S. citizen, 1994; s. Robert Henry and Priscilla (Gorton) T.; m. Margaret Elizabeth Scrase, July 26, 1958; children: Michael, Christopher, Helen. BA, U. Cambridge, Eng., 1955, ScD, 1986; PhD, Cornell U., 1958. Physicist Lawrence Berkeley Lab., Calif., 1958-59; rsch. fellow U. Birmingham, Eng., 1959-61, prof. math. physics, 1965-78; lectr., fellow Churchill Coll. U. Cambridge, Eng., 1961-65; prof. physics Queen's U., Kingston, Ont., Can., 1978; prof. applied sci. Yale U., New Haven, 1979-80; prof. physics U. Wash., Seattle, 1980—. Author: Quantum Mechanics of Many Body Systems, 2d edit., 1972. Recipient Maxwell medal Inst. Physics, 1973, Holweck prize Soc. Francaise de Physique-Inst. Physics 1980, Fritz London award for Low temperature physics, Fritz London Meml. Fund, 1984, Wolf prize in physics, 1990, Paul Dirac medal Inst. Physics, 1993; Edwin Uehling disting. scholar U. Wash., 1988—. Fellow Royal Soc., Am. Acad. Arts and Scis. Office: U Wash Dept Physics # Fm-15 Seattle WA 98195

THOW, GEORGE BRUCE, surgeon; b. Toronto, Ont., Can., Mar. 24, 1930; came to U.S., 1965; s. George and Helen Bruce (Smith) T.; m. Marion Bernice Perry, Sept. 7, 1956; children—Deborah, George, Helen, Catherine. M.D., U. Toronto, 1954. Diplomate Am. Bd. Gen. Surgery, Am. Bd. Colon and Rectal Surgery (pres. 1983-84, adv. coun. 1989—), sr. examiner 1989—). Intern Toronto East Gen. Hosp., 1954-55; gen. practice medicine Toronto, 1955-56; instr. anatomy U. Toronto; resident in gen. and colon and rectal surgery Mayo Postgrad. Sch. Medicine, Rochester, Minn., 1957-63; gen., colon and rectal surgeon Lockwood Clinic, Toronto, 1963-65; founder and dir. colon and rectal residency program U. Ill. Med. Sch. and Carle Found. Hosp., Urbana, 1974-85; dir. dept. colon and rectal surgery Carle Clinic Assocs., Urbana, Ill., 1974-85; clin. assoc. U.S. Basic Med. Scis., U. Ill., Urbana, 1973-77; clin. asst. prof. Coll. Medicine, U. Ill., Urbana-Champaign, 1975-78; clin. assoc. prof. Coll. Medicine, U. Ill., 1978-85; prof. clin. nutrition, dept. food sci. U. Ill., Urbana, 1981-85; practice medicine specializing in colon and rectal surgery Chattanooga, 1985—; vice chmn. Residency Rev. Bd. in Colon and Rectal Surgery, 1980-82; active Am. Bd. Med. Specialties, 1979-84; mem. interspecialty bd. AMA, Chgo., 1974-80. Assoc. editor Diseases of the Colon and Rectum Jour., 1978—; contbr. chpt., numerous articles to profl. publs.; inventor Thow tube, Intraseal operative irrigation tube. Community coordinator Urbana conv. Inter-Varsity Christian Fellowship, Ill., 1967-84. Recipient Med. Edn. award Carle Found., 1982. Fellow Royal Coll Surgeons (Can.) (cert. 1963), ACS (credentials com. 1980-82); mem. Priestley Surg. Soc., Mid-West Colon and Rectal Surg. Soc. (pres. 1985-86), Can. Assn. Gen. Surgeons, Am. Bd. of Colon and Rectal Surgery (chmn. exam. com.1980-83, pres. 1983-84, adv. coun. 1989), Soc. Surgery Alimentary Tract, Am. Cancer Soc. (pres. Champaign County unit 1975-77, Ill. Top Ten award 1973-74), United Ostomy Assn. (founding mem. Champaign-Urbana chpt.). Presbyterian. Home: 7142 Revere Cir Concord Highlands Chattanooga TN 37421-1205 Office: Colon & Rectal Surgery Assocs 721 Greenwood Dr Ste 473 Chattanooga TN 37404

THOW, JOHN H., music educator, composer; b. L.A., Oct. 6, 1949; s. George H. and Marie (Dykes) T.; m. Margaret Wait Thow, June 24, 1971; children: Diana Corrina, Caroline Miranda. BMus in Composition magna cum laude, U. So. Calif., 1971; MA in Music Composition, Harvard U., 1973, PhD in Music Composition, 1977; diploma d'onore (Composition), Accademia Musicale Chigiana, Siena, Italy, 1974. Asst. prof. music theory and composition Boston U. Sch. for the Arts, 1978-80; asst. prof. in music composition U. Calif. Dept. Music, Berkeley, 1981-86, assoc. prof., 1986-90, prof., 1990—. Composer: Madrone (Bklyn Philharmonic commn. 1987), Image, Double & Envoi, All Hallows 1982 (Nat. Endowment for the Arts rec. grant 1983, Boston Musica Viva/New England Fdn. for the Arts Commn. 1981), Seven Charms for a New Day, Canto del Quetzal, Chinese Poems, Divergences, Songs for the Earth 1994 (Am. Acad. award 1994), Into the Twilight 1988 (San Francisco Symphony commn. 1988), Trigon 1974 (Debut Orchestra award 1976), Live Oak (Musical Elements N.Y. commn. 1983). Guggenheim fellowship Guggenheim Fdn., 1986, Djerassi Fdn. fellowships, 1986, 87, Regents Jr. Faculty fellowship U. Calif., 1983, Goddard Lieberson fellowship Am. Acad. and Inst. of Arts and Letters, 1983, Dorland Mountain Colony fellow, 1981, Yaddo fellowships, 1976, 1980, John Knowles Paine Travelling fellowship (Harvard), 1976-77, Fulbright Grad. fellowship to Italy, 1973-74; Margaret Jory Fairbanks Copying assistance grants (The Am. Music Ctr.), 1978, 92, Meet the Composer grants, 1980, 82, 86, 87, 92, 95; Acad. award in Music Composition AAAL, 1994. Fellow Am. Academy in Rome, 1978— (Rome Prize fellowship 1977); mem. BMI, 1978—, Am. Music Ctr., 1988—, Minn. Composers Forum, 1994—. Home: 1045 Ordway St Albany CA 94706 Office: Univ of Calif-Berkeley Dept Music 104 Morrison Hall Berkeley CA 94720

THOYER, JUDITH REINHARDT, lawyer; b. Mt. Vernon, N.Y., July 29, 1940; d. Edgar Allen and Florence (Mayer) Reinhardt; m. Michael E. Thoyer, June 30, 1963; children: Erinn, Michael John. AB with honors, U. Mich., 1961; LLB summa cum laude, Columbia U., 1965. Bar: N.Y. 1966, D.C. 1984. Law libr. U. Ghana, Accra, Africa, 1963-64; assoc. Paul, Weiss, Rifkind, Wharton & Garrison, N.Y.C., 1965-75, ptnr., 1975—. Bd. dirs. Women's Action Alliance, N.Y.C., 1975-89, pro bono counsel, 1975—; mem. bd. visitors Columbia Law Sch., N.Y.C., 1991—. Mem. N.Y. County Lawyers Assn. (securities and exchs. com.), Assn. of the Bar of the City N.Y. (securities regulation com. 1976-79, recruitment of lawyers com. 1980-82), Women's Coun. Democratic Senatorial (campaign com. 1993—). Home: 1115 5th Ave Apt 3B New York NY 10128-0100 Office: Paul Weiss Rifkind Wharton & Garrison 1285 Avenue Of The Americas New York NY 10019-6064

THRALL, ARTHUR ALVIN, artist; b. Milw., Mar. 18, 1926; s. Irving and Helen (Fabich) T.; m. Winifred Rogers, 1960; children: Grant, Wade, Sara, Jay. BS, Milw. State Tchrs. Coll., 1950; MS, U. Wis., Milw., 1954; postgrad. (fellow), U. Ill., 1954-55. Tchr. art Lincoln Jr. High Sch., Kenosha, Wis., 1951-54; asst. prof. SUNY, Geneseo, 1955-56; assoc. prof. Milw.-Downer Coll., 1956-64; prof. Farrar-Marrs prof. fine arts Lawrence U., Appleton, Wis., 1964-90; prof. emeritus Lawrence U., Appleton, 1990—. One-man shows Smithsonian Instn., 1960, Silvermine Artists, New Canaan, Conn., 1964, Ohio State U., Columbus, 1967, Bergstrom-Mahler Mus., Neenah, Wis., 1973, 83, Baylor U., Waco, Tex., 1985, America Ctr. U.S. Info. Agy., Helsinki, Finland, 1986; group shows include Corcoran biennials, Washington, 1951, 53, 55, 57, 62, Bklyn. Mus. annuals, Mus. Modern Art, N.Y.C, NAD, N.Y.C., Audubon Artists, N.Y.C., 1985, S.A.G.A., N.Y.C., 1985; represented in permanent collection Tate Gallery, Victoria and Albert Mus., Brit. Mus., all London, Phila. Mus., Seattle Mus., Art Inst. Chgo., Bklyn. Mus., UCLA, Smithsonian Instn., USIA, Washington, others. Served

with U.S. Army, 1944-46, ETO. Recipient Bklyn. Mus. print awards 1952, 64; Pa. Acad. Arts award 1960; NAD awards 1956, 68); Louis Comfort Tiffany fellow, 1963. Mem. AAUP, Boston Printmakers (award 1963, 65), Soc. Am. Graphic Artists (awards 1951, 52, 60, 78), Audubon Artists Inc. (award 1977). Home: 4225 N Woodburn St Milwaukee WI 53211-1504

THRALL, DONALD STUART, artist; b. Detroit, Mar. 29, 1918; s. Ernest Lawrence and Gertrude Marie (Adams) T. B.A., Mich. State U., 1940; M.A., Columbia U. Tchrs. Coll., 1946; summer student, Skowhegan (Maine) Sch. Painting and Sculpture, 1947, Black Mountain (N.C.) Coll., 1948. Instr. painting and design Cass Tech. Sch., Detroit, 1949-55; ednl. coordinator Guggenheim Mus., N.Y.C., 1961-73; Bd. dirs. Mich. Watercolor Soc., 1950-55, Detroit Met. Art Assn., 1948-54; exhibiting mem. Detroit Inst. Arts, 1947-53. One-man exhbn., Contemporary Arts Gallery, N.Y.C., 1961, group exhbns. include, Met. Mus. Art, 1950, Detroit Inst. Arts, 1947-55 (award 1950, 53, 55), Mich. Artists invited survey show, 1951, Butler Inst. Am. Art, Youngstown, Ohio, 1950-52 (1st prize 1951), Whitney Mus., N.Y.C., 1953, Bklyn. Mus., 1961, others, group exhbns. include, Wildenstein Galleries, N.Y.C., 1952 (Hallmark Art prize), Downtown Gallery, N.Y.C., 1950-53, Detroit Artists Market, 1948-54, Scarab Gallery, Detroit, 1948-53 (award 1948, 51, 53, 54), Mich. Watercolor Soc., 1949-55 (award 1950, 52, 53, 55), Mich. State Fair, 1952 (1st prize 1952), Detroit Art Instr. Exhbn., 1946-53 (1st award 1946, 48, 50, 51, 53), 16th Serigraph Internat., N.Y.C., 1955, others; represented in permanent collections, Detroit Inst. Arts, Butler Inst. Am. Art, U. Mich. Mus. Art, Mus. Wayne State U., Cranbrook Acad. Art Mus., Bloomfield Hills, Mich., numerous pvt. collections, U.S. and abroad. Served with AUS, 1941-45. Guggenheim fellow, 1955. Mem. Mich. Acad. Sci., Arts and Letters, Beta Alpha Sigma (pres. 1940). Address: 945 West End Ave New York NY 10025

THRALL, JAMES HUNTER, radiology educator; b. Ann Arbor, Mich., 1943. MD, U. Mich. 1968. Intern Walter Reed Army Med. Ctr., Washington, 1968-69, resident in radiology, 1969-72, fellow in nuclear medicine, 1972-73, asst. chief nuclear med. svc. dept. radiology, 1973-75; asst. prof. radiology and nuclear medicine U. Mich., Ann Arbor, 1975-78, assoc. prof., 1978-81, prof., 1981-83; now Juan M. Taveras prof. radiology Harvard U., Cambridge, Mass.; cons. nuclear medicine Ann Arbor VA Hosp.; chmn. radiology dept. Henry Ford Hosp., Detroit, 1983; radiologist in chief, Mass. Gen. Hosp., Boston, 1983—. Maj. M.C., U.S. Army, 1968-75. Office: Mass General Hosp Fruit St Boston MA 02114

THRASH, EDSEL E., educational administrator; b. Lake, Miss., Aug. 28, 1925; m. Jessie McLendon, Apr. 16, 1949; children—Jane, Catherine, George. B.S. in Bus. Adminstrn, La. State U., 1950, M.B.A., 1951, Ph.D., 1963. Acct. Esso Standard Oil Co., 1951-55; dir. alumni affairs La. State U., 1957-68, mem. dept. econs., 1966-68; exec. sec., dir. bd. trustees State Instns. Higher Learning in Miss., Jackson, 1968-87; Disting. prof. health care econs. U. Miss. Med. Ctr., Jackson, 1987—. Bd. dirs. Miss. Heart Assn., 1970-76; mem. exec. council Andrew Jackson council Boy Scouts Am.; mem. council on ministries United Meth. Ch., Raymond, Miss., 1973—. Recipient Silver Beaver award Boy Scouts Am., 1977, Gold Heart award Miss. Heart Assn., 1976; elected to La. State U. Alumni Hall of Distinction, 1993. Mem. State Higher Edn. Exec. Officers (nat. pres. 1984-85), Omicron Delta Kappa, Alpha Kappa Psi. Office: U Miss Health Care Ctr PO Box 13872 Jackson MS 39236-3872

THRASH, PATRICIA ANN, association executive; b. Grenada, Miss., May 4, 1929; d. Lewis Edgar and Weaver (Betts) T. BS, Delta State Coll., 1950; MA, Northwestern U., 1953, PhD, 1959. Tchr. high sch. English Clarksdale, Miss., 1950-52; head resident Northwestern U., 1953-55, asst. to dean women, 1955-58, asst. dean women 1958-60, lectr. edn., 1959-65, dean women, 1960-69, assoc. prof. edn., 1965-72, assoc. dean students, 1969-71; asst. exec. sec. Commn. on Instns. Higher Edn., North Central Assn. Colls. and Schs., 1972-73, assoc. exec. dir., 1973-76, assoc. dir., 1976-87, exec. dir., 1988—. Author (with others): Handbook of College and University Administration, 1970; contbr. articles to ednl. jours. Mem. Nat. Assn. Women Deans and Counselors (v.p. 1967-69, pres. 1972-73), Ill. Assn. Women Deans and Counselors (sec. 1961-63, pres. 1964-66), Am. Coll. Personnel Assn. (editorial bd. jour. 1971-74), Council Student Personel Assns. in Higher Edn. (sec.-treas. 1969-71), Am. Assn. Higher Edn. (program, nominations com. 1974-75, adv. panel Am. Coll. Testing Coll. Outcome Measures project 1977-78, staff COPA project for evaluation nontraditional edn. 1977-78, mem. editorial bd. Jour. Higher Edn. 1975-80, guest editor Mar.-Apr. 1979, co-editor NCA Quar. 1988—), exec. com. Nat. Policy Bd. for Higher Edn. Inst. 1993—, Mortar Bd. (hon.), Phi Delta Theta, Pi Lambda Theta, Alpha Psi Omega, Alpha Lambda Delta. Methodist. Home: 2337 Hartrey Ave Evanston IL 60201-2552

THRASH, PURVIS JAMES, SR., retired oil field equipment and service company executive; b. Nacogdoches, Tex., Dec. 6, 1927; s. James David and Elsie Marie (Crenshaw) T.; m. Betty Jo Johnston, Mar. 7, 1931; children: Purvis James Jr., Jan Caroline Thrash Beckman, Jill Marie Thrash Denton. BS in Petroleum Engring., Texas A&M U., 1950. V.p. domestic ops. Otis Engring. Corp., Dallas, 1975-80, sr. v.p. mgf., 1980-81, pres., chief exec. officer, 1981-90, chmn. bd., 1981-90, ret., 1990; mem. exec. com. Halliburton Co., Dallas, 1981-90. Author: (with others) Gas Lift Theory and Practice, 1967; contbr. articles to profl. jours.; patentee in field. Bd. dirs. Dallas Jr. Achievement, 1985. Recipient Outstanding Safety Achievement award Safety Coun. of Greater Dallas, 1987, 89. Mem. Am. Petroleum Inst., Soc. Petroleum Engrs., Nat. Oil-Equipment Mfrs. and Dels. Soc., Dallas Petroleum Club. Republican. Methodist. Avocations: hunting, fishing, travel. Home and Office: 17101 Vista Tree Cir Dallas TX 75248-6034

THRASHER, DIANNE ELIZABETH, mathematics educator, computer consultant; b. Brockton, Mass., July 11, 1945; m. George Thomas Thrasher, Jan. 28, 1967; children: Kimberly Elizabeth, Noelle Elizabeth. BA in Math, Bridgewater State Coll., 1967, postgrad. in computer sci., 1984-87. Cert. secondary math. and history tchr., Mass., cert. Kumon instr. Tchr. math. Plymouth/Carver Regional Schs., Plymouth, Mass., 1976-78, Alden Sch., Duxbury, Mass., 1980-82, Marshfield (Mass.) High Sch., 1982-84; computer cons. TC2I-Thrasher Computer Cons. and Instrn., Duxbury, Mass., 1988—; owner Internat. Kumon Ednl. Franchise, 1991-95, Duxbury Math. Ctr. K-Adult, 1995—; owner New Eng. Regional Kumon Ednl. Franchise, 1991-95. Active U.S. Figure Skating Assn., Colorado Springs, 1978-85; 2d reader First Ch. Christ Scientist, Plymouth, 1971-73; bd. govs. Skating Club of Hingham, Mass., 1978-85, pres., 1983-85, dir. Learn to Skate program, 1983-85; mem. First Ch. Christ Scientist, Boston, 1964—; charter mem. Nat. Adv. Coun. of the U.S. Navy Meml. Found., 1992. Nominated for Presdl. award for Excellence in Math. Teaching, NSF, 1992. Oem NAFE, AAUW, Nat. Coun. Tchrs. Math., Boston Computer Soc., Duxbury Bus. Assn., New England Regional Internat. Edn. Franchise Owners. Avocations: antiques, bicycling, skating, sailing. Home: 140 Toby Garden St Duxbury MA 02332-4945

THRASHER, JERRY ARTHUR, library director; b. Fairfield, Ala., Oct. 3, 1942; s. Arthur E. and Elizabeth M. Thrasher; m. Alice Wilson, Dec. 1, 1967; children: Alexander, Andrew. BA, U. Ala., 1969; MSLS, Fla. State U., 1970. Circulation libr. R.W. Woodruff Libr., Emory U., Atlanta, 1970-72; libr. City Island Libr., Daytona Beach, Fla., 1972-74; dir. Haywood County Pub. Libr., Waynesville, N.C., 1975-77; assoc. dir. Forsyth County Pub. Libr. Winston Salem N.C., 1977-79; dir. Cumberland County Pub. Libr. and Info. Ctr., Fayetteville, N.C., 1980—; dir. N.C. Libr. Assn., 1984-85; mem. Gov.'s Confs. on Libr. and Info. Svcs. for N.C., 1990-91; mem. pub. libr. adv. com. Online Computer Libr. Ctr., 1991-93. Editor: Haywood County Public Library: An Analysis of Its Community Resources, Services and Plans for Development, 1977, The People and Their Public Library, 1983; contbr. articles to profl. jours. Adv. bd. Cape Fear Botanical Gardens, 1990-92; chmn. WFSS-FM, PBS, Fayetteville (N.C.) State U., 1990-91; v.p. United Way Cumberland County, 1991; pres. Terry Sanford H.S. PTA, 1991-92. With U.S. Army, 1961-64. Recipient Roll of Honor award Freedom to Read Found., N.C. Newspapers, 1993. Mem. ALA, N.C. Pub. Libr. Dirs. Assn. (Libr. Dir. of Yr. 1989, pres. 1984), N.C. State Libr. Comm., N.C. Info. Hwy. Libr. Com., N.C. Info. Futures Inst., Fayetteville (N.C.) Kiwanis Club (pres. 1993-94). Office: Cumberland County Pub Libr 300 Maiden Ln Fayetteville NC 28301-5000

THREEFOOT, SAM ABRAHAM, physician, educator; b. Meridian, Miss., Apr. 10, 1921; s. Sam Abraham and Ruth Frances (Lilienthal) T.; m. Virginia Rush, Feb. 6, 1954; children: Barbara Jane Stockton Mattingly, Ginny Ruth Threefoot Lindberg, Tracyann Threefoot Esenstad, Shelley Ann Threefoot Cowan. B.S., Tulane U., 1943, M.D., 1945. Diplomate: Am. Bd. Internal Medicine. Intern Michael Reese Hosp., Chgo., 1945-47; asst. vis. physician Charity Hosp. New Orleans, 1947-50, vis. physician, 1950-57, sr. vis. physician, 1957-69, cons., 1969-70, 76—; clin. asst. dept. medicine Touro Infirmary, New Orleans, 1953-56; jr. asst. Touro Infirmary, 1956-60, sr. asst., 1960-63, dir. med. edn., 1953-63, dir. research, 1953-70, sr. dept. medicine, 1963-70; fellow dept. medicine Tulane U., 1947-49, instr., 1948-53, asst. prof., 1953-59, asso. prof., 1959-63, prof., 1963-70, 76-91, prof. emeritus, 1991—, asst. dean, 1979-91, adj. prof. emeritus Sch. Pub. Health & Tropical Medicine, 1993—; chief of staff VA Hosp. (Forest Hills div.), Augusta, Ga., 1970-76; asso. chief staff VA Hosp., New Orleans, 1976-79; chief of staff VA Hosp., 1979-91, cons., 1991—; asst. dean Med. Coll. Ga., 1970-76, prof. medicine, 1970-76; Cons. physician Lallie Kemp Charity Hosp., Independence, La., 1951-53. Editor: Lymphology, 1967-70; Contbr. articles profl. jours. Served with AUS, 1943-45. La. Heart Assn. grantee, 1953-55; John A. Hartford Found. grantee, 1956-74; am. Heart Assn. grantee, 1959-61; USPHS grantee, 1953-66. Fellow A.C.P., Am. Coll. Cardiology, N.Y. Acad. Sci.; mem. Am. Heart Assn. (v.p. 1970, fellow council on circulation), Central Soc. Clin. Research, So. Soc. Clin. Investigation (pres. 1967), AAAS, Internat. Soc. Lymphology, Soc. Exptl. Biology and Medicine, Soc. Nuclear Medicine, Microcirculatory Conf., Inc., Am. Fedn. Clin. Research, La. Heart Assn. (pres. 1967), Nat. Assn. VA Chiefs of Staff (pres. 1987-88), Phi Beta Kappa, Sigma Xi. Jewish. *I am one of those fortunate individuals who has been able to approach goals set early in life. Although my achievements are far short of my aspirations, at least I have had the opportunity. In dealing with both people and things, I have always felt that no detail was too small to receive attention.*

THREET, JACK CURTIS, oil company executive; b. Dundas, Ill., Aug. 16, 1928; s. Ivy Clemon and Daryl (Curtis) T.; m. Catherine Irene Hall, Mar. 24, 1951; children—Linda Sue, Judith Ann. B.A. in Geology, U. Ill., 1951. Geologist, dist. geologist, div. exploration mgr., area exploration mgr. Shell Oil Co., various locations including Oklahoma City, Amarillo, Tex., Denver, Pitts., Lafayette, La., Billings, Mont., N.Y.C., L.A., 1951-69; gen. mgr. exploration and prodn. Shell Australia Ltd., Melbourne, 1969-71; v.p. internat. exploration and prodn. Shell Can., Calgary, Alta., 1972-74, Shell Oil Co., New Orleans, 1974-75; v.p. internat. exploration and prodn. Houston, 1975-78, corp. v.p. exploration, 1978-87, ret., 1987; v.p., dir., co-founder Energy Exploration Mgmt. Co., Houston, 1988-90; pres., owner Threet Energy, Inc., Houston, 1989—. Served with U.S. Army, 1953-55. Mem. Am. Assn. Petroleum Geologists, Lakeside Country Club (Houston), Rotary. Republican. Methodist.

THRELKELD, MARY HELEN, accountant; b. East St. Louis, June 8, 1960; d. James John and Charlette Ann (Mongan) T. BBA, Tex. Christian U., 1982; MBA, U. Chgo., 1990. CPA. Software analyst Tandy Corp./Radio Shack, Ft. Worth, 1981-84; cons. supr. Coopers & Lybrand, Austin, Tex., 1985-88; cons. mgr. Coopers & Lybrand Europe, Brussels, Belgium, 1990-92; strategic analyst Software Spectrum, Inc., Garland, Tex., 1993-94, internat. acct., 1994—. Avocations: travel, reading, music. Office: Software Spectrum 2140 Merritt Dr Garland TX 75041-6184

THRELKELD, RICHARD DAVIS, broadcast journalist; b. Cedar Rapids, Iowa, Nov. 30, 1937; s. Robert M. and Lou Jane (Davis) T.; m. Sharon A. Adams, June 11, 1960 (div. 1983); children: Susan Anne, Julia Lynn; m. Betsy Aaron, May 15, 1983. B.A., Ripon Coll., 1959; M.S. in Journalism, Northwestern U., 1961; LHD (hon.), Ripon Coll., 1989. Editor Sta. WHAS-TV, Louisville, 1961; reporter Sta. WMT-TV, Cedar Rapids, Iowa, 1961-66; corr. CBS News, N.Y.C. and San Francisco, 1966-82; nat. corr. CBS News, 1989—; chief corr. ABC News TV, N.Y.C., 1982-89. Corr.: TV news documentary Defense of America, 1981 (Emmy award); TV news report Rhodesia Remembered, 1980 (Overseas Press Club award), TV news report Vietnam Remembered, 1985 (Emmy award), TV news series Status Reports, 1984 (Dupont award), TV new report Lebanon-Grenada 1983 (Overseas Press Club award). CBS News fellow, 1964. Mem. AFTRA, Radio-TV News Dirs. Assn., Sigma Delta Chi.

THRIFT, JULIANNE STILL, academic administrator; b. Barnwell, S.C.; m. Ashley Ormand Thrift; children: Lindsay, Laura. BA, U. S.C., MEd; PhD in Pub. Policy, George Washington U. Formerly asst. exec. dir. Nat. Assn. Coll. and Univ. Attys.; ombudsman U. S.C.; exec. dir. Nat. Inst. Ind. Colls. and Univs., 1982-88; exec. v.p. Nat. Assn. Ind. Colls. and Univs., Washington, 1988-91; pres. Salem Acad. and Coll., Winston-Salem, N.C., 1991—. Office: Salem Coll Office of the President Winston Salem NC 27108-0548

THROCKMORTON, JOAN HELEN, advertising agency executive; b. Evanston, Ill., Apr. 11, 1931; d. Sydney L. and Anita H. (Pusheck) T.; m. Sheldon Burton Satin, June 26, 1982. B.A. with honors, Smith Coll., 1953. Mktg. exec. Lawrence Chait & Co., N.Y.C., 1965; mktg. exec. Cowles Communications, Inc., N.Y.C., 1968-69; founder, chief exec. officer Throckmorton Assocs., Inc., N.Y.C., 1970-83; pres. Joan Throckmorton Inc., N.Y.C., 1983—; lectr. in field; instr. Direct Mktg. Assn., Sch. Continuing Edn., NYU, N.Y.C., 1985. Author: Winning Direct Response Advertising, 1986. Bd. dirs. Halle Ravine com. Nature Conservancy, 1985; mem. expedition com. Outward Bound, 1980-83. Named Direct Mktg. Woman of Yr., 1986. Mem. Women's Dir. Response Group (founding mem.), Dir. Mktg. Assn. (bd. dirs. 1971-77, exec. com. 1972-77, mem. longrange planning com. 1977-78), Women's Forum, Dir. Mktg. Idea Exchange, Dir. Mktg. Creative Guild (bd. dirs. 1984-85), Jr. League Mexico City, Jr. League N.Y.C., Phi Beta Kappa. Office: Joan Throckmorton Inc PO Box 452 Pound Ridge NY 10576-0452

THROCKMORTON, WILLIAM ROBERT, SR., sociologist; b. Washington, Feb. 28, 1923; s. Robert William and Katharine Eleanor (Crook) T.; m. Rosemary Anne Phillips, Sept. 11, 1943; children: William Robert, Nancy Elizabeth, Peter Joseph, Patricia Anne; m. Sharon Ann Jarrett, Aug. 18, 1961; children: Theresa Cecilia, Elizabeth Jean, Thomas Caron. AB, George Washington U., 1954, postgrad., 1954-58. Br. mgr. Western Union Tel. Co., Washington and Alexandria Va., 1941-44, 46-48; libr. asst. Washington Pub. Libr., 1948-49; clk., stenographer So. Ry., Washington, 1949-50; spl. class tchr., pub. schs. Washington, 1954-56; probation officer Arlington County Juvenile Ct., 1957; rsch. asst., population rsch. project George Washington U., 1957; instr. Washington Sch. for Secs., 1958-60; asst. to counsel, office mgr. U.S. Senate, 1960-66; manpower analyst Dept. Labor, 1966-79; nat. coord. Fed. Bonding Program, 1980—; pvt. cons. in criminal justice, 1980—; asst. professorial lectr. sociology George Washington U., 1960-76. Mem Keyman, United Givers Fund, 1969-72; treas. Fairfax County Commn. for Women, 1977-81. With USAAF, 1944-46, Korea, Japan. Recipient Disting. Achievement award Dept. Labor, 1974. Mem. Lester F. Ward (treas. 1954), D.C. Sociol. Soc., Am. Sociol. Assn., Am. Soc. Criminology, George Washington Univ. Faculty Club. Democrat. Roman Catholic.

THRODAHL, MONTE CORDEN, former chemical company executive; b. Mpls., Mar. 25, 1919; s. Monte Conrad and Hilda (Larson) T.; m. Josephine Crandall, Nov. 6, 1948; children: Mark Crandall, Peter Douglas. B.S., Iowa State U., 1941. With Monsanto Co., St. Louis, 1941-84; gen. mgr. internat. div. Monsanto Co., 1964-66, v.p., 1965-84, dir. 1966-84, group v.p. tech., 1974-77, sr. v.p., 1979-84; v.p., dir. Monsanto Research Corp. Fellow AIChE, AAAS, Am. Inst. Chemists; mem. NAE, Am. Chem. Soc., Comml. Devel. Assn., Soc. Chem. Industry, Old Warson Country Club, St. Louis Club, Univ. Club, Old Warson Country Club, St. Louis Club, Alpha Chi Sigma. Home: 154 Briarcliff Ladue MO 63124-1753 Office: 7811 Carondelet Ave Saint Louis MO 63105-3317

THRONDSON, EDWARD WARNER, residential association administrator; b. Woodland, Calif., Mar. 22, 1938; s. Edward J. and Arden Warner (Law) T.; m. Marjorie Jean Waite, June 25, 1960 (div. 1993); children: Mark Edward, Kimberly Anne, Sulin Marget; m. Mary Jo Riddell Law, Jan. 13, 1994. BS, Stanford U., 1960; MBA, Harvard U., 1962. Profl. Community Assn. Mgr.; Community Assn. Inst. Asst. br. mgr. Pacific Delta Gas, Santa Rosa, Calif., 1962-65; corp. staff asst. Pacific Delta Gas, San Jose, Calif.,

1965-72; regional mgr. Pargas, San Jose, 1972-86; gen. mgr., COO The Villages Golf and Country Club, San Jose, 1986-93; sr. v.p. West Coast Community Assocs., Campbell, Calif., 1994—. Mem. Cmty. Assns. Inst. (com. chair 1991—, Pres.'s Appreciation award 1991), Calif. Assn. Cmty. Mgrs. (cert., founding mem. com. chair 1992—, author course 1992, 94). Avocations: golf, stamp collecting, geneology. Office: West Coast Community Assocs 145 Dillon Ave Ste D Campbell CA 95008

THRONE, MARILYN ELIZABETH, English educator; b. Cleve., Oct. 24, 1939; d. Charles George and Clara Elizabeth (Kieffer) T.; m. James R. Woodworth. AB, Miami U. in Oxford, 1961, MA, 1962; PhD, Miami U. in Oxford, Ohio State, 1969. Instr. Miami U., Oxford, Ohio, 1964-69; asst. prof. Miami U., Oxford, 1969-79, assoc. prof., 1979-90, prof., 1990—. Author: Walter Havighurst: Novelist of the Heartland, 1979. Office: Miami U English Dept Oxford OH 45056

THRONER, GUY CHARLES, JR., engineering executive, scientist, engineer, inventor, consultant; b. Mpls., Sept. 14, 1919; s. Guy Charles and Marie (Zechar) T.; m. Betty. Dec. 5, 1943; children—Richard, Carol Anne, Steven. BA, Oberlin Coll., 1943; postgrad., UCLA, 1960, 61. Registered profl. engr., Calif. Br. head Naval Weapon Ctr., China Lake, Calif. 1946-53; mgr. ordnance div., mgr. weapon systems div. Aerojet Gen. Corp., Azusa, Calif., 1953-64; v.p., div. mgr. FMC Corp., San Jose, Calif., 1964-74; research dir. Vacu Blast Corp., Belmont, Calif., 1976-78; v.p., devel. mfg. Dahlman, Inc., Braham, Minn., 1978-79; mgr. ordnance systems & tech. Battelle Meml. Inst., Columbus, Ohio, 1979-85; pres. Guy C. Throner & Assocs., tech. and mgmt. cons., 1985—; dir. Omron Corp. Am., Chgo., 1976-77. Inventor, patentee indls., med. and mil. systems design. Served as officer USNR, World War II. Am. Order St. Barbara medal U.S. Army Arty, 1983, Recipient IR-100 award Indsl. Research Mag., Chgo., 1971, Congl. Commendation, 1985, also various commendations. Mem. AIAA, Am. Def. Preparedness Assn. (Bronze medal 1974, Simon award 1985), Lake Wildwood Country Club, Sigma Xi. Republican. Avocations: astronomy; photography; golf. Home and Office: 17992 Jayhawk Dr Penn Valley CA 95946-9206

THROWER, ELLEN, academic administrator. BS in Bus. Adminstn., U. N.C., Greensboro, 1975, MBA, 1978; PhD, Ga. State U., 1981; postgrad., Harvard U., 1988. Instr. dept. risk mgmt. Ga. State U., Atlanta, 1978-80; asst. prof. ins. and risk mgmt. dept. ins., real estate, and law Fla. State U., Talahassee, 1981-84; assoc. prof. ins. dept. ins., actuarial sci. and stats. Drake U., Des Moines, 1984-88, dir. ins. ctr., 1985-88; pres., CEO The Coll. of Ins., N.Y.C., 1988—; dir. Profl. Ins. Agts. Nat. Ins. Sch., Oberlin, Ohio and Chico, Calif., 1986-87; mem. adv. bd. Nat Ins. Ind. Assn., 1990—; bd. dirs. Pa. Nat. Ins. Cos., 1990—; editorial adv. bd. Insurance Review, 1990-92, Risk Management, 1992. Author: (with kathy Mohr) Iowa Ins. Fact Book, 1988; (with Lisa Gardener) The Status of Insurance Education at American Colleges and Universities, 1989; contbr. numerous pubs. to profl. jours. Bd. dirs. N.Y.C Coun. on Econ. Edn., 1992, N.C. Ins. Edn. Found., 1989—, Ins. Edn. Found., 1988—, PIA Ins. Found.; active Griffith Found. Grantee Nat. Assn. Mut. Ins. Cos., 1988, 90, 91, 92, Aetna Life and Casualty Co., 1987, State of Iowa Dept. Econ. Devel., 1987, James F. Kemper Found., 1987; Rsch. grantee Fla. State Found., 1983, Fla. State U., 1982. Mem. Internat. Ins. Soc., Am. Risk and Ins. Assn. (bd. dirs.), Am. Mgmt. Assn., Risk and Ins. Mgmt. Soc., Soc. for Ins. Rsch., So. Risk and Ins. Assn. (bd. dirs.), We. Risk and Ins. Soc., Fin. Womens Assn. N.Y., Consortium. Office: The Coll of Ins 101 Murray St New York NY 10007*

THROWER, JOHN EDEN, architectural firm executive; b. Barnwell, S.C., Sept. 4, 1939. BS cum laude, Trinity Coll., 1961; BArch, U. Pa., 1964, MArch, 1965. Registered arch., Pa., N.J., Del., Md., Minn.; cert. Nat. Coun. Archtl. Registration Bd. Designer Venturi & Rauch, 1966-67; assoc. Bower and Fradley Archs., Phila., 1967-78; ptnr. Bower Lewis Thrower, Phila., 1978—; from design critic to adj. assoc. prof. architecture U. Pa., 1965-90; guest critic Temple U., Drexel U., U. of Arts. Prin. works include SKF Industries, The Eugene Ormandy Archives-U. Pa., Baldwin Sch., Boeing Helicopters Hdqrs., White Horse Village, Delaware County, Pa., Phila. Navy Yard Engring. Mgmt. Bldg., numerous others. Active Interfaith Forum on Religion, Art & Architecture. Recipient Arthur Spayd Brooke Gold medal for design; John Stewardson traveling fellow, 1964, Schenk-Woodman traveling fellow, 1965. Mem. AIA (Phila. chpt. past v.p. bd. dirs.), Nat. Assn. Sr. Living, Assn. Preservation Tech., Phi Beta Kappa, Tau Sigma Delta. Office: Bower Lewis Thrower Architects 1216 Arch St Fl 8 Philadelphia PA 19107-2835

THROWER, NORMAN JOSEPH WILLIAM, geographer, educator; b. Crowthorne, Eng., Oct. 23, 1919; came to U.S., 1947, naturalized, 1957; s. Gordon William and Ethel Daisy (Bayley) T.; m. Elizabeth McPherson Martin, Aug. 9, 1947; children: Mildred Page Mosier, Anne Bayley Leonard, Mary Elizabeth Thrower Kerr. BA with honors, U. Va., 1953; MA, U.Wis., 1955, PhD, 1958. Asst. prof. geography UCLA, 1957-61, assoc. prof., 1961-65, prof., 1965-90, prof. emeritus 1990—, Clark Libr. prof., 1972-73, dir. William Andrews Clark Meml. Library, 1981-87; founder UCLA Ctr. for 17th and 18th Century Studies, 1985; dir. Columbus Quincentenary Programs UCLA, 1989-93; adv. bd. Guggenheim Found., 1978—. Author 10 books on cartographic subjects; contbr. articles to profl. jours. Vice pres. Sir Francis Drake Commn. of State of Calif., 1973-75, pres., 1975-80. Served with Brit. Army, 1940-47. Decorated Burma Star, Orden del Mérito Civil (Spain), 1992; Guggenheim fellow, 1962-63. Mem. Assn. Am. Geographers, Soc. History of Discoveries (v.p. 1971-72, pres. 1973-74), Hakluyt Soc. (hon. sec. overseas 1993—), Internat. Cartographic Assn. (corr.), Internat. Soc. for History for Cartography, Western Soc. for 18th Century Studies (v.p. 1986-87, pres. 1987-88). Presbyterian. Office: U Calif Dept Geography Los Angeles CA 90024

THRUN, ROBERT READ, architect; b. Ossining, N.Y., June 9, 1949; s. Robert and Roberta Read (Lewis) T.; m. Rita Catherine McDermott, June 15, 1968; 1 child, Zachary. BA, Colby Coll., 1971; MArch, U. Pa., 1974. Registered architect Ohio, N.Y., Pa., Conn., Md., N.J., Ky., Tenn., Wis., Ind., Iowa. Architect Mitchell/Giurgola Assocs., Phila., 1974-75; project architect/designer The Kling Lingquist Partnership, Phila., 1975-83; studio dir., prin designer CUH2A, Princeton, 1983-89; mng. ptnr., prin. designer A.M. Kinney Assocs., Cin., 1989—. Prin. works include C.C. of Phila., 1979 (AIA medal 1980), Corp. Hdqrs. Bldg. BMW of N.Am., 1986, Rsch. complex Pfizer, Inc., 1989 (City of Groton 1990), European Corp. Hdqrs. Nalco Chem. Co., 1993. Mem. AIA (award for design excellence Ohio chpt. 1993, award 1994). Avocations: cross country skiing, sailing, painting, reading. Office: AM Kinney Assocs 2900 Vernon Pl Cincinnati OH 45219

THRUNE, ELAINE M., biotechnician; b. Faribault, Minn., Sept. 24, 1948; d. Raymond E. and Eleanor F. Kalien; m. Stephen V. Thrune, June 14, 1970. BS in Biology, Winona State Coll., 1970; MA in Biology, St. Cloud State U., 1976. Cert. wildlife rehabilitator, Minn. Biology specialist Coll. Lab. Svcs. St. Cloud (Minn.) State U. Author: (anthology) Emergence, 1990, Whisperings, 1992. Dir., educator, vol. WILD AGAIN Wildlife Rehab. Program, 1981-95. Mem. Nat. Wildlife Rehab. Assn. (founder, pres. 1987-95), Minn. Wildlife Assistance Coop. (founder, pres. 1986-89), Tri-County Humane Soc. Avocations: canoeing, horseback riding, writing, reading. Office: Nat Wildlife Rehab Assn 14 7th Ave N Saint Cloud MN 56303

THUERING, GEORGE LEWIS, industrial engineering educator; b. Milw., Sept. 2, 1919; s. Louis Charles and Elsie (Luetzow) T.; m. Lillian May Cline, Dec. 7, 1945 (dec.); 1 child; m. Betty L. McBride, Aug. 9, 1975. B.S., U. Wis., 1941, M.E., 1954; M.S., Pa. State U., 1949. Registered profl. engr., Pa. Mfg. engr. Lockheed Aircraft Corp., Burbank, Calif., 1941-47; supr. plant layout Lockheed Aircraft Corp., Marietta, Ga., 1951-52; mem. faculty Pa. State U., University Park, 1947—; assoc. prof. indsl. engring. Pa. State U., 1952-56, prof., 1956-82, prof. emeritus, 1982—; dir. mgmt. engring., 1961-82; cons. engring. Contbr. articles to profl. jours. Fellow Soc. Advancement Mgmt.; mem. ASME (vice chmn. mgmt. div. 1976-77, mem. exec. com. mgmt. div. 1973-77, chmn. papers rev. com 1969-73, v.p. gen. engring. 1982-84), Am. Inst. Indsl. Engrs. (dir. students affairs 1973-74), Am. Soc. Engring. Edn. (chmn. indsl. engring. div. 1956-57), Sigma Xi, Tau Beta Pi, Pi Tau Sigma, Alpha Pi Mu. Home: 436 Homan Ave State College PA 16801-6336 Office: 207 Hammond Bldg University Park PA 16802

THUESEN, GERALD JORGEN, industrial engineer, educator; b. Oklahoma City, July 20, 1938; s. Holger G. and Helen S. T.; m. Harriett M. Thuesen; children: Karen E., Dyan L. BS, Stanford U., 1960, MS, 1961, PhD, 1968. Engr. Pacific Telephone Co., San Francisco, 1961-62, Atlantic Richfield Co., Dallas, 1962-63; asst. prof. indsl. engring. U. Tex., Arlington, 1963, 67-68; assoc. prof. indsl. and systems engring. Ga. Inst. Tech., Atlanta, 1968-76, prof., 1976—. Author: Engineering Economy, 4th edit., 1971, 5th edit., 1977, 6th edit., 1984, 7th edit., 1989, 8th edit., 1993, Economic Decision Analysis, 1974, 2d edit., 1980; assoc. editor: The Engring. Economist, 1974-80, editor, 1981-91. NASA/Am. Soc. Engring. Edn. summer faculty fellow, 1970. Fellow Inst. Indsl. Engrs. (dept. editor Trans. 1976-80, v.p. publs. 1979-80, div. dir. 1978-80, Wellington award 1989, Publs. award 1990), Am. Soc. Engring. Edn. (bd. dirs. 1977-79, Eugene L. Grant award 1977, 89); mem. Ops. Rsch. Soc. Am., Inst. Mgmt. Sci., Ga. Tech. Athletic Assn. (bd. dirs. 1978-93), Sigma Xi. Office: Sch Indsl and Systems Engring Ga Inst Tech Atlanta GA 30332

THUILLIER, RICHARD HOWARD, meteorologist; b. N.Y.C., Apr. 3, 1936; s. Howard Joseph and Louise (Schilling) T.; m. Barbara Unger (dec. 1992); children: Stephen, David, Lawrence, Daniel. BS in Physics, Fordham U., 1959; MS in Meteorology, NYU, 1963, postgrad., 1963-66. Cert. cons. meteorologist. Instr. SUNY, 1963-66; dir. of research Weather Engrs. of Panama Inc., Panama City, Rep. Panama, 1966-68; cons. Oakland, Calif., 1968—; meteorologist and chief of research and planning Bay Area Air Quality Mgmt. Dist., San Francisco, 1968-76; sr. research meteorologist SRI Internat., Menlo Park, Calif., 1976-80, Pacific Gas & Electric, San Ramon, Calif., 1980—; Note, your military record is listed in your civic section, per style. Capt. USAF, 1959-62. Mem. Am. Meteorol. Soc., (pres. Panama Canal Zone chpt. 1967-68, San Francisco Bay chpt. 1971-72, Outstanding Contributions to Advance of Applied Meteorology award 1993), Sigma Xi (hon.). Republican. Roman Catholic. Avocations: skiing, bowling, golf, music, art.

THULEAN, DONALD MYRON, symphony conductor; b. Wenatchee, Wash., June 24, 1929; s. Elmer Edward and Mary (Myron) T.; m. Meryl Mary Parnell, Mar. 17, 1951; children—Dorcas Marie, Mark Myron, William Norton. B.A., U. Wash., 1950, M.A. in Music, 1952; Mus.D. (hon.), Whitworth Coll., 1967. Faculty Pacific U., 1955-62; dean Pacific U. (Sch. Music), 1957-62. Assoc. conductor Portland (Ore.) Symphony, 1961-62, conductor, music dir. Spokane Symphony, 1962-84; v.p. artistic affairs, orch. svcs. Am. Symphony Orch. League, 1984—; asst. conductor Seattle Symphony, 1966-69, chorus master, Aspen Music Festival, 1957-61; artistic cons. Title III project in performing arts, Wash., 1966-68, music dir. Tamarack Music Festival, 1971. Served with AUS, 1953-55. Unitarian (trustee). Office: 1156 15th St NW Washington DC 20005-3201

THULIN, WALTER WILLIS, real estate company executive; b. Mpls., Aug. 10, 1929; s. Edwin and Henrietta Helen (Kaupp) T.; m. M. Joan Thulin, Jan. 11, 1952; children: Elizabeth, Joshua K., Edwin K., Justin F. B.Chem. Engring., U. Minn., 1952, B.B.A, 1952; M.B.A., Harvard U., 1954. V.p. internat. mktg. Internat. Flavors & Fragrances, N.Y.C., 1967-78; group v.p. Mallinckrodt, Inc., St. Louis, 1978-88; chmn. Evergreen Mgmt. Inc., Jackson, Wyo., 1989—. Home: PO Box 727 Wilson WY 83014-0727 Office: PO Box 2871 Jackson WY 83001-2871

THUMANN, ALBERT, association executive, engineer; b. Bronx, N.Y., Mar. 12, 1942; s. Albert and Ella (Josephy) T.; m. Susan Stock, Jan. 23, 1966; 1 child, Brian. B.S., City U. N.Y., 1964; M.S. in Elec. Engring. N.Y. U., 1967, M.S. in Indsl. Engring. 1970. Registered profl. engr., N.Y., Ga., Ky. Project engring. mgr. Bechtel Corp., N.Y.C., Louisville, 1964-77; exec. dir., founder Assn. Energy Engrs., 1977—; Adj. prof. environmental engring. U. Louisville, 1974-75; lectr. on energy conservation. Author: Electrical Consulting-Engineering and Design, 1973, (with R.K. Miller) Secrets of Noise Control, 1976, Plant Engineers and Managers Guide to Energy Conservation, 1977, 2d edit., 1982, Biorhythms and Industrial Safety, 1977, How to Patent Without a Lawyer, 1978, Electrical Design, Safety and Energy Conservation, 1978, Handbook of Energy Audits, 1979, 3d edit., 1995, Energy Audit Sourcebook, 1983, Fundamentals of Energy Engineering, 1984, Introduction to Efficient Electrical Systems Design, 3d edit., 1990, (with Goldstick) Waste Heat Recovery, 1986, (with Miller) Introduction to Noise Control Engineering, 1986, Optimizing HVAC Systems, 1988, Lighting Efficiency Applications, 1988, (with James A. Bent) Project Management for Engineering and Construction, 1988, Plant Engineers and Managers Guide to Energy Conservation, 5th edit., 1991, Handbook of Energy Engineering, 1989, 3d edit., 1994; editor: Emerging Synthetic Fuel Industry, 1981; contbr. articles to profl. jours. Named Young Engr. of Year Ky. Soc. Profl. Engrs., 1974-75, Ky. col.; recipient Disting. Service award Assn. Energy Engrs., 1980. Mem. Nat. Soc. Profl. Engrs., Am. Soc. Assn. Execs., City Coll. Alumni Assn. Creater retng. course for unemployed aerospace engrs. Home: 931 Smoketree Dr Tucker GA 30084-1548 Office: Assn Energy Engrs Ste 420 4025 Pleasantdale Rd Atlanta GA 30340-4262 *Where am I going and what am I doing, is a phrase which I have repeated many times. Constant appraisal of what one is doing and evaluation of this action with the goal are necessary for achieving one's objective. Salesmanship is the guiding tool which helps to obtain the objective once the course is chosen.*

THUMS, CHARLES WILLIAM, designer, consultant; b. Manitowoc, Wis., Sept. 5, 1945; s. Earl Oscar and Helen Margaret (Rusch) T. B. in Arch., Ariz. State U., 1972. Ptnr., Grafic, Tempe, Ariz., 1967-70; founder, prin. I-Squared Environ. Cons., Tempe, Ariz., 1970-78; designer and cons. design morphology, procedural programming and algorithms, 1978—. Author: (with Jonathan Craig Thums) Tempe's Grand Hotel, 1973, The Rossen House, 1975; (with Daniel Peter Aiello) Shelter and Culture, 1976; contbg. author: Tombstone Planning Guide, 5 vols., 1974. Office: PO Box 3126 Tempe AZ 85280-3126

THUNBORG, ANDERS INGEMAR, ambassador; b. Stockholm, June 9, 1934; s. Albert T. and Greta A. (Lundin) T.; m. Ingalill B. Holm. Sec. bd. Social Dem. Party, Sweden, 1961-69; under sec. state dept. def. Swedish Gov., 1969-74, spl. advisor, under sec. state ministry fgn. affairs, 1974-76; amb. and permanent rep. of Sweden to UN, N.Y.C., 1977-83; minister def. Swedish Gov., 1983-85, amb. at large ministry for fgn. affairs, 1985-86; amb. Embassy of Sweden, USSR, 1986-89, Swedish Embassy, U.S.A., 1989—; chmn. 1974 def. com., UN Trust Fund for S. Africa, 1977-83; v.p. UN Gen. Assembly, 1981-82. Office: Swedish Embassy 2033 M St NW # 402 Washington DC 20036-3305

THUNE, DALE GENE, financial executive, appraiser; b. Toronto, S.D., Apr. 19, 1935; s. Carl E. and Julia (Gorder) T.; m. Lorna Gail Pierce, Dec. 21, 1958; children: Diana Carol, Cynthia Ann. BS, Calif. State U., 1964; cert., UCLA, 1969. Sr. real estate appraiser County of Los Angeles, 1964-73; v.p. property and sales tax Carter Hawley Hale Stores Inc., Los Angeles, 1973—. Sgt. USMC, 1953-57. Named to Hon. Order Ky. Cols., 1982. Mem. Inst. Property Taxation (cert. property mem., salestax mem., bd. dirs. 1978—, pres. 1986-87), Internat. Assn. Assessing Officers (Outstanding Subscribing Mem. 1986), Am. Soc. Appraisers (sr. mem.), Soc. Auditor Appraisers, Los Angeles Assessors Adv. Com., Retail Mchts. Calif. State Tax Commn., Los Angeles Taxpayers Assn. (chmn. 1987-88). Republican. Lutheran. Clubs: Jonathan (Los Angeles); Ironwood Country (Palm Desert, Calif.). Lodges: Rotary, Masons. Avocations: golf, tennis, bridge. Office: Carter Hawley Hale Stores Inc 444 S Flower St Los Angeles CA 90071-2901

THURBER, CLEVELAND, JR., trust banker; b. Detroit, Aug. 2, 1925; s. Cleveland and Marie Louise (Palms) T.; m. Elizabeth-Mary Hamilton, June 22, 1947; children: Cleveland III, Elizabeth King Thurber Crawford, David. Student, Purdue U.; B.A., Williams Coll., 1948. Asst. trust officer Comerica Bank-Detroit, 1958-61, trust officer, 1961-63, v.p., 1963-69, sr. v.p., 1969-81, exec. v.p., chief trust officer, 1981-89. Pres. Friends of Grosse Pointe Pub. Libr., 1971-72, Mich. Heart Assn., 1969-74; sec. United Community Svcs., 1968-70; bd. dirs. Cottage Hosp., 1970-94, United Found., 1975-89; Mich. Humane Soc., 1973-89, Elmwood Cemetery, pres., 1995; bd. dirs. Ctr. for Creative Studies, 1976-89, Wm. L. Clements Libr., Ann Arbor. With USMCR, 1943-46. Clubs: Bayview Yacht (Detroit), Yondotega (Detroit), Country (Detroit), Grosse Pointe. Home: 34 Edgemere Rd Grosse Pointe MI 48236-3709 Office: 21 Kercheval Ave Grosse Pointe MI 48236-3601

THURBER, CLEVELAND, JR., trust banker; b. Detroit, N.H., Aug. 2, 1925; s. George Freeman and Muriel (Davis) T.; m. Shirley Ann Amos, July 14, 1946 (dec. Jan. 1970); children: Shelley Davis, Steven Anderson, George Frederick, Matthew Thomas; m. Patricia Martin Skillas, Apr. 25, 1971. Grad., Phillips Acad., Andover, Mass., 1943; B.Naval Sci., Coll. Holy Cross, 1945; M.S., Mass. Inst. Tech., 1948. Sales engr. Amos Thompson Corp., Edinburg, Ind., 1950-55; asst. to pres. White Mountain Freezer Co. Inc., Nashua, 1955-56; with Second Nat. Bank Nashua (merged to form Bank of N.H., N.A.), 1956—, pres., 1962-87, chmn. 1972—; bd. dirs. Bank of N.H. Corp., chmn., 1981—; bd. dirs. Pennichuck Corp., Nashua, Energy North, Inc., Manchester. Bd. dirs. Tee Currier Gallery Art, Manchester, Nutt Hosp. Served to lt. (j.g.) USNR, 1943-46. Mem. Detroit Club (past pres.), Yondotega Club, Country Club, Grosse Pointe Club, Bayview Yacht Club. Republican. Episcopalian. Clubs: Mason (33 deg.), Rotarian, Nashua Country. Home: 25 Swart Ter Nashua NH 03060-1966 Office: Bank NH Corp 300 Franklin St Manchester NH 03101-2318

THURBER, DONALD MACDONALD DICKINSON, public relations counsel; b. Detroit, Feb. 3, 1918; s. Donald MacDonald Dickinson and Fayetta Cecelia (Crowley) T.; m. Margaret Worcester Dudley, June 6, 1964. A.B. magna cum laude, Harvard U., 1940. Pvt. tutor Detroit, 1937-39; house mgr. Cape Playhouse, Dennis, Mass., 1940; exec. sec. youth div. Democratic Nat. Com., 1940; membership sec. Harvard Club, N.Y.C., 1940; project supr. Detroit Council for Youth Service, 1941-43; rep. for Mich., Nat. Found. Infantile Paralysis, 1943-46; sec. administr. Wayne County (Mich.) chpt., 1946-50; exec. dir. Gov. Mich. Study Commn. on Deviated Criminal Sex Offenders, 1950-51; exec. sec. Mayor Detroit Com. Rehab. Narcotic Addicts, 1951-53; sec., asst. treas. Mich. Rotary Press, Inc., Detroit, 1953-54; pres. Mich. Rotary Press, Inc., 1954-58; exec. v.p. Pub. Relations Counselors, Inc., Detroit, 1958-61; pres. Pub. Relations Counselors, Inc., 1961—. Bd. dirs. Clan Donald Found., 1994—; mem. Mich. Crippled Children Commn., 1954-58, vice chmn., 1956-58; planning dir. Episcopal Diocese of Mich., 1958-62, mem. exec. council, 1963-66; cons. to Sec. Interior, 1962-68; mem. Nat. Park Trust Fund Bd., 1963-67; bd. regents U. Mich., 1958-63; mem. Mich. Bd. Edn., 1965-67; mem. bd. overseers com. to visit Harvard Coll., 1964-70; mem. Mich. Citizens Com. for Higher Edn. Planning, 1967-69; chmn. Wayne County Community Coll., 1968-72, trustee, 1968-74; mem. Adv. Com. on Higher Edn. Planning in Southeastern Mich. 1970-72; advisor Nat. Trust Hist. Preservation, 1972-78; bd. dirs. Nat. Park Found., 1974-80, founder and historian, 1992—; mem. adv. council to Sec. Commerce, 1976-77; former v.p. Detroit Grand Opera Assn.; mem. adv. com. Detroit Urban League; trustee Clan Donald Lands Trust, Isle of Skye, Scotland, 1979—; trustee, vice chmn. St. Gregory's Abbey Found., Three Rivers, Mich., 1984-92; trustee Mich. Hist. Ctr. Found., vice chmn., 1992—; mem. Mich. Hist. Commn., 1984-87; bd. dirs. Blue Cross-Blue Shield of Mich., 1986-92, chmn. bd., exec. com., 1988-92; Mich. exec. com. United Negro Coll. Fund; bd. dirs. Friends of U. Mich. Libr., 1988—. Mem. Detroit Symphony Orch. Hall Vol. Coun., Detroit Hist. Soc., Mich. Hist. Soc., Friends of Detroit and Grosse Pointe Pub. Libraries, Mich. Natural Areas Council, Mich. Nature Assn., Clan Donald-U.S.A. (Gt. Lakes commr. emeritus, Mich. commr. emeritus), Ancient and Honorable Artillery Co., Soc. Colonial Wars, Soc. War of 1812, State Soc. of the Cincinnati of Pa., Mil. Order Loyal Legion U.S., Order Founders and Patriots Am., Colonial Order of Acorn, St. Nicholas Soc., Prismatic Club (Detroit), Harvard Club (Ea. Mich., N.Y.C., Boston). Democrat. Episcopalian. Office: Pub Rels Counselors Inc 10 Rathbone Pl Grosse Pointe MI 48230-1914

THURBER, JOHN ALEXANDER, lawyer; b. Detroit, Nov. 9, 1939; s. John Levington and Mary Anne (D'Agostino) T.; m. Barbara Irene Brown, June 30, 1962; children: John Levington II, Sarah Jeanne. AB in History, U. Mich., 1962, JD, 1965. Bar: Ohio 1965, Mich. 1968. Assoc. Hahn, Loeser and Parks, Cleve., 1965-67, Miller, Canfield, Paddock and Stone, Birmingham, Mich., 1967-73; ptnr. Miller, Canfield, Paddock and Stone, Bloomfield Hills, Mich., 1974—. Treas. Birmingham Community House, 1971-73; pres. Birmingham Village Players, 1983-84; bd. dirs. Oakland Parks Found., Pontiac, Mich., 1984—, pres., 1989-92; mem. capital com. Lighthouse Found. Mem. Otsego Ski Club (Gaylord, Mich.). Avocations: reading, theater, walking, sports. Office: Miller Canfield Paddock & Stone 1400 N Woodward Ave Ste 100 Bloomfield Hills MI 48304-2855

THURBER, PETER PALMS, lawyer; b. Detroit, Mar. 23, 1928; s. Cleveland and Marie Louise (Palms) T.; m. Ellen Bodley Stites, Apr. 16, 1955; children—Edith Bodley, Jane Chenoweth, H. Thomas, Sarah Bartlett. B.A., Williams Coll., 1950; J.D., Harvard U., 1953. Bar: Mich., 1954. Ptnr. Miller, Canfield, Paddock and Stone, Detroit, 1953-93, of counsel, 1994—; trustee McGregor Fund, Detroit, 1979—. Bd. dirs. Detroit Symphony Orch., Inc., 1974-93; trustee Community Found. for Southeastern Mich., 1990—, Coun. Mich. Founds., 1991—. With U.S. Army, 1953-55. Fellow Am. Bar Found.; mem. ABA, Mich. Bar Assn. Roman Catholic. Club: Country of Detroit (Grosse Pointe Farms, Mich.). Avocations: reading; traveling; athletics. Home: 28 Provencal Rd Grosse Pointe MI 48236-3038 Office: Miller Canfield Paddock & Stone 150 W Jefferson Ave Ste 2500 Detroit MI 48226-4432

THURBER, ROBERT EUGENE, physiologist, researcher; b. Bayshore, N.Y., Oct. 11, 1932; s. Hallett Elliot and Mary Jean (Winkler) T.; m. Barbara Meyer, June 24, 1953 (div. 1982); children: Robert, Joseph, Karl, Michael; m. Linda Boyd, Mar. 4, 1984; stepchildren: Janet, Barbara, Karen, Robert. BS, Holy Cross Coll., Worcester, Mass., 1954; MS, Adelphi U., 1961; PhD, U. Kans., 1964. Rsch. assoc. Brookhaven Nat. Lab., Upton, N.Y., 1956-61; rsch. asst. Iowa State U., Ames, 1961-62; asst. prof. Med. Coll. Va., Richmond, 1964-69; assoc. prof. Jefferson Med. Coll., Phila., 1969-70; prof., chmn. physiology Sch. Medicine East Carolina, Greenville, N.C., 1970-94, prof., 1994—. Contbr. articles to profl. jours. Sgt. U.S. Army, 1954-56, Korea. Predoctoral fellow USPHS, 1962, postdoctoral fellow NEH, 1977. Mem. Am. Physiol. Soc., Assn. Chairmen Depts. Physiology (councilor 1989-91), Am. Heart Assn. (pres. N.C. affiliate 1979) Greenville Country Club, River Bend Country Club. Avocations: music, sailing. Home: 108 Hyde Ct New Bern NC 28562-3724 Office: E Carolina U Sch Medicine Dept Physiology Greenville NC 27858

THURLBECK, WILLIAM MICHAEL, retired pathologist, retired medical educator; b. Johannesburg, South Africa, Sept. 7, 1929; s. William and Enid Muriel (Mears) T.; m. Elizabeth Anne Tippett, Oct. 28, 1955; children—Sarah Margaret, David William, Alison Mary. B.Sc., U. Cape Town, 1951, M.B., Ch.B., 1953. Intern Groote Schuur Hosp., Cape Town, 1955; asst. prof. to prof. pathology Mass. Gen. Hosp. and Harvard U., 1955-61; asst. prof. to prof. pathology McGill U., 1961-73; sr. investigator Midhurst Med. Research Inst. and Royal Postgrad. Med. Sch., Eng., 1973-75; prof. pathology, head U. Man. and Health Scis. Centre, Winnipeg, 1975-80; prof. pathology U. B.C., 1981—, asso. dean research and grad. studies, 1981—, pathologist Children's Hosp., 1985—, acting head med. microbiol., 1992—; examiner in pathology Royal Coll. Physicians and Surgeons Can., 1964-70; mem. McGill Interdisciplinary Com. on Air Pollution, 1967-73; cons. Cardiovascular Research Inst., San Francisco; pulmonary diseases adv. com. Nat. Heart and Lung Inst., 1964-70; task force research planning in environ. health scis. NIH, mem. respiration and applied physiology study sect., 1981—; adv. fellow Indsl. Hygiene Found., Pitts. 1967-71, Paul Dudley White fellow in cardiology, 1960-61; Med. Research Council vis. scientist Oxford (Eng.) U., 1970-71; Schering travelling fellow Canadian Soc. Clin. Investigation, 1971. Author: Chronic Airflow Obstruction in Lung Disease, 1976, The Lung: Structure, Function and Disease, 1978; Contbr. articles to med. jours. Fellow Royal Coll. Physicians, Royal Coll. Pathologists, Am. Coll. Chest Physicians (medalist), Royal Coll. Pathology; mem. Am. Assn. Pathologists, Internat. Acad. Pathology, Path. Soc. Gt. Britain and Ireland, Canadian Soc. Clin. Investigation, Am. Thoracic Soc., Fleischner Soc. Clubs: Rondebosch Old Boys, Pluto. Home: 4094 W 37th Ave Vancouver, BC Canada V6N 2W7

THURMAN, KAREN L., congresswoman; b. Rapid City, S.D., Jan. 12, 1951; d. Lee Searle and Donna (Altfillisch) Loveland; m. John Patrick Thurman, 1973; children: McLin Searl and Liberty Lee. BA, U. Fla., 1973. Mem. Dunnellon City Council (Fla.), 1974-82; mayor of Dunnellon, 1979-81; mem. Monroe Regional Med. Ctr. Governancy Com., 1989—; mem. Comprehensive Plan Tech. Adv. Com.; del. Fla. Dem. Conv.; Dem. Nat. Conv., 1980; mem. Regional Energy Action com.; mem. Fla. State Senate, 1982-1992; mem.

103rd-104th Congress from 5th Fla. dist., 1993—, ranking minority mem. govt. reform & oversight subcom. nat. security, internat. affairs & criminal justice, mem. com. on aging. Recipient Svc. Above Self award Dunnellon C. of C., 1980; Regional Planning Coun. Appreciation for Svc. award. Mem. Dunnellon C. of C. (dir.), Fla. Horseman's Children's Soc. (charter). Episcopalian. Office: US Ho of Reps 130 Cannon House Office Bldg Washington DC 20515-0905*

THURMAN, MAXWELL R., retired army officer; b. High Point, N.C., Feb. 18, 1931. BSChemE, N.C. State U. Commd. officer U.S. Army, advanced through grades to gen., 1983; dir. program analysis and evaluation Office of Chief of Staff, 1977-79; comdr. U.S. Army Recruiting Command, 1979-81, dep. chief of staff for personnel, 1981-83; vice chief of staff Dept. Army, Washington, 1983-87; mem. Joint Chiefs of Staff, Washington, 1983-87; comdg. gen. Army Tng. and Doctrine Command, Ft. Monroe, Va., 1987-89; comdr. in chief U.S. Forces So. Command, Quarry Heights, Republic Panama, 1989-90; ret., 1991; exec.-in-residence N.S. State U., 1993; bd. visitors N.C. State U.; cons. in field. Decorated D.S.M. with 2 oak leaf clusters, Bronze Star with V device with oak leaf cluster, Def. Disting. Svc. medal with oak leaf cluster, N.C. award Pub. Svc., 1992. Mem. Presdl. Panama Canal Consultative Commn., Presdl. Commn. on Assignment of Women in Armed Forces. Office: Assn of US Army 2425 Wilson Blvd Arlington VA 22201-3326

THURMAN, RALPH HOLLOWAY, health care company executive; b. Chgo., July 28, 1949; s. Joseph Ralph and Jean (Holloway) T.; m. Karen Ann Eisenhart, Mar. 14, 1980; children: Kelly Ann, Kaitlin Leigh, Kyle Joseph. BA, Va. Poly. Inst., 1971; MA, Webster U., 1974; postgrad., USAF Air Command and Staff Coll., 1974. Dir. orgn. Exxon Corp., N.Y.C., 1976-82; dir. personnel Pepsico Internat., Purchase, N.Y., 1982-84; pres. Rhone-Poulenc Rorer, Ft. Washington, Pa., 1984-94; CEO Corning Life Scis., N.Y.C., 1994—, 1994—; bd. dirs. Immune Response Corp., Enzon Corp., Hannaman J., Fox Chase Cancer Ctr.; cons. on resource mgmt. Contbr. articles to profl. publs. Bd. dirs. Jr. Achievement, 1984, Phila. Bus. Attraction Commn., 1987—, Univ. City Sci. Ctr., Phila., 1987—; mem. Greater Phila. Econ. Devel. Coalition, 1987—. Avocations: fishing, golf, aviation. Home: 1483 Ponus Rdg New Canaan CT 06840-3400 Office: Corning Life Scis 450 Park Ave New York NY 10022-2605

THURMAN, SAMUEL DAVID, legal educator; b. Washington, Dec. 7, 1913; s. Sam D. and Henrietta (Young) T.; m. Emeline Nebeker, June 16, 1939 (div. Dec. 17, 1977); children: David, Sally Thurman Ware, Susan Thurman-Hart, Walter; m. Enid Ryberg, Feb. 25, 1981. A.B., U. Utah, 1935; J.D., Stanford U., 1939; LL.D., U. Pacific McGeorge Sch. Law, 1984, U. Utah, 1988. Bar: Utah 1939. Assoc. Irvine, Skeen, Thurman, Salt Lake City, 1939-42; assoc. prof. law Stanford U., 1942-47, prof. law, 1947-62, Marion Rice Kirkwood prof. law, 1961-62, assoc. dean Law Sch., 1947-49, acting dean Law Sch., 1952-53; dean Coll. Law U. Utah, Salt Lake City, 1962-75; disting. prof. law U. Utah, 1975—; advisory bd. Found. Press U. Casebook Series, 1962—; vis. prof. law U. Mich., summer 1949, NYU, 1955-56, U. Tex., 1976, La. State U., 1977, U. Calif. Hastings Coll. Law, 1984—; vis. prof. law Pepperdine U., 1981-82; Hugo L. Black lectr. U. Ala., 1980. Co-author: The Study of Federal Tax Law, (with Phillips and Cheatham) The Legal Profession; adviser: Restatement of Torts, Second, Am. Law Inst; Contbr. articles to law revs., bar assn. jours. Commr. Calif. Law Revision Commn., 1954-59; chmn. Utah appeals bd. SSS; mem. Council Legal Edn. for Profl. Responsibility, 1968-73; Sec.-treas. Assn. Am. Law Schs., 1959-61, pres., 1962; bd. dirs. Nat. Legal Services Corp., 1975-78. Recipient Stanford Law Sch. Merit award, 1992. Fellow Am. Bar Found.; mem. ABA (sec. council legal edn. and admission to bar 1965-70, 74-80, chmn. 1978-79, com. on evaluation of profl. standards, Kutak award 1990), Utah Bar Assn., San Francisco Bar Assn., State Bar Calif., Am. Law Inst. (life), Order of Coif (nat. exec. com. 1964-67, nat. pres. 1977-80), Phi Beta Kappa, Phi Kappa Phi, Sigma Chi, Delta Theta Phi. Mem. Ch. of Jesus Christ of Latter-day Saints. Clubs: Commonwealth (past. chmn. San Francisco 1955), Timpanogos. Home: 910 Donner Way Apt 302 Salt Lake City UT 84108-2103 Office: U Utah Coll Law Salt Lake City UT 84112

THURMAN, UMA KARUNA, actress; b. Boston, Apr. 29, 1970; d. Robert and Nena (von Schlebrugge) T.; m. Gary Oldman (div.). Appeared in films Kiss Daddy Good Night, 1987, Johnny Be Good, 1988, Dangerous Liaisons, 1988, The Adventures of Baron Munchausen, 1989, Where the Heart Is, 1990, Henry and June, 1990, Final Analysis, 1992, Jennifer Eight, 1992, Mad Dog and Glory, 1993, Even Cowgirls Get the Blues, 1993, Pulp Fiction, 1994 (Acad. award nom. Best Supporting Actress), A Month By the Lake, 1995; TV movies include Robin Hood, 1991. Office: care CAA 9830 Wilshire Blvd Beverly Hills CA 90212*

THURMAN, WILLIAM GENTRY, medical research foundation executive, pediatric hematology and oncology physician, educator; b. Jacksonville, Fla., July 1, 1928; s. Horace Edward and Theodosia (Mitchell) T.; m. Peggy Lou Brown, Aug. 11, 1949 (div. 1978); children—Andrew E., Margaret Anne, Mary Allison; m. Gabrielle Anne Martin, Jan. 22, 1980; 1 step child, Stephanie Anne. B.S., U. N.C., 1949; M.S., Tulane U. Sch. Pub. Health, 1960; M.D.C.M., McGill U., Montreal, 1954. Prof. pediatrics Cornell U. Sch. Medicine, N.Y.C., 1962-64; prof. pediatrics U. Va., Charlottesville, 1964-73; dean sch. medicine Tulane U., New Orleans, 1973-75; provost Health Scis. Ctr. U. Oklahoma, Oklahoma City, 1975-80; pres., chief exec. officer Okla. Med. Research Found., Oklahoma City, 1979—; sr. cons. pediatrics Surgeon Gen. USAF, Washington, 1964—; mem. Diet and Nutrition Study Com., Nat. Cancer Inst., Bethesda, Md., 1969—, Profl. Edn. Com., Am. Cancer Soc., N.Y.C., 1973—. Author: (with others) Bone Tumors in Children, 1963, Pediatric Malignant Disease, 1964; contbr. articles to profl. jours. Bd. dirs. United Way, Oklahoma City, 1977—, chmn., 1994, Community Found., Oklahoma City, 1975—, ARC, Oklahoma City, 1992—; bd. dirs. C. of C., 1984—, chmn. 1995. Served with U.S. Army, 1944-46, ETO. Markle scholar, 1959-64. Fellow Am. Acad. Pediatrics (dir. 1969-72); mem. Am. Pediatric Soc., Soc. Pediatric Rsch. (councillor 1971-75), Soc. Mil. Cons., Assn. Ind. Rsch. Insts. (pres. 1985-87), Oklahoma City C. of C. (dir. 1979, chmn. 1994-95), Alpha Omega Alpha. Baptist. Club: Petroleum. Avocations: physical fitness; sailing. Home: 1521 Westchester Dr Oklahoma City OK 73120-1307

THURMON, THEODORE FRANCIS, medical educator; b. Baton Rouge, Oct. 20, 1937; s. Theodore Francis and Gertrude Wilhemena (Arnette) T.; m. Virginia Ruth Strange, Sept. 1, 1961 (div. Oct. 1975); children: Penelope, Suzanna; m. Susonne Annette Ursin, Aug. 8, 1981 (div. Aug. 1992); children: Sarah Eileen, Amanda Aislinn; m. Suzanne Greenwood, Sept. 2, 1992. BS, La. State U., Baton Rouge, 1960; MD, La. State U., New Orleans, 1962. Diplomate Am. Bd. Pediatrics, Am. Bd. Med. Genetics. Commd. ensign USNR, 1957; transferred to USN, 1957, advanced through grades to lt. comdr., 1967; intern naval hosp. Pensacola, Fla., 1962-63; resident in pediatrics naval hosp. Phila., 1963-65, trainee in cytogenetics St. Christopher's Hosp., 1964-65; asst. cardiology naval hosp. St. Albans, N.Y., 1965-67; resigned USN, 1968; fellow in med. genetics Johns Hopkins Hosp., Balt., 1968-69; asst. prof. La. State U. Med. Ctr., New Orleans, 1969-72, chmn. electives com., 1971-74, mem. curriculum com., 1971-76, assoc. prof., 1972-78, mem. dean search com., 1974-75, mem. human experimentation com., 1974-77, prof., 1978-86; prof. La. State U. Med. Ctr., Shreveport, 1986—. Author: Rare Genetic Diseases, 1974; contbr. articles to profl. jours. Active birth defects ctr. Nat. Found./March of Dimes, New Orleans, 1969-81, La. Bd. Regents, New Orleans, 1982, La. Dept. Health, New Orleans, 1984—, La. Cancer & Lung Trust Fund, New Orleans, 1985-86. Fellow Am. Coll. Med. Genetics, Am. Acad. Pediat.; mem. AAAS, Am. Genetic Assn., Soc. Human Genetics, N.Y. Acad. Scis., La. Med. Soc. Home: 1732 Willow Point Dr Shreveport LA 71119-4108 Office: La State U Med Sch Pediat-Genetics 1501 Kings Hwy Shreveport LA 71103-4228

THURMOND, GEORGE MURAT, judge; b. Del Rio, Tex., Oct. 22, 1930; s. Roger H. and Day (Hamilton) T.; m. Elsiejean Davis, June 27, 1959; children: Carolyn Day, Georganna, Sarah Gail. BA, U. of the South, 1952; JD, U. Tex., 1955. Bar: Tex. 1955. Ptnr. Montague & Thurmond, Del Rio, 1955-69; judge Tex. Dist. Ct. (63rd dist.), Del Rio, 1970—; presiding judge 6th Adminstrv. Region, Del Rio, 1983-87; chmn. jud. sect. State Bar Tex., 1988-89. Editor: U. Tex. Law Review, 1955. Rep. Tex. Ho. of Reps., 1955-

58. Mem. ABA (chmn. rural ct. com., state trial judges conf. of jud. adminstrn. div. 1991-92), Tex. Bar Assn. Democrat. Episcopalian. Avocations: jogging, water sports. Home: PO Drawer 1089 Del Rio TX 78841-1089 Office: 63d Jud Dist of Tex PO Box 1089 243 W Strickland Del Rio TX 78841-1089

THURMOND, STROM, senator; b. Edgefield, SC, Dec. 5, 1902; s. John William and Eleanor Gertrude (Strom) T.; m. Jean Crouch, Nov. 7, 1947 (dec. Jan. 1960); m. Nancy Moore, Dec. 22, 1968; children: Nancy Moore (dec.), J. Strom, Jr., Juliana Gertrude, Paul Reynolds. B.S., Clemson Coll., 1923; 14 hon. degrees. Bar: S.C. 1930. Tchr. S.C. schs., 1923-29; city atty., county atty., supt. edn. Edgefield County, 1929-33; state senator, 1933-38, circuit judge, 1938-46, gov. of S.C., 1947-51; ret. army. So. Govs. Conf., 1950; practiced in Aiken, S.C., 1951-55; U.S. senator from S.C., 1955—; Del. Nat. Democratic Conv., 1932, 36, 48, 52, 56, 60; chmn. S.C. dels., armed svcs. com., Judiciary Subcom. on antitrust bus. rts. and competition; mem. Dem. Nat. Com., 1948, Vets. Affairs/Sen. Rep. Policy Com.; States Rights candidate for Pres. U.S., 1948; del. Nat. Republican Conv., 1968, 72, 76. Bd. dirs. Ga.-Carolina council Boy Scouts Am. Served with AUS; attached to 82d Airborne Div. for invasion 1942-46, Europe; maj. gen. Res. Decorated Legion of Merit with oak leaf cluster, Bronze Star with V, Purple Heart, Croix de Guerre France; Cross of Order of Crown Belgium; others; recipient Congl. Medal Honor Soc. Nat. Patriots award, 1974, Presdl. Medal of Freedom, 1992. Mem. S.C. (past v.p.), ABA, Clemson Coll. Alumni Assn. (past pres.), also numerous def., vets., civic, fraternal and farm orgns. Baptist. Office: US Senate 217 Russell Senate Office Bldg Washington DC 20510*

THUROW, LESTER CARL, economics educator; b. Livingston, Mont., May 7, 1938; s. Willis Carl and Alice Winefred (Hickman) T.; m. Gretchen Pfuetze, Dec. 30, 1971; children: Torben, Ethan. B.A., Williams Coll., 1960; M.A., Oxford U., 1962; Ph.D., Harvard U., 1964. Mem. staff Pres.'s Council Econ. Advisors, Washington, 1964-65; asst. prof. econs. Harvard U., Cambridge, Mass., 1965-68; mem. editorial bd. N.Y. Times, 1979; mem. faculty M.I.T., Cambridge, 1968—; prof. econs. and mgmt. MIT, Cambridge, dean Sch. of Mgmt., 1987—; contbg. editor Newsweek mag., 1981. Author: Generating Inequality, 1975, Zero Sum Society, 1980, Dangerous Currents: The State of Economics, 1983. Mem. econ. adv. bd. NAACP, from 1978. Recipient David A. Wells prize Harvard U., 1968. Mem. Am. Econ. Assn. Democrat. Methodist. Office: MIT Sloan Sch Mgmt Office of the Dean 77 Massachusetts Ave Cambridge MA 02139-4307

THURSTON, ALICE JANET, former college president; b. Milw., Mar. 20, 1916; d. Karl J. and Nellie Ann (Smith) Stouffer; children: Anne, Robert. B.A., Denison U., 1937; MA, Northwestern U., 1938; PhD, George Washington U., 1960. Mem. faculty dept. psychology, counselor, dean students Montgomery Coll., Takoma Park, Md., 1950-65; dir. counseling Met. Campus, Cuyahoga Community Coll., Cleve., 1965-66; dean of students Western Campus, Cuyahoga Community Coll., 1966-69; vis. lectr. U. Ill., 1968-69; dir. Inst. Research and Student Services Met. Jr. Coll. Dist., Kansas City, Mo., 1969-71; pres. Garland Jr. Coll., Boston, 1971-75, Los Angeles Valley Coll., Van Nuys, Calif., 1975-81; lectr. Pepperdine U., L.A., 1981-83, Calif. State U. Worthridge, 1984-95; mem. adv. com. grad. program student affairs Calif. State U., Northridge. Author works in field. Bd. dirs. New Dir. for Youth, Van Nuys, Calif.; mem. ministerial search com. Unitarian Ch., Studio City, Calif., 1991-92, chair caring com., 1994—. Recipient Disting. Alumnae award Denison U., 1987, Humanitarian award Juvenile Justice Connection Project, 1987. Mem. Kappa Alpha Theta, Mortar Bd. Democrat. Unitarian. Home: 13156 Crewe St North Hollywood CA 91605-4727

THURSTON, DAVID E., lawyer, general counsel; b. Hartford, Conn., Apr. 16, 1957; s. Robert Charles and Carol Jean (Demson) T.; m. Gaye Winifred Hennemuth, Oct. 3, 1987; children: Perry Bishop, Demson Collin. BA, George Washington U., 1979; JD, Cath. U., 1982. Bar: Tex. 1982, Pa. 1984; lic. real estate broker, Pa. Assoc. Johnson, Bromberg & Leeds, Dallas, 1982-84; assoc. Morgan, Lewis & Bockius, Phila., 1984-85, N.Y.C., 1985; assoc. Shea & Gould, N.Y.C., 1986-87; sr. v.p. nat. and internat. sales, gen. counsel The Binswanger Co., Phila., 1987—. Recipient AmJur award in property Lawyers Co-op Pub. Co. Mem. ABA, Pa. Bar Assn., Tex. Bar Assn., Vesper Club. Republican. Avocations: bicycling, swimming, golf. Office: Binswanger Co 1635 Market St 7 Penn Ctr Philadelphia PA 19103

THURSTON, DONALD ALLEN, broadcasting executive; b. Gloucester, Mass., Apr. 2, 1930; s. Joseph Allen and Helen Ruth (Leach) T.; m. Oralie Alice Lane, Sept. 9, 1951; children: Corydon Leach, Carolie Lane. Grad. Mass. Radio and Telegraph, 1949; HHD (hon.), North Adams (Mass.) State Coll., 1977; LHD (hon.), Emerson Coll., 1995. Announcer, engr. Sta. WTWN, St. Johnsbury, Vt., 1949-52; v.p., gen. mgr. Sta. WIKE, Newport, Vt., 1952-60; v.p., treas., gen. mgr. Sta. WMNB, North Adams, 1960-66; pres., treas. Berkshire Broadcasting Co., Inc., North Adams, 1966—; chmn. bd. Broadcast Capital Fund, Inc., 1981-89; dir. Berkshire Bank and Trust Co., 1967-85, Broadcast Capital Fund, Inc., 1980—, Broadcast Music, Inc., N.Y.C., 1990—; chmn. bd. 1994—. Pres. No. Berkshire Indsl. Devel. Corp., 1965-67; commr. Mass. Cmty. Antenna TV Commn., 1972-74; trustee North Adams State Coll., 1991—, vice chmn. bd. trustees, 1993—. Recipient Laymen's award Vt. Tchrs. Assn., 1958; Laymen's award Mass. Tchrs. Assn., 1962; Abe Lincoln Merit award So. Baptist Radio and TV Commn., 1975; named Man of Yr. Vt. Assn. Broadcasters, 1978. Mem. North Adams C. of C. (Hayden award 1967, pres. 1964-67), Nat. Assn. Broadcasters (dir. 1965-69, 73-77, chmn. radio 1976-77, chmn. bd., chmn. exec. com. 1977-79, Disting. Svc. award 1980), Mass. Broadcasters Assn. (pres. 1964, Disting. Svc. award 1964, 71, 78), Taconic Golf Club (Williamstown, Mass.; bd. dirs. 1975-89). Republican. Methodist. Office: 466 Curran Hwy North Adams MA 01247-3901 *My goals have been to better my community, profession and life in general because I was a positive participant, and to provide independence, a sense of responsibility and a love of humanity for my family.*

THURSTON, GEORGE BUTTE, mechanical and biomedical engineering educator; b. Austin, Tex., Oct. 8, 1924; s. Rudolph D. and Olivia Ruth (Lester) T.; m. Carol A. McWharter, Apr. 5, 1947; children—John Douglas, Mary Elizabeth. B.S., U. Tex., Austin, 1944, M.A., 1948, Ph.D., 1952. Registered profl. engr., Tex. Supr. hydroacoustics sect. Def. Research Lab., U. Tex., Austin, 1949-52; asst. prof. physics U. Wyo., Laramie, 1952-53, U. Ark., Fayetteville, 1953-54; physicist Naval Ordnance Test Sta., Inyokern, Calif., 1954-55; assoc. prof. Okla. State U. Stillwater, 1954-59; research physicist U. Mich., Ann Arbor, 1958-59; prof. Okla. State U. Ann Arbor, 1959-68; vis. scientist Centre de Recherche sur les Macromolecules, Strasbourg, France, 1963-64; prof. mech. engring. and biomed. engring. U. Tex., Austin, 1968—; vis. prof. Helmholtz Inst. fur Biomedizinische Technik, Aachen, West Germany, 1975-76; cons. for govt., industry. Contbr. articles to profl. jours. Recipient Brown U. Calculus prize, 1942; Alexander von Humboldt Found. Sr. U.S. Scientist award, 1975; NSF faculty fellow, 1963-64; numerous grants. Fellow Am. Phys. Soc., Acoustical Soc. Am.; mem. ASME, Soc. Rheology, Internat. Soc. Biorheology, Brit. Soc. Rheology, Sigma Xi, Sigma Pi Sigma. Home: 1000 Madrone Rd Austin TX 78746-4320 Office: U Tex Dept Mech Engring Austin TX 78712

THURSTON, GEORGE R., lumber company executive; b. 1942. BS, Northwestern U., 1965, MBA, 1966. With Cummins Engine Co., 1966-78; exec. v.p. fin. and treas. North Pacific Lumber Co., Portland, 1987—. Office: North Pacific Lumber Co 1505 SE Gideon St Portland OR 97202

THURSTON, MORRIS ASHCROFT, lawyer; b. Logan, Utah, May 25, 1943; s. Morris Alma and Barbara (Ashcroft) T.; m. Dawna Lyn Parker, Sept. 10, 1966; children: Morris III, David, Ashley, Tyson. BA, Brigham Young U., 1967; JD, Harvard U., 1970. Bar: Calif. 1971, U.S. Dist. Ct. (cen. dist.) Calif. 1971, U.S. Supreme Ct. 1978. Assoc. Latham & Watkins, Los Angeles, 1970-77, ptnr., 1978—; jud. arbitrator Orange County Superior Ct., Calif., 1980—. Mem. Calif. Bar Assn., Orange County Bar Assn., Assn. Bus. Trial Lawyers. Republican. Mormon. Avocations: basketball, tennis, lit. Home: 9752 Crestview Cir Orange CA 92667-3204 Office: Latham & Watkins 650 Town Center Dr Ste 2000 Costa Mesa CA 92626-1925

THURSTON, STEPHEN JOHN, pastor; b. Chgo., July 20, 1952; s. John Lee and Ruth (Hall) T.; m. Joyce DeVonne Hand, June 18, 1977; children:

Stephen John II, Nicole D'Vaugh, Teniece Rael, Christian Avery Elijah. BA in Religion, Bishop Coll., 1975; Hon. degree, Chgo. Baptist Inst., 1986. Co-pastor New Covenant Missionary Bapt. Ch., Chgo., 1975-79, pastor, 1979—; corr. sec. Nat. Bapt. Conv. Am., mem. exec. com. Christian Edn. Congress; exec. v.p. Ill. Nat. Bapt. State Conv.; mem. Northern River Dist. Bapt. Assn.; lectr. various orgns.; instr. New Covenant Bapt. Ch., Fellowship Bapt. Ch. Mng. editor The Crier (Nat. Bapt. Conv. Am. Evangelical Bd. quarterly pub.). Co-chmn. religious affairs div. Operation People United to Save Humanity (PUSH); bd. dirs. nat. alumni assn. Bishop Coll.; active NAACP; trustee, fin. chmn. Chgo. Bapt. Inst.; mem. Campus Crusade for Christ, Here's Life Black Am. Mem. Broadcast Ministers Alliance, Bapt. Ministers Conf. Chgo. (Ministerial Pioneer award). Club: Bishop Coll. (Chgo.). Office: Nat baptist Conv Am 777 S R L Thornton Fwy Ste 205 Dallas TX 75203

THURSZ, DANIEL, retired service organization executive, consultant; b. Casablanca, Morocco, Jan. 25, 1929; came to U.S., 1941; s. Jonathan and Franka (Gutlas) T.; m. Hadassah Neulander, Feb. 8, 1953; children—Deborah Thursz Bleiweis, David, Deena Thursz Klopman, Tamar. B.A., Queens Coll., 1949; M.S.W., Catholic U. Am., 1955, D.S.W., 1960; L.H.D. (hon.), U. Md., 1977, Balt. Hebrew U., 1990. Asso. prof. social welfare Sch. Social Service, Cath. U. Am., 1961-63; Assoc. prof. social welfare Sch. Social Work, U. Md., 1963-65; nat. asso. dir. VISTA, OEO, Washington, 1965-67; dean, prof. U. Md. Sch. Social Work and Community Planning, 1967-77; exec. v.p. B'nai B'rith Internat., Washington, 1977-87; pres., CEO, Nat. Coun. on Aging Inc., Washington, 1988-95, pres. emeritus, 1995—; cons. social welfare agys., mem. nat. and state commns. social welfare; internat. v.p. Internat. Fedn. Aging; bd. dirs. Sage Pubs., Beverly Hills, Calif. Author books, monographs, articles in field.; Co-editor: Meeting Human Needs, Vol. 1, 1975, Vol. II, 1977, Vol. III, Reaching People, 1978, Vol. IV, Reaching the Aged, 1979. Mem. bd. visitors U. N.C., Asheville. Served with AUS, 1951-53. Alvin Johnson scholar. Mem. Acad. Certified Social Workers, Nat. Welfare Conf. (pres. 1969-71), Nat. Assn. Social Workers (1st v.p. 1973-75), Conf. Jewish Communal Service (exec. com., pres. 1988-90), B'nai B'rith (hon. exec. v.p.). Jewish. Home and Office: 8605 Carlynn Dr Bethesda MD 20817-4310

THWAITS, JAMES ARTHUR, manufacturing executive; b. London, Apr. 3, 1923; came to U.S., 1958, naturalized, 1973; s. Arthur Roper and Iris Maud (Mason) T.; m. Joyce Holmes, July 26, 1947; children: Joanna, Philip, David, Steven. Grad., East-Ham Coll. Tech., London, 1939, Thames Poly., London, 1942; Cert. Higher Math., Poly. of South Bank, London, 1944. Higher nat. cert. in elec. engring. Project engr. Standard Telephones and Cables Ltd., Eng., 1945-46; plant engr. Kelvinator Ltd., Eng., 1946-49; with 3M, St. Paul, 1949—, v.p. Afro-Asian and Can. areas, 1968-71, v.p. Tape and Allied Products Group, 1972-74, v.p. Internat. Group, 1974-75, pres. internat. ops. and corp. staff services, 1975—, also bd. dirs.; bd. dirs. First Trust Co., St. Paul. Mem. London Inst. Elec. Engrs. Clubs: St. Paul Athletic; White Bear (Minn.); Yacht, North Oaks (Minn.) Golf; King Solomon's Lodge (London, Ont., Can.). Office: Minnesota Mining & Mfg Co 3M Center Saint Paul MN 55144-0002

THYDEN, JAMES ESKEL, professional society administrator, former diplomat, educator; b. L.A., Apr. 10, 1939; s. Eskel A. and Mildred Aileene (Rock) T.; m. Patricia Irene Kelsey, Dec. 15, 1959; children: Teresa Lynn, Janice Kay, James Blaine. BA in Biology, Pepperdine U., 1961; MA in Scandinavian Area Studies, U. Wash., 1992. Cert. secondary tchr., Calif., Wash. Tchr. Gompers Jr. High Sch., L.A., 1962-64; fgn. svc. officer U.S. Dept. State, Washington, 1964-90; rschr. U. Wash., Seattle, 1991-93; now exec. dir. Seattle chpt. UN Assn.; travel lectr. Cunard Lines, Royal Viking Sun, 1995. Editor govt. report, ann. human rights report, 1983-86; author, editor in-house govt. reports, documents. Dir. Office Human Rights, 1983-86; counselor Embassy for Polit. Affairs, Am. Embassy, Oslo, Norway, 1986-90. Named Outstanding Young Man Am., 1969, Alumnus of Yr., Pepperdine U., 1984. Mem. Am. Fgn. Svc. Assn., World Affairs Coun. Seattle. Avocations: travel, reading, gardening. Home: 5631 153 Place SW Edmonds WA 98026-4239

THYEN, HERBERT EDWARD, furniture company executive; b. Jasper, Ind., 1912; married. With Jasper Wood Products Corp., 1932-50; with Kimball Internat. Corp., Jasper, 1950—, exec. v.p., sec., 1976—, also bd. dirs.; sec., bd. dirs. Lafayette Mfg. Co., Jasper-Am. Mfg. Co., Kimball Furniture Reproductions Inc., Batesville Am. Mfg. Co., L-I Enterprises Inc., McAllen-Am. Corp., West Jefferson Wood Products Inc., Habig Found. Inc., Kimball Hospitality Furniture Inc., Kimball Electronics Inc., Kimball World Inc., Kimball Internat. Transit Inc.; bd. dirs. Springs Valley Bank and Trust, Klavierfabrik L. Bosendorfer, Vienna. Mem. KC. Home: 1742 Newton St Jasper IN 47546-1602 Office: Kimball Internat Inc 1600 Royal St Jasper IN 47549-1001

THYEN, JOHN T., furniture company executive. Sr. exec. v.p. mktg. Kimball Internat. Inc., Jasper, Ind. Office: Kimball Internat Inc 1600 Royal St Jasper IN 47549-1001

THYEN, RONALD JOSEPH, furniture company executive; b. New Albany, Ind., 1937. BS, Notre Dame U., 1959. With Kimball Internat. Inc., Jasper, Ind., 1959—, exec. v.p. office furniture divsn., 1977-92; sr. exec. v.p. ops. officer, 1992—; also bd. dirs. Kimball Internat. Inc., Jasper, Ind. Home: 1407 W 31st St Jasper IN 47546-3551 Office: Kimball Internat Inc 1600 Royal St Jasper IN 47549-1001

TIAHRT, W. TODD, congressman, former state senator; b. Vermillion, S.D., June 15, 1951; s. Wilbur E. and Sara Ella Marcine (Steele) T.; m. Vicki Lyn Holland, Aug. 14, 1976; children: Jessica, John, Luke. Student, S.D. Sch. Mines & Tech., Rapid City, 1969-72; BA, Evangel Coll., 1975; MBA, S.W. Mo. State U., 1989. Property estimator Crawford & Co., Springfield, Mo., 1975-78; project engr. Zenith Electronics, Springfield, 1978-81; cost engr. Boeing, Wichita, Kans., 1981-85; proposal mgr. Boeing, Wichita, 1985—; state senator State of Kans., Topeka, 1992—; mem. 104th Congress from 4th Kans. dist. Washington; chmn. 4th dist. Rep. party, 1990-92; exec. com. Kans. Rep. party, 1990-92, nat. security com., sci. com. Mem. Pachyderm (bd. dirs. 1991-92), Delta Sigma Phi. Republican. Home: 1329 Longworth Goddard KS 67052-9133 Office: US House Reps 2371 Rayburn House Office Bldg Washington DC 20515-1604*

TIAN, GANG, mathematics educator. BS, Nanking U., 1982; MS, Beijing U., 1984; PhD, Harvard U., 1988. Prof. math. NYU Courant Inst. Math. & Sci., 1992—. Recipient Alan T. Waterman Award, NSF, 1994. Office: NYU Courant Inst Math & Sci 70 Washington Sq S New York NY 10013-6607*

TIANO, ANTHONY STEVEN, television producer, book publishing executive; b. Santa Fe, Mar. 27, 1941; s. Joseph A. and Marian (Adlesperger) T.; m. Kathleen O'Brien, Dec. 29, 1972; children: Mark A., A. Steven. BA, U. N.Mex., 1969, MA, 1971; LittD (hon.), Calif. Sch. Profl. Psychology, 1985. Dir. programming Sta. KNME-TV U. N.Mex., Albuquerque, 1968-72; sta. mgr. Sta. WHA-TV U. Wis., Madison, 1972-76; exec. dir. Sta. KETC-TV, St. Louis, 1976-78; pres., CEO KQED, Inc., San Francisco, 1978-93; chmn., CEO Santa Fe Ventures, Inc., San Francisco, 1993—. Vice-chair bd. dirs. Calif. Sch. Profl. Psychology, San Francisco, 1985-90. Mem. Nat. Assn. Pub. TV Stas. (vice chair bd. dirs. 1986). Office: Santa Fe Ventures 450 Mission St San Francisco CA 94105

TIBBETTS, PAMELA LEE, health facility administrator. Pres. Riverside Med. Ctr., Mpls. Office: Fairview Riverside Medical Ctr 2450 Riberside Ave Minneapolis MN 55454

TIBBITTS, THEODORE WILLIAM, horticulturist, researcher; b. La Crosse, Wis., Apr. 10, 1929; s. John Wilson and Vivian Sophia (Elver) T.; m. Allison Lou Mahan, Aug. 25, 1956 (dec. June 1975); children: Scott, Tia Anne; m. Mary Florence Olmsted, June 22, 1985. BS, U. Wis., 1950, MS, 1952, PhD, 1953. Asst prof., assoc. prof., and prof. U. Wis., Madison, 1955—, dir. Biotron, 1987-92; sr. rsch. engr. N.Am. Aviation, L.A., 1965-66; cons. Johnson Space Ctr., Manned Spaceflight Ctr., Apollo Flights, 1969-70; vis. prof. U. Guelph, Ont., Can., 1981; mem. NASA Controlled Ecol. Life Support System Discipline Working Group, Washington, 1989—. Author:

Controlled Environment Guidelines for Plant Research, 1979; co-author: Growth Chamber Manual, 1978, 1995; contbr. articles to sci. jours. Elder Covenant Presbyn. Ch., Madison, 1961-65. With U.S. Army, 1953-55. Recipient Rsch. award Dept. Sci. and Indsl. Rsch., New Zealand, 1981. Fellow Am. Soc. Hort. Sci. (assoc. editor, Marion Meadows award); mem. AAAS, Am. Inst. Biol. Sci., Internat. Hort. Soc., Potato Assn. Am., Am. Soc. Gravitational and Space Biology, Am. Soc. Plant Physiologists, Internat. Commn. of Illumination (CIE). Achievements include development of guidelines for controlled environment research, optimizing growth of potatoes for life support in space, patent for use of light-emitting diodes for irradiation of plants; establishment of causal factors for physiological disorders in vegetable species; plant experiment on Biosatellite flights 1966-67, growth chamber experiments on shuttle flight, 1992, 93, 94, 95. Office: U Wis Dept Hort Madison WI 53706

TIBBLE, DOUGLAS CLAIR, lawyer; b. Joliet, Ill., May 26, 1952. BA, DePaul U., 1974; JD, Syracuse U., 1977, MPA, 1978. Bar: Ill., U.S. Dist. Ct. (no. dist.) Ill., U.S. Ct. Appeals (7th cir.), U.S. Supreme Ct. Ptnr. McDermott Will & Emery, Chgo. Mem. ABA, DuPage County Bar Assn., Chgo. Bar Assn. Office: McDermott Will & Emery 227 W Monroe St Chicago IL 60606

TIBBS, MARTHA JANE PULLEN, civic worker; b. Memphis, Feb. 12, 1932; d. John Thomas Jr. and Martha Frances (Gragg) Pullen; m. Eugene Edward Tibbs; children: Martha Katherine, Eugene Edward Jr. BSBA, U. Tenn., 1953; MA in Edn., Memphis State U., 1958. Cert. tchr., social worker, Tenn. Tchr. Lausanne Sch., Memphis, Tenn., 1954-55, Millington High Sch., Memphis, 1955-56, Presbyterian Day Sch., Memphis, 1956-57, St. Mary's Episcopal Sch., Memphis, 1958-60; social worker Tenn. Dept. Pub. Welfare, Memphis, 1962-63. Author genealogical works. Mem. Memphis Vol. Svc. Bd., 1963-64; commr. Shelby County Hist. Commn., Memphis, 1983—; block worker Cancer, Kidney and Heart Fund, Memphis, 1984—. Mem. NEA, AAUW, Tenn. Tchrs. Assn., Tenn. Geneal. Soc., Early Settlers Shelby County (sec. 1984—, registrar 1988, bd. dirs. 1992—), Nineteenth Century Club (sec. 1993—, newsletter editor 1985-88), Cleve. Jr. Aux., Cleve. Med. Aux. (sec./treas.), West Tenn. Hist. Soc, Univ. Club Memphis, Racquet Club, DAR (past chpt. regent, sec.-treas. regents coun.), Chicasaw Dist. DAR Sch. (Tenn. state vice chmn., parliamentarian, chmn. Zachariah Davies chpt.), Cleve. Garden Club (past pres.), Cleve. Woman's Club, Nat. Soc. Magna Charta Dames (Memphis chpt.), Nat. Soc. Daus. of Founders and Patriots of Am. (Tenn. chpt.), Tenn. State Registrar Founders and Patriots, Nat. Soc. Colonial Dames (Memphis Chucaqua chpt.), Nat. Soc. So. Dames Am. (Memphis chpt.), Colonial Order of Crown (descendants of Charlemagne), The Sovereign Colonial Soc. Ams. Royal Descent, Memphis Scottich Soc., Family of Bruce Soc., Alpha Omega Pi (alumnae pres., adv. collegiate chpt. Rhodes Coll.). Republican. Presbyterian. Avocations: art, genealogy, computers, dancing, tennis. Home: 2008 Massey Rd Memphis TN 38119-6404

TICE, CAROL HOFF, educator, consultant; b. Ashville, N.C., Oct. 6, 1931; d. Amos H. and Fern (Irvin) Hoff; m. (div.); children: Karin E., Jonathan H. BS, Manchester Coll., North Manchester, Ind., 1954; MEd, Cornell U., 1955. Cert. tchr., Mich., N.Y., N.J. Tchr. Princeton (N.J.) Schs., 1955-60; tchr. Ann Arbor (Mich.) Schs., 1964—; dir. intergenerational programs Inst. for Study Children and Families Eastern Mich. U., Ypsilanti, 1985—; founder, pres. Lifespan Resources, Inc., Ann Arbor, 1979—; commr. U.S. Nat. Commn. Internat. Yr. of the Child, Washington, 1979-81. Innovator: program, Tch. Learning Intergenerational Communities, 1971; author: Guide Books and articles, Community of Caring, 1980; co-producer, Film, What We Have, 1976 (award, Milan, Italy Film Festival 1982). Mem. Democratic Party, Ann Arbor; trustee Blue Lake Fine Arts Camp, Twin Lake, Mich., 1975—. Recipient Program Innovation award Mich. Dept. Edn., 1974-80, C.S. Mott Found. award, 1982, Nat. Found. Improvement in Edn. award, Washington, 1986, Disting. Alumni award Manchester Coll., 1979, A+ Break the Mold award U.S. Sec. of Edn., 1992; Ford Found. fellow, Ithaca, N.Y., 1955. Mem. Am. Soc. of Curriculum Devel., Am. Assn. U. Women (Agt. 1979), Generations United (Pioneer Award 1989), Optimist Club. Democrat. Presbyterian. Office: Scarlett MS 3300 Lorraine St Ann Arbor MI 48108-1970

TICE, CLIFFORD RAY, state legislator, oil company executive; b. Dexter, N.Mex., Aug. 18, 1927; s. Nina Sherod (Williams) Tice; m. Mary Smith, June 15, 1946 (dec. 1970); children: Karen, Thomas (dec.), Kenneth (dec.), Ronald. Student in pstroleum, I.C.S., 1946-51. With Malco Refineries, Inc., Artesia, N.Mex., 1949-53; yard foreman Malco Asphalt & Refining Co., Artesia, 1953-59; craft foreman Continental Oil Co., Artesia, 1959—; mem. N.Mex. State Sen., Santa Fe. Mem. City/County Planning and Zoning Commn., Artesia, 1968-87; pres. Parents and Boosters Club, Artesia, 1967-71. With USN, 1945-46, PTO. Decorated Victory Medal. Mem. Sertoma (membership chmn. 1989-90), Elks. Democrat. Avocations: metal figurines, home improvements. Home: 537 El Rey Dr Corrales NM 87048-7121

TICE, DOUGLAS OSCAR, JR., federal judge; b. Lexington, N.C., May 2, 1933; s. Douglas Oscar Sr. and Lila Clayton (Wright) T.; m. Janet N. Capps, Feb. 28, 1959 (div. Sept. 1976); children: Douglas Oscar III, Janet E.; m. Beverley Carole Black, Aug. 8, 1982 (div. Apr. 1995). BS, U.N.C., 1955, JD, 1957. Bar: N.C. 1957, U.S. Ct. Appeals (4th cir.) 1964, Va. 1970, U.S. Dist. ct. (ea. dist.) Va. 1976, U.S. Bankruptcy Ct. (ea. dist.) Va. 1976. Exec. sec. N.C. Jud. Coun., Raleigh, 1958-59; assoc. Baucom & Adams, Raleigh, 1959-61; trial atty. Office Dist. Coun., IRS, Richmond, Va., 1961-70; corp. atty. Carlton Industries, Inc., Richmond, 1970-75; ptnr. Hubard, Tice, Marchant & Samuels, P.C., Richmond, 1975-87; judge U.S. Bankruptcy Ct., Richmond, Norfolk, Alexandria, Va., 1987—. Vice pres. Richmond Pub. Forum, 1976-80, com. chmn. Richmond Forum, Inc., 1986—; past pres. Richmond Civil War Roundtable, mem., 1965—; bd. dirs. Epilepsy Assn. Va., Inc., 1976-87. Capt. USAR, 1957-66. Mem. ABA, Va. Bar Assn., City of Richmond Bar Assn., Am. Bankruptcy Inst., Nat. Conf. Bankruptcy Judges, Old Dominion Sertoma (pres. Richmond chpt. 1967). Home: 2037 W Grace St Richmond VA 23220-2003 Office: US Bankruptcy Ct PO Box 676 Richmond VA 23206-0676

TICE, GEORGE A(NDREW), photographer; b. Newark, Oct. 13, 1938; s. William S. and Margaret T. (Robertson) T.; m. Joanna Blaylock, 1958; m. Marie Tremmel, 1960; children: Christopher, Loretta, Lisa, Lynn, Jennifer. Instr. photography New Sch. Social Research, 1970—. One-man shows, Witkin Gallery, 1970, Met. Mus. Art, 1972, group shows include, Whitney Mus. Am. Art, 1974, Mus. Modern Art, 1979; represented in permanent collections, Mus. Modern Art, Met. Mus. Art, Art Inst. Chgo., Bibliothèque Nationale, Nihon U., Tokyo; books include Fields of Peace, 1970, Goodbye River, Goodbye, 1971, Paterson, 1972, Seacoast Maine, 1973, George A. Tice Photographs, 1953-73, 1975, Urban Landscapes, 1975, Artie Van Blarcum, 1977, Urban Romantic, 1982, Lincoln, 1984, Hometowns, 1988, Stone Walls, Grey Skies, 1991. Served with USN, 1956-59. Recipient Grand prix for best photography book of Year Arles, France, 1973; Guggenheim Found. fellow, 1973-74; Nat. Endowment for Arts fellow, 1973—; Nat. Mus. Photography and Bradford and Ilkley Community Coll. (Eng.) fellow, 1990-91. Address: 323 Gill Ln 9B Iselin NJ 08830

TICE, RAPHAEL DEAN, army officer; b. Topeka, Kans., Dec. 4, 1927; s. Arthur Taylor and Mamie (McDonald) T.; m. Eunice Miriam Suddarth, Dec. 23, 1946; children: Karen Ann Tice Claterbos, William Dean. B.S. in Mil. Sci., U. Md., 1963. M.S. in Bus. Adminstrn, George Washington U., 1970. Served as enlisted man U.S. Army, 1946-47; commd. 2d lt., 1947, advanced through grades to lt. gen., 1981; platoon leader and co. comdr. 1st Inf. div., W.Ger., 1949-52; co. comdr., regimental adj. 8th Inf. div., 1955-56; tng. advisor Vietnam, 1956-57; mem. staff Office of Dep. chief of Staff for Personnel, Dept. Army, 1960-63; chief personnel mgmt. div. Office of Under Sec. of Army, 1963-64; plans Officer So. Command, Panama, 1965-67; dep. brigade comdr. 3d Brigade, 4th Inf. Div., 1967; comdr. 2d Bn., 12th Inf. of 25th Inf. div., Vietnam, 1968; exec. for personnel procurement Office of Sec. Def. for Manpower and Res. Affairs, 1968-69; comdr. 1st Brigade, 1st Inf. div., 1970; chief of staff, 1971; dep. dir. mil. personnel mgmt. Dept. Army, 1972-73; comdg. gen. Berlin Brigade, 1974-76; dep. chief of staff personnel U.S. Army Europe, 1976-77; comdg. gen. 3d. Inf. div., 1977-79; dep. asst. sec. def. for mil. personnel and force mgmt. Dept. Def., 1979-85; dep. dir. Nat. Recreation and Park Assn., 1986—; spl. adviser Pres.'s Council on

Phys. Fitness and Sports. Decorated Silver Star, Legion of Merit with 2 oak leaf clusters, Air medal with V and 7 oak leaf clusters, Bronze Star with V, Vietnam Cross of Gallantry with Palm, Purple Heart., Def. Disting. Service medal, Army Disting. Service medal. Mem. Assn. U.S. Army, Am. Defense Found. (hon. pres.). Home: 8655 Gateshead Rd Alexandria VA 22309-4042 Office: Nat Recreation & Park Assn 2775 S Quincy St Ste 300 Arlington VA 22206-2236

TICER, PATRICIA, mayor; m. Jack Ticer; 4 children. Grad., Sweet Briar Coll. Councilwoman City of Alexandria, Va., 1982-84, vice mayor, 1984-90, appointed mayor, 1991-92, mayor, 1992—; chair COG Transp. Planning Bd., chmn. bd. dirs., 1994; mem. coordinating com. Woodrow Wilson Bridge; bd. dirs. No. Va. Transp. Commn., chmn., 1994; bd. dirs. Transp. Coordinating Coun. Founding mem. Early Childhood Devel. Commn., No. Va. Housing Coalition, Alexandria Commn. on the Arts; mem. Govs. Coun. on Child Care and Early Childhood Programs; mem. adv. coun. Alexandria Symphony Orch.; active No. Va. AIDS Mins. Mem. Nat. Assn. Regional Couns. (pres.). Office: 301 King St Alexandria VA 22314

TICHENOR, DONALD KEITH, association executive; b. Battle Creek, Mich., Apr. 14, 1937; s. Don Leighton and Sarah Sophia (Parry) T.; m. Dolores B.; children: Don Kenneth, Andrew Scott, Thomas Dwight. B.A., Hillsdale Coll., 1961; M.B.A., Loyola U., 1972. Service analyst Mich. Med. Service, Detroit, 1965-66; adminstrv. asst. Port Huron (Mich.) Hosp., 1966-70; coordinator affiliated socs. Am. Hosp. Assn., Chgo., 1970-71; dir. div. membership Am. Hosp. Assn., 1971-72, dir. div. registration and membership, 1972-73, asst. dir. Bur. of Mgmt. and Planning, 1973-75, acting dir. Bur. of Mgmt. and Planning, 1975; exec. dir. Internat. Personnel Mgmt. Assn., Washington, 1975—. Served with U.S. Army, 1958-60. Mem. Am. Soc. Assn. Execs., Greater Washington Soc. Assn. Execs.

TICHI, CECELIA, English language educator; b. Pitts., Apr. 10, 1942; d. James Francis Halbert and Mary Louise (Doherty) Tashman; m. William John Tichi, Sept. 8, 1967; children: Claire, Julia. BA, Pa. State U., 1964; MA, Johns Hopkins U., 1965; PhD, U. Calif., Davis, 1968. Asst. prof., English Boston U., 1968-75, assoc. prof., 1975-82, prof., 1982-87; prof., English Vanderbilt U., Nashville, 1987-90, William R. Kenan Jr. prof., English, 1991—; cons. Nat. Ctr. Humanities, Research Triangle Park, N.C., 1992—. Author: New World New Earth, 1979, Shifting Gears, 1987, Electronic Hearth, 1991, High Lonesome, 1994; editor: The Harper American Literature, 1986. Rsch. grantee Sci. Tech. Soc., NEH, 1985. Mem. Am. Studies Assn. (pres. 1992-93), Modern Lang. Assn. Home: 616 Hillwood Blvd Nashville TN 37205-1314 Office: Vanderbilt U Dept English Nashville TN 37235

TIDBALL, CHARLES STANLEY, computer scientist, educator; b. Geneva, Switzerland, Apr. 15, 1928; (parents Am. citizens); s. Charles Taylor and Adele (Desmaison) T.; m. Mary Elizabeth Peters, Oct. 25, 1952. B.A., Wesleyan U., 1950; M.S. (Univ. scholar), U. Rochester, 1952; Ph.D., U. Wis., Madison, 1955. M.D. (Shattuck fellow, Van Noyes scholar), U. Chgo., 1958; LHD (hon.), Wilson Coll., 1994. Rotating intern Madison (Wis.) Gen. Hosp., 1958-59; physician I Mendota State Hosp., Madison, 1959; asst. research prof. physiology dept. George Washington U. Med. Center, Washington, 1959-63; USPHS spl. fellow George Washington U. Med. Center, 1960-61, asso. prof., acting chmn. dept., 1963-64, prof., 1964-65, chmn. dept., 1964-71, Henry D. Fry prof., 1965-84, research prof. med., 1972-80; dir. Office Computer Assisted Edn. George Washington U. Med. Ctr., 1973-75, dir. Office Computer Assisted Edn. and Svcs., 1975-78; Lucie Stern disting. vis. prof. natural scis. Mills Coll., 1980; prof. edn. George Washington U. Sch. Edn., 1982-84; dir. ednl. computing tech. program George Washington U. Med. Ctr., 1982-84; prof. computer medicine George Washington U. Sch. Edn., 1984-92, prof. emeritus computer medicine, 1992, prof. neurol. surgery, 1990-92, prof. emeritus neurol. surgery, 1992, dir. ednl. computing tech. program, 1982-84; civil surgeon Immigration and Naturalization Svc., Dept. Justice, Washington, 1986-89; disting. rsch. scholar, co-dir. Tidball Ctr. for Study Ednl. Environments Hood Coll., Frederick, Md., 1994—; vis. trustee prof. Skidmore Coll., 1995. Author: (with others) Consolidated Index to For Thy Great Glory, 1993; editor: (with M. C. Shelesnyak) Frontiers in the Teaching of Physiology: Computer Literacy and Simulation, 1981; mem. editorial bd.: Jour. Applied Physiology, 1966-69, Jour. Computer-Based Instrn., 1974-89, Am. Jour. Physiology; assoc. editor physiology tchr. sect.; The Physiologist, 1979-85; contbr. articles to profl. jours. Trustee Cathedral Choral Soc., 1976-79; lay reader St Albans Parish, 1965-67; lay eucharistic min. Washington Nat. Cathedral, 1967-94, clergy asst., 1968—, homilist 1977—, info. sys. specialist, 1986-93, vol. mgr. info. sys. program, 1993—, lay eucharistic min., 1994—; mem. commn. Episcopal Diocese Washington, 1976-78; mem. com. mgmt. YMCA Camp Letts, 1968—, chmn., 1972-75; dir., chmn. Camp Letts Endowment Fund, 1977—; bd. dirs. Met. YMCA, Washington, 1972-84, trustees coun., 1984-91, fin. com., 1972-93, v.p. internat. program 1974-75, asst. treas., 1975-77, v.p., treas., 1977-79, vice-chmn., 1979-80, chmn., 1980-82, pres. of found., 1991-93, bd. dirs. Woodley Ensemble, 1993—, treas., 1993—; dir. Mid-Atlantic Region YMCA, 1974-83; pres. Mid-Atlantic Regional Assembly, 1974-76; mem. nat. coun. YMCA's, 1975-83, mem. nominating com., 1979-83; bd. dirs., vice-chmn. Cathedral West Condominium, 1983-84, chmn., 1984-87, 91-93, fin. com., 1979-94; trustee Wilson Coll., 1983-92, Everitt-Pomeroy trustee, 1993—; trustee Population Reference Bur., 1987—, chmn. bd. trustees, 1992-94, sec., 1994—. Recipient award Washington Acad. Scis., 1967, Leader of Yr. award Met. YMCA, Washington, 1974, Red Triangle award, 1976, Service award, 1979; Dakota Indian name Am. Youth Found., 1976; Research Career Devel. award USPHS, 1961-63. Mem. Am. Physiol. Soc. (emeritus). Home: 4100 Cathedral Ave NW Washington DC 20016-3584

TIDBALL, M. ELIZABETH PETERS, educator, author; b. Anderson, Ind., Oct. 15, 1929; d. John Winton and Beatrice (Ryan) Peters; m. Charles S. Tidball, Oct. 25, 1952. BA, Mt. Holyoke Coll., 1951, LHD, 1976; MS, U. Wis., 1955, PhD, 1959; MTS summa cum laude, Wesley Theol. Sem., 1990; ScD (hon.), Wilson Coll., 1973; DSc (hon.), Trinity Coll., 1974, Cedar Crest Coll., 1977; ScD (hon.), U. of South, 1978, Goucher Coll., 1979; DSc (hon.), St. Mary's-of-The-Woods Coll., 1986; LittD (hon.), Regis Coll., 1980, Coll. St. Catherine, 1980, Alverno Coll., 1989; HHD (hon.), St. Mary's Coll., 1977, Hood Coll., 1982; LLD (hon.), St. Joseph Coll., 1983; LHD (hon.), Skidmore Coll., 1984, Marymount Coll., 1985, Converse Coll., 1985, Mt. Vernon Coll., 1986. Teaching asst. physiology dept. U. Wis., 1952-55, 58-59; research asst. anatomy dept. U. Chgo., 1955-56, research asst. physiology dept., 1956-58; USPHS postdoctoral fellow NIH, Bethesda, Md., 1959-61; staff pharmacologist Hazleton Labs., Falls Church, Va., 1961; assoc. in physiology George Washington U. Med. Ctr., 1960-62; cons. Hazleton Labs., 1962; asst. research prof. dept. pharmacology George Washington U. Med. Ctr., 1962-64, assoc. research prof. dept. physiology, 1964-70, research prof., 1970-71, prof., 1971-94, prof. emeritus, 1994—; asst. M of Theol. Studies program Wesley Theol Sem., 1993-94; disting. rsch. scholar Hood Coll., Frederick, Md., 1994—; co-dir. Tidball Ctr. for Study of Ednl. Environments Hood Coll., 1994—; Lucie Stern Disting. vis. prof. natural scis. Mills Coll., 1980; scholar in residence Coll. Preachers, 1984, Salem Coll., 1985, Wesley Theol. Sem., 1992; Disting. scholar in residence So. Meth. U., 1985; vis. trustee prof. Skidmore Coll., 1995; cons. FDA, 1966-67, assoc. sci. coord. sci. assocs. tng. programs, 1966-67; mem. com. on NIH tng. programs and fellowships Nat. Acad. Scis., 1972-75; faculty summer confs. Am. Youth Found., 1967-78; founder, dir. Summer Seminars for Women Am. Youth Found., 1987-95; cons. for instl. rsch. Wellesley Coll., 1974-75; exec. sec. com. on edn. and employment women in sci. and engring. Commn. on Human Resources, NRC/NAS, 1974-75, vice-chmn., 1977-82; cons., staff officer NRC/Nat. Acad. Scis., 1974-91; NSF, 1974-91; bd. mentor Assn. Governing Bds. of Univs. and Colls., 1991—; Gale Fund for the Study of Trusteeship Adv. Comm., 1992—; cons. Assn. Am. Colls. Women's Coll. Coalition Rsch. Adv. Comm., 1992—; Single Gender Schooling Working Group, U.S. Dept. Edn., 1992-94; rep. to D.C. Commn. on Status of Women, 1972-75; nat. panelist Am. Coun. on Edn.), 1983-90; panel mem. Congl. Office of Tech. Assessment, 1986-87; mem. fellows selection com., fellows mentor Coll. Preachers, 1992—; Columnist Trusteeship, 1993—; mem. editorial bd. Jour. Higher Edn., 1979-84, cons. editor, 1984—; mem. editorial adv. bd. Religion and Intellectual Life, 1983; contbr. sci. articles and rsch. on edn. of women to profl. jours. Trustee Mt. Holyoke Coll., 1968-73, vice-chmn., 1972-73, trustee fellow, 1988—; trustee Hood Coll., 1972-84, 86-92, exec. com., 1974-84, 89-92; overseer Sweet Briar Coll., 1978-85; trustee Cathedral Choral Soc.,

1976-90, pres. bd. trustees, 1982-84, hon. trustee, 1991—; trustee Skidmore Coll., 1988—, mem. exec. com., 1993—; mem. governing bd. Coll. of Preachers, 1979-85, chmn., 1983-85; mem. governing bd. Washington Cathedral Found., 1983-85, mem. exec com., 1983-85; bd. vis. Salem Coll., 1986-93; ctr. assoc. Nat. Resource Ctr., Girls Clubs Am., 1983—. Shattuck fellow, 1955-56; Mary E. Woolley fellow Mt. Holyoke Coll., 1958-59; USPHS postdoctoral fellow, 1959-61; recipient Alumnae Medal of Honor Mt. Holyoke Coll., 1971, Award for Valuable Contbns. Gen. Alumni Assn. George Washington U., 1982, 87, Chestnut Hill Medal for Outstanding Achievement Chestnut Hill Coll., Phila., 1987; named Outstanding Grad. The Penn Hall Sch., 1988. Mem. AAAS, Am. Physiol. Soc. (chmn. task force on women in physiology 1973oms. 1977-80, mem. emeritus 1994—), Am. Assn. Higher Edn., Mt. Holyoke Alumnae Assn. (dir. 1966-70, 76-77), Histamine Club, Sigma Delta Epsilon, Sigma Xi. Episcopalian. Home: 4100 Cathedral Ave NW Washington DC 20016-3584

TIDMAN, DEREK ALBERT, physics researcher; b. London, Oct. 18, 1930; came to U.S., 1957; s. Albert Horace and Florence Violet (Oscar) T.; m. Pauline Harrell Tidman, Apr. 25, 1959; children: Katherine Fleming, Mark Harrell. BSc, London U., 1952; diploma, Imperial Coll. Sci. & Tech., 1956; PhD, 1956. Rsch. fellow U. Sydney, Australia, 1956-57; asst. prof. U. Chgo., Ill., 1957-60; rsch. assoc. prof. U. Md., College Park, 1961-64, rsch. prof., 1964-80; pres. GT-Devices subs. Gen. Dynamics, Alexandria, Va., 1980-94, Ultron Inc., Manassas, Va., 1994—; cons. NASA Goddard Space Flight Ctr., Greenbelt, Md., 1961-69, Los Alamos Sci. Lab., 1974-78, Lawrence Livermore Lab., Calif., 1977-80. Co-author: Plasma Kinetic Theory, 1963, Shock Waves in Collisionless Plasmas, 1971; co-editor: Plasma Instabilities in Astrophysics, 1969; assoc. editor: Physics of Fluids, 1970-72, Jour. Math. Physics, 1972-74; contbr. articles to profl. jours.; patentee in field. Recipient Disting. Scientist award Md. Acad. Scis., 1965. Fellow Am. Phys. Soc.; mem. IEEE. Office: Ultron Inc 8506 Wellington Rd Manassas VA 22110

TIDMARSH, KAREN MACAUSLAND, dean; b. Newton, Mass., May 19, 1949; d. Maurice William and Frances Lane (Green) T. AB, Bryn Mawr Coll., 1971; PhD, U. Va., 1988. Fellow U. Va., 1975-76, 77, teaching asst., 1976-77, 78-79; asst. dean Bryn Mawr (Pa.) Coll., 1979-80, 83-86, assoc. dir. admissions, 1980-83, assoc. dean, 1986-89, lectr. in English, 1988—, acting dean, 1989-90, dean undergrad. coll., 1990—. Trustee Baldwin Sch., Bryn Mawr, 1991—. Home: 519 Old Buck Ln Haverford PA 19041-1214 Office: Bryn Mawr Coll Bryn Mawr PA 19010

TIDWELL, GEORGE ERNEST, federal judge; b. Atlanta, Aug. 1, 1931; s. George Brown and Mary (Wooddall) T.; m. Carolyn White, July 1, 1961; children: Thomas George, Linda Carol, David Loran. LL.B., Emory U., 1954. Bar: Ga. 1954. With John J. Westmoreland Sr. and Jr., Atlanta, 1954-58, Slaton, Brookins, Robertson & Tidwell, Atlanta, 1958-66; exec. asst. atty. gen. Atlanta, 1966-68; judge Civil Ct., Fulton County, Ga., 1968-71, Superior Ct., Atlanta Jud. Circuit, 1971-79, U.S. Dist. Ct. (no. dist.) Ga., Atlanta, 1979—. Mem. ABA, State Bar Ga., Am. Judicature Soc., Atlanta Bar Assn. Office: US Dist Ct 1967 US Courthouse 75 Spring St SW Atlanta GA 30303-3309

TIDWELL, MOODY RUDOLPH, federal judge; b. Kansas City, Mo., Feb. 15, 1939; s. Moody R., Jr. and Dorothy T.; m. Rena Alexandra, Jan. 28, 1966; children—Gregory, Jeremy. B.A., Ohio Wesleyan U., 1961; J.D., Am. U., 1964; LL.M., George Washington U., 1972. Bar: U.S. Ct. Appeals (D.C. cir.) 1964, U.S. Dist Ct. D.C. 1965, U.S. Ct. Claims 1972, U.S. Ct. Appeals (10th cir.) 1979. Assoc. solicitor gen. law div. Dept. Interior, Washington, 1972-75, assoc. solicitor Energy and Resources div., 1975-78; assoc. solicitor Mine Health and Safety div. Dept. Labor, Washington, 1978-80; deputy solicitor, counsellor to the sec. Dept. Interior, Washington, 1981-83; judge U.S. Ct. Federal Claims, Washington, 1983—; dir., corporate sec. Keco, Inc., Cin. Pres. Pine Lake Corp., Glengary, W.Va., 1975—. Recipient Disting. Service award Sec. of Interior, 1983, Meritorious Service award Sec. of Labor, 1979. Mem. ABA, Fed. Bar Assn., D.C. Bar Assn. Office: US Ct Fed Claims 717 Madison Pl NW Washington DC 20005-1011

TIDWELL, THOMAS TINSLEY, chemistry educator; b. Atlanta, Feb. 20, 1939; s. Charles Spear and Helen (Frazier) T.; m. Sarah Huddleston, July 29, 1971. BS, Ga. Inst. Tech., 1960; AM, Harvard U., 1963, Ph.D., 1964. Research assoc. U. Calif., San Diego, 1964-65; research assoc. U. East Anglia, Norwich, Eng., 1966-67; asst. prof. U. S.C., Columbia, 1965-72; assoc. prof. U. Toronto, 1972-77, prof. chemistry, 1977—; assoc. dean, 1979-82, assoc. chair dept. chemistry, 1991-93; chair Iupac Commn. Phys. Orgn. Chem., 1994—. NATO research fellow, 1978, 83, 89; exch. scientist U.S. Acad. Sci., Bulgaria, 1982, USSR, 1989. Mem. Am. Chem. Soc., Am. Assn. Adv. Sci., Can. Soc. Chemistry. Office: U Toronto, Dept Chemistry, Toronto, ON Canada M5S 1A1

TIECKE, RICHARD WILLIAM, pathologist, educator, association executive; b. Muscatine, Iowa, Apr. 5, 1917; s. Harry Frederick and Nell Eola (McKibben) T. BS, U. Iowa, 1940, DDS, 1942, MS, 1947; PhD. pathology, U Chicago, 1949; postgrad. in pathology, U. Chgo., 1947-49. Diplomate Am. Bd. Oral Pathology (bd. dirs., past pres.). Jr. pathologist, asst. pathologist, dep. chief oral pathology div. Armed Forces Inst. Pathology, 1949-54; assoc. prof. pathology Georgetown, 1949-54; prof. pathology Northwestern U. Sch. Medicine, Chgo., 1954-85; prof. emeritus Northwestern U. Sch. Medicine, 1985—, head oral pathology, assoc. cancer coordinator, 1954-62; prof. dept. oral pathology U. Ill., 1965-80, prof. dept. oral diagnosis, 1980-84; adj. staff Northwestern Meml. Hosps., 1981-85; research fellow Hektoen Inst. Med. Research, Cook County Hosp., Chgo., 1965-80; dir. research inst. Am. Dental Assn., Chgo., 1968-71, asst. exec. dir., 1971-85; lectr. Royal Coll. Surgeons, London, 1958, Royal Coll. Surgeons, Copenhagen, Denmark, 1959, Royal Coll. Surgeons, Helsinki, Finland, 1959; cons. AMA, U.S. Naval Hosp., Great Lakes, Ill., VA Research Hosp., VA West Side Hosp., Pub. Health Hosp., Chgo., City Chgo. Bd. Health; surgeon gen. USPHS; head and neck cancer detection Nat. Center Chronic Disease Control-USPHS, Nat. Cancer Inst. NIH; cons. to surgeon gen. Army, 1969-80. Author: Physiologic Pathology of Oral Disease, 1959, Oral Pathology, 1964, Atlas on Oral Cytology, 1969, also research articles. Served from 1st lt. to col. U.S. Army and AUS, 1942-77; now col. Res. (ret.). Richard W. Tiecke Pathology Lab. named in his honor Northwestern U. Med. Ctr., 1987. Fellow Am. Acad. Oral Pathology (past pres.), Am. Coll. Dentists; mem. ADA (hon., asst. sec. coun. dental therapeutics 1962-68), Ill., Chgo. dental socs., Internat. Assn. Dental Rsch., Psi Omega, Omicron Kappa Upsilon. Home: 5 Major Aly Palm Beach FL 33480-4518

TIEDE, TOM ROBERT, journalist; b. Huron, S.D., Feb. 24, 1937; s. Leslie Albert and Rose (Allen) T.; children: Kristina Anne, Thomas Patrick. B.A. in Journalism, Wash. State U., 1959. Mem. staff Kalispell (Mont.) Daily Interlake, 1960-61, Daytona Beach (Fla.) News Jour., 1961-63; war corr. Newspaper Enterprise Assn., N.Y.C., 1964—; lectr. in field., 1965—. Author: Your Men at War, 1965, Coward, 1968, Calley: Soldier or Killer?, 1971, Welcome to Washington, Mr. Witherspoon, 1979, The Great Whale Rescue, 1986, American Tapestry: Eye Witness Accounts of the 1900's, 1988, The Man Who Discovered Pluto, 1990, Fosser, 1994. Served as lt., inf. AUS, 1960. Recipient Ernie Pyle Meml. award, 1965; Freedoms Found. award, 1966; George Washington medal, 1972. Mem. Internat. Platform Assn., Sigma Delta Chi, Lambda Chi Alpha. Roman Catholic. Clubs: Overseas Press, National Press, Nat. Headliners (award 1966 Atlantic City). Work collected by Boston U. Library. Office: NEA 1090 Vermont Ave NW Washington DC 20005-4905 Address: PO Box 1919 Mill Run Bourne Richmond Hill GA 31324

TIEDEKEN, KATHLEEN HELEN, health facilities administrator; b. Camden, N.J., Aug. 6, 1945; d. Joseph Henry and Katherine Rita (Byrne) T. RN, Our Lady of Lourdes Sch., Camden, 1966; BSN, U. Pa., 1974, MSN, 1979. RN, N.J. Staff nurse Our Lady of Lourdes Med. Ctr., Camden, 1966-68, head nurse, 1968-76, asst. dir. staffing, 1976-78; asst. dir. nursing Our Lady of Lourdes Med. Ctr., 1978-80, assoc. dir. nursing, 1980-83; assoc. exec. dir. nursing West Jersey Health System, Voorhees, N.J., 1983-87; assoc. adminstr. nursing Meml. Hosp. Burlington County, Mt. Holly, N.J., 1986-90, v.p. patient svcs., 1990-93, v.p. patient and hosp. ops., 1993—; clin. adj., faculty nursing Widener U.; speaker in field. Contbg. author: Emotion and Reproduction, 1979, New Directions for Nursing in the

'80s, 1980, Computer Applications in Nursing Education and Practice, 1992. Rsch. grantee State Dept. Health, 1990, 91; Johnson & Johnson Wharton fellow in mgmt. for nurses, 1992. Mem. ANA (cert. nursing advanced adminstrn.), Orgn. Am. Nurses Execs. (bd. dirs., chmn. ednl. dialogue com., newsletter), N.J. State Nurses Assn. (legis. com., role of honor com. 1980-85), N.J. Bd. Nursing (ad hoc com. on unlicensed personnel role), Vol. Hosps. Am. (N.J. nursing coun.), Am. Coll. Obstetricians and Gynecologists (nurses assn.), Nat. Perinatal Assn., Sigma Theta Tau. Roman Catholic. Avocations: travel, photography, swimming, reading. Home: 1610 Beechwood Pl Clementon NJ 08021-5801 Office: Meml Hosp Burlington County 175 Madison Ave Mount Holly NJ 08060-2038

TIEDEMAN, DAVID VALENTINE, education educator; b. Americus, Ga., Aug. 12, 1919; s. Walter Dohlen and Edna M(arie) (Komfort) T.; m. Marjorie I(da) Denman, Sept. 26, 1942 (div. Jan. 2, 1973); children—David Michael, Jeffrey Denman; m. Anna Louise Miller, Jan. 6, 1973. A.B., Union Coll., Schenectady, 1941; A.M., U. Rochester, 1943; Ed.M., Harvard, 1948, Ed.D., 1949. Staff mem. NRC com. selection and tng. aircraft pilots U. Rochester, 1941-43; staff mem. test constrn. dept. Coll. Entrance Exam. Bd., 1943-44; assoc. head statistics div. Manhattan Project, 1944-46; Milton teaching fellow, instr. edn. Harvard Grad. Sch. Edn., 1946-48, Sheldon travelling fellow, 1948-49, instr. edn., 1949-51, asst. prof. edn., 1951-52, lectr. edn., 1952-55, assoc. prof., 1955-59, prof., 1959-71, assoc. dir., research assoc. Center for Research in Careers, 1963-66, also chmn. exec. com., info. system for vocat. decisions, 1966-69; prin. research scientist Palo Alto office Am. Insts. for Research, 1971-73; prof. edn. No. Ill. U., DeKalb, 1973-80; dir. ERIC Clearinghouse in Career Edn., 1973-76; coordinator Office Vocat., Tech., and Career Edn., 1978-80; prof. career and higher edn. U. So. Calif., Los Angeles, 1981-84; prof. emeritus higher and post secondary edn. U. So. Calif., 1984—; exec. dir. Nat. Inst. Advancement of Career Edn., 1981-84; pres. Internat. Coll., 1985-86; v.p. Lifecareer Found., 1985—; provost William Lyon U., 1988-91; faculty Walden U., 1992—; mem. Adv. Council on Guidance Dept. Edn. Commonwealth Mass., 1957-63; chmn. commn. on tests Coll. Entrance Exam. Bd., 1967-70; mem. advisory screening com. in edn. Council Internat. Exchange of Scholars, 1975-79, chmn., 1978-79. Co-author 5 books.; editorial assoc.: Jour. Counseling Psychology, 1957-63; Personnel and Guidance Jour., 1960-63, Character Potential: A Record of Research, 1977-82, Jour. Career Edn., 1979-85; contbr. articles to profl. jours., chpts. to books. Bd. dirs. Mass. Com. Children and Youth, 1961-63. Fellow Ctr. for Advanced Study in Behavioral Scis.; spl. fellow NIMH, 1963-64. Fellow Am. Psychol. Soc., APA (prs. divsn. counseling psychology 1965-66); mem. ACA, Nat. Career Devel. Assn. (pres. 1965-66, Eminent Career award 1979), Nat. Coun. Measurement in Edn. (pres. 1962-63), Phi Beta Kappa, Sigma Xi, Phi Delta Kappa, Phi Kappa Phi. Office: Lifecareer Ctr 1078 La Tortuga Dr Vista CA 92083

TIEDGE-LAFRANIER, JEANNE MARIE, editor; b. N.Y.C., July 24, 1960; d. Richard Frederick and Joan Jean (Gerardo) Tiedge; m. John Daniel Lewis Lafranier, Oct. 8, 1989; children: Katelyn Ellen, John Richard. BA, Drew U., 1982. Asst. Denise Morcil Lit. Agy., N.Y.C., 1982-84; sr. editor New Am. Libr., N.Y.C., 1984-87, Warner Books, N.Y.C., 1987—. Avocation: equestrian.

TIEDJE, JAMES MICHAEL, microbiology educator, ecologist; b. Newton, Iowa, Feb. 9, 1942; married, 1965; 3 children. BS, Iowa State U., 1964; MS, Cornell U., 1966, PhD in Soil Microbiology, 1968. From asst. prof. to prof. Mich. State U., 1968-78, disting. prof., 1991—; dir. sci. and tech. ctr. microbial ecology NSF, 1988—; vis. assoc. prof. U. Ga., 1974-75; cons. NSF, 1974-77; vis. prof. U. Calif. Berkeley, 1981-82; mem. biotech. sci. adv. com. EPA, 1986-89, chair sci. adv. coun. GPA, 1988-90. Editor: Applied Microbiology, 1974—, editor-in-chief, 1980-86. Recipient Carlos J. Finley prize, UNESCO, 1993. Mem. AAAS, Am. Soc. Agronomy (Soil Sci. award 1990), Internat. Inst. Biotech., Am. Soc. Microbiology (award in applied and environ. microbiology 1992), Soil Sci. Soc. Am., Ecol. Soc. Am., Internat. Soc. Soil Sci. (chair soil biology divsn.). Achievements include research in dentrification, microbial metabolism of organic pollutants, and molecular microbiol. ecology. Office: Michigan State U Microbial Ecology Ctr 540 Plant & Soil Scis Bldg East Lansing MI 48824-1325

TIEFEL, VIRGINIA MAY, librarian; b. Detroit, May 20, 1926; d. Karl and June Garland (Young) Brenkert; m. Paul Martin Tiefel, Jan. 25, 1947; children: Paul Martin Jr., Mark Gregory. B.A. in Elem. Edn., Wayne State U., 1962; M.A. in Library Sci., U. Mich., 1968. Librarian Birmingham Schs., Mich., 1967-68; librarian S. Euclid-Lyndhurst Schs., Cleve., 1968-69; acquisitions-reference librarian Hiram Coll., Ohio, 1969-77; head undergrad. libraries Ohio State U., Columbus, 1977-84; dir. library user edn. Ohio State U., 1978—. Contbr. articles to profl. jours. Recipient Disting. Alumnus award U. Mich. Sch. Info. and Libr. Studies, 1993. Mem. ALA (v.p. Ohio sect. 1973-74, pres. 1974-75, Miriam Dudley Bibliographic Instrn. Librarian of Yr. 1986), Acad. Library Assn. Ohio (Outstanding Ohio Acad. Librarian 1984), Assn. Coll. and Research Libraries (chmn. bibliographic instrn. sect. com. on research 1983-84, chmn. com. on performance measures 1984-90). Lutheran. Home: 4956 Smoketalk Ln Westerville OH 43081-4433 Office: Ohio State U Libraries 1858 Neil Ave Columbus OH 43210-1286

TIEFEL, WILLIAM REGINALD, hotel company executive; b. Rochester, N.Y., Mar. 30, 1934; s. William Reginald and Mary Hazel (Cross) T.; m. Vada Morell, Dec. 30, 1985. Student, Williams Coll., 1952-54; B.A. with honors, Mich. State U., 1956; postgrad., Harvard Bus. Sch. Gen. mgr. Marriott Hotels, Arlington, Va., 1964-65, Saddle Brook, N.J., 1966-69, Newton, Mass., 1969-71; regional v.p. Marriott Hotels, Washington, 1971-80; corp. v.p. Marriott Corp., Washington, 1976-89; exec. v.p. Marriott Hotels and Resorts, Washington, 1980-88; pres. Marriott Hotels, Resorts and Stes., 1988—; exec. v.p., mem. exec. and fin. coms. Marriott Corp., 1988—; pres. Marriott Lodging Group, 1992—. Bd. visitors Valley Forge Mil. Acad. and Jr. Coll., 1976-79, chmn., 1979, trustee, 1982-88, 89—; chmn. Campaign for Valley Forge, 1985-88, chmn. com. on trustees, 1989-91. Mem. Am. Hotel and Motel Assn. (dir. Ednl. Inst.). Republican. Roman Catholic. Home: 2426 Wyoming Ave NW Washington DC 20008-1643 Office: Marriott Corp 1 Marriott Dr Washington DC 20058-0001

TIEFENTHAL, MARGUERITE AURAND, school social worker; b. Battle Creek, Mich., July 23, 1919; d. Charles Henry and Elisabeth Dirk (Hoekstra) Aurand; m. Harlan E. Tiefenthal, Nov. 26, 1942; children: Susan Ann, Daniel E., Elisabeth Amber, Carol Aurand. BS, Western Mich. U., 1941; MSW, U. Mich., 1950; postgrad., Coll. of DuPage, Ill., 1988-90. Tchr. No. High Sch., Flint, Mich., 1941-44, Cen. High Sch., Kalamazoo, 1944-45; acct. Upjohn Co., Kalamazoo, 1945-48; social worker Family Svc. Agy., Lansing, Mich., 1948-50, Pitts., 1950-55; sch. social worker Gower Sch. Dist., Hinsdale, Ill., 1962-70; sch. social worker Hinsdale (Ill.) Dist. 181, 1970-89, cons., 1989—; sch. social worker Villa Park (Ill.) Sch. Dist. 45, 1989; addictions counselor Mercy Hosp., 1990-92; asst. prof. sch. social work, liaison to pub. schs. Loyola U., Chgo., 1990—; field instr. social work interns U. Ill., 1979-88; impartial due process hearing officer; mem. adv. com. sch. social work Ill. State Bd. Edn. approved programs U. Ill. and George Williams Coll.; speaker Nat. Conf. Sch. Social Work, Denver, U. Tex. Joint Conf. Sch. Social Work in Ill.; founder Marguerite Tiefenthal Symposium for Ill. Sch. Social Work Interns. Co-editor The School Social Worker and the Handicapped Child: Making P.L. 94-142 Work; sect. editor: Sch. Social Work Quarterly, 1979. Sec. All Village Caucus Village of Western Springs, Ill., mem. village disaster com.; deacon Presbyn. Ch. Western Springs, Sunday sch. tchr., mem. choir; instr. Parent Effectiveness, Teacher Effectiveness, STEP; trainer Widowed Persons Service Tng. Program for Vol. Aides AARP. Recipient Ill. Sch. Social Worker of Yr., 1982. Mem. Nat. Assn. Social Workers (exec. council on social work in schs.), Ill. Assn. Sch. Social Workers (past pres., past conf. chmn., conf. program chmn.), Sch. Social Workers Supervisors Group (del. to Ill. Commn. on Children), Programs. for Licensure of Social Work Practice in Ill., LWV, DKG, PEO. Avocation: sewing. Home: 4544 Grand Ave Western Springs IL 60558-1545

TIEGS, CHERYL, model, designer; d. Theodore and Phyllis T. Student, Calif. State U., Los Angeles. Profl. model, appearing in nat. mags., including, Time, Life, Bazaar, Sports Illustrated, Glamour; appeared weekly on ABC's Good Morning America; also appearing in TV commls., Cheryl Tiegs line of sportswear, Cheryl Tiegs nationally-distributed line of women's eyeglass frames, Cheryl Tiegs Collection of 14k Gold Jewelry, Fashion Watches, Shoes and Hosiery; author: The Way to Natural Beauty, 1980; Sports Illustrated video Aerobic Interval Training with Cheryl Tiegs. Address: care Barbara Shapiro 2 Greenwich Plz Ste 100 Greenwich CT 06830-6353

TIELKE, JAMES CLEMENS, retail and manufacturing executive; b. St. Helena, Nebr., May 15, 1931; s. Joseph Hubert and Catherine Josephine (Schmidt) T.; m. Betty Merle Adams, Apr. 18, 1953; children: P. James, Michael Jay, Dawn Michelle. B.S. in Bus. Adminstrn., U.S.D., 1959, MA in Speech and Econ., 1960. Partner, Tielke Motors, Yankton, S.D., 1952-54; owner Ft. Collins Motors, Colo., 1954-56; various merchandising positions Montgomery Ward, Chgo., 1960-81, v.p. mdse. adminstrn., 1978-81; pres. Midwest div. Structured Approaches, Inc., 1981-82; v.p. nat. accounts Dupli-Color Products, Elk Grove Village, Ill., 1983-85; pres. Black Leaf Products Co., 1985-89; v.p. Hysan Corp., Des Plaines, Ill., 1985-89; v.p. sales and mktg. Koos Inc., divsn. The Vigoro Corp., Kenosha, Wis., 1989—. Recipient Honors award U. S.D. Sch. Bus., 1977. Office: 4500 13th Ct Kenosha WI 53140-2790

TIEMAN, SUZANNAH BLISS, neurobiologist; b. Washington, Oct. 10, 1943; d. John Alden and Winifred Texas (Bell) Bliss; m. David George Tieman, Dec. 19, 1969. AB with honors, Cornell U., 1965; postgrad., MIT, 1965-66, Calif. Inst. Tech., 1971-72; PhD, Stanford U., 1974. Postdoctoral fellow dept. anatomy U. Calif., San Francisco, 1974-77; rsch. assoc. Neurobiology Rsch. Ctr. SUNY, Albany, 1977-90; sr. rsch. assoc., 1990—; rsch. assoc. prof. dept. biol. scis. SUNY, Albany, 1984-90, rsch. prof., 1990—, sr. rsch. assoc., 1990—; adj. asst. prof. dept. biol. scis., SUNY, Albany, 1977-84. Contbr. articles to profl. jours., chpts. to books in field. Recipient predoctoral fellowship NSF, NIH, Stanford U., 1970-73,73-74, postdoctoral fellowship Nat. Eye Inst., U. Calif., San Francisco, 1974-77, rsch. grant SUNY, Albany, 1979-83, NSF, SUNY, 1983-86, '88-92, '92-95. Mem. AAAS, Soc. for Neurosci. (steering com. Hudson Berkshire chpt. 1980-81, pres. 1991-93), Assn. Rsch. in Vision and Ophthalmology, Am. Assn. Anatomists, Assn. Women in Sci., Women In Neurosci., Nat. Audubon Soc., Nature Conservancy. Avocations: choral music, folk music, birding, eskimo art. Office: SUNY Neurobiology Rsch Ctr 1400 Washington Ave Albany NY 12222-0001

TIEMEYER, CHRISTIAN, conductor; m. Patti Tiemeyer; children: Jeanine, Hank, Elisa. Student, The Juilliard Sch. Music, N.Y.C.; BA, MusM, Peabody Conservatory; MusD, Cath. U. Am., Washington. Former assoc. condr. Dallas Symphony Orch.; music dir. Cedar Rapids (Iowa) Symphony Orch., 1982—; interim artistic dir. Omaha Symphony Orch., 1983-84, prin. guest condr., 1984-85; guest condr. Utah Symphony Orch., Calgary Philharm., N.C. Sch. Arts Orch., and numerous symphonies from Savannah, Ga. to Seattle; faculty mem. Peabody Inst. Prin. cellist for Leopold Stokowsky, Carnegie Hall, Utah Symphony Orch.; cellist Quartet in residence, Fontainebleu, France; frequent soloist throughout Central and South Am. Avocations: skiing, fly-fishing. Office: Cedar Rapids Symphony Orch 205 2nd St SE Security Bldg Cedar Rapids IA 52401

TIEN, CHANG-LIN, chancellor; b. Wuhan, China, July 24, 1935; came to U.S., 1956, naturalized, 1969; s. Yun Chien and Yun Di (Lee) T.; m. Di Hwa Liu, July 25, 1959; children: Norman Chihnan, Phyllis Chihping, Christine Chihyih. BS, Nat. Taiwan U., 1955; MME, U. Louisville, 1957; MA, PhD, Princeton U., 1959. Acting asst. prof. dept. mech. engring. U. Calif., Berkeley, 1959-60, asst. prof., 1960-64, assoc. prof., 1964-68, prof., 1968-90—, A. Martin Berlin prof., 1987-88, 90—, dept. chmn., 1974-81, also vice chancellor for research, 1983-85; exec. vice chancellor U. Calif., Irvine, 1988-90; chancellor U. Calif., Berkeley, 1990—; tech. cons. Lockheed Missiles and Space Co., GE; trustee Princeton (N.J.) U., 1991—; bd. dirs. Wells Fargo Bank. Contbr. articles to profl jours. Guggenheim fellow, 1965; recipient Heat Transfer Meml. award, 1974, Larson Meml. award, 1975. Fellow AAAS; mem. ASME (hon., AIChE/ASME Max Jakob Meml. award 1981), AIAA (Thermophysics award 1977), NAE. Office: U Calif Berkeley Chancellor's Office 200 Calif Hall 1500 Berkeley CA 94720-1500

TIEN, H. TI, biophysics and physiology educator, scientist; b. Beijing, China, Feb. 1, 1928; came to U.S., 1947; s. Fang-cheng and Wen-tsun (Chow) T.; children: Stephen, David, Adrienne, Jennifer; m. Angelica Leitmannova, 1992. B.Sc., U. Nebr., 1953; Ph.D., Temple U., 1963. Chem. engr. Allied Chem. Corp., Phila., 1953-57; med. scientist Eastern Pa. Psychiat. Inst., Phila., 1957-63; assoc. prof. Northwestern U., Boston, 1963-66; assoc. prof. Mich. State U., East Lansing, 1966-70, prof. biophysics, 1970—, chmn. dept., 1978-82; cons. Hungarian Acad. Sci., Szeged, 1975-76; rsch. prof. Acad. Sinica, Beijing, 1978; cons. prof. Sichuan U., 1984—; cons. Tianjin Econ. Tech. Devel. Area, China; external dir. Ctr. Interface Scis. Slovak Tech. U., Slovakia; cons. prof. Jilin U., Peoples Republic China; frequent lectr. many countries. Author: Bilayer Lipid Membranes, 1974; contbr. chpts. to books. Research grantee NIH, 1964—, NSF, 1978, Dept. Energy, 1980-83, U.S. Naval Rsch. Office, 1985—. Mem. AAAS, Biophys. Soc. (council 1972-75), Nat. Inst. Peer Reviewer. Research interests include membrane biophysics, bioelectrochemistry, photobiology, solar energy conversion via semiconductor septum electrochemical photovoltaic cells (SC-SEP); biomolecular electronic devices. Office: Mich State U Physiology Dept Giltner Hall East Lansing MI 48824

TIEN, PING KING, electronics engineer; b. Chekiang, China, Aug. 2, 1919; came to U.S., 1947; s. N.S. and C.S. (Yen) T.; m. Nancy N.Y. Chen, Apr. 19, 1952; children: Emily-Ju-Psia, Julia Ju-Wen. MS, Stanford U., 1948, PhD, 1951. Fellow emeritus Photonics Rsch. Lab., AT&T, Holmdel, N.J., 1990—; hon. prof. Jiao-Tong U., Shanghai, China. Contbr. sci. and tech. articles to profl. jours. Recipient Achievement award Chinese Inst. Engrs., 1966; fellow AT&T Labs., 1983. Fellow IEEE (Morris N. Liebmann award 1979), Optical Soc. Am.; mem. Nat. Acad. Sci., Nat. Acad. Engring., Inst. Am. Physics, Acad. Sci. Republic of China, Acad. Sci. of Third World, Sigma Xi. Patentee in field. Home: 9 Carolyn Ct Holmdel NJ 07733-2070 Office: AT&T Bell Labs Holmdel NJ 07733

TIENDA, MARTA, demographer, educator; b. Tex. Ph.D. in Sociology, U. Tex., 1977. From asst. prof. to prof. rural sociology U. Wis., Madison, 1976-87; vis. prof. Stanford U., 1987; Ralph Lewis prof. sociology U. Chgo., 1987—, chmn. dept. sociology, 1994—; assoc. dir. Population Research Ctr. Co-author: Hispanics in the U.S. Economy, 1985, Hispanic Population of the United States, 1987, Divided Opporunities, 1988; contbr. articles to profl. jours. Trustee Kaiser Family Found., Russell Sage Found. Guggenheim fellow. Fellow Am. Acad. Arts and Scis., Ctr. Advanced Study Behavioral Scis.; mem. Am. Sociol. Assn., Population Assn. Am., Internat. Union for the Sci. Study Population. Office: U Chgo Dept Sociology 1126 E 59th St Chicago IL 60637-1580

TIENKEN, ARTHUR T., retired foreign service officer; b. Yonkers, N.Y., Aug. 5, 1922. B.A., Princeton U., 1947, M.A., 1949. With U.S Fgn. Svc., 1949-87; dep. chief mission U.S. Fgn. Svc., Tunis, Tunisia, 1973-75, Addis Ababa, Ethiopia, 1975-77; Ambassador to Gabonese Republic and Democratic Republic of Sao Tome and Principe, Libreville, Gabon, 1978-81; dir. Fgn. Svc. Assignments and Career devel. Dept. State, 1981-85, sr. insp., 1985-87, ret., 1987; diplomat-in-residence Marquette U., 1972-73. Served with U.S. Army, 1943-46.

TIERNAN, JAMES SCOTT, JR., association executive; b. Chgo., May 3, 1954; s. James Scott and Marion G. (Gidcumb) T. BS in Bus., Knox Coll., 1976. V.p. Internat. Union Ins. Services, Washington, 1980-88, Brokers/Cons. Inc., Chgo., 1980-88; pres. Hygienic Tech. Inc., Chgo., 1986-88; exec. dir. Am. Consumers Assn., Chgo., 1985-88; speaker Profl. Ins. Mass Mktg. Assn., Bethesda, Md., 1983-88. Founder generic life ins., 1985. Bd. dirs. Young Reps., Chgo., 1980-88, St. Joseph's Hosp. Assocs., Chgo., 1983-88. Mem. Tau Kappa Epsilon (founder 1986-88, Wall of History award, 1986), Charlie Club (weight chmn. 1986-88). Avocation: collecting cars, coins and boats. Home: 1332 Dartmouth Rd Flossmoor IL 60422-1905

TIERNEY, BILL, university athletic coach. Head coach Princeton Tigers, 1988—. NCAA Divsn. 1A Champions, 1992, 94; named Morris Touchstone Divsn. 1A Coach of the Yr.; elected to L.I. Lacrosse Hall of Fame, 1995. Office: Princeton U Dillon Gym Princeton NJ 08544*

TIERNEY, BRIAN PATRICK, advertising and public relations executive; b. Bryn Mawr, Pa., Feb. 21, 1957; s. James Richard and Claire Ella (Springfield) T.; married; 2 children. BA, U. Pa., 1979; JD, Widener U., 1987. Field person Rep. Nat. Com., Washington, 1979-82, dir. incumbent programs, 1979-81, dep. dir. edn., 1981-82; polit. dir. GOPAC, Washington, 1982-83; asst. regional adminstr. U.S. SBA, Bala Cynwyd, Pa., 1983-84; pres. Tierney & Co., Phila., 1984-86; pres., chief exec. officer, Lewis, Gilman & Kynett Pub. Rels., Phila., 1986-89; pres., chief exec. officer The Tierney Group, Phila, 1989—; pres., CEO FCB/Tierney, Phila., 1994—. ann. giving chmn. Ingls House for Disabled Persons, Phila.; bd. dirs. Wilma Theater, Phila., Moore Coll. Art and Design, Phila., Sch. Bd. Archdiocese of Phila., Ave. of Arts, Inc., Phila. Police Athletic League. Mem. ABA, Pa. Bar Assn., Phila. Bar Assn., Pub. Rels. Soc. Am., St. Anthony Club, Union League. Roman Catholic. Avocation: skydiving, Bonsai gardening. Office: 200 S Broad St 10th Fl Philadelphia PA 19102-5023

TIERNEY, GORDON PAUL, real estate broker, genealogist; b. Ft. Wayne, Ind., Oct. 17, 1922; s. James Leonard and Ethele Lydia (Brown) T.; m. Carma Lillian Devine, Oct. 17, 1946; 1 child, Paul N. Student, Ind. U., 1940-41, Cath. U. Am., 1941-42; coll. tng. detachment, Clemson U., 1943. Br. mgr. Bartlett-Collins Co., Chgo., 1956-84; prin., broker Kaiser-Tierney Real Estate, Inc., Palatine, Ill., 1984-89; pres. Tierney Real Estate, Newburgh, Ind. Author: Burgess/Bryan Connection, 1978; assoc. editor Colonial Genealogist Jour., 1976-85. Served in USAC, 1943-45, China. Decorated Legion of Honor. Fellow Am. Coll. Genealogists (pres. 1977—); mem. SAR (v.p. gen. 1984-85, genealogist gen. 1981-83, silver and bronze medals 1978-80, Patriot medal 1976, Meritorious Svc. award 1983, Minutemen award 1984), Huguenot Soc. Ill. (state pres. 1978-80), Huguenot Soc. S.C., Nat. Huguenot Soc., Huguenot Soc. Ind. (pres. 1993-95), Nat. Geneal. Soc., Ind. Hist. Soc., Soc. Ind. Pioneers, First Families Ohio, Ohio Geneal. Soc., Va. Geneal. Soc., Md. Geneal. Soc., Augustan Soc., Gen. Soc. War 1812 (state pres. 1985), Sons. and Daus. Pilgrims, Descs. Old Plymouth Colony, Mil. Order Stars and Bars, Soc. Descendants Colonial Clergy, Sons of Union Vets., Sons of Confederate Vets., Pioneer Wis. Families, Welcome Soc. Pa., Pa. Geneal. Soc., Nat. Soc. Archivists, Soc. Colonial Wars in Ill., Soc. Colonial Wars in Ind. (gov. 1992-94), Sons of Am. Colonists (nat. v.p. 1971-74), Mil. and Hospitalier Order of St. Lazarus of Jerusalem, Order of Descendants of Ancient Planters, Hump Pilots Assn., Nat. Bd. Realtors, Ill. Bd. Realtors, Sword Bunker Hill, Rolling Hill Country Club, Tri-State Geneal. Soc., Ind. Hist. Soc., Jamestowne Soc., Baronial Order of Magna Charta, Mason, Shriner. Republican. Presbyterian. Home and Office: 8766 Hanover Dr Newburgh IN 47630-9327

TIERNEY, JAMES EDWARD, attorney general; b. Bklyn., Apr. 12, 1947; s. Charles J. and Agnes V. (Quinn) T.; m. Susan Webster, Jan. 26, 1969; children: Adam, Josie, Matthew, Daniel, Kate. B.A. with highest honors, U. Maine, 1969, J.D., 1974. Bar: Maine 1974. Mem. Maine State Ho. Reps., 1972-80, majority leader, 1976-80; atty. gen. State of Maine, 1980-90; cons. state attys. gen., 1994—; bd. dirs. People for the Am. Way, Topsham, Maine, 1991-93; spl. prosecutor investigate Pa. Supreme Ct., 1992-93; mem. bd. commentators Courtroom TV Network. Wasserstein fellow Harvard Law Sch., 1992-93. Mem. Am. Judicature Soc. (bd. dirs.). Office: PO Box 417 Topsham ME 04086-0417

TIERNEY, JOHN WILLIAM, chemical engineering educator; b. Oak Park, Ill., Dec. 29, 1923; s. John William and Agnes (Shea) T.; m. Patricia A. O'Neill, June 21, 1952; children: John, Patrick, Joseph, Paul. B.S. in Chem. Engring., Purdue U., 1947; M.S. in Chem. Engring., U. Mich., 1948; Ph.D. in Chem. Engring., Northwestern U., 1951. Sr. research engr. Pure Oil Co., Crystal Lake, Ill., 1948-53; asst. prof. Purdue U., West Lafayette, Ind., 1953-56; mgr. dept. Remington Rand Univac, St. Paul, 1956-60; assoc. prof. chem. engring. U. Pitts., 1960-62, prof., 1962—, W.K. Whiteford prof. chem. engring., 1991-94, prof. emeritus, 1995—; vis. prof. U. Técnica Federico Santa Maria, Valparaiso, Chile, 1960-62; lectr. U. Barcelona (Spain), 1968-69. Fellow AIChE (chmn. Pitts. sect. 1982, McAfee award Pitts. sect. 1995); mem. Am. Chem. Soc., Am. Soc. Engring. Edn. Home: 1330 N Sheridan Ave Pittsburgh PA 15206-1760 Office: U Pitts 1230 Benedum Hall Pittsburgh PA 15261-2212

TIERNEY, KEVIN HUGH, law educator; b. Bristol, Eng., Sept. 22, 1942; came to U.S., 1966, naturalized, 1979; s. Hugh John and Margaret Ellis (Davies) T.; B.A., St. John's Coll., Cambridge (Eng.) U., 1964, LL.B., 1965, M.A., 1968; LL.M., Yale U., 1967. Barrister: Eng. 1966; bar: Mich. 1977, U.S. Dist. Ct. (ea. dist.) Mich. 1978, U.S. Ct. Appeals (9th cir.) 1984, U.S. Supreme Ct., 1990. Assoc., Donovan, Leisure, Newton & Irvine, N.Y.C., 1969-70; assoc. prof. Wayne State U. Law Sch., Detroit, 1971-75, prof., 1975-79; vis. prof. Hastings Coll. Law, U. Calif.-San Francisco, 1979-80, prof., 1980—. Mem. exec. com. Inst. for Continuing Legal Edn., Ann Arbor, Mich., 1977-80. McMahon Law studentship, 1965; Lord Mansfield scholar, 1966; Sterling fellow, 1967; Vis. fellow Ranson Ct., U. Tex., 1992, 95. Mem. Hon. Soc. Lincoln's Inn (London), State Bar Mich., Am. Law Inst., Order of Coif. Club: University (San Francisco). Author: Courtroom Testimony-A Policeman's Guide, 1970, How to Be a Witness, 1971, Darrow: A Biography, 1979; contbr. articles to profl. jours. and encys.; reporter Mich. Standard Jury Instrn. Com., 1975-79. Office: U Calif-San Francisco Hastings Coll Law 200 Mcallister St San Francisco CA 94102-4978

TIERNEY, MICHAEL STEWART, newspaper editor, journalist; b. Louisville, May 20, 1952; s. James Edmund Jr. and Mary (Mullin) T.; m. Lorri Booker; children: Shannon, Meredith, Jordan. BA, U. Ky., 1973. Sports writer, asst. sports editor St. Petersburg Times, 1973-85; asst. sports editor, exec. sports editor, Olympics editor Atlanta Jour.-Constitution, 1986—, now Olympics News reporter only; mem. nat. recognized sports staffs St. Petersburg Times, Atlanta Jour.-Constitution, Assoc. Press Sports Editors. Recipient various writing awards Assoc. Press Sports Editors, Fla. Sports Writers Assn. Mem. Assoc. Press Sports Editors. Home: 457 Nelson Ferry Rd Decatur GA 30032 Office: Atlanta Journal-Constitution PO Box 4689 Atlanta GA 30302*

TIERNEY, PATRICIA A., school system administrator. Supt. schs. Diocese of St. Augustine, Jacksonville, Fla. Office: Office Supt Schs PO Box 24000 Jacksonville FL 32241-4000

TIERNEY, PATRICK JOHN, information services executive; b. Denver, Oct. 9, 1945; s. Thomas Michael and Betty Ruth (Fairall) T.; m. Lois Bruce, Jan. 1, 1980; children: Christopher, Blake. BS, U. Colo., 1967, MBA, 1970. Pres. Gould E.P.C. Div., San Diego, 1980-84, Caterpillar Capital, San Diego, 1984-85; v.p. gen. mgr. TRW Info. Svcs., Orange, Calif., 1985-91; CEO Knight-Ridder Info. Mountain View, Calif., 1991—. Mem. Info. Industry Assn. (bd. dirs. 1992—). Republican. Office: Knight-Ridder Info Inc 2440 El Camino Real Mountain View CA 94040

TIERNEY, PAUL E., JR., investment company executive; b. Feb. 18, 1943; married. Postgrad., Harvard U. With Peace Corps., Chile, 1964-66; Starwood Corp., 1969-72; v.p., gen. mgr. Continental Ill. Ltd., London, 1972-75; sr. v.p. White Weld & Co., 1975-78; mng. dir. Gollust Tierney & Oliver, Inc., 1987-90; chmn. TW Holdings, Inc., Spartanburg, S.C., 1990-92; also bd. dirs. UAL Corp., Elk Grove, Ill. Office: Gollust Tierney & Oliver 500 Park Ave 5th Fl New York NY 10022

TIERNEY, PHILIP, lawyer; b. Boston, Nov. 29, 1933; s. Albert Gerard and Myrtle Marie (Curtin) T.; m. Bettina Rathbone Hartley, Mar. 25, 1961; children—Christopher Randolph, Philip Andrew, David Hartley. AB, Harvard U., 1956; LLB, Boston U., 1961. Bar: Mass. 1961, D.C. 1963, Va., 1964, U.S. Cts. 1964. Atty. advisor U.S. Tax Ct., Washington, 1961-63; ptnr. Boothe Prichard & Dudley, Alexandria, Va., 1963-87; prtnr. McGuire, Woods, Battle & Boothe, Alexandria, 1987—; founder, dir. Bank of Alexandria, 1980—. Bd. dirs. Alexandria Seaport Found., 1982-86 Served to It. USNR, 1956-58. Fellow Am. Coll. Probate Counsel; mem. Va. State Bar (chmn. sect. taxation 1973-75), ABA, Va. Bar Assn. Clubs: Eastern Yacht, Annapolis Yacht. Avocations: sailing, yacht racing, fly fishing, tennis, cycling. Home: 1114 Savile Ln Mc Lean VA 22101-1831 Office: McGuire Woods Battle & Boothe 1199 N Fairfax St Alexandria VA 22314-1437

TIERNEY, RAYMOND MORAN, JR., lawyer; b. Bklyn., Aug. 1, 1932; s. Raymond M. and Alice Mary (Hoag) T.; m. Kathleen Maguire, June 23, 1956; children: Kathy Snyder, Alicia Johnson, Raymond III, Michael, Christopher. BA, U. Notre Dame, 1954; LLB, Fordham U., 1961. Bar: N.J. 1962. Asst. sec. and credit loaning officer Hanover Bank, N.Y.C., 1956-61; law sec. to Hon. J.J. Francis Supreme Ct. N.J., 1961-62; assoc. Shanley & Fisher P.C., Newark, 1962-67; ptnr. Shanley & Fisher P.C., Morristown, 1967—; adj. prof. Monmouth Coll., W. Long Branch, N.J., 1985-88; master William J. Brennan Jr. Inn of Ct., 1987-92; faculty U. Va. Law Sch. Ann. Trial Inst., 1990—; speaker in field. Bd. adjustment Borough Shrewsbury, 1973-80; councilman Coun. Borough Shrewsbury, 1981-83; commr. Gateway Nat. Park Adv. Commn., 1983-86; trustee Newark Mus., 1990—, St. Peter's Coll., Jersey City, 1990—. 1st Lt. U.S. Marines, 1954-56. Recipient Trial Bar award Trial Attys. N.J., 1989, Thomas More Assn. medal Seton Hall Law Sch., 1991. Fellow Am. Coll. Trial Attys., Am. Bar Found.; mem. D.C. Bar Assn., N.J. State Bar Found. (chmn. 1990-92, pres. 1992-94), N.J. State Bar Assn. (trustee 1992-94), Monmouth County Bar Assn. Office: Shanley & Fisher 131 Madison Ave Morristown NJ 07962-1979

TIERNEY, ROBERT THOMAS, civil engineer; b. Fall River, Mass., Nov. 26, 1925; s. Thomas Aloysius and Margaret Elizabeth (Lally) T.; m. Helen Marie Orpen, May 22, 1950; children: Carol, Robert, Jr., Ellen, Nancy, John. B.S., Notre Dame U., 1949. Registered profl. engr., Mass.; registered profl. land surveyor, Mass. Dep. chief engr. Mass. Dept. Pub. Works, Boston, 1970-72, chief engr., 1972-78, commr., 1983-88; asst. administr. Boston Housing Authority, 1979-81; regional mgr. Tippetts, Abbett, McCarthy and Stratton, Boston, 1981-83; dir. Commonwealth Coop. Bank, Boston. Served with USAF, 1943-45. Fellow ASCE; mem. Moles, Boston Soc. Civil Engrs., Am. Assn. State Transp. Ofcls. (policy com. 1975-78, 83-85). Democrat. Roman Catholic. Home: 35 Magnolia Rd Melrose MA 02176-3408 Office: Mass Dept Pub Works 10 Park Plaza Boston MA 02116

TIERNEY, ROSEMARY, mayor. Mayor New Bedford, Mass. Office: 133 Williams St New Bedford MA 02740-6113

TIERNEY, SUSAN FALLOWS, federal official; married; 2 children. BA, Scripps Coll., 1973; student, L'Institut d'Etudes Politiques, Paris; MA, Cornell U., 1976, PhD, 1980; LLD (hon.), Regis Coll. Asst. prof. U. Calif., Irvine, 1978-82; sr. economist Mass. Exec. Office Energy Resources, 1983-84; exec. dir. Mass. Energy Facilities Siting Coun., 1984-88; commr. Dept. Pub. Utilities, 1988-90, sec. environ. affairs, resources authority, 1991-93; asst. sec. energy, office of policy, planning and program evaluation Dept. Energy, Washington, 1993—; chmn. transmission task force New Eng. Gov.'s Conf. Power Planning Com.; mem. Keystone Project Electric Transmission Ind. Power Prodrs. Contbr. articles to profl. jours. Mem. New Eng. Conf. Public Utility Commrs., Nat. Assn. Regulatory Utility Commrs. (energy conservation gas com.), Electric Power Rsch. (adv. com.). Office: Dept Energy Policy 1000 Independence Ave SW Washington DC 20585

TIESZEN, RALPH LELAND, SR., internist; b. Marion, S.D., Sept. 21, 1928; s. Bernard D. and Hulda J. (Thomas) T.; m. Florence Morrill Johnson, July 25, 1952; children: Ralph Leland Jr., Stuart Carl, Stephan Lee. Student, Freeman Jr. Coll., 1946-48; BS, Wheaton Coll., 1950; postgrad., U. S.D., 1950-52; MD, Loma Linda U., 1954. Diplomate Am. Bd. Internal Medicine, Am. Bd. Geriatric Medicine. Intern L.A. County Hosp., 1954-55, resident TB and Chest, 1955-56; commd. 2d lt. med. corps USAF, 1956, advanced through grades to maj., 1964; chief medicine Keesler AFB, 1956, Eglin AFB, 1962-64; ret. USAF, 1979; resident in internal medicine Mayo Found., Rochester, Minn., 1957-60; mem. active staff dept. internal medicine Carraway Meth. Med. Ctr., Birmingham, 1964—, dir. resident program, 1968-72, trustee, 1972-77, pres. staff, 1973-75, exec. com., fin. com., 1974-77, dir. geriatrics, 1989—; pvt. practice Norwood Clinic, Inc., Birmingham, Ala., 1964—; asst. clin. prof. medicine Med. Coll. Ala., 1965-69, asst. clin. prof. dept. endocrinology, 1969-70, clin. assoc. prof. medicine, 1970-81, clin. prof. medicine, 1981—; med. dir. Community Hosp., 1989—; mem. faculty joint commn. accreditation hosps., 1974-78; exec. com. Birmingham Regional Health Systems Agy.; investigator numerous clin. trials. Contbr. articles to profl. jours. Chmn. Birmingham String Quartet, 1970-74; v.p. ticket sales Ala. Symphony Assn., 1979, exec. com.; sec. men's com. Ala. Symphony, 1986-88, pres. 1990-91. Gen. Med. Officer USAR, 197984, comdr. U.S. Army Hosp., Birmingham, 1984-88, col., chief profl. svcs. 5th med. group, Birmingham, 1988-92, ret., 1992. Mem. ACP, AMA, Am. Thoracic Soc. (sr.), Med. Assn. State Ala., Jefferson County Med. Soc. (past bd. censors, del. to state med. assn.), Birmingham Acad. Medicine (pres. 1987-88), Birmingham Internists Soc. (pres. 1972-73). Democrat. Avocations: opera, symphony, philosophy, medical ethics, astronomy. Office: Norwood Clinic Inc PO Box 830230 1528 26th St N Birmingham AL 35234

TIETJEN, JAMES, research institute administrator; b. 1933. With RCA Corp., from 1963, David Sarnoff Rsch. Ctr., from 1987; sr. v.p., the exec. v.p., now pres., CEO SRI Internat., 1990—; also bd. dirs. Office: SRI Internat 333 Ravenswood Ave Menlo Park CA 94025-3493 also: David Sarnoff Rsch Ctr 201 Washington Rd Princeton NJ 08540-6449

TIETJEN, JOHN HENRY, biology and oceanography educator, consultant; b. Jamaica, N.Y., June 19, 1940; s. Reinhard L. and Emma (Wilkomm) T.; m. Theresa Mary Martin, Aug., 24, 1968; children: Theresa Emma, Mary Elizabeth. BS, CCNY, 1961; PhD, U. R.I. 1966. Asst. prof. biology CCNY, N.Y.C., 1966-71, assoc. prof., 1971-75, prof., 1975—; ecol. cons. Tex. Instruments, Dallas, 1977-79, S.W. Research Inst., Houston, 1978-80, Henderson and Bodwell Engrs., Bethpage, N.Y., 1982, N.E. Utilities, Hartford, Conn., 1968—. Author, co-author over 50 rsch. articles. V.p., pres. Leonia (N.J.) Bd. Edn., 1977-86. Research grantee NSF, Office Naval Research, Dept. Energy, Nat. Oceanic & Atmospheric Adminstrn. Mem. Am. Arbitration Assn., Sigma Xi. Roman Catholic. Avocations: outdoor activities, reading, travel. Office: CCNY Dept of Biology Convent Ave New York NY 10027-2604

TIETKE, WILHELM, gastroenterologist; b. Niengraben, Germany, Oct. 15, 1938; came to U.S., 1969, naturalized, 1979; s. Wilhelm and Frieda (Schmeding) T.; m. Imme Schmidt, Oct. 15, 1965; children: Cornelia, Isabel. MD, U Goettingen (West Germany), 1968. Diplomate Am. Bd. Internal Medicine, Am. Bd. Gastroenterology. Intern Edward W. Sparrow Hosp., Lansing, Mich., 1970; resident in internal medicine Henry Ford Hosp., Detroit, 1971-73; fellow in gastroenterology, 1973-75; practice medicine specializing in gastroenterology, Huntsville, Ala., 1975—; mem. vol. faculty, cons. U. Ala., Huntsville, 1976; clin. assoc. prof. internal medicine, 1979—; v.p. Huntsville Gastroenterology Assocs., P.C., 1979—. Fellow Coll. Gastroenterology; mem. AMA, Ala. Med. Soc., Am. Coll. Physicians, Am. Soc. Gastrointestinal Endoscopy. Lutheran. Lodge: Rotary. Home: 2707 Westminster Way Huntsville AL 35801 Office: 119 Longwood Dr Huntsville AL 35801-4205 also: PO Box 2169 Huntsville AL 35804-2169

TIETZ, NORBERT WOLFGANG, clinical chemistry educator, administrator; b. Stettin, Germany, Nov. 13, 1926; s. Joseph and Anna (Kozalla) T.; m. Gertrud Kraft, Oct. 17, 1959; children—Margaret, Kurt, Annette, Michael. Student, Tuebingen, Germany, 1945-46; D.Sc., Tech. U., Stuttgart, W.Ger., 1950. Chmn. dept. chemistry Reid Meml. Hosp., Richmond, Ind., 1956-59; prof., dir. clin. chemistry Mt. Sinai Med. Ctr. and Med. Sch., Chgo., 1959-76. U. Ky. Med. Ctr., Lexington, 1976—; research fellow and asst. U. Munich, W.Ger., 1951-54; research fellow dept. pathology U. Chgo. and St. Luke's Hosp., Chgo., 1955-56, Rockford Meml. Hosp., Ill., 1954-55; cons. Ill. Dept. Pub. Health, 1967-76, VA Hosp., Hines, Ill., 1974-76; prof. biochemistry and pathology Rush Med. Coll., Chgo., 1975-76; vol. cons. VA Hosp., Lexington, 1976—. Editor: Fundamentals of Clinical Chemistry, 1970, 76, 87, Clinical Guide to Laboratory Tests, 1983, 90, 95, Textbook of Clinical Chemistry, 1986, A Study Guide to Clinical Chemistry, 1987, Applied Laboratory Medicine, 1992; assoc. editor: Dictionary and Encyclopedia of Laboratory Medicine and Technology, 1983; contbr. numerous articles to profl. jours. Recipient A. Dubin award Nat. Acad. Clin. Biochemistry, 1995. Fellow Acad. Clin. Lab. Physicians and Scientists, Am. Inst. Chemists; mem. Am. Assn. Clin. Chemistry (clin. chemist award 1971, award for outstanding efforts in edn. and tng. 1976, Disting. Alumnus award 1977, Steuben Bowl award 1978, Bernard F. Gerulat award N.J. chpt. 1988, award for Outstanding Contbns. to Clin. Chemistry 1989, Donald D. Van Slyke award N.Y. Met. chpt. 1989), AAAS, Am. Chem. Soc., Am. Soc. Clin.

Pathologists, Man. Soc. Clin. Chemists (ann. Lectureship award 1987), Sigma Xi. Roman Catholic. Home: 2075 Bridgeport Dr Lexington KY 40502-2615 Office: U Ky Med Ctr Dept Pathology Ha # 611 Lexington KY 40536

TIETZE, LUTZ FRIEDJAN, chemist, educator; b. Berlin, Mar. 14, 1942; s. Friedrich and Hete-Irene (Kruse) T.; m. Karin Krautschneider; children: Martin, Maja, Andrea, Julia. Diploma, U. Kiel, 1966, PhD, 1968; habil. for Organic Chemistry, U. Münster, 1975; DSc (hon.), U. Szeged, Hungary, 1994. Rsch. assoc. MIT, 1969-71; lectr. U. Münster, 1971-76; prof. U. Dortmund, 1977-78; full prof. and inst. dir. U. Göttingen, Göttingen, 1978—; dean and prodean U. Göttingen, 1983-87, 91-95; vis. prof. U. Wis., 1982, U. Strasbourg, 1995; mem. Bd. of Faculties of Chemistry, Germany. Author: Reactions and Syntheses, 1981, (translated into Japanese 1984, 2d edit., 1995, English 1989), 2d edit., 1991, Basic Course in Organic Chemistry, 1993, 2d edit., 1995; contbr. numerous articles to profl. jours.; patentee in field. Recipient Karl-Winnacker award, Hoechst AG, Germany, 1976, Lit. prize, Fonds der Chem. Industry, Germany, 1982; fellow Japan Soc. Promotion Sci. Fellow Royal Soc. Chemists; mem. Gesellschaft Deutsches Chemie, Am. Chem. Soc., Chem. Soc. Argentina (hon.), Academia Scientiarum Göttingen, Chem. Soc. Eng. Home: Stumpfe Eiche 73, D-37077 Göttingen Germany Office: U Göttingen Inst Organic Chemistry, Tammannstrasse 2, D-37077 Göttingen Germany

TIFFANY, JOSEPH RAYMOND, II, lawyer; b. Dayton, Ohio, Feb. 5, 1949; s. Forrest Fraser and Margaret Watson (Clark) T.; m. Terri Robbins, Dec. 1, 1984. AB magna cum laude, Harvard U., 1971; MS in Internat. Relations, London Sch. Econs., 1972; JD, U. Calif., Berkeley, 1975. Bar: U.S. Dist. Ct. (no. dist.) 1975, U.S. Dist. Ct. (ea. dist.) 1977, U.S. Ct. Appeals (9th cir.) 1982. Assoc. Pillsbury, Madison & Sutro, San Francisco, 1975-82, ptnr., 1983—. Mem. ABA (antitrust, intellectual property, litigation sects.), Calif. Bar Assn., Harvard Club (bd. dirs. San Francisco chpt. 1990—). Office: Pillsbury Madison & Sutro 225 Bush St San Francisco CA 94104-4207

TIFFANY, SANDRA L., state legislator; b. Spokane, Wash., June 30, 1949; m. Ross M. Tonkens; 1 child, Courtney. Student, U. Calif. Mem. Nev. Assembly, 1993—. Mem. Nev. Rep. Women's Club, Green Valley Cmty. Assn. Home: 75 Quail Run Rd Henderson NV 89014 Office: Nev Assembly State Capitol Carson City NV 89710

TIFFORD, ARTHUR W., lawyer; b. Bklyn., July 7, 1943; s. Herman and Dorothy (Kessler) T.; m. Barbara J. Sinreich, Aug. 15, 1965; children: Melissa Beth, Alexandra Lynn. BA, CUNY, 1965; JD, Bklyn. Law Sch., 1967. Bar: N.Y. 1967, Fla. 1967, U.S. Dist. Ct. (so. dist.) Fla. 1968, U.S. Ct. Mil. Appeals 1968, U.S. Ct. Appeals (5th cir.) 1971, U.S. Dist. Ct. (mid. dist.) Fla. 1979, U.S. Ct. Appeals (10th cir.) 1979, U.S. Ct. Appeals (1st cir.) 1982, U.S. Ct. Appeals (9th cir.) 1982, U.S. Ct. Appeals (11th cir.) 1981, U.S. Ct. Appeals (fed. cir.) 1985, U.S. Claims Ct. 1985, U.S. Tax Ct. 1988. Researcher, mgr. clk. Cravath, Swaine & Moore, N.Y.C., 1967; asst. U.S. atty. U.S. Dept. Justice (so. dist. Fla.), Miami, 1971-72; sole practice Miami, 1972—. Served with USMC, 1968-71, USMCR, 1971-92, ret. col. Mem. ABA, Am. Trial Lawyers Asns., Fla. Trial Lawyers Assn., Nat. Assn. Criminal Def. Lawyers, N.Y. Bar Assn., Fla. Bar Assn., Marine Corps Res. Officers Assn. (pres. Greater Miami chpt. 1978-79, 81-82, 84-85, nat. bd. dirs. 1987-89). Democrat. Avocations: writing, photography, parachuting, scuba diving, running. Home: 9980 SW 128th St Miami FL 33176-5632 Office: 1385 NW 15th St Miami FL 33125-1621

TIFT, WILLIAM GRANT, astronomer; b. Derby, Conn., Apr. 5, 1932; s. William Charles and Marguerite Howe (Hubbell) T.; m. Carol Ruth Nordquist, June 1, 1957 (div. July 1964); children: Jennifer, William John; m. Janet Ann Lindner Homewood, June 2, 1965; 1 child, Amy. AB cum laude, Harvard Coll., 1954; PhD, Calif. Inst. Tech., 1958. Nat. sci. postdoctoral Australian Nat. Univ., Canberra, 1958-60; rsch. assoc. Vanderbilt U., Nashville, 1960-61; astronomer Lowell Obs., Flagstaff, Ariz., 1961-64; assoc. prof. U. Ariz., Tucson, 1964-73, prof., 1973—. Joint author: Revised New General Catalog, 1973; contbr. over 100 articles to profl. jours. NSF Predoctoral fellow, 1954-58; NSF Postdoctoral fellow, 1958-60; grantee NASA, NSF, ONR. Fellow Am. Astron. Soc.; mem. Internat. Astron. Union. Achievements include discovery of redshift quantization and correlations relating to it, including variability; mapping of large scale supercluster structure; first to detect voids. Office: U of Arizona Dept of Astronomy Tucson AZ 85721

TIFT, MARY LOUISE, artist; b. Seattle, Jan. 2, 1913; d. John Howard and Wilhelmina (Pressler) Dreher; m. William Raymond Tift, Dec. 4, 1948. BFA cum laude, U. Wash., 1933; postgrad., Art Ctr. Coll., L.A., 1945-48, U. Calif., San Francisco, 1962-63. Art dir. Vaughn Shedd Advt., L.A., 1948; asst. prof. design Calif. Coll. Arts & Crafts, Oakland, Calif., 1949-59; concert designer. San Francisco Art Inst., 1959-62. Subject of cover story, Am. Artist mag., 1980, studio article, 1980; one woman shows, Gumps Gallery, San Francisco, 1977, 1986, 90, Diane Gilson Gallery, Seattle, 1978, Oreg. State U., 1981, group shows include, Brit. Biennale, Yorkshire, Eng., 1970, Grenchen Triennale, Switzerland, 1970, Polish Biennale, Crakow, 1972, Nat. Gallery, Washington, 1973, U.S.-U.K. Impressions, Eng., 1988; represented in permanent collections, Phila. Mus. Art, Bklyn. Mus., Seattle Art Mus., Library Congress, Achenbach Print Collection, San Francisco Palace Legion of Honor. Served to lt. USNR, 1943-45. Mem. Print Club Phila., World Print Council, Calif. Soc. Printmakers, Phi Beta Kappa, Lambda Rho. Christian Scientist. Studio: 275 Los Ranchitos Rd Apt 341 San Rafael CA 94903

TIGAR, MICHAEL EDWARD, lawyer, educator; b. Glendale, Calif., Jan. 18, 1941; s. Charles Henry and Margaret Elizabeth (Lang) T.; m. Pamet Ayer Jones, Sept. 21, 1961 (div. Mar. 1973); children: Jon Steven, Katherine Ayer; m. Amanda G. Birrell, Feb. 16, 1980; 1 child, Elizabeth Torrey. BA in Polit. Sci., U. Calif., Berkeley, 1962, JD, 1966. Bar: D.C. 1967, U.S. Ct. Appeals (2d, 4th, 5th, 6th, 7th, 8th, 9th, 10th and D.C. cirs.), U.S. Tax Ct., U.S. Supreme Ct. 1972, N.Y. 1993. Assoc. Williams & Connolly, Washington, 1966-69; editor-in-chief Selective Svc. Law Reporter, Washington, 1967-69; acting prof. law UCLA, 1969-71; pvt. practice law Grasse, France, 1972-74; assoc. William & Connolly, Washington, 1974, ptnr., 1975-77; ptnr. Tigar & Buffone, Washington, 1977-84; prof. law U. Tex., Austin, 1984-87, Joseph D. Jamail centennial chair in law, 1987—; reporter 5th Cir. Pattern Jury Instrns., Austin, 1988-90. Author: Practice Manual Selective Service Law Reporter, 1968, Law and the Rise of Capitalism, 1977, Federal Appeals: Jurisdiction and Practice, 2d edit., 1993, Examining Witnesses, 1993; contbr. articles to profl. jours. Mem. ABA (vice chair 1987-88, chair elect 1988-89, chair 1989-90 sect. litigation). Avocations: sailing, cooking. Home: 1901 Yaupon Valley Rd Austin TX 78746-3418 Office: U Tex Austin Sch Law 727 E 26th St Austin TX 78705-3224

TIGAY, ALAN MERRILL, editor; b. Detroit, June 23, 1947; s. Leonard and Ethel (Cooper) T.; m. Lois Kathryn Gardian, Dec. 27, 1970; 1 child, Rafael Leonard. B.A. in Sociology, U. Mich., 1969; M.S. in Journalism, Columbia U., 1976. Feature writer United Feature Syndicate, N.Y.C., 1976-78; editor in chief Near East Report, Washington, 1978-80; exec. editor Hadassah Mag., N.Y.C., 1980—; judge Nat. Mag. Awards, 1981—, Nat. Jewish Book Awards, 1988—; adminstr. Harold U. Ribalow prize, 1983—. Editor: The Jewish Traveler, 1987, 2d edit., 1994, Myths and Facts: A Concise Record of the Arab-Israeli Conflict, 1978, 2d edit., 1980; free-lance writer various N.Y. and nat. newspapers, mags., 1972—. Pres., vol. Owners Corp., N.Y.C., 1982-86; vol. Partnership for Homeless Rodeph Sholom Winter Shelter Program, N.Y.C., 1983-85, Interfaith Hospitality Network, Montclair, N.J., 1988—. Mem. Am. Soc. Mag. Editors, Am. Jewish Press Assn. Avocation: collecting newspapers. Office: Hadassah Mag 50 W 58th St New York NY 10019-2505

TIGER, IRA PAUL, lawyer; b. Bklyn., Jan. 31, 1936; s. Sidney and Rebecca (Frankel) T.; m. Rosalind Silverman, July 4, 1957 (dec. Nov. 1972); children: Ruth, Lori; m. Ann Mae Gersh, May 5, 1974; stepchildren: Jimmie, Randy, Richard Riesenberg. B.S. in Econs., U. Pa., 1956, J.D. magna cum laude, 1959. Bar: Pa. 1960, U.S. Dist. Ct. (ea. dist.) Pa. 1960, U.S. Ct. Appeals (3d cir.) 1960, U.S. Supreme Ct. 1971. Law clk. 3d cir., 1959-60; assoc. Schnader, Harrison, Segal & Lewis, Phila., 1960-67, ptnr., 1968—; chmn.

litigation dept., 1986-90, chmn. standing com. on profl. conduct, 1992—. Research editor U. Pa. Law Rev., 1958-59. Pres. Temple Sinai Synagogue, 1989-91; mem. Planning Adv. Bd. Upper Dublin Twp., 1982-87, mem. ednl. adv. com., 1976-78; legal counsel Phila. Jr. C. of C., 1963-64, bd. dirs., 1962-66, sec. Jewish campus activities bd., 1971-73. Mem. ABA, Am. Judicature Soc., Inst. Jud. Adminstrn., Pa. Bar Assn., Phila. Bar Assn. (chmn. fed. cts. com. 1985), Lawyers Club Phila., Order of Coif (exec. com. Pa. chpt. 1981-83), Beta Alpha Psi, Beta Gamma Sigma. Democrat. Office: Schnader Harrison 1600 Market St Ste 3600 Philadelphia PA 19103-4252

TIGER, LIONEL, social scientist, anthropology consultant; b. Montreal, Que., Can., Feb. 5, 1937; s. Martin and Lillian (Schneider) T.; m. Virginia Conner, Aug. 19, 1964; 1 child, Sebastian Benjamin. BA, McGill U., 1957, MA, 1959; PhD, U. London, 1963. Instr. anthropology U. Ghana, Accra, 1960; asst. prof. dept. anthropology and sociology U. B.C., Vancouver, Can., 1963-68; assoc. prof. anthropology Rutgers U., New Brunswick, N.J., 1969-74, prof. anthropology, 1974—, Charles Darwin prof. anthropology, 1990—; cons., rsch. dir. Harry F. Guggenheim Found., N.Y.C., 1972-84; chmn. bd. social scientists U.S. News and World Report, 1986-88; sci. adv. bd. Am. Wine Inst., San Francisco. Author: Men in Groups, 1969, 2d edit., 1987; (with Robin Rox) The Imperial Animal, 1971, 2d edit., 1989; (with Joseph Shepher) Women in the Kibbutz, 1975, Optimism: The Biology of Hope, 1979, 2d edit., 1994, China's Food, 1985, The Manufacture of Evil: Ethics, Evolution, and the Industrial System, 1987; editor: Female Hierarchies, 1978, (with Michael Robinson) Man and Beast Revisited, 1991, The Pursuit of Pleasure, 1992; mem. editorial bd. Social Sci. Info, Ethology and Sociobiology jour., Jour. of Social Distress and the Homeless. Bd. dirs. David R. Graham Found., Toronto, Ont., Can. Recipient W.I. Susman award for excellence in tchg., 1985, McNaughton prize for creative writing; ASDA Found. rsch. fellow, 1985; Can. Coun. Rsch. fellow, Ford Found. Fgn. Area Tng. fellow, Can. Coun.-Killam fellow for interdisciplinary rsch., Rockefeller fellow Aspen Inst., 1979, H.F. Guggenheim Found. fellow, 1988-89. Fellow Royal Anthrop. Inst. (Eng.); mem. PEN (mem. exec. bd., treas. 1988-91, v.p. 1991-94), Am. Anthrop. Assn., Can. Anthrop. Assn., Can. Humanists Assn. (hon.), Soc. for Study of Evolution, Century Assn. Home: 248 W 23rd St Fl 4 New York NY 10011-2304 also: RR 2 Millbrook NY 12545-9802 Office: Rutgers U Douglas Coll New Brunswick NJ 08903-0270

TIGERMAN, STANLEY, architect, educator; b. Chgo., Sept. 20, 1930; s. Samuel Bernard and Emma Louise (Stern) T.; m. Margaret I. McCurry; children: Judson Joel, Tracy Leigh. Student, MIT, 1948-49; B.Arch., Yale U., 1960, M.Arch., 1961. Archtl. draftsman firm George Fred Keck, Chgo., 1949-50, Skidmore, Owings and Merrill, Chgo., 1957-59, Paul Rudolph, New Haven, 1959-61, Harry Weese, Chgo., 1961-62; partner firm Tigerman & Koglin, Chgo., 1962-64; prin. firm Stanley Tigerman & Assos., Chgo., 1964-82; ptnr. Tigerman Fugman McCurry, Chgo., 1982-88, Tigerman McCurry, 1988—; prof. architecture U. Ill.-Chgo., 1967-71, 80-93, dir. Sch. Architecture, 1985-93; vis. lectr. Yale U., 1974, Cornell U., Ithaca, N.Y., 1963, Cooper Union, 1970, U. Calif. at Berkeley, 1968, Cardiff (Wales) Coll., 1965, Engring. U., Bangladesh, 1967; chmn. AIA com. on design, coordinator exhbn. and book Chicago Architects, 1977; Charlotte Shepherd Davenport prof. architecture Yale U., 1979; architect-in-residence Am. Acad. in Rome, 1980; vis. prof. architecture Harvard U., 1982; William Henry Bishop Chair. prof. architecture Yale U., 1984; dir. post-professional grad. program U. Ill.-Chgo.; co-founder Archeworks, Design Lab., Chgo., 1993. Prin. works include: Fukuoka Apt. Complex, Japan, The Power House, Zion, Ill., The Preserve Clubhouse, New Buffalo, Mich., others; author: Versus, 1982, Architecture of Exile, 1988 (nominated Nat. Jewish Book awar 1989), Stanley Tigerman: Buildings and Projects, 1966-89, 1989; contbg. author: Design of the Housing Site, 1966, Chicago on Foot, 1969, Art Today, 1969, New Directions in American Architecture, 1969, Contemporary Jewelry, 1970, Urban Structures for the Future, 1972, Spaces for Living, 1973, Chicago 1930-70, 1974, Interior Spaces Designed by Architects, 1974, Housing, 1976, Chicago Architects, 1976, 100 Years of Architecture in Chicago, 1976, Architectural Graphics Primer, 1976, 86, Mies Reconsidered, 1986, Chicago Architecture 1872-1922, 1988 (designer exhbn.), others, also numerous articles in newspapers and profl. jours.; exhibited, Venice Biennale, 1976, 80; co-curator, author essay, Calif. Condition exhbn., 1982; curator, designer exhbn., author catalogue Chicago Architecture, The New Zeitgeist: In Search of Closure, 1989. Pres. Yale Arts Assn., 1969-70; mem. advisory com. Yale Archtl. Sch., 1976—; bd. dirs. Bangladesh Found. Served with USN, 1950-54. Recipient Alpha Rho Chi medal Yale, 1961; Archtl. Record award, 1970; Chgo. Masonry award, 1974; Masonry Gold Medal award, 1974; Alumni Art award Yale U., 1985; Graham Fedn. for Advanced Studies in Fine Arts grantee, 1965. Fellow AIA (chmn. com. design 1976-77, adv. com., Disting. Svc. award Chgo. chpt. 1982, Chgo. Honor awards 1971, 73, 75, 77-79, 82, 84, Nat. Honor award, 1987, 91, Nat. Modern Income Housing award 1970, Nat. Homes for Better Living award 1974, 75, Ill. awards 1976, named to Hall of Fame 1990, Disting. Bldg. award for pvt. residence Chgo. chpt. 1991, Nat. Interior Archtl. award of Excellence, 1992-93, Chgo. Interior Archtl. award of Excellence, 1991, Chgo. Interior Archtl. award of Excellence, 1992, Chgo. Disting. Bldg. award 1994); mem. Phi Kappa Phi Honor Soc. Clubs: Arts of Chgo, Yale of N.Y.C, Century Assn. Office: Tigerman & McCurry LTD 444 N Wells St Ste 206 Chicago IL 60610-4522

TIGGES, KENNETH EDWIN, retired financial executive; b. Sandusky, Ohio, Sept. 4, 1927; s. Edwin Ernest and Ruth Dorothea (Krapp) T.; m. Mary Anne Richardson, June 11, 1955. BSBA, Bowling Green State U., 1950. C.P.A., Ohio. With Konopak & Dalton (C.P.A.s), Toledo, 1950-57; with Owens-Illinois, Inc., 1957-84, comptr., 1963-71, v.p., comptr., 1971-84; v.p. fin. The De Vilbiss Co., Toledo, 1984-90, cons., 1990-92. Mem. fin. com. St. Vincent Hosp., Toledo, 1968—, Bowling Green State U. Bus. Adv. Council; bd. dirs. Jr. Achievement, Toledo, 1986—. Served with U.S. Army, 1946-47. Recipient Acct. of Yr.-Industry award Beta Alpha Psi, 1983. Mem. Am. Inst. C.P.A.s, Ohio Soc. C.P.A.s, Fin. Execs. Inst. (pres. Toledo chpt. 1970-71, v.p., bd. dirs. 1972-73, mem. com. on govt. liaison), Bowling Green State U. Alumni Bd. Dirs., Sigma Chi. Episcopal. Lodge: Rotary. Avocations: golf, reading. Home: 6655 Mill Ridge Rd Maumee OH 43537

TIGHE, JAMES C., publisher; b. Edmonton, Alta., Can., Sept. 30, 1950; s. James Donald and Ellen Grant (Drever) T.; m. Barbara C. Teske, Dec. 2, 1972; children: Teresa M., Jason M. Grad. high sch., Edmonton. Area supr. Edmonton Jour., 1969-73; circulation mgr. Thomson Newspapers, Western Can., 1973-79; dir. circulation Edmonton sun, 1979-81, gen. mgr.; 1981-82; gen. mgr. UP Can., Toronto, Ont., 1982-84; pub. Calgary (Alta.) Sun, 1984-88; gen. mgr. Toronto Sun, 1988-89, pub., 1991-94, v.p. corp. planning, 1994-95; pres. Island Pub. Ltd., Can., 1995—. Office: Island Pub Ltd, 1824 Store St, Victoria, BC Canada

TIGHT, DEXTER CORWIN, lawyer; b. San Francisco, Sept. 14, 1924; s. Dexter Junkins and Marie (Corwin) T.; m. Elizabeth Callander, Apr. 20, 1951; children: Dexter C. Jr., Kathryn Marie, Steven M., David C. AB, Denison U., 1948; JD, Yale U., 1951. Bar: Calif. 1951. Assoc. Pillsbury, Madison & Sutro, San Francisco, 1951-60; gen. atty. W.P. Fuller & Co., San Francisco, 1960-61; gen. counsel Schlage Lock Co., San Francisco, 1961-77; dir. govt. affairs Crown Zellerbach Corp., San Francisco, 1977-78; sr. v.p., gen. counsel The Gap Inc., San Bruno, Calif., 1978-90, legal, internat. cons., 1990—; gen. coun. The Nature Co., 1990—; bd. dirs. Shaw-Clayton Plastics, San Rafael, Calif., Granite Rock Co., Watsonville, Calif., X-L Mfg. Co., Chico, Calif., Alden Lee Ins. Co. Bd. dirs., pres. San Francisco Boys' and Girls' Club; v.p., sec. That Man May See, San Francisco; trustee Denison U., 1978—, chmn. capital fund dr. 1988-94; trustee Calvary Presbyn. Ch., 1968, 73, elder, 1969—; elder Valley Presbyn. Ch., 1992—. 1st lt. U.S. Army, 1943-45, 51-52. Mem. ABA, Calif. Bar Assn., San Francisco Bar Assn. (chmn. various coms.), Commonwealth Club Calif. (past bd. dirs., exec. com.), Menlo Country Club, Bohemian Club (San Francisco), Guardsmen Club (1st v.p. 1961), Phi Beta Kappa. Republican. Presbyterian. Avocations: hiking, fishing, tennis, golf, photography. Home: 170 Wildwood Way Redwood City CA 94062-2352

TIGNER, MAURICE, physicist, educator. Student, Webb Inst. of Naval Architecture, 1954-56; BS in Physics, Rensselaer Polytechnic Inst., 1958; PhD in Exptl. Physics and Elec. Engring., Cornell U., 1962. Prof. dept. physics Cornell U., Ithaca, N.Y.; rsch. assoc. dept. physics Cornell U., 1963-68, sr. rsch. assoc. and dir. ops., accelerator facilities dept. physics, 1968-77;

vis. scientist Deutsches Elec. Synchrotron, Hamburg, Germany, 1972-73; prof. physics and staff mem., lab. nuclear studies Cornell U., 1977—; dir. SSC Cen. Design Group Univs. Rsch. Assn., 1984-89; vis. prof. dept. physics, U. Calif., 1987-89; cons. Bechtel National, Inc., 1989—; mem. RHIC Mechm Com., BNL, 1992—; mem. dirs. adv. com. for accelerator and fusion rsch. divsn., Lawrence Berkeley Lab., 1992—; chmn. steering com. accelerator test facility, BNL, 1992—. Recipient Ernest Orlando Lawrence Meml. award U.S. Dept. Energy, Washington, 1990. Fellow AAAS, Am. Phys. Soc., Am. Acad. Arts and Scis.; mem. Nat. Acad. Sci. Office: Cornell Univ Dept Of Physics Ithaca NY 14853

TIGNOR, GEORGE, principal. B.A. Biology, St. Mary of Plains Coll., Dodge City, KS, 1965-69; M.A. Botany, Kansas U., Lawrence, KS, 1971-72; admin. training, Emporia State U., Emporia, KS, 1974-76. Sci. instr. Rosedale HS, Kansas City, KS, 1969-71, Washington HS, Kansas City, 1973-74, F.L. Schlagle HS, Kansas City, 1974-76; asst. prin., athletic dir. Wyandotte HS, Kansas City, KS, 1976-80; prin. Rosedale MS, Kansas City, 1980-81, Parsons HS, Parsons, KS, 1981—. Prin. of the Year 1995, Nat. Assn. of Secondary School Principals. office: Parsons HS 3030 Morton Parsons KS 67357*

TIGNOR, ROBERT LEE, historian, educator; b. Phila., Nov. 20, 1933; s. Robert Max and Martha Arvilla (Stalter) T.; m. Marian Ann Shaw, June 16, 1956; children: Jeffrey, Sandra. B.A., Coll. Wooster, 1955; M.A. Yale U., 1956, Ph.D., 1960. Mem. faculty dept. history Princeton U., 1960—, prof., 1976—, chmn. dept. history, 1976—; mem. faculty U. Ibadan, Nigeria, U. Nairobi, Kenya, 1965-66. Author: Modernization and British Colonial Rule in Egypt, 1882-1914, 1966, The Colonial Transformation of Kenya, 1976; Editor: (with Gouda Abdel-Khalek) The Political Economy of Income Distribution in Egypt, 1982; State, Private Enterprises, and Economic Change in Egypt, 1918-52, 1984. Ford Found. fellow, 1959-60; Rockefeller Found. fellow, 1965-66; Am. Council Learned Socs.-Social Sci. Research Council fellow, 1969-70. Mem. Am. Hist. Assn., Middle East Studies Assn. Democrat. Unitarian. Home: 69 Maclean Cir Princeton NJ 08540-5620 Office: Dept History Princeton Univ Princeton NJ 08540

TIHANY, LESLIE CHARLES, retired foreign service officer, educator; b. Hungary, Dec. 28, 1911; came to U.S., 1930; naturalized, 1940; s. Béla and Katalin (Báródy) T.; m. Elizabeth Derricott, 1936; m. 2d., Maria Dekom, 1959; children: Elizabeth, Richard, Peter. BS, Franklin and Marshall Coll., 1931; MA, Northwestern U., 1933, PhD, 1936; AM, Harvard U., 1938; PhD, U. Chgo., 1943; postdoctoral study, U. Helsinki. Rsch. fellow Am. Coun. Learned Socs., 1938-40; asst. history U. Chgo., 1941; teaching fellow Harvard U., 1942-43; prof. U. Denver, 1943; joined Fgn. Svc., Dept. State, 1943, fgn. affairs specialist, 1943-56; consul Salzburg, Austria, 1956-57, Bombay, 1957-59; 1st sec. Am. Embassy, Beirut, 1960-61, 1st sec., chief econ. officer, 1961-65; 1st sec., chief econ. officer Am. Embassy, Saigon, Vietnam, 1965-66; pub. affairs officer Bur. Far Ea. Affairs, Dept. State, 1966; counselor of embassy, assigned Dept. State, 1966-69, internat. rels. officer Bur. European Affairs, 1966-69; Am. consul gen. Antwerp, Belgium, 1969-72; Disting. prof. humanities and social sci. No. Ky. U., 1972-76, prof. emeritus, 1976—; adj. prof. history U. Cin., 1978—; vis. prof. Ecole des Hautes Etudes de l'Histoire et de la Philologie, Sorbonne, Paris, 1984; museological study, Paris, 1992, 93. Author: History of Middle Europe, 1976, The Baranya Dispute, 1978; contbr. articles, revs. to profl. jours. Bd. dirs. Inst. Mediterranean Art and Archeology. Lt. col. USAFR, ret. Decorated comdr. Order Concordia, Rome, 1949; recipient Meritorious Honor award Dept. State, 1965; Frederick Sheldon Prize and Teaching fellow Harvard U., 1938-40. Mem. Soc. Finno-Ougrienne, Cosmos Club. Home: 218 Scenic View Dr Fort Thomas KY 41075-1245 Office: 18 E 4th St Ste 211 Cincinnati OH 45202-3706

TIJUNELIS, DONATAS, engineering executive; b. Kaunas, Lithuania, Nov. 6, 1935; came to U.S. 1949; s. Juozas and Alicija (Gustaitis) T.; m. Judre Paliokas, July 7, 1962; children: Daina, Rasa, Aras, Nida. BS in Chem. Engring., Purdue U., 1958; MS in Chem. Engring., Northwestern U., 1960; DBA in Mgmt., Nova U., 1986. Registered profl. engr. Project leader Union Carbide Corp., Chgo., 1959-68; rsch. engr. Continental Can Co., Chgo., 1962; assoc. dir. Borg Warner Rsch. Ctr., Des Plaines, Ill., 1968-87; pres. DKT Engring., Buffalo Grove, Ill., 1987-88; div. mgr. USG Corp., Chgo., 1988; v.p. in rsch. and devel. VISKASE Corp., Chgo., 1988—; pres. Rsch. Dis. Assn. Chgo., 1991-92; mem. Ill. Engring. REgistration Bd., Springfield, 1992—, Indsl. Rsch. Inst., Washington, 1992—. Editor: Manufacturing High Technology, 1987; co-author: Research and Development on a Minimum Budget, 1979; contbr. articles to profl. jours. Named Outstanding Faculty Lake Forest Grad. Sch., 1988. Mem. Soc. Plastic Engrs., Tau Beta Pi. Roman Catholic. Achievements include 14 patents. Home: 419 Weidner Rd Buffalo Grove IL 60089 Office: VISKASE Corp 6855 W 65th St Chicago IL 60638

TILBERIS, ELIZABETH, editor-in-chief; m. Andrew Tilberis, 1971. Student, Jacob Kramer Coll. Arts, Leeds, England; BA in Eng., Leicester (Eng.) Poly. Fashion asst. British Vogue, 1970, fashion editor, 1974, exec. fashion editor, 1984, sr. fashion editor, 1986, editor-in-chief, 1987; dir. Conde Nast Pubs., 1991; editor-in-chief Harper's Bazaar, N.Y.C., 1992—. Recipient 2 Nat. Mag. awards for design, photography, 1993, Coun. Fashion Designers of Am. award, 1994. Office: Harper's Bazaar 1700 Broadway New York NY 10019-5905 also: care Susan Magrino Susan Magrino Agency 167 East 73rd St New York NY 10019

TILBURY, ROGER GRAYDON, lawyer, rancher; b. Guthrie, Okla., July 30, 1925; s. Graydon and Minnie (Lee) T.; m. Margaret Dear, June 24, 1952; 1 dau., Elizabeth Ann. B.S., U. So. Calif., 1945; J.D., U. Kans., 1949; LL.M., Columbia, 1950; postgrad., Oxford (Eng.) U., 1949. Bar: Mo. bar 1950, Oreg. bar 1953. Pvt. practice Kansas City, Mo., 1950-53, Portland, Oreg., 1953—; assoc. firm Rogers, Field, Gentry, Kansas City, Mo., 1950-53, Stern, Reiter & Day, Portland, 1953-56; ptnr. firm Roth & Tilbury, 1956-58, Tilbury & Kane, 1970-72, Haessler, Tilbury & Platten, 1978-81; pvt. practice Portland, 1981—; circuit judge pro tem., Oreg., 1972—, arbitrator and fact finder, 1973—; sec. Barrington Properties; mem. nat. panel arbitrators U.S. Mediation and Conciliation Svc.; arbitrator for N.Y. Stock Exch., Pacific Stock Exch. and Nat. Assn. Security Dealers; mediator U.S. Dist. Ct.; atty. Animal Defender League, 1969-73. Dep. election commr. Kansas City, Mo., 1952-53; bd. dirs. Multnomah Bar Found. Served to lt. (j.g.) USNR, 1943-45. Battenfeld scholar, 1943. Mem. Oreg. State Bar, Soc. Barristers, Am. Arbitration Assn., Save the Redwoods League, East African Wildlife League, Nat. Wildlife Found., Am. Trial Lawyers Assn., Delta Tau Delta, Phi Delta Phi. Home: 9310 NW Cornell Rd Portland OR 97229-6449 Office: Tilbury-Rothman Bldg 1123 SW Yamhill St Ste 101 Portland OR 97205-2106

TILFORD, SHELBY G., earth science director, physical chemist, meteorolgist; b. Grayson County, Kentucky, Jan. 11, 1937; married 1956; 2 children. BS, Western Ky. U., 1958; PhD in Physical Chemistry, Vanderbilt U., 1962. Rsch. assoc. spectros Naval Rsch. Lab., 1961-63, rsch. chemist, 1963-66, spectros cons. physicist, 1966-72; section head extreme ultraviolet spectros, 1972-76; space scientist solar atmospheric processes NASA Headquarters, 1976, discipline chief upper atmosphere, 1976-78, br chief atmospheric processes, 1978-81, divsn. dir. environ. ops., 1981-84, divsn. dir. earth sci. and appln., 1984—; vis. prof. U. Md., 1969-76. Recipient Special award Am. Meteorological Assn., 1993. Research in high resolution vacuum ultraviolet spectroscopy of atoms and molecules of atmospheric, laser, and astrophysical interest; mesospheric research; tropospheric and stratospheric air quality; upper atmospheric research; oceanic processes. Office: NASA Hdqs 600 Independence Ave SW Washington DC 20546 Address: 8805 Church Field Ln Laurel MD 20708-2428*

TILGHMAN, RICHARD GRANVILLE, banker; b. Norfolk, Va., Sept. 18, 1940; s. Henry Granville and Frances (Fulghum) T.; m. Alice Creech, June 28, 1969; children—Elizabeth Arrington, Caroline Harrison. B.A., U. Va., 1963. Asst. cashier United Va. Bank-Seaboard Nat., Norfolk, Va., 1968-70, asst. v.p., 1970-72; pres., chief adminstrv. officer United Va. Bank, Richmond, 1978-80; asst. v.p. United Va. Mortgage Corp., Norfolk, Va., 1972, v.p., 1972-73, pres., chief exec. officer, 1974-76; pres., chief exec. officer United Va. Leasing Corp., Richmond, Va., 1973-74; sr. v.p. bank related United Va. Bankshares, Inc., Richmond, 1976-78, exec. v.p. corp. banking, 1980-84, vice chmn., 1984-85; pres., chief exec. officer United Va. Bank-

shares, Inc., now Crestar Fin. Corp., Richmond, 1985—, chmn., 1986—; bd. dirs. Chesapeake Corp., Richmond, 1986—; chmn. Va. Pub. Bldg. Authority, Richmond, 1982-87; prin. Va. Bus. Coun., 1987—; mem. Fed. Adv. Coun., 1994—. Chmn. bd. dirs. Richmond Symphony, 1984-85; bd. dirs., gen. adv. coun. Sheltering Arms Hosp., Richmond, 1981-89; bd. dirs. Va. Free, 1989-90, Richmond Symphony Found., 1989-91, Va. Found. Ind. Colls., 1988—, Va. Literacy Found., 1986-89; bd. govs. St. Catherine's Sch. 1989—; bd. dirs. Va. Mus. Found., 1986-92, trustee, 1994—; trustee Randolph-Macon Coll., 1985-93, Richmond Renaissance, 1986—, Colonial Williamsburg Found., 1994—; co-chmn. NCCJ. 1st lt. U.S. Army, 1963-66. Mem. Bankers Roundtable, Am. Bankers Assn., Va. Bankers Assn. (bd. dirs.). Episcopalian. Clubs: Commonwealth, Country of Va. Office: Crestar Fin Corp PO Box 26665 919 E Main St Richmond VA 23219-4625

TILGHMAN, SHIRLEY MARIE, biology educator. PhD in biochemistry, Temple U., 1975. Prof. molecular biology Princeton (N.J.) U., 1986—, Howard A. Prior prof. in life scis.; investigator Howard Hughes Med. Inst. Co-editor: Gene Expression & Its Control, 1991, Genes & Phenotypes, 1991, Genetic & Physical Mapping, 1991, Genome Maps & Neurological Disorders, 1993, Genome Rearrangement & Stability, 1993, Regional Physical Mapping, 1993. Office: Princeton U Lewis Thomas Lab HHMI Washington Rd Princeton NJ 08544*

TILL, JAMES EDGAR, scientist; b. Lloydminster, Sask., Can., Aug. 25, 1931; s. William and Gertrude Ruth (Isaac) T.; m. Marion Joyce Sinclair, June 6, 1959; children: David William, Karen Sinclair, Susan Elizabeth. BA, U. Sask., 1952, MA, 1954; PhD, Yale U., 1957. Postdoctoral fellow Connaught Med. Research Labs., Toronto, Ont., Can., 1956-57; mem. physics div. Ont. Cancer Inst., Toronto, 1957-67, div. biol. rsch., 1967-89, div. head, 1969-82, with div. epidemiology and stats., 1989—; assoc. dean U. Toronto, 1981-84, Univ. prof., 1984—. Contbr. articles on biophysics, cell biology, cancer research and decision sci. to sci. jours. Recipient Gairdner Found. Internat. award, 1969, Order of Canada, 1994. Fellow Royal Soc. Can.; mem. Can. Bioethics Soc. Home: 182 Briar Hill Ave Toronto, ON Canada M4R 1H9 Office: 610 University Ave, Toronto, ON Canada M5G 2L7 Albert Einstein said: "The most beautiful thing we can experience is the mysterious. It is the source of all true art and science." And, "Concern for humanity must always form the chief interest of all technical endeavors—in order that the creations of our mind shall be a blessing and not a curse to mankind." Is there a more eloquent summary of standards for the scientist than this?

TILLERY, BILL W., physics educator; b. Muskogee, Okla., Sept. 15, 1938; s. William Earnest and Bessie C. (Smith) Freeman; m. Patricia Weeks Northrop, Aug. 1, 1981; 1 child, Elizabeth Fielding; children by previous marriage: Tonya Lynn, Lisa Gail. BS, Northeastern U., 1960; MA, U. No. Colo., 1965, EdD, 1967. Tchr. Guthrie Pub. Schs., Okla., 1960-62; tchr. Jefferson County schs., Colo., 1962-64; teaching asst. U. No. Colo., 1965-67; asst. prof. Fla. State U., 1967-69; assoc. prof. U. Wyo., 1969-73, dir. sci. and math. teaching ctr., 1969-73; assoc. prof. dept. physics Ariz. State U., Tempe, 1973-75, prof., 1976—; cons. in field. Author: (with Ploutz) Basic Physical Science, 1964; (with Sund and Trowbridge) Elementary Science Activities, 1967, Elementary Biological Science, 1970, Elementary Physical Science, 1970, Elementary Earth Science, 1970, Investigate and Discover, 1975; Space, Time, Energy and Matter: Activity Books, 1976; (with Bartholomew) Heath Earth Science, 1984; (with Bartholomew and Gary) Heath Earth Science Activities, 1984, 2d edit. 1987, Heath Earth Science Teacher Resource Book, 1987, Heath Earth Science Laboratory Activity, 1987, Physical Science, 1991, 2d edit. 1993, Physical Science Laboratory Manual, 1991, 2d edit. 1993, Physical Science Instructor's Manual, 1991, 2d edit. 1993, Physical Science Laboratory Manual Instructor's Manual, 1991, 2d edit. 1993, (with Grant) Physical Science Student Study Guide, 1991, 2d edit. (with Claassen) 1993, Introduction to Physics and Chemistry: Foundations of Physical Science, 1992, Laboratory Manual in Conceptual Physics, 1992, Physics, 1993, Chemistry, 1993, Astronomy, 1993, Earth Science, 1993; editor: Ariz. Sci. Tchrs. Jour., 1975-85, Ariz. Energy Edn., 1978-84. Fellow AAAS; mem. Nat. Sci. Tchrs. Assn., Ariz. Sci. Tchrs. Assn., Assn. Edn. of Tchrs. in Sci., Nat. Assn. Research in Sci. Teaching. Republican. Episcopalian. Home: 8986 S Forest Ave Tempe AZ 85284-3142 Office: Ariz State U Dept Physics Tempe AZ 85287-1504

TILLERY, RICHARD LEE, television executive; b. Pratt, Kans., Nov. 6, 1940; s. Donald R. and Thelma L. (Keen) T.; m. Naomi Goodman, June 7, 1967 (div. July 1984); children: Richard Craig, Mary Kathrine; m. Julia D. Rockler, June 30, 1985; 1 child, Melissa Beth. Student, Ft. Hays State U., 1958-60, 63-65. Investigative reporter, photographer, editor Sta. KZTV, Corpus Christi, Tex., 1965; asst. news dir., prodr., assignments editor, inv. reporter Sta. KIII-TV, Corpus Christi, 1972; asst. news dir., co-anchor, prodr. Sta. KRIS-TV, Corpus Christi, 1973; asst. news dir., prodr., assignment editor Sta. KETV, Omaha, 1974; news dir. Sta. KHGI-TV, Kearney, Nebr., 1976; acting news dir., exec. prodr. Sta. KWCH-TV, Wichita, Kans., 1980; exec. prodr., dir. spl. projects Sta. KENS-TV, San Antonio, 1984; freelance prodr., investigator Washington, 1986-87; coord. Newsnet satellite feed svc. CBS News, 1987-88; bur. chief The Washington Bur., Washington, 1988—; com. mem. UPI, AP, Soc. of Prof. Journalists; panelist, guest speaker in field; organizer profl. seminars in field. Bd. dirs. ARC, Campfire Girls, Boy Scouts Am., South Tex. Mental Health and Retardation. With U.S. Army, 1960-63. Recipient Pieringer award Tex. Assn. Broadcasters, Headliners award U. Tex., Gavel award Tex. Bar Assn., Sch. Bell award Tex. Classroom Tchrs. Assn., Investigative Reporting award Nat. AP, investigative reporting and regional awards from various orgns. Mem. Nebr. AP Broadcasters (past pres., regional awards), South Tex. Press Club (past v.p., regional awards), Radio and TV News Dirs. Assn. (com. mem., panelist, guest speaker). Office: The Washington Bur # 363 400 N Capitol Washington DC 20001

TILLETT, SAMUEL RAYMOND, lawyer; b. Akron, Ohio, May 4, 1951. AB, Hamilton Coll., 1973; JD, Case Western Res. U., 1977. Bar: Ohio 1977, D.C. 1978, Ill. 1988. Trior. Mayer, Brown & Platt, Chgo.; adj. prof. law DePaul U. Coll. Law, Chgo., 1992—; trustee Village of Glencoe, Ill. Libr. Bd., 1995—. Bd. dirs. Chgo. Metro History Edn. Ctr., 1989-94. Mem. ABA, Nat. Assn. Bond Lawyers, D.C. Bar Assn., Chgo. Bar Assn. Office: Mayer Brown & Platt 190 S La Salle St Chicago IL 60603-3410

TILLEY, C. RONALD, gas company executive; b. Welch, W.Va., Oct. 20, 1935; s. Clarence D. and Mildred R. (Carnes) T.; m. Janice E. Tilley, Aug. 24, 1956; children: Christopher R., Cory G., Beth Ann. B.S. in Acctg., Concord Coll., 1957. Clk. rate dept. United Fuel Gas Co., Charleston, W.Va., 1957-62, rate analyst, 1962-64; engr. rate dept. Columbia Gas Service Corp., N.Y.C., 1964-71; mgr. rate dept. Columbia Gas Service Corp., Columbus, Ohio, 1971-73; dir. rate dept. Columbia Gas Service Corp. Charleston, 1973-75; v.p. corp. Columbia Gas Service Corp., Washington, 1975-80; v.p. rate Columbia Gas Service Corp., Wilmington, Del., 1980-82; sr. v.p. Columbia Gas Distbn. Cos., Columbus, 1982-85, pres., 1985-87, chmn., chief exec. officer, 1987—; Bd. dirs. BancOhio Nat. Bank. Trustee Columbus Symphony Orch., 1988—, Children's Hosp., 1989—; Columbus Mus. Art, 1990; bd. dirs. United Negro Coll. Fund, 1987—; mem., bd. dirs. Columbus Assn. Performing Arts, 1989—; chmn. Coun. on Ethics in Econs., 1992. With U.S. Army, 1958-60. Mem. Columbus Area C. of C. (bd. dirs. 1987—). Republican. Avocations: golf; reading. Office: Columbia Gas Distbn Cos 200 Civic Center Dr S Columbus OH 43215-4138

TILLEY, CAROLYN BITTNER, technical information specialist; b. Washington, July 29, 1947; d. Klaud Kay and Margaret Louise (Hanson) Bittner; m. Frederick Edwin Dudley, June 18, 1985. B.S., Am. U., 1975; M.L.S., U. Md., 1976. With NIH, 1965-71; statis. research asst. Health Manpower Edn., Bethesda, Md., 1971-72 tech. info. specialist Nat. Libr. Medicine, Bethesda, Md., 1972-81, head medlars (med. lit. analysis and retrieval system) mgmt. sect., 1981—. Mem. editorial bd.: Med. Reference Services Quar. Mem. CENDI User Edn. Comm., Nat. Fed. Abstracting and Info. Svc. Pub. Com. Recipient Merit award NIH, 1984, Rogers award Nat. Libr. Medicine, 1991. Mem. Med. Library Assn. Presbyterian. Avocation: horseback riding. Office: Nat Libr Medicine 8600 Rockville Pike Bethesda MD 20894-0001

TILLEY, NORWOOD CARLTON, JR., federal judge; b. Rock Hill, S.C.; s. Norwood Carlton and Rebecca (Westbrook) T.; m. Greta Medlin, Sept. 25, 1970. BA, Wake Forest U., 1966, JD, 1969. Bar: N.C. 1969, U.S. Dist. Ct. (middle dist.) N.C. 1971. Law clk. to Hon. Eugene A Gordon, U.S. Dist. Judge Middle Dist. N.C., 1969-71; asst. U.S. atty. Mid. Dist. N.C. Greensboro, 1971-73, U.S. atty., 1974-77; U.S. dist. judge Mid. Dist. N.C., Durham, 1988—; ptnr. Osteen, Adams, Tilley & Walker, Greensboro, 1977-88; instr. Wake Forest U. Sch. Law, 1980. Office: US Dist Ct PO Box 3443 Greensboro NC 27402-3443

TILLEY, RICE M(ATTHEWS), JR., lawyer; b. Ft. Worth, June 21, 1936; s. Rice Matthews Sr. and Lucille Geyer (Kelly) T.; children: Marisa Lynn, Angela Ainsworth, Lisa Scott, Rice Matthews III; m. Sandra Cooper, May 13, 1994. BA, Washington & Lee U., 1958; JD, So. Meth. U., 1961; LLM in Taxation, NYU, 1962. Bar: Tex. 1961. Mem. Law, Snakard & Gambill, Ft. Worth, 1964—. Bd. dirs. Van Cliburn Found., Ft. Worth Ballet Assn., Ft. Worth Symphony Orch. Assn.; bd. trustees Tex. Wesleyan Univ.; pres. Ft. Worth Opera Assn. Mem. State Bar Tex. (chmn. real estate, probate and trust law sect.), Ft. Worth C. of C. (chmn. bd.), Century II Club (pres.), Leadership Ft. Worth (chmn. bd. dirs.), Exch. Club of Ft. Worth (pres.). Republican. Office: Law Snakard & Gambill 500 Throckmorton St Ste 3200 Fort Worth TX 76102-3859

TILLINGHAST, CHARLES CARPENTER, JR., aviation and financial consultant; b. Saxton's River, Vt., Jan. 30, 1911; s. Charles C. and Adelaide Barrows (Shaw) T.; m. Lisette Micoleau, Nov. 16, 1935; children: Charles Carpenter III, Elizabeth, Jane, Anne Shaw. Ph.B., Brown U., 1932; J.D., Columbia U., 1935; L.H.D., S.D. Sch. Mines and Tech., 1959; LL.D., Franklin Coll., 1963, U. Redlands, 1964, Brown U., 1967, Drury Coll., 1967, William Jewell Coll., 1973. Bar: N.Y. bar 1935, Mich. 1943. Assoc. Hughes, Schurman & Dwight, 1935-37; dep. asst. dist. atty. N.Y. County, 1938-40; assoc. Hughes, Richards, Hubbard & Ewing, 1940-42; ptnr. Hughes, Hubbard, Blair & Reed (and predecessor firms), N.Y.C., 1942-57; v.p., dir. The Bendix Corp., Detroit, 1957-61; pres., chief exec. officer Trans World Airlines, Inc., 1961-69, chmn. bd., chief exec. officer, 1969-76, dir. 1961-81; dir., vice chmn. bd. White Weld & Co., Inc., 1977-78; mng. dir. Merrill Lynch White Weld Capital Markets Group, 1978-82; bd. dirs. Henry Luce Found., Air Transport Assn., 1961-72, 74-75; mem. exec. com. Internat. Air Transport Assn., 1969-75. Bd. dirs. Community Welfare Fund, Bronxville, 1951-53, pres., 1953; gov. Lawrence Hosp., Bronxville, 1955-59; trustee Brown U., 1954-61, 65-79, chancellor, 1968-79, fellow, 1979—; fellow Midwest Rsch. Inst., 1963-76, The Conf. Bd., 1965-76, People to People Program, 1961-70, Com. for Econ. Devel., 1967—; bd. visitors Sch. Law, Columbia, 1962-92; bd. govs. John Carter Brown Libr., 1989—. Mem. ABA, Assn. Bar City N.Y., Brown U. Club (N.Y.C.), Hope Club (R.I.), Sakonnet Golf Club. Home: Apt 530 355 Blackstone Blvd Providence RI 02906

TILLINGHAST, CHARLES CARPENTER, III, marketing company executive; b. N.Y.C., Nov. 16, 1936; s. Charles Carpenter, Jr. and Lisette (Micoleau) T.; m. Cynthia Branch, Sept. 28, 1974; children by previous marriage: Avery D., Charles W., David C. B.S. in Mech. Engring, Lehigh U., 1958; M.B.A., Harvard U., 1963. Asst. to dir. devel. Lehigh U., Bethlehem, Pa., 1958-61; adminstrv. asst. Boise Cascade Corp., Portland, Oreg., 1961-63; asst. to v.p. Boise Cascade Corp., Boise, Idaho, 1964-65; gen. mgr. office supply div. Boise Cascade Corp., 1965-67, gen. mgr. paper distbn. div., 1966, v.p bus. products, 1967-69, sr. v.p housing group, 1969-71, sr. v.p., 1971-73; pres. CRM div. Ziff-Davis Pub. Co., Inc., Del Mar, Calif., 1971-75; pres., treas. Value Communications, Inc., La Jolla, Calif., 1975-76; pres. Oak Tree Publs., Inc., San Diego, 1976-81; pres. Advanced Mktg. Services Inc., San Diego, 1982-94, chmn., 1994—. Served to 2d lt. AUS, 1959. Home: 1762 Nautilus St La Jolla CA 92037-6413 Office: Advanced Mktg Svcs Inc 5880 Oberlin Dr San Diego CA 92121-3701

TILLINGHAST, DAVID ROLLHAUS, lawyer; b. N.Y.C., Feb. 25, 1930; s. Charles Carpenter and Josephine Dorothy (Rollhaus) T.; m. Phyllis Van Horn, Sept. 24, 1955 (div. Jan. 1984); m. Lisa Sewell, Feb. 25, 1984; children: Gregory Barrett Sewell, Lauren Alexa. AB cum laude, Brown U., 1951; LLB cum laude, Yale U., 1954. Bar: N.Y. 1955, Oreg. 1956, U.S. Supreme Ct. 1978. Assoc. Hughes, Hubbard & Reed, N.Y.C., 1954-55, 57-61; ptnr. Hughes, Hubbard & Reed, 1961-62, 65-90; assoc. King, Miller, Anderson, Nash & Yerke, Portland, Oreg., 1955-57; spl. asst. for internat. tax affairs U.S. Dept. Treasury, Washington, 1962-65; ptnr. Chadbourne & Parke, N.Y.C., 1990—; adj. prof. law NYU, 1977-87; cons. UN Ctr. on Transnat. Corps., 1978-87; reporter Am. Law Inst. Project on Internat. Aspects of U.S. Income Taxation, 1982-91; cons. to reporters Am. Law Inst. Revision of Restatement of Fgn. Relations Law of U.S., 1982-83. Author: Tax Aspects of Internat. Transactions, 1978, 2d edit., 1984; contbr. articles to profl. publs. Mem. transition team Sec. of Treasury W. Michael Blumenthal, 1977. Mem. Assn. of Bar of City of N.Y. (chmn. com. on taxation 1981-83), Internat. Bar Assn. (vice-chmn. com. on taxation bus. law sect. 1984-86), U.S. Council for Internat. Bus. (com. on taxation), Tax Forum, Council on Fgn. Relations. Democrat. Clubs: Siwanoy (Bronxville, N.Y.). Avocations: golf; tennis. Office: Chadbourne & Parke 30 Rockefeller Plz New York NY 10112-0001

TILLINGHAST, JOHN AVERY, utilities executive; b. N.Y.C., Apr. 30, 1927; s. Charles C. and Dorothy J. (Rollhaus) T.; m. Mabel Heagy, Sept. 11, 1948; children: Katherine Brickley, Susan Trainor, Abigail Ryan. BSME, Columbia U., 1948, MS, 1949. Registered profl. engr., Ky., Ind., Mich. N.Y., Ohio, Va., W.Va., N.H. With Am. Elec. Power Service Corp., N.Y.C. 1949-79, exec. v.p. engring. and constrn., 1967-72, sr. exec. v.p. engring. and constrn., 1972-79; sr. v.p. tech. Wheelabrator-Frye Inc., Hampton, N.H., 1979-83, Signal Advanced Tech. Group, The Signal Cos., Hampton, N.H., 1983-85; sr. v.p. Allied-Signal Internat., Hampton, 1985-86, Sci. Applications Internat. Corp., San Diego, 1986-88; pres. TILTEC, Portsmouth, N.H, 1987-94; CEO Great Bay Power Corp., Portsmouth, 1994—. Patentee generating unit control system. Elder Reformed Ch., 1976-79. Served with USN, 1944-46. Fellow ASME; mem. IEEE, Nat. Acad. Engring.,Sigma Xi, Tau Beta Pi. Office: Great Bay Power Corp 20 Ladd St Portsmouth NH 03801-4080

TILLIS, MEL(VIN), musician, songwriter; b. Tampa, Fla., Aug. 8, 1932; m. Judy Edwards, 1979; children: Pam, Connie, Cindy, Melvin Jr., Carrie, Hannah. Student, U. Fla. Founder Sawgrass Music, Sabal Music, Tillis Tunes, Sweet Tater Tunes, Nashville. Songwriter, Cedarwood Music, Nashville, 20 years, (Named Entertainer of Year, Country Music Assn. 1976), numerous personal and TV appearances; composer over 600 songs recorded by, Webb Pierce, Ray Price, Carl Smith, Brenda Lee, Kenny Rogers, Charlie Pride, Burl Ives, George Strait, others; (with The Statesiders) 56 albums including: Mel Tillis and the Statesiders on Stage, Best of Mel Tillis, Love Revival, Welcome to Country, California Road, 1985, American Originals, 1990, Greatest Hits, 1991, Beyond the Sunset, 1993; author: Stuttering Boy, 1986. Served in USAF. Named Comedian of Yr., Country Music Assn., 1971, 73, 74, 75, 76, 77, Entertainer of Yr., 1976. Office: Mel Tillis Theater Inc PO Box 1626 2527 Hwy 248 Branson MO 65616-9999

TILLIS, PAM, country singer, songwriter; b. Plant City, Fla., 1957; d. Mel and Doris T.; divorced; 1 child, Ben; m. Bob DiPiero, Feb. 14, 1991. Student, U. Tenn. Recording artist Arista Records, 1990—. Singer, songwriter for acts including Highway 101, Gloria Gaynor, Dan Seals, Chaka Kahn, Ricky Van Shelton, Suzy Bogguss, Conway Twitty; albums: Put Yourself in My Place, 1991, Homeward Looking Angel, 1992, Pam Tillis Collection, 1994, Sweethearts Dance, 1994; 1st single: Every Home Should Have One, 1981; #1 hit record Don't Tell Me What To Do, 1991. Grammy nomination, Best Country Vocal Collaboration for "Romeo" with Dolly Parton, Tanya Tucker, Billy Ray Cyrus, Kathy Mattea & Mary-Chapin Carpenter, 1994. Office: Arista Records 6 W 57th St New York NY 10019*

TILLMAN, ELIZABETH CARLOTTA, nurse, educator; b. Md., Aug. 31, 1929; d. Walter Monroe and Mozelle Virginia (Shugars) Brown; m. Lloyd A. Tillman, Apr. 16, 1949; children: Lloyd A. Jr., William L., Susan E. Tillman Chaires. Diploma, Md. Gen. Hosp. Sch. Nursing, 1950; student, Towson State U., U. Md., Loyola Coll., Balt., Howard C.C. RN. Psychiatric nurse Spring Grove Hosp. Ctr., Catonsville, Md.; 1950; pvt. duty home health nurse Md., 1951-60; dir., tchr., nurse Doughoregan Manor Day Sch., Ellicott City, Md., 1960-80; med.-surg. nurse Woman's Hosp., Balt., 1964, Md. Gen. Hosp., Balt., 1980; nursing instr. Howard County Dept. Edn., Ellicott City, 1981-91; nursing educator Howard County Sch. Tech., 1981-91, Howard County Gen. Hosp., 1981-91; geriatric nurse Lorien Columbia (Md.) Nursing & Rehab. Ctr., 1981-91; home health nurse Md., 1992—. Mem. NEA, Md. State Tchrs. Assn., Md. Gen. Hosp. Alumni Assn., Am. Vocat. Assn., Health Occupations Educators, Md. Vocat. Assn., Phi Eta Sigma, Iota Lambda Sigma. Home: 10002 Reed Ln Ellicott City MD 21042-2238

TILLMAN, JOSEPH NATHANIEL, engineering executive; b. Augusta, Ga., Aug. 1, 1926; s. Leroy and Canarie (Kelly) T.; m. Alice Lavonia Walton, Sept. 5, 1950 (dec. 1983); children: Alice Lavonia, Robert Bertram; m. Areerat Usahaviriyakit, Nov. 24, 1986. BA magna cum laude, Paine Coll., 1948; MS, Northrop U., 1975, MBA, 1976, DBA, Nova U., 1989. Dir. Rockwell Internat., Anaheim, Calif., 1958-84; pres. Tillman Enterprises, Corona, Calif., 1985—; guest lectr. UCLA, 1980-85. Contbr. articles to profl. jours. Capt. USAF, 1948-57, Korea. Recipient Presdl. Citation Nat. Assn. for Equal Opportunity in Higher Edn., 1986. Mem. Acad. Mgmt. (chmn. 1985-86), Soc. Logistics Engrs. (pres. 1985-86), Paine Coll. Alumni Assn. (v.p. 1976—), NAACP (pres. 1984-88). Avocations: duplicate bridge, travel, swimming, skiing, hiking. Office: Tillman Enterprises 1550 Rimpau Ave Trlr 45 Corona CA 91719-3206

TILLMAN, MASSIE MONROE, federal judge; b. Corpus Christi, Tex., Aug. 15, 1937; s. Clarence and Artie Lee (Stewart) T.; m. Karen Wright, July 2, 1993; children: Jeffrey Monroe, Holly. BBA, Baylor U., 1959, LLB, 1961. Bar: Tex. 1961, U.S. Dist. Ct. (no. dist.) Tex. 1961, U.S. Ct. Appeals (5th cir.) 1969, U.S. Supreme Ct. 1969. Ptnr. Herrick & Tillman, Ft. Worth, 1961-66; pvt. practice, Ft. Worth, 1966-70, 79-87; ptnr. Brown, Herman et al., Ft. Worth, 1970-78, Street, Swift et al., Ft. Worth, 1978-79; U.S. bankruptcy judge No. Dist. Tex., Ft. Worth Div., 1987—. Author: Tillman's Trial Guide, 1970. Fellow Am. Bd. Trial Advocates, Tex. Bar Found.; mem. Ft. Worth/Tarrant County Bar Assn. (bd. dirs. 1969-70, v.p. 1970-71), Trial Atty's. Am., Nat. Conf. Bankruptcy Judges, Am. Bankruptcy Inst., Ft. Worth Club, Phi Alpha Delta. Democrat. Baptist. Avocations: cutting horses, competition shotgun shooting.

TILLMAN, MURRAY HOWELL, instructional technology educator; b. Birmingham, Ala., Nov. 7, 1940; s. Gray Eddie and Ruby (Wood) T.; m. Dorris Collier Hogan, June 9, 1962; children: David Murray, Kathryn Collier. BA, Birmingham So. Coll., 1962; MS, U. Ga., 1965, PhD, 1966. Elem. sch. tchr. Muscogee County Bd. Edn., Columbus, Ga., 1961-62; rsch. assoc. R&D Ctr. U. Ga., Athens, 1966-70, asst. prof. Coll. Edn., 1970-71, assoc. prof., 1971-81, prof. instrnl. tech., 1981-93; prof. emeritus, 1993—; acting head dept. curriculum and instrn. U. Ga., Athens, 1983-84, acting head div. instrnl. support, 1983-84, head instrnl. tech., 1991-92; Co-author: Learning to Teach, 1976; author: Troubleshooting Classroom Problems, 1982; editor, author: Instructional Design, 1991. NDEA fellow, 1963-65. Mem. Am. Ednl. Rsch. Assn., Assn. Ednl. Comm. and Tech. (cert. of merit 1986), Humanities and Tech. Assn., Nat. Soc. Peformance and Instrn. (cert. of achievement 1989, cert. of recognition 1990). Avocations: biking, swimming, chess, music. Home: 215 Hall St Athens GA 30605 Office: U Ga 607 Aderhold Hall Athens GA 30602

TILLMAN, ROLLIE, JR., university official; b. Lake Wales, Fla., Apr. 11, 1933; s. Rollie and Louise (Johnson) T.; m. Mary Windley Dunn, June 22, 1957; children—Mary Windley, Jane Guion, Rollie. B.S., U. N.C., 1955; M.B.A., Harvard U., 1957, D.B.A., 1962. Rsch. asst. Harvard Bus. Sch., 1958-60; asst. prof. bus. adminstrn. U. N.C., Chapel Hill, 1960-63, assoc. prof., 1963-65, prof., 1965—; dir. MBA program, 1965-67, dir. exec. program, 1968-77, vice chancellor for univ. relations, 1978-84; trustee chmn. Kenan Inst. Pvt. Enterprise, Chapel Hill, 1985-90, chmn. bd., 1990—; dir. Techform Inc., U. N.C. Press, Renfro Inc., Entrepreneur of Yr. Inst., Coun. Entrepreneur Devel., Good Mark Foods, NationsBank. Author: (with C.A. Kirkpatrick) Promotion: Persuasive Communication in Marketing, 1964, (with Luther H. Hodges, Jr.) Bank Marketing: Text and Cases, 1968. Trustee St. Mary's Coll., 1968-78; dir., pres. N.C. Mus. of Art Soc. Mem. Am. Mktg. Assn. (dir. 1967-69). Democrat. Episcopalian. Office: Kenan Inst Pvt Enterprise CB 3490 Chapel Hill NC 27599

TILLMAN, BOBBI, lawyer; b. Kansas City, Kans., Dec. 29, 1952; d. Edward E. and Barbara (Wilson) T.; children: Morgan Mallory, Ryan Mallory. BA in Pol. Sci. cum laude, U. So. Calif., 1974; postgrad., Hastings Coll. Law, 1974-75; JD, U. So. Calif., 1977. Bar: Calif. 1979, U.S. Dist. Ct. (cen. dist.) Calif. 1979, U.S. Supreme Ct. 1984. Pvt. practice L.A., 1979-86; sr. ptnr. Mallory, Brown-Curtis & Mallory, L.A., 1986—; mem. Jud. Coun. Calif. Adv. Com. Family Law, subcommittee child support guidelines, 1990, Jud. Coun. Focus Group on Legal Forms, 1991, L.A. Dist. Atty.'s Child Support Adv. Coun., 1993, State Child Support Adv. Task Force, Adv. Com. Integration Child and Family Legal Proceedings, project Inst. Ct. Mgmt.-Nat. Ctr. State Cts., Denver; instr. family law Continuing Edn. of Bar, 1990-93; Judge Pro Tem L.A. Mcpl. Traffic Ct.; presenter and speaker in field. Guest: sta. KTLA TV Weekend Gallery show. Vol. mentor Harriet Buhai Ctr. Family Law. Recipient Vol. award Women's Legal Clinic, 1981, Santa Monica Gems award 1990. Mem. ABA, Nat. Bar Assn. (family law sect., comml. law sect., local coord. 1992 corp. counsel conf.), State Bar Calif. (past mem. family law sect. exec. com., mem. support com. so. Calif.), Calif. Assn. Black Lawyers (past chair family law adv. com.), Los Angeles County Bar (exec. com. family law sect.), John M. Langston Bar Assn., Corp. Counsel Conf., Black Women Lawyers Assn. L.A., Inc. (past chair family law sect., past chmn.), L.A. Legion Lex Inn of Court (chpt. VIII), U. So. Calif. Law Ctr. Legion Lex.

TILLOTSON, CAROLYN, state legislator; m. John C. Tillotson. Mem. Kans. Senate, 1993—. Republican. Home: 1606 Westwood Dr Leavenworth KS 66048 Office: Kans State Senate State Capitol Topeka KS 66612

TILLOTSON, FRANK LEE, naval officer; b. Ketchikan, Alaska, June 8, 1941; s. Frank Deforest and Helen Bernice (Gibson) T.; m. Elizabeth Ann Green, June 27, 1964; children: Matthew, Wyatt. BS, U.S. Naval Acad., 1963; MSA, George Washington U., 1971. Commd. ensign USN, 1963, advanced through grades to rear adm., 1990; ops. officer fighter squadron 124 USN, San Diego, 1974-77, commanding officer fighter squadron 51, 1977-80, comdr. carrier wing 11, 1980-82; program coord. F-14 USN, Washington, 1980-82; commanding officer USS St. Louis USN, Sasebo, Japan, 1985-86; commanding officer USS Kitty Hawk USN, Phila., 1987-89; dep. for ops. U.S. Pacific Command USN, Honolulu, 1989-90; command dir. U.S. Space Command/NORAD USN, Colorado Springs, Colo., 1990-92; comdr Naval Tng. Ct., Orlando, Fla., 1992—. Mem. editorial bd., bd. dirs. Naval Inst. Press, Annapolis, Md., 1983-84. Decorated Legion of Merit, DFC, Def. Meritorious Svc. medal, Navy Meritorious Svc. medal. Mem. Soc. Exptl. Test Pilots, Phila. Union League. Avocations: golf, fishing. Home: Quarters A Trident Ln Naval Tng Ctr Orlando FL 32803 Office: Commander Naval Tng Ctr Orlando FL 32813

TILLSON, JOHN BRADFORD, JR., newspaper publisher; b. Paris, Tex., Dec. 21, 1944; s. John Bradford Sr. and Frances (Ragland) T.; m. Patricia Hunt, June 14, 1966 (div. June 1978); children: John, Karen; m. Cynthia Wornom, Oct. 10, 1981. BA, Denison U., Granville, Ohio, 1966. Reporter Charlotte (N.C.) News, 1969-71; reporter Dayton (Ohio) Daily News, 1971-76, city editor, 1977-80, asst. mng. editor, 1980-82, mng. editor features, 1982-84; editor Dayton Daily News and Jour. Herald, 1984-88, pub., 1988—; lectr. Am. Press Inst., Reston, Va., 1980-84. Exec. com. Vietnam Vets. Meml. Park Fund, Dayton, 1985-86; community bd. advisors Jr. League Dayton 1986; trustee Dayton Art Inst., 1984—; Victory Theatre, 1986—; trustee Dayton Performing Arts Fund. Mem. Am. Soc. Newspaper Pub. Episcopalian. Home: 4833 Far Hills Ave Dayton OH 45429-2184 Office: Dayton Daily News 45th S Ludlow St Dayton OH 45401*

TILLY, JENNIFER, actress. TV series include: Shaping Up, 1984, Bodyguard, 1988; Key West, 1993; TV movies include: Heads, 1994; films include: No Small Affair, 1984, Moving Violations, 1985, He's My Girl, 1987, Inside Out, 1987, Rented Lips, 1988, High Spirits, 1988, Johnny Be Good, 1988, Remote Control, 1988, The Fabulous Baker Boys, 1989, Let It Ride, 1989, Far From Home, 1989, Scorchers, 1991, Shadow of the Wolf,

1992, Made in America, 1993, At Home With the Webbers, 1993, Double Cross, 1994, Bullets Over Broadway, 1994 (Academy award nomination best supporting actress 1994), The Getaway, 1994. Office: Agency for the Performing Arts 9000 Sunset Blvd Ste 1200 Los Angeles CA 90069*

TILLY, LOUISE AUDINO, history and sociology educator; b. Orange, N.J., Dec. 13, 1930; d. Hector and Piera (Roffino) Audino; m. Charles Tilly, Aug. 15, 1953; children: Christopher, Kathryn, Laura, Sarah. BA, Rutgers U., 1952, MA, Boston U., 1955; PhD, U. Toronto, 1974. From instr. to asst. prof. Mich. State U., East Lansing, 1972-75; from asst. prof. to prof. U. Mich., Ann Arbor, 1975-84; Michael E. Gellert prof. history and sociology New Sch. for Social Rsch., N.Y.C., 1984-94, chair com. hist. studies, 1984—, Michael E. Gellert prof. history and sociology, 1994—; assoc. dir. studies Ecole des Hautes Etudes en Scis. Sociales, Paris, 1979, 80, 88; fellow Shelby Cullom Davis Ctr., Princeton (N.J.) U., 1978; vis. mem. Inst. for Advanced Study, Princeton, 1987-88; fellow Ctr. for Advanced Studies Behavioral Scis., 1991-92; vis. scholar Russell Sage Found., 1994-95; bd. dirs. Social Scis. Rsch. Coun., N.Y.C., 1983-86. Author: Politics and Class in Milan, 1881-1901, 1992; co-author: The Rebellious Century, 1975, Women, Work and Family, 1978, rev. edit., 1987; co-editor, co-author: Class Conflict and Collective Action, 1981, Women, Politics and Change, 1990; co-editor: The European Experience of Declining Fertility: The Quiet Revolution, 1992; also articles. Active com. on women's employment and related social issues Nat. Acad. Scis., 1981-86, chmn., co-editor report Panel on Tech. and Women's Employment, 1984-86. Grantee Rockefeller Found., 1974-76, Am. Philos. Soc., 1977-78, 85-86, Russell Sage Found., 1985-86; Guggenheim Found. fellow, 1991-92. Mem. Am. Hist. Assn. (coun. 1985-87, pres. elect. 1992, pres. 1993), Social Sci. History Assn.(pres. 1981-82), Coun. on European Studies (exec. com. 1980-83), Berkshire Conf. Women Historians. Democrat. Home: 5 E 22nd St Apt 5K New York NY 10010 Office: Com on Hist Studies 64 University Pl New York NY 10003-4520

TILLY, MEG, actress; b. Long Beach, Calif., Feb. 14, 1960. Actress: (films) Fame, 1980, Tex, 1982, One Dark Night, 1983, The Big Chill, 1983, Psycho II, 1983, Impulse, 1984, Agnes of God, 1985 (Academy award nomination best supporting actress 1985), Off Beat, 1986, Masquerade, 1988, The Girl in a Swing, 1988, Valmont, 1989, The Two Jakes, 1990, Leaving Normal, 1992, Body Snatchers, 1994, Sleep with Me, 1994, (TV movies) In the Best Interest of the Child, 1990, (TV series) Winnetka Road, 1993; author: Singing Songs, 1994. Office: UTA 9560 Wilshire Blvd 5th Fl Beverly Hills CA 90212*

TILSON, DOROTHY RUTH, word processing executive; b. Bloomsburg, Pa., Mar. 24, 1918; d. Roy Earl and Mary Etta (Masteller) Derr; m. Irving Tilson, Sept. 1949. BS, Bloomsburg U., 1940. Tchr. Madison Consol. Sch., Jerseytown, Pa., 1940-42; gage checker Phila. Ordinance Gage Lab., 1942-43; tabulating asst. Remington Rand, Phila., N.Y.C., 1943-46; copy writer Sears Roebuck, Phila., N.Y.C., 1946-48; statis. asst. Ford Internat., N.Y.C., 1949-56; word processing adminstrv. asst. Coopers & Lybrand, N.Y.C., 1956-91. Life mem. Rep. Senatorial Inner Circle, Washington, 1987—. Mem. Am. Movement for World Govt. (sec. 1991—), N.Y. Theosophical Soc. (libr. 1969—), UN Assn.-USA (mem. global policy project which includes internat. econ. governance and human rights). Home: 435 W 119 St 9G New York NY 10027-7102

TILSON, HUGH HANNA, epidemiologist; b. New Kensington, Pa., Jan. 6, 1940; s. Donald Heath and Ann Coe T.; m. Judith Scullin, June 10, 1961; children: Hugh, Richard S., Ann C., Alice H. BA, Reed Coll., 1963; MD, Washington U., 1964; MPH, Harvard U., 1969, DPH, 1972. Diplomate Am. Bd. Preventive Medicine (trustee 1986-95, vice chmn. pub. health & preventive medicine, 1988-95). Intern Yale-New Haven Med. Center, 1964-65; resident in preventive medicine Harvard Sch. Pub. Health, 1968-72; research mem. John F. Kennedy Inst. Politics, 1969-70; research assoc. Health Services Research Ctr., U. N.C., Chapel Hill, 1970-81; asst. prof. preventive medicine and pub. health U. Oreg. Med. Sch., 1971-74, assoc. prof., 1974-76, clin. prof., 1976-78; asst. health officer Multnomah County, Oreg., 1971-75; health officer, dir. div. health services Multnomah County, 1975-76, health officer, dir. dept. human services, 1976-78; dir. div. health services State of N.C., Raleigh, 1979-81; with Burroughs Wellcome Co., Research Triangle Park, N.C., 1981—, internat. v.p. surveillance, epidemiology and econ. rsch., 1994—; adj. prof. epidemiology U. N.C. Sch. Pub. Health, clin. prof. family medicine U. N.C. Med. Sch., 1981—; cons. in field; examiner Am. Bd. Preventive Medicine, 1974-75; cons. Nat. Center for Health Services Research, HEW, 1975-89; mem. external adv. bd. Health Services Research Center, U. Wash. Sch. Public Health, 1977-80; mem. public health standards work group USPHS, 1977—; chmn. external adv. bd. Health Services Research Center, U. N.C., 1979-93, mut. adv. bd., 1993—; mem. med. adv. bd. Planned Parenthood of Portland, 1973-79, Planned Parenthood Greater Raleigh, 1986-95; bd. dirs. N.W. Oreg. Health Systems Agy., 1976-79; vice chmn. policy adv. bd. Joint Commn. on Accreditation of Hosps., 1980-81; mem. adv. bd. AIDS Svc. Agency; bd. health promotion and disease prevention Inst. Medicine, 1993—; Mem. editorial bd. Am. Jour. Pub. Health, 1980-85, assoc. editor, 1985—; mem. editorial bd. Jour. Community Health, 1977-86, Jour. Public Health Policy, 1979-87, Jour. Clin. Rsch. and Pharmacoepidemiol., 1986-89, Am. Jour. Preventive Medicine, 1987-93. Bd. dirs. United Way Columbia-Willamette, Oreg., 1977-78, Portland Opera Assn., 1977-79, Raleigh Chamber Music Guild, 1981—, Partnership for Prevention, 1993—; mem. Research Triangle Internat. Visitors Ctr., 1981—, bd. dirs., v.p., 1981-85. With M.C. U.S. Army, 1963-68. Fellow Am. Coll. Preventive Medicine (regent 1988-92, pres.-elect 1993-95, pres. 1995—); mem. Nat. Assn. County Health Officers (pres. 1977-79), N.C. Med. Soc., English Speaking Union, N.C. Pub. Health Assn., Am. Pub. Health Assn., Assn. Tchrs. Preventive Medicine, Pharm. Mfrs. Assn. (med. sect. steering com. 1988—, sec. 1989-92, vice chmn., 1992—, chmn. 1994—), Internat. Soc. Pharmaco-epidemiology (founding co-pres. 1990-91), Wake Count Med. Soc., Harvard Sch. Pub. Health Alumni Assn., Am. Assn. Pharm. Physicians (bd. dirs. 1994—, hon. life mem. 1994—). Democrat. Episcopalian. Home: 1116 Cowper Dr Raleigh NC 27608-2231 Office: Burroughs Wellcome Co 3030 W Cornwallis Rd Research Triangle Park NC 27709

TILSON, JOHN QUILLIN, lawyer; b. New Haven, Aug. 27, 1911; s. John Quillin and Catherine E. Jackson; m. Catherine E. Jackson, Sept. 14, 1934; children—John Quillin III, Thomas D., Rebecca E. Grad., Hotchkiss Sch., 1929; B.A., Yale, 1933, LL.B., 1936. Bar: Conn. bar 1936. Since practiced in New Haven; assoc. Wiggin & Dana, New Haven, 1936-48, ptnr., 1948—; lectr. hosp. law Yale Sch. Medicine, 1959—. Chmn. plan and zoning commn., Hamden, Conn., 1949-51; pres. Conn. Conf. Social Work, 1949-50; Bd. aldermen, New Haven, 1935-37; rep. Conn. Gen. Assembly, 1953; alternate Republican Nat. Conv., 1956, del., 1964; chmn. Hamden Rep. Town Com., 1964-68; Corporator Inst. Living, Hartford, 1959—; bd. dirs. New Haven Vis. Nurse Assn., New Haven United Fund; trustee Yale in China, 1936-62; bd. dirs. Yale New Haven Hosp., Yale Psychiat. Inst.; bd. dels. Am. Hosp. Assn. Served to lt. comdr. USNR, 1943-46, 51-53. Mem. ABA (del.), Conn. Bar Assn. (pres.), Internat. Bar Assn., Quinnipiack Club, Morys Club. Home: 88 Notch Hill Rd Apt 372 North Branford CT 06471-1853 Office: Wiggin & Dana 1 Century Tower New Haven CT 06510-7009

TILSON, M(ARTIN) DAVID, surgeon, scientist; b. Texarkana, Tex., Aug. 25, 1941; s. M. David and Leta (Martin) T.; m. Joan E. Stanescki, 1974; children: Martin David IV, William Thomas, John Wainwright. BA, Rice U., 1963; MD, Yale U., 1967. Diplomate Am. Bd. Surgery, Nat. Bd. Med. Examiners. Surg. intern Yale U., 1967-68; resident in surgery U. New Haven, 1968-72; asst. to assoc. prof. Yale U., New Haven, 1974-83, prof., 1983-89; Alisa Mellon Bruce prof. of surgery Columbia U., N.Y.C., 1989—; dir. surgery St. Lukes Roosvelt Hosp Ctr., N.Y.C., 1989—. Contbr. articles to profl. jours. Maj. USAF, 1972-74. Rsch. grantee NIH, 1983—. Mem. ACS, Soc. Univ. Surgeons, Am. Surg. Assn., Soc. Vascular Surgery, Internat. Soc. Cardiovascular Surgery, Halsted Soc., Med. Strollers. Office: St Lukes Roosevelt Hosp 1000 Tenth Ave New York NY 10019-1105

TILSON THOMAS, MICHAEL, symphony conductor; b. L.A., 1944; s. Ted and Roberta T. Studies with, Ingolf Dahl, U. So. Calif., others; student conducting, Berkshire Music Festival, Tanglewood, Mass.; student conducting (Koussevitzky prize 1968); LL.D., Hamilton Coll., L.H.D. (hon.), D'Youville Coll., 1976. Asst. condr. Boston Symphony Orch., 1969, assoc.

condr., 1970-72, prin. guest condr., 1972-74; also Berkshire Music Festival, summer 1970, 74; music dir., condr. Buffalo Philharmonic Orch., 1971-79; music dir., prin. condr. Great Woods Ctr. for Performing Arts, 1985-88; prin. condr. London Symphony Orch., 1988—; artistic dir. New World Symphony, Fla., 1988—. Condr. dir., N.Y. Philharmonic Young People's Concerts, CBS-TV, 1971-77; vis. condr. numerous orchs., U.S., Europe, Japan; chief condr. Ojai Festival, 1967, dir., 1972-77; opera debut, Cin., 1975; condr.: Am. premiere Lulu (Alban Berg), Santa Fe Opera, summer 1979; prin. guest condr., L.A. Philharm., 1981-85, Am. premiere Desert Music (Steve Reich), 1984; prin. condr. Gershwin festival London Symphony Orch., Barbcan Ctr., 1987; composer: Grace (A Song for Leonard Bernstein), 1988, Street Song (for Empire Brass Quintet), 1988, From the Diary of Anne Frank (for orchestra and narrator Audrey Hepburn and New World Symphony), 1990; commd. by UNICEF for Concerts for Life's Endangered premiere, 1991; recording artist Sony Classical/CBS Masterworks, 1973—; co-artistic dir. Pacific Music Festival, 1990—, with Leonard Bernstein 1st ann. Pacific Music Festival, Sapporo, Japan, 1990; co-artistic dir. 2d ann. Pacific Music festival, 1991, Salzburg Festival, 1991; conducted Mozart Requiem. Named Musician of Year, Musical Am. 1970; recipient Koussevitsky prize, 1968, Grammy award for Carmina Burana with Cleve. Orch., 1976, for Gershwin Live with Los Angeles Philharm., 1983, Grammy nomination, Best Classical Album - Debussy: Le Martyre de Saint Sebestien (with the London Symphony Orchestra), 1994. Office: 888 7th Ave Fl 37 New York NY 10106-0001 Office: San Francisco Symphony Davies Symphony Hall San Francisco CA 94102

TILSWORTH, TIMOTHY, retired environmental/civil engineering educator; b. Norfolk, Nebr., Apr. 6, 1939; s. Brooke and Mildred (Palmer) T.; m. Joanne Novak, Apr. 19, 1966 (div. Jan. 1984); children: Craig Scott, Patrick Joseph; m. Debbie J. May, July 20, 1984. BSCE, U. Nebr., Lincoln, 1966, MSCE, 1967; PhD, U. Kans, 1970. Registered profl. engr., Alaska; diplomate Inst. Hazardous Materials Mgmt. Instr. U. Nebr., Lincoln, 1967; prof. environ. quality and civil engring. U. Alaska, Fairbanks, 1970-94, dir. program environ. quality engring. and sci., 1972-76, 78-94, asst. to pres. for acad. affairs, 1976-78, head dept. civil engring, 1990-91, chmn. grad. coun., chmn. chancellor search com., 1990-91; co-owner Raven Press Pub. Co., Fairbanks, 1990—; prof. emeritus civil engring. and environ. quality engring., 1994—; res. faculty senate U. Alaska, 1992-93; owner Alaska Arctic Environ. Svcs., Fairbanks, 1972—, DJT's Shelties Delight, Fairbanks, 1985—, T2 Antiques, 1994—; project mgr. superconducting super collider proposal State of Alaska, Fairbanks, 1987-88. Chmn. exec. com. Cowper for Gov. Alaska, Fairbanks, 1986. Recipient commendation State of Alaska, 1988. Mem. Assn. for Environ. Engring. Profs., ASCE (Outstanding Service award 1975), Am. Water Works Assn. Water Pollution Control Fedn., Chi Epsilon. Roman Catholic. Home and Office: 1900 Raven Dr Fairbanks AK 99709-8358

TILTON, DAVID LLOYD, savings and loan association executive; b. Santa Barbara, Calif., Sept. 21, 1926; s. Lloyd Irving and Grace (Hart) T.; m. Mary Caroline Knudtson, June 6, 1953; children: Peter, Jennifer, Michael, Catharine. A.B., Stanford U., 1949, M.B.A., 1951. With Santa Barbara Savs. & Loan Assn., 1951-90, pres., 1965-84; now pres., vice chmn., bd. dir. Fin. Corp., Santa Barbara; bd. dirs. Sizzler Internat.; trustee, chmn. Calif. Real Estate Investment Trust, 1988. Served with USNR, World War II. Mem. Calif. Savs. and Loan League (dir. 1980), Delta Chi. Home: 630 Oak Grove Dr Santa Barbara CA 93108-1402 Office: 800 Santa Barbara St Santa Barbara CA 93101

TILTON, GEORGE ROBERT, geochemistry educator; b. Danville, Ill., June 3, 1923; s. Edgar Josiah and Caroline Lenore (Burkmeyer) T.; m. Elizabeth Jane Foster, Feb. 7, 1948; children—Linda Beth, Helen Elizabeth, Elaine Lee, David Foster, John Robert. Student, Blackburn Coll., 1940-42; B.S., U. Ill., 1947; Ph.D., U. Chgo., 1951; D.Sc. (hon.), Swiss Fed. Inst. Tech., Zurich, 1984. Phys. chemist Carnegie Instn., Washington, 1951-65; prof. geochemistry U. Calif.-Santa Barbara, 1965-91, emeritus, 1991—, chmn. dept. geol. scis., 1973-77; guest prof. Swiss Fed. Inst., Zurich, 1971-72; prin. investigator NSF research grant, 1965—; mem. earth scis. panel NSF, 1966-69, 82-85. Assoc. editor Jour. Geophys. Research, 1962-65, Geochimica et Cosmochimica Acta, 1973—; contbr. articles to profl. jours. Served with AUS, 1942-45. Decorated Purple Heart; recipient Sr. Scientist award Alexander von Humboldt Found., 1989. Fellow AAAS, Am. Geophys. Union, Geol. Soc. Am.; mem. Nat. Acad. Scis., Geochem. Soc. (pres. 1981), Sigma Xi. Episcopalian. Home: 3425 Madrona Dr Santa Barbara CA 93105-2652 Office: U Calif Dept Geol Scis Santa Barbara CA 93106

TILTON, GLENN F., oil company executive; b. Washington, Apr. 9, 1948. BA in Internat. Rels., U. S.C., 1970. Sales trainee U.S. mktg. ops. Texaco Inc., Washington, 1970; various assignments Texaco Inc., Washington, Pa., Conn., 1970-76; div. supr. mktg. Texaco Inc., East Brunswick, N.J., 1976-78; area mgr. resale N.Y. div. Texaco Inc., N.Y.C., 1978, asst. to gen. mgr. northeastern region, 1978-79; mktg. mgr. resale Phila. div. Texaco Inc., 1979-81; staff coord. corp. planning and econs. dept. Texaco Inc., Harrison, N.Y., 1981-83; asst. gen. mgr. sales Texaco Europe, 1983-84, gen. mgr. mktg., 1984-87; v.p. mktg. Texaco U.S.A., Houston, 1987-88; pres. Texaco Refining and Mktg. Inc., Houston, 1988-89; v.p. Texaco Inc., 1989—; chmn. Texaco Ltd., 1991-92; pres. Texaco Eruope, 1992-94, Texaco USA, Houston, 1994—. Office: TRMI Holdings Inc 1111 Bagby St Houston TX 77002

TILTON, JAMES FLOYD, theatrical designer, art director; b. Rochelle, Ill., July 30, 1937; s. Norval Bailey T. and Magdeline (Ripplinger) Marelli; m. Helga Strang, Dec. 26, 1962 (div. Nov. 1976). B.A., U. Iowa, 1959. Resident designer John Drew Theater, Easthampton, N.Y., 1963; prin. designer Assn. Producing Artists, N.Y.C., 1965-69, Phoenix Theatre, N.Y.C., 1970-80; freelance designer, 1963—; designer maj. indsl. shows Avon, Coca-Cola, ABC, NBC Affil., N.Y.C., 1974—; designer for TV, 1977—; designer mus. exhibits Guild Hall Mus., East Hampton, 1979—; set and lighting designer 30 Broadway shows including You Can't Take It With You, 1965, 83, Seascape (nomination for Antoinette Perry award), 1975. Served with U.S. Army, 1960-62. Recipient Carbonelle awards, 1987, 91, 92. Mem. United Scenic Artists 829. Democrat. Roman Catholic. Office: 10 W 15th St New York NY 10011-6752

TILTON, JOHN ELVIN, mineral economics educator; b. Brownsville, Pa., Sept. 16, 1939; s. John Elvin Sr. and Margaret Julia (Renn) T.; m. Elizabeth Martha Meier, June 18, 1966; children: Margaret Ann, John Christian. AB, Princeton U., 1961; PhD in Econs., Yale U., 1965. Staff analyst Office of Sec. of Def., Washington, 1965-67; rsch. assoc. Brookings Inst., Washington, 1967-70; asst. prof. econs. U. Md., College Park, 1970-72; assoc. prof. mineral econs. Pa. State U., University Park, 1972-75, prof., 1975-85; Coulter prof. Colo. Sch. Mines, Golden, 1985-94, dir. Divsn. Econs. and Bus., 1994—; officer econ. affairs commodities divsn. UN Conf. on Trade and Devel., Geneva, 1977; leader rsch. Internat. Inst. Applied Systems Analysis, Laxenburg, Austria, 1982-84; joint dir. mineral econs. and policy Program of Resources for Future, Colo. Sch. Mines, Washington, 1982—; vice chmn. bd. mineral and energy resources NRC, Washington, 1980-83, mem. nat. materials adv. bd., 1987-89. Author: International Diffusion of Technology, 1971, The Future of Nonfuel Minerals, 1977; editor: Material Substitution, 1983, World Metal Demand, 1990, Mineral Wealth and Economic Development, 1992; co-editor: Economics of Mineral Exploration, 1987, Competitiveness in Metals, 1992. Capt. U.S. Army, 1965-67. Fulbright scholar Ecole Nat. Supérieure des Mines de Paris, 1992. Mem. Am. Econ. Assn., Am. Inst. Mining Metall. and Petroleum Engrs. (Mineral Econs. award 1985), Mineral Econs. and Mgmt. Soc. (pres. 1993-94), Mining and Metall. Soc. Am. Avocations: skiing, hiking. Office: Colo Sch Mines Divsn Econs and Bus Golden CO 80401

TILY, STEPHEN BROMLEY, III, bank executive; b. Phila., July 7, 1937; s. Stephen Bromley Jr. and Edith Helen (Straub) T.; m. Janet Anita Walz, July 10, 1965; children: Deborah Powell, Stephen Bromley IV, James Charles II. BS in Econs., Washington and Jefferson Coll., 1960; postgrad., Temple U., 1963. Trust officer Indsl. Valley Bank & Trust Co., Phila., 1968-71; v.p. Farmers Bank of Delaware, Wilmington, 1971-77; exec. officer G&T, Inc. Ltd., Wilmington, 1977-80; pres., COO DCG&T Co., Wilmington, 1977-91, chmn., CEO, 1991-93, chmn. emeritus, 1993—; chmn. The Declaration Group, Conshohocken, Pa., 1985—; tchr. Am. Inst. Banking, 1970-79. Capt.

USAR, 1960-61. Mem. Fin. Analysts of Wilmington, Internat. Assn. Fin. Planning, Barnegat Light Yacht Club (commodore 1988-89, trustee 1989-92), Kimberton Fish and Game Assn., Waynesborough Country Club, Union League Club of Phila., Merion Golf Club, Ducks Unltd. Republican. Episcopalian. Office: The Declaration Group 555 North Ln Ste 6160 Conshohocken PA 19428

TIMBERG, SIGMUND, lawyer; b. Antwerp, Belgium, Mar. 5, 1911; came to U.S., 1916, naturalized, 1921; s. Arnold and Rose (Mahler) T.; m. Eleanor Ernst, Sept. 22, 1940; children—Thomas Arnold, Bernard Mahler, Rosamund and Richard Ernst (twins). A.B., Columbia U., 1930, A.M., 1930, LL.B., 1933. Bar: N.Y. 1935, U.S. Supreme Ct. 1940, D.C. 1954. Sr. atty., solicitors' office Dept. Agr., 1933-35, chief, soil conservation sect., 1935-38; staff mem. Temporary Nat. Econ. Com., 1938-39; sr. atty. SEC, 1938-42; chief, property relations and indsl. orgn. div., reoccupation br. Bd. Econ. Warfare and Fgn. Econ. Adminstrn., 1942-44; spl. asst. to atty. gen., antitrust div. Dept. Justice, 1944-45, chief judgments and judgment enforcement sect., 1946-52; sec. UN Com. on Restrictive Bus. Practices, 1952-53; cons. UN, 1953-55, 62-64; pvt. law practice, 1954-88; prof. law Georgetown U. Law School, 1952-54; faculty Parker Sch. Comparative Law, Columbia U., 1967-80; spl. counsel Senate Mil. Affairs Subcom. on Surplus Property Legislation, 1944; mem. Mission for Econ. Affairs, Am. Embassy, London, 1945; del. Anglo-Am. Telecommunications Conf., Bermuda, 1945, Geneva Copyright Conf., 1952; cons. Senate Patents Subcom., 1961, UN Patents Study, 1962-64, OAS, 1970; mem. adv. com. on fed. policy on indsl. innovation, patent and info. policy sub com., 1978-79, adv. com. on internat. investment, tech. and devel., 1979-85. Contbr. articles on antitrust, intellectual property and internat. law to legal periodicals. Mem. ABA, D.C. Bar Assn., Internat. Bar Assn., Internat. Law Assn., Am. Soc. Internat. Law, Washington Fgn. Law Soc., Am. Law Inst., Assn. Bar City N.Y., Copyright Soc. Am., Cosmos Club (Washington), Philosophy Club (Washington). Home: 3519 Porter St NW Washington DC 20016-3177

TIMBERLAKE, CHARLES EDWARD, history educator; b. South Shore, Ky., Sept. 9, 1935; s. Howard Ellis and Mabel Viola (Collier) T.; m. Patricia Alice Perkins, Dec. 23, 1958; children: Mark Brewster, Daniel Edward, Eric Collier. BA, Berea Coll., 1957; Calif. State Teaching Credential, Claremont Grad. Sch., 1958, MA, 1962; PhD, U. Wash., 1968. Tchr. Barstow High Sch., Calif., 1959-60, Claremont City Sch., Calif., 1960-61; teaching, rsch. asst. U. Wash., Seattle, 1961-64; asst. prof. history U. Mo., Columbia, 1967-73, assoc. prof., 1973-81, prof., 1981—, asst. dir. Honors Coll., 1988-90; exch. prof. Moscow State U., 1985, U. Manchester, Eng., 1987-88; hon. prof. history Lanzhou U., People's Republic of China, 1991; edn. coord. Revalba Russian River Cruises, 1992—. Editor: Essays on Russian Liberalism, 1972, Detente: A Documentary Record, 1978, Religious and Secular Forces in Late Tsarist Russia, 1992, Profiles of Finland series, 1991-94, (microfiche) The St. Petersburg Collection of Zemstvo Publs., 1992—; contbr. chpts. to books, articles to profl. jours. Mem. Citizens Alliance for Progress, Columbia, Mo., 1969-75, pres., 1969-70; founding mem. High Edn. Rescue Operation, Mo., 1983—; mem. Columbians Against Throw-Aways, 1980-83. Fgn. Area fellow, 1965-66, Am. Coun. Learned Socs. fellow, 1978-79; NEH grantee, 1972, 79, 87. Mem. Am. Assn. Advancement Slavic Studies (bd. dirs. 1980-82, 84-86, chmn. council regional affiliates 1981-82, 85-86, chmn. permanent membership com. 1981-84), Western Slavic Conf., Am. Hist. Assn. (exec. council Conf. on Slavic and East European History 1987-89), Central Slavic Conf. (sec.-treas. 1967-68, pres. 1968-69, 76-77, 83-84, 88-89, exec. bd. 1972—, custodian archive 1972—), Mo. Conf. History (pres. 1992), State Hist. Soc. Mo., Rocky Mountain Assn. Slavic Studies. Avocations: backpacking, travel, skiing. Home: 9221 S Rte N Columbia MO 65203-9312 Office: U Mo Dept History Columbia MO 65211

TIMBERS, MICHAEL JAMES, information technology executive; b. Evanston, Ill., Dec. 30, 1941; s. James G. Timbers and Betty (Aalseth) Fink; m. Frances D. Layer, Dec. 16, 1961; children—Michael J., Kenneth A., Suzanne T. B.S., U. Va., 1963; M.B.A., NYU, 1969. Cert. profl. contracts mgr. Mgr. mgmt. adv. services Price Waterhouse, Washington, 1968-72; dir. purchasing So. Ry. Co., Washington, 1969-72; commr. GSA, Washington, 1972-75; pres. Washington Mgmt. Group, 1975-81, pres., CEO Info. Handling Services, Englewood, Colo., 1981—. Chmn., bd. dirs. AVO Internat., bd. dirs. Colo. Uplift, 1984. Served to lt. U.S. Army, 1964-66. Mem. Info. Industry Assn. (com. chair 1984), Internat. Info. Mgmt. Congress (bd. dirs.), Assn. Info. and Image Mgmt. (bd. dirs.), Computer and Bus. Equipment Mfrs. Assn. (bd. dirs.). Republican. Roman Catholic. Clubs: Merion Golf (Ardmore, Pa.), Farmington (Charlottesville, Va.), Congl. Country (Bethesda, Md.), Castle Pines (Castle Rock, Colo.), Cherry Hills (Englewood). Home: 2500 E Quincy Ave Englewood CO 80110-4919 Office: Info Handling Svcs Inc PO Box 1154 15 Inverness Way E Englewood CO 80150

TIMBERS, STEPHEN BRYAN, financial services company executive; b. Madison, Wis., Aug. 8, 1944; s. James G. Timbers and Betty A. (Aalseth) Fink; m. Joan Phillips (div.); 1 child, Alexander C. A.; m. Elaine C. Mack, Nov. 17, 1990; children: Christopher B., Brendan C. AB in English Lit., Yale U., 1966; MBA, Harvard U., 1968. Portfolio strategist Mutual Life Ins. Co. of N.Y., N.Y.C., 1970-81; sr. portfolio mgr. Smith Barney, Harris Upham & Co., N.Y.C., 1981-84; chief investment officer The Portfolio Group, Inc., N.Y.C., 1984-87, Kemper Fin. Svcs., Inc., Chgo., 1987-92; pres., COO Kemper Corp., Long Grove, Ill., 1992—; bd. dirs. Kemper Corp. and Affiliates, LTV Corp., Gillett Holdings, Inc.; trustee Kemper Mutual Funds and Seperate Accounts; mem. NYSE Panel on Market Volatility and Investor Confidence, N.Y.C., 1990. Mgr. Yale Alumni Fund, Harvard Bus. Sch. Alumni Fund. With U.S. Army, 1968-70. Mem. Investment Analysts Soc. Chgo. (dir.), N.Y. Soc. Security Analysts, The Yale Club of N.Y.C., The Economic Club of Chgo. (membership com. 1990), Chgo. Club, Glen View Club, The Attic, The Racquet Club of Chgo. Office: Kemper Corp 1 Kemper Dr Long Grove IL 60049-0001

TIMBERS, WILLIAM HOMER, JR., nuclear fuel company executive; b. N.Y.C., Nov. 10, 1949; s. William Homer and Charlotte McLaughlin (Tanner) T.; m. Jeannette Amalie Mattson, July 14, 1979; children: Lisa Allison, Colin Mattson, Alexander Arms. BA, Allegheny Coll., Meadville, Pa., 1972; MBA, U. Pa., 1976. Assoc. Smith Barney, Harris Upham, N.Y.C., 1976-78, 2nd v.p., 1978-80, v.p., 1980-83; mng. dir. Western region Smith Barney, Harris Upham, San Francisco, 1983-86; mng. dir. Smith Barney, Harris Upham, N.Y.C., 1986-91; pres., CEO Timbers Corp., Stamford, Conn., 1991-93; apptd. transition mgr. by U.S. Pres. William J. Clinton U.S. Enrichment Corp., Washington, 1993-94; pres., CEO U.S. Enrichment Corp., Bethesda, Md., 1994—. Mem. Nuclear Energy Inst. (mem. com. 1993—). Home: 884 Oenoke Ridge New Canaan CT 06840 Office: US Enrichment Corp 6903 Rockledge Dr Bethesda MD 20817

TIMINSKI, ROBERT, sporting goods store executive. Exec. v.p., chief mdse., adminstrv. officer Herman's Sporting Goods, Carteret, N.J. Office: Herman's Sporting Goods Inc 2 Germak Dr Carteret NJ 07008-1291

TIMKEN, W. ROBERT, JR., manufacturing company executive; b. 1938; married. B.A., Stanford U., 1960; M.B.A., Harvard U., 1962. With Timken Co. (formerly The Timken Roller Bearing Co.), Canton, Ohio, 1962—, asst. v.p. sales, 1964-65, dir. corp. devel., 1965-68, v.p., 1968-73, vice-chmn. bd., chmn. fin. com., 1973-75, chmn. bd., chmn. fin. com., 1975—, chmn. exec. com., 1983—, also dir. Office: Timken Co 1835 Dueber Ave SW Canton OH 44706-2798

TIMLIN, JAMES CLIFFORD, bishop; b. Scranton, Pa., Aug. 5, 1927; s. James C. and Helen E. (Norton) T. A.B., St. Mary's Sem., Balt., 1948; S.T.B., Gregorian U., Rome, Italy, 1950. Ordained priest Roman Catholic Ch., 1951; asst. pastor St. John the Evangelist Ch., Pittston, Pa., 1952-53, St. Peter's Cathedral, Scranton, Pa., 1953-66; asst. chancellor, sec. Diocese of Scranton, 1966-71, chancellor, 1971-77, aux. bishop, vicar gen., 1976-84; pastor Ch. of Nativity, Scranton, 1979-84; bishop Diocese of Scranton, 1984—. Address: 300 Wyoming Ave Scranton PA 18503-1224*

TIMM, LAURANCE MILO, musician, educator; b. Sioux City, Iowa, Jan. 21, 1949; s. Everett Leroy and Margaret Jeanne (Anderson) T.; m. Carol Yvonne Smith, Aug. 14, 1976; 1 child, Monique Angelique. MusB, La. State U., 1971; MusM, Yale U., 1973, M. in Mus. Arts, 1974, D. Mus. Arts, 1981.

Asst. prof. music Univ. S.C., Columbia, 1974-77; prin. oboist Columbia Philharm., 1974-77, Charleston (S.C.) Symphony Orch., 1974-77; prof. Calif. State Univ., Fullerton, 1977—; prin. oboist Pacific Symphony, Orange County, Calif., 1979-86, Long Beach (Calif.) Symphony, 1980—, Los Angeles Opera Orch., 1984-86; substitute prin. oboist Los Angeles Philharm., Los Angeles Chamber Orch., Los Angeles Music Ctr. Opera; soloist chamber music recital, Alice Tully Hall, Lincoln Ctr., N.Y.C., 1988; freelance rec. artist 20th Century Fox, Paramount, Metro-Goldwyn-Mayer, NBC, ABC, CBS, Columbia Pictures, Touchstone Pictures, Burbank and Hollywood, Calif., 1978—; adj. prof. oboe Occidental Coll., Los Angeles, 1979—, Pomona Coll., 1991—. Contbr. articles to Woodwind, Brass and Percussion mag., 1983-86. Faculty advisor Phi Mu Alpha. Mem. Internat. Double Reed Soc., Soc. for the Preservation of Film Music, Pi Kappa Lambda, Omicron Delta Kappa, Phi Kappa Phi, Phi Eta Sigma, Mu Sigma Rho. Republican. Roman Catholic. Avocations: collecting books, film soundtracks, traveling, reading, swimming. Home: 636 E 9th St Upland CA 91786-5344 Office: Calif State Univ 800 N State College Blvd Fullerton CA 92631-3599

TIMME, KATHRYN PEARL, secondary education educator; b. Houston, Feb. 15, 1934; d. William Emil and Neoma Leila (Harvey) T. BA, Rice U., 1956; MA, U. Houston, 1965. Cert. secondary tchr., Tex. Tchr. Houston Ind. Sch. Dist., 1956—; rsch. fellow Houston Maths. and Sci. Consortium, 1986-87. Author: Horticultural Chemistry, 1976, Chemistry of The Sea, 1977, Textile Chemistry, 1978, Geochemistry, 1982, Exploring Electrolytes, 1987. Grantee NSF, 1970, 72, Houston Bus. Com., 1987, Impact II, 1989. Mem. Am. Chem. Soc., Phi Beta Kappa (Rice chpt.), Phi Alpha Theta. Episcopalian. Avocation: animal rights projects. Office: Robert E Lee High Sch 6529 Beverlyhill St Houston TX 77057-6499

TIMMER, BARBARA, lawyer; b. Holland, Mich., Dec. 13, 1946; d. John Norman and Barbara Dee (Folensbee) T. BA, Hope Coll., Holland, Mich., 1969; JD, U. Mich., 1975. Bar: Mich. 1975, U.S. Supreme Ct. Assoc. McCrosky, Libner, VanLeuven, Muskegon, Mich., 1975-78; apptd. to Mich. Women Commn. by Gov., 1976-79; staff counsel subcom. commerce, consumer & monetary affairs Ho. Govt. Ops. Com., 1979-82, 85-86; exec. v.p. NOW, 1982-84; legis. asst. to Rep. Geraldine Ferraro, 1984; atty. Office Gen. Counsel Fed. Home Loan Bank Bd., 1986-89; gen. counsel Com. on Banking, Fin. and Urban affairs U.S. Ho. of Reps., Washington, 1989-92; asst. gen. counsel, dir. govt. affairs ITT Corp., Washington, 1992—; bd. dirs. ITT Fed. Bank, San Francisco. Recipient Affordable Housing award Nat. Assn. Real Estate Brokers, 1990, Acad. of Women Achievers, YWCA, 1993. Mem. ABA (bus. law, exec. coun. adminstrv. law and regulatory practice sects.), Mich. Bar Assn., Fed. Bar Assn. (exec. coun. of banking law com.), Bar of Surpreme Ct., Women in Housing and Fin. (bd. dirs. 1992-94, gen. counsel 1994—), Supreme Ct. Hist. Soc. Episcopalian. Office: ITT Corp 1600 M St NW Washington DC 20036

TIMMER, CHARLES PETER, agricultural economist; b. Troy, Ohio, July 29, 1941; s. Thomas Gerhart and Rose Marie (Hoffman) T.; m. Carol Falb, Aug. 31, 1963; children: Anne Carol, Ashley Susan. A.B. in Econs. magna cum laude, Harvard U., 1963, Ph.D. in Econs, 1969. Commodity analyst W.R. Grace and Co., N.Y.C., 1964-66; asst. prof. Food Research Inst., Stanford U., 1968-74, assoc. prof., 1974-75; econ. adv. Indonesian Nat. Planning Agy., Harvard Adv. Group, Jakarta, 1970-71; H.E. Babcock prof. food econs. Cornell U., 1975-77; prof. econs. of food and agr. Sch. Public Health Harvard U., Cambridge, Mass., 1977-80, John D. Black prof. agr. and bus., 1980-86, prof. devel. studies at large, 1986-88, Thomas D. Cabot prof. devel. studies, at large, 1988—; Hibbard lectr. U. Wis., 1993; cons. on food and agr. Author: (with others) Choice of Technology in Developing Countries, 1975, (with Perkins et al) Small Scale Rural Industry in the People's Republic of China, 1977, (with Falcon and Pearson) Food Policy Analysis, 1983, (with Nelson et al) Food Aid and Development, 1981, Getting Prices Right: Scope and Limits of Agricultural Price Policy, 1986; editor, contbg. author: Rice Policy in Indonesia, 1974, The Political Economy of Rice in Asia, 1976, The Corn Economy of Indonesia, 1987, Agriculture and the State: Growth, Employment, and Poverty in Developing Countries, 1991. Recipient Bintang Jasa Utama medal Govt. Indonesia, 1992; John Harvard scholar, 1960-63; Fulbright fellow, 1963-64; NSF fellow, 1966-68. Mem. Am. Econ. Assn., Am. Agrl. Econs. Assn., AAAS, Phi Beta Kappa. Home: 15 Winnetaska Rd Newton MA 02168-1424 Office: Harvard U Inst for Internat Devel 1 Eliot St Cambridge MA 02138-5781

TIMMER, WAYNE F., architectural firm executive. BA in Pre-Architecture with High Honors, Clemson U., 1972; MArch in Urban Design, Rice U., 1975, MArch, 1978. Registered architect, Miss.; cert. Nat. Coun. Archtl. Registration Bds. Asst. planner/programmer Caudill, Rowlett, and Scott, Architects and Engrs., Houston, 1975; sr. planner divsn. urban design Oklahoma City Dept. Planning, 1976-78; project architect Barlow and Plunkett, Architects and Engrs., Jackson, Miss., 1978-83; prin., project mgr. WFT Architects, P.A., Jackson, Miss., 1983—; adj. prof. sch. architecture Miss. State U., 1981—. Mem. adv. com. neighborhood revitalization City of Jackson, 1988, mem. history city hall com., 1990; mem. Save Hist. Burwell Ho. Com., 1990-91; mem. Jackson Hist. Preservation Commn., 1990—; chmn., 1990, 91. Rsch. fellow Rice U. Mem. AIA (Miss. chpt., bd. dirs. 1992-93, sec./treas. 1994, 2d v.p. 1995), Nat. Trust Hist. Preservation, Tau Sigma Delta, Phi Kappa Phi. Office: WFT Architects PA PO Box 12344 Jackson MS 39236-2344

TIMMERHAUS, KLAUS DIETER, chemical engineering educator; b. Mpls., Sept. 10, 1924; s. Paul F. and Elsa L. (Bever) T.; m. Jean L. Mevis, Aug. 3, 1952; 1 dau., Carol Jane. BS in Chem. Engring. U. Ill., 1948, MS, 1949, PhD, 1951. Registered profl. engr., Colo. Process design engr. Calif. Rsch. Corp., Richmond, 1952-53; extension lectr. U. Calif., Berkeley, 1952; mem. faculty U. Colo., Boulder, 1953—, prof. chem. engring., 1961—, asso. dean engring., 1963-86, dir. engring. rsch. ctr. coll. engring., 1963-86, chmn. aerospace dept., 1979-80, chmn. chem. engring. dept., 1986-89, Patten Chair Disting. prof., 1986—; presdl. teaching scholar, 1989—; mem. engr. cryogenics lab. Nat. Bur. Standards, Boulder, summers 1955,57,59,61; lectr. U. Calif. at L.A., 1964-62; sect. head engring. div. NSF, 1972-73; cons. in field. Bd. dirs. Colo. Engring. Expt. Sta., Inc., Engring. Measurements Co., both Boulder. Editor: Advances in Cryogenic Engineering, vols. 1-25, 1954-80; co-editor: Internat. Cryogenic Monograph Series, 1965—. Served with USNR, 1944-46. Recipient Disting. Svc. award Dept. Commerce, 1957, Samuel C. Collins award for outstanding contbrs. to cryogenic tech., 1967, George Westinghouse award, 1968, Alpha Chi Sigma award for chem. engring. rsch., 1968, Meritorious Svc. award Cryogenic Engring. Conf., 1987, Disting. Pub. Svc. award NSF, 1984; named CASE Colo. Prof. of Yr., 1993. Fellow AAAS (Southwestern and Rocky Mountain divsn. Pres.'s award 1989), Internat. Inst. Refrigeration (v.p. 1979-87, pres. 1987-95, U.S. nat. commn. 1983—), pres. 1983-86, W.T. Pentzer award 1989), Am. Inst. Chem. Engrs. (v.p. 1975, pres. 1976, Founders award 1978, Eminent Chem. Engr. award 1983, W. K. Lewis award 1987, F. J. Van Antwerpen award 1991), Am. Soc. for Engring Edn. (bd. dirs. 1986-88, 3M Chem. Engring. divsn. award 1980, Engring Rsch. Council award 1990, Delos Svc. award 1991); mem. NAE, Am. Astron. Soc., Austrian Acad. Sci., Cryogenic Engring. Conf. (chmn. 1956-67, bd. dirs. 1956—), Soc. Automotive Engrs. (Ralph Teetor award 1991), Sigma Xi (v.p. 1986-87, pres. 1987-88, bd. dirs. 1981-89), Sigma Tau, Tau Beta Pi, Phi Lambda Upsilon. Home: 905 Brooklawn Dr Boulder CO 80303-2708

TIMMONS, EARL L., oil company executive; b. Berlin, Md., Jan. 24, 1937; s. William Earl and Mary (Lang) T.; m. Rosalie K. Timmons; children: Earl Jr., Lori Ann. BSBA, U. Md., 1960. V.p., controller Conoco Inc., Houston. Mem. Am. Petroleum Inst. (acctg. com.). Office: E I DuPont Nemours & Co 1007 N Market St Rm 8000D Wilmington DE 19898

TIMMONS, EDWIN O'NEAL, psychologist; b. West Point, Ga., May 12, 1928; s. Robert A. and Lois O. T.; m. Mary Birmingham, June 21, 1952; children: Robert A., Laura W., Jenny O., William B. B.S., Auburn U., 1951; M.A., U. Tenn., 1956, Ph.D., 1959. Staff psychologist Tuscaloosa (Ala.) VA Hosp., 1956-59; clin. psychologist Gulfport (Miss.) VA Hosp., 1960-61; asso. prof., then Alumni prof. psychology La. State U., 1961-78, prof. bus. adminstrn. and Alumni prof. psychology, 1978-83; mem. faculty Sch. Banking of South, 1975—; prin. Timmons & Assos. (Psychol. Cons.), Baton Rouge; mem. faculty So. Meth. U. Grad. Sch. Banking, 1976-83. Author

TV-based tng. series on sales, mgmt., human rels., 1979. Served with U.S. Army, 1946-48, 51-53. Mem. Am. Psychol. Assn., La. Psychol. Assn., Southeastern Psychol. Assn., AAAS, AAUP, Sigma Xi. Office: 505 L S U Ave Baton Rouge LA 70808-4643 *Assume we have a given amount of elan vital. If we overinvest it in the past, we reap guilt over what we should or shouldn't have done. If we overinvest it in the future, we gain anxiety over what may happen. How better to invest it mainly in the here-and-now, to live the most fully human life possible for each of us.*

TIMMONS, EVELYN DEERING, pharmacist; b. Durango, Colo., Sept. 29, 1926; d. Claude Elliot and Evelyn Allen (Gooch) Deering; m. Richard Palmer Timmons, Oct. 4, 1952 (div. 1968); children: Roderick Deering, Steven Palmer. BS in Chemistry and Pharmacy cum laude, U. Colo., 1948. Chief pharmacist Meml. Hosp., Phoenix, 1950-54; med. lit. rsch. librarian Hoffman-LaRoche, Inc., Nutley, N.J., 1956-57; staff pharmacist St. Joseph's Hosp., Phoenix, 1958-60; relief mgr. various ind. apothecaries, Phoenix, 1960-68; asst. then mgr. Profl. Pharmacies, Inc., Phoenix, 1968-72; mgr. then owner Mt. View Pharmacy, Phoenix and Paradise Valley, Ariz., 1972—; pres. Ariz. Apothecaries, Ltd., Phoenix, 1976—; mem. profl. adv. bd., bereavement counselor Hospice of Valley, 1983—; mem. profl. adv. bd. Upjohn Health Care and Svcs., Phoenix, 1984-86; bd. dirs. Am. Council on Pharm. Edn., Chgo., 1986-92, v.p. 1988, 89, treas., 1990-91. Author poetry; contbr. articles to profl. jours. Mem. Scottsdale (Ariz.) Fedn. Rep. Women, 1963; various other offices Rep. Fedn.; mem. platform com. State of Ariz., Nat. Rep. Conv., 1964; asst. sec. Young Rep. Nat. Fedn., 1963-65; active county and state Rep. coms.; fin. chmn. Internat. Leadership Symposium:Woman in Pharmacy, London, 1987; treas. Leadership Internat. Women Pharmacy, 1991—. Named Outstanding Young Rep. of Yr., Nat. Fedn. Young Reps., 1965, Preceptor of Yr., U. Ariz./Syntex, 1984; recipient Disting. Public Svc. award Maricopa County Med. Soc., 1962, Disting. Alumni award Wasatch Acad., 1982, Career Achievement award, 1983, Leadership and Achievement award Upjohn Labs., 1985-86, Outstanding Achievement in Profession award Merck, Sharp & Dohme, 1986, award of Merit, 1988, Disting. Coloradoan award U. Colo., 1989, Vanguard award, 1991. Fellow Am. Coll. of Apothecaries (v.p. 1982-83, pres. 1984-85; chmn. bd. dirs. 1985-86, adv. council 1986—, Chmn. of Yr. 1980-81 Victor H. Morganroth award 1985, J. Leon Lascoff award 1990); mem. Ariz. Soc. of Hosp. Pharmacists, Am. Pharm. Assn. (Daniel B. Smith award 1990), Ariz. Pharmacy Assn. (Svc. to Pharmacy award 1976, Pharmacist of Yr. 1981, Bowl of Hygeia 1989, 1st Innovative Pharmacy award 1994), Maricopa County Pharmacy Assn. (pres. 1977, Svc. to Pharmacy award 1977), Am. Soc. of Hosp. Pharmacists, Aux. to County Med. Soc. (pres. 1967-68), Am. Aircraft Owners and Pilots Assn., Air Safety Found., Nat. Assn. of Registered Parliamentarians, Kappa Epsilon (recipient Career Achievement award 1986, Vanguard award 1991, Unicorn award 1993). Lodge: Civinettes (pres. Scottsdale chpt. 1960-61). Avocations: flying, skiing, swimming, backpacking, hiking. Office: Mt View Pharmacy 10565 N Tatum Blvd Suite B-118 Paradise Valley AZ 85253

TIMMONS, GERALD DEAN, pediatric neurologist; b. Rensselaer, Ind., June 1, 1931; s. Homer Timmons and Tamma Mildred (Spall) Rodgers; m. Lynne Rita Matrisciano, May 29, 1982; 1 child, Deanna Lynne; children from previous marriage: Jane Christina Timmons Mitchell, Ann Elizabeth, Mary Catherine. AB, Ind. U., 1953, MD, 1956. Diplomate Am. Bd. Psychiatry and Neurology. Intern Lima (Ohio) Meml. Hosp., 1956-57; resident Ind. U. Hosp., Indpls., 1957-59, 61-62; instr. neurology dept. Ind. U., Indpls., 1962-64; practice medicine specializing in psychiatry and neurology Indpls., 1962-64; practice medicine specializing in pediatric neurology Akron, Ohio, 1964—; chief pediatric neurology Children's Hosp. Med. Ctr., Akron, 1964—; chmn. neurology subcouncil Coll. Medicine Northeastern Ohio Univs., Rootstown, 1978—; chief examiner Am. Bd. Neurology and Psychiatry. Contbr. articles to profl. and scholarly jours. Served to capt. USAF, 1959-61. Mem. Summit County Med. Soc., Ohio Med. Soc., AMA, Am. Acad. Pediatrics, Am. Acad. Neurology (practice com. 1980-86), Child Neurology Soc. (chmn. honors and awards com. 1978—), Am. Soc. Internal Medicine, Am. Electroencephalographic Soc. Republican. Methodist. Office: Akron Pediatric Neurology 300 Locust St Ste 460 Akron OH 44302-1804

TIMMONS, GLENN F., church administrator. Grn. sec. Parish Ministries Commn. of the Ch. of the Brethren. Office: Ch of the Brethren 1451 Dundee Ave Elgin IL 60120

TIMMONS, JOSEPH DEAN, insurance company executive; b. Hays, Kans., Feb. 27, 1948; s. Charles Everett and Darwina Marcella (Riedel) T.; m. Sharon Lucile Manley, June 6, 1970; children: Stacia Katherine, Mathew Joseph. BA, U. Kans., Lawrence, 1972. CPCU. Asst. mgr. Rusty's IGA, Lawrence, Kans., 1971-72, Manley Mailing Service, Kans. City, 1972-74, acting dept. mgr. Midwestern Gen. Agy., Inc., Kans. City, 1974-77, v.p., 1977-79; pres. Midwestern Gen. Agy., Inc., Kansas City, Mo., 1979—, ARS Mgmt. Corp., Kans. City, 1979—, Midwestern Mutual Casualty Ins. Co., 1979—, Midwestern Gen. Agy., Inc., Kans. City, 1979—, Agy. Mgmt. Corp., Kans. City, 1979—; chmn. of the bd. Garry & Assocs., Kansas City, Mo., 1986—; officer Hon. Honor of Blue Goose, Heart of Am. Pond, Kansas City, Mo., 1986—; bd. dirs. Union Bank, Kansas City; chmn. bd. Midwestern Gen. Brokerage, Kansas City. Contbr. articles to profl. jours. Scout leader Troop 109 Boy Scouts Am., Kansas City, 1985—, coun. chmn., 1989-91, Tribe of MIC-O-SAY Warrior, 1991. Mem. NAt. Assn. Profl. Surplus Lines Offices (bd. dirs. 1986-92, Pres. Cup award 1988, pres. edn. found. 1991-92), Am. Assn. Mng. Agts. (bd. dirs. Kansas City 1981-83, 84-86), Surplus LInes Assn. Mo. (bd. dirs. 1979-80, 81-83, 85-89), Nat. Honor Soc. Avocations: stamp collecting, coin collecting, racquetball. Office: Midwestern Gen Agy Inc 255 NW Blue Pky Lees Summit MO 64063-1869

TIMMONS, STEVE (RED), volleyball player; b. Newport Beach, Calif., Nov. 29, 1958. BA in Comm., U. So. Calif., 1982. Mem. U.S.A. Nat. Olympic Volleyball Team, 1983-88, 92; founder, creator volleyball clothing Redsand, 1985—; profl. volleyball tour player U.S., Il Messaggero, Italian Profl. League, Ravenna. Recipient Gold medal Olympics, 1984, 88, Bronze medal Olympics, 1992; named Most Valuable Player U.S.A. Olympic Volleyball Team, 1984. Mem. Assn. Volleyball Profls. Career-high second at 1991 Off Shore Manhattan Beach Open, 1991; only 3-time Olympic medal winner; led U.S.A. Nat. Team to bronze medal finish Olympics, Barcelona, Spain, 1992, gold medal finishes, 1984, 88; led U.S.A. Nat. Team to first Triple Crown-1984 Olympics, 1985 World Cup, 1986 World Championships; led Il Messaggero to team title, 1991, 2d place finish, 1992; team capt. Team Cup Volleyball champions, 1992; team capt. Team Coca-Cola Superstars Competition, 1993-94. Office: c/o Assn Volleyball Profls 15260 Ventura Blvd Ste 2250 Sherman Oaks CA 91003*

TIMMONS, WILLIAM EVAN, corporate executive; b. Chattanooga, Dec. 27, 1930; s. Owen Walter and Doris (Eckenrod) T.; m. Mimi Bakshian, Sept. 28, 1966; children: Karen Leigh, Kimberly Anne, William Evan. Grad., Baylor Mil. Acad., Chattanooga, 1949; B.S. in Fgn. Service, Georgetown U., 1959; postgrad., George Washington U., 1959-61. Aide to U.S. Senator Alexander Wiley, 1955-62; adminstrv. asst. to U.S. Rep. William Brock, 1963-69; dep. asst. to Pres. Richard M. Nixon, 1969-70, asst., 1970-74; asst. to Pres. Gerald R. Ford, 1974; pres. Timmons & Co. Inc., 1975-86, chmn. exec. com., 1986—; mem. Fed. Property Rev. Bd., 1972-75, Pres.'s Trade Adv. Com., 1975-80; U.S. del. to Internat. Conf. on Viet Nam, Paris, 1973. Exec. dir. Tenn. Republican Com., 1962; mgr. Brock campaigns, 1962, 64, 66, 68; dir. congl. relations Nixon-Agnew campaign, 1968; coordinator Nixon for Pres.; Rep. Nat. Conv., Miami, Fla., 1968, 72; dir. Pres. Ford com. Rep. Nat. Conv., Kansas City, 1976; nat. conv. dir. Reagan for Pres. Com., Detroit, 1980, Dallas, 1984; mem. adv. com. Rep. Nat. Com. Conv., New Orleans, 1988; mem. exec. com. Nat. Young Reps., 1965-67; nat. polit. dir. Reagan for Pres. Com., 1980; dep. dir. for transition Office of Pres.-Elect, 1980-81; presdl. appointee U.S.-Japan Adv. Commn., 1983-85; mem. faculty Nat. Rep. campaign workshops, 1963-69; bd. dirs. Radio Free Europe/Liberty, 1975-82, Georgetown U. Ctr. Strategic and Internat. Studies, 1982-85; sr. adviser Bush for Pres. Com., New Orleans, 1988. Served with USAF, 1951-55. Named Outstanding Young Rep. of Year Nat. Rep. Com., 1965; recipient 1970 Ann. Achievement award Georgetown Alumni Club; citation for Disting. Service Baylor Mil. Acad. Alumni Assn., 1970. Mem. Soc. of the Cin., Columbia Country Club, George Towne Club, F Street Club, City Club, St. Alban's Tennis Club, Sons Confederate Vets., Sons Am. Revolution, Masons (33 degree). Home: 4426 Garfield St NW

Washington DC 20007-1142 Office: Timmons & Co 1850 K St NW Washington DC 20006-2213

TIMMONS, WILLIAM MILTON, retired cinema arts educator, publisher, free-lance writer, film maker; b. Houston, Apr. 21, 1933; s. Carter Charles and Gertrude Monte (Lee) T.; m. Pamela Cadorette, Dec. 24, 1975 (div. 1977). BS, U. Houston, 1958; MA, UCLA, 1961; PhD, U. So. Calif., 1975. Child actor Houston Jr. Theater, 1945-46; staff announcer Sta. KMCO, Conroe, Tex., 1951-52; prodn. asst. Sta. KUHT-TV, Houston, 1953-54, 56-57; teaching fellow UCLA, 1960-61; ops. asst. CBS-TV, Hollywood, Calif., 1961-62; prof. speech and drama Sam Houston State U., Huntsville, Tex., 1963-67; chmn. dept. cinema Los Angeles Valley Coll., Van Nuys, Calif., 1970-91, ret., 1992; producer Sta. KPFK, Los Angeles, 1959-60, 1983—; pub. Acad. Assocs., L.A., 1976—; proofreader, conv. Focal Press Pub. Co., N.Y.C., 1983—. Author: Orientation to Cinema, 1986; contbr. articles to mags.; prodr., dir.: (radio programs) Campus Comments, 1963-67, numerous ednl. films, 1963—; prodr. ednl. series for cable TV, 1993—. With USNR, 1954-56. Named Hon. Tex. Ranger, State of Tex., Austin, 1946; U. Houston scholar, 1957. Mem. Soc. for Scholary Pub., Mensa, So. Calif. Cinema-TV Alumni Assn., Red Masque Players, Secular Humanists L.A., Alpha Epsilon Rho, Delta Kappa Alpha. Democrat. Avocations: reading, writing, viewing movies.

TIMMRECK, THOMAS C., health sciences and health administration educator; b. Montpelier, Idaho, June 15, 1946; s. Archie Carl and Janone (Jensen) T.; m. Ellen Prusse, Jan. 27, 1971; children: Chad Thomas, Benjamin Brian, Julie Anne. AA, Ricks Coll., 1968; BS, Brigham Young U., 1971; MEd, Oreg. State U., 1972; MA, No. Ariz. U., 1981; PhD, U. Utah, 1976. Program dir. Cache County Aging Program, Logan, Utah, 1972-73; asst. prof. div. health edn. Tex. Tech U., Lubbock, 1976-77; asst. prof. dept. health care administrn. Idaho State U., Pocatello, 1977-78; program dir., asst. prof. health services program No. Ariz. U., Flagstaff, 1978-84; cons., dir. grants Beth Israel Hosp., Denver, 1985; assoc. prof. dept. health scis. and human ecology, coordinator grad. studies, coordinator health adminstrn. and planning Calif. State U., San Bernardino, 1985—; pres. Health Care Mgmt. Assocs., 1985—; presenter at nat. confs.; mem. faculty Loretto Heights Coll., Denver, Dept. Mgmt. U. Denver, Dept. Mgmt. and Health Adminstrn. U. Colo., Denver. Author: Dictionary of Health Services Management, rev. 2d edit., 1987, An Introduction to Epidemiology, 1994, Handbook of Planning and Program Development for Health and Social Services, 1994; mem. editl. bd. Jour. Health Values, 1986—, Introduction to Epidemiology; contbr. numerous articles on health care adminstrn., behavioral health, gerontology and health edn. to profl. jours. Chmn., bd. dirs. Inland Counties Health System Agy.; bd. dirs. health svc. orgns. Served with U.S. Army, 1966-72, Vietnam. Mem. Assn. Advancement of Health Edn., Am. Acad. Mgmt., Assn. Univ. Programs in Health Care Adminstrn., Healthcare Forum. Republican. Mormon. Office: Calif State U Dept Health Scis and Human Ecology San Bernardino CA 92407

TIMMS, A. JACKSON, lawyer; b. Lock Haven, Pa., July 13, 1938; s. A.B. and Elizabeth (Vaughan) T.; m. Margaret R. Timms, Dec. 28, 1958 (div. 1983); children: Christie E., A. Jackson III, Margaret Shannon; m. Terrie Guille, Aug. 6, 1983; children: Matthew S., Michael G., Kelly V. BA, Yale U., 1960; LLB, U. Va., 1963. Bar: Va. 1964, U.S. Dist. Ct. (ea. dist.) Va., U.S. Ct. Appeals (4th cir.), U.S. Supreme Ct. Ptnr. Seawell, Dalton, Hughes & Timms, Norfolk, Va., 1964-87, Hunton & Williams, Norfolk, 1987—. Mem. ABA, Maritime Law Assn. U.S., Va. Bar Assn., Virginia Beach Bar Assn., Norfolk Portsmouth Bar Assn. Home: 1500 Southwick Dr Virginia Beach VA 23451-5965 Office: Hunton & Williams First Va Bank Tower 101 Saint Pauls Blvd Norfolk VA 23510-2710

TIMMS, LEONARD JOSEPH, JR., gas company executive; b. Pitts., Dec. 10, 1936; s. Leonard Joseph Sr. and Dorthea W. (Abernethy) T.; m. Annabel Phillips, Apr. 14, 1959; children: Cynthia, Rebecca, Sarah. BCE, MIT, 1958; BS in Bus. and Econs., Salem Coll., 1975. Pipeline engr. Williams Bros., Tulsa, 1958-61; planning engr. No. Natural Gas, Omaha, 1961-63; sr. engr. CNG Transmission Corp. (name formerly Consol. Gas Transmission), Clarksburg, W.Va., 1963-70, asst. chief engr., 1970-72, mgr. computer svcs., 1972-75, chief engr., 1975-80, v.p. engring. and ops. svcs., 1980-84, sr. v.p. ops., 1984-86, pres., 1986—, also bd. dirs.; bd. dirs. Empire Nat. Bank, United Hosp. Ctr. Served to capt. USAR C.E., 1958-64. Mem. ASCE, NSPE, Am. Gas Assn., So. Gas Assn. (chmn. bd. dirs.), Interstate Natural Gas Assn. Am. (bd. dirs.), Lions (pres. Clarksburg chpt. 1979-80). Republican. Presbyterian. Avocations: golf, swimming, reading. Home: 801 Worthington Dr Bridgeport WV 26330-1134

TIMMS, PETER ROWLAND, art museum administrator; b. Phila., Aug. 26, 1942; s. H. Rowland and Nancy Virginia (Shaub) T.; m. Romayne Julian Dawnay, Jan. 8, 1972; children: Matthew, Zöe, Christopher. B.A., Brown U., 1964; M.A., Harvard U., 1970, Ph.D., 1976. Instr. Internat. Coll., Beirut, Lebanon, 1967-68; dir. Fitchburg (Mass.) Art Mus., 1973—; dir. Spofford Garrison Excavations, 1978; teaching fellow Harvard U., 1969-71, MIT, 1973. Author: Flint Implements of the Old Stone Age, 1974. Mem. Fitchburg Bicentennial Com., 1974; bd. dirs. Cen. Mass. Tourist Coun., 1974-78, Fitchburg chpt. ARC, 1975-79, Spofford Garrison Excavations, 1978, 79, 80, Nashua River Watershed Assn., 1979-81, Nashua Arts and Sci. Ctr., 1983-86; trustee Applewild Sch., 1982-94, Nat. Plastics Ctr. and Mus., 1991—; pres. Fitchburg Cultural Alliance, 1979-83. Capt. USMCR, 1964-67, Vietnam. Mem. Am. Assn. Museums, Fitchburg Hist. Soc. Republican. Episcopalian. Home: 198 Lake Rd Ashburnham MA 01430-1207 Office: Fitchburg Art Mus 25 Merriam Pky Fitchburg MA 01420-7523

TIMONEY, PETER JOSEPH, veterinarian, virologist, educator, consultant; b. Dublin, Ireland, June 5, 1941; came to U.S., 1983; s. John Francis and Evelyn Norah (Whittle) T.; m. Katherine Mary Murphy, Sept. 11, 1971; children: Peter, Caroline, Sarah, David. MVB, Nat. U., Dublin, 1964; MS, U. Ill., 1966; PhD, U. Dublin, 1974. Rsch. assoc. U. Ill., Urbana, 1964-66; rsch. officer Vet. Rsch. Lab., Abbotstown, Ireland, 1966-72; sr. rsch. officer equine diseases sect. Veterinary Rsch. Lab., Abbotstown, Ireland, 1972-79; assoc. prof. diagnostic lab., dept. microbiology Cornell U., Ithaca, N.Y., 1979-81; sci. dir. Irish Equine Ctr., Johnstown, Ireland, 1981-83; assoc. prof. virology vet. sci. dept. U. Ky., Lexington, 1983-87, prof. virology, assoc. chair for rsch., 1987-89, Frederick Van Lennep prof., 1988—, acting chair, 1989-90, chair, dir. Gluck Equine Rsch. Ctr., 1990—; cons. Daryl Labs., Inc., Santa Clara, Calif., 1981-86, Ft. Dodge (Iowa) Lab., 1986-92, 94—. Fellow Royal Coll. Vet. Surgeons; mem. AAAS, Am. Assn. Equine Practitioners, Am. Soc. for Microbiology, Am. Soc. for Virology, U.S. Animal Health Assn. Avocations: reading, gardening. Office: U Ky Gluck Equine Rsch Ctr 108 Gluck Ctr Lexington KY 40506

TIMOTHY, DAVID HARRY, biology educator; b. Pitts., June 9, 1928; s. David Edgar and Harriett P. (Stein) T.; m. Marian Claire Whiteley, Sept. 5, 1953; children—Marjory J., M. Elisabeth, David W. BS, Pa. State U., 1952, MS, 1955; PhD, U. Minn., 1960. Asst. geneticist Rockefeller Found., Bogota, Colombia, 1956-58; assoc. geneticist Rockefeller Found., Bogota, 1958-61; assoc. prof. N.C. State U., Raleigh, 1961-66, prof., 1966-93, prof. emeritus, 1993—; cons. to fgn. and U.S. govts., also U.S. and internat. sci. orgns.; mem. crop adv. com. on grasses USDA, 1983-87, policy adv. com., sci. and edn. grants program, 1982-84, chief scientist Sci. and Fedn. Competitive Rsch. Grants office, 1985, 86, Nat. Plant Genetic Resources Bd., 1984-91, vice chmn., 1987; bd. dirs., treas. Genetic Resources Comms. Sys., Inc., 1985-91, pres., 1991-93; mem. bd. on agr. NAS-Nat. Rsch. Coun., work group on U.S. Nat. Plant Germplasm Sys., 1987-89. Co-author monographs, also author articles. With AUS, 1946-48, PTO. Recipient Frank M. Meyer medal for plant genetic resources Crop Sci. Soc. Am., 1994; grantee NSF, 1965, 78, Rockefeller Found., 1968, 69, Pioneer Hi-Bred Internat., 1982, 83. Fellow AAAS (electorate, nominating com. sect. O, Agr., 1988-90), Am. Soc. Agronomy, Crop Sci. Soc. Am. (editorial bd. 1982-84, assoc. editor Crop Sci. 1982-84); mem. Am. Inst. Biol. Scis. Home: 13 Furches St Raleigh NC 27607

TIMOTHY, RAYMOND JOSEPH, television executive; b. N.Y.C., Mar. 23, 1932; s. Richard and Mary Ann (O'Connor) T.; B.A. in Polit. Sci., Queens Coll., 1954; LL.B., Bklyn. Law Sch., 1963; m. Kathleen Shanahan, May, 1964; children—Matthew, Patrick, Luke. Admitted to N.Y. bar, 1964; various broadcasting positions, 1954-76; v.p.; gen. mgr. WNBC-TV, N.Y.C.,

1976-77; exec. v.p. affiliate relations NBC, N.Y.C., 1977-79, group exec. v.p., 1982-84; exec. v.p. NBC-TV Network, N.Y.C., 1979-81, pres., 1981-82; group exec. v.p. NBC Entertainment, 1984—. Active N.Y.C. affiliate Nat. Council on Alcoholism. Served with U.S. Army, 1956-58. Mem. Nat. Acad. Arts and Scis. (pres. internat. council). Office: NBC TV Network 30 Rockefeller Plz New York NY 10112-0001

TIMOTHY, ROBERT KELLER, telephone company executive; b. Gilcrest, Colo., June 27, 1918; s. Virge and Alice (Patterson) T.; m. Elaine Hurd, Oct. 23, 1941; children: Kristen, Timothy Lankester, Robert Alan. AB, U. No. Colo., 1941, LLD (hon.). 1986. High sch. sci. tchr. Ft. Lupton Colo., 1941-42; with Mountain States Tel. & Tel. Co., 1946-83, v.p. operations, 1968-69, pres., 1970-82, chmn. bd., 1982-83, also bd. dirs.; past bd. dirs. United Bank Denver, United Banks Colo.; bd. dirs. Rocky Mountain Health Care Corp. Pres., campaign chmn. United Fund, Boise, Idaho, 1962-64; Bd. dirs. Air Force Acad. Found., Bus.-Industry Polit. Action Com., 1975-82, Luth. Med. Center, 1971-84, Nat. Safety Council, 1971-80; trustee U. Denver, 1982-89, Gates Found., 1982-89; pres. Telephone Pioneers Am., 1977-78. Served to capt., Signal Corps U.S. Army, 1943-46. Mem. Newcomen Soc. (chmn. Colo. 1980-84), Civilian/Mil. Inst. (founding bd.), Rotary, Denver Country Club, University Club (Denver), Castle Pines Golf Club. Republican. Clubs: Denver Country, University (Denver). Home: 2155 E Alameda Ave Denver CO 80209-2710 Office: 931 14th St Denver CO 80202-2994

TIMOUR, JOHN ARNOLD, retired librarian, medical bibliography and library science educator; b. Hartford, Conn., Jan. 20, 1926; s. John Alfred and Karin Elizabeth (Levin) T.; m. Betty Jo Lord, Mar. 23, 1952; children—Jon, David, Alan. B.A., Miami U., Oxford, Ohio, 1951; postgrad., Fla. State U., 1951-52; M.A., George Washington U., 1960; M.L.S., U. Md., 1969. Tng. and Med. Lit. Analysis and Retrieval System liaison officer Nat. Library of Medicine, Bethesda, Md., 1966-69; dir. library services Conn. Regional Med. Program-Yale U., New Haven, 1969-73; dir. Mid-Eastern Med. Library Service Coll. Physicians of Phila., 1973-75; univ. librarian Thomas Jefferson U., Phila., 1975-87; instr. U.S. Army Reserve, Hamden, Conn., 1970-73; lectr. library sci. So. Conn. State Coll., New Haven, 1970-71; adj. prof. library sci. Drexel U., Phila., 1976-78. Contbr. articles to profl. jours. Served to RM2-c USN, 1943-46, PTO; 2d lt. USAF, 1951-53, lt. col. USAR, ret. Mem. Assn. Acad. Health Sci. Libr. Dirs., Am. Med. Writers Assn. (pres. Phila. chpt. 1986-87), Med. Libr. Assn. (bd. dirs. 1978-81, Eliot prize 1974), Acad. of Health Info. Profls. (disting. mem.), Spl. Librs. Assn. (pres. Phila. chpt. 1979-80), Conn. Assn. Health Sci. Librs. (hon. life), Sigma Xi (bull. editor Jefferson chpt. 1980-86, recognition cert. 1982), Beta Phi Mu. Episcopalian. Club: Washington Yacht and Country. Avocations: golfing; sailing; chess. Home: 209 Wedgewood Dr Washington NC 27889-9688

TIMPANE, PHILIP MICHAEL, educator, foundation official; b. Troy, N.Y., Nov. 27, 1934; s. Philip Thomas and Rita (Killeen) T.; m. Genevieve LaGrua, Nov. 30, 1957; children: Michael J., Joseph T., Paul J., David A. AB, Cath. U. Am., 1956, MA, 1964; MPA, Harvard U., 1970; LittD (hon.), Wagner Coll., 1986; LLD (hon.), Catholic U. Am., 1991. Historian Joint Chiefs of Staff Dept. Def., 1961-65; spl. asst. civil rights Office of Sec. Def., 1965-68; edn. policy planner HEW, 1968-72; sr. fellow Brookings Instn., 1972-74; dir. edn. policy ctr. Rand Corp., 1974-77; dep. dir. Nat. Inst. Edn., Washington, 1977-80; dir. Nat. Inst. Edn., 1980-81; prof. edn., dean Tchrs. Coll. Columbia U., N.Y.C., 1981—, pres., 1984; Aspen Inst. Edn. Program, 1974-77, 87—; v.p. and sr. scholar Carnegie Found. for the Advancement of Teaching, Princeton, N.J., 1994—. Author: Corporate Interest in Public Education in the Cities, 1982; co-author: Youth Policy in Transition, 1976, Business Impact on Education and Child Development Reform, 1991; co-editor: Planned Variation in Education, 1975, Work Incentives and Income Guarantees, 1975, Ethical and Legal Issues in Social Experimentation, 1975; editor: Federal Interest in Financing Schooling, 1978. Mem. Arlington (Va.) Sch. Bd., 1972-76, chmn., 1973-74; bd. dirs. Am. Assn. for Higher Edn., 1985-93, Synergos Inst., 1988—, Children's TV Workshop, 1989—, Am. Coun. Edn., 1991-94. Mem. Century Assn., Cosmos Club. Democrat. Roman Catholic. Office: Carnegie Found Advncmnt of Tchng 5 Ivy Ln Princeton NJ 08540

TIMPANO, ANNE, museum director, art historian; b. Osaka, Japan, June 17, 1950; d. A.J. and Margaret (Smith) T. BA, Coll. William and Mary, 1972; MA, George Washington U., 1983. Program mgmt. asst. Nat. Mus. Am. Art, Washington, 1977-86; dir. The Columbus (Ga.) Mus., 1986-93, DAAP Galleries, U. Cin., 1993—; grant reviewer Inst. Mus. Svcs., Washington, 1988—, Ga. Coun. for Arts, Atlanta, 1988-91. Mem. 1992 Quincentenary Commn., Columbus, 1987-92. Recipient David Lloyd Kreeger award George Washington U., 1980. Mem. Am. Assn. Mus. (surveyor mus. assessment program), Assn. of Coll. and Univ. Mus. and Galleries, Coll. Art Assn., Midwest Mus. Conf. Roman Catholic. Home: 85 Pleasant Ridge Ave Fort Mitchell KY 41017 Office: U Cin PO Box 210016 Cincinnati OH 45221-0016

TIMPERLAKE, EDWARD THOMAS, public relations executive; b. Perth Amboy, N.J., Nov. 22, 1946; s. James Elwood Timperlake Jr. and Joan Dorothy (Conkling) Maurer; m. Barbette Runckel, Aug. 10, 1969 (div. 1993); children: Tara, Kimberly. BS, U.S. Naval Acad., 1969; MBA, Cornell U., 1977. Commd. 2d lt. USMC, 1969, advanced through grades to lt. col., 1985, resigned, 1975; rsch. asst. peace studies program Cornell U., Ithaca, N.Y., 1976-77; asst. venture mgr. optical info. systems Exxon Enterprise, N.Y.C., 1977-88; sect. mgr. Analytic Svcs. Corp., Arlington, Va., 1978-81; dep. dir. Nat. Dir. Vietnam Vets. Leadership Program, The Action Agy., Washington, 1981-83; dir. mobilization plans and requirements Office of Sec. Def., Washington, 1984; campaign staff George Bush for Pres., 1988; staff asst. Dept. Navy, Washington, 1989; asst. sec. pub. and pub. affairs Dept. Vets. Affairs, Washington, 1989-91, asst. sec. pub. and intergovtl. affairs, 1991-93, apptt. spl. asst. to sec. of Vets. Affairs, 1993; pres. T-9 Group, 1993—, The Battle of Normandy Found., Washington, 1994—. Contbr. numerous articles to profl. jours. Lt. col. USMCR, 1985-88, ret., 1993. Mem. Naval Acad. Alumni Assn., Army-Navy Club, U.S. Naval Sailing Squadron, N.Y. Yacht Club, Vietnamese Meml. Assn., Bush/Quayle Alumni Assn. Home: 317 Chesapeake Ave Annapolis MD 21403 Office: Dept Vets Affairs 810 Vermont Ave NW Washington DC 20420

TINDAL, RALPH LAWRENCE, career officer; b. Columbus, Ohio, Jan. 10, 1940; s. Charles Howard and Dorthy (Limpert) T.; m. Sally Joan Tankalavage, June 17, 1961; children: Ralph Lawrence III, William Charles, John Patrick. BSEE, Pa. State U., 1961; MS, Naval Postgrad. Sch., Monterey, Calif., 1971. Commd. ensign USN, 1961, advanced through grades to rear adm., 1988; navigator, ops. officer USS Skipjack USN, Norfolk, Va., 1971-73, exec. officer USS Shark, 1973-76; mgr. enlisted nuclear programs Dept. Navy, Washington, 1976-78, mgr. nuclear power pers., 1986-88, dir. strategic and theater nuclear warfare, 1990-92; dir. ops./logistics U.S. Strategic Command, 1992-93; comdg. officer USS Dace USN, New London, Conn., 1978-82; comdg. officer USS Henry M. Jackson USN, Bangor, Wash., 1982-86; asst. chief of staff, logistics Allied Forces So. Europe USN, Naples, Italy, 1988-90; deputy comdr.-in-chief Iberian Atlantic Area Supreme Allied, Oeiras, Portugal, 1994—; mem. sci. adv. group Joint Strategic Targeting Planning Staff, Omaha, 1990-92; bd. dirs. opera Omaha, 1992-93. Mem. exec. com. No. Va. Cursillio Movement. Decorated Navy Commendation medal (2), Meritorious Svc. medal (3), Legion of Merit with two gold stars, Def. Superior Svc. medal (2). Mem. U.S. Naval Inst. Roman Catholic. Avocation: running. Home: APO AE, PSC 83 Box 4, 2765 Estoril Portugal Office: Dir Ops/Logistics Us Strategic Command Offutt A F B NE 68113 Office: Deputy CINCIBERLANT NATO, Oeiras Portugal

TINDALL, GEORGE BROWN, historian, educator; b. Greenville, S.C., Feb. 26, 1921; s. Goin Roscoe and Nellie Evelyn (Brown) T.; m. Carliss Blossom McGarrity, June 29, 1946; children: Bruce McGarrity, Blair Alston Mercer. AB, Furman U., 1942, LittD, 1971; MA, U. N.C., 1948, PhD, 1951. Asst. prof. history Eastern Ky. State Coll., 1950-51, U. Miss., 1951-52, Woman's Coll. of U. N.C., 1952-53, La. State U., 1953-58; assoc. prof. U. N.C., Chapel Hill, 1958-64, prof., 1964-69, Kenan prof., 1969-90, Kenan prof. emeritus, 1990—; vis. prof. Coll. of Charleston, 1951, Kyoto Am. Studies Sem., 1977; Fulbright guest prof. U. Vienna, 1967-68; mem. Inst. for Advanced Study, 1963-64; mem. Ctr. for Advanced Study in Behavioral Scis., 1979-80. Author: South Carolina Negroes, 1877-1900, 1952 (hon. mention John H. Dunning award 1952), The Emergence of the New South,

1913-1945, 1967 (Jules F. Landry award 1968, Mayflower Cup 1968, Lillian E. Smith award 1968, Charles S. Sydnor award 1968), The Disruption of the Solid South, 1972, The Persistent Tradition in New South Politics, 1975, The Ethnic Southerners, 1976, America: A Narrative History, 1984, 2d edit., 1988, 3d edit. (with David Shi), 1989, Natives and Newcomers: Ethnic Southerns and Southern Ethnics, 1995; editor: The Pursuit of Southern History, 1964, A Populist Reader, 1966; mem. editorial bd. Am. Hist. Rev., 1970-74. Guggenheim fellow, 1957-58, Social Sci. Rsch. Coun. fellow, 1959-60, Ctr. for Advanced Study in Behavioral Scis., 1979-80. Mem. Am. Hist. Assn., Hist. Soc. N.C. (pres. 1990), N.C. Lit. and Hist. Soc., Organ. Am. Historians, So. Hist. Assn. (pres. 1973). Home: 305 Burlage Cir Chapel Hill NC 27514-2703

TINDALL, GEORGE TAYLOR, neurosurgeon, educator; b. Magee, Miss., Mar. 13, 1928; s. George Earl and Lyda (Smith) T.; children: Catherine, George Taylor Jr., Suzanne, Annelle. BA, U. Miss., 1948; MD, Johns Hopkins U., 1952. Diplomate Am. Bd. Neurol. Surgery. Intern Johns Hopkins Hosp., Balt., 1952-53; resident in neurosurgery Duke U., Durham, N.C., 1955-61, asst. prof. neurosurgery, 1961-67, assoc. prof., 1967-68; chief neurosurgery Durham VA Hosp., 1961-68; prof., chief div. neurosurgery U. Tex. Med. Br., Galveston, 1968-73; prof. surgery, chief neurosurgery Emory U., Atlanta, 1973—; pvt. practice specializing in neurosurgery Atlanta, 1973—. Capt. USAF, 1953-55. Mem. Am. Acad. Neurol. Surgery (editor Jour. 1971-74)), Am. Assn. Neurol. Surgeons (pres. 1988-89), Congress Neurol. Surgeons (pres. 1973-74), Soc. Neurol. Surgeons, Neurosurg. Soc. Am., Soc. Univ. Neurosurgeons (pres. 1966), ACS, AMA (vice chmn. coun. neurol. surgery 1972—), Ga. Med. Assn., Johns Hopkins Med. and Surg. Assn., Alpha Omega Alpha. Home: 869 Lullwater Pky NE Atlanta GA 30307-1233 Office: 1327 Clifton Rd NE Atlanta GA 30322

TINDER, JOHN DANIEL, federal judge; b. Indpls., Feb. 17, 1950; s. John Glendon and Eileen M. (Foley) T.; m. Jan M. Carroll, Mar. 17, 1984. B.S., Ind. U., 1972, J.D., 1975. Bar: Ind. 19, U.S. Dist. Ct. (so. dist.) Ind. 19, U.S. Ct. Appeals (7th cir.) 19, U.S. Supreme Ct. Asst. U.S. atty. Dept. of Justice, Indpls., 1975-77; pub. defender Marion County Criminal Ct., Indpls., 1977-78; chief trial dep. Marion County Pros. Office, Indpls., 1979-82; litigation counsel Harrisone Moberly, Indpls., 1982-84; U.S. atty. U.S. Dist. Ct. (so. dist.) Ind., Indpls., 1984-87; judge U.S. Dist. Ct. (so. dist.) Ind., 1987—; adj. prof. Ind. U. Sch. of Law, Indpls., 1980—; mem. Supreme Ct. Character & Fitness Com., Ind., 1982—. Co-founder Turkey Trot Invitational Race, Indpls., 1980. Recipient Cert. of Appreciation award Bur. Alcohol, Tobacco & Firearms, Indpls., 1976; Service award Marion County Prosecutor, Indpls., 1981. Mem. ABA, Ind. State Bar Assn. (dir. criminal justice sect. 1984—), Indpls. Bar Assn., 7th Circuit Ct. Bar Assn., Fed. Bar Assn. Republican. Roman Catholic. Office: US Dist Ct 304 US Courthouse 46 E Ohio St Indianapolis IN 46204-1903

TINER, STANLEY RAY, business communications executive, former editor; b. Springhill, La., Aug. 22, 1942; s. Elmer Ray and Nannie Lea (Randolph) T.; m. Veronica Jo Thibodeaux, Dec. 31, 1966; children—Mark Gerard, Jon Stuart, Heather Nicole. B.A., La. Tech. U., 1969. City editor Texarkana Daily News, 1970-71; mng. editor Minden (La.) Press-Herald, 1970-71; chief editorial writer Shreveport (La.) Times, 1972-74; editor Shreveport Jour., 1974-88; dir. pub. affairs Arkla Inc., 1988—. Bd. dirs. Shreveport chpt. NCCJ, 1981—, Assn. of Retarded Citizens, Caddo-Bossier, La. 1974-87; chmn. Holocaust Commemoration, Shreveport, 1987; bd. dirs. La. Assn. for Blind, 1988—; chmn. La. State Exhibit Mus., 1991—. Served as sgt. USMC, 1962-66, Vietnam. Recipient Frank Allen award La.-Miss. AP, 1976; Silver Gavel award ABA, 1977; Robert F. Kennedy award, 1978; Social Justice award Social Justice Com., Shreveport, 1981; Nieman fellow Harvard U., 1985-86; Liberty Bell award Shreveport Bar Assn., 1985; award of merit AIA. Mem. Interstate Natural Gas Assn. Am. (state rels. com. 1988—), Internat. Assn. Bus. Communicators, La. Assn. Bus. and Industry (bd. dirs. 1989—), Soc. Profl. Journalists (pres. 1974, bd. dirs. 3 yrs.), La. Press Assn. (bd. dirs. 1975-77). Democrat. Baptist. Avocations: walking; photography. Home: 6675 N Park Cir Shreveport LA 71107-9539 Office: Arkla Inc 525 Milam St Shreveport LA 71101-3539

TING, ALBERT CHIA, bioengineering researcher; b. Hong Kong, Sept. 7, 1950; came to U.S., 1957; s. William Su and Katherine Sung (Bao) T.; m. Shirley Roung Wang, July 30, 1988. BA, UCLA, 1973; MS, Calif. State U., L.A., 1975, Calif. Inst. Tech, 1977; PhD, U. Calif., San Diego, 1983. Rsch. asst. Calif. Inst. Tech., Pasadena, 1975-77, U. Calif., San Diego, 1982-83; sr. staff engr. R&D Am. Med. Optics, Irvine, Calif., 1983-86; project engr., rsch. Allergan Med. Optics, Irvine, Calif., 1987-89; sr. project engr., rsch, 1989-92, sr. project engr., engring., 1993-94. Inventor med. and optical devices, recipient patent awards 1988, 89, 91, 92, 93; contbr. articles to sci. jours. Mem. AAAS, Biomed. Engring. Soc., Assn. for Rsch. in Vision and Ophthalmology, Biomed. Optics Soc.

TING, ROBERT YEN-YING, physicist; b. Kwei-yang, China, Mar. 8, 1942; came to U.S. 1965; s. Chi-yung and Shou-feng (Yang) T.; m. Teresa Yen-chun Ting, June 3, 1967; children: Paul H., Peggy Y. BS, Nat. Taiwan U., 1964; MS, MIT, 1967; PhD, U. Calif., San Diego, 1971. Rsch. engr. U.S. Naval Rsch. Lab., Washington, 1971-77, supervisory engr., 1977-80; supervisory physicist U.S. Naval Rsch. Lab., Orlando, Fla., 1980—; prof. George Washington U., 1972-80. Contbr. over 100 articles in rheology, polymer and acoustics to profl. jours. Fellow Acoustical Soc. Am.; mem. Am. chem. Soc., Am. Ceramics Soc., Am. Inst. Chem. Engrs. Office: US Naval Rsch Lab PO Box 568337 Orlando FL 32856-8337

TING, SAMUEL CHAO CHUNG, physicist, educator; b. Ann Arbor, Mich., Jan. 27, 1936; s. Kuan H. and Jeanne (Wong) T.; m. Susan Carol Marks, Apr. 28, 1985; children: Jeanne Min, Amy Min, Christopher M. BS in Engring. U. Mich., 1959, MS, 1960, PhD, 1962, ScD (hon.), 1978; ScD (hon.), Chinese U. Hong Kong, 1987, U. Bologna, Italy, 1988, Columbia U., 1990, U. Sci. and Tech., China, 1990, Moscow State U. 1991, U. Bucharest, China, 1993, U. Bucharest, Romania, 1993. Ford Found. fellow CERN (European Orgn. Nuclear Research), Geneva, 1963; instr. physics Columbia U., 1964, asst. prof., 1965-67; group leader Deutsches Elektronen-Synchrotron, Hamburg, W.Ger., 1966; assoc. prof. physics MIT, Cambridge, 1967-68, prof., 1969—; Thomas Dudley Cabot Inst. prof. M.I.T. 1977—; program cons. Div. Particles and Fields, Am. Phys. Soc., 1970; hon. prof. Beijing Normal Coll., 1987, Jiatong U., Shanghai, 1987, U. Bologna, Italy, 1988. Assoc. editor: Nuclear Physics B, 1970; contbr. articles in field to profl. jours.; editorial bd.: Nuclear Instruments and Methods, Mathematical Modeling; advisor Jour. Modern Physics A. Recipient Nobel prize in Physics, 1976, De Gasperi prize in Sci., Italian Republic, 1988, Ernest Orlando Lawrence award U.S. Govt., 1976, Eringen medal Soc. Engring. Sci., 1977, Gold medal in Sci. City of Brescia, Italy, 1988, Golden Leopard award Town of Taormina, 1988; Am. Acad. Sci. and Arts fellow, 1975. Mem. NAS; fgn. mem. Pakistani Acad. Sci., Academia Sinica, Russian Acad. Sci., Hungarian Acad. Sci.. Office: MIT Dept Physics 51 Vassar St Cambridge MA 02139-4308

TINGELSTAD, JON BUNDE, physician; b. McVille, N.D., Jan. 15, 1935; s. Sophus B. and Mabelle (Bunde) T.; m. Marcia Ayers, Dec. 17, 1960; children: Paul, Catherine, David. B.A., U. N.D., 1957, B.S., 1958; M.D., Harvard U., 1960. Diplomate Am. Bd. Pediatrics. Intern Children's Hosp. Med. Ctr., Boston, 1960-61, resident, 1961-62; resident U. Colo. Med. Ctr., Denver, 1962-63; fellow in pediatric cardiology Children's Hosp., Buffalo, 1965-67; asst. prof. pediatrics Med. Coll. Va., Richmond, 1967-71, assoc. prof., 1971-76; prof., vice chmn. pediatrics East Carolina U. Sch. Medicine, Greenville, N.C., 1976-77, prof., chmn. pediatrics, 1977—. Mem. Greenville City Bd. Edn., 1978-82, chmn., 1981-82. Served to capt. USAF, 1963-65. Fellow Am. Acad. Pediatrics, Am. Coll. Cardiology; mem. AAAS, So. Soc. Pediatric Research, Ambulatory Pediatric Assn., Greenville C. of C., Phi Beta Kappa, Phi Eta Sigma. Home: 208 Chowan Rd Greenville NC 27858-6321 Office: E Carolina U Sch Med Dept Pediatrics Greenville NC 27858-4354

TINGHITELLA, STEPHEN, publishing company executive; b. Bklyn., May 21, 1915; s. Michael and Carmela (Cestaro) T.; m. Inez Barbara Albertelli, May 20, 1945; children—Vilma, Stephen, John. Student, Acad. Advanced Traffic, 1946-50. Traffic mgr. John Sexton & Co. (wholesale grocery distbn.), Long Island City, N.Y., 1947-53; v.p. Rupp Trucking Co.,

N.Y.C., 1953-56; dir. transp. Commerce and Industry Assn. N.Y., N.Y.C., 1956-62; editor-in-chief Traffic Mgmt. mag. Cahners Pub. Co., N.Y.C., 1962—, pub., 1970—, v.p., 1975—. Author: Introduction of Traffic and Transportation, 1986; Sponsoring editor: Red Book on Transportation of Hazardous Materials, 1977. Served to master sgt. AUS, 1942-46. Recipient Spl. citation Pres's. Com. Employment of Handicapped, 1967, Editor's award Cahners Pub. Co., 1968, Editorial Achievement award Am. Bus. Press, 1974, 78. Mem. Delta Nu Alpha (Transp. Man of Year award 1964). Office: Freight Traffic Inst 960 Broadway Hicksville NY 11801-5028

TINGLE, AUBREY JAMES, pediatric immunologist, research administrator; b. St. Paul, Alta., Can., June 28, 1943; s. Cyril Nisbet Tingle and Margaret Lucy (Fraser) Tarbuck; m. Valerie Jean Anderson, Nov. 2, 1968; children: Heather Lynn, Brian James. MD, U. Alta., Edmonton, 1967; PhD, McGill U., Montreal, Que., Can., 1974. Asst. prof. dept. pediatrics U. B.C., Vancouver, Can., 1974-79, head div. immunology dept. pediatrics, 1974-86, assoc. prof., 1979-86, prof., 1986—, prof. dept. pathology, 1986—; dir. rsch. B.C. Rsch. Inst. for Child and Family Health, Vancouver, 1992—; asst. dean rsch. Faculty of Medicine, U. B.C., Vancouver, 1992—. Fellow Royal Coll. Physicians and Surgeons Can., Soc. Pediatric Research, Am. Acad. Pediatrics; mem. Western Soc. Pediatric Research. Office: BC Childrens Hosp-Pediatrics, 4480 Oak St, Vancouver, BC Canada V6H 3V4

TINGLE, JAMES O'MALLEY, lawyer; b. N.Y.C., June 12, 1928; s. Thomas Jefferson and Mercedes (O'Malley) T. B.S., U. Mont., 1950, B.A., 1952, LL.B., 1952; LL.M., U. Mich., 1953, S.J.D., 1958. Bar: Calif. 1959, Mont. 1952, N.Y. 1961. Asst. prof. law U. Mont., Missoula, 1955-56; atty. Shell Oil Co., N.Y.C., 1957-62; assoc. Pillsbury, Madison & Sutro, San Francisco, 1962-68, ptnr., 1969—. Author: The Stockholder's Remedy of Corporate Dissolution, 1959; editor: State Antitrust Laws, 1974. Served to 1st lt. USAF, 1953-55. William W. Cook fellow U. Mich. Mem. Mont. Bar Assn., Calif. Bar Assn., ABA. Democrat. Office: Pillsbury Madison & Sutro 225 Bush St San Francisco CA 94104-4207

TINGLEY, FLOYD WARREN, physician; b. Charlotte, N.C., Nov. 22, 1933; s. Floyd Warren Sr. and Janie (Suggs) T.; m. Sandra Carpenter, Aug. 20, 1955 (div. Dec. 1984); children: Sheryl Tingley Hagen, David Alan; m. Johnette Hill, Apr. 5, 1985. BA in English, Emory U., 1955, MD, 1959. Diplomate Am. Bd. Internal Medicine (bd. govs. 1986-92). Intern USAF Hosp., Lackland AFB, Tex., 1959-60; resident in internal medicine Parkland Meml. Hosp., Dallas, 1963-65, fellow in cardiology, 1965-66; pvt. practice specializing in internal medicine Arlington, Tex., 1966-88; med. dir. southwestern region Met. Life Ins. Co., Irving, Tex., 1988-90; regional practice leader William M. Mercer Inc., 1990-91; v.p., sr. med. dir. Provident Life and Accident Co., Chattanooga, 1991-92; v.p., nat. med. dir. Travelers Ins. Cos., Hartford, Conn., 1992-94; sr. v.p., chief med. officer Kemper Nat. Svcs., Plantation, Fla., 1995—; apptd. Tex. Commn. on Health Care Reimbursement Alternatives, 1987; bd. dirs. Riverside Nat. Bank, Grand Prairie, Tex. Contbr. articles to profl. jours. Pres. Arlington YMCA, 1971; chmn. budget com. Family Services, Ft. Worth, 1973; participant Health Policy Agenda for Am. People, Chgo., 1984-87; trustee Tex. Med. Liability Trust, Austin, 1987-88. Capt. USAF, 1958-63. Fellow ACP (Tex. chpt. 1981); mem. AMA (chmn. sect. coun. internal medicine, 1979-88), Am. Soc. Internal Medicine (Tex. Med. Assn. (treas. 1978-85, alt. del. to AMA 1985-91, commendation 1985), Tarrant County Med. Soc. (pres. Arlington br. 1974, del. to Tex. Med. Assn., Community Svc. award 1983). Presbyterian. Avocations: photography, sailing, gardening, computer hobbies. Home: 4 Laurel Crest Burlington CT 06013-1911 Office: Travelers Ins Cos One Tower Sq Hartford CT 06183

TINIC, SEHA MEHMET, finance educator; b. Istanbul, Turkey, Nov. 23, 1941; came to U.S., 1964; s. Cevad Ali and Nezihe Fatma (Bahtoglu) T.; m. Hale Hatice Yorukoglu, Aug. 27, 1964; children: Serra, Atilla. BA, Robert Coll., Istanbul, 1964; MBA, U. Tulsa, 1966; PhD, Cornell U., 1970. Instr. Middle East Tech. U., Ankara, Turkey, 1966-67; assoc. prof. U. Alta., Edmonton, Can., 1970-73, prof., 1973-85; J.L. Mosle prof. U. Tex., Austin, 1985-89, J.A. Elkins prof. fin., 1989—; vis. scholar Dartmouth Coll., Hanover, N.H., 1976-77, Merrill Lynch vis. prof., 1983-84; vis. prof. U. B.C., Vancouver, 1978-79; cons. treas. dept. Province of Alta., 1975, Alta. Govt. Telephones, 1982, 85, Columbia Securities Ltd. Calgary, Alta., Can. 1984. Co-author: Economics of the Stock Market, 1971, Investing in Securities: An Efficient Markets Approach, 1979; contbr. numerous articles to profl. jours. With Turkish Army, 1986. Mem. Am. Fin. Assn., Western Fin. Assn. (pres. 1984-85), Am. Econ. Assn., Fin. Mgmt. Assn., Phi Kappa Phi. Moslem. Avocations: tennis, swimming, reading, music. Office: U Tex Coll Bus Adminstn 21st And Speedway Austin TX 78712

TINKER, GRANT A., broadcasting executive; b. Stamford, Conn., Jan. 11, 1926. Student, Dartmouth Coll. With radio program dept. NBC, 1949-54; TV dept. McCann-Erickson Advt. Agy., 1954-58, Benton & Bowles Advt. Agy., 1958-61; v.p.-programs West Coast, NBC, 1961-66; v.p. in charge programming West Coast, NBC, N.Y.C, 1966-67; v.p. Universal TV, 1968-69, 20th-Fox, 1969-70; pres. Mary Tyler Moore (MTM) Enterprises, Inc., Studio City, Calif., 1970-81; chmn. bd., chief exec. officer NBC, Burbank, Calif., 1981-86; independent producer Burbank, Calif., from 1986; pres. GTG Entertainment, Culver City, Calif., from 1986. Author: (with Bud Rukeyser) Tinker in Television: From General Sarnoff to General Electric, 1994. Office: GTG Entertainment 9336 Washington Blvd Culver City CA 90232-2628

TINKER, H(AROLD) BURNHAM, chemical company executive; b. St. Louis, May 16, 1939; s. H(arold) Burnham and Emily (Barnicle) T.; m. Barbara Ann Lydon, Feb. 20, 1965; children: Michael B., Mary K., Ann E. BS in Chemistry, St. Louis U., 1961; MS in Chemistry, U. Chgo., 1964, PhD in Chemistry, 1966. Sr. research chemist Monsanto, St. Louis, 1966-69, research specialist, 1969-73, research group leader, 1973-77, research mgr., 1977-81; tech. dir. Mooney Chems., Inc., Cleve., 1981-90, v.p. rsch. and devel., 1991-94; v.p. corp. devel., 1994—. Patentee in field; contbr. article to profl. jours. Mem. assn. adv. coun. U. Akron, 1975—. Mem. Am. Chem. Soc. (chmn. bd. St. Louis sect. 1978-79), Cleve. Assn. Rsch. Dirs. (v.p. 1989, pres. 1990, bd. dirs. 1991—). Roman Catholic. Avocation: computers. Home: 2889 Manchester Rd Cleveland OH 44122-2570 Office: OM Group Inc 3800 Terminal Tower Cleveland OH 44113-2204

TINKER, THOMAS EATON, headmaster; b. Providence, May 24, 1941; s. George Milan and Ruth (Eaton) T.; m. Rosalyn May Silverman, Dec. 21, 1968. BA, Columbia U., 1963; MA, Brown U., 1968. English instr. Tabor Acad., Marion, Mass., 1964-66; history instr. Wheeler Sch., Providence, 1967-77; headmaster Broadmeadow Sch., Middletown, Del., 1977-82, St. Paul's Sch., Garden City, N.Y., 1982-89, The Barnard Sch., N.Y.C., 1989—; evaluator Mid. State Assn. Colls. and Schs., Phila., 1978—. bd. dirs. Univ. Club of L.I., 1984-86. With USSR, 1963-69. Mem. Nat. Assn. Ind. Schs., N.Y. State Assn. Ind. Schs., L.I. Episcopal Sch. Assn. (v.p./treas. 1984-89), Del. Assn. Ind. Schs. (sec. 1978-82). Episcopalian. Avocation: sailing. Home: 174 Howard Ave Rochelle Park NJ 07662 Office: Barnard Sch 554 Ft Washington Ave New York NY 10033

TINKHAM, MICHAEL, physicist, educator; b. Green Lake County, Wis., Feb. 23, 1928; s. Clayton Harold and LaVerna (Krause) T.; m. Mary Stephanie Merin, June 24, 1961; children: Jeffrey Michael, Christopher Gillespie. A.B., Ripon (Wis.) Coll., 1951, Sc.D. (hon.), 1976; M.S., MIT, 1951; Ph.D., 1954; M.A. (hon.), Harvard, 1966. NSF postdoctoral fellow at Clarendon Lab., Oxford (Eng.) U., 1954-55; successively research physicist, lectr., asst. prof., asso. prof., prof. physics U. Calif. at Berkeley, 1955-66; Gordon McKay prof. applied physics Harvard U., 1966—, prof. physics, 1966-80, Rumford prof. physics, 1980—, chmn. physics dept., 1975-78; cons. to industry, 1958—; participant internat. seminars and confs.; mem. commn. on very low temperatures Internat. Union Pure and applied Physics, 1972-78; vis. Miller rsch. prof. U. Calif.-Berkeley, 1987; vis. prof. Technical Univ., Delft, The Netherlands, 1993. Author: Group Theory and Quantum Mechanics, 1964, Superconductivity, 1965, Introduction to Superconductivity, 1975; also numerous articles. Served USNR, 1945-46. Recipient award Alexander von Humboldt Found. U. Karlsruhe, W. Ger., 1978-79; NSF sr. postdoctoral fellow Cavendish lab.; vis. fellow Clare Hall Cambridge (Eng.) U., 1971-72; Guggenheim fellow, 1963-64. Fellow Am. Phys. Soc. (chmn. div. solid state physics 1966-67, Buckley prize 1974, Richtmyer lectr. 1977), AAAS; mem. Am. Acad. Arts and Scis., Nat. Acad. Scis. Home: 98

Rutledge Rd Belmont MA 02178-2633 Office: Harvard Univ Physics Dept Lyman Lab of Physics 326 Cambridge MA 02138

TINKHAM, THOMAS W., lawyer; b. Milw., June 29, 1944; s. Richard Perry and Helen (Savage) T.; m. Jackie Hauser; children: Tamara, Liza, Taylor. BS with honors, U. Wis., 1966; JD with honors, Harvard U., 1969. Ptnr. Dorsey & Whitney, Mpls., 1974—. Mem. Minn. State Bar (pres. 1991), Hennepin County Bar Assn. (pres. 1980). Office: Dorsey & Whitney 220 S 6th St Minneapolis MN 55402

TINKLE, CAROLYN J., state legislative staff member; b. Henderson, Ky., Oct. 27, 1940; d. Frank Mason and Hazel LaVerne (Potts) Ploch; m. Charles Everman Tinkle II, Feb. 11, 1961; children: Charles Everman III, Christopher Mason, Amanda Lynn Tinkle Rowe. Student in Bus., Ind. U., 1958-60. Legal sec. King, Deep & Branaman, Henderson, Ky., 1960-61; sec. Jewell Tea Co., Chgo., 1961-62; sec. to state chmn. Rep. Nat. Com., Indpls., 1973-75; sec. to chmn. majority caucus Ind. State Senate, Indpls., 1980-82, sec. supr., 1982-83, legis. asst. to pres. pro tempore, 1983-85, prin. sec., 1985—. Editor: (newsletter) Reaching Out; editor, pub.: (newsletter) The Legislative Administrator, 1988. Recipient Sagamore of Wabash State Ind., 1989; named to Hon. Order Ky. Colonels, 1987. Mem. Am. Soc. Legis. Clks. and Secs. (editor, pub. Roster 1987, sec.-treas. 1989-90, v.p 1990-91, pres. nat. orgn. 1991-92). Home: 404 Beech Park Dr Greenwood IN 46142 Office: Ind State Senate 200 W Washington Indianapolis IN 46204

TINOCO, IGNACIO, JR., chemist, educator; b. El Paso, Tex., Nov. 22, 1930; s. Ignacio and Laurencia (Aizpuru) T.; 1 child. B.S., U. N.Mex., 1951, D.Sc., 1972; Ph.D., U. Wis., 1954; postgrad., Yale, 1954-56. Mem. faculty U. Calif.-Berkeley, 1956—, prof. chemistry, 1966—; Rosser-Rivera disting. lectr. in biol. chemistry Calif. State U.-Los Angeles and U. Calif.-Riverside, 1983. Guggenheim fellow, 1964. Mem. Am. Chem. Soc. (Calif. award 1965), Am. Biophysics Soc., Am. Phys. Soc., Nat. Acad. Sci. Office: Univ of Calif Dept Of Chemistry Berkeley CA 94720

TINSLEY, ADRIAN, college president; b. N.Y.C., July 6, 1937; d. Theodore A. and Mary Ethel (White) T. AB, Bryn Mawr Coll., 1958; MA, U. Wash., 1962; PhD, Cornell U., 1969. Asst. prof. English U. Md., College Park, 1968-72; dean William James Coll., Grand Valley State, Allendale, Mich., 1972-80; assoc. vice chancellor acad. affairs Minn. State U., St. Paul, 1982-85; exec. v.p., provost Glassboro (N.J.) State Coll., 1985-89; pres. Bridgewater (Mass.) State Coll., 1989—; coord. women higher edn. adminstrn. Bryn Mawr (Pa.) & Hers Summer Inst., 1977—. Editor: Women in Higher Education Administration, 1984. Office: Bridgewater State Coll Office of Pres Bridgewater MA 02325

TINSLEY, JACKSON BENNETT, newspaper editor; b. Ewing, Tex., Dec. 14, 1934; s. Henry Bine and Sallie Alberta (Jackson) T.; m. Claudia Anne Miller, Oct. 3, 1965; children: Ben, Anna. B.S., Sam Houston State U., 1958. Editor Diboll News-Bull., 1953-54, Corrigan Times, 1954; reporter Lufkin News, 1952, 56; news editor Port Lavaca Wave, 1955; mem. staff Ft. Worth Star-Telegram, 1959-60, 62—, Sunday editor, 1967-71, asst. mng. editor, 1971-74, asst. to editor, 1974-75, exec. editor, 1975-82, v.p., exec. editor, 1982-86, v.p., editor, 1986-90, sr. v.p., editor, chmn., 1990—; info. asst. S.W. Bell Telephone Co., 1960-62; part time instr., editor Tex. Christian U., 1971-72. Com. chmn. United Way Tarrant County, 1970-87, gen. chmn. Tex. Gridiron Show, 1981, 93-95; bd. dirs. Safety Coun. Ft. Worth, 1975-80; pres., bd. dirs. Parenting Guidance Ctr., 1989-90. 2d lt. U.S. Army, 1959. Recipient Nat. Writing award Am. Writers Assn., 1965, citation Tex. Conf. AAUP, 1965; named Disting. Alumnus, Sam Houston State U., 1984; named to C.E. Shuford Journalism Hall of Honor, U. North Tex., 1987. Mem. Soc. Profl. Journalists (Ft. Worth chpt. 1991-92, chmn. journalism adv. com. U. North Tex. and Sam Houston State U. 1988-93), Am. Soc. Newspapers Editors, AP Mng. Editors Assn., Tex. AP Mng. Editors Assn. (pres. 1979-80), Press Club Ft. Worth (pres. 1970-71), Colonial Country Club, Ft. Worth Club, Rotary (v.p. Ft. Worth 1981, pres. 1983-84). Home: 3550 Wind River Ct Fort Worth TX 76116-9329 Office: Ft Worth Star-Telegram 400 W 7th St Fort Worth TX 76102-4701

TINSLEY, TUCK, III, book publishing executive. With Fla. School for the Deaf & Blind, St. Augustine, Fla., 1968-89; pres. American Printing House for the Blind, Louisville, 1989—. Office: Am Print House for the Blind PO Box 6085 1839 Frandfort Ave Louisville KY 40206-0085

TINSLEY, WALTON EUGENE, lawyer; b. Vanceburg, Ky., Jan. 22, 1921; s. Wilbur Walton and Sarah Edith (Frizzell) T.; m. Joy Mae Matthews, Aug. 31, 1952; children—Merry Walton Tinsley Moore, Troy Eugene, Paul Richard. E.E., U. Cin., 1943; M.S. in Aero. Engring, NYU, 1947; J.D., U. So. Calif., 1953. Bar: Calif. 1954, U.S. Supreme Ct. 1971. Practiced in Los Angeles, 1954—; mem. firm Harris, Wallen, MacDermott & Tinsley, 1958—. Author: (book) Tasmania: Stamps and Postal History, 1986. Pres. World Philatelic Exhbn., Pacific 97 Inc. Signatory Roll of Disting. Philatelists, 1983. Fellow Royal Philatelic Soc. London; mem. IEEE (assoc.), AIAA, ABA, L.A. County Bar Assn., Am. Philatelic Soc. (v.p. 1965-69, Luff award 1986), S.R., English Speaking Union (dir. L.A. br.), Mensa. Presbyterian (elder, trustee, chmn. trustees 1972). Home: 2210 Moreno Dr Los Angeles CA 90039-3044 Office: Harris Wallen MacDermott Tinsley 650 S Grand Ave Los Angeles CA 90017-3809

TINSMAN, MARGARET NEIR, state senator; b. Moline, Ill., July 14, 1936; d. Francis Earl and Elizabeth (Lourie) Neir; m. Robert Hovey Tinsman Jr., Feb. 21, 1959; children: Robert Hovey III, Heidi Elizabeth, Bruce MacAlister. BA in Sociology, U. Colo., 1958; MSW, U. Iowa, 1974. Health care coord. Community Health Care, Inc., Davenport, Iowa, 1975-77; assoc. dir. Scott County Info., Referal, and Assistance Svc., Davenport, Iowa, 1977-79; county supr. Scott County Bd. Suprs., Davenport, Iowa, 1978-89; senate State of Iowa, Des Moines, 1989—; asst. minority leader Iowa Senate, coms. appropriations, edn., human resources, human svcs. appropriations subcom., ranking mem., 1989—; chair Iowa adv. commn. on inter-govt. rels., 1982-84; U.S. county rep. to the German-Am. Symposium German Marshall Plan, 1983; commr. Iowa Dept. Elder Affairs, Des Moines, 1983-89. Chairperson Planning Com. Quad City United Way, Davenport; bd. dirs. Bi-State Met. Planning Commn., Davenport, 1981-89, Quad City Devel. Group, Davenport, 1988-90. Named Iowa Social Worker of Yr., NASW, 1978. Mem. Am. Lung Assn. (bd. dirs. 1989—), Davenport C. of C. (local/state govt. com. 1989—), Nat. Assn. Legislators, Nat. Assn. of Counties (bd. dirs. 1984-89, pres. Women Ofcl. 1984-89), Iowa State Assn. of Counties (bd. dirs. 1983-89, chair), Jr. League (sustaining mem. 1989), Vol. Action Ctr. (pres. 1989). Republican. Episcopalian. Avocations: tennis, golf, sailing, water and snow skiing. Home: 3055 Red Wing Ct Bettendorf IA 52722 Office: c/o Twin State 3541 E Kimberly Rd Davenport IA 52807-2551

TINSMAN, DALE CLINTON, beef processing company executive; b. Chester, Nebr., May 19, 1919; s. Clinton Lewis and Elizabeth Golashin (Gretzinger) T.; m. Jean Sundell, Oct. 1, 1942; children: Thomas C., Nancy (Mrs. Ron Remington), Jane C. (Mrs. Stephen Kramer). BS, U. Nebr., 1941, JD, 1947. Bar: Nebr. 1947. Asst. sec., asst. investment dept. First Trust Co., Lincoln, Nebr., 1947-58; v.p., asst. treas. Securities Acceptance Corp., Omaha, financial v.p., treas. Central Nat. Ins. Group, Omaha, 1958-60; pres., treas. Tinsman & Co., Inc., Lincoln, 1960-61; exec. v.p. First Mid Am., Inc., Lincoln, 1961-68, pres., 1973-74, fin. cons., 1974—; pres., dir. Iowa Beef Processors, Inc., 1976-77, vice chmn., 1977-82, co-chmn., 1982-83, dir., cons., 1983—; chmn., dir. Eaton Tinsman Druliner, Inc., 1983—; bd. dirs. IBP, Inc.; past chmn. Nebr. Investment Council. Trustee, chmn. U. Nebr. Found.; trustee Lincoln Found., Nebr. Council Econ. Edn., Mall Corp., Smith Haye Trust. Served with USAAF, World War II, Korea; to col. Nebr. Air NG. Mem. Nebr. Bar Assn., Neb. Diplomats, Newcomen Soc. N.Am., Am. Legion, Nebr. State Chamber of Commerce, Lincoln Contry Club, Lincoln U. Club, Firethorn Country Club, Alpha Sigma Phi, Phi Delta Phi. Republican. Presbyterian (elder). Home: 40 Bishop Sq Lincoln NE 68502 Office: Iowa Beef Processors Inc Dakota City NE 68731

TINSTMAN, ROBERT A., construction, real estate executive. Pres. mining group Morrison Knudsen Co., Inc., Boise, Idaho, 1989-95, CEO, 1995—. Office: Morrison Knudsen Co Inc 1 Morrison Knudsen Pla Boise ID 83729

TIPPECONNIC, JOHN W., III, federal agency administrator. Dir. Office of Indian Edn. Programs Dept. of the Interior, Washington. Office: Dept the Interior/Bur Indian Affairs Office Indian Edn Programs 1849 C St NW MS-3512MIB Washington DC 20240-0001

TIPPETT, WILLIS PAUL, JR., automotive and textile company executive, retired; b. Cin., Dec. 27, 1932; s. Willis Paul and Edna Marie (Conn) T.; m. Carlotta Prichard, Jan. 24, 1959; children: Willis Paul III, Holly. AB, Wabash Coll., 1953. Brand mgr.; advt. supr. Procter & Gamble Co., Cin., 1958-64; advt. and sales promotion mgr. Ford Motor Co., Dearborn, Mich., 1964-65; gen. mktg. mgr. Ford Motor Co., 1965-69; advt. mgr. Ford Motor Co. (Ford div.), 1969-70, advt. and sales promotion mgr., 1970-72; v.p. product and mktg. Philco-Ford Corp., Phila., 1972-73; dir. sales and mktg. Ford of Europe, Inc., Brentwood, Essex, Eng., 1973-75; pres., dir. STP Corp., Ft. Lauderdale, Fla., 1975-76; exec. v.p., dir. Singer Co., N.Y.C., 1976-78; pres., chief operating officer, dir. Am. Motors Corp., Southfield, Mich., 1978-82; chmn., chief exec. officer Am. Motors Corp., Southfield, 1982-85; pres. Springs Industries, Inc., Ft. Mill, S.C., 1985-89; prin. Ann Arbor (Mich.) Ptnrs. Investment Co., 1989—; bd. dirs. Lukens, Inc., Stride Rite Corp., Just Cynthia Inc. With USN, 1953-58. Mem. Univ. Club (N.Y.).

TIPPIN, AARON, country music singer, songwriter; b. Travelers Rest, S.C., July 3, 1958; divorced; 1 child, Charla. Various positions including farm hand, welder, airplane pilot, truck driver, heavy equipment operator, factory worker; writer Acuff-Rose, 1987-90; recording artist RCA, 1990—. Albums: You've Got to Stand for Something, 1991, Read Between the Lines, 1992 (gold), Call of the Wild, 1993; #1 single There Ain't Nothing Wrong with the Radio, 1992; toured with Bob Hope to perform for troops during Persian Gulf War, 1991, 1st singer to perform, song You've Got to Stand for Something was anthem of troops. Avocation: body-building (prize winner). Office: RCA Records Nashville 1 Music Circle Nashville TN 37203*

TIPPING, WILLIAM MALCOLM, social services administrator; b. Oak Park, Ill., Mar. 31, 1931; s. William McKinley and Evelyn Amelia (Freier) T.; m. Lois A. Grife, Sept. 18, 1954 (dec. May 1986); children: William, Barbara, Robert; m. Babette J. Cumming, Oct. 10, 1987; children: Christopher Cumming, Courtney Barone. BA, Carleton Coll., Northfield, Minn., 1954. Sales rep. Gen. Mills, Inc., Mpls., 1954-56; account exec. Campbell Mithun, Inc., Mpls., 1956-63; v.p. mgmt., supr. Campbell Mithun, Inc., Mpls. and Chgo., 1965-76; account supr., v.p. Lennen & Newell, Inc., N.Y.C., 1963-65; ptnr., mgr. Heidrick & Struggles, Inc., Chgo., 1976-88; exec. v.p., chief exec. officer Am. Cancer Soc., Atlanta, 1988-91; pres. Tipping and McRae, Inc., Atlanta, 1991-93; mng. dir. Ward Howell Internat., Inc., Atlanta, 1993—. Trustee Carleton Coll., 1986-90; bd. dirs. Nat. Health Coun., 1992—, Ga. Conservancy, Families First; mem. fin. com. UICC, Geneva, 1990-91. Recipient Disting. Svc. award Carleton Coll., 1984. Mem. Skokie Country Club (Glencoe, Ill., pres. 1983-84), Capital City Club (Atlanta), Haig Pt. Club (Daufuskie Island, S.C.), Quechee (Vt.) Club. Republican. Episcopalian. Office: Ward Howell Internat Inc 3350 Peachtree Rd NE Ste 1600 Atlanta GA 30326-1040

TIPPINS, BEDELL A., lawyer; b. Berlin, Aug. 8, 1948. BA, Rutgers U., 1970; JD, John Marshall Law Sch., 1978. Bar: Ill. 1978. Ptnr. Keck, Mahin & Cate, Chgo. Editor-in-chief John Marshall Law Rev., 1977-78. Mem. ABA, Ill. State Bar Assn., Chgo. Bar Assn., Maritime Law Assn. U.S. Office: Keck Mahin & Cate 77 W Wacker Dr Ste 4900 Chicago IL 60601-1693

TIPPIT, JOHN HARLOW, lawyer; b. Marietta, Okla., July 22, 1916; s. Alva Ney and Edna Pearl (Harlow) T.; m. Ann Morse, Feb. 27, 1943; children—David H., Ann Maurine. B.A., U. Okla., 1940, LL.B., 1940. Bar: Okla., 1940, Colo., 1945, U.S. Supreme Ct., 1960. States atty. Love County, Okla., 1940; sole practice Denver, 1945-77, Boulder, Colo., 1978-83; ptnr. Tippit, Haskell & Welborn, Tippit & Haskell and Tippit & Whittington P.C., Boulder, 1947-48; dir. Buckingham Nat. Bank; pres., mng. ptnr. natural resources cos.; lectr. Rocky Mountain Mineral Law Found.; lectr. various legal confs. Co-author: American Law of Mining; contbr. articles to profl. jours. Vice pres. Denver council Boy Scouts Am.; pres. Red Rocks Assn.; bd. dirs., sec. Acad. Ind. Scholars. Served to lt. col. USAAF, 1940-44. Mem. ABA (chmn. sect. natural resources), Okla. Bar Assn., Colo. Bar Assn. (chmn. mineral law sect.), Denver Bar Assn. (trustee). Republican. Episcopalian. Clubs: Mile High Denver Country (Denver); Boulder Country. Home: 525 Aurora Ave Boulder CO 80302-7127 Office: 305 Park West Bldg 250 Arapahoe Ave Boulder CO 80302-5838

TIPPLES, KEITH HOWARD, research scientist; b. Cambridge, Eng., Feb. 4, 1936; arrived in Can., 1963; s. Arthur Lyndhurst and Violet Isobel (Brown) T.; m. Maureen Cecilia Mannall, Apr. 23, 1962; children: Neil Anthony, Megan Angela, Graham Arthur. BSc, U. Birmingham, Eng., 1959, PhD, 1962. Research scientist Grain Rsch. Lab., Can. Grain Commn., Winnipeg, Man., 1964-79, dir. rsch., 1979—. Mem. Am. Assn. Cereal Chemists (bd. dirs. 1985-87, Carl Wilhelm Brabender award 1978, William F. Geddes Meml. award 1991). Avocations: choral singing, cross-country skiing, sailing, tennis, cricket. Office: Can Grain Commn Rsch Lab, 1404-303 Main St, Winnipeg, MB Canada R3C 3G8

TIPPO, OSWALD, botanist, educator, university administrator; b. Milo, Maine, Nov. 27, 1911; s. John and Anna (Kimen) T.; m. Emmie Fernas, Sept. 21, 1934; children: Ray Ethan, Denis Robert. BS, U. Mass., 1932, DSc (hon.), 1954; MA, Harvard U., 1933, PhD, 1937; MA (hon.), Yale U., 1955. Austin teaching fellow Harvard U., Cambridge, Mass., 1932-35; teaching asst. Radcliffe Coll., Cambridge, 1935-37; instr. botany U. Ill., Urbana, 1937-39, assoc. in botany, 1939-41, asst. prof. botany, 1941-47, assoc. prof., 1947-49, prof. botany, 1949-55, acting head dept., 1947-48, chmn. dept., 1948-55, chmn. div. biol. scis., 1949-51, dean grad coll., 1953-55; Eaton prof. botany, chmn. dept. Yale U., New Haven, 1955-60, dir. Marsh Bot. Garden, 1955-60; provost U. Colo., Boulder, 1960-63; exec. dean arts and scis. NYU, 1963-64; provost U. Mass., Amherst, 1964-70, chancellor, 1970-71, Commonwealth prof. botany and higher edn., 1971-82, prof. emeritus, 1982—. Author: (with H.J. Fuller) College Botany, 1949, rev. edit., 1954, (with W.L. Stern) Humanistic Botany, 1977; editor in chief Am. Jour. Botany, 1951-53; chmn. editorial com. in biol. scis. Rinehart & Co., 1958-60; mem. com. on Handbook of Biol. Data, 1953-60; trustee Biol. Abstracts, 1957-63, pres. 1963-64; editor Econ. Botany, 1979-86; contbr. articles to profl. jours. Mem. Harvard U. bd. overseers com. to visit Arnold Arboretum, 1957-62; mem. Mass. bd. Found. for Sci. and Tech., 1970-71; trustee Hampshire Coll., 1970-71; mem. Commn. on Instns. of Higher Edn., New Eng. Assn. Schs. and Coll., 1977-81; biologist wood sect., last sch. 1958 NY Sch. Yard, Phila., 1943-45. Republican (v.p., chmn. sect. G 1958), Am. Acad. Arts and Scis. (coun. 1967-71, membership com. 1974-76); mem. AAUP (U. Ill. chpt. pres. 1952-53), Am. Inst. Biol. Scis. (chmn. edml. commn. 1956-60, chmn. steering com. on secondary sch. biology film series 1958-60), Bot. Soc. Am. (pres. 1955, Merit award 1980), Soc. for Econ. Botany (Disting. Econ. Botanist award 1988), Conn. Bot. Soc. (dir. 1955-60), New Eng. Bot. Club, Internat. Assn. Wood Anatomists, Sigma Xi (pres. U. Ill. chpt. 1951-52, Yale U. chpt. 1958), Phi Beta Kappa. Home: 95 Aubinwood Rd Amherst MA 01002-1623 Office: Univ Mass Botany Dept Amherst MA 01003

TIPTON, CLYDE RAYMOND, JR., communications and resources development consultant; b. Cin., Nov. 13, 1921; s. Clyde Raymond and Ida Marie (Molitor) T.; m. Marian Gertrude Beushausen, Aug. 6, 1942; children: Marian Page Ashley, Robert Bruce. BS, U. Ky., 1946, MS, 1947. Research engr. Battelle Meml. Inst., Columbus, Ohio, 1947-49, sr. tech. adviser, 1951-62, coordinator corporate communications, 1969-73, v.p. communications, 1973-75, asst. to pres., 1978-79, v.p., corp. dir. communications and pub. affairs, 1979-86, ret.; staff mem. Los Alamos Sci. Lab., 1949-51; dir. research Basic, Inc., Bettsville, Ohio, 1962-64; asst. dir. Battelle Pacific N.W. Labs., Richland, Wash., 1964-69; pres., trustee Battelle Commons Co. for Community Urban Redevel., Columbus, 1975-78; cons. bus. communications and devel. Columbus, 1986—; secretariat U.S. del. 2d Internat. Conf. on Peaceful

Uses Atomic Energy, Geneva, 1958; cons. U.S. AEC in Atoms for Peace Program, Tokyo, 1959, New Delhi, 1959-60, Rio de Janeiro, Brazil, 1961. Author: How to Change the World, 1982; editor: Jour. Soc. for Nondestructive Testing, 1953-57, The Reactor Handbook, Reactor Materials, vol. 3, 1955, vol. 1, 1960. Learning to Live on a Small Planet, 1974; patentee in field. Past pres. Pilot Dogs; bd. dirs., treas. Pilot Guide Dog Found. Served with U.S. Army Air Corp., 1943. U. Ky. Haggin fellow, 1947; Otterbein Coll. Sr. fellow, 1978. Mem. NSPE (pres.), Am. Soc. Metals, Ohio Soc. Profl. Engrs. (past pres.), D. Episcopalian. Home and Office: 6475 Strathaven Ct W Columbus OH 43085-2991

TIPTON, DANIEL L., religious organization executive. Gen. supt. Churches in Christ in Christian Union, Circleville, Ohio. Office: Chs of Christ in Christian Union Box 30 1426 Lancaster Pike Circleville OH 43113

TIPTON, E. LINWOOD, trade association executive; b. Adrian, Mo., Nov. 19, 1934; s. Harlow Acklin and Mary Catherine (Lacy) T.; m. Marjorie A. Wolford, Dec. 17, 1955 (div. June 1983); children: Kelly A., Mark A.; m. Constance E. Eaton Broadstone, Oct. 8, 1983. BS in Agriculture, U. Mo., 1955, MS in Agriculture and Econs., 1956. Economist USDA Fgn. Agy. Svc., Washington, 1956-57, Eastern Milk Prodrs., Syracuse, N.Y., 1960-62; exec. dir. Coop. Dairy Econ. Svc., Boston, 1962-65; v.p., exec. v.p., pres., chief exec. officer Internat. Dairy Foods Assn., Washington, 1965—; founder Nat. Economist Club, Washington, treas., chmn. bd., 1967-73; founder Nat. Economist Ednl. Found., Washington, treas., chmn. bd., 1969-74; chmn. bd. Petlin, Inc., Fredericksburg, Va.; expert witness congl. coms., regulatory agencies; founder Internat. Sweetener Colloquium; apptd. to Nat. Commn. Agrl. Trade and Export Policy, 1984; advisor Sec. Agriculture, U.S. Trade Rep.; co-founder, chmn. bd. restaurant/motel chain, 1967—; chmn. The Food Group, The Ice Cream and Milk Polit. Action Com., Food Processors Steering Com. on Wage and Price Stability. 1st lt. Army Fin. Corp., 1957-60. Recipient Citation of Merit U. Mo. Alumni Assn., 1988. Avocations: tennis, golf. Office: Internat Dairy Foods Assn 1250 H St NW Ste 900 Washington DC 20005

TIPTON, HARRY BASIL, JR., state legislator, physician; b. Salida, Colo., Mar. 14, 1927; s. Harry Basil Sr. and Nina Belle (Hailey) T.; m. Dorothy Joan Alexander, Sept. 16, 1950; children: Leslie Louise, Harry Basil III, Robert Alexander. BA, U. Colo., 1950, MD, 1953. Diplomate Am. Bd. Family Practice. Postgrad. med. tng. Good Samaritan Hosp., Phoenix., Ariz., Maricopa County Hosp., Phoenix; ptnr., dir. Lander (Wyo.) Med. Clinic, 1954—; mem. Wyo. Ho. Reps., Cheyenne, 1981—, chmn. judiciary com., 1986—; cons. Indian Health Svc., Ft. Washakie, Wyo., 1968—; dir NOWCAP Family Planning, Worland, Wyo., 1975-90. Mem., pres. Fremont County Sch. Dist. # 1, Lander, 1958-78. With USMC, 1945-46, capt. USNR Med. Corps, 1950-87. Named Capt. Med. Corps. USNR, 1974. Fellow Am. Coll. Ob.-Gyn., Am. Assn. Family Practice (charter); mem. Wyo. Med. Soc. (Physician of Yr. 1989), Rotary (pres. 1960-61), Elks. Republican. Avocations: fishing, skiing, bird hunting, military history. Office: Lander Med Clin PC 745 Buena Vista Dr Lander WY 82520-3431

TIPTON, JENNIFER, lighting designer; b. Columbus, Ohio, Sept. 11, 1937; d. Samuel Ridley and Isabel (Hanson) T. B.A., Cornell U., 1958. arist in residence Nat. Theater Artist Residency Program at Wooster Group funded by the PEW Charitable Trusts, 1994; assoc. prof. lighting Yale U. Sch. of Drama. Lighting designer Paul Taylor Dance Co., Twyla Tharp and Dancers, 1965, Am. Ballet Theater, Jerome Robbins, Dana Reitz, Guthrie Theater, Hartford Stage Co., Wooster Group, numerous others. Beck Theatre, Murder Among Friends, Biltmore Theatre, 1975, Rex, Lunt-Fontanne Theatre, For Colored Girls Who Consider Suicide When the Rainbow is Enuf (Drama Desk award), Booth Theatre, Cleve. Ballet Co., Mikhail Baryshnikov's The Nutcracker, Am. Ballet Theatre, 1976, The Landscape of the Body, Newman Theatre, The Cherry Orchard (Drama Desk award, Tony award 1977), Agamemnon, Beaumont Theatre, Happy End, Martin Beck Theatre, Agamemnon, Delacorte Theatre, 1977, Museum, Public Theatre, Runaways, Public Theatre and Plymouth Theatre, All's Well That Ends Well, Taming of the Shrew, Delacorte Theatre, After the Season, Academy Festival Theatre, A Month in the Country, Williamstown Theatre Festival, Mikhail Baryshnikov's Don Quixote, Am. Ballet Theatre, The Goodbye People, Westport Playhouse, Funny Face, Buffalo Studio Arena, Drinks Before Dinner, Public Theatre, Alice in Wonderland, The Pirates of Penzance, Public Theatre, 1978, Lunch Hour, 1980, Billy Bishop Goes to War, 1980, The Sea Gull, 1980, Sophisticated Ladies, 1981, The Wake of Jamie Foster, 1982, Uncle Vanya, 1983, Orgasmo Adulto Escapes from the Zoo, 1983, Baby with the Bathwater, 1984, Hurlyburly, 1984, Whoopie Goldberg, 1984, Endgame, 1984, The Ballad of Soapy Smith, 1984, Jerome Robbins' Broadway, (Antoinette Perry award, 1989); assoc. dir. Goodman Theatre, Chgo.; lighting instr. Yale U. Sch. Drama; lighting designer The Joffrey Ballet, N.Y.C. Recipient Chgo.'s Joseph Jefferson award, 1976-77, Obie award 1979, Brandies U. Creative Arts award medal in dance, 1982, Mpls. Kudos award 1983, N.Y. Dance and Performance award 1984, (with Ana Reitz), 1987, Guggenheim fellowship, 1986-87, Am. Theater Wing award 1989, Commonwealth award in dramatic arts, 1989, Lawrence Olivier award, 1991, Dance Magazine award, 1991, NEA Disting. Theater Artist award 1991. Home: 11 W 18th St New York NY 10011-4603

TIPTON, JOHN J., lawyer; b. Denver, Dec. 18, 1946. BS cum laude, Colo. State U., 1968; JD, U. Denver, 1974, LLM, 1978. Bar: Colo. 1975, U.S. Dist. Ct. (Colo. dist.) 1975, U.S. Ct. Appeals (10th cir.) 1975, U.S. Tax Ct. 1976, U.S. Supreme Ct. 1978. Exec. dir. Colo. Dept. Revenue, Denver, 1988-92, Colo. Dept. Adminstrn., Denver, 1990-91; cabinet officer Colo. Gov. Roy Romer, Denver, 1988-92; ptnr. Baker & Hostetler, Denver. With USAF, 1968-72. Mem. ABA (mem. sect. econs. law practice law practice mgmt. divsn., divsn. vice chmn. 1987-89, chmn. law practice mktg. of legal svcs. group 1986-89, vice chmn. nat. mktg. conf. com. 1986-89), Colo. Bar Assn., Denver Bar Assn. (mem. sects. taxation, econs. of law practice, real property, probate and trust law), Denver Estate Planning Coun. Office: Baker & Hostetler 303 E 17th Ave Ste 1100 Denver CO 80203-1264

TIPTON, JON PAUL, allergist; b. Lynchburg, Ohio, Nov. 8, 1934; s. Paul Alvin and Jeanette (Palmer) T.; m. Martha J. Johnson, Dec. 29, 1968; children: Nicole Ann, Paula Michelle. BS, Ohio U., 1956; MD, Ohio State U., 1960. Resident internal medicine Ohio State U. Hosps., Columbus, 1964-66; fellow in allergy and pulmonary disease Duke U. Med. Ctr., Durham, N.C., 1964-64, 66-67; pvt. practice medicine specializing in allergies Athens, Ohio, 1967-74; pvt. practice medicine specializing in allergy Marietta, Ohio, 1974—; dir. cardio respiratory therapy Marietta Meml. Hosp., 1983, med. dir. pulmonary rehab. program, chief of medicine; med. dir. pulmonary rehab. program, past chief of medicine; cons. Ohio U. Hudson Health Ctr., 1967—, Marietta Coll. Health Ctr., 1974—, United Mine Workers of Am. Funds, 1984—; med. lectr. for physicians groups. Vol. Marietta Rep. Hdqrs., 1978—; mem. choir St. Luke's Luth. Ch., Marietta, 1983—. Served to capt. USAF, 1961-63. Mem. Am. Acad. Allergy, Ohio State Med. Assn., Wash. County Med. Soc., Parkersburg Acad. Medicine. Republican. Methodist. Avocations: yardwork, piano, attending plays, football, children. Home: 101 Meadow Ln Marietta OH 45750-1345 Office: 100 Front St Marietta OH 45750-3142

TIPTON, KENNETH WARREN, agricultural administrator, researcher; b. Belleville, Ill., Nov. 14, 1932; s. Roscoe Roy and Martha Pearl (Davis) T.; m. Barbara Adds, Mar. 2, 1957; children: Kenneth Warren Jr., Nancy Tipton O'Neal. BS, La. State U., 1955, MS, 1959; PhD, Miss. State U., 1964. Asst. prof. Agrl. Ctr., La. State U., Baton Rouge, 1959-70, assoc. prof., 1970-75, prof., 1975—; supt. Red River Rsch. Sta., La. Agrl. Expt. Sta. Agrl. Ctr., La. State U., Bossier City, 1975-79; assoc. dir. La. Agrl. Expt. Sta. Agrl. Ctr., La. State U., Baton Rouge, 1979-89, dir. La. Agrl. Expt. Sta., vice chancellor, 1989—; mem. com. nine USDA/Coop. State Rsch. Svc., 1986-88; Expt. State Com. Orgn. Policy, 1988-91. Contbr. articles to Agronomy Jour., Jour. Econ. Entomology, Grain Sorghum Conf. Coach baseball program Am. Legion, 1969-74; scoutmaster Boy Scouts Am., Baton Rouge, 1970-75. Capt. USAF, 1955-58. Mem. Am. Soc. Agronomy, Crop Sci. Soc. Am., Coun. Agrl. Sci. Tech. Achievements include research on inheritance of fiber traits in cotton, resistance of grain sorghum hybrids to bird damage, tannin content of grain sorghum and effects of phosphorus on growth of sorghum. Home: 732 Baird Dr Baton Rouge LA 70808-5916

TIPTON, PAUL LOUIS, physicist, educator; b. Rochester, N.Y., Nov. 12, 1957; s. William L. and Joan (Rusnock) T.; m. Mary I. Daly, Aug. 13, 1983. BS, SUNY, Binghamton, 1979; MA, U. Rochester, 1983, PhD, 1987. Postdoctoral rsch. assoc. Lawrence Berkeley Lab., Berkeley, Calif., 1987-90; Wilson fellow Fermi Nat. Accelerator Lab., Batavia, Ill., 1990-91; asst. prof. physics U. Rochester, 1991—. Named Outstanding Jr. Investigator, U.S. Dept. Energy, 1992; NSF Young Investigator, 1992—. Mem. Am. Phys. Soc., Phi Beta Kappa. Office: U Rochester Dept Physics Rochester NY 14627

TIPTON, PAUL S., former college president, association executive. Joined S.J., Roman Catholic Ch., ordained priest, 1971. Pres. Spring Hill Coll., Mobile, Ala., 1972-1989, Assn. Jesuit Colls. and Univs., Washington, 1990—. Office: Assn Jesuit Colls and Univs 1 Dupont Cir Ste 405 Washington DC 20036-2211

TIPTON, WHITNEY HORD, federal agency administrator. BS in Chemistry, Morehead U., 1965; MSCE, U. Tenn., 1974. Mgmt. engr. Union Carbide Corp., Oak Ridge, Tenn., 1966-79; dep. regional dir. Fed. Office Surface Mining, Knoxville, Tenn., 1979-82; field office dir. Fed. Office Surface Mining, Lexington, Ky., 1982-89; dep. dir. Dept. Interior, Washington, 1989—. Active Project First Offender, Big Brothers Am. Recipient Nat. Indsl. Rsch. award, Presdl. award. Avocations: triathlete, karate (black belt). Home: 1637 N Abingdon St Arlington VA 22207 Office: Dept Interior Surface Mining Reclamation & Enforcement 1951 Constitution Ave NW Washington DC 20240

TIPTON-MARTIN, TONI, newspaper editor. Food section editor, wine section editor The Cleveland Plain Dealer, Ohio. Office: Plain Dealer Pub Co 1801 Superior Ave NE Cleveland OH 44114

TIRAKIS, JUDITH ANGELINA, financial company executive; b. Bristol, Conn., Oct. 11, 1938; d. Dante and Ines (Paravella) Follandri; m. George Tirakis, July 15, 1967. BA, St. Joseph Coll., West Hartford, Conn., 1956-60; postgrad., St. Joseph Coll., 1960-61. With Engelhard Minerals and Chem. Corp., Menlo Park, N.J., 1964-67; supr. Sci. Info. Ctr. Ciba Geigy Pharm. Co., Summit, N.J., 1967-78; records mgr. research info. Ortho Pharm. Corp. div. Johnsn & Johnson, Raritan, N.J., 1978-86; v.p., corp. records mgr. AMBAC Indemnity Corp., N.Y.C., 1985-90, v.p. adminstrn., 1991—. Mem. Assn. Records Mgrs. and Adminstrs., Am. Mgmt. Assn., Nat. Assn. Female Execs., Assn. Image and Info. Mgmt., Internat. Facilities Mgmt. Assn. Office: AMBAC Indemnity Corp 1 State Street Plz New York NY 10004-1505

TIRANA, BARDYL RIFAT, lawyer; b. Geneva, Dec. 16, 1937; s. Rifat and Rosamond English (Walling) T.; m. Anne Prather, June 22, 1985; children by previous marriage: Kyra, Amina. A.B., Princeton U., 1959; LL.B. Columbia U., 1962. Bar: D.C. 1962, Md. 1986, N.Y. 1986, Va. 1986, Pa. 1992. Trial atty. Dept. Justice, 1962-64; assoc. Amram, Hahn & Sundlun, Washington, 1965-68; ptnr. Amram, Hahn & Sundlun, 1969-72; dir., sec. Exec. Jet Aviation, Inc., Columbus, Ohio, 1970-77, Technics, Inc., Alexandria, Va., 1971-77; ptnr. Sundlun, Tirana & Scher, Washington, 1972-77; dir. def. civil preparedness agy. Dept. Def., Washington, 1977-79, mem. armed forces policy coun., 1977-79; chmn. bd. Technics, Inc., San Jose, Calif., 1979-85; of counsel Silverstein and Mullens, Washington, 1982-84, ptnr., 1984-90; pvt. practice law Washington, 1991—. Mem.-at-large D.C. Bd. Edn., 1970-74; treas. Jimmy Carter Inaugural Trust, Washington, 1977-87; co-chmn. 1977 Presdl. Inaugural Com., 1976-77; mem. exec. adv. coun. Calif. Commn. Indsl. Innovation, 1981-82; pres. China/USA Edn. Fund, Inc., Washington, 1981—. Recipient medal for disting. pub. svc. Dept. Def., 1979, Fuess award Phillips Acad., 1991, Svc. Commendation award YWCA of Nat. Capital Area, 1991. Mem. N.Y.C. Racquet and Tennis Club, D.C. Met. Club. Home: 3550 Tilden St NW Washington DC 20008-3121 Office: 4401 Connecticut Ave NW Ste 606 Washington DC 20008-2322

TIRRELL, JOHN ALBERT, religious organization executive, consultant; b. Boston, Feb. 11, 1934; s. George Howard and Helen Sarah (Hitchings) T.; m. Helga Ruth Eisenhauer, Jan. 29, 1966; children: Steffanie Ruth, Sabina Lisette, Monica Susanne. BA in Psychology, The King's Coll., Briarcliff Manor, N.Y., 1961; MEd, U. Ariz., 1975. Various positions for several orgns., 1962-68; analyst instrnl.-ednl. systems GE, Daytona Beach, Fla., 1969-72; dir. curriculum and program devel. Brookdale C.C., Lincroft, N.J., 1972; dir. learning and faculty resources Pima C.C., Tucson, 1972-76; dir. human resources planning and devel. Miami divsn. Cyprus Copper Co., Claypool, Ariz., 1976-79; exec. dir. Calvary Missionary Fellowship, Tucson, 1983-85; interim pastor Sagauro Evang. Ch., Tucson, 1985-86; Midvale Evang. Ch. Midvale Evangelical Ch., Tucson, 1986-87; founder, pres. The Jethro Consultancy, Birmingham, Mich., 1979—; v.p. mgmt. svc. AA Gage, Ferndale, Mich., 1987-88; pastor Desert Hills Bapt. Ch., Tucson, 1993—; mem. adv. bd. UIM Internat., Flagstaff, Ariz., 1983-92, mem. fin. com., 1983-94, sec. support svcs. field bd., 1993—, also bd. dirs.; assoc. faculty mem. Gila Evangelica Ea. Ariz. Coll., Globe, 1978; adj. prof. Montclair State Coll., Upper Montclair, N.J., 1972; chmn. Mgmt. and Pers. com. Wildwood Ranch, Inc., Howell, Mich., 1989-92; interim pres., v.p. programs, v.p. devel. Detroit Rescue Mission Ministries, 1990-92; v.p. corp. planning, tng., productivity George Instrument Co., Royal Oak. Contbr. articles to profl. jours. Mem. Ariz. Coun. for Econ. Conversion, 1992—; mem. facilities task force Grace Evang. Free Ch., Birmingham, 1988-89, chmn. by-laws revision com., 1989-90, chmn. property devel. com., 1990-92; elder 1st Evang. Free Ch., Tucson, 1986-87, Sunday sch. supt., 1981-84, Adult Sunday Sch. supt., 1992—, chmn., gen. bd., elder bd., 1979-82, short-term missions coord., missions bd., 1992—; v.p. parent-tchr. fellowship Palo Verde Christian Sch., Tucson, 1980-81; bd. dirs. Clearing House of Operational Resources for Christian Orgns., Royal Oak, Mich., 1991; interim pastor Desert Hills Bapt. Ch., Tucson, 1993—. Staff sgt. USAF, 1952-56. Mem. ASTD (treas. Old Pueblo chpt. 1988, dir. at large 1983, Human Resources Devel. award Valley of the Sun chpt. 1977), Birmingham-Bloomfield C. of C. (mem. profl. devel. edn. com. 1987-91, mem. pub. rels. mktg. com. 1989), King's Coll. Alumni Assn. (class gov. 1988—). Republican. Avocations: photography, Bible teaching. Home and Office: 2501 W Rapallo Way Tucson AZ 85741-2536

TIRRELL, MATTHEW, chemical engineering/materials science educator; b. Phillipsburg, N.J., Sept. 5, 1950; s. Matthew Vincent Tirrell Jr. and Loraine (Wier) Gonsky; m. Pamela Lavigne, Aug. 1993. BS, Northwestern U., 1973; PhD, U. Mass., 1977. Mem. coop. edn. program Cin. Milacron Chem. Inc., 1970-72; tchg. and rsch. asst. U. Mass., Amherst, 1973-77; asst. prof. U. Minn., Mpls., 1977-81, assoc. prof., 1981-85, prof. chem. engring. and materials sci., 1985—, Shell disting. chair in chem. engring., 1986-91, acting head, 1992-93, Earl E. Bakken prof. biomed. engring., 1993—; sci. advisor BIOSYM Techs., San Diego. Author: Modeling of Polymerization Processes, 1995. John Simon Guggenheim Meml. Found. fellow, 1986. Mem. AIChE (editor jour. 1991—), Profl. Progress award 1994, Allan P. Colburn award 1985), Am. Chem. Soc., Am. Phys. Soc. (John H. Dillon medal 1987), Materials Rsch. Soc. Avocations: gourmet cooking, movies, distance running. Home and Office: U Minn Dept Chem Engring & Mat Sci Minneapolis MN 55455

TIRRO, FRANK PASCALE, music educator, author, composer; b. Omaha, Sept. 20, 1935; s. Frank and Mary Carmela (Spensieri) T.; m. Charlene Rae Whitney, Aug. 16, 1961; children: John Andrew, Cynthia Anne. B.M.E., U. Nebr., 1960; M.M., Northwestern U., 1961; Ph.D., U. Chgo. 1974. Chmn. lab. schs. U. Chgo., 1961-70; fellow of Villa I Tatti Harvard U., Florence, Italy, 1971-72; lectr. U. Kans., Lawrence, 1972-73; dir. Southeastern Inst. Medieval and Renaissance Studies, Durham, N.C., 1978-80; chmn., assoc. prof. music Duke U., Durham, 1973-80; prof. Yale U., New Haven, 1980—, dean, 1980-89; reader, cons. several univ. presses; jurist Parisot Internat. Cello Competition, Sao Paolo, Brazil, 1981. Author: Jazz: a History, 1977, rev. edit., 1993, Renaissance Choirbooks in the Archive of San Petronio in Bologna, 1986; (with others) The Humanities: Cultural Roots and Continuities, 1980, 4th edit., 1992; editor: Medieval and Renaissance Studies No. 9, 1982; mem. editoral bd. Wittenberg Rev.; composer American Jazz Mass, 1960. Bd. dirs. New Haven Symphony, 1980-89, Neighborhood Music Sch., New Haven, 1982-89, Chamber Orch. New Eng., 1980-82, Ctr. for Black Music Rsch., 1985—. Recipient Standard Composer award Am. Soc. Composers, Authors and Pubs., 1966, Gustavus Fine Arts medal, 1988, Duke Ellington Fellow medal, 1989; travel grantee Am. Coun. Learned Socs., 1967; rsch. grantee Duke U., 1978. Mem. Am. Musicol. Soc. (council 1978-

80), Coll. Music Soc. (council 1980-82, mem. exec. bd. 1984-86), Nat. Assn. Schs. of Music, Internat. Soc. Jazz Research, Renaissance Soc. Am., Mory's Club, Yale Club (N.Y.C.). Republican. Lutheran. Office: Yale U Sch Music PO Box 208246 New Haven CT 06520-8246

TIRYAKIAN, EDWARD ASHOD, sociology educator; b. Bronxville, N.Y., Aug. 6, 1929; s. Ashod Haroutioun and Keghinee (Agathon) T.; m. Josefina Cintron, Sept. 5, 1953; children: Edmund Carlos, Edwyn Ashod. BA summa cum laude, Princeton U., 1952; MA, Harvard U., 1954, PhD, 1956; PhD (hon.), U. Rene Descartes, Paris, 1987. Instr. Princeton U., 1956-57, asst. prof., 1957-62; lectr. Harvard U., 1962-65; assoc. prof. Duke U., Durham, N.C., 1965-67, prof., 1967—, chmn. dept. sociology and anthropology, 1969-72, dir. internat. studies, 1988-91; vis. lectr. U. Philippines, 1954-55, Bryn Mawr Coll., 1957-59; vis. scientist program Am. Sociol. Assn., 1967-70; vis. prof. Laval U., Quebec, Que., Can., 1978, Institut d'Etudes Politiques, Paris, 1992; summer seminar dir. Nat. Endowment for Humanities, 1978, 80, 83, 89, 91; lectr. Kyoto Am. Studies Summer Seminar, 1985. Author: Sociologism and Existentialism, 1962; Editor: Sociological Theory, Values and Sociocultural Change: Essays in Honor of P.A. Sorokin, 1963, The Phenomenon of Sociology, 1971, On the Margin of the Visible: Sociology, the Esoteric, and the Occult, 1974, The Global Crisis: Sociological Analyses and Responses, 1984; co-editor: Theoretical Sociology: Perspectives and Developments, 1970; New Nationalisms of the Developed West, 1985. Recipient Fulbright Research award, 1954-55; Ford Faculty Research fellow, 1971-72. Mem. Am. Sociol. Assn., African Studies Assn., Am. Soc. for Study Religion (council 1975-78, pres. 1981-84), Assn. Internationale des Sociologues de Langue Française (v.p. 1985-88, pres. 1988-92), Soc. for Phenomenology and Existential Philosophy, Phi Beta Kappa. Clubs: Princeton, Century Assn. (N.Y.C.). Home: 16 Pascal Way Durham NC 27705-4924 *As a sociological researcher, I have sought to understand on a comparative basis the dynamics of social consciousness in the process of historical change. As a teacher, I have sought to encourage in students—undergraduates, graduates, and postgraduates— a gusto for intellectual curiosity in exploring the myriad of linkages that make up social reality, our human patrimony.*

TISCH, ANDREW HERBERT, corporate executive; b. Asbury Park, N.J., Aug. 14, 1949; s. Laurence Alan and Wilma Zelda (Stein) T.; 2 children. BS, Cornell U., 1971; MBA, Harvard U., 1977. Brand mgr. Lorillard Co., N.Y.C., 1971-75; mgr. operational analysis Loews Corp., N.Y.C., 1977-79, v.p., 1985—; pres. Bulova Corp., Woodside, N.Y., 1985-89; chmn., chief exec. officer Lorillard Tobacco Co., N.Y.C., 1989—; also bd. dirs. Lorillard Tobacco Co., Bulova Corp., Woodside, N.Y.; mem mgmt. com. Loews Corp., Bulova Systems and Instruments Corp. Contbr. articles to profl. jours. Mem. fgn. affairs com. Am. Jewish Com., N.Y.C., 1983—; bd. dirs. Outward Bound, Inc., Greenwich, Conn., 1983-88; trustee Central Synagogue, N.Y.C., 1984—; gen. chmn. United Jewish Appeal Fedn. of Jewish Philanthropies N.Y., vice chmn. United Jewish Appeal, chmn. Prime Minister's Coun., 1987—; bd. dirs. N.Y. Shakespeare Festival, 1987—; chmn. Children's Hearing Inst., 1988; bd. mem. N.Y.C. Sports Commn. Mem. 24 Karat Club N.Y., Century Country Club, Harmonie Club, Plumb Club, Achilles Track Club (bd. dirs.). Avocations: tennis, running. Office: Lorillard Tobacco Co 1 Park Ave New York NY 10016-5802 also: 666 Fifth Ave New York NY 10103

TISCH, JAMES S., diversified holding company executive; b. Atlantic City, Jan. 2, 1953; s. Laurence A. and Wilma (Stein) T.; m. Merryl Hiat; children: Jessica, Benjamin, Samuel. BA, Cornell U., 1975; MBA, Wharton Grad. Sch., U. Pa., 1976. With Loews Corp., N.Y.C., 1977—, exec. v.p., 1987-94, pres., 1994—, also mem. mgmt. com. Pres. Fedn. Employment and Guidance Svc., N.Y.C., 1985—; trustee Dalton Sch., N.Y.C., 1985—, Mt. Sinai Med. Ctr., N.Y.C., 1988—. Office: Loews Corp 667 Madison Ave New York NY 10021-8029

TISCH, JONATHAN MARK, hotel company executive; b. Atlantic City, Dec. 7, 1953; s. Preston Robert and Joan (Hyman) T. BA, Tufts U., 1976. Cinematographer, producer WBZ-TV, Boston, 1976-79; sales mgr. Loews Hotels, N.Y.C., 1980-81, dir. devel., 1981-82, v.p., 1982-85, exec. v.p., 1985-86, pres., 1986-89, pres., chief exec. officer, 1988—; mem. mgmt. com. Loews Corp. Trustee Robert Steel Found., N.Y.C., Gunnery Sch., Washington, Conn., 1983— Tufts U., Medford, Mass., 1986—; chmn. N.Y.C. host com. for 1988 Grammys, 1987-88; bd. dirs. Pediatric AIDS Found.; mem. dean's adv. coun. Sch. Hotel Adminstrn., Cornell U. Mem. Urban Land Inst., Young Pres.'s Orgn. Clubs: Century Country (Purchase, N.Y.); Friars (N.Y.C.). Avocations: tennis, snow skiing. Office: Loews Hotels 667 Madison Ave New York NY 10021-8029

TISCH, LAURENCE ALAN, broadcast corporation executive; b. N.Y.C., Mar. 5, 1923; s. Al and Sadye (Brenner) T.; m. Wilma Stein, Oct. 31, 1948; children: Andrew, Daniel, James, Thomas. BSc cum laude, NYU, 1942; MA in Indsl. Engring, U. Pa., 1943; postgrad., Harvard Law Sch., 1946; LLD (hon.), Skidmore Coll., 1994. Pres. Tisch Hotels, Inc., N.Y.C., 1946-74; chmn. bd., co-chief exec. officer Loews Corp., N.Y.C., 1960—, co-chief exec. officer, 1988—; pres., chief exec. officer, 1990—, also bd. dirs., co-chmn. bd., chmn. bd. dirs. CNA Fin. Corp., Chgo.; bd. dirs. Bulova Corp. subs. Loews Corp., N.Y.C., ADP Corp., Petrie Stores Corp., Federated Dept. Stores. Bd. dirs. United Jewish Appeal-Fedn.; chmn. bd. trustees NYU; trustee Met. Mus. Art, N.Y.C., N.Y. Pub. Libr. Mem. Coun. Fgn. Rels. Home: Island Dr N Manursing Island Rye NY 10580 Office: CBS Inc 51 W 52nd St New York NY 10019-6101 also: Loews Corp 667 Madison Ave New York NY 10021

TISCH, PRESTON ROBERT, finance executive; b. Bklyn., Apr. 29, 1926; s. Abraham Solomon and Sayde (Brenner) T.; m. Joan Hyman, Mar. 14, 1948; children: Steven E., Laurie M., Jonathan M. Student, Bucknell U., 1943-44; B.A., U. Mich., 1948. Co-chmn., co-chief exec. officer, dir. Loews Corp., N.Y.C., 1960—; postmaster gen. U.S. Postal Svc., Washington, 1986-88; chmn., co-CEO, half owner N.Y. Football Giants, 1990—; bd. dirs. CNA Fin. Corp., Bulova Watch Co. Chmn. emeritus N.Y. Conf. and Visitors Bur., Nat. Dem. Conv., 1976, 80; trustee NYU; mem. Quadrennial Commn. on Exec., Legis. and Jud. Salaries, 1988; mem. Gov.'s Bus. Adv. Coun. for N.Y. State; pres. Citymeals on Wheels. With AUS, 1943-44. Mem. Rye Racquet Club, Century Country Club, Sigma Alpha Mu. Office: Loews Corp 667 Madison Ave New York NY 10021-8029 also: NY Giants Giants Stadium East Rutherford NJ 07073

TISCH, RONALD IRWIN, lawyer; b. N.Y.C., Aug. 3, 1944; s. Joseph and Elsie (Rosler) T.; m. Eddi Gorewicz, July 1, 1973; children: Marissa, Courtney. BA, Bklyn. Coll., 1966; JD George Washington U., 1969; LLM, Harvard U., 1970. Bar: D.C. 1969. Appellate atty. NLRB, Washington, 1970-72; ptnr. Graham & James, Washington, 1987—. Mem. ABA, Am. Arbitration Assn., Immigration and Naturalization Lawyers Assn., Nat. Health Lawyers Assn., Order of Coif, Phi Alpha Delta. Contbr. to profl. publs. Home: 11005 Roundtable Ct Rockville MD 20852-4560 Office: Graham & James 2000 M St NW Ste 700 Washington DC 20036-3313

TISCH, STEVEN E., movie producer; b. Lakewood, N.J., Feb. 14, 1949; s. Preston Robert and Joan (Hyman) T.; m. Patricia Keast, Sept. 27, 1981 (div. July 1991); children: Hilary, William. BA, Tufts U., 1971. Pres. Tisch-Avnet Prodns., L.A., 1981-88, Steve Tisch Co. L.A., 1988—. Chmn. AIDS Project L.A., 1992-94. Office: The Steve Tisch Company 3815 Hughes Ave Culver City CA 90232-2715

TISCHLER, GARY LOWELL, psychiatrist, educator; b. N.Y.C., Oct. 30, 1935; s. Louis and Dorothy (Green) T.; m. Judith Post, Aug. 18, 1957; children: Laurie Dee, Marc David, Rachel Mara. AB, Hamilton Coll., 1957; MD, U. Pa., 1961; MS, Yale U., 1975. Intern Kings County Hosp., Bklyn., 1961-62; resident in psychiatry Yale U. Sch. Medicine, New Haven, 1962-65, asst. prof., 1967-70, assoc. prof., 1970-75, prof. psychiatry, 1975-90; prof. chmn. dept. psychiatry and biobehavioral scis., dir. neuropsychiatric inst. UCLA Sch. Medicine, 1990—; chmn. dept. psychiatry Yale U. Sch. Medicine, New Haven, 1986-87; dir. Yale Psychiatric Inst., New Haven, 1978-87; chief psychiatry Yale-New Haven Hosp., 1986-87; clin. dir. Hill-West Haven div. Conn. Mental Health Ctr., New Haven, 1968-70, dir., 1970-77; prof. psychiatry UCLA, 1987—; study dir. Pres.'s Commn. on Mental Health, Washington, 1977-78; cons. Arthur D. Little Inc., Boston, 1973-75,

IBM Corp., Armonk, N.Y., 1986-87; mem. profl. adv. com. Am. Med. Internat., Los Angeles, 1984-86; mem. bd. mental health and behavioral medicine Inst. Medicine, Washington, 1986—; com. on clin. evaluation Inst. Medicine, 1990—. Author: Quality Assurance Thru Utilization and Peer Review, 1982; editor: Patient Care Evaluation in Mental Health, 1985, Diagnosis and Classification in Psychiatry, 1987; contbr. articles to profl. jours. Mem. Gov.'s transition staff on mental health, Conn., 1975; vice chmn. Bd. Mental Health State of Conn., 1986. Served to capt. U.S. Army, 1965-67, Vietnam. Fellow Am. Psychiat. Assn.; Am. Coll. Mental Health Adminstrn., Am. Assn. for Social Psychiatry. Am. Coll. Psychiatry. Democrat. Jewish. Home: 16314 Meadowridge Rd Encino CA 91436-3607 Office: UCLA Dept Psychiatry 760 Westwood Plz Los Angeles CA 90024-8300*

TISCHLER, HERBERT, geologist, educator; b. Detroit, Apr. 28, 1924; s. Louis and Hermina (Leb) T.; m. Annette Zeidman, Aug. 10, 1954; children—Michael A., Robert D. B.S., Wayne U., 1950; M.A., U. Calif.-Berkeley, 1955; Ph.D., U. Mich., 1961. Instr. Wayne State U., Detroit, 1956-58; assoc. prof. No. Ill. U., DeKalb, 1958-65; prof. dept. earth scis. U. N.H., Durham, 1965—, chmn. dept., 1965-90; co-dir. No. New Eng. Jr. Sci. and Humanities Symposium, 1979—, mem. nat. adv. com., 1989-92. Trustee Mt. Washington Observatory, 1980-92. With USCG, 1943-46. Fellow Geol. Soc. Am. Home: 36 Oyster River Rd Durham NH 03824-3029 Office: U NH Dept Earth Scis James Hall Durham NH 03824

TISCHMAN, MICHAEL BERNARD, lawyer; b. Elizabeth, N.J., Oct. 8, 1937; s. Nathan and Ann (Goldberg) T.; m. Elinor Cohen, Aug. 16, 1959; children: David F., Susan F. BA, U. Pa., 1959; LLB, Harvard U., 1963; LLM in Taxation, NYU, 1968. Bar: N.J. 1964, Fla. 1979, N.Y. 1984. Law sec. Judge Walter J. Freund N.J. Appellate Div., 1963-64; assoc. Schiff, Cummis & Kent, Newark, 1964-67; ptnr. Cummis, Kent, Radin & Tischman, Newark, 1968-70, Sills, Beck, Cummis, Radin & Tischman, Newark, 1971-87, Sills, Cummis, Zuckerman, Radin, Tischman, Epstein & Gross, Newark, 1988—; panel chmn. fee arbitration com. N.J. Supreme Ct. Dist. Essex County, 1987-91. Mem. Mayor's Performing Arts Ctr. Task Force, Newark, 1983—. Mem. N.J. Bar Assn. (com. on ltd. partnership act revisions 1983-88), Phi Beta Kappa. Home: 8 Wedgewood Way Scotch Plains NJ 07076-2727 Office: Sills Cummis Zuckerman Radin Tischman Epstein & Gross One Riverfront Pla Newark NJ 07102

TISDALE, STUART WILLIAMS, holding company executive; b. Leominster, Mass., Aug. 15, 1928; s. Malcolm and Ruth (Williams) T.; m. Ann Howard, Dec. 7, 1967; children: Stuart, Walter, Malcolm, Andrew, Ward; stepchildren: Peter, Scott, Bruce. BA, Yale U., 1951. Pres. Southworth Machine Co., Portland, Maine, 1954-65; pres. climate control div. Singer Co., N.Y.C., 1965-74; exec. v.p. Dover Corp., N.Y.C., 1974-84; chmn. STA-RITE Industries, Inc., Milw., 1984-94; chmn., CEO, dir. Wicor, Inc., Milw., 1984—; bd. dirs. Wis. Gas Co., Milw., Marshall and Ilsley Bank, Marshall and Ilsley Corp., Twin Disc Inc., Modine Mfg. Co. Bd. dirs. Columbia Hosp., Greater Milw. Com. With USN, 1952-54.

TISE, LARRY EDWARD, historical organization administrator, historian; b. Winston-Salem, N.C., Dec. 6, 1942; s. Russell Edward and Lena Irene (Norman) T.; children: Larry Edward, Nicholas Allen, William Zane. A.B., Duke U., 1965, M.Div., 1968; Ph.D. (Ford Found. fellow, 1970, Research Triangle fellow, 1971), U. N.C., 1974. Part-time editor John Fries Blair, Pub., Winston-Salem, 1969-72; teaching fellow history dept. U. N.C., Chapel Hill, 1971; instr. U.N.C., 1972-73; dir. hist. publs. N.C. Bicentennial Com., 1973-74; asst. dir. N.C. Div. Archives and History, Raleigh, 1974-75; dir. N.C. Div. Archives and History, 1975-81, N.C. State Hist. Preservation officer, 1975-81; exec. dir. Pa. Hist. and Mus. Commn., 1981-87; Pa. State Hist. Preservation officer, 1981-87; dir. Am. Assn. for State and Local History, Nashville, Tenn., 1987-89; exec. dir. Benjamin Franklin Nat. Meml., Phila., 1989—; adj. prof. grad. sch. fine arts U. Pa., 1984-87; vis. prof. Vanderbilt U., 1988-89, Temple U., 1989-91; mem. Nat. Hist. Publs. and Records Commn., 1982-88; officer Preservation Action; corp. dir. Fedn. N.C. Hist. Socs., Friends of N.C. Archives, Inc., Hist. Preservation Fund of N.C., Inc., Preservation Fund of Pa., Inc., Hist. Preservation Soc. N.C., Inc., Mus. History Assocs., Inc., N.C. Inst. Applied History, Stagville Ctr. Corp., N.C., Inc. Author, co-author writings in fields of archives, hist. preservation, hist. sites and museums, history, society, religion; author: The Southern Experience in the American Revolution, 1978, The Monitor: Its Meaning and Future, 1978, Writing North Carolina History, 1979, A House Not Made with Hands, 1966, The Yadkin Melting Pot: Methodism and the Moravians in the Yadkin Valley, 1750-1850, 1968, Proslavery: The Defense of Slavery in America, 1987, A Book About Children, 1992; gen. editor: writings in fields of archives, hist. preservation, hist. sites and museums, history, society, religion including Winston-Salem in History, 13 vols, 1976; edit. bd. The Public Historian, 1980-86; editor N.C. Hist. Rev., 1974-81, Pa. Heritage, 1981-87, History News, 1987-89, Franklin Gazette, 1989—; contbr. articles to books, newsletters, jours. Recipient William R. Davie History award, 1979, Herbert L. Feis award, Am. Hist. Assn., 1989, Benjamin Franklin Nat. Meml. awards 1990; Nat. Endowment for the Humanities fellow, 1992-93. Mem. Am. Hist. Assn. (various coms.), Orgn. Am. Historians (chmn. coms.), So. Hist. Assn., Soc. Am. Archivists, Am. Assn. State and Local History (mem. council and coms.), Nat. Trust for Hist. Preservation, Nat. Assn. State Archives and Records Adminstrs. (pres. 1980-81), Nat. Council State Hist. Preservation Officers (bd. dirs. 1976-79, pres. 1979-81), Nat. Council on Public History (bd. dirs., exec. com. 1979-83, pres. 1983-85), N.C. Hist. Commn. (sec. 1975-81), N.C. Lit. and Hist. Assn. (sec., treas. 1977-81), Pa. Fedn. Hist. Socs. (sec. 1981-87), Internat. Cong. Disting. Awards (founder, pres. 1993—), Friends of Franklin, Inc. (exec. sec. 1989—). Methodist. Home: 705 Corinthian Ave Philadelphia PA 19130-2614

TISE, MARY SHACKELFORD, public librarian; b. Charlottesville, Va., Oct. 26, 1954; d. Alfred Colquitt and Mary Aston (Leavell) Shackelford; m. Frank Peine Tise, July 4, 1981; children: David, Gregory, Joseph. BA, U. Va., 1976; MLS, U. N.C., 1978. Libr. dir. Vaughan Meml. Libr., Galax, Va., 1978-81; reference libr. Concord Pike Libr., Wilmington, Del., 1981-83, divsn. mgr., 1989—; divsn. mgr. Claymont (Del.) Pub. Libr., 1983-89. Mem. ALA, AAUW, Del. Libr. Assn. (pres. 1989-90). Office: Concord Pike Libr 3406 Concord Pike Wilmington DE 19803

TISCHLER, WILLIAM HENRY, landscape architect, educator; b. Baileys Harbor, Wis., June 22, 1936; s. William John and Mary Viola (Sarter) T.; m. Betsy Lehner, Sept. 23, 1961; children—William Phillip, Robin Elizabeth. B.S. in Landscape Architecture, U. Wis., 1960; M.L.A., Harvard U., 1964. Urban planner City of Milw., 1961-62; mem. faculty dept. landscape architecture U. Wis.-Madison, 1964—; assoc. Hugh A Dega & Assos. (Landscape Architects), 1964-66; prin. Land Plans Inc. (Land and Hist. Preservation Planning Cons.), Madison 1966—; advisor emeritus Nat. Trust for Hist. Preservation; mem. Door County Land Trust, Inc., 1986-91; bd. dirs. The Hubbard Edul. Trust. Author: American Landscape Architecture: Designers and Places, 1989; contbr. articles to profl. jours. Served with C.E., U.S. Army, 1960. Recipient Design Arts Program award NEH, 1981; Attingham (Eng.) Program fellow Soc. Archtl. Historians, 1980; Dumbarton Oaks sr. fellow, 1990. Fellow Am. Soc. Landscape Architects (Horace Cleve. Vis. Prof. U. Minn. 1993, merit award 1971, nat. honor award 1980, 89); mem. Assn. Preservation Tech., Wis. Acad. Arts, Letters and Scis., Pioneer Am. Soc., Hist. Madison (hon.), Vernacular Architecture Forum, Madison Trust for Hist. Preservation, Alliance for Hist. Landscape Preservation (founder), The Clearing Landscape Inst. (co-dir.), Phi Kappa Phi, Sigma Lambda Alpha, Sigma Nu. Lutheran. Home: 3925 Regent St Madison WI 53705-5222 Office: U Wis Dept Landscape Architecture Madison WI 53706

TISHMAN, JOHN L., realty and construction company executive; b. N.Y.C., Jan. 24, 1926; s. Louis and Rose F. (Foreman) T.; m. Suzanne Weisberg; children: Daniel R., Katherine T. Chmn., chief exec. officer Tishman Realty & Constrn. Co., Inc., N.Y.C. Home: Mianus Riv Rd Bedford NY 10506 Office: Tishman Constrn Corp N Y 666 5th Ave New York NY 10103-0001

TISHMAN, ROBERT V., real estate and construction company executive; b. N.Y.C., Apr. 7, 1916; s. David and Ann (Valentine) T.; m. Phyllis Gordon (decr.); children: Lynne Tishman Speyer, Nancy Tishman Gonchar. BA, Cornell U., 1937. With Tishman Realty & Constrn. Co., Inc., N.Y.C.,

1938—, pres., 1962-78; mng. ptnr. Tishman Speyer Properties; chmn. Real Estate Bd. N.Y., 1973-75. Bd. dirs. Citizens Housing and Planning Coun.; trustee Citizens Budget Commn.; chmn. Montefiore Hosp. and Med. Ctr., 1973-79, hon. chmn., 1979—; assoc. chmn. Jewish Assn. Svcs. to Aged. Lt. comdr. USNR, World War II. Office: 520 Madison Ave New York NY 10022-4213

TISINGER, CATHERINE ANNE, college dean; b. Winchester, Va., Apr. 6, 1936; d. Richard Martin and Irma Regina (Ohl) T. BA, Coll. Wooster, 1958; MA, U. Pa., 1962, PhD, 1970; LLD (hon.), Coll. of Elms, 1985. Provost Callison Coll., U. of Pacific, Stockton, Calif., 1971-72; v.p. Met. State U., St. Paul, 1972-75; v.p. acad. affairs S.W. State U., Marshall, Minn., 1975-76, interim pres., 1976-77; dir. Ctr. for Econ. Edn., R.I. Coll., Providence, 1979-80; v.p. acad. affairs Cen. Mo. State U., Warrensburg, Mo., 1980-84; pres. North Adams State Coll., Mass., 1984-91; dean arts and scis. Shenandoah U., Winchester, Va., 1991—; cons. North Cen. Assn. Colls. and Schs., 1980-84, New Eng. Assn. Schs. and Colls., 1978-79, 85—, Minn. Acad. Family Physicians, 1973-77; mem. adv. bd. First Agrl. Bank, North Adams, 1985-91; pres. No. Berkshire Cooperating Colls., 1986-91; v.p. Coll. Consortium for Internat. Studies, 1989-90. V.p. Med. Simulation Found., 1986-88; bd. dirs. Williamstown Concerts, 1989-91, Shawnee coun. Girl Scouts U.S., 1992-93. Mem. No. Berkshire C. of C. (bd. dirs. 1984-89, v.p. 1986-89). Avocations: fiber and textile arts, photography. Office: Shenandoah U 1460 College Dr Winchester VA 22601

TISON, JOSEPH SOUTHWOOD, food products company executive; b. Savannah, Ga., June 23, 1943; s. Henry Lawton and Edna Lucille (Williamson) T.; m. Sarah Wheeler, July 22, 1967; children: Katherine Coates, Joseph Southwood, Sarah Lawton, Robert Fletcher. BA, U. N.C., 1965; MBA, Old Dominion U., 1971; cert. exec. mgmt., Pa. State U., 1982. Mktg. assoc. Continental Can Co., N.Y.C., 1971-72; sales rep. Continental Can Co., Cin., 1972-77; dist. mgr. Continental Can Co., Atlanta, Stamford, Conn., 1977-82; nat. sales mgr. TriCoast Container Corp., Stamford, 1982-85; exec. v.p. Citrus Products Inc., N.Y.C., 1985—. Vice-chmn. Ridgefield (Conn.) Parking Authority, 1989; incorporator Ridgefield Community Ctr., 1988—. Mem. Nat. Juice Processors Assn., Internat. Apple Inst., Citrus Processors Assn. (assoc.), Dairy and Food Industries Supply Assn., Brazilian-Am. C. of C. (dir. 1987—), Citrus Assocs. N.Y. N.Y. Cotton Exchange (assoc.), Oglethorpe Club (Savannah, Ga.), Lakeside Field (South Salem, N.Y.). Republican. Episcopalian. Avocations: skiing, tennis, horticulture. Office: Citrus Products Inc 499 Park 21st Ave New York NY 10022-1240

TISON-BRAUN, MICHELINE LUCIE, French language educator; b. Arras, France, Apr. 7, 1913; came to U.S., 1947, naturalized, 1964; d. Eugène and Lucie (Duchat) T.; m. Lev Braun, Apr. 1, 1948. Agregée ès lettres, 1937, Docteur ès lettres, 1972. Prof. French Education Nationale, London, 1938-47; translator BBC, London, 1941-45; translator, précis writer UN, N.Y.C., 1947-54; prof. French Lycée N.Y., City U. N.Y. Grad. Ctr. and Hunter Coll., 1961-81. Author: La Crise de l'Humanisme, vol. I, 1957, rev. edit., 1963, vol. II, 1968, Nathalie Sarraute la Recherche de l'Authenticitè, 1971, Dada et le Surréalisme, 1975, Tristan Tzara, 1977, Poetique du Paysage, 1980, L'Introuvable Origine, 1981, Ce Monstre Incomparable, A. Malraux et le Probleme de la Personnalite (Prix Jouvenel), 1982, Marquerite Duras, 1983, Le Moi décapité Lang, 1989. Decorated Palmes Academiques; Guggenheim fellow, 1978-79. Mem. MLA, Am. Assn. Tchrs. French, Pen Club, Gens de Lettres, Société d'Histoire littéraire de la France. Home: 50 Central Park W New York NY 10023

TITCOMB, CALDWELL, music and theatre historian; b. Augusta, Maine, Aug. 16, 1926; s. Samuel and Lura Elizabeth (Smith) T. AB summa cum laude, Harvard U., 1947, M.A., 1949, Ph.D., 1952. Univ. organist Brandeis U., Waltham, Mass., 1953-70. dir. undergrad. studies music, 1954-84, curator creative arts, library, 1961-64, co-chmn. music dept., 1977-84, from instr. to prof. music, 1953-88, prof. emeritus, 1988—; drama critic Harvard Crimson, 1953-82, Bay State Banner, 1975—; trustee Charles Playhouse, Boston, 1966-71. Editor: The Art of Fine Words, 1965, The Furies (Lauren Price), 1988; co-editor: Varieties of Black Experience at Harvard, 1986, Blacks at Harvard: A Documentary History of African-American Experience at Harvard and Radcliffe, 1993; contbr. articles to profl. jours., ency.; composer stage and film music scores. Bd. dirs. Cambridge Civic Symphony Orch., Mass., 1959-70; exec. bd. Mus. Fine Arts Friends Music, Boston, 1959-65; panelist Mass. Commn. Arts and Humanities, 1981-83; mem. selection com. Theater Hall of Fame, 1980—; juror Elliot Norton awards, 1985-94; pres. Boston Theater Awards, 1994—. With U.S. Army, 1944-46, PTO; with Mil. Intelligence Res., 1946-50. Mem. AAUP, Coll. Music Soc., Am. Theatre Critics Assn. (charter), New Eng. Theatre Conf. (adv. coun. 1961-81, coll. fellows 1981), Am. Guild Organists, Am. Musicol. Soc. (coun. 1965-67), Soc. for Ethnomusicology, Hist. Brass Soc., Signet Soc., Sonneck Soc., Phi Beta Kappa (sec. Mu chpt. Mass. 1984—). Avocations: philology; Afro-Am. history and culture. Office: Brandeis U Music Dept South St Waltham MA 02254-9110

TITLEY, LARRY J., lawyer; b. Tecumseh, Mich., Dec. 9, 1943; s. Leroy H. and Julia B. (Ruesink) T.; m. Julia Margaret Neukom, May 23, 1970; children: Sarah Catherine, John Neukom. BA, U. Mich., 1965, JD, 1972. Bar: Va. 1973, Mich. 1973. Assoc. Hunton & Williams, Richmond, Va., 1972-73; Varnum, Riddering, Schmidt & Howlett, Grand Rapids, Mich., 1973—. Trustee Friends Pub. Mus, 1985-94; bd. dirs. Grand Rapids Pub. Mus. Found., 1988—, pres., 1992—; bd. dirs. Camp Optimist YMCA, 1993—, Peninsular Club, 1994—. Mem. ABA, Mich. Bar Assn., Grand Rapids Bar Assn. Home: 746 San Jose Dr SE Grand Rapids MI 49506-3418 Office: Varnum Riddering Schmidt & Howlett Bridgewater Pl PO Box 352 Grand Rapids MI 49504

TITLOW, LARRY WAYNE, physical education and kinesiology educator; b. Hearne, Tex., Oct. 12, 1945; s. Stanford P. and Mary Ellen (Bostick) T. BS, U. Houston, 1969, MEd, 1970; PhD, Tex. A&M, 1977. Asst. prof. No. Ky. U., Highland Heights, 1977-82; assoc. prof. U. Cen. Ark., Conway, 1982-89, prof., 1989—; fitness cons. Acxiom, Conway, Ark., 1986-91; rsch. cons. U. Ark., Fayetteville, 1983—. Author: (with D.K. Cobb, W.G. Smith and M.E. Norman) A Resource Manual for Workshops on Presenting the Educational Improvement Plan to the Community, 1980, (with M.E. Gray) Lifetime Fitness, 1981, (with A. Maehen) Principles of Kinesiology and Physical Education, 1994, (with D.J. Johnson) Research Methods in Kinesiology and Physical Education. Instr. lifesaving ARC, Conway, 1983-91. Rsch. grantee DaVinci Lab., Burlington, Vt., 1980, Ky. Coun. on Higher Edn., Lexington, 1982, U. Cen. Ark. Rsch. Coun., 1985, 89. Mem. Am. Alliance for Health, Phys. Edn., Recreation and Dance (active various coms., assemblies, rsch. coun. so. dist.), Am. Coll. Sports Medicine (Cen. States chpt.), Ark. Assn. Health, Phys. Edn., Recreation and Dance (pres., other offices), others. Avocations: sailing, scuba diving, travel, hunting, fishing. Office: U Cen Arkansas PO Box 4991 Conway AR 72035

TITONE, VITO JOSEPH, judge; b. Bklyn., July 5, 1929; s. Vito and Elena (Ruisi) T.; m. Margaret Anne Viola, Dec. 30, 1956; children: Stephen, Matthew, Elena Titone Hill, Elizabeth. BA, NYU, 1951; JD, St. John's U., 1956, LL.D., 1984. Bar: N.Y. 1957, U.S. Dist. Ct. (ea. and so. dists.) N.Y., 1962, U.S. Supreme Ct. 1964. Ptnr. Maltese & Titone, N.Y.C., 1957-65, Maltese, Titone & Anastasi, N.Y.C., 1965-68; assoc. counsel to pres. pro tem N.Y. State Senate, 1965; justice N.Y. State Supreme Ct, N.Y.C., 1969-75; assoc. justice appellate div. 2d dept. N.Y. State Ct. Appeals, N.Y.C., 1975-85; judge N.Y. State Ct. Appeals, Albany, 1985—; adj. prof. Coll. S.I., CUNY, 1969-72, St. John's U., Jamaica, N.Y., 1969-85. Contbr. articles to law jour. Bd. govs. Daytop Village N.Y., N.Y.C.; bd. dirs. Boy Scouts Am. With U.S. Army, 1951-53, to col. N.Y. State Guard. Named Citizen of Yr. Daytop Village, N.Y.C., 1969, Disting. Citizen Wagner Coll., S.I., 1983, Outstanding Contbr. Camelot Substance Abuse Network, 1983; recipient citation of merit S.I. Salvation Army Adv. Bd., 1983, Rapollo award Columbian Lawyers Assn., 1983, Disting. Judiciary award Cath. Lawyers Guild Diocese of Bklyn., 1991, Disting. Svc. award N.Y. State Lawyers Assn., Justice William Brennan award N.Y. Assn. Criminal Def. Lawyers, 1993. Mem. ABA, N.Y. State Bar Assn., Richmond County Bar Assn., Supreme Ct. Justice Assn., VFW, Am. Legion (past comdr.), Charles C. Pinckney Tribute Def. Assn. of N.Y.C. Justice Assn., K.C. Roman Catholic. Office: NY Ct Appeals 20 Eagle St Albany NY 12207-1004 also: 60 Bay St Fl 9 Staten Island NY 10301-2514

TITTMANN, BERNHARD RAINER, engineering science and mechanics educator; b. Moshi, Tanganjika, East Africa, Sept. 15, 1935; came to U.S., 1950, naturalized, 1956; s. Gustav and Hermine Marie (Polland) T.; m. Katharine Shower, Dec. 17, 1966; children: Christine M., Heidi E., Raymond J., Monica M., Brian P.F. BS, George Washington U., 1957; MS, UCLA, 1961, PhD, 1965. Mem. staff Hughes Aircraft Co., Culver City, Calif., 1957-65; asst. prof. UCLA, 1965-66; mem. staff Rockwell Internat., Thousand Oaks, Calif., 1966-79, dept. mgr., 1979-89; Schell prof. engring. Pa. State U., University Park 1989—. Co-author 5 books; contbr. over 200 articles to profl. jours.; patentee in field. George Washington fellow George Washington U., 1953, Howard Hughes fellow Hughes Aircraft Co., 1957. Fellow IEEE (adminstrv. com. for ultrasonics, ferrolectrics, frequency control, nominating chmn. 1988—); mem. Acoustical Soc. Am. (tech. program mem. 1986-89), KC (4th degree), Phi Beta Kappa. Home: 2466 Sassafras Ct State College PA 16803-3366 Office: Pa State U 228C Hammond Bldg University Park PA 16802

TITUS, ALICE CESTANDINA (DINA TITUS), state legislator; b. Thomasville, Ga., May 23, 1950. AB, Coll. William and Mary, 1970; MA, U. Ga., 1973; PhD, Fla. State U., 1976. Prof. polit. sci. U. Nev., Las Vegas; mem. Nev. Senate, 1989—; alt. mem. legis. commn., 1989-91, mem., 1991-93; minority floor leader, 1993—; chmn. Nev. Humanities Com., 1984-86; mem. Eldorado Basin adv. group to Colo. River Commn.; active Gov. Commn. Bicentennial of U.S. Constn.; former mem. Gov. Commn. on Aging. Author: Bombs in the Backyard: Atomic Testing and American Politics, 1986, Battle Born: Federal-State Relations in Nevada during the 20th Century, 1989. Mem. Western Polit. Sci. Assn., Clark County Women's Dem. Club. Greek Orthodox. Home: 1637 Travois Cir Las Vegas NV 89119-6283 Office: Nev State Senate State Capitol Carson City NV 89710

TITUS, DAVID ANSON, political science educator; b. Cleve., Dec. 2, 1934; s. Jesse Edmond and Anne (Bonnette) T.; m. Kaoru Matsumura, Sept. 3, 1960 (div. 1966); m. Rachel Thankful Roberts, Aug. 3, 1968; children: Jeffrey, Bryan. B.A., Harvard U., 1956; M.A., Columbia U., 1962, Ph.D., 1970. Instr. Wesleyan U., Middletown, Conn., 1966-70, asst. prof., 1970-73, assoc. prof., 1973-79, prof. govt., 1979—; co-chmn. Coll. Social Studies, Wesleyan U., Middletown, Conn., 1972-75, 81-84, 93—, chmn. dept. govt., 1976-78, chmn. East Asian Studies Program, 1976-78, 1979-81, 1988-90; mem. staff Joint Com. Japanese Studies, N.Y.C., 1968-70; chmn. bd. dirs. Associated Kyoto Program, 1976-77, 79-82, resident dir., 1975-76, 84-85. Author: Palace and Politics in Prewar Japan, 1974; translator: Japan's Road to the Pacific War-The Final Confrontation: Japanis Negotiations with the United States, 1941, 1994. Founder Mattabeseck Audubon Soc., Middletown, Conn., 1974. Served to lt. (j.g.) USN, 1956-58. Recipient Ansley award Columbia U. Press, 1970; vis. scholar Corpus Christi Coll., Cambridge, Eng., 1978-79, Doshisha U., Kyoto, Japan, 1987. Mem. Assn. Asian Studies (council confs. 1983-86, chmn. studies program com. 1975). Home: 376 Main St Cromwell CT 06416-2305 Office: Wesleyan U Middletown CT 06459

TITUS, EDWARD DEPUE, psychiatrist, administrator; b. N.Y.C., May 24, 1931; s. Edward Kleinhans and Mary (Brown) Chadbourne; m. Virginia Van Den Steenhoven, Mar. 24, 1963 (div.); m. Catherine Brown, Apr. 22, 1990. BA, Occidental Coll., 1953; MS, U. Wis., 1955; MD, Stanford U., 1962; PhD, So. Calif. Psychoanalytic Inst., 1977. Mng. ptnr. Hacker Clinic Assn., Lynwood, Calif., 1968-90; chief psychiatrist parole outpatient clinic region III Calif. Dept. Corrections, L.A., 1991—; asst. clin. prof. psychiatry U. So. Calif., 1993—; chmn. dept. psychiatry St. Francis Hosp., Lynwood, 1979-80. Fellow Am. Psychiat. Assn.; mem. Calif. Med. Assn. (ho. of dels. 1982—), So. Calif. Psychiat. Soc. (sec. 1984-85), Los Angeles County Med. Assn. (dist. pres. 1980-81, pres. sect. psychiatry 1990-92). Avocations: photography, backpacking. Office: Parole Outpatient Clinic 307 W 4th St Los Angeles CA 90013-1104

TITUS, H. MARK, librarian; b. Boston, July 29, 1947; s. Harry Seferian and Isabelle Diane Titus; m Judith Marie Mundis, Aug. 15, 1968 (div. July 1976); m. Barbara Kunsela, May 3, 1986; children: Sean Michael, Jessica Barbara. BA, Boston U., 1969; MLS, U. Mich., 1971. Asst. library dir. Plymouth (Mass.) Pub. Library, 1972-73, library dir., 1973-74; exec. dir. APlymouth County Nuclear Info. Ctr., 1974-75; head processing div. New Castle County Dept. of Libraries, Wilmington, Del., 1975-83; library dir. Concord Pike Library, Wilmington, Del., 1983—; Mem. Council on Library Cooperation, Dover, Del., 1986—, long-range planning com. State Library Advisory Council, Dover, 1987—. Editor newsletters Lincs and Picnic, 1984; contbr. articles to profl. jours. Sec. Del. Coalition for Literacy, 1985-86, treas, 1986-87; mem. adult edn. com. Westminster Presbyn. Ch., Wilmington, 1986. Mem. ALA, Del. Library Assn. (treas. 1978-81, v.p. 1986-87, pres. 1987—), Libraries in New Castle County (v.p. 1985-86, pres. 1986-87). Democrat. Avocations: running, writing, music. Home: 1418 Lovering Ave Wilmington DE 19806-3018 Office: Concord Pike Library 3406 Concord Pike Wilmington DE 19803-5074

TITUS, JACK L., pathologist, educator; b. South Bend, Ind., Dec. 7, 1926; s. Loren C. and Rutha B. (Orr) T.; m. Beverly Harden, June 18, 1949; children—Jack, Elizabeth Ann Titus Engelbrecht, Michael, Matthew, Joan. B.S., Notre Dame U., 1948; M.D., Washington U., St. Louis, 1952; Ph.D., U. Minn., 1962. Practice medicine Rensselaer, Ind., 1953-57; fellow in pathology U. Minn., 1957-61; assoc. prof. pathology Mayo Grad. Sch., Rochester, Minn., 1961-72; prof. pathology Mayo Med. Sch., 1971-72, coordinator pathology tng. programs, 1964-72; W.L. Moody Jr. prof., chmn. dept. pathology Baylor Coll. Medicine, Houston, 1972-87; chief pathology service Meth. Hosp., Houston, 1972-87; pathologist-in-chief Harris County Hosp. Dist., Houston, 1972-87; chmn. dept. pathology Med. Ctr. Hosp., Conroe, Tex., 1982-87; Woodlands Community Hosp., 1984-87; dir. registry for cardiovascular diseases United Hosps., 1987—; clin. prof. pathology U. Minn., 1987—; adj. prof. pathology Baylor Coll. Medicine; sr. cons. in pathology U. Tex. System Cancer Ctr., Houston, 1974—. Mem. editorial bd.: Circulation, 1966-72, Am. Heart Jour, 1972-77, Modern Pathology, 1987—, Human Pathology, 1988—, Am. Jour. of Cardiovascular Pathology, 1987—, Cardiovascular Pathology, 1991—; contbr. articles to med. jours. Served with U.S. Army, 1945-47. Recipient Billings gold medal AMA, 1968, Hoektoen gold medal, 1969, Disting. Achievement award Soc. Cardiovascular Pathology, 1993, Scholarly Achievement award Houston Soc. Clin. Pathology, 1993. Mem. Internat. Acad. Pathology, Am. Assn. Pathologists, Am. Soc. Clin. Pathologists, AAAS, AMA, Am. Heart Assn., Coll. Am. Pathologists, Minn. Med. Assn., Minn. Heart Assn., Minn. Soc. Clin. Pathologists, Ramsey County Med. Soc., Sigma Xi, Alpha Omega Alpha. Methodist. Office: 255 Smith Ave N Ste 200 Saint Paul MN 55102-2518

TITUS, ROGER WARREN, lawyer; b. Washington, Dec. 16, 1941; s. George R. and Margaret (Merithew) T.; m. Catherine Mary Gaughen, Aug. 16, 1961; children: Paula Titus Laboy, Richard Roger, Mark William. BA, Johns Hopkins U., 1963; JD, Georgetown U., 1966. Bar: Md. 1966, D.C. 1966, U.S. Dist. Ct. Md. 1966, D.C. Dist. 1966, U.S. Ct. Appeals (4th cir.) 1966, U.S. Supreme Ct. 1970. Ptnr. Titus & Glasgow, Rockville, Md., 1966-88, Venable, Baetjer & Howard, Rockville, 1988—; asst. city atty. City of Rockville, 1966-69, city atty., 1970-82; spl. asst. Md. State Bd. of Law Examiners, 1969-72; adj. prof. law Georgetown U., Washington, 1972-78; mem. inquiry com. Atty. Grievance Commn., Annapolis, Md., 1975-80; mem. Trial Cts. Judicial Nominating Commn. Montgomery County, 1979-91; mem. standing com. on rules of practice and procedure Ct. of Appeals of Md., 1989—; mem. Appellate Jud. Nominating Commn., 1991—. Trustee Suburban Hosp., Inc. Bethesda, Md., 1986—. Fellow Am.Coll. Trial Lawyers, Am. Bar Found., Md. Bar Found. (bd. dirs. 1987—), v.p. 1990-91, pres. 1991-93); mem. ABA (del. 1987—), Nat. Conf. Bar Pres. (mem. exec. coun. 1990-93), Md. Bar Assn. (sec. 1984-87, pres. 1988-89), Md. Mcpl. Attys. Assn. (pres. 1975), Montgomery County Bar Assn. (pres. 1983-84), City Tavern Club. Office: Venable Baetjer & Howard PO Box 1906 1 Church St Ste 1000 Rockville MD 20850-4158

TITZE, INGO ROLAND, physics educator; b. Hirschberg, Silesia, Germany, July 8, 1941; came to U.S. 1955; s. Kurt Herrmann and Marta Emma (Bettermann) T.; m. R Katherine Pittard, July 19, 1969; children: Karin, Michael, Jason, Gregory. BSEE, U. Utah, 1963, MS in Elec. Engring. and Physics, 1965; Ph.D. in Physics, Brigham Young U., 1972. Rsch. engr. N. Am. Aviation, Tulsa, 1965-66, Boeing Co., Seattle, 1968-70; lectr.

Calif. State Poly. U., Pomona, 1973-74; asst. prof. U. Petroleum and Minerals Dhahran, Saudi Arabia, 1974-76, Gallaudet Coll., Washington, 1976-79; prof. physics and communication sci. U. Iowa, Iowa City, 1979—; cons. Bell Labs., Murray Hill, N.J., 1977-78; dir. rsch. Denver Ctr. Performing Arts, 1983—; pres. Voice Cons. Inc., 1985—; panelist, site visitor NRC-NAS, 1984—; regular cons. div. rsch. grants NIH, 1986—; chmn. task force on voice Nat. Inst. Deafness and Other Communication Disorders, 1989; adj. prof. Westminster Choir Coll., Princeton, N.J., 1989—; dir. Nat. Ctr. for Voice and Speech, 1990—. Author: Principles of Voice Production, 1991; editor: Vocal Fold Physiology: Biomechanics, Acoustics and Phonatory Control, 1985, assoc. editor: Jour. of Voice; editor: Vocal Fold Pysyiology: Frontiers in Basic Science, 1992; contbr. articles to profl. jours. Adv. bd. Voice Found., N.Y.C., 1980—; young men's pres. Latter Day Saints Ch. and Boy Scouts Am., Iowa City, 1982—. Jacob Javits Neurosci. Investigator grantee NIH, 1984; recipient William and Harriot Gould Found. award, 1983, Claude Pepper award, 1989, Quintant award Voice Found., 1990, fellow ASHA, 1992. Fellow Acoustical Soc. Am. (tech. council, awards com. 1989); mem. Am. Speech-Hearing-Lang. Assn., Nat. Assn. Tchrs. Singing (research council 1977—, editorial bd. 1986—), Internat. Assn. Research Singing (dir. publs. 1982—). Republican. Avocations: classical singing; tennis; choir directing; home building. Home: 2015 Glendale Rd Iowa City IA 52245-3217 Office: Nat Ctr for Voice & Speech Univ of Iowa 330 Wjshc Iowa City IA 52242-1012

TIZZIO, THOMAS RALPH, brokerage executive; b. Elmont, N.Y., Jan. 9, 1938; s. Anthony Thomas and Ann Marie (Pascale) T.; m. Mary Ann Gentile, Aug. 26, 1962; children: Anthony, Vincent, Thomas. BBA, Bklyn. Coll., 1962. Underwriter W.J. Roberts & Co., N.Y.C., 1957-65; sr. underwriter Atlantic Mut. Ins. Co., 1965-67; various positions AIG Am. Home Assurance Co., N.Y.C., 1967-74, sr. v.p. property underwriting, 1974-78; exec. v.p. AIG Transatlantic Reins. Co., N.Y.C., 1978-80, pres., bd. dirs., 1980-82; sr. v.p. reins. Am. Internat. Group, Inc., N.Y.C., 1982-85, pres. domestic brokerage divsn., 1985-91, pres. Brokerage divsn., 1986-91, pres., 1991—. Mem. Am. Inst. for Property and Liability Underwriters (trustee), Ins. Inst. Am. (trustee). Office: Am Internat Group Inc 70 Pine St New York NY 10270-0199

TJOFLAT, GERALD BARD, federal judge; b. Pitts., Dec. 6, 1929; s. Gerald Benjamin and Sarita (Romero-Hermoso) T.; m. Sarah Marie Pfohl, July 27, 1957; children: Gerald Bard, Marie Elizabeth Tjoflat. Student, U. Va., 1947-50, U. Cin., 1950-52; LL.B., Duke U., 1957; D.C.L. (hon.), Jacksonville U., 1978; LLD (hon.), William Mitchell Coll. Law, 1993. Bar: Fla. 1957. Individual practice law Jacksonville, Fla., 1957-68; judge 4th Jud. Cir. Ct. Fla., 1968-70, U.S. Dist. Ct. for Middle Dist. Fla., Jacksonville, 1970-75, U.S. Ct. Appeals, 5th Cir., Jacksonville, 1975-81; judge U.S. Ct. Appeals, 11th Cir., Jacksonville, 1981-89, chief judge, 1989—; mem. Adv. Corrections Coun. U.S., 1975-87, Jud. Conf. of U.S., 1989—, Fed. Jud. Ctr. Com. on Sentencing, Probation and Pretrial Svcs., 1988-90; mem. com. adminstrn. probation system Jud. Conf. of U.S., 1972-87, chmn., 1978-87; U.S. del. 6th and 7th UN Congress for Prevention of Crime and Treatment of Offenders. Hon. life mem. bd. visitors Duke U. Law Sch.; pres. North Fla. coun. Boy Scouts Am., 1976-85, chmn., 1985-90; trustee Jacksonville Marine Inst., 1976-90, Episc. H.S., Jacksonville, 1975-90; mem. vestry St Johns Cathedral, Jacksonville, 1969-71, 73-75, 77-79, 81-83, 85-87, 93—, sr. warden, 1975, 83, 87, 91, 92. Served with AUS, 1953-55. Recipient Merit award Duke U. 1990. Mem. ABA, Fla. Bar Assn., Am. Law Inst., Am. Judicature Soc. Episcopalian. Office: US Ct Appeals PO Box 960 Jacksonville FL 32201-0960

TLALKA, JACEK, mathematics educator; b. Krosno, Poland, Dec. 16, 1937; came to U.S. 1979; s. Antoni and Stanislawa (Rola) T.; m. Alicia S. Gaudyn, Apr. 30, 1960; children: Marek, Irena. M.Math., Jagiellonian U., Cracow, 1960; DrTech.Sci., Mining & Metall. U., Cracow, 1971. Tchr. Tech. High Sch., Cracow, 1960-63; teaching/research asst. Mining & Metall. U., Cracow, 1963-71; asst. prof. math. Mining & Metall. U., 1971-79; assoc. prof. math. Livingstone Coll., Salisbury, N.C., 1983-89; prof. math. Livingstone Coll., 1989—; chmn. math. and computer sci. Livingstone Coll., 1984—. Contbr. articles to profl. jours.; author book for coll. students, 1978. 2nd lt. Polish Army. 1Mem. Am. Math. Assn., math. Assn. Am. Republican. Roman Catholic. Office: Livingston Coll 701 W Monroe St Salisbury NC 28144-5298

TOAL, JAMES FRANCIS, academic administrator; b. N.Y.C., June 7, 1932; s. John Joseph and Catherine (Whyte) T. MA, St. John's U., 1966; PhD, Fordham U., 1976. Cert. elem. tchr., N.Y. cert. supt., adminstrn. and supervision, English 7-12. Athletic dir., tchr. English St. Francis Prep. High Sch., N.Y.C., 1957-60; tchr. Bishop Ford High Sch., N.Y.C., 1960-66, chmn. dept. English; prin. St. Francis Central Summer High Sch., N.Y.C., 1966-73, St. Francis Prep. High Sch., N.Y.C., 1966-73; exec. v.p., assoc. prof. dept. edn. adminstrn. and supervision Grad. Sch. St. Bonaventure U., N.Y., 1976-83; pres., prof. Quincy U., Ill., 1983—; also bd. trustees; mem. Springfield Diocesan Bd. of Edn., Provincial Bd. of Edn., Franciscan Friars of Chgo. and St. Louis. Trustee Siena Coll., Loudonville, N.Y., 1977-83; bd. advisors Jamestown Community Coll., Olean, N.Y., 1979-83; bd. dirs. Am. Cancer Soc., Olean, 1981-83; mem. Mental Health Assn., 1981-83; mem. state legis. com. Commn. of Ind. Colls. and Univs., Albany. N.Y., 1980-83. Grantee Colgate U., 1967; grantee SUNY-Plattsburg, 1968, St. Bonaventure U., 1980. Mem. Am. Coun. on Edn., Associated Colls. of Ill., Ill. Bus. and Edn. Forum, Assn. of Governing Bds., West Cen. Ill. Ednl. Telecommunications Corp. (bd. dirs. exec. com., pers. com.), Fedn. Ind. Ill. Colls. and Univs. (pub. rels. com.), Mid. States Accrediting Assn. (assoc., evaluation team for higher edn.), Nat. Assn. Secondary Sch. Prins., North Cen. Accrediting Assn. (evaluation team for higher edn., chair evaluation team 1986—), Soc. Coll. and U. Planning, Quincy C. of C. (transp. com. 1985—), Quincy Soc. Fine Arts (bd. dirs. 1985—), Rotary, Univ. Club, KC, Phi Delta Kappa. Office: Quincy U Office of Pres 1800 College Ave Quincy IL 62301-2699

TOAL, JEAN HOEFER, lawyer, state supreme court justice; b. Columbia, S.C., Aug. 11, 1943; d. Herbert W. and Lilla (Farrell) Hoefer; m. William Thomas Toal; children: Jean Hoefer, Lilla Patrick. BA in Philosophy, Agnes Scott Coll., 1965; JD, U. S.C., 1968; LHD (hon.), Coll. Charleston, 1991; LLD (hon.), Columbia Coll., 1992. Bar: S.C. Assoc. Haynsworth, Perry, Bryant, Marion & Johnstone, 1968-70; ptnr. Belser, Baker, Barwick, Ravenel, Toal & Bender, Columbia, 1970-88; assoc. justice S.C. Supreme Ct., 1988—; mem. S.C. Human Affairs Commn., 1972-74; mem. S.C. Ho. of Reps., 1975-88, chmn. house rules com., constitutional laws subcom. house judiciary com.; mem. parish coun. and lector St. Joseph's Cath. Ch.; chair S.C. Juvenile Justice Task Force, 1992-94; chair S.C. Rhodes Scholar Selection Com., 1994. Mng. editor S.C. Law Rev., 1967-68. Mem. bd. visitors Clemson U., 1978; trustee Columbia Mus. Art; chair S.C. Juvenile Justice Task Force, 1992-94; chair S.C. Rhodes Scholar Selection Com., 1994. Named Legislator of Yr. Greenville News, Woman of Yr., U. S.C.; recipient Disting. Svc. award S.C. Mcpl. Assn., Univ. Notre Dame award, 1991, Algernon Sydney Sullivan award U. S.C., 1991. Mem. John Belton O'Neill Inn of Ct., Phi Alpha Delta. Office: Supreme Ct SC PO Box 12456 Columbia SC 29211

TOALE, THOMAS EDWARD, school system administrator, priest; b. Independence, Iowa, Aug. 30, 1953; s. Francis Mark and Clara R. (DePaepe) T. BS in Biology, Loras Coll., 1975, MA in Ednl. Adminstrn., 1986; MA in Theology, St. Paul Sem., 1980; PhD in Ednl. Adminstrn., U. Iowa, 1988. Ordained priest Roman Cath. Ch., 1981; cert. tchr., prin., supt., Iowa. Tchr. St. Joseph Key West, Dubuque, Iowa, 1975-77; tchr. Marquette High Sch., Bellevue, Iowa, 1981-84, prin., 1984-86; assoc. supt. Archdiocese of Dubuque, 1986-87, supt. schs., 1987—; assoc. pastor St. Joseph Ch., Bellevue, 1981-84; pastor Sts. Peter and Paul Ch., Springbrook, Iowa, 1984-86, St. Peter, Temple Hill, Cascade, Iowa, 1986—. Mem. Nat. Cath. Edn. Assn. Office: Archdiocese of Dubuque 1229 Mount Loretta Ave Dubuque IA 52003-7800

TOBACH, ETHEL, retired curator; b. Miaskovka, USSR, Nov. 7, 1921; came to U.S. 1923; d. Ralph Wiener and Fanny (Schechterman) Wiener Idels; m. Charles Tobach, 1947 (dec. 1969). BA, Hunter Coll., 1949; MA, NYU, 1952, PhD, 1957; DSc (hon.), L.I. Univ., 1975. Lic. psychologist, N.Y. Rsch. fellow Am. Mus. Natural History, N.Y.C., 1958-61, assoc. curator, 1964-69, curator, 1969-90, emerita curator; rsch. fellow NYU

N.Y.C., 1961-64; adj. prof. psychology CUNY, N.Y.C., 1964—. Co-editor (series) T.C. Schneirla Conference Series, 1981, Genes & Gender, 1975; editor: Informational Jour. Comparative Psychology, 1987-93; assoc. editor: Peace and Conflict: Jour. of Peace Psychology, 1994—. Recipient Disting. Sci. Career, Assn. Women in Sci., 1974, Disting. Sci. Publ. Assn. for Women in Psychology, 1982, Kurt Lewin award Soc. for Psychol. Study of Social Issues, 1993. Fellow APA (pres. comparative psychology div. 1985); mem. Internat. Soc. Comparative Psychology (pres. 1984-86, sec. 1988-92), Ea. Psychol. Assn. (pres. 1987), N.Y. Acad. Scis. (v.p. behavioral scis. 1973-76). Office: Am Mus Natural History Central Pkwy 79th St New York NY 10024-5192

TOBE, STEPHEN SOLOMON, zoology educator; b. Niagara-on-the-Lake, Ont., Can., Oct. 11, 1944; s. John Harold and Rose T. (Bolter) T.; m. Martha Reller. BSc, Queen's U., Kingston, Ont., 1967; MSc, York U., Toronto, Ont., 1969; PhD, McGill U., Montreal, Que., Can., 1972. Rsch. fellow U. Sussex, Eng., 1972-74; asst. prof. U. Toronto, 1974-78, assoc. prof., 1978-82, prof., 1982—; assoc. dean scis. faculty arts and sci., 1988-93; vis. prof. U. Calif., Berkeley, 1981, Nat. U. Singapore, 1987, 1993-94, U. Hawaii, 1988; mem. animal biology grant selection com. Natural Scis. and Engring. Rsch. Coun. Can., 1986-89, chair, 1988-89; lectr. Internat. Congress Entomology, Vancouver, B.C., Can., 1988; cons. in hydroponics. Editor: Insect Biochemistry, 1987; mem. editl. bd.: Jour. Insect Physiology, 1980—, Physiol. Entomology, 1985—, Life Scis. Advances, 1987—, Gen. and Comparative Endocrinology, 1995-98; contbr. numerous articles to profl. jours., book chpts. Recipient Pickford medal in comparative endocrinology, 1993; E.W.R. Steacie fellow Natural Scis. and Engring. Rsch. Coun. Can., 1982-84. Fellow Royal Soc. Can., Royal Entomol. Soc.; mem. AAAS, Am. Soc. Zoologists, Entomol. Soc. Can. (C. Gordon Hewitt award 1982, Gold medal 1990), Entomol. Soc. Am., Soc. Exptl. Biology, Soc. for Neurosci, Sigma Xi. Avocations: amateur radio, gardening, hydroponics. Home: 467 Soudan Ave, Toronto, ON Canada M4S 1X1 Office: U Toronto Dept Zoology, 25 Harbord St, Toronto, ON Canada M5S 1A1

TOBER, BARBARA D. (MRS. DONALD GIBBS TOBER), editor; b. Summit, N.J., Aug. 19, 1934; d. Rodney Fielding and Maude (Grebbin) Starkey; m. Donald Gibbs Tober, Apr. 5, 1973. Student, Traphagen Sch. Fashion, 1954-56, Fashion Inst. Tech., 1956-58, N.Y. Sch. Interior Design, 1964. Copy editor Vogue Pattern Book, 1958-60; beauty editor Vogue mag., 1961; dir. women's services Bartell Media Corp., 1961-66; editor-in-chief Bride's mag., N.Y.C., 1966-94; chmn. Am. Craft Mus.; pres. Acronym, Inc., N.Y.C., 1995—, The Barbara Tober Found., 1995—; dir. Gen. Brands Corp., sec.-treas.; adv. bd. Traphagen Sch.; coordinator SBA awards; Am. Craft Council Mus. Assn., 1983—, benefit food com. chmn., 1984-87. Author: The ABC's of Beauty, 1963, China: A Cognizant Guide, 1980, The Wedding . . . The Marriage . . . And the Role of the Retailer, 1980, The Bride: A Celebration, 1984. Mem. Nat. Council on Family Relations, 1966; nat. council Lincoln Center Performing Arts, Met. Opera Guild; mem. NYU adv. bd. Women in Food Service, 1983; NYU Women's Health Symposium: Steering Com., 1983—. Recipient Alma award, 1968, Penney-Mo. award, 1972, Traphagen Alumni award, 1975, Diamond Jubilee award, 1983. Mem. Fashion Group, Nat. Home Fashions League (v.p., program chmn.), Am. Soc. Mag. Editors, Am. Soc. Interior Designers (press mem.), Intercorporate Group, Women in Communications (60 yrs. of success award N.Y. chpt. 1984), Nat. Assn. Underwater Instrs., Pan Pacific and S.E. Asia Women's Assn., Asia Soc., Japan Soc., China Inst., Internat. Side Saddle Orgn., Millbrook Hounds, Golden's Bridge Hounds, Wine and Food Soc., Chaines des Rotisseurs (chargée de press) (bd. dirs.), Dames d'Escoffier, Culinary Inst. Home: 620 Park Ave New York NY 10021-6591 Office: Acronym Inc 620 Park Ave New York NY 10021

TOBER, LESTER VICTOR, shoe company executive; b. St. Louis, Dec. 29, 1916; s. Abraham E.M. and Anna (Saifer) T.; m. Sylvia Isenburg, Aug. 4, 1940; children—Neil Steven, Robert Boyd, Cristie Elizabeth. B.S., U. Wis., 1935; postgrad., Washington U., 1936, U. Mo., 1936-39. Sec. Tober-Saifer Shoe Mfg. Co., St. Louis, 1955-65; v.p. Tober-Saifer Shoe Mfg. Co., 1966-68, exec. v.p., 1969-71, pres., 1974—; pres., chief exec. officer Tober Industries, Inc., 1977—. Active St. Louis Ambassadors, United Fund.; Trustee A.E. Tober Charitable Trust. Served to lt. (j.g.) USNR, 1944-46. Mem. Washington U. Eliot Soc., St. Louis Club, Mo. Athletic Club, Naples (Fla.) Pelican Bay Club, Hideaway Beach Club, Elks, Zeta Beta Tau. Republican. Jewish (pres. temple brotherhood 1957). Home: 19 Maryhill Dr Saint Louis MO 63124-1318 Office: Tober Industries Inc 1520 Washington Ave Saint Louis MO 63103-1817

TOBER, STEPHEN LLOYD, lawyer; b. Boston, May 27, 1949; s. Benjamin Arthur Tober and Lee (Hymoff) Fruman; m. Susan V. Schwartz, Dec. 22, 1973; children: Cary, Jamie. Grad., Syracuse U., 1971, JD, 1974. Bar: N.H. 1974, U.S. Dist. Ct. N.H. 1974, U.S. Supreme Ct. 1978, N.Y. 1981. Assoc. Flynn, McGuirk & Blanchard, Portsmouth, N.H., 1974-79; sole practice Portsmouth, 1979-81; ptnr. Aeschliman & Tober, Portsmouth, 1981-91; prin. Tober Law Offices, P.A., Portsmouth, 1992—; lectr. Franklin Pierce Law Ctr., Concord, N.H., 1978-80. Contbr. articles to law jours. Mem. Portsmouth Charter Commn., 1976, Portsmouth Planning Bd., 1977-81; del. N.H. Constl. Conv., Concord, 1984; city councilman, Portsmouth, 1977-81. Fellow ABA (del. Ho. Dels.), Am. Bar Found., Internat. Acad. Trial Lawyers, N.H. Bar Found., N.H. Bar Assn. (pres. 1988-89, chair com. to redraft code of profl. responsibility); mem. ATLA (gov. 1980-86), N.H. Trial Lawyers Assn. (pres. 1977), New Eng. Bar Assn. (bd. dirs. 1988-). Democrat. Jewish. Avocations: reading, tennis. Home: 55 T J Gamester Ave Portsmouth NH 03801-5871 Office: Tober Law Offices PA PO Box 1377 Portsmouth NH 03802-1377

TOBEY, ALTON STANLEY, artist; b. Middletown, Conn., Nov. 5, 1914; s. Saul Zilman and Rose (Aaronson) T.; m. Rosalyn S. Caplovitz, Sept. 24, 1950; children: David Seth, Judith Robin. BFA, Yale Sch. Fine Arts, 1937, MFA, 1946. Faculty mem. Yale Sch. of Fine Arts, New Haven, 1946-50, CCNY, N.Y.C., 1951-53; pvt. practice, 1953—; instr. Yale U. Sch. Fine Art, New Haven, City Coll., N.Y.C., 92nd St. Lexington Ave., YMHA, N.Y.C.; now teaching privately, Larchmont, N.Y. One-man shows include Am. Ctr., Stockholm, Alliance Gallery, Copenhagen, Cape East Gallery, Provincetown, Mass., Pietrantonis Gallery, N.Y.C., Bridge Gallery, White Plains, N.Y., Burliuk Gallery, N.Y.C., Katonah (N.Y.) Gallery, Portrait Gallery, Westport, Conn., Charles Mann Gallery, N.Y.C., Casa de Aquarella, Mexico City, Alice Tully Hall, Lincoln Ctr., N.Y.C., Riverside Mus., N.Y.C., Westchester Art Soc., White Plains, N.Y., Bloomingdales, White Plains, N.Y., U. Pa., Trinity Coll., Yale Art Sch., Sarah Lawrence Coll., U. Maine; permanent collections include Met. Opera Gallery, Lincoln Ctr., N.Y., Norfolk (Va.) Mus., Mus. City of N.Y., Goshen (N.Y.) Hall of Fame, Hillandale Mus., Chadds Ford, Pa., Sea Air Space Mus., N.Y.C. Smithsonian Inst., Washington, West Point (N.Y.) Mus., MacArthur Meml., Norfolk, Va., Jewish Mus., N.Y.C., Tazewell (Va.) Mus.; limited editions include Royal Doulton Plates, London, Lucien Piccard, N.Y.C., Franklin (Pa.) Mint, Numa Ltd., Akron, Ohio; corporate collections include ABC-TV, N.Y.C., Chas. Pfizer Co., N.Y.C., Readers' Digest, Pleasantville, N.Y., Evyan Perfumes, N.Y.C., Ciba Geigy, Ardsley, N.Y., Am. Cyanamid, Bound Brook, N.J., Gen. Foods, White Plains, N.Y.; govt. and other collections include Dept. Commerce, Washington, Am. Machine & Foundry, White Plains, N.Y., Pres. Coun. on Physical Fitness & Sports, Washington, Yonkers (N.Y.) Profl. Hosp., Iona Coll., New Rochelle, N.Y., Am. Bureau of Shipping, N.Y.C., Nat. Acad., N.Y.C., St. Patrick's Cathedral, N.Y.C., St. Francis Hosp., Hartford, Conn., Elmira (N.Y.) Coll., Hofstra Coll., L.I., St. Francis murals in public bldgs. throughout the U.S.; portraits include Albert Einstein, Pope John Paul II, Ronald Reagan, Robert Frost, Douglas MacArthur, J.F. and Robert Kennedy, Robert Merrill, E. Roland Harriman, Cardinal Cook, Golda Meir. Named Artist of the Year Westchester Council of Arts, 1987; recipient Honorary award Thornton Donovan Sch., 1989. Mem. Nat. Soc. Mural Painters (pres. emeritus 1985-89), Artists Equity N.Y (pres. emeritus), Hudson River Contemporary Artists (pres. emeritus), Internat. Artists Assn. (v.p.), Mamaronick Artists Guild (pres. emeritus), Proto V. Abraxas, League of Present Day Artists, Fine Arts Fedn. Avocations: pre-Colombian archeology, history of art. Home and Office: 296 Murray Ave Larchmont NY 10538-1239

TOBEY, CARL WADSWORTH, retired publisher; b. Meriden, Conn., Nov. 18, 1923; s. Carl W. and Prudence (Wadsworth) T.; m. Charlotte But-

terworth, Aug. 19, 1944; children: Peter Wadsworth, Carl Eric, Cheryl L. Ed., U.S. Mcht. Marine Acad. Regional sales mgr. Northeastern div. Dell Pub. Co., Inc., 1953-58; sales mgr. Dell Books, 1958-64, v.p. co., 1964-68, sr. v.p., 1968, exec. v.p., dir., 1968-76; pres. Dell Pub. Co. Inc., from 1976, chmn., 1981-83; ret., 1983; owner Greater Savannah Travel, Inc.; With U.S. Mcht. Marine, 1943-46. Mem. Landing Club on Skidaway Island. Democrat. Congregationalist. Office: Greater Savannah Travel 12-D Bishops Ct Trustees Garden Savannah GA 31401

TOBEY, JOEL NYE, insurance company executive; b. South Dartmouth, Mass., Apr. 4, 1929; s. Warren P. Jr. and Molly Nye (Gammons) T.; m. Margaret E. Pumphrey, Nov. 26, 1955; children: Mark H., James A., Judith E. BA, Brown U., 1952. Underwriter Amica Mut. Ins. Co., Providence, 1960-65; asst. br. mgr. Balt., 1965-67; asst. sec. Providence, 1967-68, sec., 1968-84, v.p., 1972-80, dir., 1975—, exec. v.p., 1980-85, pres., chief exec. officer, 1985—; bd. dirs. People's Bank, Providence. Trustee Greater Providence YMCA, R.I. Pub. Expenditure Council; bd. dirs. Jr. Achievement R.I. Inc., United Way Southeastern New Eng. Served to capt. U.S. Army, 1952-59. Mem. Am. Inst. Property and Liability Underwriters and Ins. Inst. Am. (trustee), Alliance Am. Insurers (bd. dirs.), Greater Providence C. of C. (bd. dirs., sec.). Clubs: Hope, Turks Head, Univ. (Providence), Squantum Assn. (East Providence). Avocations: gardening, sailing, skiing. Office: Am Mut Ins Co 10 Weybosset St Providence RI 02903-2808

TOBIA, RONALD LAWRENCE, lawyer; b. Newark, Oct. 25, 1944; s. Salvatore and Marie (Melillo) T.; m. Sandra A. Boutsikaris, June 15, 1969; children: Jill, Alisandra, Joseph. BA, Lafayette Coll., 1966; JD, U. Miami, 1969. Bar: Fla. 1969, N.J. 1970. Legal asst. region 22 NLRB, Newark, 1967, 68; jud. clk. to presiding justice N.J. Superior Ct., Passaic County, 1969-70; hearing officer N.J. Pub. Employment Rels. Com., Trenton, 1970-71; sr. ptnr. Schwartz, Tobia & Stanziale, P.A., Montclair, N.J., 1972—. Contbr. articles to profl. jours. Fin. co-chmn. N.J. Rep. Com. With JAGC, U.S. Army, 1967-68. Mem. ABA, N.J. Bar Assn., Fla. Bar Assn., Essex County Bar Assn., Indsl. Rels. Rsch. Assn. Republican. Roman Catholic. Avocation: skiing. Home: 64 Forest Way Essex Fells NJ 07021-1422 Office: Schwartz Tobia & Stanziale PA 22 Crestmont Rd Montclair NJ 07042-9998

TOBIA, STEPHEN FRANCIS, JR., marketing professional, consultant; b. Bronx, N.Y., Jan. 14, 1955; s. Stephen Francis and Zelinda (Caruso) T.; m. Maureen Patricia Homan, Dec. 31, 1978; children: Michael, Marc. BA, U. Dayton, 1978; MA, Occidental Coll., L.A., 1980. Project mgr. L.A. C. of C., 1978-81; mgr. pub. affairs/communications Coca Cola Bottling Co., L.A., 1981-84; dir. pub. affairs, 1984; v.p. pub. affairs Beatrice Cos. Inc., L.A., 1984-86; pres. Pacific/West Communications, L.A., 1987—; mem. adv. com. Calif. Mus. Sci. & Industry, L.A., L.A. C. of C. Edn.; guest lectr. mktg. communications UCLA, 1989, 90; panelist Nat. Recycling Congress, 1990; speaker Inst. for Internat. Rsch., 1991, World Recycling Conf. and Expn., 1991. Mem. adv. com. Sch. Pub. Adminstrn., U. So. Calif., L.A., Focus on Youth; chmn. YMCA, East L.A.; bd. dirs. Big Bros. Greater L.A.; mem. Mayor Bradley's Edn. Adv. Com. Pub. Affairs fellow CORO Found., 1978-79. Mem. RecyCAL (founding chmn.), So. Calif. Business Men's Assn. (bd. dirs.), Calif./Nev. Soft Drink Assn. (bd. dirs.), Nat. Soft Drink Assn. (govt. rels. com.), L.A. Pub. Affairs Officer Assn., CORO Assn., Rotary. Office: Pacific/West Communications Group 3435 Wilshire Blvd Ste 2850 Los Angeles CA 90010-2014

TOBIAS, ANDREW PREVIN, columnist, lecturer; b. N.Y.C., Apr. 20, 1947; s. Seth D. and Audrey J. (Landau) T. BA, Harvard U., 1968, MBA, 1972. Pres. Harvard Agys. Inc., Cambridge, Mass., 1967-68; v.p. Nat. Student Mktg. Corp., N.Y.C., 1969-70; contbg. editor N.Y. Mag., 1972-77, Esquire mag., 1977-83; columnist Playboy mag., 1982-86; contbr. Time mag., 1989—, Worth mag., 1995—. Author: The Funny Money Game, 1972, Fire and Ice, 1976, The Only Investment Guide You'll Ever Need, 1978, Getting by on $100,000 a Year and Other Sad Tales, 1980, The Invisible Bankers, 1982, Managing Your Money (software), 1984-94, Money Angles, 1984, The Only Other Investment Guide You'll Ever Need, 1987, Kids Say Don't Smoke, 1991, Auto Insurance Alert!, 1993. Recipient Gerald Loeb award, 1984, Consumer Fedn. of Am. Media Svc. award, 1993.

TOBIAS, CHARLES HARRISON, JR., lawyer; b. Cin., Apr. 16, 1921; s. Charles Harrison and Charlotte (Westheimer) T.; m. Mary J. Kaufman, June 15, 1946; children—Jean M., Thomas Charles, Robert Charles. B.A. cum laude, Harvard U., 1943, LL.B., 1949. Bar: Ohio 1949. Assoc. firm Steer, Strauss and Adair, Cin., 1949-56; ptnr. firm Steer, Strauss, White and Tobias, Cin., 1956-90; mem. Kepley MacConnell & Eyrich, Cin., 1990-93; conf. atty. U.S. Ct. Appeals (6th crct.) Ohio, Cin., 1993—. Bd. dirs. Cin. City Charter Com., 1955-75; mem. Wyoming (Ohio) City Council, 1972-77, vice mayor, 1974-77; bd. govs., sec., past chmn. Cin. Overseers, Hebrew Union Coll.-Jewish Inst. Religion; pres. Met. Area Religious Coalition of Cin., 1977-80, Jewish Fedn. Cin., 1972-74; mem. nat. bd. govs. Am. Jewish Com., 1981-87. With UNS, 1943-46. Mem. Cin. Bar Assn., Losantiville Country Club. Home: 19 Diplomat Dr Cincinnati OH 45215-2074 Office: US Ct Appeals Potter Stewart US Courthse 5th and Walnut St Cincinnati OH 45202

TOBIAS, CHARLES WILLIAM, chemical engineer, educator; b. Budapest, Hungary, Nov. 2, 1920; came to U.S., 1947, naturalized, 1952; s. Karoly and Elizabeth (Milko) T.; m. Marcia Rous, Sept. 10, 1950 (dec. Jan. 1981); children: Carla, Eric, Anthony.; m. Katalin Voros, June 19, 1982. Dipl. in chem. engring. U. Tech. Scis., Budapest, 1942, Ph.D., 1946, Dr (hon), 1992. Registered profl. engr., Calif. Research, devel. engr. United Incandescent & Elec. Co., Ujpest, Hungary, 1942-47; instr. phys. chemistry U. Tech. Scis., 1945-46; research faculty U. Calif.-Berkeley, 1947—, prof. chem. engring., 1960—, chmn. dept., 1967-72, prof. emeritus, 1991—; faculty sr. scientist Lawrence Berkeley Lab., 1954—; assoc. research prof. Miller Inst. Basic Sci., 1958-59. Editor: (with Paul Delahay and Heinz Gerischer) Advances in Electrochemistry and Electrochemical Engineering, 1961-64, (with Heinz Gerischer) Advances in Electrochem. Sci. and Engring., 1990—; mem. editorial bd. Jour. Applied Electrochemistry. Fellow AAAS, Electrochem. Soc. (assoc. editor jour. 1955-90, v.p. 1970-71, pres. 1970-71, Acheson award 1972, hon. mem. 1977—; Henry B. Linford award for disting. teaching 1982, Vittorio de Nora Diamond Shamrock award 1990); mem. NAE, Hungarian Acad. Scis. (hon.), Am. Chem. Soc., Am. Inst. Chem. Engrs. (Alpha Chi Sigma award 1983, Founders award 1991), Am. Soc. Engring. Edn., Internat. Soc. Electrochemistry (v.p. 1975-76, pres. 1977-78), Deutsche Bunsen-Gesellschaft, Sigma Xi. Researcher numerous publs. on mass and charge transport in electrochem. systems, design of electrolytic processes, batteries and fuel cells, electrolysis in non-aqueous solvents. Home: 524 Moraga Way Orinda CA 94563-4241 Office: U Calif Dept Chem Engring Berkeley CA 94720

TOBIAS, JULIUS, sculptor; b. N.Y.C., Aug. 27, 1915; s. Louis and Anna (Tabachnick) T.; m. Suzanne Tobias. Student, Atelier Fernand Leger, Paris, 1949-52. Pvt. tchr., 1950-63; tchr. Morris Davidson Sch. Modern Painting, 1947-48; instr. N.Y. Inst. Tech., 1966-70; lectr. Rutgers U., Queens Coll., N.Y.C., 1966-67, Ind. U., Bloomington, 1974. One-man shows include Esther Stuttman Gallery, 1959, Bleecker Gallery, 1961, Easthampton Gallery, 1962, 10 Downtown, 1968, Max Hutchinson Gallery, 1970, 71, 72, Alessandra Gallery, 1976, 55 Mercer St. Gallery, 1976, 77, 78, 80, all N.Y.C., Zriny-Hayes Gallery, Chgo., 1979, B4A Gallery, N.Y.C., 1991, The SUNY, Stony Brook, 1992, Artemisia Gallery, Chgo., 1992, Galerie Art In, Nürnberg, Germany, 1994; group shows include, Provincetown (Mass.) Art Assn., 1946, Roko Gallery, N.Y.C., 1946, Camino Gallery, N.Y.C., 1957, Polari Gallery, Woodstock, N.Y., 1957, Art USA, Coliseum, N.Y.C., 1957, Brata Gallery, N.Y.C., 1957-59, Pa. Acad. Fine Arts, 1958, Gallery Creuze, Paris, 1958, Knoedler Gallery, N.Y.C., 1959, Mus. Modern Art, traveling exhbn. in Tokyo, 1959, New Eng. Exhbn., Silvermine, Conn., 1960, De Aenle Gallery, N.Y.C., 1961, Bleecker Gallery, N.Y.C., 1962, Staten Island Mus., N.Y.C., 1962, Allan Stone Gallery, N.Y.C., 1962, Easthampton Gallery, N.Y.C., 1962-66, Windham Coll., Putney, Vt., 1963, Rutgers U., 1966, Park Pl. Gallery, N.Y.C., 1967, Tibor Diday Gallery, N.Y.C., 1968, Whitney Mus. Annual, N.Y.C., 1968, Parker St. 470, Boston, 1969, Everson Mus., Syracuse, N.Y., 1972, Hunter Gallery, N.Y.C., 1981, Art Park, Lewiston, N.Y., 1981, Jan Weiss Gallery, N.Y.C., 1990, numerous others; represented in numerous collections, Europe, N. and S.Am., also pvt. collections. Served to 1st lt. USAAF, 1942-45. Decorated D.F.C., Air medal with

3 oak leaf clusters; Guggenheim fellow, 1972-73, 78-79; N.Y. Found. for Arts fellow, 1985; Pollock-Krasner Found. fellow, 1986; grantee Nat. Endowment for Arts, 1975, 81; N.Y. Council Found., 1971-78; Adolf and Esther Gottlieb Found., 1980, The Penny McCall Found., 1988; recipient Oscar Williams and Gene Derwood award, 1989, award Adolph and Esther Gottlieb Found., 1991, The Pollock-Krasner Found., 1988. Address: 9 Great Jones St New York NY 10012

TOBIAS, KAL, transportation executive; b. Bklyn., Feb. 1, 1946; m. Karen Liberty, Mar. 11, 1967; children: Kristopher, Kirk. BA, CUNY, Bklyn., 1967. Mgr. dealer devel. Volkswagon Can., Toronto, Ont., 1967-72; cons. firm Toronto, Ont., Can., 1972-78; v.p. Burmah Oil Group, Toronto, Ont., Can., 1978-83; pres., C.E.O. DHL Internat. Express Ltd., Toronto, Ont., Can., 1983—; also bd. dirs., 1983—; bd. dirs DHL Customs Brokerage, Toronto, 1983—; Skyhawk Trans., Toronto, 1988—, Can. Courier Assn., pres., 1987—, C.E.O., 1987—. Office: DHL Internat Express Ltd, 6205 Airport Rd Ste 400, Mississauga, ON Canada L4V 1E1

TOBIAS, PAUL HENRY, lawyer; b. Cin., Jan. 5, 1930; s. Charles H. and Charlotte (Westheimer) T.; 1 child, Eliza L. AB magna cum laude, Harvard U., 1951, LLB, 1958. Bar: Mass. 1958, Ohio 1962. Assoc. Stoneman & Chandler, Boston, 1958-61, Goldman & Putnick, Cin., 1962-75; ptnr. Tobias, Kraus and Torchia, Cin., 1976—; instr. U. Cin. Law Sch., 1975-77. Author: Litigating Wrongful Discharge Claims, 1987; contbr. articles to profl. jours. Mem. Cin. Bd. of Park Commrs., 1973-81, Cin. Human Rels. Commn., 1980-84, Cin. Hist. Conservation Bd., 1990-91. With U.S. Army, 1952-54. Mem. Cin. Bar Assn. (past chmn. legal aid com.), Ohio State Bar Assn., ABA, Nat. Employment Lawyers Assn. (founder), Nat. Employment Rights Inst. (chmn.), Phi Beta Kappa. Home: 15 Hill And Hollow Ln Cincinnati OH 45208-3317 Office: Tobias Kraus Torchia 911 Mercantile Libr Bldg Cincinnati OH 45202

TOBIAS, RANDALL L., pharmaceutical company executive; b. Lafayette, Ind., Mar. 20, 1942; m. Marilyn Jane Salyer, Sept. 2, 1966 (dec. May 1994); children—Paige Noelle, Todd Christopher. BS in Mktg., Ind. U., 1964, LLD (hon.), Galuedette U. Numerous positions Ind. Bell, 1964-81, Ill. Bell, 1977-81; v.p. residence mktg. sales and service AT&T, 1981-82, pres. Am. Bell Consumer Products, 1983, pres. Consumer Products, 1983-84, sr. v.p., 1984-85; chmn., CEO AT&T Comm. N.Y.C., 1985-91, AT&T Internat., Basking Ridge, N.J., 1991-93; vice chmn. bd. AT&T, N.Y.C., 1993—; chmn., CEO Eli Lilly & Co., Indpls., 1993—; bd. dirs. Eli Lilly & Co., Kimberly-Clark, Dow Elanco, Guidant Corp., Knight-Ridder, Phillips Petroleum; active U.S.-Japan Bus. Couns. Trustee Duke U.; vice chmn. Colonial Williamsburg Found.; bd. govs. Skyline Club, Indpls. Mus. Art; bd. dirs. Indpls. Symphony Orch., Ind. U. Found., Econ. Club Indpls. Mem. Coun. Fgn. Rels., Bus. Roundtable, Meridian Hills Country Club (Indpls.), Woodstock Club, Amwell Valley Conservancy, Theta Chi. Avocations: skiing, fly fishing, shooting. Office: Eli Lilly & Co Lilly Corp Ctr Indianapolis IN 46285

TOBIAS, ROBERT MAX, labor leader, lawyer; b. Detroit, Aug. 4, 1943. BA, U. Mich., 1965, MBA, 1968; JD, George Washington U., 1969. Lawyer Nat. Treasury Employees Union, Washington, 1968-70, gen. counsel, 1970-79, exec. v.p. and gen. counsel, 1979-83, pres., 1983—; lectr. George Washington U. Law Sch., Washington, 1970-90. Contbr. articles to law revs. Sec., treas. Fed. Employee Edn. and Asst. Found, Washington, 1986. Mem. ABA, Soc. for Labor Relations Profls. (1st Annual Union Leader award, 1987), Fed. Bar Assn., D.C. Bar Assn., Am. Arbitration Assn. (bd. dirs.). Democrat. Episcopalian. Office: Nat Treasury Employees Union 901 E St NW Ste 600 Washington DC 20004-2037

TOBIN, BENTLEY, lawyer; b. Bklyn., N.Y., Feb. 8, 1924; s. Nathan H. and Mildred E. (Aronoff) T.; m. Nancy Gurvitz, Sept. 13, 1947; children—Patricia E., Mitchell H.; m. 2d, Beverly Ann Mucciarone, Feb. 17, 1979. B.S., CCNY, 1943; LL.B., Harvard U., 1948. Bar: N.Y. 1948, Mass. 1951, R.I. 1952. Atty. N.Y.C. Housing Authority, 1948-49; ptnr. Titiev, Greenman & Tobin, Boston, 1949-52; sr. ptnr. Tobin & Silverstein, Providence, 1952-84; ptnr. Hinckley, Allen, Tobin & Silverstein, 1984-87, Hinckley, Allen, Comen, 1987-92, Hinckley, Allen & Snyder, 1992—; chmn. bd. Landmark Health Systems, Inc. Served in USAR, 1943-46. Mem. ABA, R.I. Bar Assn., Woonsocket Bar Assn. Office: Hinckley Allen Snyder 1500 Fleet Ctr Providence RI 02903 Also: Landmark Health Systems Inc 115 Cass Ave Woonsocket RI 02895-4705

TOBIN, BRIAN, Canadian government official; b. Stephenville, Nfld., Can., Oct. 21, 1954; s. Patrick Vincent and Florence Mary (Frye) T.; m. Jodean Smith; children: Heather Elizabeth, Adam Vincent, John Joseph. Student, Meml. U. Nfld. Mem. parliament for Humber-St. Barbe-Baie Verte Ho. Commons, Can., 1980, parliamentary sec. to Min. Fisheries and Oceans, 1980-93, Min. Fisheries and Oceans, 1993—, vice chair com. on regional devel., mem. transport, fisheries and forestry, labour, emnployment and immigration, constl. coms., spl. com. on employment opportunities for 1980s; past exec. asst. to Liberal leader Liberal Party Nfld. and Labrador; opposition MP; critic for forestry, employment, regional industrial expansion, privatization; critic, assoc. critic transport. Electrd chair Nat. Liberal Caucus, 1989, mem. Liberal nat. campaign, nat. platform coms. 1993. Office: Fisheries & Oceans Can, 200 Kent St, Ottawa, ON Canada K1A 0E6

TOBIN, CALVIN JAY, architect; b. Boston, Feb. 15, 1927; s. David and Bertha (Tanfield) T.; m. Joan Hope Fink, July 15, 1951; children—Michael Alan, Nancy Ann. B.Arch., U. Mich., 1949. Designer, draftsman Arlen & Lowenfish (architects), N.Y.C., 1949-51; with Samuel Arlen, N.Y.C., 1951-53, Skidmore, Owings & Merrill, N.Y.C., 1953; architect Loebl, Schlossman & Hackl, 1957—; Chmn. Jewish United Fund Bldg. Trades Div., 1969; chmn. AIA and Chgo. Hosp. Council Com. of Hosp. Architecture, 1968-76. Archtl. works include Michael Reese Hosp. and Med. Ctr., 1954—; Prairie Shores Apt. Urban redevel., 1957-62, Louis A. Weiss Meml. Hosp., Chgo., Chgo. State Hosp., Central Cmty. Hosp., Chgo., Gottlieb Meml. Hosp., Melrose Park, Ill., West Suburban Hosp., Oak Park, Ill., Thorek Hosp. and Med. Ctr., Chgo., Water Tower Pl., Chgo., Christ Hosp., Oak Lawn, Greater Balt. Med. Ctr., Shriners Hosp. for Crippled Children, Chgo., Hinsdale Hosp., Hinsdale, Ill., South Chgo. Cmty. Hosp., Chgo., Mt. Sinai Med. Ctr., Chgo., Alexian Bros. Med. Ctr., Elk Grove Village, Ill., Luth, Gen. Hosp., Park Ridge, Ill., Evanston (Ill.) Hosp., Resurrection Medical Ctr., Chgo., alos numerous apt., comml. and cmty. bldgs. Chmn. Highland Park (Ill.) Appearance Rev. Commn., 1972-73; mem. Highland Park Plan Commn., 1973-79; mem. Highland Park City Coun., 1974-89, mayor pro-tem, 1979-89; mem. Highland Park Environ. Control Commn., 1979-84, Highland Park Hist. Preservation Commn., 1982-89; bd. dirs. Highland Park Hist. Soc., Young Men's Jewish Coun., 1953-67, pres, 1967; bd. dirs. Jewish Community Ctrs. Chgo., 1973-78, bd. dirs. 1989-93; Ill. Coun. Against Handgun Violence, 1989-94; trustee Ravinia Festival Assn., 1990—. With USNR, 1945-46. Fellow AIA (2d v.p. Chgo. chpt.); mem. U. Mich. Alumni Soc. Coll. Architecture and Urban Planning (bd. govs. 1989—), U. Mich. Alumni Assn. (bd. govs. 1990-95, v.p. 1993-95), Standard Club, Ravinia Green Country Club, Pi Lambda Phi. Jewish. Home: 814 Dean Ave Highland Park IL 60035-4749 Office: Loebl Schlossman & Hackl 130 E Randolph St Chicago IL 60601-6378

TOBIN, JAMES, economics educator; b. Champaign, Ill., Mar. 5, 1918; s. Louis Michael and Margaret (Edgerton) T.; m. Elizabeth Fay Ringo, Sept. 14, 1946; children: Margaret Ringo, Louis Michael, Hugh Ringo, Roger Gill. AB summa cum laude, Harvard U., 1939, MA, 1940, PhD, 1947; LLD (hon.), Syracuse U., 1967, U. Ill., 1969, Dartmouth Coll., 1970, Swarthmore Coll., 1980, New Sch. Social Research, 1982, NYU, 1982, Bates Coll., 1982, U. Hartford, 1984, Colgate U., 1984, Gustavus Adolphus Coll., 1986, Western Md. Coll., 1984, U. New Haven, 1986; D in Econs. (hon.), New U. Lisbon, 1980; D in Econs. (hon.), Athens U. Econ. & Bus., 1992; D in Econs. (hon.), Athens U. of Econ. and Bus., 1992; LHD (hon.), Hofstra U., 1983, Sacred Heart U., 1990; D in Social Scis. honoris causa, U. Helsinki, 1986. Assoc. economist OPA, WPB, Washington, 1941-42; teaching fellow econs. Harvard U., Cambridge, Mass., 1946-47, with Soc. Fellows, 1947-50; assoc. prof. econs. Yale U., New Haven, 1950-55, prof., 1955—, Sterling prof. econs., 1957-88, prof. emeritus, 1988—; mem. Council Econ. Advisers, 1961-62, Nat. Acad. Scis. Author: National Economic Policy, 1966, Essays

in Economics-Macroeconomics, vol. 1, 1972, The New Economics One Decade Older, 1974, Consumption and Econometrics, vol. 2, 1975, Asset Accumulation and Economic Activity, 1980, Theory and Policy, Vol. 3, 1982, Policies for Prosperity, 1987; co-author: Two Revolutions in Economic Policy, 1988. Served to lt. USNR, 1942-46. Recipient Nobel prize in econs., 1981; Social Sci. Research Council faculty fellow, 1951-54; Grand cordon Order of the Sacred Treasure, Japan, 1988; Centennial medal Harvard Grad. Sch., 1989. Fellow Am. Acad. Arts and Scis., Econometric Soc. (pres. 1958), Am. Statis. Assn., Brit. Acad. (corr.); mem. Am. Philos. Soc., Am. Econ. Assn. (John Bates Clark medal 1955, v.p. 1964, pres. 1971), Acad. Scis. Portugal (fgn. assoc.), Phi Beta Kappa. Home: 117 Alden Ave New Haven CT 06515-2109 Office: Yale U Dept Econs Box 208281 New Haven CT 06520-8281

TOBIN, JAMES MICHAEL, lawyer; b. Santa Monica, Calif., Sept. 27, 1948; s. James Joseph and Glada Marie (Meisner) T.; m. Kathleen Marie Espy, Sept. 14, 1985. BA with honors, U. Calif., Riverside, 1970; JD, Georgetown U., 1974. Bar: Calif. 1974, Mich. 1987. From atty. to gen. atty. So. Pacific Co., San Francisco, 1975-82; v.p. regulatory affairs So. Pacific Communications Co., Washington, 1982-83; v.p., gen. counsel Lexitel Corp., Washington, 1983-85; v.p., gen. counsel, sec. ALC Communications Corp., Birmingham, Mich., 1985-87, sr. v.p., gen. counsel, sec., 1987-88; of counsel Morrison & Foerster, San Francisco, 1988-90, ptnr., 1990—. Mem. ABA, Calif. Bar Assn., Mich. Bar Assn., Fed. Communications Bar Assn. Republican. Unitarian. Avocations: innkeeper (DeHaven Valley Farm, Westport, Calif.), carpentry, travel. Home: 2739 Octavia St San Francisco CA 94123-4303 Office: Morrison & Foerster 345 California St San Francisco CA 94104-2606

TOBIN, JAMES ROBERT, biotechnology company executive; b. Lima, Ohio, Aug. 12, 1944; s. J. Robert and Doris L. (Hunt) T.; m. Janet Trafton, Dec. 30, 1971; children: James Robert III, Amanda Trafton. BA in Govt., Harvard U., 1966, MBA, 1968. Fin. analyst Baxter Internat., Inc., Deerfield, Ill., 1972-73, internat. contr., 1973-75; mng. dir. Japan Baxter Internat., Inc., Tokyo, 1975-77; mng. dir. Spain Baxter Internat., Inc., Valencia, 1977-80; pres. IV Sys. Divsn. Baxter Internat. Inc., Deerfield, 1981-84; group v.p. Baxter Internat., Inc., Deerfield, 1984-88, exec. v.p., 1988-92, pres., COO, 1992-94; pres., COO Biogen, 1994—; also bd. dirs.; bd. dirs. Medisense, Creative Biomolecules. Lt. USN, 1968-72. Republican. Home: 12 Briarwood Ln Lincolnshire IL 60069-2500 Office: Biogen Inc 14 Cambridge Ctr Cambridge MA 02142-1481

TOBIN, JOHN EVERARD, retired lawyer; b. Utica, N.Y., Sept. 28, 1923; s. Michael and Julia Theresa (O'Brien) T.; m. Margaret T. Swope, June 17, 1944; children: John E. Jr., Catherine J. (dec.), Brian D., Paul C. A.B., Hamilton Coll., 1947; LL.B., Columbia U., 1950. Bar: N.Y. 1950, U.S. Supreme Ct. 1966. Practiced law N.Y.C., 1950-94; assoc. Donovan, Leisure, Newton & Irvine, 1950-59, ptnr., 1959-84; ptnr. Dorsey & Whitney, 1984-94; chief counsel subcom. administrn. internal revenue laws, ways and means com. U.S. Ho. of Reps., 1952-53; dir. Alleghany Corp. Bd. dirs Legal Aid Soc., N.Y., 1979-85; trustee Hamilton Coll., 1974—; mem. exec. com. Lawyers Com. for Civil Rights under Law. 1st lt. USAF, 1942-46. Mem. Assn. of Bar of City of N.Y., Am. Judicature Soc., Century Assn. (N.Y.C.). Home: 100 Ackerman Ave Ho Ho Kus NJ 07423-1002

TOBIN, MICHAEL EDWARD, banker; b. Newtown Square, Pa., Jan. 17, 1926; s. Michael Joseph and Emma (Roberts) T.; m. Judith Anne Brown; children: Michael E., Allegra, Corey. B.S. in Econs, U. Pa., 1948. Cons. Philco, RCA, Ebasco Services, Inc., 1950-56; sr. cons. Arthur Young & Co., N.Y.C., 1956-59; midwest dir. cons. svcs. Arthur Young & Co., Chgo., 1959-68; pres. Midwest Stock Exch., Chgo., 1968-78; pres. Am. Nat. Bank & Trust Co., Chgo., 1978, chmn. bd., chief exec. officer, 1979-90, chmn. bd., 1990-91, ret. Served with U.S. Army, World War II, ETO.

TOBIN, PAUL EDWARD, JR., naval officer; b. Detroit, Oct. 24, 1940; s. Paul Edward and Mary Margaret (Atkinson) T.; m. Lynne Dawson Carter, June 12, 1963; children: Mary Elizabeth, Patricia Carter. BS in Naval Sci., U.S. Naval Acad., 1963; MS in Computer Sys., U.S. Naval Postgrad. Sch., 1969. Commd. ensign USN, 1963, advanced through grades to rear adm., 1988; commdg. officer USS Tattnall (DDG-19), 1979-81, USS Fox (CG-33), 1984-86; chief engr. USS Forrestal (CV-59), 1986-88; commdg. officer Surface Warfare Officers Sch., 1986-88; dir. USN Info. Sys. Mgmt., 1988-90; commdr. Western Pacific USN Info. Sys., Subic Bay, The Philippines, 1990-92; asst. chief naval pers. USN, Washington, 1992-94; vice commdr. naval edn. and tng. USN, Pensacola, Fla., 1994—. Decorated D.S.M., Legion of Merit (3). Mem. U.S. Naval Inst., Surface Navy Assn., Army Navy Country Club. Presbyterian. Avocations: classical music, running, computers, boating. Home: Quarters 4 North Ave Pensacola FL 32508 Office: CNET 250 Dallas St Pensacola FL 32508

TOBIN, PETER J., financial executive; b. N.Y.C., Mar. 3, 1944; s. Patrick J. and Kathleen A. (Sweetnam) T.; m. Mary P. Gamble, June 25, 1966; children—Kristin, Peter G. B.B.A., St. John's U., N.Y.C., 1965. C.P.A. Mgr. Peat, Marwick Mitchell, N.Y.C., 1965-72; supr., controller Mfgrs. Hanover Corp., N.Y.C., 1972-85; exec. v.p., chief fin. officer Mfrs. Hanover Corp., 1985-91; exec. v.p., CFO Chem. Banking Corp., N.Y.C., 1991—. Mem. Am. Inst. C.P.A.s, N.Y. State Soc. C.P.A.s, Fin. Execs. Inst. (bd. dirs. N.Y. chpt. 1979-82), Bank Adminstrn. Inst. Republican. Roman Catholic. Avocations: tennis; golf. Office: Cehm Banking Corp 270 Park Ave New York NY 10017-2014

TOBIN, RICHARD J., lawyer; b. Boston, Aug. 1, 1934; s. Richard Charles and Eleanor Marie (Leary) T.; m. Esther Hanley, Oct. 27, 1962; children: Margaret Alicia, Joseph Hanley, Richard Neil, David Lawrence, Mary Courtney. BS, Boston Coll., 1956, LLD, 1962. Bar: Conn., 1967, Mass. 1962, Fla., 1993. Asst. corp. counsel law dept. City of Boston, 1962-65; asst. gen. counsel New Haven Redevel. Agy., 1966-67; ptnr. Cummings and Lockwood, Stamford, Conn., 1967-94; judge Superior Ct. State of Conn., 1994—. Chmn. Standard Products Intat., 1970-72; mem. Dem. City Com., Stamford, 1970-76. Capt. USMCR, 1956-60. Mem. Conn. Bar Assn. (exec. com. planning and zoning sect. 1980-94), Mass. Bar Assn., Fla. Bar Assn., Greater Stamford Bar Assn. (pres. 1977-78), Stamford Yacht Club (bd. dirs 1980-85, 90—). Roman Catholic. Office: Superior Ct Judges Chambers State of Conn Bridgeport CT 06604

TOBIN, ROBERT G., supermarket chain executive; b. 1938. With Stop & Shop Supermarket Co., 1960—, pres., COO, 1989-93; pres., COO Stop & Shop Cos., Braintree, Mass., 1993—, chmn., 1995—. Office: Stop & Stop Cos Inc 1 Bradlee Circle Braintree MA 02184*

TOBIN, STEVEN MICHAEL, insurance company executive; b. N.Y.C., Sept. 23, 1940; s. Ernest J. and Beatrice (Cohen) T.; m. Joanne Cohen, Nov. 30, 1969; children: Danielle Hope, Greer Olivia. BS, NYU, 1963; postgrad., CUNY, 1966-67. Investment acct. CIT Fin. Corp., N.Y.C., 1964-67; supr. Guardian Life Ins. Co., N.Y.C., 1967-70; controller Am. Mayflower Life Ins., N.Y.C., 1970-73; sr. v.p., CFO Beneficial Nat. Life (subs. Beneficial Std. Corp.), N.Y.C., 1973-81; sr. v.p. fin./adminstrn. Fidelity Interstate Life (subs. Beneficial Std. Corp.), L.A., 1981-83; cons. N.Y.C., 1983-85; sr. v.p., treas. Gerber Life Ins. Co., White Plains, N.Y., 1985—; bd. dirs. Gerber Life Ins. Co. Fellow Life Mgmt. Inst.; mem. Fin. Execs. Inst., Ins. Acctg. and Statis. Assn., Sigma Alpha Mu. Republican. Office: Gerber Life Ins Co 66 Church St White Plains NY 10601-1901

TOBIN, THOMAS F., lawyer; b. Chgo., Apr. 12, 1929. BSS, John Carroll U., 1951; JD, Loyola U., 1954. Bar: Ill. 1954. Ptnr. Baker & McKenzie, Chgo. Office: Baker & McKenzie 1 Prudential Plz 130 E Randolph Dr Chicago IL 60601-6206

TOBIN, WILLIAM THOMAS, retail executive; b. Cleve., May 31, 1931; s. Paul William and Ellen Louise (Fenlon) T.; m. Mary Ellen Fawcett, May 22, 1976; children: William Thomas, Bradford Fenlon. B.A., Yale U., 1949-53. With M. O'Neil Co., Akron, Ohio, 1953-73; exec. v.p. M. O'Neil Co., 1973-75, pres. 1975-79; pres., chief exec. officer Kaufmann's, Pitts., 1979—. Mem. Yale Club (N.Y.C.), Portage Country Club, Rolling Rock Club, Duquesne Club, Fox Chapel Golf Club, Laurel Valley Golf Club, Pittsburgh

Golf Club, Rivers Club. Office: Kaufmann's 400 5th Ave Pittsburgh PA 15219-1700

TOBIS, JEROME SANFORD, physician; b. Syracuse, N.Y., July 23, 1915; s. David George and Anna (Feinberg) T.; m. Hazel Weisbard, Sept. 18, 1938; children: David, Heather, Jonathan. B.S., CCNY, 1936; M.D., Chgo. Med. Sch., 1943. Diplomate: Am. Bd. Phys. Medicine and Rehab. Intern Knickerbocker Hosp., 1943-44; resident Bronx VA Hosp., 1946-48; med. dir. state fever therapy unit USPHS, Brookhaven, Miss., 1944-46; practice medicine N.Y.C., 1948-70; prof. dir. dept. phys. medicine and rehab. N.Y. Med. Coll., Flower and Fifth Av. Hosps., 1948-61; prof. rehab. medicine Albert Einstein Coll. of Medicine, 1963-70; chief div. rehab. medicine Montefiore Hosp., 1961-70; dir. vis. physician Met., Bird S. Coler hosps., 1952-61; prof., chmn. dept. phys. medicine and rehab. Calif. Coll. Medicine, U. Calif. at Irvine, 1970-82, prof., dir. program in geriatric medicine and gerontology, 1980-86; cons. Dept. Health, N.Y.C., Long Beach VA Hosp., 1970—, Fairview State Devel. Ctr., 1976—; mem. expert med. com. Am. Rehab. Found., 1961-70; mem. adv. coun. phys. medicine and rehab. for appeals com. Calif. Med. Assn., 1971-74; NIH Internat. Fogarty fellow. hon. lectr. dept. geriatric medicine U. Birmingham, 1979-80; chair ethics com. U. Calif.-Irvine Med. Ctr., 1986—. Mem. editorial bd.: Heart and Lung, 1973-76, Geriatrics, 1975-80, Archives of Phys. Medicine and Rehab, 1958-73. Named Physician of the Year, 1957; recipient Distinguished Alumnus award Chgo. Med. Sch., 1972, Acad. award Nat. Inst. on Aging, 1981-86; named hon. faculty mem. Calif. Zeta chpt. Alpha Omega Alpha, 1981; Leavitt Meml. lectureship Baylor Coll. Medicine, 1983, Griffith Meml. lectureship Am. Geriatric Soc., 1984; Australian Coll. Rehabilitation Medicine, 1984; Jerome S. Tobis Ann. Conf. on Geriatric Medicine established in his name, U. Calif. at Irvine, 1986. Fellow ACP, Am. Coll. Cardiology; mem. AMA (mem. residency rev. com. Coun. Med. Edn. 1973), AAAS, Am. Acad. Cerebral Palsy, Am. Acad. Phys. Medicine and Rehab. (Disting. Clinician award 1993), Am. Congress Rehab. Medicine (pres. 1962), Calif. Coun. Gerontology and Geriatrics (bd. dirs. 1980-86, pres. 1985), N.Y. Acad. Medicine, N.Y. Acad. Sci., Orange County Med. Soc. Home: 1115 Goldenrod Ave Corona Del Mar CA 92625-1508 Office: U Calif Dept Phys Medicine & Rehab Irvine CA 92668

TOBISMAN, STUART PAUL, lawyer; b. Detroit, June 5, 1942; s. Nathan and Beverly (Porvin) T.; m. Karen Sue Tobisman, Aug. 8, 1965; children: Cynthia Elaine, Neal Jay. BA, UCLA, 1966; JD, U. Calif., Berkeley, 1969. Bar: Calif. 1969. Assoc. O'Melveny & Myers, L.A., 1969-77, ptnr., 1977—; dir. Burton G. Bettingen Corp. Contbr. articles to profl. jours. Trustee L.A. County Bar Assn., 1983-84. With USN, 1961-63. Fellow Am. Coll. Trust and Estate Counsel; mem. Phi Beta Kappa, Order of Coif. Office: O'Melveny & Myers 1999 Ave of the Stars Los Angeles CA 90067-6035

TOBLER, D. LEE, chemical and aerospace company executive; b. Provo, Utah, July 25, 1933; s. Donald and Louise Harriet (Shoell) T.; m. H. Darlene Thueson, Nov. 21, 1956; children—Lisa, Julianne, Curtis, Craig, Denise, Bradley. BA in Fin. and Econs., Brigham Young U., 1957; MBA in Fin., Northwestern U., 1958. Mgr. planning and econs. Exxon, N.Y.C., 1958-72; v.p., treas. Aetna Life & Casualty, Hartford, Conn., 1972-81; group v.p., chief fin. officer Zapata Corp., Houston, 1981-84; exec. v.p., chief fin. officer B.F. Goodrich Co., Akron, Ohio, 1985—; also bd. dirs. B.F. Goodrich Co., Akron. Trustee, mem. exec. com. Akron Regional Devel. Bd., 1990-91, chmn., 1992-95; pres. Literacy Vols. of Conn., Hartford, 1973-81; mem. exec. bd. Sam Houston Area Boy Scouts Am., 1984; bd. trustees Ohio Ballet, 1994—. Mem. Portage Country Club (Akron). Republican. Mem. LDS Ch. Avocations: gardening; tennis; reading. Home: 16135 Warwick Rd Marshallville OH 44645 Office: BF Goodrich Co 3925 Embassy Pky Akron OH 44333-1763

TOBLER, WALDO RUDOLPH, geographer, cartographer; b. Portland, Oreg., Nov. 16, 1930; s. Verner and Hanny (Urech) T.; m. Dorothy Weix, Dec. 27, 1957 (div. 1979); children—Eric, Stephen; m. Rachel Mendenhall, Sept. 16, 1982. B.A., U. Wash., 1955, M.A., 1957, Ph.D., 1961; Dr. h.c., U. Zurich, 1988. Asst. planner Pierce County, Tacoma, 1958-59; asst. prof. to prof. U. Mich., Ann Arbor, 1961-77; prof. U. Calif., Santa Barbara, 1977-94, rsch. prof., 1994—; vis. prof. U. Minn.-Mpls., 1968, U. Zurich, Switzerland, 1973, Tech. U. Vienna, Austria, 1993; chmn. Math. Social Sci. Bd., 1974; coun. Regional Sci. Assn., 1967-69; rsch. scientist Internat. Inst. for Applied Systems Analysis, Austria, 1975. Contbr. articles on math. geography and cartography to profl. jours. Served to sgt. U.S. Army, 1948-52; ETO. Fellow Royal Geograph. Soc. (London); mem. Assn. Am. Geographers (Meritorius Svc. 1968), Assn. Computing Machinery, Am. Congress Surveying and Mapping, Nat. acad. Scis., Am. Geog. Soc. (hon., O.M. MIIler Cartographic medal 1989), Nat. Ctr. for Geographic Info. and Analysis (sr. scientist NSF Ctr. 1989—), Sierra Club, Swiss (Santa Barbara pres. 1980-82, treas. 1983-85). Avocations: skiing; hiking; swimming; classical music. Office: Univ California Dept Geography Santa Barbara CA 93106

TOBY, JACKSON, sociologist, educator; b. N.Y.C., Sept. 10, 1925; s. Phineas and Anna (Weissman) T.; m. Marcia Lifshitz, Aug. 1, 1952; children: Alan Steven, Gail Afriat. B.A., Bklyn. Coll., 1946; M.A. in Econs, Harvard U., 1947, M.A. in Sociology, 1949, Ph.D. in Sociology, 1950. Research assoc. Lab. Social Relations, Harvard, 1950-51; mem. faculty Rutgers U., 1951—; prof. sociology, chmn. dept., 1961-68, dir. Inst. for Criminological Research, 1969-94; cons. Youth Devel. Program, Ford Found., 1959-63. Author: (with H. C. Bredemeier) Social Problems in America, 1960, 2d edit., 1971; contbr. numerous articles to profl. jours., pub. policy jours., N.Y. Times, Wall St. Jour., L.A. Times, Chgo. Tribune. Cons., Pres.'s Commn. Law Enforcement and Adminstrn. Justice, 1967. Recipient numerous research grants. Mem. Am. Sociol. Assn., Am. Soc. Criminology, Univ. Centers for Rational Alternatives. Spl. research adolescent delinquency in U.S., Sweden, Japan, other countries, on violence and dropouts in Am. public schools. Home: 17 Harrison Ave Highland Park NJ 08904-1813 Office: Rutgers U Dept Sociology Lucy Stone Hall Livingston Campus New Brunswick NJ 08903

TOCCO, JAMES, pianist; b. Detroit, Sept. 21, 1943; s. Vincenzo and Rose (Tabbita) T.; 1 child, Rhoya. Prof. music Ind. U., Bloomington, 1977-91; eminent scholar, artist-in-residence U. Cin. Coll.-Conservatory Music, 1991—; prof. Musikhochschule, Lübeck, Ger., 1990—; artistic dir. Great Lakes Chamber Music Festival, 1994—. Debut with orch., Detroit, 1956, since performed with symphony orchs. including Chgo. Symphony, Los Angeles Philharmonic, Cin. Symphony, Detroit Symphony, Nat. Symphony, Balt. Symphony, Atlanta Symphony, Denver Symphony, Montreal Symphony, London Symphony, London Philharm., Berlin Philharm., Moscow Radio-TV Orch., Amsterdam Philharmonic, Munich Philharmonic, Bavarian Radio Orch., also recitals, U.S. and abroad, and performances, CBS and NBC networks; guest performer, White House; Recs. include the complete preludes of Chopin, collected piano works of Leonard Bernstein, complete piano works of Charles Tomlinson Griffes, 4 piano sonatas of Edward MacDowell, selected piano works of Aaron Copland, complete Bach-Liszt organ transcriptions. Recipient Bronze medal Tchaikovsky Competition, Moscow 1970, Bronze medal Queen Elisabeth of Belgium Competition, Brussels 1972, 1st prize Piano Competition of Americas, Rio de Janeiro 1973, 1st prize Munich Internat. Competition 1973. Office: U Cin Coll-Conservatory Music Cincinnati OH 45221-0003

TOCCO, STEPHEN, airport administrator. Exec. dir. Boston Gen. Edward Lawrence Logan Internat. Airport. Office: Mass Port Authority 10 Park Plz Boston MA 02116

TOCK, JOSEPH, lawyer; b. Cleve. Aug. 22, 1954; s. Julius Joseph and Marianna Yvonne (Carracio) T. BA, Kent State U., 1979; JD, Case Western Res. U., 1983. Bar: Ohio, 1983, U.S. Ct. Mil. Appeals, 1983, Colo. 1988. Commd. 1st lt. USAF, 1983, advanced through grades to maj., 1994; asst. staff judge advocate, chief civil law USAF, McConnell AFB, Kans., 1983-84; asst. staff judge advocate, chief civil law USAF, Yokota Air Base, Japan, 1984-85, area def. counsel 7th cir., 1985-87; dep. staff judge advocate, chief mil. justice USAF, Kelly AFB, Tex., 1987-88; dep. county atty. El Paso County, Colo., 1989-90; pvt. practice Colorado Springs, Colo., 1990-91; staff atty. Guam Legal Svcs. Corp., 1991-92; asst. atty. gen. White Collar Unit Atty. Gen. Prosecution Divsn., Agana, Guam, 1992—; dep. staff judge advocate Peterson AFB, Colo., 1990-91, Andersen AFB, Guam, 1991—; instr. family law Pikes Peak C.C., 1990-91; lectr. Continental Security Divsn.,

San Antonio, 1987-88, NCO prep course, Kelly AFB, Tex., 1987-88, Profl. Mil. Edn. Ctr., Yokota Air Base, 1984-87. Mem. ABA, Internat. Legal Soc. Japan, am. Legion, Mensa. Republican. Roman Catholic. Avocations: golf, handball. Office: Atty Gen Prosecution Divsn Jud Ctr Bldg 120 W O'Brien Dr Ste 2-200E Agana GU 96910-4911

TOCKLIN, ADRIAN MARTHA, insurance company executive, lawyer; b. Coral Gables, Fla., Aug. 4, 1951; d. Kelso Hampton and Patricia Jane (Crook) Cook Atkins; m. Gary Michael Tocklin, Nov. 23, 1974. BA, George Washington U., 1972; JD, Seton Hall U., 1994. Regional claim examiner Interstate Nat. Corp., St. Petersburg, Fla., 1973-74; branch supr. Underwriter's Adjusting Co. subs. Continental Corp., Tampa, Fla., 1974-77, asst. dir. edn. tng. adminstrn., N.Y.C., 1977, asst. regional mgr. adminstrn. ops., Livingston, N.J., 1977-78, br. mgr., Paramus, N.J., 1978-80, sr. v.p. mktg., N.Y.C., Piscataway, N.J., 1980-84, regional v.p., mgr., Livingston, N.J., 1984-86, exec. v.p., 1986-88, also bd. dirs.; sr. v.p. Continental Corp., 1988-92, exec. v.p. 1992-94, pres., N.Y.C., 1994—; pres. bd. dirs. U.S. Protection Indemnity Agy., Inc., N.Y.C.; bd. dirs. Underwriters Adjusting Co., Arbitration Forums, Inc., Tarrytown, N.Y., Continental Ins. Co., Sonat Corp.; v.p. Continental Risk Services, Inc., Hamilton, Bermuda, 1983-86; editor-in-chief Profl. Ins. Bulletin Update, N.Y.C., 1977-79. Mem. YWCA Acad. Women Achievers. Mem. Nat. Assn. Ins. Women (Outstanding Ins. Woman in N.Y.C.), NOW. Democrat. Lutheran. Office: Continental Corp 180 Maiden Ln New York NY 10038-4925

TOCKMAN, RONALD CHESTER, accountant; b. St. Louis, May 18, 1945; s. Ruben J. and Gertrude (Bensky) T.; m. Lois Joyce Koplan, Sept. 1, 1969; children: Neil D., Lee D., Gail B. BS, Suffolk U., 1971. CPA, Mass. Staff acct. Theodore Samet & Co., Boston, 1972-73; sr. acct. Miller Wachman & Co., Boston, 1973-75; pvt. practice Ronald C. Tockman CPA, Boston, 1975-83; tax prin. and v.p. Cooper & Co. P.C., Burlington, Mass., 1983-94; pvt. practice, 1994—; lectr. profl. edn. courses various topics, 1976—. Served with U.S. Army, 1965-68, Vietnam. Recipient two Purple Heart medals, Vietnamese Cross of Gallantry, U.S. Army, 1966. Fellow AICPA (tax div. 1986—), Mass. Soc. CPAs (fed. tax. com. 1979—); mem. KP (Chancellor Comdr. King Solomon Lodge 1979), Handi-Kids, Inc. (dir.). Avocations: bowling, golf. Office: Ste 213 95 Washington St Canton MA 02021

TOD, G. ROBERT, consumer marketing executive; b. Schenectady, N.Y., July 10, 1939; s. George B. and Jane (Nicholson) T.; m. JoAnn Anderson, Oct. 24, 1964; children: G. Robert Jr., Jennifer R. BME, Rensselaer Poly. Inst., 1961; MBA, Harvard U., 1967. Group mgr. Bangor Punta Corp., Boston, 1967-69; pres., chief oper. officer and co-founder CML Group Inc., Acton, Mass., 1969—; bd. dirs. SCI Systems Inc., Huntsville, Ala., EG & G Inc., Wellesley, Mass. Co-author: (with others) Chief Executive's Handbook, 1976. Trustee Rensselaer Poly. Inst., Troy, N.Y., 1981—; bd. dirs. Emerson Hosp., Concord, Mass., 1983—; former trustee Fenn. Sch., Middlesex Sch., Concord. Capt. USAF, 1961-65. Mem. Harvard Bus. Sch. Alumni Coun. (bd. dirs. 1988-92). Home: PO Box 650 Concord MA 01742-0004 Office: CML Group Inc 524 Main St Acton MA 01720-3993

TODA, KEISHI, electronics executive; b. Tokyo, Japan, 1933. Grad., Hito Tsu Bashi U., Tokyo, 1960. Pres. Hitachi Am. LTD., Tarrytown, N.Y. Office: Hitachi America LTD 50 Prospect Ave Tarrytown NY 10591-4625

TODD, BARBARA SHEEN, county commissioner; b. Phila., Mar. 10, 1942; d. Milton Roy and Jeanette (Brown) Sheen; m. Thomas C. Todd, May 18, 1973; children—Kimberly, Tamara, Tiffany. Student Instituto Tecnologico, Monterrey, Mexico, 1962; B.A. in Spanish and Sociology, Fla. State U., 1963, M.A. in Fgn. Lang. Edn., 1964. Personnel mgr. State of Fla. and pvt. industry, 1965-75; state adminstr. for spl. programs, Fla. Bd. of Regents, 1973-75; acting asst. sec. for adminstrn. Office of Sec. of Edn. and Cultural Affairs, S.D., 1975; owner, mgr. cons. firm, Pierre, S.D., 1975-79; county commr. Pinellas County, Fla., 1980—, chmn., 1983. Chmn. Met. Planning Orgn., Pinellas County Property Appraisal and Adjustment Bd., 1984—. Tourist Devel. Council, 1983, Child Safety Task Force, 1985, Leon County Sch. Bd., 1973, State Task Force on Elem. Guidance, 1972, State Adv. Panel on Differentiated Staffing; bd. dirs. League of Cities, 1985-86, Juvenile Welfare Bd., 1982-83, Mental Health Bd., 1981-86; mem. Pinellas Arts Council, Pinellas County Day Care Licensing Bd., 1985-86, Pinellas Planning Council, 1980-86; mem. steering com. Nat. Assn. of Counties, 1985-86, also men. nat. health and edn. com., 1984-85, also task force on refugees, aliens and migrants; mem. Fla. State Commn. on Child Support, 1985-86. State treas. State Assn. of County Commrs., 1984, v.p., 1985-86; pres. Fla. Assn. County Commrs., 1986-87; mem. Gov.'s Growth Mgmt. Adv. Com., 1985-86; state legis. chmn S.D. PTA, 1977-79; pres. Women's Fellowship, Congl. Ch. of Pierre, 1974-75; vice chmn. Leon County Sch. Bd., 1972. Mem. Am. Assn. of Sch. Adminstrs., Nat. U. Extension Assn., Beta Sigma Phi (past pres.), Sigma Delta Pi, Kappa Delta Pi. Recipient Outstanding Service award Pinellas County Extension Hort. Adv. Com., 1984, Award for Patriotic Services Rendered to the Community, VFW, 1984; named Outstanding Elected Ofcl. for 1983, Greater Seminole Republican Club: Pilot. Home: 1934 Arrowhead Dr NE Saint Petersburg FL 33703-1904 Office: Office Bd Commrs 315 Court St Clearwater FL 34616-5136

TODD, BRUCE M., mayor. BBA in acctg., U. Tex. CPA, Tex. Former ptnr. Mueller, Todd and Co.; commr. Travis County, Tex., 1987—; mayor City of Austin, Tex., 1991—; City of Austin chair AISD/City Coun. Joint Com., Audit Com., Conv. Ctr. Com., Opportunities for Youth subcom., Joint Debt Advisory Com., Legis. Com., Judicial Com., Policy Planning and Budget Com., Downtown subcom., So. Union Gas Rate Request subcom. bd. dirs. Tex. Mcpl. League, Austin Transp. Study Com., Capital Metro Local Govt. Approval Com.; mem. Mayor's United on Safety, Crime and Law Enforcement; chairperson Balcones Canyonlands Conservation Plan; former pres. Austin-San Antonio Corridor Coun. Mem. Tex. Soc. CPAs (former mem. bd. dirs, exec. com. Austin chpt.). Address: 1700 Wethersfield Rd Austin TX 78703-3329 Office: Office of Mayor 124 W 8th St Austin TX 78701*

TODD, CECIL WILLIAM, ministry director; b. Nashoba, Okla., Oct. 7, 1931; s. Cecil William Sr. and Emily (Cent) T.; m. Barbara Joan Patchin, May 23, 1953 (div. Sept. 1979); children: Janet, Gail, Jon, Tim, Cecil; m. Linda Lorraine Hayden, May 30, 1980. B of Sacred Lit., Ozark Christian Coll., 1954; DDiv, Midwest Christian Coll., 1972. Min. Rinehart Christian Ch., Horton, Mo., 1952-54; sr. min. Albert Pike Christian Ch., Ft. Smith, Ark., 1956-59, Christian Ch., Clayton, Okla., 1960-64; founder, pres., dir. Tide Revival Fires Ministry, Branson and Joplin, Mo., 1964—; spkr. nation wide weekly TV shows Revival Fires, 1965-92. Author: Which Way America-Atheism or Almighty God, 1969, While American Played, 1985, Blue Print for Slavery, 1971; editor Revival Fires Mag., 1964—. Avocations: hunting, fishing. Home: PO Box 1060 Kimberling City MO 65686 Office: Revival Fires Ministry PO Box 1008 Branson MO 65737

TODD, DAVID FENTON MICHIE, architect; b. Middletown, Ohio, Feb. 22, 1915; s. Robert Chalmers and Frances Fenton (Michie) T.; m. Suzanne Williams, Sept. 1, 1942; 1 child, Gregory F.W. A.B., Dartmouth, 1937; B.Arch., U. Mich., 1940. Draftsman J.R.F. Swanson, Birmingham, Mich., 1940-41; archtl. designer W. Ray Yount, Dayton, Ohio, 1941-42; architect Harrison, Ballard & Allen, N.Y.C., 1942-53; architect, prin. Ballard, Todd & Snibbe, N.Y.C., 1957-62, Ballard Todd Assos., 1962-66, David Todd & Assos., 1966—. Works include Manhattan Plaza, N.Y.C., Collegiate Sch., N.Y.C., Rye (N.Y.) Country Day Sch. Past chmn. bd. dirs. Leake & Watts Children's Home, N.Y.C.; chmn. N.Y.C. Landmarks Preservation Commn. 1989-90. Served to 1st lt. AUS, 1942-46. Recipient awards for tennis pavillion, Princeton U. AIA, 1962, Harry B. Rutkins Meml. award N.Y.C. AIA, 1963, Robert Treat Hotel, Newark Asn. Commerce and Industry, 1964, Manhattan Pla. Constrn. Industry Bd., 1978, Andrew Thomas Pioneer in Housing award N.Y.C. AIA, 1986, cert. of merit Mcpl. Art Soc. N.Y.C., 1991,. Fellow AIA (pres. N.Y.C. chpt. 1969-70, chmn. jury of fellows 1971, chmn. task force on housing policy 1974), Constrn. Specifications Inst. (pres. N.Y.C. chpt. 1960-61, regional dir. 1965-66). Clubs: Century Assn, Amateur Comedy. Home and Office: 134 E 95th St New York NY 10128-1705

TODD, DONALD FREDERICK, geologist. Recipient Michel T. Halbouty Human Needs award Am. Assn. Petroleum Geologists, 1992. Office: Constellation Group 1700 Broadway Ste 420 Denver CO 80290-0401

TODD, HAROLD WADE, retired air force officer, consultant; b. Chgo., Jan. 17, 1938; s. Harold Wade and Jeanne (Fayal) T.; m. Wendy Yvonne Kendrick, July 12, 1981; children by previous marriage: Hellen J. Wilson, Kenneth J., Stephen D., Joseph M. Michelle M. Adams, Mark A.; stepchildren: Jamie Y. White, James K. Mills, Timothy S. Emerson. B.S., U.S. Air Force Acad., 1959; grad., Nat. War Coll., 1975. Commd. 2d lt. U.S. Air Force, 1959, advanced through grades to maj. gen., 1982; aide to comdr. (2d Air Force (SAC)), Barksdale AFB, La., 1970-71; exec. aide to comdr.-in-chief U.S. Air Forces Europe, Germany, 1971-74; spl. asst. chief of staff USAF, 1975-76; chief Concept Devel. Div., 1976-77, chief Readiness and NATO Staff Group, Hdqrs. USAF, 1977-78; exec. asst. to chmn. Joint Chiefs Staff Washington, 1978-80; comdr. 25th region N. Am. Aerospace Def. Command McChord AFB, Wash., 1980-82; chief staff 4th Allied Tactical Air Force Heidelberg, 1982-85; commandant Air War Coll., 1985-89; vice comdr. Air U., 1985-89, ret., 1989; ind. cons. Colorado Springs, Colo., 1989—. Founder, pres. Bossier City (La.) chpt. Nat. Assn. for Children with Learning Disabilities, 1970-71. Decorated Def. D.S.M., Air Force D.S.M. (2), Legion of Merit (2), D.F.C., Air medal (8), Air Force Commendation medal. Mem. Air Force Assn., USAF Acad. Assn. Grads., Nat. War Coll. Alumni Assn. Home: 1250 Big Valley Dr Colorado Springs CO 80919-1015

TODD, HARRY WILLIAMS, aircraft propulsion system company executive; b. Oak Park, Ill., 1922. BSME, U. So. Calif., 1947, BSIE, 1948, MBA, 1950. With Rockwell Internat., Pitts., 1947-76, former v.p. ops.; pres., chmn., chief exec. officer, bd. dirs. The L.E. Myers Co., Pitts., 1976-80; with Rohr Industries, Inc., Chula Vista, Calif., 1980-90, chief operating officer, 1980-82, pres., chief exec. officer, chmn., 1982-90, retired, 1990; mng. ptnr. Carlise Enterprises, 1990—; bd. dirs. Rohr Industries, Pacific Scientific, Helmerich & Payne, Garrett Aviation Svcs. Trustee Scripps Clinic and Rsch. Found. With U.S. Army, 1944-46. Office: Carlisle Enterprises 7777 Fay Ave La Jolla CA 92037-4323

TODD, HENRY REYNOLDS, JR., director state tourism office; b. St. Paul, Mar. 26, 1951; s. Henry Reynolds Sr. and Ruth Elizabeth (Malm) T.; m. Sue Ann Rosen, Aug. 3, 1974; children: Alison Dawn, Mackenzie Reynolds. BBA, Mankato (Minn.) State U., 1973. Travel and tourism rep. Minn. Office Tourism, St. Paul, 1973-78, dir., 1978—. Bd. dirs. St. Paul Winter Carnival, 1983-89; trustee U.S. Travel Data Ctr., Washington, 1985-90. Mem. Nat. Coun. State Travel Dirs. (chmn. 1985-87), Travel Industry Assn. Am. (bd. dirs. 1984—, Travel Dir. Yr. award 1982, Nat. Travel Mktg. award 1986), Nat. Tour Assn., Am. Bus. Assn., Great Lakes States Tourism Mktg. Com. (chmn. 1991—), Miss. River States Internat. Mktg. Com. (chmn. 1991—). Office: Minn Office of Tourism 375 Jackson St Ste 250 Saint Paul MN 55101-1810

TODD, J. C. See COOPER, JANE TODD

TODD, J. OWEN, judge; b. Boston, Dec. 2, 1935; s. John Joseph and Barbara Veronica (Feeney) T.; m. Eileen Marie Sullivan, Dec. 26, 1959; children: Gary O., Eileen Marie, Elizabeth S., Alison C. AB, Harvard U., 1957; JD, Boston Coll., 1975; LLD (hon.), New Eng. Sch. Law, 1975. Bar: Mass. 1960, U.S. Dist. Ct. Mass. 1960, U.S. Tax Ct. 1960, U.S. Ct. Appeals (1st cir.) 1960, U.S. Supreme Ct. 1960. Law clk. to presiding justice Supreme Jud. Ct., Boston, 1960-61; sr. ptnr. Hale and Dorr, Boston, 1961-88; judge Superior Ct. Dept. Trial Ct. Mass., Boston, 1988—; instr. trial advocacy Harvard U., Boston Coll., MCLE, 1980—. Moderator Town of Sudbury, Mass., 1965-75; trustee New Eng. Sch. Law, Boston, 1975-81. Mem. ABA, Mass. Bar Assn. (mediator 1980—), Am. Coll. Trial Lawyers, Boston Bar Assn. (mediator 1980—), Bald Peak Colony Club, Clover Club, Harvard Club. Office: Commonwealth Mass Superior Ct Dept Boston MA 02108

TODD, JAMES AVERILL, JR., steel company executive; b. Beckley, W.Va., July 31, 1928; s. James A. Sr. and Effie (Whisman) T.; m. Mary Margaret Barlow; children: Candace Todd Ewert, Mark A., Jennifer E. BS in Mining Engring., W.Va. U., 1950. With sales and mktg. dept. E.I. Du Pont de Nemours & Co., 1951-75; v.p. mktg. Atlas Powder Co., 1975-77; pres. United Affiliates Corp., Dallas, 1977-80; chmn., chief exec. officer Birmingham (Ala.) Bolt Co., 1980-84; pres., chief exec. officer Birmingham Steel Corp., 1984—; bd. dirs. Cyprus Minerals Co. Pres. Birmingham Coun. Boy Scouts Am. 1985-86, mem. exec. com. Mem. Am. Mining Congress (bd. govs., dir.), Inst. Scrap Iron and Steel, N.Y. Mining Club, Ala. Productivity Ctr. (bd. dirs.), Mt. Brook Club, The Club, Shoal Creek, Rotary, Kappa Alpha. Office: Birmingham Steel Corp Ste 300 1000 Urban Pkwy Birmingham AL 35242

TODD, JAMES DALE, federal judge; b. Scotts Hill, Tenn., May 20, 1943; s. James P. and Jeanette Grace (Duck) T.; m. Jeanie M. Todd, June 26, 1965; children: James Michael, Julie Diane. BS, Lambuth Coll., 1965; M Combined Scis., U. Miss., 1968; JD, Memphis State U., 1972. Bar: Tenn. 1972, U.S. Dist. Ct. (we. dist.) Tenn. 1972, U.S. Ct. Appeals (6th cir.) 1973, U.S. Supreme Ct. 1975. Tchr. sci., chmn. sci. dept. Lyman High Sch., Longwood, Fla., 1965-68, Memphis U. Sch., 1968-72; ptnr. Waldrop, Farmer, Todd & Breen, P.A., 1972-83; cir. judge div. II 26th Jud. Dist., Jackson, Tenn., 1983-85; judge U.S. Dist. Ct. (we. dist.) Tenn., Jackson, 1985—. Named Alumnus of Yr. Lambuth Coll. Alumni Assn., 1985. Fellow Tenn. Bar Found.; mem. Fed. Judges Assn., Fed. Bar Assn., Tenn. Bar Assn., Jackson Madison County Bar Assn. (pres. 1978-79). Methodist. Office: US Dist Ct 109 S Highland Ave Jackson TN 38301-6123

TODD, JAMES S., surgeon, educator, medical association administrator; b. Hyannis, Mass., 1931. Intern Presbyn. Hosp., N.Y.C., 1957-58, resident in surgery, 1959-63; resident in surgery Delafield Hosp., N.Y.C., 1963; resident ob-gyn. Sloane Womens Hosp., N.Y.C., 1958-59; resident Valley Hosp., Ridgewood, N.J.; clin. asst. prof. surgery U. Medicine and Dentistry N.J., Newark; exec. v.p. AMA, 1993—; pres. AMA. Office: American Medical Assocation 515 N State St Chicago IL 60610-4320

TODD, JAMES STILES, surgeon, professional executive association; b. Hyannis, Mass., July 9, 1931; s. Alexander Campbell and Myra Crowell (Stiles) T.; m. Marjorie Patricia Thorn, Sept. 6, 1958; children: Kendall Scott, Christopher James. AB, Harvard U., 1953, MD, 1957. Diplomate Am. Bd. Surgery. Intern Columbia-Presbyn. Med. Ctr., N.Y.C., 1957-58, resident in surgery, 1958-64; pvt. practice Ridgewood, N.J., 1964-85; asst. in surgery Columbia Coll. of Physicians & Surgeons, N.Y.C., 1964—, Columbia-Presbyn. Hosp., N.Y.C., 1964—; sr. dep. exec. v.p. AMA, Chgo., 1985—, exec. v.p. 1990—; former chmn. bd. N.J. State Med. Underwriters, Inc. Lawrenceville; cons. physician Valley Hosp., Ridgewood, 1985—. Author: (with others) DRGs for Physicians, 1983; editor: Intensive Care, 1965; contbr. articles to profl. jours. Pres. Bergen Community Blood Bank, Paramus, N.J., 1978-85; pres. bd. mgrs. County Hosp., 1978-79. Recipient Edward J. Ill Distinguished Physician award, N.J. Acad. Medicine, 1980, Disting. Svc. award N.J. Hosp. Assn., 1984. Fellow ACS; mem. Health Care Execs., Med. Soc. N.J., AMA, pres. Physician Insurers Assn. of Am., Lawrenceville, N.J., 1984-85. Republican. Avocations: clock building and repair, boating. Office: AMA 515 N State St Chicago IL 60610-4320

TODD, JOHN, mathematician, educator; b. Carnaclly, Ireland, May 16, 1911; came to U.S. 1947, naturalized, 1953; s. William Robert and Catherine (Stewart) T.; m. Olga Taussky, Sept. 29, 1938. B.S., Queen's U., Belfast, Ireland, 1931; research student, St. John's Coll., Cambridge (Eng.) U., 1931-33. Lectr. Queen's U., 1933-37, King's Coll., London, 1937-49; chief computation lab., then chief numerical analysis Nat. Bur. Standards, 1947-57; prof. math. Calif. Inst. Tech., 1957—; Fulbright prof. Vienna, Austria, 1965. Author, editor books on numerical analysis and tables, also numerous articles; editor in chief: Numerische Mathematik, 1959—; assoc. editor: Aequationes Mathematicae, 1967-85, 89—, Jour. Approximation Theory, 1967-93. Mem. Am. Math. Soc., Soc. Indsl. and Applied Math., Math. Assn. Am. (gov. 1980-83). Office: Calif Inst Technology Mathematics 253 # 37 Pasadena CA 91125

TODD, JOHN DICKERSON, JR., lawyer; b. Macon, Ga., June 30, 1912; s. J.D. and Hazel (McManus) T.; m. Mellicent McWhorter, Mar. 7, 1943; children—Rosalind (Mrs. Jack Harding Tedards, Jr.), John D. Student, Va. Mil. Inst., 1930-32; LL.B., U. Ga., 1935. Bar: S.C. bar 1935. With firm Hingson & Todd, 1935-51; partner firm Leatherwood, Walker, Todd & Mann, Greenville, S.C., 1952—; now sr. partner; judge Greenville City Ct., 1939; atty. County of Greenville, 1948-56; mem. bd. bar examiners State of S.C. Served to maj. AUS, 1941-45. Mem. ABA, Am. Coll. Trial Lawyers, Am. Bar Found., 4th U.S. Cir. Jud. Conf., S.C. Bar Assn. (bd. govs., pres. 1978—), Greenville Jr. C. of C. (pres.), Greenville County (past pres.), Phi Delta Phi, Sigma Nu. Baptist (chmn., deacon). Clubs: Kiwanian (Greenville) (past pres.), Greenville Country (Greenville) (past pres.). Home: 200 Riverside Dr Greenville SC 29605-1133 Office: 100 E Coffee St Greenville SC 29601-2707

TODD, JOHN JOSEPH, lawyer; b. St. Paul, Mar. 16, 1927; s. John Alfred and Martha Agnes (Jagoe) T.; m. Dolores Jean Shanahan, Sept. 9, 1950; children: Richard M., Jane E., John P. Student, St. Thomas Coll., 1944, 46-47; B.Sci. and Law, U. Minn., 1949, LL.B. 1951. Bar: Minn. bar 1951. Practice in South St. Paul, Minn., 1951-72; partner Thuet and Todd, 1953-72; assoc. justice Minn. Supreme Ct., St. Paul, 1972-85; sole practice West St. Paul, 1985-92; of counsel Brenner & Glassman Ltd., Mpls., 1992—. Served with USNR, 1945-46. Mem. Am. Bar Assn., state bar assns., Am. Legion, VFW. Home: 6689 Argenta Trl W Inver Grove MN 55077-2208 Office: Brenner & Glassman Ltd 2001 Killebrew Dr #170 Minneapolis MN 55425-1822

TODD, JOHN ODELL, insurance company sales professional; b. Mpls., Nov. 12, 1902; s. Frank Chisholm and Mary Mable (Odell) T.; AB, Cornell U., 1924; CLU, Am. Coll., 1933; m. Katherine Sarah Cone, Feb. 21, 1925; children: John Odell, George Bennett. Spl. agt. Equitable Life Assurance Soc., Mpls., 1926-28; ins. broker, Mpls., 1928-31; spl. agt. Northwestern Mut. Life Ins. Co., Mpls., 1931-38, Evanston, Ill., 1938—; ptnr. H.S. Vail & Sons, Chgo., 1938-43, Vail and Todd, gen. agts. Northwestern Mut., Chgo., 1943-44; sole gen. agt., Chgo., 1944-51; pres. Todd Planning and Service Co., life ins. brokers, 1951—; founder, hon. chmn., prin. John O. Todd Orgn., Exec. Compensation Specialists and Cons., 1970-91; faculty lectr. C.L.U. Insts., U. Conn., 1952-53, U. Wis., 1955-57, U. Calif., 1956, U. Hawaii, 1966; host interviewer ednl. Films Series of the Greats, 1973-74. Pres. Evanston (Ill.) 1st. Ward Non-Partisan Civic Assn., 1956-57; trustee Evanston Hist. Soc., 1973-76; bd. dirs. First Congl Ch., Evanston, 1987-89; co-founder MDRT Charitable Found., 1959, pres., 1971, sole lifetime dir. emeritus, 1971—. Recipient Cleary award Best Gen. Agt. Devel., 1948, Golden Plate award Am. Acad. Achievement, 1969; Huebner Gold medal for contbn. to edn., 1978; named Ins. Field Man of Year, Ins. Field Pub. Co., 1965, John Newton Russell award Instn. Life Ins., 1969; Ill. Room in Hall of States dedicated to him by Am. Coll., 1981. Mem. AALU Am. Coll. John O. Nat. Assn. Life Underwriters, Assn. Advanced Life Underwriters (pres. 1963-64), Am. Coll. Life Underwriters (trustee 1957-78), Chgo. Life Underwriters Assn. (dir. 1938-41, Disting. Service award 1984), Northwestern Mut. Spl. Agts. Assn. (pres. 1955-56), Life Agy. Mgrs. Assn. (dir. 1945-48), Northwestern Mut. Assn. Agts. (pres. 1957-58, leader sr. agents 1994), Chgo. Life Trust Council, Million Dollar Round Table (pres. 1951, only 60th yr. consecutive qualifier), Top of Table (charter mem.), Psi Upsilon, Sphinx Head. Republican. Clubs: Evanston Univ.; Glen View. Author: Taxation, Inflation and Life Insurance, 1950; Ceiling Unlimited, 1965, 5th edit., 1984, Never a Dull Day, an autobiography, 1990, A Lifetime of opportunities, 1994; contbg. author to text Huebner Foundation, 1951, Secrets of the Master Sellers, Am. Mgmt. assn., 1987.

TODD, KATHLEEN GAIL, physician; b. Portland, Oreg., Aug. 31, 1951; d. Horace Edward and Lois Marie (Messing) T.; m. Andrew Richard Embick, March 31, 1980; children: Elizabeth Todd Embick, Margaret Todd Embick. BA, Pomona Coll., 1972; MD, Washington U., St. Louis, 1976. Diplomate Am. Bd. Family Practice. Resident U. Wash. Affiliated Hosps., Seattle, 1976-79; pvt. practice Valdez (Alaska) Med. Clinic, 1980—; chief of staff Valdez Community Hosp., 1986—. Mem. AMA, AAFP, Am. Acad. Family Practice, Alaska State Med. Assn. (counselor-at-large 1986-87). Democrat. Episcopalian. Avocations: skiing, kayaking, camping, music. Office: Valdez Med Clinic Box 1829 Valdez AK 99686

TODD, KENNETH S., JR., parasitologist, educator; b. Three Forks, Mont., Aug. 25, 1936; s. Kenneth S. and Anna Louise (Seeman) T. BS, Mont. State U., 1962, MS, 1964; PhD, Utah State U., 1967. Asst. prof. U. Ill., Urbana, 1967-71, assoc. prof., 1971-76, prof. vet. parasitology, 1976—, chmn. div. parasitology, 1983-90, asst. head vet. pathobiology, 1984-87, prof. vet. programs in agr., 1984-94, acting head vet. pathobiology, 1987-90, head, 1990-94; prof. emeritus, 1994; affiliate scientist Ill. State Natural History Survey, 1987—; adj. prof. microbiology Mont. State U. Served with USAF, 1954-58. NSF grad. fellow, 1966-67. Mem. AVMA, Am. Assn. Vet. Parasitologists, Am. Micros. Soc., Am. Soc. Parasitologists, Am. Soc. Tropical Medicine and Hygiene, Helminthologic Soc. Washington, Midwest Conf. Parasitologists, Wildlife Disease Assn., Soc. Protozoologists. Office: Mont State U Dept Microbiology Bozeman MT 59715

TODD, MALCOLM CLIFFORD, surgeon; b. Carlyle, Ill., Apr. 10, 1913; s. Malcolm N. and Grace (Heitmeier) T.; m. Ruth Holle Schlake, June 12, 1945; 1 son, Malcolm Douglas. AB, U. Ill., 1934; MB, Northwestern U., 1934, MD, 1938; DSc (hon.), Brown U., 1975. Diplomate Am. Bd. Surgery. Intern St. Lukes Hosp., Chgo., 1937-38; resident Cook County Hosp., Chgo., 1938-41; instr. surgery Northwestern U., 1939-46; pvt. practice Long Beach, Calif., 1946-90; clin. prof. surgery U. Calif., Irvine, 1964-85, emeritus prof. surgery, 1985—; chief surgery, hon. bd. dirs. Long Beach Meml. Hosp., 1956-57, chief of staff, 1958-60; attending surgeon Long Beach VA Hosp., 1954-80, Los Angeles County Gen. Hosp., 1964-74; bd. dirs. Harbor Bank Long Beach, Spectral Diagnostics, Toronto, Ont., Can. Contbr. sci. and socio-econ. articles to med. jours. Mem. Nat. Adv. Com. on Health Manpower; cons. to def. WHO, 1970-72; dir. Calif. Health Planning Coun., 1966-74; mem. Calif. Regional Med. Programs Coun., 1968-74, Presdl. Commn. on Refugees, 1975, Long Beach Ednl. TV Bd., 1956-70; chmn. Long Beach br. ARC, 1957-58; pres. Forward Long Beach Com., 1978—; trustee Long Beach Meml. Hosp., Sch. Medicine Morehouse U., Atlanta; chmn. Long Beach Community Svcs. Devel. Corp., 1979—; mem. health policy bd. Georgetown U.; bd. dirs. Downtown Long Beach Assocs., Medic Alert Found., Calif. Cancer Soc., Japan Am. Conf. Mayors; regent Uniformed Svcs. Health Scis. U., 1973-80; mem. Nat. Commn. Cost Health Care. Served to maj. AUS, 1942-46. Fellow ACS, Internat. Coll. Surgeons (pres. 1983-84, pres. U.S. sect. 1977), Royal Soc. Medicine, Am. Coll. Gastroenterology, Internat. Soc. Surgery; mem. AMA (trustee 1973-76, pres. 1974-75, chmn. coun. on health manpower), Calif. Med. Assn. (pres. 1968-69), Los Angeles County Med. Soc., Long Beach Med. Soc. (pres. 1953-54), Karl A. Meyer Surg. Soc. (pres.), Long Beach C. of C. (pres. 1983), Virginia County Club, Internat. City Club, Torch Internat. Club, Kiwanis, Pi Kappa Alpha (v.p. 1976,. Clubs: Virginia Country, Internat. City (Long Beach); Torch Internat. Lodge: Kiwanis. Home: 5330 E El Parque St Long Beach CA 90815-4247 Office: 2840 N Long Beach Blvd Long Beach CA 90806-1531

TODD, PATRICIA ANNE, publishing executive; b. Nashville, July 25, 1957; d. Louis B. Jr. and Patricia (Cassell) T.; m. Sean Kelly, Apr. 23, 1988; 1 child, Charles McLaughlin. BA, Brown U., 1979. Editorial asst. McGraw-Hill Book Co., N.Y.C., 1979-81, Arbor House Pub. Co., N.Y.C., 1981; assoc. editor Pocket Books, N.Y.C., 1981-85; agt. March Tenth, Inc., N.Y.C., 1986-88; sr. editor Berkley Pub. Group, N.Y.C., 1988-90; exec. editor Dell Pub., N.Y.C., 1990—. Co-author: Grosseries, 1987. Mem. Jr. League City of N.Y. Office: Dell Publishing 666 5th Ave New York NY 10103

TODD, RONALD GARY, lawyer; b. Spokane, Wash., Dec. 12, 1946; s. Theodore H. and Dorothea I. (Swanson) T.; m. Natalie A., June 16, 1973; children: Russell E., Brian N., David E. AB, Cornell U., 1969; JD, Columbia U., 1972. Bar: N.Y. 1973, U.S. Dist. Ct. (so. and ea. dists.) N.Y. 1975, U.S. Ct. Appeals (2nd cir.) 1975, U.S. Supreme Ct. 1976, D.C. 1993. Atty. Dewey Ballantine, N.Y.C., 1973-79, Simpson Thacher & Bartlett, N.Y.C., 1980-82; atty., ptnr. Golenbock & Barell, N.Y.C., 1982-89; ptnr. Reid & Priest, N.Y.C., 1989—; instr., guest lectr. NYU Sch. Continuing

Edn., 1983—; adv. bd. Commonwealth Land Title and TransAm. Title Ins. Co., N.Y.C., 1992—. Contbr. articles to profl. jours. Pres., bd. dirs. Seven Bridges Field Club, 1982-85. Mem. ABA (real property sect. 1973—), N.Y. Bar Assn. (real property sect. 1973—), D.C. Bar Assn. (real property sect. 1992—). Avocations: instrumental music, tennis. Office: Reid & Priest 40 W 57th St New York NY 10019-4001

TODD, THOMAS ABBOTT, architect, urban designer; b. North Stonington, Conn., May 5, 1928; s. James Arnold and Isabel Nisbet (Downs) T.; m. Carol Roberts, July 7, 1956; children: Christopher, Suzannah, Cassandra. B.A., Haverford Coll., 1950; M.C.P., U. Pa., 1959, M.Arch. with honors, 1959. Designer Geddes Brecher Qualls Cunningham, Phila., 1961; chief designer Eshbach Pullinger Stevens Bruder, Phila., 1962; partner Grant & Todd, Phila., 1963, Wallace McHarg Roberts Todd, Phila., 1963-79, Wallace Roberts & Todd, Phila., 1979-91. Works include The master plan for Abuja, capitol city of, Nigeria; urban design concept, master plan and public architecture for Balt. Inner Harbor; master plan U.S. Capitol Grounds, McKeldin Sq., Balt., Norfolk waterfront design, (Va.), Atlantic City Conv. Ctr./Rail Terminal, Lower Manhattan Plan, N.Y.C., Downtown L.A. devel. Plan, plan for State facilities, Annapolis, Md., master plan Haverford Coll., 6th St Market Pl., Richmond, Va., Tredegar Galleries Valentine Mus., Richmond, Waterside Festival Market, Norfolk, Va., Liberty State Pk., Jersey City, N.J., Wiggins Waterfront State Pk., Camden, N.J., Downtown Buffalo master plan, Quadrangle Life Care Community, Haverford, Liberty Pl. master plan, Phila., long range devel. plan U. Pa., Performing Arts Ctr., Haverford Coll., Assembly Hall, Germantown Friends Sch., plan for downtown Westerly, R.I., numerous pvt. residences, landscape plans, instl. and pub. master plans; contbr. numerous articles, editorials to profl.jours. Bd. dirs. Germantown Friends Sch., Phila., 1972-74, Green St. Friends Sch., Phila., 1973-75, Phila. Maritime Mus., 1986-90, Philomel Ancient Instruments, Phila., 1986-91, Maxwell Mansion, Phila., 1983-86; v.p. Haverford Coll. Arboretum, 1983; chmn. ann. giving Haverford Coll., 1987; mem. Jamestown (R.I.) Planning Bd.; advisor Ft. Adams Found., Newport, R.I. Theophilus Parsons Chandler fellow, 1959; recipient numerous design awards. Fellow AIA; mem. Am. Inst. Cert. Planners. Republican. Quaker. Home: 118 Highland Dr Jamestown RI 02835

TODD, TROY W., telecommunications company executive; b. 1929. Pres., chief exec. officer United Telephone Co. of Fla., also bd. dirs. Office: United Telephone Co Fla PO Box 3193 Orlando FL 32802

TODD, VIRGIL HOLCOMB, clergyman, religion educator; b. Jordonia, Tenn., June 22, 1921; s. George Thurman and Nellie Mai (Dutton) T.; m. Irene Rolman, Sept. 21, 1941; 1 child, Donald Edwin. BA, Bethel Coll., 1945; BD, Cumberland Presbyn. Sem., 1947; MA, Scarritt Coll., 1948; PhD, Vanderbilt U., 1956. Ordained to ministry Presbyn. Ch., 1944. Minister Cumberland Presbyn. Chs., Tenn. and Ky., 1943-52; assoc. prof. Bethel Coll., McKenzie, Tenn., 1952-54; prof. of Old Testament Memphis Theol. Sem., 1954—; interim minister Presbyn. chs. in Tenn., Ky. and Miss., 1952—; vice-moderator Gen. Assembly Cumberland Presbyn. Ch., 1984-85, moderator, 1985-86. Author: Prophet Without Portfolio (2d Isaiah), 1972, A New Look at an Old Prophet (Ezekiel), 1977, Biblical Eschatology, 1985. Active Shelby (County) United Neighbors, Memphis, 1973-74, United Way of Greater Memphis, 1974-82. Mem. Soc. Bibl. Lit., Memphis Ministers' Assn. Democrat. Lodge: Civitan (chaplain, bd. dirs. local chpt.). Avocations: travel, golf. Office: Memphis Theol Sem 168 E Parkway S Memphis TN 38104-4340

TODD, WILLIAM BURTON, English language and literature educator; b. Chester, Pa., Apr. 11, 1919; s. William Booth and Edith Hawkins (Burton) T.; m. Ann Bowden, Nov. 23, 1969; children by previous marriage: Marilyn Chestnut Todd Guinn, Susan Linda Todd Kramer, Deborah Burton, Terence Kingsley. B.A., Lehigh U., 1940, M.A., 1947, L.H.D. (hon.), 1975; Ph.D., U. Chgo., 1949. Prof., head dept. English, Salem (N.C.) Coll., 1949-54; asst. librarian Houghton Library, Harvard U., 1955-58; assoc. prof. English, U. Tex., Austin, 1958; prof., dir. bibliog. research U. Tex., 1959-82, Kerr Centennial prof. English history and culture, 1982-85, Kerr Prof. emeritus, 1985—, Ransom Ctr. scholar, 1990—; J.P.R. Lyell reader in bibliography Oxford (Eng.) U., 1969-70; Andrew D. Osborn lectr. U. Western Ont., 1978; cons. Nat. Libr. Australia, 1973; D. Nichol Smith lectr. Australian Nat. U., Canberra, 1973; Cecil Oldman Meml. lectr. Leeds (Eng.) U., 1975; mem. adv. bd. NEH Rsch. Tools Program, 1977-78; Internat. Libr. lectr., Lepsig, Germany, 1981; Internat. Lit. lectr., Budapest, 1984; nat. adv. bd. Ctr. for the Book, 1978-88. Author: New Adventures among Old Books, 1958, Prize Books: Awards Granted to Scholars, 1961, Bibliography of Edmund Burke, 1964, Directory of Printers: London 1800-1840, 1972, The White House Transcripts: An Enquiry, 1974, The Gutenberg Bible: New Evidence, 1982; editor: Goldsmith's Prospect of Society, 1954, Burke's Reflections on the Revolution in France, 1959, Thomas J. Wise Centenary Studies, 1959, (with E. Stenbock-Fermor) The Kilgour Collection of Russian Literature, 1959, Guy of Warwick, 1968, Suppressed Commentaries on the Wiseian Forgeries, 1969, Hume and the Enlightenment, 1974, (with R.H. Campbell and A.S. Skinner) Smith's Wealth of Nations, 1976, (with Paul Langford) Writings and Speeches of Burke, 1981-95, Hume's History of England, 1983-85, Papers Bibliog. Soc. Am., 1967-81, Swinburne's Character and Opinions of Dr. Johnson, 1985, (with Ann Bowden) Tauchnitz International Editions in English, 1988; contbr. articles to profl. jours. Served to maj. inf. AUS, 1941-45, ETO. Decorated Bronze Star, Purple Heart; Fulbright fellow U.K., 1952-53, Am. Coun. Learned Socs. fellow, 1961-62, Guggenheim fellow, 1965-66, vis. fellow All Souls Coll., 1970, Zachariah Poulson fellow Libr. Co. Phila., 1990, Peterson fellow Am. Antiquarian Soc., 1992; scholar-in-residence Rockefeller Conf. and Study Ctr., Villa Serbelloni, Bellagio, Italy, 1986, vis. scholar Wolfson Coll., Oxford, England, 1993; recipient Oldman Meml. award and Marc Fitch bibliography prize, 1975. Mem. MLA, Bibliog. Soc. Am. (v.p. 1981-84), Bibliog. Soc. (Eng.), Printing Hist. Soc., Johnsonians (chmn. 1985), Pvt. Librs. Assn. (Eng.) (pres. 1983-86), Assn. Internat. de Bibliophilie (France), Phi Beta Kappa. Club: Grolier. Home: 2803 Scenic Dr Austin TX 78703-1040

TODD, WILLIAM MICHAEL, lawyer; b. Cleve., Dec. 13, 1952; s. William Charles and Jennie Ann (Diana) T.; m. Sara Lynn, Jan. 4, 1986. BA, U. Notre Dame, 1973; JD, Ohio State U., 1976. Bar: Ohio 1976, U.S. Dist. Ct. (so. dist.) Ohio 1977, U.S. Supreme Ct. 1987. Assoc. Porter, Wright, Morris & Arthur, Columbus, Ohio, 1976-82, ptnr., 1983-93; ptnr. Squire, Sanders & Dempsey, Columbus, 1993—. Trustee Callvac Svcs., Columbus, 1985-91, pres. 1988. Mem. ABA (governing com. forum on health law 1988-91), Ohio Bar Assn., Columbus Bar Assn., Def. Rsch. Inst., Am. Soc. Med. Assn. Counsel, Am. Bd. Trial Advocates, Ohio Soc. Hosp. Attys., Nat. Health Lawyers Assn., Worthington Hills Country Club, Columbus Athletic Club. Roman Catholic. Avocations: music, recreational sports. Office: Squire Sanders & Dempsey 41 S High St Columbus OH 43215-6101

TODD, ZANE GREY, utility executive; b. Hanson, Ky., Feb. 3, 1924; s. Marshall Elvin and Kate (McCormick) T.; m. Marysnow Stone, Feb. 8, 1950 (dec. 1983); m. Frances Z. Anderson, Jan. 6, 1984. Student, Evansville Coll., 1947-49; BS summa cum laude, Purdue U., 1951, DEng (hon.), 1979; postgrad., U. Mich., 1965; DHL, U. Indpls., 1993. Fingerprint classifier FBI, 1942-43; electric system engine engr. Indpls. Power & Light Co., 1951-56, spl. assignments supr., 1956-60, head elec. system planning, 1960-65, head distribution design div., 1965-68, head distbn. engring. dept., 1968-70, asst. to v.p., 1970-72 v.p., 1972-74, exec. v.p., 1974-75, pres., 1975-81, chmn., chief exec. officer, 1976-89, dir. emeritus, 1989—; cons. 1989-94, chief exec. officer, 1981-89; chmn., pres. IPALCO Enterprises, Inc., Indpls., 1983-89, dir., chmn. exec. com., 1989-94; chmn. bd., chief exec. officer Mid-Am. Capital Resources, Inc. subs. IPALCO Enterprises, Inc., Indpls., 1984-89, also bd. dirs., 1984-94; gen. mgr. Mooresville Pub. Svc. Co., Inc., Ind., 1956-60; bd. dirs. Nat. City Bank Ind. (formerly Mchts. Nat. Corp.), Am. States Ins. Co.; hon. dir. 500 Festival Assocs. Inc., pres. 1987. Originator probability analysis of power system reliability; contbr. articles to tech. jours. and mags. Past pres. adv. bd. St. Vincent Hosp.; bd. dirs. Commn. for Downtown, YMCA Found., Crime Stoppers Cen. Ind., Corp. Community Coun.; past chmn., bd. trustees Ind. Cen. U. (now U. Indpls.); bd. govs. Associated Colls. of Ind.; Nat. and Greater Indpls. adv. bds. Salvation Army; mem. adv. bd. Clowes Hall. Sgt. AUS, 1943-47. Recipient William Booth award Salvation Army, 1994; named Disting. Engring. Alumnus Purdue U., 1976, Outstanding Elec. Engr. Purdue U., 1992, Knight of Malta,

Order of St. John of Jerusalem, 1986. Fellow IEEE (past chmn. power system engring. com.); mem. ASME, NSPE, Power Engring. Soc., Ind. Fiscal Policy Inst. (bd. govs.), Indpls. C. of C., Indpls. C. of C., Mooresville C. of C. (past pres.), PGA Nat. Country Club, Ulen Country Club, Columbia Club, Indpls. Athletic Club (past bd. dirs.), Meridian Hills Country Club (past bd. dirs.), Skyline Club (bd. govs.), Newcomen Soc. (chmn. Ind.), Rotary, Lions (past pres.), Eta Kappa Nu, Tau Beta Pi. Home: 7645 Randue Ct Indianapolis IN 46278-1565 Office: Indpls Power & Light Co PO Box 1595 Indianapolis IN 46206-1595

TODD COPLEY, JUDITH ANN, materials and metallurgical engineering educator; b. Wakefield, West Yorkshire, Eng., Dec. 13, 1950; came to U.S., 1978; d. Marley and Joan Mary (Birkinshaw) Booth; m. David Michael Todd, June 17, 1972 (div. June 1981); m. Stephen Michael Copley, Aug. 3, 1984; 1 child, Amy Elizabeth. BA, Cambridge (Eng.) U., 1972, MA, PhD, 1977. Research asst. Imperial Coll. Sci. and Tech., London, 1976-78; research assoc. SUNY, Stonybrook, 1978; research engr. U. Calif., Berkeley, 1979-82; asst. prof. materials sci. and mech. engring. U. So. Calif., L.A., 1982-90; assoc. prof. metall. and materials engring. Ill. Inst. Tech., Chgo., 1990—; mem. task force Materials Property Coun., N.Y.C., 1979—. Contbr. articles to profl. jours.; patentee in field. Recipient Brit. Univs. Student Travel award, 1972, Brit. Fedn. Univ. Women award, 1972, Faculty Rsch. award Oak Ridge (Tenn.) Nat. Lab., 1986, Vanadium award British Inst. Materials, 1990; Kathryn Kingswell Meml. scholar, 1972. Mem. AIME (Rsch. award 1983), ASTM, ASM Internat. (chmn. L.A. chpt. 1986-87, coun. mem. materials sci. divsn. 1984-89), ASME (chmn. materials and fabrication com. pressure vessel and piping divsn., assoc. editor Jour. Pressure Vessel & Piping Tech. 1994), Soc. Women Engrs. (sr.), Electron Microscopy Soc., Am. Assn. Women in Sci., Hist. Metallurgy Soc., Nat. Soc. Corrosion Engrs. (Seed grant award 1983), Microbeam Analysis Soc. Avocations: archaeometry, hiking. Home: 307 Briargate Ter Hinsdale IL 60521-2819 Office: Ill Inst Tech Dept Metall & Materials Engring Chicago IL 60616

TODEA, ROCKLING, organizational development consultant; b. Naschitti, N.Mex., Aug. 9, 1942; s. John Jr. and Norma (Bell) T.; m. Nancy Dine Yazzie, Nov. 13, 1962; children: Rwanda, Rachelle, Nathaniel. BA, Ft. Lewis Coll., Durango, Colo., 1986; MBA, U. Denver, 1990. Acct. Navajo Agrl. Products Industry, Farmington, N.Mex., 1975-76; plant mgr. The Navajo Tribe, Window Rock, Ariz., 1976-77; bus. mgr. acctg. The Coll. of Ganado, Ariz., 1978-79; dir. fin./adminstrn. Alamo Navajo Sch. Bd., Inc., Magdalena, N.Mex., 1979-84; policy analyst The Navajo Nation, Window Rock, 1986-87; exec. dir. Denver Indian Health & Family Svc., 1989-91; systems analyst Regional Bus. Devel., Crownpoint, N.Mex., 1991-92; bus. cons. Fundamental Mgmt. Group, Denver, 1985-87; mgmt. cons. Mgmt. Exponent, Denver, 1988—; mem. Johnson-O'Malley Adv., Ignacio, Colo., 1985-86, Denver Indian Health Bd., 1987-89. Author: Managing Volunteers, 1991. Pollster MacDonald for Chairman, Window Rock, 1986; activist Govt. for Navajos, Window Rock, 1991; founder Spring Intertribal Thanksgiving: Celebration to Advance Indian Art, Crownpoint, 1992. Avocation: Indian self-determination.

TODER, ERIC JAY, economist; b. N.Y.C., Mar. 16, 1944; s. Saul and Rose (Cohen) T.; m. Susan C. Cote, Aug. 2, 1980. BS, Union Coll., 1964; MA in Econs., U. Rochester, 1967, PhD in Econs., 1971. Asst. prof. econs. Tufts U., Medford, Mass., 1968-73; sr. rsch. assoc. Charles River Assocs., Cambridge, Mass., 1973-76; fin. economist U.S. Dept. Treasury, Washington, 1976-83; dir. fin. and tax analysis U.S. Dept. Energy, Washington, 1980-81; dep. dir. Office Tax Analysis, U.S. Treasury, Washington, 1983-84; dep. asst. dir. Congl. Budget Office, Washington, 1984-88, 91-93; cons. New Zealand Treasury, Wellington, 1988-91; dep. asst. sec. tax analysis U.S. Dept. Treasury, Washington, 1993—. Author: Trade Policy and U.S. Auto Industry, 1978; contbr. to econs. publs. Mem. Am. Econ. Assn., Nat. Tax Assn., Assn. Pub. Policy Analysis and Mgmt., Washington Tax Economists Forum. Jewish. Avocations: travel, hiking, music. Office: US Dept Treasury 15th & Pennsylvania Ave NW Washington DC 20220

TODMAN, TERENCE A., diplomat; b. St. Thomas, V.I., Mar. 13, 1926; s. Alphonso and Rachel (Callwood) T.; m. Doris T. Weston, July 26, 1952; children: Terence A., Patricia, Kathryn, Michael. BA, Poly Inst., P.R., 1951; MPA, Syracuse U., 1953; postgrad., Am. U., 1953-54; hon. degree, Colgate U., 1981; LLD (hon.), Syracuse U., 1986; D in Pub. Service (hon.), Morgan State U., 1986; LLD (hon.), Boston U., 1987. Asst. personnel officer Govt. V.I., 1951; internat. relations officer State Dept., 1952-54; fgn. affairs officer, 1955, U.S. nominee UN intern program, 1955; adviser U.S. delegation UN Gen. Assembly, 1956-57; U.S. rep. UN trusteeship council petitions com. and com. rural econ. devel., 1956-57; 2d sec., polit. officer Am. embassy Beirut, Lebanon, 1960-61, Tunis, 1961-63; counselor, dep. chief mission Am. embassy Lome, 1965-68; dir. Office E. African Affairs, State Dept., 1968-69; U.S. ambassador to Chad, 1969-72, Republic Guinea, 1972-74, Costa Rica, San Jose, 1975-77; asst. sec. state, 1977-78; ambassador to Spain, 1978-83, Denmark, 1983-89, Argentina, 1989-93. Trustee Coll. of the Virgin Islands. Served to 1st lt. AUS, 1945-49. Recipient Superior Honor award State Dept., 1966, Medal of Honor, Govt. of V.I., Grand Cross of the highest order of Isabela la Catolica (Spain), Grand Cross of Order of Dannebrog (Denmark), Grand Cross of Order of San Martin (Argentina), Presdl. Svc. award, Nat. Pub. Svc. award, Presdl. Disting. Svc. award, 1985, Sec. of State Disting. Svc. award, 1993; attained rank of Career Ambassador, 1989. Mem. Am. Fgn. Svc. Assn., Coun. on Fgn. Rels., Nat. Acad. of Pub. Adminstrn. Office: Dept of State Washington DC 20520

TODREAS, NEIL EMMANUEL, nuclear engineering educator; b. Peabody, Mass., Dec. 17, 1935; s. David and Anna (Gendleman) T.; m. Carol S. Schonberg, June 19, 1958; children: Timothy, Ian. B.S.M.E., Cornell U., 1958, M.S., 1958; Sc.D. in Nuclear Engring., MIT, 1966. Asst. prof. dept. nuclear engring. MIT, Cambridge, 1970-71, assoc. prof., 1971-75, prof., 1975—, Kepco prof. nuclear engring. and prof. mech. engring., 1992—, head dept. nuclear engring., 1981-89. Served to lt. (j.g.) USN, 1958-62. Named Outstanding Prof. Dept. Nuclear Engring., MIT, 1976, 80; recipient Effective Teaching award MIT Grad. Student Council, 1975. Fellow Am. Nuclear Soc., ASME; mem. Nat. Acad. Engring., Sigma Xi, Tau Beta Pi, Pi Tau Sigma. Office: MIT 24-219 77 Massachusetts Ave Cambridge MA 02139-4307

TODT, MALCOLM S., company finance executive; b. Newark, 1945; m. Betsey Jean Parlato; children: Blair W., Kiersten E. BBA in Acctg., The George Washington U., 1967; MBA in Fin. and Investments magna cum laude, Babson Coll., 1968. Cert. mgmt. acct. . Fin. analyst Scovill, Inc., Waterbury, Conn., 1968-70; controller Dominion Electric Corp. subs. Scovill, Inc., Mansfield, Ohio, 1970-71; treasury analyst Scovill, Inc., 1971-75; mgr. cash and banking Scovill, Inc., Waterbury, Conn., 1975-77; asst. treas. Insilco Corp., Meriden, Conn., 1977-83, treas., 1983-87, v.p., treas., 1987-89; v.p., sr. officer mcpl. equipment leasing Mcpl. Bond Investors Assurance Corp., Armonk, N.Y., 1989-91; financial, mgmt. cons., 1991-93; v.p. fin., CFO Welling Internat. Corp., Milford, Conn., 1993—; bd. dirs. Centerbank, Waterbury, Thermo-Condr. Svcs., Inc., Prospect, Conn., Amphenol Corp., Wallingford, Conn. Mem. bd. govs. Newington (Conn.) Children's Hosp. mem. Highfield, Inc., Middlebury, Conn. Mem. Fin. Execs. Inst., Inst. Mgmt. Accts. (cert. mgmt. acct.). Home: 66 Artillery Rd Middlebury CT 06762-1909

TOEDT, D(ELL) C(HARLES), III, lawyer; b. Maxwell AFB, Ala., Nov. 17, 1954; m. Maretta A. Comfort. BA with high honors, U. Tex., 1973, JD, 1981. Bar: Tex. 1982, U.S. Dist. Ct. (so. dist.) Tex. 1984, U.S. Dist. Ct. (mid. dist.) Calif. 1995, U.S.C.t. Appeals (Fed. cir.) 1984, U.S. Supreme Ct. 1991, U.S. Patent & Trademark Office 1983. Atty. Schlanger, Cook, Cohn, Mills & Grossberg, Houston, 1982-83, Arnold, White & Durkee, Houston, 1983—; adj. prof. South Tex. Coll. Law, 1988-90. Sr. assoc. editor Tex. Law Rev., 1981-82; author/editor: Licensing Law Handbook: Computer Software Issues, 1997; author: Law and Bus. of Computer Software. Served to lt. USN, 1974-79. Mem. ABA (chmn. computer-related coms. 1985—). Office: Arnold White & Durkee PO Box 4433 750 Bering Dr Houston TX 77057-2104

TOEDTMAN, JAMES SMITH, newspaper editor, journalist; b. Dayton, Ohio, Dec. 1, 1941; s. James Christian and Ella Barnes (Smith) T.; m.

Haydee N. Sicart, Aug. 23, 1969; children—Eric, Kristen. A.B., Coll. Wooster, 1963; postgrad., U. Queensland, Brisbane, Australia, 1964; M.Sc. in Journalism, Columbia U., 1967. Pub. dir. Coll. Wooster, Ohio, 1963, 65; reporter, city editor, Sunday news editor, Washington Bur. news editor Newsday, L.I., N.Y., 1967-79; exec. editor Boston Herald Am., 1979-82; editor Balt. News Am., 1982-86; mng. editor N.Y. Newsday, 1986—; radio commentator Sta. WBAL Radio, Balt., 1984-86. Recipient shared award Silurian Soc., Polk award, N.Y. Pubs. award, Pulitzer Prize, 1970, spl. citation Inter-Am. Press Assn., 1979, best editorial award Md.-Del.-D.C. Press Assn., 1984, 86; Rotary Found. fellow, 1964, Internat. fellow Columbia U., 1966-67. Mem. AP Mng. Editors, Coll. of Wooster Alumni Assn. (pres. 1980-81). Methodist. Home: 4 Kroft Ct Huntington NY 11743-2357 Office: Newsday Inc 235 Pinelawn Rd Melville NY 11747-4226 also: 2 Park Ave New York NY 10016-5603

TOENSING, VICTORIA, lawyer; b. Colon, Panama, Oct. 16, 1941; d. Philip William and Victoria (Brady) Long; m. Trent David Toensing, Oct. 29, 1962 (div. 1976); children: Todd Robert, Brady Cronon, Amy Victoriana; m. Joseph E. diGenova, June 27, 1981. BS in Edn., Ind. U., 1962; JD cum laude, U. Detroit, 1975. Bar: Mich. 1976, D.C. 1978. Tchr. English Milw., 1965-66; law clk. to presiding justice U.S. Ct. Appeals, Detroit, 1975-76; asst. U.S. atty. U.S. Atty.'s Office, Detroit, 1976-81; chief counsel U.S. Senate Intelligence Com., Washington, 1981-84; dep. asst. atty. gen. criminal div. Dept. Justice, Washington, 1984-88; spl. counsel Hughes Hubbard & Reed, Washington, 1988-90; ptnr. Cooter and Gell, Washington, 1990-91; ptnr., co-chmn. nat. white collar group Manatt, Phelps and Phillips, Washington, 1991—; mem. U.S. Sentencing Commn. Working Group on Corp. Sanctions, 1988-89; co-chair Coalition for Women's Appts. Justice Judiciary Task Force, 1988-92. Author: Bringing Sanity to the Insanity Defense, 1983, Mens Rea: Insanity by Another Name, 1984; contbg. author: Fighting Back: Winning The War Against Terrorism, Desk Book on White Collar Crime, 1991; contbr. articles to profl. jours. Founder, chmn. Women's Orgn. To Meet Existing Needs, Mich., 1975-79; chmn. Republican Women's Task Force, 1979-81; bd. dirs. Project on Equal Edn. Rights, Mich., 1980-81, Nat. Hist. Intelligence Mus., 1987—. Recipient spl. commendation Office U.S. Atty. Gen., 1980, agy. seal medallion CIA, 1986, award of achievement Alpha Chi Omega, 1992; featured on cover N.Y. Time Mag. for anti-terrorism work, April 1991. Mem. ABA (standing com. on law and nat. security, council criminal justice sect., adv. bd. com. complex crimes and litigation, vice chmn. white collar crime com., chmn. subcom. on corp. criminal liability), U. Detroit Law Sch. Alumnae (bd. dirs.).

TOEPFER, SUSAN JILL, editor; b. Rochester, Minn., Mar. 9, 1948; d. John Bernard and Helen Esther (Chapple) T.; m. Lorenzo Gabriel Carcaterra, May 16, 1981; children: Katherine Marie, Nicholas Gabriel. BA, Bennington Coll., 1970. Mng. editor Photoplay Mag., N.Y.C., 1971-72; freelance writer, N.Y.C., 1972-78; TV week editor N.Y. Daily News, N.Y.C., 1978-79, leisure editor, 1979-82, features editor, 1982-84, arts and entertainment editor, 1984-86, exec. mag. editor, 1986-87; sr. writer People Mag., 1987-89, sr. editor, 1989-91, asst. mng. editor, 1991-94, exec. editor, 1994—. Democrat. Presbyterian. Office: People Mag Time-Life Bldg Rockefeller Ctr New York NY 10020

TOEPKE, UTZ PETER, lawyer; b. Konigsberg, Germany, May 5, 1940; came to U.S., 1976; s. Gunter and Christel (Printz) T.; m. Beverley Beatrice Goldsworthy, Nov. 29, 1975; children: Christopher, Beatrice, Thomas. LLB, U. Hamburg, Fed. Republic Germany, 1965, Dr.jur., 1967, Assessor, 1970. Bar: Stuttgart, Fed. Republic Germany 1973, N.Y. 1978, Hamburg 1982. Assoc. Altstotter, Weisgerber, Kalb, Nuremberg, Fed. Republic Germany, 1967-70; bus. mgr. Aktiva, GmbH, Nuremberg, 1970-72; internat. counsel IBM Germany, Stuttgart, 1972-73; counsel internat. law IBM, London and Armonk, N.Y., 1973-81; ptnr. Schwartz, Klink & Schreiber, N.Y.C., 1982-86, Heimann, Hardenberg & Ptnrs., Hamburg, 1982—, Graham & James, N.Y.C., Frankfurt, Germany, 1986—; adj. prof. NYU. Contbr. articles to profl. jours. Mem. ABA (mem. antitrust internat. law sect., chmn. European law com.), Hanseatische Rechtsanwaltskammer Hamburg, Hamburgischer Anwaltsverein, Met. Club, Shore Club. Home: 919 3rd Ave # 4778 New York NY 10022-3903 Office: Skadden Arps 919 3rd Ave New York NY 10022-3903

TOEPLITZ, GIDEON, symphony society executive; b. Tel Aviv, Nov. 18, 1944; s. Erich and Ruth (Loeb) T.; m. Gail Ransom, Sept. 2, 1978. B.A., Hebrew U. Jerusalem, 1969; M.B.A., UCLA, 1973. Flutist, Israel Philharm. Orch., 1969-71; asst. mgr. Rochester Philharm., 1973-75; asst. mgr. Boston Symphony, 1975-79, orch. mgr., 1979-81; exec. dir. Houston Symphony Soc., 1981-87; v.p., mng. dir. Pitts. Symph. Orch., 1987—. Mem. Nat. Acad. Rec. Arts and Scis., Am. Jewish Com. (bd. dirs.). Home: 2087 Beechwood Blvd Pittsburgh PA 15217-1705

TOEPPE, WILLIAM JOSEPH, JR., retired aerospace engineer; b. Buffton, Ohio, Feb. 27, 1931; s. William Joseph Sr. and Ruth May (Hipple) T. BSEE, Rose-Hulman Inst. Tech., Terre Haute, Ind., 1953. Engr. Electronics divsn. Ralph M. Parsons Co., Pasadena, Calif., 1953-55; pvt. practice cons. Orange, Calif., 1961-62; engring. supr. Lockheed Electronics Co., City of Commerce, Calif., 1962-64; staff engr. Interstate Electronics Corp., Anaheim, Calif., 1957-61; engring. supr. Interstate Electronics Corp., Anaheim, 1964-89, ret., 1989. Author: Finding Your German Village, 1990, Gazetteers and Maps of France for Genealogical Research, 1990, GGSA Library User's Guide, 1995. Pres. Golden Cir. Home Owners' Assn., Orange, 1989-95. With U.S. Army, 1955-57. Mem. Ohio Geneal. Soc. (life), Geneal. Soc. Pa., So. Calif. Geneal. Soc., German Geneal. Soc. mem. Ohio Geneal. Soc. 1993—). Avocations: genealogy, music. Home: 700 E Taft Ave Unit 19 Orange CA 92665-4400

TOEVS, ALDEN LOUIS, management consultant; b. American Falls, Idaho, Jan. 25, 1949; s. Alden Louis and Wilma Christen (Coffee) T.; m. Coralie Norwood Sickels, July 20, 1974. BS, Lewis and Clark Coll., 1971; PhD, Tulane U., 1975. NSF fellow MIT Energy Lab., Boston, 1975-76; prof. econs. La. State U., Baton Rouge, 1976-77, U. Oreg., Eugene, 1978-83; dir. mortgage rsch. Morgan Stanley and Co., N.Y.C., 1983-90; mng. v.p. First Manhattan Cons. Group, N.Y.C., 1990—; vis. scholar Fed. Home Loan Bank, San Francisco, 1983, Fed. Reserve Bank, 1982; dir. capital market research U. Oreg., Eugene, 1982-83. Author: Innovations in Bond Portfolio Managements, 1983; editor, bd. dirs. Fin. Analysts Jour., 1983-95, Jour. Portfolio Mgmt., 1984-90; contbr. articles to profl. jours. Recipient Graham and Dodd scroll Fin. Analysts Fed., 1983.

TOFF, NANCY ELLEN, book editor; b. Greenburgh, N.Y., Aug. 29, 1955; d. Ira N. and Ruth (Bluthenthal) T. AB, Radcliffe Coll./Harvard U., 1976. Editor and producer Music Minus One, N.Y.C., 1973-75; researcher Time-Life Books, Alexandria, Va., 1976-80; editor & asst. producer Time-Life Music, Alexandria, Va., 1980-84; production mgr. Vanguard Recording Soc., N.Y.C., 1984-86; editor Grove's Dictionaries of Music, N.Y.C., 1984-85; v.p. & editor-in-chief Chelsea House Pubs., N.Y.C., 1986-89, v.p., dir. book devel., 1990; editorial dir. Julian Messner/Silver Burdett Press, Englewood Cliffs, N.J., 1990-91; exec. editor children's and young adult books Oxford U. Press, N.Y.C., 1991—; editorial cons., Music Div. Lib. of Congress, 1983; hist. cons., Dept. of Musical Instruments, Met. Mus. of Art, N.Y.C., 1986. Author: The Development of the Modern Flute, 1979, The Flute Book, 1985, Georges Barrère and the Flute in America, 1994; cons. editor Flutist Quar., 1990—; contbr. articles to profl. jours.; curator George Barrère and the Flute in America, N.Y. Pub. Libr., 1994. Bd. dirs. Radcliffe Coll. Alumnae Assn. 1979-80. Mem. Nat. Flute Assn. (asst. sec. 1988-89, sec. 1989-90, bd. dirs. 1990-92), N.Y. Flute Club (bd. dirs. 1986—, sec. 1991-92, pres. 1992-95). Home: 309 E 87th St Apt 5H New York NY 10128-4812 Office: Oxford U Press 198 Madison Ave New York NY 10016

TOFFEL, ALVIN EUGENE, corporate executive, business and governmental consultant; b. Los Angeles, July 14, 1935; s. Harry and Estelle Charlotte Toffel; m. Neile McQueen; children: Stephanie, Elizabeth, Michelle; step children: Terry, Chad. B.A., UCLA, 1957. Dir. mgmt. systems and organizational planning Rockwell Internat., 1963-69; Exec. Office for the Pres. White House, Washington, 1969-70; nat. chmn., campaign dir. McCloskey for Pres., 1971-72; polit. cons. 1971—; cons. personal bus. and govt. Norton Simon and Norton Simon, Inc., Los Angeles, 1972-80; pres. Norton Simon Found., Pasadena, Calif., 1977-80; cons. exec. asst. to pres.

Twentieth Century Fox Film Corp., 1980; bd. dirs. Geometrics, Inc.; pres. So. Shellfish Inc., Atlantic Internat. Ins. Ltd., Toffel Thoroughbred Racing; lectr. mgmt. UCLA, Stanford U. Pres. Norton Simon Museum Art, Pasadena. Served with SAC USAF, 1958-63. Recipient White House Interchange Exec. Outstanding Achievement, 1971; recipient Achievement Am. Advtg. Council, 1972. Mem. Ky. Cols., Presdl. Interchange Execs. Assn., Assn. Old Crows. Developed standard U.S. govt. program performance measurement system, aerospace engring. techniques of program mgmt., aerospace manuals. Home and Office: 2323 Bowmont Dr Beverly Hills CA 90210-1808 *My legacy derives from my grandparents leaving the familiar to come to America. Here, anything can be accomplished if one honestly defines what he wants. It then becomes a matter of choosing among the many ways to accomplish anything. The character of the individual can be seen by the choices he makes.*

TOFFLER, ALVIN, author; b. N.Y.C., Oct. 4, 1928; s. Sam and Rose (Albaum) T.; m. Adelaide Heidi Elizabeth Farrell, Apr. 29, 1950; 1 dau., Karen. AB, N.Y. U., 1949; LLD (hon.), U. Western Ont., 1972; LittD (hon.), U. Cin., 1972, Miami U., 1972; DSc (hon.), Rensselaer Poly. Inst., 1972, Keio U. Tokyo; LittD (hon.), Ripon Coll., 1975; LLD, Manhattan Coll., 1984. Washington corr. various newspapers, mags., 1957-59; assoc. editor Fortune, 1959-61; mem. faculty New Sch. for Social Research, 1965-67; vis. prof. Cornell U. Ithaca, N.Y., 1969; vis. scholar Russell Sage Found., 1969-70; Cons. Rockefeller Bros. Fund., Inst. for Future, Am. Tel. & Tel. Co., Ednl. Facilities Labs., Inc., others. Author: (with Heidi Toffler) The Culture Consumers: A Study of Art and Affluence in America, 1964, Future Shock, 1970 (McKinsey Found. Book award 1970, Prix du Meilleur Livre Etranger 1972), The Eco-Spasm Report, 1975, The Third Wave, 1980, Previews and Premises, 1983, The Adaptive Corporation, 1984, Powershift: Knowledge, Wealth and Violence at the Edge of the 21st Century, 1990, War and Anti-War, 1993; editor: The Schoolhouse in the City, 1968 (Nat. Council for Advancement Ednl. Writing award 1969), The Futurists, 1972, Learning for Tomorrow: The Role of the Future in Education, 1974; contbr. articles to nat. mags. and profl. jours. Bd. govs. Internat. Inst. Stress; mem. adv. bd. Democracy Inst., Internat. Commn. Futuribles. Recipient Playboy Mag. award for best article, 1970, Centennial award IEEE, 1984, Golden Key award People's Republic of China, 1986; named Author of Yr. Am. Soc. Jornalists and Authors, 1983; fellow Am. Assn. for Advancement of Sci., 1984; decorated Officier de l'Ordre des Arts et des Lettres, 1984.

TOFFLER, HEIDI, author, futurist; b. N.Y.C., Aug. 1, 1929; d. William and Elizabeth A. (Kraayer) Farrell; m. Alvin Toffler April 29, 1950; 1 daughter, Karen. AB, Long Island U., 1949; Doctor of Laws (hon.), Manhattan Coll.; Doctor of Letters (hon.), Dowling Coll. Pres., exec. prod. Triwave Prodns., inc., Dover, Del., 1981—; Adjunct prof. National Defense U., D.C, 1994—. Author (with Alvin Toffler) The Culture Consumers, 1964, Future Shock, 1970, The Eco-Spasm Report, 1975, The Third Wave, 1980, Previews and Premises, 1983, The Adaptive Corporation, 1986, Powershift, 1990, War and Anti-War, 1983, Creating a New Civilization, 1995; editor; Schoolhouse in the City, 1968, The Futurists, 1972, Learning for Tomorrow, 1974; contbr. articles to national and internat. journals. Mem. adv. bd. Democracy Inst. D.C. 1994—. Hon. Co-chair Unifem USA (UN Development Fund for Women) N.Y.C. 1988—; Sci. Adv. Comm. Piu Manzu Found. Italy, 1987—. Bd. Govs. Intern Inst. Stress, 1983. Recipient Prix du Meilleur Livre Etrange, France 1971, Medal for Distinguished Contribution to Management Literature, McKinsey Foundation, 1971, Golden Key Award, China, 1987, Medal of the President of the Italian Republic, Government of Italy, 1987; National Book Award (nominee) 1970. Office: Care Curtis Brown Ltd 10 Astor Pl New York NY 10003

TOFT, RICHARD P(AUL), title insurance executive; b. St. Louis, Sept. 20, 1936; s. Paul C. and Hazel F. T.; B.S.B.A., U. Mo., 1958; m. Marietta Von Etzdorf, Oct. 5, 1963; children—Christopher P., Douglas J. With Lincoln Nat. Life Ins. Co., 1959-73, group and pension sales mgr., 1969-73; 2d v.p. Lincoln Nat. Sales Corp., Ft. Wayne, Ind., 1973-74, v.p., 1974-80, v.p. treas., 1980-81; pres. Chgo. Title Ins. Co., 1981-82, pres., chief exec. officer Chgo. Title Ins. Co. and Chgo. Title and Trust Co., 1982—, also dir. both; dir. Lincoln Nat. Devel. Corp. Trustee, Chgo. Community Trust, 1982. Served to 2d lt. U.S. Army, 1958-59. Mem. Am. Land Title Assn. Congregationalist. Club: Union League (Chgo.). Office: Chgo Title & Trust Co 171 N Clark St Chicago IL 60601

TOFT, THELMA MARILYN, secondary educator; b. Balt., Sept. 15, 1943; d. George Edward and Thelma Iola (Smith) Trageser; m. Ronald Harry Toft, Aug. 27, 1966; 1 child, Joanna Lynn. BS in Med. Tech., Mt. St. Agnes Coll., Balt., 1965; BSE, Coll. Notre Dame, Balt., 1972; MEd, Pa. State U., 1983. Recreation dir. Villa Maria, Balt., 1961-65; blood bank supr. Wayman Park NIH, Balt., 1965-68; tchr. Sacred Heart, St. Mary's Govan's, Balt., 1968-74, Lincoln Intermediate Unit # 12, Adams County, Pa., 1979-80, York (Pa.) City Sch. Dist., 1980—; curriculum dir. M.O.E.S.T. Pa. State U.; curriculum dir. M.O.E.S.T. Pa. State U., 1991-93; mem. Pa. State Consortium-Team for Improving Math & Scis.; grant writer, speaker in field; writer sch. to work curriculum. Active Girl Scouts USA, Hanover, 1988-92, leader, 1984-87; mgmt. bd. Agrl. Indsl. Mus. mem. ASCD, AAUW, Nat. Ptnrs. in Edn., Am. Bus. Womens Assn. (adv. com. 1992, sec. 1993, Women of Yr. 1994), Phi Delta Kappa. Democrat. Roman Catholic. Avocations: writing, marketing. Home: 30 Panther Dr Hanover PA 17331-8888

TOFTNER, RICHARD ORVILLE, engineering executive; b. Warren, Minn., Mar. 5, 1935; s. Orville Gayhart and Cora Evelyn (Anderson) T.; m. Jeanne Bredine, June 26, 1960; children: Douglas, Scott, Kristine, Kimberly, Brian. BA, U. Minn., 1966; MBA, Xavier U., 1970. Registered environ. assessor, Calif. Sr. economist Federated Dept. Stores, Inc., Cin., 1967-68; dep. dir. EPA, Washington and Cin., 1968-73; mgmt. cons. environ. affairs, products and mktg., 1973-74; prin. PEDCo Environ., Cin., 1974-80; principal PEDCo trusts, 1974-80; pres. ROTA Mgmt., Inc., Cin., 1980-82; gen. mgr. CECOS, 1982-85, cons., 1985—; v.p. Smith, Stevens & Young, 1985-88; real estate developer, 1980—; pres., CEO Toxitrol Internat., Inc., 1988-89; dir. Environ. Svcs. Belcan Corp., Cin., 1989-92; adj. prof. U. Cin., 1975-86; lectr. Grad. fellowship rev. panel Office of Edn., 1978-79; advisor, cabinet-level task force Office of Gov. of P.R., 1973; bd. dirs. EnviroAudit Svcs., Inc., pres., CEO, 1992—; subcom. Nat. Safety Coun., 1972; mem. exec. environ. briefing panels Anderson Consulting, 1991-92; nominee commr. PUCO, Ohio; chmn. Cin. City Waste Task Force, 1987-88; co-chair Hamilton County Resource Recovery Com., 1989—. Contbr. articles on mgmt. planning and environ. to periodicals, chpts. to books; inventor, developer Toxitrol Waste Minimization; inventor EnviroAudit. With AUS, 1954-57. Mem. Nat. Registry Environ. Profl. Rep., Engring. Soc. Cin., Assn. Corp. Environ. Execs., Cin. C of C, Global Assn. Corp. Environ. Execs. (charter), Bankers Club. Republican. Lutheran. Home: 9175 Yellowwood Dr Cincinnati OH 45251-1948 Office: 4700 Ashwood Dr Ste 100 Cincinnati OH 45241-2424

TOGAFAU, MALAETASI MAUGA, judge; b. Pago Pago, Am. Samoa, June 4, 1946; s. Sefulu Mauga Togafau and Femalua'i (Manu) Sialo'i; m. Oreta Mapu, Dec. 10, 1977; children: Malaetasi Jr., Steve, June, Wayne, Heidi. BS, Peru Stat U., 1971; JD, Calif. Western Sch. of Law, 1974. Asst. pub. defender High Ct., Am. Samoa, 1974; legis. asst. Office of Del.-at-Large, Washington, 1975-80, U.S. Ho. of Reps., Washington, 1981-82; rep. Legislature of Am. Samoa, Am. Samoa, 1983-86; atty. Law Firm of Talalelei Tulafono, Am. Samoa, 1983-86; dist. ct. judge High Ct., Am. Samoa, 1986—. Legal counsel Dem. Party, Am. Samoa, 1985-86; chmn. budget com. Ho. of Reps., Am. Samoa, 1985-86; vice chmn., bd. dirs. Denm. Bank of Am. Samoa, 1985-86. Mem. Am. Samoa Bar Assn., Nat. Jud. Coll. Democrat. Mem. Congregation Christian Ch. Avocations: softball, long boat crew, farming. Office: High Ct Am Samoa PO Box 309 Pago Pago AS 96799-0309

TOGASAKI, SHINOBU, corporate executive; b. San Francisco, Aug. 17, 1932; s. Kikumatsu and Sugi (Hida) T.; m. Toshiko Kawaguchi, Nov. 24, 1959; children: John Shinobu, Ann Mariko. BS in Math., Duke U., 1954; postgrad., Stanford U., 1954-56. Math. programmer IBM, 1956—; sr. programmer IBM, Palo Alto, 1970-87; mgr. applications devel. Service Bur. Corp., Palo Alto, 1961-64, sr. analyst, 1964-68; systems architect devel. lab. Service Bur. Corp., San Jose, Calif., 1968-70; chief fin. officer Robin Hood Ranch, Inc., 1976—; mgr. architecture & strategy Hewlett Packard Corp., Cupertino, Calif., 1987-89; mgr. strategic planning 1989-93; chief architect

MFA Hewlett Packard, 1993—. Mem. Am. Mgmt. Assn., AAAS, Am. Statis. Assn., Assn. Computing Machinery, Inst. Mgmt. Sci., Palo Alto C. of C., Sigma Pi Sigma. Home: 2367 Booksin Ave San Jose CA 95125-4705 Office: 19447 Pruneridge Ave Cupertino CA 95014-0683

TOGERSON, JOHN DENNIS, computer software company executive; b. Newcastle, England, July 2, 1939; arrived in Can., 1949; s. John Marius and Margaret (McLaughlin) T.; m. Donna Elizabeth Jones, Oct. 3, 1964 (div. 1972); children: Denise, Brenda, Judson; m. Patricia Willis, May 5, 1984. BME, GM Inst., Flint, Mich., 1961; MBA, York U., Toronto, Ont., 1971. Sr. prodn. engr. GM of Can., Oshawa, Ont., 1961-69; with sales, investment banking Cochran Murray, Toronto, 1969-72; pres. Unitec, Inc., Denver, 1972-79, All Seasons Properties, Denver, 1979-81, Resort Computer Corp., Denver, 1981—; mng. dir. VCC London (subs. of Resort Computer Corp.), 1992; bd. dirs. VCC London (sub. of 1st Nat. Bank U.K.), London, 1989—, mng. dir., 1992; pres., bd. dirs. Resort Mgmt. Corp., Dillon, Colo., 1980-81; presenter Assn. of Resort Developers Nat. Conv., 1993, Internat. T.S. Found. Think Tank, 1993. Contbr. articles to profl. jours. Avocations: mountain biking, ice hockey. Office: Resort Computer Corp 2801 Youngfield St Ste 300 Golden CO 80401-2266

TOGNINO, JOHN NICHOLAS, financial services executive; b. N.Y.C., Sept. 20, 1938; s. Gennaro and Catherine (Barbieri) T.; m. Norma Lucille Borrelli, Nov. 7, 1959; children: Katherine Ann, John Nicholas Jr., Michael A. BA in Econs. summa cum laude, Fordham U., 1975. Instnl. sales trader A.G. Becker & Co., N.Y.C., 1970-72; trader Merill Lynch, N.Y.C., 1957-69, instnl. salesman, 1972-74, mgr. over-the-counter sales trading, 1974-83, dir. over-the-counter dept., 1983-87, dir. unlisted trading, 1987-88; mng. dir. nondollar equities Merill Lynch, London, 1988-91; mng. dir. global equities, ret. Merill Lynch, N.Y.C., 1991-93; exec. v.p. Charles Schwab & Co., Inc., Jersey City, 1993—; bd. dirs. Nat. Assn. Security Dealers Automated Quotations Inc. Contbg. author: Market Maker Sponsorship: A Synergistic Package of Services, 1987. Pres. Ardsley (N.Y.) Rep. Club, 1967-68; mem. Ardsley Bd. Edn., 1977-84, pres. 1979; v.p. Ardsley Sch. Dist. Bd., 1978, 81; mem. exec. com. of laity Archdiocese of N.Y.C., 1988. Named Trader of Yr., Security Traders Monthly mag., 1984, Over-the-Counter Man of Yr., Equities mag., 1986. Mem. Nat. Security Traders Assn. (various offices 1981-88, chmn. fin. com. Found. 1992—), Nat. Assn. Security Dealers (bus. conduct com. 1984-86), Security Traders Assn. N.Y. (various offices 1973-83, pres. 1980-81), St. Andrews Golf Club (Hastings, N.Y.), Grey Oaks Country Club (Naples, Fla.), Alpha Sigma Lambda. Republican. Roman Catholic. Avocations: jogging, tennis, golf. Home: 114 Boulder Ridge Rd Scarsdale NY 10583 Office: Charles Schwab & Co 111 Pavonia Ave Jersey City NJ 10281-1304

TOGO, YUKIYASU, automotive executive; b. Yokohama, Kanagawa, Japan, Nov. 13, 1924; came to U.S., 1983; s. Kinji Togo and Nobuko Watanabe; m. Misako Mineta, Apr. 2, 1948; children: Yukinori, Yumi. Gen. mgr. Toyota Motor Sales, Tokyo, Japan, 1976-78, assoc. dir., 78-79, dir., 1979-80; pres. Toyota Can. Inc., Ontario, Can., 1980-82; dir. Toyota Motor Corp., Aichi, Japan, 1982, mng. dir., 1982-83; pres. Can. Auto Parts Toyota Inc., B.C., Can., 1983—; pres., chief exec. officer Toyota Motor Sales U.S.A. Inc., Torrance, Calif., 1983—; pres. Toyota Motor Credit Corp., Torrance, Calif., 1989—, Toyota Motor Ins. Svcs., Torrance, Calif., 1989—, Toyota Aviation USA Inc., Torrance, Calif., 1989—. Bd. dirs. Los Angeles World Affairs Coun., 1989. Avocations: golf, flying, skiing. Office: Toyota Motor Sales USA Inc Ste 2991 19001 S Western AVe Torrance CA 90501-1106

TOHLEN, DAVID RAY, air force officer; b. Tulsa, Oct. 5, 1948; s. Herbert M. and Edna C. (Slack) T.; m. Diana J. Overdeer, Oct. 9, 1976; children: Heather, Kathryn, Sara. BS in Applied Math., Okla. State U., 1970; M of Space Sys. Mgmt., Webster U., 1988; grad., Squadron Officer Sch., 1976, Air Command and Staff Coll., 1983, Air War Coll., 1987. Commd. 2d lt. USAF, 1970, advanced through grades to col., 1991; mem. crew orbital analysis 1st Aerospace Control Squadron NORAD Space Def. Ctr., Cheyenne Mountain Complex, Colo., 1970-71; space surveillance sys. officer 19th Surveillance Squadron, Pirinclik, Turkey, 1971-72; orbital analyst, surveillance officer NORAD Space Def. Ctr., 1972-78, duty orbital analyst leader, tng. officer, chief analyst, 1972-78, NORAD project officer Operation Morning Light, 1978; air staff tng. officer Office Dep. Chief of Staff Plans/Ops. The Pentagon, 1978; ops. dir. Air Force Satellite Control Facility hdqs. Sunnyvale Air Force Sta., Calif., 1979; chief spacecraft control br., dep. chief staff for plans Air Force Space Command hdqs., Peterson AFB, Colo., 1982; chief space support divsn. U.S. Space Command hdqs., Peterson AFB, 1987-90; comdr. Def. Support Program Mobile Ground Sys., Holloman AFB, N.Mex., 1990-92; chief space command, control, comm. and intelligence divsn., directorate of space programs Office Asst. Sec. Air Force for Acquisition, The Pentagon, Washington, 1992—; DOD advisor Skylab Re-entry Ops. Contbr. to newspapers and mags., including People Mag., N.Y. Times, Can. edit. Reader's Digest; also appeared on radio interviews. Decorated Def. Meritorious Svc. medal with one oak leaf cluster, Air Force Meritorious Svc. medal with three oak leaf clusters, Air Force Commendation medal with one oak leaf cluster, Air Force Outstanding Unit award with four oak leaf clusters, Nat. Def. Svc. medal with one bronze svc. star. Republican. United Methodist. Avocations: fishing, traveling, gardening. Office: SAF/AQSC Rm 5C269 1060 Air Force Pentagon Washington DC 20330-1060

TOKAR, EDWARD THOMAS, manufacturing company executive; b. Passaic, N.J., June 12, 1947; s. Edward Thomas Sr. and Helen (Fabian) T.; m. Frances Deland, Sept. 30, 1972; 1 child, Adam Edward. BS with high honors, U. Md., 1969; MBA, Coll. William and Mary, 1971; postgrad., George Washington U., 1972. CPA, N.J., Md. Audit, cons. Touche Ross & Co., Washington, 1970-73; mgr. fin. div. Nat. Rural Electric Coop. Assn., Washington, 1973-77; v.p. investments Allied-Signal Inc., Morristown, N.J., 1977—; bd. dirs. Morgan Products Ltd., Noel Group Inc.; mem. bd. advisors Saugatuck Capital Co., Stamford, RFE Investment Ptnrs., Stamford, Allen Value Ptnrs.; trustee Morgan Grenfel Investment Trusts; mem. pension adv. com. N.Y. Stock Exch., N.Y.C. Trustee Newark Boys Chorus Sch., 1980-84; mem. investment adv. com. Paterson Diocese Roman Cath. Ch., Clifton, N.J. Mem. AICPA, Nat. Econs. Club, Sentinel Pension Inst. (bd. advisors), Investment Tech. Symposium, Fin. Execs. Inst., CIEBA Comm. Avocations: golf, tennis. Home: 8 Sweetbriar Rd Summit NJ 07901-3256 Office: Allied-Signal Inc PO Box 1219R Morristown NJ 07962-1219

TOKER, FRANKLIN K., art history educator, archaeologist, foundation executive; b. Montreal, Que., Can., Apr. 29, 1944; came to U.S., 1964; naturalized, 1983; s. Maxwell Harris and Ethel (Herzberg-Serchuk) T.; m. Ellen Judith Burack, Sept. 3, 1972; children: Sarah Augusta, Maxwell, Jeffrey. BA, McGill U., Montreal, 1964; AM in Fine Arts, Oberlin Coll., 1966; PhD in Fine Arts, Harvard U., 1973. Instr. Boston Sch. Architecture, 1967; archaeol. dir. Florence (Italy) Cathedral excavations, 1969-74; A.W. Mellon vis. prof. Carnegie-Mellon U., Pitts., 1974-76, assoc. prof. 1976-80; assoc. prof. fine arts U. Pitts., 1980-87, prof., 1987—; vis. prof. U. Florence, 1988-89, U. Rome, 1991; preservation cons. The Carnegie, Pitts., 1981-83; bd. dirs. Allegheny Survey, Pitts. History and Landmarks Found., 1980-85; mem. Inst. for Advanced Study, Princeton, N.J., 1985; fellow Com. to Rescue Italian Art, Florence, 1969; fellow I Tatti-Harvard U. Ctr. for Italian Renaissance Studies, Florence, 1972. Author: Notre Dame in Montreal, 1970 (Alice Davis Hitchcock award 1971), French edit., 1981, 2d English edit., 1991, S. Reparata: l-Antica Cattedrale Fiorentina, 1974, Pittsburgh: An Urban Portrait, 1986 (Pitts. History and Landmarks Found. award 1987); contbr. articles to profl. jours. Mem. econ. devel. com. Allegheny Conf. Community Devel., Pitts., 1983-85. Kress fellow, 1965; Can. Coun. fellow, 1966; Guggenheim fellow, 1979; NEH grantee 1979, 92, NEH sr. fellow, 1985, fellow Bellagio Study and Conf. Ctr., Rockefeller Found., 1994. Mem. Coll. Art Assn. (life, Arthur Kingsley Porter prize 1980), Medieval Acad. (life), Soc. Archtl. Historians (pres., 1993-94, life mem., bd. dirs. 1985-88), Archaeol. Inst. Am., Internat. Ctr. for Medieval Art. Avocations: creative writing, photography, cycling. Home: 1521 Denniston Ave Pittsburgh PA 15217-1449 Office: U Pittsburgh Dept History Art Archi Pittsburgh PA 15260

TOKER, KAREN HARKAVY, physician; b. New Haven, Conn., Oct. 23, 1942; d. Victor M. and Nedra (Israel) Harkavy; m. Cyril Toker, Sept. 1, 1968; children: David Edward, Rachel Lee. BS in Chemistry, Coll. William and Mary, 1963; MD, Yale U., 1967. Diplomate Am. Bd. Pediatrics, 1974.

Intern dept. pediatrics Bronx Mcpl. Hosp. Ctr., Albert Einstein Coll. Medicine, N.Y., 1967-68, asst. resident dept. pediatrics, 1968-69, sr. resident dept. pediatrics, 1969, 70-71, attending pediatrician, 1971-72, 73-76; pediatrician Montgomery Health Dept., Silver Springs, Md., 1976-83; pediatric cons. Head Start Program Montgomery County Pub. Schs., Rockville, Md., 1976-83; pvt. practice gen. pediatrics Rockville, 1983-89; pediatrician Nemours Children's Clinic, Jacksonville, Fla., 1991—; instr. pediatrics Albert Einstein Coll. Medicine, N.Y., 1971-74, asst. prof. pediatrics, 1974-76. Exec. bd. sec. Congregation Har Shalom, Potomac, 1989-91. Fellow Am. Acad. Pediatrics; mem. Fla. Med. Assn., Duval County Med. Soc., Ambulatory Pediatric Assn. Democrat. Jewish. Avocations: piano, opera, ballet, swimming. Home: 6030 Oakbrook Ct Ponte Vedra Beach FL 32082 Office: Nemours Child Clinic 5220-24 Pearl St Pearl Plz Jacksonville FL 32208

TOKHEIM, ROBERT EDWARD, physicist; b. Eastport, Maine, Apr. 25, 1936; s. Edward George and Ruth Lillian (Koenig) T.; m. Diane Alice Green, July 1, 1962; children: Shirley Diane, William Robert, David Eric, Heidi Jean. BS, Calif. Inst. Tech., 1958, MS, 1959; Degree of Engr., Stanford U., 1962, PhD, 1965. Rsch. assist. Hansen Labs Physics Stanford (Calif.) U., 1960-65; microwave engr. Watkins-Johnson Co., Palo Alto, Calif., 1965-73, staff scientist, head ferrimagnetic R&D dept., 1966-69; sr. physicist SRI Internat., Menlo Park, Calif., 1973—. Co-author: Tutorial Handbook on X-ray Effects on Materials and Structures, 1992; contbr. articles to Jour. Applied Physics, IEEE Transactions on Magnetics, conf. proceedings on shock compression, and others. Mem. IEEE (sr.), Am. Phys. Soc., Toastmasters, Sigma Xi, Tau Beta Pi. Achievements include discovery of nonreciprocal line-coupled microwave ferrimagnetic filters, optimum thermal compensation axes in YIG and GaYIG ferrimagnetic spheres, various shock wave equation-of-state computational models for porous materials. Home: 5 Trinity Ct Menlo Park CA 94025-6643 Office: SRI International 333 Ravenswood Ave Menlo Park CA 94025-3493

TOKOFSKY, JERRY HERBERT, film producer; b. N.Y.C., Apr. 14, 1936; s. Julius H. and Rose (Trager) T.; m. Myrna Weinstein, Feb. 21, 1968 (div.); children: David, Peter; m. Fiammetta Bettuzzi, 1970 (div.); 1 child, Tatianna; m. Karen Oliver, Oct. 4, 1981. BS in Journalism, NYU, 1957, LLD, 1959. Talent agt. William Morris Agy., N.Y.C., 1953-59; v.p. William Morris Agy., L.A., 1959-64; exec. v.p. Columbia Pictures, L.A., 1964-69; v.p. Paramount Pictures, London, 1970; exec. v.p. MGM, London, 1971; pres. Jerry Tokofsky Prodns., L.A., 1972-82; exec. v.p. Zupnik Enterprises, L.A., 1982-92; pres. Jerry Tokofsky Entertainment, Encino, Calif., 1992—; prof. Sch. TV and Film U. So. Calif. Prodr. films Where's Poppa, 1971, Born To Win, 1972, Dreamscape, 1985, Fear City, 1986, Wildfire, 1988, Glengarry Glen Ross, 1992, The Grass Harp, 1994, Indubious Battle, 1995, American Buffalo, 1995. With U.S. Army, 1959, res. 1959-63. Named Man of Yr. B'nai B'rith, 1981; recipient L.A. Resolution City of L.A. 1981. Mem. Variety Club Internat. Avocations: skiing, tennis, golf, chess.

TOKUMARU, ROBERTA, principal. Prin. Aikahi Elem. Sch. Recipient DOE Elem. Sch. Recognition award, 1989-90. Office: Aikahi Elem Sch 281 Ilihau St Kailua HI 96734-1698

TOLAN, DAVID JOSEPH, transportation executive; b. N.Y.C., Jan. 25, 1933. BS in Marine Transp., SUNY, Bronx, 1955. Deck mcht. marine officer Alcoa Steamship Co., Bklyn., 1955-61; with Sea-Land Svc., Edison, N.J., 1961—; marine mgr. to group v.p. Am., 1984-85; sr. v.p. labor rels. Sea-Land Corp., Edison, 1985—; bd. dirs. Shipping Industry Mut. Assurance Soc., Vt. Industry Mut. Assurance Soc., Sea-Land Svc. Inc. Trustee Christian Bros. Acad., Lyncroft, N.J., 1984-89. Recipient Good Scout award Greater N.Y. Coun., N.Y.C., 1987, Dir.'s award Fed. Mediation and Conciliation Svc., 1991, Humanitarian award Am. Cancer Soc. Schneider-Lerner Chpt., 1995; named Person of Yr. Seaman's House YMCA, 1994. Mem. Am. Maritime Assn. (pres. 1985—), Carriers Container Coun., Inc. (chmn. 1985—), Transp. Inst. (bd. dirs. 1985—), N.Y. Shipping Assn. Inc. (bd. dirs. 1978-82, 85—), Pacific Maritime Assn. (exec. com. 1979-82, 85—), Maritime Assn. of Port of N.Y./N.J. (bd. dirs. 1991—). Office: Sea-Land Svc Inc 600 Carnegie Blvd Charlotte NC 28209

TOLAN, JAMES FRANCIS, corporate and financial communications executive, marketing consultant, financial analyst; b. Hornell, N.Y., Oct. 3, 1934; s. Edward Bartholemew and Mercedes Irene (Welden) T.; m. Dawna Marie Sheehan, Jan. 25, 1959 (dec. June 1977); children—Jeffrey, Lyn, Craig, Leslie, Lisa, Jason, Brendan, Gavin, Lauren; m. Barbara Ann Bierowski, Apr. 9, 1983; 1 child, Timothy. B.S., Canisius Coll., 1956. Stockbroker Bache & Co., Binghamton, N.Y., 1960-66; sr. analyst Value Line Investment Service, N.Y.C., 1966-68; exec. v.p. Lyle D. Gumm & Assocs., Chgo., 1968-73; nat. sales mgr. Heinold Commodities, Inc., Chgo., 1973-79; ptnr. Fin. Rels. Bd., Chgo., 1979-91; pres. Fin. Community Contact Inc, Waukegan, Ill., 1991-92; sr. v.p. O'Connor Biro & Assocs., Northbrook, Ill., 1992—. Served to sgt. U.S. Army, 1957-58. Roman Catholic. Home: 214 Douglas Ave Waukegan IL 60085-2040 Office: O'Connor Biro & Assocs 500 Skokie Blvd Northbrook IL 60062

TOLAND, JOHN WILLARD, historian, writer; b. La Crosse, Wis., June 29, 1912; s. Ralph and Helen Chandler (Snow) T.; m. Toshiko Matsumura, Mar. 12, 1960; 1 dau., Tamiko; children by previous marriage: Diana Toland Netzer, Marcia. B.A., Williams Coll., 1936; student, Yale Drama Sch., 1936-37; L.H.D., Williams Coll., 1968, U. Alaska, 1977, Western Conn. U., 1986. Mem. adv. council Nat. Archives. Author: Ships in the Sky, 1957, Battle: The Story of the Bulge, 1959, But Not in Shame, 1961 (Best Book Fgn. Affairs award Overseas Press Club), The Dillinger Days, 1963, The Flying Tigers, 1963, The Last 100 Days, 1966 (Best Book Fgn. Affairs citation Overseas Press Club), The Battle of the Bulge, 1966, The Rising Sun, 1970 (Van Wyck Brooks award for non-fiction, Best Book Fgn. Affairs award Overseas Press Club, Pulitzer prize for non-fiction), Adolf Hitler, 1976 (Best Book Fgn. Affairs award Overseas Press Club, Gold Medal Nat. Soc. Arts and Letters), Hitler, The Pictorial Documentary of His Life, 1978, No Man's Land, 1980 (Best Book Fgn. Affairs citation Overseas Press Club), Infamy, 1982, In Mortal Combat, 1991; (novels) Gods of War, 1985, Occupation, 1987; also short stories. Served to capt. USAAF, 1942-46, 1947-49. Mem. Authors Guild, Accademia del Mediterraneo., Western Front Assn. (hon. v.p.). Home: 101 Long Ridge Rd Danbury CT 06810-8413

TOLAR, CARROLL T., paper company executive, mechanical engineer; b. Center, Tex., June 10, 1929; m. Mary Lou Small, Sept. 3, 1955; children: J. Mark, Nancy Tolar Webb, Kenneth. BS in Mech. Engring., La. Polytechnic Inst., 1959. Registered profl. engr., Ala., Calif., Conn., Oreg., Va., Wash. Engr. Bowater Engring. and Devel. Co., Calhoun, Tenn., 1959-63; project engr. Rust Internat., Inc., Birmingham, Ala., 1963-66; sr. engr. Ala. Kraft Co., Mahrt, 1966-67; v.p. Rust Internat., Inc., Birmingham, 1967-77; v.p. engring. dept. Ga.-Pacific Corp., Portland, Oreg. and Atlanta, 1977-87; sr. v.p. engring. dept. Ga.-Pacific Corp., Atlanta, 1987—. Office: Ga-Pacific Corp 133 Peachtree St NE Atlanta GA 30303-1801

TOLBERT, BERT MILLS, biochemist, educator; b. Twin Falls, Idaho, Jan. 15, 1921; s. Ed. and Helen (Mills) T.; m. Anne Grace Zweifler, July 20, 1959; children—Elizabeth Dawn, Margaret Anne, Caroline Joan, Sarah Helen. Student, Idaho State U., 1938-40; B.S., U. Calif. at Berkeley, 1942, Ph.D., 1945; postgrad., Fed. Inst. Tech., Zurich, Switzerland, 1952-53. Chemist Lawrence Radiation Lab., Berkeley, 1944-57; faculty U. Colo., Boulder, 1957-89, prof., 1961-89, prof. emeritus, 1989—, assoc. chmn. dept. chemistry and biochemistry, 1980-88; bd. dirs. Hauser Chem. Rsch., Boulder, 1983—; vis. prof. IAEA, Buenos Aires, Argentina, 1961-62; Biophysicist U.S. AEC, Washington, 1967-68; cons. pvt. cos, govt. agys. Author: (with others) Isotopic Carbon, 1948; contbr. (with others) articles to profl. jours. Fellow AAAS; mem. Am. Chem. Soc., Am. Soc. Biochemistry and Molecular Biology, Radiation Rsch. Soc., Soc. for Exptl. Biology and Medicine. Rsch. on organic chemistry, including use of isotopes in chemistry and biochemistry, radiation chemistry, radiation effects in protein, intermediary metabolism, metabolism of ascorbic acid, nutritional biochemistry, instrumentation in radioactivity. Home: 444 Kalmia Ave Boulder CO 80304-1732

TOLBERT, JAMES R., III, financial executive; b. Amarillo, Tex., Apr. 29, 1935; s. James R. and Mary (Noble) T.; m. Elizabeth McMahan, Dec. 26, 1956; children: James R. IV, Cannon Miles, Elizabeth Nelson, Lee Mitchener. Student, Stanford U., 1953-55; B.A., Okla. U., 1957; M.B.A., Stanford U., 1959. Vice pres. acquisitions Mid-Am. Corp., 1959-64; pres. James R. Tolbert & Assos., Inc., 1964-69; chmn. bd., treas., co-founder Holden Tolbert & Co., 1967—; sr. partner, co-founder Resource Analysis and Mgmt. Group, 1969-80; chmn., pres. First Okla. Corp., 1986—; trustee in bankruptcy Four Seasons Nursing Centers of Am., Inc., 1971-72; pres., treas., chmn. bd. Anta Corp., Oklahoma City, 1972-85; bd. dirs. Bonray Drilling Corp. Chmn. Okla. Higher Edn. Task Force, 1986, Oklahoma City Arts Coun., 1987-89; chmn. Okla. Futures Commn., 1988-90; trustee Casady Sch., 1989-94, Okla. Found. for Humanities, McGee Eye Inst.; chmn. Myriad Gardens Authority and Found. Recipient Exec. Leadership of Yr. award Oklahoma City U., 1975, 4th Ann. Dean A. McGee award, Downtown Now, 1989. Democrat. Home: 2321 Belleview Ter Oklahoma City OK 73112-7740 Office: First Okla Corp PO Box 1533 Oklahoma City OK 73101-1533

TOLBERT, MARGARET A., geochemistry educator. Prof. dept. chemistry U. Colo., Boulder. Recipient James B. Macelwane Young Investigator medal Am. Geophys. Union, 1993. Office: U Colo Dept Chemistry Campus Box 215 Boulder CO 80309-0215*

TOLBERT, NATHAN EDWARD, biochemistry educator, plant science researcher; b. Twin Falls, Idaho, May 19, 1919; s. Edward and Helen (Mills) T.; m. Evelynne Cedarlund, June 21, 1952 (dec. Nov. 1963); children—Helen, Carol, James; m. Eleanor Dalgleish, June 22, 1964. B.S. in Chemistry, U. Calif.-Berkeley, 1941; Ph.D. in Biochemistry, U. Wis.-Madison, 1950. Prof. biochemistry Mich. State U., East Lansing. Editor: Biochemistry of Plants, Vol. 1, 1980; editor 3 sci. jours.; contbr. numerous papers, revs., abstracts to profl. publs.; patentee in field. Served to capt. USAF, 1943-45, PTO. Named disting. prof. Mich. State U., 1963, Mich. Scientist of Yr., 1985; Fulbright fellow, 1969; grantee NSF, NIH. Mem. Nat. Acad. Sci., Am. Soc. Plant Physiology (pres. 1983-84, Stephen Hale award 1980), Am. Soc. Biol. Chemists, Am. Chem. Soc., Nat. Acad. Sci. Avocation: travel. Office: Mich State U Dept Biochemistry East Lansing MI 48824

TOLCHIN, MARTIN, newspaper reporter, author; b. N.Y.C., Sept. 20, 1928; s. Charles T. and Evelyn (Weisman) Tolchin; m. Susan Jane Goldsmith, Dec. 23, 1965; children: Charles, Karen. Student, U. Utah, 1947-49; LL.B., N.Y. Law Sch., 1951. Reporter N.Y. Times, N.Y.C., 1954-94; publisher and editor-in-chief The Hill, Washington, 1994—. Author: (with Susan Jane Tolchin) To The Victor, 1971, Clout-Woman Power and Politics, 1974, Dismantling America-The Rush to Deregulate, 1983, Buying Into America: How Foreign Money is Changing the Face of Our Nation, 1988, Selling Our Security—The Erosion of America's Assets, 1992. Served with U.S. Army, 1951-53. Recipient Schaeffer Gold Typewriter award E.M. Schaeffer Co., 1967; recipient Page One award Newspaper Guild N.Y., 1967, 69, 73, Citizens Budget Commn. award, 1967, Sigma Delta Chi award, 1973, Everett M. Dirksen award for disting. reporting of Congress, 1983. Jewish. Club: Nat. Press (Washington). Home: 5117 Wickett Ter Bethesda MD 20814-5716 Office: The Hill 733 15th St NW Washington DC 20005

TOLCHIN, SUSAN JANE, public administration educator, writer; b. N.Y.C., Jan. 14, 1941; d. Jacob Nathan and Dorothy Ann (Markowitz) Goldsmith; m. Martin Tolchin, Dec. 23, 1965; children: Charles Peter, Karen Rebecca. B.A., Bryn Mawr Coll., 1961; M.A., U. Chgo., 1962; Ph.D., N.Y.U., 1968. Lectr. in polit. sci. City Coll., N.Y.C., 1963-65, Bklyn. Coll., 1965-71; adj. asst. prof. polit. sci. Seton Hall U., South Orange, N.J., 1971-73; assoc. prof. polit. sci., dir. Inst. for Women and Politics, Mt. Vernon Coll., Washington, 1975-78; prof. pub. adminstrn. George Washington U., Washington, 1978—. disting. lectr. Industrial Coll. of the Armed Forces, 1994. Co-author (with Martin Tolchin): To The Victor: Political Patronage from the Clubhouse to the White House, 1971, Clout-Womanpower and Politics, 1974, Dismantling America-The Rush to Deregulate, 1983, Buying Into America-How Foreign Money Is Changing the Face of Our Nation, 1988, Selling Our Security-The Erosion of America's Assets, 1992. Bd. dirs. Cystic Fibrosis Foun., 1982—; county committeewoman Dem. Party, Montclair, N.J., 1969-73. Dilthey fellow George Washington U., 1983, Aspen Inst. fellow, 1979; named Tchr. of Yr., Mt. Vernon Coll., 1978; recipient Founder's Day award NYU, 1968. Fellow Nat. Acad. Pub. Adminstrn.; mem. Am. Polit. Sci. Assn. (pres. Women's Caucus for Polit. Sci. 1977-78), Am. Soc. Pub. Adminstrn. (chairperson sect. Natural Resources and Environ. Adminstrn. 1982-83). Democrat. Jewish. Office: George Washington U Dept Pub Adminstrn Washington DC 20052

TOLEDANO, RALPH DE, columnist, author, photographer; b. Internat. Zone of Tangier, Aug. 17, 1916; s. Hayim and Suzanne (Nahon) de T.; m. Nora Romaine, July 6, 1938 (div. 1964); children: James, Paul; m. Eunice Marshall, Apr. 19, 1979. Student, Fieldston Sch., N.Y.C., 1928-34; B.A., Columbia Coll., 1938. Founder, co-editor Jazz Info., 1938-39; assoc. editor The New Leader, 1941-43; editor The Standard, 1946; mng. editor Plain Talk, 1946-47; pub. dir. Dress Joint Bd., Internat. Ladies Garment Workers Union, 1947-48; asst. editor Newsweek, 1948, nat. reports editor, 1950-60, asst. chief Washington Bur., 1956-60; syndicated columnist King Features, 1960-71, nat. News Research Syndicate, 1971-74, Copley News Service, 1974-89, Heritage Features Syndicate, 1989-91, Creators Syndicate, 1991—; chief Washington Bur., Taft Broadcasting Co., 1960-61, Creator's Syndicate, 1991—; contbg. editor Nat. Rev., 1960—; pres. Nat. News-Research, 1960—, Anthem Books, 1970; editor-in-chief Washington World, 1961-62; vice chmn. Am. Conserva-Union, 1965-66; mem. 20th Century Fund Task Force on Freedom Press, 1971-72. Author: Seeds of Treason, 1950, Spies, Dupes and Diplomats, 1952, Day of Reckoning, 1955, Nixon, 1956, Lament for a Generation, 1960, The Greatest Plot in History, 1963, The Winning Side, 1963, The Goldwater Story, 1964, RFK: The Man Who Would be President, 1967, America, I-Love-You, 1968, One Man Alone: Richard M. Nixon, 1969, Claude Kirk: Man and Myth, 1970, Little Cesar, 1971, J. Edgar Hoover: The Man in His Time, 1973, Hit and Run: The Ralph Nader Story, 1975, Let Our Cities Burn, 1975, Poems: You & I, 1978, Devil Take Him, 1979, The Apocrypha of Limbo (poems), 1994; editor: Frontiers of Jazz, 1947; co-editor: The Conservative Papers, 1964; editor-in-chief: Political Success, 1968-69; mem. adv. bd.: Yale Lit. Mag, 1981-86; contbr. to nat. mags. Bd. dirs. Americans for Constitutional Action, 1966-67, Constructive Action, 1990—. With OSS, AUS, 1943-46. Recipient Freedoms Found. award, 1950, 61, 74; Americanism award VFW, 1953; Heritage Found. Disting. Journalism fellow. Mem. Internat. Mark Twain Soc. (knight), Bibl. Archeology Soc., Dutch Treat Club, Nat. Press Club, Naval and Mil. Club (London), Am. Philatelic Soc., Sigma Delta Chi. Home and Office: 500 23rd St NW Washington DC 20037-2828

TOLEDO-PEREYRA, LUIS HORACIO, transplant surgeon, researcher, historian, educator; b. Nogales, Ariz., Oct. 19, 1943; s. Jose Horacio and Elia (Pereyra) Toledo; m. Marjean May Gilbert, Mar. 21, 1974; children: Alexander Horacio, Suzanne Elizabeth. BS magna cum laude, Regis Coll., 1960; MD,Nat. U. Mex., 1967, MS in Internal Medicine, 1970; PhD in Surgery, U. Minn., 1976, PhD in Hist. Medicine, U. Minn., 1984. Intern Hosp. Juarez, Nat. U. Mex., 1966; resident in internal medicine Instituto Nacional de la Nutricion, Nat. U. Mex., 1968, 70; resident in gen. surgery U. Minn., 1970-76; resident in thoracic and cardiovascular surgery U. Chgo., 1976-77; dir. surg. research Henry Ford Hosp., Detroit, 1977-79, co-dir. transplantation, 1977-79; chief transplantation, dir. surg. research Mt. Carmel Mercy Hosp., Detroit, 1979-89; chief transplantation, dir. rsch. Borgess Med. Ctr., Kalamazoo, Mich., 1990—; clin. prof. surgery Mich. State U., 1993—; instr. biochemistry and internal medicine Nat. U. Mex., 1963, 68; adj. prof. Sch. Health Sci. Mercy Coll., Detroit, 1983-91, history Western Mich. U., 1990—, biol. sci., 1991—; prof. surgery Nat. U. Mex., 1990—. Recipient Outstanding Achievement award U. Mex., 1961, 64, 67; Resident Research award Assn. Acad. Surgery, 1974; Cecil Lehman Mayer Research award Am. Coll. Chest Physicians, 1975, Surgery Rsch. nat. award Mex. Assn. Gen. Surgery, 1993. Mem. AMA, Transplantation Soc., Assn. Acad. Surgery, Am. Soc. Transplant Surgery, Soc. Organ Sharing, Am. Assn. History Medicine, Am. Soc. Nephrology, Am. Assn. Immunologists, Am. Physiol. Soc., Soc. Exptl. Biology and Medicine, Am. Soc. Artificial Organs, Am. Diabetes Assn., European Soc. Study of Diabetes, No. Am. Soc. Dialysis Transplantation (pres., founder) Pan Am. Soc. Dialysis Transplantation (gov., founder) Roman Catholic. Guest editor various med. and transplant jours.; mem. editorial bd. Dialysis and Trans-

plantation, 1979—, Rsch. in Surgery, 1991—, Cirugia Iberoamericana, 1992—, clin. adv. bd. Transplt. Proc., 1993—, Medico Interamericano, 1993—, Cirugia Española, 1994—; assoc. editor Transplantology, 1990—; contbr. over 700 publs. on organ preservation, transplantation, other surg. and med. related areas, and the history of medicine to profl. jours.

TOLENTINO, CASIMIRO URBANO, lawyer; b. Manila, May 18, 1949; came to U.S., 1959; s. Lucio Rubio and Florence (Jose) T.; m. Jennifer Masculino, June 5, 1982; 2 children: Casimiro Masculino, Cristina Cecelia Masculino. BA in Zoology, UCLA, 1972, JD, 1975. Bar: Calif. 1976. Gen. counsel civil rights div. HEW, Washington, 1975-76; regional atty. Agrl. Labor Relations Bd., Fresno, Calif., 1976-78; regional dir. Sacramento and San Diego, 1978-81; regional atty. Pub. Employment Relations Bd., Los Angeles, 1981; counsel, west div. Writers Guild Am., Los Angeles, 1982-84; dir. legal affairs Embassy TV, Los Angeles, 1984-86; sole practice Los Angeles, 1986-87; mediator Ctr. Dispute Resolution, Santa Monica, Calif., 1986-87; asst. chief counsel Dept. of Fair Employment and Housing, State of Calif., 1986-92, adminstrv. law judge dept. social svcs., 1992—. Editor: Letters in Exile, 1976; contbr. articles and revs. to Amerasia Jour. Chmn. adv. bd. UCLA Asian Am. Studies Ctr., 1983—; chmn. bd. Asian Pacific Legal Ctr., L.A., 1983-93 (Decade award); pres. bd. civil svc. commrs. City of L.A., 1984-85, 90-93; bd. dirs. met. region United Way,; bd. dirs. Rebuild L.A., 1992—; mem. Asian-Pacific Am. adv. coun. L.A. Police Commn. Mem. State Bar Calif. (exec. com. labor law sect. 1985-88), Los Angeles County Bar Assn., Minority Bar Assn. (sec. 1984-85), Philippine Lawyers of So. Calif. (pres. 1984—, Award of Merit 1982). Democrat. Roman Catholic. Avocations: history, photography, travel.

TOLER, JAMES C., electrical engineer; b. Carthage, Ark., Jan. 31, 1936. BSEE, U. Ark., 1957; MSEE, Ga. Inst. Tech., 1970. Prin. rsch. engr. Ga. Inst. Tech., Atlanta, 1966—, dir. bioengring. ctr., 1984—, dir. ctr. rehab. tech., 1987-93. Fellow IEEE; mem. Bioelectromagnetics Soc. Achievements include research on interaction of electromagnetic waves with biological systems. Office: Office Interdisc Programs 225 North Ave NW Atlanta GA 30332

TOLER, RAY EDWARD, conductor, band director; b. Detroit, Feb. 1, 1942; s. Ralph Vivian and Neva Florence (Killough) T.; m. Catherine Virginia Hoff, Aug. 15, 1964; children: Ray Edward Jr., Eric Andrew, Bryan Alan. MusB, Tex. Christian U., 1964; MA summa cum laude, Trenton State Coll., 1975; grad., Air Command and Staff Coll., Maxwell AFB, Ala., 1982, Air War Coll., Maxwell AFB, Ala., 1984. Commd. 2d lt. USAF, 1968, advanced through grades to lt. col.; trombonist 539th Air Force Band USAF, Lackland AFB, Tex., 1966-68; condr., comdr. Air Force Logistics Command Band Wright-Patterson AFB, Ohio, 1968-71; condr., comdr. 13th Air Force Band of the Pacific Clark AFB, The Philippines, 1971-73, Air Force Band of the East, McGuire AFB, N.J., 1973-75; condr., comdr. Mil. Airlift Command Band Scott AFB, Ill., 1975-78; condr., comdr. Air Force Band of the West, Lackland AFB, 1978-81, Band of the Air Force Res., Robins AFB, Ga., 1982-85; chief of bands and music Pentagon, Washington, 1985-88; condr. USAF Band, Washington, 1985-88; ret. USAF, 1988; dir. bands Tex. A&M U., College Station, 1988—; trombonist Ft. Worth Symphony and Opera Co., 1963-65, Stan Kenton Orch., L.A., 1965, Dallas Symphony Orch., 1965-66; band dir. Weatherford (Tex.) High Sch., 1964-66. Condr. rec. Music of the King, 1971, condr./producer rec. Music of West Africa, 1977, Ready Then, Ready Now, 1982, Concert Band Classics, 1983, Recall! Step-Off on Hullabaloo, 1990, Bands of Aggieland, 1993, Texas Aggie Band Centennial, 1994; condr./composer rec. In Concert, 1985; prodr. Comin' At 'Ya, 1984; condr. rec. The Best of the Air Force Reserve, 1988. Deacon 1st Presbyn. Ch., Fairborn, Ohio, 1970; judge Miss Am. Scholarship Pageant, 1992, 94; bd. dirs. Woodcreek Homeowners Assn., College Station, 1988-91. Mem. Nat. Assn. Mil. Marching Bands, John Philip Sousa Found. (bd. dirs.), Coll. Band Dirs. Nat. Assn., Tex. Bandmasters Assn., Tex. Music Educators Assn., Tex. Band Masters Assn., World Assn. for Symphonic Bands and Ensembles, N.Am. Band Dirs. Coordinating Coun., Internat. Mil. Music Soc., Assn. Concert Bands, USAF Ret. Band Dirs. Soc., Kappa Kappa Psi, Phi Mu Alpha Sinfonia. Republican. Methodist. Avocations: reading, crossword puzzles, fishing, computers. Office: Tex A&M U Adams Band Bldg College Station TX 77843

TOLES, EDWARD BERNARD, retired judge; b. Columbus, Ga., Sept. 17, 1909; s. Alex and Virginia Frances (Luke) T.; m. Susan Evelyn Echols, Jan. 24, 1944; 1 son, Edward Bernard. A.B., U. Ill., 1932; postgrad., Law Sch., 1932-34; J.D., Loyola U., Chgo., 1936. Bar: Ill. bar 1936. Practiced in Chgo., 1936-69; asst. atty. U.S. Housing Authority, 1939-40; asst. gen. counsel, war corr. ETO; Chgo. Defender, 1943-45; U.S. bankruptcy judge No. Dist. Ill., Chgo., 1969-87. Author: Chicago Negro Judges, 1959, Negro Federal Judges, 1960, Negro Lawyer in Crisis, 1966, Black Lawyers and Judges in the U.S, 1971, also articles.; Editor: Cook County Bar News, 1961-63; Columnist: Bench and Bar, Nat. Bar Assn. Bull, 1968-75. Recipient U.S. War Dept. award for services as war corr., 1947, Ill. Jud. Coun. award, 1988; named Sr. Counsellor, Ill. State Bar Assn., 1986,. Mem. ABA, Fed. Bar Assn., Nat. Bar Assn. (Barrister of Year award 1960, C.F. Stradford award, columnist Bench and Bar Bull., historian jud. coun. 1985—), Chgo. Bar Assn. (bd. mgrs. 1969-70), Cook County Bar Assn. (Edward H. Wright award, 1962, pres. 1960-62), 7th Circuit Bar Assn. (World Peace Through Law Bar Assn.), Am. Judicature Soc., Nat. Conf. Bankruptcy Judges, Alpha Phi Alpha, Omega Psi Phi (Ode to Excellence award 1963). Democrat. Home: 4800 S Chicago Beach Dr Chicago IL 60615-2009

TOLES, THOMAS GREGORY, editorial cartoonist; b. Buffalo, Oct. 22, 1951; s. George Edward and Rose Elizabeth (Riehle) T.; m. Gretchen Amanda Saarnijoki, May 26, 1973; children: Amanda Laurel, Seth August. B.A. in English, SUNY-Buffalo, 1973. Artist Buffalo Courier-Express, 1973-80, cartoonist, 1980-82; cartoonist Buffalo News, 1982—, UPS, 1982—, The New Republic, 1992-94, U.S. News & World Report, 1994—. Author: The Taxpayer's New Clothes, 1985, Mr. Gazoo: A Cartoon History of the Reagan Era, 1987, At Least Our Bombs Are Getting Smarter: A Cartoon Preview of the 1990's, 1991, My Elected Representatives Went to Washington, 1993; creator (comic strip) Curious Avenue, 1992. Recipient John Fischetti Editorial Cartoon award Columbia Coll., Chgo., 1984, Pulitzer Prize for editorial cartooning, 1990. Mem. Am. Assn. Editorial Cartoonists. Home: 75 Central Ave Hamburg NY 14075-6219 Office: Buffalo News 1 News Plz Buffalo NY 14203-2994

TOLINO, ARLENE BECENTI, elementary education educator; b. Crownpoint, N.Mex., Dec. 26, 1942; d. Little Billie and Mary (Arviso) Becenti; m. Albert Ray Tolino, Nov. 23, 1963; children: Adrian, Nathaniel Ray, Bryan. BS, U. N.Mex., 1977; MA, No. Ariz. U., 1984. Cert. elem. tchr., N.Mex. Ednl. aide Bur. Ind. Affairs Ea. Agy., Crownpoint, 1966-77; elem. tchr. Bur. Ind. Affairs Ea. Agy., Mariano Lake, N.Mex., 1977-79; elem. tchr. Bur. Ind. Affairs Ea. Agy., Crownpoint, 1979—, adult edn. tchr., summer 1988; sch. curriculum trainer BeautyWay curriculum Navajo Tribe, Crownpoint, 1989; computer tchr. Crownpoint Community Sch., 1988-89; site coord. pilot project ICON, Crownpoint, 1986-87; mem. com., tutor Gifted and Talented Program, Crownpoint, 1989-91. Sch. coord. Girl Scouts Am., 1977-79; sec. Navajo Nation Chpt. Officers, Crownpoint, 1983-86; mem. St. Paul Parish Coun., Crownpoint, 1982—, sec., 1992—, chairperson edn. com. 1992—; pres. Crownpoint Community Sch. Staff Assn., 1992—. Recipient Appreciation award Chaparral coun. Girl Scouts U.S.A., 1978, Title I Outstanding Tchr. award Crownpoint Community Sch. Parent Action Com., 1981, Ea. Navajo Coun., 1988. Mem. Ea. Navajo Agy. Tchrs. (sch. rep. 1987-88). Democrat. Roman Catholic. Avocations: reading, computers, crocheting, ceramics, sewing. Home: PO Box 344 Crownpoint NM 87313-0344 Office: Crownpoint Community PO Box Drawer H Crownpoint NM 87313

TOLIVER, LEE, mechanical engineer; b. Wildhorse, Okla., Oct. 3, 1921; s. Clinton Leslie and Mary (O'Neall) T.; m. Barbara Anne O'Reilly, Jan. 24, 1942; children: Margaret Anne, Michael Edward. BSME, U. Okla., 1942. Registered profl. engr., Ohio. Engr. Douglas Aircraft Co., Santa Monica, Calif., 1942, Oklahoma City, 1942-44; engr. Los Alamos (N.Mex.) Sci. Lab., 1946; instr. mech. engring. Ohio State U., Columbus, 1946-47; engr. Sandia Nat. Labs., Albuquerque, 1947-82; instr. computer sci. and math. U. N.Mex., Valencia County, 1982-84; number theory researcher Belen, N.Mex., 1982—. Co-author: (computer manuals with G. Carli, A.F. Schkade, L.

Toliver) Experiences with an Intelligent Remote Batch Terminal, 1972, (with C.R. Borgman, T.I. Ristine) Transmitting Data from the PDP-10 to Precision Graphics, 1973, (with C.R. Borgman, T.I. Ristine) Data Transmission-PDP-10/Sykes/Precision Graphics, 1975. With Manhattan Project (Atomic Bomb) U.S. Army, 1944-46. Mem. Math. Assn. Am., Am. Math. Soc. Achievements include devel. of 44 computer programs with manuals. Home: 206 Howell St Belen NM 87002-6225

TOLK, NORMAN HENRY, physics educator; b. Idaho Falls, Idaho, Jan. 9, 1938; s. Henry and Merle (Ricks) T.; m. Marilyn Ann Neubauer, Dec. 19, 1961; children: Jeffrey S., Bentley J., David H., Rebecca E., Amy C. AB in Physics, Harvard U., 1960; PhD in Physics, Columbia U. 1966. Rsch. physicist Columbia Radiation Lab. N.Y.C., 1966, rsch. assoc., 1966-67, lectr., mem. staff, 1967-68; adj. asst. prof. Columbia U., N.Y.C., 1968-69; mem. tech. staff Bell Telephone Lab., Murray Hill, N.J., 1968-83, Bell Comms. Rsch., Murray Hill, 1984; prof. physics Vanderbilt U., Nashville, 1984—, prof. dept. radiology, 1993—; adj. prof. physics Fisk U., Nashville, 1991—; cons. Physitron, Inc., Huntsville, Ala., 1993—. Editor: Inelastic Ion-Surface Collisions, 1977, Desorption Induced by Elec. Trans., 1983, Atomic Collisions in Solids, 1986; N.Am. editor Radiation Effects and Def./Solids, 1987—; contbr. over 140 articles to profl. jours. Alexander von Humboldt sr. scientist, 1987. Fellow Am. Phys. Soc. Home: 314 Appomattox Dr Brentwood TN 37027-4955 Office: Vanderbilt U Dept Physics PO Box 1807 B Nashville TN 37202-1807

TOLL, DANIEL ROGER, corporate executive, civic leader; b. Denver, Dec. 3, 1927; s. Oliver W. and Merle D'Aubigne (Sampson) T.; m. Sue Andersen, June 15, 1963; children: Daniel Andersen, Matthew Mitchell. AB magna cum laude (Pyne prize), Princeton U., 1949; MBA with distinction, Harvard U., 1955. With Deep Rock Oil Corp., Tulsa, 1949-51, asst. mgr. product supply and distbn.; with Helmerich & Payne, Tulsa, 1955-64, roughneck, landman, exploration mgr., pipeline constrn. mgr., v.p. fin., 1961-64; with Sunray DX Oil Co., Tulsa, 1964-69, treas., v.p. corp. planning and devel.; v.p. Sun Oil Co., 1969; with Walter E. Heller Internat. Corp., Chgo., 1970-85, sr. v.p. fin., dir., 1970-80, pres., dir., 1980-85, corp. and civic dir., 1985—; bd. dirs. Brown Group, Inc., Mallinckrodt Group, Inc. (formerly IMCERA Group Inc.), Kemper Corp., Kemper Nat. Ins. Co., Lincoln Nat. Convertible Securities Fund, Inc., Lincoln Nat. Income Fund, Inc., NICOR, Inc., A.P. Green Industries Inc. Vice chmn. Tulsa Cmty. Chest, 1964-66; v.p. bd. dirs. Tulsa Opera, 1960-69; bd. dirs. Tulsa Little Theatre, 1963-69, Internat. House, Chgo., 1984-87; bd. dirs. Inroads, Inc., 1973—, nat. vice chmn., 1982—; bd. dirs. Chgo. Area coun. Boy Scouts Am., 1976-94, pres., 1981-83; mem. Kenilworth (Ill.) Sch. Bd. Dist. 38, 1975-81, pres., 1978-81; bd. dirs., mem. exec. com., chmn. fin. and hosp. affairs coms. Evanston (Ill.) Hosp., 1982—; bd. dirs. Chgo. Met. Planning Coun., 1989—, pres., 1991-94; bd. dirs. Northwestern Healthcare Network, Inc., 1995—; trustee Princeton U., 1990-94. Lt. (j.g.) USNR, 1951-52. Baker scholar Harvard U., 1955. Mem. Chgo. Assn. Commerce and Industry (bd. dirs. 1979-86), Chgo. Club, Comml. Club, Econ. Club, Harvard Bus. Sch. Club (past pres., bd. dirs. 1971-91), Indian Hill Club (bd. govs. 1987-90), Princeton Club (past pres., bd. dirs. 1985—), Phi Beta Kappa. Home: 125 Abingdon Ave Kenilworth IL 60043-1201 Office: 135 S La Salle St Ste 1117 Chicago IL 60603-4265

TOLL, JACK BENJAMIN, government official; b. Denver, Nov. 25, 1925; s. John B. and Vera (Calabrese) T.; m. Jean Small, Dec. 31, 1946; children: Robert John, Barbara, Susan Jean, Jack Edward, Carol. J.D., U. Denver, 1947; postgrad., Westminster Law Sch., Denver, 1950. Bar: Colo. 1950. Inland marine mgr. Gen. Adjustment Bur., Denver, 1949-53; trial legal dept. Denver Chgo. Trucking Co., 1953-65, sec., 1965-69; dir. D.C. Internat., Inc., Denver, 1966-69; v.p. D.C. Internat., Inc., 1967-69, sec., 1965-69; gen. counsel Denver Urban Renewal Authority, 1969-71; regional counsel HUD, 1971-82; regional dir. Merit Systems Protection Bd., 1982-88; ret., 1988; judge Jefferson County, Colo., 1955-59. Republican. Home: 14020 Elderberry Rd Golden CO 80401-2014

TOLL, JOHN, cinematographer. Cinematographer: (TV movies) Goodnight Sweet Wife, 1992, (films) Wind, 1992, Legends of the Fall, 1994 (Academy award best cinematography 1994). Office: care Judy Marks Judy Marks Agency 650 N Bronson Ave Ste 148 Los Angeles CA 90004*

TOLL, JOHN SAMPSON, association administrator, former university administrator, physics educator; b. Denver, Oct. 25, 1923; s. Oliver Wolcott and Merle d'Aubigne (Sampson) T.; m. Deborah Ann Taintor, Oct. 24, 1970; children: Dacia Merle Sampson, Caroline Taintor. BS with highest honors, Yale U., 1944; AM, Princeton U., 1948, PhD, 1952; DSc (hon.), U. Md., 1973, U. Wroclaw, Poland, 1975; LLD (hon.), Adelphi U., 1978; hon. doctorate, Fudan U., Peoples Republic China, 1987; LHD (hon.), SUNY, Stony Brook, 1990; LLD (hon.), U. Md., Eastern Shore, 1993. Mng. editor acting chmn. Yale Sci. mag., 1943-44; with Princeton U., 1946-49, Proctor fellow, 1948-49; Friends of Elementary Particle Theory Research grantee for study in France, 1950; theoretical physicist Los Alamos Sci. Lab., 1950-51; staff mem., assoc. dir. Project Matterhorn, Forrestal Rsch. Ctr., Princeton U., 1951-53; prof., chmn. physics and astronomy U. Md., 1953-65; pres., prof. physics SUNY, Stony Brook, 1965-78; pres., prof. physics U. Md., 1978-88, chancellor, 1988-89, chancellor emeritus, prof. physics, 1989—; pres. Univs. Rsch. Assn., Washington, 1989-94; interim pres. Wash. Coll., Chestertown, Md., 1995. Contbr. articles to sci. jours. Recipient Benjamin Barge prize in math. Yale U., 1943, George Beckwith medal for Proficiency in Astronomy, 1944, Outstanding citizen award City of Denver, 1958, Outstanding Tchr. award U. Md. Men's League, 1965, Nat. Golden Plate award Am. Acad. Achievement, 1968, Copernicus award Govt. of Poland, 1973, Stony Brook Found. award for disting. contbns. to edn., 1979, Disting. Svc. award State of Md., 1981; named Washingtonian of Yr., 1985; Silver medal Sci. Univ. of Tokyo, 1994; John Simon Guggenheim Meml. Found. fellow Inst. Theoretical Physics U. Copenhagen, U. Lund, Sweden, 1958-59. Mem. Fellow Am. Phys. Soc., Washington Acad. Scis. (pres.-elect 1994—); mem. NAACP (life), NSTA, Am. Assn. Physics Tchrs., Fedn. Am. Scientists (chmn. 1961-62), Philos. Soc. Washington, N.Y. Acad. Scis., Assn. Soc. Washington, Assn. Higher Edn., Yale Engring. Assn., Cosmos Club, Univ. Club, Phi Beta Kappa, Sigma Xi (Sci. Achievement award 1965), Phi Kappa Phi (Disting. Mem. award 1990), Omicron Delta Kappa (hon.). Achievements include research on elementary particle theory; scattering. Office: U Md Dept Physics College Park MD 20742-4111 Throughout my life I have tried mainly to do whatever seemed most important and useful.

TOLL, MAYNARD JOY, JR., investment banker; b. Los Angeles, Feb. 5, 1942; s. Maynard Joy and Ethel (Coleman) T.; m. Kathryn Wiseman, Sept. 12, 1964; children: Ian Wolcott, Adam Donahue. BA, Stanford U., 1963; MA, Johns Hopkins U., 1965, PhD, 1970. Asst. prof., asst. dean faculty U. Mass., Boston, 1968-71; legis. and adminstrv. asst. Sen. Edmund Muskie, Washington, 1971-75; from asst. v.p. to mng. dir. CS First Boston, N.Y.C., 1975—. Active Council Fgn. Relations, N.Y.C. Democrat. Episcopalian. Clubs: Links; Vineyard Haven (Mass.) Yacht.

TOLL, PERRY MARK, lawyer; b. Kansas City, Mo., Oct. 28, 1945; s. Mark Irving and Ruth (Parker) T.; m. Mary Anne Shottenkirk, Aug. 26, 1967; children: Andrea Lynne, Hillary Anne. BS in Polit. Sci. and Econs., U. Kans., 1967, JD, 1970. Bar: Mo. 1970 1970, U.S. Dist. Ct. (we. dist.) Mo. 1970, U.S. Tax. Ct. 1979, U.S. Supreme Ct. 1979. With Shughart, Thomson & Kilroy P.C., Kansas City, 1970—; asst. prof. deferred compensation U. Mo., Kansas City, 1979-83; bd. dirs., pres. Heart of Am. Tax Inst., Kansas City, 1975-87. Mem., chmn. Prairie Village, Kans., Bd. of Zoning Appeals, 1977—. Mem. ABA, Mo. Bar Assn., Lawyers Assn. Kansas City, East Kans. Estate Planning Coun. (bd. dirs., pres.), Phi Kappa Tau (bd. dirs.). Office: Shughart Thomson & Kilroy 12 Wyandotte Plz 120 W 12th St Kansas City MO 64105-1917

TOLL, ROBERT IRWIN, lawyer, real estate developer; b. Elkins Park, Pa., Dec. 30, 1940; s. Albert A. and Sylvia (Steinberg) T.; m. Norma (div.); children: Laurie, Deborah; m. Jane Snyder; children: Rachel, Jacob; stepson Joshua Goldfein. AB, Cornell U., 1963; LLB cum laude, U. Pa., 1966. Bar: Pa. 1967. Atty. Wolf, Block Schorr Solis-Cohen, Phila., 1966-67; chmn., chief exec. officer Toll Bros. Inc., Huntingdon Valley, Pa., 1967—; mem. Mayor's Coun. on Housing in Phila.; mem. bd. overseers U. Pa. Law Sch.; mem. real estate coun. Cornell U. Real Estate Coun. Bd. dirs. Pa. Campaign for Choice, Phila., Beth Sholom Synagogue, Elkins Park, Southeastern chpt.

ARC; sponsor Say Yes to Edn., Phila.; mem. bd. trustees Abington Meml. Hosp. Found. Named Profl. Builder of Yr., Builder Mag., 1988. Mem. Nat. Assn. Home Builders, Philmont Country Club (Huntingdon Valley), Equity Lodge 591. Avocations: racing J/35 sailboats, tennis, skiing. Office: Toll Brothers Inc 3103 Philmont Ave Huntingdon Valley PA 19006-4298

TOLL, SHELDON SAMUEL, lawyer; b. Phila. June 6, 1940; s. Herman and Rose (Ornstein) T.; m. Roberta Darlene Pollack, Aug. 11, 1968; children: Candice Moore, John Maitland, Kevin Scott. Bar: Pa. 1967, Mich. 1972, Ill. 1990, Tex. 1990, U.S. Dist. Ct. (ea. dist.) Pa. 1968, U.S. Ct. Appeals (3d cir.) 1970, U.S. Supreme Ct. 1971, Mich. 1972, U.S. Dist. Ct. (ea. dist.) U.S. Ct. Appeals (6th cir.) 1973, U.S. Ct. Appeals (5th cir.) 1978, U.S. Dist. Ct. (no. dist.) Calif. 1986, U.S. Ct. Appeals (9th cir.) 1987, U.S. Dist. Ct. (ea. dist.) Wis. 1989. Assoc. Montgomery, McCracken et al, Phila., 1967-72; sr. ptnr. Honigman Miller Schwartz and Cohn, Detroit, 1972—; panelist Bankruptcy Litigation Inst., N.Y.C., 1984—. Author: Pennsylvania Crime Codes, 1972, Bankruptcy Litigation Manual, 1988. Bd. dirs. Southeastern Mich. chpt. ARC, Detroit. Mem. Fed. Bar Assn. (past pres. Detroit chpt.), ABA, Pa. Bar Assn., Phila. Bar Assn., Detroit Bar Assn., Am. Bankruptcy Inst. (cert. bus. bankruptcy law specialist), Franklin (Mich.) Hills Country Club, Phi Beta Kappa. Democrat. Jewish. Office: Honigman Miller Schwartz & Cohn 2290 1st National Bldg Detroit MI 48226

TOLLENAERE, LAWRENCE ROBERT, retired industrial products company executive; b. Berwyn, Ill., Nov. 19, 1922; s. Cyrille and Modesta (Van Damme) T.; m. Mary Elizabeth Hansen, Aug. 14, 1948; children: Elizabeth, Homer, Stephanie, Caswell, Mary Jennifer. BS in Engring., Iowa State U., 1944, MS in Engring., 1949; MBA, U. So. Calif., 1969; LLD (hon.), Claremont Grad. Sch., 1977. Specification engr. Alumninum Co. Am., Vernon, Calif., 1946-47; asst. prod. indsl. engring. Iowa State U., Ames, 1947-50; sales rep. Am. Pipe and Constrn. Co. (name changed to AMERON 1970), South Gate, Calif., 1950-53; spl. rep. Am. Pipe and Constrn. Co. (name changed to AMERON 1970), S.Am., 1952-54; 2nd v.p., mgr. Columbian divsn. Am. Pipe and Constrn. Co. (name changed to AMERON 1970), Bogota, S.Am., 1955-57; divsn. v.p., mgr. Am. Pipe and Constrn. Co. (name changed to AMERON 1970), Calif., 1957-63; v.p. concrete pipe ops. Am. Pipe and Constrn. Co. (name changed to AMERON 1970), Monterey Park, Calif., 1963-65, pres. corp. hdqrs., 1965-67; pres., CEO Ameron Inc., Monterrey Park, Calif., 1967-89; CEO, pres. Ameron Inc., Pasadena, 1989-93, chmn. bd. dirs., 1989-94, ret., 1994; bd. dirs. Avery Dennison, Pasadena, Calif., Newhall Land and Farming Co., Valencia, Calif., The Parsons Corp., Padasena. Trustee The Huntington Library, Art Gallery and Bot. Gardens; emeritus mem. bd. fellows Claremont U. Ctr.; bd. gov.'s Iowa State U. Found. Mem. Newcomen Soc. N.Am., Calif. C. of C. (bd. dirs. 1977-92), Alpha Tau Omega, Calif. Club (bd. dirs.), Jonathan Club, Pauma Valley Country Club, San Gabriel Country Club, Bohemian Club, San Francisco Club, Commanderie de Bordeaux Club, L.A. Club, L.A. Confrerie des Chevaliers du Tastevin Club, Twilight Club, London Club, Beavers Club (past pres., hon. dir.), Valley of Montecito Club (Santa Barbara, Calif.). Republican. Avocations: fishing, hunting, equestrian, philately. Home: 1400 Milan Ave South Pasadena CA 91030-3930 Office: Ameron Inc 245 S Los Robles Ave Pasadena CA 91101-2894

TOLLER, WILLIAM ROBERT, chemical and oil company executive; b. Ft. Smith, Ark., Aug. 10, 1930; s. Audly Sr. and Martha (Anderson) T.; m. Jo Ella Perry, June 13, 1959; children: William R. Jr., Michelle D., Gregory A. BBA, U. Ark., 1956; postgrad., Stamford U., 1971. Various positions Conoco Inc., Okla., Tex. and Colo., 1955-77; v.p. fin. and adminstrn. Continental Carbon Co., Houston, 1977-81, pres., chief exec. officer, 1981-84; v.p., gen. mgr. Concarb div. Witco Corp., Houston, 1984-86; dir., chmn. bd., chief exec. officer Witco Corp., N.Y.C., 1990—; bd. dirs. CMA. Mem. Rep. Nat. Com., Washington, 1988-92; bd. dirs. Internat. Ctr. for Disabled, SW Area Commerce and Industry. Mem. Am. Chem. Soc., Am. Petroleum Inst., Bus. Roundtable, U.S. C. of C. (bd. dirs.). Presbyterian. Avocations: golf, skiing. Home: 53 Ridge Brook Dr Stamford CT 06903-1234 Office: Sherex Chem Co Inc 5777 Frantz Rd Dublin OH 43017*

TOLLERSON, ERNEST, newspaper editor; married; 2 children. Grad., Princeton U., Columbia U. With Wall Street Jour., N.Y.C.; gen. assignment, ct. reporter N.Y. Daily News; statehouse bur. chief Phila. Inquirer, Trenton, N.J.; with N.Y. Newsday, N.Y.C., 1986—; editl. page editor, 1990—. Recipient Silurian award, 1989. Office: NY Newsday 2 Park Ave New York NY 10016

TOLLES, BRYANT FRANKLIN, JR., history and art history educator; b. Hartford, Conn., Mar. 14, 1939; s. Bryant Franklin and Grace Frances (Ludden) T.; m. Carolyn Coolidge Kimball, Sept. 15, 1962; children: Thayer Coolidge, Bryant Franklin III. BA, Yale U., 1961, MA in Teaching, 1962; PhD, Boston U., 1970. Instr. history King Sch., Stamford, Conn., 1962-63; tchr. history St. George's Sch., Newport, R.I., 1963-65; instr., asst. dean Tufts U., Medford, Mass., 1965-71; asst. dir., libr., editor publs. N.H. Hist. Soc., Concord, 1972-74; exec. dir., libr. Essex Inst., Salem, Mass., 1974-84; dir. mus. studies program, assoc. prof. history and art history U. Del., Newark, 1984—; mem. Com. for a New England Bibliography. Author: New Hampshire Architecture, 1979, Architecture in Salem, 1983, The Grand Resort Hotels of the White Mountains: A Vanishing Architectural Legacy, 1995; editor: Leadership for the Future, 1991; contbr. articles to profl. jours. Trustee Mt. Washington Obs., N.H. Ford. Found. fellow Yale, 1962. Mem. Orgn. Am. Historians, Soc. Archtl. Historians, Soc. Indsl. Archaeology, Am. Assn. Mus., New England Mus. Assn., Mid-Atlantic Mus. Assn., Am. Assn. for State and Local History, Wilmington Rowing Club, Appalachian Mountain Club, Univ. Bridge Club (Phila.). Home: 1002 Kent Rd Wilmington DE 19807-2820 Office: U Del Mus Studies Program 301 Old Coll Newark DE 19716

TOLLESTRUP, ALVIN VIRGIL, physicist; b. Los Angeles, Mar. 22, 1924; s. Albert Virgil and Maureen (Petersen) T.; m. Alice Hatch, Feb. 26, 1945 (div. Nov. 1970); children: Kristine, Kurt, Eric, Carl; m. Janine Cukay, Oct. 11, 1986. BS, U. Utah, 1944; PhD, Calif. Inst. Tech., 1950. Mem. faculty Calif. Inst. Tech., Pasadena, 1950-77, prof. physics, 1968-77; scientist Fermi Nat. Lab., Batavia, Ill., 1977-93; co-spokesman CDF Collaboration, 1977-93. Co-developer superconducting magnets for Tevatron, Fermi Lab. Served to lt. (j.g.) USN, 1944-46. NSF fellow; Disting. Alumni award Calif. Inst. Tech., 1993. Fellow AAAS, Am. Phys. Soc. (R.R. Wilson prize 1989, Nat. medal for tech. 1989). Democrat. Home: 29W 254 Renouf Dr Warrenville IL 60555 Office: Fermi Nat Lab PO Box 500 Batavia IL 60510-5000

TOLLETT, LELAND EDWARD, food company executive; b. Nashville, Ark., Jan. 21, 1937; s. Vergil E. and Gladys V. (Sturgis) T.; m. Betty Ruth Blew, June 2, 1961; children—Terri Lynn, Gary Dwayne. B.S.A., U. Ark., 1958, M.S.A., 1959. Dir. Research Tyson Foods, Inc., Springdale, Ark., 1959-64, gen mgr. prodn., 1965-66, v.p. prodn., 1966-80, chief operating officer, 1981-83, pres., chief operating officer, 1983-91, chief exec. officer, 1991—, vice chmn., 1993-95, chmn., 1995—, also dir.; pres., chief oper. officer Spring Valley Farms Inc., Tyson Farms Tex., Inc., Poultry Growers Inc., Lane Processing Inc., Tyson-Carolina Inc., Eagle Distbg. Inc., Lane Farms Inc., Tyson Export Sales Inc.; pres. Louis Kemp Seafood Co., Arctic Alaska Fisheries Corp., Henry House, Inc. Served with USAF, 1961-62. Mem. Nat. Broiler Council (bd. dirs. 1979—). Avocations: hunting, golfing. Home: 2801 Johnson Rd Springdale AR 72762-6833 Office: Tyson Foods Inc 2210 W Oaklawn Dr Springdale AR 72762*

TOLLEY, AUBREY GRANVILLE, hospital administrator; b. Lynchburg, Va., Nov. 15, 1924; married. Student, Duke U., 1942-43; M.D. U. Va. 1952. Diplomate Am. Bd. Psychiatry and Neurology. Intern St. Elizabeths Hosp., Washington, 1952-53; asst. resident psychiatry U. Va. Hosp., Charlottesville, 1953-54; resident psychiatry VA Hosp., Roanoke, Va., 1954-56; instr. U. N.C. Sch. Medicine, 1956-61, asst. prof., 1961-66, clin. asst. prof. psychiatry, 1966-72, clin. assoc. prof., 1972-76, clin. prof., 1976—; dir. psychotherapy Dorothea Dix Hosp., Raleigh, 1962-67; dir. hosp. Dorothea Dix Hosp., 1973-88; dir. resident tng. John Umstead Hosp., Butner, N.C., 1966-67; dir. profl. tng. and edn. N.C. Dept. Mental Health, Raleigh, 1967-72, asst. dir., 1972-73; Prin. investigator USPHS grant, 1957-59; cons. VA Hosp., Fayetteville, N.C., 1957-78; sr. cons., supervising faculty, community psychiatry sect. dept. psychiatry U. N.C. Sch. Medicine, 1971—; exec. sec. Multiversity Group, 1968-73. Trustee Found. Hope, Raleigh, N.C., 1984—.

Served with USNR, 1943-46. Fellow Am. Psychiat. Assn. (rep. N.C. Dist. bd. 1969-82, 86—, mem. joint commn. on pub. affairs 1984-87, mem. constl. membership com. 1990—, mem. commn. on subspecialization 1990-94, Warren Williams award 1987), Am. Coll. Psychiatrists; mem. N.C., Durham-Orange County med. socs., N.C. Neuropsychiat. Assn. (pres. 1984-85), Am. Assn. Dirs. Psychiat. Residency Tng., N.C. Hosp. Assn. (life), George C. Ham Soc. (Disting. Alumni award 1992). Home and Office: 110 Laurel Hill Rd Chapel Hill NC 27514-4323

TOLLEY, JERRY RUSSELL, clinical laboratory executive; b. Goldsboro, N.C., Nov. 6, 1942; s. Elva Russell Tolley and Clara (Smith) Tolley-Bunch; m. Joan Morrison, June 8, 1965; children: Jerry R. Jr., Justin Clay. BS, East Carolina U., 1965, MEd, 1966; EdD, U. N.C., Greensboro, 1982; exec. mgmt. courses, Duke U. Tchr., coach Fayetteville (N.C.) Sr. High Sch., 1966; asst. football coach, head track and tennis coach Elon Coll., N.C., 1967-77, head football coach, 1977-81, dir. athletic scholarship fund, 1982, dir. corp. and ann. resources, 1983, coordinator Pride II Capital Campaign, 1984, assoc. dir. devel., 1985; asst. v.p. tng., nat. dir. tng. & pub. affairs Roche Biomed. Labs. Inc., Burlington, N.C., 1986—. Author: Intercollegiate History of Athletics and Elon College, 1982, American Football Coaches Guidebook to Championship Football Drills, 1985; contbg. author: 101 Winning Plays, 1977, Leadership Education: A Source Book, 1989; contbr. articles to profl. jours. Treas. Town of Elon Coll., 1984-87, mayor protem, 1988, mayor, 1990-94, 94—; convenor City County Govt. Assn., Alamance County, N.C., 1986—; mem. exec. bd. dirs. Cherokee Coun. Boy Scouts Am., 1986, Thomas E. Powell Jr. Biology Found., mem. exec. bd. Alamance Found.; mem. exec. bd. N.C. Health & Fitness Found; visitors Elon Coll.; mem. exec. com. Alamance County Ptnrs. in Edn.; bd. trustees Alamance County Habitat for Humanity, bd. govs. Named one of Outstanding Young Men Am., 1980, Internat. Men of Achievement, 1990, Cmty. Leaders Am., 1990, Mayors Hall of Fame, 1995; recipient Dwight D. Eisenhower award Nat. Football Hall of Fame, 1980, 81, Nat. Collegiate Football Championship award Eastman Kodak, Meritorious Svc. award Tom Sawyer-Huck Finn Tennis Classic, 1986; named Nat. Football Coach of Yr., Nat. Assn. Intercollegiate Athletics, 1980, Elon Coll. Sports Hall of Fame, East Carolina U. Athletic Hall of Fame, 1991. Mem. Am. Football Coaches Assn., Phi Delta Kappa, Sigma Delta Psi. Avocations: writing, racquet sports, jogging. Home: Box 463 1322 Westbrook Ave Elon College NC 27244 Office: Roche Biomedical Labs Inc 430 Spring St Burlington NC 27215-5865

TOLLIVER, DON L., dean library and media services; b. Louisville, Ill., Mar. 11, 1938; s. Edgar and Alene (Blair) T.; m. Ramona Sue Weber, Aug. 16, 1964. BS in Edn., Ea. Ill. U., 1960, MS in Edn. Adminstrn., 1964; MLS, U. Ill., 1967; PhD in Adminstrn., Edn. Psychology, Purdue U., 1970. Instr. edn. media Purdue U., Lafayette, Ind., 1965-69, asst. head instrn. media research, 1969-70, head instrnl. media research, 1970-74; dean library U. Wis., Whitewater, 1974-80; asst. dir. libraries U. Mich., Ann Arbor, 1980-84; dean librs. Kent State U., Ohio, 1984—. Mem. ALA, Spl. Library Assn., Assn. Ednl. and Communication Technologists. Office: Dean Kent State U Library Kent OH 44242

TOLLMAN, THOMAS ANDREW, librarian; b. Omaha, Mar. 14, 1939; s. James Perry and Elizabeth (McVey) T.; m. Teresa Ramírez, Jan. 4, 1964; children: James Daniel, Lisa Maria. BA, Carleton Coll., 1960; MA, U. Chgo., 1965, U. Minn., 1974; postgrad., U. Ariz., 1977-79. Admissions counselor Carleton Coll., Northfield, Minn., 1960-62; asst. dean of coll. Carleton Coll., Northfield, 1968-73; reference libr. N.W. Mo. State U., Maryville, 1974-77; adj. instr. U. Ariz., Tucson, 1977-79; chair libr. reference dept. U. Nebr., Omaha, 1979-88, assoc. prof., reference libr., 1988—; sr. lectr. Fulbright Commn., Quito, Ecuador, 1991. Contbr. articles to profl. jours. Trustee Dundee Presbyn. Ch., Omaha, 1987-93, deacon, 1981-86; vol. U.S. Peace Corps., Colombia, 1962-64. Mem. ALA, Nebr. Libr. Assn., Spl. Libr. Assn., Assn. Coll. and Rsch. Librs., Reference and Adult Svcs. Div., Reforma. Avocations: running, bicycling. Home: 2121 S 84 St Omaha NE 68124-2222 Office: U Nebr Omaha NE 68182-0237

TOLMIE, DONALD MCEACHERN, lawyer; b. Moline, Ill., June 21, 1928; s. Ronald Charles and Margaret Blaine (Kerr) T.; m. Joann Phillis Swanson, Aug. 15, 1953; children: David M., John K., Paul N. AB, Augustana Coll., 1950; JD, U. Ill., 1953. Bar: Ill. 1953, Va. 1968. Atty. Pa. R.R., Chgo., 1953-60; asst. gen. soliciter Pa. R.R., Phila., 1961-67; gen. atty. Norfolk & Western, Roanoke, Va., 1968; gen. solicter Norfolk & Western, Roanoke, 1968-75, gen. counsel, 1975-82; gen. counsel Norfolk (Va.) So. Corp., 1982, v.p., gen. counsel, 1983-89. Mem. Va. Bar Assn., U.S Supreme Ct. Bar Assn., Harbor Club, Cedar Point Club. Lutheran. Home: 912 Hanover Ave Norfolk VA 23508-1227

TOLMIE, KENNETH DONALD, artist, author; b. Halifax, N.S., Can., Sept. 18, 1941; s. Archibald and Mary Evelyn (Murray) T.; m. Ruth Mackenzie, Aug. 11, 1962; children: Sarah Katherine, Jane Marianna. B.F.A., Mt. Allison U., 1962. Proprietor Tolmie Gallery, Mahone Bay, N.S.; Chmn. Visual Arts Ottawa, 1975-76; founding mem. Bridgetown and Area Hist. Soc., James House Mus.; bd. dirs. Art Gallery N.S. Author: (children's book) Tale of an Egg, 1974, (art book) A Rural Life: An Artist's Portrait, 1986; 3 TV documentary films produced on his work by CBC and by TV-Ont.; one-man shows include Dorothy Cameron Gallery, Toronto, 1963, Beckett Gallery, Hamilton, 1986, Kaspar Gallery, Toronto, 1988; Mt. Allison Univ. solo cross Can. touring exbn. Bridgewater Series, 1982-84; group shows include Banfer Gallery, N.Y.C., 1963, Nat. Gallery Can., Watercolors Prints and Drawing, 1964, 66, London Art Mus., Ont., 1966, Can. Soc. Graphic Art, 1973, Art Gallery N.S., 1980, 81, N.S. Art Bank, 1981; represented in permanent collections Nat. Gallery Can., Ottawa, Montreal Mus. Fine Arts, N.S. Art Bank, Art Gallery N.S., Confedn. Centre for Arts, Hirshhorn Collection, Washington, Owens Art Gallery, Mt. Allison U., Dofasco Ltd., Husky Oil Ltd., Procter & Gamble Ltd., Slater Steels Ltd., Crownx Ltd. Mem. Writer's Union Can., Writers Fedn. N.S., Visual Arts N.S. Address: PO Box 96 16 Orchard St, Mahone Bay, NS Canada B0J 2E0

TOLOR, ALEXANDER, psychologist, educator; b. Vienna, Austria, Oct. 21, 1928; s. Stanley and Josephine (Kellner) T.; m. Belle Simon, Sept. 2, 1951; children: Karen Beth, Lori Ann, Diana Susan. B.A., NYU, 1949, M.A., 1950, Ph.D., 1954. Diplomate Am. Bd. Profl. Psychologists. Grad. asst. NYU, 1950-52; intern Neurol. Inst., N.Y.C., 1952-53; clin. psychologist Neurol. Inst., 1953-55; sr. clin. psychologist Inst. of Living, Hartford, Conn., 1957-59; dir. psychol. services Fairfield Hills Hosp., Newtown, Conn., 1959-64; clinic dir. Kennedy Center, Bridgeport, Conn., 1964-65; dir. Inst. Human Devel., Fairfield U., 1965-77, assoc. prof. psychology, 1965-68, research prof. psychology, 1968-75, prof. psychology, 1975-89, dir. school psychology div., 1975-77, dir. sch. and applied psychology program, 1982-86, prof. emeritus, 1989—; practice psychology Danbury, Conn., 1960—; clin. instr. psychology Yale U., 1963-67; cons. West Haven VA Hosp., 1962-66, Bridgeport Bd. Edn., Silver Hill Found., 1972-75, Fairfield Hills Hosp., 1973-94, Hallbrooke Hosp., 1975-92. Author: (with H.C. Schulberg) An Evaluation of the Bender-Gestalt Test, 1963, (with G.G. Brannigan) Research and Clinical Applications of the Bender-Gestalt Test, 1980, (with M. Deignan) Adjustment Problems in Children, 1984; editor: Effective Interviewing, 1985; adv. editor Jour. Cons. and Clin. Psychology; cons. editor Personality: An Internat. Jour.; contbr. articles to profl. jours. Served to 1st lt. USAF, 1955-57. Fellow Am. Psychol. Assn., Soc. Personality Assessment; mem. Conn. Psychol. Assn. (mem. council 1964, pres. 1984), Eastern Psychol. Assn., Psi Chi, Delta Phi Alpha, Beta Lambda Sigma, Phi Delta Kappa. Home: 6 Brittania Dr Danbury CT 06811-2606 Office: 57 North St Ste 309 Danbury CT 06810-5628

TOLSON, JOHN J., editor; b. Montgomery, Ala., June 28, 1948; s. John J. and Margaret Jordan (Young) T.; m. Mary Irene Bradshaw; 1 child, Benjamin Bradshaw. AB, Princeton U., 1972; MA, Am. Univ., 1977. Instr. English and history Asheville (N.C.) Sch., 1972-74, Landon Sch., Bethesda, Md., 1974-77; free-lance writer, critic Washington, 1977-81; lit. editor The Wilson Quar., Washington, 1981-89, editor, 1989—. Author: Pilgrim in the Ruins: A Life of Walker Percy (So. Book Nonfiction award 1992-93, Hugh Holman prize for best work of criticism and scholarship 1992), 1992; contbr. essays and criticism to The New Republic, The Nation, The Scis., Washington Post, The Times Lit. Supplement, Internat. Economy and other publs. Independent Scholars fellow NEH, Washington, 1989. Mem. Nat. Book

Critics Circle. Home: 2010 N Lincoln St Arlington VA 22207-3729 Office: Wilson Quarterly 901 D St SW Washington DC 20024-2169

TOLTZIS, ROBERT JOSHUA, cardiologist; b. Phila., May 6, 1949; s. Louis and Shirley (Weiner) T.; m. Catharina Kolek, 1989; 1 child, Alexander Jonah. AB, Temple U., 1970; MD, Hahnemann U., 1974. Cert. Am. Bd. Internal Medicine, Cardiovascular Diseases. Intern, resident, fellow Peter Bent Brigham Hosp., Boston, 1974-79, Children's Hosp., Boston, 1974-79; chief of service in cardiology Nat. Heart Lung and Blood Inst., Bethesda, Md., 1980-82; assoc. prof. clin. medicine and pediatrics U. Cin., 1982—; cardiologist Christ Hosp., Cin., 1988—; fellow in medicine Harvard U., Boston, 1974-79, instr. 1979-80; dir. coronary care unit U. Hosp., Cin., 1982-88, dir. electrocardiography lab., 1988—. Fellow Am. Coll. Cardiology (coun. clin. cardiology), Am. Heart Assn., Am. Coll. Chest Physicians; mem. Am. Soc. Echocardiography, Alpha Omega Alpha. Home: 7720 Annesdale Dr Cincinnati OH 45243 Office: 2123 Auburn Ave Apt 139 Cincinnati OH 45219-2966

TOMAC, STEVEN WAYNE, state senator, farmer; b. Hettinger, N.D., Nov. 23, 1953; s. Robert and Betty Ann (Schmidt) T. BS, N.D. State U., 1976. Loan officer Bank of N.D., Bismarck, 1976-79; v.p. 1st Southwest Bank, Mandan, N.D., 1979-80; dir. mktg. N.D. Dept. Agr., Bismarck, 1980-81; exec. dir. N.D. Grain Growers, Bismarck, 1981-86; rodeo clown PRCA, Colorado Springs, 1971—; farmer/rancher St. Anthony, N.D., 1982—; state rep. State of N.D., Bismarck, 1986-90, state senator, 1990—. Mem. Accredited Rural Appraisers, Am. Soc. Farm Mgrs. and Rural Appraisers (appraiser 1981—). Democrat. Roman Catholic. Home: RR 1 Box 36 Saint Anthony ND 58566-9613

TOMAINO, MICHAEL THOMAS, lawyer; b. Utica, N.Y., Dec. 1, 1937; s. Joseph Michael and Rosemary (Fragetta) T.; m. Beverly A. Meyer, Aug. 29, 1959; children—Mark, Matthew, Andrea, Michael, Julie. B.A., Holy Cross Coll., 1959; J.D., Cornell U., 1962. Bar: N.Y. 1962, U.S. Dist. Ct. (so., ea., no. and we. dists.) N.Y., U.S. Ct. Appeals (2d., 4th and 5th cirs.), U.S. Supreme Ct. 1975. Assoc. Donovan, Leisure, Newton & Irvine, N.Y.C., 1962-64; assoc. Nixon, Hargrave, Devans & Doyle, Rochester, N.Y., 1964-70, ptnr., 1971—; dir. Otetiana Coun. Boy Scouts Am., Rochester, N.Y., 1987—. Past pres., hon trustee Aquinas Inst. of Rochester, 1976—; bd. dirs. Rochester Eye Inst., 1984—. Mem. ABA, N.Y. State Bar Assn. (past chmn. com. on pub. utility law), Monroe County Bar Assn., Am. Coll. Trial Lawyers, N.Y. Telephone Assn. Republican. Roman Catholic. Avocations: squash; tennis; sailing. Home: 135 Taylor Rd Honeoye Falls NY 14472-9732 Office: Nixon Hargrave Devans & Doyle Clinton Sq PO Box 1051 Rochester NY 14603-1051

TOMAN, MARY ANN, federal official; b. Pasadena, Calif., Mar. 31, 1954; d. John James and Mary Ann Zajec T.; m. Milton Allen Miller, Sept. 10, 1988; 1 child, Mary Ann III. BA with honors, Stanford U., 1976; MBA, Harvard U., 1981. Mgmt. cons. Bain and Co., Boston, 1976-77; brand mgr. Procter & Gamble Co., Cin., 1977-79; summer assoc. E.F. Hutton, N.Y.C., 1980; head corp. planning The Burton Group, PLC, London, 1981-84; pres., founder Glendair Ltd., London, 1984-86; pres. London Cons. Group, London, Beverly Hills, Calif., 1987-88; mem. U.S. Presdl. Transition Team Bus. and Fin., 1988-89; dep. asst. sec. commerce, automotive affairs, consumer goods U.S. Dept. Commerce, Washington, 1989-93; commr., chmn. L.A. Indsl. Devel. Authority, 1993-95; dep. treas. State of Calif., Sacramento, 1995—; bd. dirs. U.S. Coun. of Devel. Fin. Agencies, 1994—. Founder, chair Stanford U. Fundraising, London, 1983-88; chair Reps. Abroad Absentee Voter Registration, London, 1983-88; bd. dirs. Harvard Bus. Sch. Assn., London, 1984-87; vol. Bush-Quayle Campaign, 1988; trustee Bath Coll., Eng., 1988—; apptd. by Gov. Wilson to State of Calif. Econ. Devel. Adv. Coun., 1994—. Mem. Stanford Club U.K. (pres. 1983-88), Harvard Club N.Y., Harvard Club Washington. Roman Catholic. Home: 604 N Elm Dr Beverly Hills CA 90210 Office: State Treasurers Office 915 Capitol Mall Rm 110 Sacramento CA 95814

TOMAN, STEPHEN E., educational publishing company executive; married. BBA, St. John's U., 1964. Pres., chief exec. officer Grolier Enterprises Inc., 1983; group v.p. direct mail Grolier Inc., Danbury, Conn., 1986-88, exec. v.p. U.S. and Can. sales mktg. ops., 1988, now sr. exec. v.p. With USMCR, 1966-72. Office: Grolier Inc Sherman Turnpike Danbury CT 06816

TOMANIC, JOSEPH P(AUL), research scientist; b. Danbury, Conn., Nov. 18, 1943; s. Joseph A. and Helen U. (Drusik) T.; m. Helen G. Brown Gannon, Apr. 15, 1967; children: Sharon A., Karen S. BEE, U. Bridgeport, 1972. Electronic technician Manson Labs., Wilton, Conn., 1964-66; assoc. rsch. scientist Schlumberger-Doll Research, Ridgefield, Conn., 1966—. Contbr. articles to profl. jours. Mem. Inst. Elec. and Electronic Engrs. Roman Catholic. Home: 36 Deepwood Dr Bethel CT 06801 Office: Schlumberger-Doll Research Old Quarry Rd Ridgefield CT 06877-4108

TOMAR, RUSSELL HERMAN, pathologist, educator, researcher; b. Philadelphia, Pa., Oct. 19, 1937; s. Julius and Ethel (Weinreb) T.; m. Karen J. Kent, Aug. 29, 1965; children: Elizabeth, David. BA in Journalism, George Washington U., 1959, MD, 1963. Diplomate Am. Bd. Pathology, Am. Bd. Allergy and Immunology, Am. Bd. Immunopathology. Intern Barnes Hosp., Washington U. Sch. Medicine, 1963-64, resident in medicine, 1964-65; asst. prof. medicine SUNY, Syracuse, 1971-79, assoc. prof., 1979-88, assoc. prof. microbiology, 1980-84, prof., 1984-88, asst. prof. pathology, 1974-76, assoc. prof., 1976-83, prof., 1983-88, dir. immunopathology, 1974-88, attending physician immunodeficiency clinic, 1982-88, acting dir. microbiology, 1977-78, 82-83, interim dir. clin. pathology, 1986-87; dir. clin. labs., prof. pathology and lab. medicine U. Wis. Ctr. for Health Scis., Madison, 1988—; dir. Div. Lab. Medicine U. Wis. Ctr. for Health Scis., Madison, 1988—; past mem. numerous coms. SUNY, Syracuse, U. Wis., Madison; mem. exec. com., mem. med. cons. AIDS Task Force Cen. N.Y., 1983-88. Assoc. editor Jour. Clin. Lab. Analysis; contbr. articles, rev. to profl. jours. Mem. pub. health com. Onondaga County Med. Soc., 1987-88. Lt. comdr. USPHS, 1965-67. Allergy and Immunology Div. fellow U. Pa. Fellow Coll. Am. Pathologists (diagnostics immunology rsch. com. 1993—, standards com. 1995—), Am. Soc. Clin. Pathology (com. on continuing edn. immunopathology 1985-91, pathology data presentation com. 1976-79), Am. Acad. Allergy (penicillin hypersensitivity com. 1973-77); mem. AAAS, Am. Assn. Immunologists, Am. Assn. Pathology, Acad. Clin. Lab. Physicians and Scientists (com. on rsch. 1979-81, chairperson immunology 1979), Clin. Immunology Soc. (coun., chair clin. lab. immunology com. 1991—). Office: U Wis Clinical Sci Ctr Rm B4/251 Madison WI 53792-2472

TOMAS, JEROLD F. V., business executive, management consultant; b. N.Y.C.; s. Samuel and Jean Tomas. BS, U. Bridgeport, 1968; MS, U. Mass., 1971, D in Mgmt. and Organizational Behaviour, 1973. Grantee in exec. devel. Ford Found. and Carnegie Found., 1970-73; fellow Ctr. for Leadership, 1970-73; dir. edn. Young Pres.'s Orgn., N.Y.C., 1975-77; chief rsch. scientist Mgmt. Decision Lab., Grad. Sch. Bus. Administrn. NYU, 1977; officer, sr. cons., mgmt. and orgn. Morgan Guaranty Trust Co. of N.Y., N.Y.C., 1978-80; corp. mgmt. resources planning Pfizer, Inc., N.Y.C., 1981-82; pres. TOMACO, Inc., Cons., N.Y.C., 1983—; mem. sr. faculty advanced mgmt. program Rutgers U., 1984—. Contbr. articles to profl. jours. Football scholar U. Bridgeport.

TOMASH, ERWIN, retired computer equipment company executive; b. St. Paul, Nov. 17, 1921; s. Noah and Milka (Ehrlich) T.; m. Adelle Ruben, July 31, 1943; children: Judith Sarada Tomash Diffenbaugh, Barbara Ann Tomash, Bussa. B.S., U. Minn. 1943; M.S., U. Md., 1950. Instr. elec. engring. U. Minn., 1946; assoc. dir. computer devel. Univac div. Remington Rand Corp., St. Paul, 1947-51; dir. West Coast ops. Univac div. Sperry Rand Corp., L.A., 1953-55; pres. Telemeter Magnetics, Inc., L.A., 1956-60; v.p. Ampex Corp., L.A., 1961; founder, pres. Dataproducts Corp., L.A. 1962-71; chmn. bd. Dataproducts Corp., 1971-80; chmn. bd. & dir. Newport Corp., Irvine, Calif., 1982-94; chmn. exec. com. Dataproducts Corp., 1980-89; chmn. Tomash Cons., Inc., cons. to high tech. industry; chmn. bd. Tomash Pubs., pubs. computer and physics works; dir. Supershuttle Internat., Inc., L.A., Pasqua Inc., San Francisco. Founder, chmn. bd. trustees Charles Babbage Found., U. Minn.; dir. and nat. gov. Coro Found., L.A.; trustee Computer Mus., Boston; dir. L.A. Ednl. Partnership. Served to capt.

Signal Corps AUS, 1943-46. Decorated Bronze Star; recipient Outstanding Grad. award U. Minn., 1983. Mem. IEEE (sr., computer entrepeneur award 1988), Assn. Computing Machinery, Am. Soc. for Technion (exec. v.p., dir.), History of Sci. Soc., Soc. for History of Tech., Assn. Internationale du Bibliophile, Grolier Club. Home: 110 S Rockingham Ave Los Angeles CA 90049-2514

TOMASI, DONALD CHARLES, architect; b. Sacramento, Calif., Oct. 24, 1956; s. Thomas M. and Anita (Migliavacca) T.; m. Loretta Elaine Goveia, Feb. 1, 1986; children: Jeffrey, Genna, Michael. AB in Architecture with honors, U. Calif., Berkeley, 1979; MArch, U. Wash., 1982. Registered architect, Calif. Project mgr. Robert Wells and Assocs., Seattle, 1982-84, Milbrandt Architects, Seattle, 1984, T.M. Tomasi Architects, Santa Rosa, Calif., 1984-86; prin. Tomasi Architects, Santa Rosa, 1986-93; Tomasi Lawry Coker De Silva Architecture, Santa Rosa, 1993—. Grad. Leadership Santa Rosa, 1992; mem. design rev. com. Sonoma County, 1988-90; chmn. Santa Rosa Design Rev. Bd., 1990—. Recipient Honor award Coalition for Adequate Sch. Housing, 1991, 93, Merit award, 1991. Mem. AIA (chpt. bd. dirs. 1990-91, Merit award 1986). Avocations: snow skiing, wine, travel.

TOMASI, THOMAS B., cell biologist, administrator; b. May 24, 1927; s. Thomas B. and Ivis (Ratazzi) T.; children—Barbara, Theodore, Anne. A.B., Dartmouth Coll., Hanover, N.H., 1950; M.D., U. Vt., Burlington, 1954; Ph.D., Rockefeller U., 1965. Intern, resident, chief resident Columbia Presbyn. Hosp., N.Y.C., 1954-58, instr. medicine, 1958-60; prof., chmn. div. exptl. medicine U. Vt., Burlington, 1960-65; prof. medicine, dir. immunology SUNY, Buffalo, 1965-73; prof., chmn. immunology dept. Mayo Med. Sch., Rochester, Minn., 1973-81; dir. Cancer Ctr., Disting. Univ. prof., chmn. dept. cell biology U. N. Mex., Albuquerque, 1981-86; pres., CEO Roswell Park Cancer Inst., Buffalo, 1986—, chmn. dept. molecular medicine. Author: The Immune System of Secretions, 1976; contbr. over 200 articles to profl. jours. Served with USN, 1945-46. Mem. Am. Soc. Cell Biology, Am. Assn. Immunologists, Am. Assn. Cancer Research, Am. Soc. Clin. Investigation, Am. Fedn. Clin. Research, Assn. Am. Physicians. Roman Catholic. Avocations: skiing, tennis, hunting, fishing, gardening. Home: 7980 E Quaker St Orchard Park NY 14127-2017 Office: Roswell Park Cancer Inst Elm and Carlton Sts Buffalo NY 14263

TOMASKO, MARK DANIEL, lawyer; b. N.Y.C., June 22, 1948; s. Daniel Paul and Ruth (Syckelmoore) T.; m. Nancy Ruth Norton, Nov. 16, 1985. BA, Yale U., 1970; JD, U. Pa., 1973. Bar: N.Y. 1974. Assoc. atty. Chadbourne, Parke, Whiteside & Wolf, N.Y.C., 1973-78; corp. counsel Singer Co., N.Y.C. and Stamford, Conn., 1978-83, group counsel, Stamford, 1983-86; v.p., gen. counsel, sec. Esselte Bus. Systems Inc., Garden City, N.Y., 1986—. Mem. ABA, Assn. of Bar of City of N.Y., Am. Soc. Corp. Secs., Am. Corp. Counsel Assn., Univ. Club, Grolier Club.

TOMASSINI, LAWRENCE ANTHONY, accounting educator, consultant; b. San Francisco, June 12, 1945; s. Charles Pasquale and Flora Joan (Novelli) T.; m. Eve Collier, July 20, 1982; children: Nicholas Charles, Anthony Domenic, Katherine Joiner. BS, U. Santa Clara, 1967; MS, UCLA, 1969, PhD, 1974. CPA, Tex. Asst. prof. acctg. U. Tex., Austin, 1973-78, assoc. prof., 1978-83, prof., 1983-85, John Arch White prof. bus., 1985-86, Peat, Marwick, Mitchell & Co. Centennial prof. acctg., 1986-87; Arthur Young Disting. prof. acctg. U. Ill., Urbana-Champaign, 1987-90, Ernst and Young Disting. prof. acctg., 1990-93; prof., Ernst & Young scholar, chmn. dept. acct. and MIS Ohio State U., Columbus, 1993—; bd. dirs. Fermentations Inc., Austin. Contbr. articles to profl. jours. Grantee for Doctoral Dissertation AICPAs, 1971-72. Mem. AICPA, Am. Acctg. Assn. (fellowship 1971-73), Ill. Soc. CPAs, Soc. for Judgment and Decision Making (founder). Avocations: collecting fine wines, antiques, golf. Home: 2035 Tremont Rd Upper Arlington OH 43221 Office: Ohio State U Dept Acctg & MIS 1775 College Rd Columbus OH 43210-1399

TOMASSON, HELGI, dancer, choreographer, dance company executive; b. Reykjavik, Iceland, 1942; m. Marlene Rizzo, 1965; children: Kristinn, Erik. Student, Sigridur Arman, Erik Bidsted, Vera Volkova, Sch. Am. Ballet, Tivoli Pantomime Theatre, Copenhagen. With Joffrey Ballet, 1961-64; prin. dancer Harkness Ballet, 1964-70, N.Y.C. Ballet, 1970-85; artistic dir. San Francisco Ballet, 1985—, also dir. Debut with Tivoli Pantomime Theatre, 1958; created roles in A Season of Hell, 1967, Stages and Reflections, 1968, La Favorita, 1969, The Goldberg Variations, 1971, Symphony in Three Movements, 1972, Coppélia, 1974, Dybbuk Variations, 1974, Chansons Madecasses, 1975, Introduction and Allegro, 1975, Union Jack, 1976, Vienna Waltzes, 1977; choreographer Theme and Variations, Polonaise, Op. 65, 1982, Ballet d'Isoline, 1983, Menuetto (for N.Y.C. Ballet) 1984, Beads of Memory, 1985, Swan Lake, 1988, Handel-a Celebration, 1989, Sleeping Beauty, 1990, Romeo and Juliet, 1994, others. Decorated Knight Order of Falcon (Iceland), 1974, Comdr. Order of Falcon, 1990; recipient Silver medal Internat. Moscow Ballet Competition, 1969, Golden Plate award Am. Acad. Achievement, 1992, Dance Mag. award, 1992. Office: care San Francisco Ballet 455 Franklin St San Francisco CA 94102-4438*

TOMASULO, VIRGINIA MERRILLS, retired lawyer; b. Belleville, Ill., Feb. 10, 1919; d. Frederick Emerson and Mary Eckert (Turner) Merrills; m. Nicholas Angelo Tomasulo, Sept. 30, 1952; m. Harrison I. Anthes, March 5, 1988. BA, Wellesley Coll., 1940; LLB (now JD), Washington U., St. Louis, 1943. Bar: Mo. 1942, U.S. Ct. Appeals (D.C. cir.) 1958, Mich. 1974, U.S. Dist. Ct. (ea. dist.) Mo. 1943, U.S. Supreme Ct. 1944, U.S. Tax Ct. 1974, U.S. Ct. Appeals (6th cir.) 1976. Atty. Dept. of Agr., St. Louis and Washington, 1943-48, Office of Solicitor, Chief Counsel's Office, IRS, Washington and Detroit, 1949-75; assoc. Baker & Hostetler, Washington, 1977-82, ptnr. 1982-89, of counsel, 1989, ret., 1989. Sec., S.W. Day Care Assn., Washington, 1971-73; mem. fin. com. Residents Assn. Village on the Green, Longwood, Fla. Mem. ABA, Mo. Bar, Fed. Bar, Village on the Green Residents Assn. (fin. com.), Wellesley Club (Ctrl. Fla.). Episcopalian. Home: 570 Village Pl Apt 300 Longwood FL 32779-6037

TOMASZEWSKI, JAMES M., electronics executive; b. 1948. BA in Fin. and Acctg., Wayne State U., 1973, MS in Fin. and Econs., 1975. With J. L. Hudson Co., Detroit, 1970-82; v.p., contr. Diamond's Dept. Store, Phoenix, 1982-84, Filene's, Boston, 1985-87; sr. v.p., CFO Filene's Basement, Boston, 1985-87; v.p., CFO Lechmere, Woburn, Mass., 1987-88, sr. v.p., CFO, 1988-92, exec. v.p. retail ops., bd. dirs., 1992—. Office: Lechmere Inc 275 Wildwood St Woburn MA 01801-6809

TOMAZINIS, ANTHONY RODOFLOS, city planning educator; b. Larissa, Greece, June 24, 1929; came to U.S., 1956, naturalized, 1966; s. Rodolfos A. and Christofily (Papamargaritou) T.; m. JoAnn R. Frank, June 24, 1962; children: Christina, Marina, Alexis. BCE, Assoc. Schs. Nat. Tech. U. Greece, 1952; M of City Planning, Ga. Inst. Tech., 1959; PhD in Planning, U. Pa., 1963. Mem. faculty U. Pa., Phila., 1962—; assoc. prof. city planning, 1966-77, prof. city and regional planning and civil engring., 1977—, chmn. transp. research group, inst. environ. studies, 1969-79, dir. Transp. Studies Center, 1969-79, chmn. univ.-wide program in transp. Transp. Studies Center, 1977—, chmn. faculty senate, 1984-87; chmn. grad. liberal studies program U. Pa., 1987-92; chmn. dynamics of orgn. U. Pa., Phila., 1990—; chmn. dept. city and regional planning dept. U. Pa., 1992—; pres. A.R. Tomazinis & Assocs., Inc., 1977-90; pres. Arista Found. Inc., 1991—, chmn. dept. city and regional planning, 1993—; cons. Inst. for Internat. Edn., 1991-92; cons. transp. and urban planning; pres. ARISTA Found., 1991—; transp. planning cons. Del. Valley Regional Commn., 1965-72, Doxiadis & Assocs., Athens, Greece, 1961-64, OECD, Paris, 1970-74, Govt. Iran, 1976; mem. travel forecasting com. transp. Rsch. Bd.; Fulbright prof. city planning U. Paris, 1973-74; cons. Institut de Recherche de Transports, Paris, 1973-74. Served with Greek Armed Forces, 1953-54. Decorated medal of Meritorious Acts King of Greece, 1949. Mem. Am. Inst. Cert. Planners, Inst. Transp. Engrs. (assoc. editor Jour. Advanced Transp., Transp. Planning and Tech.), Am. Hellenic League (Phila. pres. 1967-71, 81-85, dir. 1971-80), AAAS, Regional Sci. Assn., Am. Soc. Planning Ofcls., Univ. City Arts League, Fedn. Am. Hellenic Socs. of Greater Phila. (pres. 1977-79). Club: Hellenic University. Home: 379 Montgomery Ave Wynnewood PA 19096-1718 Office: U Pa Translab 3400 Walnut St Philadelphia PA 19104-6208 *What we call success in life is indeed relative to what we want in life. My deep commitment to city planning led me to seek gratification in the process of solving urban problems, planning for new cities and sections of older cities, and in educating the young and aspiring planners. Searching not for convention or compromise, the stress is on innovation and accomplishment. What others call success is for me simply a struggle to achieve the best solution possible to each given problem.*

TOMBAUGH, CLYDE WILLIAM, astronomer, educator; b. Streator, Ill., Feb. 4, 1906; s. Muron D. and Adella Pearl (Chritton) T.; m. Patricia Irene Edson, June 7, 1934; children: Annette Roberta, Alden Clyde. AB, U. Kans., 1936, MA, 1939; DSc (hon.), No. Ariz. U., 1960. Asst. Lowell Obs., Flagstaff, Ariz., 1929, asst. astronomer, 1938; instr. sci. Ariz. State Coll., Flagstaff, 1943-45; vis. asst. prof. astronomy UCLA, 1945-46; astronomer Aberdeen Ballistics Labs. Annex/White Sands Missile Range, Las Cruces, N.Mex., 1946—, chief optical measurement sect., 1948, chief research and evaluation br. planning dept. Flight Determination div., 1948-53, chief investigator search for natural satellites project, 1953-58, planetary astrophys. researcher, 1958—; research assoc. prof. astronomy N.Mex. State U., 1955-59, prof., 1965-73, prof. emeritus, 1973—, with planetary astrophysics research program, 1959—; discoverer planet Pluto, 1930, 1 globular star cluster, 1932, 5 galactic star clusters, variable stars, asteroids, clusters of galaxies; extensive search for distant planets and natural earth's satellites, studies in apparent distbn. extragalactic galaxies, geol. studies Mars' and Moon's surface features, prodn. telescope mirrors; mem. expdn. extension satellite research project, Quito, Ecuador, 1956-58; lectr. in field. Author: Out of the Darkness: the Planet Pluto, 1980; contbr. articles to profl. jours. Paul Harris fellow Rotary Internat.; Edward Emory Slosson scholar in sci. U. Kans., 1932-36; recipient Jackson-Guilt medal and gift Royal Astron. Soc. Eng., 1931, Fairbanks award Soc. Photog. Instrument Engrs., 1968, Bruce Blair award, 1965, Disting. Svc. citation U. Kans., 1966, Rittenhouse award, Phila., 1990, Golden Plate award Am. Acad. Achievement, 1991; named to White Sand Missile Range Hall of Fame, 1980, Internat. Space Hall of Fame; Clyde Tombaugh Scholars Endowment Fund established in his honor at N.Mex. State U., 1987. Fellow Soc. for Research on Meteorites, AIAA; mem. Am. Astron. Soc., Internat. Astron. Union, Astron. Soc. Pacific, Sigma Xi. Mem. Unitarian Ch. Avocations: grinding telescope mirrors, designing small telescopes. Home: PO Box 306 Mesilla Park NM 88047-0306

TOMBERLIN, WILLIAM G., principal. Prin. St. Simons (Ga.) Elem. Sch. Recipient DOE Elem. Sch. Recognition Program award, 1989-90. Office: St Simons Elem Sch 805 Ocean Blvd Saint Simons Island GA 31522

TOMBLIN, EARL RAY, state official; b. Logan County, W.Va., Mar. 15, 1952; s. Earl and Freda (Jarrell) T.; m. Joanne Jaeger, Sept. 8, 1979; 1 child, Brent Jaeger. BS, W.Va. U.; MBA, Marshall U.; postgrad., U. Charleston. Former sch. tchr., businessman; mem. W.Va. Ho. Dels., 1974-80; mem. W.Va. State Senate, 1980—, pres., 1995—; lt. gov. State of W.Va., Charleston; mem. exec. com. So. Legis. Conf. Former pres., bd. dirs. Appalachia Ednl. Lab., Inc.; mem. Logan County Devel. Authority. Mem. Kappa Alpha. Democrat. Presbyterian. Office: State Capitol #463M Charleston WV 25305 Address: PO Box 116 Chapmanville WV 25508*

TOMBLINSON, JAMES EDMOND, architect; b. Flint, Mich., Feb. 12, 1927; s. Carl and Edna Ethel (Spears) T.; m. Betsy Kinley, Sept. 26, 1959; children: Amy Lisa, John Timothy (dec.). B.Arch., U. Mich., 1951. Draftsman firms in Detroit, 1951-53, Flint, 1953-54, 56-57, San Francisco, 1955-56; field engr. Atlas Constructors, Morocco, 1952-53; architect Tomblinson, Harburn, & Assos., Inc. (and predecessors), Flint, 1958—; pres. Tomblinson, Harburn, & Assos., Inc. (and predecessors), 1969—; chmn. Mich. Bd. Registration Architects, 1975-77; sec. Mundy Twp. Planning Commn., 1974-85, Grand Blanc Planning Commn., City of Mich., 1985—; chmn., 1988—. Pres. Flint Beautification Commn., 1968-69; bd. dirs. Grand Blanc Beautification Commn., 1969-84; founding mem. bd. dirs. Flint YMCA, 1969-75, chmn. camp com., 1971-75; founding mem. bd. dirs. Flint Environ. Action Team, 1971-77, v.p., 1971-73; elder First Presbyn. Ch. Flint, 1983, trustee, 1986—; exec. com. Tall Pine council Boy Scouts Am., 1975—; bd. dirs. New Paths, pres., 1985-86. Served with AUS, 1945-46. Recipient various civic service awards. Fellow AIA; mem. Mich. Soc. Architects, Flint Area C. of C. Clubs: Greater Flint Jaycees (dir. 1957-63, v.p. 1963), Flint City, U. Mich. (pres. Flint chpt. 1980—). Lodge: Rotary (pres. 1984-85). Home: 686 Applegate Ln Grand Blanc MI 48439-1669 Office: Tomblinson Harburn Assocs 817 E Kearsley St Flint MI 48503-1913

TOMBRELLO, THOMAS ANTHONY, JR., physics educator, consultant; b. Austin, Tex., Sept. 20, 1936; s. Thomas Anthony and Jeanette Lilian (Marcuse) T.; m. Esther Ann Hall, May 30, 1957 (div. Jan. 1976); children: Christopher Thomas, Susan Elaine, Karen Elizabeth; m. Stephanie Carhart Merton, Jan. 15, 1977; 1 stepchild, Kerstin Arusha. B.A. in Physics, Rice U., 1958, M.A., 1960, Ph.D., 1961. Research fellow in physics Calif. Inst. Tech., Pasadena, 1961-62, 64-65, asst. prof. physics, 1965-67, assoc. prof., 1967-71, prof., 1971—; asst. prof. Yale U., New Haven, 1963; cons. in field; disting. vis. prof. U. Calif.-Davis, 1984; v.p., dir. tech. Schlumberger-Doll Rsch., Ridgefield, Conn., 1987-89; mem. U.S. V.P.'s Space Policy Adv. Bd., 1992. Assoc. editor Nuclear Physics, 1971-91, Applications of Nuclear Physics, 1980—; Radiation Effects, 1985-88, Nuclear Instruments and Methods B, 1993—. Recipient Alexander von Humboldt award von Humboldt Stiftung, U. Frankfurt, Federal Republic of Germany, 1984-85; NSF fellow Calif. Inst. Tech. 1961-62; A.P. Sloan fellow, 1971-73. Fellow Am. Phys. Soc.; mem. AAAS, Materials Rsch. Soc., Phi Beta Kappa, Sigma Xi. Avocations: reading, jogging. Democrat. Office: Calif Inst Tech Dept Physics Mail Code 20125 Pasadena CA 91125

TOMBROS, PETER GEORGE, pharmaceutical company executive; b. Oak Hill, W.Va., June 12, 1942; s. George P. and Mary Jane (Boliski) T.; m. Ann Riblett Cullen, June 12, 1965. BS, Pa. State U., 1964, MS, 1966; MBA, U. Pa., 1968. Mktg. asst. Pfizer Labs. div. Pfizer Inc., N.Y.C., 1968; asst. product mgr. Pfizer Inc., N.Y.C., 1969, product mgr., 1970-71, group product mgr., 1972-74, v.p. mktg., 1975-80; sr. v.p., gen. mgr. Roerig div. Pfizer Inc., N.Y.C., 1980-86; exec. v.p. Pfizer Pharms. div. Pfizer Inc., N.Y.C., 1986-90; v.p. corp. strategic planning, 1990-94; also corp. officer Pfizer Inc., N.Y.C.; pres., CEO Enzon, Inc., Piscataway, 1994—, also bd. dirs.; adv. panel Penn State BS/MBA, 1992—; alumni fellow Penn State, 1993; bd. dirs. Pfizer Pharm. Inc., Al Pharma Inc., Oslo, Norway. Bd. dirs. Am. Found. for Pharm. Edn., North Plainfield, N.J., 1980—, past chmn.; trustee Fisk U. Nashville, 1986—, Dominican Coll., Orangeburg, N.Y. 1987—; key campus exec. U. Pa., Phila., 1987—; trustee Bklyn. Borough Hall Restoration, 1987—; mem. corp. devel. com. Cen. Park Conservancy, N.Y.C.; bd. dirs. Vote America, 1990; bd. dirs. Cancer Care; hon. bd. mem. Reflex Sympathetic Dystrophy Assn. Am. Mem. Pharm. Mfrs. Assn. (past chmn. mktg. steering com.), Links Club, Blind Brook Club, Masons. Avocations: marathon running, golf, tennis, skiing, bridge.

TOMEI, MARISA, actress; b. Bklyn., Dec. 4, 1964. TV appearances include (series) A Different World, 1987, (films) Parker Kane, 1990; film appearances include: The Flamingo Kid, 1984, Playing for Keeps, 1986, Oscar, 1991, Zandalee, 1991, My Cousin Vinny, 1992 (Acad. award best supporting actress 1993), Chaplin, 1992, Untamed Heart, 1993, Equinox, 1993, The Paper, 1994, Only You, 1994, The Perez Family, 1994; theatre appearances include Slavs! Thinking About the Longstanding Problems of Virtue and Happiness, 1994. Office: William Morris Agy 151 S El Camino Dr Beverly Hills CA 90212-2704*

TOMEK, LAURA LINDEMANN, marketing executive; b. New Brunswick, N.J., Oct. 21, 1940; d. A. John and Jeanette (Lacey) Lindemann; m. Charles L. Tomek, Oct. 4, 1969 (div. Apr. 1990); 1 child, Gregory C. Student, U. Wis., Milw., 1958-59; BS in Mktg., U. Ariz., 1962. Market rsch. mgr. Procter & Gamble Inc., Cin., 1962-66; nat. buyer exec. tng. mgr., market rsch. analyst Sears, Roebuck & Co., Chgo., 1966-84; hdqrs. buyer Federated Dept. Stores, Chgo., 1984-85; v.p. O'Bryan Bros., Inc., Chgo., 1985-86; cons. Mktg. Connections, Chgo., 1986-88; regional sales mgr. Fabrican, Inc., Chgo., 1988-90; counsel Crouch & Fitzgerald, Oakbrook, Ill., 1991-93; with Little Switzerland Chgo., 1993-94; merchandising and mktg. cons. Mktg. Connections and Info., 1994—; mem. bd. judges Ray Coll. Design, Chgo., 1987-88, Internat. Fashion Group, 1979—. Mem. com. March of Dimes Ann. Corp. Fundraiser, Chgo., 1992. Mem. Internat. Fashion Group Assn. U. Ariz. Alumni (bd. dirs. 1990—), Lake Shore Ski Club, Snow Hawks Ski Club (banquet co-chair social com. 1991). Avocations: skiing, sailing, boating, travel, investments. Home: 675 Lake St Oak Park IL 60301

TOMEK, WILLIAM GOODRICH, agricultural economist; b. Table Rock, Nebr., Sept. 20, 1932; s. John and Ruth Genevieve (Goodrich) T. B.S., U. Nebr., 1956, M.A., 1957; Ph.D., U. Minn., 1961. Asst. prof. Cornell U., Ithaca, N.Y., 1961-66, NSF fellow, 1965, assoc. prof. agrl. econs., 1966-70, prof., 1970—, chmn. dept. agrl. econs., 1988-93; vis. econ. USDA, 1978-79; vis. fellow Stanford U., 1968-69, U. New Eng., Australia, 1988. Author: Agricultural Product Prices, 1990; editor: Am. Jour. Agrl. Econs., 1975-77; co-editor: Review of Futures Markets, 1993—; mem. editorial bd. Jour. Futures Markets, 1992—; contbr. articles to profl. jours. Served with U.S. Army, 1953-55. Recipient Earl Combs Jr. award Chgo. Bd. Trade Found. Mem. Am. Agrl. Econs. Assn. (pres. 1985-86), Am. Econ. Assn., Econometric Soc., Northeastern Agrl. Econs. Assn., Am. Agrl. Econs. Assn. (awards 1981, 89, fellow), Gamma Sigma Delta (rsch. award 1994). Democrat. Methodist. Office: Cornell U Warren Hall Ithaca NY 14853-7801

TOMIYASU, KIYO, consulting engineer; b. Las Vegas, Nev., Sept. 25, 1919; s. Yonema and Toyono (Kawamura) T.; m. Eiko Nakamizo, Aug. 31, 1947. B.S., Calif. Inst. Tech., 1940; M.S., Columbia U., 1941; M.E.S., Harvard U., 1947, Ph.D., 1948. Instr. Harvard U., 1948-49; head engring. sect. Sperry Gyroscope Co., Gt. Neck, N.Y., 1949-55; with GE, 1955-93; cons. engr. microwave techniques GE Valley Forge Space Ctr., Phila., 1969-93; with Martin Marietta Corp., Phila., 1993-95, Lockheed Martin Corp., Phila., 1995—. Author: The Laser Literature-An Annotated Guide, 1968; articles; patentee in field. Exec. bd. Friendship Hill Civic Assn., Paoli, Pa., 1972-73, pres., 1973. Recipient Steinmetz award Gen. Electric Co., 1977; Mgmt. and Data Systems fellow Martin Marietta Corp., 1993; established Tomiyasu Meml. ann. scholarship Calif. Inst. Tech., 1977. Fellow IEEE (life, hon. life mem. Microwave Theory and Techniques Soc. 1975, tech. activities bd., awards bd., publs. bd., bd. dirs. div IV 1985-86, ednl. activities bd. 1987-88, Microwave Career award, 1981, Centennial medal 1984, Geosci. and Remote Sensing Outstanding Svc. award 1986, Microwave Disting. Svc. award 1987); mem. Am. Phys. Soc. Patents. Home: 366 Hilltop Rd Paoli PA 19301-1211 Office: Lockheed Martin Corp PO Box 8048 Philadelphia PA 19101-8048

TOMJANOVICH, RUDOLPH, professional athletic coach; b. Hamtramck, Mich., Nov. 24, 1948. Scout Houston Rockets, 1981-83, asst. coach, 1983-92, head coach, 1992—. Coach NBA championship team, 1994. Office: Houston Rockets The Summit 10 Greenway Plz Houston TX 77024*

TOMKINS, ALAN, art director, production designer. Art dir.: (films) The Empire Strikes Back, 1980 (Academy award nomination best art direction 1980), The Curse of the Pink Panther, 1983, The Keep, 1983, Lassiter, 1984, Lifeforce, 1985, Haunted Honeymoon, 1986, High Spirits, 1988, A Dry White Season, 1989, (with Steve Spence) Heaven and Earth, 1991, (with Derek R. Hill) JFK, 1991, Natural Born Killers, 1994; prodn. designer: (films) National Lampoon's European Vacation, 1985, (TV movies) War and Remembrance, 1989. Office: care Art Directors Guild 11365 Ventura Blvd #315 Studio City CA 91604*

TOMKINS, CALVIN, writer; b. Orange, N.J., Dec. 17, 1925; s. Frederick and Laura (Graves) T.; m. Grace Lloyd Fanning, Sept. 11, 1948; children: Anne Graves, Susan Temple, Spencer; m. Judy Johnston, Nov. 11, 1961 (div. Feb. 1981); m. Susan Cheever, Oct. 1, 1981; 1 child, Sarah Liley Cheever; m. Dodie Kazanjian, May 28, 1988. B.A., Princeton U., 1948. Assoc. editor Newsweek mag., N.Y.C., 1955-57, gen. editor, 1957-59; staff writer The New Yorker, N.Y.C., 1960—. Author: The Bride and The Bachelors, 1965, Merchants and Masterpieces, 1970, Living Well Is the Best Revenge, 1971, Off the Wall, 1980, Post- to Neo-, 1988. Bd. dirs. Cunningham Dance Found., N.Y.C., 1963—. Served with USN. Guggenheim fellow, 1978. Mem. Authors League Am. Inc., Pen Am. Ctr. Club: Century (N.Y.C.). Home: 145 E 74th St New York NY 10021-3225 Office: New Yorker Magazine 20 W 43d St New York NY 10036

TOMKINS, FRANK SARGENT, physicist; b. Petoskey, Mich., June 24, 1915; s. Charles Frederick and Irene Eugenie (Gouin) T.; m. Mary Ann Lynch, Jan. 6, 1964; 1 son, Frank Sargent. B.S., Kalamazoo Coll., 1937; Ph.D. (Parke-Davis fellow), Mich. State U., 1941. Physicist Buick Aviation Engine Div., Melrose Park, Ill., 1941-42; scientist Manhattan Project U. Chgo., 1943-45; sr. scientist Argonne (Ill.) Nat. Lab., 1945—, group leader, 1944—; U.S. del. 2d Internat. Conf. on Peaceful Uses Atomic Energy, 1958; cons. Bendix Corp., Cin., 1963-69; assoc. Harvard Coll. Obs., 1978—; chmn. bd. Pegasus Industries, Inc. Contbr. articles to sci. jours. John Simon Guggenheim fellow Laboratoire Aime-Cotton, Bellevue, France, 1960-61; Sci. Rsc. Coun. fellow Imperial Coll., London, 1975; recipient Argonne Univs. Assn. Disting. Appointment, 1975-76, Kalamazoo Coll. Disting. Achievement award, 1990. Fellow Am. Phys. Soc., Optical Soc. Am. (William F. Meggers award 1977); mem. AAAS, Societe Francaise de Physique, N.Y. Acad. Scis., Sigma Xi. Home: 11714 S 83d Ave Palos Park IL 60464 Office: 9700 Cass Ave Lemont IL 60439-4801

TOMKOVICZ, JAMES JOSEPH, law educator; b. L.A., Oct. 10, 1951; s. Anthony Edward and Vivian Marion (Coory) T.; m. Nancy Louise Abboud, June 27, 1987; children: Vivian Rose, Michelle Evelene, Henry James. BA, U. So. Calif., 1973; JD, UCLA, 1976. Bar: Calif. 1976, U.S. Dist. Ct. (so. dist.) Calif., U.S. Ct. Appeals (9th and 10th cirs.), U.S. Supreme Ct. Law clk. to Hon. Edward J. Schwartz San Diego, 1976-77; law clk. to Hon. John M. Ferren Washington, 1977-78; atty. U.S. Dept. Justice, Washington, 1979-80; assoc. prof. law U. Iowa, Iowa City, 1982-86, prof., 1986—; vis. prof. U. Iowa, Iowa City, 1981, U. Mich., Ann Arbor, 1992; adj. prof. UCLA, 1981-82. Author: (casebook) Criminal Procedure, 2d edit., 1994; contbr. articles to profl. jours. Mem. Order of Coif, Phi Beta Kappa. Democrat. Roman Catholic. Avocations: running, tennis, creative writing. Office: U Iowa Coll Law Melrose & Byngton Iowa City IA 52242

TOMLIN, DONALD ROBERT, JR., real estate management company executive; b. Columbia, S.C., Dec. 19, 1947; s. Donald Robert and Frances (Patrick) T. B.S. in Bus. Mgmt., U. S.C.-Columbia, 1971. Pres. Columbia Mgmt. Corp., S.C., 1974-83; chmn. bd., chief exec. officer U.S. Capital Corp., Columbia, 1983—. Author: Making Time Sharing Work, 1975. Office: US Capital Corp 2730 Devine St Columbia SC 29205-2433

TOMLIN, LILY, actress; b. Detroit, 1939. Student, Wayne State U.; studied mime with Paul Curtis, studied acting with Peggy Feury. Appearances in concerts and colls. throughout U.S.; TV appearances include Lily Tomlin, CBS Spls., 1973, 81, 82; 2 ABC Spls., 1975, Edithann Animated Specials, ABC, 1994; formerly cast mem. The Music Scene, Laugh In; motion picture debut in Nashville, 1975 (N.Y. Film Critics award); also appeared in The Late Show, 1977, Moment by Moment, 1978, The Incredible Shrinking Woman, 1981, Nine to Five, 1980, All of Me, 1984, Big Business, 1987, Shadows and Fog, 1992, The Player, 1992, Short Cuts, 1993, The Beverly Hillbillies, 1993, And the Band Played On, HBO, 1993 (Best Supporting Actress Emmy nominee - Special, 1994); one-woman Broadway show Appearing Nitely, 1977 (Spl. Tony award), The Search for Signs of Intelligent Life in the Universe, 1985 (Drama Desk award, Outer Critics Circle award, Tony award 1986); recs. include This is a Recording, And That's The Truth, Modern Scream, On Stage. Recipient Grammy award 1971, 5 Emmy awards for CBS Spl. 1973, 81, Emmy award for ABC Spl. 1975.*

TOMLIN, PATRICK LESLIE, condominium development executive; b. Columbia, S.C., Jan. 12, 1949; s. Donald Leslie and Frances Marie (Patrick) T.; m. Sherryl Ann Johnson, Dec. 28, 1968; children: Leslie Ryann, Lindy Meredith. BS in Fin., U. S.C., 1971; MPH in Biostats., U. N.C., 1975. Statistician S.C. Dept. Health, Columbia, 1970-76; sr. v.p. Columbia Mgmt. Corp., 1977-80; exec. v.p. U.S. Capitol Corp., Columbia, 1981—, also bd. dirs.; bd. dirs. Resort Devel. Corp., Columbia. Republican. Presbyterian. Club: Summit (Columbia). Avocations: fishing, basketball. Home: 217 Cranewater Dr Columbia SC 29212-8215 Office: US Capital Corp 2730 Devine St Columbia SC 29205-2433

TOMLINSON, ALEXANDER COOPER, investment banker, consultant; b. Haddonfield, N.J., May 13, 1922; s. Alexander Cooper and Mary Cooper (Buzby) T.; m. Elizabeth Anne Brierley, Jan. 10, 1953 (div.); children: William Brierley, Deborah Kay, Alexander Cooper III; m. Margaret L. Dickey, Nov. 15, 1986. BS, Haverford Coll., 1943; postgrad., London Sch. Econs. and Polit. Sci., 1947-48; MBA, Harvard U., 1950; LLD (hon.), Haverford Coll., 1995. With Morgan Stanley & Co., N.Y.C., 1950-76, ptnr., 1958-76, mng. dir., 1970-76; dir., pres. Morgan Stanley Can. Ltd. div., Montreal, Que., 1972-76; chmn. exec. com. First Boston, Inc., N.Y.C., 1976-82, dir., 1976-88; pres. Nat. Planning Assn., Washington, 1982-85; exec. dir. Ctr. for Privatization, Washington, 1985-88; pres. Hungarian-Am. Enterprise Fund, Washington, 1990-93; chmn. Fund for Arts and Culture in Ctrl. and Ea. Europe, 1994—; bd. dirs. Preco Corp. Trustee Incorp Village, Cove Neck, N.Y., 1958-72, 76-82, Cold Spring Harbor Lab., 1976-84, Salisbury Sch., Conn., 1976-87, N.Y. Infirmary-Beekman Downtown Hosp., 1968-82, East Woods Sch., Oyster Bay, N.Y., 1962-70, Nature Conservancy, Long Island, N.Y., 1970-82, Carnegie Found. for Advancement Teaching, 1984-90; bd. mgrs. Haverford Coll., 1979-92; bd. dirs. Nat. Bldg. Mus., 1987-94, Nat. Planning Assn., 1982-90, Decatur House Coun., 1990-94; chmn. Am. Friends Can., Inc., 1982-91, Harvard Bus. Sch. Fund, 1981-83. Served to lt. USNR, 1943-46. Mem. Coun. on Fgn. Rels., Metropolitan Club (Washington), Links (N.Y.). Home: 3314 P St NW Washington DC 20007-2701

TOMLINSON, CHARLES WESLEY, JR., advertising executive; b. West Chester, Pa., Oct. 14, 1947; s. Charles Wesley and Kathryn Elizabeth (Madeira) T.; m. Kathy Anne Petersheim, June 7, 1969 (div.); 1 son, Alan Charles (dec. Apr. 1992); m. Carol A. Oldfield, Apr. 4, 1986; 1 stepchild, Christie. B.S. in Communications, Temple U., 1969. Announcer, then sales mgr., air personality sta. WCHE, West Chester, Pa., 1966-70; communications specialist West Chester Area Sch. Dist., 1970-71; freelance advt. cons., 1971-73; gen. mgr. sta. WCHE, 1973-75; gen. sales mgr. Sta. WJBR-AM/FM, Wilmington, Del., 1975-84; dir. mktg. svcs. Winner Group, Wilmington, 1984-93; dir. sales and mktg. Del. Today mag. Suburban Mktg. Assn., Wilmington, 1994—. Past mem. exec. com. United Fund Greater West Chester. Mem. Advt. Club Phila., Chester County Chambers Commerce Assn. (1st v.p. 1981-82, pres. 1982-84), C. of C. Greater West Chester (pres. 1977). Republican. Lodges: Masons, Elks (past exalted ruler). Office: 407 Homestead Dr West Chester PA 19382-8200

TOMLINSON, GEORGE HERBERT, retired industrial company research executive; b. Fullerton, La., May 2, 1912; emigrated to Can., 1914; s. George Herbert and Irene Loretta (Nourse) T.; m. Frances Fowler, July 17, 1937; children: Peter George, David Lester, Susan Margaret Tomlinson Goff. B.A., Bishop's U., 1931; Ph.D., McGill U., 1935; D.C.L. (hon.), Bishop's U., 1986. Chief chemist Howard Smith Chem. Ltd., Cornwall, Ont., Can., 1936-39; research dir. Howard Smith Paper Mills Ltd., Cornwall, 1939-61, Domtar Ltd., Montreal, Que., 1961-70; v.p. research and environ. tech. Domtar Ltd., 1970-77, sr. sci. adv., 1977-90. Contbr. articles to profl. jours. Recipient Gov. Gen.'s Gold medal, 1931; Laureate of UN Environ. Programme Global 500, June, 1987. Fellow Royal Soc. Can., Internat. Acad. Wood Sci., Chem. Inst. Can., TAPPI (dir. 1976-79, medal 1969, hon. life mem.); mem. Am. Chem. Soc. (emeritus), Can. Pulp and Paper Assn. (hon. life mem.), Chemists Club (N.Y.). Avocation. Patentee in field. Home: 920 Perrot Blvd N, Ile Perrot, PQ Canada J7V 3K1

TOMLINSON, GUS, biology educator; b. Bon Aqua, Tenn., Apr. 30, 1933; s. Clarence Doyle and Ina Mae (Hutcheson) T.; m. Opal Aline Bowman, May 10, 1952; children—Jeffrey Lynn, Jenifer Lynne, Tracey Eileen. BS in Math, George Peabody Coll., 1958; MA in Molecular Biology, Vanderbilt U., 1961, PhD, 1962; postgrad. (Nat. Cancer Inst. fellow), Swiss Fed. Inst., Zurich, Switzerland, 1963-64. Asst. prof. biology George Peabody Coll., Nashville, 1962-63; asso. prof. biology George Peabody Coll., 1964-67, prof., 1968-80, chmn. dept. biology, 1966-80, chmn. div. natural scis., 1967-80, dir. NSF summer insts., 1966, dir. sci. leadership devel. program, 1973-74, dir. instrnl. improvement implementation program, 1974—; prof. biology Tenn. State U., Nashville, 1980—; cons. project Reach High (Tenn.) and Project MAMOS, Mo., cardiovascular edn. Bapt. Hosp., Nashville, 1971—, U.S. Corps of Engrs., 1992-93. Contbr. articles to sci. jours. Served with AUS, 1953-55. Recipient Sci. Chair award, 1978, Sci. Leadership award, 1979; Nat. Med. Scis. rsch. grantee, 1965-70, NIH, NSF rsch. grantee, 1987-91. Fellow Tenn. Acad. Sci. (exec. com. 1970—, pres. 1987, editor jour. 1970-86, Disting. Svc. award 1989); mem. Southeastern Electron Microscopic Soc., Sigma Xi. Office: Tenn State U Arts and Scis 10th And Charlotte Ave Nashville TN 37203 *I have never met anyone from whom I could not learn.*

TOMLINSON, J. RICHARD, engineering services company executive; b. Newtown, Pa., Mar. 26, 1930; s. Robert K. and Margaret (Wright) T.; m. Barbara Elizabeth Brazill, Apr. 30, 1955; children: Karin Kathleen Tomlinson Pizzirola, Kimberly Ann Tomlinson Donahue. B.A., Swarthmore Coll., 1952; postgrad., George Washington U., 1952-53, U. Mich., 1955-57, Drexel Inst. Tech., 1954-57, Am. U., 1965. Mgmt. analyst Dept. State, Washington, 1952-53; with Old Republic Life Ins. Co., Washington, 1953-54; supr. financial analysis Ford Motor Co., Detroit, 1954-61; cons. McKinsey & Co., Washington, 1961-65; v.p. finance, dir. passenger svcs. Reading Co., Phila., 1965-69; v.p. finance Rollins Internat., Inc., 1969-71; exec. v.p. Amtrak, Washington, 1972-74; ptnr. L.T. Klauder and Assocs., 1974-75, 79-83; exec. v.p. Penn Central Transp. Co., 1975-78; pres. LTK Engring. Svcs., 1984-95. Named Man of Month, Phila. C. of C., 1977. Mem. Union League, Aronomink Golf and Country Club, Phila. Aviation Country Club. Home: 451 Inveraray Rd Villanova PA 19085-1139

TOMLINSON, JAMES FRANCIS, retired news agency executive; b. Long Beach, Calif., Oct. 18, 1925; s. Lilburn Jesse and Margaret (Roemer) T.; m. Sally JoAnne Ryan, Aug. 12, 1967; children—Elizabeth Anne, Victoria Alexandra. B.A., U. Va., 1950; student, Harvard U., Grad. Sch. Arts and Scis., 1950-51; grad., Advanced Mgmt. Program, Harvard U., 1977. With A.P., 1951-92; chief bur. A.P., Newark, 1957-63; bus. news editor A.P., N.Y.C., 1963-67; dep. treas. A.P., 1967-68, treas., 1968-87; v.p., 1972-92, sec., 1978-92, asst. to pres., 1987-92. Served with AUS, 1943-46, ETO. Mem. Phi Beta Kappa, Phi Eta Sigma. Clubs: N.Y. Athletic (N.Y.C.), Harvard (N.Y.C.). Home: 222 E 71st St New York NY 10021-5134

TOMLINSON, JAMES LAWRENCE, mechanical engineer; b. Detroit, Sept. 12, 1935; s. James Emmet and Ethel Pearl (Williams) T.; m. Marilyn Joyce Peterson, Aug. 24, 1957; children: James, Mary, Robert, Susan. BSME, Mich. Tech., 1957. Registered profl. engr., Mich. Design engr. Buick Motor div. GMC, Flint, Mich., 1960-61, project engr., 1961-66, sr. project engr., 1966-71; staff analysis engr. GM Corp., Warren, Mich., 1971-82, sr. staff analysis engr., 1983-88; pres. Eastport Engring., Grand Blanc, Mich., 1989—. Mayor City of Grand Blanc, 1985-89, city councilman, 1969-84, police liaison/commr., 1971-82, planning adv. bd., 1978-80, planning commr., 1985-89; nat. coun. mem. Boy Scouts Am., 1979-90, 93—, coun. commr., 1984—, nat. camp sch. staff, 1986-88, regional camp inspector/accreditation team, 1988—; vice chmn. Genesee County Sml. Cities and Villages Assn., 1986, chmn. 1987. Capt. USAF, 1958-60. Recipient Silver Beaver Tall Pine Coun. Boy Scouts Am., 1980. Mem. NSPE (treas. Flint chpt. 1968-72, Engr. of the Yr. Flint chpt. 1990), SAE (membership com. 1992-94), ASME (exec. bd. Saginaw Valley chpt. 1968-70). United Ch. of Christ. Home: 12536 Greenhill Dr Grand Blanc MI 48439

TOMLINSON, JOSEPH ERNEST, manufacturing company executive; b. Sycamore, Ill., Apr. 22, 1939; s. Bernie Gilbert and Elizabeth Lowe (Hoffman) T.; m. Judith Ann Worst, Sept. 20, 1969; children: Mark Joseph, Amy Ann. BS in Accy., U. Ill., 1962. CPA. Staff acct. Price Waterhouse and Co., Chgo., 1962-65, sr. acct., 1965-69; audit mgr. Price Waterhouse and Co., Indpls., 1969-74; corp. contr. Inland Container Corp., Indpls., 1974-82, v.p., treas., contr., 1982—. Congl. chmn. Carmel Luth. Ch., Ind., 1983-86, v.p., 1988-91; mem. bd. dirs. Luth. Child and Family Svcs., Indpls., 1994—. With Ill. N.G. 1963-69. Mem. Fin. Execs. Inst. (treas. Indpls. chpt. 1986-87, sec. 1987-88, 2d v.p. 1988-89, 1st v.p. 1989-90, pres. 1990-91). Republican. Club: Crooked Stick Golf. Home: 2063 St Andrews Cir Carmel IN 46032-9547 Office: Inland Container Corp 4030 Vincennes Rd Indianapolis IN 46268-3007

TOMLINSON, JULIETTE SHELL, elementary school educator; b. Atlanta, July 31, 1943; d. Robert Harold and Dorothy Anne (Johnson) Shell; m. John Arthur Tomlinson, June 6, 1964; children: Robert Tyler, Ashley Shell. BA, Trenton State Coll., 1965, MA, 1967. Tchr. Lawrenceville (N.J.) Schs., 1965-67; tchr. Cen. Bucks (Pa.) Schs., 1967—, acting prin., 1990, prin., 1993—; social studies curriculum developer, 1990-92; organizer math. workshops, Doylestown, 1989-91. Pres. Am. Field Svc., Doylestown, Pa., 1978-85; troop leader Girl Scouts U.S.A., Doylestown, 1981-82; mem. adv. bd. Civil War Svc. Assn.; chmn. pub. rels., tres. Ctrl. Bucks Edn. Assn.; active Holistic Writing Process Leader, Instrnl.Support Team, Strategic Planning Steering Comm., Performance Appraisal Task Force. Mem. NEA, Pa. State Edn. Assn., Central Bucks Edn. Assn. Republican. Presbyterian. Home: 191 Cherry Ln Doylestown PA 18901-3136 Office: Simon Butler Elem Sch 200 Brittany Dr Chalfont PA 18914-2306

TOMLINSON, KENNETH Y., periodical editor-in-chief; b. Mt. Airy, N.C., Aug. 3, 1944; s. Young and Mattie (Wingate) T.; m. Rebecca Moore, Apr. 25, 1975; children: William Moore, Lucas Young. BA in History, Randolph Macon Coll., 1966. Reporter Richmond Times Dispatch, 1965-68; corr. Reader's Digest, Pleasantville, N.Y., 1968-81, editor, 1981-82, mng. editor, 1984-85, exec. editor, 1985-90, editor-in-chief, 1990—; dir. Voice of Am., 1982-84. Co-author: History of American Prisoners of War in Vietnam, 1975. Chmn. Nat. Commn. Librs. and Info. Sci., 1986-87; active Nat. Commn. Vol. Svc., 1981-83, U.S. Bd. Internat. Broadcasting, 1987—. Episcopalian. Office: Readers Digest Assn Inc Pleasantville NY 10570*

TOMLINSON, MILTON AMBROSE, clergyman; b. Cleveland, Tenn., Oct. 19, 1906; s. Ambrose Jessup and Mary Jane (Taylor) T.; m. Ina Mae Turner, Sept. 18, 1928; children: Wanda Jean (Mrs. Hugh Ralph Edwards), Carolyn Joy (Mrs. Verlin Dean Thornton). Ed., Tenn. pub. schs. Printer, Herald Printing Co., Cleveland, ten years; pastor ch. Henderson, Ky., 1 yr.; gen. overseer Ch. of God of Prophecy, Cleveland, 1943-90, gen. overseer emeritus, 1990—; editor and pub. The White Wing Messenger; pres. Bible Tng. Inst., chmn. trustees. Author: Basic Bible Beliefs. Pres., Tomlinson Home for Children. Office: Bible Pl PO Box 2910 Cleveland TN 37320-2910

TOMLINSON, ROBERT JOHN, lawyer, energy executive; b. Detroit, May 4, 1936; s. Harry John and Helen Adele (Strauss) T.; m. Margaret Armstrong, June 9, 1962 (div. 1977); 1 child, Justin Hudspeth. BA in Econs., U. Mich., 1958; JD, Wayne State U., 1961. Bar: Mich. 1962, Wash. 1972. Internat. atty. Parke Davis & Co., Detroit, 1962-68; assoc. Heritier & Abbott, Detroit, 1969-70; atty. Mich. Consol. Gas Co., Detroit, 1970-72; sr. v.p. legal and adminstrn. Wash. Energy Co. & Wash. Nat. Gas Co., Seattle, 1972—; pres. Thermal Efficiency, 1988-94; pres., bd. dirs. Universal Synergetics, Inc., 1989-94; bd. dirs. Mercer Ins. Co., Hamilton, Bermuda, WECO Fin. Co., Seattle. Mem. ABA, Am. Soc. Corp. Secs. (pres. N.W. chpt. 1978-79), Pacific Coast Gas Assn. (legal adv. com. 1977—, legal sect. chmn. 1977, 78, 80, 85, 89), N.W. Gas Assn., Bellevue Athletic Club Wash., Rainier Club, Chi Phi. Avocations: squash, water color, sailing. Home: 11010 SE 30th St Bellevue WA 98004 Office: Wash Energy Co 815 Mercer St Seattle WA 98109-4714

TOMLINSON, WARREN LEON, lawyer; b. Denver, Apr. 2, 1930; s. Leslie Alton and Esther (Hasler) T.; m. Lois Elaine Retallack, Aug. 8, 1953 (div. 1987); children: Stephanie Lynn Huffine, Brett Louis; m. Linda Jane Beville, May 17, 1989. BA, U. Denver, 1951; JD, NYU, 1954. Bar: Colo. 1954, U.S. Dist. Ct. Colo., U.S. Ct. Appeals (10th cir.) 1958, U.S. Supreme Ct. 1960. Assoc. Holland & Hart, Denver, 1958-63, ptnr., 1963—. Contbr. numerous articles to profl. jours. Lt. U.S. Army, 1954-58. Mem. ABA (chmn. law practice mgmt. sect. 1988-89, charter fellow Coll. of Law Practice Mgmt. 1994). Republican. Episcopalian. Avocations: skiing, white-water rafting. Home: 5017 Main Gore Dr # 4 Vail CO 81657 Office: Holland & Hart 555 17th St Ste 2900 Denver CO 80202-3979

TOMLINSON, WILLIAM HOLMES, management educator, retired army officer, b. Thornton, Ark., Apr. 12, 1922; s. Hugh Oscar and Lucy Gray (Holmes) T.; m. Dorothy Payne, June 10, 1947 (dec.); children: Jane Axtell, Lucy Gray, William Payne; m. Florence Mood Smith, May 1, 1969 (div.); m. Suzanne Scollard Gill, Mar. 16, 1977. Student, Centenary Coll., 1938-39; BS, U.S. Mil. Acad., 1943; grad. Air Command Staff Coll., 1958; MBA, U. Ala., 1960; MS in Internat. Affairs, George Washington U., 1966; grad. U.S. Army War Coll., 1966; grad. Indsl. Coll. Armed Forces, 1968; PhD in Bus. Adminstrn., Am. U., 1974; postgrad. 56th Advanced Mgmt. Program, Harvard U., 1968, 69; BAS, U. N. Fla., 1988. Commd. 2d lt. U.S. Army, 1943, advanced through grades to col.; field arty., 1966; combat svc. in Leyte and Cebu, Philippines 246 Field Arty. Bn. Americal Divsn., 1945; aide de camp, comdg. gen. 8th U.S. Army, Japan, 1945-48, ops. officer 9th Divsn. Arty., Germany, 1954-56, Office of Undersec. Army, Pentagon, Washington, 1961-64; comdr. 2d Bn., 8th Arty. and 7th Div. Arty., UN Comd. S. Korea, 1964-65; faculty Indsl. Coll. Armed Forces, Ft. McNair, Washington, 1966-72, ret., 1973; faculty U. North Fla., Jacksonville, 1972—, prof. mgmt., 1993—; vis. prof. U. Glasgow, Scotland, fall 1987; vis. lectr. Moscow Linguistics U., Plekhanov Econ. U., Ulyanovsk U., Russia, fall 1993; mem. Nat. Def. Exec. Res., Fed. Emergency Mgmt. Agy., 1976—. Co-author: International Business, Theory and Practice; contbr. articles to profl. jours. and books. Exec. bd. Jacksonville Campus Ministry, 1991—. Decorated Bronze Star, Legion of Merit, Philippine Liberation medal, Japanese Occupation; recipient Freedom Found. award, 1967-71, Sr. Profl. in Human Resources, UNF Outstanding Tchr. award, 1994, Teaching Incentive award, 1994-95. Mem. Soc. Human Resource Mgmt., Acad. Mgmt., Indsl. Rels. Rsch. Assn., Acad. Internat. Bus., European Internat. Bus. Assn., Internat. Trade and Fin. Assn., Exec. Svc. Corps. Bd., Co. Mil. Historians, Nat. Eagle Scout Assn., Northeast Fla. Employee Svcs. Assn. (charter pres. 1987-89), West Point Soc. N. Fla. (pres. 1976), Mil. Order Stars and Bars (comdr. 1980-90), Army Navy Club, Fla. Yacht Club, Mason, Shriner, Rotary, Beta Gamma Sigma (pres. 1988-89), Kappa Alpha. Presbyterian (elder). Home: 1890 Shadowlawn St Jacksonville FL 32205-9430 Office: U North Fla Dept Mgmt 4567 Saint Johns Bluff Rd S Jacksonville FL 32224

TOMLINSON-KEASEY, CAROL ANN, university administrator; b. Washington, Oct. 15, 1942; d. Robert Bruce and Geraldine (Howe) Tomlinson; m. Charles Blake Keasey, June 13, 1964; children: Kai Linson, Amber Lynn. BS, Pa. State U., 1964; MS, Iowa State U., 1966; PhD, U. Calif., Berkeley, 1970. Lic. psychologist, Calif. Asst. prof. psychology Trenton (N.J.) State Coll., 1969-70, Rutgers U., New Brunswick, N.J., 1970-72; prof. U. Nebr., Lincoln, 1972-77; prof. U. Calif., Riverside, 1977-92, acting dean Coll. Humanities and Social Scis., 1986-88, chmn. dept. psychology, 1989-92; vice provost for faculty rels. U. Calif., Davis, 1992—. Author: Child's Eye View, 1980, Child Development, 1985; also numerous chpts. to books; articles to profl. jours. Recipient Disting. Tchr. award U. Calif., 1986. Mem. APA, Soc. Rsch. in Child Devel., Riverside Aquatics Assn. (pres.). Office: Office of Provost U Calif Davis CA 95616

TOMLJANOVICH, ESTHER M., judge; b. Galt, Iowa, Nov. 1, 1931; d. Chester William and Thelma L. (Brooks) Moellering; m. William S. Tomljanovich, Dec. 26, 1957; 1 child, William Brooks. AA, Itasca Jr. Coll., 1951; BSL, St. Paul Coll. Law, 1953, LLB, 1955. Bar: Minn. 1955, U.S. Dist. Ct. Minn. 1958. Asst. revisor of statutes State of Minn., St. Paul, 1957-66, revisor of statutes, 1974-77; dist. ct. judge State of Minn., Stillwater, 1977-90; assoc. justice Minn. Supreme Ct., St. Paul, 1990—. Former mem. North St. Paul Bd. Edn.; Maplewood Bd. Edn., Lake Elmo Planning Comm; bd. trustees William Mitchell Coll. Law, 1995—. Mem. Minn. State Bar Assn., Bus. and Profl. Women's Assn. St. Paul (former pres.). Office: Supreme Ct MN MN Judicial Ctr Rm 423 25 Constitution Ave Saint Paul MN 55155-1500

TOMMERAASEN, MILES, college president; b. Sioux Falls, S.D., Jan. 30, 1923; m. Marilyn Fladmark, 1945; children: Marsha Tommeraasen Heimann, Mark, Miles. B.A., Morningside Coll., 1944; M.A. (hon.), 1948; M.B.A., Northwestern U., 1948; Ph.D., U. Nebr., Lincoln, 1964. Tchr. math. secondary sch. Canton, S.D., 1943-45; staff acct. Arthur Andersen & Co., Chgo., 1946-50; mem. faculty Morningside Coll., 1950-64, chmn. dept. econs. and bus., 1951-61, prof., 1952-64, exec. v.p., 1966-84, pres., 1978-93, pres. emeritus, 1993; prof. U. Nebr., Lincoln, 1964-78; asst. dean Coll. Bus. Adminstrn. U. Nebr., 1968-69, vice chancellor for bus. and fin., 1969-78; mem. 5 corporate bds. Bd. dirs. Siouxland Found., Sunrise Manor; mem. mayor's com. Internat. Visitors; mem. Lincoln Downtown program, United Way Bd., Symphony Bd., First Luth. Ch. Mem. Am. Acctg. Assn., Am. Inst. C.P.A.s, Iowa Soc. C.P.A.s, Nebr. Soc. C.P.A.s (dir. 1966-69), Am. Fin. Assn., Fin. Analysts Soc., Inst. Chartered Fin. Analysts, Midwest Bus. Adminstrn. Assn. (pres. 1973-74), Fin. Execs. Inst. (dir. 1975-76), Lincoln C. of C. Office: Morningside Coll 1501 Morningside Ave Sioux City IA 51106-1751

TOMMEY, CHARLES ELDON, surgeon; b. Nashville, Ark., Jan. 13, 1922; s. William Robert and America Anna (Compton) T.; m. Clara Blair Newman, Aug. 28, 1948; children: Robert, Jean, Phillip, Dale, Scott. Student, Henderson State Tchrs. Coll., 1940-42; BSM, U. Ark. Sch. Medicine, 1944, MD, 1945. Diplomate Am. Bd. Surgery. Intern City Hosp., Columbus, Ga., 1945-46; surg. resident Bapt. Hosp., Little Rock, 1948-49, VA Hosp., Cleve., 1950-54; pvt. practice surgery El Dorado, Ark., 1954—; asst. clin. instr. surgery U. Ark. Coll. Medicine. Capt. U.S. Army Med. Corps, 1943-45, 46-48. Fellow ACS. Baptist. Avocations: golf, photography. Home: 123 Glenridge Pky El Dorado AR 71730-3117 Office: Surg Clinic of S Ark 518 Thompson Ave El Dorado AR 71730-4556

TOMOMATSU, HIDEO, chemist; b. Tokyo, June 8, 1929; came to U.S., 1959; s. Shinsai Nasu and Suma (Sugawara) T.; m. Yuko Ito, Nov. 12, 1967; 1 child, Tadao. BSChemE., Waseda U., 1952; MS in Chemistry, U. of the Pacific, 1960; PhD in Chemistry, Ohio State U., 1964. Registered profl. engr., Tex., U.S. patent agt. Chem. Hodogaya Chem. Co., Tokyo, 1952-59, Texaco Chems. Co., Austin, Tex., 1964-72; Quaker fellow Quaker Oats Co., Barrington, Ill., 1972—. Contbr. articles to profl. jours.; patentee in field. Mem. Am. Chem. Soc., Am. Assn. Cereal Chemists, Inst. Food Technologists. Office: Quaker Oats Co Rsch Lab 617 W Main St Barrington IL 60010-4199

TOMPKINS, CURTIS JOHNSTON, university president; b. Roanoke, Va., July 14, 1942; s. Joseph Buford and Rebecca (Johnston) T.; m. Mary Katherine Hasle, Sept. 5, 1964; children: Robert, Joseph, Rebecca. BS, Va. Poly. Inst., 1965, MS, 1967; PhD, Ga. Inst. Tech., 1971. Indsl. engr. E.I. DuPont de Nemours, Richmond, Va., 1965-67; instr. Sch. Indsl. and Systems Engring., Ga. Inst. Tech., Atlanta, 1968-71; assoc. prof. Colgate Darden Grad. Sch. Bus. Adminstrn., U. Va., Charlottesville, 1971-77; prof., chmn. dept. indsl. engring. W.Va. U., Morgantown, 1977-80, dean Coll. Engring., 1980-91; pres. Mich. Tech. U., Houghton, 1991—; mem. engring. accreditation commn. Accreditation Bd. for Engring. and Tech., 1981-86; mem. Commn. on Engring. Edn., Nat. Assn. State Univs. and Land Grant Colls., 1985-90; cons. corps., govt. agys., ednl. instns.; lectr. various univs.; mem. exec. bd. Engring. Deans Coun., 1985-89, vice chmn., 1987-89; mem. engring. adv. com., chmn. of planning com. NSF, 1988-91. Author: (with L.E. Grayson) Management of Public Sector and Nonprofit Organizations, 1983, (with others) Maynard's Industrial Engineering Handbook, 1992; contbr. chpt. to Ency. of Profl. Mgmt, 1978, 83. Co-chmn. W.Va. Gov.'s Coun. on Econ. Devel.; bd. dirs. Pub. Land Corp. W.Va., 1980-89; mem. faculty Nat. Acad. Voluntarism, United Way Am., 1976-91; mem. Morgantown Water Commn., 1981-87, Morgantown Utility Bd., 1987-91; mem. steering com. W.Va. Conf. on Environ., 1985-89; chmn. Monongalia County United Way, 1989-90. Fellow Inst. Indsl. Engrs. (life mem., sr. v.p. publs. 1983-85, v.p. edn. and rsch. 1985-87, trustee 1983-90, pres.-elect 1987-88, pres. 1988-89), Am. Soc. Engring. Edn. (chmn. indsl. engring. div. 1981-82, v.p. pub. affairs 1985-87, bd. dirs. 1985-87, 1st v.p., exec. com., fin com. 1986-87, pres.-elect 1989-90, pres. 1990-91); mem. Am. Assn. Engring. Soc. (bd. govs. 1987-90, exec. com. 1987-90, sec.-treas. 1989-90), Jr. Engring. Tech. Soc. (bd. dirs. 1988-91), Nat. Soc. for Sci., Tech. and Society (bd. dirs. 1991—), Internat. Hall of Fame of Sci. and Engring. (hon. trustee), Sigma Xi, Phi Kappa Phi, Tau Beta Pi, Alpha Pi Mu. Methodist. Home: 2 Woodland Rd Houghton MI 49931-9746 Office: Mich Tech U 1400 Townsend Dr Houghton MI 49931-1295

TOMPKINS, DANIEL D., landscape architect, horticulturist. Dir. Bayard Cutting Arboretum, Great River, N.Y. Office: Bayard Cutting Arboretum PO Box 466 Oakdale NY 11769-0466

TOMPKINS, EILEEN, state legislator; m. Patrick Tompkins; 9 children. Attended, Inver Hills C.C., U. Minn., Coll. of St. Thomas. Mem. Minn. Ho. of Reps., 1984—; mem. health and human svcs. com., mem. local govt. com., mem. met. affairs com., mem. transp. and transit com. Home: 7734 133rd St W Apple Valley MN 55124 Office: Minn Ho of Reps State Capitol Saint Paul MN 55155 also: 245 State Office Bldg Saint Paul MN 55155

TOMPKINS, JAMES ARTHUR, consulting firm executive, industrial engineer; b. Chgo., Dec. 8, 1946; s. Carroll Arthur and Evelyn Angela (Smith) T.; m. Sharon Marie Steffens, Aug. 17, 1968; children: Tiffany, Jamie, Jimmy. BS in Indsl. Engring., Purdue U., 1969, MS in Indsl. Engring., 1970, PhD, 1972. Sr. scientist Rsch. Triangle Inst., Raleigh, N.C., 1975-77; prof. N.C. State U., Raleigh, 1975-78; pres. Tompkins Assocs. Inc., Raleigh, 1978—; dir. Material Handling Edn. Found., 1990. Author: Facilities Planning, 1984 (best book 1984), Winning Manufacturing, 1989, others; editor: Warehouse Handbook, 1988; contbr. numerous articles to profl. jours. Recipient Reed Apple award Material Handling Inst., 1985, numerous others. Mem. Inst. Indsl. Engrs. (pres. 1990), Internat. Materials Mgmt. Soc. (pres. 1986), Coll. Industry Coun. on Material Handling Edn. (pres. 1984). Republican. Office: Tompkins Assocs Inc 2809 E Millbrook Rd Ste 200 Raleigh NC 27604-2849

TOMPKINS, JEANNIE KAY, special education educator; b. Portage, Wis., Feb. 8, 1944; d. Matt and Ivy (Lee) Keiller; m. Robert Jay Tompkins, June 18, 1967; children: Troy M., Lee M. BA, U. Ariz., 1966, MEd, 1970. Tchr. spl. edn. Moreno Valley Sch. Dist., Sunnymead, Calif., 1966-67; tchr. educationally handicapped Centralia Sch. Dist., Buena Park, Calif., 1967-68; pupil appraisal rm. tchr. Tucson Unified Sch. Dist., 1968-69, learning disabilities resource tchr., 1969-70; learning disabilities tchr., diagnostician Grace Christian Sch., Tucson, 1979-89; special edn. resource tchr. Vail Sch. Dist. # 20, 1989—; organizer, dir. Attention Deficit Disorders Support Group for Parents, Tucson, 1988. Mem. task force for presch. handicapped Ariz. State Dept. Edn.; precinct committeeman Pima County. Govt. scholar, 1970. Mem. Ariz. Coun. for Learning Disabilities, Coun. for Exceptional Children. Republican. Avocations: country crafts, reading, testing. Home: 600 S Avenida Los Reyes Tucson AZ 85748-6835

TOMPKINS, JOE L., costume designer. Costume Designer: (TV movies) Eleanor and Franklin: The White House Years, 1977 (Emmy award best costume design in drama spl. 1978), (films) When You Comin' Back, Red Ryder?, 1979, Coal Miner's Daughter, 1980, Foolin' Around, 1980, Raggedy Man, 1981, True Confessions, 1981, Missing, 1982, Romantic Comedy, 1983, Cross Creek, 1983 (Academy award nomination best costume design 1983), Irreconcilable Differences, 1984, The River, 1984, Swing Shift, 1984, Marie, 1985, Murphy's Romance, 1985, Big Trouble, 1986, Violets Are Blue, 1986, Howard the Duck, 1986, Nuts, 1987, Betrayed, 1988, Harlem Nights, 1989 (Academy award nomination best costume design 1989), Memoirs of an Invisible Man, 1992, Stay Tuned, 1992, Fire in the Sky, 1993, Blown Away, 1994; costume cons.: Weekend at Bernie's, 1989. Office: care Costume Designer's Guild 13949 Ventura Blvd Ste 309 Sherman Oaks CA 91423*

TOMPKINS, JOHN ANDREW, school system administrator. Supt. Salina (Kans.) Unified Sch. Dist. 305. State finalist Supt. of Yr. award, 1992. Office: Salina Unified Sch Dist 305 PO Box 797 Salina KS 67402

TOMPKINS, JOSEPH BUFORD, JR., lawyer; b. Roanoke, Va., Apr. 4, 1950; s. Joseph Buford and Rebecca Louise (Johnston) T.; m. Nancy Powell Wilson, Feb. 6, 1993; children: Edward Graves, Claiborne Forbes; 1 stepchild, Clayton Tate Wilson. BA in Politics summa cum laude, Washington and Lee U., 1971; M.P.P. in Pub. Policy, Harvard U., 1975, JD, 1975. Bar: Va. 1975, U.S. Dist. Ct. D.C. 1982, U.S. Ct. Appeals (D.C. cir.) 1976, U.S. Ct. Appeals (5th cir.) 1977, U.S. Ct. Appeals (11th cir.) 1982, U.S. Ct. Appeals (3d cir.) 1983, U.S. Ct. Appeals (6th cir.) 1985, U.S. Ct. Appeals (7th cir.) 1991, U.S. Ct. Appeals (4th cir.) 1993, U.S. Supreme Ct. 1977. Assoc. Sidley & Austin, Washington, 1975-79, ptnr., 1982—; assoc. dir.

Office of Policy and Mgmt. Analysis, criminal div. U.S. Dept Justice, Washington, 1979-81, dep. chief fraud sect. criminal div., 1981-82. Contbr. articles to legal publs. Mem. Va. Bd. of Health Professions, Richmond, Va., 1984-92, vice chmn., 1984-86, chmn., 1986-88, 90-91. Recipient Spl. Commendation, U.S. Dept. Justice, 1981. Mem. ABA (criminal justice sect., mem. white collar crime com., 1980—; chmn. task force on computer crime; 1982—), Va. Bar Assn., D.C. Bar Assn., Fed. Bar Assn., Phi Beta Kappa. Democrat. Methodist. Home: 8146 Wellington Rd Alexandria VA 22308 Office: Sidley & Austin 1722 I St NW Washington DC 20006-3705

TOMPKINS, ROBERT GEORGE, physician; b. Portland, Oreg., May 29, 1923; s. George Henry and Minnie (Davies) T.; m. Rosemarie Nowicki, June 6, 1948 (dec. 1960); children: Timothy Michael, Mary Eileen, George Henry, Robert George. B.S. U. Wash., 1943; M.B., Northwestern U., 1947; M.D. 1949; M.S., U. Minn., 1954. Diplomate Am. Bd. Internal Medicine. Intern King County Hosp., Seattle, 1948-49; resident King County Hosp., 1949-50; fellow, 1st asst. Mayo Found., Rochester, Minn., 1950-54; practice medicine specializing in cardiology and internal medicine Tulsa, 1954—; mem. staff St. Francis Hosp., chief staff, 1964, med. dir., 1968-86; clin. prof. medicine Tulsa Med. Coll. and U. Okla. Med. Coll.; v.p. med. dir. William K. Warren Med. Rsch. Ctr., med. chmn. Guatemala Mission Hosp., Diocese Oklahoma City and Tulsa; coord. planning program Okla. Regional Med. Program; mem. Tulsa Health and Hosp. Planning Coun.; bd. dirs. Okla. Ctr. Molecular Medicine; med. dir. Laureate Hosp. Rsch. Inst.; pres. Tulsa Med. Edn. Found., 1980-82; bd. dirs. Laureate Psychiatric Clinic and hosp. Contbr. articles to profl. jours; editor: Jour. Okla. State Med. Assn, 1974-86. Bd. dirs. St. Francis Hosp., Tulsa, 1969-86, 94—. Decorated Knight of the Grand Cross (Equestrian Order Holy Sepulchre of Jerusalem, Knight (Sovereign Mil. Order of Malta); recipient Dean's award U. Okla., 1991. Fellow ACP, Royal Coll. Medicine, Am. Coll. Cardiology; mem. AAAS, AMA, Am. Diabetic Assn., Am. Acad. Med. Dirs. (bd. dirs.), Am. Heart Assn., Tulsa County Heart Assn. (pres. 1959), Am. Rheumatism Assn., Mayo Alumni Assn., KC, Alpha Kappa Kappa. Home: 6551 S Darlington Ave Tulsa OK 74136-2002 Office: 6465 S Yale Ave Tulsa OK 74136-7822

TOMPKINS, RONALD GARY, surgeon, educator, biomedical investigator; b. Many, La., Sept. 24, 1951; s. Horace and Ruby (McFerrin) T.; m. Denise Marie Clougherty, Mar. 7, 1985; children: Megan Elizabeth, Ryan Coleman, Caitlin Maureen. BS in Chemistry summa cum laude, Tulane U., 1972, MD, 1976; SM in Chem. Engring., MIT, 1983, ScD in Med. and Chem. Engring., 1983. Diplomate Am. Bd. Surgery (bd. dirs. 1994—), Am. Bd. Surg. Critical Care. Intern in surgery Mass. Gen. Hosp., Boston, 1976-77, asst. resident, then resident, 1977-79, 83-85, asst. in surgery, 1985-87, asst. surgeon, 1988-90, assoc. chief trauma and burn svcs., 1987-90, chief, 1990—, assoc. vis. surgeon, then vis. surgeon, 1991—; clin. fellow in surgery Harvard Med. Sch., Boston, 1977-79, 92-85, instr., then asst. prof. surgery, 1985-90, assoc. prof., 1990—; rsch. assoc. MIT, Cambridge, Mass., 1985-86; asst. in surgery Shriners Burns Inst., Boston, 1987-88, asst. surgeon, 1988-90, chief staff, 1990—; vis. asst. prof. Rutgers U. Sch. Engring., 1988-91; surg. cons. Spaulding Rehab. Hosp., Boston, 1987-88; numerous presentations in field at regional, nat. and internat. orgns. Mem. editl. bd. Critical Care Medicine, 1991—, Jour. Tissue Engring. 1994—, Jour. Am. Soc. Artificial Internal Organs, 1994—; contbr. over 100 articles and revs. to med. jours., chpts. to books; patent pending for culturing liver cells. DuPont fellow MIT, 1979-80, E.R. Gilliland fellow, 1980-81, William Prince fellow, 1981-83; Edward D. Churchill rsch. fellow Mass. Gen. Hosp., 1981-82, fellow Am. Surg. Assn. Found., 1987-88; grantee Link Found., 1985—, NIH, 1987-91, Whitaker Found., 1988-91, Nat. Inst. Gen. Med. Scis., 1992—, Nat. Inst. Digestive Diseases and Kidney, 1987-94, Shriners Hosps., 1988—. Fellow ACS; mem. AMA, AAAS, AIChE, Assn. for Acad. Surgery, Am. Chem. Soc., Am. Burn Assn., Am. Fedn. for Clin. Rsch., Soc. Critical Care Medicine, Surg. Infection Soc., Am. Soc. for Artificial Internal Organs, Shock Soc., Am. Assn. for Surgery of Trauma, Am. Soc. for Laser Medicine and Surgery, Soc. for Cryobiology, Soc. Univ. Surgeons, Am. Assn. for Study Liver Diseases, Am. Trauma Soc., New Eng. Surg. Soc., Cell Transplant Soc., Phi Beta Kappa, Alpha Omega Alpha, numerous others. Home: 16 Emerson Pl Boston MA 02114 Office: Mass Gen Hosp Fruit St Boston MA 02114

TOMPKINS, RONALD K., surgeon; b. Malta, Ohio, Oct. 14, 1934; s. Kenneth Steidley and Mildred Lillian (Loomis) T.; m. Suzanne Colbert, June 9, 1956; children—Gregory Alan, Teresa Susan, Geoffrey Stuart. B.A., Ohio U., 1956; M.D., Johns Hopkins U., 1960; M.S., Ohio State U., 1968. Diplomate: Am. Bd. Surgery. Intern in surgery Ohio State U., 1960-61, resident in surgery, 1964-68, adminstrv. chief resident in surgery, 1968-69, NIH trainee in acad. surgery, instr. physiol. chemistry, 1966-69; asst. prof. surgery UCLA, 1969-73, asso. prof., 1973-79, prof., 1979—, chmn. basic surg. tng. program, 1970-79, asst. dean student affairs, 1979-82, chief div. gen. surgery, 1982-88, chief gastrointestinal surgery, 1986—; assoc. dean, 1988-91; cons. VA Hosps. Editor-in-chief World Jour. Surgery, 1993—. Served with M.C. USAF, 1961-64. NIH grantee, 1968-70; John A. Hartford Found. grantee, 1970-79; Royal Soc. Medicine Eng. travelling fellow, 1976-77. Fellow ACS; mem. Am. Surg. Assn., Am. Gastroenterol. Assn., Am. Fedn. Clin. Rs. cn., Am. Inst. Nutrition, AMA, Assn. Acad. Surgery, Pacific Coast Surg. Assn. (recorder 1986-91, pres. 1995), Soc. Clin. Surgery, Soc. Surgery Alimentary Tract (sec. 1982-85, pres.-elect 1985, pres. 1986, chmn. bd. trustees 1987), Soc. Univ. Surgeons, Societe Internationale de Chirurgie (sec. 1990-94), Internat. Biliary Assn. (pres. 1993-91), Bay Surg. Soc., Los Angeles Surg. Soc. (pres. 1981), ACS (So. Calif. chpt. pres. 1987), Robert M. Zollinger/Ohio State U. Surg. Soc. (pres. 1988-90), Phi Beta Kappa, Sigma Xi, Alpha Omega Alpha, Delta Tau Delta. Republican. Research, numerous publs. in gastrointestinal surgery and gastrointestinal metabolism and biochemistry. Office: Dept of Surgery University of California Los Angeles CA 90024

TOMPKINS, TAIN PENDLETON, foreign service official; b. Phila., Apr. 2, 1943; s. Pendleton Souther and Louise Agnes (Mertz) T.; m. Grace Muller, Feb. 26, 1981; children: Ann Louise, Heather Ashley Muller. BA in English, Washington & Lee U., 1964; MA in Internat. Rels., Johns Hopkins U., 1968, MA in English, 1970. Commd. Fgn. Svc., 1969; 3d sec. Am. Consulate, Can Tho, South Vietnam, 1970-71, Am. Embassy, Lisbon, Portugal, 1972-74; ceasefire observer Am. Consulate, Can Tho, South Vietnam, 1974; staff asst. U.S. Dept. State, Washington, 1974-75; fellow Inst. Politics Harvard U., Cambridge, Mass., 1976; 2d sec. Am. Embassy, Beirut, Lebanon, 1977-80; staff asst. Office of Les Aspin, Washington, 1980-81; dep. dir. staff secretariat U.S. Dept. State, 1980-83; 2d sec. Am. Embassy, Harare, Zimbabwe, 1983-85; 1st sec. Am. Embassy, Canberra, Australia, 1987-91; dep. chief of mission Am. Embassy, Bridgetown, Barbados, 1992-95; coun. Econ. Affairs Am. Embassy, Tel Aviv, Israel, 1995—; diplomat in residence U. Tex., Austin, 1991-92. Co-editor: The Challenge of NAFTA, 1992. Mem. Army and Navy Club, Phi Beta Kappa Assoc. Episcopalian. Avocations: tennis, reading. Office: Am Embassy Tel Aviv APO AE 09830

TOMPKINS, WILLIAM DAVID, corporate professional; b. Tuscaloosa, Ala., Feb. 6, 1937; s. William Collins and Susan Wilburn (Powers) T.; children from previous marriage: William David Jr., Katherine Leigh; m. Rebecca Frances Durden, Sept. 24, 1977; 1 child, Amanda Katherine. BS in Mech. Engring., U. Ala., 1961. Mech. engr., sales engr. Am. Cast Iron Pipe Co., 1962-69; midwest regional sales mgr. Ductile Iron Pipe, 1969-76, sales mgr., 1973-76; div. mgr. Am. Ductile Iron Pipe div. Am. Cast Iron Pipe Co., 1977-81, Am. Darling Valve div. Am. Cast Iron Pipe Co., 1982-85; pres., chief operating officer Donald Justice Corp., 1985-86; sr. v.p., chief ops. officer Clayton Group, Inc., Tampa, Fla., 1987-88; pres. Clayton Group, Inc., 1988—. Served to 1st lt. U.S. Army, 1958-59. Mem. Am. Water Works Assn., Water Pollution Control Assn., Ductile Iron Pipe Rsch. Assn. (com. chmn. 1976-81), Valve Mfrs. Assn. (com. chmn. 1982-85), Milburn Golf and Country (Kansas City), Vestavia Country (Birmingham). Republican. Presbyterian. Avocations: golf, fishing. Home: 2912 W Wallcraft Ave Tampa FL 33611-1615 Office: Clayton Group Inc 9501 E Hillsborough Ave Tampa FL 33610-5925

TOMPSETT, MICHAEL FRANCIS, research director; b. Coulsdon, Surrey, Eng., May 4, 1939; came to U.S., 1969; s. Francis John and Kathleen Mary Tompsett; m. Margaret Ellen Hatfield, July 8, 1967; children: Karen, Adrian, Kevin, Ellen. BA, Cambridge U., Eng. 1962, MA, PhD, 1966. Project leader English Electric Valve Co., Eng., 1966-69; supr. AT&T Bell

Labs., Murray Hill, N.J., 1969-89. Co-author: Charge Transfer Devices, 1975 (translated into Japanese and Russian); patentee in field. Fellow IEEE.

TOMPSETT, WILLIAM C., lawyer; b. N.Y.C., Dec. 22, 1948. BA, Haverford Coll., 1970; JD, Cornell U., 1974. Bar: Pa. 1974, Ill. 1978. Ptnr. Mayor, Brown & Platt, Chgo. Mem. ABA, Chgo. Bar Assn. Office: Mayer Brown & Platt 190 S LaSalle St Chicago IL 60603

TOMPSON, MARIAN LEONARD, association executive; b. Chgo., Dec. 5, 1929; d. Charles Clark and Marie Christine (Bernardini) Leonard; m. Clement R. Tompson, May 7, 1949 (dec. 1981); children: Melanie Tompson Kandler, Deborah Tompson Mikolajczak, Allison Tompson Fagerholm, Laurel Tompson Davies, Sheila Tompson Dorsey, Brian, Philip. Student public and parochial schs., Chgo. and Franklin Park, Ill. Co-founder La Leche League (Internat.), Franklin Park, 1956; pres. La Leche League (Internat.), 1956-80, dir., 1956—, pres. emeritus, 1990—; exec. dir. Alternative Birth Crisis Coalition, 1981-85; cons. WHO; bd. dirs. North Am. Soc. Psychosomatic Ob-Gyn, Natural Birth and Natural Parenting, 1981-83; mem. adv. bd. Nat. Assn. Parents and Profls. for Safe Alternatives in Childbirth, Am. Acad. Husband-Coached Childbirth; mem. adv. bd. Fellowship of Christian Midwives; mem. profl. adv. bd. Home Oriented Maternity Experience; guest lectr. Harvard U. Med. Sch., UCLA Sch. Public Health, U. Antioquia Med. Sch., Medellin, Columbia, U. Ill. Sch. Medicine, Chgo., U. W.I., Jamaica, U. N.C., Nat. Coll. of Chiropractic, Am. Coll. Nurse Midwives, U. Parma, Italy, Inst. Psychology, Rome, Rockford (Ill.) Sch. Medicine, Northwestern U. Sch. Medicine; mem. family com. Ill. Commn. on Status of Women, 1976-85; mem. perinatal adv. com. Ill. Dept. Pub. Health, 1980-83; mem. adv. bd. Internat. Nutrition Communication Service, 1980—; bd. cons. We Can, 1984—; exec. adv. bd. United Resources for Family Health and Support, 1985-86. Author: (with others) Safe Alternatives in Childbirth, 1976, 21st Century Obstetrics Now!, 1977, The Womanly Art of Breastfeeding, 3d edit., 1981, Five Standards for Safe Childbearing, 1981, But Doctor, About That Shot..., 1988, Breast Feeding, 5th edit., 1991; author prefaces and forwards in 10 books; columnist La Leche League News, 1958-80; columnist People's Doctor Newsletter, 1977-88, mem. adv. bd., cons., 1988-92; assoc. editor Child and Family Quar., 1967—; mem. med. adv. bd. East West Jour., 1980—; also articles. Recipient Gold medal of honor Centro de Rehabilitacao Nossa Senhora da Gloria, 1975, Night of 100 Stars III Achiever award Actors Fund Am., 1990. Office: 1400 N Meacham Rd Schaumburg IL 60173-4840

TOMS, JUSTINE WILLIS, educational organization executive; b. Evanston, Ill., Oct. 16, 1942; d. Robert Jacques and Ruth (Herzfeld) W.; m. Donald Carroll Welch, Nov. 1962 (div. 1969); 1 child, Robert Willis Welch; m. Michael Anthony Toms, Dec. 16, 1972. BS, Auburn U., 1967. Elem. sch. tchr. Sylacauga (Ala.) Sch. System, 1966-69; exec. dir. New Dimensions Radio, Ukiah, Calif., 1973—. Editor (quar. jour.) New Dimensions Jour., 1987—. Democrat. Buddhist. Avocation: horseback riding.

TOMS, MICHAEL ANTHONY, broadcast journalist; b. Washington, June 7, 1940; s. Austin Herman Toms and Margaret Dorothy (Pitcher) Slavinsky; m. Justine Willis, Dec. 16, 1972; children: Michael Anthony, Robert Welch. Student, U. Miami, 1959-60, U. Va., 1961-63; postgrad., Calif. Inst. Integral Studies, San Francisco, 1973-75; DrTheology, Stem. St. Basil the Great, Sydney, Australia, 1981; DHL (hon.), U. Humanistic Studies, San Diego, 1983. Field govt. rep. VariTyper Corp., Washington, 1960-64; sales mgr. VariTyper Corp., San Francisco, 1964-67; regional sales mgr. VariTyper Corp., San Bernardino, 1967-68; pres. Creative Mktg. Assocs., San Francisco, 1968-73; chmn. bd. The Response Mktg. Group, San Francisco, 1971-73; CEO Michael A. Toms & Assocs., San Francisco, 1973-76; pres. New Dimensions Found., San Francisco, 1973—; sr. acquisitions editor Harper Collins, San Francisco, 1989—; exec. prodr., host nat. pub. radio interview series New Dimensions, 1980—; chmn. bd. emeritus Calif. Inst. Integral Studies, San Francisco, 1979-83; exec. dir. Audio Inds., Inc., San Francisco, 1981-83; adj. prof. Union Grad. Sch., 1994—; founder, CEO New Dimensions Broadcasting Network, 1994—; exec. editor New Dimensions Book Series, 1993—; mem. bd. dirs. KQED, Inc., San Francisco, 1980-83, Green Earth Found., 1989—, KZYX-FM, Mendocino County, Calif., 1989-91; mem. bd. adv. The Great Mound, 1989—. Author: Worlds Beyond, 1978, The New Healers, 1980, An Open Life, 1988, At The Leading Edge 1991. Mem. Task Force to Promote Self Esteem and Personal and Social Responsibility, Mendocino County, Calif., 1988-89; mem. internat. adv. bd. Radio Peace Internat. Mem. Internat. Assn. for Socially Responsible Radio (founding dir. 1991—). Avocations: travel, writing, reading. Home: PO Box 1029 Ukiah CA 95482 Office: New Dimensions Found PO Box 410510 San Francisco CA 94141

TOMSETH, VICTOR L, ambassador; b. Eugene, Oreg., Apr. 14, 1941; s. Hersey F. and Lyla I. (Currant) T.; m. Wallapa Charoenrath, Sept. 1, 1968; 2 children. BA in History, U. Oreg., 1963; MA in History, U. Mich., 1966; student, Cornell U., 1972-73; student in Persian lang., Fgn. Svc. Inst., 1975, student exec. seminar in nat. and internat. affairs, 1981. Vol. Peace Corps, Nepal, 1964-65; joined Fgn. Svc., 1966; polit.-mil. officer Am. Embassy, Bangkok, 1967-68, staff asst. to amb., 1969-70, polit. officer, 1970-71, dep. chief of mission, 1989-92; vice consul U.S. Consulate Gen., Chiang Mai, Thailand, 1967-68, Udorn, Thailand, 1968-69; prin. officer U.S. Consulate Gen., Shiraz, Iran, 1976-79; mem. bd. examiners Dept. State, Washington, 1971-72, country officer for Thailand, 1973-75; dir. India, Nepal and Sri Lanka affairs Dept. State, 1982-84, dir. Thailand and Burma affairs, Bur. East Asian and Pacific affairs, 1986-89; polit. counselor Am. Embassy, Tehran, Iran, 1979-81; dep. chief of mission Am. Embassy, Colombo, Sri Lanka, 1984-86; U.S. amb. to Laos Am. Embassy, Vientiane, 1993—; diplomat-in-residence N.C. Consortium for Internat./Intercultural Edn., 1992-93. Active Am. Mus. Natural History. Mem. Asia Soc., Oreg. Winegrowers Assn., Sr. Seminar Alumni Assn., Westwood Country Club (Vienna, Va.). Office: AMEMB Vientiane Box V APO AP 96546

TOMSOVIC, EDWARD JOSEPH, college dean; b. San Francisco, 1922. MD, U. Calif., 1946. Intern Franklin Hosp., San Francisco, 1946-47, asst. resident internal medicine, 1948; pediatric intern Bellevue Hosp., N.Y.C., 1948-49, asst. resident in medicine, 1949-50; chief med. service 109th Field Hosp., Salzburg, Austria, 1950-52, chief pediatrician, 1954; chief pediatrician Madigan Army Hosp., Tacoma, Wash., 1954-59, Walter Reed Army Inst. Rsch., Washington, 1959-60; staff Walter Reed Gen. Hosp., Washington, 1960-61, chief pediatrician, 1961-62; chief pediatrician USA Tripler Gen. Hosp., Honolulu, 1963-66, Letterman Gen. Hosp., San Francisco, 1966-69; div. div. pediatrics Orange (Calif.) County Med. Ctr., 1969-72, med. dir., 1972-76; med. dir. U. Calif-Irvine Med. Ctr., 1976-79; dean Coll. Medicine, U. Okla., Tulsa, 1979-91, prof. pediatrics, 1979-93, prof. emeritus, 1993—, med. dir. devel. support program, 1991-93; assoc. clin. prof. pediatrics Georgetown U., Washington, 1961-62; clin. prof. U. Calif., Irvine, 1969-77, adj. prof., 1977-79, asst. dean for hosp. profl. affairs, 1972-79. Served to col., M.C., U.S. Army, 1950-69. Fellow Am. Acad. Pediatrics, ACP; mem. AMA, Assn. Mil. Surgeons of U.S., So. Med. Assn., Okla. State Med. Assn.

TON, L. EUGENE, church official. Exec. min. Ind. Bapt. Conv., Indpls. Office: American Baptist Churches 1350 N Delaware St Indianapolis IN 46202-2493

TONDEL, LAWRENCE CHAPMAN, lawyer; b. N.Y.C., Apr. 9, 1946; s. Lyman Mark and Jean (Basch) T.; m. Sharyn A. Smith, Aug. 3, 1974; children: Michael Lawrence, Kathryn Chapman. Student, The Lawrenceville Sch., 1964; AB, Wesleyan U., 1968; JD, U. Mich., 1971. N.Y. 1972. Assoc. Brown & Wood, N.Y.C., 1971-79, ptnr., 1980—; chmn. Internat. Bus. Comm. 5th, 6th and 7th Ann. Internat. Forum on Offshore Funds. Trustee Elisabeth Morrow Sch., Englewood, N.J., 1988-93. Mem. ABA, Am. Law Inst., Am. Bar Found., Assn. Bar City N.Y. Republican. Episcopalian. Office: Brown & Wood 1 World Trade Ctr New York NY 10048-0001

TONDEUR, PHILIPPE MAURICE, mathematician, educator; b. Zurich, Switzerland, Dec. 7, 1932; came to U.S., 1964, naturalized, 1974; s. Jean and Simone (Lapaire) T.; m. Claire-Lise Ballansat, Dec. 20, 1965. Ph.D., U. Zurich, 1961. Rsch. fellow U. Paris, 1961-63; lectr. math. U. Zurich, 1963-64, U. Buenos Aires, 1964, Harvard U., Cambridge, Mass., 1964-65, U. Calif., Berkeley, 1965-66; asso. prof. Wesleyan U., Middletown, Conn., 1966-

68, U. Ill., Urbana, 1968-70; prof. U. Ill., 1970—; vis. prof. Auckland U., 1968, Eidg. Techn. Hochschule U. Heidelberg, 1973, U. Zurich, 1982, U. Rome, 1984, Ecole Polytechnique, Paris, 1987, U. Santiago de Compostela, 1987, Max Planck Inst., 1987, U. Leuven, Belgium, 1990, Keio U., Yokohama, Japan, 1993; assoc. mem. Ctr. Advanced Study U. Ill., 1977-78, 91-92. Contbr. articles to profl. jours. Recipient fellowships Swiss Nat. Sci. Found., fellowships Harvard U., fellowships U. Ill. Mem. Am. Math. Soc., Schweiz Math. Gesellschaft, Société Math. de France. Office: Math Dept U Ill Urbana IL 61801

TONE, JEFFREY R., lawyer; b. Oak Park, Ill., Mar. 27, 1953. AB cum laude, Princeton U., 1975; JD summa cum laude, U. Ill., 1978. Bar: Ill. 1978. Law clk. to Hon. Prentice H. Marshall U.S. Dist. Ct. (no. dist.), Ill., 1978-80; law clk. to Hon. John Paul Stevens U.S. Supreme Ct. 1980-81; ptnr. Sidley & Austin, Chgo. Office: Sidley & Austin 1 First Nat Plz Chicago IL 60603

TONE, KENNETH EDWARD, lawyer; b. Tiffin, Ohio, July 15, 1930; s. Harry Frederick and Lucille (Wahl) T.; m. Mary Zeitzheim, July 19, 1954; children: Mary Robin Buechlein, Tygh Mathew. B.S., Miami U., Oxford, Ohio, 1950; LL.B., J.D., Ohio No. U., 1953. Bar: Ohio 1953, Fed. Ct. 1955, U.S. Supreme Ct. 1962. Practice in Sandusky, Ohio, 1953—; ptnr. firm Tone, Maddrell, Eastman, Grubbe, McGory & Vermeeren, 1960—; solicitor Village of Bay View, Ohio, also Village of Milan, Ohio, 1955-60; spl. legal counsel to atty. gen. Ohio, 1971-84; acting judge Sandusky Mcpl. Ct. Author: Sandusky Civil Service Rules, 1955-56, Your Budget and You, 1966, History of Tone Family, 1409-1978, 1978. Sec. Sandusky Planning and Zoning Commn., 1956-65, Sandusky Zoning Code Bd. Appeals, 1956-65, Sandusky Bldg. Code Bd. Appeals, 1956-65, Sandusky Civil Service Commn., 1953-72; mem. Sandusky City Charter Revision Com., 1954-55, 64; chmn. Erie County Bd. Visitors to Public Instns., 1976-82; mem. Erie County Democratic Exec. Com. and Central Com., 1962-70; bd. dirs. Goodwill Industries, 1969-79; bd. dirs. Vols. of Am., 1955-63, v.p., 1959-60, pres., 1960-62; bd. dirs. drive chmn., legal counsel Erie County chpt. Am. Heart Assn., 1956-58; chmn. Heart Ball, 1969; bd. dirs., v.p. Sandusky Area council Girl Scouts U.S.A., 1956-59; trustee Sandusky chpt. Am. Cancer Soc., 1958-60, pres., 1960; exec. bd. Firelands Area council Boy Scouts Am., 1985-92. Served with USNR, 1950-52. Mem. ABA, Ohio Bar Assn. (probate and trust com. 1964-74), Erie County Bar Assn. (pres. 1978), Fed. Bar Assn., Am. Judicature Soc., Sandusky Area C. of C. (steering, legis. coms.), Sandusky Jaycees (past treas., v.p., dir., parliamentarian), N. Central Ohio Arts Council, Internat. Platform Assn., AMVETS (life), Ohio Fire Chiefs Assn. (hon.), Ohio Protective Assn. (hon.), Nat. Eagle Scout Assn., Sandusky Power Squadron (comdr. 1981), Ohio Geneal. Soc., Phi Kappa Tau, Delta Theta Phi. Mem. United Ch. Christ (past mem. consistory). Clubs: Ski (founder), Torch (founder), Sandusky Yacht (commodore 1973), Interlake Yachting Assn. Lodges: Grotto, Elks, Masons, Shriners, Internat. Order Blue Gavel (chpt. pres. 1981, dist. 9 pres. 1984, internat. northeastern v.p. 1984-86). Home: 587 Bimini Dr Sandusky OH 44870-3942 Office: 1401 Cleveland Rd Sandusky OH 44870-4216

TONE, MICHAEL P., lawyer; b. Washington, Aug. 31, 1949. BA, Denison U., 1971; JD, U.S.C., 1974. Bar: Ill. 1974; U.S. Ct. Appeals; U.S. Dist. Ct. Atty. Peterson & Ross, Chgo. Mem. ABA, Ill. State Bar Assn. Office: Peterson & Ross 200 E Randolph Dr Ste 7300 Chicago IL 60601-6969*

TONE, PHILIP WILLIS, lawyer, former federal judge; b. Chgo., Apr. 9, 1923; s. Elmer James and Frances (Willis) T.; m. Gretchen Altfillisch, Mar. 10, 1945; children: Michael P., Jeffrey R., Susan A. B.A., U. Iowa, 1943, J.D., 1948; grad. fellow, Yale Law Sch., 1948. Bar: Iowa 1948, Ill. 1950, D.C. 1950. Law clk. Justice Wiley B. Rutledge, Supreme Ct. U.S., Washington, 1948-49; assoc. firm Covington & Burling, Washington, 1949-50; assoc., ptnr. firm Jenner & Block, Chgo., 1950-72, 80—; judge U.S. Dist. Ct., Chgo., 1972-74, U.S. Ct. Appeals (7th cir.), Chgo., 1974-80; spl. counsel Nat. Commn. on Causes and Prevention of Violence, 1968-69, U.S. Senate subcom. to investigate individuals representing interests of fgn. govts.; 1980; chmn. Ill. Supreme Ct. Rules Com., 1968-71, sec., 1963-68; mem. Com. on Jud. Br. of Jud. Conf. of U.S., 1987-91; gen. counsel U.S. Golf Assn., 1988-92; mem. Fed. Jud. Fellows Commn., 1986-92; chmn. Fed. Jud. Ctr. Found. Contbr. articles to legal periodicals. Served with AUS, 1943-46. Fellow Am. Coll. Trial Lawyers (regent 1984-87, pres. 1988-89); mem. Am. Bar Found., Am. Law Inst., ABA, Ill. Bar Assn. (bd. govs. 1960-64), Chgo. Bar Assn. (bd. mgrs. 1966-69), Ill. Soc. Trial Lawyers, Am. Judicature Soc., Law Club Chgo. (pres. 1979-80), Legal Club Chgo. Office: Jenner & Block 1 IBM Plz Chicago IL 60611-3695

TONEGAWA, SUSUMU, biology educator; b. Nagoya, Japan, Sept. 5, 1939; came to U.S., 1963; s. Tsutomu and Miyoko (Masuko) T.; m. Mayumi Yoshinari, Sept. 28, 1985; children: Hidde, Hanna, Satto. BS, Kyoto U., Japan, 1963; PhD, U. Calif., San Diego, 1968. Rsch. asst. U. Calif., San Diego, 1963-64, teaching asst., 1964-68; mem. Basel (Switzerland) Inst. Immunology, 1971-81; prof. biology MIT, Cambridge, 1981—; investigator Howard Hughes Med. Inst., 1988—; dir. MIT Ctr. for Memory and Learning, 1994; professorship Amgen, Inc., 1994. Editorial bd. Jour. Molecular and Cellular Immunology. Decorated Order of Culture, Emperor of Japan; recipient Cloetta prize, 1978, Avery Landsteiner prize Gesselschaft für Immunologie, 1981, Louisa Gross Horwitz prize Columbia U., 1982, award Gardiner Found. Internat., Toronto, Ont., Can., 1983, Robert Koch Found. prize, Bonn., Fed. Republic Germany, 1986, co-recipient Albert Lasker Med. Rsch. award, 1987, Nobel prize in Physiology or Medicine, 1987; named Person with Cultural Merit Japanese Govt., 1983. Mem. NAS (fgn. assoc.), Am. Assn. Immunologists (hon.), Scandinavian Soc. Immunology (hon.). Office: MIT 77 Massachusetts Ave Cambridge MA 02139-3594

TONELLO-STUART, ENRICA MARIA, political economist; b. Monza, Italy; d. Alessandro P. and Maddalena M. (Marangoni) Tonello; m. Albert E. Smith; m. Charles L. Stuart. BA in Internat. Affairs, Econs., U. Colo., 1961; MA, Claremont Grad. Sch., 1966, PhD, 1971. Sales mgr. Met. Life Ins. Co., 1974-79; pres. E.T.S. Rsch. and Devel., Inc., 1977—; dean internat. studies program Union U., L.A. and Tokyo; lectr. internat. affairs and mktg. UCLA Ext., Union U.; CEO, ETS Internat. Investments and ETS Publs., Inc., 1986—. Pub. editor Tomorrow Outline Jour., 1963—, The Monitor, 1988; pub. World Regionalism-An Ecological Analysis, 1971, A Proposal for the Reorganization of the United Nations, 1966, The Persuasion Technocracy, Its Forms, Techniques and Potentials, 1966, The Role of the Multinationals in the Emerging Globalism, 1978; developed the theory of social ecology and econsociometry. Organized first family assistance program Langley AFB Tactical Air Command Commandation, 1956-58. Recipient vol. svc. award VA, 1956-58, ARC svc. award, 1950-58. Mem. Corp. Planners Assn. (treas. 1974-79), Investigative Reporters and Editors, World Future Soc. (pres. 1974—), U.S.-China Journalists Fellowship Assn., Asian Bus. League, Chinese Am. Assn. (life), Japan Am. Assn., L.A. World Trade Ctr., Palos Verdes C. of C. (legis. com.), L.A. Press Club (bd. dirs.), L.A. World Trade Ctr., Zonta (chmn. internat. com. South Bay), Pi Sigma Alpha. Avocations: writing, collecting old books and maps, community service, travel.

TONER, MICHAEL F., journalist; b. LeMars, Iowa, Mar. 17, 1944; s. Francis F. and Mary Ann (Delaney) T.; m. Patricia L. Asleson, Aug. 28, 1966; children: Susan Michelle, Sharon Lynn. BA cum laude, U. Iowa, 1966; postgrad., U. Okla.; Peru; MS cum laude, Northwestern U., 1967. Reporter UPI, Chgo., 1966-67; bur. chief Miami Herald, Key West, Fla., 1967-68, reporter, 1968-69, asst. city editor, 1970-72; sci./environ. writer Miami (Fla) Herald, 1973-84; sci. editor Atlanta Journal and Constitution, 1984-91, sci. writer, 1991—. Co-author: Florida by Paddle and Pack, 1979; contbr. articles to mags. Recipient Pulitzer Prize for explanatory journalism, 1993; Stanford U. profl. journalism fellow, 1973. Avocations: hiking, swimming, photography, stamp collecting, cooking. Office: Atlanta Journal and Constn 72 Marietta St NW Atlanta GA 30303-2804

TONER, WALTER JOSEPH, JR., transportation engineer, financial consultant; b. Rutherford, N.J., July 22, 1921; s. Walter Joseph Toner and Rhea Virginia Carell; m. Barbara Jean Francis, Sept. 11, 1943; children: Sherry Francis, Walter J. III. Student, Wesleyan U., 1938-39; BS in Engring., U.S. Naval Acad., 1942. Profl. engr. Engring. mgr. Bethlehem Steel Corp.,

Boston, 1946-75; nuclear cons. Stone & Webster, Boston, 1975-77; v.p. project devel. & mgmt. Sverdrup Corp., Boston, 1977-86; cons., v.p., T.Y. Lin Internat., Boston, 1986—; v.p. Performance Index, Inc., 1991—. Lt. USN, 1942-46. Fellow Soc. Am. Mil. Engrs. (nat. trustee, v.p. 1978-85, life); mem. ASCE (life), DAV, Am. Consulting Engrs. Coun., Am. Railway Engrs. Assn., Boston Soc. Civil Engrs., Transp. Rsch. Bd., U.S. Naval Acad. Alumni Assn. (life, nat. trustee), U.S. Naval Inst. (life), Wardroom Club, Bass River Yacht Club (chair race com.), Wrinkle Point Beach Assn., Masons. Episcopalian. Office: 100 Tower Ave Needham MA 02194

TONEY, ANTHONY, artist; b. Gloversville, N.Y., June 28, 1913; s. Michael and Susan (Betor) T.; m. Edna Amadon Greenfield, Apr. 8, 1947 (wid. Apr. 1993); children: Anita Karen, Adele Susan. B.F.A., Syracuse U., 1934; M.A., Columbia Tchrs. Coll., 1952, Ed.D., 1955. Instr. art Stevenson Sch., N.Y.C., 1948-52, Hofstra Coll., Hempstead, N.Y., 1953-55, New Sch. Social Research, 1953—; No. Westchester Ctr. for Arts, 1980—; vis. artist Brandeis U., spring 1973, 74. Executed mural Gloversville (N.Y.) High Schs., 1937, Bowne Hall, 1967, Brockway Cafeteria Syracuse U., 1971; one-man shows Wakefield Gallery, 1941, Santa Barbara Mus., 1942, Artists Gallery, 1948, A.C.A. Gallery, 1949, 51, 54, 55, 57, 59, 62, 64, 68, 70, 72, 75, 77, 79, 81, 83, 87, Syracuse Mus., Roswell Mus., Kansas City Art Inst., U. N.Mex., 1956, Berkshire Mus., 1957, 60, S.I. Mus., Rochester Inst. Tech., 1958, U. So. Ill., Tyringham (Mass.) Gallery, 1960, 61, 66, Katonah Gallery, 1982-83, Albany Inst. History and Art, Lenox (Mass.) Art Gallery, Cayuga Mus., Auburn, N.Y., 1959, Harbor Gallery, L.I., N.Y., 1965, Dutchess C.C., Fordham Coll., 1967, Pace Coll., 1968, New Sch. for Social Rsch., 1970, 77, 83, St. Mary's Coll. Md., 1974, Bridge Gallery, White Plains, N.Y., 1975, Virginia Barrett Gallery, 1978, 80, 86, Amphora, La Jolla, Calif., 1979, Nardin Gallery, Crossriver, N.Y., 1986, Retrospective ACA Gallery, 1987, Rutgers U., 1987, Rose Mus., Brandeis U., 1987, No. Westchester Ctr. for the Arts, 1988, Juniper Gallery, Napa (Calif.) Art Ctr., 1991, Rasmussen Art Gallery, Angwin, Calif., 1991, Herbert Johnson, Cornell Mus., 1991, Notre Dame U., 1991, Tchrs. Coll.-Columbia U., N.Y.C., 1994 (Audubon Artists Annual prize 1994); others; exhibited many group shows including Syracuse Mus., Whitney Mus., U. Ill., U. Nebr., Carnegie Biennial, Pa. Acad., Nat. Acad., Walker Art Center, Nat. Inst. Arts and Letters, Am. Acad. Arts and Letters, Katonah Gallery, St. Lawrence U., Purchase Coll., Brandeis U., Westminster Coll., Rutgers U., Corcoran Biennial, Butler Inst. Am. Art, Youngstown, Ohio, 1979-80, Staatliche Galerie, Moritazburg Halle, Fed. Republic, Germany, 1990, Im Gemeente, J.K. Vanreekum-Museum Apeldoorn, Niederlande, 1991, Autier Gallery, Piermont, N.Y., 1992, Peel Gallery, Danbi, Vt., 1993, Nardin Galleries, Somers, N.Y., 1993-94, Triton Mus. Art, Santa Clara, Calif., 1994; works in permanent collections, U. Ill., Ind. Fine Arts Ctr., Ohio Wesleyan U., Wichita State U. Mus., U. Wyo. Mus. Art, Norton Gallery (Fla.), New Britain (Conn.) Mus., Whitney Mus. Tchrs. Coll. Columbia U. Nat. Acad., Chrysler Mus. at, Norfolk, Montgomery Community Mus., S.I. Mus., Berkshire Mus., Butler Inst. Am. Art, Hofstra Coll., No. Westchester Hosp. Ctr., Lenin Mus., USSR, Anti-War Show, Berlin, New Soc. Fine Arts, No. Westchester Ctr. for the Arts, Bklyn. Mus., Herbert Johnson, Notre Dame, Cornell U., Fordham U., Skidmore Coll., Bennington Coll., SUNY, Fleming Hall Mus. U. Vt., City Hall, Gloversville, N.Y., Katonah (N.Y.) Libr., New Eng. Ctr. Contemporary Art, Putnam Art Coun., The State Mus. N.J., Bklyn. Mus., also pvt. collections; freelance comml. artist, 1945-50; author: Creative Painting and Drawing, 1968, Painting and Drawing, 1978, Leonardo; also articles; editor: 150 Masterpieces of Drawing, 1963; contbr. to The Tune of the Calliope, 1958, Family Creative Workshop, 1975, The Palette and the Flame, 1979, Funk and Wagnalls Ency., 1980, Political Affairs, 1985. Served as sgt. AUS, 1942-45. Served in Abraham Lincoln Brigade, Spain, 1938-39. Decorated D.F.C. with clusters, Air medal with clusters; recipient purchase prize U. Ill., 1950, 1st prize Artists Equity Assn., 1952, Emily Lowe award, 1955, Mickewiecz Art Competition 1st prize, 1956, Purchase prize S.I. Mus., 1957, Ranger purchase Nat. Acad., 1966, 76, Childe Hassam purchase prize Nat. Inst. Arts and Letters, 1967, 76, Mintz Meml. award, 1974, Benjamin Altman Figure prize Nat. Acad., 1975, 80, Eggers Sr. Alumni award Syracuse U., 1989, Disting. Alumnus award Tchrs. Coll., Columbia U., 1991, 3 1st prizes Putnam Arts Coun., 1994. Mem. NEA, Nat. Soc. Mural Painters (treas. 1973-74), Artists Equity Assn. (nat. dir. 1952-56, 71-72, sec. nat. bd. 1956-57, exec. bd. N.Y. chpt. 1960-62, 71-72), Audubon Artists (mem. bd. 1959, 75-78, Grumbacher award 1954, medal of honor Nat. Show 1967, 75, 87, Judy Brenne Meml. award 1981, Ann. Emily Lowe award 1983, Ralph Fabri award 1984, Ann. Robert Phillips Meml. award 1988, Len G. Everett Meml. award 1989, 91, Silver medal 1993), Nat. Acad. (mem. council, asst. corr. spc. 1978—, membership com. 1988—), Coll. Art Assn., Kappa Delta Pi. Home: 16 Hampton Pl Katonah NY 10536-1402 *I consider persistent struggle in the context of as much awareness of all possible factors of key importance. It is necessary to be as whole as possible in one's understanding of self, life, society and one's individual endeavor. One's goal must be the survival of life, the earth and solar system that makes it possible, and the solution of the problems that threaten human survival and perhaps all existence as we know it.*

TONEY, ROBERT L., naval officer; b. Monroe, La., Aug. 30, 1934; s. James and Alice (Jackson) T.; m. Flora Jean Wallace, Jan. 26, 1963; children: Kimberly E., Kelly A., Robert N. BA in Social Sci., Chico State U., 1957; PhD (hon.), Nat. U., 1988. Commd. ensign USNR, 1957; advanced through grades to rear adm. (upper), 1988; asst. communications officer USS Bennington, 1957-59; staff officer, comdr. Tng. Command, U.S. Pacific Fleet, 1959-61; ops. officer USS Guadalupe, 1963-66; combat info. officer USS Topeka, 1966-67; sr. project officer, Destroyer Devel. Group, spl. project officer, comdr. Cruiser-Destroyer Group, Pacific Fleet, 1967-68; exec. officer USS Crowell, 1968-69; spl. asst. to chief naval ops. under comdr. Naval Recruiting Command for Minority Affairs, Arlington, Va., 1969-73; exec. officer USS Wichita, 1972-74; comdg. officer USS Kiska, 1974-76; student NATO Def. Coll., 1977; staff comdr. Allied Forces, So. Europe, 1977-79; chief staff, comdr. Svc. Group ONE, Oakland, Calif., 1979-83; comdg. officer USS Roanoke, 1983; dep. comdr. Naval Surface Force Pacific; comdr. Naval Surface Group Long Beach, Calif., 1984-85, Naval San Francisco, Logistics Group ONE, 1986-89; dir. Logistics-Security Assistance, USCINCPAC/J4, Camp H. M. Smith, Hawaii, 1989—. Bd. dirs. Boys Club Oakland, Calif., Salvation Army, San Francisco, Urban League, San Francisco, Navy Adopt Sch. Program, San Francisco Bay Area, 1986-88. Decorated Legion of Merit, Def. Meritorious Svc. medal, Armed Forces Expeditionary medal, Nat. Def. Svc. medal; Vietnam Svc. medal (Socialist Republic Vietnam), Republic of Vietnam Campaign medal. Mem. Nat. Naval Officers Assn. (sr.), Masons, Kappa Alpha Psi. Methodist. Avocation: reading. Home: 1016 Ashmount Ave Oakland CA 94610-1261 Office: US CINCPAC Code J4 Box 20 Camp H M Smith HI 96861

TONEY, SHIRLEY PUTMAN, nursing administrator, educator; b. Rutherford County, N.C., Jan. 28, 1937; d. Thomas Alonzo and Mary Grace (Johnson) Putman; m. Max Lee Toney, Sept. 23, 1962; children: Andy Lee, Victor Brian. Diploma, N.C. Bapt. Hosp. Sch. Nursing, 1961; BSN, Wake Forest U., 1961; MEd, N.C. State U., Raleigh, 1974; PhD in Nursing, U. Tex., 1989. Head nurse Harris Hosp., Ft. Worth; staff and charge nurse, asst. head nurse Cleve. Meml. Hosp., Shelby, N.C.; instr. in nursing diploma program Rutherford Hosp., Rutherfordton, N.C.; dir. assoc. degree nursing program Gardner-Webb U., Boiling Springs, N.C., 1965-90, prof., chair dept. nursing, 1992—; dir. assoc. degree nursing program Catawba Valley C.C., Hickory, N.C., 1990-92. Mem. ANA, N.C. Coun. Assoc. Degree Nursing Programs, Phi KappaPhi, Beta Beta Beta. Home: RR 1 Box 279A Forest City NC 28043-9737

TONG, HING, mathematician, educator; b. Canton, China, Feb. 16, 1922; s. Shen-Beu and Fung-Kam (Cheng) T.; m. Mary Josephine Powderly, Aug. 19, 1956; children—Christopher Hing, Mary Elizabeth, William Joseph, Jane Frances, James John. A.B., U. Pa., 1943; Ph.D., Columbia, 1947; M.A. (hon.), Wesleyan U., Middletown, Conn., 1961. NRC postdoctoral fellow Inst. Advanced Study, Princeton, 1947-48; lectr. Canton (China) U., 1949; Cutting travelling fellow Inst. Henri Poincare, Paris, France, 1950-51; asst. prof. Reed Coll., 1952-53; vis. asst. prof. Barnard Coll., 1953-54; mem. faculty Wesleyan U., 1954-67, prof. math., 1960-67, chmn. dept., 1962-64; prof. math. Fordham U., Bronx, N.Y., 1966—; chmn. dept. Fordham U., 1967-74; mem. U.S. subcom. World Orgn. Gen. Systems and Cybernetics. Contbr. profl. jours. Mem. Phi Beta Kappa, Sigma Xi. Home: 725 Cooper Ave Oradell NJ 07649-2334 Office: Fordham Univ Bronx NY 10458

TONG, ROSEMARIE, medical humanities and philosophy educator, consultant and researcher; b. Chgo., July 19, 1947; d. Joseph John and Lillian (Nedued) Behensky; m. Paul Ki-King Tong, Aug. 15, 1971 (dec. Apr. 1988); children: Paul Shih-Mien Tong, John Joseph Tong; m. Jeremiah Putnam, Aug. 1, 1992. BA, Marygrove U., 1970; MA, Cath. U., 1971; PhD, Temple U., 1978; LLD (hon.), Marygrove Coll., 1987; LHD (hon.), SUNY, Oneonta, 1993. Asst. and assoc. prof. philosophy Williams Coll., Williamstown, Mass., 1978-88; vis. disting. prof. humanities Davidson (N.C.) Coll., 1988-89, Thatcher Prof. in med. humanities and philosophy, 1989—; Louise M. Olmstead vis. prof. philosophy and women's studies, Lafayette Coll., Easton, Pa., 1993—; manuscript reviewer Wadsworth Pub. Co., 1985-92; curriculum reviewer philosophy dept. Carlton and Bowdoin Colls., 1986; honors examiner Hobart and William Smith Colls., 1990; dissertation dir., adj. faculty The Union Inst., 1992-93; cons., awards judge, panelist, organizer and speaker in field; mem. numerous U.S. coms. Author: Women, Sex and the Law, 1984, Ethics in Policy Analysis, 1985, Feminist Thought: A Comprehensive Introduction, 1989, Feminist Philosophies: Problems, Theories, and Applications, 1991, Feminine and Feminist Ethics, 1993, (with Larry Kaplan) Controlling Our Reproductive Destiny, 1994, Feminist Philosophy: Essential Readings in Theory, Reinterpretation and Application, 1994; contbr. numerous articles to profl. jours.; mem. various editl. bds. Project reviewer Annenberg/CPB Project, Washington, 1986; policy writer dvsn. health svcs. rsch. and policy U. Minn., 1988, Frank Graham Porter Early Childhood Ctr., U. N.C. Chapel Hill, 1988; mem. Charlotte task force Congl. Task Force Health Care, Congressman Alex McMillan, 1991, standards and ethics com. Hospice N.C., 1991, resource and ethics coms. McMillan-Spratt Task Force Health Care Policy, 1992, pastoral care com. Carolinas Med. Ctr., 1990—, ethics com. Presbyt. Hosp., 1990—, Cabarrus Hosp., 1991, Nat. Adv. Bd. Ethics in Reproduction, Washington, 1993; active Hastings Ctr. Project Undergrad. Values Edn., Briarcliff Manor, N.Y., 1993, N.C. Found. Humanities and Pub. Policy. Named Prof. of Yr., Carnegie Found. and Coun. Advancement and Support of Edn., 1986. Mem. Am. Cath. Philosophical Assn., Am. Philosophical Assn. (ad hoc com. computers, pub. and role of Am. Philosophical Assn. 1984, adv. com. to program com. 1986-88, nomination com. 1989-91, nat. com. on status of women 1989-93), Am. Legal Studies and Assn., Am. Soc. Pol. and Legal Philosophy, Am. Soc. Law and Medicine, Nat. Coun. Rsch. on Women, Nat. Women Studies Assn., Internat. Assn. Philosophy of Law and Social Philosophy, Assn. Practical and Profl. Ethics, Soc. Health and Human Values (faculty program chairperson 1991—), Society Christian Ethics, Soc. Women in Philosophy, Soc. Philosophy and Tech., Soc. Philosophy and Pub. Affairs, Soc. Study of Women Philosophers, Network Feminist Approaches to Bioethics, The Hastings Ctr., Triangle Bioethics Group, So. Soc. Philosophy and Psychology. Avocations: aerobics, boating, hiking. Home: 20501 Pointe Regatta Dr Davidson NC 28036-8951 Office: Davidson Coll PO Box 1719 Main St Davidson NC 28036

TONGES, MARY CRABTREE, nurse executive; b. Dixon, Ill.; d. John Charles and Marion Rita (Shields) Crabtree; m. James Alan Tonges, may 21, 1983; children: Christina Mary, James John. BSN, U. Iowa, 1973; MSN, U. Ill., Chgo., 1977; MBA, Baruch Coll., 1994. Cert. in nursing adminstrn. Asst. dir. med.-surg. nursing St. Joseph Hosp., Chgo., 1977-78; dir. specialty nursing Northwestern Meml. Hosp., Chgo., 1979-82; v.p. nursing Clara Maass Med. Ctr., Belleville, N.J., 1983-86, Robert Wood Johnson U. Hosp., New Brunswick, N.J., 1987-91; cons. dir. for Case Mgmt., Inc., South Natick, Mass., 1991—. Contbr. articles to profl. jours. Commonwealth Fund nurse exec. fellow, 1991. Mem. Am. Orgn. Nurse Execs., Orgn.Nursing Execs. N.J., Nat. Forum Women Health Care Leaders, Sigma Theta Tau. Home: 8 Fairfield St Montclair NJ 07042-4114

TONGUE, PAUL GRAHAM, financial executive; b. Phila., Dec. 30, 1932; s. George Paul and Florence Amelia (Kogel) T.; m. Marjorie Joan Meyers, May 26, 1954; children: Suzanne Marjorie, Douglas Paul. BS in Commerce, Drexel U., 1957; MBA, NYU, 1958. With Chase Manhattan Bank, N.Y.C. 1957-87; pres. Eppley-Tongue Assocs., Inc., Towson, Md., 1988—; exec. v.p. Veritas Venture Inc., Scotch Plains, N.J., 1990-91; chmn. Plus Systems Inc., Denver. Pres. Our Saviour Luth. Ch., Manhasset, N.Y., 1984; bd. dirs. Nassau Symphony Orch. With U.S. Army, 1954-55. Mem. Ford's Colony Country Club. Avocations: golf, classical music.

TONGUE, WILLIAM WALTER, economics and business consultant, educator emeritus; b. Worcester, Mass., May 24, 1915; s. Walter Ernest and Lena (Brown) T.; m. Beverly Harriet Cohan, Dec. 26, 1936; children—Barbara Tongue Duggan, Kathleen Tongue Alligood. A.B., Dartmouth, 1937, M.C.S., 1938; Ph.D., U. Chgo., 1947. Jr. acct. Price, Waterhouse & Co. (C.P.A.'s), N.Y.C., 1938; instr. Coe Coll., Cedar Rapids, Iowa, 1941-42; spl. cons. OSS, 1942; financial economist Fed. Res. Bank Chgo., 1942-44; economist Jewel Companies, Inc., Chgo., 1944-64; prof. econs. and finance U. Ill. Chgo. Circle, 1965-80, prof. emeritus, 1980—; prof. emeritus, 1980—; econ. cons. LaSalle Nat. Bank, Chgo., 1968-91; mem. com. CNA Fin. Separate Fund B.; dir. St. Joseph Light & Power Co., Mo., 1965-86; trustee Signode Employees' Savings and Profit Sharing Trust Fund, 1980-89. Author articles; contbr. to books including How We Can Halt Inflation and Still Keep Our Jobs, 1974. Bd. dirs., v.p. research and statistics Chgo. Assn. Commerce and Industry, 1968-69. Mem. Nat. Assn. Bus. Economists (pres. 1962-63), Conf. Bus. Economists, Am. Statis. Assn. (pres. Chgo. chpt. 1951-52), Econ. Club Chgo., Investment Analysts Assn. Chgo., Inst. Chartered Fin. Analysts (chartered fin. analyst 1963), Midwest Fin. Assn. (pres. 1972-73). Home and Office: 212 Shoreline Dr Park Ridge IL 60068-2934

TONJES, MARIAN JEANNETTE BENTON, education educator; b. Rockville Center, N.Y., Feb. 16, 1929; d. Millard Warren and Felicia E. (Tyler) Benton; m. Charles F. Tonjes (div. 1965); children: Jeffrey Charles, Kenneth Warren. BA, U. N.Mex., 1951, cert., 1966, MA, 1969; EdD, U. Miami, 1975. Dir. recreation Stuyvesant Town Housing Project, N.Y.C., 1951-53; tchr. music., phys. edn. Sunset Mesa Day Sch., Albuquerque, 1953-54; tchr. remedial reading Zia Elem. Sch., Albuquerque, 1965-67; tchr. secondary devel. reading Rio Grande High Sch., Albuquerque, 1967-69; asst. reading Southwestern Coop. Ednl. Lab., Albuquerque, 1969-71; assoc. dir., vis. instr. Fla. Ctr. Tchr. Tng. Materials U. Miami, 1971-72; asst. prof. U.S. Internat. U., San Diego, 1972-75; prof. edn. Western Wash. U., Bellingham, 1975-94, prof. emerita, 1994—; dir. summer study at Oxford (Eng.) U., 1975-94; vis. prof. adult edn. Palomar (Calif.) Jr. Coll., 1974; reading supr. Manzanita Ctr. U. N.Mex., Albuquerque, 1968; vis. prof. U. Guam, Mangilao, 1989-90; speaker, cons. in field; invited guest Russian Reading Assn., Moscow, 1992. Author: (with Miles V. Zintz) Teaching Reading/Thinking Study Skills in Content Classrooms, 3d edit., 1992, Secondary Reading, Writing and Learning, 1991; contbr. articles to profl. jours. Tng. Tchr. Trainers grantee, 1975; NDEA fellow Okla. State U., 1969. Mem. Am. Reading Forum (chmn. bd. dirs. 1983-85), Adult and Adolescent Literacy Confs. (spkr. 1991—), Internat. Reading Assn. (mem. travel, interchange and study tours com. 1984-86, mem. non-print media and reading com. 1988-93, workshop dir. S.W. regional conf. 1982, mem. com. internat. devel. N.Am. 1991—, Outstanding Tchr. Educator 1988-90), U.K. Reading Assn. (spkr. 1977-93), European Conf. in Reading (Berlin 1989, Edinburgh 1991, Malmo 1993, Budapest 1995 spkr.), European Coun. Internat. Schs. (The Hague, spkr. 1993), World Congress in Reading Buenos Aires (spkr. 1994), PEO (past chpt. pres.), Phi Delta Kappa, Delta Delta Delta. Avocations: miniatures, tennis, bridge, art, travel.

TONKIN, HUMPHREY RICHARD, university president; b. Truro, Cornwall, Eng., Dec. 2, 1939; came to U.S., 1962; s. George Leslie and Lorna Winifred (Sandry) T.; m. Sandra Julie Winberg, Mar. 9, 1968 (div. 1981); m. Jane Spencer Edwards, Oct. 1, 1983; 1 child, Sebastian George. BA, St. John's Coll., Cambridge, Eng., 1962, MA, 1966; AM, Harvard U., 1966, PhD, 1966. Asst. prof. English U. Pa., Phila., 1966-71, assoc. prof., 1971-80, prof., 1980-83, vice-provost undergrad. studies, 1971-75, coord. internat. programs, 1977-83, master Stouffer Coll. House, 1980-83; pres. State Univ. Coll., Potsdam, N.Y., 1983-88, U. Hartford, Conn., 1989—; vis. prof. English Columbia U., N.Y.C., 1980-81; exec. dir. Ctr. Rsch. and Documentation on World Lang. Problems, Rotterdam and Hartford, 1974—; mem. editl. bd. Spenser Studies, Duquesne Studies in Lang. and Lit.; mng. editor Lang. Problems and Lang. Planning. Author: (bibliography) Sir Walter Raleigh, 1971, Esperanto and International Language Problems, 4th edit., 1977, Spenser's Courteous Pastoral, 1972, (with Jane Edwards) The World in the Curriculum 1981, The Faerie Queene, 1989, (with Allison Keef)

Language in Religion, 1989, Esperanto: Language, Literature, and Community, 1993; contbr. articles, studies, revs. to profl. jours. Pres. Pa. Coun. Internat. Edn., 1980-81; bd. dirs. World Affairs Coun. Phila., 1979-83, Am. Forum, 1985—, Zamenhof Found., 1987—, Hartford Symphony Orch., 1989—, World Affairs Coun. Conn., 1989—, Greater Hartford Arts Coun., 1989—; chmn. Coun. Internat. Exch. Scholars, 1991-95, Esperantic Studies Found., 1991—, Partnership for Svc.-Learning, 1991—. Recipient Lindback award for disting. teaching, 1970; Frank Knox fellow Harvard U., 1962-66; Guggenheim fellow, 1974. Fellow Acad. Esperanto; mem. Universal Esperanto Assn. (pres. 1974-80, 86-89, rep. to UN 1974-93), Spenser Soc. (pres. 1983-84, former dir.), Internat. Acad. Scis. San Marino, Conn. Acad. Arts and Scis., Greater Hartford C. of C., Cosmos Club, Hartford Golf Club, Hartford Club. Home: 85 Bloomfield Ave Hartford CT 06105 Office: U Hartford Office of Pres 200 Bloomfield Ave West Hartford CT 06117

TONKIN, LEO SAMPSON, educational foundation administrator; b. Suffern, N.Y., Apr. 2, 1937; s. Leo S. and Ann (Petrone) T. A.B., Johns Hopkins, 1959; postgrad., Sch. Advanced Internat. Studies, 1962-63; J.D., Harvard, 1962; Dr. Pedagogy, St. Thomas Aquinas Coll., 1973. Legis. asst. to U.S. Congressman; then Sen. Charles McC. Mathias, Jr., of Md., 1962-63; asso. counsel U.S. Ho. of Reps. Select Com. on Govt. Research, 1964; spl. cons. Ho. Spl. Subcom. on Edn., 1965-66; exec. dir. D.C. Commrs. Council on Higher Edn., 1965-66; pres. Leo S. Tonkin Assos., Inc., 1966—; founder, dir., chmn. bd. Washington Workshops Found., 1967—; Mem. White House Conf. on Edn., 1965, White House Conf. on Youth, 1971; spl. asst. to chmn. U.S. Ho. of Reps. Select Com. on Crime, 1972; mem. bd. plebe sponsors U.S. Naval Acad., 1977—; v.p. London Fedn. Boys' Clubs, 1980—; mem. adv. panel Nat. Commn. for Protection of Human Subjects of Biomed. and Behavioral Research, HEW, 1976-77. Contbr. articles to mags. Bd. dirs. Washington Choral Arts Soc., 1971-73, Nat. Coordinating Council on Drug Edn., 1973, Nat. Student Ednl. Fund, 1974—; chmn. Wall Street Seminar Found., 1978—; chmn. bd. trustees St. Thomas Aquinas Coll., 1966-73, continuing trustee, 1973-78, trustee, chmn. emeritus, 1978—; chmn. bd. trustees City of Phila. Govt. Honors Program; trustee Southeastern U., 1966-73; asso. bd. trustees Immaculata Coll., 1966-73; mem. advisory bd. Pub. Affairs and Govt. Degree Program, Mt. Vernon Coll., 1971-74; bd. dirs. YMCA, Washington, 1969-71. Recipient Americanism award, Valley Forge Freedoms Found, 1973. Mem. Johns Hopkins Alumni Assn. of Washington (pres. 1969-72). Clubs: Georgetown (Washington), City Tavern (Washington), Nat. Press (Washington), Capitol Hill (Washington), Capitol Yacht (Washington); Harvard (N.Y.C.). Home: 4368 Sunset Ct Nokesville VA 22123 Office: 3222 N St NW Washington DC 20007-2849

TONKONOGY, JOSEPH MOSES, physician, neuropsychiatrist, researcher; b. Belaya Tserkov, Kiev, Ukraine, Oct. 22, 1925; cmae to U.S., 1979, naturalized, 1985; s. Moysey Iosifovich and Beyla (Gdalievna (Schvachkina) T.; married; children: Vitaly, Milla, Bella. MD, Military Med. Acad., Leningrad, USSR, 1947; PhD, All Union Acad. Med. Sci., Moscow, 1956; DSc, 1st Med. Inst., Leningrad, 1966. From asst. to assoc. prof. The Bechterev Inst., Leningrad, 1956-66, prof., chmn., 1966-78; assoc. Boston U. Sch. Medicine, 1980-81; physician VA Med. Ctr., Northampton, Mass., 1981-87; assoc. prof. U. Mass. Med. Ctr., Worcester, 1987—; dir. neuropsychiatry svc. Worcester State Hosp., Mass., 1989—. Author: Introduction to Clinical Neuropsychology, 1973, Vascular Aphasia, 1986; editor: Problems of Contemporary Psychoneurology, 1966, Psychological Experiment in Psychiatry and Neurology, 1969, Mathematical Methods in Psychiatry and Neurology, 1971, Current Problems of Clinical Psychology, 1975; cons.: (book) Soviet Military Psychiatry, 1986; contbr. numerous articles to profl. jours. Capt. Med. Corps, Germany, 1947-48. Recipient The Bechterev Prize, All Union Acad. Med. Scis., Moscow, 1974. Fellow The Royal Soc. Medicine (U.K.); mem. Am. Neuropsychiat. Assn., Am. Acad. Neurology, Internat. Neuropsychol. Soc., Soc. Neurosci., Internat. Psychogeriatric Soc. Jewish. Office: U Mass Med Ctr 55 Lake Ave N Worcester MA 01655-0002

TONKS, ROBERT STANLEY, pharmacology and therapeutics educator, former university dean; b. Aberystwyth, Wales; emigrated to Can., 1973; s. Robert Patrick Dennis and Prudence Violet (Williams) T.; m. Diana Mary Cownie; children: Pamela Mary, Julia Rosalind, Robert Michael, Sara Katharine. Student, U. Coll. of South Wales, Welsh Coll. Pharmacy; B.Pharm., Welsh Nat. Sch. Medicine, Cardiff, Ph.D. Organon postdoctoral fellow Med. Sch., Cardiff, Nat. Health Service postdoctoral fellow; Nat. Health Service sr. fellow Cardiff and Nevill Hall Hosp., Abergavenny; lectr. pharmacology U. Wales, Cardiff, 1958-72; vis. fellow Claude Bernard Research Assn., Faculté de Medicine, Paris, 1959; sr. lectr. pharmacology and therapeutics Med. Sch. and U. Wales Hosp., Cardiff, 1972-73; dir., prof. Coll. Pharmacy, Dalhousie U., Halifax, N.S., Can., 1973-77, dean Faculty of Health Professions, 1977-88, prof. geriatric pharmaco-therapeutics, 1988—; acting head divsn. geriatric medicine, 1991-94; cons. pharm. industry in U.K., Govt. of N.B., Can., Health and Welfare Dept. Can.; advisor health manpower Govt. of N.S.; coordinator N.E. Can./Am. Health Coun. co-chmn., 1974-91; mem. Health and Welfare Personnel Career Rev. Com.; pharm. scis. grants com. Med. Rsch. Council Can., chmn.; mem. rev. com. health protection br. fed. govt. div. pharm. chemistry, Can.; chmn. advisory com. N.B. Minister of Health; mem. joint com. on devel. rsch. in nursing Med. Rsch. Coun.-Nat. Health Rsch. Devel. Program; mem. nat. adv. panel on risk/benefit mgmt. of drugs. Contbr. articles on pharmacology and pathology to profl. jours. Fellow Pharm. Soc. Gt. Britain, Inst. Biology; mem. Brit. Pharmacol. Soc., Internat. Soc. Thrombosis and Haemostasis, Canadian Soc. Clin. Investigation, Soc. Pharm. Medicine, Can. Assn. on Gerontology, Gerontol. Soc. Am., Am. Soc. Clin. Pharm. and Therapeutics, Can. Soc. Hosp. Pharmacy (hon.), N.B. Pharm. Soc. (hon.), N.S. Pharm. Soc. (cert. of merit, coord. drug and med. supplies Ethiopia airlift), Med. Soc. N.S. (task force on pharmacare), Welsh Cultural Soc. (past pres.). Anglican. Home: 62 Kingsway Dr, Haliburton Hills, NS Canada B0J 3J0 Office: Dalhousie U, Coburg Rd, Halifax, NS Canada

TONKYN, RICHARD GEORGE, retired oil and gas company executive, researcher, consultant; b. Portland, Oreg., Mar. 26, 1927; s. William James and Gladys (Campbell) T.; m. Carol Joan Sloan, May 29, 1948 (div. 1976); children: Michael Stephen, Paula Ruth, David William, John Campbell, James Lewis, Russell George; m. Barbara Ann Friedman, May 27, 1982. BA, Reed Coll., 1948; MA, U. Oreg., 1951; PhD, U. Wash., 1960. Registered patent agt., U.S. Patent and Trademark Office. Chemist Titanium Metals Corp., Henderson, Nev., 1952-54, Allegheny Ludlum Steel, Brackenridge, Pa., 1954-55; rsch. engr. Boeing Airplane Co., Seattle, 1955-59; chemist, project scientist Union Carbide Corp., Bound Brook, N.J., 1961-69; mgr. rsch., group leader Betz Labs., Inc., Trevose, Pa., 1969-76; v.p. rsch. and devel. Mogul div. The Dexter Corp., Chagrin Falls, Ohio, 1976-85, Petrolite Corp., St. Louis, 1985-92. Patentee in field. NSF fellow, 1959, 60-61. Mem. Am. Chem. Soc., Indsl. Rsch. Inst., Cooling Tower Inst. (bd. dirs. 1982-85, pres. 1985), Physical and Chem. Soc., Sigma Xi, Phi Lambda Upsilon. Avocations: tennis, golf.

TONN, ELVERNE MERYL, pediatric dentist, dental insurance consultant; b. Stockton, Calif., Dec. 10, 1929; s. Emanuel M. and Lorna Darlene (Bryant) T.; m. Ann G. Richardson, Oct. 28, 1951; children: James Edward, Susan Elaine Tonn Yee. AA, La Sierra U., Riverside, Calif., 1949; DDS, U. So. Calif., 1955; BS, Regents Coll., 1984. Lic. dentist; cert. tchr., Calif., dental ins. cons. Pediatric dentist, assoc. Walker Dental Group, Long Beach, Calif., 1957-59, Children's Dental Clinic, Sunnyvale, Calif., 1959-61; pediatric dentist in pvt. practice Mountain View, Calif., 1961-72; from clin. instr. to assoc. prof. U. Pacific, San Francisco, 1964-84; pediatric dentist, ptnr. Pediatric Dentistry Assocs., Los Altos, Calif., 1972-83; assoc. prof. U. Calif., San Francisco, 1984-86; pediatric dentist, ptnr. Valley Oak Dental Group, Manteca, Calif., 1987—; pediatric dental cons. Delta Dental Plan, San Francisco, 1985—; chief dental staff El Camino Hosp., Mountain View, 1964-65, 84-85; lectr. in field. Weekly columnist Manteca Bull., 1987-92; producer 2 teaching videos, 1986; contbr. articles to profl. jours. Lectr. to elem. students on dental health Manteca Unified Sch. Dist., 1982-92; dental health screener Elem. Schs., San Joaquin County Pub. Health, 1989-92; dental cons. Interplast program Stanford U. Sch. Medicine. Capt. U.S. Army, 1955-57. Fellow Internat. Coll. Dentists, Internat. Assn. Pediatric Dentistry, Internat. Assn. Dental Rsch., Fedn. Dentaire Internationale, Am. Acad. Pediatric Dentistry, Am. Coll. Dentists, Royal Soc. Health (Eng.), Acad. of Dentistry for Handicapped, Pierre Fauchard Acad., Am. Dental Materials; mem. ADA, Am. Assn. Dentists Children, Am. Assn. Dental

Cons., Calif. Dental Assn., Calif. Soc. Dentistry for Children (pres. 1968). Calif. Soc. Pediatric Dentists, N.Y. Acad. Scis., Calif. Acad. Sci., Am. Bd. Quality Assurance & Utilization Rev. Physicians, Nat. Assn. for Healthcare Quality, Rotary Internat. Republican. Avocations: photography, travel, history. Home: 374 Laurelwood Cir Manteca CA 95336-7122 Office: Valley Oak Dental Group Inc 1507 W Yosemite Ave Manteca CA 95337

TONN, ROBERT JAMES, entomologist; b. Watertown, Wis., June 23, 1927; s. Harry James and Elise (Foogman) T.; m. Noemi C. Tonn; children: Sigrid M., Monica E. BS, Colo. State U., 1949, MS, 1950; MPH, Okla. Med. Sch., 1963; PhD, Okla. State U., 1959. Rsch. assoc La. State U., Costa Rica/New Orleans, 1961-63; dir. Taunton Field Sta., Taunton, Mass., 1963-65; chief PMO unit WHO, various locations, 1965-87; adj. prof. of parasitology U. Tex.-El Paso, 1988—; cons. USAID/VBC, 1987—. Contbr. numerous articles to profl. jours. Mem. Am. Soc. Tropical Medicine, Soc. Vector Ecology (pres. 1984), Am. Mosquito Control Assn., U.S./ Mex. Border Health Assn., Royal Soc. Tropical Medicine and Hygiene, Masons. Congregationalist. Home: RR 3 Box 505 Park Rapids MN 56470-9363

TONNOS, ANTHONY, bishop; b. Port Colborne, Ont., Can., Aug. 1, 1935. Ordained priest Roman Cath. Ch., 1961. Bishop Archdiocese of Hamilton, Ont., Can., 1984—. Office: Roman Catholic Church-Canada, 700 King St W, Hamilton, ON Canada L8P 1C7

TONTZ, ROBERT L., government official; b. Guthrie, Okla., May 18, 1917; s. John and Mabel (Johnson) T.; m. Hazel D. Crothers, June 10, 1944; children: John W., Brenda Kay. BS, Okla. State U., 1940, PhD, 1952; MS, Iowa State U., 1941. Asst. agrl. economist U. Tenn., 1942; assoc. agrl. economist U.S. Dept. Agr., Washington, 1942-45, agrl. economist, 1956-68, supervisory agrl. economist, 1971-80; agrl. statistician U.S. Dept. Commerce, Washington, 1946; asst. prof. Okla. State U., 1947-55; internat. economist Dept. State, Paris, 1968-71; econ. cons. Nat. Assn. Fed. and State Employees, 1980—. Editor: Foreign Agricultural Trade: Selected Readings, 1966; contbr. numerous econ. studies to profl. jours.; sr. joint author: Memberships of General Farmers' Organizations, United States, 1965-89, 1991, U.S. Agricultural Organizations The Voices of Organized Agriculture, 1991, Historical Statistics of Memberships of General Farmers' Organizations United States, 1874-1991, 1992, Organized Agriculture in the United States, 1992. Elder, chmn. bd. dirs. Christian Ch., Falls Church, Va. Recipient Superior Svc. award U.S. Dept. Agr., 1965, 75, Blue Ribbon award, 1972. Mem. Nat. Orgn. Fed.-State Employees (pres. 1988-92), Sigma Xi, Phi Kappa Phi, Alpha Phi Sigma, Alpha Zeta, Phi Eta Sigma. Home: 8712 Braeburn Dr Annandale VA 22003-3970

TOOHEY, BRIAN FREDERICK, lawyer; b. Niagara Falls, N.Y., Dec. 14, 1944; s. Matthew Frederick and Marilyn Gertrude (Hoag) T.; m. Mary Elizabeth Monihan; children: Maureen Elizabeth, Matthew Sheridan, Margaret Monihan, Mary Catherine. BS, Niagara U., 1966; JD, Cornell U., 1969. Bar: N.Y. 1969, N.Mex. 1978, Ohio 1980. Ptnr. Cohen, Swados, Wright, Hanifin & Bradford, Buffalo, 1973-77; pvt. practice, Santa Fe, 1977-79; of counsel Jones, Day, Reavis & Pogue, Cleve., 1979-80, ptnr., 1981—. Mem. Citizens League Greater Cleve., 1982—. Lt. JAG Corps, USNR, 1970-73. Mem. ABA, N.Y. State Bar Assn., State Bar N.Mex., Ohio State Bar Assn., Greater Cleve. Bar Assn. Roman Catholic. Home: 25 Pepper Creek Dr Cleveland OH 44124-5279 Office: Jones Day Reavis & Pogue N Point 901 Lakeside Ave Cleveland OH 44114-1190

TOOHEY, CYNTHIA D., state legislator; b. N.Y.C., Apr. 16, 1934; widowed; children: Camden, Sean, Kate. ADN, U. Alaska-Anchorage C.C. 1974. Co-owner, operator Crow Creek Mine, 1970—; mem. Alaska House of Reps., Anchorage, 1992—. Trustee Alaska Regional Hosp.; bd. dirs. Anchorage Conv. & Visitors Bur.; past mem. Girdwood Bd. Suprs. Office: The House of Representatives 2642 Forest Park Dr Anchorage AK 99517-1326

TOOHEY, DANIEL WEAVER, lawyer; b. St. Louis, Feb. 5, 1940; s. Jerome Vincent and Marion (Weaver) T.; m. Anne Iva Latta, Aug. 14, 1966; children: Bridget Toohey Keefe, Sean Kirkpatrick. AB, St. Louis U., 1961, JD, 1964. Prodr., dir. Sta. KETC-TV, St. Louis, 1961-64; gen. atty. FCC, Washington, 1964-65; assoc. lawyer Welch & Morgan, Washington, 1965-66; assoc. lawyer Dow, Lohnes & Albertson, Washington, 1966-71, ptnr., 1971—; mng. ptnr. Dow Lohnes & Albertson, Washington, 1985-91; Henry Marsh prof. U. Mich., Ann Arbor, 1984, vis. prof., 1985-86; dir. Bur. Nat. Affairs, Inc., Washington. Author: Legal Problems in Broadcasting, 1974; contbr. articles to profl. jours.; mem. editorial adv. bd. Pub. Telecom. Rev., 1973-81. Mem. adv. com. The Ohio State Awards, 1984-94; trustee Legal Aid Soc. of D.C., 1984—, pres. 1991-93; trustee The Washington Opera, 1986-90; bd. dirs., corp. sec. Volunteer: The Nat. Ctr., 1986-92; trustee Shakespeare Theatre of Washington, 1987—, vice chmn. and gen. counsel, 1991—; Washington trustee Fed. City Coun., 1987—, mem. exec. com., 1991—; mem. Greater Washington Bd. of Trade's Crime Task Force, 1989-90, mem. regional affairs com., 1990—; gen. counsel Greater Washington Bd. Trade, 1993—. Mem. Nat. Assn. Coll. and Univ. Attys., D.C. Bar Assn. (bd. dirs. 1976-77), Econ. Club Washington, Met. Club Washington, Columbia Country Club. Roman Catholic. Avocations: reading, writing, golf, hunting. Office: Dow Lohnes & Albertson 1255 23d St NW Ste 500 Washington DC 20037-1194

TOOHEY, JAMES KEVIN, lawyer; b. Evanston, Ill., July 16, 1944; s. John Joseph and Ruth Regina (Cassidy) T.; m. Julie Marie Crane, Nov. 1, 1969 (div. Aug. 1977); children: Julie Colleen, Jeanne Christine; m. Anne Margaret Boettigheimer, May 28, 1983; children: James Robert, Kevin John, Casey Anne. BBA, U. Notre Dame, 1966; JD, Northwestern U., 1969. Bar: Ill. 1969, Wis. 1992, U.S. Dist. Ct. (no. dist.) Ill. 1971, U.S. Dist. Ct. (ctrl. dist.) Ill. 1991, U.S. Ct. Appeals (7th cir.) 1972, U.S. Ct. Appeals (8th cir.) 1975, U.S. Supreme Ct. 1988. Assoc. Taylor, Miller, Magner, Sprowl & Hutchings, Chgo., 1970-71, Ross, Hardies, O'Keefe, Babcock & Parsons, Chgo., 1974-77; asst. U.S. atty. Office U.S. Atty., Chgo., 1971-74; ptnr. Ross & Hardies, Chgo., 1978—. Bd. dirs., commr. Edgebrook Sauganash Youth Baseball, 1993—. Mem. Ill. Bar Assn., Soc. Trial Lawyers, Assn. Advancement of Automotive Medicine, Ill. Assn. Defense Attys., Trial Lawyers Club Chgo. Office: Ross & Hardies 150 N Michigan Ave Ste 2500 Chicago IL 60601-7567

TOOHEY, MARGARET LOUISE, journal editor, researcher; b. Torrington, Conn., Mar. 18, 1925; d. Erwin Byron and Lucy Lucille (Duigou) Gabaree; m. John Michael Toohey, Nov. 25, 1950 (div. Jan. 1972); children: John Michael Jr., Michele Louise Toohey Parsons. BS, U. Rochester, 1974, MA in English, 1978, PhD in English, 1987. Rsch. asst. Sch. Medicine Psychiatry Dept. Yale U., New Haven, 1950-57; rsch. asst. administr. adult psychiatry NIMH, Bethesda, Md., 1957-71; rsch. asst. Psychiatry Dept., U. Rochester, 1972-77, data analyst coord., 1973-74, rsch. assoc., 1977—; tech. editor Family Process, Allendale, N.J., 1986—, Family Systems Medicine, N.Y.C., 1990—. Contbr. articles to profl. jours., books. Mem. MLA. Democrat. Office: U Rochester Dept Psychiatry Rm 1-9011 300 Crittenden Blvd Rochester NY 14642-8409

TOOHIG, TIMOTHY E., physicist; b. Lawrence, Mass., Feb. 17, 1928; s. Timothy Michael and Catherine Marie (Walsh) T. BS in Physics, Boston Coll., 1947; MS in Optics, U. Rochester, 1953; PhD in Physics, Johns Hopkins U., 1962; Licentiate in Philosophy, Weston Coll., 1957. Ordained priest Soc. Jesus, 1965. Rsch. asst. Johns Hopkins U., 1957-62, rsch. assoc., 1962-63; physicist 200 Be V project Lawrence Berkeley Lab., 1964-66; physicist Brookhaven Nat. Lab., 1967-70; physicist, various positions Fermi Nat. Accelerator Lab., 1970-89; physicist superconducting supercollider Ctrl. Design Group, 1984-89, dep. head conventional systems divsn.; physicist SSC Lab., 1989-94, dep. head conventional construction divsn.; chaplain Seton Hall High Sch., Patchogue, N.Y., 1967-70, St. Joseph High Sch., Westchester, Ill., 1971-89. Sgt. U.S. Army, 1946-47. Mem. Am. Phys. Soc. Roman Catholic. Achievements include discovery of eta meson. Measurement of pi meson and k meson form factors. Demonstration of charged particle steering by crystals. Demonstration of the existence of channeling radiation from crystals. Home: 12345 Inwood Dallas TX 75244

TOOKER, CARL E., department store executive; b. Allegan, Mich., 1947. Grad., Ferris State Coll., 1970. Chmn. Filene's subs. May Dept. Stores, Boston. Office: Specialty Retailers Inc 10201 Main St Houston TX 77025

TOOKER, GARY LAMARR, electronics company executive; b. Shelby, Ohio, May 25, 1939; s. William Henry and Frances Ione (Melick) T.; m. Diane Rae Kreider, Aug. 4, 1962; children: Lisa, Michael. B.S.E.E., Ariz. State U., 1962. With Motorola Inc., Phoenix, 1962—, v.p., gen. mgr. internat. semicondr. div., 1980-81, v.p., gen. mgr. semicondr. products sector, 1981-82, sr. v.p., gen. mgr. semicondr. products sector, 1982-83; exec. v.p., gen. mgr. semicondr. products sector Motorola Inc., 1983-86; sr. exec. v.p., chief corp. staff officer Motorola Inc., Schaumburg, Ill., 1986-88, sr. exec. v.p., chief operating officer, 1988-90, pres., chief oper. officer, 1990-93, chief exec. officer, 1993—, also bd. of dirs., pres.; mem. engring. adv. council Ariz. State U., Tempe, 1982-86. Bd. dirs. Scottsdale (Ariz.) Boys Club, 1980-86, Jr. Achievement Chgo., 1988—; chief crusader, major. corp. group United Way, Chgo., 1988—; mem. alumni bd., mem. Found. bd. Ariz. State U., 1991—. Named Outstanding Alumni of Yr., Ariz. State U., 1983. Mem. IEEE, Am. Mgmt. Assn., Semicondr. Industry Assn. (bd. dirs. 1981-86, chmn. bd. 1982-86), Ariz. Assn. Industries (bd. dirs. 1981-86), Am. Electronics Assn. (bd. dirs. 1988—, chmn. bd. 1991), Econ. Club of Chgo., Elec. Mfrs. Club. Republican. Office: Motorola Inc 1303 E Algonquin Rd Schaumburg IL 60196

TOOKER, GEORGE, artist; b. Bklyn., Aug. 5, 1920; s. George Clair and Angela Montejo (Roura) T. BA, Harvard U., 1942; student, Art Students League, N.Y.C., 1943-44. Instr. Art Students League, N.Y., 1965-68. One man shows include Edwin Hewitt Gallery, 1951, 55, Robert Isaacson Gallery, 1960, 62, Durlacher Bros., 1964, 67, Hopkins Center at Dartmouth Coll., 1967, Fine Arts Mus., San Francisco, 1974, Mus. Contemporary Art, Chgo., 1974, Whitney Mus., N.Y.C., 1975, Indpls. Mus. Art, 1975; exhibited in group shows at Whitney Mus., 1947-50, 53, 55-58, 61, 64, 65, 67, 75, Venice Biennale, 1956, Art Inst. Chgo., 1951, 52, 54, 59, Inst. Contemporary Arts, London, 1950, Va. Mus., 1954, 62, Pa. Acad., 1966, Marisa Del Re Gallery, 1985, 88, 92, Spoleto Festival, Gibbes Mus. Art, Charleston, S.C., 1987, Robert Hall Fleming Mus. U. Vt., 1987, Marsh Gallery, U. Richmond, Va., 1989, Addison Gallery of Am. Art, 1994; represented permanent collections at Smithsonian Nat. Mus. of Am. Art, Smithsonian Hirshhorn Mus., Whitney Mus., Dartmouth Coll., Met. Mus., Walker Art Center, Mus. Modern Art, S.C. Johnson & Sons, Inc., Art, U.S.A., Sara Roby Fund Collection Am. Art, Addison Gallery, Ariz State Univ. Gallery, Bklyn. Mus. Columbus (Ohio) Mus. Recipient Vt. gov.'s award for excellence in arts, 1983; Grantee Nat. Inst. Arts and Letters, 1960. Mem. NAD., Acad. Arts and Letters. Address: PO Box 385 Hartland VT 05048 Office: care Marisa del Re Gallery 41 East 57th St New York NY 10022

TOOLAN, BRIAN PAUL, newspaper editor; b. Carbondale, Pa., June 29, 1950; s. Walter William and Elizabeth (Cleary) T.; m. Maureen Ellen Connolly, Sept. 7, 1974; children: Brendan, Seamus, Bridget, Colin, Molly. BA in English, St. Bonaventure U., Olean, N.Y., 1972. Reporter Scranton (Pa.) Tribune, 1972-79; copy editor Dayton (Ohio) Jour. Herald, 1979-81; layout editor Balt. News Am., 1981; copy editor Phila. Daily News, 1982-84, sports editor, 1984-89, asst. mng. editor, 1989-91, mng. editor, 1991—. Mem. AP Mng. Editors, Am. Soc. Newspaper Editors, Pa. Soc. Newspaper Editors (dir. 1989-92). Roman Catholic. Office: Phila Daily News 400 N Broad Philadelphia PA 19101*

TOOLE, DAVID GEORGE, pulp and paper products executive; b. Winnipeg, Man., Can., Apr. 22, 1942; s. George Toole; m. Bette Lynn Smith, Aug. 28, 1965; children: Jennifer, Simon. BSME, U. Man., 1964; MS in Adminstrv. Scis., The City U., London, 1968. Mem. corp. devel. Can. Pacific Ltd., Montreal, 1975-79, dir. fin. analysis 1983-89, v.p. fin. analysis and planning 1989-90; gen. mgr. Can. Pacific Ltd., Bermuda, 1979-83; sr. v.p., chief fin. officer Can. Pacific Forest Products Ltd., Montreal, 1990-94; pres. White Paper Group. Avenor Inc., Montreal, 1994—. Mem. Montreal Amateur Athletic Assn., Alpine Club Can. (sec.), Viking Ski Club (past pres.). Office: 2 Kenview Blvd, Brampton, ON Canada L6T 5EH

TOOLE, JAMES FRANCIS, medical educator; b. Atlanta, Mar. 22, 1925; s. Walter O. Brien and Helen (Whitehurst) T.; m. Patricia Anne Wooldridge, Oct. 25, 1952; children: William, Anne, James, Douglas Sean. BA, Princeton U., 1947; MD, Cornell U., 1949; LLB, LaSalle Extension U., 1962. Intern, then resident internal medicine and neurology U. Pa. Hosp., Nat. Hosp., London, Eng., 1953-58; mem. faculty U. Pa. Sch. Medicine, 1958-62; prof. neurology, chmn. dept. Bowman Gray Sch. Medicine Wake Forest U., 1962-83; vis. prof. neurosci. U. Calif. at San Diego, 1969-70; vis. scholar Oxford U., 1989; mem. Nat. Bd. Med. Examiners, 1970-76; mem. task force arteriosclerosis Nat. Heart Lung & Blood Inst., 1970-81; chmn. 6th and 7th Princeton confs. cerebrovascular diseases; cons. epidemiology WHO, Japan, 1971, 73, 93, USSR, 1968, Ivory Coast, 1977, Japan, 1993; mem. Lasker Awards com., 1976-77; chmn. neuropharmacologic study com. FDA, 1979; co-chair Commn. on Presdl. Disability; cons. NASA, 1966. Author: Cerebrovascular Diseases, 4th edit., 1990; editor: Current Concepts in Cerebrovascular Disease, 1969-73, Jour. Neurol. Sci., 1990—; mem. editorial bd. Annals Internal Medicine, 1968-75, Stroke, 1972-91, Jour. AMA, 1975-77, Ann. Neurology, 1980-86, Jour. Neurol. Soc., 1990; mem. editorial bd. Jour. of Neurology, 1985-89. Pres. N.C. Heart Assn., 1976-77. Served with AUS, 1950-51; flight surgeon USNR, 1951-53. Decorated Bronze Star with V, Combat Med. badge. Fellow ACP, AAAS (life); mem. AMA, Am. Clin. and Climatol. Assn., Am. Heart Assn. (chmn. com. ethics 1970-75), Am. Physiol. Soc., Am. Neurol. Assn. (sec.-treas. 1978-82, pres. 1984-85, archivist, historian 1988—), World Fedn. Neurology (sec.-treas. 1982-89, mgmt. com. 1990—), Am. Acad. Neurology, Am. Soc. Neuroimaging (pres. 1992-94), Internat. Stroke Soc. (exec. com. 1989—, program chair 1992), Assn. Brit. Neurologists (hon.), German Neurol Soc. (hon.), Austrian Soc. Neurology (hon.), Irish Neurol. Assn. (hon.), 1992, Nat. Stroke Assn. (bd. dirs. 1993—, exec. com. 1994—), co-chair Commn. on U.S. Presdl. Disability 1994—). Home: 1836 Virginia Rd Winston Salem NC 27104-2316

TOOLE, LEE K., telecommunications company executive; b. 1936. BSBA, U. Tenn., 1961. With AT&T Long Lines, 1961-76, dep. dir. internat.; with GTE Hawaiian Tel. Co., Inc., Honolulu, 1976-83, 85—, v.p., also chief oper. officer, 1985, then v.p., chief oper. officer, mgr., v.p. nat. accounts mktg. and nat. sales, 1983-85, now pres., also bd. dirs. With U.S. Army, 1956-59. Office: GTE-Hawaiian Tel Co PO Box 2200 Honolulu HI 96841-0001

TOOMAJIAN, WILLIAM MARTIN, lawyer; b. Troy, N.Y., Sept. 26, 1943; s. Leo R. and Elizabeth (Gundrum) T.; children—Andrew, Philip. A.B., Hamilton Coll., 1965; J.D., U. Mich., 1968; LL.M., N.Y.U., 1975. Bar: N.Y. 1968, Ohio 1978. Mem. firm Cadwalader, Wickersham & Taft, N.Y.C., 1971-77, Baker & Hostetler, Cleve., 1977—. Served to lt. USCG, 1968-71. Mem. ABA, Ohio Bar Assn., Cleve. Bar Assn., Cleve. Tax Club. Home: 3582 Lytle Rd Cleveland OH 44122-4908 Office: Baker & Hostetler 3200 National City Ctr 1900 E 9th St Cleveland OH 44114-3303

TOOMBS, EUGENE MARTIN, III, manufacturing executive; b. Newark, Sept. 25, 1941; s. Eugene Martin Jr. and Dorothy Ann (Croghan) T.; m. Judith Ann Choborda, June 15, 1963; 1 child, Eugene Martin IV. BS, Fairleigh Dickinson U., 1963; postgrad., Harvard U., 1975. Various mgmt. positions to gen. mgr. Boise Cascade Corp., St. Louis, 1985-87; v.p. Sonoco Products Co., Hartsville, S.C., 1987-90; COO Mitek, Inc., St. Louis, 1990-92; pres., CEO Miter, Inc., St. Louis, 1992—. Bd. dirs. Parkway Nursery Sch., St. Louis, 1989-91, St. Louis U., 1987-89, Am. Assn. Indsl. Mgmt., St. Louis, 1990—. Sgt. U.S. Army, 1964-70. Mem. Greenbriar Hills Country Club. Republican. Avocations: golf, reading, wine collecting. Home: 1116 Templeton Pl Town and Country MO 63011 Office: Mitek Inc 14515 N Outer Forty Rd Chesterfield MO 63017

TOOMBS, KENNETH ELDRIDGE, librarian; b. Colonial Heights, Va., Aug. 25, 1928; s. Garnett Eldridge and Susie W. (Bryant) T.; m. Ada Teresa Hornsby, Aug. 29, 1949; children—Susan Elizabeth Shealy, Cheri Lynn Morris, Teresa Ann Heilman. A.A., Tenn. Wesleyan Coll., 1950; B.S., Tenn. Poly. Inst., 1951; M.A., U.Va., 1955; M.L.S., Rutgers U., 1956; student, La. State U., 1951-63. Reference asst. Alderman Library, U. Va., 1954-55; research asst. Grad. Sch . Library Sci., Rutgers U., 1955-56; mem. staff and faculty La. State U., 1956-63, asst. dir. charge pub. services, 1962-63; dir. libraries, prof. library sci. U. Southwestern La., 1963-67; dir. libraries U. S.C., Columbia, 1967—; bd. dirs. Southeastern Library Network, 1967-88; disting. dir. of librs. emeritus U. S.C., Columbia, 1988—; vice chmn. Southeastern Library Network, 1973-74, 83-84, chmn., 1974-75, treas., 1984-85; libr. cons. for bldgs. and adminstrn. for 60 colls. and univs. in past 30 yrs.; chmn. librarians sect. La. Coll. Conf., 1965-67; mem. Bd. La. Libr. Examiners, 1966-67; participant Libr. Mgmt. Inst., U. Wash., Seattle, 1969, Libr. Bldg. Problems Inst., UCLA, 1970. Contbr. articles to profl. jours.; editor: Bull. La. Library Assn., 1959-62; mng. editor: SW La. Jour., 1963-67; adv. bd.: Linguistic Atlas Am. Treas. Wesley Found.; v.p. Am. Field Services Internat. Scholarships; bd. dirs. U. S.C. Ednl. Found., 1975-82; Danforth assoc., 1967—; AIA/ALA Bldg. Awards Jury, 1987. Served to 1st lt. AUS, 1946-47, 51-53. Mem. ALA (life), La. Library Assn. (parliamentarian 1962-63, 66-67), Southeastern Library Assn. (Life mem., exec. bd. 1981-85, Rothrock award 1978), Southwestern Library Assn., S.C. Library Assn. (Life mem., pres. 1976, exec. bd. 1981-85), Assn. Southeastern Research Libraries (chmn. 1973-75, adv. com. to OCLC 1979-84), AAUP (sec.), La. Hist. Assn., La. Tchrs. Assn., Soc. Tympanuchus Cupido Pinnatus, South Caroliniana Soc., Nat. Library Bldg. Consultants List (chmn. 1981-84), Tenn. Squire. Methodist. Clubs: Mason (Shriner), Kiwanis. Home: 16 Garden Springs Rd Columbia SC 29209-1716

TOOMEY, JEANNE ELIZABETH, animal activist; b. Manhattan, N.Y., Aug. 22, 1921; d. Edward Aloysius and Anna Margaret (O'Grady) Toomey; m. Peter Terranova, Sept. 28, 1951 (dec. 1968); children: Peter Terranova, Sheila Terranova Beasley. Student, Hofstra U., 1938-40; student law sch., Fordham U., 1940-41; BA, Southampton Coll., 1976; postgrad., Monmouth Coll., 1978-79. Reporter, columnist Bklyn. Daily Eagle, 1943-52; with The Fitzgeralds, NBC Radio, N.Y.C., 1952-53; reporter, writer King Features Syndicate, N.Y.C., 1953-55; reporter, columnist N.Y. Jour.-Am., N.Y.C., 1955-61; newsman AP, N.Y.C., 1963-64; stringer; columnist News Tribune, Woodbridge, N.J., 1976-86; editor Calexico (Calif.) Chronicle, 1987-88; editor community sect. Asbury Park (N.J.) Press, 1988; pres., dir. Last Post Animal Sanctuary, Falls Village, Conn., 1991—. Author: Murder in the Hamptons, 1994. Named Woman of the Yr. N.Y. Women's Press Club, 1960. Mem. Newswomen's Club of N.Y., Overseas Press Club, N.Y. Press Club, Silurians. Roman Catholic. Home and Office: 95 Belden St Falls Village CT 06031

TOOMEY, THOMAS MURRAY, lawyer; b. Washington, Dec. 9, 1923; s. Vincent L. and Catherine V. (McCann) T.; m. Grace Donohoe, June 22, 1948; children: Isabelle Marie Toomey Hessick, Helen Marie, Mary Louise, Thomas Murray. Student, Duke U., 1943-44, Catholic U. Am., 1942-43, 45-47; J.D., Catholic U. Am., 1949. Bar: D.C. 1949, Md. 1952. Sole practice Washington and Md., 1949—; bd. dirs. Allied Capital Corp. and subs., Washington and Vero Beach, Fla., Fed. Ctr. Plz. Corp., Donohoe Cos., Inc., Washington, Nat. Capital Bank, Washington. Chmn. aviation and transp. coms. Met. Washington Bd. Trade, 1954-76, bd. dirs., 1962-77; chmn. dedication Dulles Internat. Airport, 1962; trustee Cath. U. Am., 1981—; founding trustee Heights Sch. Served to 1st lt. USMC, 1942-46, 50-52. Recipient Ann. Alumni Achievement award Cath. U., 1977, Most Disting. Alumnus award St. John's Coll. High Sch. D.C., 1994. Mem. ABA, D.C. Bar Assn., Md. Bar Assn., Bar Assn. D.C., Am. Judicature Soc., Comml. Law League Am., Friendly Sons St. Patrick (pres. 1983), Sovereign Mil. Order of Malta (Fed. Assn. U.S.A.), Congl. Golf and Country Club, Kenwood Golf and Country Club, Univ. Club, Army and Navy Club, Tower Club, Lago Mar Beach Club, Country Club. Home: 6204 Garnett Dr Bethesda MD 20815-6618 also: 2000 S Ocean Dr Apt 1410 Fort Lauderdale FL 33316-3813 Office: 4701 Sangamore Rd Bethesda MD 20816-2508

TOOMRE, ALAR, applied mathematician, theoretical astronomer; b. Rakvere, Estonia, Feb. 5, 1937; came to U.S., 1949, naturalized, 1955; s. Elmar and Linda (Aghen) T.; m. Joyce Stetson, June 15, 1958; children—Lars, Erik, Anya. B.S. in Aero. Engring., B.S. in Physics, MIT, 1957; Ph.D. in Fluid Mechanics, U. Manchester, Eng., 1960. C.L.E. Moore instr. math. dept. MIT, Cambridge, 1960-62; asst. prof. applied math. MIT, 1963-65, assoc. prof., 1965-70, prof., 1970—; fellow Inst. for Advanced Study, Princeton, N.J., 1962-63. Contbr. articles to profl. jours. Guggenheim fellow, 1969-70, MacArthur fellow, 1984-89; Fairchild scholar, 1975, Marshall scholar, 1957-60. Fellow AAAS; mem. Am. Astron. Soc. (Dirk Brouwer award 1993), Internat. Astron. Union, Am. Acad. Arts and Scis., Nat. Acad. Scis. Office: MIT Room 2-371 77 Massachusetts Ave Cambridge MA 02139

TOON, MALCOLM, former ambassador; b. Troy, N.Y., July 4, 1916; s. George and Margaret Harcomb (Broadfoot) T.; m. Elizabeth Jane Taylor, Aug. 28, 1943; children: Barbara, Alan, Nancy. A.B., Tufts U., 1937, LL.D. (hon.), 1977; M.A., Fletcher Sch. Law and Diplomacy, 1939; student, Middlebury Coll., 1950, Harvard U., 1950-51; LL.D. (hon.), Middlebury Coll., 1978, Drexel U., 1980, Am. Coll. Switzerland, 1985, Grove City Coll., 1990. Fgn. service officer, 1946-79; assigned successively Warsaw, Budapest, Moscow, Rome, Berlin, Washington, 1946-60; assigned Am. embassy, London, 1960-63; counselor political affairs Am. embassy, Moscow, 1963-67; with Dept. of State, Washington, 1967-69; ambassador to Czechoslovakia, 1969-71, to Yugoslavia, 1971-75, to Israel, 1975-76, to USSR, 1976-79; mem. U.S. del. Nuclear Test Center, Geneva, 1958-59, Four Power Working Group, Washington, London, Paris, 1959, Fgn. Ministers Conf., Geneva, 1969, Ten Nation Disarmament Com., Geneva, 1960; mem. SALT II del., 1977-79, U.S.-Soviet Summit Conf., Vienna, 1979; Brennen prof. U. N.C. Asheville, 1981; Finch prof. Miami U., Oxford, Ohio, 1982; Allis-Chalmers chair Marquette U., Milw., 1982. Trustee emeritus Tufts U.; bd. visitors Fletcher Sch. Law and Diplomacy, 1992; chmn. U.S. Delegation to Joint U.S Russian Commn. on POW's, MIA's. Served from ensign to lt. comdr. USNR, 1942-46. Recipient Freedom Leadership award Hillsdale Coll., 1980; Valley Forge Freedom award, 1981; Disting. Honor award Dept. State, 1980; Wallace award, 1984, Gold medal Nat. Inst. of Social Scis., 1987. Home: 375 Pee Dee Rd Southern Pines NC 28387-2118

TOOR, HERBERT LAWRENCE, chemical engineering educator, researcher; b. Pitts., June 22, 1927; s. Matthew G. and Jean (Mogul) T.; m. Elizabeth Margaret Weir, Dec. 1950; children: Helen Mary, John Weir, William Ramsay. BS, Drexel U., 1948; MS, Northwestern U., 1950, PhD, 1952. Rsch. chemist Monsanto Chems., Ltd., 1952-53; asst. prof. Carnegie Mellon U., Pitts., 1953-57, assoc. prof., 1957-61, prof., 1961—, head chem. engring dept., 1967-70, dean Carnegie Inst. Tech., 1970-79, Mobay prof. chem. engring., 1980-92, Mobay prof. chem. engring. emeritus, 1992—; vis. UNESCO prof. U. Madras, India, 1962-63. Contbr. numerous articles to tech. jours. With USNR, 1944-45. Recipient merit award Northwestern U. Alumni, 1973. Fellow AAAS, Am. Inst. Chem. Engrs. (Colburn award 1964); mem. NAE.

TOOT, JOSEPH F., JR., bearing manufacturing company executive; b. 1935; married. AB, Princeton U., 1957; postgrad., Harvard U. Grad. Sch. Bus. Adminstrn., 1961. With Timken Co., Canton, Ohio, 1962—; dep. mgr. Timken (France) Co., 1967—; v.p. internat. div. Timken Co., Canton, 1967-68, corp. v.p., then exec. v.p., 1968-79, pres., 1979—, also bd. dirs.; bd. dirs. Rockwell Internat. Mem. Am. Iron and Steel Inst. Office: Timken Co 1835 Dueber Ave SW Canton OH 44706-2798

TOOTE, GLORIA E. A., developer, lawyer, columnist; b. N.Y.C.; d. Frederick A. and Lillie M. (Tooks) Toote. Student, Howard U., 1949-51; J.D., NYU, 1954; LL.M., Columbia U., 1956. Bar: N.Y. 1955, U.S. Dist. Ct. (so. and ea. dists.) N.Y. 1956, U.S. Supreme Ct. 1956. With firm Greenbaum, Wolff & Ernst, 1957; mem. editorial staff Time mag., 1957-58; asst. assoc. counsel N.Y. State Workmen's Compensation Bd., 1958-64; pres. Toote Town Pub. Co. and Town Sound Studios Inc., 1966-70; asst. dir. Action Agy., 1971-73; asst. sec. Dept. HUD, 1973-75; vice chmn. Pres.'s Adv. Council on Pvt. Sector Initiatives, 1983-85; housing developer, 1976—; pres. Trea Estates and Enterprises, Inc.; newspaper columnist; chairperson The Policy Coun. Former bd. dirs. Citizens for the Republic, Nat. Black United Fund, Exec. Women in Govt., Am. Arbitration Assn., Consumer Alert; bd. overseers Hoover Inst., 1985-95; vice chair Nat. Polit. Congress of Black Women, 1984-92; former mem. Coun. Econ. Affairs. Rep. Nat. Com.; pres. N.Y.C. Black Rep. Coun.; exec. trustee Polit. Action Com. for Equality. Recipient citations Nat. Bus. League, Alpha Kappa Alpha, U.S. C. of

C., Nat. Assn. Black Women Attys. Mem. N.Y. Fedn. Civil Svc. Orgns., Nat. Assn. Real Estate Brokers, Nat. Fed. Mortgage Assn. (bd. dirs. 1992), Nat. Citizens Participation Coun., Nat. Bar Assn.,Delta Sigma Theta, others. Address: 282 W 137th St New York NY 10030-2439

TOPAZ, MURIEL, dance educator; b. Phila., May 7, 1932; d. Joseph Topaz and Rhea Rebecca Rosenbloom; m. Jacob Druckman, June 5, 1954; children: Karen Druckman, Daniel Druckman. Student, NYU, 1950-51; studies with Martha Graham, Antony Tudor, The Juilliard Sch., 1951-54; student, Dance Notation Bur., N.Y.C., 1954-56. Mem. faculty The Juilliard Sch., N.Y.C., 1959-70, dir. dance div., 1985-92; exec. dir. Dance Notation Bur., 1978-85; co-chmn. First Internat. Congress on Movement Notation Bur., Israel, 1984, 2d Internat. Congress, Hong Kong, 1990; chmn. artistic com. Dance Notation Bur.; adjudicator Reginal Dance/Am., Mid-States 1980, Pacific 1981, N.E. 1983. Author: Changes and New Developments in Labanotation, 1966, Intermediate Reading Studies, 1972, Intermediate Study Guide, 1972, Choreography and Dance: The Notation Issue, 1988, Alvin Ailey, An American Visionary, 1995; co-author (with Hackney & Manno) Elementary Study Guide, 1970, Elementary Reading Studies, 1970, (with Edelson) Readings in Modern Dance, 1972; author and editor Young Dancer sect. Dance Mag.; editorial coms. Choreography and Dance, Dance Studies; reconstructor: Lilac Garden, (Milw. Ballet), Continuo (Paris Conservatory, N.C. Sch. Arts), Notator Moor's Pavane. Mem. May O'Donnell Hon. Com., 1979; chmn. dance panel N.Y. State Coun. on Arts, 1982-83; assessor Can. Coun., 1987; auditor NEA, 1989—. Recipient fgn. travel grant Inst. Internat. Edn., 1967. Fellow Internat. Coun. Kinetography Laban.

TOPAZIO, VIRGIL WILLIAM, university official; b. Middletown, Conn., Mar. 27, 1915; s. Concetto and Corradina (Rizzo) T.; m. Juwil E. Child, July 28, 1941; 1 dau., Jula Diane. B.A., Wesleyan U., Middletown; M.A., Columbia U., 1947, Ph.D., 1951. Lectr. Columbia U., 1947-48; from instr. to prof. French lit. U. Rochester, 1948-65; prof. French, chmn. dept. Rice U., 1965-67, dean humanities and social scis., 1967—, also acad. v.p.; Favrot chair in French lit., 1973; Fulbright vis. lectr. U. Rennes, France, 1964-65. Author: D'Holbach's Moral Philosophy, 1956, Voltaire: A Critical Study of His Major Works, 1967. Served with AUS, 1945-46. Decorated Palmes Academiques France, 1966, 76. Mem. Alliance Francaise (pres. 1963-65), Modern Lang. Assn. (pres. 18th century sect. 1965), Council Fgn. Langs. (v.p. 1967-68). Home: 3 Knoll Pines Ct The Woodlands TX 77381-2690

TOPE, DWIGHT HAROLD, retired management consultant; b. Grand Junction, Colo., Aug. 29, 1918; s. Richard E. and Elizabeth (Jones) T.; m. Carolyn Stagg, Apr. 29, 1949; children: Stephen R., Chris L. AS, Mesa Coll., 1940; student, George Washington U. With Fgn. Funds Control, a Div. of U.S. Treasury Dept.; staff adjuster Fire Cos. Adjustment Bur., Denver, Albuquerque, 1946-48; br. mgr. Gen. Adjustment Bur., Deming, N.Mex., 1948-50; spl. agt. Cliff Kealey State Agy., Albuquerque, 1950-56; pres. Dwight Tope State Agy., Inc., Albuquerque, 1956-84, also chmn. bd., sr. cons., 1985-87. Mem. adv. bd. Salvation Army, Albuquerque, 1974—, Meals on Wheels, 1987—; past chmn. bd., pres. Presbyn. Heart Inst., Albuquerque, 1977—. Maj. Coast Arty. Anti-Aircraft, 1941-45. Mem. N.Mex. Ins. Assn. (past chmn.), Ins. Info. Inst. (past chmn.), N.Mex. Surplus Lines Assn. (past pres.), Air Force Assn., Assn. of U.S. Army, Am. Legion, Albuquerque C. of C. (mil. rels. com.), Rotary, Masons, Shriners, Albuquerque Country Club, Petroleum Club. Republican. Avocations: boating, fishing, hunting. Home: 1812 Stanford Dr NE Albuquerque NM 87106-2538 Office: 8100 Mountain Rd NE Ste 204E Albuquerque NM 87110-7833

TOPEL, DAVID GLEN, college dean, animal science educator; b. Lake Mills, Wis., Oct. 24, 1937; s. Walter C. and Mable (Strauss) T.; m. Jacqueline May Richardson, Nov. 21, 1964. BS, U. Wis. 1960; MS, Kans. State U., 1962; PhD, Mich. State U., 1965. Asst. prof. Iowa State U., Ames, 1965-67, assoc. prof., 1967-73, prof. dept. animal sci., 1973-88, head. dept., 1979-88, dean, Coll. Agr., 1988—; dir. Iowa Agr. Expt. Sta., Ames, 1988—, MidAm. Internat. Agrl. Consortium, Lincoln, Nebr., 1988—. Author: The Pork Industry - Problems and Progress, 1968. Secretariat World Food Prize, Iowa State U., Ames, 1991—. Recipient Outstanding Educator award Nat. Assn. Meat Purveyors, 1989, Internat. award Gamma Sigma Delta, 1994, Acad. Sci. Ukraine, 1994. Mem. Am. Soc. Animal Sci. (sec. So. sect. 1988, rsch. award 1979), Inst. Food Tech., Am. Meat Sci. Assn. (bd. dirs. 1977). Presbyterian. Avocations: fishing, golf. Home: 2630 Meadow Glen Rd Ames IA 50014-8239

TOPELIUS, KATHLEEN E., lawyer; b. July 15, 1948. BA, U. Conn., 1970; JD, Cath. U. Am., 1978. Bar: D.C. 1978, U.S. Supreme Ct. 1988. Atty. office of gen. counsel Fed. Home Loan Bank Bd., 1978-80; ptnr. Morgan, Lewis & Bockius, Washington, 1985-93, Bryan Cave, Washington, 1993—. Office: Bryan Cave 700 13th St NW Washington DC 20005-3960

TOPERZER, THOMAS RAYMOND, art museum director; b. Pitts., Aug. 12, 1939; s. Raymond Otto and Blodwyn (Roberts) T.; m. Carol Jane Reece, June 2, 1961; children: Scott Thomas, Max Otto. Student, West Liberty (W.Va.) State Coll., 1959, Sterling (Kans.) Coll., 1959-61; AB, Southwestern Coll., 1963; MFA, U. Nebr., 1970. Dir. Blanden Meml. Art Mus., Fort Dodge, Iowa, 1970-71, Rochester (Minn.) Art Ctr., 1971-72; curator univ. art gallery Ill. State U., Normal, 1972-73, asst. dir. univ. mus., 1972-73, dir. univ. art mus. and CVA art galleries, 1973-82; coordinator div. fine arts Bethel Coll., St. Paul, 1982-84; dir. Fred Jones Jr. Mus. Art. U. Okla., Norman, 1984—; arts coms. to various corps., Minn., Ill. and Okla., 1972— Nelle Cochran Woods fellow U. Nebr., 1969-70. Mem. Assn. Coll. and U. Mus. and Galleries (mem. exec. com. 1986—), Am. Assn. Mus., Coll. Art Assn. Office: Fred Jones Jr Mus Art U Okla 410 W Boyd St Norman OK 73069-4851

TOPFER, MORTON LOUIS, computer company executive; b. Bklyn., Sept. 18, 1936; s. Abraham and Sadie (Rindner) T.; m. Arlene Siegel, June 6, 1959 (div.); children: Bonnie, Jacqueline, Alan, Richard; m. Angela C. Finch, June 20, 1987. B.S. in Physics, Bklyn. Coll., 1959; M.S., Poly. Inst. Bklyn., 1962. Engr. Elec. Tran, N.J., 1959-61; physicist Kollsman Inst., Elmhurst, N.Y., 1961-62; mgr. RCA, Princeton, N.J., 1962-69; v.p. Kulite Semiconductor, Ridgefield, N.J., 1969-71; exec. v.p. sector Motorola, Inc., Schaumburg, Ill., 1971-94; vice chmn. Dell Computer, Austin, Tex., 1994—. Author: Thick Film Microelectronics, 1971. Mem. South Fla. Coordinating Council, 1979-82; mem. United Way of Broward County, 1979-81, Discovery Center, Fla., 1979-81. Mem. IEEE, Internat. Soc. Hybrid Microelectronics (Dan Hughes award 1977). Jewish. Office: Dell Computer Corp 9505 Arboretum Blvd Austin TX 78759-7299

TOPIK, STEVEN CURTIS, history educator; b. Montebello, Calif., Aug. 6, 1949; s. Kurt and Gertrude Irene (Kriszanich) T.; m. Martha Jane Marcy, Feb. 3, 1979; children: Julia, Natalia. BA, U. Calif., San Diego, 1971; MA, U. Tex., 1973, PhD, 1978. Asst. prof. Universidade Fed. Fluminense, Rio de Janeiro, 1978-81, vis. prof., 1984; asst. prof. Colgate U., Hamilton, N.Y., 1981-84; vis. prof. Univ. Ibero Americana, Mexico City, 1982; prof. U. Calif., Irvine, 1984—; vis. prof. Ecols des Hautes Etudes en Sci. Social, Paris, 1990; cons. in field; mem. editorial com. U. Calif. Press, Berkeley, 1987-89. Author: The Political Economy of the Brazilian State, 1987, Trade and Gunboats, The United State and Brazil in the Age of Empire, 1995; contbr. articles, revs. to profl. publs. Mem. Mayor's Adv. Bd. on Sister Cities, Irvine, 1989-90; mem. adv. bd. Orange County (Calif.) Com. on Latin Am., 1989-90. Fellow NEH, 1987, 89-90, Rockefeller Found., 1977, Social Sci. Rsch. Coun. Mexico City, 1982-83, Fulbright-Hayes Found., 1978-79, 84, U. Calif., 1988-89. Mem. Latin Am. Studies Assn., Am. Hist. Assn., Conf. Latin Am. History (com. on hist. statistics, com. on projects and publs., chair Brazilian studies com. 1988-90), Pacific Coast Coun. on Latin Am. Studies (bd. govs. 1987-90).

TOPILOW, CARL S., symphony conductor; b. Jersey City, N.J., Mar. 14, 1947; s. Jacob Topilow and Pearl (Roth) Topilow Josephs; 1 child, Jenny Michelle. B.Mus., Manhattan Sch. of Mus., 1968, M.Mus., 1969. Exxon/Arts Endowment Condr. Denver Symphony Orch., 1976-79, asst. condr., 1979-80; mus. dir. Denver Chamber Orch., 1976-81, Denver Youth Orch., 1977-80, Grand Junction Symphony, Colo., 1977-80, Nat. Repertory Orch., Keystone, Colo., 1978—; dir. orchs. Cleve. Inst. Mus., 1981—; condr. Summit Brass 1986—. Recipient Conducting fellowship Nat. Orch. Assn.,

N.Y.C., 1972-75, Aspen Mus. Festival, Colo., 1976; winner 1st place Balt. Symphony Conducting Competition, Md., 1976.

TOPINKA, JUDY BAAR, state official; b. Riverside, Ill., Jan. 16, 1944; d. William Daniel and Lillian Mary (Shuss) Baar; 1 child, Joseph Baar. BS, Northwestern U., 1966. Features editor, reporter, columnist Life Newspapers, Berwyn and LaGrange, Ill., 1966-77; with Forest Park (Ill.) Rev. and Westchester News, 1976-77; coord. spl. events dept. fedn. comm., AMA, 1978-80; rsch. analyst Senator Leonard Becker, 1980-82; mem. Ill. Ho. of Reps., 1981-84; mem. Ill. Senate, 1985-94; treas. State of Ill., Springfield, 1995—; former mem. judiciary com., former chmn. senate health and welfare com.; former mem. fin. instn. com.; former co-chmn. Citizens Coun. on Econ. Devel.; former co-chmn. U.S. Commn. for Preservation of Am.'s Heritage Abroad, serves on legis. ref. bur.; former mem. minority bus. resource ctr. adv. com. U.S. Dept. Transp.; former mem. adv. bd. Nat. Inst. Justice. Founder, pres., bd. dirs. West Suburban Exec. Breakfast Club, from 1976; chmn. Ill. Ethics for Reagan-Bush, 1984, Bush-Quayle 1988; spokesman Nat. Coun. State Legislatures Health Com.; former mem nat. adv. coun. health professions edn. HHS; mem., GOP chairwoman Legis. Audit Commn. of Cook County; chmn. Riverside Twp. Regular Republican Orgn., 1994—. Recipient Outstanding Civilian Svc. medal, Molly Pitcher award, Abraham Lincoln award, Silver Eagle award U.S. Army and N.G. Office: JR Thompson Ctr 100 W Randolph Ste 15-600 Chicago IL 60601

TOPOL, CLIVE M., lawyer; b. Chgo., Feb. 16, 1949. BS, U. Ill., 1971, JD, 1975. Bar: Ill. 1975. Ptnr. Winston & Strawn, Chgo. Mem. Ill. State Bar Assn., Chgo. Bar Assn. Office: Winston & Strawn 35 W Wacker Dr Chicago IL 60601-1614

TOPOL, ROBERT MARTIN, financial services executive, securities trader; b. N.Y.C., Mar. 9, 1925; s. Morris and Pearl Topol; m. D'Vera Greene, Oct. 10, 1948; children—Clifford M., Gail S., Martha E. B.A., NYU, 1948. Ptnr. Greene & Co., N.Y.C., 1948-71; dir. Harris Upham & Co, N.Y.C., 1971-76; exec. v.p., dir. Shearson Lehman Bros., N.Y.C., 1976-94. Served with USMC, 1943-46. Mem. Security Traders N.Y., Nat. Security Traders Assn., N.Y. Security Dealers Assn. (gov. 1961-77), Securities Industry Assn. (v.p. 1981-94), Investment Co. Inst., Chevalier Chaine de Rotisseurs, Hampshire Country Club. Republican. Jewish. Home: 825 Orienta Ave Mamaroneck NY 10543-4314 Office: Shearson Lehman Bros 2 World Trade Ctr New York NY 10048-0002

TOPP, GEORGE CLARKE, soil physicist; b. Canfield, Ont., Can., Nov. 12, 1937; s. G. Ernest and Rhea L. (Mehlenbacher) T.; m. Eleanor Bruce, Dec. 29, 1962; children: Karen, Bruce, Brenda. BS in Agr., U. Toronto, Ont., 1959; MSc, U. Wis., 1962, PhD, 1964. Rsch. asst. U. Wis., Madison, 1959-64; rsch. assoc. U. Ill., Urbana, 1964-65; rsch. scientist Land Resource Rsch. Ctr., Ottawa, Ont., 1965-87, rsch. mgr., 1987-91; rsch. scientist land resource div. Agr. Can., Ottawa, 1991—; sessional lectr. Carleton U., Ottawa, 1975-78; vis. assoc. prof. U. Sask., Saskatoon, Can., 1980; vis. scientist Divsns. Environment, Mechanics and Soils Commonwealth Sci. and Indsl. Rsch. Orgn., Canberra, Australia, 1992-93; cons. Can. Internat. Devel. Agy., Islamabad, Pakistan, 1985, Hyderabad, India, 1986, Campinas, Sao Paulo, Brazil, 1988. Editor: Soil Physical Measurements, 1992. Chmn. Ottawa West End Community Chaplaincy, 1984-87, bd. dirs., 1991-92; chmn. Bells Corners United Ch., Nepean, Ont., 1987-89. Fellow Can. Soc. Soil Sci. (sec. 1969-72, pres. 1978), Soil Sci. Soc. Am. (bd. dirs. 1990-91); mem. Am. Geophys. Union. Mem. United Ch. of Canada. Avocations: cross-country skiing, canoeing, sailing. Home: 45 Foothills Dr, Nepean, ON Canada K2H 6K6 Office: Agriculture Canada, 960 Carling Ave, Ottawa, ON Canada K1A 0C6

TOPPEL, HAROLD H., diversified company executive; b. Franklin, N.J., 1924; married. BA, U. Ill., 1948. Salesman Lever Bros. Co., 1944, Food Fair Corp. and Penn Fruit Co., Inc., 1945-50; pres. Nat. Grocery Co., Metuchen, N.J., 1950-54; chmn. bd., chief exec. officer Pueblo Internat., Inc., formerly Pueblo Supermarkets, Inc., 1955—. Office: Pueblo Internat Inc 1300 NW 22nd St Pompano Beach FL 33069-1426 also: Pueblo Internat Inc PO Box 3288 San Juan PR 00902-3288

TOPPING, JOHN CARRUTHERS, JR., environmental organization administrator, lawyer; b. Wilkinsburg, Pa., Apr. 18, 1943; s. John Carruthers and Barbara Anne (Murray) T.; m. Linda Marie Thompson, Dec. 1, 1974; children: John Carruthers III, Elizabeth Barrett, Alexandra LaMotte. AB, Dartmouth Coll., 1964; JD, Yale U., 1967. Bar: Mass. 1967, D.C. 1968. Counsel Adv. Coun. for Minority Enterprise, Washington, 1970-73, staff dir., 1972-73; chief counsel office minority bus. enterprise U.S. Dept. Commerce, Washington, 1973-76; ptnr. Topping and Shewer, Washington, 1977-82; cons. U.S. EPA, Washington, 1982-83, staff dir. office air and radiation, 1983-86; ptnr. Topping & Swillinger, Washington, 1986-87; pres. Climate Inst., Washington, 1986—. Co-author: Southern Republicanism and the New South, 1966, Clean Air Handbook, 1987; editor: Preparing for Climate Change, 1988, Coping with Climate Change, 1989. Pres. Ripon Soc., Washington, 1978-80. Capt. USAF, 1968-70. Recipient Pres.'s award Nat. Bar Assn., 1976. Republican. Presbyterian. Home: 220 Maryland Ave NE Washington DC 20002-5704 Office: Climate Inst 324 4th St NE Washington DC 20002

TOPPING, NORMAN HAWKINS, former university chancellor; b. Flat River, Mo., Jan. 12, 1908; s. Moses H. and Charlotte Amanda (Blue) T.; m. Helen Rummens, Sept. 2, 1930 (dec. Aug. 1989); children—Bruan, Linda. A.B., U. So. Calif., 1933, M.D., 1936. Diplomate: Am. Bd. Preventive Medicine and Pub. Health. Intern USPHS marine hosps., San Francisco, Seattle; mem. staff NIH, Bethesda, Md., 1937-52; asst. chief div. infectious diseases NIH, 1946-48; asst. surgeon gen. USPHS; asso. dir. NIH, 1948-52; v.p. for med. affairs U. Pa., 1952-58; pres. U. So. Calif., 1958-70, chancellor, 1970-80, chancellor emeritus, 1980—; engaged in med. research, viral and rickettsial diseases, 1937-48; mem. com. on virus research and epidemiology Nat. Found. Infantile Paralysis, 1950-56, chmn., 1956-58; mem. research com. Nat. Found., chmn., 1958-77; pres. Am. Soc. Tropical Medicine, 1949. Author articles on typhus, Rocky Mountain spotted fever, Q fever, pub. health. Pres. So. Calif. Rapid Transit Dist., 1971-73. Recipient Bailey K. Ashford award, 1943; Wash. Acad. Sci. award, 1944; U.S.A. Typhus Commn. medal, 1945. Mem. A.A.A.S., Assn. Am. Physicians, Am. Epidemiological Soc. Exptl. Biology and Medicine. Home and Office: 100 S Plymouth Blvd Los Angeles CA 90004-3836

TOPPING, PETER, historian, educator; b. Milw., May 13, 1916; s. William P. and Anastasia (Makri) Topitzes; m. Eva V. Catafygiotu, June 20, 1951; 1 son, John Themis. B.A., U. Wis., 1937, M.A., 1938; postgrad., U. Chi., 1939-40; Ph.D., U. Pa., 1942. Instr. history U. Wis., 1943-44, Northwestern U., 1944-45; asst. prof. history U. Calif.-Santa Barbara, 1948-53; librarian Gennadeion Am. Sch. Classical Studies, Athens, Greece, 1953-60, mem. mng. com., 1961—; vis. assoc. prof. history, library cons. U. Pa., 1960-61; assoc. prof. history, later Greek studies U. Cin., 1961-64, prof., 1964-67, Charles Phelps Taft prof., 1967-78; fellow Grad. Sch., 1972—; sr. research assoc. Dumbarton Oaks Rsch. Libr. and Collection, Washington, 1978-84; mem. bd. scholars Dumbarton Oaks Center for Byzantine Studies, 1972-74, mem. sr. fellows, 1979-86, hon. sr. research assoc., 1984—; interpreting officer U.S. staff Allied Mission to Observe Greek Elections, 1946; mem. exec. com. Frank L. Weil Inst. in Religion and Humanities, 1964-78. Author: Feudal Institutions as Revealed in the Assizes of Romania, 1949, (with Jean Longnon) Documents sur le régime des terres du principauté de Moreé au XIVme siècle, 1969, Studies on Latin Greece A.D. 1205-1715, 1977; contbr. articles, revs. to hist. jours. Advanced fellow Belgian Am. Edn. Found., 1947-48; Fulbright sr. research awardee Greece, 1950-51; sr. fellow NEH, 1974-75. Mem. Am. Hist. Assn., Mediaeval Acad. Am., Soc. Byzantine Studies (Athens, Greece) (hon.), Modern Greek Studies Assn., Phi Beta Kappa. Democrat. Mem. Greek Orthodox Ch. Home: 1823 Rupert St Mc Lean VA 22101-5434

TOPPING, SEYMOUR, publishing executive, educator; b. N.Y.C., Dec. 11, 1921; s. Joseph and Anna (Seidman) Topolsky; m. Audrey Elaine Ronning, Nov. 10, 1949; children: Susan, Karen, Lesley, Rebecca, Joanna. B.J., U. Mo., 1943; Litt.D. (hon.), Rider Coll., 1983. With I.N.S. (China civil war), 1946-47; with AP, 1948-59; corr. AP, Berlin, 1957-59; mem. staff N.Y. Times, 1959-93; chief corr. N.Y. Times, Moscow, 1960-63, Southeast Asia,

1963-66; fgn. editor N.Y. Times, 1966-69, asst. mng. editor, 1969-76, dep. mng. editor, 1976-77, mng. editor, 1977-86; dir. editorial devel. N.Y. Times Regional Newspapers, 1987-93; pres. Am. Soc. Newspaper Editors, 1992-93; prof. Grad. Sch. Journalism Columbia U., N.Y.C., 1993—; Sanpaolo prof. internat. journalism, 1994—; adminstr. Pulitzer Prizes Columbia U., N.Y.C., 1993—; adviser Ctr. Fgn. Journalists, Found. Am. Comm.; juror Pulitzer Prize com.; lectr. in field. Author: Journey Between Two Chinas, 1972. Spl. advisor to Sec.-Gen. UN to Earth Summit, Rio de Janeiro, 1992; mem. Nat. Com. U.S.-China Rels.; bd. dirs. Lamont-Doherty Earth Obs. Served with inf. AUS, 1943-46, PTO. Mem. Coun. Fgn. Rels., Asia Soc., Am. Soc. Newspaper Editors, Internat. Press Inst. (Am. com., bd. dirs.), Century Assn. Home: 5 Heathcote Rd Scarsdale NY 10583-4413

TORAN, DANIEL JAMES, insurance executive; b. Boston, Mass., Jan. 30, 1948; s. Dante Robert and Eleanor May (Slesser) T.; m. Amy Ruth Chittenden, Aug. 1, 1971; children: Jennifer, David. BA, Bates Coll., 1970. With New Eng. Mut. Life Ins. Co., Boston, 1970—, exec. v.p., 1987—. Deacon Trinitarian Congregation Ch., Wayland, Mass., 1985-89. Mem. Life Ins. Mgmt. Rsch. Assn. (chmn. bd. dirs.). Republican. Congregationalist. Avocations: fishing, boating. Office: New Eng Mut Life Ins Co 501 Boylston St Boston MA 02116-3706

TORAN, KAY DEAN, social services administrator; b. Birmingham, Ala., Nov. 21, 1942; d. Benjamin and Mary Rose Dean; children: Traci Rossi, John D. Toran. BA, U. Portland, 1964; MSW, Portland State U., 1970. Asst. prof. social work Portland (Oreg.) State U., 1971-76; mgr. Adult and Family Svcs., Salem, Oreg., 1976-79; asst. gov. Office of Gov., Salem, 1979-87; adminstr. purchasing divsn. Dept. Gen. Svcs., Salem, 1987-90; regional adminstr. Children's Svcs. Divsn., Portland, 1991-94, adminstr., 1994—; pres. Walker Inst., Portland, 1990-94, Portland chapter Links, Inc., 1990-92. Bd. trustees Catlin Gabel Sch., Portland, 1980-84, Portland State U. Found., 1980-87; bd. dirs. Oreg. Law Found., 1990-93. Office: Childrens Svcs Divsn 500 Summer St NE Salem OR 97310

TORBERT, CLEMENT CLAY, JR., state supreme court justice; b. Opelika, Ala., Aug. 31, 1929; s. Clement Clay Sr. and Lynda (Meadows) T.; m. Gene Hurt, May 2, 1952; children: Mary Dixon, Gene Shealy, Clement Clay III. Student, U.S. Naval Acad., 1948-49; B.S., Auburn U., 1951; postgrad., U. Md., 1952; LL.B., U. Ala., 1954. Bar: Ala. 1954. Practiced in Opelika, 1954-77, city judge, 1954-58; partner firm Samford, Torbert, Denson & Horsley, 1959-74; chief justice Ala. Supreme Ct., 1977-89; ptnr. firm Maynard, Cooper & Gale, 1990—; past chmn. Ala. Jud. Study Commn., Jud. Coordination Com.; past pres. Conf. Chief Justices; supervisory bd. Ala. Law Enforcement Planning Agy., 1977-83; bd. dirs. Ala. Criminal Justice Info. Systems, Nat. Inst. for Dispute Resolution, First Nat. Bank Opelika, State Justice Inst., 1986-92; mem. panel of arbitrators Am. Arbitration Assn.; panelist-at-large Ctr. for Pub. Resources; held Leslie S. Wright Chair of Law, Cumberland Sch. Law, 1989, John Sparkman Chair, U. Ala. Sch. Law. Mem. Ala. Ho. of Reps., 1958-62, Ala. Senate, 1966-70, 74-77. Served to capt. USAF, 1952-53. Elected to Ala. Acad. of Honor, 1979; recipient Disting. Svc. award Nat. Ctr. for State Cts., 1989, 1989 award, Am. Judges Assn. Mem. Am. Judicature Soc., Farrah Law Soc., Phi Delta Phi, Phi Kappa Phi, Alpha Tau Omega. Methodist. Lodge: Kiwanis. Home: 611 Terracewood Dr Opelika AL 36801-3850 Office: One Commerce St Ste 302 Montgomery AL 36104

TORBERT, PRESTON M., lawyer; b. Greenwich, Conn., Aug. 9, 1943. AB magna cum laude, Princeton U., 1966; MA, U. Chgo., 1970, PhD, 1973; JD, Harvard U., 1974. Bar: Ill. 1974. Ptnr. Baker & McKenzie, Chgo. Office: Baker & McKenzie 1 Prudential Plz 130 E Randolph St Chicago IL 60601

TORCIVIA, BENEDICT J., SR., construction company executive; b. Passaic, N.J., Sept. 8, 1929; s. Joseph and Felicia (Latteri) T.; m. Elvira Venneri, June 20, 1953; children—Benedict J., Joseph A. B.S. in Archtl. Engring., Catholic U. Am., 1951. Registered profl. engr., N.H. Estimator, project mgr. Arthur Venneri Co., Westfield, N.J., 1951-60, v.p., asst. to pres., 1960-63, pres., 1963-65; pres., treas. Torcon, Inc., Westfield, 1965-84, pres., treas., chief exec. officer, 1984-89, chmn. bd., chief exec. officer, 1990—. Trustee bd. overseers N.J. Inst. Tech., Newark, 1980—; trustee Found. U. Medicine and Dentistry N.J., Newark, 1985-88; regent St. Peter's Coll., Jersey City, 1972-80; No. N.J. Area chmn. U.S. Olympic Com., 1984—; exec. com. March of Dimes, Monmouth County, N.J., 1985, N.J. unit NCCJ, 1985; trustee Kidney Fund of N.J., Union County, 1980-85, The Pingry Sch., 1987—. Recipient Ann. Alumni Achievement in Engring. award Cath. U. Am., Washington, 1978, Humanitarian and Brotherhood award N.J. chpt. Nat. Conf. Christians and Jews, 1990; named Constrn. Man of Yr., N.J. Ready Mixed Concrete Assn., 1981, Gen. Contractor of Yr. N.J. chpt. Am. Subcontractors Assn., 1974, 82, Constrn. Mgr. of Yr., 1989. Mem. Constrn. Congress (pres. 1983-85), Union County Bldg. Contractors Assn. (pres. 1975-83), Am. Concrete Inst., Bldg. Contractors Assn. N.J. (pres. 1981-82), N.J. Alliance for Action (trustee 1980—), Navesink Country Club, Jupiter Hills Club, MetedeconK Country Club. Roman Catholic. Avocations: golf; reading. Office: Torcon Inc PO Box 609 214 E Grove St Westfield NJ 07090-1657

TORCIVIA, BENEDICT JOSEPH, JR., construction company executive; b. Buffalo, July 5, 1957; s. Benedict Joseph and Elvira (Venneri) T.; m. Judith Anne Hlavenka, May 2, 1981; children: Benedict III, Brian, Christopher, Leigh Ann. BS in Bus., Lehigh U., 1979; lic. in real estate, Union Coll., 1980. Lic. in real estate. Exec. v.p., chief oper. officer Torcon, Inc., Westfield, N.J., 1979—, exec. v.p., 1979—. Bd. dirs. N.J. Alliance for Action. Mem. Bldg. Contrs. Assn. N.J. (trustee), Constrn. Mgmt. Com., Assoc. Gen. Contrs. Am. (com. mem.), Waterfront Invest (bd. advisors), Navesink Country Club (Middletown, N.J.), Atlantic City Country Club. Roman Catholic. Office: Torcon Inc 214 E Grove St Westfield NJ 07090-1657

TORDOFF, HARRISON BRUCE, retired zoologist, educator; b. Mechanicville, N.Y., Feb. 8, 1923; s. Harry F. and Ethel M. (Dormandy) T.; m. Jean Van Nostrand, July 3, 1946; children: Jeffrey, James. B.S., Cornell U., 1946; M.A., U. Mich., 1949, Ph.D., 1952. Curator Inst. of Jamaica, Kingston, 1946-47; instr. U. Kans., 1950-52, asst. prof., 1952-57, assoc. prof., 1957; asst. prof. U. Mich., 1957-59, assoc. prof., 1959-62, prof., 1962-70; former dir. Bell Mus. Natural History; prof. ecology U. Minn., Mpls., 1970-91, dean coll. biol. scis., 1986-87. Contbr. articles in ornithology to profl. jours. Served with USAF, 1942-45. Decorated D.F.C., 17 Air medals. Fellow Am. Ornithologists Union (pres. 1978-80); mem. Nature Conservancy (chmn. bd. Minn. chpt. 1975-77), Wilson Ornithol. Soc. (editor 1952-54), Cooper Ornithol. Soc. Home: 6 Chickadee Ln North Oaks Saint Paul MN 55127 Office: 100 Ecology 1987 Upper Buford Cir Saint Paul MN 55108

TORELL, JOHN RAYMOND, III, banker; b. Hartford, Conn., July 10, 1939; s. Raymond John and Gertrude May (Bent) T.; m. Anne A. Keller, Feb. 17, 1962; children: John Raymond, Anne Elizabeth, Susan Allgood. BA, Princeton U., 1961. With Mfrs. Hanover Trust Co., N.Y.C., 1961-88, vice-chmn., 1978-82, exec. vice- chmn., 1982-85, pres., 1985-88; chmn., pres., CEO Calfed Inc., L.A., 1988-89; chmn. Calif. Fed. Savs. and Loan, L.A., 1988-89, Torell Mgmt. Inc., L.A., 1989—; chmn., CEO Fortune Bancorp., Inc., Clearwater, Fla., 1990-94; bd. dirs. Am. Home Products Inc., Volt Info. Scis. Inc., various Paine Webber investment cos. With USN, 1962-68. Mem. Blind Brook Club, Siwanoy Country Club, Clove Valley Club, Seminole Club, Nat. Golf Links Club. Republican. Office: Torell Mgmt Inc 767 Fifth Ave Ste 4605 New York NY 10153

TORG, JOSEPH STEVEN, orthopaedic surgeon, educator; b. Phila., Oct. 25, 1934; s. Jay and Elva Dorothy (May) T.; m. Barbara Jane Groenendaal, May 23, 1959; children—Joseph Steven, Elisabeth, Jay Michael. A.B. Haverford Coll., 1957; M.D., Temple U., 1961. Diplomate: Am. Bd. Orthopaedic Surgeons. Intern San Francisco Gen. Hosp., 1961-62; resident in orthopaedic surgery Temple U. Hosp., Phila., 1964-68, Shriners Hosp. for Crippled Children, Phila., 1966-67; asst. surgeon Episcopal Hosp., Phila., 1968-70; surgeon Shriners Hosp. Crippled Children, 1970-78; mem. staff Temple U. Hosp., 1970-78; instr. orthopaedic surgery, 1968-70, asst. prof., 1970-75, assoc. prof., 1976-78; dir. Center for Sports Medicine and Sci., 1974-78; chief orthopaedic sect. St. Christopher's Hosp. for Children, Phila.,

1971-74, mem. staff, 1974—; active staff St. Joseph's Hosp., Phila., 1977—; prof. U. Pa., 1978—; active staff hosp., 1978—; dir. Sports Medicine Center, 1978—; prof. orthopaedic surgery Hahnemann U., 1995; mem. active staff Children's Hosp., Phila., 1978; med. cons. Pres.'s Council on Phys. Fitness and Sports. Mem. editorial bd. Sports Medicine, Yearbook of Sports Medicine, Contemporary Orthopaedics, Jour. Clin. Sport Medicine, Am. Jour. Knee Surgery, Orthopaedic Rev.; contbr. articles to profl. jours. Served with M.C. U.S. Army, 1962-64. Recipient Layman Honor award Pa. State Assn. Health, Phys. Edn. and Recreation, 1970, Grad. Honor award, 1975; Commendation of Merit Phila. Public High Sch. Football Coaches, 1974. Fellow Am. Acad. Orthopaedic Surgeons, Am. Coll. Sports Medicine (trustee 1975-78), Phila. Coll. Physicians; mem. AMA, Eastern Orthopaedic Soc., Am. Orthopaedic Soc., Sports Medicine, Phila. County Med. Soc., Phila. Orthopaedic Soc., Pa. State Med. Soc., Pa. State Orthopaedic Soc. Home: 401 Conestoga Rd Wayne PA 19087-4811 Office: Hahnemann U Sports Medicine Center 219 N Broad St Philadelphia PA 19107

TORGERSEN, PAUL ERNEST, university president; b. N.Y.C., Oct. 13, 1931; s. Einar and Hansine Malene (Hansen) T.; m. Dorothea Zuschlag, Sept. 11, 1954; children: Karen Elizabeth, Janis Elaine, James Einar. B.S., Lehigh U., 1953, DEng (hon.); M.S., Ohio State U., 1956, Ph.D., 1959. Instr. Ohio State U., 1956-59; asst., then assoc. prof. Okla. State U., 1959-67; prof., head dept. indsl. engring. Va. Poly. Inst., 1967-70, dean Coll. Engring., 1970-90, pres. corp. rsch. ctr., 1990-93, interim pres., 1988, John W. Hancock chair, 1990—, pres., 1993—; mem. Engring. Accreditation Commn., 1980-85; chmn. engring. grad. record exam. com. Ednl. Testing Service, 1984-86. Author: (with W.J. Fabrycky) Operations Economy, 1966, A Concept of Organization, 1968, (with I. T. Weinstock) Management: An Integrated Approach, 1972, (with W.J. Fabrycky and P.M. Ghare) Industrial Operations Research, 1972 (W.H. Maynard Book of the Year award 1972), (with M.H. Agee and R.E. Taylor) Quantitative Analysis for Management Decisions, 1975. Served to 1st lt. USAF, 1953-55. Recipient Outstanding Tchr. award Okla. State U., 1963, Disting. Alumnus award Ohio State U., 1971, Lamme medal Ohio State U., 1990. Fellow Am. Inst. Indsl. Engring. (editl. bd. 1967-70, publs. policy bd. 1970-72, v.p. edn. and profl. devel. 1983-85), Am. Soc. Engring. Edn. (chmn. I.E. divsn. 1966-67, exec. bd. engring. deans coun. 1974-81, chmn. 1979-81, Lamme medal 1994), Soc. Logistics Engrs. (adv. bd. 1975-89); mem. NAFE, Nat. Assn. State Univs. and Land-Grant Colls. (chmn. engring. com. 1981-83), Nat. Acad. Engring., Alpha Pi Mu (nat. regional dir. 1962-70). Home: The Grove VA Tech Blacksburg VA 24061-0446

TORGERSEN, TORWALD HAROLD, architect, designer; b. Chgo., Sept. 2, 1929; s. Peder and Hansine Malene (Hansen) T.; m. Dorothy Darlene Peterson, June 22, 1963. B.S. in Archtl. Engring. with honors, U. Ill., 1951. Lic. architect Ill., D.C.; real estate broker, Ill.; interior designer, Ill.; registered architect Nat. Coun. Archtl. Registration Bds. Ptnr. Coyle & Torgersen (Architects-Engrs.), Washington, Chgo. and Joliet, Ill., 1955-56; project coord. Skidmore, Owings & Merrill, Chgo., 1956-60; corp. architect, dir. architecture, constrn. and interiors Container Corp. Am., Chgo., 1960-86; prin. in charge of orgn. and adminstrn. Jack Train Assocs. Inc., Chgo., 1987-88; cons. Torwald H. Torgersen, AIA, FASID, Chgo., 1988—; guest lectr. U. Wis. Capt. USNR, 1951-82. Recipient Top Ten Design award Factory mag., 1964. Fellow Am. Soc. Interior Designers; mem. AIA, Naval Res. Assn., Ill. Naval Militia, Am. Arbitration Assn., Am. Soc. Mil. Engrs., Paper Industry Mgmt. Assn. (hon.), Sports Car Club Am., Nat. Eagle Scout Assn. Club: 20 Fathoms. Home and Office: 3750 N Lake Shore Dr Chicago IL 60613

TORGERSON, DAVID FRANKLYN, chemist, research facility administrator; b. Winnipeg, Man., July 11, 1942; m. Dale Rae Evans, May 28, 1966; children: Kristen, Dara, Shauna. BSc with honors, U. Man., 1965, MSc, 1966; PhD, McMaster U., 1969; postgrad., Nat. Def. Coll., Kingston, Ont., 1987-88. Rsch. scientist cyclotron inst. Tex. A&M Univ., College Station, 1969-76; rsch. scientist cyclotron inst. Atomic Energy Can. Ltd. Rsch., Pinawa, Man., 1976-78, head containment analysis sect., 1978-79, head br. rsch. chemistry, 1979-84, dir. reactor safety rsch., 1984-89, v.p. environ. sci. and waste mgmt., 1989-91; v.p. reactor devel. Atomic Energy Can. Ltd. Rsch., Chalk River, Ont., 1991—; acting pres. Atomic Energy Can. Ltd. Rsch., Ottawa, Ont., 1994; v.p. rsch., product devel. Atomic Energy Can. Ltd., 1995—; chmn. prin. working group Orgn. Econ. Cooperation and Devel./Com. Safety Nuclear Installation, Paris, 1985-87, chmn. task force on source terms, 1986-87. Contbr. articles to profl. jours. Scholar Dow Chem. Can., 1966, Nat. Rsch. Coun. Can., 1967-69. Fellow Chem. Inst. Can. (chmn. Man. sect. 1982, regional councillor 1983), Can. Nuclear Soc. Office: Atomic Energy Can Ltd Rsch, Chalk River Labs, Chalk River, ON Canada K0J 1J0

TORGERSON, LES, bar association administrator; b. Valley City, N.D., Aug. 10, 1946; s. Kermit L. and Annie L. (McEachern) T.; m. Marcia M. Guckeen, June 7, 1969; children: Susan, Stephanie. BS, No. Ariz. U., 1968; MS, N.D. State U., 1972; JD, U. N.D., 1985. Career counselor Employment Security Bur., Bismarck, N.D., 1968-75; personnel specialist N.D. Div. Personnel, Bismarck, 1975-76; dir. personnel N.D. Dept. of Health, Bismarck, 1976-82; exec. dir. State Bar Assn of N.D., Bismarck, 1985—. Mem. Nat. Assn. Bar Execs., Nat. Conf. Bar Founds., Am. Judicature Soc., N.D. Bar Found. (sec., treas. 1985—), Bismarck C. of C. (various coms. 1985—). Roman Catholic. Lodges: Kiwanis, Elks. Avocations: golf, water sports. Home: 6165 161st St W Rosemount MN 55068-1335 Office: State Bar Assn ND PO Box 2136 Bismarck ND 58502-2136

TORGOW, EUGENE N., electrical engineer; b. Bronx, N.Y., Nov. 26, 1925; s. Frank and Blanche Anita (Revzin) T.; m. Cynthia Silver, Mar. 19, 1950; children: Joan, Martha, Ellen. BSEE, Cooper Union, 1946; MSEE, Poly. Inst. Bklyn., 1949; Engr. in E.E., Poly. Inst. N.Y., 1980; postgrad. UCLA, 1983. Rsch. assoc., sect. leader Microwave Research Inst., Poly. Inst. Bklyn., 1947-51, 53-60, instr., 1954-59; mgr. microwave lab. A.B. Dumont Labs, East Patterson, N.J., 1951-53; chief engr., mgr. microwave products Dorne & Margolin, Inc., Westbury, L.I., N.Y., 1960-64; chief engr., dir. research, dir. mktg. Rantec div. Emerson Electric, Calabasas, Calif., 1964-68; with Missile Systems Group, Hughes Aircraft Co., Canoga Park, Calif., 1968-85. assoc. labs. mgr., 1981-85; cons. various electronics firms, N.Y.C., 1956-59; cons., 1986—; lectr. Calif. State U., Northridge, 1986-91. Contbr. articles to profl. jours.; patentee in field. Am. Fair Housing Coun., San Fernando Valley, L.A., 1967—; mem. L.A. County Mus. Assn., 1976—. Served with USAAF, 1946-47. Recipient Engr. '85 Merit award San Fernando Valley Engrs. Coun., 1985. Fellow Inst. for Advancement Engring., IEEE (life); mem. WINCON (bd. dirs. 1984-89, chmn. bd. dirs. 1988-89), Microwave Theory and Techniques Soc. of IEEE (pres. 1966, mem. adminstrn. com. 1962-72, Svc. award 1978), Accreditation Bd. Engring. and Tech. (mem. engring. accreditation com. 1994—), Hughes Mgmt. Club (editl. com. chmn. 1979-80), Sigma Xi. Democrat. Office: 9531 Donna Ave Northridge CA 91324-1816

TORIAN, MERVILLE RUSSELL, SR., construction company executive; b. Birmingham, Ala., Nov. 28, 1933; s. Ezra Sullivan and Leona (Friend) T.; student U. Ala., 1956; m. Doris Willene Davis, Aug. 28, 1952; children—Merville Russell, William Michael, James Gregory. Supr., Rust Engring. Co., Birmingham, New Orleans, Cleveland, Tenn. and Escanaba, Mich., 1956-70; resident constrn. mgr. Pullman-Swindell Co., Salt Lake City and Ahwaz, Iran, 1970-76; exec. v.p., dir. John Price Assos., Inc., Salt Lake City, 1976-79; mgr. constrn. mktg. Rust Engring. Co., Birmingham, 1979—. Dir., state dir. Cleveland Jaycees, 1962-65. Recipient several public service awards Jaycees. Mem. Soc. Mining Engrs. Presbyterian. Club: Rotary. Office: Ford Bacon & Davis Cos 2675 Breckinridge Blvd Duluth GA 30136 also: FB&D Techs Inc 375 Chipeta Way Salt Lake City UT 84108

TORIBARA, TAFT YUTAKA, radiation biologist, biophysicist, chemist, toxicologist; b. Seattle, Apr. 10, 1917; s. Minekichi and Hisano (Miyata) T.; m. Masako Ono, Aug. 28, 1948; children—Lynne Suzanne, Neil Wildard. BS in Chem. Engring. summa cum laude, U. Wash., 1938, M.S. in Chem. Engring. 1939; Ph.D., U. Mich., 1942. Rsch. chemist dept. engring. rsch. U. Mich., 1942-48; from asst. prof. to prof. radiation biology and biophysics Sch. Medicine and Dentistry, U. Rochester, N.Y., 1948-89, prof. emeritus toxicology in biophysics, 1989-93; prof. emeritus dept. environ. medicine, 1993—; cons. in field. Editor: Modern Techniques for the Detection and Measurement of Environmental Pollutants, 1978, Polluted Rain,

1980; contbr. articles to profl. jours. Chmn. advancement com. Boy Scouts Am., 1964-67; pres. Jr. High Family Faculty Forum, 1964-66; mem. Gates Library Bd., 1965-75, pres., 1972-74. NIH Spl. Research fellow, 1961-62; AAAS fellow, 1966. Mem. Am. Chem. Soc., AAAS. Inventor ultrafiltration apparatus, 1953. Home: 54 Timpat Dr Rochester NY 14624-2928 Office: EHSC U Rochester Med Ctr Rochester NY 14642 My life might be summarized by the statement, "Adversity is not always bad".

TORII, SHUKO, psychology educator; b. Toyohashi, Aichi-ken, Japan, Apr. 5, 1930; m. Toshiko Mochizuki, June 19, 1975. BA, U. Tokyo, 1954, MA, 1956, PhD, 1964. Rsch. asst. Tokyo Inst. Tech., 1959-61, U. Tokyo, 1961-65; assoc. prof. Tokyo U. Agr. Tech., 1965-70; rsch. assoc. U. Mich., Ann Arbor, 1966-68; rsch. assoc. Inst. Molecular Biophysics Fla. State U., 1968-69; from assoc. prof. to prof. psychology U. Tokyo, 1970-91; prof. U. Sacred Heart, Tokyo, 1991—. Author: The World of Vision, 1979, Psychology of Vision, 1982, Visual Perception in the Congenitally or Early Blinded after Surgery, 1992; author, editor: Perception, 1983, Visually Handicapped and Technology of Sensory Substitution, 1984, The Visually Handicapped and Their Cognitive Activity, 1993. Mem. Japanese Psychonomic Soc. (assoc. editor 1981-88, editor 1988—), Japanese Psychol. Assn. (mem. editorial com. 1987-89, editor 1989-92), Optical Soc. Am., Assn. Rsch. in Vision and Ophthalmology. Home: 2-17-26-204 Takada, Toshima, Tokyo 171, Japan Office: U Sacred Heart, 4-3-1 Hiroo, Shibuya Tokyo 150, Japan

TORKILDSEN, PETER G., congressman; b. Milw., Jan. 28, 1958; s. Robert Allan and Mary Ellen (Hill) T. BA, U. Mass., 1980; MPA, Harvard U., 1990. Mem. Mass. House of reps., from 1985, 103rd Congress from 6th Mass. dist., 1993—. Chmn. Danvers (Mass.) Rep. Town Com., 1983-88; mem. Danvers Town Meeting, 1983-85, Mass. Rep. State Com., Boston, 1984-93. Mem. Am. Legis. Exchange Council, Mass. Legislator's Assn., Nat. Rep. Legislator Assn. Roman Catholic. Lodge: Sons of Norway. Home: 12 Spruce St Danvers MA 01923-2070 Office: US House of Reps 120 Cannon Washington DC 20515-2106

TORLEY, JOHN FREDERIC, iron and steel company executive; b. Pitts., June 5, 1911; s. Walter Anderson and Emma Katherine (Hacker) T.; m. Leona Helen Depp, Oct. 5, 1940; children: Lois Leona, Jane Mildred. BS in Mech. Engring., Carnegie-Mellon U., 1940; Indsl. Engr., Youngstown U., 1948. Registered profl. engr., Pa. V.p. Midland Ross Co., Sharon, Pa., Phoenix and Chgo., 1946-61; chmn. Amcast Corp., Ohio, 1961-80, also bd. dirs.; chmn. bd. Morris Bean & Co., Yellow Springs, Ohio, 1992—; bd. dirs. Monarch Machine Tool Co., Standard Register Co., Ponderosa Systems Inc., Van Dyne Crotty Corp. Chmn. Air Force Mus. Found. Served with USNR, World War II; comdr. Res. Mem. ASME. Office: 1515 Kettering Towers Dayton OH 45423

TORMAN, HOWARD ALAN, cardiologist, medical correspondent; b. Providence, Jan. 18, 1947; s. Norman and Elaine (Israel) T.; m. Julie Ann McKim, Aug. 29, 1981; children: Andrew, Alexander. BS in Engring., U. R.I., 1969, LHD (hon.), 1994; MD, Pa. State U., 1973. Instr. radiology Harvard U. Med. Sch., Boston, 1980-83; pres., cons. on cardiovascular disease Torman Med. Prodns., San Mateo, Calif., 1983—; health reporter KRON-TV, San Francisco, 1984-86; health editor KCBS-TV, L.A., 1987-93; pres., pilot Tacair Sys. Ltd., Reno, 1991—; med. corr. CBS News, N.Y.C., 1993—; clin. cons. ACAD Labs, Sunnyvale, Calif., 1984-87. Contbr. numerous articles to med. jours. Recipient Jules Bergman award AMA, 1994. Avocations: flying, skiing. Office: CBS News CBS This Morning 524 W 57th St New York NY 10019-2902

TORME, MEL(VIN) (HOWARD TORME), musician, jazz vocalist; b. Chgo., Sept. 13, 1925; m. Janette Scott (div.); 2 children. Studied drums at age seven. Acted in radio soap operas; sang with Buddy Rogers, other name bands during early years; toured with Chico Marx band, 1942-43; motion picture debut in Higher and Higher, 1943; other motion picture appearances include Pardon My Rhythm, 1944, Words and Music, 1948, Walk Like a Dragon, 1960, A Man Called Adam, 1966, The Land of No Return; leader vocal group, Mel-Tones, Calif.; solo singer, 1947—, co-founder Producers Group Ltd., 1982; numerous compositions including County Fair; solo singer Vaudeville Tour, Eng., 1956, 57; recs. include Live at the Maisonette, Mel Torme and Friends, Recorded at Marty, Back in Town, Songs of New York, Swings Shubert Alley, That's All, Easy to Remember, Velvet Fog, Songs About Love, Round Midnight, Together Again, The London Sessions, 1992, Mel Torme in Hollywood, 1992, Nothing Without You, 1993, Christmas Songs, 1993, Sixteen Most Requested Songs, 1993, Sing, Sing, Sing: Live at the Fujitsu-Concord Jazz Festival, 1993, Jazz 'Round Midnight, 1994, A Tribute to Bing Crosby, 1994; author: The Other Side of the Rainbow, 1970, autobiography It Wasn't All Velvet, 1988. Recipient Grammy award Best Male Jazz Vocal Performance, 1983, 84. Address: care Prappas Co 9201 Wilshire Blvd Ste 204 Beverly Hills CA 90210-5513*

TORMEY, DOUGLASS COLE, medical oncologist; b. Sept. 2, 1938. BS in Med. Scis., U. Wis., 1960, MD, 1964, MS in Oncology, 1966, PhD in Oncology, 1969. Intern U. Calif. Med. Ctr., San Francisco, 1964-65, resident, 1965-66; postdoctoral fellow oncology U. Wis. Med. Ctr., Madison, 1966-69; fellow in oncology Roswell Park Meml. Inst., Buffalo, 1969-70; staff oncologist Walter Reed Gen. Hosp., Washington, 1970-72; head med. breast unit NCI, NIH, Bethesda, Md., 1972-73, sr. investigator, 1972-76, head med. breast cancer svc., 1973-76; cons. rsch. cell physiology dept. biol. scis. George Washington U., Washington, 1974-76; assoc. prof. depts. human oncology and medicine U. Wis. Med. Sch., Madison, 1976-82, prof. depts. human oncology and medicine, 1982-92; cons. William S. Middleton Meml. Vets. Hosp., Madison, 1979-92; assoc. dir. clin. programs Wis. Clin. Cancer Ctr., Madison, 1985-92; exec. officer Ea. Coop. Oncology Group, 1985-90, chmn., 1990—; dir. AMC Cancer Rsch. Ctr., Denver, 1992—, Rose Med. Ctr. Cancer Ctr., Denver, 1992—; prof. dept. medicine U. Colo. Sch. Medicine, Denver, 1994—; mem. U. Colo. Cancer Ctr., 1994—. Mem. Ea. Coop. Oncology Group (chmn.). Office: AMC Cancer Rsch Ctr 1600 Pierce St Denver CO 80214-1433

TORN, RIP (ELMORE RUAL TORN, JR.), actor, director; b. Temple, Tex., Feb. 6, 1931; s. Elmore and Thelma (Spacek) T.; m. Ann Wedgeworth, Jan. 15, 1955 (div.); 1 dau., Danae; m. Geraldine Page; children: Angelica, Anthony, Jonathan. Student, Tex. A & M Coll., 1948-50; B.S.F.A., U. Tex. Performances include: (stage) Cat on a Hot Tin Roof, 1955, Orpheus Descending, 1958, Chaparral, 1958 (Theatre World award 1959), Sweet Bird of Youth, 1959, on tour, 1960, Daughter of Silence, 1961, Macbeth, 1962, Desire Under the Elms, 1963, Strange Interlude, 1963, Blues for Mr. Charlie, 1964, The Kitchen, 1966, The Country Girl, 1966, The Deer Park, 1967 (Obie award), The Cuban Thing, 1968, The Honest-to-God Schnozzola, 1969, Dream of a Blacklisted Actor, 1969, The Dance of Death, 1970-71, The Marriage Proposal, 1971, Marriage and Money, 1971, Barbary Shore, The Little Foxes, 1974, The Father, 1975, The Glass Menagerie, 1975, Fever for Life, 1975, Creditors, 1977, Night Shift, 1977, Seduced, 1979, Anna Christie, 1992; (motion pictures) Baby Doll, 1956, A Face in the Crowd, 1957, Time Limit, 1957, Pork Chop Hill, 1959, King of Kings, 1961, Hero's Island, 1962, Sweet Bird of Youth, 1962, Critic's Choice, 1963, The Cincinnati Kid, 1965, One Spy Too Many, 1966, Beach Red, 1967, You're a Big Boy Now, 1967, Beyond the Law, 1968, Sol Madrid, 1968, Coming Apart, 1969, Tropic of Cancer, 1970, Slaughter, 1972, Payday, 1973, Crazy Joe, 1974, Birch Interval, 1976, Maidstone, The Man Who Fell to Earth, 1976, Nasty Habits, 1977, Coma, 1978, The Seduction of Joe Tynan, 1979, First Family, 1980, Heartland, 1980, One Trick Pony, 1980, Jinxed, 1982, Airplane II: The Sequel, 1982, The Beastmaster, 1982, A Stranger is Watching, 1982, Cross Creek, 1983, City Heat, 1984, Misunderstood, 1984, Night Shadows, 1984, Song Writer, 1984, Flashpoint, 1984, Summer Rental, 1985, Beer, 1985, Extreme Prejudice, 1987, Defending Your Life, 1991, Beautiful Dreamers, 1992, Hard Promises, 1992, Robocop 3, 1993, Where the Rivers Flow North, 1994, How to Make an American Quilt, 1995; (TV films and miniseries) Two Plays, 1971, The President's Plane Is Missing, 1973, The FBI Versus the Ku Klux Klan, 1975, Song of Myself, 1976, Betrayal, 1976, The Gift of Love, 1978, Blind Ambition, 1979, A Shining Season, 1979, Sophia Loren: Her Own Story, 1980, Rape and Marriage: The Rideout Case, 1980, The Blue and the Gray, 1982, When She Says No, 1984, Dream West, 1986, April Morning, 1988, Sweet Bird of Youth, 1989, By Dawn's Early Light, 1990, Another Pair of Aces: Three of a Kind, 1991, My Son Johnny,

1991, Death Hits the Jackpot, 1991, T-Bone and Weasel, 1992, A Mother's Right: The Elizabeth Morgan Story, 1993, Dead Ahead: The Exxon Valdez Disaster, 1992; (TV series) The Larry Sanders Show, HBO, 1992— (Emmy nominee for best supporting actor 1993, 94, Cable Ace award for best supporting actor 1994); dir. plays: The Beard, 1968 (Obie award), Look Away, 1973. Mem. AFTRA, SAG, Actors Equity Assn., Actors' Studio (bd. dirs., prodn. bd., 1st chmn. founding com.), Dirs. Guild Am. •

TORNABENE, RUSSELL C., communications executive; b. Gary, Ind., Sept. 18, 1923; s. Samuel Tornabene and Marion (LaVorci) Roush; m. Audrey F. Shankey, June 21, 1952; children—Joseph, Leigh, David, Lynn. A.A., Gary Jr. Coll., 1941, 46-47; B.A., Ind. U., 1949, M.A., 1950. Radio, TV newswriter WRC-AM-TV, Washington, 1951-55; network supr. NBC Network News, Washington, 1955-61; network gen. mgr. NBC Network News, NYC, 1961-75; v.p. NBC News, NYC, 1975-81; exec. officer Soc. Profl. Journalists, Chgo., 1981-87; Midwest dir. Exec. TV Workshop, Chgo., 1987—. Contbr. articles on news to mags. and newspapers. Mem. N.Y. Catholic Archdiocese Sch. Bd., N.Y.C., 1972. Recipient Disting. Service award, Sigma Delta Chi, 1949; Ernie Pyle scholar, 1949. Mem. Acad. TV Arts and Scis., Radio TV News Dirs. Assn. Club: Overseas Press (former v.p.). Avocation: photography. Office: 626 Sheridan Sq # 2 Evanston IL 60202-3156

TORNABENE, THOMAS GUY, microbiologist, researcher, administrator; b. Cecil, Pa., May 6, 1937; s. Guy Thomas and Helen (Skarupa) T.; m. Maria D. Butos, June 10, 1962 (div. May 1974); children: Elene D., Demi E., Joanna M.; m. Kristi S. Broadwater, Nov. 5, 1977; children: Kari J., Miki A., Talia C. BS in Biology, St. Edwards U., 1959; MS in Immunology, U. Houston, 1962, PhD in Biol. Chemistry, 1967. Postdoctoral fellow NRC, Ottawa, Ont., Can., 1967-68; asst. prof. Colo. State U., Ft. Collins, 1968-73, assoc. prof., 1973-78, prof., 1978-81; dir., prof. Ga. Inst. Tech., Atlanta, 1981-90, assoc. dean, 1990-95, prof., 1981—. Contbr. articles to profl. jours., chpts. to books in field. Mem. Am. Soc. Microbiology. Office: Ga Inst Tech Sch Applied Biology Atlanta GA 30332-0230

TORNEK, TERRY E., real estate executive; b. Bklyn., Nov. 23, 1945; s. Allen Vernon and Gertrude (Slotkin) T.; m. Maria Elizabeth Mascoli, June 25, 1967; children: Joshua, Jessica, Rachel. BA, Princeton U., 1967; MS in Urban Planning, Columbia U., 1971. Urban renewal rep. U.S. Dept. HUD, N.Y.C., 1968-69; prin. planner, dir. Planning Dept., Springfield, Mass., 1971-75; dir. Planning Dept., Pasadena, Calif., 1982-84; adminstr. Pioneer Valley Transit Authority, Springfield, 1975-79; v.p., gen. mgr. Cannon Planning & Devel., Springfield, 1979-82; dir. devel. BWC Devel., L.A., 1984-87; exec. v.p. Haseko (Calif.) Inc., L.A., 1987—. City councillor Springfield (Mass.) City Coun., 1976-77; bd. dirs. Springfield (Mass.) Action Commn., 1975-80; bd. dirs., v.p. Pasadena (Calif.) Neighborhood Housing Svcs., 1982-88. Home: 4910 Burgoyne Ln La Canada CA 91011-3717 Office: Haseko (Calif) Inc 350 S Figueroa St Ste 601 Los Angeles CA 90071-1302

TORNG, HWA C., engineering educator, researcher; b. Yangchow, Jiangsu, China, Aug. 12, 1932; came to U.S., 1956; s. Y.C. and Yung (Chang) T.; m. Bung-fung Lee, June 10, 1960; children: Clifford, Eric. BS, Nat. Taiwan U., 1955; MS, Cornell U., 1958, PhD, 1960. Asst. prof. Cornell U., Ithaca, N.Y., 1960-62, assoc. prof., 1962-71, prof., 1971—, coord. grad. studies electrical engring., 1989-92; mem. tech. staff Bell Telephone Labs., Holmdel, N.J., 1966-67. Author: Introduction to Logic Design, 1964, Switching Circuits, 1972; patentee in field. Recipient Award for excellence in teaching, 1985. Fellow IEEE (disting. vis., 1983-86, editor, 1986—). Office: Cornell U 333 Engring Theory Ctr Ithaca NY 14853

TORO, CARLOS HANS, insurance/financial products marketing executive; b. Lima, Peru, Jan. 20, 1943; s. Charlie Toro and Eufemia (Lopez); m. Liliana Irene Perez, Feb. 7, 1967; children: Michelle V., Hans C. Student Sch. Engring., Nev. So. U., 1964-67. Enlisted USAF, 1963, advanced through grades to staff sgt., resigned, 1972; regional dir. Am. Continental Life, Frankfurt, Germany, 1972-78, Continental Am. Securities, Ltd., Frankfurt, 1973-78; stockbroker Continental Am. Securities, Ltd., Phoenix, 1978-84; owner, ins. broker C.H. Toro Internat. Ltd., Phoenix, 1978—; officer Century Pacific Internat. Corp., Phoenix, 1984-90, pres., 1987-90. Mem. Miami (Fla.) C. of C. Republican. Roman Catholic. Avocations: skiing, travel. Office: CH Toro Internat Ltd 801 Brickell Ave Fl 9 Miami FL 33131-2900

TOROK, MARGARET LOUISE, insurance company executive; b. Detroit, June 22, 1922; d. Perl Edward Ensor and Mary (Seggie) Armstrong; m. Leslie A. Torok, Aug. 14, 1952; 1 child, Margaret Mary Ryan. Lic. Ins. Agy. Ins. agy. Grendel-Wittbold Ins., Southgate, Mich., 1961-68, corp. officer, 1968-72; pres. of corp. Grendel-Wittbold Ins., Southgate, 1972—; bd. dirs. Ind. Ins. Agts. of Mich., Lansing, 1984-92, Ind. Ins. Agts. of Wayne County, Dearborn, 1979—, pres. 1978. Bd. dirs. So. Wayne County C. of C., Taylor, 1975, 2d vice chair 1995; leadership chmn. YMCA, Wyandotte, 1980—, Downriver Cmty. Alliance; lay chmn. Cath. Svc. Appeal for Archdiocese of Detroit, 1989; co-chair fundraiser Sacred Heart Ch.; chmn. MESC Employers Com., 1991—. Recipient Capital award Ind. Ins. Agents of Mich., 1988, Amb. award, 1994, Woman of Yr. AAUW, 1994, Salute to Excellence award Downriver Coun. of Arts, 1993-94, Chmn. of Yr. award MESC Job Svc. Employers Com., 1991, Robert Stewart award Wyandotte Svc. Club Coun., 1994. Mem. Wyandotte Yacht Club, Soroptimist Club of Wyandotte Southgate (pres. Taylor 1984-86, sgt., Advancing Status Women award 1988, Soroptimist of Yr. 1993-94). Roman Catholic. Office: Grendel Wittbold Agy Inc 12850 Eureka Rd Southgate MI 48195-1344

TORQUATO, SALVATORE, materials science engineer, researcher; b. Falerna, Calabria, Italy, Feb. 10, 1954; came to U.S., 1955; s. Vincent and Palma (Vaccaro) T.; m. Kim Tracey Hoberock, Nov. 8, 1975; 1 child, Michelle. BSME, Syracuse U., 1975; MSME, SUNY, Stony Brook, 1977, PhD in Mech. Engring., 1980. Rsch. engr. Grumman Aerospace Corp., Bethpage, N.Y., 1975-78; rsch. asst. dept. mech. engring. SUNY, Stony Brook, 1978-80; asst. prof. dept. mech. engring. GM Inst., Flint, Mich., 1981-82; from asst. to assoc. prof. depts. mech., aerospace & chem. engring. N.C. State U., Raleigh, 1982-90, prof. depts. mech., aerospace & chem. engring., 1991-92; prof. Civil Engring. Princeton (N.J.) U., 1992—; vis. prof. Courant Inst. Math. Scis., N.Y.C., 1990-91; cons. Eastman Kodak, Rochester, N.Y., 1989—. Contbr. articles to profl. jours. Grumman Masters fellow, 1975-77; grantee NSF, 1982—, U.S. Dept. Energy, 1986—; recipient Engring. Rsch. Achievement award Alcoa Co., 1987, Disting. Engring. Rsch. award, 1989, Gustus L. Larson Meml. award, 1994. Fellow ASME; mem. Am. Inst. Chem. Engrs., Am. Phys. Soc., Soc. Engring. Sci., Soc. for Indsl. and Applied Math. Avocations: racquetball, reading. Office: Princeton U Princeton Materials Inst Depts Civ Eng & Oper Rsch Princeton NJ 08544

TORRACO, STEPHEN FRANCIS, priest, theologian, educator; b. Watertown, Mass., Nov. 25, 1953; s. Italo and Clorinda Antoinette (Dimare) T. BA Theology/Philosophy summa cum laude, St. Francis de Sales Coll., 1975; MA in Theology, Boston Coll., 1977; MDiv magna sum laude, Harvard U., 1979; PhD in Theology, Boston Coll., 1986. Prof. Theology Boston Coll., Chestnut Hill, Mass., 1980-86, 88, Stonehill Coll., North Easton, Mass. 1986-88, Assumption Coll., Worcester, Mass., 1988—; dir. Inst. Study of Magisterial Teaching of Ch. Assumption Coll.; cons. Pope Paul VI Ctr. for Study of Human Reproduction, Omaha, 1994—. Author (book) Priests as Physicians of Souls, 1991; editor (jour.) Catholic International, 1993—; contbr. articles to profl. jours. Assoc. mem. Cath. Commn. on Intellectual and Cultural Affairs; mem. Fellowship of Cath. Scholars, Soc. of Cath. Social Scientists, Am. Acad. Natural Family Planning. Republican. Roman Catholic. Office: Assumption Coll 500 Salisbury St Worcester MA 01615

TORRANCE, ELLIS PAUL, psychologist, educator; b. Milledgeville, Ga., Oct. 8, 1915; s. Ellis Watson and Jimmie Pearl (Ennis) T.; m. Jessie Pansy Nigh, Nov. 25, 1959 (dec. Nov. 1988). B.A., Mercer U., 1940; M.A., U. Minn., 1944; Ph.D., U. Mich. 1951. Tchr. Midway Vocational High Sch., Milledgeville, 1936-37; tchr., counselor Ga. Mil. Coll. 1937-40, prin., 1941-44; counselor student counseling bur. U. Minn., 1945; counselor counseling bur. Kans. State Coll., 1946-48, dir., 1949-51; dir. survival research field unit Stead AFB, Nev., 1951-57; dir. Bur. Ednl. Research, 1958-64; prof. ednl.

psychology U. Minn., 1958-66; chmn., prof. dept. ednl. psychology U. Ga., 1966-78, Alumni Found. disting. prof., 1974-85; Alumni Found. disting. prof. emeritus, 1985—; advisor Torrance Ctr. for Creative Studies, U. Ga. Author: Torrance Tests of Creative Thinking, Thinking Creatively in Action and Movement, Style of Learning and Thinking, and Sounds and Images; contbr. articles to jours., mags., books. Trustee Creative Edn. Found.; founder Nat. Future Problem Solving Problem and Bowl, Nat. Scenario Writing Contest. Torrance Ctr. for Creative Studies, Torrance Creative Scholars, and Mentors Network established in his honor at U. Ga. Fellow Am. Psychol. Assn.; mem. Am. Ednl. Rsch. Assn., Am Soc. Group Psychotherapy and Psychodrama, Creative Edn. Leadership Coun., Nat. Assn. Gifted Children, Am. Creativity Assn., Phi Delta Kappa. Baptist. Home: 183 Cherokee Ave Athens GA 30606-4305

TORRAS, JOSEPH HILL, pulp and paper company executive; b. Americus, Ga., Nov. 14, 1924; s. Fernando Joseph and Nell Wilson (Hill) T.; m. Mary Ravenel Robertson, Sept. 20, 1952; children: Mary Martin, Fernanda Maria, Joseph Hill. S.B., Yale U., 1948; M.B.A., Harvard U., 1950. Asst. to fin. v.p. Seatrian Lines, Inc., 1950-51; with St. Regis Paper Co., 1951-60, sales mgr. printing papers div., 1956-60; exec. v.p. Brown Co., Boston, 1960-64; pres., chmn. bd. Premoid Corp., West Springfield, Mass., 1964-87; pres. Precon, Inc., Ludlow, 1967-87, Lincoln Pulp & Paper Co., Lincoln, Maine, 1968—, Astro Tissue Co., Battleboro, Vt., 1968—; chmn. bd. Whitman Products, Ltd., West Warwick, 1976-89; pres., chief exec. officer Preco Corp., Amherst, Mass., 1976—; chmn. Lincoln (Maine) Pulp and Paper Co., 1989—; mem. Nat. UN Day Com., 1977; bd. dirs. Bay Banks, Inc., Boston; chmn. Ea. Fine Paper Inc., Brewer, Maine; adv. dir. Liberty Mutual Ins. Mem. Mass. Gov.'s Bus. Adv. Coun., 1985-88, devel. bd. Yale U., 1989—; bd. govs. Mass. Gen. Hosp.; bd. dirs. Mass. Taxpayers Assn., 1976-86, U. Maine Pulp and Paper Found., 1981—; trustee Hist. Deerfield, 1990—, Piedmont Coll., Ga., 1991—. Lt. (j.g.), aviator USNR, 1943-46. Mem. Tissue Paper Mfrs. Assn. (dir. 1963-64), Am. Pulp and Paper Mill Supts. Assn., Salesman's Assn. Paper Industry, NAM (dir. 1981-85), Colony Club. Independent. Office: Preco Corp 100 University Dr Amherst MA 01004

TORRE, DOUGLAS PAUL, dermatologist; b. New Orleans, Feb. 6, 1919; s. Peter and Jeanne Renee (Mottram) T.; m. Sylvia Elizabeth Stenmark, Apr. 22, 1954 (div. May 1977); children—Eric, Jeanne; m. Catherine Babcock, May 28, 1977. B.S., Tulane U., 1940, M.D, 1943; postgrad., Cornell U., 1946-50. Intern Phila. Gen. Hosp., 1943-44; fellow Cornell U. Med. Coll.-N.Y. Hosp., 1946-50; practice medicine, specializing in dermatology N.Y.C., 1946—; instr. Cornell U. Med. Coll., N.Y.C., 1950-55; asst. prof. Cornell U. Med. Coll., 1956-59, asso. prof., 1960-65, clin. prof. dermatology, 1966—; attending physician N.Y. Hosp.; cons. Meml. Hosp. Contbr. articles to profl. jours. and chpts. to textbooks. Served to lt., M.C. USNR, 1944-46, PTO. Mem. AMA, Am. Acad. Dermatology, Soc. Investigative Dermatology, Atlantic Dermatology Assn (pres. 1969), N.Y. Dermatology Assn. (pres. 1969, 79), Am. Soc. Dermatol. Surgery (v.p. 1979, pres. 1980-81), Am. Coll. Cryosurgery (pres. 1982-83), N.Y. Acad. Medicine, Phi Beta Kappa, Delta Tau Delta. Club: University (N.Y.C.). Home: 122 Rowayton Ave Norwalk CT 06853-1409 Office: 320 E 65th St New York NY 10021-6743

TORREGROSSA, JOSEPH ANTHONY, lawyer; b. Bklyn., Sept. 23, 1944; s. Joseph and Marie (Faraone) T.; m. Ann S. Gormally, July 11, 1970; children—Brennan, Maresa. A.B., Villanova U., 1966, J.D., 1969. Bar: N.Y. 1970, Pa. 1971, U.S. Dist. Ct. (ea. dist.) Pa. 1971, U.S. Ct. Appeals (3d cir.) 1973, U.S. Supreme Ct. 1975. Law Clk. to judge U.S. Dist. Ct. (ea. dist.) Pa., 1969-71; assoc. Morgan, Lewis & Bockius, Phila., 1971-77; ptnr. Morgan, Lewis & Bockius, Phila., 1977—; lectr. in field. Mem. Phila. Bar Assn., Pa. Bar Assn., ABA. Office: Morgan Lewis & Bockius 2000 One Logan Sq Philadelphia PA 19103

TORRENCE, (JOHN) RICHARD, fundraising executive, special events producer; b. Ottumwa, Iowa, Oct. 12, 1936; s. John W. and Louise Lucy (Willey) T. BS, U. Wis., Madison, 1958. Pres. Richard Torrence Mgmt., N.Y.C., 1962-72, WTM Inc., Englewood, N.J., 1966-71, Torrence/Perrotta Mgmt. Inc., N.Y., 1972-76, Torrence Assocs., N.Y.C., 1976-78; chmn. Performance Mktg. Corp., 1978-84; exec. chmn. Creo Soc., N.Y.C., 1983-89; pres. Coleman Spl. Events Inc., N.Y.C., 1989-91; dir. devel. Am. Found. for AIDS Rsch., N.Y.C., 1991; dep. to mayor of St. Petersburg, Russia for Internat. Affairs, 1992—; also dir. St. Petersburg Partnership; dir. pub. relations Rodgers Organ Co., Hillsboro, Oreg., 1971-75, 81-82, v.p. mktg., 1975; cons. in field; mem. adv. bd. Van Cliburn Piano Competition; bd. dirs. Albert Schweitzer Fellowship, 1985-89; chmn. music com. Albert Schweitzer Inst. for the Humanities, 1990—. N.Y. producer: Fanfare for Organ, Lincoln Center, 1969-70, Heavy Organ, 1970, Albert Schweitzer Music Award, 1975, 79, 83, 85, 87, Umabatha, 1994, Frank Lloyd Wright Creativity award, 1982, 84, 86, Bach-Gesellschaft of N.Y., 1985-88, Rockefeller U. Founders Ball, 1985, A Classic Evening for AIDS Research, 1986, Music Under the Stars, 1986, 87, Dancing for Life, Lincoln Ctr., 1987, A Million Dollar Cabaret, Rainbow Rm., N.Y., 1987, Hair...for the Next Generation, UN, 1988, Treasures of Fortune, Bloomingdales, N.Y.C., 1988, World AIDS Day Masquerade, 1989, 90, 91, Night of 100 Stars III, 1990, Glitter and Be Giving, L.A. and N.Y.C., 1991-92, Bella the Ball, Music and Remembrance, 1992, First St. Petersburg Festival of American Film Treasures, 1993, St. Petersburg Festival of American Films, 1995. Mem. Carnegie Hall Nat. Endowment Fund (founding). Democrat. Home: One Lincoln Plaza New York NY 10023 Office: 20 W 64th St Ste 32P New York NY 10023 also: Smolny St 1/3, 193060 Saint Petersburg Russia

TORRENZANO, RICHARD, public affairs executive. BS, N.Y. Inst. Tech., 1972, LittD (hon.), 1990; postgrad., Standford U. With N.Y. Stock Exch., N.Y.C., 1082-91, sr. v.p., chief spokesman, mem. mgmt. com., 1982-91; sr. v.p., dir. corp. affairs SmithKline Beecham, London, 1992-94; CEO, The Torrenzano Group Ltd., N.Y.C., 1994—; coord. Pres. Reagan's Bd. Advisors on Pvt. Sector Initiatives, Washington, 1986-89; mem. pvt. sector adv. com. USIA, Washington, 1983-92; coord. program USSR-N.Y. Stock Exch., Moscow, 1990; lectr. in field. Contbr. articles to profl. jours. Trustee N.Y. Inst. Tech., 1985—. Recipient Silver Anvil award Pub. Rels. Soc. Am. Mem. Royal Soc. Medicine (London), Internat. Pub. Rels. Assn., Nat. Press Club (Washington), N.Y. Press Club, Knights of Malta. Office: The Torrenzano Group Ltd 520 E 72d St Ste 12-0 New York NY 10021

TORRES, CYNTHIA ANN, banker; b. Glendale, Calif., Sept. 24, 1958; d. Adolph and Ruth Ann (Smith) T.; m. Michael Victor Gisser, Mar. 11, 1989; 1 chld, Spencer Williams Gisser. AB, Harvard U., 1980, MBA, 1984. Research assoc. Bain & Co., Boston, 1980-82; assoc. Goldman, Sachs & Co., N.Y.C., 1984-88, v.p., 1988; v.p. First Interstate Bancorp, L.A., 1989-92; dir. Fidelity Investments Mgmt. (H.K.) Ltd., Hong Kong, 1993—. Mem. judiciary rev. bd. Bus. Sch. Harvard U., Boston, 1983-84. Rockefeller Found. scholar, 1976; Harvard U. Ctr. for Internat. Affairs fellow, 1979-80; recipient Leadership award Johnson and Johnson, 1980; by Council for Opportunity in Grad. Mgmt. Edn. fellow, 1982-84. Mem. Acad. Polit. Sci., Asia Soc., Fin. Women's Assn. Hong Kong (bd. dirs.), Harvard Club of Hong Kong. Avocation: sportswriting. Office: Fidelity Investments Mgmt, 16/F Citibank Tower 3 Garden Rd, Hong Kong Hong Kong

TORRES, DAVID, Spanish language educator; b. Laredo, Tex., Oct. 30, 1934. PhD, U. Ill., 1969. Cert. tchr., Tex. Prof. Spanish Angelo State U., San Angelo, Tex., 1979—. Author: Los Prólogos de Leopoldo Alas, 1984, Studies on Clarín, 1987; contbr. articles to profl. publs. Grantee Nat. Endowment Humanities, 1977, Angelo State U., 1981, 84; Southland Corp. scholar, 1986. Mem. Am. Assn. Tchrs. Spanish and Portuguese, Tex. Assn. Coll. Tchrs., Sigma Delta Pi. Office: Angelo State U 2601 Avenue Ave N San Angelo TX 76909

TORRES, EDWIN, state judge, writer; b. N.Y., 1931; s. Edelmiro and Ramona T.; m. Vickie; 4 children. Degree, City Coll., N.Y., Bklyn. Law Sch. Asst. dist. atty. N.Y.C., 1958-61; appt. judge Criminal Ct. Bench, N.Y. State Supreme Ct., 1980—. Author: Carlito's Way, 1974, After Hours, 1975, Q & A, 1976. Office: NY Supreme Ct 12th Judicial Dist 100 Centre St New York NY 10013

TORRES, ERNEST C., federal judge; b. 1941. AB, Dartmouth Coll., 1963; JD, Duke U., 1968. Assoc. Hinckley, Allen, Salisbury & Parsons, 1968-74, Saunders & Torres, 1974-80; assoc. justice R.I. Superior Ct., 1980-85; asst. v.p. Aetna Life and Casualty, 1985-86; assoc., then ptnr. Tillinghast, Collins & Graham, 1986-87; judge U.S. Dist. Ct. R.I., 1988—; pres. East Greenwich (R.I.) Town Coun., 1972-74; state rep. R.I. Ho. of Reps., 1975-80, dep. minority leader, 1977-80. Alfred P. Sloan scholar Dartmouth Coll. Mem. ABA, Am. Trial Lawyers Assn., R.I. Bar Assn., Jaycees (Dist. Svc. award 1974). Office: US Dist Ct 1 Exch Ter 216 Fed Bldg & US Courthouse Providence RI 02903

TORRES, ESTEBAN EDWARD, congressman, business executive; b. Miami, Ariz., Jan. 27, 1930; s. Esteban Torres and Rena Baron (Gomez) T.; m. Arcy Sanchez, Jan. 22, 1955; children: Carmen D'Arcy, Rena Denise, Camille Bianca, Selina Andre, Esteban Adrian. Student, East Los Angeles Coll., 1960, Calif. State U., Los Angeles 1963, U. Md., 1965, Am. U., 1966, PhD (hon.), Nat. U., 1987. Chief steward United Auto Workers, local 230, 1954-63, dir. polit. com., 1963; organizer, internat. rep. United Auto Workers (local 230), Washington, 1964; asst. dir. Internat. Affairs Dept., 1975-77; dir. Inter-Am. Bureau for Latin Am., Caribbean, 1965-67; exec. dir. E. Los Angeles Community Union (TELACU), 1967-74; U.S. ambassador to UNESCO, Paris, 1977-79; chmn. Geneva Grp., 1977-78; chmn. U.S. del. Gen. Conf., 1978; spl. asst. to pres. U.S., dir. White House Office Hispanic Affairs, 1979-81; mem. 98th-103rd Congresses from 34th Dist. Calif. 1983—, mem. appropriations com., subcom. fgn. ops., subcom. military constrn.; campaign coordinator Jerry Brown for Gov., 1974; Hispanic coordinator Los Angeles County campaign Jimmy Carter for Pres., 1976; mem. Sec. of State Adv. Group, 1979-81; v.p. Nat. Congress Community Econ. Devel., 1973-74; pres. Congress Mex.-Am. Unity, 1970-71, Los Angeles Plaza de la Raza Cultural Center, 1974; dir. Nat. Com. on Citizens Broadcasting, 1977; cons. U.S. Congress office of tech. assessment, 1976-77; del. to U.S. Congress European Parliament meetings, 1984—; ofcl. congl. observer Geneva Arms Control Talks; chmn. Congl. Hispanic Caucus, 1987; speaker Wrights Del. to USSR, 1987; Dem. dep. Whip, 1990. Contbr. numerous articles to profl. jours. Co-chmn. Nat. Hispanic Dems., 1988—; chmn. Japan-Hispanic Inst. Inc.; bd. visitors Sch. Architecture U. Calif. at Los Angeles, 1971-73; bd. dirs. Los Angeles County Econ. Devel. Com., 1972-75, Internat. Devel. Conf., 1976-78. Served in AUS, 1949-53, ETO. Recipient various awards for public service. Mem. Americans for Dem. Action (exec. bd. 1975-77), VFW Post 6315, Pico Rivera, Calif., Am. Legion Post 0272, Montebello, Calif. Office: House of Representatives Rm 2368 Rayburn Washington DC 20515-0534

TORRES, GERALD, law educator; b. Victorville, Calif., Sept. 29, 1952; s. Frank E. and Mary L. (Lopez) T.; m. Frances Gloria Nash. AB in Polit. Sci., Stanford U., 1974; JD, Yale U., 1977; LLM, U. Mich., 1980. Crew chief Hall's Aboveground Pool Installation, 1973-74; legal intern Ctr. for Advocacy, Rsch. and Planning, NAACP, 1976-77; staff atty. Children's Def. Fund, 1977-78; prof. law U. Pitts. Law Sch., 1980-83, U. Minn., 1983—; vis. prof. law Vt. Law Sch., 1986, U. Tex. Law Sch., 1989, Harvard U. Law Sch., 1990-91; adj. prof. law Drake Summer Agrl. Law Inst., 1986—; presenter in field; mem. Minn. Atty. Gen.'s Task Force on Agr. Contbr. articles to profl. jours.; author: (with others) Law Office Without Walls, 1987, (with J. Davidson and L.B. Kurland) Agricultural Law and Policy Institute, 1988. Appointee U. Mich. Law Sch. Com. of Visitors. Named Law Prof. of Yr. Nat. Hispanic Bar Assn., 1990-91. Mem. D.C. Bar Assn., Am. Agrl. Law Assn., Am. Law Inst., Rural Am., Rural Coalition, Am. Farmland Trust. Office: U Minn Sch Law 229 19th Ave S Minneapolis MN 55455-0400

TORRES, MILTON JOHN, industrial engineering educator; b. N.Y.C., July 28, 1931; s. Milton and Vitalia (Cabrera) T.; m. Dorothy Spaugh (div. Feb. 1971); children: Milton J. III, Geoffrey, Vicky L. Lopez; m. Dorothy Roberts. BS in Gen. Engring., U. Okla., 1963, M Aerospace Engring., 1964; DArts in Mech. Engring., U. Miami, 1989. Commd. 2d lt. USAF, 1954, advanced through grades to maj.; chief test control br. Ops. Directorate Air Force Ea. Test Range, Cape Kennedy, Fla., 1968-71; ret. USAF, 1971; indsl. engr., sr. indsl. engr. Pan Am. World Airways, Inc., Miami, Fla., 1972-73; plant supt. Am. Panel Corp., Miami, 1973-77; plant mgr. Dyplast of Fla., 1977-83; asst. prof. indsl. systems dept. Fla. Internat. U., 1983-87, rsch. scientist, lectr. dept. indsl. engring., 1987-94. Contbr. articles to profl. jours., patentee in field. Decorated DFC, Air medal (13), Air Force Meritorious Svc. medal, Air Force Commendation medal. Mem. Tau Beta Pi, Sigma Tau, Sigma Gamma Tau, Alpha Pi Mu. Home: 11200 SW 99th Ct Miami FL 33176-4123

TORRES, RALPH CHON, minister; b. San José, Calif., Oct. 18, 1948; s. Chon Poncé and Dora (Grijalva) T.; m. Pamela Ellen Hansen, Mar. 6, 1971; children: Chon, Brida, Samuel, Sarah. BTh, L.I.F.E. Bible Coll., L.A., 1970. Ordained to ministry Internat. Ch. of the Foursquare Gospel, 1981. Missionary asst. Internat. Ch. of Foursquare Gospel, Mexicali, Mex., 1970; youth pastor Internat. Ch. of Foursquare Gospel, Redondo Beach, Calif., 1971-72, Pueblo, Colo., 1972-74; sr. pastor Internat. Ch. of Foursquare Gospel, Pasadena, Calif., 1984—; youth pastor Ch. on the Way, Van Nuys, Calif., 1975-84; asst., dir. children's camps, Jr. and Sr. High camps for So. Calif. Dist. Foursquare Chs., 1978—; tchr. L.I.F.E. Bible Coll., L.A., 1979-86; bd. dirs. Holy Ghost Repair Svc., Hollywood, Calif., Centrum of Hollywood, Christians in Govt., L.A., Camp Cedar Crest, Running Springs, Calif.; bd. dirs., speaker Mainstream Inc., Tacoma, 1978-83. Composer: Kids of the Kingdom, 1976. Mem. Prop. 98 Sch. Report Card Com., Pasadena, 1989-90; adv. com. Marshall Fundamental Sch., Pasadena, 1989-90, Pasadena Unified Sch. Dist., 1990—. Recipient commendation for svc. Mayor of Pasadena, 1990. Office: Pasadena Foursquare Ch 174 Harkness Ave Pasadena CA 91106-2099

TORRES-AYBAR, FRANCISCO GUALBERTO, medical educator; b. San Juan, P.R., July 12, 1934; s. Francisco and Maria (Aybar) Torres; m. Elga Arroyo; children: Elga, JoAnn Marie. BS, U. P.R., 1956; MD, U. Barcelona, Spain, 1963. Diplomate Am. Bd. Pediatrics. Chief pediatric cardiology Ponce (P.R.) Dist. Hosp., 1970-91, chmn. dept. pediatrics, 1971-91, med. dir., 1980, prog. dir. pediatric tng. prog., 1970-91; prof., chmn. dept. pediatrics Cath. Univ. Sch. of Medicine, Ponce, 1978-80; chmn., dept. pediatrics Damas Hosp., Ponce, 1985—; prof., chmn. dept. pediatrics Ponce Sch. of Medicine, 1980—. Editorial bd.: Sci.-Ciencia jour., Ponce, 1975—; contbr. articles to profl. jours. Fellow Am. Acad. Pediatrics, Am. Coll. Physicians, Am. Coll. Cardiology, Am. Coll. Internat. Physicians, British Royal Soc. Health, InterAm. Coll. Physicians and Surgeons; mem. AAUP, Phi Delta Kappa. Republican. Roman Catholic. Home: A26 Jacaranda Ponce PR 00731 Office: 13 Calle Mayor Ponce PR 00731-5025

TORRES-GIL, FERNANDO M., federal official; b. Salinas, Calif., June 24, 1948. BA in Polit. Sci., San Jose State U., 1970; MSW, Brandeis U., 1972, PhD, 1976. Spl. asst. to sec. Dept. Health, Edn. and Welfare, Washington, 1978-79; spl. asst. to sec. Dept. Health and Human Svcs., Washington, 1979-80, asst. sec. for aging, 1993—; prof. gerontology and pub. adminstrn. U. So. Calif., 1981-91, assoc. dir. Nat. Resource Ctr. on Minority Aging Populations, 1988-92, prof. social welfare, 1991-93; staff dir. Select Com. on Aging, U.S. Ho. of Reps., Washington, 1985-87. Contbr. articles to profl. jours. White House fellow, 1978-79. Mem. Am. Soc. Aging (pres. 1989-92). Office: Dept Health and Human Svcs 200 Independence Ave SW Washington DC 20201

TORRES MEDINA, EMILIO, oncologist, consultant; b. Mexico, Aug. 8, 1934; s. Manuel Torres and Juana Medina; m. Suisa Torres Dec. 6, 1966; children: Patricia, Ana Luisa, Veronica, Jesus Manuel. MD, U. Mex., 1958-64. Internist Hosp. of Nutrition, Mex., 1965-67; oncologist Hosp. of Oncology, Mex., 1967-70; chief dept. radiation Clin. of Parque, Chih, Mexico, 1970-80, chief of med. edn., 1974-78; chief dept. radiation Centro Oncologico del Norte, Juarez, Mexico, 1981-95; chief of med. edn. I.S.S.S.T.E., Juarez, Mexico, 1984-85; oncologist I.S.S.S.T.E., Juarez 1981-85; oncology prof. Uach Y Uacj, Juarez, Mexico, 1984-90; mem. med. coun. Pensiones Civiles del Edo., Juarez, Chih. 1985-90; med. dir. Pensionesl Civiles del Edo., Juarez Chih., 1982-88, Electronic Diagnosis of Juarez, 1981-92; oncologist cons. Gen. Hosp. of Juarez City, 1988-95. Author: Policitemia on Rats by Hemolizates, 1965, Alkil beta-d Glicosias on Human Lymphs, 1970. Advisor Juarez Cancer Soc., 1986-95. Mem. Soc. Mex. Est. Oncol. Capitulo Chihuahua (pres. 1990-92), Soc. Medicina Interna Cd.

Juarez (pres. 1992). Office: Centro Oncologico del Norte, Plutarco Elias Calles 1235, 32350 Juarez Mexico

TORRES OLIVER, JUAN FREMIOT, bishop; b. San German, P.R., Oct. 28, 1925; s. Luis N. and Amalia (Oliver) Torres. B.A., St. John's Seminary, 1944-50; M.A. Musicology, Catholic U., 1952; LL.B., U. of P.R., 1959; LL.M., St. John's U., 1964, LL.D., 1995. Ordained priest Roman Cath. Ch., 1950. Instr. Catholic U., Ponce, P.R., 1952-56; vice-chancellor Diocesan Curia, 1961-64; prof., assoc. dean Catholic U. Sch. of Law, Ponce, P.R., 1961-64; bishop of Ponce P.R., 1964—; grand chancellor Pontifical Cath. U. P.R., Ponce, 1964—; pres. P.R. Episcopal Conf. 1982-94; Grand Prior, P.R. lieutenancy of Equestrian Order of the Holy Sepulchre of Jerusalem, 1984—. Decorated Cross of Order Juan Pablo Duarte, Dominican Republic. mem. Academia de Artes y Ciencias; Phi Alpha Delta. Office: Obispado de Ponce Apartado 205 Sta 6 Ponce PR 00732*

TORREY, BARBARA BOYLE, research council administrator; b. Pensacola, Fla., Nov. 27, 1941; d. Peter F. and Elsie (Hansen) Boyle; m. E. Fuller Torrey, Mar. 23, 1968; children: Michael, Martha. BA, Stanford U., 1963, MS, 1970. Vol. Peace Corps, Tanzania, 1963-65; fiscal economist Office Mgmt. and Budget, Washington, 1970-80; dept. asst. sec. HHS, Washington, 1980-81; dir. Ctr. for Internat. Rsch., Census Bur., Washington, 1984-92; pres. Population Reference Bur., Washington, 1992-93; exec. dir. Commn. on Behavioral and Social Scis. and Edn., NRC, NAS, Washington, 1993—; bd. dirs. Luxembourg Income Study, 1984—. Co-editor: The Vulnerable, 1987, Population and Land Use, 1992; contbr. articles to profl. jours. Mem. Population Assn. Am. (bd. dirs. 1993—). Office: NRC 2101 Constitution Ave NW Washington DC 20418-0007

TORREY, DAVID LEONARD, investment banker; b. Ottawa, Ont., Can., Oct. 6, 1931; s. Arthur Starratt and Josephine Edith (Leonard) T.; divorced; children: Heather Torrey Murphy, John Winthrop, Diana Bruce, Arthur Bruce, David Molson. B.A. in Econs., St. Lawrence U., 1953; diploma, Grad. Sch. Bus., U. Western Ont., 1954. With Pitfield Mackay Ross Ltd., Toronto, Ont., Can., 1954-84; v.p. Pitfield Mackay Ross Ltd., 1963-73, sr. v.p., 1973-80, vice chmn., 1980-82, pres., 1982-84, also bd. dirs.; vice chmn. Dominion Securities, Inc., 1984-88, RBC Dominion Securities, Inc., 1988-93; chmn. Phillips Cables Ltd.; bd. dirs. Total Petroleum N.Am. Ltd., Wajax Ltd., Can. Stebbins Engring. and Mfg. Co. Ltd., Provigo Inc.; mem. adv. bd. I.C.I. Can., Inc.; chmn. Montreal Stock Exch., 1971-73; mem. coun. Montreal Bd. Trade, 1971-72. Chmn. Montreal Downtown YMCA, 1972-74; trustee St. Lawrence U.; bd. dirs. Montreal Hosp. Found. Mem. Investment Bankers Assn. (gov. 1971-72), Securities Industries Assn. (bd. govs. 1972-73), Multiple Sclerosis Can. (past pres., bd. dirs.), Beta Theta Pi. Clubs: Montreal Badminton and Squash, Royal Montreal Golf, Mt. Royal (Montreal); Toronto. Home: 389 Carlyle Ave, Montreal, PQ Canada H3R 1T3 Office: Ste 525, 2000 McGill Coll Ave, Montreal, PQ Canada H3A 3H3

TORREY, JAMES D., communications executive, consultant; b. Drayton, N.D., July 16, 1940; s. Howard J. Torrey and Gertrude (Carpenter) Steenson; m. Katherine Joann Kowal, Sept. 2, 1958; children: Tamara, Timonthy (dec.), Teresa, Todd. Student, U. Oreg. Mgr. Waldport (Oreg.) Food Market, 1959-67; dist. mgr. Obie Outdoor Advt., Aberdeen, Wash., 1967-68; dir. sales Obie Media Corp., Eugene, Oreg., 1968-71, exec. v.p., 1971-78, pres., CEO, 1980-88; pres., CEO Total Comm., Inc., Eugene, Oreg., 1989—; N.W. area market mgr. 3M Nat. Advt., Eugene, Oreg., 1978-80; dir. mktg. State Accident Ins. Fund, Salem, Oreg., 1988-89; mem. exec. com. affiliate bd. Mut. Broadcasting, 1981-87. Pres. Waldport City Coun., 1962-67; coach Eugene Kidsports, 1968-92, Am. Softball Assn. Girls Softball Team, 1988; mem. adv. com. 4 J Sch. Dist., 1988-90; bd. dirs. Lane County United Way, 1983-86, dir., 1992, Lane County Goodwill Industries, 1989-90; mem. Eugene City Budget Com., 1992-94, Eugene City Coun., 1994—. Named JCI senator, Oreg. State Jaycees, 1966, Citizen of Yr., City of Waldport, 1967, Outstanding Vol., City of Eugene, 1991. Mem. Oreg. Outdoor Advt. Assn. (pres. 1971-80), Oreg. Assn. Broadcasters (dir. 1984-87), Eugene C. of C. (bd. dirs., pres. 1991-92), Eugene Rotary (dir., pres. 1984, Paul Harris fellow 1985). Republican. Roman Catholic. Avocation: youth coaching. Home: 2545 Chuckanut St Eugene OR 97401 Office: Station KUGN-AM & FM 2545 Chestnut St Eugene OR 97401

TORREY, RICHARD FRANK, utility executive; b. Saratoga Springs, N.Y., Dec. 31, 1926; s. Reginald Frank and Marian (Currey) T.; m. Betty Louise Stetson, July 2, 1949; children: Patricia Ann Torrey Simpkins, Carol Louise Torrey Kress, Barbara Jean Torrey Friedman. BA cum laude, Syracuse U., 1951. News reporter Syracuse (N.Y.) Post Standard, 1947-51; pub. rels. account exec. Syracuse, 1951-53; home sec. 35th Congl. Dist., Syracuse, 1952-53; exec. sec. to mayor Syracuse, 1954-58; dir. area devel. Niagara Mohawk Power Corp., Syracuse, 1958-66; comml. v.p. Niagara Mohawk Power Corp., Buffalo, 1966-68; adminstrv. v.p. Niagara Mohawk Power Corp., 1968-72, v.p., gen. mgr., 1972-76; sr. v.p. Niagara Mohawk Power Corp., Syracuse, 1976-88, ret., 1988; pres. Can. Niagara Power Co. Ltd., Niagara Falls, Ont., Can., 1968-88, dir., 1968-89; pres., dir. Caragh Investments Ltd., 1981-85; pres. Opinac Investments Ltd., Toronto, 1982-88, bd. dirs., 1982-89; pres. Opinac Energy Ltd., Calgary, Alta., 1983-88, bd. dirs., 1983-89. Pres., Syracuse USO, 1959-61, mem. nat. coun. 1959-62, 68-74; co-chmn. Cen. N.Y. Interim Coun. Regional Planning, 1965-66; gen. chmn. Dunbar-Huntington Bldg. Fund, Syracuse, 1963; state campaign chmn. N.Y. Job Devel. Authority, 1961; gen. chmn. United Way of Buffalo and Erie County, 1971; mem. Syracuse U. Corp. Adv. Coun., 1972-76, trustee Elmcrest Children's Ctr., 1962-63, Camp Good Will, Syracuse, 1964-66, Syracuse Area Coun. Chs., 1959-64; bd. dirs. United Way Buffalo and Erie County, 1967-76, Greater Buffalo Devel. Found., Kenmore Mercy Hosp., 1970-76, Crouse Irving Meml. Hosp. Found., 1978-87, Nat. Kidney Found., 1987-89, Venice (Fla.) Hosp. Found., 1992—; bd. dirs. Plantation Community Found., Venice, 1989-93, pres. 1990-93; mem. bd. advs. Sisters of St. Joseph, 1967-76; elder Trinity Presbyn. Ch., Venice, 1992-94; assoc. mem. Dewitt Community Ch. Served with Air Corps, U.S. Army, 1944-47. Recipient Syracuse Young Man of Yr. award, 1962; Outstanding Citizen award Buffalo Evening News, 1973. Mem. Empire State (v.p., bd. dirs. 1963-80), Buffalo Area (v.p. 1968-72, bd. dirs. 1968-76, pres. 1972-73, chmn. bd. 1973-74, Man of Yr. 1974) C. of C., Associated Industries of N.Y. (bd. dirs. 1978-80), Bus. Coun. N.Y. (bd. dirs. 1980-82), Mfrs. Assn. Cen. N.Y. (bd. dirs. 1977-88), Augusta Villa Assn. (bd. dirs. 1989-92), Buffalo Club (past 2d v.p., dir.), Syracuse Century Club (gov. 1980-83), Onondaga Golf Club, Plantation Golf and Country Club, Automobile Club Western N.Y.(bd. dirs. 1971-73, pres. 1973), N.Y.S. Automobile Assn. (dir. 1975-76). Home and Office: 705 Carnoustie Ter Venice FL 34293

TORRIANI-GORINI, ANNAMARIA, microbiologist; b. Milan, Italy, Dec. 19, 1918; came to U.S., 1955, naturalized, 1962; d. Carlo and Ada (Forti) Torriani; m. Luigi Gorini (dec. aug. 1976); 1 child, Daniel. PhD, U. Milan, Italy, 1942. Research assoc. Istituto Ronzoni Chimica-Biochimica, Milan, 1942-48; charge de recherche Institut Pasteur, Paris, 1948-56; research assoc. NYU, 1956-58, Harvard U., Cambridge, Mass., 1958-60; research assoc. MIT, Cambridge, 1960-71, assoc. prof. microbiology, 1971-76, prof., 1976—; prof. emerita, 1989. Recipient NIH Career award, 1962-72; Fulbright fellow, 1956-58. Mem. Am. Soc. Microbiology, Am. Soc. Genetics, Am. Soc. Biochemistry, Soc. Française de Microbiologie (hon.). Home: 115 Longwood Ave Brookline MA 02146-6625 Office: MIT Dept of Biology 68-371 Cambridge MA 02139

TORRICELLI, ROBERT G., congressman; b. Paterson, N.J., Aug. 26, 1951; m. Susan King Holloway, 1980. B.A., Rutgers U., 1974, J.D, 1977; M.P.A., Harvard U., 1980. Bar: N.J. 1978. Dep. legis. counsel Office Gov. N.J., 1975-77; counsel to Vice Pres. Mondale, Washington, 1978-81; sole practice law Washington, 1981-82; mem. 98th-104th Congresses from 9th Dist. N.J., Washington, D.C., 1983—; ranking minority mem. internat. rels. subcom. on the western hemisphere, mem. select com. intelligence. Bd. govs. Rutgers U., 1977-83. Mem. ABA, N.J. Bar Assn. Democrat. Office: US Ho of Reps 1026 Longworth Washington DC 20515-3009*

TORRUELLA, JUAN R., federal judge; b. 1933. BS in Bus. and Fin., U. Pa., 1954; LLB, Boston U., 1957; LLM, U. Va., 1984; MPA, U. P.R., 1984. Judge U.S. Dist. Ct. P.R., San Juan, 1974-84; chief judge, 1982-84; judge U.S. Ct. Appeals (1st cir.), San Juan, 1984-94, chief judge, 1994—; former mem. jud. conf. com. on the Adminstrn. of the Fed. Magistrate Sys; mem.

jud. conf. com. on Internat. Jud. Reform. Mem. ABA, Fed. Bar Assn., Assn. Labor Rels. Practitioners P.R. and V.I., D.C. Bar Assn., P.R. Bar Assn. Office: US Ct Appeals PO Box 3671 San Juan PR 00904 also: US Ct Appeals (1st cir) Boston MA 02109

TORSHEN, JEROME HAROLD, lawyer; b. Chgo., Nov. 27, 1929; s. Jack and Lillian (Futterman) T.; m. Kay Pomerance, June 19, 1966; children: Jonathan, Jacqueline. BS, Northwestern U., 1951; JD, Harvard U., 1955. Bar: Ill. 1955, U.S. Dist. Ct. (no. dist.) Ill. 1955, U.S. Ct. Appeals (7th cir.) 1958, (8th cir.) 1961, (9th and D.C. cirs.) 1972, U.S. Supreme Ct. 1972. Assoc. Clausen, Hirsh & Miller, Chgo., 1955-62; pres. Jerome H. Torshen, Ltd., Chgo., 1963-87, Torshen, Schoenfeld & Spreyer Ltd., Chgo., 1987-93, Torshen, Spreyer & Garmisa, Ltd., Chgo., 1994—; spl. asst. atty. gen. Ill., 1965-70; assoc. counsel Spl. Commn. Ill. Supreme Ct., 1969; counsel Ill. Legis. Redistricting Commn., 1971-72; spl. state's atty. Cook County, Ill., 1979-81, 83-86; spl. counsel Met. San. Dist. Greater Chgo., 1977-81, 84-88. Contbr. articles to profl. jours. Counsel Cook County Dem. Cen. Com., Chgo., 1982-87; bd. dirs. Jewish Family and Community Svc., Parents' Coun. Washington U., St. Louis, 1988-92; mem. collectors' group Mus. Contemporary Art; sustaining fellow Art Int. Chgo. Served with U.S. Army, 1951-52. Recipient Torch of Learning award Am. Friends of Hebrew U., 1985, Outstanding Civic Duty award, Union League Club of Chgo., 1967. Fellow Am. Coll. Trial Lawyers; mem. ABA, Chgo. Bar Assn. (commn. on jud. evaluation 1986-90), Bar Assn. 7th Cir. Appellate Lawyers Assn. (founder, pres. 1976-77), Decalogue Soc., Standard Club, Sixty Club of Chgo. Office: 105 W Adams St Ste 3200 Chicago IL 60603-6209

TORTO, RAYMOND GERALD, economist; b. Lynn, Mass., Dec. 16, 1941; s. Edward Dante and Lucy (Petrucci) T.; m. Linn Torto; children: Stephanie, Pamela. AB, Boston Coll., 1963, MA, 1967, PhD, 1969. Prof. econs. U. Mass., Boston, 1970—; spl. asst. to mayor for tax policy City of Boston, 1976-80, commr. assessing, 1980-82; pres. Torto Wheaton and Assocs., Boston, 1982-86; prin. CB Comml./Torto Wheaton Rsch., Boston, 1987—; sr. fellow, dir. McCormack Inst. U. Mass., Boston, 1984—; bd. dirs. Boston Mcpl. Rsch. Bur., Assoc. Ind. of Mass. Author: The Rich Get Richer and the Rest Pay Taxes, 1974, Money and Financial Institutions, 1981, Property Tax Reevaluation, 1983. Chmn. fiscal issues study group Commonwealth of Mass., 1988-90. Mem. Am. Soc. Real Estate Councilors, Am. Real Estate Soc., Boston C. of C. (chmn. legis. com. 1986-90), Corinthian Yacht Club. Avocations: sailing, squash, gardening. Home: 38 Foster St Marblehead MA 01945-3645 Office: CB Comml/Torto Wheaton Rsch 200 High St Boston MA 02110-3036

TORTORA, ROBERT D., mathematician; b. Youngstown, Ohio, Aug. 20, 1946. BS in Math. cum laude, Youngstown State U., 1968; MS in Math. Stats., Cath. U. Am., 1972; PhD in Probability and Stats., Bowling Green State U., 1975. Mathematician Nat. Security Agy., 1968-69; various positions ending in dir. rsch. and applications, Nat. Agrl. Stats. Svcs. USDA, 1975-90; chief statis. rsch. divsn. Census Bur., Washington, 1990-92, assoc. dir. statis. design, methodology, standards, 1992—; chair subcom. role of telephone data collection in fed. surveys Fed. Com. Statis. Methodology, 1980—; co-chair com. disclosure risk analysis Office Mgmt. and Budget; mem. stats. industrial advisory com. Ohio State U., 1990—; adv. com. George Mason Univ. Ctr. computational Stats., 1991—. Contbr. articles to profl. jours. 1st lt. U.S. Army, 1969-72. Mem. Am. Statis. Assn. (mem., chair govt. subcom. mem. com. 1986-91, ad hoc com. Office Sci. Affairs 1987-88, 91—, assoc. editor Jour. Ofcl. Stats. 1988—, program chair survey methods rsch 1992, organizer various meetings), Wash. Statis. Soc. (chmn. agr. 1980-81), Internat. Assn. Survey Statisticians. Office: Bureau of the Census Statistical Rsch Divsn Federal Center Washington DC 20233

TORTORELLA, ALBERT JAMES, public relations executive, consultant; b. Washington, Feb. 11, 1942; s. Caesar Joseph and Rose (Rosamilia) T.; m. Karen A. Bauer, Aug. 3, 1989; children by previous marriage: John Christopher, Anne Christina. BS, U. Md., 1965; postgrad., Am. U., 1970-71. Journalist Wall St. Jour., Dow Jones & Co. Inc., Cleve., 1963-68; mgr. pub. relations Gen. Electric Co., Washington and N.Y.C., 1968-78; vice pres. Burson-Marsteller, N.Y.C., 1978—; cons. Cen. Park Conservancy, N.Y.C. 1981-84; cons. on crisis mgmt. issues for various corps.; lectr. Kellogg Grad. Sch. Mgmt., Northwestern U. Served with U.S. Army, 1959-60. William Randolph Hearst Found. scholar, 1963; recipient Silver Anvil award Pub. Relations Soc. Am., 1982, 84. Mem. Nat. Press Club. Roman Catholic. Office: care Burson-Marsteller 230 Park Ave S New York NY 10003

TORTORICI, PETER FRANK, television executive; b. N.Y.C., June 19, 1949; s. Tony F. and May (Augello) T.; m. Susan Kay Dupar, June 21, 1986; children: Caitlin, Dayna, Thomas. BA, Ohio State U., 1971; JD, St. John's U., 1974. Sr. counsel grievance com. 2nd & 11th Jud. Dists., Bklyn., 1974-80; prodn. asst. ABC Sports, N.Y.C. 1980; dir. program acquisitions CBS Sports, N.Y.C., 1981-83, v.p. program planning and devel., 1983-86, v.p. programming, 1986-87; sr. v.p. program planning CBS Entertainment, L.A., 1987-91; exec. v.p. CBS Entertainment, 1991-94, pres., 1994—. Writer (TV show) Tour de France, 1987 (Emmy nomination). Mem. Hollywood Radio TV Soc. (bd. dirs. 1990-92). Avocations: golf, skiing, music, N.Y. sports teams. Home: 1148 Napoli Dr Pacific Palisades CA 90272-3112 Office: CBS Entertainment 7800 Beverly Blvd Los Angeles CA 90036-2165

TORTORIELLO, ROBERT LAURENCE, lawyer; b. Newark, Nov. 23, 1950; s. Frank and Leah L. (Megaro) T.; m. Margaret Ann F. Mullins, Sept. 29, 1979; children: Lauren Elyse, Christopher Robert, Kenneth William. BA summa cum laude, St. Peter's Coll., Jersey City, 1971; JD magna cum laude, Harvard U., 1974. Bar: N.Y. 1975, N.J. 1975, U.S. Dist. Ct. (so. and ea. dists.) N.Y. 1975, U.S. Dist. Ct. N.J. 1975, U.S. Ct. Appeals (2nd cir.) 1975, U.S. Supreme Ct. 1978. Assoc. Cleary, Gottlieb, Steen & Hamilton, N.Y.C. 1974-82, ptnr., 1982—. Contbr. articles to profl. jours. Trustee Montclair (N.J.) Adult Sch., 1990—; bd. dirs. United Congl. Weekday Nursery Sch., Upper Montclair, N.J., 1987-90. Mem. N.Y. State Bar Assn., Assn. of Bar City of N.Y. Republican. Roman Catholic. Home: 112 Heller Way Montclair NJ 07043-2512 Office: Cleary Gottlieb Steen 1 Liberty Plz New York NY 10006

TORY, JOHN A., newspaper publishing executive. Dep. chmn. The Thomson Co., Toronto, Ont., Can. Office: Thomson Newspaper Inc 3150 Des Plaines Ave Des Plaines IL 60018-4211 also: The Thomson Corporation, Toronto Dominion Ctr Box 24, Toronto, ON Canada M5K 1A1*

TOSCANO, JAMES VINCENT, medical institute administrator; b. Passaic, N.J., Aug. 8, 1937; s. William V. and Mary A. (DeNigris) T.; m. Sharon Lee Bowers; children: Shawn, Lauren, David Brendan, Dania. A.B. summa cum laude, Rutgers U., 1959; M.A., Yale U., 1960. Lectr. Wharton Sch., U. Pa., 1961-64; chief opinion analyst Pa. Opinion Poll, 1962-64; mng. dir. World Press Inst., St. Paul, 1964-68; exec. dir. World Press Inst., 1968-72; dir. devel. Macalester Coll., St. Paul, 1972-74; v.p. resource devel. and public affairs Mpls. Soc. Fine Arts, 1974-79; pres. Minn. Mus. Art, 1979-81; exec. v.p. Park Nicollet Med. Found., 1981—; corp. sec. Park Nicollet Med. Ctr., 1983-86; sr. v.p. Am. Med. Ctrs., Inc., 1985-87; adj. prof. sch. of mgmt. U. St. Thomas, 1989—. Author: The Chief Elected Official in the Penjerdel Region, 1964; co-editor: The Integration of Political Communities, 1964. Bd. dirs. emeritus Minn. Citizens Arts; sec. bd. dirs. World Press Inst., 1972—; bd. dirs., chmn. Southside Neighborhood Svcs., 1979; chmn. com. to improve student behavior St. Paul Pub. Schs., 1977-78; bd. dirs. Planned Parenthood St. Paul, 1965-72; bd. dirs. Help Enable Alcoholics Receive Treatment; mem. St. Paul heritage Preservation Commn., 1979-81, vice chmn., 1981; mem. Citizens Adv. Com. on Cable Communication; bd. dirs. Citizens League, 1980, Park Nicollet Med. Found., 1981—, African-Am. Cultural Center, 1979-82, Minn. Composers Forum, 1981-85, Sr. Paul Chamber Orch., 1976-80, 83-89, United Theol. Sem., 1985-88; bd. dirs. emeriuts; bd. dirs., past chair, mem. exec. com. Med. Alley Assn., 1986—; mem. task force on tech. assessment Medical Alley, 1992-93; mem. health affairs adv. com. Acad. Health Ctr. U. Minn., 1988—; bd. dirs. Mother Cabrini House, 1985-92, Minn. Civil Justice Coalition, 1987-91, also chmn.; chmn. Gov.'s Task Force on Health Care Promotion, mem. Gov.'s Com. Promotion Health Care Resources, 1986-87; chmn. bd. Minn. Fin. Counselling Svcs., Inc., 1990-93; mem. task force cost effectiveness Medical Alley, 1994-95. Mem. Minn. Newspaper Found. (bd. dirs. 1987-92), Minn. Coun. Nonprofits (bd. dirs. 1989—, bd. mem. Plymouth Music series 1993—, alt.

Minn. healthcare commn.; chair adv. com. on med. edn. and rsch. costs 1994—, liaison health tech. adv. com. 1993—), Skylight Club, Informal Club. Address: 1982 Summit Ave Saint Paul MN 55105 Office: Park Nicollet Med Found 5000 W 39th St Minneapolis MN 55416

TOSKES, PHILLIP PAUL, physician, educator, clinical researcher; b. Balt., Md., Jan. 4, 1940; s. John F. and Mary R. (Vonelli) T.; m. Patricia A. Sponsel, June 3, 1961; children: Tammy Lynn Price, Tracey Lynn, Steven D. BA, Johns Hopkins U., 1961; MD, U. Md., 1965. Diplomate Am. Bd. Internal Medicine (bd. dirs.), Am. Bd. Gastroenterology. Intern, resident U. Md. Hosp., Balt., 1965-68; fellow in gastroenterology Hosp. U. Pa., Phila., 1968-70; asst. prof. medicine U. Fla., Gainesville, 1973-75, assoc. prof. medicine, 1975-78, prof. medicine, 1978—, dir. divsn. gastro, hepatology, 1978—; chief gastro sect. Gainesville VA Med. Ctr., 1973-92; mem. adv. bd. Lederle Labs, Pearl River, N.Y., 1986—, Solvay Labs, Marietta, Ga., 1990—, Martek Inc., Columbia, Md., 1991—; chmn. Nat. Digestive Disease Adv. Bd., Washington, 1992-94. Author chpts. to books. Maj. U.S. Army, 1970-73. Recipient Disting. Achievement award Can. Gastroenterol. Assn., 1982. Fellow ACP (Meade Johnson scholar 1969—); mem. Am. Soc. Clin. Investigation, Am. Fedn. Clin. Rsch., Am. Gastroenterol. Assn. Avocations: travel, swimming, boating. Home: 202 NW 114 Way Gainesville FL 32607 Office: U Fla Box 100214 1600 SW Archer Rd Gainesville FL 32610

TOSTESON, DANIEL CHARLES, physiologist, medical school dean; b. Milw., Feb. 5, 1925; s. Alexis H. and Dilys (Bodycombe) T.; m. Penelope Kinsley, Dec. 17, 1949 (div. 1969); children: Carrie Marias, Heather Tosteson, Tor, Zoe Losada; m. Magdalena Tieffenberg, July 8, 1969; children: Joshua, Ingrid. Student, Harvard U., 1942-44; DSc (hon.), U. Copenhagen, 1979; Dr. hon. causa, U. Liege, 1983; DSc (hon.), Med. Coll. Wis., 1984, NYU, 1992; DHL (hon.), Johns Hopkins U., 1993. Fellow physiology Harvard Med. Sch., 1947-48; intern, then asst. resident medicine Presbyn. Hosp., N.Y.C., 1949-51; research fellow medicine Brookhaven Nat. Lab., 1951-53; lab. kidney and electrolyte metabolism Nat. Heart Inst., 1953-55, 57; research fellow biol. isotope research lab. Nat. Heart Inst., Copenhagen, 1955-56; research fellow Physiol. Lab., Cambridge, Eng., 1956-57; assoc. prof. physiology Washington U. Sch. Medicine, St. Louis, 1958-61; prof., chmn. dept. physiology and pharmacology Duke U. Sch. Medicine, 1961-75, James B. Duke Distinguished prof., 1971-75; dean div. biol. scis., dean Pritzker Sch. Medicine U. Chgo., Lowell T. Coggleshall prof. med. scis., v.p. for Med. Center, 1975-77; dean and Caroline Shields Walker prof. physiology Harvard Med. Sch., Boston, 1977—; pres. Med. Center Harvard Med. Sch., 1977; mem. molecular biology panel NSF, 1959-62; cons. sci. rev. com. NIH, 1964-67, nat. adv. gen. med. scis., 1982-86; mem. U.S. Office Tech. Assessment, 1976; ethics adv. bd. HEW, 1977-80; nat. adv. gen. med. scis. coun. NIH, 1982—; mem. governing bd. NRC, 1977; founding mem. Nat. Found. for Depression, 1982—; mem. sci. com. Found. pour l'Etude du Systeme Nerveux Central et Peripherique, 1982—; nat. adv. com. biomed. scis. PEW Scholars Program, 1984-87. Mem. Inst. Medicine NAS (coun. 1975-78, adv. bd. PEW scholars program 1984-85), AAAS, Am. Physiol. Soc. (council 1967-75, pres. 1973-74), Soc. Gen. Physiologists (pres. 1968-69), Nat. Found. for Depression (founding 1982), Biophys. Soc. (council 1970-73), Found. pour L'Etude du Systeme Nerveux Central et Peripherique (sci. com. 1982—), Assn. Am. Med. Colls. (dean adv. com. 1969-70, chmn. assembly 1973-74, chmn. physician supply task force 1988—), Assn. Am. Physicians, Red Cell Club, Soc. Health and Human Values, Danish Royal Soc. (fellow), Alpha Omega Alpha. Spl. research cellular transport processes, red cell membranes. Office: Harvard Med Sch 25 Shattuck St Boston MA 02115-6092

TOTA, FRANK PETER, educational administrator; b. Hoboken, N.J., Dec. 28, 1938; s. Frank and Jeanette (Grimaldi) T.; m. Eileen Virginia Dolan, Aug. 3, 1968; children—Frank, Christopher. BA, N.J. State Coll., 1960; MA, Columbia U., 1962; EdD, Columbia U., 1986. Tchr., coordinator pub. schs., Englewood, N.J., 1960-65; head lang. arts dept. pub. schs., Bedford, N.Y., 1965-70; dir. secondary and elem. edn. pub. schs., New Rochelle, N.Y., 1970-73; supt. for instrn., pub. schs., Rochester, N.Y., 1973-81; supt. schs., Roanoke, Va., 1981—; adj. prof. VPI, SU, guest lectr. Cambridge U. (Eng.). 1983. Bd. dirs. Roanoke Symphony Orch., United Way Roanoke Valley, Arts Council Roanoke Valley. Recipient Nat. Conf. Christians and Jews award, 1985, Leadership for Learning awd., Am. Assn. of School Administrators, 1993. Mem. Am. Assn. Sch. Adminstrs., Nat. Sch. Bds. Assn., Va. Urban Schs. Assn. (pres. 1991, exec. bd. mid-urban supts. northeast and mid-Atlantic region), Assn. for Supervision and Curriculum Devel., Nat. Forensic League, Roanoke C. of C., Phi Delta Kappa, Kappa Delta Pi, Delta Upsilon. Roman Catholic. Lodge: Rotary (chmn. youth com. Roanoke 1983-84). Home: 430 Bramble Ln SW Roanoke VA 24014-3011 Office: Roanoke City Pub Schs PO Box 13145 40 Douglas Ave NW Roanoke VA 24012-4699 also: Roanoke CSD PO Box 13145 Roanoke VA 24031-3145

TOTENBERG, NINA, journalist; b. N.Y.C., Jan. 14, 1944; d. Roman and Melanie (Shroder) T.; m. Floyd Haskell, Feb. 3, 1979. Student, Boston U.; LLD (hon.), Haverford Coll., Chatham Coll., Gonzaga U., Northeastern U., St. Mary's, SUNY; LHD, Lebanon Valley Coll., Westfield State Coll. Reporter Boston Record Am., 1965, Peabody Times, 1967, Nat. Observer, 1968-71, Newtimes, 1973, Nat. Pub. Radio, Washington, 1974—, Inside Washington, 1992—; reporter Nightline ABC, 1993—. contbr. articles to N.Y. Times Mag., Harvard Law Rev., Christian Sci. Monitor, N.Y. Mag., Parade. Recipient Alfred I. Dupont award Columbia U., 1988, George Foster Peabook award, 1991, George Polk award, 1991, Joan Barne award, 1991, Silver Gavel award ABA, 1991, Woman of Courage award Women in Film, 1991, Athena award, 1994. Mem. Sigma Delta Chi. Office: Nightline 1717 DeSales St NW Washington DC 20036

TOTENBERG, ROMAN, violinist, music educator; b. Lodz, Poland, Jan. 1, 1911; came to U.S., 1935; s. Adam and Stanislava (Vinaver) T.; m. Melanie Shroder, July 30, 1941; children: Nina, Jill, Amy. Grad., Chopin Sch. Music, Warsaw, Poland, 1928, Hochschule für Music, Berlin, 1931, Paris Inst. Instrumental Music, 1933. Head violin dept. Peabody Conservatory, Balt., 1943-44, Mannes Coll. Music, N.Y.C., 1951-57; chmn. string dept. Boston U., 1962-78, prof., 1978—, co-chmn. string dept.; Prin. soloist, dir. chamber music Interstate Broadcasting Co., N.Y.C., 1937-42; prin. soloist, head string dept. Music Acad. West, Santa Barbara, Calif., summers 1948-51; with Music Assocs., Aspen, Colo., summers 1951-62; dir. Totenberg Instrumental Ensemble, 1953-60; George Miller vis. prof. U. Ill., 1960-61; head string dept. Boston U. Tanglewood Inst., summers 1966-74; performer, tchr. Kneisel Hall Festival, Blue Hill, Maine, 1975—, acting dir., 1984-87; dir. Longy Sch. Music, Cambridge, Mass., 1978-85; judge Paganini, Wieniawski, Carnegie Hall competitions, Kreisler and Japan Internat. Competition. Performer worldwide concerts and tours; rec. artist with Vanguard, DGG, Mus. Heritage Soc. records, Titanic compact disk, Omega Records, VGR Records. Chmn. Music Project, Newton Tricentenary, 1988. Recipient Mendelssohn prize, 1932, Wieniawski medal, 1970, Eugene Ysaye Soc. medal, 1975, Polish Nat. medal of Cultural Achievement, 1988. Mem. Am. String Tchrs. Assn. (named Artist-Tchr. of yr. 1983), AAUP, Music Tchrs. Nat. Assn., Phi Kappa Lambda. Avocations: photography, tennis. Office: Boston U 855 Commonwealth Ave Boston MA 02215-1303 *Devotion to human values expressed through music as well as through daily activities in public life.*

TOTH, ROBERT CHARLES, polling consultant, journalist; b. Blakely, Pa., Dec. 24, 1928; s. John and Tillie (Szuch) T.; m. Paula Goldberg, Apr. 12, 1954; children: Jessica, Jennifer, John. B.S. in Chem. Engring., Washington U., St. Louis, 1952; M.S. in Journalism, Columbia U., 1955; postgrad., Harvard U., 1960-61. Started as engr. in Army Ordnance Dept., 1952-54; reporter Providence Jour., 1955-57; sci. reporter N.Y. Herald Tribune, 1957-62, N.Y. Times, 1962-63; mem. staff Los Angeles Times, 1963-93; bur. chief Los Angeles Times, London, 1965-70; diplomatic corr. Los Angeles Times, 1970-71, White House corr., 1972-74; bur. chief Los Angeles Times, Moscow, 1974-77; nat. security corr. Washington bur. Los Angeles Times, 1977-93; cons. opinion poll in U.S. and abroad by Times Mirror Ctr. for People and Press, 1990, sr. assoc., 1993—. Served with USMC, 1946-48. Recipient Overseas Press Club award, 1977, Sigma Delta Chi award, 1977, George Polk award in Journalism for fgn. reporting L.I. U., 1978, Columbia U. Alumni award, 1978, Wienthal award Pub. Service Inst., Georgetown U., 1986, Edwin N. Hood award Nat. Press Club, 1986; Pulitzer Travelling scholar, 1955; Nieman fellow Harvard U., 1960-61. Mem. Coun. on Fgn.

Rels. Home: 21 Primrose St Chevy Chase MD 20815-4228 Office: Times Mirror Ctr 1875 I St NW Washington DC 20006-5409

TOTLIS, GUST JOHN, title insurance company executive; b. Highwood, Ill., May 15, 1939; s. John Chris and Agape (Galelis) T.; m. Joyce Elaine Edholm, June 5, 1960; children: Kenneth Chris, Charles Gust. BA, Lake Forest Coll., 1962; MBA, U. Chgo., 1964. Fin. planning mgr. Gen. Foods Corp., Battle Creek, Mich., 1964-68; fin. analyst Irving Trust Co., N.Y.C., 1968-69; asst. sec., 1969-71, asst. v.p., 1971-72, v.p., 1972-75; corp. contr. Irving Bank Corp., N.Y.C., 1975-82; exec. v.p., CFO Fidelity Union Bancorp, Newark, 1982-85, Star Banc Corp (formerly First Nat. Cin. Corp.), Cin., 1985-93; sr. v.p., CFO Chgo. Title and Trust Co., 1993—; bd. dirs. Miami Valley Bus. Econ., Ticor Title Ins. Co., Security Union Title Ins. Co. Adv. bd. dirs. Salvation Army, Cin., 1987-93; bd. dirs. Cin. Chamber Orch. 1988-93, May Festival Assn., 1988-93, Spl. Olympics, 1990-93, SB United Way, 1991-93; bd. trustees Cin. Inst. Fine Arts, 1991-93. Mem. Fin. Execs. Inst., Univ. Club, Kenwood Country Club. Presbyterian. Home: 111 East Bellevue Place Chicago IL 60611

TOTMAN, CONRAD DAVIS, history educator; b. Conway, Mass., Jan. 5, 1934; s. Raymond Smith and Mildred Edna (Kingsbury) T.; m. Michiko Ikegami, Jan. 21, 1958; children: Kathleen Junko, Christopher Ken. B.A., U. Mass., 1958; M.A., Harvard U., 1960, Ph.D., 1964. Asst. prof. U. Calif., Santa Barbara, 1964-66; asst. prof. Northwestern U., Evanston, Ill., 1966-68; assoc. prof. Northwestern U., 1968-72, prof. Japanese history, 1972-84, chmn. dept. history, 1977-80; prof. Japanese history Yale U., New Haven, 1984—; chmn. Council on East Asian Studies, Yale U., 1985-88, acting chmn. Dept. History, 1989-90; prof. Kyoto Ctr. for Japanese Studies, 1992-93. Author: Politics in the Tokugawa Bakufu 1600-1843, 1967, paperback edit., 1988, The Collapse of the Tokugawa Bakufu 1862-1868, 1979 (John K. Fairbank prize Am. Hist. Assn. 1981), Japan Before Perry: A Short History, 1981, Tokugawa Ieyasu: Shogun, 1983, The Origins of Japan's Modern Forests, 1985, The Green Archipelago: Forestry in Preindustrial Japan, 1989, Early Modern Japan, 1993, The Lumber Industry in Early Modern Japan, 1995. Served with U.S. Army, 1953-56. Recipient Carstensen prize for essay Agrl. History Soc., 1982; Woodrow Wilson nat. fellow, 1958-59; Social Sci. Research Council-Am. Council Learned Socs. fellow, 1968-69; NEH sr. fellow, 1972-73; Fulbright-Hays research grantee, 1968-69; Japan Found. grantee, 1981-82. Mem. Assn. Asian Studies (N.E. Asia coun. 1977-80, chmn. 1978-80, exec. com. 1978-80, pres. New Eng. Conf. 1985-86, coun. of confs. 1992-95), Forest History Soc. Office: Yale U Dept History New Haven CT 06520

TOTMAN, PATRICK STEVEN, lawyer, retail executive; b. Stockton, Calif., Sept. 29, 1944; s. Mervyn Willis and Margaret Elizabeth (McDow) T.; m. Rosemarie Bachle, Aug. 27, 1966 (div. Jan. 1989); children—Michael, Jarrod; m. Nancy Choate, July 15, 1991; 1 stepson, Jason. A.B., U. San Francisco, 1966, J.D., 1969. Bar: Calif. 1969. Atty. Safeway, Inc., Oakland, Calif., 1969-72, asst. v.p., 1973-79, v.p., 1979-83, sr. v.p. treasury, 1983—; bd. dirs. Goodwill Industries; seminar leader NYU, 1983-84. Mem. ABA, Calif. Bar Assn., Nat. Assn. Corp. Retail Execs., Internat. Council Shopping Ctrs. Roman Catholic. Office: Safeway Inc 201 4th St Oakland CA 94660-0001

TOTO, MARY, elementary and secondary education educator; b. Phila., Mar. 12, 1922; d. John and Piacentina (Rossi) T. BS in Edn., Temple U., 1943; MS in Edn., U. Pa., 1951; MS in Libr. Sci., Villanova U., 1963. Cert. tchr., Pa. Tchr. Phila. Sch. Dist., 1943-81. Mem. Dem. Women of Phila. 1974, Phila. Rep. Women., 1987, LWV. Mem. NEA, AAUW, LWV, Phila. Fedn. Tchrs., Columbus Forum Lodge, Nationalities Svc. Ctr. of Phila., Italian Folk Art Fedn. of Am., Nat. Assn. Retired Tchrs., Pa. Assn. Sch. Retirees, Pa. Edn. Assn., Womens Internat. League Peace and Freedom, United We Stand Am. Roman Catholic. Avocations: needlework, interior decorating, folk dancing, travel. Home: 1210 W Ritner St Philadelphia PA 19148-3524

TOTTEN, GEORGE OAKLEY, III, political science educator; b. Washington, July 21, 1922; s. George Oakley Totten Jr. and Vicken (von Post) Totten Barrois; m. Astrid Maria Anderson, June, 1948 (dec. Apr. 26, 1975); children: Vicken Yuriko, Linnea Catherine; m. Lilia Huiying Li, July 1, 1976; 1 child, Blanche Maluk Lemes. Cert., U. Mich., 1943; AB, Columbia U., 1946, AM, 1949; MA, Yale U., 1950, PhD, 1954; docentur i japanologi, U. Stockholm, 1977. Lectr. Columbia U. N.Y.C. 1954-55; assist. prof. MIT, Cambridge, 1958-59, Boston U., 1959-61; assoc. prof. U. R.I., Kingston, 1961-64; assoc. prof. polit. sci. U. So. Calif., L.A., 1965-68, prof. 1968-92, chmn. dept., 1980-86, prof. emeritus, 1992—; bd. dirs., founder Calif. Pvt. Univs. and Colls. Yr.-in-Japan program Weseda U., 1967-73; bd. dirs. East Asian Studies Ctr., 1974-77; 1st dir. USC-UCLA Joint East Asian Studies Ctr., 1976-77; sr. affiliate scholar Ctr. for Multiethnic and Transnat. Studies, 1993—; vis. prof. U. Stockholm, 1977-79; 1st dir. Ctr. Pacific Asia Studies 1985-89, sr. counselor bd. dirs., 1989—. Author: Social Democratic Movement in Prewar Japan, 1966, Chinese edit., 1987; co-author: Socialist Parties in Postwar Japan, 1966, Japan and the New Ocean Regime, 1984; co-editor, author: Developing Nations: Quest for a Model, 1970, Japanese edit., 1975, Helen Snow's Song of Ariran, 1973, Korean edit., 1991, Chinese edit., 1993, China's Economic Reform: Administering the Introduction of the Market Mechanism, 1992. Community in Crisis: Korean American..., 1994; co-translator: Chien Mu's Traditional Government in Imperial China, 1982; contbr. The Politics of Divided Nations, 1991. Mem. U.S.-China People's Friendship Assn., Washington, 1974—; mem. Com. on U.S.-China Relations, N.Y.C., 1975—; chmn. L.A.-Pusan Sister City Assn., L.A., 1976-77; bd. dirs. L.A.-Guangzhou Sister City Assn., 1982—, Japan-Am. Soc. L.A., 1981—; mem. nat. adv. com. Japan Am. Student Conf., 1984—, Assn. of Korean Pol. Studies in N.Am., 1992—; coun. mem. China Soc. for People's Friendship Studies, Beijing, 1991—. 1st lt. AUS, 1942-46, PTO. Recipient Plaque for program on Korean studies Consulate Gen. of Republic of Korea, 1975; Social Sci. Rsch. Coun. fellow, 1952-53; Ford Found. grantee, 1955-58, NSF grantee, 1979-81, Korea Found. grantee, 1993, Rebuild L.A. grantee, 1993, Philippine Liberation medal, 1994. Mem. Assn. for Asian Studies, Am. Polit. Sci. Assn., Asia Soc., Internat. Polit. Sci. Assn., Internat. Studies Assn., Japanese Polit. Sci. Assn., European Assn. Japanese Studies, U. So. Calif. Faculty Club, Phi Beta Delta (founding mem. Beta Kappa chpt. 1993—). Episcopalian. Home: 5129 Village Grn Los Angeles CA 90016-5205 Office: U So Calif Ctr Multiethic & Transnat Studies Kerckhoff Hall 734 W Adams Blvd Los Angeles CA 90089-7724 *The two main driving forces in my life have been a desire for world peace and a fascination with Asia. I try to work for the reduction and eventual abolition of armaments and a world-wide decision making process. Domestically I try to promote democracy. I think it can be promoted in both capitalist and socialist nations, and can be compatible with modified communist ideology but not with fascism. Since childhood I have tried to work for friendship with Asian nations, especially China, Japan and Korea. My research has been on better understanding their politics, history and culture.*

TOTTEN, RANDOLPH FOWLER, lawyer; b. Washington, June 20, 1943; s. Arthur Irving and Margaret Holland (Ross) T.; m. Virginia Hunton, July 31, 1965; children—Louise, Fitz, Caroline. B.A., Yale U., 1965; LL.B., U. Va., 1968. Bar: Va. 1968. Law clk. to Justice Gordon, Va. Supreme Ct. Appeals, Richmond, 1968-69; from assoc. to mem. Hunton & Williams, Richmond, 1969—; dir. Mid-Atlantic Holdings, Inc. Chmn., Richmond Community High Sch., 1979-81; mem. exec. com. Christchurch Sch., 1982—; trustee Church Schs. Episcopal Diocese Va., 1974—, mem. standing com., 1984—. Mem. ABA, Va. Bar Assn. Clubs: Country of Va., Commonwealth. Bd. editors Va. Law Rev. Office: Hunton & Williams Riverfront Plz 951 E Byrd St Richmond VA 23219-4040

TOTTENHAM, TERRY OLIVER, lawyer; b. Dallas, June 5, 1944; s. Edwin Pier and Ruth Elizabeth (Paris) T.; m. Carolyn Sue Lewis, July 7, 1967; children: Leslie Jo, Dana Elizabeth, Jessica Leigh. Student, Blinn Jr. Coll., 1962-67; B.S. in Pharmacy with high honors, U. Tex.-Austin, 1967, J.D. with honors, 1970; LL.M., George Washington U., 1973. Bar: Tex. 1970, U.S. Ct. Mil. Appeals 1971. Assoc. firm Fulbright, Crooker & Jaworski, Houston, 1970; ptnr. Fulbright & Jaworski, Houston, 1978—; mem. faculty South Tex. Coll. Law, U. Houston; vis. prof. med. jurisprudence Baylor U.; vis. prof. health law Tex. Women's U.; adj. prof. law U. Tex. Sch. Law; speaker profl. groups. Author: Texas Medical Jurisprudence;

editor: Patients Rights Handbook, 1980. Served to capt. USMC, 1971-75. Recipient Gene Cavin award, 1992; named Outstanding Young Lawyer Houston, 1981, Outstanding Young Lawyer Tex., 1981. Fellow Tex. Bar Found. (life, trustee 1986—); mem. Tex. Assn. Def. Counsel, Am. Soc. Law and Medicine, Am. Soc. Pharmacy Law, Tex. Ex-Students Assn. (life), ABA, Nat. Health Lawyers Assn., Am. Acad. Hosp. Attys. (bd. dirs. 1989—), State Bar Tex. (chmn. health law sect., chmn. litigation sect, bd. dirs. 1985-86, chmn. continuing legal edn. com., Cert. of Merit award 1989), Houston Young Lawyers Assn. (dir. 1975-77), Tex. Young Lawyers Assn. (chmn. bd. 1979-80). Democrat. Episcopalian. Home: 25 Cicero Ln Austin TX 78746-3206 Office: Fulbright & Jaworski 600 Congress Ave Ste 2400 Austin TX 78701-3271

TOTTER, JOHN RANDOLPH, biochemist; b. Saragosa, Tex., Jan. 7, 1914; s. Mathias and Agnes (Smith) T.; m. Elizabeth Margaret Van Sant, Aug. 6, 1938; children—Lorena E. Totter Barfuss, Anita Ruth, John Alan. B.A., U. Wyo., 1934, M.A., 1935; Ph.D., State U. Iowa, 1938. Instr. biochemistry U. W.Va., 1938-39; instr. biochemistry Ark. Sch. Medicine, 1939-42, asst. prof., 1942-45, asso. prof., 1945-52; chemist Oak Ridge Nat. Lab., 1952-56; biochemist AEC, Washington, 1956-58; vis. staff mem. U. of Republic, Montevideo, Uruguay, 1958-60; prof. biochemistry, chmn. div. biol. scis. U. Ga., 1960-62; asst. dir. for biol. scis. div. biology and medicine U.S. AEC, 1962-67, dir., 1967-72, asso. dir. for research, 1963-67; asso. dir. biomed. and environ. scis. Oak Ridge Nat. Lab., 1972-74; vis. staff mem. Inst. for Energy Analysis, Oak Ridge Asso. Univs., 1976-79, staff mem., 1979-87, ret., 1987; Participant nutritional survey, Alaska, 1947. Mem. Am. Chem Soc., Am. Soc. Biol. Chemists, Soc. for Exptl. Biology and Medicine (chmn. S.W. sect. 1950), Sigma Xi. Home: 360 Laboratory Rd Apt 517 Oak Ridge TN 37830-3819 Office: Med Scis Div Oak Ridge Assoc Univs Oak Ridge TN 37830

TOU, JULIUS T., electrical and computer engineering educator; b. Shanghai, China, Aug. 18, 1926; came to U.S., 1949; married; children: Albert, Fred, Ivan, Sylvia. BS, Chiao-Tung U., Shanghai, 1947; MS, Harvard U., 1950; DEng, Yale U., 1952; hon. degree, Jiao Tong U., Shanghai, 1986. Asst. prof. U. Pa., Phila., 1954-57; assoc. prof. Purdue U., Lafayette, Ind., 1957-61, vis. prof., 1961-62; dir. computer sci. Northwestern U., Evanston, Ill., 1962-64, prof., 1961-64; dir. Batelle Meml. Inst., Columbus, Ohio, 1964-67; grad. rsch. prof. U. Fla., Gainesville, 1967-92, dir. Ctr. for Info. Rsch., 1971—, grad. rsch. prof. emeritus, 1992—; pres. CITAC Computer, Inc., Gainesville, 1992—; adj. prof. Ohio State U., Columbus, 1964-67. Author: Digital and Sampled-data Control Systems, 1959, Modern Control Theory, 1964, Optimum Digital Control, 1963, Pattern Recognition Principles, 1973; editor: Software Engineering, 1969, Information Systems, 1972, Computer-based Automation, 1984; editor Internat. Jour. Computer Info. Scis., 1972—; inventor Chinese-English translation computer. Fellow IEEE (life); mem. Academia Sinica. Office: CITAC Computer Inc 3009 SW Archer Rd Gainesville FL 32608

TOUHILL, BLANCHE MARIE, university chancellor, history-education educator; b. St. Louis, Mo., July 1, 1931; d. Robert and Margaret (Walsh) Van Dillen; m. Joseph M. Touhill, Aug. 29, 1959. BA in History, St. Louis U., 1953, MA in Geography, 1954, PhD in History, 1962. Prof. history and edn. U. Mo., St. Louis, 1965-73, assoc. dean faculties, 1974-76, assoc. vice chancellor for acad. affairs, 1976-87, vice chancellor, 1987-90, chancellor, 1991—; bd. dirs. Boatmen's Nat. Bank of St. Louis, Barnes-Jewish Christian Health Hosps. Conglomerate. Author: William Smith O'Brien and His Irish Revolutionary Companions in Penal Exile, 1981, The Emerging University UM-St. Louis, 1963-83, 1985; editor: Readings in American History, 1970, Varieties of Ireland, 1976; adv. editor Victorian Periodicals Rev. Bd. dirs. Sister City Internat., Am. Coun. Fgn. Rels., St. Louis Forum, Network Bd., Mo. State Hist. Soc., 1989—, Mo. Bot. Garden, 1980, St. Louis Symphony Soc., 1993—. Named Outstanding Educator St. Louis chpt. Urban League, 1976; recipient Leadership award St. Louis YWCA, 1986. Mem. Nat. Assn. State Univs. and Land Grant Colls. (exec. com. 1988—), Am. Com. on Irish Studies (pres. 1991—), Phi Kappa Phi, Alpha Sigma Lambda. Office: U Mo Office of the Chancellor 8001 Natural Bridge Rd Saint Louis MO 63121-4499

TOULMIN, PRIESTLEY, geologist; b. Birmingham, Ala., June 5, 1930; s. Priestley and Catharine Augusta (Carey) T.; m. Martha Jane Slason, Aug. 30, 1952; children: Catharine Bosier (Mrs. Robert G. Gibson), Priestley Chewning. A.B., Harvard U., 1951, Ph.D., 1959; M.S., U. Colo., 1953. With U.S. Geol. Survey, Washington, 1953-56, 57-89; staff geologist for exptl. geology U.S. Geol. Survey, 1966, chief br. exptl. geochemistry, 1966-71, geologist geologic div., 1971-89; geologist geologic div. U.S. Geol. Survey, Reston, Va., 1974-89, ret., 1989; also leader inorganic chemistry team NASA (Viking Project); adj. prof. Columbia U., 1966; research asso. in geochemistry Calif. Inst. Tech., 1976-77; vis. lectr. Am. Geol. Inst.; dir. petrogenesis and mineral resources program NSF, 1985; bd. dirs., treas. 28th Internat. Geol. Congress, 1985-86; Mng. sci. editor Geochemistry Internat., 1965-68; assoc. editor Am. Mineralogist, 1974-76; contbr. articles to profl. jours. Mem. advisory com. spl. edn., Alexandria, Va., 1977-80. Recipient Exceptional Service medal NASA, 1977; Meritorious Service award U.S. Dept. Interior, 1978. Fellow Geol Soc. Am., Mineral Soc. Am. (bd. assoc. editors 1974-76), Soc. Econ. Geologists; mem. AAAS, Geol. Soc. Washington (2d v.p. 1977, councillor 1973-74, 90-91, 1st v.p. 1981, pres. 1982), Am. Geophys. Union, soc. Mayflower Descendants, S.R., SAR, Aztec Club of 1847, Cosmos Club (pres. 1993-94), Sigma Xi, Sigma Gamma Epsilon. Home: 418 Summers Dr Alexandria VA 22301-2449 Office: PO Box 183 Alexandria VA 22313-0183

TOULMIN, STEPHEN EDELSTON, humanities educator; b. London, Mar. 25, 1922. BA in Math. and Physics, King's Coll., Cambridge, Eng., 1942; PhD, King's Coll., 1948; D Tech. (hon.), Royal Inst. Tech., Stockholm, 1991. Lectr. in philosophy of sci. Oxford U., Eng., 1949-55; prof., chmn. dept. of philosophy U. Leeds, Yorkshire, Eng., 1955-59; dir. unit for history of ideas Nuffield Found., London, 1960-65; prof. history of ideas and philosophy Brandeis U., Waltham, Mass., 1965-69; prof. philosophy Mich. State U., East Lansing, 1969-72; prof. humanities U. Calif., Santa Cruz, 1972-73; prof. com. social thought U. Chgo., 1973-86; Avalon prof. humanities Northwestern U., Evanston, Ill., 1986-92, Avalon prof. emeritus, 1992—; Henry R. Luce prof.Ctr. Multiethnic and Transnational Studies U. So. Calif., 1993—; vis. prof. U. Melbourne, Australia, 1954-55, Stanford U., Calif., 1959, Columbia U., N.Y.C., 1960, Hebrew U., Jerusalem, 1964, U. South Fla., 1972, DArtmouth Coll., 1979, SUNY, Plattsburgh, 1980, Colo. Coll., 1980, 82, MacMaster U., 1983, Harvard Project Physics Grad. Sch. Edn., Harvard U., 1965; counselor Smithsonian Inst., Washington, 1977; cons., staff mem. Nat. Common. Protection Human Subjects Biomed. Behavioral Rsch., 1975-78; sr. vis. scholar, fellow Inst. Soc. Ethics and Life Scis., Hastings-on-Hudson, N.Y., 1981; regent's lectr. U. Calif. Med. Sch., Davis, 1985; Mary Flexner lectr. Bryn Mawr Coll., 1977; Ryerson lectr. U. Chgo., 1979; Tate-Wilson lectr. So. Meth. U., 1980; John Nuveen lectr. U. Chgo., 1980; Or Emet lectr. Osgoode Hall Law Sch., 1981; McDermott lectr. U. Dallas, 1985; lectr. Sigma Xi, 1965-66, Phi Beta Kappa, 1978-79, Phi Beta Kappa-AAAS, 1984; guest prof. social and human scis. Wolfgang Goethe Universitat, Frankfurt, Germany, 1987; vis. fellow Internationales Forschungszentrum Kulturwissenschaften (IFK), Vienna, Austria, 1995. Author: The Place of Reason in Ethics, 1949, The Philosophy of Science: an Introduction, 1953, The Uses of Argument, 1958, Foresight and Understanding, 1961, Human Understanding, vol. 1, 1972, Knowing and Acting, 1976, The Return to Cosmology, 1982, Cosmopolis, 1989; (with J. Goodfield) The Fabric of the Heavens, 1961, The Architecture of Matter, 1963, The Discovery of Time, 1965; (with A. Janik) Wittgenstein's Vienna, 1973; (with R. Rieke and A. Janik) An Introduction to Reasoning, 1978; (with A. Jonsen) The Abuse of Casuistry, 1987; contbr. numerous sci. articles to profl. jours. Recipient Honor Cross 1st class (Austria), 1991; Getty Ctr. for History of Art and Humanities scholar, 1985-86, First Book of the Year prize Am. Soc. Social Philosophy, 1992; Ctr. for Psychosocial Studies fellow, 1974-76. Fellow Am. Acad. Arts and Scis. Office: U So Calif CMTS Kerckhoff Hall Los Angeles CA 90089-7724

TOULOUSE, ROBERT BARTELL, retired college administrator; b. Wellsville, Mo., May 8, 1918; s. Walter Eaton and Emma (Schmidt) T.; m. Virginia Lee Danford, Aug. 7, 1948; children—Samuel Phillip, Robert Bartell. Student, Central Coll., 1935-37; B.S., U. Mo., 1939, M.Ed., 1947, Ed.D., 1948. Tchr. sci. and social studies, high sch. Mountain View, Mo.,

1939-41; asst. prof. to prof. U. North Tex., 1949-54, dean Grad. Sch., 1954-82, v.p., from 1982; now ret. Contbr. articles profl. jours. State sponsor Future Tchrs. Am. Served from pvt. to lt. col. AUS, World War II. Mem. Assn. Tex. Grad. Schs. (pres.), Assn. Coll. Tchr. Edn. (v.p.), Tex. Assn. Audio-Visual Edn. Dirs. (v.p.), AAUP, NEA, Phi Delta Kappa. Democrat. Methodist. Club: Kiwanis (pres.). Home: 1218 Emerson Ln Denton TX 76201-1104

TOUMEY, HUBERT JOHN (HUGH TOUMEY), textile company executive; b. N.Y.C.; s. William Joseph and Mary Veronica (Drury) T.; m. Dorothy A. Henry, Oct. 16, 1954; children: Donald Joseph, Kenneth Drury. A.B., Fordham U., 1936; M.B.A., Harvard, 1938. With Cannon Mills, Inc., 1938-81, v.p., mgr. towel sales, 1959-60, v.p., gen. sales mgr., 1960-62, exec. v.p., 1962-67, pres., chief adminstrv. and mktg. officer, 1967-81, chmn., chief exec. officer, 1978-81, also dir.; dir. Cannon Mills Co.; Mem. mktg. com. Am. Textile Mfrs. Inst., 1967-81, chmn., 1977-78. Trustee Coll. Mt. St. Vincent, Riverdale, N.Y., 1977-89, chmn., 1979-88. Mem. Assn. Knights of Malta. Home: 29 Bank St Leefair E New Canaan CT 06840

TOUPIN, HAROLD OVID, chemical company executive; b. Hibbing, Minn., Jan. 21, 1927; s. Ovid Pascal and Ellen (Holt) T.; m. Edna F. Sallila, Feb. 8, 1948 (div. Feb. 1973); m. Colleen Beverly Lange, Apr. 18, 1981; children: James, Ronald. BS, U. Minn., 1954, MA, 1955, postgrad, 1968; PhD (hon.), Internat. Acad. Color, Las Vegas, Nev., 1982, U. Mont., 1990. Mgr. Firestone Tire Co., East Los Angeles, Calif., 1948-51; dir. vocat. edn. Hopkins (Minn.) Pub. Schs., 1955-75; with research and devel. Power-o-Peat Co., Gilbert, Minn., 1966-67; chief exec. officer, cons. Color Specialties Inc., Mpls., 1976—; pres., founder travel, meeting planners sv. co., 1990; bd. dirs. Vu-tek Inc., St. Paul, Airport Auto Sales, St. Paul, Color Specialties of Nev., Las Vegas, Instant Air Inc., Mpls., Freedom Fin.; cons. Runs Hot Cons. Service, 1966-75. Contbr. articles to profl. jours. Bd. dirs. Hopkins Jaycees, 1958-60. Served with USAAF, 1944-47. Mem. Am. Assn. Mfrs. Internat. Assn. Color, Nat. Ret. Tchrs. Assn., Am. Assn. Self Employeed, Met. Area Dist. Edn. Instrs. Assn. (pres.), Mpls. C. of C. (Super Bowl com. 1992), Am. Legion, VFW. Democrat. Roman Catholic. Lodge: Lions (sec. Hopkins club 1956-76). Avocations: traveling, golfing, writing. Office: Color Specialities Inc 6405 Cedar Ave S Minneapolis MN 55423-1836

TOURIGNY, CHRISTINE, judge; b. Quebec City, Can., June 18, 1943; d. Émile Tourigny and Yvette LeBel. BA, Laval U., Quebec City, 1966. Atty.-at-law Bard, L'Heureux, Philippon, Tourigny, et al, Quebec City, 1969-79; assoc. sec. gen. exec. coun. on status of women Quebec Govt., Quebec City, 1979-82, assoc. dep. min. justice, 1982-85, appointed to Superior Ct. Quebec, 1985-87, appointed to Quebec Ct. Appeal, 1987—. Office: Palais de Justice, 300 Blvd Jean-Lesage Rm 457, Quebec, PQ Canada G1K 8K6

TOURINO, RALPH GENE, career officer; b. L.A., Mar. 11, 1941; s. John Tourino and Zalia Rose (Perez) Chacon; m. Sherry Lane Tisdail, Sept. 5, 1964; children: Christina Marie, Rebecca Kathleen. BS, UCLA, 1964; MPA, Auburn U., 1973; MBA, U. So. Calif., 1975; postgrad. sr. officials in nat. security, Harvard U., 1988. Commd. 2d lt. USAF, 1964, advanced through grades to maj. gen., 1992; student Undergrad. Navigator Tng., James Connally AFB, Tex., 1964-65; C-97 navigator AF Western Test Range, Vanderberg AFB, Calif., 1965-66; navigator HQ 7th AF Flight Ops., Tan Son Nhut AB, Vietnam, 1966-67; mem. KC135 Crew, March AFB, Calif., 1967-70; sect. comdr. Squadron Officer Sch. Maxwell AFB, Ala., 1970-73; program control Space Div., L.A. AF Sta., 1975-78; dir. program control NAVSTAR Global Positioning System, L.A. AF Sta., 1978-80; dir. contracts Space Def. Systems Program Office, L.A. AF Sta., 1980-82; systems program dir. Inertial Upper Stage Program, L.A. AF Sta., 1982-85; asst. dep. cmdr. for Small ICBM Ballistic Missile Office, Norton AFB, Calif., 1985-87; asst. dep. chief of Staff Systems AF Systems Command, Andrews AFB, Md., 1987-88; insp. gen. AF Systems Command, Andrews AFB, 1988-89; comdr. Ballistic Missile Orgn., Norton AFB, 1989-91; program dir. B-2 System Program Office, Wright-Patterson AFB, Ohio, 1991—. Decorated Legion of Merit, Def. Meritorious Svc. medal, Meritorious Svc. medal, Air medal, Air Force Commendation medal. Mem. Air Force Assn. Republican. Avocation: exercising.

TOURLENTES, THOMAS THEODORE, psychiatrist; b. Chgo., Dec. 7, 1922; s. Theodore A. and Mary (Xenostathy) T.; m. Mona Belle Land, Sept. 9, 1956; children: Theodore W., Stephen C., Elizabeth A. BS, U. Chgo., 1945, MD, 1947. Diplomate Am. Bd. Psychiatry and Neurology (sr. examiner 1964-88, 90). Intern Cook County Hosp., Chgo., 1947-48; resident psychiatry Downey (Ill.) VA Hosp., 1948-51; practice medicine specializing in psychiatry Chgo., 1952, Camp Atterbury, Ind., 1953, Ft. Carson, Colo., 1954, Galesburg, Ill., 1955-71; staff psychiatrist Chgo. VA Clinic, 1952; clin. instr. psychiatry Med. Sch., Northwestern U., 1952; dir. mental hygiene consultation service Camp Atterbury, 1953-54, Ft. Carson, 1953-54; asst. supt. Galesburg State Research Hosp., 1954-58, supt., 1958-71; dir. Comprehensive Community Mental Health Ctr. Rock Island and Mercer Counties; dir. psychiat. services Franciscan Hosp., 1971-85; chief mental health services VA Outpatient Clinic, Peoria, Ill., 1985-88; clin. prof. psychiatry U. Ill., Chgo. and Peoria, 1955—; preceptor in hosp. adminstrn. State U. Iowa, Iowa City, 1958-64; councilor, del. Ill. Psychiat. Soc.; chmn. liaison com. Am. hosp. and psychiat. assns., 1978-79. Contbr. articles profl. jours. Mem. Gov. Ill. Com. Employment Handicapped, 1962-64; zone dir. Ill. Dept. Mental Health, Peoria, 1964-71; mem. Spl. Survey Joint Commn. Accreditation Hosps.; chmn. Commn. Cert. Psychiat. Adminstrs., 1979-81; pres. Knox-Galesburg Symphony Soc., 1966-68; bd. dirs. Galesburg Civic Music Assn., pres. 1968-70; chair Knox county United Way Campaign, 1989; pres. Civic Art Ctr., 1990-92. Capt. M.C. AUS, 1952-54. Fellow AMA, Am. Psychiat. Assn. (chair hosp. and community psychiatry award bd. 1989-90), AAAS, Am. Coll. Psychiatrists, Am. Coll. Mental Health Adminstrs.; mem. Ill. Med. Soc. (chmn. aging com. 1968-71, coun. on mental health and addictions 1987-89, chair mental health substance abuse com. 1987-89), Ill. Psychiat. Soc. (pres. 1969-70), Am. Pub. Health Assn., Soc. Biol. Psychiatry, Ill. Hosp. Assn. (trustee 1968-70), Am. Coll. Hosp. Adminstrs., Assn. for Rsch. Nervous and Mental. Home and Office: 138 Valley View Rd Galesburg IL 61401-9544 *Feeling useful and needed is the greatest recognition and reward.*

TOURNAS, METHODIOS (METHODIOS OF BOSTON), bishop, academic administrator; b. N.Y.C., Nov. 19, 1946; s. Vasilios and Stavroula (Stavropoulos) T. B.A., Hellenic Coll., Brookline, Mass., 1968; M.Div., Coll. of Holy Cross; S.T.M., Boston U., 1972, D.D. (hon.), 1985. Ordained priest Greek Orthodox Ch., 1979. Archdeacon Greek Orthodox Archdiocese, N.Y.C., 1973-79, aux. bishop, 1982-84; priest St. Spyridon Ch., N.Y.C., 1980-82; bishop Greek Orthodox Diocese of Boston, 1984—; pres. Hellenic Coll., Holy Cross Greek Orthodox Sch. Theology, Brookline, Mass., 1989—. Trustee Hellenic Coll. Inc. Mem. Nat. Coun. Chs. Office: Greek Orthodox Diocese Boston 162 Goddard Ave Brookline MA 02146-7414 also: Hellenic Coll 50 Goddard Ave Brookline MA 02146-7496

TOURNILLON, NICHOLAS BRADY, trade finance, international investments company executive; b. New Orleans, Sept. 1, 1931; s. Samuel C. and Anna Mae (Brady) T.; m. Audrey Nicosia, Dec. 15, 1956; children: Brady, Linda, Tracy, Jeffrey, Gregory, Lori. B.A., Southeastern La. U., 1958; M.B.A., La. State U., 1960. Loan officer Export Import Bank U.S., Washington, 1960-66; adminstrv. asst. to exec. officers Atlantic Gulf & Pacific Co. of Manila, 1966-68; asst. treas. GTE Internat., Stamford, Conn., 1968-76, treas., 1976-84, v.p., 1978-86; pres. GTE Fin. Corp., 1984-86; asst. treas. GTE Corp., 1985-86; chmn., chief exec. officer Am. and Internat. Investment Corp., 1986—; mgr. Dir. Trade and Investment Advisors Ltd., Hungary, 1992—; internat. adv. bd. Union Trust Co.; advisor on export fin. to Office of Pres. (U.S. trade rep.). Past chmn. Conn. Dist. Export Council of US Dept. Commerce; mem. monetary com. U.S. Council Internat. Bus.; bd. dirs. Nat. Fgn. Trade Council. Served with USNR, 1953-54, Korea. Named Outstanding Alumnus of Yr., Southeastern La. U., 1976. Mem. Soc. Internat. Treasurers, Acad. Internat. Bus., Phi Kappa Phi. Home: Midwood Dr Greenwich CT 06831-4400 Office: Am and Internat Investment Corp 25 Midwood Dr Greenwich CT 06831-4412 *Perseverance is an often mentioned but never overrated quality—the quality that prevents the substitution of expediency for excellence. Throughout life, persevering effort has been responsible for converting ideas and talents into results and recognition.*

TOURTELLOTTE, CHARLES DEE, physician, educator; b. Kalamazoo, Aug. 28, 1931; s. Dee and Helen May (Lotz) T.; m. Barbara Richwine, June 25, 1955; children: Daniel DeWitt, Elizabeth Anne, William Charles, Scott David. AB, Johns Hopkins U., 1953; MS in Biochemistry, MD, Temple U., 1957. Diplomate Am. Bd. Internal Medicine. Intern, resident in medicine U. Mich. Hosp., Ann Arbor, 1957-60; fellow in rheumatology Temple U. Hosp., Phila., 1960-61; fellow in biochemistry Rockefeller U., N.Y.C., 1961-63; faculty Sch. Medicine, Temple U., 1963—, prof. medicine, 1972—; chief rheumatology Temple U. Hosp., 1966—, pres. med. staff, bd. dirs., 1984-86; dir. Greater Delaware Valley Arthritis Control Program, 1974-77; pres. Eastern Pa. chpt. Arthritis Found., 1972-74; mem. active/cons. staff 10 area and regional hosps. Contbr. chpts. to textbooks, articles to profl. jours.; Editorial Bd.: Arthritis and Rheumatism, 1969-77, 19th-24th Rheumatism Revs, 1969-81. Mem. Haddonfield (N.J.) Bd. Edn., 1968-74, pres., 1974; mem. Borough of Haddonfield Environ. Comm., 1975-87, chmn., 1977-85; mem. Haddonfield Civic Assn., 1963—; South N.J. chmn. Johns Hopkins U. Alumni Schs. Com., 1975-90; trustee Bobby Fulton Meml. Fund, 1979—. Served with AUS, 1953-61. Helen Hay Whitney Found. fellow, 1962-63; Arthritis Found. fellow, 1963-66. Fellow ACP, Phila. Coll. Physicians, Am. Coll. Rheumatology (founding fellow); mem. Am. Fedn. for Clin. Research, Am. Soc. Internal Medicine, Pa. Soc. Internal Medicine, AMA, Pa. Med. Soc., Philadelphia County Med. Soc., Babcock Surg. Soc., Phila. Rheumatism Soc. (pres. 1968-69), Pa. Rheumatology Soc. (founding pres. 1985-86), N.J. Soc. of Pa., Huguenot Soc. Pa., Sigma Xi, Alpha Omega Alpha, Delta Upsilon, Phi Chi. Republican. Presbyterian. Clubs: Tavistock Country (N.J.); Little Egg Harbor Yacht, Wedgewood Swim, Med. of Phila. (bd. dirs. 1991—), Seabrook Island; Johns Hopkins; Diamond (Temple U.). Home: 6 Lane of Acres Haddonfield NJ 08033-3505 Office: Temple Univ Hosp Philadelphia PA 19140-5192

TOUSEY, LOUANN HOLLY, nurse administrator; b. Oconto Falls, Wis., Dec. 5, 1943; d. Gordon John and Ethel Judith (Kopitzke) T.; m. Richard E. Orchard, Aug. 3, 1964 (div.); 1 dau., Kaia Michelle. Lic. practical nurse Hinsdale (Ill.) Sanitarium and Hosp., 1963; B.S. in Nursing, U. Wis., 1974; M.S. in Health Services Adminstrn., Coll. St. Francis, Joliet, Ill., 1984. Emergency and surgery supr. Community Meml. Hosp., Oconto Falls, 1963-71; night supr. Manor House of Madison Nursing Home (Wis.), 1975; shift supr. Algoma (Wis.) Meml. Hosp. and Long Term Care Unit, 1975-76, dir. patient care services, 1976-82; dir. nursing service Langlade Meml. Hosp., Antigo, Wis., 1982—; cons. nursing adminstrn. Rural Health Systems, Chgo. Chairperson Kewaunee County (Wis.) Health Careers Adv. Com., 1978-82. Mem. Am. Orgn. Nurse Execs., Wis. Orgn. Nurse Execs., Am. Soc. Nursing Service Adminstrs., Wis. Soc. Nursing Service Adminstrs. (sec. 1981-82, pres. 1984-86), Am. Nurses Assn. (cert. nurse adminstr.), Wis. Nurses Assn., Northeastern Wis. Emergency Med. Services Council, Am. Indian Nurses Assn., Dist. 4 Nursing Service Council for Long Term Care. Home: 1021 5th Ave Antigo WI 54409-1458 Office: Langlade Memorial Hospital 112 E 5th Ave Antigo WI 54409

TOUSEY, RICHARD, physicist; b. Somerville, Mass., May 18, 1908; s. Coleman and Adella Richards (Hill) T.; m. Ruth Lowe, June 29, 1932; 1 dau., Joanna. A.B., Tufts U., 1928, Sc.D. (hon.), 1961; A.M., Harvard, 1929; Ph.D., 1933. Instr. physics Harvard, 1933-36, tutor div. phys. scis., 1934-36; research instr. Tufts U., 1936-41; physicist U.S. Naval Research Lab. optics div., 1941-58, head instrument sect., 1942-45, head micron waves br., 1945-58, head rocket spectroscopy br., atmosphere and astrophysics div., 1958-67, space sci. div., 1967-78, cons., 1978—; Mem. com. vision Armed Forces-NRC, 1944—; line spectra of elements com. NRC, 1960-72; mem. Rocket and Satellite Research Panel, 1958—; mem. astronomy subcom. space sci. steering com. NASA, 1960-62, mem. solar physics subcom., 1969-71; prin. investigator expts. including Skylab; mem. com. aeronomy Internat. Union Geodesy and Geophysics, 1958—; U.S. nat. com. Internat. Commn. Optics, 1960-66; mem. sci. steering com. Project Vanguard, 1956-58; mem. adv. com. to office sci. personnel Nat. Acad. Scis.-NRC, 1960-72. Contbr. articles to sci. jours. and books. Bayard Cutting fellow Harvard, 1931-33, 35-36; recipient Meritorious Civilian Service award U.S. Navy, 1945; E.O. Hulburt award Naval Research Labs., 1958; Progress medal photog. Soc. Am., 1959; Prix Ancel Soc. Francaise de Photographie, 1962; Henry Draper medal Nat. Acad. Scis., 1963; Navy award for distinguished achievement in sci, 1963; Eddington medal, 1964; NASA medal for exceptional sci. achievement, 1974; George Darwin lectr. Royal Astron. Soc., 1963. Fellow Am. Acad. Arts and Scis., Am. Phys. Soc., Optical Soc. Am. (dir. 1953-57, Frederic Ives medal 1960), Am. Geophys. Union; mem. Internat. Acad. Astronautics, Nat. Acad. Scis., Am. Astron. Soc. (v.p. 1964-66, Henry Norris Russell lectr. 1966, George Ellery Hale award 1992), Soc. Applied Spectroscopy, AAAS, Am. Geophys. Union, Philos. Soc. Washington, Internat. Astron. Union, Nuttall Ornithol. Club, Audubon Naturalists Soc., Phi Beta Kappa, Sigma Xi, Theta Delta Chi. Home: 10450 Lottsford Rd Apt 231 Bowie MD 20721-2742 Office: US Naval Research Lab Washington DC 20375

TOUSIGNANT, JACQUES, human resources executive, lawyer; b. Montreal, Que., Can., Sept. 20, 1948. JD, Sherbrooke U., Que., 1975. Assoc. law firm Pouliot Mercure & Assocs., Montreal, Que., 1975-85; dir. assoc. law firm Montreal Trans. Soc., Montreal, Que., 1985-87; v.p. La Presse Ltee, Montreal, Que., 1987—. Mem. Can. Bar Assn., Que. Bar Assn. Office: La Presse, 7 Rue St Jacques, Montreal, PQ Canada H2Y 1K9

TOUSSAINT, ALLEN RICHARD, recording studio executive, composer, pianist; b. New Orleans, Jan. 14, 1938; s. Clarence Matthew and Naomi (Neville) T.; children: Naomi, Clarence, Alison. Student pub. and pvt. schs., New Orleans. Pres. Sea-Saint Recording Studios, Inc., New Orleans; lectr. in field. Pianist for, Shirley & Lee, 1957, U.S. Army Soldiers Choir, 1963-65; recorded albums Tousan-Wild Sounds of New Orleans, 1958, Life, Love & Faith, 1972, Southern Nights, 1975, Motion, 1978; founder, v.p. recorded albums, Sansu Enterprises, Inc., from 1965, pres., Sea-Saint Rec. Studio, Inc., New Orleans, Marsaint Music, Inc.; composer: songs Southern Nights (Country Music Assn. Song of Yr., Broadcast Music, Inc., citation of achievement), The Greatest Love, The Optimism Blues, Viva La Money, Whipped Cream, With You In Mind, Working In A Coal Mine, Yes We Can, Can, All These Things, (Broadcast Music, Inc. citation of achievement); stage (Broadway) performer, dir., choreographer, The High Rollers Social and Pleasure Club, 1992; performer, New Orleans Jazz Festival, annually. Served with U.S. Army, 1963-65. Mem. Broadcast Music, Inc., Am. Fedn. Musicians, Contemporary Arts Ctr. Office: Sea-Saint Rec Studio Inc 3809 Clematis St New Orleans LA 70122-4801

TOUSSIENG, YOLANDA, make-up artist. television work includes: (movies) Fallen Angel, 1981, Blue de Ville, 1986, (series) Pee-wee's Playhouse, 1986, (mini-series) North and South, Book II, 1986; films include: Blue City, 1986, No Man's Land, 1987, Beetlejuice, 1988, Gross Anatomy, 1989, Three Fugitives, 1989, Farewell to the King, 1989, Edward Scissorhands, 1990, Flatliners, 1990, Everybody Wins, 1990, Hoffa, 1992, Batman Returns, 1992, Mrs. Doubtfire, 1993, Rising Sun, 1993, Ed Wood, 1994 (Acad. award for Best Make-up 1994), Being Human, 1994, Junior, 1994. Office: IATSE Local 706 11519 Chandler Blvd North Hollywood CA 91601

TOUSTER, SAUL, legal educator; b. Bklyn., Oct. 12, 1925; s. Ben and Bertha (Landau) T.; m. Helen Davidson, Nov. 23, 1954 (div. 1967); children: Natasha Ann, Jonathan Bach; m. Irene Tayler, Jan. 14, 1978. A.B. magna cum laude, Harvard U., 1944, J.D., 1948. Bar: N.Y. 1949. Practiced in N.Y.C., 1949-55; prof. law SUNY-Buffalo, 1955-69, asst. to pres., 1966-68, mem. adj. faculty in medicine, edn., psychology, 1964-69; prof. law and social scis. State Coll. at Old Westbury, 1969-71; prof., provost, acad. v.p. CCNY, 1971-73; acting pres. Richmond Coll. City U. N.Y., 1973-74; prof. law CUNY Grad. Sch. also John Jay Coll. of Criminal Justice, 1974-80; prof., dir. legal studies, humanities, professions programs Brandeis U., Waltham, Mass., 1980-93, prof. emeritus, 1993; legis. cons. N.Y. State Law Rev. Commn., 1956-61; vis. prof. U. Brussels, summer, 1968, Boston Coll. Law Sch., 1994. Author: Still Lives and Other Lives, 1966 (Devins Meml. prize 1966); Contbr. articles to legal periodicals. Served to lt. (j.g.) USNR, 1944-46. NEH fellow, 1978; Am. Bar Found. Legal History fellow, 1977-78. Mem. Internat. Inst. Boston (bd. dirs.), Phi Beta Kappa. Home: 180 Beacon St Boston MA 02116-1455 Office: Legal Studies Program Brandeis U Waltham MA 02254

TOVAR, CAROLE L., real estate management administrator; b. Toppenish, Wash., May 19, 1940; d. Harold Max and Gertrude Louisa (Spicer) Smith; m. Duane E. Clark, Aug. 1959 (div. 1963); 1 child, David Allen; m. Vance William Gribble, May 19, 1966 (div. 1989), m. Conrad T. Tovar, June 25, 1992. Student, Seattle Pacific Coll. With B.F. Shearer, Seattle, 1959-60, Standard Oil, Seattle, 1960-62, Seattle Platen Co., 1962-70; ptnr. West Coast Platen, Los Angeles, 1970-87, Waldorf Towers Apts., Seattle, 1970—, Cascade Golf Course, North Bend, Wash., 1970-88; co-owner Pacific Wholesale Office Equipment, Seattle and L.A., 1972-87; owner Pacific Wholesale Office Equip., Seattle, L.A. and San Pablo, Calif., 1988-92, Pac Electronic Service Ctr., Commerce and San Pablo, Calif., 1988-90, Waldorf Mgmt. Co. dba Tovar Mgmt. Co., 1988—; Tovar Properties, 1993—. Mem. Nat. Ctr. Housing Mgmt. (cert. occupancy specialist), Assisted Housing Mgmt. Assn. (nat. cert., Wash. bd. dirs.). Methodist. Avocations: genealogy, music, low income housing for seniors. Office: 706 Pike St Seattle WA 98101-2301

TOVISH, HAROLD, sculptor; b. N.Y.C., July 31, 1921; s. Louis Goodman and Anna (Treffman) T.; m. Marianna Pineda Packard, Jan. 14, 1946; children: Margo, Aaron, Nina. Student, WPA Art Project, 1938-40, Columbia U., 1940-43, Ossip Zadkine Sch. Drawing and Sculpture, Paris, France, 1949-50, Acad. De La Grande Chaumiere, Paris, 1950-51. Tchr. sculpture N.Y. State Coll. Ceramics, 1947-49, U. Minn., 1951-54, Sch. of Boston Mus., 1957-66; sculptor in residence Am. Acad. in, Rome, 1966; prof. art Boston U., 1971-85, prof. emeritus, 1986—; vos. prof. U. Hawaii, 1969-70. Group exhbns. include Met. Mus. of Art, 1943, Toledo Mus. Art, 1948, Galerie 8, 1949, Walker Art Center, 1951, Mpls. Inst. Art, 1953, San Francisco Art Assn., 1953, Whitney Mus. Am. Art, 1954, 58, 60, 64, 80, 28th Venice Biennial, 1956, Mus. Modern Art, 1960, Chgo. Art Inst., 1960, Carnegie Internat, 1960, Am. Fedn. Art, 1964, Decordova Mus., 1964, Internat. Exhbn. of Contemporary Metal, Paris, 1967, Boston Visual Artists Union Gallery, 1975, Boston U., 1975, 78, Colby Coll., 1975, Inst. Contemporary Art, Boston, 1975, 76, Skowhegan Sch., 1975, NYU, 1976, Boston Mus. Fine Arts, 1977, Nat. Mus. Am. Art, 1987, Nat. Acad. Design, 1987, DeCordova Mus., 1987, Howard Yezersky Gallery, 1988; one-man shows include, Walker Art Center, 1953, Swetzoff Gallery, Boston, 1957, 60, 65, Dintenfass Gallery, N.Y.C., 1965, 72, Addison Gallery Am. Art, Andover, Mass., 1965, Alpha Gallery, Boston, 1968, 73, 86, Terry Dintenfass, Inc., N.Y.C., 1980, 85, Boston U. Gallery, 1980, retrospective exhibit, Wheaton Coll., 1967, Howard Yezerski, Boston, 1993; survey exhibit, Solomon Guggenheim Meml. Mus., 1968, Fed. Res. Bank, Boston, 1991; retrospective exhbn. Addison Gallery Am. Art, 1988; survey exhibit Muscarelle Mus., Williamsburg, Va., 1990; represented in permanent collections Phila. Mus. Art, Whitney Mus. Am. Art, Walker Art Center, Mpls. Inst. Art, Addison Gallery Am. Art, Chgo. Art Inst., Mus. Modern Art, Boston Mus. Fine Art, Guggenheim Mus., Worcester Mus. Art, Hirshhorn Collection, Sara Roby Found., Colby Coll., Muscarelle Mus. William & Mary Coll., Williamsburg, Va., Nat. Gallery Am. Art, Minn. Gallery Art, Nat. Mus. Am. Art, Boston Pub. Library; (Recipient 1st prize sculpture Boston Arts Festival 1957, 1st prize drawing 1958, award Am. Inst. Arts and Letters 1971, sculpture grantee Am. Inst. Arts and Letters 1960). Guggenheim fellow, 1967; research fellow Center for Advanced Visual Studies, MIT, 1967-68. Assoc. mem. NAD.

TOWBIN, (ABRAHAM) ROBERT, investment banker; b. N.Y.C., May 26, 1935; s. Harold Clay and Minna (Berlin) T.; m. Jacqueline de Chollet; children: Minna Joyce Pinger, Abraham Robert, Zachary Harold. B.A., Dartmouth Coll., 1957. With Asiel & Co., N.Y.C., 1958-59; with L.F. Rothschild, Unterberg, Towbin Holdings, Inc. (merged with C.E. Unterberg, Towbin Co. 1977), N.Y.C., 1959-86, vice chmn., 1961-86; mng. dir. Lehman Bros. (formerly Shearson Lehman Bros., Inc.), N.Y., 1987-94; pres., CEO Russian Am. Enterprise Fund, N.Y.C., 1994—; bd. dirs. Bradley Real Estate, Inc., Russian-Am. Enterprise Fund, Gerber Sci. Inc., Globalstar Inc., K&F Industries, Very Spl. Arts; pres., CEO Russian-Am. Enterprise Fund, 1994—, Columbus New Millenium Fund, 1994. Hon. mem. N.Y. State Coun. Arts.; bd. dirs. St. David's Sch., Museum Sch. Mem. Securities Industry Assn., Bond Club N.Y., Stock Exch. Luncheon Club, Harmonie Club (N.Y.C.), Nat. Golf Links Am., N.Y. Yacht, Antigua Yacht Club, Chelsea Art Club (London), Century Assn. Home: 1010 Fifth Ave New York NY 10028-0130 Office: Russian-Am Enterprise Fund 17 State St New York NY 10004

TOWE, THOMAS EDWARD, lawyer; b. Cherokee, Iowa, June 25, 1937; s. Edward and Florence (Tow) T.; m. Ruth James, Aug. 21, 1960; children: James Thomas, Kristofer Edward. Student, U. Paris, 1956; BA, Earlham Coll., 1959; LLB, U. Mont., 1962; LLM, Georgetown U., 1965. Ptnr. Towe, Ball, Enright, Mackey & Sommerfeld, Billings, Mont., 1967—; legislator Mont. House of Rep., Billings, 1971-75, Mont. State Senate, Billings, 1975-87, 91-94; served on various coms. Mont. Senate, 1975-87, 91-94. Contbr. articles to law revs. Pres. Alternatives, Inc., Halfway House, Billings, 1985-86, mem. 1977—; mem. adv. com. Mont. Crime Control Bd. 1973-78, Youth Justice coun., 1981-83; mem. State Dem. Exec. com., 1969-71, Yellowstone County Dem. Exec. Com., 1969-73, candidate for congress, 1976; bd. dirs. Mont. Consumer Affairs Coun., Regl. Community Svcs. for the Devel. Disabled, 1975-77, Rimrock Guidance Found., 1975-80, Vols. of Am., Billings, 1984-89, Youth Dynamics Inc., 1989—, Zoo Mont., 1985—. Capt. U.S. Army, 1962-65. Mem. Mont. Bar Assn., Yellowstone County Bar Assn., Am. Hereford Assn., Billings C. of C. Mem. Soc. of Friends. Avocation: outdoor recreation. Home: 2739 Gregory Dr S Billings MT 59102 Office: 2525 6th Ave N Billings MT 59101

TOWELL, WILLIAM EARNEST, forester, former association executive; b. St. James, Mo., June 11, 1916; s. Esco Joel and Margaret (Pinto) T.; m. Virginia Ruth Dotter, Aug. 31, 1940; children: Jane Towell Darrough, Linda Towell Pinney. B.S. in Forestry, U. Mich., 1938, M.S. in Silviculture, 1938; D.Sc. (hon.), U. Mo., 1981. With Mo. Dept. Conservation, 1938-67, dir. 1957-67; exec. v.p. Am. Forestry Assn., Washington, 1967-78; adj. prof. forestry N.C. State U., 1979—. Mem. Pres.'s Water Pollution Control Adv. Bd., 1963-66, Sec. Agr. Wildlife Adv.Bd., 1965-69, Lewis and Clark Trail Commn., 1965-67; mem. conservation com. Boy Scouts Am., 1968-78, nat. chmn., 1975-78; nat. chmn. project SOAR, 1970-74; adv. mem. com. interrelations wildlife and agr. NAS, 1965-70, mem. adv. team to Indonesia, 1972; mem. Cradle of Forestry Advisory Commn., Dept. Agr., 1971-76; conservation cons. Walt Disney Prodns., 1969-78; chmn. exec. com. Internat. Assn. Fish and Wildlife Agys., 1964-65, pres., 1965-66; mem. exec. com. Fontana Conservation Roundup, 1969-80; mem. exec. com. Nat. Resources Coun. Am., 1968-78, chmn., 1975-77; bd. dirs. Nat. Wildlife Fedn., 1979-87; Forest History Soc., 1978-88;; mem. study panel Fishery Mgmt. Nat. Marine Fisheries Svc. NOAA, U.S. Dept. Commerce, 1986; mem. adv. bd. Wild Horse and Burro dept. U.S. Dept. of Interior, 1986-87; mem. diocesan coun., past sr. warden Episcopal Ch., pres. The Village Chapel, Pinehurst, N.C., 1988, 91. Lt. USNR, 1943-46. Recipient Merit de Agrico medal France, 1970; Conservationist of Year award Nat. Wildlife Fedn., 1976; Disting. Service award U. Mich. Sch. Natural Resources Alumni Soc., 1978; Lifetime Achievement award Nat. Assn. State Foresters, 1978; John Aston Warder Medal Am. Forestry Assn., 1982; J. Sterling Morton award Nat. Arbor Day Found., 1984. Fellow Soc. Am. Foresters (chmn. Ozark sect. 1950, v.p. 1982-83, pres. 1984, Sir William Schlich Meml. medal 1978); mem. Kiwanis. Democrat. Home: 4 Village Green Cir Southern Pines NC 28387-3209

TOWER, HORACE LINWOOD, III, consumer products company executive; b. New Haven, July 16, 1932; s. Horace Linwood, Jr. and Madeline Elizabeth (Davin) T.; m. Elizabeth Wright, Dec. 29, 1956; children: Cynthia, William, John. BA, Cornell U., 1955, MBA, 1960; DHL (hon.), Westfield (Mass.) State Coll., 1984. With Procter & Gamble Corp., Cin., 1960-62; mgmt. cons. Booz, Allen & Hamilton, N.Y.C., 1962-63; with Gen. Foods Corp., White Plains, N.Y., 1963-67, pres. Maxwell home divsn., 1963-78, pres., CEO, 1978-90; pres., CEO, Stanhome Inc., Westfield, Mass., 1978-90, chmn., 1982—; bd. dirs. Stanhome Inc., Tambrands, Inc., Stanley Park; formerly bd. dirs. Forman Cos. Capt. USAF, 1956-59. Mem. Air Force Assn., Sabre Pilots Assn., Thimble Island Sailing and Lit. Soc., Stony Creek Boating Club, N Agawa Fishing Club, Kappa Phi, Sigma Gamma Epsilon. Office: Stanhome Inc 333 Western Ave Westfield MA 01085-2560

TOWERS, BERNARD LEONARD, medical educator; b. Preston, Eng., Aug. 20, 1922; s. Thomas Francis and Isabella Ellen (Dobson) T.; m. Carole Ilene Lieberman (div. 1992); 1 child, Tiffany Sabrina; children from previous marriage: Helena Marianne, Celia Marguerite, Julie Carole. M.B., Ch.B., U. Liverpool, 1947; M.A., U. Cambridge, 1954. House surgeon Royal Infirmary, Liverpool, 1947; lectr. U. Bristol, 1949-50, U. Wales, 1950-54, Cambridge U., 1954-70; fellow Jesus Coll., 1957-70, steward, 1961-64, tutor, 1964-69; dir. med. studies, 1964-70; prof. pediatrics UCLA, 1971-84, prof. anatomy, 1971-91, prof. psychiatry, 1983-91, prof. emeritus anatomy and psychiatry, 1991—, convenor, moderator medicine and soc. forum, 1974-89; pvt. practice integrative medicine, 1991—; co-dir. Program in Medicine, Law and Human Values, 1977-84; cons. Inst. Human Values in Medicine, 1971-84; adv. bd. Am. Teilhard Assn. for Future of Man, 1971—; v.p. Teilhard Centre for Future Man, London, 1974—. Author: Teilhard de Chardin, 1966, Naked Ape or Homo Sapiens?, 1969, Concerning Teilhard, 1969; also articles, chpts. on sci. and philosophy.; Editor anat. sect.: Brit. Abstracts Med. Scis, 1954-56, Teilhard Study Library, 1966-70; adv. bd.: Jour. Medicine and Philosophy, 1974-84. Served to capt. RAMC, 1947-49. NIH grantee, 1974-78; NEH grantee, 1977-83. Fellow Cambridge Philos. Soc., Royal Soc. Medicine; mem. Brit. History of Medicine, Soc. Health and Human Values (pres. 1977-78), Anat. Soc. G.B., Worshipful Soc. Apothecaries London, Am. Assn. for Study Mental Imagery, Western Assn. Physicians, Societe Europeene de Culture Venise. Office: 436 N Bedford Dr Ste 302 Beverly Hills CA 90210-4320

TOWERS, GORDON THOMAS, province official; b. Red Deer, Alta., Can., July 5, 1919; s. Thomas Henry and Janet (Morrison) T.; m. Doris Roberta, Dec. 27, 1940; children: Thomas Robert, Gary Lee, Lynda Marie, Ross Gordon, Leona. LLD, U. Alta., 1992. Farmer; M.P. Ho. of Commons, 1972, re-elected, 1974, 78, 80, 84; Parliament Sec. to Solicitor Gen., Parliament Sec. to Min. of State; Lt. Gov. Province of Alta., Edmonton, Can., 1991—; appted. Dep. Critic of Veterans Affairs, 1984; del. U.N. Gen. Assembly, 1978. Past pres. Red Deer 4-H Coun. Mem. Can.-Brit. Commonwealth Parliamentary Assn. (del. Westminster 29th Parliament 1980); Red Deer Exhbn. Assn. (past pres.), Prairy Fairs Assn, River Glen Home and Sch. Assn., Masons (Grand Master Red. Deer dist.), Alta. Order of Excellence (chancellor), Knights of St. J., Rotary Internat. (Paul Harris fellow), Red Deer C. of C. (Citizen of the Year 1990). Presbyterian. Office: Legis Bldg 3rd Fl Edmonton, AB Canada T5K 2B6*

TOWERS, JAMES MC, education educator; b. Ames, Iowa, Dec. 3, 1948; s. Charles Mc and Mary Elizabeth (Peck) T.; m. Karen Ruth Lauridsen, Aug. 18, 1973; children: Devon Charles, Jaimee Faye Elizabeth. BA, U. Iowa, 1970, MA, 1974, diploma as Ednl. Specialist, 1976, PhD in Edn., 1985. Instr. English Walgett High Sch., New South Wales, Australia, 1971-73, Am. Sch. of Kuwait, 1974-75; prof. Muscatine (Iowa) Community Coll., 1976-79; program coordinator U. Iowa, Iowa City, 1979-85; dir. Title III Des Moines Area Community Coll., Ankery Iowa, 1985-86; asst. prof. edn. Monmouth (Ill.) Coll., 1986-88; assoc. prof., chmn. dept. St. Mary's Coll. of Minn., Winona, 1988—, assoc. dean sch. edn., 1993—, dean sch. edn., 1995—; cons. Am. Coll. Testing, Iowa City, 1984-85. Editor: How To Study for Academic Success, 1988; author poems; contbr. articles to profl. jours. Methodist. Avocation: traveling. Office: St Mary's Coll Winona MN 55987

TOWERS, T. GORDON, Canadian lieutenant governor; b. Red Deer, Alta., Can., July 5, 1919; s. Thomas Henry and Janet (Morrison) T.; m. Doris Roberta Nicholson, Dec. 22, 1940; children: Thomas Robert, Gary Lee, Lynda Marie, Ross Gordon, Leona. Farmer Red Deer; mem. Can. Ho. of Commons, 1972—; lt. gov. Edmonton, Alta., 1991—; del. UN Gen. Assembly, 1978, Can. br. Commonwealth Parliamentary Assn. to the 29th Parliamentary Seminar; chmn. Standing Com. on Privileges and Elections; vice chmn. Standing Com. on Agr.; official Opposition Critic for the Ministry of Supply and Svcs.; dep. official Opposition Critic for the Min. of State for Sci. and Tech. Pres. River Glen Home and Sch. Assn., Red Deer Exhib. Assn., Prairie Fairs Assn., Red Deer 4-H Coun. Named Paul Harris fellow Rotary Internat., 1989, Citizen of Yr. Red Deer C. of C., 1990. Presbyterian. Office: Office of Lt Gov, 3d Flr Legislature Bldg, Edmonton, AB Canada T5K 2B6

TOWERY, MATTHEW ALLEN, SR., lawyer; b. Atlanta, Dec. 6, 1959; s. Maurice Jean and Joan (Gilleland) T.; m. Marilea Jean Taglia; children: Matthew Allen Jr., Katherine Alexandra. M of Philosophy, Cambridge (Eng.) U., 1984; JD cum laude, Stetson U. 1987. Bar: Ga. Speechwriter, spl. asst. to Mack F. Mattingly U.S. Senate, Washington, 1981-82; ptnr. Towery, Thompson, Gulliver, and Bunch, Atlanta, 1987-; trustee Southeastern Legal Found., Atlanta, Pace Acad.; overseer coll. law Stetson U. Author: Power in the South, 1984. Rep. nominee for lt. gov. State of Ga., 1990. Recipient Nat. Bicentenniel Debate Champion award Nat. Bicentennial Commn., 1976-77; named Nat. Freshman Legis. of Yr., Nat. Rep. Party, 1993. Mem. Ga. Bar. Assn., Atlanta Bar Assn., Oxford-Cambridge Club, Cherokee Town and Country Club, Ga. House Reps., Nat. Color Graphics, Inc. (chmn 1993—), Friends of Newt Girgrili (ampaign com. 1992—).

TOWEY, RICHARD EDWARD, economics educator; b. Mount Kisco, N.Y., Sept. 22, 1928; s. William Joseph and Anna Margaret (Rumse) T.; m. Mary Ann Franusich, June 12, 1954 (dec. Mar. 1988); 1 child, John Patrick; m. Lorraine T. Miller, July 21, 1990. BS, U. San Francisco, 1954; MA, U. Calif., Berkeley, 1957, PhD, 1967. Economist Fed. Res. Bank of San Francisco, 1957-60; prof. econs. Oreg. State U., Corvallis, 1962-93, emeritus prof., 1993—; economist Fed. Deposit Ins. Corp., Washington, 1968-70. Cpl. U.S. Army, 1948-49, 1950-51. Earhart fellow U. Calif., Berkeley, 1961-62. Mem. Am. Econ. Assn., Am. Fin. Assn., Western Econ. Assn. Roman Catholic. Office: Oreg State Univ Dept. Econ Corvallis OR 97331

TOWEY, ROBERT, pharmaceutical company executive; b. Newark, Feb. 20, 1949; s. Oswald Joseph and Bertha Ann (Rinderer) T.; m. Maureen Savage, Aug. 14, 1971; children: Jeffrey, Jarid. BS in Acctg., Fairleigh Dickinson U., 1971. CPA, N.J. Mem. audit staff Coopers & Lybrand Co., Newark, 1971-73, audit supr., 1973-74; auditor Hoffmann-LaRoche, Nutley, N.J., 1975-76; mgr. acctg. policies Hoffmann-LaRoche, Nutley, 1976-78, dir. corp. acctg., 1978-86; contr. Roche Diagnostic Systems, Nutley, 1986-87, v.p. fin., 1987—; asst. prof. Fairleigh Dickinson U., Rutherford, N.J., 1976-81. Mem. fin. com. St. Thomas The Apostle Ch., Bloomfield, N.J., treas., 1986-87; advancement chmn. Bloomfield area Boy Scouts Am. Mem. Am. Inst. CPAs, N.J. Soc. CPAs, Nat. Assn. Accts. Home: 8 Carolyn Ct East Hanover NJ 07936-1802

TOWLE, LAIRD CHARLES, book publisher; b. Exeter, N.H., Sept. 13, 1933; s. Gerald Charles and Wilma Lois (Buzzell) T.; m. Marlene Ann Towne, Apr. 14, 1956; children: Karen Lee, Joel Andrew, Glenn Corbett, Leslie Kim. BS in Physics, U. N.H., 1955, MS in Physics, 1958; PhD, U. Va., 1962. Rsch. physicist AVCO Corp., Wilmington, Mass., 1962-63, Allis Chalmers Corp., West Allis, Wis., 1963-67; section head Naval Rsch. Lab., Washington, 1967-77, project mgr., 1977-81; chief exec. officer Heritage Books, Inc., Bowie, Md., 1981—. Author: N.H. Genealogical Research Guide, 1973, The Descendants of William Brown and Isabella Kennedy, 1992; editor: Genealogical Periodical Annual Index, 1974—; contbr. articles to profl. jours. Pres. NRL Fed. Credit Union, Washington, 1970-71, treas., 1972-84; pres. Prince George's County General Soc., Bowie, 1977-91; mem. Bowie Adv. Planning Bd., 1987-91. Mem. Nat. Geneal. Soc., N.E. Historic Geneal. Soc., Prince George's County General Soc., Sigma Xi. Avocations: genealogical research, sailing, gardening. Home: 3602 Maureen Ln Bowie MD 20715-2998 Office: Heritage Books Inc 1540-E Pointer Ridge Pl Bowie MD 20716-1874

TOWLE, LELAND HILL, government official; b. Boston, Mar. 29, 1931; s. Leland and Bertha Mary (Hill) T.; m. Carol Peterson, June 5, 1953; children—Peter Kimball, Gretchen Towle Maynard, Michele. B.S., U. N.H. 1952; M.S., M.I.T., 1953; Cert. in Bus. and Mgmt, U. Calif., Berkeley, 1962. Nuclear chemist Stanford Research Inst., Menlo Park, Calif., 1956-59; community systems economist, economist, nuclear economist Stanford Research Inst., 1959-68, mgr. health scis. research, 1968-74; asst. dir. Nat. Center for Alcohol Edn., Arlington, Va., 1974-75; cons. Medicine in the Pub. Interest, Washington, 1975; vis. scientist Nat. Inst. on Alcohol Abuse and Alcoholism, Rockville, Md., 1975-76, dep. dir. office of program devel. and analysis, 1976-77, assoc. dir. office of program devel. and analysis, 1977-81, dir. internat. and intergovernmental affairs, 1981-95; cons. regional and med. programs. Contbr. articles to profl. jours. Bd. dirs. Med. Resources Found., Palo Alto, Calif., 1972-73. Served with USAF, 1952-56. Mem. Am. Pub. Health Assn., Sci. Research Soc. Am., Am. Nuclear Soc., Am. Chem. Soc., Sigma Xi, Phi Kappa Phi. Home: Rt 663 Burgess VA 22432

TOWLES, DONALD BLACKBURN, retired newspaper publishing executive; b. Lawrenceburg, Ky., Sept. 10, 1927; s. Joseph Sterling and Marjorie (Blackburn) T.; m. Geraldine Gooch, Dec. 20, 1947 (dec. Nov. 1980); children: Sally Blackburn Towles Clark, Rebecca Neale Towles Brown; m. Julia Mason, Dec. 3, 1981. A.B. in Journalism, U. Ky., 1948. Asst. dir. pub-licity, editor In Ky. Mag. Commonwealth of Ky., Frankfort, 1948-55; pub. service mgr. Courier-Jour. and Louisville Times Co., Louisville, 1956-66, dir. pub. service and promotion, 1966-71, v.p., 1974-92, v.p., dir. circulation, 1971-76, v.p., dir. pub. affairs, 1976-92. Author: The Press of Kentucky 1787-1994; editor: Newspaper Promotion Handbook, 1983. Pres. Heritage Corp. of Louisville, 1982-85; chmn. Louisville area chpt. ARC, 1987-89; chmn. program adv. com. Louisville Devel. Program, 1971-80; mem. adv. bd. Salvation Army; bd. dirs. Louisville Med. Ctr., Jewish Hosp. Heart and Lung Inst. Served with U.S. Army, 1952-54, Korea. Recipient Comty. Svc. award Louisville Devel. Com., 1980; named Outstanding Chpt. Vol. Louis-ville area chpt. ARC, 1993, Outstanding State Vol., 1994; inducted into Ky. Journalism Hall of Fame, 1992. Mem. Internat. Newspaper Promotion Assn. (pres. 1980-82, Silver Shovel 1983), Ky. Press Assn. (pres. 1982, Pres.'s Cup Leadership 1982, Disting. Comty. Svc. award 1987), Journalism Alumni Assn. U. Ky. (pres. 1979—, Outstanding Alumnus award, All-Am. Alumni award 1994), Soc. Profl. Journalists (pres. Louisville chpt. 1991-92). Democrat. Disciple of Christ. Home: 3536 Norbourne Blvd Louisville KY 40207-3753

TOWLES, STOKLEY PORTER, commercial and investment banking executive; b. St. Louis, Dec. 12, 1935; s. Harold Robert Towles and Margaret (Salmon) Derrick; m. Eleanor Hollingsworth, June 19, 1960 (div. 1983); children: Stokley Porter, Amor Hollingsworth, Holly Kimbrough; m. Jeanne Glass, Dec. 28, 1983. AB, Princeton U., 1957; MBA, Harvard U., 1960. With Brown Bros. Harriman & Co., Boston, 1960—, asst. mgr., 1964-67, dep. mgr., 1967-69, mgr., 1969-78, ptnr., 1978—; bd. dirs. Norfolk & Dedham Ins., Dedham., Mass., West Newbury (Mass.) Ins., Brown Bros. Harriman S.A., Luxembourg. Trustee Boys and Girls Clubs, Boston, 1965, Vincent Meml. Hosp., Boston, 1978, Univ. Hosp., Boston, 1981, Noble & Greenough Sch., Dedham, 1985. Mem. Somerset Club, The Country Club (Brookline, Mass; gov. 1967-73), Phi Beta Kappa. Avocations: tennis, golf, jogging, reading. Office: Brown Bros Harriman & Co 40 Water St Boston MA 02109-3661

TOWNE, L. STANTON, lawyer; b. Chgo., July 16, 1952. BS, Columbia U., JD, 1976. Bar: N.Y. 1977, Ill. 1991. Ptnr. McDermott, Will & Emery, Chgo. Mem. ABA, Assn. Bar City N.Y., N.Y. State Bar Assn. Office: McDermott Will & Emery 227 W Monroe St Chicago IL 60606-5096

TOWNE, ROBERT, screenwriter; b. 1936; m. Luisa Towne; 2 children. Student, Pomona State Coll. Screenplays include The Last Woman on Earth, 1960, The Tomb of Ligeia, 1965, Villa Rides, 1968, The Last Detail, 1973, Chinatown, 1974 (Acad. award best original screenplay), (with Warren Beatty) Shampoo, 1974 (Acad. award best original screenplay), (with Paul Schrader) The Yazuka, 1975, (also prodr., dir.) Personal Best, 1981, 1981, (with Michael Austin) Greystoke, 1984, (also dir.) Tequila Sunrise, 1988, The Two Jakes, 1990, Days of Thunder, 1990, The Firm, 1992. Office: Creative Artists Agy 9830 Wilshire Blvd Beverly Hills CA 90212

TOWNER, NAOMI WHITING, fiber artist, educator; b. Providence, May 8, 1940; d. Basil J. and Nellie (Woolhouse) Whiting; B.F.A. in Textile Design, R.I. Sch. Design, 1962; postgrad. (Textron fellow) Foreningen Handarbetets Vanner, Stockholm, 1962-63; M.F.A. in Textile Design, Rochester Inst. Tech., 1965. Internat. studies with faculty Ill. State U., People's Republic of China and Thailand, 1986; Teaching grad. asst. Sch. Am. Craftsmen, Rochester (N.Y.) Inst. Tech., 1963-65, instr. textile design summer 1964; instr. Ill. State U., Normal, 1965-68, asst. prof., 1968-72, assoc. prof., 1972-76, prof. art, 1976—; lectr. various art guilds and schs., 1967—; pres., ptnr. Smiling Camel Choklits, Ltd., Bloomington; dir. workshops on weaving and textile design, 1964—. One person shows sell art fabrics include: Fox Valley Art League, St. Charles, Ill., 1968, Fine Arts Ctr. Clinton (Ill.), 1971, Old Town Gallery, St. Charles, Mo., 1973, Lincoln Coll., Lincoln, Ill., 1974, Craft Alliance Gallery, St. Louis, 1974, Unitarian Ch., Bloomington, Ill., 1975, The Art-In, Riverton, Wyo., 1975, Xavier U., Cin., 1992; numerous group shows including: Mus. Contemporary Crafts Fabrics Internat. travelling exhibit, 1961-62, Security Trust Co., Rochester, N.Y., 1965, Ill. State U., Normal, 1965-68, 71, 73-86, Old Town Art Ctr., Chgo., 1967, Brooks Meml. Art Gallery, Memphis, 1967, Lakeview Ctr. for Arts, Peoria, Ill., 1967-68, Ill. State Mus., 1968, Wis. State U., Oshkosh, 1969, Art Inst. Chgo., 1971, No. Ill. U., DeKalb, 1971, U. Mass. Art Gallery, Amherst, 1972, Evansville (Ind.) Mus. Arts and Scis., 1973, 88, Eureka Coll. (Ill.), 1973, Mills Coll., Oakland, Calif., 1974, Columbus (Ga.) Mus. Arts and Crafts, 1974, Wright Art Center, Beloit (Wis.) Coll., 1975, Lowe Art Mus., U. Miami (Fla.) Goldstein Gallery, 1976, U. Minn., St. Paul, 1977, Paul Sargent Gallery, Eastern Ill. U., Charlestown, 1977, Boise (Idaho) State U., 1978, Cin. Art Mus., 1978, Kearney (Nebr.) State Coll. Art Gallery, 1979, Coll. Art Gallery, 1979, Rahr-West Mus., Manitowoc, Wis., 1979, Ill. State Mus., Springfield, 1979, No. Calif. Handweavers, Inc., San Mateo, 1979, Ill. Arts Council Gallery, Chgo., 1979, Tex. Tech U., Lubbock, 1980, Caterpillar Internat., Peoria, Ill., 1980, No. Ill. U., Midwest Constructed Fibers, 1940-80, travelling exhibit, 1980-82, Loveland (Colo.) Mus., 1981, Ft. Collins (Colo.) Mus., 1981, Fiber Art Trends, 1982, Pyramid Arts Ctr. Rochester, 1983, U. Wis.-Green Bay travelling exhibit, 1984-85, Ariel Gallery, Naperville, Ill., 1984, Premonitions, Nashville, 1985, Ill. State Fair Profl. Art Exhbn., Springfield, 1986 (1st place award craft media, merit award 1987), 7th ann. Cen. Ill. Arts Consortium Visual Arts Touring Exhbn., 1984-86 (merit award), Juror's Exhbn.: New Dimensions in Fiber II, Coll. Du Page, Ill., 1986, U. Galleries Ill. State U., Normal, 1987, Creative Arts Guild, Dalton, Ga., 1988, No. Ill. U. Art Gallery, Chgo., 1988, Merchandise Mart, Chgo., 1988, Evansville (Ind.) Mus. Arts & Scis., 1988, Midwest Weavers Assn. Conf., Cin., 1989, Malton Gallery, Cin., 1989, U. Art Gallery/Mus. Western Ill. U., Macomb, 1989, Upper Gallery, Milw., 1990, Henderson Gallery, Yellow Springs, Ohio, 1990, Butler Inst. Am. Art, Youngstown, Ohio, 1991, Xavier U. Art Galleries, Cin., 1992, Springfield (Ill.) Art Assn., 1992, Craft Alliance Gallery, St. Louis, 1992; represented in permanent collections Ill. State Mus., Springfield, Washington U. St. Louis, Eureka (Ill.) Coll., corp. and pvt. collections; juror exhbns. Recipient numerous awards including Silver Shuttle award U. Rochester, 1964, Owens-Corning Fiberglas competition, 1964, award of excellence Ill. Craftsmen's Council Invitational, 1967, Merit award Springfield Art Assn., 1976, Hon. mention Tchr. of Yr. awards, 1986; grantee Handweavers Guild Am. and Ill. Arts Council, 1975-78. Mem. Am. Crafts Council, Midwest Weavers Conf., Am. Fedn. Tchrs., AFL-CIO, Handweavers Guild Am. (rep. 1973-77, bd. dirs. 1978-80), ACLU, Surface Design Assnontbr. articles on textile design and weaving to profl. publs.; editor Fiber News, 1975-85; mem. editorial bd. Ars Textrina, 1985—. Home: 610 E Taylor St Bloomington IL 61701-5347 Office: Ill State U Art Dept Normal IL 61761

TOWNES, CHARLES HARD, physics educator; b. Greenville, S.C., July 28, 1915; s. Henry Keith and Ellen Sumter (Hard) T.; m. Frances H. Brown, May 4, 1941; children: Linda Lewis, Ellen Screven, Carla Keith, Holly Robinson. B.A., B.S., Furman U., 1935; M.A., Duke U., 1937; Ph.D., Calif. Inst. Tech., 1939. Mem. tech. staff Bell Telephone Lab., 1939-47; assoc. prof. physics Columbia U., 1948-50, prof. physics, 1950-61; exec. dir. Columbia Radiation Lab., 1950-52, chmn. physics dept., 1952-55; provost and prof. physics MIT, 1961-66, Inst. prof., 1966-67; v.p., dir. research Inst. Def. Analyses, Washington, 1959-61; prof. physics U. Calif., Berkeley, 1967-86, 94, prof. physics emeritus, 1986-94, prof. grad. sch., 1994—; Guggenheim fellow, 1955-56; Fulbright lectr. U. Paris, 1955-56, U. Tokyo, 1956; lectr., 1955, 60; dir. Enrico Fermi Internat. Sch. Physics, 1963; Richtmeyer lectr. Am. Phys. Soc., 1959; Scott lectr. U. Cambridge, 1963; Centennial lectr. U. Toronto, 1967; Lincoln lectr. 1972-73, Halley lectr., 1976, Krishman lectr., 1992, Nishina lectr., 1992; dir. Gen. Motors Corp., 1973-86; mem. Pres.'s Sci. Adv. Com., 1966-69; chmn. sci. and tech. adv. com. for manned space flight NASA, 1964-69; mem. Pres.'s Com. on Sci. and Tech., 1976; researcher on nuclear and molecular structure, quantum electronics, interstellar molecules, radio and infrared astrophysics. Author: (with A.L. Schawlow) Microwave Spectroscopy, 1955; author, co-editor: Quantum

Electronics, 1960, Quantum Electronics and Coherent Light, 1964; editorial bd.; Rev. Sci. Instruments, 1950-52, Phys. Rev., 1951-53, Jour. Molecular Spectroscopy, 1957-60, Procs. Nat. Acad. Scis., 1978-84; contbr. articles to sci. publs.; patentee masers and lasers. Trustee Calif. Inst. Tech., Carnegie Instn. of Washington, Grad. Theol. Union, Calif. Acad. Scis.; mem. corp. Woods Hole Oceanographic Instn. Decorated officier Légion d'Honneur (France); recipient numerous hon. degrees and awards including Nobel prize for physics, 1964; Stuart Ballantine medal Franklin Inst., 1959, 62; Thomas Young medal and prize Inst. Physics and Phys. Soc., Eng., 1963; Disting. Public Service medal NASA, 1969; Wilhelm Exner award Austria, 1970; Niels Bohr Internat. Gold medal, 1979; Nat. Sci. medal, 1983, Berkeley citation U. Calif., 1986; named to Nat. Inventors Hall of Fame, 1976, Engring. and Sci. Hall of Fame, 1983; recipient Common Wealth award, 1993. Fellow IEEE (life, medal of honor 1967) Am. Phys. Soc. (pres. 1967, Plyler prize 1977), Optical Soc. Am. (hon., Mees medal 1968), Indian Nat. Sci. Acad., Calif. Acad. Scis.; mem. NAS (coun. 1968-72, 78-81, chmn. space sci. bd. 1970-73, Comstock award 1959), Am. Philos. Soc., Am. Astron. Soc., Am. Acad. Arts and Scis., Royal Soc. (fgn. mem.), Russian Acad. Scis. (fgn. mem.), Pontifical Acad. Scis., Max-Planck Inst. for Physics and Astrophysics (fgn. mem.). Office: U Calif Dept Physics Berkeley CA 94720

TOWNES, PHILIP LEONARD, pediatrician, educator; b. Salem, Mass., Feb. 18, 1927; s. Saul and Lillian (Kravetsky) T.; m. Marjorie Joan Greenstone, Aug. 27, 1956; children: Elizabeth Ann, Susan Jane, David Andrew. A.B., Harvard, 1948; Ph.D., U. Rochester, 1952, M.D., 1959. Diplomate: Am. Bd. Pediatrics, Am. Bd. Med. Genetics. Intern Strong Meml. Hosp., Rochester, 1959-60; asst. resident Strong Meml. Hosp., 1963, chief resident pediatrics, 1965; mem. faculty U. Rochester Sch. Medicine, 1952-79, prof. pediatrics, 1969-79; prof. anatomy (genetics), chmn. div. genetics, dir. Genetic Clinic, 1966-79; prof. pediatrics U. Mass. Sch. Medicine, 1979—, dir. Genetic Clinic, 1979—, dir. Cytogenetics Lab., 1981—; pediatrician Strong Meml. Hosp.; cons. attending Newark State Hosp., Genesee Hosp.; hon. research asst. Univ. Coll., London, Eng., 1965-66; mem. adv. com. for genetics services Mass. Dept. Pub. Health, 1979—, chmn. com., 1982—; mem. steering com. New Eng. Regional Genetics Group, 1981—. Contbr. articles to med. jours. Mem. com. qualifications cytogenetics N.Y. State Dept. Health, 1968-74; bd. dirs. Monroe County chpt. Nat. Found., 1965-79, chmn. med. adv. com., 1967-79, hon. bd. dirs., 1979—, also cons. Served with USNR, 1945-46. USPHS predoctoral fellow, 1951-52; sr. research fellow, 1960-61; research career devel. award, 1961-66. Mem. Am. Acad. Pediatrics, Am. Assn. Anatomists, Soc. Pediatric Research, Am. Soc. Human Genetics, Am. Pediatric Soc., Teratology Soc., Sigma Xi, Alpha Omega Alpha. Home: 14 Spring Valley Rd Worcester MA 01609-1151

TOWNLEY, JON, production company creative director. BFA, Ohio State U., 1976. Formerly dir. design Cranston/Csuri Prodns.; creative dir. MetroLight Studios, L.A., 1987—; designer, dir. numerous TV and film projects; designer animation storyboards HBO, ESPN, NBC Sports, Nat. TV comml., and feature film effects. Recipient various awards Broadcast Designers Assn., Broadcast Promotion and Mktg. Execs., Internat. Film & TV Festival of N.Y., Nicograph, Anima Acad. of TV Arts and Scis. Office: Metrolight Studios 5724 W 3rd St Ste 400 Los Angeles CA 90036-3078

TOWNLEY, ROBERT GORDON, medical educator; b. Omaha, Nebr., July 27, 1928. MD, Creighton U., 1955. Pvt. practice in internal medicine and allerty Physicians Clinic, Omaha, 1960-62; attending staff mem. Douglas County Hosp., Omaha, 1960-62; instr. dept. medicine and allergy Creighton U., 1960-62; asst. prof. medicine Creighton U., 1966-69, assoc. prof. medicine and microbiology, 1969-74, chief allergy sect., 1969—, prof. medicine, prof. microbiology, 1974—; instr. dept. medicine and allergy U. Colo. Med. Sch., 1962-66; asst. chief dept. asthma-allergy Nat. Jewish Hosp., Denver, 1962-66; mem. presdl. task NHLI, 1973-74. Contbr. numerous articles to profl. publs. Lederle fellow, 1954. Mem. Nebr. Thoracic Soc. (pres. 1970). Office: Creighton U Allergic Disease Ctr Dept Medicine Omaha NE 68178

TOWNS, EDOLPHUS, congressman; b. Chadbourn, N.C., July 21, 1934; m. Gwendolyn Forbes, 1960; children: Darryl, Deidra. B.S., N.C. A & T State U., Greensboro, 1956; M.S.W., Adelphi U., Garden City, N.Y., 1973; PhD (hon.), N.C. A&T, Shaw U. Tchr. Medgar Evers Coll., Bklyn., N.Y.C. Pub. Schs.; dep. hosp. adminstr., 1965-71; dep. pres. Borough of Bklyn., 1976-82; mem. 98th-104th Congresses from 11th (now 10th) N.Y. dist., Washington, D.C., 1982—; ranking minority mem. subcom. Human Resources and Intergovtl. Affairs; mem. Commerce com. Mem. adv. council Boy Scouts Am.; active Salvation Army. Served with U.S. Army, 1956-58. Named to Acad. of Distinction Adelphi U. Mem. Kiwanis, Phi Beta Sigma. Democrat. Office: US Ho of Reps 2232 Rayburn Ho Office Bldg Washington DC 20515*

TOWNSEND, CHARLES EDWARD, Slavic languages educator; b. New Rochelle, N.Y., Sept. 29, 1932; s. Charles Edward and Lois (Fukushima) T.; m. Janet Linner, Sept. 18, 1957; children: Erica, Sylvia, Louise. B.A., Yale U., 1954; M.A., Harvard U., 1960, Ph.D., 1962. Instr., then asst. prof. Harvard U., 1962-66; mem. faculty Princeton U., 1966—, dir. Critical Langs. Program, 1968-70, prof. Slavic langs., 1971—, chmn. dept., 1970—. Author: Russian Word Formation, 1968, Continuing with Russian, 1970, Memoirs of Princess Natalja Borisovna Dolgorukaja, 1977, Czech Through Russian, 1981, A Description of Spoken Prague Czech, 1990, Russian Readings for Close Analysis, 1993. Served with U.S. Army, 1955-58. IREX grantee, 1968, 89; Fulbright grantee, 1954-55, 71, 83, 88; Ford Found. fellow, 1958-60; NDEA fellow, 1960-62. Mem. Am. Coun. Tchrs. Russian, Am. Assn. Tchrs. Slavic and East European Langs. (Disting. Contbn. to Profession award), N.Am. Assn. Tchrs. Czech (pres. 1992—), Am. Assn. Advancement Slavic Studies, Linguistic Soc. Czech Republic (hon.), Czechoslovak Soc. Arts and Scis., Phi Beta Kappa. Home: 145 Hickory Ct Princeton NJ 08540-3434 Office: Dept Slavic Langs Princeton U 028 E Pyne Princeton NJ 08542-3810

TOWNSEND, CHARLES H., publishing executive. Pub. Glamour, Conde Nast Pub. Inc., N.Y.C. Office: Glamour Conde Nast Publication Inc. 350 Madison Ave New York NY 10017*

TOWNSEND, CRAIG ARTHUR, chemistry educator; b. Chgo., Aug. 19, 1947; s. Herbert Ward and Thelma Alice (Hayskar) T.; m. S. Darlene Dance, Aug. 7, 1971; children: Reed Lincoln, Andrew Vernon. BA cum laude with honors in Chemistry, Williams Coll., 1969; PhD in Organic Chemistry, Yale U., 1974. Internat. exch. postdoctoral fellow Swiss Fed. Inst. Tech., Zurich, 1974-76; asst. prof. chemistry Johns Hopkins U., Balt., 1976-82, assoc. prof., 1982-85, prof., 1985—, chmn. dept., 1990-94, prof. dept. biology and McCollum-Pratt Inst., 1984—; prof. Thomas C. Jenkins dept. biophysics, 1989—; vis. prof. chemistry Harvard U., Cambridge, Mass., 1987; disting. lectr. U. Hawaii, 1988; lectr. Robert A. Welch Found., 1989; H. Martin Friedman lectr. Rutgers U., 1990; Boehringer-Ingelheim lectr. Yale U., 1992; also numerous others; cons. Lederle Labs., Pearl River, N.Y., 1984-94, ChekTsc Corp., Balt., 1993—, Upjohn Co., Kalamazoo, 1995—; mem. adv. panel Office Tech. Assessment, Washington, 1994-95; organizer, co-founder bio-organic chemistry Gordon Rsch. Conf., Kingston, R.I., 1992. Mem. editl. adv. bd. Jour. Organic Chemistry, 1987-91; contbr. over 80 articles to sci. jours. Recipient award in chemistry Stuart Pharms., 1986; named Md. Chemist of Yr., 1992; NIH postdoctoral fellow Yale U., 1970-73, rsch. fellow Alfred P. Sloan Found., 1982-86; Camille and Henry Dreyfus tchr.-scholar, 1983-88. Mem. Am. Chem. Soc. (Arthur C. Cope scholar award 1995), Royal Soc. Chemistry. Research in biosynthesis of natural products; stereochemical and mechanistic studies of enzyme action; application of spectroscopic techniques to the solution of biological problems; molecular biology of secondary metabolism; activation and mechanism of DNA cleavage by calicheamicin. Office: Johns Hopkins U 3400 N Charles St Baltimore MD 21218-2608

TOWNSEND, EARL CUNNINGHAM, JR., lawyer, writer; b. Indpls., Nov. 9, 1914; s. Earl Cunningham and Besse (Kuhn) T.; m. Emily Macnab, Apr. 3, 1947 (dec. Mar. 1988); children: Starr, Vicki M. (Mrs. Christopher Katterjohn), Julia E. (Mrs. Edward Goodrich Dunn Jr.), Earl Cunningham III, Clyde G. Student, De Pauw U., 1932-34; AB, U. Mich., 1936, JD, 1939. Bar: Ind. 1939, Mich. 1973, U.S. Supreme Ct. 1973, U.S. Ct. Appeals (4th,

5th, 6th, 7th cirs.), U.S. Dist. Ct. (no. and so. dists.) Ind., U.S. Dist. Ct. (ea. dist.) Va., U.S. Dist. Ct. (ea. dist.) Mich. Sr. ptnr. Townsend & Townsend, Indpls., 1941-64, Townsend, Hovde & Townsend, Indpls., 1964-84, Townsend & Townsend, Indpls., 1984—; dep. prosecutor, Marion County, Ind., 1942-44; radio-TV announcer WIRE, WFBM, WFBM-TV, Indpls., 1940-53, 1st TV announcer Indpls. 500 mile race, 1949, 50; Big Ten basketball referee, 1940-47; lectr. trial tactics U. Notre Dame, Ind. U., U. Mich., 1968-79; chmn. faculty seminar on personal injury trials Ind. U. Sch. Law, U. Notre Dame Sch. Law, Valparaiso Sch. Law, 1981; mem. Com. to Revise Ind. Supreme Ct. Pattern Jury Instrns., 1975-83; lectr. Trial Lawyers 30 Yrs. Inst., 1986; counsel atty. gen., 1988-92. Author: Birdstones of the North American Indian, 1959; editor: Am. Assn. Trial Lawyers Am. Jour., 1964-88; contbr. articles to legal and archeol. jours.; composer (waltz) Moon of Halloween. Trustee Cathedral High Sch., Indpls., Eiteljorg Mus. Am. Indian and Western Art, Cale J. Holder Scholarship Found. Ind. U. Law Sch.; life trustee, bd. dirs., mem. fin. and bldg. coms. Indpls. Mus. Art; life trustee Ind. State Mus.; founder, dir. Meridian St. Found.; mem. dean's coun. Ind. U.; founder, life fellow Roscoe Pound/Am. Trial Lawyers Found., Harvard U.; fellow Meth. Hosp. Found. Recipient Ind. Univ. Writers Conf. award, 1960, Hanson H. Anderson medal of honor Arsenal Tech. Schs., Indpls., 1971; named to Coun. Sagamores of Wabash, 1969; Rector scholar, 1934, Ind. Basketball Hall of Fame; hon. chief Black River-Swan Creek Saginaw-Chippewa Indian tribe. Fellow Internat. Acad. Trial Lawyers, Internat. Soc. Barristers, Ind. Bar Found. (life trustee, disting. fellow award); mem. ASCAP, ABA (com. on trial techniques 1964-76, aviation and space 1977—), Assn. Trial Lawyers Am. (v.p.), Ind. State Bar Assn. (Golden Career award 1989), Indpls. Bar Found. (disting. charter 1986), Ind. Trial Lawyers Assn. (pres. 1965, pres. Coll. Fellows 1984-90, Lifetime Achievement award 1992), Am. Bd. Trial Advs. (diplomate, pres. Ind. chpt. 1980-86), Am. Arbitration Assn. (nat. arbitrators panel), Am. Judicature Soc., State Bar of Mich. (Champion of Justice award 1989), Roscommon County Bar Assn., 34th Jud. Cir. Bar Assn., Bar Assn. 7th Fed. Cir. (bd. govs. 1966-68), Mich. Trial Lawyers Assn., Soc. Mayflower Descendants (gov. 1947-49), Ind. Hist. Soc., Marion County/Indpls. Hist. Soc. (bd. dirs.), Key Biscayne C. of C., U. Mich. Pres. Club, U. Mich. Victors Club (founder, charter mem.), Trowel and Brush Soc. (hon.), Genuine Indian Relic Soc. (founder, pres., chmn. frauds com.), The Players Club, Key Biscayne Yacht Club, Columbia Club, Indpls. Athletic Club, Masons (33 degree), Shriners, Delta Kappa Epsilon, Phi Kappa Phi. Republican. Methodist. Avocations: art, Indian relics. Home: 5008 N Meridian St Indianapolis IN 46208-2624

TOWNSEND, FRANK MARION, pathology educator; b. Stamford, Tex., Oct. 29, 1914; s. Frank M. and Beatrice (House) T.; m. Gerda Eberlein, 1940 (dec. div. 1944); 1 son, Frank M.; m. Ann Graf, Aug. 25, 1951; 1 son, Robert N. Student, San Antonio Coll., 1931-32, U. Tex., 1932-34; MD, Tulane U., 1938. Diplomate: Am. Bd. Pathology. Intern Polyclinic Hosp., N.Y.C., 1939-40; commd. 1st lt. M.C., U.S. Army, 1940, advanced through grades to lt. col., 1946; resident instr. pathology Washington U., 1945-47; trans. to USAF, 1949, advanced through grades to col., 1956; instr. pathology Coll. Medicine, U. Nebr., 1947-48; asso. pathologist Scott and White Clinic, Temple, Tex., 1948-49; asso. prof. pathology Med. Br. U. Tex., Galveston, 1949-59; flight surgeon USAF, 1950-65; dir. labs. USAF Hosp. (now Wilford Hall USAF Hosp.), Lackland AFB, Tex., 1950-54; cons. pathology Office of Surgeon Gen. Hdqrs. USAF, Washington, 1954-63, chief cons. group Office of Surgeon Gen. Hdqrs., 1954-55; dep. dir. Armed Forces Inst. Pathology, Washington, 1955-59; dir. Armed Forces Inst. Pathology, 1959-63; vice comdr. aerospace med. divsn. Air Force Systems Command, 1963-65; ret., 1965; practice medicine specializing in pathology San Antonio, 1965—; dir. labs. San Antonio State Chest Hosp.; consulting pathologist Tex. Dept. Health hosps., 1965-72; clin. prof. pathology U. Tex. Med. Sch., San Antonio, 1969-72; prof., chmn. dept. pathology Health Sci. Ctr. U. Tex. Med. Sch., 1972-86, emeritus chmn., prof., 1986—; cons. U. Tex. Cancer Ctr.-M.D. Anderson Hosp., 1966-80, NASA, 1967-75; mem. adv. bd. cancer WHO, 1958-75; mem. Armed Forces Epidemiology Bd., 1983-91; bd. govs. Armed Forces Inst. Pathology, 1984-95. Mem. editorial bd. Tex. Med. Jour., 1978-86; contbr. articles to med. jours. Mem. adv. coun. Civil War Centennial Commn., 1960-65; bd. dirs. Alamo Area Sci. Fair, 1967-73. Decorated D.S.M., Legion of Merit; recipient Founders medal Assn. Mil. Surgeons, 1961. Recipient Comdr.'s award Armed Forces Epidemiol. Bd., 1990; F.M. Townsend Chair of Pathology endowed in his honor by faculty of Dept. Pathology, U. Tex. Health Sci. Ctr., 1987. Fellow ACP, Coll. Am. Pathologists (edn. advisor on accreditation, commr. lab. accreditation South Ctrl. States region 1971-84), Am. Soc. Clin. Pathologists (Ward Burdick award 1983), Aerospace Med. Assn. (H.G. Mosely award 1962); mem. AMA, AAAS, Tex. Med. Assn., Internat. Acad. Aviation and Space Medicine, Tex. Soc. Pathologists (Caldwell award 1971), Am. Assn. Pathologists, Internat. Acad. Pathology, Acad. Clin. Lab. Physicians and Scientists, Soc. Med. Cons. to Armed Forces, Torch Club. Home: PO Box 77 Harwood TX 78632-0077 Office: U Tex Health Sci Ctr Dept Pathology 7703 Floyd Curl Dr San Antonio TX 78284-7700

TOWNSEND, GREG, professional football player; b. Los Angeles, Calif., Nov. 3, 1961. Student, Long Beach City Coll., Tex. Christian U. Defensive end L.A. Raiders, 1983—. Named defensive end The Sporting News NFL All-Pro team, 1990. Played in Pro Bowl, 1990, 91, in Super Bowl XVIII, 1983. Office: L A Raiders 332 Center St El Segundo CA 90245*

TOWNSEND, HAROLD GUYON, JR., publishing company executive; b. Chgo., Apr. 11, 1924; s. Harold Guyon and Anne Louise (Robb) T.; A.B., Cornell U., 1948; m. Margaret Jeanne Keller, July 28, 1951; children: Jessica, Julie, Harold Guyon III. Advt. salesman Chgo. Tribune, 1948-51; gen. mgr. Keller-Heartt Co., Clarendon Hills, Ill., 1951-62; pub. Santa Clara (Calif.) Jour., 1962-64; chmn. bd. dirs., pub. Dispatch-Tribune newspaper Townsend Communications, Inc., Kansas City, Mo., 1964—. Chmn., Suburban Newspaper Research Commn., 1974—; dir. Certified Audit Bur. of Circulation, 1968-72. del. Rep. Nat. Conv., 1960; chmn. Mission Hills Rep. Com., 1966-77; bd. dirs. Kansas City Jr. Achievement, 1966-68, Kansas City council Girl Scouts U.S.A., 1969-71, Kansas City council Boy Scouts Am., 1974, Kansas City chpt. ARC, 1973-79, Kansas City Starlight Theater, Clay County (Mo.) Indsl. Commn.; treas., trustee Park Coll., Parkville, Mo., 1970-78. Mem. adv. com. North Kansas City Hosp.; bd. dirs. Taxpayers Research of Mo., 1978—, Nelson Gallery Friends of Art, 1980-85. Served with inf. AUS, World War II. Mem. Kansas City Advt. and Sales Club, Kansas City Press Club, Suburban Press Found. (pres. 1969-71), Suburban Newspapers Am. (pres. 1976-77), Kansas City Printing Industries Assn. (pres., dir.), Printing Industries of Am. (pres. non-heatset web sect. 1980-82), North Kansas City C. of C. (dir., pres. 1964-70), Univ. Assocs. (treas. 1977-80), Sigma Delta Chi, Pi Delta Epsilon, Phi Kappa Psi. Clubs: University (treas. 1977); Indian Hills Country; Hinsdale (Ill.) Golf; Mission Valley Country, Field (Sarasota, Fla.). Home: 829 W 54th Ter Kansas City MO 64112-2335 Office: 7007 NE Parvin Rd Kansas City MO 64117-1532

TOWNSEND, JAMES WILLIS, computer scientist; b. Evansville, Ind., Sept. 9, 1936; s. James Franklin and Elma Elizabeth (Galloway) T.; m. Leona Jean York, Apr. 20, 1958; 1 child, Eric Wayne. BS in Arts and Scis., Ball State U., 1962; PhD, Iowa State U., 1970. Rsch. technologist Neuromuscular div. Mead Johnson, Evansville, 1957-60; chief instr. Zoology dept. Iowa State U., Ames, 1965-67; asst. prof. Ind. State U., Evansville, 1967-72; cons. electron microscopy Mead Johnson Rsch. Ctr., Evansville, 1971-73; mgr. neurosci. Neurosci. Lab., Kans. State U., Manhattan, 1974-76; head electron microscopy Nat. Ctr. for Toxicology Rsch., Jefferson, Ark., 1976-82; dir. electron microscopy U. Ark. Med. Sci., Little Rock, 1982-87; dir. computer ops. pathology dept. Univ. Hosp., Little Rock, 1987—; workshop presenter Am. Soc. Clin. Pathology, 1980-81, Nat. Soc. Histotechnologists, 1984-88. With USAF, 1957. Contbr. articles to profl. jours.; reviewer Scanning Electron Microscopy, 1977-78. Nat. Def. fellowship NDEA, Iowa State U., 1962-65; recipient Chgo. Tribune award Chicago Tribune, 1955. Mem. Sigma Xi, Sigma Zeta. Baptist. Avocations: genealogy, American Civil War. Home: 4 Breeds Hill Ct Little Rock AR 72211-2514 Office: Univ Ark for Med Sci Dept Pathology Slot 517 4301 W Markham St Little Rock AR 72205-7101

TOWNSEND, JANE KALTENBACH, zoologist, educator; b. Chgo., Dec. 21, 1922; B.S., Beloit Coll., 1944; M.A., U. Wis., 1946; Ph.D., U. Iowa, 1950; m. 1966. Asst. in zoology U. Wis., 1944-47; asst. in zoology U. Iowa, 1948-50; asst., project assoc. in pathology U. Wis., 1950-53; Am. Cancer Soc. research fellow Wenner-Grens Inst., Stockholm, 1953-56; asst. prof. zoology

Northwestern U., 1956-58; asst. prof. to assoc. prof. zoology Mt. Holyoke Coll., South Hadley, Mass., 1958-70, prof., 1970-93, chmn. biol. scis., 1980-86, prof. emeritus 1993—. Fellow AAAS (sec. sect. biol. sci. 1974-78); mem. Am. Assn. Anatomists, Am. Inst. Biol. Scis., Am. Soc. Zoologists, Soc. Experimental Biology and Medicine, Soc. Devel. Biology, Corp. of Marine Biol. Lab., Sigma Xi, Phi Beta Kappa. Office: Mount Holyoke Coll Dept Biology South Hadley MA 01075

TOWNSEND, JEFFREY, production designer. Prodn. designer: (films) Baby, It's You, 1983, Old Enough, 1984, Reckless, 1984, After Hours, 1985, Maid to Order, 1987, The Fabulous Baker Boys, 1989, Straight Talk, 1993, Sleepless in Seattle, 1993. Office: care Lawrence Mirisch The Mirisch Agency 10100 Santa Monica Blvd Ste 700 Los Angeles CA 90067*

TOWNSEND, JOHN MICHAEL, lawyer; b. West Point, N.Y., Mar. 21, 1947; s. John D. and Vera (Nachman) T.; m. Frances M. Fragos, Oct. 8, 1994. BA, Yale U., 1968, JD, 1971. Bar: N.Y. 1972, U.S. Dist. Ct. (so. and ea. dists.) N.Y. 1975, U.S. Ct. Appeals (2nd cir.) 1975, U.S. Supreme Ct. 1975, U.S. Ct. Appeals (8th cir.) 1982, U.S. Ct. Appeals (7th and 10th cirs.) 1986, D.C. 1990, U.S. Dist. Ct. D.C. 1990, U.S. Ct. Appeals (D.C. cir.) 1990, U.S. Ct. Appeals (4th cir.) 1991. Assoc. Hughes Hubbard & Reed, N.Y.C., 1971-73, 1975-80, ptnr., 1980; assoc. Hughes Hubbard & Reed, Paris, 1973-74; arbitrator U.S. Dist. Ct. (ea. dist.) N.Y.; trustee U.S. Coun. Internat. Bus. 1st It. USAR, 1971-75. Mem. ABA, Internat. Bar Assn., Assn. of Bar of City of N.Y., N.Y. Lawyers for Pub. Interest, D.C. Bar Assn., Union Internat. des Advs., Univ. Club (Washington), Am. Arbitration Assn. (bd. dirs.), Yale Club (N.Y.C.). Democrat. Episcopalian. Office: Hughes Hubbard & Reed 1300 I St NW Washington DC 20005-3306

TOWNSEND, JOHN WILLIAM, JR., physicist, retired federal aerospace agency executive; b. Washington, Mar. 19, 1924; s. John William and Elenore (Eby) T.; m. Mary Irene Lewis, Feb. 7, 1948; children: Bruce Alan, Nancy Dewitt, John William III, Megan Lewis. BA, Williams Coll., 1947, MA, 1949, ScD, 1961. With Naval Research Lab., 1949-55, br. head, 1955-58; with NASA, 1958-68, dep. dir. Goddard Space Flight Ctr., 1965-68; dep. adminstrn. Environmental Scis. Services Adminstrn., 1968-70; asso. adminstrn. Nat. Oceanic and Atmospheric Adminstrn., 1970-77; pres. Fairchild Space and Electronics Co., 1977-82; v.p. Fairchild Industries, 1979-85; pres. Fairchild Space Co., 1983-85; sr. v.p. Fairchild Industries 1985-87; chmn. bd. Am. Satellite Co., 1985, sr. v.p., exec. aerospace group, 1987, exec. v.p., 1987; dir. NASA Goddard Space Flight Ctr., 1987-90; ret., 1990; mem. U.S. Rocket, Satellite Rsch. Panel, 1950-60; chmn. space applications bd. NRC, 1985-87; bd. dirs., trustee Telos Corp., 1990-92; mem. adv. bd. Loral Corp., 1990-92; mem. coms. NRC, 1990—; bd. dirs CTA, Inc. Authored numerous papers, reports in field. Pres. town council, Forest Heights, Md., 1951-55. Served with USAAF, 1943-46. Recipient Profl. Achievement award Engrs. and Architects Day, 1957; Meritorious Civilian Service award Navy Dept., 1957; Outstanding Leadership medal NASA, 1962; Distinguished Service medal, 1971, 90; recipient Arthur S. Fleming award Fed. Govt., 1963. Fellow AIAA, AAAS, Am. Meteorol. Soc.; mem. NAE (com. 1990—), Am. Phys. Soc., Am. Geophys. Union. (fin. com. 1991—), Internat. Astronautical Fedn. (mem., trustee internat., acad. astronautics), Sigma Xi. Home: 15810 Comus Rd Clarksburg MD 20871-9169

TOWNSEND, KATHLEEN KENNEDY, state official; m. David Townsend; children:Meaghan, Meave, Kate, Kerry. BA cum laude, Harvard U.; JD, U. N.Mex. Former program dir. U.S. Peace Corps; former dep. asst. atty. gen. U.S. Dept. Justice, Washington; lt. gov. State of Md., 1994—; tchr. U. Md., Balt. County, Essex. C.C., Dundalk C.C., U. Pa.; past exec. dir. Md. Student Svcs. Alliance. Editor U. N.Mex. Law Rev. Founder Robert F. Kennedy Human Rights award. Recipient 4 hon. degrees. Office: Lt Govs Office State House 100 State Circle Annapolis MD 21401

TOWNSEND, KENNETH ROSS, priest; b. Holly Grove, Ala., Oct. 31, 1927; s. James Ernest and Mary H. (Jordan) T.; m. Irene Fogleman, Mar. 18, 1951; children: Marietta, Martha, Kenneth Ross, Elizabeth. AB, Birmingham South Coll., 1956; postgrad., Union Theol. Sem., 1960-63; MDiv, Va. Theol. Sem., 1964. Ordained priest Episcopal Ch., 1965. Pastor meth. chs. N.C. and Va. Confs., 1954-63; priest Bath Priest Parish, Dinwiddie, Va., 1964-69, St. Paul's Ch., Vanceboro, N.C., 1969—; lectr. philosophy Richard Bland Coll. of Coll. William and Mary, Williamsburg, Va., 1966-68; del. to synod Province IV, 1973; mem. liturgical com. Episcopal Diocese of East Carolina, Wilmington, N.C., 1971-82, mem. prison commn., 1984. Mem. Delta Sigma Phi. Address: 2521 Paxton St Lake Ridge Woodbridge VA 22192 *Yearning for self fulfillment in a better world is the 'mother of the will' to be and to accomplish. By this will we define ourselves. This will identifies our goals in work and relationships. Such a self concept informs our minds as to what is right and correct. The yearning, the will, the goals and accomplishment are thinkable and obtainable. The world awaits our resolve.*

TOWNSEND, LEROY B., chemistry educator, university administrator, researcher; b. Lubbock, Tex., Dec. 20, 1933; s. L.B. and Ocie Mae (McBride) T.; m. Sammy Beames, Sept. 15, 1953; children: Lisa Loree, LeRoy Byron. BA in Chemistry and Math., N.Mex. Highlands U.-Las Vegas, 1955, MS, 1957; PhD, Ariz. State U.-Tempe, 1965. Assoc. prof. medicinal chemistry U. Utah, Salt Lake City, 1971-75, prof., 1975-78, adj. prof. chemistry, 1975-78; prof. medicinal chemistry U. Mich., Ann Arbor, 1979—, Albert B. Prescott prof. medicinal chemistry, 1985—, prof. chemistry, 1979—, chmn., 1979—, dir. interdept. grad. program in medicinal chemistry, 1979—, chmn. drug discovery and devel. program Comprehensive Cancer Ctr.; mem. cancer rsch. com. Nat. Cancer Inst., 1979—, com. on devel. treatments for rare genetic disease dept. human genetics; mem. nat. adv. com. on AIDS to NIAID; mem. steering com. on chemotherapy of malaria WHO; mem. study sect. on chemotherapy of cancer Nat. Am. Cancer Soc.; mem. Am. Cancer Soc. study sect. drug devel., hematology and pathology; various ad hoc site visit teams Nat. Cancer Inst.; chmn. purines and pyrimidines Gordon Rsch. Conf.; participant symposia in field; lectr. various nat. and internat. sci. congresses. Contbr. articles to profl. jours.; assoc. editor Internat. Jour. Heterocyclic Chemistry; mem. editorial bd. Jour. Carbohydrates, Nucleosides, Nucleotides, Jour. Nucleosides and Nucleotides, Jour. Chinese Pharm. Soc. Recipient Smissman-Bristol Myers-Squibb award in medicinal chemistry; various grants; named Disting. prof. MAGB. Mem. Am. Chem. soc. (chmn., counsilor medicinal chemistry div.), Internat. Soc. Heterocyclic Chemistry (treas., pres. 1973-79), Nat. Am. Chem. Soc. (chmn. divsn. of medicinal chemistry). Home: 3317 E Dobson Pl Ann Arbor MI 48105-2583 Office: U Mich Coll Pharmacy Coll Pharmacy 4563 Pharmacy CC Little Bldg Ann Arbor MI 48109

TOWNSEND, M. WILBUR, manufacturing company executive; b. Oyster Bay, N.Y., Jan. 17, 1912; s. Maurice West and Alberta (Say) T.; m. Barbara White Hayden, Oct. 1, 1938; children—Barrett Say, Philip Hayden. A.B., Wesleyan U., Middletown, Conn., 1934. With Handy & Harman, N.Y.C., 1946—; exec. v.p. Handy & Harman, 1961-64, pres., 1964-79, chmn. bd., 1967-87, chmn. emeritus, cons., 1988—; past pres. 24 Karat Club, N.Y.C. Mem. Community Ch. Club. Office: Handy & Harman 250 Park Ave New York NY 10177-0074

TOWNSEND, MARJORIE RHODES, aerospace engineer, business executive; b. Washington, Mar. 12, 1930; d. Lewis Boling and Marjorie Olive (Trees) Rhodes; m. Charles Eby Townsend, June 7, 1948; children: Charles Eby Jr., Lewis Rhodes, John Cunningham, Richard Leo. BEE, George Washington U., 1951. Electronic scientist Naval Rsch. Lab., Washington, 1951-59; rsch. engr. to sect. head Goddard Space Flight Ctr.-NASA, Greenbelt, Md., 1959-65, tech. asst. to chief systems divsn., 1965-66, project mgr. small astronomy satellites, 1966-75, project mgr. applications explorer missions, 1975-76, mgr. preliminary systems design group, 1976-80; aerospace and electronics cons. Washington, 1980-83; v.p. systems devel. Space Am., 1983-84; aerospace cons. Washington, 1984-90; dir. space systems engring. BDM Internat., Inc., Washington, 1990-91; dir. space applications BDM ESC, Washington, 1991-92; sr. prin. staff mem. BDM Fed., Inc., Washington, 1992-93; areospace cons., Washington, 1993—. Patentee digital telemetry system. Decorated Knight Italian Republic Order, 1972; recipient Fed. Women's award, 1973, EUR award for Culture, 1974, Engr. Alumni Achievement award George Washington U., 1975, Gen. Alumni Achievement award George Washington U., 1976, Exceptional Svc. medal NASA,

1971, Outstanding Leadership medal NASA, 1980, Eye-of-the-Needle award NASA, 1991. Fellow IEEE (chmn. Washington sect. 1974-75), AIAA (chmn. nat. capitol sect. 1985), Washington Acad. Sci. (pres. 1980-81); mem. AAAS (coun. del. 1985-88), Internat. Acad. Astronautics, Am. Geophys. Union, Soc. Women Engrs., DAR, Daus. Colonial Wars, Mensa, Sigma Kappa. Republican. Episcopalian. Home and Office: 3529 Tilden St NW Washington DC 20008-3122

TOWNSEND, MERTON LEROY, metal products executive; b. Omaha, July 3, 1934; s. Merton Clayton and Dorothy Fern (Blinn) T.; m. Helen Joyce Holcombe, July 11, 1957; children: Steven Lee, Lance Clayton. BSME, Iowa State U., 1956; MSME, U. So. Calif., 1964, MS in Aero. Engring., 1965. Prodn. supr. Proctor & Gamble, Dallas, 1956-57; commd. 2d lt. U.S. Army, 1956, advanced through grades to col.; 1978; various assignments, 1957-80, ret., 1980; program mgr. Aerojet Gen., Sacramento, 1980-82, dir. programs, 1982-84; v.p., gen. mgr. Chamberlain Mfg., Waterloo, Iowa, 1984-88; v.p. corp. devel. Chamberlain Mfg., Elmhurst, Ill., 1989, group v.p., 1990, pres., 1991—; cons. AVSER, Sacramento, 1984. Author: Modern Analytical Methods, 1985. Chmn. Airport Commn., Waterloo, Iowa, 1987-89. Decorated Legion of Merit, Bronze Starr, Air medal, Meritorious Svc. medal. Mem. Assn. U.S. Army (exec. com.), Am. Def. Preparedness Assn., River Forest Country Club. Avocations: flying, auto restoration, golf. Office: Chamberlain Mfg Corp 845 N Larch Ave Elmhurst IL 60126-1196

TOWNSEND, MILES AVERILL, aerospace and mechanical engineering educator; b. Buffalo, N.Y., Apr. 16, 1935; s. Francis Devere and Sylvia (Wolpa) T.; children: Kathleen Townsend Hastings, Melissa, Stephen, Joel, Philip. BA, Stanford U., 1955; BS MechE, U. Mich., 1958; advanced cert., U. Ill., 1963, MS in Theoretical and Applied Mechanics, 1967; PhD, U. Wis., 1971. Registered profl. engr., Ill., Wis., Tenn., Ont. Project engr. Sundstrand, Rockford, Ill., 1959-63, Twin Disc Inc., Rockford, 1963-65, 67-68; sr. engr. Westinghouse Electric Corp., Sunnyvale, Calif., 1965-67; instr., fellow U. Wis., Madison, 1968-71; assoc. prof. U. Toronto, Ont., Can., 1971-74; prof. mech. engring. Vanderbilt U., Nashville, 1974-81; Wilson prof. mech. and aerospace engring. U. Va., Charlottesville, 1982—, chmn. dept., 1982-91; prof. mech. engring. Endev Ltd., Can. and U.S., 1972—; cons. in field. Contbr. numerous articles to profl. jours.; 7 patents in field. Recipient numerous research grants and contracts. Fellow ASME (mem. coun. on engring., productivity com., tech. editor Jour. Mech. Design); mem. AAAS, N.Y. Acad. Scis., Sigma Xi, Phi Kappa Phi, Pi Tau Sigma. Avocations: running, reading, music. Home: 221 Harvest Dr Charlottesville VA 22903-4850 Office: U Va Dept Mech and Aerospace Engring Thornton Hall Charlottesville VA 22903-2442

TOWNSEND, NANCY CHRISTINE, secondary education educator; b. Johnson City, Tenn., Mar. 28, 1951; d. Dewey Ford and Vivian Louise (Logan) Parks; m. Worth B. Townsend, Jr., Feb. 5, 1979; stepchildren: Worth B. Townsend, III,Steven C. Townsend, Mark A. Townsend, Norman R. Townsend. BA cum laude, Francis Marion Coll., 1984, MEd, 1990. Cert. secondary tchr. English tchr. Wilson H.S., Florence, S.C., 1984—; guest lectr. So. Bell and Sch. Edn. Francis Marion Coll., Florence, 1991; mem. S.C. Educator Recruitment Task Force, 1990-94; chairperson Tchr.'s Forum Steering Com., 1990-92; rep. to policy bd. dirs. S.C. Ctr. for Tchr. Recruitment, 1990-94; mem. policy bd. dirs. S.C. Ctr. for Advancement Tchg. and Sch. Leadership, 1990—; mem. curriculum and English transition teams S.C. Supt. Edn., 1990-93. Recipient State Tchr. of Yr. award State of S.C., 1991. Mem. NEA, Nat. Coun. Tchrs. English, S.C. Coun. Tchrs. English, S.C. Edn. Assn., Phi Kappa Phi, Sigma Tau Delta (charter v.p. Nu Rho chpt.). Office: Wilson High Sch 1411 E Old Marion Hwy Florence SC 29506-7420

TOWNSEND, PHILIP W., JR., library director; b. Phila., Aug. 14, 1949; s. Philip Walsh and Eleanor (Clay) T.; m. Mary Rasmussen, Aug., 1973; children: Grace, Philip, Erica. BA, U. Utah, 1973; MSLS, Villanova U., 1988. Libr. dir. Valley Forge Mil. Jr. Coll., Wayne, Pa., 1985—. Capt. U.S. Army Res., 1973-83. Avocations: pipe major Washington Meml. Pipe Band. Office: Valley Forge Mil Jr Coll Office of Libr 1001 Eagle Rd Wayne PA 19087-3694

TOWNSEND, P(RESTON) COLEMAN, agricultural business executive; b. Salisbury, Md., Dec. 27, 1945; s. Preston Coleman and Rachel (Morris) T.; m. Susan Marshall, Dec. 8, 1968. B.S., U. Del., 1969. Chmn., CEO Townsends, Inc., Millsboro, Del., 1969—. Bd. visitors Del. State Coll. Mem. Nat. Broiler Council (bd. dirs.). Republican. Office: Townsends Inc Route 24 PO Box 468 Millsboro DE 19966

TOWNSEND, ROBERT, film director; b. Chgo., Feb. 6, 1957; s. Robert and Shirley (Jenkins) T. Actor: (stage) Take It From the Top, 1979, Bones, 1980, (films) Cooley High, 1974, Willie and Phil, 1980, Streets of Fire, 1983, A Soldier's Story, 1983, American Flyers, 1984, Odd Jobs, 1984, Ratboy, 1985, The Mighty Quinn, 1989, That's Adequate, 1990, (t.v. movies) Women At West Point, 1979, Senior Trip!, 1981, In Love With an Older Woman, 1982; actor, prod., dir.- co-writer: (films) Hollywood Shuffle, 1987, The Five Heartbeats, 1990, The Meteor Man, 1993; dir.: (films) Eddie Murphy Raw, 1987; stand-up comedian: (t.v. spls.) Robert Townsend and His Partners in Crime, Take No Prisoners, Robert Townsend and His Partners in Crime II.TV series: Townsend Television, 1992, The Parent 'Hood, 1995. Office: Tinsel Townsend 8033 W Sunset Blvd Ste 890 Los Angeles CA 90046-2427 also: CAA 9830 Wilshire Blvd Beverly Hills CA 90212-1804*

TOWNSEND, ROBERT J., lawyer; b. Charlotte, Mich., Nov. 11, 1938; s. Robert Wright and Rhea Lucille (Jennings) T.; m. Thea E. Kolb, Aug. 1, 1964; children: Melissa, Bradley. BA, Mich. State U., 1960; LLD, Harvard U., 1963. Bar: Ohio 1964, U.S. Dist. Ct. (so. dist.) Ohio 1964, U.S. Ct. Appeals (6th cir.) 1971, U.S. Supreme Ct. 1992. Assoc. Taft, Shettinus & Hollister, Cin., 1963-72, ptnr., 1972—; dir. Employers Resource Assn., Cin., 1989—. Dir. Jobs for Cin. Grads., 1990—. With U.S. Army, 1963-64, 68-69. Office: 1800 Star Bank Ctr 425 Walnut St Cincinnati OH 45202-3957

TOWNSEND, SUSAN ELAINE, social service institute administrator, hostage survival consultant; b. Phila., Sept. 5, 1946; d. William Harrison and Eleanor Irene (Fox) Rogers; m. John Holt Townsend, May 1, 1976. BS in Secondary Edn., West Chester State U., 1968; MBA, Nat. U., 1978; PhD in Human Behavior, La Jolla U., 1984. Biology tchr. Methacton Sch. Dist., Fairview Village, Pa., 1968-70; bus. mgr., analyst profl. La Jolla Research Corp., San Diego, 1977-79; pastoral asst. Christ Ctr. Bible Therapy, San Diego, 1980-82, also bd. dirs.; v.p., pub. relations World Outreach Ctr. of Faith, San Diego, 1981-82, also bd. dirs.; owner, pres., cons. Townsend Research Inst., San Diego, 1983-89; teaching assoc. La Jolla U. Continuing Edn., 1985-86, administr., assoc. registrar, adj. faculty, 1990. Author: Hostage Survival-Resisting the Dynamics of Captivity, 1983; contbr. articles to profl. jours. Instr. USN Advanced Survival Evasion Resistance Escape Sch., 1986-89; security officer Shield Security, San Diego, 1991-92; bd. dirs. Christ Fellowship Ch. of San Diego, 1987—, music dir., 1992—; religious vol. Met. Correctional Ctr., San Diego, 1983-89, San Diego County Jail Ministries, 1978—, scheduling coord., 1993—. Served to compdt. USN, 1970-76, USNR, 1976-93. Mem. Naval Res. Assn. (life), Res. Officers Assn. (Outstanding Jr. Officer of Yr. Calif. chpt. 1982), Navy League U.S. (life), West Chester U. Alumni Assn., Nat. U. Alumni Assn. (life), La Jolla U. Alumni Assn., Gen. Fedn. Women's Clubs (pres. Peninsula Woman's Club 1983-85, pres. Peninsula Woman's Club 1994-96, pres. Parliamentary law club 1984-86, Past Pres.' Assn.), Calif. Fedn. Women's Clubs (v.p.-at-large San Diego dist. 25 1982-84, recording sec. 1994—).

TOWNSEND, TERRY, publishing executive; b. Camden, N.J., Dec. 14, 1920; d. Anthony and Rose DeMarco; BA, Duke U., 1942; LHD (hon.) Dowling Coll., 1991; m. Paul Brorstrom Townsend, Dec. 8, 1961; 1 son, Kim. Pub. rels. dir. North Shore Univ. Hosp., Manhasset, N.Y., 1955-68; pres. Theatre Soc. I., 1968-70; pres. Townsend Comm. Bur., Ronkonkoma, N.Y., 1970—, L.I. Communicating Service, Ronkonkoma, 1977—; columnist, writer L.I./Bus., Ronkonkoma, 1970-75; pub. L.I. Bus. News, 1978—; v.p. Parr Meadows Racetrack, Yaphank, N.Y., 1977. Assoc. trustee North Shore U. Hosp., 1968—; bd. govs. Adelphi U. Friends Fin. Edn., 1978-85; chmn. ann. archtl. awards competition N.Y. Inst. Tech., 1970-83; trustee, vice chair Dowling Coll., 1994—, trustee L.I. Fine Arts Mus., 1984-

85; pub. broadcasting Sta. WLIW TV, Garden City, L.I., N.Y., 1990-93; bd. dirs. Family Svc. Assn. Nassau County, 1982-92; dinner chmn. L.I. 400 Ball, 1987; vice chmn. bd. trustees Dowling Coll., 1994—; trustee Mus. at Stony Brook, 1994—. Recipient Media award 110 Center Bus. and Profl. Women, 1977, Enterprise award Friends of Fin. Edn., 1981, L.I. Loves Bus. Showcase Salute, 1982, Community Svc. award N.Y. Diabetes Assn., 1983, Disting. Long Islander in Communications award L.I. United Epilepsy Assn., 1984, Spl. award Dowling Coll. Spring Tribute, 1989, Disting. Svc. award Episcopal Health Svcs., 1989, Disting. Citizen award Dowling Coll., 1991, Gilbert Tilles award Nat. Assn. Fundraising Execs., 1994; named First Lady of L.I., L.I. Public Relations Assn., 1973, L.I. Woman of Yr. L.I. Assn. Action Com., 1989. Office: LI Bus News 2150 Smithtown Ave Ronkonkoma NY 11779-7348

TOWNSEND, THOMAS PERKINS, former mining company executive; b. Bryn Mawr, Pa., Mar. 28, 1917; s. John and Mildred (Perkins) T.; m. Laura M. Trench, Sept. 14, 1940; children: Joanne Townsend Taber, Hunter, Elizabeth Townsend Ballinger. B.S. in Econs., U. Pa., 1939; postgrad., Harvard U., 1944. C.P.A., Pa. Sr. acct. Price Waterhouse & Co., 1945-48; treas., dir. Fox Products Co., 1948-53, Wilcolator Co., 1953-55; staff acct. Tex. Gulf Sulphur Co., N.Y.C., 1955-57; asst. treas. Tex. Gulf Sulphur Co., 1958-61, v.p., controller, 1961-62, v.p., treas., 1962-64, v.p. internat. ops., 1964-68; exec. v.p. Bosco Middle East Oil Corp., Greenwich, Conn., 1968-69; pres. Conn. Real Estate Corp., Greenwich, 1969-70, also bd. dirs., 1969—; v.p. finance Rosaria Resources Corp., N.Y.C., 1970-81; treas. Unidyne Corp., 1984-85; cons. AMAX, Inc., 1981-85; bd. dirs. Thermal Exploration Corp., Carlin Gold Co. Chmn. nat. com. for employment youth Nat. Child Labor Com., 1968-70; trustee, pres. South Kent Sch.; trustee Soc. to Advance Retarded, Norwalk, Conn.; bd. dirs. United Way of Tri-State, Denison Pequotsegos Nature Ctr.; mem. New Canaan Bd. Fin., Conn., 1985-89 . Served to lt. (s.g.) Supply Corps, USNR, World War II. Mem. Am. Inst. Accts., N.Y. State Soc. CPAs, Fin. Execs. Inst., Mason's Island Yacht Club, Off Soundings Club. Episcopalian (treas., vestryman 1960-72, 87-95). Home: 9 Kensington Ct Mystic CT 06355-3116 *The principal goal in my life has been to be a straight dealer, to be honest in thought, word and deed. It has paid off for me. Crooked dealing may make more money, but it does not lead to a happier life. One must live by his God.*

TOWNSEND, WARDELL C., JR., federal agency administrator; b. Balt., Oct. 16, 1952; s. Wardell Clinton Sr. and Toyoko Yonamine; m. Diane Martin, 1979; 4 children. BS in Psychology and Social Welfare, Western Carolina U., 1975; MSW with distinction, W.Va. U., 1977. Project dir. Congressman Jamie Clarke, Washington, 1983-85, Congressman Doug Applegate, Washington, 1985-87; from legis. dir. to adminstrv. asst./chief of staff Congressman Mike Espy, Washington, 1987-93; sr. adv. Presdl. Transition Team, Washington, 1992-93; asst. sec. adminstrn. USDA, Washington, 1993—. Former group counselor Boys Club, Asheville, N.C.; former health educator, outreach coord. Assn. Sickle Cell Disease, Charlotte, N.C.; former planning and devel. mgr. Human Resource Devel. Found., Morgantown, W.Va.; former dir. Community Devel. Dept., Henderson County, N.C.; former bus. mgr. Cherokee Minority Bus. Devel. Ctr., Asheville, N.C.; bd. dirs. Shepherd's Table, Inc., 1985-88, chmn. pub. rels. com., 1986-87; sr. warden ministry Ascension Episc. Ch., Silver Spring, Md., 1986-90, vestry mem., treas., chmn. fin. com., chmn. rector search com.; mem. diocesan investment com. Episc. Diocese Washington, 1991—; active YMCA, Silver Spring, 1988—. Mem. NASW, Adminstrv. Assts. Assn. (life. pres. 1991, 92, v.p. 1992), Coun. African-Am. Admistrv. Assts., Acad. Cert. Social Workers, Global Leders for the Soutn, House Adminstrv. Assts. Alumni Assn. (bd. dirs. 1994). Office: Dept Agriculture Office Asst Sec Administrn 14th & Independence Ave SW Washington DC 20250-0002

TOWNSHEND, PETER, musician, composer, singer; b. London, England, May 19, 1945. Co-founder (with Keith Moon, Roger Daltry, John Entwhistle), guitarist, composer music and lyrics for musical group, The Who (originally called The High Numbers, The Detours), 1964-82; composer: (rock operas) Tommy, 1969 (Tony Award, Best Score - Broadway prodn., 1993), Quadrophenia, 1973, (other albums) The Who Sings My Generation, 1965, Happy Jack, 1966, The Who Sell Out, 1967, Magic Bus: The Who on Tour (U.S. only), Live At Leeds, 1970, Who's Next, 1971, The Who By Numbers, 1975, Who Are You, 1978, Face Dances, 1981, It's Hard, 1982, Join Together, 1990; compositions including Behind Blue Eyes, I'm Free, Who Are You, My Generation, The Kids Are Alright, Bargain, Pure and Easy, Won't Get Fooled Again, Pinball Wizard, We're Not Gonna Take It, Dreaming From the Waist, Emminence Front, Nothing Is Everything (Let's See Action), Slit Skirts, Give Blood, Let My Love Open the Door, Cats in the Cupboard, English Boy; producer: films The Kids Are Alright, 1979, Quadrophenia, 1979, (with The Who) Meaty, Beaty, Big and Bouncy, 1971, Odds and Sods, 1974, The Kids Are Alright, 1979, Hooligans, 1981, Who's Missing, 1986, Two's Missing, 1987, Who's Better Who's Best, 1989, Who's Missing. 1986; solo albums include Who Came First, 1972, (with Ronnie Lane) Rough Mix, 1977, Secret Policeman's Ball, 1980, Empty Glass, 1980, All the Best Cowboys Have Chinese Eyes, 1982, Scoop, 1983, White City, 1985, Another Scoop, 1986, Deep End Live, 1987, The Iron Man, 1989, Psychoderelict, 1993, Psychoderelict, 1993; rec. 13 albums with The Who; author (short stories) Horse's Neck, 1985; musical dir. (film and soundtrack) Tommy, 1975 (Oscar award nomination 1975); Broadway musical The Who's Tommy (Tony award., best original score), 1993. Office: care Entertainment Corp Am 99 Park 16th Ave New York NY 10016*

TOY, ARTHUR DOCK FON, chemist; b. Canton, China, Sept. 13, 1915; came to U.S., 1927, naturalized, 1952; s. Yam Hong and Suei Hao (Loui) T.; m. Hui-I Liang, Sept. 5, 1942; children: Larry, Alan, Howard. Student, Joliet Jr. Coll., 1935-37; B.S., U. Ill., 1939, M.S., 1940, Ph.D. (Sigma Xi fellow, U. Ill. fellow), 1942. Research chemist Victor Chem. Works, Chicago Heights, Ill., 1942-52; dir. organic research Victor Chem. Works, 1952-59, asso. dir. research, 1959-63, dir. research, 1963-65; vis. scientist Cambridge U., Eng., 1965-66; sr. scientist Stauffer Chem. Co., Westport, Conn., 1965-68; mgr. splys. dept. Stauffer Chem. Co., 1968-72, chief scientist, 1972-74; dir. Eastern Research Ctr., 1975-78, dir. research, 1979-80; cons. Stamford, Conn., 1980—; cons. dept. chemistry Manhattan Coll., 1982-85; internat. sci. bd. Internat. Conf. Phosphorus Chemistry, 1974-80. Author: Phosphorus Chemistry in Everyday Living, 1976, 2d edit. (with Edward N. Walsh), 1987, The Chemistry of Phosphorus, 1975; contbr. articles to sci. jours.; holder 83 patents in field; researcher on organic phosphorus compounds for plastic applications, on allyl aryl-phosphonate flame resistant plastics, on economic processes for synthesis of organic phosphorus intermediates, on phosphorus insecticides, on aquo ammono phosphoric acids, on organic reaction mechanisms, and on new reactions leading to the formation of carbon to phosphorus bonds. Recipient Disting. Alumnus award Joliet Jr. Coll., 1985, Eli Whitney award Conn. Patent Law Assn., 1988; honoree of Symposium Phosphorus Chemistry in Am., 1991, at 202d Am. Chem. Soc. nat. meeting. Fellow AAAS; mem. Am. Chem. Soc. (chmn. N.Y. chpt. 1974-76, councilor 1973-87, Outstanding Svc. award 1978), Royal Soc. Chemistry (London), Westchester Chem. Soc. (chmn. 1970-71), Conn. Acad. Sci. and Engring., Chinese-Am. Chem. Soc., Phi Beta Kappa, Sigma Xi. Home: 14 Katydid Ln Stamford CT 06903-4813

TOY, CHARLES DAVID, lawyer; b. N.Y.C., June 29, 1955; s. Frank H.F. and Louise S.K. (Louie) T.; m. Sandra Lynn Youla, Mar. 10, 1984. BA cum laude, Harvard U., 1977, JD, 1980. Bar: N.Y. 1981. Assoc. Milbank, Tweed, Hadley & McCloy, N.Y.C., 1980-84; assoc. Kaye, Scholer, Fierman, Hays & Handler, Hong Kong, 1984-88, ptnr., 1989-91; ptnr. Kaye, Scholer, Fierman, Hays & Handler, N.Y.C., 1991-93; v.p., gen. counsel Overseas Pvt. Investment Corp., Washington, 1993—; spkr. seminars Bus. Internat., 1985, Asia Conf., 1988, Korea Fgn. Trade Assn., 1989, 90, World Trade Inst., 1992, U. Pa., 1993, 94, Washington Internat. Trade Assn., 1993, Am. Conf. Inst., 1994. Am. Soc. Internat. Law, 1994. ABA, 1994, 95, Small Bus. Exporters Assn., 1994. Contbg. editor Taxes and Investment in Asia and the Pacific, 1985, Tax News Svc., 1986—, Bull. for Internat. Fiscal Documentation, 1986—; bd. editors Strategic Alliance Alert, 1994—. Mem. ABA, Am. Arbitration Assn., N.Y. State Bar Assn., Assn. Bar City of N.Y., Nat. Asian Pacific Am. Bar Assn., Asian Am. Bar Assn. N.Y., Asia Soc., Hong Kong Assn. N.Y., Harvard Law Sch. Assn., Harvard Club (N.Y.C and Washington), Am. Club (Hong Kong), Ladies Recreation Club (Hong Kong), Phi Beta Kappa. Democrat. Roman Catholic. Office: Internat Devel Cooperation Agy Insurance Dept 1100 New York Ave NW Washington DC 20527-0001

TOYER, RICHARD HENRY, accountant; b. Snohomish, Wash., Aug. 6, 1944; s. Henry James Toyer and Bertha Maud (Darrow) Gilmore; m. Jean Ann Moore, July 1, 1966; 1 child, David K. BS in Acctg., Cen. Wash. U., 1973. CPA. Staff acct. Moss, Adams and Co., Everett, Wash., 1973-74; sr. staff acct., 1975-77; prin. Toyer and Assocs., CPAs Inc., PS, Everett, Wash., 1977—. Mayor City of Lake Stevens, Wash., 1983-91, city councilman, 1977-83; state treas. Wash. Jaycees, 1975-76; pres. Snohomish Jaycees, 1974-75; mem. Snohomish County Estate Planning Coun.; chmn. Snohomish County Subregional Coun., 1981-82; exec. bd. Puget Sound regional coun., 1981-83; chmn. City of Everett Navy Review Task Force, 1987-88, Snohomish County HUD policy adv. bd., 1982-91; chmn. Snohomish County Cities and Towns, 1983-84, Snohomish County Transp. Authority, 1987-89, Snohomish County Dept. Emergency Mgmt., 1981-91, Snohomish County Tomorrow Steering Com., 1989-91; treas. Lake Stevens Aquafest, 1983-84; sponsor Miss Lake Stevens Pageant, 1983-84; bd. dirs., treas. Josephine Sunset Home, 1993-94. Served as Sgt. U.S. Army, 1965-67, Vietnam. Mem. AICPA, Wash. Soc. CPAs, Everett C. of C. (treas. 1990-94), Marysville C. of C., Lake Stevens C. of C. (charter), Rotary (charter). Lutheran. Home: 15128 76th St SE Snohomish WA 98290-6150 Office: 3201 Broadway Ste C Everett WA 98201-4470

TOYODA, EIJI, automobile manufacturing company executive; b. Kinjo, Nishikasugai, Aichi, Japan, Sept. 12, 1913; s. Heikichi and Nao T.; m. Kazuko Takahashi, Oct. 19, 1939; children: Kanshiro, Tetsuro, Shuhei, Sonoko. B.M.E., Tokyo U., 1936. Dir. Toyota Motor Corp., Aichi, Japan, 1945—, mng. dir. 1950-53, sr. mng. dir., 1953-60, exec. v.p., 1960-67, pres., 1967-82, chmn. bd., 1982-92; hon. chmn. Toyota Motor Corp., Aichi, 1992—; chmn. Towa Real Estate Co., Ltd.; chmn. bd. Toyota Cen. R&D Lab., Inc.; dir. Aichi Steel Works Co., Ltd., Toyoda Machine Works Ltd. Author: Toyota Fifty Years in Motion, 1988. Mem. Japan Automobile Mfrs. assn. (supreme adv. 1980, pres. 1972-80), Japan Motor Indsl. Fedn. (adv. 1980), Fedn. Econ. Orgns. (Keidanren, vice chmn. 1984-90). Office: Toyota Motor Corp, 1 Toyota-cho, Toyota Aichi 471, Japan

TOZER, FORREST LEIGH, lawyer; b. Morgantown, W.Va., Oct. 29, 1922; s. Aiden Wilson and Ada Cecelia (Pfautz) T.; m. Rosemary Peacock, June 16, 1947; children: Christine, Paul, Judith, Thomas. B.A., U. Chgo., 1947, J.D., 1948. Bar: Ill. 1948. Atty. anti-trust divsn. Dept. Justice, Detroit, 1948-50; mem. firm Lord, Bissell & Brook, Chgo., 1952—, ptnr. firm, 1959-89. Contbr. articles to profl. jours. Chmn. Cook County Sheriff's Police Dept. Merit Bd., 1963-69; chmn. Ill. State Police Merit Bd., 1969-73. Served with USMCR, 1943-46, 50-52. Decorated Purple Heart. Fellow Am. Coll. Trial Lawyers; mem. Am. Bar Assn., Ill. State Bar Assn., Chgo. Bar Assn., Soc. Trial Lawyers, Attic (Chgo.), Flossmoor Country Club. Republican. Presbyterian. Clubs: Attic (Chgo.). Home: 843 Bruce Ave Flossmoor IL 60422-1213 Office: Lord Bissell & Brook 115 S La Salle St Chicago IL 60603-3801

TOZER, W. JAMES, JR., investment company executive; b. Salt Lake City, Feb. 9, 1941; s. W. James and Virginia (Somerville) T.; m. Elizabeth Farran, July 30, 1965; children: Farran Virginia, Katharine Coppins. B.A. cum laude, Trinity Coll., 1963; M.B.A., Harvard U., 1965. Investment officer First Nat. City Overseas Investment Corp., N.Y.C., 1965-70; v.p. corp. devel. Citicorp, N.Y.C., 1970-71; sr. v.p. and head Citicorp Subs. Group, 1971-74; sr. v.p. gen. mgr., head Merchant Banking Group, 1974-75, sr. v.p., gen. mgr. N.Y. banking div., 1975-77; sr. exec. v.p., dir. and head investment banking div. Shearson Hayden Stone, Inc., N.Y.C., 1977-79; exec. v.p. Marine Midland Bank and Marine Midland Banks, Inc., 1979-80, sr. exec. v.p. ops., fin. and strategic staff units, 1980-85, mem. office of chmn., sector exec. corp., instl. and internat. banking, 1985-87; chmn. Mountain West Banking Corp., Denver, 1988-89; pres., chief operating officer Prudential-Bache Securities, Inc., N.Y.C., 1989-90; mng. dir. Vectra Mgmt. Group, 1990-93; pres., CEO Lincolnshire Mgmt, Inc., N.Y.C., 1993-95; mng. dir. Vectra Mgmt. Group, 1995—; trustee Mktg. Sci. Inst., 1975-78; bd. dirs. Cobra Industries, Inc., Vectra Banking Corp., Trans-Wasatch Co., Credentials Svcs. Internat. Chmn. bd. Fellows Trinity Coll., 1972-78; trustee, treas. Community Service Soc., 1976-87; mem. Securities Industry Assn.; 1977-78; mem. Citizens Budget Commn., 1986—; adv. council Atlanta U. Sch. Bus. Adminstrn., 1985-89. Mem. N.Y. State Bankers Assn. (legis. policy com. 1981-87), Assn. Res. City Bankers (govt. rels. com. 1984-87), Am. Bankers Assn. (govt. rels. com. 1985-87), Economic Club, University Club, Bond of N.Y. Club, Millbrook Club, Mashomack Club, River Club (N.Y.C.). Home: 1112 Park Ave New York NY 10128-1235 Office: 780 3rd Ave 45th Fl New York NY 10017-2024

TOZZER, JACK CARL, civil engineer, surveyor; b. Marion, Ohio, Jan. 5, 1922; s. Carl Henry and Henrietta (Schellenbaum) T.; children: Brent Jack, Hal Jack; m. Aleta C. Lehner, July 14, 1974. BCE, Ohio No. U., 1944. Registered profl. engr., Ohio, Fla., registered surveyor, Ohio. Pres. firm Tozzer & Assocs. Inc., Marion, 1948-85; county engr. Marion County, Ohio, 1964—; city engr. Marion, 1959, Galion, Ohio, 1960-85; cons. civil engr. Mem. cons. bd. Coll. Engring. Ohio No. U., 1970; v.p. Marion Community Improvement Corp.; mem. Marion County Regional Planning Commn. Served with USNR, 1944-46. Recipient Order of Engr. Coll. Engring. Ohio No. U., 1971. Fellow ASCE; mem. NSPE, Marion C. of C., Cons. Engrs. Ohio, Profl. Land Surveyors Ohio, Ohio Hist. Soc., Marion County Hist. Soc. (past dir.), Elks, Delta Sigma Phi. Lutheran. Home: 307 Forest Lawn Blvd Marion OH 43302-5523 Office: Courthouse # 1 Marion OH 43302

TOZZI, RICHARD RAYMOND, oil and gas company executive; b. N.Y.C., June 27, 1941; s. Aurelio and Margaret (Tassille) T.; m. Sharon L. Roberts, Aug. 17, 1961 (div. 1981); children: Dina Michelle, Anna Maria, Donna Rene; m. Brenda Lee Hallberg, Jan. 29, 1982; children: Burton Anthony, Victoria Marie. BS in Acctg., Cen. State U., Edmond, Okla., 1969. CPA, Okla. Ctr. mgr. Univ. Computing Co., Oklahoma City, 1965-70; mgr. Arthur Young & Co., Oklahoma City, 1970-79; pres. Aftak, Columbus, Okla., 1979-81; treas. Alpha Energy, Oklahoma City, 1981; v.p. fin. Adams Exploration Co., Tulsa, 1981-84, Ward Petroleum Corp., Enid, Okla., 1984—; v.p. Ward Gas, Ward Drilling Co., Rambler Well Svc., Gale Force Compression. With U.S. Army, 1960-62. Named Boss of Yr. Am. Bus. Women's Club, 1987. Mem. Petroleum Accts. Assn., Cash Mgmt. Assn., Okla. Inst. CPA's, AICPA, Grand Nat. Quail Club, Ducks Unltd. Club. Home: 3540 Chickadee Ln Enid OK 73703-1423 Office: Ward Petroleum Corp PO Box 1187 Enid OK 73702-1187

TRABITZ, EUGENE LEONARD, aerospace company executive; b. Cleve., Aug. 13, 1937; s. Emanuel and Anna (Berman) T.; m. Caryl Lee Rine, Dec. 22, 1963 (div. Aug. 1981); children: Claire Marie, Honey Caryl; m. Kathryn Lynn Bates, Sept. 24, 1983; 1 stepchild, Paul Francis Rager. BA, Ohio State U., 1965. Enlisted USAF, 1954, advanced through grades to maj.; served as crew commdt. 91st Stragetic Missile Div., Minot, S.D., 1968-70; intelligence officer Fgn. Tech. Div., Dayton, Ohio, 1970-73; dir. external affairs Aero Systems Div., Dayton, 1973-75; program mgr. Air Force Armament Div., Valparaiso, Fla., 1975-80; dir. ship ops. Air Force Ea. Test Range, Satellite Beach, Fla., 1980-83; dep. program mgr. Air Force Satellite Text Ctr., Sunnyvale, Calif., 1983-84; ret., 1984; sr. staff engr. Ultrasystems Inc., 1984-86; pres. TAWD Systems Inc., Palo Alto, Calif., 1986-92, Am. Telenetics Co., San Mateo, Calif., 1992—; cons. Space Applications Corp., Sunnyvale, 1986-87, Litton Computer Svcs., Mountain View, Calif., 1987-91, Battelle Meml. Inst., Columbus, 1993-95. V.p Bd. County Mental Health Clinic, Ft. Walton Beach, Fla., 1973-75. Decorated Bronze Star. Mem. DAV (life), World Affairs Coun., U.S. Space Found. (charter), Air Force Assn. (life), Assn. Old Crows, Nat. Sojourners, Commonwealth Club Calif., Masons (32 degree). Avocations: golf, tennis, racketball, sailing, bridge. Home: 425 Anchor Rd Ste 317 San Mateo CA 94404

TRACEY, EDWARD JOHN, physician, surgeon; b. Norwalk, Conn., July 26, 1931; s. Edward John and Clara (Hammond) T.; m. Ann Marie Schenk, Sept. 7, 1957; children: Sharon, Scott. BA, Yale U., 1954; MD, N.Y. Med. Coll., N.Y.C., 1958. Diplomate Am. Bd. Surgery. Intern Bellevue Hosp., N.Y.C., 1958-59; resident in surgery NYU-Bellevue Med. Ctr., N.Y.C., 1958-63; attending surgeon Norwalk (Conn.) Hosp., 1965—, asst. dir. med. surgery, 1975-82, chief of staff, 1982-85, chief sect. gen. surgery, 1989-95, trustee, 1972, 82-85, 92—; surgeon courtesy staff St. Joseph's Hosp., Stamford, Conn., 1978-95; commr. Norwalk Bd. Health, 1979—. Lt. commdr. USNR, 1963-65. Mem. ACS, AMA, Conn. Med. Soc., Fairfield County

Med. Soc., Norwalk Med. Soc. (pres. 1976-77). Clubs: Cath. (Norwalk, Conn., pres. 1974-75), Shore and country (Norwalk, Conn.). Home: 124 East Ave Norwalk CT 06851-5713

TRACEY, JAY WALTER, JR., retired lawyer; b. Rocky Ford, Colo., June 13, 1925; s. Jay Walter and Margaret Louise (Bish) T.; m. Elizabeth Longfellow Henry, Nov. 1, 1952 (div. July 1988); children: Jay Walter III, William H., Anne E., John B.; m. Elizabeth Folk Flinn, Apr. 22, 1989. BS, Yale U., 1949; LLB, Harvard U., 1952. Bar: Colo. 1952, U.S. Dist. Ct. Colo. 1952, U.S. Ct. Appeals (10th cir.) 1958. Assoc. Holland & Hart, Denver, 1952-57, ptnr., 1957-71, 72-89; pres. Von Frellick Assocs., Inc., Denver, 1971-72; dir. Ctr. for Dispute Resolution, Denver, 1984-88. Councilman, City of Cherry Hills Village (Colo.), 1965-70, mayor pro tem, 1966-70, mem. Home Rule Charter Conv., 1966; trustee Denver Country Day Sch., 1967-70. With U.S. Army, 1943-46. Decorated Purple Heart. Mem. ABA, Colo. Bar Assn., Denver Bar Assn., Colo. Yale Assn. (pres. 1971-72), Assn. Yale Alumni (del. 1975-78), Harvard Law Sch. Assn. Colo. (pres. 1962-63), Harvard Law Sch. Assn. (v.p. 1963-64), Univ. Club (pres. 1967-69) Denver Country Club, Mile High Club, Round Hill Club (Greenwich, Conn.), Denver Rotary (sec. 1979-80, bd. dirs. 1980-82, 1st v.p. 1981-82). Republican. Episcopalian. Office: 555 17th St Ste 2900 Denver CO 80202-3929

TRACEY, MARGARET, dancer; b. Pueblo, Colo.. Student, Sch. Am. Ballet, 1982. With corps de ballet N.Y.C. Ballet, 1986-88, soloist, 1989-91, prin., 1991. Featured in ballets (Balanchine) Ivesiana, Tarantella, The Nutcracker, Symphony in C, Jewels, Square Dance, Tschaikovsky Pas de Deux, Tschaikovsky Suite No. 3, Vienna Waltzes, Apollo, Ballo Della Regina, Divertimento No. 15, Donizetti Variations, Harlequinade, A Midsummer Night's Dream, Sonatine, La Source, Stars and Stripes, Symphony in Three Movements, Valse Fantaisie, Western Symphony, Who Cares?, (Robbins) Afternoon of a Faun, The Four Seasons, The Goldberg Variations, (Martins) Les Petits Riens, Mozart Serenade, Fearful Symmetries, Zakouski, Sleeping Beauty, (Anderson) Baroque Variations; also appeared in N.Y.C. Ballet's Blanchine Celebration, 1993; toured in Europe, Asia. Recipient U.S.A. award Princess Grace Found., 1985-86; scholar Atlantic Richfield Found., 1982-85. Office: NYC Ballet NY State Theater Lincoln Ctr Plaza New York NY 10023*

TRACHSEL, WILLIAM HENRY, corporate lawyer; b. El Paso, Tex., Apr. 20, 1943. BS in Aerospace Engring., U. Fla., 1965; JD, U. Conn., 1971. Bar: Conn. 1971. With United Tech. Corp., Hartford, Conn., 1965-86, v.p., sec. and dep. gen. counsel, 1993—. Mem. ABA, Am. Corp. Counsel Assn. Office: United Tech Corp United Tech Bldg Hartford CT 06101

TRACHTA, PAMELA HALE, consulting executive; b. Sacramento, May 10, 1943; d. Robert Armstrong Hale and Mary Wilder (Richards) Hale-Lochead; adopted d. James Struthers Lochead; m. Robert Louis Weaver, June 18, 1966 (div. Oct. 1988); children: Laura Michelle, Erin Hale; m. S. Jon Trachta, June 24, 1989. BA, Stanford U., 1965; MA, Columbia U., 1966. Tchr. N.Y.C. (N.Y.) Pub. Schs., 1966-68; paraprofl. counselor Pasadena (Calif.) Mental Health Ctr., 1970-73; founder, dir., ednl. cons. Images (Ednl. Photography), So. Pasadena, Calif., 1978-85; dir. of devel. Friends of the Jr. Arts Ctr., L.A., 1985-87; assoc. dir. of devel. Stanford U., So. Calif. Office, L.A., 1987-89; dir. of devel. U. Heart Calif. U. Ariz., Tucson, 1990-94; dir. Phototherapy Assn., 1980-84; artist-in-residence Calif. Arts Coun., So. Pasadena, 1982, 83, 84. Artist, photographer various one-woman and group exhibits, 1973-84. Dir. Pasadena (Calif.) Mental Health Ctr., 1973-76, Tucson Symphony Orgn., 1991-93, Planned Parenthood So., Ariz., Tucson, 1990—; Tucson/Pima Arts Coun., 1992—, sec.; pres. bd. Stanford Alumni of So. Ariz., 1992-93; mem. Ariz.-Mexico commn.. Democrat. Episcopalian.

TRACHTENBERG, MATTHEW J., bank holding company executive; b. N.Y.C., June 20, 1953; s. Mark Trachtenberg and Joanne Horne. BA magna cum laude, NYU, 1974; JD, Bklyn. Law Sch., 1977; MBA in Fin., Fordham U., 1982. Bar: N.Y. 1979. Mgmt. trainee Mfrs. Hanover Trust Co., N.Y.C., 1977-78, credit analyst, 1978-79, corp. banking rep., 1979-80, asst. sec., 1980-82, asst. v.p., 1982, v.p., 1982—; dir. mfrs. Hanover Found., 1987-92; corp. sec. Mfrs. Hanover Trust Co., N.Y.C., 1987-92; v.p., corp. sec. Mfrs. Hanover Corp., N.Y.C., 1987-92; dir. Mfrs. Hanover Found., 1987-92; v.p., sec. regional bd. Chem. Bank, N.Y.C., 1992—; v.p., dep. corp. sec. Chem. Banking Corp., N.Y.C., 1992—, Chem. Bank, 1992—; sec. Chem. Bank Regional Bd., 1992—; v.p. Chem. Bank, 1992—, Chem. Banking Corp., 1992—. Bd. dirs., treas. Nat. Orch. Assn.; bd. dirs. Joffrey Ballet, N.Y. Eye and Ear Infirmary, U.S.O. of Met. N.Y.; mem. adv. com. Lighthouse for the Blind. N.Y. State Regents scholar. Mem. N.Y. State Bar Assn., Am. Soc. Corp. Secs., Phi Beta Kappa, Pi Sigma Alpha. Avocations: music, fishing, painting, writing. Office: Chem Banking Corp 270 Park Ave New York NY 10017-2014

TRACHTENBERG, STEPHEN JOEL, university president; b. Bklyn., Dec. 14, 1937; s. Oscar M. and Shoshana G. (Weinstock) T.; m. Francine Zorn, June 24, 1971; children: Adam Maccabee, Ben-Lev. BA, Columbia U., 1959; JD, Yale U., 1962; M in Pub. Adminstrn., Harvard U., 1966; LHD (hon.), Trinity Coll., 1986; HHD (hon.), U. Hartford, 1989; LLD (hon.), Hanyang U., Seoul, Republic of Korea, 1990; DPA (hon.), Kyonggi U., Seoul, 1994. Bar: N.Y. 1964, U.S. Supreme Ct. 1967. Atty. AEC, 1962-65; legis. asst. to Congressman John Brademas of Ind., Washington, 1965; tutor law Harvard Coll., also; teaching fellow edn. and pub. policy J.F. Kennedy Grad. Sch. Govt., Harvard U., 1965-66; spl. asst. to U.S. edn. commr. Office of Edn., HEW, Washington, 1966-68; asso. prof. polit. sci. Boston U., 1969-77, asso. dean, 1969-70, dean, 1970-74, assoc. v.p., co-counsel, 1974-76, v.p. acad. services, 1976-77; pres., prof. pub. adminstrn. U. Hartford, Conn., 1977-88, George Washington U., Washington, 1988—; mem. adv. bd. Ednl. Record; bd. dirs. Consortium of Univs. Washington Met. Area; mem. Coun. on Competitiveness; mem. Fed. City Coun.; peer reviewer NCAA Com. on Athletics Cert.; bd. dirs. Loctite Corp., NationsBank, NationsBank Trust Co., Greater Washington Bd. Trade, Nat. Edn. Telecom. Orgn., Wash. Rsch. LIbr. Consortium. Mem. editl. bd. Jour. Higher Edn. Mgmt.; consulting editor Jour. Edn.; contbr. articles to profl. jours. Bd. dirs. Urban League, Washington; mem. D.C. Mayor's Adv. Coun., Jewish Hist. Soc. Am., Jewish Pub. Soc. Am. Winston Churchill fellow Eng., 1969; named Outstanding Young Person, Boston Jr. C. of C., 1970, One of 100 Young Leaders, Acad. Am. Council Learning, 1978, Alumnus of Yr. James Madison High Sch., Bklyn., 1982, one of Fifty Outstanding Alumni Problem Solvers Harvard's John F. Kennedy Sch. Government, 1987; recipient Myrtle Wreath award Hadassah, 1982, Scopus award Am. Friends of Hebrew U., 1986, assoc. fellow Morse Coll. Yale U., 1980, Human Rels. award NCCJ, 1987, award NAACP, 1988, citation Conn. Bar Assn., 1988, Univ. medal of highest honor Kyung Hee U., Seoul, Korea, 1990, Martin Luther King, Jr. Internat. Salute award, 1992, Hannah G. Solomon award Nat. Coun. Jewish Women, 1992, Father of Yr. award Washington Urban League, 1993, Univ. Pres. medal Kyonggi U., Seoul, 1993, Am. Czech and Slovak Assn. Merit award, 1993, John Jay award Columbia U., 1995. Mem. Internat. Assn. Univ. Pres. (N.Am. coun., v.p.), Nat. Assn. Ind. Colls. and Univs., Coun. Ren. Rels., Sr. Soc. Sachems (mem., chief naval ops. exec. panel), Harvard Club, Tumblebrook Country Club, Cosmos Club, Univ. Club, Nineteen Twenty-Five F. St. Club, Inc., Scottish Rite Freemasonry, Phi Beta Kappa, Pi Alpha Alpha. Office: George Washington U Office of President Washington DC 20052

TRACI, DONALD PHILIP, retired lawyer; b. Cleve., Mar. 13, 1927; m. Lillian Traci Calafiore; 11 children. BS cum laude, Coll. of the Holy Cross, Worcester, Mass., 1950; JD magna cum laude, Cleve. State U., 1955; LLD (hon.), U. Urbino, Italy, 1989. Bar: Ohio 1955, U.S. Dist. Ct. (no. and so. dists.) Ohio 1955, U.S. Ct. Appeals (3d, 6th and 7th cirs.), U.S. Dist. Ct. (we. and ea. dists.) Pa., U.S. Supreme Ct. 1965. Ptnr. Spangenberg, Shibley, Traci, Lancione & Liber, Cleve., 1955-95; lectr. Western Res. U., Cleve. Marshall Law Sch., U. Mich., Akron U., U. Cin., Ohio No. U., Harvard U. Trustee Cath. Charities Diocese of Cleve., past pres. Bd. Cath. Edn.; former chmn. bd. regents St Ignatius H.S., Cleve.; mem. pres.'s coun. Coll. of Holy Cross; Eucharist min. St. Rose of Lima Ch. With USN 1945-46. Fellow Am. Coll. Trial Lawyers, Internat. Acad. Trial Lawyers (past pres.), Am. Bd. Trial Advocacy; mem. ABA, ATLA (trustee Lambert Chair Found., lectr. trial practice), Ohio State Bar Assn. (lectr. trial practice), Ohio Acad. Trial Lawyers (past chmn. rules seminar, lectr. trial

---

practice), Cuyahoga County Bar Assn. (lectr. trial practice), Cleve. Acad. Trial Lawyers (lectr. trial practice), Trial Lawyers for Pub. Justice (sustaining founder), Cleve. Bar Assn. (chmn. Advocacy Inst., trustee, CLE com., jud. selection com., spl. justice ctr. com., fed. ct., common pleas ct. and ct. appeals com., pres. 1986), Jud. Conf. U.S. 6th Cir. Ct. (life), Jud. Conf. 8th Jud. Dist. Ohio (life), Knights of Malta, Delta Theta Phi. Home: 10416 Lake Ave Cleveland OH 44102-1206 Office: 2400 National City Ctr Cleveland OH 44114

TRACY, ALLEN WAYNE, manufacturing company executive; b. Windsor, Vt., July 25, 1943; s. J. Wayne and Helen (Bernard) T.; m. Karla Noelte, Dec. 14, 1968; children: Tania, Tara. BA, U. Vt., 1965; MBA cum laude, Boston U., 1974. Retail salesman Exxon Corp., Boston, 1965-72; mfg. mgr. Leonard Silver Mfg. Co., Inc., Boston, 1974-78, v.p. ops., 1979-81; pres. OESM Corp., N.Y.C., 1978-81; pres. Gold Lance Inc., Houston, 1981-91, also bd. dirs.; v.p. ops. Town & Country Corp., 1989-92; sr. v.p. L.G. Balfour Co., 1990-92; asst. to pres. Syratech Corp., Boston, 1993; dir. ops. Goldman-Kolber Co., Inc., Norwood, Mass., 1994; exec. v.p., COO George H. Fuller & Son Co., Inc., Pawtucket, R.I., 1994—; bd. dirs. Verilyte Gold, Inc., L.G. Balfour Co., Inc. Mem. Bd. Selectmen, Town of Ashland, 1977-78; chmn. Ashland Study Town Govt. Com., 1976-77; vice chmn. ch. council Federated Ch. of Ashland, 1979-80, chmn., 1981; bd. dirs. Nottingham Forest Civic Assn., 1986. Served with U.S. Army, 1965-68. Mem. Nottingham Forest Club (Houston, bd. dirs. 1986), Beta Gamma Sigma. Home: 455 Prospect St Seekonk MA 02771-1503 Office: George H. Fuller & Son Co Inc 151 Exchange St Pawtucket RI 02862 *The key to economic and social mobility is education. Education, however must be coupled with perseverance, diligence, hard work and a genuine appreciation of the efforts of all the people that one interacts with.*

TRACY, CAROL COUSINS, mathematics educator; b. N.Y.C., Jan. 31, 1943; d. James Franklin and Ruth (Hubbard) Cousins; m. William Ferber Tracy, Feb. 14, 1963; children: Lisa, Scott, Jennifer. BA, Duke U., 1965. Cert. educator, math. Tchr. Thrasher Sch., Signal Mountain, Tenn., 1967-69; tchr., math. Girls Prep. Sch., Chattanooga, 1980-91; exec. dir. Psi Beta, Chattanooga, 1981—; fin. officer Psi Beta, 1991—. Vol., bd. dirs. Jr. League, Chattanooga, 1973-83; tutor Inner City, Chattanooga, 1974-75, 88-90; sec., vol. Allied Arts, Chattanooga; publicity LWV; v.p., pres. Chattanooga Ballet Bd., 1991—; sec., bd. dirs. Signal Mountain Libr. Avocation: skiing. Home: 1500 Lyndhurst Dr Chattanooga TN 37405-3121 Office: Psi Beta/Psi Chi 407 E 5th St Ste B Chattanooga TN 37403

TRACY, DAVID, theology educator; b. Yonkers, N.Y., Jan. 6, 1939. Licentiate in Theology, Gregorian U., Rome, 1964, Doctorate in Theology, 1969; hon. doctorate, U. of the South, 1982, Cath. Theol. Union, 1990. Instr. theology Cath. U. Am., Washington, 1967-69; prof. theology Divinity Sch., U. Chgo., 1969—, prof. com. analysis of ideas and methods, 1981—, Disting. Svc. prof., 1985, Andrew Thomas Greeley and Grace McNichols Greeley Disting. Svc. prof. Cath. studies, 1987, prof. com. social thought, 1990—; lectr. Beijing Inst. Sci. Study of Religion, Trinity Coll., Dublin, Gregorian U., Rome, World Coun. Chs., Geneva, Cath. U., Leuven, Belgium, Union Theol. Sem., Princeton Theol. Sem., numerous U.S. univs. including Harvard, Yale, Fordham, Notre Dame, Vanderbilt, So. Meth., Xavier, Marquette. Author: The Achievement of Bernard Lonergan, 1970, Blessed Rage for Order: The New Pluralism in Theology, 1975, The Analogical Imagination: Christian Theology and the Context of Pluralism, 1981, Plurality and Ambiguity: Hermeneutics, Religion and Hope, 1987, Religion and the Public Realm, 1987; co-author: (with John Cobb) Talking About God, 1983, (with Stephen Happel) The Catholic Vision, 1983, (with Robert M. Grant) A Short History of the Interpretation of the Bible, 1984; co-editor: (with Hans Küng and Johann Baptist Metz) Towards Vatican III: The Work That Needs to be Done, (with H. Küng) Theologie-Wohin?. German edit., 1983, English edit., 1985, (with Hans Küng) Paradigm Change in Theology, 1989; editor or co-editor various spl. vols. for Jour. Religion, Concilium jour.; co-editor Jour. Religion, Religious Studies Rev., Commonweal; past mem. editorial bd. Jour. Am. Acad. Religion, Theol. Studies jour.; current editorial bd. Theology Today, Jour. Pastoral Psychology; contbr. articles to scholarly and popular jours. including Jour. Religion, Theology Today, Critical Inquiry, Daedalus, Jour. Am. Acad. Religion, New Republic, N.Y. Times Book Rev., Christian Century. Mem. Am. Acad. Arts and Scis., Am. Acad. Religion, Am. Theol. Soc., Cath. Theol. Soc. Am. (pres. 1977-78). Office: U Chgo The Divinity Sch 1025 E 58th St Chicago IL 60637-1509

TRACY, JAMES DONALD, historian; b. St. Louis, Feb. 14, 1938; s. Leo W. and Marguerite M. (Meehan) T.; m. Nancy Ann McBride, Sept. 6, 1968 (div. 1993); children: Patrick, Samuel, Mary Ann. BA, St. Louis U., 1959; MAS, Johns Hopkins U., 1960; MA, Notre Dame U., 1961; PhD, Princeton U., 1967. Instr. U. Mich., 1964-66; instr. to prof. history U. Minn., Mpls., 1966—; dept. chmn., 1988-91; vis. prof. U. Leiden, Netherlands, spring 1987. Author: Erasmus: The Growth of a Mind, 1972, The Politics of Erasmus: A Pacifist Intellectual and His Political Milieu, 1979, True Ocean Found: Paludanus' Letters on Dutch Voyages to the Kara Sea, 1980, A Financial Revolution in the Habsburg Netherlands: Renten and Renteniers in the County of Holland, 1515-1565, 1985, Holland under Habsburg Rule: The Formation of a Body Politic. 1506-1566, 1990; editor: Luther and the Modern State in Germany, 1986, The Rise of Merchant Empires: Long Distance Trade in the Early Modern Era, 1350-1750, 1990, The Political Economy of Merchant Empires: Long Distance Trade and State Power in the Early Modern World, 1991, (with T.A. Brady and H.O. Oberman) Handbook of European History in the Late Middle Ages, Renaissance and Reformation, Vol. 1, 1994, Vol. 2, 1995; mem. editorial bd. Sixteenth Century Jour., 1979—. Guggenheim fellow, 1972-73; NEH summer grantee, 1977, 85; Fulbright rsch. grantee, Belgium, 1979, Netherlands, 1980; resident fellow Netherlands Inst. for Advanced Studies, 1993-94. Fellow Netherlands Inst. for Advanced Studies; mem. Am. Cath. Hist. Soc., Soc. Reformation Rsch., 16th Century Studies Conf. (pres. 1995-96). Republican. Roman Catholic. Home: 63 Avon St S Apt 33 Saint Paul MN 55105-3336 Office: U Minn 614 Social Sci Bldg Minneapolis MN 55455

TRACY, JAMES JARED, JR., law firm administrator; b. Cleve., Jan. 17, 1929; s. James Jared and Florence (Comey) T.; m. Elizabeth Jane Bourne, June 30, 1953 (div. 1988); children: Jane Mackintosh, Elizabeth Boyd, James Jared IV, Margaret Gardiner; m. Judith Anne Cooper, Feb. 18, 1989. AB, Harvard U., 1950, MBA, 1953. CPA, Ohio. Acct., mgr. Price Waterhouse & Co., Cleve., 1953-65; treas., CFO Clevite Corp., Cleve., 1965-69; asst. treas. Republic Steel Corp., Cleve., 1969-70, treas., CFO I. T. Corp. L.A., 1981-82; exec. dir. Hufstedler, Miller, Carlson & Beardsley, L.A., 1983-84; Shank, Irwin & Conant, Dallas, 1984-85, Pachter, Gold & Schaffer, L.A., 1985-86; v.p., sr. cons. Right Assocs., L.A., 1987-91; dir. adminstrn. Larson & Burnham, Oakland, Calif., 1991—; trustee and v.p. Miss Hall's Sch., Pittsfield, Mass., 1970-78; dir. Union Commerce Bank, Cleve., 1971-76; adv. bd. mem. Arkwright-Boston Ins. Co., Boston, 1976-81. Trustee and v.p. Cleve. Soc. for Blind, 1965-76; trustee Western Res. Hist. Soc., Cleve., 1972-76; treas. St. Peters by the Sea Presbyn. Ch., Palos Verdes, Calif., 1981-91. Recipient Alumni award Harvard U., Denver, 1981. Mem. AICPA, Ohio Soc. CPAs, Assn. Legal Adminstrs., Nat. Assn. Realtors, Piedmont Montclair Rotary Club (pres.-elect), Harvard Club of San Francisco, Harvard Bus. Sch. Club. Avocations: sailing, golf, gardening, railroad layouts. Home: 180 Lombardy Ln Orinda CA 94563-1126 Office: Larson & Burnham 1901 Harrison St Fl 11 Oakland CA 94612-3574

TRACY, JANET RUTH, legal educator, librarian; b. Denison, Iowa, July 16, 1941; d. L. M. and Grace (Harvey) T.; m. Rodd Mc Cormick Reynolds, Feb. 15, 1975 (dec. June 1993); children: Alexander, Lee. BA, U. Oreg., 1963; ML, U. Wash., 1964; JD, Harvard U., 1969. Bar: N.Y. 1970. Reference libr. Harvard Coll. Librs., Cambridge, Mass., 1964-66; assoc. Kelley Drye & Warren, N.Y.C., 1969-71; dir. data base design Mead Data Ctrl., Inc., N.Y.C., 1971-75; dir. rsch. Mvpl. Employees Legal Svc. Fund, N.Y.C., 1975-76; from asst. to assoc. prof. N.Y. Law Sch., N.Y.C., 1976-82; asst. libr. dir. Law Libr. Columbia U., N.Y.C., 1982-86; prof., law libr. dir. Fordham U., N.Y.C., 1986—; chmn. Conf. Law Librs. Jesuit Univs., 1988-89. Co-author: Professional Staffing and Job Security in Academic Law Libraries, 1989. Recipient Catalog Automation award Winston Found.,

---

1990, 91, 92. Home: 285 Riverside Dr New York NY 10025 Office: Fordham U Sch of Law 140 W 62nd St New York NY 10023

TRACY, MARY E., principal. Prin. Holy Names Acad. Recipient Blue Ribbon Sch. award, 1990-91. Office: Holy Names Acad 728 21st Ave E Seattle WA 98112-4058

TRACY, MICHAEL CAMERON, choreographer, performer; b. Florence, Italy, Feb. 1, 1952; s. Stanley B. and Elizabeth Lee (McIntosh) T. B.A. Magna cum laude, Dartmouth Coll., 1973. Instr. Yale U., New Haven, Conn., 1992—. Artistic dir. Pilobolus Dance Theatre, Washington, Conn., 1974—; choreographer Die Zauberflöte, 1995; co-choreographer: Ciona, 1974, Monkshood's Farewell, 1975, Untitled, 1976, Eve of Samhain, 1. Recipient Berlin Critics award, 1975, New Eng. Theatre Conf. prize, 1977, Brandeis award, 1978, Excellence in Arts award Conn. Commn. on the Arts, 1981; sr. fellow Dartmouth Coll., 1973. Office: PO Box 388 Washington Depot CT 06794-0388

TRACY, PHILIP R., computer company executive; b. 1940. JD, George Washington U., 1966. With FBI, Washington, 1966-69; atty. Steptoe & Johnson, Washington, 1966-69; with Burroughs Wellcome Co., Durham, N.C., 1974—, CEO, pres., 1989—. Office: Burroughs Wellcome Co 3030 W Cornwallis Rd Research Triangle Park NC 27709

TRACY, ROBERT (EDWARD), English educator, poetry translator; b. Woburn, Mass., Nov. 23, 1928; s. Hubert William and Vera Mary (Hurley) T.; m. Rebecca Garrison, Aug. 26, 1956; children: Jessica Janes, Hugh Garrison, Dominick O'Donovan. AB in Greek with honors, Boston Coll., 1950; MA, Harvard U., 1954, PhD, 1960. Teaching fellow Harvard U., Cambridge, Mass., 1954-58; instr. Carleton Coll., Northfield, Minn., 1958-60; from asst. prof. English, to assoc. prof., then prof. U. Calif., Berkeley, 1960-89, prof. English and Celtic Studies, 1989-94, assoc. dir. Dickens Project, 1994—; vis. prof., Bruern fellow in Am. studies, U. Leeds, England, 1965-66; vis. prof., Leverhulme fellow Trinity Coll., Dublin, 1971-72; vis. Kathryn W. Davis prof. slavic studies Wellesley (Mass.) Coll., 1979; Charles Mills Gayley lectr. U. Calif., Berkeley, 1989-90. Author: Trollope's Later Novels, 1978; translator (poems by Osip Mandelstam): Stone, 1981, 2d edit., 1991; editor J.M Synge's The Aran Islands, 1962, The Way We Live Now (Anthony Trollope), 1974, The Macdermots of Ballycloran (Anthony Trollope), 1989, Nina Balatka and Linda Tressel (Anthony Trollope), 1991, In A Glass Darkly (Sheridan Le Fanu) 1993, Rhapsody in Stephen's Green (Flann O'Brien), 1994; adv. editor The Recorder, 1985—, LIT (Lit., Interpretation, Theory), 1989—; contbr. articles and revs. to numerous jours. including Shakespeare Quarterly, So. Rev., Nineteenth-Century Fiction, Eire-Ireland, Irish Literary Supplement, others; poetry translations in New Orleans Rev., Poetry, N.Y. Rev. of Books, others. Appointed mem. cultural panel San Francisco-Cork Sister City Com. Fulbright travel grantee, 1965-66; recipient humanities research fellowships U. Calif., Berkeley, 1962, 69, 78, 81, 86 , 92; Guggenheim fellow, 1981-82. Mem. MLA, Philol. Assn. Pacific Coast, Am. Conf. for Irish Studies, Internat. Assn. for Study of Anglo-Irish Lit. Avocation: exploring western Ireland and no. Calif. Office: U Calif Dept English Berkeley CA 94720

TRACY, THOMAS KIT, investment company executive; b. Lufkin, Tex., Dec. 9, 1938; s. Albert Ray and Ruth (Rumsey) T.; m. Cary Jane Barrow, Feb. 22, 1964; children—Thomas Kit, Jr., Joe Barrow. B.S., Okla. State U. Fin. cons. Goodbody & Co., Atlanta, 1966-71; br. mgr. Robinson-Humphrey Co., Macon, Ga., 1971-79; divisional sales mgr. Robinson-Humphrey Co., Atlanta, 1979-88, vice chmn., 1993—; also bd. dirs.; dir. Shearson Lehman Hutton/Robinson Humphrey Co., Atlanta, 1988-93; group pres. Smith Barney/Robinson-Humphrey Co., Atlanta, 1993—. Participant Leadership Ga., 1978, Leadership Atlanta, 1981. Served to lt. USN, 1962-66. Mem. Piedmont Driving Club, Capital City Club, Buckhead Club. Republican. Episcopalian. Clubs: Piedmont Driving; Capital City (Atlanta), Commerce (Atlanta). Avocations: rowing, tennis, gardening. Office: Robinson-Humphrey Co Inc 3333 Peachtree Rd NE Atlanta GA 30326-1047

TRACY, THOMAS MILES, international health organization official; b. Great Barrington, Mass., July 8, 1936; s. Thomas Paul and Marion (Miles) T.; m. June Betts, June 17, 1967; children: Miles Christopher, Keir Thomas John. B.A., Colgate U., 1958; M.A., Stanford U., 1959; M.B.A., Columbia U., 1973. Fgn. service officer Dept. State, Washington, 1960-84; counselor Am. Embassy, Moscow, 1975-78, Bonn, Germany, 1978-79; asst. sec. Dept. State, Washington, 1979-83; chief adminstrn. Pan Am./WHO, Washington, 1983—; v.p. Pan-Am. Health and Edn. Found. Trustee, treas. Chelsea Sch.; treas. Pam Am. Health and Edn. Found. With U.S. Army, 1959-60. Recipient Superior Honor award Dept. State, 1978. Mem. Am. Fgn. Svc. Assn. (dir. 1970-72), Am. Fgn. Svc. Protective Assn. (dir. 1988—), Am. Fgn. Svc. Protective Found. (sec., treas.). Home: 5902 Devonshire Dr Bethesda MD 20816-3416 Office: Pan Am WHO 525 23d St NW Washington DC 20037

TRADER, JOSEPH EDGAR, orthopedic surgeon; b. Milw., Nov. 2, 1946; s. Edgar Joseph and Dorothy Elizabeth (Senzig) T.; m. Janet Louise Burzycki, Sept. 23, 1972 (div. Nov. 1987); children: James, Jonathan, Ann Elizabeth; m. Rhonda Sue Schultz, May 26, 1990. Student, Marquette U., 1964-67; MD, Med. Coll. Wis., 1971. Diplomate Am. Bd. Orthopaedic Surgery. Emergency rm. physician columbia, St. Joseph's Hosps., Milw., 1972-76; orthopedic surgeon Orthopaedic Assn., Manitowoc, Wis., 1978—; mem. exec. com. Holy Family Meml. Med. Ctr., Manitowoc, 1985—, chief-of-staff, 1994—, ethics com., 1995, bd. dirs. Mem., former pres. Holy Innocents Men's Choir; county del State Med. Soc. Charitable Sci. and Edn. Found.; mem. adv. bd. Manitowoc Area Cath. Schs. Endowment Fund. Lt. comdr. USN, 1976-78. Fellow Am. Acad. Orthopaedic Surgeons (orthopaedic rsch. and edn. found. state com.), ACS; mem. AMA, Wis. State Med. Soc. (del. gov. affairs com.), Wis. Orthopaedic Soc., Midwest Orthopaedic Soc., Milw. Orthopaedic Soc., Phi Delta Epsilon, Psi Chi, Crown & Anchor. Roman Catholic. Club: Manitowoc Yacht. Avocations: singing, piano, scuba diving, tennis, skiing, sailing. Home: 1021 Memorial Dr Manitowoc WI 54220 Office: Orthopaedic Assocs 501 N 10th St Manitowoc WI 54220-4039

TRAEGER, CHARLES HENRY, III, lawyer; b. Bethlehem, Pa., Sept. 30, 1942; s. Charles Henry Jr. and Dorothy Shelly (Weinberger) T.; m. Carole Lynn DeGraff, Feb. 20, 1972; children: Chad, Erin, Seth, Anna, Claire, Benjamin. AB, Coll. William and Mary, 1964; JD, Stanford U., 1967. Bar: Calif. 1967, N.Y. 1972, Mass. 1976, Ariz. 1980. Assoc. Milbank, Tweed, Hadley & McCloy, N.Y., 1967, 71-76; v.p., gen. counsel Shawmut Corp., Boston, 1976-80, Shawmut Bank of Boston, N.A., 1976-80; assoc. Snell & Wilmer, Phoenix, 1980-83, ptnr., 1983-91; v.p., gen. counsel Bank One Ariz. N.A., Phoenix, 1991—. Contbr. Stanford Law Rev. Lt. comdr. USNR, 1967-71. Phi Beta Kappa. Republican. Mem. LDS Ch. Office: Bank One Ariz NA 241 N Central Ave Phoenix AZ 85004

TRAFFORD, ABIGAIL, editor, writer, columnist; b. N.Y.C., July 14, 1940; d. William Bradford and Abigail (Sard) T.; children from previous marriage: Abigail, Victoria, Brett; m. Donald Lloyd Neff, Nov. 25, 1989. BA cum laude, Bryn Mawr Coll., 1962. Researcher Nat. Geog. Soc., Washington, 1964-67; tchr. Hermansberg Mission, Northern Ter., Australia, 1967-68; spl. corr. Time mag., The Washington Post, Houston, 1969-74; writer, asst. mng. editor U.S. News & World Report, Washington, 1975-86; health editor The Washington Post, 1986—; syndicated columnist Universal Press Syndicate. Author: Crazy Time: Surviving Divorce and Building a New Life, 1982, revised edit., 1992. Journalism fellow Harvard Sch. Pub. Health, 1980. Mem. Nat. Press Club, Washington Press Club Found. (bd. mem. 1989—, pres. 1993—). Home: 2600 Upton St NW Washington DC 20008-3826 Office: The Washington Post 1150 15th St NW Washington DC 20071-0001

TRAFICANT, JAMES A., JR., congressman; b. Youngstown, Ohio, May 8, 1941; s. James A. and Agnes T. Traficant; m. Patricia Coppa; children: Robin, Elizabeth. B.S., U. Pitts., 1963, 1973; M.S., Youngstown State U., 1976. Exec. dir. Mahoning County Drug Program, Ohio, 1971-81; sheriff Mahoning County, Ohio, 1981-85; mem. 99th-104th Congresses from 17th Ohio dist., Washington, D.C., 1985—; ranking minority mem. transp. and infrastructure subcom. on Coast Guard and maritime transp., mem. sci. com.

Office: US House of Reps Office of House Members 2446 Rayburn House Office Washington DC 20515-3517*

TRAFTON, STEPHEN J., banking executive; b. Mt. Vernon, Wash., Sept. 17, 1946; m. Diane Trafton; children: John, Roland. BS in Zoology, Wash. State U., 1968. V.p., mgr. dept. money market Seattle-First Nat. Bank, 1968-79; v.p., mgr. bank consulting group Donaldson Lufkin Jennrette, N.Y.C., 1980; exec. v.p., treas. Gibraltar Savings Bank, L.A., 1980-84; banking cons., 1984-86; v.p., treas. Hibernia Bank, San Francisco, 1986-88; sr. v.p., treas. Goldome Bank, Buffalo, N.Y., 1988-90; sr. exec. v.p., CFO Glenfed Inc., 1990-91, vice chmn., CFO, 1991—, pres., 1992—; sr. exec. v.p., CFO Glendale Fed. Bank, 1990-91, vice chmn., CFO, 1991, pres., COO, 1991-92, chmn. bd., pres., CEO, 1992—, also bd. dirs. Mem. Phi Eta Sigma. Office: Glendale Fed Bank 414 N Central Ave Glendale CA 91203-1238

TRAGER, ALAN MARTIN, financial services company executive; b. N.Y.C., Apr. 21, 1947; s. Sidney C. and Alice N. T.; m. Katherine Jones, Sept. 15, 1974; children: Carolyn, David. AB in Liberal Arts, Syracuse U., 1970; MPA, Harvard U., 1972. Sr. project mgr. Bur. of Budget City of N.Y., 1972-74; mgr. planning Pfizer Pharms., N.Y.C., 1974-78; mng. dir. Morgan Stanley, N.Y.C., 1978-91; pres. AMT Capital Advisers, Inc., N.Y.C., 1991—; speaker numerous industry confs. Contbr. articles to profl. jours. Mem. Harvard Club N.Y. Home: 175 Riverside Dr New York NY 10024-1616 Office: AMT Capital Advisers Inc 1270 Avenue Of The Americas New York NY 10020-1700

TRAGER, DAVID G., judge, lawyer, educator; b. Mt. Vernon, N.Y., Dec. 23, 1937; s. Sol and Clara (Friedman) T.; m. Roberta E. Weisbrod, May 2, 1972; children: Mara Emet, Josiah Samuel, Naomi Gabrielle. B.A., Columbia Coll., 1959; LL.B., Harvard U., 1962. Bar: N.Y. Assoc. firm Berman & Frost, 1963-65, Butler, Jablow & Geller, 1965-67; asst. corp. counsel Appeals Div. City of N.Y., 1967; law clk. Judge Kenneth B. Keating, N.Y. State Ct. Appeals, 1968-69; asst. U.S. atty. chief, appeals div., 1970-72; U.S. atty. Ea. Dist. N.Y., Bklyn., 1974-78; prof. Bklyn. Law Sch., 1992-93, dean, 1983-94; judge U.S. Dist. Ct. (ea. dist.) N.Y., Bklyn., 1994—; chmn. Mayor's Com. on Judiciary, 1982-89; N.Y. State Temp. Commn. on Investigation, 1983-90. Mem. N.Y.C. Charter Rev. Commn., 1986-89. With U.S. Army, 1962. Mem. ABA, N.Y. State Bar Assn., Assn. Bar City N.Y., Fed. Bar Council (pres. 1986-88), Am. Law Inst., Am. Judicature Soc. Office: US Courthouse 225 Cadman Plaza E Brooklyn NY 11201

TRAGER, PHILIP, photographer, lawyer; b. Bridgeport, Conn., Feb. 27, 1935; s. Bernard Harold and Mina (Rubenstein) T.; m. Ina Louise Shulkin, Sept. 2, 1957; children: Michael, Julie. B.A., Wesleyan U., Middletown, Conn., 1956; J.D., Columbia U., 1960. Bar: Conn. 1960, N.Y. 1981, U.S. Supreme Ct. 1963. With Trager & Trager, P.C., Fairfield, Conn., 1960—. Exhibited one man shows at Wesleyan U. Davison Art Ctr., 1970, 74, 81, 87, 92, Balt. Mus. Art, 1977, Mus. of City of N.Y., 1980, The Witkin Gallery, 1973, 80, 86, Jacobs Pillow, 1992, 93, Drew U., 1993, Recontres Internationales de la Photographie, Arles, France, 1994, Photographic Resource Ctr., Boston, 1995; group shows include Yale U. Art Gallery, 1979, Santa Barbara Mus. Art, Calif., 1979, Internat. Ctr. of Photography, 1987, N.Y. State Mus., Albany, 1982, The Bklyn. Mus., 1989, Bibliothèque Nationale, Paris, 1982, N.Y.U., 1985; represented in permanent collections, Balt. Mus. Art, Corcoran Gallery Art, Met. Mus. Art, Mus. Modern Art, New Orleans Mus. Art, Yale U. Gallery Art; author: Echoes of Silence, 1972, Photographs of Architecture (selected as Book of the Yr. Am. Inst. Graphic Arts), Philip Trager: New York, 1980, Wesleyan Photographs, 1982, The Villas of Palladio, 1986, Dancers, 1992. Bd. dirs. Bridgeport Hosp., 1985-95, Bridgeport Hosp. Found., 1993-95, New Eng. Found. for Arts, 1988—. Recipient Lay Person award Conn. Soc. Architects, 1980; recipient Disting. Alumnus award Wesleyan U., 1981. Mem. ABA, Conn. Bar Assn. Home: 20 Rolling Ridge Rd Fairfield CT 06430-2254 Office: Trager and Trager PC 1305 Post Rd Fairfield CT 06430-6016

TRAGER, WILLIAM, biology educator; b. Newark, Mar. 20, 1910; s. Leon and Anna (Emilfork) T.; m. Ida Sosnow, June 16, 1935; children—Leslie, Carolyn, Lillian. B.S., Rutgers U., 1930, Sc.D. (hon.), 1965; M.A., Harvard U., 1931, Ph.D., 1933; Sc.D. (hon.), Rockefeller U., 1987. Fellow Rockefeller U. N.Y.C., 1934-35, mem. faculty 1935—, assoc. prof., 1950-64, prof. biology, 1964-81, prof. emeritus, 1981—; guest investigator West African Inst. Trypanosomiasis Research, 1958-59, Nigerian Inst. Trypanosomiasis Research, 1973-74; vis. prof. Fla. State U., 1962, U. P.R. Med. Sch., 1963, U. Mex. Med. Sch., 1965; mem. study sect. parasitology and tropical medicine Nat. Inst. Allergy and Infectious Diseases, 1954-58, 67-70, mem. tng. grant com., 1961-64, mem. microbiology and infectious diseases adv. com., 1978-79; mem. malaria commn. Armed Forces Epidemiol. Bd., 1965-73; mem. study group parasitic diseases Walter Reed Army Inst. Research, 1977-79; chmn. sci. adv. council Liberian Inst. Tropical Medicine, 1965-66; rapporteur 6th, 7th Congresses Tropical Medicine; pres. Am. Found. for Tropical Medicine, 1966-69; mem. steering com. Malaria Immunology Group, WHO, 1977-80; cons. WHO, Bangkok, 1978, Panama, 1979, Shanghai, 1979; hon. pres. Asia and Pacific Conf. on Malaria, 1985. Author: Symbiosis, 1970, Living Together: The Biology of Animal Parasitism, 1986; editor Jour. Protozoology, 1954-65; contbr. articles on insect physiology and exptl. parasitology to profl. jours. Served to capt. AUS, 1943-45. Recipient Leuckart medal Deutsche Gesellschaft fur Parasitologie, 1982, First Rameshwardas Birla Internat. award in Medicine, 1982, Darling medal WHO, Manson medal Royal Soc. Tropical Medicine and Hygiene, 1986, Prince Mahidol award in Med. Sci., 1994; fellow NRC, 1933-34, Guggenheim Found., 1973-74, Avivah Zuckerman fellow Kuvin Ctr. Infections and Tropical Diseases, Hebrew U., 1982. Fellow AAAS, N.Y. Acad. Scis.; mem. Nat. Acad. Sci., Am. Soc. Parasitologist (council 1956-57, v.p. 1973, pres. 1974), Soc. Protozoologists (pres. 1961-63), Am. Soc. Tropical Medicine and Hygiene (pres. 1978-79, Le Prince medal 1991). Office: Rockefeller U York Ave At 66th St New York NY 10021

TRAHANT, MARK NEIL, newspaper editor; b. Pocatello, Idaho, Aug. 13, 1957; s. Neil Walter Trahant and Sharon Dianne (Murray) Empey; m. Lenora Ann Begay, Nov. 2, 1991; 1 child, Marvin Sam. Student, Idaho State U., 1975. Editor Sho-Ban News, Ft. Hall, Ind., 1977-79; pub. info. officer U.S. Bur. Indian Affairs, Washington, 1979-80; freelance writer Washington, 1980-83; pub. Navajo Times Today, Widow Rock, Ariz., 1983-87; reporter Ariz. Republic, Phoenix, 1989-91; pres., pub. Navajo Nation Today, Window Rock, 1991-92; exec. news editor Salt Lake Tribune, Salt Lake City, 1992—; bd. dirs. Robert C. Maynard Inst. for Journalism Edn.; mem. nat. adv. bd. Poynter Inst. for Media Studies; vis. scholar Freedom Forum's First Amendment Ctr., Vanderbilt U. Contbg. author: A Circle of Nations. Founding bd. dirs. UNITY '94. Mem. Native Am. Journalists Assn. (past pres.), Am. Soc. Newspaper Editors. Office: Salt Lake Tribune 143 S Main Salt Lake City UT 84111

TRAHERN, JOSEPH BAXTER, JR., humanities educator; b. Clarksville, Tenn., Feb. 20, 1937; s. Joseph Baxter and Margaret Dancey (Fort) T.; m. Marjorie Elizabeth Hawkins, Aug. 29, 1958; children: Sarah Margaret, Joseph Baxter III. BA, Vanderbilt U., 1958, MA, 1959; MA, Princeton U., 1962, PhD, 1963. Asst. prof. English U. Ill., Urbana, 1963-71, assoc. prof., 1971-78, acting head dept., 1976-77; prof. English U. Tenn., Knoxville, 1978—, head dept. English, 1978-88, exec. asst. to chancellor, 1989-90, acting vice chancellor for acad. affairs, 1990-92; mem. adv. coun. dept. English Princeton U., 1982—, chair, 1988-92. Editor: (annotated bibliography) Year's Work in Old English Studies, 1986—; Standardizing English: Essays in the History of Language Change, 1989; assoc. editor Old English Newsletter, 1986—; contbr. articles on Old English language and lit. to profl. jours. Trustee Webb Sch. Knoxville, 1981-87. Served to 2d lt. U.S. Army, 1958-59. Fulbright fellow Worcester Coll., Oxford, Eng., 1962-63. Mem. MLA (exec. com. Old English divsn. 1982-86), South Atlantic MLA (exec. com. 1993—), Medieval Acad. Am. (Haskins medal com. 1987-90), New Chaucer Soc., South Atlantic Assn. Depts. English (exec. com. 1986-88), Internat. Soc. Anglo-Saxonists (adv. bd. 1988-91), Phi Beta Kappa (chpt. pres. 1985-86). Democrat. Methodist. Home: 3920 Topside Rd Knoxville TN 37920-6043 Office: U Tenn Dept English Knoxville TN 37996-0430

TRAICOFF, GEORGE, college president; b. Elyria, Ohio, May 16, 1932; s. George and Lena (Szaroff) T.; m. Diane C. Schneider, Dec. 28, 1965; children: George Scott, Paula Jane, Amy Jo. BS, Miami U., Oxford, Ohio, 1954; MEd, Kent State U., 1959; EdD, Ind. U., 1967. Tchr. bus. LaGrange (Ohio) High Sch., 1956-57, Elyria High Sch., 1956-57; instr., coord. Ind. U., 1959-60, Ohio State U., 1960-63; prof., head dept. No. Mich. U., Marquette, 1963-66, dir. program gen. studies, 1966-67; dean community svcs. Cuyahoga Community Coll., Cleve., 1967-73; pres. North Shore Community Coll., Danvers, Mass., 1973—; pres. New Eng. Jr. Community and Tech. Coll. Coun.; vice chmn. regional employment bd. Pvt. Industry Coun.; bd. dirs. Century Bank and Trust Co. With U.S. Army, 1954-56. Mem. Am. Assn. Community and Jr. Colls., Nat. Coun. Community Svcs. (past pres.), Mass. Adminstrs. Community Colls., Mass. Community Coll. Assn. (treas.) Episcopalian. Office: North Shore Community Coll 1 Ferncroft Rd Danvers MA 01923-4017

TRAIN, HARRY DEPUE, II, retired naval officer; b. Washington, Nov. 5, 1927; s. Harold Cecil and May (Philipps) T.; m. Catharine Peck Kinnear, July 8, 1950; children: Louise Lucas, Catharine Philipps, Elizabeth Langdon, Cecilia Spencer. B.S., U.S. Naval Acad., 1949. Commd. ensign U.S. Navy, 1949, advanced through grades to adm., 1978; comdr. Cruiser-Destroyer Flotilla 8, 1971-72; dir. internat. security affairs East Asia and Pacific Region Office Asst. Sec. Def., 1972-73; dir. Systems Analysis Div., Office Chief Naval Ops., 1973-74; dir. joint staff Orgn. Joint Chiefs of Staff, 1974-76; comdr. U.S. 6th Fleet, 1976-78; comdr.-in-chief U.S. Atlantic Fleet and supreme allied comdr. Atlantic, 1978-82, ret., 1982; dir. Strategic Rsch. and Mgmt. Svcs. div. Sci Applications Internat. Corp.; bd. dirs. Aydin Corp.; bd. trustees Inst. for Def. Analyses. Chmn. bd. dirs. Va. divsn. Am. Cancer Soc. Decorated D.S.M. with 3 gold stars, Def. Disting. Service medal, Legion of Merit with 3 gold stars, Meritorious Service medal, Joint Services Commendation medal, Navy Commendation medal; comdr. Order Republic of Tunisia; Order Naval Merit Brazil; Pedro Campbell medal Uruguay; Order of Pres. of Republic Chile); Decorated Portuguese Mil. Order Christ; Netherlands Order Orange-Nassau; German Order Merit; French Legion of Honor; Colombian Naval Order Admiral Padilla; Mexican Order Spl. Merit; sr. fellow Inst. Higher Def. Studies Nat. Def. U. Mem. U.S. Naval Inst., Coun. on Fgn. Rels., Def. Sci. Study Group (sr. mentor). Clubs: Columbia Country (Chevy Chase, Md.); N.Y. Yacht; Town Point (chmn. bd. govs.) (Norfolk). Home: 1002 Magnolia Ave Norfolk VA 23508-1411

TRAIN, JOHN, investment counselor, writer, government official; b. N.Y.C., May 25, 1928; s. Arthur Cheney and Helen (Coster) T.; m. Maria Teresa Cini di Pianzano, 1961 (div. 1976); children: Helen, Nina, Lisa; m. Frances Cheston, July 23, 1977. BA magna cum laude, Harvard U., 1950, MA, 1951. Founder, mng. editor Paris Rev., 1952-54; staff Asst. Sec. Army, Washington, 1954-56; assoc. de Vegh & Co., 1956-58; chmn. Train, Smith Counsel (and predecessor firms), N.Y.C., 1958-94, chmn. emeritus, 1995—; co-chmn., then dir. ICAP, S.A., Athens, 1964—; pres. Chateau Malescasse, Lamarque-Margaux, Bordeaux, France, 1970-81; columnist Forbes mag., 1977-83; Fin. Times, London, 1977—; columnist Harvard mag., 1983-95, Wall St. Jour., 1984—, Worth Mag., Boston, 1991-93, Town and Country mag., 1994-95; dir. African Devel. Found., Washington, 1988-94; bd. dirs. Bulgarian-Am. Enterprise Fund, Washington, Genesis Funds, London; bd. govs. East-West Ctr., Hawaii, 1993—; chmn. Montrose Advisors, N.Y.C., 1992—; mem. Internat. Rescue Com., N.Y.C., 1994—; overseer Nat. Endowment for Democracy Internat. Forum for Democratic Studies, 1995—. Author: Dance of the Money Bees, 1973, Remarkable Names, 1977, Even More Remarkable Names, 1979, Remarkable Occurrences, 1978, Remarkable Words, 1980, The Money Masters, 1980, Remarkable Relatives, 1971, Preserving Capital, 1983, Famous Financial Fiascos, 1984, John Train's Most Remarkable Names, 1985, The Midas Touch, 1987, The New Money Masters, 1989, Valsalva's Maneuver, 1989, John Train's Most Remarkable Occurences, 1990, Wit, 1991, Love, 1993, The Craft of Investing, 1994; various articles. Chmn. Italian Emergency Relief Com., 1976-77; pres. Afghanistan Relief Com., 1986-95; trustee Harvard Lampoon, Cambridge, Mass., 1974-90, World Monuments Fund, 1988-92; chmn. Free Elections Project, 1990, Brit. Mus. Nat. Hist. Internat. Trust, 1990—. With U.S. Army, 1954-56. Decorated commendatore Ordine del Merito della Repubblica, commendatore Ordine Della Solidarieta (Italy). Mem. Order Colonial Lords of Manors, The Pilgrims, Century Club, Racquet and Tennis Club, Met. Club (Washington), Brooks's Club (London), Beefsteak Club (London), Travellers Club (Paris). Office: 667 Madison Ave New York NY 10021-8029

TRAIN, RUSSELL ERROL, environmentalist; b. Jamestown, R.I., June 4, 1920; s. Charles R. and Errol C. (Brown) T.; m. Aileen Bowdoin, May 27, 1954; children—Nancy, Emily, Bowdoin, Errol. A.B., Princeton U., 1941, LL.D. (hon.), 1970; LL.B., Columbia U., 1948, LL.D. (hon.), 1970; LL.D. (hon.), Bates Coll., 1970, Drexel U., 1970; D.E. (hon.), Worcester Poly. Inst., 1970, U. Md., 1975; Sc.D. (hon.), St. Mary's Coll., 1970, Clarkson Coll. Tech., 1973, Salem Coll., 1975, Southwestern U., 1976, Mich. State U., 1976; D.C.L. (hon.), U. of South, 1973. Bar: D.C. bar 1949. Atty. staff joint com. on internal revenue taxation U.S. Congress, 1949-53; chief counsel Ways and Means Com., U.S. Ho. of Reps., 1953-54, minority adviser, 1955-56; asst. to sec., head legal adv. staff Treasury Dept., 1956-57; judge U.S. Tax Ct., 1957-65; pres. Conservation Found., 1965-69; also trustee; undersec. Dept. Interior, 1969-70; chmn. Council on Environ. Quality, 1970-73; adminstr. EPA, Washington, 1973-77; sr. assoc. Conservation Found., 1977; pres., chief exec. officer World Wildlife Fund, Washington, 1978-85, chmn. bd., 1985; chmn. bd. Conservation Found., 1985-90, Nat. Commn. on the Environment, 1991-93; chmn. Nat. Coun. World Wildlife Found., Washington; chief exec. Washington Nat. Monument Assn.; mem. Nat. Water Commn., 1968; head U.S. del. UN Conf. Human Environment, 1972; rep. Internat. Whaling Commn., 1972, other internat. confs.; dir. Applied Energy Services Inc.; mem. Pres.'s adv. com. on trade and trade negotiations, 1991-93. Trustee emeritus African Wildlife Found.; bd. dirs. Am. Conservation Assn., Found. Philippine Environ., King Mahendra Trust for Nature Conservation in Nepal; bd. dirs. Served to maj., F.A. AUS, 1941-46. Decorated Order of Golden Ark (The Netherlands); recipient Albert Schweitzer medal Animal Welfare Inst., 1972; Aldo Leopold medal Wildlife Soc., 1975; Conservationist of Yr. award Nat. Wildlife Fedn., 1974; John and Alice Tyler Ecology award, 1978; Freese award ASCE, 1978; Public Welfare award Nat. Acad. Scis., 1981; Elizabeth Haub prize in internat. environ. law, 1981, Lindbergh award, 1985, Environ. Law Inst. award, 1986; conservationist of yr. award Nat. Wildlife Fedn., 1986; Presidential Medal of Freedom, 1991. Mem. Council Fgn. Relations, Washington Inst. Fgn. Affairs, Atlantic Coun. Office: World Wildlife Fund 1250 24th St NW Washington DC 20037-1124*

TRAINA, ALBERT SALVATORE, publishing executive; b. Bklyn., Apr. 30, 1927; s. Salvatore and Guilia (LeBarbara) T.; m. Vail Devereux, June 27, 1957; children—Caroline Vail, Robert Brooks. B.S. (N.Y. State War Service scholar), Seton Hall U., 1950; postgrad., Columbia U., 1950-51; M.B.A., NYU, 1954. Circulation promotion advt. space salesman Fairchild Publs., N.Y.C., 1951-53; Eastern advt. mgr. Modern Bride mag. Ziff-Davis, N.Y.C., 1953-58; advt. mgr. Bride and Home mag. Hearst Mags., N.Y.C., 1958-60; pub. Bride and Home mag. Hearst Mags., 1960-64; pub. Sports Afield mag., 1964-65, Town and Country mag., 1965-67, Harpers Bazaar mag., 1967-70; pres., chief exec. officer Bartell Media Corp., 1970-74; pub. Ziff-Davis Mag. Network, 1974-76, group v.p., 1976-78; sr. v.p. Ziff-Davis Pub. Co., 1978-81; pres. Ziff-Davis Consumer Mag., 1981-85; exec. v.p. mags. CBS, N.Y.C., 1985; pres. Traina Assocs., N.Y.C., 1985—. Mem. Scarsdale Bi-Partisan Com., 1975-78; bd. dirs. Crane Berkeley Assn., 1978-88, pres., 1983-84; mem. nat. bd. dirs., chmn. comms. com., treas. Goodwill Industries of Am. 1979—, chmn. bd., 1988-92; bd. dirs. Goodwill Industries of N.Y., 1983—. With USNR, 1945-47. Mem. NYU Grad. Sch. Bus. Adminstrn. Alumni Assn., NYU Alumni Fedn. (comms. com. 1970-73), Fox Meadow Tennis Club (Scarsdale), Union League Club (N.Y.C.). Home: 205 E 63rd St Apt 15D New York NY 10021-7419 Office: 205 E 63d St 15D New York NY 10021

TRAINA, RICHARD PAUL, university president; b. San Francisco, June 3, 1937; s. Frank Ignatius and Isabelle (Thomas) T.; m. Margaret Bradley Warner, June 6, 1959; children: Cristina Traina Hutchison, Michelle Traina Riecke, Matthew Warner, Michael Derek. B.A., U. Santa Clara, 1958; M.A., U. Calif.-Berkeley, 1960, Ph.D., 1964. Instr. history Wabash Coll. Crawfordsville, Ind., 1963-64, asst. prof., 1964-68, assoc. prof., 1968-74, dean, 1969-74; dean, provost Franklin & Marshall Coll., Lancaster, Pa., 1974-81, acad. v.p., dean, 1981-84; pres. Clark U., Worcester, Mass., 1984—. Author: American Diplomacy and the Spanish Civil War, 1968; co-editor: (with A. Rappaport) Present in the Past, 1972. Mem. Orgns. of Am. Historians, Soc. for Values in Higher Edn. Democrat. Roman Catholic. Home: 80 William St Worcester MA 01609-2138 Office: Clark U 950 Main St Worcester MA 01610-1400

TRAINOR, BERNARD EDMUND, journalist, educator, retired marine corps officer; b. N.Y.C., Sept. 2, 1928; s. Joseph Patrick and Ann Veronica (Whelan) T.; m. Margaret Ann Hamilton, June 13, 1959; children: Kathleen Marie, Theresa Ann, Eileen Cecile, Claire Hamilton. B.S., Coll. of Holy Cross, 1951; M.A., U. Colo., 1963, postgrad., 1970—. Commd. 2d lt. USMC, 1951, advanced through grades to lt. gen., 1983; inf. comdr. Korea, 1952; assigned USS Columbus, 1953-55, staff Marine Corps Hdqrs., 1955-58, exchange office Royal Marine Commandos, 1958-59, inf. comdr. First Marine Div., 1959-61; asst. prof. naval sci. U. Colo., Boulder, 1961-64; assigned to Marine Corps Command and Staff Coll., 1964-65; adv. Republic of Vietnam, 1965-66; instr. Marine Corps Command and Staff Coll., 1966-69; student Air War Coll., Montgomery, Ala., 1969-70; bn. comdr. Vietnam, 1970-71; staff officer Hdqrs. Marine Corps, Washington, 1970-71; dir. First Marine Corps Dist., N.Y.C., 1974-76; asst. depot comdt. Marine Corps Recruit Depot, Parris Island, S.C., 1976-78; dir. Edn. Center, Quantico, Va., 1978-81; dep. chief of staff for plans, policies and ops. Hdqrs. Marine Corps, 1981-85; cons., 1985—; mil. corr. N.Y. Times, 1986-90; dir. nat. security program Kennedy Sch. Govt. Harvard U., Cambridge, Mass., 1990—. Author: History of the U.S. Marine Corps, 1968, The Generals' War, 1995; contbg. author: American Defense Annual, 1990, Defense Beat, 1991, After the Storm, 1992, The Almanac of Seapower, 1993, Newsmen and National Defense, 1991, Perspectives on Warfighting, 1992; mem. editl. adv. bd. Naval War Coll. Rev., Harvard Jour. Internat. Affairs; mem. editl. bd. Amphibious Warfare Rev.; contbr. articles to profl. jours. Mem. adv. bd. to pres. of Naval War Coll.; mil. analyst NBC News; rsch. bd. dirs. Inst. for Fgn. Policy Analysis, Marine Toys for Tots Found. Decorated D.S.M., Legion of Merit (2), Bronze Star, Navy Commendation medal (2), others; recipient Anderson Meml. award Air War Coll., 1970. Mem. Naval Inst., Internat. Inst. Strategic Studies, Marine Corps Assn., Coun. Fgn. Rels., World Affairs Coun., Army-Navy Club. Roman Catholic. Home: 80 Potter Pond Lexington MA 02173 Office: Harvard U Kennedy Sch Govt 79 JFK St Cambridge MA 02138-3352

TRAINOR, JERRY ALLEN, vocational education professional; b. Pablo, Mont., May 19, 1937; s. Harry Frances and Eva Grace (Simonis) T.; m. Joyce Evelyn Rice, July 2, 1962 (div. 1970); 1 child, Darryn Sean; m. Helen Elizabeth Wahl, Aug. 29, 1974; children: Hillary Gay, Erin Lane Estein. BS in Edn., U. Idaho, 1987, MEd, 1989. Asst. prof. welding tech. Lewis and Clark State Coll., Lewiston, Idaho, 1983-89; coord. Cen. Idaho Vocat. Edn. Consortium, Lapwai, 1989-91; vocat. counselor Alaska Tech. Ctr., Kotzebue, 1991-93; career counselor, job devel. specialist Arctic Sivunmun Ilisagvik Coll., Barrow, Alaska; bd. dirs. Profl. Devel. for Educators, State of Idaho, 1987; presenter at profl. confs. Contbr. articles to profl. publs; author curriculum materials. Mem. Winter Carnival com., Prince George, B.C., Can., 1975; regional rep. Libertarian Party Idaho, 1986. Winner various ice racing and hill climbing competitions Can. Auto Sports Club; named New Vocat. Educator of Yr. State of Idaho, 1986. Mem. NEA, ASCD, Am. Vocat. Assn., Phi Delta Kappa. Nazarene. Avocations: automobile racing, snowmachine touring, hunting, photography. Office: Arctic Sivunmun Ilisagvik Coll Box 749 Barrow AK 99723

TRAINOR, JOHN FELIX, retired economics educator; b. Mpls., Dec. 1, 1921; s. James Patrick and Myra Catherine (Pauly) T.; m. Margaret Dolores Pudenz, July 3, 1965 (dec. 1977); children: John Anthony, Patrick James. BA cum laude, Coll. St. Thomas, 1943; MA, U. Minn., 1950; PhD, Wash. State U., 1970. Instr. high sch. Mpls., 1946-47; instr. Coll. St. Thomas, 1949-50; v.p. Trainor Candy Co., Mpls., 1946-56; instr., asst. prof. econs. Rockhurst Coll., Kansas City, Mo., 1956-62; instr. Wash. State U., Pullman, 1966-67; asst. prof. Moorhead (Minn.) State U., 1967-70, assoc. prof. econs., 1971-87, prof. econ., 1988-89, chmn. dept. econs., 1981-89; prof. emeritus, 1989—. Author: (with Frank J. Kottke) The Nursing Home Industry in the State of Washington, 1968. Ensign Lt. (j.g.) USNR, 1943-46, ETO. Mem. Minn. Econs. Assn. (pres. 1976-77), Assn. Social Econs., Omicron Delta Epsilon. Roman Catholic. Home: 1333 4th Ave S Moorhead MN 56560-2971

TRAINOR, LILLIAN (MIDGE TRAINOR), elections official; b. Norma, N.J., Oct. 30, 1936; d. Loenell Lesley and Lillie Ara (Kenyon) Barber; m. Arthur James Trainor, Mar. 9, 1959; children: Michael, Arthur, Lynn Marie. Student pub. schs., Pleasantville, N.J. Chair Burlington County Bd. Elections, Mount Holly, N.J., 1978-81, commr. of registration, 1981-83, chair, 1983-90; dir. N.J. Div. Elections, 1990—. Vice chair, mem. exec. bd. Burlington County Dem. Com., 1977-90; chair Southampton Twp. Dem. County Com., 1976-79, Bd. County Convassers, Burlington County, 1978-90; v.p. Southeastern Dem. Coalition, 1977-87; mgr. Florio for Gov. Campaign, N.J., 1981, Carter for Pres. Campaign, Burlington County area, 1980; del. Dem. Nat. Conv., 1984, 88; coord. Women for Florio Gubanatorial campaign, 1989. Served with WAC, 1955-57. Mem. Nat. Assn. State Election Dirs., N.J. State Assn. Election Ofcls., VFW Aux. Club: Big Six (pres. 1973-79). Avocations: accordian, piano, birdwatching, reading. Home: PO Box 2266 Vincentown NJ 08088-2266 Office: NJ Div Elections 315 W State St Trenton NJ 08618-5703

TRAISMAN, HOWARD SEVIN, pediatrician; b. Chgo., Mar. 18, 1923; s. Alfred Stanley and Sara (Sevin) T.; m. Regina Gallagher, Feb. 29, 1956; children—Barry D. Lifschultz, Edward S., Kenneth N. B.S. in Chemistry, Northwestern U., 1943, M.B., 1946, M.D., 1947. Intern Cook County Hosp., Chgo., 1946-47; resident in pediatrics Children's Meml. Hosp., Chgo., 1949-51; attending physician div. endocrinology Children's Meml. Hosp., 1951—; mem. faculty Northwestern U. Med. Sch., 1951—, prof. pediatrics, 1973—. Author articles in field, chpts. in books. Served to capt. M.C. AUS, 1943-46, 47-49. Mem. Am. Med. Assn. (Disting. Service award 1976), Am. Pediatric Soc., Am. Acad. Pediatrics, Endocrine Soc., Lawson Wilkins Pediatric Endocrine Soc., AMA, Midwest Soc. Pediatric Research, Ill. Med. Soc., Chgo. Pediatric Soc., Chgo. Med. Soc., Inst. Medicine Chgo. Democrat. Jewish. Office: 1325 Howard St Evanston IL 60202-3766

TRAISTER, ROBERT EDWIN, naval officer, engineer; b. Haverhill, Mass., Sept. 15, 1937; s. Frank and Anne (Schlafman) T.; m. Janet Weinberger; children: James, Jeffrey. Student, Bowdoin Coll., 1955-56; BS, U.S. Naval Acad., Annapolis, Md., 1960; MSME, U.S. Naval Postgrad. Sch., Monterey, Calif., 1967. Commd. ensign USN, 1960, advanced through grades to rear adm., 1988; surface warfare officer, chief engr. USS William R. Rush, 1962-64; ship supt. Puget Sound Naval Shipyard, Bremerton, Wash., 1969-72, shipbuilding/repair/prodns. officer, 1982-86; chief engr. USS Springfield, USS Little Rock, 1972-75; trials officer Office Comdr. Naval Sea Systems, DD963 PRGM, Washington, 1975-78; comdg. officer Pearl Harbor (Hawaii) Naval Shipyard, 1984-88; maintenance officer Office Comdr. in Chief Pacific Fleet, Pearl Harbor, 1988-90; dep. comdr. surface ships Naval Sea Systems Command, Washington, 1990-94; dir. projects and site svcs. Westinghouse Hanford Corp., Richland, Wash., 1994—. Decorated Legion of Merit. Mem. Am. Soc. Naval Engrs. Assn., Am. Def. Preparedness Assn. (bd. dirs. 1990-92), U.S. Naval Acad. Alumni Assn. (pres. 1989-90), Bowdoin Coll. Alumni Assn., Army/Navy Country Club, Meadows Spring Country Club. Avocations: photography, sports. Office: Westinghouse Hanford Co Richland WA 99352

TRAMIEL, SAM, microcomputer and video game company executive; b. 1950. With Commodore Internat. Ltd., 1974-84, Atari Corp., 1984—; now pres., chief exec. officer. Office: Atari Corp 1196 Borregas Ave Sunnyvale CA 94089-1302

TRAMMELL, GEORGE THOMAS, physics educator; b. Marshall, Tex., Feb. 5, 1923; s. George Thomas and Cordelia (Whitsitt) T.; children: Peter, David, Susan, Jonathon. BA, Rice Inst., 1944; PhD, Cornell U., 1950. Physicist Oak Ridge Nat. Lab., 1950-61; prof. physics Rice U., Houston, 1961—; vis. prof. Tech. U., Munich, Fed. Republic Germany, 1967-68; vis. scientist Internat. Laue-Langevin Inst., Grenoble, France, 1975-76. Contbr. articles to profl. jours. Lt. (j.g.) USNR, 1944-46. Fellow Am. Phys. Soc. Office: Rice U Dept Physics PO Box 1892 Houston TX 77251-1892

TRAMMELL, HERBERT EUGENE, physicist, laboratory executive; b. Laurel, Miss., Apr. 19, 1927; s. Homer Lee and Evie Louisa (Breazeale) T.; m. Jane Walker, Dec. 28, 1948; children—Carmen, Bert, Lisa, Brian. B.A. in Physics, U. Miss., 1947, M.A., 1948. With Nuclear div. Union Carbide, Oak Ridge, 1949-89, mgr. barrier devel. programs, 1967-69, dir. gaseous diffusion devel. div., 1969-77; dir. engring. tech. div. Oak Ridge Nat. Lab., 1977-89, ret., 1989; with Martin Marietta Energy Systems, 1983-89. Bd. dirs. Emory Valley Sch. for Retarded Children, 1962-68, v.p., 1966-68; mem. Tenn. Med. Malpractice Rev. Bd., 1974-80; active PTA. Served with U.S. Navy, 1944-45. Methodist. Club: Rotary (pres. 1980-81). Home: 901 Johnson St Key West FL 33040-4745

TRAMONTINE, JOHN O., lawyer; b. Iron Mountain, Mich., Sept. 21, 1932; s. Orlando F. and Susan M. (Hollar) T.; m. Nancy A. McCabe, July 14, 1956; 1 child, Margaret A. BS in Chem. Engring., U. Notre Dame, 1955; postgrad., Georgetown U., 1956-58; LLB, NYU, 1960. Bar: N.Y. 1960, U.S. Dist. Ct. (no. dist.) Ill. 1963, U.S. Dist. Ct. (so. and ea. dists.) N.Y. 1965, U.S. Ct. Appeals (2d and 5th cirs.) 1967, U.S. Supreme Ct. 1970, U.S. Ct. Appeals (8th cir.) 1970, (3d cir.) 1973, (7th cir.) 1976, (fed. cir.) 1979, U.S. Dist. Ct. (we. dist.) N.Y. 1981. Examiner U.S. Patent Office, 1956-58; patent agt. Arthur, Dry & Dole, N.Y.C., 1958-60; assoc. Arthur, Dry, Kalish, Taylor & Wood, N.Y.C., 1960-62, Wolfe, Hubbard, Voit & Osann, Chgo., 1962-63; assoc. Fish & Neave, N.Y.C., 1963-70, ptnr., 1970—. 2d lt. USMCR, 1955. Fellow Am. Coll. Trial Lawyers, Am. Bar Found.; mem. ABA, Assn. Bar City N.Y. (chmn, patent com. 1974-77), Fed. Cir. Bar Assn., N.Y. Intellectual Property Assn. (pres. 1985-86), St. Andrews Golf Club (sec. 1981-83). Office: Fish & Neave 1251 Avenue Of The Americas New York NY 10020-1104

TRAMPOSCH, WILLIAM JOSEPH, museum director, consultant; b. Bridgeport, Conn., Dec. 14, 1948; s. Emil J. and Alice Catherine Tramposch; m. Margaret Simpson, May 4, 1976; children: Emma, Molly. AB, U. Calif., Berkeley, 1970; MA, Coll. William and Mary, 1982, EdD, 1986. Coord. interpretation Old Sturbridge Village, Mass., 1976-79; dir. interpretation Colonial Williamsburg, Va., 1979-89; dir. Oreg. Hist. Soc., Portland, Oreg., 1989—. Sgt. USAFR, 1970-76. Fulbright scholar, New Zealand, 1986, 88. Mem. Am. Assn. for State and Local History (coun. 1987-91), Am. Assn. Mus., Internat. Coun. Mus. (bd. dirs. 1986, participant Moscow meeting 1986), Phi Beta Kappa. Mem. Soc. of Friends. Avocations: running, writing, drawning. Home: 65 SW Custer St Portland OR 97219-2953 Office: Oreg Hist Soc 1230 SW Park Ave Portland OR 97205-2441

TRAMUTO, JAMES ARNOLD, utilities public affairs executive, lawyer; b. Galveston, Tex., Nov. 30, 1948; s. Angelo James and Arlene (Wrba) T.; m. JoAnn Crapitto, May 20, 1979; children—Catherine, James Joseph, Laura Marie, Emily Louise. B.B.A. Tex. A&M U., 1971; J.D., S. Tex. Coll. Law, 1974; postgrad. Harvard U., 1977. Bar: Tex. 1974. Vice pres. United Energy Resources, Inc., Houston, 1984—; atty. United Gas Pipe Line Co., Houston, 1974-77, mgr., 1977-79, dir., 1979-82, v.p., 1982-84; v.p. pub. affairs United Energy Resources, 1984—. Mem. ABA, Houston Bar Assn., Tex. Bar Assn., Fed Power Bar Assn., Tex. Bar Found., Tex. Utility Lawyers Assn. (pres.), Houston Jr. Bar Assn., Houston C. of C., Houston Livestock Show and Rodeo. Office: United Energy Resources Inc 600 Travis PO Box 1478 Houston TX 77001

TRANDEL, RICHARD SAMUEL, mechanical engineer, educator; b. Chgo., Apr. 19, 1937; s. August Anthony and Helen Rose (Krug) T.; m. Barbara Swisher, June 4, 1960. BSCE, U.S. Mil. Inst., 1959; MSME, Va. Poly. Inst. and State U., 1966; PhD in Mech. Engring., U. Va., 1974. Registered profl. engr., Va. Prof. Va. Mil. Inst., Lexington, 1959—, head mech. engring. dept., 1980-90, sr. prof., 1990—; engring. div. dir., 1992—; cons. in field. 1st lt. U.S. Army, 1960-62. Home: RR 5 Box 425 Lexington VA 24450-8729 Office: Va Mil Inst Mech Engring Dept Lexington VA 24450

TRANI, EUGENE PAUL, university president, educator; b. Bklyn., Nov. 2, 1939; s. Frank Joseph and Rose Gertrude (Kelly) T.; m. Lois Elizabeth Quigley, June 2, 1962; children: Anne Chapman, Frank. BA in History with honors, U. Notre Dame, 1961; MA, Ind. U., 1963, PhD, 1966. Instr. history Ohio State U., Columbus, 1965-67; asst. prof. So. Ill. U., Carbondale, 1967-71, assoc. prof., 1971-75, prof., 1975-76; asst. v.p. acad. affairs, prof. U. Nebr., 1976-80; prof., vice chancellor acad. affairs U. Mo. Kansas City, 1980-86; prof., v.p. acad. affairs U. Wis. System, 1986-90; pres. Va. Commonwealth U., 1990—; pres., bd. dirs. Va. Biotechnology Rsch. Park, 1992—; vis. asst. prof. U. Wis. Milw., 1969; bd. dirs. Crestar Bank Richmond Met. Bd., Crestar Fin. Corp., Lawyers Title Corp., Innovative Tech. Authority; cons. various univ. presses, jours., govtl. agys.; advisor gov. La., Okla. State Regents Higher Edn.; mem. commn. Internat. Edn. Am. Coun. Higher Ed., 1991—; bd. gov. Ctr. Russian Am. Bus., Washington, 1993—; bd. advisors Inst. for U.S. Studies, I. London, 1993—; adv. coun. mem. Coun. on Grad. Studies and Rsch., U. Notre Dame, 1994—. Author, editor: Concerns of a Conservative Democrat, 1968, The Treaty of Portsmouth: An Adventure in American Diplomacy, 1969, The Secretaries of the Department of the Interior, 1849-69, 1975, (with David Wilson) The Presidency of Warren G. Harding, 3d edit., 1989; contbr. articles to profl. jours., newspapers; book reviewer. Permanent mem. Coun. Fgn. Rels., N.Y.C., 1979—; bd. dirs. Richmond Ballet, 1991—, NCCJ, Richmond, 1991—, Va. Spl. Olympics, 1991—, YMCA of Greater Richmond, 19926, Richmond Renaissance, 1992—, Met. Found., 1992-95; mem. U.S. Savs. Bond Vol. Com., chmn. higher edn. area, 1992, 93; adv. bd. Greater Richmond chpt. ARC, 1992—. Fellow Russian and East European Inst., 1964-65, Nat. Hist. Publs. Commn., 1969-70, Woodrow Wilson Internat. Ctr. Scholars, 1972-73, So. Ill. U. Sabbatical Leave, 1975-76, Coun. Internat. Exchange Scholars, 1981, U. Mo. Faculty, 1981; grantee U.S. Dept. Interior Rsch., 1965, 66, So. Ill. U. Office Rsch. and Projects, 1967-74, Am. Philos. Soc., 1968, 72, So. Ill U. Summer Rsch. 1970, 72, 75, Lilly Endowment, 1975-76, Sloan Commn. Govt. and Higher Edn., 1978, U.S. Info. Agy. Am. Participants Program, 1984, 85, 86, 88, 90; recipient Younger Humanist award NEH, 1972-73, Leadership and Achievement award Cert. Richmond Assn., 1992. Mem. Internat. Inst. Strategic Studies, Am. Assn. Advancement Slavic Studies, Orgn. Am. Historians, Soc. Historians Am. Fgn. Rels., Met. Richmond C. of C. (bd. dirs. 1991—), Va. Ctr. for Innovative Tech., Cert. Richmond Assn. (leadership award, 1992), Phi Kappa Phi. Roman Catholic. Avocations: reading, travel, basketball, golf. Office: Va Commonwealth U Box 842512 910 W Franklin St Richmond VA 23284-2512

TRANK, DOUGLAS MONTY, rhetoric and speech communications educator; b. Lincoln, Nebr., Sept. 8, 1944; s. Walter John and Hazel Elaine (Stegeman) T.; children: Heather Nicole, Jessica Celeste; m. Christine Marie Quinn, 1992. BA in English, U. Nebr., Kearney, 1967, MS in Comm., 1970; PhD in Comm., U. Utah, 1973. Tchr. Ogallala (Nebr.) High Sch., 1967-70; teaching fellow in communications U. Utah, Salt Lake City, 1970-72; prof. rhetoric and edn. U. Iowa, Iowa City, 1974—, chmn. rhetoric dept., 1984-89; chmn. bd. control athletics, faculty senate, mem. ednl. policy com., faculty adv. com., faculty assembly, exec. com. U. Iowa. Author book, chpts. books, monographs; editor Communication Edn., 1993-96; assoc. editor Communication Studies; contbr. articles to profl. jours. Recipient Admiral award Ace Adventures, Inc., Iowa, 1987, Hemingway prize, 1992. Mem. Speech Communication Assn., Iowa Communication Assn. (pres. 1980-82, editor 1977-81, mem. jour. editorial bd.), Cen. States Communication Assn. (pres. 1990-91), Fedn. Iowa Speech Orgns. (pres. 1977-79), Iowa City Optimist Club (dir. 1982-89, pres. 1987-88). Democrat. Avocations: ice sailing, hunting, fishing, canoeing. Office: U Iowa Dept Rhetoric Iowa City IA 52242

TRANQUADA, ROBERT ERNEST, medical educator, physician; b. Los Angeles, Aug. 27, 1930; s. Ernest Alvro and Katharine (Jacobus) T.; m. Janet Martin, Aug. 31, 1951; children: John Martin, James Robert, Katherine Anne. B.A., Pomona Coll., 1951; M.D., Stanford U., 1955; D.Sc. (hon.), Worcester Poly. Inst., 1985. Diplomate Am. Bd. Internal Medicine. Intern in medicine UCLA Med. Center, 1955-56, resident in medicine, 1956-57; resident Los Angeles VA Hosp., 1957-58; fellow in diabetes and metabolic diseases UCLA, 1958-59; fellow in diabetes U. So. Calif., 1959-60, asst. prof. medicine, 1960-63, assoc. prof., 1964-68, chmn. dept. community medicine, 1967-75; med. dir. Los Angeles County/U. So. Calif. Med. Center, 1969-74; regional dir. Central Region, Los Angeles County Dept. Health

Services, 1974-76; assoc. dean UCLA Sch. Medicine, 1976-79; chancellor and dean U. Mass. Med. Sch., 1979-86; dean U. So. Calif. Sch. Medicine, 1986-91; prof. medicine U. So. Calif., L.A., 1986-92, Norman Topping/Nat. Med. Enterprises prof. medicine and pub. policy, 1992—. mem., chair L.A. County Task Force on Health Care Access, 1992-94. Trustee Pomona Coll., 1969—, vice chmn., 1987-91, chmn., 1991—; mem. bd. fellows Claremont U. Ctr., 1971-79, 91—; corporator Worcester Art Mus., 1980-86; bd. dirs. Nat. Med. Fellowships, Inc., 1973—, chmn., 1980-85; trustee Charles Drew U. Medicine and Sch., 1968-79, 86—, Orthopaedic Hosp., 1986-91, Barlow Hosp., 1987-89; bd. dirs. Worcester Acad., 1984-86, Worcester County Inst. for Savs., 1982-86, U. So. Calif. Univ. Hosp., 1988-91, Alliance for Childrens Rights, 1991—; bd. dirs. Good Hope Med. Found., 1994—; mem. Ind. Commn. on L.A. Police Dept., 1991-92; mem. governing bd. L.A. County Local Initiative Health Authority, 1994—. Milbank faculty fellow, 1967-72. Fellow AAAS, Am. Antiquarian Soc.; mem. AMA, Am. Diabetes Assn., Western Soc. Clin. Investigation, Los Angeles County Med. Assn., Los Angeles Acad. Medicine, Calif. Med. Assn., Inst. Medicine of Nat. Acad. Scis., Phi Beta Kappa, Sigma Xi, Alpha Omega Alpha. Office: U So Calif VKC # 368A Los Angeles CA 90089-0041

TRANSOU, LYNDA LEW, advertising art administrator; b. Atlanta, Dec. 11, 1949; d. Lewis Cole Transou and Ann Lynette (Taylor) Putnam; m. Lue Gregg Loso, Oct. 25, 1991. B.F.A. cum laude, U. Tex.-Austin, 1971. Art dir., The Pitluk Group, San Antonio, 1971, Campbell, McQuien & Lawson, Dallas, 1973-74, Bozell & Jacobs, Dallas, 1974-75; art dir., ptnr. The Assocs., Dallas, 1975-77; art dir. Belo Broadcasting, Dallas, 1977-80; creative dir., v.p. Allday & Assocs., Dallas, 1980-85; owner Lynda Transou Advt. & Design, 1986—. Recipient Merit award N.Y. Art Dirs. Show, 1980; Gold award Dallas Ad League, 1980, Silver award, 1980, Bronze award, 1981, 82, 2 Merit awards Houston Art Dirs. Club, 1978-86; Merit award Broadcast Designers Assn., 1980, 82; Merit awards Dallas Ad League, 1978, 87; Silver award Houston Art Dirs. Show; Gold award Tex. Pub. Relations Assn., 1982, 85; Gold award N.Y. One Show, 1982, Creativity award Art Direction mag., 1986, Print award Regional Design Annual, 1988, Telly Finalist, 1987. Mem. Am. Inst. Graphic Arts, Dallas Soc. Visual Communications (Bronze award 1980, Merit awards, 1978-86), Delta Gamma (historian 1969-70).

TRAPNELL, CHRISTINE, county official; b. Tientsin, China, Feb. 4, 1945; came to U.S., 1947; d. Wallace Hamilton and Irene Renée (Teodoro) Robinson; m. Gordon Robins Trapnell, Oct. 8, 1966; children: Andrea Renée, William Todd. BS in Fgn. Svc., Georgetown U., 1966. Dir. Sleepy Hollow Sr. Ctr., 1979-83; adminstrv. asst. Fairfax County Bd. Suprs., 1984-90, Mason dist. mem., 1992—. Pres. Lake Barcroft Civic Assn., Falls Church, Va., 1984-86, Mason Dist. Coun., Annandale, Va., 1988-90; commr. No. Va. Planning Dist. Commn., 1993—; mem. bd. advisors USA-Asian Bus. Coun., 1994; bd. dirs. Savation Army Alcoholic Rehab. Ctr. Adv. Coun., Annandale, 1992—. No. Va. Dental Clinic, Bailey's Crossroads, 1994. Mem. Rotary Internat. (bd. dirs. 1991), Lake Barcroft Womens Club (pres. 1988), Greater Falls Ch. Rep. Womens Club. Office: Mason Dist Govt Ctr 6507 Columbia Pike Annandale VA 22003

TRAPOLIN, FRANK WINTER, retired insurance executive; b. New Orleans, Jan. 29, 1913; s. John Baptiste and Florence Bertha (Winter) T.; BS in Econs., Loyola U. of South, New Orleans, 1935; cert. official U.S.A. Track & Field. m. Thelma Mae Mouledoux, Oct. 27, 1937; children: Timothy, Patricia Couret, Jane Oaksmith, Anne Britt. Agt., Godchaux & Mayer, New Orleans, 1935-42, 46-51; pres. Trapolin-Couret Ins. Agy., Inc., New Orleans, 1953-92, 92-93; v.p. Gillis, Ellis & Baker, Inc., New Orleans, 1993-94, ret., 1994; mem. faculty Loyola U.; TV lectr., seamanship instr. Coast Guard Aux., New Orleans Former pres. Cath. Human Rels. Commn. Greater New Orleans, Associated Cath. Charities New Orleans, Maryland Dr. Homeowners Assn., Loyola U. Alumni Assn.; former chmn. adv. bd. Ursuline Nuns New Orleans, New Orleans Juvenile Cts.; former scoutmaster Boy Scouts Am., former chmn. Boy Scout troop com.; former v.p. Cmty. Rels. Coun. Greater New Orleans, New Orleans Jr. C.of C., La. Interch. Conf.; former trustee United Fund Greater New Orleans Area; treas. emeritus La. Interchurch Conference, dir. emeritus Catholic Book Store Found., tng. officer 8th Coast Guard Dist. Aux.; former mem. adv. bd. Coll. Bus. Adminstrn., Loyola U., Mother-house of Sisters of Holy Family, Immaculate Conception Cath. Ch.; group captain Manresa Retreats, 1947—; former bd. dirs. St. John Berchman Orphanage, New Orleans Interfaith Conf., St. Elizabeth's Home for Girls, Cath. Book Store Found., Manresa Retreat House; adv. bd. New Orleans Track Club; founder, Serra Run for Vocations. Served with USN, 1942-46, 51-53, capt. Res. ret. Recipient Merit cert. City of New Orleans, 1972; Order of St. Louis, 1976; lector Catholic Ch., 1964-87; eucharistic min., 1986—. Mem. La. Assn. Ins. Agts., Nat. Assn. Ins. Agts., New Orleans Ins. Exch., Navy League, Mil. Order World Wars, Greater New Orleans Exec. Assn. (pres. 1985, named Exec. of the Year 1985, lifetime hon. mem.), New Orleans Photog. Soc., Sierra Club, Blue Key. Democrat. Roman Catholic. Clubs: Sertoma (pres. New Orleans 1955-56), Serra (pres. New Orleans 1973-74), Internat. House, New Orleans Track, New Orleans Yacht, Pass Christian Yacht. Lodge: KC (4 deg.). Patentee gunnery, tng. and machinery devices for USN. Home: 119 Audubon Blvd New Orleans LA 70118-5538

TRAPP, FRANK ANDERSON, art educator; b. Pitts., June 13, 1922; s. Frank Louis and Mary (Anderson) T. B.A., Carnegie Inst. Tech., 1943; A.M., Harvard, 1947, Ph.D., 1952. Teaching fellow Harvard (also resident tutor Adams House), 1948-51; mem. faculty Williams Coll., 1951-56; mem. faculty Amherst (Mass.) Coll., 1956-92, prof. art, 1963-92, William R. Mead prof., 1976-89, Arms prof., 1989-92, dir. Mead Art Mus., 1969-89; rsch. assoc. fine arts U. Pitts., 1994—; vis. Mellon prof. dept. fine arts U. Pitts., 1979-80. Author: The Attainment of Delacroix, 1970, Peter Blume, 1987, The Grand Tradition: British Art in the Amherst College Collection, 1988 (with others) Clarence Holbrook Carter, 1989; contbg. author and editor Mead Mus. Publs.; contbr. articles to profl. jours. Served with AUS, 1943-46, PTO. Fulbright grantee, 1949-50; Belgian-Am. Ednl. Found. fellow, 1954; Nat. Endowment for the Humanities sr. fellow, 1971-72. Home: 4609 Bayard St Apt 51 Pittsburgh PA 15213

TRAPP, JAMES MCCREERY, lawyer; b. Macomb, Ill., Aug. 11, 1934. BA, Knox Coll., 1956; JD, U. Mich., 1961. Bar: Ill. 1961. Ptnr. McDermott, Will & Emery, Chgo. Chmn. Ill. Inst. Continuing Legal Edn., 1978-79, bd. dirs., 1980-86, pres., 1984-85. Fellow Am. Coll. Trust and Estate Coun. (Ill. chmn. 1980-83, nat. regent 1983—, treas. 1989-90, sec. 1990-91, v.p. 1991-92, pres.-elect 1992-93, pres. 1993-94, exec. com. 1986-94). Am. Bar Found., Ill. Bar Found.; mem. ABA, Ill. State Bar Assn. Chgo. Bar Assn. (chair trust law com. 1972-73, com. on coms. 1972-74), Internat. Acad. Estate and Trust Law, Am. Law Inst., Chgo. Estate Planning Coun. Office: McDermott Will & Emery 227 W Monroe St Chicago IL 60606

TRAPP, LESLIE COMBS, state legislator; b. Lexington, Ky., Sept. 18, 1954; s. David Morton and Julette (Combs) T.; m. Cynthia Benes; children: Alexandra Benes, Lucas Combs. BA, Centre Coll. Ky. Exec. asst. to dir. Ky. Dept. Pub. Info., Frankfort, Ky. Internat. Tourism Office, Brussels, 1977-78; account exec. Becker Advt., Louisville, 1979-83, William Esty Co., N.Y.C., 1985-86; account supr. Wells, Riche, Greene, Inc., N.Y.C., 1985-86; v.p., mktg. dir. Bank One, Lexington, 1987-92; pres. Trapp Comm., 1987—; mem. Ky. Ho. of Reps., 1993—. Active Lexington-Fayette Urban Coun. Dist. 10, 1990-92; exec. v.p., co-founder Jazz Arts Found., 1989. Mem. SAR, Ky. Civil War Round Table. Episcopal. Democrat. Home: 1045 Lane Allen Rd Lexington KY 40504 Office: Ky Ho of Reps State Capitol Frankfort KY 40601

TRAPPE, JAMES MARTIN, mycologist; b. Spokane, Wash., Aug. 16, 1931; s. Martin Carl and Esther Louise (Koss) T.; m. Beverly Joan Reller, Dec. 27, 1963; children: Matthew, Erica, John, Angela. B.S., U. Wash., 1953, Ph.D., 1962; M.F., SUNY, Syracuse, 1955. With U.S. Forest Service, 1954-85; prin. mycologist, project leader Pacific N.W. Forest and Range Experiment Sta., Corvallis, Oreg., 1965-85; mem. faculty Oreg. State U., Corvallis, 1965—; prof. botany-plant pathology and forest sci. Oreg. State U., 1977—; co-chmn. Corvallis FISH, 1971-73. Editor Convictions mag.; contbr. articles to profl. jours. Recipient Civil Rights accomplishment award U.S. Forest Svc., 1979, Civil Liberties award ACLU, 1990, Barrington Moore Meml. award Soc. Am. Foresters, 1995; grantee NSF, 1971—, Am.

Philos. Soc., 1968-72, Sigma Xi, 1968-72, U.S. Spain Joint Com. Sci. and Tech. Cooperation, 1985-87, Indo-Am. Sci. and Tech. Initiative, 1984-91. Fellow AAAS; mem. Mycological Soc. Am. (council 1976-77, program chmn. 1976-77, v.p. 1984-85, pres. 1986-87), N.W. Sci. Assn. (past pres., Outstanding Scientist award 1991), Oreg. Acad. Sci. Oreg. Mycological Soc. (hon. life), Soc. Mex. de Micologia, Japanese Mycological Soc., Brit. Mycological Soc., N.Am. Truffling Soc. (hon. life). Home: 2165 NW Maser Pl Corvallis OR 97330 Office: Oreg State U Dept Forest Sci Corvallis OR 97331-7501

TRASK, GROVER C., lawyer; m. Cindy, 1971; children: Natalie, Trey. BA, San Diego State U., 1970; JD, U. San Diego, 1973; degree, Nat. Coll. Dist. Attys., U. Houston, 1980. With Riverside County Dist. Atty's. Office, 1974—, dist. atty., 1982—; mem. Calif. Coun. on Criminal Justice, 1985—; mem. advisory bd. Drug Suppression in Schs., 1984—; mem. Gov's. Statewide Task Force on Gangs and Drugs and Violence, 1985—; mem. Blue Ribbon Commn. on Inmate Population Mgmt., 1988; cons. U.S. Dept. Justice, 1991, Cont. Edn. of the Bar of the State of Calif., Calif. Criminal Law Procedure and Practice (book); mem. Statewide Task Force on Victims Rights, 1987. Contbr. articles to profl. jours. Exec. bd. mem. Boy Scouts of Am. (recipient dist. citizen of the yr. award 1988, chmn. scouting for food drive 1988, 90), Citizens Advisory Com. U. Calif., Riverside County Gen. Hosp. Found. Recipient Gov's. award for Outstanding Victim/Witness Program, 1987, Annual Law Enforcement Appreciation award Alternatives to Domestic Violence, 1991, Cert. of Appreciation Am. Legion, 1992; named Prosecutor of the Yr. WE-TIP, 1989. Mem. Nat. Dist. Attys. Assn. (mem. bd. dirs. 1988, chair subcom. Child Support Automation 1992-93, v.p. bd. dirs. 1992-93), Calif. Dist. Attys. Assn. (mem. bd. dirs. 1988-84, 1990-92, pres. 1987-88), Riverside County Bar Assn. (co-chair law & media com. 1982—, chair legis. com. 1985, mem. judicial selection com., 1982-86), Riverside County Dep. Dist. Attys. Assn. (pres.), Riverside County Law Enforcement Adminstrs. Assn. (pres. 1984, 86). Office: 4075 N Main St Fl 1 Riverside CA 92501-3707

TRASK, THOMAS EDWARD, religious organization administrator; b. Brainard, Minn., Mar. 23, 1936; m. Shirley Burkhart; children: Kimberly, Bradley, Todd, Tom. BA, North Cril. Bible Coll., 1956. Ordained min. Assemblies of God, 1958. Pastor First Assembly of God, Hibbing, Minn., 1956-60; pastor First Assembly of God, Vicksburg, Mich., 1960-64; Mich. dist. A/G youth leader First Assembly of God, 1964-68; sr. pastor Saginaw (Mich.) First Assembly of God, 1968-73, Brightmoor Tabernacle, Southfield, Mich., 1976-88; supt. Mich. Dist. Coun., Dearborn, 1973-76; gen. treas. The Gen. Coun. Assemblies of God, Springfield, Mich., 1988-93, gen. supt., 1993—. Co-author: Back to the Altar: A Call to Spiritual Awakening, 1994. Office: Assemblies of God 1445 Boonville Ave Springfield MO 65802

TRAUB, J(OSEPH) F(REDERICK), computer scientist, educator; b. June 24, 1932; m. Pamela Ann McCorduck, Dec. 6, 1969; children: Claudia Renee, Hillary Anne. B.S., CCNY, 1954; Ph.D., Columbia U., 1959. Mem. tech. staff Bell Labs., Murray Hill, N.J., 1959-70; prof. computer sci. and math., head dept. computer sci. Carnegie-Mellon U., Pitts., 1971-79; Edwin Howard Armstrong prof. computer sci., chmn. dept., prof. math. Columbia U., 1979-86; prof. computer sci. Princeton (N.J.) U., 1986-87; pres. John Von Neumann Nat. Supercomputer Ctr. Consortium for Sci. Computing, Princeton, 1986-87; Edwin Howard Armstrong prof., chmn. dept. computer sci., prof. math. Columbia U., N.Y.C., 1987-89, Edwin Howard Armstrong prof. computer sci., math., 1989—; dir. N.Y. State Ctr. Computers and Info. Systems, 1982-88; disting. lectr. MIT, 1977; vis. Mackay prof. U. Calif., Berkeley, 1978-79; cons. Hewlett-Packard, 1982, IBM, 1984, Schlumberger, 1986; mem. pres.'s adv. com. computer sci. Stanford U., 1972-75, chmn., 1975-76; mem. adv. com. Fed. Jud. Center; mem. sci. council I.R.I.A., Paris, 1976-80; mem. central steering com., computing sci. and engring. research study NSF, also liaison to panel on theoretical computer sci. and panel on numerical comp., 1974-80; mem. adv. com. Carnegie-Mellon Inst. Research, 1978-79; mem. applied math. div. rev. com. Argonne Nat. Lab., 1973-75; mem. adv. com. math. and computer sci. NSF, 1978-80; chmn. computer sci. and tech. bd. NRC, 1986-90; chmn. computer sci. and telecommunications bd. NRC, 1990-92; trustee Columbia U. Press, 1983-85; founding chair Spl. Interest Group on Numerical Math., 1965-71. Author: Iterative Methods for the Solution of Equations, 1964, Russian edit., 1985; (with H. Wozniakowski) A General Theory of Optimal Algorithms, 1980, Russian edit., 1983; (with G. Wasilkowski and H. Wozniakowski) Information, Uncertainty, Complexity, 1983, Information-Based Complexity, 1988; editor: Complexity of Sequential and Parallel Numerical Algorithms, 1973, Analytical Computational Complexity, 1976, Algorithms and Complexity: New Directions and Recent Results, 1976, Jour. Assn. Computing Machinery, 1970-76, Transactions on Math. Software, 1974-76, Jour. Computer and System Scis, 1973-86, Internat. Jour. on Computers and Math. with Applications, 1974—, Cohabiting With Computers, 1985; founding editor Jour. Complexity, 1985—, Ann. Rev. Computer Sci., 1986-92. Sherman Fairchild Disting. scholar Calif. Inst. Tech. 1991, 92; recipient Award for Disting. Svc. to Computing Rsch. Computer Rsch. Assn., 1992, Lezione Lincee Acad. Nazionale dei Lincei, 1993, Sr. Scientist award Alexander Von Humboldt Found., 1992—. Fellow AAAS (coun. 1971-74), ACM (chmn. award com. 1974-76); mem. Conf. Bd. Math. Scis. (coun. 1971-74), Soc. Indsl. and Applied Math., IEEE (Emanuel R. Piore Gold medal 1991), Am. Math. Soc., NAE (membership com. for computer sci., elec. engring. and control 1986-87, membership com. for computer sci. and engring. 1987-91, presdl. search com. 1993-94), N.Y. Acad. Sci. (study on high performance computing and comm. 1994-95, exec. com., bd. govs. 1987-89), Nat. Acad. Sci. (mem. study on high performance computing and comm. 1994-95). Office: Columbia University Dept Computer Sci New York NY 10027

TRAUB, RICHARD KENNETH, lawyer; b. Lakewood, N.J., Aug. 4, 1950; s. Harold W. and Muriel N. (Zurlin) T.; m. Barbara Lynn Wright, July 9, 1972; children: Russell S., Melissa L. BBA, U. Miami, Coral Gables, Fla., 1972, JD cum laude, 1975. Bar: Fla. 1975, N.Y. 1976, N.J. 1976, U.S. Dist. Ct. N.J. 1976, U.S. Supreme Ct. 1979, U.S. Dist. Ct. (ea. & so. dists.) N.Y. 1981. Ptnr. Wilson, Elser, Moskowitz, Edelman & Dicker, N.Y.C., 1975—; ptnr. Time for Patty Stables, N.J., 1992—; officer, dir. X-Ray Duplications, Inc., N.J.; ptnr., founder Fractured Greetings, N.J.; mem. lectr. Fedn. Ins. and Corp. Counsel, 1993—; lectr. Inst. for Internat. Rsch., Washington, 1988, Engring. News Record Constrn. Claims Conf., 1991. Author: Legal and Professional Aspects of Construction Management, 1990; contbr. articles to profl. jours. Bd. dirs. Pop Warner Football Assn., Holmdel, N.J., 1989—. Mem. ABA (forum com. on constrn. industry 1989, tort and ins. practice sect. 1985—, computer litigation sect.), N.Y. State Bar Assn., N.J. Bar Assn., Fla. Bar Assn., Fedn. Ins. and Corp. Counsel (spkr. ins. coverage sect., mem. ins. coverage and industry coop. sects.). Office: Wilson Elser Moskowitz Edelman & Dicker 150 E 42d St New York NY 10017-5639

TRAUDT, MARY B., elementary education educator; b. Chgo., Jan. 1, 1930; d. Lloyd Andrews Haldeman and Adele Eleanor (MacKinnon) Haldeman-Oliver; m. Eugene Peter Traudt, Dec. 6, 1952 (dec.); 1 child, Victoria Jean. BS, Cen. Mich. U., 1951; MA, Roosevelt U., 1978; postgrad., U. Ill., 1982. Asst. editor Commerce Clearing House, Chgo., 1951-53; tchr. Cleve. Elem. Sch., 1954-56, Chgo. Sch. System, 1956-57, Community Consolidated # 54, Hoffman Estates, Ill., 1957-64, Avoca Elem. Sch., Wilmette, Ill., 1964—; ret. 1995. Recipient Computer award Apple Computer Co. Mem. Avoca Edn. Assn. (v.p. 1986-91), Alpha Psi Omega. Presbyterian. Avocations: reading, sewing, music, travel, gardening. Home: 107 Lincoln St Glenview IL 60025-4916 Office: Avoca Elem Sch 235 Beech Dr Glenview IL 60025-3274

TRAUGER, DONALD BYRON, nuclear engineering laboratory administrator; b. Exeter, Nebr., June 29, 1920; s. Charles C. and Ethel L. (Downey) T.; m. Elaine Causey, Sept. 2, 1945; children: Byron Roscoe, Thomas Charles. A.B., Nebr. Wesleyan U., 1942, D.Sc. (hon.), 1974; postgrad., Columbia U., 1942-46, U. Tenn., 1946-49; D.Sc. (hon.), Tenn. Wesleyan Coll., 1977. Supr. test equipment devel. Manhattan Dist. Project, 1942-46; supr. Devel. Lab., Oak Ridge Gaseous Diffusion Plant, 1946-54; with Oak Ridge Nat. Lab., 1954-93, assoc. dir. nuclear and engring. technologies, 1970-84, sr. staff asst. to dir., 1984-93; cons. in energy tech., 1993—. Editorial advisor Anns. Nuclear Engring., 1989—; design features editor sect. IV Nuclear Safety Jour., 1989—. Mem. Oak Ridge Bd. Edn., 1961-67; pres. Oak Ridge PTA Coun., 1969-70, Oak Ridge Parents Adv. Coun., 1958-59;

chmn. exec. com., trustee Tenn. Wesleyan Coll., 1976-81, chmn. bd. govs., 1986-90, chmn. bd. trustees, 1990-93. Recipient Alumni Achievement award Nebr. Wesleyan U., 1962. Fellow Am. Nuclear Soc. (chmn. planning com. 1981-83); mem. AAAS, Am. Phys. Soc., Sigma Xi (pres. Oak Ridge chpt. 1987-88), Sigma Pi Sigma. Methodist. Club: Rotary. Office: PO Box 2008 Oak Ridge TN 37831-6254

TRAUGOTT, ELIZABETH CLOSS, linguistics educator and researcher; b. Bristol, Eng., Apr. 9, 1939; d. August and Hannah M.M. (Priebsch) Closs; m. John L. Traugott, Sept. 26, 1967; 1 dau., Isabel. BA in English, Oxford U., Eng., 1960; PhD in English lang., U. Calif., Berkeley, 1964. Asst. prof. English U. Calif., Berkeley, 1964-70; lectr. U. East Africa, Tanzania, 1965-66, U. York, Eng., 1966-67; lectr., then assoc. prof. linguistics and English Stanford U., Calif., 1970-77, prof., 1977—, chmn. linguistics dept., 1980-85; vice provost, dean grad. studies Stanford U., 1985-91, mem. grad. record examinations bd., 1989-93, mem. test of English as a fgn. lang. bd., 1989-91; chmn. test of English as a fgn. lang. bd., 1991-92. Author: A History of English Syntax, 1972, (with Mary Pratt) Linguistics for Students of Literature, 1980, (with Paul Hopper) Grammaticalization, 1993; editor: (with ter Meulen, Reilly, Ferguson) On Conditionals, 1986, (with Heine) Approaches to Grammaticalization, 2 vols., 1991; contrb. numerous articles to profl. jours. Am. Coun. Learned Socs. fellow, 1975-76, Guggenheim fellow, 1983-84, Ctr. Advanced Study of Behavioral Scis. fellow, 1983-84. Mem. MLA, AAUP, AAUW, Linguistics Soc. Am. (pres. 1987, sec.-treas. 1994—), Internat. Soc. Hist. Linguistics (pres. 1979-81). Office: Stanford Univ Dept Linguistics Bldg 460 Stanford CA 94305-2150

TRAUM, JEROME S., lawyer; b. Newark, Sept. 26, 1935; s. Max and Evelyn (Fein) T.; m. Lynda Sturner, Apr. 16, 1972; children: David, Norman, Daniel, Edward. A.B., U. Mich., 1956, J.D. with distinction, 1959. Bar: N.Y. 1960, U.S. Supreme Ct. 1976. Assoc. Chadbourne, Parke, Whiteside & Wolff, N.Y.C., 1959-62; assoc. to ptnr. Spear and Hill, N.Y.C., 1962-67; ptnr. Janklow and Traum, N.Y.C., 1967-89; v.p., then pres. Morton L. Janklow Assocs., Inc., lit. agy., 1977-89; gen. ptnr. investment bankers The Blackstone Group, N.Y.C., 1989-91; of counsel Proskauer, Rose, Goetz & Mendelsohn, N.Y.C., 1991-95; ptnr. Moses & Singer, N.Y.C., 1995—; adj. prof. fed. securities regulation Syracuse U. Coll. Law, 1975; bd. dirs. Interep Nat. Radio Sales, Inc. Bd. dirs. McCaffery & McCall, Inc., 1987-90, Open Channel, 1971-77, Call for Action, 1978-83, Playwright's Forum, Inc., 1981—, Penny McCall Found., Inc., 1987—; trustee Jose Limon Dance Found., 1968. Mem. Assn. of Bar of City of N.Y., ABA (com. fed. regulation securities), Order of Coif. Home: 111 W 67th St Apt 30C New York NY 10023 Office: Moses & Singer 1301 Ave of Americas New York NY 10019-6076

TRAUSCHT, DONALD C., security services executive; b. 1933. BA, St. Mary's Coll., 1955; MBA, U. Chgo., 1959. With Langevin Co., 1959-67; with Borg Warner Corp., 1967—, v.p. bus. devel. and acquisitions, 1978-82, v.p. corp. planning, 1982-87, v.p. finance and strategy, 1987, COO, pres., CEO, COO, 1992-93; chair, CEO Borg-Warner Security Corp., Chgo., 1993—. Office: Borg-Warner Security Corp 200 S Michigan Ave Chicago IL 60604-2402

TRAUTMAN, DONALD W., bishop; b. Buffalo, June 24, 1936. Ed., Our Lady of Angels Sem., Niagara Falls, N.Y., Theology Faculty, Innsbruck, Austria, Pontifical Biblical Inst., Rome, Cath. U., St. Thomas Aquinas U., Rome. Ordained priest Roman Cath. Ch., 1962, consecrated bishop, 1985. Titular bishop of Sassura and aux. bishop Diocese of Buffalo, 1985; bishop Erie, Pa., 1990—; Episc. moderator Diocesan Fiscal Mgmt. Conf.; mem. com. on doctrine and migration Nat. Conf. Cath. Bishops; chmn. Bishops' Liturgy Com. Home: 205 W 9th St Erie PA 16501 Address: St Mark's Ctr PO Box 10397 Erie PA 16514-0397

TRAUTMAN, HERMAN LOUIS, lawyer, educator; b. Columbus, Ind., Sept. 26, 1911; s. Theodore H. and Emma (Guckenberger) T.; m. Marian Lucille Green, Sept. 1, 1940; children: Stephen M., Pamela C.; LLB with distinction Ind. U., 1937, BA, 1946, JD with distinction, 1946; postgrad., NYU, 1953, Ford Found. faculty fellow, Harvard U., 1954-55. Bar: Ind. 1937, U.S. Tax Ct., U.S. Ct. Appeals (6th cir.) Tenn. Sole practice, Evansville, Ind., 1937-43; pres. Crescent Coal Co., Evansville, 1941-43; prof. law U. Ala. Tuscaloosa, 1946-49; prof. law Vanderbilt U., 1949—, prof. law emeritus, 1977; NYU vis. prof., 1955, U. Mich., Ann Arbor, 1963-64; ptnr. Trautman & Trautman, Nashville, 1976-85; sole practice, Nashville, 1986—. Served to lt. comdr. USN, 1943-46. Mem. ABA, Am. Law Inst., Tenn. Bar Assn., Nashville Bar Assn., Nat. Conf. Jud. Adminstrs., Estate Planning Coun., Order of Coif, Phi Gamma Delta, Belle Meade Club, Univ. Club, Kiwanis. Methodist. Address: 5100 Stanford Dr Nashville TN 37215

TRAUTMAN, WILLIAM ELLSWORTH, lawyer; b. San Francisco, Nov. 27, 1940; s. Gerald H. and Doris Joy (Tucker) T.; m. Dorothy Williamson, June 17, 1962; children: Darcey, Torey. AB, U. Calif., Berkeley, 1962, LLB, 1965. Bar: Calif. U.S. Supreme Ct., Calif. Dist. Ct., U.S. Ct. Appeals (9th and fed. cirs.). Assoc. Chickering & Gregory, San Francisco, 1965-71, ptnr., 1972-81; ptnr. Brobeck, Phleger & Harrison, San Francisco, 1981—, mng. ptnr., 1992—, litigation dept. chair, 1984-91; panelist Fed. Ct. Practice Ins. Trial Video, Ins. Coverage Disputes. Pres. Oakland (Calif.) Mus. Assn., 1981-83; bd. dirs. Piedmont (Calif.) Campfire Girls, 1978-80; mem. budget com. United Way, San Francisco, 1972; mem. profl. ethics com. State Bar Calif., 1974-77. Fellow Am. Coll. Trial Lawyers; mem. Legal Aid Soc. (bd. dirs. 1982-93, pres. 1985-88), Bar Assn. San Francisco (bd. dirs. 1972-73), Calif. Barristers (bd. dirs., v.p.), Barrister's Club of San Francisco (v.p. 1973). Office: Brobeck Phleger & Harrison 1 Market Plz San Francisco CA 94105-1019

TRAUTMANN, CHARLES HOME, museum director, civil engineer; b. Pawtucket, R.I., Jan. 6, 1952; s. Homer Frank and Gail (Greenhalgh) T.; m. Nancy Lawson Morton, May 7, 1977; children: Nina Morton, Eric Morton. BA cum laude, Amherst Coll., 1974; MSCE, MS in Geology, Stanford U., 1976; PhD in Civil Engring., Cornell U., 1983. Registered profl. engr.; cert. profl. geologist. Geologist Geotech. Engrs., Inc., Winchester, Mass., 1976-79; grad. rsch. asst. Cornell U., Ithaca, N.Y., 1979-83; rsch. assoc. Cornell U., Ithaca, 1983-88, sr. rsch. assoc., 1988-94; adj. assoc. prof. civil and environ. engring., 1994—; exec. dir. Sciencenter, Ithaca, 1990—; cons. engr., geologist, pvt. practice, Ithaca, 1983—. Contbr. over 50 articles to profl. jours. Bd. dirs. Ithaca Montessori Sch., 1984-91, pres., 1984-86, trustee, 1995—; pres. Forest Home Assn., Ithaca, 1989-90; pres., bd. trustees First Meth. Ch., Ithaca, 1984-87; mem. adv. bd. Paleontol. Rsch. Inst., 1993—; Cayuga Nature Ctr., 1993—. Rsch. fellow Alexander von Humboldt Found., 1987-88. Mem. ASCE (pres. Ithaca sect. 1993-94), Assn. Engring. Geologists, AAAS, Am. Inst. Profl. Geologists, Nat. Assn. Sci. Tchrs., Assn. Sci-Tech. Ctrs., Sci. Tchrs. Assn. N.Y. State (exec. com. 1994-95), Am. Assn. Mus., N.Y. State Sci. and Tech. Mus. Consortium (v.p. 1993-95, pres. 1995—), Nat. Eagle Scout Assn., Sigma Xi, Chi Epsilon. Office: Sciencenter 601 1st St Ithaca NY 14850-3507

TRAUTMANN, THOMAS ROGER, history and anthropology educator; b. Madison, Wis., May 27, 1940; s. Milton and Esther Florence (Trachte) T.; m. Marcella Hauolilani Choy, Sept. 25, 1962; children: Theodore, Robert. BA, Beloit Coll., 1962; PhD, U. London, 1968. Lectr. in history Sch. of Oriental and African Studies, U. London, 1965-68; asst. prof. history U. Mich., Ann Arbor, 1968-71, assoc. prof., 1971-77, prof., 1977—; Richard Hudson rsch. prof., 1979, prof. anthropology, 1984—, prof. history and anthropology, 1984—, chmn. dept. history, 1987-90, Steelcase rsch. prof., 1993-94. Author: Kautilya and the Arthasastra, 1971, Dravidian Kinship, 1981, Lewis Henry Morgan and the Invention of Kinship, 1987, (with K.S. Kabelac) The Library of Lewis Henry Morgan, 1994; author various articles on India, kinship and history of anthropology. Sr. Humanist fellow NEH, 1984. Fellow Royal Asiatic Soc.; mem. Am. Anthrop. Assn., Assn. for Asian Studies, Am. Oriental Soc., Am. Inst. Indian Studies (trustee, Sr. rsch. fellow in India 1985), Phi Beta Kappa. Office: U Mich Dept History Ann Arbor MI 48109-1045

TRAUTWEIN, GEORGE WILLIAM, conductor; b. Chgo., Aug. 5, 1927; s. William Jacob and Hilda (Martin) T.; m. Barbara Wilson, Jan. 20, 1955; children: Paul Martin, Matthew Richard. MusB, Oberlin Conservatory, Ohio, 1951; MusM, Cleve. Inst. Music, 1955; MusD, Ind. U., 1961. mem.

faculty U. Minn., U. Tex., Austin, Armstrong (Ga.) State Coll.; arts cons. Nat. Endowment Arts. Violinist Indpls. Symphony Orch., 1947-48, Balt. Symphony Orch., 1951-52, Nat. Symphony Orch., Washington, 1952-53, Cleve. Orch., 1953-57, Chautauqua Symphony Orch., N.Y., 1953-59, Camerata Acad., Salzburg, 1957-58, Mozarteum Orch., Salzburg, 1958 (Fulbright grantee 1958), assoc. condr. Dallas Symphony Orch., 1962-66, Mpls. Symphony, 1966-73; music dir. S.D. Symphony, 1971-75, Internat. Congress Strings, Ohio, 1973-75; music dir., condr. Savannah (Ga.) Symphony Orch., 1974-77; music adv., prin. guest condr. Evansville (Ind.) Philharm., 1979-80; music dir., condr. RIAS Edn. Network, Berlin, 1979, Tucson Symphony Orch., 1977-81; artistic dir., condr. Piedmont Chamber Orch.; prin. condr. Internat. Music program; dir. orchestral programs, N.C. Sch. of Arts, 1981-83; dir. instrumental ensembles, Wake Forest U., 1983—, dir. Artists series, 1985—; guest appearances with orchs., U.S., Germany, Sweden, France, Rumania, Jugoslavia, Portugal, Hong Kong, India, P.R. Mex. Adv. bd. Avery Fisher Found., N.Y.C. Served with USN, 1948-49. Recipient Orpheus award Phi Mu Alpha, 1971, ASCAP award, 1979, 82, World Peace award Ministry of World Harmony, 1983; Fulbright grantee Mozarteum, Salzburg, 1958; Sr. Fulbright lectr., India, 1989-90. Mem. Am. Fedn. Musicians, Chamber Music Soc. Am., Sir Thomas Beecham Soc., Erich Wolfgang Korngold Soc., Wilhelm Furtwaengler Soc., Literacy Initiative Assn., Am. String Tchrs. Assn. Avocations: chamber music, art reproduction, Indian ragas, Scandinavian cuisine. Office: Wake Forest U PO Box 7411 Winston Salem NC 27109-7411

TRAVAGLINI, RAYMOND DOMINIC, corporate executive; b. Greenville, Pa., May 3, 1928; s. Perugino and Mary Ann (DiFalco) T.; children: Alan, Lynne, Debbie, Kimberly, Kristine. LHD (hon.), Youngstown State U., 1993. Mgr. Kroger Co., Meadville, Pa., 1949-62; owner Suburban Water Conditioning, Warren, Ohio, 1962-65; ptnr. Sanray Corp., Meadville, 1965—; bd. dirs. Bank One, Youngstown, Ohio. Bd. dirs. Butler State Am. Art, Youngstown, Mahoning Valley Econ. Devel. Corp., Base Cmty. Coun., Dept. of Air Force. Named Man of Yr. Boys' Towns of Italy, 1979, Italian Scholarship League, 1984, Mahoning Valley Econ. Devel. Corp., 1985, Nat. Italian-Am. Sports Hall of Fame, 1992; recipient Disting. Citizen award Youngstown State U. Alumni Assn., 1993. Office: Sanray Corp 1323 Youngstown-Warren Rd Niles OH 44446

TRAVANTI, DANIEL JOHN, actor; b. Kenosha, Wis., Mar. 7, 1940; s. John and Elvira (DeAngelis) T. BA, U. Wis.; MA, Loyola Marymount, L.A. Performances include: (TV movies) The Love War, 1970, Adam, 1983, Aurora, 1984, Murrow, 1986, Adam: His Song Continues, 1986, I Never Sang for My Father, 1988, A Case of Libel, Howard Beach: Making the Case for Murder, 1989, Fellow Traveler, 1990, Tagget, 1991, Eyes of a Witness, 1991; (TV series) appeared as Capt. Frank Furillo in Hill Street Blues, 1981-87, Missing Persons, 1993-94; (films) St Ives, 1976, Midnight Crossing, 1988, Millenium, 1989, Megaville, 1991, Weep No More My Lady, 1993, Just Cause, 1995; (stage) Othello, Who's Afraid of Virginia Woolf?, The Taming of the Shrew. Gen. Motors fellow U. Wis., 1958-61; Woodrow Wilson fellow, 1961; Yale U. Sch. Drama, 1961-62; recipient Emmy award for role as Capt. Frank Furillo in Hill Street Blues, 1981, 82; Golden Globe award, 1981. *

TRAVELSTEAD, CHESTER COLEMAN, former educational administrator; b. Franklin, Ky., Sept. 25, 1911; s. Conley and Nelle (Gooch) T.; m. Marita Hawley, Aug. 1, 1936; children—Coleman, Jimmie. A.B., Western Ky. State Coll., Bowling Green, 1933; M.Music, Northwestern U., 1947; Ph.D., U. Ky., 1950; D.Hum., Morehead (Ky.) State U., 1975; Ph.D., John F. Kennedy U., Buenos Aires, 1975; LHD, U. N.Mex., 1980. Tchr., prin. rural and consol. schs. Mecklenburg County, Va., 1931-32, 33-35; tchr. gen. sci., math., music Picadome High Sch., Lexington, Ky., 1935-37; dir. music Henry Clay High Sch., Lexington, 1937-42; personnel supr. Lexington Signal Dept., Dept. War, 1942-43; supr. music Lexington pub. schs., 1945-47; rep. Investors Diversified Services, Inc., 1947-48; coordinator in-service tchr. edn. Ky. Dept. Edn., 1950-51; asst. prof. edn., asst. dean Coll. Edn. U. Ga., Athens, 1951-53; dean Sch. Edn., U. S.C., Columbia, 1953-56; dean Coll. Edn. U. N.Mex., Albuquerque, 1956-68; v.p. acad. affairs U. N.Mex., 1968-76, provost, 1976-77; Mem. Nat. Council Accreditation Tchr. Edn., 1960-66, chmn., 1963-65. Author books; contbr. articles in field to profl. jours. Pres. bd. dirs. N.Mex. Symphony Orch., 1977-78, 84-85; treas. U.S. Senator Jeff Bingaman's re-election campaign, 1988-93. With USNR, 1943-45; PTO. Mem. NEA, Nat. Soc. Study Edn., Soc. Advancement Edn., AAUP, Phi Kappa Phi, Phi Delta Kappa., Kappa Delta Pi. Home: 320 Fontana Pl NE Albuquerque NM 87108-1167

TRAVER, COURTLAND LEE, lawyer; b. New Haven, Sept. 20, 1935; s. Courtland L. Sr. and Bertha (Wilmot) T.; (div.); children: Lee, Kim, Amy. BA, U. Conn., 1957; LLB, Georgetown U., 1966. Bar: D.C. 1966, Va. 1967. Law clk. to presiding justice Ct. of Gen. Sessions, Washington, Va., 1965-66; clk. U.S. Ct. Appeals (D.C. cir.), Washington; ptnr. McGuire, Woods, Battle & Boothe, McLean, 1967—. Contbr. articles on real estate law to jours. Lt. USN, 1957-63. Mem. ABA (various coms.), Va. State Bar Assn. (chmn. real estate com.), D.C. Bar Assn., Va. Bar Assn. (chmn. real estate sect.). Office: McGuire Woods Battle & Boothe 8280 Greensboro Dr Ste 900 Mc Lean VA 22102-3892

TRAVERS, OLIVER S., JR., manufacturing company executive; b. Balt. 1926; married. Grad., U. Md., 1949. With Nat. Dairies, 1950-52; with Schenuit Industries, 1953-80, v.p., 1953-63, pres., 1963-80; pres., chief exec. officer Allegheny Internat. Inc., 1980—. With USN, 1944-46. Office: Allegheny Internat Inc 2 Oliver Pla 650 Smithfield St # 2100 Pittsburgh PA 15222-3907

TRAVERSE, ALFRED, palynology educator, clergyman; b. Port Hill, P.E.I., Can., Sept. 7, 1925; s. Alfred Freeman and Pearle (Akerley) T.; m. Elizabeth Jane Insley, June 30, 1951; children: Paul, Martha, John, Celia. S.B., Harvard U., 1946, A.M., 1948, Ph.D., 1951; cert. in Botany, Kings Coll., Cambridge, Eng., 1947; M.Div., Episcopal Theol. Sem. S.W., 1965. Teaching fellow Harvard U., 1947-51; coal technologist U.S. Bur. Mines, Grand Forks, N.D., 1951-55; head Fuels Microscopy Lab., Denver, 1955; palynologist Shell Devel. Co., Houston, 1955-62; cons. palynologist Austin, Tex., 1962-65; asst. prof. geology U. Tex., Austin, 1965-66; assoc. prof. geology and biology Pa. State U., University Park, 1966-70; ordained to ministry Episcopal Ch., 1965; asst. priest St. Matthew's Ch., Austin, 1965-66, St. Paul's Ch., Philipsburg, Pa., 1966-75, Christuskirche (Old Cath.), Zurich, Switzerland, 1980-81; vicar St. John's Ch., Huntingdon, Pa., 1975-80; adj. prof. geobiology Juniata Coll., 1977-82; guest prof. Geol. Inst., Swiss Fed. Tech. Inst., Zurich, 1980-81; councillor Internat. Commn. Palynology, 1973-78, pres., 1977-80; archivist, historian, 1986—; on-bd. scientist Glomar Challenger, 1975; Fulbright prof. Senckenberg Rsch. Inst., Frankfurt, 1992. Author: Paleopalynology, 1988, Sedimentation of Organic Particles, 1994; mem. editorial bd.: Catalog Fossil Spores and Pollen, 1957-66, editor-in-chief, 1966-76; palynological editor: Palaeontographica, 1989—. Recipient Best Paper award Am. Assn. Stratigraphic Palynologists, 1973, Internat. prize Palaeobot. Soc. India, 1990-91, Korrespondierendes Mitglied, Senckenbergische Naturforschende Gesellschaft, 1992—; NSF rsch. grantee, 1966-87. Fellow AAAS, Geol. Soc. Am.; mem. Bot. Soc. Am. (sec.-treas. paleobot. sect. 1957-60, chmn. sect. 1960-61), Internat. Assn. Plant Taxonomists (sec.-com. fossil plants 1969-93), Am. Assn. Stratigraphic Palynologists (sec.-treas. 1967-70, pres. 1970-71, chmn. type collections com. 1989-91), Internat. Fedn. Palynol. Soc. (pres. 1976-80, archivist 1980—). Home: RR 2 Box 390 Huntingdon PA 16652-9209 Office: 435 Deike Bldg University Park PA 16802

TRAVIS, ANDREW DAVID, lawyer; b. Washington, Mar. 23, 1944; s. Don Carlos Jr. and Nevenna (Tsanoff) T. BA, Rice U., 1966; JD, U. Tex., 1969. Bar: Tex. 1969. Sole practice Houston, 1971-75; atty. Allright Corp. (formerly Allright Auto Parks Inc.), Houston, 1975-82, v.p., legal counsel, 1982—. Mem. ABA, Tex. Bar Assn., Houston Bar Assn. Home: 307 Timber Terrace Rd Houston TX 77024-5602 Office: Allright Corp 1111 Fannin St Ste 1300 Houston TX 77002-6923

TRAVIS, DAVID B., curator; b. Omaha, Jan. 31, 1948; s. Marvin B. and Zona Mae (Ruffcorn) T.; m. Leslie Joan Strauss, Sept. 19, 1970. B.A., U. Chgo., 1971. Curator of photography Art Inst. Chgo., 1972—. Author: Starting with Atget: Photographs from the Julien Levy Collection, 1976;

book-catalogue Photography Rediscovered: American Photographs, 1900-1930, 1979, The Art of Photography: Past and Present, 1984; (with others) André Kertész: Of Paris and New York, 1985; catalogue Photographs from Chicago Collections, 1982, On the Art of Fixing a Shadow: 150 Years of Photography, 1989. Decorated Chevalier de l'Ordre des Arts et des Lettres, 1987. Club: Arts of Chicago. Home: 5038 S Blackstone Ave Chicago IL 60615-3006 Office: Art Inst Chgo Michigan Ave & Adams St Chicago IL 60603

TRAVIS, DEMPSEY JEROME, real estate executive, mortgage banker; b. Chgo., Feb. 25, 1920; s. Louis and Mittie (Strickland) T.; m. Moselynne Hardwick, Sept. 17, 1949. B.A., Roosevelt U., 1949; grad., Sch. Mortgage Banking, Northwestern U., 1969; D.Econs., Olive Harvey Coll., 1974; D.B.A. (hon.), Daniel Hale Williams U., Chgo., 1976; PhD (hon.), Kennedy-King Coll., 1982. Cert. property mgr.; cert. real estate counselor. Pres. Travis Realty Co., Chgo., 1949—, Urban Rsch. Press, 1969—. Author: Don't Stop Me Now, 1970, An Autobiography of Black Chicago, 1981, An Autobiography of Black Jazz, 1983, An Autobiography of Black Politics, 1987, Real Estate is the Gold in Your Future, 1988, Harold: The People's Mayor, 1989, Racism; American Style a Corporate Gift, 1990, I Refuse to Learn to Fail, 1992, Views From the Back of the Bus During World War II and Beyond, 1995. Trustee Northwestern Meml. Hosp., Chgo., Chgo. Hist. Soc.; bd. dirs. Chgo. Bd. Roosevelt U. Served with AUS, 1942-46. Recipient award Soc. Midland Authors, 1982, Chgo. Art Deco Soc., 1985. Mem. United Mortgage Bankers Assn. Am. (pres. 1961-74), Dearborn Real Estate Bd. (pres. 1957-59, 70-71), Nat. Assn. Real Estate Brokers (1st v.p. 1959-60), Inst. Real Estate Mgmt., Soc. Profl. Journalists, Soc. Midland Authors (pres. 1988-90), NAACP (pres. Chgo. 1959-60), Beta Gamma Sigma, Lambda Alpha. Clubs: Economics, Forty of Chgo., Assembly (Chgo.). Office: Travis Realty Co 840 E 87th St Chicago IL 60619-6242

TRAVIS, FORREST, investment firm executive; b. Birmingham, Ala., Dec. 4, 1938; s. Otis F. and Carolyn (Parker) T.; m. Carol Cole, June 25, 1960; children: Mark, Holly, Robin. BMechE, Ga. Inst. Tech., 1961. CLU. Engr. Reynolds, Smith & Hills, Jacksonville, Fla., 1961-62; pres. Forrest Travis Co., Jacksonville, 1962-81; v.p. E.F. Hutton, Jacksonville, 1981-88; 1st v.p. Shearson-Lehman Bros. (merger with E.F. Hutton), Jacksonville, 1988-93; sr. v.p. Smith Barney (merger with Shearson-Lehman Bros.), 1993-94; pres. Instl. Asset Mgmt., Jacksonville, 1994—; former dir. consulting group Smith Barney. Mem. Assn. Profl. Investment Cons. (founder, bd. dirs.), Sigma Chi. Republican. Methodist. Avocations: running, tennis, hunting, skiing. Home: 4934 Prince Edward Rd Jacksonville FL 32210-8122 also: 2379 S Ponte Vedra Blvd Saint Augustine FL 32084 Office: Instl Asset Mgmt 3550 Barnett Ctr Jacksonville FL 32202

TRAVIS, LAWRENCE ALLAN, accountant; b. Bloomington, Ill., Sept. 17, 1942; s. Willard Burns and Florence May (Harvey) T.; m. Katy Quinones, Apr. 16, 1965 (div. 1978); children: Lawrence A. Jr., Matthew B.; m. Kathleen Lucas, May 24, 1995. BS in Bus. Edn., Ill. State U., 1968, MA in Pub. Adminstrn., Sangamon State U., Springfield, Ill., 1976. CPA, Ill. Staff acct. Alexander Grant & Co., Chgo., 1969; internal auditor State Farm Ins., Bloomington, 1969-73; dep. dir. Ill. Dept. Ins., Springfield, 1973-74; audit mgr. Ill. Auditor Gen., Springfield, 1974-81; pres. Lawrence Travis & Co., P.C., CPAs, Virden, Normal, Springfield, Ill., 1979—; also bd. dirs. Lawrence Travis & Co., P.C., CPAs, Virden, Normal, Springfield; v.p., bd. dirs. Virden Broadcasting Corp., 1986—; pres., bd. dirs. Travco, Inc., Virden, 1985—; Ka-Lar Enterprises, Inc., Springfield, 1991—; v.p., bd. dirs. Carlinville Broadcasting Corp., 1988—, Miller Comm., Inc., 1992—. Mem. Ill. Common Cause, Springfield. Fellow Internat. Biog. Assn., Am. Biog. Inst. (life); mem. AICPAs, Assn. Govt. Accts., Ill. CPA Soc., Internat. Platform Assn., Nat. Space Soc., Smithsonian Inst. Assoc., Internat. Biog. Ctr., World Future Soc., Internat. Traders. Democrat. Roman Catholic. Avocation: sports. Home: 2409 Idlewild Dr Springfield IL 62704-5403 Office: 300 S Walnut St Springfield IL 62704-1914

TRAVIS, MARTIN BICE, political scientist, educator; b. Iron Mountain, Mich., Sept. 22, 1917; s. Martin Bice and Helen (Carrett) T.; m. Olivia Brewster Taylor, Nov. 29, 1942; children: Elizabeth Nichols (Mrs. Usama Mugharbil), Helen Willard. A.B., Amherst Coll., 1939; student, Heidelberg (Germany) U., 1937; M.A., Fletcher Sch. Law and Diplomacy, 1940; Ph.D., U. Chgo., 1948. Asst. prof. internat. relations Syracuse U., 1948-49; asst. prof. polit. sci. Duke U., 1949-52; asst. prof., then asso. prof. polit. sci. Stanford U., 1953-61; prof. polit. sci. SUNY-Stony Brook, 1961-92; coordinator SUNY Program Am. U., Beirut, Lebanon, 1972-73; chmn. dept., 1961-68; dir. Inst. Am. Studies SUNY-Stony Brook, 1965-93; vis. prof. Sch. Internat. Affairs, Columbia, 1956-57; vis. summer prof. U. Guadalajara, Mex., 1959, 62, U. Wash., 1961; Bd. dirs. State U N.Y. Inst. Am. Studies in France, 1966-77; cons. to industry. Author: (with E.E. Robinson) Powers of the President in Foreign Affairs, 1966; Co-editor, contbr.: (with Philip W. Buck) Control of Foreign Relations in Modern Nations, 1957; bd. editors: Western Polit. Quar., 1956-58; adv. bd.: Almanac of Current World Leaders, 1957—; editorial critic for book pubs. Mem. sch. bd., Cold Spring Harbor, N.Y., 1965-71, v.p., 1967-68, pres., 1968-69; trustee Village of Laurel Hollow, 1983—, police com., 1983-85, mayor, 1985—. Served with USAAF, 1942-45. Ford Found. grantee, 1960-61. Mem. Acad. Polit. Sci., Am. Soc. Internat. Law, Council Fgn. Relations, Phi Delta Theta, Phi Delta Kappa. Home: 533 Cold Spring Rd Syosset NY 11791-1206 Office: Dept Polit Science Suny Stony Brook NY 11794

TRAVIS, NANCY, actress; b. New York, NY, Sept. 21, 1961. BA, NYU. stage appearances include: Brighton Beach Memoirs (touring prodn.), It's Hard to Be a Jew, 1984, I'm Not Rappaport, 1986, The Signal Season of Dummy Hoy, 1987-88; television appearances include: High School Narc, 1985, Malice in Wonderland, 1985, Harem, 1986, I'll Be Home for Christmas, 1988, Almost Perfect, 1995—; films include: Three Men and a Baby, 1987, Eight Men Out, 1988, Married to the Mob, 1988, Air America, 1990, Internal Affairs, 1990, Loose Cannons, 1990, Three Men and a Little Lady, 1990, Passed Away, 1992, Chaplin, 1992, The Vanishing, 1993, So I Married an Ax Murderer, 1993, Greedy, 1994, Fluke, 1995, Destiny Turns On the Radio, 1995. Office: UTA 9560 Wilshire Blvd 5th Fl Beverly Hills CA 90212*

TRAVIS, NEIL, film editor. Editor: (TV movies) Roots, 1977 (Emmy award outstanding film editing of drama series for Part 1 1977), The Atlanta Child Murders, 1985, Shannon's Deal, 1989, (films) Jaws II, 1978, Die Laughing, 1980, The Idolmaker, 1980, Nobody's Perfekt, 1981, Second Thoughts, 1983, The Philadelphia Experiment, 1984, Cujo, 1984, Marie, 1985, No Way Out, 1987, Cocktail, 1988, Dances with Wolves, 1990 (Academy award best film editing 1990), Patriot Games, 1992, Bopha!, 1993, Clear and Present Danger, 1994. Office: care Motion Picture Editors 7715 Sunset Blvd #220 Los Angeles CA 90046*

TRAVIS, RANDY BRUCE, musician; b. Monroe, N.C., 1959; married. Musician Country City U.S.A., 1977-82, Nashville Palace, 1982-85. Rec. artist Warner Bros. Records, 1985—; albums include debut Storms of Life, 1986 (Album of Yr., Acad. Country Music 1987, Album of Yr., Music City News 1987), Always & Forever, 1987 (Album of Yr., Country Music Assn. 1987), Old 8x10, 1988, No Holdin' Back, 1989, An Old Time Christmas, 1989, Heroes and Friends, 1990, High Lonesome, 1991, Greatest Hits, 1992, Wind in the Wire, 1993, This is Me, 1994; songs include On the Other Hand (Best Song, Acad. Country Music 1987, Best Single, Acad. Country Music 1987, Single of Yr., Music City News 1987), Diggin' Up Bones, No Place Like Home, Forever and Ever, Amen (Single of Yr., Song of Yr.,Country Music Assn. 1987, Best Country Record, AMOA Jukebox 1987), I Won't Need You Anymore, No Holding Back, 1989; film appearances include: Frank and Jesse, 1994. Named Top Male Vocalist, Acad. Country Music, 1987, Male Vocalist of Yr., Music City News, 1987, Star of Tomorrow, Music City News, 1987, Male Vocalist of Yr., Country Music Assn., 1987, Entertainer of Yr. Music City News, 1988, Male Artist of Yr., 1988, Favorite Entertainer, Favorite Entertainer, Nashville Network Viewers Choice Awards, 1988; recipient Horizon award Country Music Assn., 1986, Grammy award, 1987, Am. Music award, best country album, 1988, Am. Music award, best country single, 1988, Country Music Assn. best male vocalist, 1988. Mem. Grand Ole Opry. *

TRAVIS, VANCE KENNETH, petroleum business executive; b. Coriander, Sask., Can., Jan. 30, 1926; s. Roy Hazen and Etta Orilla (Anderson) T.; m. Louise Mary, Nov. 30, 1948 (div. 1979); children: Stuart, Shirley, Gordon, Donald, Marian; m. Mildred Elaine, June 29, 1979; stepchildren: Susan, Nancy, Gordon, Sandra, Karen. Chmn. bd. Turbo Resources Ltd., 1970-83, Challenger Internat., 1977-83, Bankeno Mines Ltd., 1977-83, Queenston Gold Mines Ltd., Toronto, Ont., Can., 1977-84, Health Risk Mgmt. Inc., Mpls., 1984-86, Triad Internat. Inc., 1985—; dir. Health Resource Mgmt. Ltd., Edmonton, 1990—; bd. dirs. Vencap Equities Alta. Ltd., Edmonton, 1981-86, L.K. Resources Ltd., Calgary, 1973-84. Mem. Young. Pres.'s Orgn., Calgary, 1964-76, World Pres. Orgn. Recipient Presdl. pin Jr. Achievement, 1963, Best Pitcher award Petroleum Fastball League, 1955. Clubs: Calgary Petroleum, Ranchmen's. Office: Triad Internat Inc, 4600 5th St NE # 200, Calgary, AB Canada T2E 7C3 also: Health Resource Mgmt Ltd, 10104-103rd Ave Ste 800, Edmonton, AB Canada T5J 4R5 also: Med Tech Computer Systems, 3015 5th Ave NE Ste 150, Calgary Can T2A6T8 also: Hars Sys Inc, 707 7th Ave SW Ste 600, Calgary, AB Canada T2P 3H6

TRAVIS, W. VANCE, JR., architect; b. Chattanooga, July 1, 1947; s. Willard V. and Betty (Donoughy) T.; m. Ruth Rodgers, Sept. 4, 1971; children: Dana Leigh, Todd Rodgers. BArch, U. Tenn., 1970. With Hensley-Schmidt, Inc., Chattanooga, 1967, Harrison Gill & Assocs., Chattanooga, 1968, Earl Swenson & Assocs., Nashville, 1969, Bost and Assocs., Knoxville, Tenn., 1970; with Franklin Design Group, Inc., Chattanooga, 1971-83, v.p., 1973-83; with Vance Travis Architects, Chattanooga, 1983-85; pres. TWH Architects, Inc., Chattanooga, 1985-89. Bd. dirs. Chattanooga C. of C., 1988; v.p. Health House, Chattanooga, 1986-90; v.p. phys. arrangements Riverbend Festival, Chattanooga, 1991; mem. Ptnrs. for Econ. Progress, Chattanooga; bd. dirs. YMCA 1991—. Mem. AIA (pres. 1978), Tenn. Soc. Architects (pres. 1983), Chattanooga Jaycees, Rotary. Home: 4907 Sawyer Rd Signal Mountain TN 37377-2819 Office: TWH Architects Inc 651 E 4th St Ste 500 Chattanooga TN 37403-1924

TRAVISANO, FRANK PETER, professional management consultant/business broker; b. Newark, Feb. 5, 1921; s. Peter Fountain and Carmela Elizabeth (Tellone) T.; m. Nancy Jean Drees; children: Peter, Thomas, James, Theresa, Patricia. BS in Bus., Rutgers U., 1943, postgrad. in mktg., 1945, postgrad. in real estate, 1946; Cert. Computers, morris C.C., Morris County, Randolph, 1985. Cert. profl. mgmt. cons. Various to pres. Rochester Lubricator Co., Newark, 1943-71, Franklin Hosp. Equipment Co., Newark, 1955-71, Acme Plating Works, Newark, 1961-72, Micro Machine Co., Union, N.J., 1962-72, Darwin Phoenix Co., Cranbury, N.J., 1972—; Darwin Safety Packaging Co., Cranbury, 1986—; exec. v.p. Logos Group, Chester, N.J., 1987—; mktg. mgr. Artisan Controls Corp., Parsippany, N.J., 1991—; cons. dir. TPI Inc., Lodi, N.J., 1991—; sr. cons. Solutions Group, Madison, N.J., 1991—; cons. MAN-ROLAND, OM Internat. Superior MPM Plastics. Inventor in field of hosp. products and safety packaging materials. Co-founder Essexfields Youthful Offenders Program, pres. 1965. Recipient various svc. awards Rutgers U. Mem. Inst. Chem. Physics (chmn. bd. dirs. 1993—), Rutgers U. Alumni Assn. (bd. dirs., pres. 1966-67), Kiwanis (bd. dirs.), Newark Execs. Assn. (pres. 1960). Avocations: inventions in field.

TRAVOLTA, JOHN, actor; b. Englewood, N.J., Feb. 18, 1954; s. Salvatore and Helen (Burke) T.; m. Kelly Preston; one child, Jett. Appeared in TV series Welcome Back Kotter, 1975-79; TV movies: The Boy in the Plastic Bubble, 1976; films: Carrie, 1976, Saturday Night Fever, 1977 (Best Actor award Nat. Bd. of Rev. 1977, Best Actor Acad. award nominee 1977, Best Actor Golden Globe award nominee 1977), Grease, 1978 (Golden Globe World Film Favorite 1978), Moment-By-Moment, 1978, Urban Cowboy, 1980, Blow Out, 1981, Staying Alive, 1983 (Male/Box Office Star of Yr., Nat. Assn. Theatre Owners ShowWest 1983), Two of a Kind, 1983, Perfect, 1985, The Experts, 1989, Chains of Gold, 1989, Look Who's Talking, 1989 (Male/Box Office Star of Yr., Nat. Assn. Theatre Owners ShowEast 1989), Look Who's Talking Too, 1990, The Tender, 1991, Shout, 1991, Look Who's Talking Now, 1993, Pulp Fiction, 1994 (Best Actor Acad. award nominee 1994, Best Actor award nominee Brit. Acad. Film and TV Arts 1994, Golden Globe Best Actor award nominee 1994, Best Actor award nominee SAG 1994, Best Actor award nominee Chgo. Film Critics 1994, Best Actor award nominee Comedy Awards 1994, Best Actor award L.A. Film Critics 1994, Best Actor award Stockholm Film Festival 1993, Best Actor award London Film Critics Cir. 1994); author: Staying Fit, 1984; rec. artist album, 1976, 77. Recipient Best Male Vocalist Billboard award, 1976, Best Male Vocalist award Record World and Music Retail mag., 1976, Best Actor Golden Apple award Cue mag., Juno award Can. Acad. Rec. Arts and Scis., 1978; nominated Best New Male Star, Women's Press Club, 1970; named Man of Yr., Hasty Pudding Club, Harvard U., 1981.

TRAWICK, LEONARD MOSES, English educator; b. Decatur, Ala., July 4, 1933; s. Leonard M. and Frances (Earle) T.; m. Kerstin Ekfelt, July 16, 1960; children: Eleanor, Matthew. BA, U. of South, 1955; MA in English, U. Chgo., 1956; PhD in English, Harvard U., 1961. Asst. prof. Columbia U., N.Y.C., 1961-69; from assoc. prof. to prof. English Cleve. State U., 1969—; editor Poetry Ctr., Cleve. State U., 1971—, dir., 1990-92. Editor: Backgrounds of Romanticism, 1968, World, Self, Poem, 1990, (poems) Beastmorfs, 1994; editor, prin. translator: German Literature of the Romantic Era and Age of Goethe, 1993; author (opera libretto) Mary Stuart: A Queen Betrayed, 1991; founding editor mag. The Gamut, 1980-92 (Ohioana award for Editl. Excellence 1991). Recipient Individual Artist award Ohio Arts Coun., 1980; Ohioana Poetry award, 1994. Office: Cleve State U Dept English Cleveland OH 44115

TRAXLER, WILLIAM BYRD, lawyer; b. Greenville, S.C., July 10, 1912; s. David Byrd and Mary Willey (Gatling) T. Student The Citadel, 1929-30, U. Tex., 1930-32; JD, George Washington U., 1940. Bar: D.C. 1940, S.C. 1940, U.S. Ct. Appeals (4th cir.) 1960. Ptnr. Hinson, Traxler and Hamer, Greenville, 1950-58, Rainey, Fant, Traxler and Horton, 1958-60; sole practice, Greenville, 1960—. Bd. dirs. Phyllis Wheatly Assn., 1954, Vis. Nurse Assn., Greenville, 1957-59, United Way, Greenville, 1976; vice-chmn. bd. health City of Greenville, 1960-68; life mem. The Citadel Endowment Fund; prosecutor So. Bavaria Mil. Govt., asst. to reopening German civil cts. Capt. U.S. Army, 1942-46. Recipient Alumni Achievement award George Washington U., 1946. Fellow S.C. Bar Found.; mem. S.C. State Bar Assn. (sec.), Greenville County Bar Assn. (pres. 1976), Greenville C. of C. (Chmn. of Yr. 1967, chmn. taxation com.), Law Sci. Acad., George Washington U. Law Assn. (life), Phi Alpha Delta (justice 1939), Beta Theta Pi, Torch Club (pres. 1956), Greenville Country Club (bd. govs. 1982-85). Author: Military Government in Germany, 1960, Political Third Parties, 1968, History of the Fourteenth Amendment, 1974, The Jury Numbers Game, 1976, Medieval Harmony, 1982, Presumptions of Life and Death, 1989. Home: 100 Trails End Greenville SC 29607-1741

TRAXLER, WILLIAM BYRD, JR., federal judge; b. Greenville, S.C., May 1, 1948; s. William Byrd and Bettie (Wooten) T.; m. Patricia Alford, Aug. 21, 1971; children: William Byrd III, James McCall. BA, Davidson Coll., 1970; JD, U. S.C., 1973. Assoc. William Byrd Traxler, Greenville, 1973-75; asst. solicitor 13th Jud. Ct., Greenville, 1975-78, dep. solicitor, 1978-81, solicitor, 1981-85, resident crct. judge, 1985-92; U.S. Dist. judge Dist. of S.C., Greenville, 1992—. Recipient Outstanding Svc. award Solicitors Assn., S.C., 1987, Leadership award Probation, Parole & Pardon Svcs., S.C., 1990. Office: US Dist Ct 300 E Washington St Greenville SC 29601-2800

TRAYLOR, ANGELIKA, stained glass artist; b. Munich, Bavaria, Fed. Republic of Germany, Aug. 24, 1942; came to U.S. 1959; d. Walther Artur Ferdinand and Berta Kreszentia (Boeck) Klau; m. Lindsay Montgomery Donaldson, June 10, 1959 (div. 1970); 1 child, Cameron Maria Greta; m. Samuel William Traylor III, June 12, 1970. Student, Pvt. Handelsschule Morawetz Jr. Coll., Munich, 1958. came to U.S., 1959;. Freelance artist, 1980—. Works featured in profl. jours. including The Dayliily Jour., 1987, Design Jour., South Korea, 1989, The Traveler's Guide to American Crafts, 1990, Florida Mag., 1991, Florida TODAY, 1993, Melbourne Times, 1994. Recipient Fragile Art award Glass Art mag., 1982, 1st Yr. Exhibitor award Stained Glass Assn., 1984, 2d pl. Non-figurative Composition award Vitraux des USA, 1985, Best of Show Stained Glass Assn. mem., 1989, 3d pl., 1989, Merit award George Plimpton All-Star Space Coast Art Open, 1994; named Hist. Woman of Brevard Brevard Cultural Alliance, 1991, one of 200 Best Am. Craftsmen Early Am. Life mag., 1994, 95. Home and Office: 100 Poinciana Dr Indian Harbor Beach FL 32937-4437

TRAYLOR, JOAN SADLER, interior design educator; b. Pique, Ohio; d. Carl E. and Mary E. (Bond) Sadler; children: Douglas Traylor, Michelle Traylor. BS in Interior Design and Art, Western Ky. U., 1981, MS in Interior Design, 1984. Interior designer Interiors By Biggers, Glasgow, Ky., 1981-83; teaching fellow Western Ky. U., Bowling Green, 1983-84, instr. interior design, 1985; asst. prof. interior design U. So. Miss., Hattiesburg, 1985-91, assoc. prof. interior design, 1991—, interior design program coord., 1990—; prof. Brit. studies abroad program, 1989—; presenter profl. assn. meetings. Contbr. articles and abstracts to profl. publs. Mem., officer Warren County Arts Alliance, Bowling Green, 1977-85; mem. Jr. Woman's Club, Bowling Green, 1970-76. Mem. Interior Design Educators Coun., Am. Soc. Interior Designers (La. chpt. presdl. citation 1991), Inst. Bus. Designers (officer Delta chpt. 1992-94), Nat. Trust for Hist. Preservation, New Orleans Preservation Resource Ctr., Hattiesburg Hist. Soc., Internat. Interior Design Assn., Designed Comm. Assn., Internat. Interior Design Assn. (Ms. dir. 1994—), Phi Upsilon Omicron, Phi Delta Kappa, Delta Kappa Gamma. Avocations: travel, drawing and painting, textile design. Home: 315 Woodshire Dr Hattiesburg MS 39402 Office: U So Miss SS Box 5035 Hattiesburg MS 39406-5035

TRAYLOR, ORBA FOREST, economist, lawyer, educator; b. Providence, Ky., June 16, 1910; s. Eddie Ewing and Dillie (Stuart) T.; m. Josephine Zananiri, Nov. 17, 1945; children—Joseph Marion, Robert Forest, John Christopher. B.A., Western Ky. U., 1930; M.A., U. Ky., 1932, Ph.D., 1948; J.D., Northwestern U., 1936. Bar: Ky. 1941. Head dept. econs. Ashland Coll., 1935-36; legal asst. trust dept. 1st Nat. Bank, Chgo., 1936-37; assoc. prof. econs., sociology Western Ky. U., 1938-40; research asst. Bur. Bus. Research, U. Ky., 1939; research dir. Ky. Legislative Council, 1939-41; dir. research and statistics Ky. Dept. Welfare, 1941; assoc. econ. analyst div. tax research U.S. Treasury Dept., 1942; acting chief acctg. UNRRA, Balkan Mission, 1944-45; asst. prof. econs. and bus. U. Denver, 1946-47, U. Mo., 1947-50; tax specialist, asst. econ. commr. ECA, Greece, 1950-53; coordinator exec. devel. programs Ordnance Corps, Dept. Army, 1954; pub. fin. expert UN; lectr. fin. adminstrn. Inst. Pub. Adminstrn., Egypt, 1954-56; exec. asst. to lt. gov. Ky. Legislative Research Commn., Frankfort, 1956-58; commr. fin. State of Ky., Frankfort, 1958-59; dir. finance Office High Commr., Ryukyu Islands, 1960-64; dir. econ. affairs Office High Commr., 1964-65; prof. econs. and pub. adminstrn. U. Ala., Huntsville, 1965-75; chmn. dept. bus. and pub. adminstrn. U. Ala., 1966-68, chmn. econs., 1968-70; vis. prof. pub. adminstrn. San Diego State U., 1975-76, Western Ky. U., 1976-77; fin. economist AID, U.S. State Dept., 1977-78; adj. prof. Ala. A&M U., 1978-81, N.Y. U. and Rider Coll., 1981-82, Columbia Coll., 1982—; cons. economist Am. Tech. Services, Inc., 1982-91; cons. ops. research Johns Hopkins U., 1957-61; fiscal cons. various orgns.; vis. lectr. econs. various univs. and colls.; lectr. U. Md. Far East Div., 1960-65, Ala. A&M U., 1976-77, Fla. Inst. Tech., 1977; sr. adv. Bank of Ryukyus, 1960-65, Joint Fgn. Investment Bd., 1964-65; chmn. bd. Ryukyuan Devel. Loan Corp., 1960-65, Joint Petroleum Bd., 1960-65; counsellor Oak Ridge Asso. Univs., 1966-67. Mem. editorial bd.: Public Adminstrn. Rev, 1973-79; contbr. articles to profl. publs. Mem. Ala. Edn. Study Commn. Fin. Task Force, 1968-69; chmn. fin. com. Top of Ala. Health Planning Agy., 1974-75; mem. adv. com. Ala. Legislature, 1981-94. With AUS, 1942-46; lt. col. Res. (ret.). Mem. Am., So. econs. assns., Am. Soc. for Pub. Adminstrn. (council 1973-75), Am., Ky. bar assns., Nat. Tax Assn. (dir. 1971-74), local C. of C., Res. Officers Assn., Mil. Order World Wars, Beta Gamma Sigma, Delta Sigma Pi. Democrat. Baptist. Club: Rotary. Address: 216 Westmoreland Huntsville AL 35801

TRAYNHAM, JAMES GIBSON, chemist, educator; b. Broxton, Ga., Aug. 5, 1925; s. James G. and Eddie Louise (Greer) T.; m. Margaret A. Egert, 1948; children: David F., Peter C.; m. Gresdna A. Doty, 1980. Student, South Ga. Coll., 1942-43; B.S., U. N.C., 1946; Ph.D., Northwestern U., 1950. Instr. Northwestern U., 1949-50; asst. prof. Denison U., 1950-53; mem. faculty La. State U., Baton Rouge, 1953—; prof. chemistry La. State U., 1963-88, prof. emeritus, 1988—, chmn. dept. chemistry, 1968-73, vice chancellor for advanced studies and rsch., dean Grad. Sch., 1973-81; postdoctoral research fellow Ohio State U., 1951-53. Author: Organic Nomenclature: A Programmed Introduction, 1966, 4th edit., 1991; editor: Essays on the History of Organic Chemistry, 1987; contbr. articles to profl. jours. Bd. dirs. Council Grad. Schs. in, U.S., 1981. Recipient Petroleum Research Fund Am. Chem. Soc. Type D award Eidg. Technische Hochschule, Zurich, Switzerland, 1959-60; Charles E. Coates award Baton Rouge sects. Am. Chem. Soc. and Am. Inst. Chem. Engrs., 1965; NATO sr. fellow in sci. Universität des Saarlandes, Saarbrücken, Fed. Republic Germany, 1972. Mem. Am. Chem. Soc. (councilor, past chmn. Baton Rouge sect., chmn. divsn. history of chemistry 1988), La. Acad. Sci., Internat. Union Pure and Applied Chemistry (titular mem. commn. on nomenclature of organic chemistry, sec. 1994—), Phi Beta Kappa, Sigma Xi, Phi Lambda Upsilon, Phi Kappa Phi (past pres. La. State U. chpt.). Home: 628 Polytech Dr Baton Rouge LA 70808-4755

TRAYNOR, HARRY SHEEHY, engineering consultant; b. Lexington, Ky., Sept. 4, 1911; s. John Hanrahan and Augusta (Sheehy) T.; m. Helen Mae Ingalls, June 28, 1941; children: Martha Ingalls (Mrs. Paul J. Sweeney), Harry Sheehy. B.S. in Mech. Engring., U. Ky., 1935. Test engr. Aerofin Corp., Newark, 1935; air conditioning, refrigeration engr. Carrier Corp., Syracuse, N.Y., 1935-42; pres. gen mgr. Regent Knitting Co., Inc., Syracuse, N.Y., 1946-50; contract sales mgr. Remington Corp., Auburn, N.Y., 1950-54; spl. asst. to gen. mgr., asst. gen. mgr. adminstrn. AEC, 1954-64, asst. to gen. mgr., 1964-71; asst. to dean Grad. Sch. U. Ky., Lexington, 1972-73; cons. Inst. Mining and Minerals Research, 1974-79, Ky. Center for Energy Research, 1976-78; ret., 1971; mem. U.S. Intelligence Bd., 1954-64; exec. officer U.S. del. Internat. Conf. on Peaceful Uses of Atomic Energy, Geneva, 1955. Chmn. Met. Environ. Improvement Commn., Lexington, 1975; mem. U. Ky. Rsch. Found.; SCORE, 1987-89. Col., C.E. AUS, 1952. Decorated Legion of Merit; recipient Disting. Alumni award U. Ky., 1965. Mem. ASHRAE (asso.), AAAS, Ky. Hist. Soc., Pi Kappa Alpha, Pi Tau Sigma. Roman Catholic. Clubs: Lafayette (Lexington), Kiwanis (Lexington), Spindletop (Lexington). Home: 1336 Prather Rd Lexington KY 40502-2421

TRAYNOR, J. MICHAEL, lawyer; b. Oakland, Calif., Oct. 25, 1934; s. Roger J. and Madeleine (Lackmann) T.; m. Shirley Williams, Feb. 11, 1956; children: Kathleen Traynor Millard, Elizabeth Traynor Fowler, Thomas. B.A., U. Calif., Berkeley, 1955; J.D., Harvard U., 1960. Bar: Calif. 1961, U.S. Supreme Ct. 1966. Dep. atty. gen. State of Calif., San Francisco, 1961-63; spl. counsel Calif. Senate Com. on Local Govt., Sacramento, 1963; assoc. firm Cooley Godward Castro Huddleson & Tatum, San Francisco, 1963-69, ptnr., 1969—; adviser 3d Restatement of Torts: Product 5 Liability, 1992—, Apportionment, 1994—, 1988 Revs. 2d Restatement of Conflict of Laws, 2d Restatement of Restitution, 1981-85; lectr. U. Calif. Boalt Hall Sch. Law, Berkeley, 1982-89; chmn. Sierra Club Legal Def. Fund, 1989-91, pres., 1991-92, trustee. Mem. bd. overseers Inst. for Civil Justice The RAND Corp., 1991—; bd. dirs. Environ. Law Inst., 1992—. Served to 1st lt. USMC, 1955-57. Fellow Am. Bar Found. (life); mem. Am. Law Inst. (coun. 1985—, 2d v.p. 1993—), Bar Assn. San Francisco (pres. 1973). Home: 3131 Eton Ave Berkeley CA 94705-2713 Office: Cooley Godward Castro Huddleson & Tatum Ste 2000 1 Maritime Plz San Francisco CA 94111-3580

TRAYNOR, SEAN GABRIAL, manufacturing executive; b. Waterford, Ireland, Jan. 6, 1950; came to U.S., 1974; s. Sean Gerard and Norah Mary (Gower) T.; m. Geraldine Margaret Turner, Aug. 21, 1974; children: Kevin, Patrick, Tara. BA in Chemistry magna cum laude, Trinity Coll., 1971, PhD in Chemistry, 1974. Rsch. chemist SCM Glidco Organics, 1975, mgr. devel., 1980, dir. devel. and engring., 1984, dir. mktg., 1986, v.p. sales and mktg., 1986-93; chmn., CEO Garden State Tanning Inc., King of Prussia, Pa., 1993—. Co-author (chpt.) Chemistry of Turpentine, 1989; contbr. over 30 articles to profl. jours. Pres. Irish Cultural Assn., Jacksonville, Fla., 1980. Recipient Exec. Achievement award Hanson Industries, 1990. Fellow Am. Inst. Chemists, Am. Chem. Soc.; mem. Anethole Task Force (co-chmn. 1989-92), Rotary (bd. dirs. Jacksonville chpt. 1991-92). Achievements include 12 patents in field organic chemistry. Office: Garden State Tanning Inc 630 Freedom Bus Ctr King Of Prussia PA 19406

TRCZINSKI, ROBERT A., public relations executive. Ptnr., treas. Fin. Rels. Bd., Chgo. Office: Fin Rels Bd John Hancock Ctr 875 N Michigan Ave Chicago IL 60611-1779*

TREACY, VINCENT EDWARD, lawyer; b. Mass., Jan. 30, 1942; m. Edith Barnett. AB, Boston Coll., 1964; JD with honors, George Washington U., 1971. Bar: Va. 1972, D.C. 1973. Atty. Fed. Labor Relations Council, Washington, 1971-73; legis. atty. Am. law div. Congressional Research Service, Library of Congress, Washington, 1973—. Mem. law rev. staff George Washington Law Rev., 1970. Mem. ABA, Fed. Bar Assn., George Washington Law Alumni Assn. (pres. Capitol Hill chpt. 1986-87), Order of the Coif. Office: Congl Rsch Svc Am Law Divsn Libr Of Congress Washington DC 20540

TREADWAY, DOUGLAS MORSE, academic administrator; b. San Diego, Apr. 23, 1942; s. Thelma Lillian (Lindsay) T.; m. Carole Rae Culp, June 5, 1964; children: Christine, Paul. BA, Calif. Western U., 1964; MT, Claremont Grad. Sch., 1967; PhD, Northwestern U., 1971. Asst. dean students Northwestern U., Evanston, Ill., 1969-71; asst. prof. psychology U.S. Internat. Univ., Maui, Hawaii, 1971-73; dir. coop. edn. Maui Community Coll., 1973-74; dean of students Ea. Oreg. State Coll., La Grande, 1974-79, dean continuing edn., 1979-85; pres. Western Mont. Coll., Dillon, 1985-87, S.W. State U., Marshall, Minn., 1987-91; chancellor N.D. U. System, 1991-94; supt., pres. Shasta Coll., Redding, Calif., 1994—; chmn. Nat. Conf. Rural Edn., Washington, 1987; mem. rsch. coun. USDA. Author: Higher Education in Rural America, 1985; contbr. numerous articles on higher edn. and rural programs to profl. jours. Mem. Big Bros., Maui, 1971-74. Mem. Am. Assn. Higher Edn., Am. Assn. State Colls. and Univs., Nat. Univ. Continuing Edn. Assn. Republican. Methodist. Lodge: Rotary. Avocations: swimming, fishing, hunting. Home: 2113 Western Oak Dr Redding CA 96002

TREADWAY, JAMES, hotel chain executive; b. Southbridge, Mass., May 14, 1947; s. Richard Fowle and Martha Cecil (Chamberlin) T.; m. Patricia Helen Hancock, Apr. 14, 1973 (div. May 1985); children: Jean, Heather. BS in Hotel Adminstrn., Cornell U., 1971. Gen. mgr. The Olympic, Seattle, 1979-80, The Westin Hotel Seattle, 1980-84; on spl. assignment Westin Corp. Mktg., Seattle, 1984-85; mng. dir. The Westin Bonaventure, L.A., 1985-86, The Westin Hotel Kauai, Hawaii, 1986-90; sr. v.p. hotel ops. Westin Corp., Seattle, 1991; pres. N.Am. Westin Hotel & Resorts, Seattle, 1991—; guest lectr. Cornell U., Fla. State U., Nova U. Mem. Am. Hotel and Motel Assn (cert. hotel adminstr.). Avocations: golf, tennis, skiing. Office: Westin Hotels & Resorts Westin Bldg 2001 6th Ave Seattle WA 98121

TREADWAY, JAMES CURRAN, investment company executive, lawyer, former government official; b. Anderson, S.C., May 21, 1943; s. James C. and Maxine (Hall) T.; m. Susan Pepper Davis, Sept. 6, 1969; children: Elizabeth Pepper Hall, Caroline Worrell Harper. A.B., U. Ga., 1964; JD summa cum laude, Washington and Lee U., 1967. Bar: Ga. 1967, Mass. 1968, D.C. 1970. Assoc. Candler, Cox, McClain & Andrews, Atlanta, 1967-68, Gadsby & Hannah, Boston and Washington, 1968-72; ptnr. Dickstein, Shapiro & Morin, Washington, 1972-82; commr. SEC, Washington, 1982-85; ptnr. Baker & Botts, Washington, 1985-87; exec. v.p. PaineWebber Group Inc., N.Y.C., 1987—; chmn. Nat. Commn. on Fraudulent Fin. Reporting, 1985-87; mem., bd. dirs. AICPA, 1994—. Mem. Mass. Bar Assn., Ga. Bar Assn., D.C. Bar Assn., Order of Coif, Phi Beta Kappa, Omicron Delta Kappa, Omicron Delta Epsilon (hon.), Chevy Chase (Md.) Club, Bedford (N.Y.) Golf and Tennis Club, City Tavern Club, Met. Club, University Club (D.C.), Verbank Hunting and Fishing Club (Uniondale, N.Y.). Republican. Roman Catholic. Home: Laurel Ledge RD 4 Croton Lake Rd Bedford Corners NY 10549 Office: PaineWebber Group Inc 1285 Ave Of The Americas New York NY 10019-6028

TREADWAY, JOHN DAVID, history educator; b. San Bernardino, Calif., June 30, 1950; s. Emery Russell and Mabel A. (Batchelor) T.; m. Sandra Gioia, Sept. 4, 1976; 1 child, Robyn. BA summa cum laude, Fla. State U., 1972; PhD, U. Va., 1980. Prof. History U. Richmond, Va., 1980—. Author: The Falcon and the Eagle, 1983; co-editor: The Soviet Union under Gorbachev, 1987; editor Ind. Slavic Studies/Balkanistica, 1991-92; book reviewer Am. Hist. Rev., Historian, Choice, Slavic Rev., Serbian Studies; contbr. articles to profl. jours. Recipient Disting. Educator award U. Richmond, 1985, 88, 91, Outstanding faculty award Va., 1993; fellow ITT Internat., 1975-76, Fulbright, 1985, 90, Woodrow Wilson Ctr., 1989; grantee NDFL, 1976-77, ACLS, 1981, Internat. Rsch. and Exch. Bd., 1981. Mem. Am. Hist. Assn., Southern Hist. Assn. (Snell prize 1985-87), Va. Hist. Soc., Am. Assn. for Advancement Slavic Studies, Am. Assn. Southeast European Studies (pres. 1987-89), North Am. Soc. Serbian Studies (exec. com. 1985-88), Library Svc. and Construction Act Adv. Coun., Va. Social Sci. Assn. (exec. bd. 1987-89), Am. Com. to Promote Studies of History of Habsburg Monarchy. Lutheran. Home: 8201 Gaylord Rd Richmond VA 23229-4121 Office: U Richmond Dept History Richmond VA 23173

TREADWAY, STEPHEN JOSEPH, investment banking and brokerage executive; b. N.Y.C., Aug. 11, 1947; s. Joseph and Dorothy (Overbaugh) T.; m. Beth Heydinger, Nov. 26, 1971; children: Joseph, Peter, James. BS, Cornell U., 1969; JD, Columbia U., 1972. Bar: N.Y. 1972. Assoc. Findle, Kuimble, Heine, Underbury and Casey, N.Y.C., 1972-77; investment banker Smith Barney Harris Upham & Co., Inc., N.Y.C., 1977—, now exec. v.p., also bd. dirs.; bd. dirs. real estate investment trusts. Mem. Investment Partnership Assn., Securities Industry Assn. (direct participation com.), N.Y. State Bar Assn. Republican. Roman Catholic. Avocations: golf, tennis, piano. Office: Smith Barney Harris Upham & Co 21st 23rd & 32nd Fls 1345 Avenue Of The Americas New York NY 10105-0216

TREADWELL, HUGH WILSON, publishing executive; b. Waurika, Okla., Nov. 21, 1921; s. Hugh and Jessie Ellen (Cogdell) T.; m. Edith Albena Doolittle, June 20, 1959; children—Pamela, Hugh, Cynthia. B.A., U. Okla., 1949, M.A., 1952; diploma in French Studies (Rotary Found. fellow), Institut de Touraine, U. Poitiers, France, 1950. Asst. editor internat. lit. quar. Books Abroad, U. Okla., 1952-53; field rep. coll. dept. The Macmillan Co., 1953-60, Holt, Rinehart & Winston, Inc. Okla. and Tex., 1960-62; mgr. coll. programs in fgn. lang. dept. Holt, Rinehart & Winston, Inc., N.Y.C., 1962-67; sr. editor coll. dept. Random House-Knopf, N.Y.C., 1967-72; dir. U. N.Mex. Press, Albuquerque, 1973-80, Tex. Western Press, U. Tex., El Paso, 1981-85; pvt. practice cons., 1985—; field rep. coll. dept. W. W. Norton & Co., Tex., N.Mex. Okla., 1988-93; instr. ESL El Paso C.C., 1994—; instr. French U. Okla., 1952-53; Industry rep. Nat. Com. Support of Fgn. Langs., 1971. Pres. El Paso Council for Internat. Visitors, 1987-88. Served with USAAF, 1943-46. Decorated Air medal. Mem. Phi Beta Kappa. Democrat. Club: Alliance Francaise (El Paso). Home: 6832 La Cadena Dr El Paso TX 79912-2810 In my mind, the pursuit of happiness has always been bound up with the pursuit of knowledge—knowledge not in a purely abstract sense, but purposeful knowledge humanely applied. The professions of teaching and publishing, if practiced in the light of the highest ethical standards associated with each, make this pursuit possible and offer the greatest satisfaction to those who view life as I do. I consider myself fortunate to have served in both of these professions.

TREANOR, CHARLES EDWARD, scientist; b. Buffalo, Oct. 22, 1924; s. William Michael and Margaret Mary (Powers) T.; m. Ruth Ziegelmaier, Jan. 28, 1950; children: Timothy, John, Peter, Michael, Melissa. B.A., U. Minn., 1947; Ph.D., U. Buffalo, 1956. Instr. physics U. Buffalo, 1952-53; physicist Cornell Aero. Lab., Buffalo, 1954-68, head aerodynamic research dept., 1968-78; v.p. phys. sci. group Calspan Corp., Buffalo, 1978-83, v.p., chief scientist, 1983-90; pres. CTSA, Inc., 1990—. Contbr. articles to profl. jours. Patentee in field. Served to lt. U.S. Army, 1943-46. Recipient C.C. Furnas award SUNY, Buffalo, 1989. Fellow Am. Phys. Soc. (chmn. 1977), AIAA (com. chmn. 1975-76, 87-89, Fluid and Plasma Dynamics award 1978); mem. NAE. Home: 140 Segsbury Rd Buffalo NY 14221-3425 Office: Calspan UB Rsch Ctr 4455 Genesee St PO Box 400 Buffalo NY 14225

TREAS, JUDITH KAY, sociology educator; b. Phoenix, Jan. 2, 1947; d. John Joseph and Hope Catherine (Thomas) Jennings; m. Benjamin C. Treas II, May 14, 1969; children: Stella, Evan. BA, Pitzer Coll., Claremont, Calif. 1969; MA, UCLA, 1972, PhD, 1976. Instr. U. So. Calif., L.A., 1974-75, asst. prof., 1975-81, assoc. prof., 1981-87, dept. chair, 1984-89, prof., 1987-

89; prof. U. Calif., Irvine, 1989, dept. chair, 1989-94; bd. overseers Gen. Social Survey, 1986-88; cons. social sci. and population study sect. NIH, 1989-92. Contbr. articles to profl. jours. Trustee Pitzer Coll., 1977-79. Recipient Rsch. award NSF, 1978-81, 84-91, NIH, 1979-81; Univ. scholar U. So. Calif., 1982-83. Fellow Gerontological Assn. Am.; mem. Golden Key (hon.), Am. Sociol. Assn., Population Assn. Am., Internat. Union for Sci. Study Population. Office: U Calif-Irvine Dept Sociology Irvine CA 92717

TREASTER, JOSEPH B. (BLAND), journalist; b. Mt. Union, Pa., May 19, 1941; s. Ellsworth F. and Anna Katherine (Chalupka) T.; m. Barbara A. Gluck, June 6, 1970 (div. Aug. 1976); m. Barbara J. Dill, Feb. 24, 1990. BA, U. Miami, 1965; student, Sorbonne, Paris, 1971, San Francisco de Marroquin, Guatemala, 1988. Reporter Miami (Fla.) Herald, 1963; staff asst. Saigon bur. N.Y. Times, 1965-67, Vietnam corr., 1968-69, 72-74; reporter N.Y. Times, N.Y.C., 1969-70; chief Conn. bur. N.Y. Times, 1970-72, investigative reporter N.J. bur., 1974-75, crime/youth violence writer, 1975-76, rewrite desk and spl. assignments to Washington, L.Am. and Mid. East, 1976-84, chief Caribbean bur., 1984-90, drug policy corr., 1990—; freelance corr. Atlantic Monthly, Rolling Stone, the Nation, others; fellow Poynter Inst., St. Petersburg, Fla., 1993, U. Nev. Bus. Journalism, 1995. Co-author: No Hiding Place: Inside Report on the Hostage Crisis (in Iran), 1981; contbg. author: Encyclopedia Britannica, Insight Guide to Caribbean Youth Violence, 1992. Served with U.S. Army, 1963-65, Vietnam. Recipient Page One award N.Y. Newspaper Guild, 1977, 79; Tom Wallace award Inter-Am. Press Assn., 1980, citation and awards Overseas Press Club Am., 1977, 80, 85, News Analysis award Soc. of Silurians, 1993, others; Poynter fellow Yale U., 1975. Mem. Mystery Writers Am. Avocations: skiing, sport fishing, running, bicycling. Office: NY Times 229 W 43d St New York NY 10036

TREASURE, JOHN ALBERT PENBERTHY, advertising executive; b. Usk, Monmouthshire, Eng., June 20, 1924; s. Harold Paul and Constance (Shapl) T.; m. Valerie Bell, Apr. 1954; children—Jonathan, Julian, Simon. Ph.D., Cambridge U., 1956. Research officer Brit. Market Research Bur., Ltd., London, 1952-56; mng. dir. Brit. Market Research Bur., Ltd., 1957-60; dir. research and mktg. J. Walter Thompson Co., Ltd., London, 1960-66; chmn. J. Walter Thompson Co., Ltd., 1967-77, John Treasure and Partners, London, 1981-83; dean City U. Bus. Sch., London, 1978-81; vice chmn. Saatchi & Saatchi Advt. Ltd., 1983-89; chmn. Taylor Nelson AGB plc, 1992—. Contbr. articles to profl. jours. Friend Royal Coll. Physicians; trustee Found. for Bus. Responsibilities. Fellow Inst. Practitioners in Advt. (past pres.); mem. Market Research Soc. (past pres.). Home: 20 Queensberry House, Friars Ln, Richmond, Surrey TW9 1NT, England Office: Taylor Nelson AGB, AGB House, West Gate, Hanger Ln, London W5 1UA, England

TREAT, JAMES J., accountant, business executive; b. Pittsfield, Mass., May 8, 1942; s. Orion F. and Gladdis A. (Whittsley) T.; m. Marcelle Joanne Felker, Sept. 8, 1967; children: James Matthew, Jessica Ann. BS, Butler U., 1965; student, U. New Haven, 1969-79, MIT, 1976. Cost acctg. mgr. Sperry Products, Inc., Danbury, Conn., 1969-70; chief acct. Automation Industries, Inc., Danbury, 1970-73, asst. controller, 1974-75, group controller, 1976-80; controller Nuclear Energy Services Inc., Danbury, 1975-76; gen. mgr. Conam Inspection, Midland, Tex., 1980-81; v.p. Conam Inspection, Longview, Tex., 1981-84; controller, v.p. Longview Inspection, Inc., 1984-90; pres., dir., 1990—; treas. Automation Fedn. Credit Union, Danbury, 1973-75, v.p., 1975-80. Inventor (with others) ultrasonic testing device, 1986. Fund raiser YMCA, Danbury, 1978, dir. regional YMCA, Danbury, 1978-79; fin. chmn. United Meth. Ch., Hallsville, Tex., 1984-85. Served with USN, 1965-69. Mem. Am. Welding Soc., Nat. Assn. Accts., Am. Soc. Nondestructive Testing, Nondestructive Mgmt. Assn. Avocations: sports, collectibles.

TREAT, JOHN ELTING, management consultant; b. Evanston, Ill., June 20, 1946; s. Carlin Alexander and Marjorie Ann (Mayland) T.; adopted s. Howard Elting Jr.; m. Barbara Laflin, May 27, 1984; children: Charles, Luli, Tyler. BA, Princeton U., 1967; MA, Johns Hopkins U., 1969. Legis. asst. U.S. Senate, 1966; assoc. ops. officer Office of Sec., U.S. Dept. State, 1971-73; research coordinator Presdl.-Congressional Commn. on Orgn. of Govt. for Conduct of Fgn. Policy, Washington, 1973-74; dir. research trade U.S. Fed. Energy Adminstrn., Washington, 1974-78; dep. asst. sec. U.S. Dept. Energy, Washington, 1979-80; staff mem. Nat. Security Council, 1980-81; sr. v.p. N.Y. Merc. Exchange, N.Y.C., 1981-82, pres., 1982-84; ptnr. Bear Stearns & Co., Los Angeles, 1984-85; exec. pub. Petroleum Intelligence Weekly, N.Y.C., 1985-87; pres. Regent Internat., Washington and The Hague, 1987-89; v.p., ptnr. Booz, Allen & Hamilton, Inc., San Francisco, 1989—. Chmn. spl. gifts Am. Cancer Soc., 1983; chmn. bd. dirs. Mirror Repertory Co., 1987—; trustee, mem. exec. com., chmn. corp. rels. com. No. Calif. World Affairs Coun.; mem. San Francisco Fgn. Rels. com.; bd. trustees Am. U. of Cairo. With USNR, 1969-71. Decorated AF Commendation medal; Ford Found. European Area Travel grantee, 1972; Woodrow Wilson fellow, 1967; McConnell fellow, 1966. Mem. Coun. Fgn. Rels., Internat. Assn. for Energy Econs. Democrat. Unitarian. Clubs: Colonial (Princeton, N.J.), St. Francis Yacht Club, Bankers (San Francisco). Home: 42 San Carlos Ave Sausalito CA 94965-2048

TREAT, LAWRENCE, author; b. N.Y.C., Dec. 21, 1903; s. Henry and Daisy (Stein) Goldstone; m. Rose Ehrenfreund, 1943. B.A., Dartmouth Coll., 1924; LL.B., Columbia U., 1927. Author: fiction Run Far, Run Fast, 1937, B as in Banshee, 1940, D as in Dead, 1941, H as in Hangman, 1942, O as in Omen, 1943, The Leatherman, 1944, V as in Victim, 1945, H as in Hunted, 1946, Q as in Quicksand, 1947, Over the Edge, 1948, F as in Flight, 1948, Trial and Terror, 1949, Big Shot, 1951, Weep for a Wanton, 1956, Lady, Drop Dead, 1960, Venus Unarmed, 1961, P as in Police, 1970, True Crime with Judge Norbert Ehrenfreund: You're the Jury, 1992; originator of police procedurals and pictorial mysteries, Bringig Sherlock Home, 1931, Crime and Puzzlement, 1981, Crime and Puzzlement 2, 1982, You're the Detective, 1983, The Clue Armchair Detective, 1983, Crime and Puzzlement 3, 1988, Cherchez le Coupable, 1 and 2, 1989, Crime and Puzzlement, My Cousin Phoebe, 1991, Crime and Puzzlement on Martha's Vineyard, 1993; editor: Murder in Mind, 1967; The Mystery Writer's Handbook, 1976, A Special Kind of Crime, 1982; contbr. numerous short stories to mags. including Alfred Hitchcock's Mystery Mag., Ellery Queen's Mystery Mag., Red Book, others, also numerous anthologies. Recipient Ceremonial sword Mystery Writers Japan, 1961, Edgar Allan Poe award Mystery Writers of Am., 1965, 78, Spl. Edgar Allan Poe award for story in Alfred Hitchcock TV Hour, 1986; prize Internat. Crime Writer's Conv., Stockholm, 1981. Mem. Mystery Writers Am. (founder, past pres.), Boston Author's Club, Crime Writers' Assn., Phi Beta Kappa. Office: RFD Box 475A Edgartown MA 02539 also: care Vicky Bijur 333 West End Ave New York NY 10023

TREAT, SHARON ANGLIN, state legislator; b. Brattleboro, Vt., Jan. 30, 1956; d. Robert Sherman and Mary Lou (Strassburger) T. AB, Princeton U., 1978; JD cum laude, Georgetown U., 1982. Bar: Maine, N.J. Asst. dep. pub. adv. N.J. Dept. of the Pub. Adv., Trenton, 1982-85; assoc. atty. Ball, Livingston & Tykulsker, Newark, 1985-86; staff atty. Natural Resources Coun. Maine, Augusta, 1986-90; state rep. Maine State Legis., Augusta, 1991—; pvt. practice Hallowell, Maine, 1991—; leader Ctr. for Policy Alternatives, Washington, 1992—. Bd. dirs. N.J. Environ. Lobby, Trenton, 1984-86, Maine People's Resource Ctr., Augusta, 1991—, N.E. Citizen Action Resource Ctr., Hartford, Conn., 1992—, Maine Assn. Conservation Commns., 1994—; co-founder, dir. Alliance, Portland, Maine, 1987; trustee Class of 1978 Found., White Plains, N.Y., 1988—; mem. adv. bd. Augusta Area Rape Crisis Ctr., 1992—, Divsn. of Deafness, 1994—; mem. Natural Resources Coun. Maine, Maine Women's Lobby. Mem. Gardiner Libr. Assn., Rotary. Democrat. Office: 222 Water St Hallowell ME 04347-1391 also: Maine Ho of Reps State House Augusta ME 04333-0002

TREBEK, ALEX, television game show host; b. Sudbury, Ont., Can., July 22, 1940; came to U.S. 1973; s. George Edward and Lucille (Lagacé) T.; m. Elaine Callei (div. 1981); m. Jean Currivan, Apr. 30, 1990; 2 children. BA and PhB, U. Ottawa, Ont., 1961. Staff announcer CBC, Toronto, Ont., 1961-73; game show host Wizard of Odds for NBC, Calif., 1973-74, High Rollers for NBC, Calif., 1974-79, Stars on Ice for Can. TV, 1974-77, $128,000 Question for Global TV, Can., 1976-77, Double Dare for CBS, Calif., 1977-78, Battle Stars for NBC, Calif., 1981-82; game show host, producer Jeopardy!, Calif., 1984-87, game show host, 1987—; game show host Classic Concentration, Calif., 1987-90, To Tell the Truth, 1991, film appearances

include: Short Cuts, 1993. Mem. Screen Actors Guild, AFTRA, Assn. Can. TV and Radio Artists. Roman Catholic. Avocations: golf, hockey, tennis, water skiing. Office: Jeopardy! 1020 W Washington Blvd Culver City CA 90232

TREBILCOCK, WILLIAM EVERETT, food products executive; b. Calumet, Mich., Aug. 13, 1945; s. Everett Robert and Jane Mary (Baccus) T.; m. Ann Helen Hoekema, June 22, 1968; children: Heather, Dereck, Damen. BA, Mich. State U., 1967; MBA, Western Mich. U., 1968. Sales mgr. Coca Cola Bottling of Calif., Oakland, 1968-70; v.p. adminstrn. Coca Cola of Wis., Milw., 1970-72; v.p., gen. mgr. Pacific Coca Cola Corp., Portland, Oreg., 1972-78; sales v.p. Coca Cola Mich.-Ohio, Grand Rapids, Mich., 1978-82; regional v.p. Mid Continent Bottlers, Des Moines, 1982-84, chmn., pres., bd. dirs., 1987—; v.p. 7up Beverage Div., Des Moines, 1984-86; bd. dirs. Beverage Assn. Coop., Holland, Mich., Royal Crown Bottlers Assn., Louisville; pres. 7up Bottlers Assn., Chgo., 1985—. Mem. Rotary, West Des Moines Golf Club (bd. dirs.). Republican. Avocations: tennis, skiing, golf. Office: Mid Continent Bottlers Inc 4500 Westwn Pkwy West Des Moines IA 50266

TREBILCOTT, JAMES JOSEPH, former utility executive; b. Kansas City, Mo., June 20, 1917; s. William Henry and Catherine (Curran) T.; m. Maureen E. Ball, Dec. 16, 1944; children: Katherine, Michael, Ronald. B.S., U. Mo., 1938; postgrad., Harvard U., 1942, Mass. Inst. Tech., 1942, U. Mich., 1952. With Pub. Service Co., Okla., 1946-48, Mich. Wis. Pipe Line Co., Detroit, 1948-80; v.p., chief ops. officer, dir. Mich. Wis. Pipe Line Co., 1960-72, exec. v.p., dir., 1973-80; exec. v.p. Am. Nat. Resources Co., 1980-82; pres., dir. Am. Nat. Service Co., 1980-82, Worldwide Profl. Mgmt., 1982—; chmn. Thermo Electric Co., 1982-87; v.p., chief ops. officer, dir. Am. La. Pipe Line Co., Detroit, 1960-66; v.p., dir. Am. Natural Gas Prodn. Co., 1962-80; exec. v.p., dir. Am. Nat. Alaskan Co., 1979-80, pres., dir., 1981-82; chmn. Oumic Thermo-Electric Co.; pres., dir. Am. Nat. LNG Corp., ANR LaSalle LNG Transmission Corp., ANR Elba LNG Transmission Corp., all 1979-82, Mich. Med. Properties, 1985—; exec. v.p., dir. Energy Conversion Devices Inc., 1983-87; dir. Gt. Lakes Gas Transmission Co., St. Clair Group Money Market Funds. Served to capt. USAAF, 1942-46. Mem. Engring. Soc. Detroit, Greater Detroit Bd. Commerce, Detroit Econ. Club, Newcomen Soc., Am. Gas Assn., Midwest Gas Assn. (dirs.), So. Gas Assn., Ind. Natural Gas Assn., Internat. Gas. Union (com. mem.). Clubs: Detroit Athletic, Detroit, Detroit Golf, Circumnavigators (pres., dir.) (Detroit). Lodges: K.C., Rotary (Detroit). Home: 3 Alger Pl Grosse Pointe MI 48230-1908

TRECKELO, RICHARD M., lawyer; b. Elkhart, Ind., Oct. 22, 1926; s. Frank J. and Mary (Ferro) T.; m. Anne Kosick, June 25, 1955; children: Marla Treckelo Buck, Mary Treckelo Lucchesi. AB, U. Mich., 1951, JD, 1953. Bar: Ind. 1953, U.S. Dist. Ct. (no. and so. dists.) Ind. Pvt. practice, Elkhart, 1953-70; ptnr. Barnes & Thornburg, Elkhart, South Bend, Indpls., Ft. Wayne, of counsel, 1992—; sec. Skyline Corp., Elkhart, 1959-94, bd. dirs., 1961-91. Bd. dirs. Elkhart Gen. Hosp. Found., Elkhart Park Found.; co-chmn. Elkhart Constl. Bicentennial Commn. Served with USAF, 1945-46. Mem. ABA, Elkhart City Bar Assn. (pres. 1975), Ind. Bar Assn., Elkhart County Bar Assn., Pres.'s Club (U. Mich.), Rotary. Republican. Office: Barnes & Thornburg 301 S Main St Ste 305 Elkhart IN 46516-3285

TREDWAY, THOMAS, college president; b. North Tonawanda, N.Y., Sept. 4, 1935; s. Harold and Melanya (Scorby) T.; m. Catherine Craft, Jan. 12, 1991; children: Daniel John, Rebecca Elizabeth. BA, Augustana Coll., 1957; MA, U. Ill., 1958; BD, Garrett Theol. Sem., 1961; PhD, Northwestern U., 1964. Instr. history Augustana Coll., Rock Island, Ill., 1964-65, asst. prof., 1965-69, assoc. prof., 1969-71, prof., 1971—, v.p. acad affairs, 1970-75, pres., 1975—; vis. prof. ch. history Waterloo Lutheran Sem., 1967-68. Mem. Am. Hist. Assn., Am. Soc. Ch. History, Phi Beta Kappa, Omicron Delta Kappa. Lutheran. Office: Augustana Coll Office of President 639 38th St Rock Island IL 61201-2296

TREE, DAVID L., advertising agency executive. Formerly sr. v.p., creative dir. D'Arcy Masius Benton & Bowles, Inc., N.Y.C.; chmn., corp. chief creative officer Campbell Mithun Esty, 1989—. Office: Campbell Mithun Esty 222 S 9th St Minneapolis MN 55402-3310

TREE, MICHAEL, violinist, violist, educator; b. Newark, Feb. 19, 1934; s. Samuel and Sada (Rothman) Applebaum; m. Johanna Kreck, Sept. 8, 1966; children: Konrad Efrem, Anna Louise. Diploma, Curtis Inst. Music, Phila., 1955; DFA (hon.), U. South Fla., 1975, SUNY, Binghamton, 1983. Faculty Harpur Coll., Binghamton, 1965-70, Curtis Inst. Music, 1970—, U. Md. College Park, 1981—, St. Louis Conservatory Music, 1982-88, Rutgers U., 1988—, Manhattan Sch. Music, 1993—; co-artistic dir. Phila. Chamber Orch., 1985-88; Misha Elman chair Manhattan Sch. Music, 1991. Violin recital debut at Carnegie Hall, 1954; soloist with major orchs. and at maj. internat. festivals, 1958—; founding mem. Guarneri String Quartet, 1964—; rec. artist for Philips, RCA, Columbia, Nonesuch, Vanguard, Sony Classics records. Recipient Seal of Recognition City of N.Y., 1982. Avocations: hiking, tennis. Home: 45 E 89th St New York NY 10128-1232 Office: care Herbert Barrett Mgmt Inc 1776 Broadway New York NY 10019

TREECE, JOHN W., lawyer; b. Madison, Wis., Oct. 2, 1952. BA magna cum laude, Harvard U., 1975; JD, Columbia U., 1978. Bar: Ill. 1978. Ptnr. Sidley & Austin, Chgo. With Army NG, 1972-78. Harlan Fiske Stone scholar. Office: Sidley & Austin 1 First Nat Plz Chicago IL 60603

TREECE, JOSEPH CHARLES, insurance broker; b. Loma Linda, Calif., Sept. 1, 1934; s. Roy G. and Jeane L. (Reade) T.; children: Debbie, Mike, David. BA, Chapman Coll., 1956. Cert. Ins. Counselor, Assoc. in Risk Mgmt. Comml. banker Security Pacific Nat. Bank, Hemet, Calif., 1959-72; ins. broker H.I.S./Kent & Hamilton, Hemet, 1972-89, Russell & Kaufmann, Hemet, 1989—. Dir. YMCA, Hemet. Lt. USN, 1956-59. Recipient Associate Achievement award Am. Assn. Mng. Gen. Agts., 1991, Disting. Svc. award Cert. Profl. Ins. Agents Soc., 1995. Mem. Ramona Pageant Assn. (life, chmn.-supr. 1962—), Profl. Ins. Assn. (state dir. 1988-91), Profl. Ins. Agts. (pres. Riverside and San Bernardino, Calif. 1989-90), Joint Ins. Assn. (pres. Riverside and San Bernardino 1991), Ind. Ins. Agts. (pres.), Cert. Profl. Ins. Agts. (nat. pres. 1992, Disting. Svc. award 1995), Hemet C. of C. (pres. 1970), Kiwanis Club (life, Hemet chpt. pres. 1971, lt. gov. divsn. 6 Cal-Na-Ha 1972). Avocations: golf, camping, fishing, canoeing. Home: PO Box 1731 San Jacinto CA 92581-1731 Office: Russell & Kaufmann Ins Agts 400 S State St Hemet CA 92543

TREFFERT, DAROLD ALLEN, psychiatrist, author, hospital director; b. Fond du Lac, Wis., Mar. 12, 1933; s. Walter O. and Emma (Leu) T.; m. Dorothy Marie Sorgatz, June 11, 1955; children: Jon, Joni, Jill, Jay. B.S., U. Wis., 1955, M.D., 1958. Diplomate: Am. Bd. Psychiatry and Neurology. Resident in psychiatry U. Wis. Med. Sch., 1959-62, assoc. clin. prof. psychiatry, 1965—; chief children's unit Winnebago (Wis.) Mental Health Inst., 1962-64, supt., 1964-79; supt. Central State Hosp., Waupun, Wis., 1977-78; dir. Dodge County Mental Health Center, Juneau, Wis., 1994—; mem. staff St. Agnes Hosp., Fond du Lac, 1963—; exec. dir. Fond du Lac County Mental Health Center, 1979—; chmn. Controlled Substances Bd. Wis.; mem. critical health problems com. Wis. Dept. Pub. Instrn. Author: Extraordinary People: Understanding Savant Syndrome, U.S. and U.K. edits., 1989; contbr. articles to profl. jours. in Italy, Japan, The Netherlands, Sweden; autism cons. movie Rainman, 1988. Fellow Am. Coll. Psychiatrists; mem. AMA, Wis. Med. Soc. (pres. 1979-80), Wis. Psychiat. Assn. (pres.), Am. Assn. Psychiat. Adminstrs. (pres.), Alpha Omega Alpha. Home: W 4065 Maplewood Ln Fond Du Lac WI 54935-9562 Office: 481 E Division St Fond Du Lac WI 54935-3775 *People often spend too much time regretting what they are not and far too little time savoring that which they are.*

TREFFINGER, KARL EDWARD, architectural firm executive; b. Columbus, Ohio, Oct. 21, 1927; s. Raymond Hartman and Eldred (Ruffner) T.; m. Beverly Jean Becke, Mar. 21, 1957 (dec. 1994); children: Kathy Anne, Julia Frances Wirth, Karl Raymond, Frederick Charles. BA, Yale U., 1948, MArch, 1952. Registered arch. Calif., Oreg. Wash., Nev., Ohio, Ill., Fla. Okla.; cert. Nat. Coun. Archtl. Registration Bds. Draftsman Stanley Morse, Denver, 1955-56; pvt. practice Columbus, Ohio, 1956-57; apprentice Edward

Durrell Stone, Palo Alto, Calif., 1957-58; designer Wurster, Bernardi and Emmons, San Francisco, 1959-60; arch. Karl Treffinger & Assoc., San Francisco, 1960-78; prin. Treffinger, Walz and MacLeod, San Francisco and San Rafael, Calif., 1978-92. Prin. works include Harbor Point Beach Club, Strawberry Peninsula, Calif.; Telegraph Hill Apts., San Francisco, Peninsula Squash Club, San Mateo, Calif., Sheraton Inn-Walden, Schaumburg, Ill., Court of Flags Complex, Orlando, Fla., Growers Sq., Walnut Creek, Calif. Walden Office Sq., Schaumburg, Wescot Internat., San Rafael, Treffinger, Walz & MacLeod Offices, San Rafael, Remillard Brick Yard, Larkspur, Calif., Walden Market Sq. Project, Schaumburg, Walden Lakes, Bensenville, Ill., Smith Ranch Master Plan, San Rafael, Bon Air Project, Greenbrae, Calif., Ridgeland Devel. Project, Marin City, Calif., condominiums, townhouses, apts.; contbr. articles to profl. jours. Lt. USN, 1952-55, Korea. Recipient civic awards for design excellence. Fellow AIA (corp., pres. No. Calif. chpt. 1974, sec. Calif. coun., awards design excellence). Home: 700 SW Schaeffer Rd West Linn OR 97068

TREFIL, JAMES S., physicist, educator; b. Chgo., Sept. 10, 1938; s. Stanley James and Sylvia (Mestek) T.; m. Elinor Pletka; children: James Karel, STefan; m. Jeanne L. Waples, Oct. 17, 1972; children: Dominique, Flora, Tomas. BS, U. Ill., 1960; BA, MA, Oxford (Eng.) U., 1962; MS, Stanford U., 1964, PhD, 1966. Rsch. assoc. Stanford (Calif.) Linear Accelerator Ctr., 1966; postdoctoral fellow Air Force Office Sci. Rsch., Geneva, 1966-67; asst. prof. physics U. Ill., Urbana, 1968-70; assoc. prof. physics U. Va., Charlottesville, 1970-75, prof. physics, 1975-87, Univ. prof. physics, 1987; C.J. Robinson prof. physics George Mason U., Fairfax, Va., 1987—; sci. adv. bd. Nat. Pub. Radio; cons. Smithsonian Mag.; tech. cons. Am. Heritage Dictionary. Author: The Dark Side of the Universe, 1988, Dictionary of Cultural Literacy, 1988, 2d edit., 1993, Reading the Mind of God, 1989, Science Matters, 1991, Facts of Life: Science and the Abortion Controversy, 1992, A Scientist in the City, 1994, The Sciences: An Integrated Approach, 1995. NSF fellow Stanford U., 1966; recipient Sci. Journalism award AAAS-Westinghouse, 1983; John Simon Guggenheim fellow, 1987-88; Marshall scholar Oxford U., 1962. Fellow Am. Phys. Soc. Office: George Mason U 207 E Bldg Fairfax VA 22030

TREFRY, ROBERT J., healthcare administrator; b. Springfield, Vt., Mar. 29, 1947; married. Bachelors' degree, Ga. Inst. Tech., 1970; Masters' degree, George Washington U., 1974. With Greater Southeast Community Hosp., Washington, 1973, adminstrv. asst., 1973-74, asst. administr., 1974-79; sr. v.p. North Kansas City (Mo.) Community Hosp., 1979-83; exec. v.p., chief exec. officer St. Agnes Hosp., White Plains, N.Y., 1983-88; exec. v.p., chief operating officer Carle Found. Hosp., Urbana, Ill., 1988-91; exec. v.p., chief oper. officer Bridgeport (Conn.) Hosp., 1991—. With U.S. mil. 1970-71. Office: Bridgeport Hosp 267 Grant St Bridgeport CT 06610-2870

TREGDE, LORRAINE C., hospital administrator; b. Bklyn., Aug. 19, 1928. MA, St. John's U., 1955, NYU, 1966. Asst. exec. dir. Hosp. Holy Family, Bklyn., 1955-62, exec. dir., 1962-65; cons. MDC Systems, Cherry Hill, N.J., 1968-73; adminstr. Calvary Hosp., Bronx, N.Y., 1973-76; exec. dir. Calvary Hosp., Bronx, 1976-80, Coler Meml. Hosp., N.Y.C., 1980-82, Queens Hosp. Ctr., Jamaica, N.Y., 1982-87, Bronx (N.Y.) Mcpl. Hosp. Ctr., 1992—; acting exec. dir. Bellevue Hosp. Ctr., N.Y.C., 1991-92. Office: Bronx Mcpl Hosp Ctr Pelham Pky S & Eastchester Rd Bronx NY 10461

TREGOE, BENJAMIN BAINBRIDGE, management consultant, researcher; b. San Francisco, Dec. 23, 1927; s. Benjamin Bainbridge and Marianne (West) T.; m. Jeannette Sylvia Gill, Aug. 4, 1956; children: Cynthia West, Elizabeth Gill, Benjamin Bainbridge III. BA, Whittier Coll., 1951, HHD (hon.), 1990; PhD, Harvard U., 1957. Rsch. assoc. Rand Corp., Santa Monica, Calif., 1955-58; co-founder Kepner-Tregoe, Inc., Princeton, N.J., 1958—, also chmn. bd. dirs.; lectr. UCLA, Westwood, 1956-57, UCLA, 1955-58; bd. dirs. J.M. Smucker Co., Orrville, Ohio, World Affairs Coun. of Phila., 1992—; mem. exec. com., bd. dirs. Nat. Alliance Bus., Washington; pres., founder Bainbridge Ednl. Found., 1993. Author: The Rational Manager, 1965, The New Rational Manager, 1980, Top Management Strategy, 1980, Vision in Action, 1989. Trustee Whittier Coll., 1980—, St. Simon's-by-the-Sea, Mantoloking, N.J., 1988—; Princeton Day Sch., 1976-85; dir. Princeton U. Libr., 1986-89, YWCA Exec. Assn., Princeton, 1975-86; elder Nassau Presbyn. Ch., Princeton, 1990—. With USMC, 1946-47. Mem. Chief Execs. Orgn., World Affairs Coun. (bd. dirs. Phila.), ASTD (dir. 1975-79), Harvard Club N.Y.C., Harvard Club Princeton (dir. 1987-89), Nassau Club, BayHead Yacht Club, Mantoloking Yacht Club. Republican. Avocations: skiing, swimming, reading, fly fishing. Office: Kepner-Tregoe Inc 17 Research Rd PO Box 704 Princeton NJ 08542-0704

TREGURTHA, PAUL RICHARD, marine transportation and construction materials company executive; b. Orange, N.J., 1935; married. BSME, Cornell U., 1958; MBA, Harvard U., 1963. V.p., controller Brown & Sharpe Mfg. Co., 1969-71; v.p. fin. Moore McCormack Resources, Inc., Stamford, Conn., 1971-73, exec. v.p. fin. 1973-78, pres., chief operating officer, from 1978, pres., chief exec. officer, chmn., 1987-88; chmn., co-owner Mormac Marine Group, Inc., Stamford, 1988—; vice chmn., co-owner The Interlake Steamship Co., 1988—; chmn. Meridian Aggregates Acquisitions, Inc., Moran Transp. Co., 1994—; bd. dirs. Shawmut Nat. Corp., Brown and Sharpe Mfg. Co., FPL Group, Inc. Trustee Cornell U., Ithaca, N.Y.; trustee Tchrs. Ins. and Annuity Assn. Served to 1st lt. USAF, 1958-61. Named Baker Scholar, Harvard U., 1963. Office: Mormac Marine Group Inc Three Landmark Sq Stamford CT 06901

TREICHEL, PAUL MORGAN, JR., chemistry educator; b. Madison, Wis., Dec. 4, 1936; s. Paul Morgan and Irene (Wells) T.; m. Isabel Walk, June 4, 1961; children: Janet R., David A. BS, U. Wis., 1958; AM, Harvard U., 1960, PhD, 1962. Asst. prof. chemistry U. Wis., Madison, 1963-66, assoc. prof. chemistry, 1966-71, prof. chemistry 1971—, chmn. dept. chemistry, 1986—; cons. Goodyear Chem. Co., Oscar Mayer Co. Contbr. numerous articles to profl. jours. Mem. Am. Chem. Soc., Sigma Xi. Avocations: woodworking, tennis. Home: 1121 Amherst Dr Madison WI 53705-2201 Office: U Wis Dept Chemistry Madison WI 53706

TREIGER, IRWIN LOUIS, lawyer; b. Seattle, Sept. 10, 1934; s. Sam S. and Rose (Steinberg) T.; m. Betty Lou Friedlander, Aug. 18, 1957; children: Louis H., Karen I., Kenneth B. BA, U. Wash., 1955, JD, 1957; LLM in Taxation, NYU, 1958. Bar: Wash. 1958, D.C. 1982, U.S. Dist. Ct. (we. dist.) Wash., U.S. Ct. Appeals (9th cir.), U.S. Supreme Ct. Assoc. Bogle & Gates, Seattle, 1957-63, ptnr., 1964-. Mem. 1986-94. Pres. Jewish Fedn. Greater Seattle, 1993-95; chmn. Mayor's Symphony Panel, 1986, Corp. Coun. for the Arts, 1987-88; pres. Seattle Symphony Found., 1986—; trustee, co-chmn. Cornish Coll. of the Arts, 1990—; trustee The Seattle Found., 1992—, Samis Found., 1989—; chmn. King County Baseball Pk. Commn., 1995—. Fellow Am. Coll. Tax Counsel; mem. ABA (chmn. taxation sect. 1988-89, sect. del. 1990—), Wash. State Bar Assn. (chmn. taxation sect. 1975), Greater Seattle C. of C. (chmn. 1993-94), Seattle Rotary Svc. Found. (v.p. 1995—). Jewish. Office: Bogle & Gates 601 Union St Seattle WA 98101-2327

TREIMAN, SAM BARD, physics educator; b. Chgo., May 27, 1925; s. Abraham and Sarah (Bard) T.; m. Joan Little, Dec. 27, 1952; children—Rebecca, Katherine, Thomas. Student, Northwestern U., 1944; S.B., U. Chgo., 1948, S.M., 1949, Ph.D., 1952. Mem. faculty Princeton U., 1952—, instr., 1952-54, asst. prof. 1954-58, assoc. prof. 1958-63, prof. physics 1963—, Eugene Higgins prof., 1977—, chmn. dept., 1981-87, chmn. univ. rsch. bd., 1988—. Author: (with M. Grossjean) Formal Scattering Theory, 1960, (with R. Jackiw and D.J. Gross) Current Algebra and Its Applications, 1972; Contbr. articles to profl. jours. Served with USNR, 1944-46. Recipient Oersted medal Am. Assn. Physics Tchrs. Mem. NAS, Am. Phys. Soc., Am. Acad. Arts and Scis. Home: 60 Mccosh Cir Princeton NJ 08540-5627

TREISTER, GEORGE MARVIN, lawyer; b. Oxnard, Calif., Sept. 5, 1923; s. Isadore Harry and Augusta Lee (Bloom) T.; m. Jane Goldberg, Jan. 24, 1946; children: Laura, Neil, Dana. BS., UCLA. 1943, S. JD, Yale U., 1949. Bar: Calif. 1950. Law clk. to chief justice Calif. Supreme Ct., 1949-50; law clk. to Assoc. Justice Hugo L. Black U.S. Supreme Ct., 1950-51; asst. U.S. atty. So. Dist. Calif., 1951-53; dep. atty. gen. Calif., 1953; practiced in Los Angeles, 1953—; mem. Stutman, Treister and Glatt,

1953—; instr. U. So. Calif. Law Sch., 1954—, Stanford U. Law Sch., 1977-81; mem., former vice chmn. Nat. Bankruptcy Conf.; former mem. adv. com. on bankruptcy rules Jud. Conf. U.S. Contbr. articles to profl. jours. Served with USNR, 1943-46. Mem. Am. Law Inst., Am. Judicature Soc. Home: 1201 Neil Creek Rd Ashland OR 97520-9778 Office: 3699 Wilshire Blvd Los Angeles CA 90010-2719

TREISTER, KENNETH, architect, artist; b. N.Y.C., Mar. 5, 1930; s. Arthur and Anita (Weinberg) T.; m. Helyne Bressler, Jan. 31, 1954; children: Charles, Alan, Eliot. Student, U. Miami, 1948-49; BArch, U. Fla., 1953. Adj. prof. U. Fla. Sch. Architecture; lectr. in field; guest lectr. numerous univs. One-man shows Mirell Gallery, Miami, Fla., 1964, 66, 67; exhibited in group shows Greenwich Gallery, N.Y.C., Columbus (Ga.) Mus. Fine Arts, Lowe Art Gallery (1st prize for ceramics), Coral Gables, Fla., Houston Contemporary Art Mus., Atlanta High Mus.; represented in permanent collections Norton Gallery, Palm Beach, Fla., Miami Mus. Modern Art, Fla. Supreme Ct. Bldg; designer, sculptor Holocaust Meml., Miami Beach; author: Chinese Architecture, Urban Planning, and Landscape Design, 1987, A Sculpture of Love and Anguish, 1993; contbr. numerous articles to art and archtl. mags. and books. Chmn. Miami Citizen's Adv. Com., 1965-67; bd. dirs. Am. Jewish Com., Dade County Conf. on Urban Affairs, Friends U. Miami Libr.; trustee Fla. Gov.'s Mansion Found., 1985. With USNR, 1953-57. Recipient numerous awards for archtl. designs including Gold medal S.E. Regional Conf. HUD, 1968, Beautification award City of Miami, 1974, 85, Award of Excellence and Design, Internat. Council of Shopping Ctrs., 1985, award of service, Fla. Architects, 1987, Samuel Kruse Silver medal, 1990. Fellow AIA (svc. award Fla. South chpt. 1984, Fla. media award 1985), Fla. Assn. AIA; mem. Guild Religious Architecture (nat. merit award 1968), Richard J. Nautra Inst., Blue Dome Soc., Fla. Concrete and Products Assn. (award of excellence 1985), Fla. Sculpture Soc., So. Assn. Sculptors, Real Academia de Belles Artes de Sant Jorge (academico correspondente), Lambda Alpha, Zeta Beta Tau. Home and Office: 3660 Battersea Rd Miami FL 33133-6805

TREITLER, LEO, musicologist, educator; b. Dortmund, Fed. Republic Germany, Jan. 26, 1931; came to U.S., 1938.; s. Ben and Regina (Knoll) T.; m. Ruth Elizabeth Wijkman, Sept. 12, 1956 (div. Nov. 1984); children: Christopher, Inga, Alexander, Max. BA, U. Chgo., 1950, MA, 1957; MFA, Princeton U., 1960, PhD, 1966. Instr. Princeton U., N.J., 1961-62; asst. prof. U. Chgo., 1962-66; assoc. prof. then prof. Brandeis U., Waltham, Mass., 1966-75; prof. SUNY-Stony Brook, 1975-87; disting. prof. Grad. Ctr. CUNY, N.Y.C., 1987—. Author: Music and the Historical Imagination, 1989; contbr. articles to profl. publs. Fellow Am. Council Learned Socs., 1974, NEH, 1983; recipient Research prize Humbolt Found., 1982. Fellow Am. Acad. Arts and Scis.; mem. Am. Musicol. Soc., Internat. Musicol. Soc. Home: 139 W 19th St New York NY 10011-4105 Office: Music Program Grad Ctr CUNY 33 W 42nd St New York NY 10036-8003

TRELEASE, ALLEN WILLIAM, historian, educator; b. Boulder, Colo., Jan. 31, 1928; s. William, Jr. and Helen (Waldo) T.; children—William C. (dec. 1990), Mary E., John A. A.B., U. Ill., 1950, M.A., 1951; Ph.D., Harvard U., 1955. Mem. faculty Wells Coll., Aurora, N.Y., 1955-67; prof. history Wells Coll., 1965-67, chmn. dept. history and govt., 1963-67; prof. history U. N.C., Greensboro, 1967-94, head dept., 1984-92, prof. emeritus, 1994—. Author: Indian Affairs in Colonial New York: The Seventeenth Century, 1960, White Terror: The Ku Klux Klan Conspiracy and Southern Reconstruction, 1971, Reconstruction: The Great Experiment, 1971, The North Carolina Railroad, 1849-1871, and the Modernization of North Carolina, 1991, Changing Assignments: A Pictorial History of the U. of N.C. at Greensboro, 1991. Mem. Am., So. Hist. assns., Orgn. Am. Historians, Hist. Soc. N.C. (pres. 1986-87), AAUP, Phi Beta Kappa, Phi Kappa Phi, Phi Eta Sigma, Phi Kappa Psi.

TRELEAVEN, PHILLIPS ALBERT, retired publishing company executive; b. Oak Park, Ill., July 20, 1928; s. Harry William and Mary Elizabeth (Gregory) T. BA, Duke U., 1950; AM, Boston U., 1959; DBA (hon.), Unity Coll., 1988; graduate geologist, Gemological Inst. Am., 1994. With G. K. Hall & Co., Boston, 1956-60, 61-67, 69-79; pres. G. K. Hall & Co., 1969-78, chmn. bd., 1970-78; underwriter mcpl. bonds Scharff & Jones, New Orleans, 1959-61; instr. in polit. economy Boston U., 1967-69; vis. lectr. econs. Unity Coll., 1979-90; owner Odyssey Hill Farms, Thorndike, Maine, 1971-75; pres., pub. Thorndike Press, 1977-87, chmn. bd. dirs., 1988-89; pres. pubs./info. group Sr. Svc. Corp., 1987-89; bd. dirs. Marco Polo Pasta House, Inc., 1989-92, pres., 1991-92. Selectman, Thorndike, 1979-81; trustee Unity Coll., 1985-90, 92—, chmn., 1988-90. Served with AUS, 1950-53. Mem. Phi Beta Kappa. Home: PO Box 40 Thorndike ME 04986 *The biggest blunders in I have made in my life have usually resulted from taking myself or my circumstances too seriously.*

TRELFA, RICHARD THOMAS, paper company executive; b. Alpena, Mich., July 5, 1918; s. Fred R. and Mable (Hagen) T.; m. Heidi Brigitte Ruckstuhl, Dec. 3, 1965; children: Thomas W., Barbara E., Jeffrey C., Michael F. B.S., U. Mich., 1940. With Hercules Powder Co., 1941-52, Watervliet Paper Co., Mich., 1952-58; exec. v.p., treas., dir. Perkins-Goodwin Co., Inc., N.Y.C., 1958-70; v.p., treas., chief fin. officer Perkins-Goodwin Co., Inc., 1970, sr. v.p., 1974—82; chmn. bd. Elcon, Inc., Houston, 1983-91, also bd. dirs., 1983-93; vice chmn. bd. B.S. & W Whiteley Ltd., Eng., 1983-88; bd. dirs. B.S. & W Whiteley Ltd.; treas., dir. Kennebec River Pulp & Paper Co., Madison, Maine, 1967-69, chmn. bd., treas., 1969-72, chmn. bd., mem. exec. com., 1972-73, dir., mem. exec. com., 1973-75; pres. Castle & Overton (Can.) Ltd., 1971-82; chmn. bd. EHV Weidmann Industries, Inc., St. Johnsbury, Vt., 1974-84, Franconia Paper Co. Inc., Lincoln, N.H., 1978-80; bd. dirs. Elcon Mgmt. Svcs. Co., chmn. bd. 1984-91, Old Forge Pulp and Paper Co., chmn. bd. 1985-91; N.H. State rpe. to Gen. Ctr., 1990—; water commr. Lisbon, N.H., 1990—, selectman, Lisbon, 1995—. Fellow Am. Soc. Quality Control, TAPPI (former div. chmn., dir.); mem. Paper Industry Mgmt. Assn. (former div. chmn.), Am. Inst. Chem. Engrs., Am. Chem. Soc., Soc. Rheology. Republican. Club: U. Mich. Lodge: Masons. Home: Northey Rd PO Box 245 Lisbon NH 03585-0245 Office: 46 Main St Saint Johnsbury VT 05819-2216

TREMAIN, ALAN, hotel executive; b. Kent, England, Aug. 18, 1935; came to U.S., 1966; s. Archibalt and Elizabeth (Morris) T.; divorced; 1 child, Warren. Grad., Westminster Hotel Sch., 1952, Canterbury Sch. Econs., 1962; LL.B., La Salle Sch., Chgo., 1971. Chef de Pertie Grosvenor House, London, 1954-55; food and beverage mgr. Peninsula, Hong Kong, 1956-57; gen. mgr. Warners Hotel, also The Russley, Christchurch, New Zealand, 1958-64, Menzies, Sydney, Australia, 1964-65, Empress Hotel, Vancouver, B.C., Can., 1966-69; pres. Planned Food Facilities (Internat.) Ltd., Toronto, 1970-72; resident mgr. Sheraton Boston, 1972; mng. dir. Copley Plaza Hotel, Boston, 1972—; chmn. Hotels of Distinction, Inc., Boston. Author: A Guide to the Fine Art of Living, 1963, A Meal for To-Night, 1965. Decorated officer Order Brit. Empire (U.K.); recipient Culinary Merit award from Cercle Epicurien Mondel, Paris, 1956. Fellow Hotel and Catering Inst. (U.K.); founding mem. Internat. Soc. Chefs de Cuisine (chmn. 1964). Clubs: Mason, Montreal Badminton and Squash, The Beach Club, Palm Beach, Les Ambs., London, Rolls Royce Owners. Address: Hotels of Distinction Inc 380 S County Rd 200 Palm Beach FL 33480

TREMAINE, SCOTT DUNCAN, astrophysicist; b. Toronto, Ont., Can., May 25, 1950; s. Vincent Joseph and Beatrice Delphine (Sharp) T. BSc, McMaster U., Hamilton, Ont., 1971; PhD, Princeton U., 1975. Postdoctoral fellow Calif. Inst. Tech., Pasadena, 1975-77; rsch. assoc. Inst Astronomy, Cambridge, Eng., 1977-78; long-term mem. Inst. for Advanced Study, Princeton, N.J., 1978-81; assoc. prof. MIT, Cambridge, 1981-85; prof., dir. Canadian Inst. for Theoretical Astrophysics U. Toronto, 1985—. Author: Galactic Dynamics, 1987; contbr. articles to profl. jours. E.W.R. Steacie fellow Natural Scis. and Engring. Rsch. Coun., 1988; recipient H.B. Warner prize Am. Astron. Soc., 1983, Steacie prize, 1989, C.S. Beals award Canadian Astron. Soc., 1990, Rutherford medal Royal Soc. Can., 1990. Fellow Royal Soc. London, Royal Soc. Can.; mem. Am. Acad. Arts and Scis. (fgn. hon.). Office: U Toronto-CITA McLennan Lab, 60 St George St, Toronto, ON Canada M5S 1A7

TREMAYNE, BERTRAM WILLIAM, JR., lawyer; b. St. Louis, Feb. 23, 1914; s. Bertram William and Pearl Inez (Flory) T.; m. Frances Lewis, July 6, 1940 (dec. Jan. 1964); children: Pamela L., Eric F.; m. Clara Tarling Marsalek, Jan. 2, 1966. A.B., Washington U., St. Louis, 1935, J.D., 1938. Bar: Mo. 1938, U.S. Dist. Ct. (ea. dist.) Mo. 1938, U.S.Ct. Appeals (8th cir.) 1938. With firm Neuhoff & Millar, St. Louis, 1938-41; dist. rationing atty. OPA, 1941-43; partner firm Neuhoff, Millar, Tremayne & Schaefer, St. Louis, 1946-54, Tremayne, Lay, Carr & Bauer (and predecessors), St. Louis, 1954-93; ret. Mem. St. Louis County Parks and Recreation Bd., 1956-63, chmn., 1959-63; mem. met. bd. dirs. Met. St. Louis YMCA, 1960—, pres., 1970-73; mem. nat. council YMCAs, 1970-77; bd. dirs. Washington U., 1961-65; trustee Deaconess Hosp., St. Louis, 1973-82. Served to capt. AUS, 1943-46. Recipient Distinguished Eagle Scout award Boy Scouts Am., 1973, Disting. Law Alumni award Wash. U. Sch. Law, 1989, Disting. Alumni award Wash. U., 1990. Fellow Am. Bar Found.; mem. ABA (Ho. of Dels. 1981-84), St. Louis County Bar Assn. (disting. service award 1982), Mo. Bar (bd. govs. 1973-80, pres. 1978-79), Mo. Bar Found. (pres. 1987-89), Bar Assn. Met. St. Louis, Am. Coll. Trust and Estate Counsel, Am. Judicature Soc., Judge Advs. Assn., Phi Delta Phi, Omicron Delta Kappa. Congregationalist (pres. 1960-63). Club: Algonquin Golf. Home: 58 Frederick Ln Saint Louis MO 63122-1929

TREMAYNE, WILLIAM HOWARD, insurance company executive; b. Nanticoke, Pa., Nov. 26, 1935; s. William Howard and Dorothy (Davis) T.; m. Lora Christensen, July 3, 1958; children—Cuyler, Carter, Kerry. B.S. in Acctg., Wilkes U., 1957. CLU. With The Prudential Ins. Co. Am., Newark, 1957—, v.p.; tax adminstr., 1972-74, v.p.; asst. comptroller, 1974-77, v.p. pub. relations and advt., 1977-78, v.p. 1978-84, sr. v.p. pub. affairs, 1984—. Pres. Piscataway Bd. Edn., N.J., 1966-70, Wilkes U. Alumni Assn., Wilkes-Barre, Pa., 1967-69, N.J. Taxpayers Assn., Trenton, 1974-77; exec. dir. Gov.'s Commn. to Evaluate Capital Needs of N.J., 1975; mem. N.J. Econ. Devel. Council, 1976-79; vice chmn. New Brunswick Devel. Corp., N.J., 1976-85, chmn., 1986—; trustee New Brunswick Cultural Ctr., N.J., 1983—; project mgr. Pres.'s Pvt. Sector Survey on Cost Control, Washington, 1982-83; mem. policy bd. N.J. Cert. Pub. Mgr. Program, Trenton, 1983—; bd. dirs. N.J. Audubon Soc., 1977-83, ; prin. Ctr. for Excellence in Govt., 1986—; chmn. bd. trustees N.J. Council Chs., East Orange, 1977-85; mem. adv. bd. N.J. chpt. Nat. Huntington Disease Assn., Madison, 1980-85; trustee Pub. Affairs Research Inst. N.J., 1986—, Robert Wood Johnson Hosp., 1987-89; bd. dirs. Bus. Exec. for Nat. Security, 1988—. Republican. Methodist. Avocations: birding; tennis. Home: 109 Haywood Ave Piscataway NJ 08854-3515 Office: The Prudential Ins Co Am 15 Prudential Plz Newark NJ 07102

TREMBLAY, ANDRE GABRIEL, lawyer, educator; b. Jonquiere, Que., Can., Nov. 10, 1937; s. Jean-Charles T. and Julienne (Tremblay) Laberge; children: Jean-Francois, Frederic, Alexandre Reynold. B.A., U. Laval-Que. Can., 1959, LL.L., 1962; D.E.S. in Law, U. Ottawa-Ont. Can., 1964, LL.D., 1966. Bar: Que. 1963. Asst. law U. Ottawa, 1966-70; assoc. U. Montreal, Que., 1970-75, prof., 1972—, pres. Gen. Assn. Profs.; of Pub. Law Ctr., Que., 1972-76, vice dean Sch. Law, 1982-86; dir. grad. studies U. Ottawa, 1968-70; pres. Com. on Human Rights, Montreal, 1981—; legal adv. to bar, govts., law firms, cos. Can., 1972—; sr. Constl. adviser to Que. Govt., 1986-92. Author: Les competences legislatives, 1967 (1st prize Govt. of Que. 1968), Precis de droit municipal, 1973, Precis de droit constitutionnel, 1982, Droitconstitutional-Principles, 1993, La Revision Constitution Nelle, 1995; contbr. articles, chpts. to legal publs. Sec. Polit. Chmn., Que. Liberal Party, Montreal, 1977-81; mem. observer's mission, Internat. Commn. Jurists, Geneva, 1981—, mem. coun. Can. sect., Ottawa, 1981—; v.p. Can. Human Rights Found., Montreal, 1982—. Mem. Assn. Can. Law Tchrs. (pres. Ottawa Chpt. 1974-75). Christian Scientist. Office: Faculty Law U Montreal, CP 6201 succ A, Montreal, PQ Canada H3C 3T1

TREMBLAY, ANDRÉ-MARIE, physicist; b. Montreal, Que., Can., Jan. 2, 1953; m. Marié à Guylaine Séguin; children: Noémie, Rachel. BSc, U. Montreal, 1974; PhD, MIT, 1978. With Energie Atomique du Can. Limitée, 1973-74, MIT, Boston, 1974-75, Inst. de Recherche de l'Hydro-Que., 1976, Cornell U., Ithaca, N.Y., 1978-80; prof. physics U. Sherbrooke, Que., 1980—, dir. Rsch. Ctr. Physics of Solids, 1991—; cons. Cornell U., 1981, Ohio State U., 1982, IBM, 1984; vis. scientist Cornell U., 1986-87; vis. rsch. physicist Inst. for Theoretical Physics, Santa Barbara, Calif., 1989; vis. scientist Brookhaven (N.Y.) Nat. Lab, 1984; assoc. prof. U. Provence, France, 1982, 83. Contbr. articles to profl. publs. Recipient Herzberg medal Can. Assn. Physics, Steacie prize Natural Scis. and Engring. Rsch. Coun., 1987; Killam fellow, 1992-94. Mem. Can. Inst. Advanced Rsch. Office: Sherbrooke U, Dept Physics, Sherbrooke, PQ Canada J1K 2R1

TREMBLAY, MARC ADÉLARD, anthropologist, educator; b. Les Eboulements, Que., Can., Apr. 24, 1922; s. Willie and Laurette (Tremblay) T.; m. Jacqueline Cyr, Dec. 27, 1949; children: Geneviève, Lorraine, Marc, Colette, Dominique, Suzanne. A.B., U. Montreal, 1944, L.S.A., 1948; M.A., Laval U., 1950; Ph.D., Cornell U., 1954; PhD (hon.), Ottawa U., 1982, Guelph U., U. N.B.C., 1983, Carleton U., 1995. Research asso. Cornell U., 1953-56; mem. faculty Laval U., 1956-93, prof. anthropology, 1963-68, 81-93, prof. emeritus, 1994, vice dean social scis., 1969-71, dean Grad. Sch., 1971-79, also mem. univ. council; pres. Quebec Coun. Social Rsch., 1988-93; dir. Inuit and Circu;ndar Study Group, Laval U., 1991-93. Author 20 books in social scis., about 200 articles. Recipient Que. Lit. prize, 1965, Innis-Gerin prize Royal Soc. Can., 1979, Molson prize Can. Coun., 1987, Prix Marcel Vincent ACFAS, 1988, Contbn. exceptionnelle Societé de sociologie et d'anthropolotie, 1990, Esdras Minville award Soc. St.-Jean Baptiste, 1991; named Officer of Order of Can., 1980, Gt. Officer of Order of Que., 1995; named to Internat. Order of Merit, Internat. Biog. Inst., Cambridge, Eng., 1990. Mem. Royal Soc. Can. (pres. 1981-84), Acad. des Scis. Morales et Politiques (sec.), Rsch. Inst. Pub. Policy, Am. Anthrop. Assn. (past fellow), Can. Soc. Applied Anthropology, Can. Sociology and Anthropology Assn. (founding pres.), Can. Ethnology Soc. (past pres.), Assn. Can. Intern. for Northern Studies (past pres.), Assn. Internat. Sociology, Societe des savants et sci. Can. (v.p.). Home: 835 N Orléans St, Sainte Foy, PQ Canada G1X 3J4 Office: Laval Univ, Dept Anthropology, Quebec, PQ Canada G1K 7P4

TREMBLAY, RODRIGUE, economics educator; b. Matane, Que., Can., Oct. 13, 1939; s. George and Germaine (St. Louis) T.; m. Carol Howard, Sept. 5, 1964; children: Jean-Paul, Alain, Joanne. BA, Laval U., Quebec City, 1961; BS in Econs., U. de Montreal (Que.), 1963; MA in Econs., Stanford U., 1965, PhD in Econs., 1968. Prof. Univ. de Montreal, 1967—; mem. nat. assembly Parliament of Que., 1976-81; min. industry and commerce Govt. of Que., 1976-79; mem. arbitrage panel Can.-U.S. Free Trade Agreement Ottawa (Can.) and Washington, 1989—. Woodrow Wilson Found. fellow, 1964-65. Mem. N.Am. Econs. and Fin. Assns. (pres. 1986-87). Office: U Montreal, Dept of Economics, Montreal, PQ Canada H3C 3J7

TREMBLY, DENNIS MICHAEL, musician; b. Long Beach, Calif., Apr. 16, 1947; s. Fred Lel and Jewel Fern (Bouldin) T. Student, Juilliard Sch. Music, 1965-68. Asst. adj. prof. U. So. Calif., 1981—. Bass player, 1959—, with Los Angeles Philharmonic Orch., 1970-73, co-prin. bass, 1973—. Recipient 2d pl. Internat. Solo Bass competition, Isle of Man, 1978. Mem. Internat. Soc. Bassists. Office: L A Philharm Orch 135 N Grand Ave Los Angeles CA 90012-3013

TREMERE, ARNOLD WESLEY, agricultural institute executive; b. Shaunavon, Sask., Can., Apr. 14, 1941; s. Lesley Albert and Ruth Evelyn (Anderson) T.; m. Marcella Shirley Fritz, Aug. 7, 1962; children: Lisa Anne, Evelyn Marie. BS in Agr., U. Sask., Saskatoon, 1962, MSc in Agr., 1964; PhD in Agr., Cornell U., 1968. Nutritionist Maple Leaf Mills Ltd. Toronto, Can., 1967-71, dir. nutrition and rsch., 1971-72, dir. agrl. rsch., 1972-76, mgr. mktg., 1976-79; gen. mgr. Maple Leaf Mills Ltd., Calgary, Can., 1979-82; dir. feed tech. Can. Internat. Grains Inst., Winnipeg, Can., 1982-89, exec. dir., 1989—. Office: Can Internat Grains Inst, 303 Main St 10th Fl, Winnipeg, MB Canada R3C 3G7

TREML, VLADIMIR GUY, economist, educator; b. Kharkov, USSR, Mar. 27, 1929; came to U.S., 1950, naturalized, 1953; s. Guy Alexey and Lydia Vladimir (Timofeev) T.; m. Emma Miro, July 12, 1952; children—Irene Treml Cagney, Tatiana, Alexey. B.A. in Econs, Bklyn. Coll., 1955; M.A. in Econs, Columbia U., 1956; Ph.D. in Econs, U. N.C., 1963. Dept. supr.

Bache & Co., N.Y.C., 1953-58; research asso. Inst. for Social Scis., U. N.C., Chapel Hill, 1958-61; asso. prof. econs. Franklin and Marshall Coll., 1961-66; research asso. Inst. Study USSR, Munich, Germany, 1966-67; prof. econs. Duke U., 1967—; cons. in field; expert Dept. Commerce, other fed. agys., 1971—; vis. Ford research prof. U. Calif., Berkeley, 1984-85; vis. research prof. U. Hokkaido, Sapporo, Japan, 1985. Author: (with others) Structure of the Soviet Economy, 1972, Input-Output Analysis and the Soviet Economy, 1975; contbr. reports to publs. of Joint Econ. Com., U.S. Congress; contbr. articles to profl. publs.; editor: Soviet Economic Statistics, 1972; editor, contbg. author: Studies in Soviet Input-Output Analysis, 1977, Alcohol in the USSR, 1982; contbg. editor: Soviet Economy Jour. Trustee Nat. Council for Soviet and East European Research, Inc., Washington, 1978-84. Served with USMC, 1951-53. Ford Found. grantee, 1972-81, Dept. Def.-Advanced Rsch. Project Agy. grantee, 1975-76, Dept. State grantee, 1976-77, Dept. Def. grantee, 1985-90, Georgetown U. grantee, 1984-86, Olin Found. grantee, 1989; Fulbright fellow Moscow U., 1992. Mem. So. Econ. Assn., Am. Econ. Assn., Assn. Comparative Econ. Studies (exec. com. 1972-74), Am. Assn. Advancement Slavic Studies, So. Conf. on Slavic Studies (pres. 1977-78), Phi Beta Kappa. Democrat. Eastern Orthodox. Home: 603 Longleaf Dr Chapel Hill NC 27514-3039

TREMPER, KEVIN K., anesthesiologist, educator; b. Phila., Jan. 5, 1948; s. Henry Stever and Sheila Tremper; m. Amy Louise Opheim, Dec. 19, 1987; children: Theodore Tyler, Connor Keefe. BSChemE, U. Denver, 1971; MS in Chem. Engring., U. Calif., Berkeley, 1973, PhD in Chem. Engring., 1975; MD, U. Calif., Irvine, 1978. Diplomate Am. Bd. Anesthesiologists; lic. physician, Mich., Calif. Intern/surg. resident Harbor/UCLA Med. Ctr., 1978-79, surg. ICU rsch. fellow, 1979-81; resident in anesthesiology UCLA Sch. Medicine, 1981-83; asst. prof. anesthesiology U. Calif., Irvine, 1983-84, assoc. prof., chmn. dept. anesthesiology, 1984-90; prof., chmn. dept. anesthesiology U. Mich., Ann Arbor, 1991—; extensive lectr. in field. Editl. bd. Anesthesiology News, Critical Care Medicine, Jour. Clin. Monitoring, Jour. Intensive Care Monitoring, 1986-88; reviewer for A.I.Ch.E. Jour., Anesthesiology, Anesthesia and Analgesia, Chest, Critical Care Medicine, IEEE Transactions, Jour. Applied Physiology, Jour. Clin. Engring., Jour. Clin. Anesthesia, Pediatrics, Pediatric Rsch., Obstetrics and Gynecology, Med. Instrumentation, Surgery; contbr. 89 articles and 55 abstracts to profl. jours., 33 chpts. to books; author: Perfluorochemical Oxygen Transport, 1985, Advances in Oxygen Monitoring, 1987. With USAR, 1971-77. Fellow Am. Coll. Chest Physicians, Am. Coll. Anesthesiologists; mem. AMA, Am. Soc. Anesthesiologists (chmn. subcom. on equip., monitoring and engring. tech. 1992—), adj. mem. com. on sci. papers 1992—), Internat. Anesthesia Rsch. Soc., Mich. Soc. Anesthesiologists, Internat. Soc. of Oxygen Transport to Tissue, Am. Soc. Critical Care Anesthesiologists, Calif. Med. Assn. (sci. adv. panel 1984-90), Orange County Anesthesia Soc. (treas. 1985-86, pres. 1986-87), Alpha Omega Alpha. Republican. Home: 7227 Pleasant Lake Rd Ann Arbor MI 48103 Office: U of Mich Med Sch 1301 Catherine Rd Ann Arbor MI 48109-0624

TRENBERTH, KEVIN EDWARD, atmospheric scientist; b. Christchurch, New Zealand, Nov. 8, 1944; came to U.S., 1977; s. Edward Maurice and Ngaira Ivy (Eyre) T.; m. Gail Neville Thompson. Mar. 21, 1970; children: Annika Gail, Angela Dawn. BSc with honors, U. Canterbury, Christchurch, 1966; ScD, MIT, 1972. Meteorologist New Zealand Meteorol. Service, Wellington, 1966-76, supt. dynamic meteorology, 1976-77; assoc. prof. meteorology U. Ill., Urbana, 1977-82, prof., 1982-84; scientist Nat. Ctr. Atmospheric Research, Boulder, Colo., 1984-86, sr. scientist, 1986—, leader empirical studies group, 1987, head sect. climate analysis, 1987—; dep. dir. climate and global dynamics divsn. Nat. Ctr. Atmospheric Rsch., Boulder, Colo., 1991—; cons. NOAA, 1980—, NASA, 1981—; mem. joint sci. com. for world climate programme, com. climate changes and the ocean Tropical Oceans Global Atmosphere Program Sci. Steering Group, 1990-94. Editor: Climate System Modeling, 1992; contbr. articles to profl. jours. Grantee NSF, NOAA, NASA. Fellow Am. Meteorol. Soc. (editor sci. jour. 1981-86, com. chmn. 1985-87, editor's award 1989), AAAS (coun. del. sect. atmosphere and hydrosphere sci. 1993—); mem. NAS (earth scis. com. 1982-85, tropical oceans global atmosphere adv. panel 1984-87, polar rsch. bd. 1986-90, climate rsch. com. 1987-90, global oceans atmosphere land sys. panel 1994—), Atmosphere Obs. Panel of Globe Climate Observing Sys., Royal Soc. New Zealand, Meteorol. Soc. New Zealand. Home: 1445 Landis Ct Boulder CO 80303-1122 Office: Nat Ctr Atmospheric Research PO Box 3000 Boulder CO 80307-3000

TRENCH, WILLIAM FREDERICK, mathematics educator; b. Trenton, N.J., July 31, 1931; s. George Daniel and Anna Elizabeth (Taylor) T.; m. Lucille Ann Marasco, Dec. 26, 1954 (div. Dec. 1978); children: Joseph William, Randolph Clifford, John Frederick, Gina Margaret; m. Beverly Joan Busenshut, Nov. 22, 1980. B.A. in Math., Lehigh U., 1953; A.M., U. Pa., 1955, Ph.D., 1958. Applied mathematician Moore Sch. Elec. Engring., U. Pa., 1953-56 with Gen. Electric Corp., Phila., 1956-57, Philco Corp., Phila., 1957-59, RCA, Moorestown, N.J., 1957-64; assoc. prof. math. Drexel U., Phila., 1964-67; prof. Drexel U., 1967-86; Andrew G. Cowles disting. prof. math. Trinity U., San Antonio, 1986—. Author: Advanced Calculus, 1971, (with Bernard Kolman) Elementary Multivariable Calculus, 1971, Multivariable Calculus with Linear Algebra and Series, 1972; contbr. rsch. articles in numerical analysis, ordinary differential equations, smoothing, prediction and spl. functions to profl. jours. Mem. Math. Assn. Am., Am. Math. Soc., Soc. Indsl. and Applied Math., Phi Beta Kappa, Eta Kappa Nu, Pi Mu Epsilon. Achievements include development of Trench's Algorithm for inversion of finite Toeplitz matrices, of fast algorithms for computing eigenvalues of structured matrices, of asymptotic theory of solutions of nonlinear functional differential equations under mild integral smallness conditions. Home: 211 W Rosewood Ave San Antonio TX 78212-2332 also: 413 Lake Drive W Divide CO 80814 Office: Dept Math Trinity U 215 Stadium Dr San Antonio TX 78212 also: 413 Lake Dr W Divide CO 80814

TRENERY, MARY ELLEN, librarian; b. Conran, Mo., Jan. 10, 1939; d. John Herman and Stella Cecelia (Durbin) Hulshof; m. Frank E. Trenery, June 10, 1967. BA in Classics, Coll. New Rochelle, 1962; MALS, Rosary Coll., River Forest, Ill., 1966; postgrad., Fla. Atlantic U., Boca Raton, 1986-89. Tchr. grades 6, 8 Archdiocesan Sch. System, St. Louis, 1962-64; serials and acquisition libr. U. Ill., Chgo., 1966-69; acquisitions, circulation and cataloging libr. Rosary Coll., River Forest, Ill., 1964-66, 70-72; libr. media specialist St. Coleman Cath. Sch., Pompano Beach, Fla., 1973-94; coord. for self study St. Coleman Schs., 1982, 83, 89, 90; cons. Pompano Beach City Libr. Author: Policies and Procedures for School Libraries, 1976, UICC Call Number (founding editor), 1967-68, NIUCLA Newsletter (editor 1969-72). Fed. Funding liaison with Broward County Sch. Bd., 1974-94. Mem. Ill. Libr. Assn. (rsch. and tech. svcs. div. chair 1967-69), Cath. Libr. Assn. (No. Ill. unit chair, sec. 1969-72)

TRENNEPOHL, GARY LEE, finance educator, consultant; b. Detroit, Dec. 6, 1946; s. Leo Donald and Wilma Mae (Tiensvold) T.; m. Sandra K. Yeager, June 9, 1968; children: Paige E., Adrienne A. BS, U. Tulsa, 1968; MBA, Utah State U., 1971; PhD, Tex. Tech U., 1976. Asst. prof. aero. studies Tex. Tech U., Lubbock, 1972-74; asst. prof. fin. Ariz. State U., Tempe, 1977-80, assoc. prof., 1980-82; prof. U. Mo., Columbia, 1982-86, dir. Sch. Bus., 1984-86; prof. fin., dept. head Tex. A&M U., College Station, 1986-91, assoc. dean Coll. Bus., 1991-93, Peters prof. fin., 1992—, exec. assoc. dean, 1994—; mem. faculty Options Inst., Chgo. Bd. Options Exchange, 1987—. Author: An Introduction to Financial Management, 1984, Investment Management, 1993; assoc. editor Jour. Fin. Research, 1983—, Rev. Bus. Studies, 1992—; contbr. chpts. Encyclopedia of Investments; contbr. articles to profl. jours. Capt. USAF, 1968-72. Decorated Commendation medal with oak leaf cluster, Vietnam svc. medal. Mem. Fin. Mgmt. Assn. (v.p. program 1993, pres. 1993-94), So. Fin. Assn., Southwestern Fin. Assn. (bd. dirs. 1983-84, pres. 1986), Midwest Fin. Assn. (bd. dirs. 1985-89). Republican. Lutheran. Home: 2010 Pebblestone Ct College Station TX 77845-5562 Office: Tex A&M U Bus Coll College Station TX 77843

TRENT, DARRELL M., academic and corporate executive; b. Neosho, Mo., Aug. 2, 1938; s. Clarence Melvin and Edna Ruth T.; m. Judith Mercy Turner; children: Darrell Michael, Derek Montgomery, Mercy Ruth. A.B. Stanford U., 1961; postgrad., Internat. Law Sch., The Hague, Netherlands, summer 1961, Wharton Grad. Sch. Bus., U. Pa., summer 1962; M.B.A.,

Columbia U., 1964. Owner, mgr. Trent Enterprises, Kans. and Mo., 1963-66; pres., chief exec. officer N.Am. Carmen, Ltd., Del., 1965-68, Assoc. Stores, Inc., Okla., 1967-69, Plaza Supermarkets, Inc., Kans. 1966-69, Food Service, Inc., Kans., 1966-69, Supermarkets, Inc., Kans., 1966-69, Acton Devel. Co., Inc., Kans., 1966-81; research/writer Nixon for Pres., 1968; staff dir. for personnel Presdl. Transition, 1968-69; commr. Property Mgmt. and Disposal Service, GSA, 1969; dep. asst. to Pres. U.S., 1969-70; exec. dir. Property Rev. Bd., Exec. Office of Pres., 1969-73; dep. dir. Office Emergency Preparedness, 1970-72, acting dir., 1973; mem. Cost of Living Council, 1973, Oil Policy Com., 1973; chmn. Joint Bd. Fuel Supply and Fuel Transp., 1973; mem. NSC, 1973; chmn. Pres.'s Adv. Council CD, 1973; U.S. mem. NATO Sr. Civil Emergency Planning Com., 1973; sr. research fellow Hoover Inst., Stanford U., 1974-81, 89—, assoc. dir., 1974-81, bd. overseers, 1985-89; dep. campaign mgr. Citizens for Reagan, 1976; dep. campaign mgr., cons. Reagan for Pres. Com., 1979-80, sr. policy advisor, 1980; dir. Office Policy Coordination, Presdl. Transition, 1980-81; U.S. alt. rep. Nato Com. Challenges of Modern Soc., 1982-83; dep. sec. Dept. Transp., 1981-83; chmn. U.S. del. European Civil Aviation Com. with rank ambassador, 1983-88; chmn. Action Devel. Corp., Inc., 1988—; chmn., chief exec. officer Rollins Environ. Svcs., Inc., 1983-88, TEC Systems, Inc., 1990-91, Clean Earth Techs., Inc., 1992—; chmn. Fed. Home Loan Bank Pitts., 1983-91; cons. ACDA, 1974-81, HUD, 1974, Dept. Commerce, 1974-76; bd. advisors Chronicle Info. Svcs., Inc., 1984-87. Author: The U.S. and Transnational Terrorism, 1980, Transportation: Policy, Goals, Accomplishments, 1984; co-author: Terrorism: Threat, Reality, Response, 1979; contbr. articles to profl. publs. Bd. regents Pepperdine U., 1985—; bd. dirs. Found. Teach Econs., 1988-90; dep. chmn. Ronald Reagan Presdl. Found., 1985-88. Mem. Mt. Pelerin Soc. Republican. Methodist. Club: Bohemian. Office: Ste S 115 520 N St SW Washington DC 20024

TRENT, ROBERT HAROLD, business educator; b. Norfolk, Va., Aug. 3, 1933; s. Floyd Murton and Myrtle Eugenia (White) T.; m. Joanne Bell, Aug. 17, 1951; 1 child, John Thomas. B.S., U. Richmond, 1963; Ph.D., U. N.C. 1968. Asst. prof. U. N.C., Chapel Hill, 1968-69; assoc. prof. commerce McIntire Sch. Commerce U. Va., Charlottesville, 1970-74, prof. commerce, 1975-84, Ralph A. Beeton prof. free enterprise, 1985-91; C. & P. Telephone Co. prof. commerce U. Va., Charlottesville, 1991—. Co-author: Marketing Decision Making, 1976, 4th edit.; 1988; editor: Developments in Management Information Systems, 1974. Mem. Inst. Mgmt. Scis., Soc. Info. Mgmt., Assn. Comp. Machinery, Decision Scis. Inst., Beta Gamma Sigma, Omicron Delta Kappa. Office: U Va Monroe Hall Charlottesville VA 22903

TRENT, WENDELL CAMPBELL, business owner; b. Sneedville, Tenn. Nov. 1, 1940; s. William Campbell and Inez Hall (Daugherty) T.; m. Donna Lee Posey, May 31, 1964. BA, Berea Coll. 1963; MPH, UCLA, 1971; D in Pub. Adminstrn., Nova U., 1980. Asst. USPHS, UCLA, 1969; pres. Lockwood MacDonald Hosp., Petoskey, Mich., 1971-75, Allegan Gen. Hosp., Mich., 1975-79, Bethany Meth. Hosp., Chgo. 1979-84, St. Ansgar Hosp., Moorhead, Minn., 1984-85; pres. Meml. Hosp., Lawrenceville, Ill., 1985-89; midwest devel. dir. Brim Healthcare, 1989-90; prin. Larson & Trent Assocs., Sumner, Ill., 1990—; mem. Gov.'s Health Care Task Force; mem. Govs. Com. on Healthcare. Contbr. articles to profl. jours. Maj. USAF, 1963-69. Decorated Bronze Star. Fellow Am. Coll. Hosp. Adminstrs. (article of year com.); mem. Rotary, Kiwanis. Republican. Presbyterian. Avocations: photography, amateur radio. Home: RR 1 Box 120 Sumner IL 62466-9704

TRENT-OTA, JANE SUZANNE, elementary school educator; b. Long Beach, Calif., June 10, 1935; d. George Lionel and Jennie Bolton (Rundio) Heap; children from previous marriage: Katharine Trent, Cecily Finegan; m. William T. Ota, Sept. 27, 1991; stepchildren: William N. Ota, Douglas W. Ota. BA, Mary Washington Coll., Fredericsburg, Va., 1957; MA in Edn., Azua-Pacific U., 1978; student, Calif. Western-USIU, San Diego. 1970. Cert. elem. tchr. K-8, Calif., Level I Orff-Schulwerk nat. cert; cert. in master gardening, Calif. Tchr. 5th and 6th grades Chula Vista (Calif.) Elem. Sch. Dist., kindergarten tchr., ret., 1991; cons. bargaining team Chula Vista Edn. Assn. Vol. with U. Calif. Cooperative Extension/U.S. Dept. Agr. Vol. numerous civic orgns. Recipient Instruction grant, ORFF Instrumentarium, We Honor Ours award San Diego county svc. ctr. coun. Calif. Tchrs. Assn., 1991. Mem. Calif. Ret. Tchrs. Assn., NSF Math. Inst. Univ. Calif. San Diego, Am. ORFF-Schulwerk Assn. (bd. sec. San Diego chpt. 1991-93), Delta Kappa Gamma (chpt. exec. bd., chmn. scholarship). Home: 620 First St Coronado CA 92118

TREPEL, MINDY J., county official, lawyer; b. N.Y.C., Dec. 20, 1955; d. Jerome and Anita Lee (Kalish) Trepel; m. Ronald F. Harnisch, Apr. 12, 1986; 1 child, Matthew Charles. BA, SUNY, Stony Brook, 1977; JD, Vt. Law Sch., 1980. Law asst. Queens County Civil Ct., Kew Gardens, N.Y., 1982-83; prin. law clk. to surrogate Queens County Surrogate's Ct., Jamaica, N.Y., 1984-91; pub. administr. Queens County, Jamaica, 1992—. Mem. Queens County Bar Assn., Queens County Women's Bar Assn. (pres. 1994—). Home: 153 Beach 131 St Belle Harbor NY 11694 Office: Queens County Office Pub Administr 88-11 Sutphin Blvd Jamaica NY 11435

TREPPLER, IRENE ESTHER, state senator; b. St. Louis County, Mo., Oct. 13, 1926; d. Martin H. and Julia C. (Bender) Hagemann; student Meramec Community Coll., 1972; m. Walter J. Treppler, Aug. 10, 1950; children: John M., Steven A., Diane V. Anderson, Walter W. Payroll chief USAF Aero. Chart Plant, 1943-51; enumerator U.S Census Bur., St. Louis, 1960, crew leader, 1970; mem. Mo. Ho. of Reps., Jefferson City, 1972-84; mem. Mo. Senate, Jefferson City, 1985—; chmn. Minority Caucus, 1991-92. ActiveGravois Twp. Rep. Club, Concord Twp. Rep. Club; alt. del. Rep. Nat. Conv., 1976, 84. Recipient Spirit Enterprise award Mo. C. of C., 1992, Appreciation award Mo. State Med. Assn., Nat. Otto Nuttli Earthquake Hazard Mitigation award, 1993; named Concord Twp. Rep. of Yr., 1992. Mem. Nat. Order Women Legislators (rec. sec. 1981-82, pres. 1985), Nat. Fedn. Rep. Women. Mem. Evangelical Ch. Office: Mo State Senate Rm 433 Jefferson City MO 65101

TRESNOWSKI, BERNARD RICHARD, retired health insurance company executive; b. Chgo., Oct. 14, 1932; s. Al and Luella (Stewart) T.; m. Beverly Ann Gesmond, Nov. 26, 1955; children: Linda, Judy, Mark, Tom, MaryBeth, David; m. Leanne Patricia Irish, Aug. 1985; 1 child, Megan. B.S., U. Mich. 1955; M.P.H. in Hosp. Adminstrn, U. Pitts., 1958. Second asst. administr., then asst. administr. Albert Einstein Med. Center, Phila., 1958-61; research asso. U. Mich., 1961-62; assoc. administr. St. Joseph Mercy Hosp., Pontiac, Mich., 1963-67; sr. v.p. Blue Cross Assn., Chgo., 1967-78; exec. v.p. Blue Cross Assn., 1977-78; pres. Blue Cross and Blue Shield Assn., Chgo., 1978-81, pres., 1981-94; ret. Blue Cross and Blue Shield Assn., 1994; mem. Health Adminstrs. Study Soc. Author articles in field. Mem. Am. Hosp. Assn., Am. Coll. Health Care Execs., Am. Pub. Welfare Assn. Found. Employee Benefit Plans, Internat. Fedn. Vol. Health Svc. Funds. (pres.), Am. Health Planning Assn., The Conf. Bd.

TRESTMAN, FRANK D., distribution company executive; b. Mpls., Sept. 3, 1934; s. Saul and Rose (Hyster) T.; m. Carol Lynn Wasserman, Apr. 3, 1960; children—Lisa Ellen, Jill Susan. B.B.A. with high distinction, U. Minn., 1955. Exec. v.p., treas. Napco Industries, Inc., Mpls., 1965-74, pres., dir., 1974-84; chmn, CEO Mass Merchandisers, Inc., Hopkins, Minn., 1984-86; pres. Trestman Enterprises, Golden Valley, Minn., 1987—; bd. dirs. Best Buy Co., Mpls., Western Container Corp., Mpls., Insignia Systems, Inc., T.C.F. Industries. Mem. bd. govs. Mt. Sinai Hosp., Mpls., 1978-91, Abbott Northwestern Hosp., 1993—; chmn. bd. trustees Mpls. Fedn. Endowment Fund. With USN, 1957-58. Jewish. Clubs: Oak Ridge Country (Hopkins); Presidents Country (West Palm Beach, Fla.). Home: 4544 Woodridge Rd Minnetonka MN 55345-3936 Office: Trestman Enterprises 5500 Wayzata Blvd Ste 1045 Minneapolis MN 55416-1241

TRETTER, JAMES RAY, pharmaceutical company executive; b. Boone, Iowa, June 7, 1933; s. Raymond J. and Freda E. (Ohge) T.; m. Neltje Van Loon; 1 child, Elsa. BS in Chemistry, Loras Coll., 1956; PhD in Chemistry, U. Calif., Berkeley, 1960. Chemist Pfizer, Inc., Groton, Conn., 1960-72, dir. med. chem. dept., 1972-74, dir. central chem. process rsch., 1975-77, exec. dir. devel. rsch., 1977-80; v.p. R&D William H. Rorer, Inc., Ft. Washington, Pa., 1980-90; pres. Cen. Rsch. div. Rhone-Poulenc Rorer, Paris, 1990-92; pres. CEO

Ixsys Inc., San Diego, 1992—. Avocation: sailing. Office: Rhone-Poulenc Rorer Ctr Rsch 500 Arcola Rd Collegeville PA 19426-3909

TREU, JESSE ISAIAH, venture capitalist; b. N.Y.C., Apr. 10, 1947. BS, Rensselaer Poly. Inst., 1968; MS, Princeton U., 1971, PhD, 1973. Physicist, liaison sci. components, materials group Gen. Electric Co., Schenectady, N.Y., 1973-77; tech. dir. Technicon Corp., Tarrytown, N.Y., 1977-82; v.p. Channing Weinberg-CW Ventures, N.Y.C., 1982-85; gen. ptnr. Domain Assocs., Princeton, N.J., 1986—. Office: Domain Assocs 1 Palmer Sq Princeton NJ 08542-3718

TREUHOLD, CHARLES RICHARD, investment banker; b. Bklyn., May 24, 1930; s. Eugene and Selma (Straus) T.; m. Kerstin Margareta Nevrell, July 28, 1956; 1 child, Robert Charles. BA, Yale U., 1952; postgrad., U. Paris, 1955-56. Syndicate assoc. Lehman Bros., N.Y.C., 1956-61; syndicate mgr. Paribas Corp., N.Y.C., 1961-66; sr. v.p., syndicate mgr. Arnhold & S. Bleichroedet, N.Y.C., 1966—. Editor: Bawl St. Jour., 1977, 88. Lt. (j.g.) USN, 1952-55). Mem. Assn. Internat. Bond Dealers (bd. dirs. 1979-86), Bond Club N.Y. (gov. 1988—), City Midday Club. Home: 200 E 66th St New York NY 10021-6728 Office: Arnhold & S Bleichroeder Inc 45 Broadway New York NY 10006-3007

TREUMANN, WILLIAM BORGEN, university dean; b. Grafton, N.D., Feb. 26, 1916; s. William King and Dagny Helen (Borgen) T.; m. Mildred Elizabeth Jenkins, Aug. 14, 1948; children—Richard Roy, Robert Evan, Beverly Kay. B.S., U. N.D., 1942; M.A., U. Ill., 1944, Ph.D., 1947. Teaching asst. chemistry U. Ill., 1942-45, teaching asst. math., 1945-46, vis. prof., summers 1948-50; from asst. prof. to prof. chemistry N.D. State U., 1946-55; mem. faculty Moorhead (Minn.) State U., 1960—, prof. chemistry, 1962—, asso. dean acad. affairs, 1968-70, dean faculty math. and sci., 1970—. Contbr. to profl. jours. Research Corp. Am. grantee, 1954; Minn. U. Bd. grantee, 1967. Fellow Am. Inst. Chemists; mem. Am. Chem. Soc., Am. Assn. U. Profs., Minn. Acad. Sci., Fedn. Am. Scientists, Phi Beta Kappa, Sigma Xi. Home: One 2nd St S Apt 5-204 Fargo ND 58103-1921 Office: Moorhead State U Moorhead MN 56560

TREUTING, EDNA GANNON, retired nursing administrator; b. New Orleans, Dec. 16, 1925; d. Alphonse Joseph and Clara Josephine (David) Gannon; m. August Raymond Treuting, Sept. 4, 1948 (dec.); children: Keith, Karen Treuting Stein, Madeline Treuting LeBlanc, Jaime Treuting Gonzales, Jay (dec.). Diploma, Charity Hosp. Sch. Nursing, New Orleans, 1946; BS in Nursing Edn., La. State U., 1953; MPH, Tulane U., 1972, DPH, 1978. RN, La.; cert. family nurse practitioner Tulane U. Head nurse premature nursery Charity Hosp., New Orleans, 1946-47, head nurse pediatrics 1947-49; instr. pediatrics Charity Hosp. Sch. Nursing, New Orleans, 1949-52, 54, instr., 1953; pvt. duty Touro, Hotel Dieu, New Orleans, 1957-59; instr. maternal and child health La. State U. Sch. Nursing, New Orleans, 1960, 65, 69-71; from instr. to prof., sect. head Tulane Sch. Pub. Health and Tropical Medicine, New Orleans, 1972-83; dean, prof. Our Lady Holy Cross Coll. Nursing Div., New Orleans, 1983-84; chief nurse Dept. Health and Hosp., New Orleans, 1987-94; region IV nurse practitioner Baylor U., Health Edn. and Welfare, 1974-76; citizen amb. to South Am. People to People, 1979; presentor U. Hawaii Pub. Health and Nursing, 1977; planner, advisor, reviewer continuing edn. U. Tenn., Memphis, 1990-95. Author: editor: Occupation Health Nursing, 1979; sect. head, prin. investigator Practitioner Programs Family and Pediatric, 1973-83; item writer Nurse Practitioners, Community Health and Occupational Nursing, 1974-80; mem. editorial bd. to sci. jours. Pres. Oti-Mrs. Internat., New Orleans, 1955-68; sponsor bd. dirs. Holy Cross H.S. Treuting Scholarship, New Orleans, 1966—; hurricane and disaster nurse ARC, New Orleans, 1966-77; v.p. Pandora Carnival Club, New Orleans, 1968-78; alternate state health dept. Commn. Nursing Supply and Demand by Legislation, 1991-94; planner, presentor La. State Rsch. Day, 1990-92. Named outstanding woman in the mainstream world's fair women of achievement, 1984. Mem. New Orleans Dist. Nurses Assn. (First J.B. Hickey Meml. Community award 1985, Great 100 Nurse-First Yr. 1987), La. Pub. Health Assn. (Dr. C.B. White Merritorious Diligent Svc. 1990), La. Nurse Practitioners Assn.(Edna Treuting scholarship named in her honor), Tulane U. Alumni Assn. (past pres.), Tulane Med. Alumni Assn. (past pres.), Delta Omega (past pres. nat.,Eta chpts.), Sigma Theta Tau (Epsilon Nu chpt.). Republican. Roman Catholic. Avocations: traveling, dancing, swimming, photography, reading. Home: 5100 Rebecca Blvd Kenner LA 70065-3250

TREVES, SAMUEL BLAIN, geologist, educator, administrator; b. Detroit, Sept. 11, 1925; s. Samuel and Stella (Stork) T.; m. Jane Patricia Mitoray, Nov. 24, 1960; children: John Samuel, David Samuel. BS, Mich. Tech. U., 1951; postgrad., U. Otago, New Zealand, 1953-54; MS, U. Idaho, 1953; PhD, Ohio State U., 1959. Geologist Ford Motor Co., 1951, Idaho Bur. Mines and Geology, 1952, Otago Catchment Bd., 1953-54; mem. faculty U. Nebr., Lincoln, 1958—, prof. geology, 1966, chmn. dept., 1964-70, 74-89, assoc. dean Coll. Arts and Scis., 1989—; curator geology Nebr. State Mus., 1964—; participant expdns. to Antarctica and Greenland, 1960-61,63, 65, 70, annually 72-76. Rsch. and publs. on geology of igneous and metamorphic rocks of Idaho, New Zealand, Mich., Antarctica, Nebr., Can., Greenland with emphasis on origin of Precambrian granite complexes and basaltic volcanic rocks. Fulbright scholar U. Otago, New Zealand, 1953-54. Fellow Geol. Soc. Am., AAAS, Explorers Club; mem. Am. Mineral Soc., Sigma Xi, Tau Beta Pi, Sigma Gamma Epsilon. Home: 1710 B St Lincoln NE 68502-1524

TREVILLIAN, WALLACE DABNEY, economics educator, retired dean; b. Charlottesville, Va., May 1, 1918; s. Robert Carr and Mary Anna (Perry) T.; m. Mary Lou McEachern Moody, Nov. 28, 1963; children: Malcolm McEachern, Edward Dabney. BS, U. Va., 1940, MA, 1947, PhD, 1954; postgrad., U. Calif., 1950-51. Mem. faculty Clemson (S.C.) U., 1947—, successively instr. econs., asst. prof., assoc. prof., 1947-55, prof. econs., head dept. indsl. mgmt., 1955-63, founding dean Coll. Commerce and Industry, 1963-80, prof., dean emeritus, 1983—; vis. scholar U. Sussex, Eng., 1980—; mem. Regional Export Expansion Council, 1965-77; sec. commn. on edn. for bus. professions Nat. Assn. State Univs. and Land-Grant Colls., 1975-77; pres. Nat. Council for Textile Edn., 1978-80. Master sgt. AUS, 1941-45. Mem. St. Andrews Soc. Upper S.C., Newcomen Soc., Thomas Jefferson Soc. of Alumni U. Va. Mem. Cradle Episcopalian Ch. Home: PO Box 1258 Clemson SC 29633-1258

TREVINO, JERRY ROSALEZ, secondary school principal; b. Mathis, Tex., July 9, 1943; s. Geronimo R. and Hilaria (Rosalez) T.; m. Juanita Escalante, Jan. 1, 1985; 1 child, John-Michael. BA, U. Houston, 1967, MEd, 1974; PhD, Kennedy-Western U., 1988; postgrad., U. Tex., Odessa, 1988-92. Cert. tchr., adminstr., Tex. Tchr. N.E. Houston Sch. Dist., 1966-70, pub. rels. officer, 1970-72, asst. prin., 1972-76; tchr. Harris County Dept. Edn., Houston, 1968-72, Austin (Tex.) Ind. Sch. Dist., 1977-87; asst. prin. Tex. Youth Commn., Pyote, 1987-91, prin., 1991—; Title VII project dir. U.S. Dept. Edn., Pyote 1988-95; instr. Austin C.C., 1980-84, chair, Prin. Coun. for Edn. of Lang. Minority Students, S.W. Ednl. Delel. Lab., Austin. Editor newsletter The Flyer, 1970-72; contbr. articles to profl. publs. Mem. Community Adv. Coun., Pyote, 1987—; mem. planning com. Permian Basin Quality Work Force, Midland, Tex., 1992—; mem. Supt.'s Coun., Pyote, 1987—. Named Outstanding Adminstr. of Permian Basin (Golden Apple award) Permian Basin Private Industry Coun., 1994. Mem. ASCD, Nat. Assn. for Bilingual Edn., Am. Biog. Inst. (rsch. bd. advisors 1992—, Recognition plaque 1992, diploma of honor 1992, Commemorative Medal of Honor). Presbyterian. Avocations: flying, travel, reading, landscaping. Home: 12009 Rotherham Dr Austin TX 78753 Office: Tex Youth Commn Box 415 Pyote TX 79777

TREVINO, LEE BUCK, professional golfer; b. Dallas, Dec. 1, 1939; s. Joe and Juanita (Barrett) T.; m. Claudia Bove; children: Ricky Lee, Lesley Ann, Tony Lee, Troy Liana, Olivia Leigh, Daniel Lee. Ed. pub. schs. Head profl. Hardy's Driving Range, Dallas, 1961-65; asst. profl. Horizon Hills Country Club, El Paso, Tex., 1966-67; chmn. bd. Lee Trevino Enterprises, Inc., 1967—. Hon. chmn. Christmas Seal campaign, 1969-72, sports ambassador, 1971; mem. Pres.'s Conf. on Phys. Fitness and Sports; grand marshal Sun Carnival Parade, 1976-77. mem. sports com. Nat. Multiple Sclerosis Soc. Served with USMCR, 1956-60. Recipient Hickok Belt award, 1971; named Golf Rookie of Yr., 1967, PGA Player of Yr., 1971, Tex. Pro

Athlete of Yr., 1970, Gold Tee award, 1971, AP Pro Athlete of Yr., 1971, Player of Yr. Golf Mag., 1971, Sportsman of Yr. Sports Illustrated, 1971, PGA Sr. Tour Players of Yr., 1990, 92, 94, Internat. Sports Personality of Yr. Brit. Broadcasting Assn., 1971, Rookie and Player of Yr., Sr. PGA Tour, 1990; mem. Tex. Hall of Fame, Am. Gulf Hall of Fame, World Golf Hall of Fame. Tournament winner Tex. Open, 1965, 66, N.Mex. Open, 1966, U.S. Open, 1968, 71, Amana Open, 1968, 69, Hawaiian Open, 1968, Tucson Open, 1969, 70, World Cup, 1969, 71, Nat. Airlines Open, 1970, Brit. Open, 1971, 72, Canadian Open 1971, 77, 79, Can. PGA, 1979, Danny Thomas-Memphis Classic, 1971, 72, 80, Tallahassee Open, 1971, Sahara Invitational, 1971, St. Louis Classic, 1972, Hartford Open, 1972, Jackie Gleason Classic, 1973, Doral-Eastern Open, 1973, Mexican Open, 1973, 75, Chrysler Classic, Australia, 1973, PGA Championship, 1974, 84, World Series Golf, 1974, Greater New Orleans Open, 1974, Fla. Citrus Open, 1975, Colonial Nat. Invitational, 1976, 78, Colgate Mixed Team Matches, 1979, Brit. Masters, 1985, U.S. Sr. Open, 1990; King Hassan Moroccan trophy II, 1977; Lancome trophy Benson & Hedges, 1978, 80; 1st golfer to have scored four sub-par rounds in U.S. Open Competition, 1968; leading Money winner, 1970, 2d pl. money winner 1971, 1972; Vardon trophy winner, 1970 1972, 74, 80; Can. PGA, 1983; PGA Seniors Championship, 1994; capt. Ryder Cup Matches, 1985; first golfer to have scored 4 sub-par rounds in PGA competition. Office: 5757 Alpha Rd Ste 620 Dallas TX 75240-4668

TREVOR, ALEXANDER BRUEN, computer company executive; b. N.Y.C., Apr. 12, 1945; s. John B. Jr. and Evelyn (Bruen) T.; m. Ellen Ruth Armstrong, Sept. 21, 1974; children: Anne Wood, Alexander Jay Bruen. BS, Yale U., 1967; MS, U. Ariz., 1971. Rsch. asst. U. Ariz., Tucson, 1971; systems analyst CompuServe Inc., Columbus, Ohio, 1971-73; dir. systems, 1973-74, v.p., 1974-81, exec. v.p., chief tech. officer, 1981—, also bd. dirs., 1985—. Author (software program) CB Simulator, 1980. Trustee Trudeau Inst., Saranac Lake, N.Y., Aviation Safety Inst., Worthington, Ohio. 1st lt. Signal Corps, U.S. Army, 1968-70, Vietnam. Decorated Bronze Star. Mem. IEEE, Assn. for Computing Machinery, SAR (N.Y.), Union Club (N.Y.), Scioto Country Club. Republican. Episcopalian. Office: CompuServe Inc 5000 Arlington Centre Blvd Columbus OH 43220-5439

TREVOR, BRONSON, economist; b. N.Y.C., Nov. 12, 1910; s. John Bond and Caroline Murray (Wilmerding) T.; A.B., Columbia Coll., 1931; m. Eleanor Darlington Fisher, Nov. 8, 1946; children—Eleanor, Bronson, Caroline. Own bus., 1931-; dir., asst. sec. Northwestern Terminal R.R., 1952-58; chmn. bd. Texinia Corp., 1959-92. Former dir. chmn. fin. com. Gen. Hosp. of Saranac Lake mem. Council for Agrl. and Chemurgic Research, Am. Forestry Assn. Mem. Republican County Com. of N.Y. County, 1937-39; leader in primary election campaigns N.Y. County, 1937, 38, 39 to free local Rep. party orgn. from leftwing affiliations. Served with U.S. Army, 1942, World War II. Mem. S.A.R., Soc. Colonial Wars. Clubs: Union, Knickerbocker, Racquet and Tennis, Piping Rock, Bath and Tennis. Author: (pamphlet) The United States Gold Purchase Program, 1941; also numerous articles on econ. subjects. Home: Heron Ln Paul Smiths NY 12970 Office: PO Box 182 Oyster Bay NY 11771-0182

TREVOR, KIRK DAVID NIELL, orchestra conductor, cellist; b. London, Feb. 8, 1952. Student, Dartington Coll., 1968-69; grad. with distinction, Guildhall Sch. Music and Drama, 1974; student, N.C. Sch. Arts, 1975-77. Asst. condr. Guildhall Opera Sch., 1973-74; music dir. Youth Symphony of Carolinas, 1978-82; music dir., condr. Knoxville (Tenn.) Symphony Orch., 1984—; chief condr. Martinu Philharmonic Czech Rep., 1995—; assoc. condr. Charlotte (N.C.) Symphony Orch., 1978-82, Exxon Art Endowment and Dallas Symphony, 1982-85; former resident condr. Dallas Symphony; dir. music Indpls. Chamber Orch., 1988—; instr. U. Tenn., 1985—; guest condr. U.S., S.Am., USSR, Czech Republic, Poland, Romania, Switzerland; tchr. Condrs. Symphonic Workshop in Zlin, Czech Republic, 1991—, Artistic Dir. Recipient Libottom Meml. prize, 1972, Kappilis Condr. prize, 1974, Toussant prize, 1974; winner Am. Condrs. Program, 1990; Fulbright Exchange grantee U.K. and U.S. Dept. State, 1975, Am. Condrs. Program grantee, 1990. Mem. Condrs. Guild, Am. Symphony Orch. League. Office: Knoxville Symphony Orch 623 Market St Ste 600 Knoxville TN 37902

TREVOR, LEIGH BARRY, lawyer; b. Galesburg, Ill., Aug. 29, 1934; s. Dean Spaulding and Jean Elizabeth (Barry) T.; m. Mary Witherell, Aug. 8, 1978; children: John W. Hoffman, Ann Kete, Stephen S., Julia B. Kramer, Elizabeth P. Grad., Phillips Acad., 1952; AB magna cum laude, Harvard U., 1956, LLB, 1962. Bar: Ohio 1963, U.S. Dist. Ct. D.C. 1970. Assoc. Jones, Day, Reavis & Pogue, Cleve., 1962-68, ptnr., 1969—, ptnr.-in-charge, 1990-93; dir., sec. Dix & Eaton, Inc., Cleve.; lectr. on hostile corp. takeovers, other corp. law topics. Contbr. articles to profl. jours. Trustee, sec. State Troopers of Ohio, 1985—; pres. Stakeholders in Am., Mpls., 1987-88; trustee Cleveland State U. Found., 1990-94, Gt. Lakes Theater Festival, 1991-94. Lt. (j.g.) USN, 1956-59. Fellow Ohio State Bar Found.; mem. Ohio State Bar Assn. (mem. tender offer subcom. 1982—, corp. governance subcom. 1986—, chmn. corp. law com. 1989-91, coun. of dels. 1991—), Cleve. Bar Assn., D.C. Bar Assn., Nat. Investor Rels. Inst. (bd. dirs. local chpt. 1985-92, pres. Cleve.-Akron chpt. 1990-91), Phi Beta Kappa. Republican. Episcopalian. Home: 3 Hidden Vly Rocky River OH 44116-1143 Office: Jones Day Reavis & Pogue 901 Lakeside Ave Cleveland OH 44114-1190

TREXLER, EDGAR RAY, minister, editor; b. Salisbury, N.C., Sept. 17, 1937; s. Edgar Ray and Eula Belle (Farmer) T.; m. Emily Louise Kees, Aug. 21, 1960; children—David Ray, Mark Raymond, Karen Emily. AB, Lenoir-Rhyne Coll., 1959, LittD, 1978; MDiv, Luth. Theol. So. Sem., 1962; MA, Syracuse U., 1964; postgrad., Boston U., 1960, Luth. World Fedn. Study Project, Geneva, 1977, 81, 95; LittD (hon.), Midland Coll., 1990; DD, Wittenberg U., 1994. Ordained to ministry United Luth. Ch. Am., 1962; pastor St. John's Luth. Ch., Lyons, N.Y., 1962-65; features editor Luth. Mag., Phila., 1965-72, assoc. editor, 1972-78, editor, 1978-87; editor Luth. Mag., Chgo., 1988—; sec. Commn. Ch. Papers, Luth. Ch. Am., 1971-72, mem. staff team communications, 1972-78; chmn. Interch. Features, 1971-76; chmn. postal affairs com. Assoc. Ch. Press, 1983-90, Work Group on New Ch. Periodical, 1985-86; Evangelical Luth. Ch. Am. Cabinet of Execs., 1988—. Author: Ways to Wake Up Your Church, 1969, Creative Congregations, 1972, The New Face of Missions, 1973, Mission in a New World, 1977, LWF/6, 1978, Anatomy of a Merger, 1991; mem. editorial adv. bd. The New World, Roman Cath. Archdiocese of Chgo., 1994—. Pres. Lyons Council Chs., 1964; trustee Lenoir Rhyne Coll., 1975-84. Recipient Disting. Alumnus award Lenoir-Rhyne Coll., 1991, Disting. Svc. award Newberry Coll., 1992, Bachman award for disting. Luth. Theol. So. Sem., 1993, award of merit for editorials Assoc. Ch. Press, 1991, award of merit for articles in mission mags. Assoc. Ch. Press, 1974. Mem. Nat. Luth. Editors Assn. (pres. 1975-77). Home: 1401 Sequoia Rd Naperville IL 60540-6391 Office: Luth Mag 8765 W Higgins Rd Chicago IL 60631-4101

TREXLER, WYNN RIDENHOUR, paralegal; b. Salisbury, N.C., Sept. 15, 1941; d. Lee R. and Olena (Ludwig) Reinhour; m. Frederick C.D. Trexler, June 14, 1959; children: Dale, Wendy, Chris, Matt. Grad. high sch., Salisbury. Legal sec. Woodson & Woodson and successor firm Woodson, Hudson & Busby, Salisbury, 1961-63; legal sec. Burke, Donaldson & Holshouser, Salisbury, 1968-77, Carlton, Rhodes & Wallace, Salisbury, 1977-81; paralega Mona Lisa Wallace, Salisbury, 1981-86; freelance paralegal Piedmont Paralegal Svc., Salisbury, 1986—. Mem. Nat. Assn. Legal Assts. (cert.), Nat Assn. Legal Secs. (cert.), N.C. Paralegal Assn. (charter, bd. dirs. 1980-86, liaison), N.C. Acad. Trial Lawyers (assoc., legal assts. sect., edn. com. 1984—), Profl. Legal Assts. Democrat. Lutheran. Avocations: photography, collecting and restoring antiques, driving and showing British cars, raising ostrich. Home: PO Box 275 Faith NC 28041-0275 Office: Piedmont Paralegal Svc 2450 Artz Rd Salisbury NC 28146-1164

TREYBIG, JAMES G., computer company executive; b. Clarendon, TX, 1940. BS, Rice U., 1963; MBA, Stanford, 1968. Mkgt. mgr. Hewlett-Packard Co., 1968-72; with Kleiner and Perkins, 1972-74; with Tandem Computer Inc., Cupertino, Calif., 1974—, now pres., chief exec. officer, dir. Office: Tandem Computers Inc 19333 Vallco Pky Cupertino CA 95014-2506

TREYNOR, JACK LAWRENCE, financial advisor, educator; b. Council Bluffs, Iowa, Feb. 21, 1930; s. Jack Vernon and Alice (Cavin) T.; m. Elizabeth Glassmeyer, Aug. 29, 1968; children: Elizabeth Childs, Wendy

F.C., Thomas Pirrie. BA, Haverford Coll., 1951; MBA with distinction, Harvard U., 1955; postgrad., MIT, 1961-62. Jr. faculty Harvard U. Sch. Bus., Cambridge, Mass., 1955-56; ops. research staff Arthur D. Little, Cambridge, 1956-66; mgr. computer applications Merrill Lynch, N.Y.C., 1966-69; editor Fin. Analysts Jour., N.Y.C., 1969-81; chief investment officer Treynor-Arbit Assocs., Chgo., 1981-85; assoc. vis. prof. of fin. and bus. econs. U. So. Calif., Los Angeles, 1985-88; pres. Treynor Capital Mgmt., Palos Verdes Estates, Calif.; gen. ptnr., trustee, dir. certain mutual funds Eaton Vance, 1970—. Author: (with Patrick Regan and William Priest) The Financial Reality of Pension Funding Under ERISA, 1976; mem. editl. bd. Fin. Analysts Jour., 1969—; co-author and contbr. numerous articles in fin. jours. (Graham and Dodd Scroll award 1968, 82, twice in 1987, Graham and Dodd Plaque for best paper in Fin. Analysts Jour. 1981). Trustee Fin. Analysts Research Found., 1970-85; mem. vis. com. Grad. Sch. Bus. Adminstrn. U. Chgo., 1984-89. Served with U.S. Army, 1951-53. Mem. Inst. for Quantitative Rsch. in Fin. (Disting. fellow, bd. dirs. 1970—), Fin. Analysts Fedn. (Nicholas Molodovsky award 1985), Am. Fin. Assn. (bd. dirs. 1979-81); fellow Haverford Varsity Club, Manursing Island Club (Rye, N.Y.), The Winter Club (Lake Forest, Ill.), Longwood Cricket Club (Chestnut Hill, Mass.), N.Y. Athletic Club, Palos Verdes Beach and Athletic Club, Palos Verdes Tennis Club. Episcopalian. Avocations: jazz piano, sports cars, antique trains.

TREYZ, JOSEPH HENRY, librarian; b. Binghamton, N.Y., Nov. 23, 1926; s. Joseph Henry and Edna Belle (Leonard) T. B.A., Oberlin Coll., 1950; postgrad., Harvard U., 1951; M.L.S., Columbia U., 1952. Circulation asst. N.Y. Acad. Medicine Library, 1950-51; cataloger Columbia Libraries, N.Y.C., 1951-53, Stevens Inst. Tech., Hoboken, N.J., 1953-54; administrv. asst. Yale Library, 1955, asst. head catalogue dept., 1955-61; head new campuses program U. Calif., La Jolla, 1961-65; asst. dir. U. Mich. Library, Ann Arbor, 1965-71; dir. libraries U. Wis., Madison, 1971-83, asst. to chancellor, 1983-85; sec.-treas. L.D. Repos, Inc., 1985-87, pres., 1987—; univ. rep. Consumer Reaction Project for Catalog Card Reprodn. Study, 1961; condr. survey tech. services Fordham U. Libraries, 1967-69, Brandeis U. Libraries, 1970-71; mem. Wis. Gov.'s Com. on Library Devel., 1973-81, Wis. com. Library Services and Constrn. Act, 1979-81; del. U.S. Mission to China on Libraries, 1979. Author: Books for College Libraries, 1967, also articles. Bd. dirs. Wis. Center for Theatre Research (founder with AUS, 1945-46). Mem. Universal Serials and Book Exchange (v.p. 1976, pres., chmn. bd. dirs. 1977), ALA (councilor 1970-74, 77-81, chmn. various coms. 1967-69, recipient Melvil Dewey medal 1970), Assn. Research Libraries (commn. orgn. materials, dir. 1975-78), Midlnet (v.p. 1978-79, pres. 1979-80), Assn. Coll. and Research Libraries (chmn. editorial bd. Choice 1968-70), Wis. Library Consortium (pres. 1975-76), Wis. Assn. Acad. Libraries (chmn. 1973-74), Council U. Wis. Librarians (chmn. 1975-76, 79-80, 81-83), Wis. Library Assn. (bd. dirs. 1973-74, mem. White House Conf. com. 1977-78), Madison Area Library Council (v.p. 1973-74), Mich. Library Assn. (chmn. tech. services sect. 1968-69), N.Y. Tech. Services Librarians (pres. 1959-60). Methodist. Home: 801 N Venetian Dr Miami FL 33139-1007

TREZEK, GEORGE JAMES, mechanical engineer; b. Chgo., July 10, 1937; s. George A. T.; m. Joan A. Arcieri, Aug. 18, 1962; children: Wendy Marie, Keith R., Cynthia Ann. B.M.E., Gen. Motors Inst., 1960; M.S., U. Ill., 1962, Ph.D., 1965. Asst. prof. mech. engring. Northwestern U., 1965; asst. prof. U. Calif., Berkeley, 1966-70, assoc. prof., 1970-74, prof., 1974-90; prof. emeritus, 1990—; v.p. R&D Greenfield Environ.; dir. recycling ops. BKK Corp., 1990—; cons. to industry, state and fed. govtl. agys. Contbr. numerous articles on heat transfer, bio-engring. and environ. engring., solid waste mgmt. and hazardous waste mgmt., heavy metals treatment tech., marine sediments remediation, plastics recycling tech. to profl. jours. Mem. ASME, ASTM. Roman Catholic. Home: 2210 Canyon Oak Ln Danville CA 94506-2014

TREZISE, PHILIP HAROLD, government official; b. Calumet, Mich., May 27, 1912; s. Norman and Emma (Anderson) T.; m. Ruth Elenor Dorsey, Nov. 26, 1938; children: John Dorsey, David Philip. A.B., U. Mich., 1936, M.A., 1939; student, Nat. War Coll., 1949-50. Research asso. U. Mich., 1940-41; fellow Social Sci. Research Council, 1941-42; ofcl. Office Def. Transportation, 1942-43; with Dept. State, 1946-71; advisor U.S. delegation to U.N. Commn. on Indonesian question, 1948, cons. report to Pres. on fgn. econ. policy, 1950; dep. asst. sec. for econ. affairs Dept. State, 1961-65; U.S. ambassador to OECD, Paris, France, 1966-69; asst. sec. state econ. affairs, 1969-71; mem. Washington Policy Council Internat. Mgmt. and Devel. Inst., Trilateral Commn., 1976-83; sr. fellow Brookings Instn., 1971—; Adj. prof. dept. polit. sci. Columbia U., 1978; Dir. Bank of Tokyo Trust Co., 1976, Atlantic Council; mem. Nat. Commn. Supplies and Shortages, 1975-76. Contbg. editor: Yomiuri Shimbun, 1979-86. Pres. Japan-Am. Soc., 1973-76. Served as lt. OSS USNR, 1943-46. Decorated Order of Rising Sun (Japan); recipient Pres.'s award for disting. fed. civilian svc., 1965, Disting. Honor award Dept. State, 1971, Disting. Alumnus award U. Mich., 1980. Mem. Council Fgn. Relations, Phi Beta Kappa. Episcopalian. Club: Internat. Nat. Economists (Washington). Home: 6900 Broxburn Dr Bethesda MD 20817-4716 Office: 1775 Massachusetts Ave NW Washington DC 20036-2188

TREZZA, ALPHONSE FIORE, librarian, educator; b. Phila., Dec. 27, 1920; s. Vincent and Amalia (Ferrara) T.; m. Mildred Di Pietro, May 19, 1945; children: Carol Ann Trezza Johnston, Alphonse Fiore. B.S., U. Pa., 1948, M.S., 1950; postgrad.; librarian cert., Drexel Inst., 1949. Page Free Library, Phila., 1940-41, 45-48; library asst. Free Library, 1948-49; cataloger, asst. reference librarian Villanova U., 1949-50, instr., 1956-60; head circulation dept. U. Pa. Library, 1950-56; lectr. Drexel Inst. Sch. Library Sci., 1951-60; editor Cath. Library world, 1956-60; exec. sec. Cath. Library Assn., 1956-60; assoc. exec. dir. ALA, exec. sec. library adminstrn. div., 1960-67, assoc. dir. adminstrv. services, 1967-69; dir. Ill. State Library, Springfield, 1969-74; lectr. Grad. Sch. Library and Info. Sci., Cath. U., 1975-82; exec. dir. Nat. Commn. on Libraries and Info. Scis., Washington, 1974-80; dir. intergovt. library Cooperation Project Fed. Library Com./Library of Congress, Washington, 1980-82; assoc. prof. Sch. Library and Info. Studies Fla. State U., Tallahassee, 1982-87, prof., 1987-93, emeritus prof., 1993—; mem. Ill. Library LSCA TITLE I-II Adv. Commn., 1963-69; mem. network devel. com. Library of Congress, 1977-82; bd. visitors Sch. Library and Info. Sci., U. Pitts., 1977-80; cons. Becker & Hayes, Inc., 1980-84, King Research, Inc., 1981-82; mem. planning com and steering com. Fla. Gov.'s Conf. on Library and Info. Svcs., 1988-91. Mem. chmn. Cath. Book Week, 1954-56; pres. Joliet Diocesan Bd. Edn., 1966-68; Democratic committeeman, Lombard, Ill., 1961-69; auditor Borough of Norwood (Pa.), 1958-60. Served to 1st lt. USAAF, 1942-45. Decorated Air medal; recipient Ofcl. commendation White House Conf. on Libr. and Info. Svc., 1979. Mem. ALA (coun. 1973-82, 88-92, mem. exec. bd. 1974-79, chmn. stats. coordinating com. 1970-74, mem. pub. com. 1975-78, 81-83, 87-89, mem. adv. com. interface, 1979-83, chmn. membership com. 1983-84, chmn. nominating com. 1988-89, mem. legis. com. 1989-91, adv. bd. ALA Yearbook 1976-91, Assn. Specialized and Coop. Library Agys. legis. com., 1987-89, ad hoc com. White House Conf. on Libr. and Info. Svcs. 1989-91, chmn. awards com. 1990-92, Exceptional Achievement award 1981, J.B. Lippincott award 1989), Cath. Library Assn. (life, adv. coun. 1960—), Ill. Library Assn. (chmn. legis.-library devel. com. 1964-69, mem. exec. bd., libr's. citation 1974), Fla. Library Assn. (bd. dirs. 1987-93, pres. 1991-92, intellectual freedom com., chmn. com. on Fla. Librs. publ., editor, publ. com., planning com., 1991, site com.), Continuing Libr. Edn. Network and Exchange (pres. 1982-83), Internat. Fedn. Library Assns. and Institutions (statistics standing com. 1976-85, planning com.), Coun. Nat. Library Assns. (chmn. 1959-61), Assn. Coll. and Research Librarians (pres. Phila. chpt. 1953-55), Drexel Inst. Library Sch. Alumni Assn. (pres. 1955-56, exec. bd. 1956-60, chmn. chief officers State Library Agys. 1973-74), Chgo. Library Club (pres. 1969), Assn. Library and Info. Sci. Edn. (govt. relation com. 1985-87), Drexel U. Alumni Assn. (Outstanding Alumnus award 1963), Kappa Phi Kappa (chpt. pres. 1948), Beta Phi Mu (hon.). Lodge: K.C. Office: Fla State U Sch Libr and Info Studies Tallahassee FL 32306

TRIANTAFYLLOU, MICHAEL STEFANOS, ocean engineering educator; b. Athens, Greece, Oct. 27, 1951; came to U.S., 1974; s. Stefanos M. and Penelopi I. (Koutras) T.; m. Joan L. Kimball, Sept. 22, 1985; children: Stefanos R., Kimon K. MS in Ocean Engring., MIT, 1977, MSME, 1977,

ScD, 1979. Rsch. assoc. MIT, Cambridge, Mass., 1978-79, asst. prof., 1979-83, assoc. prof., 1983-86, tenured assoc. prof., 1986-90, prof., dir. ocean engring. testing tank, 1990—; vis. scientist Woods Hole (Mass.) Oceanographic Inst., 1990—. Contbr. articles to profl. jours. Rsch. grantee OFfice NAval Rsch., Office Naval Tech., NSF, Doherty Found. Dept. Commerce, 1979—. Mem. Internat. Soc. Offshore and Polar Engrs. (founding mem.), Soc. Naval Architects and Marine Engrs. (papers com., vice chmn. OC-2 com.), Am. Phys. Soc. Office: MIT 77 Massachusetts Ave Rm 5-323 Cambridge MA 02139-3594

TRIANTAPHYLLOU, HEDWIG HIRSCHMANN, plant pathologist; b. Fuerth, Bavaria, Germany, Jan. 16, 1927; came to U.S., 1954; d. Friedrich and Ferdinandine (Schonleben) Hirschmann; m. Anastasios Christos Triantaphyllou, July 9, 1960; 1 child, Christos F. PhD, U. Erlangen, Erlangen, Germany, 1951. From tech. asst. to prof. N.C. State Univ., Raleigh, N.C., 1954-92; ret. Contbr. articles to profl. jours., chpts. to books in field. Recipient rsch. award Soc. Sigma Xi, 1962, Ruth Allen award Am. Phytopathol. Soc., 1993, Soc. Nematologists fellowship, 1981. Mem. Helminthological Soc. Wash., Soc. European Nematologists, Soc. of Nematologists, Soc. Sigma Xi. Avocations: sailing, music, piano. Office: N C State U Dept Plant Pathology Box 7616 Raleigh NC 27695-7616

TRÍAS-MONGE, JOSE, lawyer, former territory supreme court chief justice; b. San Juan, P.R., May 5, 1920; s. José and Belén Monge; m. Jane G. Trías, June 3, 1943; children: Jose Enrique, Peter James, Arturo Trías. B.A., U. P.R., 1940; M.A., Harvard U., 1943, LL.B., 1944; J.S.D., Yale U., 1947. Bar: P.R. 1945, U.S. Supreme Ct 1949. Teaching fellow Harvard U., 1943-44; practiced law San Juan, 1950-52, 57-74; atty. gen. P.R., 1953-57; chief justice Supreme Ct. P.R., San Juan, 1974-85; of counsel Trías, Acevedo & Otero, San Juan, 1989—; mem. P.R. Constl. Conv., 1951-52, Inter-Am. Juridical Commn., OAS, 1966-67; pres. P.R. Acad. Legislation and Jurisprudence, 1985—; lectr. U. P.R., 1947-49. Author: El Sistema Judicial de Puerto Rico, 1978, La Crisis del Derecho en Puerto Rico, 1979, Historia Constitucional de Puerto Rico, Vol. I, 1980, Vol. II, 1981, Vol. III, 1982, Vol. IV, 1983, Vol. V, 1994; Sociedad, Derecho y Justicia, 1985, El Choque de Dos Culturas Juridicas en Puerto Rico, 1991. Mem. nat. com. ACLU, 1958-74; v.p. Festival Casals, Inc., 1957-69, 73-74; trustee U. P.R., 1962-72. Mem. Bar Assn. P.R., ABA, Soc. de Legislation Comparée, French Acad. Comparative Law, Royal Acad. Spanish Lang. (life). Roman Catholic. Office: PO Box 366283 San Juan PR 00936-6283

TRIBE, LAURENCE HENRY, lawyer, educator; b. Shanghai, Republic of China, Oct. 10, 1941; s. George Israel and Paulina (Diatlovitsky) T.; m. Carolyn Ricarda Kreye, June 20, 1964; children: Mark Alexander, Kerry Katrina. A.B. summa cum laude in Math., Harvard U., 1962, J.D. magna cum laude, 1966; LL.D. (hon.), Gonzaga U., 1980, Pacific U. 1987, Am. U. 1987, Ill. Inst. Tech., 1988. Bar: Calif. 1966, U.S. Supreme Ct. 1966. Law clk. Calif. Supreme Ct., 1966-67, U.S. Supreme Ct., 1967-68; exec. dir. tech. assessment panel Nat. Acad. Scis., 1968-69; asst. prof. law Harvard U., 1969-72, prof., 1972-82, Ralph S. Tyler, Jr. prof. constl. law, 1982—; chmn. Marshall Islands Jud. Service Commn., 1979-80; chief appellate counsel Calif. Nuclear Litigation, 1978-83; spl. dep. atty. gen. Hawaii, 1983-84; cons. NSF, Nat. Endowment Humanities, White House, others; cons. Marshall Islands for drafting new constitution, 1978-79. Author: American Constitutional Law, 1978 (recipient awards), 2d edit., 1988, Constitutional Choices, 1985, God Save this Honorable Court, 1985, Abortion: The Clash of Absolutes, 1990, (with Michael Dorf) On Reading the Constitution, 1991; contbr. articles to profl. jours. Nat. scholar; recipient Triennial Coif award for the outstanding work of legal scholarship in U.S., 1978-80, Scribe award, 1980, Beale prize; 1966 Detur prize, 1969; nat. debate champion, 1961; NSF fellow, 1962-63. Fellow Am. Acad. Arts and Scis.; mem. ABA (Silver Gavel award 1991), ACLU, Phi Beta Kappa. Office: Harvard U Law Sch Hauser Hall 420 Cambridge MA 02138

TRIBETT, BRENDA DIANE BELL, religious organization administrator; b. Richmond, Va., Oct. 3, 1947; d. Ervin George Jr. and Claudia (Miller) Bell; m. Louis Tribett Jr., Sept. 2, 1967 (div. 1973); 1 child, Diondrea Nichelle. BS in Juvenile Justice, Va. Commonwealth U., 1978; MA in Legal Studies, Antioch Sch. Law, 1981; MA in Christian Edn., Presbyn. Sch. Christian Edn., 1991, EdS in Christian Edn., 1992. Ch. sec., youth coord. Mt. Olive Bapt. Ch., Richmond, 1973-89; acad. skills coord. Va. Union U., Richmond, 1987-89; ESL/adult basic edn. tchr. Richmond Pub. Schs., 1982-92; dir. Joseph Nash Multicultural Ctr., Richmond, 1990-92; exec. dir. Christian edn. Prog. Nat. Bapt. Conv., Washington, 1992—; workshop facilitator Bapt. Gen. Conv., Richmond, 1974-92, mem. leadership team, 1980-92; cons. Commonwealth Girl Scouts, Richmond, 1988; tchr. Adult Basic Edn., 1991-92. Named one of 100 Most Influential Black Women, Koinonia Ind. Meth. Ch., 1993; Educator's fellow Ecumenical Resource Ctr. Mem. Nat. Coun. Chs., Religious Edn. Assn. Democrat. Avocations: jogging, reading, cooking, skating. Office: Prog Nat Bapt Conv Inc Dept of Christian Edn 601 50th St NE Washington DC 20019-5499

TRIBLE, PAUL SEWARD, JR., former senator; b. Balt., Dec. 29, 1946; s. Paul Seward and Katherine (Schilpp) T.; m. Rosemary Dunaway; children: Mary Katherine, Paul Seward III. B.A., Hampden-Sydney Coll., 1968; J.D., Washington and Lee U., Lexington, Va., 1971. Bar: Va. 1971. Law clk. to U.S. dist. judge Albert V. Bryan, Jr., 1971-72; asst. U.S. atty. Office U.S. Atty. Eastern Dist. Va., 1972-74; commonwealth's atty. Essex County, Va., 1974-76; mem. 95th-97th Congresses from 1st Va. Dist.; U.S. Senator from Va., 1982-89; of counsel Shuttle Worth, Ruloff, Giordano & Kahle, 1989—; pres. Jefferson Group, Washington, 1991—. Mem.: Washington and Lee Law Rev. Republican. Episcopalian. Office: The Jefferson Group 603 Pilot House Dr Newport News VA 23606

TRIBUS, MYRON, management consultant, engineer, educator; b. San Francisco, Oct. 30, 1921; s. Edward and Marie D. (Kramer) T.; m. Sue Davis, Aug. 30, 1945; children—Louanne, Kamala. B.S. in Chemistry, U. Calif. at Berkeley, 1942; Ph.D. in Engring. U. Calif. at Los Angeles, 1949; D.Sc. (hon.), Rockford (Ill.) Coll., 1965, Oakland (Mich.) U., 1971. Registered profl. engr., Mass. Instr. to prof. engring. U. Calif. at Los Angeles, 1946-61; dir. aircraft icing research U. Mich., 1951-54; dean engring. Thayer Sch. Engring., Dartmouth Coll., 1961-69; asst. sec. sci. and tech. Dept. Commerce, Washington, 1969-70; sr. v.p. tech. and engring. info. tech. group Xerox Corp., Rochester, N.Y., 1970-74; dir. Center for Advanced Engring. Study, Mass. Inst. Tech., Cambridge, 1974-86; cons. in quality mgmt., 1986—; dir. rsch. Exergy, Inc., Hayward, Calif., 1987—; cons. heat transfer Gen. Electric Co., 1950; cons. Fed. Office Saline Water; tech. adv. bd. Dept. Commerce; adviser to NATO, 1953; mem. Nat. Adv. Com. Oceans and Atmosphere, 1971-72; bd. dirs. Exergy, Inc., Hayward, Calif. Author: Thermostatics and Thermodynamics, 1961, Rational Descriptions, Decisions and Designs, 1969; Contbr. articles to profl. jours. Bd. govs. Technion, Haifa, Israel, 1973-84. Served to capt. USAAF, 1942-46. Recipient Thurman H. Bane award Inst. Aero. Scis. 1945; Wright Bros. medal Soc. Automotive Engrs., 1945; Alfred Noble prize Engring. Socs., 1952; named U. Calif. at Los Angeles Alumnus Year, 1972. Mem. Am. Soc. M.E., IEEE, Am. Soc. for Engring. Edn., Nat. Soc. Profl. Engrs. Home: 350 Britto Terrace Fremont CA 94539 Office: Exergy Inc 22320 Foothill Blvd Hayward CA 94541-2700

TRICE, THOMAS GRANVILLE, library director, history educator; b. Reedley, Calif., Mar. 7, 1945; s. Granville Jones Trice and Orine Marie (Price) Trice-Paul; m. Gwennyth Susannah Noroian, May 4, 1968; children: Bronwen Verity, Megan Angharad. BA, Stanford U., 1967; MA, Calif. State U., Hayward, 1969; PhD, U. Wis., 1974; M Libr. and Info. Studies, U. Calif., Berkeley, 1981. C.C. tchg. credential, Calif. Tchr. Chadwick Sch., Palos Verde Peninsula, Calif., 1969-70; tchr. reading and math. St. Patrick's Sch., Madison, Wis., 1970-72; instr. assoc. Napa (Calif.) City-County Pub. Libr., 1975-81, reference libr., 1981-86, head tech. svcs., 1986, asst. libr. dir., 1986-90, dir. libr., 1990—; instr. history Solano CC, Napa Valley Coll., Coll. of Marin, 1974—; mem. Police Power, Inc., Napa, 1983-88. Author: Spanish Liberalism in Crisis, 1991; also articles. Mem., chmn. Napa Cultural Heritage Commn., 1983-86; participant Leadership Napa Valley, 1988-89; chmn. site coun. Napa H.S., 1992-94. Fellow Coun. for European Studies, Spain, 1972-73, Sidney B. Mitchell fellow U. Calif. 1980-81. Mem. ALA, Calif. Libr. Assn. (chmn. legis. com. 1981—), Napa Valley Stanford Club, Kiwanis, Beta Phi Mu (life). Home: 1509 Maxwell Ave Napa CA

94559 Office: Napa City-County Pub Libr 580 Coombs St Napa CA 94559-3396

TRICE, WILLIAM HENRY, paper company executive; b. Geneva, N.Y., Apr. 4, 1933; s. Clyde H. T.; m. Sandra Clayton, July 16, 1955; children—Russell, Amy. B.S. in Forestry, State U. N.Y., 1955; M.S., Inst. Paper Chemistry, Appleton, Wis., 1960, Ph.D., 1963. With Union Camp Corp., 1963—, tech. dir. bleached div., 1972-74; v.p., corp. tech. dir. research and devel. Union Camp Corp., Wayne, N.J., 1974-79; v.p. tech. Union Camp Corp., 1979-85, exec. v.p., 1985—; chmn. bd. dirs. Bush Boake Allen, Inc. Trustee, pres. Western Mich. U.-Paper Tech. Found., Syracuse Pulp and Paper Found. With USAF, 1955-57. Fellow TAAPI (bd. dirs. 1978-81), Indsl. Rsch. Inst. (alt. rep.), Inst. Paper Sci. and Tech. (trustee, exec. commn. alumni assn.). Home: 6 Hanover Rd Mountain Lakes NJ 07046-1004 Office: Union Camp Corp 1600 Valley Rd Wayne NJ 07470

TRICK, TIMOTHY NOEL, electrical and computer engineering educator, researcher; b. Dayton, Ohio, July 14, 1939; s. Edmund Louis and Roberta Elizabeth (Heckel) T.; m. Dorothe Lee Jacobs, Feb. 18, 1958; children: Patricia, Michael, Thomas, William, Gregory, Andrew. BSEE, U. Dayton, 1961; MSEE, Purdue U., 1962, PhD, 1966. Instr. Purdue U., W. Lafayette, Ind., 1963-65; asst. prof. elec. and computer engring. U. Ill., Urbana, 1965-70, assoc. prof., 1970-75, prof., 1975—; dir. Coordinated Sci. Lab., 1984-86, head dept. elec. and computer engring., 1985—. Author: Introduction to Circuit Analysis, 1978. Fellow IEEE (bd. dirs. 1986-89, v.p. publs. 1988-89, Guillemin-Cauer award 1976, Centennial medal 1984, Meritorious Svc. award 1987); mem. Circuits and Systems Soc. IEEE (pres. 1979, Van Valkenburg award 1994), Am. Soc. Engring. Educators, NSPE. Roman Catholic. Avocations: hiking, camping. Office: U Ill Dept Elec & Computer Engring 1406 W Green St Urbana IL 61801-2918

TRICOLES, GUS PETER, electromagnetics engineer, physicist, consultant; b. San Francisco, Oct. 18, 1931; s. Constantine Peter and Eugenia (Elias) T.; m. Beverly Mildred Ralsky, Dec. 20, 1953 (dec. Dec. 1974); children: Rosanne, Robin; m. Aileen Irma Aronson, Apr. 1, 1980 (div. June 1980). BA in Physics, UCLA, 1955; MS in Applied Math., San Diego State U., 1958; MS in Applied Physics, U. Calif., San Diego, 1962, PhD in Applied Physics, 1971. Engr. Convair div. Gen. Dynamics, San Diego, 1955-59, engr. Electronics div., 1962-75, engring. mgr. Electronics div., 1975-89, sr. engring. staff specialist, 1989-92; sr. engring. staff specialist GDE Systems Inc., 1992—; engr. Smyth Rsch. Assn., San Diego, 1959-61; rsch. asst. Scripps Instn. Oceanography, La Jolla, Calif., 1961-62; sr. engring. staff specialist G.D.E. Systems, Inc., San Diego, 1992—; cons. Ga. Inst. Tech., Atlanta, 1972, 79-80, Transco Industries, L.A., 1973, Aero Geo Industries, San Antonio, 1980-82, Vantage Assocs., San Diego, 1988; rsch. reviewer NRC, NAS, Boulder, Colo., 1986-88. Author: (with others) Radome Engineering Handbook, 1970, Antenna Handbook, 1988; contbr. articles to profl. jours.; holder 18 patents. With USN, 1952-53. Fellow IEEE (antenna standards com. 1980—, advancement com. 1988), Optical Soc. Am. (local sect. v.p. 1966); mem. N.Y. Acad. Scis., Am. Geophys. Union. Avocations: woodworking, photography. Home: 4633 Euclid Ave San Diego CA 92115-3226 Office: GDE Sys Inc PO Box 92150 San Diego CA 92150-9009

TRIENENS, HOWARD JOSEPH, lawyer; b. Chgo., Sept. 13, 1923; s. Joseph Herman and Myrtle (Wilsberg) T.; m. Paula Miller, Aug. 27, 1946; children: John, Thomas, Nancy. BS, Northwestern U., 1945; JD, 1949. Bar: Ill. 1949, N.Y. 1980, U.S. Dist. Ct. (no. dist.) Ill., U.S. Dist. Ct. (so. and ea. dists.) N.Y., U.S. Ct. Appeals (2d, 3d, 7th, 8th, 10th, 11th and D.C. cirs.), U.S. Supreme Ct. 1954. Assoc. firm Sidley, Austin, Burgess & Harper, Chgo., 1949-50; law clk. to Chief Justice Vinson, 1950-52; assoc. Sidley, Austin, Burgess & Smith, Chgo., 1952-56; ptnr. Sidley & Austin, Chgo., 1956—; v.p., gen. counsel AT&T, 1980-86. Trustee Northwestern U., 1967—. With USAAF, 1943-46. Mem. ABA, Ill. Bar Assn., Chgo. Bar Assn., N.Y. State Bar Assn., Am. Coll. Trial Lawyers, Legal Club (Chgo.), Law Club (Chgo.), Chgo. Club, Casino Club (Chgo.), Mid-Day Club, Skokie Country Club, Shoreacres Club, Glen View Club (Golf, Ill.), Met. Club (Washington), Old Elm Country Club, Sigma Chi. Democrat. Home: 690 Longwood Ave Glencoe IL 60022-1761 Office: Sidley & Austin 1 First National Plz Chicago IL 60603

TRIER, JERRY STEVEN, gastroenterologist, educator; b. Frankfurt, Germany, Apr. 12, 1933; came to U.S., 1938, naturalized, 1943; s. Kurt J. and Alice L. (Cahn) T.; m. Laurel M. Baw, June 8, 1957; children: Stanley, Jeryl, Stephen. M.D., U. Wash., 1957; M.A. (hon.), Harvard U., 1973. Diplomate: Am. Bd. Internal Medicine. Intern U. Rochester, N.Y., 1957-58; resident in medicine U. Rochester, 1958-59; clin. assoc. Nat. Cancer Inst., Bethesda, Md., 1959-61; trainee in gastroenterology U. Wash., Seattle, 1961-63; assoc. prof. medicine U. Wis., Madison, 1963-67; assoc. prof. U. N.Mex., Albuquerque, 1967-69, Boston U., 1969-73, Harvard U. Med. Sch., Cambridge, Mass., 1973-76; prof. Harvard U. Med. Sch., 1976—; sr. physician Brigham and Women's Hosp.; cons. Sidney Farber Cancer Ctr., Boston VA Hosp., W. Roxbury VA Hosp. Nat. Inst. Diabetes and Digestive and Kidney Disease; adv. coun. NIH, 1986-90. Editor: Internal Medicine; mem. editorial bd.; Anatomical Record, 1969—; Gastroenterology, assoc. editor, 1971-77, mem. editorial bd., 1967-71, 78-83, 93—; chmn., 1988-93, Am. Jour. Medicine, 1978-87, Current Opinion in Gastroenterology, 1990—; contbr. articles to chpts. on gastrointestinal histology, pathology, devel. and disease to med. jours. and books. Served as surgeon USPHS, 1959-61. USPHS-NIH grantee, 1963—. Mem. Am. Soc. Clin. Investigation, Assn. Am. Physicians, Am. Gastroent. Assn. (pres. 1985-86), Am. Soc. Cell Biology, Am. Fedn. Clin. Research. Home: 119 Pine St Weston MA 02193-1178 Office: Brigham and Women's Hosp 75 Francis St Boston MA 02115-6195

TRIEWEILER, TERRY NICHOLAS, lawyer; b. Dubuque, Iowa, Mar. 21, 1948; s. George Nicholas and Anne Marie (Oastern) T.; m. Carol M. Jacobson, Aug. 11, 1972; children: Kathryn Anne, Christina Marie, Anna Theresa. BA, Drake U., 1970, JD, 1972. Bar: Iowa 1973, Wash. 1973, U.S. Dist. Ct. (so. dist.) Iowa 1973, U.S. Dist. Ct. (we. dist.) Wash. 1973, Mont. 1975, U.S. Dist. Ct. Mont. 1977. Staff atty. Polk County Legal Services, Des Moines, 1973; assoc. Hullin, Roberts, Mines, Fite & Riveland, Seattle, 1973-75, Morrison & Hedman, Whitefish, Mont., 1975-77; sole practice, Whitefish; now justice Mont. Supreme Ct., Helena; lectr. U. Mont. Law Sch., 1981—; mem. com. to amend civil proc. rules Mont. Supreme Ct., Helena, 1984, commn. to draft pattern jury instrns., 1985; mem. Gov.'s Adv. Com. on Amendment to Work Compensation Act, adv. com. Mont. Work Compensation Ct. Mem. ABA, Mont. Bar Assn. (pres. 1986-87), Wash. Bar Assn., Iowa Bar Assn., Assn. Trial Lawyers Am., Mont. Trial Lawyers Assn. (dir., pres.). Democrat. Roman Catholic. Home: 1615 Virginia Dale St Helena MT 59601-5823 Office: Mont Supreme Ct Justice Bldg 215 N Sanders St Rm 323 Helena MT 59620 also: 215 N Sanders St Helena MT 59620

TRIFFIN, NICHOLAS, law librarian, law educator; b. Boston, May 30, 1942; s. Robert and Lois (Brandt) T.; m. Mary M. Bertolet, June 1, 1965 (div. June 1975); children: Amyk (dec.), A. Robert; m. Madeleine J. Wilken, May 30, 1981. BA cum laude, Yale U., 1965, JD, 1968; MLS, Rutgers U., 1978. Bar: N.Y. 1969, Conn. 1973, U.S. Dist. Ct. Conn. 1973, U.S. Ct. Appeals (2nd cir.) 1973, U.S. Tax Ct. 1974. Assoc. Willkie Farr & Gallagher, N.Y.C., 1968-70; dean students Johnson (Vt.) State Coll., 1970-72; assoc. Di Sesa & Evans, New Haven, 1972-76; head pub. services, instr. law U. Conn., W. Hartford, 1977-81; law library dir., assoc. prof. Hamline U. St. Paul, 1982-84; dir. law library, prof. Pace U., White Plains, N.Y., 1984—; bd. dirs. Hale Found.; bd. advisors Oceana Pub., Inc., 1987—; chief info. svcs. Inst. Internat. Comml. Law, 1993-94, dir., 1994—; adj. prof. Hartford Coll., 1978-80. Author: Law Books Published, 1984—, Law Books in Print, 5th edit., 1987, 6th edit., 1991, 7th edit., 1995, Law Books in Review, 1984-92, Drafting History of the Federal Rules of Criminal Procedure, 1991; columnist Law Libr. Jour., 1983-84. Justice of the Peace, Conn., 1976-78. Mem. Am. Assn. Law Librs. (chmn. reader svcs. spl. interest sect. 1982-83, chmn. legal history and rare books spl. interest sect. 1991-92, chmn. constitution and bylaws com. 1994-95), Westchester Acad. Libr. Dirs. Orgn., Inc. (v.p. 1990-91, pres. 1991-92, exec. bd. dirs. 1992-94), Law Libr. New Eng. (pres. 1981-82), Minn. Assn. Law Librs. (v.p. 1983-84), Westchester Libr. Assn. (exec. bd. 1990-91), Body Myositis Assn., Mory's Club, Beta Phi Mu. Mem. Soc. of Friends. Avocations: kayaking, rare books, opera. Office: Pace U Law Sch 78 N Broadway White Plains NY 10603-3796

TRIGERE, PAULINE, fashion designer; b. Paris, Nov. 4, 1912; came to U.S., 1937, naturalized, 1942; d. Alexandre and Cecile (Coriene) Trigere; children: Jean-Pierre, Philippe Radley. Student, Victor Hugo Coll., Paris. Began career at Martial et Armand, Paris, 1937; became asst. designer at Hattie Carnegie, N.Y.C.; started House of Trigere, N.Y.C., 1942. Recipient Coty Am. Fashion Critics award, 1994, Return award, 1951, Neiman-Marcus award, 1950, Cotton award Nat. Cotton Coun., 1959, award Filene's, 1959, Coty Hall of Fame award, 1959, Silver medal City of Paris, 1972, medal of Vermeil City of Paris, 1982, Lifetime Achievement award, 1992, Nat. Arts Club award, 1993, CFDA Lifetime Achievement award Lincoln Ctr., 1994; celebrated 50 yrs. in the bus. at Fashion Inst. Tech., 1992. Office: Trigere Inc 498 7th Ave New York NY 10018

TRIGG, DONALD CLARK, lawyer, insurance company executive; b. Flint, Mich., Aug. 22, 1949; s. Samuel Clark and Rose Mary (Solomen) T.; m. Carol Lawmaster, Oct. 28, 1978. AB in Polit. Sci., Ind. U., 1971, JD, 1974, MBA, 1987. Bar: Ind. 1974, U.S. Dist. Ct. Ind. 1974, U.S.Ct. Appeals (7th cir.) 1974, U.S. Supreme Ct. 1979. Dep. atty. gen. Ind. Attys. Gen.'s Office, Indpls., 1974-76; assoc. gen. counsel Blue Cross/Blue Shield Ind., Indpls., 1976-86, dir. health care ops. support, 1986-87, v.p., asst. gen. counsel, 1988, sr. v.p., gen. counsel, corp. sec., 1988—. Vice-precinct committeeman Ind. Reps., 1976. Mem. ABA, Ind. Bar Assn., Indpls. Bar Assn. Office: The Associated Group 120 Monument Cir Indianapolis IN 46204-2802

TRIGG, PAUL REGINALD, JR., lawyer; b. Lewistown, Mont., Mar. 25, 1913; s. Paul Reginald and Opal Stella (Fay) T.; m. Helen Ruth Leake, Dec. 25, 1938; children: Paul Reginald III, Mary Adra. BA, Grinnell Coll., 1935; JD, U. Mich., 1938. Bar: Mich. 1938. Practiced law in Detroit; ptnr. Dykema, Gossett (and predecessor), 1938—. Mem. ABA, Mich. Bar Assn., Detroit Bar Assn., Detroit Country Club, Yondotega Club. Clubs: Detroit, Detroit Country, Yondotega.

TRIGG, ROGER HUGH, philosophy educator; b. Pontypridd, Wales, Aug. 14, 1941; s. Ivor and Muriel Grace (Collins) T.; m. Julia Gibbs, July 23, 1972; children: Nicholas (dec.), Alison. MA, Oxford U., Eng., 1967, PhD, 1968. From lectr. to sr. lectr. then reader U. Warwick, Coventry, Eng., 1966-87; dir. Ctr. for Rsch. in Philosophy and Lit., Coventry, Eng., 1985-91; prof. philosophy U. Warwick, Coventry, Eng., 1987—; chmn. Dept. Philosophy, 1994-95; vis. fellow St. Cross Coll., Oxford U., 1986-87, 91-92. Author: Pain and Emotion, 1970, Reason and Commitment, 1973, Reality At Risk, 1980, The Shaping of Man, 1982, Understanding Social Science, 1985, Ideas of Human Nature, 1988, Rationality and Science, 1993. Justice of the Peace, Warwickshire, Eng., 1981-91. Mem. British Soc. for Philosophy of Religion (pres. 1993—), Royal Inst. Philosophy (of coun.). Office: U Warwick, Dept Philosophy, Coventry West Midlands CV4 7AL, England

TRIGGER, BRUCE GRAHAM, anthropology educator; b. Cambridge (formerly Preston), Ont., Can., June 18, 1937; s. John Wesley and Gertrude Elizabeth (Graham) T.; m. Barbara Marian Welch, Dec. 7, 1968; children: Isabel Marian, Rosalyn Theodora. BA, U. Toronto, 1959; PhD, Yale U., 1964; DSc (hon.), U. N.B. 1987; LittD (hon.), U. Waterloo, 1990; LLD (hon.), U. Western Ont., 1995. Assoc. prof. Northwestern U., 1963-64; asst. prof. McGill U., 1964-67, assoc. prof., 1967-69, full prof. anthropology, 1969—, chmn. dept., 1970-75; V.G. Childe Meml. lectr. U. London, 1982; Harry Hawthorn Disting. lectr., 1988; Disting. lectr. in archaeology Am. Anthrop. Assn., 1990; Disting. vis. prof. Am. U. in Cairo, 1992. Author: History and Settlement in Lower Nubia, 1965, Beyond History, 1968, The Huron: Farmers of the North, 1969, 2d edit., 1990, Cartier's Hochelaga, 1972, Nubia Under the Pharaohs, 1976, The Children of Aataentsic, 1976, Time and Traditions, 1978, Gordon Childe: Revolutions in Archaeology, 1980, Natives and Newcomers, 1985, A History of Archaeological Thought, 1989, Early Civilizations, 1993; vol. editor: Handbook of North AMerican Indians, Vol. 15, 1978; editor Native and Northern Series. Recipient Can. Silver Jubilee medal, 1977, Cornplanter medal, 1979, John Porter prize, 1987, Prix Victor-Barbeau Acad. Canadienne-française, 1991, Prix Leon-Gérin (Prix du Québec), 1991, James R. Wiseman Book award Archaeol. Inst. Am., 1991; Woodrow Wilson fellow, 1959-60, Woodrow Wilson dissertation fellow, 1962-63, Can. Coun. Leave fellow, 1968-69, 76-77, Killam rsch. fellow Can. Coun., 1970-71, 90, 91, leave fellow Social Scis. and Humanities Rsch. Coun. of Can., 1983. Fellow Royal Soc. Can. (Innis-Gerin medal 1985), Soc. Antiquaries of Scotland (hon.); mem. Prehistoric Soc. U.K. (hon.), Huron Great Turtle Clan (adopted), Sigma Xi. Home: Apt 603, 3495 Mountain St, Montreal, PQ Canada H3G 2A5 Office: McGill U Dept Anthropology, 855 Sherbrooke St W, Montreal, PQ Canada H3A 2T7

TRIGGER, KENNETH JAMES, manufacturing engineering educator; b. Carsonville, Mich., Sept. 6, 1910; married, 1939; 3 children. BS, Mich. State U., 1933, MS, 1935, ME. 1943. Asst. Mich. State Coll., 1933-34, instr. mech. engring., 1935-36; instr. mech. engring. Swarthmore (Pa.) Coll., 1937-38, Lehigh (Pa.) U., 1938-39; assoc. U. Ill., Urbana, 1939-45, from asst. prof. to prof., 1945-70, prof. mech. and indsl. engring.; cons. nuclear divsn. Union Carbide Corp., Continental Can Co., Aeroprojects Inc., Atlantic Richfield Co., numerous others. Fellow Soc. Mfg. Engrs. (medal 1959), Am. Soc. Mech. Engrs. (life), (Blackall award 1957, William T. Ennor Mfg. Tech. award 1992), Am. Soc. Metals (life); mem. Am. Soc. Engring. Edn. Achievements include research in metal cutting and machinability, physical metallurgy, cutting temperatures and temperature distribution in cutting of metals and mechanism of tool wear. Office: U Illinois Dept Mech Engr Indust Engr 140 1206 W Green St Urbana IL 61801-2906

TRIGGIANI, LEONARD VINCENT, corporate executive; b. Paterson, N.J., June 24, 1930; s. Mario and Theresa (Tierno) T.; m. Aldona Witko, Apr. 24, 1965; 1 son, Paul. BA, Drew U., 1952; MS, Cath. U. Am., 1954, PhD, 1958; postgrad., Duke U. Sch. Medicine, 1956. Instr. Cath. U. Am., Washington, 1958-60; with rsch. div. W.R. Grace & Co., Columbia, Md., 1960-84, sr. rsch. chemist, rsch. supr., 1960-66, mgr.-dir. nuclear rsch., 1967-72, dir. inorganic rsch., 1972-73, dir. indsl. rsch., 1973-74, pres. rsch. div., 1974-83, v.p. co., 1978-84, v.p. for tech. ventures, 1983-84; symposium chmn. nuclear fuels, 1967, 70; exec. v.p., chief tech. officer B.F. Goodrich Co., Akron, Ohio, 1984-87; pres., chief exec. officer Amoco Tech. Co., Amoco Corp., Naperville, Ill., 1987—; Chmn. Basic Industry Rsch. Lab. Adv. Bd., Northwestern U. Author and patentee in field. Recipient Alumni Achievement award Cath. U. Am., 1977, Drew U., 1978. Mem. Am. Chem. Soc., Comml. Devel. Assn., Dirs. Indsl. Rsch., Am. Inst. Chem. Engrs. Licensing Execs. Soc., Electrochem. Soc., Sigma Xi. Methodist. Home: 419 Le Provence Cir Naperville IL 60540-8127 Office: Amoco Tech Co 55 E Shuman Blvd Naperville IL 60563-8467

TRIGGIANI, ROBERTO, mathematics educator; b. Bolzano, Italy, Mar. 28, 1942; came to U.S., 1968; s. Giuseppe and Maria (Ugenti) T.; m. Irena Lasiecka. Doctoral Degree, U. Padova, Italy, 1967; PhD, U. Minn., 1973. Asst. prof. SUNY, Albany, 1974-75, Iowa State U., Ames, 1975-78; assoc. prof. Iowa State U., Ames, 1978-81, U. Fla., Gainesville, Fla., 1981-83; prof. U. Fla., Gainesville, 1983-87; prof. math U. Va., Charlottesville, 1987—. Grantee NSF, 1978—, USAF Office Sci. Rsch., 1979—. Office: Dept of Applied Mathematics University of Virginia Charlottesville VA 22903

TRIGGLE, DAVID JOHN, university dean, consultant; b. U.K., Apr. 5, 1935; came to U.S., 1962; s. William John and Maud F. (Henderson) T.; m. Ann. M. Jones, Sept. 22, 1959; children: Andrew B., Jocelyn A. BSc in Chemistry, U. Southampton, United Kingdom, 1956; PhD, U. Hull, United Kingdom, 1959. Research fellow U. Ottawa, Ont., Can., 1959-61, U. London, 1961-62; asst. prof. SUNY Sch. of Pharmacy, Buffalo, 1962-65, assoc. prof., 1965-69, prof., 1969—, chmn. dept., 1971-85, dean, 1985—; Disting. prof. Author: Chemical Aspects of Autonomic Nervous System, 1965, Neurotransmitter-Receptor Interactions, 1971, Chemical Pharmacology of the Synapse, 1976. Recipient Volwiler Rsch. Achievement award Am. Assn. Colls. Pharmacy, 1988, 89, George Koepf award Biomed. Rsch. Med. Found. Buffalo, 1994. Fellow AAAS; mem. Am. Chem. Soc., Am. Soc. Pharmacology and Therapeutics (Otto Krayer award), Soc. Neurosci., Brit. Pharmacology Soc. Office: SUNY 126 Cooke Sch of Pharmacy Buffalo NY 14260

TRILLIN, CALVIN MARSHALL, writer, columnist; b. Kansas City, Mo., Dec. 5, 1935; s. Abe and Edyth T.; m. Alice Stewart, Aug. 13, 1965;

children: Abigail, Sarah Stewart. BA, Yale U., 1957; DLitt (hon.), Beloit Coll., 1987; LHD (hon.), Albertus Magnus Coll., 1990. Reporter, writer Time mag., 1960-63; staff writer New Yorker mag., 1963—; columnist Nation mag., 1978-85; syndicated columnist, 1986—; trustee N.Y. Pub. Libr. Author: An Education in Georgia, 1964, Barnett Frummer is an Unbloomed Flower, 1969, U.S. Journal, 1971, American Fried, 1974, Runestruck, 1977, Alice, Let's Eat, 1978, Floater, 1980, Uncivil Liberties, 1982, Third Helpings, 1983, Killings, 1984, With All Disrespect, 1985, If You Can't Say Something Nice, 1987, Travels With Alice, 1989, Enough's Enough, 1990, American Stories, 1991, Remembering Denny, 1993, Deadline Poet, 1994, Too Soon to Tell, 1995; author, performer one-man show Calvin Trillin's Uncle Sam, Am. Place Theatre, N.Y.C., 1988, Calvin Trillin's Words, No Music, Am. Place Theatre, 1990. Office: care New Yorker 20 W 43rd St New York NY 10036

TRILLING, DIANA, writer; b. N.Y.C., July 21, 1905; d. Joseph and Sadie Helene (Forbert) Rubin; m. Lionel Trilling, June 12, 1929; 1 son, James Lionel. A.B., Radcliffe Coll., 1925. Fiction critic: The Nation, 1941-49; free-lance writer on lit., social and polit. subjects, 1949—; author: Claremont Essays, 1964, We Must March My Darlings, 1977, Reviewing The Forties, 1978, Mrs. Harris: The Death of the Scarsdale Diet Doctor, 1981, The Beginning of the Journey: The Marriage of Diana and Lionel Trilling, 1993; contbr. numerous articles to mags.; Editor: Viking Portable D. H. Lawrence, 1947, Selected Letters of D. H. Lawrence, 1958, Uniform Edition of the Works of Lionel Trilling, 1978-80. Guggenheim fellow, 1950-51, 91-92; Rockefeller-NEH grantee, 1977-79. Fellow Am. Acad. Arts and Scis.; mem. Phi Beta Kappa (hon.).

TRILLING, DONALD R., federal agency administrator; b. Phila., Jan. 23, 1928; s. David Morris and Shirley (Siskin) T.; m. Jane Hunter, June 6, 1954 (div.); m. Shirley Morlan, Aug. 8, 1975; children: Jeffrey, James, Terry, Greg, Randy. BA in Economics, U. Pa., 1956, MA in Economics, 1959, PhD in Bus. Applied Economics, 1969. Mgr. mgmt. scis. Westinghouse Electric Corp., Pitts., 1967-69; dir. Washington ops. Westinghouse Pub. Mgmt. Svc., 1969-73; dir. policy rev., office sec. U.S. Dept. Transp., Washington, 1973-81; acting dep. asst. sec. policy office OST, Washington, 1978-79; exec. asst. to dep. sec. U.S. Dept. Transp., Washington, 1981-83; dir. environ. and safety policy office OST, Washington, 1986-94; mgr. industry policy Commercial Space Trans., Washington, 1983-86; acting dir. Comml. Space Transp., Washington, 1992-93; dir., environ. and safety office OST, 1994—. Co-author: (handbook) New Horizons for Air Traveler, 1991. 1st lt. US Army, 1950-53, Korea. Decorated Bronze Star, 1953. Mem. AIAA, Nat. Economists Club. Republican. Home: 5903 Mount Eagle Dr Apt 1418 Alexandria VA 22303-2532 Office: Dept of Transp Environment, Engery, & Safety 400 7th St SW Washington DC 20590-0001

TRILLING, GEORGE HENRY, physicist, educator; b. Bialystok, Poland, Sept. 18, 1930; came to U.S., 1941; s. Max and Eugenie (Walfisz) T.; m. Madeleine Alice Monic, June 26, 1955; children: Stephen, Yvonne, David. BS, Calif. Inst. Tech., Pasadena, 1951, PhD, 1955. Research fellow Calif. Inst. Tech., Pasadena, 1955-56; Fulbright post-doctoral fellow Ecole Polytechnique, Paris, 1956-57; asst. to assoc. prof. U. Mich., Ann Arbor, 1957-60; assoc. to prof. dept. physics U. Calif., Berkeley, 1960—. Fellow Am. Phys. Soc., Am. Acad. Arts and Scis.; mem. NAS. Research in high energy physics. Office: Lawrence Berkeley Lab Berkeley CA 94720

TRILLING, HELEN REGINA, lawyer; b. Boston, May 13, 1950; d. Charles Alexander and A. Lillian Trilling. AB magna cum laude, Radcliffe Coll., 1973; JD, Harvard U., 1976. Bar: Mass. 1977, U.S. Dist. Ct. Mass. 1978, U.S. Supreme Ct. 1980, D.C. 1984, U.S. Ct. Appeals (10th cir.) 1984. Asst. gen. counsel Blue Cross/Blue Shield, Boston, 1976-79; sp. asst. to gen. counsel HHS, Washington, 1979-83; assoc. Hogan & Hartson, Washington, 1983-86, ptnr., 1987—. Mem. ABA (health law forum com.), Nat. Health Lawyers Assn., Women and Health Roundtable, Women's Legal Def. Fund, Wash. Council Lawyers.

TRILLING, LEON, aeronautical engineering educator; b. Bialystok, Poland, July 15, 1924; came to U.S., 1940, naturalized, 1946; s. Oswald and Regina (Zakhejm) T.; m. Edna Yuval, Feb. 17, 1946; children: Alex R., Roger S. B.S., Calif. Inst. Tech., 1944, M.S., 1946, Ph.D., 1948. Research fellow Calif. Inst. Tech., 1948- 50; Fulbright scholar U. Paris, 1950-51, vis. prof., 1963-64; mem. faculty MIT, Cambridge, 1951—, prof. aeros. and astronautics, 1962-94, prof. emeritus, 1994—, mem. coun. on primary and secondary edn., 1992—; mem. Program in Sci. Tech. and Society, Engring. Edn. Mission to Soviet Union, 1958; vis. prof. U. Delft Tech. U., 1974-75; vis. prof. engring. Carleton Coll., 1987;. Pres. Met. Com. Ednl. Opportunity, 1967-70, Council for Understanding of Tech. in Human Affairs, 1984—. Guggenheim fellow, 1963-64. Fellow AAAS. Home: 180 Beacon St Boston MA 02116-1455 Office: MIT 77 Massachusetts Ave Cambridge MA 02139-3594

TRIM, CYNTHIA MARY, veterinarian, educator; b. Uxbridge, Eng., Apr. 12, 1947; came to U.S., 1976; d. Ettrick and Katherine Theodocia (Bradburne) T.; m. James Neil Moore, Sept. 2, 1979; children: Breanna Kathleen, Jamianne Marie. B Vet. Sci., U. Liverpool (Eng.), 1970. Rsch. asst. Coll. Medicine, U. Cambridge (Eng.), 1970-72; pvt. practice Nixon and Ptnrs., Bury St. Edmunds, Eng., 1972-74; asst. prof. Ont. Vet. Coll., U. Guelph (Can.), 1974-76, U. Ill., Urbana, 1976-77; assoc. prof. U. Mo., Columbia, 1977-81; assoc. prof. U. Ga., Athens, 1981-85, prof., 1985—. Contbr. articles to profl. jours., chpts. to books. Mem. Royal Coll. Vet. Surgeons, Am. Vet Med. Assn., Am. Coll. Vet. Anesthesiologists (pres. 1985, diplomate). Episcopalian. Avocations: gardening, horseback riding. Office: Coll Vet Medicine U Ga Athens GA 30602

TRIM, DONALD ROY, consulting engineer; b. Saginaw, Mich., June 23, 1937; s. Roy E. and Agnes (Kontranowski) T.; m. Dorothy Mae Franek, Aug. 11, 1962; children—Jeffrey D., Gregory S., Christopher M. B.S. in Civil Engring., U. Mich., 1959. Registered profl. engr., Mich., Ohio, Fla.; registered land surveyor, Mich. Engr., Francis Engring., Saginaw, 1959-64, Edwin M. Orr, Inc., Dearborn, Mich., 1964-66; pres. Wade-Trim Group, Plymouth, Mich., 1966—; pres. Wade-Trim Inc., Tampa, Fla., 1984—. Vice pres. Plymouth Canton Basketball Assn., 1980-84; bd. govs. Greater Mich. Found., Lansing, 1983-85. Mem. Nat. Soc. Profl. Engrs., Cons. Engrs. Council Mich. (dir. 1972-73, pres. 1983-84), Am. Cons. Engrs. Council (v.p. 1986-88), Am. Waterworks Assn. Roman Catholic. Office: Wade-Trim Group PO Box 701428 Plymouth MI 48170-0964

TRIMBLE, CHARLES R., electronics executive; b. 1941. BS in Engring. Calif. Inst. Tech., 1963, MS in Elec. Engring., 1964. Mgr. integrated circuit rsch. and devel. Hewlett-Packard Co., Santa Clara, Calif., 1964-78; pres., CEO Trimble Navigation Ltd., Sunnyvale, Calif., 1978—. Recipient Engr. Gen. Aviation award Am. Inst. Aeronautics and Astronautics, 1994. Office: Trimble Navigation Limited 585 N Mary Ave Sunnyvale CA 94086

TRIMBLE, GEORGE SIMPSON, industrial executive; b. Phila., Oct. 12, 1915; s. George Simpson and Edna Mae (Mytinger) T.; m. Janet Anna Bogue, Apr. 15, 1939; children: Robert Bogue, Frank George. S.B., Mass. Inst. Tech., 1936. With The Martin Co., Balt., 1937-67; successively draftsman, design engr., chief fluid dynamics, mgr. aerodynamics, mgr. advanced design, v.p. advanced design The Martin Co., 1937-55, v.p. engring., 1955-60, v.p. advanced programs, 1960-67; dir. Advanced Manned Missions Program, NASA, Washington, 1967; dep. dir. Johnson Spacecraft Center, Houston, 1967-69; pres., dir. Bunker Ramo Corp., Oak Brook, Ill., 1970-80; dir. Richardson Co., Des Plaines, Ill., 1978-82, Martin Marietta Corp., 1970-78; owner, pres. Carefree Engine Co. (Ariz.), 1981—; cons. Sci. Adv. Bd. Aero Vehicle Panel, 1959-61, Office Dir. Def., Research and Engr. ing. Trustee Devereux Found., 1968—, chmn. bd. trustees, 1976-79. Fellow AIAA; mem. Tau Beta Pi. Home: PO Box 1355 Carefree AZ 85377-1355 Office: Carefree Engine Co Carefree AZ 83577

TRIMBLE, JAMES T., JR., federal judge; b. Bunkie, La., Sept. 13, 1932; s. James T. Sr. and Mabel (McNabb) T.; m. Murel Elise Biles, Aug. 18, 1956; children: Lise Ann Reed, Mary Olive Beacham, Martha McNabb Elliott, Sarah Palmer Trimble. Attended, U. Southwestern La. (formerly Southwestern La. Inst.), 1950-52; BA in Law, La. State U., 1955, JD, 1956. Bar: La. 1956. With Gist, Murchison & Gist (now Gist, Methvin, Hughes & Mun-

sterman), 1959-78, Trimble, Percy, Smith, Wilson, Foote, Walker & Honeycutt, 1979-86; U.S. magistrate U.S. Dist. Ct. (we. dist.) La., 1986-91, judge, 1991—. Lt. USAF, 1956-59. Mem. Fed. Judges Assn., Southwest La. Bar Assn., La. Bar Assn., La. Bar Found. Avocations: jogging, gardening, tennis. Office: 611 Broad St Ste 237 Lake Charles LA 70601

TRIMBLE, JOHN LEONARD, sensor psychophysicist, biomedical engineer; b. Detroit, Feb. 27, 1944. BS, U. Ill., 1968; PhD in Physiology and Bioengineering, U. Ill. Med. Ctr., 1972. Rsch. assoc., asst. prof. Eye Rsch. Labs., U. Chgo., 1972-79, engring. dir., 1979-83; dir. rehab. R&D ctr. Hines (Ill.) VA Hosp., 1983—; pres. IMT, Inc., 1984—; vis. assoc. biology Calif. Inst. Tech., 1977-79; cons. Nat. Ctr. Health Care Tech., NIH, 1980—, office productivity, tech. and innovation and ctr. utilization fed. tech. U.S. Dept. Commerce, 1984—; clin. assoc. prof. dept. orthopedic surgery Loyola Med. Sch., 1983—; adj. assoc. prof. Pritzker Inst. Med. Engring., 1984—. Mem. AAAS, Inst. Elec. and Electronics Engrs., Soc. Neuroscience, Assn. Rsch. Vision and Ophthalmology, Sigma Xi. Achievements include research on neural modeling, biological signal processing, intelligent systems. Office: Hines VA Hosp Rehab R&D Ctr PO Box 20 Hines IL 60141-0020

TRIMBLE, MARIAN ALICE EDDY, mutual fund executive; b. Cleve., Dec. 23, 1933; d. Gilbert H. and Velma O. (Frech) Eddy. B.A., Wittenberg U., Springfield, Ohio, 1955. With Nationwide Fin. Services Inc., Columbus, Ohio, 1957—, v.p., treas., 1973-78, gen. mgr., 1978—, pres., 1981—; also pres. Nationwide Investors Svcs. Inc.; treas. Nationwide Investing Found., Columbus, 1973—, Nationwide Investing Found. II, Nationwide Separate Account Trust. Bd. dirs. Pvt. Industry Council of Columbus and Franklin County, 1981—. Named Woman of Year Capitol City Bus. and Profl. Women's Club, 1980. Woman of Distinction Seal of Ohio Girl Scouts U.S., 1992; named to Ohio Women's Hall of Fame, 1984. Mem. Investment Co. Inst. (bd. govs.), Fin. Execs. Inst. (past pres., bd. dirs. Ctrl. Ohio chpt.), Treasurers Club (past pres.), Contrs. Club. Office: One Nationwide Plz Columbus OH 43216

TRIMBLE, PAUL JOSEPH, lawyer; b. Springfield, Mass., Oct. 9, 1930; s. Peter Paul and Bernnese (Myrick) T.; m. Suzanne Hrudka; children: Troy, Derrick, Andrew. B.A., Am. Internat. U., Springfield, Mass., 1952; LL.B. U. Tex., Austin, 1955. Bar: Calif., Tex., Ill., Alaska. Counsel Mobil Oil Corp., Joliet, Ill., 1964-72; assoc. counsel Fluor Corp., Irvine, Calif., 1972-73, corp. counsel, 1973-74, sr. corp. counsel, 1974, asst. gen. counsel, 1974-80, gen. counsel, 1980-82, sr. v.p., gen. counsel, 1982—, sr. v.p. law, gen. counsel, 1984—, corp. sec., 1992—. Mem. ABA, Calif. Bar Assn., Tex. Bar Assn., Ill. Bar Assn., Alaska Bar Assn. Republican.

TRIMBLE, PHILLIP RICHARD, law educator; b. Springfield, Ohio, Nov. 12, 1937; s. Melvin R. and Dorothy (Lang) T.; m. Stephanie Gardner, July 20, 1963 (div. 1977); children: John, William. BA, Ohio U., 1958; MA, Tufts U., 1959; JD, Harvard U., 1963. Bar: NY 1964. Legal writing instr. U. Calif., Berkeley, 1963-64; assoc. Cravath, Swaine & Moore, N.Y.C., 1964-70; staff mem. senate fgn. rels. com. Dept. State, Washington, 1971-72, asst. legal adviser, 1973-78; counsel to the mayor N.Y.C., 1978, dep. mayor, 1979; U.S. ambassador Nepal, 1980-81; prof. law UCLA, 1981—; mem. exec. com. Asia Soc. So. Calif. Ctr., L.A., 1981—; vis. prof. law Stanford U., 1988-89, U. Mich. 1995—; U.S. panelist under U.S.-Can. Free Trade Agreement; cons. ACDA, 1989-92. Bd. editors Am. Jour. Internat. Law. Fellow Explorers Club; mem. Am. Soc. Internat. Law, Am. Alpine Club (bd. dirs. 1978-87). Democrat. Avocation: mountaineering. Office: UCLA Law Sch 405 Hilgard Ave Los Angeles CA 90024-1301

TRIMBLE, PRESTON ALBERT, retired judge; b. Salina, Okla., Aug. 27, 1930; s. James Albert and Winnie Louella (Walker) T.; m. Patricia Ann Beadle; children: Todd, Beth, Amy. B.A., U. Okla., 1956, LL.B., 1960. Bar: Okla. 1960. Practice law, 1960; asst. county atty. Cleveland County, Okla., 1960-62; county atty., 1962-67, dist. atty., 1967-79, dist. judge, 1979-91; spl. instr. S.W. Center Law Enforcement Edn.; cons. prosecution mgmt. Mem. Jud. Council Okla.; chmn. Okla. Corrections Workshop; mem. planning com. Nat. Inst. Crime and Delinquency; mem. com. on multi-agy. problems in criminal justice Appellate Judges Conf. Bd. dirs. Okla. U. Crisis Ctr., 1970—, ARC, Lake Murray Conservation Assn.; trustee Nat. Assn. Pretrial Svc. Agys. Resource Ctr., Sarkeys Found., 1994—. With USNR, 1948-52; col. USAFR. Mem. Okla., Cleveland County bar assns., Nat. Dist. Attys. Assn. (past pres.), Okla. Dist. Attys. Assn. (past pres.), Nat. Coll. Dist. Attys. (bd. regents), Am. Legion. Democrat. Methodist. Club: Lion. Home: 1886 Trailview Dr Norman OK 73072-6655 Office: 231 S Peters Ave Norman OK 73069-6035 An elected public official must remember that the people own his position and he only holds it in trust for them.

TRIMBLE, STANLEY WAYNE, hydrology and geography educator; b. Columbia, Tenn., Dec. 18, 1940; s. Stanley Drake and Clara Faye (Smith) T.; m. Alice Erle Gunn, Aug. 16, 1964; children: Alicia Anne, Jennifer Lusanne. BS, U. North Ala., 1964; MA, U. Ga., 1970, PhD, 1973. Asst. prof. hydrology and geography U. Wis., Milw., 1972-75; from assoc. prof. to prof. UCLA, 1975—; vis. asst. prof. U. Chgo., 1978, vis. assoc. prof., 1981, vis. prof. environ. geography, 1990—; vis. lectr. U. London, 1985; hydrologist U.S. Geol. Survey, 1974-84; vis. prof. U. Vienna, 1994; 1st lectureship Brit. Geomorphological Rsch. Group, Durham, Eng., 1994; vis. rsch. lectr. Oxford U., 1995; Fulbright scholar in U.K., 1995; vis. fellow Keble Coll., Oxford U., 1995. Author: Culturally Accelerated Sedimentation on the Middle Georgia Piedmont, 1971, Man-Induced Erosion on the Southern Piedmont, 1700-1970, 1974, Soil Conservation and the Reduction, 1982, Sediment Characteristics of Tennesee Streams, 1984. Served to 1st lt. U.S. Army, 1963-65. Fulbright Fellow, 1995; Grantee U.S. Geol. Survey, Washington, 1974-79, Wis. Dept. Nat. Resources, Madison, 1978, 82, 93, 94, NSF, Washington, 1976, Agrl. Research Service of USDA, Washington, 1972, Nat. Geographic Soc., 1993. Mem. Assn. Am. Geographers, Am. Geophys. Union, Soil Conservation Soc. Am., Brit. Geomorphol. Rsch. Group, Sigma Xi. Republican. Avocations: historic houses, documentation and restoration. Office: UCLA Dept Geography 405 Hilgard Ave Los Angeles CA 90024-1301

TRIMBLE, THOMAS JAMES, utility company executive, lawyer; b. Carters Creek, Tenn., Sept. 3, 1931; s. John Elijah and Mittie (Rountree) T.; m. Glenna Kay Jones, Sept. 3, 1957; children: James Jefferson, Julie Kay. BA, David Lipscomb U., 1953; JD, Vanderbilt U., 1956; LLM, NYU, 1959. Bar: Tenn. 1956, Ariz. 1961, U.S. Dist. Ct. Ariz. 1961, U.S. Dist. Ct. D.C. 1963, U.S. Ct. Appeals (10th cir.) 1971, U.S. Supreme Ct. 1972, U.S. Ct. Appeals (9th cir.) 1975. From assoc. to ptnr. Jennings, Strouss & Salmon, Phoenix, 1960-85, mng. ptnr., 1985-87; sr. v.p., gen. counsel, corp. sec. S.W. Gas Corp., Las Vegas, Nev., 1987—, gen. counsel, 1987-92; corp. sec. Primerit Bank, 1990-92, pres., 1994—; exec. v.p., bd. dirs. Energy Ins. (Bermuda) Ltd., 1992-94; pres.; bd. dirs. Energy Ins. Mut. Ltd., vice chmn., 1992-94, chmn., 1994—. Mem. editorial bd. Vanderbilt U. Law Rev., 1954-56. Mem. Pepperdine U. Bd. Regents, Malibu, Calif., 1981—, sec., 1982—, mem. exec. com., 1982-89; bd. visitors Pepperdine Sch. Law, Malibu; pres. Big Sisters Ariz., Phoenix, 1975, bd. dirs., 1979-82; chmn. Sunnydale Children's Home, Phoenix, 1966-69, bd. dirs., 1965-75; pres. Clearwater Hills Improvement Assn., Phoenix, 1977-79, bd. dirs., 1975-80; trustee Nev. Sch. of Arts, 1988-92, chmn., 1989-90. 1st lt. JAGC, USAF, 1957-60. Fellow Ariz. Bar Found. (founding); mem. ABA, Ariz. Bar Assn. (editorial bd. Jour. 1975-80), Am. Gas. Assn. (legal sect. mng. com. 1987—), Order of Coif, Phi Delta Phi. Republican. Mem. Ch. Christ. Club: Spanish Trail Country (Las Vegas). Lodge: Kiwanis (pres. Phoenix 1972-73). Home: 5104 Turnberry Ln Las Vegas NV 89113-1394 Office: SW Gas Corp PO Box 98510 5241 Spring Mountain Rd Las Vegas NV 89150-8510

TRIMBLE, VANCE HENRY, retired newspaper editor; b. Harrison, Ark., July 6, 1913; s. Guy L. and Josephine (Crump) T.; m. Elzene Miller, Jan. 9, 1932; 1 dau., Carol Ann. Student pub. schs., Wewoka, Okla. Cub reporter Okemah (Okla.) Daily Leader, 1928; worked various newspapers in Okmulgee, Muskogee, Tulsa and, Okla.; successively reporter, rewrite man, city editor Houston Press, 1939-50, mng. editor, 1950-55; news editor Scripps-Howard Newspaper Alliance, Washington, 1955-63; editor Ky. Post and Times-Star, Covington, 1963-79. Author: The Uncertain Miracle, 1974, Sam M. Walton, 1990, (biography) E.W. Scripps, 1992, Frederick Smith of Federal Express, 1993; editor: Scripps-Howard Handbook, 1981; co-author Happy Chandler autobiography, 1989. Trustee Scripps-Howard Found.,

1974-79. Recipient Pulitzer prize for nat. reporting, 1960, Raymond Clapper award, 1960, Sigma Delta Chi award for disting. Washington correspondence, 1960, Frank Luther Mott award for journalism book rsch. U. Mo., 1993; named to Okla. Journalism Hall of Fame, 1974. Mem. Am. Soc. Newspaper Editors. Baptist. Clubs: Nat. Press (Washington); Press (Houston); Cincinnati, Ft. Mitchell Country. Home: 1013 Sunset Rd Covington KY 41011-1168

TRIMBLE, WILLIAM CATTELL, JR., lawyer; b. Buenos Aires, Argentina, Feb. 7, 1935; s. William Cattell and Nancy Gordon (Carroll) T.; m. Barbara Janney, June 19, 1960; children: William C., Margery M. Kennelly. A.B., Princeton U., 1958; LL.B., U. Md., 1964. Bar: Md. 1965. With firm Ober, Grimes & Shriver, Balt., 1965-87, ptnr., 1970-87, mng. ptnr., 1973-77; counsel Semmes, Bowen & Semmes, Balt., 1987—; mem. Gov.'s Commn. to Revise Annotated Code of Md., 1975-83. Pres. bd. trustees Valley Sch., 1968-73; trustee Garrison Forest Sch., 1975-95, Gilman Sch. 1980-84; hon. consul of The Netherlands, 1986—. Lt. USNR, 1958-61. Mem. Am., Md., Balt. bar assns. Episcopalian. Clubs: Colonial (Princeton); Md, Greenspring Valley Hunt, Soc. of Cin. Home: 409 Chattolanee Hill Rd Owings Mills MD 21117-4318 Office: 17th Fl 250 W Pratt St Baltimore MD 21201

TRIMMER, HAROLD SHARP, JR., lawyer, international telecommunications consultant; b. Somerville, N.J., July 27, 1938; s. Harold Sharp and Mary Elizabeth (Knox) T. B.A., Wesleyan U., 1960; J.D., Harvard U., 1963. Instr. law UCLA, 1963-64; Congl. fellow Am. Polit. Sci. Assn., Washington, 1964-65; assoc. Royall, Koegel & Rogers, Washington and N.Y.C., 1965-66, McCutchen, Doyle, Brown & Enersen, San Francisco, 1966-69; with GSA, Washington, 1969-75; exec. asst. to adminstr. GSA, 1969-70, asst. adminstr., 1970-72, commr. automated data and telecommunications, 1972-73, assoc. adminstr. fed. mgmt. policy, 1973, gen. counsel, 1974-75; sec., gen. counsel Garfinckel, Brooks Bros., Miller & Rhoads, Inc., Washington, 1976-82, v.p., 1979-82; v.p. internat. MCI Communications Corp., Washington, 1982-83, v.p. regulatory policy, 1983-84, v.p. fin. and adminstrn. M.A. div., 1984-86, v.p. govt. systems, 1986-87; pres. Pacific div. MCI Communications Corp., San Francisco, 1987-89, sr. v.p. internat. devel., 1990-91; cons. internat. communications, 1991—. Trustee World Affairs Council No. Calif., 1969-70, Wesleyan U., 1971-74. George F. Baker scholar. Mem. State Bar Calif., Phi Beta Kappa. Home: 169 Filbert Ave Sausalito CA 94965-1846

TRIMMIER, ROSCOE, JR., lawyer; b. Charlotte, N.C., July 22, 1944; s. Roscoe and Susie Elizabeth (Stitt) T.; divorced; 1 child, Leigh Snowden. AB, Harvard U., 1971, JD, 1974. Bar: Mass. 1974, U.S. Dist. Ct. Mass. 1975, U.S. Ct. Appeals (1st cir.) 1975, U.S. Supreme Ct. 1979, U.S. Claims Ct. 1983. Assoc. Ropes & Gray, Boston, 1974-83, ptnr., 1983—; mem. hearing com. Bd. Bar Overseers 1983-89; bd. dirs. v.p. Family Counseling & Guidance Ctr., Inc., Boston, 1980-93; overseer Mus. of Sci., 1981-93; mem. exec. com. Jud. Nominating Commn., 1991—; corp. mem. Mass. Gen. Hosp., 1992—; overseer N.E Med. Ctr. Hosps., 1992—. Served to 1st lt. U.S. Army, 1965-68. Fellow Am. Bar Found. (life), Mass. Bar Found. (life); mem. ABA, Mass. Bar Assn., Boston Bar Assn., Mass. Soc. for Prevention of Cruelty to Children, Mass. Black Lawyers Assn. (life). Home: 1265 Beacon St Brookline MA 02146-5243 Office: Ropes & Gray 1 International Pl Boston MA 02110-2600

TRINH, VICTOR, small business owner; b. Vientiane, Laos, Apr. 7, 1941; came to U.S., 1975; s. Thu and Mao (Nguyen) T.; m. Tuyet Mai Nguyen, Jan. 19, 1972; children: Nancy H., Wiliam Q. Grad. high sch., Vientiane. Electronic assembler Anilam Electronics, Miami, Fla., 1978-80; owner Kim-Do Food, Pitts., 1981-85, Jensen Food Mart, Houston, 1986—; pub. Vic Pub., Houston, 1993—. Author: Student Assignments Notebook, 1993. Avocations: biking, swimming. Office: 7202 Jensen Dr Houston TX 77093-8705

TRINKAUS, JOHN PHILIP, cell and developmental biologist; b. Rockville Centre, N.Y., May 23, 1918; s. Charles Edward and Fransiska Magdalena (Krueger) T.; m. Madeleine Francine Marguerite Bazin, Oct. 6, 1963; children: Gregor, Tanya, Erik. B.A. with honors and high distinction in Biology, Wesleyan U., Middletown, Conn., 1940; M.A. (Cramer fellow in genetics), Columbia U., 1941; Ph.D., Johns Hopkins U., 1948. Mem. faculty Yale U., New Haven, 1948—; prof. cell and devel. biology Yale U., 1964—; dir. grad. studies in biology, 1965, master of Branford Coll., 1966-73, also dir. undergrad. studies in biology, prof. emeritus biology, 1988—, sr. rsch. scientist, 1988—; chmn. Gordon Rsch. Conf. on Cell Contact and Movement, 1979; mem. staff embryology course Woods Hole (Mass.) Marine Biol. Lab., 1953-57, 78, trustee, 1991—; mem. space biology adv. panel NASA, 1976-79; lectr. internat. symposia, including Internat. Inst. Embryology, Moscow, 1969, Ciba, London, 1972, Devl. Biol Fishes, Tampa, 1979, 500th anniversary U. Uppsala, Sweden, 1977, Conf. on Malignancy, Keystone, Colo., 1979, Conf. on Cell Behaviour, London, 1982 and Oxford, 1987, Gastrulation, Louisville, 1982, Biol. Fundulus, Phila., 1983, Conf. Cell Traffic, Zurich, 1984, Cellular Basis of Morphogenesis, Woods Hole, 1988, Experimental Embryology of Aquatic Plants and Animals, Banyuls-sur-Mer, 1989, Gastrulation: Movements, Patterns and Molecules, Bodega Bay, 1990, Cytoskeleton, in Devel. Biology, Kingston, Ont., 1991, Gastrulation, Brighton, U.K., 1992, Devl. and Genetics of Zebrafish, Cold Spring Harbor, 1994, Soc. Devel. Biology, La Jolla, 1995. Author: Cells into Organs-The Forces that Shape the Embryo, 1969, 2d rev. edit., 1984, On the Mechanism of Metazoan Cell Movements, 1976; also articles on cell motility, invasiveness, morphogenesis, gastrulation and differentiation; assoc. editor: Jour. Exptl. Zoology, 1964-68. Served to capt. USAAF, 1942-46. Recipient citation for distinction in scholarship and teaching Wesleyan U., 1960; John Simon Guggenheim fellow Coll. de France, 1959-60; NSF grantee, 1952-76; NIH grantee, 1974—; Merit award NIH, 1987-96. Mem. Am. Soc. Zoologists, Am. Soc. Cell Biology, Am. Soc. Developmental Biology (Edwin Grant Conklin medal 1995), Internat. Inst. Embryology, ACLU, Phi Beta Kappa, Sigma Xi. Clubs: Yale (N.Y.C.); Mory's. Home: Moose Hill Rd Guilford CT 06437-2356 Office: Osborn Meml Lab Yale Univ Dept Biology New Haven CT 06520

TRIOLO, PETER, advertising agency executive, marketing educator, consultant; b. N.Y.C., Feb. 20, 1927; s. Antonino and Cira T.; m. Audrey Sullivan, Aug. 7, 1954; children—Stuart, Bruce, Ellen, Leslie. A.B., Adelphi U., Garden City, N.Y., 1952; exec. program, Columbia U. Grad. Sch. Bus., 1966. Vice pres. Ogilvy & Mather, Inc., N.Y.C., 1952-64; sr. v.p. Ketchum, MacLeod & Grove Inc., Pitts. and N.Y.C., 1964-68; founder, exec. v.p. Marketronics Inc., N.Y.C., 1968-72; chief adminstrv. officer Rosenfeld, Sirowitz & Lawson Inc., N.Y.C., 1972-76; sr. v.p. media dir. William Esty Co., Inc., N.Y.C., 1976-87; cons. Internat. Exec. Svc. Corps, Stamford, Conn., 1987—; adj. prof. mktg. Baruch Coll., City U. N.Y., 1980-86, Fordham U., N.Y.C., 1987—. Guest editor: Mktg. and Media Decisions, 1967. Served with USAAF, 1945-47. Mem. Assn. Nat. Advertisers (TV workshops), Advt. Age Media Workshops Faculty, Mktg. and Media Decisions Faculty.

TRIPATHY, SUKANT KISHORE, chemistry educator; b. Chakradharpur, Bihar, India, Aug. 4, 1952; came to U.S., 1976; s. Jyotish C. and Usha (Pani) T.; m. Susan Thomson, Sept. 5, 1981; children: Sheila, Aneil. MS, I.I.T. Kharagpur, 1974; PhD, Case Western Res. U., 1981. Tech. staff mem. GTE Labs., Waltham, Mass., 1981-83; rsch. mgr. GTE Labs., Waltham, 1983-86; assoc. prof. chemistry U. Lowell, Mass., 1986-87; prof. chemistry U. Lowell, 1987—; dir. ctr. advanced materials U. Mass., Lowell, 1992-94, vice chancellor for acad. affairs, 1994—; dir. Molecular Technologies, Inc., Lowell, 1997—. Contbr. over 200 articles to profl. jours. Mem. AAAS, Am. Chem. Soc. (Carl S. Marvel Creative Polymer Chemistry award 1993), Am. Phys. Soc., Sigma Xi, MRS, SPE. Achievements include 14 patents. Home: 8 Northbriar Rd Acton MA 01720-5826 Office: U Mass Ctr for Advanced Materials 1 University Ave Lowell MA 01854

TRIPLEHORN, CHARLES A., entomology educator, insects curator; b. Bluffton, Ohio, Oct. 27, 1927; s. Murray E. and Alice Irene (Lora) T.; m. Wanda Elaine Neiswander, June 12, 1949 (dec. Nov. 1985); children: Bradley Alyn, Bruce Wayne; m. Linda Sue Parsons, July 11, 1987. B.sc., Ohio State U., 1949, M.S., 1952; Ph.D., Cornell U., 1957. Asst. prof. entomology U. Del., Newark, 1952-54; teaching assoc. entomology Cornell U., Ithaca, N.Y.,

1954-57; asst. prof. entomology Ohio Agri. Research and Devel. Ctr., Wooster, Ohio, 1957-61; asst. prof. entomology Ohio State U., Columbus, 1961-62, assoc. prof. entomology, 1962-66, prof. entomology, 1966-92, prof. emeritus, 1992—; econ. entomologist U.S. AID/Brazil, Piracicaba, Sao Paulo, 1964-66; vis. curator Can. Nat. Collection, Ottawa, Ont., 1977. Co-author: Introduction to the Study of Insects, 6th edit., 1989. Cubmaster Boy Scouts Am., Wooster, Ohio, 1959-60, scoutmaster, Columbus, 1971-72; football coach Upper Arlington Football Assn., Ohio, 1968-71. Grantee Am. Philos. Soc., 1963, NSF, 1979, 85. Mem. Entomol. Soc. Am. (pres. 1985), Coleopterists Soc. (pres. 1976), Royal Entomol. Soc. London, Entomol. Soc. Washington, Sigma Xi, Gamma Sigma Delta. Republican. Methodist. Club: Wheaton (pres.). Avocations: sports; music; reading; writing. Home: 3943 Medford Sq Hilliard OH 43026-2219 Office: Mus Biol Diversity Div Insects 1315 Kinnear Rd Columbus OH 43212-1157

TRIPLETT, ARLENE ANN, travel company executive; b. Portland, Oreg., Jan. 21, 1942; d. Vincent Michael and Lorraine Catherine (Starr) Jakovich; m. William Karrol Triplett, Jan. 27, 1962; children: Stephen Michael, Patricia Ann. B.A. in Bus. Adminstrn., U. Calif., Berkeley, 1963. Budgets and reports analyst Cutter Labs., Berkeley, 1963-66; controller Citizens for Reagan, 1975-76; dir. adminstrn. Republican. Nat. Com., 1977-80; asst. sec. Dept. Commerce, Washington, 1981-83; assoc. dir. mgmt. Office Mgmt. and Budget, Exec. Office of Pres., Washington, 1983-85; prin. assoc. McManis Assocs., Inc., 1985-87, v.p., 1987-89, sr. v.p., 1989-93; v.p. Am. Tours International., Inc., L.A., 1993—, exec. v.p., 1994—. Roman Catholic. Office: Am Tours Internat Inc 6053 W Century Blvd Los Angeles CA 90045-6430

TRIPLETT, E. EUGENE, editor; b. LaJolla, Calif., Mar. 12, 1949; s. Erbin Eugene Triplett and Marjorie Ann (Aldrich) Heath; m. Vannie Carol Crow, July 19, 1968; 1 child, Aaron Eugene. BA in Journalism, Ctrl. State U., 1975. Reporter, columnist The Okla. Jour., Oklahoma City, 1976-80; entertainment editor The Daily Oklahoman, Oklahoma City, 1981-85, asst. city editor, 1985-89, city editor, 1989—. Comm. com. Okla. Heart Assn., 1989-92. With U.S. Army, 1969-71, Vietnam. Recipient 1st. Place Feature Writing award Soc. Profl. Journalist, 1987, 2nd. Place Feature Writing award AP/One, 1988. Mem. AP/Okla. News Exec. (pres.-elect 1994-95, pres. 1995-96). Democrat. Avocations: collecting recorded music, feature films, vintage TV shows. Home: 2821 Tealwood Dr Oklahoma City OK 73120 Office: The Daily Oklahoman 9000 N Broadway Oklahoma City OK 73114

TRIPLETT, KELLY B., chemist; b. Cin., BA, Northwestern U., 1968; PhD in Chemistry, U. Mich., 1974. Rsch. assoc. Mich. State U., 1974-76; rsch. chemist Stauffer Chem. Co., Dobbs Ferry, N.Y., 1976-78, supr., 1978-82, tech. mgr., 1982-84, bus. mgr., 1984-87; program mgr., bus. mgr. Akzo Chem. Inc., Dobbs Ferry, N.Y., 1987-90, mgr. rsch. ctr., 1990—, dir. rsch., 1992—. Mem. Am. Ceramic Soc., Industry Rsch. Inst. Achievements include development of new research and development methodologies; research in new polymerization products and process, organometallics and transition metal chemistries; investigation of chemical routes to advanced ceramics. Office: Akzo Nobel Chems Inc 1 Livingstone Ave Dobbs Ferry NY 10522

TRIPLETT, LOREN O., religious organization administrator; b. San Jose, Calif., July 5, 1926; m. Mildred Triplett; children: Donald, Debora, Marcus, Timothy. Grad., Bethany Bible Coll., 1946; student, Ctrl. Bible Coll., Evangel Coll., Dade Jr. Coll. Ordained min. Assemblies of God, 1950. Pastor various orgns., Oreg. and Nebr., 1947-54; missionary Life Pubs., Nicaragua, 1954-73; field dir. Divsn. Fgn. Ministries, Springfield, Mo., 1973-89, exec. dir., 1990—. Contbr. articles to profl. jours. Office: Assemblies of God 1445 N Boonville Ave Springfield MO 65802-1805

TRIPODI, LOUIS ANTHONY, advertising agency executive; b. N.Y.C., July 7, 1931; m. Mary Gail Ennis; children: Pascal, William, Louis, James, Stephen, Michela, Gian, Christian, Blanid, Theresa, Michael. B.A., Bklyn. Coll., 1952. Dir. corp. pub. relations Kenyon & Eckhardt, N.Y.C., 1965-68; sr. v.p., corp. dir. pub. relations Needham Harper Worldwide, N.Y.C., 1968-87; exec. v.p., corp. dir. pub. affairs DDB Needham Worldwide, N.Y.C., 1987—. Mem. ASCAP, Am. Assn. Advt. Agys. (chmn. pub. relations com. 1982-83), Am. Advt. Fedn. (chmn. pub. relations com.). Home: 565 Kiowa Dr Franklin Lakes NJ 07417-1208 Office: DDB Needham Worldwide Inc 437 Madison Ave New York NY 10022-7001

TRIPP, DAVID RICHARD, lawyer; b. Denver, May 27, 1946; m. Cathy A. Tripp, Sept. 4, 1982; children: Megan E., Jessica C. BA, Washburn U., 1968, JD, 1971; LLM, U. Mo., Kansas City, 1973. Bar: Kans. 1971, U.S. Dist. Ct. Kans. 1971, Mo. 1988. Dep. regional coun. U.S. EPA, Kansas City, 1971-82; regional counsel, 1982-88; ptnr., chair environ. law practice group Stinson, Mag & Fizzell, P.C., Kansas City, 1988—; adj. prof. Kansas U. Sch. Law, Lawrence, 1979-80. Mem. Kansas City Met. Bar Assn. (chair environ. law com. 1991-92). Office: Stinson Mag & Fizzell PC PO Box 419251 Ste 2800 Kansas City MO 64141

TRIPP, FREDERICK GERALD, investment advisor; b. Chgo., Oct. 1, 1936; s. Gerald F. and Kathryn Ann (Siebold) T.; m. Terry Anne Shull, Aug. 27, 1967; children: Mark A., Karin M., Tracy L. Clark, Tricia L., Patrick G. BS in Econs., Purdue U., 1958; MBA, Lehigh U., 1964; PhD, The Am. U., 1974. Sr. v.p. CRI, Inc., Rockville, Md., 1979-82, Security Pacific, Inc., Seattle, 1982-83; pres. Frederick G. Tripp & Assocs., Inc., Rockville, 1983—; instr. Troy State U., 1965-67, Am. U., 1975-77, Indsl. Coll. Armed Forces, 1975-80; mem. pres.'s coun. Investment Mgmt. and Rsch., Inc., 1985—. Pres. Doctoral Assn., The Am. U., 1973. Maj. U.S. Army, 1958-67 Vietnam. Mem. Internat. Assn. Fin. Planning, Investment Mgmt. Cons. Assn., Sigma Pi. Methodist. Avocations: skiing, boating, racquetball. Office: Frederick G Tripp & Assocs 3200 Tower Oaks Blvd # 300 Rockville MD 20852-4216

TRIPPE, KENNETH ALVIN BATTERSHILL, shipping industry executive; b. Kansas City, Mo., Jan. 3, 1933; s. Alvin C. and Blanche (Battershill) T.; m. Jane Muir Mitchell, June 11, 1955 (dec. Jan. 1988); children: Kenneth, Tracy, Robert; m. Josphine M. Kling, May, 12, 1990. B.S. in Bus. Adminstrn, Kans. U., 1955; LL.B., U. Mo., 1958; postdoctoral mgmt. program, MIT, 1972. Bar: Mo. 1958. With Miss. River Corp., St. Louis, 1958-68, asst. sec., 1958-64, sec., 1964-65, asst. to pres., 1965-68; asst. treas. Internat. Utilities Corp. (name IU Internat. Corp. 1973), Phila., 1968-69; asst. treas. corporate and internat. fin. Internat. Utilities Corp. (name IU Internat. Corp. 1973), 1970-72, v.p. treas., 1972-75; exec. v.p. dir. subs. Gotaas-Larsen Shipping Corp., 1975-77, pres., chief exec. officer, dir., 1977-82; founder, chmn. Cruiseship Info. Systems Inc., Coral Gables, Fla., 1982-91, Cruise Brokers Inc., 1990—, Trippe & Co., 1990—; v.p. fin. Kans. Gas & Electric Co., Wichita, 1969-70. Patentee cruise info. and booking data processing system. Mem. Mo. Bar Assn., Fisher Island Club, Union League N.Y.C., Phi Beta Phi, Sigma Chi. Republican. Episcopalian. Home: 2134 Fisher Island Dr Fisher Island FL 33109

TRIPPLEHORN, JEANNE, actress; b. Tulsa, Okla., 1963; d. Tommy and Suzanne (Ferguson) T. Student, Juilliard Sch. Appeared in (theatre off-Broadway) The Big Funk, 1990, 'Tis Pity She's A Whore, 1992; (film) Basic Instinct, 1991, The Firm, 1993, The Night We Never Met, 1993, Reality Bites, 1994, Waterworld, 1995. *

TRIPPY, DONALD R., illustrator; b. Denver, May 19, 1934; s. Fred Esta and Agnes Wilma (Van Duesen) T.; m. Mary Catherine Karnes, Jan. 27, 1961; children: Lynn Mary, Matthew Allen. Student, Colo. Inst. of Art, 1956-59. Illustrator tng. aids Ft. Carson Co., Colorado Springs, Colo., 1964-65; illustrator, supr. aerospace def. command USAF, Colorado Springs, 1965-74; illustrator, supr. graphics tactical fighter weapons ctr. USAF, Nellis AFB, Nev., 1974—, chief of graphics, 1979—. Mem. tech. skills adv. com. Clark County Sch. Dist., Nev., 1987-88; bd. dirs. Las Vegas (Nev.) Art Mus., 1987-88, Desert Sculptors, Las Vegas, 1988; mem. adv. bd. Clark County Community Coll., 1987-88. Democrat. LDS Ch. Avocation: sculptor with the lost wax method of bronze casting. Home: 4027 Maple Hill Rd Las Vegas NV 89115-0115 Office: USAF Tactical Fighter Weope Ctr Nellis AFB NV 89191 also: Las Vegas Art Mus 3333 W Washington Ave Las Vegas NV 89107-2255

TRISCO, ROBERT FREDERICK, church historian, educator; b. Chgo., Nov. 11, 1929; s. Richard E. and Harriet Rose (Hardt) T. B.A., St. Mary of Lake Sem., Mundelein, Ill., 1951; S.T.L., Pontifical Gregorian U., Rome, 1955, Hist. Eccl.D., 1962; LHD (hon.), Belmont Abbey Coll., 1992. Ordained priest Roman Catholic Ch., 1954. Mem. faculty Cath. U. Am., Washington, 1959—; prof. ch. history Cath. U. Am., 1975—; expert 2d Vatican Coun., 1962-65; pres. Am. subcom. Internat. Commn. Comparative Ch. History, 1978-80, assesseur, 1980—; mem. subcoms. Nat. Conf. Cath. Bishops, 1966-76, 87-92; mem. Pontifical Com. Hist. Scis., 1982—; hon. mem. Accademia di San Carlo (Milan), 1986—; hon. prelate (monsignor), 1992. Author: The Holy See and Nascent Church in the Middle Western U.S., 1826-1850, 1962, Bishops and Their Priests in the United States, 1988; co-author: A Guide to American Catholic History, 2d edit., 1982; editor: Catholics in America, 1976; editor CAth. Hist. Rev., 1963—; co-editor, contbr.: Studies in Catholic History in Honor of John Tracy Ellis, 1985; contbr. articles to profl. publs. Named Knight, Equestrian Order of the Holy Sepulchre of Jerusalem, 1993. Mem. Am. Soc. Ch. History (coun. 1980-82), Am. Cath. Hist. Assn. (exec. sec. 1961—, sec., treas. 1983—). Office: Cath U Am Mullen Library Rm 318 Washington DC 20064

TRISKA, JAN FRANCIS, retired political science educator; b. Prague, Czechoslovakia, Jan. 26, 1922; came to U.S., 1948, naturalized, 1955; s. Jan and Bozena (Kubiznak) T.; m. Carmel Lena Burastero, Aug. 26, 1951; children: Mark Lawrence, John William. J.U.D., Charles U., Prague, 1948; LL.M., Yale U., 1950, J.S.D., 1952; Ph.D., Harvard U. T. Co-dir. Soviet treaties Hoover Instn., Stanford, Calif., 1956-58; lectr. dept. polit. sci. U. Calif.-Berkeley, 1957-58; asst. prof. Cornell U., Ithaca, N.Y., 1958-60; assoc. prof. Stanford U., Calif., 1960-65, prof. polit. sci., 1965-89, assoc. chmn. dept., 1965-66, 68-69, 71-72, 74-75, emeritus prof. polit. sci., 1990—. Co-author: (with Slusser) The Theory, Law and Policy of Soviet Treaties, 1962, (with Finley) Soviet Foreign Policy, 1968, (with Cocks) Political Development and Political Change in Eastern Europe, 1977, (with Ike, North) The World of Superpowers, 1981, (with Gati) Blue Collar Workers in Eastern Europe, 1981, Dominant Powers and Subordinate States, 1986; bd. editors: East European Quar. Comparative Politics, Internat. Jour. Sociology, Jour. Comparative Politics, Studies in Comparative Communism, Soviet Statutes and Decisions, Documents in Communist Affairs. Recipient Rsch. award Ford Found., 1963-68, Josef Hlavka Commemorative medal Czechoslovak Acad. Scis., 1992, M.A. Comenius 1592-1992 Meml. medal Czechoslovak Pedagogical Mus., Prague, 1991; fellow NSF, 1971-72, Sen. Fulbright fellow, 1973-74, Woodrow Wilson fellow Internat. Ctr. for Scholars, 1980-81. Mem. Am. Polit. Sci. Assn. (sec. pres. conf. on communist studies 1970-76), Assn. Advancement Slavic Studies (bd. dirs. 1975-83), Am. Soc. Internat. Law (exec. coun. 1964-67), Czechoslovak Soc. Arts and Scis. (pres. 1978-80, 90-92), Inst. for Human Scis. Vienna (acting for Commn. European Communities, Brussels, com. experts on transformation of nat. higher edn. and rsch. system in Ctrl. Europe, Brussels 1991—). Democrat. Club: Fly Fishers (Palo Alto, Calif.). Home: 720 Vine St Menlo Park CA 94025-6154 Office: Stanford U Dept Polit Sci Stanford CA 94305

TRITES, DONALD GEORGE, human service foundation executive; b. Boston, Sept. 26, 1941; s. George Herman and Ada Christena (Patten) T.; m. Ruth Ann Lewis, June 15, 1963 (div. 1987); children: Sarah Jeanne, Amy Bray; m. Beverly Jean Baker, Apr. 8, 1989; children: Erica Christena, Philip Jameson Granville. AB, Colgate U., 1963; EdM, Tufts U., 1964; PhD, Syracuse U., 1976. Thcr., then chair history dept. Hamilton (Mass.)-Wenham Regionial High Sch., 1964-70; instr. div. ednl. studies Emory U., Atlanta, 1973-76; asst. prof. ednl. studies Emory U., 1976-81, vis. faculty, 1981-86; exec. dir. Ga. Advocacy Office, Inc., Atlanta, 1981-86, Devel. Svcs. Strafford County, Inc., Dover, N.H., 1986—; cons. in human svc. mgmt. and evaluation, U.S. and Europe, 1978—. Editor, author: The College and A Human Future, 1986; contbr. articles to profl.publs. Deacon, First Bapt. Ch., Melrose, Mass., 1968-69, Syracuse, N.Y., 1972-73; deacon, cons. Congl. Ch., Atlanta, 1984-86. Mem. Assn. for Persons with Severe Handicaps, Delta Upsilon. Democrat. Mem. United Ch. of Christ. Avocations: reading, gardening. Home: 42 Rollingwood Rd Eliot ME 03903-1508 Office: Devel Svcs Strafford County 1 Forum Ct Dover NH 03820

TRITT, TRAVIS, country music singer, songwriter; b. Marietta, Ga., 1963. Recording artist Warner Bros., 1990—. Albums include Country Club, 1990 (platinum), It's All About to Change, 1991 (platinum), T-R-O-U-B-L-E, 1992 (platnium), A Travis Tritt Christmas: Loving Time of the Year, 1992 (with Marty Stuart, Hank Williams Jr., Waylon Jennings) Ten Feet Tall and Bulletproof, 1994; #1 singles The Whiskey Ain't Workin' (Grammy award with Marty Stuart 1993), Here's a Quarter (Call Someone Who Cares), Anymore, Can I Trust You with my Heart; author: (with Michael Bane) 10 Foot Tall and Bullet Proof, 1994. Named Billboard's Top New Male Country Artist, 1990; recipient Horizon award Country Music Assn., 1991, (with Marty Stuart) Vocal Event of Yr. award Country Music Assn., 1992; inductee Grand Ole Opry, 1992. Office: Warner Bros Records 3300 Warner Blvd Burbank CA 91505-4694*

TRITTER, RICHARD PAUL, strategic consulting executive; b. Boston, Sept. 30, 1945; s. Herman Louis and Rose (Greenblatt) T.; 1 child, Melissa Rosanne; m. Marcy Lynn Kroll, June 17, 1984; children: Matthew Alexander, Rachel Danielle, Adam Levi. AB, Columbia U., N.Y.C., 1967; JD, Northeastern U., 1976. Bar: Mass. 1977, U.S. Supreme Ct. 1980. Mktg. mgr./cons. Digital Equipment Corp., Merrimack, N.H., 1979-81, 83-86; nat. dir. high-tech. industry program Coopers & Lybrand, Boston, 1981-83; pres. Video/Demo Ctrs., Inc., Burlington, Mass., 1986-88; v.p. bus. devel. Info. Resources, Inc., Boston, 1988-91; dir. facilitation consulting methodologies Arthur Andersen, Boston, 1991-93; dir. self-assessment practices Arthur Andersen, Chgo., 1993—; panelist MIT Enterprise Forum, Cambridge, 1983-89; pres. Samali Lobster Exports Co., 1995. Creator software application Compliance Testing and Verification, 1981. UN rep. Jubaland Relief and Rehab. Soc., Somalia; dir. Save Somalia Livestock Campaign, 1993. Facilitated meetings between opposite clans in the Juba region of southern Samalia. Home: 2000 Arrow Ln Deerfield IL 60015 Office: Arthur Andersen LLP 33 W Monroe St Chicago IL 60603

TRIVELPIECE, ALVIN WILLIAM, physicist, corporate executive; b. Stockton, Calif., Mar. 15, 1930; s. Alvin Stevens and Mae (Hughes) T.; m. Shirley Ann Ross, Mar. 23, 1953; children: Craig Evan, Steve Edward, Keith Eric. B.S., Calif. Poly. Coll., San Luis Obispo, 1953; M.S., Calif. Inst. Tech., 1955, Ph.D., 1958. Fulbright scholar Delft (Netherlands) U., 1958-59; asst. prof., then assoc. prof. U. Calif. at Berkeley, 1959-66; prof. physics U. Md., 1966-76; on leave as asst. dir. for research div. controlled thermonuclear research AEC, Washington, 1973-75; v.p. Maxwell Labs. Inc., San Diego, 1976-78; corp. v.p. Sci. Applications, Inc., La Jolla, Calif., 1978-81; dir. Office of Energy Research, U.S. Dept. Energy, Washington, 1981-87; exec. officer AAAS, Washington, 1987-88; dir. Oak Ridge (Tenn.) Nat. Lab., 1988—; v.p. Martin Marietta Energy Systems, 1988—; head del. for joint NAS and Soviet Acad. Scis. meeting and conf. in the USSR on energy and global ecol. problems, 1989; chmn. math. scis. ednl. bd. NAS, 1990-93; chmn. coord. coun. for edn. NRC, 1991-93; bd. dirs. Bausch & Lomb, Inc., Rochester, N.Y.; active State of Tenn. Sci. and Tech. Adv. Commn., 1993—; adv. com. Fed. Networking Coun., 1992—; mem. NRC Commn. on Phys. Scis., Math. and Applications, 1993—. Author: Slow Wave Propagation in Plasma Wave Guides, 1966, Principles of Plasma Physics, 1973; also articles. Named Disting. Alumnus Claif. Inst. Tech., Pasadena, Calif., 1987; recipient U.S. Sec. of Energy's Gold medal for Disting. Svc., 1986, Outstanding Engr. award IEEE Region 3, 1995; Guggenheim fellow, 1966. Fellow AAAS, IEEE, Am. Phys. Soc.; mem. AAUP, Nat. Acad. Engring., Am. Nuclear Soc., Am. Assn. Physics Tchrs., Capital Hill Club, Nat. Press Club, Sigma Xi. Achievements include research in plasma physics. Home: 8 Rivers Run Way Oak Ridge TN 37830-9004 Office: Oak Ridge Nat Lab Office of Dir PO Box 2008 Oak Ridge TN 37831-6255

TRIVISONNO, NICHOLAS LOUIS, communications company executive, accountant; b. Bklyn., Apr. 10, 1947; s. Nicholas John and Anne (Mucciardi) T.; m. Doris Frances Conaty; children: Drew Michael, Danielle Marie. BBA in Acctg., St. Francis Coll., Bklyn., 1968. CPA, N.Y., Conn., La. Ptnr. Arthur Andersen & Co., N.Y.C., 1979-85, mng. ptnr, Stamford, Conn., 1985-88; sr. v.p. fin. GTE Corp., Stamford, 1988—, bd. dirs. St. Joseph Med. Ctr., Stamford, 1986—, Jr. Achievement, Stamford, 1986—; mem. Gov.'s Task Force Am. Shakespeare Theatre, Conn., 1987-88. Mem. Am.

Inst. CPA's, N.Y. State Soc. CPA's. Conn. Soc. CPA's, La. Soc. CPA's, Conn. Golf Club (Easton) (treas. 1986—). Republican. Roman Catholic. Avocation: Golf. Office: GTE 1 Stamford Forum Stamford CT 06901-3516

TROCCOLI, JOAN CARPENTER, museum director; b. Jan. 28, 1953; d. Charles Lidstone and Elizabeth (Hayes) Carpenter; m. Robert C. Troccoli, Apr. 29, 1983. BA summa cum laude, Middlebury Coll., 1975; MA, NYU, 1977, PhD, 1984. Free-lance curator, lectr., 1983-89; art curator Gilcrease Mus., Tulsa, 1989-92; adj. prof. U. Tulsa, 1989; organizer, moderator Okla. Art Ctr., 1984; spkr. in field; panelist Mus. and Hist. Orgns. Program NEH, 1993; visual arts scholar Adult Insts. in Arts Okla. Arts Inst., 1990; visual arts adv. panelist Okla. Arts Inst., 1990-92; visual arts project assistance adv. panelist State Arts Coun. Okla., 1985— Contbr. articles to profl. jours.; reader U. Okla. Press. Pres. Okla. Art Ctr. Assn. 1987-88; co-pres. Com. of Twenty, Arts Place II, Okla. City, 1985-86; ex officio trustee Okla. Art Ctr., 1985-89; mem. Visionmakers adv. bd. State Arts Coun. Okla., 1988-89, Arts Commn. City of Tulsa, 1992—; master lectr. Tulsa Opera, 1991. Inst. Fine Arts fellow NYU; Okla. Found. Humanities grantee, 1985-86, 87, 90, State Arts Coun. Okla. grantee. Mem. Assn. Art Mus. Dirs., Mortarboard, Phi Beta Kappa. Home: 2116 E 32d Pl Tulsa OK 74105 Office: Gilcrease Mus 1400 N Gilcrease Museum Rd Tulsa OK 74127-2105

TRODDEN, STEPHEN ANTHONY, federal agency administrator; b. Washington, D.C., Dec. 13, 1939; s. Stephen Albertson and Margaret Mary (Myers) T.; m. Regina Lee Miller, Dec. 26, 1962; children: Mark Andrew, Sharon Ruth. BS in Engring., U. Mich., 1962; JD, Georgetown U., 1965. Bar: Va. 1965. Indsl. engr. U.S. Army Materiel Command, 1962-66; staff officer missile systems U.S. Army Missile Command, 1966-69; tech. advisor, budget analyst Directorate for Procurement, Office of Sec. Def., 1969-73; dep. dir. R & D Office Asst. Sec. Defense, 1973-75, dep. dir., 1975-81, dir. procurement, 1981-83; dir. major acquisition programs Dept. Defense, 1983-86; asst. insp. gen. auditing Office of Insp. Gen., 1986-90; insp. gen. Dept. Vets. Affairs, 1990—; chmn. inspection com. Pres. Coun. Integrity and Efficiency, Washington, 1990-94. Lay dir. No. Va. Cursillo Movement, 1988-91. Recipient Meritorious Civilian Svc. award Sec. Defense, Washington, 1983, Disting. Civilian Svc. award, 1990, Meritorious Exec. Pres. rank award U.S. Govt., 1990. Mem. Va. State Bar. Avocations: basketball, jogging, beach, reading, bicycling. Office: IG Dept Vets Affairs 810 Vermont Ave NW Washington DC 20420-0002

TROEGER, CURTIS RALPH, advertising executive; b. St. Louis, Jan. 24, 1931; s. Alfred Donald and Bernice Elizabeth (Kleisley) T.; m. Joyce Earline Thurmon, 1953; children: Melody Beth, Susan Elaine, Curtis Ralph Jr., Elizabeth Ann. BA, Culver-Stockton Coll., Canton, Mo., 1953; postgrad., Pace U., 1966-67. Credit mgr. Chase Manhattan Bank, N.Y.C., 1955-56; advt. sales rep. N.Y. Times, 1956-61, resort and travel mgr., 1961-65, radio and TV advt. mgr., 1965-69, fin. advt. mgr., 1970-71; v.p. Doremus & Co., N.Y.C., 1971-74; sr. v.p., 1974-82, exec. v.p., 1982-85, pres., 1985-86, chmn., chief exec. officer, 1986—. Served as cpl. U.S. Army, 1953-55. Mem. Fin. Communications Soc. (pres.), Advt. Club N.Y. Republican. Episcopalian. Clubs: Downtown Assn., Bond of N.Y. Avocations: classical music, chess, bridge, tennis, squash, singing. Home: 65 Diamond Hill Rd West Redding CT 06896-2224 Office: Doremus & Co 200 Varick St New York NY 10014-4810

TROELSTRA, ARNE, physics educator; b. Zelhem, The Netherlands, Mar. 30, 1935; came to U.S., 1965; m. Louise M. Van de Meent; 1 child, Catherine. BS in Physics and Math., Utrecht U., The Netherlands, 1955, MS in Physics, 1958, PhD in Physics, 1964. Rsch. scientist Applied Physics Rsch. TNO, Soesterberg, The Netherlands, 1959-65; assoc. prof. U. Ill., Chgo., 1965-69; assoc. prof. Rice U., Houston, 1969-76, prof., 1976-80; instr. physics Okla. Sch. Sci. and Math., Oklahoma City, 1989—. Postdoctoral fellow NATO, MIT, 1962-63. Home: 501 NE 15th St Oklahoma City OK 73104-1221 Office: Okla Sch Sci and Math 1141 N Lincoln Blvd Oklahoma City OK 73104-1298

TROEN, PHILIP, physician, educator; b. Portland, Maine, Nov. 24, 1925; s. Ben and Gertrude (Cope) T.; m. Betty Ann Zelig, Mar. 22, 1953 (dec.); children: Mark Lawrence, Bruce Robert, Gail Sheri. A.B., Harvard U., 1944, M.D., 1948. Diplomate: Nat. Bd. Med. Examiners, Am. Bd. Internal Medicine. Intern Boston City Hosp., 1948-49, asst. resident in medicine, 1949-50; resident in medicine Beth Israel Hosp., Boston, 1950, 52-53; chief resident Beth Israel Hosp., 1953-54, asst. in medicine, 1955-56, USPHS research fellow, 1955-56, assoc. in med. research, 1956-64, assoc. in medicine, 1956-58, asst. vis. physician, 1959-64; teaching fellow Harvard Med. Sch., 1952-53, asst. in medicine, 1953-54, research fellow, 1955-56, instr. medicine, 1956-59, asso. in medicine, 1959-60, asst. prof., 1960-64; prof. medicine U. Pitts. Sch. Medicine, 1964—, assoc. chmn. dept. medicine, 1969-79, vice chmn. dept. medicine, 1979-90, physician in chief Montefiore Univ. Hosp., 1964-90, physician in chief emeritus, 1990—; sci. counselor NIH, key cons. contraceptive devel. br., 1980; sci. counselor rev. Intramural Reproductive Biology Program, Nat. Inst. Child Health and Human Devel., 1977; cons. male fertility and infertility Nat. Inst. Occupational Safety and Health, 1977; mem. med. res. service merit rev. bd. in endocrinology VA, 1979-82; mem. contract rev. com. Nat. Inst. Child Health and Human Devel., 1975-84, chmn., 1976-89, reviewer intramural site visit devel. endocrinology br., 1983, 87; mem. endocrinologic and metabolic drugs adv. com. FDA, 1984-88, chmn. 1987-88; mem. expert advisor panel on occupational health, WHO, 1987—. Mem. editorial bd. Jour. Andrology, Jour. Clin. Endocrinology and Metabolism, Internat. Jour. Andrology, Andrologia; contbr. articles to profl. jours. Served to capt. M.C., AUS, 1950-52. Fellow in endocrinology and metabolism Mayo Clinic, Rochester, Minn., 1954-55; Kendall-Hench research fellow, 1955; Ziskind teaching fellow, 1956-59; Med. Found. Greater Boston research fellow, 1959-63; Guggenheim fellow Stockholm, 1960-61. Mem. AAAS, Assn. Am. Physicians, Am. Soc. Clin. Investigation, Am. Soc. for Biochemistry and Molecular Biology, Am. Fedn. Clin. Research, Am. Soc. Andrology (program and publs. com., exec. coun. 1977-79, v.p. 1979-80, pres. 1980-81, chmn. publ. com. 1990-93, Disting. Andrologist award 1991), Internat. Soc. Andrology (sec. 1981-89, pres. 1989-93), Endocrine Soc. (publ. com. 1984-90, chmn. 1987-90), N.Y. Acad. Scis., Central Soc. Clin. Research, Soc. Study of Reproduction. Office: Montefiore U Hosp U Pitts Med Ctr 200 Lothrop St Pittsburgh PA 15213-3241

TROFINO, JOAN ALHANATI, health care facility administrator; b. N.Y.C.; d. Manoel and Mary (Yurecic) Alhanati; m. Michael Trofino, Sept. 28, 1968. BS in Nursing, Adelphi Coll., 1955-59; MS in Nursing, Adelphi U., 1967; MEd, Columbia U., 1987, EdD, 1988. Supr. obstetrics Wyckoff Hosp., Bklyn., 1960-61; instr. Brookdale Hsop., Bklyn., 1962-64, supr. surgery, 1964-65; dir. nursing emergency room and outpatient dept. Hackensack (N.J.) Hosp., 1969-72; dir. nursing Raritan Valley Hosp., Greenbrook, N.J., 1972-74; v.p. patient care Riverview Med. Ctr., Red Bank, N.J., 1974—. Contbr. articles to profl. jours. Named Nurse Adminstr. of Yr. Mgmt. Forum N.J. State Nurses Assn., Trenton, 1985. Fellow Am. Orgn. Nurse Execs.; mem. Orgn. Nurse Execs. N.J. (legis. chmn. 1981—), Soc. Nursing Service Adminstrs. N.J. (pres. 1980), Nat. Ctr. Nursing Research, NIH, Bethesday, Md. (mem. adv. council), Nat. League for Nursing (bd. dirs.), Sigma Theta Tau. Avocations: reading, walking, dog shows. Home: 19 Wildhedge Ln Holmdel NJ 07733-2115 Office: Riverview Med Ctr 35 Union St Red Bank NJ 07701-1846

TROGANI, MONICA, ballet mistress; b. Newark, Sept. 2, 1963; m. Jay Brooker, July 3, 1993. Grad. high sch., 1980. Ballet dancer N.J. Ballet, West Orange, 1980-83; field asst., coder Reichman Rsch., Inc., N.Y.C., 1984-86; ballet mistress, prin. dancer Dance Theatre of L.I., Port Washington, N.Y., 1984-88; exec. sec. programming dept. The First N.Y. Internat. Festival of the Arts, N.Y.C., 1987-89; guest regisseur Alta. Ballet, Edmonton, Can., 1988-89, ballet mistress, asst. to artistic dir., 1989-93; guest regisseur Ballet du Nord, Roubaix, France, 1991, Dance Theatre of Harlem, N.Y.C., 1993-94; ballet mistress Les Grands Ballets Canadiens, Montreal, 1994—. Avocation: singing. Office: Les Grands Ballets Canadien, 4816 Rue Rivard, Montreal, PQ Canada H2J 2N6

TROGDON, DEWEY LEONARD, JR., textile executive; b. Summerfield, N.C., Feb. 17, 1932; s. Dewey Leonard and Ethel (Miller) T.; m. Barbara Jean Ayers, Sept. 10, 1955; children: Mark, Leonard. AB in Econs.,

Guilford Coll., 1958; postgrad., U. N.C., 1967-68, U. Va., 1970, Advanced Mgmt. Program, Harvard U., 1978. With Cone Mills Corp., Greensboro, 1958—, staff asst. to chief exec. officer, 1970-74, exec. v.p., 1978, pres., 1979—, chief exec. officer, 1980-90, chmn., 1981—; pres. subs. co. Otto B. May, 1974-78; v.p. Cone Mills Mktg. Co., 1977-78; dir. First Union Corp. With USNR, 1949-53. Mem. Am. Textile Mfrs. Inst. (pres. 1986-87), N.C. Textile Mfrs. Assn. (past pres., dir.). Methodist. Office: Cone Mills Corp 1201 Maple St Greensboro NC 27405-6939*

TROIDL, RICHARD JOHN, banker; b. Buffalo, July 2, 1944; s. Henry Albert and Lola Julian (Davern) T.; m. Diane Budney, Nov. 20, 1982; children: Nicholas, Holly. AAS, SUNY, Buffalo, 1973. Sr. v.p. Empire Am. Fed. Savs. Bank, Buffalo, 1969-93; pres. Express Svcs. of Am., Inc., Las Vegas, Nev., 1993—. With U.S. Army, 1965-71. Home: 5004 S Rainbow Blvd Las Vegas NV 89118-1124 Office: Express Svcs Am Inc 6120 W Tropicana Ave Ste A-16 Las Vegas NV 89103-4694 also: PO Box 848 Buffalo NY 14228

TROLANDER, HARDY WILCOX, engineering executive, consultant; b. Chgo., June 2, 1921; s. Elmer Wilcox and Freda Marie (Zobel) T.; m. Imogen Davenport, July 3, 1946; children: Megan, Patricia. BS in Engring., Antioch Coll., 1947. Instr. Antioch Coll., Yellow Springs, Ohio, 1947-48; co-founder, CEO Yellow Springs Instrument Co., Inc., 1948-86; dir. co-founder Cook Design Ctr., Dartmouth Coll., Hanover, N.H., 1975-88; bd. dirs. Deban Inc., Yellow Springs. Contbr. articles to profl. jours.; patentee in field. Co-founder, trustee Yellow Springs Community Found., 1974-83; trustee Autioch Coll., 1968-74, chmn. bd., 1972-74; trustee Engring. and Sci. Found., Dayton, 1982—, Engring. and Sci. Hall of Fame, 1994—; bd. dirs. united Way Greater Dayton Area, 1984-92. 1st lt. U.S. Army Air Corps., 1943-46. Named Outstanding Engr., Dayton Affiliate Socs., 1967, 89. Fellow Dayton Engrs. Club; mem. ACLU, Nat. Acad. Engring., Amnesty Internat. Democrat. Avocations: restoring antique radios and automobiles. Home and Office: 1475 President St Yellow Springs OH 45387

TROLINGER, JAMES DAVIS, laser scientist; b. Shelbyville, Tenn., Mar. 2, 1940; s. Winston Perry and Euna Mae (Davis) T.; children: James D. Jr., Kristina Lin, Jonathan P. BS, U. Tenn., 1963; MS, La. State U., 1964; PhD, U. Tenn., 1967. Scientist Sverdrup Tech., Tullahoma, Tenn., 1967-73, Sci. Applications, Tullahoma, 1973-75; chief scientist, founder Spectron, Costa Mesa, Calif., 1975-88; gen. ptnr., founder MetroLaser, Irvine, Calif., 1988—; cons. Adv. Group for Aerospace R & D, NATO, Chatillon, France, 1985-88. Recipient George W. Goddard award Internat. Soc. Optical Engring., 1992. Home: 3417 Wimbledon Way Costa Mesa CA 92626-1645 Office: MetroLaser 18006 Sky Park Cir Irvine CA 92714-6429

TROLLER, FRED, graphic designer, painter, visual consultant, educator; b. Zurich, Switzerland, Dec. 12, 1930; came to U.S., 1961; s. Albert and Katherina (Iseli) T.; m. Beatrice Stocklin, Nov. 22, 1952; children—Simon, Meret. B.A. in Graphic Design, Kunstgewerbeschule, Zurich, 1950. Art dir. Geigy Corp., Ardsley, N.Y., 1961-66; pres. Fred Troller Assoc., Visual Communications Cons., Rye, N.Y., 1966—; chmn., prof. design div. design Sch. Art and Design N.Y. State Coll. Ceramics at Alfred U., 1991—. Author and illustrator articles. Served to pvt. 1st class Inf. Swiss Army, 1949-60. Mem. Am. Inst. Graphic Arts, Alliance Graphique Internationale, Ptnrs. Livable Places. Home & Office: Fred Troller Assocs 12 Harbor Ln Rye NY 10580-2213

TROMBINO, ROGER A., investment banker; b. Kenosha, Wis., Sept. 23, 1939; s. Paul and Lena T.; m. Joann M. Buchholtz, 1961; children: Tracey, Suzanne, Steven. B.S., U. Wis., 1962. CPA. Audit mgr. Ernst & Young, Chgo., 1962-73; sr. v.p., exec. officer Norin Corp./Norris Cos., Miami, Fla., 1973-85; executor, trustee Norris Group, Miami, 1986-92; mng. dir. AIBC Investment Bank, Miami, 1993—. Chmn. bd. Bon Secours Hosp., Miami, 1979-94. Mem. AICPA. Club: Riviera Country.

TROMP, JEROEN, earth scientist. Asst. prof. dept. earth scis. Harvard U., Cambridge, Mass. Packard fellow David and Lucile Packard Found., 1994. Office: Harvard U Dept Earth Science Cambridge MA 02138-6502*

TRONCHON, CLAUDE, chemical executive. Chrmn., ceo Big Three Industries Inc., Houston. Office: Big Three Inds 3535 W 12th St Houston TX 77008

TROOBOFF, PETER DENNIS, lawyer; b. Balt., June 22, 1942; s. Benjamin M. and Rebecca C. (Cohen) T.; m. Rhoda Morss, Aug. 10, 1969; children: Hannah, Abigail. BA cum laude, Columbia U., 1964; LLB cum laude, Harvard U., 1967; LLM, London Sch. Econs., 1968; diploma cum laude, Hague (Netherlands) Acad. Internat. Law, 1968. Bar: N.Y. 1968, D.C. 1970. Rsch. assoc., Harvard U. Law Sch., 1968-69; asst. to exec. editor for The Advocates, Sta. WGBH-TV, Boston, 1969; assoc. Covington & Burling, Washington, 1969-75, ptnr., 1975—; lectr.; dir. seminars The Hague Acad. Internat. Law, 1972, 82, lectr.; 1986, mem. curatorium, 1991—; lectr. The Hague Acad. External Program Beijing, 1987, Harare, 1993, internat. orgns. U. Va. Sch. Law, 1973; head U.S. del. 3d Inter-Am. Specialized Conf. Pvt. Internat. Law, La Paz, Bolivia, 1984; mem. U.S. del. Hague Conf. private internat. law, 1993; mem. sec. of state adv. com. private internat. law, 1990—. Frank Knox Meml. fellow. Mem. Coun. Fgn. Rels., Am. Soc. Internat. Law (pres. 1990-92, bd. editors Am. Jour. of Internat. Law 1980-92, 94—, hon. v.p. 1992—), Internat. Law Assn., Washington Inst. Fgn. Affairs. Club: Cosmos, City (Washington). Contbr. chpts., articles to profl. publs.; editor: Law and Responsibility in Warfare-The Vietnam Experience, 1975. Office: Covington & Burling PO Box 7566 1201 Pennsylvania Ave NW Washington DC 20044

TROSINO, VINCENT JOSEPH, insurance company executive; b. Upland, Pa., Nov. 19, 1940; s. Sylvester N. and Stella Trosino; m. Patricia Ann Gibney, June 18, 1960; children: Laura, Valerie, Vincent Jr. BS in Psychology, Villanova U., 1962; MS in Psychology, Ill. State U., 1973. Ops. supr. State Farm Mut. Auto Ins. Co., Springfield, Pa., 1962-67; personnel mgr. State Farm Mut. Auto Ins. Co., Bloomington, Ill., 1970-72, dir. personnel, 1972-74, corp. v.p., 1974-86-87, exec. v.p., 1987—, COO, 1990—; also bd. dirs.; div. mgr. State Farm Mut. Auto Ins. Co., Costa Mesa, Calif., 1974-75, dep. regional v.p., 1976-80; regional v.p. State Farm Mut. Auto Ins. Co., Wayne, N.J., 1981-85; bd. dirs. State Farm Fire & Casualty Co., State Farm Life Ins. Co., State Farm Internat. Services, State Farm Investment Mgmt. Corp., all Bloomington. Bd. dirs. Chilton Hosp., Pompton Lakes, N.J., 1982-85, Jr. Achievement, McLean County, Ill., 1971, McLean County Law and Justice Com., 1970, McLean County Alcohol and Drug Assistance Corp., 1970-74. Mem. N.J. Ins. News Svc. (pres. 1984-85, bd. dirs.), N.J. Joint Underwriting Assn. (bd. dirs. 1982-85), Jud. Inquiry Bd. State of Ill. (apptd. by Gov. Edgar, 1992—). Avocations: trout fishing, tennis, golf. Office: State Farm Ins Cos 1 State Farm Plz Bloomington IL 61710-0002

TROST, BARRY MARTIN, chemist, educator; b. Phila., June 13, 1941; s. Joseph and Esther T.; m. Susan Paula Shapiro, Nov. 25, 1967; children: Aaron David, Carey Daniel. B.A. cum laude, U. Pa., 1962; Ph.D., MIT, 1965; D (hon.), U. Claude Bernard, Lyons, France, 1994. Mem. faculty U. Wis., Madison, 1965—, prof. chemistry, 1969—, Evan P. and Marion Helfaer prof. chemistry, from 1976; Vilas rsch. prof. chemistry U. Wis.; cons. Merck, Sharp & Dohme, E.I. duPont de Nemours.; Chem. Soc. centenary lectr., 1982. Author: Problems in Spectroscopy, 1967, Sulfur Ylides, 1975; editor-in-chief Comprehensive Organic Synthesis, 1991—, Chem-Tracts/Organic Chemistry, 1993—; editor: Structure and Reactivity Concepts in Organic Chemistry series, 1972—; assoc. editor Jour. Am. Chem. Soc., 1974-80; mem. editorial bd. Organic Reactions Series, 1971—; contbr. numerous articles to profl. jours. Recipient Dreyfus Found. Tech.-Scholar award, 1970, 77, Creative Work in Synthetic Organic Chemistry award, 1981, Baeckland medal, 1981, Alexander von Humboldt award, 1984, Guenther award, 1990, Janssen prize, 1990, Roger Adams award, 1995; named Chem. Pioneer, Am. Inst. Chemists, 1983; NSF fellow, 1963-65, Sloan Found.fellow, 1967-69, Am. Swiss Found. fellow, 1975—; Cope scholar, 1989. Mem. AAAS, Am. Chem. Soc. (award in pure chemistry 1977, Roger Adams award 1995), Nat. Acad. Scis., Am. Acad. Arts and

Scis., Chem. Soc. London. Office: Stanford U Dept Chemistry Stanford CA 94305

TROST, CARLISLE ALBERT HERMAN, retired naval officer; b. Valmeyer, Ill., Apr. 24, 1930; s. Elmer Herman and Luella Caroline (Hoffman) T.; m. Pauline Louise Haley, May 1, 1954; children—Carl, Laura Lee, Steven, Kathleen. Student, Washington St. Louis, 1948-49; B.S., U.S. Naval Acad., 1953; Olmsted scholar, U. Freiburg, W. Ger., 1960-62. Commd. ensign U.S. Navy, 1953, advanced through grades to adm., 1985; exec. officer U.S.S. Scorpion, 1962-63, U.S.S. Von Steuben, 1963-65; mil. asst. to Dep. Sec. Def., 1965-68; comdg. officer U.S.S. Sam Rayburn, 1968-69; staff Comdr. Sub Force Atlantic, 1969-70; exec. asst. to Sec. Navy, 1970-73; comdr. Submarine Group Five, 1973-74; asst. chief Bur. Naval Personnel, 1974-76; dir. systems analysis div. Office Chief Naval Ops., Washington 1976-78; dep. comdr.-in-chief U.S. Pacific Fleet, 1978-80; comdr. U.S. Seventh Fleet, 1980-81; dir. Navy program planning Office Chief Naval Ops., 1981-85; comdr.-in-chief U.S. Atlantic Fleet, 1985-86, chief naval ops., 1986-90; bd. dirs. Lockheed Corp., L.A. Land & Exploration, Gen. Pub. Utility Corp., GPU Nuclear Corp., Bird-Johnson Co., Gen. Dynamics Corp., Precision Components Corp. Trustee U.S. Naval Acad. Found. Decorated Def. D.S.M. with cluster, Navy D.S.M. with 2 clusters, Army D.S.M., Air Force D.S.M., Legion of Merit with 2 oak leaf clusters, Navy Achievement medal, Def. Disting. Svc. medal; named Outstanding Young Man of Am. Nat. Jr. C. of C., 1964. Mem. U.S. Naval Inst., U.S. Naval Alumni Assn. (trustee). Episcopalian. Home: 10405 Windsor View Dr Rockville MD 20854-4025

TROST, EILEEN BANNON, lawyer; b. Teaneck, N.J., Jan. 9, 1951; d. William Eugene and Marie Thelma (Finlayson) Bannon; m. Lawrence Peter Trost Jr., Aug. 27, 1977; children: Lawrence Peter III, William Patrick, Timothy Alexander. BA with great distinction, Shimer Coll., 1972; JD cum laude, U. Minn., 1976. Bar: Ill. 1976, U.S. Dist. Ct. (no. dist.) Ill. 1976, Minn. 1978, U.S. Tax Ct. 1978, U.S. Supreme Ct. 1981. Assoc. McDermott, Will & Emery, Chgo., 1976-82, ptnr., 1982-93; v.p. No. Trust Bank Ariz. N.A., Phoenix, 1993—. Mem. Minn. Bar Assn., Internat. Acad. Estate and Trust Law. Roman Catholic. Office: Northern Trust Bank Ariz NA 2398 E Camelback Rd Phoenix AZ 85016-9001

TROST, J. RONALD, lawyer; b. Fresno, Calif., Nov. 27, 1932; s. David Trost and Betty (Shapiro) Buno; m. Florence Stern; children: Gregory, Larry, Leslie, Jacqueline. BA, Rice U., 1954; JD, U. Tex., 1957. Bar: Tex. 1957, D.C. 1960, Calif. 1963. With U.S. Dept. Justice, Washington, 1957-59; pvt. practice law Washington, 1959-62; pvt. practice L.A., 1963—; ptnr. Sidley & Austin, L.A., 1980—; adj. prof. law UCLA; instr. law U. So. Calif., Los Angeles. Contbr. articles to law revs. and jours.; contbg. editor Collier on Bankruptcy. Served with U.S. Army, 1957-63. Mem. ABA, Am. Law Inst., Nat. Bankruptcy Conf. Office: Sidley & Austin 875 3rd Ave New York NY 10022

TROSTEL, MICHAEL FREDERICK, architect; b. Balt., May 19, 1931; s. Louis Jacob and Katharine (Fisher) T. BArch, U. Pa., 1954, MArch, 1957; diploma, Ecole des Beaux Arts, Fontainebleau, France, 1957. Registered architect, Md., D.C., Va. Draftsman Taylor & Fisher, Balt., 1958-59, Fisher, Nes, Campbell & Ptnrs., Balt., 1959-60; assoc. James R. Edmunds, Jr., Balt., 1960-73; v.p. Edmunds & Hyde, Balt., 1973-81; prin. Michael F. Trostel, FAIA, Balt., 1981-94, Trostel & Pearre, 1995—; mem. adv. bd. Md. House and Garden Pilgrimage, 1982—; archtl. advisor Hammond-Harwood House Assn., 1988-94. Author: Mount Clare, 1981, Domestic Maryland Architecture, 1984, Wines and Other Potables in Maryland, 1987, Mondawmin: Baltimore's Last Country Estate, 1991; editor Architect's Report mag., 1963-65. Bd. dirs. Balt. Heritage, Inc., 1970-73, Am. wing Balt. Mus. Art, 1994—; mem. art commn. City of Balt., 1972-80, chmn., 1978-80; mem. gov.'s com. for Nat. Register Hist. Places, State of Md., 1984—, vice chmn., 1987-92, chmn., 1993. Recipient Award of Excellence, Balt. Bldg. Congress, 1980, 83, 87, Honor award Balt. Heritage, 1986, 90, Commendation award Preservation Md., 1986, 90, Preservation award Md. Hist. Trust, 1991, 92. Fellow AIA (mem. com. on hist. preservation); mem. Soc. for Preservation of Md. Antiques (bd. dirs. 1965-68, 81-84, sec. 1968-79), Nat. Trust for Hist. Preservation (mem. bd. advisors 1990—, Honor award 1992), Assn. for Preservation of Tech., Soc. Archtl. Historians, Vernacular Architecture Form, Soc. Colonial Wars, Md. Club. Home and Office: 1307 Bolton St Baltimore MD 21217-4102

TROSTEN, LEONARD MORSE, lawyer; b. Bklyn., Jan. 25, 1932; s. David and Anne Bertha (Belkin) T.; m. Arthea Howell Dickson, Aug. 21, 1954 (dec. Jan. 1978); children: Amanda Trosten-Bloom, Jessica Trosten Forrest; m. Addie Jane Tyner Harris, Jan. 12, 1979; children: Hope Harris Pampillonia, Arthur F.M. Harris. A.B., Columbia U., 1953, LL.B., 1955. Bar: N.Y. 1955, D.C. 1965. Assoc. Dwight, Royall, Harris, Koegel & Caskey, N.Y.C., 1955-58; with Office of Gen. Counsel AEC, Washington, 1958-64; staff counsel Joint Congrl. Com. on Atomic Energy, Washington, 1964-67; ptnr. LeBoeuf, Lamb, Leiby & MacRae, Washington, 1968-90, of counsel, 1991—. Contbr. articles to profl. jours.; editor Columbia Law Rev., 1953-55. Mem. University Club (Washington), Columbia Country Club (Chevy Chase, Md.), First City Club (Savannah, Ga.), The Landings Club (Savannah, Ga.), Rotary, Phi Beta Kappa. Episcopalian. Avocations: bridge, walking, bowling. Home: 3 Mainsail Crossing Savannah GA 31411 Office: LeBoeuf Lamb Greene MacRae 1875 Connecticut Ave NW Washington DC 20009-5728

TROSTORFF, ALEXANDER PETER, lawyer; b. Queens, N.Y., Apr. 6, 1951; s. Peter W. and Cecilia (Rott) T.; m. Danielle Lombardo, June 30, 1984. BA, Davidson Coll., 1973; JD, Washington U., 1976; LLM in Taxation, Georgetown U., 1981. Bar: N.Y. 1978, La. 1981. Tax law specialist IRS, Washington, 1978-80; assoc. Jones, Walker, Waechter, Poitevant, Carrere & Denegre, New Orleans, 1980—, ptnr., 1984—. Lutheran. Avocations: tennis, basketball, golf. Home: 1414 Eleonore St New Orleans LA 70115-4318 Office: Jones Walker Waechter Poitevant Carrere & Denegre 201 Saint Charles Ave New Orleans LA 70170-5100

TROTMAN, ALEXANDER J., automobile manufacturing company executive; b. 1933; married. MBA, Mich. State U., 1972. Various positions Ford Motor Co., Europe, 1955-69, Dearborn, Mich., 1969-71, dir. sales and mktg. planning, 1971-72, exec. dir. product planning and research, 1972-75, chief car planning mgr. Car Product Devel. Group, 1975-77, exec. dir. ops. planning, 1977-78, asst. gen. mgr. truck and recreational products ops., 1978-79, corp. v.p., from 1979, mgr. truck ops. Ford of Europe, Inc., then pres. Ford Asia-Pacific Inc., 1983-84, pres., chmn. Ford of Europe, Inc., from 1984, then exec. v.p. No. Am. auto ops., now chmn. bd., pres., CEO, dir. Ford Motor Co., 1993—; bd. dirs. IBM Corp., Armonk, N.Y. Served with RAF, 1951-55. Office: Ford Motor Co The American Rd Dearborn MI 48121*

TROTT, SABERT SCOTT, II, marketing professional; b. Concord, N.C., Nov. 21, 1941; s. Sabert Scott and Mary Welker (Crooks) T.; m. Brenda Lee Bost, Nov. 27, 1964; children—Sabert Scott III, David Lee. B.S. in Textile Tech., N.C. State U., 1964; MBA, U. N.C., 1969. Mgr. trainee Cannon Mills Co., Kannapolis, N.C., 1969-70, mktg. mgr., 1970-75, v.p. mktg., 1975-82, sr. v.p. mktg., 1982-86, dir. telemktg. and premium sales, 1987-89; mgr. spl. markets, mktg. & sales Fieldcrest Cannon Inc., mktg. mgr., telemarketing sales mgr., 1989-92; v.p. mktg. and sales Spencer's Inc., Mt. Airy, N.C., 1992-93; v.p. mktg. Carpenter Co., Richmond, Va., 1994—. Chmn. Cabarrus-Rowan Parks and Recreation Commn., N.C., 1982-86; mem. Cabarrus County Parks and Recreation Commn., N.C., 1980-88; Rep. candidate County Commr., Cabarrus County, 1990; bd. dirs. Cabarrus Meml. Hosp., 1992, N.C. Ctr. for Applied Textile Tech.; vestryman local Episcopal ch., 1988-93. Capt. U.S. Army, 1965-70. Decorated Commendation medal (2). Republican. Lodge: Rotary. Avocations: canoeing; rafting; golf; basketball; racquetball. Home: PO Box 18062 Richmond VA 23226 Office: Carpenter Co 5016 Monument Ave Richmond VA 23230

TROTT, STEPHEN SPANGLER, federal judge, musician; b. Glen Ridge, N.J., Dec. 12, 1939; s. David Herman and Virginia (Spangler) T.; divorced; children: Christina, Shelley. B.A., Wesleyan U., 1962; LL.B., Harvard U., 1965; LLD (hon.), Santa Clara U., 1992. Bar: Calif. 1966, U.S. Dist. Ct. (cen. dist.) Calif. 1966, U.S. Ct. Appeals (9th cir.) 1983, U.S. Supreme Ct. 1984. Guitarist, mem. The Highwaymen, 1958—; dep. dist. atty. Los Angeles County Dist. Atty.'s Office, Los Angeles, 1966-75; chief dep. dist.

atty. Los Angeles County Dist. Atty.'s Office, 1975-79; U.S. dist. atty. Central Dist. Calif., Los Angeles, 1981-83; asst. atty. gen. criminal div. Dept. Justice, Washington, 1983-86; mem. faculty Nat. Coll. Dist. Attys., Houston, 1973—; chmn. central dist. Calif. Law Enforcement Coordinating Com., Houston, 1981-83; coordinator Los Angeles-Nev. Drug Enforcement Task Force, 1982-83; assoc. atty. gen. Justice Dept., Washington, 1986-88; chmn. U.S. Interpol, 1986-88; judge U.S. Ct. of Appeals 9th Cir., Boise, Idaho, 1988—; chmn. U.S. Interpol. Trustee Wesleyan U., 1984-87; bd. dirs. Children's Home Soc. Idaho, 1990—; bd. dirs. Boise Philharmonic Assn., 1995—. Recipient Gold record as singer-guitarist for Michael Row the Boat Ashore, 1961, Disting. Faculty award Nat. Coll. Dist. Attys., 1977. Mem. Am. Coll. Trial Lawyers, Wilderness Fly Fishers Club (pres. 1975-77), Brentwood Racing Pigeon Club (pres. 1977-82), Magic Castle, Idaho Classic Guitar Soc. (founder, pres. 1989—). Republican. Office: US Ct Appeals for 9th Cir 550 W Fort St Boise ID 83724-0101

TROTTER, F(REDERICK) THOMAS, retired university president; b. L.A., Apr. 17, 1926; s. Fred B. and Hazel (Thomas) T.; m. Gania Demaree, June 27, 1953; children—Ruth Elizabeth, Paula Anne (dec.), Tania, Mary. AB, Occidental Coll., 1950, DD, 1968; STB, Boston U., 1953, PhD, 1958; LHD, Ill. Wesleyan U., 1974, Cornell Coll., 1985, Westmar Coll., 1987; LLD, U. Pacific, 1978, Wesleyan Coll., 1981; EdD, Columbia Coll., 1984; LittD, Alaska Pacific U., 1987. Exec. sec. Boston U. Student Christian Assn., 1951-54; ordained elder Calif.-Pacific, Methodist Ch., 1953; pastor Montclair (Calif.) Meth. Ch., 1956-59; lectr. So. Calif. Sch. Theology at Claremont, 1957-59, instr., 1959-60, asst. prof., 1960-63, assoc. prof., 1963-66, prof., 1966, dean, 1961; prof. religion and arts, dean Sch. Theology Claremont, 1961-73; mem. Bd. Higher Edn. and Ministry, United Meth. Ch., 1972-73, gen. sec., 1977-87; pres. Alaska Pacific U., Anchorage, 1988-95; ret., 1995; dir. Inst. for Antiquity and Christianity at Claremont. Author: Jesus and the Historian, 1968, Loving God with One's Mind, 1987, weekly column local newspapers; editor-at-large: Christian Century, 1969-84. Trustee Dillard U. Served with USAAF, 1944-46. Kent fellow Soc. for Values in Higher Edn., 1954; Dempster fellow Meth. Ch., 1954. Mem. Rotary Internat. (Anchorage Downtown), Commonwealth North. Home: 75-136 Kiowa Dr Indian Wells CA 92210

TROTTER, HAYNIE SEAY, lawyer; b. Clarksville, Va., Feb. 24, 1931; s. William Augustus and Frances (Seay) T.; m. Marguerite Stapleford, Feb. 6, 1958; (dec. Feb. 1981); children: Richard Haynie, Frances Patricia; m. Katrin Gunnarsdottir, May 31, 1986. AB, Coll. of William & Mary, 1952; LLB, U. Va., 1957. Bar: Va. 1957, U.S. Dist. Ct. (ea. dist.) Va. 1957, U.S. Ct. Appeals (4th cir.) 1963, U.S. Supreme Ct. 1963. Sole practice Vienna, Va., 1957-58; assoc. William C. Bauknight, Fairfax, Va., 1958-59; ptnr. Bauknight, Williams, Swann & Trotter, Fairfax, 1959-61, Bauknight, Prichard, McCandlish & Williams, Fairfax, 1961-71, Boothe, Prichard & Dudley, McLean, Va., 1971-87, McGuire, Woods, Battle & Boothe, 1987—; bd. trustees Nat. Hosp. Orthopaedics and rehab., Alexandria, Va., 1981-93; bd. dirs. Network Health Plan, Alexandria. Mem. ABA, Va. Bar Assn., Fairfax Bar Assn., Assn. Trial Lawyers Am. Republican. Episcopalian. Avocations: tennis, fishing. Home: 9185 Old Dominion Dr Mc Lean VA 22102-1018 Office: McGuire Woods Battle & Boothe 8280 Greensboro Dr Ste 900 Mc Lean VA 22102-3892

TROTTER, HERMAN EAGER, JR. (HERMAN TROTTER), music critic; b. Providence, Sept. 25, 1925; s. Herman Eager, Sr. and Shelley Fern (Jones) T.; m. Johanne Marguerite Haberstro, Sept. 22, 1956; children: Kim Avery. Holly Anne. Joy Caroline. BA, Yale U., 1946. Pub. utility sec. analyst Mass. Mut. Life Ins. Co., Springfield, 1947-51; sales engr. B-I-F Industries, Providence, 1951-56; asst. sec. Buffalo Batt and Felt Co, Depew, N.Y., 1956-68; account exec. Harold Warner Advt., Buffalo, N.Y., 1968-77; freelance music critic Buffalo News, 1968-77, staff critic, 1977—. Contbr. articles to profl. and popular jours. Program annotator Buffalo Philharm., 1964-70. Lt. (j.g.) USN, 1943-46, PTO. Mem. Music Critics Assn. (v.p. 1988-93). Avocations: skiing, record collecting. Home: 125 Edward St No 1 J Buffalo NY 14201 Office: The Buffalo News PO Box 100 Buffalo NY 14240-0100

TROTTER, LESLIE EARL, operations research educator, consultant; b. Muskogee, Okla., Nov. 17, 1943; s. Leslie Earl and Sylvia Helene (Freeze) T.; m. Jomi Tuggle, July 19, 1968; children: Colleen Nicole, Eamonn Scott. AB in Math., Princeton U., 1965; MS in Indsl. and Systems Engring., Ga. Inst. Tech., 1971; PhD in Ops. Rsch., Cornell U., 1973. Sci. computer programmer Lockheed-Ga. Co., Marietta, 1965-68; computer applications analyst Control Data Corp., Atlanta, 1968-70; postdoctoral rsch. assoc. Math. Rsch. Ctr., U. Wis., Madison, 1973; asst. prof. Yale U. Sch. Orgn. and Mgmt., New Haven, 1974-75; assoc. prof. ops. rsch. Cornell U. Sch. Ops. Rsch. and Indsl. Engring., Ithaca, N.Y., 1975-84, dir. of Sch., 1983-87, prof., 1984—; vis. prof. Bonn (Germany) U., 1977-79, math dept. E.P.F.L., Lausanne, Switzerland, 1984-85, 91-92, Math. Inst., Augsburg (Germany) U., 1987-88; vis. cons. Bell Labs., Holmdel, N.J., 1981. Editor optimization area Jour. Ops. Rsch., 1982-87; contbr. numerous articles to profl. jours. Recipient teaching excellence awards Cornell U., 1977, 81, 93, sr. U.S. scientist award Alexander von Humboldt Found., Germany, 1988; numerous rsch. grants NSF, 1974—. Mem. Ops. Rsch. Soc. Am., Math. Programming Soc. (treas. 1988-94), Soc. for Indsl. and Applied Math. Avocations: running, skiing, music. Home: 161 Highgate Rd Ithaca NY 14850-1469 Office: Cornell Univ School of Operations Research Engineering Theory Ct Ithaca NY 14853

TROTTER, THOMAS ROBERT, lawyer; b. Akron, Ohio, Apr. 11, 1949; s. Fred and Josephine (Daley) T. BA, Ohio U., 1971; JD, Tulane U., 1975. Bar: Ohio 1975, U.S. Dist. Ct. (no. dist.) Ohio 1975. Assoc. Squire, Sanders & Dempsey, Cleve., 1975-80; mem. Buckingham, Doolittle & Burroughs, Akron, 1980—; chmn. taxation and legis. com. Akron Regional Devel. Bd., 1988-95. Trustee Akron Symphony Orch., 1984-93, Cascade CDC, Inc., Akron, 1983—; Akron/Summit Solid Waste Mgmt. Authority, 1994—. Mem. ABA, Ohio Bar Assn. (chair local govt. law com.), Akron Bar Assn., Cleve. Bar Assn., Nat. Assn. Bond Lawyers, Sigma Alpha Epsilon. Democrat. Home: 589 Avalon Ave Akron OH 44320-2048 Office: Buckingham Doolittle & Burroughs PO Box 1500 50 S Main St Akron OH 44308-1828

TROTTI, JOHN BOONE, librarian, educator; b. Asheville, N.C., Dec. 11, 1935; s. Clarence Trotti and Janice Trotti Lyon; m. Joan Thompson, June 12, 1957; children: Elizabeth, Margaret, Michael. Ba, Davidson Coll., 1957; BD cum laude, Union Theol. Sem. Va., 1960; MA, Yale U., 1961, PhD, 1964; MLS, U. N.C., 1964. Ordained to ministry Presbyn. Ch. in the U.S., 1964; instr. O.T. Yale Div. Sch., 1961-62; minister ch. Altavista, Va., 1964-68; asst. prof. religion Randolph Macon Woman's Coll., Lynchburg, Va., 1965-68; asst. librarian, asst. prof. Union Theol. Sem. Va., 1968-70, librarian, 1970—, assoc. prof. bibliography, 1972-80, prof. bibliography, 1980—; mem. library adv. com., Va.; mem. Va. State Networking Users Adv. Council, 1983-88; pres. Altavista Area Ministerial Assn., 1967. Author: Lesser Festivals 2, 1980; editor: Aids to a Theological Library, 1977; editor: Scholar's Choice, Building a Pastor's Library, 1991; contbr. articles to religious and profl. jours., ch. sch. curriculum. Trustee Stillman Coll., 1969-78, Richmond Baptist Theological Seminary, 1989—; bd. dirs. Hist. Found. Presbyn. and Ref. Chs., 1979-86. Mem. Am. Theol. Library Assn. (exec. com. 1971-74, 78-79, pres. 1977-78), Va. Library Assn., Presbyterian Library Assn. (pres. 1973), Soc. Bibl. Lit., Beta Phi Mu. Home: 1222 Rennie Ave Richmond VA 23227-4723 Office: 3401 Brook Rd Richmond VA 23227-4514 Life is a gift from God to be expended with zest, joy, and a concern for others. In our free society achieving an education appropriate for one's vocation involves seizing opportunities when they come and much hard work. An effective education puts one more, not less, in touch with our common humanity.

TROTTIER, BRYAN JOHN, professional sports team coach, former professional hockey player; b. Val Marie, Sask., Can., July 17, 1956; s. Eldon J. and Mary (Gardner) T.; m. Laura Lynn Theis, July 14, 1976; children: Bryan John, Lindsay Ann. Student public schs., Val Marie; student, Swift Current Comprehensive High Sch. Mem. N.Y. Islanders Hockey Club, Farmingdale, 1975-90; owner, operator Bryan Trottier Skating Acad., Port Washington, N.Y.; player Pitts. Penguins, 1990-93; asst. coach Pittsburgh Penguins, 1993—; hockey cons. Right Guard Corp., Phila; spokesman 1980 Winter Olympics, Lake Placid, N.Y.; pres. NHL Player's Assn. Recipient Calder Meml. trophy as Rookie of Yr. Nat. Hockey League, 1976; Hart Meml. trophy as Most Valuable Player, 1979; Art Ross trophy as Leading

Scorer; Conn Smythe trophy as Most Valuable Player in Nat. Hockey League Playoffs, 1979-80. Office: Pitts Penguins Civic Arena Gate 9 Pittsburgh PA 15219*

TROTTY, WILLIE FRANCIS, university dean; b. Nacogdoches, Tex., Mar. 26, 1947; s. Luther Sr. and Hattie Marion (Anderson) T.; m. Sarah Ann Gamble, Dec. 21, 1974; children: Laurette Marion, Willette Francine, William Martin. BS in Biology and Polit. Sci., Stephen F. Austin State U., 1970, MS in Biology and Secondary Edn., 1972; PhD in Ednl. Adminstrn. and Indsl. Mgmt., Purdue U., 1977. Cert. biology and govt. tchr., prin., sch. supt., Tex. Asst. prof. edn. Prairie View (Tex.) A & M, 1977-79, asst. dir. tchr. certification, 1977-82, assoc. prof. edn., 1977-91, assoc. dean coll. edn., head dept. sch. svcs., 1988-90, dir. rsch. and sponsored projects, 1990—, dean Grad. Sch., 1991—; assoc. dir. So. Consortium Colls. and Tchr. Edn., 1977-79; chmn. self-study steering com. So. Assn. Colls., 1989-90; exec. com. Tex. Coun. Faculty Governance Orgns., 1990. Author: (with Louis Aikens) Theory into Practice: A Casebook for Students of School Administration, 1986; contbr. articles to profl. jours. Vice-chair adv. bd. Johnson-Phillip All Faiths Chapel, 1988—; mem. adv. com. Aldine Ind. Sch. Dist., 1991-92. Recipient Disting. Svc. award Houston Tchrs. Assn., 1974, Key Achiever award E.J. Campbell High Sch. Alumni Assn., 1992, Leadership award Prairie View A&M U., 1993. Mem. Nat. Coun. Univ. Rsch. Adminstrs., Tex. Profs. Assn., Tex. Assn. Sch. Adminstrs., Purdue U. Ednl. Adminstrn. Alumni Assn. (charter), Kiwanis (charter), Kappa Delta Pi, Phi Delta Kappa (treas., past pres., Disting. Svc. award 1974). Baptist. Avocations: computers, reading. Home: 5926 Black Maple Ln Houston TX 77088-6617 Office: Prairie View A&M U PO Box 2355 Prairie View TX 77446-2355

TROUBETZKOY, ALEXIS SERGE, foundation administrator, educator; b. Paris, Mar. 6, 1934; came to U.S., 1936; s. Serge G. and Luba A. (Obolensky) T.; m. Helene de Klebnikoff, July 8, 1967; children: Anne, Andrew. BA, Sir George William U., 1958; grad. diploma in Edn., Bishop's U., 1960. Tchr. Stanstead Coll., 1959-60, Bishop's Coll. Sch., Lennoxville, Que., Can., 1960-66; registrar St. Stephen's Sch, Rome, 1966-68; asst. headmaster Appleby Coll., Oakville, Ont., Can., 1968-71, headmaster, 1981-87; headmaster Selwyn House Sch., Montreal, Que., 1971-81, Toronto (Ont.) French Sch., 1987-92; exec. dir. Tolstoy Found., N.Y.C., 1992—. Author: The Road to Balaklava, 1986. Regent Cathedral St. John the Divine, N.Y.C.; bd. overseers CARE, N.Y.C.; mem. lt.-gov.'s conservation award selection com., Ont.; active Sir Edmund Hillary Found. Mem. Can. Assn. Internat. Affairs (pres. Sherbrooke br. 1964-66), Assn. Russian-Am. Scholars, Can. Assn. Ind. Schs. (pres. 1980-81), European Coun. Internat. Schs., Quebec Assn. Ind. Schs. (pres. 1979-81), Amities Internat. Napoleoniennes. Mem. Orthodox Ch. in Am. Avocations: hist. reading and writing, music. Home: 7 E 75th St New York NY 10021 Office: Tolstoy Found 200 Park Ave S New York NY 10003-1503

TROUILLOT, MICHEL-ROLPH, anthropology educator, educational administrator; b. Port-au-Prince, Haiti, Nov. 26, 1949; s. Ernst and Anne-Marie (Morisset) T.; children: Jean-Philip, Claude; m. Anne-Carine Séide; 1 child, Canel. BA, CUNY, 1978; PhD, Johns Hopkins U., 1985. Mem. adj. faculty Bklyn. Coll. CUNY, N.Y.C., 1982-83; instr. dept. anthropology Duke U., Durham, N.C., 1983-84, asst. prof., 1984-87, assoc. prof., 1987; assoc. prof. dept. anthropology Johns Hopkins U., Balt., 1987-89, prof., 1989—, now Krieger/Eisenhower prof. anthropology, dir. Program in Atlantic history, culture and society, 1991-93, dir. Inst. for Global Studies in Culture, Power and History, 1993—; mem. acad. coun. for Latin. Am. and Carribean program Woodrow Wilson Ctr., Smithsonian Instn., 1987-89; mem. screening com. for predissertation fellowships Social Sci. Rsch. Coun., N.Y.C., 1991—; reviewer, cons. Am. Coun. Learned Socs., Guggenheim Found., NSF, Woodrow Wilson Internat. Ctr. for Scholars, UN, Can. Coun. for Learned Socs., Ford Found. Author: (books) Ti dife boule son Istoua Ayiti, 1977, Les racines historiques de l'état duvaliérien, 1986, Peasants and Capital: Dominica in the World Economy, 1988, Haiti: State against Nation, 1990, Silencing the Past: Power and the Production of History, 1995, (monograph) Nation, State and Society in Haiti (1804-84), 1984; co-editor: (monograph series) Studies in Atlantic History and Culture, 1989—; co-editor, staff writer Les Cahiers du Vendredi, 1987—. Rsch. fellow Nat. Humanities Ctr., 1985-86, Guggenheim Found., 1990-91, Ctr. for Advanced Study in the Behavioral Sci., 1995-96; Guest scholar Woodrow Wilson Inst./ Smithsonian Instn., 1992. Mem. Am. Anthrop. Assn., Carribean Studies Assn., Hatian Resource Consortium, Hatian Studies Assn., Wenner-Gren Found. for Anthrop. Rsch. (mem. adv. coun. 1991—, reviewer, cons.), Transafrica. Office: Johns Hopkins U Dept Anthropology 3400 N Charles St Baltimore MD 21218

TROUNSTINE, PHILIP J., editor, journalist; b. Cin., July 30, 1949; s. Henry P. and Amy May (Joseph) Trounstine; children: Jessica, David; m. Deborah Williams, May 1, 1993; children: Amy, Ryan, Patrick Wilkes. Student, U. Vt., 1967-68, Stanford U., 1968-70; BA in Journalism, San Jose State U., 1975. Graphic artist Eric Printing, San Jose, Calif., 1972-75; reporter Indpls. Star, Ind., 1975-78; reporter San Jose Mercury News, Calif., 1978-83, editorial writer, 1983-86, political editor, 1986—. Co-author: Movers & Shakers: The Study of Community Power, 1981. Creator, writer SPJ Gridiron Show, San Jose, 1981-91. Pulliam fellow, 1975, Duke U., 1991, J.S. Knight Stanford U., 1993-94. Mem. Soc. Profl. Journalist (mem. nat. ethics com. 1993—). Jewish. Avocations: golf, fishing. Home: 960 Asbury St San Jose CA 95126-1805 Office: San Jose Mercury News 750 Ridder Park Dr San Jose CA 95190*

TROUP, THOMAS JAMES, electronics company executive; b. Council Bluffs, Iowa, Sept. 4, 1923; s. Ralph Leslie and Ruth (Beaumont) T.; m. Marjory Alice Suelflow, Feb. 2, 1946; children: Robert, Patricia Alice, James Thomas. B.Sc. in Chem. Engring. U. Wis., 1945; M.B.A. with high distinction, Harvard U., 1952. With Internat. Minerals & Chem. Corp., 1945-53; asst. to gen. mgr. Internat. Minerals & Chem. Corp., Chgo., 1950-53; sales rep. Foxboro Co., Los Angeles, 1949-50; with W.R. Grace Co., 1954-68; v.p. chem. group W.R. Grace Co., N.Y.C., 1965-68; treas. Burr-Brown Corp., Tucson, 1968-71; dir. Burr-Brown Research Co., 1967—, vice-chmn., 1981—; v.p., treas. Akzona, Inc., Asheville, N.C., 1971-82; bd. dirs. Dynamics Research Corp., Wilmington, Mass. Mem. Biltmore Forest Country Club (Asheville), Red Fox Country Club (Tryon, N.C.), Farmers Club (London), Ventana Golf and Racquet Club (Tucson, Tucson Country Club. Home: 7278 E Camino Vly Verde Tucson AZ 85715-3408 Office: PO Box 11400 Tucson AZ 85734-1400

TROUPE, TERRY LEE, holding company banker; b. Ephrata, Pa., Apr. 17, 1947; s. Jacob I. and Mary J. (Shober) T.; m. Judy A. Hagy, May 28, 1966; children—Todd L., Brenda R. B.S., Pa. State U. C.P.A. Conn. Auditor Arthur Andersen & Co., Hartford, Conn., 1969-73; exec. v.p., chief fin. officer Am. Bank and Trust Co. Pa., Reading, 1973-85; vice chmn. Meridian Bancorp, Inc., Reading, 1985-93; v.p., CFO Irex Corp., Lancaster, Pa., 1993—. Mem. adv. bd. Pa. State U., Berks Campus. Mem. AICPA, Bank Adminstrn. Inst. (rep.), Fin. Execs. Inst. Republican. Mem. United Ch. of Christ. Avocations: sailing, skiing, tennis, golf. Office: Irex Corp PO Box 1268 120 N Lime St Lancaster PA 17602-2951

TROUT, CHARLES HATHAWAY, historian, educator; b. Seattle, Nov. 3, 1935; s. Charles Whyron and Elizabeth (Hathaway) T.; m. Margot Stevens, Dec. 30, 1961 (div. 1983); children: Nicholas H., Benjamin C.; m. Katherine Taylor Griffiths, Oct. 6, 1984. B.A., Amherst Coll., 1957; M.A., Columbia U., 1961, Ph.D., 1972. History instr. Hill Sch., Pottstown, Pa., 1958-59, Philips Exeter Acad., (N.H.), 1960-69; prof. history Mt. Holyoke Coll., South Hadley, Mass., 1969-80; provost, dean faculty Colgate U., Hamilton, N.Y., 1980-90; pres. Washington Coll., Chestertown, Md., 1990—; now pres./chancellor; vis. prof. U. Mass. Labor Rels. and Rsch. Ctr., 1974-80. Author: Boston, The Great Depression, and the New Deal. Trustee Md. Citizens for the Arts, Chesapeake Bay Maritime Mus.; Pickering Creek Environ. Ctr. Columbia U. Pres.'s scholar, 1959-60; NEH rsch. fellow, 1975-76; Charles Warren fellow Harvard U., 1978-79. Democrat. Episcopalian. Home: Hynson-Ringold House Chestertown MD 21620 Office: Washington Coll Office of President Chestertown MD 21620-1197

TROUT, MAURICE ELMORE, foreign service officer; b. Clifton Hill, Mo., Sept. 17, 1917; s. David McCamel and Charlotte Temple (Woods) T.; m. Margie Marie Mueller, Aug. 24, 1943; children—Richard Willis, Babette

Yvonne. B.A., Hillsdale Coll., 1939; M.A. in Pub. Adminstrn, St. Louis U., 1948, Ph.D. in Polit. Sci., 1950. Joined U.S. Fgn. Service, 1950; assigned Paris, France, 1950-52, Vienna, Austria, 1952-55, London, Eng., 1955-59, Vientiane, Laos, 1959-61; with Office Exec. Dir. Bur. Far Eastern Affairs, Dept. State, Washington, 1961-65; Am. consulate gen. Munich, Germany, 1965-69; 1st sec., consul Am. embassy, Bangkok, Thailand, 1969-72; dep. office dir. Bur. Politico-Mil. Affairs, Dept. State, Washington, 1972-75; Dept. State advisor Armed Forces Staff Coll., Norfolk, Va., 1975-77. Bd. dirs. Internat. Sch., Bangkok, 1970-72. Served with USCG, 1939-45; capt. USAFR, 1951-55. Recipient Achievement award diplomacy and internat. affairs Hillsdale Coll., 1962. Mem. Am. Fgn. Service Assn., Diplomatic and Consular Officer, Delta Tau Delta, Delta Theta Phi, Pi Gamma Mu. Home: 6203 Hardy Dr Mc Lean VA 22101-3114

TROUT, MONROE EUGENE, hospital systems executive; b. Harrisburg, Pa., Apr. 5, 1931; s. David Michael and Florence Margaret (Kashner) T.; m. Sandra Louise Lemke, June 11, 1960; children: Monroe Eugene, Timothy William. AB, U. Pa., 1953, MD, 1957; LLB, Dickinson Sch. of Law, 1964, JD, 1969; LLD (hon.), Bloomfield Coll., 1994. Intern Great Lakes (Ill.) Naval Hosp., 1957-58; resident in internal medicine Portsmouth (Va.) Naval Hosp., 1959-61; chief med. dept. Harrisburg State Hosp., 1961-64; dir. drug regulatory affairs Pfizer, Inc., N.Y.C., 1964-68; v.p. med. dir. Winthrop Labs., N.Y.C., 1968-70; med. dir. Sterling Drug, Inc., N.Y.C., 1970-74, v.p., dir. med. affairs, 1974-78, sr. v.p., dir. med. affairs, bd. dirs., mem. exec. com., 1978-86; pres., CEO Am. Healthcare Sys., Inc., 1986-95, chmn., 1987-95; also bd. dirs. Am. Healthcare Systems, Inc.; chmn. emeritus Am. Healthcare Sys., Inc., 1995—; chmn. bd. dir. Am. Excess Ins. Ltd., 1990-95; adj. assoc. prof. Bklyn. Coll. Pharmacy; spl. lectr. legal medicine, trustee Dickinson Sch. Law, 1970-93; trustee Ariz. State U. Sch. Health Adminstrn., 1988-91; mem. Sterling Winthrop Rsch. Bd., 1977-86; sec. Commn. on Med. Malpractice, HEW 1971-73, cons., 1974; mem. Joint Commn. Prescription Drug Use, 1976-80; co-chmn. San Diego County Health Commn., 1992-94; dir. Biotransplantation, Inc., 1994-95. Mem. editorial bd. Hosp. Formulary Mgmt, 1969-79, Forensic Science, 1971—, Jour. Legal Medicine, 1973-79, Reg. Tox. and Pharmac, 1981-87, Medical Malpractice Prevention, 1985—; contbr. articles to profl. jours. Exec. com. White House mini conf. on aging, 1980; Rep. dist. leader, New Canaan, Conn., 1966-68; mem. Town Coun. New Canaan, 1978-86, vice chmn., 1985-86; bd. dirs. New Canaan Interchurch Svc. com., 1965-69, Athletes Kidney Found., Circle in Sq. Theatre Inc., 1984-86, Baxter Internat., 1995—, SAIC, 1995—; trustee U. Calif.-San Diego Thornton Hosp. and Med. Ctr., Albany Med. Coll., 1977-86, St. Vincent DePaul Ctr. for the Homeless, 1987-90, Cleveland Clinic, 1971-87; trustee, vice chmn. Morehouse Med. Sch., 1980-89; assoc. trustee U. Pa.; bd. visitors U. Pa. Sch. Nursing, 1988-92; vice chmn. Med. Commn. for Food and Shelter, Inc.; mem. Nat. Health Adv. Bd. AAA, N.Y. State Commn. Substance Abuse, 1978-80; chmn. bd. ACLM Found., 1983-87; chmn. Internat. B'nai B'rith Dinner, 1989, 94. Recipient Alumni award of merit U. Pa., 1953, Disting. Alumni award Dickinson Sch. Law, 1989, Nat. Healthcare award Internat. B'nai B'rith, 1991, Entrepreneur of Yr. award San Diego, 1994, Horatio Alger award 1995; named to Hon. Order Ky. Cols., Tenn. Cols. Fellow Am. Coll. Legal Medicine (v.p., pres., bd. govs.); mem. AMA (Physicians Recognition awards 1969, 72, 76, 82, 85, 88, 92), Med. Execs. (pres. 1975-76), Delta Tau Delta. Lutheran. Office: Box 8052 Rancho Santa Fe CA 92067

TROUTMAN, E. MAC, federal judge; b. Greenwood Township, Pa., Jan. 7, 1915; s. Emmett Theodore and Kathryn (Holman) T.; m. Margaret Petrick, Nov. 23, 1944; children—Jane A., Jean K. A.B., Dickinson Coll., 1934, LL.B., 1936. Bar: Pa. 1937. With Phila. and Reading Coal and Iron Co., 1937-58, gen. counsel, 1954-58; gen. atty. Phila. and Reading Corp., 1958-67; gen. counsel Reading Anthracite Co., 1958-61, Reserve Carbon Corp., 1961-66, So. Carbon Corp., 1966-67; solicitor Blue Mountain Sch. Dist., 1963-67, Blue Mountain Area Sch. Authority, 1963-67, Orwigsburg Municipal Authority, 1966-67, Am. Bank and Trust Co., Reading and Pottsville, Pa., 1957-67; exec. sec., gen. counsel Pa. Self-Insurers Assn., 1962-67; U.S. judge Eastern Dist. Pa., from 1967, now sr. judge. Bd. dirs. Greater Pottsville Indsl. Devel. Corp., 1963-67, Pa. C. of C., 1955-65, Greater Pottsville Area C. of C., 1961-64, Orwigsburg Community Meml. Assn., 1950-66, Schuylkill County Soc. Crippled Children, 1945-67; v.p., dir. Pottsville Hosp. and Warne Clinic, 1960-67. Served with AUS, World War II. Mem. ABA, Pa. Bar Assn., Schuylkill County Bar Assn. (vice chancellor 1955-57, chmn. jud. vacancies and unauthorized practice coms. 1960, chmn. medico-legal com. 1963-65). Lutheran (pres. coun. 1961—). Club: Lion (bd. dirs. Orwigsburg 1964). Home: Kimmel's Rd Orwigsburg PA 17961 Office: US District Ct The Madison Bldg 400 Washington St Rm 400 Reading PA 19601-3908

TROUTMAN, RONALD R., electrical engineer; b. Lewisburg, Pa., Oct. 4, 1940; m. Roy Marlin and Dorothy Irene (Savidge) T.; m. Gail McCarthy Owen, July 30, 1966; children: Kelby Scott, Ramsay Owen. BS, MIT, 1962; PhD, NYU, 1966. Staff engr. gen. tech. div. IBM, Essex Junction, Vt., 1969-73, adv. engr., 1973-81, sr. engr., 1981-87; sr. engr. IBM T.J. Watson Rsch. Ctr., Yorktown Heights, N.Y., 1987-91, engring. staff mem., 1991—; Fellow MIT Ctr. for Advanced Engring. Studies, Cambridge, 1983-84. Author: Latchup in CMOS Technology: The Problem and Its Cure, 1986; contbr. over 60 articles to profl. jours. Lt. USN, 1966-68. Fellow IEEE. Achievements include patents on random access memory design, semiconductor technology development, others; analysis and characterization of short channel effects, subthreshold behavior and hot electron phenomena in field-effect transistors, modeling and control of latchup in CMOS technology, management of TFT/LCD materials and devices research and of TFT/LCD array tester development. Home: 38 Deer Hill Dr Ridgefield CT 06877-5308 Office: IBM TJ Watson Rsch Ctr PO Box 218 Yorktown Heights NY 10598-0218

TROVA, ERNEST TINO, artist, sculptor; b. St. Louis, Feb. 19, 1927. One-man exhbns. include: Pace Gallery, Boston and N.Y.C., 1963, 69, 70, 71, 73, 75, 82, Hanover Gallery, London, Eng., 1964, 68, 70, Harcus/Krakow Gallery, Boston, 1968, Dunkelman Gallery, Toronto, Ont., Can., 1969, Hanover-Gimpel, Zurich, Switzerland, 1970, Galerie Der Spiegel, Cologne, Germany, 1970, Block Gallery, St. Louis, 1970, Galerie Brusberg, Hanover, Germany, 1970, Venezuela, 1971, Israel, 1971, Makler Gallery, Phila., 1972, Phoenix Art Mus., 1974, Hokin Gallery, Palm Beach, Fla., 1975, 83, 84, 87, So. Ill. U. Mus., 1982, Greenberg Gallery, St. Louis, 1983, 84, Hokin Gallery, Miami, 1988-90, Mangel Gallery, Phila., 1989, The Exbn. Space at 112 Greene St, N.Y.C., 1989, Galeria Freites, Caracas, Venezuela, 1989-90, Philharmonic Ctr. for the Arts, Naples, Fla., 1991, Philip Samuels Fine Art, St. Louis, 1991, Ariji Gasiunasen Fine Art, Palm Beach, Fla., 1993, Bruce R. Lewin Gallery, N.Y.C., 1993; others; numerous group exhbns. including: Chgo. Art Inst., 1964, Pasadena (Calif.) Art Mus., 1964, De Cordova Mus., Documenta IV, Kassel, Germany, 1968, Mus. Modern Art, 1968, Internat. Biennale, Warsaw, 1968, Whitney Mus. Modern Art, 1968, Cleve. Inst. Art, 1969, Jewish Mus., N.Y.C., 1969, Contemporary Arts Center, Cin., 1970, 72, Princeton, 1970, U. Wis.-Milw., 1973, Hirshorn Mus. and Sculpture Garden, 1974, The Anchorage Mus. History and Art, 1987, 88, The Anchorage Mus., Juneau, Alaska, 1988, U. Alaska Mus., Fairbanks, 1988, Hanson Galleries, La Jolla, Calif., 1989, ACA Galleries, N.Y.C., 1990, Hokin Galleries, Miami, 1990, Galeria Freites, Caracas, Venezuela, 1990, Philharm. Ctr. for Arts, Naples, Fla., 1991, Art Chgo., 1991, 93, Art Miami, 1992, 93, 94, Art L.A., 1992, Isetan Mus. Art, Tokyo, 1992, Daimaru Mus., Umeda-Osaka, Japan, 1992, Hiroshima (Japan) Mus. Contemporary Art, 1992, Internat. Biennale, Monte Carlo, 1993, Asian Internat. Contemporary Art Fair, 1993, Art Basel, 1993, others; represented in permanent collections including Mus. Modern Art, Aldrich Mus. of Contemporary Art, Israel Mus.-Jerusalem, Met. Mus. of Art, Guggenheim Mus., Hirshorn Mus., Nat. Mus. of Art, the St. Louis Art Mus., Phoenix Art Mus., Atkins Mus. Fine Art, Laumeier Sculpture Garden, Springfield Art Mus.-Mo., Tate Gallery-London, Whitney Mus. of Am. Art, Nat. Mus. Am. Art, Smithsonian Instn., Washington, also pvt., Whitney Mus., and corporate collections. Office: Trova Found 8112 Maryland Ave Ste 200 Saint Louis MO 63105-3700 also: Exclusive Reps Philip Samuels Fine Art 8112 Maryland Ave Saint Louis MO 63105

TROW, JO ANNE JOHNSON, retired university official; b. Youngstown, Ohio, Feb. 10, 1931; d. Raymond Leonard Johnson and Mary Belle Beede; m. Clifford W. Trow, Oct. 10, 1969. BA, Denison U., 1953; MA, Ind. U., 1956; PhD, Mich. State U., 1965. Case worker Office Pub. Assistance, Cleve., 1953-54; asst. dean women Denison U., Granville, Ohio, 1956-59, Wash. State U., Pullman, 1959-63; asst. dir. resident program Mich. State U., East Lansing, 1964; dean women Oreg. State U., Corvallis, 1965-69, assoc. dean students, 1969-83, v.p. student affairs, 1983-95, program dir., 1993-95; presenter, speaker in field. Contbr. articles to profl. jours. Bd. dirs. Benton County Mental Health Assn., 1975-79, United Way Benton County, 1977—, United Way Oreg., 1977-80; mem. adv. bd. Old Mill Sch., 1979-95, chmn., 1983, 94-95; mem. Oreg. Cmty. Corrections Adv. Bd., 1988-95; moderator 1st Congl. Ch., 1977, trustee, 1979-83, 91-95; mem. Oreg. Gov.'s Com. on Status of Women, 1972-78, vice chmn., 1976-77; mem. fund campaign Good Samaritan Hosp. Found. Cancer Care Ctr., 1982-83. Recipient Corvallis Woman of Achievement award, 1974, Boss of Yr. award Oreg. State U. Office Personnel Assn., 1979, White Rose award March of Dimes, 1987, Elizabeth A Greenleaf Disting. Alumna award Ind. U., 1987, Scott Goodnight award, 1989, Disting. Alumni Citation, Denison U., 1993, Coun. Woman of Distinction award Oreg. State U. Meml. Union Program, 1993. Mem. Nat. Assn. Women Deans, Adminstrs. and Counselors (pres. 1981-82), Am. Coll. Personnel Assn. (sec. 1969-70), Nat. Assn. Student Personnel Adminstrs., Am. Coun. on Edn., N.W. Assn. Schs. and Colls. (comn. on colls. 1989-95), Am. Assn. for Higher Edn., N.W. Coll. Personnel Assn. (life, pres. 1969-70), Assn. Oreg. Faculties, AAUW (state and local bd. dirs.), LWV (bd. dirs., v.p. Corvallis 1966-69, 79-80), Corvallis Area C. of C. (bd. dirs. 1972-74, 78-80), Mortar Bd., Phi Delta Kappa, Phi Kappa Phi, Alpha Lambda Delta. Democrat.

TROWBRIDGE, ALEXANDER BUEL, JR., corporate director, consultant; b. Englewood, N.J., Dec. 12, 1929; s. Alexander Buel and Julie (Chamberlain) T.; m. Eleanor Hutzler, Apr. 18, 1981; children by previous marriage: Stephen C., Corrin S., Kimberly. Grad., Phillips Acad., Andover, Mass., 1947; AB cum laude, Princeton U., 1951; LLD (hon.), D'Youville Coll., 1967, Hofstra U., 1968, Hobart Coll., William Smith Coll., 1975. With Calif. Tex. Oil Co. 1954-59; ops. mgr. Esso Standard Oil S.A. Ltd., Panama C.Z., 1959-61; div. mgr. Esso Standard Oil S.A. Ltd., El Salvador, 1961-63; pres. Esso Standard Oil Co., P.R., 1963-65; asst. sec. commerce for domestic and internat. bus. U.S., 1965-67; sec. of commerce, 1967-68; pres. Am. Mgmt. Assn., N.Y.C., 1968-70; The Conf. Bd., Inc., N.Y.C., 1970-76; vice chmn. bd. Allied Chem. Corp., 1976-80; bd. dirs. NAM, Washington, 1978—, pres., 1980-90; bd. dirs. New Eng. Mut. Life Ins. Co., PHH Corp., WMX Technologies, Inc., Rouse Co., Harris Corp., Gillette Co., Sun Resorts Internat. Ltd., Warburg Pincus Funds, Sun Co. Inc., ICOS Corp. Trustee Phillips Acad., Andover, Mass.; mem. Pres.'s Task Force on Pvt. Sector Initiatives, Nat. Commn. on Social Security Reform, 1982; mem. Nat. Commn. on Exec., Legis. and Jud. Salaries, 1985, Nat. Commn. on Pub. Svcs.; mem. Competitiveness Policy Coun., 1991. With USMCR, 1951-53, maj. Res. Decorated Bronze Star with combat V; recipient Arthur Flemming award, 1966, Pres.'s E cert for export service, 1968, Bryce Harlow award for Bus.-Govt. Rels., 1988. Mem. Coun. Fgn. Rels., Met. Club, Georgetown Club, Univ. Club. Home: 1823 23rd St NW Washington DC 20008 Office: 1155 Connecticut Ave NW Ste 700 Washington DC 20036-4307

TROWBRIDGE, EDWARD KENNETH, insurance executive; b. Phila., Nov. 17, 1928; m. Marie Cassidy; 3 children. Certificate of proficiency in bus. adminstrn., U. Pa., 1956; student, Harvard U. Grad. Sch. Bus. Adminstrn., 1976-77. With William H. McGee Co., Phila., 1951-52; with Atlantic Cos., 1952—; marine sec. Atlantic Cos., N.Y.C., 1965-67; v.p. marine underwriting Atlantic Cos., 1967-73, sr. v.p. mktg. adminstrn., 1973-77, sr. exec. v.p., 1977-85, pres., 1985-88, chmn., 1988—; trustee Atlantic Mut. Ins. Co.; bd. dirs. Centennial Ins. Co., DCNY Corp.; governing com. IRM Inc. Trustee N.Y. coun. Boy Scouts Am., Coll. Ins.; mem. Am. Bur. Shipping. With U.S. Army, 1948-51. Mem. Am. Inst. Property and Liability Underwriters Am.-Ins. Inst. Am. (trustee), Life Saving Benevolent Assn. (pres.), Maritime Law Assn. U.S., India House Club (bd. govs.), Spring Brook Country Club (Morristown, N.J.). Office: Centennial Mutual Ins Co 45 Wall St New York NY 10005-1918

TROWBRIDGE, PHILLIP EDMUND, surgeon, educator; b. Hartford, Conn., Oct. 17, 1930; s. John Henry and Isabelle Story (Warren) T.; m. Fay Elaine Russell, June 23, 1956; children: Kimberly, Heather, Allison, John, David. BA, Trinity Coll., 1952; postgrad., Harvard U., 1955; MD, Tufts Med. Sch., 1959. Diplomate Am. Bd. Surgery. Intern Hartford Hosp., 1959-60, resident in gen. surgery, 1960-65, from mem. surg. staff to sr. surgeon, 1965—; clin. asst. prof. Surgery U. Conn. Med. Sch., Farmington, 1986—; adj. asst. prof. Surgery Dartmouth Med. Sch., Hanover, N.H. 1986—. Contbr. 17 articles to profl. jours. Corporator Hartford Sem., Hartford, 1975-77, 86—, trustee, 1977-86; dir. West Hartford Street Ministry, 1974-79. With USAF, 1952-54. Mem. ACS, Hartford Med. Soc. (pres. 1988, trustee 1989-93, Loving Cup award 1994), Am. Soc. Gen. Surgeons (chmn. Conn. chpt. 1993—), New Eng. Surg. Soc., New Eng. Cancer Soc., Internat. Surg. Soc., Soc. for Surgery Alimentary Tract. Republican. American Baptist. Avocations: golf, tennis, skiing, photography, painting. Home: 11 Lucy Way Simsbury CT 06070 Office: 85 Seymour St Hartford CT 06106

TROWBRIDGE, RONALD LEE, college administrator; b. Ft. Wayne, Ind., Dec. 4, 1937; s. Perry and Arola May (Erb) T.; m. Pamela Gay Chapman, Aug. 11, 1962; children: Andrew Lee, Stephen Scott, Elizabeth Chapman. BA, U. Mich., 1960, MA, 1962, PhD in English Lang. and Lit., 1967. Prof. English Ea. Mich. U., Ypsilanti, 1965-78; v.p. Hillsdale (Mich.) Coll., 1978-81, 90—; assoc. dir. U.S. Info. Agy., Washington, 1981-86; dir. fed. and internat. programs Commn. on Bicentennial of U.S. Constitution, Washington, 1986-88, staff dir., 1988-90. Contbr. articles to profl. jours. Mem. Ann Arbor (Mich.) City Coun., 1975-79. Recipient George Washington Honor medal Freedoms Found. Valley Forge, 1979. Mem. Mont Pelerin Soc., Phila. Soc. Republican. Presbyterian. Avocations: politics, writing, speaking. Home: 1500 Lake Pleasant Rd S Osseo MI 49266-9636 Office: Hillsdale Coll Hillsdale MI 49242

TROWBRIDGE, THOMAS, JR., mortgage banking company executive; b. Troy, N.Y., June 28, 1938; s. of Thomas and Elberta (Wood) T.; m. Delinda Bryan, July 3, 1965; children: Elisabeth Tacy, Wendy Bryan. BA, Yale U., 1960; MBA, Harvard U., 1965. V.p. James W. Rouse & Co., Balt., 1965-66, Washington, 1966-68, San Francisco, 1968-73, 76-78; pres. Rouse Investing Co., Columbia, Md., 1973-76, Trowbridge, Kieselhorst & Co., San Francisco, 1978—. Bd. dirs. Columbia Assn., 1973-76; trustee, treas. The Head-Royce Sch., Oakland, Calif., 1980-84; trustee, pres. Gen. Alumni Assn. Phillips Exeter Acad., 1984-90. Lt. USNR, 1960-63. Mem. Urban Land Inst., Calif. Mortgage Bankers Assn. (bd. dirs. 1991—), Mortgage Bankers Assn. Am. (bd. govs. 1993—), Olympic Club, Pacific Union Club, Lambda Alpha Internat. Republican. Presbyterian. Avocations: running, mountain climbing, golf. Home: 4 Ridge Ln Orinda CA 94563-1318 Office: Trowbridge Kieselhorst & Co 555 California St Ste 2850 San Francisco CA 94104-1604

TROXEL, DONALD EUGENE, electrical engineering educator; b. Trenton, N.J., Mar. 11, 1934; s. Shirley Monroe and Emma Ruth (Marvel) T.; m. Eileen Millicent Cronk, Aug. 23, 1963; children: Gregory, Jocelyn, Andrea. BS, Rutgers U., 1956; SM, MIT, 1958, PhD, 1962. Ford Found. postdoctoral fellow, asst. prof. MIT, Cambridge, Mass., 1962-64, asst. prof. dept. elec. engring., 1964-67, assoc. prof. 1967-85, prof. elec. engring., 1985—; asst. prof. Tufts U., Medford, Mass., 1963; bd. dirs. ECRM, Inc., Tewksbury, Mass. 1st lt. U.S. Army, 1956-58. Mem. IEEE (sr. mem., Leonard G. Abraham Prize Paper award 1971), Assn. for Computing Machinery, Sigma Xi, Tau Beta Pi, Eta Kappa Nu, Pi Mu Epsilon. Home: 4 Madison St Belmont MA 02178-3536 Office: MIT 36-287 77 Massachusetts Ave Cambridge MA 02139-3594

TROY, ANTHONY FRANCIS, lawyer; b. Hartford, Conn., Apr. 16, 1941; children: Anthony John, Francis Gerard II. BA in Govt., St. Michael's Coll., Vt., 1963; LLB, T.C. Williams, U. Richmond, Richmond, Va., 1966. Bar: Va. 1966, D.C. 1972, U.S. Dist. Ct. (ea. dist.) Va. 1966, U.S. Dist. Ct. (we. dist.) Va. 1967, U.S. Ct. Appeals (4th cir.) 1967, U.S. Supreme Ct. 1969. Asst. atty. gen. Commonwealth of Va., Richmond, 1966-72, dep. atty. gen., 1974-75, chief dep. atty. gen., 1975-76, atty. gen., 1977-78; assoc. Colson & Shapiro, Washington, 1972-74; ptnr. Mays & Valentine, Richmond, 1978—. Contbr. articles to profl. jours. Trustee Sci. Mus. Va. Home: 1814 Park Ave Richmond VA 23220 Office: Mays & Valentine 1111 East Main St PO Box 1122 Richmond VA 23208

TROY, B. THEODORE, direct mail advertising executive; b. Huntington Park, Calif., Jan. 16, 1932; s. Bernard and Florence Ruth (Stillman) T.; m. Pauline Pearson, Feb. 25, 1960; 1 child, Kevin. B.A. in Econs, U. Calif.-Santa Barbara, 1953; B.Fgn. Trade, Am. Grad. Sch. Internat. Mgmt., 1957. Brand mgr. Procter & Gamble, Eng., 1957-61; account exec. McCann-Erickson, Los Angeles, 1961-62; with R.J. Reynolds Co., 1962-77, pres. Mexican subs., 1968-75, pres. Brazilian subs., 1976-77; pres. Burlington Export Co. Inc., 1977-78, Kayser-Roth Internat., Kayser-Roth Corp., N.Y.C., 1978-82, Am. Advt. Distbrs. of Central Fla., 1983-92, Fla. Mail, Inc., 1992—. Trustee U. Calif.-Santa Barbara Found., 1980-86. Served with U.S. Army, 1953-55. Recipient Disting. Achievement award U. Calif., Santa Barbara Alumni Assn., 1979.

TROY, J. EDWARD, bishop; b. Chatham, N.B., Can., Sept. 2, 1931; s. J. Thomas and Lilian Mary (Barry) T. BA, St. Francis Xavier U., Antigonish, N.S., 1951; lic. philosophy, Louvain (Belgium) U., 1953, PhD, 1962; BD, Holy Heart Sem., Halifax, N.S., 1959; LLD (hons), St. Thomas U., Fredericton, N.B. 1985. Ordained priest Roman Cath. Ch., 1959. Prof. philosophy St. Thomas U., Chatham, N.B., 1959-63; commd. Canadian Armed Forces, 1963, advanced through grades to col, 1979, ret., 1984, chaplain, 1963-84; dir. personnel adminstrn. Can. Forces Chaplaincy, Ottowa, Ont., 1981-84; bishop Roman Cath. Ch., St. John, N.B., 1984—; episcopal promoter Apostleship of the Sea, Can., 1985—. Columnist New Freeman newpaper, 1984—. Chancellor St. Thomas U., 1986—. Mem. Canadian Conf. Cath. Bishops, Anglican/Roman Cath. Dialogue. Avocations: reading, bird watching. Office: Diocese St John, 1 Bayard Dr, Saint John's, NF Canada E2L 3L5

TROY, JOSEPH FREED, lawyer; b. Wilkes-Barre, Pa., Aug. 16, 1938; s. Sergei and Shirley Jean T.; m. Brigitta Ann Balos, June 9, 1962; children: Darcy Kendall, Austin Remy. BA, Yale U., 1960; LLB, Harvard U., 1963. Bar: Calif. 1964, D.C. 1979. Assoc. Hindin, McKittrick & Marsh, Beverly Hills, Calif., 1964-68, ptnr., 1968-70; pres. Troy & Gould, Los Angeles, 1970—; lectr. Calif. Continuing Edn. of Bar, 1972-80, 94; dir. World Trade Bank N.A., 1983—, Amerigon Inc., 1993—, Movie Gallery, Inc., 1994—. Author: Let's Go: A Student Guide to Europe, 1962, Accountability of Corporate Management; co-author: Protecting Corporate Officers and Directors from Liability, 1994. Pres. L.A. Chamber Orch. Soc., 1968-75, chmn. bd. dirs., 1975-78, vice chmn. bd. dirs., 1978-81; bd. dirs. Music Ctr. Opera Assn., 1972—, v.p., mem. exec. com., 1987—; hon. consul of Tunisia, L.A., 1984-88; pres. Internat. Festival Soc.; active L.A. Com. Fgn. Rels., 1991—; bd. dirs. Brentwood Pk. Property Owners Assn., 1988-93. Reid Hall fellow U. Paris, 1958. Mem. ABA, Calif. State Bar Assn. (chmn. bus. ct. com.), D.C. Bar Assn., L.A. County Bar Assn. (chmn. bus. and corp. law sect. 1977-78), French Am. C. of C. U.S. (exec. v.p. 1983-85), French Am. C. of C. L.A. (pres. 1982-84), Wine and Food Soc. Calif. Inc. (sec., bd. dirs.), Beach Club, Calif. Club. Office: 1801 Century Park E Ste 1600 Los Angeles CA 90067-2318

TROY, RICHARD HERSHEY, lawyer; b. Boston, Sept. 24, 1937; married. AB, Georgetown U., 1959; postgrad., U. Munich, Fed. Republic Germany, 1959-60; LLB, Harvard U., 1963. Bar: Mass. 1963, N.Y. 1965, U.S. Dist. Ct. (so. and ea. dists.) N.Y. 1965, U.S. Ct. Appeals (2d cir.) 1968, U.S. Supreme Ct. 1969, Conn. 1985. Law clk. to presiding justice U.S. Dist. Ct. N.H., Concord, 1963-64; assoc. Shearman & Sterling, N.Y., 1964-73; asst. gen. counsel, asst. sec. Combustion Engring., Inc., Stamford, Conn. 1974-81, v.p., assoc. gen. counsel, 1982-85, v.p., dep. gen. counsel, 1985-90; v.p., dep. gen. counsel Asea Brown Boveri, Inc., Stamford, 1990; v.p., assoc. gen. counsel UST, Inc., Greenwich, Conn., 1990-92; v.p. fin., law and adminstrn. Cell Pathways, Inc., Denver and Tucson, 1992—; speaker in field. Contbr. articles to profl. publs. Mem. Am. Soc. Corp. Secs. (bd. dirs. 1988-91, chmn. securities law com. 1984-89, chmn. proxy system com. 1990-93), Conn. Bar Assn. (mem. exec. com. corp. sect. 1986—), Westchester Fairfield Corp. Counsel Assn. (bd. dirs. 1978-83, pres. 1982). Office: Cell Pathways Inc 1700 Broadway Ste 2000 Denver CO 80290-2001

TROYER, ALVAH FORREST, seed corn company executive, plant breeder; b. LaFontaine, Ind., May 30, 1929; s. Alvah Forrest and Lottie (Waggoner) T.; m. Joyce Ann Wigner, Sept. 22, 1950; children: Anne, Barbara, Catherine, Daniel. B.S., Purdue U., 1954; M.S., U. Ill., 1956; Ph.D., U. Minn., 1964. Research assoc. U. Ill., Urbana, 1955-56; research fellow U. Minn., St. Paul, 1956-58; research sta. mgr. Pioneer Hi-Bred Internat., Inc., Mankato, Minn., 1958-65, research coordinator, 1965-77; dir. research and devel. Pfizer Genetics, St. Louis, 1977-81, v.p. and dir. research and devel., 1981-82; v.p. research and devel. DEKALB Plant Genetics, Ill., 1982-93; cons.Hybrid Seed Divsn. Cargill, Mpls., 1993—; researcher corn breeding, econ. botany, crop physiology, increasing genetic diversity, recent corn evolution. Contbr. articles to numerous publs.; developer of popular corn inbred lines and hybrids. Master sgt. U.S. Army, 1951-53, Korea. Recipient Nat. Coun. Comml. Plant Breeders Genetics and Plant Breeding award, 1992. Fellow AAAS, Am. Soc. Agronomy, Crop Sci. Soc. Am.; mem. Am. Genetic Assn., Genetic Soc. Am., N.Y. Acad. Sci., CAST, Sigma Xi, Gamma Sigma Delta, Alpha Zeta, Lambda Chi Alpha, Gamma Alpha, VFW. Methodist. Lodge: Masons. Home: 611 Joanne Ln De Kalb IL 60115-1862

TROYER, LEROY SETH, architect; b. Middlebury, Ind., Nov. 23, 1937; s. Seth and Nancy (Miller) T.; m. Phyllis Eigsti, May 24, 1958; children: Terry, Ronald, Donald. BArch, U. Notre Dame, 1971. Prin. LeRoy Troyer and Assocs., South Bend, 1971; sr. ptnr. LeRoy Troyer and Assocs., Mishawaka, Ind., 1977; pres. Southfield, Inc., 1988, The Troyer Group, Inc., Mishawaka, 1988—; bd. dirs. Lead Devel., Inc. Pres. Environic Found. Internat., Inc.; bd. dirs. Habitat for Humanity Internat. Americus, 1987-91, Coalition for Christian Colls. and Univs., 1991—, Habitat for Humanity St. Joseph County, Ind., 1992—; mem. adv. bd. Archtl. Sch. Berrien Springs, Mich., 1986—, Andrews (Mich.) U., 1987-88, Bethel Coll., Mishawaka; chmn. bd. dirs. Concerned Parents. Mem. Ind. Soc. Archs. (No. Ind. chpt.), AIA Practice Mgmt. Co. (chmn. 1978-80), Nat. AIA (pratice mgmt. com., chmn. 1983-84), Mennonite Econ. Devel. Assn. Internat. (chmn. bd. 1987-91). Avocations: photography, traveling, reading. Home: 1442 Deerfield Ct South Bend IN 46614-6429 Office: The Troyer Group Inc 415 Lincolnway E Mishawaka IN 46544

TROYER, THOMAS ALFRED, lawyer; b. Omaha, Aug. 15, 1933; s. Robert Raymond and Dorothy (Darlow) T.; m. Sally Jean Brown, June 28, 1958; children: Kenneth D., Robert C., Virginia D., Thomas C. BA, Harvard U., 1955; JD, U. Mich., 1958. Bar: Colo. 1958, U.S. Ct. Appeals (D.C. cir.) 1967. Assoc. Holme, Roberts, More & Owen, Denver, 1958-61; USAF, Denver, 1961-62; trial atty. U.S. Dept. Justice, Washington, 1962-64; mem. legal staff Asst. Sec. Treasury for Tax Policy, Washington, 1964-66; assoc. tax legis. counsel U.S. Dept. Treasury, Washington, 1966-67; mem. Caplin & Drysdale, Washington, 1967—; pres. Stern Fund, N.Y.C., 1985-86; bd. dirs., Children's Def. Fund, Washington, Mineral Policy Ctr., Washington, Am. Tax Policy Inst., Washington; mem. bd. trustees Natural Resources Def. Coun., N.Y.C., 1977—, Carnegie Corp., N.Y.C., 1983-91, Found. Nat. Capital Region, 1992—. Contbr. numerous articles to profl. jours. Mem. Treasury Adv. Commn. on Pvt. Philanthropy and Pub. Needs, Washington, 1976-77; mem. adv. group to Commr. Internal Rev., Washington, 1978-80; mem. com. of visitors U. Mich. Law Sch., Ann Arbor, 1982—; mem. IRS Commr.'s Exempt Orgn. Adv. Group, Washington, 1987-90. Fellow Am. Bar Found., Am. Coll. Tax Counsel; mem. Coun. for Excellence in Govt., Am. Law Inst., ABA (vice chmn. govt. rels. tax sect. 1989-91, Commn. on Homelessness and Poverty 1992—). Democrat. Home: 16 Primrose St Chevy Chase MD 20815-4229 Office: Caplin & Drysdale Chartered 1 Thomas Cir NW Washington DC 20005-5801

TROZZOLO, ANTHONY MARION, chemistry educator; b. Chgo., Jan. 11, 1930; s. Pasquale and Francesca (Vercillo) T.; m. Doris C. Stoffregen, Oct. 8, 1955; children: Thomas, Susan, Patricia, Michael, Lisa, Laura. BS, Ill. Inst. Tech., 1950; MS, U. Chgo., 1957, PhD, 1960. Asst. chemist Chgo. Midway Labs., 1952-53; assoc. chemist Armour Rsch. Found., Chgo., 1953-56; mem. tech. staff Bell Labs., Murray Hill, N.J., 1959-75; Charles L. Huisking prof. chemistry U. Notre Dame, 1975-92, Huisking prof. emeritus, 1992—, Charles L. Huisking prof. emeritus, 1992—; asst. dean Coll. Sci., 1993—, P.C. Reilly lectr., 1972, Hesburgh Alumni lectr., 1986, Disting. lectr. sci., 1986; vis. prof. Columbia U., N.Y.C., 1971, U. Colo., 1981, Katholieke

U. Leuven, Belgium, 1983, Max Planck Inst. für Strahlenchemie, Mülheim/Ruhr, Fed. Republic Germany, 1990; vis. lectr. Academia Sinica, 1984, 85; Phillips lectr. U. Okla., 1971; C.L. Brown lectr. Rutgers U., 1975; Sigma Xi lectr. Bowling Green U., 1976, Abbott Labs., 1978; M. Faraday lectr. No. Ill. U., 1976; F.O. Butler lectr. S.D. State U., 1978; Chevron lectr. U. Nev., Reno, 1983; plenary lectr. various internat. confs.; founder, chmn. Gordon Conf. on Organic Photochemistry, 1964; trustee Gordon Rsch. Confs., 1988-92; cons. various chem. cos. Assoc. editor Jour. Am. Chem. Soc., 1975-76; editor Chem. Revs., 1977-84; editorial adv. bd. Accounts of Chem. Rsch., 1977-85; cons. editor Encyclopedia of Science and Technology, 1982-92; contbr. articles to profl. jours.; patentee in field. Fellow AEC, 1951, NSF, 1957-59. Fellow N.Y. Acad. Scis. (chmn. chem. scis. sect. 1969-70, Halpern award in photochemistry 1980), AAAS, Am. Inst. Chemists (Student award 1950); mem. Am. Chem. Soc. (Disting. Svc. award St. Joseph Valley sect. 1979, Coronado lectr. 1980, 93, N.Y. state lectr. 1993, Hoosier lectr. 1994), AAUP, Sigma Xi. Roman Catholic. Home: 1329 E Washington St South Bend IN 46617-3340 Office: U Notre Dame Notre Dame IN 46556

TRPIS, MILAN, vector biologist, scientist, educator; b. Mojsova Lucka, Slovakia, Dec. 20, 1930; came to U.S., 1971, naturalized, 1977; s. Gaspar and Anna (Sevcikova) T.; m. Ludmila Tonkovic, Dec. 15, 1956; children: Martin, Peter, Katarina. M.S., Comenius U., Bratislava, 1956; Ph.D., Charles U., Prague, 1960. Research asst. Slovak Acad. Sci., Bratislava, 1953-56; sci. asst. Slovak Acad. Sci., 1956-60, scientist, 1960-62, ind. scientist, 1962-69; ecologist-entomologist Wast Africa-Aedes Rsch. Unit, WHO, Dar es Salaam, Tanzania, 1969-71; asst. faculty fellow dept. biology U. Notre Dame, 1971-73, assoc. faculty fellow, 1973-74; assoc. prof. med. entomology Johns Hopkins U. Sch. Hygiene and Pub. Health, 1974-78, prof., 1978—; dir. labs. med. entomology; rsch. assoc. U. Ill., Urbana, 1966-67, Can. Dept. Agr., Lethbridge, Alta., 1967-68; dir. Biol. Rsch. Inst. Am. 1971-79; external dir. rsch. Liberian Inst. Biomed. Rsch., 1981—; dir. AID project on transmission of river blindness in areas of Liberia and Sierra Leone; dir. WHO rsch. grant; tech. adv. com. AID Vector Biology and Control Project, 1986-91; dir. Johns Hopkins U./Fed. U. Tech. Akure Onchocerciasis Project in Nigeria, 1991—, Johns Hopkins U./Organisation de Coordination et de Cooperation pour la Lutte les Grandes Endemies-Pierre Richet Inst. Onchocerciasis Project, Bouaké, Ivory Coast, 1993—; dir. Johns Hopkins U./Pierre Richet Inst./ORSTOM onchocerciasis project in Ivory Coast, 1993—; trainer doctoral students, Africa, Asia, Cen. Am., 1979—. Editor: Jour. Biologia, 1956-71, Jour. Entomol. Problems, 1960-72; zool. sect.: Jour. Biol. Works, 1960-71; Contbr. articles to profl. jours. Dir. WHO project on prophylactic drugs for river blindness, Liberia, 1985-87. Recipient Slovak Acad. Sci., 1st prize for research project. Mem. AAUP, AAAS, Am. Inst. Biol. Soci., Am. Mosquito Control Assn., Am. Soc. Parasitologists, Helminthol. Soc. Washington, Am. Soc. Tropical Medicine and Hygiene, Entomol. Soc. Am., Am. Genetic Assn., Soc. of Vector Ecology, N.Y. Acad. Scis., Johns Hopkins U. Tropical Medicine Club, Smithsonian Assocs., Royal Soc. Tropical Medicine and Hygiene, Royal Entomol. Soc. of London, Sigma Xi, Delta Omega (Alpha chpt.). Home: 1504 Ivy Hill Rd Cockeysville MD 21030-1418 Office: Johns Hopkins U 615 N Wolfe St Baltimore MD 21205-2103

TRSTENSKY, SISTER JOMARY, hospital administrator; b. Springfield, Ill., June 12, 1938. BA, Marillac Coll., 1970; MA, Catholic U. of Am., 1972, Ohio State U., 1984. Nursing coord. St. John's Hosp., Springfield, Ill., 1962-65; head nurse St. Mary's Hosp., Streator, Ill., 1965-68; clin. specialist St. John's Hosp., Springfield, Ill., 1972-76; mgr. human resources Sisters Health System, Springfield, Ill., 1976-82; resident Mercy Health Ctr., Dubuque, Iowa, 1983; asst. adminstr. St. Vincent Hosp., Green Bay, Wis., 1984-88; exec. v.p. Hosp. Sisters Health System, Springfield, Ill., 1988-89, pres., CEO, 1989—. Home: 2101 Shabbona Springfield IL 62702 Office: Hosp Sisters Health System PO Box 19431 Springfield IL 62794

TRUBECK, WILLIAM LEWIS, air transportation company executive; b. Chgo., July 5, 1946; s. G. William and Priscilla Jeanne (Nelson) T.; m. Judith Carpenter Williams, Aug. 17, 1969; 1 child, William Andrew. BA, Monmouth Coll., Ill., 1968; MBA, U. Conn., 1976. Fin. sales mgr. Ford Motor Credit Co., Walnut Creek, Calif. and Stamford, Conn., 1971-74; v.p. Aetna Bus. Credit (Barclays Am. Corp.), East Hartford, Conn., 1974-81; corp. v.p., treas. Armco Inc., Middletown, Ohio and Parsippany, N.J., 1981-89; exec. v.p. fin. and chief fin. officer Northwest Airlines Inc. and NWA Inc., St. Paul, 1989—; bd. dirs. IAMS Co., Dayton, Ohio. Served to capt. C.E., U.S. Army, 1968-70, Vietnam. Mem. Fin. Execs. Inst., Nat. Assn. Corp. Treas., Blue Key, Pi Gamma Mu. Republican. Presbyterian. Avocations: golf, tennis. Office: NW Airlines Inc Mpls-St Paul Internat Airport Saint Paul MN 55111

TRUBIN, JOHN, lawyer; b. East Orange, N.J., Aug. 1, 1917; s. Albert J. and Fanny (Babetch) T.; m. Edna Glassman, June 24, 1945; children—Priscilla Jo, Andrew James. Student, Johns Hopkins U., 1935-36, Coll. City N.Y., 1936-39; J.D., N.Y.U., 1943. Bar: N.Y. 1943. Clerk firm Strauss, Reich & Boyer, N.Y.C. 1943-46; pvt. practice N.Y.C., 1946-48; asst. atty. gen. N.Y. State, 1948-50; law sec. to Surrogate George Frankenthaler, 1950-53; chief counsel to Moreland Act Commn. on Workmen's Compensation, N.Y.C., 1953-54; first asst. atty. gen. N.Y. State, 1955-57; partner firm Trubin Sillcocks Edelman and Knapp, N.Y.C., 1958-84; counsel firm Parker Chapin Flattau & Klimpl., 1984-86; pvt. practice N.Y.C., 1986-90; mem. chief investigative counsel N.Y. State Senate Com. on Investigation, 1986-90; mem. N.Y.C. Housing Authority, 1990-94; commr. N.Y.C. Tax Appeals Tribunal, 1994—; mem. com. on character and fitness First Jud. Dept., 1976—. Trustee-at-large Fedn. Jewish Philanthropies; trustee N.Y.C. Police Found., Inc.; bd. dirs. Citizen's Com. For N.Y.C., Inc.; bd. overseers Center for N.Y.C. Affairs, New Sch. for Social Research; bd. dirs. United Jewish Appeal Greater N.Y. Mem. N.Y. County Lawyers Assn. (dir. 1967-73), Assn. Bar City N.Y., N.Y. State, Am. bar assns., Am. Judicature Soc. Home: 26 E 10th St New York NY 10003-5945 Office: 1 Centre St #2400 New York NY 10007-2516

TRUBY, JOHN LOUIS, corporate executive; b. New Kensington, Pa., Nov. 28, 1933; s. George N., Sr. and Bertha (Deyber) T.; m. Mary Ann Holmes Dec. 10, 1952; children: Leslie Ann, Jacque Lee, Barbara Holmes. B.B.A. cum laude, U. Pitts., 1959. Fin. analyst Union R.R., East Pittsburgh, Pa., 1959-64; adminstrn. mgr. Westvaco, Luke, Md., 1964-70; controller Lehigh Portland Cement Co., Allentown, Pa., 1970-72; v.p. finance Lehigh Portland Cement Co., 1972-74; pres. J. Truby Co., Zanesville, Ohio, 1974—, Truby Enterprises, Inc., Zanesville, 1981—, TruCom Inc., 1989—. Past pres. Keyser Jaycees, Mineral County Sch. Bd. Levy; class of 1959 agt. U. Pitts.; v.p. treas. Zanesville Habitat for Humanity; elder Cen. Presbyn. Ch. 1st lt. AUS, 1953-56. Named Outstanding Personality of the South, 1967. Mem. Am. Inst. Individual Investors, Fin. Execs. Inst., Zanesville Country Club. Home: 225 W Willow Dr Zanesville OH 43701-1252 Office: PO Box 2519 Zanesville OH 43702-2519

TRUCANO, MICHAEL, lawyer; b. Washington, May 28, 1945; s. Peter Joseph and Fern Margaret (Bauer) T.; m. Doreen E. Struck, 1969; children: Michael, David. BA, Carleton Coll., 1967; JD, NYU, 1970. Assoc. Dorsey & Whitney, Mpls., 1970-75, ptnr., 1976—. Office: Dorsey & Whitney 220 S 6th St Minneapolis MN 55402-4500

TRUCE, WILLIAM EVERETT, chemist, educator; b. Chgo., Sept. 30, 1917; s. Stanley C. and Frances (Novak) T.; m. Eloise Joyce McBroom, June 16, 1940; children—Nancy Jane, Roger William. B.S., U. Ill., 1939; Ph.D., Northwestern U., 1943. Mem. faculty Purdue U., 1943-88, prof. chemistry, 1956-88, prof. chemistry emeritus, 1988—; asst. dean Grad. Sch., 1963-66; Mem. numerous univ. dept. and profl. coms.; chmn. various profl. meetings. Co-author book; contbr. articles to profl. jours., chpts. to books. Guggenheim fellow Oxford U., 1957. Mem. Am. Chem. Soc., Phi Beta Kappa. Research in new methods of synthesis, devel. new kinds of compounds and reactions. Home: 156 Creighton Rd West Lafayette IN 47906-2102 Office: Purdue U Dept Chemistry Lafayette IN 47907

TRUCKSIS, THERESA A., library director; b. Hubbard, Ohio, Sept. 1, 1924; d. Peter and Carmella (DiSilverio) Pagliasotti; m. Robert C. Trucksis, May 29, 1948 (dec. May 1980); children: M. Laura, Anne, Michele, Patricia, David, Robert, Claire, Peter; m. Philip P. Hickey, Oct. 19, 1985 (dec. May 1993). BS in Edn., Youngstown Coll., 1945; postgrad., Youngstown State

U., 1968-71; MLS, Kent State U., 1972. Psychometrist Youngstown (Ohio) Coll., 1946-49; instr. ltd. svc. Youngstown State U., 1968-71; libr. Pub. Libr. Youngstown & Mahoning County, Youngstown, 1972-73, asst. dept. head, 1973-74, asst. dir., 1985-89, dir., 1989—; dir. NOLA Regional Libr. System, Youngstown, 1974-85. Contbr. articles to profl. jours. Mem. bd. Hubbard Sch. Dist., 1980-85. Mem. ALA, Ohio Libr. Assn. (bd. dirs. 1979-81), Pub. Libr. Assn. Office: Pub Libr Youngstown & Mahoning Co 305 Wick Ave Youngstown OH 44503-1079

TRUDEAU, GARRETSON BEEKMAN (GARRY TRUDEAU), cartoonist; b. N.Y.C., 1948; m. Jane Pauley, June 14, 1980; children: 1 son, Ross, 1 dau., Rachel (twins). M.F.A., Yale U., 1970, D.H.L., 1976. Artist graphics studio, New Haven, CT; syndicated cartoonist, writer. Creator: comic strip Doonesbury; syndicated nationwide comic strip; author: Still a Few Bugs in the System, 1972, The President is a Lot Smarter Than You Think, 1973, But This War Had Such Promise, 1973, Call Me When You Find America, 1973, Guilty, Guilty, Guilty, 1974, Joanie, 1974, The Doonesbury Chronicles, 1975, What Do We Have for the Witnesses, Johnnie?, 1975, Dare to Be Great, Ms. Caucus, 1975, Wouldn't A Gremlin Have Been More Sensible?, 1975, We'll Take it From Here, Sarge, 1975, Speaking of Inalienable Rights, Amy..., 1976, You're Never Too Old for Nuts and Berries, 1976, An Especially Tricky People, 1977, As the Kid Goes For Broke, 1977, Stalking the Perfect Tan, 1978, Any Grooming Hints for Your Fans, Rollie?, 1978, Doonesbury's Greatest Hits, 1978, But The Pension Fund was Just Sitting There, 1979, We're Not Out of the Woods Yet, 1979, A Tad Overweight, but Violet Eyes to Die For, 1980, And That's My Final Offer!, 1980, The People's Doonesbury, 1981, He's Never Heard of You, Either, 1981, In Search of Reagan's Brain, 1981, Ask for May, Settle for June, 1982, Unfortunately, She Was Also Wired for Sound, 1982, Adjectives Will Cost You Extra, 1982, Gotta Run, My Government is Collapsing, 1982, The Wreck of the Rusty Nail, 1983, You Give Great Meeting, Sid, 1983, Guess Who Fish Face, 1983, It's Supposed to be Yellow Pinhead: Selected Cartoons From Ask For May, Settle For June, Vol. I, 1983, Do All Birders Have Bedrooms, 1983, Farewell to Alms, 1984, Doonesbury Dossier: The Reagan Years, 1984, Doonesbury: A Musical Comedy, 1984, Check Your Egos at the Door, 1985, That's Doctor Sinatra, You Little Bimbo, 1986, Death of a Party Animal, 1986, Doonesbury Deluxe: Selected Glances Askance, 1987, Downtown Doonesbury, 1987, Calling Dr. Whoopee, 1987, The Doonesbury Desk Diary 1988, 1987, Talking Bout My G-G-Generation, 1988, We're Eating More Beets, 1988, Read My Lips, Make My Day, Eat Quiche & Die! A Doonesbury Collection, 1989, Small Collection, 1989, The Doonesbury Stamp Album, 1990, 1990, Recycled Doonesbury: Second Thoughts on a Gilded Age, 1990, You're Smokin' Now, Mr. Butts! A Doonesbury Book, 1990, Welcome to Club Scud: A Doonesbury Book, 1991, The Portable Doonesbury, 1993, In Search of Cigarette Holder Man: A Doonesbury Book, 1994, Doonesbury Nation, 1995; co-author: Talks From the Margaret Mead Taproom, 1979; contbr.: includ Nicholas von Hoffman) publs. including The People's Doonesbury; many others (recipient Pulitzer prize 1975) plays include: Doonesbury, 1983, Rapmaster Ronnie, A Partisan Review (with Elizabeth Swados), 1984. Pulitzer Prize for Editorial Cartooning, 1975. *

TRUDEAU, GARRY See TRUDEAU, GARRETSON BEEKMAN

TRUDEAU, PIERRE ELLIOTT, lawyer, former Canadian prime minister; b. Montreal, Que. Can., Oct. 18, 1919; s. Charles-Emile and Grace (Elliott) T.; m. Margaret Sinclair, Mar. 4, 1971 (div.); children: Justin Pierre, Alexandre Emmanuel, Michel Charles-Emile. B.A., Jean de Brebeuf Coll., Montreal, 1940; LL.L., U. Montreal, 1943; M.A., Harvard U., 1946; student, Ecole des Sciences Politiques, Paris, London Sch. Econs.; LLD (hon.), U. Alta., 1968, Queen's U., Kingston, 1969, U. Ottawa, 1974, Duke U., 1974, U. Keio, Japan, 1976, St. Xavier U., N.S., 1982, Notre Dame U., 1982, Dalhousie U., 1983, McGill U., 1985, U. B.C., 1986, U. Montreal, 1987, U. East Asia, Macau, 1987, Mt. Allison U., 1989, U. Toronto, 1991; LittD (hon.), U. Moncton, 1969. Bar: Que. 1944, Ont. 1967; created Queen's counsel 1969. Practiced law in Montreal, 1952—; jr. economist staff Privy Council, Ottawa, Ont., Can., 1949; assoc. prof. law, mem. Inst. Pub. Law U. Montreal, 1961-65; former mem. Ho. of Commons from 1965; parliamentary sec. to prime minister, 1966-67; minister justice, atty. gen. Can., 1967-68; leader Liberal party, from 1968; prime minister Can., 1968-79, 80-84; leader of opposition in parliament, 1979-80, mem. Privy Council., from 1979; mem. Heenan Blaikie and predecessor firms, 1984—; co-founder Cité Libre (monthly rev.); del. France-Can. Interparliamentary Assn., 1966, UN, 1966. Author: Towards a Just Society: The Trudeau Years, 1990, Memoirs, 1993. Decorated Order of Companions of Honor (Gt. Britain). Recipient Order of Merit U. Montreal, 1975, Berkeley citation U. Calif., 1977, Family of Man award N.Y.C. Council Chs., 1981, Ralston prize Faculty of Law Stanford U., Calif., 1990; Albert Einstein Internat. Peace prize, 1984; named Freeman of City of London, 1975, Companion of Honour, 1984, Companion of the Order of Can., 1985, hon. dean Faculty of Law U. Poitiers, France, 1975; hon. fellow London Sch. Econs., 1968. Mem. Canadian Bar Assn., Montreal Civil Liberties Union, Royal Soc. Can. Liberal. Roman Catholic. Office: Heenan Blaikie y Assocs Bur 2500, 1250 boul René-Lévesque Ouest, Montreal, PQ Canada H3B 4Y1

TRUDEL, MARC J., botanist. PhD, Cornell U. Prof. plant physiology and horticulture Laval U., former dean sch. agrl. and food scis., dir. gen. continuing edn. Office: Universite Laval, Ctr Continuing Edn, Quebec, PQ Canada G1K 7P4

TRUDNAK, STEPHEN JOSEPH, landscape architect; b. Nanticoke, Pa., Feb. 25, 1947; s. Stephen Adam and Marcella (Levulis) T.; m. Arden Batchelder Weill, Sept. 6, 1980. BS in Landscape Architecture, Pa. State U., 1970. Jr. landscape architect Kling Partnership, Phila., 1970-72; landscape architect firm Keith French Assocs., Washington, 1972-73; head dept. landscape architecture Linganore Center Design, Frederick, Md., 1973-74; head dept. landscape architecture Toups and Loiederman, Rockville, Md., 1974-76; project landscape architect Dade County Transit Improvement Program, Kaiser Transit Group, So. Calif. Rapid Transit Dist., Metro Rail Transit Cons.; v.p. Harry Weese & Assocs., Ltd., Miami, Fla., 1976-84; v.p. landscape architecture Canin Assocs., Orlando, Fla., 1984-87; dir. planning and design Bonita Bay Properties Inc., Bonita Springs, Fla., 1987-91; prin. Stephen J. Trudnak, P.A., Landscape Architecture and Land Planning, 1991—. V.p. bd. dirs. Koreshan State Hist. Site, 1989-94; mem. 'not for profit' com. Bonita Springs Cmty. Redevel. Agy., 1994—. Fellow Am. Soc. Landscape Architects (pres. Fla. chpt. 1983, chpt. adv. bd. 1984-85, elections task force 1986, publs. task force 1987, trustee 1987-89, membership task force, chmn. 1989-90, nat. v.p. chpt. and mem. svcs. 1992-94, non-dues renewal task force 1994-95), Nat. Xeriscape Coun. (Fla. steering com.), Nat. Speleol. Soc. SCARAB; mem. Bonita Springs C. of C. (chair beautification com. 1991-92, 1994-95). Home: 554 104th Ave N Naples FL 33963-3225 Office: 3461 Bonita Bay Blvd Bonita Springs FL 33923

TRUE, EDWARD KEENE, architectural engineer; b. Boston, July 12, 1915; s. Edward Payson and Laura Keene (Darling) T.; m. Mildred Louise Richenburg, Aug. 31, 1940; children: Edward Bartlett, Robert Payson, Peter Keene, James Duncan. B.S., MIT, 1939. Engr. Concrete Steel Co. Boston, 1939-40; instr. architecture U. Oreg., 1940-42; sr. engr. Raytheon Mfg. Co., Waltham, Mass., 1943-45; mem. faculty Grad. Sch. Design, Harvard U., 1945-76, prof. architecture, 1958-76; trustee, mem. bd. investment Middlesex Savs. Banks, Natick, Mass., 1954-88; cons. engr. and architect, 1947-59; ptnr. Souza and True, engrs., Cambridge, 1959—; engr. Souza and True Inc., 1970, pres. 1970-86; chmn. bd. Souza, True and Ptnrs. Inc., 1986—. Mem. Concord Planning Bd., 1948-58, chmn. 1954-58; mem. Concord Bd. Appeals, 1959-68, chmn., 1959-61; mem. Concord Bd. Selectmen, 1970-76, chmn., 1972-73; mem. exec. com. Mass. League of Cities and Towns, 1974-76. Club: Searsport Yacht. Home: PO Box 483 Searsport ME 04974-0483 Office: 653 Mount Auburn St Watertown MA 02172-2017

TRUE, JEAN DURLAND, entrepreneur, oil company executive; b. Olney, Ill., Nov. 27, 1915; d. Clyde Earl and Harriet Louise (Brayton) Durland; m. Henry Alfonso True, Jr., Mar. 20, 1938; children: Tamma Jean (Mrs. Donald G. Hatten), Henry Alfonso III, Diemer Durland, David Lanmon. Student, Mont. State U., 1935-36. Ptnr. True Drilling Co., Casper, Wyo., 1951—, True Oil Co., Casper, 1951-94, Eighty-Eight Oil Co., 1955-94, True Geothermal Energy Co., 1980—, True Ranches, 1981-94; officer, dir. White Stallion Ranch, Inc., Tucson, Smokey Oil Co., Casper; officer Toolpushers

Supply Co., Belle Fourche Pipeline Co., Black Hills Trucking, True Geothermal Drilling Co., Casper. Mem. steering com. YMCA, Casper, 1954-55, bd. dirs., 1956-58; mem. bd. dirs. Gottsche Rehab. Ctr., Thermopolis, Wyo., 1966-93, mem. exec. bd. 1966-93, v.p., 1973-90; mem. adv. bd. for adult edn. U. Wyo., 1966-68; mem. Ft. Casper Commn., Casper, 1973-79; bd. dirs. Mus. of Rockies, Bozeman, Mont., 1983-87, bd. dirs. Nicolaysen Art Mus., 1988-93; mem. Nat. Fedn. Rep. Women's Clubs; del. Rep. nat. conv., 1972. Mem. Rocky Mountain Oil and Gas Assn., Casper Area C. of C., Alpha Gamma Delta, Casper Country Club, Petroleum Women's Club (Casper). Episcopalian. Office: Rivercross Rd PO Box 2360 Casper WY 82602-2360

TRUE, LELAND BEYER, civil engineer, consultant; b. Cheyenne, Wyo., Aug. 20, 1921; s. James Beaman and Mary Laura (Beyer) T.; m. Janet R. Hill (dec. Aug. 1976); 1 child, Patricia Ann; m. Alef Collins, May 8, 1977. BSCE, U. Wyo., 1943. Hydrographic field asst. U.S. Geol. Survey, Cheyenne and Laramie, Wyo., 1942-43; engr. P.1 Boysen Dam U.S. Bur. Reclamation, Thermopolis, Wyo., 1946-52; with Morrison-Knudsen Co., Inc., 1952-70, 77-86; project mgr. Greer's Ferry Dam Morrison-Knudsen Co., Inc., Heber Springs, Ark., 1961-63; project mgr. Blue Ridge Dam Morrison-Knudsen Co., Inc., Payson, Ariz., 1963-65; project mgr., estimator home office Morrison-Knudsen Co., Inc., Boise, Idaho, 1965-69; project mgr. Toa Vaca Dam Morrison-Knudsen Co., Inc., Villalba, P.R., 1969-70; resident area engr. metro subway A.A. Mathews, Inc., Washington, 1970-77; asst. chief engr. Morrison-Knudsen Co., Inc., Boise, 1977-86; pvt. practice constrn. cons. Boise, 1986—. Staff sgt. U.S. Army Corps Engrs., 1943-46. Mem. ASCE (life). Avocations: fishing, hunting, golf, rocks, RV travel. Home and Office: 1143 Santa Maria Dr Boise ID 83712

TRUE, RICHARD BROWNELL, scientist; b. Framingham, Mass., Apr. 4, 1943; s. Charles Richard and Marjorie Brownell (Clapp) T.; m. Sarah Jellison, Feb. 5, 1966; children: Christopher Edmund, Jonathan Richard. BSEE, Brown U., 1966; MS in Microwave Engring., U. Conn., 1968, PhD in Electrophysics, 1972. Elec. engr. Raytheon Co., Inc., Portsmouth, R.I., 1966; lectr., rschr. U. Conn., Storrs, 1966-72; tech. cons., elec. engr. Microwave Assocs., Inc., Burlington, Mass., 1972-73; sr. engr., dept. analyst Litton Systems, Inc., San Carlos, Calif., 1973-78, sr. scientist, 1978-90, chief scientist, 1990—; cons. True Sci., Sunnyvale, 1985—; bd. dirs. AFTER Program U. Utah, 1980-85, chmn. recruiting brochure, 1981, organizer spl. topics course, 1982, 83, lectr. spl. topics course, 1982-86, indsl. thesis advisor, 1982-87; bd. dirs. AFTER Program Stanford U., 1979-81, organizer spl. topics course, 1980, 81, lectr. spl. topics course, 1978-81, indsl. thesis advisor, 1978-81. Patentee in field; contbr. articles to profl. jours. and papers to meetings. Recipient Paul Rappaport ward for best paper of yr. in IEEE Electron Devices Soc. publ., 1987, Litton Industries Corp. Advanced Tech. award for electron beam dynamics software, 1992; NDEA fellow, 1967-70, NSF fellow, 1970-71. Fellow IEEE (mem. adminstrv. com. electron devices soc. 1988-94, assoc. editor IEEE Transactions on Electron Devices 1986-90); mem. Sigma Xi. Republican. Home: 1760 Karameos Dr Sunnyvale CA 94087-5226 Office: Litton Systems Inc 960 Industrial Rd San Carlos CA 94070-4116

TRUE, ROY JOE, lawyer; b. Shreveport, La., Feb. 20, 1938; s. Collins B. and Lula Mae (Cady) T.; m. Patsy Jean Hudsmith, Aug. 29, 1959; children: Andrea Alane, Alyssa Anne, Ashley Alisbeth. Student, Centenary Coll., 1957; BS, Tex. Christian U., 1961; LLB, So. Meth. U., 1963, postgrad., 1968-69. Bar: Tex. 1963. Pvt. practice Dallas, 1963—; pres. Invesco Internat. Corp., 1969-70, True Rohde & Sewell and predecessor firms, 1975—; bus. adviser, counselor Mickey Mantle, 1969—. Editorial bd.: Southwestern Law Jour, 1962-63. Served with AUS, 1956. Mem. Am., Dallas bar assns., Tex. Assn. Bank Counsel, Phi Alpha Delta. Home: 5601 Ursula Ln Dallas TX 75229-6429 Office: 8080 N Central Expy Fl 9 Dallas TX 75206-1806

TRUEBA, FERNANDO, film director and producer, screenwriter; b. Madrid, Jan. 18, 1955; s. Maximo Rodriguez and Palmira Trueba; m. Cristina Huete, Oct. 8, 1982; 1 child, Jonas-Groucho. Film critic El Pais, newspaper, Madrid, 1976-79; editor, dir. Casablanca, film mag., Madrid, 1981-83. Dir., screenwriter Opera Prima, 1980 (Silver Hugo award Chgo. Film Festival 1980), Mientras el Cuerpo Aguante, 1982, Sal Gorda, 1983, Se Infiel y No Mires con Quien, 1985, El Año de Las Luces, 1986 (Silver Bear award Berlin Film Festival 1987), The Mad Monkey, 1989, Belle époque, 1992 (Academy Award, Best Foreign Language Film, 1993); producer, screenwriter A Contratiempo, 1981, De Tripas Corazon, 1984, La Mujer de tu Vida, 1988-89; producer Lulu de Noche, 1985, El Juego Mas Divertido, 1987, Earth Magicians, 1989—; Amo tu cama rica, 1991, Alas de mariposa, 1991 (Concha of Gold award San Sebastian Film Festival 1991), Sublet, 1992; also dir. short films. Mem. Acad. Motion Pictures Spain (pres. 1988). Home: Bueso Pineda 29, 28043 Madrid Spain Office: Antonio Cavero 37, 28043 Madrid Spain*

TRUEBLOOD, ALAN STUBBS, former modern language educator; b. Haverford, Pa., May 3, 1917; s. Howard M. and Louise (Nyitray) T. B.A., Harvard U., 1938, M.A., 1941, Ph.D.; 1951; M.A. (hon.), Brown U., 1957. Ednl. dir. Chile-U.S. Cultural Inst., Santiago, 1942-43; mem. faculty Brown U., 1947—, prof. Spanish, 1963-82, prof. comparative lit., 1972-82, adj. prof., 1982-87, prof. emeritus, 1987—, chmn. dept. Hispanic and Italian studies, 1967-72, chmn. dept. comparative lit., 1973-77; Fulbright lectr. Am. studies, Colombia, 1972; Sr. Resident scholar Merton Coll., Oxford (Eng.) U., 1973. Author: Experience and Artistic Expression in Lope de Vega, 1974, Antonio Machado, Selected Poems, 1982, (with E. Honig) Lope de Vega, La Dorotea, 1985, Letter and Spirit in Hispanic Writers: Selected Essays, 1986, A Sor Juana Anthology, 1988; transl. Gongora (Picasso), 1985, Garcia Lorca, Complete Poems, 1991, Songs, Lament for Ignacio Sanchez Mejias, Villegas, Colombia from the Air, 1993, Villegas, The Route of Humboldt: Colombia and Venezuela, 2 vols., 1994. Served to lt. USNR, 1943-46. Fulbright research scholar Chile, 1958; Guggenheim fellow, 1965-66; Nat. Endowment for Humanities grantee, 1977-81; recipient Spanish Govt. award Order of Isabel la Catolica, 1990. Home: 54 Willow Ave College Station RI 02837-1532 Office: Brown U PO Box 1961 Providence RI 02912-1961

TRUEBLOOD, HARRY ALBERT, JR., oil company executive; b. Wichita Falls, Tex., Aug. 28, 1925; s. Harry A. and Marguerite (Barnhart) T.; m. Lucile Bernard, Jan. 22, 1953; children: Katherine T. Astin, John B. Student, Tex. A&M Coll., 1942-43; BS in Petroleum Engring., U. Tex., 1948. Petroleum engr. Cal. Co., 1948-51; chief engr. McDermott & Barnhart Co., Colo., Tex., 1951-52; cons. petroleum and geol. engr. Denver, 1952-55; pres. Colo. Western Exploration Inc., Denver, 1955-58; pres. Consol. Oil and Gas., Inc., 1958-88, chmn. bd., chief exec. officer, 1969-88; chmn. bd., chief exec. officer Princeville Devel. Corp., 1979-87, pres., 1984-86; chmn. bd., chief exec. officer Columbus Energy Corp., 1983—; chmn. bd., CEO Princeville Airways, Inc., 1979-87; pres., CEC Resources, Ltd., 1984—. With USNR, 1944-46, ensign, 1949-52. Mem. Soc. Petroleum Engrs., Am. Petroleum Inst., World Bus. Council and Chief Execs. Group. (bd. dirs.), Ind. Petroleum Assn. Am. (exec. com.), Natural Gas Supply Assn. (exec. com.), Denver Petroleum Club, Cherry Hills Country Club, Univ. Club, One Hundred Club. Roman Catholic. Office: Columbus Energy Corp 1660 Lincoln St Ste 2400 Denver CO 80264-2401

TRUEBLOOD, PAUL GRAHAM, retired English educator, author, editor; b. Macksburg, Iowa, Oct. 21, 1905; s. Charles E. and Adele (Graham) T.; m. Helen Churchill, Aug. 19, 1931; children—Anne Williams, Susan Stuart. BA, Willamette U., 1928; MA, Duke U., 1930, Ph.D., 1935; Litt.D. (hon.), Willamette U., 1984. Instr. Friends U., 1931-34; English master Mohonk Sch. Boys, Lake Mohonk, N.Y., 1935-37; instr. U. Idaho, 1937-40; asso. prof. Stockton Coll., 1940-46; asst. prof. U. Wash., 1947-52; vis. prof. U. Oreg., 1954-55; prof. English, head dept. Willamette U., 1955-70, prof. emeritus, 1971—; vis. lectr. U. B.C., summer 1963. Author: The Flowering of Byron's Genius, 2d edit, 1962, Lord Byron, 2d edit, 1977; Editor: Byron's Political and Cultural Influence in Nineteenth-Century Europe: A Symposium, 1981; Contbr. to charter issues Keats-Shelley Jour, 1952, Byron Jour, 1973. Pendle Hill fellow, 1934-35; fellow Am. Council Learned Socs., 1952-53; recipient Disting. Alumni citation Willamette U., 1975. Mem. MLA, Keats-Shelley Assn. Am., Philol. Assn. Pacific Coast (exec. com. 1964-65), Byron Soc. (founding mem. Am. com. 1973, bd. dirs. 1975, delivered lecture to Byron Soc. in Ho. of Lords 1975). Home: Capitol Manor 1955 Dallas Rd NW # 903 Salem OR 97304

TRUEHEART, CHARLES, journalist, university administrator; b. Washington, Sept. 5, 1951; s. William Clyde and Phoebe (Everett) T. A.B., Amherst Coll., 1973. Editorial writer, book editor Greensboro Daily News, N.C., 1973-78; book editor, columnist The News Am., Balt., 1978-81; editorial page editor The News Am., 1979-81; western corr. Publishers Weekly, Los Angeles, 1982-83; contbr. editor Publishers Weekly, 1983—; mag. columnist USA Today, Cambridge, Mass., 1982—; assoc. dir. Inst. Politics John F. Kennedy Sch. Govt. Harvard U., Cambridge, 1983—. Author: Kyrie: Letters to a Friend, 1971; contbr. articles to profl. jours., mags., newspapers. Mem. Nat. Book Critics Circle. Democrat. Episcopalian. Home: 11 Berkeley St Cambridge MA 02138-3409 Office: The Wash Post 1150 15th St NW Washington DC 20071

TRUEHEART, HARRY PARKER, III, lawyer; b. Rochester, N.Y., Mar. 27, 1944; s. Harry Parker and Bertha (Hendryx) T.; m. Karen Ellingson, June 26, 1965; children: Eric Parker, Kathryn Marie. BA, Harvard U., also JD. Bar: N.Y. 1970, Fla. 1975. Assoc. Nixon, Hargrave, Devans & Doyle, Rochester, 1969-77, ptnr., 1977—; spkr. fed. ct. practice, 1979-83; arbitrator, mediator CPR, AAA. Trustee Sta WXXI Broadcasting; bd. dirs. Rochester Downtown Devel. Corp., High Tech. of Rochester, Inc., Park Ridge Found. Mem. ABA, N.Y. State Bar Assn. (chair commal. and fed. litigation sect. 1992-93, house of del.), Monroe County Bar Assn., Fed. Bar Coun (v.p.), Am. Arbitration Assn. Co-author: Federal Civil Practice; contbr. articles on fed. ct. litigation, microfilm records, profl. liability in connection with use of computers to profl. jours. Office: Nixon Hargrave Devans & Doyle Clinton Sq Rochester NY 14604 also: Nixon Hargrave Devans & Doyle 437 Madison Ave New York NY 10022

TRUEHEART, WILLIAM E., academic administrator; b. Stamford, Conn., July 10, 1942. BA in Polit. Sci., U. Conn., 1966; MPA, Harvard U., 1973, EdD in Edn. and Social Policy, 1979. Asst. dir. admissions U. Conn., Storrs, 1966-68, Am. Coun. on Edn. fellow, 1968-69, asst. to pres., 1969-70, dean undergrad. acad. affairs Liberal Arts and Scis., 1970-72; asst. dean, dir. MPA program John F. Kennedy Sch. Govt. Harvard U., Cambridge, Mass., 1980-83; assoc. sec. to univ. Office Governing Bds. Harvard U., Cambridge, 1983-86; exec. v.p. Bryant Coll., Smithfield, R.I., 1986-89, pres., 1989—; cons. Ford Found., 1979-80, 82, Nat. Park Svc., 1983, Lilly Endowment, 1982, Mary Reynolds Babcock Found., 1979-80, Lincoln U., Pa., 1977, Arthur D. Little, Inc., 1974-75; bd. dirs. Fleet Nat. Bank, Blackstone Valley Devel. Found., New Eng. Edn. Loan Mktg. Corp., Nellie Mae, Inc. Roxbury Comprehensive Community Health Ctr., Boston, Narragansett Electric, Wood Hole Oceanographic Instn.; expert witness U.S. vs. Ala. ct. case, HEW vs. N. Carolina adminstrv. hearing; mem. adv. bd. Dorcas Place, Assn. Governing Bds. Author: (with George Weathersby) Production Function Analysis in Higher Education: General Methodology and Applications to Four Year Black Colleges, 1977; contbr. articles to profl. jours. Trustee Pub. Edn. Fund, 1987-93, Bryant Coll., 1981-86, Pomfret (Conn.) Sch., 1972-76; rep. Consortium on Fin. Higher Edn., 1983-86; bd. visitors, vice chmn. Fed. Emergency Mgmt. Inst., 1986-88; chmn. exec. bd., prin. architect Conn. Talent Assistance Coop., 1967-68. Littauer, Travelli fellow John F. Kennedy Sch. Govt. Harvard U., Ford Found. fellow Harvard U. Mem. R.I. Commodores (bd. dirs. 1991), R.I. Ind. Higher Edn. Assn. (vice chmn.). Office: Bryant Coll Office of Pres Smithfield RI 02917-1284

TRUEMAN, WALTER, retired advertising agency executive; b. N.Y.C., Oct. 20, 1928; s. David Frank and Bertha H. T.; m. Enid Prussman, Nov. 7, 1953; children—Beth, Deborah, Glenn, Richard. B.A., N.Y. U., 1951. Advt. services dir. Pepsi-Cola Co., Purchase, N.Y., 1966-74; advt. dir. Royal Crown Cola Co., Columbus, GA., 1974-76; sr. v.p., creative mgr. SSC&B, Inc., N.Y.C., 1976-81; sr. v.p., dir. creative ops. McCann-Erickson, N.Y.C., 1981-87; seminar leader, guest speaker in field. Exec. v.p. H.S. Richards Boys Club, Yonkers, N.Y., 1972-74. Served with AUS, 1946-48. Jewish. Home: 11 Balint Dr Yonkers NY 10710-3942 Office: 485 Lexington Ave New York NY 10017-2630

TRUEMAN, WILLIAM PETER MAIN, broadcaster, newspaper columnist; b. Sackville, N.B., Can., Dec. 25, 1934; s. Albert William and Jean Alberta (Miller) T.; m. Eleanor Joy Wark, Dec. 22, 1956; children: Anne, Mark, Victoria. Student, U. N.B., 1951-54. UN corr. Montreal Star, 1957-62, Washington corr., 1962-65; Parliamentary corr. Toronto Star, Ottawa, Ont., 1965-67; nat. dir. UN Assn. in Can., 1967-68; nat. news writer CBC, Toronto, 1968-69; exec. producer news, head network news CBC, 1969-72; freelance reporter, 1972-73; anchorman Global TV News, Don Mills, Ont., 1974-88; free lance broadcaster, 1988—; media critic Toronto Star's Starweek mag., 1988—; Kingston Whig-Standard, 1989—. Contbg. editor This Country, Can. mag., 1993—. Recipient Bowater award for journalism, 1962, Sam Ross award, 1983.

TRUEMPER, JOHN JAMES, JR., retired architect; b. Helena, Ark., June 18, 1924; s. John James and Mary Ann (Jacob) T.; m. Julia Clare Wood, Nov. 21, 1956; children: Zachary Wood, John James III, Ann Rutland Penick. BS in Arch., U. Ill., 1950; DHL (hon.), Lyon Coll., 1995. With archtl. firm Cromwell, Truemper, Levy, Thompson, Woodsmall Inc. (and predecessors), Little Rock, 1950-94; v.p. Cromwell, Truemper, Levy, Thompson, Woodsmall Inc. (and predecessors), 1972-74, pres., 1974-81, chmn. bd., 1980-89; ret., 1994; mem. Ark. Bd. Architects, 1974-82. Prin. works include Ark. system for edn. and tng. mentally retarded, 1956-78, Winrock Farm, Morrilton, Ark., 1953-58, Ark. State Parks, 1955-75, Ark. Power 7 Light Co., 1961-89, Lyon Coll., Batesville, 1988-94; author: A Century of Service, 1885-1985, 1985. Pres. Ark. Arts Center, 1979, chmn. bd., 1980; mem. Little Rock Bldg. Code Bd. Appeals, 1961-86, chmn. 1971-86; mem. Ark. Hist. Preservation Rev. Bd.; bd. dirs. Little Rock Met. YMCA, 1975-84. Served with USAAF, 1943-46. Recipient Winthrop Rockefeller Meml. award Ark. Arts Center, 1980. Fellow AIA, Greater Little Rock C. of C. (dir. 1979-88). Roman Catholic. Home: 5216 Crestwood Dr Little Rock AR 72207-5404

TRUESDALE, JOHN CUSHMAN, government executive; b. Grand Rapids, Mich., July 17, 1921; s. John Cushman and Hazel (Christianson) T.; m. Karin A. Nelson, Feb. 10, 1957; children—John Cushman, Charles N., Margaret E., Andrew C. A.B., Grinnell Coll., 1942; M.S., Cornell U., 1948; J.D., Georgetown U., 1972. Bar: Md. bar 1972, D.C. bar 1973. Field examiner NLRB, Buffalo and New Orleans, 1948-52; adminstrv. analyst NLRB, Washington, 1952-57, assoc. exec. sec., 1963-68; dep. exec. sec. NLRB, 1968-72, exec. sec., 1972-77, 81-94, mem., 1977-81, 94, 95; dir. info. dir. World Data Center/Rockets and Satellites, IGY, Nat. Acad. Scis., Washington, 1957-63. Served with USCG, 1942-46. Recipient Presdl. award Pres. of U.S., 1988. Mem. ABA, D.C. Bar Assn., Assn. Labor Rels. Agys. (pres. 1992-93). Democrat. Congregationalist. Office: Nat Labor Relations Board 1717 Pennsylvania Ave NW Washington DC 20570-0002

TRUESDELL, CAROLYN GILMOUR, lawyer; b. Oak Park, Ill., July 15, 1939; d. William Bonney and Gladys (Chapman) Gilmour; m. J. Richard Cheney, June 26, 1982; children by previous marriage—Kelly Truesdell Robbins, Robin Trusdell Sher. Student Stanford U., 1957-59; B.A., Case Western Res. U., 1961; J.D., U. Houston, 1975. Bar: Tex. 1975. Law clk. Chief Judge John R. Brown, U.S. Ct. Appeals, 5th Cir., Houston, 1975-76; assoc. Vinson & Elkins, Houston, 1976-83, ptnr., 1983—. Mem. ABA, Nat. Assn. Bond Attys. Office: Vinson & Elkins 2500 First City Tower 1001 Fannin Houston TX 77002

TRUESDELL, CLIFFORD AMBROSE, III, author, editor; b. Los Angeles, Feb. 18, 1919; s. Clifford Ambrose and Yetta Helen (Walker) T.; m. Beverly Poland, Nov. 18, 1939 (dec.); 1 child, Clifford Ambrose IV; m. Charlotte Janice Brudno, Sept. 16, 1951. B.S. in Math, Calif. Inst. Tech., 1941, B.S. in Physics, 1941, M.S., 1942; cert. in mechanics, Brown U., 1942; Ph.D. in Math, Princeton U., 1943; Dottr. ing. honc., Politecnico di Milano, 1965; D.Sc., Tulane U., 1976; Fil.D. (hon.), Uppsala U., 1979; Dr.Phil. (hon.), Basel U., 1979; Dottore di Matematica (hon.), U. Ferrara, 1992. Asst. in history, debating and math. Calif. Inst. Tech., Pasadena, 1940-42; asst. in mechanics Brown U., Providence, 1942; instr. math. Princeton U., 1942-43, U. Mich., Ann Arbor, 1943-44; mem. staff radiation lab. MIT, Cambridge, 1944-46; chief theoretical mechanics subdiv. U.S. Naval Ordnance Lab., White Oak, Md., 1946-48; head theoretical mechanics sect. U.S. Naval Rsch. Lab., Washington, 1948-51; prof. math. Ind. U., Bloomington, 1950-61; prof. rational mechanics Johns Hopkins U., Balt., 1961-89, prof. emeritus, 1989—; hon. prof. applied math. and mechanics Shanghai Inst., 1985. Author or co-author 25 books including Mechanical Foundations, 1952, Kinematics of Vorticity, 1954, Classical Field Theories, 1960, Rational Mechanics of Flexible or Elastic Bodies 1638-1788, 1960, Nonlinear Field Theories of Mechanics, 1965, 2d edit., 1992, Essays in the History of Mechanics, 1968, Rational Thermodynamics, 1969, 2d edit., 1984, Introduction to Rational Elasticity, 1973, Rational Continuum Mechanics, 1977, 2d edit., 1991, Concepts and Logic of Classical Thermodynamics, 1977, Maxwell's Kinetic Theory, 1980, Tragicomical History of Thermodynamics, 1980; An Idiot's Fugitive Essays on Science, 1984, Great Scientists of Old as Heretics in "The Scientific Method", 1987; co-founder, co-editor: Jour. Rational Mechanics and Analysis, 1952-56; editor or co-editor: Leonhardi Euleri Opera Omnia Series II, vols. 11-13, 18, 19, 1952-71; co-editor: Handbuch der Physik, vols. 6a, 8-9, 1956-74; founder, editor: Archive for Rational Mechanics and Analysis, 1957-67; co-editor, 1967-85, editor, 1985-89; founder, editor Archive for History of Exact Sciences, 1960—, Springer Tracts in Natural Philosophy, 1962-66; co-editor, 1967-78, editor, 1979—; editorial bd.: Rendiconti del Circolo Matematico di Palermo, 1971—; Annali della Scuola Normale Superiore, Pisa, 1974—, Meccanica, 1974—, Bollettino di Storia delle Scienze Matematiche, 1979—, Speculations in Science and Technology, 1980-87. Recipient Euler medal USSR Acad. Sci, 1958, 83, Bingham medal Soc. of Rheology, 1963, gold medal and internat. prize Modesto Panetti, Accademia di Scienze di Torino, 1967; Birkhoff prize Am. Math. Soc., 1978; Ordine del Cherubino U. Pisa, Italy, 1978; Guggenheim fellow, 1957; NSF Sr. Postdoctoral fellow, 1960-61; Japan Soc. Sci. fellow, 1981, U.S. Sr. Scientist award Alexander von Humboldt Stiftung, Fed. Republic of Germany, 1986. Fellow Am. Acad. Arts and Scis.; mem. Soc. for Natural Philosophy (founding mem., dir. 1963-85), Socio Onorario dell'Accademia Nazionale di Scienze, Lettere ed Arti (Modena, Italy), Académie Internationale d'Histoire des Sciences (Paris, France), Istituto Lombardo Accademia di Scienze e Lettere (Milano, Italy), Istituto Veneto di Scienze, Lettere ed Arti (Venice, Italy), Accademia delle Scienze dell'Istituto di Bologna (Italy), Accademia Nazionale dei Lincei (Rome, Italy), Académia Brasileira de Ciencias, Académie Internationale de Philosophie des Sciences (Bruxelles, Belgium), Accademia delle Scienze di Torino (Italy), Polish Soc. Theoretical and Applied Mechanics (hon. fgn. mem.), Regia Societas Scientiarum Upsaliensis (Sweden). Home: 4007 Greenway Baltimore MD 21218-1153 Office: Johns Hopkins Univ Computer Sci Rm 222 New Engring Bldg Baltimore MD 21218

TRUESDELL, WESLEY EDWIN, public relations and investor relations consultant; b. Bklyn., Dec. 16, 1927; s. Wesley Edwin and Anna Josephine (Gippert) R.; m. Mabel Johnsen, Oct. 4, 1957. BBA, St. John's U., Jamaica, N.Y., 1956. With Doremus & Co. (advt. and pub. rels.), N.Y.C., 1953-88; v.p. Doremus & Co., 1969-74; dir. Doremus & Co. (advt. and pub. rels.), 1970-88, sr. v.p., mgr. public relations dept., 1974-81, exec. v.p., 1981-88, mem. exec. com., 1978-88, chmn. profit sharing com., 1975-81; dir. Creamer, Dickson, Basford (subs. EuroRSCG, Paris), N.Y.C., 1988-91, exec. v.p., gen. mgr., 1988-89, dep. chmn., 1989-91, also bd. dirs.; pres. The W.E. Truesdell Co., 1991—. Contbg. author: Dealing With The Business and Financial Media, 1989; contbr. articles profl. jours. V.p. S.I. Citizens Planning Com., 1965-72; trustee S.I. Inst. Arts and Scis., 1970-88; chmn. High Rock Park Conservation Ctr., 1970-75. Served with USAR, 1950-52, Korea. Mem. Pub. Rels. Soc. Am. (editor newsletter Fin. Communications Report 1990—), Nat. Investor Rels. Inst. (pres. N.Y.C. chpt. 1979-80), Women Execs. in Pub. Rels. (dir. 1993), Downtown-Lower Manhattan Assn. (dir. 1975-88), Profl. Communicators N.Y., Bklyn. Tech. Rsch. Found. Inc. (bd. dirs. 1988—). Republican. Home: Silver Ct Staten Island NY 10301 Office: The W E Truesdell Co 1633 Broadway 27 Fl New York NY 10019

TRUETT, LILA FLORY, economics educator; b. Emporia, Kans., June 30, 1947; d. Ulysses Earl and Ursula Mabel (Schwindt) Matile; m. Donald Gene Flory, May 26, 1967 (div. 1973); m. Dale Brian Truett, Apr. 4, 1977; stepchildren: Katherine, Patrick. BA in Math., Kans. State U., 1968; MA in Econs., U. Iowa, 1971, PhD in Econs., 1972. Teaching asst., then part-time instr. U. Iowa, Iowa City, 1969-71; asst. prof. Iowa Wesleyan Coll., Mt. Pleasant, 1971-73, Appalachian State U., Boone, N.C., 1973-75; asst. prof. U. Tex., San Antonio, 1975-78, assoc. prof., 1978-80, prof., dir. econs. and fin., 1981—; outside reviewer dept. econs., Colo. State U., Colorado Springs, 1988. Co-author: Intermediate Microeconomics, 1984, Economics, 1987, Managerial Economics, 5th edit., 1995; contbr. numerous articles to profl. jours. Mem. Fin. Execs. Inst., Fin. Mgmt. Assn., Am. Econ. Assn., So. Econ. Assn., Ea. Fin. Assn., Midwest Fin. Assn., Western Econs. Assn., Ea. Econs. Assn., Omicron Delta Epsilon, Beta Gamma Sigma. Brethren. Avocations: reading, music, travel, gardening. Home: 16402 NW Military Hwy San Antonio TX 78231-1224 Office: U Tex at San Antonio Divsn Econs and Fin San Antonio TX 78249-0633

TRUEX, DOROTHY ADINE, retired university administrator; b. Sedalia, Mo., Oct. 6, 1915; d. Chester Morrison and Madge (Nicholson) T. AB, William Jewell Coll., 1936; MA, U. Mo., 1937; EdD, Columbia U., 1956. Asst. dean women N.W. Mo. State U., Maryville, 1939-43; dean women N.W. Mo. State U., 1943-45, Mercer U., Macon, Ga., 1945-47, U. Okla., Norman, 1947-69; assoc. prof. U. Okla., 1969-72, dir. rsch. and program devel., 1969-74, prof. edn., 1972-74, dir. grad. program in student pers. svcs., 1969-74; vice chancellor for student affairs U. Ark., Little Rock, 1974-83; alumni specialist U. Ark., 1983-84, acad. adviser, 1984-87; exec. bd. N. Cen. Assn. Schs. and Colls., 1977-83. Mem. Nat. Assn. Women Deans, Adminstrs. and Counselors (pres. 1973-74), So. Coll. Pers. Assn. (pres. 1970), Okla. Coll. Pers. Assn. (pres. 1972-73), William Jewell Coll. Alumni Assn. (pres. 1970-73), Pi Beta Phi, Alpha Lambda Delta, Mortar Bd., Sigma Tau Delta, Cardinal Key, Gamma Alpha Chi, Kappa Delta Pi, Pi Lambda Theta, Alpha Psi Omega, Pi Gamma Mu, Delta Kappa Gamma, Phi Delta Kappa, Phi Kappa Phi. (nat. v.p. 1986-89). Avocation: novelist. Home: 14300 Chenal Pky Apt 7422 Little Rock AR 72211-5819

TRUHLAR, DONALD GENE, chemist, educator; b. Chicago, Ill., Feb. 27, 1944; s. John Joseph and Lucille Marie (Vancura) T.; m. Jane Teresa Gust, Aug. 28, 1965; children: Sara Elizabeth, Stephanie Marie. B.A. in Chemistry summa cum laude (scholar), St. Mary's Coll., Winona, Minn., 1965; Ph.D. in Chemistry, Calif. Inst. Tech., 1970. Asst. prof. chemistry and chem. physics U. Minn., Mpls, 1969-72; assoc. prof. U. Minn., 1972-76, prof., 1976-93, Inst. of Tech. prof., 1993—; cons. Los Alamos Sci. Lab.; vis. fellow Joint Inst. for Lab. Astrophysics, 1975-76; sci. dir. Minn. Supercomputer Inst., 1987-88, dir., 1988—. Editor: Theoretica Chimica Acta, 1985—, Computer Phys. Comms., 1986—, Topics Physics Chem., 1992—, Understanding Chem. Reactivity, 1990-92; mem. editl. bd. Jour. Chem. Physics, 1978-80, Chem. Physics Letters, 1982—, Jour. Phys. Chemistry, 1985-87, Advances in Chem. Physics, 1993—, IEEE Computational Sci. and Engring., 1994—. Ruhland Walzer Meml. scholar, 1961-62; John Stauffer fellow, 1964-66, NDEA fellow, 1966-68, Alfred P. Sloan Found. fellow, 1973-77; grantee NSF, 1971—, NASA, 1987—, U.S. Dept. of Energy, 1979—. Fellow AAAS, Am. Phys. Soc.; mem. Am. Chem. Soc. (sec.-treas. theoretical chemistry subdivsn. 1980-89, councilor 1985-87, editor jour. 1984—). Achievements include research, numerous publications in field. Home: 5033 Thomas Ave S Minneapolis MN 55410-2240 Office: U Minn Minn Supercomputer Inst 1200 Washington Ave S Minneapolis MN 55415-1284

TRUHLSEN, STANLEY MARSHALL, physician, educator; b. Herman, Nebr., Nov. 13, 1920; s. Henry and Lola Mollie (Marshall) T.; m. Ruth Haney, June 2, 1943 (dec. Dec. 1976); children: William, Nancy, Stanley M., Barbara; m. Dorothy D. Johnson, Jan 10, 1981. AB, U. Nebr., 1941, MD, 1944. Diplomate Am. Bd. Ophthalmology. Intern Albany (N.Y.) Hosp., 1944-45; resident Barnes Hosp., St. Louis, 1948-51; practice medicine specializing in ophthalmology Omaha, 1951—; mem. staff U. Nebr., Clarkson, Immanuel; pres. med. staff Immanuel Hosp., 1961, Clarkson Hosp., 1972-73; prof. ophthalmology U. Nebr. Coll. Medicine, 1974-81, clin. prof., 1981-93, interim chmn. dept. ophthalmology, 1989-90; dir. Nebr. Blue Cross and Blue Shield, 1971-95, vice chmn. bd., 1986—; dir. Health Planning Council Midlands, 1972-75, Clarkson Hosp., 1974-76, Nebr. Soc. Prevention Blindness, Lions Eye Bank of Nebr., 1983-91. Trustee Omaha Home of Boys, 1966— Brownell Talbot Sch., 1966-69, Omaha Citizens Assbmely, 1972—, U. Nebr. Found., 1985—, Action Internat., Inc. 1994— With AUS, 1946-48. Recipient Alumni Achievement award U. Nebr., 1986, Disting. Alumnus Achievement award U. Nebr. Med. Ctr., 1989, Ann. Hon. awards for civic and community contbns.; named Omaha Health Citizen of Yr., 1989; named King Aksarben XCI for outstanding contbns. to Nebr.

community, 1985. Fellow ACS (bd. govs. 1985-91); mem. Am. Ophthal. Soc. (asst. editor transactions 1973-79, editor 1979-84, coun. 1987-92, v.p. 1994), Am. Acad. Ophthalmology and Otolaryngology (assoc. editor transactions 1968-75, editor 1975-80), Am. Acad. Ophthalmology (1st v.p. 1981, pres. 1983, vice chmn. AAO Found. 1992—), Nebr. Acad. Ophthalmology (pres. 1975), Am. Eye Study Club (pres. 1962), Omaha Med. Soc. (pres. 1973), Omaha Country Club (pres. 1977-78), U. Nebr. Med. Ctr. Alumni Assn. (pres. 1958), Masons, Rotary (pres. local club 1981-82), Sigma Xi, Alpha Omega Alpha, Sigma Nu, Phi Rho Sigma. Republican. Home: 10086 Fieldcrest Dr Omaha NE 68114-4939

TRUITT, ANNE DEAN, artist; b. Balt., Mar. 16, 1921; d. Duncan Witt and Louisa Folsom (Williams) Dean; m. James McConnell Truitt, Sept. 19, 1947 (div.); children—Alexandra, Mary McConnell, Samuel Rogers. B.A., Bryn Mawr Coll., 1943; postgrad., Inst. Contemporary Art, Washington, 1948-50. Exhibited in one woman shows at, Andre Emmerich Gallery, N.Y.C., 1963, 65, 69, 75, 80, 86, 91, Minami Gallery, Tokyo, 1964, 67, Balt. Mus. Art, 1969, 75, 92, Pyramid Galleries, Washington, 1971, 73, 75, 77, Whitney Mus. Am. Art, N.Y.C., 1973-74, Corcoran Gallery, Washington, 1974, Osuna Gallery, Washington, 1979, 81, 86, 89, 91-92, Neuberger Mus., Purchase, N.Y., 1986; exhibited in group shows at, Balt. Mus. Art, 1970, 72-73, 82, Whitney Mus. Am. Art, 1970-71, 72, 77, Phillips Collection, Washington, 1971-72, Pyramid Galleries, 1972, 73, Mus. Contemporary Art, Chgo., 1974, 77, Indpls. Mus. Art, 1974, Nat. Gallery Art, Washington, 1974, Corcoran Gallery Art, Washington, 1975, numerous others.; Translator: (with C.J. Hill): Marcel Proust and Deliverance from Time (Germaine Brée), 1955; author: Daybook: The Journal of an Artist, 1982, Turn: The Journal of an Artist, 1986. Guggenheim fellow, 1970; Nat. Endowment for Arts fellow, 1971, 77; Australia Council for Arts fellow, 1981. Home: 3506 35th St NW Washington DC 20016-3114

TRUITT, JOHN H., insurance agency executive; b. Tallassee, Ala., Feb. 19, 1938; s. Woodrow Wilson and Nora Gladys (Taylor) T.; m. Gail Ward, Jan. 31, 1962: children: John Alan, Lee Anthony. LLB, Faulkner U., 1972. Asst. sec. Gulf Am. Fire & Casualty, Montgomery, Ala., 1962-70; mgr. product line Ins. Co. N.Am., Birmingham, Ala., 1970-74; mgr. Reliance Ins. co., Birmingham, 1974-75; sr. v.p. Molton, Allen & Williams, Birmingham, 1975-85; v.p. Krent-Truitt Ins. Agy., Birmingham, 1985-91; pres. Truitt Ins. Agy., Inc., Birmingham, 1991—; bd. dirs. Fire Mark Cir. Americus, Chamblee, Ga. Mem. Ind. Ins. Agts. Am., Ala. Ind. Ins. Agts., Birmingham Ind. Ins. Agts., The Club, Inc., C of C, Sigma Delta Kappa (sec. 1969-70). Baptist. Office: Truitt Ins Agy Inc 3520 7th Ave S Birmingham AL 35222-3211

TRUITT, RICHARD HUNT, public relations agency executive; b. Chgo., June 12, 1932; s. Richard Braeme and Cleon (Johnson) T.; m. Ruth Young, Oct. 4, 1958 (div. June 1983); children: Susan, Thomas, Stephen. B.S. in Polit. Sci., Northwestern U., 1953, M.S. in Journalism, 1957. Reporter, editor Chgo. Tribune, 1957-59; account exec. Carl Byoir & Assocs., Inc., N.Y.C., 1959-67, v.p., 1967-75, sr. v.p., 1975-76, group v.p., 1976-78, exec. v.p., 1978-85; pres. Doremus Pub. Relations, N.Y.C., 1985-91, Arnold & Truitt, N.Y.C., 1992—; adj. assoc. prof. Mgmt. Inst., NYU, k1992—. Author: Strategic Public Relations Counseling, 1987, (with others) History of U.S. Marine Corps Reserve, 1965; contbg. editor Pub. Relations Quar.; contbr. articles on pub. relations counseling to profl. jours. Pres. Winnebago Day Sch., Menasha, Wis., 1969; mem. bd. edn., Neenah, Wis., 1970-71; v.p. Ind. Soc., Chgo., 1976—. Served to maj. USMC, 1953-55, Korea, Japan. Recipient CeeBee award Carl Byoir & Assocs., 1974. Fellow PRSA; mem. Pub. Relations Soc. Am. (sec.-treas. Counselors Acad. 1982, chmn. 1983, chmn. ann. conf. 1985, Silver Anvil award 1973, 74, Thoth award Washington chpt. 1973, elected fellow 1991). Republican. Clubs: Norwalk Yacht (Conn.); N.Y. Yacht; Internat. (Washington). Avocations: sculpting; sailboat racing. Home: 27 Craw Ave Rowayton CT 06853-1608 Office: Arnold & Truitt 171 Madison Ave New York NY 10016-5110

TRUITT, THOMAS HULEN, lawyer; b. St. Louis, Apr. 24, 1935; s. Max O'Rell and Marian (Barkley) T.; m. Nancy Leigh Jenkins, Mar. 7, 1985; children: Anne O'Rell, Lindsey, Sally, Kendall, Elly, Paul, Rebecca. BA, George Washington U., 1960; LLB, U. Va., 1964. Bar: Va. 1964, D.C. 1964, U.S. Supreme Ct. 1976. Assoc. Sellers, Conner & Cuneo, Washington, 1964-70; ptnr. Rowley & Scott, Washington, 1970-71; dir. legal support div. EPA, Washington, 1971-72; ptnr. Truitt, Fabrikant, Bucklin & Lenzner, Washington, 1973-76, Wald, Harkrader & Ross, Washington, 1977-85, Piper & Marbury, Washington, 1986—; mem. adv. bd. Hazardous Substances. Author: (with others) Environmental Audit Handbook: Basic Principles of Environmental Compliance Auditing, 1981; mem. editorial bd. Environ. Analyst, 1980-86; contbr. articles to profl. jours. Sgt. U.S. Army, 1953-56. Mem. ABA, Fed. Bar Assn, Am. Constrn. Owners Assn. (chmn. environ. law com.). Jewish. Avocations: biking, backpacking, reading, hunting. Home: Shadow Valley Farm RR 3 Box 275C Berkeley Springs WV 25411-9561 Office: Piper & Marbury 1200 19th St NW Washington DC 20036

TRUITT, WILLIAM HARVEY, private school educator; b. Alton, Ill., May 27, 1935; s. Howard Earl and Mary Margaret (Haper) T.; m. Janetha Mitchell, Aug. 5, 1961; children: Joy Elizabeth, Janita Ann. BA, Principia Coll., 1957; MA, So. Ill. U., 1964. Headmaster Forman Schs., Litchfield, Conn.; prin. upper and lower sch. The Principia, St. Louis, headmaster. Mem. NASSP, Mo. Assn. Secondary Prins., St. Louis Ind. Sch. Heads, Mo. Ind. Schs. (pres. 1983-84), Am. Coun. for Am. Pvt. Edn. (v.p. 1983-84), North Cen. Accrediting Assn. (exec. bd. dirs. 1988-91). Home: 13201 Clayton Rd Saint Louis MO 63131-1099

TRUKENBROD, WILLIAM SELLERY, banker; b. Orange, N.J., June 19, 1939. B.B.A. U. Wis., 1961; M.B.A. U. Chgo., 1969. Account officer No. Trust Co., Chgo., 1962-71, v.p., 1972-81, sr. v.p., 1981-94, exec. v.p., 1994—. Chmn. Bannockburn (Ill.) Plan Commn., 1979-89, trustee, 1989-91, pres. bd. trustees, 1991—; bd. dirs. Bank Rsch. Ctr., 1988—, Chgo. Crime Commn., 1994—, Pilsen Devel. Corp., 1993—. Mem. Am. Inst. Banking, Alumni Bd. U. Wis. Bus. Sch. (emeritus), Tennaqua Club (Deerfield, Ill.), Univ. Club (bd. dirs. 1985-88), Econ. Club (Chgo.). Republican. Episcopalian. Avocations: tennis; skiing. Office: No Trust Co 50 S La Salle St Chicago IL 60675-0001

TRULL, FRANCINE SUE, research foundation administrator, lobbyist; b. Lawrence, Mass., Sept. 14, 1950; d. Irving M. and Shirley Ann (Barenboim) Leoff; m. David J. Trull, Oct. 22, 1978 (div. 1985). BA cum laude, Boston U., 1972; MA, Tufts U., 1980. Dir. extramural programs Tufts Dental Sch., Boston, 1972-76; asst. dir. office health planning Tufts U., Boston, 1976-80; assoc. dir. Nat. Health Professions Placement Network, Boston, 1978-80; pres. Nat. Assn. Biomed. Research, Washington, 1980—, Found. for Biomed. Research, Washington, 1985-86. Jewish. Avocations: horseback riding, racquetball. Office: Nat Assn Biomedical Rsch 818 Connecticut Ave NW Ste 303 Washington DC 20006-2702

TRULUCK, JAMES PAUL, JR., dentist, vintner; b. Florence, S.C., Feb. 6, 1933; s. James Paul and Catherine Lydia (Nesmith) TruL.; m. Kay Bowen (dec. Oct. 1981); children: James Paul III, David Bowen, Catherine Ann; m. Amelia Nickels Calhoun, Apr. 26, 1983; 1 child, George Calhoun. BS, Clemson (S.C.) U., 1954; DMD, U. Louisville, 1958. Pvt. practice Lake City, S.C., 1960—; founder, pres. TruLuck Vineyards & Winery, Lake City, 1976, Chateau TruLuck Natural Water Co., Lake City, 1990. Member bd. advisors Clemson U., 1978-84; mem. bd. visitors Coker Coll., Hartsville, S.C., 1978-84; pres., bd. dirs. Lions Club, Lake City, 1960-73; chmn. Greater Lake City Lake Commn., 1967-84. Capt. USAF, 1958-67. Recipient S.C. Bus. and Arts Partnership award S.C. State Arts Commn., 1988. Mem. ADA, Am. Assn. Vinters (bd. dirs. 1982-86), Am. Wine Soc. (nat. judge 1982-88), Am. Soc. Clin. Hypnosis (emeritus), Internat. Acad. Laser Dentistry (chartered), S.C. Dental Assn., Florence County Dental Assn., Soc. First Families of S.C. (exec. sec. 1991—), Descs. Colonial Govs. of Am., Descs. Magna Carta Barons Runnymede. Episcopalian. Avocations: genealogy, tennis, sailing, writing. Home: 1036 McCutcheon Rd Lake City SC 29560-1265 Office: 125 Epp St Lake City SC 29560-2449

TRUMAN, MARGARET, author; b. Independence, Mo., Feb. 17, 1924; d. Harry S. (32nd Pres. U.S.) and Bess (Wallace) T.; m. E. Clifton Daniel Jr., Apr. 21, 1956; children: Clifton T., William, Harrison, Thomas. LHD, Wake Forest U., 1972; HHD, Rockhurst Coll., 1976. Concert singer, 1947-54, actress, broadcaster, author, 1954—; author: Souvenir, 1956, White House Pets, 1969, Harry S. Truman, 1973, Women of Courage, 1976, Murder in the White House, 1980, Murder on Capitol Hill, 1981, Letters from Father, 1981, Murder in the Supreme Court, 1982, Murder in the Smithsonian, 1983, Murder on Embassy Row, 1985, Murder at the FBI, 1985, Murder in Georgetown, 1986, Bess W. Truman, 1986, Murder in the CIA, 1987, Murder at the Kennedy Center, 1989, Murder in the National Cathedral, 1990, Murder at the Pentagon, 1992, Murder on the Potomac, 1994; editor: Where the Buck Stops: The Personal and Private Writings of Harry S. Truman, 1989. Trustee and v.p. Harry S. Truman Inst.; sec. bd. trustees Harry S. Truman Found.

TRUMBLE, ROBERT ROY, business educator; b. Wabeno, Wis., Mar. 21, 1940; s. Clarence Lincoln and Celia (Ward) T.; children: Eric, Monica. BA, Hamline U., 1962; MA, U. Minn., 1963; PhD, 1971. Vol. Peace Corps., Lima, Peru, 1963-65; mgr. Latin Am. programs U. Minn., Mpls., 1965-67; asst. dir. internat. programs Cooperative League USA, Washington, 1967-69; program dir. Ops. Research Inc., Washington, 1969-71; chief party Ohio State U., Caracas, Venezuela, 1971-72; div. dir. NIH, Bethesda, Md., 1972-76; sect. head NSF, Washington, 1976-84; dean grad. sch. mgmt. Kent (Ohio) State U., 1984-88; dean sch. bus. Va. Commonwealth U., Richmond, 1988-93; dir. Va. Labor Studies Ctr., 1993—; adj. faculty George Washington U., Washington, 1976-84; pres. Ctr. for Applied Studies, Kent, 1971—; CEO Trumble Investments, St. Croix, V.I., 1987—; bd. dirs. Cen. Allied Ent., Willmar, Minn. Contbr. articles to profl. jours. U.S. State Dept. grantee, 1971-72, State of Ohio grantee, 1986-87. Mem. Am. Assembly Collegiate Schs. Bus., Indsl. Relations Research Assn., Ohio Bus. Deans, Fgn. Policy Assn. (Outstanding Young Person 1968), Mensa, LWV (fin. com. 1987), Delta Sigma Pi, Beta Gamma Sigma, Phi Gamma Mu, Tau Kappa Epsilon (trustee 1960—). Presbyterian. Avocations: Spanish lang., sports, music, painting. Home: 8101 Spencely Pl Richmond VA 23229-8426 Office: VCU Sch of Bus 1015 Floyd Ave Richmond VA 23284-4000

TRUMBULL, DOUGLAS, film director, writer, creator special effects; b. Apr. 8, 1942. Created spl. effects for films including: 2001: A Space Odyssey, 1968, Silent Running, 1971 (also dir.), Close Encounters of the Third Kind, 1977, Star Trek, 1979, Blade Runner, 1982, Brainstorm, 1983 (also prodr., dir.), Spaced Invaders, 1990; inventor Showscan process. Address: c/o Larry Goldberg Goldberg, Nagler & Schnieder 9460 Wilshire Blvd Beverly Hills CA 90212*

TRUMBULL, RICHARD, psychologist; b. Johnstown, N.Y., Apr. 6, 1916; s. Milton Elmer and Hazel (Busse) T.; m. Alice Esther McDaniel, June 17, 1939; children—Judith Trumbull Townsend, Joanne Trumbull Titus, Janice Trumbull Smith, Joyce Ellen Trumbull Setzer. A.B., Union Coll., 1937; M.S., Union U., 1939; Ph.D., Syracuse U., 1951. Asst. prof. psychology Green Mountain Jr. Coll., Poultney, Vt., 1939-41; chmn. dept. psychology, 46-49; lectr. Syracuse U., 1941-43; chmn. undergrad. program psychology, 49-51; mem. research staff Sch. Aviation Medicine, U.S. Navy, 1951-53, asst. head physiol. psychology br., Office of Naval Research, 1953-54, head, 1954-61, dir. psychol. scis., 1961-67; dir. research Office Naval Research, Washington, 1967-70; dep. exec. officer AAAS, 1970-74; exec. dir. Am. Inst. Biol. Scis., Arlington, Va., 1974-79, Renewable Natural Resources Found., Bethesda, Md., 1979-80; chmn. adv. group on human factors NATO; research advisory com. NASA; surgeon gen. advisory com. FAA. Author: Research and Its Management, 1984; joint editor: Sensory Deprivation, 1961, Psychological Stress: Issues in Research, 1966, The Dynamics of Stress, 1986, Scientific Freedom and Responsibility in Psychology, Science and Human Affairs, 1994; contbr. articles to profl. jours. Trustee Green Mountain Jr. Coll.; Biol. Scis. Info. Service. Served with USNR, 1943-46, 51-53. Recipient Navy Distinguished Civilian Service award, 1961, Longacre award in aerospace medicine, 1966; Sustained Super Accomplishment award, 1966. Mem. AAAS, Aerospace Med. Assn., Natural Resources Council Am. (sec. 1977), Sigma Xi. Home: 4708 N Chelsea Ln Bethesda MD 20814-3714

TRUMKA, RICHARD LOUIS, labor leader, lawyer; b. Waynesburg, Pa., July 24, 1949; s. Frank Richard and Eola Elizabeth (Bertugli) T.; m. Barbara Vidovich, Nov. 27, 1982; 1 child, Richard L. BS, Pa. State U., 1971; JD, Villanova U., 1974. Bar: U.S. Dist. Ct. (D.C.) 1974, U.S. Ct. Appeals (3d, 4th and D.C. cirs.) 1975, U.S. Supreme Ct. 1979. Atty. United Mine Workers Am., Washington, 1974-77, 78-79, internat. pres., 1982—; miner, operator Jones & Laughlin Steel, Nemacolin, Pa., 1977-78, 79-81; internat. exec. bd. Dist. 4 United Mine Workers Am., Masontown, Pa., 1981-82; bd. dirs. Am. Coal Found.; mem. Nat. Coal Council, 1985. Trustee Pa. State U. Democrat. Roman Catholic. Office: UMWA 900 15th St NW Washington DC 20005-2503*

TRUMP, DONALD JOHN, real estate developer; b. N.Y.C., 1946; s. Fred C. and Mary Trump; m. Ivana Zelnicek, 1977 (div. 1991); children: Donald Jr., Ivanka, Eric; m. Marla Maples, Dec. 20, 1993; one child, Tiffany. Student, Fordham U.; BA, U. Pa., 1968. Pres. Trump Orgn., N.Y.C.; owner Trump Enterprises Inc., N.Y.C., The Trump Corp., N.Y.C., Trump Devel. Co., N.Y.C., Wembly Realty Inc., Park South Co., Land Corp. of Calif., Plaza Hotel, Trump Tower, Trump Parc, Trump Palace, all N.Y.C., Trump Pla., Trump Castle, Trump Taj Mahal, casinos, hotels, Atlantic City, West Side Rail Yards to be devel. as Riverside South, N.Y.C. Author: The Art of the Deal, 1987, Surviving at the Top, 1990. Co-chmn. N.Y. Vietnam Vets. Meml. Fund; founding mem. constrn. com. Cathedral of St. John the Divine; mem. N.Y. Citizens Tax Coun., Fifth Ave Assn., Realty Found. of N.Y., Met. Mus. of Art's Real Estate Coun.; bd. dirs. Police Athletic League; mem. adv. bd. Lenox Hill Hosp., United Cerebral Palsy; spl. advisor to Pres.'s Coun. on Phys. Fitness and Sports; mem. N.Y. Sportsplex Commn.; bd. of overseers Wharton Sch.; mem. adv. bd. Wharton Real Estate Ctr.; bd. dirs. Fred C. Trump Found.; chmn. N.Y. citizens com. 78th Ann. NAACP Conv., 1987. Recipient Entrepreneur of Yr. award Wharton Entrepreneurial Club, 1984, Ellis Island Medal of Honor, 1986; inducted Wharton Hall of Fame. *

TRUMP, EDDIE, holding company executive; b. 1946. With John Scott & Co. Pty. Ltd., South Africa, 1967-71; chmn. bd. dirs. Woolfson Holdings Ltd., South Africa, 1971-78, Trump Securities Pty. Ltd., South Africa, 1971-78; bd. dirs. Bond Industries Inc., N.Y.C., 1974-91; with Bokap Investments Inc., L.A., 1976-90; with No. Holdings Corp., Seattle, 1985—, now pres. Office: No Holdings Corp 1511 6th Ave Seattle WA 98101

TRUMP, JULIUS, holding company executive; b. 1943; married. Dir. John Scott & Co. Pty. Ltd., South Africa, 1966-71; mng. dir. Woolfson Holdings Ltd., South Africa, 1971-78, Trump Securities Pty. Ltd., South Africa, 1971-78; chmn. bd. dirs. Bond Industries, Inc., N.Y.C., 1974-91; formerly with Bokap Investments Co., L.A.; with No. Holdings Corp., Seattle, 1985—, now chmn. Office: No Holdings Corp 1511 6th Ave Seattle WA 98101

TRUNDLE, W(INFIELD) SCOTT, publishing executive newspaper; b. Maryville, Tenn., Mar. 24, 1939; s. Winfield Scott and Alice (Smith) T.; m. Elizabeth Latshaw, Oct. 14, 1989; children: Stephen, Allison. B.A., Vanderbilt U., 1961, J.D., 1967. Bar: Tenn. 1967. Spl. agt. U.S. Secret Service, 1963-66; asso. to partner firm Hunter, Smith, Davis & Norris, Kingsport, Tenn., 1967-72; pub. Kingsport (Tenn.) Times-News, 1972-78; pres. Greensboro (N.C.) Daily News, 1978-80; exec. v.p. Jefferson Pilot Publs., Inc., Greensboro and Clearwater, Fla., 1980-82; v.p., bus. mgr. Tampa Tribune (Fla.), 1982-91; sr. v.p. Hillsborough Community Coll., 1991-93; publisher Ogden (Utah) Standard Examiner, 1993—; assoc. prof. E. Tenn. State U., 1973-77. Bd. dirs. Downtown Ogden, Inc.; trustee Utah Opera. Mem. Tenn. Bar Assn., Ogden Press Assn. (sec., bd. dirs.), Weber Ogden C. of C. (bd. dirs.). Methodist. Home: 1580 Maule Dr Ogden UT 84403 Office: Ogden Publ Corp 455 23d St PO Box 951 Ogden UT 84402

TRUOG, DEAN-DANIEL WESLEY, educator, consultant; b. Denver, Apr. 1, 1938; s. George Calvin and Zelma Elizabeth (Bennett) T.; m. Dorothy Anne Harding, May 31, 1961; children: David Robert, Denise Dawne. Student, Bethel Coll., 1960-61, L'Abri Fellowship Found., Switzerland, 1967-68; diploma in Bible and Leadership Devel., The Navigators Internat.

Tng. Inst., 1968; BA in European History, U. Colo., 1971; Diploma in Gen. Univ. Studies in French Civilization, U. Strasbourg, France, 1977; MA in Liberal Edn., St. John's Coll., 1986; M of Liberal Arts in History of Sci., Harvard U., 1987; postgrad. Boston U., 1987-93. Sr. resident adv. U. Colo., Boulder, 1964-65; rep., tutor, lectr. biblical studies and practical christianity The Navigators, 1965-93; rep. for greater Washington area, 1965-67; training asst. The Navigators, Colorado Springs, Colo., 1968; rep. at U. Colo. The Navigators, Boulder, 1968-70, No. Colo. dir., 1970-71; spl. adv. The Navigators, Birmingham, Eng., 1971-72; rep. at large The Navigators, Boulder, Colo., 1979-80; founding dir., pres. Les Navigateurs, France, 1972-84; v.p. Les Navigateurs, France, 1984-85, rep. to U. Strasbourg, 1973-79, rep. to U. Grenoble, 1980-85; sr. teaching fellow in non-deptmental studies Harvard U., Cambridge, Mass., 1987-90; tutor North House, Harvard U., 1987-91; founding chmn. Harvard Christian Assocs., 1987-92; speaker, tchr. profl. confs.; designer, dir. leadership devel. programs, Boston, Washington, Colo., Austria, France, Switzerland; founding pres., life mgmt. cons./counselor Cornerstone Inst. for Values and Relationships, 1990—; v.p. U.S.-Bulgaria Inst., Cambridge, 1991—; spl. cons. to mems. U.S. Congress, 1993—. With USN, 1958-59. Mem. History of Sci. Soc., Am. Sci. Affiliation, Soc. of Christian Philosophers, Assn. for Religion and Intellectual Life, Inst. on Religion in an Age of Sci., Ctr. for Theology and the Natural Scis., Rotary Internat., Nat. Assn. Scholars. Presbyterian. Avocations: cycling, gardening, skiing, tennis, reading. Home and Office: 15 Sheridan Rd Swampscott MA 01907

TRURAN, JAMES WELLINGTON, JR., astrophysicist; b. Brewster, N.Y., July 12, 1940; s. James Wellington and Suzanne (Foglesong) T.; m. Carol Kay Dell'Acy, June 26, 1965; children—Elaina Michelle, Diana Lee, Anastasia Elizabeth. B.A. in Physics, Cornell U., 1961; M.S. in Physics, Yale U., 1963, Ph.D. in Physics, 1966. Postdoctoral rsch. assoc. NAS-NRC Goddard Inst. Space Studies, NASA, N.Y.C., 1965-67; asst. prof. physics Belfer Grad. Sch. Sci., Yeshiva U., 1967-70; rsch. fellow in physics Calif. Inst. Tech., 1968-69; assoc. prof. Belfer Grad. Sch. Sci., Yeshiva U., 1970-72, prof., 1972-73; prof. astronomy U. Ill., Urbana, 1973-91; sr. vis. fellow, Guggenheim Meml. Found. fellow Inst. Astronomy, U. Cambridge, Eng., 1979-80; trustee Aspen Ctr. Physics, 1979-85, 91-93, v.p., 1985-88; assoc. U. Ill. Center for Advanced Study, 1979-80, 86-87; prof. astronomy astrophysics U. Chgo., 1991—; Alecander von Humboldt-Stiftung sr. scientist Max-Plank Inst., Munich, Germany, 1986-87, 94. Contbr. articles to profl. jours.; co-editor: Nucleosynthesis, 1968, Nucleosynthesis— Challenges and New Developments, 1985, Nuclear Astrophysics, 1987; editor: Physics Letters B, 1974-80. Co-recipient Yale Sci. and Engring. Assn. annual award for advancement basic or applied sci., 1980. Fellow Am. Phys. Soc.; mem. Am. Astron. Soc., Meteoritical Soc., Am. Phys. Soc., Internat. Astron. Union. Home: 210 Wysteria Dr Olympia Fields IL 60461 Office: U Chgo Dept Astronomy Astrophysics 5640 S Ellis Ave Chicago IL 60637-1467

TRUS, BENES LOUIS, structural chemist; b. Tyler, Tex., May 9, 1946; s. Joseph N. and Ruthie (Mosier) T.; m. Susan Gale Evans, Apr. 23, 1972; children—Aaron Baram, Anthony Phillip. B.S. cum laude with honors, Tulane U., 1968; Ph.D., Calif. Inst. Tech., 1972. Jane Coffin Childs postdoctoral fellow Calif. Inst. Tech., Pasadena, 1972-75; research fellow NIH, Bethesda, Md., 1975-77, sr. research fellow, 1977-80, research chemist, 1980-93; chief image processing rsch. sect., computational biosci. and engring. lab., computer rsch. and tech. divsn. NIH, 1993—; mem. steering com. NIH wide image processing group, Bethesda, 1984— (NIH Dirs. award, 1987, 94). Contbr. articles to profl. jours.; chpt. to book. Tulane U. scholar and fellow 1965-68. Mem. Am. Crystallographic Assn., Chesapeake Soc. Electron Microscopy, Electron Microscope Soc. Am., N.Y. Acad. Scis., Phi Beta Kappa, Sigma Xi. Mem. NIH 1986-88 Marathon Team (1st Place Marine Corps Marathon, Govt. Team Competition 1986, 3d place 1987, 88, 3d place Masters Team, 1993). Clubs: Montgomery County Road Runners, NIH Health's Angels Running. Avocations: music, running, carpentry. Office: NIH Rm 2033 Bethesda MD 20892

TRUSHEIM, H. EDWIN, insurance executive; b. Chgo., May 3, 1927; s. H. Edwin and Lucy (Genslein) T.; m. Ruth M. Campbell; children—John E., Mark R. BS in Edn., Concordia Tchrs. Coll., Chgo., 1948; MA in Polit. Sci., Northwestern U., 1955; postgrad. in polit. sci. and econs., Washington U., St. Louis, 1951-54. With Gen. Am. Life Ins. Co., St. Louis, v.p., 1966-67, sr. v.p., 1974, exec. v.p., 1974-79, pres., 1979—, also chief exec. officer, 1981—, chmn., 1986—; chmn. bd. Fed. Res. Bank of St. Louis; bd. dirs. Am. Coun. Life Ins., Washington. Bd. dirs. Angelica Corp., St. Louis, Civic Progress, St. Louis, United Way Greater St. Louis. Office: Gen Am Life Ins Co 700 Market St Saint Louis MO 63101-1829

TRUSKOWSKI, JOHN BUDD, lawyer; b. Chgo., Dec. 3, 1945; s. Casimer T. and Jewell S. (Kirk) T.; m. Karen Lee Sloss, Mar. 21, 1970; children: Philip K., Jennifer B. BS, U. Ill., 1967; JD, U. Chgo., 1970. Bar: Ill. 1970, U.S. Dist. Ct. (no. dist.) Ill. 1970, U.S. Tax Ct. 1977. Assoc. Keck, Mahin & Cate, (Chgo.), 1970-71, 74-78, ptnr., 1978—. Author, editor Callaghan's Federal Tax Guide, 1987. Served to lt, USNR, 1971-74. Mem. ABA, Ill. State Bar Assn., Chgo. Bar Assn. Republican. Presbyterian. Avocations: model railroading, stamp collecting. Home: 251 Kimberly Ln Lake Forest IL 60045-3862 Office: Keck Mahin & Cate 77 W Wacker Dr 49th Fl Chicago IL 60601

TRUSSELL, CHARLES TAIT, columnist; b. Balt., May 9, 1925; s. Charles Prescott and Beatrice (Tait) T.; m. Woodley Grizzard, Dec. 27, 1953 (div. 1990); children: Galen Tait, Thomas Marshall; m. Nancy Rathbun Billington, Dec. 19, 1990. B.A. in Journalism, Washington and Lee U., 1949. Reporter St. Petersburg (Fla.) Times, also; writer Congl. Quar. News Features, 1951-54; reporter Wall St. Jour., 1954-56, Washington Evening Star, 1956; asso. editor Nation's Business mag., 1956-64, mng. editor, 1964-69; sr. editor Congressional Quar., Inc., 1969-70; dir. pub. relations and advt. Investment Co. Inst., Washington, 1970-72; free-lance writer, real estate investor, 1972-74; v.p. Am. Forest Inst., Washington, 1974-79, sr. v.p., 1980-81; v.p. Am. Enterprise Inst., 1981-86; dir. communications Constitution Bicentennial Commn., 1986-88; free-lance writer, syndicated columnist, 1988—. Producer: documentary record album The Best of Washington Humor, 1963; author: Beating the Competition, 1992; editor: (with others) Successful Management, 1964, (with Paul Hencke) Dear NASA Please Send Me a Rocket, 1964. Served with USNR, 1944-46. Recipient Loeb Spl. Achievement award for mags. U. Conn., 1961, Benjamin Fine Journalism award, 1992. Mem. Washington Assembly (exec. com. 1961-65, chmn. 1965), Soc. Profl. Journalists, Country Club of Mt. Dora, Beta Theta Pi. Home: 6014 Spring Creek Ct Mount Dora FL 32757

TRUST, TREVOR JOHN, microbiology educator and researcher; b. Melbourne, Australia, June 24, 1942. BSc, U. Melbourne, Australia, 1964; MSc, U. Melbourne, 1966, PhD in Microbiology, 1969. Lectr. microbiology Royal Melbourne Inst. Tech., Australia, 1969; from asst. prof. to assoc. prof., 1969-80; prof. microbiology U. Victoria, B.C., Can., 1980—; vis. rsch. fellow Southampton Fac. Med., 1977-78. Mem. Can. Soc. Microbiology, Am. Soc. Microbiology, Brit. Soc. Gen. Microbiology. Research in fish diseases; molecular basis for bacterial virulence and immunogenicity; campylobacter, salmonella, and enteric pathgens. Office: Dept Biochemistry & Microbiology U Victoria, PO Box 1700, Victoria, BC Canada V8W 2Y2*

TRUSTY, ROY LEE, former oil company executive; b. Paris, Ark., Nov. 27, 1924; s. Bennie Otis and Katy Jane (Williamson) T.; m. Caroline Sue Thibaut, Nov. 23, 1950; children: Rebecca Sue, Sara Elizabeth, Jane Ellen, Roy Lee. B.S. in Chem. Engring. La. State U., 1949. Engr. Esso Standard Oil Co., Baton Rouge, 1949-61; mgr. Humble Oil and Refining Co., Houston, 1961-64, Standard Oil of N.J., N.Y.C., 1964-68; pres. Lago Oil and Transp. Co. Ltd., Aruba, Netherlands Antilles, 1970-73; various exec. positions Exxon Co. U.S.A., Houston, 1973-76, sec., 1976-83; trustee, exec. dir. Exec. Service Corps, Houston, 1983—. Served with U.S. Army, 1943-46, ETO. Republican. Methodist. Home: PO Box 103 Round Top TX 78954-0103 Office: Exec Service Corps Ste 910 2401 Fountainview Houston TX 77057

TRUTA, MARIANNE PATRICIA, oral and maxillofacial surgeon, educator, author; b. N.Y.C., Apr. 28, 1951; d. John J. and Helen Patricia (Donnelly) T.; m. William Christopher Donlon, May 28, 1983; 1 child Sean Liam Riobard Donlon. BS, St. John's U., 1974; DMD, SUNY, Stonybrook,

1977. Intern The Mt. Sinai Med. Ctr., N.Y.C., 1977-78, resident, 1978-80, chief resident, 1980-81; asst. prof. U. of the Pacific, San Francisco, 1983-85, clin. asst. prof., 1985—; asst. dir. Facial Pain Rsch. Ctr., San Francisco, 1986-92; pvt. practice oral and maxillofacial surgery Peninsula Maxillofacial Surgery, South San Francisco, Calif., 1985—, Burlingame, Calif., 1988—, Redwood City, Calif., 1990-95, San Carlos, Calif., 1995—. Contbr. articles to profl. jours., chpts. to textbooks. Mem. Am. Assn. Oral Maxillofacial Surgeons, Am. Dental Soc. Anesthesiology, Am. Soc. Cosmetic Surgery, Am. Assn. Women Dentists, Western Soc. Oral Maxillofacial Surgeons, No. Calif. Soc. Oral Maxillofacial Surgeons, San Mateo County Dental Soc. (bd. dirs. 1995). Office: Peninsula Maxillofacial Surgery 1860 El Camino Real Ste 300 Burlingame CA 94010-3114

TRUTTER, JOHN THOMAS, consulting company executive; b. Springfield, Ill., Apr. 18, 1920; s. Frank Louis and Frances (Mischler) T.; m. Edith English Woods II, June 17, 1950; children: Edith English II, Jonathan Woods. BA, U. Ill., 1942; postgrad., Northwestern U., 1947-50, U. Chgo., 1947-50; LHD (hon.), Lincoln Coll., 1986. Various positions Ill. Bell, Chgo., 1946-58, gen. traffic mgr., from asst. v.p. pub. rels. to gen. mgr., 1958-69, v.p. pub. rels., 1969-71, v.p. operator svcs., 1971-80, v.p. community affairs, 1980-85; mem. hdqs. staff AT&T, N.Y.C., 1955-57; pres. John T. Trutter Co., Inc, Chgo., 1985—; pres., CEO Chgo. Conv. and Visitors Bur., 1985-88; pres. Chgo. Tourism Coun., 1988-90; mem. adv. bd. The Alford Group, Chgo., 1984—, Bozell-Worldwide, Chgo.; chancellor Lincoln Acad. of Ill., 1985—. Co-author: Handling Barriers in Communication, 1957, The Governor Takes a Bride, 1977. Past chmn., life trustee Hull House Assn.; honorary chmn. United Cerebral Palsy Assn. Greater Chgo., chmn. Canal Corridor Assn., 1991—; bd. dirs. Chgo. Crime Commn., Abraham Lincoln Assn., Lyric Opera Chgo.; v.p. English Speaking Union, 1989-91, bd. govs., 1980—; chmn. bd. City Colls. Chgo. Found., 1987-91; past chmn. Children's Home and Aid Soc. Ill.; v.p. City Club Chgo.; treas. Chgo. United, 1970-85; mem. Ill. Econ. Devel. Commn., 1985, Commn. on Improvement Cook County Cir. Ct. System, 1985—; past presiding co-chmn. NCCJ; v.p., bd. dirs. Ill. Humane Soc. Found.; numerous others; bd. gov's. Northwestern U. Libr. Coun., 1984—; trustee Lincoln (Ill.) Coll., 1987-90, Mundelein Coll., 1988-91; mem. sch. problems coun. State Ill. Assembly, 1985-91, spl. commn. on adminstrn. of justice in Cook County, 1986-92. Lt. col. U.S. Army. Decorated Legion of Merit; recipient Laureate award State of Ill., 1980, Outstanding Exec. Leader award Am. Soc. Fundraisers, Humanitarian of Yr. award, New Directions award SSMD, 1987, Jane Addams award The Hull House Assn., 1991. Mem. Pub. Rels. Soc. Am., Sangamon County Hist. Soc. (founder, past pres.), Ill. State Hist. Soc. (pres. 1985-87), Coun. on Ill. History (chmn. 1991—), U. Ill. Alumni Assn. (bd. dirs. 1990-94), Tavern Club, Econ. Club, Mid-Am. Club, Alpha Sigma Phi (Nat. Merit Achievement award 1994), Phi Delta Phi.

TRYBUS, RAYMOND J., academic administrator, psychologist; b. Chgo., Jan. 9, 1944; s. Fred and Cecilia (Liszka) T.; m. Sandra A. Noone, Aug. 19, 1967; children: David, Nicole. BS, St. Louis U., 1965, MS, 1970, PhD, 1971. Lic. psychologist, Md., D.C., Calif. Clin. psychologist Jewish Vocat. Svc., St. Louis, 1968-71; clin. psychologist Gallaudet U., Washington, 1971-72, rsch. psychologist, 1972-74, dir. demographic studies, 1974-78, dean grad. studies and rsch., 1978-88; provost, prof. psychology Calif. Sch. of Profl. Psychology, 1988—, chancellor, 1992—; dir. mental health for persons hard of hearing or late deafened Rsch. and Tng. Ctr., 1994—; mem. Sci. Rev. Bd. Dept. Vets. Affairs Rehab. Rsch. and Devel. Program, 1991—; cons. Mental Health Ctr. for Deaf, Lanham, Md., 1982-88, Congl. Rsch. Svc., 1982-84, McGill U. Nat. Study Hearing Impairment in Can., 1984-88. Contbg. author: The Future of Mental Health Services for the Deaf, 1978, Hearing-impaired Children and Youth with Devel. Disabilities, 1985; editor Jour. Am. Deafness and Rehab. Assn., 1988-91. Grantee NIMH, Nat. Inst. Disability and Rehab. Rsch., Spencer Found., Tex. Edn. Agy., W.K. Kellogg Found. Mem. APA, Am. Assn. Univ. Adminstrs., Calif. Psychol. Assn. (pres. div. edn. and tng. 1990-92), San Diego Psychol. Assn., Am. Coun. Edn., Am. Deafness and Rehab. Assn., Am. Assn. Higher Edn., Am. Psychol. Soc. Roman Catholic. Home: 6342 Cibola Rd San Diego CA 92120-2124 Office: 6212 Ferris Sq San Diego CA 92121-3250

TRYGG, STEVE LENNART, advertising executive; b. Ludvika, Sweden, Sept. 19, 1947; came to U.S., 1982; s. Lennart Tore Roland and Ingrid Linnea (Widèn) T.; m. Karin Margareta Hammarstrand, May 31, 1969; children: Tobias, Jenny, Carl. övningselev, Sch. Visual Arts, Stockholm, 1967; cert. interpretation, Tolkskolan (Swedish Army Lang. Sch.), Uppsala, Sweden, 1968; Kandidat in Philosophy, Stockholm U., 1970. Copywriter Anderson & Lembke, Stockholm, 1970-72, pres., creative dir., 1977-82; pres., creative dir. Anderson & Lembke, Stamford, 1985—; creative dir. Lenskog & Co., Stockholm, 1972-77; v.p., creative dir. Anderson Lembke Welinder, Stamford, Conn., 1982-85; mem. specialist adv. bd. ADS mag. Recipient over 60 internat. and nat. advt. awards including The One Show, Clio, Andy, Guldägg. Lutheran. Avocations: boating, carpentry. Home: 74 Gardiner St Darien CT 06820-5114 Office: Anderson & Lembke Inc 79 5th Ave # 17 New York NY 10003-3034

TRYGSTAD, LAWRENCE BENSON, lawyer; b. Holton, Mich., Mar. 22, 1937. B.A., U. Mich., 1959; JD, U. So. Calif., 1967. Bar: Calif. 1968, U.S. Supreme Ct. 1974. Legal counsel Calif. Tchrs. Assn., United Tchrs. L.A., L.A., 1968-71; ptnr. Trygstad & Odell, L.A., 1971-80; pres. Trygstad Law Corp., L.A. 1980—; instr., tchr. negotiation U. Calif.-Northridge; panelist TV shows Law and the Teacher. Bd. dirs. George Washington Carver Found., L.A. Mem. ABA, Calif. Bar Assn., L.A. County Bar Assn., Calif. Trial Lawyers Assn., L.A. Trial Lawyers Assn., Nat. Orgn. Lawyers for Edn. Assns., Am. Trial Lawyers Assn., Phi Alpha Delta. Home: 4209 Aleman Dr Tarzana CA 91356-5405 Office: 1880 Century Park E Bldg 404 Los Angeles CA 90067-1604

TRYHANE, GERALD, newspaper publishing executive. V.p. finance New York Newsday, N.Y.C. Office: New York Newsday 2 Park Ave New York NY 10016

TRYTHALL, HARRY GILBERT, music educator, composer; b. Knoxville, Tenn., Oct. 28, 1930; s. Harry Gilbert and Clara Hannah (Akre) T.; m. Jean Marie Slater, Dec. 28, 1951 (div. 1976); children: Linda Marie, Karen Elizabeth; m. Carol King, Sept. 19, 1985. BA, U. Tenn., 1951; MusM, Northwestern U., 1952; DMA, Cornell U., 1960. Asst. prof. music Knox Coll., Galesburg, Ill., 1960-64; prof. music theory and composition George Peabody Coll. Tchrs., Nashville, 1964-75; dean Creative Arts Ctr., 1975-81; prof. music W.Va. U., Morgantown, 1975—; pres. Luxikon Music, Pandora-Synthe Records, Westover, W.Va., 1983—. Author: Principles and Practice of Electronic Music, 1974, Eighteenth Century Counterpoint, 1993, Sixteenth Century Counterpoint, 1994; past mem. editorial bd. Music Educators Jour.; composer orchestral music, chamber and electronic music. With USAF, 1953-57. Home: 41 W Main St Morgantown WV 26505-4561 Office: Pandora-Synthe Records PO Box 2281 Westover WV 26502-2281

TRZCINSKI, RONALD E., mattress and bedding company executive; b. 1944; married. MBA, Univ. Va., 1971. Pres., dir. Ohio Mattress Co., Cleve.; v.p. Ohio Sealy Mattress Mfg. Co., Cleve., 1975-77, exec. v.p., from 1977, now pres., chief operating officer. Home: 16600 W Sprague Rd Ste 280 Cleveland OH 44130-6318

TRZEBIATOWSKI, GREGORY L., education educator; b. Buena Vista, Wis., May 19, 1937; s. Bert Bernard and Amelia O. (Brychell) T.; m. Maxine Eder, June 18, 1960 (dec. Sept. 1991); children: Peggy, Heidi, Molly; m. Ana Virginia Mangili Godoy, June 5, 1992; 1 child, Gregory L., Jr. BS, U. Wis., Stout, 1959; PhD, Mich. State U., 1967. Tchr. Madison (Wis.) Pub. Schs., 1959-62; asst. prof. U. So. Calif., Los Angeles, 1965-67; from asst. to assoc. prof. Coll. Edn. Ohio State U., Columbus 1967-74, prof. edn. Coll. Edn., 1974-92, asst. dean, 1970-77, assoc. dean med. and grad. edn., Coll. Medicine, 1978-87, prof. emeritus, 1992; rector, pres., chief exec. officer The Thomas Jefferson Sch., Concepción, Chile; dir. Office Geriatrics and Gerontology, 1985-92, Alzheimer's Disease Rsch. Ctr. 1987-92, Ohio State U.; cons. U. Concepcion, Chile, 1979—, Meml. Hosp. Union County, Marysville, Ohio, 1978-87; mem. peer rev. com. Nat. Cancer Inst., Bethesda, Md., 1979-84; cons., sci. rev. com. Pan Am. Health Orgn., Rio de Janeiro, 1978-82; pres., CEO Inmobiliaria Monticello S.A., Talcahuano, Chile. Author: Medical Education for the 21st Century, 1985; contbr. articles to profl. jours.

V.p. Friends of Upper Arlington (Ohio) Library, 1987, pres. 1988-91; bd. dirs. Ohio State U. Friends of Library, 1987-92. Recipient Stout Medallion, U. Wis., 1959, Outstanding Alumni award Mich State U., 1979, Disting. Alumni award U. Wis. Stout, 1980; named hon. prof. U. Concepcion, Chile, 1981. Mem. Alzheimer's Assn. (trustee Columbus chpt. 1988-92), Am. Fedn. Aging Research (bd. dirs. Ohio affiliate 1982-92), Phi Beta Delta (pres. Hon. Soc. for Internat. Scholars Ohio State U. 1989-90, nat. pres. 1990-91). Roman Catholic. Avocations: bicycling, jogging, woodworking, collecting books. Home: Casilla #2532, Concepcion Chile Office: Thomas Jefferson Sch. #26, Avenida Jorge Alessandri Rd, Casilla 2532 Concepción Chile

TRZETRZELEWSKA, BASIA See BASIA

TRZNADEL, FRANK DWIGHT, JR., leasing company executive; b. Chgo., Feb. 7, 1942; m. Sandra S. Murphy; children: Kelly Ann, Daniel Adam, C. Marc. B.S in Bus. and Econs., Ill. Inst. Tech., 1968; M.S. in Taxation, De Paul U., 1974. C.P.A., Ill. Prodn. control exec. Anchor Coupling Co., Libertyville, Ill., 1961-67; asst. treas. J.B. Carroll, Chgo., 1967-68; tax exec. N.W. Industries, Chgo., 1968-72; sr. v.p. fin., treas. Comdisco, Inc., Rosemont, Ill., 1972-84, also bd. dirs.; sr. v.p. Comdisco, Inc., 1976-87; pres. Comdisco Investment Group, Inc., Rosemont, 1987—; pres. Mizzen, Inc., also bd. dirs. Mem. adv. coun. DePaul U. Coll. Commerce, Chgo.; founder, pres. FDT Charitable Found.; bd. dirs. Human Effective Living Program, Chgo., Scottsdale (Ariz.) Prevention Inst. Fellow AICPA, Ill. Soc. CPAs, Gainey Ranch Country Club (Scottsdale, Ariz.), Merit Country Club (Libertyville, Ill.), Paradise Valley Country Club (Ariz.). Avocations: tennis, travel, sailing, golf. Office: Comdisco Investment Group 6111 N River Rd Rosemont IL 60018-5158

TRZYNA, THOMAS NICHOLAS, college dean; b. Evanston, Ill., Nov. 30, 1946; s. Thaddeus and Irene (Giese) T.; m. Martha Hannah Deutsch, Sept. 13, 1969; children: Alexander, Margaret. BA, U. Calif., Berkeley, 1968; PhD, U. Wash., 1977. Asst. prof. Ohio State U., Columbus, 1978-80; from asst. prof. to prof. Seattle Pacific U., 1980—, dean Sch. Humanities, 1987-94, dean Coll of Arts and Sci, 1994—; editor Aquaseed Press, Seattle, 1989—, Calif. Inst. Pub. Affairs, Claremont, 1979. Author: Writing for Technical Professionals, 1987, also poems and textbooks in field; contbr. articles to profl. publs. Episcopalian. Office: Seattle Pacific U 3307 3rd Ave W Seattle WA 98119-1997

TSAI, JAMES TARNG, chemical and plastics company executive; b. Taiwan, China, Nov. 20, 1943; came to U.S., 1966, naturalized, 1976; s. Chin-To Tsai; m. Nancy Lin Tsai, Feb. 1, 1975; children: Jason V., Conne E. BSChemE, U. Tex., Austin, 1968; MSChemE, N.C. State U., 1970, PhD, 1972; postgrad., Research Triangle Inst., N.C., 1973. Sr. engr. plastics divsn. polyolefins group plastics divsn. Mobil Corp., Rochester, N.Y., 1973-79; group leader radiation processing dept., project mgr. conductive heat trace group Raychem Corp., Menlo Park, Calif., 1980-86; sect. mgr. engring. plastics divsn. GE Plastics Tech. Ctr., Washington, W.Va., 1986-90; tech. mgr. vision product divsn. Johnson & Johnson, Jacksonville, Fla., 1989-95; heat shrinkable material tech. dir., Irradiated Wire/Cable Saiplas Co., 1990-94; pres. conductive polymer divsn. Saiplas Corp., 1994—; dir., tech. cons. Saiplastic Radiation Co., 1985—; pres. electron beam radiation divsn. Saiplas Corp., 1989—; CEO Saiplas Material Corp., 1992—; cons., lectr. UN Tech. Exch. Program, 1980-89, Polymer Process Tech. Plastics Material & Engring., Joint Venture E-Beam Process & Material Tech. in U.S., Europe, China, Taiwan, 1990—. Contbr. articles to profl. jours.; patentee in field. Ch. music dir., 1982—. Mem. Am. Chem. Soc., Soc. Plastics Engrs. (sr.). Home: 8544 Hunters Creek Dr N Jacksonville FL 32256

TSAI, TSU-MIN, surgeon; b. Taipei, Taiwan, Dec. 15, 1936; arrived in U.S., 1976; m. Fu-Mei Tsai; children: Yi-Yi Tsai Chen, Ring-Ring Tsai, Berlin Tsai. MD, Taiwan U., 1961. Diplomate Am. Bd. Orthopedic Surgeons with added qualifications in surgery of the hand. Intern Nat. Taiwan U. Hosp., China, 1961-62, resident in urology, surgery and orthopedics, 1964-70; intern U. Louisville, 1976-77, resident in orthopedics, 1977-79; Christine Kleinert fellow in hand surgery U. Louisville Affiliated Hosps., 1976; clin. prof. orthopaedic surg. Louisville Sch. Medicine, 1980—; presenter in field, including dept. orthopedics, Okinawa, Japan, Nat. Taiwan U. Hosp., dept. plastic surgery, Chang Gung Hosp., Taipei, Moscow, Hand Forum, Silverado, Calif., Hua Shan Hosp., Shanghai Med. U., Shanghai, Shenyang (China) Ctr. Hosp., all in 1990, presenter Malaysian Hand Conf., Kuala Lumpur, Internat. Fedn. European Hand Socs., Brussels, others, 1993; Disting. Vis. Prof. Divsn. Plastic and Reconstructive Surgery, Washington Hosp. Ctr., 1990, others. Contbr. articles to profl. jours. and publs. Fellow Am. Coll. Surgeons, Am. Acad. Orthopedic Surgeons; mem. Jefferson Count Med. Soc., Jefferson County Orthopaedic Soc., Ky. Orthopaedic Soc., Ky. Med. Soc., Ky. Pediat. Soc., AMA, Internat. Soc. Reconstructive Microsurgery, Am. Soc. Reconstructive Microsurgery, Western Pacific Orthopedic Assn., Am. Soc. Surgery of the Hand, Hand Forum, Clin. Orthopedic Soc., Japanese Orthopaedic Assn. SICOT Soc. Avocations: fishing, tennis. Office: Kleinert Kutz & Assocs 225 Abraham Flexner Way Louisville KY 40202-1817

TSAI, WEN-YING, sculptor, painter, engineer; b. Xiamen, Fujian, China, Oct. 13, 1928; came to U.S., 1950, naturalized, 1962; s. Chen-Dak and Ching-Miau (Chen) T.; m. Pei-De Chang, Aug. 7, 1968; children: Lun-Yi and Ming Yi (twins). Student, Ta Tung U., 1947-49; BSME, U. Mich., 1953; postgrad., Art Students League N.Y., 1953-57, Faculty Polit. and Social Sci., New Sch., 1956-58. cons. engr., 1953-63; project mgr. Cosentini Assocs., 1962-63; project engr. Guy B. Panero, Engrs., 1956-60. Creator cybernetic sculpture based on prin. harmonic motion, stroboscopic effects; one-man shows include, Ruth Sherman Gallery, N.Y.C., 1961, Amel Gallery, N.Y.C., 1964, 65, Howard Wise Gallery, N.Y.C., 1968, Kaiser Wilhelm Mus. Haus Lange, Krefeld, Germany, 1970, Hayden Gallery of MIT, Cambridge, Ont. Sci. Centre, Toronto, Can., 1971, Corcoran Gallery Art, 1972, Denise René Gallery, 1972, 73, Musée d'Art Contemporain, Montreal, 1973, Museo de Arte Contemporáneo, Caracas, 1975, Wildenstein Art Center, Houston, 1978, Museo de Bellas Artes, Caracas, 1978, Hong Kong Mus. Art, 1979, Isetan Mus. Art, Tokyo, 1980, Galerie Denise René, Paris, 1983, Nat. Mus. History, Taipei, Taiwan, 1989, Taiwan Mus. of Art, Taichung, 1990; represented maj. internat. exhbns., also numerous group exhbns., in permanent collections, Centre Georges Pompidou, Paris; Tate Gallery, London, Albright-Knox Gallery, Buffalo Mus., Addison Gallery Am. Art, Andover, Mass., Museo de Arte Contemporáneo, Caracas, Museo de Bellas Artes, Caracas, Whitney Mus., Chrysler Art Mus., Orlando Sci. Ctr., MIT, Hayden Gallery, Kaiser Wilhelm Mus., Mus. Modern Art, Israel Mus., Jerusalem, Artware, Kunst und Elektronik, Honnover-Messe, Great Exploration-The Hands on Mus., Taiwan Mus. Art, Saibu Gas Mus., Nagoya City Mus., Mus. fü Holographie, Kanagawa Sci. Pk., Hong Kong Sci. Mus., others; commd. works include: fountain at Land Mark, Hong Kong, 1980, water sculpture at Shell Tower, Singapore, 1982, cybernetic upward falling fountains (2), Paris; creator spatial dynamic hydro-cybernetic systems for 42d Internat. Exhbn. Art-La Biennale di Venezia, 1986, Digital Visions-Computers and Art, Everson Mus. of Art, 1987, Contemporary Arts Ctr. Cin., 1987, IBM Gallery of Sci. and Art. N.Y.C., 1988, Phenomena Art Expo, Fukuoka, Japan, 1989, Artec '91, Wonderland of Sci.-Art Kanagawa Internat. Art Sci. Exhbn., Kawasaki, Japan, 1989, Nagoya, Japan, 1989, Vienna Messe-Wiener Festwochen, 1989, Kanagawa Internat. Art & Sci. Exhbn., Kawasaki, Japan, 1989, Artec Grandprix, Internat. Biennale in Nagoya, Japan, 1991 (Artec Grand Prix winner); featured: Art for Tomorrow-The 21st Century, CBS-TV, 1969, Video Variation, WGBH-TV, 1971, Science and Art, Japan TV Man Union, 1982, Art and Sci.-Innovation, Sta. WNET-TV, 1988, The World of Wen-Ying Tsai, Taiwan Pub. TV, 1991. John Hay Whitney fellow, 1963; MacDowell fellow, 1965; fellow Center Advanced Visual Studies, MIT, 1969, 70. Inventor upward falling fountain, computer mural, multiple light computer array, utilizing environ. feedback control system.

TSAPOGAS, MAKIS J., surgeon; b. Athens, Greece, May 7, 1926; m. Lily Philossopoulou. M.D., U. Athens, 1954; MChir magna cum laude, U. London, 1960, DSc, 1967, PhD (hon.), 1991; DM (hon.), U. France, 1993. Intern Ryhope Gen. Hosp., Durham, Eng., 1954-55; resident in surgery Meml. Hosp., London, 1955-56, London Jewish Hosp., 1956, Blackburn Royal Infirmary, 1957-58; resident in surgery Aberdeen Royal Infirmary Med. Sch., Scotland, 1958-59, sr. resident in surgery, 1959-60; research fellow King's Coll. Hosp. Med. Sch., U. London, 1960-61, lectr. in surgery, 1961-63, chief resident in vascular and gen. surgery, 1961-63, sr. lectr. in surgery, 1963-67, attending surgeon, 1963-67; attending surgeon Albany Med. Center, N.Y., 1967-75; assoc. prof. surgery Albany Med. Coll., 1967-70, prof. surgery, 1970-75; chief surg. dept. VA Hosp., Albany, 1967-73; adj. prof. biomed. scis. Rensselaer Poly. Inst., 1970-80; chmn. dept. surgery Ellis Hosp., Schenectady, 1973-75; cons. surgeon St. Clare's Sunnyview, Glenridge and VA hosps., 1973-75, UN, 1993—; prof. surgery, chief vascular surgery Rutgers Med. Sch., 1976; prof. surgery Sch. Medicine, SUNY-Stony Brook, 1977—; also attending surgeon Univ. Hosp.; founding dir. NE Regional Med. Edn. Ctr., Northport, N.Y., 1976—; Hunterian prof. Royal Coll. Surgeons Eng., 1964—; academician (c.m.) Acad. Athens, 1984—; advisor WHO, 1987—, Inst. Internat. Edn., 1993—; vis. prof. Univs. London, Athens, Salonica, Patras, Ioannina, Alexandroupolis, Crete, Nice, Alexandria, 1980—; cons. devel. program UN, 1993—. Contbr. chpts. to books, articles to med. jours. Fellow ACS; mem. Internat. Soc. Surgery, Central Surg. Assn., Soc. Vascular Surgery, Internat. Cardiovascular Soc., Vascular Surg. Soc. Gt. Britain and Ireland (founding mem.), Surg. Research Soc. Gt. Britain and Ireland, Nat. Assn. VA Chiefs of Staff, Assn. VA Surgeons, Brit. Med. Assn., Hellenic Surg. Soc., Hellenic Med. Assn., Pan Am. Med. Assn., Assn. Am. Med. Colls., N.Y. Regional Vascular Soc. (founding mem., councillor), Ea. Vascular Soc. Home and Office: PO Box 457 Northport NY 11768-0457

TSCHANTZ, BRUCE ALLEN, civil engineer, educator; b. Akron, Ohio, Sept. 15, 1938; s. Miles Emerson and Gladys Marcella (Krichbaum) T.; m. Penelope Ann Ford, Dec. 20, 1962; children: Peter Allen, Michael Ford. B.S., Ohio No. U., 1960; M.S., N.Mex. State U., 1962, Sc.D., 1965. Registered profl. engr., Ohio, Tenn., Va. San. engr. Bur. Indian Affairs, Albuquerque, 1962-63; civil engr. White Sands (N.Mex.) Missile Range, 1965; asst. prof. civil engring. U. Tenn., Knoxville, 1965-69; asso. prof. U. Tenn., 1969-74, prof., 1974—, M. E. Brooks Disting. prof., 1978, R.N. Condra Disting. prof.; acting dir. Tenn. Water Resources Rsch. Ctr., 1991-94; cons. hydrologist U.S. Geol. Survey, Knoxville, 1973-76; cons. Exec. Office of Pres. Office Sci. Tech. Policy, Washington, 1977-80, Tenn. Dept. Transp., 1976—, Tenn. Dept. Conservation, 1978; chief fed. dam safety Fed. Emergency Mgmt. Agy., Washington, 1979-80; mem. Tenn. Gov.'s Adv. Com. on Dams, 1972; adviser, cons. Coun. of State Govts., Lexington, Ky.; mem. U.S. Com. on Large Dams; mem. bd. on radioactive waste mgmt. NAS/NRC; mem. Ward Valley, Calif. Rvw. Commn. on LLRW. Contbr. articles on dam safety, flood control, hydrologic impacts of strip mining to profl. jours., chpts. to books. Recipient Engring. Coll. Faculty Achievement award U. Tenn., 1977, Robert Shaw Fulton Engring. Prof. award, 1980, Outstanding Tchr. award, 1985, 89, 91, 92, 93, 94, Engring. Coll. Leon and Nancy Cole Outstanding Tchg. award, 1995; President's award Assn. State Dam Safety Ofcls., 1986, Centennial Distinguished Alumnus award N.Mex. State U., 1988. Mem. ASCE (Faculty of Year award Student chpt. 1968), Am. Soc. Engring. Edn. (civil engr. chmn. S.E. sect. 1972, Dow Chem. award 1969, Western Electric award 1980), Nat. Soc. Profl. Engrs., Tenn. Soc. Profl. Engrs. (v.p., pres. Knoxville br. 1973-75), U.S. Com. on Large Dams, Knoxville Tech. Soc. (Knoxville Young Engr. award 1970), N.Mex. Acad. Civil Engring., Sigma Xi, Tau Beta Pi, Chi Epsilon. Home: 1508 Meeting Ridge Rd Knoxville TN 37931-4427 Office: U Tenn 63 Perkins Hall Knoxville TN 37996

TSCHERNY, GEORGE, graphic designer; b. Budapest, Hungary, July 12, 1924; s. Mendel and Bella (Heimann) T.; m. Sonia Katz, July 7, 1950; children—Nadia, Carla. Student, Pratt Inst., Bklyn., 1947-50. Staff designer Donald Deskey & Assocs., N.Y.C., 1950-53; designer, assoc. George Nelson & Assocs., N.Y.C., 1953-55; pres. George Tscherny, Inc., N.Y.C., 1955—; instr. Pratt Inst., Bklyn., 1956, bd. advisors, 1979; instr. Sch. Visual Arts, N.Y.C., 1955-64; curriculum cons. Phila. Coll. Art, 1967; Mellon vis. prof. Cooper Union, N.Y., 1978. Retrospective exhbn. Visual Art Mus., N.Y.C., 1992; exhibited in group shows, Germany, 1962-67, Italy, 1974, U.S., 1975; represented in permanent collections Mus. Modern Art, N.Y.C., Cooper Hewitt Mus., N.Y.C., Libr. of Congress, Washington, Kunstgewerbeschule der Stadt Zurich. Contbr. design svcs. to UN Assn., Sta. WNET Pub. TV, Am. Lung Assn., Peace Corps, Cystic Fibrosis Found., L.I. State Park Commn. With U.S. Army, 1943-46, ETO. Recipient numerous awards, Am. Inst. Graphic Arts medal, 1988, Art Dirs. Club N.Y., N.Y. Type Dirs. Club; Silver medal Warsaw Biennale, 1976. Mem. Am. Inst. Graphic Arts (pres. 1966-68), Alliance Graphique Internationale. Office: 238 E 72nd St New York NY 10021

TSCHINKEL, ANDREW JOSEPH, JR., law librarian; b. Catskill, N.Y., Aug. 8, 1952; s. Andrew Joseph and Marie Frances (O'Connor) T.; m. Frances K. Quigley, Nov. 4, 1989. BA summa cum laude, St. John's Coll., Jamaica, N.Y., 1975, MLS, 1977; MBA, Fordham U., 1983. Grad. asst. div. libr. sci. St. John's Coll., Jamaica, 1975-77, asst. law libr., 1977-79, adj. law librarian, 1983-87; head librarian Christ the King High Sch., Middle Village, N.Y., 1979-80; sr. law librarian Bklyn. Supreme Ct., 1980-81; prin. law librarian N.Y. Supreme Ct., Jamaica, 1981—. Recipient Pub. Svc. award Queens Borough Pres. and N.Y. Tel. Co., 1986; named Alumnus of Yr. Grad. Sch. Arts & Scis. Divsn. Libr. & Info. Sci. St. John's U., 1993. Mem. Am. Assn. Law Librs., Law Libr. Assn. Greater N.Y., Elks, Beta Phi Mu. Republican. Office: NY Supreme Ct Libr 88-11 Sutphin Blvd Jamaica NY 11435

TSCHINKEL, SHEILA LERNER, banker, economist; b. N.Y.C., Nov. 21, 1940; d. Abraham and Mira (Nevelova) Lerner. BA, Hunter Coll., 1961; MA, Yale U., 1963, postgrad., 1967-68; grad. advanced mgmt. program, Harvard Bus. Sch., 1988. Asst. prof. U. Alaska, Fairbanks, 1963-65, U. Conn., Storrs, 1967-68; instr. Yale U., New Haven, 1968-69; asst. v.p. Fed. Res. Bank, N.Y.C., 1970-79; v.p., dir. global asset mgmt. Chase Manhattan Bank, N.Y.C., 1979-81; exec. v.p. MPH Commodities Corp., N.Y.C., 1982-83; sr. v.p., dir. research Fed. Res. Bank Atlanta, 1984—. Active Com. on Future of the South, 1986, 92; trustee Literacy Action, Inc.; bd. dirs. Atlanta Symphony Orch.; also treas.; mem. exec. bd. Boy Scouts Am. Yale U. fellow, 1961-63; Ossabaw Island Project fellow, Ga., 1977. Mem. Am. Econ. Assn., So. Econ. Assn., So. Fin. Assn., Money Marketeers N.Y. (bd. govs. 1979-82), Internat. Women's Forum, Rotary, Phi Beta Kappa. Avocation: harpist. Office: Fed Res Bank of Atlanta 104 Marietta St NW Atlanta GA 30303-2706

TSCHIRHART, PAUL M., corporate lawyer. BS, UNotre Dame, 1963; JD, Wayne State U., 1968. Bar: Mich. 1968, D.C. 1971, Ill. 1978. Hearing counsel Fed. Maritime Commn., 1968-69; assoc. Coles and Goertner, Washington, 1969-71, Bebchick Sher & Kushnick, Washington, 1971-73; asst. U.S. Atty. Office of the U.S. Atty., Washington, 1973-76; sr. trial atty.civil divsn. U.S. Dept. Justice, 1976-77; trial atty. United Airlines, 1977-82; sr. counsel The Hertz Corp., Park Ridge, N.J., 1982-86; sr. v.p., gen. counsel The Hertz Corp., Park Ridge, 1986—. Office: Hertz Corp 225 Brae Blvd Park Ridge NJ 07656-1870*

TSCHOEPE, THOMAS, bishop; b. Pilot Point, Tex., Dec. 17, 1915; s. Louis and Catherine (Sloan) T. Student, St. Thomas Sch. Pilot Point, 1930, Pontifical Coll. Josephinum, Worthington, Ohio, 1943. Ordained priest Roman Cath. Ch., 1943; asst. pastor in Ft. Worth, 1943-46, Sherman, Tex., 1946-48, Dallas, 1948-53; adminstr. St. Patrick Ch., Dallas, 1953-56; pastor St. Augustine Ch., Dallas, 1956-62, Sacred Heart Cathedral, Dallas, 1962-65; bishop San Angelo, Tex., 1966-69; bishop Dallas, 1969-90, ret. bishop, 1990; asst. pastor St. Joseph Parish, Waxahachie, Tex., 1990—. Home and Office: St Joseph Ch PO Box 190 504 E Marvin St Waxahachie TX 75165-3406

TSE, EDMUND SZE-WING, insurance company executive; b. Hong Kong, Jan. 2, 1938; s. Kai-Sum and Chao-Sui (Chui) T.; m. Peggy Pik-Kin Wai, Dec. 18, 1965; children: Ada Koon-Hang, Elaine Koon-Ming. BA, U. Hong Kong, 1960; diploma, Life Ins. Agy. Mgmt. Assn., 1972, Stanford U., 1980. Mng. supr. Nan Shan Life Ins. Co., Ltd., Taipei, Taiwan, 1970-74, pres., mng. dir., 1975-83; various positions Am. Internat. Assurance Co., Ltd., Hong Kong, 1961-70, pres., chief exec. officer, 1983—, also bd. dirs.; pres. dir. Am. Internat. Assurance Co. (Bermuda), Ltd.; exec. v.p. life ins. Am. Internat. Group Inc, N.Y., 1991—; bd. dirs. Australian Am. Assurance Co. Ltd., dep. chmn., 1988—; bd. dirs. dep. chmn. Australian Am. Superannuation Co., Ltd.; chmn. Nan Shan Life Ins. Co., Ltd., 1990—; vice-chmn. Philippine Am. Life Ins. Co.; pres., chmn. bd. dirs. Green Heights Inc.,

Panama; dir. Met. Land Co., Ltd., Hong Kong; mem. ins. adv. com. Govt. of Hong Kong, 1988; bd. dirs. Am. Internat. Data Ctr. Ltd., USI Far East Corp., Life Ins. Mktg. & Rsch. Assn., Inc.; chmn. Universal Fin. Co., others. Mem. Gen. Ins. Coun. Hong Kong (chmn. 1989-90, chmn. legis. subcom. 1988-89), Hong Kong Fedn. Inst. (dep. chmn. 1991-92, chmn. 1992-93), Chief Execs. Orgn. (U.S.), Pacific Ins. Conf. (nat. area chmn. 1985—), Bus. and Profls. Fedn. Hong Kong (mem. exec. com., fin. specialist group 1993—), Pres. Orgn. (U.S.). Home: 10C Headland Rd, Repulse Bay Hong Kong Office: Am Internat Assurance Co Lt, No 1 Stubbs Rd, Hong Kong Hong Kong

TSE, STEPHEN YUNG NIEN, insurance executive; b. Shanghai, China, Feb. 14, 1931; came to U.S., 1949; s. Koong Kai and Teh-Ying Koo T.; m. Margaret Miray Lock, Sept. 7, 1957; children: Chida, Chiming, Chiyung, Chikai. Student Ripon Coll., 1951-52; BBA, U. Wis., 1955. V.p. investments Am. Internat. Assurance Co., Hong Kong, 1962-64, fin. v.p., 1964-70; v.p. fgn. investments Am. Internat. Group, Inc., N.Y.C., 1971-82, sr. v.p., 1982—; pres., chief exec. officer AIG Assocs., 1986—; bd. dirs. Am. Internat. Assurance Co., Am. Internat. Underwriters, Ltd., Tai Ping Carpets Internat. Ltd., Worldwide Looms, Ltd., AIG Realty Inc., C.V. Starr & Co., Inc. Mem. Sky Club, Club at the World Trade Ctr., India House Club, Hong Kong Country CLub, Am. Club of Hong Kong, Royal Hong Kong Golf Club, Beta Theta Pi. Office: Am Internat Group Inc 70 Pine St New York NY 10270-0001

TSIAPERA, MARIA, linguistics educator; b. Cyprus, July 26, 1935; naturalized, 1964; d. Anastasis and Aphrodite T.; m. Jeff Beaubier, May 1, 1969; 1 dau., Nike Tsiapera. B.A., U. Tex., Austin, 1957, M.A., 1959, Ph.D., 1963. Asst. prof. linguistics Fresno (Calif.) State U., 1964-66; asst. prof. U. N.C., Chapel Hill, 1966-67, assoc. prof., chmn. dept., 1967-72, prof., chmn., 1972-73, prof., 1973—. Author: Maronite Cypriot Arabic, 1969, Generative Studies in Historical Linguistics, 1971; The Port-Royal Grammar: Sources and Influences, 1993; contbr. articles to profl. jours. NSF travel grantee, 1977; U. N.C. research grantee, 1967, 69, 72, 74, 77. Mem. Linguistic Soc. Am. (exec. com.), Southeastern Conf. Linguistics (founder, pres.), Am. Oriental Soc., Modern Greek Studies Assn., Am. Assn. Tchrs. Arabic, N.Am. Assn. for History of Lang. Scis. (v.p., pres.-elect 1992). Democrat. Greek Orthodox. Research on history and philosophy of linguistics and human scis. since 1660. Home: 1051 Burning Tree Dr Chapel Hill NC 27514-5657 Office: U NC Dept Linguistics Chapel Hill NC 27514

TSIEN, RICHARD WINYU, biology educator; b. Tating, Kweichow, People's Republic China, Mar. 3, 1945; s. Hsue-Chu and Yi-Ying (Li) T.; m. Julia Shiang; children: Sara Shiang-Ming, Gregory Shiang-An, Alexa Tsien-Shiang. BS, MIT, 1965, MS, 1966; DPhil, Oxford U., Eng., 1970. Rsch. student Eaton Peabody Lab. Auditory, Physiology, Mass. Eye and Ear Infirmary, 1966; asst. prof. dept. physiology, Yale U. Sch. Medicine, New Haven, 1970-74, assoc. prof., 1974-79, prof., 1979-88; George D. Smith prof. molecular and cellular physiology Stanford (Calif.) U., 1988—, chmn. dept., 1988—; established investigator Am. Heart Assn., 1974-79. Author: Electric Current Flow in Excitable Cells, 1975. Recipient Otsuka award internat. Soc. Heart Rsch., 1985; Rhodes Scholar, 1966; Weir Rsch. fellow, 1966-70 Univ. Coll., Oxford, 1966-70, lecturing fellow Balliol Coll., Oxford, 1969-70. Mem. Gen. Soc. Physiologists (pres. 1988), Biophys. Soc. (Kenneth S. Cole award 1985), Soc. for Neurosci. Democrat. Home: 866 Tolman Dr Palo Alto CA 94305-1026 Office: Stanford U Dept Molecular and Cellular Physiology 300 Pasteur Dr Stanford CA 94305

TSINA, RICHARD VASIL, chemistry educator; b. Boston, Aug. 13, 1941; s. Vasil Anastas and Theodora (Kasuli) T.; m. Irene Wang, Nov. 28, 1970; children: Lesley, Katherine. BA, Boston U., 1963; MA, Duke U., 1965; PhD, Tufts U., 1968. Asst. prof. chemistry Rutgers U., New Brunswick, N.J., 1970-73; v.p. Sultra Corp., N.Y.C., 1973-76; dean continuing edn. Cogswell Coll., San Francisco, 1976-79; asst. dean, chmn. engring. ext. U. Calif., Berkeley, 1979—. Contbr. articles to profl. jours. Mem. IEEE (chmn. San Francisco sect. 1984-85, chmn. fin. council 1985-86, cert. appreciation 1984), Am. Soc. Engring. Edn. (chmn. continuing devel. 1978-85), Am. Chem. Soc., Sigma Xi, Tau Beta Pi (eminent engr. com.). Avocations: music, reading, hiking. Home: 1424 Dana Ave Palo Alto CA 94301-3149 Office: U Calif Continuing Edn Engring 2223 Fulton St Berkeley CA 94720-2307

TSIPIS, KOSTA MICHAEL, science educator; b. Athens, Greece, Feb. 12, 1934; s. Michael Kosta and Zoe (Alexiou) T.; m. Judith Ebel, Dec. 20, 1970; children: Mikael, Andreas, Yanni. BSc, Rutgers U., 1958, MSc, 1960; PhD, Columbia U., 1966. From asst. prof. to sr. rsch. sci. MIT, Cambridge, 1966—; dir. program in sci. and tech. internat. security. Author: Tactical and Strategic Antisubmarine Warfare, 1974, Arsenal-Understanding Weapons in the Nuclear Age, 1985, Kosta Tsipis on the Arms Race-A Collection of Critical Essays, 1987, New Technologies, Defense Policy and Arms Control, 1989; editor: The Future of the Sea-Based Deterrent, 1973, Military R&D., 1977, Tutorials on Nuclear Weapons, 1983, Annual Review of Military Research and Development, 1983, and others; contbr. articles to profl. jours. and chpts. in books. Fellow Am. Physical Soc. (Szilard award 1983), AAAS; mem. N.Y. Acad. Scis. Office: MIT 77 Massachusetts Ave Cambridge MA 02139-4307

TSIRPANLIS, CONSTANTINE N., theology, classics and history educator; b. Kos, Greece, Mar. 18, 1935; came to U.S., 1957; m. Sophia Pappas, July 12, 1975; children: Kalliope-Chrysoula, Nike. BA, STM, lic. in theology magna cum laude, Halke Theol. Sem., Istanbul, Turkey, 1957; ThM, Harvard U., 1962; ThD, Union Theol. Sem., 1963; MA, Columbia U., 1966, PhD, 1970; PhD, Fordham U., 1973. Instr., organizer Greek-Am. communities, 1958-63; founder, chmn., prof. modern Greek studies NYU, 1963-70; prof. world history N.Y. Inst. Tech. N.Y.C. and Delaware County Coll., Media, Pa., 1967-75; disting. prof. theology, history and Greek studies Union Theol. Sem., Barrytown, N.Y., 1976—; chmn., prof. classics Collegiate Sch., N.Y.C., 1967-69; prof. modern Greek lang. and lit. New Sch. for Social Rsch., N.Y.C., 1968-70; prof. classical mythology Hunter Coll. CUNY, 1968-70. Author numerous books including A Short History of the Greek Language, 1966, rev. edit., 1970, A Modern Greek Reader for Americans, 1967, rev. edit., 1968, A Modern Greek Idiom and Phrase Book, 1978, Mark Eugenicus, 1979, N. Cabasilas, 1979, Greek Patristic Theology, 9 vols.; editor The Patristic and Byzantine Rev., 1981—; contbr. articles to profl. jours. Decorated Medal of Nat. Rebirth 1821 (Greece), medals of Byzantine Nobility, including count, baron, G. chevalier, Gt. Prior of N.Am., medal of Accademia Ferdinandea. Mem. Am. Soc. Neohellenic Studies (founder, v.p.), Pan Dodecanisian Fedn. U.S., Am. Hist. Assn., Am. Philog. Assn., Am. Acad. Medieval Studies, Internat. Assn. Byzantine Studies, Am. Philos. Assn., N.Am. Patristic Soc., Hellenic Philog. Assn., Am. Soc. Papyrologists. Home: 12 Minuet Ln Kingston NY 12401-9801

TSIVIDIS, YANNIS P., electrical engineering educator; b. Piraeus, Greece, Dec. 22, 1946; came to U.S., 1970; s. Pelopidas I. and Maria (Filippa) T. BS, U. Minn., 1972; MS, U. Calif., Berkeley, 1973, PhD, 1976. Asst. prof. elec. engring. Columbia U., N.Y.C., 1976-81, assoc. prof., 1981-84, prof., 1984-92; adj. prof. Nat. Tech. U. Athens, Greece, 1992—; cons. AT&T Bell Labs., Murray Hill, N.J., 1977-88. Author: Operation and Modeling on the Mos Transistor, 1987; co-editor: Design of Mos VLSI Circuits for Telecommunications, 1985; also over 100 articles; patentee in field. Recipient best paper award European Solid State Cirs. Conf., 1986, Great Tchr. award Columbia U., 1991. Fellow IEEE (Baker best paper award 1984, Darlington award 1987). Office: Columbia Univ Dept Elec Engring New York NY 10027

TS'O, PAUL ON-PONG, biophysical chemist, educator; b. July 17, 1929. B.S., Lingnan U., 1949; M.S., Mich. State U., 1951; Ph.D., Calif. Inst. Tech., 1955. Teaching asst. Calif. Inst. Tech., 1952-55, rsch. fellow biology div., 1955-61, sr. rsch. fellow, 1961-62; assoc. prof. biophys. chemistry dept. radiol. scis. Johns Hopkins U., Balt., 1962-67; prof. Johns Hopkins U., 1967-73, prof. dir. div. biophysics Sch. Hygiene and Pub. Health, 1973-90, prof. dept. biochemistry, 1973—; cons. Nat. Cancer Inst., 1972-75; mem. study sect. A on biophysics and biophys. chemistry NIH, 1976-80; mem. Clearinghouse on Environ. Carcinogens, Nat. Cancer Inst., 1976-80; mem. European expert com. on biophysics UNESCO; mem. sci. com. of the consortium Internat. Biomed. Inst., Bari, Italy. Editor: Basic Principles in

Nucleic Acid Chemistry, Vol. I and II, 1974, The Molecular Biology of the Mammalian Genetic Apparatus, Vol. I and II, 1977; co-editor: The Nucleohistones, 1964, Chemical Carcinogenesis, Part A and Part B, 1974, Polycyclic Hydrocarbons and Cancer: Environment, Chemistry and Metabolism; and Molecular and Cell Biology, Vol. 1 and 2, 1978, Vol. 3, 1981, Carcinogenesis: Fundamental Mechanisms and Environmental Effects, 1980, Interrelationship Among Aging, Cancer and Differentiation, 1985, Structure and Function of the Genetic Apparatus, 1986; mem. editorial bd. Molecular Pharmacology, 1964-83, Biophys. Jour, 1969-72, Biochimica et Biophysica Acta, 1971-81, Cancer Rev, 1973-84, Jour. Environ. Health Scis, 1969-81; assoc. editor: Cancer Research, 1975-87; mem. editorial adv. bd. Biochemistry, 1966-74, Biopolymers, 1979-85; contbr. over 350 articles and revs. to profl. jours. Named Md. Chemist of Yr., 1981; named One of 1000 Most Cited Scientists, Citation Index, 1965-78. Fellow AAAS; mem. Biophys. Soc. (chmn. pub. sci. policy com. 1972-76, coun. mem. 1975-78, exec. bd. 1975), Am. Soc. Biol. Chemists, Am. Soc. Microbiology, Am. Soc. Cell Biology, Biology Alliance for Pub. Affairs (chmn. organizing com. 1973-76), Am. Assn. Cancer Rsch., Am. Chem. Soc., Acadmia Sinica (1st dir. inst. molecular biology, chmn. adv. com. 1982-94), European Acad. Arts, Scis. and Humanities, Sigma Xi. Office: Johns Hopkins U Sch Hygiene and Pub Health Dept Biochemistry Rm 3102 Baltimore MD 21205

TSO, TIEN CHIOH, federal agency official, plant physiologist; b. Hupeh, China, July 25, 1917; came to U.S., 1947, naturalized, 1961; s. Ya Fu and Suhwa (Wang) T.; m. Margaret Lu, Aug. 28, 1949; children: Elizabeth, Paul. B.S., Nanking U., China, 1941, M.S., 1944; Ph.D., Pa. State U., 1950; postgrad., Oak Ridge Inst. Nuclear Studies. Supt. exptl. farm Ministry Social Affairs, China, 1944-46; exec. sec. Tobacco Improvement Bur., 1946-47; research chemist Gen. Cigar Research Lab., 1950-51; with U.S. Dept. Agr., 1952—; prin. plant physiologist crop research div. Agrl. Research Service, Beltsville, Md., 1964-66; leader tobacco quality investigations, tobacco and sugar crops research br. Agrl. Research Service, 1966-71, chief tobacco lab., 1972-83, sr. exec. service, 1974-83, collaborator, 1984—; exec. dir. Internat. Devel. and Edn. in Agr. and Life Scis., 1984—; cons. Nat. Cancer Inst., Ky. Tobacco Health Rsch. Inst., China Nat. Tobacco Corp., Philippine Tobacco Rsch. Ctr., Philip Morris Tobacco Corp. Author: Physiology and Biochemistry of Tobacco Plants, 1972, Production, Physiology and Biochemistry of Tobacco Plants, 1991; contbg. author: Ann. Rev. Plant Physiology, Vol. 9, 1958, The Chemistry of Tobacco and Tobacco Smoke, 1972, Toward Less Harmful Cigarettes, 1968, 71, 75, 80; editor: Structural and Functional Aspects of Phytochemistry, 1972, Recent Advances in Tobacco Science, vol. 1, 1975. Fellow AAAS, Am. Soc. Agronomy (chmn. colloquium on agr. and life scis. in China 1983, 84, 85, 86, 87, 88-89), Am. Inst. Chemists; mem. Am. Chem. Soc., Am. Soc. Plant Physiologists, Phytochem. Soc. N.Am. (pres. 1971, life mem.), Tobacco Chemists Rsch. Conf. (symposium chmn. 1965, 79, chmn. 1975, 83), World Conf. Smoking and Health (sect. chmn. 1967, 71, 75), Tobacco Workers Conf. N.Y. Acad. Scis., Interagy. Smoking and Health Forum (chmn. 1979-83), Nat. Coordinating Com. on Tobacco-Related Rsch., Sigma Xi, Gamma Sigma Delta. Research publs. on establishment of loci of alkaloid formation, biosynthetic pathway, interconversion and fate of alkaloids in tobacco plants, chem. composition as affected by macro and micro elements, homogenized leaf curing, health-related factors including mycotoxins and phenolics. Home: 4306 Yates Rd Beltsville MD 20705-2758 Office: Beltsville Agr Rsch Ctr Bldg 005 Beltsville MD 20705 also: Ideals Inc 5010 Sunnyside Ave Beltsville MD 20705-2320 *We are thankful to those fools. They are the only ones who dare to dream of something new and seemingly impossible.*

TSOI, EDWARD TZE MING, architect, interior designer, urban planner; b. New Orleans, Aug. 7, 1943; s. Edward Mong Yok and Ruby Liu Wei (Hsia) T.; m. Louise Smoyer, June 15, 1968; children: Laura Li Ling, Alison Li Mei. BArch, MIT, 1966; MArch, U. Pa., 1968, M in City Planning, 1968, cert. in urban design, 1969. Registered architect, Mass., La. Assoc. Serf/Jackson & Assocs., Cambridge, Mass., 1969-76; assoc. prin. Skidmore Owings & Merrill, Boston, 1976-83; prin. Tsoi/Kobus & Assocs., Inc., Cambridge, 1983—, pres., 1983—, 93—; instr. Sch. Design, Harvard U., Cambridge, 1980-84. Designer Marine Resource Ctr., 1994. Chmn. Arlington (Mass.) Redevel. Bd., 1972—; past chair First Parish Unitarian Universalist Ch., Arlington, 1990; bd. dirs. Cambridge Salvation Army, 1990-94; mem. Boston Civic Design Commn., 1993—. Recipient Best New Med. Facility award, Symposium on Healthcare, 1993, Grand Honor award, Assn. Gen. Contractors, 1993, Lotus Devel. Corp. Landscape award, Urban Design, 1991. Fellow AIA; mem. Boston Soc. Architects (pres. 1993-94). Democrat. Avocations: windsurfing, boating, woodworking, carpentry. Home: 16 Devereaux St Arlington MA 02174-8114 Office: Tsoi/Kobus & Assocs Inc PO Box 9114 Cambridge MA 02238-9114

TSONGAS, PAUL EFTHEMIOS, lawyer, former senator; b. Lowell, Mass., Feb. 14, 1941; s. Efthemios and Katina Tsongas; m. Nicola Sauvage, Dec. 21, 1969; children: Ashley, Katina, Molly. BA, Dartmouth Coll., 1962; LLB, Yale U., 1967. Bar: Mass. Tng. coord. Peace Corps, W.I., 1967-68; mem. Gov.'s Com. on Law Enforcement, 1968-69; dep. asst. atty. gen. Mass. 1969-71; pvt. practice, 1971-74; mem. 94th-95th Congresses from 5th Mass. dist., 1975-79; U.S. senator from Mass., 1979-85; ptnr. Foley, Hoag & Eliot, Boston, 1985—; Dem. candidate for U.S. pres., 1992; mem. energy and natural resources com., mem. com. on small bus., mem. fgn. rels. com., co-chmn. ad-hoc Congl. monitoring group on So. Africa. Author: The Road from Here, 1981, Heading Home, 1984, A Call to Economic Arms, 1992. Vol. Peace Corps, Ethiopia, 1962-64; city councillor City of Lowell, 1969-72; county commr. Middlesex County, 1973-74; chmn. Mass. Bd. Regents of Higher Edn., 1989-91. Democrat. Greek Orthodox. Office: Foley Hoag & Eliot 1 Post Office Sq Boston MA 02109-2103

TSORIS, STEPHEN A., lawyer; b. Milw., July 26, 1957; s. Athan John Tsoris and Lillian Marian (Ribish) Groothousen; m. Elizabeth Mintor Lennihan, June 25, 1983. BA, Marquette U., 1979; JD, Cornell U., 1982. Bar: Ill. 1982, U.S. Dist. Ct. (no. dist.) Ill. 1982. Assoc. Jenner & Block, Chgo., 1982-84; assoc. McDermott, Will & emery, Chgo., 1984-87, ptnr., 1988—. Author (note) Great Britain's Protection of Trading Interests, 1982, Act: The Claw and the Lever, 1982; editor-in-chief Cornell Internat. Law Jour., Ithaca, N.Y., 1981-82. Mem. ABA, Chgo. Bar Assn. (chmn. corp. law com. 1992-93). Office: McDermott Will & Emery 227 W Monroe St Chicago IL 60606-5016

TSOU, TANG, political science educator, researcher; b. Canton, Guangdong, China, Dec. 10, 1918; came to U.S., 1941; s. Lu and Chien-yun (Hsu) T.; m. Yi-chuang Lu. BA, Nat. Southwest Associated U., Kunming, Yunnan, China, 1940; PhD, U. Chgo., 1951. Rsch. assoc. Ctr. for Study Am. Fgn. Policy, U. Chgo., 1955-62, asst. prof. dept. polit. sci., 1959-62, assoc. prof., 1962-66, prof., 1966-84, Homer J. Livingston prof., 1984-88, assoc. prof., 1962-66, prof., 1966-84, Homer J. Livingston prof., 1984-88, Homer J. Livingston prof. emeritus, 1989—; bd. dirs. Nat. Com. on U.S.-China Rels., N.Y.C., 1971-87, emeritus, 1987—; mem. Joint Com. on Contemporary China, Social Sci. Rsch. Coun. and Am. Coun. Learned Socs., 1972-74. Author: America's Failure in China, 1963 (Gordon J. Laing prize 1965), The Cultural Revolution and Post-Mao Reforms, 1986, Chinese Politics in the Twentieth-Century: Macrohistory and Micro-mechanisms, 1994; co-author, co-author: China in Crisis, 1968; mem. editorial bd. World Politics, China Quarterly, Asian Survey, Modern China; contbr. articles to profl. jours. Named Hon. Prof. Peking U, Beijing, 1986; rsch. grantee Joint Com. on Contemporary China, Social Sci. Rsch. Coun. and Am. Coun. Learned Socs., 1962-63, 68-69, 75-76; fellow Rockefeller Found., 1966-67, Luce Found., 1982-83. Mem. Am. Polit. Sci. Assn. Office: U Chgo Dept Polit Sci 5828 S University Ave Chicago IL 60637-1515

TSOUCALAS, NICHOLAS, federal judge; b. N.Y.C., Aug. 24, 1926; s. George Michael and Maria (Monogenis) T.; m. Catherine Aravantinos, Nov. 21, 1954; children: Stephanie, Georgia. BSBA, Kent State U., 1949; LLB, N.Y. Law Sch., 1951. Bar: N.Y. 1953. Sole practice, N.Y.C., 1953-55, 59-68; asst. U.S. atty. So. Dist. N.Y., 1955-59; judge Criminal Ct., City of N.Y., 1968-86; acting supreme ct. judge State of N.Y., N.Y.C., 1975-82; judge U.S. Ct. Internat. Trade, N.Y.C., 1986—. Dist. leader Republican Party N.Y. County, 1961-68; mem. Rep. Exec. Com., N.Y.C., 1961-68. Served with USN, 1944-46, 51-52. Recipient Proficiency in Constl. Law award N.Y. Law Sch., N.Y.C., 1951, Man of Yr. award St. Paul Soc., N.Y.C., 1971. Mem. ABA, N.Y. County Lawyers Assn., Queens County Bar Assn., Fed. Bar Assn., Greek Am. Lawyers Assn., Am. Hellenic Ednl. Prog. Assn.

Republican. Greek Orthodox. Lodges: Parthenon, Masons. Avocations: basketball, racquetball, stamp collecting, walking, dancing. Office: US Ct Internat Trade 1 Federal Plz New York NY 10278-0001

TSOULFANIDIS, NICHOLAS, nuclear engineering educator; b. Ioannina, Greece, May 6, 1938; came to U.S., 1963; s. Stephen and Aristea (Ganiou) T.; m. Zizeta Koutsombidou, June 21, 1964; children: Stephen, Lena. BS in Physics, U. Athens, Greece, 1960; MS in Nuclear Engring., U. Ill., 1965, PhD in Nuclear Engring., 1968. Registered profl. engr., Mo. Prof. nuclear engring. U. Mo., Rolla, 1968—, vice chancellor acad. affairs, 1985-86, asst. dean School of Mines and Metallurgy, 1989—; sr. engr. Gen. Atomic Co., San Diego, 1974-75; engr. Ark. Power and Light Co., 1976-80; researcher Cadarache France, 1986-87. Author: Measurement and Detection of Radiation, 1984, 2d edit. 1995; co-author: Nuclear Fuel Analysis and Management, 1990. Electric Power Research Inst. grantee, 1980-84. Mem. Am. Nuclear Soc. (chmn. radiation protection shielding div. 1987-88), Health Physics Soc., Nat. Soc. Profl. Engring., Rotary. Office: U of Mo Rolla Dept Of Nuclear Engrin Rolla MO 65401

TSUBAKI, ANDREW TAKAHISA, theater director, educator; b. Chiyoda-ku, Tokyo, Japan, Nov. 29, 1931; s. Ken and Yasu (Oyama) T.; m. Lilly Yuri, Aug. 3, 1963; children: Arthur Yuichi, Philip Takeshi. BA in English, Tokyo Gakugei U., Tokyo, Japan, 1954; postgrad. in Drama, U. Saskatchewan, Saskatoon, Canada, 1958-59; MFA in Theatre Arts, Tex. Christian U., 1961; PhD in Speech & Drama, U. Ill., 1967. Tchr. Bunkyo-ku 4th Jr. High Sch., Tokyo, Japan, 1954-58; instr., scene designer Bowling Green (Ohio) State U., 1964-68; asst. prof. speech & drama U. Kans., Lawrence, 1968-73, assoc. prof., 1973-79; visiting assoc. prof. Carleton Coll., Northfield, Minn., 1974; lectr. Tsuda U., Tokyo, Japan, 1975; visiting assoc. prof. theatre Tel-Aviv (Israel) U., 1975-76; visiting prof. theatre Mo. Repertory Theatre, Kansas City, Mo., 1976, Nat. Sch. Drama, New Delhi, India, 1983; prof. theatre, film, east Asian Languages and Cultures U. Kans., Lawrence, 1979—; dir. Internat. Theatre Studies Ctr., U. Kans., Lawrence, 1971—, Operation Internat. Classical Theatre, 1988—; Benedict disting. vis. prof. Asian studies Carleton Coll., 1993; area editor Asian Theatre Jour., U. Hawaii, Honolulu, 1982-94; chmn. East Asian Langs. and Cultures, U. Kans., Lawrence, 1983-90; mem. editl. bd. Studies in Am. Drama, Oxford, Miss., 1985—. Dir. plays Kanjincho, 1973, Rashomon, 1976, King Lear, 1985, Fujito and Shimizu, 1985, Hippolytus, 1990, Busu and the Missing Lamb (Japan) 1992, Suehirogari and Sumidagawa, 1992, 93; choreographed Antigone (Greece), 1987, Hamlet (Germany), 1989, The Resistible Rise of Arturo Ui, 1991, Man and the Masses (Germany), 1993, The Children of Fate (Hungary) 1994, The Great Theatre of the World (Germany); editor Theatre Companies of the World, 1986; contributing author to Indian Theatre: Traditions of Performance, 1990; contributed 7 entries in Japanese Traditional plays to the Internat. Dictionary of Theatre, vol. 1, 1992, vol 2, 1994. Recipient World Univ. Svc. Scholarship U. Saskatchewan, 1958-59, University fellow U. Ill., 1961-62, Rsch. fellow The Japan Found., 1974-75, 90, Rsch. Fulbright grantee, 1983. Mem. Am. Theatre Assn., Asian Theatre Program (chair 1976-79), Assn. for Asian Studies, Assn. Kans. Theatres., Assn. Kans. Theatres U/C Div. (chmn. 1980-82), Assn. for Theatre in Higher Edn., Assn. for Asian Performance. Democrat. Buddhist. Avocations: Ki-Aikido (3d Dan), photography, travel. Home: 924 Holiday Dr Lawrence KS 66049-3005 Office: U Kans Theatre And Film Lawrence KS 66045

TSUI, LAP-CHEE, molecular genetics educator; b. Shanghai, Dec. 21, 1950; arrived in Can., 1981; s. Jing Lue Hsue and Hui Ching Wang; m. Ellen Lan Fong, Feb. 11, 1977; children: Eugene, Felix. BS, Chinese U. Hong Kong, 1972, MPhil, 1974, DSc (hon.), 1991, DLL (hon.), 1994; PhD, U. Pitts., 1979. Postdoctoral investigator Oak Ridge (Tenn.) Nat. Lab., 1979-80; postdoctoral fellow Hosp. for Sick Children, Toronto, Ont., Can., 1981-83; asst. prof. depts. genetics and med. genetics Hosp. for Sick Children and U. Toronto, 1983-88, assoc. prof., 1988-90; prof., Sellers chair cystic fibrosis rsch., 1990—, univ. prof., 1994—; chmn. chromosome 7 subcom. Human Gene Mapping Workshop, 1986—; mem. mammalian genetics study sect. NIH, Bethesda, Md., 1988-93; dir. Cystic Fibrosis Rsch. Ctr., Hosp. for Sick Children Spl. Rsch. Ctr., 1994—; scientist Med. Rsch. Coun. Can., 1989—; advisor European Jour. Human Genetics, 1992—, Molecular Medicine Today, 1995—. Editor Cytogenetics and Cell Genetics, 1988-92, Internat. Jour. Genome Rsch., 1990—; assoc. editor Am. Jour. Human Genetics, 1990-93, Genomics, 1994—; mem. editl. bd. Mammalian Genome, 1990, PCR Methods and Application, 1991—, Clin. Genetics, 1991—, Human Molecular Genetics, 1991—; communictaing editor Human Mutation, 1991—; contbr. over 150 articles to sci. jours.; co-discoverer cystic fibrosis gene, 1989. Trustee Edn. Found., Fedn. Chinese Canadian Profls., Toronto, 1987—. Recipient Paul di Sant Agnese Disting. Achievement award Cystic Fibrosis Found., 1989, Gold medal of honor Pharm. Mfrs. Assn. Can., 1989, award of excellence Genetics Soc. Can., 1990, Gairdner Internat. award, 1990, Cresson medal Franklin Inst., 1992, E. Mead Johnson award, 1992, Disting. Scientist award The Can. Soc. Clin. Investigators, 1992, Canadian Conf. medal 1992, Sarstedt Rsch. prize 1993, Sanremo Internat. award for Genetic Rsch. 1993; scholar Can. Cystic Fibrosis Found., 1984-86. Fellow Royal Soc. Can., Royal Soc. London, Academia Sinica; mem. Human Genome Orgn., Am. Soc. Human Genetics. Office: Hosp for Sick Children, 555 University Ave, Toronto, ON Canada M5G 1XG

TSUNEISHI, WARREN MICHIO, librarian; b. Monrovia, Calif., July 4, 1921; s. Satoru and Sho (Murakami) T.; m. Betty Takeuchi, Nov. 16, 1946; children: David, Kenneth, Julia Tsuneishi Jordan. BA, Syracuse Univ., 1943; MA, Columbia U., 1948, MS in Lib. Sci., 1950; PhD, Yale U., 1960. Cataloger/research assoc. Yale U. Libr., New Haven, Conn., 1950-52, curator far-eastern collection, 1953-57, curator East Asian collection, 1960-66; curator East Asian collection Yale U. Libr., New Haven, 1978-89; head far-eastern lang. sect. Libr. of Congress, Washington, 1957-60, chief orientalia div., 1966-78, dir. area studies, 1979-85, chief Asian div., 1989-93; lectr. dept. polit. sci. Yale U., 1963-64; grad. lib. sch. U. Hawaii, 1967, 68, 71, Inst. Far Eastern Librarianship, U. Chgo., 1969. Author: Japanese Political Style, 1966; joint editor: Univesity and Research Libraries, 1972, Issues in Library Adminstration, 1974, Strengthening the U.S.-Japan Library Partnership in the Golbal Information Flow, 1990, Japan-U.S. Collaboration in Enhancing International Access to Scholarly Information, 1993. Bd. trustees Japan-Am. Soc. 1968-72. With U.S. Army, 1943-46 (Pacific theater, Bronze Star 1945). Recipient: Superior Svc. Award, Library of Congress, 1979, 89. Mem. ALA, Assn. for Asian Studies, Internat. Assn. of Orientalist Libr. (pres. 1983-88). Home: 5703 Maiden Ln Bethesda MD 20817-6267

TUAN, DEBBIE FU-TAI, chemistry educator; b. Kiangsu, China, Feb. 2, 1930; came to U.S., 1958; d. Shiau-gien and Chen (Lee) T.; m. John W. Reed, Aug. 15, 1987. BS in Chemistry, Nat. Taiwan U., Taipei, 1954, MS in Chemistry, 1958; MS in Chemistry, Yale U., 1960, PhD in Chemistry, 1961. Rsch. fellow Yale U., New Haven, 1961-64; rsch. assoc. U. Wis., Madison, 1964-65; asst. prof. Kent (Ohio) State U., 1965-70, assoc. prof., 1970-73, prof., 1973—; rsch. fellow Harvard U., Cambridge, 1969-70; vis. scientist SRI Internat., Menlo Park, Calif., 1981; rsch. assoc. Cornell U., Ithica, N.Y., 1983; vis. prof. Yeshiva U., N.Y.C., 1966, Academia Sinica of China, Nat. Taiwan U. and Nat. Tsing-Hwa U., summer 1967, Ohio State U., 1993, 95. Contbr. articles to profl. jours. Recipient NSF Career Advanced award, 1994—; U. Grad. fellow Nat. Taiwan U., 1958, F.W. Heyl-Anon F fellow Yale U., 1960-61, U. Faculty Rsch. fellow Kent State U., 1966, 68, 71, 85; Pres. Chiang's scholar Chinese Women Assn., 1954, 58, Grad. scholar in humanity and scis. China Found., 1955. Mem. Am. Chem. Soc., Am. Phys. Soc., Sigma Xi. Office: Kent State U Chemistry Dept Williams Hall Kent OH 44242

TUAN, SAN FU, theoretical physics, political science educator; b. Tientsin, China, May 14, 1932; came to U.S., 1954; naturalized, 1967; s. Mao Lan and Lu Kung (Tao) T.; m. Loretta Kan, Dec. 15, 1963; children: Katherine Tsung Yen, Melinda Tsung Tao, Priscilla Tsung Pei, David Tsung Lien. BA, U. Oxford, Eng., 1954, MA, 1958; PhD, U. Calif. at Berkeley, 1958. Rsch. assoc. U. Chgo., 1958-60; asst. prof. Brown U., R.I., 1960-62; assoc. prof. Purdue U., 1962-65; prof. physics U. Hawaii, Honolulu, 1966—; vis. prof. physics U. Hawaii, 1965-66, Purdue U., 1973, Beijing U. and Inst. Theoretical Physics, 1979-80, U. Wis.-Madison, spring 1982; vis. scientist Inst. Theoretical Physics Acad. Sinica, 1987, Inst. Physics Academia Sinica, Taipei, City Poly., Hong Kong, Inst. High Energy Physics Acad. Sinica,

Beijing, fall 1993, Weizmann Inst., Rehovot, spring 1994; mem. Inst. Advanced Study, Princeton, 1966, 72; prin. investigator Theoretical High Energy Program AEC, 1967-80; cons. Argonne Nat. Lab., 1963-70; dir. Hawaii Topical Conf. in Particle Physics, 1967, 69, 73, 75, 77; vis. lectr. Bariloche Summer Sch., Argentina, 1969-70, U.S.-China Sci. Coop. Program NSF, 1970-71; participant exploratory mission to China U. Hawaii-China Sci. Coop., 1973. Editor: Modern Quantum Mechanics, 1985, rev. edit., 1994; co-editor Procs. of Hawaii Topical Confs. in Particle Physics, 1967, 69, 73, 75, 77, Procs. of 10th Hawaii Conf. in High Energy Physics, 1985; reviewer Math. Rev., 1962-70, Phys. Rev., 1963—; contbr. articles to profl. jours. Coord. State Hawaii on initial planning for projected Internat. Sci. Found., 1970; mem. Hawaii Gov.'s Alt. Energy Sources Com., 1974. John S. Guggenheim fellow, 1965-66; Mackinnon scholar Magdalen Coll., Oxford, 1951-54. Fellow Am. Phys. Soc.; mem. Phi Beta Kappa. Home: 3634 Woodlawn Terrace Pl Honolulu HI 96822-1475 Office: U Hawaii Dept Physics 2505 Correa Rd Honolulu HI 96822-2219

TUAN, YI-FU, geography educator. Prof. dept. geography U. Wis., Madison. Recipient Cullum Geog. medal Am. Geog. Soc., 1987. Office: U Wisconsin Dept Geography M 383 Science Hall 550 North Park St Madison WI 53706-1491*

TUBB, JAMES CLARENCE, lawyer; b. Corsicana, Tex.; s. Cullen Louis and Sarah Elmore (Chapman) T.; m. Suzanne Alice Smith, Nov. 22, 1954; children: James Richard, Sara Elizabeth, Daniel Chapman. BA, So. Meth. U., 1951, JD, 1954. Bar: Tex. 1954, U.S. Dist. Ct. (no. dist.) Tex. 1955, U.S. Ct. Appeals (5th cir.) 1959, U.S. Supreme Ct. 1978; cert. comml. real estate specialist. With legal dept. Schlumberger Well Surveying Corp., Houston, 1954-55; claims atty. Franklin Am. Ins. Co., Dallas, 1957-58; ptnr. Vial, Hamilton, Koch, Tubb & Knox and predecessor firm Akin, Vial, Hamilton, Koch & Tubb, Dallas, 1958-84, Winstead, McGuire, Sechrest & Minick, Dallas, 1984-90; pvt. practice Dallas, 1990—. Bd. dirs. Christian Concern Found., 1965-71; ruling elder Highland Park Presbyn. Ch., Dallas, 1978-84, 88-91; mem. permanent jud. commn. Grace Presbytery, 1984-90; bd. dirs. Am. Diabetes Assn. Dallas County affiliate, 1991—. 1st lt. JAGC, SAC, USAF, 1955-57, 1st lt. USAFR, ret. Fellow Tex. Bar Found.; mem. ABA (chmn. comml. law com. gen. practice sect. 1982-84), Tex. Bus. Law Found., Tex. Bar Assn., Am. Arbitration Assn., Soc. Profls. in Dispute Resolution Dallas Country Club, Dallas County Rep. Men's Club (sec. 1978-79). Home: 3407 Haynie Dallas TX 75205 Office: 5956 Sherry Ln Ste 1000 Dallas TX 75225-8021

TUBESING, RICHARD LEE, library director; b. Kansas City, Mo., Nov. 25, 1937; s. Clarence and Letha (Thacker) T. BA, Yale U., 1959; MA, U. Chgo., 1969; MSL, Western Mich. U., 1972. Asst. to dir. U. Louisville, 1972-73; reference libr. Ga. Tech. Libr., Atlanta, 1973-76; head bus. and sci. Atlanta Pub. Libr., 1976-79; libr. dir. Lewis U., Romeoville, Ill., 1979-81; collection devel. coord. U. Toledo Libr., 1981-86; libr. dir. Coll. of the Southwest, Hobbs, N.Mex., 1986-89; libr. dir., libr. sci. program Glenville (W.Va.) State Coll., 1989—. Author: Architectural Preservation, 1978, Architectural Preservation and Urban Renovation, 1982. Program coord. Lea County Archaeol. Soc., Hobbs, 1987-89. Lt. j.g. USNR, 1960-63. Mem. W.Va. Libr. Assn., Lea County Libr. Assn. (v.p. 1987-88, pres. 1988-89). Avocation: collecting primitive and peasant art. Home: Rte 76 Box 17 Glenville WV 26351 Office: Glenville State Coll Robert F Kidd Libr Glenville WV 26351

TUBMAN, WILLIAM CHARLES, lawyer; b. N.Y.C., Mar. 16, 1932; s. William Thomas and Ellen Veronica (Griffin) T.; m. Dorothy Rita Krug, Aug. 15, 1964; children: William Charles Jr., Thomas Davison, Matthew Griffin. BS, Fordham U., 1953, JD, 1960; postdoctoral, NYU Sch. Law, 1960-61. Bar: N.Y. 1960, U.S. Ct. Appeals (2d cir.) 1966, U.S. Supreme Ct. 1967, U.S. Ct. Customs and Patent Appeals 1971. Auditor Peat, Marwick Mitchell & Co., N.Y.C., 1956-60; sr. counsel Kennecott Corp., N.Y.C., 1960-82; sr. counsel Phelps Dodge Corp., N.Y.C., 1982-85, sec., 1985-87, v.p., 1987—; pres. Phelps Dodge Found., Phoenix, 1988—. Author: Legal Status of Minerals Beyond the Continental Shelf, 1966. Mem. scholarship adv. coun. U. Ariz., 1990-92; active Big Bros., Inc., N.Y.C., 1963-73; trustee Phoenix Art Mus., 1989-94; chmn., bd. dirs. St. Joseph Hosp. Found.; bd. dirs. The Phoenix Symphony. Recipient Cert. Disting. Service, Big Brothers Inc., 1968. Mem. ABA, N.Y. State Bar Assn., Maricopa County Bar Assn. Democrat. Roman Catholic. Office: Phelps Dodge Corp 2600 N Central Ave Phoenix AZ 85004-3014

TUCCI, JOSEPH M., computer software and services executive; b. 1947. BA, Manhattan Coll.; MBA, Columbia U. With Sperry Corp., 1970-86; pres. U.S. ops. Unisys Corp., 1986-90; exec. v.p. ops. Wang Labs., Inc., 1990-93; chmn. bd., CEO Wang Labs., Inc., Lowell, Mass., 1993—. Office: Wang Labs Inc 1 Industrial Ave Lowell MA 01851

TUCCI, MARK A., state agency administrator; b. Trenton, N.J., Dec. 14, 1950; s. William F. and Theresa M. (Miccio) T.; m. Carolyn J. Bilecki, July 10, 1971; children: Nicholas A., Anthony M., Vincent J. BS, Trenton State Coll., 1972, MEd, 1978; cert. pub. mgr., Rutgers U. Cert. N.J. chief sch. adminstr., prin., supr., tchr. of deaf, tchr. of handicapped, N.J. Tchr. of deaf Katzenbach Sch. for the Deaf, West Trenton, N.J., 1972-82; spl. asst. to supt. Katzenbach Sch. for the Deaf, West Trenton, 1982-85; exec. asst. to asst. commr. edn. N.J. Dept. Edn., Trenton, 1985-87; chief of enterprise license bur. N.J. Casino Control Commn., Atlantic City, 1987-91, dir. organizational devel., 1991—, dir. adminstrn., 1992-93; examiner N.J. Quality Achievement Award Program, 1993, sr. examiner, 1994; judge N.J. Exemplary State and Local Awards Program, 1994; chmn. N.J. Quality Achievement Award Focus Group, 1994—. Mem. editorial bd. periodical for Trenton chpt. Phi Delta Kappa, 1986-88; columnist Total Quality Management, 1994; contbr. articles to profl. pubs. Cub Scout leader Trenton chpt. Boy Scouts Am., 1981-84, mem. dist. com. Jersey Shore Coun., 1995—; pres. Katzenbach (N.J.) chpt. N.J. State Employees' Assn., 1979; co-chair adv. coun. Mercer County Spl. Edn. Assn., 1984; mem. bus. adv. coun. Atlantic Cmty. Coll., 1990—; chmn. bd. trustees AIDS Support Found., Inc., 1994—. Mem. Cert. Pub. Mgrs. Soc. N.J. (fellow trustee), Phi Delta Kappa, Kappa Delta Pi. Roman Catholic. Avocations: reading, journalism, martial arts, photography, songwriting. Home: 273 Neptune Dr Manahawkin NJ 08050-5026 Office: NJ Casino Control Commn Tennessee Ave Atlantic City NJ 08401-4602

TUCHMAN, AVRAHAM, physicist, researcher; b. N.Y.C., July 1, 1935; s. Max and Rebecca (Brick) T.; m. Sylvia Crystal, Dec. 26, 1957; children: Davida, Ari, Sima, Pnina. BA, Yeshiva U., 1956; PhD, MIT, 1963. Scientist, group leader to sect. chief Avco Rsch. and Advanced Devel., Wilmington, Mass., 1963; prin. scientist, staff scientist to prin. staff scientist Avco Systems Div., Wilmington; chief scientist Textron Def. Systems, Wilmington, 1988—; vis. prof. Weizmann Inst. Sci., Rehovot, Israel, 1974, 78, 82. Contbr. numerous articles to profl. jours. Founder, pres. Kehilla Day Camp of Jewish Community Ctrs., Westwood, Mass., 1975-86; chmn. Brookline (Mass.) Traffic Commn., 1975-81; pres. Mikvah Rescue Svc., Brighton, Mass., 1969-77; mem. Temple Beth Avraham, Brookline, 1969—. Recipient award for outstanding cantorial artistry Am. Soc. Forktwangers, Detroit, 1970. Fellow AIAA (sr.). Avocations: computers, gardening, softball, homecraft. Office: Textron Def Systems 201 Lowell St Wilmington MA 01887-2969

TUCHMAN, MAURICE SIMON, library director; b. Bklyn., Sept. 14, 1936; s. William and Rose (Luria) T.; m. Helene Lillian Bodner, Aug. 30, 1959; children: Joel Aron, Miriam Auri. BA, CUNY, 1958; MLS, Columbia U., 1959; B Hebrew Lit., Jewish Theol. Sem., N.Y.C., 1964; D of Arts in LS, Simmons Coll., 1979. Cataloger. svcs. Buffalo and Erie County, 1959-60; asst. libr. N.Y. State Maritime Coll., Ft. Schuyler, 1962-64; libr. cons. Mid-Hudson Librs., Poughkeepsie, N.Y., 1964-66; libr. dir. Hebrew Coll., Brookline, Mass., 1966—; book appraiser, Auburndale, Mass., 1980—; book reviewer Libr. Jour., 1970—. With U.S. Army, 1960-62. N.Y. Regents scholar, 1959. Mem. ALA, Assn. Jewish Librs., Coun. Archives and Rsch. Librs. Jewish Studies, Ch. and Synagogue Libr. Assn. (pres. 1974-75), Fenway Libr. Consortium (coord. 1980-82, treas. 1990—). Home: 16 Duffield Rd Newton MA 02166-1004 Office: Hebrew Coll 43 Hawes St Brookline MA 02146-5495 *It is our most difficult task and our greatest accomplishment to reach our potential as a thinking and ethical human being.*

TUCHMANN, ROBERT, lawyer; b. N.Y.C., July 7, 1946; s. Frederick C. and Hildegard (Jung) T.; m. Naomi R. Walfish, June 1, 1969; children: David, Paul. AB, Oberlin Coll., 1967; JD, Harvard Coll., 1971. Bar: Mass. 1971, U.S. Dist. Ct. Mass. 1971. Assoc. Hale and Dorr, Boston, 1971-76, jr. ptnr., 1976-80, sr. ptnr., 1980—; lectr. Mass. Continuing Legal Edn., 1976—. Pres. Project Bread-The Walk for Hunger, Boston, 1990—; mem. com. Oberlin Coll., 1990; chair Ctrl. Artery Environ. Oversight Com., 1992—; mem. New Fed. Courthouse Task Force, 1993—. Mem. Boston Bar Assn. (com. chairperson 1977-81), Mass. Conveyancers Assn. (com. chairperson 1984-89), Abstract Club. Office: Hale and Dorr 60 State St Boston MA 02109-1801

TUCK, EDWARD HALLAM, lawyer; b. Brussels, June 27, 1927; s. William Hallam and Hilda (Bunge) T.; m. Liliane Solmsen, June 8, 1978; children by previous marriage—Edward, Jessica, Matthew. B.A., Princeton U., 1950; LL.B., Harvard Law Sch., 1953. Bar: N.Y. Assoc. Shearman & Sterling, N.Y.C., 1953-62, ptnr., 1962-86, of counsel, 1986—; bd. dirs. The French-Am. Found.; bd. dirs. Lafarge Corp., Comml. Bank. Bd. dirs. Belgian Am. Ednl. Found., Fgn. Policy Discussion Group, Am. Assn. for Internat. Commn. of Jurists; trustee French Inst. Alliance Francaise; chmn. bd. North Country Sch., Inc., 1974-78, The Drawing Ctr., Gateway Citizens Com., 1972-74; pres. The Parks Council, 1970-74; chmn. N.Y. State Parks and Recreation Commn., City of N.Y., 1971-76. Served with USN, 1945-46. Mem. Assn. Bar City N.Y., Council on Fgn. Relations, Racquet and Tennis Club, The Brook Club, The Ivy Club, Pilgrims Club, Soc. of the Cin. Episcopalian. Office: Shearman & Sterling 599 Lexington Ave New York NY 10022-6069

TUCK, GRAYSON EDWIN, real estate agent, former natural gas transmission executive; b. Richmond, Va., May 11, 1927; s. Bernard Okly and Erma (Wiltshire) T.; m. Rosalie Scroggs, June 6, 1947; children—Janice Lorrain, Kenneth Edwin, Carol Lynn. B.S., U. Richmond, 1950. Payroll clk., cost clk. Gen. Baking Co., Richmond, 1948-51; jr. accountant Commonwealth Natural Gas Corp., Richmond, 1951-55; sr. accountant Commonwealth Natural Gas Corp., 1956-57, accounting supr., 1957-58, asst. treas., 1959-62, asst. sec., asst. treas., 1963-64, treas., asst. sec., 1965-77; treas. Commonwealth Natural Resources, Inc., 1977-81, CNG Transmission Co. subs., 1977-79; sec.-treas. Air Pollution Control Products, Inc., Richmond, 1970-73; asst. treas., asst. sec. Commonwealth Gas Distbn. Corp., Richmond, 1969-79; mgr. taxes and cash mgmt. Commonwealth Gas Pipeline Corp., subs. Columbia Gas System Inc., 1981-86; investor, realtor Bill Eudailey & Co., 1986—. Active Boy Scouts Am., 1965-69; bd. dirs. Henrico Area Mental Health Retardation Services, 1983-85. Served with USNR, 1945-46. Mem. Nat. Assn. Accts. (assoc. dir. 1963-64). Presbyn. (deacon 1958-86, elder 1986—, treas. 1968-70). Home: 2923 Oakland Ave Richmond VA 23228-5827 Office: 6401 Mallory Dr Richmond VA 23226-2911

TUCK, JOHN CHATFIELD, former federal agency administrator, public policy advisor; b. Dayton, Ohio, May 28, 1945; m. Jane McDonough; 3 children. BS, Georgetown U., 1967. Various positions as asst. to Rep. leaders Ho. of Reps., Washington, 1974-77, chief Rep. floor ops., 1977-81; asst. sec. to majority U.S. Senate, 1981-86, spl. asst. then dep. asst. to pres. for legis. affairs, 1986-87; dep. asst. to Pres. of U.S. and exec. asst. to chief of staff Office Chief of Staff, The White Ho., 1987-88; asst. to Pres. and dir. Office Chief of Staff, 1988-89, also asst. to Pres. of U.S.; under sec. Dept. Energy, Washington, 1989-92; sr. pub. policy advisor Baker, Donelson, Bearman & Caldwell, Washington, 1992—. With USN, 1968-73; capt. USNR, 1973-94. Office: Baker Donelson Bearman & Caldwell 801 Pennsylvania Ave NW Washington DC 20004

TUCK, RUSSELL R., JR., past college president; b. June 9, 1934; m. Marjorie Gay Tuck; children: Russell R. III, Catherine Elizabeth. BS in Chemistry, Union U., 1956; MS in Biology, Vanderbilt U., 1957, PhD in Curriculum and Instrn., 1971; study, Wash. U., 1960-61. Instr. biology, asst. coordinator Korean Tchr. Edn. Program George Peabody Coll. Vanderbilt U., Nashville, 1957-59; tchr. biology, chmn. sci. dept. University City (Mo.) Sr. High Sch., 1960-63, from asst. prin. to prin., 1963-70; prin. Parkway North Sr. High Sch., St. Louis County, Mo., 1971-78; asst. supt. Parkway Sch. Dist., St. Louis County, 1979-81, assoc. supt., 1981-84; pres. Calif. Bapt. Coll., Riverside, 1984-95, pres. emeritus, 1994—. Contbr. articles to profl. jours. Bd. dirs. Opera Assn.; pres. Riverside County chpt. ARC, 1989-90; active Bapt. Ch., local hosp. assn. bd., local edn. com.; World Affairs Coun. Mem. Calif. Bapt. Hist. Soc. (bd. dirs.), Calif. Bapt. Devel. Found. (bd. dirs.), Am. Assn. Sch. Adminstrs., Inland Empire Higher Edn. Coun. (pres. 1987-88), Kappa Delta Pi, Phi Delta Kappa. Lodge: Rotary.

TUCKER, ALAN CURTISS, mathematics educator; b. Princeton, N.J., July 6, 1943; s. Albert William and Alice Judson (Curtiss) W.; m. Amanda Almira Zeisler, Aug. 31, 1968; children: Lisa, Kathryn. BA, Harvard U., 1965; MS, Stanford U., 1967, PhD, 1969. Asst. prof. applied math. SUNY, Stony Brook, 1970-73, assoc. prof. applied math., 1973-78, prof. applied math., chmn., 1978-89, SUNY Disting. Teaching prof., 1989—; vis. asst. prof. math. U. Wis., Madison, 1969-70; vis. assoc. prof. computer sci. U. Calif., San Diego, 1976-77; vis. prof. ops. research Stanford U., 1983-84; cons. Sloan Found., 1981-85; acad. cons. 40 colls. and univs. Author: Applied Combinatorics, 1980, Unified Introduction to Linear Algebra, 1987, Linear Algebra, 1993; assoc. editor Math. Monthly, 1977-81, Applied Maths. Letters, 1986—; contbr. 45 rsch. articles to profl. jours. Ga. U. Consortium Disting. Visitor, 1982; NSF grantee, 1972-86. Mem. Math. Assn. Am. (chmn. publs. 1982-86, editor Studies in Math. series 1979-86, v.p. 1988-90, chmn. ednl. coun. 1990—, Disting. Tchr. award 1994), U.S. Commn. Math. Instrn., Am. Math. Soc., Ops. Rsch. Soc. Am., Soc. Indsl. Applied Maths., Sigma Xi (chpt. pres. 1987—). Home: 36 Woodfield Rd Stony Brook NY 11790-1112 Office: SUNY At Stony Brook Dept Of Math Stats Stony Brook NY 11794

TUCKER, ALAN DAVID, publisher; b. Erie, Pa., Mar. 9, 1936; s. Meredith LaDue and Monica (Klocko) T.; m. Kiyoko Iizuka, Feb. 8, 1963; 1 child, Kumi Tucker. A.B., Princeton U., 1957. Assoc. editor Hawthorn Books, N.Y.C., 1964-66; editor John Day Co., Inc., N.Y.C., 1966-72; mng. editor David McKay Co., Inc., N.Y.C., 1972-75, v.p. 1975-78, exec. v.p., editorial dir., 1978-84; editorial dir. Fodor's Travel Guides, Inc., N.Y.C., 1978-84; producer, Penguin Travel Guides and other pubs. N.Y.C., 1984-91; gen. editor Root Pub. Co. and Berlitz Travellers Guides, N.Y.C., 1991—. Served to USNR, 1957-60. Mem. Soc. Am. Travel Writers, N.Y. Travel Writers Assn. Office: 186 Riverside Dr New York NY 10024-1007

TUCKER, ALLEN BROWN, JR., computer science educator; b. Worcester, Mass., Feb. 19, 1942; s. Allen Brown and Louise (Woodberry) T.; m. Maida Somerville, Dec. 18, 1965; children: Jennifer, Brian. BA, Wesleyan U., Middletown, Conn., 1963; MS, Northwestern U., 1969, PhD, 1970. Asst. prof. computer sci. U. Mo., Rolla, 1970-71; assoc. prof. computer sci. Georgetown U., Washington, 1971-76, assoc. prof., chmn., 1976-83; MacArthur prof., chmn. Colgate U., Hamilton, N.Y., 1983-88, assoc. dean faculty, 1986-88; prof., chmn. Bowdoin Coll., Brunswick, Maine, 1988—; dir. acad. computing Georgetown U., 1976-83; cons. in field, 1976—. Author: Programming Languages, 1977, 2d rev. edit., 1986, Text Processing, 1979, Computer Science: A Second Course, 1988, Fundamentals of Computing I, 1992, 2d edit., 1995, Fundamentals of Computing II, 1993, 2d edit., 1995; assoc. editor Jour. of Computer Langs., 1979—, Jour. of Machine Translation, 1986—; contbr. articles to profl. jours. NSF fellow, 1984-86, ACM fellow, 1994—, Fulbright lectureship, 1986, 92. Fellow Assn. for Computing Machinery (Outstanding Contrb. award 1991); mem. Computer Soc. of IEEE, N.Y. Acad. Scis., Sigma Xi. Democrat. Episcopalian. Avocations: squash, golf, jogging, music, travel. Home: 1 Boody St Brunswick ME 04011-3005 Office: Bowdoin Coll Dept of Computer Sci Brunswick ME 04011

TUCKER, ALVIN LEROY, federal government executive; b. Bklyn., Sept. 7, 1938; s. Alvin Leroy and Alveria (Klune) T.; m. Jacqueline Twiggs, Aug. 27, 1966; children: Hazel, Pluma, Jacqueline, Alvin. BS, U. Md., 1965. CPA, Md. cert. internal auditor. Auditor Dept. Army, Washington, 1965-67; auditor Dept. Def., Washington, 1967-72, budget analyst, 1972-79, dir. tng. and edn., 1979-83, dep. asst. inspector gen., 1983-86, dep. comptr., 1989-94, dep. CFO, 1991—; dep. inspector gen. HUD, Washington, 1989; mem. steering com. Joint Fin. Mgmt. Improvement Program, 1990-93; mem.

Chief Fin. Officers Coun., 1989—; chair fin. sys. com., 1989—; mem. Fed. Acctg. Stds. Adv. Bd., 1991—. With U.S. Army, 1958-61. With U.S. Army, 1958-61. Mem. AICPA, Am. Soc. Mil. Comptrs., Assn. Govt. Accts. (nat. exec. com. 1993-94), Kiwanis (club pres. 1981-82, 86-87). Avocation: genealogy. Office: Undersec of Defense Pentagon Rm 3E831 Washington DC 20301

TUCKER, ANNE WILKES, curator, photographic historian and critic, lecturer; b. Baton Rouge, Oct. 18, 1945. A.A.S. in Photographic Illustration, Rochester Inst. Tech., 1968; B.A. in Art History, Randolph-Macon Woman's Coll.; M.F.A. in Photographic History, SUNY-Buffalo, 1972. Rsch. asst. Internat. Mus. Photography at the George Eastman House, Rochester, N.Y., 1968-70; rsch. assoc. Gernsheim Collection U. Tex., Austin, summers 1969, 79; curatorial intern (N.Y. State Coun. on the Art grant) dept. photography Mus. Modern Art, N.Y.C., 1970-71; photography cons. Creative Artists Pub. Svc. program, N.Y.C., 1971-72; vis. lectr. New Sch. for Social Rsch., Photography spring 1973; dir. photography lecture series Cooper Union Forum, N.Y.C., 1972-75; lectr. Cooper Union for the Advancement of Arts and Sci., N.Y., 1972-75; vis. lectr. Phila. Coll. Art, 1973-75; affiliate artist U. Houston, 1976-80; curator of photography Mus. Fine Arts, Houston, 1976—, also Gus and Lyndall Wortham curator, photographic historian and critic, lectr.; trustee Visual Studies Workshop, 1980—, Houston Ctr. Photography, 1991—, Houston Foto Fest, 1988—; visual arts panel The Houston Festival, 1981-83; adv. bd. Randolph-Macon Woman's Coll. Art Gallery, 1982-84. Author of books and catalogues: The Woman's Eye, 1973, (with William C. Agee) The Target Collection of American Photography, 1977, Target II: 5 American Photographers, 1981; Target III: In Sequence, 1982; (with Philip Brookman) Robert Frank: New York to Nova Scotia, 1986, (with Maggie Olvey) The Sonia and Kaye Marvins Portrait Collect, 1986; Photo Notes and Filmfront, 1977; (with other curators) The Museum of Fine Arts, Houston: A Guide to the Collection, 1981; Unknown Territory: Photography by Ray K Metzker, 1957-83, 1984; Fifth Annual International Fine Art Photograpy Exposition, 1984; (with Andy Grundberg) American Prospects: The Photographs of Joel Slernfeld, 1987; (with Willie Morris) American Classroom: The Photographs of Catherine Wagner, 1988; (with Pamela Allara) Crosscurrents/Crosscountry, 1988; (with other authors) Money Matters: A Critical Look at Bank Architechture, 1990, The Blue Moon: Photographs by Keith Carter, 1990; (with Pete Daniel) Carry Me Home: Photographs by Debbie Fleming Caffery, 1990, George Krauze, 1991, Tradition & the Unpredictable The Allan Chasanoff Photographic Collection, 1994; co-prodr. video: Fire in the East: The Portrait of Robert Frank, 1986; editor: The Anthony G. Cronin Memorial Collection, 1979; Susanne Bloom and Ed Hill (Manual), 1980; The Photo League, 1987, Czech Modernism 1900-1945, 1990, Paul Strand: Essays on his Life and Work, 1991, George Krause, 1992, also articles to profl. jours. and mags. Director of numerous exhbns. and workshops; lecturer; mem. numerous juries and panels. Recipient Third Ann. Publ. award Internat. Ctr. Photography, 1987; Nat. Endowment Arts grantee, 1976, 86, 89; John Simon Guggenheim Meml. Alumna Achievement award Randolph-Maeon Woman's Coll., 1993. Found fellow, 1983-84. Mem. Soc. Photographic Edn. (nat. bd. dirs. 1976-80), sec., 1977-79), Coll. Art Assn., Art Table, Inc., Houston Ctr. for Photograpy (adv. bd. 1980—). Office: Mus Fine Arts 1001 Bissonnet St Houston TX 77005

TUCKER, ARLIE G., manufacturing executive; b. 1939. Pres. Haulpak Division, Peoria, Ill., 1964-90; with Komatsu Dresser Co., Lincolnshire, Ill., 1990-91, chmn., CEO, 1991—. Office: Komatsu Dresser Co 200 Tri State Intl Lincolnshire IL 60069

TUCKER, BOBBY GLENN, minister; b. Grand Saline, Tex., Sept. 11, 1954; s. Glen Burton and Edna LaFaye (Phillips) T. BS, Tex. A&M U., 1979; student, Southwestern Bapt. Theol., Seminary, Ft. Worth, 1980-83. Minister of music and youth First Missionary Bapt. Ch., Terrell, Tex., 1980; minister of youth Farley St. Bapt. Ch., Waxahachie, Tex., 1980-83; assoc. pastor First Bapt. Ch., Magnolia, Ark., 1983-86; youth ministry cons. Dept. Ch. Ministries Bapt. Missionary Assn. of Am., Waxahachie, 1986-87; exec. dir. Nat. Youth Dept. Bapt. Missionary Assn. of Am., Texarkana, Tex., 1987—; dir. Nat. Christian Youth Leadership Conf., Washington, 1984-87; trustee Found. for Christian Youth Leadership, 1983—; cons. to denominational curriculum com., 1987—. Named Outstanding Young Religious Leader, Jaycees, Magnolia, 1986, Outstanding Young Man of Am., 1976. Republican. Home: PO Box 871 College Station TX 77841-0871 Office: National Youth Dept PO Box 3376 Texarkana TX 75504-3376

TUCKER, CYNTHIA ANNE, journalist; b. Monroeville, Ala., Mar. 13, 1955; m. Michael Pierce, Dec. 26, 1987 (div. 1989). BA, Auburn U., 1976. Reporter The Atlanta Jour., 1976-80, editorial writer, columnist, 1983-86; reporter The Phila. Inquirer, 1980-82; assoc. editorial page editor The Atlanta Constitution, 1986-91, editorial page editor, 1992—. Bd. dirs. ARC, 1989-93, Families First, 1988—. Internat. Women's Media Found., 1994—. Nieman fellow Harvard U., 1988-89. Mem. Am. Soc. Newspaper Editors. Mem. United Ch. Christ. Office: Atlanta Jounal Constitution 72 Marietta St NW Atlanta GA 30303

TUCKER, CYNTHIA DELORES NOTTAGE (MRS. WILLIAM M. TUCKER), political party official, former state official; b. Phila., Oct. 4, 1927; d. Whitfield and Captilda (Gardiner) Nottage; m. William M. Tucker, July 21, 1951. Student, Temple U., Pa. State U., U. Pa.; student hon. degrees, Villa Maria Coll., Erie, Pa., 1972, Morris Coll., Sumter, S.C., 1976. Sec. of state Commonwealth of Pa., Harrisburg, 1971-77; nat. pres. Fedn. Democratic Women, 1979-81; v.p. Pa. chpt. NAACP, nat. v.p. bd. trustees; mem. nat. adv. bd. Nat. Women's Polit. Caucus; now chair Black Caucus Nat. Dem. Com.; mem., vice chair Pa. Black Dem. Com., 1966—; chair Women for Dem. Action, 1967; founding vice chair Nat. Polit. Congress of Black Women, Inc., 1984-92, nat. chair, 1992—; sec., mem. Phila. Zoning Bd. Adjustment, 1968-70; vice chair Pa. Dem. State Com., 1970-76; mem. exec. com. Dem. Nat. Com., 1972-76; Dem. candidate lt. gov., Pa., 1978; v.p. Phila. Tribune Newspaper. Del. to White Ho. Conf. on Civil Rights; bd. dirs. Phila. YWCA, New Sch. Music, Martin Luther King Ctr. for Social Change; pres., founder Phila. Martin Luther King Assn.; mem. Commonwealth bd. Med. Coll. Pa.; bd. assocs. Messiah Coll.; founder, pres. Bethune-DuBois Fund. Recipient Service and Achievement award NAACP, 1964, Phila. Tribune Charities Ann. award, Community Svc. award Opportunities Industrialization Ctr., Emma V. Kelley Achievement award Nat. Elks, 1971, Lincoln U. Nat. Leadership award, 1993, Community Svc. award Quaker City chpt. B'nai B'rith; named Best Dressed Woman of Yr., Ebony mag., One of 100 Most Influential Black Ams., 1973-77. Mem. Nat. Assn. Secs. State (v.p.), Bus. and Profl. Women's Club, Links (dir.), Alpha Kappa Alpha (hon.). Home: 6700 Lincoln Dr Philadelphia PA 19119-3155

TUCKER, DAVID, newspaper editor. Sports editor Phila. Inquirer, now city editor. Office: Phila Inquirer 400 N Broad St Philadelphia PA 19103*

TUCKER, DON EUGENE, retired lawyer; b. Rockbridge, Ohio, Feb. 3, 1928; s. Beryl Hollis and Ruth (Primmer) T.; m. Elizabeth Jane Parke, Aug. 2, 1950; children: Janet Elizabeth, Kerry Jane, Richard Parke. B.A., Aurora Coll., 1951; LL.B., Yale, 1956. Bar: Ohio 1956. Since practiced in Youngstown, Ohio; asso. Manchester, Bennett, Powers & Ullman, 1956-62, ptnr., 1962-73, of counsel, 1973-87; gen. counsel Comml. Intertech Corp., Youngstown, 1973-73, of counsel, 1975-83, also dir., sr. v.p., gen. counsel, 1983-87, sr. v.p., 1987-93; ret., 1993; bd. dirs. Bank One of Youngstown Ohio. Solicitor Village of Poland, Ohio, 1961-63; former chmn. bd., pres., trustee United Cerebral Palsy Assn., Youngstown and Mahoning County; trustee Mahoning County Tb and Health Assn.; former trustee, pres. Indsl. Info. Inst.; former chmn., trustee Ea. Ohio Lung Assn.; trustee, former chmn. Cmty. Corp.; trustee, former pres. Butler Inst. Am. Art. With USMCR, 1946-48, 51-53. Mem. Ohio Bar Assn., Mahoning County Bar Assn. (pres. 1972, trustee 1970-73), Youngstown Area C. of C. (bd. dirs. 1979). Methodist. Home: 7850 Garfield Rd W Salem OH 44460-9227 Office: Comml Intertech Corp PO Box 239 Youngstown OH 44501-0239

TUCKER, FREDERICK THOMAS, electronics company executive; b. Herkimer, N.Y., May 27, 1940; s. Edmond and Martha R. (Rich) T.; m. Mary McDonald; children: Michael, Lisa. BSEE, Rochester Inst. Tech., 1963. Coop. student designer Delco Products div. Gen. Motors, Rochester, N.Y., 1960-65; salesman Motorola, N.Y., N.J., Conn., 1965-70; prodn. engr.

Motorola, Phoenix, 1970-73, prodn. mgr., 1973-78, from ops. mgr. to v.p., div. ops., 1978-79, v.p., gen. mgr. power products div., 1981-84; v.p., gen. mgr. bipolar i.c. div. Motorola, 1984-87; corp. v.p., asst. gen. mgr. automotive and indsl. electronics group Motorola, Schaumburg, Ill., 1987-88; sr. v.p., gen. mgr. Motorola, Northbrook, Ill., 1988-92, exec. v.p., gen. mgr. automotive and inds. electronics group, 1992-93; exec. v.p., gen. mgr. automotive, energy and controls group, 1993—. Patentee in field. Active Jr. Achievement Bd., 1983-87; trustee Rochester Inst. Tech., 1986. Named Disting. Alumnus Coll. Engring., Rochester Inst. Tech., 1983; Alumni Honor Roll of Excellence, Rochester Inst. Tech., 1986. Mem. ITS Am. (chmn. bd. 1993). Republican. Lutheran. Office: Motorola Inc 4000 Commercial Ave Northbrook IL 60062-1840

TUCKER, GARDINER LUTTRELL, physicist, former paper company executive; b. N.Y.C., June 9, 1925; s. Ernest Eckford and Katherine May (Luttrell) T.; m. Helen Caldwell Harwell, July 24, 1954; children: Patricia Leigh Tucker Stroh, Gardiner Luttrell, James Busbee. A.B. with honors and spl. distinction in Math. and Physics, Columbia U., 1947, Ph.D. in Physics, 1953. Dir. research IBM, Yorktown Heights, N.Y., 1963-67; dep. dir. research and engring. U.S. Dept. Def., Washington, 1967-69, prin. dept. dir. research and engring., 1969-70, asst. sec. def. systems analysis, 1970-73; asst. sec. gen. def. support NATO, Brussels, 1973-76; v.p. sci. and tech. Internat. Paper Co., N.Y.C., 1976-85; bd. dirs. Motorola, Inc., Schaumburg, Ill. Contbr. articles to profl. jours.; patentee in field. Bd. dirs. Schola Cantorum of N.Y., 1985-91. Recipient Disting. Civilian Service award Dept. Def., 1972. Mem. Phi Beta Kappa, Sigma Xi. Democrat. Episcopalian. Home: 13 Quarter Mile Rd Westport CT 06880-1422

TUCKER, GARY JAY, physician, educator; b. Cleve., Mar. 6, 1934; s. Isadore Martin and Blanche Hanna (Luftig) T.; m. Sharon Ruth Pobby, June 10, 1956; children: Adam, Clare. AB, Oberlin Coll., 1956; MD, Case Western Res. U., 1960; postdoctoral fellow, Yale U., 1961-64; MA (hon.), Dartmouth Coll., 1977. Diplomate Am. Bd. Psychiatry and Neurology. Asst. prof. psychiatry Sch. Medicine Yale U., New Haven, 1967-70, assoc. prof. psychiatry, 1970-71; with Dartmouth Med. Sch., Hanover, N.H., 1971-85, prof. psychiatry, 1974-85, chmn. dept., 1978-85; prof., chmn. psychiatry and behavioral scis. Sch. Med. U. Wash., Seattle, 1985—; bd. dirs. Am. Bd. Psychiatry and Neurology. Co-author: Rational Hospital Psychiatry, 1974, Behavioral Neurology, 1985; contbr. articles to profl. jours. Lt. Commdr. USN, 1964-67. Fellow Am. Psychiat. Assn.; mem. W. Coast Coll. Biol. Psychiatry, Sigma Xi, Alpha Omega Alpha. Democrat. Jewish. Avocations: photography, motorcycles. Office: Univ of Washington Dept of Psychiatry RP-10 Seattle WA 98195

TUCKER, H. RICHARD, oil company executive; b. Streator, Ill., Oct. 2, 1936; s. H.L. and Dorothy A. (Miller) T.; children by previous marriage: Randall R., Brian A.; m. Cheryl L. Kirk, Jan. 14, 1984. BS in Chem. Engring., Purdue U., 1958; MBA, Northwestern U., 1962. Project engr. crude oil supply Amoco Corp., Chgo., 1958-64, specialist product supply, 1965-66, coord. fgn. crude oil supply, 1967-68; coord. orgn. planning Amoco Internat. Corp., Chgo., 1969-70; coord. orgn. planning Amoco Corp., Chgo., 1970-72, mgr. adminstrv. svcs., 1972-84, mgr. real estate svcs., 1984-86, coord. spl. studies, 1986-89, dir. quality mgmt., 1989-92; mgr. cost mgmt., 1992-94; v.p. Amoco Realty Co., 1984-91, Amoco Devel. Co., 1984-91. Mem. adv. com. Sch. Bd. Wheaton, Ill., 1966; mem. Citizen's Nominating Com., Wheaton, 1972; leader Boy Scouts Am., Wheaton, 1979-82; dir. Oak Brook Colony Condominium Assn., 1992-94. Mem. Westhaven Home Owners Assn. (pres. 1965-67), Phi Eta Sigma, Omega Chi Epsilon, Beta Gamma Sigma, Tau Beta Pi. Avocations: tennis, bridge, hiking.

TUCKER, HAL BEALL, retired electric utility executive; b. Ocilla, Ga., Oct. 12, 1928; s. Warren Hubert and Sarah Elizabeth (Beall) T.; m. Louise Godbee, Oct. 14, 1950; children: Julia Elizabeth, Mary Louise. BEE, Ga. Inst. Tech., 1949. Test engr. Duke Power Co., Mt. Holly, N.C., 1949-56; plant engr. Duke Power Co., Belmont, N.C., 1956-59; plant mgr. Duke Power Co., Mt. Holly, 1959-67; mgr. operation and maintenance Duke Power Co., Charlotte, N.C., 1967-74, mgr. nuclear div., 1974-82, v.p. nuclear prodn., 1982-90, sr. v.p. nuclear generation, 1990-93, ret., 1993; Southeastern Electric Exch., Atlanta, 1975-76; chmn. ops. com. Atomic Indsl. Forum, Washington, 1980-82; mem. tech. issues com., bd. dirs. Nuclear Utility Mgmt. and Resources Coun., Washington, 1989-92. Mem. sec. I boiler and pressure vessel com. ASME, N.Y.C., 1971-73; dist. officer Lions Internat., Mt. Holly, 1966; bd. dirs. Habitat for Humanity, Charlotte, 1988. 1st lt. U.S. Army, 1951-53. Mem. Am. Nuclear Soc. (corp.), Nuclear Utility Mgmt. and Resources Coun. (tech. issues com.), Civitan Internat. (bd. dirs. 1978-79), Myers Park Country Club, Charlotte City Club. Republican. Methodist. Avocations: traveling, golf, swimming, genealogy.

TUCKER, HOWARD MCKELDIN, investment banker, consultant; b. Washington, Apr. 1, 1930; s. Howard Newell and Bessie Draper (McKeldin) T.; m. Julia Spencer Merrell, Feb. 1, 1952; children: Deborah, Mark, Alexander, H. David; m. Megan Evans, Aug. 17, 1979. BA, U. Va., 1954; MBA, NYU, 1956. CFA. Investment rsch. J.P. Morgan & Co., N.Y.C., 1954-59; pension investment dept. Morgan Guaranty Trust Co., N.Y.C., 1959-61; registered rep.-analyst Mackall & Coe, Washington, 1962-69; dir. internat. dept., analyst Legg Mason Wood Walker & Co., Washington, 1969-79; with Govt. Rsch. Corp./Nat. Jour., 1979-82, Potomac Asset Mgmt., 1982-91; ptnr., mng. dir. Capital Insight's Group, Washington, 1992—; cons. County Natwest (Washington Analysis Corp.), 1985-90; bd. dirs. Monarch Enterprises, Inc., Uniflight, Inc., Sci. Mgmt. Assocs., Inc., Jeffrey Bigelow Assocs.; mem. task force on balance-of-payments U.S. Dept. Treasury, 1967—; co-organizer U.S.-Ger. Parliamentary Exchange, 1980-82; observer OECD, 1980-82; spl. overseas visitor Australian Govt., 1982. Author: Literature in Medicine; writer London Investment Jour.; contbr. articles to fin. jours. Trustee Nat. Cathedral Sch. for Girls, 1972-78; chmn. Missionary Devel. Fund Episcopal Diocese of D.C., 1974; vestryman Christ Episcopal Ch., Georgetown, 1962-65; trustee Washington Nat. Cathedral, 1966-72; del. Va. Republican Conv., 1968; co-dir. Andover-Exeter Washington Intern Program, 1976-86; patron West Europe program Woodrow Wilson Ctr., 1985-86. Served with USNR, 1950-56. Mem. Washington Soc. Investment Analysts, Nat. Economists Club, Cogswell Soc. Clubs: Naval and Mil. (London), Nat. Press, Georgetown Visitation Tennis, Saints and Sinners, Beta Theta Pi. Home: 4 Potomac Ct Alexandria VA 22314 Office: Capital Insights Group 1700 K St NW Ste 1200 Washington DC 20006

TUCKER, JACK RANDOLPH, JR., architectural firm executive; b. Little Rock, Feb. 6, 1939. BArch, BA, U. Ark., 1963. Registered arch., Ark., Tenn.; cert. Nat. Coun. Archtl. Registration Bds. Designer, draftsman, field inspector U. Ark., 1962-64, 66-68; arch., planner Peace Corps, Tunisia, 1964-66; designer, project mgr. Roy P. Harrover and Assocs. Archs., Memphis, 1968-79; prin. Jack. R. Tucker, Jr., Arch., Memphis, 1979-82; prin., owner Jack R. Tucker Jr. and Assocs., Memphis, 1982—. Mem. Shelby County mayor's task force The Econs. of Amenity, 1983; pres. Downtown Neighborhood Assn., 1984, also mem. exec. bd.; mem. exec. bd. Memphis Heritage; mem. selection com., mem. pub. works com. Center City Commn. Policy Com. Downtown Devel. Plan; chmn. Memphis Landmarks Commn.; bd. dirs. Greater Memphis Soc.; mem. profl. adv. bd. U. Ark. Sch. Architecture; active Brooks Meml. Art Gallery, Downtown Transit Task Force, Union Ave. Task Force, Mud Island Found. Support Group. Recipient 30 awards for design. Fellow AIA (past pres. Memphis chpt., Francis Gassner award Memphis chpt. 1994). Office: 81 S Front St Memphis TN 38103

TUCKER, JACK WILLIAM ANDREW, writer, film editor; b. Portland, Oreg., May 1, 1944; s. Admyrl Foster and Aileen Eloise (McDaniels) T. BA in English, Portland State U., 1964. Film editor MGM TV, Culver City, Calif., 1984-86, Cannon Film Group, Beverly Hills, Calif., 1988, Columbia TV, Burbank, Calif., 1988, Paramount Pictures, Hollywood, Calif., 1990—. Editor: (TV) Winds of War, 1982 (Emmy award nominee 1983), The Fifth Missile, 1986, 240-Robert, 1979, Flatbed Annie and Sweetpie, 1979, (films) Shogun, 1980, Salsa, 1988, They're Playing with Fire, 1983, Viper, 1988, Nightmare on Elm Street IV, 1988, Distortions, 1987, Diplomatic Immunity, 1991, Illusions, 1992, Double-O-Kid, 1993, A Million to Juan, 1994, Cinemeditor mag. Sgt. USAF, 1964-68, Vietnam. Mem. NATAS, Am. Cinema Editors (former bd. dirs., treas. 1993—).

TUCKER, JAMES RAYMOND, elementary educator; b. Pueblo, Colo., Apr. 18, 1944; s. James George and Pauline F. (Sena) T.; m. Kathie Owens; 1 child, Brittany. BA, U. So. Colo., 1966; MA, U. No. Colo., 1990, postgrad., 1991. Tchr. Sinclair Mid. Sch., Englewood, Colo., 1971-93, Denver Pub. Schs., 1993—; co-dir. Nick Bolleteri Tennis Acad., Boulder, Colo., 1986; head tennis coach Englewood High Sch., 1971—. Sgt. U.S. Army, 1967-70. Mem. NEA, U.S. Profl. Tennis Assn., U.S. Profl. Tennis Registry, Internat. Platform Assn., Colo. Edn. Assn., Meadow Creek Tennis and Fitness, Colo. H.S. Coaches Assn. (Achievement award 1989, 92, Tchr. of Yr. 1973, 78, 86, Coach of Yr. 1986, 87, 90, 93, Franklin award 1988, 89). Home: 2316 S Harlan Ct Lakewood CO 80227

TUCKER, JIM GUY, JR., governor; b. Oklahoma City, Okla., June 13, 1943; s. James Guy and Willie Maude (White) T.; m. Betty Allen; children: Lance, Kelly, Anna Rebecca, Sarah Allen. BA, Harvard U., 1964; JD, Univ. Arkansas, 1968. Assoc. atty. Rose, Barron, Nash, Williamson, Carroll and Clay, Little Rock, Ark., 1968-70; prosecuting attorney 6th Jud. Dist., Ark., 1971-72; attorney general State of Ark., 1973-75, 1975-77; ptnr. Tucker and Stafford Attys., 1979-82, Mitchell, Williams, Selig and Tucker Attys., from 1982; congressman U.S. Ho. Reps., Ark.-2, 1977-79; lt. gov., pres. of the Senate Ark., 1991-92; governor, state of Ark., 1992—; mem. Ho. Ways and Means Com.; chmn. White House Conf. on Families, 1979-80. Author: Arkansas Men at War, 1968. Presbyterian. Office: Office of the Governor State Capitol Rm 250 Little Rock AR 72201*

TUCKER, JOHN MARK, librarian, educator; b. Natchez, Miss., Oct. 25, 1945; s. Paul Marlin and Edith (Upton) T.; m. Barbara Ann Wilson, Mar. 22, 1968. BA, David Lipscomb Coll., 1967; MLS, George Peabody Coll. Tchrs., 1968, specialist in edn., 1972; PhD, U. Ill., 1983. Head libr. Freed-Hardeman Coll., Henderson, Tenn., 1968-71; reference libr. Wabash Coll., Crawfordsville, Ind., 1973-79; reference libr. Purdue U., West Lafayette, Ind., 1979-82, asst. prof. libr. sci., 1979-85, assoc. prof. libr. sci., 1985-89, sr. reference libr. Humanities, Social Sci. and Edn. Libr., 1982-90, prof. libr. sci., 1989—, libr. Humanities, Social Sci. and Edn. Libr., 1990—; grantee com. on instnl. coop. NEH, 1991-94. Co-editor: Reference Services and Library Education, 1983, User Instruction in Academic Libraries, 1986, American Library History, 1989; contbr. articles to profl. publs. Thomas S. Wilmeth grantee for innovative excellence, 1988, Frederick B. Artz rsch. grantee Oberlin Coll. Archives, 1991; Coun. on Libr. Resources rsch. fellow, 1990. Mem. ALA (chair Libr. History Round Table 1993-94), Assn. for Bibliography of History, Assn. Coll. and Rsch. Librs., Disciples of Christ Hist. Soc., Soc. for Historians of the Gilded Age and Prog. Era, So. Hist. Assn., Friends of Univ. Ill. Libr., Phi Kappa Phi, Beta Phi Mu. Democrat. Mem. Chs. of Christ. Home: 1055 Southernview Dr S Lafayette IN 47905 Office: Purdue U Humanities Social Sci & Edn Libr 1530 Stewart Center West Lafayette IN 47907-1530

TUCKER, KATHLEEN M., lawyer; b. Carroll, Iowa, Feb. 28, 1944; d. Veldon M. and Florence C. (Mahoney) Payne; m. Charles H. Tucker, Jan. 27, 1967 (div.); children: Shawn Donnelly, Kerry A. Tucker; m. Robert J. Alvarez, Oct. 13, 1974; 1 child, Amber N. BS, U. Wis., 1967; JD, Antioch Sch. Law, Washington, 1979. Bar: D.C. 1979. Exec. dir. Health and Energy Inst., Washington, 1980-87; pvt. practice law Washington; pres. Health and Energy Inst., Washington, 1987—. Co-author: Plutonium and the Workplace, 1980, Food, High Water and Rock Instability, 1982, Food Irradiation: Who Wants It?, 1987; author: Uranium and the Nuclear Cycle, 1979. Sec. Nat. Com. for Radiation Victims, Takoma Park, Md., 1980—. Stout scholar U. Wis., 1962-66. Democrat. Soc. Friends. Avocations: gardening, reading. Home: 615 Kennebec Ave Takoma Park MD 20912 Office: Health & Energy Inst PO Box 5357 Takoma Park MD 20912

TUCKER, KEITH E., pension fund executive, portfolio manager; b. N.Y.C., Jan. 31, 1933; s. Frederick Randall and Eula (Edwards) T.; m. Lindsey Ann Sale, July 7, 1936 (div. May 1977); children: Bruce Douglas, Craig Randall, Janis Lynne; m. Mary Ethel Willoschat, Aug. 31, 1937. BS in Commerce and Fin., Bucknell U., 1955; postgrad., NYU, 1958-60. Comml. banker Irving Trust Co., N.Y.C., 1957-63; fin. analyst Met. Life Ins. Co., N.Y.C., 1963-68; portfolio mgr. J. Aron & Co., N.Y.C., 1969, Shawmut Trust Co., Boston, 1970-71, Hartford (Conn.) Nat. Bank, 1971-73; portfolio mgr., sr. investment officer E.I. DuPont de Nemours & Co., Wilmington, Del., 1973—; bd. dirs. EQK Realty I, Bala Cynwyd, Pa. Mem. exec. bd. 1st Ch. Christ Scientist, Newark, Del., 1987. Served with U.S. Army, 1955-57. Avocations: sailing, bridge, tennis. Office: E I du Pont de Nemours & Co 1007 N Market St Wilmington DE 19898-0001

TUCKER, LAUREY DAN, lawyer; b. El Dorado, Ark., Oct. 23, 1936; s. Floyd A. and Harriet Kathleen (Graves) T.; m. Katherine Ellen Washburn, June 21, 1958; children: Laurie Kathleen, Dana Elizabeth. B.S. in Chem. Engring., U. Okla., 1959, LL.B., 1962. Bar: Okla., Tex., U.S. Dist. Ct. Tex., U.S. Ct. Appeals (5th, 11th, fed. cir.), U.S. Supreme Ct. Patent atty. Phillips Petroleum Co., Bartlesville, Okla., 1963-67; patent atty., then patent mgr. Monsanto Co., 1967-74; ptnr. firm Hubbard, Tucker & Harris, Dallas, 1974-94; shareholder firm Harris, Tucker & Hardin, P.C., Dallas, 1994—; lectr. environ. sci. U. Tex., Dallas, 1974-76. Trustee Episcopal Community Svc. Bd., Diocese of Dallas, 1977-84, v.p., 1981-84; vestryman Episcopal Ch. of Epiphany, Richardson, Tex., sr. warden, 1980-82. 1st lt. U.S. Army, 1962-64, capt. Res. ret. Mem. Okla. Bar Assn., State Bar Tex., Dallas Bar Assn., Am. Intellectual Property Law Assn., Internat. Trademark Assn., Dallas-Ft. Worth Patent Assn. (pres. 1978-87). Republican. Office: 2100 One Galleria Towers Dallas TX 75240

TUCKER, LOUIS LEONARD, historical society administrator; b. Rockville, Conn., Dec. 6, 1927; s. Joseph and Dora (Conn) T.; m. Beverley Jones, Mar. 27, 1953; children—Mark T., Lance K. B.A., U. Wash., 1952, M.A., 1954, Ph.D., 1957. Instr. history U. Calif., Davis, 1958; fellow Inst. Early Am. History and Culture, Williamsburg, Va., 1958-60; instr. history Coll. William and Mary, 1958-60; dir. Cin. Hist. Soc., 1960-66; asst. commr., state historian of N.Y., N.Y State Edn. Dept., 1966-76; also dir. N.Y. State Bicentennial Commn., 1969-76; dir. Mass. Hist. Soc., Boston, 1977—. Author: Puritan Protagonist, 1962, Cincinnati During Civil War, 1962, Cincinnati's Citizen Crusaders, 1967, Our Travels, 1968, Cincinnati: Students Guide to Local History, 1969, James Allen, Jr.: From Elkins to Washington, 1969, Connecticut's Seminary of Sedition, Yale College, 1974, Clio's Consort: Jeremy Belknap and the Founding of the Massachusetts Historical Society, 1990. Dir. Shaker Mus., 1967-74; dir. Am. Heritage Co., 1973-75. Served with AUS, 1946-47. Winston Churchill fellow, 1969. Mem. Am. Assn. State and Local History (pres. 1972-74). Home: 11 Colburn Rd Wellesley MA 02181-3019 Office: Massachusetts Historical Society 1154 Boylston St Boston MA 02215-3695

TUCKER, MARCIA, museum director, curator; b. N.Y.C., Apr. 11, 1940; d. Emanuel and Dorothy (Wald) Silverman; student Ecole du Louvre, Paris, 1959-60; BA, Conn. Coll., New London, 1961; MA, Inst. Fine Arts, N.Y U., 1969; hon. doctorate San Francisco Art Inst. Curator, William N. Copley Collection, N.Y.C., 1963-66; editorial asso. Art News mag., N.Y.C., 1965-69; collection cataloger Alfred H. Barr, Jr., N.Y.C., 1966-67, catalog raisonée Howald Collection Am. Art, Ford Found., Columbus (Ohio) Gallery Fine Arts, 1966-69; curator painting and drawing Whitney Mus. Am. Art, N.Y.C., 1969-77; dir./founder The New Museum, N.Y.C., 1977—; faculty U. R.I., Kingston, 1966-68, City U. N.Y., 1967-68, Sch. Visual Arts, 1969-73, Columbia U. Sch. Arts and Scis., N.Y.C., 1977; guest lectr. San Francisco Art Inst., Yale U., Balt. Mus. Art, Art Inst. Chgo., Smithsonian Instn., Princeton U.; U.S. commr. 1984 Venice Biennale Mem. Coll. Art Assn., Am. Assn. Mus. (dir.), Phi Beta Kappa. Author: Anti-Illusion: Procedures/Materials, 1969; Catalogue of Ferdinand Howald Collection, 1969; Robert Morris, 1970; The Structure of Color, 1971; James Rosenquist, 1972; Bruce Nauman, 1973; Al Held, 1974; Richard Tuttle, 1975; Early Work by 5 Contemporary Artists, 1977; Bad Painting, 1978; Barry Le Va, 1979; John Baldessari, 1981; Not Just For Laughs: The Art of Subversion, 1981; Earl Staley: 1973-83, 1984; Paradise Lost/Paradise Regained catalog for Am. exhbn. at Venice Biennale, commr., 1984; Series editor: Art After Modernism: Rethinking Representation, 1984; Choices: Making An Art Out of Everyday Life, 1986, Pat Steir, Self Portrait: An Installation, 1987; Blasted Allegories: An Anthology of Writings by Contemporary Artists, 1987; Markus Raetz: In the Realm of the Possible, 1988; Out There: Marginalization & Contemporary Cultures, 1990; Discourse: Conversations In

Postmodern Art & Culture, 1992; Bad Girls, 1994; catalog for Am. exhbn. at Venice Biennale; also articles. Office: New Mus Contemporary Art 583 Broadway New York NY 10012-3228

TUCKER, MARCUS OTHELLO, judge; b. Santa Monica, Calif., Nov. 12, 1934; s. Marcus Othello Sr. and Essie Louvonia (McLendon) T.; m. Indira Hale, May 29, 1965; 1 child, Angelique. BA, U. So. Calif., 1956; JD, Howard U., 1960. Bar: Calif. 1962, U.S. Dist. Ct. (cen. dist.) Calif. 1962, U.S. Ct. Appeals (9th cir.) 1965, U.S. Ct. Internat. Trade 1970, U.S. Supreme Ct. 1971. Pvt. practice, Santa Monica, 1962-63, 67-74; dep. atty. City of Santa Monica, 1963-65; asst. atty. U.S. Dist. Ct. (Cen. Dist.) Calif, 1965-67; commr. L.A. Superior Ct., 1974-76; judge mcpl. ct. Long Beach (Calif.) Jud. Dist., 1976-85; judge superior ct. L.A. Jud. Dist., 1985—; supervising judge L.A. County Dependency Ct. L.A. Superior Ct., 1991-92, presiding judge Juvenile divsn., 1993—; asst. prof. law Pacific U., Long Beach, 1984, 86; justice pro tem U.S. Ct. Appeals (2d cir.), 1981; exec. com. Superior Ct. of L.A. County, 1995—. Mem. editorial staff Howard U. Law Sch. Jour., 1959-60. Pres. Community Rehab. Industries Found., Long Beach, 1983-86, Legal Aid Found., L.A., 1976-77; bd. dirs. Long Beach coun. Boy Scouts Am., 1978-92. With U.S. Army, 1960-66. Named Judge of Yr. Juvenile Cts. Bar Assn., 1986, Disting. Jurist Long Beach Trial Trauma Coun., 1987, Honoree in Law Handy Community Ctr., L.A., 1987, Bernard S. Jefferson Jurist of Yr. John M. Langston Bar Assn. Black Lawyers, 1990, Judge of Yr. Long Beach Bar Assn., 1993; recipient award for Law-Related Edn. Constl. Rights Found./L.A. County Bar Assn., 1992. Mem. ABA, Calif. Judges Assn. (chmn. juvenile law com. 1986-87), Langston Bar Assn. (pres. bd. dirs. 1972, 73), Calif. Assn. Black Lawyers, Santa Monica Bay Dist. Bar Assn. (treas. 1969-71), Am. Inns of Ct., Selden Soc. Avocations: comparative law, traveling. Office: 201 Centre Plaza Dr Ste 3 Monterey Park CA 91754-2142

TUCKER, MICHAEL, actor; b. Balt., Feb. 6, 1944; m. Jill Eikenberry, 1973. Grad., Carnegie-Mellon Univ., 1966. Theatre appearances include Long Wharf Theatre, Milw. Repertory Theatre, 1960's, Arena Stage, Washington, 1970, N.Y. Shakespeare Fest. prodn. of A Comedy of Errors, 1976; Broadway appearances include Trelawney of the Wells, Moonchildren, The Goodbye People; feature films include Purple Rose of Cairo, Diner, An Unmarried Woman, The Eyes of Laura Mars, Radio Days, Tin Men, Checking Out, For Love or Money, D2: The Mighty Ducks; TV work includes regular role on series L.A. Law, NBC; also TV movies Assault and Matrimony, Day One, Spy, Too Young to Die?, Casey's Gift: For Love of a Child, The Secret Life of Archie's Wife, In the Nick of Time, A Town Torn Apart. Office: care The Gersh Agency 232 N Canon Dr Beverly Hills CA 90210*

TUCKER, MICHAEL, elementary school principal. Prin. Grace Abbott Elem. Sch., Omaha. Recipient Elem. Sch. Recognition award U.S. Dept. Edn., 1989-90. Office: Grace Abbott Elem Sch 1313 N 156th St Omaha NE 68118

TUCKER, PAUL THOMAS, information systems executive; b. Evanston, Ill., Apr. 9, 1948; s. Charles E. Jr. and Francine G. Tucker; m. Carolyn K. Montgomery, 1967 (div. 1981); 1 child, Sean P.; m. Patricia M. Merlie, 1984. BEE, U. Ill., 1970, MEE, 1971, PhD in elec. engring., 1975. Founder, ptnr., primary design engr. HAL Devices, 1968-71; pres., dir. engring., and chmn. bd. HAL Communications Corp., 1971-83; sr. rsch. engr., assoc. prof. U. Ill. Grad. Coll., 1971-83, 1983-87; sr. v.p. Commodity News Svcs., Inc., subs. Knight-Ridder, Inc., 1983-88; sr. v.p. Bus. Info. Svcs. div. Knight-Ridder, Inc., 1985-90; COO Knight-Ridder Fin., Inc., N.Y.C., 1990-91, pres., CEO, 1991—; cons. Magnavox Corp., 1974-78, Control Data Corp., 1978, TDK Corp., Tokyo, Japan, 1976-82, Commodity News Svcs., Inc., 1980-82; tchr. Parkland Jr. Coll., 1980-81; mem. U. Ill. President's Coun., 1978—. Patentee (4) in field. Strategic tech. planning bd. Mercy Hosp. Found., 1978-82; bd. dirs. Urbana C. of C., 1980-82. Office: Knight-Ridder Fin Inc 75 Wall St 23d Fl New York NY 10006 also: Knight-Ridder Fin 2020 W 89th St Shawnee Mission KS 66206

TUCKER, PAUL WILLIAM, retired petroleum company executive; b. Liberty, Mo., Dec. 21, 1921; s. Nova William and Georgia May (Cuthbertson) T.; m. Beverly Caryl Livingston, June 2, 1943; children: Ann Caryl Tucker Worland, Linda Tucker Smith. B.S., William Jewell Coll., 1942, LL.D., 1968, DSc, 1992; M.S. in Chemistry, La. State U., 1944; Ph.D. in Chemistry, (George Breon fellow), U. Mo., 1948; postgrad., U. Ill., 1946. Registered profl engr., Okla. Chemist, spectroscopist Tenn. Eastman Corp., Oak Ridge, 1944-46; chemist Phillips Petroleum Co., Bartlesville, Okla., 1948-49; tech. rep. Phillips Petroleum Co., 1949-60, asst. dir. public affairs, 1960-62; mng. dir. U.K. Ltd., London, 1962-68; v.p. gas and gas liquids U.K. Ltd., Europe-Africa, London, 1969-73; v.p. gas and gas liquids public affairs and govt. relations Europe-Africa, London, 1973-74; mgr. internat. gas and gas liquids Bartlesville, 1974-78; v.p. gas and gas liquids div., natural resources group, 1978-80, v.p. gas and gas liquids group, 1980-85. Contbr. articles to profl. jours. Recipient Disting. Services award N.Mex. Petroleum Industries Com., 1956, Citation of Achievement William Jewell Coll., 1979. Fellow Inst. Petroleum (U.K.), Instn. Gas Engrs. (U.K.); mem. NSPE (life), Am. Chem. Soc. (emeritus), Okla. Soc. Profl. Engrs., Hillcrest Country Club, Sigma Xi, Alpha Chi Sigma, Phi Lambda Upsilon. Republican. Baptist.

TUCKER, RANDOLPH WADSWORTH, engineering executive; b. Highland Pk., Ill., Dec. 3, 1949; s. Thomas Keith and Nancy Ellen (Jung) T.; m. Jean Marjorie Zenk, June 30, 1973 (div. 1991); 1 child, Nicholas Randolph; m. Lori Kaye Hicks, June 21, 1991. BS in Fire Protection Engring., Ill. Inst. Tech., 1972; M in Mgmt., Northwestern U., 1979. Registered profl. engr., Ill., Tex., Fla., La., Ga. With Ins. Svcs. Office of Ill., Chgo., 1972-74, bldg. insp., fire protection cons., 1972-74; with Rolf Jensen & Assocs., Inc., Deerfield, Ill., 1974—, cons. engr., 1974-77, mktg. mgr., 1977-81, mgr. Houston office, 1981-83, v.p. engring., mgr. Houston, 1983-89, v.p., tech. officer for Atlanta, Houston, N.Y.C., and Washington offices, 1989-90, sr. v.p., 1990-94, sr. v.p. internat. devel., 1994—; mem. adv. coun. Tex. State Fire Marshal, Austin, 1983-91; Dept. of Justice/Nat. Inst. Corrections cons. to Tex. Commn. on Jail Stds., 1993—. Editorial advisor Rusting Publs., N.Y.C., 1981—, Cahners Pub., 1993—; author articles in field. V.p. Juvenile Fire Setters Program, Houston, 1982-84. Named one of Outstanding Young Men Am., U.S. Jaycees, 1981. Mem. Soc. Fire Protection Engrs. (chmn. nat. qualifications bd. 1985, pres. Houston chpt. 1983-84), Soc. Mktg. Profl. Svcs. (pres. Houston chpt. 1985, nat. pres. 1989-90), Nat. Fire Protection Assn., Urban Land Inst., Internat. Conf. Bldg. Ofcls., So. Bldg. Code Cong. Internat., Inc., Bldg. Ofcls. and Code Administrs. Internat., Bldg. Ofcls. Assn. Tex., AIA (profl. affiliate), Tex. Soc. Architects (profl.affiliate), Houston C. of C. (vice chmn. fire protection com. 1983, govt. rels. com. 1984—), Aircraft Owners and Pilots Assn., Waller Country Club. Republican. Episcopalian. Avocations: flying, golf. Office: Rolf Jensen & Assoc Inc 13831 Northwest Fwy Ste 330 Houston TX 77040-5215

TUCKER, RAY MOSS, agricultural products cooperative executive. BS, U. Ky. Pres. Dairymen Inc., Louisville, also bd. dirs. Office: Dairymen Inc 10140 Linn Station Rd Louisville KY 40223-3813

TUCKER, RICHARD LEE, civil engineer, educator; b. Wichita Falls, Tex., July 19, 1935; s. Floyd Alfred and Zula Florence (Morris) T.; m. Shirley Sue Tucker, Sept. 1, 1956; children: Brian Alfred, Karen Leigh. BCE, U. Tex., 1958, MCE, 1960, PhD in Civil Engring., 1963. Registered profl. engr., Tex. Instr. civil engring. U. Tex., 1960-62; from asst. prof. to prof. U. Tex., Arlington, 1962-74, assoc. dean engring., 1963-74; v.p Luther Hill & Assoc., Inc., Dallas, 1974-76; C.T. Wells prof. project mgmt. U. Tex., Austin, from 1976, dir. Constrn. Industry Inst., from 1983, dir. Constrn. Engring. and Project Mgmt. Program, 1976—; pres. Tucker and Tucker Cons., Inc., Austin, 1976—. Contbr. numerous articles and papers to profl. jours. Named Outstanding Young Engr., Tex. Soc. Profl. Engrs., 1965, Outstanding Young Man, City of Arlington, 1967, Michael Scott Endowed Rsch. fellow Inst. for Constructive Capitalism, 1990-91, Ronald Reagan award for Individual Initiative, Constrn. Industry Inst., 1991, Disting. Grad., Coll. Engring. U. Tex. Austin, 1994. Fellow ASCE (R.L. Peurifoy award 1984, Thomas Fitch Rowland prize 1987, Tex. sect. award of honor 1990); mem. NSPE (Constrn. Engring. Educator award of the Profl. Engrs. in Constrn. 1993), NRC, Soc. Am. Mil. Engrs., The Moles (hon.). Baptist.

Office: U Tex at Austin Dept Civil Engring 3208 Red River St Ste 300 Austin TX 78705-2650

TUCKER, RICHARD LEE, financial executive; b. Boston, Jan. 16, 1940; s. Frank Lee and Dorothy (Mansell) T.; m. Melinda Nichols, 1970 (div. 1987); children: Anne P., John M.; m. Elizabeth M. Lyne, 1988; children: Christopher B., William M. AB, Harvard U., 1962. CFA. Portfolio mgr. Scudder Stevens & Clark, Boston, 1963-72, v.p. investments, 1972-80; sr. v.p., mgr. trust div. The Boston Co., 1980-86; supervising portfolio mgr., v.p Trinity Investment Mgmt. Corp., Boston, 1986—, mng. dir., 1992—; dir. Data Gen. Corp., 1994—. Trustee Phillips Exeter (N.H.) Acad., 1975-86. Served with U.S. Army, 1962-63. Mem. Inst. Chartered Fin. Analysts, Somerset Club (pres.), The Country Club (Brookline). Home: 23 Woodman Rd Chestnut Hill MA 02167-1221 Office: Trinity Investment Mgmt 75 Park Plz Boston MA 02116-3934

TUCKER, ROBERT ARNOLD, electrical engineer; b. Atlanta, Jan. 30, 1941; s. Robert Drury and Mary M. (Dobbs) T.; m. Judy Elizabeth Henley, Sept. 18, 1964 (div. Sept. 13, 1979); children: Paige Elizabeth, Priscilla Elaine, Matthew Arnold; m. Joan Janet Ashton, Nov. 18, 1983; children: Beth Bennett, Russell E. McKenna III. BEE, Ga. Inst. Tech., 1964. Registered profl. engr., Ala., Fla., Ga., Tenn. Engr. in tng. Patterson & Dewar Engrs. Inc., 1964; substation design engr. Ga. Power Co., 1964-65, comml. sales engr., sr. engr., 1965-67, 72-73; dist. sales engr. Sylvania Elec. Products, Inc., 1967-71; regional sales mgr. The J.H. Spaulding Co., 1971-72; gen. sales mgr. Perimeter Lighting, Inc., 1973-74; utility mgmt. engr. Colonial Stores, Inc., 1975-76; prin. R. Arnold Tucker & Assocs., P.C., 1977-82; dist. sales engr. GTE Products Corp., 1982-86, mgr. tech. programs, 1986-90, engr. regional lighting/energy mgmt., 1990-93; comml. engr. Osram Sylvania Inc., Atlanta, 1993—. Contbr. articles to profl. jours. Mem. Kiwanis. Mem. NSPE, Illuminating Engring. Soc., Assn. Energy Engrs. Republican. Baptist. Home: 2130 Wynfield Point Dr Buford GA 30519 Office: Osram Sylvania Inc 5169 Pelican Dr Atlanta GA 30349-5979

TUCKER, ROBERT DENNARD, health care products executive; b. Tifton, Ga., July 18, 1933; s. Robert Buck and Ethel Margaret (Dennard) T.; m. Peggy Angelyn Smith, June 23, 1957; children: Robert Barron, Jennifer Lee. BBA, Ga. State U., 1958. With sales and mgmt. mgmt. Johnson & Johnson Inc., New Brunswick, N.J., 1958-68; v.p., gen. mgr. ASR Med. Industries, N.Y.C., 1968-72, Howmedica Suture div. Pfizer Inc., N.Y.C., 1972-75; exec. v.p., chief operating officer R. P. Scherer Corp., Detroit, 1976-79; pres., chief operating officer Scherer Sci. Inc., Atlanta, 1980—, also bd. dirs; chmn., chief exec. officer Scherer Health Care Inc., Atlanta, 1980—, also bd. dirs. Nat. Travel Mgmt., Atlanta Biofor Inc., Waverly, Pa., Clean Air Corp. Am., Atlanta, U.S. Environ. Compliance Corp., Atlanta, Body Care Inc., Atlanta, Marquest Med. Products, Inc., Denver. Pub: Tuckers of Devon, 1983; author, pub.: Descendants of William Tucker of Throwleigh, Devon. Chmn. bd. Health Industries Mfrs. Assn. polit. action com., Washington, 1983-85; trustee, past pres. Ga. Horse Found., Atlanta; trustee Brenau Coll. Gainesville, Ga., 1985—. Served with USN, 1951-54, Korea. Decorated Knight of Malta, Imperial Russian Order of St. John; recipient Disting. Service award Brenau Coll., 1987. Mem. Nat. Assn. Mfrs., Health Industries Mfrs. Assn. (bd. dirs. 1979-86, disting. service recognition 1981, 86), Pharm. Mfrs. Assn., Thoroughbred Owners and Breeders Assn. Ky. and Ga. (Man of Yr. 1984). Republican. Methodist. Clubs: Cherokee (Atlanta); Big Canoe (Ga.). Avocations: scuba diving, tennis, genealogical research. Home: 405 Townsend Pl NW Atlanta GA 30327-3037 Office: Scherer Healthcare Inc Ste 300 2859 Paces Ferry Rd NW Atlanta GA 30339-5740

TUCKER, ROBERT KEITH, environmental scientist, research administrator; b. Santa Ana, Calif., Feb. 22, 1936; s. Lloyd Levi and Margaret Corinne (Skiles) T.; m. Sharon Penney Langs, 1961 (div. 1974); children: Katherine Penney, Lee Ann; m. Joan Cook Luckhardt, Oct. 9, 1977. BA in Biochemistry, U. Calif., Berkeley, 1963; MA in Marine Biology, Humbolt State U., 1967; PhD in Zoology, Physiological Ecology, Duke U., 1971. Rsch. biologist Sandy Hook Lab. NOAA Nat. Marine Fisheries Svc., Highlands, N.J., 1971-77; rsch. scientist N.J. Dept. Environ. Protection and Energy, Trenton, 1977-78, mgr. water and biota unit Office Cancer and Toxic Substances Rsch., 1978-80, asst. dir. Office Cancer and Toxic Substance Rsch., 1980-83, dep. dir. Office Sci. and Rsch., 1983-86, dir. Divsn. Sci. and Rsch., 1986—; chmn. environ. task force Gov.'s Coun. Prevention Mental Retardation and Devel. Disabilities, 1984-86, Interagy. Task Force Prevention Lead Poisoning, 1986—; mem. bd. trustees N.J. Marine Scis. Consortium, 1987—; mem. N.J. Commn. Cancer Rsch., 1984—; mem. adv. bd. Environ. and Occupational Health Scis. Inst. U. Medicine and Dentistry N.J., 1987—; N.J. Comprehensive Cancer Ctr., 1991—, Greater N.Y. Bight Marine Rsch., 1992—; mem. external adv. bd. Nat. Inst. Occupational Safety and Health, 1990-92; mem. review panel estuarine rsch. northeast ctr. NOAA, Nat. Marine Fisheries Svc., 1989; organizer, dir. session 100th anniversary meeting Am. Soc. Testing and Materials, 1984; external com. mem. for PhD candidates Ruthers U., CUNY, Hunter Coll., U. Medicine and Dentistry N.J., 1972—. Contbr. over 50 articles to profl. jours. Fellow USPHS, 1967-70; recipient Merit citation NOAA, 1975, Outstanding Scientist award N.J. DEP, 1980. Mem. AAAS, Am. Chem. Soc. (organizer, dir. sessions on environ. chemistry Mid-Atlantic regional meeting 1979), Internat. Soc. Environ. Epidemiology, Soc. Occupational and Environ. Health, Crustacean Soc. Democrat. Unitarian. Achievements include reasearch in lead poisoning, problems dealing with petroleum contaminated soils, toxics in drinking water and groundwater, effects of toxic contaminants on marine resources. Office: NJ Dept Environ Protection & Energy Divsn Sci & Rsch CN409 Trenton NJ 08625

TUCKER, ROY NELSON, mathematics educator, minister; b. LaGrange, Ga., Aug. 12, 1941; s. Henry Patrick Jr. and Katherine Irene (Irwin) T.; m. Sharon Elizabeth Knapp, May 10, 1974; children: Cheryl, Tina, David. PhD in Clin. Psychology, Ohio Christian U., 1967; MDiv, Southeastern Bapt. Theol. Sem., 1970; PhD in Psychology of Religion, Baylor U., 1978; MS in Math., Prairie View A&M U., 1983; MEd, Pan Am. U., 1987. Salesman, divsn. mgr. Sears, Roebuck & Co., Macon, Ga., 1962-66; learning lab coord. W.W. Holding Tech Inst., Raleigh, N.C., 1968-70; teaching asst. Baylor U., Waco, Tex., 1970-73; instr. Tex. State Tech. Inst., Waco, 1976-80, Blinn Coll., Bryan-College Station, Tex., 1982-84, Tex. Southmost Coll., Brownsville, 1984-87, Embry-Riddle Aero. U., Beeville, Tex., 1988-89; asst. prof. math. Palo Alto Coll., San Antonio, 1988—. Author: Social Structures, 1978, Human Relations in Industry, 1979, A Time to Laugh, A Time to Cry, 1992, (play) The Innkeeper's Christmas, 1991. Pastor First Bapt. Ch., Jewell, Ga., 1965-67, Cmty. Bapt. Ch., Wake Forest, N.C., 1967-70, Marquez (Tex.) Bapt. Ch., 1975-79, Evang. U. C.C., Lyons, Tex., 1980-84, First Christian Ch., Aransas Pass, Tex., 1988-91, First Christian Ch., Devine, Tex., 1994—; pres. Boosters Assn., Waco, 1978-79; v.p. Family Abuse Ctr., Waco, 1978-79; pres. faculty senate Palo Alto Coll., 1995—; city councilman City of Hewitt, Tex., 1980. Maj. USAR, 1942-69. Mem. Tex. Faculty Assn., Tex. Jr. Coll. Tchrs. Assn., Masons. Republican. Avocations: travel, sports. Home: 6208 Sawyer Rd San Antonio TX 78238-2205 Office: Palo Alto Coll 1400 W Villaret Blvd San Antonio TX 78224-2499

TUCKER, SHIRLEY LOIS COTTER, botany educator, researcher; b. St. Paul, Apr. 4, 1927; d. Ralph U. and Myra C. (Knutson) Cotter; m. Kenneth W. Tucker, Aug. 22, 1953. BA, U. Minn., 1949, MS, 1951; PhD, U. Calif. Davis, 1956. Asst. prof. botany La. State U., Baton Rouge, 1967-71, assoc. prof., 1971-76, prof., 1976-82, Boyd prof., 1982-95, prof. emerita, 1995—; adj. prof. dept. ecology, evolution and marine biology U. Calif., Santa Barbara, 1995—. Co-editor: Aspects of Floral Development, 1988, Advances in Legume Systematics, Vol. 6, 1994; Contbr. more than 90 articles on plant devel. to profl. jours. Fellow Linnean Soc., London, 1975—; Fulbright fellow Eng. 1952-53. Mem. Bot. Soc. Am. (v.p. 1979, program chmn. 1975-78, pres.-elect 1986-87, pres. 1987-88, Merit award 1989), Am. Bryological and Lichenological Soc., Brit. Lichenological Soc., Am. Inst. Biol. Scis., Am. Soc. Plant Taxonomists (pres.-elect 1994-95, pres. 1995—), Phi Beta Kappa, Sigma Xi. Home: 3987 Primavera Rd Santa Barbara CA 93110 Office: Dept Ecology Evolution and Marine Biology U Calif Santa Barbara CA 93101

TUCKER, STANLEY R., headmaster. Headmaster Girls Prep. Sch., Chattanooga. Office: Girls Prep Sch 200 Barton Ave PO Box 4736 Chattanooga TN 37405

TUCKER, STEFAN FRANKLIN, lawyer; b. Detroit, Dec. 31, 1938. Assoc. in Bus., Flint Jr. Community Coll., 1958; BBA, U. Mich., 1960, JD, 1963. Bar: U.S. Dist. Ct. D.C. 1964, U.S Ct. Appeals (D.C. cir.) 1964, U.S. Ct. Claims 1964, U.S. Tax Ct. 1964. Clk. to judge U.S. Tax Ct., Washington, 1963-64; assoc. Arent, Fox, Kintner, Plotkin & Kahn, Washington, 1964-69, ptnr., 1970-74; ptnr. Tucker, Flyer & Lewis, Washington, 1975—; speaker in field; profl. lectr. law George Washington U. Nat. Law Ctr., 1970—; adj. prof. law, Georgetown U. Law Ctr., 1990—; adj. profl. lectr. law U. Miami Law Ctr., 1975-78; mem. adv. com. Ann. Inst. Real Estate Planning, U. Miami, 1978-91; chmn. bd. trustees Mass. Sch. Law, Andover, 1989—; mem. visitors com. U. Mich. Law Sch., 1989—. Author: Tax Planning for Real Estate Transactions, 1989; mem. editorial bd. Taxation for Lawyers, 1972—; mem. adv. bd. Bur. Nat. Affairs Housing and Devel. Reporter, 1973-76, Mertens on Federal Income Taxation, 1985—, The Tax Times, 1986-87; mem. editorial adv. bd. Jour. Real Estate Taxation, 1975—, Practical Real Estate Lawyer, 1984—. Mem. nat. com. U. Mich. Law Sch. Fund, 1972-78. Mem. ABA (tax sect., chmn. real estate tax problems com. 1977-79, chmn. continuing legal edn. com. 1984-86, coun. mem 1987-91, vice chmn. com. ops. 1991-93), Fed. Bar Assn., D.C. Bar Assn. (taxation div., steering com. 1980-82), Nat. Trust Hist. Preservation (com. legal svcs. 1978-85). Office: 1615 L St NW Ste 400 Washington DC 20036-5610 *I believe that each person has an obligation to share with others, whether through teaching, lecturing or writing, the knowledge and experience gained through his life's work. Such sharing provides a greater reward than monetary gain can ever provide.*

TUCKER, STEPHEN LAWRENCE, health administration educator, consultant; b. Cin., Oct. 18, 1940; s. Lawrence Henry and Blanche Virginia (Greenwood) T.; m. Lucille Frances Dinda, June 15, 1968; children: Gregory Lawrence, David John. BA, Dartmouth Coll., 1962; MBA, Xavier U., Cin., 1966; D Bus. Adminstrv., George Washington U., 1970. Adminstrv. asst. Presbyn.-U. Pa. Med. Ctr., Phila., 1966-67; assoc. adminstr. Harrisburg (Pa.) Hosp., 1970-73; assoc. prof. Xavier U., 1973-76; prof. chmn. Trinity U., San Antonio, 1976-81, prof. healthcare adminstrn., 1981-87, 94—, dean, 1987-94; cons. on healthcare adminstrn., San Antonio, 1976—. Co-author: Analysis Manual for Hospital Information Systems, 1980; contbr. articles to profl. jours., chpts. to books. Bd. dirs. Bexar County Mental Health and Mental Retardation Ctr., San Antonio, 1979-85; bd. dirs., chmn. S.W. Neuropsychiat. Inst., San Antonio, 1986-92. 1st lt. U.S. Army, 1962-64. Recipient Disting. Alumni Svc. award Xavier U., 1984; fellow Accrediting Commn. Grad. Edn. in Hosp. Adminstrn., 1974, WHO, Eng., 1975. Fellow Am. Coll. Healthcare Execs. (various coms. 1966—); mem. Soc. for Healthcare Planning and Mktg. (bd. dirs. 1983-86). Home: 347 Tophill Rd San Antonio OH 78209 Office: Trinity U 58 Dept of Hlth Adm 715 Stadium Dr San Antonio TX 78212

TUCKER, TANYA DENISE, singer; b. Seminole, Tex., Oct. 10, 1958; d. Boe and Juanita Tucker; 2 children, Presley, Beau. Regular on Lew King Show; rec. artist formerly with Columbia Records, MCA Records, Capitol Records; albums include Tear Me Apart, Changes, Delta Dawn, Dreamlovers, Here's Some Love, TNT, Girls Like Me, Greatest Hits, 1989, Greatest Hits (1972-1975), Greatest Hits Encore, 1990, Greatest Country Hits, 1991, Greatest Hits 1990-92, 1993, Love Me Like You Use To, 1987, Strong Enough to Bend, 1988, Tanya Tucker Live, Tennessee Woman, 1990, What Do I Do With Me, 1991, (with Delbert McClinton) Can't Run From Yourself, 1992, Soon, 1993; TV appearances include A Country Christmas, 1979, The Georgia Peaches, 1980; actress: (mini-series) The Rebels, 1979, (film) Jeremiah Johnson, 1968. Recipient: Country Music Assn. award, 1991, female vocalist of the year; 2 Grammy nominations, 1994. Office: care Chapple Fin Svcs Inc 5200 Maryland Way Ste 103 Brentwood TN 37027-5018*

TUCKER, THOMAS JAMES, investment manager; b. Atlanta, Sept. 5, 1929; s. Thomas Tudor and Carol (Govan) T.; m. Margaret Guerard. B.A. U. of the South, 1952. With CIT Corp, N.Y.C., 1957-72; pres., chief exec. officer AmSouth Fin. Corp., Birmingham, Ala., 1972-82; chmn. bd. AmSouth Fin. Corp., 1982, also dir., 1972-93; exec. v.p. AmSouth Bank N.A., Birmingham, 1982-93, chief credit officer, 1992; ret. Tucker Investments, Birmingham, 1993, prin.; exec. v.p. AmSouth Bankcorp, Birmingham, 1982-93; bd. dirs. Alabanc Properties Corp., Birmingham, chmn., 1991-93; bd. dirs. Birmingham Broadway Series Inc. Contbr. articles on credit and leasing to trade jours.; photographer gen. interest mags., 1970—. Bd. dirs. Birmingham Community Devel. Corp.; chmn. bd., 1990-93. 1st lt. USAF, 1952-56. Mem. Vulcan Trail Assn., Birmingham Art Mus. Assn., Birmingham Canoe Club (bd. dirs. 1990—), Photography Guild, Shades Valley Camera Club, Cahaba River Soc. (adv. bd. 1991-92, bd. dirs 1993), Ala. Growth Strategies Task Force, Regional Open Space and Trails Alliance, The Club, Jefferson Club, Summit Club. Episcopalian. Avocations: photography, high altitude hiking, white water canoeing. Home and Office: Tucker Investments 4132 Old Leeds Rd Birmingham AL 35213-3210

TUCKER, THOMAS WILLIAM, mathematics professor; b. Princeton, N.J., July 15, 1945; s. Albert William Tucker and Alice Judson (Curtiss) Beckenbach; m. Mollie Dalton; children: Thomas John, Emily McDonnell. AB magna cum laude, Harvard U., 1967; PhD, Dartmouth U., 1971. Instr. Princeton (N.J.) U., 1971-73; asst. prof. Colgate U., Hamilton, N.Y., 1973-78; assoc. prof. Colgate U., Hamilton, 1979-83, prof., 1983—, Charles G. Hetherington prof. math., chmn. math. dept., 1982-86; acting dean coll. Colgate U., Hamilton, N.Y., 1991-92; dir. divsn. nat. sci. Colgate U., Hamilton, 1993—; vis. assoc. prof. Dartmouth Coll., Hanover, N.H., 1978-79; cons. field. Testing Svc. 1973—; Inst. for Def. Analyses, Princeton, (summers) 1974, 75, 78, 79, 84, 85; chmn. advanced placement calculus com. Coll. Bd., N.Y.C., 1983-87. Co-author: Topological Graph Theory, 1987; editor: Priming the Calculus Pump, 1990; contbr. numerous articles to profl. jours. NSF grantee, 1976-77, 80-82, 86-88, 89, 90—. Mem. Math. Assn. Am. (mem., chmn. many coms., v.p. 1990—), Am. Math. Soc. Home: 21 Hamilton St Hamilton NY 13346-1329 Office: Colgate U Dept Math Hamilton NY 13346

TUCKER, WALTER RAYFORD, III, congressman, lawyer, former mayor; b. Compton, Calif., 1957; s. Walter Rayford Jr. and Martha H. Tucker; m. Robin Tucker; children: Walter Rayford IV, Autumn Monet. BA in Polit. Sci. cum laude, U. So. Calif., 1978; JD, Georgetown U., 1981. Ordained Christian minister. Staff Segrue, Rothwell, McPeak, Washington; dep. dist. atty. County of Los Angeles, 1984-86; pvt. practice Compton 1986—; mayor City of Compton, Calif., 1991-92; mem. 103rd-104th Congresses from 37th Calif. dist., 1993—; mem. transp. and infrastructure com., mem. small bus. com. Active Compton Juvenile Delinquency Panel; Sunday Sch. teacher. Mem. NAACP (life), Calif. Bar Assn., South Crtl. Bar Assn., L.A. Bar Assn., Langston Bar Assn., Kiwanis Club of Compton. Democrat. Office: US Ho of Reps 419 Cannon Office Of Ho Mems Washington DC 20515-0531*

TUCKER, WATSON BILLOPP, lawyer; b. Dobbs Ferry, N.Y., Nov. 16, 1940; s. Watson Billopp and Mary (Prema) T.; m. Ann Bryant Cramer, June 19, 1981; children: Robin, Craig, Christopher, Alexander, John. BS, Northwestern U., Evanston, Ill., 1962; JD, Northwestern U., 1965. Bar: Ill. 1965, U.S. Dist. Ct. (no. dist.) Ill. 1966, U.S. Supreme Ct. 1971, U.S. Dist. Ct. (no. dist.) N.Y. 1976, U.S. Ct. Appeals (7th cir.) 1970, U.S. Ct. Appeals (2d cir.) 1976, U.S. Ct. Appeals (3d cir.) 1981. Ptnr. Mayer, Brown & Platt, Chgo., 1965—. Fellow Am. Coll. Trial Lawyers. Office: Mayer Brown & Platt 190 S La Salle St Chicago IL 60603-3410

TUCKER, WILLIAM EDWARD, university chancellor, clergyman; b. Charlotte, N.C., June 22, 1932; s. Cecil Edward and Ethel Elizabeth (Godley) T.; m. Ruby Jean Jones, Apr. 8, 1955; children: Janet Sue, William Edward, Gordon Vance. BA, Barton Coll., Wilson, N.C., 1953, LLD (hon.), 1978; BD, Tex. Christian U., 1956; MA, Yale U., 1958, PhD, 1960; LHD (hon.), Chapman Coll., 1981; DH (hon.), Bethany Coll., 1982; DD (hon.), Austin Coll., 1985; LHD (hon.), Kentucky Wesleyan Coll., 1989. Ordained to ministry Disciples of Christ Ch., 1956; prof. Barton Coll., 1959-66, chmn. dept. religion and philosophy, 1961-66; mem. faculty Brite Div.

Sch., Tex. Christian U., 1966-76, prof. ch. history, 1969-76, dean, 1971-76, chancellor, 1979—; pres. Bethany (W.Va.) Coll., 1976-79; dir. Justin Industries, Inc., Tandy Corp., Brown and Lupton Found.; mem. gen. bd. Christian Ch. (Disciples of Christ), 1971-74, 75-87, administrv. com., 1975-81, chmn. theol. edn. commn., 1972-73, mem. exec. com., chmn. bd. higher edn., 1975-77; dir. Christian Ch. Found.; 1980-83; moderator Christian Ch. (Disciples of Christ), 1983-85. Author: J.H. Garrison and Disciples of Christ, 1964, (with others) Journey in Faith: A History of the Christian Church (Disciples of Christ), 1975; also articles. Bd. dirs. Ft. Worth Symphony Orch. Assn., 1980—, Van Cliburn Internat. Piano Competition, 1981—. Mem. Newcomen Soc. N.Am., Exch. Club, Phi Beta Kappa. Home: 2900 Simondale Dr Fort Worth TX 76109-1250 Office: Tex Christian U Office of Chancellor Fort Worth TX 76129

TUCKER, WILLIAM PHILIP, lawyer, writer; b. Kingston, N.Y., Jan. 26, 1932; s. Philip and Mary (McGowan) T.; m. Dolores F. Beaudoin, June 10, 1961; children: Andrew M., Thomas B., Mary A. BA with honors, Hunter Coll., 1958; JD with honors, St. John's U., 1962. Bar: N.Y. 1962, U.S. Dist. Ct. (ea. dist.) N.Y. 1962, Fla. 1980. Assoc. Mendes & Mount, N.Y.C., 1962-63; ptnr. Cullen and Dykman, Bklyn. and Garden City, N.Y., 1963—; gen. counsel Broadway Nat. Bank, Roosevelt Savs. Bank, Olympian Bank, CrossLand Savs., FSB, The Green Point Savs. Bank, Ridgewood Savs. Bank, Atlantic Liberty Savs., F.A., Bethpage Fed. Credit Union, Episcopal Health Svcs., Inc., St. John's Episcopal Hosp., Smithtown, St. John's Home for the Aged and Blind, St. John's Episcopal Nursing Home, Interfaith Med. Ctr.; spl. counsel Bklyn. C. of C., Downtown Bklyn. Bus. Assoc., Marine Midland Bank, N.A., Bank of N.Y., Chemical Bank, Nat. Westminster Bank, Travelers Mortgage Svcs., Cititrust, North Fork Bank, Am. Express Credit Union, Mcpl. Credit Union. Mem. Selective Svc. Bd.; past pres. St. Vincent Ferrer Home Sch. Assn.; del. Diocesan Union Holy Name Socs.; mem. coun. St. John's U.; mem. coun. of regents St. Francis Coll., Bklyn.; bd. dirs. Faith Home Found. Mem. N.Y. State Bar Assn. (real estate exec. com.), Fla. Bar Assn., Savs. Banks Lawyers Assn. of Bklyn., N.Y. Land Title Assn., Suffolk County Bar Assn., Savs. Bank Assn. N.Y. State (law com.), Bklyn. Mpcl. Club, Knight of Malta. Avocations: co-ownership of baseball team, writing. Home: 23 Bunker Hill Dr Huntington NY 11743-5705 Office: Cullen and Dykman 100 Quentin Roosevelt Blvd Garden City NY 11530-4850 also: 177 Montague St Brooklyn NY 11201

TUCKER, WILLIAM THOMAS, III, computer software company executive; b. Milw., June 26, 1942; s. William Thomas and Shirley Audrey (Holmes) T.; m. Barbara Ann Granof, Sept. 8, 1965 (dec. Sept. 1982); children: Pamela Ann, Penelope Lynn, Matthew Louis. BS cum laude, U. Wis., 1969. Lic. real estate broker, Wis. Dir. pub. rels. Jr. Achievement S.E. Wis., Milw., 1969-71; exec. dir. Jr. Achievement Fox Valley, Appleton, Wis., 1971-74; mktg. dir. Southridge Mall, Milw., 1974-81; asst. mall mgr. Southridge and Northridge Malls, Milw., 1981-83; pres. Buyer Publs., Inc., San Diego, 1983-86; mall mgr. Mayfair Mall, Milw., 1987-89; pres. ML-Asst., Inc., real estate computer software, Milw., 1989—; cons. House Trader mag. Home Buyer Inc., San Diego, 1986—; instr. Waukesha County Tech. Coll. Design engr. computer software Home Search System, 1989. Dep. state dir. Naval Acad. Info. Program, Milw., 1981—; mem. nominating com. Sen. Kasten Acad., Milw., 1990-93, Congressman Kleczka Acad., Milw., 1990-93, Senator Kohl Acad., Milw., 1991—; mem. Naval Recruiting Dist. Coun., 1977—. Comdr. USNR. Lutheran. Avocations: desktop publishing, genealogy, history, psychology, salesmanship. Home: 6065 Doyle St Greendale WI 53129 Office: ML-Asst Inc 6065 Doyle St Greendale WI 53129

TUCKER, WILLIAM VINCENT, vocational evaluator, former college president; b. Beatrice, Nebr., May 23, 1934; s. Custer Augustine and Mary Margaret (Carmichael) T.; m. Marian Elizabeth Cooper, Aug. 9, 1958; children: Catherine, Jean, Rose Marie, Alan. B.A., Benedictine Coll., 1955; M.S., Emporia State U., 1963; Ed.D., U. S.D., 1968. Tchr. Kelly (Kans.) High Sch., 1958-61; grad. asst. Emporia State U., 1960-61, instr., 1961-63; instr. Briar Cliff Coll., 1963-65, asst. prof. ednl. psychology, assoc. prof., 1968-70, prof., 1970-71, acad. v.p., 1967-71; pres., prof. St. Mary of the Plains Coll., 1971-75; pres. Mt. Marty Coll., 1975-83; sr. devel. rep. State of S.D., 1983-84; pres. Greater Huron Devel. Corp., 1984-87; owner Career Devel., Inc., 1987—; cons. Social Security Adminstrn., 1962—; vocat. evaluator Goodwill Rehab., 1992—. Contbr. articles on ednl. rehab., placement of physically handicapped to profl. jours. Trustee Dodge City Area Hosp. Assn., Kans.; chmn. bd. Colls. of Mid Am.; pres. S.D. Found. Private Colls. Served with U.S. Army, 1955-57. Mem. Am. Econ. Devel. Council, Yankton C. of C. (dir.), Phi Delta Kappa. Roman Catholic. Clubs: Elks, Rotary. Home: 2605 W 37th St Sioux Falls SD 57105-5201

TUCKER, WILLIS CARLETON, retired academic administrator, retired journalism educator; b. Beckley, W.Va., Mar. 14, 1907; s. Charles Cherrington and Bessie Alma (Willis) T.; m. Julia Belle Infield, Mar. 15, 1941. B.A., W.Va. Inst. Tech., 1930; M.A., W.Va. U., 1931; postgrad., U. So. Calif., 1940, Ohio State U., summers 1931, 33, 35, 37, 41. Reporter daily newspapers, editor and bus. mgr. weekly, press assn. corr., coll. publicity, 1924-33; asst. prof. Marshall Coll., 1934-37, co-editor quar., 1936-37; asst. prof. journalism U. Ky., 1938-42, asso. prof., 1943-47; telegraph, news editor daily newspapers, 1942-47; Nat. Assn. Broadcasters radio news intern Sta. WGAR, Cleve., summer 1945; prof., head dept. journalism U. Tenn., 1947-57, prof., 1972-74, dir. Sch. Journalism, 1957-72, dir. emeritus, 1974—; pres. U. Tenn. Pub. Assn., 1955-70; univ. dir. Indsl. Editing Inst., 1948-72; editorial cons., trade and indsl. publs., 1952—; pres. Precision Editing, 1977-91; sec. U. Tenn.-Tenn. Press Assn. Press Inst., 1952-73; cons. Am. Assn. Indsl. Editors, 1963-70; exec. dir. Tenn. High Sch. Press Assn., 1948-74. Co-author books; contbr. articles to profl. jours. Recipient Gov.'s Merit award, 1972. Mem. Assn. Edn. in Journalism and Mass Communication, Kappa Tau Alpha, Phi Kappa Phi, Kappa Alpha, Sigma Delta Chi, Omicron Delta Kappa. Home: 39 Canyon Rd Bella Vista AR 72714-3036 *I think whatever we touch we should try to leave a little better than before—whether an organization, public facility, student's paper, historical record, or shade tree. I value people whose work is paced not by timepieces but by a high regard for accuracy and quality—professionals who are happy in giving more than they receive.*

TUCKER-KETO, CLAUDIA A., academic administrator; b. Phila., Jan. 24, 1948; d. Arthur and Erma (Miller) Tucker; m. Clement T. Keto (div. 1993); children: Victor Lefa, James Lefanyana (twins). BA, Temple U., 1982. With adminstrv. office Pa. Supreme Ct., Phila.; coll. adminstr., family resource specialist Camden County Coll., Blackwood, N.J.; coord. women's programs Camden County Dept. Health and Human Svcs., Camden, N.J. mem. ethics com. Dist. IV Supreme Ct., 1993-95. Legis. chairwoman N.J. Fed. Dem. Women, Trenton, N.J.; mem. planning com. U.S. Dept. Labor Women's Bur. Region II, N.Y.; commr. N.J. Martin Luther King Jr. Organization, Trenton; bd. dir. N.J. Women's Summit, Sicklerville, N.J.; chairwoman Camden County Commn. on Women, N.J. Recipient Women in Bus. award Nat. Hookup of Black Women, 1992, Outstanding Svc. to Women award African Am. Women's Network, 1994. Mem. AAUW. Baptist. Home: 3211 Arborwood III Lindenwold NJ 08021 also: Commission on Women 2101 Ferry Ave 4th fl Camden NJ 08104

TUCKMAN, BRUCE WAYNE, educational psychologist, educator, researcher; b. N.Y.C., Nov. 24, 1938; s. Jack Stanley and Sophie Sylvia (Goldberg) T.; m. Darby Godwin, July 24, 1980; children by previous marriage: Blair 2., Bret A. BS, Rensselaer Poly. Inst., 1960; MA, Princeton U., 1962, PhD, 1963. Rsch. assoc. Princeton U., 1963; rsch. psychologist Naval Med. Rsch. Inst., Bethesda, Md., 1963-65; assoc. prof. edn. Rutgers U., New Brunswick, N.J., 1965-78; dir. Bur. Research and Devel.-Rutgers U., New Brunswick, 1975-78; dean Coll. Edn. Baruch Coll., CUNY, 1978-82; sr. rsch. fellow CUNY, 1982-83; dean Coll. Edn. Fla. State U., Tallahassee, 1983-85, prof., 1985—. Author: Preparing to Teach the Disadvantaged, 1969 (N.J. Assn. Tchrs. of English Author's award 1969), Conducting Educational Research, 1972, 4th rev. edit., 1994 (Phi Delta Kappa Rsch. award 1973), Evaluating Instructional Programs, 1979, 2d rev. edit., 1985, Analyzing and Designing Educational Research, 1979, Effective College Management, 1987, Testing for Teachers, 1988; (novel) Long Road to Boston, 1988, Educational Psychology: From Theory to Application, 1992. Rsch. dir. Task Force on Competency Standards, Trenton, N.J., 1976. N.Y. State Regents scholar, 1956; Kappa Nu grad. scholar, 1960; NIMH predoctoral fellow, 1961, 62; Rutgers U. faculty study fellow, 1974-75;.

Fellow APA, Am. Psychol. Soc.; mem. Am. Ednl. Rsch. Assn., Phi Delta Kappa. Office: Fla State Univ Dept Edn Rsch 307 Stone Bldg Tallahassee FL 32306-3030

TUCKSON, REED V., university president. Pres. Charles R. Drew U., L.A. Office: Charles R Drew U Office of President 1621 E 120th St Los Angeles CA 90059-3025

TUCKWELL, BARRY EMMANUEL, musician, music educator; b. Melbourne, Australia, Mar. 5, 1931; s. Charles Robert and Elizabeth (Hill) T.; children: David Michael, Jane Madeleine, Thomas James; m. Susan Levitan, June 21, 1992. Grad., Sydney (Australia) State Conservatorium; DMus (hon.), Sydney U., Australia, 1994. Prof. French horn Royal Acad. Music, 1962-74; mem. mgmt. com. London Symphony Orch. Trust, 1963-69; mem. faculty congregation arts Dartmouth Coll., 1968-69; guest prof. Harvard U., Yale U., others. With Melbourne, Sydney, Halle, Scottish Nat. and Bournemouth symphony orchs., 1947-55; solo French horn, London Symphony Orch., 1955-68; tchr., soloist and chamber music player, 1968—; mem. Chamber Music Soc. of Lincoln Ctr., N.Y.C., 1974-81, dir. London Symphony Orch. Ltd., 1957-68, chmn., 1961-68, mem. Tuckwell Wind Ensemble, Tuckwell Wind Quintet, Tuckwell Horn Quartet, chief condr. Tasmanian Symphony Orch., 1980, condr., music dir. Md. Symphony Orch., 1982—; rec. artist for RCA, CRI, Angel, London, Argo.; author: Playing the Horn, 1978, The Horn, 1983; editor: Horn Lit. for G. Schirmer, Inc; leader ann. French horn workshop, Fla. State U., Claremont Music Festival, 1970-71. Decorated Order Brit. Empire; companion Order of Australia; recipient Harriet Cohen Meml. medal for soloists, 1968. Fellow Royal Coll. Music, Royal Soc. arts; mem. Internat. Horn Soc. (hon., pres. 1969-77, 92-94), Royal Acad. Music (hon.), Guildhall Sch. Music (hon.). Address: 13140 Fountain Head Rd Hagerstown MD 21742-2839

TUDOR, DONALD NORRIS, state government administrator; b. Raleigh, N.C., Mar. 15, 1947; s. Owen Shell and Rubelle Catherine (Norris) T.; m. Melba Elaine Buckner Spencer, Aug. 15, 1970 (div. Apr. 1988); children: James Dwight, Lauren Burdette, William Brandon Norris; m. Leah Annette McNeely, Apr. 2, 1994. BS, East Carolina U., 1969; MPA, Golden Gate U. 1976. Urban planner Gov.'s Office, Columbia, S.C., 1969-71; dir. planning orgn. Santee-Wateree Regional Planning Coun., Sumter, S.C., 1971-78; exec. asst. Inter-Agy. Coun. on Pub. Transp., Columbia, 1978-79; dir. transp. policy Gov.'s Office, Columbia, 1979-86; dir. trans. cons. Carter Goble Associates., Columbia, 1986-90; pub. transit cons. Don Tudor Assocs., Columbia, 1990-91; sr. exec. asst. for support svcs. S.D. Dept. Edn., Columbia, 1991—; charter chmn. Nat. Transp. Acctg. Consortium, Lansing, Mich., 1980-86; mem. bd. dirs. Southeastern Pupil Transp. Conf. Mem. adminstrv. bd. Shandon United Meth. Ch., Columbia, 1988-91, 93—; bd. dirs. Internat. Trade Conf., Charleston, S.C., 1982-92, Inter-Modal Transp. Program, Coll. of Charleston, 1982-92. Decorated Order of the Palmetto, Gov. of S.C., 1986; recipient ann. award Transp. Assn. S.C., 1986. Mem. AICP, S.C. Assn. Pupil Transp. (pres. 1995—), Nat. Assn. State Dirs. Pupil Transp. Svcs. Avocations: home repair, reading, travel. Home: 833 Adger Rd Columbia SC 29205 Office: SC Dept Edn 1429 Senate St Columbia SC 29201

TUDRYN, JOYCE MARIE, professional society administrator; b. Holyoke, Mass., July 27, 1959; d. Edward William and Frances Katherine (Bajor) T.; m. William Wallace Friberger III, Sept. 18, 1982; 1 child, Kristen. BS in Comm., Syracuse U., 1981. Asst. editor Nat. Assn. Broadcasters, Washington, 1981-83; dir. programs Internat. Radio and TV Soc. Found., N.Y.C., 1983-87; assoc. exec. dir. Internat. Radio and TV Soc., N.Y.C., 1988-94, exec. dir., 1994—; spkr. in field; nat. adv. bd. Alpha Epsilon Rho Broadcasting Soc., 1988-93, 93-94, hon. trustee, 1994—; v.p. Corp. for Ednl. Radio and TV, 1988-94. Editor-in-chief IRTS News, 1983—; columnist TV Facts, Figures and Film mag., 1983-88. Recipient Mass. Kodak Photography award, 1977; S.I. Newhouse scholar Syracuse U., 1980-81. Mem. N.Y. Media Roundtable, Gamma Phi Beta. Avocations: photography. Home: 602 Bennington Dr Union NJ 07083-9104 Office: Internat Radio and TV Soc Found/Ste 1714 420 Lexington Ave New York NY 10170-0001

TUELL, JACK MARVIN, retired bishop; b. Tacoma, Nov. 14, 1923; s. Frank Harry and Anne Helen (Bertelson) T.; m. Marjorie Ida Beadles, June 17, 1946; children—Jacqueline, Cynthia, James. B.S., U. Wash., 1947, LL.B., 1948; S.T.B., Boston U., 1955; M.A., U. Puget Sound, 1961, DHS, 1990; D.D., Pacific Sch. Religion, 1966; LLD, Alaska Pacific U., 1980. Bar: Wash. 1948; ordained to ministry Meth. Ch., 1955. Practice law with firm Holte & Tuell, Edmonds, Wash., 1948-50; pastor Grace Meth. Ch., Everett, Wash., 1950-52, South Tewksbury Meth. Ch., Tewksbury, Mass., 1952-55, Lakewood Meth. Ch., Tacoma, 1955-61; dist. supt. Puget Sound dist. Meth. Ch., Everett, 1961-67; pastor 1st United Meth. Ch., Vancouver, Wash., 1967-72; bishop United Meth. Ch., Portland, Oreg., 1972-80, Calif.-Pacific Conf. United Meth. Ch., L.A., 1980-92; interim sr. pastor First United Meth. Ch., Boise, Idaho, 1995; Mem. gen. conf. United Meth. Ch., 1964, 66, 68, 70, 72; pres. coun. of Bishops United Meth. Ch., 1989-90. Author: The Organization of the United Methodist Church, 1970, 7th edit. 1993. Pres. Tacoma U.S.O., 1959-61, Vancouver YMCA, 1968; v.p. Ft. Vancouver Seamens Cnt., 1969-72; vice chmn. Vancouver Human Rels. Commn., 1970-72; pres. Oreg. Coun. Alcohol Problems, 1972-76; trustee U. Puget Sound, 1961-73, Vancouver Meml. Hosp., 1967-72, Alaska Meth. U., Anchorage, 1972-80, Willamette U., Salem, Oreg., 1972-80, Willamette View Manor, Portland, 1972-80, Rogue Valley Manor, Medford, Oreg., 1972-76, Sch. Theology at Claremont, Calif., 1980-92, Methodist Hosp., Arcadia, Calif., 1983-92; pres. nat. div. bd. global ministries United Meth. Ch., 1972-76, pres. ecumenical and interreligious concerns div., 1976-80, Commn. on Christian Unity and interreligious concerns, 1980-84, Gen. Bd. of Pensions,1984-92, Calif. Coun. Alcohol Problems, 1985-88. Jacob Sleeper fellow, 1955. Mem. Lions. Home and Office: 2697 S North Bluff Rd Greenbank WA 98253-9718

TUERFF, JAMES RODRICK, insurance company executive; b. Gary, Ind., Jan. 17, 1941; m. Julie K. Luttinen; children: Brian J., Kevin A., Jeffrey J., Gregory S. BA in Econs., St. Joseph's Coll., 1963. CLU. Asst. v.p. Life and Casualty Ins. Co., Nashville, 1967-75; v.p. Commonwealth Life Ins. Co., Louisville, 1975-77; v.p. Am. Gen. Life Ins. Co., Houston, 1977-78, sr. v.p., exec. v.p., 1979-83; v.p. Am. Gen. Corp., Houston, 1978-79, exec. v.p., 1983-88, pres., chief exec. officer Gulf Life Ins. Co., 1988-90; pres., chief exec. officer Am. Gen. Life and Accident Ins. Co., Nashville, 1990-93, also bd. dirs.; pres. Am. Gen. Corp., Houston, 1993—; mem. adv. com. to bd. trustees St. Joseph's Coll.; bd. dir. YMCA Greater Houston, Sam Huston Coun. Boy Scouts Am., St. Joseph Hosp. Found., Am. Coun. Life Ins. Fellow Life Mgmt. Inst. Soc. Houston (life). Republican. Roman Catholic. Office: Am Gen Corp 2929 Allen Pky Houston TX 77019-2119

TUERK, RICHARD CARL, English language educator; b. Balt., July 10, 1941; s. Isadore and Helen (Blumberg) T.; m. Rosalind Paula Lerner, June 24, 1963; children: Michael Aaron, Rebekah Felice. AB, Columbia Coll., 1963; MA, Johns Hopkins U., 1964, PhD, 1967. Asst. prof. U. Calif., Riverside, 1967-72; assoc. prof. East Tex. State U., Commerce, 1972-77, prof., 1977—, Piper prof., 1991. Author: Central Still, 1975; co-author: Adventures in Appreciation, Annotated Teacher's Edition, 1989; contbr. articles to profl. publs. Leader Boy Scout Am., Commerce, 1976-93. Mem. MLA, Soc. for Study of Multi-Ethnic Lit. of U.S. (treas. 1976-79, nat. chmn. 1980-81, spl. award 1981), Thoreau Soc., Am. Assn. Profs. of Yiddish, Am. Studies Assn., Popular Culture Assn., Am. Studies Assn. Tex. (v.p. 1992, pres. 1993). Democrat. Jewish. Avocations: swimming, raising dogs. Home: 2808 Washington St Commerce TX 75428-3844 Office: East Tex State U Lit and Langs Dept Commerce TX 75429

TUFARIELLO, JOSEPH JAMES, chemistry educator; b. Bklyn., Oct. 3, 1935; s. Joseph and Louise Katherine (Jacino) T.; m. Agnes Patricia Matze, June 25, 1960; children: Catherine, JoAnn, Donna, Jennifer. BA, Queens Coll., 1957; PhD, U. Wis., 1961. Post-doctoral assoc. Purdue U., West Lafayette, Ind., 1962; NIH post-doctoral fellow Cornell U., Ithaca, N.Y., 1963; asst. to assoc. prof. chemistry SUNY, Buffalo, 1963-80, prof. chemistry, 1980—, chmn. dept. chemistry, 1984-91, dean faculty of natural scis. and math., 1991—; cons. Allied Chem. Corp., Buffalo, 1986—, Laser Photonics Inc., 1991—. Contbr. articles to profl. jours. Named Merck Lectr. Bucknell U., Lewisburg, Pa., 1986; recipient Excellence in Teaching award Students' Assn. SUNY, Buffalo, 1982, Chancellor's award for Excellence in Teaching, SUNY, 1981. Mem. Am. Chem. Soc., Sigma Xi, Phi Beta

Kappa. Roman Catholic. Avocations: baseball, tennis, chess. Home: 257 Hunters Ln Buffalo NY 14221-3331 Office: SUNY Natural Scis and Math Fac Capen Hall Buffalo NY 14260

TUFARO, RICHARD CHASE, lawyer; b. N.Y.C., July 9, 1944; s. Frank P. and Stephania A. (Maida) T.; m. Helen M. Tufaro, June 25, 1977; children: Mary C., Edward F., Paul R., Cynthia M. AB magna cum laude, Dartmouth Coll., 1965; LLB cum laude, Harvard U., 1968. Bar: N.Y. 1969, D.C. 1992, Md. 1994; U.S. Dist. Ct. (so. dist.) N.Y. 1973, U.S. Dist. Ct. (ea. dist.) N.Y. 1978, U.S. Dist Ct. (D.C. dist.), 1994; U.S. Ct. Apls. (2d cir.) 1973, (5th cir.) 1976, (9th cir.) 1979, (6th cir.) 1980, (4th cir.), 1995; U.S. Ct. Claims, 1985, U.S. Ct. Appeals (fed. cir.) 1988, U.S. Ct. Appeals (3d cir.) 1990, U.S. Ct. Appeals (D.C. cir.) 1992, U.S. Dist. Ct. D.C., 1994; U.S. Sup. Ct., 1975; U.S. Claims Ct., 1985. Law clk. Appellate-Div. N.Y. State, N.Y.C., 1970-71, assoc. Milbank, Tweed, Hadley & McCloy, N.Y.C., 1971-72, adminstrv. asst. White House Domestic Coun., Washington, 1972-73, assoc. Milbank, Tweed, Hadley & McCloy, N.Y.C., 1973-77, ptnr. 1978—. Served to capt. U.S. Army, 1968-70. Decorated Bronze Star with oak leaf cluster. Mem. ABA, Am. Mgmt. Assn., Phi Beta Kappa. Home: 7109 Heathwood Ct Bethesda MD 20817-2915 Office: 1825 I St NW Ste 1100 Washington DC 20006-5403

TUFT, MARY ANN, former association executive; b. Easton, Pa., Oct. 11, 1934; d. Ben and Elizabeth (Reibman) T. B.S., West Chester (Pa.) State Coll., 1956; M.A., Lehigh U., 1960. Cert. assn. exec. Nat. trainer Girl Scouts U.S.A., N.Y.C., 1965-68; cons. Nat. League for Nursing, N.Y.C., 1968-69; exec. dir. Nat. Student Nurses Assn., N.Y.C., 1970-85; mem. Commn. on Dietetic Registration, Am. Dietetic Assn., 1981-85; pres. Specialized Cons. Ltd., 1983-85; exec. dir. Radiol. Soc. N.Am., Oak Brook, Ill., 1985-88; prin. Tuft & Assocs., 1989—. Bd. dirs. Nurses House, Inc., 1981-85; bd. dirs. Chgo. Sinai Cong., 1987-91, v.p., 1988. Mary Ann Tuft Scholarship Fund named in her honor Found. Nat. Student Nurses Assn.; Kepner-Tregoe scholar, 1966. Mem. ALA (pub. mem. com. on accreditation 1993-95), Am. Soc. AAssn. Execs. (bd. dirs. 1980-83, trustee for cert. 1980-83, vice chmn. 1983-84), N.Y. Soc. Assn. Execs. (pres. 1978-79, bd. dirs. 1975-78, 1st Outstanding Exec. award 1982), Continuing Care Accreditation Assn. (bd. dirs. 1983-85), Specialized Cons. in Nursing (faculty).

TUFTE, EDWARD ROLF, statistics educator, publisher; b. Kansas City, Mo., Mar. 14, 1942; s. Edward E. and Virginia (James) T.; m. Inge Druckrey. BS, Stanford U., 1963, MS, 1964; PhD, Yale U., 1968; HHD (hon.), Cooper Union, 1992, Conn. Coll., 1995. Asst. prof. pub. policy Princeton U., 1967-71, assoc. prof., 1971-74, prof., 1974-77; prof. polit. sci., stats., computer sci. and graphic design Yale U., New Haven, 1977—; pres. Graphics Press, Cheshire, 1983—; cons. in field; mem. com. on nat. stats. NRC, 1979-84. Author: Quantitative Analysis of Social Problems, 1970, Size and Democracy, 1973, Data Analysis, 1974, Political Control of the Economy, 1978 (Kammerer award 1979, Citation Classic 1989), The Visual Display of Quantitative Information, 1983 (Citation Classic 1992), Envisioning Information, 1990. Pres. Cheshire Neighborhood Assn., 1984-87. Recipient Best Graphic Design award Internat. Design, 1990, Wittenborn award, 1991, Best Book Design award Assn. Ind. Publs., Computer Press Assn. award, 1991, Sci. award Phi Beta Kappa, 1991; Ctr. for Advanced Study in Behavioral Scis. fellow, 1973-74; Guggenheim fellow, 1977. Fellow Am. Acad. Arts and Scis., Am. Statis. Assn. Office: Yale U PO Box 208301 New Haven CT 06520-8301

TUFTE, OBERT NORMAN, retired research executive; b. Northfield, Minn., May 30, 1932; s. Ole Nels and Stella Josephine (Lundene) T.; m. Doris Helen Wisbroecker, Dec. 29, 1956; children, Keith, Brian, Stephen, Jon. BA in Physics, St. Olaf Coll., 1954; PhD in Physics, Northwestern U., 1960. Rsch. scientist Honeywell Inc., Hopkins, Minn., 1960-69; rsch. mgr. Honeywell Inc., Bloomington, Minn., 1969-84; rsch. fellow Honeywell Inc., Bloomington, 1984-87, chief scientist, 1987-93; ret., 1994. Contbr. articles to profl. jours., 1960-88; inventor 7 U.S. patents, 1962-89. Mem. IEEE (sr.), Am. Phys. Soc., Sigma Xi. Home: 14937 Manitou Rd Prior Lake MN 55372-1112 Office: Honeywell Tech Ctr 10701 Lyndale Ave S Minneapolis MN 55420-5601

TUFTS, DAVID ALBERT, JR., securities company executive; b. Winchester, Mass., Sept. 9, 1945; s. David Albert and Florence Ida (Watters) T.; m. Jocelyne Maggiar-Nash, Aug. 21, 1971; children: Stephanie Elizabeth, Natalie Alexandra. BA, Hobart Coll., 1967. Dir. sales Kennedy Ctr. for Performing Arts, Washington, 1970-71; mgr. Merrill Lynch, Washington, 1971-81; asst. mgr. Oppenheimer & Co., N.Y.C., 1981-84, mng. dir., 1984—; mem. mgmt. com. Oppenheimer & Co., N.Y.C., 1986—. Bd. dirs. Brunswick Sch., Greenwich, Conn., 1986—; alumni council Hobart Coll., Geneva, N.Y., 1985—. Served to lt. USN, 1968, Vietnam. Mem. Kappa Alpha. Republican. Congregational. Clubs: Rocky Point (Greenwich); U. (Washington). Home: 37 Lockwood Rd New York NY 10012-1149 Office: Oppenheimer & Co Inc Oppenheimer Tower World Financial Ctr New York NY 10081

TUFTS, DONALD WINSTON, electrical engineering educator; b. Yonkers, N.Y., Mar. 5, 1933; s. Fletcher Gorham Tufts and Myrtle (Ayers) Gordon; m. Barbara Michelsen, Mar. 24, 1956; children: Cynthia Tufts Anderson, David Jost, John Lawrence. MS; Diploma, The Hotchkiss Sch., Lakeville, Conn., 1951; BA, Williams Coll., 1955; BS, MS, MIT, 1957, DSc, 1960. Engr. Sanders Assocs., Nashua, N.H., summer 1960; cons. Sanders Assocs., Nashua, 1960—; asst. prof. applied math. Harvard U., Cambridge, Mass., 1960-67; prof. elec. engring. and computer sci. U.R.I., 1967—; cons. NASA, AT&T, others, 1966-75. Contbg. author books, papers in field. Chmn. East Greenwich (R.I.) Sch. Commn., 1976, 77; bd. dirs. East Greenwich Acad. Found., 1989-91. Recipient Bell Fellowship AT&T, 1957-60, Rsch. award URI, 1987, 90. Fellow IEEE (chmn. providence sect. 1987-88, 93—, CNEC div. 1990-91); mem. Assn. Computer Mach., Tau Beta Pi, Sigma Si, Eta Kappa Nu. Democrat. Unitarian. Achievements include four patents and one patents pending. Home: 490 Carrs Pond Rd East Greenwich RI 02818-1007 Office: Univ RI 199 Kelly Hall Kingston RI 02881

TUFTS, ROBERT B., registrar; b. Cleve., Nov. 5, 1940; s. Robert L. and Dora Mae (Yingling) T.; m. Nancy Intihar, June 22, 1968 (div. Feb. 1990); children: Therese, Kevin R. BA cum laude, Cleve. State U., 1967; MA, Case Western Res. U., 1972; postgrad., U. Akron, 1973-76. Admissions counselor Cleve. State U., 1967-69, asst. registrar, 1969-70; asst. registrar Youngstown (Ohio) State U., 1970-73; asst. registrar U. Akron (Ohio), 1973-75, assoc. registrar, 1975-78; registrar Portland (Oreg.) State U., 1978—; com. mem. Park Recreation Adv. Bd., W. Linn., Oreg., 1981-84; presenter on fraudulent credentials, 1987—. Contbr. articles to profl. jours. With U.S. Army, 1959-62, Korea. Mem. Oreg. Assn. Registrars and Admissions Officers (sec.-treas. 1988-90), Pacific Assn. Collegiate Registrars and Admissions Officers (mem. program com. 1986-87, exec. bd., chair local arrangement 64th Ann. Mtg., Portland 1990), Am. Assn. Collegiate Registrars and Admissions Officers (local arrangements com., chair pub. com. 82nd Ann. Mtg., Reno, 1996, mem. facilities planning mgmt. com. 1975-78, chmn. of com. 1977-78), Nat. mem. Assn. Coll. and Univ. Bus. Officers, Theta Rho. Democrat. Mem. Unitarian Ch. Avocations: mountaineering, camping, home projects. Home: 4981 Prospect St West Linn OR 97068-3116 Office: Portland State U PO Box 751 Portland OR 97207-0751

TUFTY, HAROLD GUILFORD, editor, publisher; b. Chgo., Sept. 1, 1922; s. Harold and Esther (Van Wagoner) T.; m. Barbara Jean Taeusch, Dec. 29, 1948; children: Christopher, Karen, Steven. BME, U. Va., 1949; postgrad., Sorbonne/Alliance Franciase, 1949-50. Corr. Tufty News Svc., Washington, 1946—; reporter Denver Post, 1949-51; European corr. Denver Post, Paris, 1951-52; pub. rels. Grant Advt., N.Y.C., 1953-55; info. officer U.S. Info. Agy., Madras, India, 1955-58, Bombay, India, 1958-59; pub. affairs officer, press attache U.S. Info. Agy., Conakry, Guinea, 1960, Abidjan, Ivory Coast, 1961-63; dir. French speaking African programs Peace Corps, Washington, 1963-64; pres. Tufty & Assoc., Washington, 1964—; bureau chief Tufty News Svc., Washington, 1984—; comml. pilot, single engine, land and sea, 1947—; mem. media staff conf. on civil rights White House, Washington, 1964; cons. U.S. Senate Com. Pub. Works, Washington, 1966-80; dir. The Ad Agy., Inc., Washington, 1970-78; pres. The Value Found., Washington, 1979—; congl. value engring. witness, testimony rschr., 1967—; presenter value engring. workshops in Bombay, Madras, Delhi, Hyderabad, Bangalore, and Calcutta. Author: Compendium on Value Engineering, 1983; editor, pub. Value Engrng. and Mgmt. Digest, 1972—; columnist Interactions, 1988—. Nat. v.p. Soc. Am. Value Engrs., Washington, 1970-72; bd. dirs. SAVE Nat. Capital, Washington, 1964—, chmn., 1973—; congl. receptions. Lt. USN, 1944-46. Fellow Soc. Am. Value Engrs., 1985; recipient Capital Honor award, SAVE, 1971, Disting. Svc. award SAVE, 1977-78. Mem. Soc. Am. Valve Engrs. (nat. pres. 1990-92), Nat. Dem. Club. Avocations: reading, understanding my computer, haiku, chess, instructing sailing using aerodynamic principles. Home: 3812 Livingston St NW Washington DC 20015-2803 Office: Tufty Comm Co 2107 National Press Bldg Washington DC 20045

TUGGLE, FRANCIS DOUGLAS, management educator; b. Portsmouth, Va., Jan. 19, 1943; s. Francis Joyner and Florence Eleanor (Dahlgren) T.; m. Mary Ann Tredway, June 3, 1967; children: Wendy Elizabeth, Laura Michelle. SB, MIT, 1964; MS, Carnegie-Mellon U., 1967, PhD, 1971. Prof. bus. adminstrn. and computer sci. U. Kans., Lawrence, 1968-78; Jesse H. Jones prof. mgmt. Rice U., Houston, 1978-90; dean Kogod Coll. Bus. Adminstrn., Am. U., Washington, 1990—; bd. dirs. Equus II Inc., Houston, Internat. Expert Systems Inc., Houston; mem. coun. acad. advisors Bryce Harlow Found., 1994—. Author: How to Program a Computer, 1975, Organizational Processes, 1978. Com. chmn. United Way Tex. Gulf Coast, Houston, 1985-88. Ford Found. fellowship, 1966. Mem. AAAS, Inst. Mgmt. Scis. (v.p. 1992-94), Informs (dir. 1995), Am. Assn. of Artifical Intelligence, Assn. for Computing Machinery, Acad. of Mgmt., Sigma Xi, Beta Gamma Sigma, Alpha Kappa Psi. Episcopalian. Avocations: golf, bicycling, jogging. Home: 4709 Ft Sumner Dr Bethesda MD 20816-2466 Office: Am U Kogod Coll Bus Adminstrn 4400 Massachusetts Ave NW Washington DC 20016-8044

TUGWELL, JOHN, bank executive; b. 1940. With Nat. Westminster Bancorp., Inc., chmn. bd., pres., CEO, 1991; chmn. Natwest Bank N.A. Office: Nat Westminster Bancorp Inc 10 Exchange Pl Jersey City NJ 07302

TUKEY, HAROLD BRADFORD, JR., horticulture educator; b. Geneva, N.Y., May 29, 1934; s. Harold Bradford and Ruth (Schweigert) T.; m. Helen Dunbar Parker, June 25, 1955; children: Ruth Thurbon, Carol Tukey Schwartz, Harold Bradford. B.S., Mich. State U., 1955, M.S., 1956, Ph.D, 1958. Research asst. South Haven Expt. Sta., Mich., 1955; AEC grad. research asst. Mich. State U., 1955-58; NSF fellow Calif. Inst. Tech. 1958-59; asst. prof. dept. floriculture and ornamental horticulture Cornell U., Ithaca, N.Y., 1959-64, assoc. prof., 1964-70, prof., 1970-80; prof. urban horticulture U. Wash., Seattle, 1980—, dir. Arboreta, 1980-92, dir. Ctr. Urban Horticulture, 1980-92; cons. Internat. Bonsai mag., Electric Power Rsch. Inst., P.R. Nuclear Ctr., 1965-66; lectr. in field; mem. adv. com. Seattle-U. Wash. Arboretum and Bot. Garden, 1980-92, vice chmn., 1982, chmn., 1987-93; vis. scholar U. Nebr., 1982; vis. prof. U. Calif.-Davis 1973; mem. various coms. Nat. Acad. Scis.-NRC; bd. dirs. Arbor Fund Bloedel Res., 1980-92, pres., 1983-84. Mem. editorial bd. Jour. Environ. Horticulture, Arboretum Bull. Mem. nat. adv. com. USDA, 1990—; pres. Ithaca PTA; troop advisor Boy Scouts Am., Ithaca. Lt. U.S. Army, 1958. Recipient B.Y. Morrison award USDA, 1987; NSF fellow, 1958-59; named to Lansing (Mich.) Sports Hall of Fame, 1987; grantee NSF, 1962, 75, Bot. Soc. Am., 1964; hon. dr. Portuguese Soc. Hort., 1985. Fellow Am. Soc. Hort. Sci. (dir. 1970-71); mem. Internat. Soc. Hort. Sci. (U.S. del. to coun. 1971-90, chmn. commn. for amateur horticulture 1974-83, exec. com. 1974-90, v.p. 1978-82, pres. 1982-86, 86-90, chmn. commn. Urban Horticulture 1990—, hon. mem. 1994), Internat. Plant Propagators Soc. (ea. region dir. 1969-71, v.p. 1972, pres. 1973, internat. pres. 1976), Am. Hort. Soc. (dir. 1972-81, exec. com. 1974-81, v.p. 1978-80, citation of merit 1981), Royal Hort. Soc. (London, v.p. hon. 1993—), Bot. Soc. Am., N.W. Horticulture Soc. (dir. 1980-92), Wash. State Nursery and Landscape Assn. (hon. mem., 1995), Arboretum Found. (dir. 1980-92), Rotary, Sigma Xi, Alpha Zeta, Phi Kappa Phi, Pi Alpha Xi, Xi Sigma Pi. Presbyterian. Home: 3300 E St Andrews Way Seattle WA 98112-3750 Office: U Wash Ctr for Urban Horticulture Ctr Frst # Gf-15 Seattle WA 98144

TUKEY, LOREN DAVENPORT, pomology educator, researcher; b. Geneva, N.Y., Dec. 4, 1921; s. Harold Bradford and Margaret (Davenport) T.; m. Louise Arleyne Young, Feb. 2, 1952; children: David Davenport, Barbara Ann Tukey Shea. B.S., Mich. State U., 1943, M.S., 1947; Ph.D., Ohio State U., 1952. Asst. prof. pomology Pa. State U., University Park, 1950-57, assoc. prof., 1957-66, prof., 1966-91, prof. emeritus pomology, 1991—; fruit rsch. cons. Nat. Inst. Agrl. Tech., Argentina, 1965-70; rsch. cons. Instituto Interamericano Cooperacion Agricultura, Argentina, 1988; rsch. cons. cocoa Malaysian Agr. Rsch. and Devel. Inst., Malaysia, 1993. Editor: Pa. State Hort. Revs., 1962-91; assoc. editor: Jour. Hort. Sci. (Eng.), 1978-92; researcher numerous publs. in field. Bd. dirs. State College chpt. ARC, 1963-82; mem. Borough of State College Traffic Commn., 1976-80. Served to capt. Q.M.C., U.S. Army, 1943-46, ETO. Named Outstanding Horticulturist State Hort. Assn. Pa., 1986; recipient Milo Gibson award N.Am. Fruit Explorers, 1989. Fellow Am. Soc. Hort. Sci., AAAS; mem. Internat. Soc. Hort. Sci., Am. Soc. Plant Physiologists, Plant Growth Regulator Soc. Am., Am. Pomological Soc. (sec. 1968-74, Paul Howe Shepard award 1964, treas. and bus. mgr. 1968-89), Internat. Dwarf Fruit Tree Assn. (Svc. and Leadership award 1988), Academie d'Agriculture de France (corr.), Brit. Soc. for Plant Growth Regulation, Sigma Xi, Gamma Sigma Delta (pres. chpt. 1967-68), Phi Epsilon Phi, Theta Chi, Rotary, pres. State Coll. 1971-72, Paul Harris fellow). Republican. Presbyterian. Growth and development of tree fruits: growth regulating chemicals, environ. factors in fruit sizing, orchard productivity, intensive orchard systems and rootstocks. Developer of Penn State low-trellis hedgerow system for apple culture. Home: 549 Glenn Rd State College PA 16803-3473 Office: 103 Tyson Bldg University Park PA 16802

TULCHIN, DAVID BRUCE, lawyer; b. N.Y.C., Dec. 2, 1947; s. Philip Tulchin and Mary (Weiner) Black; m. Nora Barrett, Aug. 20, 1972; children: Rachel, Daniel, Laura. BA, U. Rochester, 1970; JD, Harvard U., 1973. Bar: N.Y. 1974, U.S. Dist. Ct. (so. & ea. dists.) N.Y. 1975, U.S. Ct. Appeals (2d cir.) 1975, U.S. Supreme Ct. 1977, U.S. Ct. Appeals (5th cir.) 1983, U.S. Ct. Appeals (1st & 6th cirs.) 1984, U.S. Dist. Ct. (no. dist.) Ohio 1984, U.S. Ct. Appeals (3d, 4th & Fed. cirs.) 1988, U.S. Ct. Appeals (7th cir.) 1991. Law clk. to Judge Frederick V.P. Bryan U.S. Dist. Ct. So. Dist. N.Y., N.Y.C., 1973-75; assoc. Sullivan & Cromwell, N.Y.C., 1975-82, ptnr., 1982—. Mem. ABA, Assn. Bar of City of N.Y., Fed. Bar Coun., N.Y. State Bar Assn., Fed. Cir. Bar Assn. Office: Sullivan & Cromwell 125 Broad St New York NY 10004

TULCHIN, STANLEY, banker, lecturer, author, business reorganization consultant. Founder, chmn. bd. Stanley Tulchin Assocs., Westbury, N.Y., 1955-95; bd. dirs. N.Y. Inst. Credit, Topps Corp., PCA Internat.; founder, chmn. Reprise Capital Corp. Recipient Leadership in Credit Edn. award N.Y. Inst. Credit, 1990. Mem. Comml. Law League Am. (Pres'. Cup award 1975, past bd. govs., vice-chmn. bd. editors Comml. Law Jour., bd. dirs. Fund for Pub. Edn.), Nat. Assn. Credit Mgmt. Office: Stanley Tulchin Assocs 400 Post Ave PO Box 185 Westbury NY 11590

TULEY, SISTER MARGARET, hospital administrator; b. Boston. BS in Nursing, St. Joseph's Coll., Emmitsburg, Md., 1961; MS Nursing Svc. Adminstrn, Boston U., 1969; MA in Hosp. and Health Care Adminstrn., St. Louis U., 1976. Lic. to practice nursing, Mass., Va., Maine, N.Y., Mo., Tex., Washington. Staff nurse, head nurse DePaul Hosp., Norfolk, Va. 1961-62; med.-surgical nursing supr. DePaul Hosp., 1962-67; dir. nursing svcs., bd. dirs. Seton Hosp., Waterville, Maine, 1969-70; adminstrv. asst. St. Mary's Hosp., Rochester, N.Y., 1970-71; assoc. adminstr. sec. bd. trustees St. Mary's Hosp., Rochester, 1971-74; pres., chief exec. officer, chmn. bd. trustees Carney Hosp., Boston, 1976-85; pres., chief exec. officer, chmn. bd. dirs. Our Lady of Lourdes Meml. Hosp., Binghamton, N.Y., 1985-89; pres., chief exec. officer, vice chmn., bd. dirs. 1989—; adv. bd. SUNY-Ctr. for Leadership Studies, Binghamton, 1988—; bd. dirs. St. Mary's Hosp., Rochester, Good Samritan Hosp., Pottsville, Pa. Mem. United Way, Binghamton, 1987—; State U. Binghamton Found., 1996—. Recipient Leboure medal Laboure Coll., 1986. Fellow Am. Coll. Healthcare Execs. (nominating com. 1987—); mem. Am. Hosp. Assn. (search com. for pres. 1985—, regional adv. bd. II Chgo. 1985-87), N.Y. State Cathtolic Healthcare Coun. (exec. com. 1987—), Hosp. Assn. N.Y. State (strategic planning com.

1987—), Cen. N.Y. Hosp. Assn. (exec. com. 1986—), Broome County C. of C., Rotary. Office: Good Samaritan Reg Med Ct 700 E Norwegian St Pottsville PA 17901

TULEY, THOMAS WAYNE, newspaper executive; b. Evansville, Ind., May 15, 1940; s. Russell Lee and Mildred (Rodger) T.; m. Barbara Helen Capin, June 22, 1963; children: Tracy, Brent, Brandon. AB, U. Evansville, 1962. Sports writer Evansville Press, 1962-68, asst. sports editor, 1968-75, mng. editor, 1980-83, editor, pres., 1983-86; exec. sports editor Cin. Post, 1975-80; mng. editor Evansville Press, 1980-83, editor, 1983-86; editor, pres. Evansville Courier, 1986—. Bd. dirs. Evansville Arts and Edn. Coun., 1983-88, Evansville Blind Assn., 1986-88, U. Evansville, 1982-86, Youth Resources, 1993—, Comty. Found. Alliance, 1991—; trustee U. Evansville, 1993—. Recipient Alumni Excellence award U. Evansville, 1988. Mem. Am. Soc. Newspapers Editors, Evansville C. of C. (bd. dirs. 1983-88), Evansville Country Club, Petroleum Club, Sigma Delta Chi. Avocations: jogging, gardening, reading, antique-collecting. Home: 8522 Framewood Dr Newburgh IN 47630-2348 Office: Evansville Courier Co Inc PO Box 268 300 E Walnut St Evansville IN 47713-1938

TULL, DONALD STANLEY, marketing educator; b. Mo., Oct. 28, 1924; s. Raymond Edgar and Ethel (Stanley) T.; m. Marjorie Ann Dobbie, May 15, 1948; children: Susan Margaret, David Dobbie, Brooks William. S.B., U. Chgo., 1948, M.B.A., 1949, P.h.D., 1956. Analyst U.S. Steel Corp., 1949-50; instr. U. Wash., 1950-52; mgr. adminstrn. N.Am. Aviation, 1954-61; prof. mktg. Calif. State U., Fullerton, 1961-67; dean Sch. Bus. Adminstrn. and Econs., 1966-67; prof. mktg. Coll. Mgmt. and Bus. U. Oreg., 1967-90, chmn. dept. mktg., transp. and bus. environment), 1969, 73-81. Author: (with P.E. Green and G.S. Albaum) Research for Marketing Decisions, 1987, (with G.S. Albaum) Survey Research, 1973, (with L.R. Kahle) Marketing Management, 1989, (with D.I. Hawkins) Marketing Research: Measurement and Method, 1993, Essentials of Marketing Research, 1994. Served to lt. (j.g.) USNR, 1943-46. Mem. AAUP (pres. 1978-79), Beta Gamma Sigma. Home: 2310 Trillium St Eugene OR 97405-1343

TULL, THERESA ANNE, ambassador; b. Runnemede, N.J., Oct. 2, 1936; d. John James and Anna Cecelia (Paull) T. B.A., U. Md., 1972, M.A., U. Mich., 1973; postgrad., Nat. War Coll., Washington, 1980. Fgn. svc. officer Dept. State, Washington, 1963, Brussels, 1965-67, Saigon, 1968-70; dep. prin. officer Am. Consulate General, Danang, Vietnam, 1973-75; prin. officer Cebu, Philippines, 1977-79; dir. office human rights, 1980-83; charge d'affaires Am. Embassy, Vientiane, Laos, 1983-86; Dept. State Senior Seminar, 1986-87; ambassador to Guyana, 1987-90; diplomat-in-residence Lincoln U., Pa., 1990-91; dir. office regional affairs, bur. East Asian & Pacific affairs Dept. State, Washington, 1991-93; amb. to Brunei Bandar Seri Begawan, 1993—. Recipient Civilian Service award Dept. of State, 1970, Superior Honor award, 1977. Mem. Am. Fgn. Svc. Assn. Home: care Waldis 416 N Washington Ave Moorestown NJ 08057-2411 Office: Am Embassy Box B APO AP 96440 also: Am Embassy, Bandar Seri Begawan, Brunei Darussalam

TULLER, HARRY LOUIS, materials science and engineering educator; BS, Columbia U., 1966, MS, 1967, DSc in Engring., 1973. Rsch. assoc. physics Technion, Haifa, Israel, 1974-75; from asst. to assoc. prof. materials sci. and engring. MIT, Cambridge, 1975-81, prof. materials sci. and engring., 1981—, dir. Crystal Physics and Optical Electronics Lab., 1985—; vis. prof. U. Pierre et Marie Curie, Paris, 1990; faculty chair Sumitomo Electric Industries, 1992. Co-editor: High Temperature Superconductors, 1988, Electroceramics and Solid State Ionics, 1988, Science and Technology of Fast Ion Conductors, 1989, Solid State Ionics, 1992. Fulbright travel grantee, 1990. Fellow Am. Ceramic Soc. (N.E. chair 1983); mem. IEEE, Electrochem. Soc. (co-organizer 1st and 2d internat. symposium ionic and mixed conducting ceramics 1991, 94), Materials Rsch. Soc., Am. Phys. Soc. Jewish. Avocations: photography, gardening. Office: MIT 77 Massachusetts Ave Cambridge MA 02139-3594

TULLIS, DAVID ALLEN, municipal official, safety consultant; b. Madison, S.D., Sept. 10, 1938; s. Ralph and Millie Grace (Hanneman) T.; m. Celia Kathleen Hagan (div. 1970); children: Christine Louise, David Bradford; m. Linda Pauline Sweat, Sept. 10, 1972; 1 child, Larry Allan. Student, U. Wash., 1963, Centralia (Wash.) Coll., 1969, South Sound Coll., 1975. Customer engr. IBM Corp., Seattle, 1963-69; bus. machine technician State of Wash.. Olympia, 1969-77, safety compliance officer, 1977-80, sr. safety compliance officer, 1980-83; safety/risk City of Tacoma, 1983—; mem. gov.'s adv. bd. Indsl. Safety and Health, 1989—, v.p. bd., 1993—, pres. bd. 1994; mem. Employers Elec. Safety commn., State of Wash., 1983—; chmn. utilities panel Gov.'s Conf. on Safety, State of Wash., 1985-86. Scoutmaster Boy Scouts Am., Olympia, 1977. Served with U.S. Army Security Agy., 1959-62. Mem. Am. Water Works Assn. (chmn. N.W. sect. 1985-91), Am. Soc. Safety Engrs., Am. Pub. Power Assn. (chmn. safety com. 1993-94, co-author chlorine manual, nat. safety manual), Am Pub. Power, Day Island Yacht Club, Capital Cruising Club, Elks. Home: 2111 Tina Ct SE Olympia WA 98513-9413 Office: City of Tacoma PO Box 11007 Tacoma WA 98411-0007

TULLIS, EDWARD LEWIS, retired bishop; b. Cin., Mar. 9, 1917; s. Ashar Spence and Priscilla (Daugherty) T.; m. Mary Jane Talley, Sept. 25, 1937; children: Frank Loyd, Jane Allen (Mrs. William Nelson Offutt IV). AB, Ky. Wesleyan Coll., 1939, LHD, 1975; BD, Louisville Presbyn. Theol. Sem., 1947; DD, Union Coll., Barbourville, Ky., 1954, Wofford Coll., 1976; LHD, Claflin Coll., 1976, Lambuth Coll., 1984. Ordained to ministry Methodist Ch., 1941; service in chs. Frenchburg, Ky., 1937-39, Lawrenceburg, Ky., 1939-44; asso. pastor 4th Ave. Meth. Ch., Louisville, 1944-47, Irvine, Ky., 1947-49; asso. sec. ch. extension sect. Bd. Missions, Meth. Ch., Louisville, 1949-52; pastor First Meth. Ch., Frankfort, Ky., 1952-61, Ashland, Ky., 1961-72; resident bishop United Meth. Ch., Columbia, S.C., 1972-80 Nashville area, 1980-84; ret. United Meth. Ch., 1984; instr. Ky. Wesleyan Coll., 1947-48; instr. Louisville Presbyn. Theol. Sem., 1949-52; mem. Meth. Gen. Conf., 1956, 60, 64, 66, 68, 70, 72, Southeastern Jurisdictional Conf., 1952, 56, 60, 64, 68, 72, bd. mgrs. Bd. Missions, 1962-72, mem. bd. discipleship, 1972-80, v.p. Gen. Council on Fin. and Adminstrn., 1980-84; Chaplain Ky. Gen. Assembly, 1952-61; chmn. Frankfort Com. Human Rights, 1956-61, Mayor's Advisory Com. Human Relations, Ashland, 1968-72. Author: Shaping the Church from the Mind of Christ, 1984. Contbr. articles to religious jours. Sec. bd. dirs. Magee Christian Edn. Found.; trustee Emory U., 1973-80, Alaska Meth. U., 1965-70, Ky. Wesleyan Coll., Martin Coll., Lambuth Coll., McKendree Manor, Meth. Hosps., Memphis, Lake Junaluska Assembly, 1966-88; chair adv. bd. Found. for Evangelism, United Meth. Ch., 1991—. Recipient Outstanding Citizen award Frankfort VFW, 1961, Mayor's award for outstanding service. Ashland, 1971. Club: Kiwanis. Home: PO Box 754 Lake Junaluska NC 28745-0754

TULLIS, JOHN LEDBETTER, retired wholesale distributing company executive; b. Quanah, Tex., May 9, 1911; s. John Ledbetter and Coral (Horton) T.; m. Bettye Bishop Winston, Mar. 22, 1980; children—Tom, Jeff, Alan Winston. B.S. in Elec. Engring, U. Tex., Austin, 1933. With AMF, Inc. and predecessors, 1947-74, pres., chief oper. officer, 1967-74; gen. mgr. Interstate Electric Co., Inc., Shreveport, La., 1974-83, ret., 1983; cons. in field. Chmn. devel. council Schumpert Med. Center, Shreveport, 1974-82; mem. chancellor's council U. Tex., Austin, 1974—. Recipient Disting. Engring. Grad. award U. Tex., Austin, 1963. Mem. Tex. Hist. Assn. Methodist. Clubs: Shreveport Country, Shreveport. Home: 1806 Hunter Cir Shreveport LA 71119-4104

TULLIS, JULIA ANN (JAN TULLIS), structural geologist, educator; b. Swedesboro, N.J., Feb. 21, 1943; d. Frank MacIvor and Julia Ann (Upson) Conway; m. Terry Edson Tullis, June 19, 1965. B.A., Carleton Coll., 1965; Ph.D., UCLA, 1971. Asst. prof. rsch. dept. geol. scis. Brown U., Providence, 1971-77, assoc. prof. rsch., 1977-78, assoc. prof. structural geology, 1978—. Contbr. articles to profl. jours. Editor Tectonophysics, 1978—. Bd. dirs. LWV, Rehoboth, Mass., 1975-77. Grantee NSF, 1972—, U.S. Geol. Survey, 1975-81, 85—. Fellow Mineral Soc. Am.; mem. Geol. Soc. Am., Am. Geophys. Union. Avocations: hiking, gardening, reading, quilting. Office: Brown U Dept Geol Sci Providence RI 02912

TULLOCH, GEORGE SHERLOCK, JR., electrical equipment distribution company executive, lawyer; b. Bklyn., Aug. 18, 1932; s. George Sherlock and

Dorothy (Gooch) T.; m. Edyth Benson Woodroofe, June 16, 1956; children: Michael, Daniel, Lindsay. BA in History, Amherst Coll., 1954; LLB, U. Mich., 1959. Bar: N.Y. 1960, Mo. 1983. Assoc. Breed, Abbott & Morgan, N.Y.C., 1959-66; sec., asst. gen. counsel Westvaco Conn., N.Y.C., 1966-78; v.p., sec., gen. counsel, dir. Graybar Electric Co., N.Y.C., 1978—. Dir. World Affairs Coun., St. Louis, Repertory Theatre of St. Louis. Served to 1st lt. USMCR, 1954-56. Mem. ABA, Assn. Bar City N.Y., Met. St. Louis Bar Assn., Am. Soc. Corp. Secs. Home: 4954 Lindell Blvd Saint Louis MO 63108-1500 Office: Graybar Electric Co Inc 34 N Meramec Ave PO Box 7231 Saint Louis MO 63177

TULLOS, JOHN BAXTER, banker; b. Morton, Miss., Dec. 3, 1915; s. William Baxter and Mell (Roberts) T.; m. Maxine Stone, Sept. 20, 1941. Student, Miss. Coll., 1934, Am. Inst. Bank, Jackson, Miss., 1936-40, Sch. Banking South, La. State U., 1955-57. With Trustmark Nat. Bank, Jackson, 1935-88; exec. agt. Trustmark Corp. (formerly 1st Capital Corp.); faculty Sch. Banking South La. State U.; 1st pres. Miss. Young Bankers Assn.; mem. Miss. Valley World Trade Council, 1965—; mem. La.-Miss. Regional Export Expansion Council div. U.S. Dept. Commerce, 1967-74; vice-chmn. Ala.-Miss. Dist. Export Council, 1975-80; chmn. Miss. Dist. Export Council, 1980-85. Former chmn. budget com. United Givers Fund. Served with AUS, World War II. Mem. Miss. Bankers Assn. (past chmn. operations/automation com.). Methodist. Clubs: Lion, Capitol City Petroleum. Home: 8 Eastbrooke St Jackson MS 39216-4714 Office: PO Box 2343 Jackson MS 39225-2343

TULLY, DANIEL PATRICK, financial services executive; b. 1932; married. BBA, St. Johns U., 1953. With Merrill Lynch, Pierce, Fenner & Smith, N.Y.C., 1955—, mem. acctg. dept., 1955-59, acct. exec. trainee, 1959-63, asst. to mgr. Stamford, Conn. office, 1963-70, mgr., 1970-71, v.p., 1971-79, dir. individual sales, 1976-79, exec. v.p., 1979-82, pres. individual services group, 1982-84, pres. consumer mktg., from 1984; pres., COO Merrill Lynch & Co., Inc., N.Y.C., 1985; former exec. v.p. Merrill Lynch & Co. (parent), N.Y.C., 1979, CEO, chmn. bd., 1992—, chmn., CEO, pres., 1993—. Served U.S. Army, 1953-55. Office: Merrill Lynch & Co Inc World Fin Ctr No Tower 250 Vesey St New York NY 10281

TULLY, DARROW, newspaper publisher; b. Charleston, W.Va., Feb. 27, 1932; s. William Albert and Dora (McCann) T.; m. Victoria Lynn Werner; children: Bonnie Tully Paul, Michael Andrew. Student, Purdue U., 1951; BA in Journalism, St. Joseph's Coll., 1972; PhD in Journalism (hon.), Calumet (Ind.) Coll., 1975. V.p., gen. mgr. Stas. WDSM-AM-FM and WDSM-TV, Duluth, Minn., 1956-59; bus. mgr. Duluth Herald & News Tribune, 1960-62; gen. mgr. St. Paul Dispatch & Pioneer Press, 1962-66; pub. Gary (Ind.) Post-Tribune, 1966-73; v.p., pub. Wichita (Kans.) Eagle & Beacon, 1973-75; pres. San Francisco Newspaper Agy., 1975-78; exec. v.p., pub. Ariz. Republic & Phoenix Gazette, 1978-85; editor., pub., chief exec. officer Ojai (Calif.) Valley News, 1987-90; pres., pub., CEO Beacon Comms., Acton, Mass., 1990-92; asst. to pres. newspaper divsn. Chronicle Pub. Co., 1992-94. Author: Minority Representation in the Media, 1968. Trustee Calumet Coll. Recipient Disting. Achievement award Ariz. State U., 1982, Disting. Journalist award No. Ariz. U./AP, 1983, 1st Pl. Editorial Writing award Ariz. Planned Parenthood, 1983. Mem. Am. Soc. Newspaper Editors, Soc. Profl. Journalists. Office: 3001 Barret Ave Plant City FL 33567-7278

TULLY, JOHN CHARLES, research chemical physicist; b. N.Y.C., May 17, 1942; s. Harry V. and Pauline (Fischer) T.; m. Mary Ellen Thomsen, Jan. 23, 1971; children: John Thomsen, Elizabeth Anne, Stephen Thomsen. BS, Yale U., 1964; PhD, U. Chgo., 1968. NSF postdoctoral fellow U. Colo. and Yale U., 1968-70; mem. tech. staff AT&T Bell Labs., Murray Hill, N.J., 1970-82, disting. mem. tech. staff, 1982-85, head phys. chemistry rsch. dept. 1985-90, head materials chem. rsch. dept., 1990—; vis. prof. Princeton (N.J.) U., 1981-82, Harvard U., Cambridge, Mass., 1991. Contbr. articles to sci. jours.; author. prodr. movie Dynamics of Gas-Surfact Interactions, 1979. NSF predoctoral fellow, 1965-68. Fellow AAAS, Am. Phys. Soc. (chem. physics exec. com. 1983-86); mem. Am. Chem. Soc. (chmn. theoretical chemistry suvdivsn. 1991-92, phys. chemsitry divsn. 1993-94, Peter Debye award 1995), Sigma Xi. Achievements include patent on Method and Apparatus for Surface Characterization Utilizing Radiation from Desorbed Particles; fundamental theoretical contributions towards atomic level understanding of chemical reaction dynamics. Office: AT&T Bell Labs ID346 600 Mountain Ave Murray Hill NJ 07974-2008

TULLY, MICHAEL J., JR., state senator; b. N.Y.C., June 23, 1933; s. Michael and Elizabeth (Carpenter) T.; children: Michael, Christpher, Maura, Brian. J.D., St. John's U. Town councilman Town of North Hempstead, Manhasset, N.Y., 1967-71, town supr., 1971-82; senator State of N.Y., Roslyn, 1982—; chmn. Senate Environ. Conservation Com., Coun. Health Care Financing; mem. health com. Nat. Conf. State Legislators; mem. coun. state Govts.' Health Policy Task Force. Com. mem. Boy's Town of Italy, Inc., Boy Scouts Am.; bd. dirs. NCCJ, Save the Books Corp., Am. Com. on Italian Migration, Manhasset-Great Neck Econ. Opportunity Commn., Econ. Devel. Dist. Com., L.I. Area Devel. Agy.; adv. bd. Assn. for Help of Retarded Children; mem. Am. Legis. Exchange Council; hon. trustee Great Neck Symphony Soc., Inc., others. Served with U.S. Army, USAR. Recipient Hon. Law Enforcement Man of Year award, Nassau County Police Dept. Detectives Assn. 1984, Outstanding Community Service award, United Jewish Y's L.I., Frank A. Gulotta Criminal Justice award, Former Asst. Dist. Atty.'s Assn. 1980 award, 1976, 1975, medal for assistance Displaced Homemakers, 1988, Pres.' medal N.Y. Inst. Tech., 1988, Leadership award N/S Health Systems Agy., 1988, Health Care Leader Yr. award N.C. Helath Facilities Assn., 1992, plaque Am. Acad. Pediatrics, Med. Soc. N.Y. State, Am. Coll. Obstetrics and Gynecologists, 1992 Lodge: K.C., Ancient Order of Hibernians, Order Sons of Italy. Republican. Roman Catholic. Avocations: golf; reading. Office: NY State Senate 201 Expressway Roslyn Heights NY 11577

TULLY, RICHARD LOWDEN, architect; b. New Orleans, May 24, 1911; s. Thomas James and Elizabeth (Lowden) T.; m. Frances Louise Gross, Oct. 3, 1942; children: Mary Elizabeth Tully Pratt, Richard Lowden. BArch, Ohio State U., 1937, spl. degree safety engring., 1943. Registered architect, Ohio, N.Y., Fla. Architect Thomas J. Tully, Columbus, Ohio, 1937-41; plant architect Denison Engring. Co., Columbus, 1941-46; partner F.H. Hobbs, Jr. (architects), Columbus, 1966, Tully, Hobbs (and partners), Columbus, 1966-72, Tully, Ames, Elzey & Thomas, 1972—; pres. A. Consulting, Inc., 1981—; mem. design adv. panel Gen. Services Adminstrn., 1970—; mem. Columbus Bldg. Com., 1961-63; mem. adv. com. (Capitol Dist.), 1969—; past chmn. Capitol Sq. Commn.; chmn. Land Use Planning-Devel. Com. Columbus, 1971—. Prin. archtl. works include Thurber Village Urban Renewal, Sci. Campus Ohio U., Athens, Federated Dept. Stores, (Lazarus and Gold Circle), office bldg., Blue Cross Central Ohio, 7th Ave. Ch. of Christ (P.L.A.N. award, Architects Soc. Ohio award 1966), Ohio State U. married housing (AIA award), City Nat. Bank, Columbus (Man of Year award Columbus Citizen Jour. 1972). Chmn. Devel. Com. for Greater Columbus, 1975; vice chmn. Gov.'s Com. on Nuclear Emergency, 1968—; v.p., treas. Planned Parenthood Columbus, Architects Soc. Ohio Found. Recipient Silver Shovel award Am. Subcontractors Assn., 1976; Constrn. Man of Yr. award Builders Exchange Central Ohio, 1985, Builders Exchange Corner Stone award, 1992. Fellow AIA (past pres. Columbus chpt.), Architects Soc. Ohio (past pres., Gold medal 1975); mem. Constrn. Specifications Inst. (past pres. Columbus), Newcomen Soc. N.Am., Am. Srs. Golf Assn., Internat. Srs. Amateur Golf Soc., Columbus Country Club, Gold Club (Columbus), Delta Chi. Episcopalian (sr. warden). Home: 74 S Stanwood Rd Columbus OH 43209-1871

TULLY, SUSAN BALSLEY, pediatrician, educator; b. San Francisco, July 12, 1941; d. Gerard E. Balsley Sr. and Norma Lilla (Hand) Carey; m. William P. Tully, June 19, 1965; children: Michael William, Stephen Gerard. BA in Premed. Studies, UCLA, 1963, MD, 1966. Diplomate Am. Bd. Pediatrics, Am. Bd. Pediatric Emergency Medicine. Intern L.A. County-U. So. Calif. Med. Ctr., 1966-67, jr. resident pediatrics, 1967-68; staff pediatrician, part-time Permanente Med. Group, Oakland, Calif., 1968; sr. resident pediatrics Kaiser Found. Hosp., Oakland, 1968-69; sr. resident pediatrics Bernalillo County Med. Ctr., Albuquerque, 1969-70, chief resident pediatric outpatient dept., 1970; instr. pediatrics, asst. dir. (OPD) U. NMex. Sch. Medicine, 1971-72; asst. prof. pediatrics, dir. (ambulatory pediatrics) U.

Calif., Irvine, 1972-76, asst. prof. clin. pediatrics, vice chair med. edn., 1977-79; staff pediatrician Ross-Loos Med. Group, Buena Park, Calif., 1976-77; assoc. prof. clin. pediatrics and emergency medicine U. So. Calif. Sch. Medicine, 1979-86; dir. pediatric emergency dept. L.A. County/U. So. Calif. Med. Ctr., 1979-87; prof. clin. pediatrics and emergency medicine U. So. Calif. Sch. Medicine, 1986-89; dir. ambulatory pediatrics L.A. County/U. So. Calif. Med. Ctr., 1987-89, L.A. County-Olive View/UCLA Med. Ctr., 1989—; clin. prof. pediatrics U. Calif., L.A., 1989-93, prof. clin. pediatrics, 1993—; pediatric toxicology cons. L.A. County Regional Poison Control Ctr. Med. Adv. Bd., 1981—; faculty exec. com., clin. faculty rep. UCLA Sch. Medicine, 1992-93, strategic planning action com. subcom. on ednl. structure, 1992-93, dept. pediatrics alliance-wide rev. and appraisal com., 1992-93, steering com., 1993—; pediatric liaison dept. emergency medicine Olive View/UCLA Med. Ctr., 1989—, dir. lead poisoning clinic, 1993—; L.A. County Dept. Health Svcs., 1990—; mem. quality assurance com. L.A. County Community Health Plan, 1986-89; mem. survey team pediatric emergency svcs. L.A. Pediatric Soc., 1984-86; mem. adv. bd. preventive health project U. Affiliated Program Children's Hosp. L.A., 1981-83; active numerous coms. Author: (with K.E. Zenk) Pediatric Nurse Practitioner Formulary, 1979; (with W.A. Wingert) Pediatric Emergency Medicine: Concepts and Clinical Practice, 1992; (with others) Educational Guidelines for Ambulatory/General Pediatrics Fellowship Training, 1992, Physician's Resource Guide for Water Safety Education, 1994; reviewer Pediatrics, 1985-89; editorial cons. Advanced Pediatric Life Support Course and Manual, 1988-89; dept. editor Pediatric Pearls Jour. Am. Acad. Physician Assts., 1989-94; tech. cons., reviewer Healthlink TV Am. Acad. Pediatrics, 1991; reviewer Pediatric Emergency Care, 1992—; question writer sub-bd. pediatric emergency medicine Am. Bd. Pediatrics, 1993—; cons. to lay media NBC Nightly News, Woman's Day, Sesame Street Parents, Parenting, Los Angeles Times; author numerous abstracts; contbr. articles to profl. jours. cons. spl. edn. programs Orange County Bd. Edn., 1972-79; mem. Orange County Health Planning Coun., 1973-79; co-chairperson Orange County Child Health and Disability Prevention Program Bd., 1975-76; mem. Orange County Child Abuse Consultation Team, 1977-79; mem. project adv. bd. Family Focussed "Buckle Up" Project, Safety Belt Safe, U.S.A., 1989—; Fellow Am. Acad. Pediatrics (life, active numerous sects. and coms., active Calif. chpt.); mem. APHA, Ambulatory Pediatric Assn., L.A. Pediatric Soc. (life), L.A. Area Child Passenger Safety Assn. Democrat. Avocations: art needlework, reading. Office: Olive View UCLA Med Ctr Pediatrics 3A108 14445 Olive View Dr Sylmar CA 91342-1495

TULLY, THOMAS ALOIS, building materials executive, consultant, educator; b. Dubuque, Iowa, Nov. 11, 1940; s. Thomas Aloysius and Marjorie Mae (Fosselman) T.; m. Joan Vonnetta Dubay, Nov. 30, 1963; children: Thomas Paul, Maureen Elizabeth. BA, Loras Coll., 1962; postgrad., Georgetown U., 1963-66; MPA, Harvard U., 1968. Mgmt. trainee Office of Sec. Def., Washington, 1962-63, fgn. affairs officer, 1963-70; v.p. Dubuque Lumber Co., 1970-84, pres., 1984-91; pres. Tully's, 1991-92, LBM Mktg. Assocs., Inc., 1992—; adj. instr. Divine Word Coll., 1971, Loras Coll., 1972; adj. instr. Clarke Coll., 1987-89, instr., 1989-91, asst. prof., 1992—, chmn. dept. acctg. and bus., 1993—, dir. small bus. inst., 1994—; pres. Hills and Dales Child Devel. Ctr., Inc., 1992—. Mem. Dubuque Human Rights Commn., 1974-75, chmn., 1975, Iowa State Com. for Employer Support of Guard and Res. Forces, 1988—; city councilman, Dubuque, 1975-79; bd. dirs. League Iowa Municipalities, 1977-79; mayor City of Dubuque, 1978; vice chmn. Iowa Temporary State Land Pres. Policy Com., 1978-79; pres. N.E. Iowa Regional Coordinating Council, 1985-93, East Cen. Intergovtl. Assn. Bus. Growth, Inc., 1987—, chmn., 1993—; bd. dirs. Pvt. Industry Council of Dubuque and Delaware Counties, Inc., 1983-86; trustee Divine Word Coll., 1986—; pres. Barn Community Theatre, 1988-89; chmn. bd. trustees United Way Svcs. of Dubuque, 1990, campaign chmn., 1991, bd. mem., 1980-94. Recipient Meritorious Civilian Svc. award Sec. of Def., 1970, Gov.'s Vol. award, 1989. Mem. Nat. Lumber and Bldg. Material Dealers Assn. (exec. com. 1988-90), Iowa Lumbermen's Assn. (pres. 1984, chmn. legis. com. 1985-90), Northwestern Lumbermen Assn. (bd. dirs. 1984-87, 2d v.p. 1988, 1st v.p. 1989-90, pres. 1990-91). Democrat. Roman Catholic. Home: 838 Stone Ridge Pl Dubuque IA 52001-1362 Office: LBM Mktg Assocs PO Box 771 Dubuque IA 52004-0771

TULLY, WILLIAM P., civil engineer, academic administrator; b. 1940. BCE, Northeastern U., MCE; PhD in Civil Engring., Syracuse U. Registered profl. engr., N.Y. Former engr. E.H. Porter Co., Peabody, Mass.; former structural engr. LeMessurier Assocs., Boston; with SUNY Coll. Environ. Sci. and Forestry, Syracuse, N.Y., 1966—, v.p. program affairs, provost, former dept. chmn. civil engring., 1987—, former v.p. academic affairs, now v.p. program affairs, provost. Office: SUNY Coll of Environ Sci Office VP Program Affairs/Provost 1 Forestry Dr Syracuse NY 13210-2778*

TULSKY, ALEX SOL, physician; b. Chgo., Aug. 10, 1911; s. Solomon and Clara (Tarnipolsky) T.; m. Klara Glottmann, July 20, 1948; children—Shayne Lee, Steven Henry, Asher Arthur, James Aaron. B.S., U. Ill., 1932, M.D., 1934. Intern Michael Reese Hosp., Chgo., 1934-36; attending obstetrician and gynecologist Michael Reese Hosp., 1938—, pres. med. staff, 1962-64; house officer Bklyn. Jewish Hosp., 1937-38; pvt. practice Chgo., 1938—; clin. prof. obstetrics and gynecology Abraham Lincoln Sch. Medicine, U. Ill., 1980—. Served to lt. col. M.C. AUS, 1941-45. Decorated Bronze Star. Mem. A.M.A., Chgo., Ill. med. socs., Chgo. Gynecol. Soc., Chgo. Inst. Medicine, Chgo. Oriental Inst., Pan Am. Med. Assn., Chgo. Soc. History Medicine. Home: 442 W Wellington Ave Chicago IL 60657-5804 Office: 111 N Wabash Ave Chicago IL 60602-1903

TULSKY, FREDRIC NEAL, journalist; b. Chgo., Sept. 30, 1950; s. George and Helen (Mailick) T.; m. Kim Rennard, June 20, 1971; children: Eric George, Elizabeth Rose. B.J., U. Mo., 1972; J.D. cum laude, Temple U., Phila., 1984. Bar: Pa. 1984. Reporter Saginaw News, Mich., 1973-74, Port Huron Times Herald, Mich., 1974-75, Jackson Clarion-Ledger, Miss., 1975-78, Los Angeles Herald Examiner, 1978-79, Phila. Inquirer, 1979-93; mng. editor Ctr. for Investigative Reporting, San Francisco, 1993-94, exec. dir., 1994; reporter L.A. Times, 1995—; adj. prof. urban studies U. Pa., 1990-93. Recipient nat. awards including Robert F. Kennedy Found. award, 1979, Heywood Broun award Newspaper Guild, 1978, Disting. Svc. medal Sigma Delta Chi, 1978, Pub. Svc. award AP Mng. Editors, 1978, Silver Gavel award ABA, 1979, 87, Pulitzer prize for investigative reporting, 1987, Pub. Svc. award Nat. Headliners Club, 1987; Nieman fellow Harvard U., 1989. Mem. Investigative Reporters and Editors (pres. 1988-91, chair 1991-93), Reporters Com. for Freedom of Press, Kappa Tau Alpha. Office: LA Times 388 Market St 12th Fl San Francisco CA 94111

TULVING, ENDEL, psychologist, educator; b. Estonia, May 26, 1927; s. Johannes and Linda T.; m. Ruth Mikkelsaar, June 24, 1950; children: Elo Ann, Linda. BA, U. Toronto, Ont., Can., 1953, MA, 1954; PhD, Harvard U., 1957; MA (hon.), Yale U., 1969; FD (hon.), U. Umea (Sweden), 1982; DLitt (hon.), U. Waterloo, 1987, Laurentian U., 1988; D Psychology (hon.), U. Tartu, Estonia, 1991. Lectr. U. Toronto, 1956-59, asst. prof., 1959-62, asso. prof., 1962-65; prof., 1965-70; prof. psychology Yale U., New Haven, 1970-75; prof. psychology U. Toronto, 1972-85, chmn. dept., 1974-80, univ. prof., 1985-92, Univ. prof. emeritus psychology, 1992—; vis. scholar U. Calif., Berkeley, 1964-65; fellow Ctr. Advanced Study in Behavioral Scis., Stanford, Calif., 1972-73; Commonwealth vis. prof. Oxford (Eng.) U., 1977-78; Tannenbaum chair in cognitive neurosci. Rotman Rsch. Inst. of Baycrest Ctr., Can., 1992—; disting. vis. prof. neurosci., disting. rsch. prof. psychology U. Calif., Davis, 1994—. Author: Elements of Episodic Memory, 1983; editor Jour. Verbal Learning and Verbal Behavior, 1969-72, Psychol. Rsch., 1976-88; co-editor: Organization of Memory, 1972, Memory Systems 1994, 1994; mem. editorial bd. Oxford Psychology Series, 1979—; contbr. numerous articles on memory to sci. jours. Recipient Izaak Walton Killam Meml. prize Can. Coun., 1994, Meml. scholar, 1976-77, Gold medal award for life achievemnt in psychol. sci. Am. Psychol. Found., 1994; Guggenheim fellow, 1987-88. Fellow Can. Psychol. Assn. (Disting. Sci. Contbn. award 1983), APA (Disting. Sci. Contbn. award 1983), Am. Psychol. Soc. (William James fellow), Royal Soc. Can., Am. Acad. Arts and Scis. (fgn. hon.), Soc. Exptl. Psychologists (Warren medal 1982), Royal Soc. London; mem. NAS (fgn. assoc.), Soc. for Neuroscis., Psychonomic Soc. (governing bd. 1974-80), Royal Swedish Acad. Scis. (fgn.), Cogn. Neurosci. Soc. Home: 45 Baby Point Crescent, Toronto, ON Canada M6S 2B7 Office: Rotman Rsch Inst of Baycrest Ctr, Bathurst St, North York, ON Canada M6A 2E1

TUMAY, MEHMET TANER, geotechnical consultant, educator, research director; b. Ankara, Turkey, Feb. 2, 1937; came to U.S., 1959; s. Bedrettin and Muhterem (Uybadin) T.; m. Karen Nuttycombe, June 15, 1962; children: Peri, Suna. BS in Civil Engring., Robert Coll. Sch. Engring. (Turkey), 1959; MCE, U. Va., 1961; postgrad. UCLA, 1963-64; PhD, Tech. U. Istanbul (Turkey), 1971; Fugro-Cesco postdoctoral research fellow U. Va., Gainesville, 1975-76. Instr. civil engring. U. Va., Charlottesville, 1961-62; asst. prof. civil engring. U. Louisville, 1962-63; teaching fellow UCLA, 1963-64; asst. prof. civil engring. Robert Coll. Sch. Engring., Istanbul, 1966-71; assoc. prof. dept. civil engring. Bogazici U., Istanbul, 1971-75; assoc. prof. then prof. civil engring., coord. geotech. engring. La. State U., Baton Rouge, 1976—; adv. prof. U. Vicosa, Minas Gerais, Brazil, 1991—, Tongji U., Shanghai, China, 1991—; dir. Geomechanics Program NSF, Washington, 1990-94; dir. rsch. Louisiana Transp. Rsch. Ctr., Baton Rouge, 1994—; maitre de conferences Ecole Nationale des Ponts et Chaussees, Paris, 1980—; geotech. cons. Sauti, Spa, Cons. Engrs., Istanbul, 1974-75, BOTEK, Ltd., Istanbul, 1975—, Senler-Campbell Assos., Louisville, 1972-73, D.E.A., Cons. Engrs., Istanbul, 1974-75, SOFRETU-RATP, Paris, 1972-73, D.E.A., Cons. Engrs., Italy, 1969-72, SOFRETU-RATP, Paris, 1972-73, D.E.A., Cons. Engrs., Istanbul, 1974-75, BOTEK, Ltd., Istanbul, 1975—; Senler-Campbell Assos., Louisville, 1975—; cons. Turkish Soil Mechanics Group (charter), Turkish Chamber Civil Engrs., Internat. Soc. Soil Mechanics and Found. Engring., Sigma Xi, Chi Epsilon, Tau Beta Pi. Home: 1915 W Magna Carta Pl Baton Rouge LA 70815-5521 Office: La State U Dept Civil Engring Baton Rouge LA 70803

TUMBLESON, ARTHUR LOUIS, civil engineer, contractor; b. Cin., Oct. 9, 1934; s. Albert Newton and Clara Mae T.; m. Shirley Richardson, Oct. 4, 1953 (div. June 1974); children: Michael L., Steven A.; m. Nancy C. Palmer, Feb., 1983 (div. Oct. 1987); m. Janice K. Sligh, Apr. 1989. BCE, U. Cin., 1957. With C.E., U.S. Army; with engring dept. City of Cin., 1953-63; dir. pub. works, bldg. and zoning ofcl. City of Temple Terrace, Fla., 1963-73; gen. contractor Temple Terrace, 1974-76; civil engr., project and constrn. mgr. Tomasino and Assocs., Temple Terrace, 1976—.

TUMMALA, RAO RAMAMOHANA, engineering educator; b. Nandamuru, India, Feb. 15, 1942; came to U.S., 1966; s. Venkateswara Rao and Subbamma (Paladugu) T.; m. Anne Mitran, Dec. 30, 1966; children: Dinesh, Vijay, Suneel. BSc, Loyola Coll., Vijayawada, India, 1961; BE, Indian Inst. of Sci., 1963; MS, Queen's U., Kingston, Can., 1964; PhD, U. Ill., 1968. IBM fellow, 1984-93; process engr. Norton Co., Niagara Falls, Can., 1965-66; rsch. asst. U. Ill., Urbana, 1966-68; staff engr. IBM Corp., East Fishkill, N.Y., 1968-70, adv. engr., 1970-76, sr. engr., 1976-84, fellow, 1984—, dir., 1987-89; Pettit chair prof. Ga. Inst. Tech., Atlanta, 1993—; mem. selection com. Inventors Hall of Fame, Washington, 1984—. Contbr. articles to profl. jours.; patentee in field. Mem. adv. bd. U. Ill., Urbana, 1980-83; chmn. adv. bd. U. Calif., Berkeley, 1987-89, MIT, Cambridge, 1990-93. Recipient Disting. Alumni award U. Ill., 1991, David Sarnoff award IEEE, John Wagnon award; named one of 50 in U.S. in indsl. policy Industry Week. Fellow IEEE, Am. Ceramic Soc.; mem. NAE. Avocations: tennis, golf, skiing, international travel. Home: 1748 Tilling Way Stone Mountain GA 30087-2329 Office: Ga Inst Tech MARC Ctr Atlanta GA 30332-0560

TUMMINELLO, STEPHEN CHARLES, consumer electronics manufacturing executive; b. Paterson, N.J., Nov. 7, 1936. Grad., Fairleigh Dickinson U., 1958. Former pres. N.Am. Philips Lighting Corp.; exec. v.p., former v.p., group exec. Philips Electronics N.Am. Corp. (formerly N.Am. Philips Corp.), 1984-90; pres., chief exec. officer Philips Electronics N.Am. Corp. (formerly N.Am. Philips Corp.), N.Y.C., 1990—. Office: Philips Electronics N Am Corp 100 E 42nd St New York NY 10017-5613

TUNAC, JOSEFINO BALLESTEROS, biotechnology administrator; b. Vintar, Philippines, Nov. 11, 1942; came to U.S., 1966; s. Ireneo and Corazon (Ballesteros) T.; m. Corrie D., Sept. 7, 1968; children: Brooks, Corinna. MS, S.D. State U., 1968; PhD, Rutgers U., 1975. Rsch. microbiology Merck, Sharp & Dohme, Rahway, N.J., 1974-77; rsch. dir. Warner Lambert subs. Parke-Davis, Ann Arbor, Mich., 1977-86; pres., founder Fermical, Inc., Detroit, 1987—; cons. Nat. Cancer Inst. Bethesda, Md., 1985-86, Met. Ctr. for High Tech., Detroit, 1986-87, Mycosearch, Inc., Chapel Hill, N.C., 1985-88. Contbr. articles to Jour. of Fermentation & Bioengring., Jour. of Antibiotics, Drugs of the Future, Antimicrobial Agt. & Chemotherapy, Jour. Nat. Cancer Inst. Nat. Cancer Inst. grantee, 1987. Mem. Am. Assn. Cancer Rsch., Am. Soc. Microbiology, Soc. Indsl. Microbiology. Achievements include discovery of new antibacterial (epithienamycins), antifungal (hydroheptin), and anticancer (chloropentostatin, veractamycin, elactocin, fostriecin, others) agents; developement of fermentation process of athelmintic agent (avermectin); manufacture of antiviral agents (vidarabine, pentostatin); invention of a novel culture flask (Tunair flask system) and a high-aeration capacity bioreactor (Airmentor). Home: 5284 Collington Dr Troy MI 48098-2442 Office: Fermical Inc 2727 2nd Ave Detroit MI 48201-2654

TUNE, BRUCE M., pediatrics educator, renal toxicologist; b. N.Y.C., Aug. 26, 1939; s. Buford M. and Sylvia (Newman) T.; m. Nancy Carter Doolittle, Sept. 13, 1969; children: Sara E., Steven M. AB, Stanford U., 1963, MD, 1965. Diplomate Am. Bd. Pediatrics, Am. Bd. Pediatric Nedhrology, Nat. Bd. Med. Examiners. Intern in medicine and pediatrics Strong Meml. Hosp., Rochester, N.Y., 1965-66; rsch. assoc. Lab. Kidney and Electrolyte Metabolism, Nat. Heart Inst., NIH, Bethesda, Md., 1967-69, clin. assoc., 1968-69; resident in pediatrics Stanford (Calif.) U. Sch. Medicine, 1966-67, chief resident, 1969-70, fellow in pediatric renal and metabolic disease, 1970-71, asst. prof., 1971-77, assoc. prof., 1977-83, prof., 1983—, acting chmn. dept., 1991-93; dir. pediatric nephrology, 1971—; attending physician, chief pediatric renal svcs Stanford U. Hosp., Palo Alto, Calif., 1971-91, Children's Hosp. at Stanford, Palo Alto, 1971-91; cons. physician Santa Clara Valley Med. Ctr., San Jose, Calif., 1973—; attending physician, chief pediatric renal svcs. Lucile Salter Packard Children's Hosp. at Stanford, 1991—, acting chief pediatric medicine, 1991-93; mem. internat. study kidney diseases in children NIH, N.Y.C., 1973, 74, mem. polycystic kidney disease study group, Albuquerque, 1984, mem. spl. study sect. on genetics and kidney maturation, Bethesd, Md., 1992; cons. Lilly Rsch. Labs., Indpls., 1980, Merck Sharp and Dohme Labs., Rahway, N.J., 1980, Bristol Labs., Syracuse, N.Y., 1982, ICI Pharms., Cheshire, Eng., 1992, Gilead Scis., Foster City, Calif., 1993, Zeneca Pharms., Mereside, Eng., 1994—; organizing mem., chmn. session on antibiotics NIH and EPA Conf. on Nephrotoxicity of Drygs and Environ. Toxicants, Pinehurst, N.C., 1981; co-dir. Coop. Study Terhapy of Steroid-Resistant Focal Glomerulosclerosis in Children, 1988—; mem. rsch. grant rev. panel Ont. (Can.) Ministry Health, 1992—, Wellcome Trust, London, 1994—; reviewer bd. environ. studies and toxicology NRC, 1994. Mem. editl. bd. Am. Jour. Kidney Diseases, 1981—; guest editor Contemporary Issues in Nephrology, 1984, Jour. Am. Soc. Nephrology, 1991; contbr. articles to med. jours. Grantee NIH, 1985-89, 90-95. Mem. Am. Soc. Nephrology, Internat. Soc. Nephrology, Am. Soc. Pediatric Nephrology (coun. 1978-82, rsch. subcom. 1993—), Internat. Pediatric Nephrology Assn., Western Soc. for Pediatric Rsch., Soc. for Pediatric Rsch., Am. Pediatric Soc., Am. Heart Assn. (coun. on kidney diseases, grantee 1985-88, 89-92), Am. Soc. for Pharmacology and Exptl. Therapeutics, Am. Soc. Renal Biochemistry and Metabolism, Phi Beta Kappa, Alpha Omega Alpha. Office: Stanford U Sch Medicine Dept Pediatrics 300 Pasteur Dr Stanford CA 94305

TUNE, TOMMY (THOMAS JAMES TUNE), musical theater director, dancer, choreographer, actor; b. Wichita Falls, Tex., Feb. 28, 1939; s. Jim P. and Eva Mae (Clark) T. Student, Lon Morris Jr. Coll., 1958-59; BFA, U. Tex., 1962; postgrad., U. Houston, 1962-63. Dancer, choreographer, dir. various prodns. N.Y.C., 1963—. Dancer (Broadway prodns.): Baker Street, 1965, A Joyful Noise, 1966, How Now Dow Jones, 1967, Seesaw, 1973 (Tony award Best Featured Actor musical 1974), (films): Hello Dolly, 1964, The Boyfriend, 1971; dir. choreographer Broadway prodns.: The Best Little Whorehouse in Texas, 1978 (Tony award nominations Best Dir. musical 1979, Best Choreography 1979, Drama Desk award Best Dir. musical 1979), A Day in Hollywood/A Night in the Ukraine, 1980 (Tony award Best Choreography 1980, Tony award nomination Best Dir. musical 1980, Drama Desk awards Best Musical Staging, 1980, Best Choreography 1980), Nine,

1982 (Drama Desk award Best Dir. musical 1982, Tony award Best Dir. musical 1982, Tony award nomination Best Choreography 1982), Grand Hotel, 1989 (Tony awards Best Choreography 1990, Best Dir. 1990, Drama Desk awards Best Choreography 1990, Best Dir. musical 1990); dir., actor, choreographer My One and Only, 1983 (Tony awards Best Actor musical 1983, Best Choreography 1983, Tony award nomination Best Dir. musical 1983, Drama Desk award Outstanding Choreography 1983), The Will Rogers Follies, 1990 (Tony awards Best Choreography 1991, Best Dir. 1991, Drama Desk award Best Choreography 1991); tour Bye, Bye Birdie, 1991-92; dir. Broadway prodn.: Stepping Out, 1987; dir. Off-Broadway prodns.: The Club, 1976 (Obie award 1977), Sunset, 1977, Cloud 9, 1981 (Drama Desk award Best Dir. 1982, Obie award Disting. Direction 1982); performed in the USSR, 1988. Recipient Drama League Musical Achievement award, 1990. Mem. Dirs. Guild Am., Stage Soc. Dirs. and Choreographers, Actors Equity Assn. Office: care Internat Creative Mgmt 40 W 57th St New York NY 10019-4001

TUNG, DAVID HSI HSIN, consulting civil engineer, emeritus engineering educator; b. Hong Kong, Sept. 2, 1923; came to U.S., 1948, naturalized, 1958; s. Hok Nin and Sheung-Yee (Ho) T.; m. Vera Gien, June 7, 1949; children: Leslie, Ronald Stanley, Elaine, Thomas. B.S in Civil Engring, Chiao Tung U., 1947; M.Civil Engring., Cornell U., 1950; Ph.D., U. Mich., 1953. Registered profl. engr., N.Y. Designer Giffels & Vallet, Detroit, 1950-52; sr. designer Hardesty & Hanover, N.Y.C., 1953-56, Severud-Elstad-Krueger, N.Y.C., 1956-57; project mgr., project engr. Praeger-Kavanagh-Waterbury, N.Y.C., 1957-65; assoc. prof. Cooper Union, N.Y.C., 1965-68; prof. civil engring. Cooper Union, 1968-83, prof. emeritus, 1983—, chmn. curriculum dept. civil engring., 1974-76; cons. engr., 1965—; chmn. bd. Jing Tech Inc., 1983-87, dir., 1987-92; ptnr. Tung & Assocs., Cons. Engrs., 1983-91. Contbr. articles to profl. jours. Fellow ASCE, Inst. Structural Engrs.; mem. Sigma Xi, Tau Beta Pi, Chi Epsilon (hon.). Achievements include research on both straight and curved reinforced (prestressed) concrete as well as composite steel box girder bridges; project manager and engineer in charge of design and construction of Arecibo Radio Obs., P.R., others. Home: 461 Park Ave Rye NY 10580-1211 To guide and not to force; To be strong but not to suppress; To enlighten and not to saturate; To be intellectual but not to become intolerant.

TUNG, KO-YUNG, lawyer; b. Peking, Peoples Republic China, Feb. 20, 1947; came to U.S., 1964; s. Tien-chung and Hung-Fang (Wong) T.; m. Alison Heydt, Feb. 2, 1975; children: Vanessa, Adrian, Cameron, Gregory. BA, Harvard U., 1969; JD, U. Tokyo, 1971. Bar: N.Y. 1973. Assoc. Debevoise & Plimpton, N.Y.C., 1973-76; ptnr. Tung, Drabkin & Boynton, N.Y.C., 1976-84, O'Melveny & Myers, N.Y.C., 1985—; adj. assoc. prof. sch. law NYU, 1974-88. Mem. Coun. on Fgn. Rels., N.Y.C., 1986—, Inst. Asian Studies, 1989, The Brookings Inst., 1990, Overseas Devel. Coun., Washington, 1990—, The Japan Soc., 1990; N.Am. mem. Trilateral Commn., N.Y.C., 1990—; vice-chmn., bd. govs. East West Ctr., Honolulu, 1990—; U.S. Nat. Commn. for Pacific Econ. Coop., 1991—; bd. dirs. Asian Am. Legal Def. and Edn. Fund, 1990. Law Faculty fellow Harvard U., 1993. Mem. Phi Beta Kappa. Office: O'Melveny & Myers Citicorp Ctr 153 E 53d St New York NY 10011

TUNG, ROSALIE LAM, business educator, consultant; b. Shanghai, China, Dec. 2, 1948; came to U.S., 1975; d. Andrew Yan-Fu and Pauline Wai-Kam (Cheung) Lam. BA (Univ. Admin.), York U., 1972; MBA, U. B.C., 1974, PhD in Bus. Adminstrn. (Univ. fellow, Seagram Bus. fellow, H.R. MacMillan Family fellow), 1977; m. Byron Poon-Yan Tung, June 17, 1972; 1 child, Michele Christine. Lectr. diploma div. U. B.C., 1975, lectr. exec. devel. program, 1975; asst. prof. mgmt. grad. sch. mgmt. U. Oreg., Eugene, 1977-80; assoc. prof. U. Pa., Phila. 1981-86; prof., dir. internat. bus. ctr. U. Wis., Milw., 1986-90; endowed chaired prof. Simon Fraser U., 1991—; vis. scholar U. Manchester (Eng.) Inst. Sci. and Tech., 1980; vis. prof. UCLA, 1981, Harvard U., 1988; Wis. disting. prof. U. Wis. System, 1988-90, Ming and Stella Wong chair in internat. bus., 1991—. Mem. Acad. Internat. Bus. (mem. exec. bd., treas. 1985-86), Acad. Mgmt. (bd. govs. 1987-89), Internat. Assn. Applied Psychology, Am. Arbitration Assn. (comml. panel arbitrators). Author: Management Practices in China, 1980, U.S.-China Trade Negotiations, 1982, Chinese Industrial Society After Mao, 1982, Business Negotiations with the Japanese, 1984, Key to Japan's Economic Strength: Human Power, 1984, The New Expatriates: Managing Human Resources Abroad, 1988; editor: Strategic Management in the U.S. and Japan, 1987, International Management in International Library of Business and Management Series, 1994. Oppenheimer Bros. Found. fellow, 1973-74, U. B.C. fellow, 1974-75, H.R. MacMillan Found. fellow, 1975-77; named Wis. Disting. Prof., 1988, Ming and Stella Wong Prof., 1991. Roman Catholic; recipient Leonore Rowe Williams award U. Pa., 1990, U. B.C. Alumni 75th Anniversary award, 1990. Avocation: creative writing. Office: Simon Fraser U, Faculty Bus Adminstrn, Burnaby, BC Canada V5A 1S6

TUNG, THEODORE HSCHUM, banker, economist; b. Beijing, Aug. 28, 1934; came to U.S., 1959; s. R. T. and C. (Lin) Dong; m. Patrica C. Hsu, Dec. 24, 1966; children: Candice H., Roderick. BA, Nat. Taiwan U., Taipei, 1956; MBA, U. Okla., 1962; PhD, U. Pa., 1965. Asst. prof. econs. Colo. State U., Ft. Collins, 1964-66, U. Pa., Phila., 1966-68; economist Bank of N.Y., N.Y.C., 1968-70; v.p., economist Continental Bank, Chgo., 1971-80; v.p., chief economist Cen. Nat. Bank, Cleve., 1980-83; sr. v.p., chief economist Nat. City Corp., Cleve., 1983—; cons. economist Richard Howes & Assocs., Washington, 1966-68. Co-author: General Theory: Economic, Social, Political and Regional, 1966; author Nat. City Corp.'s fin. letter, 1983—. Bd. dirs. Family Health Assn., Cleve., 1987-89. Grantee USDA, 1964-66. Mem. Nat. Assn. Bus. Economists, Am. Econs. Assn. Home: 3735 Middle Post Ln Cleveland OH 44116-3935 Office: Nat City Corp 1900 E 9th St Cleveland OH 44114-3303

TUNGATE, DAVID E., lawyer, educator; b. Columbus, Ohio, Apr. 22, 1945; s. Ernest O. and Diantha (Woltz) T.; m. Mary Ann V. Montaleone, Jan. 27, 1968; children: David, Melissa. BA, U. Ill., Champaign, 1967, JD, 1970. Bar: U.S. Dist. Ct. (we. dist.) Pa. 1970, Superior Ct. Pa., 1971, Supreme Ct. Pa., 1971, U.S. Ct. Appeals (3d cir.) 1973, U.S. Ct. Claims 1987, U.S. Dist. Ct (ea. dist.) Wis. 1989, U.S. Ct. Appeals (fed. cir.) 1990. Assoc. Eckert, Seamans, Cherin & Mellott, Pitts., 1976-75, ptnr., 1976—; bd. dirs. Rokop Corp., Pitts.; adj. prof. Carnegie Mellon U., Pitts., 1991—. Contbr. articles to profl. jours; author bus. book revs. Pitts. Post-Gazette, 1986—. Chmn. Zoning Hearing Bd. Upper St. Clair, 1991—. Mem. ABA, Penn. Bar Assn., Allegheny County Bar Assn. Office: Eckert Seamans Cherin & Mellott 42d Fl USX Tower 600 Grant St Pittsburgh PA 15219

TUNHEIM, JERALD ARDEN, academic administrator, physics educator; b. Claremont, S.D., Sept. 3, 1940; s. Johannes and Annie (Ness) T.; m. Patricia Ann Witham, June 7, 1963; children: Jon, Angie, Alec. BS in Engring. Physics, S.D. State U., 1962, MS in Physics, 1964; PhD in Physics, Okla. State U., 1968. Vis. scientist Sandia Corp., Albuquerque, 1970-71, Ames (Iowa) AEC Labs., 1972; asst. prof. S.D. State U., Brookings, 1968-73, assoc. prof., 1973-78, prof., 1978-80, prof., head physics dept., 1980-85; dean Ea. Wash. U., Cheney, 1985-87; pres. Dakota State U., Madison, S.D., 1987—; bd. dirs. NSF Systemic Initiative. Co-author: Elementary Particles and Unitary Symmetry, 1966, Quantum Field Theory, 1966; contbr. articles to profl.jours. Bd. dirs. Madison Devel. Found., 1987—. Named Tchr. of Yr. S.D. State U., 1972, 80, grantee USDA, 1987-88, S.D. Govt. Office Econ. Devel., 1988-89, U.S. Dept. Edn. Eisenhower Program, 1985-86, 87-90, 92-93, 95-96, U.S. Dept. Edn. Math. and Sci. Program, 1989-92. Mem. NSPE, Am. Phys. Soc., Am. Assn. Physics Tchrs., Madison C of C. (bd. dirs. 1990—), Rotary. Republican. Lutheran. Office: Dakota State U Office of President 820 N Washington Ave Madison SD 57042-1735

TUNISON, ELIZABETH LAMB, education educator; b. Belfast, Northern Ireland, Jan. 7, 1922; came to U.S., 1923; d. Richard Ernest and Ruby (Hill) Lamb; m. Ralph W. Tunison, Jan. 24, 1947 (dec. Apr. 1984); children: Eric Arthur, Christine Wait, Dana Paul. BA, Whittier Coll., 1943, MEd, 1963. Tchr. East Whittier (Calif.) Schs., 1943-59; tchr. T.V. Stas. TV Channels 13 and 28, So. Calif. Counties, 1960-75; dir. curriculum Bassett (Calif.) Schs., 1962-65; elem. sch. prin. Rowland Unified Schs., Rowland Heights, Calif., 1965-68; assoc. prof. edn. Calif. State Poly. U., Pomona, 1968-71; prof. Whittier Coll., 1968-88, prof. emerita, 1988—. Bd. dirs. Presbyn. Intercommunity Hosp. Found. Recipient Whittier Coll. Alumni Achievement award 1975; Helen Hefernan scholar 1963. Mem. AAUP, Assn. Calif. Sch. Adminstrs. (state bd., chmn. higher edn. com. 1983-86, region pres. 1981-83, Wilson Grace award 1983), PEO (pres. 1990-92), Assistance League of Whittier (v.p. 1994—), Delta Kappa Gamma. Home: 5636 Ben Alder Ave Whittier CA 90601-2111

TUNLEY, ROUL, author; b. Chgo., May 12, 1912; s. Joseph Hartley and Lillian (Boyd) T. BA, Yale, 1934. Reporter N.Y. Herald Tribune, 1934-37; asst. circulation mgr. Look mag., 1937-39; syndicated columnist, 1939-41; mem. English faculty Yale, 1946-47; fellow Jonathan Edwards Coll., 1946—; dir. editorial promotion Look mag., 1948-50; staff writer, assoc. editor Am. mag., 1951-56; asst. mng. editor Woman's Home Companion, 1956; assoc. editor Sat. Eve. Post, 1961-63. Author: Kids, Crime and Chaos, 1962, The American Health Scandal, 1966, (with Anne Wahle) Ordeal by Fire, 1966; frequent contbr. to nat. mags. including Reader's Digest, 1951—. Lt. comdr. USNR, 1942-45. Mem. Authors Guild (coun.), Elizabethan Club (adjoining chmn.). Address: PO Box T Stockton NJ 08559-0993

TUNNER, WILLIAM SAMS, urological surgeon; b. San Antonio, Nov. 14, 1933; s. William Henry and Sarah Margaret (Sams) T.; m. Sallie Berry Woodul, Dec. 4, 1965; children: William Woodul, Jonathan Sams. Student Washington and Lee U., 1952-55; MD, U. Va., 1960. Diplomate Am. Bd. Urology. Intern in surgery, then asst. surg. resident Duke Hosp., 1960-62; fellow cancer surgery Cancer Inst. NIH, Bethesda, Md., 1962-64; resident in urol. surgery Cornell-N.Y. Hosp., 1964-68, fellow transplantation, dialysis and biochemistry, instr. surgery, 1968-70; asst. prof. urol. surgery U. Tex. Med. Sch., San Antonio, 1970-72; pvt. practice medicine specializing in pediatric and adult urology, Richmond, Va., 1972—; mem. staff Henrico County St. Marys Hosp., Chippenham, Johnston-Willis hosps.; asst. clin. prof. urology Med. Coll. Va., 1972—. Valentine research fellow, 1970-72; grantee Hearst Research Found., 1970-72. Fellow ACS, (past pres. Va. chpt., gov.-at-large), Am. Acad. Pediatrics (affiliate); mem. AMA, SociétéInternationalde Urologié, Transplantation Soc., Soc. Pediatric Urology, Am. Urol. Assn., Am. Nephrology Assn., SR, Country Club of Va., Deep Runt Hunt Club, Alpha Epsilon Delta, Beta Theta Pi. Episcopalian. Contbr. articles to med. jours., Home: Braedon Farm 1240 Shallow Well Rd Manakin Sabot VA 23103-2300 Office: St Mary's Hosp Profl Bldg 5855 Bremo Rd Richmond VA 23226-1926

TUNNESSEN, WALTER WILLIAM, JR., pediatrician; b. Hazleton, Pa., July 25, 1939; s. Walter William and Grace Louise (Schaller) T.; m. Nancy Louise Layton, Aug. 24, 1963; children: Walter William III, Anne L. BA, Lafayette Coll., Easton, Pa., 1961; MD, U. Pa., 1965. Diplomate Am. Bd. Pediatrics (bd. dirs. 1986—). Resident Children's Hosp. of Phila., 1965-67; chief resident in pediatrics Hosp. U. Pa., Phila., 1967-68; isntr., dir. newborn nurseries Hosp. U. Pa./U. Pa. Sch. Medicine, Phila., 1970-72; from asst. prof. to assoc. prof. pediatrics SUNY Health Sci. Ctr., Syracuse, 1972-85, prof. pediatrics, acting chair dept., 1985-86; assoc. prof. pediatrics and dermatology Johns Hopkins U. Sch. Medicine, Balt., 1986-90, dir. pediatric dermatology, dir. pediatric diagnostic clinic, 1980-90; assoc. chmn. for med. edn. Children's Hosp. of Phila., 1990-95; prof. pediatrics U. Pa. Sch. Medicine, Phila., 1990-95; sr. v.p. Am. Bd. Pediatrics, Chapel Hill, N.C., 1995—; Robert Wood Johnson clin. Scholar Yale U. Sch. Medicine, New Haven, 1978-79; mem. Nat. Bd. Med. Examiners, 1989-91; mem. sci. bd. Nat. Found. for Ectodermal Dysplasia, 1989-93. Author: Signs and Symptons in Pediatrics, 1983, 2d edit., 1988; editor monthly jour. sects. Capt. USAF, 1968-70. Mem. Am. Acad. Pediatrics (sect. on dermatology exec. com. 1993—), Soc. for Pediatric Dermatology (pres. 1988-89, bd. dirs.), Am. Pediatric Soc. Avocation: furniture refinishing. Office: Am Bd Pediatrics 111 Silver Cedar Ct Chapel Hill NC 27514-1651

TUNNEY, FRANCIS RICHARD, JR., lawyer, corporate executive; b. Phila., Aug. 10, 1947; s. Francis Richard and Agatha (Danowski) T.; m. Doris Jean Fosler, Sept. 7, 1968; children: Noah, Michael. BA, Franklin and Marshall Coll., 1969; JD, Duquesne U., 1973. Bar: Pa. 1973, American Samoa 1974, U.S. Dist. Ct. Pa. (ea. dist. 1976, we. dist. 1979), Calif. 1987. Law clk. to chief justice Am. Samoa, Pago Pago, 1973-75; assoc. Feldman & Feldman, Phila., 1978-79; supervising atty. Pa. Securities Commn., Phila., 1978-79; sr. internat. atty. Smithkline Beckman Corp., Phila., 1979-85; corp. v.p., sec., gen. counsel Allergan, Inc., Irvine, Calif., 1985—. Assoc. editor Duquesne Law Rev., 1972-73. Democrat. Roman Catholic. Home: 815 Via Lido Soud Newport Beach CA 92663-5532 Office: Allergan Inc 2525 Dupont Dr Irvine CA 92715-1599

TUNNEY, JOHN VARICK, lawyer, former senator; b. N.Y.C., June 26, 1934; s. Gene and Mary (Lauder) T.; m. Kathinka Osborne, April 1977; children: Edward Eugene, Mark Andrew, Arianne Sprengers, Tara Theodora. B.A. in Anthropology, Yale, 1956; J.D., U. Va., 1959; student, Acad. Internat. Law, The Hague, Netherlands, 1957. Bar: N.Y. 1959, Calif. 1963, Va. 1963. With firm Cahill, Gordon, Reindel & Ohl, N.Y.C., 1959-60; tchr. bus. law U. Calif., Riverside, 1961-62; practice law Riverside, 1963—; mem. 89th-91st Congresses from Calif. 38th Dist., U.S. Senate from Calif., 1971-77; mem. firm Manatt, Phelps, Rothenberg & Tunney, Los Angeles, 1977-86; chmn. bd. Cloverleaf Group, Inc., Los Angeles, 1986—; political commentator Sta. K-ABC TV; bd. dirs. Prospect Group Inc., Garnet Resources Corp., Ill. Central Railroad, The Forschner Group Inc. Trustee Westminster Sch., St. Matthews Sch.; bd. visitors Loyola Law Sch.; mem. nat. adv. council Multiple Sclerosis Soc.; mem. Lawyers Adv. Council Constl. Rights Found., Citizens Research Found., Commn. on Soviet Jewry. Served to capt. USAF, 1960-63. Chubb fellow Yale U., 1967. Mem. Am. Bar Assn. Democrat. Episcopalian. Office: 1819 Ocean Ave Santa Monica CA 90401-3223

TUNNICLIFF, DAVID GEORGE, civil engineer; b. Ord, Nebr., Sept. 18, 1931; s. George Thomas and Ada Ellen (Ward) T.; m. Elaine Jean Interrante, Oct. 17, 1959 (div.); children: Martha Allison Tunnicliff Lude, Vivian Jean Tunnicliff Perez; m. Joan Elizabeth Duchesneau, Oct. 26, 1975. BS, U. Nebr., 1954; MS, Cornell U., 1958; PhD, U. Nebr., 1972. Registered profl. engr., Nebr., Mass. Engr. Nebr. Dept. Rds., Lincoln, 1954-60; asst. prof., then assoc. prof. Wayne State U., Detroit, 1960-67; chief tech. svcs. Warren Bros. Co., Cambridge, Mass., 1967-79; prin., cons. engr. D.G. Tunnicliff, Cons. Engr., Omaha, 1979—. Contbr. to profl. publs. Rep. precinct del., Detroit, 1965-66. With U.S. Army, 1955-56. Mem. ASTM (chair subcom. 1973-94), ASCE, Assn. Asphalt Paving Tech. (bd. dirs. 1976-78), Transp. Rsch. Bd. (com. chair 1983-89). Mem. Evangel. Covenant Ch. Home: 9624 Larimore Ave Omaha NE 68134-3038 Office: DG Tunnicliff Cons Engr 9624 Larimore Ave Omaha NE 68134-3038

TUNSTALL, SHARON SUE, advertising executive; b. Houston, Oct. 19, 1949; d. O. Ray and Etta Mae (Stodghill) T. BA, U. Houston, 1973, MA, 1977, PhD, 1981. Tchr. Dulles High Sch, Stafford, Tex., 1974-77; asst. prof. Oakland U., Rochester, Mich., 1980-85; v.p., dir. human resources D'Arcy Masius Benton & Bowles, Bloomfield Hills, Mich., 1985-91, dir. corp. tng. N.Am. div., 1986-90; v.p., dir. human resources B.H. and Corp, Tng., 1990-91; sr. v.p., dir. human resources N.Am. and Corp. Tng. Worldwide, 1991—; polit. cons. U. Houston; guest speaker Advt. Ednl. Found., N.Y.C., 1988—. Mem. Am. Soc. Tng. and Devel., Am. Mgmt. Assn. Democrat. Avocations: cooking, wine expert. Office: 1725 N Woodward PO Box 811 Bloomfield Hills MI 48303-0811

TUOHEY, MARK HENRY, III, lawyer; b. Rochester, N.Y., Sept. 27, 1946; s. Mark Henry T.; m. Martha; children—Brendan, Sean, Devin. B.A. in History, St. Bonaventure U., 1968; J.D., Fordham U., 1973. Bar: D.C. 1973, U.S. Supreme Ct. 1980, U.S. Ct. Appeals (D.C. cir.) 1974, U.S. Dist. Ct. D.C. 1974, N.Y. 1984. Asst. U.S. atty. U.S. Atty.'s Office, Washington, 1973-77; spl. trial counsel U.S. Dept. Justice, Washington, 1977-79; spl. counsel to U.S. Atty. Gen., Washington, 1979; ptnr. Reed, Smith, Shaw & McClay, Washington, 1987—. Served to 1st lt. U.S. Army, 1970-71. Fellow Am. Law Inst., Am. Bar Found. (bd. dirs. 1988-95); mem. ABA (litigation sect. coun. 1980-90, chair standing com. on continuing edn. of bar, chair 1980-85, Am. Law Inst./ABA com. on continuing profl. edn. 1983—), D.C. Bar (pres. 1993—, bd. govs. 1988—), Jud. Conf. U.S. Ct. Appeals (D.C. cir.), Wm. Bryant Inn of Ct. (master). Home: 1655 Kalmia Rd NW Washington DC 20012-1125 Office: Reed Smith Shaw & McClay Ring Bldg 1200 18th St NW Washington DC 20036-2506

TUOHEY, WILLIAM F., federal judge; b. Bayonne, N.J., Aug. 20, 1941; s. William E. J. and Dorothy (Heppner) T.; m. Eileen Corbett. BS in History, St. Peters Coll., 1964; JD, Rutgers U., 1967. Bar: N.J. 1968, U.S. Dist. Ct. N.J. 1968. Atty. Milton, Keane & DeBona, Jersey City, 1968-76; ptnr. Milton, Keane & Brady, Jersey City, 1976-81; pvt. practice Hawthorne, N.J., 1981-86; judge N.J. dist. U.S. Bankruptcy Ct., Newark, 1986—; counsel to trustee of Cen. RR Reorgn.; speaker in field. Counsel to Hawthorn Bd. Edn., 1981-86. Mem. ABA, Nat. Conf. Bankruptcy Judges. Office: US Bankruptcy Ct King Fed Bldg 50 Walnut St Newark NJ 07102-3506

TUOHY, WILLIAM, correspondent; b. Chgo., Oct. 1, 1926; s. John Marshall and Lolita (Klaus) T.; m. Mary Ellyn Dufek, 1955 (div.); m. Johanna Iselin, Nov. 24, 1964; 1 son, Cyril Iselin. B.S., Northwestern U., 1951. Reporter, night city editor San Francisco Chronicle, 1952-59; assoc. editor, nat. polit. corr., fgn. corr. Newsweek mag., 1959-66; Vietnam corr. L.A. Times, 1966-68; Middle East corr. L.A. Times, Beirut, 1969-71; bur. chief L.A. Times, Rome, 1971-77, London, 1977-85, Bonn, Fed. Republic Germany, 1985-90; European security corr. L.A. Times, London, 1990—. Author: Dangerous Company, 1987. Served with USNR, 1944-46. Recipient Nat. Headliner award for Vietnam bur. coverage, 1965, Pulitzer prize internat. reporting (Vietnam), 1969, Overseas Press Club award for best internat. reporting (Middle East), 1970, various others. Office: c/o L A Times Fgn Desk, 150 Brompton Rd, London SW3 1HX, England

TUOMINEN, F(RANCIS) WILLIAM, research and engineering company executive; b. Floodwood, Minn., Mar. 1, 1943. BS, U. Minn., Duluth, 1965; MS, U. Minn., Mpls., 1968, PhD, 1970. Rsch. fellow Oak Ridge Nat. Lab., Oakridge, Tenn., 1970-71; rsch. chemist Gen. Mills, Mpls., 1971-76; rsch. mgr. Henkel Corp., Mpls., 1977-79, dir. rsch., 1979-80, v.p., 1980-85; v.p. Ecolab Inc., St. Paul, 1985—. Contbr. articles to sci. jours. Undergrad. and postgrad. fellow NSF. Mem. Indsl. Rsch. Inst. (chmn. editorial bd. 1986—), Am. Chem. Soc., Am. Oil Chemists Soc. Avocations: athletics, outdoors, music. Office: Ecolab Inc Ecolab Ctr 840 Sibley Memorial Hwy Saint Paul MN 55118-1708

TUPPER, CHARLES JOHN, physician, educator; b. Miami, Ariz., Mar. 7, 1920; s. Charles Ralph and Grace (Alexander) T.; m. Mary Hewes, Aug. 4, 1942; children: Mary Elizabeth, Charles John. B.A in Zoology, San Diego State Coll., 1943; M.D., U. Nebr., 1948. Diplomate: Am. Bd. Internal Medicine. Intern U. Mich. Hosp., Ann Arbor, 1948-49; asst. resident U. Mich. Hosp., 1949-50, resident, 1950-51, jr. clin. instr., 1951-52; pvt. practice specializing in internal medicine Ann Arbor, 1954-66; practice medicine specializing internal medicine Davis, Calif., 1966—; asst. inst. Indsl. Health, U. Mich., 1951-52, rsch. assoc., 1954-56, instr. internal medicine, 1954-56, asst. prof., 1956-59, assoc. prof., 1959-66, sec. Med. Sch.), 1957-59, asst. dean, 1959-61, assoc. dean, 1961-66, dir. periodic health appraisal program univ. faculty, 1956-66; prof. internal medicine Sch. Medicine U. Calif., Davis, 1966—, dean, 1966-80, prof. community health, 1980—, prof. family practice, 1981—, acting chair dept. community health, 1989-91; mem. adv. bd. Golden State Transplant Svcs. Dir. consultation services U. Mich. Health Service, 1956-66, 73-76; pres. Calif. Med. Assn., 1979-80; vice chmn. U. Calif. Davis Found., 1993—; Sacramento Regional Found., 1993. Served from 1st lt. to capt. USAF, 1952-54. Fellow ACP; mem. AMA (trustee 1985-89, pres. elect 1989-90, pres 1990-91, immediate past pres. 1991-92, chmn. coun. sci. affairs 1977-79, coun. sect. med. schs 1977-78), Internat., Am., Calif. socs. internal medicine, Am. Coll. Health Assn., Assn. Am. Med. Colls., Am. Assn. Automotive Medicine, Yolo County Med. soc., Calif. Med. Assn. (pres. 1979-80, chmn. sci. bd. 1970-78, chmn. liaison to state bar com., chmn. com. on state legislation 1975-85, del. to AMA 1975-85), Sci. Rsch. Club. Club: El Macero Country (dir.). Home: PO Box 2007 El Macero CA 95618-0007 Office: U Calif Med Sch Dept Community Health Davis CA 95616

TURAJ, FRANK, university dean, literature and film educator; b. Derby, Conn., May 31, 1934; m. Nancy Burge, Nov. 28, 1962; children: Kristyn, Julie. B.A., U. Conn., 1959, M.A., 1960; Ph.D., Brown U., 1968. Instr. George Washington U., 1962-65; asst. prof. lit. Am. U., Washington, 1965-68, assoc. prof., 1969-74, prof., 1975—, chmn. dept. lit., 1974-76, acting dean Coll. Arts and Scis., 1976-77, dean, 1977-85, founder Am. studies program, 1970, cinema studies program, 1975; Polish exchange and Italian study program Am. U.; trustee Am. U. Rome, 1978-85; bd. dirs. Coun. Internat. Nontheatrical Events, Washington, 1978-85, William Moss Inst., Washington, 1980-85, Polish Inst. Arts and Scis., 1992—; founder, organizer, bd. dirs. N.Am. Festival Contemporary Polish Cinema, 1979—. Author: H.L. Mencken and American Literature, 1968, The Modern Cinema of Poland, 1988; (with others) Post New Wave Cinema in the Soviet Union and Eastern Europe, 1988; co-writer and co-producer: USIA documentary The Impact of Film, 1973. Served with USAF, 1951-55. Recipient Disting. Teaching award Am. U., 1968, Media Achievement award Perspectives mag., Washington, 1980, medal for svc. to Polish culture Govt. of Poland, 1981, Spl. award Polish Filmmakers Assn., 1983, Presdl. citation Am. U., 1985; Disting. Svc. medal Adam Mickiewicz U., Poznan, Poland, 1986, Spl. 70th Ann. of Univ. award, 1989. Mem. Am. Assn. Higher Edn., Am. Assn. Slavic Studies, Assn. Am. Colls., Polish Inst. Arts and Scis. (bd. dirs.). Office: Am U Coll Arts and Scis 4400 Massachusetts Ave NW Washington DC 20016-8001

TURANO, DAVID A., lawyer; b. Ashtabula, Ohio, Sept. 9, 1946; s. Egidio A. and Mary Agnes (Bartko) T.; m. Karen J. Emmel, Aug. 29, 1970; children: Aaron, Thad, Bethen, Kyle. BS, Kent State U., 1968; JD, Ohio State U., 1971. Bar: Ohio 1971. Staff atty. The Pub. Utilities Commn. Ohio, Columbus, 1971-72; assoc., then ptnr. George, Greek, King, McMahon & Mcconnaughey, Columbus, 1972-79; ptnr. Baker & Hostetler, Columbus, 1979—. Mem. ABA, Ohio State Bar Assn., Columbus Bar Assn., Transp. Lawyers Assn. Roman Catholic. Office: Baker & Hostetler 65 E State St Columbus OH 43215-4213

TURANO, EMANUEL NICOLAS, architect; b. Bklyn., Mar. 1, 1917; s. Dominick and Ann (Girordi) T.; m. Sybyl Rosmarin, July 1, 1951; children: Lisa, Laurie, Leslie. Cert. in architecture, Cooper Union, 1941, Profl. Achievement citation (hon. Ph.D.), 1964; BArch, Harvard, 1947, MArch, 1963. Designer Skidmore, Owings & Merrill, 1947-50; chief design Kelly & Gruzen, N.Y.C., 1950-52; prin. E.N. Turano (architects and planners), N.Y.C., 1952—; dir. T-4 Studios, N.Y.C., 1965; tchr. 3d, 4th, 5th and master studios Pratt Inst., Bklyn., 1959-62; archtl. instr. 4th yr. studio Columbia, N.Y.C., 1959-60; Cons. HUD, 1963-67, Sussex Woodlands, Inc., N.J., 1963-66. Mem. Boca Raton (Fla.) Bd. Adjustments and Appeals, 1979—; chmn. Boca Raton Code Enforcement Bd. Served with USAAF, 1941-45, PTO. Decorated D.F.C., Air medal. Recipient several awards including Pub. Housing Authority awards, Archtl. award excellence for Pan Am. Passenger Terminal Bldg., Archtl. award excellence for Am. Inst. Steel Constrn., 1961; Fulbright fellow, 1950. Fellow AIA (exec. com. N.Y.C. 1962-66); mem. N.Y. State Assn. Architects, Nat. Inst. Archtl. Edn. (past sec. treas.), N.Y. Soc. Architects, Municipal Art Soc., Cooper Union Alumni Assn. (gov. 1964-67), Cooper Union Adv. Council (chmn. edn. com. 1957-59). Home and Office: 1900 Isabel Rd Este Boca Raton FL 33486-6734

TURBEVILLE, GUS, emeritus college president; b. Turbeville, S.C., Jan. 20, 1923; s. William Jasper and Ila Lucile (Morris) T.; m. Joanne Beverly Johnson, June 7, 1950; children—David Baxter, William Jackson, Sara Ellen. B.A., Vanderbilt U., 1944; M.A., La. State U., 1946; Ph.D., Mich. State U., 1948, LL.D., Columbia Coll., 1982. Head sociology dept. U. Minn., Duluth, 1948-53; pres. Northland Coll., Ashland, Wis., 1953-61; chmn. sociology dept. U. Wis., Superior, 1962-69; pres. Coker Coll., Hartsville, S.C., 1969-74, Emerson Coll., Boston, 1975-78, William Penn Coll., Oskaloosa, Iowa, 1979-84; pres. emeritus William Penn Coll., Oskaloosa, Iowa, 1984—. Co-author: Social problems, 1955; If You Smoke, What Have You?, 1970; The Best of Pogo, 1982; contbr. articles to profl. jours. Bd. dirs. St. Joseph's Hosp., Superior, Wis., 1960-69, Intercomputer Communications Corp., Phoenix, 1970-79. Fellow Am. Sociol. Assn. Quaker. Lodge: Rotary (Ashland, Wis. and Hartsville, S.C.). Avocations: hiking; swimming; reading; writing; philately. Home: 1350 SW 13th Dr Boca Raton FL 33486-5367

TURBEVILLE, ROBERT MORRIS, engineering executive; b. Cleve., May 2, 1951; s. Wilfred and Patricia Alice (Lamb) T.; m. Lisa Edelman, Apr. 2, 1977; children: Adam, Dennis, Diana. Student, Drew U., London, 1971-72;

BA in History, W. Va. Wesleyan, 1973. Mgmt. trainee U.S. Steel, Pitts., 1973-74, foreman, 1975-79; mgr. standard products Heyl & Patterson, Inc., Pitts., 1979-83, sales mgr. to gen. mgr., 1983-88, v.p., 1988-91, pres., CEO, 1991—; dir. Heyl & Patterson, Inc., Pitts., 1988—; chmn. Bridge & Crane Inspection, Inc., Pitts., 1990—. Asst. leader Cub Scouts Am., Pitts., 1991—; coach Mt. Lebanon Soccer Assn., Pitts., 1990—. Mem. AIME, Coal Prep Adv. Bd. (co-chmn. 1985-89), Process Equipment Mfrs. Assn., Young Pres. Orgn. Republican. Methodist. Avocations: car restoration, travel, music. Office: Heyl & Patterson Inc PO Box 36 Pittsburgh PA 15230-0036

TURBIDY, JOHN BERRY, investor, management consultant; b. Rome, Ga., Oct. 18, 1928; s. Joseph Leo and Louyse (Berry) T.; m. Joan Marsales, Dec. 19, 1958; children: John Berry, Trevor Martin. Grad., Darlington Sch., 1945; B.A., Duke U., 1950; postgrad., NYU, 1952, Emory U., 1954-56. Pers. positions Lockheed Aircraft, Marietta, Ga., 1951-56; gen. mgmt. cons. McKinsey & Co., N.Y.C. and London, 1956-63; v.p. adminstrn. ITT Europe, Inc., Brussels, 1963, v.p., group exec. European consumer products, 1964-65, v.p., group exec. for No. Europe, 1965-67; corp. v.p. adminstrn. Celanese Corp., N.Y.C., 1967-68; pres., mng. dir. SIACE, SP.A. subias., Milan, Italy, 1968-69; chmn. bd., pres. Vecta Group, Kalamazoo, Mich., 1970-74; v.p. corp. devel. IU Internat. Corp., Phila., 1974-76, sr. v.p., 1976-77, exec. v.p., 1978-83; exec. v.p. Pitcairn Inc., Jenkintown, Pa., 1984-85; pres., chief exec. officer Pitcairn Fin. Mgmt. Group, 1986-89; chmn. Office John Turbidy, 1990—. Bd. dirs. Statute of Liberty Ellis Island Found. Served with USNR, 1952. Clubs: Merion Golf, Merion Cricket. Office: 909 Morris Ave Bryn Mawr PA 19010-1821

TURBIN, RICHARD, lawyer; b. N.Y.C., Dec. 25, 1944; s. William and Ruth (Fiedler) T.; m. Rai Saint Chu-Turbin, June 12, 1976; children—Laurel Mei, Derek Andrew. B.A. magna cum laude, Cornell U., 1966; J.D., Harvard U., 1969. Bar: Hawaii 1971, U.S. Dist. Ct. Hawaii 1971. Asst. atty. gen. Western Samoa, Apia, 1969-70; dep. pub. defender Pub. Defender's Office, Honolulu, 1970-74; dir. Legal Aid Soc. Hawaii, Kaneohe, 1974-75; sr. atty., pres. Law Offices Richard Turbin, Honolulu, 1975—; legal counsel Hawaii Crime Commn. 1980-81. Co-author: Pacific; editor Harvard Civil Rights-Civil Liberties Law Rev., 1969. Legal counsel Democratic Party, Honolulu County, 1981-82; elected Neighborhood Bd., 1985, elected chair, 1990-93; bd. dirs. Hawaii chpt. ACLU, 1974-78. East-West Ctr. grantee, 1971, 72. Mem. Hawaii Bar Assn., ABA (chair internat. torts and ins. law and practice com.), Am. Trial Lawyers Assn., Hawaii Trial Lawyers Assn. (bd. govs.), Hawaii Jaycees (legal counsel 1981-82), Chinese Jaycees Honolulu (legal counsel 1980-81), Honolulu Tennis League (undefeated player 1983). Jewish. Club: Hawaii Harlequin Rugby (sec., legal counsel 1978-82). Lodge: Elks. Home: 4557 Kolohala St Honolulu HI 96816-4953 Office: 737 Bishop St Ste 1850 Honolulu HI 96813-3209

TURBYFILL, JOHN RAY, railway executive; b. Newland, N.C., Sept. 28, 1931; s. Thomas Manuel and Della Isabell (Braswell) T.; m. Joyce Lorraine Wainwright Bolton, Aug. 14, 1954; children: Karen Denise, John Ray. BA, Roanoke Coll., 1953; LLB, U. Va., 1956. Bar: Va. 1956, N.Y. 1956. Assoc. Cravath, Swaine & Moore, N.Y.C., 1956-60; mem. law dept. Norfolk & Western Ry. Co., Roanoke, Va., 1960-70; v.p. Erie Lackawanna Ry. Co. and Delaware & Hudson Ry. Co., Cleve., Va., 1970-72; v.p. Dereco, Inc., Cleve., Va., 1970-72, 73—; v.p. adminstrn. Norfolk & Western Ry. Co., Roanoke, Va., 1972-74, v.p. fin., 1974-80, exec. v.p. 1980—; exec. v.p. fin. Norfolk So. Corp., Roanoke, Va., 1982-93, vice chmn., 1993—; also with Norfolk So. Railway Corp., 1982—, exec. v.p. fin., 1984—; v.p. Va. Holding Corp., Roanoke, 1973—; v.p. fin. Pochahontas Land Corp., Bluefield, W.Va. Mem. ABA, Roanoke Valley C. of C. (v.p. 1974-76, pres. 1976), Phi Delta Phi. Democrat. Office: Norfolk So Corp 3 Comml Pl Norfolk VA 23510

TURCHIN, CAROLYN, judge; m. Marc Turchin. Grad., U. Calif., Berkeley, 1967; JD, Loyola U., 1978. Tchr. pub. sch., 1967-77; formerly with Santa Monica (Calif.) City Atty.'s Office, U.S. Atty.'s Office, L.A.; magistrate judge US Dist. Ct. (ctrl. dist.) Calif., L.A., 1991—. Office: US Courthouse 312 N Spring St Rm 1031 Los Angeles CA 90012

TURCO, ALFRED, JR., English language educator; b. Providence, Aug. 11, 1940; s. Alfred and Delia Maria (DiMeo) Tu.; m. Elizabeth Nora Davis, 1969 (div. 1981); children—Ellen, Jeffrey. A.B., Brown U., 1962; A.M., Harvard U., 1963, Ph.D., 1969; M.A. ad eundem gradum (hon.), Wesleyan U., 1981. Instr. English Wesleyan U., Middletown, Conn., 1967-69, asst. prof., 1969-74, assoc. prof., 1974-80, prof., 1980—; vis. assoc. prof. Cornell U., Ithaca, N.Y., 1980; cons. Cornell U. Press, Hartford Stage Co. Author: Shaw's Moral Vision, 1976; guest editor: Shaw's Neglected Plays (Shaw: Vol. 7), 1987; contbr. articles on Scandinavian lit. to profl. jours.; mem. editorial bd. Ann. of Bernard Shaw Studies, 1985. Danforth Found. fellow, 1963-67; Woodrow Wilson Found. hon. fellow, 1963. Mem. Phi Beta Kappa. Avocation: gourmet cooking. Home: 62 Prospect St Portland CT 06480 Office: Wesleyan U Middletown CT 06457

TURCO, LEWIS PUTNAM, English educator; b. Buffalo, N.Y., May 2, 1934; s. Luigi and May Laura (Putnam) T.; m. Jean Cate Houdlette, May 29, 1934; children: Melora Ann, Christopher Cameron. BA, U. Conn., 1959; MA, U. Iowa, 1962. Instr. Cleve. State U., 1960-64; asst. prof. Hillsdale (Mich.) Coll., 1964-65; asst. prof. to full prof. SUNY, Oswego, 1965—, poet-in-residence, 1995; grad. asst. English, U. Conn., 1959; editorial asst. Writer's Workshop, U. Iowa, 1959-60; vis. prof. SUNY, Potsdam, 1968-69; Bingham Poet in Residence U. Louisville, 1982; Writer in Residence, Ashland U., 1991; founding dir. Cleve. State U. Poetry Ctr., 1962, program in writing arts, SUNY Oswego, 1968. Author: First Poems, 1960, Awaken, Bells Falling: Poems 1959-67, 1968, The Inhabitant, 1970, Pocoangelini: A Fantography and Other Poems, 1971, American Still Lifes, 1981, numerous other poetry books including The Shifting Web: New and Selected Poems, 1989; author numerous non-fiction books including The Book of Forms: A Handbook of Poetics, 1968, The New Book of Forms, 1986, Visions and Revisions of American Poetry, 1986, Dialogue, 1989, Emily Dickinson, Woman of Letters, 1993, others; articles. Sec. City of Oswego Charter Revision Commn. 1990-91; active Oswego Opera Theater Chorus, Oswego Festival Chorus, 1986—. With USN, 1952-56. Recipient scholarship Meriden Record-Jour. Pub. Co., U. Conn., 1957-58, 58-59, Resident fellowships Yaddo Found., Saratoga Springs, N.Y., 1959, 1977, Faculty fellowships Rsch. Found. of SUNY, 1966-67, 69, 71, 73, 78, grant-in-aid, 1969, others; inducted into the Meriden (Conn.) Hall of Fame, 1993, Disting. Alumnus award U. Conn. 1992. Mem. P.E.N. Am. Ctr., Poetry Soc. Am. (Melville Cane award 1986), Assoc. Writing Programs. Avocation: singing. Home: PO Box 362 Oswego NY 13126-0362 Office: SUNY College 39A Swetman Hall Oswego NY 13126

TURCO, RICHARD PETER, atmospheric scientist; b. N.Y.C., Mar. 9, 1943; s. Salvatore Joseph and Mary Louise (Cuocolo) T.; m. Barbara Marie Bren, July 1, 1967 (div. Sept. 1990); 1 child, Richard Cameron; m. Linda Stevenson Newman, July 27, 1991. BSEE, Rutgers U., 1965; PhDEE and Physics, U. Ill., 1971. Research fellow Ames Research Ctr., NASA, Moffett Field, Calif., 1971; research scientist R&D Assocs., Los Angeles, 1971-88; prof. UCLA, 1988—. Disting. Faculty Rsch. lectr., 1992—; dept. chair, 1993—. Author: Environmental Consequences of Nuclear War, 1986, (with Carl Sagan) A Path Where No Man Thought: Nuclear Winter and the End of the Arms Race, 1990, Earth Under Seige: From Air Pollution to Global Change, 1997; proposed nuclear winter theory, 1983; contbr. numerous articles to profl. jours. Recipient H. Julian Allen award NASA, 1983, 88, Peace Garden award U. N.D., 1984, Leo Szilard award Am. Phys. Soc., 1985; MacArthur Found. fellow, 1986. Mem. Am. Geophys. Union (press. atmospheric scis. sect. 1992-94, assoc. editor Jour. Geophys. Rsch. 1982-91, fellow 1993), Sigma Xi. Avocations: hiking, handball.

TURCOTTE, DONALD LAWSON, geophysical sciences educator; b. Bellingham, Wash., Apr. 22, 1932; s. Lawson Phillip and Eva (Pearson) T.; m. Joan Meredith Luecke, May 17, 1957; children: Phillip Lawson, Stephen Bradford. BS, Calif. Inst. Tech., 1954, PhD, 1958; M in Aero. Engring., Cornell U., 1955. Asst. prof. aero. engring. U.S. Naval Postgrad. Sch., Monterey, Calif., 1958-59; asst. prof. aero. engring. Cornell U., Ithaca, N.Y., 1959-63; assoc. prof. Cornell U., 1963-67, prof., 1967-73, prof. geol. scis., 1973-85, Maxwell Upson prof., 1985—, chmn., 1981-90. Author: (with others) Statistical Thermodynamics, 1963, Space Propulsion, 1965, Geodynamics, 1982, Fractals and Chaos in Geology and Geophysics, 1992.

Trustee U. Space Research Assn., 1975-79. NSF sr. postdoctoral research fellow, 1965-66; Guggenheim fellow, 1972-73. Mem. Am. Geophys. Union (Charles A. Whitten Medal, 1995), Geol. Soc. Am. (Day medal 1982), Seismol. Soc. Am., Nat. Acad. Scis., Am. Acad. Arts and Scis. Club: Ithaca Country. Home: 703 Cayuga Heights Rd Ithaca NY 14850-1463 Office: Cornell U Snee Hall Ithaca NY 14853

TURCOTTE, JEAN-CLAUDE, archbishop; b. Montreal, Que., Can., June 26, 1936; s. Paul-Emile and Rita (Gravel) T. Ordained priest Roman Catholic Ch., consecrated bishop. Aux. bishop Diocese of Montreal, Que., Can., 1982-90, archbishop, 1990—; cardinal Diocese of Montreal, Que., Can., 1994. Home: 1071 de la Cathedrale St, Montreal QC Canada H3B 2V4 Office: Diocese de Montreal, 2000 Sherbrooke ouest, Montreal, PQ Canada H3H 1G4

TURCOTTE, JEREMIAH GEORGE, physician, surgery educator; b. Detroit, Jan. 20, 1933; s. Vincent Joseph and Margaret Campau (Meldrum) T.; m. Claire Mary Lenz, July 5, 1958; children: Elizabeth Margaret, Sarah Lenz, John Jeremiah, Claire Meldrum. BS with high distinction, U. Mich., 1955, MD cum laude, 1957. Diplomate Am. Bd. Surgery (dir. 1982-88); added qualification in surg. critical care, 1986. Intern U. Mich. Med. Ctr., 1957-58, resident in surgery, 1958-60, 61-63; research asst. USPHS grant U. Mich. surgery dept., 1960-61; mem. faculty U. Mich. Med. Sch., 1963—, prof. surgery, 1971—, chmn. dept., 1974-87, head sect. gen. surgery, 1974-81; mem. Residency Rev. Com. for Surgery, Am. Coun. for Grad. Med. End., 1980-86; dir. Transplant and Health Policy Ctr., U. Mich. 1985-95, U. Mich. Organ Transplant Ctr., 1984—; Liver Transplant Program; chmn. ethics com. United Network for Organ Sharing, 1987-91. Author 7 books, 49 book chpts.; contbr. over 184 articles to profl. jours. Recipient Henry Russell award U. Mich., 1970, Mich. State Med. Soc. award, 1991. Fellow ACS (gov. 1982-92, pres. Mich. chpt. 1979-80); mem. Transplantation Soc. Am. (pres. 1973-75), Am. Acad. Surgeons, Am. Surg. Assn. Soc. Univ. Surgeons, Internat. Transplantation Soc., Ctrl. Surg. Assn. (pres. 1990-91), Midwest Surg. Assn., Am. Gastroenterol. Assn., Western Surg. Assn., Soc. Surgery Alimentary Tract, Am. Soc. Transplant Surgeons (pres. 1979-80, chmn. ethics com. 1991-94), Frederick A. Coller Soc. (pres. 1982-83), Am. Trauma Soc. (founder), Halsted Soc., Western State Med. Soc. (Pres.'s award 1991), Am. Liver Found., Am. Coun. on Transplantation (bd. dirs. 1987-90), Ctrl. Surg. Assn. Found. (executor and sec. 1992—). Roman Catholic. Home: One Regent Dr Ann Arbor MI 48104-1738

TURE, NORMAN BERNARD, public policy research organization executive; b. Cleve., Sept. 8, 1923; s. Albert Abel and Anne T.; m. Donna Jeanne Cramer, Oct. 23, 1979; children: Martha Elizabeth, Peter Douglas, Heather, Julianne, Keli, Anne Claire. Student, Ohio State U., 1941-43; M.A., U. Chgo., 1947, Ph.D. in Econs., 1968. Mem. staff Treasury Dept., 1951-55, Joint Econ. Com., 1955-61, Nat. Bur. Econ. Research, 1961-68, Planning Research Corp., 1968-71; pres. Norman B. Ture, Inc., Washington, 1971-80, Inst. Research Econs. Taxation, Washington, 1977-80; undersec. tax and econ. affairs Treasury Dept., 1981-82; pres. Inst. Research on Econs. of Taxation, 1983—. Author: Accelerated Depreciation in the United States 1954-60, 1967, Tax Policy, Capital Formation, and Productivity, 1973, The Future of Private Pension Plans, 1976, The Effects of Tax Policy on Capital Formation, 1977, Wealth Redistribution and the Income Tax, 1978, The Value Added Tax: Facts and Fancies, 1979, Measuring the Benefits and Costs of Section 936. Served with AUS, 1943-44. Republican. Roman Catholic. Club: Capitol Hill. Office: 1300 19th St NW Ste 240 Washington DC 20036-1609

TURECK, ROSALYN, concert artist, author, editor, educator; b. Chgo., Dec. 14, 1914; d. Samuel Tureck and Mary (Lipson) Tureck-Wise; (w. 1964). Studies with Sophia Brilliant-Liven, 1925-29, with Jan Chiapusso, 1929-31, with Gavin Williamson, 1931-32; BA cum laude, The Juilliard Sch. Music, 1935; studies with Olga Samaroff; MusD (hon.), Colby Coll., 1964, Roosevelt U., 1968, Wilson Coll., 1968, Oxford U., Eng., 1977, Music and Arts Inst., San Francisco, 1987. Mem. faculty Phila. Conservatory Music, 1935-42, Mannes Sch., N.Y.C., 1940-44, Juilliard Sch. Music, N.Y.C., 1943-55, Columbia U., N.Y.C., 1953-55; prof. music, Univ. U. Calif., San Diego, 1966-72; vis. prof. Washington U., St. Louis, 1963-64, U. Md., 1981-85, Yale U., 1991-93; vis. fellow St. Hilda's Coll., Oxford (Eng.) U., 1974, hon. life fellow, 1974—; vis. fellow Wolfson Coll., Oxford, 1975—; lectr. numerous ednl. instns., U.S., Eng., Spain, Denmark, Holland, Can., Israel, Brazil, Argentina, Chile; lectr. Royal Inst. Great Britain, 1993, Boston U., 1993, 94, Smithsonian Instn., 1994, Rockefeller U., 1994, U. Calif., Santa Barbara, 1995; hon. mem. adv. coun. Ams. for Music Libr., Hebrew U., Israel., Royal Inst. Great Britain, London, U. Southampton, Oxford U., 1993, 10th Internat. Congress Logic, Methodology and Philosophy Sci., 1995; bd. dirs., founder Internat. Bach Soc., Inst. for Bach Studies; founder Composers of Today, 1949-53, Tureck Bach Players, 1955, London, 1981, New York, Tureck Bach Inst., Inc., 1981, Symposia 1983, 84, 86—; 1st woman invited to conduct N.Y. Philharm., 1958, San Antonio Symphony, Okla. Symphony, 1962, World Tour, U.S., Eng., Holland, Turkey, Israel, 1985-86; soloist at White House State Dinner for Can. Prime Minister, 1986, Casals Festival Tour Italy, 1991; conv. organizer Symposium on Structure, U. Internat. Menendez Pelayo, Spain, 1990. Debut 2 solo recitals, Chgo., 1924; soloist Chgo. Symphony Orch., 1926, 2 all-Bach recitals, Chgo., 1930; N.Y.C. debut Carnegie Hall with Phila. Orch., 1936; series 6 all-Bach recitals, Town Hall, N.Y.C., 1937, ann. U.S-Can. tours, 1937—, ann. series 3 all-Bach recitals, N.Y.C., 1944-54, 59—; European debut Copenhagen, 1947; organizer, dir. soc. for performance internat. contemporary music, Composers of Today, Inc, 1951-55; extensive European tours, 1947—; condr., soloist, London Philharmonia, 1958; founder, dir. Tureck Bach Players, London, 1957, N.Y.C., 1981, Bach festivals cities, Eng., Ireland, Spain, 1959—, Carnegie Hall Ann. Series, N.Y.C., 1975—; TV series Well-Tempered Clavier, Book 1, Granada TV, Eng., 1961; BBC series Well-Tempered Clavier, Books 1 and 2, 1976; numerous TV appearances, U.S., 1961—, including Wm. F. Buckley's Firing Line, 1970, 85, 87, 89, Today Show, Camera Three, Bach recitals on piano, harpsichord, clavichord, antique and electronic instruments, 1963—; concert Teatro Colon, Buenos Aires, 1992, Rome, Florence, Imola, Italy, Sevilla and Alicante, Spain, 1993, 94; concert tour, recitals, master classes in Spain, Italy, Switzerland, Eng., S.Am., 1994; world tours in Far East, India, Australia, Europe, 1971, S.Am., 1986, 87, 88, 89, Europe, Israel, Turkey, Spain, 1986, 90, Argentina, Chile, 1989, 90, 91, 92, Casals Festival, 1991, Italy, 1991, 92, Eng., Italy, Spain, 1992-93; N.Y.C. series, Met. Mus. Art and Carnegie Hall, 1969—; appeared with leading orchs. U.S., Can., Europe, South Africa, S.Am., Israel; recs. for HMV, Odeon, Decca, Columbia Masterworks., Everest, Allegro, Classical Music, Inc; condr., soloist N.Y. Philharmon., 1960, London Philharmon. Orch., 1959—, Tureck Bach Players, London, 1960-72, Israel Philharmon., Tel Aviv, Haifa and Kol Israel orchs., 1963, Israel Festival, Internat. Bach Soc. Orchs., 1967, 69, 70, Washington Nat. Symphony, 1970, Madrid Chamber Orch., 1970, Carnegie Hall, N.Y., 1975-86, N.Y. 1981, 84, 85; numerous solo recitals including U. Kansas, 1992, N.Y.C., 1992; author: Introduction to the Performance of Bach, 3 vols., 1960, Video Artists Internat.eo Teatro Color CD's, 1992—, Authenticity, 1994; contbr. articles to various mags.; editor Bach-Sarabande, C minor, 1960, Tureck Bach Urtext Series: Italian Concerto, Schirmer Music, Inc., 1983, 2d edit., 1991, Lute Suite, E minor, 1984, C minor, 1985, Carl Fischer Paginini-Tureck: Moto Perpetuo, A. Scarlatti: Air and Gavotte, Bach and Tureck at Home series, 1990; films: Fantasy and Fugue: Rosalyn Tureck Plays Bach, 1972, Rosalyn Tureck plays on Harpsichord and Organ, 1977, Joy of Bach, 1978, Camera 3: Bach on the Frontier of the Future, CBS film, Ephesus, Turkey, 1985. Decorated Officers Cross of the Order of Merit, Fed. Republic Germany, 1979; recipient 1st prize Greater Chgo. Piano Playing Tournament, 1928, 1st Town Hall Endowment award, 1937, Phi Beta award, 1946; named Schubert Meml. Contest winner, 1935, Nat. Fedn. Music Clubs Competition winner, 1935, Musician of Yr., Music Tchrs. Nat. Assn., 1987; NEH grantee. Fellow Guildhall Sch. Music and Drama (hon.); mem. Royal Mus. Assn. London, Am. Musicological Soc., Inc. Soc. Musicians (London), Royal Philharmonic Soc. London, Sebastian Bach de Belgique (hon.), Am. Bach Soc., Oxford Soc. Clubs: Century (N.Y.C.), Oxford and Cambridge, London), Bohemians (N.Y.C.) (hon.). Office: care Christa Phelps, Lies Askonas Ltd 6 Henrietta St, London WC2 EALA, England also: Tureck Bach Inst 215 E 68th St New York NY 10021 *My work in Bach is not a specialization, although concentration on a single composer may seemingly give that impression. It spreads to performance on antique instruments, harpsichord, clavichord, Fortepiano, to the contemporary piano and electronic Moog, to the organ, to conducting, writing, editing,*

and research. The years of concertizing in compositions of all periods—pre-Bach, romantic, contemporary, and electronic music—have all brought a rich tapestry of understanding to the magisterial requirements for interpreting music of a past era authentically and significantly as a contemporary artist.

TUREK, SONIA FAY, journalist; b. N.Y.C., Aug. 2, 1949; d. Louis and Julia (Liebson) T. BA in English, CCNY, 1970; MSLS, Drexel U., 1972; MS in Journalism, Boston U., 1979. Children's libr. Wissahickon Valley Pub. Libr., Ambler, Pa., 1973; supr. children's svcs. Somerville Pub. Libr., 1973-78; stringer The Watertown (Mass.) Sun, 1979, The Bedford (Mass.) Minuteman, 1979; reporter The Middlesex News, Framingham, Mass., 1979-82, county bur. chief, 1982-83; reporter The Boston Herald, 1983, asst. city editor, city editor, 1985-86, asst. mng. editor features, 1986-89, asst. mng. editor Sunday, 1989-93, dep. mng. editor, arts and features, 1993—; tchr. Cambridge (Mass.) Ctr. for Adult Edn., 1982, 83; adj. prof. Boston U., 1986; travel writer The Boston Herald, 1984-88, wine columnist, 1984—. Avocations: wine and food, travel, sailing. Office: The Boston Herald One Herald Sq Boston MA 02106

TUREKIAN, KARL KAREKIN, geochemistry educator; b. N.Y.C., Oct. 25, 1927; s. Vaughan Thomas and Victoria (Guleserian) T.; m. Arax Roxanne Hagopian, Apr. 22, 1962; children: Karla Ann, Vaughan Charles. A.B., Wheaton (Ill.) Coll., 1949; M.A., Columbia U., 1951, Ph.D., 1955; DSc (hon.), SUNY, Stony Brook, 1989. Lectr. geology Columbia U., 1953-54, rsch. assoc. Lamont-Doherty Earth Obs., 1954-56; faculty, asst. prof. Yale U., 1956-61, assoc. prof., 1961-65, prof. geology and geophysics, 1965-72, Henry Barnard Davis prof. geology and geophysics, 1972-85, Benjamin Silliman prof., 1985—, chmn. dept., 1982-88, curator meteorites, archaeology coun., dir. Ctr. for the Study of Global Change; chmn. studies in the environment, 1992-93; cons. Pres.'s Commn. Marine Sci. Engring. and Resources, 1967-68; oceanography panel NSF, 1968-70; NASA exobiology panel, Am. Inst. Biol. Scientists, 1966-69; mem. NAS-NRC climate rsch. bd., 1977-80, ocean sci. bd., 1979-82, ocean studies bd., 1989-92, bd. on global change, 1992-95, Com. Phys. Scis., Math. Resources, 1986-90, Com. Geoscis., Environment, Resources, 1990-92; mem. group experts sci. aspects Marine Pollution UN, 1971-73. Author: Oceans, 1968, 2d edit., 1976, Chemistry of the Earth, 1972, (with B.J. Skinner) Man and the Ocean, 1973 (with C.K. Drake, J. Imbrie and J.A. Knauss) Oceanography, 1978; editor: Late Cenozoic Glacial Ages, 1971; editor Jour. Geophys. Rsch., 1969-75, Earth Planet. Sci. Letters, 1975≈89, Global Biogeochem. Cycles, 1990-95; assoc. editor Geochim. et Cosmochim. Acta, 1967-70, Jour. Geophys. Rsch., 1967-69; editor Discovery, Yale Peabody Mus., 1978-81; contbr. articles to profl. jours. Served with USNR, 1945-46. Guggenheim fellow Cambridge U., 1962-63; Fairchild Disting. scholar Calif. Inst. Tech., 1988. Fellow AAAS, Geol. Soc. Am., Meteoritical Soc., Am. Geophys. Union, Am. Acad. Arts and Scis.; mem. NAS, Am. Chem. Soc., Geochem. Soc. (pres. 1975-76, V.M. Goldschmidt medal 1989), Sigma Xi (pres. Yale chpt. 1961-62). Home: 555 Skiff St North Haven CT 06473-3013 Office: Yale U Dept Geology and Geophysics PO Box 208109 New Haven CT 06520-8109

TURGEON, EDGAR LYNN, economics educator; b. Mitchell, S.D., Aug. 26, 1920; s. Edgar Franklin and Margie (Fellows) T.; m. Livia Racko, Oct. 13, 1950 (div. 1988); 1 child, Danielle Kim. AB, U. Calif., Berkeley, 1942, MA, 1948; PhD, Columbia U., 1959. With Rand Corp., Santa Monica, Calif., 1950-57; prof. econs. Hofstra U., Hempstead, N.Y., 1957-90, prof. emeritus, 1991—; Fulbright lectr. Moscow State U., 1978, Acad. for Fgn. Trade, Moscow, 1991. Author: The Contrasting Economies, 1963, The Advanced Capitalist System, 1980, State and Discrimination, 1989. Lt. USN, 1942-46, PTO. Home: 30 Duncan Rd Hempstead NY 11550-4616 Office: Hofstra U Dept Econs Hempstead NY 11550

TURILLO, MICHAEL JOSEPH, JR., management consultant; b. Hartford, Conn., Aug. 22, 1947; s. Michael Joseph and Alice (Vargas) T.; m. Deborah Marchand; children: Stephanie, Christopher. BS, Providence Coll., 1969; MBA, Syracuse U., 1972; MS, U. Mass., 1973. Cons. Peat, Marwick, Mitchell & Co. (name changed to KPMG Peat Marwick), Boston, 1974-77, mgr., 1977-82, ptnr., 1982—, nat. cons. practice dir. for fin. svc. cos., 1985-91; chmn. Internat. Mgmt. Cons. Practice Com. on Banking and Fin., 1986—; nat. ptnr.-in-charge Fin. Svcs.-Specialized Cons., 1990-93, Capital Strategies, 1995—, nat. lead ptnr. in charge Global Capital Group, 1993-94. Com. mem. United Way, Boston, 1981-83; trustee Elliot Montessori, South Natick, Mass., 1984-85; dir. Greater Boston coun. Boy Scouts Am., 1988—. Capt. U.S. Army, 1969-71, Vietnam. Decorated Bronze Star. Mem. Bank Mktg. Assn., Assn. Planning Execs., Assn. Corp. Planners, Beta Gamma Sigma. Roman Catholic. Avocations: tennis, photography, travel, golf. Home: 47 South St South Natick MA 01760-3710 Office: KPMG Peat Marwick 1 Boston Pl Boston MA 02108 also: 345 Park Ave New York NY 10154

TURIN, GEORGE LEWIS, electrical engineering educator, university dean; b. N.Y.C., Jan. 27, 1930; s. Meyer H. and Lillian (Podolsky) T.; m. Helen F. Green, Sept. 11, 1964; children: David, Abigail. BS, MIT, 1952, MS, 1952, ScD, 1956. Engr. Philco Corp., Phila., 1948-51; staff mem. Mass. Inst. Tech. Lincoln Lab., Lexington, 1952-56; mem. staff Hughes Aircraft Co., Culver City, Calif., 1956-60; mem. faculty U. Calif., Berkeley, 1960-90, prof. elec. engring. and computer sci. emeritus, 1990—; vice chmn. dept. elec. engring. and computer sci. U. Calif., 1975-77, chmn., 1980-83; dean Sch. Engring. and Applied Sci. UCLA, 1983-86; dir. engring. sci. div. Tecknekron Corp., Menlo Park, Calif., 1970-73, v.p., 1988-94; v.p. engring. Ins. Tech. Co., Berkeley, 1973-74; exec. v.p. Tera Corp., N.Y.-74-76; dir. Tera Corp., Berkeley, 1983-86, Tenera MLP, Berkeley, 1995—; cons. to numerous corps. and govt. agys. Author: Notes on Digital Communication, 1969; Contbr. articles to profl. jours. Recipient Berkeley Citation, U. Calif., 1991; Guggenheim fellow, 1966-67, U.K. Sci. and Engring. Rsch. Coun. fellow, 1983. Fellow IEEE; mem. Nat. Acad. Engring. Home: 763 San Diego Rd Berkeley CA 94707-2025

TURINO, GERARD MICHAEL, physician, medical scientist, educator; b. N.Y.C., May 16, 1924; s. Michael and Lucy (Arciero) T.; m. Dorothy Estes, Aug. 25, 1951; children: Peter, Phillip, James. A.B., Princeton U., 1945; M.D., Columbia U., 1948. Diplomate: Am. Bd. Internal Medicine. Intern Columbia U., Bellevue Hosp., 1948-49, asst. resident in medicine, 1949-50; resident in medicine New Haven Hosp., 1950-51; chief resident in medicine Columbia U. Bellevue Hosp., 1953-54; sr. fellow N.Y. Heart Assn., 1956-60; career investigator Health Research Council City of N.Y., 1961-71; asst. prof. medicine Columbia U., 1960-67, assoc. prof., 1967-72, prof. medicine, 1973-83, John H. Keating prof. medicine, 1983—; mem. staff Presbyn. Hosp., N.Y.C., 1960—; attending physician Presbyn. Hosp., 1983—; dir. med. svcs. St. Lukes-Roosevelt Hosp., N.Y.C., 1983-92; cons. on sci. affairs Am. Thoracic Soc., 1992—; mem. sci. adv. com. Nat. Heart, Lung, and Blood Inst., Am. Lung Assn., Am. Heart Assn., N.Y. Lung Assn., N.Y. Heart Assn.; mem. staff divsn. med. sci. Nat. Rsch. Coun., Washington; cons. VA Hosp., East Orange, N.J., 1962-67; cons. in medicine Englewood (N.J.) Hosp., Hackensack (N.J.) Hosp., pres.-elect Am. Bur. Med. Advancement in China, 1994, pres., 1994—. Contbr. articles to med. jours. Mem. Bd. Edn., Alpine, N.J., 1960-67. Served to capt. USAF, 1951-53. Recipient Joseph Mather Smith prize Columbia U., 1965, Alumni medal, 1983; Silver medal Alumni Assn. Coll. Physicians and Surgeons Columbia U., 1979, gold medal, 1986. Fellow AAAS; mem. Assn. Am. Physicians, Am. Soc. Clin. Investigation, Harvey Soc., Am. Fedn. Clin. Rsch., Am. Physiol. Soc., Am. Heart Assn. (award of merit 1980, Disting. Achievement award 1989, bd. dirs.), N.Y. Heart Assn. (pres. 1981-83, dir.), N.Y. Lung Assn. (dir.), Am. Physiol. Soc. (chmn. steering com. respiration sect.), Am. Thoracic Soc. (pres. 1987-88), N.Y. Med.-Surg. Soc., N.Y. Clin. Soc. Clubs: Princeton (N.Y.C.); Maidstone, Devon Yacht, Century Assn. Home: 66 E 79th St New York NY 10021-0233 Office: St Lukes-Roosevelt Hosp W 114th St and Amsterdam Ave New York NY 10025

TURINSKY, PAUL JOSEF, nuclear engineer, educator; b. Hoboken, N.J., Oct. 20, 1944; s. Paul J. and Wilma A. (Budig) T.; m. Karen Ann DeLuca, Aug. 29, 1966; children: Grant Dean, Beth Noelle. BS, U. R.I., 1966; MSE, U. Mich., 1967, PhD, 1970; MBA, U. Pitts., 1979. Asst. prof. Rensselaer Poly. Inst., Troy, N.Y., 1971-73; engr., mgr. nuclear design Westinghouse Elec. Corp., Pitts., 1973-78, mgr. core devel., 1978-80; head dept. nuclear engring. N.C. State U., Raleigh, 1980-88, prof., 1980—, dir. Electric Power Rsch. Ctr., 1989—; pres. Nuclear Fuel Mgmt. Assocs., 1994—; bd. dirs.

Quantum Rsch. Svcs.; cons. Electric Power Rsch. Inst., Palo Alto, Calif., 1980—, Sci. Applications Internat. Corp., 1990-92, U.S. Dept. of Energy, 1993; tech. specialist Internat. Atomic Energy Agy., Vienna, Austria, 1982—; mem. nuclear safety rev. bd. Duke Power Co., Charlotte, N.C., 1986—. Author: (with others) CRC Handbook of Nuclear Reactor Calculations, 1986; contbr. more than 75 articles to tech. jours. Recipient Outstanding Tchr. award N.C. State U., 1985, Alcoa Disting. Rschr. award, 1993, Supercomputer award IBM, 1991. Fellow Am. Nuclear Soc. (chmn. reactor physics div. 1987-88, Mark Mills award 1971, bd. dirs. 1990-93); mem. AAAS, IEEE Computer Soc., Am. Soc. Engring. Educators (chmn. nuclear engring. div. 1984-85, Glenn Murphy award 1990), Edison Electric Inst. (Power Engring. Educator award 1992), Soc. Indsl. and Applied Math. Office: NC State U Dept Nuclear Engring PO Box 7909 Raleigh NC 27695-7909

TURK, AUSTIN THEODORE, sociology educator; b. Gainesville, Ga., May 28, 1934; s. Hollis Theodore and Ruth (Vandiver) T.; m. Janet Stuart Irving, Oct. 4, 1957 (div. 1977); children: Catherine, Jennifer; m. Ruth-Ellen Marie Grimes, July 27, 1985. BA cum laude, U. Ga., 1956; MA, U. Ky., 1959; PhD, U. Wis., 1962. Acting instr. sociology U. Wis., Madison, 1961-62; from instr. to prof. sociology Ind. U., Bloomington, 1962-74; prof. U. Toronto, Can., 1974-88; prof. U. Calif., Riverside, 1988—, chmn. dept. sociology, 1989-94; interim dir. Robert B. Presley Ctr. for Crime and Justice Studies, 1994-95. Author: Criminality and Legal Order, 1969, Political Criminality, 1982; gen. editor crime and justice series SUNY Press, Albany, 1990—; contbr. articles to jours. in field. Mem. Calif. Mus. Photography, 1988—, Friends of the Bot. Gardens, 1988, Citizens Univ. Com., 1990—. Recipient Paul Tappan award Western Soc. Criminology, 1989. Fellow Am. Soc. Criminology (pres. 1984-85); mem. Am. Sociol. Assn. (chair criminology sect. 1975-76), Law and Soc. Assn. (trustee 1982-85), Acad. Criminal Justice Scis. Democrat. Avocations: gardening, reading, swimming, tennis. Office: Dept Sociology U Calif Riverside Riverside CA 92521

TURK, HERMAN, sociologist, educator, researcher; b. N.Y.C., May 29, 1924; s. Leo F. and Lotta A.L. (Jaenke) T.; m. Elizabeth L. Branstrom, Aug. 5, 1978; children—Lawrence, Gregory, Norman; 1 stepchild, Mark. B.S. in Elec. Engring., U. Nebr., 1947; M.A. in Sociology, Columbia U., 1952; Ph.D. in Sociology, Am. U., Washington, 1959. Safety engr. Royal Liverpool Group, N.Y.C., 1947-51; research asst. Bur. Applied Social Research Columbia U., N.Y.C., 1951-52; research asst., research assoc., research scientist Human Resources Research Office, George Washington U., Washington, 1952-58; social sci. contractor U.S. Dept. State, Washington, 1957-58; social sci. analyst NIMH, Bethesda, Md., 1958-59; faculty research assoc., asst. prof. sociology and psychiatry Duke U., Durham, N.C., 1959-63; assoc. prof., dir. Bur. Sociol. Research U. Nebr., Lincoln, 1963-66; prof. sociology, dir. lab. for orgnl. rsch. U. So. Calif., L.A., 1966-91; scholar in residence Lab. for Orgnl. Research, 1966—, dir. grad. studies in sociology, 1988-89; vis. prof. U. Wis., Madison, 1969, Social Sci. Research Inst., U. Cologne, U. Kiel, Fed. Republic of Germany, 1972-73, U. Stockholm, 1973-74, 80, U. P.R., 1979-80, 83, U. Haifa, 1992; rev. panelist NSF, Washington, 1972-79; mem. exec. com. Social Sci. Adv. Com. 1977-78; cons. NIH, 1964-74, Nat. Acad. Sci., 1973-75, White House Office of Budget, 1974, U. P.R. Med. Sch., 1979—, U. Trieste, 1988—. Author: (with Thelma Ingles) Clinic Nursing: Explorations in Role Innovation, 1963, (with others) Social Aspects of Aging, 1966, Interorganizational Acivation in Urban Communities: Deductions from the Concept of System, 1973 (Am. Sociol. Assn. Rose award 1973), , Organizations in Modern Life: Cities and Other Large Networks, 1977; author, editor: (with R.L. Simpson) Institutions and Social Exchange: The Sociologies of Talcott Parsons and George C. Humans, 1970; editor: Commentaries on the Social Research and Theorems of George C. Homans, 1981; assoc. editor Sociol. Inquiry, 1961-64, editor Jours. assoc. editor Sociology and Social Research, 1966-85, book rev. editor, 1974-77; assoc. editor Sociol. Quar., 1970-72, 75-80, Sociol. Symposium, 1972-89, Connections, 1978-88, Social Welfare, Social Planning and Social Devel., 1980—, Social Forces, 1983-86 ; contbr. articles to profl. jours. and chpts. to books. NIH-Nat. Library Medicine health sci. scholar, 1968. Fellow Am. Sociol. Assn. (exec. councils sect. on theoretical sociology 1970-74, sect. on community 1975-78, chmn. com. on publs. 1981-83), Internat. Sociol. Assn. (research council 1976—), Pacific Sociol. Assn. (chmn. publs. 1968-73, 1st v.p. 1976-78), Internat. Network for Social Network Analysis (exec. com. 1977-88), Fedn. Am. Scientists, AAUP, Alpha Kappa Delta (exec. council 1964-74, 80, pres. 1968-70). Avocations: tennis; computers. Office: U So Calif Dept Sociology MC2539 Los Angeles CA 90089

TURK, JAMES CLINTON, federal judge; b. Roanoke, Va., May 3, 1923; s. James Alexander and Geneva (Richardson) T.; m. Barbara Duncan, Aug. 21, 1954; children—Ramona Leah, James Clinton, Robert Malcolm Duncan, Mary Elizabeth, David Michael. A.B., Roanoke Coll., 1949; L.L.B., Washington and Lee U., 1952. Bar: Va. bar 1952. Assoc. Dalton & Poff, Radford, Va., 1952-53; ptnr. Dalton, Poff & Turk, Radford, 1953-72; U.S. senator from Va., 1959-72; judge U.S. Dist. Ct. (we. dist.) Va., Roanoke, 1972-73, chief judge, 1973—; dir. 1st & Mchts. Nat. Bank of Radford. Mem. Va. Senate, from 1959, minority leader.; Trustee Radford Community Hosp., 1959—. Served with AUS, 1943-46. Mem. Order of Coif, Phi Beta Kappa, Omicron Delta Kappa. Baptist (deacon). Home: 1002 Walker Dr Radford VA 24141-3018 Office: US Dist Ct PO Box 2796 Roanoke VA 24001-2796

TURK, MILAN JOSEPH, chemical company executive; b. Baton Rouge, Nov. 25, 1938; s. Frank P. and Zdenka (Cop) T.; m. Margot Genre, Sept. 10, 1937; children: Milan J. Jr., Margot J., Richard P. BS in Chem. Engring., La. State U., 1960, MBA, 1962; grad. advanced mgmt. program, Harvard U., 1985. Process engring. and bus. analyst Exxon Corp., Baton Rouge, 1960-64; with Stauffer Chem. Co., 1965-85; asst. to v.p. mfg. Consol. Chem. Div. Houston, 1965-67; with Stauffer Chem. Co., 1967-85; asst. to v.p. corp. planning Stauffer Chem. Co., N.Y.C., 1967-69; fin. administr. ind. chem. div. Stauffer Chem. Co., 1969-72; dir. corp. devel. Stauffer Chem. Co., N.Y.C., 1972-73; dir. ops. Latin Am. div. Stauffer Chem. Co., Westport, Conn., 1972-3; gen. mgr. Latin Am. div. Stauffer Chem. Co., 1973-75; dep. gen. mgr. Europe div. Stauffer Chem. Co., Geneva, 1975-76, corp. v.p., gen. mgr. Europe div., 1976-80; corp. v.p. spl. projects Stauffer Chem. Co., Westport, Conn., 1980-81; corp. v.p., gen. mgr. food ingredients div. Stauffer Chem. Co., 1981-82, corp. group v.p. agr./food products, 1982-85; pres. agr. products div., corp. v.p. Chesebrough-Pond's Inc., Westport, Conn., 1985-88; exec. v.p., mem. exec. com., div. Mobay Corp., Pitts., 1988-90; corp. v.p., group exec. Internat. Paper Co., Purchase, N.Y., 1990-92; sr. v.p. Internat. Paper Co., 1992—. Mem. Am. Inst. Chem. Engring., Soc. Chem. Ind., Nat. Agrl. Chem. Assn. (bd. dirs. 1986-88, exec. com. 1986-88). Republican. Roman Catholic. Club: Patterson (Fairfield, Conn.). Home: 553 Silvermine Rd New Canaan CT 06840-4322 Office: Internat Paper Co 2 Manhattanville Rd Purchase NY 10577-2118

TURK, PATRICIA AVEDON, dance company executive. Gen. mgr. N.Y.C. Ballet. Office: NYC Ballet New York State Theatre 20 Lincoln Ctr Plz New York NY 10023*

TURK, RICHARD ERRINGTON, retired psychiatrist; b. Staten Island, N.Y., Oct. 6, 1925; s. Richard Jason and Marian (Errington) T.; m. Dec. 30, 1948 (widowed Dec. 23, 1978); children: Stephanie, Jeffrey, Alan. BS, Dartmouth Coll., 1945; MD, Johns Hopkins Med. Sch., 1948. Diplomate Am. Bd. Psychiatry. Intern Highland-Alameda County Hosp., Oakland, Calif., 1948-49; resident Herrick Meml. Hosp., Berkeley, Calif., 1949-50; fellow psychiatry Harvard Med. Sch., Boston, 1950-54; clin. instr. UCLA Med. Sch., 1954-70; pvt. practice psychiatry Berkeley, 1954—; pvt. practice psychiatry Walnut Creek, Calif., 1972-88; staff Herrick Meml. Hosp., 1984-85, Walnut Creek Hosp., 1972-78, John Muir Meml. Hosp., Walnut Creek, 1980-88. Capt. USAF, 1951-53, Korea. Mem. AMA, Am. Psychiat. Assn., No. Calif. Psychiat. Assn., Calif. Med. Assn., Alameda-Contra Costa County Med. Assn. Avocations: travel, bicycling, boating, car camping.

TURK, RUDY HENRY, artist, retired museum director; b. Sheboygan, Wis., June 24, 1927; s. Rudolph Anton and Mary Gertrude (Stanisha) T.; m. Wanda Lee Borders, Aug. 4, 1956; children: Tracy Lynn, Maria Teresa, Andrew Borders, Jennifer Wells. BS in Edn., U. Wis., 1949; MA in History, U. Tenn., 1951; postgrad., Ind. U., 1952-56. Instr. art history, gallery dir. U. Mont., Missoula, 1957-60; dir. Richmond (Calif.) Art Ctr., 1960-65; asst. dir.

San Diego Mus. Art, 1965-67; dir. Ariz. State U. Art Mus., 1967-92; from assoc. prof. to prof. art Ariz. State U., 1967-77. Painter, paintings exhibited in solo and group exhbns.; mus. cons., juror, art cons., art lectr; author: (with Cross and Lamm) The Search for Personal Freedom, 2 vols., 1972, 76, 80, 85, Merrill Mahaffey: Monumental Landscapes, 1979, (with others) Scholder, 1983, also commentaries and critiques. Bd. dirs. Chandler Arts Com., 1983-86, Friends of Mex. Art, Ariz., 1986—, pres. 1988-90; mem. Tempe Arts Com., 1987-89, Ariz. Living Treasures Com., 1988-93; bd. dirs. Ariz. Mus. for Youth, 1993—. Recipient merit award Calif. Coll. Arts and Crafts, 1965, Senator's Cultural award State of Ariz., 1987, Golden Crate award Western Assn. Art Mus., 1974, Ariz. Gov.'s Art award, 1992; named Hon. Ariz. Designer Craftsman, 1975; named dir. emeritus Ariz. State U. Art Mus., 1992, Rudy Turk Gallery at Ariz. State U. Art Mus. named in his honor, 1992; Fulbright scholar U. Paris, 1956-57; hon. fellow Am. Craft Coun., 1988. Mem. Nat. Coun. Edn. Ceramic Arts (hon. mem. coun. 1991), Phi Alpha Theta, Phi Kappa Phi. Democrat. Home: 760 E Courtney Ln Tempe AZ 85284-4003 Office: Ariz State U U Art Museum Tempe AZ 85287-2911

TURK, S. MAYNARD, lawyer; b. Roanoke County, Va., Oct. 14, 1925; s. James Alexander and Geneva (Richardson) T.; m. Patricia A. Tucker, June 1, 1957; children—Heather F., William A., Thomas M.T. B.A. in Econs., Roanoke Coll., 1949; LL.B., Washington and Lee U., 1952. Bar: Va. 1951, Del. 1961, U.S. Patent and Trademark Office 1975. With Hercules Inc., 1954-90; sr. counsel Hercules Inc., Wilmington, Del., 1966-70, sr. patent counsel, 1972, dir. patent dept., 1972-76, gen. counsel, 1976-90, sec., 1980-82, v.p., 1982—, also bd. dirs.; of counsel Morris, Nichols, Arsht & Tunnel, Wilmington, 1990—; bar examiner State of Del. Bd. Examiners, 1987-91. Mem. Assn. Gen. Counsel, ABA, Phila. Patent Law Assn., Mfg. Chemists Assn. (legal adv. com.), Atlantic Legal Found. (bd. dirs.), Southwestern Legal Found. (adv. bd.), Licensing Execs. Soc., N.A.M., Assn. Corp. Patent Counsel (emeritus), Nat. Security Indsl. Assn. Home: PO Box 3958 Wilmington DE 19807-0958 Office: Morris Nichols Arsht & Tunnell 1201 N Market St Wilmington DE 19801-1147

TURK, STANLEY MARTIN, advertising agency executive; b. Newark, N.J., June 4, 1934; s. Jack and Sylvia (Rachmiel) T.; m. Helga Louise Haberle, Dec. 1, 1962; children: Russell, Laura. BS, Purdue U., 1956; MBS, UCLA, 1989. Sr. account exec. Cunningham & Walsh Advt. Agy., N.Y.C. 1964-68; mgr., v.p. Meltzer Aaron & Lemon, N.Y.C. and San Francisco, 1968-70; pres. Promotion Devel. Specialists, N.Y.C., 1970-75; sr. v.p., ptnr. Chalek & Dreyer, N.Y.C., 1975-80; exec. v.p. Korhausen & Calene, N.Y.C., 1980-88; pres. The Turk Group, N.Y.C., 1991—; sr. v.p. Carafiello Deihl & Assoc., N.Y.C., 1991—; tchr. N.Y. Inst. Advt., N.Y.C., 1968-75. Capt. U.S. Army, 1958-60. Recipient Jesse Neal award Am. Bus. Publs. Assn., 1963. Mem. Nat. Assn. Chain Drug Stores, Am. Mktg. Assn. (Effie award 1982). Office: The Turk Group 90 N Broadway Irvington NY 10533-1251

TURKEL, STANLEY, hotel consultant, management executive; b. N.Y.C., Sept. 2, 1925; s. Nathan and Mollie (Kurtzman) Turkeltaub; m. Barbara Bell, June 12, 1955 (div. Apr. 1971); children: Marc Alexander, Allison Lee; m. Rima Sokoloff, Apr. 26, 1971; stepchildren: Joshua Bernard Forrest, Benay Debra Forrest. BS, NYU, 1947; MBA, St. Johns U., Jamaica, N.Y., 1980. Laundry cons. Victor Kramer Co. Inc., N.Y.C., 1952-59; v.p. space planner Michael Saphier Assocs., N.Y.C., 1959-62; with spl. hotel svcs. Loews Hotel Corp., N.Y.C., 1962-63; res. mgr. Americana Hotel, N.Y.C., 1963-64; gen. mgr. Drake Hotel, N.Y.C., 1964-66; mng. dir. Summit Hotel, N.Y.C., 1966-67; product line mgr. hotels ITT, N.Y.C., 1968-73; pres. Stanley Turkel Co., Hotel Cons., N.Y.C., 1973—; mem. faculty NYU Ctr. Hospitality Industry Studies. Contbr. articles to N.Y. Times, Wall St. Jour., N.Y. NEwsday, Washington Post, Crain's N.Y. Bus., N.Y. Observer, Smithsonian Mag., N.Y. Mag., N.Y. Post, N.Y. Daily News, Hotel and Motel Mgmt., World's-Eye View, Cornell Quar., Lodging Hospitality, Lodging Mag., Hotel & Resort Industry, The Bottomline, Ariz. Hospitality Trends. Mem. free speech mem. com. ACLU. With USAAF, 1943-45. Mem. Am. Hotel and Motel Assn. (MHS cert.), Internat. Soc. Hospitality Cons., Civic Affairs Forum (chmn. 1987-93), City Club N.Y. (trustee 1964—, pres. 1966-68, chmn. 1977-88, chmn. exec. com. 1988-91). Avocations: Reconstruction period of Am. history, civic affairs, autograph collecting, tennis. Office: 10 Rockefeller Plz Ste 1250 New York NY 10020-1903

TURKEVICH, ANTHONY LEONID, chemist, educator; b. N.Y.C., July 23, 1916; s. Leonid Jerome and Anna (Chervinsky) T.; m. Ireene Podlesak, Sept. 20, 1948; children: Leonid, Darya. B.A., Dartmouth Coll., 1937, D.Sc., 1971; Ph.D., Princeton U., 1940. Research assoc. spectroscopy physics dept. U. Chgo., 1940-41; asst. prof., research on nuclear transformations Enrico Fermi Inst. and chemistry dept, 1946-48, assoc. prof., 1948-53, prof., 1953-86, James Franck prof. chemistry, 1965-70, Distinguished Ser. prof., 1970-86, prof. emeritus, 1986; war research Manhattan Project, Columbia U., 1942-43, U. Chgo., 1943-45, Los Alamos Sci. Lab., 1945-46; Participant test-first nuclear bomb, Alamogordo, N.Mex., 1945, in theoretical work on test of thermonuclear reactions, 1945—, chem. analysis of moon, 1967—; cons. to AEC Labs.; fellow Los Alamos Sci. Lab., 1972—. Del. Geneva Conf. on Nuclear Test Suspension, 1958, 59. Recipient E.O. Lawrence Meml. award AEC, 1962; Atoms for Peace award, 1969. Fellow Am. Phys. Soc.; mem. N.Y. Acad. Sci. (Pregel award 1988), AAAS, Am. Chem. Soc. (nuclear applications award 1972), Am. Acad. Arts and Scis. Mem. Russian Orthodox Greek Cath. Ch. Clubs: Quadrangle, Cosmos. Home: 175 Briarwood Loop Oak Brook IL 60521-8713 Office: U Chicago Dept Chemistry 5640 S Ellis Ave Chicago IL 60637-1467

TURKIN, MARSHALL WILLIAM, symphony orchestra, festival and opera administrator, arranger, composer; b. Chgo., Apr. 1, 1926; 4 children. Student, U. Kans., 1946-48; Mus. B. in Music Composition, Northwestern U., 1950, Mus. M., 1951; postgrad., Juilliard Sch. Music, Columbia U., U. Ind. Record rev. columnist, classical music commentator, gen. mgr., Honolulu Symphony and Opera Co., 1959-66; orch. festival mgr.; Ravinia Festival for Chgo. Symphony, 1966-68; founding mgr.; Blossom Festival for Cleve. Orch., 1968-70; gen. mgr. Detroit Symphony, 1970-73, exec. dir., 1973-79, mng. dir., Pitts. Symphony Orch., 1979-88; gen. dir. Hawaii Opera Theatre, Honolulu, 1988-91. Served with USN, World War II. Avocation: jazz musician.

TURKLE, SHERRY, sociologist, psychologist, educator; b. N.Y.C., June 18, 1948; d. Milton and Harriet (Bonowitz) T.; m. Ralph Willard, Aug. 16, 1987; 1 child, Rebecca Ellen Turkle Willard. AB, Radcliffe Coll., 1970; PhD, Harvard U., 1976; PhD (hon.), Claremont Coll., 1990. Lic. psychologist, Mass. Asst. prof. sociology MIT, Cambridge, Mass., 1976-80, assoc. prof. sociology, 1980-91, prof. sociology, 1991—, mem. Lab. for Computer Sci., 1976—. Author: Psychoanalytic Politics: Freud's French Revolution, 1978, 2d edit., 1992, The Second Self: Computers and the Human Spirit, 1984. Fellow Guggenheim Found., 1981-82, Rockefeller Found., 1980-81; named Woman of Yr., Ms. Mag., 1984. Fellow AAAS. Office: MIT 70 Memorial Dr Rm E51-201C Cambridge MA 02142-1318

TURKO, ALEXANDER ANTHONY, biology educator; b. Bridgeport, Conn., Aug. 19, 1943; s. Alexander I. and Elizabeth K. (Kulcsar) T.; m. Nancy Bally Hoinacky, Dec. 30, 1967; children: Michelle Lynn, Mark A. BA, So. Conn. State U., 1965, MS, 1967, postgrad., 1976. Assoc. prof. So. Conn. State U., New Haven, 1965—. Mem. AAUP. Home: 11 Birchwood Ln Monroe CT 06468-1025

TURKUS, ALBERT H., lawyer; b. Newark, 1945. BS cum laude, U. Pa., 1967; JD, Harvard U., 1971. Bar: D.C. 1971, Md. 1978. Asst. U.S. atty. U.S. Attys. Office, Washington, 1972-78; ptnr. Dow, Lohnes & Albertson, Washington. Office: Dow Lohnes & Albertson 1255 23rd St NW Ste 500 Washington DC 20037

TURLEY, CLARENCE M., JR., finance company executive; b. 1928. Grad., Washington U., St. Louis. With Turley Corp., St. Louis, 1950-72; vice chmn. bd. dirs. Turley-Martin Co. Inc., St. Louis, 1972—; chmn. Roosevelt Fin. Group, Chesterfield, Mo., 1991—. Office: Roosevelt Fin Group 900 Roosevelt Pky Chesterfield MO 63017

TURLEY, MICHAEL ROY, lawyer; b. St. Louis, Mar. 7, 1945; s. W. Richard and Mary Jeanne (Ogle) T.; m. Patricia Ederle, Aug. 21, 1968; children: James, Alisyn. AB, Princeton U., 1967; JD, Mo. U., 1970. Bar: Mo. 1970, U.S. Dist. Ct. (ea. dist.) Mo. 1975. Assoc. Lewis, Rice & Fingersh (formerly Lewis & Rice), St. Louis, 1970-71, 74-80, ptnr., 1980—; bd. dirs. St. Louis Tech. Ctr., Inc., 1989—, St. Louis Mfg. Resource Ctr., 1994—. Mem. Planning and Zoning Commn., Jefferson County, 1987—. Mem. ABA, Mo. Bar Assn., St. Louis Met. Bar Assn., Princeton Club. Episcopalian. Office: Lewis Rice & Fingersh 500 N Broadway Ste 2000 Saint Louis MO 63102-2130

TURLEY, STEWART, retail company executive; b. Mt. Sterling, Ky., July 20, 1934; s. R. Joe and Mavis S. Turley; m. Linda A. Mulholland; children from previous marriage: Carol, Karen. Student, Rollins Coll., 1952-53, U. Ky., 1953-55. Plant mgr. Crown Cork & Seal Co., Orlando (Fla.), Phila., 1955-66; mgr. non-drug ops., dir. corporate employee rels. and spl. svcs. Eckerd Corp. (formerly Jack Eckerd Corp.), Clearwater, Fla., 1966-68; v.p. Eckerd Corp., Clearwater, Fla., 1968-71, sr. v.p., 1971-74; dir. Jack Eckerd Corp., Clearwater, Fla., 1971—, pres., chief exec. officer, 1974—, chmn. bd., 1975—; bd. dirs. Sprint Corp., Barnett Banks, Inc., Springs Industries, Inc. Trustee Eckerd Coll., St. Petersburg, US Ski Team. Mem. Fla. Coun. Econ. Edn. (bd. dirs.), Nat. Assn. Chain Drug Stores (bd. dirs., chmn. bd. 1978-79, 88-89), Fla. Coun. 100 (bd. dirs.), World Pres.'s Orgn., Chief Execs. Orgn., Inc., Carlouel Yacht Club, Belleair Country Club, Bayou Club, Kappa Alpha. Office: Eckerd Corp PO Box 4689 Clearwater FL 34618

TURLINGTON, CHRISTY, model; b. Walnut Creek, Calif., Jan. 2, 1969; d. Dwain and Elizabeth T. With Ford Models, Inc., 1985; model Calvin Klein, 1986; face of Calvin Klein's Eternity Fragrance, 1988—; with Maybelline Cosmetics, 1992; rep. (abroad) Ford Models, Paris; beauty spread with Vogue, 1987; has worked with Herb Ritts, Patrick Demarchelier, Steven Meisel; has worked for Anne Klein, Michael Kors, Chanel, Perry Ellis; appeared in George Michael's "Freedom" video. Office: Ford Models Inc 344 E 59th St New York NY 10022

TURLISH, MOLLY BUFFUM, academic administrator; b. Washington, Mar. 28, 1942; d. Fenwick Noble and Mildred Cora (Streeter) Buffum; m. Lewis Afton Turlish, Dec. 29, 1966; children: Cora Marie, Hannah Buffum. AB in Am. Lit., Middlebury Coll., 1964; MA in Am. Civilization, U. Wyo., 1965; PhD in English and Am. Lit., U. Mich., 1971. Internat. student advisor, lectr. in English Bates Coll., Lewiston, Maine, 1970-74; exec. dir. L-Arts, Lewiston, Maine, 1973-78; dir. devel. and univ. rels. U. Maine, Farmington, 1982-89; sr. devel. officer U. So. Maine, Portland, 1989-90, Boston U., 1990-92; dir. devel. Pine Manor Coll., Chestnut Hill, Mass., 1992-93; v.p. for coll. advancement Wheelock Coll., Boston, 1993—. Seminar leader Landmark Edn. Corp., 1992—; bd. dirs. Western Maine Mountains C. of C., 1982-89; mem. Maine Humanities Coun., 1974. Mem. Coun. for Advancement and Support of Edn. (dist. I chair opportunity and equity 1988-91, chair minority internship com. 1993—, moderator ann. assembly 1990, mem. forum for women instnl. advancement officers 1989), Nat. Soc. Fund-Raising Execs. Office: Wheelock Coll 200 the Riverway Boston MA 02215

TURMAN, GEORGE, former lieutenant governor; b. Missoula, Mont., June 25, 1928; s. George Fugett and Corinne (McDonald) T.; m. Kathleen Hager, Mar. 1951; children—Marcia, Linda, George Douglas, John, Laura. B.A., U. Mont., 1951. Various positions Fed. Res. Bank of San Francisco, 1954-64; mayor City of Missoula, 1970-72; mem. Mont. Ho. of Reps. from (Dist. 18), 1973-74; Mont. Pub. Service commr. (Dist. 5), 1975-80; lt. gov. State of Mont., 1981-88, resigned; apptd. Pacific NW Electric Power & Conservation Council, 1988; pres. Nat. Ctr. for Appropriate Tech., Butte, Mont., 1989—; sr. advisor, adj. staff mem., dir. New Horizon Techs., Inc., 1995. Served with U.S. Army, 1951-53. Decorated Combat Inf. badge. Home: 1525 Gerald Ave Missoula MT 59801-4227

TURMEL, JEAN BERNARD, banker; b. Lac Etchemin, Que., Can., Dec. 17, 1944; s. Joseph N. and Rose Marie (Chabot) T.; m. Lorraine Louise Langevin, June 4, 1966; children—Andree, Elaine, Johanne. B.Commerce, Laval U., Quebec, Can., 1966, M.C.S., 1967. Salesman Macmillan Bloedel, Montreal and Vancouver, Can., 1967-68; money market trader Dominion Securities, Montreal, Que., 1968-78, Merrill Lynch Can., Montreal and Toronto, Can., 1978-81; v.p. treasury Nat. Bank Can., Montreal, 1981-83, sr. v.p. treasury and exchange, 1983-86, exec. v.p. treasury, 1986-89, sr. exec. v.p., 1989—; chmn. bd. Trust Gen. du Can., 1993—, Sherbrooke Trust Co., 1993—, Nat. Bank Securities, Inc., Levesque Beaubien & Co.; bd. dirs. Levesque Beaubien, Natcan Investment Mgmt. Inc., Cartons St.-Laurent; outside adviser investment com. Assn. bienfaisance et retraite de communauté urbaine de Montreal. Liberal. Roman Catholic. Avocations: music; squash; fishing; chess; stamp collecting. Office: Nat Bank Can, 600 ouest de la Gauchetière, Montreal, PQ Canada H3B 4L2

TURNAGE, FRED DOUGLAS, lawyer; b. Ayden, N.C., Sept. 24, 1920; s. Fred C. and Lou (Johnson) T.; m. Margaret Futrell, Aug. 21, 1943 (div. Nov. 1980); children: Betty Lou Griffith, Douglas C.; m. Elizabeth Louisa Turnage, Jan. 23, 1981. Grad. Naval Sch. on Far Eastern Civil Affairs, Princeton U., 1945; LLB, Wake Forest U., 1948, LLD, 1970. Bar: N.C. 1948, U.S. Supreme Ct. 1953, U.S. Dist. Ct. D.C. 1965, U.S. Ct. Appeals (D.C. cir.) 1967, U.S. Ct. Appeals (4th and 7th cirs.) 1979. Trial atty. antitrust div. U.S. Dept. Justice, Kansas City, Mo., 1948-51; sr. trial atty. antitrust div. U.S. Dept. Justice, Washington, 1951-65, spl. asst. to atty. gen., 1965; sr. ptnr. Cleary, Gottlieb, Steen & Hamilton, Washington, 1968—; lectr. continuing legal edn. courses, 1973-77. Contbr. articles to profl. jours. Bd. Visitors Wake Forest U. Sch. Law, Winston-Salem, N.C., 1980—. Served to 1st lt. AUS, 1942-46. Recipient Disting. Service in Law citation Wake Forest U., 1979. Mem. ABA (antitrust and litigation sects.), Fed. Bar Assn., Adv. Bd. Antitrust Bulletin, Wake Forest U. Alumni Assn. (pres. 1977), Nat. Lawyers Clubs. Methodist. Avocations: fishing, golf, writing. Home: 209 N Liberty St Arlington VA 22203-1050 Office: 1752 N St NW Washington DC 20036-2806

TURNAGE, JEAN A., state supreme court chief justice; b. St. Ignatius, Mont., Mar. 10, 1926. JD, Mont. State U., 1951. Bar: Mont. 1951, U.S. Supreme Ct. 1963. Formerly ptnr. Turnage, McNeil & Mercer, Polson, Mont.; formerly Mont. State senator from 13th Dist.; pres. Mont. State Senate, 1981-83; chief justice Supreme Ct. Mont., 1985—. Mem. Mont. State Bar Assn., Nat. Conf. Chief Justices (past pres.), Nat. Ctr. State Courts (past chair). Office: Mont Supreme Ct 215 N Sanders St Helena MT 59601-4522

TURNBAUGH, DOUGLAS BLAIR, arts administration executive, author; b. Lewiston, Idaho, May 17, 1934; s. Orville Wendelle and Geneva Violet (Blair) T. BA, U. Wash., 1956. Exec. dir. Fine Arts Workshop, Inc., 1963-73, Brandon Films, Inc., 1966, Dance Notation Bur., Inc., 1967, Dance Theatre Found., Inc., for Alvin Ailey Dance Theatre, 1970; pres. Am. Inst. Choreology, Inc., N.Y.C., 1970—; exec. dir., treas. Ludwig Vogelstein Found., Inc., N.Y.C., 1973-83; pres. Direct From Broadway: Theater History Films, 1983-86; exec. dir. Poetry Soc. Am., Inc., 1978-80, Manhattan Festival Ballet, 1984; former dir. Inst. Choreology, London, Four Winds Theatre of Cooper Hewitt Mus. of Smithsonian Instn., Dance Theatre Workshop, Inc., Alt. Center for Internat. Arts, Inc., Alternative Mus.; exec. dir. Musica Reservata, Inc., 1979-81; dir. to the U.S.A., UNESCO's Coun. Internat. de la Danse, 1994—; bd. dirs. Actors Enclave, N.Y.C., 1982; past faculty mem. NYU, N.Y.C.; guest lectr. York U., Toronto; chmn. bd. Vertices, Inc./D.J. McDonald & Dancers. Author: The Use of Notation in the Dance Theatre, 1970, Notating Asian Dance, 1975, Beat It, 1983, Duncan Grant and the Bloomsbury Group, 1987, Private: The Erotic Art of Duncan Grant (1885-1978), 1989, Le Rôle D'Otto Kahn Dans la Libération de Nijinsky et sa Tournée a Travers les États-Unis, 1992, Strip Show: The Paintings of Patrick Angus, 1992; curator: The Private World of Duncan Grant (exhibit held The Nat. Arts Club 1987), Duncan Grant, Paintings and Drawings: 1922-60 (exhibit held 303 Gallery, N.Y.C., 1989); curator exhbns. Ralph Parks Gallery, N.Y.C., 1992, Leslie-Lohman Gallery, N.Y.C., 1992; contbr. articles to various publs. including N.Y. Mag., Atlantic, Playbill, Asia Mag., Poetry Soc. Am. Bull., Appearances mag., others. Nat. Endowment for Arts grantee, 1968; recipient Vaslav Nijinsky medal, Poland, 1994, Sergei Diaghilev medal Diabhilev House Found., Perm, Russia, 1994. Mem. Assn.

Internat. des Amis de Waslaw Nijinsky, Nat. Arts Club (sec. dance com., chmn. Hommage a Nijinsky, 1993). Home: 96 Grand St New York NY 10013-2633

TURNBAUGH, ROY CARROLL, archivist; b. Peoria, Ill., Oct. 16, 1945; s. Roy Carroll and Zora (Alexander) T.; m. Donna Marie Chase, Mar. 28, 1970; children: Andrew, Peter. BA, Aurora Coll., 1969; AM, U. Ill., 1973, PhD, 1977. Asst. prof. U. Ill., Urbana, 1977-78; archivist Ill. State Archives, Springfield, 1978-85; dir. Oreg. State Archives, Salem, 1985—. Office: Oreg State Archives 800 Summer St NE Salem OR 97310-1347

TURNBULL, ADAM MICHAEL GORDON, financial executive, accountant; b. Dumfries, Scotland, Dec. 29, 1935; emigrated to Canada, 1977; s. Robert Wilson and Catherine Russell (Strang) T.; m. Karen Margaret Walker, June 12, 1965; children: Candida Louise, Andrew Robert. M.A., Edinburgh U., 1956, LL.B., 1958. Chartered acct., Scotland, 1960. With Price Waterhouse Co., Paris, 1960-62, U.S. Time Corp., France and U.S., 1962-64; group chief acct. Formica Internat. Ltd., London, 1965-70; group fin. dir. Donald Macpherson Group Ltd., London, 1970-77; controller, asst. treas. Indal Ltd., Weston, Ont., Can., 1978-81; controller Indal Inc., Weston, 1978-81; v.p., treas. Indal Ltd., Weston, Ont., Can., 1981-90; v.p. fin., CFO, Hawker Siddeley Can. Inc., Mississauga, Ont., Can., 1990-94, sr. v.p. fin., CFO, 1994—. Mem. Inst. Chartered Accts. Scotland. Home: 2610 Hammond Rd, Mississauga, ON Canada L5K 2M3 Office: Hawker Siddeley Can Inc, 3 Robert Speck Pkwy, Mississauga, ON Canada L4Z 2G5

TURNBULL, ANN PATTERSON, special education educator, consultant; b. Tuscaloosa, Ala., Oct. 19, 1947; d. H. F. and Mary (Boone) Patterson; m. H. Rutherford Turnbull III, Mar. 23, 1974; children: Jay, Amy, Kate. BS in Edn., U. Ga., 1968; MEd, Auburn U., 1971; EdD, U. Ala., 1972. Asst. prof. U. N.C., Chapel Hill, 1972-80; prof., co-dir. Beach Ctr. U. Kans., Lawrence, 1980—; cons. Dept. of Edn., Washington, 1987—, Australian Soc. for Study of Intellectual Disability, Adelaide, Washington, 1990; dir. Nat. Ctr. for Clin. Infant Programs, Washington, 1988-90. Author: Meeting The Challenge of Chronic Illness and Disability, 1986, Disability and the Family, 1989, Families, Professionals and Exceptionality, 1990. Recipient Rose Kennedy Internat. Leadership award, Kennedy Found., 1990; Joseph P. Kennedy Jr. Found. fellow, 1987-88. Mem. Am. Assn. on Mental Retardation (bd. dirs. 1986-88), Assn. for Retarded Citizens (named Educator of Yr. 1982), Assn. for Persons with Severe Handicaps, Internat. League Socs. for Persons with Mental Handicap (com. chair 1986-90). Democrat. Avocations: travel, gardening. Home: 1636 Alvamar Dr Lawrence KS 66047 Office: Univ Kans Beach Ctr 3111 Haworth Hall Lawrence KS 66045

TURNBULL, CHARLES VINCENT, real estate broker; b. Mpls., May 13, 1933; s. Charles Vivien and Lucille Frances (Dallas) T.; m. Gloria Marlene Tilley, July 21, 1956; children—Charlene Kay, Charles Vincent II, Terry Lucille, Mary Marlene. B.A., U. Minn., 1960, M.S.W., 1962. Unit dir. Mental Health Treatment Service, Cambridge (Minn.) State Hosp., 1962-67, dir. rehab. therapies, 1967-68, program dir., 1973-74; program dir. Minn. Valley Social Adaptation Center, St. Peter, Minn., 1968-73; chief exec. officer Faribault (Minn.) State Hosp., 1974-84; owner Turnbull's Shady Acres Resort, 1976-85; adminstr. Minn. Vets. Homes, Mpls. and Hastings, 1984-85; owner, broker Turnbull Realty, Faribault, Minn., 1986—; program cons. Rochester (Minn.) Social Adaptation Center, 1970-71; cons. St. Louis State Sch. and Hosp., 1973-74. Chmn. United Fund Drive, St. Peter, 1971; scoutmaster Twin Valley council Boy Scouts Am., 1973-75; co-chmn. Faribault Bi-Centennial Horizons Subcom., 1975-76; pres. River Bend Nature Center, 1981-84, bd. dirs. 1976-87; mem. Minn. Developmental Disabilities Planning Council, 1975-79, chmn. comprehensive plan subcom., 1977-78; mem. Cannon River Adv. Council, 1978-79; Mayor, Village of Lexington, Minn., 1962-64; candidate for U.S. rep. 2d Dist. Minn., 1972, 74. Served with USMC, 1953-56. Mem. Democratic Farmer Labor party. Lutheran. Home: 5351 Elkton Trl Faribault MN 55021-8453

TURNBULL, DAVID, physical chemist, educator; b. Elmira, Ill., Feb. 18, 1915; s. David and Luzetta Agnes (Murray) T.; m. Carol May Cornell, Aug. 3, 1946; children: Lowell D., Murray M., Joyce M. B.S., Monmouth (Ill.) Coll., 1936, Sc.D. (hon.), 1958; Ph.D., U. Ill., 1939; A.M. (hon.), Harvard U., 1962; Sc.D. (hon.), Case-Western Res. U., 1990; Sc.D. (hon.), Claude Bernard U., Lyon, France, 1993. Tchr. research Case Sch. Applied Sci., 1939-46; scientist Gen. Electric Co. Research Lab., 1946-62, mgr. chem. metallurgy sect., 1950-58; adj. prof. metallurgy Rensselaer Poly. Inst., 1954-62; Gordon McKay prof. applied physics Harvard U., 1962-85, prof. emeritus, 1985—; chmn. Gordon Conf. Physics and Chemistry Metals, 1952; Internat. Conf. Crystal Growth, 1958; Internat. Conf. Chem. Physics of Non-metallic Crystals, 1961; Office Naval Research panel study growth and morphology crystals, 1959-60. Editor: (with Seitz, Ehrenreich) Solid State Physics, 35 vols., 1955-92, co-founding editor (with Seitz), 1993—; editor: (with Doremus, Roberts) Growth and Perfection of Crystals, 1958; assoc. editor: Jour. Chem. Physics, 1961-63; editorial adv. bd.: Jour. Physics and Chemistry Solids, 1955-93. Chmn. citizens curriculum com. Niskayuna (N.Y.) Sr. High Sch., 1954. Recipient von Hippel award, 1979, Japan Prize in Materials Sci. and Tech., 1986, Franklin medal, 1990. Fellow Am. Phys. Soc. (Internat. prize new materials 1983), N.Y. Acad. Scis., Am. Soc. Metals (chmn. seminar com. 1954), Am. Inst. Mining and Metall. Engrs. (lectr. Inst. Metals div. 1961, Hume-Rothery award 1986, Bruce Chalmers award 1991); mem. Am. Chem. Soc., Nat. Acad. Scis., Am. Acad. Arts and Scis., Am. Ceramic Soc. (hon.). Home: 29 Concord Ave Apt 715 Cambridge MA 02138 Office: Harvard Univ Applied Physics Dept Cambridge MA 02138

TURNBULL, DAVID JOHN (CHIEF PIERCING EYES-PENN), cultural association executive; b. Hornell, N.Y., May 18, 1930; s. Gerald and Dorothy Esther (Badgley) T.; m. Martha Lillian Crouse, Aug. 12, 1949 (div. 1960); children: Garry David, Mary Jane Stuhr, Dorothy Grace Houde; m. Frances Early Spring Vickery, May 4, 1985. Degree in ministry, Elim Bible Coll., 1964. Dir. pub. rels. Elim Bible Inst., Lima, N.Y., 1960-61; pastor Eagle Harbor (N.Y.) Ch., 1962-65, South Lima (N.Y.) Gospel Ch., 1962-66; ind. ins. agent, 1965-82; chief, counselor, performer weddings and funerals Pan-Am. Indian Assn., Nocatee, Fla., 1980—, pub. Pan.-Am. Indian Assn. News, 1984—; pastor Cherokee Bapt. Ch., Arcadia, Fla., 1994. Mem. Ministerial Assn. Libertarian. Mem. LDS Ch. Avocation: experimental gardening. Home and Office: 2596 SE Durrance St Arcadia FL 33821

TURNBULL, FRED GERDES, electronics engineer; b. Oakland, Calif., Apr. 12, 1931; s. Fred and Gertrude Turnbull; m. Nancy Greene, Aug. 22, 1959; children: Fred, David. BSEE, U. Calif., Berkeley, 1953, MSEE, 1959. Electronics engr. corp. rsch. devel. ctr. GE, Schenectady, N.Y., 1959-93; cons. Scotia, N.Y., 1993—. Co-author: Power Electronic Control Of AC Motors, 1988. Lt. (j.g.) USN, 1954-57. Fellow IEEE; assoc. mem. Sigma Xi.

TURNBULL, GORDON KEITH, metal company executive, metallurgical engineer; b. Cleve., Nov. 10, 1935; s. Gordon Gideon and Florence May (Felton) T.; m. Sally Ann Ewing, June 15, 1957; children: Kenneth Scott, Stephen James, Lynne Ann, June Patricia, James Robert. BS in Metall. Engring., Case Western Res. U., 1957, MS in Metall. Engring., 1959, PhD in Phys. Metallurgy, 1962. Engr. then sr. engr. casting and forgings div., Cleve. Research ALCOA, 1962-67, sr. metallurgist quality assurance, Cleve. Forge Plant, 1967-68; group leader fabricating metallurgy div. ALCOA Tech. Ctr., Pitts., 1968-71; sect. head, mgr. ingot casting div., 1971-78, mgr. fabricating metallurgy div., 1978-79, asst. dir. finishes engring. properties and design, 1979-80; mgr. bus. planning services, corp. planning dept. ALCOA, Pitts., 1980-82, dir. tech. planning, 1982-86, v.p. tech. planning, 1986-91, exec. v.p. strategic analysis/planning and info., 1991—. Patentee method of not compacting titanium powder. Governing bd. Allegheny Ctr. Christian & Missionary Alliance Ch., Pitts. Mem. AIME, ASM, Nat. Acad. Engring., Am. Foundrymen's Soc., Beta Beta Pi, Sigma Xi. Avocation: hockey. Home: 550 Fairview Rd Pittsburgh PA 15238-1745 Office: Aluminum Co Am 31st Fl 1501 Alcoa Bldg 31st Fl Pittsburgh PA 15219-1819

TURNBULL, H. RUTHERFORD, III, law educator, lawyer; b. N.Y.C., Sept. 22, 1937; s. Henry R. and Ruth (White) T.; m. Mary M. Slingluff, Apr. 4, 1964 (div. 1972); m. Ann Patterson, Mar. 23, 1974; children: Jay, Amy, Katherine. BA, Johns Hopkins U., 1959; LLB with hon., U. Md., 1964; LLM, Harvard U., 1969. Bar: Md., N.C. Law clerk to Hon. Emory H.

Niles Supreme Bench Balt. City, 1959-60; law clerk to Hon. Roszel C. Thomsen U.S. Dist. Ct. Md., 1962-63; assoc. Piper & Marbury, Balt., 1964-67; prof. instr. Govt. U. N.C., Chapel Hill, 1969-80, U. Kans., Lawrence, 1980-93. Editor-in-chief Md. Law Review. Cons., author, lectr., co-dir. Beach Ctr. on Families and Disability, U. Kans.; pres. Full Citizenship Inc., Lawrence, 1987-93; spl. staff-fellow U.S. Senate subcom. on disability policy, Washington, 1987-88; bd. dirs. Camphill Assn. N.Am., Inc., 1985-87; trustee Judge David L. Bazelon Ctr. Mental Health Law, 1993-95. With U.S. Army, 1960-65. Recipient Nat. Leadership award Nat. Assn. Private Residential Resources, 1988; Public Policy fellow Joseph P. Kennedy, Jr. Found., 1987-88. Fellow Am. Assn. on Mental Retardation (pres. 1985-86); mem. ABA (chmn. disability law commn. 1991-95), U.S.A. Assn. for Retarded Citizens (sec. 1981-83), Assn. for Persons with Severe Handicaps (treas. 1988), Nat. Assn. Rehab. Rsch. and Tng. Ctrs. (chair govt. affairs com. 1990-93), Internat. Assn. Scientific Study of Mental Deficiency, Internat. League of Assns. for Persons with Mental Handicaps, Johns Hopkins U. Alumni Assn. Democrat. Episcopalian. Home: 1636 Alvamar Dr Lawrence KS 66047 Office: U Kans University of Kansas 3111 Haworth Hall University Of Kansas KS 66045

TURNBULL, JOHN CAMERON, pharmacist, consultant; b. Regina, Sask., Can., Sept. 5, 1923; s. Cameron Joseph and Lillian Irene (Pentz) T.; m. Hazel Evelyn Rockwell, July 31, 1948; children—Lillian Elizabeth, John Rockwell, Jocelyn Hazel. B.S. in Pharmacy, U. Sask., 1949. Pharmacist with village and city pharmacies, 1945-50; supr. pharm. services Dept. Pub. Health, Province of Sask., Regina, 1950-52; ops. mgr. Nat. Drugs, Ltd., Winnipeg, and Saskatoon, 1953; exec. dir. Can. Pharm. Assn., Toronto, Ont., 1953-78; sec.-treas., mng. dir. Canadian Pharm. Realty Co. Ltd.; mem. provisional bd. Pharmacare Ltd.; registrar-treas. Pharmacy Examining Bd. of Can., 1963-68, mem. bd., 1963-78; pharmacy cons., dir. drug service Ministry of Health, Barbados, 1979-84; staff assoc. Mgmt. Scis. for Health, Boston, 1984-85; cons. logistics and pharma. USAID, East Caribbean, PanAm. Health Orgn./WHO (Belize, Cen. Am.), 1985—. Chmn. Govt.'s Spl. Com. on Acetylsalicylic Poisonings, 1967; mem. Emergency Health Services Advisory Com. Served to squadron leader RCAF, 1941-45. Decorated D.F.C., Order of Can.; recipient Can. Centennial medal, 1967, Queen's Jubilee medal, 1977, Can. 125th Anniversary medal, 1992, John C. Turnbull rsch. ann. award in socio-econs. pharmacy established in his honor Can. Pharm. Assn., 1990. Mem. Fedn. Internationale Pharmaceutique (v.p.), Inst. of Assn. Execs. (hon. life), Conf. on Pharmacy Registrars of Can. (sec.), Commonwealth Pharm. Assn. (coun. 1969-78); hon. mem. Am., Canadian, Saskatchewan, B.C., Alta., Ont., Man., N.S. Pharm. Assns., Sask. Pharm. Assn., Ont. Pharmacists Assn., Canadian Soc. Hosp. Pharmacists, Rho Pi Phi. Mem. United Ch. of Canada. Club: Bayview Country (past dir.). Home: 40 Banstock Dr, Willowdale, ON Canada M2K 2H6

TURNBULL, JOHN NEIL, retired chemical company executive; b. South Shields, U.K., Feb. 13, 1940; s. John Smith and Kathleen Bernadette (Higgins) T.; m. Aloysia Lindemann, Feb. 9, 1966; children: John Michael, David Stephen. BSChemE with honors, Kings Coll./Univ. Durham, Eng., 1961. Chartered engr., U.K. Process engr. Brit. Petroleum PLC, Sunbury, Eng., 1961-64; engr. Deutsche B.P., Dinslaken, Fed. Republic Germany, 1964-66; rsch. project mgr. Brit. Petroleum PLC, Sunbury, 1967-70; prodn. mgr. BP Chems., Port Talbot, Eng., 1975-80; pres. BP Chems. Suisse, Geneva, 1982-84; dir. BP Chems., London, 1984-89, dep. chief exec. officer, 1991-93; pres. BP Chems., Cleve., 1989-91; cons. in field. Patentee in field; contbr. articles to profl. jours. Bd. dirs. Playhouse Square Found., Cleve., 1990. Fellow Instn. Chem. Engrs., Royal Acad. Engring. Avocations: skiing, theatre, reading, walking, music.

TURNBULL, KENNETH W., bank executive. Pres., chief exec. officer United Nat. Bank, Plainfield, N.J. Office: United Nat Bank 202 Park Ave Plainfield NJ 07060-1200

TURNBULL, RENALDO, professional football player; b. St. Thomas, V.I., Jan. 5, 1966. Degree in Comm., W.Va. U. Linebacker New Orleans Saints, 1990—. Named to Pro Bowl Team, 1993. Office: New Orleans Saints 6928 Saints Dr Metairie LA 70003-5187*

TURNBULL, ROBERT SCOTT, manufacturing company executive; b. North Dumfries, Ont., Can., Dec. 19, 1929; s. Leslie William and Marjorie Clara (Scott) T.; m. Dawna Rose Sinclair, Feb. 17, 1956. Sr. Matriculation, Galt U., Ont., 1950; M.T.C., U. Waterloo, 1975. Credit mgr Can. Gen. Tower, Cambridge, Ont., 1951-53, gen. acct., 1953-62, comptroller, 1962-68, v.p. mktg., 1968-78, v.p., gen. mgr., 1978-80, pres., 1980—, also bd. dirs. Mem. Chem. Fabrics and Films Assn. (bd. dirs.), Soc. Plastics Industry (bd. dirs.). Home: 26 Lansdowne Rd S, Cambridge, ON Canada N1S 2T3 Office: Can Gen Tower, 52 Middleton St, Cambridge, ON Canada N1R 5T6

TURNBULL, WILLIAM, JR., architect; b. N.Y.C., Apr. 1, 1935; s. William and Elizabeth (Howe) T. A.B., Princeton U., 1956, M.F.A. in Architecture, 1959; student, Ecole des Beaux Arts Fontainebleau, 1956. With Skidmore, Owings & Merrill, San Francisco, 1960-63; founding ptnr. Moore, Lyndon, Turnbull, Whitaker, 1962; partner-in-charge Moore, Turnbull (San Francisco office), 1965-69; mem. design group Pres.'s Adv. Coun. Pennsylvania Ave., 1963; lectr. U. Calif.-Berkeley, 1965-69; vis. prof. U. Oreg., 1966-68; dir. MLTW/Turnbull Assocs., 1970-83; dir. William Turnbull Assocs., 1983—; lectr. Stanford U., 1974-77; vis. design critic MIT, 1975, U. Calif., Berkeley, 1977-81, 95; Mobil vis. design critic Yale U., 1982; Bishop vis. prof. archtl. design, 1986; Hyde prof. excellence U. Nebr. 1994; design cons. Formica Corp., 1978-85, World Savs. and Loan, 1976—; mem. design rev. bd. U. Calif., San Diego, 1988-93, City of Sausalito, Calif., 1976-77. Author: Global Architecture Series: Moore, Lyndon, Turnbull & Whitaker: The Sea Ranch, The Sea Ranch Details, The Poetics of Gardens, 1988; illustrator: The Place of Houses; prin. works include Sea Ranch Condominium I, 1965, Sea Ranch Swim Tennis Club, 1966, Lovejoy Fountain Plaza, Portland (assoc. architect), Faculty Club at U. Calif.-Santa Barbara, Kresge Coll. at U. Calif.-Santa Cruz, Biloxi (Miss.) Library, Am. Club, Hong Kong, Ariz. State U. Sonora Ctr., Tempe, Foothill Student Housing, U. Calif., Berkeley, Mountain View City Hall and Community Theater, Calif.; mem. editorial adv. bd. Architecture California, 1986-92. Mem. tech. adv. com. Calif. Legislature Joint Com. Open Space Lands, 1968-71; mem. regional honor awards (90) jury AIA, 1968—, nat. honor awards jury, 1969, chmn. jury, 1977, 1988; chmn. jury C.E. honor award, 1973, 79; mem. Progressive Architecture Honor Awards Jury, 1975, Pres.'s Jury for Nat. Design Excellence, 1984; bd. dirs. Pub. Sculpture Pub. Places, 1981-85. Served with AUS, 1959-60. Recipient Calif. Gov. award planned communities, 1966; citation Progressive Design awards, 1962-66, 68-70, 81; 1st honor award, 1971, 74; First honor award Homes for Better Living, 1963; Merit award, 1966; Honor award Western Home awards, 1961-62, 62, 63, 66-67, 88, 89; Merit award, 1966-67; House of Year award Archtl. Record, 1961, 67, 69, 70, 72, 83; award of Honor San Francisco Art Commn., 1982; Am. Wood Council Design award, 1984, Honor award, 1985, 89, 92, 94, 95; Firm of the Yr. award Calif. Council AIA, 1986, Maybeck award 1993, cited for continuous distinctive practice of architecture in Calif. by an individual; Am. Wood Coun. Merit award, 1991; Honor award San Francisco AIA, 1991. Fellow AIA (dir. chpt. 1981, Nat. Honor award 1967, 68, 73, 79, 90, 95, award of merit, bay region honor awards 1963, 67, 74, 78, 82, Nat. 25 Yr. Honor award 1991), Am. Acad. in Rome. Office: William Turnbull Assocs Pier 1 1/2 The Embarcadero San Francisco CA 94111

TURNER, ALMON RICHARD, art historian, educator; b. New Bedford, Mass., July 28, 1932; s. Louis Alexander and Margaret (Mather) T.; m. Jane Beebe; children: Louis Hamilton, David Alexander. AB, Princeton U., 1955, MFA, 1958, PhD, 1959. Instr. in fine arts U. Mich., Ann Arbor, 1959-60; from instr. to prof. art and archaeology Princeton (N.J.) U., 1960-68; prof. fine arts Middlebury (Vt.) Coll., 1968-74, dean faculty, 1970-74; prof. fine arts, pres. Grinnell (Iowa) Coll., 1975-79; prof., dir. Inst. Fine Arts NYU, N.Y.C., 1979-82, dean faculty arts and scis., 1982-85, prof. dept. fine arts 1985—, dir. N.Y. Inst. Humanities, 1986-93, Paulette Goddard prof. in arts and humanities, 1994—. Author: Vision of Landscape in Renaissance Italy, 1966, 73, (With G. Andres and J. Hunisak) Art of Florence (L'Art de Florence), 1988 (prix 1989), Inventing Leonardo, 1993. Mem. Coll. Art Assn., Century Assn., N.J. Audubon Soc. (1st v.p. 1990-93, pres. 1993—), Phi Beta Kappa. Democrat. Unitarian Universalist. Avocations: birding,

photography. Home: PO Box 2322 Cape May NJ 08204-7322 Office: NYU Dept Of Fine Arts New York NY 10003

TURNER, ARTHUR CAMPBELL, political science educator, author; b. Glasgow, Scotland, May 19, 1918; naturalized, 1958; s. Malcolm and Robina Arthur (Miller) T.; m. Anne Gordzialkowska, Jan. 21, 1950; 1 child, Nadine (Mrs. M.J. O'Sullivan). M.A. with 1st class honors, U. Glasgow, 1941; B.A. with 1st class honors in Modern History, Queen's Coll., Oxford U., 1943, M.A., 1947, B.Litt., 1948, M.Litt., 1979; Ph.D., U. Calif., Berkeley, 1951. Lectr. history U. Glasgow, 1945-51; asst. prof. history U. Toronto, 1951-53; Commonwealth Fund fellow U. Calif., Berkeley, 1948-50, vis. prof., summers 1950, 66, 71, 78; assoc. prof. polit. sci. U. Calif., Riverside, 1953-58, prof., 1958—, chmn. div. social scis., 1953-61, dean grad. div., 1960-61, chmn. dept. polit. sci., 1961-66; prof. internat. relations, govt. Claremont Grad. Sch., part-time 1962-72; vis. prof. UCLA, 1967, Pomona Coll., 1977; Exec. com. Inst. World Affairs, 1960—, dir., 1965. Author: The Post-War House of Commons, 1942, Free Speech and Broadcasting, 1944, Mr. Buchan, Writer: A Life of the First Lord Tweedsmuir, 1949, Scottish Home Rule, 1952, Bulwark of the West: Implications and Problems of NATO, 1953, Towards European Integration, 1953, Pakistan: The Impossible Made Real, 1957, The Unique Partnership: Britain and the United States, 1971; co-author: Control of Foreign Relations, 1957, (with L. Freedman) Tension Areas in World Affairs, 1964, The Regionalization of Warfare, 1985, Power and Ideology in the Middle East, 1988, Fights of Fancy: Armed Conflict in Science Fiction, 1993; contbr.: Ency. Americana Annual, 1957—; mem. editorial com. U. Calif. Press, 1959-65, 80-83, 90, chmn., U. Calif. Press, 1962-65. Recipient Cecil prize, 1939, Blackwell prize U. Aberdeen, 1943, 51; Wilton Park fellow, 1966, 76, Santa Barbara Seminar on Arms Control fellow, 1983; Rockefeller rsch. grantee Cambridge, Eng., 1959-60, NSF travel grantee Geneva, Switzerland, 1964. Mem. Am. Soc. Internat. Law, Am., Canadian hist. assns., Am. Polit. Sci. Assn., Am. Hist. Assn.), Phi Beta Kappa. Republican. Home: 1992 Rincon Ave Riverside CA 92506-1628 Office: U Calif Dept Polit Sci Riverside CA 92521 *It is now popular to say that we are nothing but the playthings of large, impersonal forces. Actually people, and peoples, bring most of their troubles on themselves. Our success and happiness are, to a large extent, in our own hands.*

TURNER, BARRY EARL, radio astronomer; b. Victoria, B.C., Can., Sept. 8, 1936; married, 1962. BSc, U. B.C., 1959; MSc, 1962; PhD in Astronomy, U. Calif., Berkeley, 1967. Rsch. off. electrical engr. Nat. Rsch. Coun. Can., 1962-64; from rsch. assoc. radio astronomer to assoc. scientist, 1967-74; scientist Nat. Radio Astron. Observ., 1974—; mem. site rev. team Space Telescope Assoc. U., Inc., 1980, NSF, 1981; titulaire, chmn. vis. com. Observ. Paris, 1981. Recipient Laurels award Space Missiles Aviation Week & Space Tech., 1991. Mem. Internat. Astron. Union, Am. Astron. Soc., Union Radio Sci. Internat. Research in theoretical and observational studies of interstellar molecules, interstellar chemistry, physics of the interstellar medium. Office: Nat Radio Astronomy Observatory 520 Edgemont Rd Charlottesville VA 22903*

TURNER, BERT S., construction executive; b. 1921. Grad., La. State U., 1943, Harvard U., 1949. With Esso Standard Oil Co., 1946-57, Nichols Constrn. Inc., Baton Rouge, 1957-61, Nichols Constrn. Corp., Baton Rouge, 1961—; now pres. Turner Industries Ltd., Baton Rouge. Office: Turner Inds Ltd PO Box 2750 Baton Rouge LA 70821-2750

TURNER, BILLIE B., chemical company executive; b. Whitesboro, TX, 1930. BS, Tex. A&M U., 1952. V.p. Internat. Minerals & Chem. Corp., Northbrook, Ill., 1954-87; chmn., pres., ceo IMC Fertilizer Inc Group, Northbrook, Ill., 1987-93; chrm. IMC, 1993—. Served with U.S. Army, 1952-54. Office: IMC Fertilizer Inc Group 2100 Sanders Rd Northbrook IL 60062-6139

TURNER, BILLIE LEE, botanist, educator; b. Yoakum, Tex., Feb. 22, 1925; s. James Madison and Julia Irene (Harper) T.; m. Virginia Ruth Mathis, Sept. 27, 1944 (div. Feb. 1968); children: Billie Lee, Matt Warnock; m. Pauline Henderson, Oct. 22, 1969 (div. Jan. 1975); m. Gayle Langford, Apr. 18, 1980; children (adopted)—Roy P., Robert L. B.S., Sul Ross State Coll., 1949; M.S., So. Meth. U., 1950; Ph.D., Wash. State U. 1953. Teaching asst. botany dept. Wash. State U., 1951-53; instr. botany dept. U. Tex., Austin, 1953; asst. prof. U. Tex., 1954-58, assoc. prof., 1958-61, prof., 1961—, now S.F. Blake prof. botany, chmn., 1967-75, dir. Plant Resources Ctr., 1957—; Asso. investigator ecol. study vegetation of, Africa, U. Ariz., Office Naval Research, 1956-57; vis. prof. U. Mont., summers 1971, 73, U. Mass., 1974. Author: Vegetational Changes in Africa Over a Third of a Century, 1959, Leguminosae of Texas, 1960, Biochemical Systematics, 1963, Chemotaxonomy of Leguminosae, 1972, Biology and Chemistry of Compositae, 1977, Plant Chemosystematics, 1984; Asso. editor: Southwestern Naturalist, 1959—. Served to 1st lt. USAAF, 1943-47. NSF postdoctoral fellow U. Liverpool, 1965-66. Mem. Bot. Soc. Am. (sec. 1958-59, 60-64, v.p. 1969), Tex. Acad. Sci., Southwestern Assn. Naturalists (pres. 1967, gov.), Am. Soc. Plant Taxonomists (Asa Gray award 1991), Internat. Assn. Plant Taxonomists, Soc. Study Evolution, Phi Beta Kappa, Sigma Xi. Office: U Tex Plant Resources Ctr Main Bldg 228 Austin TX 78712

TURNER, CAL, SR. (H. CALISTER TURNER), discount stores executive; widowed. With Neely Harwell Co., 1931-36; operated Retail Goods Store, 1936-39; with Dollar Gen. Corp., Scottsville, Ky., from 1939, chmn. emeritus, bd. dirs. Office: Dollar Gen Corp 427 Beech St Scottsville KY 42164-1670

TURNER, CAROLINE, theatre manager; b. Anniston, Ala.; d. Thomas Coleman and Caroline Dale (Carter) T. AB in English, Princeton U., 1982. Treas. box office Manhattan Theatre Club, N.Y.C., 1982-83; bus. mgr. CSC Repertory, N.Y.C., 1983-85; gen. mgr. Va. Stage Co., Norfolk, 1985-89; mng. dir. Portland (Maine) Stage Co., 1989-92; gen. mgr. Yale Repertory Theatre, New Haven, Conn., 1992—; treas. Uptown & Co., Portland, 1989-92. Mem. advancement panel Nat. Endowment for the Arts, Washington, 1990, mem. challenge panel, 1990-91; chair Portland Arts Alliance, 1991. Mem. League of Resident Theatres (exec. com. 1990-92, negotiating com. 1991). Office: Yale Repertory Theatre PO Box 1903A New Haven CT 06520-8244

TURNER, CATHY, Olympic athlete; b. Apr. 10, 1962. BS in Computer Sys., No. Mich. U., 1991. Gold medal 500 meter short-track speedskating Albertville Olympic Games, 1992, also silver medal 3000 meters relay, 1992; Star made in Am. tour Ice Capades, 1992-93; Gold medalist 500 meter speedskating Winter Olympics, Lillehammer, Norway, 1994, Bronze medalist 3000 meter relay, 1994; owner, pres. Cathy Turner's Empire Fitness; motivational spkr. Olympic recordholder 500 meter speedskate: 45.98. Address: US Olympic Committee 1750 E Boulder St Colorado Springs CO 80909

TURNER, CLYDE T., service executive; b. Las Vegas, Nev., July 18, 1937; s. Benjamin Joseph and Ruby (Denny) T.; m. Vivian Lee (div.); children: Gregory Einor, Blair Alexander, Susan Irene Keefe; m. Vera M., June 16, 1963. BS, U. Nev., Reno, 1960. Gaming commr. Nev. State Gaming commn., 1970-73; bd. dirs., mng. ptnr. Kafoury, Armstrong, Turner & Co. CPAs, Las Vegas, Nev., 1966-79; exec. v.p., chief fin. officer, treas. Golden Nugget Inc., Las Vegas, 1979—; chmn., pres. CEO Circus Circus Enterprises, Inc., Las Vegas, NV, Now; bd. dirs. Golden Nugget subs., Las Vegas. Mem. Am. Bd. CPAs. Home: 3035 Ashby Ave Las Vegas NV 89102-1948 Office: Circus Circus Enterprises 2880 Las Vegas Blvd S Las Vegas NV 89109*

TURNER, CRAIG, journalist; b. Pasadena, Calif., May 24, 1949; s. Donald Leslie and Dorothy A. (Kupseck) T.; m. Ellen Bevier, Oct. 10, 1973 (div. Dec. 1983); m. Joyce Huyett, Sept. 10, 1988. BS in Journalism, San Jose State U., 1971. Reporter L.A. Times, Orange County, Calif., 1971-79; asst. city editor L.A. Times, San Diego, 1979-83; asst. met. editor L.A. Times, L.A., 1983-89, met. editor, 1989-93; fgn. corr. L.A. Times, Toronto, Ont., 1994—. Co-recipient Pulitzer Prize for journalism, 1993, George Polk award Long Island U. 1993. Mem. Soc. Profl. Journalists. Episcopalian. Avocations: outdoor activities, travel, theatre. Office: Los Angeles Times, 890 Yonge St St 400, Toronto, ON Canada M4W 3P4

TURNER, DAVID REUBEN, publisher, author; b. N.Y.C., Dec. 9, 1915; s. Charles and Eva (Turner) Moskowitz; m. Ann Louise Perkins, Apr. 29, 1946 (div. 1976); children—Eve (Mrs. William Watters), Ruth. B.S., Coll. City N.Y., 1936, M.S. in Edn. 1937. Co-founder Arco Pub. Co., N.Y.C., 1937; pub., dir. Arco Pub. Co., 1937-78; v.p. parent co. Prentice-Hall, Inc. 1979-80; pres. Turner Pub., 1980-92; pub. cons. under Ford Found. contract Burma Translation Soc., Rangoon, 1959-60. Author: more than 300 books on tests and testing, including High School Equivalency Diploma Tests, 1951, 75, How to Win a Scholarship, 1955, Scoring High On College Entrance Tests, 1969, 71, Food Service Supervisor, 1968, Bank Examiner, 1968, Accountant-Auditor, 1960, 77, Officer Candidate Tests, 1978, Professional-Administrative Career Exams, 1979, English Grammar and Usage for Test-Takers, 1976, College Level Examination Program, 1979. Adviser bd. publs. Union Am. Hebrew Congregations. Home and Office: 13 Glengary Rd Croton On Hudson NY 10520-2139

TURNER, DOUGLAS LAIRD, writer, editor, columnist; b. Buffalo, N.Y., Jan. 5, 1932; s. Henry Albert and Effie Donna (McIndoo) T.; m. Mary Joan Hassett, July 7, 1962; children: Christopher Henry, Mary Julia, Albert William. BA, Brown U., 1954; postgrad., Stanford U., 1968. Reporter Buffalo (N.Y.) Courier-Express, 1957-60, state capital corr., 1960-64, fin. editor, 1964, city editor, 1964-70, exec. editor, 1971-80, Washington bur. chief, 1981-82; Washington corr. Buffalo (N.Y.) Evening News, 1982, Washington columnist, 1983, Washington bur. chief, 1989—; publs. com. Canisius Coll., Buffalo, 1975-80; founders' com. Niagara Frontier Chpt. Profl. Journalism Soc., N.Y. State Commn. on Pub. Access to Records, 1976-81; mem. cmty. adv. coun. State U. Buffalo, N.Y., 1976-79. Mem. U.S. Olympic Rowing Team, 1956; founder Erie County Forensic Psychiatry Svc., Buffalo, 1975, Area Leadership Group, Buffalo, 1977-79. Spl. agt. U.S. Army Counter Intelligence Corps, 1956-57. Nation champion four-oared shell with cox, 1956; winner Hanlan Trophy, Royal Can. Henley Regatta, 1956; recipient numerous awards Am. Newspaper Guild, N.Y. State Associated Press Assn., personal citations Erie County Legislature, N.Y. State Assembly, Buffalo Common Coun. Mem. Nat. Press Club (former gov. 1988), Potomac Boat Club, Occoquan Boat Club. Roman Catholic. Avocations: classical guitar, piano, voice, rowing, sailing. Home: 7923 St George Ct Springfield VA 22153 Office: Buffalo News Washington Bur 1141 National Press Bldg Washington DC 20045

TURNER, E. DEANE, lawyer; b. Auburn, N.Y., Aug. 4, 1928; s. Alfred Edward and Bertha (Deane) T.; A.B. summa cum laude, Princeton U., 1950; LL.B. cum laude, Harvard U., 1953. Bar: N.Y. 1953. Assoc., Dewey Ballantine and predecessor firms, N.Y.C., 1953-63, ptnr., 1963—, of counsel, 1991-93; treas. Harvard Law Sch. Assn. N.Y.C., 1964-83. Elder, trustee Brick Presbyn. Ch., N.Y.C., 1976—, pres. bd. trustees, 1988-90. Fellow Am. Coll. Investment Counsel; mem. ABA, N.Y. Bar Assn., Union Club, John's Island Club, Phi Beta Kappa. Republican. Home: 1120 Fifth Ave New York NY 10128-0144 also: 381 Llwyds Ln Johns Island Vero Beach FL 32963 Office: Dewey Ballantine 1301 Ave Of The Americas New York NY 10019-6092

TURNER, ED SIMS, broadcast executive, writer; b. Bartlesville, Okla., Sept. 25, 1935; s. Ed and Dee (Sims) T.; m. Beth Coburn, June 25, 1964; 1 child, Christopher. BA in Journalism, U. Okla. 1957. Producer, dir. documentary films Okla U., Norman, 1957-59; reporter Sta. KWTV, Oklahoma City, 1959-64; v.p. news Sta. WTTG, Washington, 1966-68; v.p. news and pub. affairs Metromedia, N.Y.C., 1968-74; v.p. news United Press Internat. TV News, N.Y.C., 1975; news producer CBS, N.Y.C., 1975-78; news dir. Sta. KWTV, Oklahoma City, 1978-79; managing editor Cable News Network, Atlanta, 1979-81, exec. producer, 1982, chief Wash. bur., 1983, exec. v.p., 1984—; spl. instr. Okla. U., 1968, Mary Mount Coll., N.Y.C., 1978. Dir. ednl. documentary (Best Documentary award Cannes Film Festival 1958); creative producer (TV spl.) Crossfire; creator, engr. (TV spl.) Novak Reports. Press sec. Bud Wilkinson for U.S. Senate campaign, 1964-65. Recipient Best Reporting award UPI, 1959-64, 8 Emmys, 1966-72, Channels mag. Award of Excellence, 1987, Peabody awards, 1983, 87, 89, 91, 6 Ace awards for cable excellence; named Producer of Yr. Millmeter mag., 1984, Outstanding Alumni, Okla. U. Sch. Journalism, 1985, One of 25 Who Count in TV/Motion Picture Industry, View mag., 1986. Mem. Radio TV News Dirs. Assn., Sigma Delta Chi (nat. reporting awards 1963), Phi Gamma Delta. Republican. Home: 1897 Breckenridge Dr NE Atlanta GA 30345-4049 Office: CNN One CNN Ctr PO Box 105366 Atlanta GA 30348*

TURNER, EDWIN LEWIS, astronomy educator, researcher; b. Knoxville, Tenn., May 3, 1949; s. George Lewis and Gladys Love (Gregory) T.; m. Joyce Beldon, Aug. 15, 1971; children: Alexander, Daniel. SB in Physics, MIT, 1971; PhD in Astronomy, Calif. Inst. Tech., 1975. Fellow Inst. for Advance Study, Princeton, N.J., 1975-76; asst. prof. dept. astronomy Harvard U., Cambridge, Mass., 1977-78; asst. prof. dept. astrophysics Princeton U., 1978-81, Alfred P. Sloan Found. Rsch. fellow, 1980-84, assoc. prof., 1981-86, prof., 1986—, assoc. chmn., 1988—; counselor Space Telescope Inst. Counsel, Balt., 1989—; vis. prof. Nat. Astron. Obs. Japan, Tokyo, 1990. Contbr. over 85 articles to astron. publs. Bd. dirs. Assn. Univs. for Rsch. in Astronomy, Inc., Tucson, 1980-89. Mem. Internat. Astron. Union, Am. Astron. Assn. Achievements include research in galaxy masses, cosmic structure formation, quasars, gravitational lenses, and cosmology. Office: Princeton U Obs Ivy Ln Princeton NJ 08544-0001

TURNER, ELIZABETH ADAMS NOBLE (BETTY TURNER), healthcare executive, former mayor; b. Yonkers, N.Y., May 18, 1931; d. James Kendrick and Orrel (Baldwin) Noble; m. Jack Rice Turner, July 11, 1953; children: Jay Kendrick, Randall Ray. BA, Vassar Coll., 1953; MA, Tex. A&I U., 1964. Ednl. cons. Noble & Noble Pub. Co., N.Y.C., 1956-67; psychometrist Corpus Christi Guidance Ctr., 1967-70; psychologist Corpus Christi State Sch., 1970-72, dir. programs, asst. supt., 1972, dir. devel. and vol. svc., 1972-76, dir. rsch. and tng., 1977-79, psychologist Tex. Mental Health and Mental Retardation, 1970-79; pres. Turner Co., 1979—; program cons. Tex. Dept. Mental Health and Mental Retardation, 1979-85; mayor pro tem. Corpus Christi, 1981-85, mayor, 1987-91; CEO, pres. Corpus Christi C. of C., 1991-94; v.p. bus. and govt. rels. Columbia Healthcare Corp., 1994—. Dir. alumni Corpus Christi State U. 1976-77; coord. vols. Summer Head Start Program, Corpus Christi, 1967; chmn. spl. gifts coml United Way, Corpus Christi, 1970; mem. Corpus Christi City Coun., 1979-91; family founded Barnes and Noble, N.Y.C.; with Leadership Corpus Christi II; founder Com. of 100 and Goals for Corpus Christi; pres. USO; bd. dirs. Coastal Bends Coun. Govts., Corpus Christi Mus., Harbor Playhouse, Communities in Schs., Del Mar Coll. Found., Pres.' Coun., Food Bank, Salvation Army, Jr. League; bd. govs. Southside Community Hosp., 1987-93, Gulfway Nat. Bank, 1985-92, Bayview Hosp., 1992—, strategic planning com. Meml. Hosp., 1992, Bayview Psychiatric Hosp., 1993—, Tex. Capital Network Bd., 1992—, Humana Hosp., Rehab. Hosp. South Tex., Admiral Tex. Navy; apptd. Gov.'s Commn. for Women, 1984-85, Leadership Tex. Class I; founder Goals for Corpus Christi, Bay Area Sports Assn., Assn. Coastal Bend Mayor's Alliance; founder Mayor's Commn. on the Disabled, Mayor's Task Force on the Homeless; active Port Arkansas Cmty. Ch. Recipient Love award YWCA, 1970, Y's Women and Men in Careers award, 1988, Commander's Award for Pub. Svc. U.S. Army, Scroll of Honor award Navy League, award Tex. Hwy. Dept., Road Hand award Tex. Hwy. Commn., 1989; named Corpus Christi Newsmaker of Yr., 1987. Mem. Tex. Psychol. Assn. (pres., mem. exec. bd.), Psychol. Assn. (pres., founder), Tex. Mcpl. League (bd. dir.), Corpus Christi C. of C. (pres., CEO), Jr. League Corpus Christi, Tex. Bookman's Assn., Tex. Assn. Realtors, Kappa Kappa Gamma, Corpus Christi Town Club, Corpus Christi Yacht Club, Jr. Cotillion Club. Home: 4600 Ocean Dr Apt 801 Corpus Christi TX 78412-2542

TURNER, EUGENE ANDREW, manufacturing executive; b. Bridgeton, N.J., Aug. 7, 1928; s. Benjamin Homer and Pearl Irene (Wolbert) T.; m. Paula Ann Webb, 1987; children: Mary Ann, John-Reed. BA, Rutgers U., 1966; student, Columbia U., 1980. With Owens Ill., 1950-73, regional mgr. West Coast, 1970-73; v.p. adminstrn. Midland Glass Co., Cliffwood, N.J., 1973-76, pres., chief operating officer, 1981-82, also bd. dirs.; v.p. gen. mgr. Anchor Hocking Corp., Lancaster, Ohio, 1976-81; dir. ops. Theo Chem. Labs., Tampa, Fla., 1988-90, Profit Counselors Inc, Sarasota, Fla. 1990—; mng. cons. 1987-88. Mem. Harbor Island Club, Seaview Country Club, Navesink Country Club. Home: Regency House # 205 1103 Tedford Way Oklahoma City OK 73116-6006 Office: Profit Engr Sys Inc 191 Mitchell Ct

Addison IL 60101 *Take time to learn the chosen business then develop credibility by doing what you say you will do.*

TURNER, EVAN HOPKINS, retired art museum director; b. Orono, Maine, Nov. 8, 1927; s. Albert Morton and Percie Trowbridge (Hopkins) T.; m. Brenda Winthrop Bowman, May 12, 1956; children: John, Jennifer. A.B. cum laude, Harvard U., 1949, M.A., 1950, Ph.D., 1954. Head docent svc. Fogg Mus., Cambridge, Mass., 1950-51; curator Robbins Art Collection of Prints, Arlington, Mass., 1951; teaching fellow fine arts Harvard U., 1951-52; lectr., research asst. Frick Collection, N.Y.C., 1953-56; gen. curator, asst. dir. Wadsworth Atheneum, Hartford, Conn., 1956-59; dir. Montreal Mus. Fine Arts, Que., Can., 1959-64, Phila. Mus. Art, 1964-77, Ackland Art Mus., 1978-83, Cleve. Mus. Art, 1983-93; adj. prof. art history U. Pa., U. N.C., Chapel Hill, 1978-83; disting. vis. prof. Oberlin Coll., 1993—. Mem. Assn. Art Mus. Dirs., Coll. Art Assn., Am. Mus. Assn., Century Assn. Club. Home: 3071 N Park Blvd Cleveland OH 44118-4114

TURNER, FLORENCE FRANCES, ceramist; b. Detroit, Mar. 9, 1926; d. Paul Pokrywka and Catherine Gagal; m. Dwight Robert Turner, Oct. 23, 1948; children: Thomas Michael, Nancy Louise, Richard Scott, Garry Robert. Student, Oakland C.C., Royal Oak, Mich., 1975-85, U. Ariz., Yuma, 1985, U. Las Vegas, 1989—. Pres., founder Nev. Clay Guild, Henderson, 1990-94, mem. adv. bd., 1994—; workshop leader Greenfield Village, Dearborn, Mich., 1977-78, Plymouth (Mich.) Hist. Soc., 1979, Las Vegas Sch. System, 1989-90, Detroit Met. area, 1977-85. Bd. dirs. Las Vegas Art Mus., 1987-91; corr. sec. So. Nev. Creative Art Ctr., Las Vegas, 1990-94. Mem. Las Vegas Gem Club, Nev. Camera Club, Golden Key, Phi Kappa Phi. Avocations: photography, collecting gems, travel. Office: Nev Clay Guild PO Box 50004 Henderson NV 89016

TURNER, FRANK MILLER, historian, educator; b. Springfield, Ohio, Oct. 31, 1944; s. Ronald O. and Mary Elizabeth (Miller) T.; m. Margaret Good, Aug. 26, 1967 (div. 1981); m. 2d, Nancy Rash, July 29, 1984. BA, Coll. of William and Mary, 1966; MPhil, Yale U., 1970, PhD, 1971; LHD (hon.), Coll. William and Mary, 1991. Asst. prof. Yale U., New Haven, Conn., 1972-77, assoc. prof., 1977-82, prof., 1982—, provost, 1988-92. Author: Between Science and Religion, 1974, The Greek Heritage in Victorian Britain, 1981, Contesting Cultural Authority: Essays in Victorial Intellectual Life, 1993; co-author: The Western Heritage, 1979, 83, 87, 91, 94, Heritage of World Civilizations, 1985, 90, 93. Guggenheim fellowship, 1983; recipient Brit. Coun. prize Conf. on Brit. Studies, 1982, Yale Press Gov.'s award, 1983. Office: Yale U History Dept PO Box 1504a West Haven CT 06520-3554

TURNER, FRANKLIN DELTON, bishop; b. Norwood, N.C., July 19, 1933; s. James T. and Dora (Streeter) T.; m. Barbara Dickerson, July 6, 1963; children: Jennifer, Kimberly, Franklin. AB, Livingstone Coll., 1956, DD (hon.), 1993; MDiv, Yale U., 1965; DD (hon.), Berkeley Div. Sch., Yale U., 1977. Ordained deacon and priest Episcopal Ch., 1965, consecrated bishop, 1988. Vicar Epiphany Ch., Diocese of Dallas, 1965-66; rector St. George's Ch., Diocese of Washington, 1966-72; officer nat. staff Episcopal Ch. Ctr., N.Y.C., 1972-83; mem. bishop's staff for congl. devel. Episcopal Diocese of Pa., 1983-86, suffragan bishop, 1988—. Author: Black Leaders in the Episcopal Church, 1975. 1st It. U.S. Army, 1966-72. Office: Diocese of Pa 240 S 4th St Philadelphia PA 19106-3722

TURNER, GENE, religious organization administrator. Dir. Dept. of Governing Body Ecumenical and Agy. Relationship of the Presbyn. Ch., USA, Louisville. Office: Presbyterian Church 100 Witherspoon St Louisville KY 40202-1396

TURNER, GEORGE PEARCE, consulting company executive; b. Dallas, Aug. 22, 1915; s. Fred Horatio and Florence (Phillips) T.; m. June Lori Haney, Feb. 4, 1943 (div. 1976); children: Bruce Haney, Brian Phillips, Mark Richardson; m. Kathryn Blank Hauf, June 1976. Student, U. Tex., 1932-33, 35-36, 40-41, So. Methodist U., 1934; BA in Internat. Rels. cum laude, U. So. Calif., 1962, MS in Internat. Pub. Adminstrn. summa cum laude, 1966; PhD in Econs. and Internat. Rels., Columbia Pacific U., 1982, PhD in Pub. Adminstrn. and Internat. Rels., 1985. Archtl. designer L.A., 1946-48; prin. Lieburg & Turner (cons. engrs.), Pasadena, Calif., 1947-48; pres. Radiant Heat Engring., Inc., Pasadena, 1948-53; exec. asst. to dir. fgn. subsidiaries S.Am. Fluor Corp. Ltd., L.A., 1953-54; mem. exec. staff Coast Fed. Savs. & Loan Assn., 1954-55; exec. staff Holmes & Narver, Inc., L.A., 1955-61; mgr. project devel. S.Am. ops. Southwestern Engring. Co., L.A., 1962; pres. Haney Devel. Corp., 1964-90, Fomento e Inversiones Quisqueyanos C. por A., Santo Domingo de Guzman, Dominican Republic, 1967—; gen. mgr. for Venezuelan ops. Hale Internat. Inc., Caracas, 1970-71; dir., mgr. Consortium Lomas de La Lagunita, Caracas, 1970, Consortium Desarrollos Urbanos, Valencia, Venezuela, 1970; pres. Haney Investment Corp. (HANCO), 1974-90, Casa FOMIQ, 1978—, Caribbean Vagabond Ltd., Grand Cayman Island, B.W.I., 1981-90, Kay Pearce & Turner, Ltd., Newtown Square, Pa., 1981—; sec. Integrated Industries of Atlantic County, N.J.; gen. ptnr. N.Y. Ave. Parking Assocs., Atlantic City, 1980-91; cons. econ. devel., 1963—; adviser, provisional pres., Dominican Republic, 1965-66, constl. pres. of republic, 1966-68; projects programmer Nat. Planning Inst. Peru Tri-Partite Mission, 1962-65; ofcl. OAS adviser Nat. Office Tourism Dominican Republic, 1966-67, Nat. Office Cultural Patrimony, Liga Mcpl. Dominicana, 1967-68; cons., dir. projects, programming, tech. matters Mission Recovery and Rehab., Dominican Republic, 1965-67; dep. dir. Tech. Assistance Mission Dominican Republic, 1967-68; cons. assignments for program assistance Inter-Am. Tng. Ctr., Fed. U. Ceara, Brazil; OAS adviser on tech. assistance to Chile, Argentina, Uruguay, Peru, Brazil, 1962-68; cons. Wildwood Ocean Towers, N.J., 1969-70, Capital Investment Devel. Corp., Downing Ctr., Downingtown, Pa., 1971-77; dir. for Project Monitor and owners agt., hosp. tower Hahnemann Med. U. and Hosp., Phila., 1975-78; pres. Urban Planning and Devel. Corp., Exton, Pa., 1978-79; cons., corp. sec., v.p. Constrn., Devel. and Properties Mgmt. Group, Integrated Industries Inc., Exton, 1978-90; ltd. ptnr. Marsh Creek Assocs. Two, 1985—; appointed to faculty Columbia Pacific U., 1987; cons. internat. consortium for multi-billion dollar econ. devel. program with projects in countries of Pacific Rim and Ea. Europe, 1993—. Author: An Analysis of the Economy of El Salvador, 1961, The Alliance for Progress: Concept Versus Structure, 1966, Some Observations on the Decade of the 1960s - U.S. vis-a-vis Latin America, 1982, Latin American Odyssey, 1985, Third Generation, 1990, Growing Up Male in America: With the Prince Charming Mystique, 1993; pub., editor Casa FOMIQ Quarterly Report, 1994; contbr. articles to profl. publs. With USAF, 1941-45. Decorated OAS Medal of Honor; recipient Citation for Valiant Svc. in Dominican Republic, 1965-66, Ofcl. OAS Commendation for Program Contbns., Peru, Dominican Republic, Brazil, Venezuela, 1969. Mem. Delta Phi Epsilon, Alpha Sigma Lambda. Home: 8 Fox Run Ln Newtown Square PA 19073-1004 Office: Kay Pearce & Turner Ltd PO Box 419 Newtown Square PA 19073-0419

TURNER, GERALD PHILLIP, hospital administrator; b. Winnipeg, Man., Can., May 13, 1930; s. Lorry and Shirley (Litman) Turbovsky; m. Clare Henteleff, June 12, 1955 (dec.); children: Robin Joy, Neil Lindsay, Daryl Lyon; m. Donna Ireland, May 22, 1994. B.Sc. in Pharmacy, U. Man., Winnipeg, 1953; Diploma in Hosp. Adminstrn., U. Toronto, Ont., Can., 1955. Asst. adminstr. Mt. Sinai Hosp., Toronto, 1955-62; assoc. adminstr. Mt. Sinai Hosp., 1962-66, adminstr., 1966-74, exec. dir. 1974-84, pres., chief exec. officer, 1984-93, pres. emeritus, 1993—; exec. v.p. Mt. Sinai Inst., Toronto, 1976-86; pres. Mt. Sinai Hosp. Found. (formerly Inst.), Toronto, 1987-88, vice chmn., 1988—; assoc. prof. health adminstrn. U. Toronto, 1971-90, prof., 1990—; chmn. rsch. bd. Samual Lunenfeld Rsch. Inst. Author: (with Joseph Mapa) The Choice is Yours: Making Canada's Medical System Work for You, 1981; co-editor: (with Joseph Mapa) Humanizing Hospital Care, 1979; Humanistic Health Care: Issues for Caregivers, 1988. Recipient Queen's Silver Jubilee medal, Pres.'s Achievement award, Extendicare award, Toronto Chpt. award for Disting. Svcs., Can. Coll. Health Svc. Execs., 1993. Fellow Am. Coll. Healthcare Execs., Can. Coll. Health Service Execs. (founder mem., cert. mem.), Ont. Hosp. Assn. (chmn. elect 1986-87, chmn. 1987-88). Office: Mt Sinai Hospital, 600 University Ave, Toronto, ON Canada M5G 1X5

TURNER, HAROLD EDWARD, education educator; b. Hamilton, Ill., Nov. 22, 1921; s. Edward Jesse and Beulah May (White) T.; m. Catherine

Skeeters, Apr. 5, 1946; children: Michele Turner Nimerick, Thomas, Barbara Turner McMahon, Krista Turner Landgraf. A.B., Carthage Coll., 1950; M.S., U. Ill. - Urbana, 1951, Ed.D. (George Peabody fellow), 1956. Tchr., Taylorville Jr. High Sch., Ill., 1951-52, Moline Jr. High Sch., Ill., 1952-54; dir. elem. edn. Jefferson County, Colo., 1955-57; prin. Jefferson County High Sch., 1957-60; asst. prof. edn. N. Tex. State U., Denton, 1960-63; asst. supt. curriculum Sacramento City Schs., 1963-66; asso. prof., chmn. dept. curriculum and instrn. U. Mo. - St. Louis, 1966-69, prof., 1971-85, prof. emeritus, 1985—, chmn. dept. adminstrn., founds., secondary edn., 1977-78, dept. chmn., 1983-85; vis. prof. Adams State Coll., Alamosa, Colo., 1959, U. Ga., Athens, 1981-82; adj. prof. NYU, 1965, U. Ill., 1980; cons. various sch. dists., Tex., Mo.; spl. cons. Mo. State Dept. Edn., 1973. Author: (with Adolph Unruh) Supervision for Change and Innovation, 1970; contbr. articles to profl. jours. Served with USNR, 1942-46. Mem. Profs. Supervision. Presbyterian (elder). Home: 3155 Calle Pueblo Green Valley AZ 85614-3307 Office: U Mo St Louis Sch Edn 8001 Natural Bridge Rd Saint Louis MO 63121-4499

TURNER, HARRY EDWARD, lawyer; b. Mt. Vernon, Ohio, Dec. 25, 1927; s. Paul Hamilton and Harriett (Krafft) T.; m. Shirley Marilyn Eggert, July 8, 1950; children: Harry Edward, Thomas Frederick. B.A., Baldwin Wallace Coll., 1951; J.D., Ohio No. U., 1954. Bar: Ohio 1954, U.S. Supreme Ct. 1966. Practice in Mt. Vernon, 1954—; state rep. Ohio Gen. Assembly, 1973-85; solicitor Mt. Vernon, 1958-62; Prosecutor Mt. Vernon Municipal Ct., 1955-58. Mem. Mt. Vernon City Sch. Bd., 1964-70, pres., 1965-70; trustee Ohio Sch. Bd. Assn., 1968-70, Hannah Browning Home, 1987—, Sta. Break/Commn. on Planning Svcs., 1989—; mem. Knox County Pub. Defender Commn., 1987-91. Served with USN, 1946-47. Mem. Ohio State Bar Assn., Knox County Bar Assn. (pres. 1970), Alpha Sigma Phi, Sigma Delta Kappa. Republican. Lutheran. Home: 400 E Vine St Mount Vernon OH 43050-3442 Office: 118 E High St Mount Vernon OH 43050-3402

TURNER, HARRY WOODRUFF, lawyer; b. Blairsville, Pa., May 2, 1939; s. James McKinnie and Dorothy Elizabeth (Tittle) T.; m. Mary Elizabeth Phelan, Dec. 30, 1972; children: James William, David Woodruff. AB, U. Pitts., 1961; JD, Harvard U., 1964. Bar: Pa., 1965, U.S. Supreme Ct., 1979. Assoc. Kirkpatrick & Lockhart, Pitts., 1964-71, ptnr., 1971—; bd. dirs., sec. Imperial Harbor Corp., 1988—, IH Utility Co., 1975—, IH Properties Co., 1980-87; mem. Fed. Jud. Selection Commn. Pa., 1995—. Trustee U. Pitts., 1995—; trustee, sec. Adoptive Rights Coun., Wilson Coll., Chambersburg, Pa., 1978-89; pres. U. Pitts. Nat. Alumni Assn., 1990-91; alt. del. Rep. Nat. Conv., Miami, Fla., 1989, Houston, 1992; trustee, v.p. Torrance (Pa.) State Hosp., 1969-73; trustee ann giving fund Pitts., 1982—; chair distbn. com. William L. Benz Found., 1985—; dir. Pitts. divsn. Am. Heart Assn., 1993—; trustee Aspinwall Baseball Assn., 1985—. Mem. ABA, Pa. Bar Assn., Am. Law Inst., Internat. Acad. Trial Lawyers, Allegheny County Bar Assn., Allegheny County Acad. Trial Lawyers, SAR (v.p. 1994), Fox Chapel Golf Club, Duquesne Club, Harvard-Yale-Princeton Club, Univ. Club, Allegheny Club. Presbyterian. Office: Kirkpatrick & Lockhart 1500 Oliver Bldg Pittsburgh PA 15222-2404

TURNER, HENRY A., political science educator, author; b. King City, Mo., Jan. 2, 1919; s. Henry A. and Bessie Marie (Claxton) T.; m. Mary Margaret Tilton, May 23, 1943; children—John Andrew, Nancy Ellen, Stephen Heald. B.S., N.W. Mo. State U., 1939; M.A., Mo. U., 1941; Ph.D., U. Chgo., 1950. Jr. coll. instr., 1940-42; instr. Iowa State U., 1945-46; from instr. to assoc. prof. U. Calif.-Santa Barbara, 1948-62, prof., 1962—, chmn. dept. polit. sci., 1960-65, acad. vice chancellor, 1971-73; mem. summer faculty U. Mo., 1951, U. Nebr., 1959, U. Calif.-Berkeley, 1958; vis. prof. polit. sci. U. Khartoum, Sudan, 1962-63; Fulbright lectr. U. Witwatersrand, Republic South Africa, 1968, U. Teheran, Iran, 1974; cons. Bur. Budget, 1953; mem. staff White House, 1953. Author: (with J.A. Vieg) The Government and Politics of California, 4th edit., 1971, American Democracy: State and Local Government, 1968, 2d edit., 1970; co-author: American Democracy in World Perspective, 1967, 5th edit., 1980, The Wilson Influence on Public Administration, 1990; editor: Politics in the United States, 1955; contbr. articles to profl. jours. Staff mem. Democratic Nat. Com., 1952. Served from ensign to It. USNR, 1942-45. Mem. Am. Polit. Sci. Assn., Western Polit. Sci. Assn. Home: 703 Foxen Dr Santa Barbara CA 93105-2516

TURNER, HENRY BROWN, finance executive; b. N.Y.C., Sept. 3, 1936; s. Henry Brown III and Gertrude (Adams) T.; m. Sarah Jean Thomas, June 7, 1958 (div.); children: Laura Eleanor, Steven Bristow, Nancy Carolyn. A.B., Duke U., 1958; M.B.A., Harvard U., 1962. Controller Fin. Corp. of Ariz., Phoenix, 1962-64; treas., dir. corporate planning Star-Kist Foods, Terminal Island, Calif., 1964-67; dir., 1st v.p. Mitchum, Jones & Templeton, Los Angeles, 1967-73; asst. sec. Dept. Commerce, Washington, 1973-74; v.p. fin. N-Ren Corp., Cin., 1975-76; v.p. Oppenheimer & Co., N.Y.C., 1976-78; exec. v.p., mng. dir. corporate fin. Shearson Hayden Stone Inc., N.Y.C., 1978-79; sr. mng. dir. Ardshiel Inc., 1980-81, pres., 1981-93, chmn. emeritus, 1994—; vis. lectr. U. Va. Sch. of Bus.; bd. dirs. MacDonald & Co., Pembrook Mgmt., Inc., Golden State Vintners, Inc., Cellu-Tissue Corp., Wrangler Cowboy Adventures McDowell Reservation, Phoenix. Sponsor Jr. Achievement, 1964-67. Served to It. USNR, 1958-60. Coll. Men's Club scholar Westfield, N.J., 1954-55. Mem. Fed. Govt. Accountants Assn. (hon.), Duke Washington Club, Omicron Delta Kappa.

TURNER, HESTER HILL, management consultant; b. San Antonio, Jan. 31, 1917; d. Orvin A. and Edna Lee (Guerguin) Hill; m. William Hoag Turner, Mar. 7, 1939 (div. Aug. 1957); children: William Hoag, John Daniel, Mary Lee, Jane Livingston (Mrs. S. Thomas Toleno). B.S., Our Lady of Lake U., 1938; M.A., S.W. Tex. State Coll., 1940; J.D., U. Ariz., 1945; Ed.D., Oreg. State U., 1956; L.H.D. (hon.), Drury Coll., Our Lady of the Lake, Salem Coll. Faculty Lewis and Clark Coll., Portland, 1947-66, dean students, 1961-66; nat. exec. dir. Camp Fire Girls, Inc., Kansas City, Mo., 1966-79; vis. instr. Oreg. State U., Western Wash. Coll., Portland State Coll.; dir. profl. services Oreg. Edn. Assn., Portland, 1959-61. Contbr. articles and chpts. to profl. publs. Mem. Oreg. Commn. on Status of Women, 1964-65; del. White House Conf. on Status of Women, 1965; mem. Portland met. steering com. OEO, 1965-66, Nat. Citizens Adv. Com. Vocat. Rehab., 1966-68; mem. Def. Adv. Com. Women in Services, 1966-69, chmn., 1968-69; mem. N.Y. State Vocat. Rehab. Planning Council, 1967-68; trustee Council for Advancement and Support of Edn.; chmn. Accreditation Commn., Nat. Home Study Council, 1983-89; mem. Army Adv. Council on ROTC Affairs, 1974-75; bd. dirs. Nat. Wildlife Fedn., 1982-88, Yosemite Inst., 1983-90; bd. dirs. Lincoln Found. and Lincoln Inst. Land Planning, 1983-89, New Century Conservation Trust, Inc., 1992—. Recipient Dept. Def. medal for disting. pub. service, 1970; named Disting. Citizen U. Ariz. Mem. NEA, Oreg. Assn. Health and Phys. Edn. (pres. 1959-60), Oreg. Bar Assn., Ariz. Bar Assn., Am. Forestry Assn. (v.p. 1977-79, pres. 1980-82), Forest History Soc. (pres. 1991-93), Gemological Inst. Am. (bd. dirs. 1989-92), Phi Kappa Phi, Delta Kappa Gamma. Home and Office: 601 E 20th St New York NY 10010-7622 *One learns to make decisions only by making them. All adults who care about young people are presented with a special challenge: If we want to help them become responsible adults, we must have both the courage to stand for our own beliefs, and the faith to allow them to discover their own.*

TURNER, HUGH JOSEPH, JR., lawyer; b. Paterson, N.J., Oct. 5, 1945; s. Hugh Joseph and Louise (Sullivan) T.; m. Charlene Chiappetta, Feb. 11, 1983; children: Cristin, Brian, James. BS, Boston U., 1967; JD, U. Miami, Coral Gables, Fla., 1975. Bar: Fla. 1975, U.S. Dist. Ct. (so. & mid. dists.) Fla. 1975, U.S. Ct. Appeals (11th cir.) 1981, U.S. Supreme Ct. 1984. Tchr. Browne & Nichols, Cambridge, Mass., 1968-72; ptnr. Smathers & Thompson, Miami, Fla., 1981-87, Kelley Drye & Warren, Miami, 1987-93, English, McCaughan & O'Bryan, Ft. Lauderdale, 1993—; chmn. Fla. Bar internat. law sect., 1988-89. Contbg. author book on internat. dispute resolution Fla. Bar, 1989; contbr. articles to profl. jours. Bd. dirs. Japan Soc. South Fla., Miami, 1989—. Mem. ABA, Def. Rsch. Inst., Internat. Bar Assn. Avocation: running. Office: English McCaughan O'Bryan 100 NE 3rd Ave Fort Lauderdale FL 33301-1176

TURNER, JACK HENRY, can manufacturing company executive; b. Peru, Ill., July 18, 1934; s. Henry W. and Ruth (Pearsen) T.; m. Judy Batchelder, June 20, 1954; children—Jon Scott, Jeff. B.S., U. Ill. C.P.A., Ill. Auditor

Arthur Andersen, 1959-64; controller Internat. Tube Co., 1964-65; mgr. gen. acctg., asst. treas., sec. Thor Power Tool Co., 1965-69; exec. v.p. internat. Am. Nat. Can Co., Chgo., 1969-92, pres., 1992—. Bd. dirs. Am. Athletic Assn., Glen Ellyn, Ill., 1966-72, Glenbard South Boosters, Glen Ellyn, 1975-76; pres. St. Luke Luth. Ch., Glen Ellyn, 1972; Served with U.S. Army, 1957-59. Republican. Lutheran. Clubs: Glen Oak Country (Glen Ellyn); Economic (Chgo.). Avocation: golf. Office: Am Nat Can Corp 8770 W Bryn Mawr Ave Chicago IL 60631-3515

TURNER, JAMES P., lawyer; b. Pueblo, Colo., Oct. 27, 1930; s. James C. and Florence E. (Sturtevant) T.; m. Jean M. Curtis, June 7, 1952 (dec. Mar. 1975); children: James C., R. Curtis, Barbara J., Amy Phillips; m. Anita J. Stephens, Aug. 6, 1977; stepchildren: Kevin J., Cory A. McCarthy. BJ, U. Mo., 1952, LLB, U. Colo., 1957. Bar: Colo. 1957, D.C. 1972, U.S. Ct. Appeals (4th cir.) 1957, U.S. Ct. Appeals (10th cir.) 1958, U.S. Ct. Appeals (7th cir.) 1959, U.S. Ct. Appeals (5th. and 11th cirs.) 1981, U.S. Supreme Ct. 1960. Appellate atty. Tax Div., 1957-61; sec. chief Civil Rights Div., 1965-69; dep. asst. atty. gen. Civil Rights Div. U.S. Dept. Justice, Washington, 1969—; acting asst. atty. gen. U.S. Dept. Justice, Washington, 1988-89; assoc. Calkins, Kramer, Grimshaw and Harring, Denver, 1961-64; pvt. practice Westminster, Colo., 1964-65. Contbr. articles to profl. jours. Mem. ABA. Avocations: golf, ballroom dancing.

TURNER, JAMES THOMAS, judge; b. Clifton Forge, Va., Mar. 12, 1938; s. James Thomas and Ruth (Greene) T.; m. Patricia Sue Renfrow, July 8, 1962; 1 child, James Thomas. BA, Wake Forest Coll., 1960; JD, U. Va., 1965. Bars: Va. 1965, U.S. Ct. Appeals (4th and fed. cirs.), U.S. Supreme Ct. Assoc. firm Williams, Worrell, Kelly & Greer, Norfolk, Va., 1965, ptnr., 1971-79; U.S. magistrate U.S. Dist. Ct., Eastern Dist. Va., Norfolk, 1979-87; judge, U.S. Ct. Fed. Claims, 1987—. Mem. ABA, FBA, Va. Bar Assn., Norfolk and Portsmouth Bar Assn. (sec. 1975-79). Office: US Ct Fed Claims 717 Madison Pl NW Washington DC 20005-1086

TURNER, JANINE, actress; b. Lincoln, Nebr., Dec. 6, 1963; d. Janice Gaunt. Appearances include (TV) Behind the Screen, 1981-82, General Hospital, 1982-83, Northern Exposure, 1990-95 (Hollywood Fgn. Press Assn. award 1992, Emmy award nominee 1993), (films) Young Doctors in Love, 1982, Knights of the City, 1985, Tai-Pan, 1986, Monkey Shines: An Experiment in Fear, 1988, Steel Magnolias, 1988, The Ambulance, 1990, Cliffhanger, 1993. Office: CAA 9830 Wilshire Blvd Beverly Hills CA 90212*

TURNER, JEROME, federal judge; b. Memphis, Feb. 18, 1942; s. Cooper and Eugenia (Morrison) T.; m. Shirley Broadhead, Oct. 18, 1969 (div. July 1986); children: Alexandra Cox, Christian Annette; m. Kay Farese, Aug. 22, 1987. BA, Washington and Lee U., 1964, LLB cum laude, 1966. Bar: Tenn. 1966. Law clk. to judge U.S. Dist. Ct., Memphis, 1966-67; assoc. Canada, Russell & Turner, Memphis, 1967-73, ptnr., 1974-78; ptnr. Wildman, Harrold, Allen, Dixon & McDonnell, Memphis, 1978-87; judge U.S. Dist. Ct. (we. Dist.) Tenn., Memphis, 1988—. Author: Law Rev. Comment, Washington and Lee Law Rev., 1964, 65; editor: Law Rev., 1966. Treas. Elect Don Sundquist to Congress Com., 1981-82, Reelect Don Sundquist to Congress Com., 1983-86. Fellow Tenn. Bar Found.; mem. ABA, Memphis and Shelby County Bar Assn. (pres. 1988, treas. 1984, bd. dirs. 1978-79), Fed. Bar Assn., Tenn. Bar Assn., Leo Bearman Sr. Am. Inn of Ct. (pres. 1995-96), Order of Coif, Omicron Delta Kappa. Roman Catholic. Avocations: hunting, tennis, reading, gardening. Office: Clifford Davis Fed Bldg 167 N Main St Ste 1107 Memphis TN 38103-1830

TURNER, JOHN GOSNEY, insurance company executive; b. Springfield, Mass., Oct. 3, 1939; s. John William and Clarence Oma (Gosney) T.; m. Leslie Corrigan, June 23, 1962; children: John Fredric, Mary Leslie, James Gosney, Andrew William. B.A., Amherst Coll., 1961; student, Advanced Mgmt. Program, Harvard U., 1980. Assoc. actuary Monarch Life Ins. Co., Springfield, Mass., 1961-67; group actuary Northwestern Nat. Life Ins. Co., Mpls., 1967-75, sr. v.p. group, 1975-79, sr. v.p., chief actuary, 1979-81, exec. v.p., chief actuary, 1981-83, pres., chief operating officer, 1983—, chmn., CEO; dir. NWNL Reins. Co., NWNL Gen. No. Life, North Atlantic Life Ins. Co. N.Y. Trustee Abbott-Northwestern Hosps., Evans Sch. Found.; chmn. Minn. Trustees of the Evans Scholars Found. Fellow Soc. Actuaries; mem. Am. Acad. Actuaries, Western Golf Assn. (dir.), Minn. Golf Assn. Club: Minikahda (Mpls.). Office: Northwestern Nat Life Ins Co PO Box 20 20 Washington Ave S Minneapolis MN 55401

TURNER, JOHN NAPIER, former prime minister of Canada, legislator; b. Richmond, Eng., June 7, 1929; s. Leonard and Phyllis (Gregory) T.; m. Geills McCrae Kilgour, May 11, 1963; children: Elizabeth, Michael, David, Andrew. BA with honors in Polit. Sci., U. B.C., Can., 1949; BA, Oxford U., Eng., 1951, BCL 1952; MA, Oxford U., 1957; postgrad., U. Paris, 1952-53; LLD (hon.), U. New Brunswick, 1968, York U., Toronto, 1969, U. B.C., 1994, U. Toronto, 1995; D. of Civil Law (hon.), Mt. Allison U., N.B., 1980. Bar: Eng. 1953, Que. 1954, Ont. 1968, B.C. 1969, Y.T. 1969, N.W.T. 1969, Barbados 1969, Trinidad 1969. With Stikeman, Elliot, Tamaki, Mercier and Turner, Montreal, Que., 1953-65, McMillan Binch, Toronto, 1976-84; M.P. for St. Lawrence-St. George Montreal, 1962-68, Ottawa-Carleton, 1968-75; parliamentary sec. to Minister of Northern Affairs and Nat. Resources, 1963-65; minister without portfolio, 1965-67; registrar-gen. Govt. of Can., 1967-68, minister of consumer and corp. affairs, 1968, solicitor-gen., 1968, minister of justice and atty.-gen. of Can., 1968-72, minister of fin., 1972-75, prime minister of Can., 1984; leader Liberal Party Can., 1984-90; mem. parliament Vancouver Quadra, 1984-93; Miller Thomson Toronto; created Queen's Counsel, Ontario and Quebec, 1968; former positions include minister without portfolio, registrar gen., minister consumer and corp. affairs, solicitor gen., minister justice and atty. gen., minister fin. Author: Senate of Canada, 1961, Politics of Purpose, 1968. Can. Track Field Champion, 1948; mem. English Track and Field Team, 1950-51. Mem. Eng. Bar Assn., Grey's Inn London, Bar. Assns. of Ont., Que., B.C., Barbados, Trinidad, Mt. Royal Club, Montreal Racquet Club, Cercle Universitaire d'Ottawa Club, Aylmer (Que.) Country Club, Queen's Club, Badminton and Racquet Club, York Club, The Vancouver Club. Liberal. Roman Catholic. Avocations: tennis, canoeing, skiing. Home: 27 Dunloe Rd Toronto, ON Canada M4V 2W4 Office: Miller Thomson, 20 Queen St W Box 27 Ste 2700, Toronto, ON Canada M5H 3S1

TURNER, JOHN SIDNEY, JR., otolaryngologist, educator; b. Bainbridge, Ga., July 25, 1930; s. John Sidney and Rose Lee (Rogers) T.; m. Betty Jane Tigner, June 5, 1955; children: Elizabeth, Rebecca, Jan Marie. BS, Emory U., 1952, MD, 1955. Diplomate Am. Bd. Otolaryngology. Intern U. Va. Hosp., 1955-56; resident in otolaryngology Duke U. Med. Ctr., 1958-61; prof. otolaryngology Emory U., Atlanta, 1961—, chmn. dept., 1961—; cons. Healthcare Partnership Cons., Atlanta, 1995—; car separatist, chief otolaryngology Emory Clinic, 1961—; area cons. in field U.S. 3d Army, 1962-69; assoc. dir. heart disease control program Fla. Bd. Health, 1956-58; Ga. state chmn. Deafness Rsch. Found., 1968—; v.p. Clifton Casualty Ins. Co., Atlanta; cons. Healthcare Partnership Cons., 1995. Mem. internat. editorial bd. Drugs jour., 1982—; Ethicals in Med. Progress, 1982—; Dialogue jour., 1988—; mem. editorial bd. Otolaryngology—Head and Neck Surgery, 1991; contbr. chpts. to books, articles to profl. jours. With USPHS, 1956-58. Recipient Appreciation award Children of Fulton County and Fulton County Health Dept., 1975. Mem. AMA, So. Med. Assn. (chmn. otolaryngology sect. 1974, cert. of appreciation 1974), Am. Acad. Otolaryngology--Head and Neck Surgery (Honor award 1994), Triological Soc. (v.p., chmn. so. sect. 1991—), Am. Acad. Otolaryngic Allergy, Ga. Soc. Otolaryngology (pres. 1973), Med. Assn. Ga., Med. Assn. Atlanta, Assn. Acad. Depts. Otolaryngology, Optimists (pres. Atlanta 1975), Alpha Omega Alpha. Democrat. Methodist. Home: 1388 Council Bluff Dr NE Atlanta GA 30345-4132 Office: Emory U Dept Otolaryngology 1365 Clifton Rd NE Atlanta GA 30307-1013

TURNER, JOSEPH FRANCIS, JR., hospital executive; children: Kathleen, Joseph, Beth and Amy (twins). BS in Fin., Gannon U.; MBA, George Washington U. Pres., CEO Cen. Suffolk Hosp., Riverhead, N.Y.; mem. various coms. Nassau/Suffolk Hosp. Coun.; appointee Suffolk County Bd. Health, 1993—. Host: (weekly cable talk show) Health Monitor. Named Man of Yr., Suffolk County Boy Scouts, 1994. Mem. Am. Hosp. Assn. (regional adv. bd.), Am. Coll. Healthcare Execs. (chair ethics com., membership com., chair task force that established Learning Resource Ctr., Sr.-level Healthcare Exec. award 1994), Healthcare Assn. of N.Y. State (various coms.), Riverhead C. of C. (bd. dirs., 2d v.p.) Office: Central Suffolk Hosp 1300 Roanoke Ave Riverhead NY 11901-2058

TURNER, KATHLEEN, actress; b. Springfield, Mo., June 19, 1954; m. Jay Weiss, 1984; 1 child, Rachel Ann. Student, Cen. Sch. of Speech and Drama, London, Southwest Mo. State U.; BFA, U. Md. various theater roles, Broadway debut: Gemini, 1978, Cat on a Hot Tin Roof, 1990, Indiscretions, 1995; appeared in TV series The Doctors, 1977; films include Body Heat, 1981, A Breed Apart, 1982, The Man With Two Brains, 1983, Crimes of Passion, 1984, Romancing the Stone, 1984, Prizzi's Honor (Golden Globe award for best actress), 1985, The Jewel of the Nile, 1985, Peggy Sue Got Married, (D.W. Griffith award for best actress, Oscar nomination for best actress) 1986, Julia and Julia, 1988, Switching Channels, 1988, Who Framed Roger Rabbit, 1988, Accidental Tourist, 1988, The War of the Roses, 1989, V.I. Warshawski, 1991, Undercover Blues, 1993, House of Cards, 1993, Serial Mom, 1994, Naked in New York, 1994; dir. (Showtime Cable movie) Leslie's Folly, 1994; also performed in radio shows with the BBC, 1992, 93. Office: ICM 8942 Wilshire Blvd Beverly Hills CA 90211*

TURNER, LANA (JULIA JEAN MILDRED FRANCES TURNER), actress; b. Wallace, Idaho, Feb. 8, 1921; d. Virgil and Mildred T.; m. Artie Shaw, Feb. 8, 1940 (div.); m. Steven Crane, 1942 (div.); m. Bob Topping (div.); m. Lex Barker (div.); m. Fred May, Nov. 27, 1960 (div.); m. Robert Eaton (div.); m. Ronald Dante. Ed. pub. schs.; Presentation Convent, San Francisco. Motion picture actress 1937—; appeared in motion pictures including Love Finds Andy Hardy, 1938, Dramatic School, 1938, Calling Dr. Kildare, Those Glamour Girls, Dancing Co-ed, 1939, Two Girls on Broadway, We Who Are Young, 1940, Ziegfeld Girl, Dr. Jekyll and Mr. Hyde, Honky Tonk, Johnny Eager, 1941, Somewhere I'll Find You, Slightly Dangerous, 1942, Marriage Is a Private Affair, Women's Army, 1944, Keep Your Powder Dry, Week End at the Waldorf, Cass Timberlane, Homecoming, 1947, The Merry Widow, 1951, The Bad and the Beautiful, 1952, Latin Lovers, Flame and the Flesh, Betrayed, The Sea Chase, The Prodigal, Rains of Ranchipur, Another Time, 1958, Imitation of Life, 1959, By Love Possessed, 1961, Bachelor in Paradise, Who's Got the Action, Love Has Many Faces, Madame X, The Big Cube, Persecution, Portrait in Black, Bittersweet Love, 1976; appeared in TV series The Survivors, 1969, Falcon Crest, 1982-83; also numerous theatrical appearances. Author: The Lady, The Legend, The Truth, 1983. *Died June 29, 1995.*

TURNER, LARRY WILLIAM, agricultural engineer, educator; b. Cin., Dec. 18, 1954; s. Roy Obertate and Martha Lucille (McNeely) T.; m. Lois V. Lynch, Oct. 23, 1976; children: Molly Elizabeth, Amy Rebekah, Clay Matthew. BS, Purdue U., 1976, MS in Agrl. Engring., 1978; PhD, U. Ky., 1984. Lic. profl. engr., 1980. Grad. instr. Purdue U., West Lafayette, Ind. 1976-78; cons. engr. Turner Engring., Rising Sun, Ind., 1980-81; extension agrl. engr. U. Ky., Lexington, 1978-80, rsch. specialist, 1981-84, asst. extension prof., 1984-89, assoc. extension prof., 1989-94, extension prof., 1994—; vis. scientist Silsoe Rsch. Inst., England, 1992-93; cons. Smith Constrn., State of Ky. Contbr. articles to profl. jours. Chmn. bd. Christ United Meth. Ch., Lexington, 1980, lay leader, 1983; evangelism chmn. St. Andrew's United Meth. Ch., 1989-90, chmn. bd., 1990-91. Mem. Am. Soc. of Agrl. Engrs., Am. Soc. of Heating, Refrigerating and Air Conditioning Engrs., Tau Beta Pi, Alpha Epsilon, Phi Kappa Phi, Gamma Sigma Delta. Republican. Methodist. Avocations: painting, drawing, fishing, basketball. Office: U Ky Agrl Engring Dept Lexington KY 40546

TURNER, LEE, travel company executive; b. 1952. BS, Worcester Polytechnic Inst., 1974; MBA, Dartmouth, 1976. With Baxter Healthcare, Deerfield, Ill., 1976-79, 82-87, Southeastern Pub. Svc. Co., Miami Beach, Fla., 1979-82; exec. v.p., CFO BTI Ams., Inc., Northbrook, Ill., 1987—. Office: BTI Ams Inc 400 Skokie Blvd Fl 8 Northbrook IL 60062-2816

TURNER, LEE S., JR., chemical engineer,consultant, former utilities executive; b. Dallas, Nov. 5, 1926; s. James A. and Fay Sims; m. Donetta Mae Johnson, Jan. 17, 1947. BCE, Tex. A&M U., 1948; JD, So. Meth. U., 1957. Engr. Dallas Power & Light Co., 1948, various exec. positions, pres., chief exec., 1967-76; dir. Tex. Utilities Co., 1967-82; exec. v.p. Tex. Utilities Co., Dallas, 1976-84; cons., 1989—. Trustee Com. for Econ. Devel., Southwestern Med. Found.; past pres., bd. dirs. Dallas Citizens Coun.; bd. dirs. So. Meth. U. Found. for Sci. and Engring.; past chmn. Children's Med. Ctr.; past chmn. United Way, YMCA, Community Coun. of Greater Dallas; past pres. Greater Dallas Ahead, Inc., Dallas Assembly. With U.S. Army, 1945-46. Mem. ABA, Am. Arbitration Assn. Presbyterian.

TURNER, LESLIE MARIE, federal official; b. Neptune, N.J., Oct. 2, 1957. BS, NYU, 1980; JD, Georgetown U., 1985. Law clk. Cole, Raywid & Braverman, Washington, 1984-85; jud. clk. to Hon. William C. Pryor U.S. Ct. Appeals (D.C. cir.), Washington, 1985-86; assoc. Akin, Gump, Strauss, Hauer & Feld, L.L.P., Washington, 1986-93; asst. sec. for territorial and internat. affairs Dept. Interior, Washington, 1993—. Office: Dept Interior Territorial & Internat Affairs 1849 C St NW Washington DC 20240

TURNER, LISA PHILLIPS, human resources executive; b. Waltham, Mass., Apr. 10, 1951; d. James Sinclair and Virginia (Heathcote) T. BA in Edn. and Philosophy magna cum laude, Washington Coll., Chestertown, Md., 1974; AS in Electronics Tech., AA in Engring., Palm Beach Jr. Coll., 1982; MBA, Nova U., 1986, DSc, 1989; PhD, Kennedy Western U. 1990. Cert. pers. adminstr., quality engr., human resource profl.; lic. USCG capt. Founder, pres. Turner's Bicycle Svc., Inc., Delray Beach, Fla., 1975-80; electronics engr., quality engr. Audio Engring. and Video Arts, Boca Raton, 1980-81; tech. writing instr. Palm Beach Jr. Coll., Lake Worth, Fla., 1981-82; adminstr. tng. and devel. Mitel Inc., Boca Raton, 1982-88; mgr. communications and employee rels. Modular Computer Systems, Inc., Ft. Lauderdale, Fla., 1988-89; U.S. mktg. project mgr. Mitel, Inc., Boca Raton, Fla., 1990-91; v.p. human resources Connectronics, Inc., Ft. Lauderdale, Fla., 1991-93; mgr. human resources Sensormatic Electronics Corp., Boca Raton, Fla., 1993—. With USCG Aux. Mem. ASTD, Am. Soc. for Pers. Adminstrn., Internat. Assn. Quality Circles, Am. Soc. Quality Control, Fla. Employment Mgmt. Assn., Am. Acad. Mgmt., Employment Assn. Fla., Am. Capts. Assn., Citizens Police Acad. Home: PO Box 4687 Boynton Beach FL 33424-4687 Office: Sensormatic Electronics Corp 6600 Congress Ave Boca Raton FL 33487

TURNER, LOYD LEONARD, advertising executive, public relations executive; b. Claude, Tex., Nov. 5, 1917; s. James R. and Maude (Brown) T.; m. Lee Madeleine Barr, Apr. 13, 1944; children: Terry Lee, Loyd Lee. Student, Tex. Tech. U., 1935-36, Okla. Bapt. U., 1936-37; BA, Baylor U., 1939, MA, 1940; postgrad., U. Pa., 1940-42. Instr. dept. English U. Pa., Phila., 1940-42; pub. relations coordinator Consol. Vultee Aircraft Corp., San Diego, 1946-48; dir. pub. relations Consol. Vultee Aircraft Corp., Fort Worth, 1948-53; asst. to pres. Fort Worth div. Gen. Dynamics Corp., 1953-72; exec. asst. to pres. and chmn. bd. Tandy Corp., Fort Worth, 1972-76; v.p. Tandy Corp., 1976-83; sr. v.p. Witherspoon and Assocs., Inc.,, Fort Worth, 1986—, also bd. dirs.; mem. Gov.'s Com. on Public Sch. Edn., Tex., 1966-69; pres. Tex. Council Major Sch. Dists., 1968-69. Author: The ABC of Clear Writing, 1954. Bd. dirs. Tarrant County chpt. ARC, 1956-59; bd. dirs. Pub. Communication Found. for North Tex., 1970-76, Tex. Com. Pub. Edn., 1961-69; bd. dirs. Ft. Worth Child Study Ctr., 1974-81, 85-88, v.p., 1986-88; bd. dirs. Parenting Guidance Ctr., 1976-78, Longhorn coun. Boy Scouts Am., 1976-91, One Broadway Plaza, 1978-88; planning and research coun. United Way, Tarrant County, 1976-80; bd. dirs. Casa Manana Musicals, 1978—, pres., 1978-80; bd. dirs. Fort Worth Citizens Organized Against Crime, 1976-90, vice chmn., 1978-89; bd. dirs. Jr. Achievement Tarrant County, 1982-87, North Central chpt. March of Dimes, 1983-84; mem. Christian edn. coordinating bd. Bapt. Gen. Conv., Tex., 1976-80; trustee Ft. Worth Pub. Libr. Bd., 1953-63, pres., 1958-63; trustee Ft. Worth Bd. Edn., 1959-71, pres., 1965-71; trustee Baylor U., Waco, Tex., 1980-89. Served with USAAF, 1942-46. Named Library Trustee of Yr. Tex. Library Assn., 1961, Paul Harris fellow Rotary Internat., 1983; recipient Silver Beaver award Boy Scouts Am., 1986. Mem. Pub. Relations Soc. Am. (pres. N.Tex. chpt. 1977), Pub. Rel. Soc. Am. (Paul M. Lund Pub. Service award 1980), Nat. Mgmt. Assn., Tex. Congress of Parents and Tchrs. (hon. life mem.), West Tex. C. of C. (bd. dirs. 1982-87, v.p. 1985-87, Leadership award 1966, 69), NEA (pres.

Best Bd. of Large Sch. Systems in U.S. 1968), Tex. Assn. of Sch. Bds. (bd. dirs. 1966-71, Outstanding Service award 1971), Advt. Club of Fort Worth (pres. 1977-78), Air Force Assn. (Spl. citation 1962), Assn. for Higher Edn. of N. Tex. (vice chmn. 1979-82), Fort Worth C. of C. (bd. dirs. 1974-76, 78-81, 83-87, vice chmn. 1985-87), Arts Council of Fort Worth (dir. 1973-75, 80-89), Tex. Assn. Bus. (bd. dirs. 1977-82, 83-86), Tex. Research League (bd. dirs. 1979-87), Baylor U. Devel. Council (pres. 1975-77), Baylor U. Alumni Assn. (bd. dirs. 1958-61), Fort Worth Safety Council (bd. dirs. 1980-83), Am. Advt. Fedn. (Silver Medal award 1981), Soc. Profl. Journalists (pres. Fort Worth chpt. 1961-62). Baptist. Clubs: Admirals, Bear, Frog. Lodge: Rotary (pres. 1974-75; William B. Todd Service Above Self award 1987). Home: 3717 Echo Trail Fort Worth TX 76109-3432 Office: Witherspoon and Assocs Inc 1000 W Weatherford St Fort Worth TX 76102-1842

TURNER, LYNNE ALISON (MRS. PAUL H. SINGER), harpist; b. St. Louis, July 31, 1941; d. Sol and Evelyn (Klein) T.; m. Paul H. Singer, June 2, 1963; children: Bennett Lloyd, Rachel E. Singer Sullivan. Student, Paris Conservatory Music (Premier Prix Hors Concours-Harp), 1959-60; studied with Pierre Jamet. Harpist Chgo. Symphony Orch., 1962—, acting prin. harpist, 1994—; soloist Chgo. Symphony Orch., Israel Philharm. Orch., other maj. orchs. in U.S. and Europe, also chamber groups; founding mem. L'Ensemble Recamier, The Chgo. Duo (harp and violin); instr. harp Sch. Music, DePaul U., Chgo., 1976-86; instr. harp Lake Forest Coll., 1988-90; instr. pvt. students. Recipient 1st prize 2d Internat. Harp Competition, Israel, 1962. Mem. Am. Harp Soc., Chgo. Hist. Soc. (costume com.), Women's Assn. Chgo. Symphony Orch., Antiquarian Soc. Art Inst. Chgo., Internat. Visitors Ctr. Chgo., Chgo. Arts Club, The Casino Club. Office: Orch Hall 220 S Michigan Ave Chicago IL 60604-2508

TURNER, MALCOLM ELIJAH, biomathematician, educator; b. Atlanta, May 27, 1929; s. Malcolm Elijah and Margaret (Parker) T.; m. Ann Clay Bowers, Sept. 16, 1948; children: Malcolm Elijah IV, Allison Ann, Clay Shumate, Margaret Jean; m. Rachel Patricia Farmer, Feb. 1, 1968; children: Aleta van Riper, Leila Samantha, Alexis St. John, Walter McCamy. Student, Emory U., 1947-48; B.A., Duke U., 1952; M.Exptl. Stats., N.C. State U., 1955, Ph.D., 1959. Analytical statistician Communicable Disease Center, USPHS, Atlanta, 1953; rsch. assoc. U. Cin., 1955, asst. prof., 1955-58; asst. statistician N.C. State U., Raleigh, 1957-58; assoc. prof. Med. Coll. Va., Richmond, 1958-63, chmn. div. biometry, 1959-63; prof., chmn. dept. statistics and biometry Emory U., Atlanta, 1963-69; chmn. dept. biomath., prof. biostats. and biomath. U. Ala., Birmingham, 1970-82, prof. biostats. and biomath., 1982—; instr. summers Yale U., 1966, U. Calif. at Berkeley, 1971, Vanderbilt U., 1975; prof. U. Kans., 1968-69; vis. prof. Atlanta U., 1969; cons. to industry. Mem. editorial bd. So. Med. Jour., 1990—; contbr. articles to profl. jours. Fellow Ala. Acad. Sci., Am. Statis. Assn. (hon.), AAAS (hon.); mem. AAUP, AMA (affiliate), Biometrics Soc. (mng. editor Biometrics 1962-69), Soc. for Indsl. and Applied Math., Mensa, Sigma Xi, Phi Kappa Phi, Phi Delta Theta, Phi Sigma. Home: 1734 Tecumseh Trl Pelham AL 35124-1012 *The logic of induction is the quest.*

TURNER, MARGERY AUSTIN, government agency administrator; b. Ithaca, N.Y., July 10, 1955; d. William Weaver and Elizabeth Jane (Hallstrum) Austin; m. James Charles Turner, Aug. 26, 1979; children: James Austin, Benjamin Phillip. BA, Cornell U., 1977; M Urban Planning, George Washington U., 1984. Rschr. Urban Inst., Washington, 1977-88, dir. housing rsch., 1988-93; dep. asst. sec. for rsch. U.S. Dept. HUD, Washington, 1993—. Author: Housing Market Impacts of Rent Control, 1990; co-author: Urban Housing in the 1980's, 1985, Future U.S. Housing Policy, 1987, Opportunities Denied, Opportunities Diminished, 1991, Housing Markets and Residential Mobility, 1993. Mem., coach Boys and Girls Club, Camp Springs, Md., 1990—. Mem. Lambda Alpha.

TURNER, MARSHALL CHITTENDEN, JR., venture capitalist; b. Santa Monica, Calif., 1941; s. Marshall C. and Winifred K. Turner; m. Ann Curran, 1965; children: Erin, Benjamin, Brian. BSME, Stanford U., 1964, MS in Product Design, 1965; MBA, Harvard U., 1970. Indsl. designer Mattel Toy Co., Hawthorne, Calif., 1965; rsch. engr. GM Defense Rsch. Lab., Santa Barbara, Calif., 1965-66; mng. engr. NIH, Bethesda, Md., 1966-68; White House fellow Washington, 1970-71; asst. to dep. adminstr. EPA, Washington, 1971-73; assoc. Crocker Assocs., L.P., San Francisco, 1973-75; v.p. fin., chief oper. officer Sierra R.R., 1973-75; chmn., pres. Liquid Crystal Tech., Inc., San Leandro, Calif., 1975-80; gen. ptnr. Taylor & Turner Assocs., Ltd., San Francisco, 1981—; bd. dirs. Image Data Corp., San Antonio, CongniSeis Devel. Corp., Houston, Alliance Tech. Fund, N.Y., Remanco Internat., Inc., Wilmington, Mass.; bd. dirs. Corp. Pub. Broadcasting, Washington, chmn., 1990-92. Contbr. articles to profl. jours. Bd. dirs. Sta. KQED, Inc., San Francisco, 1977-87, chmn., 1985-87, acting CEO, 1993; trustee Reed Union Sch. dist., Tiburon, Calif., 1977-81, chmn., 1979-81; bd. dirs. George Lucas Ednl. Found., San Rafael, Calif., 1992—, PBS, Alexandria, Va., 1993—, PBS Enterprises, Inc., 1992—; trustee Mus. TV and Radio, N.Y.C., 1991-92. Lt. USPHS, 1966-68. Recipient Creative design award Machinery Inst., 1965. Avocations: fly fishing, theatrical set design. Office: Penthouse 10 220 Montgomery St San Francisco CA 94104

TURNER, MARTA DAWN, youth program specialist; b. Morgantown, W.V., Oct. 7, 1954; d. Trubie Lemard and Dorothy Genevieve (Helmick) T.; m. David Michael Dunning, Mar. 1, 1980. Student, Royal Acad. Dramatic Art, London, 1975; BA with honors, Chatham Coll., 1976; grad. cert. in arts adminstrn., Adelphi U., 1982; MA Devel. Drama, Hunter Coll., 1988. Cert. video prodn. specialist. Asst. dir. Riverside Communications, N.Y.C., 1985-88; dir. drama, video youth environ. group Water Proof, Cornell Coop. Extension, 1989-91; playwright, dir. Awareness Players, The Disabled Theatre of Maine, 1993-95. Exec. prodr. video projects including Hispanic City Sounds, Time for Peace, Home, Home in Inwood, 1985—; asst. dir., dir. video series Riverside at Worship, 1985-88. Mem. bd. dirs. Trinity Presbyn. Ch., N.Y.C., 1980-90, Am. Diabetes Assn., 1986-87. Avocations: swimming, Scrabble, karate, Marilyn Monroe fan/memoribilia collection. Home and Office: 818 Ohio St Apt 90 Bangor ME 04401-3859

TURNER, MARY LEE, data processing executive; b. Nashville, Dec. 20, 1945; d. William Hutcheson and Lorene (Clark) Hunter; m. Edward L. Turner III, Aug. 29, 1968; 1 child, E. Brantley. BA in Math., Vanderbilt U. 1967. Various field positions IBM, N.Y.C., 1967-79, br. mgr. securities br. office, 1979-81; adminstrv. asst. of Office Chief Exec. Officer, IBM, Armonk, N.Y., 1981-82; dir. mktg. N.W. region IBM, San Francisco, 1982-83, regional mgr. N.W. region, 1983-85; dir. bus. evaluation Corp. Hdqrs., IBM, Armonk, 1985-87; v.p. ops. Data Systems div. IBM, White Plains, N.Y., 1987-88; asst. gen. mgr. mktg. Enterprise Systems Line of Bus. Data Systems div., Somers, N.Y., 1988-89; dir. communications corp. hdqrs., IBM, Armonk, 1989-90, v.p. communications, 1990—; bd. govs. Pacific Stock Exch., San Francisco, 1983—; bd. dirs. IBM Credit Corp., Stamford, Conn. Episcopalian. Office: IBM Old Orchard Rd Armonk NY 10504

TURNER, MICHAEL GRISWOLD, advertising executive; b. Pitts., Mar. 2, 1925; s. James Jewett and Madelaine Eunice (Griswold) T.; m. Elizabeth Anne Tufel, Sept. 8, 1951; children: Jason A., Michael G., Nanci S. Turner Steveson, James A., Craig C., Ashley S. BA cum laude, Princeton U., 1949. Rsch. asst. to mgmt. supr. Benton & Bowles, N.Y.C., 1950-60; dir. Benton & Bowles, London, 1960-63; mgmt. supr. Benton & Bowles, N.Y.C., 1963-66; exec. v.p. dir. Ogilvy & Mather, N.Y.C., 1966-70, Houston, 1970-85, Washington, 1985-86; vice chmn. Earle Palmer Brown, Bethesda, Atlanta, Md., 1986-91; chmn. Turner & Turner Comm., Inc., Atlanta, 1992—; cons. and lectr. in field. Contbr. articles to trade jours. With USNR, 1943-46, PTO. Mem. Gipsy Trail Club (vice commodore 1968-76), Bay Head Yacht Club (N.J.). Home: 750 Olde Clubs Dr Alpharetta GA 30202 Office: Turner & Turner Comm Inc 1168 14th Pl Atlanta GA 30309

TURNER, MICHAEL STANLEY, physics educator; b. L.A., July 29, 1949; s. Paul Joseph and Janet Mary (Lindholm) T.; m. Terri Lee Shields, Aug. 1978 (div. Sept. 1980); m. Barbara Lynn Ahlberg, Sept. 10, 1988; children: Rachel Mary, Joseph Lucien. BS in Physics, Calif. Inst. Tech., 1971; MS in Physics, Stanford U., 1973, PhD in Physics, 1978. Enrico Fermi fellow U. Chgo., 1978-80, from asst. to assoc. prof., 1980-85, prof., 1985—; scientist Fermi Nat. Accelerator Lab, Batavia, Ill., 1983—; trustee Aspen (Colo.) Ctr. Physics, 1984—, pres., 1989-93; Halley lectr. Oxford U., 1994. Author: (with E.W. Kolb) The Early Universe, 1990; contbr. over 150 articles to

profl. jours. Sloan fellow A.P. Sloan Found., 1983-88. Fellow Am. Phys. Soc. (mem. exec. bd. 1992-94, chmn. publ. oversight com. 1993-94); mem. Am. Astron. Soc. (Helen B. Warner prize 1984), Internat. Astron. Union, Sigma Xi. Office: U Chgo Enrico Fermi Inst 5640 S Ellis Ave Chicago IL 60637-1433*

TURNER, NORRIS, marketing professional; b. Angelina, Tex., May 3, 1934; s. Ezra and Frankie Turner; m. Katherine Fields, Aug. 16, 1962; 1 child, Tammie Diatrice. BS, Fisk U., 1968. Cert. real estate appraiser; lic. notary pub., ins. agt. Admission officer West Point N.Y., L.A., 1971; dir. vets. programs, profl. recorder, in-sch. coord. L.A. Urban League, 1983; loan officer Empire of Am., Inglewood, Calif., 1983-86; account exec. Imperial Thrift & Loan, Burbank, Calif., 1986-88; v.p., dir. The Mortgage Acad., Ventura, Calif., 1988—; instr. Compton (Calif.) Coll., 1977-78. Author: A Balance Approach to Career Training, 1992. HAC mem. Century Freeway, State of Calif., 1982; chairperson L.A. City Vets. Svcs., 1980-81; treas. reelection svc. L.A. Calif. Reps., 1983; pres. L.A. Calif. Day-Care Sch., 1988-89; mem., vol. L.A. Urban League, 1990-92; v.p. local dist. Rep. party, 1987-88. With U.S. Army, 1956-58. Recipient awards L.A. City Coun., 1980, Pres. U.S.A., 1978-79, Cert. of Appreciation U.S. Mil. Acad., 1980, Hon. Admissions Officer award U.S. Mil. Acad., 1980, award L.A. Urban League, 1981-82. Mem. Am. Banking Assn. (treas. 1980-81). Lutheran. Home: 8813 S 4th Ave Inglewood CA 90305-2811

TURNER, NORV, professional football coach. Head coach Washington Redskins, 1994—. Office: Washington Redskins PO Box 17247 Washington DC 20041

TURNER, PETER MERRICK, retired manufacturing company executive; b. Toronto, Ont., Can., July 4, 1931; s. William Ian MacKenzie and Marjorie (Merrick) T.; m. Beverley Brophey, Sept. 13, 1958 (dec.); children: Peter Merrick, Christopher Harold, David MacKenzie; m. Alix Johanna Houston, Aug. 17, 1991. B.A.Sc., U. Toronto, 1954; M.B.A., Harvard U., 1956. Staff asst. controllers dept. Bridgeport Brass Co., Conn., 1956-57; sec. treas. Perkins Paper Products Co., Montreal, Que., Can., 1957-58; with Texaco Can. Ltd., Montreal, 1958-68, treas., 1966-68; dir. budgeting and planning, corp. devel. Molson Breweries Ltd., Montreal, 1968—; v.p. planning Molson Breweries Can. Ltd., 1968-70; v.p. corp. devel. Molson Industries Ltd., Toronto, 1970-72; exec. v.p. Bennett Pump Inc., Muskegon, Mich., 1972-73, pres., chief exec. officer, 1973-78; v.p. corp. planning and devel. Sealed Power Corp., Muskegon, 1978-83, group v.p. internat., 1981-83, group v.p. Gen. Products Group, 1984-89; v.p. bus. devel. SPX Corp., Muskegon, 1989-91, v.p. ops., 1991-92, v.p. corp. planning and devel., 1992-94; ret., 1994; bd. dirs. Grand Trunk Corp., Grand Trunk Western Ry., Domestic Four Leasing Corp.; lectr. extension dept. McGill U., 1960-67, Grand Valley State Coll., 1979. Gen. chmn. red shield appeal Montreal Salvation Army, 1969-70; chmn. McGill Assocs., Montreal, 1969-70; bd. dirs. Hackley Hosp., 1975-94, West Shore Symphony Orch., 1976-94; bd. dirs. Muskegon C.C. Found., 1976-94. Mem. Mount Royal Club, Granite Club, Lake O'Hara Trail Club, Zeta Psi. Episcopalian. Home: 66 Rathnelly Ave, Toronto, ON Canada M4V 2M6

TURNER, PHILIP MICHAEL, university official and dean, author; b. West Acton, Mass., Nov. 26, 1948; s. William Albert and Evelyn Olena (Peterson) T.; m. Lis Jane VanderBeke, Aug. 16, 1969; children: Gabrielle, Adrienne. BS in Edn., Boston State Coll., 1970; MS, U. Wis. at La Crosse, 1972; MSLS, East Tex. State U., 1977, EdD, 1977. Tchr. math. Edgewood Jr. High Sch., Merritt Island, Fla., 1969-71; ptnr. Video Guide Prodn. Co., Denver, 1973; libr. media specialist Edison Jr. High Sch., Green Bay, Wis., 1973-76; prof. libr. sci. U. Ala., Tuscaloosa, 1977-88; dean Grad. Sch. Libr. and Info. Studies, asst. vice chancellor for acad. affairs U. Ala. System, Tuscaloosa, 1988—. Author: Handbook for In-School Media Personnel, 1980, Helping Teachers Teach, 1985, 2d edit., 1993, Casebook for Helping Teachers Teach, 1988. Vol. Meals on Wheels, Tuscaloosa, 1987—. Recipient Outstanding Commitment To Teaching award U. Ala. Alumni Assn., 1979, Outstanding Svc. award Ala. Libr. and Media Prodrs., 1987, publ. award Div. Sch. Libr. Media Specialists, 1987, award for mng. info. tech., 1994; named Libr. of Yr., Beta Phi Mu, 1991. Mem. ALA, Assn. Sch. Librs. (chair rsch. com. 1987-90, bd. dirs. 1990—), Assn. for Ednl. Communication and Tech. (chair evaluation com. 1979). Unitarian. Office: Univ Ala Sch Libr 2d Info Studies PO Box 870252 Tuscaloosa AL 35487-0252

TURNER, RALPH HERBERT, sociologist, educator; b. Effingham, Ill., Dec. 15, 1919; s. Herbert Turner and Hilda Pearl (Bohn) T.; m. Christine Elizabeth Hanks, Nov. 2, 1943; children: Lowell Ralph, Cheryl Christine. B.A., U So. Calif., 1941, M.A., 1942; postgrad., U. Wis., 1942-43; Ph.D., U. Chgo., 1948. Rsch. assoc. Am. Coun. Race Relations, 1947-48; faculty UCLA, 1948—, prof. sociology and anthropology, 1959-90, prof. emeritus, 1990—, chmn. dept. sociology, 1963-68; chmn. Acad. Senate U. Calif. System, 1983-84; bd. dirs. Founds. Fund for Rsch. in Psychiatry; vis. summer prof. U. Wash., 1960, U. Hawaii, 1962; vis. scholar Australian Nat. U., 1972; vis. prof. U. Ga., 1975, Ben Gurion U., Israel, 1983; vis. fellow Nuffield Coll. Oxford U., 1980; disting. vis. prof. Am. U., Cairo, Egypt, 1983; adj. prof. China Acad. Social Scis., Beijing, People's Republic China, 1986; faculty rsch. lectr. UCLA, 1986-87. Author: (with L. Killian) Collective Behavior, 1957, 2d edit., 1972, 3d edit., 1987, The Social Context of Ambition, 1964, Robert Park on Social Control and Collective Behavior, 1967, Family Interaction, 1970, Earthquake Prediction and Public Policy, 1975, (with J. Nigg, D. Paz, B. Young) Community Response to Earthquake Threat in Southern California., 1980, (with J. Nigg and D. Paz) Waiting for Disaster, 1986; editorial cons., 1959-62; editor: Sociometry, 1962-64; acting editor: Ann. Rev. of Sociology, 1977-78; assoc. editor, 1978-79, editor, 1980-86; adv. editor: Am. Jour. Sociology, 1954-56, Sociology and Social Research, 1961-74; editorial staff: Am. Sociol. Rev., 1955-56; assoc. editor: Social Problems, 1959-62, 67-69; cons. editor: Sociol. Inquiry, 1968-73, Western Sociol. Rev., 1975-79; mem. editorial bd. Mass Emergencies, 1975-79, Internat. Jour. Critical Sociology, 1974-76, Symbolic Interaction, 1977-90. Mem. behavioral scis. study sect. NIH, 1961-66, chmn., 1963-64; dir.-at-large Social Sci. Rsch. Coun., 1965-66; chmn. panel on pub. policy implications of earthquake predictions Nat. Acad. Scis., 1974-75, also mem. earthquake study del. to Peoples Republic of China, 1976; mem. policy adv. bd. So. Calif. Earthquake Preparedness program, 1987-92, mem. com. social edn. and action L.A. Presbytery, 1954-56. Served to lt. (j.g.) USNR, 1943-46. Recipient Faculty prize Coll. Letters and Scis. UCLA, 1985; Faculty Rsch. fellow Social Sci. Coun., 1953-56; Sr. Fulbright scholar U.K., 1956-57; Guggenheim fellow, U.K., 1964-65. Mem. AAAS (exch. del. to China 1988), AAUP, Am. Sociol. Assn. (coun. 1959-64, chmn. social psychology sect. 1960-61, pres. 1968-69, chmn. sect. theoretical sociology 1973-74, chmn. collective behavior and social movements sect. 1983-84, Cooley-Mead award 1987), Pacific Sociol. Assn. (pres. 1957), Internat. Sociol. Assn. (coun. 1974-82, v.p. 1978-82), Soc. Study Social Problems (exec. com. 1962-63), Soc. for Study Symbolic Interaction (pres. 1982-83, Charles Horton Cooley award 1978, George Herbert Mead award 1990), Sociol. Rsch. Assn. (pres. 1989-90), Am. Coun. of Learned Soc. (exec. com. of coun. 1990-93), UCLA Emeriti Assn. (pres. 1992-93). Home: 1126 Chautauqua Blvd Pacific Palisades CA 90272-3808 Office: UCLA 405 Hilgard Ave Los Angeles CA 90024-1301

TURNER, RICHARD STANLEY, health care financial executive; b. Adak, Alaska, June 22, 1948; s. John Paul and Roselyn (Duncan) T.; m. Carla Ann Williams, Sept. 7, 1969; children: Allison Leigh, Evan Patrick. AA in Bus. Administrn., DeKalb Community Coll., Clarkston, Ga., 1976; BBA in Accounting summa cum laude, Ga. State U., 1977. CPA, Ga. Mgr. br. office Volunteer Contracting Inc. (a div. H.E. Collins Contracting, Inc. of Chattanooga), Atlanta, 1973-74; asst. bus. mgr. Ben Jernigan Chevrolet Co. (now Tom Jumper Chevrolet Co.), Atlanta, 1974; audit mgr. Arthur Young & Co. Atlanta, 1977-82; v.p. controller Health Group, Inc., Nashville, 1982-85; v.p. fin./chief fin. officer Healthdyne, Inc., Marietta, Ga., 1985-87; v.p. fin., chief fin. officer Care Plus, Inc., Ft. Lauderdale, Fla., 1987—. Served with USAR, 1968-74. Mem. Fin. Execs. Inst., Am. Mgmt. Assn., Healthcare Fin. Mgmt. Assn., Am. Inst. CPA's, Ga. Soc. CPA's, Nat. Assn. Accts. Home: 390 Camelot Dr Fayetteville GA 30214-3641 Office: Care Plus Inc 6700 N Andrews Ave Suite 700 Fort Lauderdale FL 33309

TURNER, ROBBY, guitarist; b. Apr. 6, 1962; s. Doyle and Bernice R.; m. Tonda Williams, Jan. 16, 1994; 1 child, Bobby. Albums include:

Highwaymen II (The Highwaymen), Dixie Narco (Primal Scream), Otis (Mojo Nixon), Cowboys, Sister, Rascals & Dirt (Waylon Jennings), Across the Borderline (Willie Nelson), Music for Lovers (Ace Cannon), Sweet Dreams (Ace Cannon), Two Dumb for New York City (Waylon Jennings), Rhythm, Country and Blues (various artists), Elvis, The Tribute (various artists), Waymore Blues Part II (Waylon Jennings), New Miserable Experience (Gin Blossoms); motion picture soundtracks: Dick Tracy, Harley Davidson and the Marlboro Man, Honeymoon in Vegas, 8 Seconds, Maverick; live performances and recs. with major stars including Johnny Cash, Bob Dylan, Vince Gill, Chet Atkins, Clint Black, Reba McEntire, Roy Clark, Glen Campbell, Lyle Lovett, Mickey Gilley, Paul Simon, Bonnie Raitt, Kris Kristofferson, Ray Charles, Aaron Neville, Charlie Rich, B.B. King, Emmylou Harris, Tricia Yearwood, Waylon Jennings, Natalie Cole, Patti La Belle, Mary Chapin Carpenter, Jerry Lee Lewis, Charlie Pride, Ronnie Milsap, Patti Smythe, many others; TV appearances include Farm Aid, Saturday Night Live, CNN, New Country, Nashville Now, The Tonight Show, Dick Clark, The Late Show with David Letterman, many others. Recipient Premier Player award NARAS, 1986. Office: 543 Doral Country Dr Nashville TN 37221

TURNER, ROBERT COMRIE, composer; b. Montreal, Que., Can., June 6, 1920; s. William Thomson and Myrtle Wellsteed (Snowdon) T.; m. Sara Nan Scott, June 30, 1949; children: Alden, Martin, Carolyn. BM, McGill U., 1943, MusD, 1953; student, Royal Coll. Music, 1947-48; MusM, George Peabody Coll. Tchrs., 1950. Sr. music producer Canadian Broadcasting Corp., Vancouver, B.C., 1952-68; lectr. in music U. B.C., Vancouver, 1955-57; asst. prof. music Acadia U., Wolfville, N.S., Can., 1968-69; prof. composition U. Manitoba, Winnipeg, 1969-85; prof. emeritus U. Manitoba, 1985—. Over 70 compositions including Opening Night: A Theatre Overture, 1955, The Third Day (Easter Cantata), 1962, Symphony for Strings, 1960, Capriccio Concertante, 1975, Third String Quartet, 1975, opera The Brideship, 1967, Trio Transition for Violin, Cello and Piano, 1969, The Phoenix and the Turtle, 1964, Concerto for Two Pianos and Orchestra, 1971, Johann's Gift to Christmas, 1972, Eidolons, 1972, Variations on the Prairie Settler's Song, 1974, From a Different Country, 1976, Lament for Linos, 1978, Amoroso Canto, 1978, Shadow Pieces I (after Joseph Cornell), 1981, opera Vile Shadows, 1983, Symphony in One Movement, 1983, Encounters I-IX, 1984, Time for Three, 1985, Playhouse Music, 1986, Concerto for Viola and Orchestra, 1987, Shades of Autumn, 1987, Manitoba Memoir, 1989, Third Symphony, 1990, A Group of Seven, 1991, The River of Time, 1994, House of Shadows, 1994; All-Turner concert, 1989, Canada House, London; com. mem. Vancouver Internat. Festival; adjudicator Met. and San Francisco Opera auditions; MacDowell Colony resident, 1987. Served with Royal Can. Air Force, 1943-45. Recipient Commemorative medal for 125th Anniversary of Confedn. of Can., 1993; overseas scholar Royal Coll. Music, 1947-48; fellow Can. Coun., 1966-67; grantee Man. Arts Coun., 1982-83, 85, Can. Coun. Artists, 1990-92. Mem. Soc. Composers, Authors and Music Pubrs. of Can., Can. League Composers, Can. Music Ctr., MacDowell Colony.

TURNER, ROBERT EDWARD, psychiatrist, educator; b. Hamilton, Ont., Can., June 8, 1926; s. Robert William and Alice May (Johnson) T.; m. Gene Anne Stewart, Sept. 27, 1952; children: Margaret, John, Robert, Richard. B.A. with honors in Zoology and Chemistry, McMaster U., 1948; M.D., U. Toronto, 1952. Intern Hamilton Gen. Hosp., 1952-53; resident Bristol (Eng.) Mental Hosps. Group, 1953-55; practice medicine specializing in psychiatry Toronto, Ont.; dir. Forensic Clinic Toronto Psychiat. Hosp., 1958-66; sr. psychiatrist forensic service Clarke Inst. Psychiatry, Toronto, 1966; chief forensic service Clarke Inst. Psychiatry, 1967-69, med. dir., 1969-76; asst. prof. dept. psychiatry U. Toronto, 1964-68, prof., 1973-77, prof. forensic psychiatry, 1977-91, prof. emeritus, 1991—; cons. in psychiatry Law Reform Commn. Can., 1972-85; staff psychiatrist, 1987—; dir. Met. Toronto Forensic Service, 1977-87; hon. cons. Clarke Inst. Psychiatry, 1991—. Author: Pedophilia and Exhibitionism, 1964; contbr. articles on psychiatry and law to profl. jours. Pres. Kenneth G. Gray Found., 1971—; mem. legal task force Com. on Mental Health Svcs. for Ont., Ont. Coun. Health, 1978-79; dep. warden Cathedral Ch. of St. James, Toronto, 1978-79, 92-94, rector's warden, 1994-96; bd. dirs. Clin. Inst. Addiction Rsch. foun. Ont., 1973-86, chmn., 1985-86; bd. dirs. Addiction Rsch. Found., 1982-86. Fellow Royal Coll. Physicians and Surgeons Can., Am. Psychiat. Assn. (life), Can. Psychiat. Assn. (life, bd. dirs. 1974-77), Ont. Psychiat. Assn. (life, pres. 1975-76), Can. Med. Assn., Ont. Med. Assn., Med.-Legal Soc. Toronto (coun. 1979-82), Royal Coll. Psychiatrists. Home: 18 Rolph Rd, Toronto, ON Canada M4G 3M6 Office: U Toronto Dept Psychiatry, 250 College St, Toronto, ON Canada M5T 1R8

TURNER, ROBERT EDWARD See TURNER, TED

TURNER, ROBERT FOSTER, lawyer, educator, former government official, writer; b. Atlanta, Feb. 14, 1944; s. Edwin Witcher and Martha Frances (Williams) T. AB, Ind. U., Bloomington, 1968; postgrad. Stanford U., 1972-73; JD, U. Va., 1981. Bar: Va. 1982, U.S. Supreme Ct. 1986. Rsch. assoc., pub. affairs fellow Hoover Instn. on War, Revolution and Peace, Stanford U., 1971-74; spl. asst., legis. asst. U.S. Sen. Robert P. Griffin, 1974-79; assoc. dir. for Nat. Security Law U. Va., Charlottesville, 1981, 87—; sr. fellow, 1985-86; spl. asst. undersec. for policy Dept. Def., 1981-82; counsel Pres.'s Intelligence Oversight Bd., White House, 1982-84; prin. dep. asst. sec. for legis. and intergovtl. affairs Dept. State, 1984-85; pres. U.S. Inst. Peace, Washington, 1986-87; lectr. in law and in govt. and fgn. affairs U. Va., Charlottesville, 1988-93, assoc. prof., 1993—; Charles H. Stockton prof. internat. law Naval War Coll., 1994—. Author: Myths of the Vietnam War: The Pentagon Papers Reconsidered, 1972, Vietnamese Communism: Its Origins and Development, 1975, The War Powers Resolution: Its Implementation in Theory and Practice, 1983, Nicaragua v. United States: A Look at the Facts, 1987, Repealing the War Powers Resolution: Restoring the Rule of Law in U.S. Foreign Policy, 1991, (with John Norton Moore) The Legal Structure of Defense Organization, 1986, International Law and the Brezhnev Doctrine, 1987, (with John Norton Moore and Frederick Tipson) Nat. Security Law, 1990, (with John Norton Moore and Guy B. Roberts) Nat. Security Law Documents, 1995; contbr. articles to profl. jours. Pres. Endowment of U.S. Inst. Peace, 1986-87; trustee Intercollegiate Studies Inst., 1986-92. Capt. U.S. Army, 1968-71, Vietnam. Grantee Hoover Press, 1972, Earhart Found., 1980, 1989-90, Inst. Ednl. Affairs, 1980, Carthage Found., 1980. Mem. ABA (chmn. com. on exec.-congl. rels., sec. internat. law and practice 1983-86, adv. com. on law and nat. security 1984-86, standing com. on law and nat. security 1986-92, chmn. 1989-92, editor Nat. Security Law Report 1992—), Bd. Rsch. Cons., Inst. Fgn. Policy Analysis, Mensa, Am. Soc. Internat. Law, Nat. Eagle Scout Assn., Coun. on Fgn. Rels. Home: RR 18 Box 59 Charlottesville VA 22901 Office: Univ Va Sch of Law Ctr for Nat Security Law Charlottesville VA 22903-1789

TURNER, ROBERT GERALD, university chancellor; b. Atlanta, Tex., Nov. 25, 1945; s. Robert B. and Oreta Lois (Porter) T.; m. Gail Oliver, Dec. 21, 1968; children: Angela Jan, Jessica Diane. AA, Lubbock Christian Coll., 1966, LLD (hon.), 1985; LLD (hon.), Pepperdine U., 1989; BS, Abilene Christian U., 1968; MA, U. Tex., 1970, PhD, 1975. Tchr. Weatherford High Sch., Tex., 1968-69; tchr. Lanier High Sch., Austin, Tex., 1969-70; instr. psychology San Antonio Coll., 1970-72; instr. Prairie View A & M U., Tex., 1973-75; asst. prof. psychology Pepperdine U., Malibu, Calif., 1975-78, assoc. prof. psychology, 1978-79, dir. testing, 1975-76, chmn. social sci. div., 1976-78, assoc. v.p. univ. affairs, 1979; assoc. prof. psychology U. Okla., Norman, 1979-84, exec. asst. to pres., 1979-81, acting provost, 1982, v.p. exec. affairs, 1981-84; chancellor U. Miss., University, 1984-95; pres. So. Meth. U., Dallas, 1995—; chmn. pres. coun. Miss. Assn. Colls., 1985-86; pres. Southeastern Conf., 1985-87; bd. dirs., mem. exec. com. Inst. Tech. Devel.; rsch. asst. Tex. Adoption Study, 1973-75; mem. chancellor's coun. Pepperdine U.; mem. Commn. on Telecomm., Nat. Assn. State Univs. and Land-Grant Colls. 1985-86, chmn. Commn. on Edn. for Teaching Profession, 1990-91; mem. Pres.'s Commn., NCAA, 1989-92, chmn., 1991-92; mem. Knight Commn. on Intercollegiate Athletics, 1991-93; chmn. pres. coun. Miss. Assn. Colls., 1985-86; mem. def. adv. com. Svc. Acad. Athletic Programs, 1992—. Author: (with L. Willerman) Readings About Individual and Group Differences, 1979. Contbr. articles to profl. jours. Dir. area 2 Miss. Econ. Coun.; bd. dirs. First Miss. Corp., 1987; mem. Yocona Area coun. Boy Scouts Am. NIMH grantee, 1972; recipient Outstanding Alumni award Abilene Christian U., 1989, Communicator of Yr. award Toastmasters Club, 1987; named Miss. Amb. 1986; inducted New Boston High Sch. Athletic Hall of Fame.

1993. Mem. Am. Assn. Univ. Adminstrs., Am. Psychol. Assn., Western Psychol. Assn., Southwestern Psychol. Assn., Am. Coun. on Edn. for Advancement Women, Miss. Psychol. Assn., Young Pres. Orgn., Coun. on Competitiveness, Newcomen Soc., Am. Inst. for Pub. Svc. (bd. nominators 1989), Sigma Xi, Beta Alpha Psi, Phi Theta Kappa, Alpha Chi, Phi Kappa Phi. Mem. Ch. of Christ. Avocations: tennis; golf; reading; traveling. Office: So Meth U Office of Pres Dallas TX 75275

TURNER, ROBERT LLOYD, state legislator; b. Columbus, Miss., Sept. 14, 1947; s. Roosevelt and Beatrice (Hargrove) T.; m. Gloria Harrell; children: Roosevelt, Robert, Ryan. BS, U. Wis., Racine, 1976. Mgr. French Quarter Restaurant, Racine, 1989; legislator Wis. State Assembly, Madison, 1990—, chmn. transp. com. bldg. commn., mem. ways and means com., hwy. com., elections, correction & constitution com., excise fees and license com.; br. sales mgr. ETG Temporaries, Inc., Racine, 1989—; pub. Communicator News, Racine, 1989—; v.p. Racine Raider Football Team. State chmn. Dem. Black Polit. Caucus, Madison; pres. Bd. Health, Racine; chmn. Wis. State Elections Bd., Madison, 1990; alderman Racine City Coun., 1976—; chair Econ. Devel. Com., Racine; regional dir. Badger State Games, Racine; active Pvt. Industry Coun. Southeastern Wis., 1988-89, bd. dirs. Racine County Youth Sports Assn.; active Racine Juneteenth Day Com., bd. advisors Big Bros./Big Sisters. Sgt. USAF, 1967-71, Vietnam. Decorated Commendation medal; named Man of Yr. 2d Missionary Bapt. Ch., 1983. Mem. Urban League (pres. bd. dirs.), NAACP (2d v.p.), VFW, Am. Legion, Masons, Shriners. Home: 36 Mckinley Ave Racine WI 53404-3414 Office: Wis Assembly PO Box 8953 Madison WI 53708-8953

TURNER, RODERICK L., retired consumer packaged products manufacturing company executive; b. Mineola, N.Y., June 1, 1931; s. Claude E. and Eulalia (Rodriguez) T.; m. Teresa C. Vadetaire, May, 1957; children—R. Bradford, Melissa A. B.A., Cornell U., 1952. Vice-pres. Benton & Bowles, Inc., N.Y.C., 1958-63; group product mgr. personal products div. Colgate-Palmolive Co., N.Y.C., 1963-67; group product mgr. household products div. Colgate-Palmolive Co., 1967-68; pres., gen. mgr. Colgate Canadian Co., 1969-72, v.p. mktg. services div., 1973; corp. v.p., gen. mgr. Western hemisphere div. Colgate-Palmolive Co., 1974-76, gen. mgr. European div., 1977-78, group v.p., internat. ops., 1979-81, exec. v.p., 1981-85, sr. exec. v.p., 1985-92; ret., 1992. Served to 1st lt. AUS, 1952-54, Korea. Office: Colgate-Palmolive Co 300 Park Ave New York NY 10022-7402

TURNER, ROSS JAMES, investment corporation executive; b. Winnipeg, Man., Can., May 1, 1930; permanent U.S. resident, 1980; s. James Valentine and Gretta H. (Ross) T.; children: Ralph, Rick, Tracy. U. Man. Extension, 1951, Banff Sch. Advanced Mgmt., 1956. Various sr. operating and mgmt. positions Genstar Corp., San Francisco, 1961-76, chmn./pres., CEO, 1976-86, also bd. dirs.; chmn. Genstar Investment Corp., San Francisco, 1987—; bd. dirs. Rio Algom Ltd., Gt. West Life Assurance Co., Blue Shield of Calif., Guy F. Atkinson Co. of Calif., Wolverine Tube, Inc. Fellow Soc. Mgmt. Accts. Can.; mem. Toronto Club, Pacific Union Club, Rancho Santa Fe Golf Club, Peninsula Golf and Country Club. Office: Genstar Investment Corp Metro Tower Ste 1170 950 Tower Ln Foster City CA 94404-2121

TURNER, STANSFIELD, former government official, lecturer, writer, teacher; b. Chgo., Dec. 1, 1923; s. Oliver Stansfield and Wilhelmina Josephine (Wagner) T.; m. Eli Karin Gilbert, Mar. 16, 1985. Student, Amherst Coll., 1941-43, DCL, 1975; BS, U.S. Naval Acad. 1946; MA (Rhodes scholar), Oxford U., 1950; LHD, Sierra Nev. Coll., 1984; HumD, Roger Williams Coll., 1975; DSc in Edn, Bryant Coll., 1977; LLD, Salve Regina Coll., 1977, The Citadel, 1980, Pace U., 1980. Ensign USN, 1946, advanced through grades to adm., 1975, ret., 1979; served primarily in destroyers; commd. U.S.S. Horne, guided missile cruiser, 1967-68; aide to Sec. Navy; comdr. carrier task group 6th Fleet, 1970-71; dir. systems analysis div. Office Chief Naval Ops., Navy Dept., Washington, 1971-72; pres. Naval War Coll., Newport, R.I., 1972-74; comdr. U.S. Second Fleet, 1974-75; comdr.-in-chief Allied Forces So. Europe, NATO, 1975-77; dir. CIA, Washington, 1977-81; prof. U. Md. Grad. Sch. Pub. Affairs, 1991—. Author: Secrecy and Democracy, 1985, Terrorism and Democracy, 1991. Decorated Nat. Security medal, Legion of Merit, Bronze Star; John M. Olin Disting. Prof. nat. security U.S. Mil. Acad., West Point, 1989-90. Home and Office: 1320 Skipwith Rd Mc Lean VA 22101-1834

TURNER, STUART, paper company executive; b. 1944. MBA, Adelphi U., 1965. CPA. Prin. Stuart Turner, CPA, N.Y.C., 1966-69; ptnr. Turner, Imowitz & Co., N.Y.C., 1969-81; sr. exec. P&E Properties Inc., N.Y.C., 1981—; exec. v.p., treas., CFO Western Pub. Group Inc., N.Y.C., 1984—; Penn Corp., N.Y.C., 1986—. Office: Penn Corp 444 Madison Ave 6th Fl New York NY 10022*

TURNER, TED (ROBERT EDWARD TURNER), television executive; b. Cin., Nov. 19, 1938; s. Robert Edward and Florence (Rooney) T.; m. Judy Nye (div.), m. Jane Shirley Smith, June 1965 (div. 1988); children: Beau, Rhett, Jennie; children by previous marriage: Laura Lee, Robert Edward IV; m. Jane Fonda, Dec. 21, 1991. Grad. in classics, Brown U.; DSc in Commerce (hon.), Drexel U., 1982; LLD (hon.), Samford U., 1982, Atlanta U., 1984; D Entrepreneurial Sci. (hon.), Cen. New Eng. Coll. Tech., 1983; D in Pub. Adminstrn. (hon.), Mass. Maritime Acad., 1984; D in Bus. Adminstrn. (hon.), U. Charleston, 1985. Account exec. Turner Advt. Co., Atlanta, 1961-63, pres., chief oper. officer, 1963-70; pres., chmn. bd. Turner Broadcasting System, Inc., Atlanta, 1970—. Chmn. bd. Better World Soc., Washington, 1985-90; bd. dirs. Martin Luther King Ctr., Atlanta. Won America's Cup in his yacht Courageous, 1977; named Yachtsman of Yr. 4 times.Recipient Outstanding Entrepreneur of Yr. award Sales Mktg. and Mgmt. Mag., 1979, Salesman of Yr. award Sales and Mktg. Execs., 1980, Pvt. Enterprise Exemplar medal, Freedoms Found. at Valley Forge, 1980, Communicator of Yr. award Pub. Rels. Soc. Am., 1981, Communicator of Yr. award N.Y. Broadcasters, 1981, Internat. Communicator of Yr. award Sales and Mktg. Execs., 1981, Nat. News Media award VFW, 1981, Disting. Svc. in Telecommunications award Ohio U. Coll. Communication, 1982, Carr Van Anda award Ohio U. Sch. Journalism, 1982, Spl. award Edinburgh Internat. TV Festival, Scotland, 1982, Media Awareness award United Vietnam Vets. Orgn., 1983, Bd. Govs. award Atlanta chpt. NATAS, 1982, Spl. Olympics award Spl. Olympics Com., 1983, Dinner of Champions award Ga. chpt., Multiple Sclerosis Soc., 1983, Praca Spl. Merit award N.Y. Puerto Rican Assn. for Community Affairs, 1983, World Telecommunications Pioneer award, N.Y. State Broadcasters Assn., 1984, Golden Plate award Am. Acad. Achievement, 1984, Outstanding Supporter Boy Scouting award Nat. Boy Scout Coun., 1984, Silver Satellite award Am. Women in Radio and TV, Lifetime Achievement award N.Y. Internat. Film and TV Festival, 1984, Corp. Star of Yr. award Nat. Leukemia Soc., 1985, Disting. Achievement award U. Georgia, 1985, Tree of Life award Jewish Nat. Fund, 1985, Bus. Exec. of Yr. award Ga. Security Dealers Assn., 1985, Life Achievement award Popular Culture Assn., 1986, George Washington Disting. Patriot award S.R., 1986, Mo. Honor medal Sch. Journalism, U. Mo., 1987, Golden Ace award Nat. Cable TV Acad., 1987 Sol Taishoff award Nat. Press Found., 1988, Citizen Diplomat award Ctr. for Soviet-Am. Dialogue, 1988, Chmn.'s award Cable Advt. Bur., 1988, Directorate award NATAS, 1989, Paul White award Radio and TV News Dirs. Assn., 1989 Bus. Marketer of Yr. Am. Mktg. Assn., 1989, Disting. Svc. award Simon Wiesenthal Ctr., 1990, Glasnost award Vols. Am. and Soviet Life mag., 1990, numerous others; inducted into Hall of Fame, Promotion and Mktg. Assn., 1990, Dubuque (Iowa) Bus. Hall of Fame, 1983, Nat. Assn. for Sport and Phys. Edn. Hall of Fame, 1986. Mem. Nat. Cable TV Assn. (Pres.'s award 1979, 89, Ace Spl. Recognition award 1980), NAACP (life, bd. dirs. Atlanta chpt., Regional Employer of Yr. award 1976), Nat. Audubon Soc., Cousteau Soc., Bay Area Cable Club (hon.). Avocations: sailing, fishing. Office: Turner Broadcasting 1 CNN Ctr PO Box 105366 Atlanta GA 30348-5366

TURNER, TERRY MADISON, architect; b. Bastrop, La., Apr. 5, 1938; s. Eugene Campbell and Anna Pauline (Terry) T.; m. Mary Alice Fischer, June 20, 1964; children: Mat Madison, Paul Alison, William Terry. BBA, Memphis State U., 1958; BS in Archtl. Scis., Washington U., St. Louis, 1961, BArch, 1963. Registered architect, Mo., N.C.A.R.B. Asst. prof. Sch. Architecture Auburn (Ala.) U., 1965-66, U. Va., Charlottesville, 1966-69; chief architect HUD-FHA, St. Louis, 1969-79; prin. Terry M. Turner, Architect, Clayton, Mo., 1979—. Regent Harris-Stowe State Coll., St.

Louis, 1992—. 1st lt. USAR, 1963-70. Republican. Episcopalian. Avocation: reading. Home and Office: 50 Hillvale Dr Clayton MO 63105

TURNER, THOMAS PATRICK, architect; b. Gaffney, S.C., May 13, 1926; s. Thomas Patrick and Lily Mae (Clarke) T.; m. Lola Ann Love, Aug. 17, 1950; children: Sheryl A., Thomas P. III, A. Bryan. BS in Archtl. Engring., Clemson U., 1951, postgrad., 1952. Registered architect; lic. real estate broker; lic. contractor. Draftsman John H. Truluck, Walterboro, S.C., 1951-52, M.R. Marsh, Charlotte, N.C., 1953-55; architect in tng. Holroyd, Folk and Gray, Charlotte, 1955-57; architect A.G. Odell & Assocs., Charlotte, 1957-77; pres., owner ADEP Architects, Charlotte, 1977—. Precinct chmn. Dem. Party, 1993-94; elder Myers Park Presbyn. Ch. With U.S. Navy, 1943-45. Fellow AIA (nat. bd. dirs. 1987—, v.p. 1990, pres. Charlotte sect. 1966), N.C. Inst. Architects (bd. dirs. 1970, 71, 76, 77, v.p. 1972-73, pres. 1985), Rotary. Office: ADEP Architects 401 S Independence Blvd Ste 72 Charlotte NC 28204-2638

TURNER, TINA (ANNA MAE BULLOCK), singer; b. Brownsville, Tenn., Nov. 26, 1939; m. Ike Turner, 1956 (div. 1978); children: Craig, Ike Jr., Michael, Ronald. Singer with Ike Turner Kings of Rhythm, and Ike and Tina Turner Revue; appeared in films: Gimme Shelter, 1970, Soul to Soul, 1971, Tommy, 1975, Mad Max Beyond Thunderdome, 1985, Break Every Rule, 1986; concert tours of Europe, 1966, Japan and Africa, 1971; albums with Ike Turner include Hunter, 1970, Ike and Tina Show II, Ike and Tina Show, 1966, Ike and Tina Turner, Bad Dreams, 1973, Ike and Tina Turner Greatest Hits, vol. 1.2 and 3, 1989, Greatest Hits, 1990, Proud Mary, 1991, The Ike and Tina Turner Collection, 1993; solo albums include Let Me Touch Your Mind, 1972, Tina Turns the Country On, 1974, Acid Queen, 1975, Love Explosion, 1977, Rough, 1978, Airwaves, 1979, Private Dancer, 1984, Break Every Rule, 1986, Tina Live In Europe, 1988, Foreign Affair, 1989, Simply the Best, 1991, What's Love Got to Do With It? (soundtrack), 1993, The Collected Recordings: Sixties to Nine Ties, with others, 1994; performed with USA for Africa on song We are the World, 1985; author (autobiography) I, Tina, 1985 (filmed as What's Love Got To Do With It?, 1993). Recipient Grammy award, 1972, 85 (three), 86, Grammy nomination (Best Pop Female Vocal) for "I Don't Wanna Fight", 1994; inducted into Rock and Roll Hall of Fame, 1991. Address: care CAA 9830 Wilshire Blvd Beverly Hills CA 90212*

TURNER, WALLACE L., reporter; b. Titusville, Fla., Mar. 15, 1921; s. Clyde H. and Ina B. (Wallace) T.; m. Pearl Burk, June 12, 1943; children: Kathleen Turner, Elizabeth Turner Everett. B.J., U. Mo., 1943; postgrad. (Nieman fellow), Harvard U., 1958-59. Reporter Springfield (Mo.) Daily News, 1943, Portland Oregonian, 1943-59; news dir. Sta. KPTV, Portland, 1959-61; asst. sec. HEW, Washington, 1961-62; reporter N.Y. Times, San Francisco, 1962—; bur. chief N.Y. Times, 1970-85, Seattle bur. chief, 1985-88. Author: Gamblers Money, 1965, The Mormon Establishment, 1967. Recipient Heywood Broun award for reporting, 1952, 56; Pulitzer Prize for reporting, 1957. Office: Box 99269 Magnolia Sta Seattle WA 98199-4260

TURNER, WARREN AUSTIN, state legislator; b. Berkeley, Calif., Dec. 21, 1926; s. Warren Mortimer and Rebecca Oline (Noer) T.; m. Beverly Daune Mackay, Mar. 29, 1952; children: Daune Scott, Warren Adair, Alan Corey. BA, U. Calif., Berkeley, 1950, BS, 1952, MPH, 1958. Pub. acct. Price Waterhouse, San Francisco, 1951-52, AW Blackman, Las Vegas, Nev., 1952-56; asst. adminstr. Marin Gen. Hosp., San Rafael, Calif., 1958-60; assoc. dir. UCLA Hosp., 1960-68; founding adminstr. Walter O. Boswell Meml. Hosp., Sun City, Ariz., 1968-81; pres. Sun Health Corp., 1981-89; mem. Ariz. Senate, Phoenix, 1993—, chmn. rules com., vice chair health com., mem. appropriations, family svcs. and transp. com., 1993—; chmn. rules com., appropriation subcom. K-12, C.C.'s and natural resources, vice chmn. health com. Chmn. rules com. USN, 1944-46. Mem Ariz. Acad. Rotary Internat. Republican. Avocations: breeding and showing Siamese cats, fishing, mining. Home: 18432 W Glendale Ave Waddell AZ 85355 Office: Ariz State Senate Capital Complex Phoenix AZ 85007

TURNER, WAYNE CONNELLY, industrial engineer, educator; b. West Point, Va., May 7, 1942; s. Percy Lee and Evelyn Mae (Connelly) T.; m. Kathleen Patricia McCawley, June 28, 1969; children: Travis Lee, Drew Scott. BS in Indsl. Engring., Va. Poly. Inst., 1964, MS in Indsl. Engring., 1969; PhD, Va. Poly Inst., 1971. Registered profl. engr., Okla; cert. energy mgr.; cert. hazardous materials mgr. Mgr. mfg. engring. Modine Mfg. Co., Buena Vista, Va., 1964-67; instr. Va. Poly. Inst., Blacksburg, 1969-71; asst. prof. Okla. State U., Stillwater, 1971-74, assoc. prof., 1974-77, prof., 1977—; Regents prof., 1990—; cons. numerous mfg. cos., 1969—; adv. bd. World Energy Congress, Atlanta, 1981—. Author: Introduction to Industrial Engineering, 1978 (Joint Pub. Book of Yr. 1979), Energy Management, 1983, 93; author, editor: Energy Management Handbook, 1982, 92; cons. editor Prentice Hall, Englewood Cliffs, N.J., 1976—; cons. author John Wiley and Sons, N.Y.C., 1980—; contbr. more than 170 articles to profl. jours. Mem. parish council St. John's Cath. Ch., Stillwater, 1977; coach Parks and Recreation Dept., Stillwater, 1974-84. Named Outstanding Prof. Coll. of Engring., Okla. State U., 1977, 88, Outstanding Tchr. Indsl. Engring., 1977, 88, 90; recipient Regional Fund award Western Electric, 1978, Neal award Assn. Bus. Pubs., 1980, Free Enterprise award Merrick Found., 1983, Outstanding Faculty award U. Extension, 1989. Fellow Inst. Indsl. Engrs. (numerous coms. 1969—, div. dir. 1985-86); mem. Am. Soc. Engring. Educators, Assn. Energy Engrs. (adv. bd. 1981-87, Energy Proficiency Devel. award 1983), Am. Inst. Plant Engrs., Ducks Unltd. Home: 2024 N Husband St Stillwater OK 74075-2813 Office: Okla State U Indsl Engring & Mgmt Dept Indsl Engring Mgmt Dept 322E Stillwater OK 74075

TURNER, WILLIAM BENJAMIN, electrical engineer; b. Bklyn., Sept. 23, 1929; s. Jacob Joshua and Mollie (Klein) T. BEE, CCNY, 1955; MBA, NYU, 1964; DD (hon.), UCLA, 1978. Cert. tchr., N.Y. Chief engr. Esan Electronic Labs., Fla. and N.Y., 1969—; cons. in field, 1965—. Author: Theology-The Quintessence of Science, 1981, Nothing and Non-Existence, 1986, Hyper Light Speed Technology, 1992, Outer Space Communications, 1994, Eulogy for Our Dying World, 1994, Advanced Concepts and Limitations in Science, 1994. Sgt. U.S. Army, 1951-53, Korea. Decorated Bronze Star. Mem. Mensa, Boynton Beach C. of C. Achievements include invention of world's fastest computers, advanced concepts in time theory, development new physics method that exceeds speed of light, research into hyper light speed communications equiptment to probe far off regions of outer space. Home and Office: 1916 Palmland Dr # B Boynton Beach FL 33436-6019

TURNER, WILLIAM COCHRANE, international management consultant; b. Red Oak, Iowa, May 27, 1929; s. James Lyman and Josephine (Cochrane) T.; m. Cynthia Dunbar, July 16, 1955; children: Scott Christopher, Craig Dunbar, Douglas Gordon. BS, Northwestern U., 1952, LLD (hon.), Am. Grad. Sch. Internat. Mgmt., 1993. Pres., chmn. bd. dirs. Western Mgmt. Cons., Inc., Phoenix, 1955-74, Western Mgmt. Cons. Europe, S.A., Brussels, 1968-74; U.S. amb., permanent rep. OECD, Paris, 1974-77, vice chmn. exec. com., 1976-77, U.S. rep. Energy Policy Com., 1976-77, mem. U.S. dels. internat. meetings, 1974-77; mem. western internat. trade group U.S. Dept. Commerce, 1972-74; chmn., CEO Argyle Atlantic Corp., Phoenix, 1977—; chmn. European adv. coun., 1981-88, Asia Pacific adv. coun. AT&T Internat., 1981-88; bd. dirs Microtest, Inc., Phoenix; founding mem. Pacific Coun. Internat. Policy, L.A., 1995—; mem. U.S-Japan Bus. Coun., Washington, 1987-93, European adv. coun. IBM World Trade Europe/Mid. East/Africa Corp., 1977-80; mem. Asia Pacific adv. coun. Am. Can Co. Greenwich, Conn., 1981-85, GE of Brazil adv. coun. GE Co., Coral Gables, Fla., 1979-81, Caterpillar of Brazil adv. coun. Caterpillar Tractor Co., Peoria, Ill., 1979-84, Caterpillar Asia Pacific Adv. Coun., 1984-90, U.S. adv. com. Trade Negotiations, 1982-84; bd. dirs. Goodyear Tire & Rubber Co., Akron, Ohio, 1978—, Rural/Metro Corp., 1993—, Microtest, Inc., Phoenix, 1995—; chmn. internat. adv. coun. Avon Products, Inc., N.Y.C., 1985—; mem. Spencer Stuart adv. council Spencer Stuart and Assocs., N.Y.C., 1984-90; chmn., mem. internat. adv. council Advanced Semiconductor Materials Internat. NV., Bilthoven, The Netherlands, 1985-88; bd. dirs. The Atlantic Coun. of the U.S., Washington, 1977-92; co-chmn. internat. adv. bd. Univ. of Nations, Kona, Hawaii, 1985—; bd. dirs. World Wildlife Fund/U.S., 1983-85, World Wildlife Fund/The Conservation Found., 1985-89, Nat. Coun., 1989—; bd. govs. Joseph H. Lauder Inst. Mgmt. and Internat. Studies, U. Pa., 1983—; trustee Heard Mus., Phoenix, 1983-86, mem. nat. adv. bd.,

1986-93; trustee Am. Grad. Sch. Internat. Mgmt., 1972—, chmn. bd. trustees, 1987-89; bd. govs. Atlantic Inst. Internat. Affairs, Paris, 1977-88; adv. bd. Ctr. Strategic and Internat. Studies, Georgetown U., 1977-81; dir. Atlantic Inst. Found., Inc., N.Y.C., 1984-90; mem. European Cmty.-U.S. Businessmen's Coun., 1978-79; bd. govs. Am. Hosp. of Paris, 1974-77; trustee Nat. Symphony Orch. Assn., Washington, 1973-83, Am. Sch., Paris, 1976-77, Orme Sch., Mayer, Ariz., 1970-74, Phoenix Country Day Sch., 1971-74; mem. nat. coun. Salk Inst., 1978-82; mem. U.S. Adv. Com. Internat. Edn. and Cultural Affairs, 1969-74; nat. rev. bd. Ctr. Cultural and Tech. Interchange between East and West, 1970-74; mem. vestry Am. Cathedral, Paris, 1976-77; pres. bd. dirs Phoenix Symphony Assn., 1969-70; chmn. Ariz. Joint Econ. Devel. Com., 1967-68; exec. com., bd. dirs. Ariz. Dept. Econ. Planning and Devel., 1968-70; chmn. bd. Ariz. Crippled Children's Services, 1964-65; treas. Ariz. Rep. Com., 1956-57; chmn. Ariz. Young Rep. League, 1955-56; chmn. bd. Mercy Ships Internat., Inc., A Ministry of Youth With A Mission, Lindale, Tex., 1985—; mem. trade and environment com. Nat. Adv. Coun. for Environ. Policy and Tech.-U.S. EPA, Washington, 1991—; dir. exec. com. internat. com. Ariz. Econ. Coun., Phoenix, 1989-93; dir. exec. com. Orgn. for Free Trade and Devel., Phoenix, 1991-93; chmn. Internat. Adv. Coun. Plasma Tech., Inc., Sante Fe, 1992—. Recipient East-West Ctr. Disting. Svc. award, 1977. Mem. U.S. Coun. Internat. Bus. (trustee, exec. com.), Coun. Fgn. Rels., Coun. of Am. Ambs. (vice chmn. bd.), Nat. Adv. Coun. on Bus. Edn., Coun. Internat. Edn. Exchange, Greater Phoenix Leadership, Govs. Strategic Partnership Econ. Devel., Phoenix, 1992—, Met. Club, Links Club (N.Y.C.), Plaza Club (Phoenix), Paradise Valley (Ariz.) Country Club. Episcopalian. Office: 4350 E Camelback Rd Ste 240B Phoenix AZ 85018-2722

TURNER, WILLIAM J., data processing company executive; b. 1944; married. Grad., U. Maine, 1965; MBA, Northeastern U., 1969. With Digital Equipment Co., 1973-80, Tex. Instruments, 1980-83; pres. Automatic Data Processing Inc., Roseland, N.J., 1983—, now also chief operating officer, also. Office: ADP Inc 1 A D P Blvd Roseland NJ 07068-1728 also: Lear Siegler Holdings Corp 220 S Orange Ave Livingston NJ 07039

TURNER, WILLIAM WEYAND, author; b. Buffalo, N.Y., Apr. 14, 1927; s. William Peter and Magdalen (Weyand) T.; m. Margaret Peiffer, Sept. 12, 1964; children: Mark Peter, Lori Ann. BS, Canisius Coll., 1949. Spl. agt. in various field offices FBI, 1951-61; free-lance writer Calif., 1963—; sr. editor Ramparts Mag., San Francisco, 1967—; investigator and com. Nat. Wiretap Commn., 1975. Author: The Police Establishment, 1968, Invisible Witness: The Use and Abuse of the New Technology of Crime Investigation, 1968, Hoover's F.B.I.: The Men and the Myth, 1970, Power on the Right, 1971, (with Warren Hinckle and Eliot Asinof) The Ten Second Jailbreak, 1973, (with John Christian) The Assassination of Robert F. Kennedy, 1978, (with Warren Hinckle) The Fish is Red: The Story of the Secret War Against Castro, 1981, updated, expanded, retitled as Deadly Secrets: The CIA-Mafia War Against Castro and the Assassination of JFK, 1992; contbg. author: Investigating the FBI, 1973; contbr. articles to popular mags. Dem. candidate for U.S. Congress, 1968. Served with USN, 1945-46. Mem. Authors Guild, Internat. Platform Assn., Press Club of San Francisco. Roman Catholic. Avocation: tennis. Home and Office: 163 Mark Twain Ave San Rafael CA 94903-2820

TURNER, WILLIAM WILSON, hospital administrator; b. Valley Mills, Tex., Apr. 21, 1916; s. Will S. and Nettie A. (Vickrey) T.; m. Wilma David, Feb. 22, 1945; 1 child, Elizabeth Ann. B.B.A., Baylor U., 1938; postgrad., Grad. Sch. Bus., Northwestern U., 1939. Bus. mgr. Hillcrest Meml. Hosp., Waco, Tex., 1941-47; asst. adminstr. Meml. Bapt. Hosp. (name changed to Meml. Hosp. System), Houston, 1947-50; adminstr. Meml. Bapt. Hosp. (name changed to Meml. Hosp. System), 1955-63, exec. dir. hosp. system, 1963-71, pres. system, 1971-81, pres. emeritus, cons., 1981—; adminstr. Bapt. Hosp., Alexandria, La., 1950-54, Miss. Bapt. Hosp., Jackson, 1954-55; hon. life dir. Blue Cross-Blue Shield Tex., Group Life and Health Ins. Co.; mem. Council on Manpower and Ben., 1974-77. Served to 1t. USNR, 1942-45, PTO, ATO. Recipient Collier award for distinguished hosp. adminstrn., 1974, Tex. Assn. Hosp. Governing Bds. Founders award, 1980, Meml. Stewardship award, 1992. Fellow Am. Coll. Hosp. Adminstrs.; mem. Am. Prostestant Hosp. Assn. (del. 1970—, council ch.-hosp. relations 1962-66, council on edn. 1972-75, Hosp. Adminstrn. award 1979), Am. Hosp. Assn. (del. 1969-75), Tex. Hosp. Assn. (trustee 1961-68, treas. 1969, pres. 1971-72), Bapt. Hosp. Assn. (past pres., trustee), Houston Area Hosp. Assn. (past pres.), Mental Health Assn. Houston (profl. adv. com.), Tex. Assn. Hosp. Accountants (past pres., disting. life mem.), Houston Area Hosp. Council (past pres.), Houston C. of C., Tex. League Nursing (dir. 1961-63), Delta Sigma Pi. Baptist (deacon). Lodge: Masons. Developer satellite hosp. concept. Home: 7480 Beechnut St Apt 303 Houston TX 77074-4507 Office: 7737 Southwest Fwy Ste 595 Houston TX 77074-1800

TURNHEIM, PALMER, banker; b. S.I., N.Y., June 30, 1921; s. Gustav and Helga (Hansen) T.; m. Gloria Freer, June 1948 (dec.); 1 child, Joy Karen. BS magna cum laude, NYU, 1960; Am. Inst. Banking, 1947; grad., Stonier Grad. Sch. Banking, Rutgers U., 1958, Advanced Mgmt. Program, Harvard, 1962. Asst. mgr. credit dept. Chase Nat. Bank, 1951-55, asst. treas., 1955; asst. v.p. Chase Manhattan Bank, N.Y.C., 1956-61; v.p. Chase Manhattan Bank, 1961-71, sr. v.p., 1971-86; sr. v.p. Chase Manhattan Capital Markets Corp.; exec. v.p. 1st Fidelity Bank, Newark, 1990—; instr. mgmt. decision lab. Stern Grad. Sch. Bus. NYU, 1986—; pres. Chasex Asso cs., Inc. Author: International Finance Corporation, 1958. Nat. pres. United Cerebral Palsy Assns., Inc., 1967-70; dir. United Cerebral Palsy Research and Ednl. Found.; Mem. U.S. govt. com. on cash mgmt. Gen. Services Adminstrn., Washington, Am. Bankers Assn. task force advising Dept. Energy on gasoline rationing, 1979-81; Bd. dirs. Fund for Theol. Edn., 1957-84, N.Y. Inst. Credit, 1971-84. Served with USAAF, 1942-46. Mem. N.Y. State Bankers Assn. (dir. 1972-75), N.Y.U. Stern Sch. Bus. Alumni Assn. (pres. 1982-83), N.Y.U. Alumni Fedn. (v.p., dir., mem. alumni coun.), Am. Legion, Beta Gamma Sigma, Phi Alpha Kappa. Lutheran. Clubs: Harvard Bus. Sch., Union League, NYU Fin. (pres., dir. 1982-83). Home: 23 Oak Ln Mountain Lakes NJ 07046-1311

TURNLEY, DAVID CARL, photojournalist; b. Fort Wayne, Ind., June 22, 1955; s. William Loyd and Elizabeth Ann (Protsman) T.; m. Karin Nicolette, Apr. 15, 1989. BA in French, U. Mich., 1977; student, Sorbonne, Paris, 1975; DMus (hon.), Keele (Eng.) U., 1991. Staff photographer Sliger Home Newspapers, Northville, Mich., 1978-80, Detroit Free Press, 1980—; European based photographic corr. Detroit Free Press/Black Star Paris, 1988—. Author: Why Are They Weeping? South Africans under Apartheid, 1988, Beijing Spring, 1989, Moments of Revolution: Eastern Europe, 1990; artist London Decca Records. Recipient Canon essay award for S. African coverage, 1985, World Press Picture of Yr. award for Earthquake in Armenia, 1988, Robert Capa Gold medal for China, Romania coverage, 1990, Pulitzer prize for China, E. Europe coverage, 1990. Office: Detroit Free Press 321 W Lafayette Blvd Detroit MI 48226-2703*

TURNLUND, JUDITH RAE, nutrition scientist; b. St. Paul, Sept. 28, 1936; d. Victor Emanuel and Vida Mae (Priddy) Hanson; m. Richard Wayne Turnlund, Nov. 9, 1957; children: Michael Wayne, Mark Richard, Todd Hanson. BS in Chemistry and Psychology, Gustavus Adolphus Coll., 1958; PhD in Nutrition, U. Calif., Berkeley, 1978. Registered dietitian. Postdoctoral fellow U. Calif., Berkeley, 1978-80, lectr., 1984-92, adj. assoc. prof., 1989—; rsch. nutrition scientist Western Regional Rsch. Ctr./Western Human Nutrition Rsch., USDA, San Francisco and Albany, Calif., 1980-92, rsch. leader, 1992—; vis. asst. prof. Am. U. Beirut, Lebanon, 1979, 80. Editor: Stable Isotopes in Nutrition, 1984; contbr. articles to profl. jours. Recipient Cert. of Merit, USDA/ARS, 1984, 1993, Disting. Alumni citation Gustavus Adolphus Coll., 1988; USDA grantee, 1982-90, Nat. Dairy Coun. grantee, 1986. Mem. Am Inst. Nutrition, Am. Soc. Clin. Nutrition, Am. Dietetic Assn. Home: 2276 Great Hwy San Francisco CA 94116-1555 Office: USDA/ARS PO Box 29997 San Francisco CA 94129-0997

TURNOCK, JAMES MCCLYMONDS, healthcare executive; b. Pitts., Mar. 5, 1951; s. Enock Hill and Ann Louise (McClymonds) T. BA cum laude, U. Pitts., 1973; MBA, U. Pa., 1977. Fin. analyst Ford Motor Co., Dearborn, Mich., 1977-80; sr. cons. Touche Ross & Co., Washington, 1980-84; dir. planning and devel., sec. HealthCare Corp. of the Mid-Atlantic, Balt., 1984—; sec. HealthCare Corp. Am., Balt., 1986—; pres. Physicians Health Plan, Inc., 1989—. Author: 1983 Investors Guide to HMOs, (with others) Investor's Guide to HMOs, 1982. Vol. Multiple Sclerosis Soc., Washington, 1982-86. Mem. Am. Mktg. Assn. Republican. Presbyterian. Avocation: auto racing. Office: HealthCare Corp of Mid-Atlantic 100 S Charles St Fl 4 Baltimore MD 21201-2725

TURNOFF, WILLIAM CHARLES, judge; b. Phila., Nov. 19, 1948; s. David and Frieda (Kleiman) T.; m. Joy Rahinsky, Aug., 1971; children: Wendy, Dana. A.B. cum laude, Franklin and Marshall Coll., 1970; J.D., Cornell U., 1973. Bar: Pa. 1973, Fla. 1977, U.S. Dist. Ct. (ea. dist.) Pa. 1973, U.S. Dist. Ct. (so. dist.) Fla. 1980; U.S. Ct. Appeals (5th cir.) 1980, U.S. Ct. Appeals (11th cir.) 1981. Asst. dist. atty., Phila., 1973-80; asst. U.S. atty. office of U.S. Atty., Miami, Fla., 1980-86, chief maj. crimes sect., 1982-86; apptd. magistrate judge U.S. Dist. Ct. (so. dist.) Fla., 1986—, chief magistrate judge, 1994—. Chmn. Fla. Bar Grievance Com., 1985-86. Recipient Judicial Distinction award Miami chpt. Fla. Assn. Criminal Defense Lawyers, 1992. Mem. B'nai B'rith (pres. bench-bar unit 1991-92), Phi Beta Kappa.

TURNOVSKY, STEPHEN JOHN, economics educator; b. Wellington, New Zealand, Apr. 5, 1941; came to U.S. 1981; s. Frederick and Liselotte Felicitas (Wodak) T.; m. Michelle Henriette Louise Roos, Jan. 21, 1967; children: Geoffrey George, Jacqueline Liselotte. BA, Victoria U., Wellington, 1962, MA with honors, 1963; PhD, Harvard U., 1968. Asst. prof. economics U. Pa., Phila., 1968-71; assoc. prof. economics U. Toronto, Ont., Can., 1971-72; prof. economics Australian Nat. U., Canberra, 1972-82; IBE Disting. prof. economics U. Ill., Champaign, 1982-87; prof. economics U. Wash., Seattle, 1987—, chmn. dept., 1990—; rsch. assoc. Nat. Bur. Econ. Rsch., Cambridge, Mass., 1983-93. Author: Macroeconomic Analysis and Statistical Policy, 1977, International Macroeconomic Stabilization Policy, 1990, Methods of Macroeconomic Dynamics, 1995; mem. editl. bd. several jours.; contbr. numerous articles to profl. jours. Fellow Econometric Soc., Acad. Social Scis. in Australia; mem. Soc. Econ. Dynamics and Control (pres. 1982-84, editor Jour. Econ. Dynamics and Control 1981-87). Avocations: skiing, hiking, music. Home: 6053 NE Kelden Pl Seattle WA 98105-2045 Office: U Wash Coll Arts and Scis Dept Econs 301 Savery Hall Seattle WA 98195

TURNQUIST, DONALD KEITH, orthodontist; b. Pitts., Mar. 8, 1943; s. Arvid Gunnar and Ethel Elizabeth (Waddell) T.; m. Kathryn Druce, June 17, 1967; children: Juliana, Erik. AB, U. Pa., 1965; DMD, U. Pitts., 1972, MSD in Orthodontics, 1975. Cert. othodontist. Pvt. practice specializing in orthodontics, Winter Haven, Fla., 1975—. Bd. Elders Grace Luth. Ch., Winter Haven, 1975-85. Mem. ADA, Polk County Dent Assn., Am. Assn. Orthodontists, Fla. Assn. Orthodontists, Rotary, Omicron Kappa Upsilon. Republican. Lutheran. Avocations: tennis, jogging, softball, travel, reading. Home: 700 Island Way Winter Haven FL 33884 Office: 1153 1st St S Winter Haven FL 33880

TURNQUIST, PAUL KENNETH, agricultural engineer, educator; b. Lindsborg, Kans., Jan. 3, 1935; s. Leonard Otto and Myrtle Edith (Ryding) T.; m. Peggy Ann James, Dec. 22, 1962; children: Todd, Scott, Greg. BS Agrl. Engring., Kans. State U., 1957; MS in agrl. engring., Okla. State U., 1961, PhD agrl. engring., 1965. Registered profl. engr., Okla. Rsch. engr. Caterpillar Tractor Co., Peoria, Ill., 1957; instr., asst. prof. Okla. State U., Stillwater, 1958-62; assoc. prof., prof. S.D. State U., Brookings, 1964-76; prof., dept. head Auburn (Ala.) U., 1977—; mem. ABET Engring. Accreditation Commn., 1992—. Co-author: Tractors & Their Power Units, 1989; contbr. articles to profl. jours. Fellow Am. Soc. Agrl. Engrs. (life, trustee found. 1990-93, bd. dirs. edn. com. 1992-94); mem. NSPE, Am. Soc. for Engring. Edn., Coun. Forest Engrs., Sigma Xi. Methodist. Home: 1216 Nixon Dr Auburn AL 36830-6302

TURO, JOANN K., psychoanalyst, psychotherapist, consultant; b. Westerly, R.I., Feb. 13, 1938; d. Angelo and Anna Josephine (Drew) T. BS in Biology and Chemistry, U. R.I., 1959; MA in Human Rels. and Psychology, Ohio U., 1964; postgrad., NYU, 1966-71, N.Y. Freudian Inst., N.Y.C., 1977-85, Mental Health Inst., N.Y.C., 1977-80. Rsch. asst. biochemistry studies on schizophrenia Harvard U. Med. Sch., Boston, 1959-60; indsl. psychology asst. studies on managerial success N.Y. Telephone Co., N.Y.C., 1964-66; staff psychologist Testing and Advisement Ctr. NYU, 1966-70; staff psychologist M.D.C. Psychol. Svcs., N.Y.C., 1971-72; clin. dir. Greenwich House Substance Abuse Clinic, N.Y.C., 1973-76; cons. psychotherapist Mental Health Consultation Ctr., N.Y.C., 1977-82; pvt. practice psychoanalysis and psychotherapy N.Y.C., 1981—; mental health cons. Bklyn. Ctr. for Psychotherapy, 1976-78; with Psychoanalytic Consultation Svcs., 1994—; presenter in field. Mem. Internat. Psychoanalytic Assn. (cert.), Soc. for Personality Assessment (cert.), N.Y. Freudian Soc. (cert., co-chmn. grad. com. 1985-86, mem. continuing edn. com 1986—, pub. rels. com. 1992-93, psychoanalytic consult svc. 1994—), N.Y. Coun. Psychoanalytic Psychotherapists (cert.), Met. Assn. for Coll. Mental Health Practitioners (cert.). Office: 175 W 12th St Apt 9H New York NY 10011-8221

TUROCI, MARSHA MAY, county official; b. East Chicago, Ind., Mar. 21, 1940; d. Marshall W. and Georgia May Burrell; m. Les Turoci, Aug. 6, 1960 (div. 1994). Field rep. San Bernardino (Calif.) County, mem. bd. suprs. 1988—; chmn. Victor Valley Econ. Devel. Authority; active Mojave Desert Air Quality Control Bd., Southwestern Low Level Radiation Waste Commn. Active Calif. State Rep. Ctrl. Com. Recipient Law Enforcement award Optimists Club, 1985, Disting. Citizen award Boy Scouts Am., 1993; named Hesperian of Yr., Hesperia C. of C., 1981, Woman of Achievement, Victor Valley Bus. and Profl. Women, 1989. Mem. Nat. Assn. Counties (mem. pub. lands com.), So. Calif. Regional Assn. County Suprs., So. Calif. Associated Govts., Calif. State Assn. Counties, Calif. Elected Women's Assn. for Edn. and Rsch. Office: San Bernardino County Bd Suprs 385 N Arrowhead Ave San Bernardino CA 92415-0110

TUROCK, BETTY JANE, library and information science educator, educational association administrator; b. Scranton, Pa., June 12; d. David and Ruth Carolyn (Sweetser) Argust; BA magna cum laude (Charles Wesson scholar), Syracuse U., 1955; postgrad. (scholar) U. Pa., 1956; MLS, Rutgers U., 1970, PhD, 1981; m. Frank M. Turock, June 16, 1956; children: David L., B. Drew. Library and materials coordinator Holmdel (N.J.) Public Schs., 1963-65; story-teller Wheaton (Ill.) Public Library, 1965-67; ednl. media specialist Alhambra Public Sch., Phoenix, 1967-70; br. librarian, area librarian, head extension service Forsyth County Public Library System, Winston-Salem, N.C., 1970-73; asst. dir. Montclair (N.J.) Public Library, 1973-75, dir., 1975-77; asst. dir. Monroe County Library System, Rochester, N.Y., 1978-81; asst. prof. Rutgers U. Grad. Sch. Communications, Info. and Library Studies, 1981-87, assoc. prof. 1987-93, prof. 1994—, dept. chair, 1989—, dir. MLS program, 1990—; vis. prof. Rutgers U. Grad. Sch. Library and Info. Studies, 1980-81; adviser U.S. Dept. Edn. Office of Libr. Programs, 1988-89. Trustee, Raritan Twp. (N.J.) Public Library, 1961-62, Keystone Jr. Coll., 1991—, Freedom to Read Found., 1994—; mem. Bd. Edn. Raritan Twp., 1962-66; mem. Title VII Adv. Bd., Montclair Public Schs., 1975-77; ALA coord. Task Force on Women, 1978-80, mem. action coun.; treas. Social Responsibilities Round Table, 1987-88. Recipient N.J. Libr. Leadership award, 1994; named Woman of Yr., Raritan-Holmdel Woman's Club, 1975. Mem. AAUP, Am. Soc. Info. Sci., Am. Libr. and Info. Sci. Edn., Am. Libr. Assn. (pres. 1995—, pres.-elect 1994-95, exec. bd. 1991—, coun. 1988—), Rutgers U. Grad. Sch. Library and Info. Studies Alumni Assn. (pres. 1977-78, Disting. Alumni award 1994), Phi Theta Kappa, Psi Chi, Beta Phi Mu, Pi Beta Phi. Unitarian. Author: Serving Older Adults, 1983, Creating a Financial Plan, 1992; editor: The Bottom Line, 1984—; contbr. articles to profl. jours. Home: 39 Highwood Rd Somerset NJ 08873 Office: Rutgers U 4 Huntington St New Brunswick NJ 08901-1071

TUROCK, JANE PARSICK, nutritionist; b. Peckville, Pa., Apr. 15, 1947; d. Paul Charles and Elizabeth Dorothy (Mistysyn) Parsick; m. Michael John, July 12, 1968; children: Eric Matthew, Nathan Andrew, J. Seth, Melanie Kay. BS, Marywood Coll., Scranton, 1969; MS, Marywood Coll., 1982. Registered dietitian; cert. nutrition specialist. Registered dietitian Jane P. Turock, Scranton, Pa., 1985—; founder and chief dietitian Gastric Bubble, Scranton, Pa., 1986—; prof. Penn State Coll., Scranton, Pa., 1987—; dietitian & presenter WNEP TV Healthwatch, Avoca, Pa., 1988—; dir. & chief dietitian Vascular Inst. of Northeast Pa., Pa., 1989—; owner, mgr. Nutri-

tion...Plus/Fitness Unlimited, Scranton, Pa., 1991—; cons. Home Health Care Assn., Clarks Summit, 1985—; dietitian Clarks Summit, 1985—; founder Nat. Nutrition Month Bakeoff; dir. Camp Jane. Treas. Lackawanna County Med. Soc. Aux., 1974-76, pres., 1979-80, bd. dirs., 1987-93; allocations com. United Way Lackawanna County, 1990—. Mem. Am. Dietic Assn., Northeast Dist. Pa. Dietic Diet Therapy, Consulting Nutritionists in Pvt. Practice, Am. Diabetic Assn., Northeast Womens Network, Allied Wedding Firm. Republican. Roman Catholic. Avocations: skiing, tennis, gourmet cooking, jogging, swimming. Office: Nutrition Plus Fitness Unltd 815 Smith St Scranton PA 18504-3150 also: Abington Family Svcs 211 N State St Clarks Summit PA 18411-1087 also: Lady Jane Inc Chesterbrook Plz Wayne PA 19087

TUROFSKY, CHARLES SHELDON, landscape architect; b. Chgo., Oct. 1, 1942; s. Joseph and Lillian R. (Brownstein) T.; m. Diane Adrienne Haber, Aug. 22, 1971; children: Benjamin, Alexi, Nicole. BFA, U. Ill., 1964; M Landscape Architecture, U. Mich., 1966; student, Harvard Grad. Sch. Design, 1971. Registered landscape architect, N.Y., Conn., N.J., Mass., N.C. Assoc. landscape architect Sasaki Office, Watertown, Mass., 1966-71; prin. landscape architect Charles Turofsky, P.C., Great Neck, N.Y., 1971—; pres. Turlab Constrn. Corp., Great Neck, N.Y., 1984—; prof. Rutgers U., 1975-76, Westchester Community Coll., Valhalla, N.Y., 1971-75, N.Y. Bot. Garden, Bronx, N.Y., 1975-81; tchr. Yonkers (N.Y.) Pub. Schs., 1973-85; teaching fellow U. Mich., Ann Arbor, 1965. Prin. works include Tarry Town Corp. Ctr., GE World Hdqrs., Fairfield, Conn., Rosecliff Condominiums, Briarcliff, N.Y., Tarry Elm Bus. Ctr., Elmsford, N.Y., Woodmere (N.Y.) Country Club, Hampshire Country Club, Mamaroneck, N.Y., adult handicapped playground Young Adult Inst., Tarrytown, N.Y., Hebrew Hosp., Valhalla, N.Y., Mita Corp., Fairfield, N.J., AT&T Switching Ctr., Rego Park, Horizon Ho., Great Neck, N.Y., 104 Corporate Dr., Purchase, N.Y., others. Recipient award Garden Clubs of Am., 1982, award N.Y. State Nurserymen Assn., 1987, 88. Mem. Am. Soc. Landscape Architects, N.Y. State United Tchrs. (rep. 1983-85), Westchester-Putnam Builders Inst. (Excellence in Landscaping award 1986). Jewish. Avocations: painting, fishing, gardening, travel, theatre, museums. Office: 6 Bly Ct Great Neck NY 11023-1706

TUROK, PAUL HARRIS, composer, music reviewer; b. N.Y.C., Dec. 3, 1929; s. Joseph and Esther (Pashman) T.; m. Susan Kay Frucht, Mar. 24, 1967. BA, Queens Coll., N.Y.C., 1950; MA, U. Calif., Berkeley, 1951; MS, Baruch Coll., 1986. Music dir. Sta. KPFA, Berkeley, 1955-56; lectr. CCNY, 1959-63; vis. prof. Williams Coll., Williamstown, Mass., 1963-64; music critic New York Herald-Tribune, 1964-65; critic, columnist Music Jour., New York, 1964-79, Ovation mag., New York, 1980—; critic, contbr. New York Times, 1984—, Sta. WQXR, First Hearing, New York, 1985—; pub. Turok's Choice, 1990—. Composer musical compositions, premiered Indpls. Symphony, 1971, Louisville Orch., 1973, Cleve. Orch., 1973, Phila. Orch., 1976; opera Richard III, 1975; Sousa Overture, 1976; Lanier Songs, 1978; English Horn Quintet, 1982; Cello Sonata, 1984, Organ Toccata, 1984, Tourist Music, 1985, String Quartet No. 4, 1986, Rhapsody for Band, 1987, Piano Dance, 1988, Saxophone Sonata, 1988, Gypsy Airs, 1988, Violin Sonata, 1989, From Sholem Aleichem, 1990, Abac for trumpet and organ, 1990, Partita for three winds, 1991, Concerto for two violins and orch., 1991, Piano Trio, 1992, C.C. 6 for bassoon and orchestra, 1992, Fantasy for 4 Flutes and Piano, 4 hands, 1994. Served with U.S. Army, 1953-55. Hertz travelling scholar, U. Calif., 1956-58; Grammy nominee 1992, 93. Jewish. Avocations: world travel, computing.

TUROW, JOSEPH GREGORY, communication educator; b. Bklyn., Apr. 5, 1950; s. Abraham and Danuta (Chaikin) T.; m. Judith Anne Forrest, June 17, 1979; children: Jonathan, Marissa, Rebecca. BA, U. Pa., 1971, MA, 1973, PhD, 1976. Asst. prof. Purdue U., West Lafayette, Ind., 1976-86; from assoc. prof. to prof. comms. U. Pa., 1986—. Author: Getting Books to Children, 1979, Entertainment, Education and the Hard Sell, 1981, Media Industries, 1984, Playing Doctor, 1989, Media Systems in Society, 1992. Recipient Russell Nye award Popular Culture Assn., 1982; NEH grantee, 1986, 94; FCC grantee, 1978. Mem. Speech Comm. Assn. (div. head 1987), Internat. Comm. Assn. (div. chair 1995), Phi Beta Kappa. Avocation: viewing residential architecture. Office: U Pa Annenberg Sch Philadelphia PA 19104

TUROW, SCOTT F., lawyer, author; b. Chgo., Apr. 12, 1949; s. David D. and Rita (Pastron) T.; m. Annette Weisberg, Apr. 4, 1971; 3 children. BA magna cum laude, Amherst Coll., 1970; MA, Stanford U., 1974; JD cum laude, Harvard U., 1978. Bar: Ill. 1978, U.S. Dist. Ct. (no. dist.) Ill. 1978, U.S. Ct. Appeals (7th cir.) 1979. Asst. U.S. atty. U.S. Ct. Appeals (7th dist.), Chgo., 1978-86; ptnr. Sonnenschein Nath & Rosenthal, Chgo., 1986—; E. H. Jones lectr. Stanford U., 1972-75. Author: One L: An Inside Account of Life in the First Year at Harvard Law School, 1977, Presumed Innocent, 1987 (Silver Dagger award Crime Writers Assn. 1988), The Burden of Proof, 1990, Pleading Guilty, 1993; contbr. articles to profl. jours. Edith Mirrielees fellow, 1972. Mem. Chgo. Bar Assn., Fed. Bar Assn., Chgo. Coun. of Lawyers. Office: Sonnenschein Nath Rosenthal Ste 8000 Sears Tower 233 S Wacker Dr Chicago IL 60606*

TURPEN, LOUIS A., airport terminal executive. Dir. San Francisco Internat. Airport; dir., San Franciso Airports Commn. Office: San Francisco Intl Airport PO Box 8097 San Francisco CA 94128*

TURPEN, MICHAEL CRAIG, lawyer; b. Tulsa, Nov. 10, 1949; s. Wallace Kendall and Marjorie Allyce (Kinkaid) T.; m. Susan Lynn Haugor; children: Sean Michael, Patrick Michael, Sarah Allyce. BS in History Edn., U. Tulsa, 1972, JD, 1974. Bar: Okla. 1975. Legal advisor Muskogee Police Dept., Okla., 1975-76; asst. dist. atty. City of Muskogee, 1976, dist. atty., 1977-82; atty. gen. State of Okla., 1983-87; ptnr. Riggs, Abney, Neal & Turpen, Oklahoma City, 1987—; conf. speaker; mem. Okla. Spl. Legis. Com. on Criminal Justice System, 1978-79; adj. prof. bus. law N.E. Okla. State U.-Tahlequah, 1977; adj. prof. criminal law Connors State Coll., 1977-79. Author: Police-Prosecutor Training Manual, 1975; contbr. articles to profl. jours. Mem. Gov.'s Alternatives to Incarceration Com., 1980-81; bd. dirs. Call Rape, Inc.; vice chmn. Okla. Crime Commn., 1980-81; commr. Okla. State Bur. Investigation, 1978—; bd. dirs., coach Muskogee Green Country Girls Softball Assn.; mem. Muskogee High Sch. Booster Club; mem., coach Muskogee Knothole League Boys Baseball Assn.; mem. Muskogee County Human Soc., Muskogee County Women's Dem. Club; hon. mem. Okla. Hwy. Patrol, 1980; co-chmn. Clinton/Gore Okla., 1992, Al Gore for Pres., 1988; chmn. State Dem. Party Okla. Recipient Maurice Merrill Golden Quill award Okla. Bar Jour., 1981, Donald Santarelli award Nat. Orgn. Victim Assistance, Toronto, 1981, Mayor's commendation City of Muskogee, 1976, Mayor's commendation City of Owasso, 1975, $10,000 Cash award Found. for Improvement Justice, Inc., Achievement award Found. for Improvement Justice, Inc., 1986; named Outstanding Young Oklahoman, Okla. Jaycees, 1979, Outstanding Young Lawyer, Okla. Bar Assn., 1975, Outstanding Young Man, Muskogee Jaycees, 1979, One of Ten Outstanding Nat. Leaders in field of victim rights, Nat. Orgn. for Victim Assistance, 1986, One of Men and Women Under 40 Who are Changing Nation, Esquire Mag., 1985. Mem. ABA, Okla. Bar Assn., Muskogee County Bar Assn. (past sec.), Okla. Dist. Attys. Assn. (pres. 1980-81, bd. dirs.), Tulsa U. Alumni Assn., Rotary, Tulsa U. Hurricane Club, Fraternal Order of Police. Presbyterian. Office: Riggs Abney Neal & Turpen Ste 101 5801 Broadway Ext Oklahoma City OK 73118-7489 also: 502 W 6th St Tulsa OK 74119-1010

TURPIN, CHERYL NIDO, retail executive; b. Port Huron, Mich., Sept. 13, 1947; d. James N. and Lillian Mary (Forbes) N.; m. James M. Turpin, Apr. 26, 1980; children: Nicholas Nido, Jessica Rose. BA in English and Philosophy, U. Mich., 1969. Buyer, div. mdse. mgr. Rike's, Dayton, Ohio, 1969-74; div. mdse. mgr. Gimbels, Phila., 1974-75; v.p., gen. mdse. mgr. Weinstock's, Sacramento, 1975-78, chmn., chief exec. officer, 1982—; exec. v.p. Broadway Dept. Stores, Los Angeles, 1978-82. Mem. adv. bd. Sacramento Area Spl. Olympics, 1982—; bd. dirs. Sacramento Area United Way, 1985—, mem. Com. of 200, Sacramento YWCA, 1985-87, Pvt. Industry Coun. Sacramento, 1984-85. Recipient YWCA Outstanding Woman award, Sacramento, 1985, Disting. Bus. Woman's award, Sacramento C. of C., 1984-85. Mem. Fashion Group, Calif. C. of C. (bd. dirs.), The Trusteeship.

Avocation: skiing. Office: Ltd Lndn-Pris NY Inc PO Box 16528 Columbus OH 43216

TURPIN, DAVID HOWARD, biology educator, educational administrator; b. Duncan, B.C., Can., July 14, 1956; s. George Howard and Marilyn Elizabeth (Jones) T.; m. S. Laurene Clark, Oct. 4, 1985; children: Chantal, Josuha. BSc in Biology, U. B.C., 1977, PhD in Botany, Oceanography, 1980. Post-doctoral rsch. fellow Natural Sci. & Engring. Coun., 1980-81; rsch. assoc. Simon Fraser U., 1980; v.p. Sigma Resource Cons., Vancouver, B.C., 1980-81; from asst. prof. to assoc. prof. Queen's U., Kingston, Ont., Can., 1981-90; prof. biology Queen's U., Kingston, Ont., 1990-91, dean arts & sci., 1993-95, vice prin. acad., 1995—; prof., head botany U. B.C., 1991-93; invited speaker profl. meetings, univs. worldwide. Co-editor: Plant Physiology, Biochemistry and Molecular Biology, 1990; mem. editorial bd. Jour. Phycology, 1992—, Plant Physiology, 1988-92; contbr. chpts. books, numerous papers jours., conference proceedings. V.p. Great Lakes Tomorrow, 1986-90; mem. program com. Great Lakes Course-Ont. Sci. Ctr., 1988; Kingston City rep. Cataraqui Regional Conservation Authority, 1984-96. Recipient Excellence in Teaching Alumni award Queen's U., 1989, Outstanding Alumni award U. B.C., 1990; Darbaker prize Phycology Am. Botanical Assn., 1991; Natural Sci. & Engring. Rsch. Coun. Can. E.W.R. Stacie Meml. fellow 1989-90; Capt. T.S. Byrne Meml. scholar Dept. Oceanography U. B.C., 1980, postgrad. scholar Natural Scis. and Engring. Rsch. Coun., 1979-81, Edith Ashton Meml. scholar Dept. Botany U. B.C., 1979, Nat. Rsch. Coun. scholar, 1978-79, summer rsch. scholar U. B.C., 1978; many Natural Scis. and Engring. Rsch. Coun. grants, 1982—. Mem. Phycological Soc. Am., Am. Soc. Limnology & Oceanography, Can. Soc. Plant Physiologists (C.D. Nelson award 1989), Am. Soc. Plant Physiologists (cert. recognition 1992). Office: Queen's Univ, Office of Vice Prin (Acad), F407 Mackintosh Corry Hall, Kingston, ON Canada K7L 3N6

TURPIN, JACK A., electronics executive. Chmn. Hall-Mark Electronics Corp., Dallas, Tex. Office: Hall-Mark Electronics Corp PO Box 660091 11333 Pagemill Rd Dallas TX 75243-8305

TURRELL, EUGENE SNOW, psychiatrist; b. Hyattsville, Md., Feb. 27, 1919; m. Denise Deuprey, Dec. 26, 1942 (div. Jan. 1976); children: David Hillyer, Gregory Sherman (dec.); m. Zenobia A. Hopper, Apr. 16, 1988; stepchildren: Elizabeth Ann Crofoot, Mary Jane Cooper. BS, Ind. U., 1939, MD, 1947. Diplomate Am. Bd. Psychiatry and Neurology. Intern Peter Bent Brigham Hosp., Boston, 1947-48; resident physician Kandakee (Ill.) State Hosp., 1948-49; clin. asst. psychiatry U. Calif., San Francisco, 1949-51; asst. prof. Ind. U. Sch. Medicine, 1952-53, assoc. prof., 1953-58; prof., chmn. dept. psychiatry Marquette U. Sch. Medicine, 1958-63, clin. prof. psychiatry, 1963-69; lectr. U. Calif., San Francisco, 1969-75; assoc. prof. Ind. U., 1975-80, prof., 1980-89, prof. emeritus, 1989—; staff psychiatrist San Diego County Psychiat. Hosp., 1990—; assoc. clin. prof. U. Calif., San Diego, 1991—; mem., bd. dirs. Community Addictions Svcs. Agy, Indpls., 1975-79, pres. bd., 1976-77. Contr. articles to profl. jours. Lt. USNR, 1950-52. Recipient Certs. of Appreciation Office Sci. Rsch. and Devel., 1945, VA, 1964, Ind. U. Found., 1966. Fellow Am. Psychiat. Assn. (life); mem. AMA (Physician's Recognition award 1978-94), AAAS, Calif. State Med. Assn., Calif. State Psychiatric Assn., San Diego County Med. Soc., San Diego County Soc. Psychiat. Physicians, Sigma Xi, Alpha Omega Alpha. Democrat. Episcopalian. Avocations: tennis, motorcycling, bridge, literature, arts. Office: San Diego County Psychiat Hosp 3851 Rosecrans St San Diego CA 92110-3115

TURRELL, RICHARD HORTON, SR., retired banker; b. Kingston, Pa., Apr. 9, 1925; s. George Henry and Margaret (Clark) T.; m. Sally Wolfe, May 28, 1955; children: Richard H. Jr., David C., Douglas W. (dec.). Student, Cornell U., 1943; BS in Commerce, Washington and Lee U., 1949. Rep. sales Del. Lackawanna and Western Coal Co., Phila., 1949-51; asst. to pres. N.Y.C., 1951-58; broker Auchincloss Parker & Redpath, N.Y.C., 1958-61; mgr. investments Fiduciary Trust Co. Internat., N.Y.C., 1961-94, v.p., 1968-94, sr. v.p., 1968-94, sec., 1971-84; asst. sec. Blue Coal Corp., N.Y.C., 1953-58; v.p., bd. dirs. Pine Raleigh (N.C.) Corp., 1966-93. Trustee, overseer Simon's Rock of Bard Coll., Gt. Barrington, Mass., 1968-93; trustee Monmouth Coll., West Long Branch, N.J., 1980—, chmn. bd. trustees, 1989-92; chmn. Millburn-Short Hills (N.J.) Rep. Com., 1973-78; trustee Children's Specialized Hosp. Found., Mountainside, N.J., 1989-95. With Signal Corps, U.S. Army, 1943-46, PTO. Named Disting. Alumnus, Washington and Lee U., 1986. Mem. Baltusrol Golf Club (Springfield, N.J., gov. 1977), Capitol Hill Club (Washington), Turtle Creek Club (Tequesta, Fla.), Masons, Irem Temple Aaonms, Phi Beta Kappa, Phi Eta Sigma, Alpha Kappa Psi, Omicron Delta Kappa (hon.), Beta Gamma Sigma, Phi Delta Theta. Presbyterian. Avocations: golf, history, education. Home: 114 Turtle Creek Dr Tequesta FL 33469-1547

TURRENTINE, STANLEY WILLIAM, musician; b. Pitts., Apr. 5, 1934; m. Shirley Scott. Plays tenor saxophone; played with, Ray Charles, 1952, Earl Bostic, 1953, Max Roach, 1959-60; led group with wife, organist Shirley Scott, 1960-71; solo artist thereafter; rec. numerous albums including: Straight Ahead, 1985, Turrentine Again, Tender Togetherness!, Betcha Use the Stairs, What About You?, West Side Highway, Night Wings, The Man with the Sad Face, Everybody Come on Out, Have You Ever Seen the Rain?, In the Pocket, Pieces of Dreams, Salt Song, Cherry, Don't Mess with Mr. T., The Sugar Man, Sugar, Another Story, Common Touch, Always Something There, Easy Walker, The Spoiler, Rough'n Tumble, Joyride, Hustlin', A Chip Off the Old Block, Never Let Me Go, Jubelee Shouts, That's Where It's At, Dearly Beloved, Up at Minton's, Blue Hour, Ain't No Way, Mr. Natural, In Memory Of, New Time Shuffle, Straight Ahead, Wonderland, The Best of Stanley Turrentine, 1989, More Than A Mood, 1993. Office: care Associated Booking Corp 1955 Broadway New York NY 10023-6504*

TURRI, JOSEPH A., lawyer; b. Seneca Falls, N.Y., July 24, 1943; s. Louis Arthur and Assunta (Faiola) T.; m. Susan Ruth Testa, Dec. 29, 1975; 1 child, Michael James. BA, SUNY, Buffalo, 1965; JD, Cornell U., 1970. Bar: N.Y. 1971, U.S. Dist Ct. (we. dist.) N.Y. 1971, U.S. Supreme Ct. 1974. Ptnr. Harris, Beach & Wilcox, Rochester, N.Y., 1970—; mgmt. ptnrs. com. Harris, Beach & Wilcox, Rochester, 1991—, chmn. litigation dept., 1994—; bd. dirs. Thousand Island Park Corp., N.Y., Castle Bay Ltd., Rochester, N.Y.; arbitrator Am. Arbitration Assn., Syracuse, 1985—. Bd. dirs. Rochester Downtown Devel. Corp., 1992—. Mem. N.Y. Bar Assn., Monroe County Bar Assn., Assn. Gen. Contractors, Met. Forum (trustee). Avocations: horseback riding, antique wooden boats. Home: 110 Merriman St Rochester NY 14607 Office: Harris Beach & Wilcox 130 E Main St Rochester NY 14604

TURRO, NICHOLAS JOHN, chemistry educator; b. Middletown, Conn., May 18, 1938; s. Nicholas John and Philomena (Russo) T.; m. Sandra Jean Misenti, Aug. 6, 1960; children: Cynthia Suzanne, Claire Melinda. BA, Wesleyan U., 1960, DSc (hon.), 1984; PhD, Calif. Inst. Tech., 1963. Instr. chemistry Columbia U., N.Y.C., 1964-65, asst. prof., 1965-67, assoc. prof., 1967-69, prof. chemistry, 1969—, William P. Schweitzer prof. chemistry, 1982—, chmn. chemistry dept., 1981-84; Cons. E.I. duPont de Nemours and Co., Inc. Author: Molecular Photochemistry, 1965, (with G.S. Hammond, J.N. Pitts, D.H. Valentine) Survey of Photochemistry, vol. 1, 1968, vol. 2, 1970, vol. 3, 1971, (with A.A. Lamola) Energy Transfer and Organic Photochemistry, 1971, Modern Molecular Photochemistry, 1978; mem. editorial bd. Langmuir Macromolecules, Ency. of Phys. Sci. and Tech., Jour. of Reactive Intermediates. Fellow NSF, Alfred P. Sloan Found., Guggenheim fellow Oxford U., 1985; recipient Eastman Kodak award for excellence in grad. rsch. award for pure chemistry, 1973, E. O. Lawrence U.S. Dept. Energy, 1983, Porter medal European Photochem. Assn., Japanese Photochem. Soc., Inter-Am. Photochem. Soc., 1994, Havinga medal Leiden, The Netherlands, 1994; Fairchild scholar Calif. Inst. Tech., 1984-85. Mem. NAS, Am. Chem. Soc. (mem. editl. bd. jour. 1984—, Harrison Howe award Rochester, N.Y. sect. 1986, Arthur C. Cope award 1986, Fresenius award 1973, award for pure chemistry 1974, James Flack Norris award 1987), Am. Acad. Arts and Scis., Chem. Soc. (London), N.Y. Acad. Scis. (Freda and Gregory Halpern award in photochemistry 1977), Inter-Am. Photochemistry Soc. (award 1991, 94), European Photo-Chem. Assn. (Porter medal), Phi Beta Kappa, Sigma Xi. Home: 125 Downey Dr Tenafly NJ 07670-3005 Office: Columbia U 116th St and Broadway New York NY 10027

TURSI, FRANK VINCENT, journalist; b. Bklyn., Apr. 30, 1951; s. Dominick and Grace (Berardi) T.; m. Doris Ann Foster, Nov. 12, 1973; 1 child, Diana. BA in English, East Carolina U., 1973. Reporter Clemmons (N.C.) Courier, 1973-74, Key Biscayne (Fla.) Island News, 1974-75; news editor Coral Gables (Fla.) Times-Guide, 1975-77; sports writer, copy editor Miami (Fla.) Herald, 1977-79; sports writer, copy editor Winston-Salem (N.C.) Jour., 1979-81, copy editor, layout editor, 1981-85, med./sci. reporter, 1985-88, spl. projects reporter, 1988—. Author: Where the Land Meets the Sea, 1990, Winston-Salem: A History, 1994. Pres. Old Meadowbrook Homeowners Assn., 1991-92; mem. Winston-Salem Mayor's Com. for Handicapped, 1989-90; vol. camp counselor Muscular Dystrophy Assn. Recipient Media award N.C. chpt. Am. Planning Assn., 1987, Environ. Media award for Excellence N.C. Sierra Club, 1987, Conservation Communicator award N.C. Wildlife Fedn., 1988. Roman Catholic. Home: 3851 Willowood Dr Clemmons NC 27012 Office: Winston Salem Journal 418 N Marshall St Winston Salem NC 27102

TURTELL, NEAL TIMOTHY, librarian; b. N.Y.C., Nov. 1, 1949; s. Richard Roland and Ann Grace (Glover) T. AB, Fordham U., 1971; MLS, Pratt Inst., 1975. Cataloger-libr. Ford Found., N.Y.C., 1972-75, U.S. Dept. Transp., Washington, 1975-77; spl. projects libr. Smithsonian Instn., Washington, 1977-81, chief catalogue records, 1981-82; asst. dir. tech. svcs. U. Wis., Oshkosh, 1982-83, asst. prof. libr. sci., 1982-83; asst. chief libr. Nat. Gallery of Art, Washington, 1983-87, exec. libr., 1987—. Contbr. to book revs. Libr. Jour., 1972-75, exhbn. catalogue. Bd. trustees Pyramid Atlantic Ctr. for Printmaking and the Art of the Book, Riverdale, Md., 1988—, v.p. bd. trustees, 1991—. Mem. Art Librs. Soc. N. Am., Rsch. Librs. Group (steering com. for art and arch.a 1988-89). Home: 1631-B S Hayes Arlington VA 22202 Office: Nat Gallery of Art 4th & Constitution Ave NW Washington DC 20565-0001

TURTURRO, JOHN, actor; b. Brooklyn, Feb. 28, 1957; s. Nicholas and Katherine Turturro; m. Katherine Borowitz; 1 child, Amadeo. Grad., SUNY (New Paltz), 1978; student, Yale Drama Sch. Worked in regional theater and off-Broadway in Danny and the Deep Blue Sea (Obie Award, 1985), Men Without Dates, Tooth of the Crime, La Pata Viva, Chaos and Hard Times, The Bald Soprano, Of Mice and Men, The Resistable Rise of Arturo Ui, 1991; appeared in Broadway prodn. Death of a Salesman, 1984; appeared in films Raging Bull, 1980, Exterminator II, 1984, The Flamingo Kid, 1984, To Live and Die in L.A., 1985, Desperately Seeking Susan, 1985, Hannah and Her Sisters, 1986, Gung Ho, 1986, Offbeat, 1986, The Color of Money, 1986, The Sicilian, 1987, Five Corners, 1988, Do the Right Thing, 1989, Miller's Crossing, 1990, Men of Respect, Mo Better Blues, 1990, Jungle Fever, 1991, Barton Fink, 1991, (winner best actor award, Cannes Film Festival, 1991), Backtrack, 1991, Brain Donors, 1992, Fearless, 1993, Being Human, 1994, Quiz Show, 1994, Search and Destroy, 1995, Unstrung Heroes, 1995; film dir. (debut) Mac (Camera d'Or award Cannes Film Festival, 1992). Office: care ICM 8942 Wilshire Blvd Beverly Hills CA 90211*

TUSCHMAN, JAMES MARSHALL, lawyer; b. Toledo, Nov. 28, 1941; s. Chester and Harriet (Harris) T.; m. Ina S. Cheloff, Sept. 2, 1967; children: Chad Michael, Jon Stephen, Sari Anne. BS in Bus., Miami U., Oxford, Ohio, 1963; JD, Ohio State U., 1966. Bar: Ohio 1966, U.S. Ct. Appeals (6th and 7th cirs.), U.S. Supreme Ct. Assoc. Shumaker, Loop & Kendrick, Toledo, 1966-84, ptnr. 1970-84; co-founder, chmn. ops. com. Jacobson Maynard Tuschman & Kalur, Toledo, Cleve., Cin., Columbus, Youngstown and Dayton, Ohio, Morgantown, W.Va. and Louisville, Kansas City, Mo., Columbia, Md., St. Louis 1984—; chmn. bd., sec. Tuschman Steel Co., Toledo, 1969-76; vice chmn. bd. Kripke Tuschman Industries, Inc., 1977-85, dir. 1977-86; chmn. bd., sec. Toledo Steel Supply Co., 1969-86; ptnr. Starr Ave. Co., Toledo, 1969-86; bd. dirs. Capital Holdings Inc., Toledo, Capital Bank, Toledo, Fetal Devel. Eval., Ltd., Toledo. Past trustee, chmn. fin. com., former treas. Maumee Valley Country Day Sch.; past trustee, v.p., treas. Temple B'nai Israel, 1984-88. Mem. ABA, Am. Bd. Trial Advocates, Ohio Bar Assn., Toledo Bar Assn., Def. Rsch. and Trial Lawyers Assn., Ohio Civil Trial Lawyers Assn., Toledo Club, Inverness Country Club, Zeta Beta Tau, Phi Delta Phi. Home: 2579 Olde Brookside Rd Toledo OH 43615-2233 Office: 333 N Summit St Toledo OH 43604-2617

TUSHER, THOMAS WILLIAM, apparel company executive; b. Oakland, Calif., Apr. 5, 1941; s. William C. and Betty J. (Brown) T.; m. Pauline B. Kensett, Jan. 1, 1967; children: Gregory Malcolm, Michael Scott. B.A., U. Calif., Berkeley, 1963; M.B.A., Stanford U., 1965. Asst. to v.p. internat. Colgate Palmolive Co., N.Y.C., 1965-67; product mgr. Colgate-Palmolive P.R., 1967-68; supt. corp. planning Levi Strauss & Co., San Francisco, 1969; pres. Levi Strauss Internat., 1977-84; sr. v.p. Levi Straus & Co., before 1984, exec. v.p., chief operating officer, dir., from 1984, now pres., chief oper. officer; regional gen. mgr.; Australia/N.Z., Levi Strauss Australia, 1970-74; area gen. mgr. Levi Strauss No. Europe, London, 1974-75; pres. European div. Levi Strauss Internat., San Francisco, 1976; dir. various subs's. Levi Strauss Internat.; dir. Gt. Western Garment Co., Can. Bd. dirs. Calif. Council Internat. Trade, 1977—, U. Calif. Grad. Bus. Sch. Served with Intelligence Corps. USAR, 1966-67. Mem. San Francisco C. of C. (dir.). Republican. Presbyterian. Clubs: World Trade, Bay. Office: Levi Strauss & Co 1155 Battery St San Francisco CA 94111-1230*

TUSHINGHAM, (ARLOTTE) DOUGLAS, museum administrator; b. Toronto, Ont., Can., Jan. 19, 1914; s. Arthur Douglas and Lottie Elizabeth (Betts) T.; m. Margaret McAndrew Thomson, Apr. 9, 1948; children: Margaret Elizabeth, Ian Douglas. B.A., U. Toronto, 1936; B.D., U. Chgo., 1941, Ph.D., 1948, LL.D. 1982. Instr. U. Chgo. 1948-51; ann. prof. Am. Sch. Oriental Research, Jerusalem, 1951-52; dir. Am. Sch. Oriental Research, 1952-53; assoc. prof. Queen's U., 1953-55; head art and archaeology div. Royal Ont. Mus., Toronto, 1955-64; chief archaeologist Royal Ont. Mus., 1964-79, head Jerusalem project, 1979—, trustee, 1984-90; prof. emeritus dept. Nr. Eastern studies U. Toronto, Ont., 1955-79; Asst. dir. Jericho Excavations, 1952, 53, 56; dir. Dhiban Excavations, 1952-53; assoc. dir. Jerusalem Excavations, 1962-67; mem. Toronto Hist. Bd., 1960—, chmn., 1967-73. Author: (with V.B. Meen) Crown Jewels of Iran, 1968, (with Denis Baly) Atlas of the Biblical World, 1971, The Excavations at Dibon (Dhibân) in Moab, 1952-53, 1972, Gold for the Gods, 1976, Ancient Peruvian Metalworking, 1979, Excavations in Jerusalem, I, 1985. Served as lt. Royal Canadian Navy, 1942-45. Fellow Soc. Antiquaries of London, Royal Soc. Can., Canadian Museums Assn. (pres. 1964, 65), Archaeol. Inst. Am. Home: Apt 501, 20 Baif Blvd, Richmond Hill, ON Canada L4C 8T1

TUSHMAN, MICHAEL, business educator; b. Worcester, Mass., Dec. 28, 1947; s. Harry and Doris (Kneutzman) T.; children: Jonathan, Rachel. BS, Northeastern U., 1970; MS, Cornell U., 1972; PhD, MIT, 1976. bd. dirs. IBM Credit Corp., Stamford, Conn. Prof. Columbia U., N.Y.C., 1975—; exec. dir. Delta Consulting Group, N.Y.C., 1982—. Office: Columbia U Grad Sch Bus 719 Uris Hall New York NY 10027

TUSHNET, MARK VICTOR, law educator, associate dean; b. Newark, N.J., Nov. 18, 1945; s. Leonard and Fannie (Brandchaft) T.; m. Elizabeth Alexander, Aug. 23, 1969; children: Rebecca, Laura. BA magna cum laude, Harvard U., 1967; JD, MA in History, Yale U., 1971. Law clk. for Judge George Edwards, Detroit, 1971-72; law clerk for Justice Thurgood Marshall SD, Washington, 1972-73; law clk. for Justice Thurgood Marshall, Washington, 1973-81; prof. Georgetown U. Law Ctr., Washington, 1981—, assoc. dean rsch. and scholarship; vis. prof. U. Tex., 1977-78, U. So. Calif., 1989, U. Chgo. 1994. Author: (with Stone, Seidman and Sunstein) Constitutional Law, 1986, 2nd ed., 1991, (with Fink) Federal Jurisdiction: Policy and Practice, 1984, 2nd ed., 1987, The American Law of Slavery, 1981, The NAACP's Legal Strategy Against Segregated Education 1925-1950, 1987 (Littleton-Griswold prize Am. Hist. Assn.), Red, White, and Blue: A Critical Analysis of Constitutional Law, 1988; editor: Comparative Constitutional Federalism: Europe and America, 1990, Making Civil Rights Law: Thurgood Marshall and the Supreme Ct., 1936-61, 1994; contbr. articles to profl. jours. Jewish. Office: Georgetown U Law Ctr 600 New Jersey Ave NW Washington DC 20001

TUSIANI, JOSEPH, foreign language educator, author; b. Foggia, Italy, Jan. 14, 1924; came to U.S., 1947, naturalized, 1956; s. Michael and Maria (Pisone) T. Dottore in Lettere summa cum laude, U. Naples, 1947, Litt.D., 1971. Lectr. in Italian lit. Hunter Coll., 1950-62; chmn. Italian dept. Coll.

Mt. St. Vincent, 1948-71; vis. assoc. prof. NYU, 1956-64, CUNY, 1971-83; prof. Herbert H. Lehman Coll., 1971-83; NDEA vis. prof. Italian Conn. State Coll., 1962. Author: Dante in Licenza, 1952, Two Critical Essays on Emily Dickinson, 1952, Poesia Missionaria in Inghilterra Ed America, 1953, Sonettisti Americani, 1954, Melos Cordis; poems in Latin, 1955, Lo Speco Celeste, 1956, Odi Sacre; poems, 1958, The Complete Poems of Michelangelo, 1960, Rind and All, 1962, Lust and Liberty (The Poems of Machiavelli), 1963, The Fifth Season, 1963, Dante's Inferno (Introduced to Young People), 1964, Envoy from Heaven, 1965, Dante's Purgatorio (Introduced to Young People), 1969, Dante's Paradise (Introduced to Young People), 1970, Tasso's Jerusalem Delivered; verse transl., 1970, Boccaccio's Nymphs of Fiesole, 1971, Italian Poets of the Renaissance, 1971, From Marino to Marinetti, 1973, The Age of Dante, 1973, America the Free, 1976, Tireca Tàreca, 1978, Tasso's Creation of the World, 1982, Rosa Rosarum, poems in Latin, 1984, In Exilio Rerum, poems in Latin, 1985; poems, 1978, Gente Mia and Other Poems, 1978; (au obiography) La Parola Difficile, vol. I, 1988, (poems in Latin) Confinia Lucis et Umbrae La Parola Nuova, vol. II, 1991, La Parola Antica, vol. III, 1992, (poems in Italian) Il Ritorno, 1992, Bronx America, 1992, Annemale Parlante, 1994, Carmina Latina, 1994. Recipient Greenwood Prize for poetry in Eng., 1956, Outstanding Tchr. award, 1969, cavaliere ufficiale Italian Republic, 1973, Leonardo Covello's Educator award, 1980, Leone di San Marco award, 1982, Avis award, 1983, Joseph Tusiani scholarship fund established in his honor at Lehman Coll., 1983, Congl. Medal merit, 1984, Progresso Medal Liberty, 1986, Gold plaque from City Hall of San Marco, 1986, Outstanding Tchr. award Am. Assn. Tchrs. Italian, 1986, Renoir Literary award, 1988; Joseph Tusiani, Poet, Translator, Humanist (An Internat. Homage), 1995. Mem. Poetry Soc. Am. (v.p.), Cath. Poetry Soc. Am. (dir. 1958, Spirit gold medal 1968). Home: 2140 Tomlinson Ave Bronx NY 10461-1202 Strange how this continually re-edited Who's Who forces one to work and achieve.

TUTHILL, JOHN WILLS, former diplomat, educator; b. Montclair, N.J., Nov. 10, 1910; s. Oliver Bailey and Louise Jerolomen (Wills) B.; m. Erna Lueders, July 3, 1937; children: Carol Anne, David. S.B., Coll. William and Mary, 1932, LL.D., 1978; M.B.A., N.Y. U., 1936; A.M., Harvard U., 1943; LL.D., MacMurray Coll., 1967. Teller First Nat. Bank, Paterson, N.J., 1932-34; corporate trust adminstr. Bankers Trust Co. N.Y., 1934-36; investment counsel Fiduciary Counsel, N.Y.C., 1936-37; instr. Northeastern U., 1937-39, asst. prof. banking and finance, 1939-40; apptd. fgn. service officer Dept. State, 1940; served as vice counsul Windsor, Ont., Can., 1940-41, Mazatlan, Mexico, 1942; 3d sec. embassy Ottawa, Ont., 1942-44; sec. mission Office U.S. Polit. Adviser SHAEF, 1944-45; sec. mission and Am. Mil. Govt. for Germany, 1945-47, Am. consul, 1947; asst. chief shipping div. Dept. State, 1948, adviser, 1949; counselor of embassy Stockholm, 1949-51; spl. asst. ambassador London, 1952; dep. dir. Office Econ. Affairs, Bonn, W. Ger., 1952-54, USOM, Bonn, 1954; dir. USOM, 1954-56, counselor of embassy for econ. affairs, 1955-56; counselor embassy for econ. affairs with personal rank of minister Paris, 1956-59; dir. Office European Regional Affairs, Dept. State, 1959; minister-counselor econ. affairs U.S. Mission to NATO, European Regional Orgns., U.S. rep. prep. com. for OECD; also dep. U.S. rep. OEEC, 1960; U.S. rep. OECD with personal rank of ambassador, 1960-62; U.S. ambassador to European Communities, 1962-66, Brazil, 1966-69; prof. internat. politics Johns Hopkins U., Bologna Center, Italy, 1969; pres. Salzburg Seminar in Am. Studies, Cambridge, Mass., 1977-85; vis. fellow Woodrow Wilson Nat. Fellowship Found., Princeton, 1978-80; exec. dir., trustee The Am.-Austrian Found., 1985-88. Author: Some Things to Some Men: Serving in the Foreign Service, 1995. Gov. Atlantic Inst. for Internat. Affairs, Paris, 1969-86, dir. gen. 1969-76. Recipient All Am. Silver Anniversary award Sports Illustrated, 1956; named to Athletic Hall of Fame Coll. William and Mary, 1979; Dir. Gen.'s Cup Dept. State, 1983. Mem. N.Y. Coun. Fgn. Rels., Washington Inst. Fgn. Policy, Am. Acad. Diplomacy (bd. dirs.), Jean Monnet Coun. (bd. dirs.), Harvard Club (N.Y.C.), Cosmos Club (Washington), Flat Hat of William and Mary, Omicron Delta Kappa, Theta Delta Chi. Clubs: Harvard (N.Y.C.); Cosmos (Washington); Flat Hat of William and Mary. Home: 2801 New Mexico Ave NW Washington DC 20007-3921

TUTHILL, WALTER WARREN, retail executive; b. Madison, N.J., Nov. 28, 1941; s. Walter Warren and Elizabeth Emma (Kniskern) T.; m. Barbara Ann Stephens, Apr. 22, 1967. BSBA, U. N.C., 1964. CPA, N.Y., N.J., N.C.; cert. info systems auditor, cert. internal auditor. Sr. mgr. Price Waterhouse, N.Y.C., 1964-77; dir. internal audit Carter Hawley Hale Stores Inc., L.A., 1977-82, gen. auditor, 1982-85, v.p., 1985-94; v.p. retail control Broadway Stores, Inc., L.A., 1994—; lectr. in field. Contbr. articles to profl. jours. Pres. Twin W Rescue Squad, Princeton Junction, N.J., 1976-77. Mem. AICPA, N.Y. Soc. CPA's, Am. Statis. Assn., Am. Acctg. Assn., Inst. Internal Auditors, Nat. Retail Mchts. Assn. (chmn. bd. internal audit group 1982-84, bd. dirs.), EDP Auditors Assn. Avocations: travel, computers, classical music. Office: Broadway Stores Inc 3880 N Mission Rd Los Angeles CA 90031-3179

TUTINO, ROSALIE JACQUELINE, college administrator; b. Bklyn., Dec. 28, 1937; d. Peter Rocco and Rose (Oliva) T. BA, St. Joseph's Coll., 1959; MA, NYU, 1964. Licensed ins. broker, N.Y. Publ., annuity mgr. Equitable Life Assurance, N.Y.C., 1959-62; instr., dept. chmn. Our Lady Perpetual Help High Sch., Bklyn., 1962-70; dir. coll. relations St. Joseph's Coll., Bklyn., 1970-75, devel. and coll. rels. dirs., 1975-77, v.p. devel. and coll. rels., 1977—; pres. Rosalie Tutino Assocs., Hampton Bays, N.Y., 1980. Bd. dirs. Suffolk coun. Boy Scouts Am., 1988—, Suffolk Coun., 1988, Archtl. Review Bd., Town of Southampton. Mem. L.I. Coalition for Fair Broadcasting, Nat. Soc. Fundraising Execs., Pub. Rels. Soc. Am., L.I. Assn., CASE. Republican. Roman Catholic. Avocations: oil painting, sailing, photography, golf. Home: 49 Romana Dr Hampton Bays NY 11946-3718 Office: Saint Josephs Coll 155 W Roe Blvd Patchogue NY 11772-2399

TUTTLE, CLIFFORD HORACE, JR., electronics manufacturing company executive; b. Teaneck, N.J., Aug. 3, 1930; s. Clifford Horace Sr. and Mary (Rodman) T.; m. Martha M. Greene, Apr. 23, 1952; children: Deborah Tuttle Fox, Michael R., Sandra, Mary Tuttle Faucher. BA in Psychology, Amherst, 1952. V.p. mktg. Vitramon, Inc., Monroe, Conn., 1957-63; pres. Mktg. Assistance, Inc., Weston, Mass., 1963-70; v.p. mktg. AVX Corp., New Bedford, Mass., 1970-72; pres., chmn. Aerovox, Inc., New Bedford, 1973—; chmn. Electronic Industries Assn., Washington; bd. dirs. NBB Bank; exec. com. New Bedford Inst. for Savs. Trustee St. Luke's Hosp., New Bedford, 1984—. Served to lt. USCG, 1953-55. Mem. IEEE, C. of C. (v.p. New Bedford 1982—). Republican. Avocation: boating. Office: Aerovox Inc 370 Faunce Corner Rd North Dartmouth MA 02747

TUTTLE, DANIEL WEBSTER, retired political science educator; b. Quincy, Ill., Feb. 25, 1925; s. Daniel Webster and Nellie Blanche (Hampton) T.; m. Elsie Eleanor Smith, June 28, 1947; children: Vera Kay, Daniel Webster, David B.H. AB, Ill. coll., 1945; MA, U. Minn., 1947, PhD, 1964. Instr. polit. sci. U. Wyo., Laramie, 1947-50; from asst. prof. to assoc. prof. U. Hawaii, Honolulu, 1950-66, prof., 1971-89, prof. emeritus, 1989—; vis. faculty Stephens Coll., Columbia, Mo., 1956-57, UCLA, 1961; exec. dir. Hawaii Edn. Assn., Honolulu, 1966-71, 89—; polit. analyst Sta. KGMB-TV-Radio, Honolulu, 1958-86. Author: State Elections Prior to Admittance to Union, 1951, Hawaii Voting Behavior, 1964-73, Papers on Hawaiian Politics, 1952-62, Religion and Politics, 1981; columnist Honolulu Star Bull. Advertiser, 1959-66, 81-87. Chmn. bd. dirs., pres., dir. Pub. Affairs Adv. Svc., Honolulu, 1973—; mem. Honolulu Charter Commn., 1971-72, Hawaii Edn. Council, 1967-70; active PTA; bd. dirs. Big Bros. of Hawaii, 1964-79, advisor, 1979—, Aloha United Fund, 1967-71, Honolulu Youth Symphony Assn., 1965-71. Eagleton Found. grantee U. Hawaii, 1962. Mem. NEA, AAUP, Am. Polit. Sci. Assn., Western Polit. Sci. Assn., Am. Soc. Pub. Adminstrn., Phi Beta Kappa, Alpha Phi Omega, Tau Kappa Epsilon. Lodge: Kiwanis. Home: 14 Akilolo St Honolulu HI 96821-1502

TUTTLE, ELBERT PARR, federal judge; b. Pasadena, Calif., July 17, 1897; s. Guy Harmon and Margie Etta (Parr) T.; m. Sara Sutherland, Oct. 22, 1919; children: Elbert Parr, Jane T. (Mrs. John J. Harmon). Student, Punahou Acad., Honolulu, 1909-14; AB, Cornell U., 1918, LLB, 1923; LLD (hon.), Emory U., 1958, Harvard U., 1965, Georgetown U., 1978, Atlanta U., 1984. Bar: Ga. 1923. News and editl. writer N.Y. Evening World, N.Y.C.; also Army and Navy Jour. and Am. Legion Weekly, Washington, 1919; practiced in Atlanta and Washington, 1923-52; mem. firm Sutherland,

Tuttle & Brennan; gen. counsel, head legal div. Treasury Dept., 1953-54; judge U.S. Ct. Appeals (5th cir.), 1954-81; chief judge U.S. Ct. Appeals, 1961-67; judge U.S. Ct. Appeals (11th cir.), 1981—, now sr. justice; Chmn. adv. com. on civil rules Jud. Conf. U.S., 1972-78, chmn. adv. com. on jud activities, 1969-77. Trustee Atlanta Community Chest, 1947-49; v.p. Atlanta Community Planning Council, 1951; Past trustee Interdonominational Theol. Center, Cornell U., Atlanta U., Spelman Coll., Morehouse Coll., Piedmont Hosp. Served to col. F.A., 77th Inf. Div. U.S. Army, 1941-46; comdg. gen. 108th Airborne Div. (res.), 1947-50; brig. gen. U.S. Army Res. Decorated Legion of Merit, Bronze Star, Purple Heart with oak leaf cluster; recipient Presdl. medal of freedom, 1981, Devitt Disting. Svc. to Justice award, 1989. Mem. ABA, Atlanta Bar Assn. (pres. 1948), Atlanta C. of C. (pres. 1949), Phi Kappa Phi, Pi Kappa Alpha (nat. pres. 1930-36), Order of Coif. Episcopalian. Office: US Ct Appeals 11th Cir 56 Forsyth St NW Atlanta GA 30303-3147

TUTTLE, FRANK JAMES, bank executive; b. N.Y.C., Apr. 17, 1941; s. Franklin B. and Esther (Leeming) T.; m. Nora Veress, June 27, 1964; children: Franklin, Thomas, Christopher. BA, Denison U., 1963; MBA, Suny, Albany, 1970. Various positions Key Bank N.A., Albany, 1970—; sr. adminstrv. v.p., 1980-89; sr. v.p. KeyCorp, Cleve., 1989—. Served to capt. USAF, 1963-68. Clubs: Old Chatham Hunt (N.Y.) (pres. 1982-85). Office: Key Corp 127 Public Sq Cleveland OH 44114

TUTTLE, JON F., lawyer; b. Cin., 1940. BSEE, Ohio U., 1964; JD, U. Pitts., 1969. Bar: Minn. 1969, U.S. Dist. Ct. (Minn. dist.) 1970, U.S. Ct. Appeals (7th and 8th cirs.) 1970, U.S. Supreme Ct. 1970, U.S. Ct. Appeals (5th and fed. cirs.) 1973, D.C. 1985. Mng. ptnr. Dorsey & Whitney, Washington; instr. legal writing U. Minn., 1970-73; adj. prof. law William Mitchell Coll., 1974-80. Mng. editor, mem. editorial bd. U. Pitts. Law Rev., 1968-69. Mem. ABA (mem. intellectual property law sect.), Minn. State Bar Assn. (mem. sect. coun., computer law sect. 1983-88), ITC Trial Bar Assn. Office: Dorsey & Whitney 1330 Connecticut Ave NW Ste 20 Washington DC 20036-1704

TUTTLE, WILLIAM G(ILBERT) T(OWNSEND), JR., research executive; b. Portsmouth, Va., Nov. 26, 1935; s. William Gilbert and Edith Inez (Ritter) T.; m. Helen Lynn Warren, Dec. 27, 1959; children: Lynn, Robert, Jonathan. B.S., U.S. Mil. Acad., 1958; M.B.A., Harvard U., 1963. Commd. 2d lt. U.S. Army, 1958, advanced through grades to gen., 1989; dir. combat service support (Office Combat Devels., Hdqrs. Tng. and Doctrine Command), Ft. Monroe, Va., 1976-77; comdr. 3d Armored Div. Support Command Frankfurt, W. Ger., 1977-79; comdr. Mil. Traffic Mgmt. Command Eastern Area Bayonne, N.J., 1979-81; dir. force mgmt. Hdqrs. Dept. Army, Washington, 1981-82; chief policy and programs br. Supreme Hdqrs. Allied Powers Europe, 1982-84; comdr. U.S. Army Operational Test and Evaluation Agy., 1984-86; dep. comdg. gen. Logistics, Tng. and Doctrine Command and comdg. gen. U.S. Army Logistics Ctr., Ft. Lee, Va., 1986-89; comdg. gen. U.S. Army Materiel Command, Alexandria, Va., 1989-92; ret., 1992; pres., CEO, bd. trustees Logistics Mgmt. Inst., McLean, Va., 1993—; U.S. Army Kermit Roosevelt lectr., 1991; bd. dirs. Procurement Round Table; mem. bd. advisors Nat. Contract Mgmt. Assn. Prin., Coun. on Excellence in Govt.; nat. councillor Atlantic Coun. Decorated Def., USAF, USN, USA, D.S.M. (3), Bronze Star (3), Legion of Merit, Def. Superior Service medal. Mem. Nat. Def. Transp. Assn., Assn. U.S. Army (Pres.'s award 1992). Lutheran. Office: Logistics Mgmt Inst 2000 Corporate Ridge Mc Lean VA 22102-7805

TUTTLE, WILLIAM MCCULLOUGH, JR., history educator; b. Detroit, Oct. 7, 1937; s. William McCullough and Geneva (Duvall) T.; m. Linda Lee Stumpp, Dec. 12, 1959 (div.); children: William McCullough III, Catharine D., Andrew S. BA, Denison U., 1959; MA, U. Wis., 1964, PhD, 1967. Faculty mem. U. Kans., Lawrence, 1967—; prof. history, 1975—, intra-univ. prof., 1982-83; sr. fellow in So. and Negro history Johns Hopkins U., 1969-70; Charles Warren fellow Harvard U., Cambridge, Mass., 1972-73; vis. prof. U. Sc., Columbia, 1980; assoc. fellow Stanford Humanities Ctr., 1983-84; research assoc. U. Calif., Berkeley, 1986-88. Author: Race Riot: Chicago in the Red Summer of 1919, 1970, W.E.B. Du Bois, 1973, (with David M. Katzman) Plain Folk, 1982, (with others) A People and A Nation, 1982, 4th edit., 1994, "Daddy's Gone to War": The Second World War in the Lives of America's Children, 1993; contbr. chpts. to books, numerous articles to profl. jours. Dem. precinct committeeman, Lawrence, 1980-90. Lt. USAF, 1959-62. Recipient Merit award Am. Assn. for State and Local History, 1972; Younger Humanist fellow NEH, 1972-73, Guggenheim fellow, 1975-76, NEH fellow, 1983-84, rsch. fellow Hall Ctr., 1990; grantee Evans, 1975-76, Beveridge, 1982, NEH, 1986-89. Mem. Soc. Am. Historians, Am. Hist. Assn., Orgn. Am. Historians, Am. Studies Assn., So. Hist. Assn., Lawrence Trout Club, Golden Key (hon.), Omicron Delta Kappa, Phi Gamma Delta. Unitarian. Home: 713 Louisiana St Lawrence KS 66044 Office: U Kans Dept History Lawrence KS 66045

TUTTLETON, JAMES WESLEY, English educator; b. St. Louis, Aug. 19, 1934; s. Clarence M. and Nora Belle (Sutt) T. B.A., Harding U., Searcy, Ark., 1955; M.A., U. N.C., 1957, Ph.D., 1963. Instr. Clemson U., S.C., 1956-59, U. N.C., Chapel Hill, 1962-63; asst. prof. U. Wis., Madison, 1963-68; assoc. prof. English NYU, N.Y.C., 1968-74, prof., 1974—, chmn. dept., 1974-83; assoc. dean Grad Sch. Arts & Scis. NYU, 1988-89. Author: The Novel of Manners in America, 1972, Thomas Wentworth Higginson, 1978; editor: The American (Henry James), 1978, Washington Irving: History, Tales, and Sketches, 1983, Voyages and Discoveries of the Companions of Columbus (Washington Irving), 1986, The Sweetest Impression of Life: The James Family and Italy, 1990, Edith Wharton: The Contemporary Reviews, 1992, Washington Irving: The Critical Reaction, 1993. Served with USAFR, 1956-63. Mem. Century Assn. Home: 37 Washington Square W 11-D New York NY 10011 Office: NYU Dept English New York NY 10003

TUTTON, BETTY JANE, humanities educator; b. Buffalo, N.Y., June 16, 1924; d. George W. and Beatrice (Hosken) T. AB, Houghton Coll., 1947; EdM, U. Buffalo, 1951; Phd, U. Minn., 1979. Dir. youth and music Princeton (W.Va.) Presbyn. Ch., 1947-48; asst. to assoc. prof. English Bob Jones U., Greenville, S.C., 1950-55; bible tchr. Beaver High Sch., Bluefield, W.Va., 1955-57; asst. prof. English, acting dean of women Agl.-Tech. Inst. SUNY, Alfred, N.Y., 1957-59; assoc. prof. English Taylor U., Upland, Ind., 1959-60; teaching asst. English U. Minn., Mpls., 1960-61; assoc. prof. to prof. English Bethel Coll., St. Paul, 1961-66; prof. humanities St Petersburg Jr. Coll., Clearwater, Fla., 1966—; chmn. humanities dept. St Petersburg Jr. Coll., Clearwater, 1986-88; bd. dirs. Samaritan Counseling Ctr., Clearwater, 1991—; exec. com. Clearwater (Fla.) Pub. Libr. Found., 1993—; cons. art edn. Manatee County Pub. Schs., Bradenton and Sarasota, Fla., 1987-88. Ruling elder Trinity Presbyn. Ch., Clearwater, 1981-84; edn. work in area chs., 1966—. Recipient rsch. grant, assistantship U. Minn., Mpls., 1967-69, Excellence in Teaching Alfred and Lisl Schick award, Clearwater, 1980. Mem. Community Coll. Humanities Assn., Nat. Coun. for Excellence in Teaching of Critical Thinking, Pi Lambda Theta. Democrat. Avocations: hiking, sailing, woodworking, astronomy, travel. Home: 406 N Mars Ave Clearwater FL 34615 Office: St Petersburg Jr Coll Drew St Clearwater FL 34625

TUTUN, EDWARD H., retired retail executive; b. Boston, Jan. 26, 1924; s. J.J. and Esther L. T.; m. Joan M. Bocoffer, Oct. 23, 1953. B.S. in chem. Engring., Northeastern U., 1947. V.p. W.R. Grace & Co., N.Y.C., 1978-82, sr. v.p., 1982-83, exec. v.p., 1983-87, ret., 1987; vice chmn. Herman's Sporting Goods, Inc., Cartaret, N.J., 1983. Served with USAAF, 1942-45, ETO. Mem. Nat. Retail Mchts. Assn. (dir. 1983), DIY Inst. (dir. 1983). Club: N.Y. Yacht (N.Y.C.). Home: 544 Pinellas Bayway S Tierra Verde FL 33715 also: 237 Guinea Rd Stamford CT 06903 Office: WR Grace & Co 1114 Avenue Of The Americas New York NY 10036-7701

TUTWILER, MARGARET DEBARDELEBEN, communications executive; b. Birmingham, Ala., Dec. 28, 1950; d. Temple Wilson and Margaret (DeBardeleben) Tutwiler, II. Student, Finch Coll., 1969-71; B.A., U. Ala., 1973. Sec. Ala. Rep. Party, Birmingham, 1974; scheduler Pres. Ford Com., Birmingham, 1975-78; asst. dir. Pres. Ford Com. Ala., Birmingham, 1976; pub. rels. rep. Nat. Assn. Mfrs. for Ala. and Miss., Birmingham and Washingtoon, 1977-78; dir. scheduling George Bush for Pres. Com., Houston and Washington, 1978-80; spl. assist. to Pres. Reagan and exec. to Chief of Staff

The White House, Washington, 1981-85; asst. sec. Dept. Treasury, 1985-88; sr. advisor transition team U.S. Dept. State, Washington, 1988-89, asst. sec. pub. affairs, spokesman, 1989-92; ptnr. Fitzwater & Tutwiler, Inc., Washington, 1993—; dep. chmn. Bush-Quayle '88, Washington, 1988. Recipient Woman of Yr. award Wake Forest U., 1986, Alexander Hamilton award, 1988, Am. Ctr. for Internat. Leadership's Marshall award for outstanding leadership Birmingham Sothern's GALA 10, 1991. Republican. Episcopalian.

TUYAKBAEV, ZHARMAKHAN AITBAJEVICH, prosecutor; b. Kazgurt District, South Kazakhstan Region, Kazakhstan, Nov. 22, 1947; s. Aitbaj and Tynyn (Kenshymbaeva) T.; m. Bagila Nagometovna Aptaeva, May 19, 1972; children: Aziza, Tchingiz, Adilzhan. Degree, Kazakh State U., Almaty, Kazakhstan, 1971. Cert. lawyer. Asst. chief inquiry dept. Office of the Prosecutor, South Kazakhstan Region, Tchimkent, Kazakhstan, 1971-78; with South Kazakhstan Region Office, Tchimkent, Kazakhstan, 1978-81; dep. to gen. prosecutor Office of the Prosecutor, Republic of Kazakhstan, Almaty, Kazakhstan, 1981-87; prosecutor of Atyrau Office of the Prosecutor, Atyrau Region, Atyrau, Kazakhstan, 1987-90; gen. prosecutor Office of the Prosecutor, Republic of Kazakhstan, Atyrau, Kazakhstan, 1990—; dep. of Oblast Soviet Atyrau Region, Atyrau, 1989-91; dep. Parlament of Kazakhstan Supreme Coun. of Kazakhstan, Almaty, 1990-93. Recipient Devoted Work medal USSR, 1982, Honorary Worker badge USSR, 1984; named State Counsellor of Justice Republic of Kazakhstan, 1982. Avocation: tennis. Home: Internationalnaya Street 120-16, Almaty Kazakhstan Office: Embassy of Kazakhstan 3421 Massachusetts Ave NW Washington DC 20007-1446

TUZLA, KEMAL, mechanical engineer, scientist; b. Adapazari, Sakarya, Turkey, Feb. 23, 1943; came to U.S., 1974; s. Hayrettin and Muberra (Horozlu) T.; m. Asuman Fatma Cokmez. MME, Istanbul (Turkey) Tech. U., 1966, PhD in Mech. Engring., 1972. Instr. Istanbul Tech. U., 1966-72, asst. prof., 1974, assoc. prof., 1978-81; instr. Air Force Coll., Istanbul, 1973-74; rsch. asst. prof. U. Wash., Seattle, 1974-78; sr. rsch. scientist Lehigh U., Bethlehem, Pa., 1981—; mem. organizing com. 2d Thermal Sci. Conf., Istanbul; 1979, 3d Conf., Trabzon, Turkey, 1981; cons. Goodyear Tire & Rubber Co., Akron, Ohio, 1984-86, Exxon Nuclear, Richland, Wash., 1985-88. Editor Proc. 2d Thermal Sci. Conf., 1979; contbr. articles in area of thermal scis. to profl. jours. Co-founder Turkish Am. Cultural Assn. Seattle, 1977. Rsch. grantee Goddyear Tire & Rubber Co., 1985-86, Los Alamos (N.Mex.) Nat. Lab., 1989-91, Ben Franklin Tech. Ctr., Bethlehem, 1989-95, Gas Rsch. Inst., 1987-91, Elec. Power Rsch. Inst., 1991-94. Mem. ASHRAE, AIChE. Achievements include research in heat transfer in two-phase flows, boiling, fluidized beds, electronic components and nuclear safety. Avocations: skiing, tennis, chess, bridge. Home: 344 Valley Park S Bethlehem PA 18018-1360 Office: Lehigh U Chem Engring Iacocca Hall 111 Research Dr Bethlehem PA 18015

TWA, CRAIGHTON OLIVER, power company executive; b. Drumheller, Alta., Can., Oct. 15, 1937; s. Joe Philander and Freda Alice (Fowler) T.; m. Irene Adam, May 7, 1960; children: Tracy, Robert, Carey. BSEE, U. Alta., Edmonton, 1959. Registered profl. engr., Alta. Engr. Can. Utilities Ltd., Edmonton, 1959-80; v.p. customer svcs. Alta Power Ltd., Edmonton, 1980-85, sr. v.p., gen. mgr., 1985-86, pres., 1986-93; pres. CU Power div. Can. Utilities Ltd., Edmonton, 1988-93; exec. v.p. Can. Utilities Ltd., Edmonton, 1994—, Can. Utilities Ltd. and ATCO Ltd. Office of the Chmn., 1995—; bd. dirs. Alta. Power ltd., CU Power Internat. Ltd., Northland Utilitiess Enterprises Ltd., The Yukon Elec. Co. Ltd., Thames Power Ltd., Frontec Logistics Corp., Can. Western Natural Gas Co. Ltd., Northwestern Utilities Ltd. Mem. Assn. Profl. Engrs., Geologists and Geophysicists Alta. Office: Can Utilities Ltd, 10035-105th St, Edmonton, AB Canada T5J 2V6

TWADDELL, WILLIAM HARTSTHORNE, diplomat; b. Madison, Wis., Jan. 25, 1941; s. William Freeman and Helen (Johnson) T.; m. Susan J. Hardy; children: William Sanderson, Ellen Johnson. BA, Brown U., 1963. Vol. Peace Corps, Brazil, 1963-65; U.S. Army, 1965-67; journalist N.Y. Daily News, 1967-69; fgn. svc. officer U.S. Dept. State, since 1969; amb. to Mauritania Nouakchott, 1988-91; amb. to Liberia, 1992—. With U.S. Army, 1965-67. Office: Liberia Dept of State Monrovia Washington DC 20521

TWADDLE, ANDREW CHRISTIAN, sociology educator; b. Hartford, Conn., Apr. 21, 1938; s. Paul Holmes and Ruth Bridenbaugh (Christian) T.; m. Sarah A. Wolcott, June 15, 1963; children: Lisa, Kristin. AB, Bucknell U., 1961; MA, U. Conn., 1963; PhD, Brown U., 1968. Instr. sociology Coll. of Holy Cross, Worcester, Mass., 1966-67; instr. preventive medicine Harvard U. Med. Sch., Boston, 1967-69; asst. prof. sociology and community medicine U. Pa., Phila., 1969-71; assoc. prof. sociology and family and community medicine U. Mo., Columbia, 1971-74, prof. sociology, 1974—, chmn. dept., 1988-93; guest prof. U. Göteborg, Sweden, 1978-79; Fulbright rsch. fellow Linköping U., Sweden, 1993; guest lectr. Uppsala U., Sweden, 1993. Author: Sickness Behavior and the Sick Role, 1979; co-author: A Sociology of Health, 1987, Disease, Illness and Sickness, 1994, Salvaging Medical Care, 1994. Chair Columbia Bd. Health, 1980-83. Recipient John Kosa Meml. prize Pergamon Press, Eng., 1974. Mem. Internat. Sociol. Assn., Am. Sociol. Assn., Midwest Sociol. Soc., Muleskinners Club (v.p. 1985-87, 94—). Democrat. Unitarian-Universalist. Avocations: genealogy, sailing. Home: 919 Edgewood Ave Columbia MO 65203-2823 Office: U Mo Dept Sociology 109 Sociology Columbia MO 65211

TWARDOWICZ, STANLEY JAN, artist, photographer; b. Detroit, July 8, 1917; s. Joseph and Anna Ligenski; m. Lillian Dodson, Mar. 15, 1971. Student, Meinzinger Art Sch., Detroit, 1940-44, Skowhegan (Maine) Sch. Painting and Sculpture, summer 1946. Instr. Ohio State U., 1946-51; prof. Hofstra U., 1965-87. Exhibited paintings, Mus. Modern Art, Guggenheim Mus., Whitney Mus., Art Inst. Chgo., Carnegie Internat., Pa. Acad. Fine Arts, Am. Acad. Arts and Letters, Houston Mus., Milw. Art Center, Peridot Gallery, N.Y.C., others; retrospective exhbn., Heckscher Mus., Huntington, N.Y., 1974, Emily Lowe Gallery, Hempstead, N.Y., 1979, 40 Yr. Retrospective of Paintings Firehouse Gallery, Garden City, N.Y.; exhibited photographs Images Gallery, N.Y.C.; one man show: Odeon Gallery, Sag Harbor, N.Y., 1993; represented in permanent collections Mus. Modern Art, Los Angeles County Mus., Newark Mus., Milw. Art Center, Ball State Tchrs. Coll., Harvard U., Vassar Coll., Hirshhorn Mus. and Sculpture Garden, others. Guggenheim fellow, 1956. Home: 133 Crooked Hill Rd Huntington NY 11743-3811

TWARDY, STANLEY ALBERT, JR., lawyer; b. Trenton, N.J., Sept. 13, 1951; s. Stanley Albert Twardy and Dorothy M. Stonaker. BS with honors, Trinity Coll., 1973; JD, U. Va., 1976; LLM, Georgetown U. 1980. Bar: Conn. 1976, D.C. 1978, U.S. Supreme Ct. 1979, U.S. Ct. Appeals (2d cir.) 1984. Assoc. Whitman & Ransom, Greenwich, Conn., 1976-77; counsel com. on small bus. U.S. Senate, 1977-79, counsel to Senator Lowell Weicker Jr., 1979-80; ptnr. Silver, Golub & Sandak, Stamford, Conn., 1980-85; U.S. atty. Dist. of Conn., New Haven, 1985-91; chief of staff Office of Gov. Lowell Weicker, Conn., 1991-93; ptnr. Day, Berry & Howard, Stamford, Conn., 1993—. Vestryman St. John's Episc. Ch., Stamford, 1983-86; bd. dirs. Nat. Alumni Exec. Com. Trinity Coll., 1985-90, Drugs Don't Work, 1989-91, Spl. Olympics World Summer Games, 1995. Mem. ABA, Conn. Bar Assn., Assn. Trial Lawyers Am., Conn. Trial Lawyers Assn., Phi Beta Kappa. Office: One Canterbury Green Stamford CT 06901

TWEEDIE, RICHARD LEWIS, statistics educator, consultant; b. Leeton, NSW, Australia, Aug. 22, 1947; came to U.S., 1991; s. Lewis Chabaud and Nel (Dahlenburg) T.; m. Catherine Robertson, Sept. 13, 1971; 1 child, Marianne Louise Robertson. BA, Australian Nat. U., Canberra, 1968, MA, 1969, DSc, 1986; PhD, Cambridge (Eng.) U., 1972. Sr. rsch. scientist Commonwealth Sci. and Indsl. Rsch. Orgn., Canberra, 1971-79, prin. rsch. scientist Commonwealth Sci. and Indsl. Rsch. Orgn., Melbourne, Australia, 1979-81; assoc. prof. U. Western Australia, Perth, 1978; gen. mgr. Statistical Pty. Ltd., Sydney, Australia, 1981-83, mng. dir., 1983-87; profl., dean Bond U., Gold Coast, Australia, 1987-91; prof. stats. Colo. State U., Ft. Collins, 1991—, chair dept. stats., 1992—. Author: Markov Chains and Stochastic Stability, 1993; also over 80 articles. Fellow Inst. Math. Stats., Internat. Statis. Inst.; mem. Statis. Soc. Australia (pres. 1984-85). Avocations: squash, science fiction. Office: Colo State U Dept Stats Fort Collins CO 80523-1877

TWEEDY, ROBERT HUGH, equipment company executive; b. Mt. Pleasant, Iowa, Mar. 24, 1928; s. Robert and Olatha (Miller) T.; B.S. in Agrl. Engring., Iowa State U., 1952; m. Genevieve Strauss, Aug. 15, 1969; children—Bruce, Mark; 1 stepdau., Mary Ellen Francis. Sr. engr. John Deere Waterloo Tractor Works, Waterloo, Iowa, 1953-64; mktg. rep. U.S. Steel Corp., Pitts., 1964-68; mgr. product planning agrl. equipment div. Allis-Chalmers Corp., Milw., 1969-76, mgr. strategic bus. planning Agrl. Equipment Co., 1976-85; mgr. strategic bus. planning Deutz-Allis Corp., 1985-89; project mgr. AGCO Corp., Batavia, Ill., 1989-93; chmn. agrl. research com. Farm and Indsl. Equipment Inst., Chgo., 1974-76, mem. safety policy adv. com., 1972-89; mem. farm conf. Nat. Safety Council, Chgo., 1973-89; mem. industry sector adv. com. No. 16, U.S. Dept. Commerce, 1982-83; bd. dirs. C.V. Riley Meml. Found. Recipient citation in engring. Iowa State U., 1983. Fellow Am. Soc. Agrl. Engrs. (v.p. 1974-78, pres. 1981-82, gen. chmn. hdqrs. bldg. project 1968-70; chmn. Found. Trustees 1983-88, Wis. Engr. of Year award 1980, McCormick-Case Gold medal 1989); mem. Soc. Automotive Engrs., Masons. Patentee in field. Home: 1340 Bonnie Ln Brookfield WI 53045 Office: AGCO Corp 1500 N Raddant Rd Batavia IL 60510

TWEITO, ELEANOR MARIE, social services administrator, educator; b. Westgate, Iowa, Dec. 25, 1909; d. Henry Christopher and Amanda Marie (Fink) Frese; m. Thomas E. Tweito, Aug. 26, 1936; children: David Henry, Thomas Elling. Student, Wartburg Coll., 1926-28; BA, Morningside Coll., 1940; MA, U. Mo., 1966. Tchr. Pub. Rural Sch., Waverly, Iowa, 1928-30; pvt. sec. to Frank Gruber, editor, author, TV writer, pub., 1930-31; exec. sec. Century Life Ins. Co., Waverly, 1930-36, State U. Iowa, Iowa City, 1938-40; prof. Tri-State Bus. Coll., Sioux City, Iowa, 1940-42; tchr. Bronson Consolidated High Sch., Bronson, Iowa, 1942-59; founder, prof., chair bus. edn. dept. Mo. Valley Coll., Marshall, 1960-77; adminstr. Sr. Ctr. Dist. III Area Agy. on Aging, Marshall, 1987—; sec. of faculty Mo. Valley Coll., Marshall, 1965-70; lectr. workshop St. Paul's Coll., Concordia, Mo., 1979. Editor, contbr. The Evangel, 1976-86; co-author: Lest We Forget, 1988; contbr. articles to newspapers. Pres. Luth. Daus. of Reformation, Sioux City, 1957-60; sec., fin. sec. Luth. Ch., Marshall, 1976-86; bd. dirs., sec.-treas. Dist. III Area Agy. on Aging, Marshall, 1980—; sec. Saline County Coun. on Aging, 1986—. Recipient several disting. svc. citations Mayor of City of Marshall, 1990, Area Agy. on Aging, 1990, Family div. Mo. Dept. Social Svcs., 1987, resolution Mo. Ho. of Reps., 1990. Fellow AAUW (bd. dirs. Marshall chpt. 1970-90, hon. life); mem. AAUP, AARP (sec.-treas. 1977-88, chpt. 1936 v.p., program chairwoman 1988-92, pres. 1992—), Nat. Assn. Retired Tchrs., Sorosis Club, Faculty Women Club, Pi Gamma Mu, Zeta Sigma, Pi Lambda Theta. Avocations: vol. work, writing. Home: 1108 Sunrise Dr Marshall MO 65340-2844

TWELL, NICHOLAS J., financial analyst; b. Huntington, W.Va. Grad. high sch., Huntington; student, Marshall U., 1934-36. Clk. U.S. Post Office Dept., Huntington, 1935-42; prin. Mayflower Distbrs., Huntington, 1946-50, Ceredo (W.Va.) Drive-In Theatres, 1949-52, Purchasing Corp. Am., Alexandria, Va., 1949-53, Am. Vending Corp., Lexington, Ky., 1949-52, Waterford Park Race Track, Pitts., 1952-55; co-owner Tanforan Race Track, San Francisco, 1957-63; prin. Continental Tobacco Co., N.Y.C., 1959-64, Charles Town (W.Va.) Race Track, 1961-64, Atlantic Vending Corp., Huntington, W. Va., 1965-86, Tropical Park Racetrack, Miami, Fla., 1968-71; co-owner Holiday Inns, Huntington and Ft. Lauderdale, Fla., 1969-82; prin. River Downs Race Track, Cin., 1973-77; prin Gen. Mgmt. Co., N.Y.C., 1965—; prin. Entertainment/USA, Beverly Hills, Calif., 1987—. Served to capt. US Army, 1942-46. Recipient hon. recognition awards Damon Runyon Cancer Fund, Am. Vets. Assn., N.Y. Athletic Club, Shriner's Crippled Children's Hosp., Royal Dames of Cancer Rsch., Nat. Geo. Soc., U.S. Olympics, Swimming Pool Hall of Fame, Thoroughbred Racing Assn., Horsemen's Benevolent and Protective Assn. Mem. Am. Legion, Am. Vets. Assn., Phoenicians Internat., Thoroughbred Racing Assn., Horsemen's Benevolent and Protective Assn., Masons (32 degree), Shriners, Protestant Episcopal Ch., N.Y. Athletic Club, Knight of Malta (honored), N.Y. Yacht Club, Army and Navy Club, Army Officers Club, Le Club Internat., Coral Ridge Country Club, Lago Mar Beach and Tennis Club. Democrat. Episcopalian. Home and Office: The Hampshire House 150 Central Park S New York NY 10019-1566

TWENTYMAN, LEE, foreign service officer, economist; b. Cortland, N.Y., June 12, 1947; s. Gerald L. and Esther (Forbes) T. BS, Cornell U., 1969; MS, U. Md., 1973. Mktg. specialist Export Mktg. Svc., USDA, Washington, 1973; internat. devel. intern U.S. AID, Asuncion, Paraguay, 1973-75; capital projects officer U.S. AID, Santiago, Chile, 1975-76; dir. devel. resources U.S. AID, Lima, Peru, 1976-81; dir. Food for Peace U.S. AID, Washington, 1981-83; dir. for Lebanon U.S. AID, Beirut, 1983-84; dep. dir. for Thailand U.S. AID, Bangkok, 1984-88; dep. dir. for Indonesia U.S. AID, Jakarta, 1988-91; AID dir. to Cambodia U.S. AID, Phnom Penh, 1991—. Mem. Royal Bangkok Sports Club. Office: Box 66 Homer NY 13077

TWERSKY, VICTOR, mathematical physicist, educator; b. Lublin, Poland, Aug. 10, 1923; came to U.S., 1928, naturalized, 1940; s. Israel and Gertrude (Levinson) T.; m. Shirley Fine, Feb. 26, 1950; children: Lori, Mark, Nina. B.S., CCNY, 1947; A.M., Columbia U., 1948; Ph.D., N.Y. U., 1950. Assoc. guidance project, biology dept. CCNY, 1946-49; teaching asst. physics N.Y. U., 1949; research assoc. electromagnetic theory Courant Inst. Math. Scis., 1950-53; assoc. Nuclear Devel. Assocs., 1951-53; with Sylvania Electric-Gen. Telephone Electronics, 1953-66; head research Electronic Def. Labs., 1958-66, Electronics Systems-West, 1964-66; prof. math. U. Ill. at Chgo., 1966-90, prof. emeritus, 1991; lectr. Stanford U., 1956-58; vis. prof. Technion-Israel Inst. Tech., Haifa, 1962-63, Hebrew U., Jerusalem, summer 1972, Tel Aviv U., summer 1972, Weizmann Inst. Sci., Rehovoth, 1979, Ben-Gurion U., Beersheva, 1979, Stanford U., 1972, 73, 79-80, summers 1967-89, vis. scholar, 1991-94, others; summer mem. Courant Inst. Math. Scis., 1963; assoc. Ctr. for Advanced Study U. Ill., 1969-70; cons. in field. Editor jours. in field.; contbr. articles to profl. jours. Mem. tech. research com. Am. Found. for Blind, 1947-49; mem. Sch. Math. Study Group, 1964-66, U.S. com. B. Internat. Sci. Radio Union; mem.-at-large Conf. Bd. Math. Scis., 1975-77. Served with AUS, 1943-46. Guggenheim fellow, 1972-73, 79-80. Fellow AAAS, Am. Phys. Soc., Acoustical Soc. Am., Optical Soc. Am. (dir.-at-large 1961), IEEE; mem. Am. Math Soc., Soc. Indsl. and Applied Math., Sci. Research Soc. Am. (pres. Sequoia br. 1958). Address: 14848 Manuella Rd Los Altos CA 94022-2026

TWICHELL, CHASE, poet; b. New Haven, Conn., Aug. 20, 1950; d. Charles P. and Anne (Chase) T. BA, Trinity Coll., Hartford, 1973; MFA, U. Iowa, 1976. Editor Pennyroyal Pr., W. Hatfield, Mass., 1976-84; assoc. prof. English U. Ala., 1984-88; asst. prof. Hampshire Coll., 1983-84; co-editor Alabama Poetry Series, 1984-88. Author: (poetry) Northern Spy, 1981, The Odds, 1986, Perdido, 1991; editor: The Practice of Poetry, 1992, Borderlands, 1993. Nat. Endowment for Arts fellow, 1987; recipient Academy award in literature Am. Acad. Arts and Letters, 1994. Office: HCRI PO Box 54A East Hill Rd Keene NY 12942*

TWIDALE, C(HARLES) R(OWLAND), geomorphologist, educator; b. Lincolnshire, Eng., Apr. 5, 1930; s. George Wilfred and Gladys May (West) T.; m. Kathleen Mary Gargini, Apr. 21, 1956; children: Nicholas, Richard Jonathan, Amanda Elizabeth. Ed. Wintringham Grammar Sch., Grimsby; BSc, U. Bristol, 1951, MSc, 1953, DSc, 1977; PhD, McGill U., 1957; D. Honoris Causa, U. Complutense, Madrid, 1991. Rsch. officer, div. land rsch. Commonwealth Sci. and Indsl. Rsch. Orgn., Canberra, 1952-57; mem. faculty dept. geography, geology, U. Adelaide, 1958—; vis. prof. geology and geophysics U. Calif., Berkeley, 1971; vis. prof. geology U. Tex., Austin, 1979. Nuffield Commonwealth bursary, 1965; NSF sr. fgn. scientist fellow, 1965-66, also vis. prof. Rensselaer Poly. Inst., Troy, N.Y.; mem. engring. and earth scis. panel Australian Rsch. Coun., 1992—. Author: Geomorphology, 1968, Structural Landforms, 1971, Analysis of Landforms, 1976, Granite Landforms, 1982; contbr. articles to profl. jours. Recipient Mueller medal Australian and New Zealand Assn. Advancement Sci., 1993. Fellow Royal Soc. South Australia (pres., 1975-76, Verco medal 1977), Geol. Soc. Am.; mem. Geol. Soc. Australia. Home: 7 Brecon Rd, Aldgate SA 5154, Australia Office: U Adelaide, Dept Geology & Geophysics, Adelaide SA 5005, Australia

TWIFORD, TRAVIS W., school system administrator. Supt. Elizabeth City-Pasquotank Schs., Elizabeth City, N.C. Recipient Nat. Superintendent of the Yr. awd., North Carolina, Am. Assn. of School Administrators, 1992. Office: Elizabeth City Pasquotank Schs PO Box 2247 1200 Halstead Blvd Elizabeth City NC 27909

TWIGG-SMITH, THURSTON, newspaper publisher; b. Honolulu, Aug. 17, 1921; s. William and Margaret Carter (Thurston) Twigg-S.; m. Bessie Bell, June 9, 1942 (div. Feb. 1983); children: Elizabeth, Thurston, William, Margaret, Evelyn; m. Laila Roster, Feb. 22, 1983 (div. Dec. 1994). B.Engring., Yale U., 1942. With Honolulu Advertiser, 1946—, mng. editor, 1954-60, asst. bus. mgr., 1960-61, pub., 1961-86; pres., dir., chief exec. officer Honolulu Advertiser, Inc., 1962-93, chmn., 1993—; pres., dir., CEO Persis Corp.; bd. dirs. Atalanta/Sosnoff Capital Corp., N.Y. Trustee Punahou Sch., Old Sturbridge Inc., Honolulu Acad. Arts, The Contemporary Mus., Hawaii, Mus. Contemporary Art, L.A., The Skowhegan Sch., Maine, Yale Art Gallery, New Haven, Philatelic Found., N.Y., Whitney Mus. Am. Art, N.Y. Maj. AUS, 1942-46. Mem. Honolulu C. of C., Waialae Country Club, Pacific Club, Oaho Country Club, Outrigger Canoe Club. Office: Persis Corp PO Box 3110 96802 605 Kapiolani Blvd Honolulu HI 96813

TWINAME, JOHN DEAN, minister, health care executive; b. Mt. Kisco, N.Y., Dec. 27, 1931; s. C.G. and Constance Jean (Ulmer) T.; m. Carolyn Anderson, Aug. 6, 1955; children: Karen, Jeanne, Julia. A.B., Cornell U., 1953; M.B.A., Harvard U., 1957; M.Div., Union Theol. Sem., 1983. Ordained to ministry Presbyn. Ch. 1983. Sales rep. Am. Hosp. Supply Corp., Evanston, Ill., 1957-60; dir. product research Am. Hosp. Supply Corp., 1961, sales mgr., 1962, asst. to div. pres., 1963, product mgr., 1964, mktg. mgr., 1965-67, mktg. v.p., 1968-69; dep. administr. Social and Rehab. Service, HEW, Washington, 1969-70; administr. Social and Rehab. Service, HEW, 1970-73; administr. Office Health Office Health, Cost of Living Coun., 1973-74; pvt. cons. Mott-McDonald Assocs., Inc., Washington, 1974-76, pres., 1976-78; exec. v.p. Am. Health Found., N.Y., 1978-81; co-pres. The Hosp. Chaplaincy, Inc., N.Y.C., 1983-93, co-chair exec. com., 1993-94, life trustee, 1995—; voting mem. Empire Blue Cross/Blue Shield, 1994. Chmn. bd. Chgo. Bus.-Indsl. Project, 1967-68, People to People Com. for Handicapped, 1976-78, Bauman Bible Telecasts, Inc., 1976-80; treas. U.S. com. Internat. Council Social Welfare, 1977-80; sec. bd. dirs. U.S. Council Internat. Year of Disabled Persons, 1979-81; founding bd. mem. Am. Paralysis Assn. (formerly Paralysis Cure Research), 1976-83; bd. dirs. Epilepsy Found. Am., 1978-85, N.Y. Regional Transplant Program, 1988-92; mem. pres. coun. United Hosp. Fund, 1991—. 1st lt. AUS, 1953-55. Recipient Disting. Svc. award Coll. Chaplains, 1992, Baker scholar, Harvard U. Home: 163 Harbor Rd Southport CT 06490-1320 Office: The Hosp Chaplaincy 434 E 70th St New York NY 10021-5336

TWISDALE, HAROLD WINFRED, dentist; b. Roanoke Rapids, N.C., Apr. 28, 1933; s. James Robert and Elma (Smith) T.; m. Barbara Ann Edmonds, Aug. 2, 1958 (div. Apr. 1974); children: Harold Winfred, Leigh Ann.; m. Frances Jean Winstead, July 1983. B.S. in Dentistry, U. N.C. 1955, D.D.S. 1958. Individual practice dentistry Charlotte, N.C., 1961—; head, dept. dental prosthetics Meml. Hosp., 1964-66; lectr. dental subjects.; pres., gen. mgr. WCTU-TV, Charlotte Telecasters, Inc., 1967-69, WATU-TV, Augusta, Ga., Augusta Telecasters, Inc., 1968-69, Television Presentations, Inc., Charlotte, 1967-69; partner Twisdale and Steel Assocs., Charlotte, 1965-70; propr. Twisdale Enterprises, Charlotte, 1965-70; Pres. Memphis Telecasters, Inc., 1966-76, Va. Telecasters, Inc., Richmond, 1966—, Durham-Raleigh Telecasters, Inc., Durham, N.C., 1966-70, Gentil Elite, Inc., 1979—. Transp. chmn. Miss N.C. Pageant, 1965; v.p. N.C. Jaycees, 1963-64; Trustee Boys Home, Lake Waccomaw, N.C., 1966-67. Served to capt. USAF, 1958-60. Recipient various awards Charlotte Jaycees, 1962-66. Mem. ADA, N.C. Dental Found., N.C. Dental Soc., Charlotte Dental Soc. (chmn. various coms. 1961—), Am. Analgesia Soc., Internat. Analgesic Soc. (dir. 1980-85), N.C. Dental Soc. Anesthesiology (v.p. 1983-84), Charlotte Analgesia Study Club (co-founder 1970), N.C. 2d Dist Dental Soc. Metrolina Dental Soc. (founder 1994, pres. 1994-95), U. N.C. Dental Alumni Assn., Southeastern Analgesia Soc. (founder 1972, pres. 1972-74), Lambda Chi Alpha, Delta Sigma Delta. Republican. Methodist. Home: 4212 Burning Tree Dr 2221 Streatley Ln Mathews NC 28105 Office: Executive Circle #110 PO Box 25528 Charlotte NC 28212 *I must give the full credit for any achievement I might have accomplished in life to my mother and father. They not only provided me the means and direction one needs to make even the slightest accomplishment in our mortal life, but most of all, they gave me love, understanding, and a sense of values. These values have never deserted me, nor have they been compromised, even in the darkest hours of depression or during the brightest times of accomplishment. They have been my steady companions.*

TWISS, JOHN R., JR., federal government agency executive; b. N.Y.C., Sept. 16, 1938; s. John R. and Edith Jordan (Liddell) T.; m. Mary Hawthorne Sheldon, Jan. 20, 1973; children: John Stewart, Alison McIntosh, Emily Ellsworth. BA, Yale U., 1961. Polar rschr. U.S. Govt., 1961-63; NSF rep. in charge U.S. Sci. Programs in Antarctica, 1964-65; mem. staff internat. divsn. Smith Kline & French Labs., 1966-67; v.p. EPC Labs., 1967-68; sci. leader So. Ocean expdn. NSF, 1968-69, spl. asst. to head Internat. Decade Ocean Exploration, 1970-74; exec. dir. Marine Mammal Commn., Washington, 1974—; mem. strategic adv. coun. Sch. Forestry and Environ. Studies Yale U., New Haven, 1990—, assoc. fellow Branford Coll., 1990—; mem. administrv. bd. Michael C. Rockefeller Meml. fellowship Harvard U., 1991—; chmn. bd. dirs. Kokrobitey Sch., Ghana, 1992—; bd. overseers Leadership Decisions Inst., 1992—; lectr., cons. in field; mem. numerous adv. coms. and U.S. dels. V.p. Turkey Run Citizens Assn., 1989-92, pres., 1994—. Mem. ASPA, Met. Club, Army and Navy Club, Squadron A Club, Ends of the Earth Club. Office: Marine Mammal Commn Rm 512 1825 Connecticut Ave NW Washington DC 20009

TWISS, PAGE CHARLES, geology educator; b. Columbus, Ohio, Jan. 2, 1929; s. George Ransom and Blanche (Olin) T.; m. Nancy Homer Hubbard, Aug. 29, 1954; children—Stephen Ransom, Catherine Grace, Thomas Stuart. B.S. in Geology, Kans. State U., 1950, M.S., 1955; Ph.D., U. Tex. at Austin, 1959. Mem. faculty dept. geology Kans. State U., Manhattan, 1959—; assoc. prof. Kans. State U., 1964-69, prof., 1969—, also head dept., 1968-77; geologist agrl. research service U.S. Dept. Agr., 1966-68; research scientist U. Tex., Austin, 1966-67. Contbr. articles to profl. jours. Chmn. Manhattan Council Human Relations, 1960-61; vice pres. Riley County Democratic Club, 1970-71; mem. Dem. Precinct Com., Manhattan, 1970-72, 74-80. Served with USAAF, 1951-53. Fellow Pan Am. Petroleum Found., 1957-58; Shell Found. fellow, 1958-59. Fellow Geol. Soc. Am. (chmn. South Central sect. 1972-73, 1995, sec.-treas. 1980-89, vice-chmn. 1994-95); mem. Am. Assn. Petroleum Geologists (geologic maps com. 1968-70), Soc. Econ. Paleontologists and Minerologists, Kans. Acad. Sci. (mem. research awards com. 1966-70, assoc. editor 1977-92), AAAS, Am. Soc. Archaeology, Clay Minerals Soc., Kans. Geol. Soc., W. Tex. Geol. Soc., Am. Soc. Agronomy, Soil Sci. Soc. Am., Internat. Soc. Soil Sci., Internat. Assn. Sedimentologists, Assn. Internationale pour l'Etude des Argiles, Am. Quaternary Assn., AAUP (chpt. v.p. 1971-72, chpt. pres. 1972-73), Nat. Assn. Geology Tchrs., Mineral. Soc. Am., Soc. Phytolith Rsch. (organizing com. 1990-92, mem.-at-large, exec. com. 1992-93, pres.-elect 1993-94, pres. 1994-95), Sigma Xi, Sigma Gamma Epsilon, Gamma Sigma Delta. Home: 2327 Bailey Dr Manhattan KS 66502-2733

TWISS, ROBERT HAMILTON, JR., environmental planning educator; b. Chgo., May 8, 1934; s. Robert Hamilton and Helen (Ball) T.; m. Amy O. Skewes-Cox, Aug. 5, 1984; children—Robert Gregory, Gail. A.B., San Jose State U., 1955; M.S., U. Mich., 1958, Ph.D., 1962. Resource planner U.S. Forest Service, Dept. Agr., Berkeley, Calif., 1962-68; prof. environ. planning U. Calif.-Berkeley, 1968—; planning cons. UN, Titograd, Yugoslavia, 1983-85, numerous local, regional and state agys. Contbr. articles to profl. jours. Chmn. Calif. Mining and Geology Bd., Sacramento, 1977-80; chmn. governing bd. Calif./Tahoe Regional Planning Agy., 1980-83. Served to 1st lt. USAF, 1956-58. Democrat. Office: U Calif Dept Landscape Architecture 202 Wurster Hall Berkeley CA 94720-0001*

TWIST, PAUL FRANCIS, JR., neonatologist; b. Buffalo, Nov. 6, 1946; s. Paul Francis and Hazel Mary (Schoetz) T.; m. Angela Margaret McNerney, Aug. 7, 1970; children: Patrick, Michael, Brendan. BS in Pharmacy, St. John's U., Jamaica, N.Y., 1969; DO, U. Osteo. Medicine, Des Moines, 1973. Lic. physician Ohio, Ill., N.Y.; lic. pharmacist, Iowa. Resident in pediatrics

Good Samaritan Hosp., Cin., 1973-75, fellow in neonatology, 1975-76; fellow in neonatology Loyola Med. Ctr., Maywood, Ill., 1976-77; dir. neonatology and newborn medicine Winthrop-Univ. Hosp., Mineola, N.Y., 1977—; attending physician dept. pediatrics and obstetrics, 1978—; assoc. clin. prof. sch. nursing Adelphi U., Garden City, N.Y., 1985—; asst. prof. pediatrics N.Y. Coll. Osteo. Medicine, Westbury, 1980-85, assoc. prof. pediatrics, 1985—; attending physician Mercy Hosp., Rockville Centre, N.Y., 1978—; Nassau County Med. Ctr., East Meadow, N.Y., 1980—; cons. Glen Cove (N.Y.) Community Hosp., 1980—, St. Francis Hosp., Roslyn, N.Y., 1983—; lectr. in field. Contbr. articles to profl. jours. Bd. dirs. Little Village Sch., Garden City, 1980—; mem. internal rev. bd. St. John's U., Jamaica, 1981—; pres. St. Pius X Sch. Bd., Plainview, N.Y.; treas. Sch. of the Holy Child Fathers Club, Old Westbury, N.Y. Mem. Am. Pharm. Assn., N.Y. State Med. Soc., Nassau County Pediatric Soc. (rep. dist. II 1987-90), Am. Osteo. Assn., N.Y. State Osteo. Soc., Am. Acad. Pediatrics, Nat. Perinatal Assn. (com. on fetus and newborn 1979, chpt. 2 dist. II, N.Y.), N.Y. State Perinatal Soc., Assn. of N.Y. State Regional Perinatal Ctr., Am. Soc. for Parenteral and Enteral Nutrition. Roman Catholic. Home: 1 Equestrian Ct Huntington NY 11743 Office: Winthrop-Univ Hosp 259 First St Mineola NY 11501

TWITTY, JAMES WATSON, artist; b. Mt. Vernon, N.Y., Apr. 13, 1916; s. James Chapman and Amelia Madelon (Lang) T.; m. Anne Marsh Butler, May 18, 1952; children—James Watson, Gary Lee. Student, U. Miami, 1958-59, Art Students League, N.Y.C., 1960-61. Asso. prof. painting Corcoran Sch. Art, Washington, 1964-74; lectr. George Washington U., 1964-74; exchange prof. Leeds Coll. Art, Eng., 1967-68; vis. prof. painting San Antonio Art Inst. One man exhibitions include, Corcoran Gallery Art, Washington, 1966, Lehigh U., Bethlehem, Pa., 1967, David Findlay Gallery, N.Y.C., 1971, 73, 74, 76, 78, 81, McNay Art Inst., San Antonio, 1972, George Washington U., 1975, Bettina Gallery, Zurich, Switzerland, 1977, numerous others; represented in permanent collections, Nat. Gallery Art, Nat. Collection Fine Arts, Corcoran Gallery Art, Balt. Mus. Art, Bklyn. Mus., San Francisco Mus. Art, Dallas Mus. Fine Arts, Mus. Fine Arts, Houston, Minn. Mus. Art, Oxford U., White House and, others. Bd. dirs No. Va. Art League, 1974-77. Served with USAF, World War II and Korea. Club: Pinehurst Country. Home: PO Box 4000 Pinehurst Hotel Pinehurst NC 28374

TWOMBLY, CY, artist; b. Lexington, Va., Apr. 25, 1929. Student, Boston Mus. Sch. Fine Arts, 1948-49, Washington and Lee U., 1950, Art Students League, 1951; studied with, Frank Kline and Robert Motherwell, Black Mountain Coll., 1952. Head dept. Art So. Sem. and Jr. Coll., Buena Vista, Va., 1955-56. One man shows include: Milw., 1968, Nicholas Wilder Gallery, 1969, Herron Inst. Art, Indpls., 1969, Guggenheim Mus., N.Y.C., 1976, Mus. Modern Art, N.Y.C., 1976, Vancouver Art Gallery, 1982, Mus. Hans Lange, Krefeld, W.Ger., 1982, Santa Barbara Contemporary Arts Forum, 1984; retrospective exhbn. Whitney Mus. Art, N.Y.C., 1979; group exhbns. include N.Y.U., 1967, Whitney Mus. Am. Art Annual, 1967, Royal Acad. Arts, 1981, Larry Gagosian Gallery, Los Angeles, 1982, Young Hoffman Gallery, Chgo., 1982, Blum Gallery, N.Y.C., 1982; represented in permanent collections R.I. Sch. Design, Whitney Mus. Am. Art, Mus. Modern Art, N.Y.C., Ludwig Collection, Aachen, Thomas Segal Gallery, Tavelli Gallery, Adler Gallery, also pvt. collections N.Y.C., Chgo., Washington and Europe. Va. Mus. Fine Arts fellow 1952-53. Fellow Am. Acad. Arts and Letters. Office: care Gagosian Gallery 980 Madison Ave New York NY 10021-1848 Address: care Sperone Westwater 142 Greene St New York NY 10012

TWOMEY, JANET LOUISE WILKOV, banker; b. Washington, Oct. 17, 1952; d. Harry and Minnie S. Wilkov; m. Thomas N. Twomey, June 6, 1981. Student, Inst. d'Etudes Politiques, Paris, 1972-73; AB, Mt. Holyoke Coll., 1974; MBA, Columbia U., 1980. Corp. lending officer Chem. Bank, N.Y.C., 1980-84; asst. v.p. SE Bank, N.A., Melbourne, Fla., 1984-85, v.p. dept. mgr. corp. bank, 1985-87; sr. v.p. Chem. N.J., 1987—. Mary Vance Young scholar Mt. Holyoke Coll., 1972, Falk Found scholar Mt. Holyoke Coll., 1974. Club: Mt. Holyoke Coll. (South Hadley, Mass., class treas. 1984-89, class agt. 1989—).

TWOMEY, WILILAM ELDRED, JR., lawyer; b. Washington, Nov. 3, 1940; s. William E. and Clara Marie (Humpries) T.; m. Joyce Ann Cartwright, Apr. 25, 1959; children: Amanda, Raymond, Teresa. BS summa cum laude, Old Dominion U., 1974; JD, U. Va., 1977. Bar: Va. 1977, D.C. 1983. Assoc. McGuire Woods Battle & Boothe, Richmond, Va., 1977-83, ptnr., 1983—; mem. exec. com. Assn. Gen. Contractors Lawyers Coun., 1992—, chmn., 1995—. Contbr. articles to profl. jours. Chmn. Old Dominion U. Lawyers Alumni chpt., 1990-92, 94-95. Mem. Va. Bar Assn., D.C. Bar Assn., Va. C. of C. (employment rels. com. 1987—), Old Dominican U. Alumni Assn. (bd. dirs.). Republican. Methodist. Avocations: civic activities. Home: 4903 New Kent Rd Richmond VA 23225 Office: McGuire Woods Battle & Boothe 1 James Ctr 901 E Cary St Richmond VA 23219

TWYMAN, JACK, wholesale grocery company executive, management services company executive; b. May 11, 1934; married. Ed., U. Cin. Basketball player Cin. Royals, 1955-67; announcer ABC, 1967-72; vice-chmn. Super Food Services, Inc., Dayton, Ohio, from 1972, formerly pres., chief operating officer, now chmn., chief exec. officer. Office: Super Food Svcs Inc 3233 Newmark Dr Miamisburg OH 45342*

TYABJI, HATIM AHMEDI, computer systems company executive; b. Bombay, Mar. 12, 1945; came to U.S., 1967, naturalized, 1976; came to U.S., 1967, naturalized,. BSEE, Coll. Engring. Poona, India, 1967; MSEE, SUNY, Buffalo, 1969; MBA in Internat. Fin., Syracuse U., 1975; grad. exec. program, Stanford U., 1981. Program mgr. Mohawk Data Scis. Corp., Herkimer, N.Y., 1969-73; pres. Info. Systems Products and Techs. Group, Sperry Corp. (now Unisys Corp.), Roseville, Minn., 1973-86; chmn., pres., CEO VeriFone, Inc., Redwood City, Calif., 1986—. Contbr. articles to profl. publs. Islam. Avocations: skiing, tennis. Office: VeriFone Inc 3 Lagoon Dr Redwood City CA 94065-1565

TYACK, DAVID B., education educator; b. Beverly, Mass., Nov. 17, 1930; married, 1951; 2 children. AB, Harvard U., 1952, MA in Teaching, 1953, OhD, 1958. Instr. history and edn. Harvard U., Cambridge, Mass., 1958-59; from asst. prof. to prof. Reed Coll., 1959-66; assoc. prof. history edn. U. Ill., Urbana, 1967-69; assoc. prof. Stanford (Calif.) U., 1969-80, prof. edn. and history, 1980—. Author: Turning Points in American Educational History, 1967, George Ticknor and the Boston Brahmins, 1967, Nobody Knows: Black Americans in the Twentieth Century, 1968, The One Best System, 1974; contbr. articles to profl. jours. Trustee Nat. Humanities Faculty, 1973—. Com. Role Edn. Am. History research grantee, 1966. Fellow Am. Council Learned Soc., Ctr. Advanced Study Behavioral Sci.; mem. Hist. Edn. Soc. (v.p. 1968-69, pres. 1970-71), Am. Edn. Research Assn. (v.p. 1970-71), Am. Hist. Assn., Orgn. Am. Historians, Soc. Religious Higher Edn. Office: Stanford U Sch Education Stanford CA 94305

TYDINGS, JOSEPH DAVIES, lawyer, former senator; b. Asheville, N.C., May 4, 1928; s. Millard E. and Eleanor (Davies) T.; married; children: Mary Tydings Smith, Millard E. II, Emlen, Eleanor Davies, Alexandra. Grad. McDonogh (Md.) Sch., 1946; B.A., U. Md., 1951, LL.B., 1953. Bar: Md. bar 1952. Assoc. firm Tydings, Sauerwein, Benson & Boyd, Balt., 1952-57; ptnr. Tydings & Rosenberg, Balt., 1958-61; U.S. atty. Dist. Md., 1961-64; U.S. senator from Md., 1965-71; ptnr. Danzansky, Dickey, Tydings, Quint & Gordon, Washington, 1971-81, Anderson, Kill, Olick and Oshinsky, Washington, 1988—; spl. sr. cons. UN Fund for Population Activities, 1971-91; Del., Internat. Penal Conf., Bellagio, Italy, 1963, Interpol Conf. Helsinki, 1963, Mexican-U.S. Interparliamentary Conf., Mexico City, 1965, Council Intergovtl. Com. for European Migration, Geneva, 1966, NATO Assembly, Brussels, 1968, Atlantic Conf., P.R., 1970; bd. regents U. Md., 1974-83, vice chmn. 1978-81, chmn. 1981-83, co-chmn. population crisis com. 1971—. Mem. Md. Ho. of Dels. from Hartford Country, 1955-61; campaign mgr. for John F. Kennedy in Md. Primary, 1960. Served with AUS, 1946-48, ETO. Cited as outstanding legislator Md. Press Corr., 1961; named One of 10 Outstanding Young Men Balt. Jr. Assn. Commerce, 1962; recipient August Volmer award Am. Soc. Criminology, 1969; Nat. Brotherhood citation Washington chpt. NCCJ, 1970; Margaret Sanger award for distinguished pub. service Planned Parenthood-World Population. Mem. ABA, D.C. Bar Assn., Md. Bar Assn., Center Club, Univ. Club, Elkridge-Hartford Hunt

Club, Met. Club, Chevy Chase Club, Md. Club, Lotos Club. Democrat. Episcopalian. Office: Anderson Kill Olick & Oshinsky 2000 Pennsylvania Ave NW Suite 7500 Washington DC 20006

TYER, TRAVIS EARL, librarian; b. Lorenzo, Tex., Oct. 23, 1930; s. Charlie Earl and Juanita (Travis) T.; m. Alma Lois Davis, Nov. 6, 1951; children: Alan Ross, Juanita Linn. BS, Abilene Christian U., 1952; BLS, U. North Tex., 1959; AdM in LS, Fla. State U., 1969, postgrad., 1969-71. Librarian tchr. pub. schs. Gail, Lubbock, and Seminole, Tex., 1952-61; with Dallas Pub. Library, 1961-66, coordinator young adult services, 1962-66; library dir. Lubbock Pub. Library, 1966, Lubbock City-County Libraries, 1967-68; grad. library sch. faculty-state personnel coordinator Emporia (Kans.) State U., 1971-72; sr. cons. profl. devel. Ill. State Library, Springfield, 1972-80; exec. dir. Great River Libr. Sys., Quincy, Ill., 1980-94; cons. pub. rels. and comm. Alliance Libr. Sys., Quincy, 1994—; lectr. summer workshops Tex. Woman's U., U. Okla., U. Utah, Fla. State U., U. North Tex.; cons. in field; mem. adv. com. Ill. State Libr., 1984-87, 93—; pres. Resource Sharing Alliance West Ctrl. Ill., Inc., 1981-94, sec., 1994—; pres. Ill. Libr. System Dirs. Orgn., 1992-94. Contbr. articles to library jours. Inductee U. North Tex. Libr. and Info. Sci. Hall of Fame, 1990. Mem. ALA, Ill. Libr. Assn., Med. Libr. Assn., U. North Tex. Sch. Libr. and Info. Sci. (life), Friends Lubbock City-County Libraries (life), Assn. Ednl. Comm. and Tech., Ill. Assn. for Ednl. Comm. and Tech. Democrat. Mem. Ch. of Christ. Home: 2008 Arrowood Ct Quincy IL 62301-8961 Office: 515 York St Quincy IL 62301-3937

TYERS, GEDDES FRANK OWEN, surgeon; b. Giroux, Man., Can., Nov. 6, 1935; s. William Frederick and Catherine Marguerite (Stoddart) T.; m. Phyllis Amelia Randall, May 14, 1960; children: Randall Geddes, Owen Frank. M.D., U. B.C., 1962. Research and teaching fellow pharmacology U. B.C. Faculty Medicine, 1959-60; intern Vancouver Gen. Hosp., Vancouver, B.C., 1962-63; from asst. instr. to instr. surgery U. Pa. Med. Sch., 1963-68; asst. prof., then assoc. prof. surgery Pa. State U. Coll. Medicine, Hershey, 1970-77; prof., chief div. cardiovascular and thoracic surgery U. Tex. Med. Br., Galveston, 1977-79; prof., head div. cardiovascular and thoracic surgery U. B.C. Faculty Medicine, 1979—; cons. pacemaker power sources, telemetry monitoring cardiac pacemakers, med. device reliability; dir. tng. program cardiovasc. and thoracic surgery, chmn. residency tng. com.; mem. adv. com. on med. devices Health and Welfare Can., 1993-94. Contbr. articles to profl. jours. Recipient 1st prize essay contest Phila. Acad. Surgery, 1966, 1st prize essay contest Pa. Assn. Thoracic Surgery, 1977; Hamish Haney MacIntosh Meml. prize Dr. W.A. Whitelaw scholarship, 1962. Fellow Royal Coll. Surgeons Can. (nucleus com. cardiovascular and thoracic surgery, exam. com. cardiovascular and thoracic surgery), ACS, Am. Heart Assn. (council cardiovascular surgery), Am. Coll. Cardiology; mem. Am. Surg. Assn., N.Am. Soc. Pacing and Electrophysiology (founder), Am. Assn. Thoracic Surgery (mem. com., reviewer JTCS), Can. Cardiovascular Soc. (med. devices com.), Soc. Univ. Surgeons, Can. Med. Assn., Soc. Vascular Surgery, Assn. Acad. Surgery, Western Thoracic Surg. Patentee in field. Office: Vancouver Hosp, 700 W 10th Ave Fl C-314, Vancouver, BC Canada V5Z 4E5

TYGESSON, GARY LINCOLN, lawyer; b. Bryn Mawr, Pa., Nov. 16, 1955; s. Herbert Lincoln and Winnifred Grace (Abrams) Tygesson; m. Jane Cline Kringlee, June 10, 1978; children: Nicholas Kringlee, Anna Cline. BA, Northwestern U., 1977, JD, 1980. Bar: Ill. 1980, Minn. 1984. Assoc. Sidley and Austin, Chgo., 1980-84; assoc. Dorsey and Whitney, Mpls., 1984-87, ptnr., 1988—. Mem. ABA, Minn. State Bar Assn., Mortar Bd., Phi Beta Kappa, Phi Eta Sigma. Presbyterian. Office: Dorsey & Whitney 2200 First Bank Pl E Minneapolis MN 55402

TYGRETT, HOWARD VOLNEY, JR., lawyer; b. Lake Charles, La., Jan. 12, 1940; s. Howard Volney and Hazel (Wheeler) T.; m. Linda Lee; children: Carroll Diane, Howard V. III. BA, Williams Coll., 1961; LLB, So. Methodist U., 1964. Bar: Tex. 1964. Gen. atty. SEC, 1964-65; law clk. to chief judge U.S. Dist. Ct. No. Dist. Tex., 1965-67; partner Tygrett & Walker (and predecessors), Dallas, 1968—. Bd. dirs. Routh St. Center, 1976-83, Theatre Three, 1974-75, Shakespeare Festival, 1978-81, Suicide and Crisis Ctr., 1983-86. Mem. Am., Tex., Dallas bar assns., Delta Phi, Delta Theta Phi. Episcopalian. Clubs: Park City, Civitan (lt. gov. Tex. dist. 1976-77, gov. 1979-80). Home: 8530 Jourdan Way Dallas TX 75225-3214 Office: Tygrett & Walker 8111 Preston Rd Ste 600 Dallas TX 75225-6315

TYKESON, DONALD ERWIN, broadcasting executive; b. Portland, Oreg., Apr. 11, 1927; s. O. Ansel and Hillie Martha (Haveman) T.; m. Rilda Margaret Steigleder, July 1, 1950; children: Ellen, Amy, Eric. BS, U. Oreg., 1951. V.p., dir. Liberty Communications, Inc., Eugene, Oreg., 1963-67; pres., chief exec. officer, dir., 1967-83; pres. Bend Cable Communications, Inc., 1983—; chmn. bd. Telecomm Systems, Inc., 1983—, Telecomm Svcs. Inc., 1988—; Ctrl. Oreg. Cable Advt., Inc., 1992—; pres. Northwest TV Inc., 1985—. Bd. dirs. Nat. Coalition Rsch. in Neurol. and Communicative Disorders, 1984-89; mem. Nat. Coalition in Rsch. pub. and govt. info. com., 1986-89, C-SPAn, 1980-89; mem. bus. U. Oreg. Coll. Bus. Adminstrn., 1973—; vice-chmn. we. area Nat. Multiple Sclerosis Soc., 1983—, dir., mem. rsch. and med. programs com., 1986—; trustee Eugene Art Found., 1980-85, Oreg. Health Scis. U. Found., 1988-91, mem. investment com., 1992—; mem. Oreg. Investment Coun. State of Oreg., vice chmn., 1988-92. Mem. Nat. Assn. Broadcasters, Nat. Cable TV Assn. (dir. 1976-83), Chief Execs. Orgn., Vintage Club (pres. Custom Lot Assn. 1992—), Country Club Eugene (dir. 1975-77, sec. 1976—, v.p. 1977), Multnomah Athletic Club, Arlington Club, Rotary, Elks. Home: 447 Spyglass Dr Eugene OR 97401-2091 Office: PO Box 70006 Eugene OR 97401-0101

TYL, NOEL JAN, baritone, astrologer; b. West Chester, Pa., Dec. 31, 1936. BA, Harvard U., 1958. Bus. mgr. Houston Grand Opera Assn., 1958-60; account exec. Ruder and Finn Pub. Rels., N.Y.C., 1960-62; profl. astrologer, 1970—; editor Astrology Now mag., 1974-79; pres. Tyl Assocs., Inc. pub. rels. and advt., 1980-89; media spokesman; internat. lectr., locations including U.S., Moscow, London, Oslo, Copenhagen, Berlin, Amsterdam, The Netherland, Toronto, Ont., Can. Winner Am. Opera Auditions, 1964; opera singer U.S. and Europe, 1964-80; Wagner specialist; appearances include Vienna State Opera, Düsseldorf, Rome, Milan, Barcelona, N.Y.C. Opera, also throughout U.S.; author: Principles and Practice of Astrology, 12 vols., 1973-75, Teaching and Study Guide, 1976, The Horoscope as Identity, 1974, Holistic Astrology, 1980, Prediction in Astrology, 1991, Synthesis and Counseling in Astrology, 1994. Home: 17005 Player Ct Fountain Hills AZ 85268

TYLER, ANNE (MRS. TAGHI M. MODARRESSI), author; b. Mpls., Oct. 25, 1941; d. Lloyd Parry and Phyllis (Mahon) T.; m. Taghi M. Modarressi, May 3, 1963; children: Tezh, Mitra. B.A., Duke U., 1961; postgrad., Columbia U., 1962. Author: If Morning Ever Comes, 1964, The Tin Can Tree, 1965, A Slipping-Down Life, 1970, The Clock Winder, 1972, Celestial Navigation, 1974, Searching for Caleb, 1976, Earthly Possessions, 1977, Morgan's Passing, 1980, Dinner at the Homesick Restaurant, 1982, The Accidental Tourist, 1985, Breathing Lessons, 1988 (Pulitzer Prize for fiction 1989), Saint Maybe, 1991, (juvenile) Tumble Tower, 1993, Ladder of Years, 1995; contbr. short stories to nat. mags. Home: 222 Tunbridge Rd Baltimore MD 21212-3422

TYLER, CARL WALTER, JR., physician, health research administrator; b. Washington, Aug. 22, 1933; s. Carl Walter and Elva Louise (Harlan) T.; m. Elma Hermione Matthias, June 23, 1956 (dec. Dec. 1991); children: Virginia Louise, Laureen, Jeffrey Alan, Cynthia T. Crenshaw. A.B., Oberlin Coll., 1955; M.D., Case-Western Res. U., 1959. Diplomate Am. Bd. Ob-Gyn. Rotating intern Univ. Hosps. of Cleve., 1959-60, resident in ob-gyn, 1960-64; med. officer USPHS, 1964; obstetrician-gynecologist USPHS Indian Health Service, Tahlequah, Okla., 1964-66; epidemic intelligence service officer Bur. Epidemiology, Ctrs. for Disease Control, Atlanta, 1966-67; dir. family planning evaluation div. Bur. Epidemiology, Ctrs. for Disease Control, 1967-80, asst. dir. for sci., 1980-82, acting dir. Ctr. for Health Promotion and Edn., 1982, dir. epidemiology program office, 1982-88, med. epidemiologist Office of Dir., 1988-90, asst. dir. for acad. programs, pub. health practice program office, 1990—; clin. assoc. prof. ob.-gyn Emory U. Sch. Medicine, Atlanta; clin. asst. prof. ob-gyn Emory U. Sch. Medicine, Atlanta, 1966-80, clin. assoc. prof., 1980—, also clin. assoc. prof. preventive medicine and community health, adj. assoc. prof. sociology Coll. Arts and Scis., 1977-90; adj.

assoc. prof. pub. health Sch. Pub. Health, 1990—; clin. prof. pub. health and community medicine Morehouse Sch. Medicine, Atlanta, 1990—; mem. Nat. Sleep Disorders Rsch. Commn., 1990—; mem. adv. com. on oral contraception WHO, Geneva, 1974-77, mem. adv. com. maternal and child health, 1982-88; lectr. in field. Editor: (monograph) Venereal Infections; assoc. editor: Maxcy-Rosenau Textbook of Public Health and Preventive Medicine, 13th edit., 1992; contbr. articles to profl. jours. Chmn. Dekalb County Schs. com. on instruction programs, subcom. on health, phys. edn. and safety, (Ga.), 1967-68; active Ga. State Soccer Coaches Assn., Atlanta, 1973-79, DeKalb County YMCA. Josiah Macy Found. fellow, 1956-58; NIH grantee, 1961-64; recipient Superior Service award, 1974, Meritorious Service medal USPHS, 1984, Disting. Service medal, 1988; Carl S. Shultz Population award APHA, 1976, medal of Excellence Ctrs. for Disease Control, 1984. Fellow Am. Coll. Ob-Gyn (chmn. community health com. 1974-77), Am. Coll. Preventive Medicine, Am. Coll. Epidemiol.; mem. Am. Epidemiologic Soc., Internat. Epidemiologic Assn., Assn. Tchrs, Preventive Medicine (bd. dirs. 1988-89), Am. Public Health Assn. (governing council 1976-78), Assn. Planned Parenthood Profls., Population Assn. Am., Sierra Club. Avocations: photography; camping. Office: HHS Ctrs for Disease Control Mailstop E-42 1600 Clifton Rd NE Atlanta GA 30307-1276

TYLER, DAVID ALAN, auction house executive; b. Woking, Surrey, U.K., Jan. 23, 1953; married; 2 children. MA in Econs., Cambridge U., Eng., 1974. With Unilever plc London, 1974-86; group fin. controller, dir. county NatWest Nat. Westminster Bank plc, London, 1986-89; group fin. dir. Christie's, London, 1989-94; pres. Christie's, N.Y.C., 1994—; bd. dirs. Christie's Internat. plc, also fin. dir. Office: Christies Inc 502 Park Ave New York NY 10022-1108

TYLER, DAVID EARL, veterinary medical educator; b. Carlisle, Iowa, July 12, 1928; s. Guy Earl and Beatrice Virginia (Slack) T.; m. Alice LaVon Smith, Sept. 6, 1952; children: John William, Anne Elizabeth. B.S., Iowa State U., 1953, D.V.M., 1957, Ph.D., 1963; M.S., Purdue U., 1960. Instr. dept. vet. sci. Purdue U., 1957-60; asst. prof. dept. pathology Coll. Vet. Medicine, Iowa State U. 1960-63, assoc. prof., 1963-66; prof., head dept. pathology and parasitology Coll. Vet. Medicine, U. Ga., 1966-71, head dept. pathology, 1971-79, prof., 1971-91, prof. emeritus, 1991—, ret., 1991; co-founder internat. vet. pathology slide bank, 1984, co-dir., 1984—; apptd. discussant Charles L. Davis Found. for Advancement Vet. Pathology, 1977-91. Cub Scout master, 1967-69, scout com. chmn., 1970-72; elder Disciples of Christ Ch., 1968—, chmn. ch. bd., 1973-74, 92-94; mem. citizens com. to County Bd. Edn., 1968-70; bd. dirs. Christian Coll., Ga., 1974-77. With AUS, 1946-48. Recipient Borden award Gail Borden Co., 1956; Norden Disting. teaching award Norden Labs., 1964, 1969, 81, 85, 91; Prof. of Yr. award Coll. Vet. Medicine, Iowa State U., 1965; Outstanding Prof. award Coll. Vet. Medicine, U. Ga., 1970, 76, 80-81, 83, 86, 87-88, 90, Joshia Meigs Teaching award, 1985, Stange award Coll. Vet. Medicine Iowa State U., 1987, Phi Zeta Teaching award, 1985, N.Am. Outstanding Tchr. award, 1991, also Omicron Delta Kappa Outstanding Prof. award U. Ga., 1981. Mem. AVMA, Farm House, Am. Coll. Vet. Pathologists (mem. council 1975-77, exam. com. 1982-85), Am. Assn. Vet. Med. Colls. (chmn. com. teaching-learning materials 1975-77), Nat. Program for Instructional Devel. in Vet. Pathology (adv. com. 1976-77), Aghon, Sigma Xi, Phi Beta Sigma, Alpha Zeta, Gamma Sigma Delta, Phi Kappa Phi, Phi Zeta (chpt. sec.-treas. 1982-84), Omega Tau Sigma. Home: 160 Sunnybrook Dr Athens GA 30605-3348

TYLER, G. LEONARD, electrical engineering educator; b. Bartow, Fla., Oct. 18, 1940; s. George Leonard and Mable Leona (Bethea) T.; m. Joanne Lynne Phelps, Nov. 17, 1977; children: Virginia L., Matthew L. BEE, Ga. Inst. Tech., 1963; MS, Stanford U., 1964, PhD in Elec. Engring., 1967. Engr. Lockheed Aircraft Corp., Marietta, Ga., 1963; rsch. assoc. Ctr. for Radar Astronomy, Stanford (Calif.) U., 1967-69, rsch. engr., 1969-72, sr. rsch. assoc., 1972-74, rsch. prof. elec. engring., 1974-90, prof., 1990—, dir. Space, Telecom. and Radiosci. Lab., 1993—; cons. SRI-Internat., NASA, Jet Propulsion Lab., also other orgns., 1972—; mem. com. on planetary exploration of space sci. bd. NAS, 1983-87, mem. naval studies bd. panel on advanced radar tech., 1990-91. Contbr. over 150 articles to sci. jours., chpts. to books. Recipient Medal for Exceptional Sci. Achievement, NASA, 1977, 81, 86, Pub. Svc. medal, 1992; fellow NSF, 1964-66. Fellow IEEE; mem. Am. Geophys. Union, AAS, IAU, URSI, Phi Kappa Phi, Tau Beta Pi. Achievements include co-discovery of Crab Nebula pulsar, first high-resolution measurement of the directional spectrum of the sea, development and application of occultation technique for outer planets, measurement of Titan's atmosphere. Office: Stanford U Ctr for Radar Astronomy Dept Elec Engring Stanford CA 94305-4055

TYLER, GEORGE RANDOLPH, government official; b. Roanoke, Va., July 26, 1943; s. George William and Hazel Everaline (Ramsey) T.; m. Sarah Payne Gravely, Mar. 15, 1968 (div. June 1983); children: Carter Randolph, Campbell Gravely; m. Marcia Blessard, June 22, 1985; 1 child, Matthew George William. BS in Fin., U. Colo., 1966; ABD in Econs., U. Va., 1969. Asst. prof. Va. Commonwealth U., Richmond, 1969-72; mem. legis. housing study commn. Commonwealth of Va., Richmond, 1973; economist U.S. Senator Hubert H. Humphrey, Washington, 1974-77, U.S. Senator Lloyd Bentsen, Washington, 1983-92; economist Joint Econ. Com. U.S. Senate, Washington, 1978-82; dep. asst. sec. internat. fin. U.S. Dept. Treasury, Washington, 1993-95; counsel World Bank, Washington, 1995—; v.p. Tyler Land Co., Arlington, Va., 1986—. Contbr. articles to profl. publs. Mem. Soc. of the Cin., First Families of Va., Washington Golf and Country Club. Home: 3120 N Monroe St Arlington VA 22207 Office: World Bank 1818 H St Washington DC 20433

TYLER, GEORGE THOMAS, lawyer; b. Spartanburg, S.C., Dec. 4, 1933; s. George Thomas and Wathen Dallas (Strong) T.; m. Millicent Ann Rosenberg, Mar. 15, 1961; children: Millicent Ann, George Thomas, John Paul. AB, Randolph Macon Coll., 1955; LLB, Georgetown U., 1963. Bar: Md. 1963, D.C. 1978, U.S. Dist. Ct. Md., U.S. Ct. Appeals (4th cir.), U.S. Supreme Ct. Ptnr. Ober Kaler Grimes & Shriver, Balt., 1968—. Lt. USNR, 1956-60. Office: Ober Kaler Grimes & Shriver 120 E Baltimore St Baltimore MD 21202-1643

TYLER, H. RICHARD, physician; b. Bklyn., Oct. 16, 1927; s. Max M. and Beatrice F. T.; m. Joyce Colby, June 17, 1951; children—Kenneth, Karen, Douglas, Lori. AB, Syracuse U., 1947; BS in Medicine, Washington U., 1951, MD, 1951; MA (hon.), Harvard U., 1989. Diplomate Am. Bd. Neurology and Psychiatry. Intern Peter Bent Brigham Hosp., Boston, 1951-52; resident in neurology Boston City Hosp., 1952-54; public health fellow Neurol. Inst., Queen's Sq., London, Salpétriére, Paris, 1954-55; asst. in pediatrics and neurology Johns Hopkins Hosp., Balt., 1955-56; neurologist Peter Bent Brigham Hosp., Boston, 1956-74; asst. in neurology Harvard Med. Sch., Boston, 1956-59; assoc. in neurology Harvard Med. Sch., 1959-61, instr., 1961-64, asst. prof., 1964-68, assoc. prof., 1968-73, prof., 1974—; sr. physician Brigham and Women's Hosp., Boston, 1974—, dir. neurol. svc., 1979-88. Co-editor: Current Neurology I and II, 1979, 80; mem. editorial bd.: Jour. Neurology, 1979-84, Classics on Neurology and Neurosurgery Libr., 1983—; contbr. articles in field to profl. jours. Trustee Brookline Pub. Library, 1970—, chmn. bd. trustees, 1985-86, 90-91. Served with U.S. Army, 1946-47. Fellow Am. Neurol. Assn., Am. Acad. Neurology, Mass. Med. Soc. Office: 1 Brookline Pl Brookline MA 02146

TYLER, HAROLD RUSSELL, JR., lawyer, former government official; b. Utica, N.Y., May 14, 1922; s. Harold Russell and Elizabeth (Glenn) T.; m. Barbara L. Eaton, Sept. 10, 1949; children: Bradley E., John R., Sheila B. Grad., Philips Exeter Acad., 1939; AB, Princeton U., 1943; LLB, Columbia U., 1949. Bar: N.Y. 1950. Pvt. practice N.Y.C., 1950-53, 55-60; mem. firm Gilbert & Segall, 1957-60, 61-62; asst U.S. atty., 1953-55, asst. atty. gen. U.S. charge civil rights div., 1960-61; commr. N.Y.-N.J. Waterfront Commn., 1961-62; U.S. dist. judge So. Dist., N.Y., 1962-75; dep. atty. gen. U.S., 1975-77; mem. firm Patterson, Belknap, Webb & Tyler, N.Y.C., 1977—; adj. prof. NYU Law Sch., 1966-75, Albany (N.Y.) Law Sch., 1991—; vis. lectr. Inst. Criminology, Cambridge, 1968; vice chmn. Adminstrv. Conf. USA, 1975-77. Bd. dirs. Fed. Jud. Center, Washington, 1968-72; trustee Practising Law Inst., N.Y.C.; chmn. William Nelson Cromwell Found., Law Center Found. Home: 2 Beekman Pl New York NY

10022 Office: Patterson Belknap Webb & Tyler 1133 Avenue of the Americas New York NY 10036

TYLER, JOHN RANDOLPH, lawyer; b. Canandaigua, N.Y., Aug. 3, 1934; s. John Randolph and Helen McGregor (Twinkle) T.; m. Carroll Smith, Apr. 1, 1962 (div. Sept. 28, 1981); children: John R. III, Carroll Barrett; m. Janet MacAdam, June 5, 1982. BA cum laude, Amherst Coll., 1956; JD, Harvard U., 1963. Bar: N.Y. 1983. Assoc. Nixon, Hargrave, Devans & Doyle, Rochester, N.Y., 1963-70, ptnr., 1971—. Contbr. articles to profl. jours. Bd. dirs. Geva Theater, 1990—, treas. 1993—, Flower City Habitat, 1992—. Lt. USNR, 1956-59. Mem. ABA, N.Y. State Bar Assn. (chmn. exec. com. bus. corp. banking sect. 1981-82, ho. of dels. 1984-87, opinion com. 1986—), Chi Psi. Republican. Epicopalian. Clubs: Genesee Valley (Rochester); Ski Valley (Naples, N.Y.) (bd. dirs. 1980-83). Avocations: sailing, skiing, environ. matters. Home: 25 Oak Ln Rochester NY 14610-3133 Office: Nixon Hargrave Devans & Doyle PO Box 1951 Clinton Sq Rochester NY 14604-1729

TYLER, JOHN W., historic site administrator. Supt. Fort McHenry Nat. Monument and Hist. Shrine, Baltimore, Md. Office: Ft McHenry Nat Monument & Hist Shrine End Of E Fort Ave Baltimore MD 21230

TYLER, LLOYD JOHN, lawyer; b. Aurora, Ill., May 28, 1924; s. Lloyd J. and Dorothy M. (Curtis) T.; m. Inez Chappell Busener, Feb. 25, 1970; children by previous marriage: Barbara Tyler Miller, John R., Benjamin C., Robert B., Amy C. B.A., Beloit Coll., 1948; J.D., U. Mich., 1951. Bar: Ill., Mich. bars 1951. Mem. firm Sears, Streit, Tyler and Dreyer and (predecessors), Aurora, Ill., 1951-62, Tyler and Hughes (P.A.), Aurora, 1962—; lectr. speaker on profl. subjects, 1964—. Contbr. chpts. to profl. books, articles to profl. jours. Democratic precinct committeeman, 1954-59; mem. Batavia (Ill.) Sch. Bd., 1959-62. Served with USAAF, 1943-46. Fellow Am. Bar Found.; mem. Am. Bar Assn. (Ho. of Dels. 1975-79), Ill. Bar Assn. (gov. 1970-78, pres. 1978-79, chmn. legislative com. 1980, task force on alternative forms of legal service 1981-82, long range planning com. 1982-88, fed. judiciary appointment com. 1984-90, spl. com. on merit selection 1987—), Ill. Bar Found. (pres. 1972-75), Ill. Inst. Continuing Legal Edn. (dir. 1971-75, 77-79), Ill. Lawyers Polit. Action Com. (trustee 1982—, chmn. 1987-88), Soc. Trial Lawyers Ill., Appellate Lawyers Assn., Phi Beta Kappa, Omicron Delta Kappa. Presbyterian. Home: 701 Fargo Blvd Geneva IL 60134-3227 Office: Tyler and Hughes PO Box 4425 Aurora IL 60507-4425

TYLER, RICHARD, fashion designer; m. Doris Taylor (div.); 1 child, Sheridan; m. Lisa Trafficante, 1989; 1 child, Edward Charles. Prin. Zippity-doo-dah, Melbourne, Australia, Tyler-Trafficante, L.A., 1988—; design dir. Anne Klein Collection, N.Y.C., 1993—. Recipient New Fashion Talent Perry Ellis award Coun. Fashion Designers Am., 1993, Womenswear Designer of the Yr. Coun. Fashion Designers Am., 1994. Office: 146 E 37th St New York NY 10016

TYLER, RICHARD DALE, JR., air conditioning manufacturing company executive; b. Binghamton, N.Y., Aug. 21, 1944; s. Richard Dale and Irene Elizabeth (Brown) T.; m. Mary Jane Salamone, Apr. 12, 1969; children: Richard Dale III, Matthew James, Christopher Frank, Luke Michael. BA in Psychology, Amherst Coll., 1967; MBA, Harvard U., 1971. With fin. mgmt. program GE, Schenectady, N.Y., 1967-69; owner Tyler Mgmt. Co., Inc., Boston, 1970-76; pres. KuBar Bearings Inc., Cambridge, Mass., 1976-81; pres., chief operating officer Fedders Corp., Peapack, N.J., 1981—, also bd. dirs. Bd. dirs. Assn. for Retarded Citizens, Washington, N.J.; mem. Clinton Twp. (N.J.) Bd. Edn., 1988-90. Mem. Assn. MBA Execs. Office: Fedders Corp 156 Highway 206 Peapack NJ 07977

TYLER, RONNIE CURTIS, historian; b. Temple, Tex., Dec. 29, 1941; s. Jasper J. and Melba Curtis (James) T.; m. Paula Eyrich, Aug. 24, 1974. BSE, Abilene (Tex.) Christian Coll., 1964; MA, Tex. Christian U., 1966, PhD (Univ. fellow), 1968; DHL, Austin Coll., 1986. Instr. history Austin Coll., Sherman, Tex., 1967-68; asst. prof. Austin Coll., 1968-69; asst. dir. collections and programs Amon Carter Mus., Ft. Worth, 1969-86; dir. Tex. State Hist. Assn., 1986—; prof. history U. Tex., Austin, 1986—; adj. prof. history Tex. Christian U., 1971-72; cons. visual materials Western. Am. art. Author: Santiago Vidaurri and the Confederacy, 1973, The Big Bend: The Last Texas Frontier, 1975, The Image of America in Caricature and Cartoon, 1975, The Cowboy, 1975, The Mexican War: A Lithographic Record, 1974, The Rodeo Photographs of John Addison Stryker, 1978, Visions of America: Pioneer Artists in a New Land, 1983, Views of Texas: The Watercolors of Sarah Ann Hardinge, 1852-56, 1988, Nature's Classics: John James Audubon's Birds and Animals, 1992, Audubon's Great National Work: The Royal Octave Edition of the Birds of America, 1993, Prints of the West, 1994; (with Paula Eyrich Tyler) Texas Museums: A Guidebook, 1983; editor: (with Lawrence R. Murphy) The Slave Narratives of Texas, 1974, Posada's Mexico, 1979, Alfred Jacob Miller: Artist on the Oregon, 1982, Wanderings in the Southwest in 1855 (J.D.B. Stillman), 1990. Pres. Tarrant County (Tex.) Hist. Soc., 1975-77. Good Neighbor Commn. scholar Instituto Tecnologico Monterrey, Mex., 1967; Am. Philos. Soc. grantee, 1970-71; recipient H. Bailey Carroll award, 1974; Coral H. Tullis award, 1976. Mem. Am. Antiquarian Soc., Tex. Inst. Letters (Friends of Dallas Pub. Libr. award), Philos. Soc. Tex. (sec. 1990—), Phi Beta Kappa. Home: 4400 Balcones Dr Austin TX 78731-5710 Office: Ctr Studies Tex Hist 2/306 Richardson Hall University Station Austin TX 78712

TYLER, STEVEN, singer; b. Yonkers, N.Y., Mar. 26, 1948; children: Liv, Mia. Lead singer Aerosmith 1970—. Albums include Aerosmith, 1973, Get Your Wings, 1974, Toys in the Attic, 1975, Rocks, 1976, Pure Gold, 1976, Draw the Line, 1977, Live Bootleg, 1978, A Night in the Ruts, 1979, Greatest Hits, 1980, Rock in a Hard Place, 1982, Done with Mirrors, 1986, Classics Live, 1986, Permanent Vacation, 1987, Gems, 1989, Pump, 1989, Pandora's Box, 1991, Get a Grip, 1993, Big Ones, 1994, Box of Fire, 1994. recipient w/Aerosmith: MTV Video of the Year for "Cryin'", 1994, Grammy award Best Rock Group. Office: c/o Aerosmith Geffen/GDC Records 9130 Sunset Blvd Los Angeles CA 90069*

TYLER, THOMAS SHEPHARD, lawyer; b. Chgo., Jan. 30, 1911; s. Theodore Robb Tyler and Louise (Shephard) Shaw; m. Marian Phelps. BA, Yale U., 1932; JD, Northwestern U., 1935. Bar: Ill. 1936. Gen. ptnr. Winston & Strawn, Chgo., 1936-89, ret. Bd. dirs. Lyric Opera Chgo.; active English-Speaking Union. Lt. Col. USAF, 1942-46. Named to Order of British Empire Queen of England, 1973. Mem. Chgo. Casino Onwentsia, Shoreacres. Republican. Episcopalian. Office: Winston & Strawn 35 W Wacker Dr Chicago IL 60601-1614

TYLER, W(ILLIAM) ED, printing company executive; b. Cleve., Nov. 3, 1952; s. Ralph Tyler and Edith (Green) Kauer; m. Vickie Sue Boggs, Feb. 7, 1976; children: Stacia Leigh, Adam William. BS in Elec. Engring., Ind. Inst. Tech., 1974; MBA, Ind. U., 1977; postgrad., Harvard U., 1981; postgrad. in bus., Baruch U., 1988. Electronic engr. to various mgmt. positions R.R. Donnelley & Sons Co., Warsaw, Ind., 1974-89; group pres. R.R. Donnelley & Sons Co., N.Y.C., 1989—, sector pres., 1993—. Office: R R Donnelley & Sons Co 77 W Wacker Dr Chicago IL 60601

TYLER, WILLIAM HOWARD, JR., advertising executive, educator; b. Elizabethtown, Tenn., May 21, 1932; s. William Howard and Ethel Margaret (Schueler) T.; m. Margery Moss, Aug. 31, 1957; children: William James, Daniel Moss. Student, Iowa State U., 1950-52, U. Iowa, 1952; AB in Lit. BJ in Advt., U. Mo., 1958, MA in Journalism, 1966. Advt. mgr. Rolla (Mo.) Daily News, 1958-59; instr. sch. journalism U. Mo., Columbia, 1959-61; copy writer, then v.p. copy dir. D'Arcy Advt. Agy., St. Louis, 1961-67; writer, producer, creative supr. Gardner Advt. Co., St. Louis, 1967-69; sr. v.p., creative dir. D'Arcy, McManus, Masius, St. Louis, 1969-77; exec. v.p., creative dir. Larson Bateman Advt. Agy., Santa Barbara, Calif., 1977-80; v.p. advt. Pizza Hut, Inc., Wichita, Kans., 1980-82; v.p., creative dir. Frye-Sills/Y&R, Denver, 1980; exec. v.p., creative dir. Gardner Advt. Co., St. Louis, 1982-88; exec. v.p., ptnr., creative dir. Parker Group, St. Louis, 1988-91; pres. TYLERtoo Advt./Communications, St. Louis, 1991—; instr. St. Louis U., 1993—; mng. editor St. Louis Advt. Mag., 1992-95. Mem. bd. adjustment City Des Peres, Mo., 1976-77; trustee Blackburn Coll., Carlinville, Ill., 1983-84; bd. advisors U. Mo. Journalism Sch., 1986-91. 1st lt. USMC, 1952-

55, Korea. Mem. St. Louis Advt. Club (bd. dirs. 1987-90), U. Mo. Alumni Assn. (bd. dirs. 1969-70, publs. com 1990-93), Mensa, Phi Delta Theta. Episcopalian. Office: TYLERtoo Advt/Communications 13705 Corrington Ct Ballwin MO 63011-2949

TYMM, WILLIAM E., lawyer; b. Chgo., Jan. 17, 1945. BS, DePaul U., 1967, JD, 1970. Bar: Ill. 1970. Ptnr. Kirkland & Ellis, Chgo. Office: Kirkland & Ellis 200 E Randolph Dr Chicago IL 60606-1809

TYMON, LEO F., JR., banker; b. Jersey City, June 2, 1942; s. Leo F. and Mary E. (Sutton) T.; m. Marie-France Leveque, June 18, 1966; 3 children. AB, St. Peter's Coll., Jersey City, 1963; postgrad., Pace U. Trainee to group sr. v.p. First Jersey Nat. Bank (name changed to Nat. Westminster Bank N.J. 1988), Jersey City, 1967—. Served to 1st lt. U.S. Army, 1964-66. Mem. Robert Morris Assocs. Roman Catholic. Office: Natwest Bancorp 10 Exchange Pl Jersey City NJ 07302-3905

TYNDALL, DAVID GORDON, business educator; b. Bangalore, India, Nov. 19, 1919; s. Joseph and Gladys E. (Pickering) T.; m. Margaret Patricia Davies, Apr. 4, 1942; children: Caroline Lee, David Gordon, Benjamin. B.Comm., U. Toronto, 1940, M.A., 1941; Ph.D., U. Calif., 1948. Asst. prof. bus. adminstrn. Cornell U., Ithaca, N.Y., 1947-49; assoc. prof. Carnegie-Mellon U., Pitts., 1949-53; assoc. prof., dir. analytical studies U. Calif., Berkeley, 1955-67; lectr. U. Calif., 1979-82; v.p. fin. and adminstrn., investment officer U. Alta., Edmonton, 1967-74; prof. fin., 1974-79; investment adv. Berkeley, 1979—. Served with Royal Can. Air Force, 1942-45. Fulbright fellow, 1952. Unitarian-Buddhist. Home: 88 Clarewood Ln Oakland CA 94618-2243 Office: 2718 Telegraph Ave Ste 102 Berkeley CA 94705-1142

TYNDALL, MARSHALL CLAY, JR., banker; b. Wilmington, Del., Feb. 20, 1943; s. Marshall Clay Sr. and Dorothy Mabel (Batten) T.; m. Bonnie Gay Blankenburg, June 19, 1965; children: Steven Marshall, Michael Edward, Julie Anne. BS, U. Del., 1965, MBA, 1975. With First Pa. Bank, Phila., 1965-73; sr. mktg. officer First Pa. Bank, 1971-73; v.p., dir. mktg. Tex. Commerce Bank, Houston, 1973-76; sr. v.p. Tex. Commerce Bank, 1976-89, exec. v.p., 1989—; v.p. Tex. Commerce Bancshares, Inc., Houston, 1976-82, exec. v.p. mktg., 1982—; bd. dirs. Tex. Commerce Bank-Lubbock. Bd. dirs. Houston Regional Mobility Assn., Buffalo Bayou Partnership, Tex. Bankers Assn.; active Greater Houston Conv. and Vis. Bur.; chmn. New Foundations, Regional Bankers Assn. Mem. Bank Mktg. Assn. (bd. dir. 1977-80), Tex. Bankers Assn. (bd. dirs.), Houston C. of C. Methodist. Office: Tex Commerce Bancshares Inc PO Box 2558 707 Travis St Houston TX 77002-3224

TYNDALL, RICHARD LAWRENCE, microbiologist, researcher; b. Mt. Joy, Pa., Mar. 29, 1933; s. William Leroy and Reba May (Ream) T.; m. Thelma Mae Sherk, June 19, 1955; children: Sharon Tyndall Headley, Michael L., Sandra Tyndall Holland. BS in Microbiology, Pa. State U., 1955, MS in Microbiology, 1959, PhD in Microbiology, 1961. Rsch. staff biology div. Oak Ridge (Tenn.) Nat. Lab., 1961-73; rsch. staff med. div. Oak Ridge Assoc. Univs., 1973-76; assoc. prof. rsch. zoology dept. U. Tenn., Knoxville, 1976-87; adj. rsch. assoc. Biology and Environ. Scis. div. Oak Ridge Nat. Lab., 1976-87; rsch. staff mem. Health and Safety Rsch. div. Oak Ridge Nat. Lab., 1988—; founder, CEO Microbial Monitoring, Clinton, Tenn., 1985—; co-founder Reprotech Inc., Knoxville, 1981; cons. in field. Contbr. numerous articles to profl. jours.; patentee in field. Mem. com. for control of Legionella, State of Wis. With U.S. Army, 1955-57. AEC postdoctoral fellow. Mem. ASHRAE (subcom on Legionella), AAAS, Am. Soc. Microbiology, Phi Sigma, Gamma Sigma Delta (awards). Methodist. Avocations: travel, humor, jazz, the Arts. Home: 209 Woodland View Rd Clinton TN 37716 Office: Oak Ridge Nat Lab PO Box 2009 Oak Ridge TN 37831-8077

TYNER, HOWARD A., newspaper editor, journalist; b. Milw., May 30, 1943; s. Howard Arthur and Katharine Elizabeth Tyner; m. Elizabeth Jane Adams, May 3, 1969; children: Sophie Elizabeth, Ian Adams. BA, Carleton Coll., 1965; MSJ, Northwestern U., 1967. Sports editor Chippewa Herald-Telegram, Chippewa Falls, Wis., 1965-66; fgn. corr. UPI, Europe, 1967-77; with Chgo. Tribune, 1977—; fgn. corr. Chgo. Tribune, Moscow, 1982-85; fgn. editor Chgo. Tribune, Chgo., 1985-88, asst. mng. editor, 1988-90, dep. mng. editor, 1990-92, assoc. editor, 1992-93, editor, 1993—; mem. adv. bd. Alfred Friendly Press Fellowships, Washington, 1988—; mem. exec. bd. World Press Inst., 1994—. Home: 2700 Park Pl Evanston IL 60201-1337 Office: Chgo Tribune Co 435 N Michigan Ave Chicago IL 60611-1337

TYNER, NEAL EDWARD, retired insurance company executive; b. Grand Island, Nebr., Jan. 30, 1930; s. Edward Raymond and Lydia Dorothea (Kruse) T.; children: Karen Tyner Redrow, Morgan. BBA, U. Nebr., 1956. Jr. analyst Bankers Life Nebr., Lincoln, 1956-62, asst. v.p. securities, 1962-67, v.p. securities, treas., 1967-69, fin. v.p., treas., 1970-72, sr. v.p. fin., treas., 1972-83, pres., chief exec. officer, 1983-87, chmn., pres., chief exec. officer, 1983-88, chmn., CEO, 1988-95; bd. dirs. Am. Coun. Life Ins., Union Bank & Trust Co. Trustee U. Nebr. Found., Lincoln Found., Investment Banking Inst., NYU; bd. govs. Nebr. Wesleyan U.; mem. Rep. Inner Circle. Capt. USMC, 1950-54, Korea. Fellow Chartered Fin. analysts; mem. Omaha/Lincoln Soc. fin. Analysts, Newcomen Soc. U.S., Nebr. Diplomats, Pres. Assn., Country Club Lincoln (bd. dirs. 1980-83), Nebr. Club, Paradise Valley Country Club. Lutheran. Avocations: tennis, computers. Office: Ameritas Life Ins Corp Ste 324 6940 O St Lincoln NE 68510

TYNER, WALLACE EDWARD, economics educator; b. Orange, Tex., Mar. 21, 1945; s. Richard D. and Jeanne (Gullahorn) T.; m. Jean M. Young, May 2, 1970; children: Davis, Jeffrey. BS in Chemistry, Tex. Christian U., 1966; MA in Econs., U. Md., 1972, PhD in Econs., 1977. Vol. Peace Corps., India, 1966-68; math, sci., cdnl. skill desk chief Peace Corps., Washington, 1968-70; grad. teacher asst. U. Md., Balt., 1971-73; assoc. scientist Earth Satellite Corp., Washington, 1973-74; rsch. assoc. Cornell U., Ithaca, N.Y., 1974-77; asst. prof., assoc. prof. natural resource econs. and policy Purdue U., West Lafayette, Ind., 1977-84, prof., asst. dept. head, 1983-88, dept. head, 1989—; cons. UN Food and Agrl. Orgn., Rome, Office Tech. Assessment, Washington, U.S. Dept. Interior, Washington, OECD, Paris, World Bank, Washington, USDA, Washington. Author: Energy Resources and Economic Development in India, 1978, A Perspective on U.S. Farm Problems and Agricultural Policy, 1987. Mem. Am. Assn. Agrl. Economists, Am. Econs. Assn., Internat. Assn. Energy Economists, Assn. Environmental and Resource Economists, Gamma Sigma Xi, Gamma Sigma Delta. Home: 116 Arrowhead Dr West Lafayette IN 47906-2105 Office: Purdue U Krannert Bldg West Lafayette IN 47907-1145

TYNES, PAMELA ANNE, federal judge; b. Natchitoches, La., Dec. 3, 1958; d. Robert Jerrell and Carol Ann (Murphy) T.; m. Joseph Henderson Hidalgo, Aug. 8, 1988. BA, Northwestern State U., Natchitoches, 1978; JD, La. State U., 1983. Law clk. U.S. Dist. Ct. (we. dist.) La., Opelousas, 1983-85; assoc. Hunter & Plattsmier, Morgan City, La., 1985-86, Paul Guilliot, Lafayette, La.; pvt. practice Lafayette; U.S. magistrate U.S. Dist. Ct. (we. dist.) La., Lafayette, 1988—. Mem. Nat. Assn. Women Judges, Am. Inns of Ct., La. Bar Found., La. Bar Assn., Lafayette Parish Bar Assn., Acadiana Assn. Women Attys. Republican. Avocations: reading, antique collecting and shopping, traveling, walking. Office: US District Court 705 Jefferson St St 178 Lafayette LA 70501-7059

TYNES, THEODORE ARCHIBALD, educational administrator; b. Portsmouth, Va., Sept. 24, 1932; s. Theodore Archibald and Mildred Antonette (Lee) T.; m. Bettye Chalmon, June, 1955 (div. June 1970); children: Karen A. Culbert, David Lee, Tammy Alecia Simpers; m. Cassandra Washington, Nov. 17, 1989; 1 child, Jordan Alexandria. BS in Edn., W.Va. State Coll., 1954; postgrad., Calif. State U., L.A., 1959, Mt. San Antonio Coll, 1962, Chaffey Coll., 1962, Azusa Pacific Coll., 1967; MA in Ednl. Adminstrn., U. Calif., Berkeley, 1969; PhD in Adminstrn. and Mgmt., Columbia Pacific U., 1989. Tchr., athletic dir., coach Walker Grant High Sch., Fredericksburg, Va., 1958-59; dir. programs and aquatics L.A. Times Boys Club, L.A. 1959-62; tchr., dir. recreation, acting edn. supr. youth tng. sch. Calif. Youth Authority, Chino, 1962-68; tchr., dir. drug abuse program Benjamin Franklin Jr. High Sch., San Francisco, 1968-70; asst. prin. Pomona (Calif.)

High Sch., 1970-72; prin. Garey High Sch., Pomona, 1972-75; adminstrv. asst. to supt. Bd. Edn., East Orange, N.J.; asst. to commr. U.S. Dept. Edn., Washington; Rockefeller fellow, supt. adminstrv. intern Rockefeller Found., N.Y.C., 1975-76; supervising state council. sch. programs Office Essex County Supt. N.J. State Dept. Edn., East Orange, 1976-77; rsch. asst., dir. tech. assistance career info. system U. Oreg., Eugene, 1977-79; dir. ednl. placement U. Calif., Irvine, 1979; prin. sch. devs. Woodrow Wilson Rehab. Ctr., Fisherville, Va., 1980-87; med. courier Urology Inc., Richmond, Va., 1988-90; vice prin. Ithaca (N.Y.) High Sch., 1991—; cons. Fielder and Assocs., Berkeley, 1969-80, Jefferson High Sch., Portland, Oreg., 1970, U. Calif., Berkeley, 1972, U. Calif., Riverside, 1972, Calif. Luth. Coll., 1972, Compton Unified Sch. Dist., 1973, Goleta Unified Schs., 1973, Rialto Sch. Dist., 1973, Grant Union Sch. Dist., Sacramento, Calif., 1973-75, San Mateo Sch. Dist., Tri Dist. Drug Abuse project, 1973, North Ward Cultural Ctr., Newark, N.J., 1976, Nat. Career Conf., Denver, 1978, Opportunities Industrialization Ctrs. Am., Phila., Bklyn., Detroit, Poughkeepsie, N.Y., 1980, Tynes & Assocs., 1988; lectr. seminar San Francisco City Coll., 1968-69. Author various curricula, monitoring procedures, grants. 1965—. City commr. Human Rels., Pomona, Calif., 1972-74; pres San Antonio League, Calif., 1972-75. With USAF, 1954-57. Named Coach of Yr. L.A. Times Boys Club, 1959; fellow Rockefeller Found., 1975; recipient Administrv. award for Excellence Woodrow Wilson Rehab., 1987. Mem. NAACP, Am. Assn. Sch. Adminstrs., Nat. Assn. Secondary Sch. Prins., Nat Alliance Black Sch. Adminstrs., Assn. Supervision and Career Devel., Assn. Ednl. Data Systems., Assn. Calif. Sch. Adminstrs., Va. Govtl. Employees Assn., Va. Rehab. Assn., South Bay Pers. Guidance Assn., Pomona Adminstrs. Assn., Ithaca Prins. Assn., Fisherville Ruritan, Phi Delta Kappa, Omega Psi Phi (Basilius Pi Rho chpt. 1965). Democrat. Episcopalian. Avocations: video and still photogrphy, music, art, sports. Home: 115 Salem Dr Ithaca NY 14850-1944 Address: 102 Sherwood Dr Waynesboro VA 22980

TYNG, ANNE GRISWOLD, architect; b. Kuling, Kiangsi, China, July 14, 1920; d. Walworth and Ethel Atkinson (Arens) T. (parents Am. citizens); 1 child, Alexandra Stevens. AB, Radcliffe Coll., 1942; M of Architecture, Harvard U., 1944; PhD, U. Pa., 1975. Assoc. Stonorov & Kahn, Architects, 1945-47; assoc. Louis I. Kahn Architect, 1947-73; pvt. practice architecture Phila., 1973—; adj. assoc. prof. architecture U. Pa. Grad. Sch. Fine Arts, 1968—; assoc. cons. architect Phila. Planning Commn. and Phila. Redevel. Authority, 1952-54, Mill Creek Redevel. Plan, 1954; vis. disting. prof. Pratt Inst., 1979-81, vis. critic architecture, 1969; vis. critic architecture Rensselaer Poly. Inst., 1969, 78, Carnegie Mellon U., 1970, Drexel U., 1972-73, Cooper Union, 1974-75, U. Tex., Austin, 1976; lectr. Archtl. Assn., London, Xian U., China, Bath U., Eng., Mexico City, Hong Kong U., 1989, Baltic Summer Sch. Architecture and Planning, Tallinn, Estonia, Parnu, Estonia, 1993; panel speaker Nat. Conv. Am. Inst. Architects, N.Y.C., 1988, also numerous univs. throughout U.S. and Can.; asst. leader People to People Archtl. del. to China, 1983. Subject of films Anne G. Tyng at Parsons Sch. of Design, 1972, Anne G. Tyng at U. of Minn., 1974, Connecting, 1976, Forming the Future, 1977; work included in Smithsonian Travelling Exhbn., 1979-81, 82, Louis I. Kahn: In the Realm of Architecture, 1990-94; contbr. articles to profl. publs.; prin. works include Walworth Tyng Farmhouse (Hon. mention award Phila. chpt. AIA 1953); builder (with G. Yanchenko) Probability Pyramid. Fellow Graham Found. for Advanced Study in Fine Arts, 1965, 79-81. Fellow AIA (Brunner grantee N.Y. chpt. 1964, 83, dir., mem. exec. bd. dirs. Phila. chpt. 1976-78, John Harbeson Disting. Svc. award Phila. chpt. 1991); mem. Nat. Acad. Design (nat. academician), C.G. Jung Ctr. Phila. (planning com. 1979—), Form Forum (co-founder, planning com. 1978—). Democrat. Episcopalian. Home: 2511 Waverly St Philadelphia PA 19146-1049 Office: Univ Pa Dept Architecture Grad Sch Fine Arts Philadelphia PA 19107

TYPERMASS, ARTHUR G., insurance company executive; b. N.Y.C., May 15, 1937; s. Carl and Estelle (McClain) T.; m. Joan L. ALspach, May 16, 1964; children: Laurie, David. AB, Wesleyan U., Middleton, Conn., 1957; MBA, Columbia U., 1959. Chartered fin. analyst. Fin. analyst Met. Life Ins. Co., N.Y.C., 1960-67, loan officer, 1967-71, v.p. 1971-80, v.p., treas., 1980-83, sr v.p., treas., 1983—. Bd. dirs., treas. Met Life Fund, 1976—; bd. dirs. Pueblo Internat., 1988—. Mem. N.Y. Soc. Security Analysts, Inst. Chartered Fin. Analysts. Office: Met Life Ins Co 1 Madison Ave New York NY 10010

TYRE, NORMAN RONALD, lawyer; b. Boston, Aug. 28, 1910; s. Samuel and Fannie (Spector) T.; m. Margery Cayton, Mar. 10, 1935; children: Joy Tyre Coburn, Patricia Ann Tyre Tanenbaum. BA with highest distinction, Stanford, 1930; LLB, Harvard U., 1933. Bar: Calif. 1933. Practiced in L.A., 1933—; mem. Gang, Tyre, Ramer & Brown, Inc. and predecessor firm Gang, Tyre & Brown, 1941—; v.p., dir. Motion Picture and TV Tax Inst. Mem. Hillcrest Country Club. Home: 801 N Linden Dr Beverly Hills CA 90210-3007 Office: Gang Tyre Ramer & Brown Inc 132 S Rodeo Dr Beverly Hills CA 90212

TYREE, ALAN DEAN, clergyman; b. Kansas City, Mo., Dec. 14, 1929; s. Clarence Tillman and Avis Ora (Gross) T.; m. Gladys Louise Omohundro, Nov. 23, 1951; children: Lawrence Wayne, Jonathan Tama, Sharon Avis. B.A., U. Iowa, 1950; postgrad., U. Mo.-Columbia, 1956-58, U. Mo.-Kansas City, 1961-62. Ordained min. Reorganized Ch. of Jesus Christ of Latter Day Saints, 1947; appointee min. Lawrence, Kans., 1950-52; mission adminstr. (Mission Sanito) French Polynesia, 1953-64; regional adminstr. Denver, 1964-66; mem. Council Twelve Apostles, Independence, Mo., 1966-82; sec. Council Twelve Apostles, 1980-82, mem. First Presidency, 1982-92; ret., First Presidency, Council Twelve Apostles, 1992; mem. Joint Coun. and Bd. Appropriations, 1966-92; originator music appreciation broadcasts Radio Tahiti, 1962-64, Mission Sanito Radio Ministry, 1960-64; instr. Music/Arts Inst., 1992—, Met. C.C.'s, 1994—. Editor: Cantiques des Saints French-Tahitian hymnal, 1965, Exploring the Faith: A Study of Basic Christian Beliefs, 1987; mem. editing com.: Hymns of the Saints, 1981; author: The Gospel Graced by a People: A Biography of Persons in Tahiti, 1993. Bd. dirs. Outreach Internat. Found., 1979-82, mem. corp. body, 1982-92; mem. corp. body Independence Regional Health Ctr., 1982-92, v.p., 1983-92, bd. dirs., 1984-93; mem. bd. publs. Herald House, 1984-92; mem. corp. body Restoration Trail Found., 1982-92; chmn. Tempe Art Com., 1988-94; bd. dirs. Independence Symphony Orch., 1992—, pres., 1995—. Recipient Elbert A. Smith Meml. award for publ. articles, 1968, 72. Mem. Phi Beta Kappa, Phi Eta Sigma. Home and Office: 3408 S Trail Ridge Dr Independence MO 64055-1984

TYREE, LEWIS, JR., retired compressed gas company executive, inventor, technical consultant; b. Lexington, Va., July 25, 1922; s. Lewis Sr. and Winifred (West) T.; m. Dorothy A. Hinchcliff, Aug. 21, 1948; children: Elizabeth Hinchcliff, Lewis III, Dorothy Scott. Student, Washington & Lee U., 1939-40; BS, MIT, 1947. Cryogenic engr. Joy Mfg. Co., Michigan City, Ind., 1947-49; v.p. Hinchcliff Motor Service, Chgo., 1949-53; cons. engr. Cryogenic Products, Chgo., 1953-76, Liquid Carbonic Corp., Chgo., 1960-76; exec. v.p. Liquid Carbonic Industries, Chgo., 1976-87; bd. dirs. Liquid Carbonic Industries, Chgo., Worldwide Cryogenics (MVE), New Prague, Minn. Patentee in cryogenics. Served to 1st lt. U.S. Army, 1943-46, PTO. Mem. Soc. Cin., ASME, Am. Soc. Heating, Refrigeration, and Air Conditioning Engring., Hinsdale Golf Club, Lexington Golf and Country Club. Republican. Episcopalian. Home: Mulberry Hill Liberty Hall Rd Lexington VA 24450-1703

TYRER, JOHN LLOYD, retired headmaster; b. Brockton, Mass., Jan. 16, 1928; s. Lloyd Perkins and Dorothy (Nicholson) T.; m. Jeanne Irene Dunning, June 7, 1952; children: Alison Jane, John Lloyd, David Dunning, Jill Anne. A.B., Bowdoin Coll., 1949; M.A., Middlebury (Vt.) Coll., 1959. Tchr. Wilbraham (Mass.) Acad., 1949-53; tchr., adminstr. Hill Sch., Pottstown, Pa., 1953-64; headmaster Asheville (N.C.) Sch., 1964-92; headmaster emeritus, 1994—; cons. Ind. Ednl. Svcs., 1994—; mem. adv. bd. Warren Wilson Coll., 1987-92. Bd. dirs. Asheville Community Concert Assn., 1970-93, chmn., 1988-90; bd. dirs. Asheville Country Day Sch., 1965-68, A Better Chance, 1988-92, St. Genevieve/Gibbons Hall Sch., 1970-77, Webb Sch., Tenn., 1986-89, Ind. Ednl. Svcs., 1990-97, Coun. Religion in Ind. Schs., 1969-78, ASSIST, 1991—, Ft. Myers Community Concert Assn., 1993—. With U.S. Army, 1946-47. Mem. Nat. Assn. Ind. Schs. (bd. dirs., chmn. com. on boarding schs., chmn. membership com.), So. Assn. Ind. Schs. (pres., bd. dirs.), Mid.-South Assn. Ind. Schs. (bd. dirs.), N.C. Assn. Ind.

Schs. (pres., bd. dirs.), Headmasters Assn., So. Headmasters Assn., English-Speaking Union (bd. dirs., pres. Asheville br., chmn. secondary sch. exchange com.), Theta Delta Chi. Episcopalian. Home: 1353 Kingswood Court Fort Myers FL 33919

TYRRELL, GERALD GETTYS, banker; b. Canton, China, Dec. 27, 1938; came to U.S., 1940.; s. Gerald Fraser and Virginia Lee (Gettys) T.; m. Jane Haldeman, June 1961 (div. Aug. 1975); children: Gerald F., Jane N., Robert M.; m. Elizabeth Ann Drautman, Mar. 31, 1978. BA, Yale U., 1960; MA, Rutgers U., 1971. Cert. real estate financier. With 1st Nat. Bank of Louisville, 1961-89, sr. v.p., 1975-81, exec. v.p., 1981-89; pres., chmn. Churchill Mortgage Corp., 1975-77; chief fin. cons. City of Louisville Office of Downtown Devel., 1989—. Author: A Positive Approach to Financing Black Business, 1972. Trustee, treas. Patton Mus., Ft. Knox, Ky., 1970; treas. Soc. Colonial Wars in Commonwealth of Ky., 1970; mem. exec. bd. Boy Scouts Am., 1983; bd. dirs. The Louisville Orch., 1984. Served to capt. U.S. Army, 1960-68. Recipient Disting. Service Ribbon Ky. Nat. Guard, 1966. Mem. Robert Morris Assocs., Nat. Soc. Real Estate Fin. (bd. govs). Democrat. Clubs: Louisville Country, Pendennis. Avocations: fine wines, tennis. Office: City of Louisville Office Downtown Devel Republic Bldlg Ste 300 Louisville KY 40202

TYRRELL, JOSEPH PATRICK, public utility executive; b. Webster, Mass., Mar. 28, 1925; s. Richard F. and Mary A. (Harbort) T.; married, Sept. 1, 1951; children: Ann Marie, Patricia, Joseph, James, Mary Therese. B.S. in Bus. Adminstrn., Boston U., 1949; J.D., Boston Coll., Newton, Mass., 1955. Bar: Mass. 1955. Exec. v.p. Boston Edison Co., from 1975, cfo, from 1986, now ret.; dir. Boston Harbor Marina, Quincy, Mass., Bay Bank Norfolk County Trust, Dedham, Mass., Boston Edison Co., Ofcl. Industries, Brockton, Mass., Boston Mut. Life Ins. Co., Conn. Yankee Atomic Power Co., Yankee Atomic Electric Co. Trustee St. Elizabeth's Hosp., Brighton, Mass., 1973; trustee Brigham & Women's Hosp., Boston. Served to lt. USAF, 1943-46. Mem. ABA, Mass. Bar Assn. Club: Weston Golf (Mass.). Home: 241 Bristol Rd Wellesley MA 02181-2603 Office: Boston Edison Company 800 Boylston St Boston MA 02199-8001

TYRRELL, THOMAS NEIL, metal processing executive; b. Valdosta, Ga., Feb. 5, 1945; s. Thomas W. and Marilynn (Bowler) T.; children from previous marriage: Tracey, Torrey, Taryn; m. Diane Montague, 1994. BA in Bus. Adminstra., Elmhurst Coll., 1967; LLD (hon.), Baldwin-Wallace Coll., 1992. Sales loop trainee Bethlehem (Penn.) Steel Corp., 1967; gen. product sales person Bethlehem Steel Sales Office, Greensboro, N.C., 1968-73; product specialist Bethlehem Steel Corp., 1973-78; v.p. mktg. Raritan River Steel, Perth Amboy, N.J., 1978-86; CEO Am. Steel & Wire Corp., Cuyahoga Hgts., Ohio, 1986—; vice chmn., CAO Birmingham (Ala.) Steel Corp., 1994—; bd. dirs. Birmingham Steel Corp. Contbr. articles to profl. jours. Vol. Leadership Cleve., 1987, Baldwin Wallace Coll., 1989—, Elmhurst Coll., 1990—, Ohio Valley Corridor Commn. emeritus, 1990—. Named Entrepreneur of Yr. Northeast Ohio, Venture Inc. mag., 1988; recipient Register award for Bus. and Commerce, Esquire mag., 1988. Mem. Wire Assn. Internat., Cold Finished Bar Inst., Am. Wire Producers Assn., Indsl. Fastener Inst., Concrete Reinforced Steel Inst., Am. Inst. Steel Engrs., Summit Club (Birmingham), Old Overton C. of C. Roman Catholic. Avocations: running, fishing, scuba diving, weight training. Office: Birmingham Steel Corp Ste 300 100 Urban Ctr Dr Birmingham AL 35242

TYSON, CICELY, actress; b. N.Y.C., Dec. 19, 1933; d. William and Theodosia Tyson; m. Miles Davis, 1981 (div.). Student, N.Y.U., Actors Studio; hon. doctorates, Atlanta U., Loyola U., Lincoln U. Former sec., model; cofounder Dance Theatre of Harlem; bd. dirs. Urban Gateways. Stage appearances include: The Blacks, 1961-63, off-Broadway, Moon on a Rainbow Shawl, 1962-63, Tiger, Tiger, Burning Bright, Broadway; films include: Twelve Angry Men, 1957, Odds Against Tomorrow, 1959, The Last Angry Man, 1959, A Man Called Adam, 1966, The Comedians, 1967, The Heart is a Lonely Hunter, 1968, Sounder, 1972 (Best Actress, Atlanta Film Festival, Nat. Soc. Film Critics, Acad. award nominee, Best Actress, Emmy award, Best Actress in a spl., 1973), The Blue Bird, 1976, The River Niger, 1976, A Hero Ain't Nothin' but a Sandwich, 1978, The Concorde-Airport 79, 1979, Bustin' Loose, 1981, Fried Green Tomatoes, 1991, Jefferson in Paris, 1995; TV appearances include: (series) East Side, West Side, 1963, Sweet Justice, 1994-95; (films) Marriage: Year One, 1971, The Autobiography of Miss Jane Pittman, 1974, Just an Old Sweet Song, 1976, Wilma, 1977, Roots, 1977, A Woman Called Moses, 1978, King, 1978, The Marva Collins Story, 1981, Benny's Place, 1982, Playing With Fire, 1985, Samaritan: The Mitch Snyder Story, 1986, Acceptable Risks, 1986, Intimate Encounters, 1986, The Women of Brewster Place, 1989, Heat Wave, 1990, Winner Takes All, 1990, The Kid Who Loved Christmas, 1990, When No One Would Listen, 1992, Duplicates, 1993, House of Secrets, 1993, Oldest Living Confederate Widow Tells All, 1994 (Emmy Awd., Best Supporting Actress - Miniseries); other appearances include: Wednesday Night Out, 1972, Marlo Thomas and Friends in Free to Be...You and Me, 1974; CBS: On the Air, 1978, Liberty Weekend, 1986, The Blessings of Liberty, 1987, Without Borders, 1989, Visions of Freedom: A Time Television Special, 1990, Clippers, 1991, A Century of Women, 1994. Trustee Human Family Inst.; trustee Am. Film Inst. Recipient Vernon Price award, 1962; also awards NAACP Nat. Council Negro Women; Capitol Press award. Address: care CAA 9830 WIlshire Blvd Beverly Hills CA 90210*

TYSON, DONALD JOHN, food company executive; b. Olathe, Kans., Apr. 21, 1930; s. John W. and Mildred (Ernst) T.; m. Twilla Jean Womochil, Aug. 24, 1952; children: John H., Cheryl J., Carla A. Student, U. Ark. Plant mgr. Tyson Foods, Inc., Springdale, Ark., 1951-55, pres., 1955-67, chmn., chief exec. officer, 1967-95, sr. chmn., 1995—; chief exec. officer Eagle Distbg. Co., Tyson Export Sales Inc., Poultry Growers Inc., Tyson Carolina Inc., Spring Valley Farms Inc., Lane Processing Inc., Lane Farms Inc. Lodge: Elks. Home: 2210 W Oaklawn Dr Springdale AR 72762-6999 Office: Tyson Foods Inc PO Box 2020 Springdale AR 72765*

TYSON, GAIL L., health federation administrator; b. Havre de Grace, Md., Dec. 28, 1954; d. William Alva Way and Virginia Lorena Tyson; m. Joseph Matthew Pease, May 17, 1986; 1 child, Loren Juliette Tyson Pease. BA, Dickinson Coll., 1976. Dir. edn Harrisburg (Pa.) Area Rape Crisis Ctr., 1976-77; community response specialist CONTACT Harrisburg, 1978-81, asst. dir., 1981-85; pub. info. coord. Dauphin County Human Svcs., Harrisburg, 1985-87; unit exec. dir. Am. Cancer Soc., Harrisburg, 1988-92; exec. dir. Nat. Voluntary Health Agys. Pa. Com., Harrisburg, 1992—; v.p. Human Svcs. Program, 1987. Mem. adv com. Harrisburg Area C.C., 1985-87; mem. adv. bd. Ret. Sr. Vol. Program, Harrisburg, 1986-88, sec., 1987; lifetime mem. Girl Scouts U.S.; bd. dirs. Hemlock coun., 1977-91, v.p., 1982-88, pres., 1988-91, chmn. diversity task force, 1992. Recipient Thanks badge Hemlock coun. Girl Scouts U.S., 1991. Mem. Wheel and Chain Hon. Soc. Methodist. Office: Nat Voluntary Health Agy Pa Ste 2-C 4775 Linglestown Rd Harrisburg PA 17112

TYSON, H. MICHAEL, bank executive; b. Houston, Aug. 16, 1938; s. Howard Ellis and Myrle (Daunoy) T.; m. Judith O. Gilbert, June 24, 1960; children: H. Michael II, Michelle Lee. B.B.A. cum laude, U. Tex., 1962; postgrad., Stonier Grad Sch. Banking, Rutgers U., 1974. Personnel mgr. Foods div. Anderson Clayton Co., Dallas, 1962-70; exec. v.p. adminstrn. Tex. Commerce Bancshares, Houston, 1970-79; v.p. fin. and adminstrn., chief fin. officer, dir. Financial Chronicle Pub. Co., 1979-87; vice chmn., dir. Tex. Commerce Bank-Houston; exec. v.p., exec. trust officer Tex. Commerce Bancshares, 1987—. Bd. dirs. Harris County Heritage Soc., Houston Symphony, Tax Rsch. Assn., Sam. Houston coun. Boy Scouts Am., Houston Festival Found., Lighthouse for the Blind, Goodwill Industries; trustee Gulf Coast United Way; chmn. The Houston Parks Bd. Served with USMCR, 1961-67. Mem. Houston C. of C. (com. chmn.), Pers. Round Table, Am. Newspaper Pub. Assn., Houston Indsl. Rels. Group, Fin. Execs. Inst. (bd. dirs.), Internat. Newspaper Fin. Execs., Houston Club (dir., pres.), River Oaks Country Club (dir.), Inns of Ct. Methodist.

TYSON, HARRY JAMES, investment banker; b. Bklyn., Aug. 17, 1945; s. George William and Eileen Regina (Dunphy) T.; m. Sarah Lorretta Halloran, Mar. 9, 1969; children: Kelly J., Stacey L., Harry D. BS in Math., St. Francis Coll., Brooklyn Heights, N.Y., 1968. Analyst Smith Barney, Harris Upham & Co., N.Y.C., 1968, 2d v.p., 1974-76, v.p., 1976-78, 1st v.p., 1978-

83, sr. v.p., 1983-90, mem. bd. dirs., 1987-90, exec. v.p., 1990-92; mng. dir. Dillon Read & Co. Inc., N.Y.C., 1992—, also bd. dirs., 1992—. Author: Harah's Universal Bond Basis Converter, 1970. Mem. Assn. for Help Retarded Children, Nassau, N.Y., 1987—, N.Y. Zool. Soc., 1978—, St. Christopher Ottille Guardian Club, Nassau, 1987—. Trans. named Deal of the Yr., Inst. Investor, 1984, 85. Mem. Govt. Fin. Officers Assn., P.R.C. of C. (bd. dirs. 1990-92), N.Y. Athletic Club, North Hempstead Country Club. Republican. Roman Catholic. Avocations: skiing, tennis, golf. Office: Dillon Read & Co Inc 535 Madison Ave New York NY 10022-4212

TYSON, KENNETH ROBERT THOMAS, surgeon, educator; b. Houston, July 30, 1936; s. Howard Ellis and Myrle Henrietta (Daunoy) T.; m. Sue Ann Delahoussaye, Nov. 20, 1971; children: Deborah, Kenneth, Michael, Jill. B.A., U. Tex., 1956; M.D., U. Tex. Med. Br., 1960. Diplomate: Am. Bd. Surgery, Am. Bd. Thoracic Surgery. Intern Ind. U. Med. Ctr., Indpls., 1960-61; resident in gen. and thoracic surgery Ind. U. Med. Center, 1961-66; resident in pediatric surgery Children's Hosp. Med. Center, Boston, 1966-67; chief pediatric gen., thoracic surgery U. Tex. Med. Br., Galveston, 1967-80; asst. prof. surgery U. Tex. Med. Br., 1967-71, asso. prof., 1971-75, prof., 1975-80; surgeon-in-chief Child Health Center, 1974-80; clin. prof. surgery U. Calif., Davis, 1980-91, U. Tex. Med. Br., Galveston, 1991—. Contbr. articles to profl. jours. Fellow A.C.S., Am. Acad. Pediatrics, Am. Coll. Cardiology; mem. Am. Assn. Thoracic Surgery, Soc. Surgery Alimentary Tract, So. Thoracic Surg. Assn., Am. Pediatric Surg. Assn., Soc. Univ. Surgeons, So. Surg. Assn., Pacific Coast Surg. Assn., Sigma Xi, Alpha Omega Alpha, Delta Kappa Epsilon, Alpha Kappa Kappa. Episcopalian. Home: 7126 Las Ventanas Dr Austin TX 78731-1814 Office: U Tex Med Br Dept Pediatric Surgery Galveston TX 77550

TYSON, KIRK W. M., business consultant; b. Jackson, Mich., July 2, 1952; s. George Carlton and Wilma Marion (Barnes) T.; m. Janice Lynn Lorimer, Aug. 25, 1979 (div. Dec. 1984); m. Kathryn Margit Kennell, June 24, 1986; 1 child, Robert. BBA, Western Mich. U., 1974; MBA, DePaul U., Chgo., 1982. CPA, Ill.; cert. mgmt. cons., 1985. Bus. cons. Arthur Andersen & Co., Chgo., 1974-84; v.p. cons. First Chgo. Corp., 1984; pres. Kirk Tyson Internat., Oak Brook, Ill., 1984—. Author: Business Intelligence: Putting It All Together, 1986, Competitor Intelligence: Manual and Guide, 1990. Pres., Chgo. Jr. Assn. Commerce and Industry Found., 1977-79; active Easter Seals Soc., 1977, Am. Blind Skiing Found., 1977-78, Jr. Achievement, 1976-77, United Way Met. Chgo., 1979-80, Urban Gateways, 1975; Rep. Precinct Committeeman Downers Grove township, precinct 114, 1985-88. Mem. Am. Inst. CPAs, Ill. Soc. CPAs, The Planning Forum, Soc. Competitive Intelligence Profls., Assn. Global Strategic Info., Inst. Mgmt. Cons., Am. Mktg. Assn., Assn. for Corp. Growth, Alpha Kappa Psi (Disting. Service award 1982). Office: Kirk Tyson International Ltd 4343 Commerce Ct Ste 615 Lisle IL 60532-3619

TYSON, LAURA D'ANDREA, economist, government adviser, educator; b. Bayonne, N.J., June 28, 1947; m. Erik Tarloff; 1 child, Elliot. BA, Smith Coll., 1969; Ph.D., Mass. Inst. Tech., 1974. Prof. econ. and bus. admn. Univ. of Calif., Berkeley, 1977—; chmn. President's Coun. Econ. Advisors, Washington, 1993—; dir. Inst. of Internat. Studies and Research, Univ. of Calif., Berkeley Roundtable on the Internat. Economics, Univ. of Calif.; visiting scholar Inst. for Internat. Economics; Subcom. on a global Economic Strategy for the U.S.. Editor: (with John Zysman) American Industry in International Competition, 1983, (with Ellen Comisso) Power, Purpose and Collective Choice: Economic Strategy in Socialist States, 1986, (with William Dickens and John Zysman) The Dynamics of Trade, 1988, (with Chalmers Johnson and John Zysman) Politics and Productivity: The Real Story of How Japan Works, 1989, Who's Bashing Whom? Trade Conflict in High Technology Industries, 1992. Office: President's Coun Economic Advs Old Exec Office Bldg Rm 314 17th St and Pennsylvania Ave NW Washington DC 20500

TYSON, MIKE G., professional boxer; b. N.Y.C., June 30, 1966; s. John Kilpatrick and Lorna Tyson; m. Robin Givens, Feb. 7, 1988 (div. Feb. 1989);. Defeated Trevor Berbick to win World Boxing Coun. Heavyweight Title, Nov. 1986, defeated James Smith to win World Boxing Assn. Heavyweight Title, 1987, defeated Tony Tucker to win Internat. Boxing Fedn. Heavyweight Title, Aug. 1987, defeated Michael Spinks to win Internat. Boxing Fedn. Heavyweight Title, June 1988, undisputed heavyweight champion 1988-90 (defeated by James "Buster" Douglas). Hon. sports chmn. Cystic Fibrosis Assn. N.Y., 1987—, Young Adult Inst., N.Y.C., 1987—. Youngest heavyweight champion in history. Office: Tyson Enterprises 32 E 69th St # 308 New York NY 10021-5016

TYTELL, JOHN, humanities educator, writer; b. Antwerp, Belgium, May 17, 1939; came to U.S., 1941; s. Charles and Lena (Gano) T.; m. Mellon Gregori, May 28, 1967. BA, CCNY, 1961; MA, NYU, 1963, PhD, 1968. Grad. reader NYU, 1963-67; lectr. Queens Coll., N.Y.C., 1963-68, assoc. prof., 1968-73, 1973-76, prof. English, 1977—; exec. editor Am. Book Rev., 1979—; vis. prof. Rutgers U., 1980, U. Paris, 1983; cons. Nat. Humanities Faculty, Ga., 1975—. Author: The American Experience, 1970, Naked Angels, 1976, Ezra Pound: The Solitary Volcano, 1987, Passionate Lives, 1991, The Living Theatre: Art, Exile and Outrage, 1995; contbr. articles to mags. including Am. Scholar, Partisan Rev., Vanity Fair, Fame. NEH fellow, 1974. Home: 69 Perry St New York NY 10014-3297 Office: Queens College Flushing NY 11367

TYTLER, LINDA JEAN, communications and public affairs executive; b. Rochester, N.Y., Aug. 31, 1947; d. Frederick Easton and Marian Elizabeth (Allen) T.; m. George Stephen Dragnich, May 2, 1970 (div. July 1976); m. James Douglas Fisher, Oct. 7, 1994. AS, So. Sem., Buena Vista, Va., 1967; student U. Va., 1973; student in pub. adminstrn. U. N. Mex., 1981-82. Spl. asst. to Congressman John Buchanan, Washington, 1971-75; legis. analyst U.S. Senator Robert Griffin, Washington, 1975-77; ops. supr. Pres. Ford Com., Washington, 1976; office mgr. U.S. Senator Pete Domenici Re-election, Albuquerque, 1977; pub. info. officer S.W. Community Health Service, Albuquerque, 1978-83; cons. pub. relations and mktg., Albuquerque, 1983-84; account exec. Rick Johnson & Co., Inc., Albuquerque, 1983-84; dir. mktg. and communications St. Joseph Healthcare Corp., 1984-88; mktg. and bus. devel. cons., 1987-90; mgr. communications and pub. affairs Def. Avionics Systems div., Honeywell Inc., 1990—; sgt. N.Mex. Mounted Patrol, 1993—; mem. N.Mex. Ho. of Reps., Santa Fe, 1983-95, ret. 1995, vice chmn. appropriations and fin. com., 1985-86, interim com. on children and youth, 1985-86, mem. consumer and pub. affairs com., transp. com., 1992-95; chmn. Rep. Caucus, 1985-88; chmn. legis. campaign com. Rep. Com.; del. to Republic of China, Am. Council of Young Polit. Leaders, 1988. Bd. dirs. N. Mex. chpt. ARC, Albuquerque, 1984. Recipient award N.Mex. Advt. Fedn., Albuquerque, 1981, 82, 85, 86, 87. Mem. Am. Soc. Hosp. Pub. Relations (cert.), Nat. Advt. Fedn., Soc. Hosp. Planning and Mktg., Am. Mktg. Assn. Republican. Baptist.

TZAGOURNIS, MANUEL, physician, educator, university dean and official; b. Youngstown, Ohio; came to Oct. 20, 1934; s. Adam and Argiro T.; m. Madeline Jean Kalos, Aug. 30, 1958; children: Adam, Alice, Ellen, Jack George. BS, Ohio State U., 1956, M.D., 1960, M.S., 1967. Intern Phila. Gen. Hosp., 1960-61; resident Ohio State U., Columbus, 1961-63, chief med. resident, 1966-67, instr., 1967-68, asst. prof., 1970-74, prof., 1974—; asst. dean Sch. Medicine, 1973-75, assoc. dean, med. dirs. hosps., 1975-80, v.p. health scis., dean of medicine, 1981—; gen. practice medicine Columbus, 1967—; mem. staff Ohio State U. Hosps.; mem. Coalition for Cost Effective Health Services Edn. and Research Group State of Ohio, 1983. Contbg. author: textbook Endocrinology, 1974, Clinical Diabetes: Modern Management, 1980; co-author: Diabetes Mellitus, 1983, 88. Citation Ohio State Senate Resolution No. 984, 1989. Capt. U.S. Army, 1962-64. Recipient Homeric Order of Ahepa Cleve. chpt., 1976, Phys. of Yr. award Hellenic Med. Soc. N.Y., 1989; citations Ohio Stae Senate and Ho. of Reps., 1975, 83. Mem. Franklin County Acad. Medicine, Assn. Am. Med. Colls., Deans' Council. Mem. Greek Orthodox Ch. Home: 4335 Sawmill Rd Columbus OH 43220 Office: Ohio State U Coll Medicine 200 Meiling Hall 370 W 9th Ave Columbus OH 43210-1238

TZIMAS, NICHOLAS ACHILLES, orthopedic surgeon, educator; b. Greece, Apr. 18, 1928; came to U.S., 1955, naturalized, 1960; s. Archilles Nicholas and Evanthia B. (Exarchou) T.; m. Helen J. Papastylopoulos, Apr.

22, 1958; children: Yvonne, Christina. M.D., U. Athens, Greece, 1952. Intern St. Mary's Hosp., Hoboken, N.J., 1955-56; resident in gen. surgery Misericordia Hosp., N.Y.C.; resident in orthopedic surgery Bellevue Hosp., N.Y.C., 1957-60; instr. orthopedic surgery N.Y. U. Sch. Medicine, 1961-63, asst. clin. prof., 1963-65, asso. clin. prof., 1965-71; clin. prof., 1971—; mem. staff Univ. and Bellevue Hosps.; chief children's orthopedics, Hosp., White Plains, N.Y., 1972—; advisory com. Bur. Handicapped Children, N.Y.C., 1975—; spl. invitations for teaching, Osaka, Japan, 1970, Jerusalem, 1974, São Paolo, Brazil, 1976, Taranto, Italy, 1977, Bari, Italy, 1978, Barquisimeto, Venezuela, 1979, Bogotá, Colombia, 1983, Buenos Aires, Argentina, 1983. Author articles on spina bifida child mgmt. Served with M.C. Greek Army, 1952-55. Named ofcl. Knight of Italian Republic, 1979. Fellow Am., Internat. colls. surgeons; mem. N.Y. Acad. Medicine, N.Y. State, N.Y. County med. socs., Am. Acad. Orthopedic Surgeons, Am. Congress Rehab. Medicine, Am. Acad. Cerebral Palsy. Mem. Greek Orthodox Ch., Archon of the Ecumenical Patriarchate of Constantinople. Home: 33 Edgewood St Tenafly NJ 07670-2909 Office: 530 1st Ave New York NY 10016-6402

TZIMOPOULOS, NICHOLAS D., science and mathematics education specialist; b. Eptachorion, Greece, Feb. 19, 1941; came to U.S., 1956; s. Demetrius and Soultana (Davos) T. BA in Chemistry and Math., U. N.H., 1965; MS in Analytical Chemistry, Boston Coll., 1967, PhD in Phys. Chemistry, 1971. Dir. research So. N.H. Services, Manchester, 1978-80; prof. phys. chemistry U. Northern Fla., Jacksonville, 1981-82; chmn. math and sci. The Bartram Sch., Jacksonville, Fla., 1982-83; prof. chemistry Valencia Community Coll., Orlando, Fla., 1983-84; dir. sci. info. Schs. of the Tarrytowns, North Tarrytown, N.Y., 1984-91; dir. sci., math. and tech. Lexington (Mass.) Pub. Schs., 1989—. Author: Modified Null-Point Potentiometry, 1967, Irreversible Processes, 1971, Mathematics-Science Curricula, 1982, Modern Chemistry, 1990, 93, (with others) Life, Earth, Physical Sciences, 1987, 90, General Sciences Books 1 and 2, 1987, 90, The Next Generation: Teachers Resources Curriculum Guide, 1993, The Stuff of Dreams: Teachers Resource Curriculum Guide, 1993. N.H. rep. N.E. Metric Action Council, 1978-80; Tufts U. del. New Eng. Energy Congress, 1978; liaison Kiwanis Regional Sci. and Engring. Fair, Jacksonville, 1983; founder N.H. Legis. Acad. Sci. and Tech., Concord, 1980. Recipient Outstanding commendations in sci. achievement Internat. Sci. and Engring. Fair, 1986, CMA Catalyst award, 1987, Tufts U. Presdl. award for excellence in sci. and math., 1989. Fellow Sigma Xi; mem. AAAS, ASCD, Am. Chem. Soc. (Fla. congl. del. 1984, treas. Fla. sect. 1983, 84, chmn. Jacksonville sect. 1982-83, dir. Westchester County, N.Y. sub-sect. 1986—, high sch. exams. com. 1982-86, Outstanding Chemistry Tchr. Fla. 1982, S.E. U.S. 1983, Nichols award 1986), N.Y. Acad. Sci., Fla. Acad. Sci., Nat. Sci. Tchrs. Assn., Greek Orthodox Youth Assn. (pres. Manchester, N.H. 1963-65). Democrat. Avocations: photography, classical music, guitar, travel, soccer.

UBELL, DONALD PAUL, lawyer; b. Rome, N.Y., Dec. 16, 1945; s. Carl C. and Mary (De Cristo) U.; m. Nancy Sting, Aug. 23, 1969; children: Brian Donald, Matthew Lee, Karen Elizabeth. AB, U.N.C., 1967; JD, U. Mich., 1969. Bar: Mich. 1970, Ga. 1984, N.C. 1993. Rsch. atty. Mich. Ct. Appeals, 1969-71, asst. clk., 1971-73; dir. Pros. Attys. Appellate Svc., Lansing, Mich., 1973-74; commr. Mich. Supreme Ct., Lansing, 1974-83; ptnr. Kutak Rock, Atlanta, 1983-93, Parker, Poe, Adams & Bernstein, L.L.P., Charlotte, N.C., 1993—; adj. prof. law Thomas M. Cooley Law Sch., 1972-79; jud. fellow U.S. Supreme Ct., 1979-80. Contbr. articles to profl. jours. Mem. ABA (coun. young lawyers div. 1976-78, coun. legal edn. and admissions to bar sect. 1977-78, consortium profl. competence 1983-84, bd. dirs. gen. practice sect. 1986-87, budget officer 1986-89, standing com. on continuing edn. of bar 1991-94), Mich. Bar Assn. (rep. assembly 1972-76, 78-79, bd. commrs. 1978-79, chmn. young lawyers sect. 1978-79), Ga. Bar Assn., N.C. Bar Assn., Phi Beta Kappa, Phi Eta Sigma. Office: Parker Poe Adams & Bernstein LLP 2500 Charlotte Pl Charlotte NC 28244

UBELL, EARL, television science editor; b. Bklyn., June 21, 1926; s. Charles and Hilda (Kramer) U.; m. Shirley Leitman, Feb. 12, 1949; children—Lori Ellen, Michael Charles. B.S., CCNY, 1948. With N.Y. Herald Tribune, 1943-66, successively messenger, asst. to mng. editor, reporter, 1943-53, sci. editor, 1953-66, syndicated columnist, 1956-66; sci. commentator MBS, 1958-59; spl. sci. editor WNEW, N.Y., 1962; health and sci. editor WCBS-TV, N.Y.C., 1966-72, 78—; health editor PARADE mag., 1983—. Dir. TV news NBC News, N.Y.C., 1972-76; producer spl. broadcasts TV news, 1976-78; producer documentaries Medicine in America, 1977, Escape from Madness, 1977; author: The World of Push and Pull, 1964, The World of The Living, 1965, The World of Candle and Color, 1969, How to Save Your Life, 1972, (with Carol C. Flax) Mother/Father/You, 1980. Pres. Council Advancement Sci. Writing, Inc., 1960-66, bd. dirs., 1960—; chmn. Center Modern Dance Edn., Inc., 1962-82; pres. North Jersey Cultural Council, 1966-72; bd. dirs. Dance Notation Bur., 1968—; bd., 1975-94; bd. dirs. Sex Info. and Edn. Council U.S., 1967-69, YMHA, Bergen County, 1968-73, Nat. Center Health Edn., 1977. Served as aviation radioman USNR, 1944-46. Recipient Mental Health Bell award N.Y. State Soc. Mental Health, 1957, Albert Lasker med. journalism award, 1958, Nat. Assn. Mental Health award for radio program, 1962, Sci. Writers award Am. Psychol. Found., 1965, Westinghouse award AAAS, 1960, Empire State award, 1963, TV Reporting award N.Y. Assoc. Press, 1969, 71, N.Y. Emmy award, 1971, Samuelson award N.Y. League for Hard of Hearing, Legal-Med. award Milton Helpern Library of Legal Medicine, Spl. Achievement award Deadline Club, 1982, Disting. Contbn. award, 1983, Nat. Media award Am. Diabetes Assn., 1985, N.Y. State Mental Health Council award, 1987, Ann. Svc. award Dance Notation Bur., 1990. Mem. Nat. Assn. Sci. Writers (pres. 1960-61), Nuclear Energy Writers Assn. (pres. 1965-66), Phi Beta Kappa (pres. Gamma chpt. 1976-77). *I learn something new, in depth, every 5 years—x-ray crystallography, French, statistics, polling, stock market—I am refreshed.*

UBELL, ROBERT NEIL, editor, publisher, consultant, literary agent; b. Bklyn., Sept. 14, 1938; s. Charles and Hilda (Kramer) U.; m. Rosalyn Deutsche, Sept. 24, 1976; children: Jennifer, Elizabeth A., Bklyn. Coll., 1961; student, Acad. Fine Arts, Rome, Italy, 1959-60, City U. N.Y., 1961-62, Pratt Graphic Arts Workshop, N.Y.C., 1972-73. Asso. editor Nuclear Industry, Atomic Industrial Forum, 1962-64; editor Plenum Pub. Corp., N.Y.C., 1965-68; sr. editor Plenum Pub. Corp., 1968-70, v.p., editor in chief, 1970-76; editor The Sciences, N.Y. Acad. Scis., N.Y.C., 1976-79; Am. pub. Nature, N.Y.C., 1979-83; founding pub. BioTech, 1983; pres. Robert Ubell Assocs., N.Y.C., 1983—. Author: (with Marvin Leiner) Children Are the Revolution, 1974, Negotiating Networked Licensing Agreements (with Mark Tesoriero), 1995; editor Physics Today Buyers' Guide, 1984-89; exec. editor: Liguistics: The Cambridge Survey, 1987-88, Pre-Med Handbook, 1986, International Encyclopedia of the Social Sciences, Vol. 19, 1991, Encyclopedia of Astronomy and Astrophysics, 1991, Triumph of Discovery, 1995; cons. editor ISI Press, 1985-87, Am. Inst. of Physics Book Program, 1986—, Am. Chem. Soc. Book Program, 1989—; cons. pub. Computers in Physics, 1987-91; series editor Masters of Modern Physics, 1991—, Creators of Modern Chemistry, 1994—, Scientific American Focus, 1995—; contbr. articles to mags. Mem. AAAS, N.Y. Acad. Scis., Nat. Assn. Sci. Writers, Soc. Scholarly Pubs. Office: Robert Ubell Assocs Inc 111 8th Ave New York NY 10011-5201

UBERALL, HERBERT MICHAEL STEFAN, physicist, educator; b. Neunkirchen, Austria, Oct. 14, 1931; came to U.S., 1953, naturalized, 1963; s. Michael and Stefanie (Hacker) U.; m. Reyna Tosta, 1981; children by previous marriage: Bernadette, Bertrand. Ph.D., U. Vienna, Austria, 1953, Cornell U., 1956; PhD (honoris causa), U. Le Havre, France, 1987. Staff mem. Signal Corps. Labs., Ft. Monmouth, N.J., 1953-54; research asst. Cornell U., 1954-56; research fellow Nuclear Physics Research Lab., U. Liverpool, Eng., 1956-57; Ford Found. fellow CERN, Geneva, Switzerland, 1957-58; research physicist Carnegie Inst. Tech., Pitts., 1958-60; asst. prof. U. Mich., Ann Arbor, 1960-64; assoc. prof. Cath. U. Am., Washington, 1964-65, prof. physics, 1965-84, prof. emeritus, 1984—; vis. prof. U. Paris VII Jussieu, 1984-85, U. Le Havre, 1990, 92, 94, U. Bordeaux, 1993; cons. Naval Rsch. Lab., Washington, 1966—. Author: Electron Scattering from Complex Nuclei, 1971; co-author: Giant Resonance Phenomena, 1980, Nuclear Pion Photoproduction, 1991; editor: Acoustic Resonance Scattering, 1992; co-editor: Long Distance Neutrino Detection, 1979, Classical and Quantum Dynamics, 1991, Coherent Radiation Sources, 1985, Coherent

Radiation Processes in Strong Fields, 1991, Radar Target Imaging, 1994; contbr. 300 articles to profl. jours. Recipient Achievement award Washington Acad. Scis., 1984. Fellow IEEE, Am. Phys. Soc., Acoustical Soc. Am., Washington Acad. Scis.; mem. AAUP, Am. Acad. Mech., Internat. Union Radio Sci. Home: 5101 River Rd Apt 1417 Bethesda MD 20816-1571 Office: Catholic U Dept Physics Washington DC 20064

UBEROI, MAHINDER SINGH, aerospace engineering educator; b. Delhi, India, Mar. 13, 1924; came to U.S., 1945, naturalized, 1960; s. Kirpal Singh and Sulaksha (Kosher) U. B.S., Punjab U., Lahore, India, 1944; M.S., Calif. Inst. Tech., 1946; D.Eng., Johns Hopkins U., 1952. Registered profl. engr. Mem. faculty U. Mich., Ann Arbor, 1953-63, prof. aeros., 1959-63, vis. prof., 1963-64; prof. aerospace engring. U. Colo., Boulder, 1963—, chmn. dept. aerospace engring., 1963-75; fellow F. Joint Inst. for Lab. Astrophysics, Boulder, 1963-74; hon. research fellow Harvard U., 1975-76; invited prof. U. Que., Can., 1972-74. Author numerous rsch. pubs. on dynamics of ionized and neutral gases and liquids with and without chem. reactions, gravity and electromagnetic fields; editor Cosmic Gas Dynamics, 1974. Council mem. Ednl. TV Channel 6, Inc., Denver, 1963-66. Guggenheim fellow Royal Inst. Tech., Stockholm, Sweden, 1958; exchange scientist U.S. Nat. Acad. Scis.; exchange scientist Soviet Acad. Scis., 1968. Mem. Am. Phys. Soc., Tau Beta Pi. Home: 819 6th St Boulder CO 80302-7418

UBINGER, JOHN W., JR., lawyer; b. Pitts., Jan. 31, 1949. BBA, Ohio U., 1970; JD, U. Notre Dame, 1973. Bar: Pa. 1973. Ptnr. Jones, Day, Reavis & Pogue, Pitts.; instr. environ. dispute resolution Duquesne U. Sec. Pa. Environ. Coun., chmn. task force on reuse of indsl. sites; bd. dirs., treas. Allegheny Land Trust; environ. adv. com. Hampton Township; adv. com. Allegheny County Dept. Air Pollution Control, Allegheny County Contaminated Sites REdevelopment Study. Mem. ABA (natural resources, energy and environ. law sect.) Pa. Bar Assn. (chmn. environ., mineral and natural resources law sect. 1990-91), Allegheny County Bar Assn. (chmn. environ. law sect. 1991), Air and Waste Mgmt. Assn. (chmn. We. Pa. Sect. 1989-90), Environ. Law Inst. (assoc.). Office: Jones Day Reavis & Pogue 1 Mellon Bank Ct 500 Grant St Pittsburgh PA 15219-2502

UBUKA, TOSHIHIKO, biochemistry educator; b. Kagaminocho, Okayama, Japan, Jan. 31, 1934; s. Yoshio and Shigeko (Hashimoto) U.; m. Satoko Iwamiya, Oct. 18, 1960; children: Takayoshi, Hiromi, Atsue. MD, Okayama U., 1959, PhD, 1964. With Okayama U., 1964-73, asst. prof., 1973-80, assoc. prof. Med. Sch., 1980-81, prof. Med. Sch., 1981—; rsch. assoc. Med. Coll. Cornell U., N.Y.C., 1968-71. Co-author: Methods in Enzymology, vol. 143, 1987; editor Acta Med Okayama, 1980—, Physiol Chem Phys and Med NMR, 1982—, Amino Acids, 1991—; chief editor Acta Med Okayama, 1987-90. Fellow Japanese Biochem. Soc., Japanese Soc. Nutrition and Food Sci.; mem. AAAS, N.Y. Acad. Scis., Internat. Soc. Amino Acid Rsch., Soc. Study Inborn Errors Metabolism. Achievements include research in sulfur biochemistry, sulfur nutrition, cysteine metabolism in mammals, protein modification with mixed disulfides, inborn errors of cysteine metabolism. Home: 527-1 Nishikarakawa, Okayama 701-12, Japan Office: Okayama U Med Sch Dept Biochemistry, 2-5-1 Shikatacho, Okayama 700, Japan

UCCELLO, VINCENZA AGATHA, artist, director, educator emerita; b. Hartford, Conn., May 11, 1921; d. Salvatore and Josephine (Bordonaro) U. B.S., St. Joseph Coll., West Hartford, Conn., 1956; M.A. in Liberal Studies, Wesleyan U., 1961; M.F.A., Villa Schifanoia, Florence, Italy, 1963. Tchr. art Glastonbury High Sch., Conn., 1957-61, East Hartford Pub. Schs., Conn., 1963-64; prof. fine arts St. Joseph Coll., 1964—, chmn. dept. fine arts, 1967-85, acting curator, dir. coll. art collections, 1978—. One-woman shows Villa Schifanoia, Florence, 1963, St. Joseph Coll., 1965, 81, Pump House Gallery, Hartford, Conn., 1986; group shows Am. Painters in Paris Exhbn., Nat. Print and Drawing Exhbn., Ohio U., Athens, Ball State U., Muncie, Ind., Austin Art Ctr., Trinity Coll., Hartford, Munson Gallery, New Haven; represented in permanent collections St. Joseph Coll., N.Y. Pub. Libr., Ctr. for Book Arts, Conn. Nat. Bank, Hartford; pvt. collections. Recipient Harper Meml. award in painting, 1969; fellow Venice Artists Workshop, 1965; Yale U. fellow Andrew U. Mellon Found., 1980; second prize Atria Gallery Blues Show. Mem. Coll. Art Assn. Am., Conn. Women Artists (pres. 1974-76), Canton Artists Guild, Ctr. for Book Art. Home: 51 Hilltop Dr West Hartford CT 06107-1434

UCHIDA, IRENE AYAKO, cytogenetics educator, researcher; b. Vancouver, B.C., Can., Apr. 8, 1917; d. Sentaro and Shizuko (Takano) U. B.A., U. Toronto, Ont., Can., 1946; Ph.D., U. Toronto, 1951. Rsch. assoc. Hosp. Sick Children, Toronto, 1951-59; dir. med. genetics Children's Hosp., Winnipeg, Man., Can., 1960-69; asst. prof. U. Man., 1963-67, assoc. prof., 1967-69; dir. cytogenetics lab. McMaster U. Med. Ctr., Hamilton, Ont., Can., 1969-91; prof. pediatrics, pathology McMaster U., 1969-85, prof. emeritus, 1985—; dir. cytogenetics Oshawa (Ont.) Gen. Hosp., 1991—; mem. sci. adv. com. Inst. for Basic Research, Staten Island, N.Y., 1984—; vis. scientist Med. Research Council Can., U. London and Harwell Radiobiol. Research Unit, 1969; vis. prof. Med. Research Council Can., U. Western Ont., 1973. Author medcom slide tape series, 1987; contbr. articles to profl. jours. and chpts. to books. Mem. Sci. Council Can., Ottawa, 1970-73; mem. adv. com. Ont. Ministry Health, Toronto, 1979-85. Decorated officer Order of Can.; recipient Woman of Yr. award Women's Advt. Sales Club, 1963, Woman of Century award Nat. Coun. Jewish Women, 1967, achievement award Altrusa Club, 1969; Ramsay Wright scholar, 1947; fellow Rockefeller Found., 1959; grantee Nat. Found. March of Dimes, 1962-69, 71-77, NIH, 1962-69, 89-91, Nat. Heart, Lung and Blood Inst., 1977-79. Fellow Can. Coll. Med. Geneticists (emeritus 1992), Am. Coll. Med. Genetics (emeritus 1993); mem. Am. Soc. Human Genetics (pres. 1968), Peruvian Soc. Med. Genetics (hon.). Office: McMaster U, 1200 Main St W, Hamilton, ON Canada L8N 3Z5

UCHITELLE, LOUIS, journalist; b. N.Y.C., Mar. 21, 1932; s. Abraham and Alice Lee (Cronbach) U.; m. Joan Eva Shapiro, Oct. 7, 1966; children: Isabel Anne, Jennifer Emily. B.A., U. Mich., 1954. Reporter Mt. Vernon (N.Y.) Daily Argus, 1955-57; with AP, 1957-80; fgn. corr. and bur. chief AP, San Juan, P.R., 1964-67, Buenos Aires, 1967-73; supervising editor AP Newsfeatures, N.Y.C., 1974-76; bus. news editor AP, 1977-80; asst. bus. and fin. editor N.Y. Times, 1980-87, econ. writer, 1987—; instr. journalism Sch. Gen. Studies, Columbia U., 1976-89. Home: 11 Ridgecrest W Scarsdale NY 10583-2046 Office: NY Times 229 W 43rd St New York NY 10036-3913

UCKO, DAVID ALAN, museum director; b. N.Y.C., July 9, 1948; s. Lawrence L. and Helen H. U.; m. Barbara Alice Clark, Aug. 13, 1977; 1 child, Aaron. BA, Columbia Coll., N.Y.C., 1969; PhD, MIT, 1972. Asst. prof. chemistry Hostos Community Coll., CUNY, Bronx, 1972-76; asst. prof. chemistry Antioch Coll., Yellow Springs, Ohio, 1976-79, assoc. prof. chemistry, 1979; rsch. coord. Mus. Sci. and Industry, Chgo., 1979-80, dir. sci., 1981-87, v.p., 1986-87; dep. dir. Calif. Mus. Sci. and Industry, L.A., 1987-90; pres. Kansas City (Mo.) Mus., 1990—; rsch. assoc. chemistry dept. Columbia U., 1973-76; rsch. assoc. assoc. prof. dept. edn. U. Chgo., 1982-87; adj. staff scientist C.F. Kettering Rsch. Lab., Yellow Springs, 1977-79. Author: (book) Basics for Chemistry, 1982, Living Chemistry, 2d edit., 1986; contbr. articles to profl. jours.; host, producer (radio program) Science Alive!, 1983-87; developer numerous mus. exhibits. Vice pres., bd. dirs. Heritage League Greater Kansas City, 1991-92; mem. Mid-Am. Regional Coun., Regional Amenities Task Force, Kansas City, 1990—; mem. edn. com. Greater Kansas City C. of C., 1993—. Woodrow Wilson fellow, 1969, NIH postdoctoral fellow, 1972; grantee NSF, NEH, U.S. Dept. Edn., Ill. Humanities Coun., 1976-88; recipient Up and Comers award Jr. Achievement of Mid.-Am., 1992. Fellow AAAS (mem.-at-large sect Y 1987-93); mem. Assn. Sci. Tech. Ctrs. (pubs. com. 1984-94, chmn. 1988-94, ethics com. 1990—), Alpha Sigma Nu (hon.). Home: 1007 W 66th St Kansas City MO 64113-1815 Office: Kansas City Mus 3218 Gladstone Blvd Kansas City MO 64123-1199

UDALL, CALVIN HUNT, lawyer; b. St. Johns, Ariz., Oct. 23, 1923; s. Grover C. and Dora (Sherwood) U.; m. Doris Fuss, Dec. 11, 1943; children: Fredric, Margaret Udall Learn, Julie (Mrs. Blair M. Nash), Lucinda (Mrs. Douglas Johnson), Tina (Mrs. Bret Petersen). LL.B., U. Ariz., 1948. Bar: Ariz. 1948. Ptnr. Fennemore Craig, 1953—; Ariz. spl. counsel Arizona v. California, 1954-62; mem. Coun. on Legal Edn. Opportunity, 1983-93. Mem. cast Phoenix Mus. Theatre, 1959-65. Fellow Am. Bar Found. (bd.

dirs. 1986-89, fellows chmn. 1988-89), Ariz. Bar Found. (Disting. Svc. award 1993), Am. Coll. Trial Lawyers; mem. ABA (ho. dels. 1962-92, bd. govs. 1981-84, exec. com. 1983-84, chmn. task force on minorities 1984-86), Maricopa County Bar Assn. (pres. 1957, Disting. Pub. Svc. award 1986), State Bar Ariz. (bd. govs. 1960-65), Ariz. Law Coll. Assn. (founding bd. dirs. 1967-80, pres. 1978-79, U. Ariz. Disting. Citizen award 1984, bd. visitors 1991—). Office: Fennemore Craig One Renaissance Sq 2 N Central Ave, Ste 2200 Phoenix AZ 85004

UDALL, MORRIS KING, former congressman; b. St. Johns, Ariz., June 15, 1922; s. Levi S. and Louise (Lee) U.; m. Norma Gilbert, 1989; children by previous marriage: Mark, Judith, Randolph, Anne, Bradley, Katherine. LL.B. with distinction, U. Ariz., 1949. Bar: Ariz. 1949. Player Denver Nuggets, 1948-49; ptnr. firm Udall & Udall, Tucson, 1949-61; chief dep. county atty. Pima County, 1950-52, county atty., 1953-54; lectr. labor law U. Ariz., 1955-56; mem. 87th-101st Congresses, 2d Dist. Ariz., 1961-91; chmn. House Com. on Interior and Insular Affairs; mem. Com. on Post Office and Civil Service; vice chmn. Office Tech. Assessment; mem. Com. on Fgn. Affairs; a founder Bank of Tucson, 1959, former dir.; former chmn. bd. Catalina Savs. and Loan Assn.; chmn. Ariz. Com. for Modern Cts., 1960. Author: Arizona Law of Evidence, 1960, Education of a Congressman, 1972, Too Funny to Be President, 1988; co-author: The Job of the Congressman, 1966. Del. Democratic Nat. Conv., 1956; chmn. Ariz. delegation, 1972, Ariz. Volunteers for Stevenson, 1956; candidate for Dem. nomination for Pres., 1976; keynote speaker Dem. Nat. Conv., 1980. Served to capt. USAAF, 1942-46, PTO. Mem. ABA, Ariz. Bar Assn. (bd. govs.), Pima County Bar Assn. (exec. com.), Am. Judicature Soc., Am. Legion, Phi Kappa Phi, Phi Delta Phi. *

UDALL, THOMAS, state attorney general; b. Tucson, May 18, 1948; s. Stewart and Lee Udall; m. Jill Z. Cooper; 1 child, Amanda Cooper. BA, Prescott Coll., 1970; LLB, Cambridge U., Eng., 1975; JD, U. N.Mex., 1977. Law clk. to Hon. Oliver Seth U.S. Ct. Appeals (10th cir.), Santa Fe, 1977-78; asst. U.S. atty. U.S. Atty.'s Office, 1978-81; pvt. practice Santa Fe, 1981-83; chief counsel N.Mex. Health & Environ. Dept., 1983-84; ptnr. Miller, Stratvert, Togerson & Schlenker, P.A., Albuquerque, 1985-88; atty. gen. State of N.Mex., 1990—. Dem. candidate U.S. Ho. Reps., 1988; past pres. Rio Chama Preservation Trust; mem. N.Mex. Environ. Improvement Bd., 1986-87; bd. dirs. La Compania de Teatro de Albuquerque, Santa Fe Chamber Music Festival, Law Fund. Mem. Kiwanis. Office: Office of Atty Gen PO Box 1508 Galisteo St Santa Fe NM 87504-1508

UDCOFF, GEORGE JOSEPH, financial executive; b. Bklyn., Dec. 26, 1946. BS in Acctg., CUNY, 1968. Staff acct. Deloitte, Haskins & Sells, N.Y.C., 1968-74, mgr., 1974-77; mgr. Deloitte, Haskins & Sells, Bergen County, N.J., 1977-80; contr. Cabot Mineral Resources, N.Y.C., 1981-83; v.p. fin. Metallurg, Inc., N.Y.C., 1983-93; mng. dir. Ferrolegeringar A.G., Dübendorf, Switzerland, 1994—; exec. com. Metallurg Inc., N.Y. Mem. AICPAs, N.J. Soc. CPAs, Fin. Execs. Inst., Am. Mgmt. Assn.

UDELL, RICHARD, lawyer; b. Bklyn., Dec. 27, 1932; s. Alvin and Gertrude (Langsam) U.; BA, Reed Coll., 1955; LLB, U. Pa., 1958; m. Marguerite Hartshorne, July 3, 1955; children: Benjamin Alan, Edward H. Bar: N.Y. 1958, Fla. 1984. Pvt. practice, N.Y.C., 1959-65; counsel RCA Records, N.Y.C., 1965-69; assoc. firm Machat & Kronfeld, N.Y.C., 1969-71; counsel Famous Music Corp., N.Y.C., 1971-72, Random House, Inc. subs. RCA, N.Y.C., 1972-75; gen. counsel Simon & Schuster, Inc., subs. Gulf & Western Industries, Inc., N.Y.C., 1975-77; adminstrv. v.p., chief counsel Harcourt Brace Jovanovich, Inc., N.Y.C., 1977-92; v.p. gen. coun. McGraw Hill Sch. Pub. Co., 1992—. Mem. Bar Assn. City N.Y., Orange County Bar Assn., Fla. Bar Ass. Jewish. Office: McGraw-Hill Sch Pub Co 1221 Ave of the Americas New York NY 10020-1095

UDEN, DAVID ELLIOTT, cardiologist, educator; b. Montreal, Sept. 7, 1936; s. Reginald and Elsie Ada (Elliott) U.; m. Virginia Anne Lawe, June 6, 1964; children: Thomas Elliott, Linda Ann. BSc, McGill U., 1958, MD, 1962. Diplomate Am. Bd. Internal Medicine, Am. Bd. Cardiovascular Disease. Attending cardiologist Toronto Western Hosp., 1972-93, The Wellesley Hosp., Toronto, 1990-93; asst. prof. medicine U. Toronto, 1975-93; chief of cardiology Oconee Meml. Hosp., Seneca, S.C., 1993—; chief of medicine, 1994—. Contbr. articles to sci. and profl. jours. With RCAF, 1963-66. Fellow Am. Coll. Cardiology, Am. Heart Assn. Coun. on Clin. Cardiology. Avocations: travel, photography. Office: 103 Omni Dr # B Seneca SC 29678-9448

UDENFRIEND, SIDNEY, biochemist; b. N.Y.C., Apr. 5, 1918; s. Max and Esther (Tabak) U.; m. Shirley Frances Reidel, June 20, 1943; children: Aliza, Elliot. B.S., Coll. City N.Y., 1939; M.S., N.Y. U., 1942, Ph.D., 1948; D.Sc. honoris causa, N.Y. Med. Coll., 1974, Coll. Medicine and Dentistry of N.J., 1979, Mt. Sinai Sch. Medicine, City U. N.Y., 1981. Lab. asst. N.Y.C. Dept. Health, 1940-42; jr. chemist NYU Rsch. Svc., 1942-43, asst. chemist, 1943-44, research chemist, 1944-46; research asst. Med. Sch., 1946-47, instr., 1947-48; instr. Washington U. Med. Sch., 1948-50; biochemist Nat. Heart Inst., Bethesda, Md., 1950-53; head sect. cellular pharmacology lab. chem. pharmacology Nat. Heart Inst., 1953-56, chief lab. clin. biochemistry, 1956-68; dir. Roche Inst. Molecular Biology, N.J., 1968-83, head lab. molecular neurobiology, 1983—; professorial lectr. George Washington U., 1962-69; adj. prof. human genetics and devel. dept. Columbia U., 1969—; adj. prof. biochemistry City U. N.Y., 1968—; dept. pharmacology Emory U., 1976-78; adj. prof. biochemistry Cornell U. Med. Sch., 1982—; mem. sci. adv. bd. Scripps Clinic and Research Found., 1974-78; mem. adv. com. to dir. NIH, 1976-78; mem. Sci. Adv. Com. for Cystic Fibrosis; mem. adv. council of sci. and engring. City U. N.Y., 1980—; mem. sci. adv. com. Mass. Gen. Hosp., 1980-84. Trustee Wistar Inst., 1968-71; mem. adv. bd. Weizmann Inst. Scis. 1978-79, bd. govs., 1979—. Recipient Cert. of Merit for studies on malignant carcinoid A.M.A., 1956, Arthur S. Flemming award, 1958; City of Hope research award, 1975; NIH fellow St. Mary's Hosp. Med. Sch., London, Eng., 1957; Harvey lectr., 1964; recipient Superior Service award Dept. HEW, 1963, Distinguished Service award, 1966; Gairdner Found. award, 1967; Heinrich Waelsch lectr. in neurosci., 1978; recipient Townsend Harris medal CCNY Alumni Assn., 1979; Rudolph Virchow gold medal, 1979; Chauncey Leake lectr. U. Calif., 1980. Fellow N.Y. Acad. Scis. (trustee 1978—); mem. NAS, AAAS, Am. Soc. Biol. Chemists, Am. Soc. Pharmacology and Exptl. Therapeutics (sec.), Soc. Exptl. Biology and Medicine, Am. Assn. Clin. Chemists (Van Slyke award 1967, Ames award 1969), Am. Chem. Soc. (Hillebrand award 1962, Torald Sollmann award 1975), Am. Acad. Arts and Scis., Japanese Pharmacol. Soc. (hon.), Japanese Biochem. Soc. (hon.), Czechoslovak Pharmacology Soc. (hon.), Congress Internat. Neuropsychopharmacologists (hon.), Instituto de Investigaciones Citológicas (corr.) (Spain), Phi Beta Kappa, Sigma Xi. Office: Roche Inst Nutley NJ 07110

UDEVITZ, NORMAN, publishing executive; b. Cheyenne, Wyo., Jan. 22, 1929; s. Jay and Edith (Stienberg) U.; m. Marsha Rae Dinner, Dec. 17, 1960; children: Jane, Kathryn, Andrew. Student, U. Colo., 1946-49. With Cheyenne Newspapers Inc. Cheyenne, 1949-54; editor-pub. Wyo. Buffalo, Cheyenne, 1954-63; account supr. Tilds & Cantz Advt. Agy., L.A., 1963-66; exec. v.p. Fitzgerald, Maahs & Miller, L.A., 1966-71; staff writer The Denver Post, 1971-88; dir. pubs. Am. Water Works Assn., Denver, 1988—. Sgt. USNG, 1950-53. Named Colo.'s Outstanding Journalist, U. Colo., 1977; recipient Pulitzer Prize Gold medal Columbia U., 1986. Mem. Investigative Reporters and Editors Inc., (bd. dirs. 1978-80, 81-83), The Newspaper Guild (McWilliams award 1976, 77). Jewish. Home: 4677 E Euclid Ave Littleton CO 80121-3224 Office: Am Water Works Assn 6666 W Quincy Ave Denver CO 80235-3098

UDICK, ROBERT E., newspaper executive; b. Colorado Springs, Colo., May 27, 1922; s. Albert Earl and Edna (Young) U. Student, Colo. Coll. Staff corr. Rocky Mountain News, Denver, 1947-49, United Press, Denver and Santa Fe, 1950-51; war corr. United Press, Korea, 1951-53; later became mgr. Hong Kong and Manila burs.; then mgr. for Southeast Asia, hdqrs., Singapore; editor, pub. Bangkok World, until 1967; pub. Pacific Daily News, Agana, Guam, until 1985; cons. Gannett Co., Inc., 1985—; Mem. civilian adv. bd. 8th Air Force; mem. Navy League, Guam Stock Exchange. Bd. regents U. Guam. Served with Coast Arty., Inf., Signal Corps, World War II. Mem. Fgn. Corr. Assn. Thailand (pres.), Phi Delta Theta. Club: Rotary.

Office: Pacific Daily News PO Box Dn Agana GU 96910-9017 *Given the opportunities and options actually available to you, you always do what you want to do most. 'Most' is the operative word. Anyone who acts or makes a decision and says, "I didn't want to do that" is trying to fool someone, perhaps, tragically, himself.*

UDLER, RUBIN JAKOVLEVITCH, linguist; b. Braila, Muntenia, Romania, Sept. 27, 1925; came to U.S., 1992; s. Jakov Aronovitch and Dina Vladimirovna (Gleizer) U.; m. Malka Il'nitchna Alexenberg, July 8, 1956; children: Arthur, Angela. B Philol. Sci., U. Chernovtsy, Ukrainian S.S.R., 1951; M Philol. Sci., USSR Acad. Scis., Moscow, 1961; D Philol. Sci., USSR Acad. Scis., Leningrad, 1974. Dep. chmn. fgn. langs. dept. Chernovtsy State Pedagogical Inst., 1951-56; jr. sci. researcher dialectology sect. Moldavian br. USSR Acad. Scis., Kishinev, Moldavian S.S.R., 1956-61; chief dialectology and exptl. phonetics sect. Moldavian Acad. Scis., Kishinev, Moldavian S.S.R., 1961-80, chief dialectology and history of lang. sect., 1980-86, chief dialectology and linguistic geography dept., 1986-92, dep. of academician-sec. of social studies dept., 1989-92; ctr. assoc. U. Ctr. for Internat. Studies U. Pitts., 1994—; translator Soviet Bucovina newspaper, Chernovtsy, 1951-52; mem. editorial bd. Moldavian Lang. and Lit., 1961-91, Jour. of Linguistics and Study of Literature, 1991-92; sr. sci. researcher All-Union Cert. Com., Moscow, 1963; corr. mem., pres. Moldavian Acad. Scis., Kishinev, 1989. Author: Moldavian Dialects of the Chernovtsy Area Consonantism, 1964, Dialectological Division of the Moldavian Language, Parts 1 and 2, 1976; co-author: The Moldavian Linguistic Atlas, 4 parts, 1968-73, Dialectological Dictionary, 5 vols., 1985-86, Dialectological Texts, 6 parts, 1969-87, The Historical Grammar of the Moldavian Language, 1964, Notes on Modern Moldavian Literary Language, 1967, Moldavian Dialectology, 1976, The Carpathian Dialectological Atlas, 5 vols., 1987-93, also articles. Corr. mem. Moldavian Acad. Scis. Presidium of Moldavian Acad. Schs.; mem. MLA, Am. Soc. Romanian Studies. Jewish. Avocations: collecting old books, coins, travel. Home: 1535 Shady Ave Pittsburgh PA 15217-1455 Office: Univ Ctr Internat Studies U Pittsburgh 4 G40 Gorves Quadrangle Pittsburgh PA 15260

UDOUJ, HERMAN J., diversified industries company executive; b. 1917. With Riverside Furniture Corp., 1946—, now chmn. bd. dirs.; with Twin Rivers Corp. (now Ark. Best Corp.), 1946—, formerly v.p. furniture mfg. ops. now vice-chmn. bd. dirs.; vice-chmn. Ark. Best Corp., Ft. Smith. Office: Ark Best Corp 1000 S 21st St Fort Smith AR 72901-4098 also: Riverside Furniture Corp 1400 S 6th St Fort Smith AR 72901-4398

UDOVITCH, ABRAHAM LABE, historian, educator; b. Winnipeg, Man., Can., May 31, 1933; came to U.S., naturalized, 1966; s. Benjamin Alexander and Minnie (Benson) U.; m. Lucette Valensi; children—Tamar, Miriam Esther. B.S., Columbia, 1958, M.A., 1959; Ph.D., Yale, 1965. Asst. prof. Middle East history Brandeis U., 1964-65, Cornell U., 1965-67; asso. prof. Middle East history Princeton, 1968-71, prof., 1971—, chmn. dept. Nr. Eastern studies, 1973-77, 80—; Bd. govs. Am. Research Inst. in Turkey, 1969—; dir. Middle East study panel Commn. on Critical Choices for Americans, 1974-76; mem. exec. com. Internat. Ctr. for Peace in Middle East, 1989—. Author: Partnership and Profit in Medieval Islam, 1970; 2Editor: Studia Islamica, 1975; Editorial bd.: Jour. of Interdisciplinary History, 1970—, Internat. Jour. of Middle East Studies, 1975—; mem. exec. com.: Ency. of Islam. Trustee N.E. Pooled Common Fund. Guggenheim fellow, 1970-71. Mem. Am. Oriental Soc. (chmn. Islamic sect. 1972—), Middle East Studies Assn., Econ. History Assn., Council on Fgn. Relations. Home: 7 Mccosh Cir Princeton NJ 08540-5626

UDRY, J. RICHARD, sociology educator; b. Covington, Ky., Oct. 12, 1928. BS in Sociology, Northwestern U., 1950; MA in Social Sci., Long Beach State Coll., 1956; PhD in Sociology, U. So. Calif., 1960. Instr. Chaffey Coll., 1960-62; asst. prof. Calif. State Poly. Coll., 1962-65; assoc. prof. maternal and child health and sociology U. N.C., Chapel Hill, 1965-69, prof., 1969—, dir. demographic rsch. unit Carolina Population Ctr., 1973-77, dir. Carolina Popluation Ctr., 1977-92, Kenan prof., 1992—. Author: The Social Context of Marriage, 1966, 3rd edit., 1974, The Media and Family Planning, 1974; editor: (with Earl Huyck) The Demographic Evaluation of Domestic Family Planning Programs, 1975; contbr. over 120 articles and reports ot profl. publs. Mem. AAAS, APHA, Am. Sociol. Assn., Population Assn. Am., Nat. Coun. on Family Rels., Sociol. Rsch. Assn. Office: U NC Carolina Population Ctr Univ Sq CB 8120 Chapel Hill NC 27516-3997

UDVARHELYI, GEORGE BELA, neurosurgery educator emeritus, cultural affairs administrator; b. Budapest, Hungary, May 14, 1920; came to U.S., 1955; s. Bela and Margaret (Bakacs) U.; m. Elspeth Mary Campbell, July 24, 1956; children: Ian Steven, Susan Margaret, Jane Elizabeth. BS, St. Stephen Coll., 1938; MD, U. Budapest, 1944, U. Buenos Aires, 1952; D honoris causa, Semmelweis Med. Sch., Budapest, 1988. Diplomate Am. Bd. Neurol. Surgery. Intern resident in surgery Red Cross Hosp./11th Mil. Hosp., Budapest, 1942-44; asst. resident Neurol. Univ. Clinic, Budapest, 1944-46; postdoctoral fellow U. Vienna, Austria, 1946-47; fgn. asst. Psychiat. Clinic, U. Berne, Switzerland, 1947-48; asst. resident in neurosurgery Hosp. Espanol, Cordoba, Argentina, 1948-50; resident neurosurgeon Inst. Neurosurgery, U. Buenos Aires, 1950-53; asst. Neurolsurgical Clinic, U. Cologne, Fed. Republic Germany, 1953-54; registrar Royal Infirmary, Edinburgh, Scotland, 1954-55; from fellow to full prof. Johns Hopkins U., Balt., 1955-84, prof. emeritus, dir. cultural affairs, 1984—, assoc. prof. radiology, 1963-84, Phi Beta Kappa lectr., 1980; neurosurg. cons. Social Security Adminstrn., Balt., 1962-89, Disability Determination Svc., Balt., 1991—; vis. prof., guest lectr. U. Va., Charlottesville, 1977, Children's Hosp. Ea. Ont., Ottawa, Can., 1977, U. Salzburg, Austria, 1981, U. Vienna, Austria, 1983, Mayo Clinic, Rochester, Minn., 1983, U. Cape Town, Republic of South Africa, 1984, U. Porto, Portugal, 1985; vis. prof. Temple U., Phila., 1979, U. Vt., Burlington, 1980, Aukland (New Zealand) Gen. Hosp., 1989, George Washington U., 1991, U. Mainz, Fed. Republic Germany, 1991, numerous others; lectr. in field. Contbr. numerous articles to profl. jours., book chpts. Mem. program com. Balt. Symphony Orch., 1972-80, edn. com. Walters Art Gallery, Balt., 1985-88. Recipient Lincoln award Am. Hungarian Found., 1980; Humanities grantee NEH, 1984-91. Fellow ACS; mem. AAUP, Am. Assn. Neurol. Surgeons (life, Humanitarian award 1991), Congress Neurol. Surgeons (sr.), Am. Assn. Neuropathologists, Pan-Am. Med. Assn., Soc. Brit. Neurol. Surgeons (corr.), Pavlovian Soc. N.Am., German Neurol. Soc. (corr.), Internat. Soc. Pediatric Neurosurgery (founding), Hungarian Neurosurg. Soc. (corr.), Argentine Acad. Sci. (corr.), Am. Soc. for Laser Medicine and Surgery (charter), Johns Hopkins Med. Assn., Johns Hopkins Faculty Club, 14 West Hamilton Club (chair steering com. 1977-83), Cosmos Club (chair program subcom. 1991—), Landsdowne Club (London), Alpha Omega Alpha. Roman Catholic. Avocations: music, literature, travel, chess. Home and Office: 1055 W Joppa Rd Ste 614 Towson MD 21204-3732

UDWADIA, FIRDAUS ERACH, engineering educator, consultant; b. Bombay, Aug. 28, 1947; came to U.S., 1968.; s. Erach Rustam and Perin P. (Lentin) U.; m. Farida Gagrat, Jan. 6, 1977; children: Shanaira, Zubin. BS, Indian Inst. Tech., Bombay, 1968; MS, Calif. Inst. Tech., 1969, PhD, 1972; MBA, U. So. Calif., 1985. Mem. faculty Calif. Inst. Tech., Pasadena, 1972-74; asst. prof. engring. U. So. Calif., Los Angeles, 1974-77, assoc. prof., 1977-83, prof. mech. engring., civil engring. and bus. adminstrn., 1983-86; prof. engring. bus. adminstrn. U. So. Calif., 1986—; also bd. dirs. Structural Identification Computing Facility U. So. Calif.; cons. Jet Propulsion Lab., Pasadena, Calif., 1978—, Argonne Nat. Lab., Chgo., 1982-83, Air Force Rocket Lab., Edwards AFB, Calif., 1984—, vis. prof. of Applied Mechanics and Mech. Engring., Calif. Inst. Tech., 1993. Assoc. editor: Applied Mathematics and Computation, Jour. Optimization Theory and Applications, Jour. Franklin Inst., Nonlinear Digest, Jour. of Mathematical Analysis and Applications, Jour. Mathematical Problems in Engineering; mem. adv. bd. Internat. Jour. Tech. Forecasting and Social Change; mem. publs. com. Jour. Aerospace Engring.; contbr. articles to profl. jours. Bd. dirs. Crisis Mgmt. Ctr., U. So. Calif. NSF grantee, 1976—; recipient Golden Poet award, 1990. Mem. AIAA, ASCE, Am. Acad. Mechanics, Soc. Indsl. and Applied Math., Seismological Soc. Am., Sigma Xi (Earthquake Engring. Research Inst., 1971, 74, 84). Avocations: writing poetry, piano, chess. Home: 2100 S Santa Anita Ave Arcadia CA 91006-4611 Office: U So Calif 430K Olin Hall University Park Los Angeles CA 90007

UEBERROTH, JOHN A., air transportation executive; b. Phila., 1944. Student, U. Calif., Berkeley, U. So. Calif. Formerly pres. Ask Mr. Foster Travel, Encino, Calif.; formerly v.p. TCU Travel Corp.; formerly pres., COO 1st Travel Corp., Van Nuys, Calif.; with Carlson Travel Group, Mpls., 1983-89, Contrarian Group Inc., Newport Beach, Calif., 1989—; chmn. bd., CEO Hawaiian Airlines, Inc., 1990—, also bd. dirs. Office: Hawaiian Airlines Inc PO Box 30008 Honolulu HI 96820 also: First Travel Corp 7833 Haskell Ave Van Nuys CA 91406-1908 also: Carlson Cos Inc 12755 State Hwy 55 Minneapolis MN 55441

UECKER, BOB, actor, radio announcer, former baseball player, TV personality; b. Milw., Jan. 26, 1935; m. Judy Uecker. Major league baseball player Milw. Braves, Nat. League, 1962, 63; major league baseball player St. Louis Cardinals, 1964, 65, Phila. Phillies, 1966-67, Atlanta Braves, 1967; radio-TV announcer Milw. Brewers, 1971—; commentator ABC Monday Night Baseball, 1976-82. Co-star TV series Mr. Belvedere, ABC-TV, 1985—; guest TV appearances include: Late Night with David Letterman, The Tonight Show, Midnight Special; also numerous commls.; author: Catcher in the Wry, 1985; films include: Major League, 1989, Major League 2, 1994. Office: care Milw Brewers Publicity Office County Stadium Milwaukee WI 53214*

UECKER, WILFRED CHARLES, accountant, educator; b. San Antonio, Sept. 13, 1944; s. Fred and Hilda (Poss) U.; m. Susan Laura Persons, Apr. 29, 1967; 1 child, Christopher. BA, U. Tex., 1968, MBA, 1970, PhD, 1973. CPA, Tex. Staff acct. Touche Ross & Co., Austin, Tex., 1969-70; prof. acctg. U. Iowa, Iowa City, 1973-84; Whittington prof. of acctg. Jesse H. Jones Grad. Sch. Rice Univ., Houston, 1984—, assoc. dean, 1986—, dir. masters of acctg. program, 1986—; lectr. various colls. and univs. Contbr. articles to profl. jours. Doctoral Dissertation fellow Arthur Andersen Found., 1972; auditing grantee Peat Marwick Mitchell Found., 1979; Taxation grantee Arthur Young Found., 1984; Acctg. Edn. grantee Touche Ross Found., 1982; recipient manuscript award Am. Taxation Assn. 1988, Arthur Young tax manuscript award 1989. Mem. Am. Inst. CPAs, Am. Acctg. Assn., Sigma Xi. Club: Sweetwater Country (Sugarland, Tex.). Office: Rice Univ PO Box 1892 Houston TX 77251-1892

UEHLEIN, E(DWARD) CARL, JR., lawyer; b. Boston, May 7, 1941; s. Edward Carl and Elizabeth (Thatcher) U.; m. Judith Taylor, June 16, 1962; children: Christine, Sara. Student, Bowdoin Coll., Brunswick, Maine, 1958-59; BA, Swarthmore Coll., 1962; LLB, Boston Coll., 1965. Bar: Mass. 1965, D.C. 1968. Atty. Nat. Labor Relations Bd., Atlanta, 1965-68; assoc. Morgan, Lewis & Bockius, Washington, 1968-71; exec. asst. to sec. U.S. Dept. Labor, Washington, 1971-73; ptnr. Morgan Lewis & Bockius, Washington, 1973—; sec.-treas. Carlou Corp., Wilmington, Del., 1975-76. Fellow Ford Found., 1961. Mem. ABA, D.C. Bar Assn., Fed. Bar Assn., Bellehaven Country Club, Ballybunion Golf Club, Royal Dornoch Golf Club. Republican. Avocations: travel, golf, reading. Office: Morgan Lewis & Bockius 1800 M St NW Washington DC 20036-5869

UEHLING, BARBARA STANER, academic administrator; b. Wichita, Kans., June 12, 1932; d. Roy W. and Mary Elizabeth (Hilt) Staner; children: Jeffrey Steven, David Edward. B.A., U. Wichita, 1954; M.A., Northwestern U., 1956, Ph.D., 1958; hon. degree, Drury Coll., 1978; LLD (hon.), Ohio State U., 1980. Mem. psychology faculty Oglethorpe U., Atlanta, 1959-64, Emory U., Atlanta, 1966-69; adjl. prof. U. R.I., Kingston, 1970-72; dean Roger Williams Coll., Bristol, R.I., 1972-74; dean arts scis. Ill. State U., Normal, 1974-76; provost U. Okla., Norman, 1976-78; chancellor U. Mo.-Columbia, 1978-86, U. Calif., Santa Barbara, 1987-94; sr. vis. fellow Am. Council Edn., 1987; interim dir. bus./higher edn. forum, 1994—; mem. Pacific Rim Pub. U. Pres. Conf., 1990—; cons. North Ctrl. Accreditation Assn., 1974-86; mem. nat. educator adv. com. to Compt. Gen. of U.S., 1978-79; mem. Commn. on Mil.-Higher Edn. Rels., Am. Coun. on Edn., 1978-86, bd. dirs. 1979-83, treas., 1982-83, mem. Bus.-Higher Edn. Forum, 1980-94, exec. com. 1991-94; Commn. on Internat. Edn., 1992-94, vice chair 1993; bd. dirs. Coun. on Postsecondary Edn., 1986-87, 90-93, Meredith Corp., 1980—; mem. Transatlantic Dialogue, PEW Found., 1991-93. Author: Women in Academe: Steps to Greater Equality, 1979; editorial bd. Jour. Higher Edn. Mgmt., 1986—; contbr. articles to profl. jours. Bd. dirs., chmn. Nat. Ctr. Higher Edn. Mgmt. Sys., 1977-80; trustee Carnegie Found. for Advancement of Teaching, 1980-86, Santa Barbara Med. Found. Clinic, 1989-94; bd. dirs. Resources for the Futrue, 1985-94; mem. select com. on athletics NCAA, 1983-84, also mem. presdl. commn.; mem. Nat. Coun. on Edn. Rsch., 1980-82. Social Sci. Research Council fellow, 1954-55; NSF fellow, 1956-57; NIMH postdoctoral research fellow, 1964-67; named one of 100 Young Leaders of Acad. Change Mag. and ACE, 1978; recipient Alumni Achievement award Wichita State U., 1978, Alumnae award Northwestern U., 1985, Excellence in Edn. award Pi Lambda Theta, 1989. Mem. Am. Assn. Higher Edn. (bd. dirs. 1974-77, pres. 1977-78), Western Coll. Assn. (pres.-elect 1988-89,k pres. 1990-92), Golden Key, Sigma Xi. Office: Bus-Higher Edn Forum One Dupont Cir Ste 250 Washington DC 20036

UEHLINGER, JOHN CLARK, marketing executive; b. Annapolis, Md., June 28, 1929; s. Archibald Emil and Maran Hazel (Clark) U.; m. Patsy Ann Stewart, Jan. 24, 1959 (dec. Jan. 9, 1991); children: James Williamson, Jennifer Ann, David Douglas, Sarah Elizabeth, Susannah Rachel; m. Gloria Kent Haggard, Sept. 19, 1992. BA, George Washington U., Washington, 1951; MS in Mgmt., USN Postgrad. Sch. Monterey, Calif., 1966; postgrad., Naval War Coll. Newport, R.I., 1970-71, George Washington U., Washington, 1972-73. Cert. pers. subspecialist, USN. Commd. ensign USN, 1951, advanced through grades to comdr., 1973; comdg. officer USS Moctobi, 1960-62, USS Alfred A. Cunningham, 1969-70; adminstrv. officer Leonard Wood Meml., Washington, 1973-77; asst. exec. dir. Am. Congress on Surveying and Mapping, Falls Church, Va., 1977-81, exec. dir., treas., 1981-86; mktg. dir. Systems, Analyses, Instrumentation and Devel., Inc., Falls Church, 1986—. Mem. Alexandria Rep. City Com., 1978-84. Recipient Sec of Navy Commendation medal, 1969. Mem. Delta Tau Delta.

UELAND, SIGURD, JR., lawyer; b. Mpls., June 1, 1937; s. Sigurd and Harriet (Scofield) U.; m. Harriet Moulton, Dec. 27, 1963; children: Scott, Leif, Tora, Sigurd III. B.A., Yale U., 1959; LL.B., U. Minn., 1962. Bar: Minn. 1963. Asso. firm Neville, Johnson & Thompson, Mpls., 1963-67; corp. atty. Whirlpool Corp., Benton Harbor, Mich., 1968-69, Honeywell Inc., Mpls., 1969—; sec. Honeywell Inc., 1977—, asst. gen. counsel, 1980—, v.p., 1983—. Mem. ABA, Am. Soc. Corp. Secs., Minn. Bar Assn., Hennepin County Bar Assn. Congregationalist. Home: 4900 Mongan Ave S Minneapolis MN 55409 Office: Honeywell Plaza Minneapolis MN 55408

UELSMANN, JERRY NORMAN, photographer; b. Detroit, June 11, 1934; s. Norman Charles and Florence Gertrude (Crossman) U. B.F.A., Rochester (N.Y.) Inst. Tech., 1957; M.S., Ind. U., 1958, M.F.A., 1960. Mem. faculty U. Fla., Gainesville, 1960—; grad. research prof. photography U. Fla., 1974—; William A. Reedy meml. lectr. Rochester Inst. Tech., 1988; mem. Kodak Ednl. Adv. Coun., 1987-90. One-man exhbns. include, Mus. Modern Art, N.Y.C., 1967, Art Inst. Chgo., 1972, Phila. Mus. Art, 1970, San Francisco Mus. Modern Art, 1977, The Crown Gallery, Houston, 1978, Worchester (Mass.) Art Mus., 1978, Nova Gallery, Vancouver, B.C., Can., 1979, Photographers Gallery, South Yarra, Australia, 1979, Columbia Coll., Chgo., 1980, Impressions Gallery of Photography, London, 1980, Atlanta Gallery of Photography, 1980, Deja Vue Gallery, Toronto, Ont., Can., Stephen White Gallery, Los Angeles, 1980, Baker Art Gallery, Kansas City, Mo., 1981, JEB Gallery, Inc., Providence, 1981, Eclipse Gallery, Boulder, Colo., 1982, Keystone Gallery, Santa Barbara, Calif., 1982, Images Gallery, Cin., 1982, Virginia Miller Galleries, Coral Gables, Fla., 1983, Weston Gallery, Carmel, Calif., 1983, G.H. Dalsheimer Gallery, Balt., 1983, Silver Images Gallery, Seattle, 1984, Cultural Ctr. of U.S.A., Istanbul, Turkey, 1984, Susan Spiritus Gallery, Newport Beach, Calif., 1984, 87, Daytona Beach (Fla.) Community Coll., 1985, Scheinbaum & Russek Gallery, Santa Fe, 1985, Boston Athenaeum, 1985, U. Fla., Gainesville, 1986, Mus. Fine Arts, St. Petersburg, 1986, Wesleyan U., Middleton, Conn., 1986, Gallery for Fine Photography, New Orleans, 1986, Gail Severn Gallery, Ketchum, Idaho, 1987, Photo Forum Gallery, Pitts., 1987, Carl Solway Gallery, Cin., 1987, Cheekwood Fine Arts Ctr., Nashville, 1988, 89, 90, Galerie Zur Stockeregg, Zurich, 1988, A Gallery for Fine Photography, New Orleans, 1989, Jacques Baruch Gallery, Ltd., Chgo., 1989, Dayton Art Inst., 1990, Kennesaw State Coll., Marietta, Ga., 1990,

Spectrum Gallery, Rochester, N.Y., 1990, Fay Gold Gallery, Atlanta, 1991, Orange County Ctr. Contemporary Art, Santa Ana, Calif., 1991, Witkin Gallery, N.Y.C., 1991, Fla. Sch. of Arts, Palatka, 1992, Joslyn Art Mus., Omaha, 1992, Gallery at City Hall, Orlando, Fla., 1992, Ctr. Photographic Art, Carmel, Calif., 1992, Morgan Gallery, Kans. City, Mo., 1993, Photo Gallery Internat., Tokyo, 1993, Robert Klein Gallery, Boston, 1993, others; retrospective Harn Mus. Art U. Fla., 1994; rep. permanent collections, Mus. Modern Art, Nat. Gallery Can., Victoria and Albert Mus., London, Fogg Mus. at Harvard U., Mus. Fine Arts, Boston., George Eastman House, Rochester, N.Y., Art. Inst. Chgo., Phila. Mus. Art, Mpls. Art Inst., San Francisco Mus. Modern Art, Ctr. for Creative Photography, Tucson, Moderna Museet, Stockholm, Royal Photog. Soc., London, Bibliotheque Nat., Paris, Musee Reattu, Arles, France, Nat. Gallery Australia, Melbourne, Nihon U., Tokyo, Art Mus., Ind. U., Bloomington, Princeton (N.J.) U. Art Mus., Nat. Mus. Am. Art, Washington, Chgo. Ctr. for Contemporary Photography, Chgo., Nat. Mus. Modern Art, Kyoto, Japan, Seattle Art Mus., Gallery of Modern Art of Nat. Galleries Scotland, Polaroid Collection, Cambridge, Mass., St. Petersburg (Fla.) Mus. Art, Tampa (Fla.) Mus. Art, Tokyo Met. Mus. Photography, Danforth Mus. Art, Framingham, Mass., Met. Mus. Art N.Y. (poster made of one photograph 1988); subject of monograph: Jerry N. Uelsmann, 1970, Jerry N. Uelsmann: Silver Meditations, 1975, Jerry N. Uelsmann Twenty-five Years: A Retrospective, 1982; author: Process and Perception, 1985, Photo-Synthesis, 1992. Recipient Photographer award for Outstanding Achievement Photographic Soc. Japan, 1992, First Place Photographic Book of Yr. award Maine Photographic Workshops, Rockport, 1992; NEA photographer's fellow, 1972, U. Fla. grantee, 1971, Guggenheim fellow, 1967; inducted into the Fla. Artists Hall of Fame, 1994. Fellow Royal Photog. Soc. Gt. Britain; mem. Soc. Photog. Edn. (a founder, bd. dirs.), Friends of Photography, Internat. Mus. Photography at George Eastman House. Home: 5701 SW 17th Dr Gainesville FL 32608-5365 Office: Art Dept Univ Fla Gainesville FL 32611

UENO, HIROSHI, biochemist; b. Sakai, Osaka, Japan, Dec. 9, 1950; s. Haruko (Hachihama) U.; m. Naomi Matsuzaki, Feb. 11, 1978; 1 child, Leo Dale. BE, Kyoto U., 1974; MA, Brandeis U., 1976; PhD in Biochemistry, Iowa State U., 1982. Rsch. assoc. Rockefeller U., N.Y.C., 1982-83, Rockefeller Found. fellow, 1984-85, asst. prof. biochemistry, 1986—; summer investigator Woods Hole Marine Biology Laboratory, 1984—; vis. scientistPop Coun., 1984—; mem. Ad Hoc com Nat. Heart, Lung, & Blood Inst. NIH, Bethesda, Md., 1987—; mem. organizing com. 8th Internat. Congress on Vitamin B6 and Carbonyl Catalysis, Osaka, 1990; vis. prof. Kumamoto U., Japan, 1990. Recipient Molly Berns Meml. Investigator, Am. Heart Assn., 1989—. Mem. Am. Soc. Biochemistry and Molecular Biology, Am. Chem. Soc., Harvey Soc., N.Y. Acad. Scis. Research in chemistry of Gossypol, transaminases, hemoglobins. Home: 500 E 63rd St New York NY 10021-7946 Office: Dept Med Chem Lab Osaka Med Coll, 2-7 Daigakumachi Takatsuki, Osaka 569, Japan

UFFELMAN, MALCOLM RUCJ, electronics company executive, electrical engineer; b. Clarksville, Tenn., Oct. 22, 1935; s. Malcolm C. and Margaret Lillian (Davidson) U.; m. Sarah White Barksdale, June 11, 1957; children: Malcolm Rucj Jr., Katharina White, Davidson Barksdale, Jefferson Churchill. BS, Vanderbilt U., 1957; MS, George Washington U., 1963. Engr. Melpar, Inc., Falls Church, Va., 1957-60; v.p. Scope, Inc., Reston, Va., 1960-73; sr. cons. MRI, Inc., McLean, Va., 1973-78; v.p. Racal Communications Inc., Rockville, Md., 1978-80; sr. cons. MRJ, Inc., Fairfax, Va., 1980-82; v.p., gen. mgr., Ctr. Advanced Planning and Analysis E-Systems Inc., Fairfax, 1982—; pvt. practice patent agt., Vienna, Va., 1975—. Contbr. numerous articles to profl. jours.; holder 7 patents in field. Scoutmaster Troop 183 Boy Scouts Am., Oakton, Va., 1973-79. Capt. USAR, 1957-69. Fellow IEEE, AIAA (assoc.); mem. N.Y. Acad. Scis., Assn. Old Crows, Navy League, Cosmos Club (Washington). Republican. Episcopalian. Avocations: tennis, sailing, reading, travel. Office: E-Systems Inc Ctr Advance Planning 10530 Rosehaven St Fairfax VA 22030-2840

UFFEN, ROBERT JAMES, geophysics educator, engineer; b. Toronto, Ont., Can., Sept. 21, 1923; s. James Frederick and Elsie May (Harris) U.; m. Mary Ruth Paterson, May 3, 1949; children: Joanne, Robert. B Applied Sci., U. Toronto, 1949, MA, 1950; PhD, U. Western Ont., 1952, DSc (hon.), 1970; DSc (hon.), Queen's U., 1967, Royal Mil. Coll., 1978, McMaster U., 1983. Registered profl. engr., Ont. Prin. univ. coll U. Western Ont., London, 1961-65, dean Coll. Sci., 1965-66; chmn. def. research bd. Govt. of Can., Ottawa, Ont., 1967-69, chief sci. advisor to cabinet, 1969-71; dean applied sci Queen's U., Kingston, Ont., 1971-80, prof. geophysics, 1971-89, prof. emeritus, 1989—, coordinator summer program for sci. tchrs., 1986-89; bd. dirs. Ctr. for Resource Studies; mem. NRC Can., 1963-66, Sci. Council Can., 1967-71; chmn. Can. Engring. Manpower Council, 1972-74; mem. Fisheries Research Bd. Can., 1975-78. Contbr. articles to profl. jours. Bd. regents Colls. Applied Arts and Tech., Ont., 1966-75; mem. com. on Hydro, 1975-79; mem. Royal Commn. on Asbestos, Ont., 1980-84, Truck Safety Commn., Ont., 1981-83; chmn. Ont. Exploration Tech. Fund, 1980-83; mem. com. on nuclear waste mgmt. Atomic Energy Can. Ltd., 1988-91; adv. bd. Extendicare, Kingston, 1993—. Lt. Royal Can. Arty., 1941-45. Decorated officer Order of Can., 1983; named to U. Toronto Engring. Alumni Hall of Distinction, 1990; recipient Centennial Medal, Can., 1967, Disting. Svc. award Queen's U., 1990, 125th Anniversary medal Can., 1992, John Orr award Queen's U., 1993. Fellow AAAS, Royal Soc. Can., Geol. Soc. Am., Can. Acad. Engring.; mem. Assn. Profl. Engrs. Ont. (councillor 1975-79, Citizenship award 1985). Avocations: old bottles, painting. Home: 1504 185 Ontario St, Kingston, ON Canada K7L 2Y7 Office: Queen's U, Bruce Hall, Kingston, ON Canada K7L 3N6

UFFORD, CHARLES WILBUR, JR., lawyer; b. Princeton, N.J., July 8, 1931; m. Isabel Letitia Wheeler, May 20, 1961; children: Eleanor Morris Ufford Léger, Catherine Latourette Ufford-Chase, Alison Wistar Ufford Salem. BA cum laude (Francis H. Burr scholar), Harvard U., 1953, LLB, 1959; postgrad. (Lionel de Jersey Harvard studentship), Cambridge U., Eng., 1953-54. Bar: N.Y. 1961, U.S. Tax Ct. 1963. Assoc. Riggs, Ferris & Geer, N.Y.C., 1959-61; assoc. Jackson, Nash, Brophy, Barringer & Brooks, 1961-69, ptnr., 1969-78; ptnr. Skadden, Arps, Slate, Meagher & Flom, N.Y.C., 1978-92, of counsel, 1993—. Contbr. articles to legal jours. Trustee Nat. Squash Racquets Ednl. Found., N.Y.C., 1972-81; mem. Princeton monthly meeting Soc. of Friends, clk., 1986-88. Nat. Intercollegiate Squash Racquets champion, 1952-53; mem. NCAA All-Am. Soccer lst team, 1952. Fellow Am. Coll. Trust and Estate Counsel (transfer tax study com. 1990-93); mem. ABA, N.Y. Bar Assn. (chmn. trusts and estates law sect. 1984), Assn. Bar City N.Y., Internat. Acad. Trusts and Estates Law, U.S. Squash Racquets Assn. (hon. life; trustee endowment fund 1984—), Internat. Lawn Tennis Club U.S.A. (dir. 1982—). Home: 150 Mercer St Princeton NJ 08540-6827 Office: Skadden Arps Slate Meagher & Flom 919 3d Ave New York NY 10022-3903 *Integrity, perseverance, compassion and humor are all very well—but the key is to be blessed by a Divine Improvidence.*

UFIMTSEV, PYOTR YAKOVLEVICH, physicist, electrical engineer, educator; b. Ust'-Charyshskaya Pristan', Altai Region, Russia, Russia, July 8, 1931; s. Yakov Fedorovich and Vasilisa Vasil'evna (Toropchina) U.; m. Vera M. Umnova, 1958 (div. 1968); 1 child, Galina; m. Tatiana Vladimirovna Sinelschikova, May 3, 1986; children: Ivan, Vladimir. Grad., Odessa State U., USSR, 1954; PhD, Cen. Rsch. Inst. of Radio Industry, Moscow, 1959; DSc, St. Petersburg State U., Russia, 1970. Engr., sr. engr., sr. scientist Cen. Rsch. Inst. of Radio Industry, Moscow, 1954-73; sr. scientist Inst. Radio Engring. & Electronics Acad. Scis., Moscow, 1973-90; vis. prof., adj. prof. UCLA, 1990—; mem. Sci. Bd. of Radio Waves, Acad. Scis., Moscow, 1960-90. Author: Method of Edge Waves in the Physical Theory of Diffraction, 1962; contbr. articles to profl. jours. Recipient USSR State Prize, Moscow, 1990, Leroy Randle Grummann medal for outstanding sci. achievement, N.Y.C., 1991. Mem. AIAA, IEEE, Electromagnetics Acad. (U.S.), A.S. Popov Sci. Tech. Soc. Radio Engring., Electronics & Telecommunication (Russia). Achievements include origination of the Physical Theory of Diffraction, used for design of American stealth aircrafts and ships; for radarcross-section calculation and antenna design. Office: UCLA Dept Elec Engring 405 Hilgard Ave Los Angeles CA 90095-1594

UGHETTA, WILLIAM CASPER, lawyer, manufacturing company executive; b. N.Y.C., Feb. 8, 1933; s. Casper and Frieda (Bohland) U.; m. Mary L. Lusk, Aug. 10, 1957; children: William C., Robert L., Edward F., Mark

R. A.B., Princeton U., 1954; LL.B. Harvard U., 1959. Bar: N.Y. 1959. Assoc. Shearman & Sterling, N.Y.C., 1959-67; asst. sec. Corning Glass Works, N.Y., 1968-70, sec., counsel, 1971-72, v.p., gen. counsel, 1972-82, sr. v.p., gen. counsel, 1983—; bd. dirs. Corning Internat. Corp., Siecor Corp., Corning Europe Inc., Corning France, Chemung Canal Trust Co. Bd. dirs. Steuben Area coun. Boy Scouts Am.; officer Corning Mus. Glass, Corning Glass Works Found.; trustee Corning Community Coll. Served to lt. (j.g.) U.S. Navy, 1954-56. Mem. Am. Bar. City N.Y., ABA, N.Y. State Bar Assn., Am. Corp. Counsel Assn. (trustee 1982-85). Clubs: Princeton (N.Y.C.), Univ. (N.Y.C.); Corning Country. Home: 13 North Rd Corning NY 14830-3235 Office: Corning Inc 1 Riverfront Plz Corning NY 14831

UGRIN, BÉLA, video producer; b. Endröd, Hungary, July 19, 1928; came to U.S., 1962, naturalized, 1967; s. Gáspár and Regina (Gyuricza) U.; m. Emmanuella Caravageli, Feb. 12, 1964; 1 son, Gregory Alexander. Grad., Inst. Photojournalism, Munich, N.Y., mem., 1960; BA, U. Houston, 1977; MA, Tex. So. U., 1980; PhD in Edn., Southwest U., 1994. Freelance mag. photographer Munich, and N.Y.C., 1959-66; chief photographer Westport (Conn.) News, 1967-69; staff photographer Houston Post, 1969-77, chief photographer, 1978-84; pres., exec. producer Belvideo & Mult-Media Inc., 1992—; producer-dir. Houston Ind. Sch. Dist. Media Svcs. TV, 1988—; pres. Belvideo & MUltimedia Inc., 1992—; lectr. in field. Ind. film producer, 1985—; assoc. dir. Houston ISD Dept. Tech. 1986-88; producer-dir., cultural TV documentary Andre Kertesz: A Poet With the Camera, 1986 (Silver award Houston Internat. Film Festival, 1986); edn. video series including Take Command, 1986-87, Technology and Education Today, 1988; single TV programs including Tomorrow's Teacher, 1989, Visual Literacy, 1989, Top Teachers, 1989, Profession at Risk, 1990, Photo Fence, 1990, Cinco de Mayo, 1990, People Place, 1990, Global Schoolhouse, 1990 (Gold award Pub. Rels. Soc. Am. 1991), Teacher Induction: The Houston Model, 1991, Alternative Certification Program, 1991, Partners in Education, 1991, The Business Connection, 1991, Communities in Schools, 1992, Teachers for America 2000, 1992, Multimedia Instruction, 1992, A New Source for Teachers, 1992, Distance Learning, 1993, Doing Business with Hungary, 1993, School Safety and Violence, 1993, ACP's Growth and Success, 1994, Media Literacy, 1993, Armadillos on the Superhighway, 1994, Foreign Languages, 1994, Dual Language Class, 1995, "PEER"-HISD's Major Checkup, 1995; contbr. articles on video prodns., photography and travel to various publs. Mem. Soc. Profl. Journalists, Internat. TV Assn.

UGWU, DAVID EGBO, academic director, consulting company executive; b. Enugu, Anambra, Nigeria, Dec. 6, 1950; came to U.S., 1974; s. Ugwu Nwamba Enyiduru and Ujo (Nnaji) Ugwu; m. Patricia Ifeoma, Jan. 5, 1979; children: Chiugo, Adaeze, Oguejiofor, Chidiebere. BS in Chem. Engring., Mich. Tech. U., 1978; MBA, Gov.'s State U., 1981; PhD in Higher Edn., So. Ill. U., 1985, MS in Mech. Engring., 1991, MSME, 1991. Chem. analyst Nigerian Cement Co., Nkalagu, 1971-74; sales rep. Southwest Pub. Co., Nashville, 1975-76, Dumbo Enterprises, Inc., Detroit, 1977-78; plant engr., project engr. Union Carbide Corp., East Chicago, Ind., 1978-83; rsch. devel. specialist Coal Rsch. Ctr./So. Ill. U., Carbondale, 1983-85; researcher dept. mech. engring. So. Ill. U., Carbondale, 1985-87; dir. rsch. and grants Ariz. Western Coll., Yuma, 1987-89; dir. Inst. Planning and Rsch. Lorain County Community Coll., Elyria, Ohio, 1990—; pres. Eagle Consulting and Contracting Svcs. Co., Elyria, 1990—; cons. U.S. Dept. Edn., Washington, 1990—. Co-author: Chemical Desulfurization of Coal, 1987; contbr. to profl. jours. Fellow Post Doctoral Acad. Higher Edn.; mem. Am. Inst. Chem. Engring., Assn. Instl. Researchers, Toastmasters Internat., Kappa Delta Pi. Avocations: tennis, soccer. Home: 107 Dorset Ct Elyria OH 44035-3840 Office: Lorain County 1005 Abbe Rd N Elyria OH 44035-1613

UHDE, GEORGE IRVIN, physician; b. Richmond, Ind., Mar. 20, 1912; s. Walter Richard and Anna Margaret (Hoopes) U.; m. Maurine Elizabeth Whitley, July 27, 1935; children—Saundra Uhde Seelig, Thomas Whitley, Michael, Janice. M.D., Duke U., 1936. Diplomate: Am. Bd. Otolaryngology. Intern Reading (Pa.) Hosp., 1936-37, resident in medicine, 1937-38; resident in otolaryngology Balt. Eye, Ear, Nose and Throat Hosp., 1938-40, U. Oreg. Med. Sch., Portland, 1945-47; practice medicine specializing in otolaryngology Louisville, 1948—; asst. prof. otolaryngology U. Louisville Med. Sch., 1945-62, prof. surgery (otolaryngology), head dept., 1963-92, prof. emeritus, 1992—; dir. otolaryngology services, 1963—; mem. staffs Meth., Norton's-Children's, Jewish, St. Joseph's, St. Anthony's, St. Mary and Elizabeth's hosps.; cons. Ky. Surg. Tb Hosp., Hazlewood, VA Hosp., Louisville, U. Louisville Speech and Hearing Center. Author 4 books.; Contbr. articles to profl. jours. Bd. dirs. Easter Seal Speech and Hearing Ctr. Lt. col. M.C. U.S. Army, 1940-45, ETO, Gen. Eisenhower staff, 1943-45. Recipient Disting. Service award U. Louisville, 1972. Fellow A.C.S., Am. Acad. Ophthalmology and Otolaryngology, So. Med. Soc.; mem. N.Y. Acad. Scis., Am. Coll. Allergists, Am. Acad. Facial Plastic and Reconstructive Surgery, AAAS, Assn. U. Otolaryngologists, AAUP, Assn. Mil. Surgeons U.S., Am. Laryngol., Rhinol. and Otol. Soc., Am. Audiology Soc., Soc. Clin. Ecology, Am. Soc. Otolaryngology Allergy, Centurian Otol. Research Soc. (Ky. rep.), Am. Council Otolaryngology (Ky. rep. 1968-), Hoopes Quaker Found., SAR (life), Gen. Soc. Colonial Wars (hereditary mem.), Alpha Kappa Kappa. Democrat. Methodist. Clubs: Filson, Big Spring Country, Jefferson. Home: 708 Circle Hill Rd Louisville KY 40207-3627 Office: Med Towers Louisville KY 40202

UHER, RICHARD A., rail transportation executive; b. McKeesport, Pa., June 8, 1939; s. John Richard and Josephine Constance (Stewart) U.; m. Janice Joy Smith, June 17, 1961; children: Christopher Richard, Keith David, Michaeleen Marie. BS Physics, Carnegie Mellon U., 1961, MS Physics, 1963, PhD, 1966. Project mgr. Westinghouse Electric Corp., Pitts., 1968-75; dep. dir. Transp. Rsch. Inst. Carnegie Mellon U., Pitts., 1975-78, dir. Rail Systems Ctr., 1978—, dir. High Speed Grand Transp. Ctr., 1988—. Contbr. numerous articles, reports to profl. jours. Mem. ASME, ASCE, Am. Inst. Physics, Assn. R.R. Engrs., Inst. Electrical & Electronic Engrs. (chmn. land transp. com. 1979-80). Avocations: walking, biking. Office: Carnegie Mellon U Rail Sys Ctr PO Box 2950 700 Technology Dr Pittsburgh PA 15230-2950

UHLENBECK, KAREN KESKULLA, mathematician, educator; b. Cleve., Aug. 24, 1942; d. Arnold Edward and Carolyn Elizabeth (Windeler) Keskulla; m. Olke Cornelis, June 12, 1965 (div.). B.S. in Math., U. Mich., 1964; Ph.D. in Math., Brandeis U., 1968. Instr. math. MIT, Cambridge, 1968-69; lectr. U. Calif.-Berkeley, 1969-71; asst. prof., then assoc. prof. U. Ill., Urbana, 1971-76; assoc. prof., then prof. U. Ill., Chgo., 1977-83; prof. U. Chgo., 1983-88; Sid W. Richardson Found. Regents' Chair in Math. U. Tex., 1988—; speaker plenary address Internat. Congress Maths., 1990; mem. com. women on sci. and engring. Nat. Rsch. Coun., 1992-94; mem. steering com. dir. mentoring program for women IAS/PCMI. Author: Instantons and Four Manifolds, 1984. Contbr. articles to profl. jours. NSF Grad. fellow, 1964-68, Sloan Found. fellow, 1974-76, MacArthur Found. fellow, 1983-88; recipient Alumni Achievement award Brandeis U., 1988. Mem. AAAS, NAS, Alumni Assn. U. Mich. (Alumnae of Yr. 1984), Am. Math. Soc., Assn. Women in Math., Phi Beta Kappa. Avocations: gardening, canoeing, hiking. Office: U Tex Dept Math Austin TX 78712

UHLENHUTH, EBERHARD HENRY, psychiatrist, educator; b. Balt., Sept. 15, 1927; s. Eduard Carl Adolph and Elisabeth (Baier) U.; m. Helen Virginia Lyman, June 20, 1952; children: Kim Lyman, Karen Jane, Eric Rolf. BS in Chemistry, Yale U., 1947; MD, Johns Hopkins U., 1951. Intern Harborview Hosp., Seattle, 1951-52; resident in psychiatry Johns Hopkins Hosp., Balt., 1952-56; asst. psychiatrist in charge outpatient dept. Johns Hopkins Hosp., 1956-61, psychiatrist in charge, 1961-62; chief adult psychiatry clinic U. Chgo. Hosps. Clinics, 1968-76; instr. psychiatry Johns Hopkins U., 1956-59, asst. prof., 1959-67, assoc. prof., 1967-68; assoc. prof. U. Chgo., 1968-73, prof., 1973-85, acting chmn. 1983-85; prof. psychiatry U. N.Mex., Albuquerque, 1985—, vice chmn. of dept. in field., 1991-94; cons. in field; mem. clin. psychopharmacology rsch. rev. com. NIMH, 1968-72, treatment devel. and assessment rev. com., 1987; mem. psychopharmacology adv. com. FDA, 1974-78; mem. adv. group to Treatment of Depression Collaborative Rsch. Program, NIMH, 1978-92; study rev. com. Xanax Discontinuation Program, The U.pJohn Co., 1988-92, Nat. Adv. Coun. on Drug Abuse, NIDA, 1989-92, Coop. Studies Evaluation Com., VA, 1989-92. Mem. editorial bd. Jour. Affective Disorders, 1978—, Psychiatry Rsch., 1979—, Behavioral Medicine,

1982—, Neuropsychopharmacology, 1992—; Exptl. and Clin. Psychopharmacology, 1992—, Anxiety, 1993—; contbr. articles to profl. jours. Recipient Research Career Devel. award USPHS, 1962-68, Research Scientist award, 1976-81. Fellow Am. Coll. Neuropsychopharmacology (pres. 1986), Am. Psychiat. Assn., Am. Psychopath. Assn.; mem. AAAS, Balt.-Washington Soc. for Psychoanalysis, Collegium Internat. Neuro-Psychopharmacologicum, Soc. for Neurosci., Psychiat. Rsch. Soc., Am. Soc. Clin. Psychopharmacology. Office: U NMex Dept Psychiatry 2400 Tucker NE Albuquerque NM 87131

UHLIR, ARTHUR, JR., electrical engineer, university administrator; b. Chgo., Feb. 2, 1926; s. Arthur and Helene (Houghteling) U.; m. Ingeborg Williams, July 24, 1954; children—Steven, Donald, David. B.S., Ill. Inst. Tech., 1945, M.S. in Chem. Engring., 1948; S.M. in Physics, U. Chgo., 1950, Ph.D. in Physics, 1952. Process analyst Douglas Aircraft, Chgo., 1945; asst. engr. Armour Research Found., Chgo., 1945-48; mem. tech. staff Bell Telephone Labs., Murray Hill, N.J., 1951-58; dir. semi- condr. research and devel., mgr. semicondr. div., group v.p. engring. Microwave Assos., Inc., Burlington, Mass., 1958-69; dir. research Computer Metrics, Rochelle Park, N.J., 1969-73; prof. elec. engring. Tufts U., Medford, Mass., 1970-94; chmn. dept. elec. engring. Tufts U., 1970-75, dean of engring., 1973-80. AEC fellow, 1949-51. Fellow IEEE, AAAS; mem. Am. Phys. Soc., Sigma Xi. Home: 45 Kendal Common Rd Weston MA 02193-2159 Office: Elec Engring Dept Tufts Univ Medford MA 02155

UHLMANN, FREDERICK GODFREY, commodity and securities broker; b. Chgo., Dec. 31, 1929; s. Richard F. and Rosamond G. (Goldman) U.; m. Virginia Lee Strauss, July 24, 1951; children: Richard, Thomas, Virginia, Karen, Elizabeth. B.A., Washington and Lee U., 1951. Ptnr. Uhlmann Grain Co., Chgo., 1951-61; v.p. Uhlmann & Co., Inc., Chgo., 1961-65; sr. v.p. H. Hentz & Co., Chgo., 1965-73, Drexel Burnham Lambert Inc., Chgo., 1973-84; exec. v.p., dir. bus. futures Dean Witter Reynolds Inc., Chgo., 1984-85; sr. v.p., mgr. commodity dept. Bear, Stearns & Co., Inc., Chgo., 1985-88; exec. v.p. Rodman & Renshaw, Inc., 1988—; chmn. Chgo. Bd. Trade, 1973-74. Trustee Highland Park Hosp., Ill.; bd. dirs. Dist. 113 H.S. Found., 1990—. Mem. Nat. Futures Assn. (dir. 1981—), Futures Industry Assn. (bd. dirs., chmn. 1975-76). Clubs: Lake Shore Country (Glencoe, Ill.) (dir.); Standard (Chgo.). Home: 783 Whiteoaks Ln Highland Park IL 60035-3656

UHRICH, RICHARD BECKLEY, hospital executive, physician; b. Pitts., June 11, 1932; s. Leroy Earl and Mabel Hoffer (Beckley) U.; m. Susan Kay Manning, May 25, 1985; children by previous marriage—Mark, Karen, Kimberly. B.S., Allegheny Coll., 1954; M.D., U. Pa., 1958; M.P.H., U. Calif.-Berkeley, 1966. Diplomate: Am. Bd. Preventive Medicine. Intern Lancaster Gen. Hosp., (Pa.), 1958-59; commd. asst. surg. USPHS, 1959, advanced through grades to med. dir., 1967; resident U. Calif., 1965-66; various adminstrv. positions regional and service unit levels Indian Health Services, until 1971; dir. div. programs ops. Indian Health Service, Health Services Adminstrn. USPHS, Washington, 1971-73; assoc. dir. div. profl. resources Office Internat. Health, Office Asst. Sec. for Health, HEW, Washington, 1973-74; assoc. dir. for program devel. and coordination Office Internat. Health, 1974-78; dir. Phoenix Indian Med. Ctr. and Phoenix Services Unit, 1978-81, ret.; mgr. sr. adminstr. Good Samaritan Med Ctr., Phoenix, 1981-82, chief exec. officer, 1982-89; v.p. for managed care programs Samaritan Health Svcs., Phoenix, 1989-90; cons. health care systems Phoenix, 1990-93; dir. S.E. Asia, internat. dir. Med. Ambs. Internat., Modesto, Calif., 1993—; mem. Phoenix Regional Hosp. Coun., 1981-88, pres., 1982-83; bd. dirs. Med. Ctr. Redevel. Corp., Phoenix; v.p. Samaritan Redevel. Corp., 1983-88. Bd. dirs. Phoenix Symphony Orch., 1984-89, Ariz. Sr. Olympics Bd., 1985-89. Recipient Meritorious Service medal USPHS, 1973; recipient citation USPHS, 1973, Commd. Officers award, 1981. Mem. Ariz. Hosp. Assn. (bd. dirs. 1980-86, chmn. council on planning 1980-81, council on human resources 1982-83, council on patient care 1983-84, fin. com. 1984-86), Am. Coll. Health Care Adminstrs., Am. Pub. Health Assn., Christian Med. Soc.

UHRIG, ROBERT EUGENE, nuclear engineer, educator; b. Raymond, Ill., Aug. 6, 1928; s. John Matthew and Anna LaDonna (Fireman) U.; m. Paula Margaret Schnepf, Nov. 27, 1954; children: Robert John, Joseph Charles, Mary Catherine, Charles William, Jean Marie, Thomas Paul, Frederick James. B.S. with honors, U. Ill., 1948; M.S. Iowa State U., 1950, Ph.D. 1954; grad. Advanced Mgmt. Program, Harvard U., 1976. Registered profl. engr., Iowa, Fla. Instr. engring. mechanics Iowa State U., 1948-51; assoc. engr., research asst. Inst. Atomic Research (at univ.), 1951-54, assoc. prof. engring. mechanics and nuclear engring., also group leader, 1956-60; prof. nuclear engring., chmn. dept. U. Fla., Gainesville, 1960-68; on leave U. Fla., 1967-68, dean Coll. Engring., 1968-73; dean emeritus, 1989—; dep. asst. dir. research Dept. Def., Washington, 1967-68; dir. nuclear affairs Fla. Power & Light Co., Miami, 1973-74; v.p. for nuclear affairs Fla. Power & Light Co., 1974-75, v.p. nuclear and gen. engring., 1976-78, v.p. advanced systems and tech., 1978-86; disting. prof. engring. U. Tenn., Knoxville, 1986—; disting. scientist Oak Ridge Nat. Lab., 1986—; Rep. Dept. Def. to com. on acad. sci. and engring. Fed. Council Sci. and Tech., 1967; chmn. engring. adv. com. NSF, 1972-73; bd. dirs. Engring. Council Profl. Devel., 1968-72; mem. commn. edn. for engring. profession Nat. Assn. State Univs. and Land Grant Colls., 1969-72. Author: Random Noise Techniques in Nuclear Reactor Systems, 1970, trans. into Russian, 1974. Served to 1st lt. USAF; instr. engring. mechanics U.S. Mil. Acad. 1954-56. Recipient Sec. of Def. Civilian Service award, 1968, Outstanding Alumni award U. Ill. Coll. Engring., 1970, Alumni Profl. Achievement award Iowa State U., 1972, President's medallion U. Fla., 1973; Disting. Achievement citation Iowa State U. Alumni Assn., 1980, Glenn Murphy awd., Am. Soc. for Engineering Education, 1992. Fellow ASME (life, Richards Meml. award 1969), AAAS, Am. Nuclear Soc. (chmn. edn. com. 1962-64, chmn. tech. group for edn. 1964-66, dir. 1965-68, exec. com. bd. 1966-68); mem. Am. Soc. Engring. Edn. (pres. S.E. sect. 1972-73, chmn. nuclear engring. divsn. 1966-67, 88-89, rsch. award S.E. sect. 1962, Glenn Murphy award as Outstanding Educator 1992), John Henry Newman Honor Soc., Sigma Xi, Tau Beta Pi, Phi Mu Epsilon, Pi Tau Sigma, Phi Kappa Phi. Home: 113 Connors Dr Oak Ridge TN 37830-7662 Office: U Tenn Pasqua Nuclear Engring Bldg Knoxville TN 37996-2300

UHRY, ALFRED FOX, playwright; b. Atlanta, Dec. 3, 1936; s. Ralph Kahn and Alene (Fox) U.; m. Joanna Kellogg; children: Emily Uhry Rhea, Elizabeth Uhry MacCurrach, Katharine, Nell. BA, Brown U., 1958. worked with composer Frank Loesser, 1960-63; instr. Eng., drama Calhoun High Sch., 1963-80; instr. lyric writing NYU, 1985-88. Author: (play) Driving Miss Daisy, 1987 (Drama Desk award nomination for best play 1987, Pulitzer Prize for drama 1988, L.A. Drama Critics Circle award for best play 1989); (musicals) Chapeau, 1977, (adapter) Little Johnny Jones, 1982, (adapter) Follow Thru, 1984; (lyrics) Here's Where I Belong, 1968, Swing, 1980; (lyrics, libretto) The Robber Bridegroom, 1978 (Drama Desk award nomination for best play 1975, Tony award nomination for best book of a musical 1976), America's Sweetheart, 1985; (screenplays) Mystic Pizza, 1988, Driving Miss Daisy, 1989 (Academy award for best adapted screenplay 1989, WGA award 1989), Rich in Love, 1993. Mem. Dramatists Guild (coun. 1989—, Elizabeth Martow prize 1987). Office: care Flora Roberts 157 W 57th St PH A New York NY 10019*

UICKER, JAMES LEO, mechanical engineer; b. Detroit, Feb. 5, 1943; s. John Joseph and Elizabeth Josephine (Flint) U.; divorced; children: James, John, Mary, William, Martha, Margaret. BSME, U. Detroit, 1966; MS in Mech. Engring., Pa. State U., 1971. Registered profl. engr., Mich. Grad. asst. Pa. State U., Univ. Pk., 1969-71; fuel engr. to combustion engr. Nat. Steel Great Lakes Div., Ecorse, Mich., 1971-79; sr. engr. rotating equipment Detroit Edison, 1979—. Treas. Birmingham (Mich.) PTO, 1985, Boy Scouts Am., Southfield, Mich., 1986; pres. Block Club, Southfield, 1989; v.p. Parent Group, Bloomfield Hills, 1989. 1st lt. U.S. Army, 1967-69 Vietnam. Mem. ASME, NSPE, Engring. Soc. Detroit, Vibration Inst. Republican. Roman Catholic. Avocations: camping, photography, wood working, fishing. Home: 19785 W Twelve Mile Ste 229 Southfield MI 48076 Office: Detroit Edison 6200 W Warren H35A WSC H43 WSC Detroit MI 48210

UICKER, JOSEPH BERNARD, engineering company executive; b. State College, Pa., Mar. 29, 1940; s. John Joseph and Elizabeth Josephine (Flint) U.; m. Mary Catherine Howze, June 5, 1965 (div. Oct. 1971); children:

Patricia, Suzzane; m. Janet Ann Ballman, Sept. 22, 1973. B.S.M.E., U. Detroit, 1963, M.S., 1965. Registered profl. engr., Mich. Engr., Smith Hinchman & Grylls, Detroit, 1964-72, chief mech. engr. health facilities, 1972-73, asst. dir. health facilities, 1973-75, v.p., dir. mech. engring., 1975-82, v.p., dir. profl. staff, 1983—; also dir.; dir. Smith Group, Detroit, 1984—. Served to capt. U.S. Army, 1966-67. Mem. Nat. Soc. Profl. Engrs., ASME, ASHRAE, Soc. Am. Mil. Engrs. Clubs: Engring. Soc., Athletic (Detroit). Avocations: golf; photography; gardening. Home: 15250 Knolson Livonia MI 48154 Office: Smith Group Inc 150 W Jefferson Ave Detroit MI 48226-4429

UILKEMA, GAYLE BURNS, mayor, councilwoman, business educator; b. Detroit, Sept. 2, 1938; d. Joseph A. and Pearl (Rasmussen) Burns; children: Lynn, Sharon. BS in Edn., U. Mich., 1959; MPA, Calif. State U. Hayward, 1987. Instr. bus. edn. and mgmt. subjects Heald Coll., Oakland, Calif., 1961-62; tchr. bus. edn. dept. Oakland High Sch., 1962-66; lectr. Calif. State U. Grad. Sch. Pub. Adminstrn., Hayward; mem. coun. City of Lafayette, 1978—, mayor, 1981-84, 90-91, 94-95; lectr. in field; cons. U. Calif. Ext., Berkeley; adj. prof. John F. Kennedy U. Sch. of Mgmt., Orinda, Calif., 1989—; v.p. Dimensional Resources, Inc., Telecomms. Cons. Mem. Contra Costa Local Agy. Formation Commn., 1986—, commr., former chair, 1986, 95; mem. exec. bd. dirs. state bd. Calif. Assn. Local Agy. Formation Commn.; Lafayette dir., former chair, bd. dirs. Cen. Contra Costa Transit Authority, 1980—, chmn. fin. com., 1981-85, 94, chmn. ops. and scheduling, 1986, dir. ops. and scheduling com., 1987, chmn., 1989, bd. dirs., 1990—. Recipient award Met. Transp. Commn. Bay Area, 1981. Mem. AAUW (bd. dirs. 1971-78, pres. 1972-73, state bd. dirs. 1974-76, nat. rep. 1977-78, Disting. Woman award 1978), Soroptimists Internat. Republican. Roman Catholic. Avocations: tennis, gardening, interior decorating, piano, sewing. Home: 670 Sky Hy Cir Lafayette CA 94549-5228 Office: City of Lafayette PO Box 1968 Lafayette CA 94549-4342

UITTI, KARL DAVID, language educator; b. Calumet, Mich., Dec. 10, 1933; s. Karl Abram and Joy (Weidelman) U.; m. Maria Esther Clark, Feb. 15, 1953 (div. Feb. 1973); children: Maria Elisabeth, Karl Gerard (dec.); m. Michelle Alice Freeman, Mar. 13, 1974; children: David Charles, Jacob Christian. AB, U. Calif., Berkley, 1952, AM, 1952, PhD, 1959; postgrad., Nancy and Bordeaux U., 1952-54. Instr. Princeton U., 1959-61, asst. prof., 1961-65, class of 1936 preceptor, 1963-66, assoc. prof., 1965-68, prof., 1968—, John N. Woodhull prof. modern langs., 1978—, chmn. dept. Romance langs., 1972-78; vis. prof. Universidad de P.R., U. Pa., Queens Coll., U. Iowa, U. Wash., Rutgers U., UCLA, Johns Hopkins U., Ecole Normale Superieure de Saint-Cloud, de Sevres, Paris, U. Warwick, England; corr. Romance Philology, 1970-85; NEH dir. summer seminars for coll. tchrs., 1983, 87, 94, cons., 1976-78, bd. dirs.; bd. dirs. Alumni Coll. Princeton U., Paris, Fontevraud, France. Author: The Concept of Self in the Symoblist Novel, 1961, La Passion Littéraire de Remy de Gourmont, 1962, Linguistics and Literary Theory, 1969, Story, Myth and Celebration in Old French Narrative Poetry (1050-1200), 1973, (with A. Foulet) Chrétien de Troyes, Le Chevalier de la Charrette, 1989, Letteratura europea: dalle origini a Dante, 1993, Chrétien de Troyes, Le Chevalier au Lion, 1994, Chrétien de Troyes Revisited, 1995; contbr. numerous articles and revs. to scholarly jours.; editor: Edward C. Armstrong Monographs on Medieval Literature; mem. edit. bd. Romance Philology, French Forum; mem. adv. coun. Dictionary of the Middle Ages. Chmn. bd. elders Luth. Ch. of Messiah, Princeton, N.J., 1978-81. With AUS, 1954-56. Decorated officier des Palmes Académiques, France; Guggenheim fellow, 1964-65, sr. fellow Nat. Endowment for Humanities, 1974-75, vis. fellow All Souls Coll., Oxford (Eng.) U., 1975. Mem. MLA, Linguistic Soc. Am., Medieval Acad. Am. Société de linguistique romane, Phi Beta Kappa. Club: Codrington (Oxford, Eng.). Home: 50 Grover Ave Princeton NJ 08540-3654 Office: Dept Romance Langs and Lits Princeton U 309 E Pyne Princeton NJ 08544-5264

UKROPINA, JAMES R., lawyer; b. Fresno, Calif., Sept. 10, 1937; s. Robert J. and Persida (Angelich) U.; m. Priscilla Lois Brandenburg, June 16, 1962; children—Michael Steven, David Robert, Mark Gregory. A.B., Stanford U., 1959, M.B.A., 1961; LL.B., U. So. Calif., 1965. Bar: Calif. 1966, D.C. 1980. Assoc. firm O'Melveny & Myers, Los Angeles, 1965-72, ptnr., 1972-80, 92—; exec. v.p., gen. counsel Santa Fe Internat. Corp., Alhambra, Calif., 1980-84, dir., 1981-86; exec. v.p., gen. counsel Pacific Enterprises, Los Angeles, 1984-86, pres. and dir., 1986-89, chmn. bd. and chief exec. officer, 1989-91; bd. dirs. Lockheed Martin Corp., Pacific Mut. Life Ins. Co. Editor in chief So. Calif. Law Rev. 1964-65. Trustee Stanford U. Served with USAF, 1961-62. Mem. ABA, Calif. Bar Assn., Los Angeles County Bar Assn., Annandale Golf Club, Calif. Club, Beta Theta Pi. Office: O'Melveny & Myers 400 S Hope St Los Angeles CA 90071

ULABY, FAWWAZ TAYSSIR, electrical engineering and computer science educator, research center administrator; b. Damascus, Syria, Feb. 4, 1943; came to U.S. 1964; s. Tayssir Kamel and Makram (Ard) U.; m. Mary Ann Hammond, Aug. 28, 1968; children: Neda, Aziza, Laith. BS in Physics, Am. U. Beirut, 1964; MSEE, U. Tex., 1966, PhDEE, 1968. Asst. prof. elec. and computer engring. U. Kans., Lawrence, 1968-71, assoc. prof., 1971-76, prof., 1976-84; prof. elec. engring. and computer sci. U. Mich., Ann Arbor, 1984—, dir. NASA Ctr. for Space Terahertz Tech., 1988—, Williams Disting. prof., 1993—. Author: Microwave Remote Sensing, Vol. 1, 1981, Vol. 2, 1982, Vol. 3, 1986, Radar Polarimetry, 1990. Recipient Kuwait prize in applied scis. Govt. of Kuwait, 1987, NASA Group Achievement award, 1990. Fellow IEEE (gen. chmn. internat. symposium 1981, Disting. Achievement award 1983, Centennial medal 1984); mem. IEEE Geosci. and Remote Sensing Soc. (exec. editor jour., pres. 1979-81), Internat. Union Radio Sci. Avocations: flying kites, racketball. Office: U Mich 3228 EECS 1301 Beal Ave Ann Arbor MI 48109-2102

ULAM, ADAM B., history and political science educator; b. Lwow, Poland, Apr. 8, 1922; came to U.S., 1939, naturalized, 1949; s. Jozef and Anna (Auerbach) U.; children—Alexander Stanislaw, Joseph Howard. A.B., Brown U., 1943, LL.D.(hon.), 1983; Ph.D., Harvard U., 1947. Mem. Harvard U., Cambridge, Mass., 1947—; prof. govt. Harvard U., 1959-92, Gurney prof. history and polit. sci., 1979-92, prof. emeritus, 1992—, rsch. assoc. Russian Rsch. ctr., 1948—, ctr. dir., 1973-76, 80-92, mem. exec. com. Russian research ctr., 1968—. Author numerous books including: The Bolsheviks and Lenin, 1965, Stalin, 1972, 2nd edit., 1987, Expansion and Coexistence, 1973, The Unfinished Revolution, rev. edit., 1979, The Kirov Affair, 1988, Dangerous Relations: The Soviet Union in World Politics, 1970-1982, 1983, The Communists: The Story of Power and Lost Illusions, 1948-91, 1992. Guggenheim fellow, 1956, 69, Rockefeller fellow, 1957, 60. Mem. Am. Acad. Arts and Scis., Am. Philos. Soc. Clubs: The Signet, Harvard U. Eliot House (assoc.) (Cambridge). Avocation: tennis. Office: Harvard U Russian Research Ctr 1727 Cambridge St Cambridge MA 02138-3016

ULANOV, BARRY, author, educator; b. N.Y.C., Apr. 10, 1918; s. Nathan A. and Jeanette (Askwith) U.; m. Joan Bel Geddes, Dec. 16, 1939; children—Anne, Nicholas, Katherine; m. Ann Belford, Aug. 21, 1968; 1 son, Alexander. A.B., Columbia U., 1939, Ph.D., 1955; Litt.D., Villanova U., 1965. Editor Swing mag., 1939-41, Listen mag., 1940-42, Metronome mag., 1943-55, Metronome Yearbook, 1950-55; columnist Down Beat mag., 1955-58; instr. English Princeton U., 1950-51; instr. English Barnard Coll., 1951-56, asst. prof., 1956-60, assoc. prof., 1959-66, McIntosh prof., 1986-88, prof., 1966-88, McIntosh prof. emeritus — chmn. English dept., 1967-71, 79-82, chmn. program in the arts, 1975-79, 82-88; adj. prof. religion Columbia U., 1966; asso. editor The Bridge Yearbook of Inst. Judaeo-Christian studies, 1955-68; lectr. in psychiatry and religion Union Theol. Sem., 1992—. Author: The Recorded Music of W.A. Mozart, 1942, Duke Ellington, 1946, The Incredible Crosby, 1948, A History of Jazz in America, 1952, A Handbook of Jazz, 1957, Sources and Resources, 1960, Death: A Book of Preparation and Consolation, 1959, Makers of the Modern Theater, 1961, The Way of St. Alphonsus Liguori, 1961, Seeds of Hope in the Modern World, 1962, (with Robert C. Roby) Introduction to the Drama, 1962, Contemporary Catholic Thought, 1963, The Two Worlds of American Art, 1965, The Making of a Modern Saint, 1966, (with James B. Hall) Modern Culture and the Arts, 1967, 72, Where Swing Came From, 1970, Swing Lives!, 1972, (with Ann Ulanov) Religion and the Unconscious, 1975, (with Ann Ulanov) Primary Speech: A Psychology of Prayer, 1982, (with Ann Ulanov) Cinderella and Her Sisters: The Envied and the Envying, 1983, The Prayers of St. Augustine, 1984; (with Ann Ulanov) The Witch and The

Clown: Two Archetypes of Human Sexuality, 1986, Essay in Men and Women: Sexual Ethics in Turbulent Times, 1989, (with Ann Ulanov) The Healing Imagination, 1991, Jung and the Outside World, 1992, (with Ann Ulanov) Transforming Sexuality: The Archetypal World of Anima and Animus, 1994; co-translator: (with Joan Ulanov) The Last Essays of George Bernanos, 1955, (with Frank Tauritz) Joy Out of Sorrow, (by Mere Marie des Douleurs), 1958; co-editor Jour. Religion and Health, 1994—. Bd. dirs. Gandy Brody Sch., 1980—. C.G. Jung Found., 1992-94. Guggenheim fellow, 1962-63. Mem. Conf. Anglican Theologians, St. Thomas More Soc. (pres. 1955-56, 64-65), Cath. Renascence Soc. (pres. 1960-66), Conf. on Humanities (sec. 1957-58, chmn. 1958-59), Medieval Acad., Renaissance Soc., PEN, The Keys (vice chmn. 1959). Office: Barnard Coll Columbia Univ New York NY 10017

ULBRECHT, JAROMIR JOSEF, chemical engineer; b. Ostrava, Czechoslovakia, Dec. 16, 1928; s. Josef and Leopolda U.; m. Vera Krafneter, July 10, 1952; children: Jan Stanislav, Magdalena Vera. Ing., Czech Inst. Tech., Prague, 1952, Ph.D., 1958. Dept. head Research div. synthetic rubber co. Zlin, Czechoslovakia, 1963-68; head lab. engring. rheology Czechoslovak Acad. Scis., Prague, 1963-68; prof. chem. engring. U. Salford, Eng., 1968-78; prof., chmn. dept. chem. engring. SUNY, Buffalo, 1978-83; chief div. chem. process metrology Nat. Bur. Standards, Washington, 1984-88; dep. dir. office tech. evaluation and assessment Nat. Inst. Standards and Tech. (formerly Nat. Bur. Standards), Washington, 1989-90, dir. tech. programs, tech. svcs., 1991-94; prin. OFI Tech Svcs., Rockville, Md., 1994—. Author: Non-Newtonian Liquids, 1967, Mixing of Liquids by Mechanical Agitation, 1985, Process Sensing and Diagnostics, 1989, Competitiveness of the U.S. Chemical Industry in International Markets, 1990; editor: Chemical Engineering Communications, 1976-86; contbr. numerous articles to profl. jours. Recipient Outstanding Scholarship award Czech Acad. Scis., 1965, 67; Alexander von Humboldt fellow, 1967. Fellow Am. Inst. Chem. Engrs.; mem. Soc. Rheology, Am. Chem. Soc., Sigma Xi. Office: OFI Tech Svcs Inc 2407 McCormick Rd Rockville MD 20850

ULBRICHT, JOHN, artist; b. Havana, Cuba, Nov. 6, 1926; s. Tomlinson Carlile and Beatrice (Himely) U.; m. Angela von Neumann, July 25, 1950; children: Alexandra, John R. Student, Art Inst. Chgo., 1946-50. Asst. to dir. Denver Art Mus., 1952-54. Exhbns. include Spanish Contemporary Art, Brussels, Helsinki, Berlin, 1961, 63, Homage to Miro, Palma de Mallorca, 1973, Masterpieces of 20th Century Portraiture, Carlton House, London, 1978, one-man shows, Pavilion of Spain, N.Y. World's Fair, 1965, Richard deMarco Gallery, Edinburgh, 1969, Iolas-Velasco Gallery, Madrid, 1972, Bollhagen Gallery, Bremen, 1979, Pelaires Gallery, Palma de Mallorca, 1981, Biosca Gallery, Madrid, 1993; represented in permanent collections, Dallas Art Mus., Nat. Portrait Gallery, London, European Parliament, Strasbourg, SUNY, Buffalo, Pasadena Art Mus., Columbus Gallery Fine Arts; portraits include Robert Graves, Betty Ford, Lord Mountbatten, Joan Miro, Simon Weil, Carmen Romero, others. Served with U.S. Army, 1945-46. Address: 10 Es Clapes, 07195 Galilea, Mallorca Spain *I have always believed that the primary goal of life is simply the realization of its potentials and that each human being possesses the potential for some form of self-realization. My own road to this end is painting and therein I have dedicated my whole life. Perhaps the full attainment of this goal isn't possible, but certainly the striving towards it provides one of the most enriching experiences that life can offer.*

ULBRICHT, ROBERT E., lawyer, savings and loan executive; b. Chgo., Dec. 1, 1930; s. Emil Albert and Vivian June (Knight) U.; m. Betty Anne Charleson, June 20, 1953; 1 dau., Christine Anne. A.B., U. Ill., 1952, M.A., 1953; J.D., U. Chgo., 1958. Bar: Ill. 1958, U.S. Dist. Ct. (no. dist.) Ill. 1959. Research atty. Am. Bar Found., Chgo., 1957-59; asst. trust counsel Continental Ill. Nat. Bank & Trust Co., Chgo., 1959-60; assoc. law firm Cummings and Wyman, Chgo., 1960-68; gen. counsel, sec., sr. v.p. Bell Fed. Savs. & Loan Assn., Chgo., 1968—; gen. counsel, sec. sr. v.p., Bell Bancorp., Inc., Chgo., 1991—. instr. Aurora Coll., Coll. DuPage. Mem. nominating com. Dist. 41 Sch. Bd., 1970-71, vice chmn., 1971; chmn. dist. area fund raising Glen Ellyn council Girl Scouts Am., 1970. Bd. dirs. Glen Ellyn (Ill.) Pub. Library, 1979-85, pres., 1983-84. Served with AUS, 1953-55. Mem. Chgo. Bar Assn., Ill. Bar Assn., ABA. Clubs: Glen Oak Country, Glen Ellyn Tennis. Bd. editors Chgo. Bar Record, 1970-73; contbr. articles to legal jours. Office: Bell Bancorp Inc 79 W Monroe St Chicago IL 60603-4901

ULCHAKER, STANLEY LOUIS, public relations consultant; b. Cleve., July 6, 1938; s. Stanley and Anna (Zaletal) U.; m. Margaret Eleanor, Aug. 5, 1961; children: Margaret Mary, James C. B in Social Sci., John Carroll U., 1960. Reporter, clk. Cleve. Plain Dealer, 1957-61; reporter Fairchild Publs., Cleve., 1961-62; account exec. Edward Howard & Co., Cleve., 1962-69, v.p., 1969-72, sr. v.p., 1972-77, exec. v.p., 1977-86, pres., chief exec. officer, 1987-89, chmn., chief exec. officer, 1989—. Mem. Pub. Relations Soc. Am. (pres. Greater Cleve. chpt. 1993). Office: Edward Howard & Co 1 Erieview Plz Fl 7 Cleveland OH 44114-1706

ULERICH, WILLIAM KEENER, publishing company executive; b. Latrobe, Pa., Apr. 18, 1910; s. William Wesley and Anna (Keener) U.; m. Edith O. Orton, May 26, 1934 (div. 1950); 1 dau., Constance K.; m. Alethea M. Jones, Aug. 23, 1950. A.B., Pa. State U., 1931; LL.D., Dickinson Sch. Law, 1977. Editor Daily Times, State College, Pa., 1931-45; assoc. prof. journalism Pa. State U., 1934-45; pub. Clearfield (Pa.) Daily Progress, 1946; chmn. bd. dirs., chief exec. officer Progr. Pub. Co., Inc., Clearfield, Pa.; dir. emeritus County Nat. Bank, Clearfield. Bd. dirs., past pres. Clearfield Meml. Hosp.; trustee Pa. State U., 1952-57, 64-85, v.p. bd. trustees, 1973-76, pres. bd. trustees, 1976-79, pres. emeritus, 1985. Served with AUS, World War II. Mem. Pa. Newspaper Pubs. Assn. (pres. 1952). Methodist. Home: 724 S 2D St Clearfield PA 16830 Office: 206 E Locust St Clearfield PA 16830-2445

ULETT, GEORGE ANDREW, psychiatrist; b. Needham, Mass., Jan. 10, 1918; s. George Andrew and Mabel Elizabeth (Caswell) U.; m. Pearl Carolyn Lawrence; children: Richard Carlton, Judith Anne, Carol Lynn. BA in Psychology, Stanford U., 1940; MS in Anatomy, U. Oreg., 1943, PhD in Anatomy, 1944, MD, 1944. Diplomate Am. Bd. Psychiatry and Neurology. Asst. psychiatrist Barnes Hosp., St. Louis, 1950-64; med. dir. Malcolm Bliss Hosp., St. Louis, 1951-61; dir. Mo. Div. Mental Health, Jefferson City, Mo., 1962-72; prof., chair Mo. Inst. Psychiatry, St. Louis, 1964-73; dir. psychiatry Deaconess Hosp., St. Louis, 1973-94; interim dir. Mo. Inst. of Mental Health, St. Louis, 1990-91; assoc. dir. for policy and ethics Mo. Inst. of Mental Health, 1991-94; mem. adv. coun. Mental Health Assn. St. Louis, 1965-66, 69-70, mem. profl. adv., 1965; chair health and hosp. com. Health & Welfare Coun. St. Louis, 1960; mem. alcohol rev. com., psychopharmacology study sect., alcoholism study sect., 1993 grants rev. com. for alternative medicine NIMH, Rockville, Md. prof. psychiatry Washington U. Sch. Medicine, St. Louis, 1956-61; clin. prof. dept. psychiatry St. Louis U. Sch. Medicine, 1981-89, U. Mo. Sch. Medicine, 1990—. Author eight books; contbr. over 200 articles to profl. jours. Capt. U.S. Air Force, 1946-47. Recipient Ann. award Mo. Assn. for Mental Health, 1966, Recognition award, 1970, AMA Honorable Mention award Foster Com. Exhibit, 1974, Pax Mundi Fellowship award for profl. excellence, 1989; named hon. mem. Turkish Coll. Neuropharmacology, 1969. Fellow Am. Psychiat. Assn.; mem. Am. Acupuncture (past pres.), Am. Soc. of Med. Psychiatry (past pres.), Mo. Acad. Psychiatry (past pres.). Office: Mo Inst Mental Health 5247 Fyler Ave Saint Louis MO 63139-1361

ULEVICH, NEAL HIRSH, photojournalist; b. Milw., June 18, 1946; s. Ben and Leah Jean (Klitsner) U.; m. Maureen Ann Vaughan, Sept. 25, 1974; children—Jacob Vaughan, Sarah Beatrice. B.A. in Journalism, U. Wis., 1968. Reporter A.P., 1968-69, photographer, photo editor, 1971-78, Asia photo editor, 1978-83; freelance writer, Vietnam, Hong Kong, 1969-71; fellow in journalism U. Wis.-Madison, 1971-72. Recipient Pulitzer prize for news photography, 1977. Jewish. Home: 2841 Perry St Denver CO 80212-1442

ULLBERG, KENT JEAN, sculptor; b. Gothenburg, Sweden, July 15, 1945; came to U.S., 1974; s. Jean Wilgot and Kerstin Aina (Axelson) U.; m. Veerle Rufina Vermeir, May 5, 1978; children: Robert, Gerald. Diploma in sculpture, Swedish State Sch. Art, 1966. Cert. conservator German Assn. Museology. Curator Nat. Mus. and Art Gallery, Botswana, Africa, 1971-74; curator III Mus. Natural History, Denver, 1974-75. Sculptor: monument

Lincoln Ctr. Eagle, Dallas, 1981, Wind in the Sails, Corpus Christi, Tex., 1983, Genesee Eagle, Mumford, N.Y., 1984, Deinonychus Dinosaurs, Phila., 1987, Whooping Cranes Fountain, Washington, 1989, Broward Conv. Ctr., Fountain, Ft. Lauderdale, Fla., Rudor Monument bronze, Stockholm, 1991, Monumental Triptych Art Mus. South Tex., 1993, Bird Mountain Telecom. Hdqs., Stockholm, 1994. Recipient Gold medal Tex. Rangers Hall of Fame, 1980; named Master Wildlife Artist, 1987. Fellow Nat. Sculpture Soc. (Percival Dietsch award 1979, gold medal 1983, Hering award 1993), NAD (academician 1990, Barnett prize 1975, Speyer prize 1995), Nat. Acad. Western Art (gold medal 1981, 82, 88, 90), Am. Soc. Marine Artists; mem. Soc. Animal Artists (medal of merit 1979, 80, 82, 87), Allied Artists of Am. (N.Y. Silver medal 1989), Soc. for Wildlife Art of the Nations. Home: 14337 Aquarius St Corpus Christi TX 78418-6003

ULLIAN, JOSEPH SILBERT, philosophy educator; b. Ann Arbor, Mich., Nov. 9, 1930; s. Hyman Benjamin and Frieda G. (Silbert) U.; m. Theresa Helen Ridilla, July 26, 1990. AB, Harvard U., 1952, AM, 1953, PhD, 1957. Instr. philosophy Stanford U., Calif., 1957-58; asst. prof. philosophy Johns Hopkins U., Balt., 1958-60; vis. asst. prof. philosophy U. Pa., Phila., 1959-60, rsch. assoc. in linguistics, 1961-62; vis. asst. prof. philosophy U. Chgo., 1962-63; asst. prof. U. Calif., Santa Barbara, 1964-66; assoc. prof. Washington U., St. Louis, 1965-70, prof., 1970—; lectr. U. Calif., Berkeley, 1961; cons. Rsch. Directorate System Devel. Corp., Santa Monica, Calif., 1962-70. Co-author: The Web of Belief, 1970, 2d edit., 1978; contbr. articles to profl. jours. Mem. Am. Philos. Assn., Assn. for Symbolic Logic (exec. com. 1974-77), Am. Soc. for Aesthetics, Phi Beta Kappa. Democrat. Avocations: sports, theatre, music. Home: 984 Tornoe Rd Santa Barbara CA 93105-2229 Office: Washington U Dept Philosophy 1 Brookings Dr Saint Louis MO 63130-4862

ULLMAN, EDWIN FISHER, research chemist; b. Chgo., July 19, 1930; s. Harold P. and Jane F. Ullman; m. Elizabeth J. Finlay, June 26, 1954; children—Becky L., Linda J. B.A., Reed Coll., Portland, Oreg., 1952; M.A., Harvard U., 1954, Ph.D., 1956. Research chemist Lederle Labs., Am. Cyanamid, Pearl River, N.Y., 1955-60; group leader central research div. Am. Cyanamid, Stamford, Conn., 1960-66; sci. dir. Synvar Research Inst., Palo Alto, Calif., 1966-70; v.p., dir. research Syva Co., Palo Alto, 1970—; mem. sci. adv. bd. EnSys Inc., Research Triangle Park, N.C., 1992—; mem. adv. bd. San Francisco State U. Coll. of Sci. and Engring., 1994—. Edit. bd.: Jour. Organic Chemistry, 1969-74, Jour. Immunoassay, 1979—, Jour. Clin. Lab., Analysis, 1986-87; contbr. articles to sci. jours. Patentee in field. NSF predoctoral fellow, 1952-53; U.S. Rubber Co. fellow, 1954-55. Recipient Clin. Ligand Assay Soc. Mallinckrodt award, 1981, Can. Soc. Clin. Chemists Health Group award, 1982, Inventor of Yr. award Peninsula Patent Law Assn., 1987. Fellow AAAS; mem. Am. Chem. Soc., Am. Assn. Clin. Chemists (Van Slyke award N.Y. sect. 1984, No. Calif. sect. award 1991), Am. Soc. Biol. Chemists, Clin. Ligand Assay Soc., Phi Beta Kappa. Office: Syva Co PO Box 10058 900 Arastradero Rd Palo Alto CA 94304-1332

ULLMAN, FRANK GORDON, electrical engineering educator; b. N.Y.C., Dec. 14, 1926; s. Samuel Robert and Ella (Fischl) U.; m. Deborah Halpern, July 15, 1951; children: Diane Ella, Marian Ruth, Eileen Jane. BA, NYU, 1949; MS, Poly. Inst. Bklyn., 1951, PhD, 1958. Rsch. fellow Poly. Inst. Bklyn., N.Y.C., 1949-51; jr. engr. Sylvania Electric Products, Inc., Mineola, N.Y., 1951-54; rsch. asst. Poly. Inst. Bklyn., N.Y.C., 1954-57, rsch. assoc., 1957-58; sr. rsch. physicist Nat. Cash Register Co., Dayton, Ohio, 1958-66; prof. elec. engring. and physics U. Nebr., Lincoln, 1966—, assoc. chmn. dept. elec. engring., 1987-91; instr. U. Dayton, 1960-62; vis. prof. Hebrew U., Jerusalem, 1982; co-dir. Ctr. Laser-Analytical Studies of Trace Gas Dynamics, 1988—. Mem. editorial bd. Ferroelectrics, Ferroelectrics Letters; contbr. articles in field to profl. jours. With U.S. Army, 1945-46. Mem. AAUP, IEEE (sr. mem.), Am. Phys. Soc., Sigma Xi. Democrat. Jewish. Avocations: handball, tennis. Office: U Nebr Dept Elec Engring Lincoln NE 68588

ULLMAN, JEFFREY DAVID, computer science educator; b. N.Y.C., Nov. 22, 1942; s. Seymour and Nedra L. (Hart) U.; m. Holly E., Nov. 19, 1967; children: Peter, Scott, Jonathan. B.S., Columbia U., 1963; Ph.D., Princeton U., 1966; Ph.D. hon., U. Brussels, 1975, U. Paris-Dauphine, 1992. Mem. tech. staff Bell Labs., Murray Hill, N.J., 1966-69; cons. Bell Labs., 1969-89; prof. elec. engring., computer sci. Princeton U., 1969-79; prof. computer sci. Stanford (Calif.) U., 1979—, chmn. dept. computer scis., 1994—; Stanford W. Ascherman prof. computer sci. Stanford U., 1994—, Stanford (Calif.) U., 1994—; cons. Bell Labs., 1969-89; mem. computer sci. adv. panel NSF, 1974-77, info., robotics and intelligent systems adv. panel, 1986-88; mem. examination com. for computer sci. grad. record exam Ednl. Testing Svcs., 1978-86; cons. editor Computer Sci. Press, 1982—; chmn. doctoral rating com. for computer sci. N.Y. State Regents, 1989-93. Author: Principles of Database and Knowledge-Base Systems, 1988, 89, (2 vols.), (with A.V. Aho and J.E. Hopcroft) Data Structures and Algorithms, 1983, (with J.E. Hopcroft) Introduction to Automata Theory, Languages and Computation, 1979, (with A.V. Aho, R. Sethi) Compilers: Principles, Techniques and Tools, 1986, (with A.V. Aho) Foundations of Computer Science, 1992, Elements of ML Programming, 1994. Guggenheim fellow, 1989. Fellow Assn. Computing Machinery (mem. coun. 1987-89). mem. Spl. Interest Group on Automata and Computability Theory (sec.-treas. 1973-77), Spl. Interest Group on Mgmt. Data (vice-chmn. 1983-85, Computing Rsch. Assn. bd. 1994—), Nat. Acad. Engring. Home: 1023 Cathcart Way Palo Alto CA 94305-1048 Office: Stanford U 332 Margaret Jacks Hall Stanford CA 94305

ULLMAN, LOUIS JAY, financial executive; b. N.Y.C., Sept. 3, 1931; s. Abraham and Clara (Matava) U.; m. Doris Betty Weiner, Sept. 26, 1954; children: Barbara, Alan, Howard. BBA, U. Cin., 1954. CPA, Ohio. Auditor Alexander Grant & Co., Cin., 1957-60; pres. Internat. TV, Cin., 1960-62; mgmt. cons. Alexander Grant & Co., Cin., 1962-63; dir., sr. v.p. fin. Frisch's Restaurants, Inc., Cin., 1963—; former Chmn. bd. trustees Better Bus. Bur., Cin.; pres. United Jewish Cemeteries; former pres. Isaac M. Wise Temple. Mem. AICPA, Ohio Soc. CPAs. Jewish. Office: Frischs Restaurants Inc 2800 Gilbert Ave Cincinnati OH 45206-1206

ULLMAN, MYRON EDWARD, III, retail executive; b. Youngstown, Ohio, Nov. 26, 1946; s. Myron Edward Jr. and Jane (Cunningham) U.; m. Cathy Emmons, June 20, 1969; children: Myron Cayce, Denver Tryan, Peter Brynt, Benjamin Kyrk, Kathryn Kwynn. BS in Indsl. Mgmt., U. Cin., 1969; postgrad. Inst. Ednl. Mgmt., Harvard U., 1977. Internat. account mgr. IBM Corp., Cin., 1969-76; v.p. bus. affairs U. Cin., 1976-81; White House fellow The White House, Washington, 1981-82; exec. v.p. Sanger Harris div. Federated Stores, Dallas, 1982-86; mgr. dir., chief oper. officer Wharf Holdings Ltd., Hong Kong, 1986-88; chmn., CEO, dir. R.H. Macy & Co. Inc., N.Y.C., 1986-95; dir. Federated Dept. Stores, Inc.; chmn., CEO, dir. DFS Group Ltd., San Francisco, 1995—; mng. dir. Lane Crawford Ltd., Hong Kong, 1986-88; bd. advisors Gt. Traditions Corp., Cin.; dep. chmn. Omni Hotels, Hampton, N.H., 1988; vice chmn. bd. dirs. Mercy Ships Internat. Internat. v.p. U. Cin. Alumni Assn., 1980—; bd. dirs. Nat. Multiple Sclerosis Soc., N.Y.C.; bd. dirs. Brunswick Sch., Greenwich, Conn., U. Cin. Found., Lincoln Ctr. Devel. Mem. White House Fellow Alumni Assn., Econ. Club N.Y.C. (bd. dirs., exec. com. 1993—), Nat. Retail Fedn. (vice chmn., bd. dirs., exec. com. 1993—), Delta Tau Delta (treas. 1967-68). Republican. Office: DFS Group Ltd 655 Montgomery St San Francisco CA 94111-2633

ULLMAN, NELLY SZABO, statistician, educator; b. Vienna, Austria, Aug. 11, 1925; came to U.S., 1939; d. Viktor and Elizabeth (Rosenberg) Szabo; m. Robert Ullman, Mar. 20, 1947 (dec.); children: Buddy, William John, Martha Ann, Daniel Howard. BA, Hunter Coll., 1945; MA, Columbia U., 1948; PhD, U. Mich., 1969. Rsch. assoc. MIT Radiation Lab, Cambridge, Mass., 1945; instr. Polytechnic Inst. of Bklyn., 1945-63; asst. prof. to prof. Ea. Mich. U., Ypsilanti, 1963—. Author: Study Guide To Actuarial Exam, 1978; contbr. articles to profl. jours. Mem. Am. Math. Assn., Am. Stat. Assn., Biometric Soc., Am. Assn. Univ. Profs. Office: Ea Mich Univ Dept Math Ypsilanti MI 48197

ULLMAN, RICHARD HENRY, political science educator; b. Balt., Dec. 12, 1933; s. Jerome E. and Frances (Oppenheimer) U.; m. Margaret Yoma Crosfield, July 4, 1959 (div.); children: Claire Frances, Jennifer Margaret; m. Susan Sorrell, May 6, 1977 (div.); m. Gail Marie Morgan, Dec. 24, 1983. A.B., Harvard U., 1955; B. Phil., Oxford (Eng.) U., 1957, D.Phil.,

1960. Rsch. fellow European history and politics St. Antony's Coll., Oxford U., 1958-59; instr. govt. Harvard U., 1960-63, asst. prof., 1963-65; assoc. prof. politics and internat. affairs Princeton (N.J.) U., 1965-69, prof., 1969-77, 79—, David K.E. Bruce prof. internat. affairs, 1988—; George Eastman vis. prof. Oxford U., 1991-92; mem. policy planning staff Office Asst. Sec. Def., 1967-68; mem. staff Nat. Security Coun., Exec. Office Pres., 1967; dir. studies Coun. Fgn. Rels., 1973-76, dir. 1980's project, 1974-77. Author: Intervention and the War, 1961, Britain and the Russian Civil War, November 1918-January 1920, 1968, The Anglo-Soviet Accord, 1972, vols. I, II and III Anglo-Soviet Relations, 1917-21, Securing Europe, 1991; editor: Fgn. Policy Jour., 1978-80, Western Europe and the Crisis in U.S.-Soviet Relations, 1987, (with others) Theory and Policy in International Relations, 1972; mem. editorial bd. N.Y. Times, 1977-78; contbr. articles to profl. jours. Rhodes scholar, 1955-58; recipient George Louis Beer prize Am. Hist. Assn., 1969. Fellow Am. Acad. Arts and Scis.; mem. Coun. Fgn. Rels., Internat. Inst. Strategic Studies. Home: 12 Maple St Princeton NJ 08542-3852 Office: Ctr Internat Studies Bendheim Hall Princeton Univ Princeton NJ 08544

ULLMAN, TRACEY, actress, singer; b. Slough, Eng., Dec. 30, 1959; m. Allan McKeown, 1984; children: Mabel Ellen, John Albert Victor. Student, Itaia Conti Stage Sch., London. Appeared in plays Gigi, Elvis, Grease, The Rocky Horror Show, Four in a Million, 1981 (London Theatre Critics award), The Taming of the Shrew, 1990, The Big Love, (one-woman stage show) 1991; films include The Young Visitors, 1984, Give My Regards to Broad Street, 1984, Plenty, 1985, Jumpin' Jack Flash, 1986, I Love You To Death, 1990, Household Saints, 1993, I'll Do Anything, 1994, Bullets over Broadway, 1994, Ready to Wear (Prêt-à-Porter), 1994; Brit. TV shows include Three of a Kind, A Kick Up the Eighties, Girls on Top; actress TV series: The Tracey Ullman Show, from 1987-90 (Emmy award Best Performance, Outstanding Writing, 1990, Golden Globe award Best Actress, 1987); album You Broke My Heart in Seventeen Places (Gold album). Recipient Brit. Acad. award, 1983, Am. Comedy award, 1988, 90, 91, Emmy award for Best Performance in a Variety/Music Series for "Tracey Ullman Takes on New York", 1994. Office: Creative Artists Agy Inc 9830 Wilshire Blvd Beverly Hills CA 90212*

ULLMANN, LIV, actress; b. Tokyo, Japan, Dec. 16, 1938; d. Viggo and Janna (Lund) U.; m. Hans Stang, 1960 (div. 1965); 1 dau., Linn, by Ingmar Bergman; m. Donald Saunders, Sept. 7, 1985. Student pub. sch.; studies with dramatic coach, London, Eng.; 8 hon. doctoral degrees in arts and humanities. Starred in Diary of Anne Frank, repertory troup, Stavanger, Norway; became established actress of classic stage and film roles in Norway; appeared as Ingmar Bergman's leading lady in film Persona, 1966; many other films directed by Bergman; also films in U.S., Can., Mex., France, Italy, Germany, S.Am., Switzerland, England; starred as Nora in A Doll's House in N.Y. Shakespeare Festival prodn. Vivian Beaumont Theater, Lincoln Ctr., N.Y.C.; appeared on Broadway in Anna Christie, 1977, I Remember Mama, 1979, Ghosts, other stage appearances include Old Times, West End, London, 1985-86, Mother Courage, Nat. Theatre, Oslo, Norway; dir. Sofie, 1992; author: Changing, 1977, translated into over 20 langs (Book-of-Month Club), Choices, 1984, translated into over 20 langs. Ofcl. goodwill ambassador UNICEF, 1980—. Decorated officer of Arts and Letters, France, The Order of St. Olaf, King of Norway; recipient Dag Hammarskjold Hon. medal; named best actress by either N.Y. Film Critics or Nat. Soc. Film Critics U.S. for 6 yrs. in a row. *

ULLMARK, HANS, advertising agency executive; b. Stockholm, Sept. 2, 1946; came to U.S., 1984; s. Gustaf and Britten (Jansson) U.; m. Marie-Louise, July 2, 1977; children: Louise, Christian. M in Psychology, Stockholm U., 1971. Tchr. Bus. Sch. Stockholm, 1971-73; media planner Anderson & Lembke Group, Stockholm, 1973-74, media dir., 1974-75, account supr., 1975-76, v.p. account services, 1976-79; pres. Ehrenstrahle/BBDO, Stockholm, 1979-84; v.p. account services Anderson & Lembke, Inc., Stamford, Conn., 1984-88, pres., 1988—. Author, editor: Direct Marketing Handbook, 1979. Mem. Swedish Direct Mktg. Assn. (bd. dirs. 1977-82). Avocations: tennis, skiing, reading, sailing. Office: Anderson & Lembke Inc 79 5th Ave Fl 7 New York NY 10003-3034

ULLOA, JUSTO CELSO, Spanish educator; b. Havana, Cuba, Oct. 20, 1942; came to U.S., 1960; s. Derby Celso Ulloa and Margo (Hernandez) Usame; m. Leonor Rosario Alvarez, July 17, 1971; children: Sandra Leonor, Justin Alfonso. BS, Fla. State U., 1966; MA, U. Ga., 1969; PhD, U. Ky., 1973. With Va. Poly. Inst. and State U., Blacksburg, 1972-74, asst. prof., 1974-79, prof., 1987—; vis. prof. U. Ky., Lexington, Spring 1989. Author: Graded Spanish Reader, 1981, 2d edit., 1987, Lezama Lima y sus Lectores: guia y compendio bibliografico, 1987; assoc. editor, book rev. editor Critica Hispanica, 1979—; editor-in-chief Cuban Literary Studies, 1990. Recipient Acad. Teaching Excellence, Va. Tech., 1992, Alumni Teaching award, 1992. Mem. South Atlantic MLA, Mountain Interstate Fgn. Lang. Conf. (v.p. 1975-76, 82-83, pres. 1976-77, 83-84, 92-93), Order of the Discoverers, Phi Kappa Phi, Sigma Delta Pi (state dir. 1976-86, v.p. 1986-90). Office: Va Poly Inst and State U Dept Fgn Lang Lit Blacksburg VA 24061

ULLRICH, JOHN FREDERICK, diversified manufacturing company executive; b. Kalamazoo, Aug. 27, 1940; s. Frederick John and Opal Louise (Confer) U.; m. Susan K. Brundage, July 16, 1962; children: Frederick, Kathryn, Amy. BS in Engring. Physics, U. Mich. 1962, MS in Nuclear Engring., 1963, PhD in Nuc. Engring., 1967. Mgr. ignition systems dept. Ford Motor Co., Dearborn, Mich., 1975-76, mgr. vehicle evaluation, 1976-77, exec. engr. elec. and electronics div., 1977-79; v.p. sci. and tech. Internat. Harvester Co., Hinsdale, Ill., 1979-81, v.p. components engring. and devel., 1981-82, v.p. quality and reliability, 1982-83, v.p. mfg. engine and foundry div., 1983-86; v.p. strategic mgmt. Ex-Cell-o Corp., Troy, Mich., 1986, group v.p. Textron, Inc., Providence, R.I., 1987, v.p. ethics and environ. affairs, 1987-88; v.p. tech. and support svcs. Masco Corp., Taylor, Mich., 1988—. Mem. Mich. Rep. State Ctrl. Com., 1971-75; chmn. Reps. of Dearborn, 1972-74; alt. del. Rep. Nat. Conv., 1972; mem. bd. regents Ea. Mich. U., 1974-79, trustee Ea. Mich. U. Found., 1990—; mem. nat. adv. bd. Coll. Engring., U. Mich., corp. rels. and nat. campaign coms. U. Mich., 1981—; alumni mem. Coll. Engring. planning com., 1993-94; divsn. chmn. Chgo. United Way, 1983, Detroit United Way, 1986; mem. guarantor's com. Goodman Theatre, Chgo., 1980-83; mem. editorial adv. bd. Mfg. Engring. Mag., 1983-90; mem. nat. adv. bd. Nat. Kidney Found., 1989—; mem. corp. devel. com. Univ. Mus. Soc., Univ. Mich. Mus. Art, Rackham Grad. Sch., 1990—; pres. Ann Arbor Art Assn., 1993-95; bd. dirs. Ind. Tech. Inst., 1993—, Ann Arbor Hands on Mus., 1994—; Mich. Artrain, 1995—. Named Outstanding Alumnus, 1984, Alumni Soc. award, 1992; recipient Cmty. Svc. award Ford Motor Co., 1969, 73. Mem. Soc. Automotive Engrs., Soc. Mfg. Engrs., Engring. Soc. Detroit (chmn. membership com. 1989-90, Cmty. Svc. award 1991, bd. dirs. 1992—, treas. 1994—; mem. chair IPC 1995), Barton Hills Country Club, Hinsdale Golf Club, L'Arbre Croche Club, Sigma Xi, Tau Beta Pi, Kappa Kappa Psi. Republican. Presbyterian. Office: Masco Corp 21001 Van Born Rd Taylor MI 48180-1340

ULLRICH, ROBERT ALBERT, business management educator; b. Port Jefferson, N.Y., Mar. 25, 1939; s. Albert Herman and Marie Kathryn (Miller) U.; divorced; children: Karl Albert, Eleanor Marie. BS, U.S. Mcht. Marine Acad., 1960; MBA, Tulane U., 1964; D in Bus. Adminstrn., Washington U., 1968. Marine engr. Lykes Bros. Steamship Co., New Orleans, 1960-62; trainee IBM Corp., New Orleans, 1964-65; sr. rsch. officer London Sch. Econs., 1968-69; prof. Vanderbilt U., Nashville, 1969-88; dean Clark U., Worcester, Mass., 1988—. Author: Motivation Methods, 1981, Robotics Primer, 1983; co-author: Organization Theory and Design, 1980; editor: The American Work Force, 1984. Lt. j.g. USNR, 1960-66. Mem. Beta Gamma Sigma. Office: Grad School Management Clark University 950 Main St Worcester MA 01610-1400

ULMAN, LOUIS JAY, lawyer; b. Balt., Mar. 24, 1946; s. Erwin Ira And Rose (Clayman) U.; m. Diana Lynn Milford, Aug. 17, 1969; children: Kenneth, Douglas. BA, Dickinson Coll., 1967; JD, Am. U., 1970. Bar: Md. 1970. Assoc. Ulman & Cohan, Balt., 1970-75; ptnr. Ulman & Ulman, Balt., 1975-80, Weinberg & Green, Columbia, Md. 1980-92; prin. Hodes, Ulman, Pessin & Katz, Columbia, 1992—. Pres. Santa Claus Anonymous, Balt., 1975; mem. Howard County Bd. Social Svc., Ellicott City, Md., 1990. Mem. Md. State Bar Assn. (com. on rels. with fin. profls. 1985-92), Howard

County Bar Assn., Internat. Assn. for Fin. Planning. Democrat. Jewish. Office: 10500 Little Patuxent Pky Columbia MD 21044

ULMER, DANIEL C., JR., diversified financial services company executive. Vice chmn. PNC Financial Corp., Pitts., PA, now chmn. Office: PNC Fin Corp 5th Wood St Pittsburgh PA 15265

ULMER, DEBORAH LUXTON, medical training administrator, nurse, consultant; b. Phila., Apr. 1, 1953; d. Elvin Lamar and Charlotte Mabel (Herring) Luxton; m. David Dewitt Ulmer, Jan. 10, 1976. BS in Nursing, W.Va. Wesleyan U., 1975; MEd, Va. Commonwealth U., 1980; PhD in Urban Services, Va. Commonwealth U., 1987. RN, Va. Staff nurse St. Francis Hosp., Pitts., 1976; pub. health nurse Va. Health Dept., Richmond, 1977; head nurse Corrections Commn. of Va., Richmond, 1978, dir. edn. and tng. Chippenham Hosp., Richmond, 1978—; mem. faculty mgmt. tng. Ctr. for Health Studies, Nashville, 1980—; cons., 1982—. Author: (tng. programs) Communication by Caring, 1979, Why Bother?, 1984. John Tyler Community Coll., Richmond, 1983. Mem. Am. Soc. Tng. and Devel., Am. Soc. for Health, Edn. and Tng., Phi Delta Kappa. Democrat. Methodist. Home: 607 Coralview Ter Midlothian VA 23113-3319 Office: Chippenham Hosp 7101 Jahnke Rd Richmond VA 23225-4044

ULMER, FRAN, state official; m. Bill Council; children: Amy, Louis. B in Econs. and Polit. Sci., U. Wis.; JD with honors, Wis. Sch. Law. Polit. advisor Gov. Jay Hammond, Alaska, 1973-83; former mayor City of Juneau, Alaska; mem. 4 terms, minority leader Alaska Ho. Reps.; lt. gov. State of Alaska, 1995—. Home: 1700 Angus Way Juneau AK 99801-1411 Office: State Capitol PO Box 110015 Juneau AK 99811

ULMER, MELVILLE JACK, economist, educator; b. N.Y.C., May 17, 1911; s. Saul and Lillian (Ulmer) U.; m. Naomi Zinken, June 1, 1937; children: Melville Paul, Stephanie Marie. BS, NYU, 1937, MA, 1938; Ph.D., Columbia, 1948. Writer N.Y. Am., 1930-37; chief, price research sect. Bur. Labor Statistics, 1940-45; sr. economist Smaller War Plants Corp., 1945; chief financial analysis sect. Dept. Commerce, 1946-48; editor Survey of Current Bus., 1948-50; asso. prof. econs. Am. U., 1950-52, prof., 1952-61, chmn. dept., 1953-61; prof. econs. U. Md., 1961-86, emeritus prof., 1986—; vis. prof. econs. Netherlands Sch. Econ., Rotterdam, 1958-59, 65-66; research asso. Nat. Bur. Econ. Research, 1950-60; cons. OAS, 1954, Dept. Commerce, 1955, Gen. Services Adminstrn., 1957, Dept. State, 1962, Bur. Budget, 1967-69. Author: numerous books including The Economic Theory of Cost of Living Index Numbers, 1949, Trends and Cycles in Capital Formation by U.S. Railroads, 1870-1950, 1954, Economics: Theory and Practice, 2d edit., 1965, Capital in Transportation, Communications and Pub. Utilities, 1960, The Welfare State: U.S.A. 1969, The Theory and Measurement of International Price Competitiveness, 1969; co-author: (with John M. Blair) Wartime Prices, 1944, (with C. Wright Mills) Small Business and Civic Welfare, 1946; contbg. editor: The New Republic, 1970-80; contbr. articles in Am. Econ. Rev., Jour. Am. Statis. Assn., Commentary, Atlantic Monthly, Challenge, Am. Spectator, Pub. Interest, Jour. of Econ. Issues, also others. Recipient Sr. Fulbright award, 1958, 65, Medal of Honor Free U. of Brussels, 1986; Merrill Found. fellow, 1957; Wilton Park fellow Gt. Britain, 1966; Peoples Coll. fellow Denmark, 1966; Nuffield fellow Can., 1971; Nat. Endowment for Humanities sr. fellow, 1973; NSF grantee, 1973; State Dept. econ. specialist grantee, 1977, 78. Fellow AAAS; mem. Am. Econ. Assn., Am. Statis. Assn., Econometric Soc., Assn. Evolutionary Econs. (exec. bd.), Atlantic Econ. Soc. (disting assoc.), Artus Soc., Pi Gamma Mu. Club: Cosmos (Washington). Home: 10401 River Rd Potomac MD 20854-4912 Office: U Md Dept Econs College Park MD 20742 *Failure must be taken as an instructive experience that aids in exposing the pitfalls to achievement.*

ULMER, MELVILLE PAUL, physics and astronomy educator; b. Washington, Mar. 12, 1943; s. Melville Jack and Naomi Louise (Zinkin) U.; m. Patricia Elifson, Dec. 28, 1968; children: Andrew Todd, Jeremy John, Rachel Ann. BA, Johns Hopkins U., 1965; PhD, U. Wis., 1970. Asst. research U. Calif., San Diego, 1970-74; astrophysicist Harvard Smithsonian Ctr. for Astrophysics, Cambridge, Mass., 1974-76; asst. prof. Dept. Physics and Astoronomy, Northwestern U., Evanston, Ill., 1976-82, assoc. prof., 1982-87, dir. astrophysics program, 1982—, prof., 1987—; dir. Lindheimer and Dearborn Obs. Northwestern U., 1982—; co-investigator on Gamma Ray Ob. experiment and Orbiting Solar Ob. 7. Contbr. articles to profl. jours. Fellow Am. Phys. Soc.; mem. Am. Astron. Soc., Soc. Photo-optical Instrumentation Engrs., Internat. Astron. Union. Home: 2021 Noyes St Evanston IL 60201-2556 Office: Northwestern U Dearborn Obs 2145 Sheridan Rd Evanston IL 60208-3112

ULMER, SHIRLEY SIDNEY, political science educator, researcher, consultant; b. North, S.C., Apr. 15, 1923; s. Shirley S. and Anna R. (Reed) U.; m. Margaret Anel Lipscomb, Mar. 18, 1946; children: Margaret, William, Susan, John, Mary. BA cum laude, Furman U., 1952, LLD (hon.), 1981; MA, Duke U., 1954, PhD, 1956. Rockefeller fellow Duke U., 1952-53, instr. polit. sci., 1954-55, Ottis Greene fellow, 1955-56; instr. U. Houston, summer 1956; mem. faculty Mich. State U., 1956-63, asst. prof., 1956-59, assoc. prof. polit. sci., 1960-63, chmn. dept., 1961-62; prof. polit. sci., chmn. dept. U. Ky., Lexington, 1963-69, Disting. prof. arts and scis., 1975-76, Alumni prof., 1978-88, prof. emeritus, 1988—; mem. polit. sci. panel NSF, 1968-70; chmn. bd. overseers NSF Supreme Ct. data base project, 1984-87; vis. prof. SUNY, Buffalo, summer 1969, U. Wis.-Milw., summer, 1974, Ariz. State U., 1980; lectr. in field. Author: Military Justice and the Right to Counsel, 1971, Courts as Small and Not so Small Groups, 1971, Supreme Court Policy Making and Constitutional Law, 1986; editor: Introductory Readings in Political Behavior, 1961, Political Decision Making, 1969, Courts, Law and Judicial Processes, 1981; Contbr. articles to profl. jours. Served with USAAF, 1942-45, PTO. Decorated Air medal with 4 oak leaf clusters, Phila. Liberation medal; recipient Sang award for outstanding contbns. to grad. edn., 1973-74, Outstanding Polit. Sci. Tchr. award Pi Sigma Alpha, 1983, 87; Social Sci. Rsch. Coun. fellow, summers 1958, 67; NSF grantee, 1969-71, 78-82, 87-90. Mem. Am. Polit. Sci. Assn. (editorial assoc. rev. 1963-67), So. Polit. Sci. Assn. (exec. council 1965-68, v.p. 1966-67, pres. 1971-72), editorial bd. jour. (1965-72), Midwest Polit. Sci. Assn. (editorial bd. jour. 1963-64, 84-85), Ky. Polit. Sci. Assn. (v.p. 1966-67), Inter-Univ. Consortium Polit. Research (exec. council 1966-67, council chmn. 1967-68), Omicron Delta Kappa, Phi Beta Kappa. Home: 1701 Williamsburg Rd Lexington KY 40504-2013

ULMER, WALTER FRANCIS, JR., consultant, former army officer; b. Bangor, Maine, Apr. 2, 1929; married; 3 children. B.S. in Engring., U.S. Mil. Acad., 1952; M.Regional Planning, Pa. State U., 1973. Commd. 2d lt. U.S. Army, 1952, advanced through grades to lt. gen., 1982; dep. comdr. U.S. Army Armor Ctr., Ft. Knox, Ky., 1974-75; comdr. of cadets U.S. Mil. Acad., West Point, N.Y., 1975-77; dir. human resources devel. U.S. Army, Washington, 1978-79; comdr. 3d Armored Div. Frankfurt, Germany, 1979-82; comdg. gen. III Corps and Ft. Hood, Tex., 1982-85, ret., 1985; pres., CEO Ctr. for Creative Leadership, Greensboro, N.C., 1985-94; ind. cons., 1995—; lectr. in field. Contbr. articles to profl. jours. Home: 250 Riverbay Dr Moneta VA 24121

ULRICH, JOHN ROSS GERALD, aerospace engineer; b. Kalispell, Mont., Nov. 25, 1929; s. Alva Austin and Hattie Lenora (Kingston) U.; m. Virginia Jean Breinholt, June 19, 1954; children: Virginia, John, Annette, Lenora, James. BS in Engring., Northrup U., 1952. Registered profl. engr., Colo. Engr. Lockheed Aircraft, Burbank, Calif., 1952-54, Radioplane, Van Nuys, Calif., 1956-57; sect. head Aerojet-Gen., Sacramento, 1957-65; chmn. of SCUT Martin Marietta, Denver, 1965-92. Lectr. Arapahoe County Pub. Schs. With U.S. Army, 1954-56. Mem. AIAA. Achievements include invention of skyline technique for the solution to simultaneous equations, Photographic Strain Measurement Technique. Home: 3435 E Arapahoe Littleton CO 80122

ULRICH, LARS, drummer. Drummer Metallica, 1981—. Albums include Kill 'em All, 1983, Ride the Lightning, 1984, Master of Puppets, 1986, ...And Justice for All, 1988, Metallica, 1991, Live Sh*t: Binge and Purge, 1993, Garage Days Re-visited. Recipient Grammy award, 1990, 91. Office: c/o Metallica Elektra Records 75 Rockefeller Plz New York NY 10019-6907*

ULRICH, LAUREL THATCHER, historian, educator; b. Sugar City, Idaho, July 11, 1938; d. John Kenneth and Alice (Siddoway) Thatcher; m. Gael Dennis Ulrich, Sept. 22, 1958; children: Karl, Melinda, Nathan, Thatcher, Amy. BA in English, U. Utah, 1960; MA in English, Simmons Coll., 1971; PhD in History, U. N.H., 1980. Asst. prof. humanities U. N.H., Durham, 1980-84, asst. prof. history, 1985-88, assoc. prof. history, 1988-91, prof. history, 1991-95; prof. history and woman's studies Harvard U., Cambridge, Mass., 1995—; audiocourse cons. Annenberg Found.; cons., participating humanist numerous exhibits, pub. programs, other projects; project humanist Warner (N.H.) Women's Oral History Project; bd. editors William & Mary Quar., 1989-91, Winterthur Portfolio, 1991—. Author: Good Wives: Image and Reality in the Lives of Women in Northern New England, 1650-1750, 1982, A Midwife's Tale: The Life of Martha Ballard Based on Her Diary, 1785-1812, 1990 (Pulitzer Prize for history 1991); contbr. articles, abstracts, essays and revs. to profl. publs. Coun. mem. Inst. Early Am. History and Culture, 1989-91; trustee Strawberry Banke Mus. 1987-93. John Simon Guggenheim fellow, 1991-92, NEH fellow, 1982, 84-85; women's studies rsch. grantee Woodrow Wilson Fellowship Found., 1979; co-recipient Best Book award Berkshire Conf. Women's Historians, 1990; recipient Best Book award Soc. for History of Early Republic, 1990, John S. Dunning prize and Joan Kelly Meml. prize Am. Hist. Assn., 1990, Bancroft Prize for Am. History, 1991. Mem. Orgn. Am. Historians (nominating com. 1992—, ABC-Clio award com. 1989), Am. Hist. Assn. (rsch. coun. 1993-96). Office: Harvard U Dept History Cambridge MA 02138

ULRICH, MAX MARSH, executive search consultant; b. Kokomo, Ind., Mar. 21, 1925; s. Max Dan and Esther Stone (Marsh) U.; m. Mary Ellen Fisher, Sept. 12, 1950; children—Max Dwight, Jeanne Nanette; m. Geraldine A. Kidd, Jan. 25, 1973; 1 child, Amanda Marsh. B.S., U.S. Mil. Acad., 1946; M.S. in Civil Engring., Mass. Inst. Tech., 1951. Comd. 2d lt. C.E. U.S. Army, 1946, advanced through grades to capt., 1950; resigned, 1954; asst. to mng. dir. Edison Electric Inst., 1954-58; with Consol. Edison Co., N.Y.C., 1958-71; asst. v.p. Consol. Edison Co., 1962-63, v.p. charge advt. and pub. relations, 1963-67, v.p. customer service, 1968-69, v.p. Bklyn. div., 1969-71; prin., dir. Ward Howell Internat. Inc., N.Y.C., 1971-74; pres., chief exec. officer Ward Howell Internat. Inc., 1974-84, chmn., chief exec. officer, 1984-88; pres. Ward Howell Internat. Group, Inc., 1988-92, cons., 1992—. Mem. Sigma Xi. Home: 2 Kingswood Dr Orangeburg NY 10962-1806 Office: Ward Howell Internat Inc 99 Park Ave New York NY 10016-1503

ULRICH, PAUL GRAHAM, lawyer, author, publisher, editor; b. Spokane, Wash., Nov. 29, 1938; s. Donald Gunn and Kathryn (Vandercook) U.; m. Kathleen Nelson Smith, July 30, 1982; children—Kathleen Elizabeth, Marilee Rae, Michael Graham. B.A. with high honors, U. Mont., 1961; J.D., Stanford U., 1964. Bar: Calif. 1965, Ariz. 1966, U.S. Supreme Ct. 1969, U.S. Ct. Appeals (9th cir.) 1965, U.S. Ct. Appeals (5th cir.) 1981. Law clk. judge U.S. Ct. Appeals, 9th Circuit, San Francisco, 1964-65; assoc. firm Lewis and Roca, Phoenix, 1965-70; ptnr. Lewis and Roca, 1970-85; pres. Paul G. Ulrich PC, Phoenix, 1985-92, Ulrich, Thompson & Kessler, P.C., 1992-94; Ulrich, Kessler & Anger, 1995—; pres. Ulrich & Kessler, P.C., 1994-95, Ulrich, Kessler & Anger, P.C., 1995—; owner Pathway Enterprises, 1985-91; judge pro tem Div. 1, Ariz. Ct. Appeals, Phoenix, 1986; instr. Thunderbird Grad. Sch. Internat. Mgmt., 1968-69, Ariz. State U. Coll. Law, 1970-73, 78, Scottsdale Community Coll., 1975-77, also continuing legal edn. seminars. Author and pub: Applying Management and Motivation Concepts to Law Offices, 1985; editor, contbr.: Arizona Appellate Handbook, 1978—, Working with Legal Assistants, 1980, 81, Future Directions for Law Office Management, 1982, People in the Law Office, 1985-86; co-author and pub.: Arizona Healthcare Professional Liability Handbook, 1992, supplement, 1994, Arizona Healthcare Professional Liability Update Manual, 1992, 2d edit., 1995, Arizona Healthcare Professional Liability Update Newsletter, 1992—; co-author: Federal Appellate Practice Guide: Ninth Circuit, 1994; contbg. editor Law Office Economics and Management, 1984—; contbr. articles to profl. jours. Mem. Ariz. Supreme Ct. Task Force on Ct. Orgn. and Adminstrn., 1988-89; mem. com. on appellate cts. Ariz. Supreme Ct., 1990-91; bd. visitors Stanford U. Law Sch., 1974-77; adv. com. legal assisting program Phoenix Coll., 1985-95. With U.S. Army, 1956. Recipient continuing legal edn. award State Bar Ariz., 1978, 86, 90, Harrison Tweed spl. merit award Am. Law Inst./ABA, 1987. Fellow Ariz. Bar Found. (founding 1985—); mem. ABA (chmn. selection and utilization of staff personnel com., econs. of law sect. 1979-81, mem. standing com. legal assts. 1982-86, co-chmn. joint project on appellate handbooks 1983-85, co-chmn. fed. appellate handbook project 1985-88, chmn. com. on liaison with non-lawyer orgns. Econs. of Law Practice sect. 1985-86), Am. Acad. Appellate Lawyers, Am. Law Inst., Am. Judicature Soc. (Spl. Merit Citation 1987), Ariz. Bar Assn. (chmn. econs. of law practice com 1980-81, co-chmn. lower ct. improvement com. 1982-85, co-chmn. Ariz. appellate handbook 1976—), Coll. Law Practice Mgmt., Maricopa County Bar Assn. (bd. dirs. 1994—), Calif. Bar Assn., Phi Kappa Phi, Phi Alpha Delta, Sigma Phi Epsilon. Republican. Presbyterian. Home: 107 E El Caminito Dr Phoenix AZ 85020-3503 Office: 3030 N Central Ave Ste 1000 Phoenix AZ 85012-2717

ULRICH, PETER HENRY, banker; b. Munich, Germany, Nov. 24, 1922; s. Hans George and Hella (Muschweck) U.; m. Carol A. Peek, Oct. 21, 1944; children: Carol Jean (Mrs. D. Scott Hewes), Patricia (Mrs. Damon Eberhart), Peter James. Student, Northwestern U. 1941-42, U. Iowa, 1943, Sch. Mortgage Banking, 1954-56. Lic. real estate broker, cert. mortgage banker; cert. rev. appraiser; cert. mortgage underwriter. Escrow officer Security Title Ins. Co., Riverside, Calif., 1946-53; asst. cashier Citizens Nat. Trust & Savs., Riverside, 1953-57; v.p. Security First Nat. Bank, Riverside, 1957-63; sr. v.p. Bank of Calif. (N.A.), Los Angeles, 1963-72; pres. Ban Cal Mortgage Co., 1972-74, Ban Cal Tri-State Mortgage Co., 1974-75; cons., 1975-76; pres., dir. Beneficial Standard Mortgage Co., 1976-88; real estate cons., 1988—; instr. real estate and bus. San Bernardino Valley Coll., Riverside City Coll., Pasadena City Coll. Pres. Residential Rsch. Com. So. Calif., 1965, Riverside Opera Assn., 1956-59, Riverside Symphony Soc., 1959-61; trustee Idyllwild Arts Found., 1957—, pres., 1970-73, sec., 1986-87; mem. adv. bd. Salvation Army, 1959—, vice chmn., 1971-74, chmn., 1975; chmn. Harbor Light com., 1965-68; convocator Calif. Luth U., 1976-80, 81-83, regent, 1981-90; bd. dirs. Guild Opera Co., 1983—, v.p. 19916, Lark Ellen Lions Charities, 1976—, pres., 1987-90, 94—; treas. Opera Buffs, 1983—; commr. Arcadia Beautiful Commn., 1989—, vice chair, 1991-92, chmn., 1992-93; trustee Calif. Luth. Edn. Found., 1989—; dir. Arcadia Tournament Roses Assn., 1994—; dir. Arcadia Heart Assn., 1995—. Served with AUS, 1943-46. Recipient Resolution of Commendation Riverside City Council, 1963; Resolution of Appreciation Los Angeles City Council, 1968, 1973. Mem. Nat. Mortgage Bankers Assn. (chmn. Life Ins. Co. com. 1986-87), Calif. Mortgage Bankers Assn. (sec. 1965, dir. 1972-75), So. Calif. Mortgage Bankers Assn. (dir. 1975, 80-81, v.p. 1982, pres. 1983), Indland Empire Mortgage Bankers Assn. (pres. 1962, hon. dir.), Assn. Real Estate Execs. (sec. 1967-75, treas. 1975-77, v.p. 1995—). Lutheran. Home: 447 Fairview Ave Unit 2 Arcadia CA 91007-6877 Office: 201 S Lake Ave Ste 409 Pasadena CA 91101-3017 *Being of foreign birth, I particularly appreciate and cherish the American way of life. I am grateful for the opportunities which it has afforded me. I also feel strongly that we who have had the benefit of these opportunities owe something in return to our communities and to our country. I have tried to the best of my abilities to conduct myself and my business affairs in an honorable and forthright manner, thus helping to preserve what I feel is still the best life style in the world.*

ULRICH, RICHARD WILLIAM, finance executive; b. Toledo, Oct. 30, 1950; s. Richard William Josef and Vera (Bender) U.; m. Pamela Ann Momenee, Apr. 19, 1974; 1 child, Nathanial Richard James. BBA, U. Toledo, 1973; postgrad., Stanford U., 1987. CPA, Ill. Sr. acct. Assocs. Mgmt. Co., South Bend, Ind., 1973-76; acquisition analyst Assocs. Fin. Svcs., South Bend, 1975-76; sr. v.p., contr. Assocs. Comml. Corp., Chgo., 1976-87; sr. v.p. corp. fin. Assocs. Corp. N.Am., Dallas, 1987—. Mem. AICPA, Ill. CPA Soc.

ULRICH, ROBERT GARDNER, retail food chain executive, lawyer; b. Evanston, Ill., May 6, 1935; s. Charles Clemens and Nell Clare (Stanley) U.; m. Diane Mary Granzin, June 6, 1964; children—Robert Jeffrey, Laura Elizabeth, Meredith Christine. LL.B. (Law Rev. key), Marquette U., Milw., 1960. Bar: Wis. 1960, Ill. 1960, N.Y. 1981. Law clk. to fed. dist. judge Milw., 1961-62; atty. S.C. Johnson & Son, Inc., Racine, Wis., 1962-65, Motorola, Inc., Franklin Park, Ill., 1965-68; atty., then asst. gen. counsel

Jewel Cos., Inc., Melrose Park, Ill., 1968-75; v.p., gen. counsel Gt. Atlantic & Pacific Tea Co., Inc., Montvale, N.J., 1975—; v.p., gen. counsel Gt. Atlantic & Pacific Tea Co., Inc., 1981—. Mem. Am. Bar Assn., N.Y. State Bar Assn. Home: 500 Weymouth Dr Wyckoff NJ 07481-1217 Office: Gt Atlantic & PacificTea Co Box 418 2 Paragon Dr Montvale NJ 07645-1718

ULRICH, ROBERT GENE, judge; b. St. Louis, Nov. 23, 1941; s. Henry George Ulrich and Wanda Ruth (Engram) Webb; m. JoAnn Demark, July 3, 1965; children—Jill Elizabeth, Jane Ashley. B.A., William Jewell Coll., 1963; J.D., U. Mo.-Kansas City, 1969; LLM, U. Mo., 1972. Bar: Mo. 1969. Assoc. Von Erdmannsdorff, Voigts & Kuhlman, North Kansas City, Mo., 1969-72; pvt. practice Raytown, Mo., 1972; asst. U.S. atty. Dept. Justice, Kansas City and Springfield, Mo., 1973-76, 78-81; ptnr. Pine & Ulrich, Warrensburg, Mo., 1976-77; litigation atty. Shifran, Treiman, et al., Clayton, Mo., 1977-78; U.S. atty. We. Dist. Mo., Kansas City, 1981-89; judge Mo. Ct. Appeals (we. dist.), Kansas City, 1989—; mem. U.S. Atty. Gen.'s Econ. Crime Council, 1983-89 , Atty. Gen.'s Adv. Com. of U.S. Attys., chmn. 1986-89, adv. com. U.S. Ct. Appeals (8th cir.), 1983-86. Appointed mem. steering com. Protect our Children Campaign, Gov. of Mo., chmn. legis. subcom., 1985; mem. resource bd., personnel mgmt. bd. Dept. Justice, 1985-89; trustee Liberty Meml. Assn., 1989—; vice chmn. Orgn. Crime Drug Enforcement Task Force Nat. Program, Dept. Justice, 1987-89. Col. USMC, 1963-66. Mem. Am. Judicature Soc., Inst. Jud. Adminstrn., Mo. Bar Assn., Kansas City Met. Bar Assn., Marine Corps Res. Officers' Assn. (exec. councillor 1986-87), U. Mo-Kansas City Law Sch. Alumni Assn. (v.p. 1994—). Office: Missouri Ct Appeals 1300 Oak St Kansas City MO 64106-2970

ULRICH, ROBERT J., retail discount chain stores executive; b. 1944. Grad., U. Minn., 1967, Stanford U. 1978. Chmn., chief exec. officer, dir. Dayton Hudson Corp.; with Dayton Hudson Corp., Mpls., 1967—; exec. v.p. dept. stores divsn., 1981-84, pres. dept. stores divsn., 1984-87, chmn., CEO Target stores divsn., 1987-93, dir., 1993—, chmn, CEO, 1994—. Office: Dayton Hudson Corp 777 Nicollet Mall Minneapolis MN 55402*

ULRICH, THEODORE ALBERT, lawyer; b. Spokane, Wash., Jan. 1, 1943; s. Herbert Roy and Martha (Hoffman) Ulrich; m. Nancy Allison, May 30, 1966; children: Donald Wayne, Frederick Albert. BS cum laude, U.S. Mcht. Marine Acad., 1965; JD cum laude, Fordham U., 1970; LLM, NYU, 1974. Bar: N.Y. 1971, U.S. Ct. Appeals (2nd cir.) 1971, U.S. Supreme Ct. 1974, U.S. Ct. Claims 1977, U.S. Customs Ct. 1978, U.S. Ct. Internat. Trade 1981, U.S. Ct. Appeals (5th cir.) 1988, U.S. Ct. Appeals (D.C. cir.) 1992, Colo. 1993, U.S. Ct. Appeals (10 cir.) 1994. Mng. clk. U.S. Dept. Justice, N.Y.C., 1968-69, law clk. to federal dist. judge, 1969-70; assoc. Cadwalader, Wickersham & Taft, N.Y.C., 1970-80; ptnr. 1980-94; ptnr. Popham, Haik, Schnobrich & Kaufman, Ltd., Denver, 1994—. Author, editor Fordham Law Rev., 1969. Leader Boy Scouts Am., Nassau County, N.Y., 1984-94. Lt. comdr. USCGR, 1965-86. Mem. ABA, Colo. Bar, Denver Bar, Maritime Law Assn., Fed. Bar Coun., Am. Soc. Internat. Law, Soc. Naval Architects and Marine Engrs., U.S. Naval Inst., Am. Arbitration Assn. Office: Popham Haik 1200 17th St Denver CO 80202

ULRICH, WERNER, patent lawyer; b. Munich, Germany, Mar. 12, 1931; came to U.S., 1940, naturalized, 1945; s. Karl Justus and Grete (Rosenthal) U.; m. Ursula Wolff, June 28, 1959; children—Greta, Kenneth. B.S. Columbia U., 1952, M.S. (NSF fellow 1952-53), 1953, Dr.Engring. Sci., 1957; M.B.A., U. Chgo., 1975; J.D., Loyola U., Chgo, 1985. Bar: Ill. 1985. With AT&T Bell Labs, Naperville, Ill., 1953—; head electronics switching dept. AT&T Bell Labs., Inc., Naperville, Ill., 1964-68; dir. Advanced Switching Tech., Naperville, 1968-77, head maintenance architecture dept., 1977-81; sr. atty. Intellectual Property Law Group, Naperville, 1981—; vis. lectr. U. Calif., Berkeley, 1966-67. Inventor of over 20 telecommunications inventions; patentee electronic switching systems. Fellow IEEE; mem. ABA, Ill. State Bar Assn., Am. Intellectual Property Law Assn., Tau Beta Pi, Beta Gamma Sigma. Office: AT&T Bell Labs Naperville-Wheaton Rd Naperville IL 60566

ULRICH, WERNER RICHARD, union education administrator; b. N.Y.C., Sept. 26, 1941; s. Werner and Erna (Schreiner) U.; m. Marie Sciacca, July 18, 1965; children: Kenneth, Clifford, Richard. AAS, Voorhees Tech. Inst., 1969; BA, SUNY, Old Westbury, 1985; MS, N.Y. Inst. Tech., 1990. Mechanic "A" Con Edison of N.Y., N.Y.C., 1963-68; apprentice steamfitter Steamfitters'; Local Union # 638, Long Island City, N.Y., 1968-73, journeyman steamfitter, 1973-85; dir. edn. Steamfitters' Edn. Fund, N.Y.C., 1985—. Blood dr. coord. Steamfitters', Local Union # 638, Long Island City, 1987—; usher, capt. Holy Name of Mary Roman Cath. Ch., 1984—; mem. steering coun. L.I. Women's Coun., 1992—; skilled worker member emeritus N.Y. State Tng. Partnership Coun., 1993—; mem. S.I. Job Svc. Employer Com., 1993—. With U.S. Army, 1959-62. Recipient John J. Theobald award N.Y. Inst. Tech., 1989, Commr.'s award N.Y. State Dept. Labor, 1991, L.I. Women's award L.I. Women's Coun., 1991, Nassau Civic Club award, 1990. Mem. ASME, Nat. Fire Protection Assn., U.S. Apprenticeship Assn., Am. Legion, K.C. Avocations: horticulture. Office: Steamfitters Tng Ctr 48-03 32d Pl Long Island City NY 11101

ULSAMER, ANDREW GEORGE, federal agency manager; b. Yonkers, N.Y., Nov. 13, 1941; s. Andrew George and Ann Caroline (Bell) U.; m. Mary Ellen Conroy, July 31, 1965; children: Andrew William, Caroline Marie, Stephanie Ann. BS, Siena Coll., 1963; PhD, Albany Med. Coll., 1967. Postdoctoral fellow Nat. Heart and Lung Inst., NIH, Bethesda, Md., 1967-70; biochemist FDA, Washington, 1970-72; chief biochemistry br. Consumer Product Safety Commn., Washington, 1972-80; dir. div. health effects Consumer Product Safety Commn., Bethesda, 1980-86; dir. health scis. Consumer Product Safety Commn., Bethesda, Md., 1987—. Contbr. 50 articles/presentations to profl. jours./socs. Mem. exec. com. Nat. Toxicology Program, 1984—, Nat. Cancer Adv. Bd., Bethesda, Md., 1984—, Com. on Indoor Air Quality, Washington, 1984-87. Mem. Soc. of Toxicology, Assn. Govt. Toxicologists, Nat. Assn. of Watch and Clock Collectors, Sigma Xi. Republican. Roman Catholic. Avocations: malacology, horology. Home: 17 S Duke St Rockville MD 20850-1015 Office: Consumer Product Safety Commn Office of Health Sci 5401 Westbard Ave Washington DC 20207

ULTAN, LLOYD, historian; b. Bronx, N.Y., Feb. 16, 1938; s. Louis and Sophie U. BA cum laude, Hunter Coll., 1959; MA, Columbia U., 1960. Assoc. Edward Williams Coll. Fairleigh Dickinson U., Hackensack, N.J., 1964-74; asst. prof. history Edward Williams Coll. Fairleigh Dickinson U., Hackensack, 1974-75, assoc. prof. Edward Williams Coll., 1975-83, prof. Edward Williams Coll., 1983—; cons. in field. Editor Bronx County Hist. Soc. Press, 1981—; author: The Beautiful Bronx, 1920-50, 1979, Legacy of the Revolution: The Valentine-Varian House, 1983, The Bronx in the Innocent Years, 1890-1925, 1985, The Presidents of the United States, 1989, The Bronx in the Frontier Era: From the Beginning to 1696, 1993, The Bronx: It Was Only Yesterday, 1935-65, 1993. Gen. sec. Bronx Civic League, 1964-67; v.p. bd. trustees Bronx County Hist. Soc., 1965-67, 77-84, curator, 1968-71, pres., 1971-76, historian, 1986—; founding mem. bd. dir. Bronx Coun. on Arts, 1968-71; chmn. Bronx County Bicentennial Commn., 1973-76, Bronx Borough Pres.'s Bicentennial Adv. Com., 1974-76; vice chmn. Commn. Celebrating 350 Yr. of the Bronx, 1989; program guidelines com. N.Y.C. Dept. Cultural Affairs, 1976-77; bd. dirs. Nat. Shrine Bill of Rights, Mt. Vernon, N.Y., 1983—; mem. N.Y.C. Com. on Cultural Concerns, 1982-88; bd. sponsors Historic Preservation com. St. Ann's Ch. Morrisania, 1987—; bd. dirs. 91 Van Cortlandt Owners Corp., 1986—. Recipient Fairleigh Dickinson U. 15-Yr. award, 1979, 20-Yr. award, 1984, 25-Yr. award, 1989, 30-Yr. award, 1994, Outstanding Tchr. of Yr. award, 1994; named to Hunter Coll. Alumni Hall of Fame, 1974; N.Y. State Regents Coll. Teaching fellow, 1959. Mem. AAUP (v.p. Teaneck chpt. 1992-93, sec. coun. of FDU chpts. 1992-93), Am. Hist. Assn., N.Y. Hist. Soc., Phi Alpha Theta, Alpha Chi Alpha, Sigma Lambda. Home and Office: 91 Van Cortlandt Ave W Bronx NY 10463-2712

ULTMANN, JOHN ERNEST, physician, educator; b. Vienna, Austria, Jan. 6, 1925; came to U.S., 1938, naturalized, 1943; s. Oskar and Hedwig (Schechter) U.; m. Ruth E. Layton, May 25, 1952; children: Monica, Michelle, Barry. Student, Bklyn. Coll., 1946, Oberlin Coll., 1946-48; M.D., Columbia U., 1952; Dr honoris causa, Heidelberg U., Fed. Republic

Germany, 1986, Vienna U., Austria, 1991. Diplomate Nat. Bd. Med. Examiners, Am. Bd. Internal Medicine. Intern N.Y. Hosp.-Cornell Med. Center, N.Y.C., 1952-53; resident N.Y. Hosp., 1953-55; Am. Cancer Soc. fellow in hematology Columbia, 1955-56; practice medicine specializing in internal medicine N.Y.C., 1956-68, Chgo., 1968—; mem. staff Francis Delafield Hosp., 1955-68, Presbyn. Hosp., 1956-68, Bellevue Hosp., 1961-68; career scientist Health Research Council City N.Y., 1959-68; cons. Harlem Hosp., N.Y.C., 1966-68; dir. clin. oncology Franklin McLean Meml. Research Inst., 1968-91; prof. medicine Sch. Medicine U. Chgo., 1970—; dir. Cancer Rsch. Ctr., 1973-91, assoc. dir., 1991-94, dir. emeritus, 1994—; dean for rsch. and devel., 1978-88; hon. prof. Cancer Inst. Chinese Acad. Med. Scis., People's Republic of China, 1988; chmn. bd. sci. counselors div. cancer treatment Nat. Cancer Inst., 1976-80, mem. bd. sci. counselors div. cancer prevention and control, 1985-88; mem. adv. bd. Cancer Control to Gov. of Ill., 1976-93, chmn., 1985-93. Asso. editor: Cancer Research, 1974-78; editorial bd.: Annals Internal Medicine, 1974-81, Blood, 1975-77; cons. editor: Am. Jour. Medicine, 1975—; Contbr. articles to profl. jours. Bd. dirs. Assn. Cancer Insts., 1974-75, pres.-elect, 1983-84, pres., 1984-85, chmn. bd., 1985-86; bd. dirs. at-large Ill. div. Am. Cancer Soc., 1976-79; trustee Ill. Cancer Coun., 1976-93; chmn. Nat. Coalition for Cancer Rsch., 1985-90. With AUS, 1943-46. Fellow A.C.P., Inst. Medicine Chgo.; mem. Am. Fedn. Clin. Investigation, Soc. Study Blood, Am. Assn. Cancer Rsch., Am. Socs. Hematology, AAUP, AAAS, Harvey Soc., Am. Soc. Clin. Oncology (dir. 1978-83, pres.-elect 1980-81, pres. 1981-82, past pres. 1982-83), Chgo. Soc. Internal Medicine, Central Soc. Clin. Rsch., Sociedad Chilena de Cancerologia, Sociedad Chilena de Hematologia, Phi Beta Kappa, Alpha Omega Alpha. Home: 5632 S Harper Ave Chicago IL 60637-1872 Office: U Chgo Cancer Rsch Ctr 5841 S Maryland Ave Chicago IL 60637-1470

UMAN, MARTIN ALLAN, electrical engineering educator, researcher, consultant; b. Tampa, Fla., July 3, 1936; s. Morrice S. and Edith G. (Brown) U.; m. Dorit Brigitta Kalbas, Mar. 6, 1962; children: Jon, Mara, Derek. BS in Engring., Princeton U., 1957, MA, 1959, PhD, 1961. Assoc. prof. elec. engring. U. Ariz., Tucson, 1961-65; fellow physicist Westinghouse Rsch. Labs., Pitts., 1965-71; prof. dept. elec. engring. U. Fla., Gainesville, 1971-91, prof., chmn. dept., 1991—; pres. Lightning Location & Protection, Inc., Tucson, 1975-83; mem. Internat. Commn. on Atmospheric Electricity, 1975-92; cons. Boeing Aircraft, Patrick AFB, Mobil Oil Corp., McDonnell Douglas, United Techs., IBM, Flamex Corp., NOAA, NASA, No. Telecom Can., Tampa Cable TV, Bonneville Power Adminstrn., Martin Marietta, Sandia Nat. Labs., Walt Disney World, SRI, other cos. Author: Introduction to Plasma Physics, 1964, Lightning, 1969, rev. edit., 1984, Understanding Lightning, 1971, All About Lightning, 1986, The Lightning Discharge, 1987; also over 125 articles; assoc. editor Jour. Geophys. Rsch., 1980-83; patentee in field. Mem. senate U. Fla., 1988-90, 93—, bd. dirs. div. sponsored rsch., 1989-91. Recipient Outstanding Svc. award Coll. Engring. U. Fla., 1975, Disting. Faculty award Blue Key, 1979-80, Outstanding Tchr. award, 1985-86, Faculty Advisor award, 1986, 88, Tchr.-Scholar of Yr. award, 1988-89; editor's citation Jour. Geophys. Rsch., 1989, Outstanding Fla. Scientist award Fla. Acad. Scis., 1991, Group Achievement award for Galileo Probe Spacecraft NASA, 1992; rsch. grantee various orgns. Fellow IEEE (com. mem. working group on lightning performance distbn. lns. 1979—, working group on estimating performance transmission lns. 1985—), Am. Geophys. Union, Am. Meteorol. Soc.

UMANS, ALVIN ROBERT, manufacturing company executive; b. N.Y.C., Mar. 11, 1927; s. Louis and Ethel (Banner) U.; m. Nancy Jo Zadek, June 28, 1953 (div.); children: Kathi Lee Umans Lind, Craig Joseph; m. Madeleine Sayer, Sept. 21, 1985; 1 child, Valentine Brett. Student, U. Rochester, 1945. Sales mgr. Textile Mills Co., Chgo., 1954-56; regional sales mgr. Reflector Hardware Corp., Melrose Park, Ill., 1956-58; nat. sales mgr. Reflector Hardware Corp., 1959-62, v.p., 1962-65, pres., treas., dir., 1965-92; pres., CEO RHC/Spacemaster Corp., 1992—; chmn. bd., pres. Garcy Corp., Ala.; v.p., bd. dirs. Goer Mfg. Co., Inc., Charleston, S.C., Discovery Plastics, Oreg.; pres., treas., dir. Spacemaster Corp., Del.; dir., v.p. Spartan Showcase Inc., Mo.; dir. Adams Comm., Chgo.; bd. dirs. Monroe Communications, Chgo. Trustee Mt. Sinai Hosp. Med. Ctr., Chgo., chmn. bd. 1987-89; trustee Schwab Rehab. Hosp., Chgo., chmn. bd. 1987-89; dir. Mount Sinai Health System, Chgo.; com. Cook County Bur. Adv. Com.; bd. dirs. Milton & Rose Zadek Fund, 1965-78; governing bd. mem. Cinema/Chgo., 1988-89. Served with AUS, 1945-46. Mem. Nat. Assn. Store Fixture Mfrs. (dir. 1969-70), Chgo. Pres.'s Orgn. Club: Standard (Chgo.). Home: 132 E Delaware Pl Chicago IL 60611-1429 Office: RHC/Spacemaster Corp 1400 25th Ave Melrose Park IL 60160-3001

UMBREIT, WAYNE WILLIAM, bacteriologist, educator; b. Markesan, Wis., May 1, 1913; s. William Traugott and Augusta (Abendroth) U.; m. Doris McQuade, July 31, 1937; children: Dorayne Loreda, Jay Nicholas, Thomas Hayden. B.A., U. Wis., 1934, M.S., 1936, Ph.D., 1939. Instr. soil microbiology Rutgers U., 1937-38; faculty U. Wis., Madison, 1938-44; asst. prof. bacteriology and chemistry U. Wis., 1941-44; faculty Cornell U., 1944-47, prof. bacteriology, 1946-47; head dept. enzyme chemistry Merck Inst., Rahway, N.J., 1947-58; asso. dir., 1958; chmn. dept. bacteriology Rutgers U., New Brunswick, N.J., 1958-75; prof. microbiology, dir. grad. programs Rutgers U., 1969-83, prof. emeritus microbiology, 1983—; dir. labs. So. Br. Watershed Assn., 1983-89. Author: (with Burris, Stauffer) Manometric Techniques, 1945, 5th edit., 1972, (with Oginsky) An Introduction to Bacterial Physiology, 1954, Metabolic Maps, 1960, Modern Microbiology, 1962, Essentials of Bacterial Physiology, 1976; Editor: Advances in Applied Microbiology, vols. 1-10, 1959-68; Contbr. articles to profl. jours. Recipient Biochem. Congress Symposium medal Paris, France, 1952. Fellow Am. Acad. Microbiology, N.Y. Acad. Sci., A.A.A.S.; mem. Am. Soc. for Microbiology (Eli Lilly award in bacteriology 1947, Carski Found. award for distinguished teaching 1968), Soc. Biol. Chemists, Am. Chem. Soc., Theobald Smith Soc. (Waksman award in microbiology 1957, past pres.), AAUP, Sigma Xi. Home: 826 Covered Bridge Rd Holland PA 18966

UMEZAWA, HIROOMI, physics educator, researcher; b. Saitama-ken, Japan, Sept. 20, 1924; came to Can., 1975; s. Junichi and Takako (Sato) U.; m. Tamae Yamagami, July 30, 1958; children: Rui, Ado. B of Engring., U. Nagoya, Japan, 1947, DSc in Physics, 1952. Research asst. U. Nagoya, 1947-53, assoc. prof., 1953; assoc. prof. U. Tokyo, 1955, prof., 1960-64; prof. U. Napoli Inst. Theoretical Physics, Italy, 1964-66; prof. U. Wis., Milw., 1967-67, disting. prof., 1967-75; dir. Inst. Theoretical Physics, Helsinki, Finland, 1965; group leader on structure of matter Centre of Nat. Research Naples div., Italy, 1964-66; Killam Meml. prof. sci., prof. physics U. Alta., Edmonton, Can., 1975-92, Killam prof. emeritus, 1992—; vis. prof. U. Wash., Seattle, 1956, U. Md., College Park, 1957, U. Iowa, Iowa City, 1957, U. Marseille, France, 1959. Mem. editorial bd. Physics Essays, NRC Can.; contbr. numerous articles to profl. jours. ICI fellow U. Manchester, Eng., 1953-55; Lady Davis Sr. scholar, Israel, 1989; Two books published in honor of his 60th birthday, 1985, 86; several internat. workshops held in his honor. Fellow N.Y. Acad. Scis., Am. Phys. Soc., Royal Soc. Can.; mem. Japan Phys. Soc. (life). Office: U Alta, Dept of Physics, Edmonton, AB Canada T6G 2J1

UMMEL, STEPHEN L., health facility administrator; b. Des Moines, Nov. 20, 1941; married; 4 children. BA, Drake U., 1963; MA in Hosp./Health Adminstrn., U. Iowa, 1965. Adminstrv. resident North Colo. Med. Ctr., Greeley, 1964-65; asst. adminstr. Ohio Valley Hosp., Steubenville, 1965-68; asst. dir. Rockford (Ill.) Meml. Hosp., 1968-70, assoc. dir., 1970-73, v.p. adminstrn., 1973; assoc. dir. U. Iowa Hosps. & Clinics, Iowa City, 1973-79; pres. Meml. Hosp./Meml. Health System, South Bend, Ind., 1979—; pres., CEO Luth. Gen. HealthSystem, Park Ridge, Ill.; bd. dirs. Luth. Gen. Health-System, Park Ridge, Ill. Mem. Assn. World Health, Washington, Park Ridge Ctr., Chgo.; chmn., bd. dirs. InterHealth, Mpls.; mem. nominating com., nat. adv. com. The Healthcare Forum, San Francisco; mem. policy com. Nat. Com. for Quality Health Care, Washington; adj. faculty, preceptor grad. program in hosp. and health adminstrn. U. Iowa; mentor J.L. Kellogg Grad. Sch. Bus., Northwestern U.; speaker nat. health convs. Mem. editorial bd. Topics in Health Care Financing; contbr. articles to profl. jours. and mags. Fellow Inst. Medicine Chgo.; mem. Am. Hosp. Assn. (Coll. award 1992), Am. Coll. Healthcare Execs. Office: Luth Gen Hosp 1775 Dempster St Park Ridge IL 60068

UMMINGER, BRUCE LYNN, government official, scientist, educator; b. Dayton, Ohio, Apr. 10, 1941; s. Frederick William and Elnora Mae (Waltemathe) U.; m. Judith Lackey Bryant, Dec. 17, 1966; children: Alison Grace, April Lynn. BS magna cum laude with honors in biology, Yale U., 1963, MS, 1966, MPhil, 1968, PhD, 1969; postgrad., U. Calif., Berkeley, 1963-64; cert. univ. adminstrv./mgmt. tng. program, U. Cin., 1975; cert., Fed. Exec. Inst., 1984. Asst. prof. dept. biol. scis. U. Cin., 1969-73, assoc. prof. dept. biol. scis., 1973-75, acting head dept. biol. scis., 1973-75, prof. dept. biol. scis., 1975-81, dir. grad. affairs, 1978-79; program dir. regulatory biology program NSF, Washington, 1979-84, dept. dir. cellular bioscis. divsn., 1984-89, mem. sr. exec. svc., 1984—, acting divsn. dir., 1985-87, 88-89, divsn. dir. cellular bioscis. divsn., 1989-91, divsn. dir. integrative biology and neurosci. divsn., 1991—; sr. advisor on health policy Office of Internat. Health Policy Dept. State, Washington, 1988; sr. advisor on biodiversity Smithsonian Instn., 1993-94; exec. sec. Nat. Sci. Bd. Com. on Ctrs. and Individual Investigator Awards, 1986-88; mem. NSF rev. panel Exptl. Program to Stimulate Competitive Rsch, 1989, Rsch. Improvement in Minority Instns., 1986, 87, U.S.-India Coop. Rsch. Program, 1981-82, U.S.-India Exchange of Scholars Program, 1979-81; vice chmn. biotech. rsch. subcom. Fed. Coord. Coun. on Sci. Engring. and Tech., 1994, Office Sci. and Tech. Policy, 1991-94; exec. sec. subcom. biodiversity and ecosystem dynamics, com. on environment and natural resources Nat. Sci. and Tech. Coun., 1994; mem. group nat. experts on safety in biotech., OECD, 1988-89; mem. sr. exec. panel Exec. Potential Program, Office Pers. Mgmt., 1988-89; mem. space shuttle proposal rev. panel in life scis. NASA, 1978, rsch. assocs. in space biology award com., 1985-91, chmn. cell and devel. biology discipline working group, space biology program, 1990-91, chmn. gravitational biology panel, NASA Specialized Ctrs. Rsch. and Tng., 1990, mem. exec. steering com. in life scis., 1991, mem. gravitational biology facility sci. working group, 1992—, mem. NASA neurolab. steering com., 1993; mem. panel study biol. diversity, Bd. Sci. and Tech. Internat. Devel. NRC, 1989; exec. sec. adv. planning bd. Nat. Biodiversity Info. Ctr., Smithsonian Instn., 1993-94; mem. adv. screening com. in life scis. Council for Internat. Exchange of Scholars, 1978-81; liaison rep. nat. heart, lung and blood adv. council NIH, 1979-87, nat. adv. child health and human devel. coun., 1990—; recombinant DNA adv. com., 1988; liaison rep. agrl. biotech. rsch. adv. com. USDA, 1989-94, mem. interagy. rsch. animal com., 1984-88; interagy. working group internat. biotech., 1988-94. Author book chpts. and contbr. articles to profl. jours.; assoc. editor Jour. Exptl. Zoology, 1977-79; editorial adv. bd. Gen. and Comparative Endocrinology, 1982. Mem. world mission com. Ch. of the Redeemer, New Haven, 1967-68; Sun. sch. steering com. Calvary Episcopal Ch., Cin., 1972-73, sr. acolyte, 1972-77, adult edn. com., 1975-76; adv. com. mem. Wakefield High Sch., 1991-92, PTA exec. bd., 1991-92; sci. adv. com. Arlington Pub. Schs., 1987-92, adv. coun. on instrn., 1991-92; adv. bd. mem. Campbell Comml. Coll., Cin., 1977-79. Recipient George Rieveschl, Jr. Rsch. award U. Cin., 1973, Outstanding Performance award and Sustained Superior Performance NSF, 1981, spl. achievement award 1985, Sr. Exec. Svc. Performance award 1986, 87, 90, 91, Presdl. Rank Meritorious Exec. award 1992; U. Cin. Grad. Sch. fellow 1977—, NSF fellow 1964; rsch. grantee NSF 1971-79. Fellow AAAS (coun. 1980-83, 89-90, mem. programm com. for 1989 annual meeting 1988, chairperson-elect sect. G.-Biol. Scis. 1987-88, chairperson 1988-89, ret. 1989-90, mem. steering group sect. com. G 1987-90), N.Y. Acad. Scis.; mem. Am. Soc. Zoologists (sec., mem. exec. com. 1979-81, chmn. nominating com. 1981, sec. divsn. of comparative physiology and biochemsitry 17, chmn. Congl. Sci. Fellow Program com. 1986-89, mem. 1991-93), Am. Physiol. Soc. (program adv. com. 1978-81, program sec. com. 1983-86, mem. steering com., comparative physiology sect. 1978-81, sec. Am. Physiol. Soc.-Am. Soc. Zoologists Task Force on Comparative Physiology 1977-78), Am. Inst. Biol. Scis. (chmn. selection com. congl. fellow liaisons com. 1991), Am. Soc. for Gravitational and Space Biology, Sr. Execs. Assn., Assn. of Yale Alumni (del. 1990-93), Mory's Assn., Yale Club (Washington), Masons (32 degree), K.T., Shriners, Sigma Xi (Disting. Rsch. award U. Cin. chpt. 1973, pres. U. Cin. chpt. 1977-79), Mensa. Presbyterian. Achievements include development of science policy in biodiversity, space biology, integrative biology, neuroscience, and biotechnology; research in low temperature biology, in comparative physiology, endocrinology and biochemistry of fish, and in visual orientation of crustacea. Home: 4087B S Four Mile Run Dr Arlington VA 22204-5604 Office: NSF Divsn Integrative Biology and Neuroscience 4201 Wilson Blvd Arlington VA 22230-0001

UMSCHEID, LUDWIG JOSEPH, computer specialist; b. N.Y.C., Dec. 30, 1937; s. Ludwig and Bertha (Gruber) U.; m. Carole Patricia Fisher, Apr. 22, 1967. BS, Fordham U., 1959; MS, Adelphi U., 1963, NYU, 1967. Computer programmer Svc. Bur. Corp., IBM, N.Y.C., 1962; systems analyst Computer Applications Inc., N.Y.C., 1963-71; rsch. meteorologist, maj. systems specialist Environ. Rsch. Labs., NOAA, U.S. Dept. Commerce, Princeton, N.J., 1971—. Contbr. articles to profl. jours. Bd. dirs. Stony Brook Millstone Watershed Assn., Princeton; co-founder, v.p. Friends of Hopewell Valley Open Space, Pennington, N.J.; mem. Pennington Planning Bd.; chair Pennington Environ. Commn. 1st lt. USAF, 1959-62. Mem. AAAS, IEEE Computer Soc., Am. Meteorol. Soc., Assn. Computer Machinery, Assn. N.J. Environ. Commns., N.Y. Acad. Scis. Achievements include pioneering use of Fast Fourier Transforms for polar filtering in numerical weather prediction. Office: US Dept Commerce GFDL/NOAA PO Box 308 Princeton NJ 08542-0308

UMSTED, LOUIS FRANKLIN, manufacturing executive; b. Phila., Oct. 31, 1928; s. Louis Franklin and Alyce Benson (Rutherford) U.; m. Peggy J. Hatmaker, Aug. 6, 1955; children: Nancy Sullivan, Eric Umsted, Jennifer McKinley. BA, U. Washington, 1951. Sales rep. Nat. Can Corp., San Francisco, 1958-62, dist. sales mgr., 1962-68; gen. sales mgr. Nat. Can Corp., Chgo., 1968-71, v.p. sales and mktg., 1971-77, sr. v.p. sales and mktg., 1977-83, exec. v.p. sales and mktg., 1983-86, vice-chmn., 1986-88; vice-chmn. corp. mktg. Am. Nat. Can Co., Chgo., 1988—; also bd. dirs.; bd. dirs. Barry-Wehmiller Co., St. Louis, 1980—; mem. standing com. Can Mfrs. Inst., Washington, 1982—. bd. dirs., chmn. compensation com. King Bruwaert House, Hinsdale, Ill., 1987. Lt. (j.g.) USNAC, 1951-55. Mem. Hinsdale Golf Club. Republican. Mem. Evangelical Covenant Ch. Avocations: tennis, golf, woodworking. Office: Am Nat Can Corp 8770 W Bryn Mawr Ave Chicago IL 60631-3515

UNAKAR, NALIN JAYANTILAL, biological sciences educator; b. Karachi, Sindh, Pakistan, Mar. 26, 1935; came to U.S., 1961; s. Jayantilal Virshankar and Malati Jaswantrai (Buch) U.; m. Nita Shantilal Mankad; children: Rita, Rupa. BS, Gujerat U., Bhavnagar, India, 1955; MSc, Bombay U., 1961; PhD, Brown U., 1965. Research asst. Indian Cancer Research Ctr., Bombay, 1955-61; USPHS trainee in biology Brown U., Providence, 1961-65; research assoc. in pathology U. Toronto, Ont., Can., 1965-66; asst. prof. biology Oakland U. Rochester, Mich., 1966-69, assoc. prof., 1969-74, prof., chmn. biology dept., 1974-87; prof., 1974—; adj. prof. biomed. scis. Oakland U., Rochester, Mich., 1984—; mem. coop. cataract research group Nat. Eye Inst., Bethesda, Md., 1977—; mem. visual scis. study sect. NIH, Bethesda, 1982-86, mem. cataract panel, 1980—. Mem. vis. bd. Lehigh U., Bethlehem, Pa., 1986-89. Grantee Nat. Cancer Inst., NIH, 1967-70, Nat. Eye Inst., NIH, 1976—. Mem. AAAS, Am. Soc. Cell Biology, Assn. Rsch. in Vision and Ophthalmology, Sigma Xi. Home: 2822 Rhineberry Rd Rochester Hls MI 48309-1912 Office: Oakland U Dept Of Biol Scis Rochester MI 48309

UNANUE, JOSEPH, food products executive. Chmn., CEO Goya Foods, Secaucus, NJ. Office: Goya Foods Inc 100 Seaview Dr Secaucus NJ 07094-1887

UNDERBERG, ALAN J., lawyer; b. Rochester, N.Y., Oct. 12, 1929; s. Henry and Anne (Landau) U.; m. Joyce Wisbaum, Oct. 19, 1952; children: Mark A., Amy Allen, Lisa Hamburg, Kathryn Zimmerman. BS, Cornell U., 1951; JD, Harvard U., 1956. Bar: N.Y. 1956, U.S. Dist. Ct. (we. dist.) N.Y. 1957, U.S. Supreme Ct. 1961. Ptnr. Underberg & Kessler, Rochester, 1963—; cons. to Commn. on Govt. Procurement, Washington, 1970-71. Commr., co-founder Monroe County Human Rels. Commn., Rochester, 1961-64; trustee The Harley Sch., Rochester, 1972-75; mem. bd. mgrs. Meml. Art Gallery, Rochester, 1978—, pres., 1990-92; mem. N.Y. State Bd. Equalization and Assessment, Albany, 1976-84; mem. Nat. Pk. Sys. Adv. Bd., Dept. Interior, 1981-85, chmn., 1983-84; bd. govs. The Genesee Hosp., Rochester, 1984—, chmn., 1987-89; chmn. The Genesee Hosp. Health Sys. Inc., 1989-94; vice chmn. Greater Rochester Health Sys., Inc., 1994—; bd.

dirs. Managerial Econs. Rsch. Ctr., William E. Simon Grad. Sch. Bus. Adminstrn.; bd. trustees U. Rochester, 1986, mem. exec. com., 1988—; chmn. U. Rochester Assocs., 1976-77; bd. dirs. YMCA Greater Rochester, 1980-86, mem. exec. com., 1982-86. 1st lt. USAF, 1951-53. Mem. ABA, Monroe County Bar Assn. (bd. dirs. Found. 1985-88), N.Y. Bar Assn. (lectr. continuing legal edn. program 1962-69, com. corp. law, banking, corp. and bus. law sect. 1963—), Genesee Valley Club (pres. 1985-87), Country Club Rochester, Cornell Club N.Y.C., Harvard Club N.Y.C. Avocations: golf, tennis, skiing. Office: Underberg & Kessler 1800 Chase Sq Rochester NY 14604-1989

UNDERBERG, MARK ALAN, lawyer; b. Niagara Falls, N.Y., July 9, 1955; s. Alan Jack and Joyce Love (Wisbaum) U.; m. Diane Englander, Mar. 22, 1986; children: Andrew Englander, James Englander. BA, Cornell U., 1977, JD, 1981. Bar: N.Y. 1981. Law clk. to chief judge U.S. Ct. Appeals (3d cir.), Wilmington, Del., 1981-82; assoc. Debevoise & Plimpton, N.Y.C., 1982-87; mng. dir., dep. gen. counsel Henley Group, Inc., N.Y.C., 1987-90, mng. dir., gen. counsel, 1990-92; v.p., gen. counsel Abex Inc., Hampton, N.H., 1992—; v.p., gen. counsel Fisher Sci. Internat. Inc., Hampton, N.H., 1991—. Editor-in-chief Cornell Law Rev., 1980-81. Mem. ABA, Assn. of Bar of City of N.Y., Genesee Valley Club, University Club. Office: Abex Inc 645 Fifth Ave 12th Fl New York NY 10022

UNDERCOFLER, J(ONAS) CLAYTON, lawyer; b. Phila., June 11, 1940; s. Jonas Clayton and Margaret (Huff) U.; m. Lesley Mowlds, Aug. 28, 1965; children: James C., Randall T. BS, Drexel U., 1962; JD, Villanova U., 1966. Bar: Pa. 1967. Law clk. Judge Thomas J. Clary, Phila., 1966-67; assoc. Clark, Ladner, Fortenbaugh & Young, Phila., 1967-69; asst. U.S. atty. U.S. Atty.'s Office, Phila., 1969-76, U.S. atty., 1976; vis. asst. prof. Villanova (Pa.) U., 1976-77; mem. Undercofler & Hannum, West Chester, Pa., 1977, Dilworth, Paxon, Kalish & Kauffman, Phila., 1977-86, Saul, Ewing, Remick & Saul, Phila., 1986—; mem. Civil Justice Reform Act Adv. Group, Phila., 1991—. Chmn. Southeastern Pa. Transp. Authority, 1988-94; bd. dirs. Greater Phila. Econ. Devel. Coalition, 1989—, Citizens Crime Commn., Delaware Valley, 1992, Greater Phila. First Partnership for Econ. Devel., 1994—. Named Citizen of the Yr. Delaware Valley March of Dimes, 1991. Fellow Am. Coll. Trial Lawyers; mem. ABA, Fed. Bar Assn. (Outstanding Younger Fed. Lawyer 1973), Phila. Bar Assn., Pa. Bar Assn., nat. Assn. of Former U.S. Attys., Greater Phila. C. of C. Office: Saul Ewing Remick & Saul 3800 Centre Square W Philadelphia PA 19102

UNDERDOWN, DAVID EDWARD, historian, educator; b. Wells, Eng., Aug. 19, 1925; s. John Percival and Ethel Mary (Gell) U. B.A., U. Oxford, 1950, M.A., 1951; M.A., Yale U., 1952; B.Litt., U. Oxford 1953; D.Litt. hon., U. of South, 1981. Asst. prof. U. of South, Sewanee, Tenn., 1953-58, assoc. prof., 1958-62; then assoc. prof. U. Va., Charlottesville, 1962-68; prof. Brown U., Providence, 1968-85, Munro-Goodwin Wilkinson prof., 1978-85; vis. prof. Yale U., New Haven, 1979; prof. Yale U., 1986-94, George Burton Adams prof., 1994—; dir. Yale Ctr. Parliamentary History; vis. Mellon prof. Inst. for Advanced Study, 1988-89; vis. fellow All Souls Coll., Oxford, 1992; Ford's lectr. Oxford U., 1992. Author: Royalist Conspiracy in England, 1960, Pride's Purge, 1971, Somerset in the Civil War and Interregnum, 1973, Revel, Riot and Rebellion, 1985, Fire from Heaven, 1992. Guggenheim fellow, 1964-65, 91-92, fellow Am. Coun. Learned Socs., 1973-74, NEH fellow, 1980-81. Fellow Royal Hist. Soc., Brit. Acad. (corrs.); mem. Am. Hist. Assn., Conf. Brit. Studies. Office: Yale U Dept History New Haven CT 06520

UNDERDUE, MARILYN ROSETTA, special education educator; b. Washington, Apr. 20, 1944; d. Houston Cohen Green and Rosetta Virginia (Blackwell) Green Mitchell; m. Hollowell Shields Jones, May 10, 1969 (div. Apr. 1976); 1 child, Alia Michele; m. William Henry Underdue, May 29, 1982. BS, D.C. Tchrs. Coll., 1967. Cert. tchr., D.C. Tchr. 3d grade Washington Pub. Schs., 1967-69; tchr. spl. edn. Dept. of Edn., Wahiawa, Hawaii, 1969-71; tchr. spl. edn. resource D.C. Pub. Schs., Washington, 1972—. Mem. Coun. for Exceptional Children, Blackwell Family Assn. (recording sec. 1973-90, corres. sec. 1990-92, scholarship co-chair 1990-92), P.G. Jack and Jill Am. (fin. sec. 1984-86, treas. 1986-88, Svc. award 1984, 86, 89, 90), Phi Delta Kappa. Democrat. Episcopalian. Avocations: shopping, reading, gardening, cooking, walking. Home: 11306 White House Rd Upper Marlboro MD 20772

UNDERHILL, ANNE BARBARA, astrophysicist; b. Vancouver, B.C., Can., June 12, 1920; d. Frederic Clare and Irene Anna (Creery) U. BA, U. B.C., 1942, MA, 1944, DSc (hon.), 1992; PhD, U. Chgo., 1948; DSc (hon.), York U., Toronto, Ont., 1969. Sci. officer Dominion Astrophys. Obs., Victoria, B.C., 1949-62; prof. astrophysics U. Utrecht, The Netherlands, 1962-70; lab chief Goddard Space Flight Ctr./NASA, Greenbelt, Md., 1970-77, sr. scientist, 1978-85; hon. prof. U. B.C., Vancouver, 1985—. Author: The Early-type Stars, 1966; author/editor: B Stars with and without Emission Lines, 1982, O, Of and Wolf-Rayet Stars, 1988; contbr. articles to profl. jours. Fellow NRC, 1948, Can. Fedn. Univ. Women, 1944, 47. Fellow Royal Soc. Can., Royal Astron. Soc.; mem. Internat. Astron. Union (pres. commn. #36 1963-66), Am. Astron. Soc., Can. Astron. Soc. Anglican. Avocation: church choir singing. Office: U BC, Dept Geophysics & Astronomy, Vancouver, BC Canada V6T 1Z4

UNDERHILL, JACOB BERRY, III, retired insurance company executive; b. N.Y.C., Oct. 25, 1926; s. Jacob Berry, Jr. and Dorothy Louise (Quinn) U.; m. Cynthia Jane Lovejoy, Sept. 9, 1950 (div. Sept. 1962); children: David Lovejoy, Kate Howell Underhill Kerwin, Benedict Quinn; m. Lois Beachy, Nov. 2, 1963 (div. July 1987); m. Betsy F. Ashton, Oct. 17, 1987. Grad., Phillips Exeter Acad., 1944; A.B., Princeton U., 1950. Editor Courier & Freeman, Potsdam, N.Y., 1950-53; reporter Democrat & Chronicle, Rochester, N.Y., 1953-56; chief editorial writer St. Petersburg (Fla.) Times, 1956-59; assoc. editor McGraw Hill Publ. Co., N.Y.C., 1959-61, Newsweek, N.Y.C., 1961-63; assoc. press sec. to Gov. N.Y., 1963-67; dep. supt., 1st dep. supt. State N.Y. Ins. Dept., 1967-72; v.p., sr. v.p., exec. v.p., dir., vice chmn. bd., pres. N.Y. Life Ins. Co., N.Y.C., 1972-86. Chmn. bd. dirs. Manhattan Eye, Ear and Throat Hosp.; trustee emeritus Nat. Trust for Hist. Preservation. With USNR, 1944-46. Mem. Players Club, Links Club, Piping Rock Club (Locust Valley, N.Y.). Home: 410 E 57th St New York NY 10022-3059

UNDERHILL, ROBERT ALAN, consumer products company executive; b. Columbus, Ohio, June 9, 1944; s. Robert Alan and Grace Ruth (Smith) U.; m. Lynn Louise Stentz, Oct. 18, 1963; children: Robert Alan III, Richard Louis. Student, Case Western Res. U., 1962-64, Ohio State U., 1965. With tech. svc. dept. Gen. Tire & Rubber Co., Akron, Ohio, 1966-69; quality control engr. Edmont-Wilson Co., Canton, Ohio, 1969-70; mgr. quality assurance Pharmaseal Labs., Massillon, Ohio, 1970-72; mgr. R&D Internat. Playtex Corp., Paramus, N.J., 1972-78; mgr. R&D Kimberly-Clark Corp., Neenah, Wis., 1978-80, dir. R&D, 1980-83, v.p. R&D, 1983-93, sr. v.p. R&D, sr. tech. officer, 1994—; trustee United Health Group, 1994—, chmn. compensation com., 1994—; trustee Novus Health Group, 1993-94; bd. dirs. Appleton (Wis.) Med. Ctr., 1993—. Patentee (U.S. and fgn.) med. device. Mem. exec. bd. Bay Lakes coun. Boy Scouts Am., 1988-92; bd. dirs. Outagamie County (Wis.) Chpt. ARC, 1993—, chmn. nominations com., 1993—; mem. exec. com., 1994—. Mem. Pi Delta Epsilon. Republican. Avocations: stock market investment analysis, travel. Home: 1225 W Cedar St Appleton WI 54914 Office: Kimberly-Clark Corp 2100 Winchester Rd Neenah WI 54956 also: 1400 Holcomb Bridge Rd Roswell GA 30076-2199

UNDERWEISER, IRWIN PHILIP, mining company executive, lawyer; b. N.Y.C., Jan. 3, 1929; s. Harry and Edith (Gladstein) U.; m. Beatrice J. Kortchmar, Aug. 17, 1959; children: Rosanne, Marian, Jeffrey. B.A., CCNY, 1950; LL.D., Fordham U., 1954; LL.M., NYU, 1961. Bar: N.Y. 1954. With firm Scribner & Miller, N.Y.C., 1951-54, 56-62; partner firm Feuerstein & Underweiser, 1962-73, Underweiser & Fuchs, 1973-77, Underweiser & Underweiser, 1977—; v.p., sec. Sunshine Mining Co., Kellogg, Idaho, 1965-70, chmn. bd., 1970-78, pres., 1971-74, 77, v.p., 1977-83; vice chmn., dir. Underwriters Bank and Trust Co., N.Y.C., 1969-73; dir. Anchor Post Products, Inc. Bd. dirs. Silver Inst. Inc.; gen. counsel, mem. bus. council Friends City Center Music and Drama, N.Y.C., 1966-67; pres. W. Quaker Ridge Assn., 1969-70; treas. Scarsdale Neighborhood Assn. Presidents, 1970-71. Served with AUS, 1954-56. Mem. Am. N.Y. State bar assns., Bar Assn. City N.Y., Phi Beta Kappa, Phi Alpha Theta. Home: 7 Rural Dr Scarsdale NY 10583-7701 Office: 405 Park Ave New York NY 10022-4405

UNDERWOOD, BERNARD EDWARD, religious organization administrator; b. Bluefield, W.Va., Oct. 26, 1925; s. W. B. and Annie Theresa (Bain) U.; m. Esther Parramore, Dec. 22, 1947; children: Paul, Karen, Pam. BA, Emmanuel Coll., Franklin Springs, Ga., 1947; MA, Marshall U., 1954. Lic. to ministry Pentecostal Holiness Ch., 1942; ordained, 1944. Mem. Pentecostal Holiness Youth Soc. bd. Va. conf. Pentecostal Holiness Ch., Kingsport, Tenn., 1946-53; Christian edn. dir. Pentecostal Holiness Ch., Conf., 1951-60, asst. supt., 1958-64; supt. Va. conf. Pentecostal Holiness Ch., Roanoke, 1964-69, 74-78; exec. dir. world missions Pentecostal Holiness Ch., Oklahoma City, 1969-73, 77-89, vice chmn., 1981-89, gen. supt., 1989—. Author: Gifts of the Spirit, 1967, Spiritual Gifts: Ministries and Manifestations, 1984, 16 New Testament Principles for World Evangelization, 1988; contbr. numerous articles to profl. jours. Phi Alpha Theta scholar, 1954. Mem. Nat. Assn. Evangelicals (mem. exec. com. 1989—), Pentecostal Fellowship N.Am. (pres. 1991—), Pentecostal Renewal Svcs. (chmn. 1987—), Evang. Fgn. Missions Assn. (bd. adminstrn. 1981—). Republican. Avocation: reading. Office: Pentecostal Holiness Ch PO Box 12609 Oklahoma City OK 73157-2609

UNDERWOOD, CECIL H., company executive, past governor of West Virginia; b. Josephs Mills, W.Va., Nov. 5, 1922; s. Silas and Della (Forrester) U.; m. Hovah Hall, July 25, 1948; children: Cecilia A., Craig Hall, Sharon. AB, Salem (W.Va.) Coll., 1943; AM, W.Va. U., 1952; AM research fellow, Amelia Earhart Found., Ann Arbor, Mich., 1954-56; LLD, Marietta (Ohio) Coll., 1957, Bethany (W.Va.) Coll., 1957, W.Va. U., 1957, W.Va. Inst. Tech., 1957, W.Va. State Coll., 1961, Concord Coll., 1960; D of Humanics, Salem Coll., 1957; Dr. Pub. Administrn., W.Va. Wesleyan Coll., 1958; LHD (hon.), Shepherd Coll., 1964; LittD, Western New Eng. Coll., 1969. Tchr. high sch., 1943-46; mem. staff Marietta Coll., 1946-50; v.p. Salem Coll., 1950-56; gov. State of W.Va., 1957-61; v.p. Island Creek Coal Co., 1961-64; dir. civic affairs Monsanto Co., 1965-67, v.p., 1967; pres. Cecil H. Underwood Assocs., 1965-80, Franswood Corp., 1968-75, Bethany (W.Va.) Coll., 1972-75, Princess Coals, Inc., Huntington, 1978-81, Morgantown (W.Va.) Indsl. Park, Inc., 1983—; Software Valley, 1989-92, Mon View Heights of W.Va., 1993—; field underwriter N.Y. Life Ins. Co., 1976-78;, 1994; chmn. bd. Princess Coals, Inc., Huntington, 1981-83; sec. bd. dirs. Huntington Fed. Savs. and Loan Assn.; bd. dirs. Huntington Found. Mem. W.Va. Ho. Dels., 1944-56, minority floor leader, 1949, 51, 53, 55; Mem. exec. com. Gov.'s Conf., 1959; chmn. So. Regional Edn. Bd., 1959-60; Pres. Young Republican League of W.Va., 1946-50; parliamentarian Young Rep. Nat. Conv., Boston, 1951; del.-at-large Rep. Nat. Conv., 1960, 64, 72, 76, 80, 84, 88, temporary chmn., 1960; Chmn. bd. dirs. W.Va. Found. Ind. Colls.; Appalachian Regional Hosps.; chmn. bd. dirs. W.Va. div. Am. Cancer Soc., nat. bd. dirs., chmn. nat. crusade com., 1976-77, chmn. com. on legacies and planned giving, 1979; chmn. bd. dirs. Salem Coll., 1978-89, Salem Teikyo U., 1989—; bd. dirs. Higher Edn. Loan Program of W.Va., 1980-94; chair W.Va. Coun. on Vocat. Edn., 1982—; chair W.Va. State Coll. System, 1991; regional vice chmn. Boy Scouts Am., 1961-67. With U.S. Army Enlisted Res. Corps, 1942-43. Mem. Nat. Assn. State Coun. Vocat. Edn. (pres. 1994—), Masons, Shriners, Elks, Rotary, Sigma Phi Epsilon, Pi Kappa Delta. Methodist. Home: 609 13th Ave Huntington WV 25701-3227 Office: PO Box 2685 Huntington WV 25726-2685

UNDERWOOD, HARRY BURNHAM, II, financial executive, accountant; b. Easton, Pa., Jan. 6, 1943; s. Harry Burnham and Edythe (Walters) U.; m. Nancy Chostner, Nov. 23, 1963; children: Cheryl, Cathy A., Davidson Coll., 1964; MBA, U. N.C., 1966. CPA, N.C. Sr. auditor Haskins & Sells, Charlotte, N.C., 1968-72; controller Chadbourn, Inc., Charlotte, 1972-73, Rose's Store, Inc., Henderson, N.C., 1973-78; v.p., treas. Best Products Co., Inc., Richmond, Va., 1978-81; v.p., treas. Lowe's Cos., Inc., North Wilkesboro, N.C., 1981-84, sr. v.p., treas., chief fin. officer, 1985—. Pres. United Way, Wilkes County, N.C., 1986-87, chmn. bd. dirs. United Way of N.C., 1991-92. Served to 1st lt. U.S. Army, 1966-68. Fellow Am. Inst. CPA's, Fin. Exec. Inst. Presbyterian. Lodge: Rotary (pres. N. Wilkesboro 1985-86). Home: 371 Pine Valley Rd Winston Salem NC 27104-1809 Office: Lowe's Cos Inc PO Box 1111 North Wilkesboro NC 28656

UNDERWOOD, JAMES MARTIN, business executive; b. Pitts., Feb. 27, 1909; s. Fred P. and Jean (Martin) M.; m. Anne E. Saxman, Dec. 31, 1931 (dec. Mar. 1974); children: Ann Eliza, James Martin, Thomas Saxman, Charles; m. Alice A. Clemens, Dec. 1976 (dec. Apr. 1985); m. Evelyn Crane, Oct. 1985. B.S., U. Pitts., 1930; M.B.A., Harvard, 1932. Asst. sec.-tres. Vulcan Mold & Iron Co. (name changed to Vulcan, Inc. 1967), 1935-40, pres., dir., 1946-74, chmn. bd., 1946-81; exec. v.p. Toyad Corp., Latrobe, 1941; founder, pres. Halund Co., 1941-45; gen. sales mgr. Latrobe Electric Steel Co., 1945-46, dir., 1948-75; chmn. bd. Umec Corp., Latrobe, 1983—, Shepard Niles Crane & Hoist Co., Montour Falls, N.Y., 1988—; chmn. The Underwood Group, Latrobe, 1989—. Mem. Western Pa. Hosp. Coun., 1969-79, v.p., 1972-76; exec. com. Economy League Western Pa., 1974-80; Republican nominee 21st Congl. Dist. Pa., 1940; councilman, Latrobe, 1943-69, pres., 1953-69; del. Rep. Nat. Conv., 1960, 68; dir. Westmoreland Airport Authority, 1951-76, chmn., 1951-68; bd. dirs. Latrobe Hosp., 1948-82, pres., 1961-66; trustee Community Chest, St. Vincent Coll., 1954-71, U. Pitts., 1964-71. Mem. Am. Iron and Steel Inst., Young Presidents Orgn., Def. Orientation Conf. Assn. (dir.), Phi Delta Theta. Presbyn. (trustee). Clubs: Rolling Rock (Ligonier, Pa.); University, Duquesne, Oakmont Country (Pitts.); Latrobe Country; Sea Island (Ga.); Cottage Owners. Lodges: Masons (32 deg.), Shriners, Jesters, Elks. Home (summer): Saxman Dr Ext 13 Saxman Dr Latrobe PA 15650 Home (winter): Cottage 164 Sea Island GA 31561 Office: Box 29 Latrobe PA 15650

UNDERWOOD, JANE HAINLINE HAMMONS, anthropologist, educator; b. Ft. Bliss, Tex., Oct. 30, 1931; d. Frank and Lydia (Williams) Hammons; m. Van K. Hainline, Oct. 20, 1947 (div. 1966); children: Michael K., Susan J.; m. John W. Underwood, July 4, 1968; 1 dau., Anne K. A.A., Imperial Valley Coll., 1957; B.A., U. Calif., Riverside, 1960; M.A., UCLA, 1962, Ph.D., 1964. Asst. prof. U. Calif., Riverside, 1963-68; research anthropology Yap Islands, 1964, 65-66; prof. anthropology U. Ariz., Tucson, 1968—; assoc. dean Grad. Coll. U. Ariz., 1979-80, asst. provost for grad. studies, 1980-82, acting dir. Sch. Health Related Professions, 1980-82, asst. v.p. research, assoc. dean Grad. Coll., 1982-87; assoc. Micronesian Area Research Ctr., 1987—. Contbr. articles to profl. jours. Woodrow Wilson fellow, 1960-61; UCR Sr. Faculty fellow, 1968. Fellow AAAS; mem. Am. Assn. Phys. Anthropologists (v.p. 1980-82), Assn. Study Human Biology, Pacific Sci. Assn. (life), Sigma Xi (pres. U. Ariz. chpt. 1981-82). Home: 2228 E 4th St Tucson AZ 85719-5118 Office: Dept Anthropology U Ariz Tucson AZ 85721

UNDERWOOD, JOANNA DEHAVEN, environmental research and education organizations president; b. N.Y.C., May 25, 1940; d. Louis Ivan and Helen (Guiterman) U.; m. Saul Lambert, July 31, 1982; stepchildren: Jonathan Whitty, Katherine Aviva. B.A., Bryn Mawr Coll., 1962; Diplome d'etudes de Civilisation francaise with honors, Sorbonne U., Paris, 1963. Audio-visual dir. Planned Parenthood World Population, N.Y.C., 1968-70; co-dir. Council on Econ. Priorities, N.Y.C., 1970-73; pres. INFORM, Inc., N.Y.C., 1973—; bd. dirs. N.Y. State Energy R&D Authority, Albany, Hampshire Rsch. Inst., Clean Sites, Rocky Mountain Inst.; mem. Dow Environ. Adv. Coun., 1992—; awards com. Pres.'s Coun. on Environ. Quality, 1991. Author (with others) Voices from the Environmental Movement: Perspectives for a New Era, 1991; co-author: Paper Profits, 1971; editor: The Price of Power, 1972; contbr. articles to profl. jours. Circle of dirs. Planned Parenthood of N.Y. Recipient U.S. EPA Environ. Achievement award, 1987, 92. Home: 138 E 13th St New York NY 10003-5306 Office: Inform Inc 120 Wall St 16th Fl New York NY 10005-4001

UNDERWOOD, PATRICIA RUTH, clinical nursing educator, consultant; b. Lubbock, Tex., Dec. 7, 1939; d. Thomas S. Underwood and Lilian (Baker) Davis. BS in Nursing, U. Colo., 1962; MA, NYU, 1965; D Nursing Sci., U. Calif., San Francisco, 1978. Lectr. U. San Francisco, 1969-73; clin. specialist Langley Porter Inst., San Francisco, 1973-79; clin. cnslt. U. Calif., San Francisco, 1979-88, prof. clin. nursing, 1988—; cons. VA. Western Region, 1975—; Hasegawa Hosp., Japan, 1984—; dept. nursing Tel Aviv U., 1986—,

N.Mex. State Hosp., 1988-92; commr. San Francisco Health Commn., 1989-91. Fellow Am. Acad. Nursing; mem. Am. Nurses Assn., Calif. Nursing Assn. (pres. 1983-85), Sigma Theta Tau. Democrat. Office: U Calif San Francisco Dept Mental Health Community Adminstry Nu San Francisco CA 94143

UNDERWOOD, PAUL, brokerage house executive; b. N.Y.C., Jan. 23, 1940; s. Charles U. and Louise (Saunders) U. B.A., St. John's U., Jamaica, N.Y., 1964. Sr. v.p. E.F. Hutton & Co. Inc., N.Y.C., to 1986; mng. dir. Smith Barney, Harris Upham, N.Y.C., 1986—, exec. v.p., 1991—; also bd. dirs. Smith Barney, Harris Upham; past chmn. bd. NSCC, N.Y.C.; past pres. SOD, N.Y.C.; dir. Fin. Industry Securities Council. Trustee, chmn. Am. Composers Orchestra; bd. dirs. N.Y. Found. Arts. Served with U.S. Army. Office: Smith Barney Harris Upham & Co 21st 23rd & 32nd Fls 1345 Avenue Of The Americas New York NY 10105-0216

UNDERWOOD, PAUL BENJAMIN, obstetrician, educator; b. Greer, S.C., Aug. 8, 1934; s. Paul Benjamin and Gladys (Guest) U.; m. Peggy Joyce Outen, July 7, 1957; children: Paul Benjamin III, Mary Barton. MD, Med. U. S.C., 1959. Diplomate Am. Bd. Ob-Gyn, Am. Bd. Gynecol. Oncology. Intern Med. U. S.C., Charleston, 1959-60, resident, 1960-64; fellow M.D. Anderson Hosp. and Tumor Inst., Houston, 1966-67; asst. prof. U. S.C., 1967-70, assoc. prof., 1970-74, prof., 1974-79; chmn. dept. ob-gyn U. Va. Sch. Medicine, Charlottesville, 1979—. Contbr. numerous articles to med. jours. With USN, 1964-66. Recipient Alumni of Yr. award Med. U. S.C., 1989. Mem. Am. Coll. Ob.-Gyn., Soc. Gynecol. Oncologists (coun. 1972-75, v.p. 1977-78, pres. 1983), Am. Assn. Gyn.-Obs. (sec. 1992—), Felix Rutledge Soc. (pres. 1977), So. Med. Soc., Charlottesville Med. Soc., S.C. Obstet. and Gynecol. Soc., Thegos Soc., Alpha Omega Alpha. Office: U Va School Medicine Med Ctr PO Box 387 Charlottesville VA 22908

UNDERWOOD, RICHARD ALLAN, English language educator; b. Plymouth, Mich., Mar. 28, 1933; s. Harold Raymond and Yvonne Clara (Foster) U.; m. Sandra Jane Hayes, Nov. 17, 1962; 1 child, Eric Michael. BA, U. Mich., 1955, MA, 1967, PhD, 1970. Asst. prof. Clemson (S.C.) U., 1970-77, assoc. prof., 1977-84, prof. English, 1984—. Author: A Little Bit of Love, 1963, Shakespeare's "The Phoenix and Turtle": A Survey of Scholarship, 1974, Shakespeare on Love: The Poems and the Plays, 1985, The Two Noble Kinsmen and Its Beginnings, 1993; translator: En Smula Karlek, 1969, 81; editor: Phoenix with a Bayonet: A Journalist's Interim Report on the Greek Revolution (by Bayard Stockton), 1971. 1st lt. U.S. Army, 1955-57. Fellow Bread Loaf Writers Conf., 1963; vis. scholar Rackham Sch. Grad. Studies, U. Mich., 1983-85, 90-91, 91-92, 92-93, 93-94. Avocation: piano music. Home: 106 Blue Ridge Dr Clemson SC 29631-1713 Office: Clemson U 809 Strode Clemson SC 29631-1436

UNDERWOOD, ROBERT A., congressional delegate, university official; b. Tamuning, Guam, July 13, 1948; m. Lorraine Aguilar; 5 children. BA with honors in History, Calif. State U., 1969, MA in History, 1971; cert. edn. adminstrn., U. Guam, 1976; DEd, U. So. Calif., 1987. Loader, sorter United Parcel Svc., L.A., 1966-72; tchr. George Washington High Sch., 1972-74, asst. prin. for bus. and student pers., 1974-76; asst. and acting prin. Inarajan Jr. High Sch., 1976; instr., dir. bilingual bicultural tng. program U. Guam, 1976-81, asst. prof., 1981-83, dir. bilingual edn. assistance for Micronesia project, 1983-88, dean Coll. Edn., 1988-90, acad. v.p., 1990—; del. 103d Congress from Guam, 1993—; part-time curriculum writer Guam Bilingual Edn. Project, 1973-76. Roman Catholic. Office: US Delegate 424 Cannon Ho Office Bldg Washington DC 20515-5301

UNDERWOOD, SANDRA JANE, university administrator; b. Highland Park, Mich., Dec. 14, 1941; d. Donald Earl and Delores Irene (Campbell) Hayes; m. Richard Allan Underwood, Nov. 17, 1962; 1 child, Eric Michael. BA in Polit. Sci. and Pub. Adminstrn., Stephens Coll., 1987. Data mgr., rsch. analyst, div. bus. and fin. Clemson (S.C.) U., 1977-81, higher edn. project adminstr., planning/budgets, 1981-84, planning and rsch. coord., planning/budgets, 1984-86, dir. mgmt. svcs., 1986-88, asst. to v.p. bus. and fin., 1988-90, dir. univ. planning, 1989-90, dir. strategic planning and quality mgmt., 1990—; cons. colls. and univs. S.C. and Calif., 1989—. Author: Economic Development in S.C.--The Research University Link, 1987; co-editor: Alternatives for Growth, 1978. W.K. Kellogg Found. co-grantee, 1994. Mem. Am. Mgmt. Assn., World Future Soc., Assn. Women Profls., Soc. Coll. and Univ. Planning, Clemson Lions (bd. dirs. 1991-92). Avocations: poetry, philosophy, chaos theory. Home: 106 Blue Ridge Dr Clemson SC 29631 Office: Clemson U 201 Brackett Hall Clemson SC 29634-5160

UNDERWOOD, STEVEN CLARK, publishing executive; b. Arlington Heights, Ill., Dec. 1, 1960; s. Donald William and Mary Frances (Clark) U. BBA, U. Tex., 1982, MBA, 1987; JD, So. Meth. U., 1985. Bar: Tex. 1985. Sr. fin. analyst CBS, Inc., N.Y.C., 1987-89; assoc. bus. mgr. Supplementary Edn. Group Simon & Schuster, Englewood Cliffs, N.J., 1989-90; bus. mgr. Fearon/Janus/Quercus divsn. Simon & Schuster, Belmont, Calif., 1990-92, pres. Fearon/Janus/Quercus divsn., 1992-93; pres. Globe Fearon divsn. Simon & Schuster, Upper Saddle River, N.J., 1993—. Mem. ABA, Am. Mgmt. Assn. (pres.'s assn.), Assn. Am. Pubs., Nat. Eagle Scout Assn., Coll. Bus. Adminstrn. Found., Tex. Bar Assn., Tex. Alumni Assn., U. Tex. Century Club, Alpha Phi Omega, Beta Gamma Sigma, Phi Kappa Phi, Phi Eta Sigma, Golden Key. Republican. Methodist. Avocations: sailing, scuba diving, camping, rafting. Home: 123 Magnolia Rd Ramsey NJ 07446-1145

UNDERWOOD, VERNON O., JR., grocery stores executive; b. 1940. With Youngs Market Co., L.A., pres., from 1976, chmn. bd., 1989—; also chief exec. officer. Office: Young's Market Co 500 S Central Ave Los Angeles CA 90013-1715

UNDLIN, CHARLES THOMAS, banker; b. Madison, Minn., Mar. 4, 1928; s. Jennings C. and Alice M. (Berg) U.; m. Lois M. Anderson, June 23, 1953; children: Sarah, Mary Lee, Margaret, Thomas. BA, St. Olaf Coll., 1950. Asst. cashier Northwestern State Bank, Osseo, Minn., 1950-55, N.W. Bancorp., Mpls., 1955-57, Security Bank & Trust Co., Owatonna, Minn., 1957-59, Norwest Bank Black Hills, Rapid City, S.D., 1959-67; pres. and chief exec. officer Norwest Bank S.D., Rapid City, 1967-84, vice-chmn., 1984-85; pres. Norwest Bank Nebr., Omaha, 1985-88, also bd. dirs.; vice-chmn. Rushmore State Bank, Rapid City, 1988—; bd. dirs. Black Hills Corp. Past bd. dirs. Fed. Res. Bank, Mpls.; bd. dirs. Children's Hosp., Omaha, 1986. Sgt. U.S. Army, 1951-52. Mem. S.D. Bankers Assn. (past pres.), Arrowhead Country Club. Republican. Lutheran. Avocations: golf, skiing, fishing. Office: Rushmore State Bank PO Box 2290 Rapid City SD 57709-2290

UNGAR, ERIC EDWARD, mechanical engineer; b. Vienna, Austria, Nov. 12, 1926; came to U.S. 1939; s. Irwin Isidor and Sabina (Schlesinger) U.; m. Goldie Edna Becker, July 1, 1951; children: Judith Fishman, Susan Green, Ellen Borgenicht, Sharon Ungar Lane. BSME, Washington U., St. Louis, 1951; MS, U. N.Mex., 1954; Eng.Sc.D., NYU, 1957. Aero-ordnance engr. Sandia Corp., Albuquerque, 1951-53; research scientist/asst. prof. NYU, 1953-58; chief cons. engr. Bolt Beranek & Newman, Inc., Cambridge, Mass., 1958—; chief engring. scientist Acentech Inc., Cambridge, part-time 1993—. Co-author: Structure-Borne Sound, 1973, 2nd edit. 1988; contbr. articles to profl. jours., chpts. to books. 1st lt. U.S. Army, 1945-48; ETO. Fellow ASME (life fellow, chmn. design engring. div. 1978-80, Centennial medallion 1981, Per Bruel Gold medal for noise control and acoustics 1994), AIAA (assoc. fellow), Acoustical Soc. Am. (pres. 1991-92, Trent-Crede Silver medal 1983); mem. Inst. for Noise Control and Engring. (bd. dirs.). Home: 15 Considine Rd Newton MA 02159-3603 Office: BBN Systems & Tech 10 Moulton St Cambridge MA 02138-1119

UNGAR, IRWIN ALLAN, botany educator; b. N.Y.C., Jan. 21, 1934; s. Isador and Gertrude (Fageles) U.; m. Ana Celia Del Cid, Aug. 10, 1959; children: Steven, Sandra, Sharon. BS, CCNY, 1955; MA, U. Kans., Lawrence, 1957, PhD, 1961. Instr. U. R.I., Kingston, 1961-62; asst. prof. Quincy Coll., Ill., 1962-66; asst. prof. Ohio U., Athens, 1966-69, assoc. prof., 1969-74, prof. botany, 1974—, chmn. dept., 1984-89—; dir. Dysart Woods Lab., 1985—, dir. Environ. Studies Program, 1991—; vis. prof. dept. plant scis. and vis. fellow Wolfson Coll., Oxford U., Eng., 1990-91; panelist Nat. Sea Grant Program, 1984; grant proposal reviewer NSF, 1980-92; manuscript

reviewer Am. Jour. Botany, 1972-92, Bot. Gazette, 1976-92; contbr. articles to profl. jours. NSF grantee, 1974-76, 76-78, 80-83, 94-95. Fellow Ohio Acad. Sci.; mem. AAAS, Bot. Soc. Am., Ecol. Soc. Am., Sigma Xi. Home: 44 Walker St Athens OH 45701-2252 Office: Ohio Univ Dept Of Botany Athens OH 45701

UNGAR, MANYA SHAYON, volunteer, education consultant; b. N.Y.C., May 30, 1928; d. Samuel and Ethel M. (Liese) Shayon; m. Harry Fireman Ungar, June 25, 1950; children: Paul Benedict, Michael Shayon. BA, Mills Coll., 1950. Actress TV and radio NBC, CBS, N.Y.C., 1950-58; founder chpt. AFS, Scotch Plains-Fanwood, N.J., 1958-60; vol. project dir. Boy Scouts Am., Plainfield, N.J., 1958-61; founder, co-dir. Summer Theater Workshop, Scotch Plains, 1967-78; legis. v.p. N.J. State PTA, 1977-79, pres., 1979-81; legis. v.p. Nat. PTA, Chgo., 1981-85, 1st v.p., 1985-87, pres., 1987-89; Mem. arts edn. adv. panel Nat. Endowment Arts, Washington, 1988-91, panel Nat. Inst. Work and Learning, 1988-91; adv. coun. Nat. Panel Drug Free Schs., Washington, 1989-91, edn. adv. bd. NDIC, 1988-92, PBS, 1988-91, Scholastic, Inc., 1990-94; bd. dirs. Math. Sci. Edn. Bd., 1988-92. Trustee N.J. Children's Specialized Hosp., 1990—, N.J. Pub. Edn. Inst., 1987—; mem. adv. coun. Natural Resources Def. Coun., Mothers and Others, 1990—; mem. geography assessment adv. coun. Nat. Assessment Edn. Progress, 1991-92, mem. nat. oversite commn. on geog. stds., 1992-94; mem. N.J. Basic Skills Coun., 1990-94; chmn. N.J. Math. Coalition, 1994—; mem. accreditation com. APA, 1992—; mem. tchr. programs adv. panel Ednl. Testing Svc., 1990-94; mem. external rev. com. Ctr. Disease Control Preventing Risk Behaviors in Adolescents, 1993; voters svc. dir. N.J. LWV, 1995—; bd. dirs. Washington Rock Girl Scout Coun., 1995—. Manya Shayon Ungar Scholarship and Auditorium named in her honor, 1989; named Outstanding Citizen N.J. Jaycees, 1979, Scotch Plains Twp., 1989, 92, State of N.J., 1987, Bd. of Freeholders, 1987; named life mem. nat. PTA, 45 state PTAs. Mem. LWV (chmn. voter svc. Westfield area 1991, voters svc. Westfield area 1991—). Avocations: piano, acting, singing, recording talking books. Home: 10 Brandywine Ct Scotch Plains NJ 07076-2550

UNGARO, EMANUEL MATTEOTTI, fashion designer; b. Aix-en-Provence, France, Feb. 13, 1933; s. Cosimo and Concetta (Casalino) U.; m. Laura; 1 dau. Student, Lycée, Aix-en-Provence, 1943-50. Worked with father as tailor Aix-en-Provence, 1951-54; then for Camps Paris, 1955-57; with Cristobal Balenciaga, Paris, 1957-64, dir. Balenciaga br., Madrid, 1958-60; worked for André Courréges, Paris, 1964; ind. couturier, Paris, 1965. Designer of both couture and ready-to-wear men's and women's fashions; also fragrance designer since 1977. Office: 2 Ave Montaigne, F 75008 Paris France also: 650 Fifth Ave 20th fl New York NY 10019

UNGARO, JOSEPH MICHAEL, newspaper publishing executive, consultant; b. Providence, Nov. 4, 1930; s. Rocco and Lucy (Mott) U.; m. Evelyn Short, Apr. 15, 1961; children: Elizabeth Anne, Joseph Michael, Ellen Lucia. B.A., Providence Coll., 1952; M.S. in Journalism, Columbia, 1953. With Providence Jour.-Bull., 1951-73, mng. editor Evening Bull., 1967-72; mng. editor Eve. Bull., also dir. planning and devel. Providence Jour. and Bull., 1972-73; mng. editor Westchester-Rockland Newspapers, White Plains, N.Y., 1974-75, v.p., exec. editor, 1975-84, pres., gen. mgr., 1984-86, pres., publisher, 1986-90; pres., chief exec. officer Detroit Newspaper Agy., 1990-91; cons., 1991—. Mem. Am. Newspaper Pubs. Assn. (past chmn. research inst., conv. program com.), Am. Soc. Newspaper Editors, AP Mng. Editors Assn. (past pres.). Home: 379 Pond Shore Dr Charlestown RI 02813-0824

UNGARO, SUSAN KELLIHER, magazine editor. Editor-in-chief Family Circle mag., N.Y.C. Office: Family Circle 110 Fifth Ave New York NY 10011*

UNGARO-BENAGES, URSULA MANCUSI, federal judge; b. Miami Beach, Fla., Jan. 29, 1951; d. Ludivico Mancusi-Ungaro and Ursula Berliner; m. Michael A. Benages, Mar., 1988. Student, Smith Coll., 1968-70; BA in English Lit., U. Miami, 1973; JD, U. Fla., 1975. Bar: Fla. 1975. Assoc. Frates, Floyd, Pearson et al, Miami, 1976-78, Blackwell, Walker, Gray et al, Miami, 1978-80, Finley, Kumble, Heine et al, Miami, 1980-85, Sparber, Shevin, Shapo et al, Miami, 1985-87; cir. judge State of Fla., Miami, 1987-92; U.S. dist. judge Miami, 1992—; mem. Fla. Supreme Ct. Race & Ethnic & Racial Bias Study Commn., Fla., 1989-92, St. Thomas U. Inns of Ct., Miami, 1991-92. Bd. dirs. United Family & Children's Svcs., Miami, 1981-82; mem. City of Miami Task Force, 1991-92. Mem. ABA, Fed. Judges Assn., Fla. Assn. Women Lawyers, Dade County Bar Assn. Office: US Dist Ct 300 NE 1st Ave Rm 243 Miami FL 33132-2126

UNGER, BARBARA, educator, poet; b. N.Y.C., Oct. 2, 1932; d. David and Florence (Schuchalter) Frankel; m. Bernard Unger, 1954 (div. 1976); m. Theodore Sakano, 1987. B.A., CCNY, 1955, M.A., 1957; advanced cert. NYU, 1970; children: Deborah, Suzanne. Grad. asst. Yeshiva U., 1962-63; edn. editor County Citizen, Rockland County, N.Y., 1960-63; tchr. English, N.Y.C. Pub. Schs., 1955-58, Nyack (N.Y.) High Sch., 1963-67; guidance counselor Ardsley (N.Y.) High Sch., 1967-69; prof. English, Rockland Community Coll., Suffern, N.Y., 1969—; poetry fellow Squaw Valley Community of Writers, 1980; writer-in-residence Rockland Ctr. for Arts, 1986. Author: (poetry) Basement, 1975, Learning to Fox Trot, 1989, The Man Who Burned Money, 1980, Inside the Wind, 1986, Blue Depression Glass in Troika One, 1991; (fiction) Dying for Uncle Ray, 1990; contbr. poetry to over 50 lit. mags. including: Kans. Quar., Carolina Quar., Beloit Poetry Jour., Minn. Rev., Poet and Critic, The Nation, Poetry Now, Invisible City, Thirteenth Moon, So. Poetry Rev., Mass. Rev., Nebr. Rev., Wis. Rev., So. Humanities Rev., Denver Quarterly, Mississippi Valley REv., The G.W. Rev. Wordsmith; contbr. to Anthology Mag. Verse, Yearbook Am. Poetry, 1984, 89; contbr. poetry (anthologies) Two Worlds Walking, Life on the Line, Looking for Home, 80 on the Eighties, Disenchantments, Women and Work, If I Had a Hammer, Sexual Harassment: Women Speak Out; contbr. fiction to True to Life Adventure Stories, Midstream, Esprit, Beloit Fiction Jour., Am. Fiction '89 and numerous others; poetry reading in colls. and libraries throught N.Y. and elsewhere; critical reviewer Contact II. Ragdale Found. fellow, 1985, 86, 89, SUNY Creative Writing fellow, 1981-82, Edna St. Vincent Millay Colony fellow, 1984, Djerassi Found. fellow, 1991, Hambidge Ctr. for Creative Arts and Scis. fellow, 1988; NEH grantee, 1975. Recipient Goodman Poetry award, 1989, Anna Davidson Rosenberg award Judah Magnes Mus., 1989, Roberts Writing award, 1990, New Letters Literary awards, 1990; finalist Am. Fiction Competition, 1989, W.Va. Writing Competition, 1982, John Williams Narrative Poetry Competition, 1992; honorable mention Chester Jones Nat. Poetry Contest. Mem. Poets and Writers, Poetry Soc. Am., Writers' Community. Office: Rockland Community Coll 145 College Rd Suffern NY 10901-3611

UNGER, HOWARD ALBERT, artist, photographer, educator; b. Mt. Vernon, N.Y., Oct. 13, 1944; s. Howard Albert and Florence A. (Peterson) U.; m. Anrita Abelow, Aug. 25, 1972; 1 son, Christopher Howard. Student, Art Students League, N.Y.C., 1972; l son, Christopher Howard. Student, N.Y. Inst. Holography, 1976; B.F.A., Kent State U., 1966, M.A., 1968; M.Ed., Columbia U., 1972, Ed.D., 1975; MA, N.Y. Inst. Tech., 1994. Cert. open water diver, 1988, advanced scuba diver, 1989. Grad. teaching fellow in photo-journalism Kent State U., 1966-67, instr. in art, 1966-67, grad. teaching fellow in art, 1967-68; head program in art, tchr. art Kew-Forest Prep. Sch., Kew Gardens, N.Y., 1968-69; technician TV sta. Tchrs. Coll., Columbia U., 1971-72, instr. art and edn., 1972-75, instr. curriculum and teaching, 1976-82, instr. dept. communication, computing and tech. in edn., 1982—; asst. prof. visual communications tech. dept. humanities Ocean County Coll., 1972-78, assoc. prof., 1979-82, prof., 1982—; gallery coordinator Fine Arts Ctr., Ocean County Coll., 1972—; instr. communications and edn. sch. Edn. NYU, 1974-76; design and photograph coordination RCA Records, N.Y.C., 1969-70; freelance designer, 1965—. Exhibitor photography in one-man shows, Photographis Societas Photographis, Columbia U., 1971, Ziegfeld Gallery, N.Y.C., 1972, group shows, Kent State U., 1965-68, Ocean County Coll., 1973-83, permanent collections, Internat. Ctr. Photography, N.Y.C., Mus. Holography, N.Y.C., Kent State U., Ocean County Coll., Tchrs. Coll., Columbia U., pvt. collections; lectr. in photography; co-author: (with William Maxwell) photog. illustrator Printmaking: A Beginner's Handbook, 1977; photog. illustrator: The Fourth R. Stewart Kranz, 1971; contbg. author: A Tour Through The Realm of Science Plus Art, 1974; photography critic: Village Voice, 1976-77;

photography columnist Soho Weekly News, 1977-78. Recipient 1st place award Am. Greeting Card Competition, 1966; recipient honararium dept. curriculum and teaching Tchrs. Coll., Columbia U., 1973. Mem. Soc. Photography Educators, NEA, Mus. Modern Art, N.J. Edn. Assn., Met. Mus. Art, Am. Mus. Natural History, Profl. Assn. Diving Instrs. (lic. advanced scuba diver), Am. Assn. Underwater Instrs. (lic. advanced scuba diver). Republican. Lutheran. Home: 437 E 76th St New York NY 10021-2564 Office: Ocean County Coll College Dr Toms River NJ 08753-2102

UNGER, IRWIN, historian, educator; b. Bklyn., May 2, 1927; s. Elias C. and Mary (Roth) U.; m. Bernate Myra Spaet, Feb. 1956 (div.); children—Brooke David, Miles Jeremy, Paul Joshua; m. Debi Irene Weisstein, May 11, 1970; stepchildren—Anthony Allen, Elizabeth Sarah. B.Social Scis., City Coll. N.Y., 1948; M.A., Columbia, 1949, Ph.D., 1958; student, U. Wash., 1949-51. Instr. Columbia, 1956-58; vis. lectr. U. P.R., 1958-59; asst. prof. Long Beach (Calif.) State Coll., 1959-62; assoc. prof. U. Calif., Davis, 1962-66; prof. history NYU, NYC, 1966—. Author: The Greenback Era: A Social and Political History of American Finance, 1865-1879, 1964, The Movement: A History of the American New Left, 1974: (with Debi Unger) The Vulnerable Years: The United States, 1896-1917, Turning Point: 1968, 1988. Served with AUS, 1952-54. Recipient Pulitzer prize for history, 1965; Guggenheim fellow, 1972-73, Rockefeller humanities fellow, 1980-81, Harry Frank Guggenheim fellow, 1987-88. Home: 473 West End Ave New York NY 10024

UNGER, PAUL A., packaging executive; b. San Diego, Sept. 10, 1914; s. Louis A. and Ray (Seidman) U.; m. Sonja Franz, Jan. 2, 1947; children Alan, Gerald, Tamara Hyman. AB, Harvard U., 1936. With pub. rels. dept. Works Progress Adminstrn., Washington, 1936-39; with community rels. Dept. U.S. Housing Authority, Washington, 1939-44; relief adminstr. UN Relief and Rehab. Adminstrn., Egypt and Yugoslavia, 1944-47; deputy asst. sec. U.S. Dept. of Interior, Washington, 1947-50, internat. specialist, 1950-53; devel. mgr. The Unger Co., Cleve., 1953-57, pres., 1957-62, 64-88, chmn., 1988-93; sr. advisor, 1994—, The Unger Co., Cleve., 1994—; dep. adminstr. U.S. Dept. Commerce, Washington, 1962-63; mem. U.S. com. Internat. Coun. on Social Welfare; organizer, leader tours to Yugoslavia, Hungary, Austria, Czechoslovakia, East Germany, Poland, USSR, China. Pres. Coun. Internat. Programs; chmn. Cleve. adv. subcom. U.S. Commn. on Civil Rights; chmn. Mayor's Urban Renewal Task Force, Presdl. Campaign Coms. for No. Ohio, Gov.'s Internat. Trade Coun. Recipient Recognition award, Rotary, 1974, Neighborhood Ctrs. Assn. 1978, Inernat. Exch. award Coun. Internat. Programs, 1985. Mem. City Club (trustee 1972-75, v.p. 1975), Forum Found. (pres. 1988-91), Cleve. Coun. on World Affairs (program chmn., v.p., mem. exec. com.), English Speaking Union (past pres. Cleve. br., nat. v.p.), Cleve. Skating Club, Cleve. Playhouse Club, Cleve. Blue Book. Home: 15830 S Park Blvd Cleveland OH 44120-1671 Office: Ste 241 13110 Shaker Sq Cleveland OH 44120-9999

UNGER, PAUL WALTER, soil scientist; b. Winchester, Tex., Sept. 10, 1931; s. Edwin Herman and Elsie Anna (Schmidt) U.; m. Barbara Charlene Dutton, Sept. 13, 1960; children: Gary Robert, Paula Dianne. BS, Tex. A&M U., 1961; MS, Colo. State U., 1963, Ph.D. Soil scientist USDA Agrl. Rsch. Svc., Bushland, Tex., 1965-81, soil scientist/rsch. leader, 1981-87, supervisory soil scientist/rsch. leader, 1987-93, soil scientist, 1994—; cons. Food and Agrl. Orgn. UN, Rome, 1986. Author or co-author bulls. and articles; co-editor conf. proc.; editor book. With U.S. Army, 1952-55. Recipient Disting. Svc. award Great Plains Agrl. Coun., 1984; named Scientist of Yr., USDA-Agrl. Rsch. Svc., So. Plains Area, 1987. Fellow Am. Soc. Agronomy (select com. 1988-89), Soil Sci. Soc. Am. (assoc. editor 1977-82, div. chmn. 1986, mem. selection com. 1994—, applied rsch. award 1991), Soil and Water Conservation Soc. (various local and state offices, photog. awards 1990-92); mem. Internat. Soil Tillage Rsch. Orgn., Internat. Soil Sci. Soc., World Assn. Soil and Water Conservation, Coun. Agrl. Sci. and Tech. Lutheran. Avocations: photography, gardening, woodworking. Office: USDA Agrl Rsch Svc PO Box 10 Bushland TX 79012-0010

UNGER, PETER KENNETH, philosophy educator; b. N.Y.C., Apr. 25, 1942; s. Sidney and Naomi (Fein) U.; m. Susan Gill, June 2, 1977; 1 child, Andrew. BA, Swarthmore Coll., 1962 DPhil, Oxford U., Eng., 1966. Instr. U. Wis., Madison, 1965-66, asst. prof., 1966-70, assoc. prof., 1970-72; assoc. prof. NYU, N.Y.C., 1972-75, prof., 1975—. Author: Ignorance, 1975, Philosophical Relativity, 1984, Identity, Consciousness and Value, 1990; contbr. articles to profl. jours. Guggenheim fellow, 1974, NEH fellow, 1993. Mem. Am. Philos. Assn., Oxfam Am. (mem. N.Y. com.). Democrat. Home: 100 Bleecker St New York NY 10012-2202 Office: Dept Philosophy NYU 503 Main Bldg Washington Sq New York NY 10003

UNGER, RICHARD WATSON, history educator; b. Huntington, W.Va., Dec. 23, 1942; s. Abraham I. and Marion Patterson (Simons) U.; m. Katharine Lawrence, June 4, 1966; 1 child, Emily Patterson. B.A., Haverford Coll., Pa., 1963; A.M., U. Chgo., 1965; M.A., Yale U., 1967, M.Phil., 1969, Ph.D., 1971. Prof. dept. history U. B.C., Vancouver, Can., 1969—. Author: Dutch Shipbuilding Before 1800, 1978; The Ship in the Medieval Economy, 600-1600, 1980; The Art of Medieval Technology: The Image of Noah the Shipbuilder, 1991; editor: Cogs, Caravels and Galleons, 1994; co-editor: Nautical Archaeology: Progress and Public Responsibility, 1984; co-editor: Studies in Medieval and Renaissance History, 1978—; contbr. articles to profl. jours. Trustee Vancouver Maritime Mus., 1979-83. Mem. Medieval Assn. Pacific pres. 1994—, Econ. History Soc., Soc. Nautical Rsch. Office: U BC, Dept of History, Vancouver, BC Canada V6T 1Z1

UNGER, ROBERT MARTIN, lawyer, author, professional speaker, singer; b. N.Y.C., Jan. 26, 1954; s. Alex and Rose (Stuchinsky) U.; m. Phyllis Hollander; children: Adam Paul, Samantha Faye. BA magna cum laude, John Jay Coll., 1976; JD, Fordham U., 1979. Ptnr. Kupillas, Unger & Kupillas, Great Neck, N.Y., 1982—; counsel State Sen. Frank Padavan, Queens, 1985—; counsel Ins. Dept. Chgo. Tribune in N.Y., 1982—. Author: Tune In To Success: Strategies For Achieving Your Greatest Potential; talk show host WMCA Radio N.Y.; spokesman for Hooked on Phonics. Pres. 25 A.D. Rep. Club, Queens, 1989—; bd. dirs. Anti-Defamation League-L.I. chpt., 1989—, Queens Farm Mus., 1988—, Playing It Safe, Pride of Judea. Mem. N.Y. State Trial Lawyers Assn., Queens County Bar Assn., Great Neck Village Assn., Nat. Speakers Assn., Great Neck C. of C., Rotary, KP. Republican. Jewish. Avocation: family activities. Home: 38 Windsor Rd Great Neck NY 11021-2740 Office: Kupillas Unger & Kupillas 316 Great Neck Rd Great Neck NY 11021

UNGER, RONALD LAWRENCE, lawyer; b. Flushing, N.Y., June 8, 1930; s. Joseph and Rose (Weinstein) U.; m. Benita Kronish, July 11, 1954; children: Paul S., Thomas A. A.B., Bucknell U., 1951; LL.B. Harvard U., 1954. Office: Kaye Scholer Fierman Hays & Handler 425 Park Ave New York NY 10022-3506

UNGER, SONJA FRANZ, package company executive, travel consultant, ceramist; b. Zagreb, Croatia, former Yugoslavia, Oct. 28, 1921; came to U.S., 1947; d. Karl Dragutin and Elisabeth (Bihler) Franz; m. Paul A. Unger, Jan. 2, 1947; children: Alan, Gerald, Tamara. BS in Engring., U. Zagreb, 1944, MS in Architecture, 1945. City planner Ministry of Constrn., Zagreb, 1945-47; architect Don Graham, Washington, 1947-53; corp. sec., designer The Unger Co., Cleve., 1953-94; travel cons. Kollander World Travel, Cleve., 1985—; vis. com. mem. Case Western Res. U., Cleve. Mem. citizens adv. com. Juvenile Ct. Cuyahoga County, Ohio; asst. sec. Glenville Neighborhood Ctr., Cleve.; vice chmn., sec. Cuyahoga County Dem. Exec. Com., Cleve.; ward leader Shaker Heights Dem. Party, 1958-78; forelady Grand Jury Cuyahoga County; v.p. Nationalities Svc. Ctr., Cleve.; mem. Cercle/Confs. Francaises. Recipient Golden Door award Nationalities Svc. Ctr., 1975, Community Svc. award Cuyahoga County Commrs., 1975; Sonja F. Unger Day proclaimed by Mayor of Cleve., 1975. Mem. Il Cenacolo Italiano (pres.), Croatian Found. of Am. (v.p.), Am Croatian Acad. Club (v.p.), Print Club of Cleve., Cleve. Skating Club, Cleve. Playhouse Club, City Club of Cleve. Blue Book Club.

UNGER, STEPHEN HERBERT, electrical engineer, computer scientist; b. N.Y.C., July 7, 1931; s. Julius I. and Rebecca (Cooper) U.; m. Marion Ruth Baker, Apr. 8, 1960 (div. July 1978); children—Donald N., Debra Susan; m. Shirley Aronson, July 5, 1986. B.E.E., Poly. Inst. Bklyn., 1952; S.M., MIT,

1953, Sc.D., 1957. Research asst. MIT Rsch. Lab. of Electronics, 1954-57; mem. tech. staff Bell Telephone Labs., Whippany, N.J., 1957-61; assoc. prof. elec. engring. and computer sci. Columbia U., 1961-68, prof., 1968—, prof. computer sci., 1980—; vis. prof. U. Calif.-Berkeley, 1967; vis. prof. computer sci. Danish Tech. U., Lyngby, 1974-75; sr. research assoc. Center for Policy Research, N.Y.C., 1970-74; cons. in field. Author: Asynchronous Sequential Switching Circuits, 1969, Controlling Technology: Ethics and the Responsible Engineer, 1982, The Essence of Logic Circuits, 1989; research, numerous articles on computer sci. Bd. dirs. Morris County Urban League, N.J., 1959-60. Guggenheim fellow,1967, IEEE fellow, 1975, AAAS fellow, 1989; NSF grantee, 1966-70, 71-74, 79-81. Mem. IEEE (chmn. Com. on Social Implications Tech. working group on ethics and employment practices 1971-78, chmn., 1979-80, pres. 1985-86, U.S. Activities Bd. ethics com. 1987—, Centennial medal 1984, Disting. Contbns. Engring. Professionalism award 1987), AAAS (mem. com. on sci. freedom and responsibility 1981-84), IEEE Soc. on Social Implications Tech.(adminstrv. com. 1983—), Assn. Computing Machinery, AAUP, Sigma Xi, Eta Kappa Nu, Tau Beta Pi. Patentee parallel data processing apparatus. Home: 135 Van Houten Fields West Nyack NY 10994-2525 Office: Columbia U Dept Computer Sci New York NY 10027 *Unless, in doubtful situations, we act as though good may triumph, it surely won't.*

UNGERS, OSWALD M., architect, educator; b. Kaisersesch, Germany, July 12, 1926; came to U.S., 1969; s. Anton and Maria (Michels) U.; m. Liselotte Gabler, July 4, 1956; children: Simon, Sibylle, Sophia. Diploma Tng., Tech. U., Karlsruhe, Germany, 1950. Archtl. practice Cologne, Germany, 1950-62, Berlin, 1962-69, Itahaca, N.Y., 1969—; prof. architecture Tech. U. Berlin, 1963-73, dean faculty architecture, 1965-67; prof. architecture emeritus Cornell U., Ithaca, 1968—; chmn. dept. Cornell U., 1968-74; vis. prof. Harvard U., 1972, 77, UCLA, 1973; prof. emeritus Kunstakademie Dusseldorf, 1986-90; organizer 1st and 2d Berlin Summer Acads. for Architecture. Author: (with wife) Megastructure in Habitation; also numerous articles on architecture to internat. mags., numerous chpts. in books; subject of O.M. Ungers 1951-94, Bauten und Projekte; exhibited in biennale, Venice, Italy, 1976, also Berlin, London, N.Y.C.; prin. works include Mus. Architecture, Frankfurt, high rise bldg. and gallery, Frankfurt, Alfred-Wegener-Institut für Polarforschung, Bremerhaven, Badische Landesbibliothek, Karlsruhe, Supreme Ct., Karlsruhe, family court Berlin-Kreuzberg, art mus. Hamburg, Bayerische Hypotheken-und Wechselbank Düsseldorf, thermae mus. Trier, German Embassy Residential Washington, Friedrichstadt-Passagen Berlin, new fair building, Berlin. Recipient prizes in several urban design competitions, BDA Prize, GroBer, 1987, Prix Rhénan d'Architecture, 1989. Mem. AIA, Acad. di San Luca (Rome), BDA Berlin (hon.), Moscow Br. Internat. Acad. Architecture. Research on cast optimisation in large-scale housing, urban pattern devel. in N.Y. State, subsystems of cities. Designer large-scale pub. housing projects in Germany. Office: 60 Belvederestrasse, 50933 Cologne Germany also: 34 Guiöllettstrasse, 60325 Frankfurt am Main Germany also: Marienstrasse 10, 10117 Berlin Germany also: 17 Jay St New York NY 10013

UNIS, RICHARD L., state supreme court justice; b. Portland, Oreg., June 11, 1928. Grad., U. Va., U. Oreg. Bar: Oreg. 1954, U.S. Dist. Ct. Oreg. 1957, U.S. Ct. Appeals (9th cir.) 1960, U.S. Supreme Ct. 1965. Judge Portland Mcpl. Ct., 1968-71; judge Multnomah County Dist. Ct., 1972-76, presiding judge, 1972-74; former judge Oreg. Cir. Ct. 4th Judicial Dist., 1977; former sr. dep. city atty. City of Portland; adj. prof. of local govt. law and evidence Lewis & Clark Coll. Northwestern Sch. Law, 1969-76, 77—; faculty mem. The Nat. Judicial Coll., 1971—; former faculty mem. Am. Acad. Judicial Edn. Author: Procedure and Instructions in Traffic Court Cases, 1970, 101 Questions and Answers on Preliminary Hearings, 1974. Bd. dirs. Oreg. Free from Drug Abuse; mem. Oreg. Adv. Com. on Evidence Law Revision, chmn. subcom., 1974-79. Maj. USAFR, JAGC, ret. Recipient Meritorius Svc.award U. Oregon sch. Law, 1988; named Legal Citizen of Yr. Oreg. Law Related Edn., 1987; inducted into The Nat. Judicial Coll. Hall of Honor, 1988. Mem. Am. Judicature Soc. (bd. dirs. 1975), Am. Judges Assn., Multnomah Bar Found., Oregon Judicial Conf. (chmn. Oreg. Judicial Coll. 1973-80, legis. com. 1976—, exec. com. of judicial edn. com., judicial conduct com.), N.Am. Judges Assn. (tenure, selection and compensation judges com.), Dist. Ct. Judges of Oreg. (v.p., chmn. edn. com.), Nat. Conf. Spl. Ct. Judges (exec. com.), Oreg. State Bar (judicial adminstrn. com., sec. local govt. com. com. on continuing certification, uniform jury instrn. com., exec. com. criminal law sect., trial practice sect. standards and certification com., past chmn., among others), Oreg. Trial Lawyers Assn. (named Judge of Yr. 1984). Office: Oreg Supreme Ct Supreme Ct Bldg Salem OR 97310

UNITHAN, DOLLY, visual artist; came to U.S., 1976; BFA, Hornsey Coll. Art, 1975; MFA, Pratt Inst., 1978; postgrad., Brit. Coun. Fine Arts Exch., 1974, Ecole Nationale des Beaux Arts de Nancy, France, 1974. Summer intern Guggenheim Mus., N.Y.C., 1976; panelist, artist in residence Asian Am. Arts Ctr., N.Y.C., 1993; lectr. in field. One-person shows include Internat. Art Ctr., London, 1975, Am. Assn. State Colls. and Univs., Orlando, Fla., 1977, Sloan Gallery, Lock Haven State Coll., Pa., 1978, Permanent Mission of Malaysia to UN, N.Y.C., 1987, Kerr Gallery, N.Y.C., 1987, Lyman Allyn Art Mus., New London, Conn., 1990, Secretariat Bldg UN, N.Y.C., 1991, Gracie Mansion, N.Y.C., 1994; exhibited in group shows including Palace of Westminster, Ho. of Parliament, London, 1978, City Mus. and Art Gallery, Gloucester, Eng., 1978, Mus. Art, Hove, Eng., 1978, Contemporary Gallery, Warsaw, 1978, Arts Coun. Gallery, Belfast, No. Ireland, 1978, Parrish Art Mus., Southampton, N.Y., 1979, Modern Art Ctr., Guadalajara, Mex., 1979, Alternative Mus., N.Y.C., 1981, Nat. Mus. Fine Arts, Havana, Cuba, 1986, Hillwood Art Mus., Brookville, N.Y., 1988, PS 1 Mus., N.Y.C., 1990, Nat. Art Gallery, Kuala Lumpur, 1991-92, League of Nations Archives, Palais des Nations, Geneva, 1993, Jewish Mus., Vienna, Austria, 1993, Peace Mus., Remagen, Germany, Westbeth Galleries, N.Y.C., Tweed Courthouse Gallery, N.Y.C., 1994; represented in permanent collections including Lock Haven State Coll., Pa., Alternative Mus., N.Y.C., Am. Assn. State Colls. and Univs., Washington, Permanent Mission of Malaysia to UN, Wilfredo Lam Ctr., Havana, Malaysian Embassy, Washington, Spirit Found., N.Y.C., Asian Am. Arts Ctr., N.Y.C.; artwork included in (jours.) Multicultural Edn., 1994, Artspiral, 1994, (book) Sculpture, Technique, Form, Content. Recipient Artist award Rainbow Art Found., N.Y.C., 1985, Art award ArtQuest '88 Internat. Art Competition, Calif., 1988; named to Archives of Contemporary Arts Venice Biennale, 1990; grantee Lee Found., Singapore, 1972, 76, Pollock-Krasner Found., 1991-92; grad. scholar MARA, Malaysia, 1976-78. Avocation: collecting antiques.

UNKLESBAY, ATHEL GLYDE, geologist, educator; b. Byesville, Ohio, Feb. 11, 1914; s. Howard Ray and Madaline (Archer) U.; m. Wanda Eileen Strauch, Sept. 14, 1940 (dec. 1971); children: Kenneth, Marjorie, Carolyn, Allen; m. Mary Wheeler Myhre, June 8, 1973 (dec. 1980). A.B., Marietta Coll., 1938, D.Sci. (hon.), 1977; M.A., State U. Iowa, 1940, Ph.D., 1942. Geologist U.S. Geol. Survey, 1942-45, Iowa Geol. Survey, 1945-46; asst. prof. Colgate, 1946-47; mem. faculty U. Mo., Columbia, 1947—; prof. geology U. Mo., 1954-present, dep. chief, 1959-67, v.p. adminstrn., 1967-79; exec. dir. Am. Geol. Inst., 1979-85; cons. in field. Author: Geology of Boone County, 1952, Common Fossils of Missouri, 1955, Pennsylvanian Cephalopods of Oklahoma, 1962, Missouri Geology, 1992; also articles. Mem. Columbia Bd. Edn., 1954-70, Columbia Parks and Recreation Commn., 1954-57, Wilton Park fellow, 1968, 72, 76. Mem. Am. Assn. Petroleum Geologists, Paleontol. Soc. Am., Geol. Soc. Am., Nat. Assn. Geology Tchrs., Kiwanis. Methodist. Home: 37 Broadway Village Dr Apt G Columbia MO 65201-8662

UNPINGCO, JOHN WALTER SABLAN, federal judge; b. 1950. BA, St. Louis U., 1972; MBA, JD, NYU, 1976; LLM, Georgetown U., 1983. Bar: Guam 1977, D.C. 1983, Calif. 1992. Atty. Ferenz, Bramhall, Williams & Gruskin, Guam, 1976-77; atty. Office Staff Judge Advocate USAF, 1977-85, 85-87; counsel Office U.S. Naval Air Warfare Ctr., China Lake, Calif., 1987-92; fed. judge U.S. Dist. Ct. (Guam dist.), 1992—; part-time instr. U. Md. Far East divsn., Yokota Air Base, Tokyo, 1983-87. European divsn., RAF Mildenhall, Suffolk, U.K., 1979-82. Mem. ABA, State Bar Calif., Guam Bar Assn., internat. Legal Soc. Japan, D.C. Bar Assn., NWC Community Fed. Credit Union (bd. dirs. 1991-92). Office: Pacific News Bldg 238 Archbishop FC Flores St 6th Fl Agana GU 96910

UNRUH, JAMES ARLEN, business machines company executive; b. Goodrich, N.D., Mar. 22, 1941; m. Candice Leigh Voight, Apr. 28, 1984; children: Jeffrey A., Julie A. BSBA, Jamestown Coll., 1963; MBA, U. Denver, 1964. Dir. corp. planning and analysis Fairchild Camera & Instrument, Calif., 1974-76, v.p. treasury and corp. devel., 1976-79, v.p. fin., 1979-80; v.p. fin. Memorex Corp., Santa Clara, Calif., 1980-82; v.p. fin. Burroughs Corp. (now known as Unisys Corp.), Detroit, 1982-84, sr. v.p. fin., 1984-86, exec. v.p. fin., 1986, exec. v.p., 1986-89, pres., chief oper. officer, 1989-90, pres., chief exec. officer, 1990-91, chmn. bd. dirs., chief exec. officer, 1991—. Bd. dirs. Detroit Renaissance Ctr., U. Mich. vis. Com., Greater Phila. First Corp.; bd. trustees Jamestown Coll., N.D., Franklin Inst.; bd. overseers Wharton Sch. Bus., U. Pa. Mem. Greater Phila. C. of C. (exec. com.), Pa. Bus. Roundtable. Home: 208 Rose Ln Haverford PA 19041-1605 Office: Unisys Corp PO Box 500 Blue Bell PA 19424-0001*

UNRUH, LEON DALE, newspaper editor; b. Larned, Kans., Dec. 26, 1956; s. Elgie Larey Unruh and Anita Faye Byers; m. Margaret E. Jones, Apr. 30, 1988. BS in Journalism, U. Kans., 1979. Copy editor Austin (Tex.) Am-Statesman, 1979-83; copy desk chief Wichita (Kans.) Eagle-Beacon, 1983-86; asst. news editor Dallas Morning News, 1986-90; travel editor Anchorage Daily News, 1990—; freelance coll. textbook editor Harcourt Brace & Co., The Dryden Press, 1989—. Vol. Dallas Soc. Visually Impaired Children, 1986-90; active Alaska Photographic Ctr. Mem. Soc. Newspaper Design (Excellence award 1982). Office: Anchorage Daily News 1001 Northway Dr Anchorage AK 99508

UNRUH, WILLIAM G., physics educator, researcher; b. Winnipeg, Man., Can., Aug. 28, 1945; m. Patricia Truman, Apr. 19, 1974; 1 child, Daniel B. B.Sc. (hons.), U. Man., Winnipeg, 1967; M.A., Princeton U., 1969, Ph.D., 1971. Postdoctoral fellow NRC Can., London, Eng., 1971-72; Miller fellow U. Calif., Berkeley, 1973-74; asst. prof. McMaster U., Hamilton, Ont., Can., 1974-76; asst. prof. to prof. physics U. B.C., Vancouver, Can., 1976—; rsch. fellow Can. Inst. Advanced Rsch., Toronto, Ont., 1986—, dir. Cosmology Program, 1986—. Contbr. tech. papers to profl. publs. Rutherford Meml. fellow Royal Soc. Can., 1971; Alfred P. Sloan research fellow U. B.C., 1978-80; Steacie fellow Nat. Sci. and Eng. Research Council, 1984-86; Japan Soc. Promotion Sci. sr. fellow Japan, 1986; recipient Rutherford medal, Royal Soc. Can., 1982, Hertzberg medal Can. Assn. Physics, 1983, Steacie medal, 1984, Medal of Achievement, 1995, Gold medal B.C. Sci. Coun., 1991; Rutherford lectr. Royal Soc. Can. to Royal Soc. London, 1985. Fellow Royal Soc. Can. Office: Univ BC Dept Physics, 6224 Agricultural Rd, Vancouver, BC Canada V6T 1Z1

UNSELD, WESTLEY SISSEL, professional sports team executive, former professional basketball coach, former professional basketball player; b. Louisville, Mar. 14, 1946; m. Connie Martin; children: Kimberly, Westley. Student, U. Louisville, 1964-68. Basketball player Balt. Bullets (name changed to Washington Bullets), 1968-81; v.p. Washington Bullets, 1981-94, head coach, 1988-94, exec. v.p., 1994—. Office: Washington Bullets USAir Arena Landover MD 20785*

UNSELL, LLOYD NEAL, energy organization executive, former journalist; b. Henryetta, Okla., May 12, 1922; s. John William and Rhoda Elizabeth (Martinez) U.; m. Nettie Marie Rogers, Sept. 24, 1944 (dec.); children: Lloyd Neal, Jonna Kay Unsell Wilhelm, James Allan (dec.). Student, U. Ill., Kalamazoo Coll., 1942-43. Mem. editorial staff Tulsa Daily World, 1947-48; successively staff writer, dir. communications, v.p. pub. affairs, exec. v.p., pres. and chief exec. officer Ind. Petroleum Assn. Am., Washington, 1948-87; chmn. selection com. for Milburn Petty award Am. Petroleum Inst.-Assn. Petroleum Writers, 1972-86. Author reports and articles in field. Co-chmn. corp. adv. com. Vietnam Vets. Meml., 1981-82. Served with U.S. Army, 1942-46, ETO, PTO. Recipient Spl. award as outstanding petroleum industry communicator Assn. Petroleum Writers, 1960, Russell B. Brown Meml. award, 1981, Robert J. Enright award Am. Petroleum Inst./Assn. Petroleum Writers, 1986, Disting. Service award Nat. Energy Resources Orgn., 1987; named Hon. Chief Roughneck U.S. petroleum industry, 1986. Mem. Nat. Press Club, Rocky Mountain Oil and Gas Assn. (hon. life), The Jefferson Energy Found. (co-founder 1987). Republican. Baptist. Club: Washington Golf and Country. Home: Point Breeze Rd Coltons Point MD 20626 Office: 1101 16th St NW 5th Fl Washington DC 20036

UNSER, AL, professional auto racer; b. Albuquerque, May 29, 1939; s. Jerry H. and Mary C. (Craven) U.; m. Wanda Jesperson, Apr. 22, 1958 (div.); children: Mary Linda, Debra Ann, Alfred; m. Karen Barnes, Nov. 22, 1977 (div.). Auto racer U.S. Auto Club, Speedway, Ind., 1964-94. Placed 3d in nat. standings, 1968, 2d in 1969, 77, 78, 1st in 1970, 4th in 1976; winner Indpls. 500, 1970, 71, 78, 87, Pocono 500, 1976, 78, Ont. 500, 1977, 78; placed 3d in U.S. Auto Club Sports Car Club Am. Formula 5000, 1975, 2d place, 1976; Internat. Race of Champions champion, 1978; 2d pl. Indpls. Motor Speedway, 1983; CART/PPG Indy Car champion, 1983, 85. Home: 7625 Central NW Albuquerque NM 87121*

UNSER, ALFRED, JR., professional race car driver; b. Apr. 19, 1962; s. Al Sr. U.; m. Shelley Unser; children: Al, Cody, Shannon. Runner-up Indpls. 500, 1989, 4th in USAC Gold Crown Standings, 1990-91. Winner Indianapolis 500 1992, 94, Indy Car Champion 1990-94. Office: c/o US Auto Club 4910 W 16th St Speedway IN 46224-5703*

UNSER, BOBBY (ROBERT WILLIAM UNSER), professional auto racer, television commentator; b. Albuquerque, Feb. 20, 1934; s. Jerry and Mary (Craven) U.; m. Barbara Schumacher, 1953 (div. 1966); m. Norma Davis, 1967 (div. 1970); m. Marsha Sale, Oct. 20, 1990; children: Bobby Jr., Cyndi, Robby, Jeri. Former modified stock car race driver; now driver profl. racing cars; commentator ABC, 1987—; cons. Expert Accident Reconstructionist, U.S., 1985—. Co-author: The Unbelievable Unsers, 1970, The Bobby Unser Story, 1978, Unser: An American Family Portrait, 1988. Served with USAF, 1953-56. Recipient 1st pl. Indy 500 award U.S. Auto Club, 1968, 75, 81, 1st pl. Calif. 500 award U.S. Auto Club, 1974, 76, 79, 80, 1st pl. Pocono 500 award Championship Auto Racing Teams, Pa., 1980; named U.S. Auto Club Nat. Driving Champion, 1969, 75, Martini and Rossi Driver of Yr., 1974. Avocations: snowmobiling, motorbiking. Home and Office: 656 N Macdonald St Mesa AZ 85201-5020*

UNSWORTH, RICHARD PRESTON, minister, school administrator; b. Vineland, N.J., Feb. 7, 1927; s. Joseph Lewis and Laura (MacMillan) U.; m. Joy Merritt, Aug. 20, 1949; children: Sarah, John, Mary, Lucy. BA, Princeton U., 1948; BD, Yale U., 1954; ThM, Harvard U., 1963; STD, Dickinson Coll., 1971; LHD, Washington and Jefferson Coll., 1971; LLD, Smith Coll., 1992. Ordained to ministry Presbyn. Ch., 1953. Tchr. Bible and English Mt. Hermon Sch., 1948-50; asst. chaplain Yale U., New Haven, Conn., 1950-54; chaplain, assoc. prof. Smith Coll., Northampton, Mass., 1954-64, chaplain, prof. religion, 1967-80; dean William Jewett Tucker Found. and prof. religion Dartmouth (N.H.) Coll., 1963-67; headmaster Northfield (Mass.) Mt. Hermon Sch., 1980-88, pres., 1989-91, headmaster emeritus; headmaster Berkshire Sch., Sheffield, Mass., 1991—; pres. Critical Langs. and Area Studies Consortium, 1987—; bd. dirs. Bank of New Eng.-West, 1984-90; cons. Ednl. Assocs., Inc., 1967-69, U.S. Office Edn. 1969-77. Author: Sexuality and the Human Community, 1970, Dignity and Exploitation: Christian Reflections on Images of Sex in the 1970s, 1974, A Century of Religion at Smith College, 1975, (with Arnold Kenseth) Prayers for Worship Leaders, 1978; contbg. author; Sex Edn. and the Schs., 1967. Leader Operation Crossroads Africa unit, Nigeria, 1961, mem. adv. bd., 1961-66; mem. adminstrv. com. Student Christian Movement New Eng., 1964; mem. Mass. unit So. Christian Leadership Conf., 1968; trustee Conf. on Religion in Ind. Schs., 1961-63; pres. Am. Friends of Coll. Cevenol, France, 1957-63, 90-94, Am. rep., 1958-82; trustee Mt. Holyoke Coll., 1982-89, chair, 1984-89, chmn. emeritus, 1989—, Am. Sch. Tangier, Morocco, 1982-87, Eaglebrook Sch., 1992—, Mus. Sci., Boston, 1993-95; bd. dirs. Family Planning Coun. Western Mass., 1972-81; bd. dirs. Ind. Schs. Assn. Mass., 1992—. Mem. AAUP, Nat. Assn. Coll. and Univ. Chaplains, Am. Acad. Religion, Assn. Ind. Schs. New Eng. (pres. 1993—), Headmasters Assn. Home and Office: Berkshire Sch Sheffield MA 01257

UNTENER, KENNETH E., bishop; b. Detroit, Aug. 3, 1937. Ed., Sacred Heart Sem., St. John's Provincial Sem., Plymouth, Mich., Gregorian U., Rome. Ordained priest Roman Cath. Ch., 1963, ordained bishop, 1980.

Bishop Diocese of Saginaw, Mich., 1980—. Office: Chancery Office 5800 Weiss St Saginaw MI 48603-2762*

UNTERBERGER, BETTY MILLER, history educator, writer; b. Glasgow, Scotland, Dec. 27, 1923; d. Joseph C. and Leah Miller; m. Robert Ruppe, July 29, 1944; children: Glen, Gail, Gregg. B.A., Syracuse U., N.Y., 1943; M.A., Harvard U., 1946; Ph.D., Duke U., 1950. Asst. prof. E. Carolina U., Greenville, 1948-50; assoc. prof., dir. liberal arts ctr. Whittier Coll., Calif., 1954-61; assoc. prof. Calif. State U.-Fullerton, 1961-65, prof., chmn. grad. studies, 1965-68; prof. Tex. A&M U., College Station, 1968—; vis. prof. U. Hawaii, Honolulu, summer 1967, Peking U., Beijing, 1988; vis. disting. prof. U. Calif., Irvine, 1987—; Patricia and Bookman Peters prof. history, 1991—; vis. prof. Charles U., Prague, Czechoslovakia, summer 1992; mem. adv. com. fgn. rels. U.S. Dept. State, 1977-81, chair, 1981; mem. hist. adv. com. U.S. Dept. Army, 1980-81, USN, 1991—; mem. Nat. Hist. Publs. and Records Commn., 1980-84. Author: America's Siberian Expedition 1918-1920: A Study of National Policy, 1956, 69 (Pacific Coast award Am. Hist. Assn. 1956); editor: American Intervention in the Russian Civil War, 1969, Intervention Against Communism: Did the U.S. Try to Overthrow the Soviet Government, 1918-20, 1986, The United States, Revolutionary Russia and the Rise of Czechoslovakia, 1989; contbr.: Woodrow Wilson and Revolutionary World, 1982; editorial adv. bd.: The Papers of Woodrow Wilson, Princeton U., 1982-92; bd. editors: Diplomatic History, 1981-84, Red River Valley Hist. Rev., 1975-84. Trustee Am. Inst. Pakistan Studies, Villanova U., Pa., 1981—; sec., 1989-92; mem. League of Women Voters. Fellow Woodrow Wilson Found., 1979; named Disting. Univ. Teacher State of Calif. Legislature, 1966; recipient All-Univ. Disting. Teaching award Tex. A&M U., 1975. Mem. LWV, NOW, AAUW, Am. Hist. Assn. (chair 1982-83, nominating com. 1980-83), Orgn. Am. Historians (govt. relations com.), Soc. Historians of Am. Fgn. Relations (exec. council 1978-81, 86-89, govt. relations com. 1982-84, v.p. 1985, pres. 1986, co-winner Myrna F. Bernath prize 1991), Am. Soc. for Advancement Slavic Studies, Coordinating Com. on Women in Hist. Profession, Rocky Mountain Assn. Slavic Studies (program chair 1973, v.p. 1973-74), So. Hist. Assn., Asian Studies Assn., Assn. Third World Studies, Czechoslovak Soc. Arts and Scis., Czechoslovak History Conf., Women's Fgn. Policy Coun., Beyond War, Peace History Soc., Sierra Club, Phi Beta Kappa, Phi Beta Delta. Office: Tex A&M U College Station TX 77843

UNTERMAN, THOMAS E., lawyer; b. Newport, R.I., Oct. 23, 1944; s. Martin D. and Ruth (Marcus) U.; m. Janet M. Mead, Sept. 27, 1980; children: Rebecca, Amy. AB, Princeton U., 1966; JD, U. Chgo., 1969. Bar: Calif. 1970. Assoc. Orrick, Herrington & Sutcliffe, San Francisco, 1969-75, ptnr., 1975-86; ptnr. Morrison & Foerster, San Francisco, 1986-92; v.p., gen. counsel The Times Mirror Co., L.A., 1992—. Democrat. Jewish. Office: The Times Mirror Co Times Mirror Sq Los Angeles CA 90053

UNTERREINER, C. MARTIN, financial advisor; b. St. Louis, Mar. 17, 1940; s. Caspar M. and Frances C. (Walck) U.; m. Jane Marie Buxton, July 23, 1966; children: C. Michael, Jeffrey J., Teresa Lynne. BS in Commerce, St. Louis U., 1962, MEd, 1966. Registered fin. planner, master. Bus. edn. tchr. Assumption High Sch., O'Fallon, Mo., 1962-64, Lafayette High Sch., Ellisville, Mo., 1964-68; registered rep. Capital Planning Corp., St. Louis, 1966-73; registered rep., registered prin. All Am. Mgmt. Corp., Des Plaines, Ill., 1973-87; pres., chief exec. officer Security Rsch. Assocs., Inc., St. Louis, 1973-90; pres., chief exec. officer, registered prin. Forth Fin. Network, Richmond, Va., 1987-90, FFP Securities, Inc., Chesterfield, Mo., 1990-94; rep., prin. 1st Fin. Planners, Inc., Chesterfield, 1990—; money mgr., registered prin. FFP Advs. Svcs., Inc., Chesterfield, 1990—; bd. govs. Internat. Assn. Registered Fin. Planners, Tampa, 1986-90. Contbr. articles to profl. jours. Bd. dirs. Christians in Commerce, St. Louis, 1987—, Inst. for Peace & Justice, St. Louis, 1985-86; pres. Creve Coeur Area Jaycees, St. Louis, 1970. Named one of Outstanding Young Men of Am., Jaycees, Mo., 1971; recipient Project of Yr. award Jaycees, Mo., 1971. Mem. Internat. Assn. Fin. Planning (v.p. 1977-78, bd. dirs. St. Louis chpt. 1977-87), Soc. Asset Allocators and Fund Timers (bd. dirs. 1994—). Roman Catholic. Avocations: antique cars, boating. Home: 9 Andre Dr Saint Louis MO 63131-3901 Office: Proactive Money Mgmt Inc 500 Chesterfield Ctr Ste 250 Chesterfield MO 63017-4823

UNTHANK, TESSA See NELSON-HUMPHRIES, TESSA

UOTILA, URHO ANTTI KALEVI, geodesist, educator; b. Pöytyä, Finland, Feb. 22, 1923; came to U.S., 1951, naturalized, 1957; s. Antti Samuli and Vera Justina (Kyto) U.; m. Helena Vanhakartano, Aug. 6, 1949; children: Heidi, Kirsi, Elizabeth, Julie, Trina, Caroline. B.S., Finland's Inst. Tech., 1946, M.S., 1949; Ph.D., Ohio State U., 1959. Surveyor, geodesist Finnish Govt., 1944-46, 46-51; geodesist Swedish Govt., 1946; research asst. Ohio State U., 1952-53, research assoc., 1953-58, research supr., 1959-88, lectr. in geodesy, 1955-57, asst. prof., 1959-62, assoc. prof., 1962-65, chmn. dept. geodetic sci., 1964-84, prof., 1965-89, chmn., prof. emeritus, 1989—; mem. Solar Eclipse Expdn. to Greenland, 1954; mem. adv. panel on geodesy U.S. Coast and Geodetic Survey, Nat. Acad. Sci., 1964-66; mem. geodesy and cartography working group, space sci. steering com. NASA, 1965-67, mem. geodesy/cartography working group, summer conf. lunar exploration and sci., 1965, mem. geodesy and cartography adv. subcom., 1967-72; mem. ad hoc com. on N.Am. datum div. earth scis. Nat. Acad. Scis.-N.A.E., 1968-70; bd. dirs. Internat. Gravity Bur., France, 1975-83; mem. com. on geodesy Nat. Acad. Scis., 1975-78. Mem. editorial adv. com.: Advances in Geophysics, 1968-77; Contbr. articles to profl. jours., encys. Served with Finnish Army, 1942-44. Recipient Kaarina and W.A. Heiskanen award, 1962, Apollo Achievement award NASA, 1969, Disting. Svc. award Surveyor's Inst. Sri Lanka, Earle J. Fennell award Am. Congress on Surveying and Mapping, 1989. Fellow Am. Geophys. Union (v.p. geodesy sect. 1964-68, pres. 1968-70), Am. Congress Surveying and Mapping (nat. dir. 1970-73, 2d v.p. 1977-78, pres.-elect 1978-79, pres. 1979-80), Internat. Assn. Geodesy (pres. spl. study group 5.30 1967-71, pres. sect. V 1971-75, exec. com. 1971-79); mem. Am. Assn. Geodetic Surveying (pres. 1984-86), Am. Soc. Photogrammetry, Can. Inst. Surveying, Univs. Space Research Assn. (trustee 1973-75), Finnish Nat. Acad. Scis. (fgn.), Profl. Land Surveyors Ohio (hon.), Ala. Soc. Profl. Land Surveyors (hon.), Tenn. Assn. Profl. Surveyors (hon.). Research in geometric geodesy, phys. geodesy and statis. analysis of data. Home: 4329 Shelbourne Ln Columbus OH 43220-4243 Office: Ohio State U Dept Geodetic Science and Surveying 1958 Neil Ave Columbus OH 43210-1247

UPADHYAY, YOG PRASAD, former diplomat; b. Shillong, India, Feb. 26, 1927; m. Bimal Upadhyay, 1948; children: Usha, Manisha. BS, Banaras Hindu U., Varanasi, India, 1950; postgrad., Am. U.ban U., Washington Nepal, 1952; LLB, Tribhuban U., Kathmandu, Nepal, 1963; PhD, U. N.C., 1972. Dep. sec. Ministry of Home, Nepal, 1951-53, Ministry of Edn., Ministry of Def., Nepal, 1953-58; sec. Ministry of Transp., Nepal, 1958-60; with Congress Party in exile, mem. negotiating team to restore multi-pary Dem. system Nepal, 1961-90; min. in charge Ministry of Home and Community in Interim Cabinet, 1990-91; amb. to U.S. Royal Nepalese Embassy, Washington, 1991—; rector Tribhuban U., Kathmandu, 1973-76; permanent mem. Nat. Planning Commn., Kathmandu, 1976-82, vice-chmn., 1982-88; amb. to U.S. Royal Nepalese Embassy, Washington, 1988—; also accredited to Can., Mex., Costa Rica, Panama, and Colombia. Contbr. articles to profl. jours. Fulbright scholar, 1952. Home: 2730 34th Pl NW Washington DC 20007-1403 Office: Royal Nepalese Embassy 2131 Leroy Pl NW Washington DC 20008-1891

UPATNIEKS, JURIS, optical engineer, researcher, educator; b. Riga, Latvia, May 7, 1936; came to U.S., 1951; s. Karlis and Eleonora (Jegers) U.; m. Ilze Induss, July 13, 1968; children: Ivars, Ansis. BSEE, U. Akron, Ohio, 1960; MSEE, U. Mich., 1965. Rsch. asst., then rsch. assoc. Willow Run Labs. U. Mich., Ann Arbor, 1960-69; rsch. engr. Inst. Sci. and Tech., U. Mich., Ann Arbor, 1969-72, Environ. Rsch. Inst. Mich., Ann Arbor, 1973-93; sr. engr. Applied Optics, Ann Arbor, 1993—; lectr. elec. engring. dept. U. Mich., 1971-73, adj. assoc. prof. elec. engring. and computer sci. dept., 1974—. Contbr. articles to profl. jours.; patentee in field. 2d lt. U.S. Army, 1961-62. Recipient Holley medal ASME, 1976, Inventor of Yr. award Assn. for Advancement Invention and Innovation, 1976. Fellow Optical Soc. Am. (R.W. Wood prize 1975), Soc. Photographic Instrumentation Engrs. (Robert

Gordon award 1965), Am. Latvian Assn., Acad. Soc. Austrums, Latvian Acad. Sci. (elected 1991). Avocations: camping, gardening, hiking. Office: Applied Optics 2662 Valley Dr Ann Arbor MI 48103

UPBIN, HAL JAY, consumer products executive; b. Bronx, N.Y., Jan. 15, 1939; s. David and Evelyn (Sloan) U.; m. Shari Kiesler, May 29, 1960; children: Edward, Elyse, Danielle. BBA, Pace Coll., 1961. CPA, N.Y. Tax sr. Peat, Marwick, Mitchell & Co., N.Y.C., 1961-65; tax mgr. Price Waterhouse & Co., N.Y.C., 1965-71; dir. taxes Wheelabrator-Frye Inc., N.Y.C., 1971-72, treas., 1972-74; pres. Wheelabrator Fin. Corp., N.Y.C., 1974-75; v.p., chief fin. officer Chase Manhattan Mortgage and Realty Trust (became Triton Group Ltd. 1980), N.Y.C., 1975-76, pres., 1976-78, pres., chmn., 1978-83, also dir.; chmn., pres., dir. Isomedics, 1983-85; chmn., pres. Fifth Ave. Cards, Inc., Fifth Retail Corp., Ashby's Stores, Ashby's Outlet Stores, 1984-88; bd. dirs. Stacy Industries, 1988; vice chmn. Am. Recreation Products, St. Louis, 1985-88, vice chmn., pres., 1988—, chmn., 1992—; v.p. corp. devel., chmn. acquistion com. Kellwood Co., Chesterfield, Mo., 1990—, exec. v.p. corp. devel., chmn. acquisition com., 1992-94, pres., CEO, 1994—. Alumni advisor to bd. trustees Pace U.; past pres. Jewish Temple. Mem. AICPA, N.Y. State Soc. CPA's, Franklin Jaycees (v.p.). Home: 15812 Spears Ridge Dr Chesterfield MO 63017-8728 Office: Kellwood Co 600 Kellwood Pky Chesterfield MO 63017-5800 Also: Am Recreation Products 1224 Fern Ridge Pky Saint Louis MO 63141

UPBIN, SHARI, theatrical producer, director, agent, educator; b. N.Y.C.; m. Hal J. Upbin, May 29, 1960; children: Edward, Elyse, Danielle. Master tap instr. Talent mgr. Goldstar Talent Mgmt., Inc., N.Y.C., 1989-91; guest tchr. Total Theatre Lab., N.Y.C.; faculty Nat. Shakespeare Conservatory, N.Y. Asst. dir. 1st Black-Hispanic Shakespeare prodn. Julius Ceasar, Coriolanus at Pub. Theatre, N.Y., 1979; dir., choreographer Matter of Opinion, Players Theatre, N.Y., 1980, Side by Side, Sondheim Forum Theatre, N.J., 1981 (Nominated Best Dir. of Season N.J. Theatre Critics); producer, dir. Vincent, The Passions of Van Gogh, N.Y., 1981; producer Bojangles, The Life of Bill Robinson, Broadway, 1984, Captain America, nat. Am. tour; dir. Fiddler on the Roof, Cabaret, Life with Father, Roar of the Grease Paint, regional theatre, 1979-82; co-producer One Mo' Time, Village Gate, N.Y., nat. and internat. tour.; producer/dir. off-Broadway musical Flypaper, 1991-92, Women on Their Own, Things My Mother Never Told Me, Theatre East, N.Y. Founded Queens Playhouse, N.Y., Children's Theatre, Flushing, N.Y.; mem. Willy Mays' Found. Drug Abused Children. Recipient Jaycees Service award Jr. Miss Pageants Franklin Twp., N.J., 1976. Mem. League Profl. Theatre Women (pres.), Soc. Stage Dirs. and Choreographers, Actors Equity Assn., Villagers Barn Theatre (1st woman pres.), N.Y. Womens Agenda, Faculty Nat. Shakespeare Conservatory (N.Y.). Address: Shari Upbin Prodns 45 E 89th St New York NY 10128

UPCHURCH, PAUL, principal. Prin. Centerfield Elem. Sch., Crestwood, Ky. Recipient DOW Elem. Sch. Recognition award, 1989-90. Office: Centerfield Elem Sch 4512 S Hwy 393 Crestwood KY 40014

UPCHURCH, SAMUEL E., JR., lawyer; b. Birmingham, Ala., Jan. 29, 1952; s. Samuel E. Sr. and Ann Upchurch; m. Cheryl Upchurch; children: Shannon, Jeanne, Kathryn. AB, Davidson Coll., 1974; MAT, Rollins Coll., 1975; JD, U. Ala., 1978. Bar: Ala. 1978, U.S. Ct. Claims, U.S. Dist. Ct. (no. dist.) Ala., U.S. Ct. Appeals (11th cir.), U.S. Supreme Ct. Assoc. Lange, Simpson, Robinson & Somerville, Birmingham, 1978-83, ptnr., 1984; v.p., assoc. counsel Torchmark Corp., Birmingham, 1985, v.p., gen. counsel, 1986, v.p., gen. counsel, sec., 1987—, also bd. dirs.; bd. dirs. United Investors Mgmt. Co., Kansas City, Mo. Mem. Mt. Brook (Ala.) City Coun., 1988-90. Mem. ABA, Ala. State Bar Assn., Birmingham Bar Assn. Avocations: tennis, jogging, reading. Office: Torchmark Corp 2001 3rd Ave S Birmingham AL 35233-2186

UPDEGRAFF SPLETH, ANN L., church executive, pastor; b. Newark, Ohio, Sept. 15, 1949; d. John C. and Lela V. (Mervine) Updegraff; m. Randall Alan Spleth; children: Andrew Alan, Claire Campbell. BA, Transylvania Coll., 1971; MDiv, Vanderbilt U., 1974; DMin, Claremont Sch. Theology, 1985. Ordained min. Christian Ch. (Disciples of Christ), 1973. Assoc. min. First Christian Ch., New Castle, Ind., 1974-75, Sacramento, 1975-78; sr. assoc. regional min. Pacific S.W. region Christian Ch., L.A., 1978-85; exec. v.p. Christian Ch. Homeland Ministries, Indpls., 1985-89, pres., 1990—. Author: Youth Ministry Manual, 1980; co-author: Congregation: Sign of Hope, 1989, Worship and Spiritual Life, 1992; editor Vanguard, 1990—; contbr. articles to profl. jours. Founding mem. Profl. Women's Forum, L.A., 1978-85. Mem. Ind. Soc. of Washington. Democrat. Home: 8961 Sawmill Ct Indianapolis IN 46236-9171 Office: Divsn Homeland Ministries PO Box 1986 Indianapolis IN 46206

UPDEGRAFT, KENNETH E., JR., lawyer; b. Ft. Meade, Md., Sept. 30, 1946. BSBA, Am. U., 1967; MS, U. Pa., 1968; LLB, U. Va., 1971. Bar: Ohio 1971, CPA, Va. Ptnr. Jones, Day, Reavis & Pogue, Cleve. Fellow Am. Coll. Tax Counsel; mem. ABA (chmn. natural resources com. 1987-89). Office: Jones Day Reavis & Pogue North Point 901 Lakeside Ave E Cleveland OH 44114-1190

UPDIKE, HELEN HILL, economist, investment manager, financial planner; b. N.Y.C., Mar. 27, 1941; d. Benjamin Harvey and Helen (Gray) Hill; m. Charles Bruce Updike, Sept. 7, 1963 (div. 1989); children: Edith Hill, Nancy Lamar. B.A., Hood Coll., 1962; Ph.D., SUNY, Stony Brook, 1978; postgrad., Harvard U., 1986. Asst. prof. Suffolk U., Boston, 1965-67; lectr. SUNY-Stony Brook, 1969-75, vis. asst. prof., 1977-78; asst. prof. U. Mass., Boston, 1975-77; asst. prof. Hofstra U., Hempstead, N.Y., 1978-85, assoc. prof., 1985-90, chmn. dept. econs. and geography, 1981-84; assoc. dean Hofstra Coll. Hofstra U., 1984-87; pres. Interfid Capital Corp., 1987—; dir. McCrory Corp., 1987—; cons. on econ. policy, 1973—. Author: The National Banks and American Economic Development, 1870-1900, 1985. Trustee, v.p. L.I. Forum for Tech., 1979-85; trustee Madeira Sch. Greenway, Va., 1984-88, N.Y. Outward Bound, 1988—; mem. nat. adv. bd. Outward Bound USA, 1984-92. Mem. AAAS, Cosmopolitan Club, Cold Spring Harbor Beach Club. Office: Interfid Capital Corp 27th Fl 150 E 58th St New York NY 10155-2798

UPDIKE, JOHN HOYER, writer; b. Shillington, Pa., Mar. 18, 1932; s. Wesley R. and Linda G. (Hoyer) U.; m. Mary E. Pennington, June 26, 1953 (div. 1976); children: Elizabeth, David, Michael, Miranda; m. Martha Bernhard, Sept. 30, 1977. AB, Harvard U., 1954; student, Ruskin Sch. Drawing and Fine Art, 1954-55. With New Yorker mag., N.Y.C., 1955-57. Author: (fiction) The Poorhouse Fair, 1959 (Richard and Hinda Rosenthal Found. award Am. Acad. and Nat. Inst. Arts and Letters 1960), The Same Door, 1959, Rabbit, Run, 1960, Pigeon Feathers, 1962, The Centaur, 1963 (Nat. Book award 1963, Prix Medicis Etranger 1966), Olinger Stories, 1964, Of the Farm, 1965, The Music School, 1966, Couples, 1968, Bech: A Book, 1970, Rabbit Redux, 1971, Museums and Women, 1972, Warm Wine, 1973, A Month of Sundays, 1975, Marry Me, 1976, Couples, 1976, The Coup, 1978, From the Journal of a Leper, 1978, Problems, 1979, Too Far to Go: The Maples Stories, 1979 (Am. Book award nomination 1980), Three Illuminations in the Life of an American Author, 1979, Your Lover Just Called: Stories of Joan and Richard Maple, 1980, The Chaste Planet, 1980, Rabbit Is Rich, 1981 (Pulitzer prize for fiction 1982, Nat. Book Critics Circle award 1982, Am. Book award 1982), Invasion of the Book Envelopes, 1981, Bech Is Back, 1982, The Beloved, 1982, The Witches of Eastwick, 1984, Confessions of a Wild Bore, 1984, Roger's Version, 1986 (Nat. Book Critics Circle award nomination 1986), Trust Me, 1987, More Stately Mansions, 1987, S., 1988, Rabbit at Rest, 1990 (Pulitzer prize for fiction 1991, Nat. Book Critics Circle award 1991), Memories of the Ford Administration, 1992, Brazil, 1994, The Afterlife, 1994, (poetry) The Carpentered Hen and Other Tame Creatures, 1958, Telephone Poles, 1963, A Child's Calendar, 1965, The Angels, 1968, Bath after Sailing, 1968, Midpoint, 1969, Seventy Poems, 1972, Six Poems, 1973, Tossing and Turning, 1977, Sixteen Sonnets, 1979, Five Poems, 1980, Spring Trio, 1982, Jester's Dozen, 1984, Facing Nature, 1985, Collected Poems 1953-1993, 1993, (play) Buchanan Dying, 1974, (non-fiction) Assorted Prose, 1965, On Meeting Authors, 1968, Three Texts from Early Ipswich, 1968, A Good Place, 1973, Picked-Up Pieces, 1975, Hub Fans Bid Kid Adieu, 1977, Talk from the Fifties, 1979, Ego and Art in Walt Whitman, 1980, Hawthorne's Creed, 1981, Hugging the Shore, 1983 (Nat. Book Critics Circle award 1984), Emersonianism, 1984, Just

Looking, 1989, Self-Consciousness, 1989, Odd Jobs, 1991; adapter: (librettos) The Magic Flute, 1962, The Ring, 1964, (plays) Bottom's Dream, 1969; author words and music: (with Gunther Schuller) The Fisherman and His Wife, 1970; editor: Pens and Needles, 1970, (with S. Ravenel) The Best American Short Stories 1984, 1984. Recipient O. Henry First Short Story award, 1966, 91, MacDowell medal for literature, 1981, Medal of Honor for literature Nat. Arts Club, 1984, PEN/Malamud Meml. prize PEN/Faulker award Found., 1988, Nat. Medal of Arts, 1989; Guggenheim fellow, 1959. Mem. AAAL, Am. Acad. Arts. and Scis. Democrat. Episcopalian. •

UPGREN, ARTHUR REINHOLD, JR., astronomer, educator, outdoor lighting consultant; b. Mpls., Feb. 21, 1933; s. Arthur Reinhold and Marion (Andrews) U.; m. Joan Koswoski, Jan. 7, 1967; 1 child, Amy Joan. BA, U. Minn., 1955; MS, U. Mich., 1958; PhD, Case Western Res. U., 1961. Research assoc. Swarthmore Coll., Pa., 1961-63; astronomer U.S. Naval Obs., Washington, 1963-66; asst. prof. Wesleyan U., Middletown, Conn., 1966-73, assoc. prof., 1973-81, dir. Van Vleck Obs., 1973-93, John Monroe Van Vleck prof., 1981—, chmn. dept. astronomy, 1986-88, 90-93; v.p. Fund Astrophys. Research, N.Y.C., 1971—, chmn. grants com., 1985—; vis. prof. Yale U., 1979-80; adj. prof. U. Fla., 1984—; vis. lectr. U. Md., 1964-66, George Washington U., 1965-66, Thames Sci. Ctr., New London, Conn., 1990, 92; outdoor lighting cons. Wesleyan U., 1991—, Vt. State Agy. Natural Resourses, 1993—; reviewer books in astronomy, meteorology, classical music and urban demographics. Editor: The Nearby Stars and the Stellar Luminosity Function, 1983, Mapping the Sky-Past Heritage and Future Directions, 1988, Star Catalogues: A Centennial Tribute to A.N. Vyssotsky, 1989, Fundamentals of Astromony, 1990, Precision Photometry: Astrophysics of the Galaxy, 1991, Objective Prism and Other Surveys, 1991, Databases for Galactic Structure, 1993, Hot Stars in the Halo, 1994. Conn. state chair New Eng. Light Pollution Adv. Group, 1994—. Grantee NSF, 1967—. Fellow Royal Astron. Soc.; mem. Internat. Astron. Union (commn. v.p. 1982-85, pres. commn. 24 1985-88), Am. Astron. Soc. (Harlow Shapley lectr. 1977—, vice-chmn. dynamical astronomy div. 1988-89, chmn. 1989-90), Astron. Soc. Pacific, Illuminating Engring. Soc. N.Am., Sigma Xi. Office: Van Vleck Obs Wesleyan U Middletown CT 06459-0123

UPHAM, STEADMAN, anthropology educator, university dean, academic administrator; b. Denver, Apr. 4, 1949; s. Albert Tyler and Jane Catherine (Steadman) U.; m. Margaret Anne Cooper, Aug. 21, 1971; children: Erin Cooper, Nathan Steadman. BA, U. Redlands, 1971; MA, Ariz. State U., 1977, PhD, 1980. Dist. sales mgr. Ind. News Co. Inc., Los Angeles, 1971-72; regional sales mgr. Petersen Pub. Co, Los Angeles, 1972-74; archeologist, researcher Bur. Land Mgmt., Phoenix, 1979; research asst. Ariz. State U., Tempe, 1979-80; chief archeologist Soil Systems Inc., Phoenix, 1980-81; chief archeologist N.Mex. State U., Las Cruces, N.Mex., 1981-85, asst. prof. to assoc. prof., 1982-87, assoc. dean, 1987-90; prof. anthropology, vice provost for rsch., grad. dean U. Oreg., Eugene, 1990—; interim dir. Cultural Resources Mgmt. div, N.Mex. State U., Las Cruces, 1988. Author: Polities and Power, 1982, A Hopi Social History, 1992; editor: Computer Graphics in Archaeology, 1979, Mogollon Variability, 1986, The Sociopolitical Structure of Prehistoric Southwest Societies, 1989, The Evolution of Political Systems, 1990; also articles. Advanced seminar grantee Sch. of Am. Research, 1987, research grantee NSF, 1979, 1984-85, Hist. Preservation grantee State of N.Mex., 1982-84, 1991, 92, Ford Found. 1991-92, U.S. Dept. Edn. 1991-93. Mem. Nat. Nat. Phys. Sci. Consortium (pres. 1992-95), We. Assn. Grad. Schs. (pres. 1994-95). Office: U Oreg Office Acad Affairs 207 Johnson Hall Eugene OR 97403

UPHOFF, JAMES KENT, education educator; b. Hebron, Nebr., Sept. 1, 1937; s. Ernest John and Alice Marie (Dutcher) U.; m. Harriet Lucille Martin, Aug. 6, 1962; 1 child, Nicholas James. BA, Hastings Coll., 1959; MEd, U. Nebr., 1962, EdD, 1967. Tchr., Walnut Jr. High Sch., Grand Island, Nebr., 1959-65, dept. chmn., 1962-65; instr. dept. edn. U. Nebr., Lincoln, 1965-66; curriculum intern Bellevue (Nebr.) Pub. Schs., 1966-67; asst. prof. edn. Wright State U., Dayton, Ohio, 1967-70, assoc. prof., 1970-75, prof. edn., 1975—, co-dir. pub. edn. religion studies ctr., 1972-75, dean br. campuses, 1974-79, dir. lab. experiences, 1982-91, chmn. dept. tchr. edn., 1994—; vis. prof. U. Dayton, 1968-69. Author: (with others) Summer Children: Ready or Not For School, 4th edit., 1986; School Readiness and Transition Programs: Real Facts from Real Schools, 1990, 2nd edit., 1995; editor: Dialogues on Develop. Curriculum K and I, 1987, Changing to a Developmentally Appropriate Curriculum-Successfully: 4 Case Studies, 1989; weekly columnist Oakwood Register newspaper, monthly columnist Dayton Parent newspaper. Recipient Disting. Rsch. award Coll. Edn. and Human Svcs. Wright State U., 1988, 91, Deans' award, 1991; Phi Delta Kappa scholar, 1969; Malone fellow in Arab Islamic studies, 1989. Bd. dirs. pub. edn. fund Dayton Found., 1985—; mem. Luth. Ch. coun., 1987-90, chair 1988-90; mem. Oakwood City Schs. Bd. Edn., 1989—, v.p., 1994—. Mem. Am. Ednl. Rsch. Assn., Nat. Coun. Tchrs. English, Western Ohio Edn. Assn. (pres. 1974-75, exec. com. 1979-85), Assn. Supervision and Curriculum Devel. (dir. 1974-79, editor early childhood network 1989—, co-editor pub. edn. and religion network 1992—), Assn. Tchr. Educators, Assn. Childhood Edn. Internat., Ohio Assn. Supervision and Curriculum Devel. (v.p. 1972-73), Nat. Coun. Social Studies, Ohio Coun. Social Studies, Ohio Sch. Bds. Assn. (chair rules com. 1993-94, mem. policy and legislation com. 1994—), Nat. Assn. Edn. Young Children, Dayton Area Coun. Social Studies (pres. (1970-71, 85-87), Ohio Assn. Edn. Young Children (com. chair 1992—), Dayton Assn. for Young Children (exec. bd. 1988-94), Nat. Coun. on Religion and Pub. Edn. (co-editor newsletter 1991—), LWV Greater Dayton (edn. dir. 1985-85), Ohio Council Chs. (edn. com. 1973-75), Optimists Club (pres. 1983-85, sec./treas. 1988—), Golden Key (chpt. advisor 1991—), Phi Delta Kappa (chpt. pres. 1983-84, chpt. advisor 1988-94), Kappa Delta Pi. Republican. Home: 150 Spirea Dr Dayton OH 45419-3409 Office: Wright State U 322 Millett Edn Dayton OH 45435

UPLEDGER, JOHN EDWIN, osteopath, physician; b. Detroit, Feb. 10, 1932; s. Edwin Chauncey and Eleanor Bernice (Cave) U.; divorced; children from previous marriage; Leslie, John, Mark, Michael; m. Dianne Lucille Dennison, Nov. 23, 1970 (div. Feb. 1994). BA, Wayne State U, 1953; DO, Kirkville Coll. Osteo. Surgery; DSc, Medicine Alternativa, Sri Lanka, 1987. Pvt. practice Clearwater, Fla., 1964-75; prof. biomechs. Mich. State U., East Lansing, 1975-82; med.dir., clin. researcher Unity Ctr. for Health, Edn. and Rsch., West Palm Beach, Fla., 1982-85; clin.dir. Upledger Inst., Upledger Found., Palm Beach Gardens, Fla., 1985—; mem. adv. coun. NIH Office of Alt. Medicine, 1993-95. Author: Craniosacral Therapy, Vol. I-II, 1982, 85, Somato Emotional Release and Beyond, 1990, Craniosacral Therapy Somatoemotional Release Your Inner Physician and You, 1993, A Brain is Born, 1995; contbr. articles to profl. jours. Bd. dirs. Cleatwater/St. Petersburg Free Clinics, Fla., 1968-75. Fellow Am. Acad. Osteopathy; mem. Soc. Osteopathes (acad. fellow 1978). Achievements include craniosacral therapy; somato emotional release; therapist-patient electrocircuitry; neurocircuitry redevel. Office: Upledger Inst 11211 Prosperity Farms Rd West Palm Beach FL 33410-3446

UPPMAN, THEODOR, concert and opera singer, voice educator; b. San Jose, Calif., Jan. 12, 1920; s. John August and Hulda Maria (Thörnström) U.; m. Jean Seward, Jan. 31, 1943; children: Margot, Michael. Student, Coll. of Pacific, 1938-39, Curtis Inst. Music, 1939-41, Stanford U., 1941-42, U. So. Calif., 1948-50. mem. prof. com. regional auditions Met. Opera; voice faculty Mannes Coll. Music, 1977—, Manhattan Sch. Music., 1988—; tchr. master classes Britten-Pears Sch. Advanced Mus. Studies, 1985—, master classes Glimmerglass Opera, Cooperstown, N.Y., 1990, 93, Opera Theatre of St. Louis, 1993; dir. vocal dept. Music Acad. of the West, Santa Barbara, Calif., 1988. Profl. debut as baritone, No. Calif. Symphony, 1941, appeared with, San Francisco Symphony, 1947; performed in: Pelleas et Melisande, City Ctr. Opera Co., N.Y., 1948; debut, San Francisco Opera Co., 1948, N.Y. recital, Times Hall, 1950; appeared: title role Billy Budd opera premiere, Royal Opera House, London, Eng., 1951, Theatre des Champs Elysees, Paris, France, 1952; performed in: Billy Budd, NBC-TV Opera Theatre 1952, Pelleas et Melisande, Met. Opera Co., 1953-62, Magic Flute, 1956-77, La Perichole, 1956-71, Don Giovanni, 1957-73, Madam Butterfly, 1961-78, Cosi fan Tutte, 1962-71, L'Italiana in Algeri, 1973-75; world premieres of Floyd's The Passion of Jonathan Wade, N.Y.C. Opera, 1962, Villa Lobos' Yerma, Santa Fe Opera, 1971, Pasatieri's Black Widow, Seattle Opera, 1972, Barab's Philip Marshall, Chautauqua, 1974; Aix en Provence Festival, summer 1964, Aldeburgh Festival, summer 1975, Chgo. Lyric Opera debut, 1964, War Requiem by Britten, Dallas, Cleve., Cin. orchs.,

1965, Damnation of Faust, N.Y. Philharmonic, 1966; Am. premiere: Billy Budd, Chgo. Lyric Opera, 1970, Death in Venice (Britten), Geneva Opera, 1983; World premiere: A Quiet Place (Bernstein), Houston Opera, 1983, A Quiet Place, LaScala, 1984, A Quiet Place, Vienna Staatsoper, 1986; recordings include world premiere broadcast Billy Budd, 1951; concert opera symphony appearances throughout, U.S., also radio, TV. Hon. dir. Britten-Pears Sch. for Advanced Mus. Studies, 1987—. With U.S. Army, 1943-46, World War II. Recipient 1st prize Atwater Kent Found. Auditions, Gainsborough Found. award, 1947. Address: 201 W 86th St New York NY 10024

UPRIGHT, DIANE WARNER, auction house executive; b. Cleve.; d. Rodney Upright and Shirley (Warner) Lavine. Student, Wellesley Coll., 1965-67; BA, U. Pitts., 1969; MA, U. Mich., 1973, PhD, 1976. Asst. prof. U. Va., Charlottesville, 1976-78; assoc. prof. Harvard U., Cambridge, Mass., 1978-83; sr. curator Ft. Worth Art Mus., 1984-86; dir. Jan Krugier Gallery, N.Y.C., 1986-90; sr. v.p.; head contemporary art dept. Christie's, N.Y.C., 1990—. Author: Morris Louis: The Complete Paintings, 1979, Ellsworth Kelly: Works on Paper, 1987, various exhbn. catalogues; contbr. articles to art jours. Mem. Coll. Art Assn., Art Table, Inc. Office: Christies 502 Park Ave New York NY 10022-1108

UPSHAW, DAWN, soprano; b. Nashville, Tenn., July 17, 1960. BA, Ill. Wesleyan Univ., 1982; MA, Manhattan Sch. Music, 1984; studied with Jan DeGaetani at Aspen, Colo., Music Sch. Recitalist, opera singer; sang in 1983 premiere performance, Sancta Susanna (Hindemith); with Met. Opera, 1985—; other appearances include Salzburg Festival, 1987, Aix-en-Provence, 1988-89; recordings include Ariadne auf. Naxos, Mass in G (Schubert), Knoxville Summer of 1915, The Girl With Orange Lips (songs for solo voice and chamber ensemble). Winner Young Concert Artist auditions; co-winner, Naumburg Competition, N.Y.C., 1985. Office: CAMI ARBIB Div 165 W 57th St New York NY 10019-2201 also: Electra Nonesuch c/o Electra Entertainment WEA 111 N Hollywood Way Burbank CA 91505*

UPSHAW, GENE, sports association executive; b. Robstown, Tex., Aug. 15, 1945; s. Eugene and Cora (Riley) U.; 1 son, Eugene; m. Teresa Buich, 1986; 1 son, Justin. B.S., Tex. A&I U., 1968; postgrad., Calif. State U., 1969, Golden Gate U., 1980. Player Los Angeles (formerly Oakland) Raiders, 1967-82; player rep.-alt. NFL Players Assn., Oakland, Calif., 1970-76, mem. exec. com., 1976—, exec. dir., 1980—; ptnr. Gene Upshaw & Assocs., Mgmt. Cons. Firm, Oakland, 1970-78. Mem. Calif. Gov.'s Council Wellness and Phys. Fitness; mem. Calif. Bd. Govs. for Community Colls.; former planning commr. Alameda County, Calif., coordinator voter registration and fund raising. Served with U.S. Army, 1967-73. Named Offensive Lineman of Yr., Am. Football Conf., 1973, 74, 77; named Lineman of Yr., NFL, 1977, Pro Bowl selection 6 times, All Pro selection Sporting News, 1967-77, All Pro selection UPI, 1967-77, All Pro selection AP, 1967-77, All Pro selection TV Guide, 1967-77, All Pro selection Profl. Football Writers, 1967-77; mem. NFL Championship Team, 1976, 1980; recipient Byron (Whizzer) White Humanitarian award NFL Players Assn., 1980, A. Philip Randolph A. Philip Randolph Inst., 1982. Mem. Alpha Phi Alpha. Democrat. Baptist. Office: Fedn Professional Athletes 2021 L St NW Fl 6 Washington DC 20036-4909

UPSHAW, HARRY STEPHAN, psychology educator; b. Birmingham, Ala., July 10, 1926; s. N.H. and Florence (Arnold) U.; m. Paula Binyon, June 18, 1950; children: Alan Binyon, Phyllis, David Arnold, Stephan Lipner. Student, U. Ala., 1946-47; A.B., U. Chgo., 1949; M.A., Northwestern U., 1951; Ph.D., U. N.C., 1956. Asst prof. psychology U. Ala., 1954-57; spl. instr. psychology Simmons Coll., Boston, 1957-58; research asso. Ednl. Research Corp., Cambridge, Mass., 1957-58; asst. prof., then assoc. prof. pub. health U N.C., 1958-61, lectr., assoc. prof. psychology, 1958-64, rsch. prof. psychology, 1991—; assoc. prof. Bryn Mawr (Pa.) Coll., 1964-65; assoc. prof., then prof. emeritus psychology U. Ill., Chgo., 1965-91, prof. emeritus, 1991—; dept. head, 1968-72; assoc. dir. Office of Social Sci. Rsch., 1981-87; guest prof. U. Mannheim, Germany, 1975, Fulbright scholar Technische Universitaet Berlin, 1978-79; vis. scholar Inst. for Rsch. in Social Sci., U. N.C., 1991-92. Editorial cons., Jour. Expll. Social Psychology, Research in Personality, Jour. Applied Social Psychology, Jour. Personality Social Psychology; Contbr. articles to profl. jours. Served with AUS, 1944-46. Fellow Am. Psychol. Assn., Soc. Exptl. Social Psychol. Home: 209 Kirkwood Dr Chapel Hill NC 27514-5136

UPSON, DONALD V., financial executive; b. Hutchinson, Kans., Feb. 8, 1934; s. William Ernest and Luella Beatrice (Hutchison) U.; m. Janis Carol Anderson, Sept. 16, 1956; children: Mark Steven, Brent William. B.S. Kans. State U., 1956. C.P.A. With Peat, Marwick, Mitchell & Co., 1956, 60-81, ptnr., 1974-81; exec. v.p., dir. internal audit Del E. Webb Corp., Phoenix, 1981-85; mgr. info. systems Tiernay Turbines Inc., Phoenix, 1986; chief fin. officer Schomac Corp., Tucson, 1986-88; adminstr. U. Ariz., Tucson, 1988-90; pres., chief exec. officer Ariz. Commerce Bank, Tucson, 1990-91; chief fin. officer O'Connor, Cavanagh, Anderson, Westover, Killingsworth & Beshears, P.A., Phoenix, 1991-94; fin. cons., 1995—. Pres. Community Orgn. for Drug Abuse, Alcohol and Mental Health Services, Inc., 1977-78; bd. dir. Phoenix council Boy Scouts Am., elder Presbyterian Ch. Served to lt. USAF, 1956-59. Mem. Am. Inst. C.P.A.s, Ariz. Soc. C.P.A.s, Beta Theta Pi (pres. 1955-56). Republican. Home and Office: 407 W Stacey Ln Tempe AZ 85284

UPSON, STUART BARNARD, advertising agency executive; b. Cin., Apr. 14, 1925; s. Mark and Alice (Barnard) U.; m. Barbara Jussen, Nov. 2, 1946; children: Marguerite Nichols, Anne Marcus, Stuart Barnard. BS, Yale U., 1945. With Dancer, Fitzgerald, Sample, Inc., N.Y.C., 1946—; sr. v.p. 1963-66, exec. v.p., 1966-67, pres., 1967-74, chmn., 1974-86; chmn. DFS-Dorland, N.Y.C., 1986-87, Saatchi & Saatchi Advt. Inc., N.Y.C., 1987—; bd. dirs. Manhattan Life Ins. Co. Bd. dirs. Fresh Air Fund, N.Y., Advt. Coun. With USNR, 1943-46. Mem. St. Elmo Soc. Clubs: Wee Burn Country (Darien); Sky (N.Y.C.); Blind Brook, Pine Valley Golf. Home: 16 Wrenfield Ln Darien CT 06820-2201 Office: Saatchi & Saatchi Advt Inc 375 Hudson St New York NY 10014-3658

UPSON, THOMAS FISHER, state legislator, lawyer; b. Waterbury, Conn., Sept. 30, 1941; s. J. Warren and Grace (Fisher) U.; m. Barbara Secor (div. Jan. 1979); children: Secor, Chauncey Julius. BA in History, Washington and Jefferson Coll., 1963; LLB, U. Conn., 1968. Bar: Conn., 1969, U.S. Dist. Ct. (2d dist.), 1969. Lawyer Upson & Secor, Waterbury, 1969-70, 74-76; lawyer, spl. asst. U.S. Dept. Commerce, Washington, 1970-72; lawyer, spl. asst. to adminstr. GSA, Washington, 1973-74; dir. admissions St. Margaret's McTernan Sch., Waterbury, 1977-78; with div. spl. revenue State of Conn., Hartford, 1978-82; assoc. Moynahan & Ruskin, Waterbury, 1979-8l; pvt. practice, Waterbury, 1981—; mem. Conn. Senate, Hartford, 1985—, dep. majority leader, chmn. jud. com., 1995—. Moderator 1st Congl. Ch., Waterbury, 1986-91; bd. dirs. Easter Seals-United Way, Waterbury, 1984-88; mem. Conn. Rep. Ctrl. com., 1983-91; dir. Mattatuck Mus., 1993—. Mem. ABA, Conn. Bar Assn., Waterbury Bar Assn., SAR, Soc. Colonial Wars, Phi Gamma Delta. Republican. Congregationalist. Lodge: Kiwanis (former pres., lt. gov. SW New Eng. dist.). Elks. Avocations: hiking, music, history. Home: Bldg 10 Unit 1 827 Oronoke Rd Waterbury CT 06708-3939 Office: Conn Senate Capitol Bldg Hartford CT 06106 also: 52 Holmes Ave Waterbury CT 06710

UPTON, ARTHUR CANFIELD, experimental pathologist, educator; b. Ann Arbor, Mich., Feb. 27, 1923; s. Herbert Hawkes and Ellen (Canfield) U.; m. Elizabeth Bache Perry, Mar. 1, 1946; children: Rebecca A., Melissa P., Bradley C. Grad., Phillips Acad., Andover, Mass., 1941; BA, U. Mich., 1944, MD, 1946. Intern Univ. Hosp., Ann Arbor, 1947; resident Univ. Hosp., 1948-49; instr. pathology U. Mich. Med. Sch., 1950-51; pathologist Oak Ridge (Tenn.) Nat. Lab., 1951-54, chief pathology-physiology sect., 1954-69; prof. pathology SUNY Med. Sch. at Stony Brook, 1969-77, chmn. dept. pathology, 1969-70, dean Sch. Basic Health Scis., 1970-75; dir. Nat. Cancer Inst., Bethesda, Md., 1977-79; prof., chmn. dept. environ. medicine NYU Med. Sch., N.Y.C., 1980-92, prof. emeritus, 1993—; clin. prof. pathology & radiology Sch. Medicine, U. N.Mex., Albuquerque, 1991—; clin. prof. environ. and cmty. medicine UMDNJ-Rogert Wood Johnson Med. Sch., 1995—; attending pathologist Brookhaven Nat. Lab., 1969-77; dir. Inst. Environ. Medicine, Med. Sch., NYU, 1980-91; mem. various coms.

nat. and internat. orgns.; lectr. in field. Assoc. editor: Cancer Research; mem. editorial bd.: Internat. Union Against Cancer. Served with AUS, 1943-46. Recipient Ernest Orlando Lawrence award for atomic field, 1965, Comfort-Crookshank award for cancer rsch. Inst. Med., NAS, 1979, Claude M. Fuess award 1980, Sarah L. Poilley award for pub. health, 1983, CHUMS Physician of Yr. award 1985, Basic Cell Rsch. in Cytology Lectureship award 1985, Fred W. Stewart award, 1986, Ramazzini award, 1986, Lovelace Med. Found. award, 1993; Sigma Xi nat. lectr., 1989-91. Fellow N.Y. Acad. Scis., Soc. for Risk Analysis; mem. AAAS, Asm. Assn. Pathologists and Bacteriologists, Internat. Acad. Pathology, Inst. Medicine NAS, Radiation Rsch. Soc. (councilor 1963-64, pres. 1965-66), Internat. Assn. Radiation Rsch. (pres. 1983-87), Am. Assn. Cancer Rsch. (pres. 1963-64), Am. Soc. Exptl. Pathology (pres. 1963-64), Gerontol. Soc., Sci. Rsch. Soc. Am., Soc. Exptl. Biology and Medicine, Peruvian Oncology Soc. (hon.), Japan Cancer Assn. (hon.), N.Y. State Health Rsch. Coun. (chmn. 1982-90), Internat. Assn. for Radiation Rsch. (pre. 1983-87), Assn. Univ. Environ. Health Sci. Ctrs. (pres. 1982-90), Ramazzini Inst. (pres. 1992—), Phi Beta Kappa, Sigma Xi, Phi Gamma Delta, Alpha Omega Alpha, Nu Sigma Nu. Achievements include research on pathology of radiation injury and endocrine glands, on cancer, on carcinogenesis, on experimental leukemia, on aging. Home: 1424 Seville Rd Santa Fe NM 87505

UPTON, FREDERICK STEPHEN, congressman; b. St. Joseph, Mich., Apr. 23, 1953; s. Stephen E. and Elizabeth Brooks (Vial) U.; m. Amey Richmond Rulon-Miller, Nov. 5, 1983; 2 children. BA in Journalism, U. Mich., 1975. Staff asst. to Congressman David A. Stockman, Washington, 1976-81; legis. asst. Office Mgmt. and Budget, Washington, 1981-83, dep. dir. legis. affairs, 1983-84, dir. legis. affairs, 1984-85; mem. 100th-104th Congresses from 4th (now 6th) Mich. dist., Washington, 1986—; mem. commerce com. Field mgr. Stockman for Congress, St. Joseph, 1975; campaign mgr. Globensky for Congress, St. Joseph, 1981. Republican. Office: US House of Reps 2333 Rayburn Bldg Washington DC 20515*

UPTON, HOWARD B., JR., management writer, lawyer; b. Tahlequah, Okla., May 17, 1922; s. Howard B. and Marjorie (Ross) U.; m. Jean Devereaux, June 14, 1945; children—Pamela, Barbara, Martha, Brian. BA, U. Okla., 1943, LLB, 1948. Cert. assn. exec. Dir. indsl. relations Western Petroleum Refiners Assn., Tulsa, 1948-51; exec. v.p. Petroleum Equipment Inst., Tulsa, 1951-87; dir. Telex Corp., Tulsa, 1972-88; mgmt. columnist Nat. Petroleum News, 1988—, Inflight Mag. of Southwest Airlines, 1988-93; lectr. dept. engrng. profl. devel. U. Wis., 1988—, U. Alaska, Fairbanks, 1991—. Frequent contbr. to Wall St. Jour. Dir., mem. exec. com. Tulsa Zoo Friends, Inc., 1993—. Mem. Am. Soc. Assn. Execs. (bd. dirs 1964-68, Gold Circle award 1977, 82), Okla. Bar Assn., Mens Forum of Tulsa. Republican. Home: 5133 E 25th Ct Tulsa OK 74114-3749 Office: Upton Comm PO Box 4634 Tulsa OK 74159-0634

UPTON, RICHARD THOMAS, artist; b. Hartford, Conn., May 26, 1931; s. Ray Granville and Helen Marie (Colla) U.; 1 son, Richard Thomas, II. BFA, U. Conn., 1960; MFA, Ind. U., 1963. Artist-in-residence Artists for the Environ., Del. Water Gap, 1972, UGA Program Abroad, Corona, Italy, 1982-85. Exhbns. include E'stampe Contemporaine, Galerie Mansart, Bibliot Nat., France, 1969, 74, L'estampe aujourd'hui, 1973-78, Sala Internat., Palacio de Bellas Artes, Mexico City, 1969, Sept. Graveures un Sculpteur de Medailles, Mus. Deonon, Chalon-Sur Saone, France, 1973, Brit. Internat. Print Biennale, U.S. sect. touring Eng., 1973, Del. Water Gap, Corcoran Gallery Art, Washington, 1975, Everson Mus. Art, Syracuse, N.Y., 1975, Nat. Collection Prints and Poetry, Library of Congress, 1976-77, U. Ga., Palazzo Vignoli, Cortona, Italy, retrospective prints from, Atelier 17, Paris, 1977, Okla. Art Center, Oklahoma City, 1977, Tweed Mus. Art, Duluth, Minn., 1977, Weatherspoon Art Gallery, Greensboro, N.C., 1977, Chiesadi San Stae, Venice, Italy, 1989, Grey Gallery, N.Y.C., 1990, Everson Mus. of Art, Krannert Mus. Art, 1990—, Paysage Demoralise: Landscape at the End of the Century, Grey Art Gallery and Study Ctr., N.Y.C., 1990, Tuscany Rediscovered: Richard Upton at Cortona, Everson Mus. Art, Syracuse, 1991, Richard Upton: Italian Landscapes, Krannert Art Mus., Champaign, Ill., 1992, The Italian Landscapes: Richard Upton at Cortona, Mus. Am. Art, New Britain, Conn., 1992, Richard Upton: Ten Years of Italian Landscapes, James Michener Art Mus., Pa., 1994, Phila. Art Alliance, 1994, Condeso/Lawler Gallery, N.Y.C., 1995; represented in permanent collections Nat. Mus. of Am. Art at Smithsonian Instn., Mus. Modern Art, N.Y.C., Victoria and Albert Mus., London, Bibliot Nat., Paris, Montreal Mus. Fine Arts; commns. include Eros Thanatos Suite (German poem and woodcuts), Interlaken Corp., Providence, 1967, Salamovka Poster, Okla. Art Ctr., 1974, (with poems by Stanley Kunitz) River Road Suite, 1976; suite of drawing Robert Lowell at 66, 1977; suite of drawings Salmagundi mag. for humanities; The Anxious Landscape, paintings, drawings Bellarmine Coll., Louisville, 1989. With USNR, 1950-54. Recipient designer award Interlaken Corp., 1967; subject of monograph Richard Upton and the Rhetoric of Landscape, Paul Hayes Tucker, U. Mass., U. Wash. Press; fellow Fulbright Found., 1964, Ballinglen Arts Found., Ireland, 1994; grantee Nat. Endowment for Arts Artists for Environ., 1972, Richard Florsheim Fund, 1992; elected to Nat. Acad. of Design, 1995. Home: 113 Regent St Saratoga Springs NY 12866-4323 Office: Skidmore Coll Art Dept Saratoga Springs NY 12866

URAKAMI, AKIO, manufacturing company executive; b. Tokyo, Apr. 17, 1942; came to U.S. in 1991; s. Yutaka and Tomiko (Nagai) U.; m. Keiko Tanaka, Feb. 7, 1971; children: Yuji, Masako, Kota. BS, Tokyo Inst. Tech., 1965; MS, Northwestern U., 1967, PhD, 1970. Rsch. engr. Ryobi Ltd., Hiroshima, Japan, 1970-72, corp. planning mgr., 1972-76, v.p. internat., 1976-84, exec. v.p., 1984-91; chmn., pres. Ryobi N.Am., Inc., Easley, S.C., 1991—; mem. pres.'s adv. coun. Clemson (S.C.) u., 1992—. Trustee The Urakami Found., Hiroshima, 1978—; bd. dirs. Japan Am. Assn. of We. S.C., Greenville, 1992—. Mem. Keizai Doyu Kai. Office: Ryobi NAm Inc PO Box 1947 101 Grace Dr Easley SC 29641-1947

URBACH, FREDERICK, physician, educator; b. Vienna, Austria, Sept. 6, 1922; s. Erich and Josepha (Kronstein) U.; m. Nancy Ann Phillips, Dec. 20, 1952; children: Erich J., Gregory M., Andrew D. AB cum laude, U. Pa., 1943; MD, Jefferson Med. Coll., 1946; MD (hon.), U. Göttingen, Fed. Republic Germany, 1987. Diplomate: Am. Bd. Dermatology. Intern Jefferson Hosp., 1946-47; fellow in dermatology U. Pa. Hosp., 1949-52; fellow pediatric dermatology Children's Hosp., Phila., 1950-52; asst. vis. physician Phila. Gen. Hosp., Skin and Cancer Hosp., U. Pa. Hosp., 1952-54; assoc. chief cancer research (dermatology) Roswell Park Meml. Inst., Buffalo, 1954-55, chief cancer research (dermatology), 1955-58; asst. med. dir. Skin and Cancer Hosp. Phila., 1958-67, med. dir., 1967-88; research prof. physiology U. Buffalo Grad. Sch., 1955-58; assoc. prof. dermatology Temple U. Sch. Medicine, 1958-60, prof. research dermatology, 1960-67, chmn. dept. dermatology, 1967-88; dir. Ctr. for Photobiology, 1977-89, prof. dermatology emeritus, 1989—; dep. dir. Health Rsch. Inc., Buffalo, 1954-58; mem. U.S. nat. com. photo-biology Nat. Acad. Scis., 1973-80. Author: The Biology of Cutaneous Cancer, 1963, The Biologic Effects of Ultraviolet Radiation, 1969, (with Parrish, Anderson and Pitts) UVA, 1978; (with Gange) Biologic Effects of UVA Radiation, 1985, Responses to UVA Radiation, 1992; contbr. articles to profl. jours. Served with AUS, 1943-46; with USAAF, 1947-49. Recipient Ritter Meml. medal German Dermatology Soc., 1980. Fellow AAAS, N.Y. Acad. Sci.; mem. AMA, ACP, FACP, Am. Soc. Photobiology (councilor 1973-76, pres. 1977), Am. Assn. Cancer Rsch. Soc. Am. Soc. Exptl. Biology and Medicine, Internat. Soc. Tropical Dermatology, Internat. Assn. Photobiology (v.p. 1976-79, pres. 1980-84, Finsen medal 1992); hon. mem. Danish Soc. Dermatology, Swedish Soc. Dermatology (Hellerstrom medal 1977), Polish Soc. Dermatology, Austrian Soc. Dermatology, German Soc. Dermatology, Philippine Soc. Dermatology. Research epidemiology of cancer, photobiology, phototherapy. Home: 438 Clairemont Rd Villanova PA 19085-1706 Office: Temple Med Practices 220 Commerce Dr Fort Washington PA 19034-2404

URBACH, FREDERICK LEWIS, chemistry educator; b. New Castle, Pa., Nov. 21, 1938; s. Lewis Loraine and Helen Myrtle (Spann) U.; m. Carrie Marie Grimm, June 26, 1960; children: Deborah Ann, Allison Jean. BS, Pa. State U., 1960; PhD, Mich. State U., 1964. Research assoc. Ohio State U., Columbus, 1964-66; asst. prof. Case Western Res. U., Cleve., 1966-73, assoc. prof., 1973-80, prof., 1980—. Contbr. articles to profl. jours. and book chpts.

Mem. Am. Chem. Soc. Methodist. Office: Case Western Res U Dept Chemistry Cleveland OH 44106-7078

URBAITIS, ELENA, artist; b. Kaunas, Lithuania, June 4, 1922; came to U.S., 1950; d. Ignas and Elena (Brazionyte) U. Student, Akademie der Bildenden Kunst, Munich, 1946-48; Diploma in Fine Arts, Ecole des Arts et Metiers, Freiburg, Germany, 1950; BA in Fine Arts, Montevallo U., 1951; MA, Tchrs. Coll., Columbia U., 1960. One-woman show includes Space Flight/stainless steel sculpture, Press Ctr., Vilnius, Lithuania, 1992; others; groups shows include Outdoor Sculpture Now, Islip Art Mus., East Islip N.Y., 1989, Lights: Recent Issues in Illuminating Sculpture, Morris Mus. of Arts and Sci., Morristown, N.J., 1982, 83, Works on Paper -- Women Artists, The Bklyn. Mus., 1976, numerous others; contbr. articles/interviews to profl. jours. French Ministry Cultural Affairs Arts fellow Paris, 1950; recipient award of Excellence L.I. Artists League, Heckscher Mus., L.I., N.Y., 1975, Gold medal Lithuanian Cultural Ctr., N.Y.C., 1977, 1st prize Lituanian-Am. Cultural Coun., Chgo., 1993. Mem. Am. Soc. Contemporary Artists (award in sculpture 1988), Artists Equity. Home: 2292 Willow St Wantagh NY 11793

URBAN, CARLYLE WOODROW, retired lawyer; b. Beverly, Kans., Dec. 14, 1914; s. Joseph William and Anna Bell (Murphy) U.; m. Lois Ball, June 10, 1946 (dec. Mar. 1987); children: Elizabeth Anne Urban Alexander, Michael Joseph; m. Zara Walker, Feb. 11, 1989. Student, Kans. Wesleyan U., 1931-33; LL.B., U. Tex., Austin, 1941. Bar: Tex. 1941. Practiced in Austin, 1941-42, Houston, 1944-86; assoc. firm Powell, Wirtz, Rauhut & Gideon, Austin, 1941-42; partner firms Elledge, Urban & Bruce, Houston, 1944-62, Urban & Coolidge, Houston, 1963-85. Scoutmaster Sam Houston Area council Boy Scouts Am., 1959-61; Precinct committeeman Harris County (Tex.) Democratic Exec. Com., 1957-63. Served with USAAF, 1942-44. Mem. Order of Coif, Delta Theta Phi. Methodist (trustee, chmn. bd. trustees dist. conf.). Lodge: Lion. Home: 1610 Stonegate Dr Cleburne TX 76031-4554 *Have we done our children any favor by making life easier for them than for us as parents? I think not. I fear we have done our children a disservice by depriving them of the "right to struggle". We have created an environment of leniency. Being required to suffer the consequences of failure has gone out of fashion. Even our courts have pursued a policy of leniency. If our system is to be preserved, I sincerely believe that greater respect must be given to personal self-discipline, pride in personal achievement and excellence of performance.*

URBAN, FRANK HENRY, dermatologist, state legislator; b. St. Louis, May 24, 1930; s. Frank and Helen Gertrude (Zingsheim) U.; m. Lois Elaine Thurwachter, June 18, 1954 (dec. 1991); children: James, Barbara, Michael, Mark, David, Bruce, John; m. Kathryn Calvert Bloomberg, Nov. 28, 1992. BS in Med. Sci., U. Wis., 1951, MD, 1954; MS, U. Minn., 1960. Diplomate Am. Bd. Dermatology. Intern Beaumont Army Hosp., El Paso, 1954-55; resident Mayo Clinic, Rochester, Minn., 1957-60; pvt. practice dermatology Wauwatosa, Wis., 1960-93; asst. clin. prof. Med. Coll. Wis., Wauwatosa, 1964—; mem. Wis. State Assembly, Madison, 1989—. Trustee Village Bd. of Elm Grove, Wis., 1985-87, pres., 1987-89; bd. dirs. ARC of Greater Milw.; pres. Friends U. Wis.-Milw. Sch. Edn., 1995—, bd. dirs., 1990—; mem. adv. bd. Potawatomi coun. Boy Scouts Am. pres., 1974-76. Capt. U.S. Army, 1954-57. Recipient Silver Beaver award East Cen. Region Boy Scouts Am., 1972, Silver Antelope award, 1979, Civic Leadership award State Med. Soc. Wis., 1990, Disting. Svc. award U. Wis. Med. Sch. Alumni Assn., 1991. Fellow Am. Acad. Dermatology; mem. Wis. Dermatol. Soc. (pres. 1969-70), Wis. State Med. Soc. (dir. 1987-92, 93—), Milw. County Med. Soc. (caucus chmn. 1987-92, pres.-elect 1992-93, pres. 1993-94), Brookfield C. of C. (Outstanding Mem. award 1992). Republican. Roman Catholic. Avocations: tennis, walking, photography, music. Office: State Capitol PO Box 8953 Madison WI 53708-8953

URBAN, GILBERT WILLIAM, banker; b. Silver Lake, Minn., Oct. 20, 1928; s. William and Alice (Polak) U.; m. Elvera Mattson, Feb. 23, 1954; children: Lisa Alice Marie, Leann Kay. BBA, U. Minn., 1949. Sr. acct. Price Waterhouse and Co., Chgo., 1949-50; chief acct. Calif. Bank, L.A., 1950-51; asst. contr. 1st Nat. Bank, Mpls., 1951-63, contr., 1963-69; v.p., cashier La. Nat. Bank, Baton Rouge, 1969-73, v.p. assets and liabilities, 1973-86; sr. v.p. fin. policy Premier Bancorp Inc., Baton Rouge, 1986—; instr. evening sch. U. Minn., 1956-69, La. State U., 1970—, So. U., Baton Rouge, 1989—; instr. Nat. Assn. Bank Auditors and Contrs. Sch., U. Wis., 1960-63, sect. leader, 1963-69; chmn. dept. controllership Bank Adminstrn. Inst., 1970—; course coord. Banking Sch. of South, 1970, 79—. Mem. Beta Alpha Psi, Alpha Kappa Psi. Lutheran. Office: Premier Bank PO Box 1511 Baton Rouge LA 70821-1511

URBAN, GLEN L., management educator; b. Wausau, Wis., Apr. 15, 1940. BSME, U. Wis., 1963, MBA, 1964, PhD, Northwestern U., 1966. Asst. prof. MIT, Cambridge, Mass., 1966-70, assoc. prof., 1970-77, prof. mktg. and mgmt. sci., 1977—, Dai-Ichi Kangyo Bank prof. mgmt., 1987-93, dep. dean Sloan Sch. Mgmt., 1987-91; co-dir. Internat. Ctr. for Rsch. on Mgmt. of Tech., 1992-93, dean Sloan Sch. Mgmt., 1993—; co-founder Mgmt. Decision Systems, Inc., 1970, Mgmt. Sci. for Health, Inc., 1972, Mktg. Tech. Interface, Inc. Author: (with D.B. Montgomery) Management Science in Marketing, 1969, (with J.R. Hauser and N. Dholakia) Essentials of New Product Development, 1987, (with Steven H. Star) Advanced Marketing Stragety: Phenomena, Analysis and Decisions, 1991, Design and Marketing of New Products, 2d edit., 1993; mem. editl. bd. Mktg. Sci.; reviewer for Mgmt. Sci. (Best Paper award 1986), Jour. Mktg. Rsch. (O'Dell award 1983, 88), Ops. Rsch.; contbr. over 30 articles to profl. jours. Mem. Inst. Mgmt. Sci., Ops. Rsch. Soc. Am., Am. Mktg. Assn. Office: MIT Sloan Sch Mgmt 50 Memorial Dr E52-473 Cambridge MA 02142-1347

URBAN, HENRY ZELLER, newspaperman; b. Buffalo, July 11, 1920; s. George Pennock and Florence Lenhard (Zeller) U.; m. Ruth deMoss Wickwire, Apr. 28, 1948; children: Ruth Robinson Urban Smith, Florence de Moss Urban Hunn, Henry Zeller, Ward Wickwire. Grad., Hotchkiss Sch., 1939; B.S., Yale U., 1943. Treas. George Urban Milling Co., 1946-53; with Buffalo Eve. News, 1953—, asst. bus. mgr., 1957-62, bus. mgr., 1962-71, treas., dir., 1971-74, pres., pub.-1974-83; dir. G. F. Zellers Sons, Inc., 1948-53. Bd. dirs. Travelers Aid Soc., 1953-59, Buffalo Fine Arts Acad., 1960-63, 73-76, 82-85, 86-89, YMCA, 1955-68; trustee Elmwood-Franklin Sch., 1967-70; trustee Canisius Coll., 1977-83, bd. regents, 1972-78; adv. bd. Medaille Coll., 1968-83; chmn. parents council Hamilton Coll., 1977. Served to lt. USNR, 1942-46. Mem. Buffalo C. of C., N.Y. State Pubs. Assn. (dir. 1970-73, 76-79). Mid-day (Buffalo), Tennis and Squash (Buffalo), Buffalo (Buffalo), Buffalo Country (Buffalo), Saturn (Buffalo), Pack (Buffalo); Sankaty Head (Nantucket); Nantucket Yacht. Home: 57 Tudor Pl Buffalo NY 14222-1615 Office: 1 News Plz Buffalo NY 14203-2994

URBAN, JAMES ARTHUR, lawyer; b. West Palm Beach, Fla., Feb. 18, 1927; s. Arthur Joseph and Elsie Elizabeth (Wespeaker) U.; m. Alice Burmah Steed, June 21, 1952; children: James Arthur, Katherine Elizabeth. A.B. Duke U., 1950; J.D. with high honors, U. Fla., 1953. Bar: Fla. 1953. Of counsel Carlton, Fields, Ward, Emmanuel, Smith & Cutler (P.A.), Orlando, Fla.; dir. Fla. Legal Services, Inc., 1975-76. Bd. visitors Coll. Law Fla. State U., Tallahassee, 1973-79, mem. council advisers, 1975-79; mem. pres.'s council U. Fla., Gainesville, 1976-77; charter mem. Indsl. Devel. Commn. Mid-Fla., 1977—. Served with U.S. Army, 1945-47. Recipient Outstanding Alumnus award U. Fla. Law Rev. Alumni Assn., 1975. Fellow Am. Coll. Trust and Estate Counsel, Am. Coll. Real Estate Lawyers, Am. Bar Found.; mem. ABA (Ho. of Dels. 1976-80), Am. Law Inst., Fla. Bar Assn. (bd. dirs 1975-84, pres. 1977-84), Bar Founds. (bd. dirs 1979-90), Orlando C. of C. (bd. dirs 1971-73), Phi Kappa Phi, Theta Chi. Episcopalian. Clubs: Rotary (Orlando), Citrus (Orlando), Univ., Country (Orlando). Home: 1614 Pepperidge Dr Orlando FL 32806-1524 Office: Carlton Fields Ward Emmanuel Smith & Cutler PA PO Box 1171 Orlando FL 32802-1171 also: 1601 CNA Tower Orlando FL 32801

URBAN, JOHN S., engineering company executive; b. Newark, July 1, 1933; s. John Urban and Julia (Ostenski) Cahoon; m. Janet Ann Scott, June 23, 1956; children: Debra Sue Urban Doolittle, John Stanley, Gregg Scott, Jeffrey Scott. BS in Civil Engring., N.J. Inst. Tech., 1956. Registered profl. engr., N.Y., N.J., Mass., Pa., Del., Ga. Jr. engr. Edwards & Kelcey, 1956-59, engr., 1959-61, sr. engr., 1961-65, prin. engr., 1965-69, with, 1969-71, asst. v.p., 1971-74, v.p., 1974-84, sr. v.p., 1984-88, exec. v.p., 1988-90, pres., CEO, 1990-94, chmn., 1994—. Mem. bd. overseers N.J. Inst. Tech. With Army, 1957. Fellow ASCE (mem. hwy. divsn. rsch. com., Robert Ridgeway award), Am. Consulting Engrs. Coun.; mem. Am. Rd. & Transp. Builders Assn. (bd. dirs.), Soc. Am. Mil. Engrs., N.Y. Assn. Consulting Engrs. (mem. transp. com.), N.J. Soc. Profl. Engrs., N.J. Alliance Action (bd. dirs.), N.J. C. of C. (mem. transp. com.), Consulting Engrs. Coun. N.J. (past pres.), Regional Plan Assn. (mem. N.J. com.), Internat. Bridge, Tunnel and Turnpike Assn. (mem. engring. design com.), Scotch Ball Assn., Basking Ridge Golf Club (pres.), Highlander Club (N.J. Inst. Tech., pres.). Avocations: gardening, photography, golfing. Office: Edwards and Kelcey Inc Box 1936 299 Madison Ave Morristown NJ 07960

URBAN, PATRICIA A., former elementary school educator; b. Chgo., Oct. 15, 1932; d. Clifford and Caroline (Viegi) Brocken; m. Francis C. Urban, Oct. 20, 1956; children: Jim, David, Anthony, Mary Joan, Barbara, Margaret, Judy, Sharon, Jennifer. BA, Rosary Coll., River Forest, Ill., 1954; MS in Edn., Chgo. State U., 1979; MEd, Loyola U., Chgo., 1986. Cert. tchr., reading tchr., Ill. Tchr. St. Joseph Ch. Sch., Summit, Ill., 1954-56; profl. reading tutor Loyola U., 1986-90; tchr. social studies and reading Dist. 104 Schs., Summit, 1974-94; ret., 1994. Named. Dist. 104 Tchr. of Yr., 1987. Mem. ASCD, Internat. Reading Assn., Am. Fedn. Tchrs., West Suburban Tchrs. Union, Alpha Upsilon Alpha. Home: 7433 W 56th St Summit Argo IL 60501-1333

URBAN, RICHARD, newspaper editor. Metro editor Cleveland Plain Dealer. Office: Cleveland Plain Dealer 1801 Superior Ave NE Cleveland OH 44114-2192•

URBAN, STANLEY T., hospital administrator; b. Buffalo, Jan. 29, 1945; married. BA, Boston Coll., 1966; MA, Xavier U., 1969. Adminstrv. resident Colo. Gen. Hosp., Denver, 1968-69; adminstr. Colo. Psychiatric Hosp., Denver, 1969-72; asst. dir. Colo. Gen. Hosp., Denver, 1972-73, assoc. dir., 1973-76; adminstr. Oreg. Health Scis. U. Hosp., Portland, Oreg., 1976-80; dep. adminstr. St. Vincent Hosp. and Med. Ctr., Portland, Oreg., 1980-85; sr. v.p. Franciscan Health System, Aston, Pa., 1985-90, exec. v.p., 1990-92; pres., CEO Sisters of Charity Health Care Systems, Houston, 1992—. Mem. Hosp. Assn. Pa., Oreg. Assn. Hosp. Home: 161 Grogans Point Rd The Woodlands TX 77380 Office: Sisters Charity Incarnate World Health Care System 2600 N Loop W Houston TX 77092

URBAN, THOMAS NELSON, agricultural products company executive; b. 1934; married. MBA, Harvard U., 1960. Began at Pioneer Hi-Bred Internat., Inc., Des Moines, 1960, now chmn., pres., also bd. dirs.; mayor Des Moines, 1968-71. Office: Pioneer Hi-Bred Internat Inc 400 Locust Des Moines IA 50309

URBANIAK, JAMES RANDOLPH, orthopaedic surgeon; b. Fairmont, W.Va., May 15, 1936; s. Cecil and Patricia (Morgan) U.; m. Martha Helen Shawger, Dec. 20, 1970; children: Julie Kathleen, Michael James. BS, U. Ky., 1958; MD, Duke U., 1962. Diplomate Am. Bd. Orthop. Surgery, Am. Bd. Hand Surgery. Intern Duke U., Durham, N.C., 1962-63; resident in orthopaedic surgery Duke U. Hosps., Durham, N.C., 1965-69; asst. prof. Div. Orthopaedic Surgery, Duke U., Durham, 1969-73, assoc. prof., 1973-77, prof., 1977—, chief, 1985—; chief orthopaedics VA Med. Ctr., Durham, 1969-76; dir. replantation team, orthopaedic research Duke U. Med. Ctr. Editor: Microsurgery, 1987; co-editor: AAOS Symposium Microsurgery, 1979; contbr. over 110 articles to profl. jours. and 30 chpts. to books. Served to lt. comdr. USN, 1963-65. Camp Orthopaedic Travel fellow, 1968, Am. Orthopaedic Assn. Travel fellow; named N.C. Physician of Yr., 1985; recipient Disting. Alumni award U. Ky., 1985. Mem. Am. Soc. Reconstructive Microsurgery (founder, pres. 1985), Am. Soc. for Surgery of Hand (sec. 1985—), Am. Bd. Orthopaedic Surgery (bd. dirs. 1985, pres.-elect. 1988—), Joint Com. of Surgery of Hand (chmn. exam. com. 1986), Am. Orthopaedic Assn., Am. Acad. Orthopaedic Surgeons, Eastern Orthopaedic Assn. (pres. 1981), Phi Beta Kappa, Alpha Omega Alpha. Avocations: golf, skiing, sports. Home: 2600 Vintage Hill Ct Durham NC 27712-9492 Office: Duke U Med Ctr PO Box 2912 Durham NC 27715-2912•

URBANOWSKI, FRANK, publishing company executive; b. Balt., Mar. 5, 1936; s. Frank and Tofilia (Jakubik) U.; children: Alexandra, Tasha. B.S. in Ceramic Engring., Va. Poly. Inst.; postgrad., Columbia U. Rep. Ronald Press, 1960-61; editor coll. dept. Macmillan Co., 1961-66; editorial dir. Glencoe Press, 1966-68, v.p. 1968-72, pub., 1972-73; dir. market planning Ednl. Testing Service, 1973-75; dir. Mass. Inst. Tech. Press, Cambridge, 1975—; chmn. exec. council Profl. Scholarly Publs. div., 1979-81; bd. dirs. Cambridge Insight Meditation Ctr., 1985—. Mem. Am. Assn. Publs. (bd. dirs. 1979-81), Assn. Am. Univ. Press (dir. 1979-81, pres. 1990-91), Cambridge Boat Club. Home: 129 Franklin Cambridge MA 02139 also: Mountain Rd Cornwall VT 05753 Office: MIT Press 55 Hayward St Cambridge MA 02142-1399

URBIK, JEROME ANTHONY, financial consultant; b. Chgo., Oct. 30, 1929; s. Anthony Frank and Sophie Elizabeth (Stripeikis) U.; married, 1956; children: Laura M. Kern, Michael A., Anthony J., Mary L. King, John T., Maria M. BA in Philosophy, St. Mary's Coll., Techny, Ill., 1953; CLU degree, Am. Coll., 1970, ChFC degree, 1979. CLU, Chartered Fin. Cons. Field underwriter MONY Fin. Svcs., Chgo., 1955-59; merchandising specialist Mut. of N.Y., N.Y.C., 1959; pvt. practice brokerage cons. Northfield, Ill., 1960-64; CEO Hinsdale (Ill.) Assocs. Fin. Svcs. Corp, 1964—; v.p. Interstate Coll. Personology, San Diego, 1982-87; pres. Gen. Agts. Mgrs. Conf., 1967-68. Mem. publ. com. Crisis mag., 1989—; contbr. articles on industry to profl. jours.; mem. editorial bd. Leaders mag., 1981-90. Mem. adv. coun. Congressman Henry Hyde, Nat. Rep. Com., Washington; mem. Small Bus. Devel. Ctr., exec. bd. advisors Lewis U., Lockport, Ill., 1984-90; exec. coord. Legatus (Cath. chief exec. officer) Bd.; bd. dirs. United Rep. Fund, 1987-92; bd. advisors Am. Life League, Washington; bd. dirs. Nat. Coalition Reps. for Life. Named Small Bus. Acct. of Yr. for State of Ill. SBA, 1987. Mem. Am. Soc. CLUs, Am. Life League (bd. advisers), Chgo. Orchestral Assn., Chgo. Lyric Opera. Roman Catholic. Avocations: reading, writing, power boating, classical music. Home: 474 South St Elmhurst IL 60126-4120 Office: Hinsdale Assoc Fin Svc Corp 15 Spinning Wheel Dr # 414 Hinsdale IL 60521-3541

URBINA, MANUEL II, legal research historian, history educator; b. Rodriguez, Nuevo Leon, Mex., Sept. 23, 1939; came to U.S., 1947; s. Manuel and Irene (Salce) de Urbina. BA, Howard Payne Coll., 1962; postgrad., Nat. Autonoma U. Mex., Mexico City, 1963-64; MA, U. Tex., 1967, PhD, 1976; postgrad., Cambridge (Eng.) U., 1982; JD, U. Houston, 1983. Prof. Latin Am. history Coll. of the Mainland, Texas City, Tex., 1967—; founder, curator Urbina Mus. History of Mex., Houston, 1990—; chmn., legal counsel Urbina Found., Houston, 1985—; chmn., CEO Urbina Pub. Co. Inc, Houston and Mexico City, 1985—. Editor, interviewer history videos, oral history interviews with participants in the Mexican Revolution. Founder Cinco de Mayo Assn., Galveston County, Tex., 1976; founder, faculty sponsor Mex. Am. Student Assn., Coll. of Mainlan, 1974—. Named Hispanic of Yr. Galveston County League of United Latin Am. Citizens, 1982; NEH grantee, 1971-72; U.S. Dept. State scholar diplomat, 1979. Mem. League of United Latin Am. Citizens, Tex. State Hist. Assn., Howard Payne U. Alumni Assn., U. Houston Law Alumni Assn., Interam. C. of C. Democrat. Baptist. Avocations: reading, research, travel, trumpet playing, volunteer work. Home: 889 Old Genoa Red Bluff Rd Houston TX 77034-4010 Office: Museo Urbina de Historia de Mexico 889 Old Genoa Red Bluff Rd Houston TX 77034-4010

URBOM, WARREN KEITH, federal judge; b. Atlanta, Nebr., Dec. 17, 1925; s. Clarence Andrew and Anna Myrl (Irelan) U.; m. Joyce Marie Crawford, Aug. 19, 1951; children: Kim Marie, Randall Crawford, Allison Lee, Joy Renee. AB with highest distinction, Nebr. Wesleyan U., 1950, LLD (hon.), 1984; JD with distinction, U. Mich., 1953. Bar: Nebr. 1953. Mem. firm Baylor, Evnen, Baylor, Urbom, & Curtiss, Lincoln, Nebr., 1953-70; judge U.S. Dist. Ct. Nebr., 1970—; chief judge U.S. Dist. Ct. Dist. Nebr., 1972-86, sr. judge, 1991—; mem. com. on practice and procedure Nebr. Supreme Ct., 1965—; mem. subcom. on fed. jurisdiction Jud. Conf. U.S., 1975-83; adj. instr. trial advocacy U. Nebr. Coll. Law, 1979-90; bd. dirs. Fed. Jud. Ctr., 1982-86; chmn. com. on orientation newly apptd. dist.

---

judges Fed. Jud. Ctr., 1986-89; mem. 8th Cir. Com. on Model Criminal and Civil Jury Instrns., 1983—; mem. adv. com. on alternative sentences U.S. Sentencing Com., 1989-91. Contbr. articles to profl. jours. Trustee St. Paul Sch. Theology, Kansas City, Mo., 1986-89; pres. Lincoln YMCA, 1965-67; bd. govs. Nebr. Wesleyan U., chmn., 1975-80. With AUS, 1944-46. Recipient Medal of Honor, Nebr. Wesleyan U. Alumni Assn., 1983. Fellow Am. Coll. Trial Lawyers; mem. ABA, Nebr. Bar Assn. (ho. of dels. 1966-70, Outstanding Legal Educator award 1990), Lincoln Bar Assn. (Liberty Bell award 1993, pres. 1968-69), Kiwanis (Disting. Svc. award 1993). United Methodist (bd. mgrs., bd. global ministries 1972-76, gen. com. on status and role of women 1988—, gen. conf. 1972, 76, 80, 88, 92). Club: Masons (33 deg.). Home: 4421 Ridgeview Dr Lincoln NE 68516-1516 Office: US Dist Ct 586 Fed Bldg 100 Centennial Mall N Lincoln NE 68508-3803

URCIUOLI, J. ARTHUR, investment executive; b. Syracuse, N.Y., Nov. 13, 1937; s. Joseph R. and Nicoletta Anne (Phillips) U.; m. Margaret Jane Forelli, Aug. 13, 1966; children: Karen Sloan, Christian J.A. B.S., St. Lawrence U., 1959; J.D., Georgetown U., 1966; grad. Advanced Mgmt. Program, Harvard Bus. Sch., 1982. Bar: N.Y. 1966. Atty. Brown, Wood, Fuller, Caldwell & Ivey, N.Y.C., 1966-69; internat. investment banker, dir. internat. fin. Merrill Lynch, N.Y.C., Paris, 1970-78; pres. Merrill Lynch Internat., 1978-82; chmn. Merrill Lynch Internat. Bank, London; dir. banking div. Merrill Lynch Capital Markets, 1980-84; dir. Merrill Lynch Bus. Fin. Services, Merrill Lynch Co., 1984-93; dir. mktg. group Merrill Lynch Pvt. Client, 1993—. Contbr. articles to profl. jours. Trustee St. Lawrence U., 1976-89, Bruce Mus., Greenwich, Conn., 1990-94; bd. dirs. United Way, Greenwich, 1978-81. Capt. USMC, 1959-63. Mem. Securities Assn. (chmn. sales and mktg. com. 1987-89), River Club (N.Y.C.), N.Y. Yacht Club, Riverside (Conn.) Yacht Club, Rocky Point Club (Old Greenwich, Conn.). Republican. Congregationalist. Clubs: River (N.Y.C.); N.Y. Yacht, Riverside (Conn.) Yacht; Rocky Point (Old Greenwich, Conn.). Office: Merrill Lynch 800 Scudders Mill Rd Plainsboro NJ 08536

URDANG, ALEXANDRA, book publishing executive; b. N.Y.C., June 29, 1956; d. Laurence Urdang and Irena (Ehrlich) Urdang de Tour. BA in English Lit., U. Conn., 1977. Customer svc. and fulfillment mgr. Universe Books, N.Y.C., 1978-79, sales mgr., assoc. mktg. mgr., 1980-82; asst. v.p., dir. spl. sales Macmillan Pub. Co., N.Y.C., 1982-88; v.p. new markets Warner Books, Inc., N.Y.C., 1988—. Avocations: architecture, art, antiques. Office: Warner Books Inc Time and Life Bldg 1271 Avenue Of The Americas New York NY 10020-1300

URDANG, LAURENCE, lexicographer, publisher; b. N.Y.C., Mar. 21, 1927; s. Harry Rudman and Annabel (Schafran) U.; m. Irena B. Ehrlich vel Sluszny, May 23, 1952 (div.); children: Nicole Severyn, Alexandra Stefanie. B.S. Columbia U., 1954, postgrad., 1954-58. Lectr. gen. linguistics NYU, 1956-61; assoc. editor dictionary dept. Funk & Wagnalls, Inc., N.Y.C., 1957; reference editor Random House, Inc., N.Y.C., 1957-61, dir. reference dept., 1962-69; pres. Laurence Urdang, Inc., Old Lyme, Conn. and Aylesbury, Eng., 1969—; chmn. bd. Laurence Urdang Assocs., Ltd., Aylesbury, 1969-78; editor Verbatim, Old Lyme and Aylesbury, 1974—. Compiler, editor, author numerous books; mng. editor: Random House Unabridged Dictionary, 1966; editor in chief: Random House College Dictionary, 1968, Random House Dictionary of Synonyms and Antonyms, 1960, N.Y. Times Everday Reader's Dictionary of Misunderstood, Misused, Mispronounced Words, 1972, 2d edit., 1985, Dictionary of Advertising Terms, 1977, Official Associated Press Almanac, 1973, 74, 75, CBS News Almanac, 1976, Hammond Almanac, 1977, Picturesque Expressions, 1980, 2d edit., 1985, Illustrated Children's Dictionary, 1979, Basic Dictionary of Synonyms and Antonyms, 1979, 2d edit., 1986, The Synonym Finder, 1979, Collins English Dictionary, 1979, Verbatim: Vols. I, II, 1978, Vols. III, IV, V, VI, and Index, 1981, -Ologies & -Isms, 1978, 81, 86, Twentieth Century American Nicknames, 1979, A Treasury of Biblical Quotations, 1980, The Timetables of American History, 1981, Mosby's Medical and Nursing Dictionary, 1983, Allusions, 1982, 86, Modifiers, 1982, Suffixes, 1982, Prefixes, 1984, Mottoes, 1986, Holidays and Anniversaries, 1985, Slogans, 1984, Numerical Allusions, 1986, Names and Nicknames of Places and Things, 1987, Loanwords Dictionary, 1987, The Whole Ball of Wax, 1988, The Dictionary of Confusable Words, 1988, A Fine Kettle of Fish, 1990, The Oxford Thesaurus, 1992. Served with USNR, 1944-45. Mem. Linguistic Soc. Am., Am. Name Soc., Am. Dialect Soc., Brit. Name Soc., Assn. Computational Linguistics, N.Y. Acad. Scis., Dictionary Soc. N.Am., Soc. Indexers, Euralex. Clubs: Athenaeum, Naval (London); Century Assn.

URENECK, LOUIS ADAM, newspaper editor, newspaper executive; b. New Brunswick, N.J., Dec. 28, 1950; s. Eugene and Helen (Kallas) U.; m. Patricia Yeager, Nov. 1974; children: Elizabeth, Adam. BA, U. N.H., 1972. Reporter Providence Jour.-Bull., 1972-73; reporter Press Herald and Maine Sunday Telegram, Portland, 1974-75, copy editor, 1975-76, asst. city editor, 1976-82, mng. editor, 1982-87, asst. exec. editor, 1987-89, exec. editor, 1989-93; editor, v.p. Press Hearld and Maine Sunday Telegram, Portland, 1993—; tchr. U. So. Maine, Portland, summer 1993. Contbr. articles to profl. jours. Mem. alumni publs. com. U. N.H., Durham, 1991-93; founder Maine Quality Ctr., Skowhegan, 1992. Mem. Am. Soc. Newspaper Editors, New Eng. Newspaper Assn. (chmn. editorial com. 1992—), New Eng. AP News Execs. Assn. (pres. 1985). Episcopalian. Avocations: fly fishing, hunting, sailing. Home: Rowes Station Rd New Gloucester ME 04260 Office: The Portland Newspapers 390 Congress St Portland ME 04101•

URENOVITCH, JOSEPH VICTOR, chemical company executive; b. Freeland, Pa., Nov. 21, 1937; s. Joseph Charles and Victoria (Zike) U.; m. Maryjane Walsh; children: Sharon, Lori, Joseph, Michael. BA in Chemistry, U. Pa., 1959, PhD, 1963. Postdoctoral resident U. Wis., Madison, 1964; rsch. scientist Olin Mathieson Chem. Corp., New Haven, 1964-65; sect. mgr. Air Products and Chems., Trexlertown, Pa., 1965-70, gen. mgr. splty. chems., 1970-80; v.p. R & D Atlas Powder Co., Tamaqua, Pa., 1980—. Mem. Am. Chem. Soc., Soc. Explosives Engrs. Republican. Roman Catholic. Office: Tamaqua Tech Ctr PO Box 577 Tamaqua PA 18252-0271

URGENSON, LAWRENCE A., lawyer. BBA, CCNY, 1968; JD cum laude, Bklyn. Law Sch., 1975. Assoc. Mudge, Rose, Guthrie, Alexander & Ferdon, N.Y.C., 1975-79; chief criminal divsn., econ. crime divsn. U.S. Atty.'s Office (ea. dist.) N.Y., 1979-83; chief asst. U.S. atty. U.S. Atty.'s Office (ea. dist.) N.Y., 1986-90; ptnr. Anderson, Laino & Urgenson, N.Y.C., 1983-86; chief fraud sect., exec. dir. econ. crime coun., criminal divsn. Dept. Justice, Washington, 1990-92, acting dep. asst. dist. atty., criminal divsn., 1992—; adj. prof. law, trial advocacy, Bklyn. Law Sch.; lectr. trial advocacy programs Hofstra U., Practicing Law Inst.; former vice chmn. Chief Judge's com. criminal litigation U.S. Dist. Ct. (ea. dist.) N.Y. Sr. editor Bklyn. Law Review, 1975. Recipient Edmund J. Randolph award for Outstanding Svc. Mem. ABA (vice-chair com. white-collar crime), Fed. Bar Coun. (planning com.), Assn. Bar City N.Y. (criminal advocacy, criminal ops. com.). Office: Department of Justice Criminal Division 10th & Constitution Ave NW Washington DC 20005

URHAUSEN, JAMES NICHOLAS, real estate developer, construction executive; b. Berwyn, Ill., Oct. 6, 1943; s. Jack Nicholas and Florence Frances (Stalzer) U.; m. Philomena Anne Malizia, July 16, 1966 (div. 1980); children: Kristen Anne, James Nicholas III; m. Anne Siegert, July 22, 1983; children: Bradley James, Samantha Elise. BA, St. Procopius Coll., Lisle, Ill., 1965. High sch. tchr. Nazareth Acad., LaGrange Park, Ill., 1965-66; asst. village mgr. Village of Hinsdale, Ill., 1966-69; village mgr. Village of Oak Brook, Ill., 1969-73; v.p., sec.-treas. Collins Devel. Corp., St. Charles, Ill., 1973-80; exec. v.p. Westway Constrn. Corp., St. Charles, Ill., 1980-84, pres., chief exec. officer, 1984—; guest lectr. No. Ill. U., Dekalb, 1976—; expert witness Ill. Dept. Transp., Chgo., 1976-81; dir. Harris Bank/St. Charles, Ill., 1992—. Chmn. Hotel Baker Bd. Gov.'s, St. Charles, 1982-84, Bd. of Fire and Police Commrs., St. Charles, 1986—; mem. 708 Community Mental Health Bd., St Charles, 1986—, Kane County Selective Svc. System Bd., St. Charles, 1981—, Kane County Solid Waste Adv. Com., Geneva, 1990—, Metra Citizen's Adv. Bd., 1993—; bd. dirs. Neighborhood Improvement Assn. St. Charles Twp., 1992—, Delnor Community Hosp. Found., 1993—. Mem. Home Bldrs. Assn. Greater Chgo. (dir. 1989—), Nat. Assn. Home Bldrs., No. Ill. Home Bldrs. Assn., Fox Valley Polit. Action Group, St. Charles C. of C. (amb. 1988, Community Devel. award 1989, Charlemagne award 1993). Republican. Roman Catholic. Avocations: golf, rail photography, power

---

boating, model trains. Home: 3103 Greenwood Ln Saint Charles IL 60175 Office: Westway Constrn Corp 214 West River Dr Saint Charles IL 60174-5599

URI, GEORGE WOLFSOHN, accountant; b. San Francisco, Dec. 8, 1920; s. George Washington and Ruby (Wolfsohn) U.; m. Pamela O'Keefe, May 15, 1961. A.B., Stanford U., 1941, I.A., 1943, M.B.A., 1946; postgrad., U. Leeds, Eng., 1945. CPA, Calif.; chartered fin. cons.; CFP; accredited estate planner, Nat. Assn. Estate Planning Coun. Mem. acctg., econs. and stats. depts. Shell Oil Co., Inc., San Francisco, 1946-48; ptnr. Irelan, Uri, Mayer & Sheppie, San Francisco; pres. F. Uri & Co., Inc.; instr. acctg. and econs. Golden Gate Coll., 1949-50. Contbr. articles to profl. jours. Chmn. San Rafael Redevel. Adv. Com., 1977-78, mem., 1978-91, mem. emeritus, 1991—; bd. dirs. San Francisco Planning and Urban Renewal Assn., 1958-60. Served with AUS, 1942-46, to col. Res. (ret.). Recipient Key Man award San Francisco Jr. C. of C.; Meritorious Service medal Sec. of Army, 1978. Mem. AICPA (hon. 1991), Inst. Mgmt. Scis. (treas. No. Calif. chpt. 1961-62), Calif. Soc. CPAs (sec.-treas. San Francisco chpt. 1956-57, dir. 1961-63, state dir. 1964-66, mem. Forbes medal com. 1968-69, chmn. 1969-71, hon. 1991), Am. Econs. Assn., Inst. Mgmt. Accts., San Francisco Estate Planning Coun. (dir. 1965-68), Am. Soc. Mil. Comptrollers, Execs. Assn. San Francisco (pres. 1965-66), Inst. Cert. Mgmt. Accts. (cert. mgmt. acctg., Disting. Performance cert. 1978), Inst. Cert. Fin. Planners, Am. Soc. CLUs and Chartered Fin. Cons. Clubs: World Trade (San Francisco), Commonwealth (quar. chmn. 1971), Stanford (dir. 1990—); Army and Navy (Washington). Home: 11 McNear Dr San Rafael CA 94901-1545 Office: 160 Pine St Ste 710 San Francisco CA 94111-5530

URIBE, HECTOR R., state senator, lawyer; b. Brownsville, Tex., Jan. 17, 1946; s. Blas M. and Aida (Del Leon) U.; divorced; children: Echo, Brandan, Alan, Danu. BA, U. Miami (Fla.), 1967, JD, 1970. Atty. Tex. Legal Aid, El Paso, 1967-70; assoc. Law Offices of Homero Lopez, Brownsville, 1971-75, Law Offices of Jack Weich, Brownsville, 1976-82; sole practice, Brownsville, 1982—; mem. Tex. Ho. of Reps., 1978-81; mem. Tex. Senate, 1981—, mem. fin., health and human resources, and natural resources coms. Bd. dirs. Rio Grande Valley Marine Inst., 1985—. Reginald Herber fellow, 1967. Mem. Tex. Bar Assn., Brownsville C. of C. Democrat. Roman Catholic. Avocation: running. Office: 1325 Palm Blvd Ste F Brownsville TX 78520-7268 also: Tex Senate PO Box 12068 Austin TX 78711-2068

URICH, ROBERT, actor; b. Toronto, Ohio, Dec. 19, 1947; m. Heather Menzies; 2 children. B.A. in Radio and TV Communications, Fla. State U.; M.A. in Communications Mgmt., Mich. State U., 1971. Formerly sales account sta. exec. WGN, Chgo. 1st stage appearance in Lovers and Others Strangers, Pheasant Run Playhouse, other appearances at Ivanhoe Theatre, Chgo., Arlington Park (Ill.) Theatre, Burt Reynolds Theatre, Jupiter, Fla., 1983; TV appearances in series Bob and Carol and Ted and Alice, 1973, S.W.A.T., 1975-76, Tabitha, 1977-78, Soap, 1977-78; star of TV series Vega$, 1978-81, Gavilan, 1982, Spenser for Hire, 1985-88, American Dreamer, 1990, It Had to be You, 1993; other TV appearances include Fighting Back, 1980, miniseries Princess Daisy, 1983, Amerika, 1987; TV movies include Bunco, 1977, Leave Yesterday Behind, 1978, Vega$, 1978, When She Was Bad, 1979, Killing at Hell's Gate, 1981, Take Your Best Shot, 1982, Invitation to Hell, 1984, April Morning, 1988, She Knows Too Much, 1989, Murder by Night, 1989, Night Walk, 1989, Blind Faith, 1990, A Quiet Little Neighborhood, A Perfect Little Murder, 1990, Stranger At My Door, 1991, ...And Then She Was Gone, 1991, Survive the Savage Sea, 1992, Blind Man's Bluff, 1992, Double Edge, 1992, Revolver, 1992, Deadly Relations, 1993, Spenser: Ceremony, 1993; motion pictures include Magnum Force, 1973, Endangered Species, 1981, Ice Pirates, 1983, Turk 182!, 1985. Mem. Bd. Regents Cath. U. Recipient Best Actor nomination Golden Globe awards, 1980-81; People's Choice awards, 1980; named Best Actor, Bravo awards, Germany, 1980. Office: care ICM 8942 Wilshire Blvd Beverly Hills CA 90211•

URIE, JOHN JAMES, lawyer, retired Canadian federal judge; b. Guelph, Ont., Can., Jan. 2, 1920; s. G. Norman and Jane A. U.; m. Dorothy Elizabeth James; children: David, Janet, Alison. B.Commerce, Queen's U.; LL.B., Osgoode Hall Law Sch. Bar: Ont. 1948. Ptnr. firm Burke-Robertson, Urie, Weller & Chadwick, Ottawa, Ont., 1948-73; judge Fed. Ct. Can., Ottawa, 1973-90; counsel Scott and Aylen, Ottawa, 1991—; gen. counsel to Joint Com. of Senate and House of Commons on Consumer Credit; chmn. planning com. First Nat. Conf. on Law, Ottawa, 1972; judge Ct. Martial Appeal Ct., 1973-90. Past pres. County of Carleton Law Assn.; past v.p. Children's Aid Soc.; past pres. Eastern Ottawa Hockey League. Served with Cameron Highlanders of Ottawa Can. Army, 1942-45. Mem. Royal Can. Mil. Inst., Phi Delta Phi. Mem. United Ch. of Canada. Clubs: Cameron Highlanders of Ottawa Assoc. (Ottawa), Ottawa Hunt and Golf (Ottawa), Rideau (Ottawa). Office: Scott and Aylen, 60 Queen St, Ottawa, ON Canada K1P 5Y7

URIOSTE, FRANK J., film editor. Cert. Am. Cinema Editors. Films include Whatever Happened to Aunt Alice, The Grissom Gang, Boys in Company C, Fast Break, Loving Couples, Jazz Singer, The Entity, Trenchcoat, Amityville 3-D, Conan II, The Destroyer, Red Sonja, The Hitcher, Robocop (Acad. award nomination), Total Recall, Basic Instinct, Cliffhanger, (co-editor) Midway, Hoosiers, Die Hard (Acad. award nomination). Office: care Lawrence Mirisch The Mirisch Agency 10100 Santa Monica Blvd Ste 700 Los Angeles CA 90067 also: 1610 Highland Ave Glendale CA 91202

URIS, LEON MARCUS, author; b. Balt., Aug. 3, 1924; s. Wolf William and Anna (Blumberg) U.; m. Betty Katherine Beck, Jan. 5, 1945 (div. 1968); children: Karen Lynn, Mark Jay, Michael Cady; m. Margery Edwards, 1968 (dec. 1969); m. Jill Peabody, Feb. 15, 1970; 1 child, Rachael Jackson. Ed., Balt. City Coll.; hon. doctorate, U. Colo., 1976, Santa Clara U., 1977, Wittenberg U., 1980, Lincoln Coll., 1985. Author: Battle Cry, 1953, The Angry Hills, 1955, Exodus, 1957, Exodus Revisited,1959, Mila 18, 1960 (Calif. Literature Silver Medal award 1962), Armageddon, 1964 (Calif. Literature Gold Medal award 1965), Topaz, 1967, The Third Temple, 1967, QB VII, 1970, Ireland: A Terrible Beauty, 1975, Trinity, 1976, (with Jill Uris) Jerusalem, Song of Songs, 1981, The Haj, 1984, Mitla Pass, 1988, Redemption, 1995; screenwriter: (films) Battle Cry, 1954, Gunfight at the O.K. Corral, 1957; adaptor: (musical play) Ari, 1971. Served with USMCR, 1942-46. Recipient Daroff Meml. award, 1959, John F. Kennedy medal Irish/Am. Soc. of N.Y., 1977, Eire Soc. of Boston Gold medal, 1978, Jobotinsky medal State of Israel, 1980, Scopus award Hebrew U. of Jerusalem, 1981; Nat. Inst. Arts and Letters grantee, 1959; Hall fellow (with Jill Uris) Concord Academy, 1980. •

URKOWITZ, MICHAEL, banker; b. Bronx, N.Y., June 18, 1943; s. David and Esther (Levy) U.; m. Eleanor Naomi Dreazen, July 2, 1966; children—Brian, Denise. B.Engring., CCNY, 1965, M.M.E., 1967. Project engr. Lunar Module program Grumman Corp., Bethpage, N.Y., 1964-72; asst. to dep. commr. for housing code compliance, project mgr. City of N.Y., 1972-74; 2d v.p. Chase Manhattan Bank, N.Y.C., 1974-77, v.p. group exec. ops. dept., money transfer group, 1977-80, sr. v.p., 1980—, group exec. internat. bank services, 1981-82, product and prodn. risk mgmt. exec., 1982-85, exec. v.p., corp. ops. and systems exec., 1985-87; sector exec. Chase InfoServ Internat., N.Y.C., 1987—; chmn. bd. Participants Trust Co., N.Y.C., 1990-92; bd. mem. Depository Trust Co., N.Y.C., 1992-95; bd. dirs. CEDEL, Luxembourg, 1992—; lectr. CCNY, 1967-68. Contbg. author: Thermal Control and Radiation, 1972. Mem. advv. bd. N.Y.C. chpt. Salvation Army, 1989—. Mem. Tau Beta Pi, Pi Tau Sigma. Office: Chase Manhattan Corp 1 Chase Manhattan Plz Fl 17 New York NY 10081-1000 *Working against my own standards as opposed to the standards set by others, presents the greater challenge but yields greater satisfaction.*

URMY, NORMAN B., hospital administrator; b. Ft. Smith, Ark., June 26, 1944; married. BA, Williams Coll., 1966; MA, U. Chgo., 1969. Various positions Mass. Gen. Hosp., Boston, 1966-67; adminstrv. resident NYU Med. Ctr., 1968, adminstrv. asst., 1969-70, asst. adminstr., 1970-76, assoc. adminstr., 1976-79, adminstr., v.p. ops., 1979-82; exec. dir. Vanderbilt Univ. Hosp. & Clinic, Nashville, 1985—. Mem. ACHE. Office: Vanderbilt U Hosp & Clinic 1161 21st Ave S Nashville TN 37203

UROFSKY, MELVIN IRVING, historian, educator; b. N.Y.C., Feb. 7, 1939; s. Philip and Sylvia (Passow) U.; m. Susan Linda Miller, Aug. 27, 1961; children: Philip Eric, Robert Ian. AB, Columbia U., 1961, MA, 1962, PhD, 1968; JD, U. Va., 1983. Instr. history Ohio State U., 1964-67; asst. prof. history and edn., then asst. dean SUNY, Albany, 1967-74; prof. history Va. Commonwealth U., Richmond, 1974—; Harrison vis. prof. Coll. William and Mary, 1990-91; adj. prof. law U. Richmond, 1989—. Author: Big Steel and Wilson Administration, 1969, Why Teachers Strike, 1970, A Mind of One Piece, 1971, American Zionism from Herzl to The Holocaust, 1976, We Are One!, 1978, Louis D. Brandeis and the Progressive Tradition, 1980, A Voice that Spoke for Justice: The Life and Times of Stephen S. Wise, 1981, The Supreme Court, the Bill of Rights and the Law, 1986, A March of Liberty, 1987, The Douglas Letters, 1987; A Continuity of Change, 1990, A Conflict of Rights, 1991, Felix Frankfurter, 1991, Letting Go, 1993; co-editor: Brandeis Letters, 5 vols., 1971-78, Half Brother, Half Son, 1991. Chmn. exec. com. Zionist Academic Council, 1976-79; mem. nat. bd. Am. Zionist Fedn., 1976-79; co-chmn. Am. Zionist Ideological Commn., 1976-78; nat. bd. Assn. Reform Zionists Am., 1978-84. Mershon Found. fellow, 1965, sr. rsch. fellow NEH, 1976-77; recipient Kaplun award Jewish Book Coun., 1976; grantee NEH, Am. Coun. Learned Socs.; NEH scholar-in-residence, 1994-95. Mem. Am. Jewish Hist. Soc. (chmn. acad. coun. 1979-83), Am. Legal History Soc. (bd. dirs., exec. com. 1991—), Orgn. Am. Historians, Va. Hist. Soc. (trustee 1992—). Office: Va Commonwealth U Dept History Richmond VA 23284-2001

UROWSKY, RICHARD J., lawyer; b. N.Y.C., June 28, 1946; s. Jacob and Anne (Granick) U. BA, Yale U., 1967, JD, 1972; BPhil, Oxford U., Eng., 1970. Bar: N.Y. 1973, U.S. Dist. Ct. (so. dist.) N.Y. 1973, U.S. Ct. Appeals (2d cir.) 1973, U.S. Supreme Ct. 1977. Law clk. to Justice Reed U.S. Supreme Ct., Washington, 1972-73; assoc. Sullivan & Cromwell, N.Y.C., 1973-80, ptnr., 1980—. Mem. ABA, Assn. of the Bar of the City of N.Y., Fed. Bar Coun., N.Y. County Lawyers Assn., Yale Club. Office: Sullivan & Cromwell 125 Broad St New York NY 10004

URQUHART, ANDREW WILLARD, engineering and business executive; b. Burlington, Vt., Aug. 24, 1939; s. John Wardrop and Dorothy Helen (Hefflon) U.; m. Carolyn Fay Powell, Mar. 9, 1963; children: Marion, Dorothy. AB, Dartmouth Coll., 1961, MS, 1964, PhD, 1971. Engr. Div. of Naval Reactors, AEC, 1962-67, Creare, Inc., Hanover, N.H., 1967-68; metallurgist Gen. Electric Corp Rsch. and Devel., Schenectady, 1971-75, br. mgr., 1975-84; v.p. rsch., devel. and engring. Lanxide Corp., Newark, Del., 1984-89, sr. v.p. tech.; 1989-93; pres., CEO Lanxide Electronic Components, L.P., 1993—. Contbr. articles to profl. jours.; more than 30 patents in the field. Lt. USN, 1962-67. Mem. ASM Internat. (chmn. Ea. N.Y. sect. 1978-79), Am. Ceramic Soc., Phi Beta Kappa, Sigma Xi. Avocations: outdoor and family activities. Home: 48 Bridleshire Rd Newark DE 19711-2454 Office: Lanxide Electronic Components LP 1300 Marrows Rd PO Box 6077 Newark DE 19714-6077

URQUHART, GLEN TAYLOR, investment and development executive; b. Pitts., Nov. 10, 1948; s. George Taylor and Bernice (Wasserman) U.; m. Angela Margaret Boleyn, Dec. 3, 1977; children—Robert Andrew, Caroline. B.S., U. Va., 1971. Fin. mgr. Victor Wilburn & Assocs., Washington, 1972-74; v.p. Chantilly Devel. Corp., Va., 1976-79; pres. Urquhart & Co., Inc., Washington, 1979—; chmn. Nat. Capital Planning Commn., Washington, 1983—; dir. Pennsylvania Ave. Devel. Corp., Washington, 1983—; mem. Council Govts., Washington, 1983—; trustee Fed. City Council, Washington, 1983—. Mem. Com. for Dulles, Dulles Internat. Airport, Washington, 1983—; active, founding mem. Ctr. Internat. Security Studies, Washington, 1984—, World Strategy Network, Washington, 1984—; mem. U.S. Global Strategy Coun., Washington, 1984—; bd. dirs. Am. Def. Found., Washington, 1984—; mem. bd. endowment Comty. Leadership, 1989—. Republican. Avocation: flying. Office: Urquhart & Co 7601 Lewinsville Rd Mc Lean VA 22102

URQUHART, JOHN, medical researcher, educator; b. Pitts., Apr. 24, 1934; s. John and Wilma Nelda (Martin) U.; m. Joan Cooley, Dec. 28, 1957; children: Elizabeth Urquhart Vdovjak, John Christopher (dec. 1965), Robert Malcolm, Thomas Jubal. BA with honors, Rice U., 1955; MD with honors, Harvard U., 1959. Lic. physician, Calif. Walter B. Cannon fellow in physiology Harvard Med. Sch., Boston, 1956, Josiah Macy, Jr. fellow, 1956-58, 59-61; intern in surgery Mass. Gen. Hosp., Boston, 1959-60, asst. resident, 1960-61; investigator Nat. Heart Inst., NIH, Bethesda, Md., 1961-63; asst. prof. physiology U. Pitts. Sch. Medicine, 1963-66, assoc. prof., 1966-68, prof., 1968-70; prof. biomed. engring. U. So. Calif., Los Angeles, 1970-71; prin. scientist ALZA Corp., Palo Alto, Calif., 1970-86, dir. biol. scis., 1971-74, pres. research div., 1974-78, chief scientist, 1978-82, sr. v.p., 1978-85; co-founder APREX Corp., Fremont, Calif., pres., 1986-88, dir. 1986-95, chmn., 1988-91, chief scientist, 1988-95; vis. prof. pharmacology U. Limburg Sch. Medicine, Maastricht, The Netherlands, 1984-85, vis. prof. pharmaco-epidemiology, 1986-91; prof. pharmaco-epidemiology, 1992—; adj. prof. pharmacy U. Calif.-San Francisco, 1984—; mem. dir.'s adv. com. NIH, 1986-88; Boerhaave lectr. U. Leiden, The Netherlands, 1991, 94, 95. Co-author: Risk Watch, 1984; contbr. numerous articles to sci. jours.; patentee therapeutic systems for controlled drug delivery and regimen compliance monitoring (43). Trustee GMI Engring. and Mgmt. Inst., Flint, Mich., 1983—. Served with USPHS, 1961-63. NIH grantee, 1963-70; Bowditch lectr. Am. Physiol. Soc., 1969. Mem. Biomed. Engring. Soc. (pres. 1976), Boylston Med. Soc., Internat. Soc. Pharmaco-epidemiology, Am. Soc. Clinical Pharmacology and Therapeutics, Soc. for Clinical Trials, Endocrine Soc., Saturday Morning club Palo Alto., Am. Physiol. Soc., Soc. Risk Analysis. Home and Office: 975 Hamilton Ave Palo Alto CA 94301-2213

URQUHART, JOHN ALEXANDER, management consultant; b. Savannah, Ga., Aug. 26, 1928; s. George Walter and Helen Catherine (Ruwe) U.; m. Mary Anne Harvey, Apr. 23, 1954; children: Jane Harvey Urquhart Lowe, John Alexander. B.S. in Ind. Engring., Va. Poly. Inst. and State U., 1948. Registered profl. engr., Mass. With GE, 1949-90, sr. v.p. Indsl. & Power Systems, exec. v.p. Power Systems Sector, exec. v.p. Internat. Sector; vice chmn. Enron Corp., 1991—; bd. dirs. Aquarion Co., Enron Corp., Hubbell, Inc., TECO Energy Inc., The Weir Group, PLC. Mem. Brit.-N.Am. com. Fgn. Policy Assn.; trustee Am. U. of Cairo, ASME Found., Inc. 1st lt. C.E., U.S. Army, 1952-54. Mem. ASME, Country Club of Fairfield, Black Rock Yacht Club (Bridgeport, Conn.), Peguot Yacht Club (Southport, Conn.), Philanthropic Lodge (Marblehead, Mass.). Office: 111 Beach Rd Fairfield CT 06430-6668

URQUHART, TONY, artist, educator; b. Niagara Falls, Ont., Can., Apr. 9, 1934; s. Archer Marsh and Maryon Louise (Morse) U.; m. Madeline Mary Jennings, July 1958 (div. 1976); children: Allyson, Robin, Marsh, Aidan; m. Mary Jane Carter Keele, May 1976; 1 dau., Emily. B.F.A., U. Buffalo, 1958. Artist-in-residence U. Western Ont., London, 1960-63, 64-65, asst. prof. fine arts, 1967-70, assoc. prof., 1970-72; prof. fine art U. Waterloo, Ont., 1972—; chmn. dept. U. Waterloo, 1977-79, 82-85, 1994—; lectr. McMaster U., Hamilton, Ont., 1966-67. One-man shows Winnipeg Art Gallery, 1959, Walker Art Gallery, Mpls., 1960, Richard Demarco Gallery, Edinburgh, Scotland, 1975, group shows, Pitts. Biennial, 1958, Guggenheim Internat., N.Y.C., 1958, Art of the Ams. and Spain, Madrid, Barcelona, Rome, Paris, 1964, Nat. Gallery Can., Toronto, 1972, Mus. Modern Art, Paris, 1976; represented permanent collections, Nat. Gallery Can., Art Gallery, Ont., Fed. Art Bank of Ottawa, Montreal Mus., Vancouver Art Gallery, Mus. Modern Art, Victoria and Albert Mus., London, Museo Civico, Lugano, Switzerland; chmn., Jack Chambers Meml. Found. 1978-85; resident artist, Kitchener-Waterloo Art Gallery, Kitchener, Ont., 1981-83; illustrator: The Broken Ark: A Book of Beasts, 1969, I Am Walking in the Garden of His Imaginary Palace by Jane Urquhart, 1982, False Shuffles by Jane Urquhart, 1982; (50 drawings) Cells of Ourselves (text G.M. Dault), 1989, Memories of a Governor General's Daughter, 1990, Warbrain: poems by Stuart MacKinnon, 1994. Recipient Edits, I Arts Coun. grant, 1974, Kilchener Waterloo Visual Arts award, 1994; winner Nat. Outdoor Sculpture Competition MacDonald Stewart Art Ctr., 1987; appointed mem. Order of Can., 1995; grantee Can. Coun. award, 1963, 79, travel trantee, 1967, 69, 70, 74, 75, 76, 88, 91, project cost grantee, 1981, 82, short-term grantee, 1991, All Can. Coun. Mem. Can. Artists Representation (founding, sec. 1968-71). Office: Dept Fine Arts U Waterloo, Waterloo, ON Canada N2L 3G1

URQUIA, RAFAEL, II, lawyer; b. San Salvador, El Salvador, May 11, 1944; came to U.S., 1950; s. M. Rafael and Luz (Bolaños) U.; m. Thelma Louise Faught; 1 child, Alexandra. BS, Georgetown U., 1966, JD, 1969; LD, U. Madrid, 1972. Bar: N.Y. 1975, U.S. Ct. Appeals (2d cir.) 1975. Sr. assoc. Curtis, Mallet-Prevost, Colt & Mosle, N.Y.C., 1972-78; special counsel Internat. Multifoods Corp., Mpls., 1979-82; pvt. practice N.Y.C., 1983-87; ptnr. Thomas Re & Ptnrs., N.Y.C., 1987-90; of counsel Fox & Horan, N.Y.C., 1990—. Author book rev. Speaker Rep. Presdl. Campaign, 1988. Fellow OAS, 1967, Inst. Spanish Culture, 1970. Mem. ABA, Assn. of Bar of City of N.Y. (mem. inter.-Am. affairs com. 1984-87). Roman Catholic. Avocations: rare books, art. Home: 200 E 66th St D-1802 New York NY 10021-6728 Office: Fox & Horan 1 Broadway New York NY 10004-1007

URRY, DAN WESLEY, research biophysicist, educator, science facility administrator; b. Salt Lake City, Sept. 14, 1935; m. Janet Mills, July 1957 (div. Oct. 1970); children: Weston, Douglas (dec.), David; m. Kathleen Lake, June 8, 1974; 1 child, Kelley Danielle. BA, U. Utah, 1960, PhD in Phys. Chemistry, 1964. Postdoctoral fellow U. Utah, 1964, Harvard U., Cambridge, Mass., 1964-65; vis. investigator Chem. Biodynamics Lab. U. Calif.-Berkeley, 1965-66; prof. lectr. dept. biochemistry U. Chgo., 1967-70; prof. biochemistry U. Ala., Birmingham, 1970—; dir. molecular biophysics div., Lab. Molecular Biology, 1970-72, dir. lab., 1972—; vis. prof. U. Padua, Italy, 1977, U. Palermo, Italy, 1988; chmn. Bioelastics Inc.; gen. ptnr. Bioelastics Rsch. Ltd., 1989—; disting. faculty lectr. U. Ala., Birmingham, 1987. Contbr. articles to over 420 sci., publs. Recipient Alexander von Humboldt Found. preis, 1979-80, Wright A. Gardner award Ala. Acad. of Sci., 1991; named 1988 Scientist of the Yr., R&D mag.; one of 1000 Most cited scientists all disciplines worldwide, 1981; one of 10 most cited within discipline of biophysics, 1982. Fellow Am. Inst. Med. and Biol. Engring.; mem. AAAS, Am. Soc. Biol. Chemistry, Am. Chem. Soc., Biophys. Soc. Home: 2423 Vestavia Dr Birmingham AL 35216-1333 Office: U Ala at Birmingham 1670 University Blvd # 300 Birmingham AL 35233-1709*

URRY, GRANT WAYNE, chemistry educator; b. Salt Lake City, Mar. 12, 1926; s. Herbert William and Emma (Swanner) U.; m. Lillian Alibertini, Sept. 4, 1946; children—Lisa, Claudia, Serena, Anthony. S.B., U. Chgo., 1947, Ph.D., 1953. Research asst., then research assoc. U. Chgo., 1949-53, research assoc., asst. prof., 1954-55; asst. prof. Washington U., St. Louis, 1955-58; assoc. prof. Purdue U., Lafayette, Ind., 1958-64, prof., 1964-68; prof. chemistry Tufts U., Medford, Mass., 1968-92, Robinson prof. chemistry, 1970-92, chmn. dept., 1968-73, Robinson prof. emeritus chemistry, 1992—. Alfred P. Sloan fellow, 1956-58. Fellow N.Y. Acad. Scis., Am. Inst. Chemists, AAAS; mem. Am. Chem. Soc., Am. Soc. Sci. Glassblowers, Fedn. Am. Scientists, Sigma Xi, Phi Lambda Upsilon. Office: Tufts U Dept Chemistry Medford MA 02155

URSACHE, VICTORIN (HIS EMINENCE THE MOST REVEREND ARCHBISHOP VICTORIN), archbishop; b. Manastioara-Siret, Dist. of Suceava, Romania, 1912. Grad., State Lyceum of Siret; L.Th., U. Cernauti, Romania; postgrad., Bibl. Inst. Jerusalem. Ordained deacon Romanian Orthodox Ch., 1937, ordained priest, 1937. Consecrated bishop Romanian Orthodox Ch., 1966, elevated to archbishop, 1973; prof. religion Orthodox Lyceum of the Romanian Orthodox Metropolis of Cernautsi, 1936-37; prof. theology Seminary of Neamtzu Monastery, 1937-46, asst. dir. sem., 1937-40, dir. sem., superior of monastery, 1940-44; rep. Romanian Orthodox Ch. at Holy Places in, Jerusalem, 1946-56; bishop Romanian Orthodox Missionary Episcopate in Am., 1966-73; archbishop Romanian Orthodox Archdiocese in Am., 1973—; mem. Holy Synod, Romanian Orthodox Ch. of Romania; bd. dirs. U.S. Conf., World Council Chs.; mem. central com.; mem. Standing Conf. Canonical Orthodox Bishops in, Ams. Editor: Locurile Sfinte. Address: Romanian Orthodox Ch in Am 19959 Riopelle St Detroit MI 48203-1249

URSHAN, NATHANIEL ANDREW, minister, church administrator; b. St. Paul, Aug. 29, 1920; s. Andrew David and Mildred (Hammergren) U.; m. Jean Louise Habig, Oct. 1, 1941; children: Sharon, Annette, Nathaniel, Andrew. Student, Columbia U., 1936-39; DTh (hon.), Gateway Coll. Evangelism, 1976. Ordained to ministry United Pentecostal Ch. Internat. Evangelist, 1941-44; assoc. pastor Royal Oak, Mich., 1944-46, N.Y.C., 1947-48, Indpls., 1948-49; pastor Calvary Tabernacle, Indpls., 1949-78; presbyter Ind. Dist. United Pentecostal Chs., 1950-77; asst. gen. supt. United Pentecostal Ch. Internat., 1971-77; gen. supt. United Pentecostal Ch. Internat., Hazelwood, Mo., 1977—; host radio show Harvestime, 1961-78, 81—; chaplain Ind. Ho. of Reps., 1972. Author: Consider Him, 1962, These Men Are Not Drunk, 1964, Book of Sermons of the Baptism of the Holy Spirit, 1968, Major Bible Prophecy, 1971. Mem. internat. com. YMCA, 1958-79, bd. dirs. Indpls. chpt. 1961-79, world service chmn. Region L, 1969-71; chmn. Heart Fund Campaign, 1968-69; mem. screening com. Marion County Reps., Ind., 1973-74; chmn. Ministerial Com. of Richard Lugar for May of Indpls., 1968, William Hudnut for Mayor, 1975; bd. dirs. Little Red Door, Cancer Soc. Indpls., 1974-77. Recipient gold and brass medallion Heart Fund., Indpls., 1968-69; Nathaniel A. Urshan Day named in his honor, Nov. 3, 1979, Mayor Hudnut, Indpls. Mem. Indpls. Ministerial Assn. Office: United Pentecostal Ch Internat 8855 Dunn Rd Hazelwood MO 63042-2212

URSTADT, CHARLES JORDAN, real estate executive; b. N.Y.C., Oct. 27, 1928; s. Charles G. and Claire C. (Jordan) U.; m. Elinor McClure Funk, Mar. 23, 1957; children: Charles Deane, Catherine Urstadt Biddle. BA, Dartmouth Coll., 1949, MBA, 1951; LLB, Cornell U., 1953; LLD honors. Pace U., 1990. Bar: N.Y. 1953. assoc. Nevius Brett & Kellogg, N.Y.C., 1953-58; asst. sec. Webb & Knapp, Inc., N.Y.C., 1958-63; v.p., sec., counsel Alcoa Residences, Inc., N.Y.C., 1963-67; commr. N.Y. State Div. Housing and Community Renewal, N.Y.C., 1967-73 ; chmn., Battery Park City Authority, N.Y.C., 1968-78; chmn. bd., pres., dir. Urstadt Property Co. Inc. (formerly Pearce, Urstadt, Mayer & Greer, Inc.), N.Y.C., 1979—; trustee HRE Properties (formerly Hubbard Real Estate Investments), N.Y.C., 1975—, chmn., 1986—, pres., chief exec. officer, 1989—; trustee Tchrs. Ins. and Annuity Corp., 1985—; N.Y. Trustee, Pace U., 1973—; mem. fin. com. N.Y. Rep. State Com., 1981—, del. Rep. Nat. Conv., 1988; mem. Gov.'s Task Force on N.Y. Housing, 1988-90; bd. dirs. N.Y.C. Partnership, Inc., 1984-93, chmn. Realty Found. of N.Y., 1989—; chmn. N.Y. State Statue of Liberty Celebration Found., 1983-84, N.Y. State Housing Fin. Agy., 1969, Tri-State Regional Planning Commn., 1969-70; mem. Pres.'s Commn. on Housing, 1981-82, others. Lt. USNR, 1954-56. Recipient Man of Yr. award Realty Found. N.Y., 1979. Exec. v.p. Assoc. Builders and Owners Greater N.Y., dir. 1979—. Mem. Nat. Soc. Real Estate Fin. Mem. Reformed Church. Clubs: Links, Union League (N.Y.C.); Siwanoy Country (Bronxville); Bohemian (San Francisco). Office: HRE Properties 530 5th Ave New York NY 10036-5101

URSU, JOHN JOSEPH, lawyer; b. 1939. AB, U. Mich., 1962, JD, 1965. Bar: Mich. 1966, Ky. 1970, Minn. 1972. Trial atty. Bur. of Competition FTC, 1965-67; staff mem. Pres.'s Commn. on Civil Disorders, 1967; advisor to commr. FTC, 1968-69; legal counsel GE, 1969-72; divsn. atty. GM, 1972-74, sr. atty., 1974-76, assoc. counsel, 1976-81, asst. gen. counsel, 1981-86, assoc. gen. counsel, 1986-90, dep. gen. counsel, 1990-92, gen. counsel, 1992-93; v.p. legal affairs & gen. counsel GM, St. Paul, 1993—; adj. faculty William Mitchell Coll. Law, 1978-82. Office: 3M Exec Offices 3M Ctr 220 14W 07 PO Box 33220 Saint Paul MN 55133-3220

USDIN, GENE LEONARD, physician, psychiatrist; b. N.Y.C., Jan. 31, 1922; s. I. L. and Eva (Miller) U.; m. Cecile Weil, Nov. 8, 1947; children: Cecile Catherine Burka, Linda Ann, Steven William, Thomas Michael. Student, U. N.C., 1939-40, U. Fla., 1940-41; B.S., Tulane U., 1943; M.D., 1946. Diplomate: Am. Bd. Psychiatry and Neurology (asst. examiner, 1956—), Am. Bd. Legal Medicine. Intern Touro Infirmary, New Orleans, 1946-47; resident psychiatry Cin. Gen. Hosp., 1949-51; fellow psychiatry Tulane Sch. Medicine, 1951-52; pvt. practice psychiatry New Orleans, 1952-86; asst. prof. clin. psychiatry Tulane U., 1959-62, assoc. clin. prof., 1962-67; assoc. clin. prof. La. State U., 1967-71, clin. prof., 1971—; sr. psychiatrist Ochsner Clinic, 1986—; prof. Notre Dame Sem., 1969-75; chief div. neurology and psychiatry Touro Infirmary, New Orleans, 1962-66; dir. psychiat. services Touro Infirmary, 1966-71; McLaughlin-Gallie vis. prof. Royal Coll. Physicians and Surgeons of Can., 1983; Robert O. Jones lectr. Atlantic Maritime Provinces Psychiat. Assn. (Can.), 1976; sr. psychiatrist DePaul and Charity Hosps.; sr. psychiat. cons. Oshsner Med. Found., New Orleans, 1980-85, Timberlawn Psychiat. Hosp., Dallas, 1979-93; chmn. psychiat. cons. com. Am. Bar Found., 1970-73; mem. nat. psychiatric adv. bd. Achievement and Guidance Ctrs. Am., 1991-92. Editor in chief Psychiatry Digest, 1964-71, 75-79, Psychiatry Digest (Europe), 1981-92, ACP-Psychiatric Update, 1980-94, co-editor, 1994-95, editor 1995—; editor Medilex Digest of Psychiatry, 1980—; mem. editorial bd. Academic Psychiatry, 1989-92, Mental Hygiene, 1969-76, Clin. Medicine, 1965-71, 75-88, Med. Digest, 1965-71, Jour. Hosp. and Community Psychiatry, 1975, chmn., 1980-81, Jour. Psychiat. Edn., 1975-89, Am. Jour. Family Therapy, 1978—, Am. Jour. Social Psychiatry, 1981-87, Swiss Med. Digest, Psychiatry, 1981—, Extracta Medica Practica Psychiatrie, 1981—, Behavioral Scis. and the Law, 1982-92, Dynamic Psychotherapy, 1982-90, Psychiat. Medicine, 1982-88, Advances in Therapy, 1983—; Clin. Psychiatry News, 1983-92, Contemporary Psychiatry, 1984-93, Health Disease, 1986—, The Psychiat. Times, 1985—, Clinical Advances in the Treatment of Psychiatric Disorders, 1987—, Jour. Ottawa Med. Sch. 1976-90, Psychiatry Bookshelf, 1976-78, Women's Psychiat. Health, 1992—; mem. internat. adv. bd. Jour. Psicopatologia, Madrid, 1989-94; editor: Psychoneurosis and Schizophrenia, 1966, Practical Lectures in Psychiatry for the Medical Practitioner, 1966, Adolescence: Care and Counseling, 1967, Perspectives on Violence, 1972, (with Peter A. Martin and A.W. Swipe) A Physician in the General Practice of Psychiatry, 1970, The Psychiatric Forum, 1973, Sleep Research and Clinical Practice, 1973, Psychiatry: Education and Image, 1973, Overview of the Psychotherapies, 1975, Schizophrenia: Biological and Psychological Perspective, 1976, Depression: Clinical, Biological and Psychological Perspectives, 1977, Psychiatric Medicine, 1977, (with Charles K. Hofling) Aging: The Process and the People, 1978, (with Jerry M. Lewis, II) Psychiatry in General Medical Practice, 1979, (with David R. Hawkins) The Office Guide to Sleep Disorders, 1980, (with Jerry M. Lewis) Treatment Planning in Psychiatry, 1982; Contbr. articles to profl. jours. Bd. trustees United Fund Greater New Orleans, 1966-70. Served to lt. (j.g.) USNR, 1947-49. Recipient Physician of Yr. award Orleans Parish Med. Soc., 1984, Outstanding Alumni Lectr. award Tulane U. Sch. Medicine, 1986, Seymour Pollack Disting. Svc. award Am. Acad. Psychiatry and the Law, 1988, Outstanding Contbrn. to Social Psychiatry award Am. Assn. for Social Psychiatry, 1993; named Psychiatrist of Yr., La. Psychiat. Med. Assn., 1994. Fellow Am. Psychiat. Assn. (chmn. com. on psychiatry and law 1964-68, mem. com. on ethics 1970-74, com. on membership 1970-74, com. on evaluation svcs. bd. 1974-77, com. on pub. affairs 1976-78, chmn. ad hoc com. on election procedures, 1980-81, trustee at large81, coun. on internat. affairs 1986-91, sec. gen. Interamerican Coun. of Psychiatric Orgns. 1990—; recipient 3d ann. Certificate of Recognition for Excellence in Med. Student Edn. 1993, Warren Williams award, 1995), So. Psychiat. Assn. (bd. regents 1969-72, chmn. 1971-72, pres. 1973-74), La. Psychiat. Assn. (past pres.), Am. Coll. Psychiatrists (bd. regents 1967-70, pres. 1978-79, E.B. Bowis award for Outstanding Contbns. 1973, Disting. Service award for Oustanding Contbns. in Am. Psychiatry 1980), Acad. Psychosomatic Medicine (mem. exec. council 1974-76), New Orleans Soc. Psychiatry and Neurology (past pres.), Group Advancement Psychiatry (bd. dirs. 1970-75, treas. 1973-77), Am. Assn. Social Psychiatry (pres. 1986-88), World Assn. for Social Psychiatry (exec. coun. 1988-90); mem. La. Med. Soc. (chmn. com. on mental health 1966-70), Orleans Parish Med. Soc., Nat. Assn. Mental Health (mem. profl. advisory counc. 1968-75), Inst. of Mental Hygiene (pres. 1978-79). Home: 3 Newcomb Blvd New Orleans LA 70118-5527 Office: Dept Psychiatry Ochsner Clinic 1514 Jefferson Hwy New Orleans LA 70121-2483

USEEM, JOHN HEARLD, sociologist, anthropologist; b. Buffalo, N.Y., Oct. 15, 1910; s. Abram and Sema (Ross) Usem; m. Ruth Marie Hill, June 6, 1940; children: Michael, Howard, Bert. B.A., UCLA, 1934; student, Harvard U., 1934-36; Ph.D., U. Wis., 1939. Prof. U. S.D., 1939-42; vis. lectr. Barnard Coll., Columbia U., 1946; assoc. prof. U. Wis., 1946-49; prof. sociology and anthropology Mich. State U., 1949-81, prof. emeritus, 1981—; head dept., 1958-65; lectr., cons. Fgn. Svc. Inst., U.S. Dept. State, 1950—; cons. Nat. Inst. Growth and Devel.; mem. adv. com. Edward W. Hazen Found., Social Sci. Rsch. Coun., NIMH, Conf. Bd. Assoc. Rsch. Coun.; sr. fellow East-West Ctr., 1972, mem. internat. adv. panel, 1978-79; rsch. on transnat. roles of higher educated in periods of internat. conflict and change. Author: The Western-Educated Man in India, 1955; contbg. author: Human Problems in Technological Change, 1952, Cultural Patterns and Technical Change, 1953, Reconstituting the Human Community, 1972, Bonds Without Bondage, 1979, Study Abroad: The Experiences of American Undergraduates in Western Europe and in the United States, 1990; contbr. articles to profl. jours. Bd. govs. Arctic Inst. Served as lt. USNR, World War II; mil. gov. in South Pacific. Recipient Mich. State U. Disting. Faculty award, 1962, Disting. Scholar award in internat., cultural and sci. affairs Internat. Soc. Ednl., Cultural and Sci. Interchange, 1979, Disting. Profl. Service award North Central Sociol. Assn., 1982, Research in Internat. Ednl. Exchange, Council on Internat. Ednl. Exchange, 1986. Mem. Am. Sociol. Assn., Am. Anthrop. Assn., North Central Sociol. Assn. (pres. 1971), Soc. Applied Anthropology, Sociol. Research Assn., Soc. Study Social Problems (chmn. internat. div., Lee Founders' award for disting. career 1987), Central States Anthrop. Soc., Phi Beta Kappa, Phi Kappa Phi, Alpha Kappa Delta, Pi Gamma Mu, Pi Sigma Alpha. Home: 227 Chesterfield Pky East Lansing MI 48823-4110

USEEM, RUTH HILL, sociology educator; b. Hamilton, Ohio, May 31, 1915; d. William E. and Anna E. (Starlin) Hill; m. John Hearld Useem, June 6, 1940; children: Michael, Howard Sheldon, Bert. B.A., Miami U., Oxford, Ohio, 1936; Ph.D., U. Wis., 1947. Asst. prof. Queens Coll., N.Y.C., 1942-43, 1944-45; research cons. Mich. State U., East Lansing, 1951-52; instr. Mich. State U., 1952-58, asst. prof., 1958-60, asso. prof., 1960-70, prof. sociology and edn., 1970-85; Sr. fellow East-West Center, 1970. Author: (with J. Useem) The Western-Educated Man in India, 1955, (with F. Kempf) Psychology: Dynamics of Behavior in Nursing; contbr. articles to profl. jours. Disting. scholar Internat. Soc. Ednl., Cultural and Sci. Interchanges, 1979; recipient Excellence award Mich. State U. Faculty Women's Assn., 1979, award for Research in Internat. Ednl. Exchange, Council Internat. Ednl. Exchange, 1986; Edward W. Hazen Found. grantee India, 1952-53, 58; Edward W. Hazen Found. grantee Philippines, 1968-75; recipient Lee Founders' award for disting. career Soc. for Study of Social Problems, 1987, Pioneering Rsch. on Third Culture Kids award Global Nomads Internat. 1988. Mem. Am. Sociol. Assn. (council 1973-75, com. on coms. 1975-76, com. world sociology 1975-77, com. nominations 1979-81, liaison AAAS com. 1983-87), North Cen. Sociol. Assn. (council 1976-77, v.p./program chmn. 1977-78, pres. 1979-80, Disting. Profl. Service award 1984), Sociologists for Women in Soc., Soc. Internat. Edn., Tng. and Research (council 1978-81), Internat. Soc. Ednl., Cultural and Sci. Interchanges, Sociol. Research Assn., Mortar Bd.; fellow Am. Anthrop. Assn. Home: 227 Chesterfield Pky East Lansing MI 48823-4110

USELTON, JAMES CLAYTON, engineering executive; b. Tullahoma, Tenn., Oct. 2, 1939; s. Hubert and Edna Mae (Fagg) U.; m. Janice Marie Widner, Oct. 30, 1959; children: Debra Leigh, Clayton Seth, Arnold Jay. BS, U. Tenn. 1962; MS, U. Tenn. Space Inst., Tullahoma, 1966, postgrad., 1966-70. Registered profl. engr. Tenn., Mo., Fla., Mich., Tex., Mass., Ohio. Project engr. Sverdrup Tech., Tullahoma, 1962-70, lead engr., 1971-74, asst. br. mgr., 1974-77, br. mgr., 1978-79, dir., 1979-81, v.p., 1981-85, sr. v.p., 1985-86, v.p., 1986-88; exec. v.p., dir. Sverdrup Corp., Maryland Heights, Mo., 1989—; pres. Sverdrup Investments, Inc., Maryland Heights, Mo., 1992—; now exec. v.p.; chmn. CEO Sverdup Tech., Inc., Maryland Heights, 1993—; bd. dirs. Trans Fin. Savs. Bank Tenn., Tullahoma. Contbr. articles to profl. jours. Fellow AIAA (assoc.); mem. Nat. Mgmt. Assn. Methodist. Avocations: golf, skiing. Home: 16333 Wilson Farm Dr Chesterfield MO 63005 Office: Sverdrup Corp 13723 Riverport Dr Maryland Heights MO 63043*

USHER, ELIZABETH REUTER (MRS. WILLIAM A. SCAR), retired librarian; b. Seward, Nebr.; d. Paul and Elizabeth (Meyer) Reuter; m. Harry Thomas Usher, Feb. 25, 1950; m. William Arthur Scar, Mar. 28, 1992. Diploma, Concordia Tchrs. Coll., Seward, Litt.D. (hon.), 1981; BS in Edn., U. Nebr., 1942; B.S. in library sci., U. Ill., 1944. Tchr. Zion Luth. Sch., Platte Center, Nebr. and; St. Paul's Luth. Sch., Paterson, N.J.; library asst. charge rec. book reading room U. Nebr., 1942-43; asst. circulation librarian Mich. State U., 1944-45; librarian Cranbrook Acad. Art, Bloomfield Hills, Mich., 1945-48; catalog and reference librarian Met. Mus. Art, N.Y.C., 1948-53; head cataloger and reference librarian Met. Mus. Art, 1953-54, asst.

librarian, 1954-61, chief of art reference library, 1961-68, chief librarian, Thomas J. Watson Library, 1968-80, chief librarian emeritus, 1980—; acting librarian, 1954-57. Contbr. articles to profl. periodicals, library publs. Trustee N.Y. Met. Reference and Research Library Agy., 1968-80, sec. to bd., 1971-77, v.p., 1977-80; 1st v.p. Heritage Village Library, 1982-88, 91-92, pres., 1988-91, 95—. Mem. Spl. Libraries Assn. (pres. 1967-68, dir. 1960-63, 66-69, Hall of Fame 1980—), Coll. Art Assn. (chmn. libraries session 1972-73), N.Y. Library Club, Archons of Colophon (convener 1980-82), Heritage Village Rep. Club (pres. 1992-95), PEO (v.p. chpt. Q 1994—). Lutheran. Home: 711B Heritage Vlg Southbury CT 06488-1606

USHER, SIR LEONARD GRAY, retired news association executive; b. Paeroa, New Zealand, May 29, 1907; s. Robert and Mary Elizabeth (Johnston) U.; m. Mary Gertrude Lockie, Nov. 30, 1940 (div. 1962); children: Lala Athene Frazer, Miles Gray; m. Jane Hammond Derne, July 11, 1962 (dec. 1984). Tchrs. certificate, Auckland Tng. Coll., 1926-27; B.A., Auckland U., 1934. Headmaster schs. Fiji, 1930-43; pub. relations officer Govt. of Fiji, 1943-56; exec. dir. Fiji Times & Herald, Suva, 1956-73; dir. Fiji Times & Herald, 1973-77; editor Fiji Times, 1958-73; organizing dir. Pacific Islands News Assn., 1974-85, councillor, life mem., 1985—; chmn. bd. Fiji Devel. Bank, 1978-82, Suva Stock Exch., 1979-92, Island Lottlers Ltd., Fiji, 1980-86; dep. chmn. Nat. Bank Fiji, 1974-82; bd. dirs Connoisseur Products (Pacific) Ltd., Bus. Mgmt. Group Ltd., Mt. Pleasant Ltd. Mem. Fiji Broadcasting Commn., 1954-56, Fiji Visitors Bur., 1953-56; pres. Fiji Bd. Fire Commrs., 1967-70, 75-76; councillor Suva, 1962-71, 75-77, mayor, 1967-70, 75-76; mem. council U. South Pacific, 1975-78; trustee Fiji Crippled Children Soc., 1965—, pres., 1971-74; sec. Fiji Press Council, 1986-94; chmn. Fiji Coll. Honour, 1995—. Served with inf. Fiji Army, 1942-45. Decorated comdr. and knight comdr. Order Brit. Empire. Mem. Commonwealth Trust (sec. Fiji), Fiji Arts Club (pres.), Royal Suva Yacht Club, 1961. Methodist. Clubs: Masons (master Fiji 1949-50, 74-75), United Grand Lodge Eng. (past grand, dir. ceremonies 1991), Defence (life mem., trustee), Fiji Arts (pres., life mem., trustee), United (life mem., trustee) (Suva), Royal Automobile (Sydney). Home: GPO Box 13250, Suva Fiji Office: 24 Des Voeux Rd, GPO Box 13250, Suva Fiji *I would like to be worthy of C.E. Montague's tribute to three friends: "They were not ruled by fear or desire, and you could believe what they said".*

USHER, PHYLLIS LAND, state official; b. Winona, Miss., Aug. 29, 1944; d. Sandy Kenneth and Ruth (Cottingham) L.; m. William A. Usher (dec. Dec. 1993). B.S., U. So. Miss., Hattiesburg, 1967; M.S. (Title II-B fellow 1968-69), U. Tenn., Knoxville, 1969; postgrad. Purdue U., Ind. U., Utah State U. Librarian, Natchez (Miss.)-Adams County schs., 1967-68; materials specialist Fulton County Bd. Edn., Atlanta, 1969-71; cons. div. instructional media Ind. Dept. Public Instrn., Indpls., 1971-74, dir. div., 1974-82, dir. fed. resources and sch. improvement, 1982-85; acting assoc. supt. Ind. Dept. Edn., 1985; sr. officer Ctr. for Sch. Improvement, Ind. Dept. Edn., 1985—; pres. bd. dirs. INCOLSA, mcpl. corp., 1980-82; pres., owner Usher Funeral Home, Inc.; mem. task force sch. Libraries Nat. Commn. Libraries and Info. Sci.; dir., pres. NURC; cons. in field. Mem. Gov. Inst. Conf. Children and Youth Task Force. Recipient citation Internat. Reading Assn., 1975. Mem. ALA, Nat. Assn. State Ednl. Media Profls., West Deanery Bd. Edn., Indpls. Archdioces, Delta Kappa Gamma. Adv. bd. Booklist. Office: Room 229 State House Indianapolis IN 46204

USHER, W. DAVID, earth scientist. Recipient L.C. Charlesworth award Assn. Profl. Engrs., Geologists and Geophysicists Alta., 1993. Home: 6412 131 St NW, Edmonton, AB Canada T6H 3Y3°

USHIJIMA, JOHN TAKEJI, state senator, lawyer; b. Hilo, Hawaii, Mar. 13, 1924; s. Buhachi and Sano (Nitahara) U.; m. Margaret Kunishige, June 6, 1954. B.A., Grinnell Coll., 1950; J.D., George Washington U., 1952. Bar: Hawaii, 1953. Ptnr. Pence & Ushijima, Hilo, 1953-61, Ushijima & Nakamoto, Hilo, 1961-69; mem. Hawaii Senate, 1959—, pres. pro tem, 1974—; bd. dirs. Cyanotech Corp., Woodinville, Wash. Bd. dirs. Waiakea Settlement YMCA. With AUS, 1943-46, ETO. Mem. Am. Bar Assn., Phi Delta Phi. Democrat. Home: 114 Melani St Hilo HI 96720-2766 Office: 192 Kapiolani St Hilo HI 96720-2646

USRY, MILTON FRANKLIN, accounting educator; b. Mineola, Tex., Aug. 31, 1931; s. Milton F. and Luciel (Weaver) U.; m. Dona Esther White, Nov. 25, 1951; children: Milton Wayne, Mark Lester. B.B.A., Baylor U., 1952; M.B.A., U. Houston, 1959; Ph.D., U. Tex.-Austin, 1964. C.P.A., Tex. Acct. Shell Chem. Co., Houston, 1955-59; asst. prof. U. Houston, 1959-61; regents prof. Okla State U., Stillwater, 1961-86; Mary Ball Washington prof. U. West Fla., Pensacola, 1986—. Chmn. bd. dirs. Bapt. Health Care, Pensacola. Mem. Am. Acctg. Assn., Inst. Mgmt. Accts., Fla. Inst. CPAs, Gulf Coast Econs. Club (past pres. Pensacola Club), Masons, Rotary. Republican. Baptist. Home: 6553 Terrasanta Pensacola FL 32504 Office: U West Fla Pensacola FL 32514

USSERY, LUANNE, communications consultant; b. Kershaw, S.C., Feb. 20, 1938; d. Ralph Thurston and Mary Elizabeth (Haile) U. B.A., Winthrop Coll., 1959. Assoc. editor Kershaw News-Era, 1959-61; advt. saleswoman Nonpareil newspaper, Coun. Bluffs, Iowa, 1961-67; mag. editor Mutual of Omaha-United of Omaha Ins. Co., 1968-78, asst. v.p., 1977-82, 2d v.p., 1982-87. Editor: The Presbyterian, Presbytery of Missouri River Valley, Omaha, 1988-88, Presbyterian Times, Providence Presbytery, Rock Hill, S.C., 1990-93, co-editor 1993—; weekly columnist Kershaw News Era, 1988-92. Elder, clk. of session First Presbyn. Ch. U.S.A., Coun. Bluffs, 1974-88, Beaver Creek Presbyn. Ch., Kershaw, 1990-92; chair communications com. Presbytery of Missouri River Valley, 1985-87, moderator, 1988; trustee Christian Home Assn./Children's Sq. U.S.A., Coun. Bluffs, 1985-88, Internat. Assn. Bus. Communicators (pres. Omaha chpt. 1972, Communicator of Yr. award Omaha chpt. 1973).

USTINOV, SIR PETER ALEXANDER, actor, director, writer; b. London, Apr. 16, 1921; s. Iona and Nadia (Benois) U.; m. Isolda Denham, 1940 (div.); 1 child, Tamara; m. Suzanne Cloutier, Feb. 15, 1954 (div. 1971); children: Pavla, Igor, Andrea; m. Hélène du Lau d'Allemans, 1972. Student, Westminster Sch., London, Mr. Gibbs Prep. Sch., London, London Theatre Sch.; D.Mus. (hon.), Cleve. Inst. Music, 1967; LL.D. (hon.), U. Dundee, 1969, LaSalle Coll. of Phila., 1971, U. Ottawa, 1991; Litt.D. (hon.), U. Lancaster, 1972; Doctorate (hon.), U. Toronto, 1984, 95; LHD (hon.), Georgetown U., 1988; Doctorate (hon.), U. Brussels, 1995. Stage appearances include The Wood Demon, 1938, The Bishop of Limpopoland, 1939, Madame Liselotte Beethoven-Fink, 1939, White Cargo, Rookery Nook, Laburnum Grove, Pygmalion, 1939, First Night, 1940, Swinging the Gate, 1940, Fishing For Shadows, 1940, Hermione Gingold Revue, 1940, Diversion No. 1 Revue, 1940, Squaring the Circle, 1941, Crime and Punishment, 1946, Frenzy, 1948, Love in Albania, 1949, The Love of Four Colonels, 1951-52 (N.Y. Critics award, Donaldson award), Romanoff and Juliet, 1956 (Evening Standard drama award), Photo Finish, 1962, 63, The Unknown Soldier and His Wife, 1968, 73, Who's Who in Hell, 1974, King Lear, 1979, 80, Beethoven's Tenth, 1983, 83-84, 87-88; currently appearing worldwide in An Evening with Peter Ustinov; film appearances include One of Our Aircraft Is Missing, 1941, The Way Ahead, 1944, Private Angelo, 1949, Odette, 1950, Quo Vadis (Acad. award nomination for Best Supporting Actor), 1950, Hotel Sahara, 1952, Beau Brummel, 1953-54, The Egyptian, 1954, We're No Angels, 1955, Lola Montez, 1955, The Spies, 1955, An Angel Flew Over Brooklyn, 1955, I Girovaghi, 1955, The Sundowners, 1960, Spartacus, 1960-61 (Acad. award for Best Supporting Actor), Romanoff and Juliet, 1961, Billy Budd, 1962, Topkapi, 1963, John Goldfarb, Please Come Home!, 1964, Blackbeard's Ghost, 1967, The Comedians, 1967, Hot Millions, 1968, Viva Max, 1969, Hammersmith Is Out, 1971, Big Truck and Poor Clare, 1971, One of Our Dinosaurs Is Missing, 1974, Logan's Run, 1975, Treasure of Matecumba, 1975, The Last Remake of Beau Geste, 1976, Purple Taxi, 1977, Death on the Nile, 1977, The Thief of Baghdad, 1978, Ashanti, 1979, Charlie Chan and the Curse of the Dragon Queen, 1980, Evil Under the Sun, 1981, Memed, My Hawk, 1982, Appointment With Death, 1988, The French Revolution, 1989, Lorenzo's Oil, 1992, The Phoenix and The Magic Carpet, 1993; dir.: (plays) Squaring the Circle, 1941, Love in Albania, 1949, No Sign of the Dove, 1952, A Fiddle at the Wedding, 1952, Romanoff and Juliet, 1956, Photo Finish, 1962, 64, Half Way Up the Tree, 1967, The Unknown Soldier and His Wife, 1968, 73, (operas) L'Heure Espagnole (Ravel), Covent Garden, 1962, Gianni Schicchi (Puccini), Covent Garden, 1962, Erwartung

(Schoenberg), Covent Garden, 1962, The Magic Flute (Mozart), Hamburg Opera, 1968; dir., scenery and costume designer: Don Giovanni (Mozart), Edinburgh Festival, 1973; dir., producer, set and costume designer: Don Quichotte (Massenet), Paris Opera, 1973; dir., producer: The Brigands (Offenbach), The German Opera, Berlin, 1978; dir., writer libretto: The Marriage (Moussorgsky), Piccola Scala, 1981; dir.: Mavra and The Flood (Stravinsky), Piccola Scala, 1982, Katja Kabanowa (Janacek), Hamburg Opera, 1985, The Marriage of Figaro, Mozarteum and the Hamburg Opera, 1987, Jolanthe (Tchaikovsky) and Francesca da Rimini (Rachmaninoff), Dresden Opera, 1993; appeared on radio, London (BBC), Germany, Belgium, Rome, Paris, N.Y.C., Hollywood; TV appearances include In All Directions (host, producer, co-star), BBC, History of Europe, BBC, Einstein's Universe, PBS and BBC, 1979, Barefoot in Athens (Emmy award), Storm in Summer (Emmy award), The American Revolution, CBS (George Peabody award), Omnibus (Emmy award), The Well Tempered Bach (Emmy award nomination), PBS, 1984, 13 at Dinner, CBS, 1985, Deadman's Folly, CBS, 1985, Peter Ustinov's Russia, 1985, Appointment with Death, 1987, Around the World in Eighty Days, NBC, 1988-89, Secret Identity of Jack the Ripper, 1989-90, Monet: Legacy of Light, 1990, Ustinov Aboard the Orient Express, 1991-92, Ustinov Meets Pavarotti, 1993, Inside the Vatican, 1994, The Old Curiosity Shop, 1995, occasional political commentaries, BBC; recordings include Mock Mozart, The Grand Prix of Gibralter, Peter and the Wolf, Nutcracker Suite, The Soldier's Tale (Stravinsky) (with Jean Cocteau), Hary Janos (Kodaly), London Symphony Orch., The Little Prince (St. Exupéry), (narration) Grandpa, Babar and Father Christmas, The Old Man of Lochnagar, Grandpa, Peter Ustinov Reads the Orchestra; author: (plays) Fishing for Shadows, 1940, House of Regrets, 1942, Blow Your Own Trumpet, 1943, Beyond, 1943, The Banbury Nose, 1944, The Tragedy of Good Intentions, 1945, The Indifferent Shepherd, 1948, Frenzy, 1948, The Man in the Raincoat, 1949, The Moment of Truth, 1951, The Love of Four Colonels, 1951, High Balcony, 1952, No Sign of the Dove, 1953, Romanoff and Juliet, 1956, The Empty Chair, 1956, Paris Not So Gay, 1958, Photo Finish, 1962, The Life in My Hands, 1964, The Unknown Soldier and His Wife, 1967, Halfway Up the Tree, 1967, Who's Who in Hell, 1974, Overheard, 1981, Beethoven's Tenth, 1983, 87-88, others, (films) The Way Ahead (with Eric Ambler), 1942-43, School for Secrets, 1946, Vice Versa, 1947, Private Angelo, 1949, Romanoff and Juliet, 1961, Billy Budd (with DeWitt Bodeen), 1962-63, The Lady L (with Ira Wallach), 1964, Hot Millions (with Ira Wallach), 1968, Memed, My Hawk, 1982, (cartoon) We Were Only Human, 1960, (short stories) Add a Dash of Pity, 1960, Frontiers of the Sea, 1966, (novels) The Loser, 1961, Krumnagel, 1971, The Disinformer, 1989, The Old Man and Mr. Smith, 1991, (autobiography) Dear Me, 1977, My Russia, 1983, Ustinov in Russia, 1987, Ustinov at Large, 1991, Still at Large, 1993. Chancellor U. Durham, 1992; pres. World Federalist Movement, 1992. With Brit. Army, 1942-46. Comdr. Order of Brit. Empire, 1975; recipient Disting. Svc. award UNICEF, 1978, Prix de la Butte, 1978, Best Actor award Variety Club Gt. Britain, 1979, medal of Honor Charles U., 1991, Britannia award, 1992, Critic's Circle award, 1993, German Cultural award, 1994, German Bambi, 1994, Internat. Child Survival award, 1995; named rector U. Dundee, 1971-73, Commandeur des Arts et Lettres, 1985, Knight of the Realm, 1990; elected to Acad. Fine Arts Paris, 1988. Office: care William Morris Agy, 31/32 Soho Sq, London W1V 5DG, England

UTHOFF, MICHAEL, dancer, choreographer, artistic director; b. Santiago, Chile, Nov. 5, 1943; came to U.S., 1962; s. Ernst and Lola (Botka) U.; m. dau., Michelle. Grad. biology, high sch., Chile; dance tng. with Juilliard Sch., 1962-65, Martha Graham, 1962-63, Joffrey Ballet, 1965-68, Sch. Am. Ballet, 1962-64; Laureate in Humanities, St. Joseph Coll., Hartford, Conn. Leading dancer Jose Limon Dance Co., 1964-65, City Center Joffrey Ballet, 1965-68, N.Y.C. Opera, 1968-69; leading dancer, asst. dir. First Chamber Dance Co. N.Y., from 1969; artistic dir. Hartford Ballet Co., 1972-92, Ballet Ariz., 1992—; mem. faculty Juilliard Sch. Music, N.Y.C., from 1969; guest artist, tchr. Princeton Ballet Soc.; prof. dance SUNY, Purchase, 1972-74; instr. dance and drama movement, Yale U.; works premiered by Compania Nacional de Danzas, Mexico City, 1989; guest choreographer Shanghai Ballet, Republic of China, 1986; led Hartford Ballet on 3-week 11-city tour of Peoples Republic of China by invitation of Shanghai Internat. Culture Assn., 1988, 5-week 9-country tour Latin Am., 1991. Choreography, dancer-actor film Seafall, 1968; opera prodns. Aida and La Cenerentola, Honolulu, 1972, Conn. Opera Romeo et Juliette, 1989, Pitts. Opera Aida, 1988; choreographer Quartet, City Center Joffrey Ballet, 1968, The Pleasure of Merely Circulating, Juilliard Sch. Music, 1969, Windsong, Reflections, Dusk, Promenade, First Chamber Dance Co., 1969-70, Mozart's Idomeneo for Caramoor Music Festival, 1970, Concerto Grosso for Ballet Clasico 70 of Mexico, also restaged Dusk, 1972, Aves Mirabiles, 1973, Danza a Quattro, 1973, Maroszzek Dances, 1973, Duo, 1974, Pastorale, 1974, Brahms Variations, 1974, Autumalal, 1975, Mir Ken Geharget Veren, 1976, Tom Dula, 1976, Unstill Life, 1977, Songs of a Wayfarer, 1977, White Mountains Suite, 1978, Bach Cantata, 1978, The Nutcracker, 1979, Romeo and Juliet, 1981, Cachivaches, 1981, Reflections on the Water, 1981, Weeping Willow, 1982, Carmencita Variations, 1982, Hansel and Gretel, 1983, Coppelia, 1986, Speak Easy, 1986, New England Triptych, 1986, Los Copihues, 1988, Petrouchka, 1988, RFD #1, 1989, Classical Symphoniette, 1990, Alice in Wonderland, 1991, Nocturnes, 1991, Sinfonia Danzante, 1991; Nat. Endowment Arts commns. for choreography: Primavera, Minn. Dance Theatre, 1975, Panvezitos, Greater Houston Civic Ballet, 1976, Sonata, The Prodigal Son, Hartford Ballet, 1977, 79. Recipient award for best choreography for Murmurs of the Stream, Chilean Nat. Press, 1983, Critic's Circle Best of Yr. in Arts award, Chile, 1984. Office: Ballet Ariz 3645 E Indian School Rd Phoenix AZ 85018

UTIGER, ROBERT DAVID, medical editor; b. Bridgeport, Conn., July 14, 1931; s. David Alfred and Adeline (Frey) U.; m. Sally Baldwin, Nov. 27, 1953; children: Jane, David, Nancy. A.B., Williams Coll., 1953; M.D., Washington U., 1957. Intern, resident in medicine Barnes Hosp., St. Louis, 1957-61; investigator Nat. Cancer Inst., Bethesda, Md., 1961-63; asst. prof. medicine Washington U. Medicine, 1963-69; assoc. prof. U. Pa. Sch. Medicine, Phila., 1969-73; prof. U. Pa. Sch. Medicine, 1973-79; prof. medicine U. N.C. Sch. Medicine, Chapel Hill, 1979-89; clin. prof. medicine Harvard Med. Sch., Boston, 1989—; dep. editor New Eng. Jour. Medicine, Boston, 1989—. Editor-in-chief Jour. Clin. Endocrinology and Metabolism, 1983-89. Mem. Am. Soc. Clin. Investigation, Assn. Am. Physicians, Nat. Bd. Med. Examiners, Endocrine Soc., Phi Beta Kappa, Alpha Omega Alpha. Office: New Eng Jour Medicine 10 Shattuck St Boston MA 02115-6011

UTKU, SENOL, civil engineer, computer science educator; b. Suruc, Turkey, Nov. 23, 1931; s. Sukru and Sukufe (Gumus) U.; m. Bisulay Bereket, May 9, 1964; children: Ayda, Sinan. Dipl. Ing., Istanbul Tech. U., 1954; M.S., MIT, 1959, Sc.D., 1960. Civil engr., Istanbul, Turkey, 1954. Research engr. IBM, 1959-60; asst. prof. structural engring MIT, 1960-62; assoc. prof. Middle East Tech U., Ankara, Turkey, 1962-63; exec. dir. Computation Ctr., Istanbul Tech. U., 1963-65; mem. tech. staff Jet Propulsion Lab., Pasadena, Calif., 1965-70; assoc. prof. civil engring Duke U., Durham, N.C., 1970-72, prof., 1972-79, prof. civil engring, prof. computer sci., 1979—, dir. undergrad. studies, 1980-87, dir. grad. studies, 1987-89. Author: Linear Analysis of Discrete Structures, 1991; co-author: Elementary Structural Analysis, 4th edit., 1991, Dynamics of Offshore Structures, 1984, Finite Element Handbook, 1987; contbr. articles to profl. jours. Fulbright scholar, 1957; recipient Pres.'s fund Calif. Inst. Tech., 1981, award NASA, 1969, 71, 77, 84, 86, 87, Internat. Joint Rsch. award NSF, 1991-92. Fellow ASCE; mem. Acad. Mechanics, Sigma Xi, Chi Epsilon. Home: 1843 Woodburn Rd Durham NC 27705-5754 Office: Duke U 134 Hudson Hall Durham NC 27708

UTLAUT, WILLIAM FREDERICK, electrical engineer; b. Sterling, Colo., July 26, 1922; s. Frederick Ernst and Francis Ruth Hanna U.; m. Jeanne Elizabeth Pomeroy, Aug. 4, 1946; children—Mark William, Niles Frederick, Paige Elizabeth. Utlaut Moore. B.S.E.E., U. Colo., 1944, M.S.E.E., 1950, Ph.D. in Elec. Engring. 1966; diploma, Naval Radar Sch., 1945. Engr. Gen. Electric Co., Schenectady, 1946-48, Nat. Bur. Standards, Boulder, Colo., 1952-53; instr. U. Colo., 1948-52, 53-54; dir. Inst. for Telecommunications Scis., U.S. Dept. Commerce, Boulder, 1954—; assoc. administr. Nat. Telecom and Info. Adminstrn., Boulder, 1980—; chmn. U.S. study group 1, Internat. Radio Consultative Com., 1975—, mem. U.S. nat. com., 1970-81; mem. electromagnetic wave propagation panel, adv. group aerospace research and devel. NATO, 1978-81, adv. com. Nat. Research Council, 1986—; chmn.

ANSI-ECSA tech. com. on Integrated Services Digital Network, 1984—, U.S. nat. com. Internat. Consultative Com. on Telegraph and Telephone Joint Working Party, 1986—. Guest co-editor spl. joint issue: IEEE Trans. on Spectrum Mgmt, 1981, IEEE Trans. on Communications, 1975; guest editor spl. issue: Radio Sci, 1974; contbr. numerous articles to profl. jours. Bd. dirs. YMCA, 1955—; mem. bd. mgmt. 1st Congl. Ch., 1960-66, 78—; mem. engring. devel. council U. Colo., 1969-81. Served in USN, 1943-46. Recipient Gold medal U.S. Dept. Commerce, 1971; Disting. Engring. Alumnus award U. Colo., 1973. Fellow IEEE (Harry Dimond Meml. award leadership radio sci. and engring. 1989, Oresdk, Rank award 1990, policy bd. Communications Soc.), Internat. Sci. Radio Union, Am. Nat. Standards Inst., Exchange Carriets Standards Assn. Office: Inst for Telecom Scis US Dept Commerce 325 Broadway·St Boulder CO 80303-3328°

UTLEY, EDWARD H., insurance company executive; b. 1929. BS, U. Colo., 1951. With USMC, 1951-71, Group Hospitalization, Inc., Washington, 1971-73; sr. v.p. Govt. Employees Ins. Co., Washington, 1973—; with Geico Co., Washington, 1987—, pres., 1989—, now also vice chmn. Office: Geico Corp 1 Geico Plz Washington DC 20076°

UTLEY, F. KNOWLTON, library director, educator; b. Northampton, Mass., May 4, 1935; s. Frederick K. and Florence M. (Moore) U.; m. Faith E. Green, July 2, 1960; children: Richard F., Stephen R., David E. BS, Castleton State Coll., 1960; MA, U. Conn., 1967; EdD, Boston U., 1979; MLS, U. Ala., 1983. Tchr. indsl. arts Montpelier (Vt.) High Sch., 1960-61, Southwick (Mass.) High Sch., 1961-63; tchr., drafting instr. Putnam (Conn.) High Sch., 1963-68; media specialist Cen. Conn. State U., New Britain, 1968-69, dir. media svcs., 1969-72; doctoral teaching fellow Boston U., 1972-73; dir. libr., media svcs. Manchester (Mass.) Pub. Schs., 1973-79; assoc. prof. libr. scis. U. Maine, Farmington, 1979-80; dir. grad. program libr. media Livingston (Ala.) U., 1980-83; dir. libr. media svcs. Am. Internat. Coll., Springfield, Mass., 1983—; pres. C/W Mars-Ctrl. and Western Mass. Auto. Res., 1987-88; chmn. bd. dirs. Cooperating Librs. of Great Springfield, 1988-89; chmn. bd. dirs. Western Mass. Media Coun., 1991-93. Mem. ALA, Assn./Edn. Commun. and Tech. New England Edn. Media Assn., New England Libr. Assn., Sch. Libr. Medic. Assn., Mass. Libr. Assn., Phi Delta Kappa. Home: 11 Canal Dr Belchertown MA 01007-9224 Office: Am Internat Coll 1000 State St Springfield MA 01109-3151

UTLEY, JOHN EDDY, automotive supplies executive; b. Evanston, Ill., Feb. 20, 1941; s. John Eddy and Grace Millicent (Turnock) U.; m. Frances Elizabeth von Manr, Aug. 17, 1963; children: John Eddy III, Josephine Laurel Shaya, Robin Frances. BS in Indsl. Engring., U. Mich., 1964; MBA, Wayne State U., 1972. Sales engr. The Timken Co., Canton, Ohio, 1964-73, dist. mgr., 1973-78, asst. gen. mgr., 1978-82; v.p. sales and mktg. Kelsey-Hayes Co., Romulus, Mich., 1982-84, pres. auto group, 1984-88, pres., chief operating officer, 1988-89, vice chmn., 1989-92; chmn., CEO, 1992-94; chmn. Hayes Wheels Internat., 1993—; sr. v.p. Varity Corp.; pres. Automotive Original Equipment Mgrs. Assn., Detroit, 1987; bd. dirs. Walbro Corp. Mem. Soc. Automotive Engrs. (nat. chmn. passenger car meeting 1984), Bloomfield Hills Country Club. Republican. Methodist. Avocations: golf, tennis, boating. Office: Kelsey-Hayes Co 11878 Hubbard Livonia MI 48150

UTLEY, JOHN M., corporate professional; b. Henderson, Ky., Sept. 19, 1937; s. John M. and Thelma (Nunlley) U.; m. Katherine J.; children: John A., Michael A., Stephen M., Rebecca K., James M. Student, Ind. U. So. Tex. Jr. Coll., Houston, Am. Coll., Omaha, Nebr. Wireman helper U.S. Steel, Gary, Ind., 1956-58; ins. investigator Am. Svc. Bur., Gary, 1958-59, asst. mgr., 1959-60, mgr., 1960-61; asst. v.p. Am. Svc. Bur., Chgo., 1961-62; dist. mgr. Am. Svc. Bur., Houston, 1963-67; regional v.p. Am. Svc. Bur., Omaha, 1967-71; v.p. Am. Svc. Bur., Chgo., 1971-75, sr. v.p., 1975-76; chief exec. officer, owner Examination Mgmt. Svc. Inc., Dallas, 1976—. Mem. H.O. Life Underwriters Assn., Tex. H.O. Life Underwriters Assn., Ins. Inst. Assn., Jaycees (exec. v.p. 1967, Gary, Ind. chpt.), Rep. Nat. Com., Rep. Party 500 Club. Home: 5601 Willow Bend Ct Plano TX 75093-4206 Office: Examination Mgmt Svcs 1111 W Mockingbird Ln Dallas TX 75247

UTROSKA, WILLIAM ROBERT, veterinarian; b. Greenwood, Miss., Oct. 21, 1946; s. Robert Julius and Ruth (McNeal) U.; m. Dian Anderson, Aug. 3, 1968; 1 child, Amy Elizabeth. BS, Miss. State U., 1968; DVM, Auburn U., 1971. Diplomate Am. Bd. Vet. Practitioners. Staff veterinarian Animal Hosp.-Brooks Rd., Memphis, 1971-73, Whitehaven Animal Hosp., Memphis, 1973-75; owner, operator Stateline Animal Clin., Southaven, Miss., 1975—; cons. VIP Products/Pet Chems., Memphis, 1984. Contbr. articles to profl. jours. Alderman City of Southaven, 1989—, mem. planning commn., 1980-89. Mem. Exchange Club (pres. 1978). Republican. Methodist. Avocations: flight instructor, golf. Home: 577 Litchfield Pl Southaven MS 38671-5926 Office: Stateline Animal Clin 100 Guthrie Dr Southaven MS 38671-5828

UTSEY, JOHN BLAINE, retail store executive; b. Kilgore, Tex., Dec. 19, 1938; s. John Henry and Gertrude Pauline (Hensley) U.; m. Lavelle Watkins, June 4, 1960; children: John David, Jennifer Lynn. B.B.A. (scholar), Baylor U., 1960; M.S. (scholar), N.Y. U., 1961. With Foley's Dept. Store, Houston, 1961—; chmn., chief exec. officer Foley's Dept. Store, 1987—; dir. Asso. Merchandising Corp.; bd. dirs. Federated Dept. Stores Found. Bd. dirs. Tex. Research League, United Way of Tex. Gulf Coast. Mem. Greater Houston Conv. and Visitors Council (bd. dirs.). Baptist. Clubs: Heritage, Forum. Office: Foley's Dept Store 1110 Main St Houston TX 77002-6303

UTT, GLENN S., JR., motel investments and biotech industry company executive; b. Neodesha, Kans., Aug. 7, 1926; s. Glenn S. and Reba Pauline (White) U.; m. Mary Lou Ford, Aug. 8, 1948; 1 child, Jan A. B.S.E.E., BSBA, Kans. State U., 1949; M.B.A., Harvard U., 1951. Salesman Drexel Furniture Co., N.C., 1951-55; v.p. Booz Allen & Hamilton, Chgo. and Zurich, switzerland, 1955-62; exec. v.p. Abbott Labs., North Chicago, Ill., 1962-83, also dir., ret., 1983; chmn. bd. Glendon Enterprises, Iron Mountain, Mich., Janmar Enterprises, Minocqua, Wis., Marjan Inc., Houghton, Mich., U.P. Hotel Group Inc., Houghton; bd. dirs. Sugen, Inc., Redwood City, Calif., Synergen, Boulder, Colo., Selectide Inc., Tuscon. Co-author: Lalique Perfume Bottles, 1990. Alderman City of Lake Forest, Ill., 1972-76, chmn. recreational bd., 1975-78; mem. exec. com. Lake County Republican Fedn., Waukegan, Ill., 1974-83. With USN, 1944-46. Mem. Beta Theta Pi. Avocations: antiques; objects of art. Home: PO Box 292 Palm Desert CA 92261-0292 Office: Janmar Enterprises PO Box 575 Minocqua WI 54548-0575

UTTAL, WILLIAM R(EICHENSTEIN), psychology and engineering educator, research scientist; b. Mineola, N.Y., Mar. 24, 1931; s. Joseph and Claire (Reichenstein) U.; m. Michiye Nishimura, Dec. 20, 1954; children: Taneil, Lynet, Lisa. Student, Miami U. Oxford, Ohio, 1947-48; B.S. in Physics, U. Cin., 1951; Ph.D. in Exptl. Psychology and Biophysics, Ohio State U., 1957. Staff Psychologist, mgr. behavioral sci. group IBM Research Center, Yorktown Heights, N.Y., 1957-63; assoc. prof. U. Mich., Ann Arbor, 1963-68, prof. psychology, 1968-86, research scientist, 1963-86, prof. emeritus, 1986—; grad. affiliate faculty dept. psychology U. Hawaii, 1986—; research scientist Naval Ocean Systems Ctr.-Hawaii Lab., Kailua, 1985-88; prof., chmn. dept. psychology Ariz. State U., Tempe, 1988-92, prof. dept. indsl. and mgmt. systems engring., 1992—; affiliated prof., Dept. of Computer Sci. and Engring., 1993—; vis. prof. Kyoto (Japan) Prefectural Med. U., 1965-66, Sensory Sci. Lab., U. Hawaii, 1968, 73, U. Western Australia, 1970-71, U. Hawaii, 1978-79, 80-81; pres. Nat. Conf. on On-Line Uses Computers in Psychology, 1974. Author: Real Time Computers: Techniques and Applications in the Psychological Sciences, 1968, Generative Computer Assisted Instruction in Analytic Geometry, 1972, The Psychobiology of Sensory Coding, 1973, Cellular Neurophysiology and Integration: An Interpretive Introduction, 1975, An Autocorrelation Theory of Visual Form Detection, 1975, The Psychobiology of Mind, 1978, A Taxonomy of Visual Processes, 1981, Visual Form Detection in Three Dimensional Space, 1983, Principles of Psychobiology, 1983, The Detection of Nonplanar Surfaces in Visual Space, 1985, The Perception of Dotted Forms, 1987, On Seeing Forms, 1988, The Swimmer: A Computational Model of a Perceptual Motor System, 1992; also numerous articles; editor: Readings in Sensory Coding, 1972; assoc. editor Behavioral Research Method and Instrn., 1968-90, Computing: Archives for Electronic Computing, 1963-75, Jour. Exptl. Psychology: Perception and Performance, 1974-79. Served to 2d lt. USAF, 1951-53. USPHS spl. postdoctoral fellow, 1965-66; NIMH research scientist award, 1971-76. Charter fellow Am. Psychol. Soc.; fellow AAAS, Soc. Exptl. Psychologists; mem. Psychonomics Soc. Patentee in field. Office: Ariz State U Dept Indsl and Mgmt Systems Engring Tempe AZ 85287-1104

UTTER, ROBERT FRENCH, state supreme court justice; b. Seattle, June 19, 1930; s. John and Besse (French) U.; m. Elizabeth J. Stevenson, Dec. 28, 1953; children: Kimberly, Kirk, John. BS, U. Wash., 1952; LLB, 1954. Bar: Wash. 1954. Pros. atty. King County, Wash., 1955-57; individual practice law Seattle, 1957-59; ct. commr. King County Superior Ct., 1959-64, judge, 1964-69; judge Wash. State Ct. Appeals, 1969-71; judge Wash. State Supreme Ct., 1971—, chief justice, 1979-81; lectr. in field; leader comparative law tour Peoples Republic of China, 1986, 87, 88, 91, USSR, 1989; adj. prof. constl. law U. Puget Sound, 1987, 88, 89, 90, 91, 92, 93, 94; cons. CEELI, 1991, 93—, USIA, 1992; visitor to Kazakhstand and Kyrgystan Judiciary, 1993, 94; lectr. to Albanian Judiciary, 1994. Editor books on real property and appellate practice. Pres., founder Big Brother Assn., Seattle, 1955-67; pres., founder Job Therapy Inc., 1963-71; mem. exec. com. Conf. of Chief Justices, 1979-80, 81-86; pres. Thurston County Big Bros./Big Sisters, 1984; lectr. Soviet Acad. Moscow, 1991; USIA visitor to comment on jud. system, Latvia, 1992, Kazakstan, 1993-94,. Named Alumnus of Yr., Linfield Coll., 1973, Disting. Jud. Scholar, U. Ind., 1987, Judge of Yr., Wash. State Trial Lawyers, 1989, Outstanding Judge, Wash. State Bar Assn., 1990, Outstanding Judge, Seattle-King County Bar Assn., 1992, Conder-Faulkner lectr. U. Wash. Sch. Law, 1995. Mem. ABA (commentator on proposed constns. of Albania, Bulgaria, Romania, Russia, Lithuania, Azerbaijan, Uzbekistan, Byelarus, Kazakhstan & Ukraine), Am. Judicature Soc. (Herbert Harley award 1983, sec. 1987—, chmn. bd. dirs., mem. exec. com.), Order of Coif. Baptist. Office: Wash Supreme Ct Temple of Justice (AV-11) Olympia WA 98504

UTZ, SARAH WINIFRED, nursing educator; b. San Diego; d. Frederick R. and Margaret M. (Gibbons) U.; BS, U. Portland, 1943, EdM, 1958; MS, UCLA, 1970; PhD, U. So. Calif., 1979. Clin. instr. Providence Sch. Nursing, Portland, Oreg., 1946-50, edn. dir., 1950-62; edn. dir. Sacred Heart Sch. Nursing, Eugene, Oreg., 1963-67; asst. prof. nursing Calif. State U., L.A., 1969-74, assoc. prof., 1974-81, prof., 1981—, assoc. chmn. dept. nursing, 1982—; cons. in nursing curriculum, 1978—; healthcare cons., 1991—; past chmn. ednl. adminstrs., cons., tchrs. sect. Oreg. Nurses Assn., past pres. Oreg. State Bd. Nursing; mem. rsch. program Western Interstate Commn. on Higher Edn. in Nursing; chmn. liaison com. nursing edn. Articulation Coun. Calif. Author articles and lab manuals. Served with Nurse Corps, USN, 1944-46. HEW grantee, 1970-74, Kellogg Found. grantee, 1974-76, USDHHS grantee, 1987—; R.N., Calif., Oreg. Mem. Am. Nurses Assn., Calif. Nurses Assn. (edn. commr. reg 6 1987—, chair edn. interest group region 6 , 1987—), Am. Ednl. Rsch. Assn., AAUP, Phi Delta Kappa, Sigma Theta Tau. Formerly editor Oreg. Nurse; reviewer Western Jour. Nursing Rsch. Home: 1409 Midvale Ave Los Angeles CA 90024-5454 Office: 5151 State University Dr Los Angeles CA 90032

UVEGES, GEORGE, company executive; b. Cleve., Jan. 2, 1948; s. George and Irene (Merker) U.; m. Reneé Butler, July 30, 1971; children: Tom, Paul. BBA, Cleve. State U., 1970; MBA, Baldwin-Wallace U., 1978. CPA, Ohio. Sr. audit mgr. Ernst & Whinney, Cleve., 1971-85; treas., corp. controller Invacare Corp., Elyria, Ohio, 1985-91; CFO, v.p. adminstrn. Indsl. Gen. Corp., Elyria, 1991—. With U.S. Army, 1970-71. Mem. Fin. Execs. Inst., Treas. Club, AICPAs, Ohio Soc. CPAs, Cleve. State U. Alumni Assn. (pres. 1984-85), Elyria C. of C. (bd. dirs.). Republican. Roman Catholic. Office: Indsl Gen Corp Olive & Taylors Sts Elyria OH 44035

UVENA, FRANK JOHN, retired printing company executive, lawyer; b. Ernest, Pa., Feb. 2, 1934. A.B., Ohio U., Athens, 1959; LL.B., Ohio State U., Columbus, 1963. Bar: Ill. 1963. Assoc. firm McDermott, Will & Emery, Chgo., 1963-68; atty. R.R. Donnelley & Sons, Chgo., 1968-75, v.p., gen. counsel, 1975-84, sr. v.p. law and corp. staffs, 1984-95. Bd. dirs. Chgo. Crime Commn., Joseph Holmes Chgo. Dance Theatre, 1992, United Charities Chgo. With AUS, 1954-56. Mem. ABA, Ill. Bar Assn., Chgo. Bar Assn., Ill. Mfrs. Assn. (bd. dirs. 1994), Union League Club. Office: RR Donnelley & Sons Co 77 W Wacker Dr Chicago IL 60601-1629

UVILLER, H. RICHARD, lawyer, educator; b. N.Y.C., July 3, 1929; m. Rena K. Uviller; 1 dau., Daphne R. B.A., Harvard U., 1951; LL.B., Yale U., 1953. Legal counsel U.S. Dept. Justice, 1953-54; asst. dist. atty. N.Y. County, 1954-68; prof. law Columbia U. Sch. of Law, N.Y.C., 1968—. Author: Tempered Zeal, 1988; contbr. articles to profl. jours. Office: Columbia U Sch Law 435 W 116th St New York NY 10027-7201

UYEDA, SEIYA, geophysics educator; b. Tokyo, Nov. 28, 1929; s. Seiichi and Hatsuo (Okino) U.; m. Mutsuko Kosaka, July 6, 1952; children: Taro, Makiko, Naoko. BS, U. Tokyo, 1952, DSc, 1958. Rsch. assoc. Earthquake Rsch. Inst. U. Tokyo, 1957-64, assoc. prof. Geophys. Inst., 1964-69, prof. Earthquake Rsch. Inst., 1969-90; prof. dept. marine sci. and tech. Tokai U., Shimizu, Japan, 1990—; prof. Tex. A&M U., College Station, 1990—. Author: Debate About the Earth, 1966, Island Arcs, 1973, The New View of the Earth, 1978. Recipient Tanakadte prize Soc. Terrestrial Magnetism and Electricity, 1985, Acad. prize, Japan Acad., 1987, G.P. Woollard award Geol. Soc. Am., 1989, Matsumae Prize for Academic Accomplishment, Tokai Univ., 1992. Fellow AAAS (hon.), Nat. Acad. Sci. (fgn. assoc., A Agassiz medal 1972), Russian Acad. Sci. (fgn.), Geol. Soc. London (hon.), European Union Geoscis. (hon.), Am. Geophys. Union (Walter Bucher medal 1991); mem. Am. Acad. Arts and Scis. (fgn.), Soc. Geology France (assoc.). Home: 2-39-6 Daizawa, Setagaya-ku, Tokyo 155, Japan Office: Tokai U, 3-20-1, Orido, Shimizu 424, Japan also: Tex A&M U Dept Geophysics College Station TX 77843

UYEHARA, HARRY YOSHIMI, library educator; b. Honolulu, Jan. 6, 1934; s. Saburo and Uto (Yamashiro) U. BEd, U. Hawaii, 1958; AMLS, U. Mich., 1965; MA, Columbia U., 1970, EdD, 1978. Cert. sch. libr., media specialist. Tchr., libr. Waiakea-Kai Elem. & Intermediate Sch., Hilo, Hawaii, 1960-61; libr. Wahiawa (Hawaii) Intermediate Sch., 1961-66; program specialist Hawaii State Dept. of Edn., Honolulu, 1966-76; asst. prof. library studies U. Hawaii, Honolulu, 1976-83; dean U. Guam, Mangilao, 1983-89; assoc. prof. libr. and info. studies U. Hawaii, Honolulu, 1989-91; assoc. prof. Edn. U. Guam, Mangilao, 1991-93; prof. libr. faculty Guam C.C., Mangilao, 1994—; mem. in-svc. adv. coun. Hawaii State Dept. of Edn., Honolulu, 1977-80, adv. coun. of librs. Guam Pub. Libr., Agana, 1983-89. Editor (jours.) HLA Jour., 1978, The Golden Key, 1981, 82. With U.S. Army, 1958-60. Mem. Hawaii Libr. Assn. (pres. 1977-78), Hawaii Assn. Sch. Librs. (pres. 1982-83), Guam Libr. Assn. (pres. 1984-85), Phi Delta Kappa, Kappa Delta Pi. Home: PO Box 20820 Barrigada GU 96921-0820 Office: Guam CC PO Box 23069 Barrigada GU 96921

UYTERHOEVEN, HUGO EMIL ROBERT, business educator and consultant; b. Eindhoven, The Netherlands, Aug. 6, 1931; came to U.S., 1955, naturalized, 1967; s. Willem and An (Von der Nahmer) U.; children: Monique, An, Sonia, Laura. D Iur, U. Zurich, 1955; D in law, U. Ghent, 1955; MBA, Harvard U., 1957, DBA, 1963. Mem. faculty Grad. Sch. Bus. Adminstrn. Harvard U., 1960—, Timken prof. bus. adminstrn. Grad. Sch. Bus. Adminstrn., 1974—, sr. assoc. dean Grad. Sch. Bus. Adminstrn., 1980-89; bd. dirs. Brown, Boveri & Co. Ltd., The Stanley Works, Harcourt Gen., Inc., Ciba-Geigy AG, Bombardier, Inc., Ecolab, Inc.; mem. internat. adv. coun. Degussa Corp. Author: (with others) Strategy and Organization: Text and Cases in General Management, 1973, 2d edit., 1977, Business Policy, 8th edit., 1995. Mem. Planning Bd. Weston (Mass.), 1969-72, Conservation Commn., 1972-76; pres. Weston Forest and Trail Assn., 1970-77; trustee Concord Acad., 1982-88. Belgian-Am. Ednl. Found. fellow, 1955-57. Office: Harvard U Sch Bus Boston MA 02163

UZAN, BERNARD FRANCK, general and artistic director; b. Tunis, Tunisia, Dec. 5, 1944; Arrived in Can., 1967; s. Henri and Elise Gabrielle (Pansieri) U.; m. Diana Soviero, Nov. 9, 1984. PhD, Paris U., 1968. Gen. & artistic dir. Théâtre français d'Amérique, Boston, 1973-83, Tulsa Opera, 1987-88, L'Opéra de Montreal, Que., Can., 1988—; adminstr., exec. dir. Alliance français de Boston, 1974-83; stage dir.: U.S.: Detroit, Dallas, Phila., L.A.; Can.: Montreal, Toronto, Vancouver; Europe: Monte-Carlo, Zurich, Palermo, Turin. Office: L'Opéra de Montréal, 260 de Maisonneuve W, Montreal, PQ Canada H2X 1Y9

UZENDA, JARA CARLOW, technical writer; b. Brookline, Mass., May 24, 1946; d. Roscoe William and Gloria Pauline (St. Jacques) Carlow; m. William Anthony Perry, June 1, 1963 (dec. Dec. 1971); children: Troy Anthony, William Lance, Richard A. Student, R.I. Jr. Coll., 1965-67, U. R.I., 1967-68; BS in Journalism, U. Colo., 1975, MS in Telecommunications, 1978. Mktg. mgr. Humidor Smoke Shoppes, Warwick, R.I., 1965-69; telecommunication cons. Arthur D. Little, Inc., Boston, 1976-78; dir. research Horizon House Internat., Boston, 1978-80; market analyst Internat. Telecommunications, Boulder, Colo., 1980-81; field service engr. Allied Info. Systems, Boulder, 1981-83; gen. ptnr. Kentucky Gold Ltd., San Jose, Calif., 1984; sr. tech. writer Paradyne Corp., Largo, Fla., 1984-86; sales and mktg. Piedmont Airlines Golf Resort Directory, Myrtle Beach, S.C., 1986-87; cons. Data Security, Little River, S.C., 1987—; v.p. mktg. So. Golfer, 1989—; pres. 110% Inc., Myrtle Beach, 1994—; vis. prof. Prescott Coll., Flagstaff, Ariz., 1972; film dir. Niel Minority News, Estes Park, Colo., 1973-74; featured artist Denver Post, 1973; spl. expert Latin Am. Telecommunications, Washington, 1980. Author: Electronic Fund Transfer, 1978; contbr. articles to jours. Grantee Nat. Endowment Arts, 1973. Mem. Coun. Internat. Rels. and UN Affairs, Internat. Rels. Club, Soc. Women Engrs., U. Colo. Alumni Assn., Mortar Bd., Optimists, Civitans. Lodge: Optimists. Avocations: golf, computer programming, flying, boating. Home: PO Box 603 Little River SC 29566-0603

UZMAN, BETTY GEREN, pathologist, retired educator; b. Fort Smith, Ark., Nov. 17, 1922; d. Benton Asbury and Myra Estelle (Petty) Geren; m. L. Lahut Uzman, Dec. 17, 1955 (dec.); 1 dau., Betty Tuba. Student, Fort Smith Jr. Coll., 1939-40; B.S., U. Ark., 1942; M.D., Washington U., 1945; postgrad., M.I.T., 1948-50; M.A. (hon.), Harvard U., 1967. Intern Childrens Hosp., Boston, 1945-46; resident in pathology Barnes Hosp., St. Louis, 1946-48; Am. Cancer Soc. research fellow MIT, Cambridge, Mass., 1948-50; chief biol. ultrastructure and exptl. pathology Children's Cancer Research Found., Boston, 1950-71; instr. Harvard Med. Sch., Boston, 1949-53, assoc., 1953-56, research assoc., 1956-67, assoc. prof., 1967-71, prof., 1971-72; head research dept. Sparks Regional Med. Center, Fort Smith, 1972-74; prof. pathology La. State U., Shreveport, 1974-77, U. Tenn., Memphis, 1978-89; assoc. chief staff rsch. VA, Shreveport, 1974-77; staff pathologist VA, Memphis, 1978-89, chief lab. svc., 1986-87; chief field ops., spl. asst. to dir. VA Central Office, Washington, 1978-79; dir. med. rsch. svcs., 1979-80; chmn. pathology A Study sect. NIH, 1973-76; cons. to sci. dir. Children's Cancer Rsch. Found., Boston, 1971-73; mem. adv. com. on prevention, diagnosis and treatment Am. Cancer Soc., 1970-73, 77-80; mem. adv. bd. Office Regeneration Rsch., VA, 1985-89; disting. vis. investigator Inst. Venezolano Investigation Cientificas, Caracas, 1972-74. Decorated Order of Andres Bello 1st class Venezuela; recipient Weinstein award United Cerebral Palsy, 1964; Am. Cancer Soc. research fellow, 1948-50. Mem. AAAS, Am. Soc. Cell Biology, Soc. Devel. Biology, Am. Acad. Neurology (assoc.), Am. Soc. Neurochemistry, Microscopy Soc. Am. (Diatome poster award 1985), Internat. Acad. Pathology, Am. Assn. Neuropathology (assoc.), Soc. Neurosci., Am. Assn. Cancer Rsch. Home and Office: Geren Farm 16048 E State Hwy 197 Scranton AR 72863

VAADIA, BOAZ, sculptor; b. Petah-Tiqva, Israel, Nov. 13, 1951; s. Nissim and Rivka Vaadia; m. Kim Turner, Sept. 10, 1989; children: Rebecca Danielle, Sara Madeline. Student, Avni Inst. Fine Art, Tel Aviv, 1971. vis. artist Appalachian State U., Boone, N.C., 1982; resident Internat. Tel-Hai '80 Internat. Meeting, Israel, 1980. One-person shows include O.K. Harris Works of Art, N.Y.C., 1986, 88, 89, 94, Birmingham, Mich., 1990, Phila. Mus. Judaica, 1987, Helander Gallery, Palm Beach, Fla., 1988, Jewish Mus., N.Y.C., 1988-89, Hokin Kaufman Gallery, Chgo., 1989, 90, Fay Gold Gallery, 1993, others; exhibited group shows at Helander Gallery, 1989-90, Phyllis Rothman Gallery, Fairleigh Dickinson U., Madison, N.J., 1990, Margulies Taplin Gallery, Bar Harbor Islands, 1990, Utsukushi-ga-hara Open Air Mus., Japan, 1992, First Lady's Sculpture Garden, White House, 1995, more. Grantee NEA, 1988, Ariana Found. for Arts, 1986, Artists Space, 1983, Am.-Israel Cultural Found., 1975-76, Am. the Beautiful Fund, Palisades Interstate Park, 1977; Beeckman scholar, 1976-77. Home: 475 Broadway # 7flr New York NY 10013-5905 Studio: 104 Berry St Brooklyn NY 11211

VACANO, JOST, cinematographer. Cinematographer: (films) Soldier of Orange, 1977, Spetters, 1980, Das Boot, 1981, The Neverending Story, 1984, 52 Pick-up, 1986, Robocop, 1987, Rocket Gibraltar, 1988, Total Recall, 1990, Untamed Heart, 1993. Office: care Spyros Skouras Sanford Skouras Gross & Assocs 1015 Gayley Ave 3rd Fl Los Angeles CA 90024*

VACCA, JOHN JOSEPH, JR., television executive; b. Chgo., Apr. 7, 1922; s. John Joseph and Caroline (Bain) V.; m. Alice Isabel Ure, May 2, 1944; children: John Joseph, Dawn Susan, Kim Frances. Student, Northwestern U., 1940-42, Internat. Corr. Schs., 1950-54, Harvard U., 1966. Editor, Midwest Times, Chgo., 1940-41; with prodn. dept. NBC Radio, 1946-47; news dir. sta. KECK, Odessa, Tex., 1947-49; chief announcer sta. KECK, 1948-49; program mgr. KOSA-Radio, Odessa, 1949-55; sta. mgr. KOSA-TV, 1955-61, gen. mgr., 1962-72; v.p., dir. Trigg Vaughn Stas., Inc., Odessa, 1962-67; sec. Odessa Broadcasting Co., 1950-72; asst. sec. Doubleday Broadcasting Co., 1967-77, v.p., 1967-75, sr. v.p., 1975-77; gen. mgr. KDTV, Dallas, 1972-73; TV cons. Dallas, 1978—; v.p., dir., gen. mgr. Heart O'Texas Broadcasting, Waco, Tex., 1978-83; v.p. Dunn Prodns., Inc., Dallas, 1984-88, pres., 1989-92; indl. TV producer Dallas, 1992—. Author: Seven Keys to Success, 1981. Bd. dirs. Odessa Community Chest, 1964-72, Better Bus. Bur., 1956-72; campaign maj. ARC, 1951-72; publicity adviser Ector County chpt. Nat. Found. for Infantile Paralysis, 1949-72; campaign coordinator Civic Music Assn., 1950-72; sponsor, adviser Permian Playhouse, 1959-72, v.p., bd. dirs., 1971-72, City councilman, Odessa, 1962-64; Bd. dirs. Am. Cancer Soc. Served with USAAF, 1942-46. Recipient Zeus award Epsilon Sigma Alpha, 1971. Mem. Nat. Tex. assns. broadcasters, Tex. AP Broadcasters Assn., Advt. Club Odessa (pres. 1960-61, dir. 1960-63), C. of C. (publicity adviser 1950-72), Holy Name Soc. Roman Catholic. Club: K.C (sec. Odessa 1950-51). Home and Office: 646 Harvest Hill St Lewisville TX 75067-3588 *A philosophy of service, personal and through broadcasting, coupled with a sincere approach to excellent Human Relations have formed the keystone of my career. Consistent honesty and a constant effort to give and produce much more than required have always been guiding principles. My goals have been set with flexible policies to implement them, ever mindful that 'change' is an integral part of life and progress.*

VACCARELLI, MARIE C., lawyer; b. Long Branch, N.J., Sept. 29, 1948; d. Anthony J. and Assunta J. (Vaccaro) V. BA in English, Cabrini Coll., Radnor, Pa., 1970; JD, Suffolk U., 1980. Bar: R.I. 1980, Mass. 1980, U.S. Dist. Ct. R.I. 1980, Fla. 1981, U.S. Dist. Ct. Mass. 1986, U.S. Ct. Appeals (1st cir.) 1988, U.S. Supreme Ct. 1988. With corp. pub. affairs Time, Inc., N.Y.C., 1970-72; cons. advt. and pub. rels. Boston, 1972-77; assoc. Selya & Iannuccillo, Providence, 1980-81; pvt. practice Newport, R.I., Palm Beach, Fla., 1981-86; chief domestic rels. dept. Friedman & Atherton, Boston, 1986—. Mem. ABA (exec. mem. family law sect., com. domestic violence, publicity, mental health com.), Fla. Bar Assn. (family law sect.), R.I. Bar Assn. (family ct. bench and bar com.), Mass. Bar Assn. Office: Friedman & Atherton 53 State St 27th Fl Boston MA 02109

VACCARO, CHARLES G., federal judge; b. Sept. 15, 1940; married. BS, Calif. State U., 1962; MS, Fla. State U., 1963; JD, U. Colo., 1973. Bar: Ark. 1974, U.S. Dist. Ct. (ea. and we. dists.) Ark. 1978, U.S. Supreme Ct. 1978, Fla. 1989. Engr. Bethlehem (Pa.) Steel Corp.; tchr. in U.S. and France, CEO of wood products mfg. co.; tech. projects coord. U.S. Govt., Washington; polit/econs. officer U.S. Govt., Nigeria; sr. dist. advisor U.S. Fgn. Svc., Vietnam; dep. dist. atty., U.S. Magistrate judge U.S. We. Dist. Ct., Hot Springs Nat. Park, Ark. Office: US Dist Ct 514 Ouachita Ave Hot Springs National Park AR 71901-5107

VACCARO, LOUIS CHARLES, college president; b. L. A., July 25, 1930; s. Louis Charles and Louise (Vinciguerra) V.; m. Jean Hudak, Jan. 29, 1955 (div. Aug. 1983); children: Mary Lou, Theresa, Victoria, Frances, Michelle, Justin; m. Linda Lasher, July, 1987. A.B., U. So. Calif., 1957, M.Ed. 1961; M.A., Calif. State U.-Northridge, 1960; Ph.D., Mich. State U., 1963; Litt.D. (hon.), St. Martin's Coll., Olympia, Wash., 1969; L.H.D. (hon.), Vt. Coll. of Norwich U., Montpelier, 1978. Asst. to prof. acad. affairs Marquette U., Milw., 1963-67; v.p. acad. affairs U. Portland, Oreg., 1967-70; pres.

Marycrest Coll., Davenport, Iowa, 1970-72, Colby-Sawyer Coll., New London, N.H., 1972-77, Siena Heights Coll., Adrian, Mich., 1977-83, Coll. St. Rose, Albany, N.Y., 1983—; bd. dirs. Inst. Internat. Edn., N.Y.C., Key Bank Trust Corp., Albany. Author: Notes from a College President, 1976, Planning in Small Colleges, 1979, In Search of Wisdom, 1994; editor: Student Freedom in American Higher Education, 1969, Reshaping American Higher Education, 1969. Bd. dirs. Albany Strategic Planning, 1983—; Albany Symphony Orch., 1984—; mem. Tricentennial Commn. City of Albany, 1986—; chmn. Bicentennial Commn. U.S. Constn. City of Albany, 1987. Served with USAF, 1951-52. W. K. Kellogg Found. fellow Mich. State U., East Lansing, 1961-63; Exxon Found. grantee, 1975. Mem. Nat. Cath. Edn. Assn. (exec. com.), Hudson-Mohawk Consortium Colls. Roman Catholic. Clubs: Fort Orange, University (Albany). Avocations: reading; walking; Italian cooking; travel; racquet sports. Home: 90 S Manning Blvd Albany NY 12203-1733 Office: Coll St Rose 432 Western Ave Albany NY 12203-1419

VACCARO, NICHOLAS CARMINE, English language and media educator; b. Bklyn., July 16, 1942; s. Joseph Anthony Vaccaro and Carmela (Tallarico) Chicorelli; m. Jane Elizabeth Forgiel, July 7, 1973; children: Stephen Nicholas, Christopher Joseph. BA in English, St. John's U., 1964, MS in Edn., 1966, Profl. Diploma in Adminstrn., 1978. Tchr. English South Huntington (N.Y.) Schs., 1965-68, Elwood Schs., East Northport, N.Y., 1968-69; tchr. English and media Massapequa (N.Y.) Schs., 1969—; novelist Sterling Lord-Literistic Lit. Agy., N.Y.C., 1984—; screenwriter Sterlinglord-Literistic Literary Agy., N.Y.C., 1984—; curriculum rsch. & program devel. Massapequa Schs., 1971-72, 78, 82, 84, 88; drama club dir. Berner and Massapequa High Schs., 1970-73, 78-82, 91, creative writing advisor, 1982-93; in-svc. educator Tchr. Effectiveness Inst. Contbr. articles to profl. jours. Mgr. Little League Baseball, Northport, 1984-91, Youth Ctr. Soccer, 1989. Recipient Nat. Tchrs. award NBC and Carnegie Found. for Advancement of Teaching, 1990, NEH and Coun. for Basic Edn. fellow, 1991. Mem. Mensa, Nat. Coun. Tchrs. English, Massapequa Fedn. Tchrs., Phi Delta Kappa. Roman Catholic. Avocations: textbook writing, novelist, screenwriter, directing theatre productions. Home: 208 Highland Ave Northport NY 11768-1657 Office: Massapequa High Sch 4925 Merrick Rd Massapequa NY 11758-6297

VACCARO, NICK ANTHONY, principal; b. New Orleans, July 17, 1944; s. Nick A. Sr. and Rose (Giovingo) V.; m. Linda L. Lavigne, Jan. 21, 1968; 1 child, David A. BS, Southeastern La. U., 1969, MEd, 1975, postgrad., 1986. Cert. secondary tchr., La. Tchr. sci. Independence (La.) Boys Sch., 1969-78; tchr. sci. Independence High Sch., 1978-91, asst. prin., 1991—, acting prin., 1994-95; head sci. dept. Independence High Sch., 1978-91; vol. VISTA Office Econ. Opportunity, Washington, 1966-67; chmn. steering Com. for Accreditation, So. Assn., 1984-85. Mem. zoning com. Town of Independence, 1977-78, planning bd., 1985-86; pres. mem. Mater Dolorosa Sch. Bd., Independence, 1984-90. Mem. NEA, La. Assn. Edn., La. Assn. Sch. Execs., Tangipahoa Assn. Edn. Democrat. Avocations: reading, home repairs. Home: PO Box 376 Independence LA 70443-0376

VACCARO, RALPH FRANCIS, marine biologist; b. West Somerville, Mass., Apr. 30, 1919; s. Angelo Ralph and Adelaide (Alberlini) V.; m. Martha Ann Walsh, Apr. 19, 1955; children: Christopher Ralph, Adelaide Marie, John Michael, Mark Joseph, Thomas James (dec.), Peter Anthony. B.S., Tufts U., 1941; M.P.H., MIT, 1943. Sanitary engring. aide Commonwealth of Mass., Boston, 1946-47; pub. health bacteriologist Assn. Am. Railroads, Balt., 1947-48; sr. rsch. scientist Woods Hole Oceanographic Inst. (Mass.), 1948-86, chmn. dept. biol., 1984-85; cons. environ. quality; assoc. math.-sci. staff Falmouth (Mass.) High Sch., 1989—. Patentee in field. Served with USPHS, 1956—; served with U.S. Army, 1943-46. Mem. Am. Soc. Limnology and Oceanography, AAAS. Republican. Roman Catholic. Home: PO Box 245 West Falmouth MA 02574-0245

VACCO, DENNIS C., lawyer; b. Buffalo, Aug. 16, 1952; s. Carmen A. and Mildred V.; m. Adrianne Venczel (div.). BA, Colgate U., 1974; JD, SUNY, Buffalo, 1978. Bar: N.Y. 1978, Fed. Ct. 1978, 82. Asst. dist. atty. Office of Erie County Dist. Atty., Buffalo, 1978-82, chief Atty. Gen.'s bureau, 1982-88; U.S. Atty. We. Dist. N.Y. Buffalo, 1988—; chmn. Atty. Gen.'s Environ. Subcom., U.S. Atty.'s Subcom. on Organized Crime and Violent Crime; mem. Nat. Environ. Enforcement Coun. Co-chair Erie County Community Commn. on Alcohol and Substance Abuse; bd. dirs. United Way of Erie County. Recipient Environ. Enforcement Leadership award Atty. Gen. Dept. of Justice, Washington, 1991. Mem. N.Y. State Bar Assn., Erie County Bar Assn., Nat. Dist. Attys. Assn., N.Y. State Dist. Attys. Assn., NCCJ, Hamburg Devel. Corp., 100 Club of Buffalo, U. Buffalo Law Alumni Assn. (bd. dirs.). Republican. Roman Catholic. Avocations: travel, sports. Office: US Atty's Office 68 Court St Rm 502 Buffalo NY 14202-3492

VACHHER, PREHLAD SINGH, psychiatrist; b. Rawalpindi, Punjab, Pakistan, Nov. 30, 1933; came to U.S., 1960; s. Thakar Singh and Harbans Kaur (Ghai) V.; m. Margaret Mary Begley, Oct. 9, 1963; children: Paul, Sheila, Mary Ann, Eileen, Mark. Grad., Khalsa Coll., India, 1950; MD, Panjab U., Amritsar, India, 1956. Diplomate Am. Bd. Psychiatry. Staff N.J. State Hosp., Trenton, 1965-66, Wayne County Gen. Hosp., Eloise, Mich., 1966-68; pvt. practice Livonia, Mich., 1966-75, Woodstock, Va., 1991—; pres. Vachher Psychiat. Ctr., P.C., Livonia, 1975-91; dir. community psychiatry Northville (Mich.) State Hosp., 1968-71; cons. staff Kingswood Hosp., Ferndale, Mich., 1967-72, Annapolis Hosp., Wayne, 1967-88, St. Joseph Mercy Hosp., Ann Arbor, 1970-89; westland staff Margaret Montgomery Hosp., 1988-91; bd. dirs. Oakland Rental Housing Assn., 1990-91; med. dir. mental health unit Shenandoah County Meml. Hosp., Woodstock, Va., 1991-94. Mem. Am. Psychiat. Assn., Va. Psychiat. Soc., Sikh Physicians in Mich. (bd. dirs. 1987), Canton C. of C. (pres. 1975), Sikh Bus. Profl. Coun. (pres. 1988—), Rotary (Canton and Plymouth, Mich., Woodstock), Prince William County C. of C. Office: 14573 Potomac Mills Rd Woodbridge VA 22192

VACHON, LOUIS-ALBERT CARDINAL, archbishop; b. St. Frederic, Que., Can., Feb. 4, 1912; s. Napoleon and Alexandrine (Gilbert) V. D.Ph., Laval U., 1947, hon. degree, 1982; D.Th., St. Thomas Aquinas U., Rome, 1949; hon. degrees, U. Montreal, McGill and Victoria, 1964, Guelph U., 1966, Moncton U., 1967, Bishop's, Queen's and Strasbourg U., 1968, U. Notre Dame, 1971, Carleton U., 1972, Laval U., 1982. Superior Grand Seminaire Quebec, 1955-59; superior gen. Le Séminaire de Qué., 1960-77; prof. philosophy Laval U., 1941-47, prof. theology, 1949-55, vice-rector, 1959-60, rector, 1960-72; protonotary apostolic, 1963-77, aux. bishop of Que., 1977-81, archbishop of Que. and primate of Can., 1981-90, apptd. Cardinal with title St. Paul of the Cross, 1985; Past pres. Corp. Laval U. Med. Centre; mem. Sacred Congregation for Clergy, Vatican, 1986—; adminstrv. bd. Nat. Order of Qué., 1985—, Can. Conf. Cath. Bishops, 1981—. Author: Espérance et Présomption, 1958, Verité et Liberte, 1962, Unité de l'universite, 1962, Apostolat de l'universitaire catholique, 1963, Memorial, 1963, Communauté universitaire, 1963, Progres de l'universite et consentement populaire, 1964, Responsabilite collective des universitaires, 1964, Les humanites aujourd'hui, 1966, Excellence et loyauté des universitaires, 1969, Pastoral Letters, 1981—. Hon. pres. La Société des etudes grecques et latines du Québec; assoc. mem. bd. Quebec Symphony Orch.; bd. govs. Laval U. Found. Decorated officier de l'Ordre de la Fidelité française, companion Order of Can., du Conseil de langue française, Ordre nat. du Qué., officier de la Légion d'honneur, France. Fellow Royal Soc. Can.; mem. Canadian Assn. French Lang. Educators (pres. 1970-72), Assn. Univs. and Colls. Can. (pres. 1965-66), Conf. Rectors and Prins. Que. Univs. (pres. 1965-68), Internat. Assn. Univs. (dep. mem. adminstrv. bd. 1965-70), Assn. des universites partiellement ou entierement de langue française (adminstrv. bd. 1961-69), Internat. Fedn. Cath. Univs. (adminstrv. bd. 1963-70), Ordre des francophones d'Amérique. *

VACHON, MARILYN ANN, retired insurance company executive; b. Fort Wayne, Ind., Dec. 12, 1924; d. Robert J. and Maude (Shaffer) V. Asst. treas Lincoln Nat. Life Ins. Co., Fort Wayne, Ind., 1961-81, assst. v.p., 1973-87; sec. Lincoln Nat. Life Ins. Co., Fort Wayne, 1980-87; asst. sec. Lincoln Nat. Corp., Fort Wayne, 1977-80, asst. treas., 1977-87, sec., 1980-87. Home: 1825 Cortland Ave Fort Wayne IN 46808-2446

VACHON, ROGATIEN ROSAIRE (ROGIE VACHON), professional hockey team executive; b. Palmarolle, Que., Can., Sept. 8, 1945; m. Nicole Vachon; children: Nicholas, Jade, Mary Joy. Goaltender Montreal (Que.) Canadiens, NHL, 1966-72, Los Angeles Kings, NHL, 1972-78, Detroit Red Wings, NHL, 1978-80, Boston Bruins, 1980-82; asst. coach Los Angeles Kings, 1982-84, gen. mgr. 1984—, alt. gov., now asst. to chmn. Co-recipient Vezina Trophy, 1968. Office: care Los Angeles Kings PO Box 17013 3900 W Manchester Blvd Inglewood CA 90306

VACHON, RUSSELL BERTRAND, transportation executive; b. Portsmouth, N.H., Apr. 3, 1945; s. Bertrand Joseph and Claire Agnes (Bouchard) V.; m. Linda Diane Holmes, Aug. 10, 1968; children: Gregory Russell, Gretchen Elise. BSCE, Merrimack Coll., North Andover, Mass., 1967; ME, Rensselaer Poly. Inst., 1969. Jr. engring. aide Haverhill (Mass.) City Engr. and City Planner's Office, 1967; jr. engr. N.Y. State Dept. Transp., Albany, 1967-69, sr. transp. analyst, 1969-73, assoc. airport devel. specialist Aviation Bur., 1973-83, dir. airport ops., 1983-89, dir. aviation div., 1989—. Recipient Aviation Modal award Am. Assn. State Highway and Transp. Officials, 1985, Most Innovative State Program award Nat. Assn. State Aviation Officials, 1991. Mem. Am. Assn. Airport Execs., Airports Assn. Coun. Internat. (govt. affairs com. 1985-92). Roman Catholic. Avocations: golf, woodworking, gardening. Office: NY State Dept Of Transp 1220 Washington Ave Rm 115 Albany NY 12232-0001

VACHON, SERGE JEAN, bank executive; b. Montreal, Que., Can., May 15, 1939; s. Adrien Joseph and Helene Marie (Contre) V. M.Econ. Sci. U. Montreal, 1963; diploma, Inst. IMF, Washington, 1966. Asst. prof. U. Montreal, Que., Can., 1962-63; adviser to gov. Bank of Can., Ottawa, Ont., 1980—, officer, 1981-83; chmn. Can. Payments Assn., Ottawa, Ont., 1981—. Recipient 1st prize Best Thesis in Econs. and Fin. Montreal Stock Exchange, 1963; recipient medal Lt. Gov. Que., 1963; Can. Council fellow, 1964. Mem. Societe Canadienne de Science Economique (dir. 1975-77). Roman Catholic. Club: Cercle Universitaire (Ottawa, Ont., Can.).

VACIK, JAMES PAUL, university administrator; b. North Judson, Ind., Nov. 30, 1931; s. George J. and Elsie E. (Paulsen) V.; m. Dorothy M. Nobles, Dec. 27, 1967; children: Deborah, Pamela, James, Stephen, Joshua, Jonathan. BS in Pharmacy, Purdue U., 1955, MS in Medicinal Chemistry, 1957, PhD in Bionucleonics, 1959. Cert. hazard control mgr.; registered pharmacist, Ind., N.D., Ala. Asst. prof. bionucleonics dept. Purdue U., Lafayette, Ind., 1959-60; assoc. prof., dept. chmn. pharm. chemistry & bionucleonics N.D. State U., Fargo, 1960-63; prof., dept. chmn. pharm. chemistry & bionucleonics N.D. State U., Fargo, 1963-76; assoc. prof. pharmacology Univ. S. Ala., Mobile, 1976-82; adj. prof., dir. environ. safety Univ. S. Ala., 1982—; Pub. Health Svc. grant dir. N.D. State U., Fargo, 1963-71; VA Hosp. cons. VA Hosp. System, Washington, 1966; vis. prof. Nat. Reactor Testing Sta., Idaho Falls, Idaho, 1968; pvt. cons. to various indsl. firms, 1970—. Contbr. articles to profl. Mem., first dir. "Showboat on the Red," Jaycees, Fargo, 1965. With U.S. Army, 1949-52, ETO. Named Outstanding Educator Am., Fuller & Dees, Washington, 1975. Mem. Am. Chem. Soc., Am. Pharm. Assn., Health Physics Soc. (chmn. com.), Am. Biol. Safety Assn. (bd. dirs. 1985-87), Health Physics Soc. (pres., treas., bd. dirs. Ala chpt. 1977—, pres., bd. dirs. N. Ctrl. chpt. 1966—), Masons. Baptist. Avocations: camping, fishing, woodworking. Home: 1220 Vendome Dr W Mobile AL 36609-3326 Office: U South Ala CC CB 307 University Blvd N Mobile AL 36688-0001

VACKETTA, CARL LEE, lawyer; b. Danville, Ill., Aug. 3, 1941; s. Peter G. and Julia M. (Columbus) V. BS, U. Ill., 1963, JD, 1965. Bar: Ill. 1965, D.C. 1968, U.S. Dist. Ct. D.C. 1968, U.S. Ct. Fed. Claims 1968, U.S. Supreme Ct. 1970. Tax lawyer GM, Detroit, 1965-66; ptnr. Sellers, Conner & Cuneo, Washington, 1968-74; ptnr. Pettit & Martin, Washington, 1974-94, Piper & Marbury, Washington, 1994—; adj. prof. law Georgetown U., 1971—. Capt. U.S. Army, 1966-68. Fellow ABA (sec. pub. contract law sect. 1978-79, coun. 1979-82, contract law sect. 1993), Nat. Contract Mgmt. Assn.; mem. Fed. Bar Assn., D.C. Bar Assn., Nat. Assn. Purchasing Mgrs. Roman Catholic. Club: University (Washington). Co-author: Government Contract Default Termination, 1991, 93; co-editor Extraordinary Contractual Relief Reporter, 1974—. Office: Piper & Marbury 7th Fl 1200 19th St NW Washington DC 20036-2430 also: Piper & Marbury 11th Fl 36 S Charles St Baltimore MD 21201

VADEN, FRANK SAMUEL, III, lawyer, engineer; b. San Antonio, Nov. 13, 1934; s. Frank Samuel Jr. and Helen Alyne (Roberts) V.; m. Caroline Chittenden Gerdes, Feb. 20, 1960; children: Christina Louise, Olivia Anne, Cecilia Claire Vaden Johnson. BSEE and BS in Indsl. Engring., Tex. A&M U., 1957; JD, So. Meth. U., 1963. Bar: Tex. 1963, U.S. Dist. Ct. (we. and so. dists.) Tex. 1963, U.S. Ct. Appeals (5th, 9th, 11th and Fed. cirs.) 1963, U.S. Supreme Ct. 1963. Assoc. Arnold & Roylance, Houston, 1963-66; ptnr. Arnold, White & Durkee, Houston, 1966-73, mng. ptnr., 1973-78; prin. Frank S. Vaden III, P.C., Houston, 1978-80; sr. ptnr. Vaden, Eickenroht, Thompson, Boulware, Feather, Houston, 1980—; bd. dirs. Phoenix Anydrous, Inc., Houston; lectr. in field. Author: Invention Protection for Practicing Engineers, 1971; contbr. numerous articles to profl. jours. Capt. S.C., U.S. Army, 1957-67. Fellow Tex. Bar Found. (sustaining), Houston Bar Found. (sustaining); mem. ABA (mem. standing com. on specialization), Tex. Bar Assn. (chair intellectual property law sect. 1984-85), Houston Bar Assn., Am. Intellectual Property Law Assn. (chair inventor rels. com.), Houston Intellectual Property Law Assn. (pres. 1985-86), U.S. Trademark Assn., Licensing Exec. Soc. (chmn. Houston chpt. 1987-88). Republican. Episcopalian. Office: Vaden Eickenroht Thompson Boulware & Feather 1 Riverway Ste 1100 Houston TX 77056-1982

VAETH, NANCY ANN, sales executive; b. Mineola, N.Y., Oct. 21, 1954; d. Jerome Marcus and Mary Teresa (MacStoker) V. B.A., Syracuse U., 1976. Advt. salesperson Sta. WEZG/WSOQ, Syracuse, N.Y., 1976-78, KMJQ, Houston, 1978-80; advt. salesperson Sta. WPLX/KLIF, Dallas, 1980-81, nat. sales mgr., 1981-82, gen. sales mgr., 1982—. Republican. Roman Catholic. Office: Sta KRBE-AM 9801 Westheimer Rd Ste 700 Houston TX 77042-3955

VAGELOS, PINDAROS ROY, pharmaceutical company executive; b. Westfield, N.J., Oct. 8, 1929; s. Roy John and Marianthi (Lambrinides) V.; m. Diana Touliatos, July 10, 1955; children: Randall, Cynthia, Andrew, Ellen. AB, U. Pa., 1950; MD, Columbia U., 1954; DSc (hon.), Washington U., 1980, Brown U., 1982, U. Medicine and Dentistry of N.J., 1984, NYU, 1989, Columbia U., 1990; LLD (hon.), Princeton U., 1990; LHD (hon.), Rutgers U., 1991; DSc (hon.), N.J. Inst. Tech., 1992, SUNY, 1994. Intern medicine Mass. Gen. Hosp., 1954-55, asst. resident medicine, 1955-56; surgeon Lab. Cellular Physiology, NIH, 1956-59; surgeon Lab. Biochemistry, 1959-64, head sect. comparative biochemistry, 1964-66; prof. biochemistry, chmn. dept. biol. chemistry Washington U. Sch. Medicine, St. Louis, 1966-75; dir. div. biology and biomed. scis. Washington U. Sch. Medicine, 1973-75; sr. v.p. research Merck, Sharp & Dohme Research Labs., Rahway, N.J., 1975-76, pres., 1976-84; corp. sr. v.p. Merck & Co., Inc., Rahway, N.J., 1982-84, exec. v.p., 1984-85, CEO, 1985-86, chmn., CEO, 1986-94, also bd. dirs.; chmn. Regeneron Pharms., Inc., Tarrytown, N.Y., 1995—; mem. Inst. Medicine, NAS, 1974—; chmn. sci. adv. bd. Ctr. for Advanced Biotech. and Medicine, 1985-94; bd. dirs. Prudential Ins. Co., PepsiCo, Inc., McDonnell Douglas Corp. Rsch. Trustee U. Pa., 1988—; mem. 1994, Rockefeller U., 1976-94, Danforth Found., 1978—; mem. Pres.'s Commn. on Environ. Quality, 1991-93, Adv. Com. Trade Policy and Negotiations, 1992—; Bus. Coun., 1987—; bd. mng. dirs. Met. Opera Assn., Inc., 1989-95; chmn. bd. dirs. N.J. Performing Arts Ctr., 1989—; co-chmn. 1992; chmn. bd. trustees U. Pa., 1994—. Recipient Award for Distinction in Service to Society, NAS, 1995. Mem. Am. Chem. Soc. (Enzyme Chemistry award 1967), Am. Soc. Biol. Chemists, Nat. Acad. Scis., Am. Acad. Arts and Scis., Am. Philosophical Soc., 1993—, Bus. Roundtable (policy com. 1987-94). Avocations: jogging, tennis, sculling. Discoverer of acyl-carrier protein. Home: 82 Mosle Rd Far Hills NJ 07931-2228 Office: Regeneron Pharms Inc 777 Old Saw Mill River Rd Tarrytown NY 10591

VAGET, HANS RUDOLF, language professional, educator; b. Marienbad, Czekoslovakia, Feb. 2, 1938; came to U.S., 1964; s. Hans Ernst and Berta (Isop) V.; m. Ann Leone; children: Melanie Claudine, Erec Alexander. MA, U. Tübingen, Fed. Republic Germany, 1964; PhD, Columbia U., 1969.

Instr. Columbia U., N.Y.C., 1964-67, vis. prof., 1985; from instr. to prof. Smith Coll., Northampton, Mass., 1967—; vis. prof. U. Calif., Irvine, 1979, Columbia U., 1985, Princeton U., 1986-87, Yale U., 1991, U. Hamburg, 1992. Author: Dilettantismus bei Goethe, 1971, Goethe. Der Mann von 60 Jahren, 1982, Thomas-Mann Kommentar, 1984; author, editor: Briefwechsel T. Mann-Agnes Meyer, 1992; contbr. articles to profl. and ednl. publs. Recipient Thomas Mann-Medaille, 1994; grantee NEH, 1985, Am. Coun. Learned Socs., 1986. Mem. MLA, Assn. Tchrs. of German, Deutsche Schillergesellschaft, Thomas-Mann-Gesellschaft, Goethe Soc. N.Am. (co-founder), Wagner Soc., Am. Musicol. Soc. Office: Smith Coll Dept German Northampton MA 01063-0001

VAGLEY, ROBERT EVERETT, insurance association executive; b. New Eagle, Pa., Jan. 31, 1940; s. William S. and Lillian (Tesi) Vagli; children: Erin S., Beth A. BS, Pa. State U., 1961, MA, 1963; JD, Georgetown U., 1977. With CIA, Washington, 1963-64; counsel, staff dir. U.S. Ho. Reps. Com. on Edn. and Labor, Washington, 1965-80; ptnr. Preston, Thorgrimson, Ellis & Holman, Washington, 1980-86; pres. Am. Ins. Assn., Washington, 1986—; chmn. Am. Ins. Services Group, N.Y.C., 1986—. Editor Georgetown Law Jour., 1975-77; contbr. articles to profl. jours. Mem. D.C. Bar Assn., Met. Club (Washington), Univ. Club, George Town Club (Washington), Congl. Country Club. Roman Catholic. Avocations: skiing, squash, biking, reading. Home: 1035 Bellview Pl Mc Lean VA 22102-1551 Office: American Insurance Assn 1130 Connecticut Ave NW Washington DC 20036-3904

VAGLIANO, ALEXANDER MARINO, banker; b. Paris, France, Mar. 15, 1927; came to U.S., 1940, naturalized, 1945; s. Andre M. and Barbara (Allen) V.; children: Barbara A., Andre M., Justin C. Grad., St. Paul's Sch., Concord, N.H., 1944; B.A., Harvard, 1949, LL.B. cum laude, 1952. Bar: N.Y. bar 1952. Asso. firm White & Case, N.Y.C., 1952-58; asst. treas. J.P. Morgan & Co., Inc., N.Y.C., 1959; v.p. Morgan Guaranty Trust Co., N.Y.C., 1959-62, 65-66; sr. v.p. Morgan Guaranty Trust Co., 1968-76, exec. v.p., 1976-81; chief exec. officer Banca Vonwiller, Milan, Italy, 1967-68; chmn. Morgan Guaranty Internat. Finance Corp., 1976-81, J.P. Morgan Overseas Capital Corp., 1976-81; ptnr. Price Waterhouse and Ptnrs., 1983-85; chmn. Sunset Ridge Farm, Inc., 1983—; Michelin Fin. Corp., Greenville, S.C., 1985—; chmn. bd. advisors Equity Linked Investors, N.Y.C., 1985—; pres. The N.Y. Farmers, 1992-94; bd. dirs. Optimum Resource, S.C., Holographics, Inc., N.Y., Ea. States Exposition; dir. office of capital devel. and fin. Near East and South Asia. AID, 1963-65; adviser Yale Econ. Growth Ctr., 1973—, NYU Inst. French Studies, 1979—; trustee Coun. for Excellence in Govt., 1990—. Pres. Parks Council N.Y., 1971-73; bd. dirs. French Am. Found., N.Y.C., 1986—; gov. The Atlantic Inst. Internt. Affairs, 1986-90. Served with AUS, 1945-47. Mem. Council Fgn. Relations. Clubs: Brook (N.Y.C.); Travellers (Paris). Home and Office: Sunset Ridge Farm Inc Norfolk CT 06058

VAGTS, DETLEV FREDERICK, lawyer, educator; b. Washington, Feb. 13, 1929; s. Alfred and Miriam (Beard) V.; m. Dorothy Larkin, Dec. 11, 1954; children: Karen, Lydia. Grad., Taft Sch., 1945; AB, Harvard U., 1948, LLB, 1951. Bar: Mass. 1961. Assoc. Cahill, Gordon, Reindel & Ohl, N.Y.C., 1951-53, 56-59; asst. prof. law Harvard Law Sch., 1959-62, prof., 1962—, Eli Goldston prof., 1981-84, Bemis prof., 1984—; counselor internat. law Dept. State, 1976-77. Author: (with others) Transnational Legal Problems, 1968, 4th edit., 1994, Basic Corporation Law, 1973, 3d edit., 1989; editor: (with others) Secured Transactions Under the Uniform Commercial Code, 1963-64; assoc. reporter: (with others) Restatement of Foreign Relations Law; book rev. editor Am. Jour. Internat. Law, 1986-93, co-editor-in-chief, 1993—. 1st lt. USAF, 1953-56. Recipient Max Planck Rsch. award, 1991. Mem. ABA, Am. Soc. Internat. Law, Phi Beta Kappa. Home: 29 Follen St Cambridge MA 02138-3502 Office: Sch Law Harvard U Cambridge MA 02138

VAGUE, JEAN MARIE, physician; b. Draguignan, France, Nov. 25, 1911; s. Victor Francois and Marie (Voiron) V.; m. Denise Marie Jouve, Sept. 3, 1936; children: Philippe, Thierry, Irene (Mrs. Claude Juhan), Maurice. Baccalaureat, Cath. Coll., Aix en Provence, France, 1928; MD, Marseilles (France) U., 1935. Intern, Hotel Dieu Conception, Marseilles, 1930, resident, 1932-39; practice medicine specializing in endocrinology, Marseilles, 1943—; assoc. prof. Marseilles U., 1946-57, prof., clinic endocrinology, 1957—. Dir. Ctr. Alimentary Hygiene and Prophylaxis Nutrition Diseases Nat. Rys. Mediterranean region, 1958—; expert chronic degenerative diseases (diabetes) WHO, 1960—. Served to lt. French Army, 1939-40. Decorated Cross Legion Honor, Acad. Palms, knight pub. health, knight mil. merit, War Cross. Mem. Endocrine Soc. U.S., am. Diabetes Assn., Royal Soc. Medicine (London), European Assn. for Study Diabetes, Spanish, Italian, French (past pres.) socs. endocrinology, French Acad. Medicine, Spanish Acad. Medicine, Italian Acad. Medicine, Belgian Acad. Medicine, French Lang. Diabetes Assn. (past pres.). Author: Human Sexual Differentiation, 1953, Notions of Endocrinology, 1965, Obesities, 1991, Dawn on Iaboc's Ford, History of Man, History of Men, 1993, others. Achievements include first identification of the metabolic and vascular complications of android obesity and their mechanism; research in demonstration of diabetogenic and atherogenic power of obesity with topographic distbn. fat in upper and deep part of body, evolution of android diabetogenic obesity from 1st stage of efficacious hyperinsulinism to less efficacious hyperinsulinism and hypoinsulinism-neurogerminal degeneration, degenerative lesions of germinal epithelium and nervous system. Home: 6 Prado Parc, 411 Ave du Prado, 13008 Marseilles France Office: Hopital U Timone Clin Endocrinologique, Blvd Jean-Moulin, 13385 Marseilles France

VAHAVIOLOS, SOTIRIOS JOHN, electrical engineer, scientist, corporate executive; b. Mistra, Greece, Apr. 16, 1946; s. John Apostolos and Athanasia (Pavlakos) V.; m. Aspasia Felice Nessas, June 1, 1969; children: Athanasia, Athena, Kristy. BSEE, Fairleigh Dickinson U., 1970; MSEE, Columbia U., 1972, M in Philosophy, 1975, PhDEE, 1976. Mem. tech. staff Bell Telephone Labs., Princeton, N.J., 1970-75, supr., 1975-76, dept. head, 1976-78; founder, pres., chief exec. officer Phys. Acoustics Corp., Princeton, 1978—; pres., CEO Mistras Holdings Corp., 1984—; adviser Greece Ministry Def., Athens, 1986-88; bd. dirs. Orthosonics, Inc., N.Y.C. Contbr. more than 100 papers to profl. publs. 13 U.S. patents, 7 fgn. patentsin field. Bd. dirs. Holy Cross Greek Orthodox Sch. Theology, Boston, 1989—; pres. bd of trustees St. George Greek Orthodox Cmty., Trenton, N.J.; adv. bd. Trenton State Coll., N.J., 1983—; chmn. Princeton sect. United Fund, 1976-78. Recipient Spartan Merit award Spartan World Soc., 1987, Entrepreneur of Yr. award Arthur Young/Inc. Mag., N.J., 1989. Fellow IEEE (Centennial medal award 1984, Dr. Ing Eugene Mittlemen Achievement award 1993), Am. Soc. Nondestructive Testing (bus. and fin. com. 1984-87, 88—, bd. dirs. 1985, sec. 1989, treas. 1990, v.p. 1991, pres. 1992, chmn. bd. 1993, chmn. internat. com. nondestructive testing 1994—, editor handbook on Acoustic Emission, 1988), Acoustic Emission Working Group; mem. ASTM, IEEE Indsl. Electronics Soc. (sr. mem. adminstrv. com. 1988, founder, v.p. conf. 1974-78, 2d prize Student Paper Contest 1970, Outstanding Young Engr. award 1984, editor Trans. on Indsl. Electronics 1976-82), N.Y. Acad. Scis. Independent. Greek Orthodox. Avocations: bird hunting, soccer, technical writing, gardening. Home: 7 Ridgeview Rd Princeton NJ 08540-7601 Office: Phys Acoustics Corp PO Box 3135 Princeton NJ 08543-3135

VAI, MARJORIE THERESA, language educator, university administrator; author; b. Jersey City, Feb. 24, 1947; d. Mario and Grace (Nolan) V.; 1 child, Daniel V. AB, Rutgers U., 1968; MA, NYU. Instr. Am. Coll. Greece, Athens, 1974-76, N.Y. Inst. Tech., N.Y.C., 1977-79; product mgr. Litton Ednl. Publs. Internat., N.Y.C., 1979-81; dir. product devel. Atlantis Publishers, N.Y.C., 1981-82; instructional design cons., N.Y.C., 1982—; instructional designer/author courseware English on Call!, McGraw-Hill Pubs., N.Y.C., 1989; dir. English Lang. Studies Ctr. The New Sch., N.Y.C., 1988—; freelance writer Dow Jones Inc., South Brunswick, N.J., 1983-92. Author: (with L. Ferreira) Read On! Speak Out!, 1979; contbg. editor Dowline Mag, 1986-88. Mem. Tchrs. of English as a Second Lang. Home: 340 W 28th St New York NY 10001-4732

VAI, STEVE, guitarist; b. Carle Place, NY, June 6, 1960; married; 1 child. Student, Berklee Coll. of Music. Transfer & stunt guitarist for Frank Zappa, 1979-83; guitarist Alcatrazz, 1984, David Lee Roth, 1986-89, Whitesnake, 1990; solo artist, 1991—. albums include Flex-able, 1984, Pas-

sion & Warfare, 1990, Sex & Religion, 1994; (with Frank Zappa) Tinsel Town Rebellion, 1980, You Are What You Is, 1981, The Man From Utopia, 1982, Ship Arriving Too Late to Save a Drowning Witch, 1983, Them or Us, 1984; (with Alcatrazz) Disturbing the Peace, 1984; (with David Lee Roth) Eat 'Em and Smile, 1986, Skyscraper, 1988; (with Whitesnake) Slip of the Tongue, 1990, (with Frank Zappa) Shut Up N' Play Yer Guitar, 1986, (with Shanker) The Epidemics; film appearances include: Crossroads, 1986. Recipient Rock Instrumental Grammy Award for "Sofia" from Zappa's Universe, 1993. Office: c/o Relativity Records 18707 Henderson Ave Hollis NY 11423-3133*

VAICAITIS, RIMAS, civil engineering and engineering mechanics educator; b. Sakiai, Lithuania, Apr. 30, 1941; came to U.S., 1960; s. Kostas and Marcele (Vaivada) V.; m. Jone Aukse Paplenas, June 19, 1965; children: Rima, Krista. BS, U. Ill., 1966, MS, 1967; D (hon.), Kaunas Tech. U., 1993, Kans. Tech. U., 1993. Asst. professor civil engring. Columbia U., N.Y.C., 1970-75, assoc. prof., 1975-80, dir. inst. flight structures, 1977—, prof., 1980—; research engr. NASA, Hampton, Va., 1976-77; pres. Vibroacoustics, Inc., West Nyack, N.Y., 1984—. Contbr. numerous articles to profl. jours. Named Disting. Alumnus U. Ill., 1984; fellow NASA, 1975-77. Mem. AIAA, ASCE, KASA Lithuanian Fed. Credit Union (pres. 1987-92, bd. dirs. 1981-92). Roman Catholic. Office: Columbia U Dept Civil Engring 610 Mudd Bldg New York NY 10022-1620

VAIL, CHARLES DANIEL, veterinarian, consultant; b. Denver, June 11, 1936; s. Allan Paden and Katherine Marie (Phillips) V.; m. Jean Williams Ebsen, June 15, 1963; children: Ellen Marie, David Elston. BS, Colorado A&M, 1958. DVM, Colo. State. U., 1960. Asst. veterinarian Colo. Racing Commn., Littleton, 1958-60; equine practitioner Littleton Large Animal Clinic, 1960—; track veterinarian Centennial Race Track, Littleton, 1962-63. Editor in chief Equine Practice, 1986—; contbr. articles to profl. jours. Mem. selection com. Outstanding Biology Tchr. award Colo., 1978-80, 88—, Arapahoe Fair Assn., Littleton, 1965-84, gallery disting. grads. Colo. State U. Coll. Vet. Medicine, 1989; chmn. Littleton Rotary Western Heritage Art Fair; bd. dirs. Animal Assistance Found. Denver, 1991—. Recipient Honor Alumni award Coll. Vet. Medicine, Colo. State U., 1991. Mem. AVMA (publs. com. 1987-89), Am. Assn. Equine Practitioners (pres. 1985), Colo. Vet. Medicine Assn. (pres. 1980, Veterinarian of Yr. award 1987), Denver Area Vet. Medicine Soc. (pres. 1975), Arapahoe Town and Gown Soc., Nottingham Club, Rotary (pres. Littleton 1992-93), Sigma Alpha Epsilon, Omicron Delta Kappa. Home: 5921 S Cherrywood Cir Littleton CO 80121-2465 Office: Littleton Large Animal Clinic PC 8025 S Santa Fe Dr Littleton CO 80120-4305

VAIL, PATRICIA, lawyer; b. Worcester, Mass., Apr. 7, 1941; d. Jeremiah Hamilton and Gladys (Conner) V.; children: Nathan, Norman. BA, Wilson Coll., 1963; JD, Cleve. Marshall Law Sch., 1977; MBA, Jacksonville U., 1987. Bar: Ohio 1977, Fla. 1988, U.S. Dist. Ct. Ohio (south dist.) 1978, U.S. Dist. Ct. Ohio (north dist.) 1981, U.S. Dist. Ct. (mid. dist.) Fla., U.S. Dist. Ct. Fla. (north dist.) 1993, U.S. Ct. Appeals (6th, 7th, 11th cirs.). Staff atty. Ohio Atty. Gen. Office, Columbus, Ohio, 1977-80, C&O R.R., Cleve., 1980-83, Seaboard System R.R., Jacksonville, Fla., 1983-86; sr. counsel CSX Transp., Jacksonville, 1986—. Bd. dirs. Jacksonville Area Legal Aid, 1990—, pres. 1995, Uptown Civitan, Jacksonville, 1988-90, Pine Castle, Inc., Jacksonville, 1989-90, Planned Parenthood NE Fla., 1993—. Mem. Jacksonville Coalition for Visual Arts (officer 1988-89), Jacksonville Women Lawyer's Assn. (pres. 1989-91), Fla. Assn. Women Lawyers (sec. 1991—). Home: 5709 St Isabel Dr Jacksonville FL 32277 Office: CSX Transp 500 Water St J-150 Jacksonville FL 32202-4420

VAIL, PETER ROBBINS, geologist; b. N.Y.C., Jan. 13, 1930; s. Donald Bain and Eleanor (Robbins) V.; m. Carolyn Flesher, Sept. 15, 1956; children: Andrea, Susan, Timothy Edward. A.B., Dartmouth Coll., 1952; M.S., Northwestern U., 1955, Ph.D. (Shell fellow), 1959. Asst. geologist U.S. Geol. Survey, Spokane, Wash., 1952-56, Evanston, Ill.; research geologist Carter Oil Co., Tulsa, 1956-58, Jersey Prodn. Research Co., Tulsa, 1958-62; sr. research geologist Jersey Prodn. Research Co., 1962-65; sr. research specialist Exxon Prodn. Research Co., Houston, 1965-66; research assoc. Exxon Prodn. Research Co., 1966, research supr., 1966-70, sr. research assoc., 1970-72, sr. research adv., 1972-75, research scientist, 1975-81, sr. research scientist, 1981—; mem. Consortium for Continental Reflection Profiling Site Selection Com., 1974-81; mem. internat. subcom. on stratigraphic classification Internat. Union Geol. Seismology com. on Stratigraphy, 1976—; mem. ocean sci. bd. U.S. Nat. Acad. Scis., 1979-82; mem. Joint Oceanography Insts. Deep Earth Sampling Passive Margin Panel, 1978-84; William Smith lectr. Geol. Soc. London, 1978; Bullerwell lectr. U.K. Geophys. Soc., 1983; mem. Am. Petroleum Inst., 1978—; mem. Eur. Assn. Exploration Geophysicists, 1983. Contbr. to profl. jours. articles on seismic stratigraphy, global changes of sea level, tectonics. Recipient Offshore Tech. Conf. Individual Disting. Achievement Award, 1983, William H. Twenhofel medal Soc. Sedimentary Geology, 1992. Fellow Geol. Soc. Am. (research grants com. 1977-79, chmn. 1979, councilor 1979-82), AAAS; mem. Am. Assn. Petroleum Geologists (disting. lectr. 1975-76, marine geology com. 1977, research com. 1978-84, co-recipient Pres.'s award for best pub. paper 1979, co-recipient Matson award for author of best paper 1980 ann. conv. 1981), Soc. Exploration Geophysicists (Virgil Kaufmann Gold medal for advancement of science of geophys. exploration 1976, Disting. lectr. 1985, hon. mem. 1985—), Soc. Econ. Paleontologists and Mineralogists (Disting. speaker 1984 ann. meeting luncheon), Houston Geophys. Soc. (hon. mem.), Houston Geol. Soc. (Best Paper award 1982-83), Mayflower Soc., Sigma Xi. Home: 3745 Del Monte Dr Houston TX 77019-3017 Office: Exxon Production Research Co PO Box 2189 Houston TX 77252-2189 also: Rice University PO Box 1892 6100 South Main Houston TX 77251

VAIL, VAN HORN, German language educator; b. Buffalo, Dec. 23, 1934; s. Curtis Churchill and Faith Newbrook (Ely) V.; m. Michele Juliette Edelstein, May 5, 1969; 1 son, Mark Curtis. B.A., U. Wash., 1956; M.A., Princeton U., 1961, Ph.D., 1964. Instr. Princeton U., 1962-65, asst. prof., 1965-66; asst. prof. German Middlebury (Vt.) Coll., 1966-69, assoc. prof., 1969-75, prof., 1975—; chmn. dept. Middlebury Coll., Vt., 1970-73, 87-88; dir. studies Middlebury Sch. in Germany Middlebury Coll., 1967-68, 70-71, 74-75, 85-86, 88-89, 92-93, 95—; mem. nat. screening com. Fulbright Scholarships, 1979-81. Author: German in Review, 1967, 2d edit., 1986, Der Weg zum Lesen, 1967, 2d edit., 1974, 3d edit., 1986, Modern German, 1971, 2d edit., 1978, 3d edit., 1992, Tonio Kröger als Weg zur Litertur, 1974, Workbook for Modern German, 1992. Served to 1st lt. M.I., U.S. Army, 1956-58. Fulbright scholar U. Heidelberg, 1958-59. Mem. MLA. Home: Cider Mill Rd Middlebury VT 05753 Office: Middlebury Coll Middlebury VT 05753

VAILAS, ARTHUR C., biomechanics educator. BS in Exercise Physiology, U. N.H., 1973; PhD in Exercise Physiology, U. Iowa, 1979, postgrad., 1979-82. Asst. prof. dept. kinesiology UCLA, 1982-88, assoc. prof., 1988; assoc. prof. U. Wis. Madison, 1988-91, prof., 1991—, dir. biodynamics lab., 1988—; session chair Gordon Rsch. Conf.; mem. life sci. adv. com. NASA, life sci. del. to COSMOS 1887, 2044 Missions; com. chair Musculoskeletal Implementation Group EDO and Countermeasure Sci. Plan; SLS-1 scientist. Contbr. 60 articles to profl. jours. Recipient Rsch. Svc. award NIH, Outstanding Sci. award USSR-NASA; named Disting. Scientist, CSU. Mem. Nat. Rsch. Coun. (mem. NASA com.). Office: U Wis Biodynamics Lab 2000 Observatory Dr Madison WI 53706-1189

VAILLANCOURT, JEAN-GUY, sociology educator; b. Chelmsford, Ont., Can., May 24, 1937; s. Royal A. and Marie (Lavallée) V.; m. Pauline Hansen, June 6, 1966 (div. 1983); 1 child, Véronique. BA magna cum laude Laurentian U., Sudbury, Ont., 1957; licenciate in philosophy, Faculté des Jésuites, Montreal, Que., Can., 1961; licenciate in sociology, Gregorian U., Rome, 1964; PhD in Sociology, U. Calif., Berkeley, 1975. Lectr. St. Boniface (Man.) Coll., Can., 1964-65; asst. prof. U. de Montréal, Que., Can., 1969-76, assoc. prof., 1976-83, prof. sociology, 1983—, chmn. dept., 1984-87; mem. consultative com. Can. ambassador for disarmament, Ottawa, Ont., 1984-91, consultative com. on environ. Hydro-Que., 1984-89. Author: Papal Power, 1980, Essais d'écosociologie, 1982; co-editor: Le processus électoral au Québec, 1976, Roots of Peace, 1986, Environment et dévelopement Problems Socio-Politiques, 1991, Gestion de l'environment, éthique et société, 1992, Instituer le déevelopement durable, 1994, Aspects Sociaux des récipitations acides au Quebec, 1994; editor-in-chief Sociologie et Sociétés, 1978-87. Mem. coun. City of Durham, Que., 1976-80; bd.dirs. Oxfam-Que., 1976-79, Can. Inst. Internat. Peace and Security, Ottawa, Ont., 1986-89, European Iniv. Ctr. for Peace Studies, Burg Schlaining, Burgenland, Australia, 1989-93. Grantee Counseil de Recherche en science sociale du Quebec, 1982, FCAR, 1989—, Social Sci. Rsch. Coun., 1983-86, 90-96, Can. Inst. Internat. Peace and Security, 1985, 91; fellow Can. Coun., 1965-68. Mem. Internat. Sociol. Assn., Assn. Can. des sociologues et anthropologues de langue francaise, Sci. for Peace, Pugwash, Group 78. Roman Catholic. Avocations: tree farming, travelling. Home: 953 Cherrier #2, Montréal, PQ Canada H2L 1J2 Office: U Montreal, Dept Sociology, Montreal, PQ Canada H3C 3J7

VAILLANT, GEORGE EMAN, psychiatrist; b. N.Y.C., June 16, 1934; s. George Clapp and Mary Suzannah (Beck) V.; m. Leigh McCullough, Dec. 4, 1993; children: George Emery, John Holden, Henry Greenough, Anne Liberty, Caroline Joanna. A.B., Harvard U., 1955, M.D., 1959; postgrad., Boston Psychoanalytic Inst., 1967-76. Resident in psychiatry Mass. Mental Health Center, Boston, 1960-63; from asst. prof. to asso. prof. psychiatry Tufts U. Sch. Medicine, 1966-71; asso. prof. psychiatry Harvard Med. Sch., 1971-77, prof., 1977-82, 93—; dir. tng. Cambridge (Mass.) Hosp., 1976-81, Mass. Mental Health Center, Boston, 1981-83; prof. Dartmouth Sch. Medicine, 1983-92; dir. study of adult devel. Harvard U. Health Services, 1972—. Author: Adaptation to Life, 1977, Natural History of Alcoholism, 1983, Wisdom of the Ego, 1993; contbr. articles to profl. jours. Served with USPHS, 1963-65. Fellow Center for Advanced Study in Behavioral Scis., 1978-79. Fellow Am. Psychiat. Assn.; mem. Boston Psychoanalytic Soc. Episcopalian. Home: 943 High St Dedham MA 02026 Office: Brigham Women's Hosp 75 Francis St Boston MA 02115-6195

VAINSTEIN, ROSE, librarian, educator; b. Edmonton, Alta., Can., Jan. 7, 1920; d. Rabbi Nathan and Jane (Simenstein) V. A.B., Miami U., Oxford, Ohio, 1941; B.L.S., Western Res. U., 1942; M.S., U. Ill., 1952. Jr. librarian Cuyahoga County Library, Cleve., 1942-43; young people's librarian Bklyn. Public Library, 1943-44; br. librarian Contra Costa County Library, Martinez, Calif., 1948-51; library cons. Calif. State Library, Sacramento, 1953-55; head extension dept. Gary (Ind.) Public and Lake County Library, 1955-57; public library specialist U.S. Office Edn., Washington, 1957-61; asso. prof. Sch. Librarianship, U. B.C., Vancouver, 1961-64; dir. Bloomfield Twp. Pub. Library, Bloomfield Hills, Mich., 1964-68; prof. library sci. U. Mich., Ann Arbor, 1968-82, Margaret Mann prof. emeritus, 1982—; dir. Middle Mgmt. Inst. for Pub. Librs., 1969, 1st Margaret Mann Disting. prof. libr. sci., 1974—; libr. U.S. Armed Forces U.S., Hawaii, Japan, 1944-48; dir. B.C. (Can.) Pub. Librs. Rsch. Study, 1963-64; mem. steering com. Kendal Corp. Strategic Planning and Orgnl. Devel. Project Phase II, 1993. Contbr. articles to profl. jours. Mem. Jewish Community Coun. of Washtenaw County, Mich., 1981-84; bd. dirs. Jewish Community Ctr., 1986-89; mem. geriatric svcs. steering com. U. Mich. Med. Ctr., 1988-89. Fulbright Research scholar Eng., 1952-53; Council on Library Resources fellow, 1974-75; scholar-in-residence Sch. Librarianship, U. B.C., 1981. Mem. ALA (mem. public libr. stds. com. 1969-73, chmn. public libr. activities com. 1974-76, mem. coun. 1975-79, mem. coun. budget assembly 1977-79, chmn. nominating com. 1976-77), Mich., Canadian library assns., U. Mich. Women's Rsch. Club (treas. 1971-72, chmn. loan fund com. 1976-79, Spl. 75th Anniversary award 1978), LWV, Hadassah (life, co-chmn. study group Ann Arbor chpt. 1982-83), Crossland Residents Assn. (bd. dirs. 1992-94, chair genealogy study group 1990-95, forum com. 1990-93, treas. 1992-93, long range planning group 1993-94, pres. 1995-96), Phi Beta Kappa (Alumnus mem. Iota of Ohio chpt. 1976), Beta Phi Mu (dir. 1974-77). Home: Apt 179 Crosslands Kennett Square PA 19348-2019

VAIRA, PETER FRANCIS, lawyer; b. McKeesport, Pa., Mar. 5, 1937; s. Peter Francis and Mary Louise (Bedogne) V.; m. Mary Hohler, 1981. B.A., Duquesne U., 1959, J.D., 1962. Bar: Pa. 1963, D.C. 1968, Ill. 1984, U.S. Ct. Appeals (D.C. cir.) 1964, Ill. Supreme Ct. Ill. 1984, U.S. Dist. Ct. (no. dist.) Ill., U.S. Dist. Ct. (ea. dist.) Pa. Atty. Chgo. Strike Force, Justice Dept., 1968-72; atty. in charge Phila. Strike Force, 1972-73, Chgo. Strike Force on Organized Crime, 1973-78; U.S. atty. Phila., 1978-83; ptnr. firm Lord Bissel & Brook, Chgo., 1983-86; ptnr. Fox, Rothschild, O'Brien & Frankel, Phila., 1986-90, Buchanan Ingersoll, Phila., 1990-92, Vaira & Assocs., Phila., 1992-93, Vaira, Backstrom, Riley, Smith, Phila., 1993—; exec. dir. President's Commn. on Organized Crime, 1983. Author: Corporate Responses to Grand Jury Investigation, 1984; contbr. articles to profl. jours. Mem. Mayor's Search Com. for Police Commr., Phila., 1992. Served with USNR, 1965-68. Recipient Spl. Commendation award Justice Dept., 1976. Fellow Am. Coll. Trial Lawyers (chmn. criminal procedure com.); mem. ABA (mem. criminal justice coun. 1986), Am. Law Inst., Union League, Phila. Country Club. Office: Vaira Backstrom & Riley Ste 2650 1600 Market St Philadelphia PA 19103

VAIRO, ROBERT JOHN, insurance company executive; b. Bklyn., Sept. 27, 1930; s. John and Antonietta (DeRose) V.; m. Carol P. Andross, Apr. 8, 1951 (div. Feb. 1979); children: Robert J., Gregory J.; m. Inge R. Buhlbecker, Feb. 20, 1979. Student, Coll. Ins., N.Y.C., 1953-62; Exec. Program in Bus. Adminstrn., Columbia U., 1973. CPCU. Under asst. mgr. Atlantic Cos., N.Y.C., 1952-62; underwriter mgr., v.p. Fireman's Fund Ins. Co., N.Y.C., 1962-75; v.p., sr. v.p. underwriting C & F Ins. Cos., Morristown, N.J., 1975-79; exec. v.p., pres. U.S. Ins. Group, Morristown, N.J., 1979-82; chmn., chief exec. officer C & F Underwriters Group and The North River Ins. Co., Morristown, N.J., 1982-86; pres., chief oper. officer Crum and Forster, Inc., Morristown, 1987-88, pres., chief exec. officer, 1988-90, chmn., pres., chief exec. officer, 1990-92, also bd. dirs.; chmn. Ins. Services Office, N.Y.C., 1983, Am. Ins. Assn., Washington, 1990. Pres. Lincoln Park City Council, N.J., 1971-76. Served with USMC, 1951-53. Mem. Soc. CPCUs, Am. Inst. for Chartered Property Casualty Underwriters (dir., chmn. 1991-92), Desert Highlands Golf Club. Roman Catholic. Home: 9294 E Palm Tree Dr Scottsdale AZ 85255

VAISHNAVI, VIJAY KUMAR, computer science educator, researcher; b. Srinagar, Kashmir, India, Mar. 25, 1948; came to U.S., 1980; s. Nand Lal and Prabhawati (Hakhu) V.; m. Kirti Ganju, July 17, 1972; children: Sandeep, Sanjeev. BEE, Regional Engring. Coll., Srinagar, 1969; MEE, Indian Inst. Tech., India, 1972, PhD, 1976. Asst. prof. IIT Kanpur, 1973-77; postdoctoral fellow McMaster U., Hamilton, Ont., Can., 1977-79; vis. asst. prof. Concordia U., Montreal, 1979-80; asst. prof. Ohio U., Athens, 1980-81; assoc. prof. Ga. State U., Atlanta, 1981-87, prof., 1987—; vis. scientist U. Dortmund, Fed. Republic Germany, 1980; cons. AT&T, others 1990—. Contbr. articles to profl. jours. Recipient rsch. grants; collegiate faculty recognition, Coll. of Bus. Adminstrn., Ga. State U., Atlanta, 1989, 93. Mem. Assn. for Computing Machinery, Computer Soc. of IEEE (software engring. tech. com.), IEEE (sr.). Avocations: reading, gardening, table-tennis. Office: Ga State U Computer Info Systems Dept PO Box 4015 Atlanta GA 30302-4015

VAITKEVICIUS, VAINUTIS KAZYS, foundation administrator, medical educator; b. Kaunas, Lithuania, Jan. 12, 1927; came to U.S., 1951; s. Henrikas and Camille Vaitkevicius; m. Ingeborg Jausen; children: Eva, Henri, Peter, Camille, Walter, Martin. Diploma, Lithuanian Coll., Eichstett, Germany, 1946; MD, J.W. Goethe U., Frankfurt, Germany, 1951. Diplomate Am. Bd. Internal Medicine, Am. Bd. Med. Oncology. Intern Grace Hosp., Detroit, 1951-52, resident, 1955-56; resident Detroit Receiving Hosp., 1956-58; fellow in cancer rsch. Detroit Inst. Cancer Rsch., 1958-59; from asst. to assoc. prof. medicine sch. medicine Wayne State U., Detroit, 1962-72, prof., 1972—, dir. divsn. conjoint svcs. and curricula oncology, 1966-72, chmn. dept. oncology, 1972-82, chmn. dept. internal medicine, 1982-89; clin. dir. Detroit Inst. Cancer Rsch., 1962-66; acting chief medicine Detroit Gen. Hosp., 1970-71; chief divsn. medicine Grace Hosp., 1973-76; chief oncology Harper-Grace Hosps., Detroit, 1977-82, chief medicine, 1982-89; assoc. dir. clin. activities Comprehensive Cancer Ctr. Met. Detroit, 1978-82; physician-in-chief Detroit Med. Ctr., 1982-89; pres. Mich. Cancer Found., Detroit, 1991—; mem. com. human and animal experimentation Wayne State U., 1968-73, chmn, 1971-73, mem. presdl. selection adv. com., 1981, mem. univ. coun., 1981-83, mem. budget com. of univ. coun., 1981-83, mem. presdl. com. cancer programs, 1981—; mem. Nat. Colorectal Cancer Adv. Com., 1971-73, Com. Evaluate Cancer Curricula Am. Med. Sch., 1971-79; mem. exec. com. S.W. Cancer Chemotherapy Study Group, 1972-73; mem. evaluation adv. coun. Southeastern Regional Cancer Programs, 1972-74; chmn.

gastrointestinal com. S.W. Oncology Group, 1974-79; mem. exec. bd. Wayne State U./U. Mich. Inst. Gerontology, 1975-86; mem. oper. com. Comprehensive Cancer Ctr. Met. Detroit, 1978—; mem. commd. jury Saint-Vincent Internat. Prize Med. Scis., Rome, 1979, 83; chmn. coun. dept. chairmen sch. medicine Wayne State U., 1979-81, mem. dean's coun. grad. med. edn. program, 1983-89, mem. dean's rev. com., 1986, mem. pharmacy and medicine task force, 1986, chmn. radiation oncology search com., 1987; mem. med. staff fin. and budget com. Harper-Grace Hosps., 1983-84, mem. gerontology svcs. planning com., 1984-87, chmn. NMR adv. com., 1984—; mem. transplantation com. Detroit Med. Ctr., 1985-86, mem. med. bd., 1985-89, chmn. task force cancer programs, 1987; presenter in field. Contbr. chpts. to books and articles to profl. jours.; mem. adv. bd. Cancer Treatment Reports, 1980-82. Mem. exec. com. bd. trustees Mich. Cancer Found., 1975-85; mem. blood svc. com. ARC Southeastern Mich., 1981-84; bd. dirs. Wayne County unit Am. Cancer Soc., 1976-79; trustee Hospice Southeastern Mich., 1991—. Capt. U.S. Army, 1953-55. Recipient Life award Am. Cancer Soc. Met. Detroit, 1981, Mercy Medallion, 1983, Tree-of-Life award Nat. Jewish Fedn., 1987, Michiganian-of-Yr. award The Detroit News, 1987, Hospice Humanitarian award, 1989; inductee Internat. Heritage Hall of Fame, Inst. Met. Detroit, 1989; honored by Am. Cancer Soc., 1989, Weizmann Inst. Sci., 1992. Mem. AAAS, ACP, Am. Assn. Cancer Rsch., Am. Fedn. Clin. Rsch., Am. Soc. Hematology, Am. Soc. Clin. Oncology (mem. program com. 1981), Am. Assn. Cancer Edn. (mem. exec. coun. 1971—, pres. 1976-77), Mich. State Med. Soc. (mem. cancer com. 1965-73, Flag award 1992), N.Y. Acad. Scis., Mich. Soc. Internal Medicine, Wayne County Med. Soc. (mem. del. body 1981-87, mem. task force referral edn. 1986, mem. physician tech. svcs. 1986—), Detroit Physiol. Soc., Detroit Acad. Medicine, Ctrl. Soc. Clin. Rsch., James Ewing Soc., Aesculapian Soc. (hon.), Alpha Omega Alpha, Phi Lambda Kappa (hon.). Office: Mich Cancer Found 110 E Warren Ave Detroit MI 48201

VAITUKAITIS, JUDITH LOUISE, medical research administrator; b. Hartford, Conn., Aug. 29, 1940; d. Albert George and Julia Joan (Vaznikaitis) V. BS, Tufts U., 1962; MD, Boston U., 1966. Investigator, med. officer reproductive rsch. Nat. Inst. Child Health and Human Devel., NIH, Bethesda, Md., 1971-74; assoc. dir. clin. rsch. Human Reprodn. Resources NIH, Bethesda, Md., 1986-91, dir. gen. clin. rsch. ctr., 1986-91, dep. dir. extramural rsch., 1991; acting dir. Nat. Ctr. Rsch. Resources NIH, Bethesda, 1991-92, dir., 1993—; from assoc. prof. to prof. medicine Sch. Medicine Boston U., 1974-86, assoc. prof. physiology, 1975-80, assoc. prof. ob-gyn., 1977-80, program. dir. gen. clin. rsch. ctr., 1977-86, prof. physiology, 1980-86; head sect. endocrinology and metabolism Boston City Hosp., 1974-86. Mem. editorial bd. Jour. Clin. Endocrin. and Metabolism, 1973-80, Proc. Soc. Exptl. Biol. and Medicine, 1978-87, Endocrine Rsch., 1984-88. Author: Clinical Reproductive Neuroendocrinology, 1982; contbr. articles to profl. jours. Recipient Disting. Alumna award Sch. Medicine, Boston U., 1983, Mallincrodt award for Inv. Rsch. Clin. Radiossay Soc., 1980. Mem. Am. Fedn. Clin. Rsch., Endocrine Soc., Am. Soc. Clin. Rsch., Soc. Exptl. Biology and Medicine, Am. Physicians, Soc. for Study of Reproduction, Am. Soc. Andrology. Office: Nat Ctr Rsch Resources NIH Bldg 12A Rm 4007 12 South Dr MSC 5660 Bethesda MD 20892-5660

VAJEEPRASEE THONGSAK, THOMAS, business planning executive; b. Udonthani, Thailand, Feb. 10, 1935; came to U.S., 1970; s. Chanmar and Pee Vajeeprasee; m. Somchit; 1 child, Rosarine. BS in Sociology, BA in Philosophy, Mahamakut U., Bangkok, 1968; MA in Edn., Kean Coll. of N.J., 1976; MA in Philosophy, NYU, 1989; PhD in Mgmt., AMA Mgmt. Inst., 1987. Tchr. Machimavas Sch., Udonthani, 1958-65; spl. instr. Chana Songkram Sch., Bangkok, 1965-68; tchrs. staff Thai Straipratoom U., Bangkok, 1968-70; salesman Met. Life of N.Y., 1974-76; rep. Mut. Life of N.Y., 1976-78; agt. Equitable Life Ins., N.Y.C., 1983-84; insp. IBI Security Svc. Inc., L.I., 1979-85; security police insp. Brandeis U., Waltham, Mass., 1985-86; U.S. chief legal investigator, pvt. investigator U.S. Legal Investigation, Inc., U.S. Bur.'s Security Agy., Boston, N.Y.C., Fresno, Calif., 1987—; advisor Thai N.E. Assn., N.Y.C., 1980—, Rep. Nat. Com., Washington, 1980—; state advisor U.S. Congl. Adv., Washington, 1980; assoc. mem. Nat. Security Ctr., Citizen's Adv. Coun., Washington, 1989; pres., chief security agt. U.S. Bur. Security Agy., 1991; mem. Pres. Pvt. Sector Survey on Cost Control, Washington, 1989—; mem. Am. Security Coun. Adv. Bd., Washington, 1983-88; U.S. chief legal investigator, pvt. investigator U.S. Legal Investigation, Inc., U.S. Bureau's Security Agy. under Million Mutual Corp., Inc. Mem. G.O.P. Republican Conservative Party (recommendation pres. Gerald R. Ford 1977), 1977—, Nat. Republican Congl. Com. Victory Fund, Washington, 1982—, Republican Presdl. Task Force and Comsn. (recommendation chmn. Nat. Republican Senatorial Com. 1982, 93), 1982—, Am. Security Coun. Found., 1978—, Defense Dept., Defense Inst., 1982—, Nat. Rep. Senatorial Com., Washington, Chiefs of Police Nat. Drug Task Force, 1982—, Nat. Law Enforcement Officers Meml. Fund, Washington, 1982—, Natl. Wildlife Fedn., 1982—; apptd. state adviser U.S. Congl. Adv. Bd., 1979, 93; priest asst. U.S.A. Buddhayaram Temple, Bronx, 1970—; pres. S.E. Asia Found., 1970; mem. Citizens Against Govt. Waste, Washington; mem. U.S. Def. Com., Washington, 1982-86; sec. Wat Buddhamonthol United Buddhist Meditation Ctr., 1992—. Recipient Presdl. Seal, Rep. Orgn., 1983, 84, Rep. Presdl. Legion of Merit highest level of Govts. for Lifetime, 1993. Mem. Internat. Assn. Chiefs of Police, President's Club, Senator's Club, Rep. Presdl. Legion of Merit.

VAJK, HUGO, manufacturing executive; b. Ljubljana, Slovenia, Mar. 26, 1928; emigrated to Can., 1947, naturalized, 1953; s. Hugo and Magda (Slatnar) V.; m. Barbara Lois Hallin, June 13, 1953; children: Tanja Astrid, Hugo Anthony, Madeleine Louise, Anita Marie, Nicolette Cecile, Moira Suzanne. Student, Institut Polytechnique, Grenoble, France, 1947; B.Eng. with honors, McGill U., Montreal, 1951; M.S., Carnegie Mellon U., Pitts., 1953. Product mgr. Joy Mfg. Co., Buffalo, 1957-59; dir. gen. Joy Mfg. Co., Paris, 1960-63; with Massey-Ferguson, Ltd., 1964-78; pres. Moteurs Perkins S.A., Paris, 1964-65, Massey-Ferguson Ltd., Paris, 1966-69; v.p. logistics parent co. Massey-Ferguson Ltd., Toronto, 1970-72, exec. v.p., 1973-78; dir. GEC Inc., subs. Gen. Electric Co., Eng., 1979; chmn. English Electric Corp., Elmsford, N.Y., 1979; with Garret Corp. div. Signal Cos., 1980-84; v.p. Garrett Automotive Products; pres. Garrett Automotive Group, Allied-Signal, Inc., 1985-87; chmn. Inovatek Advisors, Inc., Tarpon Springs, Fla., 1988—; pres. ATM Communications Engrs., Inc., Wilmington, Del., 1991—. Mem. ASME, Soc. Automotive Engrs., Assn. Profl. Engrs. Ont., Inst. Mgmt. Sci., Inst. Dirs., Inst. Mgmt. Cons., Nat. Assn. Corp. Dirs., Univ. Club (Toronto), Royal Can. Yacht Club (Toronto), Union Interaliée (Paris), Royal Thames Yacht Club (Paris), Royal Thames Yacht Club (London). Office: Inovatek Advisors Inc Ste 200 905 M L King Dr Tarpon Springs FL 34689-4827

VAJNA, ANDREW G., film company executive. Chmn., CEO Cinergi Pictures Entertainment Inc., Santa Monica, Calif. Office: Cinergi Pictures Ent Inc 2308 Broadway Santa Monica CA 90404-2916

VAKY, VIRON PETER, diplomacy educator, former foreign service officer; b. Tex., Sept. 13, 1925; m. Luann Colburn. BS, Georgetown U., 1947; MA, U. Chgo., 1948. Vocat. appraiser VA, Washington, 1948-49; joined Fgn. Svc. Dept. of State, Washington, 1949; consular officer Guayaquil, Ecuador, 1949-51; econ. officer Buenos Aires, 1951-54; internat. rels. officer Washington, 1955-57, info. specialist, 1958-59; polit.officer Bogota, Colombia, 1959-61; detailed to Nat. War Coll., 1963-64; counsellor-dep. chief mission Guatemala, 1964-67; mem. Policy Planning Coun. Dept. of State, 1967-68; dep. asst. sec. Bur. Inter-Am. Affairs, 1968-69, acting asst. sec., 1969; detailed to NSC, 1969-70; diplomat-in-residence Georgetown U., Washington, 1970-71; ambassador to San Jose, Costa Rica, 1972-74, Bogota, Colombia, 1974-76, Caracas, Venezuela, 1976-78; asst. sec. Inter-Am. Affairs Washington, 1978-89; sr. assoc. Carnegie Endowment for Internat. Peace, Washington, 1985-92; asst. dean, rsch. prof. diplomacy Sch. Fgn. Svc., Georgetown U., Washington, 1980-84, adj. prof. diplomacy, 1985-95; sr. fellow Inter-Am. Dialogue, Washington, 1994—. With U.S. Army, 1944-46.

VALADE, ALAN MICHAEL, lawyer; b. Berwyn, Ill., Jan. 26, 1952; s. Merle F. and Verna M. (Gildersleeve) V.; m. June 17, 1978. BA, U. Mich., 1974; JD, Wayne State U., 1977; LLM in Taxation, NYU, 1978. Bar: Mich. 1978, Fla. 1987. Assoc. Kemp, Klein, Endelman & Beer, Birmingham, Mich., 1978-79; shareholder Valade, MacKinnon & Higgins, P.C., Detroit, 1979-84, Schwendener & Valade, P.C., Mason, Mich., 1985-91; ptnr.

Honigman Miller Schwartz and Cohn, Lansing, Mich., 1991—. Co-author: The Michigan Single Business Tax, 1991; contbr. articles to profl. jours. Mem. ABA, State Bar Mich. (chmn. state and local tax com. 1991, tax coun. 1989-92), State Bar Fla., Univ. Club of Mich. State U., Oak Pointe Country Club. Avocations: reading, traveling, running, skiing. Office: Honigman Miller Schwartz & Cohn 222 Washington Sq N Ste 400 Lansing MI 48933-1800

VALADE, ROBERT CHARLES, apparel company executive; b. Detroit, Apr. 19, 1926; s. Cyril K. and Marion I. (Anderson) V.; m. Gretchen Carhartt, Sept. 18, 1948; children: Gretchen Garth, Mark R. Degree in bus. adminstrn., Mich. State U., 1947. Salesman Royal Typewriter, Detroit, 1947-50; v.p. Carhartt Inc., Detroit, 1950-59; pres., CEO Carhartt Inc., Dearborn, Mich., 1959—; bd. dirs. Rep. Bank S.E., Grosse Pointe, Mich. with USN, 1944-46, PTO. Mem. World Pres.'s Orgn. (dir. 1980-82), Detroit Racquet Club (pres. 1950-54), Country Club Detroit, Fiddle Sticks Country Club (Ft. Myers, Fla.). Republican. Roman Catholic. Avocations: golf, hunting, fishing.

VALBERG, LESLIE STEPHEN, medical educator, physician, researcher; b. Churchbridge, Sask., Can., June 3, 1930; s. John Stephen and Rose (Vikfusson) V.; m. Barbara Tolhurst, Sept. 14, 1954; children: John, Stephanie, Bill. M.D., C.M., Queens U., 1954, M.S.C., 1958. Cert. internal medicine specialist Royal Coll. Physicians and Surgeons of Can. Asst. prof. Queens U. Kingston, Ont., Can., from 1960—, prof., until 1975; prof. medicine U. Western Ont., London, 1975-95, chmn. dept., 1975-85; dean faculty of medicine U. Western Ont., 1985-92; prof. emeritus, 1995—; cons. Univ. Hosp., 1975-95. Rsch. Assoc. Med. Council of Can., 1960-65. Fellow Royal Coll. Physicians and Surgeons; mem. Am. Gastroent. Assn., Med. Rsch. Coun. Can. (v.p. 1980-82). Home: 1496 Stoneybrook Crescent, London, ON Canada N5X 1C5 Office: U Western Ont, London, ON Canada N6A 5C1

VALBUENA-BRIONES, ANGEL JULIAN, language educator, author; b. Madrid, Spain, Jan. 11, 1928; naturalized, 1963; s. Angel Valbuena-Prat and Francisca Briones; m. Barbara Northrup Hobart, Nov. 9, 1957; children: Teresa, Vivian. Licenciado summa cum laude, Murcia (Spain) U., 1949; PhD. with honors, Madrid U., 1952. Prof. Ayudante Murcia U., 1949-51; lectr. Oxford (Eng.) U., 1953-55; prof. Ayudante Madrid U., 1955-56; vis. lectr. U. Wis., 1956-58; asst. prof. Yale U., 1958-60; Elias Ahuja prof. Spanish lit. U. Del., 1960—; lecture tour S.Am., summer 1957, vis. summer prof., NYU, 1960, 61; vis. prof. Madrid U., summer 1965, 1970-71, summer 1977, U. Mexico at Aragon, summer 1979, Instituto Caro y Cuervo, Bogota, Colombia, summer 1980; mem. Fulbright-Hays nat. screening com., 1981-83, 89-90; bd. dirs. Publs. of Univs. of Barcelona, Spain, Bull. of Comediantes U. Calif. (Riverside), Hispanic Jour., Pa., Juan de la Cuesta Editions Del.; profl. cons. NEH. Author: Nueva Poesia de Puerto Rico, 1952, Comedias de Capa y Espada de Calderón, 1954, Dramas de Honor de Calderón, 2 vols., 1956, Obras Completas de Calderón, vol. I, 1959, Vol. II, 1956, 6th edit. 2 vols., 1988, Literatura Hispanoamericana, 1962, Perspectiva crítica de los dramas de Calderón, 1965, Ideas y Palabras, 1968, El alcalde de Zalamea de Calderón, 1971, Primera Parte de Comedias de Pedro Calderón de la Barca, Vol. 1, 1974, Vol. 2, 1981, La Dama Duende de Calderón, 1976, Calderón y la comedia nueva, 1977, La vida es sueño. Antes que todo es mi dama. Pedro Calderón de la Barca, 1988; contbr. articles to profl. jours., book chpts. Founder, pres. Valbuena Inst. Spanish Lit., Inc., 1986. Consejo Superior de Investigaciones Científicas fellow, 1951, 70-71, Instituto de Cultura Hispánica fellow, 1951-52; recipient Excellence in Teaching award U. Del., 1988. Mem. AAUP, Assn. Tchrs. Spanish and Portuguese, MLA, Instituto de Literatura Iberoamericana, Internat. Fedn. Modern Langs. and Lits., Asociación Internacional de Hispanistas, Am. Comparative Lit. Assn., Assn. for Hispanic Classic Theatre, Philol. Assn. of the Pacific Coast, Sigma Delta Pi (hon.), Phi Kappa Phi. Club: Greenville Country. Home: 203 Nottingham Rd Newark DE 19711-7402

VALCIC, SUSAN JOAN, lawyer; b. N.Y.C., Mar. 23, 1956; d. Joseph and Eve Manderville; m. Alexander C. Valcic, July 28, 1979. BA magna cum laude, Columbia U., 1983; JD, Cardozo Sch. Law, 1986. Assoc. attorney Bailey, Marshall & Hoeniger, N.Y.C., 1986-87, Zalkin, Rodin & Goodman, N.Y.C., 1987-89; pvt. practice N.Y.C., 1989—. Apptd. adminstrv. law judge, N.Y. 1990. Mem. Assn. Bar City N.Y., N.Y. County Lawyers Assn., N.Y. State Bar. Assn., Fed. Bar. Assn., Columbia Club, Phi Beta Kappa.

VALDEPEÑAS, JOAQUÍN MARIO, clarinetist, conductor; b. Torreón, Mex., Jan. 19, 1955; came to Can., 1980; s. Joaquín Ignacio and Maria Del Carmen (Estrada) V.; m. Mi-Hyon Kim, Dec. 23, 1988; 1 child, Josué. B.Mus., Calif. State U., Fullerton, 1978; M.Mus. with honors, Yale U., 1980. Adj. prof. music U. Toronto, Ont., Can., 1980—; faculty Aspen (Colo.) Music Festival, 1977—; Banff (Alta.) Sch. Fine Arts, 1985; mem. Marlboro (Vt.) Music Festival, 1980-81, Casals Festival, P.R., 1985, Nagano (Japan) Festival, 1990—, Norfolk (Conn.) Chamber Festival, 1994, Mostly Mozart Festival, N.Y.C.; founding mem., bd. dirs. Amici music ensemble; condr. Toronto Symphony Youth Orch., 1985—; clarinetist Toronto Symphony Orch. Numerous compact discs; soloist with many symphony orchs. including English Chamber Orch., BBC Symphony Orch., Buffalo Philharmonic, Toronto Symphony. Can. Coun. Career Devel. grantee, 1992-95. Avocations: oil painting, reading. Office: Toronto Symphony Orchestra, 212 King St W Ste 550, Toronto, ON Canada M5H 1K5

VALDÉS, DAVID CHURCHILL, motion picture producer; b. Los Angeles, Aug. 12, 1950; s. Armand George de Valdés and Joan Rosemary Churchill; m. Susan Margaret Jones, Sept. 14, 1974; children: Summer Diana, Julia Margaret. AA, Orange Coast Coll., 1970; BA magna cum laude, UCLA, 1976. Asst. dir. Universal Studios, Universal City, Calif., 1977-78, Warner Bros., Burbank, Calif., 1978-84; assoc. producer Warner Bros., Burbank, 1984-86; producer Tri-Star Pictures, Century City, Calif., 1986-87, Warner Bros., Burbank, 1987-90, 91-94; exec. producer Hollywood Pictures, 1990-91. Mem. Dirs. Guild Am., Acad. Motion Pictures Arts and Scis., Am. Film Inst. Democrat. Avocations: music, tennis, raquetball, swimming, movies. Home: 4017 Nogales Dr Tarzana CA 91356-5004 Office: Rysher Entertainment 3400 Riverside Dr Ste # 600 Burbank CA 91505

VALDÉS, KAREN W., art gallery director, educator; b. L.A., May 25, 1945; d. Richard Victor and Eleanor M. (Tomte) V.; m. Thomas E. Schwarz, Oct. 14, 1989. BFA, U. Calif., Irvine, 1968; MFA, Fla. State U., 1974. Dir. cultural events Fla. State U., Tallahassee, 1973-75; curator exhbn. Art Mus. So. Tex., Corpus Christi, 1975-76; assoc. curator, dir. gallery Miami (Fla.)-Dade Community Coll., 1976-84; dir. Gloria Luria Gallery, Miami, 1985; curator exhbn. Mus. Art, Ft. Lauderdale, Fla., 1985-89; assoc. prof., dir. univ. galleries U. Fla., Gainesville, 1989—; panelist NEA, Ft. Lauderdale, 1978-80, Dade County Art in Pub. Places, Miami, 1980-83, GSA Commn., 1982, Arts in State Bldgs., Gainesville, 1989—. Mem. Am. Assn. Mus., Coll. Art Assn., U. Fla. Hispanic Faculty Assn. Democrat. Avocation: sailing. Office: U Fla Galleries 102 Fab Gainesville FL 32611

VALDES, MAXIMIANO, conductor. Student, Conservatory of Music, Santiago, Chile, Accademia Santa Cecilia, Rome. Asst. condr. Teatro Fenice, Venice, Italy, 1976; worked as conducting fellow with Leonard Bernstein and Seiji Ozawa, 1977; condr. Buffalo Philharm. Orch., 1989—. Operatic debut with La Traviata, Nice Opera, France; Paris Opera debut with Romeo and Juliet, 1986; London debut with English Chamber Orch., 1987; other opera appearances include The Barber of Seville in Lausanne, Le Nozze di Figaro and Werther in Barcelona, Agnese di Hohenstaufen and The Barber of Seville at Rome Opera, Eugene Onegin at Bonn Opera, Faust in Copenhagen; condr. orchs. of Spain, Denmark, Italy, S.Am.; leader London Philharm. Orch. on tour to Spain, Monte Carlo Philharm. on tour to Italy; prin. condr. Nat. Orch. of Spain, 1986-87; recs. with Monte Carlo Philharm., London Symphony, Nice Philharm., New Zealand Symphony; N.Am. debut with Buffalo Philharm., 1987; appointed music dir. Buffalo Philharm. Orch., 1989, asst. conductor at the Teatro Fenice in Venice, 1976. Recipient 2d prize Rupert Found. Conducting Competition, London, 1978, 1st prize Nicolai Malko Competition, Copenhagen, 1980, 1st prize Vittorio Gui Competition, Florence, Italy; awarded the Del Carlo Tanglewood fellowship, 1977. Office: Buffalo Philharm Orch 71 Symphony Circle PO Box 905 Buffalo NY 14213*

VALDES, MIGUEL A., lawyer; b. Habana, Cuba, Sept. 14, 1943. BSBA cum laude, Loyola U., 1972; MST, DePaul U., 1974, JD, 1978. Bar: Ill. 1978, Fla. 1978. Ptnr. Mayer, Brown & Platt, Chgo. Mem. Fla. Bar. Office: Mayer Brown & Platt 190 S LaSalle St Chicago IL 60603

VALDES-DAPENA, MARIE AGNES, pediatric pathologist, educator; b. Pottsville, Pa., July 14, 1921; d. Edgar Daniel and Marie Agnes (Rettig) Brown; m. Antonio M. Valdes-Dapena, Apr. 6, 1945 (div. Oct. 1980); children: Victoria Maria Valdes-Dapena Dead, Deborah Anne Valdes-Dapena Malle, Maria Cristina, Andres Antonio, Antonio Edgardo, Carlos Roberto, Marcos Antonio, Ricardo Daniel, Carmen Patricia Valdés-Dapena Fater, Catalina Inez Valdés-Dapena Amram, Pedro Pablo. BS, Immaculata Coll., 1941; MD, Temple U., 1944. Diplomate: Am. Bd. Pathology (spl. qualification-pediatric pathology 1990). Intern Phila. Gen. Hosp., 1944-45, resident in pathology, 1945-49; asst. pathologist Fitzgerald Mercy Hosp., Darby, Pa., 1949-51; dir. labs. Woman's Med. Coll. Pa., Phila., 1951-55; instr. pathology Woman's Med. Coll. Pa., 1947-51, asst. prof., 1951-55, assoc. prof., 1955-59; assoc. pathologist St. Christopher's Hosp. for Children, Phila., 1959-76; dir. sect. pediatric pathology U. Miami (Fla.)-Jackson Meml. Hosp., 1976-81, pediatric pathologist, dir. div. edn. in pathology, 1981-93, co.-dir. edn. in pathology, 1993—; cons., lectr. U.S. Naval Hosp., Phila., 1972-76; instr. pathology Sch. Medicine U. Pa., 1945-49; instr. Sch. Medicine U. Pa. (Sch. Dentistry), 1947, Sch. Medicine U. Pa. (Grad. Sch. Medicine), 1948-55, vis. lectr., 1960-62; asst. prof. Temple U. Med. Sch., 1959-63, assoc. prof., 1963-67, prof. pathology and pediatrics, 1967-76; prof. pathology and pediatrics U., Miami, 1976-93, prof. emeritus pathology and pediatrics, 1993—; cons. pediatric pathology div. med. examiner Dept. Pub. Health Phila., 1967-70; mem. perinatal biology and infant mortality research and tng. com. Nat. Inst. Child Health and Human Devel., NIH, 1971-73; mem. sci. adv. bd. Armed Forces Inst. Pathology, 1976-82; assoc. med. examiner, Dade County, Fla., 1976—; chmn. med. bd. Nat. Sudden Infant Death Syndrome Found., 1961-81, 87-91, pres., 1984-87, chmn. bd., 1985-88; mem. med. and sci. adv. coun. The SIDS Alliance, 1990—. Contbr. articles to profl. jours. NIH grantee. Mem. U.S. and Can. Acad. Pathology, Coll. Physicians Phila., Internat. Assn. Pediatric Pathology, Soc. for Pediatric Pathology (pres. 1980-81), Alpha Omega Alpha. Roman Catholic. Home: 179 Morningside Dr Miami FL 33166-5240 Office: Dept Pathology U Miami Sch Medicine PO Box 016960 Miami FL 33101-6960

VALDEZ, ABELARDO LOPEZ, lawyer; b. Floresville, Tex., Aug. 31, 1942; 1 child, Felipe Alejandro. BS, Tex. A&M U., 1965; postgrad., The Hague (Netherlands) Acad. Internat. Law, 1969; JD, Baylor U., 1970; LLM, Harvard U., 1974. Bar: Tex., U.S. Supreme Ct. Mil. aide to Pres. Lyndon Johnson Washington, 1965-67; atty. Overseas Pvt. Investment Corp., Washington, 1971-73; gen. counsel Inter-Am. Found., Washington, 1973-75; asst. administr. Latin-Am. and Caribbean Region U.S Agy. for Internat. Devel., Washington, 1977-79; U.S. amb. and chief of protocol The White House, Washington, 1979-81; of counsel Squire, Sanders & Dempsey, Washington, 1981—. Editor Harvard Internat. Law Jour.; contbr. articles to profl. jours. Trustee Am. U. Washington, Coun. Am. Ambs., Pan Am. U. Found., Edinburg, Tex., Congl. Hispanic Caucus Inst., Inc., Washington, Meridian House Internat., Washington; mem. adv. bd. Sch. Bus. Tex. A&M U., Nat. Bank, Washington; chmn. internat. com. Greater Washington Bd. Trade; mem. U.S. Christopher Columbus Quincentenary Commn. Decorated hon. mem. U.S. Christopher Columbus Quincentenary Commn. Decorated hon. mem. Order of Isabel La Catolica King Juan Carlos, Spain. Mem. Am. Soc. Internat. Law, U.S. C. of C. (bd. dirs.), Bar Assn. D.C., Coun. Fgn. Rels., Ibero-Am. C. of C. Home: 4810 Sedgewick St NW Washington DC 20016-2324 Office: Squire Sanders & Dempsey 1201 Pennsylvania Ave NW Ste 5 Washington DC 20004-2401

VALE, MARGO ROSE, physician; b. Balt., June 16, 1950; d. Henry and Pauline Esther (Koplow) Hausdorff; m. Michael Allen Vale, Aug. 22, 1971; children: Edward, Judith. BA magna cum laude, Brandeis U., 1971; MD, Albert Einstein Coll. Medicine, 1975. Diplomate Am. Bd. Dermatology. Resident in internal medicine and dermatology NYU, N.Y.C., 1975-79, Bellevue Hosp., N.Y.C., 1975-79, VA Hosp., N.Y.C., 1975-79; staff physician HIP Greater N.Y., Bay Shore, 1979-81; pvt. practice medicine Huntington, N.Y., 1981—; cons. in dermatology Huntington Hosp., 1981—, Gurwin Jewish Geriatric Ctr., Commack, N.Y., 1990—. Contbr. articles to profl. jours. Mem. Am. Acad. Dermatology, Med. Soc. State N.Y., Long Island Dermatology Soc., Suffolk County Med. Soc., Suffolk Dermatology Soc. (pres. 1990-92), Phi Beta Kappa. Avocations: cooking, photography, sketching, music. Office: 205 E Main St Huntington NY 11743-2923

VALE, NORMAN, advertising executive; b. N.Y.C., Jan. 19, 1930; s. Henry and Evelyn (Spaulder) Vale; m. Irene Loebenson Vale, Dec. 22, 1957; children: Margaret, Jennifer. BBA, CCNY, 1952. Actg. exec. Grey Adv'l., N.Y.C. 1954-60, SSCB Co., N.Y.C., 1960-62; sr. asst. to chief exec. officer Lennen & Newell, N.Y.C., 1962-67; dep. dir. internat. Needham Harper, N.Y.C., 1967-73; mng. dir. Grey Internat., N.Y.C., 1974-90; dir. gen. IAA, N.Y.C., 1990—. Chmn. Dunewood Fire Dist., Fire Island, N.Y. Cpl. U.S. Army, 1952-54. Mem. Internat. Advt. Assn. (world bd. 1986—), Am. Assn. Advt. Agys. (chmn. internat. com. 1987-89), Achilles Track Club. Avocations: triathlons, skiing, ballet, theater. Office: IAA 521 Fifth Ave Ste 1807 New York NY 10175

VALENCIA, JAIME ALFONSO, chemical engineer; b. Arequipa, Peru, Apr. 2, 1952; came to the U.S., 1970; s. Luis A. and Julia (Chavez) V.; m. Cecelia Ann Ingram, Nov. 21, 1987; 1 child, Julia Nicole. BSChE, U. Md., 1974; DSc in Chem. Engring., MIT, 1978. Registered profl. engr., Tex. Mem. cons. staff Arthur D. Little, Inc., Cambridge, Mass., 1978-82; group leader Exxon Prodn. Rsch. Co., Houston, 1982-86; dir. tech. devel. Novatec, Inc., Houston, 1986-89; v.p. Novatec Prodn. Systems, Inc., Houston, 1988-91; dir. strategic tech. devel. Aspen Tech., Inc., Houston, 1995—; prin. NOVI Enterprises, Houston, 1986-95; cons. Exxon, Houston, 1990-95. Contbr.: Flue Gas Desulfurization, 1982; contbr. articles to Internat. Jour. Heat and Mass Transfer, Hydrocarbon Processing; author: Initial Symposium Series, 1977. Mem. bd. advisors Entrepreneurial Devel. Ctr., Houston, 1993—. Mem. AIChE, MIT Alumni Club South Tex. (bd. dirs. 1990—, pres. 1994-95), Houston Inventors Assn. Roman Catholic. Achievements include patents for cryogenic processing; invention of CFZ process for cryogenic separations; development of Novatec process for cleaning oil contaminated cuttings from drilling operations; basic principles for Ryan-Holmes technology for processing natural gas. Home: 9830 Stableway Dr Houston TX 77065-4368 Office: Aspen Tech Inc PO Box 22807 Houston TX 77227-2807

VALENS, EVANS GLADSTONE, sculptor, printmaker, author, former television producer, director; b. State College, Pa., Apr. 17, 1920; s. Evans G. and Mabel (Grazier) V.; m. Winifred A. Crary, Oct. 11, 1941 (div. 1976); children: Thomas Crary, Marc John, Jo Anne, Dan Malcolm.; m. Anne Kent Curtis, Dec. 18, 1980 (div. 1987). BA, Amherst Coll., 1941; MFA, San Francisco Art Inst., 1990. Reporter El Paso Herald-Post, 1942-43; corr. UPI, Central Pacific, U.S. and Europe, 1943-48; bur. chief UPI, Munich, 1946-48; producer-dir. KQED, San Francisco, 1954-62, 70-71. Author: (non-fiction): (with others) Elements of the Universe, 1958 (Thomas Alva Edison award); The Number of Things, 1963, A Long Way Up, The Story of Jill Kinmont, 1966, (with others) Viruses and the Nature of Life, 1961, The Attractive Universe, 1969, (with others) People-reading, 1975; poetry includes Cybernaut, 1968; juvenile books include Me and Frumpet, 1957; Wingfin and Topple, 1962, Wildfire, 1963, Magnet, 1965, Motion, 1965, The Other Side of the Mountain, 1975; Part II, 1978; producer-writer numerous films and TV prodns.; sculpture commn. Napa (Calif.) Town Ctr., 1988. Decorated Purple Heart.

VALENSTEIN, SUZANNE GEBHART, art historian; b. Balt., July 17, 1928; d. Jerome J. and Lonnie Cooper Gebhart; m. Murray A. Valenstein, Mar. 31, 1951. With dept. Asian Art Met. Mus. Art, N.Y.C., 1965—; rsch. curator Asian Art. Author: Ming Porcelains: A Retrospective, 1970, A Handbook of Chinese Ceramics, 1975, rev. and enlarged, 1989, Highlights of Chinese Ceramics, 1975, (with others) Oriental Ceramics: The World's Great Collections: The Metropolitan Museum, 1977, rev., 1983, The Herzman Collection of Chinese Ceramics, 1992. Mem. Oriental Ceramic Soc. (London), Oriental Ceramic Soc. (Hong Kong). Office: Met Mus Art Dept Asian Art Fifth Ave at 82nd St New York NY 10028

VALENTA, ZDENEK, chemistry educator; b. Havlickuv Brod, Czechoslovakia, June 14, 1927; came to Can., 1950; s. Karel Valenta and Jindra (Komers) Valentova; m. Noreen Elizabeth Donahoe, July 29, 1957; children—Katherine Elizabeth, Richard Karel, Michael Francis. Dipl. Ing. Chem., E.T.H., Zurich, Switzerland, 1950; M.S., U. N.B., 1952, Ph.D., 1953. Spl. lectr. dept. chemistry U. N.B., Fredericton, Can., 1953-54, lectr., 1954-56, asst. prof., 1957-58, assoc. prof., 1958-63, prof., 1963-90; rsch. prof. U. N.B., Fredericton, 1990—; head chemistry dept. U. N.B., Fredericton, Can., 1963-72; cons. Delmar Chems., LaSalle, Que., Can., 1970—, Ayerst Research Labs., Montreal, Que., Can., 1980-85, Torcan Chem., Toronto, Ont., Can., 1980—. Contbr. articles to profl. jours. Recipient Excellence in Teaching award U. N.B., 1974, Sci. Teaching award Atlantic Provinces Coun. on Scis./Northern Telecom 1987, award for chem. edn. Union Carbide, 1989. Fellow Chem. Inst. Can. (Merck, Sharp and Dohme award 1967), Royal Soc. Can. Home: 872 Windsor St, Fredericton, NB Canada E3B 4G5 Office: U NB Dept Chemistry, Bag Service 45222, Fredericton, NB Canada E3B 6E2

VALENTE, LOUIS PATRICK (DAN VALENTE), technical corporation executive; b. Somerville, Mass., July 26, 1930; s. Luigi and Mary Constance (Fedele) V.; m. Jeanne Barbara Peters, Oct. 3, 1992; children: Louis, Marianne, Steven, Diane, Richard, Carol, Susan. Cert., Bentley Coll., Boston, 1955. Cost acct. Cambridge Corp., Lowell, Mass., 1953-55; sr. acct. Flaherty, Bliss & Co., CPAs, Boston, 1956-61; fin. analyst Sanders Assocs., Nashua, N.H., 1961-62; fin. cons. Burlington, Mass., 1961-68; contract audit adminstr. Dept. Def. Audit Agy., Boston, 1962-66, DOE, Las Vegas, 1966-68; asst. controller EG&G, Inc., Wellesley, Mass., 1968-71, asst. v.p., treas., 1971-74, dir. fin., 1974-79, officer, corp. treas., 1979-83, v.p. bus. devel., 1985-91, sr. v.p. mergers, acquisitons and investments, 1991—; bd. dirs. Meditech Inc., Westwood, Mass., Micrion Corp. Selectman Town of Burlington, 1970-73, 76-79, chmn., 1972-79; trustee, mem. fin. com. Choate-Symmes Hosp., Woburn, Mass., 1972—; pres.'s adv. coun. Bentley Coll. With USAF, 1951-53. Mem. AICPA, Fin. Execs. Inst., Mass. Soc. CPAs, Bentley Coll., Bentley Alumni Assn., New Eng. Council. Roman Catholic. Lodge: K.C. Home: 44 Concord Rd Weston MA 02193-1223 Office: E G & G Inc 45 William St Wellesley MA 02181-4004

VALENTI, CARL M., newspaper publisher. Pres., pub.-info. svc. Wall St. Jour., N.Y.C.; also sr. v.p. Dow Jones & Co., N.Y.C. Office: The Wall Street Journal Dow Jones & Co Inc 200 Liberty St New York NY 10281-1003*

VALENTI, JACK JOSEPH, motion picture executive; b. Houston, Sept. 5, 1921; m. Mary Margaret Wiley, June 1, 1962; children: Courtenay Lynda, John Lyndon, Alexandra Alice. BA, U. Houston, 1946; MBA, Harvard U., 1948. Co-founder, formerly exec. v.p. Weekley and Valenti, Inc. (advt.), 1952-63; spl. asst. to Pres. Johnson, 1963-66; pres., chief exec. officer Motion Picture Assn. Am., Inc., 1966—; chmn. Alliance Motion Picture and TV Producers, Inc., 1966—; chmn., chief exec. officer Motion Picture Export Assn. Am.; adj. prof. govt. and pub. adminstrn. Am. U., 1977; bd. dirs. Riggs Nat. Corp. Washington. Author: Bitter Taste of Glory, 1971, A Very Human President, 1976, Speak Up With Confidence: How To Prepare, Learn and Deliver an Effective Speech, 1982, Protect and Defend, 1992; contbr. articles to mags. Trustee, bd. dirs. Am. Film Inst. Served with USAAF, 1942-45. Decorated D.F.C., Air medal with five oak leaf clusters, Disting. Unit Citation with cluster, European Theater Ribbon with 4 battle stars, Chevalier de la Legion d'honneur (France). Address: Motion Picture Assoc 1600 I St NW Washington DC 20006-4010 also: MPAA 1133 Avenue Of The Americas New York NY 10036-6710

VALENTI, LEO FRANK, electronics company executive; b. Cleve., Dec. 23, 1925; s. Joseph and Concetta (Giallanza) V. m. Rosalie Regina Caputo, Oct. 29, 1949; children: Thomas, Paul, Mark, Cynthia. BEE, Case Inst. Tech., 1946. Chief engr. Brush-Devel. (Clevite), Cleve., 1947-58; engring. mgr. RCA, Moorestown, N.J., 1958-61; v.p. engring. Techni-Rite, Inc., East Greenwich, R.I., 1961-69, Gulton Industries, Inc., East Greenwich, 1969—; co-owner, bd. dir. Techni-Rite Electronics, Inc.; faculty adviser Hall Inst., Providence. Patentee in field. With USAAF, 1946-47. Mem. Instrument Soc. Am. Republican. Roman Catholic. Home: PO Box 190 East Greenwich RI 02818 Office: Rte 2 and Middle Rd E Greenwich RI 02818

VALENTI, RITA, critical care nurse; b. Pelham, N.Y., Oct. 14, 1948; d. Frank D. and Edythe (McCaffrey) V. Student, Newton (Mass.) Coll., 1966-69; ADN, Clayton State Coll., Jonesboro, Ga., 1983. RN, Ga. Staff and charge nurse DeKalb Gen. Hosp., Decatur, Ga.; staff and charge nurse trauma intermediate ICU, Grady Meml. Hosp., Atlanta; Ga. Ho. of Reps. Dist 52, 1990—; mem. health care adv. com. to Congressman Ben Jones of Ga., 1989—; presenter to numerous profl. and community orgns. on health care crisis, 1985-88. Coord. So. Project on Women's Econ. Rights, 1980-83; chmn. Com. for Health Care Access in Ga., 1986—; del. Nat. Dem. Conv., 1988; mem. exec. com. DeKalb County Dem. Com., 1988; mem. Com. for Nat. Health Plan, 1989—, Physicians for Nat. Plan, 1989—, Nat. Women's Polit. Caucus, 1987—, Ga. Women's Polit. Caucus, 1987—, Rainbow Coalition, 1985—. Recipient Nurses Make a Difference dist. award Ga. Hosp. Assn., 1989, hon. award Ga. Hosp. Assn., 1989, hon. award Rosalyn Carter fellow pub. policy and global affairs Emory U., Mary K. Taylor award, 1992. Mem. ANA, APHA, Ga. Pub. Health Assn., Ga. Nurses Assn. (exec. bd. 1985—, bd. dirs. polit. action com. 1985—, chmn. cabinet on govtl. affairs 1985—, rep. Access to Health Care Commn. of Ga. Gen. Assembly 1989—, honoree 5th dist. 1986, recognition award 1988). Home: 660 Northern Ave Clarkston GA 30021-1914

VALENTIN ACEVEDO, FREDDY, senator; b. Mayaguez, P.R., Nov. 18, 1951; s. Ramon Valentin Cruz and Gloria (Acevedo) Cruz; m. Lourdes Perez Torres, Dec. 13, 1974; children: Lexandra, Freddy, Frederick Valentin Perez. B in Arts and Scis., U.P.R., 1971. Mem. Mayaguez County Assembly, 1972-76; rep. at large Commonwealth of P.R., San Juan, 1976-84; exec. dir. Republican Party, San Juan, 1985-91; sen. at large Commonwealth of P.R., 1992—; chmn. natural resources, environ. and energy affairs com., chmn. nominations com. Senate of P.R.; cons. fed. affairs, San Juan, 1986-90. Nat. del. 4 convs. Rep. Party; mem. appt. and orgn. com. New Progressive Party, San Juan, 1968—. Named Youth of Yr. by P.R. C. of C., 1977. Mem. Nat. State Legislature Conf. (energy com.0. Avocations: reading, swimming, motorcycling, water sports. Office: Senate of Puerto Rico El Capitolio San Juan PR 00901

VALENTINE, ALAN DARRELL, symphony orchestra executive; b. San Antonio, July 18, 1958; s. Lonnie Darrell Jr. and Marjorie (Childs) V.; m. Jari Ann Ruhl, Aug. 10, 1979 (div. 1987); children: Brandon Darrell, Chelsea Michelle; m. Karen Kay Bingham, Oct. 21, 1989; 1 child, Nathan Lee. MusB, U. Houston, 1981. Orch. mgr. U. Houston Symphony, 1977-81; gen. mgr. Mid-Columbia Symphony Soc., Richland, Wash., 1981-83, Greensboro (N.C.) Symphony Soc., 1983-85; orch. mgr. Symphony Soc. San Antonio, 1985-87; mng. dir. Chattanooga Symphony and Opera, 1987-88; exec. dir. Okla. Philharm. Soc., Oklahoma City, 1988-; mem. adj. faculty Arts Administrn., Oklahoma City U., 1992—. Bd. dirs. Classen Sch. for Artistically and Academically Gifted, Arts Festival Okla. Mem. Am. Symphony Orch. League (bd. dirs. Community and Urban Symphony Orch. divsn. 1981-83), Met. Orch. Mgrs. Assn. (cons.), Rotary, Phi Mu Alpha. Presbyterian. Avocations: computers, racquetball, reading. Office: Okla City Philharm 428 W California Ave Ste 210 Oklahoma City OK 73102-2454

VALENTINE, DE WAIN, artist; b. Fort Collins, Colo., Aug. 27, 1936; s. Glenn and Rouine (Lass) V.; m. Jeanne C. Clayman, Feb. 14, 1985; children by previous marriage: Christopher, Sean, Nelsen. BFA, U. Colo., 1958, MFA, 1960; Yale Norfolk fellow, Yale U., 1958. Instr. U. Colo., 1958-61, 64, UCLA, 1965-67; artist-in-residence Aspen Inst., Colo., 1967, 68. One man shows include U. Colo., 1958, 60, The Gallery, Denver, 1964, Douglas Gallery, Vancouver, Can., 1968, Ace Gallery, L.A., 1968, Galerie Birschofberger, Zurich, Switzerland, 1969, Pasadena Mus. Modern Art, Calif. 1970, San Jose Mus., Calif., 1974, Long Beach Mus. Art, Calif., 1975, La Jolla Mus. Contemporary Art, Calif., 1975, Santa Barbara Mus. Art, Calif., 1977, Los Angeles County Mus. Art, 1979; U. Calif.-Irvine, 1979, Inst. Art and Urban Resources, N.Y.C., 1981, Thomas Babcor Gallery, La Jolla, 1982, Laumeier Internat. Sculpture Park, St. Louis, 1982, Madison Art Ctr., Wis., 1983, Honolulu Acad. Arts, 1985, Contemporary Arts Ctr., Honolulu, 1985; group exhbns. include Whitney Ann. Exhibit, 1966, 69, 70, Walker Art Ctr., Mpls., 1969, Milw. Art Ctr., 1971, Am. Ann. Exhbit, Chgo. Art Inst., 1973; represented in permanent collections Los Angeles County Mus. Art, Milw. Art Ctr., Whitney Mus. Am. Art, Chgo. Art Inst., Joslyn Mus. Art, Mus. Contemporary Art., L.A., San Diego Mus. Art, San Diego Mus. Contemporary Art, Plam Springs (Calif.) Desert Mus., Honolulu Acad of Arts, Contemporary Mus., Honolulu, Laguna Beach (Calif.) Mus. Art, Pasadena (Calif.) Art Mus. John Simon Guggenheim fellow, 1980; Nat. Endowment for Arts awardee, 1981. Address: 59-230 Alapio Rd Haleiwa HI 96712

VALENTINE, FOY DAN, clergyman; b. Edgewood, Tex., July 3, 1923; s. John Hardy and Josie (Johnson) V.; m. Mary Louise Valentine, May 6, 1947; children: Mary Jean, Carol Elizabeth, Susan Foy. BA, Baylor U., 1944, LLD (hon.), 1979; ThM, Southwestern Baptist Theol. Sem., 1947, ThD, 1949; DD, William Jewell Coll., 1966, Louisiana Coll., 1989. Ordained to ministry Bapt. Ch., 1942. Dir. Bapt. student activities colls. in Houston, 1949-50; pastor First Bapt. Ch., Gonzales, Tex., 1950-53; dir. Christian life commn. Bapt. Gen. Conv. Tex., 1953-60; exec. dir. treas. Christian life commn. So. Bapt. Conv., 1960-87, exec. officer for devel., 1987-88; chmn. So. Bapt. inter-agy. council, 1965-67; Willson lectr. applied Christianity Wayland Bapt. Coll., 1963; Christian ethics lectr. Bapt. Theol. Sem., Ruschlikon-Zurich, Switzerland, 1966; Layne lectr. New Orleans Bapt. Theol. Sem., 1974; Jones lectr. Union U., 1976; Staley Disting. Christian scholar/lectr. La. Coll., 1981; Simpson lectr. Acadia Divinity Coll., Nova Scotia, 1982; H.I. Hester lectr. on preaching Midwestern Bapt. Theol. Sem., 1984; Belote lectr. Christian ethics Hong Kong Bapt. Theol. Sem., 1990; co-chmn. commn. religious liberty and human rights Bapt. World Alliance, 1966-75, chmn. commn. Christian ethics, 1976-80, mem. gen. coun., 1976-80; mem. Nashville Met. Human Rels. Commn., 1966-78, Pres.'s Commn. for Nat. Agenda for the Eighties, 1980; guest columnist USA Today; lectr. on Christian ethics Bible Inst. for Evangelism and Missions, St. Petersburg, USSR, 1991; pres. Ctr. for Christian Ethics, 1990—. Author: Believe and Behave, 1964, Citizenship for Christians, 1965, The Cross in the Marketplace, 1966, Where the Action Is, 1969, A Historical Study of Southern Baptists and Race Relations 1917-1947, 1980, What Do You Do After You Say Amen?, 1980, Hebrews, James, 1 and 2 Peter: Layman's Bible Book Commentary, 1981; editor: Christian Faith in Action, 1956, Peace, Peace, 1967; contbr. to numerous anthologies; also author articles. Trustee Ams. United for Separation of Ch. and State, 1960-93, pres., 1989-93; bd. dirs. Bapt. Joint Com. Pub. Affairs, 1960-87, Chs. Ctr. Theology and Pub. Policy, 1976-87, T.B. Maston Found., 1988—, Texans Against Gambling, 1990—; mem. bd. fellows Interpreter's House, 1967-78, Ctr. for Dialogue and Devel., 1987—. Recipient Disting. Alumnus award Southwestern Bapt. Theol. Sem., 1970, Brooks Hays Meml. Christian Citizenship award, 1983, Disting. Alumni award Baylor U., 1987. Mem. Am. Soc. Christian Ethics. Democrat. Home and Office: 12527 Matisse Ln Dallas TX 75230-1741

VALENTINE, H. JEFFREY, legal association executive; b. Phila., Sept. 28, 1945; s. Joshua Morton and Olga W. (Wilson) V.; 1 child, Karyn. BS, St. Louis U., 1964, postgrad., 1966-68. Programmer, systems analyst Honeywell Electronic Data Processing, Wellesley Hills, Mass., 1964-66; account exec. Semiconductor div. Tex. Instruments, New Eng., 1966-68; New Eng. sales exec., Mid-Atlantic regional mgr. Electronic Instrumentation Co., 1968-70; pres. Nat. Free Lance Photographers Assn., Doylestown, Pa., 1970-89; pres., dir. Towne Print & Copy Ctrs. Inc.; exec. dir. Nat. Paralegal Assn., 1982—; pres. Paralegal Assocs., Inc., 1982—; chief operating officer Doylestown Parking Corp., 1977-88; bd. dir. Law Enforcement Supply. Co., Solebury, Valtronics Supply Co., Towne Print & Copy Ctrs. Inc., Solebury, Doylestown Stationery and Office Supply, Energy Mktg. Assocs. Inc., Solebury, Paralegal Placement Network; pres. Paralegal Pub. Corp., 1983-90; pub. Paralegal Jour.; pres. Valco Enterprises Inc., 1986—; Paralegal Employment Systems, Inc., 1988, Solebury Press Inc., 1989—. Author: Photographers Bookkeeping System, 1973, rev. edit., 1978, Photographers Pricing Guides, 1971, 72, 74, 75, Available Markets Director's - 4 Vols., 1973-77, National Model Sources Directory, Nat. Paralegal Salary and Employment Survey, 1985-86, 88, 90-92, 93-94; also articles, bulls. and pamphlets. Exec. sec. Doylestown Bus. Assn., 1972-78, pres., 1979, 83, v.p., 1981. Recipient Internat. Men of Achievement award, 1988; named Personalities of the Am., 1988. Mem. London Coll. Applied Scis., Nat. Fedn. Paralegal Assns., Photog. Industry Coun., Nat. Assn. Legal Assts., Am. Soc. Assn. Execs., Soc. Assn. Mgrs., Nat. Fedn. Ind. Business (mem. action coun. com.), Nat. Parking Assn., Nat. Office Products Assn., Graphic Arts Assn. Delaware Valley, Nat. Assn. Federally Licensed Firearms Dealers, Nat. Compostition Assn., Internat. Platform Assn. Office: PO Box 406 Solebury PA 18963-0406

VALENTINE, HERMAN EDWARD, computer company executive; b. Norfolk, Va., June 26, 1937; s. Frank and Alice Mae (Heigh) V.; m. Dorothy Jones, Nov. 27, 1958; children: Herman Edward, Bryce Thomas. BS in Bus. Adminstrn., Norfolk State Coll., 1967; postgrad., Am. U., 1968; grad. student, Coll. William and Mary. Asst. bus. mgr. grad. sch. Dept. Agr., 1967, exec. officer grad. sch., 1967-68; bus. mgr. Norfolk State Coll. 1968; chmn., pres. Systems Mgmt. Am. Corp., Norfolk, 1969—; chmn. Century Capitol Holders, Inc. Bd. dirs. PUSH Internat. Trade Bur., Cooperating Hampton Roads Orgn. for Minorities in Engring., Operation Smile, Greater Norfolk Corp.; mem. president's coun. Old Dominion U.; mem. adv. bd. Tidewater Vets. Meml. Project; mem. adv. coun. Va. Stage Co. Named Entrepreneur of Yr. Dept. Commerce Minority Bus. Devel. Agy., 1984, one of 10 Top Minority Owned Fed. Govt. Contractors Govt. Computer News, 1988, Outstanding Business Person of Yr. Va. Black Pres.'s Roundtable Assn., 1987, Amb. City of Norfolk, Va., 1986, Citizen of Yr. William A. Hunton YMCA, 1986, Pres.'s Coun. Am. Inst. Mgmt.; recipient Cert. of Merit City of Chg., 1985, McDonald's Hampton Roads Black Achievement award United Negro Coll. Fund., 1986, Colgate Whitehead Darden award, U. Va., 1987, cert. recognition Lt. Gov. Commonwealth of Va., 1987, Class III Supplier of Yr. award Nat. Minority Supplier Devel. Coun., 1987, Regional Minority Mfr. of Yr. award Minority Bus. Devel. Agy., 1988, Patriotic Svc. award U.S. Treasury Dept., 1989, Black Diamond award Operation Push, 1989; recognized by Upscale Mag., 1993. Mem. Armed Forces Communications and Electronics Assn., Tidewater Regional Minority Purchasing Coun., Downtown Norfolk Devel. Corp., Air Traffic Control Assn., Soc. Logistics Engrs., U.S. Navy League, Hampton Roads C. of C. Office: Systems Mgmt Am Corp 5 Koger Ctr Ste 219 Norfolk VA 23502

VALENTINE, JAMES WILLIAM, paleobiology, educator, author; b. Los Angeles, Nov. 10, 1926; s. Adelbert Cuthbert and Isabel (Davis) V.; m. Grace Evelyn Whysner, Dec. 21, 1957 (div. 1972); children—Anita, Ian; m. Cathryn Alice Campbell, Sept. 10, 1978 (div. 1986); 1 child, Geoffrey; m. Diane Mondragon, Mar. 16, 1987. B.A., Phillips U., 1951; M.A., UCLA, 1954, Ph.D., 1958. From asst. prof. to assoc. prof. U. Mo., Columbia, 1958-64; from assoc. prof. to prof. U. Calif., Davis, 1964-77; prof. geol. scis. U. Calif., Santa Barbara, 1977-90; prof. integrative biology U. Calif., Berkeley, 1990—. Author: Evolutionary Paleoecology of the Marine Biosphere, 1973; editor: Phanerozoic Diversity, 1985; co-author: Evolution, 1977, Evolving, 1979; also numerous articles, 1954—. Served with USNR, 1944-46; PTO. Fulbright research scholar, Australia, 1962-63; Guggenheim fellow Yale U., Oxford U., Eng., 1968-69; Rockefeller Found. scholar in residence, Bellagio, Italy, summer 1974; grantee NSF, NASA. Fellow Am. Acad. Arts and Scis., AAAS, Geol. Soc. Am.; mem. Nat. Acad. Scis., Paleontol. Soc. (pres. 1974-75). Avocation: collecting works of Charles Darwin. Home: 1351 Glendale Ave Berkeley CA 94708-2025 Office: U Calif Dept Integrative Biolo Berkeley CA 94720

VALENTINE, JOHN LESTER, state legislator, lawyer; b. Fullerton, Calif., Apr. 26, 1949; s. Robert Lester and Pauline C. (Glood) V.; m. Karen Marie Thorpe, Jan. 7, 1972; children: John Robert, Jeremy Reid, Staci Marie, Jeffrey Mark., David Emerson, Patricia Ann. BS in Acctg. and Econs., Brigham Young U., 1973, JD, 1976. Bar: Utah 1976, U.S. Dist. Ct. Utah, U.S. Ct. Appeals (10th cir.), U.S. Tax Ct.; CPA. Atty. Howard, Lewis & Petersen, Provo, Utah, 1976—; mem. Utah Ho. Reps., 1988—; instr. probate and estates Utah Valley State Coll.; instr. film. planning., adj. prof. law Brigham Young U.; mem. exec offices, cts., corrections and legis. appropriations subcom., 1988-90, capital facilities subcom., 1988-90, retirement com., 1988-90, judiciary com., 1988—, strategic planning steering com., 1988-90, interim appropriations com., 1988—, tax. review commn., 1988-92, ethics com., 1990-92, human svcs. and health appropriations subcom., 1990-92, revenue and taxation com., 1988—, vice chmn. 1990-92; vice chmn. exec. appropriations., 1990-92, chmn. 1992—; chmn. exec. appropriations com.,

1992-94, chmn. rules com., 1994, higher edn. appropriations com. 1994; bd. dirs. Utah Corrections Industries. Mem. adv. bd. Internat. Sr. Games, 1988—; active Blue Ribbon Task Force on Local Govt. Funding, Utah League Cities and Towns, 1990—, Criminal Sentencing Guidelines Task Force, Utah Judicial Coun., 1990-92, Access to Health Care Task Force, 1990-92, Utah County Sheriff Search and Rescue, Orem Met. Water Bd., Alpine Sch. Dist. Boundary Line Com., Boy Scouts Am.; bd. regents Legis. Adv. Com. UVCC.; mem. exec. bd. Utah Nat. Parks Coun.; mem. adv. coun. Orchard Elem. Sch., Mountainlands Com. an Aging; bd. trustees Utah Opera Co.; judge nat. and local competitions Moot Ct.; voting dist. chmn.; state, county del.; lt. incident command sys. Utah County Sheriff. Recipient Silver Beaver award Boy Scouts Am., Taxpayer Advocate award Utah Taxpayer Assn. Mem. ABA (tax sect.), Utah State Bar, CPA Com., Tax Sect. Specialization Com., Bicentennial Com. Republican. Mormon. Avocation: mountain climbing. Office: Howard Lewis & Petersen 120 E 300 N Provo UT 84603-0778

VALENTINE, RALPH SCHUYLER, chemical engineer, research director; b. Seattle, Nov. 3, 1932; s. John Campbell and Elizabeth Florence (Patterson) V.; m. Jeanne Marie Belanger, June 15, 1957; children: Susan Diana, Jacqueline Leigh, John Campbell. BSChemE, U. Wash., 1955, PhDChemE, 1963; MSChemE, U. Ill., 1956. Registered profl. engr., Calif., Va., Wash. Rsch. engr. Chevron Rsch. Corp., Richmond, Calif., 1956-61; instr. U. Wash., Seattle, 1961-63; mgr. fluid dynamics Aerojet-Gen., Sacramento, 1963-69; mgr. chem. tech. Atlantic Rsch. Corp., Alexandria, Va., 1969-79; mgr. United Techs. Chem. Systems, San Jose, Calif., 1979-91; lectr. U.S. Naval Postgrad. Sch., Monterrey, Calif., 1968, UCLA Modern Devels. in Propulsion, L.A., 1967-68, USAF Astronautics Labs., Lancaster, Calif., 1967, U.S. Army R & D Unit, Sacramento, 1966. Contbr. 23 tech. articles to profl. jours.; patentee in field. Recipient NASA commendation for Apollo work, Houston, 1969, 1st prize Ceramographic Exhbn. Am. Ceramics Soc., 1974. Mem. Am. Inst. Chem. Engrs. (life). Republican. Home: 7242 Via Mimosa San Jose CA 95135-1413

VALENTINE, STEVEN RICHARDS, lawyer; b. Memphis, Jan. 30, 1956; s. William Robert and Lenita Joanne (Nelms) V.; m. Susan Marie Burke, Jan. 14, 1984; children: Christina Michele, William Robert II, Steven Richards Jr., Thomas Burke. Student, Earlham Coll., 1974-77; BGS with distinction, Ind. U., 1979, JD, 1982. Bar: Ill. 1983, D.C. 1985, U.S. Ct. Appeals (D.C. cir.) 1986, U.S. Supreme Ct. 1986, U.S. Ct. Appeals (9th cir.) 1989. Chief investigator consumer protection div. Office Atty. Gen., State of Ind., 1980-82; exec. dir. Ams. United for Life Legal Def. Fund, Chgo., 1982-83; chief counsel subcom. on separation of powers U.S. Senate, Washington, 1983-85, chief counsel subcom. on cts., 1985; adminstrv. asst. Senator John P. East, 1985-86; dir. Office of Policy Devel. Legal Svcs. Corp., 1986-87; counselor to asst. atty. gen. Civil div. U.S. Dept. Justice, 1987-88; dep. asst. atty. gen. Civil div. U.S. Justice Dept., 1988-93; gen. counsel U.S. Senator Robert C. Smith, 1993—; sec. bd. dirs. Deluxe West, Inc., Yokefellows Internat., Inc.; D. Elton Trueblood Acad. Endowment, Inc. Author: Each Time A Man, 1978, All Shall Live, 1980, (with others) Abortion and the Constitution, 1987; contbr. articles to profl. jours. Recipient U.S. Atty. Gen.'s Spl. Commendation award, 1993. Mem. SAR, Federalist Soc., Sons of Union Vets. of the Civil War, Capitol Hill Club. Republican. Roman Catholic. Avocations: history, baseball. Home: 6513 Old Coach Ct Alexandria VA 22315-5045 Office: 332 Dirksen Ofc Bldg Washington DC 20510-2903

VALENTINE, WILLIAM EDSON, architect; b. Winston-Salem, N.C., Sept. 3, 1937; s. Howard Leon and Sally (Cunningham) V.; m. Jane Dorward, Aug. 13, 1939; children: Anne, Karen, William. BArch, N.C. State U., 1960; MArch, Harvard U., 1962. Prin. Hellmuth, Obata & Kassabaum Inc., San Francisco, 1962—; chmn. Hellmuth, Obata & Kassabaum Design Bd., also bd. dirs. Served to 1st lt. U.S. Army, 1960-61. Fellow AIA. Club: Harvard. Office: Hellmuth Obata & Kassabaum Inc 71 Stevenson St Ste 2200 San Francisco CA 94105

VALENTINE, WILLIAM NEWTON, physician, educator; b. Kansas City, Mo., Sept. 29, 1917; s. Herbert S. and Mabel W. (Watson) V.; m. Martha Hickman Winfree; children: William, James, Edward. Student, U. Mich., Ann Arbor, 1934-36, U. Mo., Columbia, 1936-37; MD, Tulane U., New Orleans, 1942. Diplomate: Am. Bd. Internal Medicine. Intern Strong Meml. Hosp., Rochester, N.Y., 1942-43, asst. resident in medicine, 1943, chief resident in medicine, 1943-44; specialist, attending physician in internal medicine Wadsworth Hosp., L.A., 1949-88, VA Ctr., L.A., 1949-88; specialist, attending physician in internal medicine Ctr. Health Scis. UCLA, 1949—, prof. medicine, 1957-88, chmn. dept., 1963-71; prof. emeritus medicine UCLA, Los Angeles, 1988—. Contbr. articles to profl. jours. Served to capt. MC, AUS, 1944-47. Recipient Mayo Soley award for excellence in research Western Soc. Clin. Research, 1978; 53d Annual UCLA faculty research lectr., 1978; Henry Stratton lectr. Am. Soc. Hematology, 1978; John Phillips Meml. award for Disting. Achievements in Internal Medicine, ACP, 1979. Fellow Am. Soc. Hematology, Internat. Soc. Hematology (v.p. U.S. 1976-80); mem. Am. Bd. Internal Medicine, ACP (master), Am. Soc. Clin. Investigation (v.p. 1962), Assn. Am. Physicians, Nat. Acad. Scis., Western Assn. Physicians (pres. 1969-70), Western Soc. Clin. Research. Am. Acad. Arts and Scis. Republican.

VALENTINI, ROBERT M., telecommunications industry executive; b. 1943. Grad., Rider Coll. 1965. With Bell Atlantic, 1965—; now pres., CEO Bell Telephone Co. Pa. Office: Bell Telephone Co of PA 1 Parkway # 16B Philadelphia PA 19102-1589*

VALENTINO (VALENTINO GARAVANI), fashion designer; b. Voghera, Italy, May 11, 1932. Student, Academia Dell'Arte, Paris, Ecole des Beaux-Arts, Paris. Asst. designer Fashion Ho. of Jean Desses, 1950-55, Fashion Ho. of Guy Laroche, 1956-58; co-owner Valentino Fashion Ho., Rome, 1960; developer Valentino Più, 1973; owner various boutiques, Rome, Milan, other cities. Exhibited at Victoria and Albert Mus., London, 1971, La Jolla Mus. Art, Calif., 1982; costume designer (films) Wild and Wonderful, 1964, Hello-Goodbye, 1970. Recipient Neiman-Marcus award, 1967. Office: Via Gregoriana 24, 00187 Rome Italy also: 823-825 Madison Ave New York NY 10021

VALENTINO, F. WILLIAM, energy executive. Pres. N.Y. State Energy Rsch. and Devel., Albany. Office: NY State Energy Rsch 2 Rockefeller Plz Albany NY 12223

VALENZUELA, JULIO SAMUEL, sociologist, educator; b. Concepción, Chile, Mar. 30, 1948; came to U.S., 1970; s. Raimundo Arms and Dorothy Dueul (Bowie) V.; m. Erika Fresia Maza, Mar. 22, 1969. Licenciatura, Universidad de Concepcion, 1970; PhD, Columbia U., 1979. Asst. prof. Yale U., New Haven, 1977-80; asst. prof. Harvard U., Cambridge, Mass., 1980-85, assoc. prof., 1986; assoc. prof. U. Notre Dame, Ind., 1987-89, prof., dept. chairperson, 1989-92, fellow Kellogg Inst., 1987—; sr. assoc. fellow St. Antony's Coll., Oxford U., 1992-93. Author: Democratizacion via Reforma, 1986; co-editor: Chile: Politics And Society, 1976, Military Rule In Chile, 1986, Issues In Democratic Consolidation, 1992; contbr. chpts. to books, articles to profl. jours. Fellow NEH ind. scholarship rsch. 1983-84, conf. grant 1987. Mem. Am. Sociol. Assn., Internat. Sociol. Assn. (v.p. rsch. com. #44 1990—), Latin Am. Studies Assn. (nominating com. 1987-88); New Eng. Coun. Latin Am. Studies (pres. 1984-85). Methodist. Office: U Notre Dame Dept Sociology Notre Dame IN 46556

VALERIANI, RICHARD GERARD, news broadcaster; b. Camden, N.J., Aug. 29, 1932; s. Nicholas and Christine (Camerota) V.; m. Kathie Berlin, Apr. 20, 1980; 1 child, Kimberly. BA, Yale U., 1953; postgrad., U. Pavia, Italy, 1953-54, U. Barcelona, Spain, 1954. Reporter The Trentonian, Trenton, 1957; with AP, 1957-61; corr. AP, Havana, Cuba, 1959-61; with NBC-TV News, 1961—; corr. NBC-TV News, Washington, 1964-83; nat. corr. NBC-TV News, N.Y., 1983-88; free-lance journalist, 1988—; participant 2d Carter-Ford debate, 1976. Author: Travels With Henry, 1979; actor: (feature film) Crimson Tide, 1995. With AUS, 1955-56. Recipient Overseas Press Club award for best radio reporting, 1965. Mem. Elihu Soc., Yale Club (N.Y.C.). Home: 23 Island View Dr Sherman CT 06784-2036

VALERIO, JOSEPH M., architectural firm executive, educator; b. Dec. 26, 1947; m. Linda A. Searl; children: Joseph Jr., Anthony. BArch, U. Mich. 1970; MArch, UCLA, 1972. Registered architect, Wis., Ill., Ind., Mo., Calif., Tex., Ariz., Minn., Ala., Iowa, Ind.; cert. Nat. Coun. Archtl. Registration Bds. Pres. Chrysalis Corp. Architects, 1970-85; assoc. prof. U. Wis. 1973-86; design dir. Swanke Hayden Connell Architects, 1985-86; v.p. architecture A. Epstein and Sons, Inc., 1986-88; pres. Valerio-Assocs. Inc., 1988-94; prin. Valerio Dewalt Train Assocs., Inc., Chgo., 1994—; speaker Ariz. State U., UCLA, U. Ariz., U. Cin., others; cons. USG Interiors, Formica Corp., AAAS, NAS, NEA: vis. critic and lectr. in field. Prin. works include corp., retail, health and residential bldgs.; author: Movie Palaces, 1983; editor: Architectural Fabric Structures, 1985. Mem. exec. bd. men's coun. Mus. Contemporary Art, 1989-91; mem. exec. bd. Contemporary Arts Coun., 1994. Recipient Honor awards Wis. Soc. Architects, 1975, 81, 84, 85, Gov.'s Award for Design Excellence, State of Mich., 1979, Gold medal Inst. Bus. Designers, 1988, Design award Progressive Architecture, 1991, Disting. Interior award Inst. Bus. Designers, Chgo., 1993; honored by Emerging Voices series Archtl. League N.Y., Met. Home mag., Interiors mag. Fellow AIA (programs chmn. design com. Chgo. chpt. 1990, mem. long range planning com. 1992, Nat. Honor award 1981, 93, Interiors award Chgo. chpt. 1988, 90, 92, Disting. Bldg. award 1991, 93, Nat. Interior award 1993), Chgo. Architecture Club (pres. 1994). Office: Valerio Dewalt Train Assocs 200 N La Salle St Ste 2400 Chicago IL 60601

VALERIO, MICHAEL ANTHONY, financial executive; b. Detroit, Sept. 20, 1953; s. Anthony Rudolph and Victoria (Popoff) V.; m. Barbara Ann Nabozny, Oct. 8, 1983. BA, U. Mich. Dearborn, 1975. CPA, Mich. Jr. acct. Carabell, Bocknek CPA's, Southfield, Mich., 1975-76; sr. acct. Purdy, Donovan & Beal, CPA's, Detroit, 1976-77; mgr. Buctynck & Co., CPA's, Southfield, 1978-79; controller Transcontinental Travel, Harper Woods, Mich., 1979-80; exec. v.p. Holland Cons., Inc., Detroit, 1980-85; controller, CFO SLC Recycling Industries, Inc., Warren, Mich., 1985—; owner Pinnacle Fin. Consulting, 1994—. Mem. AICPA, Mich. Soc. CPAs, Acctg. Rsch. Found. Roman Catholic. Office: SLC Recycling Industries Inc 21000 Hoover Rd Warren MI 48089-3183

VALERO, RENÉ ARNOLD, clergyman; b. N.Y.C., Aug. 15, 1930; s. Caesar J. and Maria Luisa (Cordova) Valero; BA. in Liberal Arts, Immaculate Conception-Cathedral Coll., 1952; M.S.W., Fordham U., 1962. Ordained to ministry Roman Cath. Ch., 1956; asso. pastor St. Michael-St. Edward, Bklyn., 1956-57, St. Agatha, Bklyn., 1957-60; dir. Bklyn. Cath. Charities Family Service, 1960-69; dir. Bklyn. Diocesan Office for Aging, 1969-74; coordinator Bklyn. Diocesan Hispanic Apostolate, 1974-79; pastor Blessed Sacrament, Jackson Heights, N.Y., 1979—; aux. bishop Diocese of Bklyn., 1980—; vicar for immigrants and refugees Diocese of Bklyn., 1983-90; regional bishop Queens, 1990-94, Queens North, 1994—. Home: 34-43 93rd St Jackson Heights NY 11372 Office: Immaculate Conception Ctr 7200 Douglaston Pkwy Flushing NY 11362

VALESIO, PAOLO, Italian language and literature educator, writer; b. Bologna, Italy, Oct. 14, 1939; came to U.S., 1963; s. germano and Maria (Galletti) V.; 1 child, Sara. Dottorato in Lettere, U. Bologna, 1961, Libera Docenza in Glottologia, 1969; MA (hon.), Yale U., 1976. Lectr. Istituto di Glottologia, U. Bologna, 1961-62, 67-68; teaching fellow dept. Romance langs. and lit. Harvard U., Cambridge, Mass., 1964-65; lectr., 1969-70, assoc. prof., 1970-73; assoc. prof. Italian, dir. grad. studies dept. French and Italian NYU, 1973-75; prof. Italian, chmn. dept. Yale U., New Haven, Conn., 1976-88, dir. grad. studies dept. Italian, 1989—. Author: Novantiqua, 1980, Ascoltare il Silenzio, 1986, Gabriele d'Annunzio: The Dark Flame, 1992, (novel) I Regno Doloroso, 1983, (poems) La Rosa Verde, 1987, Le Isole del Lago, 1990, Analogia del Mondo, 1992, (stories) S'Ilcontrano Gli Amanti, 1993; co-editor: Vocabolario Zingarelli, Bologna, 1970; am. corr. MagazinePoesia, Milan, 1992—. Recipient first prize Biennial Nat. Poetry Competition San Vito, 1992, Lit. prize Am. Assn. Italian Studies, 1993; named Cavaliere Ufficiale, Order of Merit of Republic of Italy, 1994. Roman Catholic. Office: Yale Univ Dept Italian PO Box 208311 New Haven CT 06520-8311

VALETTE, REBECCA MARIANNE, Romance languages educator; b. N.Y.C., Dec. 21, 1938; d. Gerhard and Ruth Adelgunde (Bischoff) Loose; m. Jean-Paul Valette, Aug. 6, 1959; children: Jean-Michel, Nathalie, Pierre. BA, Mt. Holyoke Coll., 1959, LHD (hon.), 1974; PhD, U. Colo., 1963. Instr., examiner in French and German U. So. Fla., 1961-63; instr. NATO Def. Coll., Paris, 1963-64, Wellesley Coll., 1964-65; asst. prof. Romance Langs. Boston Coll., 1965-68, assoc., 1968-73, prof., 1973—; lectr., cons. fgn. lang. pedagogy; Fulbright sr. lectr., Germany, 1974; Am. Council on Edn. fellow in acad. adminstrn., 1976-77. Author: Modern Language Testing, 1967, rev. edit., 1977, French for Mastery, 1975, rev. edit., 1988, Contacts, 1976, rev. edit., 1993, C'est Comme Ça, 1978, rev. edit., 1986, Spanish for Mastery, 1980, rev. edit., 1989, 94, Album: Cuentos del Mundo Hispanico, 1984, rev. edit., 1992, French for Fluency, 1985, Statistics, 1988, rev. edit., 1994, Discovering French, 1994, A votre tour, 1995; contbr. articles to fgn. lang. pedagogy and lit. publs. Decorated Palmes académiques (France). Mem. Modern Lang. Assn. (chmn. div. on teaching of lang. 1980-81), Am. Coun. on Teaching Fgn. Langs., Am. Assn. Tchrs. French (v.p. 1980-86, pres. 1992-94), Am. Assn. Tchrs. German, Phi Beta Kappa, Alpha Sigma Nu, Palmes Academiques. Home: 16 Mt Alvernia Rd Chestnut Hill MA 02167-1019 Office: Boston Coll Lyons 311 Chestnut Hill MA 02167

VALIANT, LESLIE GABRIEL, computer scientist; b. Mar. 28, 1949; s. Leslie and Eva Julia (Ujlaki) V.; m. Gayle Lynne Dyckoff, 1977; children—Paul A., Gregory J. M.A., Kings Coll., Cambridge, U.K., 1970; D.I.C., Imperial Coll., London, 1971; Ph.D., U. Warwick, U.K., 1974. Vis. asst. prof. Carnegie-Mellon U., Pitts., 1973-74; lectr. U. Leeds, Eng., 1974-76; lectr., reader U. Edinburgh, Scotland, 1977-82; vis. prof. Harvard U., 1982, Gordon McKay prof. computer sci. and applied math., 1982—. Guggenheim fellow, 1985-86; recipient Nevanlinna prize Internat. Math. Union, 1986. Fellow Royal Soc., Am. Assn. for Artificial Intelligence. Office: Harvard U 33 Oxford St Cambridge MA 02138-2901

VALINSKY, MARK STEVEN, podiatrist; b. Chgo., May 24, 1951; m. Michelle Susan Morgan; children: Cara Linda, Erin Abra, Noah Allen, Hannah Rae, Arielle Lauren. Student in biology and pre-medicine, Ohio State U., 1969-71, SUNY, Buffalo, 1971-72; BS, D in Podiatric Medicine, Ill. Coll. Podiatric Medicine, 1976; MD (hon.), Inst. Orthopaedics & Traumatology China Acad. Traditonal Medicine, Beijing, 1989. Lic. podiatrist, Ill., Calif., N.Y.; diplomate Am. Bd. Podiatry Examiners, Am. Bd. Ambulatory Foot Surgery; cert. Am. Coun. Cert. Podiatric Physicians and Surgeons. Pvt. practice podiatric surgery Oak Park, Ill., 1977—; founder, dir. The Foot Care Ctr., P.C., Oak Park; mem. 1st foot surg. team to China, 1983, also 1987; instr. minimal incision foot surgery to orthopaedic surgeons in China; lectr. 1st Sino Nat. Am. Treatise of Foot Disorders, Beijing, 1987, vis. prof., 1989; pres., founder Biol. Scis. Rsch. Inst., Inc.; lectr. on minimal incision and radiowave foot surgery in Australia and throughout U.S.; internat. lectr. and tchr. on health care of feet, also radio and TV appearances. Columnist Focus on the Foot; contbr. articles to profl. and popular publs.; author video tapes in field. Former mem. Chgo. Mayor's Coun. for Sr. Citizens and Handicapped. Mem. Am. Inst. Foot Medicine (cert.), Ill. Podiatric Soc. (sec. Zone I, 1980-82, zone pres. 1981-82, del. to bd. dirs. 1980-82), Am. Podiatric Soc., Podiatric Med. Assn., Acad. Ambulatory Foot Surgeons (pres. midwest region 1986), Oak Park-River Forest C. of C. (bd. dirs.), Am. Karate Assn. Office: 163 S Oak Park Ave Oak Park IL 60302-2901 also: 4600 N Harlem Ave at Wilson Harwood Heights IL 60656 also: Water Tower 845 N Michigan Ave Chicago IL 60611

VALK, HENRY SNOWDEN, physicist, educator; b. Washington, Jan. 26, 1929; s. Henry Snowden and Dorothy (Blencowe) V.; m. Gillian Wedderburn, June 20, 1968; children—Alison, Diana, Robert. Richard. B.S. George Washington U., 1953, M.S. (Agnes and Eugene Meyer scholar), 1954; postgrad., Johns Hopkins, 1953-54; Ph.D. (Shell fellow), Washington U., St. Louis, 1957. Profl. asst. NSF, 1957, asst. program dir. physics, 1959-60; asst. prof. physics U. Oreg., 1957-59; mem. faculty U. Nebr., 1960-70, prof. physics, 1964-70, chmn. dept., 1966-70; prof. physics Coll. Scis. and Liberal Studies, Ga. Inst. Tech., Atlanta, 1970—, acting dir. physics, 1991—, dean, 1970-82; cons. physics sect. NSF, 1961-62, program dir. theoretical physics, 1965-66; chmn. Gordon Rsch. Conf. Photonuclear Reactions, 1969;

vis. prof. U. Frankfurt/Main, Germany, 1970, Rensselaer Poly. Inst., 1982, 88, Cath. U. Am., 1982-83, 88-89; chmn. SE regional Marshall scholarship com., 1974-92. Author: (with M. Alonso) Quantum Mechanics: Principles and Applications, 1973; contbr. articles to profl. jours. Decorated Most Excellent Order Brit. Empire. Fellow Am. Phys. Soc.; mem. Am. Math. Soc., Am. Assn. Physics Tchrs., Math. Assn. Am., Cosmos Club (Washington), Phi Beta Kappa, Sigma Xi. Home: 3032 St Helena Dr Tucker GA 30084-2227

VALK, ROBERT EARL, corporate executive; b. Muskegon, Mich., Aug. 21, 1914; s. Allen and Lulu (Schuler) V.; m. Ann Parker, August 9, 1941 (div. July 1959); children: James A., Sara C.; m. Alice Melick, Dec. 29, 1960; children: Marie, Susan. B.S. in Mech. Engring. U. Mich., 1938. With Nat. Supply Co., 1938-55; plant mgr. Nat. Supply Co., Houston, 1945-48; works mgr. Nat. Supply Co., Toledo, Houston and Gainesville, Tex., 1949-55; asst. v.p. prodn. Electric Auto-Lite Co., Toledo, 1956, v.p., group exec. gen. products, 1960-66; gen. mgr. mfg. automotive div. Essex Internat., Inc., 1960-66, v.p. corp., gen. mgr. automotive div., 1966-74; pres. ITT Automotive Elec. Products Div., 1974-80; v.p. ITT N.Am. Automotive Ops. Worldwide, 1980-86; chmn. Chamberlin, Davis, Rutan & Valk, 1986—; bd. dirs. Breed Techs., Inc., Lakeland, Fla.; trustee Henry Ford Health Care System, Detroit. Trustee Cottage Hosp., Grosse Pointe; chmn. adv. bd. St. Luke's Episcopal Ch. Home; bd. dirs. Ecumenical Theological Ctr. Mem. Am. Soc. Naval Engrs., Soc. Automotive Engrs., Am. Ordnance Assn., Am. Mgmt. Assn., Air Force Assn., Am. Mfrs. Assn., Wire Assn., Nat. Elec. Mfrs. Assn., Engring. Soc. Detroit. Republican. Episcopalian. Clubs: Country (Detroit), Yondotega, Economics (Detroit); Grosse Pointe, Bay View Yacht; Little Harbor (Harbor Springs, Mich.). Home: 80 Renaud Rd Grosse Pointe MI 48236-1742 Office: 21 Kercheval Ave Ste 270 Grosse Pointe MI 48236-3601

VALLANCE, JAMES, church administrator, religious publication editor. Dir. Master's Men Dept. of the Nat. Assn. of Free Will Baptists, Antioch, Tenn.; pub. Attack, A Magazine for Christian Men. Office: Natl Assn of Free Will Baptists PO Box 5002 Antioch TN 37011

VALLAT, LOUISE MARIE, elementary school educator, poet; b. Bklyn., Jan. 13, 1945; d. Joseph Anthony and Marie (Curcio) DeRiggi; m. Bruce Robert Vallat, Sept. 3, 1966; children: Anthony Joseph, Deborah Maria. BA, CUNY-Queens Coll., 1976, MS in Elem. Edn., 1991. Cert. elem. tchr., elem. English tchr., N.Y. Tchr. Bd. Edn., N.Y.C. Pub. Schs., Bklyn., 1990—. Author: (poetry) From Kindergarten to Graduate School, 1992; contbr. poetry to Am. Poetry Anthologies, 1990. Named Poet of Merit, finalist Poet of Yr. contest Am. Poetry Assn., Santa Cruz, Calif., 1990; recipient Editor's Choice award Nat. Libr. Congress, 1993. Mem. Nat. Writing Project. Avocations: writing, painting, organ and guitar, storytelling, poetry.

VALLBONA, RIMA-GRETEL ROTHE, foreign language educator, writer; b. San Jose, Costa Rica, Mar. 15, 1931; d. Ferdinand Hermann and Emilia (Strassburger) Rothe; m. Carlos Vallbona, Dec. 26, 1956; children: Rima-Nuri, Carlos-Fernando, Maria-Teresa, Maria-Luisa. BA/BS, Colegio Superior de Senoritas, San Jose, 1948; diploma, U. Paris, 1953; diploma in Spanish Philology, U. Salamanca, Spain, 1954; MA, U. Costa Rica, 1962; D in Modern Langs., Middlebury Coll., 1981. Tchr. Liceo J.J. Vargas Calvo, Costa Rica, 1955-56; faculty U. St. Thomas, Houston, 1964—, prof. Spanish, 1978—, Cullen Found. prof. Spanish, 1989, head dept. Spanish, 1966-71, chmn. dept. modern fgn. lang., 1978-80, prof. emeritus, 1980—; vis. prof. U. Houston, 1975-76, Rice U., 1980-83, U. St. Thomas, Argentina, 1972, vis. prof. U. St. Thomas Merida program, 1987-91; vis. prof. Rice U. program in Spain, 1974. Author: Noche en Vela, 1968, Yolanda Oreamuno, 1972, La Obra en Prosa de Eunice Odio, 1981, Baraja de Soledades, Las Sombras que Perseguimos, 1983, Polvo del Camino, 1972, La Salamandra Rosada, 1979, Mujeres y Agonias, 1982, Cosecha de Pecadores, 1988, El arcangel del perdon, 1990, Mundo, demonio y mujer, 1991, Los infiernos de la mujer y algo mas, 1992, Vida i sucesos de la Monja Alférez, critical edition, 1992, Flowering Inferno-Tales of Sinking Hearts, 1994; mem. editorial bd. Letras Femeninas, Alba de America, U.S.; co-dir. Foro Literario, Uruguay, 1987-89; contbg. editor The Americas Review, 1989—; contbr. numerous articles and short stories to lit. mags. Mem. scholarship com. Inst. Hispanic Culture, 1978-79, 88, 91, chmn., 1979, bd. dirs., 1974-76, 88-89, 91-92, chmn. cultural activities, 1979, 80, 85, 88-89; bd. dirs. Houston Pub. Libr. 1984-86; bd. dirs. Cultural Arts Coun. of Houston, 1991-92. Recipient Aquileo J. Echeverria Novel prize, 1968, Agripina Montes del Valle Novel prize, 1978, Jorge Luis Borges Short Story prize, Argentina, 1977, Lit. award S.W. Conf. Latin Am. Studies, 1982; Constantin Found. grantee for rsch. U. St. Thomas, 1981; Ancora Lit. award, Costa Rica, 1984, Civil Merit award King Juan Carlos I of Spain, 1989. Mem. MLA, Am. Assn. Tchrs. Spanish and Portuguese, Houston Area Tchrs. of Fgn. Langs., South Cen. MLA, S.W. conf. Orgn. Latin Am. Studies, Latin Am. Studies Assn., Inst. Internat. de Lit. Iberoam., Latin Am. Writers Assn. of Costa Rica, Inst. Hispanic Culture of Houston, Casa Argentina de Houston, Inst. Lit. y Cultural Hispanico, Phi Sigma Iota, Sigma Delta Pi (hon.), Nat. Writers Assn. Roman Catholic. Home: 3706 Lake St Houston TX 77098-5522 Office: 3800 Montrose Blvd Houston TX 77006

VALLE, LAURENCE FRANCIS, lawyer; b. N.Y.C., Feb. 16, 1943; s. Mario John and Marian Josephine (Longinotti) V.; m. Joan Strachan, June 11, 1966; children: Christopher John, Stacia Lynn. BS, U. Miami, 1966, JD, 1969. Bar: Fla. 1969, U.S. Ct. Mil. Appeals 1970, U.S. Dist. Ct. (so. and mid. dists.) Fla. 1975, U.S. Ct. Appeals (D.C. cir.) 1975, U.S. Ct. Appeals (5th and 11th cirs.) 1981, U.S. Dist. Ct. (we. dist.) Tex. 1989. Assoc. Underwood, Gillis & Karcher PA, Miami, Fla., 1973-77; ptnr. Underwood, Gillis, Karcher & Valle PA, Miami, 1977-87, Dixon, Dixon, Nicklaus & Valle, Miami, 1987-90, Nicklaus, Valle, Craig & Wicks, Miami, 1990—; of counsel Greater Miami Marine Assns., 1993—. Contbr. articles to profl. jours. Served to capt. U.S. Army, 1970-74. Mem. ABA, Fla. Bar Assn. (chmn. grievance com., 1982-85), Assn. Trial Lawyers Am., SE Admiralty Law Inst., Maritime Law Assn. of U.S., Bankers Club Miami. Republican. Roman Catholic. Avocations: tennis, running, water skiing, snow skiing. Office: 100 N Biscayne Blvd #1500 Miami FL 33132

VALLEE, BERT LESTER, biochemist, physician, educator; b. Hemer, Westphalia, Germany, June 1, 1919; came to U.S., 1938, naturalized, 1948; s. Joseph and Rosa (Kronenberger) V.; m. Natalie T. Kugris, May 29, 1947. ScB, U. Berne, Switzerland, 1938; MD, NYU, 1943; AM (hon.), Harvard, 1960; MD (honoris causa), Karolinska Institutet, Stockholm, Sweden, 1987; prof. (hon.), Tsinghua U., Beijing, 1987; DSC honoris causa, Naples, Italy, 1991; PhD in Chemistry (honoris causa), Ludwig-Maximilians U., Munich, 1995. Rsch. fellow Harvard Med. Sch., Boston, 1946-49; rsch. assoc. Harvard Med. Sch., 1949-51, assoc., 1951-56, asst. prof. medicine, 1956-60, assoc. prof., 1960-64, prof. biol. chemistry, 1964-65, Paul C. Cabot prof. biol. chemistry, 1965-80, Paul C. Cabot prof. emeritus, biochem. scis., 1980—, Disting. Sr. prof. biochem. scis., 1989-90, Edgar M. Bronfman Disting. sr. prof., 1990—; rsch. assoc. dept. biology MIT, Cambridge, 1948—; physician Peter Bent Brigham Hosp., Boston, 1961-80; biochemist-in-chief Brigham & Women's Hosp., Boston, 1980-89, emeritus, 1989—; sci. dir. Biophysics Rsch. Lab., Harvard Med. Sch., Peter Bent Brigham Hosp., 1954-80; head Ctr. for Biochem. and Biophys. Scis. and Medicine, Harvard Med. Sch. and Brigham & Women's Hosp., 1980—; Messenger lectr. Cornell U., 1988. Author 9 books; contbr. articles and chpts. to sci. publs. Founder, trustee Boston Biophysics Research Found., 1957—; founder, pres. Endowment for Research in Human Biology, Inc., 1980—. Recipient Warner-Chilcott award, 1969, Buchman Meml. award Calif. Inst. Tech., 1976; Linderstøm-Lang award and gold medal, 1980; Willard Gibbs Medal award, 1981, William C. Rose award in biochemistry, 1982; Order Andres Bello First Class of Republic of Venezuela. Fellow NAS, AAAS, Am. Acad. Arts and Scis., N.Y. Acad. Scis.; mem. Am. Soc. Biol. Chemists, Am. Chem. Soc. (Willard Gibbs gold medal 1981), Optical Soc. Am., Biophys. Soc., Swiss Biochem. Soc. (hon. fgn. mem.), Royal Danish Acad. Scis. and Letters, Japan Soc. for Analytical Chemistry (hon.), Alpha Omega Alpha. Home: 56 Browne St Brookline MA 02146-3445

VALLEE, JUDITH DELANEY, environmentalist, fundraiser; b. N.Y.C., Mar. 14, 1948; d. Victor and Sally Hammer; m. John Delaney, Apr. 9, 1974 (div. 1978); m. Henry Richard Vallee, May 15, 1987. BA, CUNY, 1976.

Exec. dir. Save the Manatee Club, Maitland, Fla., 1985—; mem. U.S. Manatee Recovery Plan Team, Jacksonville, Fla., 1988—, Fla. Manatee Tech. Adv. Coun., Tallahassee, 1989—, Save the Manatee Com., Orlando, Fla., 1985-92; advisor Save the Wildlife Inc., Chuluota, Fla., 1992-93; bd. dirs. Environ. Fund for Fla. Lobbyist Save the Manatee Club, 1989; vol. Broward County Audubon Soc., Ft. Lauderdale, 1983, 84, Wild Bird Care Ctr., Ft. Lauderdale, 1984. Recipient Refuge Support award Chassahowitzka Nat. Wildlife Refuge, 1989. Mem. Coop. Am., Fla. Coalition for Peace and Justice, People for Ethical Treatment of Animals, Animal Activists of Ctrl. Fla. Democrat. Avocations: creative writing, antiques, wildlife observation, canoeing. Office: Save the Manatee Club Inc 500 N Maitland Ave Maitland FL 32751-4482

VALLES, JEAN-PAUL, finance company executive; b. Paris, Oct. 17, 1936; came to U.S., 1963; s. Jacques Pierre and Simone (Bourlinski) V.; m. Carol Ann Bennett, Dec. 28, 1935; children: Alain, Suzanne, Sandra. BA, Lycee Corneille, Rouen, France, 1956; Diplome D'enseignement Comml. Superieur, Ecole Supérieure de Commerce de Paris, 1960; MBA, NYU, 1961, PhD, 1967. Bus. economist W.R. Grace, N.Y.C., 1963-68; asst. to chmn. Pfizer Inc., N.Y.C., 1968-70, dir. corp. planning, 1970-72, controller, 1972-80, v.p. fin., 1980—, also bd. dirs.; bd. dirs. Mach Trucks Inc., Allentown, Pa., 1984—, Nat. Assn. Mfrs. Author: The World Market For Bananas, 1968. Dir. Jr. Achievement N.Y., 1986. Served to sgt. French USAF, 1960-61. Mem. Fin. Execs. Inst., Am. Econ. Assn. Club: Econ. of N.Y. Home: RR 2 Box 176 Bedford NY 10506-9775 Office: Pfizer Inc 235 E 42nd St New York NY 10017-5703

VALLETTA, AMBER, model; b. Tulsa, Feb. 9, 1973; m. Hervé Le Bihan. With Boss Models, N.Y.C. Office: Boss Models 317 W 13th St New York NY 10014

VALLEY, GEORGE EDWARD, JR., physicist, educator; b. N.Y.C., Sept. 5, 1913; s. George Edward and Edith Ringgold (Cummins) V.; m. Louisa King Williams, July 19, 1941 (div. Dec. 1960); children—George Cummins, John Williams, Katharine; m. Shea LaBonte. BS, Mass. Inst. Tech., 1935; Ph.D., U. Rochester, 1939. Optical engr. with Bausch & Lomb Optical Co., 1935-36; teaching asst. U. Rochester, 1936-39; research asso. Harvard, 1939-41, NRC fellow nuclear physics, 1940-41; project supr., sr. staff Radiation Lab., Mass. Inst. Tech., 1941-45; editorial bd. Radiation Lab. Tech. Series, 1945; successively asst. prof., asso. prof. Mass. Inst. Tech., 1946-57, prof. physics, 1957-78; now prof. emeritus, assisted founding Lincoln Lab., 1949, asso. dir., 1953-57, undergrad. planning prof., 1965-68; Mem. Air Force Sci. Adv. Bd., 1946-64; chmn. Air Def. Systems, Enging. Com. for Chief Staff USAF, 1950-51, chief scientist, 1957-58. Author and editor books and monographs. Recipient U.S. Army Sci. award of appreciation; President's certificate of merit; Air Force Assn. Sci. award; exceptional civilian service medal USAF, 1956, 58, 64. Fellow Am. Phys. Soc.; Inst. Elec. and Electronics Engrs.; mem. Sigma Xi. Address: 607 Main St Concord MA 01742-3303

VALLONE, JOHN CHARLES, motion picture production designer; b. Phila., June 23, 1953; s. Louis Phillip and Laura Anne (Gaglione) V.; divorced; children: Gabriella, Lilli. BFA, NYU, 1975. Prodn. designer: (feature films) Southern Comfort, 1981, 48 Hours, 1982, Brainstorm, 1983, Streets of Fire, 1984, Brewster's Millions, 1985, Commando, 1985, Predator, 1987, Red Heat, 1988, The Adventures of Ford Fairlane, 1990, Die Hard 2, 1990, Rambling Rose, 1991, Cliffhanger, 1993, Bad Boys, 1995, (TV pilots) Private Eye, 1987, Sweet Justice, 1994, (TV movies) Shannon's Deal, 1989, Angel City, 1990; art dir.: (film) Star Trek: The Motion Picture, 1979 (Academy award nomination best art direction 1979). Mem. AOPA, SMPTUAD, Acad. Motion Picture Arts and Scis. (Best Art Direction award nomination 1981). Republican. Avocations: restoration of wooden yacht, pilot, sailing, woodworking, skiing.

VALOIS, CHARLES, bishop; b. Montreal, Apr. 24, 1924. Ordained priest Roman Cath. Ch., 1950; ordained bishop St. Jerome, Que., Can., 1977—. Office: 355 St George St, Saint Jerome, PQ Canada J7Z 5V3

VALOT, DANIEL L., oil industry executive; b. 1944. Student, Ecol Nationale d'Administration, Paris. Mng. dir., head corp. planning divsn. Total Petroleum South East Asia, 1981—; chmn. bd., pres., CEO Total Petroleum, Inc., Denver, 1992—; chmn. Total Petroleum N.Am. Ltd. Office: Total Petroleum Inc 900 19th St Ste 2201 Denver CO 80202-2523*

VAMMEN, JAMES OLIVER, human services administrator; b. Green Bay, Wis., June 23, 1932; s. Peter Jens and Virga Christine (Andersen) V.; m. Gladys Bernice Helland, June 17, 1954 (div. Apr. 1974); children: Calvin, Connie, Charlton; m. Jean Brooks, May 5, 1975. BS in Edn., Dana Coll., 1958; postgrad., U. Iowa, 1959, 62, U. Nebr., Omaha, 1962-63, No. Colo. U., 1963, DePauw U., 1961; MEd, Temple U., 1965; postgrad., S.E. Nebr. Community Coll., 1975, DePauw U., 1961. Lic. nursing home administr., Nebr. Tchr. Thurston (Nebr.) Pub. Schs., 1958-59, Westside Community Schs., Omaha, 1959-64, Phila. Pub. Schs., 1964-65; exec. dir. Ken-Crest Ctrs., Plymouth Meeting, Pa., 1965-74, Cheyenne Village, Manitou Springs, Colo., 1975-79; exec. v.p. ISS Found., Denver, 1979-83; administr. Martin Luther Home, Beatrice, Nebr., 1984-86; pres., CEO North Cen. Human Svcs., Forest City, Iowa, 1987—, Devel. Resources Inc., Forest City, 1992—. Bd. dirs. Forest City 2000. With USN, 1950-54. Recipient award Chapel of Four Chaplains, 1971. Mem. Am. Assn. on Mental Retardation, Am. Network of Cmty. Options and Resources, Rotary Internat. Avocations: gardening, travel, sightseeing, cooking. Home: 135 Woodland Dr Forest City IA 50436-2419 Office: North Central Human Svcs 106 E Park St # 368 Forest City IA 50436-2103

VAMVAKETIS, CAROLE, nursing educator; b. Bklyn., Mar. 1, 1943; d. William and Helen (Calacanis) Vamvaketis; 1 child, William. AA, Parker Collegiate Inst., Bklyn., 1962; BS, Columbia U., 1964; MA, Columbia Tchrs. Coll., 1969; AAS in Nursing, Rockland C.C., Suffern, N.Y., 1981; BSN, Dominican Coll., 1991. Tchr. elem. sch. A Fantis Parochial Sch., 1964-67; nurse Nyack (N.Y.) Hosp., 1981-91; nurse mgr. Kings Harbor Care Ctr., 1991-93; assoc. dir. nursing Port Chester Nursing Home, 1993-94; CQI/edn. coord. Highbridge Woodycrest Ctr., 1994—; assoc. dir. nursing Port Chester Nursing Home, 1993-94; edn. coord. Highbridge Woodycrest Ctr., 1994—. Home: 102 Poplar St Nanuet NY 10954-2007

VAN, DIRK, radio newscaster, talk show host; b. Rye, N.Y., Apr. 22, 1951; s. Lyle and Lyvonne (Clinton) V.; m. Paula Crozier, June 2, 1974; 1 child, Peter. Student, Duke U., 1969-72; BS, NYU, 1973, MS, 1975. News dir. WGCH Radio, Greenwich, Conn., 1976-78; reporter WCBS-AM, N.Y.C., 1978-80; news dir. WHN, N.Y.C., 1980-89; host, anchor NBC Radio, Arlington, Va., 1989—; host First Light on NBC Radio, Arlington, 1989—. Recipient award Best News Mag., N.Y. Radio Festival, 1990, 94, Personality of Yr., 1991; award for Best Documentary, Ohio State/Clarion, 1989, Gold Cindy/Gabriel, 1988. Avocations: music (singing, piano, guitar), sports (squash, rollerblading). Office: Westwood One 1775 S Jefferson Davis Pky Arlington VA 22202

VAN, GEORGE PAUL, international money management consultant; b. Isle Maligne, Que., Can., Feb. 12, 1940; s. Raymond Murdoch and Germaine Marie (Brassard) V.; m. Janine Marie Irene Therese Yvette Boily, Sept. 15, 1962; children: John, Robert, Caroline. BA, McGill U., 1961; DHA, U. Toronto, 1963. Sr. cons. Agnew Peckham and Assos., Toronto, Ont., Can., 1963-65; chief exec. officer, exec. dir. Misericordia Corp., Edmonton, Alta., Can., 1965-68; chief operating officer, exec. v.p. Texpack, Ltd., Brantford, Ont., 1968-70, also bd. dirs.; group v.p. Will Ross, Inc., Milw., 1970-73; exec. v.p. Nortek, Inc., Cranston, R.I., 1973-77, also bd. dirs.; pres., chief operating officer Hosp. Affiliates Internat. Inc. subs. INA Corp., Nashville, 1977-80, also bd. dirs.; chmn., pres., chief exec. officer Health Group Inc., Nashville, 1980-84; chmn., chief exec. officer Columbia Corp. (formerly Franklin Corp.), Nashville, 1984-88; pres. Grinders Farms, Grinders Switch Shooting Club, Centerville, Tenn., 1990—; chmn. Internat. Adv. Group, Nashville, 1992—. Bd. dirs Tulane U. Med. Ctr., 1977-80, Nashville Inst. for the Arts, 1987-88, Nashville Symphony, 1987-88, Fedn. Internat. de Tir aux Armes Sportives de Chasse, Paris, 1990-92; mem. Internat. Tech. Commn. for Sporting Clays, Paris, 1990; bd. overseers U. Pa. Sch. of

Nursing, 1979-82, 84-88, assoc. trustee U. Pa., 1979-82, 84-88; chmn. internat. com. U.S. Sporting Clays Assn., 1989-92; active pres.'s coun. Andrew Jackson Inst., 1993—; adv. bd. Fin. Mktg. Rsch. Ctr. Vanderbilt U. Recipient several scholarships. Mem. Westside Club, Grinders Switch Club. Contbr. articles to profl. jours. Home and Office: 1608 Chickering Rd Nashville TN 37215-4906

VAN, PETER, lawyer; b. Boston, Sept. 7, 1936; s. Frank Lewis and Ruth (Spevack) V.; m. Faye Anne Zinck, 1991; children: Jami Lynne, Robert Charles. BA, Dartmouth, 1958; LLD, Boston Coll., 1961. Bar: Mass. 1962. Assoc. Brown, Rudnick, Freed and Gesmer, Boston, 1961-63; assoc. Fine and Ambrogne, Boston, 1963-65, ptnr., 1966-73, sr. ptnr., 1973—, mng. ptnr., chmn. exec. com., 1988-90; ptnr., mem. exec. com. Mintz, Levin, Cohn, Ferris, Glovsky and Popeo, P.C., Boston, 1990—. Mem. fin. com., trustee Beth Israel Hosp. Boston. Mem. Masons. Office: One Financial Ctr Boston MA 02111

VAN ACKEREN, MAURICE EDWARD, college administrator; b. Cedar Rapids, Nebr., Aug. 21, 1911; s. Edward M. and Frances (O'Leary) Van A. B.A. in Chemistry, Creighton U., 1932; M.A. in Edn., St. Louis U., 1946; LL.D. (hon.), Benedictine Coll., 1976. Ordained Jesuit priest Roman Cath. Ch., 1943. Tchr. Campion High Sch., Prairie du Chien, Wis., 1937-40; prin. St. Louis U. High Sch., 1946-51; pres. Rockhurst Coll., Kansas City Mo., 1951-77, chancellor, 1977—. Recipient Knight of Holy Sepulchre award Catholic Ch., Chgo., 1968, Chancellor's medal U. Mo.-Kansas City, 1981, Mr. Kansas City award Greater Kansas City C. of C., 1983; named to Creighton U. Athletic Hall of Fame, Omaha, 1971; named Mktg. Exec. of Yr., Sales and Mktg. Club Kansas City, 1979. Mem. C. of C. of Greater Kansas City. Lodge: Rotary (Paul Harris fellow 1983). Avocations: fishing; golf; baseball; football. Home and Office: 1100 Rockhurst Rd Kansas City MO 64110-2508

VAN ALLEN, JAMES ALFRED, physicist, educator; b. Mt. Pleasant, Iowa, Sept. 7, 1914; s. Alfred Morris and Alma E. (Olney) Van A.; m. Abigail Fithian Halsey, Oct. 13, 1945; children: Cynthia Schaffner, Margot Cairns, Sarah Trimble, Thomas, Peter. BS, Iowa Wesleyan Coll., 1935; MS, U. Iowa, 1936, PhD, 1939; ScD (hon.), Iowa Wesleyan Coll., 1951, Grinnell Coll., 1957, Coe Coll., 1958, Cornell Coll., Mt. Vernon, Iowa, 1959, U. Dubuque, 1960, U. Mich., 1961, Northwestern U., 1961, Ill. Coll., 1963, Butler U., 1966, Boston Coll., 1966, Southampton Coll., 1967, Augustana Coll., 1969, St. Ambrose Coll., 1982, U. Bridgeport, 1987. Research fellow, physicist dept. terrestrial magnetism Carnegie Instn., Washington, 1939-42; physicist, group and unit supr. applied physics lab. Johns Hopkins U., 1942, 46-50; organizer, leader sci. expdns. study cosmic radiation Peru, 1949, Gulf of Alaska, 1950, Arctic, 1952, 57, Antarctic, 1957, prof. physics, head dept. U. Iowa, Iowa City, 1951-85, Carver prof. physics, 1985-90, Regent disting. prof., 1990—; Regents fellow Smithsonian Instn., 1981; rsch. assoc. Princeton U., 1953-54; mem. devel. group radio proximity fuze Nat. Def. Rsch. Coun., OSRD; pioneer high attitude rsch. with rockets, satellites and space probes. Author: Origins of Magnetospheric Physics, 1983, First to Jupiter, Saturn and Beyond, 1981; 924 Elementary Problems and Answers in Solar System Astronomy, 1993; contbg. author: Physics and Medicine of Upper Atmosphere, 1952, Rocket Exploration of the Upper Atmosphere; editor: Scientific Uses of Earth Satellites, 1956, Cosmic Rays, the Sun, and Geomagnetism: The Works of Scott E. Forbush, 1993; acting editor Jour. Geophys. Rsch.-Space Physics, 1991-92; contbr. numerous articles to profl. jours. *. Lt. comdr. USNR, 1942-46, ordnance and gunnery specialist, combat observer. Recipient Physics award Washington Acad. Sci., 1949, Space Flight award Am. Astronautical Soc., 1958, Louis W. Hill Space Transp. award Inst. Aero. Scis., 1959, Elliot Cresson medal Franklin Inst., 1961, Golden Omega award Elec. Insulation Conf., 1963, Iowa Broadcasters Assn. award, 1964, Fellows award of merit Am. Cons. Engrs. Coun., 1978, Nat. Medal of Sci., 1987, Vannevar Bush award NSF, 1991; named comdr. Order du Merit Pour la Recherche et l'Invention, 1964; Guggenheim Found. rsch. fellow, 1951. Fellow Am. Rocket Soc. (C.N. Hickman medal devel. Aerobee rocket 1949), IEEE, Am. Phys. Soc., Am. Geophys. Union (pres. 1982-84, John A. Fleming award 1963, William Bowie medal 1977); mem. NAS, AAAS (Abelson prize 1986), Iowa Acad. Sci., Internat. Acad. Astronautics (founding), Am. Philos. Soc., Am. Astron. Soc., Royal Astron. Soc. U.K. (gold medal 1978), Royal Swedish Acad. Sci. (Crafoord prize 1989), Am. Acad. Arts and Scis., Cosmos Club, Sigma Xi (Procter prize 1987), Gamma Alpha. Presbyterian. Avocations include discovery of radiation belts around earth. Office: Univ Iowa 701 Van Allen Hall Iowa City IA 52242-1403

VAN ALLEN, WILLIAM KENT, lawyer; b. Albion, N.Y., July 30, 1914; s. Everett Kent and Georgia (Roberts) Van A.; m. Sally Schall, Nov. 11, 1944; children: William Kent, Jr., George Humphrey, Peter Cushing. A.B., Hamilton Coll., 1935; LL.B., Harvard U., 1938. Bar: N.Y. 1938, D.C. 1939, N.C. 1951, U.S. Dist. Ct. (we. dist.) N.C. 1951, U.S. Dist. Ct. (mid. dist.) N.C. 1953, U.S. Ct. Appeals (4th cir.) 1951, U.S. Ct. Claims 1946, U.S. Tax Ct. 1940, FCC 1939, ICC 1940, U.S. Supreme Ct. 1946. With Hanson, Lovett & Dale, Washington, 1938-41, 46-50; ptnr. Lassiter, Moore and Van Allen and Moore and Van Allen, Charlotte, N.C., 1951-87; of counsel Moore & Van Allen, Charlotte, 1988—; permanent mem. Jud. Conf. 4th Jud. Circuit. Vestryman Episc. Ch., 1957-60, 66-69; mem. Mecklenburg County Bd. Public Welfare, 1954-59; chmn. 1957-59; bd. dirs. N.C. Found. Commerce and Industry, 1965-73, Found. U. N.C. at Charlotte, 1979-89, Charlotte Symphony Orch., 1981-82, Mercy Health Svcs., 1983-88; chmn. Charlotte Area adv. coun. Am. Arbitration Assn., 1967-76; bd. dirs. United Community Svcs., 1972-77, v.p., 1972; bd. mgrs. Charlotte Country Day Sch., 1956-61, chmn., 1959-61, bd. visitors, 1978—, chmn., 1987-88; bd. advisers U. N.C.-Charlotte, 1983-84; trustee Spastics Hosp., 1951-60, Mint Mus. Art, 1976-79, Surtman Found., 1955-90, Mercy Hosp. Found., 1979-84; bd. visitors Johnson C. Smith U., 1978-89; pres. Charlotte Symphony League, 1980-81, Friends of U. N.C. at Charlotte, 1990-91. Served with USNR, 1941-45, commdg. officer destroyer escort ATO and PTO; released to inactive duty as lt. comdr. Mem. ABA, Charlotte C. of C. (bd. dirs. 1971-75, v.p. 1972-75). Mil. Order of Carabao, Charlotte Country Club, Charlotte City Club, Chevy Chase Club (Md.), Mullett Lake Country Club (Mich.), Phi Beta Kappa, Chi Psi. Office: Moore & Van Allen 4700 Nations Bank Corp Ctr Charlotte NC 28202-4003

VAN ALLSBURG, CHRIS, author, artist; b. Grand Rapids, Mich., June 18, 1949; s. Richard Allen and Doris Marie (Christiansen) Van A.; m. Lisa Carol Morrison, Aug. 17, 1976. BFA, U. Mich., 1972; MFA, R.I. Sch. Design, 1975. Tchr. R.I. Sch. Design, Providence. Author, illustrator: The Garden of Abdul Gasazi, 1979 (Caldecott Honor Book 1980, Irma Simonton Black award Bank St. Coll. Edn. 1980, Boston Globe/Horn Book award 1980), Jumanji, 1981 (Caldecott medal 1982, Boston Globe/Horn Book award 1982, Children's Choice award Internat. Reading Assn. 1982, Am. Book award, 1982, Ky. Bluegrass award No. Ky. U. 1983, Buckeye Children's Book award Ohio State Libr. 1983, Wash. Children's Choice Picture Book award Wash. Libr. Media Assn. 1984, W. Va. Children's Book award 1985), Ben's Dream, 1982 (Parents Choice award for illustration Parents' Choice Found. 1982), Wreck of the Zephyr, 1983 (Silver medal Soc. Illustrators 1983), The Mysteries of Harris Burdick, 1984 (Parents Choice award for illustration Parents' Choice Found. 1984, Irma Simonton Black award Bank St. Coll. Edn. 1985, Boston Globe/Horn Book award 1985, World Fantasy award 1985), The Polar Express, 1985 (Parents Choice award for illustration Parents' Choice Found. 1985, Caldecott medal 1986, Boston Globe/Horn Book award 1986, Ky. Bluegrass award No. Ky. U. 1987), The Stranger, 1986 (Parents Choice award for illustration Parents' Choice Found. 1986), The Z Was Zapped: A Play in Twenty-Six Acts, 1987, Two Bad Ants, 1988, Just A Dream, 1990, The Wretched Stone, 1991, The Widow's Broom, 1992, The Sweetest Fig, 1993, The Two Figs, 1993, Bad Day at River Bend, 1995; illustrator: Swan Lake, 1989; exhibited works at Whitney Mus. Art, N.Y.C., Mus. Modern Art, N.Y.C., Alan Stone Gallery, N.Y.C., Grand Rapids (Mich.) Art Mus., Port Washington (N.Y.) Pub. Libr.; permanent collections include Kerlan Collection at U. Minn. Recipient Hans Christian Andersen award nomination, 1985. Jewish. *

VAN ALSTYNE, JUDITH STURGES, English language educator; b. Columbus, Ohio, June 9, 1934; d. Rexford Leland and Wilma Irene (Styan) Van A.; m. Dan C Duckham (div. 1994); children: Kenton Leland, Jeffrey Clarke. BA, Miami U., Oxford, Ohio, 1956; MEd, Fla. Atlantic U., 1967.

Sr. prof. Broward C.C., Ft. Lauderdale, Fla., 1967-93, ret., 1993; spl. asst. for women's affairs Broward C.C., 1972-93, dir. cmty. svcs., 1973-74, dir. cultural affairs, 1974-75, dir. Broward C.C. Found., Inc., 1973-89; spkr., cons. Malaysian Coll., 1984; ednl. gravel group tour guide, 1992—; v.p., ptnr. Downtown Travel Centre, Ft. Lauderdale, Fla., 1994—. Author: Professional and Technical Writing Strategies, 3d edit., 1994, Write it Right, 1980; freelance writer travel articles; contbr. articles to profl. jours. Active Sister Cities/People to People, Ft. Lauderdale, 1988—; docent Ft. Lauderdale Mus. Art, 1988—; officer Friends of Mus., Ft. Lauderdale, 1992—; bd. dirs. Broward Friends of the Libr., 1994—, Broward Friends of Miami City Ballet, 1994—. Recipient Award of Achievement Soc. for Tech. Communication, 1986, Award of Distinction Fla. Soc. for Tech. Communication, 1986. Mem. English-Speaking Union (bd. dirs. 1984-89). Democrat. Episcopalian. Avocations: writing, reading, travel. Home: 1688 S Ocean Ln # 265 Fort Lauderdale FL 33316-3346

VAN ALSTYNE, W. SCOTT, JR., lawyer, educator; b. East Syracuse, N.Y., Sept. 21, 1922; s. Walter Scott and Cecil Edna (Folmsbee) Van A.; m. Margaret Reed Hudson, June 23, 1949 (div.); children: Gretchen Anne, Hunter Scott; m. Marion Graham Walker, May 3, 1980. B.A., U. Buffalo, 1948; M.A., U. Wis., 1950, LL.B., 1953, S.J.D., 1954. Bar: Wis. 1953. Assoc. Shea & Hoyt, Milw., 1954-56; asst. prof. law U. Nebr., 1956-58; pvt. practice Madison, Wis., 1958-72; prof. law U. Fla., 1973-90, prof. emeritus, 1990—; lectr. law U. Wis., 1958-72; lectr. Cambridge-Warsaw Trade Program Cambridge U. (Eng.), 1976; vis. prof. law Cornell U., 1977, U. Leiden, Netherlands, 1988, 91; spl. lectr. U. Utrecht, Netherlands, 1991; spl. counsel Gov. of Wis., 1966-70; bd. dirs. non-resident div. State Bar Wis., 1981—, pres., 1988-90, bd. govs., 1988-90. Prin. author: Goals and Missions of Law Schools, 1990; contbr. articles to profl. jours. Mem. Gov.'s Commn. on Edn., Wis., 1969-71. Served with AUS, 1942-45, 61-62; col. Res., ret. Decorated Legion of Merit. Mem. SR (N.Y.), Holland Soc. (N.Y.), Madison (Wis.) Club, Ft. Rennselaer (N.Y.) Club, Netherland Club (N.Y.C.), Order of Coif, Phi Beta Kappa, Omicron Delta Kappa. Republican. Presbyterian. Office: U Fla Holland Law Ctr Gainesville FL 32611

VAN ALSTYNE, WILLIAM WARNER, legal educator; b. Chico, Calif., Feb. 8, 1934; s. Richard Warner and Margaret (Ware) Van A.; BA, U. So. Calif., 1955; JD, Stanford U., 1958; certificate Hague Acad. Internat. Law, 1961; LLD, Wake Forest U., 1976, Coll. William and Mary, 1979. Bar: Calif. 1958. m. Carol Frances Engstrom, Sept. 18, 1955 (div. 1979); children: Marshall, Allyn, Lisa; m. Pamela Gann, Jan. 1980. Dep. atty. gen. Calif., 1958; atty. civil rights div. U.S. Dept. Justice, Washington, 1959; from asst. prof. to prof. Ohio State U. Law Sch., 1959-63; prof. Duke U. Law Sch., Durham, N.C., 1965-73, William R. Perkins prof. law, 1974—. Mem. nat. bd. dirs. ACLU, 1972-76; mem. adv. council Carnegie Found. for Advancement Teaching, 1974-76. With USAF, 1959. Mem. AAUP (nat. pres. 1974-76, gen. counsel 1988-90). Author: Interpretations of the First Amendment, 1984, First Amendment Cases and Materials, 1991; contbr. articles to profl. jours. Office: Duke U Sch Law Rm 106 Durham NC 27706

VANAMAN, CHARLES ARTHUR, lawyer; b. Heidelberg, Fed. Republic of Germany, July 15, 1954; s. Nathan E. and Eula Mae (Cummins) V. BA, Baylor U., 1976, JD, 1977; LLM in Taxation, Southern Meth. U., 1984. Bar: Tex. 1978, U.S. Dist. Ct. (so. dist.) Tex. 1979, U.S. Ct. Appeals (5th cir.) 1980, U.S. Tax Ct. 1986. Asst. atty. City of Corpus Christi, Tex., 1978-79; asst. dist. atty. Nueces County, Corpus Christi, 1979-83; sole practice Corpus Christi, 1984—; mcpl. ct. judge City of Corpus Christi, 1986—. Mem. ABA, Tex. Bar Assn. Club: Exchange (Corpus Christi, Tex.) (bd. dirs. 1986—). Office: Berry Contracting Inc 1414 Corn Products Rd Corpus Christi TX 78409

VAN AMRINGE, JOHN HOWARD, retired oil industry executive, geologist; b. L.A., Oct. 11, 1932; s. Edwin Verne and Viola (Hail) Van A.; m. Mary Jane Lothras, Jan. 29, 1955; children: Kathryn Jean Van Amringe Ball, Kenneth Edwin. AA, Pasadena City Coll., 1954; BA, UCLA, 1956, MA, 1957. Geologist Unocal Corp., Santa Maria, Calif., 1957-58, Santa Fe Springs, Calif., 1958-64, New Orleans, 1964-66; dist. geologist Unocal Corp., Lafayette, La., 1966-68, dist. exploration mgr., 1968-79; exploration mgr. western region Unocal Corp., Pasadena, Calif., 1979-88; v.p. exploration Unocal Corp., L.A., 1988-92. Editor: Typical Offshore Oil and Gas Fields, 1973; author profl. paper. Bd. dirs. Pasadena City Coll. Found., 1986—; treas., 1992-95; pres. Pasadena Cmty. Orch., 1990-94. With U.S. Army, 1949-52, Korea. Named Geologist of Yr., Lafayette chpt. Am. Inst. Profl. Geologists, 1972. Mem. Am. Assn. Petroleum Geologists (del. 1972-73), Pacific Sect. of Am. Assn. Petroleum Geologists (editor 1961-63), Lafayette Geological Soc. (pres. 1971-72), Petroleum Club L.A., Jonathan Club. Republican. Avocations: tennis, travel, sailing, collecting, photography. Home: 1455 Old House Rd Pasadena CA 91107-1518

VAN ANDEL, JAY, home and personal products company executive; b. Grand Rapids, Mich., June 3, 1924; s. James and Nella (Vanderwoude) Van A.; m. Betty J. Hoekstra, Aug. 16, 1952; children: Nan, Stephen, David, Barbara. Student, Pratt Jr. Coll., 1945, Calvin Coll., 1942, 46, Yale, 1943-44; DBA (hon.), No. Mich. U., 1976, Western Mich. U., 1979, Grand Valley State U., 1992; LLD (hon.), Ferris State Coll., 1977. Co-founder, chmn. bd. Amway Corp., Ada, Mich.; U.S. amb., commr. gen. Genoa Expo '92, 1992 World's Fair marking 500th Anniversary of Columbus Journey to Am.; chmn. bd. Amway Internat., Amway Hotel Corp., Amway Environ. Found., Nutrilite Products, Inc.; chmn. Ja-Ri Corp., Ada, Mich.; mem. adv. coun. Am. Private Edn. Participant White Ho. Conf. Indsl. World Ahead, 1972; chmn. Mich. Rep. fin. com., 1975-81; Founding chmn. Right Place Com. Grand Rapids, Mich.; mem. adv. council Nat. 4H Found.; trustee Hillsdale (Mich.) Coll., Citizens Rsch. Coun. Mich., Hudson Inst., Indpls. and Washington; dir. Jamestown Found., Gerald R. Ford Found.; bd. dirs., trustee, treas. Washington, Heritage Found., Washington; pres. Van Andel Found.; co-chmn. Mich. Botanic Garden Capital Campaign; founding chmn. Citizen's Choice, Washington; former bd. dirs. BIPAC, Washington, former chmn. Netherlands-Am. Bicentennial Commn. Served to 1st lt. USAAF, 1943-46. Knighted Grand Officer of Orange-Nassau, The Netherlands; recipient Disting. Alumni award Calvin Coll., 1976, Golden Plate award Am. Acad. Achievement, Gt. Living Am. award and Bus. and Profl. Leader of the Yr. award Religious Heritage Am., George Washington medal of Honor Freedom Found., Gold medals Netherland Soc. of Phila. and N.Y.C., Disting. Citizen award Northwood Inst., Patron award Mich. Found. for Arts, 1982, Achievement award UN Environment Programme, 1989, UN Environment Programme Achievement award Amway, 1989, Adam Smith Free Enterprise award Am. Legis. Exchange Coun., 1993, Disting. Svc. award Rotary Grand Rapids, Gold Medal Netherlands Soc. N.Y., Edison Achievement award Am. Mktg. Assn., 1994; named Bus. Person Yr. Econ. Club Grand Rapids, 1990; named to Grand Rapids Bus. Hall of Fame; World fellow Duke of Edinburgh's award. Mem. Sales and Mktg. Execs. Internat. Acad. Achievement (charter), Direct Selling Assn. (bd. dirs., named to Hall of Fame), U.S. C. of C. (past chmn. bd.), Right Place Com. (founding chmn.), de Tocqueville Soc. (former chmn.), Nat. Chamber Found. (dir.), Mensa Soc. USA, Peninsular Club, Cascade Hills Country Club, Lotus Club, Capitol Hill Club (Washington), Macatawa Bay Yacht Club (Holland, Mich.), Le Mirador Country Club (Switzerland), Carlton Club (Chgo.), Econ. Club (Grand Rapids), Omicron Delta Kappa (hon.). Mem. Christian Reformed Ch. (elder). Home: 7186 Windy Hill Dr SE Grand Rapids MI 49546-9745 Office: Amway Corp Fulton St E Ada MI 49355

VAN ANTWERPEN, FRANKLIN STUART, federal judge; b. Passaic, N.J., Oct. 23, 1941; s. Franklin John and Dorothy (Hoedemaker) Van A.; m. Kathleen Veronica O'Brien, Sept. 12, 1970; children: Joy, Franklin W., Virginia. BS in Engring. Physics, U. Maine, 1964; JD, Temple U., 1967; postgrad., Nat. Jud. Coll., 1980. Bar: Pa. 1969, U.S. Dist. Ct. (ea. dist.) Pa. 1971, U.S. Ct. Appeals (3d cir.) 1971, U.S. Supreme Ct. 1972. Corp. counsel Hazeltine Corp., N.Y.C., 1967-70; chief counsel Northampton County Legal Aid Soc., Easton, Pa., 1970-71; assoc. Hemstreet & Smith, Easton, 1971-73; ptnr. Hemstreet & VanAntwerpen, Easton, 1973-79; judge Ct. Common Pleas of Northampton County (Pa.), 1979-87, U.S. Dist. Ct. (ea. dist.) Pa., Phila., 1987—; appointed to U.S. Sentencing Commn. Judicial Working Group 1992-93; trial judge U.S. vs. Scarfo, 1988-89; adj. prof. Northampton County Area Community Coll., 1976-81; solicitor Palmer Twp., 1971-79; gen. counsel Fairview Savs. and Loan Assn., Easton, 1973-79. Recipient Booster award Bus. Indsl. and Profl. Assn., 1979, George Palmer award

Palmer Twp., 1980, Man of Yr. award, 1981, Law Enforcement Commendation medal Nat. Soc. SAR, 1990; named an Alumnus Who Has Made a Difference in the World, U. Maine, 1991. Mem. ABA (com. on jud. edn.), Fed. Bar Assn. (hon.), Pa. Bar Assn., Northampton County Bar Assn., Am. Judicature Soc., Fed. Judges Assn., Pomfret Club, Nat. Lawyers Club (Washington), Union League Club. Office: US Dist Ct Holmes Bldg 2nd and Ferry St Easton PA 18042

VAN ANTWERPEN, REGINA LANE, underwriter, insurance company executive; b. Milw., Aug. 16, 1939; d. Joseph F. Gagliano and Sophia B. (Johannik) Wolfe; widowed; children: Thomas II, Victoria. Student, U. Wis., Milw., 1954-57. Office mgr. Gardner Bender Inc., Milw., 1972-80; mfg. rep. Rosenbloom & Co., Chgo., 1980-81; spl. agt. Northwestern Mut. Life Equities Inc., Milw., 1981-88, registered rep., 1985-88; account rep. Fin. Instn. Mktg. Co., Milw., 1988-93; investment specialist Fimco Securities Group, Inc., Milw., 1993—; pres. Anvers Ltd., 1990—, 1990—. Author: (poetry) One More Time Its Christmas, 1978, True Friendship, 1979, Beautiful Brown Eyes, 1990 (award 1992). Mgr. Sch. Bd. Elections, Fox Point, 1969; v.p. Suburban Rep. Women's CLub, Milw., 1968-72; vol. tchr. St. Eugene Sch., Milw., 1968-72. Mem. AAUW, Milw. Life Underwriters, Women's Life Underwriters (v.p. 1982-83), Legis. Orgn. Life Underwriters, Nat. Assn. Securities Dealers (lic.), Investment Club (sec. 1989-90, pres. 1990—). Republican. Roman Catholic. Avocations: writing, service work, gardening. Office: Fin Instn Mktg Co 111 E Kilbourn Ave Ste 1850 Milwaukee WI 53202-6611

VAN ARK, JOAN, actress; d. Carroll and Dorothy Jean (Hemenway) Van A.; m. John Marshall, Feb. 1, 1966; 1 child, Vanessa Jeanne. Student, Yale Sch. Drama. Appeared at Tyrone Guthrie Theatre, Washington Arena Stage, in London, on Broadway; performances include: (stage) Barefoot in the Park, 1965, School for Wives, 1971, Rules of the Game, 1974, Cyrano de Bergerac, Ring Round the Moon, Three Tall Women, 1995; (TV series) Temperatures Rising, 1972-73, We've Got Each Other, 1977-78, Dallas, 1978-81, Knots Landing, 1979-92 (also dir. episodes Letting Go, Hints and Evasions); (TV movies) The Judge and Jake Wyler, 1972, Big Rose, 1974, Shell Game, 1975, The Last Dinosaur, 1977, Red Flag, 1981, Shakedown on the Sunset Strip, 1988, My First Love, 1989, Murder at the PTA, 1990, To Cast a Shadow, 1990, Always Remember I Love You, 1990, Grand Central Murders, 1992, Tainted Blood, 1992, Someone's Watching, 1993; (TV miniseries) Testimony of Two Men, 1978; dir., star ABC-TV Afterschool Spl. Boys Will Be Boys, 1994. Recipient Theatre World award, 1970-71, L.A. Drama Critics Circle award, 1973, Outstanding Actress award Soap Opera Digest, 1986, 89. Mem. AFTRA, SAG, Actors Equity Assn., San Fernando Valley Track Club. Address: care William Morris Agy Inc 151 S El Camino Dr Beverly Hills CA 90212-2704 also: 1350 Avenue Of The Americas New York NY 10019-4701*

VAN ARNEM, HAROLD LOUIS, capital and technology equipment leasing company executive; b. Cin., Dec. 19, 1940; s. Harold Louis and Elizabeth (Smith) Van A.; m. Karen Schram, Aug. 31, 1963 (div. 1980); children: Aleise, Heidi, Heather, Harold Louis IV; m. Bridget Elizabeth Sahlin, Feb. 17, 1990; children: Adam, Maxwell, Brandon. BBA, U. Cin., 1964; postgrad., U. Detroit, 1968, 69, 71. With fin. and mktg. depts. GE Computers, Phoenix, 1964-67; chief exec. officer Acts Computing Corp., Southfield, Mich., 1967-74, Van Arnem, Birmingham, Mich., 1974-88, Finalco Group, Inc., Boca Raton, Fla., 1988—; gen. ptnr. Finalco Ltd., Birmingham, 1988—, Gemini Equities Ltd. Boca Raton, 1989—; chmn., chief exec. officer Gemini Group, Inc., Boca Raton, 1989—; gen. ptnr. Detroit Express, profl. soccer team, Pontiac, Mich., 1978-84; bd. dirs. N.Am. Soccer League, Pontiac, N.Y., 1978-80; commr. Am. Soccer League, Pontiac, N.Y., 1980. Co-producer feature film Love at First Bite, 1979; assoc. producer feature film Quick and The Dead, 1978; producer video Jump Rope Aerobic Work-Out, 1991. Co-chmn. Mich. Rep. Legis. Com., 1977-81; fin. chmn. Murphy for Oakland (Mich.) City Exec. Campaign, 1976-80, Patterson for Mich. Gov. Campaign, 1984. Mem. Young Pres. Orgn., Computer Dealer Lessor Assn., World Bus. Coun., Oakland Hills Country Club (Birmingham). Avocations: jump rope, aerobics, water sports, golf. Office: Gemini Group Inc 1301 W Newport Ctr Dr Deerfield Beach FL 33441

VAN ARSDALE, DICK, professional basketball team executive; b. Indpls., Feb. 22, 1943; m. Barbara V.; children: Jill, Jason. AB in economics, Indiana U., 1965. Player New York Knicks (Nat. Basketball Assn.), N.Y.C., 1965-68; with Phoenix Suns, Phoenix, Ariz., 1968-77; color commentator, TV broadcasts Phoenix Suns, from 1977, interim mgr., 1987, from v.p., player personnel. Named "Mr. Basketball" of Indiana during high school, NCAA All-American, Indiana U. Office: care Phoenix Suns 201 E Jefferson Phoenix AZ 85004*

VAN ARSDALL, ROBERT ARMES, engineer, retired air force officer; b. Omaha, Oct. 5, 1925; s. Samuel Peter and Althea (Armes) Van A.; m. Margaret Cooper Kiersted, June 9, 1948; children: Robert Armes, Janet Althea, Susan DeBaun, Kathryn Ann. BS, U.S. Mil. Acad., 1948; postgrad., U. Colo., spring 1961; MS, George Washington U., 1968. Commd. 2d lt. USAF, 1948, advanced through grades to col., 1968; grad. Randolph AFB, Tex., 1949; assigned 5th Air Rescue Group, Westover AFB, Mass., 1949-51; student USAF Squadron Officer Sch., Maxwell AFB, Ala., 1950; pilot, ops. officer 9th Air Rescue Group, Burton-Wood, Manston and Bushy Park, Eng., 1951-55; ops. officer Hdqrs. Air Rescue Service, Orlando AFB, Fla., 1955-57; plans officer Hdqrs. Air R & D Command, Balt., also Andrews AFB, Md., 1957-60; grad. USAF jet qualification course, Randolph AFB, 1959; tng.-with-industry Air Force Inst. Tech., Martin Co., Denver, 1960-61; chief plans div. Hdqrs. Space Systems Div., L.A., 1961-63; exec. officer Office Space Systems, Office Sec. Air Force, 1963-67; assoc. Air War Coll. program, Washington, 1964-66; student Naval War Coll., 1967-68; dep. dir. Dept. Def. Manned Space Flight Support Office, Patrick AFB, Fla., 1968-69; dir. range engring., 1969-70; dir. range ops. Air Force Eastern Test Range, 1970-72; comdr. USAF Satellite Test Ctr., Sunnyvale, Calif., 1972-73; vice comdr. USAF Satellite Control Facility, L.A., 1973-74; comdr. USAF Satellite Control Facility, 1974-76; staff engr. Pan Am. World Airways, Cocoa Beach, Fla., 1976-78; project dir. Pan Am. World Airways, 1978-79, program mgr., 1980-85, dir. internat. projects, 1985-88; program dir. Diego Garcia, 1989, ret., 1989. Decorated Air Force Commendation medal with two oak leaf clusters, Legion of Merit with oak leaf cluster. Life mem. Assn. Grads. U.S. Mil. Acad.; charter mem. Nat. Soujourners, USAF Acad. Athletic Assn. Republican. Methodist. Clubs: Mason, Burtonwood Air Force (gov.), Bushy Park Air Force (gov.), Orlando Air Force (gov.), Andrews Air Force (gov.), Space Systems Division Air Force (gov.). Home: 660 Cinnamon Ct Satellite Beach FL 32937-4391

VAN ARSDEL, EUGENE PARR, tree pathologist, consultant meteorologist; b. Emaus, Pa., Dec. 4, 1925; s. William Campbell and Mabel Elizabeth (Hedde) Van A.; m. Rose Price, Aug. 23, 1948 (div. Aug. 1991); children: Jonathan Eugene, Elizabeth Rose. BS in Forestry, Purdue U., 1947; MS, U. Wis., 1952, PhD, 1954. Plant pathologist Lake States Forest Expt. Sta. U. Wis., Madison, 1956-59, plant pathologist, 1959-62; prin. plant pathologist, project leader No. Conifer Disease Rsch., No. Ctrl. Forest Expt. Sta. U. Minn., St. Paul, 1962-68, prof. plant pathology, 1967-68; assoc. prof. plant sci. Tex. A&M U., College Station, 1968-80; plant pathologist, forester Profl. Tree Svc., Inc., Bryan, Tex., 1981—; vis. prof. Yale U., New Haven, 1965-66. Assoc. editor Ecol. Soc. Am. Jour., 1968-71; contbr. chpts. to books, articles to Am. Meteorol. Soc., Am. Soc. Foresters, Am. Phytopath. Soc. others. An organizer, mem. Brazos Chorale, Bryan, Tex., 1970—. Grantee NSF, 1962-63, Tex. Peanut Producers Bd., 1972, USDA Forest Svc., 1973-77, Mrs. Lyndon B. Johnson, 1977-82, I.S.A. Rsch. Trust, 1988. Fellow AAAS; mem. Soc. Am. Foresters, Internat. Soc. Arboriculture, Am. Phytopath Soc. (emeritus). Achievements include development of effective treatment for wilt diseases in oaks of Texas; study of climatic.microclimatic relationship of the spread of white pine blister rust; research in long-distance transport of fungous spores. Office: Profl Tree Svc Inc 2112 Cavitt Dr Bryan TX 77801

VAN ARTSDALEN, DONALD WEST, federal judge; b. Doylestown, Pa., Oct. 21, 1919; s. Isaac Jeans and May Mable (Danenhower) Van A.; m. Marie Catherine Auerbach, June 20, 1953. Student, Williams Coll., 1937-40; LL.B., U. Pa., 1948. Bar: Pa. 1948, U.S. Supreme Ct. 1956. Practiced in Doylestown, 1948-70; dist. atty. Bucks County (Pa.), 1954-58; judge U.S. Dist. Ct. Pa. (ea. dist.), Phila., from 1970, now sr. judge, 1987. Served with

Canadian Army, 1940-42; Served with AUS, 1942-45. Mem. Orde of the Coif. Office: US District Court 14614 US Courthouse Ind Mall W 601 Market St Philadelphia PA 19106-1510

VAN ARTSDALEN, ERVIN ROBERT, physical chemist, educator; b. Doylestown, Pa., Nov. 13, 1913; s. Isaac J. and May M. (Danenhower) Van A.; m. Mary Louise Naylor, June 14, 1945. B.S. in Chemistry cum laude, Lafayette Coll., 1935; Internat. Exchange fellow U. Munich, Germany, 1935-36; A.M., Harvard, 1939, Ph.D. in Phys. Chemistry, 1941. Instr., then asst. prof. chemistry Lafayette Coll., 1941-45; on leave to Nat. Def. Research Com., Johns Hopkins Med. Sch., 1943-45; group leader Los Alamos Atomic Bomb Lab., 1945-46; asst. prof. chemistry Cornell U., 1946-51; adminstrv. group leader Oak Ridge Nat. Lab., 1951-56; asst. dir. research, basic lab. Union Carbide Corp., Cleve., 1956-63; John W. Mallet prof. chemistry, chmn. dept. U. Va., 1963-68; prof. chemistry U. Ala., 1968-84, prof. emeritus, 1984—, head dept., 1968-72; with Inst. Energy Analysis, Oak Ridge, 1975-76; cons. to govt. and industry; mem. chemistry adv. com. USAF Office Sci. Rsch., 1958-72, chmn., 1963-70; mem. Radiation Safety Bd. of Health, State of Ala., 1980—. Contbr. to profl. jours., govt. reports; Mem. editorial bd.: Jour. Phys. Chemistry, 1958-62. Dir. High Sch. Students and Tchrs. Sci. Workshops and Seminars, Cleve., 1957-60; bd. dirs. Oak Ridge Sch. Music, 1953-56, Oak Ridge Asso. Univs., 1969-75; mem. 1st Presbyn. Ch., Tuscaloosa. Recipient Distinguished Alumni Sci. Tchr. citation Lafayette Coll., 1966. Fellow Am. Inst. Chemists; mem. AAAS, Am. Chem. Soc., Am. Phys. Soc., Va. Acad. Sci., Oak Ridge Country Club, Indian Hills Country Club (Tuscaloosa, Ala.). Exch. Club, Phi Beta Kappa, Alpha Chi Sigma, Gamma Alpha, Gamma Sigma Epsilon, Kappa Delta Rho. Clubs: Oak Ridge Country; Indian Hills Country (Tuscaloosa, Ala.). Spl. research reaction kinetics and photochemistry, thermodynamics, fused salts, nuclear energy, energy analysis. Home: 1512 Bellingrath Dr Reston Pl Tuscaloosa AL 35406

VAN ASPEREN, MORRIS EARL, banker; b. Wessington, S.D., Oct. 5, 1943; s. Andrew and Alyce May (Flagg) Van A.; m. Anne Virginia Merritt, July 2, 1966; 1 child, David Eric. BS in Math., U. Okla., 1966; MBA, Pepperdine U., 1979. Mgr. western dist. Sec. Rev. Inc., Northbrook, Ill., 1970-77; v.p. Hooper Info. Systems Inc., Tustin, Calif., 1977-78; v.p., chief fin. officer ATE Assocs. Inc., Westlake Village, Calif., 1978-84; mgmt. cons. Thousand Oaks, Calif., 1984—; sr. v.p. Nat. Bank Calif., L.A., 1986—; chmn. liaison com. region IX SBA, 1990-94. Nat. advocate fin. svcs. SBA, 1989. Lt. USN, 1966-70. Mem. Nat. Assn. Govt. Guaranteed Lenders (bd. dirs. 1990-93), Robert Morris Assocs., Nat. Assn. Credit Mgmt. Avocations: art, music. Office: Nat Bank Calif 145 S Fairfax Ave Los Angeles CA 90036-2171

VANATTA, BOB, athletic administrator; b. Columbia, Mo., July 7, 1918; s. Claude W. and Viola (Toler) V.; m. Lois A. Williams; children: Robert, Thomas, Timothy. BA, Ctrl. Meth. Coll., 1942; MEd, U. Mo., 1949. Tchr., coach Boonville (Mo.) High Sch., 1942-43, Kemper Mil. Sch., Boonville 1943-44, Springfield (Mo.) High Sch., 1944-47; tchr., dir. athletics, coach Ctrl. Meth. Coll., Fayette, Mo., 1947-50, S.W. Mo. State U. Springfield, 1950-53; coach U.S. Mil. Acad., West Point, N.Y., 1953-54; dir. athletics, coach Bardley U., Peoria, Ill., 1954-56; tchr., coach Memphis State U., 1956-62, U. Mo., Columbia, 1962-68; bank mktg. officer Empire Bank, Springfield, 1968-71; profl. basketball exec. dir. Memphis Pros, 1971-72; tchr., coach Delta State U. Cleve., 1972-73; dir. athletics Oral Roberts U., Tulsa, 1973-77; commr. Ohio Valley Athletic Conf., Nashville, 1977-80, Trans Am. Athletic Conf., Shreveport, La., 1980-83; dir. athletics La. Tech. U., Rustin, 1983-86; commr. Sunshine State Athletic Conf., Jupiter, Fla., 1986—; cons., speaker in field. Author: Coaching Patterson Play Basketball, 1959; contbr. articles to profl. jours. Named to Ctrl. Meth. Coll. Hall of Fame, S.W. Mo. State U. Hall of Fame, Nat. Athletic Intercollegiate Assn. Hall of Fame, Greater Springfield Hall of Fame, John Q. Hammons Mo. Sports Hall of Fame, Nat. Football Found. Hall of Fame. Mem. Nat. Assn. Basketball Coaches. Office: Sunshine State Conf 745 N A 1 A # C205 Jupiter FL 33477-4581

VANATTA, CHESTER B., business executive, educator; b. Bartlesville, Okla., Sept. 3, 1935; s. Benjamin Franklin and Iona Ruth (Hayes) V.; m. Patsy Lou Straub, May 29, 1958; children—Tracy Ann, Christopher B., John Scott. B.S. in Mktg., U. Kans., Lawrence, 1959, M.S. in Acctg., 1962; Advanced Mgmt. Program, Harvard U., Cambridge, 1972. Mem. staff Arthur Young & Co., Kansas City, Mo., 1962-69; regional dir, Arthur Young & Co., Dallas, 1969-72, ptnr., 1969-85; mng. ptnr. Arthur Young & Co., Chgo., 1972-76, dir., 1973-85; mng. ptnr., vice chmn. ops. Arthur Young & Co., N.Y.C., 1976-81; mng. ptnr., vice chmn. S.W. Region Arthur Young & Co., Dallas, 1981-85; pres. Exec. Cons. Group, Lawrence, Kans., 1985—; exec. in residence, Paul J. Adam Disting. lectr. U. Kans. Sch. Bus., Lawrence, 1985-90; bd. dirs. Oread Labs., Lawrence, Atlantis Group Inc., Miami, Fla., Arcadian Corp., Memphis, Adams Bus. Forms, Topeka. Trustee, exec. com., fin. com. Kans. U. Endowment Fund, 1983—; bd. dirs. Kans. Alumni Assn., 1984-91, pres. 1986-87. Mem. Am. Inst. CPA's, Kans. Soc. CPA's (Gold Key 1962). Republican. Clubs: Alvamar Country (Lawrence), Tournament Players-Summerlin (Las Vegas), Elkhorn Country (Sun Valley, Idaho). Avocations: golf, travel, photography. Home: # 356 2251 N Rampart Blvd Las Vegas NV 89128-7640

VAN ATTA, DAVID MURRAY, lawyer; b. Berkeley, Calif., Oct. 20, 1944; s. Chester Murray and Rosalind (Eisenstein) Van A.; m. Jo Ann Masaoka; 1 child, Lauren Rachel. BA, U. Calif., Berkeley, 1966; JD, U. Calif., Hastings, 1969. Bar: Calif. 1970. Asst. gen. counsel Boise Cascade Corp., Palo Alto, Calif., 1970-73; ptnr. Miller, Starr & Regalia, San Francisco, 1973-87, Graham & James, San Francisco, 1987-93, Hanna & Van Atta, Palo Alto, Calif., 1993—; instr. Golden Gate U., San Francisco, 1984-85; U. Calif., Berkeley, 1976-84. Mem. ABA, Calif. Bar Assn. (vice chmn. exec. com. real property law sect 1982-85, chmn. condo. and subdiv. com. real property law sect. 1981-83), Community Assn. Inst., Urban Land Inst., Am. Coll. Real Estate Lawyers. Avocations: skiing, tennis, painting. Office: Hanna & Van Atta 525 University Ave Ste 705 Palo Alto CA 94301-1921

VANATTA, JOHN CROTHERS, III, physiologist, physician, educator; b. Lafayette, Ind., Apr. 22, 1919; s. John Crothers and Ida Lahr (Raub) V.; m. Carol Lee Geisler, July 30, 1944; children: Lynn Ellen, Paul Richard. B.A., Ind. U., 1941, M.D., 1944. Intern Wayne County Gen. Hosp., Eloise, Mich., 1944-45, resident in internal medicine, 1946-47; fellow in physiology, pharmacology Southwestern Med. Coll., Dallas, 1947-48, fellow in exptl. and internal medicine, 1948-49; instr. physiology U. Tex. Southwestern Med. Sch., 1949-50, asst. prof., 1950-53, assoc. prof., 1953-57, prof. physiology, 1957—, Robert W. Lackey prof. physiology, 1987-89; prof. physiology So. Meth. U. Dallas, 1969-80, Baylor Coll. Dentistry, Dallas, 1992-94; mem. staff Parkland Meml. Hosp., Dallas, 1953-57, VA Hosp., Dallas, McKinney, Tex., 1956-58; cons. div. nuclear edn. tng. AEC, 1964-67. Author: Oxygen Transport, Hypoxia and Cyanosis, 1974, Fluid Balance - A Clinical Manual, 1988; contbr. articles to profl. jours. Scouter, Circle 10 council Boy Scouts Am., Dallas, 1963-78; v.p. Luth. Health Care Council N. Tex., 1975-80, pres., 1980-81. Served as lt. (j.g.) M.C., USNR, 1945-46, PTO. Mem. AMA, AAAS, Am. Physiol. Soc., Am. Soc. Exptl. Biology and Medicine, Phi Beta Pi, Sigma Xi, Delta Tau Delta. Lutheran (councilman 1951-91, v.p. 1974-75). Home: 10416 Remington Ln Dallas TX 75229-5262

VAN AUKEN, ROBERT DANFORTH, business administration educator, management consultant; b. Chgo., Oct. 31, 1915; s. Howard Robert and Mable (Hanlon) Van A.; student Guilford Coll., 1933-35, Gen. Motors Inst. Tech., 1936-38, U. Pitts., 1953-54; BS, U. Dayton, 1958; MA, U. Okla., 1967; m. Ruth Bowen Cutler, Nov. 24, 1939 (dec.); children: Robert Hanlon, Joseph Marshall, David Danforth, Howard Evans, Jonathan Lewis; m. Vernia Maurine Long, July 9, 1993. Commd. aviation cadet U.S. Air Force, 1938; advanced through grades to lt. col., 1961; fighter pilot, squadron comdr., ops. officer, 1939-45; asst. air attaché, Paris, 1946-49; staff officer, Pentagon 1950-53; procurement-prodn. staff officer Wright-Patterson AFB, 1954-58, Tinker AFB, 1958-60, Holloman AFB, 1960-61, ret., 1961; personnel officer U. Okla., Norman, 1962-65, mem. faculty, 1965—, asst. prof. mgmt., 1979-83, prof. emeritus bus. adminstrn., 1983—; dir. student programs and career devel. Coll. Bus. Adminstrn., 1975-79; cons. seminars mgmt. amd compensation, 1963—; adj. instr. Park Coll., 1991—; instr. Park Coll., 1991—; cattle rancher, 1970—; owner VA Farms. Mem. Oklahomans

for Improvement in Nursing Care Homes; ombudsman vol. Okla. Areawide Aging Agy., 1992—. Decorated Silver Star, Purple Heart. Mem. DAV, Oklahoma City Human Resources Assn., Acad. Mgmt., Internat. Platform Assn., Nat. Cattlemans Assn., Okla. Cattlemans Assn., Okla. Alliance Aging, Am. Legion, Ret. Officers Assn., Mil. Order of World Wars, Order of Deadalians, 5th Air Force Meml. Found., 49th Fighter Group Assn., 31st Fighter Officers Assn., Disabled Am. Vets., Masons, Beta Gamma Sigma, Delta Sigma Pi. Republican. Contbr. monographs in field. Home: 420 S Highland Rd Oklahoma City OK 73110-2138 Office: U Okla 307 W Brooks St Norman OK 73069-8822

VAN BEBBER, GEORGE THOMAS, federal judge; b. Troy, Kans., Oct. 21, 1931; s. Roy Vest and Anne (Wenner) V.; m. Alleen Sara Castellani. AB, U. Kans., 1953, LLB, 1955. Bar: Kans. 1955, U.S. Dist. Ct. Kans. 1955, U.S. Ct. Appeals (10th cir.) 1961. Pvt. practice, Troy, 1955-58, 1961-82; asst. U.S. atty. Topeka, Kansas City, Kans., 1958-61; county atty. Doniphan County, Troy, 1963-69; mem. Kans. House of Reps., 1973-75; chmn. Kans. Corp. Commn., Topeka, 1975-79; U.S. magistrate Topeka, 1982-89; judge U.S. Dist. Ct., Kansas City, Kans., 1989—. Mem. ABA, Kas. Bar Assn. Episcopalian. Home: 6701 W 66th Ter Shawnee Mission KS 66202-4146 Office: US Dist Ct 529 US Courthouse 500 State Ave Kansas City KS 66101-3037

VAN BEEK, GUS WILLARD, archaeologist; b. Tulsa, Mar. 21, 1922; s. Gus Willard and Dovie Lucille (Crupper) Van B.; children: John Phillip, Christopher Hicks, Stephen Dart; m. Ora Braunstein, Sept. 25, 1972. BA with honors, U. Tulsa, 1943; BD, McCormick Theol. Sem., Chgo., 1945; PhD, Johns Hopkins U., 1953. Fellow Hebrew Union Coll., Cin., 1947-49, Am. Schs. Oriental Research, Jerusalem, 1952; research assoc. Johns Hopkins U., Balt., 1954-59; assoc. curator Smithsonian Instn., Washington, 1959-67, curator, 1967—; dir. archeol. expdn. Hadhramaut, Arabia, 1961-62, Nejran, Saudi Arabia, 1968, Tell Jemmeh, Israel, 1970—; trustee Am. Schs. Oriental Rsch., 1988-93, mem. adv. bd., 1993—. Author: Hajar Bin Humeid, 1969; editor: The Scholarship of William Foxwell Albright: An Appraisal, 1989; also 150 articles on archeology, history; producer/curator exhibits: Dead Sea Scrolls of Jordan, 1965, Arabia Felix, 1972. Recipient Disting. Alumnus award U. Tulsa Coll. Arts. Scis., 1971. Mem. Archeol. Inst. Am., Am. Inst. Yemeni Studies, Am. Schs. Oriental Research. Democrat. Presbyterian. Office: Smithsonian Inst Mus Natural History Mrc Nhb # 112 Washington DC 20560

VANBIESBROUCK, JOHN, professional hockey player; b. Detroit, Sept. 4, 1963; m. Rosalinde V. With N.Y. Rangers, 1981-93, Vancouver Canucks, 1993, Florida Panthers, 1993—; mem. NHL All-Star team, 1985-86; player NHL All-Star game, 1994. Recipient Vezina Trophy (NHL outstanding goaltender), 1985, 86, (with Ron Scott) Terry Sawchuk trophy, 1983-89, (with Marc D'Amour) F.W. Dinty Moore trophy, (with D. Bruce Affleck) Tommy Ivan trophy, 1983-84; named NHL All-Star, 1985-86, Sporting News NHL All-Star, 1985-86, 93-94. Office: Florida Panthers 100 North East Third Ave 10th Fl Fort Lauderdale FL 33301*

VAN BOKKELEN, WILLIAM REQUA, health facility administrator; b. Indpls., Mar. 27, 1946; s. Robert William and Wilma Louise (Reynolds) Van B.; m. Cheryl Lyn Steiling, June 12, 1972; children: Audrey Leigh, Adriane Lisa. BA, DePauw U., 1968; MBA, Northwestern U., Evanston, Ill., 1973. Adminstrv. intern Lake Forest (Ill.) Hosp., 1972; student assoc. VA Lakeside Hosp., Chgo., 1973; asst. adminstr. St. Francis Hosp., Evanston, Ill., 1973-76, v.p. clin. svcs., 1976-79; v.p. adminstrn. Louis A. Weiss Meml. Hosp., Chgo., 1979-83; adminstr. Christian hosp. Northeast, St. Louis, 1983-86; exec. v.p. Christian Hosp. Northeast/Northwest, St. Louis, 1986-90, pres., 1990—; bd. dirs. Durable Med. Equipment Co., Maryland Heights, Mo., Citizens Bank Florissant, Mo., Midwest Stone Inst., St. Louis. Chairperson Friends of Scouting, St. Louis, 1989—. Am. Coll. Healthcare Execs. fellow, 1983. Mem. Res. Officers Am., Florissant Valley C. of C. (bd. dirs. 1990—), Marygrove (bd. dirs. 1990), Norwood Hills Country Club, Florissant Rotary (bd. dirs. 1990-91). Methodist. Avocations: running, snow skiing, golf, fishing. Office: Christian Hosp NE-NW 11133 Dunn Rd Saint Louis MO 63136-6192

VAN BORTEL, HOWARD MARTIN, automarketing consultant; b. Canandaigua, N.Y., May 29, 1930; s. Kenneth and Edna (Martin) Van B.; m. Patricia Gamble, June 26, 1953; children: Mary Catherine, Howard, George, John. Grad. high sch., Palmyra, N.Y. Used car dealer Town Auto Sales Owner, Palmyra, 1951-53; new car dealer Palmyra (N.Y.) Motors Pres., 1954-81; cons. Van Bortel Auto Mktg., Fairport, N.Y., 1982-94; pres., cons. Van Bortel Auto Mktg., Rochester, N.Y., 1992—. Democrat. Avocation: tennis. Home: 696 Moseley Rd Fairport NY 14450-3622 Office: Van Bortel Auto Mktg 696 Mosley Rd Fairport NY 14450

VANBRODE, DERRICK BRENT, IV, association executive; b. Elgin, Ill., Sept. 3, 1940. Grad., N.Y. Inst. Criminology, 1963. Sr. v.p. Am. Fraternal Programmers, Inc., North Miami, Fla., 1977—; mgmt. cons. Am. Fedn. Police, Am. Law Enforcement Officers Assn., Nat. Assn. Chiefs of Police, Am. Police Acad. Editor: Who's Who in American Law Enforcement, 1976-93, Crime Watch mag, 1981—, Police Times/Command, 1975—. Pres. Greater Miami Assn. Licensed Beverage Owners, 1973—. Decorated Grand Cross Knights of St. Michael; comdr. Royal Knights of Justice. Mem. Greater North Port Fla. C. of C. (founder, pres.). Clubs: Miami Millionaires (founder, past pres.), Millionaires Internat. (pres. 1983—), Miami Shores Country, Racquet. Office: 3801 Biscayne Blvd Miami FL 33137-3732

VAN BRUGGEN, ARIENA HENDRIKA CORNELIA, plant pathologist; b. Delfzyl, The Netherlands, Dec. 7, 1949; came to U.S., 1980; d. Adriaan and Nelly (Meerwald) Van B. MS, Agr. U., Wageningen, The Netherlands, 1976; PhD, Cornell U., 1985. Assoc. expert Food and Agriculture Orgn. of UN, Ethiopia, 1976-80; grad. asst. Cornell U., Ithaca, N.Y., 1980-84; postdoctoral Boyce Thompson Inst., Ithaca, N.Y., 1984-86; asst. prof. U. Calif., Davis, 1986-92, assoc. prof., 1992—. Contbr. articles to profl. jours. Recipient Ciba Geigy award Am. Phytopathology Soc.; Eriksson Gold medal Agr. U., Sweden, 1993; USDA grantee, 1988-92, 95-96. Achievements include discovery of a new plant pathogen, rhizomonas suberifaciens. Office: U Calif Dept Plant Pathology Davis CA 95616

VAN BRUNT, ALBERT DANIEL, advertising agency executive; b. N.Y.C., Nov. 13, 1920; s. Ernest Robert and Helen (Rothschild) Isaacs. B.S. in Mktg., NYU, 1942. Dir. advt. Air France, N.Y.C., 1947-50; v.p. Buchanan Advt. Agy., N.Y.C., 1951-57; pres. Van Brunt & Co. Advt.-Mktg., Inc., N.Y.C., 1958-88, chmn. bd., 1989-90; pres. IMAA, Inc., N.Y.C., 1965-70; sr. v.p. IMAA, Inc., 1970-89; exec. v.p. Van Brunt & Co., Chgo., Inc., 1969-76, Van Brunt/Schaeffer, 1979-89; v.p. HBC/Van Brunt, Chgo., 1976-77; pres., chief exec. officer WDB Advt., Inc., N.Y.C., 1990—. Trustee N.Y. chpt. Leukemia Soc. Am., 1979-80; bd. dirs. Leukemia program Coll. Physicians and Surgeons, Columbia U. Served to lt. USNR, 1942-46. Mem. Am. Assn. Advt. Agys. (mem. N.Y. council 1969-74), Internat. Advt. Assn., SAR. Clubs: Wings (N.Y.), Lotos (N.Y.C.) (dir. emeritus 1987—), Internat. 1987—; sec. 1972-75, treas. 1975-76). Home: 315 E 68th St New York NY 10021-5692 also: Jason's Ln East Hampton NY 11937 Office: WDB Prodns Inc 419 E 57th St New York NY 10022

VAN BUREN, ABIGAIL (PAULINE FRIEDMAN PHILLIPS), columnist, author, writer, lecturer; b. Sioux City, Iowa, July 4, 1918; d. Abraham and Rebecca (Rushall) Friedman; m. Morton Phillips, July 2, 1939; children: Edward Jay, Jeanne. Student, Morningside Coll., Sioux City, 1936-39; Litt.D. (hon.), Morningside Coll., 1965; L.H.D. (hon.), U. Jacksonville, Fla., 1984. Vol. worker for causes of better mental health Nat. Found. Infantile Paralysis; tng. Gray Ladies, ARC, 1939-56; pres. Minn.-Wis. council B'nai B'rith Aux., 1945-49; columnist Dear Abby San Francisco Chronicle, 1956, McNaught Syndicate, 1956-74, Chgo. Tribune Syndicate, 1974-80, Universal Press Syndicate, 1980—; syndicated U.S. Brazil, Mex., Japan, Philippines, Fed. Republic Germany, India, Holland, Denmark, Can., Korea, Thailand, Italy, Hong Kong, Taiwan, Ireland, Saudi Arabia, Greece, France, Dominican Republic, P.R., Costa Rica, U.S. Virgin Islands, Bermuda, Guam; host radio program The Dear Abby Show, CBS, 1963-75; life-time cons. Found for Advancement Psychiatry, 1987—. Author: Dear Abby, 1957 (also translated into Japanese, Dutch, German, Spanish, Danish, Italian, Finnish), Dear Teen Ager, 1959, Dear Abby on Marriage, 1962, The

Best of Dear Abby, 1981, reissued, 1989, Dear Abby on Planning Your Wedding, 1988, Where Were You When President Kennedy Was Shot?: Memories and Tributes to a Slain President as Told to Dear Abby, 1993. Mem. nat. adv. council on aging NIH, HEW, 1978-81; hon. chairwoman 1st Nat. Women's Conf. on Cancer, Am. Cancer Soc., Los Angeles, 1979; mem. public adv. council Center for Study Multiple Gestation, 1981; trustee, mem. adv. bd. Westside Community for Ind. Living, 1981; bd. dirs. Guthrie Theatre, Mpls., 1970-74; charter mem. Franz Alexander Research Found., Los Angeles; charter trustee Armand Hammer United World Coll. of Am. West; bd. dirs. Am. Fedn. for Aging Research Inc.; mem. nat. bd. Goodwill Industries, 1968-75; nat. chmn. Crippled Children Soc., 1962; founding mem. The Amazing Blue Ribbon 400; hon. chmn. Easter Seal campaign Nat. Soc. Crippled Children and Adults, Washington, 1963; del. to Democratic Nat. Conf. from Calif., 1964; Calif. del. White House Conf. on Children and Youth, 1974; non. life mem. Concern for Dying-Am. Ednl. Council; mem. White House Conf. on Physically Handicapped, 1976, NIH, 1976; mem. adv. council Suicide Prevention Ctr., Los Angeles, 1977; mem. com. on aging HHS, 1977-82; council sponsor Assn. Vol. Sterilization, 1981; mem. Women's Trusteeship, 1980; sponsor Mayo Found., Rochester, 1982; bd. dirs. Lupus Found. Am., 1983; mem. adv. com. Ams. for Substance Abuse Prevention, 1984; participant XIII Internat. Congress Gerontology, N.Y.C., 1985; mem. adv. bd. Young Writer's Contest Found., 1985; bd. dirs. Am. Found. for AIDS Research, 1985—; mem. adv. bd. Nat. Council for Children's Rights, Washington, 1988; mem. adv. bd. San Diego Hospice, 1990; mem. adv. bd. Rhonda Fleming Mann Clinic for Women's Comprehensive Care, 1991; mem. Scripps Rsch. Coun. Recipient Times Mother of Yr. award, Los Angeles, 1958; Golden Kidney award, Los Angeles, 1960; Sarah Coventry award, Miami, 1961; Woman of Yr. award Internat. Rotary Club, Rome, 1965; award NCCJ, St. Louis, 1968; award for disting. service to sightless Internat. Lions Club, Dallas, 1972; Disting. Service award Suicide Prevention Center, San Mateo, Calif., 1975; Good Samaritan award Salvation Army, San Francisco, 1970; Margaret Sanger award Nat. Planned Parenthood, 1974; award for outstanding services in mental health So. Psychiat. Assn., 1974; Robert T. Morse writer's award Am. Psychiat. Assn., 1977; Tex. Gov.'s award in recognition of exceptional service to youth of Am. for Ops. Peace of Mind, 1979; Humanitarian award Gay Acad. Union, Los Angeles, 1979, Braille Inst. So. Calif., 1981, Gay and Lesbian Community Services Ctr., 1984; pub. Awardness trophy for Living Will, Soc. for Right to Die, 1983; citation of commendation Simon Weisenthal Found., 1984; Internat. Image in Media award Gay Fathers Coalition, 1985; 1st ann. Woman of Yr. Humanitarian award Rainbow Guild of Amy Karen Children's Cancer Clinic, Cedars-Sinai Med. Ctr., Los Angeles, 1985; Pub. Service award Nat. Kidney Found., 1985, John Rock award Ctr. Population Options, 1986, Serve Am. award Ladies Auxiliary to the VFW, 1986, Genesis award Fund for Animals, 1986, Disting. Service award Inst. Studies Destructive Behavior and Suicide Prevention Ctr., 1986, Citizen of Yr. award Beverly Hills, Calif. C. of C., 1988, Humanitarian award Nat. Council on Alcoholism, 1988, Helen B. Taussig medal Internat. Socs. for the Right to Die with Dignity, 1988, Media award So. Psychiat. Soc., 1988; named Hon. Dir. Found. for Craniofacial Deformities, 1988; Disting. Achievement award Nat. Assn. to Advance Fat Acceptance, 1988, Hand to Hand award Episc. Charities San Francisco, 1989; Nat. Media award for print Nat. Down Syndrome Congress, 1991; Sec.'s award for excellence in communication HHS, 1992; Dove award Assn. Retarded Citizens, 1992. Mem. Women in Communications (hon.), Am. Coll. Psychiatrists (hon. life mem.). Nat. Council Jewish Women (hon. life mem.), Newspapers Features Council, Soc. Profl. Journalists, Nat. Orgn. Women, "Women For", Nat. Com. Preserve Social Security and Medicare, Korean War Vets. Assn. (hon.), Sigma Delta Chi. Office: Phillips-Van Buren Inc 9200 W Sunset Blvd Ste 1003 West Hollywood CA 90069-3605 "If a man loves the labor of his trade, apart from any question of success of fame, the gods have called him." (Robert Louis Stevenson.) The same holds true for women and I am one of them.

VAN BUREN, WILLIAM BENJAMIN, III, retired pharmaceutical company executive; b. Bklyn., Mar. 25, 1922; s. William Benjamin and Dorothy Marjorie (Way) Van B.; m. Joan Cottrell Whitford, Sept. 11, 1948; children—Susan (a), Patricia, William S., Richard W. B.A., Washington & Lee U., 1944; LL.B., Yale U., 1949. Bar: N.Y. 1950. V.p., sec. Merck & Co., Inc., 1976-86; pres. Merck & Co. Found., 1982-86. Served with USNR, 1943-46. Mem. Phi Beta Kappa. Home: 8 Point North Dr Salem SC 29676-4113

VANBUTSEL, MICHAEL R., real estate developer; b. Alma, Nebr., Dec. 7, 1952; s. Julius and Margaret (McCorkle) VanB.; divorced; children: Vanessa, Stephanie, Jamie; m. Kimberly Peters. BArch, U. Nebr., 1975. Lic. real estate rep., Ariz., Fla. Asst. to v.p. cen. adminstrn. U. Nebr., Lincoln, 1975-76; architect Consol. Architects Engrs., Omaha, 1976-77; project mgr. Dana, Larson, Roubal Architects, Phoenix, 1977-79; mktg. dir. Dick, Fritsche Architects, Phoenix, 1979-81; mktg. mgr. Lendrum Design Group, Phoenix, 1981-85; owner Developers Mgmt. Group, Phoenix, 1985-86; mktg. mgr. Turner Constrn., Phoenix, 1986-87; v.p. devel., mktg. The Bay Plaza Co., St. Petersburg, Fla., 1987—; bd. dirs. Cen. Ariz. Health Systems Agy. Commr. Housing Commn., City of Phoenix; mem. Paradise Valley Planning Com.; pres. The Mariners for Senator John McCain, Ariz.; surrogate speaker for Congressman Eldon Rudd; mem. Senate roundtable Senator Connie Mack, Fla.; bd. dirs. Am. Stage Theater; adv. bd. U. South Fla., St. Petersburg, chmn. beautification com.; bd. dirs. Pinellas Econ. Devel. Coun. Mem. Urban Land Inst., Valley Leadership (Phoenix), Am. Planning Assn. Republican. Avocations: cooking, body building, reading geo-political books.

VAN CAMP, BRIAN RALPH, lawyer; b. Halstead, Kans., Aug. 23, 1940; s. Ralph A. and Mary Margaret (Bragg) Van C.; m. Diane D. Miller, 1992; children: Megan M., Laurie E. A.B., U. Calif., Berkeley, 1962, LL.B., 1965. Bar: Calif. 1966. Dep. atty. gen. State Calif., 1965-67; agy. atty. Redevel. Agy., City of Sacramento, 1967-70; asst./acting sec. Bus. and Transp. Agy., State Calif., 1970-71; commr. of corps. State of Calif., Sacramento, 1971-74; partner firm Diepenbrock, Wulff, Plant & Hannegan, Sacramento, 1975-77, Van Camp & Johnson, Sacramento, 1978-90; sr. ptnr. Downey, Brand, Seymour & Rohwer, 1990—; lectr. Continuing Edn. Bar, Practicing Law Inst., Calif. CPA Soc., others; mem. adv. bd. UCLA Securities Law Inst., 1978. Contbr. articles to profl. jours. State Ctrl. Com. Calif., 1974-78, exec. com., 1974-78; pres. Sacramento Area Commerce and Trade Orgn., 1986-87; mem. electoral coll. Presdl. Elector for State of Calif., 1976, Calif. Health Facilities Fin. Authority, 1985-89, Capital Area Devel. Authority, 1989—, chmn., 1990—; bd. dirs. Sacramento Symphony Assn., 1973-85, 92—, Rep. Assocs. Sacramento County, 1975-79, Sacramento Valley Venture Capital Forum, 1986-90, League to Save Lake Tahoe, 1988—; elder Fremont Presbyn. Ch., 1968—. Recipient Sumner-Mering Meml. award Sacramento U. of Calif. Alumni Assn., 1962, Thos. Jefferson award Am. Inst. Pub. Svc., 1994; named Outstanding Young Man of Yr. Sacramento Jaycees, 1970, Internat. Young Man of Yr. Active 20-30 Club Internat., 1973. Mem. ABA, Calif. State Bar (mem. com. on corps. 1977-80, partnerships and unincorporated bus. assns. 1983-87), Sacramento County Bar Assn., Calif. C. of C. (chmn. statewide energy task force 1979-85, bd. dirs. 1982—, chmn. edn. com. 1988-90), Sacramento Met. C. of C. (co-chmn. econ. devel. com. 1979, bd. dirs. 1986-88), Boalt Hall Alumni Assn. (bd. dirs. 1991-94), Lincoln Club of Sacramento Valley (bd. dirs., pres. 1984-86), U. Calif. Men's Club (pres. 1968), Sutter Club, Kandahar Ski Club, Rotary Club of Sacramento (pres. 1993-94). Republican. Presbyterian. Office: 555 Capitol Mall 10th Fl Sacramento CA 95814

VAN CAMP, DARRELL ROBERT, chemist; b. Two Buttes, Colo., July 15, 1935; s. Robert Lewis and Pauline (Comer) Van C.; m. Orlene Crone, Sept. 8, 1958 (div. 1977); children: Anthony, Bryan; m. Judith Ann Gorsky, June 27, 1978; 1 child, John. BS, Colo. State U., 1957; MS, N.C. State U., 1960, PhD, 1962. Postdoctoral fellow Cornell U., Ithaca, N.Y., 1962-63; rsch. chemist USDA ARS, Ithaca, 1964-80, lab. dir., 1980—. Contbr. articles and revs. to profl. jours. and chpts. to books. NIH fellow, 1962. Mem. Sigma Xi, Alpha Zeta, Phi Kappa Phi. Avocations: golf, gardening, numismatics. Home: 117 Simsbury Dr Ithaca NY 14850-1728 Office: USDA ARS Plant Soil & Nutrition Lab Tower Road Ithaca NY 14853

VAN CAMPEN, STEPHEN BERNARD, executive recruiter, consultant; b. East Stroudsburg, Pa., Oct. 1, 1941; s. Bernard Allen and Marion (Van Whye) Van C.; m. Ellen Baars, July 22, 1989; children: Brendon, Regan, Meghan, Taylor, Hannah. BS in Sci. and Pre-Veterinary Med., Pa. State U.,

1959-64; postgrad. in indsl. rels., George Washington U. Grad. Sch, 1965-68; law student, U. Balt., 1966-68. With FDA, Balt., Washington, 1964-66; indsl. rels. officer Joseph E. Seagrams & Sons, Balt., N.Y.C., San Francisco, 1966-72; worldwide dir. exec. staffing RCA/Hertz Corp., N.Y.C., 1972-74; dir. internat. indsl. rels. Revlon Internat., N.Y.C., 1974; pres./owner/cons. Gilbert & Van Campen Exec. Search, Internat. (subs.: J.B. Gilbert Assocs., Inc., Amtrade Assocs., Internat., GVC Fin. Svcs.), N.Y.C., 1974—; owner, pres. Lillagaard Hotel Corp., Ocean Grove, N.J., 1992—; owner N.J. Profl. Meeting Planners Group, No. Shore Region Convention and Vis. Bur.; appointed to N.J. Gov.'s Commn. on Internat. Trade, 1992; White House nominee to Nat. Parks Adv. Commn., Dept. Interior; chmn. internat. trade subcom. ad hoc N.J. Assembly Small Bus. Adv. Coun.; bd. dirs. N.J. SBDC, N.J. Shore Region Tourism Coun.; named to Commerce and Econ. Devel. Transition Team for Gov.-elect Christine Todd Whitman; chmn. Econ. Devel. Task Force, Warren County, N.J., 1994. Rep. fundraiser; active N.J. Rep. Gov.'s Club, N.J. State Fin. Com.; appointed to Congressman Zimmer's Warren County N.J. Fed. Adv. Com., Warren County Econ. Adv. Coun., N.J. Gov.'s appointee and chmn. fed. enacted Del. Water Gap Nat. Recreation Area citizens adv. com., Gov.-elect Christie Todd Whitman Transition Team-Commerce and Econ. Devel.; elected to Warren County Rep. Com.; chmn. adv. bd. Warren Presdl. Correctional Facility; chmn. Calno Cemetery Assn.; chmn. Warner County Econ. Devel. Blue Ribbon Task Force; vice chmn. bd. trustees Warren County C.C., chmn. found. bd.; exec. bd. Tri-County Washington coun. Boy Scouts Am.; bd. dirs. N.J. Shore Regional Tourism Coun., N.Y. SBDC, N.J. Juvenile Justice Adv. Bd.; mem. 1st N.J. Trade Del. Soviet Union; mem. commerce and econ. devel. transition team Gov.-elect Christie Whitman, N.J., 1994; chmn. N.J. assembly bus. retention com. of Task Force for Bus. Rentention, Attrition, Expansion and Internat. Trade; chmn. N.J. Gov.'s Conf. Travel and Tourism, Atlantic City, 1994; chmn. N.J. No. Shore Region CUB Allaire Airport Conv. Ctr.; pres.-elect Warren County Econ. Partnership. Recipient medal of honor Ellis Island, 1994. Mem. ASTD, Am. Mgmt. Assns., Am. Coun. on Germany, U.S.C. of C., Nat. Fgn. Trade Coun., World Trade Inst., U.S.-USSR Trade and Econ. Coun., N.Y. C. of C. and Industry, N.J.C. of C., Commerce and Industry Assn. N.J., Am. C. of C.s and U.S. Bus. Couns. Abroad, Soc. Human Resource Mgmt., Nat. Assn. Corp. and Profl. Recruiters, Employment Mgmt. Assn., N.J. Hotel/Motel Assn. (bd. dirs., mem. exec. bd.), N.J. Travel Industry Assn. (bd. dirs., v.p. exec. bd.), N.Y. Pers. Mgmt. Assn., Soc. Plastics Engrs., Soc. Cosmetic Chemists, Small Bus. Adv. Coun., Ocean Grove C. of C. (vice chmn.). Republican. Methodist. Home: 37 Petersburg Rd Hackettstown NJ 07840-4903 Office: Gilbert & Van Campen Intl 420 Lexington Ave New York NY 10170 also: Gilbert & Van Campen Intl Conference Ctr 393 Lake Dr Belvidere NJ 07823

VAN CASPEL, VENITA WALKER, financial planner; b. Sweetwater, Okla.; d. Leonard Ransom and Ella Belle (Jarnagin) Walker; m. Lyttleton T. Harris IV, Dec. 26, 1987. Student, Duke, 1944-46; B.A., U. Colo., 1948, postgrad., 1949-51; postgrad., N.Y. Inst. Fin., 1962. Cert. fin. planner. Stockbroker Rauscher Pierce & Co., Houston, 1962-65, A.G. Edwards & Sons, Houston, 1965-68; founder, pres., owner Van Caspel & Co., Inc., Houston, 1968—, Van Caspel Wealth Mgmt.; owner, mgr. Van Caspel Planning Service, Van Caspel Advt. Agy.; sr. v.p. investments Raymond James and Assocs.; owner Diamond V Ranch; moderator PBS TV show The Money Makers and Profiles of Success, 1980; 1st women mem. Pacific Stock Exchange. Author: Money Dynamics, 1978, Money Dynamics of the 1980's, 1980, The Power of Money Dynamics, Money Dynamics for the 1990's, 1988; editor: Money Dynamics Letter. Bd. dirs. Boy Scouts Am., Horatio Alger Assn., Robert Schuller Ministries. Recipient Matrix award Theta Sigma Phi, 1969, Horatio Alger award for Disting. Americans, 1982, Disting. Woman's medal, Northwood Univ., 1988, Georgia Norlin award U. Colo. Alumni Assn., 1987. Mem. Internat. Assn. Fin. Planners, Inst. Cert. Fin. Planners, Phi Gamma Mu, Phi Beta Kappa. Methodist. Office: Raymond James & Assocs Inc 2700 Post Oak Blvd Ste 2325 Houston TX 77056-5705

VANCE, ANDREW PETER, lawyer; b. Detroit, Jan. 23, 1925; s. Peter Andrew and Anna (Maktos) V.; m. Olvia Cambourelis, Nov. 23, 1952; children: Peter, Cathy, Penny, Dorothy. BA, Harvard Coll., 1948; LLB, Harvard Law Sch., 1952. Trial atty. U.S. Dept. Justice, Washington, 1953-62; chief customs sect. U.S. Dept. Justice, N.Y.C., 1962-76; sr. ptnr. Barnes, Richardson & Colburn, N.Y.C., 1976-93, of counsel, 1994—; mem. adv. com. U.S. Ct. Appeals (fed. cir.), Washington, 1983—, chmn., 1992—; mem. adv. com. Ct. Internat. Trade, N.Y.C. 1987-93. Contbr. articles to profl. jours. Trustee Greenwood Union Cemetary, Rye, N.Y., 1984—, St. Photios Found., St. Augustine, Fla., 1990—, Juanita Coll., Huntingdon, Pa., 1990—. Recipient St. Paul's medal Greek Orthodox Archdiocese N. Am. and S. Am., 1976. Mem. ABA (chmn. Standing Com. on Customs Law 1991-93), Customs and Internat. Trade Bar Assn. (pres. 1990-92), Fed. Cir. Bar Assn. (pres. 1989-90), Order of St. Andrew. Greek Orthodox. Office: Barnes Richardson & Colburn 475 Park Ave S New York NY 10016

VANCE, BERNARD WAYNE, lawyer, government official; b. Meridian, Miss., May 31, 1947; s. Jack Bernard and Marjorie Opal (Ezell) V. BBA, U. Miss., 1969, JD, 1975. Bar: Miss. 1975, D.C. 1975. Trial atty. admiralty sect. Dept. Justice, Washington, 1975-77, dep. asst. atty. gen., 1982-85; chief of staff Sec. Transp., Washington, 1985-87; general counsel Dept. of Transp., Washington, 1987-89; ptnr. Dykema & Gossett, Washington, 1989-93. Editor-in-chief Miss. Law Jour., 1975, articles editor, 1974. Mem. 1969-72. Mem. ABA, D.C. Bar Assn., Phi Delta Phi, Phi Delta Theta, Phi Kappa Phi, Omicron Delta Kappa. Republican. Episcopalian. Office: 1203 Essex Manor Alexandria VA 22308

VANCE, CAROL STONER, lawyer; b. Beaumont, Tex., July 26, 1933; s. Carol Stoner and Fanelle (Philp) V.; m. Carolyn Ruth Kongabel, Dec. 6, 1954; children: Lynnell, Carroll III, Karen, Harold, Cheryl. BBA, U. Tex., 1955, LLB, 1958. Bar: Tex. 1957, U.S. Dist. Ct. (so. dist.) Tex. 1960, U.S. Dist. Ct. (no. dist.) Tex. 1964, U.S. Ct. Appeals (5th cir.) 1964, U.S. Supreme Ct. 1964. Asst. dist. atty. Harris County Dist. Atty.'s Office, Houston, 1958-66, dist. atty., 1966-79; sr. ptnr. Bracewell & Patterson, Houston, 1979—; adj. prof. law U. Houston Sch. Law, 1972-79; chmn. Tex. Dept. Criminal Justice, 1992—. Recipient Outstanding Young Man of Houston award Houston Jr. C. of C., 1967. Mem. ABA (spl. com. on criminal justice standards 1975-77, coun. sect. criminal justice 1972-79), Am. Coll. Trial Lawyers, Tex. Bar Assn. (chmn. criminal law sect. 1969-70), Houston Bar Assn. (appellate judiciary com.), Houston Bar Found., Nat. Coll. Dist. Attys. (bd. regents), Tex. Bar Found. (life), Tex. Assn. Def. Counsel, Tex. Young Lawyers Assn. (bd. dirs. 1963-66, Outstanding Young Lawyer of Tex. award 1970), Tex. Dist. Atty.'s Assn. (pres. 1969-70), Nat. Dist. Atty.'s Assn. (pres. 1972-73, Outstanding Dist. Atty. award 1972), Houston Young Lawyers' Assn. (pres. 1964), Nat. Coll. Dist. Attys. (chmn. bd. regents 1979-80, mem. bd. 1973—), Houston C. of C. (crime control com., chmn. legis. com.), Phi Alpha Delta. Avocations: tennis, golf. Office: Bracewell & Patterson South Tower Pennzoil Pl 711 Louisiana St Ste 2900 Houston TX 77002-2721

VANCE, CHARLES FOGLE, JR., lawyer; b. Winston-Salem, N.C., Oct. 4, 1924; s. Charles Fogle and Margaret (Vaughn) V.; m. Eleanor James, May 10, 1952; children: Lucy, Charles, Burton, Margaret. BA in Physics, U. N.C., 1946, JD, 1949. Bar: N.C. 1949, U.S. Dist. Ct. (mid. dist.) N.C. 1949, U.S. Ct. Appeals (4th cir.) 1949. Pvt. practice Winston-Salem, 1949-52; assoc. Womble Carlyle Sandridge & Rice, Winston-Salem, 1952-57, ptnr., 1957—; asst. solicitor Mcpl. Ct. Winston-Salem, 1951-52. Trustee Moravian Coll., Bethlehem, Pa., 1953-59, Salem Coll., Winston-Salem, 1974-80, chmn., 1977-80. With U.S. Army, 1944-45. Recipient Whitney North Seymour medal Am. Arbitration Assn., 1984. Fellow Am. Coll. Trial Lawyers; mem. ABA, Am. Bar Found., Am. Judicature Soc., Nat. Assn. R.R. Trial Counsel, N.C. Bar Assn., N.C. State Bar Coun. (councilor 1986-95), Forsythe County Bar Assn. (pres. 1966), 4th Cir. Jud. Conf. Democrat. Avocations: coastal fishing, piano. Office: Womble Carlyle Sandridge & Rice So Nat Fin Ctr PO Box 84 200 W 2d St Winston Salem NC 27102-0084

VANCE, CYRUS ROBERTS, lawyer, former government official; b. Clarksburg, W.Va., Mar. 27, 1917; s. John Carl and Amy (Roberts) V.; m. Grace Elsie Sloane, Feb. 15, 1947; children: Elsie Nicoll, Amy Sloane, Grace, Camilla, Cyrus Roberts. Student, Kent Sch.; B.A., Yale U., 1939, LL.B., 1942, LL.D. (hon.), 1968; LL.D. (hon.). Marshall U., 1963, Trinity Coll., 1968, W.Va. U., 1969, Bowling Green U., 1969, Salem Coll., 1970, Brandeis

U., 1971, Amherst Coll., 1974, W.Va. Wesleyan U., 1974, Harvard U., 1981, Colgate U., 1981, Gen, Theol. Sem., 1981, Williams Coll., 1981, Notre Dame U., 1982, Mt. Holyoke Coll., 1982, Brown U., Davidson Coll., U. Haifa, Fairfield U., NYU, Northwestern U. Bar: N.Y. State 1947, U.S. Supreme Ct. 1970. Asst. to pres. Mead Corp., 1946-47; assoc. Simpson Thacher & Bartlett, N.Y.C., 1947-56; ptnr. Simpson Thacher & Bartlett, 1956-61, 67-77, 80—; spl. counsel preparedness investigating subcom. Senate Armed Services Com., 1957-60; gen. counsel Dept. Def., 1961-62; sec. of army, 1962-63, dep. sec. def., 1964-67; spl. rep. of Pres. Johnson in Cyprus crisis, 1967, Korea, 1968; U.S. negotiator Paris Peace Conf. on Vietnam, 1968-69; sec. state, 1977-80, personal envoy UN Sec. Gen. on Yugoslavia crisis, 1991-92, personal envoy UN Sec. Gen. on South Africa and Nagorno-Karabakh, 1992; co-chmn. UN-EC Internat. Conf. on Former Yugoslavia, 1992-93; cons. counsel Spl. Com. on Space and Astronautics, U.S. Senate, 1958; chmn. com. on adjudication of claims Adminstrv. Conf. U.S.; mem. Com. To Investigate Alleged Police Corruption in N.Y.C., 1970-72; chmn. UN Devel. Corp., 1976; mem. Ind. Com. on Disarmament and Security Issues, N.Y. State Commn. on Govt. Integrity, N.Y. State Jud. Commn. on Minorities in the Ct.; bd. dirs. N.Y. Times; bd. dirs. Fed. Res. Bank of N.Y., 1989-93, chmn., 1989-91. Trustee Yale Corp., 1968-78, 80-87; trustee Rockefeller Found., 1970-77, 80-82, chmn., 1975-77; chmn. Am. Ditchley Found., 1981-94. Lt. USNR, 1942-46. Recipient Medal of Freedom, 1969, Grand Cordon of Order of Rising Sun Govt. of Japan, 1990, Legion of Honor French Rep.; 1993; apptd. Hon. Knight Comdr. in Civil div. of Most Excellent Order of British Empire, 1994. Fellow Am. Coll. Trial Lawyers; mem. ABA, Assn. of Bar of City of N.Y. (pres. 1974-76), Council on Fgn. Relations (dir., vice chmn. 1985-87), Japan Soc. (chmn. 1985-93). Office: Simpson Thacher & Bartlett 425 Lexington Ave New York NY 10017-3954

VANCE, DENNIS EDWARD, biochemistry educator; b. St. Anthony, Idaho, July 14, 1942; s. Russell Ernest and Josephine (Renner) V.; m. Jean Stuart Eaton, June 10, 1967; children—Russell Eaton, Fiona Natalie. B.S., Dickinson Coll., 1964; Ph.D., U. Pitts., 1968. Postdoctoral fellow U. Pitts., 1968-70; postdoctoral fellow Harvard U., Cambridge, Mass., 1970-72, U. Warwick, Coventry, Eng., 1972-73; asst. prof. biochemistry U. B.C., Vancouver, Can., 1973-77; assoc. prof. U.B.C., Vancouver, Can., 1977-82; prof. U. B.C., Vancouver, Can., 1982-86, assoc. dean medicine, 1978-81, head dept., 1982-86; prof. biochemistry U. Alta., Edmonton, 1986—; dir. Lipid/Lipoprotein Group U. Alta., 1986—. Author: (with others) Principles of Biochemistry, 1995; editor: Phosphatidylcholine Metabolism, 1989, Biochemistry of Lipids, Lipoproteins and Membranes, 1991, Phospholipid Biosynthesis, 1992. Grantee Med. Rsch. Coun., 1973—; Heart and Stroke Found. Can., 1974—. Mem. Am. Soc. Biochem. and Molecular Biology, Can. Soc. of Biochemistry and Molecular-Biology (Boeringer Mannheim Can. Prize, 1989), Biochem. Soc. (U.K.). Avocations: fishing, skiing, golf. Office: Univ Alta Faculty of Medicine, Lipid/Lipoprotein Rsch Group, Edmonton, AB Canada T6G 2S2

VANCE, DON KELVIN, baking industry consultant; b. Detroit, Jan. 3, 1935; s. George Paul and Marie Jo (Nichols) V.; children—James Delano, Sarah Elizabeth, David Paul. B.B.A., U. Mich., 1957, M.B.A., 1958. Various positions ITT Continental Baking Co., 1958-72; v.p. ITT Continental Baking Co., Rye, N.Y., 1972-83; sr. v.p., div. pres. Am. Bakeries Co., N.Y.C., 1983-86; cons. to baking industry; pres., chief oper. officer Country Home Bakers, Bridgeport, Conn., 1991-94; COO Quality Bakers of Am., Greenwich, Conn., 1994—. Served with USAFR, 1958-64. Methodist. Club: Pensacola (Fla.) Country. Avocations: sailing; skiing; golfing. Office: Quality Bakers of Am 70 Riverdale Ave Greenwich CT 06831

VANCE, ELBRIDGE PUTNAM, mathematics educator; b. Cin., Feb. 7, 1915; s. Selby Frame and Jeannie (Putnam) V.; m. Margaret Gertrude Stoffel, Aug. 5, 1939 (div. 1975); children: Susan (Mrs. Timothy Griffin), Peter Selby, Douglas Putnam, Emily (Mrs. Charles Harold Beynon III); m. Jean Haigh, Jan. 1975. Student, Haverford Coll., 1932-33; A.B., Coll. Wooster, 1936; M.A., U. Mich., 1937, Ph.D., 1939. Asst. U. Mich., 1937-39; instr. U. Nev., 1939-41, asst. prof., 1941-43; vis. lectr. Oberlin (Ohio) Coll., 1943-46, asst. prof., 1946-50, assoc. prof., 1950-54, prof., 1954-83, prof. emeritus, 1983—, chmn. dept., 1948-77, acting dean Coll. Arts and Scis., 2d semester, 1965-66, 1st semester, 1970-71; chmn. advanced placement com. Coll. Entrance Exam. Bd., 1961-65, chief reader, 1956-61; chmn. com. examiners math. Comprehensive Coll. Tests, Ednl. Testing Service, 1965-67. Author: Trigonometry, 2d edit, 1969, Unified Algebra and Trigonometry, 1955, Fundamentals of Mathematics, 1960, Modern College Algebra, 3d edit, 1973, Modern Algebra and Trigonometry, 3d edit, 1973, An Introduction to Modern Mathematics, 2d edit, 1968, Mathematics 12, 1968, Solution Manual for Mathematics 12, 1968; Book review editor: Am. Math. Monthly, 1949-57; asso. editor, 1964-67. Mem. Oberlin Sch. Bd., 1952-60, pres., 1957-60. NSF Faculty fellow, 1960-61. Mem. Math. Assn. Am., Nat. Council Tchrs. of Math., Am. Math. Soc., Phi Beta Kappa, Sigma Xi, Phi Kappa Phi. Home: 315 Yorktown Pl # 4D Vermilion OH 44089-2104

VANCE, JAMES, retired manufacturing company executive, lawyer; b. Cleve., May 20, 1930; m. Dolores Bernadette Doyle, July 6, 1957; 1 child, James J. BA cum laude, Baldwin Wallace Coll., 1955; JD magna cum laude, Cleve. State U., 1960. Bar: Oct. 1960. Asst. treas., asst. to v.p. fin. and adminstrn., financial analyst Repr. Steel Corp., 1956-68; treas. Addressograph & Multigraph Corp., Cleve., 1968-72; v.p. fin. Cin. Milacron Inc., 1972-77; vice chmn., dir. Dayton-Walther Corp., 1977-87; sr. v.p., gen. counsel, sr. bus. advisor Varity Corp., Toronto, 1987-88, sr. v.p., chief fin. officer, chief legal officer, 1988-89; ret., 1990; bd. dirs. Citation Cos., Amertool Corp., Gen. Automation, Min-Cer (S.A.), Mexico, Dwisa of Paris, Dayton-Est of Vesoul, Fiday of Asnieres, France, Polygon Reinsurance Corp., Bermuda, Massey Ferguson Co., Kelsey Hayes Co. Vice chmn. United Appeal, 1959; mem. Citizens League Cleve., 1960—; mem. fin. com. YMCA, 1961—; mem. Greater Cleve. Growth Center, 1963—; Vice chmn. fin. com. Cuyahoga Rep. Com., 1968-69. With AUS, 1951-52. Decorated Bronze Star. Mem. Cleve. Soc. Security Analysts, Am., Ohio Bar Assn., Fin. Execs. Inst., Am. Ordnance Assn., Nat. Machine Tool Builders Assn., Machinery and Allied Products Assn., Am. Mgmt. Assn., Cin. Indsl. Inst., Ohio C. of C., Alpha Tau Omega, Delta Theta Phi, Cleve. Club, Treas.' Club (bd. dir.). Cleve. Treasurers (dir.). Home: 6600 Wyman Ln Cincinnati OH 45243-2724 Office: Varity Corp, 595 Bay St, Toronto, ON Canada M5G 2C3

VANCE, JOAN EMILY JACKSON (MRS. NORVAL E. VANCE), elementary school educator; b. Anderson, Ind., Feb. 25, 1925; d. Virgil S. and Hannah (Hall) Jackson; B.A., Ball State U., 1947, M.A., 1955; m. Norval E. Vance, Aug. 17, 1955; 1 son, Bill E. Tchr. art and phys. edn. Winchester (Ind.) High Sch., 1948-50, 50-52, Wheatfield (Ind.) Elem. Sch., Wheatfield High Sch., 1952-54; tchr. Eaton (Ind.) Elementary Sch. and High Sch., 1954-90; tchr. elem. art, Elwood, Ind., 1954-90, bilingual-bi-cultural migrant sch., summers 1969-90; exhibited in group shows at Erica's Gallery, John Herron, Anderson Fine Art Ctr., state shows, street fairs. Mem. council Hoosier Salon, Indpls. Mus. Art. Recipient First prize Anderson Fine Arts Center show, 1975, 77; vol. Anderson Community Concerts, Anderson Fine Arts Ctr., Historic Home and Gruenwald House living history tours. Mem. NEA, Nat. Art Edn. Assn., Western Art Edn. Assn., Ind Art Edn. Assn. (council), Ind. Art Tchrs. Assn. (mem. council), Anderson Art League (pres. 1967-68, 76—) Anderson Soc. Artists (v.p.), Ind. Weavers Guild, Elwood Art League (pres. 1960-70), Brown County Gallery, Brown County Guild, Ind. Artists and Craftsmen Assn., Anderson Artists Assn. (treas.), Ind. State Tchrs. Assn., Elwood Classroom Tchrs. Assn., Ind. Ret. Tchrs. Assn., Delta Kappa Gamma (v.p.), Delta Theta Tau. Home: 9348 N 625 W Frankton IN 46044-9716 Office: Elwood Community Sch State Rd 13 N Elwood IN 46036

VANCE, RALPH BROOKS, oncologist and educator; b. Jackson, Miss., Dec. 4, 1945; s. Brooks C. and Chrystine G. (Gober) V.; m. Mary Douglas Allen, June 18, 1979; children: Brooks, Barrett. BA in Biology and German, U. Miss., 1968, MD, 1972. Asst. prof. medicine U. Miss., Jackson, 1978-86, assoc. prof. medicine, 1986-93; prof. medicine, 1993—; chief of staff U. Miss. Hosp. and Clinics, Jackson, 1989-90; pres. faculty senate Univ. Med. Ctr., Jackson, 1986-87, univ. clin. assoc., pres., 1987-89. Author (with others) Development in Molecular Virology: Herpes Virus DNA, 1982; contbr. numerous articles and abstracts to profl. jours. Bd. dirs. Am. Cancer Soc., Atlanta, nat. bd. dirs., exec. com.; bd. dirs. ARC, Jackson; med. adv. bd. Blue Cross/Blue Shield, Jackson, 1989-92. Named to Hall of Fame, U.

Miss., 1968. Mem. Am. Assn. for Cancer Edn., Am. Fedn. for Clin. Rsch., Am. Soc. Clin. Oncology, Am. Assn. for Cancer Rsch., Miss. Acad. Scis., S.W. Oncology Group, Sigma Xi. Episcopalian. Office: Univ of Miss Sch Medicine 2500 N State St Jackson MS 39216-4505

VANCE, ROBERT MERCER, textile manufacturing company executive, banker; b. Clinton, S.C., July 9, 1916; s. Robert Berly and Mary Ellen (Bailey) V.; m. Virginia Sexton Gray, Dec. 27, 1949; children: Mary Bailey Vance Suitt, Robert Mercer, Russell Gray. BSBA, Davidson Coll., 1937; postgrad., Northwestern U., 1942; postgrad. Carolina Bankers Conf., U. N.C., 1948-57; HHD (hon.), Presbyn. Coll., 1968. Trainee Clinton Cotton Mills, summers, 1931-36; paymaster Lydia Cotton Mills, Clinton, 1937-41; dir., asst. treas. Clinton Cotton Mills Inc. and Lydia Cotton Mills, 1948-53, v.p., 1953-58, pres., treas. 1958-75; pres., treas. Clinton Mills, Inc. (merger Clinton Cotton Mills and Lydia Cotton Mills), 1975, chmn. bd., 1975—; with M.S. Bailey & Son, Bankers, Clinton, S.C., 1946—; pres. M.S. Bailey & Son, Bankers, Clinton, 1948, chmn. bd., 1975—; dir. Clinton Mills Sales Corp., N.Y.C., 1948, v.p., asst. treas., 1953, treas., 1958-86; bd. dirs. Palmetto Expo. Ctr., Greenville, S.C.; trustee J.E. Sirrine Textile Found., Inst. Textile Tech., 1959—; mem., advisor Nat. Cotton Coun., 1970—; mem. N.Y. Cotton Exch., 1965—. Mem. orgn. com., dir., treas Community Chest Greater Clinton, 1952-55, pres., 1958; former mem. nom. com. for S.C. Carolinas United Community Svcs.; trustee exec. com. Edn. Resources Found., 1965; sec. bd. trustees Thornwell Orphanage, Clinton, 1959-67; mem. state adv. com. Commn. on Higher Edn., Clinton, 1965-67; mem. S.C. Commn. on Higher Edn., 1967-71, chmn., 1968-71; trustee S.C. Found. Ind. Colls.; trustee Presbyn. Coll., Clinton, 1953-76, chmn., 56-67, 73-93; bd. visitors Davidson (N.C.) Coll., 1959-62, 77—; mem. S.C. Water Resources Commn., 1981-83; deacon, elder First Presbyn. Ch., Clinton, 1950—, treas., 1950-58, past pres. Men's Sunday Sch. Class, other coms. With U.S. Army, 1941; lt. USN, 1942-46; lt. comdr. USNR, 1946-54. Decorated 17 battle stars; Named Clinton Man of Yr. Lions Club, 1955, Textile Man of Yr. N.Y. Bd. Trade, 1978. Mem. S.C. Bankers Assn. (v.p. 1953-55, pres. 1963-64), S.C. Textile Mfrs. Assn. (dir., v.p. 1966-67, pres. 1967-68), S.C. C. of C. (dir. 1959-60), Laurens County C. of C. (dir. 1982-86), Am. Legion, Poinsett Club (Greenville, S.C.), Lakeside Club (Clinton), Litchfield Club (Pawleys Island, S.C.), Musgrove Mill Golf Club, Moose. Masons, Kiwanis (former dir., pres. 1955), Shriners, Kappa Alpha. Presbyterian. Home: 311 S Broad St Clinton SC 29325 Office: MS Bailey & Son Bankers 211 N Broad St Clinton SC 29325-2303 also: Clinton Mills Inc 600 Academy St Clinton SC 29325

VANCE, ROBERT PATRICK, lawyer; b. Birmingham, Ala., Feb. 12, 1948; s. James Robert and Lucy Juanita (McMath) V.; m. Sarah Elizabeth Savoia, June 11, 1971; 1 son, Robert Patrick, Jr. B.A. with honors, La. State U., 1970, J.D., 1975. Bar: La. 1975, U.S. Dist. Ct. (ea. dist.) La. 1975, U.S. Dist. Ct. (mid. dist.) La. 1978, U.S. Dist. Ct. (we. dist.) La. 1979, U.S. Ct. Appeals (5th cir.) 1975, U.S. Ct. Appeals (11th cir.) 1981, U.S. Supreme Ct. 1981. Assoc. Jones, Walker, Waechter, Poitevent, Carrere & Denegre, New Orleans, 1975-80, ptnr., 1980—, exec. com. 1991—, mng. ptnr., 1994—. Author, editor: Bankruptcy Rules: Parts I, II, VII, VIII and IX, 1983; Overview of the Bankruptcy Code and the Court, 1983. Co-author: Bankruptcy-Current Developments, 1983, Current Developments in Commercial Law, 1984, Basic Bankruptcy of Louisiana, 1989, Fundamentals of Bankruptcy Law & Procedure in La., 1993. Contbr. articles to profl. jours. Fellow Am. Coll. Bankruptcy; mem. ABA (mem. creditors rights litigation com. coun., vice chair bankruptcy litigation, subcom. of bus. bankruptcy com.), commi. Law League Am. (mem. sect. bankruptcy and insolvency), Am. Law Inst., Am. Bankruptcy Inst., Fed. Bar Assn. (mem. bankruptcy law com., polit. campaign and election law com., editorial bd. Bankruptcy Briefs), La. State Bar Assn. (pres. consumer and bankruptcy law sect., chmn. CLE com.), New Orleans Bar Assn., La. Bankers Assn. (chmn. bank counsel com. 1992-93), Pi Sigma Alpha, Phi Beta Kappa, Phi Kappa Phi. Democrat. Roman Catholic. Home: 1821 State St New Orleans LA 70118-6219 Office: Jones Walker Waechter Poitevent Carrere & Denegre 201 Saint Charles Ave New Orleans LA 70170-1000

VANCE, SHELDON BAIRD, lawyer, former diplomat; b. Crookston, Minn., Jan. 18, 1917; s. Erskine Ward and Helen (Baird) V.; m. Jean Chambers, Dec. 28, 1939; children: Robert Clarke and Stephen Baird. A.B., Carleton Coll., 1939; J.D., Harvard U., 1942. Bar: Mass. 1942, D.C. 1977, U.S. Supreme Ct. 1977. Practiced in Boston, 1942; assoc. firm Ropes, Gray, Best, Coolidge & Rugg; joined Fgn. Service; econ. analyst, 3d sec. Am. embassy, Rio de Janeiro, Brazil, 1942-46; U.S. vice consul Nice, France and Monaco, 1946-49; U.S. consul Martinique, W.I., 1949-51; Swiss Desk officer, 1951-52; Belgium-Luxemburg desk officer Dept. State, Washington, 1952-54; 1st sec. Am. embassy, Brussels, Belgium, 1954-58; chief personnel placement br. Africa, Middle East and South Asia, 1958-60; student Sr. Seminar in Fgn. Relations, 1960-61; dir. Office Central African Affairs, 1961-62; dep. chief mission Am. embassy, Addis Ababa, Ethiopia, 1962-66; sr. fgn. service insp., 1966-67; U.S. ambassador to Republic of Chad, 1967-69, to Republic of Zaire, Kinshasa, 1969-74; promoted to rank of career minister, 1971; sr. adviser to sec. state, coordinator internat. narcotics matters, also exec. dir. President's Cabinet Com. on Internat. Narcotics Control, Dept. State, 1974-77; ptnr. Vance, Joyce, Carbaugh and Fields, Washington, 1977-87; of counsel Vance, Joyce, Carbaugh & Fields, Washington, 1987-89; bd. dirs. Sun Co. Inc., 1977-87. Vice-chmn. Mayor's Adv. Com. on Drug Abuse, Washington, 1980-91; mem. com. of four internat. experts advising UN Conf. on Narcotic Drugs, 1987; keynote speaker Western Hemisphere Conf. on Narcotic Drugs Inter Parliamentary Union, Carcas, Venezuela, 1987. Mem. Fgn. Svc. Assn., DACOR, Columbia Country Club (Chevy Chase, Md.). Presbyterian. Home and Office: 8510 Lynwood Pl Chevy Chase MD 20815-6810

VANCE, STANLEY CHARLES, management educator; b. Minersville, Pa., May 5, 1915; s. Stanley and Margaret (Zelin) V.; m. Regina Dober, Mar. 4, 1946. A.B., St. Charles Sem., 1937; M.A., U. Pa., 1944, Ph.D., 1951. Instr. U. Pa., 1945-47; asst. prof. U. Conn., 1947-52; prof. U. Mass., 1952-56; dean Coll. Bus. Adminstrn., Kent State U., 1956-60; H.T. Miner prof. bus. adminstrn. U. Oreg., Eugene, 1960-75; head dept. personnel and indsl. mgmt. U. Oreg., 1963-71; also acting dean Coll. Bus. Adminstrn.; William B. Stokely prof. mgmt. U. Tenn., Knoxville, 1975—; Mem. nat. council Nat. Planning Assn.; bd. dirs., pres. Inst. Adminstrv. Research. Author: American Industries, 1955, Industrial Administration, 1959, Management Decision Simulation, 1960, Industrial Structure and Policy, 1961, Quantitative Techniques for Operations Management, 1962, Board of Directors Structure and Performance, 1964, The Corporate Director, 1968, Managers and Mergers, 1971, Corporate Leadership: Boards, Directors and Strategy, 1983; Editor book revs.; scanning editor: Dirs. and Bds. Fellow Nat. Acad. Mgmt. (dean of fellows, pres. Western div., editor Jour. 1966-70, newsletter, 1971—, pres. 1975—), Internat. Acad. Mgmt. (vice chancellor); mem. AIM, C. of C., Am. Soc. Personnel Adminstrn., N.Am. Simulation and Gaming Assn. (dir.), Assn. Bus. Simulation and Exptl. Learning (pres.), N.Am. Simulation and Gaming Assn. (gov.), Dirs. Coun. Corp. Bds., Nat. Assn. Corp. Dirs., N.Am. Mgmt. Coun. (pres.), Rotary. Home: 1701 Cherokee Blvd Knoxville TN 37919-8335

VANCE, THOMAS CARTER, historic site director; b. Danville, Ill., Oct. 19, 1946; s. John DeWitt and Maxine Margaret (Sherman) V.; m. Susan Ellen Addams Vance, Feb. 25, 1972; 1 child, Erin Katherine. BS in Wildlife Biology, U. Ill., 1969, MS in Entomology, 1971; MA in Historical Adminstrn., Ea. Ill. U., 1979. Rsch. asst. Ill. Natural History Survey, Urbana, Ill., 1969-71; naturalist Kickapoo State Park, Oakwood, Ill., 1971-73, park ranger, 1973-74; historic site mgr. Lincoln Log Cabin State Hist., Lerna, Ill., 1974—. Author: (rsch. periodical) Ill. Nat. History Survey Bulletin, 1974; editor: (mag.) Midwest Open Air Mus. Mag., 1986-91. mem. bd. dirs. Charleston Tourism Com., 1989—; mem. adv. bd. Coles Together Econ. Devel. Corp. Coles Co., 1991—. Recipient GOS Grant award Inst. Mus. Svcs., 1983, 85; MAP Grant award Am. Assn. Mus., 1988. Mem. Midwest Open Air Mus. (past pres. 1982-83), Assn. Living Hist. Farms (mem. bd. dirs. 1984-87), Charleston Rotary Club. Mem. The Universal Ch. Avocations: guitar, banjo, American Indian, personal development, firewalking. Home and Office: Lincoln Log Cabin State Hist Site RR 1 Box 172A Lerna IL 62440-9757

VANCE, VERNE WIDNEY, JR., lawyer; b. Omaha, Mar. 10, 1932; s. Verne Widney and June Caroline (Henckler) V.; m. Anita Paine, June 27,

1970; children: Lisa Joy, Charles Hebard Paine, Virginia Caroline. A.B., Harvard U., 1954, J.D., 1957. Bar: D.C. 1957, Mass. 1964. Law clk. U.S. Dist. Judge, Mass., 1957-58; assoc. Covington & Burling, Washington, 1958-60; atty. adv. Devel. Loan Fund, Washington, 1960-61; legal counsel AID, Washington, 1961-63; assoc. Foley, Hoag & Eliot, Boston, 1963-67, ptnr., 1967—; lectr. law Boston U., 1964-66; corp. clk. S.S. Pierce Co., 1971-72. Pres. UN Assn. Greater Boston, 1964-66, 77-78, treas., 1974-77; mem. Mass. Adv. Council on Edn., 1969-75, chmn., 1977-95; mem. Democratic City Com., Newton, Mass., 1972—; Gov.'s Local Govt. Adv. Commn., 1986-90; alderman City of Newton, 1982-91; pres. Newton Bd. of Aldermen, 1988-91; mem. Newton Sch. Com., 1994—; trustee Judge Baker Children's Ctr., 1994—; trustee Mass. Bay Community Coll., 1987—, vice chmn., 1989-91, chmn. 1991—. Mem. Boston Bar Assn. (bd. of editors bar jour. 1986-90) bd. dir. Boston Archtl. Ctr., 1991-92. Unitarian. Club: Longwood Cricket (Chestnut Hill, Mass.). Editor Harvard Law Rev., 1955-57; bd. editors Boston Bar Jour., 1986-90; contbr. articles to profl. jours. Home: 101 Old Orchard Rd Chestnut Hill MA 02167-1202 Office: Foley Hoag & Eliot 1 Post Office Sq Boston MA 02109-2103

VANCE, ZINNA BARTH, artist, writer; b. Phila., Sept. 28, 1917; d. Carl Paul Rudolph Barth and Dorothy Ellice (Wilson) Hart; m. Nathan E. Curry (div. 1959); m. Samuel Therrel Vance, Dec. 2, 1960; children: Barry, Scott Hart. BS in Edn. summa cum laude, Southwestern U., Georgetown, Tex., 1965; MA in Communications, U. Tex., 1969. Cert. in teaching langs., Tex. Freelance writer various pubs., 1946-56; assoc. editor, newspaper Canacao Clipper, Philippines, 1956-58; dir. Region One Tex. Fine Arts Assn., Austin, 1962-63; curricular cons. U. Tex. Curricular Conf., 1966; sec. Tex. Fgn. Langs. Assn., 1967; publicity dir. Burnet (Tex.) Creative Arts, 1983—; freelance portrait artist, Liberty Hill, Tex.; owner Gallery Zinna Portrait Studio, Liberty Hill, Tex., 1978—; artist registry Hill Country Arts Found., Ingram, Tex., 1984—; art columnist two newspapers Burnet, 1983—. Contbr. numerous articles to profl. jours.; exhibited in pvt. and corp. collections; illustrator children's books; numerous one-woman shows. Active Hill Country Arts Found., 1978—, Burnet Creative Arts, 1980—, Hill Country Council of Arts, 1986—. Named one of Tex. Emerging Artists, Hill Country Arts Found., 1985; featured as Cover Story Philippines Internat. mag., 1957, featured in book Artists of Texas, 1989, 94. Mem. Nat. Mus. Women in Arts (charter mem.), Nat. Portrait Inst., Alpha Chi, Phi Kappa Phi. Republican. Episcopalian. Avocations: ranching, figure skating, Chinese brush painting. Home: RR 2 Box 135 Liberty Hill TX 78642-9501

VANCE SIEBRASSE, KATHY ANN, newspaper publishing executive; b. Kansas City, Kans., Oct. 28, 1954; d. Donald Herbert Vance and Barbara June (Boris) Vance-Young; m. Charles Richard Siebrasse, Mar. 8, 1980; 1 stepson, Michael; 1 child, Bradley. BS in Journalism, No. Ill. U., 1976. Reporter Des Plaines (Ill.) Suburban Times and Park Ridge Herald, 1974-75, DeKalb (Ill.) Daily Chronicle, 1976-78; stringer Rockford (Ill.) Register Star, 1978; editor The MidWeek Newspaper, DeKalb, 1978-81, owner and pub., 1982—. Active No. Ill. U. Found., 1992—, mem. exec. bd., 1994—, chair bus. and industry for No. Ill. U. campaign, 1993-94; chair Kishwaukee Hosp. Health Coun., 1984-92, DeKalb County Partnership for a Substance Abuse Free Environment, 1990—; bd. dirs. DeKalb Edn. Found., sec., 1987-89, pres., 1989-93, active, 1987-94; sponsor Big Bros./Big Sisters Bowl-a-Thon. Recipient Comty. Svc. award Nat. Assn. of Advt. Pubs., 1980, Athena award Oldsmobile, DeKalb C. of C., 1990, Bus. of Yr., 1994. Mem. Ill. Press Assn., No. Ill. Newspaper Assn., Ind. Free Papers Am. (Community Svc. award 1992-93), Free Papers of Am., DeKalb County Farm Bur., DeKalb and Sycamore C. of C. (editor Sycamore newsletter 1994—, mem. Dekalb Athena award com., Dekalb bd. dirs.). Avocations: photography, reading, swimming, skiing, sailing. Office: The MidWeek Newspaper 121 Industrial Dr De Kalb IL 60115-3977

VANCE-STRAKER, MARILYN, costume designer. Costume designer: (films) Fast Times at Ridgemont High, 1982, 48 Hours, 1982, Jeckyll and Hyde...Together Again, 1982, Streets of Fire, 1984, (with Winnie Brown and Ronald I. Caplan) The Wild Life, 1984, Romancing the Stone, 1984, Weird Science, 1985, The Breakfast Club, 1985, Ferris Bueller's Day Off, 1986, Jo Jo Dancer, Your Life is Calling, 1986, Pretty in Pink, 1986, Predator, 1987, Some Kind of Wonderful, 1987, The Untouchables, 1987, Throw Momma From the Train, 1987, Cross My Heart, 1987, Die Hard, 1988, The Great Outdoors, 1988, Action Jackson, 1988, Road House, 1989, Uncle Buck, 1989, The Package, 1989, Little Monsters, 1989, Pretty Woman, 1990, The Last of the Finest, 1990, The Adventures of Ford Fairlane, 1990, Die Hard 2: Die Harder, 1990, Predator 2, 1990, The Rocketeer, 1991, Ricochet, 1991, The Last Boy Scout, 1991, Hudson Hawk, 1991, Medicine Man, 1992, Sommersby, 1992, Year of the Comet, 1992, Used People, 1993; visual cons.: The Wraith, 1986; exec. prodr., wardrobe cons.: The First Power, 1990. Office: care Costume Designer's Guild 13949 Ventura Blvd Ste 309 Sherman Oaks CA 91423*

VAN CLEAVE, WILLIAM ROBERT, international relations educator; b. Kansas City, Mo., Aug. 27, 1935; s. Earl Jr. and Georgiana (Offutt) Van C.; children: William Robert II, Cynthia Kay. B.A. in Polit. Sci. summa cum laude, Calif. State U. Long Beach, 1962; M.A. in Govt. and Internat. Relations, Claremont (Calif.) Grad. Sch., 1964, Ph.D., 1966. Mem. faculty U. So. Calif., 1967-87, prof. internat. rels., 1974-87, dir. def. and strategic studies ctr., 1971-87; prof. dept. head, dir. Ctr. for Def. and Strategic Studies Southwest Mo. State U., 1987—; sr. rsch. fellow Hoover Instn. Stanford U., 1981—; chmn. Strategic Alternatives Team, 1970; acting chmn. Pres.'s Gen. Adv. Com. on Arms Control, 1981-82; spl. asst. Office Sec. Def. mem. Strategic Arms Limitation Talks (SALT) delegation, 1969-71; mem. B team on Nat. Intelligence Estimates, 1976; mem. exec. panel, bd. dirs. Com. Present Danger, 1980-93; dir. transition team Dept. Def., 1980-81; nat. security advisor to Ronald Reagan, 1979-80; mem. nat. security affairs adv. council Republican Nat. Com., 1979—; research council Fgn. Policy Research Inst., Inst. Fgn. Policy Analysis; co-dir. Ann. Internat. Security Summer Seminar, Fed. Republic Germany; trustee Am. com. Internat. Inst. Strategic Studies, 1980—; vis. prof. U.S. Army Advanced Russian Inst., Garmisch, Fed. Republic Germany, 1978-79; chmn. adv. bd. Internat. Security Coun., 1991—; cons. in field, mem. numerous govt. adv. coms. Co-author: Strategic Options for the Early Eighties: What Can Be Done?, 1979, Tactical Nuclear Weapons, 1978, Nuclear Weapons, Policies, and the Test Ban Issue, 1987; author: Fortress USSR, 1986; bd. editors: Global Affairs. Co-chmn. Scholars for Reagan, 1984. Served with USMC, 1953-57. Recipient Freedom Found. award, 1976, Outstanding Contbn. award Air War Coll., 1979, award teaching excellence U. So. Calif., 1980, 86; named Outstanding Prof. U. So. Calif., 1977, Disting. Alumnus Claremont Colls., 1978; Woodrow Wilson fellow, 1962, NDEA fellow, 1963-65. Mem. Internat. Strategic Studies (U.S. com.). Home: RR 3 Box 691 Rogersville MO 65742-9126 Office: Ctr for Def and Strategic Studies Southwest Mo State U Springfield MO 65804-0095

VAN CLEVE, JOHN VICKREY, history educator; b. Evanston, Ill., Apr. 8, 1947; s. John William and Mildred Madelane (Vickrey) Van C. Student, U. Ill., 1965-67; BA, Western State Coll. Colo., 1970; MA, PhD, U. Calif., Irvine, 1976. Instr. history Gallaudet U., Washington, 1976-77, asst. to assoc. prof. history, 1977-84, chmn. dept. history, 1983-95, prof. history, 1984—. Author: (with Barry A. Crouch) A Place of Their Own: Creating the Deaf Community in America, 1989; chmn. editorial bd. Gallaudet U. Press, 1985—; editor in chief Gallaudet Encyclopedia of Deaf People and Deafness, 1987 (Pres.' award); editor Deaf History Unveiled: Selections from the new Scholarship, 1993; contbr. articles to profl. jours. Mem. Orgn. Am. Historians, History Edn. Soc., Soc. Historians of Am. Fgn. Relations, Conv. Am. Instrs. of the Deaf. Office: Gallaudet Univ Dept of History 800 Florida Ave NE Washington DC 20002-3600

VAN CLEVE, RUTH GILL, retired lawyer, government official; b. Mpls., July 28, 1925; d. Raymond S. and Ruth (Sevon) Gill; m. Harry R. Van Cleve, Jr., May 16, 1952; children: John Gill, Elizabeth Webster, David Hamilton Livingston. Student, U. Minn., 1943; A.B. magna cum laude, Mt. Holyoke Coll., 1946, LL.D., 1976; LL.B., Yale, 1950. Bar: D.C. 1950, Minn. 1950. Internat Nat. Inst. Pub. Affairs, 1946-47; atty. Dept. Interior, 1950-54, asst. solicitor, 1954-64; dir. Office Territorial Affairs, 1964-69, 1977-80, dep. asst. sec., 1980-81, acting asst. sec., 1993; atty. Solicitor's Office, 1981-93; atty. FPC, 1969-75, asst. gen. counsel, 1975-77. Author: The Office of Territorial Affairs, 1974, The Application of Federal Laws to the Territories,

1993. Recipient Fed. Woman's award, 1966, Disting. Service award Dept. Interior, 1968, Presdl. Rank award, Pres. U.S., 1989. Mem. Phi Beta Kappa. Unitarian. Home: 4400 Emory St Alexandria VA 22312-1321

VAN CLEVE, WILLIAM MOORE, lawyer; b. Mar. 17, 1929; s. William T Van Cleve and Catherine (Baldwin) Moore Van Cleve; m. Georgia Hess Dunbar, June 27, 1953; children: Peter Dunbar, Robert Baldwin, Sarah Van Cleve Van Doren, Emory Basford. Grad., Phillips Acad., 1946; AB in Econs., Princeton U., 1950; JD, Washington U., St. Louis, 1953. Bar: Mo. 1953. Assoc. Dunbar and Gaddy, St. Louis, 1955-58; ptnr. Bryan Cave (and predecessor firm), St. Louis, 1958—, chmn., 1973-94; bd. dirs. Emerson Electric Co. Trustee Washington U., 1983—, vice chmn. bd. trustees, 1988-93, 95—, chmn., 1993-95, mem. exec. com., 1985—; pres. Eliot Soc., 1982-86; chmn. Law Sch. Nat. Coun., 1986-93; commr. St. Louis Sci. Ctr., 1993—; bd. dirs., v.p. Parents As Tchrs. Nat. Ctr., 1991—. Mem. ABA, Bar Assn. Met. St. Louis, Mound City Bar Assn., St. Louis County Bar Assn., Order of Coif (hon.). Democrat. Episcopalian. Clubs: Princeton (pres. 1974-75), Noonday (pres. 1985), St. Louis Country, Bogey (pres. 1990-91), Round Table (St. Louis). Home: 8 Dromara Rd Saint Louis MO 63124-1816 Office: Bryan Cave 211 N Broadway 36th Fl Saint Louis MO 63102-2750

VANCO, JOHN L., art museum director; b. Erie, Pa., Aug. 21, 1945; s. John Jr. and Alice (Crozier) V.; m. Kathleen Merski, 1971; children: John H., Jesse L. BA, Allegheny Coll., 1967. Dir. Erie (Pa.) Art Mus., 1968—; mem. adv. panels Pa. Coun. on the Arts, Harrisburg, 1974—, Mid Atlantic Arts Found., Balt., 1992. Photographer miscellaneous exhbns.; curator miscellaneous exhbns. including Teco: Art Pottery of the Prairie Sch. in Harmony with the Earth; author: A Roycroft Desktop: Musings on Elbert Hubbard and the Roycroft Shops, 1994. Chief adminstrv. officer Discovery Square, Erie, 1991-92. Office: Erie Art Mus 411 State St Erie PA 16501

VAN CULIN, SAMUEL, religious organization administrator; b. Honolulu, Sept. 30, 1930; s. Samuel and Susie (Mossman) Van C. A.B., Princeton U., 1952; B.D., Va. Theol. Sem., 1955, D.D. (hon.), 1955. Curate St. Andrew's Cathedral, Honolulu, 1955-56; Canon precentor, rector Hawaiian Congregation, Honolulu, 1956-58; asst. rector St. John's Ch., Washington, 1958-60; gen. sec. Lyman Internat., Washington, 1960-61; asst. sec. overseas Exec. Council of Episcopal Ch., N.Y.C., 1962-68, sec. for Africa, Middle East, 1968-76; exec. for world mission Episcopal Ch. U.S.A., N.Y.C., 1976-83; sec. gen. Anglican Consultative Council Eng., London, 1983-95; asst. priest All Hallows Ch., London, 1995—. Named Hon. Canon Canterbury, 1983, Jerusalem, 1983, Ibadan, 1984, Ch. Province of So. Africa, 1989, St. Andrew's Cathedral, Honolulu, 1994. Clubs: Atheneum (London); Princeton (N.Y.). Avocations: Music; travelling. Home: 16a Burgate, Canterbury 2HG, England Office: All Hallows Ch, 43 Trinity Sq, London EC3N 4DJ, England

VAN DALEN, PIETER ADRIAAN, broadcast equipment executive; b. Sprang-Capelle, Netherlands, Mar. 12, 1942; arrived in Fed. Republic Germany, 1988; s. Rokus and Lucia Elisabeth (Rijkers) van D.; m. Hendrika Geertje Visscher, May 3, 1968; children: Rokus H.J., Karsten E., Elmer C. M Phys. Engring., Tech. U. Eindhoven, Netherlands, 1963; PhD in Tech. Scis., Tech. U. Eindhoven, 1966. Postdoctoral rsch. fellow Faculty Scis., U. Paris, 1966-67; researcher Philips Rsch. Labs., Eindhoven, 1967-72; product mgr. Philips Med. Systems Div., Eindhoven, 1972-73, 75-80; mktg. mgr. Philips Med. Systems, Best, Netherlands, 1980-81; systems cons., med. systems div. N.Am. Philips, N.Y.C., 1981-82; mktg. mgr., med. systems div. N.Am. Philips, Shelton, Conn., 1982-88; dir. S&I div., then mng. dir. I&E div. Philips, Eindhoven, 1982-88; pres., chief exec. officer Broadcast Television Systems GmbH, Darmstadt, Fed. Republic Germany, 1988—; mem. program com. for commi. tng. of univ.-educated engrs., Tech. U. Eindhoven. Mem. Dutch Phys. Soc. Avocations: reading, history, travel, sports, music. Home: Amselweg 18, 6240 Königstein Fed Republic Germany Office: Broadcast Television System 2300 S 2300 W Salt Lake City UT 84119

VAN DAM, ANDRIES, computer scientist, educator; b. Groningen, The Netherlands, Dec. 8, 1938; came to U.S., 1952; s. Levie and Mietje (Rosenbaum) van D.; m. Deborah Kurmes, Oct. 18, 1961; children: Elisa, Lori, Katrin. BS, Swarthmore Coll., 1960; MS, U. Pa., 1963, PhD, 1966. Asst. prof. applied math. Brown U., Providence, 1965-68, assoc. prof. applied math. and computer sci., 1968-72, prof. computer sci., 1972—, chmn. dept. computer sci., 1979-85, L. Herbert Ballou Univ. Prof. computer sci., 1992—; vis. sci. assoc. CERN, Geneva, 1978-79; sr. scientist Stardent Computer, 1985-88, BLOC devel., 1988—; Prime Computer/Computer Vision, 1990-91. Co-author: The Man-Made World, 1968; Fundamental of Interactive Computer Graphics, 1982, Pascal on the Macintosh: A Graphical Approach, 1987; Computer Graphics: Principles and Practice, 1990; Computing the Future: A Broader Agenda For Computer Science and Engineering. Mem. com. to assess the scope and direction of computer sci. and tech. Nat. Rsch. Coun. Recipient Spl. Recognition Soc. Info. Display, 1974, R.I. Gov.'s Sci. and Tech. award, 1988, acad. award Nat. Computer Graphics Assn., 1990, Centennial medal IEEE, 1984, Steven A. Coons award SIG-GRAPH, 1991. Mem. Assn. Computing Machinery, IEEE Comp. Soc. Home: 106 Highland Ave Barrington RI 02806-4748 Office: Brown U Computer Sci Dept PO Box 1910 Providence RI 02912-0001

VAN DAM, HEIMAN, psychoanalyst; b. Leiden, The Netherlands, Feb. 5, 1920; s. Machiel and Rika (Knorringa) van D.; m. Barbara C. Strona, Oct. 6, 1945; children: Machiel, Claire Ilena, Rika Rosemary. A.B., U. So. Calif., 1942, M.D., 1945. Fellowship child psychiatry Pasadena (Calif.) Child Guidance Clinic, 1950; instr. Los Angeles Psychoanalytic Inst., 1959—, co-chmn. com. on child psychoanalysis, 1960-67, tng. and supervising psychoanalyst, 1972—; supr. child and adolescent psychoanalysis So. Calif. Psychoanalytic Inst., 1986—; cons. Reiss Davis Child Study Center, 1955-76, Neighborhood Youth Assn., Los Angeles, 1964-69; assoc. clin. prof. psychiatry UCLA Sch. Medicine, 1960—, asso. clin. prof. pediatrics, 1980—; vis. supr. child psychoanalysis San Francisco Psychoanalytic Inst., 1969-79, Denver Psychoanalytic Inst., 1972-74; mem. adv. bd. Western State U. Coll. Law, Fullerton, Calif., 1965-83. Corr. editor Arbeits Hefte Kinderanalyse, 1985—; contbr. articles to profl. jours. Trustee, mem. adm. com. Center for Early Edn., 1964-92, v.p., 1978-79; bd. dirs. Child Devel. and Psychotherapy Tng. Program, Los Angeles, 1975-80, pres., 1975-77; bd. dirs. Los Angeles Child Devel. Center, 1977-86, treas., 1978-80; mem. cult clinic Jewish Family Service, Los Angeles, 1978-86; bd. dirs. Lake Arrowhead Crest Estates, 1990—. Served to capt. M.C. AUS, 1946-48. Mem. Am. Psychoanalytic Assn. (com. on ethics 1977-80), Assn. Child Psychoanalysis (councillor 1966-69, sec. 1972-74, mem. nominating com. 1978-84, membership com. 1988—), Internat. Assn. Infant Psychiatry (co-chmn. program com. 1980-83), Internat. Soc. Adolescent Psychiatry (sci. adv. com. 1988—), Phi Beta Kappa. Office: 1100 Glendon Ave Ste 941 Los Angeles CA 90024-3513

VANDAMENT, WILLIAM EUGENE, academic administrator, educator; b. Hannibal, Mo., Sept. 6, 1931; s. Alva E. and Ruth Alice (Mahood) V.; m. Margery Vandament, Feb. 2, 1952; children: Jane Louise, Lisa Ann. BA, Quincy Coll., 1952; MS, So. Ill. U., 1953; MS in Psychology, U. Mass., 1963, PhD, 1964. Psychologist Bacon Clinic, Racine, Wis., 1954-61; NDEA fellow U. Mass., Amherst, 1961-64; asst. prof. SUNY, Binghamton, 1964-69, univ. examiner and dir. instl. research, 1969-73, asst. v.p. planning, instl. research, 1972-76; exec. asst. to pres., dir. budget and resources Ohio State U., Columbus, 1976-79, v.p. fin. and planning, 1979-81; sr. v.p. adminstrn. NYU, N.Y.C., 1981-83; provost, vice chancellor acad. affairs Calif. State U. System, Long Beach, 1983-87; Trustees prof. Calif. State U., Fullerton, 1987-92; pres. No. Mich. U., 1991—. Contbr. articles to psychol. jours. and books on higher edn. Home: 1440 Center St Marquette MI 49855-1625 Office: 1401 Presque Isle Ave Marquette MI 49855-5302

VAN DAMME, JEAN-CLAUDE (JEAN-CLAUDE VAN VARENBERG), actor; b. Brussels, 1961; m. Darcy LaPier, Feb. 3, 1994; children: Kristopher, Bianca. Former European karate champion. Performances include: (films) Rue Barbar, No Retreat, No Surrender, 1986, Predator, 1987, Bloodsport, 1988, Black Eagle, 1988, Cyborg, 1989, Kickboxer, 1989, Death Warrant, 1990, Lionheart, 1991, Double Impact, 1991, Universal Soldier, 1992, Hard Target, 1993, Time Cop, 1994, Street Fighter, 1994, The Quest, 1995, Sudden Death, 1995. Winner Middleweight Championship, European Karate Assn. Office: ICM 8942 Wilshire Blvd Beverly Hills CA 90211*

VANDEGRIFT   4268   WHO'S WHO IN AMERICA

VANDEGRIFT, JOHN RAYMOND, priest, librarian; b. Wilmington, Del., Apr. 27, 1928; s. Ira Ambers and Florence (Metzler) V. AB in Chemistry, Princeton U., 1949; STB, Dominican House, 1959, STL/STLr, 1962; MLS, Columbia U., 1975. Ordained priest, Roman Cath. Ch., 1960. Lab. asst. Merck & Co., Inc., Rahway, N.J., 1949-52; instr. in theology Xaverian Coll., Silver Spring, Md., 1961-62, Aquinas Coll., Grand Rapids, Mich., 1962-65, Mercy Cen. Nursing Sch., Grand Rapids, 1963-65, Albertus Magnus Coll., New Haven, 1968-70; instr. in theology and philosophy St. Catharine (Ky.) Coll., 1965-68; dir. Dominican Coll. Libr., Washington, 1970—; instr. theology Aquinas Inst. for Religion, Grand Rapids, summers 1963-70; spiritual moderator Dominican Laity Chpt., McLean, Va., 1989—; chaplain Team of Our Lady, Arlington, Va., 1984—; preacher Sunday Eucharist, Washington, 1960—; confessor Shrine of Immaculate Conception, Washington, 1980—. Mem. ALA, D.C. Libr. Assn., Am. Theol. Libr. Assn., Washington Theol. Consortium (chmn. com. of librs. 1981), Cluster Periodical Ctr. (com. librs.). Avocations: mountain climbing, backpacking, hiking, jogging. Home: 487 Michigan Ave NE Washington DC 20017-1584 Office: Dominican Coll Libr 487 Michigan Ave NE Washington DC 20017-1584

VANDE HEY, JAMES MICHAEL, corporate executive; former air force officer; b. Maribel, Wis., Mar. 15, 1916; s. William Henry and Anna (Zimmerman) VandeH.; m. Jean Margretta Schilleman, June 23, 1944; children: James Todd, Dale Michael, Dean Clark. Student, U. Wis., 1947-49; BA, U. Philippines, 1955; postgrad., Air War Coll., Maxwell AFB, Montgomery, Ala., 1956-57. Commd. 2d lt. USAAF, 1941; advanced through grades to brig. gen. USAF, 1967; fighter pilot PTO, 1941-45; including Hawaii, Dec. 7, 1941; duty in command and USAF level including duty in Europe (NATO) and Philippines, 1945-69; dep. chief of staff Hdqrs. USMACV, Saigon, Vietnam, 1969-71; assigned Hdqrs. Tactical Air Command, 1971—; mem. faculty Air War Coll., 1957-59, dep. for acads., dean of faculty, 1959-61; ret., 1971; pres. Vanson Inc., 1971—, Vande Hey Inc., 1976—. Decorated D.S.M., Legion of Merit with two oak leaf cluster, D.F.C. with two oak leaf cluster, Bronze Star, Air medal with 7 oak leaf clusters, decorations from Philippine, Vietnamese and Korean govts. Mem. USAF Hist. Found., Air Force Assn. Roman Catholic. Home: 3374 S El Dorado Austin TX 78734-5232

VAN DE KAMP, JOHN KALAR, lawyer; b. Pasadena, Calif., Feb. 7, 1936; s. Harry and Georgie (Kalar) Van de K.; m. Andrea Fisher, Mar. 11, 1978; 1 child, Diana. BA, Dartmouth Coll., 1956; JD, Stanford U., 1959. Bar: Calif. 1960. Asst. U.S. atty. L.A., 1960-66, U.S. atty., 1966-67; dep. dir. Exec. Office for U.S. Attys., Washington, 1967-68, dir., 1968-69; spl. asst. Pres.'s Commn. on Campus Unrest, 1970; fed. pub. defender L.A., 1971-75; dist. atty. Los Angeles County, 1975-83; atty. gen. State of Calif., 1983-91; ptnr., chmn. litigation dept. Dewey Ballantine, L.A., 1991—; bd. dirs. United Airlines. Mem. Calif. Dist. Attys. Assn. (pres. 1975-83), Nat. Dist. Attys. Assn. (v.p. 1975-83), Peace Officers Assn. L.A. County (past pres.), Nat. Assn. Attys. Gen. (exec. com. 1983-91), Conf. Western Attys. Gen. (pres. 1986). Office: Dewey Ballantine 333 S Hope St Ste 3000 Los Angeles CA 90071-3039

VANDE KROL, JERRY LEE, architect; b. Oskaloosa, Iowa, Oct. 5, 1949; s. Glen Vande Krol and Nola Fern (Monsma) Emmert; m. Constance Louise Wood, May 30, 1970; children: Sarah Lynn, Rachel Ann, Molly Jayne. BArch, Iowa State U., 1972. Registered architect, Iowa. Designer City of Akron, Ohio, 1972-76; architect Brooks Borg and Skiles, Des Moines, 1976-90; founder VOV Architecture and Design, P.C., Des Moines, 1990—. Recipient Merit Design award Ohio Chpt. Soc. Landscape Architects, 1977. Mem. AIA (Iowa chpt., Design award 1984, 90, regional chpt. Design award 1985, 91), Des Moines Architects Coun. Republican. Mem. Brethren Ch. Avocations: music, classical guitar, reading, golf. Office: Vov Architecture Design 108 Third St 200 Des Moines IA 50309

VANDELL, DEBORAH LOWE, educational psychology educator; b. Bryan, Tex., June 5, 1949; d. Charles Ray and Janice (Durrett) Lowe; m. Kerry Dean Vandell, May 16, 1970; children: Colin Buckner, Ashley Elizabeth. AB, Rice U., 1971; EdM, Harvard U., 1972; PhD, Boston U., 1977. Tchr. Walpole (Mass.) Pub. Schs., 1972-73; rschr. Ralph Nader Congress Project, Washington, 1972; asst. prof. U. Tex., Dallas, 1976-81, assoc. prof., 1981-89; prof. ednl. psychology U. Wis., Madison, 1989—; vis. scholar MacArthur Rsch. Network, Cambridge, Mass., 1985-86, U. Calif., Berkeley, 1988-89; mem. steering com. NICHD Study of Early Child Care. Assoc. editor Child Devel., 1993-95; mem. editl. bd. Child Devel., 1980-93, Jour. Family Issues, 1983-89, Devel. Psychology, 1989-93; co-author books; contbr. articles to profl. jours. Mem. bd. Infant Mental Health Assn., 1988-89, Community Coord. Child Care, Madison, Wis., 1990-93, chair, 1991-93; Sunday sch. tchr. Ch. of the Epiphany, Richardson, Tex., 1990—; mem. altar guild St. Andrew's Ch., also vestry, 1992-95. Named Outstanding Young Scholar, Found. for Child Devel., 1982; grantee infant child and family processes NIH, 1989. Mem. Am. Psychol. Assn. (exec. com. div. 7 1985-88), Southwestern Soc. Rsch. in Human Devel. (pres. 1988-90), Am. Psychol. Soc., Soc. for Rsch. in Child Devel., Phi Beta Kappa. Episcopalian. Office: U Wis Dept Ednl Psychology 1025 W Johnson St Madison WI 53706-1706

VANDELL, KERRY DEAN, real estate and urban economics educator; b. Biloxi, Miss., Jan. 8, 1947; s. Benedict Sandy and Eleanor Ruby (Lenhart) V.; m. Deborah Ann Lowe, May 16, 1970; children: Colin Buckner, Ashley Elizabeth. BA, MME, Rice U., 1970; M City Planning, Harvard U., 1973; PhD, MIT, 1977. Assoc. engr. Exxon Co., USA, Houston, 1970-71; asst. prof. So. Meth. U., Dallas, 1976-80, assoc. prof., 1980-86, prof., chmn. dept., 1986-89; prof. real estate and urban land econs., chm. dept. U. Wis., Madison, 1989-93; dir. Ctr. for Urban Land Econs. rsch., 1989—; vis. assoc. prof. Harvard U., Cambridge, Mass., 1985-86; vis. prof. U. Calif., Berkeley, 1988-89; bd. dirs. Park Bank, Madison, U. Rsch. Park, Domus Equity Corp.; mem. real estate coms. adv. com. Salomon Bros., N.Y.C., 1988-90; cons. in field. Mem. editorial bd. Jour. Real Estate Fin. and Econs., 1989—, Land Econs., 1989—, Jour. Property Rsch., 1989—; contbr. numerous articles on mortgage default risk, neighborhood dynamics, econs. of architecture, and appraisal theory to profl. jours. Fellow Homer Hoyt Advanced Studies Inst. (faculty 1989—, bd. dirs.), Urban Land Inst.; mem. Am. Real Estate and Urban Econs. Assn. (2d v.p. 1989, 1st v.p. 1990, pres. 1991, co-editor jour. 1991—). Episcopalian. Home: 3301 Topping Rd Madison WI 53705-1436 Office: U Wis Sch Bus 975 University Ave Madison WI 53706-1323

VANDEMAN, GEORGE ALLEN, lawyer; b. Muncie, Ind., Jan. 16, 1940; s. George Edward and Nellie Florence (Johnson) V.; m. Judith Ellen Meyers, June 16, 1959 (div. 1976); m. Winifred Margaret Hayward, Jan. 15, 1977; children: Shelli, Bradley, Craig. AB, U. So. Calif., 1963, JD, 1966. Bar: Calif. 1966. Atty., ptnr. Latham & Watkins, L.A., 1966—. Mem. bd. councilors U. So. Calif. Sch. Law, 1988—. Mem. Calif. State Bar (com. on takeover and corp. govt. 1987—). Avocations: travel, water sports, skiing. Office: Latham & Watkins Ste 1130 1900 Avenue Of The Stars Los Angeles CA 90067-4503

VAN DEMARK, ROBERT EUGENE, SR., orthopedic surgeon; b. Alexandria, S.D., Nov. 14, 1913; s. Walter Eugene and Esther Ruth (Marble) Van D.; m. Bertie Thompson, Dec. 28, 1940; children: Ruth Elaine, Robert, Richard. B.S., U. S.D., 1936; A.B., Sioux Falls (S.D.) Coll., 1937; M.B., Northwestern U., 1938, M.D., 1939; M.S. in Orthopedic Surgery, U. Minn., 1943. Diplomate Am. Bd. Orthopedic Surgery; cert. addl. qualifications surgery of the hand. Intern Passavant Meml. Hosp., Chgo., 1938-39; fellow in orthopedic surgery Mayo Found., 1939-43; 1st asst. orthopedic surgery Mayo Clinic, 1942-43; orthopedic surgeon Sioux Falls; hon. mem. past pres. staff McKennan Hosp.; hon. mem. Sioux Valley Hosp., past pres. staff; clin. prof. orthopedic surgery U.S.D., Sioux Falls, 1953—; adj. prof orthopedic anatomy, 1983—; med. dir. Crippled Children's Hosp. and Sch., 1956-84; chief hand surgery clinic VA Hosp., Sioux Falls, 1978-90; bd. dir. S.D. Blue Shield, 1976-88. Editor: S.D. Jour. Medicine, 1956-70; contbr. articles to med. jours. Bd. dirs. S.D. Found. for Med. Care, 1976-83; hon. chmn. S.D. Lung Assn., 1982. Maj. U.S. Army, 1943-46. Recipient citation for outstanding svc. Pres.'s Commn. for Employment Physically Handicapped, 1960; Svc. to Mankind award Sertoma Internat., 1963; award for dedicated svcs. to handicapped S.D. Easter Seal Soc., 1969; Robins award for outstanding community svc., 1971; Humanitarian Svc. award United Cerebral Palsy, 1976; Alumni Achievement award U. S.D., 1977, Disting. Alumnus award, 1992; Disting. Citizen award S.D. Press Assn., 1978; U. S.D. Med.

Sch. Faculty Recognition award, 1980; outstanding contbns. to Handicapped Children award S.D. State Dept. Health, 1985, Community Svc. Health award Sioux Valley Hosp. Found., 1991; named Humanitarian of Yr. S.D. Human Svcs. Forum, 1987; Robert E. Van Demark Inst. Anat. Rsch. at U. S.D. named in his honor, 1989; named Disting. Alumnus U. S.D. Med. Sch. Fellow ACS (first pres. S.D. chpt. 1952-53); mem. Am. Acad. Orthopedic Surgery, Am. Soc. Surgery Hand, Am. Assn. Hand Surgery (cert.), Am. Coll. Sports Medicine, Am. Orthopedic Assn., Am. Soc. Surgery Hand, Am. Acad. Cerebral Palsy, Clin. Orthopedic Soc., Doctors Mayo Soc., S.D. Med. Assn. (pres. 1974-75, Disting. Svc. award 1987, Spl. Presdl. award 1991), Sioux Falls Dist. Med. Soc., SAR, 500 First Families, Optimists, Minnehaha Country Club, Sigma Xi, Alpha Omega Alpha, Phi Chi. Lutheran. Home: 2803 Ridgeview Way Sioux Falls SD 57105-4243 Office: 1301 S 9th Ave Sioux Falls SD 57105-1042

VANDEMARK, ROBERT GOODYEAR, retired retail company executive; b. Youngstown, Ohio, Sept. 1, 1921; s. Arthur Glenn and Lola (Goodyear) V.; m. Jean Chapman, Sept. 19, 1943; children: Ann (Mrs. William K. Butler), Peggy Lynn (Mrs. Michael Murray). B.Sc., Ohio U., 1943. Dept. mgr. F. & R. Lazarus, Columbus, Ohio, 1947-54; asst. controller Boston Store, Milw., 1954-57; v.p., treas. Cleland Simpson Co., Scranton, Pa., 1957-65; asst. to exec. v.p. Bergdorf Goodman, N.Y.C., 1965-68; treas. Garfinckel, Brooks Bros., Miller & Rhoads, Inc., Washington, 1968-69; v.p. Garfinckel, Brooks Bros., Miller & Rhoads, Inc., 1969-73, exec. v.p., 1973-79, vice chmn., 1979-83; chmn., chief exec. officer Garfinckel's, 1983-87. Head dept. and specialty stores div. United Fund, Scranton, Pa., 1960-65; bd. dirs. Goodwill Industries, 1964-65; treas. Washington Nat. Cathedral. Served to 1st lt. AUS, 1943-46; col. Res. Decorated Bronze Star with V and cluster, Mil. Order of Wilheim. Mem. Fin. Execs. Inst., Nat. Retail Mchts. Assn. (sec., treas., 1st v.p., pres., dir., mem. exec. fin. exec. divsn.), Delta Tau Delta, City Club Washington, Washington Golf and Country Club, Army-Navy Club, Burning Tree Golf Club, Laurel Oak Country Club (Fla.), Masons (32d degree), Kiwanis (Fla.). Home: 670 Potomac River Rd Mc Lean VA 22102

VAN DEMARK, RUTH ELAINE, lawyer; b. Santa Fe, N. Mex., May 16, 1944; d. Robert Eugene and Bertha Marie (Thompson) Van D.; m. Leland Wilkinson, June 23, 1967; children: Anne Marie, Caroline Cook. AB, Vassar Coll., 1966; MTS, Harvard U., 1969; JD with honors, U. Conn., 1976. Bar: Conn. 1976, U.S. Dist. Ct. Conn. 1976, Ill. 1977, U.S. Dist. Ct. (no. dist.) Ill. 1977, U.S. Supreme Ct. 1983, U.S. Ct. Appeals (7th cir.) 1984. Instr. legal research and writing Loyola U. Sch. Law, Chgo., 1976-79; assoc. Wildman, Harrold, Allen & Dixon, Chgo., 1977-84, ptnr., 1985-94; prin. Law Offices of Ruth E. Van Demark, Chgo., 1995—; bd. dirs., sec. Systat, Inc., Evanston, Ill., 1984-94. Assoc. editor Conn. Law Rev., 1975-76. Mem. adv. bd. Horizon Hospice, Chgo., 1978—; del.-at-large White House Conf. on Families, Los Angeles, 1980; mem. adv. bd. YWCA Battered Women's Shelter, Evanston, Ill., 1982-86; mem. alumni coun. Harvard Divinity Sch., 1988-91; vol. atty. Pro Bono Advocates, Chgo., 1982-92, bd. dirs. 1993—, chair devel. com., 1993; bd. dirs. Friends of Pro Bono Advocates Orgn., 1987-89, New Voice Prodns., 1984-86, Byrne Prevn Theater Workshop, 1987-90; founder, bd. dirs. Friends of Battered Women and their Children, 1986-87; chair 175th Reunion Fund Harvard U. Div. Sch., 1992. Mem. ABA, Ill. Bar Assn., Conn. Bar Assn., Chgo. Bar Assn., Appellate Lawyers Assn. Ill. (bd. dirs. 1985-87, treas. 1989-90, sec. 1990-91, v.p. 1991-92, pres. 1992-93), Women's Bar Assn. Ill., AAUW, Jr. League Evanston (chair State Pub. Affairs Com. 1987-88, Vol. of Yr. 1983-84). Clubs: Chgo. Vassar (pres. 1979-81), Cosmopolitan (N.Y.C.). Home: 1127 Asbury Ave Evanston IL 60202-1136

VAN DEN AKKER, KOOS, fashion designer; b. The Hague, Netherlands, Mar. 16, 1939; came to U.S., 1968, naturalized, 1982; Student, Royal Acad. Arts, The Hague, 1956-58, Ecole Guerre Lavigne, Paris, 1961. Apprentice designer Christian Dior Fashion House, Paris, 1963-65; freelance designer, est. custom fashion boutique The Hague, 1965-68; designer Eve Stillman lingerie co., N.Y.C., 1969-70; freelance designer, est. boutique, 1971—, freelance designer, est. showroom, 1978—. Works include: collaged fur coat range, Ben Kahn Furs, 1981—, handbag range, Meyers Manufacturing, 1986-88; couture lingerie collections, La Lingerie stores, 1987—; collaged upholstery furniture ranges James II Galleries, 1988—. Recipient Gold Coast award, 1978, Tommy award Am. Painted Fabrics Coun., 1982. Office: 215 W 10th St New York NY 10014-3203

VANDENBERG, EDWIN JAMES, chemist, educator; b. Hawthorne, N.J., Sept. 13, 1918; s. Albert J. and Alida C. (Westerhof) V.; m. Mildred Elizabeth Wright, Sept. 9, 1950; children: David James, Jean Elizabeth. M.E. with distinction, Stevens Inst. Tech., 1939, Dr.Engring. (hon.), 1965. Rsch. chemist Hercules Inc. Rsch. Ctr., Wilmington, Del., 1939-44, asst. shift supr. Sunflower Ordnance Works, Kans., 1944-45, rsch. chemist Research Ctr., Wilmington, 1945-57, sr. research chemist, 1958-64, rsch.assoc., 1965-77, sr. rsch. assoc., 1978-82; adj. prof. chemistry Ariz. State U., Tempe, 1983-91, rsch. prof. chemistry, 1992—. Author: Polyethers, 1975; Coordination Polymerization, 1983; Contemporary Topics in Polymer Science V, 1984, Catalysis in Polymer Synthesis, 1992. Patentee in field. Mem. adv. bd. Jour. Polymer Sci., 1967-93, Macromolecules, 1979-81; chmn. Gordon Rsch. Conf. on Polymers, 1978. Recipient Internat. award Soc. Plastics Engrs., 1994. Mem. Am. Chem. Soc. (councillor Del. sect. 1974-81, chmn. 1976, chmn. div. polychemistry 1979, coord. indsl. sponsors 1982—, Del. sect. award 1965, 79, Indsl. Rsch. 100 award 1965, Polymer Chemistry award 1981, Exceptional Svc. award 1983, 95, Applied Polymer Sci. award 1991, Charles Goodyear medal, 1991, Herman F. Mark award 1992). Home: 16223 E Inca Ave Fountain Hls AZ 85268-4518 Office: Ariz State U Dept Chemistry and Biochemistry Tempe AZ 85287-1604

VANDENBERG, JOHN DONALD, entomologist; b. Benton Harbor, Mich., Jan. 24, 1954; s. Robert Landis and Madelaine Louise (Westendorf) V.; m. Alice C. L. Churchill, Oct. 8, 1983. B.S. with Honors, U. Mich., 1975; M.S., U. Maine, 1977; Ph.D., Oreg. State U., 1982. Grad. rsch. asst. U. Maine, Orono, 1975-77; grad. teaching asst. Oreg. State U., Corvallis, 1977-78, grad. rsch. asst., 1978-82; postdoctoral assoc. Boyce Thompson Inst., Ithaca, N.Y., 1982-83; rsch. entomologist Agrl. Rsch. Svc., U.S. Dept. Agr., Beltsville, Md., 1983-87, rsch. leader Agrl. Rsch. Svc., Logan, Utah, 1987-93; lead scientist Agrl. Rsch. Svc., Ithaca, N.Y., 1993—; acting asst. dir. Midwest area Agrl. Rsch. Svc., Peoria, Ill., 1991; equal employment opportunity counsellor, 1985-87. Contbr. articles to profl. jours. Mem. AAAS, Soc. for Invertebrate Pathology, Entomol. Soc. Am., Am. Soc. for Microbiology, Sigma Xi (sec. 1989-90, chpt. pres. 1991). Avocations: singing, guitar, softball, gardening. Office: USDA-ARS Plant Protection US Plant Soil & Nutrition Lab Tower Rd Ithaca NY 14853

VANDENBERG, SISTER PATRICIA CLASINA, health system executive; b. N.Y.C., Mar. 15, 1948; d. Paul John and Alice Margaret (Walter) V. BSN cum laude, CUNY, 1970; MHA, Duke U., 1979. Nurse critical care staff Roosevelt Hosp., N.Y.C., 1967-69, St. Vincent's Hosp., N.Y.C., 1970; nurse specialist, instr. Meth. Hosp. Bklyn., 1970-71; cons., instr. St. John's Hosp., Anderson, Ind., 1972; nurse critical care, ambulatory svcs. Mt. Carmel Med. Ctr., Columbus, Ohio, 1974-77; v.p. clin. svcs., apostolic devel. Holy Cross Hosp., Silver Springs, Md., 1979-83; pres., chief exec. officer St. Alphonsus Regional Med. Ctr., Boise, Idaho, 1983—; trustee St. Alphonsus Regional Med. Ctr., Boise, 1983-88; sr. v.p. Holy Cross Health System Corp., South Bend, Ind., 1988-89; pres., chief exec. officer Holy Cross Health System Corp., South Bend, 1989—; trustee Holy Cross Hosp., Blue Cross Idaho, Boise, 1986—. Mem. task force United Way, Boise, 1985; bd. dirs. ARC, Boise, 1984-85. Mem. Idaho Hosp. Assn. (trustee), Greater Boise C. of C. (bd. dirs. 1987), Sigma Theta Tau. Roman Catholic. Office: Holy Cross Health System Corp 3606 E Jefferson Blvd South Bend IN 46615-3097

VANDENBERG, PETER RAY, magazine publisher; b. Geneva, Ill., Sept. 8, 1939; s. Don George and Isabel (Frank) V.; m. Kathryn Stock, June 1973 (div. Apr. 1977). BBA, Miami U., 1962. Creative adminstr. E.F. McDonald Incentive Co., Dayton, Ohio, 1966-73; mfrs.' rep. Denver, 1974-75; mgr. Homestake Condominiums, Vail, Colo., 1975-76; desk clk. Vail Run Resort, 1976-77; sales rep. Colo. West Advt., Vail, 1977-79, pres., 1980-83; pres. Colo. West Publ., Vail, 1983—. With U.S. Army, 1963-66. Mem. Sigma Chi. Avocations: sports, music, reading.

VAN DEN BERGH, SIDNEY, astronomer; b. Wassenaar, Netherlands, May 20, 1929; emigrated to U.S., 1948; s. Sidney J. and Mieke (van den Berg) vandenB.; m. Paulette Brown; children by previous marriage: Peter, Mieke, Sabine. Student, Leiden (The Netherlands) U., 1947-48; A.B., Princeton U., 1950; M.Sc., Ohio State U., 1952; Dr. rer. nat., Goettingen U., 1956. Asst. prof. Perkins Obs., Ohio State U., Columbus, 1956-58; research assoc. Mt. Wilson Obs., Palomar Obs., Pasadena, Calif., 1968-69; prof. astronomy David Dunlap Obs., U. Toronto, Ont., Can., 1958-77; dir. Dominion Astrophys. Obs., Victoria, B.C., 1977-86; prin. rsch. officer NRC Can., 1977—; adj. prof. U. Victoria, 1977—. Decorated officer Order of Can. Fellow Royal Soc. London, Royal Soc. Can.; mem. Am., Royal Astron. Soc. (assoc.), Canadian Astronomy Soc. (sr. v.p. 1988-90, pres. 1990-92). Home: 418 Lands End Rd, Sidney, BC Canada V8L 5L9

VAN DEN BERGHE, PIERRE LOUIS, sociologist, anthropologist; b. Lubumbashi, Zaire, Jan. 30, 1933; s. Louis and Denise (Caullery) van den B.; m. Irmgard C. Niehuis, Jan. 21, 1956; children—Eric, Oliver, Marc. B.A., Stanford U., 1952, M.A., 1953; Ph.D., Harvard U., 1960. Asst. prof. sociology Wesleyan U., Middletown, Conn., 1962-63; assoc. prof. sociology SUNY, Buffalo, 1963-65; prof. sociology and anthropology U. Wash., Seattle, 1965—; vis. prof. U. Natal, South Africa, 1960-61, Sorbonne, Paris, 1962, U. Nairobi, Kenya, 1967-68, U. Ibadan, Nigeria, 1968-69, U. Haifa, Israel, 1976, U. New South Wales, Australia, 1982, U. Strasbourg, France, 1985, U. Tuebingen, Fed. Republic Germany, 1986, Tel Aviv U., 1988, U. Cape Town, South Africa, 1989; fellow Advanced Study in Behavioral Scis., Stanford, Calif., 1984-85. Author: 22 books including South Africa, A Study in Conflict, 1965, Race and Racism, 1967, Academic Gamesmanship, 1970, Man in Society, 1978, Human Family Systems, 1979, The Ethnic Phenomenon, 1981, Stranger in Their Midst, 1989, State Violence and Ethnicity, 1990, The Quest for the Other, 1994. Served with M.C. U.S. Army, 1954-56. Mem. Am. Sociol. Assn., Am. Anthrop. Assn., Social Research Assn., Human Behavior and Evolution Soc. Home: 2006 19th Ave E Seattle WA 98112-2902 Office: U Wash Dept Sociology DK-40 Seattle WA 98195

VANDENBOS, GARY ROGER, psychologist, publisher; b. Grand Rapids, Mich., Dec. 16, 1943; s. Paul Martin and Irene (Dorenbos) V.; m. Jane Annunziata, Dec. 16, 1983; 1 child, Bret. BS, Mich. State U., 1967, MA, 1969; PhD, U. Detroit, 1973. Dir. Howell (Mich.) Area Community Mental Health Ctr., 1973-77; dir. nat. policy studies Am. Psychol. Assn., Washington, 1977-82, exec. dir. for pubs., 1984—; prof. U. Bergen, Norway, 1982-84; project cons. Rand Corp., Santa Monica, Calif., 1984-89; bd. dirs. Am. Biodyne Found., San Francisco; newspaper pub. APA Monitor, 1985—. Author: Psychotherapy with Schizophrenic, 1981; editor Pscynology and National Health Insurance, 1979; assoc. editor Am. Psychologist Jour. Office: Am Psychol Assn 750 1st St NE Washington DC 20002-4242

VANDEN BOUT, PAUL ADRIAN, astronomer, physicist, educator; b. Grand Rapids, Mich., June 16, 1939; s. Adrian and Cornelia (Peterson) Vanden B.; m. Rachel Ann Eggebeen, Sept. 1, 1961; children—Thomas Adrian, David Anton. A.B., Calvin Coll., 1961; Ph.D., U. Calif.-Berkeley, 1966. Postdoctoral fellow U. Calif., Berkeley, 1966-67; postdoctoral fellow Columbia U., N.Y.C., 1967-68; instr. Columbia U., 1968-69, asst. prof., 1969-70; asst. prof. U. Tex., Austin, 1970-74; assoc. prof. U. Tex., 1974-79, prof., 1979-84; dir. Nat. Radio Astronomy Obs., Charlottesville, Va., 1985—; cons. NSF, NASA. Fellow Fulbright Found., Heidelberg, Fed. Republic Germany, 1961-62, Leiden, Netherlands, 1977. Fellow AAAS, Am. Phys. Soc.; mem. Am. Astron. Soc., Internat. Astron. Union, Internat. Radio Sci. Union. Office: Nat Radio Astronomy Obs 520 Edgemont Rd Charlottesville VA 22903

VANDENBROUCKE, RUSSELL JAMES, theatre director; b. Chgo., Aug. 16, 1948; s. Arthur C. Sr. and Ardelle (Barker) V.; m. Mary Allison Dilg, Sept. 7, 1974; children: Aynsley Louise, Justin Arthur. BA, U. Ill., 1970; MA, U. Warwick, Coventry, Eng., 1975; MFA in Drama, Yale U., 1977, DFA in Drama, 1978. Case worker Cook County Dept. Pub. Aid, Chgo., 1970-71; family worker Alliance of Cambridge Settlement Houses, Cambridge, Mass., 1971-72; child care worker Cambridge/Sommerville Catholic Charities, Cambridge, Mass., 1972-73; asst. literary mgr. Yale Repertory Theatre, New Haven, 1977-78; lit. mgr., dramaturg Mark Taper Forum, Los Angeles, 1978-85; assoc. producing dir. Repertory Theatre St. Louis, 1985-87; artistic dir. Northlight Theatre, Evanston, Ill., 1987—; vis. prof. Yale U., 1978, La. State U., 1981, U. Calif.-San Diego, 1983, Middlebury Coll., 1985, Washington U., 1986; adj. assoc. prof. Northwestern U., 1987—; on site evaluator, peer panelist Nat. Endowment for Arts, Washington, 1981—. Author: Truths the Hand Can Touch: The Theatre of Athol Fugard, 1985; adapted play Eleanor: In Her Own Words (for TV), 1985 (Emmy award 1986) (dir. for stage 1990), Los Alamos Revisted (for stage and radio), 1984, 87, Atomic Bombers, 1995, Holiday Memories (from Truman Capote), 1991; adapted, stage dir. Feiffer's America, 1988, Eleanor: In Her Own Words, 1990; adapted An Enemy of the People, 1991; stage dir. Lucky Lindy, Love Letters on Blue Paper, 84 Charing Cross Road, Three Women Talking (also radio), Smoke on the Mountain, The White Rose, Betrayal, My Other Heart, Later Life, Hedda Gabler; contbr. articles to mags. and newspapers. Recipient L.A. Drama Critics Circle award, 1984, Spl. Actors Equity Assn. award, 1990. Avocation: basketball. Office: Northlight Theatre 600 Davis St Evanston IL 60201-4419

VAN DEN-NOORT, STANLEY, physician, educator; b. Lynn, Mass., Sept. 8, 1930; s. Judokus and Hazel G. (Van Blarcom) van den N.; m. June Le Clere, Apr. 17, 1954; children—Susanne, Eric, Peter, Katherine, Elizabeth. A.B., Dartmouth, 1951; M.D., Harvard, 1954. Intern then resident Boston City Hosp., 1954-56, resident neurology, 1958-60; research fellow neurochemistry Harvard, 1960-62; instr. medicine Case Western Res. U., Cleve., 1962-66; asst. prof. Case Western Res. U., 1966-69, assoc. prof., 1969-70; prof. neurology U. Calif., Irvine, 1970—; chair dept. neurology U. Calif., 1970-72, 86—, assoc. dean Coll. Medicine, 1972-73, dean, 1973-85; mem. cons. staff U. Calif., Irvine Med. Center; mem. Long Beach (Calif.) Meml. Hosp., Long Beach VA Hosp.; mem. com. of revision U.S. Pharmacopoeial Conv., 1990-95. Mem. med. adv. bds. Orange County Epilepsy Svc., 1971—, Nat. Multiple Sclerosis Soc./Myasthenia Gravis, 1971—, Orange County chpt. Nat. Multiple Sclerosis Soc., 1971—, Orange County Health Planning Coun., 1971-85, Nat. Com. Rsch. in Neurol. Disease, 1982-87. Lt. MC USNR, 1956-58. Fellow ACP, Am. Acad. Neurol.; mem. AAUP, AMA, Am. Neurol. Assn., Orange County Med. assn., Calif. Med. Assn., Am. Heart Assn. Home: 17592 Orange Tree Ln Tustin CA 92680-2353 Office: U Calif Dept Neurology 100 Irvine Hall Irvine CA 92717-4275

VANDERBEKE, PATRICIA K., architect; b. Detroit, Apr. 3, 1963; d. B. H. and Dolores I. VanderBeke. BS in Architecture, U. Mich., 1985, MArch, 1987. Registered architect, Ill. Archtl. intern Hobbs & Black, Assocs., Ann Arbor, Mich., 1984-86, Fry Assocs., Ann Arbor, 1988; architect Decker & Kemp Architecture/Urban Design, Chgo., 1989-92; prin. founder P. K. VanderBeke, Architect, Chgo., 1992—. Contbr. photographs and articles to Inland Architect mag.; contbr. photographs to AIA calendar. Chair recycling com. Lake Point Tower Condo. Assn., Chgo., 1990T, chair, ops. com., 1993. George S. Booth travelling fellow, 1992. Mem. AIA (1st place photog. contest award 1992, hon. mention 1994), Chgo. Archtl. Club. Office: P K VanderBeke Architect 505 N Lake Shore Dr Apt 808 Chicago IL 60611-3402

VAN DER BIJL, WILLEM, meteorology educator; b. Alphen, The Netherlands, Aug. 15, 1920; came to U.S., 1956; s. Coenraad Johannes and Hillegonda Maria (Evenblij) Van Der B.; m. Godefrieda Judith Lemkes, Sept. 24, 1946; children: Joan Elizabeth, Baldwin John William. BS, Free U., Amsterdam, The Netherlands, 1941, MS, 1943; PhD, State U. Utrecht, The Netherlands, 1952. Research assoc. Royal Netherlands Meteorol. Inst., de Bilt, 1946-56; prof. meteorology Kans. State U., Manhattan, 1956-61, Naval Postgrad. Sch., Monterey, Calif., 1961—. Author: Long Range Weather Forecasts, 1951, Statistics in Climatology, 1952; contbg. author: Academic American Encyclopedia, 1980. Fellow U. Chgo., 1954-55. Mem. Am. Meteorol. Soc., Am. Geophys. Union., Naval Postgrad. Sch. Soccer Club, Sigma Chi. Home: 791 Toyon Dr Monterey CA 93940-4226 Office: Naval Postgrad Sch Dept Meteorology Monterey CA 93943

VANDERBILT, HUGH BEDFORD, SR., mineral and chemical company executive; b. N.Y.C., Apr. 23, 1921; s. Robert Thurlow and Mildred (Bedford) V.; m. Claire Frances McKiernan, Apr. 27, 1946; children: Laura V. Ernst, Linda V. Allen, Hugh B. Jr. Student, Trinity Coll., Hartford, Conn., 1940-42. With News Syndicate Corp., N.Y.C., 1946-54; chmn. bd. R.T. Vanderbilt Co., Inc., Norwalk, Conn., 1954—. Hon. trustee Greenwich (Conn.) Hist. Soc., 1957—; trustee hist. Deerfield (Mass.) Inc., 1976-93. 1st lt. U.S. Army, 1942-46. Mem. Chem. Mfrs. Assn. (bd. dirs. 1975-79), Blind Brook Club, Greenwich Country Club, Lyford Country Club, Everglades Club, Round Hill Club. Republican. Avocations: golf, skiing. Office: R T Vanderbilt Co Inc 30 Winfield St Norwalk CT 06855-1395

VANDERBILT, KERMIT, English language educator; b. Decorah, Iowa, Sept. 1, 1925; s. Lester and Ella (Qualley) V.; m. Vivian Osmundson, Nov. 15, 1947; 1 dau., Karen Paige. B.A., Luther Coll., Decorah, 1947, Litt. D. (hon.), 1977; M.A., U. Minn., 1949, Ph.D., 1956. Instr. English U. Minn., 1954-57; instr. U. Wash., 1958-60, asst. prof. English, 1960-62; asst. prof. San Diego State U., 1962-65, assoc. prof., 1965-68, prof., 1968-90, prof. emeritus, 1990—; vis. prof. Am. lit. U. B.C., Can., Vancouver, summer 1963; vis. prof. U. Oreg., summer 1968. Author: Charles Eliot Norton: Apostle of Culture in a Democracy, 1959, The Achievement of William Dean Howells: A Reinterpretation, 1968, American Literature and the Academy: The Roots, Growth and Maturity of a Profession, 1986 (Choice award for outstanding acad. books), Theodore Roethke in A Literary History of the American West, 1987; editor: (with others) American Social Thought, 1972, April Hopes (W.D. Howells), 1975, The Rise of Silas Lapham, 1983, spl. issue Am. Literary Realism, winter 1989, La Litterature Americaine, 1991, 2nd edit., 1994; mem. edit. bd. U. Wash. Press, 1960-62, Twentieth Century Lit., 1969—; contbr. numerous articles to profl. jours. Served with USNR, 1943-46. Outstanding Prof. San Diego State U., 1976; Guggenheim fellow, 1978-79; Huntington Library fellow, 1980; Am. Philos. Soc. grantee, 1964, Am. Council Learned Socs. grantee, 1972, Nat. Endowment for Humanities grantee, 1986. Mem. Am. Studies Assn. (exec. council 1968-69), So. Calif. Am. Studies Assn. (pres. 1968-69), Philol. Assn. Pacific Coast (chmn. sect. Am. lit. 1968), MLA, Internat. Mark Twain Soc. (hon.), United Profs. of Calif. (Disting. prof. 1978). Home: 6937 Coleshill Dr San Diego CA 92119-1920

VANDERBILT, OLIVER DEGRAY, financier; b. N.Y.C., Oct. 25, 1914; s. Oliver Degray Jr. and Madelon (Weir) V.; m. Frances Philips, Nov. 11, 1939; children: Oliver Degray IV, Madelon V. Peck. AB, Princeton U., 1937. With Tenn. Coal Iron & R.R. Co., Birmingham, Ala., 1939-40; v.p. Weir Kilby Corp., Cin., 1940-49; exec. v.p. Taylor Wharton Iron & Steel Co., Cin., 1949; pres. Taylor Wharton Iron & Steel Co., 1954-55; v.p. Harrisburg Steel Corp., 1954; pres. Twisco Corp., 1954-55; v.p., dir. Baldwin-Lima-Hamilton Corp., 1955-56; exec. v.p., dir. Blair & Co. Inc., Phila., 1957-62; chmn. Blair & Co. Inc., 1963-70; founder, pres. Vanderbilt Corp., Phila., 1963-68, Capitol Mgmt. Corp., 1968—, Innovest Group Inc., 1970—; pres., chief exec. officer Ecolaire Inc., 1971-74; founder, pres. Dorsey Corp., 1959, Standard Computers Inc., 1965, Systems Capital Corp., 1967, Marina City Corp., 1968; founder, chmn. bd. Tierra Corp., San Francisco, 1977—, Vanderbilt Energy Corp., N.Y.C., 1978—; founder, chmn. Seaborad Savs. Bank, Stuart, Fla., 1983—. Maj. AUS, 1942-45, ETO, NATOUSA. Decorated Croix de Guerre (France); Bronze Star (U.S.). Mem. Links, Commonwealth Club, Jupiter Island Club, Racquet and Tennis Club, Gulph Mills Golf Club, Ivy Club, Nassau Club, Seminole Club, Maidstone Club. Republican. Episcopalian. Avocation: golf. Home: 111 Gomez Rd Hobe Sound FL 33455-2427

VANDER CLUTE, NORMAN ROLAND, lawyer; b. N.Y.C., Nov. 14, 1932; s. Carl Frederick and Agnes (Hansen) Vander C.; m. Sandra Sheffey, Dec. 30, 1978; children: William Bowditch, Edward Carl, Jeffrey. BA, Amherst Coll., 1954; LLB, Harvard U., 1957. Bar: N.Y. 1958, D.C. 1967. Law clk. 1st Cir. Ct. Appeals, Boston, 1957-58; atty. Standard Vacuum Oil Co., Hartsdale, N.Y., 1958-60; sr. atty. Am. Airlines, Inc., N.Y.C., 1960-63; asst. gen. counsel Agy. for Internat. Devel., Washington, 1963-65, office dir., 1965-67; ptnr. Surrey & Morse, Washington, 1967-85, Jones, Day, Reavis & Pogue, Washington, 1986-93, Winston & Strawn, 1993—. Mem. ABA. Presbyterian. Avocations: boating. Office: Winston & Strawn 1400 L St NW Washington DC 20005-3509

VAN DER EB, HENRY GERARD, retired packaging company executive; b. Hartford, Conn., May 11, 1918; s. Henry Johan and Harriet (Krug) V. d. E.; m. Janet Susan Land, Sept. 6, 1941; children: Janet Susan Van der Eb Greene, Henry Gerard, Peter Johan. SB, Harvard U., 1942. With Container Corp. Am., 1946-79, mem. mgmt. com., 1960-79, exec. v.p., 1965-68, pres., 1968-79, chief exec. officer, 1970-79, chmn., 1974-79, also bd. dirs.; bd. dirs. Baxter Internat., Bell & Howell Co., Nat.-Standard Co., Graphic Packaging Co., SFN Cos., Mobil Corp. Chmn. gen. mfg. sect. Chgo. Crusade of Mercy, 1963; trustee Loomis-Chaffee Sch., 1972-73, Chgo. Zool. Soc.; trustee, chmn. oper. bd. Paperboard Packaging Coun., 1967; bd. dirs. Nat. Ctr. for Resource Recovery Inc. Lt. USNR, 1942-46. Mem. Folding Paper Box Assn. Am. (pres. 1966-68, dir., exec. com.), Am. Paper Inst. (dir., exec. com., chmn. 1975-76), Harvard Alumni Assn. (pres. 1980-81, com. on univ. resources, bd. overseers 1986-92, chmn. Harvard Coll. Fund 1984-87), Harvard Club (N.Y.C., Boston, Chgo., Harvard medal 1994), Chgo. Club, Mid-Day Club, Comml. Club (Chgo.), Chgo. Commonwealth Club, Hole in the Wall Club (Naples, Fla.), Royal Poinciana Club (Naples), Old Elm Club (Ft. Sheridan, Ill.). Home: The Glenview at Pelican Bay 100 Glenview Pl # 708 Naples FL 33963-3130

VANDERET, ROBERT CHARLES, lawyer; b. Bklyn., Apr. 12, 1947; s. James Gustav and Bernadette Cecelia (Heaney) V.; m. Sharon Kay Brewster, Oct 3, 1970; children: Erin Anne Brewster, Aidan McKenzie Brewster. AB, UCLA, 1969; JD, Stanford U., 1973. Bar: Calif. 1973, U.S. Dist. Ct. (cen. and so. dists.) Calif. 1974, U.S. Ct. Appeals (9th cir.) 1976, N.Y. 1978, U.S. Supreme Ct. 1978, U.S. Dist. Ct. (no. dist.) Calif. 1980, U.S. Dist. Ct. (ea. dist.) Calif. 1981. Extern law clk. to Justice Tobriner Calif. Supreme Ct., 1972-73; assoc. O'Melveny & Myers, Los Angeles, 1973-80, ptnr., 1980—; transition aide Chief Justice Rose Bird, Calif. Supreme Ct., 1976. Del. Dem. Nat. Conv., 1968; bd. dirs. Legal Aid Found. L.A., 1978-90, Constnl. Rights Found., 1990. Mem. ABA (chair media law and defamation torts com. 1991-92), L.A. Bar Assn. (pro bono coun. chair 1993—). Democrat. Home: 834 Greentree Rd Pacific Palisades CA 90272-3911 Office: O'Melveny & Myers 400 S Hope St Los Angeles CA 90071 Notable cases include: Galloway vs. CBS, 14 Media L. Rep. 1161, 1987, in which he represented Dan Rather and CBS in celebrated libel case; Martha Raye vs. David Letterman, 14 Media L. Rep. 2047, 1987, in which he represented David Letterman and NBC; Robert Mahev vs. CBS, 201 Calif. App. 3d 662, 1988, in which he represented CBS, Playboy and other pubs.; Crane vs. The Ariz. Republic, 729 F. Supp. 698 Ct. Dist. Calif., 1989, in which he represented The Ariz. Republic; Kruse vs. Bank of Am., 202 Calif. App. 3d 38, 1988, in which he represented Bank of Am. in successful appeal of leading lender liability case; CHH vs. The Limited, 587 F. Supp. 246, Ct. Dist. Calif., 1984, in which he represented Carter Hawley Hale Stores, Inc. in major takeover battle.

VANDERGRIFF, JERRY DODSON, computer store executive; b. Ft. Leonard Wood, Mo., Nov. 6, 1943; s. Oliver Wyatt Vandergriff and Mary Ella (Perkins) Myers; m. Donna Jean Niehof, Aug. 14, 1976 (div. Nov. 1987); children: Robert Lee II, William Oliver. BS in Bus., Emporia State U., 1974. Customer serv. mgr. Pictures, Inc., Anchorage, 1975-83, v.p., gen. mgr., 1983-87; gen. mgr. Pictures-The Computer Store, Anchorage, 1987—. Bd. dirs. Community Schs. Coun., Anchorage, 1986-87; mem. v.p.'s Coun. on Edn., 1989-90; bd. dirs. Romig Jr. High Sch., 1989-90, pres. PTSA, 1990-92; mem. exec. bd. Alaska's Youth Ready for Work, 1989-92. Mem. VFW, Moose. Republican. Avocations: movies, reading, pool, fishing, scuba diving. Home: 3831 Balchen Dr Anchorage AK 99517-2446 Office: The Computer Store 601 W 36th Ave Ste 19 Anchorage AK 99503-5849

VANDERHAEGHE, GUY CLARENCE, writer, creative writing educator; b. Esterhazy, Sask., Can., May 4, 1951; s. Clarence Earl and Alma Beth (Allen) V.; m. Margaret Elizabeth Nagel, Sept. 2, 1972. BA in History with great distinction, U. Sask., Saskatoon, 1971, BA honours diploma with high honors, 1972, MA in History, 1975; BEd with great distinction, U. Regina, Sask., 1978. Freelance writer and editor, 1975-77; tchr. English and history Herbert (Sask.) H.S., 1978-79; project officer Access Cons., Saskatoon, 1979-82; teaching asst. dept. history U. Sask., 1982-83; writer-in-residence Saskatoon Pub. Libr., 1983-84; writer-in-residence U. Ottawa, Ont., Can., 1985, vis. prof. creative writing, 1985-86; mem. faculty writing program Banff (Alta., Can.) Ctr. for Arts, 1990-91; mem. faculty SAGE Hills (Sask.) Creative Writing Program, 1992; vis. prof. creative writing St. Thomas More Coll., U. Sask., 1993—; mem. adv. bd. New Can. Libr., McClelland and Stewart, 1988—. Author: Man Descending, 1982, The Trouble with Heroes, 1983, My Present Age, 1984, Homesick, 1989 (co-winner City of Toronto Book award 1990), Things As They Are; translator: Het volmaakte einde van een volmaakte dag, 1989, En Chute Libre, 1991, Min Nutid, 1986, Se Menee Ohi, 1986, Min Natid, 1987, Tegen de morgen in slaap gevallen, 1987, Une histoire de mon temps, 1990, Een soort heimwee, 1992. Mem. Sask. Arts Bd., 1984; hon. trustee Inst. for Society and Humanity, U. Sask., 1993—. Recipient 1st prize short story competition Sask. Dept. Culture, 1976, ann. contbr.'s prize Can. Fiction mag., 1980, Gov.-Gen.'s award for fiction, 1982, award Ont. Arts Coun., 1986, Geoffrey Faber Meml. prize, Gt. Britain, 1987, award for short story Western mag., 1991, award for drama I Had a Job I Liked. Once, Canadian Authors Assn., 1993, sr. artist's award Can. Coun., 1988, 93; scholar, 1969-71, 78; grad. fellow, 1972-74; grantee Can. Coun., 1981-83, Sask. Arts Bd., 1983, 85, 92-93, 94-95. Avocations: hockey, golf. Home: 44 Welker Cresent, Saskatoon, SK Canada S7H 3M4

VANDERHOEF, LARRY NEIL, university administrator; b. Perham, Minn., Mar. 20, 1941; s. Wilmar James and Ida Lucille (Wothe) V.; m. Rosalie Suzanne Slifka, Aug. 31, 1963; children: Susan Marie, Jonathan Lee. B.S., U. Wis., Milw., 1964, M.S., 1965; Ph.D., Purdue U., 1969. Postdoctorate U. Wis., Madison, 1969-70; research assoc. U. Wis., summers 1970-72; asst. prof. biology U. Ill., Urbana, 1970-74; assoc. prof. U. Ill. 1974-77, prof., 1977—; head dept. plant biology, 1977-80; provost Agrl. and Life Scis., U. Md., College Park, 1980-84; exec. vice chancellor U. Calif. Davis, 1984-91, exec. vice chancellor, provost, 1991-94; chancellor, 1994—; vis. investigator Carnegie Inst., 1976-77, Edinburgh (Scotland) U., 1978; cons. in field. NRC postdoctoral fellow, 1969-70, Eisenhower fellow, 1987; Dimond travel grantee, 1975, NSF grantee, 1972, 74, 76, 77, 78, 79, NATO grantee, 1980. Mem. AAAS, Am. Soc. Plant Physiology (bd. editors Plant Physiology 1977-82, trustee, mem. exec. com., treas. 1982-88, chmn. bd. trustees 1994—), Nat. Assn. State Univ. and Land Grant Colls. Home: 615 Francisco Pl Davis CA 95616-0210 Office: U Calif Davis Office Chancellor Davis CA 95616

VANDERHOOF, IRWIN THOMAS, life insurance company executive; b. Newark, Dec. 4, 1927; s. Irwin and Dora (Blanchard) V.; m. Ruth Elizabeth Green, Feb. 18, 1949; children: Thomas Arthur Irwin, Karen McNeill Brundage. B.S., Worcester (Mass.) Poly. Inst., 1948; Ph.D in Fin., NYU, 1987. C.L.U.; chartered fin. analyst. Asst. actuarial supr. Met. Life Ins. Co., 1951-55; assoc. actuary U.S. Life Ins. Co., 1955-59; exec. v.p., treas. Standard Security Life Ins. Co., 1959-73; sr. v.p. Equitable Life Assurance Soc. U.S., N.Y.C., 1973-87; pres. Actuarial Investment Cons. Inc., Towaco, N.J., 1987—; prof. Stern Sch. Bus., NYU; bd. dirs. Life Ins. Co. of the Southwest, Dallas, Analytic Risk Mgmt., Louisville. Author papers in field. Pres. Montville (N.J.) Twp. Bd. Edn., 1962. Fellow Soc. Actuaries, Life Officer Mgmt. Inst.; assoc. Casualty Actuarial Soc., Inst. Actuaries; mem. N.Y. Soc. Security Analysts, Am. Acad. Actuaries. Republican. Episcopalian.

VANDER HORST, KATHLEEN PURCELL, nonprofit association administrator; b. Glen Rock, N.J., Jan. 15, 1947; d. John Francis Ralph and Elizabeth Jeanne (Burnett) Purcell; m. John Vander Horst Jr., Feb. 12, 1972 (div. Oct. 1993). Dir. devel. svcs Johns Hopkins U., Balt., 1968-71; dir. devel. Union of Colls. of Art, Kansas City, Mo., 1971-72; dir. pub. rels. Md. Ballet and Ctr. Stage, Balt., 1973-76; dir. program devel. Joint Ctr. for Polit. and Econ. Studies, Washington, 1976-90, v.p. for program devel., 1990—. Dir., chmn. fin. com. Roland Park Community Found., Balt., 1990—. Office: Joint Ctr for Polit & Econ 1090 Vermont Ave NW Washington DC 20005-4905

VAN DER KROEF, JUSTUS MARIA, political science educator; b. Djakarta, Indonesia, Oct. 30, 1925; came to U.S., 1942, naturalized, 1952; s. Hendrikus Leonardus and Maria Wilhelmina (van Lokven) van der K.; m. Orell Joan Ellison, Mar. 25, 1955 (dec.); children: Adrian Hendrick, Sri Orell. B.A., Millsaps Coll., 1944; M.A., U. N.C., 1947; Ph.D., Columbia U., 1953. Asst. prof. fgn. studies Mich. State U., 1948-55; Charles Dana prof. coord. dept. polit. sci. and sociology U. Bridgeport, Conn., 1956-92, prof. emeritus, 1992—; vis. prof. Nanyang U, Singapore, U. Philippines, Quezon City, Vidyodaya U, Sri Lanka Colombo; dir. Am.-Asian Ednl. Exchange, 1969—; chmn. editorial bd. Communications Research Services, Inc., Greenwich, Conn., 1971-80; mem. internat. adv. bd. Union Trust Bank, Stamford, Conn., 1974-88, adv. bd., 1988-94; mem. nat. acad. adv. council Charles Edison Meml. Youth Fund; bd. dirs. WUBC-TV, Bridgeport, Conn., 1978-80. Author: Indonesia in the Modern World, 2 vols., 1954-56, Indonesian Social Evolution. Some Psychological Considerations, 1958, The Communist Party of Indonesia: Its History, Program and Tactics, 1965, Communism in Malaysia and Singapore, 1967, Indonesia Since Sukarno, 1971, The Lives of SEATO, 1976, Communism in Southeast Asia, 1980, Kampuchea: The Endless Tug of War, 1982, Aquino's Philippines: The Deepening Security Crisis, 1988, Territorial Claims in the South China Sea, 1992, The South China Sea Problem: Some Alternative Scenarios, 1994; mem. editorial bd. World Affairs, 1975—, Jour. Asian Affairs, 1975—, Asian Affairs, 1980—, Asian Profile, 1983—, Jour. of Govt. and Adminstrn., 1985—, Jour. of Econ. and Internat. Relations, 1987—, Asian Affairs Jour. (Karachi), 1992—; mng. editor: Asian Thought and Society, 1986—; book rev. editor: Asian Thought and Soc, 1976-85. Mem. City Charter Revision Com. City of Bridgeport, 1983-86, 90-92. Served with Royal Netherlands Marine Corps, 1944-45. Sr. fellow Research Inst. Communist Affairs, Columbia U., 1965-66, Rockefeller Found.; fellow U. Queensland, Brisbane, Australia, 1968-69; research fellow Inst. Strategic Studies, Islamabad, Pakistan, 1982—; research fellow Mellon Research Found., 1983, 90; research fellow Internat. Ctr. Asian Studies, Hong Kong, 1983—. Mem. Univ. Profs. Acad. Order (nat. pres. 1970-71), Pi Gamma Mu, Phi Alpha Theta, Lambda Chi Alpha, Alpha Sigma Lambda Phi Sigma Iota. Home: 165 Linden Ave Bridgeport CT 06604-5730

VANDER LAAN, MARK ALAN, lawyer; b. Akron, Ohio, Sept. 14, 1948; s. Robert H. and Isabel R. (Bishop) Vander L.; m. Barbara Ann Ryzenga, Aug. 25, 1970; children: Aaron, Matthew. AB, Hope Coll., 1970; JD, U. Mich., 1972. Bar: Ohio 1973, U.S. Dist. Ct. (so. dist.) Ohio 1973, U.S. Ct. Appeals (6th cir.) 1978, U.S. Supreme Ct. 1981. Assoc. Dinsmore, Shohl, Coates & Deupree, Cin., 1972-79; ptnr. Dinsmore & Shohl, Cin., 1979—; spl. counsel Ohio Atty. Gen.'s Office, 1983—; spl. prosecutor State of Ohio, 1985-94; city solicitor City of Blue Ash, Ohio, 1987—; trustee Cin. So. Railway, 1994—. Mme. Cin. Human Rels. Commn., 1980-86; mem. Leadership Cin. Class XIII, 1989-90; trustee Legal Aid Soc. of Cin., 1981—, pres., 1988-90. Mem. ABA, Ohio Bar Assn., Cin. Bar Assn. (ethics com. 1983—), Potter Stewart Inn of Ct. (master), Queen City Club. Office: Dinsmore & Shohl 1900 Chemed Ct 255 E 5th St Cincinnati OH 45202-4700

VANDERLAAN, ROBERT D., lawyer; b. Grand Rapids, Mich., Aug. 22, 1952; s. Donald Gene and Elizabeth Jo (Stankiewicz) V.; m. Betty Jane Thomas, June 25, 1983. BA, U. Detroit, 1974, JD, 1977. Bar: Mich. 1977, U.S. Dist. Ct. (we. dist.) Mich. 1977, U.S. Ct. Appeals (3d cir.) 1983, U.S. Ct. Appeals (6th cir.) 1978, U.S. Supreme Ct. 1981. Ptnr., pres., dir. firm Mohney, Goodrich & Titta, P.C., Grand Rapids, Mich., 1977-86; ptnr. Miller, Canfield, Paddock and Stone, Grand Rapids, 1986—. Bd. dirs. St. John's Home, Grand Rapids, 1980-87, Mercy Respite Care Corp., Grand Rapids, 1980-83, Grand Rapids Cath. Secondary Sch. Bd. Edn., 1982-89, treas. 1985-88, pres. 1988-89, Nat. Kidney Found. of Mich., trustee, 1988—, exec. com., 1989—; bd. dirs. Citizens League Greater Grand Rapids, 1988—, sec., treas., 1992-93, v.p. 1993—. Named One of Outstanding Young Men of Am., 1985. Mem. Nat. Inst. Trial Advocacy (faculty 1982—), Grand Rapids Bar Assn. (sec. 1988-89), Fed. Bar Assn. (western dist. Mich. v.p. programs, 1992-93, sec. 1993-94, v.p. ops. 1994—), Grand Rapids Jaycees (dir. 1979-80, legal counsel 1978-79, 82-83, v.p. 1985-86, pres. 1986-87, chmn. bd. 1987-88, Disting. Svc. award 1984). Roman Catholic. Office: Miller Canfield Paddock 1200 Campau Sq Plz 99 Monroe NW Grand Rapids MI 49503-2661

VANDERLEEST, DIRK, airport executive. Exec. dir. Jackson (Miss.) Mcpl. Airport Authority, Jackson Internat. Airport. Office: Jackson Internat Airport PO Box 98109 Jackson MS 39298-8109

VANDERLINDE, RAYMOND EDWARD, clinical chemist; b. Newark, N.Y., Feb. 28, 1924; s. Isaac Edward and Hazel Effie (Robinson) V.; m. Ruth Louise Hansen, June 19, 1948; children: Susan Kay, Jeanne, William Edward. AB magna cum laude, Syracuse U., 1944, MS, 1945, PhD in Med. Biochemistry, 1950. Diplomate: Am. Bd. Clin. Chemistry. Asst. prof. biochemistry U. Md. Sch. Medicine, 1950-53, assoc. prof., 1953-57; lab. dir.; asst. prof. Syracuse Meml. Hosp.-Upstate Med. Center, Syracuse, 1957-62; clin. chemist Meml. Hosp., Cumberland, Md., 1962-65; dir. labs. for clin. chemistry N.Y. State Dept. Health, Albany, 1965-76; prof. pathology and lab. medicine Hahnemann U., Phila., 1977-90, prof. emeritus, 1990; mem. lab. tech. adv. com. Pa. Dept. Health, 1981-85; mem. Coun. Nat. Reference Sys. in Clin. Chemistry, 1978—, vice chair holder, 1987, 91-93, chair holder, 1988-90; mem. Commn. on Accreditation in Clin. Chemistry, 1980-93; mem. enzyme subcom. Commn. on World Standardization, World Assn. Socs. of Pathology, 1978-90. Editor: Selected Methods of Clinical Chemistry, 1977-83, Annals of Clinical and Laboratory Science, 1981-93, Clinical Chemistry 1983-92. Chmn. council on ministries, lay del. to ann. conf. Berwyn United Methodist Ch., 1979-82. Nat. Inst. Arthritis, Metabolism and Digestive Diseases grantee, 1977-81; NIH Lab. Standardization Panel for Lipids, 1986-90. Fellow Am. Assn. for Clin. Chemistry (bd. dirs. 1979-81, Fisher award 1985, Rheinhold award 1992); mem. Am. Chem. Soc., Am. Soc. Clin. Pathologists (assoc.), Acad. Clin. Lab. Physicians and Scientists, Assn. of Clin. Scientists, Soc. Mayflower Descs. of Am., Masons, Rotary (past pres. Delmar, N.Y.), Phi Beta Kappa, Sigma Xi. Republican. Methodist. Home: Brookside #636 719 Maiden Choice Ln Catonsville MD 21228

VAN DER MARCK, JAN, art historian; b. Roermond, The Netherlands, Aug. 19, 1929; s. Everard and Anny (Finken) van der M.; m. Ingeborg Lachmann, Apr. 27, 1961 (dec. Dec. 1988); m. Sheila Stamell, May 24, 1990. BA, U. Nijmegen, The Netherlands, 1952, MA, 1954, PhD in Art History, 1956; postgrad., U. Utrecht, The Netherlands, 1956-57, Columbia U., 1957-59. Curator Gemeentemuseum, Arnhem, The Netherlands, 1959-61; asst. dir. fine arts Seattle World's Fair, 1961-62; curator Walker Art Center, Mpls., 1963-67; dir. Mus. Contemporary Art, Chgo., 1967-70; assoc. prof. art history U. Wash., 1972-74; dir. Dartmouth Coll. Mus. and Galleries, 1974-80, Center for Fine Arts, Miami, 1980-85; curator 20th century art, chief curator Detroit Inst. Arts, 1986—. Author: Romantische Boekillustratie in Belgie, 1956, George Segal, 1975, Arman, 1984, Bernar Venet, 1988; contbr. articles to art jours., essays to catalogues. Netherlands Orgn. Pure Rsch. fellow, 1954-55, Rockefeller Found. fellow, 1957-59, Aspen Inst. fellow, 1974, 94; vis. sr. fellow Ctr. for Advanced Study in Visual Arts, Washington, 1986. Mem. Internat. Art Critics Assn., Internat. Council Mus., Internat. Com. Modern Mus.'s. Office: Inst Arts 5200 Woodward Ave Detroit MI 48202-4008

VANDER MEER, HARRY, church administrator. Fin. co-ordinator Christian Ref. Ch. in N Am. Office: Chirstian Ref Ch in N Am 2850 Kalamazoo Ave SE Grand Rapids MI 49560

VAN DER MERWE, NIKOLAAS JOHANNES, archaeologist; b. Riviersonderend, Republic of South Africa, Aug. 11, 1940; came to U.S., 1958; s. Johannes Abraham and Rachel Maria (Burger) van der M.; m. Julia Ann Feeny, Nov. 11, 1962 (div. 1969); 1 child, Kerstin; m. Karen Elaine Bardou, Feb. 19, 1973; 1 child, Nicolina Thandiwe. BA cum laude, Yale U., 1962, MA, 1965, PhD, 1966; MA (hon.), Harvard U., 1988. Curatorial asst. Yale Peabody Mus., New Haven, 1962-64; rsch. asst. Yale Radiocarbon Lab. New Haven, 1963-66; asst. prof. anthropology SUNY, Binghamton, 1966-69, assoc. prof., 1969-74; prof. archaeology U. Cape Town, Republic of South Africa, 1974-88; Landon Clay prof. sci. archaeology, earth and planetary scis. Harvard U., Cambridge, Mass., 1988—; dir. African Studies, U. Cape Town, 1976-80. Author: The Carbon 14 Dating of Iron, 1969; co-editor: (collection of essays) Perspectives on South Africa's Future, 1979, Iron Age in Southern Africa, 1979; contbr. numerous articles to profl. jours. Fellow U. Cape Town, 1986; Ford Found. Fgn. Area fellow, 1964-66. Fellow AAAS, Royal Soc. South Africa (John F.W. Herschel medal 1994),, Am. Anthrop. Assn., Explorers Club, Soc. Antiquaries (London); mem. South African Archaeol. Soc. (life), Soc. Am. Archaeology, Hist. Metallurgy Group, South African Assn. Archaeologists (founder), West African Assn. Archaeology (founder), Soc. Archaeol. Sci. (life), Owl Club (Cape Town), Concord (Mass.) Rod and Gun, Sigma Xi. Avocations: flying, diving, shooting, hiking, cooking. Home: 475 River Rd Carlisle MA 01741-1819 Office: Harvard Univ Peabody Mus/Dept Anthropology 11 Divinity Ave Cambridge MA 02138-2096*

VAN DER MEULEN, JOSEPH PIERRE, neurologist; b. Boston, Aug. 22, 1929; s. Edward Lawrence and Sarah Jane (Robertson) VanDer M.; m. Ann Irene Yadeno, June 18, 1960; children—Elisabeth, Suzanne, Janet. A.B., Boston Coll., 1950; M.D., Boston U., 1954. Diplomate: Am. Bd. Psychiatry and Neurology. Intern Cornell Med. div. Bellevue Hosp., N.Y.C., 1954-55; resident Cornell Med. div. Bellevue Hosp., 1955-56; resident Harvard U., Boston City Hosp., 1958-60, instr., fellow, 1962-66; assoc. Case Western Res. U., Cleve., 1966-67; asst. prof. Case Western Res. U., 1967-69, assoc. prof. neurology and biomed. engring., 1969-71; prof. neurology U. So. Calif., L.A., 1971—; also prof. neurology Los Angeles County/U. So. Calif. Med. Center; chmn. dept. U. So. Calif., 1971-78, v.p. for health affairs, 1977—, dean Sch. Medicine, 1985-86, dir. Allied Health Scis., 1991—; vis. prof. Autonomous U. Guadalajara, Mex., 1974; pres. Norris Cancer Hosp. and Research Inst., 1983—. Contbr. articles to profl. jours. Mem. med. adv. bd. Calif. chpt. Myasthenia Gravis Found., 1971-75, chmn., 1974-75, 77-78; med. adv. bd. Amyotrophic Lateral Sclerosis Found., Calif., 1973-75, chmn., 1974-75; mem. Com. to Combat Huntington's Disease, 1973—; bd. dirs. Calif. Hosp. Med. Ctr., Good Hope Med. Found., Doheny Eye Hosp., House Ear Inst., L.A. Hosp. Good Samaritan, Children's Hosp. of L.A., Barlow Respiratory Hosp., USC U. Hosp., chmn., 1991—; bd. govs. Thomas Aquinas Coll.; bd. dirs. Assn. Acad. Health Ctrs., chmn., 1991-92; pres. Scott Newman Ctr., 1987-89; pres., bd. dirs. Kenneth Norris Cancer Hosp & Rsch. Inst. Served to lt. M.C. USNR, 1956-58. Nobel Inst. fellow Karolinska Inst., Stockholm, 1960-62; NIH grantee, 1968-71. Mem. AMA, Am. Neurol. Assn., Am. Acad. Neurology, L.A. Soc. Neurology and Psychiatry (pres. 1977-78), L.A. Med. Assn., Mass. Med. Soc., Ohio Med. Soc., Calif. Med. Soc., L.A. Acad. Medicine, Alpha Omega Alpha (councillor 1992—), Phi Kappa Phi. Home: 39 Club View Ln Palos Verdes Peninsula CA 90274-4208 Office: U So Calif 1540 Alcazar St Los Angeles CA 90033-1058

VANDER MOLEN, THOMAS DALE, lawyer; b. Ann Arbor, Mich., Oct. 30, 1950; s. John and Eleanor Ruth (Driesens) Vander M.; m. Marlese Kay Alden, June 29, 1974; children: Laura, David, Eric. BA, Calvin Coll., 1972; JD magna cum laude, Harvard U., 1975. Bar: Minn. 1976, U.S. Dist. Ct. Minn. 1981, U.S. Claims Ct. 1983, U.S. Tax Ct. 1977, U.S. Ct. Appeals 1988. Law clk. to judge U.S. Ct. Appeals-First Cir., Boston, 1975-76; assoc. Dorsey & Whitney, Mpls., 1976-81; ptnr. Dorsey & Whitney, P.L.L.P., Mpls., 1982—; gen. counsel, 1993—. Mem. editorial bd. Harvard Law Rev., 1973-75. Mem. Christian Reformed Ch. Office: Dorsey & Whitney PLLP 2100 Pillsbury Ctr S 220 S 6th St Minneapolis MN 55402-1498

VANDER MYDE, PAUL ARTHUR, engineering services executive; b. Estherville, Iowa, Feb. 9, 1937; s. Louis John and Anna Marie (Pals) Vander M.; m. Jeanne Elizabeth Russell, Sept. 8, 1973. BA, U. Minn., 1959; MA, U. Iowa, 1966. Staff asst. Nat. Security Agy., Ft. Meade, Md., 1962-68; congressional fellow U.S. Rep. George Bush/U.S. Senator Bob Packwood, Washington, 1968-69; legis. asst. U.S. Senator Bob Packwood, Washington, 1969-71; exec. asst. Office of Vice-Pres., White House, Washington, 1971-73; staff mem. domestic council White House, Washington, 1973; dep. asst. sec. for conservation, research and edn. U.S. Dept. Agr., Washington, 1973-77; minority staff dir. Sci. and Tech. Com., Ho. of Reps., 1977-81; asst. sec. for congressional and inter-govtl. affairs U.S. Dept. Commerce, Washington, 1981-87; v.p. corp. affairs VSE Corp., Alexandria, Va., 1987—; guest speaker numerous profl. confs. and seminars. Contbr. articles to profl. jours. Bd. dirs. Profl. Svcs. Coun., Washington, U.S. Naval Aviation Mus., Pensacola, Fla; vice chmn. Adminstrv. Conf. of U.S., Washington. With USN, 1959-61; capt. USNR (ret.). Decorated Meritorious Svc. medal. Mem. Naval Res.

Assn., U.S. Navy League, Sovreign Mil. Order Knights Templar of Jerusalem, Belle Haven Country Club, Rotary Club Alexandria. Episcopalian. Office: VSE Corp 2550 Huntington Ave Alexandria VA 22303-1499

VANDERPOOL, ROBERT LEE, JR., banker; b. Galveston, Tex., Nov. 10, 1918; s. R.L. and Felicia (Hussey) V.; m. Mildred Frances Loscalzo, Sept. 23, 1946; children: Janet Ann Vanderpool Haedicke, Robert Lee III. Student, Tex. A&M U., 1935-36; B.B.A., Tulane U., 1941. V.p., dir. Citizens State Bank, Dickinson, Tex., 1946-50; v.p., dir. Ouachita Nat. Bank, Monroe, La., 1951, pres., dir., 1952-85, chmn. bd., 1985-88; chmn. exec. com., dir. La. Bancshares, Inc., Baton Rouge, 1985—. Past pres., bd. dirs. Monroe C. of C., La., 1953; past chmn. ARC fund campaign, Ouachita Parish, 1954, United Givers Fund, 1960; past pres. N.E. La. U. Found., Monroe, 1980. Recipient David C. Silverstein Citizens of Yr. Monroe C. of C., 1975. Mem. La. Bankers Assn. (past pres.), Am. Bankers Assn. Episcopalian. Clubs: Bayour DeSiard Country (Monroe, La.) (past pres.); Lotus (Monroe, La.); Plimsoll (New Orleans).

VANDER PUTTEN, LEROY ANDREW, insurance company executive; b. Appleton, Wis., Aug. 20, 1934; s. Theo S. and Lorraine M. (Quella) Vander P.; m. Evon Marie Schumacher, July 3, 1956; children: Suzanna, Dale, Lisa, Carole, Kim. BS in Math. and Psychology, Wis. State U., 1961; Advanced Mgmt. Program, Harvard U., 1983-84. asst. sec. EDP research Aetna Life & Casualty, Hartford, Conn., 1968-69, asst. cashier, 1969-74, dir. investment planning, 1974-79, asst. v.p. investment planning, 1979-81, v.p. investment planning, 1981-82, v.p. corp. fin., 1982-86, v.p. and deputy treas., 1986-87, chmn., pres., chief exec. officer Exec. Re Idemnity Inc., Simsbury, Conn., 1987-93; chmn., chief exec. officer Exec. RE, Inc., Simsbury, Conn., 1994—, also bd. dirs., 1986—; adv. bd. Conn. Nat. Bank, 1988—; Chmn. South Windsor Econ. Devel. Com., Conn., 1977; trustee Talcott Mountain Sci. Ctr., Avon, Conn. Recipient Distinguished Alumni award U. Wis., 1987—. With USCG, 1952-56. Mem. Fin. Exec. Inst., Am. Council Life Ins. Cos. (chmn. investment reporting sub-com. 1982-83), AMP 91 Assocs. of Boston (treas. 1982—). Republican. Roman Catholic. Avocations: sailing, sports car restoration, canoeing. Office: Exec Risk Inc 82 Hopmeadow St PO Box 2002 Simsbury CT 06070

VANDERRYN, JACK, philanthropic foundation administrator; b. Groningen, The Netherlands, Apr. 14, 1930; came to U.S., 1939; s. Herman Gabriel and Henrietta S.E. (Hartog) V.; m. Margrit Wolfes, Mar. 18, 1956; children: David, Judith, Amy, Daniel. BA, Lehigh U., 1951, MS, 1952, PhD, 1955. Rsch. and grad. teaching asst. Lehigh U., Bethlehem, Pa., 1952-55; asst. prof. chemistry Va. Poly. Inst., Blacksburg, 1955-58; rsch. participant Oak Ridge (Tenn.) Nat. Lab., 1957; chemist AEC, Oak Ridge, 1958-62, tech. adviser to asst. gen. mgr. R & D, Washington, 1962-67, asst. to gen. mgr., 1971-72, tech. asst. to dir. div. applied tech., 1972-73, chief energy tech. br., div. applied tech., 1973-75; acting dir. div. energy storage Energy Rsch. and Devel. Adminstrn., Washington, 1975, dir. Office Internat. R & D Programs, 1975-77; dir. Office Internat. Programs Dept. Energy, Washington, 1977-82; dir. energy and natural resources AID, Washington, 1982-91; program dir. environment Moriah Fund, Chevy Chase, Md., 1991—; sr. sci. adviser U.S. Mission to Internat. Atomic Energy Agy., Dept. State, Vienna, Austria, 1967-71; lectr. Brookings Instn., 1965-66. Mem., dep. pres., exec. bd. Am. Internat. Sch., Vienna, 1968-71; v.p. Oak Ridge Civic Music Assn., 1959-60; pres. Washington Print Club, 1986-91. Fellow AAAS. Home: 8112 Whittier Blvd Bethesda MD 20817-3123 Office: Moriah Fund 35 Wisconsin Cir Chevy Chase MD 20815

VANDERSALL, JOHN HENRY, dairy science educator; b. Helena, Ohio, July 20, 1928; s. Clarence C. and Ida M. (Barnhope) V.; m. Patricia L. King, May 11, 1963; children: Eric John, Karen Susan. BS, Ohio State U., 1950, M.S., 1954, PhD, 1959. Farm researcher Ralston Purina Co., 1950; from research asst. to instr. Ohio State U. Agrl. Expt. Sta., 1953-59; mem. faculty U. Md., 1959—; prof. dairy sci., 1971-93, prof. emeritus, 1993—. Contbr. articles to profl. jours. Served with AUS, 1950-52. Mem. Am. Dairy Sci. Assn., Am. Soc. Animal Sci., AAAS, Sigma Xi. Home: 10906 Ashfield Rd Hyattsville MD 20783-1003 Office: Dept Animal Sci Univ Md College Park MD 20742

VANDERSLICE, JOSEPH THOMAS, chemist; b. Phila., Dec. 21, 1927; s. Joseph R. and Mae (Daly) V.; m. Patricia Mary Horstmann, Nov. 20, 1954; children—Sharon, Joseph, Julie, Peter, John, Polly, Jeffrey, Amy. B.S. in Chemistry, Boston Coll., 1949; Ph.D. in Phys. Chemistry (Allied Chem. and Dye fellow), Mass. Inst. Tech., 1953. Mem. faculty Cath. U. Am., 1952-56, asst. prof., 1955-56; mem. faculty U. Md., College Park, 1956-79, prof. emeritus, 1978—; prof. chem. physics U. Md., 1963-79; dir. U. Md. (Inst. Molecular Physics), 1967-69, chmn. chemistry dept., 1968-76; research chemist Nutrition Inst., U.S. Dept. Agr., Beltsville, Md., 1974-94. Author: (with Schamp and Mason) Thermodynamics, 1966; mem. editorial bd. Jour. Micronutrient Analysis, 1985-91, Food Chemistry, 1992, Food Research International, 1992—; contbr. articles to profl. jours. Inducted into Boston Latin Sch. Athletic Hall of Fame, 1992. Fellow Washington Acad. Scis., Am. Phys. Soc.; mem. AAAS, Am. Inst. Food Technologists, Cosmos Club, Sigma Xi. Home: PO Box 221 Cobb Island MD 20625-0221

VANDERSLICE, THOMAS AQUINAS, electronics executive; b. Phila., Jan. 8, 1932; s. Joseph R. and Mae (Daly) V.; m. Margaret Hurley, June 9, 1956; children: Thomas Aquinas, Paul Thomas Aquinas, John Thomas Aquinas, Peter Thomas Aquinas. BS in Chemistry and Philosophy, Boston Coll., 1953; PhD in Chemistry and Physics, Cath. U. Am., 1956. With GE, Fairfield, Conn., 1956-70, gen. mgr. electronic components bus. div., 1970-72, v.p., 1970, group exec. spl. systems and products group, 1972-77, sr. v.p., sector exec. Power System Sector, 1977-79, exec. v.p. Power System Sector, 1979-84; chief oper. officer, dir. Gen. Tel. & Electronics Corp., Stamford, Conn., 1979-83; chmn., CEO, Apollo Computer, Inc., Chelmsford, Mass., 1984-89, M/A COM, Inc., Lowell, Mass., 1989—; bd. dirs. Texaco, Inc., Storage Tech., Inc. Patentee low pressure gas measurements and analysis, gas surface interactions and elec. discharges; co-author: Ultra High Vacuum and Its Applications, 1963; reviser: Scientific Foundations of Vacuum Technique, 1960; contbr. to profl. jours. Trustee Boston Coll., past chmn.; trustee Com. Econ. Devel. Recipient Bicentennial medal Boston Coll., 1976; Fulbright scholar, 1953-56. Mem. NAE, ASTM, Am. Vacuum Soc., Am. Chem. Soc., Am. Inst. Physics, St. Andrews Golf Club (Scotland), Patterson Club (Fairfield), Royal Poinciana Golf Club (Naples, Fla.), Oyster Harbors Club, Sigma Xi, Tau Beta Pi, Alpha Sigma Nu, Sigma Pi Sigma. Office: M/A COM inc 100 Chelmsford St Lowell MA 01853-3294

VAN DER SMISSEN, M. E. BETTY, educator; b. Great Bend, Kans., Dec. 27, 1927; d. Theodor Alwin and Margaret (Dirks) van der S. AB, U. Kans., 1949, JD, 1952; MS, Ind. U., 1954, D. Recreation, 1955. Bar: Kans. 1952. Asst. prof. U. Iowa, Iowa City, 1956-65; prof. Pa. State U., University Park, 1965-79; dir. sch. health physical edn./prof. recreation Bowling Green (Ohio) State U., 1979-90; prof., chmn. park, recreation and tourism resources Mich. State U., East Lansing, 1990—; mem., 1st chair Nat. Com. for Accreditation of Parks and Recreation Agys. Author: Legal Liability and Risk Management of Public & Private Entities, 1990. Recipient Disting. Fellow award Soc. Park and Recreation Educators, 1974, W.W. Palty Disting. Alumni award Ind. U. Sch. Health, Phys. Edn. and Recreation, 1993. Fellow Acad. Leisure Scis. (founder); mem. AAHPERD (R. Tait McKenzie award 1991), Nat. Recreation and Park Assn. (trustee 1988-90), Am. Acad. Park and Recreation Administration. (bd. dirs. 1990-93), Am. Assn. Leisure and Recreation (Jay B. Nash award 1987), Am. Camping Assn. (nat. pres. 1980-82), Assn. for Experiential Edn. (Kurt Hahn award 1987). Home: 1920 Opaline Dr Lansing MI 48917-8639 Office: Mich State U 131 Natural Resources East Lansing MI 48824-1222

VAN DER SPIEGEL, JAN, engineering educator; b. Aalst, Belgium, Apr. 12, 1951; came to U.S., 1980; s. Robert and Celestine Van der Spiegel. BSEE, U. Leuven, 1971, MSEE, 1974, PhD in Elec. Engring., 1979; M of Arts and Sci., U. Pa., 1988. 2d lt. Belgian Air Force, 1979-90; asst. prof. elec. engring. U. Pa., Phila., 1981-87, assoc. prof., 1987—, dir. Ctr. Sensor Tech., 1989—; Sec., treas. Corticon, Inc., Phila., 1991—; faculty master Ware Coll. Ho., U. Pa., Phila., 1992—. Patentee integ. ambient sensing, radiation sens. retina sens., gen prupost neural comp., novel ferroelectric sensors; editor Sensors and Actuators, 1986—. Postdoctoral fellow

U. Pa., 1980-81; named Presdl. Young Investigator The White House, 1984. Mem. IEEE (sr.), Neural Network Soc., Tau Beta Pi. Office: U Pa Ctr Sensor Techs 200 S 33rd St Rm 308 Moor Philadelphia PA 19104-6314

VANDERSTAPPEN, HARRIE ALBERT, Far Eastern art educator; b. Heesch, The Netherlands, Jan. 21, 1921; came to U.S., 1959; s. Johannes and Johanna (van de Poel) V. Student, Theol. Sch., Helvoirt and Teteringen, The Netherlands, 1939-45, Chinese Lang. Sch., Peking, People's Republic of China, 1946-48; Ph.D. in Far Eastern Art, U. Chgo., 1955. Ordained priest Roman Catholic Ch., 1945. Student lang., also tchr., writer Tokyo, 1955-57; tchr. Nansan U., Nagoya, Japan, 1957-59; prof. Far Eastern art U. Chgo., 1959-92, chmn. dept. art, 1964-69. Author: The T.L. Yuan Bibliography of Chinese Art and Archaeology, 1975; author, editor: Ritual and Reverence, 1989; assoc. editor Monumenta Serica, 1955—; contbr. articles to profl. jours. Recipient Teaching of Art History award Nat. Coll. Art Assn. Am., 1985. Mem. Asia Soc., Assn. Asian Arts. Home: 2147 Bennett Ave Evanston IL 60201-2158

VANDERSTAR, JOHN, lawyer; b. Jersey City, Sept. 17, 1933; s. John Vanderstar and Rosemarie (Torraco) Legette; m. Beth S. Vanderstar, Nov. 7, 1956 (div. Oct. 1984); children: Pippa, Alexandra, Thankful, Eliza. M. Elizabeth Culbreth, Mar. 16, 1985. BSE, Princeton U., 1954; LLB cum laude, Harvard U., 1961. Bar: D.C. 1961, U.S. Dist. Ct. (D.C. dist.) 1961, U.S. Dist. Ct. Md. 1985, U.S. Ct. Claims 1976, U.S. Ct. Appeals (8th cir.) 1966, U.S. Ct. Appeals (5th cir.) 1969, U.S. Ct. Appeals (1st cir.) 1971, U.S. Ct. Appeals (4th cir.) 1974, U.S. Ct. Appeals (3d cir.) 1979, U.S. Ct. Appeals 11th cir.) 1981, U.S. Ct. Appeals (Fed. cir.) 1983, U.S. Supreme Ct. 1966. Assoc. Covington & Burling, Washington, 1961-70, ptnr., 1970—. Pres. ACLU Nat. Capital Area, Washington, 1976-78, bd. dirs., 1971-78; bd. dirs. NOW Legal Def. and Edn. Fund, N.Y.C., 1974-84. Lt. USNR, 1954-58. Recipient Alan Barth award, ACLU Nat. Capital Area, 1984. Mem. ABA, D.C. Bar (bd. govs. 1985-88). Episcopalian. Home: 3642 N Monroe St Arlington VA 22207-5317 Office: Covington & Burling 1201 Pennsylvania Ave NW PO Box 7566 Washington DC 20044

VANDERVEEN, JOHN E., federal agency administrator; b. Prospect Park, N.J., May 13, 1934; m. Ernestine Neuhardt, June 3, 1967; children: Keith Bradley, Kimetha Leigh. BS, Rutgers U., 1956; PhD, U. N.H., 1961. Nutritionist USAF, 1961-75; dir. divsn. nutrition FDA, Washington, 1975-92, dir. office plant & dairy foods and beverages, 1992—. 1st lt. USAF, 1961-64. Office: FDA-Center for Food Safety & Applied Nutrition 200 C St SW Washington DC 20204-0001

VANDERVEEN, PETER, wholesale grocery company executive; b. 1931; married. LLB, U. Fla., 1949. With Hood Chem. Co., 1955-62; sales mgr. Fox Grocery Co., 1962-72; asst. to pres. Super Rite Foods, Inc., Harrisburg, Pa., 1977-80, pres., dir., 1980—. Office: Super Rite Foods Inc 3900 Industrial Rd Harrisburg PA 17110-2945

VAN DERVEER, TARA, university athletic coach. Coach women's basketball Stanford U. Cardinals, 1985—, U.S. Nat. Women's Team, 1995—. Champions NCAA Divsn. 1 A, 1990, 92. Office: c/o Stanford Univ Stanford CA 94305*

VANDERVELD, JOHN, JR., waste disposal company executive; b. Chgo., Oct. 24, 1926; s. John J. and Rose (Renkema) V. Pres. Nat. Disposal Contractors, Barrington, Ill., 1952-71; sr. v.p., dir. Browning Ferris Industries, Houston, 1971-78; pres. Pioneer Equities, Inc., 1975-90, C.J.V. Corp., Dallas, 1990-92; sr. corp. advisor Vector Environmental Techs., Inc., 1993—; dir. Am. Far East, Inc., Dallas and Tokyo; adv. bd. Southwestern Legal Found. Bd. dirs., exec. com. Internat. Bible Soc. Mem. Nat. Solid Waste Mgmt. Assn. (former chmn. govt. industry coordinating council, mem. environ. research com.). Home: 7031 Brookshire Dr Dallas TX 75230-4248

VANDER VELDE, WALLACE EARL, aeronautical and astronautical educator; b. Jamestown, Mich., June 4, 1929; s. Peter Nelson and Janet (Keizer) Vander V.; m. Winifred Helen Bunai, Aug. 29, 1954; children—Susan Jane, Peter Russell. B.S. in Aero Engring., Purdue U., 1951; Sc.D., Mass. Inst. Tech., 1956. Dir. applications engring. GPS Instrument Co., Inc., Newton, Mass., 1956-57; mem. faculty Mass. Inst. Tech., 1957—, prof. aero. and astronautics, 1965—; Cons. to industry, 1958—. Author: Flight Vehicle Control Systems, Part VII of Space Navigation, Guidance and Control, 1966, (with Arthur Gelb) Multiple-Input Describing Functions, 1968; also papers. Served to 1st lt. USAF, 1951-53. Recipient Edn. award Am. Automatic Control Coun., 1988. Fellow AIAA; mem. IEEE. Home: 50 High St Winchester MA 01890-3314 Office: MIT Rm 9-321 Cambridge MA 02139

VANDERVER, TIMOTHY ARTHUR, JR., lawyer; b. Birmingham, Ala., Jan. 25, 1944; s. Timothy Arthur and Jeanette (Grimes) V.; m. Virginia Cassandra Nye, Oct. 1, 1966; children: Timothy A. III, Glenn Bruce, Benjamin Richard. BA, Washington and Lee U., 1965; BA in Law, Oxford (Eng.) U., 1967, MA, 1983; JD, Harvard U., 1969. Bar: D.C., U.S. Ct. Appeals (D.C. cir.) 1969, U.S. Ct. Appeals (5th cir.) 1984, U.S. Ct. Appeals (3d and 11th cirs.) 1989, U.S. Supreme Ct. 1978. Assoc. Covington & Burling, Washington, 1969-72, Dept. of Interior, Washington, 1972-76; ptnr. Patton Boggs L.L.P., Washington, 1976—. Editor: Clean Air Law and Regulation, 1992, Environmental Law Handbook, 1994. Capt. U.S. Army, 1970-71. Presbyterian. Home: 9000 Congressional Ct Potomac MD 20854 Office: Patton Boggs L.L.P. 2550 M St NW Washington DC 20037

VAN DER VOO, ROB, geophysicist; b. Zeist, The Netherlands, Aug. 4, 1940; came to U.S., 1970; s. Maximiliaan and Johanna Hendrika (Baggerman) Van der V.; m. Tatiana M. C. Graafland, Mar. 26, 1966; children—Serge Nicholas, Bjorn Alexander. B.S., U. Utrecht, Netherlands, 1961, M.S., 1965, Ph.D., 1969. Research asst. U. Utrecht, 1964-65, research asso., 1965-69, sr. research asso., 1969-70; vis. asst. prof. U. Mich., Ann Arbor, 1970-72; asst. prof. U. Mich., 1972-75, asso. prof., 1975-79, prof. geophysics, 1979—, chmn., 1981-88, 91-95, Arthur F. Thurnau prof., 1994—; guest prof. ETH, Zurich, Switzerland, 1978, Kuwait U., 1979. Author: Paleomagnetism of the Atlantic, Tethys and Iapetus Oceans, 1993; contbr. articles to profl. jours. Recipient Russel award U. Mich., 1976, Disting. Faculty Achievement award U.Mich., 1990. Mem. Geol. Soc. Am., Am. Geophys. Union, Geologische Vereiningug (W.Ger.), Royal Dutch Geol. and Mining Soc., Royal Acad. Scis. (Netherlands), Sigma Xi, Phi Kappa Phi. Home: 2305 Devonshire Ann Arbor MI 48104-2703 Office: U Mich 4528 CC Little Bldg Ann Arbor MI 48109

VANDER VOORT, DALE GILBERT, textile company executive; b. Paterson, N.J., Feb. 7, 1924; s. Gilbert H. and Lillian (Hatton) Vander V.; m. Florine E. Storey, Aug. 6, 1944; children: Lydia Ann, Dale Gilbert, Roy Lee. B.M.E., Clemson U., 1944. Gen. mgr., dir. Stevens Line Assos., Webster, Mass., 1954-56; gen. mgr. Montreal Cottons Ltd., Valleyfield, Que., Can., 1951-54; supt. Mill 4 Dan River Mills, Danville, Va., 1946-51; sr. v.p. United Merchants & Mfrs. Inc., N.Y.C., 1972-77; chmn. bd. Asso. Textiles Can. Ltd., 1969-77; pres., chief exec. officer Arnold Print Works, Inc., Adams, Mass., 1977-83, Alton Fabrics, Allentown, Pa., 1983-85; pres. Asheville Dye & Finishing, Swannanoa, N.C., 1985-87; pres., chief exec. officer River Dyeing and Finishing Co., Asheville, N.C., 1988—; dir. Northwestern Bank, Asheville, N.C., Western Carolina Industries Inc., Brit. Silk Dyeing Co., Valchem Australia, Profile Sports Corp., West Lebanon, N.H. Mem. coun. Luth. Ch., 1962—. Lt. AUS, 1943-46. Decorated Bronze Star, Purple Heart. Mem. ASME, Am. Assn. Textile Chemists and Colorists, Can. Textile Inst. (dir.), Soc. Advancement of Mgmt. (nat. gov. 1961-62), Can. Club (N.Y.), Asheville Country Club. Home: 214 Stratford Rd Asheville NC 28804-1440 also: 131 Riverside Dr Asheville NC 28801

VANDERVOORT, PETER, lawyer; b. Paterson, N.J., Dec. 15, 1929; s. Vincent and Jeannette Barbara (Scott) V.; m. Elena Drake, June 26, 1971. BA, Williams Coll., 1951; LLB, U. Va., 1954. Bar: Va. 1953, N.J. 1958. Assoc. Evans Hand, Paterson, 1958-62; ptnr. Evans Hand, West Paterson, N.J., 1963—; asst. sec. Essex Chem. Corp., Clifton, N.J., 1963-83, sec., 1983-88. Trustee West Side Presbyn. Ch., Ridgewood, N.J., 1961-67, Family Counselling Service of Ridgewood, 1968-77, Soc. Valley Hosp., Ridgewood, 1976-88; vice chmn. Valley Care Corp., 1988—; bd. dirs.

Paterson YMCA, 1959-76, pres. 1967-74, trustee 1978—, chmn. 1984-88. Fellow Am. Coll. Trust and Estate Counsel; mem. ABA, N.J. Bar Assn., Va. Bar Assn., Ridgewood Country Club, Upper Ridgewood Tennis Club (sec. 1960-61), Williams Club (N.Y.C.), Union League Club (N.Y.C.), Order of Coif, Phi Beta Kappa. Home: 376 Beechwood Rd Ridgewood NJ 07450-2308 Office: Evans Hand 8th Fl 1 Garret Mountain Plz West Paterson NJ 07424-3318

VANDER WEELE, RAY, religious organization administrator. Adminstr. Min. Pension Fund. Office: Christian reformed ch in N Am 2850 Kalamazoo Ave SE Grand Rapids MI 49560

VANDERWEIL, RAIMUND GERHARD, JR., consulting firm executive, mechanical engineer; b. Neptune, N.J., Nov. 21, 1940; s. Raimund Gerhard and Janet Stelle (Letson) V.; m. Anne Stuart Hinshaw, Oct. 10, 1970; children: Alexander Raimund, Shelley McMillan, Stefan Gerhard. AB in Engring. and Applied Physics, Harvard U., 1961; MSME, MIT, 1963. Registered profl engr. 20 states. Research asst. MIT, Cambridge, Mass., 1961-63; engr. Lockheed MSC, Sunnyvale, Calif., 1963-65, Atomic Power Dept. Gen. Electric, San Jose, Calif., 1965-67; pres. R.G. Vanderweil, Engrs., Boston, 1967—. Mem. ASME, ASHRAE, Nat. Soc. Profl. Engrs., Mass. Soc. Profl. Engrs. (Young Engr. of Yr., 1976). Club: Harvard (Boston). Home: 500 Jerusalem Rd Cohasset MA 02025-1148 Office: R G Vanderweil Engrs Inc 266 Summer St Boston MA 02210-1112

VANDER WIEL, KENNETH CARLTON, computer services company executive; b. Sheldon, Iowa, July 6, 1933; s. Sylvan Vander Wiel and Irene F. (Weekley) Taylor; m. Loretta Marie Smith, Aug. 28, 1969; children: Gretchen G., Alison June, Joseph W., Carol Ann, Andrea., Beth L., David. BA, Bowling Green U., 1955. With mgmt. devel. Dayton (Ohio) Power & Light, 1955-68; cons. G.W. Young & Assocs., Dayton, 1968-69; pres. Datamac Corp., Dayton, 1970-84, Carlton Leasing Co., 1975—, The Carlton Systems Group, Dayton, 1984-89, Carlton Computer Systems, Inc., Dayton, 1989-95; CEO Carlton Computer Systems, Inc., Tampa, Fla., 1993-95; pres. Interlogic Systems of Dayton, Inc., 1995—. Chmn. Montgomery County Data Processing Task Force, Dayton, 1982. With USN, 1955-57. Recipient Commendations, Montgomery County Commn., Dayton, 1982, Dayton Execs. Club, 1986. Mem. Dayton Area C. of C. (nat. affairs com., state legis. com.), Nat. Assn. Mfg. (nat. affairs com.), Dayton Engrs. Club. Avocations: sailing, fishing, travel.

VANDER WILT, CARL EUGENE, banker; b. Ottumwa, Iowa, Aug. 17, 1942; s. John Adrian and Wilma (Hulsbos) V w. Carol Anne Szymanski, Jan. 29, 1977; children—Dirk Francis, Neal Adrian. BS, Iowa State U., 1964, PhD, 1968; grad. Advanced Mgmt. Program, Harvard U., 1986. Research economist Fed. Res. Bank, Chgo., 1970-73, asst. v.p., 1973-74, v.p., 1974-79, sr. v.p., 1979-84, sr. v.p., chief fin. officer, 1984—. Chmn. bd. dirs. Goodwill Industries Met. Chgo. Served to capt. U.S. Army, 1968-70. Mem. Execs. Club Chgo. (dir., chmn. reception com.), Banker's Club Chgo., Econ. Club Chgo. Home: 663 Garland Ave Winnetka IL 60093-3911 Office: Fed Res Bank 230 S La Salle St Chicago IL 60604-1496

VANDERWOUDE, J. STEPHEN, communications company executive; b. 1944. BS, Ohio U., 1967; MBA, U Chgo., 1978. Engr. Gen. Ry. Signal Co., 1955-66; with N.Y. Tel. Co., 1967-71, Centel Corp. (now Sprint Corp.), Chgo., 1971-93; group v.p. Centel Corp., Chgo., 1982-86; pres. Centel Bus. Systems, Chgo., 1986-87; exec. v.p. Centel Corp., Chgo., 1987-89; pres., dir. Centel Corp. (now Sprint Corp.), Chgo., 1989-93; pres. local telecom divsn. Sprint Corp., Kansas City, Mo., 1993, Westwood, Kans., 1993; bd. dirs. Rehab. Inst. Chgo., First Midwest Bancorp Inc. Home: Secret Keel Farm PO Box 1735 Southern Pines NC 28388-1735

VANDEUSEN, BRUCE DUDLEY, company executive; b. Lorain, Ohio, Aug. 20, 1931; s. Clarence Elmer and Margaret (Richards) VanD.; m. Ann Marie Groves, Aug. 17, 1957; children: David Bruce, Elizabeth Ann. Janet Marie. B.A., Ohio Wesleyan U., 1952; M.S., U. Mich., 1958, Ph.D., 1971; M.A.E., Chrysler Inst. Engring., Highland Park, Mich., 1958. Registered profl. engr., Mich. Fellow Ohio State U., Columbus, 1953-54; student engr. Chrysler Corp., Highland Park, 1956-58, sr. research scientist, 1958-67; chief engr. Chrysler Def., Inc., Center Line, Mich., 1967-79, mgr. advanced devel., 1979-82; dir. advanced devel. Gen. Dynamics, Warren, Mich., 1982-87, program dir., 1987-93; pres. Edn. Svcs., Birmingham, Mich., 1994—. Contbr. numerous articles to profl. publs.; patentee electronic cirs. Trustee Birmingham Bd. Edn., Mich., 1976-88, pres., 1979-84, 87-88; trustee Birmingham Community House, 1981-87. Mem. Soc. Automotive Engrs. (chmn. sci. engring. activity 1967-69 Arch T. Colwell), Am. Def. Preparedness Assn., Assn. U.S. Army. Republican. Methodist. Home: 1492 W Lincoln St Birmingham MI 48009-1830 Office: Edn Svcs PO Box 170 Birmingham MI 48012-0170

VANDEVEER, MICHAEL D., city official; b. Evansville, Ind., Aug. 22, 1941; s. Adolphus William and Mary Lucinda (Smith) V.; m. Melissa Lois Malone; children—Lee, Emily. A.B. in Polit. Sci., Washington U., St. Louis, 1963; postgrad., Georgetown U., 1964-66. At-large rep. Evansville (Ind.) City Council, 1975-79; mayor City of Evansville, Ind., 1979—; chmn. urban hwys. com. U.S. Conf. Mayors, 1982—, Evansville Urban Transp. Study, 1986—, Vanderburgh County (Ind.) Dem. Central Com., 1982—. Chmn. Ind. Democratic Mayor's Caucus, 1980-85. Served to SP4 USAR, 1966-72. Recipient upper dir. honor scholarship Washington U., 1961-63, Disting. Leadership Award Ind. Planning Assn., 1986. Mem. Nat. League Cities (transp. com.), Ind. Assn. Cities and Towns (chmn. legis. com.). Presbyterian. Avocations: reading, tennis, travel, politics, cooking. Office: City Hall Civic Ctr Rm 302 Evansville IN 47708

VANDEVENDER, BARBARA JEWELL, elementary education educator, farmer; b. Trenton, Mo., Dec. 4, 1929; d. Raleigh Leon and Rose Rea (Dryer) S.; m. Delbert Lyle Vandevender, Aug. 15, 1948; children: Lyle Gail, James R. BS, N.E. Mo. State U., 1971, MA, 1973. Elem. tchr. Williams Sch., Spickard, Mo., 1948-49; reading specialist Spikard R-2 Sch., 1971-74, Princeton (Mo.) R-5 Sch., 1974-89; spkr. Mo. State Coun. of IRA, Columbia, 1987-89, Plains area IRA, 1988; mem. ad hoc com. Mo. State Dept. Edn., Jefferson City, 1994. Pres. Spickard PTA, 1963-64, Women's Ext. Club, Galt, Mo.; foster mother Family Svcs., Trenton, Mi., 1972-79; mem. ad hoc com. State Dept. of Edn., Jefferson City, Mo., 1994-95. Pres. Spickard PTA, 1963-64, Women's Ext. Club, Galt, Mo.; foster mother Family Svcs., Trenton, Mo., 1972-79; mem. ad hoc com. State Dept. Edn., Jefferson City. Recipient Mo. State Conservation award Goodyear Tire Co., Akron, Ohio, 1972, Balanced Farming award Gulf Oil Co., N.Y.C., 1972, Mo. State Farming award Kansas City C. of C., 1974, FHA State Farming award, Jefferson City, Mo., 1974, Outstanding Leadership Mo. U., Columbia, 1976, Ednl. Leadership award MSTA, Columbia, 1984, Outstanding Contbn. to Internat. Reading Assn., Newark, Del., 1988. Mem. Internat. Reading Assn. (pres. North Ctrl. coun. 1985-86). Republican. Baptist.

VAN DEVENDER, J. PACE, physical scientist; b. Jackson, Miss., Sept. 12, 1947; m. Nancy Jane Manning, 1971; 3 children. BA in Physics, Vanderbilt U., 1969; MA in Physics, Dartmouth Coll., 1971; PhD in Physics, U. London, 1974. Physicist diagnostics devel. Lawrence Livermore Lab., 1969; mem. tech. staff pulsed power rsch. and devel. Sandia Nat. Labs., 1974-78, divsn. supr. pulsed power rsch. divsn., 1978-82, dept. mgr. fusion rsch., 1982-84; dir. pulsed power scis. Sandia Nat. Labs., Albuquerque, 1984-93, dir. corp. comm., 1993, dir. Nat. Indsl. Alliances Ctr., 1993—; mem. rev. bd. Compact Ignition Tokomak, Sandia Labs. rep., 1988—. Mem. editorial bd. Laser and Particle Beams, 1987-90. Mem. bd. trust Vanderbilt U., 1969-73. With U.S. Army, 1969-71. Recipient Ernest Orlando Lawrence Meml. award U.S. Dept. Energy, 1991; named one of 100 Most Promising Scientists Under 40, Sci. Digest, 1984; Marshal scholar U. London, 1971-74. Fellow Am. Phys. Soc.; mem. NAS (mem. bd. naval studies 1990-93), Phi Beta Kappa, Omicron Delta Kappa, Sigma Xi. Home: 7604 Lamplighter Ln NE Albuquerque NM 87109 Office: Sandia Nat Lab Nat Industrial Alliance Ctr Albuquerque NM 87185-5800

VAN DEVENTER, ARIE PIETER, agricultural engineer; b. Hardinxveld-Giessendam, The Netherlands, June 11, 1963; m. Corine Margreet Geljon,

Aug. 25, 1989; 1 child, Raisa Céline. BS, MS in Soil and Water Engring., Agrl. U. Wageningen, The Netherlands, 1981-88; PhD in Agrl. Engring., Ohio State U., 1992. Rsch. assoc. Ohio State U., Columbus, 1989-92, postdoctoral rsch. dept. agrl. engring., 1992-93; cons. dept. remote sensing and digital photogrammetry Grontmij Geogroep, Roosendaal, The Netherlands, 1993-95, head dept. geodata, 1995—; chmn. Interest Group on Global Understanding, 1991-93; treas. Stichting Auto Reizen Indonesia, 1993—. Contbr. articles to profl. jours. Mem. Am. Soc. Agrl. Engrs. (Robert E. Stewart Engring. Humanities award 1993), Am. Soc. Photogrammetry and Remote Sensing, Gamma Sigma Delta, Alpha Epsilon, Phi Kappa Phi, Phi Beta Delta. Home: Zuivelstraat 35a, 4611 PE Bergen op Zoom The Netherlands Office: Grontmij Geogroep, Postbus 1747, 4700 BS Roosendaal The Netherlands

VANDEVER, WILLIAM DIRK, lawyer; b. Chgo., Aug. 1, 1949; s. Lester J. and Elizabeth J. V.; m. Kathi J. Zellmer, Aug. 26, 1983; children: Barton Dirk, Brooke Shelby. BS, U. Mo., Kansas City, 1971, JD with distinction, 1974. Bar: Mo. 1975, U.S. Dist. Ct. (we. dist.) Mo. 1975. Dir. Popham Law Firm, Kansas City, Mo., 1975—; lectr. medicine, engring. and multiple CLE various hosps. and colls., Kansas City Mo. 1979—. Issue editor U. Mo.-Kansas City Law Rev., 1974. Mem. ABA, Am. Trial Lawyers Assn., Mo. Assn. Trial Attys., Kansas City Met. Bar Assn. (treas., sec., pres., exec. com. 1986—, elected to 16th Jud. Commn. 1988—), Kansas City Bar Found. (treas. 1992, sec. 1994), Interest on Lawyer Trust Accts. of Mo. (bd. govs.), Kansas City Mem. Svcs. (pres. 1988—, commr. 16th jud. cir. selection com.), Phi Delta Phi, Beta Theta Pi. Avocations: tennis, skiing, running, reading. Home: 11380 W 121st Ter Shawnee Mission KS 66213-1978 Office: Popham Law Firm 1300 Commerce Trust Bldg Kansas City MO 64106

VAN DE VYVER, SISTER MARY FRANCILENE, academic administrator; b. Detroit, Sept. 6, 1941; d. Hector Joseph and Irene Cecilia (Zygailo) V. BA, Madonna Coll., 1965; MEd, Wayne State U., 1970, PhD, 1977. Joined Sisters of St. Felix of Cantalice, Roman Cath. Ch., 1967. Tchr. Ladywood High Sch., 1965-74; adminstrv. asst. to pres. Madonna Coll., Livonia, Mich., 1974-75, acad. dean, 1975-76; now pres. Madonna U., Livonia, Mich. Office: Madonna U Office of President 36600 Schoolcraft Rd Livonia MI 48150-1176

VAN DE WALLE, ETIENNE, demographer; b. Namur, Belgium, Apr. 29, 1932; came to U.S., 1961; s. Arnould and Yolande (Blommaert) Van De W.; m. Francine Robyns de Schneidauer, Aug. 24, 1955; children: Dominique, Nicolas, Jean-Francois, Patrice. Dr. in Law, U. Louvain, Belgium, 1956, MA in Econs., 1957, PhD in Demography, 1973. Researcher Irsac, Rwanda, Burundi, 1957-61; rsch. assoc. Princeton (N.J.) U., 1962-64, rsch. staff, 1964-67, rsch. demographer, 1967-72; vis. lectr. U. Calif., Berkeley, 1971-72; prof. U. Pa., Phila., 1972—; dir. Population Studies Ctr., U. Pa. 1976-82; sr. assoc. The Population Coun., Bamako, Mali, 1982. Author: The Female Population of France, 1974; co-author: The Demography of Tropical Africa, 1968. Fellowship Woodrow Wilson Ctr. for Scholars, 1976. Mem. Internat. Union for Scientific Study of Population, Population Assn. of Am. (pres. 1992). Home: 261 Sycamore Ave Merion Station PA 19066-1545 Office: Population Studies Ctr 3718 Locust Walk Philadelphia PA 19104-6209

VANDEWALLE, GERALD WAYNE, state supreme court chief justice; b. Noonan, N.D., Aug. 15, 1933; s. Jules C. and Blanche Marie (Gits) VandeW. B.Sc., U. N.D., 1955, J.D., 1958. Bar: N.D., U.S. Dist. Ct. N.D. 1959. Spl. asst. atty. gen. State of N.D., Bismarck, 1958-75, 1st asst. atty. gen., 1975-78; justice N.D. Supreme Ct., 1978-92, chief justice, 1993—; mem. faculty Bismarck Jr. Coll., 1972-76. Editor-in-chief N.D. Law Rev, 1957-58. Active Bismarck Meals on Wheels. Recipient Sioux award U. N.D., 1992. Mem. State Bar Assn. N.D., Burleigh County Bar Assn., ABA (co-chair bar admissions com.), Am. Contract Bridge League, Order of Coif, N.D. Jud. Conf. (exec. com.), Phi Eta Sigma, Beta Alpha Psi, Beta Gamma Sigma, Phi Alpha Delta. Roman Catholic. Clubs: Elks, K.C. Office: ND Supreme Ct State Capitol 600 E Boulevard Ave Bismarck ND 58505-0660

VANDEWATER, DAVID, hospital administrator. With Clearlake Hospital, 1975-78, Hospital Affiliates Internat., 1978-82, Republic Health Corp., 1982-90; pres. Columbia Healthcare Corp, Louisville, 1992—. Office: Columbia/HCA Healthcare Corp 201 West Main St PO Box 740033 Louisville KY 40201-7433

VAN DE WETERING, JOHN E(DWARD), college president; b. Bellingham, Wash., Jan. 20, 1927; s. John and Jessie Van De W.; m. Maxine Schorr, Mar. 7, 1961; 1 son, Josh. B.A in History, U. Wash., 1950, M.A. in History, 1953, Ph.D. in History, 1959. Instr. U. Idaho, 1959; instr. U. Wash., 1959-61, vis. asst. prof. history, 1963; asst. prof. U. Mont., 1961-64, asso. prof., 1964-69, prof., chmn. dept. history, 1969-76; acting pres. Eastern Mont. Coll., 1976-77, pres., 1977-81; pres. SUNY, Coll. at Brockport, 1981—; mem. Mont. Com. for Humanities, 1972-74; Danforth asso. Author: (with Jack Bumsted) What Must I Do to Be Saved? : The Great Awakening in Colonial America, 1976; contbr. articles to profl. jours. Bd. dirs. Park Ridge Hosp., Rochester, N.Y., George Eastman House Mus. Photography, Rochester, Rochester Area Ednl. TV Assn. Served with C.E. U.S. Army, 1955-57. Home: 230 Holley St Brockport NY 14420-2124 Office: SUNY Coll at Brockport Office of Pres Brockport NY 14420

VANDE WOUDE, GEORGE FRANKLIN, molecular biologist, cancer researcher; b. Brooklyn, N.Y., Dec. 25, 1935; s. George Franklin Sr. and Alice Beatrice (Leudesdorff) V.W.; m. Dorothy Helen Stapel, Apr. 5, 1959; children: Susan Joan, Gail Louise, Cynthia Irene, Alice Helene. Student, Hope Coll., 1953-54; BA, Hofstra U., 1959; MS, Rutgers U., 1962, PhD, 1964. Postdoctoral rsch. assoc. USDA Plum Island, Greenport, N.Y., 1964-65, rsch. scientist, 1965-72; chief virus tumor biochemistry Nat. Cancer Inst. NIH, Bethesda, Md., 1972-81, chief lab. molecular oncology, 1981-83; dir. basic rsch. program Nat. Cancer Inst.-Frederick (Md.) Cancer R & D Ctr., 1983—. Contbr. over 100 articles and sci. papers to profl. publs., 35 book chpts. Recipient Robert J. and Claire Pasarow Found. award, 1989. Mem. AAAS, Am. Soc. for Microbiology, Am. Assn. for Cancer Rsch. Achievements include research in fields of biology and cancer. Office: NCI Frederick Cancer R & D Ctr-Basic Rsch Program PO Box B Frederick MD 21702-1201

VAN DINE, HAROLD FORSTER, JR., architect; b. New Haven, Aug. 28, 1930; s. Harold Forster and Marguerite Anna (Eichstedt) Van D.; m. Maureen Kallick, Mar. 1, 1983; children by previous marriage: Rebecca Van Dine, Stephanie Van Dine Natale, Gretchen Van Dine Natale. BA, Yale U., 1952, MArch, 1958. Registered architect. Designer Minoru Yamasaki & Assocs., Detroit, 1958-60; chief designer Gunnar Birkerts & Assocs., Detroit, 1960-67; prin. Straub, Van Dine & Assocs., Troy, Mich., 1967-80; chief architecture and design officer Harley Ellington, Pierce, Yee & Assocs., Southfield, Mich., 1980-95; archtl. design cons. Birmingham, Mich., 1995—; v.p. Fields, Devereaux, HEPY, L.A., 1984-95. Prin. works include Mcpl. Libr., Troy, Mich., campuses for Oakland (Mich.) Community Coll., North Hills Ch., Troy, First Ctr. Office Plaza, chemistry bldgs at. U. Mich. and Ind. U., G.M.F. Robotics Hdqrs., Flint Ink Rsch. and Devel. Ctr., Comerica Bank Ops. Ctr., Christ the King Mausoleum, Chgo., Resurrection Mausoleum, Staten Island, Mich. Biotech Inst., Ford Sci. Rsch. Labs, Fetzer Inst. Hdqrs. and Retreat Ctr., Cen. Mich. U. Music Sch., Oakland U. Sci. Techs. Bldg., Mead Corp. Rsch. Ctr., Dayton, Ohio, Corning (N.Y.) Credit Union. Bd. dirs. Cultural Coun. Birmingham/Bloomfield, 1990—. Served to lt. (j.g.) USN, 1952-55. Recipient Book award AIA, 1958, Excellence in Architecture Silver medal AIA, 1958, Gold medal Detroit chpt. AIA, 1987, Mich. Soc. of Architects gold medal, 1991, over 50 major design awards; William Wirt Winchester travelling fellowship Yale U. Sch. Architecture, 1958; elect. to AIA Coll. Fellows, 1979. Mem. Pewabic Soc. (bd. dirs. 1983—). Home and Office: 544 S Bates St Birmingham MI 48009-1423

VAN DINE, VANCE, investment banker; b. San Francisco, July 2, 1925; s. Melvin Everett and Grace Winifred (Harris) Van D.; m. Isabel Erskine Brewster, Sept. 8, 1956; 1 dau., Rose M. (dec.). BA, Yale U., 1949; LLB, NYU, 1955. Assoc. Morgan Stanley & Co., N.Y.C., 1953-59, 61-63; ptnr. Morgan Stanley & Co., 1963-75; mng. dir. Morgan Stanley & Co., N.Y.C., 1970-83, adv. dir., 1983—; cons. Internat. Bank for Reconstn. and Devel., 1959-61; chmn. Doane Western Co. Author: The Role of the Investment Banker in International Transactions, 1970, The U.S. Market After Controls,

1974. Bd. dirs. Yale U. Alumni Fund, Rec. for Blind, Inc., N.Y.C., 1979-89; trustee L.I. U., 1979-91, Cancer Rsch. Inst., N.Y.C., Nassau County Art Mus.; gov. dir. Fgn. Policy Assn., 1980-89. With USN, 1943-46. Recipient Yale Class of 1949 Disting. Service award, 1983. Mem. The Pilgrims of the U.S. Republican. Episcopalian. Clubs: Union, Piping Rock, N.Y. Yacht, Seawanhaka Corinthian Yacht, Church, Yale of N.Y.C, Met. Opera, Pilgrims of U.S. Office: Morgan Stanley & Co 1251 Avenue Of The Americas New York NY 10020-1104

VANDIVER, FRANCES, principal. Prin. Coral Springs (Fla.) Mid. Sch. Recipient Blue Ribbon Sch. award, 1990-91. Office: Coral Springs Mid Sch 10300 Wiles Rd Coral Springs FL 33076-2003

VANDIVER, FRANK EVERSON, institute administrator, former university president, author, educator; b. Austin, Tex., Dec. 9, 1925; s. Harry Shultz and Maude Folmsbee (Everson) V.; m. Carol Sue Smith, Apr. 19, 1952 (dec. 1979); children: Nita, Nancy, Frank Alexander; m. Renée Aubry, Mar. 21, 1980. Rockefeller fellow in humanities, U. Tex., 1946-47, Rockefeller fellow in Am. Studies, 1947-48, MA, 1949; PhD, Tulane U., 1951; MA (by decree), Oxford (Eng.) U., 1963; HHD (hon.), Austin Coll., 1977; DHL (hon.), Lincoln Coll., 1989, BA (hon.), 1994. Apptd. historian Army Service Forces Depot, Civil Service, San Antonio, 1944-45, Air U., 1951; prof. history La. State U., summers 1953-57; asst. prof. history Washington U., St. Louis, 1952-55; asst. prof. history Rice U., Houston, 1955-56, assoc. prof., 1956-58, prof., 1958-65, Harris Masterson Jr. prof. history, 1965-79, chmn. dept. history and polit. sci., 1962-63, dept. history, 1968-69, acting pres., 1969-70, provost, 1970-79, v.p., 1975-79; pres., chancellor N. Tex. State U., Denton and Tex. Coll. Osteo. Medicine, 1979-81; pres. Tex. A&M U., College Station, 1981-88, pres. emeritus, disting. U. prof., 1988—; founding pres. Acad. Marshall Plan, 1992; Harmsworth prof. Am. history Oxford U., 1963-64; vis. prof. history U. Ariz., summer 1961; master Margarett Root Brown Coll., Rice U., 1964-66; Harman lectr. Air Force Acad., 1963; Keese lectr. U. Chattanooga, 1967; Fortenbaugh lectr. Gettysburg Coll., 1974; Phi Beta Kappa assoc. lectr., 1970—; vis. prof. mil. history U.S. Mil. Acad., 1973-74; hon. pres. Occidental U., St. Louis, 1975-80; chmn. bd. Am. U. Cairo, 1992—. Editor: The Civil War Diary of General Josiah Gorgas, 1947, Confederate Blockade Running Through Bermuda, 1861-65: Letters and Cargo Manifests, 1947, Proceedings of First Confederate Congress, 4th Session, 1953, Proceedings of Second Confederate Congress, 1959, A Collection of Louisiana Confederate Letters; new edit, J.E. Johnston's Narrative of Military Operations; new edit, J.A. Early's Civil War Memoirs, The Idea of the South, 1964; author: Ploughshares Into Swords: Josiah Gorgas and Confederate Ordnance, 1952, Rebel Brass: The Confederate Command System, 1956, Mighty Stonewall, 1957, Fields of Glory, (with W. H. Nelson), 1960, Jubal's Raid, 1960, Basic History of the Confederacy, 1962, Jefferson Davis and the Confederate State, 1964, Their Tattered Flags: The Epic of the Confederacy, 1970, The Southwest: South or West?, 1975, Black Jack: The Life and Times of John J. Pershing, 1977 (Nat. Book Award finalist 1978), (address) The Long Loom of Lincoln, 1986, Blood Brothers: A Short History of the Civil War, 1992; also hist. articles.; mem. bd. editors: U.S. Grant Papers, 1973—. Mem. bd. trustees Am. U. in Cairo, 1988, chmn., 1992—. Recipient rsch. grants Am. Philos. Soc., 1953, 54, 60; Guggenheim fellow, 1955-56; Huntington Libr. rsch. grant, 1961; laureate Lincoln Acad., Ill., 1973; Carr P. Collins prize Tex. Inst. Letters, 1958, Harry S. Truman award Kansas City Civil War Round Table, Jefferson Davis award Confederate Meml. Lit. Soc., 1970, Fletcher Pratt award N.Y. Civil War Round Table, 1970, First Outstanding Alumnus award Tulane U. Grad. Sch., 1974, Outstanding Civilian Service medal Dept. Army, 1974, Nevins-Freeman award Chgo. Civil War Round Table, 1982, T. Harry Williams Meml. award, 1985; hon. Knight San Jacinte, 1993; hon. mem. Sons of Republic of Tex., 1986. Fellow Tex. Hist. Assn.; mem. Am. Hist. Assn., So. Hist. Assn. (assoc. editor jour. 1959-62, pres. 1975-76), Tex. Inst. Letters (past pres.), Jefferson Davis Assn. (pres., chmn. adv. bd. editors of papers), Soc. Am. Historians (councillor), Tex. Philos. Soc. (pres. 1978), Civil War Round Table (Houston), Orgn. Am. Historians, Phi Beta Kappa, SAR of Tex. (hon., Knight San Jacinto 1993). Clubs: Cosmos, Army and Navy (Washington); Briarcrest Country (College Station); Austin. Office: Tex A&M U Mosher Inst Internat Policy Studies College Station TX 77843-2400

VANDIVER, RICHARD WHITE, judge; b. Marion, Ind., Jan. 31, 1932; s. Hugh E. and Verne (White) V.; m. Martha Roth, Aug. 25, 1956; m. 2d, Linda Gates, May 19, 1966; children—Elizabeth, Jennifer, Hugh, David, Mary Jayne. B.A. in Journalism, Franklin Coll., 1956; J.D., Ind. U.-Indpls., 1967. Bar: Ind. 1967, U.S. Dist. Ct. (so. dist.) Ind. 1967. Local govt. and ct. reporter Indpls. News, 1962-64; press sec. Ind. Gov. Roger D. Branigan, Indpls., 1964-66; exec. sec. Ind. Pub. Service Commn., Indpls., 1966-67; ptnr. Young & Vandiver, Franklin, Ind., 1967-74; judge U.S. Bankruptcy Ct., So. Dist. Ind., Indpls., 1974—. Office: US Bankruptcy Ct 46 E Ohio St Rm 320 Indianapolis IN 46204

VAN DOMELEN, JOHN FRANCIS, academic administrator; b. Havana, Cuba, Oct. 19, 1942; s. Floyd and Sara (Molina) Van D.; m. Naomi Ruth Kittlesen. BS in Applied Physics, Mich. Tech. U., 1964; MS in Water Res. Mgmt., U. Wis., Madison, 1972; PhD in Civil Engring., U. Wis., 1974. Commd. 2nd lt. USAF, 1964, advanced through grades to col., 1988; mgr. engring. Charmin Paper Products Co., Green Bay, Wis., 1969-70; asst. prof. Norwich U., Northfield, Vt., 1974-79, head engring. and tech. dept., 1979-83, head engring. and tech. div., 1983-85, v.p. acad. affairs, dean of faculty, 1985-90; pres. Wentworth Inst. Tech., Boston, 1990—; mem. Engring. Workforce Commn. Contbr. articles to profl. jours. Mem. MassPep, Boston, 1990—. Decorated Cross of Gallantry (Vietnam); recipient Centennial medal IEEE, 1984. Mem. ASCE, Am. Soc. Engring. Edn., Sci. Rsch. Soc. N.Am., New Eng. Assn. Schs. and Colls. (commr. for inst. higher edn. 1994—). Avocations: racquetball, golf, science fiction. Office: Wentworth Inst Tech 550 Huntington Ave Boston MA 02115-5998

VAN DOMMELEN, DAVID B., artist, educator; b. Grand Rapids, Mich., Aug. 21, 1929; s. Henry and Thelma (Brown) Van D.; m. Michal Bohnstedt; children: Erica, Dorn. Diploma in interior design, Harrington Inst., Chgo., 1951; BA, Mich. State U., 1956, MA, 1957. Art cons. Warren (Mich.) Schs., 1957-59; instr. home art Pa. State U., State College, 1959-62; assoc. prof. interiors Pa. State U., 1964-73, prof. art edn., 1973-87, prof. emeritus, 1987—; asst. prof. design, U. Maine, Orono, 1962-64; instr., Haystack Mountain Crafts Schs., Deer Isle, Maine, 1963, 64, 74, Arrowmont Arts and Crafts, Gatlinburg, Tenn., 1971-82; vis. prof., U. Iowa, Iowa City, 1967, 68, 70. Author: Decorative Wall Hangings: Art with Fabric, 1962, Walls: Enrichment & Ornamentation, 1965, Designing & Decorating Interiors, 1965, New Uses for Old Cannonballs, 1966, Doughboy Letters, 1977; contbr. articles to various publications; represented in numerous art exhbns. Cpl. U.S. Army, 1952-54. Grantee for craft rsch., Ford Found., 1972, OAS, 1976, Pa. State U., 1986; recipient Eleanor Fishborn award, Ednl. Press Am., 1973. Mem. Am. Craft Coun., Am. Home Econs. Assn. (bd. dirs. 1966-71), Pa. Home Econs. Assn. (pres. 1970), Am.-Scandinavian Found. Internat. Home Econs. Assn. Avocation: stamp collecting. Home: RR 1 Box 631 Petersburg PA 16669-9216 Office: Pa State U 207 Arts Coll University Park PA 16802

VAN DOREN, EMERSON BARCLAY, administrative judge; b. Rahway, N.J., Dec. 30, 1940; s. Emerson Maynard and Jacqueline Pendleton (Hicks) Van D.; m. Janet Elisabeth Bumbarger, Dec. 28, 1963; children: Pendleton Barclay, Virginia Cary. BA, Harvard U., 1962; JD, U. Mich., 1965; postgrad. degree (hon.), Air War Coll., Maxwell AF Base, Ala., 1985. Bar: Ky. 1965, N.H. 1971, U.S. Dist. Ct. (we. dist.) Ky. 1966, U.S. Dist. Ct. N.H. 1972. Assoc. Brown, Ardery, Todd & Dudley, Louisville, 1965-66; judge adv. USAF, 1966-71, 72-76; pvt. practice N. Conway, N.H., 1971-72; sr. procurement atty. U.S. Dept. Energy, Washington, 1976-81, dep. asst. gen. counsel for procurement, 1981-85; adminstrv. judge U.S. Energy Bd. Contract Appeals, Arlington, Va., 1985, chmn., chief adminstrv. judge, 1985—; Capt. USAF, 1966-75, col. USAFR, command mobilization asst. to staff judge adv., 1988-90, ret., 1990. Decorated Meritorious Svc. medal with one oak leaf cluster, Commendation medal with one oak leaf cluster, Legion of Merit award; Leckie fellow, Resident fellow U. Mich.; named Outstanding Young Judge Adv., AF Systems Command, 1975. Mem. ABA, St. Execs. Assn. (chpt. pres. 1993—), Bd. Contract Appeals Judges Assn. (bd. govs.), Fed. Bar Assn., N.H. Bar Assn., Ky. Bar Assn. Avocation: surf and fly

fishing. Home: 6916 Arbor Ln Mc Lean VA 22101-1542 Office: Energy Contract Appeals Bd 4040 N Fairfax Dr Arlington VA 22203

VAN DOREN, GLENN HENRY, professional association executive, management consultant; b. Detroit, Oct. 8, 1927; s. Hendrik Hubert and Suzanne (Orval) Van D.; m. Nicky Wright (div. 1978); children: Suzanne Marrie, Frederick Michael; m. Phyllis Elaine Delp, 1980. BA, Wayne State U., 1951. Contr. Security Aluminum Co., Detroit, 1951-54; plant mgr. Detroit Hardware Mfg. Co., 1954-60; dir. mfg. engring. Detroit Steel Products, 1960-62; with Arthur Young & Co., 1962-88, ptnr., dir. of cons., Detroit, 1962-74, ptnr., dir. edn., Reston, Va., 1974-80, ptnr., asst. nat. dir., N.Y.C., 1980-88; pres. Inst. of Mgmt. Cons., N.Y.C., 1988-90, Assn. Exec. Search Cons., N.Y.C., 1990—. Author: Management Services Advisory Manual, 1987 (award Best Bus. Publ. in Binder Format Book Pub. Assn. 1988); editor quar. mag. The Mgmt. Advisor, 1986-89. With U.S. Army, 1945-47. Office: Assn Exec Search Cons 230 Park Ave Ste 1549 New York NY 10169-1549

VAN DOVER, ROBERT BRUCE, physicist; b. Eatontown, N.J., Apr. 30, 1952. BS, Princeton U., 1974; MS, Stanford U., 1975, PhD, 1980. Mem. tech. staff AT&T Bell Labs., Murray Hill, N.J., 1980—. Mem. IEEE, Am. Phys. Soc., Materials Rsch. Soc. Office: AT&T Bell Labs 600 Mountain Ave Rm 1t-106 Murray Hill NJ 07974-2008

VANDOVER, SAMUEL TAYLOR, lawyer; b. St. Louis, Jan. 28, 1942; s. Lewis Samuel and Mary Lou (Dimond) V.; m. Gail L. Chartrand, Sept. 9, 1966; children: Sally Billimack, Virginia G., Lewis S. BS, St. Louis U., 1964, JD, 1967. Bar: Mo. 1967, U.S. Dist. Ct. (ea. dist.) Mo. 1968, U.S. Ct. Appeals (8th cir.) 1974, U.S. Supreme Ct. 1977. Assoc. Law Offices of Edward L. Dowd, St. Louis, 1967-69; asst. pub. defender St. Louis County, 1969-71; assoc. Heneghan, Roberts & Godfrey, St. Louis, 1971-73; ptnr. Godfrey & Vandover, St. Louis, 1973-77; prin. Godfrey, Vandover & Burns, Inc., St. Louis, 1977—; prosecuting atty. City of Kirkwood, Mo., 1977-80; mem. com. on rules Mo. Supreme Ct., Jefferson City, 1980-82. Recipient Lon O. Hocker Meml. Trial Lawyer award Mo. Bar Found., 1973. Mem. Am. Bd. Trial Advs., Internat. Assn. Def. Counsel, St. Louis Metro Bar Assn. (award of merit 1977), Media Club. Roman Catholic. Avocations: hunting, fishing. Home: 530 Gray Barn Ln Wilson Woods MO 63122-1602 Office: Godfrey Vandover & Burns Inc 720 Olive St Fl 21 Saint Louis MO 63101-2338

VAN DRESER, MERTON LAWRENCE, ceramic engineer; b. Des Moines, June 5, 1929; s. Joseph Jerome and Victoria (Love) Van D.; m. Evelyn Lenore Manny, July 12, 1952; children: Peter, Jennifer Sue. BS in Ceramic Engring., Iowa State U., 1951. Tech. supt. Owens-Corning Fiberglas Corp., Kansas City, Mo., 1954-57; rsch. engr. Kaiser Aluminum & Chem. Corp., Milpitas, Calif., 1957-60, rsch. sect. head, 1960-63, lab. mgr., 1963-65, assoc. dir. rsch., 1965-69; dir. refractories rsch. Kaiser Aluminum & Chem. Corp., Pleasanton, Calif., 1969-72; dir. non-metallic materials rsch. Kaiser Aluminum & Chem. Corp., 1972-83; v.p., dir. rsch. Indsl. Chem. div. and Harshaw/Filtrol Partnership Kaiser Aluminum & Chem. Corp., Cleve., 1983-85; dir. bus. devel. Kaiser Aluminum & Chem. Corp., Pleasanton, 1985-88, cons., 1988—; mem. adv. bd. dept. ceramic engring. U. Ill., 1974-78; chmn. tech. adv. com. Refractories Inst., 1980-84; mem. nat. materials adv. bd. Nat. Acad. Sci.; mem. Indsl. Rsch. Inst. Contbr. articles to sci. jours. Sustaining membership chmn. local dist. Boy Scouts Am., 1980; pres. PTA, 1967-68; vol. exec. Pakistan Internat. Exec. Svc. Corps, 1990-91. Aviator C.E., U.S. Army, 1951-54. Recipient Profl. Achievement citation Iowa State U., 1978. Fellow Am. Ceramic Soc. (v.p. 1973-74); mem. ASTM (hon. com.), Brit. Ceramic Soc., Nat. Inst. Ceramic Engrs., Keramos (pres. 1976-78, helad 1980-84, Greaves Walker Roll of Honor award), Metall. Soc., AIME. Lodges: Rotary (Paul Harris fellow), Masons. Patentee in field. Avocation: comml. pilot.

VANDROSS, LUTHER, singer; s. Mary Ida Vandross. Albums include The Best of Luther Vandross...The Best of Love, Busy Body, Forever, For Always, For Love, Give Me The Reason, 1986, Never Too Much, The Night I Fell In Love, Any Love, 1989, The Power of Love, 1991, Never Let Me Go, 1993 (Grammy nomination: Best Rhythym & Blues Male Vocal for "How Deep Is Your Love"), Luther, 1993. *

VAN DUSEN, ALBERT CLARENCE, university official; b. Tampa, Fla., Aug. 30, 1915; s. Charles H. and Maude E. (Green) Van D.; m. Margaret Davis, Jan. 3, 1943; children: Margaret Anne (Mrs. Joseph J. Pysh), Jane Katherine , Sally Elizabeth (Mrs. Frank J. Matyskiela). BS, U. Fla., 1937, AM, 1938; PhD, Northwestern, 1942; LittD, U. Tampa, 1959; LL.D. Duquesne U., 1967. Instr., asst. prof. dept. psychology U. Fla., 1938-41; asso. prof. psychology Northwestern U., 1946, dir. summer session, 1948-52, v.p. pub. relations, 1952-56; prof. psychology, bus. adminstrn. and edn. U. Pitts., 1956-85, asst. chancellor for planning and devel., 1956-59, vice chancellor the professions, 1959-67, vice chancellor program devel. and pub. affairs, 1967-71, vice chancellor, sec. univ., 1971-80, vice chancellor emeritus, spl. asst. for pub. affairs, 1980-85, vice chancellor emeritus, prof. emeritus psychology, bus. adminstrn. and edn., 1985—, ctr. assoc. univ. ctr. for internat. studies, 1986—; bd. dirs. Dollar Bank, Pitts. Editor: Proc. Am. Coll. Personnel Assn; contbr. articles to profl. jours. Bd. govs. Pinchot Inst. Conservation Studies; vice chmn., bd. dirs. The Buhl Found., World Affairs Coun. Pitts., vice chmn. bd. dirs. Duquesne U., acting chmn., 1987-88; bd. dirs. Pitts. YMCA, ACTION Housing, Inc., Assn. Am.'s Pub. TV Stas., QED Communications Inc., chmn. 1981-88; bd. dirs. Japan-Am. Soc. Pa.; mem. Pa. Pub. TV Network Commn.; chmn., bd. trustees Pitts. History and Landmarks Found.; pres. bd. trustees H.C. Frick Ednl. Commn., United Way Pa.; dir. South Hills Child Guidance Ctr.; chmn. selfcare study Health Edn. Ctr., Pitts., 1979-80. Lt. USNR, 1942-46. Fulbright sr. scholar Australian-Am. Ednl. Found., 1980. Fellow Am. Psychol. Assn., Am. Psychol. Soc., Pa. Psychol. Assn., Internat. Found. Social Econ. Deve.; mem. Internat. Assn. Schs. Insts. Adminstrn., C of C. (dir. 1953-55), Am. Coll. Pub. Rels. Assn. (v.p. 1956-58), Assn. Deans and Dirs. Summer Sessions (sec. 1950-51), Profll. Schs. and World Affairs Com. (chmn. edn. and world affairs 1965-67), Am. Pers. and Guidance Assn., Midwest Psychol. Assn., Ea. Psychol. Assn., Pitts. Psychol. Assn., Internat. Assn. Applied Psychology, Western Pa. Coun. Econ. Edn., Internat. Assn. Schs. and Insts. Adminstrn., Friends of Art for Pitts. Schs. (charter mem.), Phi Beta Kappa, Sigma Xi, Beta Theta Pi, Beta Gamma Sigma. Clubs: Univ. (Pitts.), Duquesne (Pitts.). Home: 108 Blue Spruce Cir Pittsburgh PA 15243-1026

VAN DUYN, MONA JANE, poet; b. Waterloo, Iowa, May 9, 1921; d. Earl George and Lora G. (Kramer) Van D.; m. Jarvis A. Thurston, Aug. 31, 1943. B.A., U. No. Iowa, 1942; M.A., U. Iowa, 1943; D.Litt. (hon.), Washington U. St. Louis, 1971, Cornell Coll., Iowa, 1972, U. No. Iowa, 1991, U. of the South, Sewanee, Tenn., 1993, George Wash. U., 1993; LHD, Georgetown U., 1993. Instr. in English U. Iowa, Iowa City, 1943-46; instr. in English U. Louisville, 1946-50; lectr. English Univ. Coll., Washington U., 1950-67; poetry editor, co-pub. Perspective, A Quar. of Lit., 1947-67; lectr. Salzburg (Austria) Seminar Am. Studies, 1973; adj. prof. poetry workshop Washington U., Spring 1983; vis. Hurst prof. 1987; poet-in-residence Sewanee Writers Conf., 1990, Breadloaf Writing Conf., Mass., 1974. Author: Valentines to the Wide World, 1959, A Time of Bees, 1964, To See, To Take, 1970, Bedtime Stories, 1972, Merciful Disguises, 1973, Letters from a Father and Other Poems, 1983, Near Changes, 1990 (Pulitzer Prize for poetry 1991), Firefall, 1993, If It Be Not I, 1993. Recipient Eunice Tietjens award, 1956, Helen Bullis prize, 1964, 76, Harriet Monroe award, 1968, Hart Crane Meml. award, 1968, Borestone Mountains 1st prize, 1968, Bollingen prize, 1970, Nat. Book award, 1971, Sandburg prize Cornell Coll., 1982, Shelley Meml. prize Poetry Soc. Am., 1987, Lilly prize for poetry, 1989, Mo. Arts award, 1990, Golden Plate award Am. Acad. Achievement, 1992, Arts and Edn. Coun. St. Louis award, 1994; named U.S. Poet Laureate, 1992-93; grantee Nat. Coun. Arts, 1967, NEA, 1985, Guggenheim fellow, 1972. Fellow Acad. Am. Poets (chancellor 1985); mem. Nat. Acad. Arts and Letters (Loines prize 1976).

VAN DUYNE, RICHARD PALMER, analytical chemistry and chemical physics educator; b. Orange, N.J., Oct. 28, 1945; s. John Palmer and Lorraine Montgomery (Stoller) Van D.; m. Jerilyn Elise Miripol. B.A., Rensselaer Poly. Inst., 1967; Ph.D., U. N.C., 1971. Asst. prof. analytical chemistry and chem. physics Northwestern U., Evanston, Ill., 1971-76, assoc.

prof., 1976-79, prof., 1979-87, Charles E. and Emma H. Morrison prof. chemistry, 1987—; cons. Beckman Instrument Co., Fullerton, Calif., 1982-86, Eastman Kodak Co., Rochester, N.Y., 1978—; disting. vis. prof. U. Tex., Austin, 1979; chmn. Vibrational Spectroscopy Gordon Conf., 1982; Camille and Henry Dreyfus lectr. U. Colo., Boulder, 1981; Kilpatrick lectr. Ill. Inst. Tech., 1982; O.K. Rice lectr. U. N.C., 1984; Henry Werner lectr. U. Kans., 1986. Mem. adv. bd. Jour. Phys. Chemistry, 1983—; contbr. chpts. to books, articles to profl. jours. Recipient Coblentz award, 1980; Fresenius award, 1981. Sloan Found. fellow, 1974-78. Fellow AAAS, Am. Phys. Soc.; mem. Am. Chem. Soc., Electrochem. Soc. Home: 1520 Washington Ave Wilmette IL 60091-2417 Office: Northwestern Univ 2145 Sheridan Rd Evanston IL 60201-2926

VAN DYCK, NICHOLAS BOORAEM, minister, foundation official; b. Pasadena, Calif., Aug. 10, 1933; s. David Bevier and Anna Booraem (Richardson) van D.; m. Marcia Perera, June 14, 1958; children: Karen Rhoads, Jennifer Bevier, Sarah Paxson, Rebecca Booraem. BA, Rutgers U., 1959; BD, Union Theol. Sem., N.Y.C., 1962; PhD, U. St. Andrews, 1965. Ordained to ministry Presbyn. Ch., 1962. Pastor Palisades (N.Y.) Presbyn. Ch., 1964-68; tchr., adminstr. Princeton (N.J.) Theol. Sem., 1968-76; exec. dir. Action Research Corp., Princeton, 1976-77; exec. dir., founder Nat. Council for Children & TV, Princeton, N.Y.C. and Los Angeles, 1977-82; pres. Nat. Council for Families and TV, Princeton, N.Y.C. and Los Angeles, 1982-87; pres., chief exec. officer Religion In Am. Life, Princeton, Phila, N.Y.C., 1988—; chmn. bd. Action Research Corp., Princeton, 1987—; chmn. Assn. for Theol. Field Edn., U.S. and Can., 1975-76. Pub., editor TV and Families, 1982-87; contbr. articles to profl. jours. Bd. dirs. ARC, Princeton, 1984-89, Princeton Youth Fund, 1983-89, YMCA, Princeton, 1986-89, George H. Gallup Internat. Inst., 1990—. Lt. USNR, 1954-58. Scholar-in-residence Aspen (Colo.) Inst. for Humanistic Studies, 1985. Mem. Soc. for Psychol. Study Social Issues, Ind. Sector. Clubs: Princeton (N.Y.C.) Nassau (Princeton). Lodge: Rotary (pres. Princeton club 1981-82, bd. dirs. found. 1985—). Avocation: collecting antique autos.

VAN DYCK, WENDY, dancer; b. Tokyo. Student, San Francisco Ballet Sch. With San Francisco Ballet, 1979—, prin. dancer, 1987—. Performances include Forgotten Land, The Sons of Horus, The Wonderer Fantasy, Romeo and Juliet, The Sleeping Beauty, Swan Lake, Concerto in d: Poulenc, Handel-a Celebration, Menuetto, Intimate Voices, Hamlet and Ophelia pas de deux, Connotations, Sunset, Rodin, In the Night, The Dream: pas de deux, La Sylphide, Beauty and the Beast, Variations de Ballet, Nutcracker, The Comfort Zone, Dreams of Harmony, Rodeo, Duo Concertant, Who Cares; performed at Reykjavik Arts Festival, Iceland, 1990, The 88th Conf. of the Internat. Olympic Com., L.A., 1984, with Kozlov and Co. Concord Pavilion; guest artist performing role Swan Lake (Act II), San Antonio Ballet, 1985, Giselle, Shreveport Met. Ballet, 1994; featured in the TV broadcast of Suite by Smuin. Office: San Francisco Ballet 455 Franklin St San Francisco CA 94102-4471

VAN DYK, FREDERICK THEODORE, corporate executive; b. Bellingham, Wash., Oct. 6, 1934; s. Ted and June Ellen (Williams) Van D.; m. Julia Jean Covacevich, Nov. 22, 1957; children: Theodore, Robert, Terry Jean, Sue Ellen. B.A., U. Wash., 1955; M.S., Columbia U., 1956. Reporter, editor Seattle Times, 1956-57; advt. public relations exec. Boston and N.Y.C., 1958-62; acting dir. European Community Info. Service, Washington, 1962-64; asst. to Hubert Humphrey, Vice Pres. of U.S., 1964-68; v.p. Columbia U., N.Y.C., 1968-69; pres. Van Dyk Assocs., Washington, 1969-76; asst. adminstr. AID, Washington, 1977; v.p. Weyerhaeuser Co., Tacoma, 1978-80; pres. Center for Nat. Policy, Washington, 1981-85, Van Dyk Assocs., 1985—. Contbr. essays on govt. and politics to gen. publs. including L.A. Times, N.Y. Times, Wall St. Jour., Washington Post. Bd. dirs. Com. for Study of Am. Electorate, Franklin and Eleanor Roosevelt Inst., Jean Monnet Coun.; mem. Coun. on Fgn. Rels., Presdl. Commn. on Fgn. Assistance. Served with M.I. AUS, 1957, 61-62. Mem. Delta Upsilon (nat. trustee). Clubs: Fed. City, Army Navy (Washington), Rainier (Seattle). Home: 7500 Masters Dr Potomac MD 20854-3854 Office: Van Dyk Assocs 1250-24th St NW Washington DC 20037

VAN DYK, STEPHEN HENRY, librarian; b. Paterson, N.J., June 19, 1950; s. George Disler and Lillian Jeanette (Bogert) Van D. BA, William Paterson Coll., 1972; MLS U, N.C., 1973; postgrad., Rutgers U., 1982—. Ref. libr. Bloomfield (N.J.) Coll., 1973-73; architecture libr. N.J. Inst. Tech., Newark, 1974-81; art and architecture libr. N.Y. Inst. Tech., Old Westbury, 1981-84; art dept. head libr. Mid-Manhattan Libr. N.Y. Pub. Libr., 1984-88; chief libr. Cooper-Hewitt Mus., N.Y.C., 1988—. Editor: World of Work, 1985, Future of Education, 1983. Mem. First Presbyn. Ch., Palisades, N.Y., 1990—. Recipient Exceptional Svc. award Smithsonian Inst. Librs., 1992, 93; grantee Smithsonian Rsch. Resources, 1991, Smithsonian Inst. Women's Com., 1989. Mem. Spl. Librs. Assn. (rep. to ARLIS 1993—), ARLIS/NA (chair dec. arts com. 1985—). Avocations: marathon running, square dancing. Home: 139 W 94th St New York NY 10025-7051 Office: Cooper-Hewitt Mus 2 E 91st St New York NY 10128-0606

VAN DYKE, CLIFFORD CRAIG, retired banker; b. Ft. Madison, Iowa, June 23, 1929; s. Charles Clifford and Frances Mary (Butterwick) Van D.; m. Edith Ellicott Powers, Aug. 4, 1951 (dec. Oct. 1980); children: Carol Elizabeth, Deborah Ellicott, Jill Anne, Lisa Ellicott. BA, Knox Coll., 1951; MBA, Harvard U., 1955. Asst. v.p. Nat. Bank of Detroit, 1962-65; v.p. 1965-76; pres. Peoples Nat. Bank & Trust Co. of Bay City, Mich., 1976-78, chmn. bd., pres., 1979-86; chmn. bd., pres., chief exec. officer New Ctr. Bank Corp., Bay City, Mich., 1986; chmn. First of Am. Bank-Bay City, N.A., 1987-89; sr. v.p. First of Am. Bank-Mid Mich. N.A., 1990-94; ret., 1994. Trustee Kantzler Found., Bay City, 1979—; bd. dirs., pres. Bay County Growth Alliance, 1987—. 1st lt. U.S. Army, 1951-53, Korea. Mem. Bay City Country Club, Saginaw Valley Torch Club, Saginaw Bay Yacht Club, Rotary, Elks. Republican. Unitarian. Office: Bay County Growth Alliance PO Box 369 Bay City MI 48707-0369

VAN DYKE, DAVID, broadcast executive; b. Jersey City, N.J., Mar. 1, 1949; s. Sidney Arthur and Wilma Patricia (Heilbrunn) Hass; m. Denise Lynn Spinney, Feb. 14, 1988. BA in Comm., U. Miami, 1971. Air personality Sta. WMFQ-FM, Miami, Fla., 1971, Sta. WWWW-FM, Detroit, 1971-72, Sta. WDAI-FM, Chgo., 1972-76; program dir. Sta. KFWD-FM, Dallas, 1976-78, Sta. KAZY-FM, Denver, 1978-82, Sta. KLUV-FM, Dallas, 1983-87; program dir. Sta. WODS-FM, Boston, 1987-89, v.p., gen. mgr. Sta. KCBS-FM, L.A., 1991—; cons. Sta. WOGL-FM, Phila., Sta. KLOU-FM, St. Louis, 1988, Sta. KOJD-FM, L.A., 1989. Mem. So. Calif. Broadcasters (bd. dirs.), Alpha Epsilon Rho. Avocations: music, reading, outdoor activities, magic. Office: Station KCBS-FM 6121 W Sunset Blvd Los Angeles CA 90028-6455

VAN DYKE, DICK, actor, comedian; b. West Plains, Mo., Dec. 13, 1925; m. Marjorie Willett, Feb. 12, 1948; children: Christian, Barry, Stacey, Carrie Beth. Ed. high sch. With Wayne Williams, founded advt. agy. Danville, Ill., 1946; chmn. Nick at Nite, 1992—. Appeared school plays, civic theatre prodns.; appeared with Philip Erickson in pantomine act The Merry Mutes, Eric and Van, 1947-53; TV master ceremonies The Music Shop, Atlanta; TV variety show Dick Van Dyke Show, New Orleans; master ceremonies: Morning Show, CBS, 1955, Cartoon Show, 1956; guest appearances nat. TV shows, 1958; host Flair, weekly TV show, ABC, 1960; Broadway debut in The Girls Against the Boys, 1959; performed in Broadway musical Bye Bye Birdie, 1960-61 (also motion picture version); weekly comedy program Dick Van Dyke Show, CBS-TV, 1961-66; star weekly comedy program New Dick Van Dyke Show, 1971-74; performer weekly comedy program Carol Burnett Show; host weekly comedy program Van Dyke and Company, 1976, The Van Dyke Show, CBS, 1988; appeared in TV series Diagnosis Murder, 1993-94; numerous TV guest appearances; performed in motion pictures including What a Way To Go, 1964, Mary Poppins, 1965, Divorce American Style, 1967, Chitty, Chitty, Bang, Bang, 1968, The Comic, 1969, Some Kind of Nut, 1969, Cold Turkey, 1971, The Morning After, 1974, The Runner Stumbles, 1979, Drop-Out Father, 1982, Found Money, 1983, Dick Tracy, 1990; Author: Faith, Hope, and Hilarity, 1970. With USAAC, World War II. Recipient Theater World award 1960, Antoinette Perry award for best mus. comedy actor 1961, Emmy award for comedy Nat. Acad. TV Arts and Scis. 1962, 64, 65. Office: William Morris Agy Inc care Sol Leon 151 S El Camino Dr Beverly Hills CA 90212-2775

VAN DYKE, JERRY, actor, comedian; b. Danville, Ill.. Stand-up comedian for years, performing in Las Vegas, Atlantic City, other major showrooms; TV work includes (series) The Judy Garland Show, My Mother The Car, 1964, Coach, ABC-TV, 1990— (Emmy nomination, Supporting Actor - Comedy Series, 1994); film work includes The Courtship of Eddie's Father, Palm Springs Weekend. With USAF, 1952-54. Office: Sutton Barth Vennari 145 S Fairfax Ave Ste 310 Universal City CA 90036*

VAN DYKE, JOSEPH GARY OWEN, computer consulting executive; b. N.Y.C., Dec. 21, 1939; s. Donald Wood and Gladys Ann (Tague) Van D.; m. Lynne Diane Lammers; June 25, 1966; children: Alison Baird, Jeremy Wood, Matthew Kerr. BA, Rutgers U., 1961; postgrad., R.I. Sch. of Design, 1962, Am. U., 1964-67. Computer programmer System Devel. Corp., Paramus, N.J., 1962-64; sect. head computer tech. div. System Devel. Corp., Falls Church, Va., 1964-67; project mgr. Informatics Inc., Bethesda, Md., 1967-70; dept. dir. Informatics Inc. Rockville, Md., 1970-74, v.p., gen. mgr., 1974-78; owner, pres. J G Van Dyke and Assoc., Inc., Bethesda, 1978—; chmn. bd., chief exec. officer The Outreach Group, Inc., 1987—. Bd. dirs. Westbrook Sch., Bethesda, 1981-82, St. Columba's Ch., Washington, 1980-84; founder Computer Edn. Workshop, Bethesda, 1981; coach MSI soccer, Bethesda, 1979-89. Mem. Inst. Elec. Engring. Democrat. Episcopalian. Avocations: coaching soccer, sailing, graphic designing. Home: 5117 Dalecarlia Dr Bethesda MD 20816-1801 Office: JG Van Dyke & Assocs Inc 6550 Rock Spring Dr # 360 Bethesda MD 20817-1813

VAN DYKE, MILTON DENMAN, aeronautical engineering educator; b. Chgo., Aug. 1, 1922; s. James Richard and Ruth (Barr) Van D.; m. Sylvia Jean Agard Adams, June 16, 1962; children: Russell B., Eric J., Nina A., Brooke A. and Byron J. and Christopher M. (triplets). B.S., Harvard U., 1943; M.S., Calif. Inst. Tech., 1947, Ph.D, 1949. Research engr. NACA, 1943-46, 50-54, 55-58; vis. prof. U. Paris, France, 1958- 59; prof. aero. Stanford, 1959—; prof. emeritus, 1992—; pres. Parabolic Press. Author: Perturbation Methods in Fluid Mechanics, 1964, An Album of Fluid Motion, 1982; editor: Ann. Rev. Fluid Mechanics, 1969—. Trustee Soc. For Promotion of Sci. and Scholarship, Inc. Served with USNR, 1944-46. Guggenheim and Fulbright fellow, 1954-55. Mem. Am. Acad. Arts and Scis., Nat. Acad. Engring., Am. Phys. Soc., Phi Beta Kappa, Sigma Xi, Sierra Club. Office: Stanford U Div Applied Mechanics Stanford CA 94305-4040

VAN DYKE, THOMAS WESLEY, lawyer; b. Kansas City, Mo., May 12, 1938; s. Harold Thomas and Elizabeth Louise (Barritt) Van D.; m. Sharon Edgar, Jan. 30, 1960; children: Jennifer Van Dyke Winters, Jeffrey. BA, U. Kans., 1960; JD, U. Mich., 1963. Bar: Mo. 1963, Kans. 1983. Atty. SEC, Washington, 1963-64; legal asst. to commr. Hamer E. Budge, Washington, 1964-65; from assoc. to ptnr. Linde Thomson Langworthy Kohn & Van Dyke (P.C.), Overland Park, Kans., 1965-91; co-chmn. ALI-ABA Tax and Bus. Planning Seminar, 1987-95; mem. securities adv. panel Sec. of State of Mo., 1984-89. Mem. ABA (fed. regulation securities com bus. law sect. 1982-95, negotatiated acquisitions com. 1989-95), Kans. Bar Assn., Mo. Bar Assn. (corp. banking and bus. law com.), chmn. full com. 1983-84, past chmn. securities law subcom.), Carriage Club (bd. dirs. 1986-89). Republican. Avocations: tennis, reading. Office: Bryan Cave Ste 1100 7500 College Blvd Overland Park KS 66210

VAN DYKE, WILLIAM GRANT, manufacturing company executive; b. Mpls., June 30, 1945; s. Russell Lawrence and Carolyn (Grant) Van D.; m. Karin Van Dyke; children: Carolyn Julie, Colin Grant, Alexander Grant, Stephanie Joyce. BA in Econs., U. Minn., 1967, MBA, 1972. V.p., CFO Northland Aluminum Co., Mpls., 1977-78; controller Donaldson Co., Inc., Mpls., 1978-80, v.p. controller, 1980-82, v.p., CFO, 1982-84, pres., COO, 1984—, also bd. dirs. Served to lt. U.S. Army, 1968-70, Vietnam. Mem. Kappa Sigma Alumni Assn. Avocations: running; bicycling. Office: Donaldson Co Inc 1400 W 94th St Minneapolis MN 55431-2370

VANE, DENA, magazine editor-in-chief. Editor-in-chief First for Women, Englewood Cliffs, N.J. Office: First for Women Bauer Pub Co 270 Sylvan Ave Englewood NJ 07632*

VANE, TERENCE G., JR., finance and insurance company executive, lawyer; b. Elgin, Ill., Jan. 17, 1942; s. Terence Gregory and Velma Mary (Mersman) V.; m. Patricia Bryant, Aug. 29, 1964; children: Terence Gregory III, Lourdene DeLynne, Christopher Theodore. BA, Ind. U., 1964, JD 1967. Bar: Ind. 1967, Tex. 1977, N.C. 1992. Staff atty. Assocs. Discount Corp., South Bend, Ind., 1967-69; asst. gen. counsel Assocs. Mgmt. Corp., South Bend, 1969-74, Assocs. Comml. Corp., South Bend, 1974-76, Assocs. Ins. Group, Inc., Dallas, 1976-77; gen. counsel, v.p. ins. ops. Assocs. Corp. N.Am., Dallas, 1977-80, gen. counsel, sr. v.p. ins. ops., 1981-82, gen. counsel, sr. v.p. consumer fin. and ins. ops., 1982-86, gen. counsel, sr. v.p. diversified consumer fin. services and credit card ops., 1986-88; exec. v.p., gen. counsel, sec., dir. Barclays Am. Corp., Charlotte, N.C., 1988-91; pres. Vector Fin. Svcs., Inc., Charlotte, 1991—, also bd. dirs. Chmn. bd. dirs., sec. Youth Concert Found. for Promotion Creative Arts, 1981—; bd. dirs. N.C. Bus. Com. Edn., 1988-91. Mem. ABA, Ind. Bar Assn., Tex. Bar Assn., N.C. Bar Assn., Mecklenburg County Bar Assn., Nat. Assn. Ind. Insurers (laws com. 1978-86), Consumer Credit Ins. Assn. (chmn. property ins. legis. com. 1979-85), Am. Fin. Svcs. Assn. (law com., chmn. environ. law subcom.), Conf. Consumer Fin. Law (gen. com.). Republican. Home: 5930 Laurium Rd Charlotte NC 28226-5616 Office: Two First Union Ctr 101 N McDowell St Ste 114 Charlotte NC 28204

VANECKO, ROBERT MICHAEL, surgeon, educator; b. Chgo., Aug. 15, 1935; s. Michael and Raphael Regina (Burns) V.; m. Mary Carol Daley; children: Robert G., Mark G., Richard J., Mary Clare. BS, Georgetown U., 1957; MS, Northwestern U., 1960, MD, 1961. Diplomate Am. Bd. Surgery, Am. Bd. Thoracic Surgery. Intern Cook County Hosp., Chgo., 1961-62, resident in gen. surgery, 1962-66; intern surgery U. Ill., 1966-66; resident in cardiothoracic surgery Cook County Hosp., Chgo., 1966-67, Hines (Ill.) VA Hosp., 1969-70; attending surgeon VA Rsch. Hosp., Chgo., 1970—; attending surgeon Cook County Hosp., Chgo., 1972—, chief sect. thoracic trauma, 1972-78; assoc. attending Northwestern Meml. Hosp., Chgo., 1970-77, attending, 1977—; assoc. in surgery Northwestern U. Med. Sch., Chgo., 1970-71, asst. prof. surgery 1971-75, assoc. prof. surgery, 1975-88, prof. clin. surgery, 1988-93, prof. surgery 1993—, asst. dean, then assoc. dean grad. med. edn., 1988—; mem. numerous hosp. coms. Creator, writer numerous surgical movies, 1963-84; contbr. articles to profl. jours. Bd. govs. Chgo. Heart Assn., 1980-86, 88—, mem. phys. fitness com., 1973-80, mem. pub. policy and govt. rels. com., 1980—; mem. alumni coun. Northwestern U. Med. Sch., mem. instl. rev. bd.; mem. adv. com. Ill. Dept. Pub. Health, 1990—; bd. gov. Chgo. Access Corp., 1984-90, Crescent County Med. Found., 1984-87. Mem. AAAS, ACS (mem. motion picture com. 1974-80, mem. credentials com. 1978-86, chmn. met. credentials com. 1986—), AMA (alt. del. to ho. of dels. 1984-86, del. to ho. of dels. 1986—, mem. sect. med. schs. 1987—), Am. Assn. Thoracic Surgery, Am. Coll. Chest Physicians (chmn. motion picture com. 1977-80, treas. 1980-85, pres. Ill.-Great Lakes chpt. 1981-82, dir. edn. found. 1985—), Am. Hosp. Assn. (mem. nat. congress hosp. gov. bd. 1984—, mem. coordinating com. med. 1989—), Am. Med. Writers Assn., Am. Trauma Soc., Ctrl. Surg. Assn., Chgo. Med. Soc. (mem. health planning com., mem. health care delivery com. 1982-86, mem. health system agy. com. 1978-84, bd. trustees 1984-89, sec. 1984-86, pres. 1987-88, chmn. bd. trustees 1986-87), Chgo. Surg. Soc. (rep. to Ill. State Med. Soc. 1984-86), Ill. Med. Soc., Ill. Surg. Soc., Ill. Hosp. Assn. (bd. trustees 1986—), Inst. Medicine Chgo. (bd. govs. 1984—, mem. grad. and undergrad. med. edn. com. 1975-79, treas. 1986-89), Soc. Med. History Chgo., Soc. Thoracic Surgeons, Western Surg. Assn. Office: Northwestern Med Sch 303 E Chicago Ave Chicago IL 60611

VANEGAS, JORGE ALBERTO, civil engineering educator; b. Bogota, Colombia, Oct. 17, 1956; came to U.S., 1983; s. Carlos Enrique and Cecilia (Pabon) V.; m. Adriana Martinez, Dec. 18, 1987 (div. Dec. 1992); m. Loretta Sanders, Dec. 22, 1992). BS in Architecture, U. de los Andes, Bogota, 1979; MSCE, Stanford U., 1985, PhD in Civil Engring., 1988. Rsch. and teaching asst. Stanford (Calif.) U., 1984-87, acting asst. prof, 1988; asst. prof. Purdue U., West Lafayette, Ind., 1988-93; assoc. profl. civil engring. Ga. Inst. Tech., Atlanta, 1993—; cons. U.S. and Colombia, 1982—. Mem. ASCE (assoc.), Am. Soc. Engrs. in Edn. (assoc.), Soc. Hispanic Profl. Engrs. (assoc.).

Roman Catholic. Avocation: gourmet cooking. Home: 4205 Newpond Trail Kennesaw GA 30144 Office: Sch Civil Engring Dept Civil Engring Ga Inst Tech Atlanta GA 30332-0355

VANEK, CYNTHIA WILKINSON, administrator; b. Quincy, Mass., Nov. 2, 1950; d. Harold F. Jr. and Priscilla (Coleman) Wilkinson; m. James E. Vanek, Dec 18, 1976; children: James E., Terence M. BSN, U. Rochester, 1972, MS, 1975. Cert. nursing adminstrn. advanced. V.p. nursing Good Samaritan Med. Ctr., West Palm Beach, Fla.; assoc. clin. chief pediatric nursing U. Rochester, N.Y. Recipient Rochester Acad. Medicine award. Mem. South Fla. Orgn. Nurse Execs., Fla. Hosp. Assn. Nursing Adv. Coun. Home: 202 Thornton Ct West Palm Beach FL 33418-8037

VANEK, JAROSLAV, economist, educator; b. Prague, Czechoslovakia, Apr. 20, 1930; came to U.S., 1955, naturalized, 1963; s. Josef and Jaroslava (Tucek) V.; m. Wilda M. Marraffino, Dec. 26, 1959; children: Joseph, Francis, Rosemarie, Steven, Teresa. Degree in stats., Sorbonne, Paris, 1951; license in econ., U. Geneva, 1954; Ph.D., MIT, 1957. Instr., then asst. prof. Harvard U., 1957-63; adviser AID, 1964; mem. faculty Cornell U., 1964—, prof. econs., 1966—, Carl Marks prof. internat. studies, 1969—, dir. program comparative econ. devel., 1968-73, dir. program participation and labor-managed systems, 1969—; mem. nat. adv. bd. econs. NSF, 1969-70; founder, pres. S.T.E.V.E.N. Found. (Solar Tech. and Energy for Vital Econ. Needs), 1985—. Author: International Trade: Theory and Economic Policy, 1962, The Balance of Payments, Level of Economic Activity and the Value of Currency, 1962, The Natural Resource Content of United States Foreign Trade, 1870-1955, 1963, General Equilibrium of International Discrimination, 1965, Estimating Foreign Resource Needs for Economic Development, 1966, Maximal Economic Growth, 1968, The General Theory of Labor-Managed Market Economies, 1970, The Participatory Economy, 1971, Self-Management: Economic Liberation of Man, 1975, The Labor-Managed Economy, 1977, Crisis and Reform: East and West; Essays in Social Economy, 1989, Toward Full Democracy, Political and Economic, In Russia, 1993; also manuscripts on solar tech.; contbr. to Advances in the Economic Analysis of Participatory and Labor-Managed Firms, Vol. 2, 1987; inventor several solar tech. designs including solar steam engines, pumps, refrigerators, cookers; holder 1 patent. Roman Catholic. Home: 414 Triphammer Rd Ithaca NY 14850-2521 Office: Cornell U Prog Participation Labor Managed Systems Uris Hall # 490 Ithaca NY 14853-7601

VAN EKRIS, ANTHONIE CORNELIS, trading corporation executive; b. Rotterdam Netherlands, June 3, 1934; came to U.S., 1963; s. Cornelis and Evertje (Mulder) van E.; m. Heather Frances Button, Sept. 7, 1960; children: Anthonie Cornelis, Marijke Karin. Trainee Van Rees, Ltd., Rotterdam, 1952-57; mgr. African Coffee Trading Ops., Mombasa, E. Africa, 1957-63, Ralli Trading Co., N.Y.C., 1963-67; pres. Van Ekris & Stoett, Ltd., N.Y.C., 1967-70; pres., dir. Ralli-Am. Ltd., N.Y.C., 1970-72; pres. Kay Corp. (now Balfour Maclaine Corp.), N.Y.C., 1972—, chief exec. officer, chmn., 1988—, also bd. dirs.; chmn. Kay Jewelers, Inc., Balfour, Maclaine Internat. Ltd., Van Ekris & Stoett, Inc., Marcus & Co., Inc. Served with Royal Dutch Navy, 1951-53. Address: Hilltop Pl Rye NY 10580

VAN EMBURGH, JOANNE, lawyer; b. Palmyra, N.J., Nov. 18, 1953; d. Earl Henry and Clare (Kemmerle) Van E.; m. Samuel Michael Surloff, July 6, 1993. BA summa cum laude, Catholic U., 1975; JD cum laude, Harvard Law Sch., 1978. Assoc. atty. Agnew Miller & Carlson, L.A., 1978-82; ptnr. Sachs & Phelps, L.A., 1982-91, Heller, Ehrman, White & McAuliffe, L.A., 1991—. Mem. ABA, L.A. County Bar (exec. com., bus. and corp. law sect. 1993—). Avocations: reading, cooking, sports. Office: Heller Ehrman White & McAuliffe 601 S Figueroa St Los Angeles CA 90017

VAN ES, RICHARD JOHN, JR., electronics executive; b. South Bend, Ind., Aug. 3, 1957; s. Richard John Sr. and Barbara Jean (Frick) Van E.; m. Mary Elizabeth Sartini, June 6, 1982. BBA, U. Notre Dame, Ind., 1980. CPA, Ind. Staff acct. Price Waterhouse, South Bend, 1980-82; asst. controller St. Joseph Bank and Trust Co., South Bend, 1982-84; sr. acct. McGladrey, Hendrickson & Pullen, Elkhart, Ind., 1984-87; v.p. fin. and acctg. Am Electronic Components, Elkhart, 1987—. Mem. Am. Inst. CPA's, Ind. Soc. CPA's. Avocations: tennis, music. Home: 1560 Durham Way W Granger IN 46530 Office: Am Electronic Components 1010 N Main St Elkhart IN 46514-3205

VAN ESELTINE, WILLIAM PARKER, microbiologist, educator; b. Syracuse, N.Y., Aug. 21, 1924; s. Glen Parker and Florence Marie (Lamb) Van E.; m. Marian Louise Vanderburgh, Aug. 25, 1948; children—Kenneth Leslie, Karen Elaine. A.B., Oberlin Coll., 1944; M.S., Cornell U., 1947, Ph.D., 1949. Asst. in bacteriology N.Y. State Agrl. Expt. Sta. Geneva, 1944-45, summer 1944; Asst. in bacteriology N.Y. State Coll. Agr., Cornell U., Ithaca, 1946-48; asso. prof. bacteriology Clemson (S.C.) Agrl. Coll., 1948-52; asst. prof. vet. hygiene U. Ga., Athens, 1952-59, asso. prof. microbiology and preventive medicine, 1959-67, prof. med. microbiology, 1967-87, prof. emeritus, 1987—. Contbr. articles on microbiology to profl. jours. Mem. Am. Soc. Microbiology, N.Y. Acad. Sci., Ga. Acad. Sci., Am. Leptospirosis Research Conf. (pres. 1987), AAAS, Sigma Xi, Phi Kappa Phi. Home: 237 Woodlawn Ave Athens GA 30606-4353

VANESS, CAROL, soprano; b. L.A., July 27, 1952; d. William Anthony and Dorothea Jean (Whitsun) V. BA, Calif. Poly. U., 1974; MA, Calif. State U., Northridge, 1976; student, Merola and Affiliate Artist programs, San Francisco, 1976-78. Made debut N.Y.C. Opera as Vitellia in La Clemenza di Tito, 1979; prodns. include Don Giovanni, 1980, Merry Wives of Windsor, 1981, La Boheme, Rigoletto, Pearl Fishers, Traviata and Alcina, 1983; revivals San Francisco Opera Don Giovanni, 1981, Dialogues of the Carmelites, 1982, La Traviata, 1991, Don Carlo, 1992; European debut Clemenza, Bordeaux, France, 1981, Buffalo Philharm., Rossini Stabat Mater, 1981; debut Phila. Opera as Countess in Figaro, 1982, N.Y.C. Opera in Figaro, Covent Garden debut as Mimi in La Boheme, 1982, Glyndebourne Festival Don Giovanni, 1982, Idomeneo, 1983, Cosi, 1984, Boccanegra, 1986; Paris Opera debut as Nedda in Pagliacci, 1982, Idomeneo & Clemenza, 1986, Berlin, Munich and Vienna debut in Don Giovanni, Met. Opera debut as Armida in Rinaldo, 1984, Australian debut in a Masked Ball, 1985, Rome debut in Faust, 1987, Barcelona, Spain debut in Tito, 1988, Salzburg Festival debut as Vitellia, Austria, 1988, Tito, 1988-89, Donna Elvira, 1990, Lyric Opera of Chbo. debut, 1988, Don Giovanni, 1989, N.Y. Philharm. debut, 1991, La Scala (Milan) debut Idomeneo, 1990; Met. Opera Figaro, 1985, Samson, 1986, Faust, 1990, Don Giovanni, 1990; recital debut, Liberty, Mo., 1986, Carnegie Hall debut Strauss 4 Last Songs, 1987, Live from Lincoln Ctr. Pavarotti Plus, 1986, 90, numerous recs. with EMI; rec. complete Giovanni and Cosi with Glyndebourne/Haitink; N.Y. recital debut Alice Tully Hall, 1987, , Carol Vaness Mozart An'as, Don Giovanni-Muti Mozart Duets with Placido Domingo, Rossini Stabat Mater Tosca-Muti, Verdi Requiem Iphigenie en Tauride, 1992. Winner San Francisco Opera Audition, 1976. Office: IMG Artists Europe Medin House, 3 Burlington Lane, London W4 2TH, England*

VAN EYS, JAN, pediatrician, educator, administrator; b. Hilversum, The Netherlands, Jan. 25, 1929; came to U.S., 1951; s. Jan and Geertruida (Floor) van E.; m. Catherine Travis; children: Jan Peter, D. Catherine. PhD in Biochemistry, Vanderbilt U., 1955; MD, U. Wash., 1966. Diplomate Nat. Bd. Med. Examiners, Am. Bd. Pediatrics, Am. Bd. Pediatric Hematology/Oncology. Postdoctoral fellow McCollum Pratt Inst., Johns Hopkins U., Balt., 1955-57; asst. prof. biochemistry Vanderbilt U., Nashville, 1957-62, assoc. prof., 1962-71, prof., 1971-73; intern, resident in pediatrics Vanderbilt U. Hosps., Nashville, 1966-69; pediatrician M.D. Anderson Hosp. U. Tex., Houston, 1973—; prof. pediatrics 1973—; Mosbacher prof. pediatrics, 1979-87, Mosbacher chmn., 1988-90, chmn. dept., 1983-88, head div., 1983-90, chmn. dept. exptl. pediatrics 1983-90; David R. Park prof. pediatrics U. Tex. Med. Sch., Houston, 1973-90, chmn. dept.; 1987-94; clin. prof. pediat. Sch. Medicine, Vanderbilt U., Nashville, 1994—; cons. Cancer Info. Svcs. for Code Ethics and Pediatric Cancers, 1986-89. Author: (with T.S. Carter and C. Jordan) The Howell Kindred, 1979; Humanity and Personhood. Personal Reactions to a World in Which Children Can Die, 1981; (with M. Weiner) Nicotinic Acid, Drug, Nutrient and Cofactor, 1983; contbr. numerous articles, abstracts, papers, book chpts. and revs. to profl. publs.; editor: (with J.T. Truman and C. Pochedly) Human Values in Pediatric Hematology/Oncology, 1986; (with R.A. Dowell and D. Copeland) The Child with

Cancer in the Community, 1988; Cancer in the Very Young, 1989; chief editor pediatric sect. Year Book of Cancer, 1978-87, cons. editor, 1974-78; assoc. editor Nutrition and Cancer, 1978—, Jour. Pediatric Hematology/Oncology, 1982-92, Houston Med. Jour., 1986-93, Cancer Prevention Interanat., 1993—; also editor/co-editor proc. of workshops, clin. and mental health confs., ann. symposiums, etc. Pres. bd. trustees Inst. Religion, Houston, 1989—; mem. adminstrv. bd. Westbury United Meth. Ch., Houston. Fellow Am. Acad. Pediatrics, Am. Coll. Nutrition; mem. Am. Pediatric Soc., Am. Soc. Hematology, Am. Soc. Clin. Oncology, Am. Med. Writers Assn., Am. Soc. for Parental and Enteral Nutrition, So. Med. Assn., World Fedn. for Hemophilia, Tex. Pediatric Soc., Houston Pediatric Soc. (pres. 1981-82), Houston Acad. Medicine, Harris County Med. Assn., U. Tex. M.D. Anderson Cancer Ctr. Assocs., Sigma Xi, Alpha Omega Alpha. Home and Office: 3504 Ruland Pl Nashville TN 37215

VAN EYSINGA, FRANS W., publisher; b. The Hague, The Netherlands, June 7, 1940; m. Anja Moret, Apr. 4, 1964; 3 children. D.R.S. in Earth Sci., Leyden U., 1966. Dep. mng. dir. Elsevier Sci. Publ., Amsterdam, Netherlands, 1968-78; pres. Kluwer Acad. Pubs., Hingham, Mass., 1978-93, Wolters Kluwer U.S. Corp., N.Y.C., 1994—. Editor Geol. Time Table, 1975. Served with Royal Dutch Navy, 1966-68. Mem. Royal Dutch Pubs. Assn. (v.p. export coun. 1982-93), chmn. S.T.M., 1992-94. Office: Wolters Kluwer US Corp 1185 6th Ave 36th fl New York NY 10036

VAN FLEET, GEORGE ALLAN, lawyer; b. Monterey, Calif., Jan. 20, 1953; s. George Lawson and Wilma Ruth (Williams) Van F.; m. Laurie Elise Koch, July 20, 1975; children: Katia Elaine, Alexander Lawson. BA summa cum laude, Rice U., 1976; JD, Columbia U., 1977. Bar: Tex. 1978, U.S. Dist. Ct. (so. dist.) Tex. 1978, U.S. Dist. Ct. (we. dist.) Tex. 1987, U.S. Dist. Ct. (no. dist.) Tex. 1988, U.S. Dist. Ct. (ea. dist.) Tex. 1991, U.S. Tax Ct., 1984, U.S. Ct. Appeals (5th cir.) 1978, U.S. Ct. Appeals (11th cir.) 1981, U.S. Ct. Appeals (D.C. cir.) 1982, U.S. Ct. Appeals (fed. cir.) 1993, U.S. Supreme Ct. 1981. Law clk. U.S. Ct. Appeals (2d cir.), N.Y.C., 1977; assoc. Vinson & Elkins, Houston, 1977-84, ptnr., 1984—. Editor: Compliance Manuals for the New Antitrust Era, 1989, quarterly rev. Litigation News, 1983-86; contbr. articles to profl. jour. Regional dir. Anti-Defamation League, 1990-94; bd. visitors Columbia U., 1992—; mem. City of Houston Ethics Com., 1992—. Recipient Ordroneaux prize Columbia U., 1977; James Kent scholar Columbia U., 1974-77. Fellow Tex. Bar Assn.; mem. ABA (com. chmn. 1987—), Houston Bar Assn. (sect. chair 1991-93), Tex.-Mex. Bar Assn. (com. chmn. 1994—), Phi Beta Kappa. Democrat. Jewish. Home: 4323 N Roseneath Dr Houston TX 77021-1623 Office: Vinson & Elkins 1001 Fannin Ste 2500 Houston TX 77002-6760

VAN FOSSAN, KATHRYN RUTH, library director; b. Elmhurst, Ill., Feb. 24, 1948; d. Norman Harvey and Ruth Marion (Shoger) Zurbrigg; m. Randy Eugene Van Fossan, Feb. 15, 1969; children: Karen Irene, David Bryan. BA in Music, U. Ill., 1969; MA in Musicology, Ill. State U., 1979; MLS, U. Ill., 1983. Interlibr. loan libr. Garrett Theol. Sem., Evanston, Ill., 1970-71; acquisitions asst. Olivet Nazarene U., Kankakee, Ill., 1978-80, cataloger, 1980-83, head tech. svcs., 1983-92, libr. dir., 1992—. Bd. dirs. Bur Oak Libr. Sys., Shorewood, Ill., 1990-93. Mem. ALA, Ill. Libr. Assn., Assn. Coll. and Rsch. Librs., Assn. Libr. Collections and Tech. Svcs. Avocations: church organist, choir director. Office: Olivet Nazarene U Benner Libr and Resource Ctr PO Box 592 Kankakee IL 60901

VAN FOSSEN, LARRY JACK, service company executive; b. Sidney, Ohio, Sept. 27, 1937; s. Carl Anderson and Bessie Lena (Laws) Van F.; m. Emily Jane Brockmann, Oct. 14, 1961; children: Elizabeth, William. B.B.A., U. Cin., 1960; J.D. summa cum laude, Ohio State U., 1963. Bar: Ohio 1963. Mem. firm Porter, Wright, Morris & Arthur, Columbus, Ohio, 1965-74; chmn., pres., CEO Chem Lawn Corp., Columbus, 1974-88, chmn.; pres. Nessoff Corp.; Columbus; pres. CEO Red Roof Inns Inc., also bd. dirs.; bd. dirs. Cardinal Distbn. Inc., Famous-Fraternity Sportswear, Inc. Mem. nat. coun. Coll. Law, Ohio State U., 1980—; trustee Paul G. Duke Found. Capt. U.S. Army, 1963-65. Mem. ABA, Ohio Bar Assn., The Golf Club, Worthington Hills Country Club. Republican. Office: Nessoff Corp 4355 Davidson Rd Hilliard OH 43026-2438

VANG, TIMOTHY TENG, church executive; b. Xieng Khouang, Laos, May 10, 1956; came to U.S., 1976; s. Nao Chai and Mai (Yang) V.; m. Chee Yang, Jan. 1, 1974 (dec. June 1975); m. Lydia Joua Vang, July 9, 1979; children: Jennifer P., Nathan K. BS in Missions, Cin. Bible Coll., 1984; MDiv in Ch. Ministries, Can. Theol. Sem., Regina, Sask., 1991; postgrad., Fuller Theol. Sem., Pasadena, Calif., 1993—. Machine operator Pellet Co., Green Bay, Wis., 1977-78; mental health worker Inst. Human Design, Oshkosh, Wis., 1978-80; ch. planter Ch. of Christ, Eau Claire, Wis., 1984-86; pastor Boulder (Colo.) Hmong Alliance Ch., 1986-87; dir. Christian edn. Hmong dist. Christian and Missionary Alliance, Brighton, Colo., 1986-87, dist. supt., 1991—; Ordained to ministry Ch. of Christ, 1984, Christian and Missionary Alliance, 1986. Organizer Fox Valley Lao/Hmong Assn., Appleton, Wis., 1979. Lt. U.S./Hmong Allied Army, 1971-75. Avocations: reading, writing, walking. Office: Hmong Dist 108 W Walnut St Brighton CO 80601-2827

VANGER, MILTON ISADORE, history educator; b. N.Y.C., Apr. 11, 1925; s. Max Manuel and Rose (Rothstein) V.; m. Elsa M. Oribe, Sept. 10, 1956; children: John, Mark, Rachel. A.B., Princeton U., 1948; M.A., Harvard U., 1950, Ph.D., 1958. Teaching fellow history Harvard U., 1952-56; instr. Okla. State U., 1956-58; asst. prof. history Sacramento State Coll., 1958-62; mem. faculty Brandeis U., Waltham, Mass., 1962—; prof. history Brandeis U., 1973-84, prof. emeritus, 1984—; chmn. Latin Am. studies, 1971-81; invited lectr. 50th anniversary conf. commemorating death of Battle y Ordóñez of Uruguay, 1979; invitee to inauguration of pres. Sanguinetti, Uruguay, 1985; Barnette Miller vis. prof. history, Wellesley Coll., 1990. Author: José Battle y Ordóñez of Uruguay: The Creator of His Times, 1902-1907, 1963, 2d edit., 1980, Spanish transl., 1968, 2d edit., 1992, The Model Country: José Battle y Ordóñez of Uruguay, 1907-1915, 1980, Spanish transl., 1983, 2d edit., 1991, Reforma o Revolución La Polémica Batlle-Mibelli, 1917, 1989; outside reviewer NEH, Radcliffe Inst.; contbr. articles to profl. jours. Juror for Lindahl Prize, Inst. Latin Am. Studies, Stockholm. With AUS, 1943-45. Doherty Found. fellow, 1950-52; grantee Am. Philos. Soc., 1966; recipient Hermes prize for best history pub. in Uruguay, 1983. Mem. New Eng. Council Latin Am. Studies (sec.-treas. 1970-72), Am. Hist. Assn., Conf. on Latin Am. History, Amnesty Internat., Phi Beta Kappa. Democrat. Jewish. Address: 931 Massachusetts Ave Ste 503 Cambridge MA 02139

VAN GESTEL, ALLAN, lawyer; b. Boston, Dec. 3, 1935. B.A., Colby Coll., 1957; LL.B., Boston U., 1961. Bar: Mass. 1961, U.S. Dist. Ct. Mass. 1963, (no. dist.) N.Y. 1980, (we. dist.) N.Y. 1993, U.S. Ct. Claims 1979, U.S. Ct. Appeals (1st cir.) 1969, (2d cir.) 1980, (3d cir.) 1993, U.S. Supreme Ct. 1972. Assoc. firm Goodwin, Procter & Hoar, Boston, 1961-70; ptnr. Goodwin, Procter & Hoar, 1970—; spl. counsel Boston Fin. Commn., 1974; spl. counsel to Mass. Commn. on Jud. Conduct, 1986; mem. Scituate (Mass.) Bd. Zoning Appeals, 1970, Scituate Planning Bd., 1972; spl. counsel Gov. of N.Y. on Indian Land Claims, 1985—; spl. counsel to Gov. and Atty. Gen. of Vt. on Indian Claims, 1987-90; chmn. standing adv. com. Mass. Rules Civil Procedure, 1986-93 ; overseer Colby Coll. Contbr. numerous articles on Eastern Indian land claims, ct. administrn., capital punishment to profl. jours. Fellow Am. Coll. Trial Lawyers; mem. ABA, Mass. Bar Assn., Boston Bar Assn. (chmn., task force on drugs and the cts.), Supreme Jud. Ct. Hist. Soc. (chmn. bd. overseers 1993—). Office: Goodwin Procter & Hoar Exchange Pl Boston MA 02109-2808

VAN GILDER, JOHN CORLEY, neurosurgeon, educator; b. Huntington, W.Va., Aug. 14, 1935; s. John Ray and Sarah Pool (Corley) Van G.; m. Kerstin Margarita Olesson, Mar., 1965; children: Sarah, John, Rachel, David. BA, W.Va. U., 1957, BS, 1959; MD, U. Pitts., 1961. Diplomate Am. Bd. Neurol. Surgery (examiner 1976, 79, 84). Intern Pa. Hosp., Phila., 1961, asst. resident in surgery 1964-65; asst. resident in surgery Wilkes-Barre (Pa.) Hosp., 1962; asst. resident neurosurgery Barnes Hosp., St. Louis, 1966-68, sr. resident, 1968-69; instr. neurosurgery Yale U. Sch. Medicine, New Haven, 1970, assoc. prof., 1970-73, assoc. prof., 1973-76; prof. neurosurgery U. Iowa, Iowa City, 1976—, chmn. div. neurosurgery, 1976—, exec. com. dept. surgery, 1978-81; fellow neurosurgery Wash. U. Sch. Medicine, St.

Louis, 1965 -66, instr., 1966; attending neurosurgeon VA Hosp., New Haven, 1970-73, cons. 1973-76; assoc. to attending neurosurgeon Yale-New Haven Med. Ctr. 1970-76; cons. VA Hosp., Iowa City, 1976—; mem. clin. coordinating com. U. Iowa Cancer Ctr., 1979—; presenter numerous papers at profl. meetings., confs., symposia; vis. prof. U. Tenn., 1984, Tufts U. Med. Ctr., Boston, 1986, U. Tex., San Antonio, 1987, U. Mich., Ann Arbor, 1988, People's Republic China at Hunan Med. Coll., Beijing Neurol. Inst., Tianjin Med. Coll. Hosp., Tiantan Xili, Xian Gen. Hosp., 2d Mil. Coll., Shanghai, Suzhou Med. Coll. Shanghai, 1985, USSR at Burdenk Inst., Kiev Neurol. Inst., Leningrad Neurol. Soc., 1989, Western Reserve U., Cleve., 1993, Yale U., New Haven, Conn., 1994. Author: (with others): Principles of Surgery, 2d edit., 1973, Brief Textbook of Surgery, 1976, Aneurysmal Subarachnoid Hemorrhage, 1981, Operative Neurosurgical Techniques, Indications, Methods, and Results, 1982, Sports Medicine, 1982, Neurosurgery, 1982, Clinical Neurosurgery, 1982, Operative Neurosurgical Technique, Vol. II, 1982, 88, Vol. III, 1995, Current Therapy in Neurosurgical Surgery, 1985, 2d edit. , 1987, Craniovertebral Junction Abnormalities, 1987, Decision Making in Neurological Surgery, 1987, Neurological Surgery, 3d edit., 1988, Anterior Cervical Spine Surgery, 1993, Brain Surgery: Complication Avoidance and Management, 1993, Neurosurgical Emergencies, 1994, Techniques of Spinal Fusion and Instrumation, 1995, Somatic Gene Therapy, 1995; contbr. numerous articles and abstracts to profl. jours.; co-author teaching films; mem. editorial bd. Neurosurgery jour., 1978-84. Capt. USAF, 1962-64. Grantee NIH, 1973-78, Nat. Cancer Inst., 1980-88. Fellow ACS (membership com. Iowa dist. #1 1983—); mem. AMA (Physicians Recognition award), Am. Physiol. Soc., Congress Neurol. Surgeons (resident placement com. 1970), Am. Assn. Neurol. Surgeons (bd. dirs. 1986-90, awards com. 1986-87, chmn. 1987-88), Rsch. Soc. Neurol. Surgeons, Neurol. Soc. Am. (long range planning com. 1984—, v.p. 1985), Iowa Med. Soc., Johnson County Med. Soc. (program com. 1984-88, chmn. 1985-86), Iowa-Midwest Neurosurg. Soc. (pres. 1978-79), Soc. Neurol. Surgeons (chmn. membership com. 1986-87, treas. 1991—), Midwest Surg. Assn., Am. Acad. Neurol. Surgery (v.p. 1995—), Ga. Neurosurg. Soc. (hon. life), Am. Board Neurol. Surg. (dir. 1992—; residency rev. com.-neurol. surgery 1995—), Sigma Xi. Home: 330 S Summit St Iowa City IA 52240-3220 Office: U Iowa Hosps & Clinics Dept Neurosurgery 459 Newton Rd Iowa City IA 52240

VAN GINKEL, BLANCHE LEMCO, architect, educator; b. London, Dec. 14, 1923; d. Myer and Claire Lemco; m. H. P. Daniel van Ginkel, 1956; children: Brenda Renee, Marc Ian. B.Arch., McGill U., 1945; M.C.P., Harvard U., 1950. Tech. asst. Nat. Film Bd. Can., 1943-44; mgr. City Planning Office, Regina, Sask., Can., 1946; architect Atelier Le Corbusier, Paris, 1948; asst. prof. architecture U. Pa., 1951-57; ptnr. van Ginkel Assocs., Montreal, Que., Can., also Toronto, Ont., Can., 1957—; prof. architecture U. Toronto, 1977—, dir. Sch. Architecture, 1977-80, dean faculty architecture and landscape architecture, 1980-82; vis. critic Harvard U., 1958, 70; vis. prof. Universite de Montreal, McGill U.; curator exhbns. RCA, U. Toronto, and others. Contbr. articles to profl. jours. Mem. adv. com. Nat. Capital Planning Com., Ottawa; mem. adv. com. Nat. Mus.'s Corp.; mem. Que. Provincial Planning Commn. Recipient Lt. Gov.'s medal McGill U., 1945, Internat. Fedn. Housing and Planning Grand Prix award, 1956, Massey medal, 1962, Mademoiselle Mag. award, 1957, Queen's Silver Jubilee medal, 1977, Citizenship award Can. Govt., 1991, Alumni award U. Toronto, 1991. Fellow Royal Archtl. Inst. Can (exec. com. 1971-74), AIA (hon.); mem. Can. Inst. Planners (bd. dirs. 1961-64), Assn. Collegiate Schs. Architecture (bd. dirs. 1981-84, v.p. 1985-86, pres. 1986-87, Disting. prof. award 1989), Assn. Royal Inst. Brit. Architects (assoc.), Royal Can. Acad. Art. Office: 38 Summerhill Gardens, Toronto, ON Canada M4T 1B4

VAN GORKOM, JEROME WILLIAM, financial executive; b. Denver, Aug. 6, 1917; s. A.G. and Elizabeth (Laux) Van G.; m. Betty Jean Alexander, June 27, 1942; children: Gayle, Lynne. BS, U. Ill., 1939, JD, 1941. Bar: Ill. 1941; C.P.A., 1950. Law assoc. Kix Miller, Baar & Morris, Chgo., 1945-47; accountant Arthur Andersen & Co., 1947-54, ptnr., 1954-56; treas., contr. Trans Union Corp., Chgo., 1956—; dir. Trans Union Corp., 1957—, v.p., 1958-60, exec. v.p., 1960-63, pres., 1963-78, chmn. bd., 1978-82; under sec. Dept. State, 1982-83; mng. dir. Chgo. Housing Authority, 1987-88. Chmn. bd. Lyric Opera of Chgo.; chmn. Chgo. Sch. Fin. Authority, 1980-89. With USNR, 1941-45. Clubs: Chicago, Mid America, Comml, Onwentsia, Old Elm, Pauma Valley Country. Home: 245 W Westminster Rd Lake Forest IL 60045-2126

VAN GRAAFEILAND, ELLSWORTH ALFRED, federal judge; b. Rochester, N.Y., May 11, 1915; s. Ivan and Elsie (Gohr) VanG.; m. Rosemary Vaeth, May 26, 1945; children—Gary, Suzanne, Joan, John, Anne. A.B., U. Rochester, 1937; LL.B., Cornell U., 1940. Bar: N.Y. 1940. Practiced in Rochester; now sr. judge U.S. Ct. Appeals for 2d Cir. Fellow Am. Bar Found.; mem. ABA (ho. dels. 1973-75), N.Y. State Bar Assn. (v.p. 1972-73, pres. 1973-74, chmn. negligence compensation and ins. sect. 1968-69), Monroe County Bar Assn. (past pres.), Am. Coll. Trial Lawyers, Masons, Kent Club, Oak Hill Country Club. Home: 76 Ramsey Park Rochester NY 14610-1333 Office: Fed Bldg 100 State St Ste 423 Rochester NY 14614-1369

VAN GRAAFEILAND, GARY P., lawyer. BA, Union Coll., 1968; JD, Cornell U., 1972. Bar: N.Y. 1973. Asst. gen. counsel Eastman Kodak, Rochester, N.Y., 1989-92, sr. v.p., gen. counsel, sec., 1992—. Office: Eastman Kodak Co 343 State St Rochester NY 14650-0001*

VAN GUNDY, GREGORY FRANK, lawyer; b. Columbus, Ohio, Oct. 24, 1945; s. Paul Arden and Edna Marie (Sanders) Van G.; m. Lisa Tamara Langer. B.A., Ohio State U., Columbus, 1966, J.D, 1969. Bar: N.Y. bar 1971. Asso. atty. firm Willkie Farr & Gallagher, N.Y.C., 1970-74; v.p. legal, sec. Marsh & McLennan Cos., Inc., N.Y.C., 1974-79; v.p., sec., gen. counsel Marsh & McLennan Cos., Inc., 1979—. Mem. ABA, Phi Beta Kappa. Roman Catholic. Club: University (N.Y.C.). Home: 232 Fox Meadow Rd Scarsdale NY 10583-1640 Office: Marsh & McLennan Cos Inc 1166 Ave Of The Americas New York NY 10036-2774

VAN GUNDY, JAMES JUSTIN, biology educator; b. Peoria, Ill., Jan. 29, 1939; s. George Christian and Beatrice (Baird) Van G.; m. Judith V. Mobley, Sept. 5, 1964; children: Douglas, Susan. MS, Pa. State U., 1969; PhD, U. Utah, 1973. Prof. biology U. Bridgeport, Conn., 1972-75; prof. biology, environ. scis. Davis and Elkins (W.va.) Coll., 1975—; cons. Gannet, Fleming, Inc., Harrisburg, Pa., 1986-87; dir. W.Va. Highlands Conservancy, Charleston, 1984-88, W.Va. Pub. Lands Corp., Charleston, 1989-91. With U.S. Army, 1959-61, Korea. Recipient Appalachian Scholar award U. Ky., 1991. Mem. AAAS, Nat. Speleol. Soc., W.Va. Acad. Sci. Democrat. Home: 240 Boundary Ave Elkins WV 26241-3902 Office: Davis and Elkins Coll 100 Sycamore St Elkins WV 26241-3971

VAN GUNDY, SEYMOUR DEAN, nematologist, plant pathologist, educator; b. Toledo, Feb. 24, 1931; s. Robert C. and Margaret (Holloway) Van G.; m. Wilma C. Fanning, June 12, 1954; children: Sue Ann, Richard L. BA, Bowling Green State U., 1953; PhD, U. Wis., 1957. Asst. nematologist U. Calif., Riverside, 1957-63, assoc. prof., 1963-68, prof. nematology and plant pathology, 1968-73, assoc. dean rsch., 1968-70, vice chancellor rsch., 1970-72, chmn. dept. nematology, 1972-84, prof. nematology and plant pathology, assoc. dean rsch. Coll. Natural and Agrl. Scis., 1985-88, acting dean, 1986, interim dean, 1988-90, dean, 1990-93, emeritus dean and prof, 1993—. Former mem. editorial bd. Rev. de Nematologie, Jour. Nematology and Plant Disease; contbr. numerous articles to profl. jours. NSF fellow, Australia, 1965-66; grantee Rockefeller Found., Cancer Res., NSF, USDA. Fellow AAAS, Am. Phytopathol. Soc. Nematologists (editor-in-chief 1968-72, v.p. 1972-73, pres. 1973-74). Home: 1188 Pastern Rd Riverside CA 92506-5619 Office: U Calif Dept Nenatology Riverside CA 92521

VAN HALEN, EDDIE, guitarist, rock musician; b. Nijmegan, The Netherlands, Jan. 26, 1957; came to U.S., 1967; s. Jan and Eugenia Van Halen; m. Valerie Bertinelli, Apr. 1981. Student, Pasadena City Coll.; studied piano. Formed group Broken Combs, name later Mammoth, with bro. Alex.; leader group Van Halen, 1974—; albums include Van Halen, 1978, Van Halen II, 1979, Women and Children First, 1980, Fair Warning, 1981, Diver Down, 1982, 1984, (1984), 5150, 1986, OU812, 1988, For Unlawful Carnal Knowledge, 1991, Van Halen Live: Right Here Right Now, 1993, Balance,

1995. Office: care Premier Talent Agy 3 E 54th St New York NY 10022-3108*

VANHANDEL, RALPH ANTHONY, librarian; b. Appleton, Wis., Jan. 17, 1919; s. Frank Henry and Gertrude Mary (Schmidt) Van H.; m. Alice Catherine Hogan, Oct. 27, 1945; children: William Patrick, Karen Jean, Mary Jo. BA, U. Wis., 1946; AB in Libr. Sci., U. Mich., 1947. Head libr. Lawrence (Kans.) Free Pub. Libr., 1947-51, Hibbing (Minn.) Pub. Libr., 1951-54; libr. dir. Gary (Ind.) Pub. Libr., 1954-74; libr. dir. Wells Meml. Pub. Libr., Lafayette, Ind. (name now Tippecanoe County Pub. Libr.), 1974-84, libr. cons., 1963—; mem. Ind. Library Cert. Bd., 1969-84, Ind. State Library and Hist. Bldg. Expansion Commn., 1973-81. Named Ind. Librarian of Year, 1971, Sagamore of Wabash, 1984. Mem. ALA, Anselm Forum (sec. 1964, v.p. 1965), Ind. Library Assn. (pres. 1963-64), Kans. Library Assn. (v.p. 1951), KC, Rotary. Home: 3624 Winter St Lafayette IN 47905-3838

VANHARN, GORDON LEE, college administrator and provost; b. Grand Rapids, Mich., Dec. 30, 1935; s. Henry and Edna (Riemersma) VanH.; m. Mary Kool, June 12, 1958; children—Pamela L., Mark L., Barbara A. B.A., Calvin Coll., 1957; M.S., U. Ill., 1959, Ph.D., 1961. Asst. prof. biology Calvin Coll., Grand Rapids, Mich. 1961-68, prof., 1970-82, acad. dean, 1982-85, provost, 1985-94, sr. v.p., provost, 1994—; assoc. prof. biology Oberlin Coll., Ohio, 1968-70; research assoc. U. Va., Charlotteville, 1975-76. Contbr. articles to profl. jours. Mem. sci. adv. com. Gerald R. Ford, 1972-73, Blodgett Hosp. research and review com., 1978-84; pres. bd. Grand Rapids Christian Sch. Assn., 1982-85; v.p. Christian Schs. Internat., 1987-93. Grass Found. fellow, 1969. Mem. AAAS, Am. Assn. Higher Edn., Phi Kappa Phi. Mem. Christian Reformed Ch. Home: 1403 Cornell Dr SE Grand Rapids MI 49506-4103 Office: Calvin Coll Office of the Provost Grand Rapids MI 49546

VAN HASSEL, HENRY JOHN, dentist, educator, university dean; b. Paterson, N.J., May 2, 1933; s. William Cornelius and Ina (Sturr) Van H.; m. Ann Newell Wiley, Dec. 28, 1960. BA, Maryville Coll., Tenn., 1954; DDS, U. Md., 1963; MSD, U. Wash., 1967, PhD, 1969. Diplomate Am.Bd. Endodontics. Dental dir. USPHS, Seattle, 1965-81; prof., chmn. dept. endodontics U. Md., Balt., 1981-84; dean dental sch. Oreg. Health Scis. U., Portland, 1984—, v.p. instl. affairs, 1989-91. Recipient Schlack award Assn. Mil. Surgeons U.S., 1976, Borrish award Acad. Gen. Dentistry, 1989. Mem. Am. Assn. Endodontists (pres. 1981-82, Grossman Gold medal 1984), Oreg. Dental Assn. (pres. 1990). Office: Oreg Health Scis U Dental Sch 611 SW Campus Dr Portland OR 97201-3001

VAN HAUER, ROBERT, former health care company executive; b. Chgo., June 9, 1910; s. Francis Anthony and Della Agnes (Mulhern) Van H.; m. Elaine Greenwood, July 24, 1944 (dec. Nov. 1961); children: Peter, Jan, Mary, Christopher, Gretchen, Juliana; m. Margaret Ann St. Pierre Viehman, May 4, 1968; stepchildren: Gayle, Edwin, Thomas, John, Michael, Daniel. B.A. in Econs; B.B.A. in Accounting (Reiman scholar), U. Mont., Missoula, 1938; M.A. in Econs, U. Minn., Mpls., 1940. Jr. Auditor Peat Marwick Mitchell, C.P.A.'s, Mpls., 1938-40; asst. sales mgr. North Star Woolen Mill, Mpls., 1940-42; dir. contracts Mpls. regional office VA, 1946-51; with Health Central, Inc., Mpls., 1951-78; exec. v.p. Health Central, Inc., 1965, pres., chief exec. officer, 1970-78; exec. dir. Health Found., Mpls., 1979-81. Mem. planning commn. Golden Valley, Minn., 1959-66; past trustee St. Margaret's Acad., Benilde-St. Margaret's High Sch. Served to maj. AUS, 1941-46. Decorated Commendation ribbon; Rieman fellow, 1938-40. Mem. Am. Hosp. Assn., Minn. Hosp. Assn. (trustee, com. chmn. 1974-79), War Meml. Blood Bank (pres., dir. 1967), Physicians Health Plan Mpls. (dir., exec. com.), Am. Legion. Republican. Roman Catholic. Clubs: Mpls. Athletic, Minn. Valley Country, Elks; Union Hills Country (Sun City, Ariz.). Home: 6837 Olson Memorial Hwy Golden Valley MN 55427-4951

VAN HENGEL, MAARTEN, banker; b. Amsterdam, The Netherlands, Mar. 29, 1927; came to U.S., 1950, naturalized, 1957; s. Adrianus J. and Helena (Gips) van H.; m. Drusilla Drake Riley, Dec. 1, 1951; children: Maarten, Virginia, Hugh, Drusilla. Student, Kennemer Lyceum, Bloemendaal, Holland, 1939-45. With tng. programs of Amsterdamsche Bank, N.V., Amsterdam, Lazard Bros. & Co. Ltd., London and Canadian Bank of Commerce, Montreal, Que., Can., 1945-49; with Brown Bros. Harriman & Co., 1950—, ptnr., 1968—; chmn. Brown Bros. Harriman Trust Co. Bd. dirs. Netherlands-Am. Found., Phelps Meml. Hosp. Served with AUS, 1951-53. Clubs: India House, Netherland (N.Y.C.); Fishers Island Country, Hay Harbor (Fishers Island); Sleepy Hollow Country (Scarborough, N.Y.). Home: 350 River Rd Briarcliff Manor NY 10510-2418 Office: Brown Bros Harriman & Co 59 Wall St New York NY 10005-2818

VAN HEYDE, J. STEPHEN, lawyer; b. Columbus, Ohio, May 22, 1943. BBA magna cum laude, U. Notre Dame, 1965; JD cum laude, Ohio State U., 1968. Bar: Ohio 1968. Ptnr. Baker & Hostetler, Columbus, Ohio. Mem. ABA, Columbus Bar Assn. (bd. govs. 1989-90), Beta Gamma Sigma, Beta Alpha Psi, Phi Delta Phi. Office: Baker & Hostetler Capital Sq 65 E State St Ste 2100 Columbus OH 43215-4260

VAN HOESEN, BETH MARIE, artist, printmaker; b. Boise, Idaho, June 27, 1926; d. Enderse G. and Freda Marie (Soulen) Van H.; m. Mark Adams, Sept. 12, 1953. Student, Escuela Esmaralda, Mexico City, 1945, San Francisco Art Inst., 1946, 47, 51, 52, Fontainbleau (France) Ecole des Arts, Acad. Julian and Acad., 5Grande Chaumier, Paris, 1948-51; B.A., Stanford U., 1948; postgrad., San Francisco State U., 1957-58. One-Woman shows include, De Young Mus., San Francisco, 1959, Achenbach Found., Calif. Palace Legion of Honor, San Francisco, 1961, 74, Santa Barbara (Calif.) Mus., 1963, 74, 76, Oakland (Calif.) Mus., 1980, John Berggruen Gallery, San Francisco, 1981, 83, 85, 88, 91; traveling exhibit Am. Mus. Assn., 1983-85; group shows include, Calif. State Fair, Sacramento, 1951 (award), Library of Congress, Washington, 1956, 57, San Francisco Mus. Modern Art, 70 (award), Boston Mus. Fine Arts, 1959, 60, 62, Pa. Acad. Fine Arts, Phila., 1959, 61, 63, 65, Achenbach Found., 1961 (award), Bklyn. Mus., 1962, 66, 68, 77, Continuing Am. Graphics, Osaka, Japan, 1970, Hawaii Nat. Print. Exhbn., Honolulu, 1980 (award), Oakland Mus. 1975 (award); represented in permanent collections, including, Achenbach Found., San Francisco, Fine Arts Mus., Bklyn. Mus., Mus. Modern Art N.Y.C., Oakland Mus., San Francisco Mus. Modern Art, Victoria and Albert Mus., (London), Chgo. Art Inst., Cin. Mus., Portland (Oreg.) Art Mus. (Recipient award of Honor, San Francisco Art Commn. 1981); author: Collection of Wonderful Things, 1972, Beth Van Hoesen Creatures, 1987, Beth Van Hoesen Works on Paper, 1995. Mem. Calif. Soc. Printmakers (award 1993), San Francisco Women Artists. Office: care John Berggruen 228 Grant Ave Fl 3D San Francisco CA 94108-4612

VAN HOFTEN, JAMES DOUGAL ADRIANUS, business executive, former astronaut; b. Fresno, Calif., June 11, 1944; s. Adriaan and Beverly (McCurdy) van H.; m. Vallarie Davis, May 31, 1975; children—Jennifer Lyn, Jamie Juliana, Victoria Jane. B.S., U. Calif.-Berkeley, 1966; M.S., Colo. State U., 1968, Ph.D., 1976. Asst. prof. U. Houston, 1976-78; astronaut NASA, Houston, 1978-86; sr. v.p., mgr. advanced systems line Bechtel Nat., Inc., San Francisco, 1986-93; project mgr. Hong Kong New Airport projects. Served with USN, 1969-74; lt. col. Air N.G. 1984—. Recipient Disting. Service award Colo. State U., 1984; Disting. Citizen award Fresno Council Boy Scouts Am., 1984; Disting. Achievement award Pi Kappa Alpha, 1984. Assoc. fellow AIAA; mem. ASCE (Aerospace Sci. and Tech. Application award 1984). Republican. Home: 46 Tai Tam Rd House C, Hong Kong Hong Kong Office: Internat Bechtel Inc, 8 Harbour Rd, Wanchai Hong Kong

VAN HOLDE, KENSAL EDWARD, biochemistry educator; b. Eau Claire, Wis., May 14, 1928; s. Leonard John and Nettie (Hart) Van H.; m. Barbara Jean Watson, Apr. 11, 1950; children: Patricia, Mary, Stephen, David. B.S., U. Wis., 1949, Ph.D., 1952. Research chemist E.I. du Pont de Nemours & Co., 1952-55; research assoc. U. Wis. 1955-56; asst. prof. U. Wis. at Milw., 1956-57; mem. faculty U. Ill., Urbana, 1957-67; prof. dept. biochemistry and biophysics Oreg. State U., Corvallis, 1967; Am. Cancer Soc. rsch. prof., 1977-93, disting. prof., 1988-93, disting. prof. emeritus, 1993—; instr.-in-charge physiology course Marine Biol. Lab., Woods Hole, Mass., 1977-80; mem. research staff Centre des Recherches sur les Macromolecules, Strasbourg, France, 1964-65; mem. study sect. USPHS, 1966-69, 91—; staff Weizmann Inst., Israel, 1981, Lab. Léon Brillouin, Saclay, France, 1989-90. Author: Physical Biochemistry, 1971, Chromatin, 1988; (with C. Mathews) Biochemistry, 1989; editor: Biochemica Biophysica Acta, 1966-68; mem. editorial bd. Jour. Biol. Chemistry, 1968-75, 81-87, 91-92, assoc. editor, 1992—, Biochemistry, 1973-76, 82-89; contbr. profl. jours. Trustee Marine Biol. Lab., Woods Hole, 1979-82, 84-92. NSF sr. postdoctoral fellow, 1964-65; Guggenheim fellow, 1973-74; European Molecular Biology Orgn. fellow, 1975. Mem. NAS, Am. Chem. Soc., Am. Soc. Biol. Chemists, Biophys. Soc. Home: 229 NW 32nd St Corvallis OR 97330-5020 Office: Oreg State U Dept Biochemistry Corvallis OR 97331

VANHOLE, WILLIAM REMI, lawyer; b. Denver, June 25, 1948; s. Joseph L. and Mildred M. (DeKoevend) VanH.; m. Gemma Irene Rice, Feb. 7, 1971; 3 children. B.S., Colo. State U., 1970; J.D., U. Idaho, 1976. Bar: Idaho 1976, U.S. Dist. Ct. Idaho 1976, U.S. Ct. Appeals (9th cir.) 1983. Law clk. to judge U.S. Dist. Ct. Idaho, Boise, 1976-78; assoc. Quane, Smith, Howard & Hull, Boise, 1978-81, Langroise, Sullivan & Smylie, Boise, 1981-83; asst. U.S. atty. U.S. Dept. of Justice, Boise, 1983-87; U.S. atty. Dist. of Idaho, 1984-85; assoc. gen. counsel Boise Cascade Corp., 1987—. Served with U.S. Army, 1970-72. Mem. ABA, Fed. Bar Assn., Idaho Bar Assn., Idaho Assn. Def. Counsel, Def. Rsch. Inst., Am. Corp. Counsel Assn. Republican. Avocations: skiing, fishing, tennis. Office: Boise Cascade Corp 1111 W Jefferson PO Box 50 Boise ID 83702

VAN HOOMISSEN, GEORGE ALBERT, state supreme court justice; b. Portland, Oreg., Mar. 7, 1930; s. Fred J. and Helen F. (Flanagan) Van H.; m. Ruth Madeleine Niedermeyer, June 4, 1960; children: Geroge T., Ruth Anne, Madeleine, Matthew. BBA, U. Portland, 1951; JD, Georgetown U., 1955, LLM in Labor Law, 1957; LLM in Jud. Adminstrn., U. Va., 1986. Bar: D.C. 1955, Oreg. 1956, Tex. 1971, U.S. Dist. Ct. Oreg. 1956, U.S. Ct. Mil. Appeals 1955, U.S. Ct. Customs and Patent Appeals 1955, U.S. Ct. Claims 1955, U.S. Ct. Appeals (9th cir.) 1956, U.S. Ct. Appeals (D.C. cir.) 1955, U.S. Supreme Ct. 1960. Law clk. for Chief Justice Harold J. Warner Oreg. Supreme Ct., 1955-56; Keigwin teaching fellow Georgetown Law Sch., 1956-57; dep. dist. atty. Multnomah County, Portland, 1957-59; pvt. practice Portland, 1959-62; dist. atty. Multnomah County, 1962-71; dean natl. coll. dist. attys. U. Houston, 1971-73; judge Cir. Ct., Portland, 1973-81, Oreg. Ct. Appeals, Salem, 1981-88; assoc. justice Oreg. Supreme Ct., Salem, 1988—. Mem. Oreg. Ho. of Reps., Salem, 1959-62, chmn. house jud. com. With USMC, 1951-53; col. USMCR (ret.). Recipient Disting. Alumnus award U. Portland, 1972. Mem. ABA, Oreg. State Bar, Tex. Bar Assn., Multnomah Athletic Club, Univ Club. Roman Catholic. Office: Oreg Supreme Ct 1163 State St Salem OR 97310-0260

VAN HOOSIER, GERALD LEONARD, veterinary science educator; b. Weatherford, Tex., June 4, 1934; s. Gerald L. Sr. and Louise (Ashcroft) Van H.; m. Marlene M., Aug. 2, 1959; children: Gunther, Paul. DVM, Tex. A&M, 1957. Diplomate Am. Coll. Lab. Animal Medicine. Postdoctoral fellow U. Calif., Berkeley, 1959-60, Wash. State U., Pullman, 1969-71; chief applied virology NIH, Bethesda, 1960-62; assoc. prof. Baylor U. Coll. Medicine, Houston, 1962-69; assoc. prof., dir. Wash. State U., Pullman, 1969-75; prof., chmn. U. Wash., Seattle, 1975—; cons. VA Med. Ctr., Seattle, Tacoma, Boise, Seattle Biomed. Rsch. Inst. Editor: Laboratory Hamsters, 1987; contbg. author: The Hamster, Clin. Chemistry of Lab. Animals, 1989; contbr. articles to profl. jours. With USPHS Res., 1959—. Recipient Disting. Alumni award Tex. A&M, 1991, Animal Investigation and Diagnosis Lab award NIH, 1979-91, Comparative Med. Tng. NIH, 1982-91. Mem. Am. Assn. Lab. Animal Sci. (pres. 1991-92, Charles A. Griffin award 1986). Office: U Wash Dept Comparative Med S # 42 Seattle WA 98195

VAN HORN, LECIA JOSEPH, legal secretary; b. L.A., Jan. 19, 1963; d. McKinley Joe and Opal Geneva (Ivie) Joseph; m. Philip Dale Van Horn, Apr. 19, 1986; children: Kari Christine, Brandon Joseph. BA in Journalism, U. Southern Calif., 1984. News reporter Sta. KSCR Radio, L.A., 1983; consumer news researcher Sta. KCBS-TV, L.A., 1983, Sta. KABC-TV, L.A., 1983-84; newswriter Headline News, Atlanta, 1984-85; editorial asst., newswriter, field producer Sta. KNBC-TV, Burbank, Calif., 1985-86; newswriter, assoc. producer Sta. WYFF-TV, Greenville, S.C., 1986; freelance newswriter, assoc. producer Sta. WSB-TV, Atlanta, 1987-88; newswriter CNN, Atlanta, 1987-94. Author: Thoughts and Inspirational Sayings, 1985; contbr. poetry and articles to newspapers. Mem. U. So. Calif. Alumni. Mem. Science of Mind. Avocations: reading, music, dancing, gymnastics (Class III Calif. State Champion 1977).

VAN HORN, RICHARD LINLEY, university administrator; b. Chgo., Nov. 2, 1932; s. Richard Linley and Mildred Dorothy (Wright) Van H.; m. Susan Householder, May 29, 1954 (dec.); children: Susan Elizabeth, Patricia Suzanne, Lynda Sue; m. Betty Pfefferbaum, May 29, 1988. BS with highest honors, Yale U., 1954; MS, MIT, 1956; PhD, Carnegie-Mellon U., 1976; D of Bus. (hon.), Reitsumeikan U., Kyoto, Japan, 1991. Asst. dir. Army EDP Project, MIT, Cambridge, 1956-57; research staff Rand Corp., Santa Monica, Calif., 1957-60; head mgmt. systems group Rand Corp., 1960-67; dir., prof. mgmt. systems European Inst. Advanced Studies in Mgmt., Brussels, Belgium, 1971-73; asso. dean Grad. Sch. Indsl. Adminstrn., Carnegie-Mellon U., Pitts., 1967-71; dir. budget and planning, 1973-74, v.p. for bus. affairs, 1974-77, v.p. for mgmt., 1977-80, provost and prof. mgmt., 1980-83; chancellor U. Houston, 1983-86, pres., 1986-89; pres. U. Okla., 1989-94; pres. emeritus and regent's prof. Coll. of Bus. U. Okla., Norman, 1994—. Author: (with Robert H. Gregory) Automatic Data Processing Systems, 1960, 2nd edit. 1963, (with R.H. Gregory) Business Data Processing and Programming, 1963, (with C.H. Kriebel and J.T. Heames) Management Information Systems: Progress and Perspectives, 1971; contbr. articles to profl. jours.; assoc. editor: Jour. Inst. Mgmt. Scis, 1964-78. Bd. dirs. Last Frontier coun. Boy Scouts Am., Kirkpatrick Ctr., Nelson-Atkins Art Mus., Truman Libr. Inst., State Fair Okla., Okla. Futures Commn., Okla. Health Scis. Ctr. Found., Inc., Okla. Ednl. TV Authority. Mem. Inst. Mgmt. Sci. (nat. council mem. 1963-65, sec.-treas. 1964), Assn. for Computing Machinery (nat. lectr. 1969-70), Council on Govt. Relations (bd. dirs. 1981-83). Avocation: commercial pilot. Home: 701 NW 14th St Oklahoma City OK 73103 Office: U Okla Coll of Bus Norman OK 73019

VAN HORN, VERNE HILE, III, retail executive; b. Tulsa, July 27, 1938; s. Verne Hile and Vonnie Hoffman (King) Van H.; m. Anne Burkhalter; children: Tracy, Melissa, David, William. Student, U. Okla., 1957; BS in Bus., U. Tulsa, 1962. Salesman Phillips Petroleum Co., Dallas, 1963-66; with Nat. Convenience Stores, Houston, 1966—; v.p. stores div. Nat. Convenience Stores Inc., 1971-75, exec. v.p., 1975, pres., dir., 1975—, also chief exec. officer.; bd. dirs. Southdown Inc., Tex. Rsch. League. Bd. dirs. Houston Pks. Bd., United Way of Tex. Gulf Coast, United Way of Am., Sam Houston area coun. Boy Scouts Am., Houston Ballet, Houston Better Bus. Bur., Greater Houston Partnership. Mem. Tex. Assn. Taxpayers (bd. dirs.), Am. Leadership Forum (bd. dirs.), Forum Club of Houston (bd. dirs.), Young Pres.'s Assn. Republican. Office: Nat Convenience Stores Inc 100 Waugh Dr Houston TX 77007-5850

VAN HORNE, JAMES CARTER, economist, educator; b. South Bend, Ind., Aug. 6, 1935; s. Ralph and Helen (McCarter) Van H.; m. Mary A. Roth, Aug. 27, 1960; children: Drew, Stuart, Stephen. AB, De Pauw U., 1957, DSc (hon.), 1986; MBA, Northwestern U., 1961, PhD, 1964. Comml. lending rep. Continental Ill. Nat. Bank, Chgo., 1958-62; prof. fin. Stanford U. Grad. Sch. Bus., 1965-75, A.P. Giannini prof. fin., 1976—, assoc. dean, 1973-75, 76-80; dep. asst. sec. Dept. Treasury, 1975-76; bd. dirs. Sanwa Bank Calif., BB&K Internat. Fund, BB&K Fund Group; chmn. Montgomery St. Income Securities; commr. workers compensation Rate Making Study Commmn., State of Calif., 1990-92. Author: Function and Analysis of Capital Market Rates, 1970, Financial Market Rates and Flows, 1994, Financial Management and Policy, 1995; co-author: Fundamentals of Financial Management, 1995; assoc. editor Jour. fin. and Quantitative Analysis, 1969-85, Jour. Fin., 1971-73, Jour. Fixed Income, 1990—. Mem. bd. trustees DePauw U. With AUS, 1957. Mem. Am. Econ. Assn., Am. Fin. Assn. (past pres., dir.) Western Fin. Assn. (past pres., dir.) Fin. Mgmt. Assn. Home: 2000 Webster St Palo Alto CA 94301-4049 Office: Stanford U Grad Sch Bus Stanford CA 94305

VAN HORNE, JON W., lawyer; b. Chgo., Apr. 6, 1945. BA, Andrews U. (formerly Emmanuel Missionary Coll.), 1967; JD, Harvard U., 1971; MPA, Kennedy Sch. Govt., 1971. Bar: Ohio 1971, Pa. 1979, D.C. 1988. Ptnr. McDermott, Will & Emery, Washington; chmn. Bus. Coun. Reduction of Paperwork, 1990—. Mem. D.C. Bar. Office: McDermott Will & Emery 1850 K St NW Washington DC 20006-2213

VAN HORNE, R. RICHARD, oil company executive; b. Milw., June 7, 1931; s. Ralph Rupert and Edna (Benson) Van H.; m. Elizabeth Whitaker Dixon, July 3, 1954; children—Ann Van Horne Arms, R. Ross, Margaret Van Horne Shuya. B.B.A., U. Wis., 1953. Various positions Anaconda Am. Brass Co., Milw. and Kenosha, Wis., 1955-72; pres., chief exec. officer Anaconda Am. Brass Co., Waterbury, Conn., 1972-74, Anaconda Aluminum Co., Louisville, 1974-82; sr. v.p. pub. affairs Atlantic Richfield Co., Los Angeles, 1982-85; bd. dirs Citizens Fidelity Corp. Bd. visitors Sch. Bus., U. Wis., Madison; mem. U. Wis. Found.; trustee Brooklawn, Louisville Community Found. Served to 1st lt. U.S. Army, 1953-55. Sr. fellow Bellarmine Coll. Mem. Mchts. and Mfrs. Assn. (bd. dirs. 1983-85), Am. Petroleum Inst., Nat. Planning Assn. (com. on new Am. realities 1982-84), Bascom Hill Soc., Minocqua Country Club. Republican. Episcopalian. Avocations: golf; reading; gardening. Home: 5520 Tecumseh Cir Louisville KY 40207 Office: Atlantic Richfield Co 515 S Flower St Los Angeles CA 90071-2200

VAN HORSSEN, ARDEN DARRELL, retired manufacturing executive; b. Cottonwood County, Minn., June 14, 1917; s. Charles and Mabel Rosina (Schaffer) Van H.; m. Margaret Eleanor Ellingsen, Nov. 29, 1941; children: Charles A., Ronald D. Student, U. Minn., 1935-38, DePauw U., 1938-40, Lawson Sch. Engring., Chgo., 1941. Trainer Nunn Mfg., Evanston, Ill., 1941-42; dept. supr. Mpls. Moline Mfg., Mpls., 1942-44; plant mgr. Indsl. Tool & Die, Mpls., 1944-47; part owner Tonka Toys, Minnetonka, Minn., 1947-49; plant supt. Woodmark Industries, St. Louis Park, Minn., 1949-51; owner Nu-Line Industries, Mpls., 1951-65; pres. Cinch Nu-Line divsn. United Carr, Mpls., 1965-67; cons. mgmt. and engring., 1968-73. Patentee in field. Home: 10015 Royal Oak Rd Apt 150 Sun City AZ 85351

VAN HOUSE, NANCY ANITA, library educator; b. Ogden, Utah, Aug. 3, 1950. AB, U. Calif., Berkeley, 1971, MLS, 1972, PhD, 1979. Reference libr. San Mateo County Libr., Belmont, Calif., 1972-75; coord. East Bay Info. Svc., Oakland, Calif., 1975-76; sr. rsch. assoc. King Rsch., Inc., Rockville, Md., 1979-81; asst. prof. U. Calif., Berkeley, 1981-87, assoc. prof., 1987-93, prof., 1993—, acting dean, 1991—. Author: Public Library User Fees, 1983; co-author: Output Measures for Public Libraries, 1987, Planning and Role-Setting for Public Libraries, 1987, Measuring Academic Library Performance, 1990, What's Good, 1993, Public Library Effectiveness Study, 1993; contbr. articles to profl. jours. Redcipient Young Investigators award NSF, grantee, 1984, U.S. Dept. Edn., 1987-88, 92-93, 93-94. Mem. ALA, Assn. for Libr. and Info. Sci. Edn. (rsch. award 1983, 84). Office: U Calif Sch Libr & Info Studies Berkeley CA 94720-4600

VAN HOUSEN, THOMAS CORWIN, III, architect, designer, builder; b. Oak Park, Ill., Jan. 2, 1927; s. Thomas Corwin and Dorothea (Saunders) Van H.; children: Deborah, Victoria, Constance. BA, Lawrence U., 1951; BArch, U. Minn., Mpls., 1954; MArch in Urban Design, Harvard U., 1962. Registered architect, Minn., Wis. Architect in tng. Ellerbe Assocs., Inc., St. Paul, 1951-61; architect, prin. Progressive Design Assocs., Inc., St. Paul, 1961-71; architect, developer, v.p. Landmark Devel. Corp./Appletree Enterprises, Inc., Bloomington, Minn., 1971-85; architect, developer Mortenson Devel. Co., Mpls., 1985-88; architect, design, bldg. dir. D&B Collaborative, Inc., Mpls., 1989—. Bldg. official City of North Oaks, Minn., 1964-78; mem. Minn. League of Municipalities-Metro, St. Paul, 1970-72, Gov.'s Open Space Adv. Com., St. Paul, 1972-74. With U.S. Air Force, 1945-47, ETO. Recipient Outstanding House award St. Paul Jaycees, 1958, 62; named finalist (team mem.) Archtl. competition Boston City Hall, 1962. Fellow AIA (bd. dirs. 1985-88, v.p., pres.-elect Minn. chpt. 1994-95, pres. 1995—, spl. award 1981, Presdl. citation 1988, 90); mem. N.W. Racquet and Swim Club. Republican. Lutheran. Avocations: tennis, skiing, swimming, music. Home: 6322 45th Place N Minneapolis MN 55428-5152

VAN HOUTEN, FRANKLYN BOSWORTH, geologist, educator; b. N.Y.C., July 14, 1914; s. Charles Nicholas and Hessie Osborne (Bosworth) Van H.; m. Jean Oliver Sholes, Feb. 18, 1943; children: Jean S., F. Bosworth, David Gordon. B.S., Rutgers U., 1936; Ph.D., Princeton U., 1941. Instr. dept. geology Williams Coll., 1939-42; asst. prof. Princeton U., 1946-51, assoc. prof., 1951-55, prof., 1955-85, prof. emeritus, 1985—; vis. prof. geology UCLA, 1964, State U. N.Y. at Binghamton, 1971; geologist U.S. Geol. Survey, 1948-67; temporary geologist Geol. Survey Can., 1953, Yukon Expdn., geol. expdns. to Morocco, Tunisia, Libya, Egypt, Madagascar. Author reports and articles on geology. Served as lt. USN, 1942-46. Fellow Geol. Soc. Am.; mem. Am. Assn. Petroleum Geologists, Soc. Econ. Paleontologists and Mineralogists (hon. mem., Twenhofel medal), Internat. Assn. Sedimentologists, Colombia Geol. Soc. (hon.), Delta Upsilon. Home: 168 Fitzrandolph Rd Princeton NJ 08540-7224

VAN HOUTEN, STEPHEN H., manufacturing company executive; b. Toronto. BA Honours, U. Western Ont., 1974; LLB, U. Ottawa, 1977; LLM, Osgoode Hall, Toronto, 1984. Bar: Ont. 1979. Legal counsel Gen. Motors, Can., 1980-84, mgr. bus. planning, 1984-87, dir. govt. rels., trade policy, 1987-88, dir. pub. rels., 1988-89; pres. Automotive Parts Mfrs'. Assn., Can., 1989-91, Can. Mfrs'. Assn., 1991—; mem., bd. dirs. numerous mfg. assns. Contbr. numerous articles to profl. jours. V.p. Traffic Injury Rsch. Found. Can. Office: Can Mfrs Assn, 75 International Blvd, Toronto, ON Canada M9W 6L9

VAN HOUTTE, RAYMOND A., financial executive; b. Detroit, Aug. 1, 1924; s. Maurice and Gabrielle (Hoorelbeke) Van H.; m. Margaret Graves, June 17, 1950; children—Raymond C., Jonathan P., Nancy J. B.B.A., U. Mich., 1949; J.D., U. Conn., 1955. Bar: N.Y. 1963; CPA, Conn. Sole practice Hartford, Conn., 1955-58; mem. new product devel. staff Nestle Co., White Plains, N.Y., 1958-60; pres. Ithaca Gun Co., N.Y., 1960-68; v.p. Tompkins County Trust Co., Ithaca, 1968-73, pres., chief exec. officer, 1973-89, pres. emeritus, counselor, 1990—; pres. Tompkins County Area Devel., Ithaca, 1985; trustee Mut. Funds for Bank Trust Depts., Boston; bd. dirs. Ithaco, Inc., Evaporated Metal Product, Inc. Author: Responsibilities of Bank Directors, 1974. Bd. dirs. Ithaca City Sch. Dist., 1965-66, Tompkins Comty. Hosp.; trustee Paleontol. Rsch. Instn., Kendal at Ithaca. With USAF, 1944-45. Mem. AICPA, N.Y. State Bankers Assn. (2d v.p. 1985-86, pres. 1987-88), Chi Phi (treas.). Lodge: Rotary (chmn.). Home: 1 Strawberry Ln Ithaca NY 14850-1413

VAN HOUWELING, DOUGLAS EDWARD, university administrator, educator; b. Kansas City, Mo., Sept. 20, 1943; s. Cornelius Donald and Roberta Irene (Olson) Van H.; m. Andrea Taylor Parks, Aug. 28, 1965; children: Robert Parks, Benjamin Parks. BS, Iowa State U., Ames, 1965; PhD, Ind. U., 1974. Asst. prof. Cornell U., Ithaca, N.Y., 1970-81; dir. acad. computing Cornell U., 1978-81; vice provost Carnegie-Mellon U., Pitts., 1981-84; adj. assoc. prof. Carnegie-Mellon U., 1981-84; vice provost, adj. prof. U. Mich., Ann Arbor, 1984—; mem. research adv. com. Online Coll. Library Consortium, Dublin, Ohio, 1984-87; trustee EDUCOM, vice chmn. bd. dirs., 1987-91; Princeton vice chmn., 1987, council chmn., 1986-87; co-founder Interuniv. Consortium for Ednl. Computing, 1984; chmn. bd. MERIT computer network, 1986-90, Advanced Network and Svcs., 1990—; state of Mich. del. Midwest Tech. Inst., 1986-87. Contbr. chpts. in books, articles to profl. publs. NSF fellow, 1968; Indiana U. fellow, 1969; CAUSE nat. leadership award, 1986. Mem. Simulation and Gaming Assn. Home: 920 Lincoln Ave Ann Arbor MI 48104-3508 Office: U Mich 503 Thompson St Ann Arbor MI 48109-1340

VANÍČEK, PETR, geodesist; b. Sušice, Czechoslovakia, July 18, 1935; emigrated to Can., 1969, naturalized, 1975; s. Ivan and Irena (Blahovcová) V.; m. Valeria Vásáriová, 1991; children from previous marriage: Filip, Štěpán, Naninka. Degree in Engring., Czech Tech. U., Prague, 1959; PhD in Math. Physics, Czechoslovak Acad. Scis., Prague, 1968; DSC in math. and physical scis., Czech. Acad. Scis., 1993. Lic. profl. engr. Geodesist Inst. Surveying, Prague, 1959-63; computer cons. Czech Tech. U., 1963-67; Natural Environ. Research Council sr. research fellow Tidal Inst., U.

Liverpool, Eng., 1967-68; sr. sci. officer Natural Environ. Research Council, U.K., 1968-69; NRC Can. postdoctoral fellow Fed. Govt., Ottawa, 1969-71; prof. geodesy U. N.B., Fredericton, 1971—; prof. geodesy Erindale Coll., U. Toronto, 1980-83, adj. prof., 1983-89; vis. prof. U. Parana, Brazil, summers 1975-76, 79, 87, U. Stuttgart, Germany, 1981, 82, U. São Paulo, Brazil, 1981, 84, 87; vis. scientist U.S. Geol. Survey, Menlo Park, Calif., 1977; sr. vis. scientist NAS, 1978; pres. Can. Geophys. Union, 1987-89; v.p. IAG Commn. on Recent Crustal Movements, 1991—; sr. vis. scientist Royal Inst. Tech., Stockholm, 1986; sr. vis. fellow Council of Sci. and Indsl. Research, South Africa, 1986. Author: (with V. Pleskot and others) Základy Programování Pro Ural, vol. I, 1964, (with J. Čulík, T. Miklošová), vol. II, 1965, (with E.J. Krakiwsky) Geodesy: The Concepts, 1982, rev. edit., 1986, (with others) Guide to GPS Positioning, 1986; editor: Proc. Internat. Symposium on N.Am. Geodetic Networks, 1974, Proc. Can. Geophys. Union Symposium on Satellite Geodesy and Geodynamics, 1975, (with S. Cohen) Slow Deformation and Transmission of Stress in the Earth, 1989, (with N. Christou) Geoid and its Geophysical Interpretations, 1993; editor-in-chief Manuscripta Geodaetica, Bull. Geodisique; mem. internat. editorial bd. Studia Geofisica et Geodetica; contbr. articles to profl. jours. Recipient Humboldt sr. rsch. award Federal Republic of Germany; Am. Geophys. Union fellow. Fellow Geol. Assn. Can., Internat. Assn. Geodesy, Explorers Club; mem. Can. Geophys. Union (past pres.), Czechoslovak Soc. Arts and Scis. Am., Sigma Xi. Home: 667 Golf Club Rd, Fredericton, NB Canada E3B 4X4 *As one coming from communist central Europe, I cannot stop marveling at the opportunities this society offers to anyone willing to work earnestly. One must feel sorry for those who do not conduct their lives to take an advantage of this offer.*

VANIER, JACQUES, physicist; b. Dorion, Que., Can., Jan. 4, 1934; s. Henri and Emma (Boileau) V.; m. Lucie Beaudet, July 8, 1961; children: Lyne, Pierre. BA, U. Montreal, 1955, BSc, 1958; MSc, McGill U., 1960, PhD, 1963. Lectr. U. Montreal, 1961-63, McGill U., 1960-63; physicist Varian Assocs., Beverly, Mass., 1963-67, Hewlett Packard Co., Beverly, 1967; prof. elec. engring. U. Laval, Que., 1967-83; physicist Nat. Rsch. Coun., Ottawa, 1983-94, head elec. and time standards, 1984-86, dir. Lab. Basic Standards, 1986-90, dir. gen. Inst. for Nat. Measurement Standards, 1990-93; cons. Commn. Components Corp., Costa Mesa, Calif., 1974-76, EGG Co., Salem, Mass., 1979-82; chmn. com. A URSI, 1990-93; chmn. exec. com. CPEM, 1990-94; mem. Internat. Com. Weights and Measures, 1992—. Author: Basic Theory of Lasers and Masers, 1971, (with C. Audoin) The Quantum Physics of Atomic Frequency Standards, 1989; contbr. articles to profl. jours.; inventor nuclear quadrupole resonance thermometer. Fellow IEEE (Centennial medal 1984, Rabi award 1994), Royal Soc. Can., Am. Phys. Soc.

VANIER, KIERAN FRANCIS, business forms printing company executive; b. Alliance, Ohio, May 10, 1914; s. Joseph A. and Johanna Mary (McCarthy) V.; m. Marjory S. Kitchen, 1937 (dec.); children: Denis K., Annette Vanier Fritzenkotter; m. June Day, 1975 (dec. 1995). B.S., Loyola U., 1937. Salesman Moore Bus. Forms, to 1946; founder Vanier Graphics Corp., 1946, ret. chmn. bd.; ret. vice chmn. Am. Bus. Products, Inc., Atlanta; founder, chmn. Kieran Label Corp. Founder Amoyotrophic Lateral Sclerosis Found. San Diego; past chmn. San Diego chpt. Muscular Dystrophy; past pres. San Diego Employers Assn. Knight Order of Holy Sepulcher, Pope John Paul II. Mem. San Diego Yacht Club, San Diego Country Club, De Anza Country Club. Office: 8765 Olive Ln Santee CA 92071-4137

VAN INWAGEN, PETER JAN, philosophy educator; b. Rochester, N.Y., Sept. 21, 1942; s. George Butler and Mildred Gloria (Knudson) van I; m. Margery Bedford Naylor, Mar. 31, 1967 (div. Apr. 1988); 1 child, Elizabeth Core; m. Elisabeth Marie Bolduc, June 3, 1989. B.S., Rensselaer Poly. Inst., 1965; Ph.D., U. Rochester, 1969. Vis. asst. prof. U. Rochester, N.Y., 1971-72; asst. prof. Syracuse U., N.Y., 1972-74, assoc. prof., 1974-80, prof. philosophy, 1980-95; John Cardinal O'Hara prof. of philosophy U. Notre Dame, South Bend, Ind., 1995—; vis. prof. U. Ariz., Tucson, 1981. Author: An Essay on Free Will, 1983, Material Beings, 1990, Metaphysics, 1993, God, Knowledge and Mystery, 1995; editor: Time and Cause, 1980, Alvin Plantinga, 1985; mem. editl. bd. Jour. Faith and Philosophy, Philos. Perspectives, Nous, Philos. Studies; contbr. articles to profl. jours. Served to capt. U.S. Army, 1969-71. NEH grantee, 1983-84, 89-90. Mem. Am. Philos. Assn., Soc. Christian Philosophers. Democrat. Episcopalian. Home: 517 Scott Ave Syracuse NY 13224-1909 Office: U Notre Dame Dept Philosophy South Bend IN 46556

VAN ITALLIE, JEAN-CLAUDE, playwright; b. Brussels, May 25, 1936; came to U.S., 1940; s. Hughes Ferdinand and Marthe Mathilde Caroline (Levy) van I. BA, Harvard U., 1958; PhD (hon.), Kent State U., 1977. Tchr. theater, playwriting New Sch. for Social Research, N.Y.C., 1966, Yale U. Sch. Drama, New Haven, 1969, 84, Naropa Inst., Boulder, Colo., 1976-83, 87-88, Princeton U., N.J., 1976-88, NYU, 1982-88, U. Colo., Boulder, 1985, 89, 91, Columbia U., 1986, Am. Repertory Theatre, Cambridge, Mass., 1990; vis. Mellon prof. Amherst Coll., Mass., fall 1976. Playwright for Open Theatre ensemble, N.Y.C., 1963-68; playwright War, 1963, Almost Like Being, 1965, I'm Really Here, 1965, America Hurrah, 1966 (Drama Desk award, Outer Circle Critics award 1967), The Serpent, 1968 (Obie award 1969), A Fable, 1975, King of the United States, 1972, Mystery Play, 1973, Medea, 1979, Bag Lady, 1979, Tibetan Book of the Dead, 1983, Early Warnings, 1983, The Traveler, 1986, new English versions Chekhov's The Seagull, 1973, Cherry Orchard, 1977, Three Sisters, 1982, Uncle Vanya, 1983, Paradise Ghetto, 1981, Struck Dumb (with Joseph Chaikin), 1987, Ancient Boys, 1989; transl. Genet's The Balcony, 1986, The Odyssey (musical), 1991, Bulgahov's Master & Margarita, 1993. Grantee Rockefeller Found., 1973, Ford Found., 1979, Creative Artists Pub. Service, 1975; recipient Playwrights award NEA, 1986, Creative Artists Pub. Service award, 1975; Guggenheim fellow, 1963, 83. Buddhist.

VANITALLIE, THEODORE BERTUS, physician; b. Hackensack, N.J., Nov. 8, 1919; s. Dorus Christian and Lucy M. (Pohle) VanI.; m. Barbara Cox, Sept. 25, 1948 (div. Mar. 1992); children: Lucy M., Theodore Bertus, Christina M., Elizabeth B., Katharine K.; m. Sallie Newton Calhoun, Mar. 11, 1992. B.S., Harvard U., 1941; M.D., Columbia U., 1945. Diplomate: Am. Bd. Internal Medicine. Intern in medicine St. Luke's Hosp., N.Y.C., 1945-46, asst. resident in internal medicine, 1948-49, resident, 1949-50, dir. nutrition and metabolism rsch. lab., 1952-55; assoc. Peter Bent Brigham Hosp., Boston, 1955-57; dir. medicine St. Luke's Hosp. Center, N.Y.C., 1957-75; dir. Obesity Rsch. Ctr., 1974-85, co-dir., 1986-88; asst. prof. Sch. Pub. Health, Harvard U., 1955-57; assoc. clin. prof. medicine Columbia, N.Y.C., 1957-65, clin. prof., 1965-71, prof., 1971-88, prof. emeritus 1988—; vis. prof. internal medicine Am. U. Beirut, 1968-69, trustee, 1976-93; spl. advisor on human nutrition Surgeon Gen. 1980-81; mem. sci. adv. bd. Nutrition Found., 1967-71; pres. Am. Bd. Nutrition, 1968-71; mem. food and nutrition bd. NRC, 1970-76; med. adv. com. on cyclamates HEW, 1969-70; mem. gastrointestinal and nutrition tng. com. NIH, 1969-73, mem. adv. coun. Nat. Arthritis, Diabetes, Digestive and Kidney Diseases, NIH, 1978-81; mem. joint nutrition monitoring evaluation com. USDA and HHS, 1982-86; dir. Miles Labs., 1976-84; vis. physician Rockefeller U. Hosp., 1986-89; adj. prof. Rockefeller U., 1986-89; vis. prof. medicine in psychiatry, U. Pa., 1990-94. Mem. editorial bd.: Diabetes, 1960-71; editor-in-chief: Am. Jour. Clin. Nutrition, 1979-81. Mem. Englewood (N.J.) Bd. Edn., 1960-65, v.p., 1964-65; trustee St. Luke's-Roosevelt Hosp. Ctr., 1988-94. Lt. (j.g.) USNR, 1946-68. Recipient citation FDA, 1983. Fellow ACP (Disting. Physicians award 1987), AAAS, Am. Inst. Nutrition; mem. AMA (mem. coun. on foods and nutrition 1967-74, vice chmn. 1974, Joseph B. Goldberger award 1985), Am. Soc. Clin. Investigation, Am. Soc. Clin. Nutrition (mem. coun. 1970-73, pres. 1976-77, Elmer V. McCollum award 1985), Soc. Study Ingestive Behaviour (Disting. Sci. award 1994), Order of Malta (knight comdr. Quebec priory 1990—), Century Assn. Research and contbr. numerous publs. on obesity, body composition, pancreatic hormone, glucagon, mechanism of energy balance regulation, treatment of pruritus and hypercholesteremia in biliary cirrhosis, physiology and clin. use of medium chain triglyceride. Address: PO Box 775 1678 Jose Gaspar Dr Boca Grande FL 33921

VAN KIRK, JOHN ELLSWORTH, cardiologist; b. Dayton, Ohio, Jan. 13, 1942; s. Herman Corwin and Dorothy Louise (Shafer) Van K.; m. Patricia L.

Davis, June 19, 1966 (div. Dec. 1982); 1 child, Linnea Gray. BA cum laude, DePauw U., Greencastle, Ind., 1963; BS, Northwestern U., Chgo., 1964, MD with distinction, 1967. Diplomate Am. Bd. Internal Medicine, Am. Bd. Internal Medicine subspecialty in cardiovascular disease; cert. Nat. Bd. Med. Examiners. Intern Evanston (Ill.) Hosp., 1967-68; staff assoc. Nat. Inst. of Allergy & Infectious Diseases., Bethesda, Md., 1968-70; resident internal medicine U. Mich. Med. Ctr., Ann Arbor, 1970-72, fellow in cardiology, 1972-74; instr. internal medicine, 1973-74; staff cardiologist Mills Meml. Hosp., San Mateo, Calif., 1974—; vice-chief medicine, 1977-78, dir. critical care, 1978—; critical care utilizaton rev., 1988—; dir. pacemaker clinic, 1976—; mem. active staff Peninsula Hosp. and Med. Ctr.; mem. courtesy staff Sequoia Hosp. Contbr. rsch. articles to profl. jours. Recipient 1st prize in landscaping Residential Estates, State of Calif., 1977, Physician's Recognition award AMA, 1968, 72, 75, 77, 80, 82, 85, 87, 89, 93. Fellow Am. Coll. Cardiology; mem. AMA, Calif. Med. Assn., San Mateo County Med. Soc., Am. Heart Assn., San Mateo County Heart Assn. (bd. dirs. 1975-78, bay area rsch. com. 1975-76, edn. com. 1975-77, pres. elect 1976-77, pres. 1977-79), Alpha Omega Alpha. Republican. United Brethren. Avocations: gardening, computer science, tennis, woodworking, electronics, ham radio. Office: Unified Med Clinics of Peninsula 50 S San Mateo Dr Ste 270 San Mateo CA 94401-3859

VAN KIRK, ROBERT JOHN, nursing administrator, educator; b. Jersey City, N.J., Sept. 18, 1944; s. Robert and Doris V.; m. Marjorie Ann Carroll, Mar. 23, 1968 (div. 1993); children: Walther, Michael, Robert Jr., Peggy. BA cum laude, U. Conn., 1974; MEd, Kent State U., 1983; D of Nursing, Case Western Reserve U., 1986. RN. Sales mgr. Nutmeg Home Protection, Middlebury, Conn., 1972-74; theater mgr. SBC Mgmt. Corp., Boston, 1974; dist. supr. Selected Theatres Mgmt. Corp., Lyndhurst, Ohio, 1974-86; nat. sales mgr. ZBS Video, Inc., Lyndhurst, Ohio, 1981-82; staff nurse Cleve. Clinic Found., 1986-87, clin. instr., 1987-88, head nurse, 1988-93; asst. clin. prof. Case Western Reserve U., Frances Payne Bolton Sch. Nursing, Cleve., 1990—; case mgr. Cleve. Clin. Home Care, 1993—. Health officer Lake County (Ohio) Bd. Alcohol, Drug Addiction and Mental Health Svcs., 1991—; co-chmn. United Way, Cleve., 1991-93. Staff Sgt. U.S. Army, 1964-71, Vietnam. Recipient Achievement award Greater Cleve. Nurses Assn., 1986. Mem. AACCN, Am. Assn. Tchrs. German, Am. Assn. Tchrs. Portuguese and Spanish, Assn. Specialists in Aging, Kappa Delta Pi, Sigma Theta Tau, Frances Payne Bolton Sch. Nursing Alumni Assn. (pres. 1992-93). Avocations: pocket billiards, furniture making. Home: 5011 Nob Hill Dr # 9C Chagrin Falls OH 44022 Office: Cleve Clinic Found 9555 Rockside Rd Valley View OH 44125

VAN KIRK, THOMAS L., lawyer; b. Pa., June 25, 1945; s. Theodore and Mary Jane (Young) Van K.; children: Thomas Jr., Christopher. BA, Bucknell U., 1967; JD cum laude, Dickinson U., 1970. Bar: Pa., U.S. Dist. Ct. (we. and ea. dists.) Pa. 1971, U.S. Ct. Appeals (3d cir.) 1972, U.S. Supreme Ct. 1976. Clk. Pa. Superior Ct., 1970-71; assoc. Buchanan Ingersoll, Pitts., 1971-77, ptnr., 1978—, chief oper. officer, 1985—; bd. dirs. Buchanan Ingersoll P.C., Civic Light Opera, State Pa. Economy League, Allegheny County Am. Heart Assn. Devel. Fund, Pitts., Pitts. Downtown Partnership; v.p. Western Pa. Economy League. Chmn. Allegheny County Heart Assn. Walk, 1992; bd. dirs. Rivers Club; vice chmn. Pitts. Downtown Partnership; sec.-treas., bd. dirs. Capital divsn. Pa. Economy League. Mem. ABA, Allegheny County Bar Assn., Duquesne Club, Rivers Club, Racquet Club Phila., The Club at Nevillewood. Democrat. Lutheran. Home: 1010 Osage Rd Pittsburgh PA 15243-1014 Office: Buchanan Ingersoll PC 600 Grant St 58th Fl Pittsburgh PA 15219-2701

VAN KLEEK, PETER ERIC, college dean; b. St. Petersburg, Fla., Mar. 15, 1929; s. John R. and Joan (Hill) Van K.; m. Barbara Jane King, June 4, 1954; children: Laura, Jennifer, Erica. BS, Cornell U., 1955; LHD (hon.), Schiller Internat. U., 1984. Mgr. hotels, various locations, 1955-59; gen. mgr., v.p. Barringer Hotel and VIP Hotels, Charlotte, N.C., 1959-62; mgmt. cons. Jack Tar Hotels, Galveston, Tex., 1962-65; owner, operator Mimosa Inn, Tryon, N.C., 1965-69; assoc. prof. SUNY, Alfred, 1969-76; founding dean Sch. Hotel and Restaurant Mgmt. Jonson Wales Coll., Providence, 1976-86; founding dean Sch. Hotel and Restaurant Mgmt. No. Ariz. U., Flagstaff, 1986-92, prof. emeritus, 1992—; ednl. cons. Govt. of St. Maarten, 1983-84, Schiller Internat. U., London, 1983-84; bd. dirs. Rainbow Tech. Group, Phoenix; cons. in field. Author: Anthology/Vegetable Cooking, 1966, Cooking With Pride, 1975, Beverage and Bartending, 1981; co-author: Menu Planning, 1974; assoc. editor mag. Cooking For Profit, 1983-85. Sgt. U.S. Army, 1950-52, Korea. Mem. Am. Hotel and Motel Assn. (cert. hotel adminstr., Outstanding Educator of Yr. 1988, Amb., trustee Ednl. Inst.), Internat. Hotel Assn., Coun. Hotel, Restaurant Instl. Edn., Internat. Exec. Svc. Corps. Avocations: cooking, travel. Home: 7397 E Wandering Rd Tucson AZ 85715

VAN LANDINGHAM, LEANDER SHELTON, JR., lawyer; b. Memphis, July 15, 1925; s. Leander Shelton and Bertha (Shumaker) Van L.; m. Henrietta Adena Stapf, July 5, 1959; children: Ann Henrietta, Leander Shelton III. B.S. in Chemistry, U. N.C., 1948, M.A. in Organic Chemistry, 1949; J.D., Georgetown U., 1955. Bar: D.C. 1955, Md. 1963, Va. 1976. Patent adviser Dept. Navy, Washington, 1953-55; sole practice comml. law and patent, trademark and copyright law, Washington met. area, 1955—. Served to lt. USNR, 1943-46, 51-53. Mem. Am. Chem. Soc., Sci. Assn., Fed. Bar Assn., ABA, D.C. Bar Assn., Va. Bar Assn., Md. Bar Assn., Am. Intellectual Property Law Assn., Am. Judicature Soc., Sigma Xi, Phi Alpha Delta. Home: 10726 Stanmore Dr Potomac MD 20854-1518 Office: 2001 Jefferson Davis Hwy Arlington VA 22202

VANLANDINGHAM, WILLIAM JENNINGS, banker; b. Louisville, Sept. 10, 1937; s. Zack Jennings and Corinne (Brown) V.; m. Barbara McMillan, Feb. 16; children—William Jennings II, Teri Leigh, Joseph Templeton. Grad. Ga. Tech., 1959; postgrad., Emory U. Law Sch., 1964-67; P.M.D., Harvard U., 1972. Prodn. mgr. Procter & Gamble, Cin. and Dallas, 1962-64; asst. to v.p. Rich's Inc., Atlanta, 1964-66; pres., chief exec. officer C&S Ga. Corp., Atlanta, 1966—; bd. dirs. Ga. Interchange Network, Inc. Mem. Atlanta Bd. Edn., 1971-74; bd. dirs. Rsch. Atlanta, Inc., Vol. Atlanta, Ga. Safety Coun., Metro Atlanta chpt. ARC; chmn. bd. trustees Pace Acad.; chmn. Ga. Coun. Econ. Edn.; trustee Ga. Inst. Tech. Found. With USNR, 1959-61. Mem. Ga. Bankers Assn. (bd. dirs.). Methodist. Home: 3100 Argonne Dr NW Atlanta GA 30305-1948 Office: Nationsbank of Georgia 55 Nationsbank Plz Atlanta GA 30319

VAN LEUVEN, ROBERT JOSEPH, lawyer; b. Detroit, Apr. 17, 1931; s. Joseph Francis and Olive (Stowell) Van L.; student Albion Coll., 1949-51; B.A. with distinction Wayne State U., 1953; J.D., U. Mich., 1957; m. Holly Goodhue Porter, Dec. 31, 1976; children—Joseph Michael, Douglas Robert, Julie Margaret. Bar: Mich. 1957. Since practiced in Muskegon, Mich.; ptnr. Hathaway, Latimer, Clink & Robb, 1957-68, ptnr. McCroskey, Libner & Van Leuven, 1968-81, ptnr. Libner, Van Leuven & Kortering, 1982—; past mem. council negligence law sect. State Bar Mich. Bd. dirs. Muskegon Children's Home, 1965-75. Served with AUS 1953-55. Fellow Mich. Bar Found., Mich. Trial Lawyers Assn., Am. Coll. Trial Lawyers; mem. Assn. Trial Lawyers Am., Delta Sigma Phi. Club: Muskegon Country. Home: 2142 Easthill Dr Muskegon MI 49441-4428 Office: Libner Van Leuven & Kortering Muskegon Mall 400 Comerica Muskegon MI 49443

VAN LINT, VICTOR ANTON JACOBUS, physicist; b. Samarinda, Indonesia, May 10, 1928; came to U.S., 1937; s. Victor J. and Margaret (DeJager) Van L.; m. M. June Woolhouse, June 10, 1950; children: Lawrence, Kenneth, Linda, Karen. BS, Calif. Inst. Tech., Pasadena, 1950, PhD, 1954. Instr. Princeton (N.J.) U., 1954-55; staff mem. Gen. Atomic, San Diego, 1957-74; physics cons. San Diego, 1974-75; staff mem. Mission Research Corp., San Diego, 1975-82, 83-91; cons., 1991—; spl. asst. to dep. dir. sci. and tech. Def. Nuclear Agy., Washington, 1982-83. Author, editor: Radiation Effects in Electronic Materials, 1976; contbr. articles to profl. jours. Served with U.S. Army, 1955-57. Recipient Pub. Service award NASA, 1981. Fellow IEEE. Republican. Mem. United Ch. of Christ. Home and Office: 1032 Skylark Dr La Jolla CA 92037-7733

VAN LOPIK, JACK RICHARD, geologist, educator; b. Holland, Mich., Feb. 25, 1929; s. Guy M. and Minnie (Grunst) Van L.; 1 son, Charles Robert (dec.). B.S., Mich. State U. 1950; M.S., La. State U., 1953, Ph.D.,

1955. Geologist, sect. chief, asst. chief, chief geology br. U.S. Army C.E., Waterways Expt. Sta., Vicksburg, Miss., 1954-61; chief engrs. environ. adv. bd. U.S. Army C.E., 1988—; chief area evaluation sect., tech. dir., mgr. Space and Environ. Sci. Programs, tech. requirements dir. geosciences ops. Tex. Instruments, Inc., Dallas, 1961-68; chmn. dept. marine sci. Tex. Instruments, Inc., 1964-70; prof. dept. marine sci., dir. sea grant devel., dean Center for Wetland Resources, La. State U., Baton Rouge, 1968—; chmn. Coastal Resources Directorate of U.S. Nat. Com. for Man and Biosphere, U.S. Nat. Comm. for UNESCO, 1975-82; dir. Gulf South Research Inst., 1974-89; mem. Nat. Adv. Com. Oceans and Atmosphere, 1978-84; mem. Lower Miss. River Waterway Safety Com. USCG 8th dist., 1983—; mem. adv. council Nat. Coastal Resources Research and Devel. Inst., 1985—; ofcl. del. XX Congreso Internacional, Mexico City, 1956, XII Gen Assembly Internat. Union Geodesy and Geophysics, Helsinki, 1960; chmn. panel on geography and land use Nat. Acad. Scis.-NRC, com. on remote sensing programs for earth resources surveys, 1969-77. Fellow Geol. Soc. Am., A.A.A.S.; mem. Am. Astronautical Soc. (dir. S.W. sect. 1967-68), Am. Soc. Photogrammetry (dir. 1969-72, chmn. photo interpretation com. 1960, 65, rep. earth scis. div. NRC 1968-71), Am. Geophys. Union, Am. Assn. Petroleum Geologists (acad. adv. com. 1973-78), Assn. Am. Geographers, Soc. Econ. Paleontologists and Mineralogists (mem. research com. 1962-65), Am. Mgmt. Assn., Soc. Research Adminstrs., Marine Tech. Soc., Am. Water Resources Assn., Soc. Am. Mil. Engrs., Sea Grant Assn. (exec. bd. 1972-74, 80-82, pres.-elect 1988-89, pres. 1989—), Nat. Ocean Industries Assn. (adv. council 1973—), Nat. Conf. Advancement Rsch., La. Partnership for Tech. and Innovation (bd. dirs. 1989—), Sigma Xi. Home: 9 Rue Sorbonne Baton Rouge LA 70808-4682 Office: La State U Office Sea Grant Devel Baton Rouge LA 70803

VAN LOUCKS, MARK LOUIS, venture capitalist, business advisor; b. Tampa, Fla., June 19, 1946; s. Charles Perry and Lenn (Bragg) Van L.; m. Eva Marianne Forsell, June 10, 1986; children: Brandon, Charlie. BA in Comm. and Pub. Policy, U. Calif., Berkeley, 1969. Sr. v.p. mktg., programming and corp. devel. United Cable TV Corp., Denver, Colo., 1970-81, advisor, 1983-89; sr. v.p., office of chmn. Rockefeller Ctr. TV Corp., N.Y.C., 1981-83; advisor United Artists Commun. Corp., Englewood, 1989-91; investor, business advisor in pvt. practice Englewood, 1983—; founder, prin. owner Glory Hole Saloon & Gaming Hall, Central City, Colo., 1990—, Harrah's Casino, Black Hawk, Colo., 1990—; chmn., CEO Bask Internat., Englewood, 1990—; bd. dirs. Wild West Devel. Corp., Denver; sr. v.p., bd. dirs. GSI Cable TV Assocs., Inc., San Francisco, 1984-90; guest lectr. on cable TV bus., 1985-91; cons. Telecommunications, Inc., Denver, 1989-93. Producer HBO spl. Green Chili Showdown, 1985; producer TV spl. 3 Days for Earth, 1987; producer, commd. artist nuclear war armament pieces; contbr. articles to profl. jours. Chmn. Cops in Crisis, Denver, 1990—; bd. dirs. The NOAH Found., Denver, 1976—; founding dir. Project for Responsible Advt., Denver, 1991-92; chmn. mayor's mktg. adv. bd., Central City, Colo. Named hon. capt. Denver Police Dept., 1991—, fin. advisor L. Rose Co., 1995—. Mem. Casino Owners Assn. (founding dir. 1989—), Colo. Gaming Assn. (dir. 1990—), recipient S'nnaeel Evol award, 1995), Glenmoor Country Club, The Village Club. Republican. Jewish. Avocations: music, woodworking, philanthropy, vintage autos. Office: MLVL Inc 333 W Hampden Ave Ste 1005 Englewood CO 80110-2340

VANLUVANEE, DONALD ROBERT, electronics executive; b. Neosho, Mo., July 3, 1944; s. Harry Earl and Joyce Elizabeth (Skillen) VanLuvanee; m. Lynne Marie Hodge; children: Kenneth Richard, Daryl Robert. BSEE, Rensselaer Poly. Inst., 1966, MEEE, 1972. Sr. engr., br. mgr. Tex. Instruments, Dallas, 1972-80; v.p. product design, research and devel. Syntex Dental Products, Valley Forge, Pa., 1980-82; v.p. research and devel. Kulicke and Soffa Industries, Inc., Willow Grove, Pa., 1982, v.p. domestic ops., 1982-84, pres., chief operating officer, 1984—, also bd. dirs. Contbr. articles to profl. jours.; patentee in field. Varsity coach Methacton Ice Hockey Assn., Eagleville, Pa.; head coach, exec. v.p. Colonials of Valley Forge Ice Hockey Assn. Mem. Nat. Assn. Corp. Dirs., Am. Mgmt. Assn., IEEE. Avocations: fishing, model aircraft, folk guitar and banjo, ice hockey. Office: Kulicke & Soffa Industries Inc 2101 Blair Mill Rd Willow Grove PA 19090-1795

VANMARCKE, ERIK HECTOR, civil engineering educator; b. Menen, Belgium, Aug. 6, 1941; came to U.S., 1965, naturalized, 1976; m. Louis Eugene and Maria Louisa (van Hollebeke) V.; m. Margaret Maria Delesie, May 25, 1965; children: Lieven, Ann, Kristien. BS, U. Louvain, Belgium, 1965; MS, U. Del., 1967; PhD in Civil Engring., MIT, 1970. From instr. to prof. civil engring. MIT, Cambridge, 1969-85; Gilbert W. Winslow Career Devel. prof. MIT, 1974-77, dir. civil engring. systems group, 1976-80; prof. civil engring. and ops. rsch. Princeton U., 1985—, dir. grad. studies civil engring. and ops. rsch., 1990—; cons. Office Sci. and Tech. Policy, 1978-80; vis. scholar in engring. Harvard U., 1984-85; Shimizu Corp. vis. prof. Stanford U., 1991; cons. various govt. agys. and engring. firms; mem. exec. com. Princeton Materials Inst., 1991-93. Author: Random Fields: Analysis and Synthesis, 1983, Predictive Cosmology: Embryonic Inflation and the Origin of Cosmic Structure, 1995; editor: Internat. Jour. Structural Safety, 1981-91. Recipient Sr. Scientist award for study in Japan, Japan Soc. for Promotion of Sci., 1991. Mem. ASCE (Raymond C. Reese rsch. award 1975, Walter L. Huber rsch. prize 1984, chair com. on safety and reliability in geotech. engring. 1993—), Am. Geophys. Union, Seismol. Soc. Am., Internat. Soc. Soil Mechanics and Found. Engring., Sigma Xi. Home: 50 Brooks Bnd Princeton NJ 08540-7530 Office: Room E311 Engring Quadrangle Princeton U Princeton NJ 08544

VAN MASON, RAYMOND, dancer, choreographer. Prin. dancer Ballet West, Salt Lake City. Dance performances include Swan Lake, Gisells, Sleeping Beauty, Romeo & Juliet, Anna Karenina, The Nutcracker, Carmina Burana, White Mourning, Ophelia; choreographer: Requiem: A Liturgical Ballet, 1990, A Pilgrimage: A Liturgical Ballet, 1992, Lady Guinevere, Chameleon, Carmina Burana, Symphony # 7, 1992, others. Office: Ballet West 50 West 200 South Salt Lake City UT 84101*

VAN METER, ABRAM DEBOIS, lawyer, retired banker; b. Springfield, Ill., May 16, 1922; s. A.D. and Edith (Graham) Van M.; m. Margaret Schlipf, Dec. 1, 1956; children: Andy, Alice, Ann. BS, Kings Point Coll., 1946; JD, Northwestern U., 1948. Bar: Ill. 1949. Ptnr. Van Meter, Oxtoby & Funk, Springfield, 1949—; adminstrv. asst. to treas. State of Ill., Springfield, 1963; v.p. Ill. Nat. Bank, Springfield, 1964-65, pres., 1965-88, chmn. bd. dirs., 1988-90, also bd. dirs.; chmn. bd. dirs. First of Am.-Springfield, N.A., 1990-93, dir. emeritus, 1993—. Chmn. bd. dirs. Ill. Housing Devel. Authority, 1977—; chmn. bd. trustees So. Ill. U., 1989—; bd. dirs., mem. exec. com. Meml. Med. Ctr. (emeritus). Mem. ABA, Ill. Bar Assn., Sangamon Bar Assn., Chgo. Club, Chgo. Athletic Club, Sangamo Club, Island Bay Yacht Club,. Home: 6 Fair Oaks St Springfield IL 62704-3222 Office: First of Am Springfield NA 1 Old State Capitol Pla N Springfield IL 62701

VAN METER, JOHN DAVID, lawyer; b. Owensboro, Ky., Oct. 30, 1951; s. Leslie Evan and Agnes Regina (Gropp) Van M.; m. Laura Ann Isbell, May 19, 1984; children: Katherine Leigh, Elizabeth Grace, Jennifer Marie. BA in Journalism, U. Ky., 1973, JD, 1978. Bar: Ky. 1978. Atty. Ashland (Ky.) Oil Inc., 1978-83, exec. asst. to chmn., 1983-88; adminstrv. v.p. Valvoline Oil Co. div. Ashland Oil, Inc., Lexington, Ky., 1988-90; pres. Ashland Internat. Ltd. subs. Ashland, Inc., London, 1990—. Bd. dirs. London City Ballet. Mem. ABA, Ky. Bar Assn., Boyd County Bar Assn., Fayette County Bar Assn., Carlton Club, Buck's Club, Pilgrim's Club (bd. dirs.). Roman Catholic. Home: 8 Reston Pl Hyde Park Gate, London SW7 5DY, England Office: 58 St James's St, London SW1A 1PR, England

VANMETER, VANDELIA L., library director; b. Seibert, Colo., July 17, 1934; d. G.W. and A. Pearl Klockenteger; m. Victor M. VanMeter, Jan. 21, 1954; children: Allison C., Kristopher C. BA, Kansas Wesleyan U., 1957; MLS, Emporia State U., 1970; PhD, Tex. Woman's U., 1986. Cert. libr. media specialist. Tchr. Ottawa County Rural Sch., Kans., 1954-55; social scis. tchr. McClave (Colo.) High Sch., 1957-58, Ellsworth (Kans.) Jr. High Sch., 1959-68; libr., media specialist Ellsworth (Kans.) High Sch., 1968-84; asst. prof. libr. sci. U. Wis.-Oshkosh, Hattiesburg, 1986-90; chair dept. libr./info. sci. Spalding U., Louisville, 1990—, libr. dir., 1991—; cons. to sch., pub. and spl. librs., Kans., Miss., Ky., 1970—; mem. Ky. NCATE Bd. Examiners.

Author: American History for Children and Young Adults, 1990, World History for Children and Young Adults, 1992; editor: Mississippi Library Media Specialist Staff Development Modules, 1988, Library Lane Newsletter, 1991—; contbr. chpts. to books; contbr. articles to profl. jours. Active City Coun., Ellsworth, Kans., 1975-79, Park Bd., Ellsworth, 1975-79; bd. dirs. Robbins Meml. Libr., 1977-79. Grantee Kans. Demonstration Sch. Libr., 1970-72, Miss. Power Found., 1989; named Women of Yr. Bus. and Profl. Women of Ellsworth, Kans., 1976. Mem. ALA, Am. Assn. Sch. Librs., Nat. Assn. State Ednl. Media Profls., Assn. Coll. & Rsch. Librs., Ky. Libr. Assn., Ky. Sch. Media Assn., Ky. Assn. Tchr. Educators, Assn. for Libr. and Info. Sci. Educators. Office: Spalding U Libr 851 S 4th St Louisville KY 40203-2115

VAN METRE, MARGARET CHERYL, artistic director, dance educator; b. Maryville, Tenn., Nov. 24, 1938; d. Robert Fillers and Margaret Elizabeth (Goddard) Raulston; m. Mitchell Robert Van Metre II, Aug. 25, 1956; 1 child, Mitchell Robert. Elem., intermediate and advanced teaching certs. Dir. Van Metre Sch. of Dance, Maryville, 1958—; artistic dir. Appalachian Ballet Co., Maryville Coll., 1972—; chmn. dance panel Tenn. Arts Commn.; 1973-74; chmn. Bicentennial Ballet Project, Tenn., 1975-76. Choreographer ballets: DeLusion, 1965; Hill Heritage Suite, 1972; Dancing Princesses, 1983. Mem. Tenn. Assn. of Dance (pres. 1972). Democrat. Episcopalian. Home: 609 Kendrick Pl Knoxville TN 37902-2019 Office: Appalachian Ballet Co 215 W Broadway Ave Maryville TN 37801-4705

VAN METRE, THOMAS EARLE, physician, allergist; b. Newport, R.I., Jan. 11, 1923; s. Thomas Earle and Anne Heap (Gleaves) Van M.; m. Mary Rosalie Evans, Sept. 7, 1947 (dec. Jan. 1967); children: Rosalie Van Metre Baker, Anne Gleaves Van Metre Kibbe, Mary Evans Van Metre Chodroff, Elizabeth Bowyer Van Metre Domowski, Helen Jenkins Van Metre Weary; m. Adéla Bell Hurst Winand, June 29, 1968; stepchildren: William Thomas Winand III, Bruce Hurst Winand. BS cum laude, Harvard U., 1943; MD cum laude, Harvard Med. Sch., 1946. Diplomate Am. Bd. Internal Medicine, Am. Bd. Allergy. Intern in internal medicine Johns Hopkins Hosp., 1946-47, resident in internal medicine, 1947-48, 50, 1951-52, Am. Cancer Soc. fellow virology and bacteriology, 1952-53, physician diagnostic clin., asst. physician allergy clinic, 1954-56, physician, 1956—; physician OPD, allergy and infectious disease clinic, 1956—, pediatrician, 1957-66, physician-in-charge allergy clinic, 1966-84; pvt. practice in internal medicine and allergy Balt., 1954—; asst. in medicine Johns Hopkins U. Med. Sch., 1947-48, 51-52, 54-56, part-time instr. in medicine 1953-63, part time asst. prof. medicine 1963-70, part-time assoc. prof. medicine, 1970-94, part-time prof., 1994—; attending physician Balt. City Hosp. (now Johns Hopkins Bayview Med. Ctr.), 1954—; active staff The Union Meml. Hosp., 1959—; courtesy staff Church Home and Hosp., 1956-66. Contbr. numerous articles to profl. jours. John Harvard fellowship Harvard Med. Sch., 1945. Fellow ACP, Am. Acad. of Allergy and Immunology (pres. 1978-79, exec. com. 1973-81, other coms., Disting. Svc. award 1986, Disting. Clinician award 1994), Am. Acad. of Allergy; mem. Am. Assn. for Certified Allergists (co-chmn. allergen and immunotherapy com. 1973-77), Am. Bd. of Internal Medicine, Am. Clin. and Climatol. Assn., Am. Fedn. for clin. Rsch., Am. Soc. of Internal Medicine, Asthma and Allergy Found. of Am. (coms.), Balt. City Med. Soc. (coms.), Joint Coun. of Allergy and Immunology (bd. dirs. 1975-84, treas. 1976-84), Md. Blue Cross and Blue Shield, Md. Found. for Health Care, Md. Soc. of Allergy (pres. 1973-74), Md. Soc. of Internal Medicine (pres. elect 1971-73, pres. 1973-75), So. Med. Assn., U.S. FDA (adv. com.), Sigma Xi. Achievements include contributions to understanding risk factors for pneumococcal pneumonia, longitudinal growth of children treated with corticosteroids, inflammatory diseases of eye, severe asthma and immunotherapy for hay fever and asthma. Home: 1902 A Indian Head Rd Baltimore MD 21204 Office: Ste 4 E 11 E Chase St Baltimore MD 21204

VAN MOL, LOUIS JOHN, JR., public relations executive; b. Knoxville, Tenn., Oct. 7, 1943; s. Louis John and Evelyn (Ramsay) Van M.; m. Deborah Ruth Boyd, Nov. 1, 1969; children: Derek, Millicent. BS, U. Tenn., 1966. Staff writer, editor AP, Knoxville and Nashville, 1963-66, 69; account exec. to exec. v.p. Holder, Kennedy & Co., Nashville, 1970-74, exec. v.p., 1978-79; dir. info. TVA, Knoxville, 1974-78; co-founder, ptnr. Dye, Van Mol & Lawrence, Nashville, 1980—; bd. dirs. Fogel & Assocs., Columbia, Tenn. Bd. dirs. East Tenn. Children's Hosp., Knoxville, 1977-78, Martha O'Bryan Ctr., Nashville, 1985-87, United Way Comm. Com., 1987-91, Am. Heart Assn. Mid. Tenn., Nashville, 1991-92, Leadership Nashville, 1992-93, Goodwill Industries Mid. Tenn., Crime Stoppers Nashville, 1986-92, Alcohol and Drug Coun. Mid. Tenn., Nashville, 1991-93. Lt. U.S. Army, 1966-68. Decorated Bronze Star. Mem. Richland Country Club, Cumberland Club, Sigma Delta Chi. Presbyterian. Home: 712 Bowling Ave Nashville TN 37215-1049 Office: Dye Van Mol & Lawrence Public Relations 209 7th Ave N Nashville TN 37219 Office: Dye, Van Mol & Lawrence 209 7th Ave N Nashville TN 37219

VAN MOLS, BRIAN, publishing executive; b. L.A., July 1, 1931; s. Pierre Matthias and Frieda Caryll (MacArthur) M.; m. Barbara Jane Rose, Oct. 1, 1953 (dec. 1968); children—Cynthia Lee, Matthew Howard, Brian; m. Nancy Joan Martell, June 11, 1977; children—Thomas Bentley, Cynthia Bentley, Kristi. A.B. in English, Miami U., Oxford, Ohio, 1953. Media supr. McCann-Erickson Inc., 1955-58; salesman Kelly Smith Co., 1959; with sales Million Market Newspaper Inc., 1959-63; sales mgr. Autoproducts Mag., 1964; sr. salesman True Mag., 1965-68, Guns Mag., 1969-70; regional advt. dir. Petersen Pub. Co., Los Angeles, 1971-74; pub. Motor Trend, 1982-84; nat. automotive mktg. mgr. Playboy Enterprises, Inc., N.Y.C., 1984-85, nat. sales mgr., 1985—; western advt. dir. Playboy mag., 1985-86; assoc. pub., advt. dir. Cycle World CBS, Inc., Newport Beach, Calif., 1986-88; pub., 1981; v.p., advt. dir. Four Wheeler Mag., Canoga Pk., Calif., 1986-88; v.p., dir. advt. western div. Gen. Media, Inc., 1988-91; v.p., dir. new bus. devel. Paisano Pub., Inc., Agoura Hills, Calif., 1991-92; dir. mktg. Crown Publs., 1993-94; exec. v.p. Voice Mktg. Inc., Thousand Oaks, Calif., 1994, DMR The Reis Co., Thousand Oaks, Calif., 1995—. Served with U.S. Army, 1953-55. Mem. Los Angeles Advt. Club, Adcraft Club Detroit, Advt. Sportsmen of N.Y. Republican. Episcopalian. Home and Office: 1453 Valecroft Ave Thousand Oaks CA 91361

VANN, JOHN DANIEL, III, university dean, historian; b. Raleigh, N.C., July 14, 1935; s. John Daniel Jr. and Sybil Dean (Wilson) V.; m. Helen Jane Rogers, June 21, 1969; children: John Daniel IV, Justin Fitz Patrick. BA with honors, U. N.C., 1957; MA, Yale U., 1959, PhD, 1965; M in Librarianship, Emory U., 1971; postgrad., Columbia U., 1962-63, Stanford U., 1977-78. Ordained deacon, elder Presbyn. Ch. Assoc. prof. history Campbell Coll., Buie's Creek, N.C., 1961-63; bibliographer European history and lit. Newberry Libr., Chgo., 1963-65, asst. reference librarian, 1963-65; prof. history Calif. Bapt. Coll., Riverside, 1965-66; dir. libr., prof. history Bapt. Coll. at Charleston, S.C., 1966-69; libr. Keuka Coll., Keuka Park, N.Y., 1969-71; chief libr., prof. history, chmn. libr. dept. S.I. Community Coll. CUNY, 1971-76; prof. libr. Coll. S.I. CUNY, 1976-79; head libr. Lockwood Libr./SUNY, Buffalo, 1979-80; asst. dir. for planning, univ. librs. SUNY, Buffalo, 1980-81; exec. dir. librs. and learning resources, prof. U. Wis., Oshkosh, 1981-87; libr. svcs. Bloomsburg U. Pa., 1987-89, dean libr. svcs., 1989—; resident planner, cons. on libr. bldgs. and collection devel; bd. dirs. Coun. Wis. Librs., 1983-86, Susquehanna Libr. Coop., 1987—; sec./treas., 1993—. Contbr. chpts. to books, articles to profl. jours. Trustee Maplewood (N.J.) Meml. Libr., 1977-79, v.p., 1979; bd. dirs. Coun. Wis. Librs., 1983-86, Midwest Rotary Multi-Dist. Short Term Internat. Youth Exch., 1987, Oshkosh (Wis.) Symphony Assn., 1986-87, United Cerebral Palsy of Winnebagoland, Oshkosh, 1986-87; active coms. Winnebago Presbytery, Presbyn. Ch., 1984-87; com. on min. Northumberland Presbytery, Presbyn. Ch., 1992—; commd. lay preacher, 1994—. Acad. Libr. Mgmt. intern Coun. on Libr. Resources Stanford U., 1977-78. Mem. ALA (com. mem.), Am. Hist. Assn., Archons of Colophon, Assn. for Libr. Collections and Tech. Svcs., Assn. Coll. and Rsch. Librs. (com. chmn., sec. chmn. 1977-78, editorial bd., bd. dirs. 1976-78)), Bibliog. Soc. Am., Libr. Adminstrn. and Mgmt. Assn., Libr. and Info. Tech. Assn., Medieval Acad. Am., Pa. Libr. Assn. (sect. dir.), Bloomsburg Rotary Club, Beta Phi Mu, Phi Alpha Theta. Republican. Home: 810 E Second St Bloomsburg PA 17815-2011 Office: Bloomsburg U Pa Harvey A Andruss Libr Bloomsburg PA 17815

VAN NELSON, NICHOLAS LLOYD, business council executive; b. Milw., Feb. 28, 1942. BS, Jacksonville U., 1964, MA, 1967; MA, Am. U., Washington, 1970; postgrad., Harvard U. Kennedy Sch. Govt., 1980. Adminstrv. asst. to Congressman Charles E. Bennett Washington, 1967-74; dir. Owens Ill. Corp., Washington, 1974-77; v.p., gen. mgr. Am. Paper Inst., Washington, 1977-80; v.p. govt. Champion Internat. Corp., Washington, 1980-89; pres. U.S.-Korea Bus. Coun., 1990—; bd. dirs., mem. exec. com. Tysons Nat. Bank, 1990-92. State chmn. Fla. Jaycees, Jacksonville, 1966; scoutmaster Boy Scouts Am. Named Outstanding Civic Leader in Am., 1967; Jacksonville U. pres.'s scholar, 1961-63. Mem. Pub. Affairs Coun. (bd. dirs. 1982-85), Washington Golf and Country Club, Dem. Club. Democrat. Roman Catholic. Home: 1023 15th St NW Washington DC 20005-2602

VANNEMAN, EDGAR, JR., lawyer; b. El Paso, Ill., Aug. 24, 1919; s. Edgar and Fern (Huffington) V.; m. Shirli Thomas, Apr. 28, 1951 (dec.); children: Jill, Thomas. BS, BA, Northwestern U., 1941, J.D., 1947. Bar: Ill. 1947. Mem. firm Campbell, Clark & Miller, 1947-48; gen. atty. Chgo. and NorthWestern R.R. Co., 1949-62; gen. atty., asst. sec. Brunswick Corp., Skokie, Ill., 1962-89, ret.; sec. Sherwood Med. Industries, Inc., 1976-82. Pres. Northeastern Ill. Planning Commn., 1978-82; dir. Suburban Health Systems Agy., 1976-82; mayor City of Evanston (Ill.), 1970-77; alt. del. Republican Nat. Conv., 1952, 56. Served with USAF, 1942-46. Decorated Bronze Star. Mem. ABA, Ill. Bar Assn. (past bd. govs.), Chgo. Bar Assn., Soc. Trial Lawyers. Presbyterian. Club: Law (Chgo.). Home: 715 Monticello Pl Evanston IL 60201-1745

VAN NESS, JAMES EDWARD, electrical engineering educator; b. Omaha, June 24, 1926; s. Hubert James and Jean (Woodruff) Van N.; m. Mary Ellen Dolvin, Dec. 28, 1948; children: Rebecca Ellen, Barbara Jean, Margaret Ann, Julie Lynn. B.S., Iowa State U., 1949; M.S., Northwestern U., 1951, Ph.D., 1954. Faculty elec. engring. dept. Northwestern U., 1952—, now prof., chmn. dept., 1969-72; dir. Computer Center, 1962-65; vis. assoc. prof. U. Calif., Berkeley, 1958-59; vis. prof. MIT, 1973-74, Ariz. State U., winter 1984. Contbr. Articles to profl. jours. Served with USNR, 1944-46. Fellow IEEE; mem. AAUP. Home: 2601 Noyes St Evanston IL 60201-2170

VAN NESS, JOHN RALPH, university foundation administrator; b. Columbus, Ohio, Oct. 22, 1939; s. Ralph Taylor and Norma Gertrude (Thorp) Van N.; children: Heather Thorpe, Hilary Clark. BA, The Colo. Coll., Colo. Springs, 1965; MA, U. Pa., 1969, PhD, 1979. Instr. West Chester (Pa.) U., 1969-70, Knox Coll., Galesburg, Ill., 1970-73, Fort Lewis Coll., Durango, Colo., 1974-76; cons. fund raising pvt. practice Phila., 1977-79; capital campaign con. John F. Rich Co., Phila., 1979-84; v.p. for coll. relations, adjunct prof. Anthropology Ursinus Coll., Collegeville, Pa., 1984-89; exec. v.p., prof. Moore Coll. Art and Design, Phila., 1989-90, pres., 1990-92; pres. Mus. N.Mex. Found., Santa Fe, 1992-93, N.Mex. State U. Found., 1995—; bd. dirs. Ctr. for Land Grant Studies, Santa Fe, 1978-94; editl. bd. Jour. of the West, Manhattan, Kans., 1980-88. Co-author: Cañones: Values, Crisis and Survival in a Northern New Mexico Village, 1981; author: Hispanos in Northern New Mexico, 1991; co-editor: Spanish and Mexican Land Grants in New Mexico and Colorado, 1980, Land, Water and Culture, 1987; editor: New Mexico Land Grant Series, vols. 1-5, 1983, 84, 87, 89, 94. Recipient Teaching Fellowship U. Pa.; grantee Ford Found., Nat. Sci. Found. Mem. Am. Anthrop. Assn., Am. Assn. Museums, Coun. for Advance and Support Edn., Nat. Soc. Fund Raising Execs., Pi Gamma Mu. Democrat. Avocations: architecture, art, ballet, running, tennis.

VANNICE, M. ALBERT, chemical engineering educator, researcher; b. Broken Bow, Nebr., Jan. 11, 1943; s. Duane M. and Eugenia R. (Farmer) V.; m. Bette Ann Clark, Jan. 2, 1971. BSChemE, State Univ., 1964; MS, Stanford Univ., 1966, PhD, 1970. Engr. Dow Chemical Co., Midland, Mich., 1966, Sun Oil Co., Marcus Hook, Pa., 1970; sr. rsch. engr. Esso Rsch. & Engr. Co., Linden, N.J., 1971-76; assoc. prof. Pa. State Univ., State Coll., 1976-80, prof., 1980—, disting. prof., 1991—; cons. Eastman Chem. Co., Kingsport, Tenn., 1980—, DuPont Chem. Co. Wilmington, Del., 1993—; adv. bd. Adsorption Sci. & Tech., 1982-95. Mem. editorial bd. Jour. of Catalysis, 1988-94, assoc. editor, 1994—; contbr. articles to profl. jours. Recipient N.Y. Catalysis Soc. award, 1985, P.H. Emmett award, 1987, Pa. Cleve. Catalysis Soc., 1988, Humboldt Rsch. award, 1990. Mem. AIChE (Profl. Progress award 1986), ACS, MRS, N.Am. Catalysis Soc. Achievements include 9 patents; effects of strong metal-support interactions on catalytic behavior; studies of CO hydrogenation, NOx reduction, catalyst characterization. Office: Pa State Univ 107 Fenske Lab University Park PA 16802

VAN NORTWICK, THOMAS H., radio broadcast executive; b. Syracuse, N.Y., Aug. 4, 1949; s. Howard J. and Virginia (Trost) Van N.; m. Linda Maccarone, Mar. 23, 1973; children: Melissa, Ryan, Jonathan. BS in Acctg., Canisius Coll., 1971. CPA, N.Y. Staff acct. Haskins and Sells, CPA, Buffalo, 1971-74; exec. dir. sub-bd. SUNY, Buffalo, 1974-78; contr. Sta. WBEN Algonquin Broadcasting Corp., Buffalo, 1978-84, v.p. fin. Sta. WBEN, 1984-90, exec. v.p., gen. mgr. Sta. WBEN, 1990—. Pres. Lancaster (N.Y.) Sch. Bd., 1990-91; bd. dirs. Jr. Achievement of Western N.Y., Buffalo, 1991—; town councilman, Lancaster, 1992—. Mem. AICPA, Nat. Assn. Broadcasters, N.Y. State Soc. CPAs, Rotary (dir. Buffalo chpt. 1991—). Avocations: skiing, golf. Home: 11 Shadyside Ln Lancaster NY 14086-1157 Address: WBEN(AM) 2077 Elmwood Ave Buffalo NY 14207-1903

VAN NOSTRAND, MORRIS ABBOTT, JR., publisher; b. N.Y.C., Nov. 24, 1911; s. Morris Abbott and Margaret Adrianna (Edwards) Van N.; m. Jane Alexander, Dec. 28, 1934 (dec. 1944); children: Pamela George, Patricia Abbott; m. Julia de La Roche Eaton, July 3, 1953; children: Deborah Randall, Abbie Eaton. B.A., Amherst Coll., 1934. With Samuel French, Inc., N.Y.C., from 1934; sec. Samuel French, Inc., 1948-52, pres., from 1952; pres. Samuel French Canada, Ltd., Toronto, Ont., 1952—, Walter H. Baker Co., Boston and Denver, 1952—; Hugo & Luigi-Samuel French Music Pubs., Inc.; chmn. bd. Samuel French, Ltd., London. Bd. dirs. New Dramatists Com., mem. coun. Friends of Amherst (Mass.) Library. Mem. ANTA (dir.), Chi Phi. Clubs: Amherst, Doubles (N.Y.C.); Nassau Country (Glen Cove) (gov.); Les Ambassadeurs, Clermont (London). Home: 131 E 66th St New York NY 10021-6129 Office: Samuel French Inc 45 W 25th St New York NY 10010-2003

VANONI, VITO AUGUST, hydraulic engineer; b. Calif., Aug. 30, 1904; s. Battista and Mariana V.; m. Edith Maria Falcinella, June 23, 1934. B.S. in Civil Engring, Calif. Inst. Tech., 1926, M.S. in Civil Engring, 1932, Ph.D., 1940. Supr. research lab. U.S. Soil Conservation Service, Pasadena, Calif., 1935-47; asst. prof. hydraulics Calif. Inst. Tech., 1942-49, asso. prof., 1949-55, prof., 1955-74, prof. emeritus, 1974—. Contbr. numerous articles on hydraulics and sedimentation to profl. jours.; editor: Sedimentation Engineering, 1975. Mem. ASCE (hon.), Internat. Assn. Hydraulic Research, Nat. Acad. Engineering, Sigma Xi. Home: 3545 Lombardy Rd Pasadena CA 91107-5628 Office: 1201 E California Blvd Pasadena CA 91125-0001

VAN ORDEN, PHYLLIS JEANNE, librarian, educator; b. Adrian, Mich., July 7, 1932; d. Warren Philip and Mabel A. Nancy (Russell) Van O. BS, Ea. Mich. U., 1954; AMLS, U. Mich., 1958; EdD, Wayne State U., 1970. Sch. librarian East Detroit (Mich.) Pub. Schs., 1954-57; librarian San Diego Pub. Library, 1958-60; media specialist Royal Oak (Mich.) Pub. Schs., 1960-64; librarian Oakland U. Rochester, Mich., 1964-66; instr. Wayne State U., Detroit, 1966-70; asst. prof. Rutgers U., New Brunswick, N.J., 1970-76; prof. library science Fla. State U., Tallahassee, 1977-91, assoc. dean for instrn., 1988-91; prof. libr. sci. program Wayne State U., Detroit, 1991-93; dir. Grad. Sch. of Libr. and Info. Sci. U. Wash., Seattle, 1993—. Editor: Elementary School Library Collection, 1974-77; author: Collection Program in Schools, 1995, Library Service to Children, 1992. Fla. State Libr. grantee, 1984, 86, 88; Lillian Bradshaw scholar Tex. Woman's U., 1993. Mem. Assn. Library Svc. to Children (past pres.), ALA (library resources and tech. svcs. div. Blackwell/N.Am. Scholarship award 1983), Assn. for Library and Info. Sci. Edn. (pres. 1990), Pi Lambda Theta. Avocations: music, knitting, physical fitness, cooking, travel. Office: U Wash Box 352930 133 Suzzallo Libr Seattle WA 98195-2930

VAN PATTEN, DICK VINCENT, actor; b. Kew Gardens, N.Y., Dec. 9, 1928; s. Richard Byron and Josephine (Acerno) Van P.; m. Patricia Poole,

Apr. 25, 1954; children: Nels, Jimmy, Vince. Broadway debut in Tapestry in Gray, 1935; other stage appearances include Ah, Wilderness!, 1939, 40, Watch on the Rhine, 1942, The Skin of Our Teeth, 1942, Mister Roberts, 1948, 51, 53, The Tender Trap, 1955, Will Success Spoil Rock Hunter?, 1957, Don't Drink the Water, Next, 1969; films include Reg'lar Fellers, 1941, Charly, 1968, Making It, 1971, Joe Kidd, 1972, Dirty Little Billy, 1972, Snowball Express, 1972, Westworld, 1973, Soylent Green, 1973, Superdad, 1974, Freaky Friday, 1976, High Anxiety, 1977, Spaceballs, 1986, The New Adventures of Pippi Longstocking, 1988, Robin Hood: Men in Tights, 1993; radio series Young Widder Brown, 1941; also radio plays Kiss and Tell, 1947, State Fair, 1950, 53, Father of the Bride, 1951, Good Housekeeping, 1951; regular TV series Mama, 1949-58, Final Ingredient, 1959, The Partners, 1971-72, The New Dick Van Dyke Show, 1973-74, When Things Were Rotten, 1975, Eight is Enough, 1977-81, WIOU, 1990; TV spl. Grandpa Max, 1975; drama Ladies of the Corridor, 1975, A Memory of Two Mondays, 1971; TV movies Hec Ramsey, 1972, The Crooked Hearts, 1972, The Love Boat, 1976, With This Ring, 1978, Diary of a Hitchhiker, 1979, Eight is Enough: A Family Reunion, 1987, Going to the Chapel, 1988, An Eight is Enough Wedding, 1989, Jake Spanner: Private Eye, 1989. Mem. SAG, Actors Equity Assn. Office: care Artists Agy 10000 Santa Monica Blvd Ste 305 Los Angeles CA 90067*

VAN PATTEN, JOYCE BENIGNIA, actress; b. Bklyn.; d. Richard Byron and Josephine (Acerno) Van P.; divorced; children: T. Casey King, Talia Balsam. Appeared in Broadway plays including Loves Old Sweet Song, 1941, Tomorrow the World, 1943, The Perfect Marriage, 1944, Wind is Ninety, 1945, Desk Set, 1956, Hole in the Head, 1957, Same Time Next Year, 1975, Murder at the Howard Johnson, 1978, The Supporting Cast, Rumors, Brighton Beach Memoirs, I Ought To Be In Pictures, Jake's Women (with daughter Talia Balsam), 1992, L.A. prodn., 1993, (off Broadway plays) Ivanov, The Seagull, All My Sons, (films) Trust Me, Monkey Shines, St. Elmo's Fire, Falcon and the Snowman, Billy Galvin, Mame, Blind Date, Infinity (TV shows) The Haunted, Sirens, Under The Influence, Malice In Wonderland, First Lady of the World; (TV movie) Breathing Lessons; (TV series) Unhappily Ever After; writer (play) Donuts, (screenplay) Would You Show Us Your Legs Please?. Co-founder The Workshop Theatre West; fund raiser AIDS Project L.A., West Hollywood, 1989, 90. Mem. Am. Film Inst. Avocations: tennis, needlework, painting, writing.

VAN PRAAG, HERMAN MEIR, psychiatrist, educator, administrator; b. Schiedam, The Netherlands, Oct. 17, 1929; came to U.S., 1982; s. Marinus and Charlotte (Leverpoll) van P.; m. Cornelia Elkens, Nov. 17, 1956; children: Marinus, Gido, Charlotte, Bart. M.D., State U. Leiden, Netherlands, 1956; Ph.D., U. Utrecht, 1962. Resident Found. Advanced Clin. Teaching, Rotterdam, Netherlands, 1958-63; chief of staff dept. psychiatry Dijkzigt Hosp., Rotterdam, Netherlands, 1963-66; founder, head dept. biological psychiatry Psychiat. U. Clinic, Groningen, Netherlands, 1966-77; assoc. prof. State U. Groningen, Netherlands, 1968, prof., 1970-77; prof., head dept. psychiatry Acad. Hosp. State U. Utrecht, 1977-82; Silverman prof., chmn. dept. psychiatry Albert Einstein Coll. Medicine, Bronx, N.Y., 1982-92; chief psychiatrist Montefiore Med. Ctr., Bronx, N.Y., 1982-92; prof., head Acad. Psychiat. Ctr. U. Limburg, Maastricht, The Netherlands, 1992—; head WHO Collaborating Ctr. for Residency Tng., Utrecht, 1974; vis. prof. Hebrew U., Jerusalem, 1976-77. Editor in chief: (6 vols.) Handbook of Biological Psychiatry, 1975-81; mem. editorial bd. numerous jours.; contbr. numerous articles to profl. jours. Decorated knight, Queen Beatrix, The Netherlands, 1990; recipient Anna-Monika prize Anna-Monika Found., 1973, Cramer award Columbia U. Coll. Physicians and Surgeons, 1983, Reynier de Graaf award Dutch Soc. for Advancement Biol. and Med. Scis., 1983, Lily Ctrl. Nervous Sys. award, 1990, 1st Sylvia Best Hunter Disting. Svc. award 1991, Open Mind award Janssen Rsch. Coun., 1992, Albert Einstein award for rsch. in psychiatry and related disciplines, 1993, Lily award European Coll. Neuropsycho-Pharmacology, 1995. Mem. Soc. Biol. Psychiatry, N.Y. Acad. Medicine, Psychiat. Research Soc., Am. Coll. Neuropsychopharmacology, Internat. Group Study Affective Disorders, Internat. Assn. Suicide Prevention, Sierra Club. Home: Proost Willemsstraat 34, 6231CW Meerssen The Netherlands Office: Univ Limburg, PO Box 616, 6200MD Maastricht The Netherlands

VAN RAALTE, JOHN A., research and engineering management executive; b. Copenhagen, Apr. 10, 1938; came to U.S., 1955; s. John A. and Laura W.M. (Louwerier) van R.; m. Andrée Valentine Greene, Dec. 28, 1963; children: Kirsten A., James E. BSEE, MIT, 1960, MSEE, 1960, elec. engrs. degree, 1962, PhD, 1964. Rsch. asst. MIT, Cambridge, 1960-64; mem. tech. staff RCA David Sarnoff Rsch. Ctr., Princeton, N.J., 1964-70, head display rsch., 1970-79, head videodisc record and playback, 1979-83, dir. videodisc systems rsch., 1983-84, dir. display systems rsch., 1984-87; dir. materials and process tech. lab. David Sarnoff Rsch. Ctr. subs. SRI Internat., Princeton, N.J., 1987-90; mgr. CRT engring. Thomson Consumer Electronics N.Am. Tube Div., Lancaster, Pa., 1990-92; dir. electron optics lab. Thomson Tubes & Displays, Genlis, Francs; mem. steering com. Internat. Display Rsch. Conf., U.S., Europe, Japan, 1981-88. Author: (with others) Electronic Engineer's Reference Handbook, 4th and 5th edits. Chmn. ednl. coun. MIT, N.J., 1978-83. Fellow IEEE, Soc. for Info. Display (pres., v.p., treas., sec. 1981-88, chmn. and program chmn. Internat. Symposium 1973-78); mem. MIT Club of Princeton, Chevalier du Tastevin, Sigma Xi, Tau Beta Pi, Eta Kappa Nu (pres. Boston chpt. 1964). Home: 24 rue des Templiers, 21121 Fontaine les Dijon France Office: Thomson Tubes & Displays, Ave du Gen de Gaulle, 21110 Genlis France

VAN REES, CORNELIUS S., lawyer; b. N.Y.C., May 29, 1929; s. Cornelius Richard and Beatrice Martin (Shreve) Van R.; m. Virginia Vandewater, Mar. 15, 1953 (div. 1984); children: Pamela Millet Van Rees Lundquist, Claire Katherine; m. Alix McIvor, Jan. 2, 1985. BA, Denison U., 1951; JD, Columbia U., 1954. Bar: N.Y. 1956, U.S. Dist. Ct. (so. dist.) N.Y. 1956, Conn. 1994. Assoc. Thacher Proffitt & Wood, N.Y.C., 1956-62, ptnr., 1963-93, of counsel, 1994—; mem. exec. com., officer, bd. dirs. Graham Corp.; lectr. in field. Writer in field. Trustee, sec. Williston Northhampton Sch.; mem. senate, honors and prizes com. Columbia U. Harlem Fisk Stone scholar Columbia U., 1954. Mem. ABA (coms. on internat. fin. trans., export credits, maritime fin. and devel. in bus. fin.), Maritime Law Assn. (com. on underseas devel. and exploration), Alumni Fedn. Columbia U., Inc. (Alumni medal 1984, pres. 1979-81), N.Y. Yacht Club. Avocation: sailing. Home and Office: 35 Cove Side Ln Stonington CT 06378-2902

VAN REMOORTERE, FRANCOIS PETRUS, chemical company research and development executive; b. Haasdonk, Belgium, Dec. 16, 1943; came to U.S., 1968; s. Jozef Frederik and Celine (van de Vyner) van R.; m. Jane Louise Evans; children: Kier, Pieter, David. BS in Chemistry, U. Louvain, Belgium, 1965, PhD in Phys. Chemistry, 1968. Rsch. chemist The Dow Chem. Co., Midland, Mich., 1968-74, group leader, 1974-77, rsch. mgr., 1977-79; dir. R & D planning Am. Can Co., Greenwich, Conn., 1979-83; v.p. tech. and planning W.R. Grace & Co., Columbia, Md., 1983-86, pres. rsch. div., 1986—; mem. adv. coun. Johns Hopkins U. Whiting Sch. Engring. Bd. visitors U. Md., College Park, 1988—; trustee Howard County Gen. Hosp. 1989-93, Howard County Hosp. Found., 1993—. Mem. AAAS, Am. Chem. Soc., Indsl. Rsch. Inst., N.Y. Acad. Sci. Chem. Industry, Cosmos Club (Washington). Office: W R Grace & Co Rsch Div Washington Rsch Ctr 7379 State Route 32 Columbia MD 21044-4098

VAN RIPER, PAUL KENT, marine corps officer; b. Brownsville, Pa., July 5, 1938; s. James Frederic and Mary Katherine (Davis) Van R.; m. Lillie Catherine Alford, Jan. 27, 1968; children: Stephen Kent, Cynthia Leigh. BA in Edn., California (Pa.) State Coll., 1963. Enlisted USMCR, 1956; commd. 2d lt. USMC, 1963, advanced through grades to brig. gen., 1990; platoon comdr., co. exec. officer, asst. ops. officer 1st Bn. 8th Marines, Dominican Republic, 1965; Marine advisor Vietnamese Marine Corps, 1965-66; instr. The Basic Sch., 1966-68; student Amphibious Warfare Sch., 1968; co. comdr., asst. ops. officer 3d bn. 7th Marines, 1st Marine Div., Vietnam, 1968-69; instr., staff officer JFK Inst. for Mil. Assistance, Ft. Bragg, N.C., 1969-71; spl. projects officer Office Chief of Staff, Hdqrs. Marine Corps, 1971-72; mil. ops. specialist Tng. Div., Washington, 1972-74; ops. officer 3d bn. 8th Marines, Camp Lejeune, N.C. 1974-75, regt ops officer 1975-76; exec. officer 1st bn. 8th Marines, 1976-77; student Naval War Coll., Newport, R.I., 1977-78; mil. observer U.S. Mil. Observer Group, UN Truce

Supervision Orgn., Palestine, 1978-79; comdg. officer Marine Barracks, Naval Air Sta., Cecil Field, Fla., 1979-81; student Army War Coll., Carlisle, Pa., 1981-82; regtl. exec. officer 7th Marines, 1st Marine Div., Camp Pendleton, Calif., 1982-83, comdr. 2d bn., 1983-84; exercise, readiness and tng. officer I Marine Amphibious Force, Camp Pendleton, 1984-85; regtl. comdr. 4th Marines, 3d Marine Div., Okinawa, Japan, 1985-86; asst. chief of staff, then chief of staff 3d Marine Div., Okinawa, 1986-88; dir. Command and Staff Coll., Quantico, Va., 1988-89; pres. Marine Corps U., Quantico, 1989-90; dir. Marine Air-Ground Tng. and Edn. Ctr., Quantico, 1990-91; comdg. gen. 2d Marine Div., Camp LeJeune, N.C., 1991—. Contbr. numerous articles to profl. mil. jours. Tchr. Sunday sch. Mil. Chapels. Decorated Silver Star medal with gold star (2), Legion of Merit, Bronze Star meda with Combat V, Purple Heart, Meritorious Svc. medal, Joint Svc. Commendation medal, Army commendation medal, Navy Achievement medal, Combat Action Ribbon with gold star, Nat. Def. Svc. medal with one bronze star (2), Vietnam Svc. medal with one silver and one bronze star, others; UN medal; Gallantry Cross and Campaign medal (Republic of Vietnam); Southwest Asia Svc. meda., Kuwaiti Liberation medal. Presbyterian. Avocations: history, running, fishing. Address: USMC GOQ 2001 Camp Lejeune NC 28542-1314

VAN RIPER, PAUL PRITCHARD, political science educator; b. Laporte, Ind., July 29, 1916; s. Paul and Margaret (Pritchard) Van R.; m. Dorothy Ann Dodd Samuelson, May 11, 1964; 1 child, Michael Scott Samuelson. A.B., DePauw U., 1938; Ph.D., U. Chgo., 1947. Instr. Northwestern U., 1947-49, asst. prof. polit. sci., 1949-51; mgmt. analyst Office Comptroller Dept. Army, 1951-52; mem. faculty Cornell U., 1952-70, prof., 1957-70; chmn. gov. bd., exec. com. Cornell Social Sci. Research Center, 1956-58; prof., head dept. polit. sci. Tex. A&M U., 1970-77, prof., 1977-81, prof. emeritus, 1981—; coordinator M.P.A. program, 1979-81; vis. prof. U. Chgo., 1958, Ind. U., 1961, U. Strathclyde, Scotland, 1964, U. Mich., 1965, U. Okla., 1989—, U. Utah, 1979. Author: History of the United States Civil Service, 1958, Some Educational and Social Aspects of Fraternity Life, 1961, (with others) The American Federal Executive, 1963, Handbook of Practical Politics, 3d edit., 1967; editor and co-author: the Wilson Influence on Public Administration, 1990. Mem. Econ. Adv. com. Civil Svc. Refor Assn. N.Y., 1960-64; mem. hist. adv. com. NASA, 1964-66; bd. dirs. Brazos Valley Community Action Agy., 1975-79, Brazos County Hist. Commn., 1976—. Served to maj. AUS, 1942-46; lt. col. USAR, ret. Decorated Croix de Guerre (France). Mem. Am. Polit. Sci. Assn., So. Polit. Sci. Assn., S.W. Polit. Sci. Assn. (exec.com. 1975-77), Am. Soc. Pub. Adminstrn. (nat adv. com. 1957-60, Dimock award 1984, Waldo award 1990), Internat. Personnel Mgmt. Assn., Rotary (pres. Bryan club 1991-92), Phi Beta Kappa, Beta Theta Pi (v.p. 1962, gen. sec. 1963-65), Pi Alpha Alpha, Pi Sigma Alpha, Phi Kappa Phi, Sigma Delta Chi. Republican. Baptist. Home: 713 E 30th St Bryan TX 77803-4789 Office: Tex A and M Univ Dept Polit Sci College Station TX 77843-4348

VAN ROOIJ, VINCENT A. M., university president. Pres. Bayamon (P.R.) Ctrl. U. Office: Bayamon Central U Office of President PO Box 1725 Bayamon PR 00960-1725

VAN ROOY, JEAN-PIERRE, international executive; b. Louvain, Belgium, Dec. 11, 1934; came to U.S., 1982; s. Félix C. and Betty H. (van Weelden) van R.; m. Marie Claire Duquesne, Oct. 8, 1960; children: Ann M., Eric M., Martine M. BA, Inst. Universitaire, St. Louis, Brussels, 1954; JD, Cath. U. of Louvain, 1958, M in Fin., 1960. Mng. dir. Otis Elevator Cy, Belgium, 1971-74, Italy, 1973-75; v.p. Otis Elevator Europe, Africa, Middle East, Paris, 1975-82; pres. Carrier Internat. Corp., Syracuse, N.Y., 1982-86; exec. v.p. Carrier Corp., Syracuse, 1986; sr. v.p. Otis Elevator ETO, Paris, 1987-89; pres. Otis N.Am. Ops., Farmingtpm, Conn., 1989-90, Otis Elevator Co., Farmington, 1990—; bd. dirs. of numerous corps. worldwide. Served to lt. Belgium Navy, 1958-60. Republican. Roman Catholic. Club: Cercle Union Interalliée (Paris). Avocations: history, sailing. Office: Otis Elevator Co. 10 Farm Springs Farmington CT 06032

VAN RUNKLE, THEADORA, costume designer. Costume designer: (films) Bonnie and Clyde, 1967 (Acad. award nomination best costume design 1967), Bullitt, 1968, I Love You, Alice B. Toklas!, 1968, (with Ron Postal and Alan Levine) The Thomas Crown Affair, 1968, The Arrangement, 1969, (with Enrico Sabbatini) A Place for Lovers, 1969, (with Levine and Joanne Haas) The Rivers, 1969, Myra Breckinridge, 1970, Johnny Got His Gun, 1971, Ace Eli and Rodger of the Skies, 1973, Kid Blue, 1973, Mame, 1974, The Godfather, Part II, 1974 (Acad. award nomination best costume design 1974), Nickelodeon, 1976, New York, New York, 1977, Same Time, Next Year, 1978, The Jerk, 1979, (with Madeline Graneto) Heartbeeps, 1981, S.O.B., 1981, The Best Little Whorehouse in Texas, 1982, (with Ron Heilman and Linda M. Henrikson) Rhinestone, 1984, Peggy Sue Got Married, 1986 (Acad. award nomination best costume design 1986), Native Son, 1986, Wildfire, 1988, Everybody's All American, 1988, Troop Beverly Hills, 1989, Stella, 1990, The Butcher's Wife, 1991, Leap of Faith, 1992, (TV series) "Dungeon of Death" episode of Wizards and Warriors, 1983 (Emmy award best costume design 1983). Office: 8805 Lookout Mountain Rd Los Angeles CA 90046*

VAN RYSSELBERGE, CHARLES H., organization administrator; b. Evanston, Ill., Oct. 8, 1945; s. John F. Van Rysselberge and Marguerite Irene (Van Witzenburg) Van Rysselberge-Yaple; m. Joan E. Roberts, June 22, 1968; children: Denise, Michelle. ABJ, U. Ga., 1968, MA, 1971, cert. in mgmt., 1977. Membership mgr. Shreveport (La.) C of C, 1972-74, exec. v.p., 1986-88; group mgr. Chattanooga (Tenn.) C of C, 1974-79; exec. 1979-81; exec. v.p. Monroe (La.) C. of C., 1977-79, Dalton-Whitfield (Ga.) C. of C., 1981-86, Atlanta C. of C., 1988-93; pres. Oklahoma City C of C, 1993—. Communications mgr. Greenville (S.C.) C. of C., 1969-70. 1st lt. Signal Corps, U.S. Army, 1970-72, USAR, 1972-73. Mem. Am. C of C. Execs. Assn., Ga. Assn. C of C. Execs. (bd. dirs. 1983-86), So. Assn. C of C. Execs. (bd. dirs. 1988-90), Century Club (chmn. 1984-86), Phi Kappa Tau. Lutheran. Avocation: jogging. Home: 5017 Misty Glen Cir Oklahoma City OK 73142 Office: C of C of Oklahoma City 123 Park Ave Oklahoma City OK 73102

VAN SANT, GUS, JR., director, screenwriter; b. Louisville, 1952. BA in Filmmaking, RISD, 1975. Films include Mala Noche, 1985 (L.A. Film Critics award 1987), Drugstore Cowboy, 1989 (with Daniel Yost: Nat. Soc. Film Critics Best Dir. award 1989, Best Screenplay award 1990, N.Y. Film Critics Best Screenplay award 1990, Best Screenplay award 1990, L.A. Film Critics Best Screenplay award 1989), Internat. PEN Literary award for Screenplay Adaptation (with Daniel Yost 1989), My Own Private Idaho, 1991 (Best Screenplay 1992, Best Film 1992), Even Cowgirls Get the Blues, 1993, To Die For, 1995. Office: William Morris Agency Inc 151 S El Camino Dr Beverly Hills CA 90212-2775

VANSANT, JOANNE FRANCES, academic administrator; b. Morehead, Ky., Dec. 29, 1924; d. Lewis L. and Dorothy (Greene) VanS. BA, Denison U., Granville, Ohio; MA, The Ohio State U.; postgrad., U. Colo. and The Ohio State U.; LLD (hon.), Albright Coll., 1975. Tchr., health and phys. edn. Mayfield, Kentucky High Sch., 1946-48; instr. Denison U., Granville, Ohio, 1948; instr. women's phys. edn. Otterbein Coll., Westerville, Ohio, 1948-52, assoc. prof., 1955-62, dept. chmn., 1952-60, chmn. div. profl. studies, 1961-65, dean of women, 1952-60, 62-64, dean of students, 1964-93, v.p. student affairs, 1968-93, v.p., dean student affairs emeritus, 1993—, cons. Instnl. Advancement, 1993—. Co-pres. Directions for Youth, 1983-84, pres., 1984-85; bd. dirs North Area Mental Health; trustee Westerville Civic Symphony at Otterbein Coll., 1983-88; active numerous other community orgns.; ordained elder Presbyn. Ch., 1967. Named to hon. Order of Ky. Cols., 1957; recipient Focus on Youth award Columbus Dispath, 1983, Vol. of the Yr. award North Area Mental Health Svcs., 1982. Mem. Am. Assn. Counseling and Devel., Ohio Personnel and Guidance Assn., Ohio Assn. Women Deans, Adminstrs., Counselors (treas., exec. bd. 1972-73), Nat. Assn. Student Personnel Adminstrs., Ohio Coll. Personnel Assn., Mortar Bd. (hon.), Zonta Internat. (pres. Columbus, Ohio club 1988-85, dist. gov. 1988-90), Vocal Arts Resource Network (chair bd. dirs. 1994-96), Cap and Dagger Club, Torch and Key Hon., Order Omega, Alpha Lambda Delta, Theta Alpha Phi, others. Avocations: musical and children's theater production, choreography. Home: 9100 Oakwood Pt Westerville OH 43081-9643 Office: Otterbein Coll Instnl Advancement Westerville OH 43081

VAN SANT, PETER RICHARD, news correspondent; b. Seattle, Feb. 21, 1953; s. Richard Murdock and Joy Marie Van Sant; m. children: Erik, Jeffrey, Stefani, Kristina; m. Sarma Anete Dindzans, Apr. 20, 1994. BS in Comm. cum laude, Washington State U., 1975. Reporter, anchor KMVT-TV, Twin Falls, Idaho, 1976; reporter KCRG-TV, Cedar Rapids, Iowa, 1976-77, KETV-TV, Omaha, 1977-78; anchor, reporter KOOL-TV, Phoenix, 1978-82; reporter WFAA-TV, Dallas, 1982-84; corr. CBS News, Atlanta, 1984-89, London, Eng., 1989-92, N.Y.C., 1992—. Recipient Emmy Investigative Reporting NATAS, 1987, Alfred I. Dupont award Columbia U., 1989-90. Avocations: hiking, fishing, travel. Office: CBS News/Street Stories 524 W 57th St New York NY 10019-2902

VAN SANT, ROBERT WILLIAM, manufacturing company executive; b. Iowa Falls, Aug. 19, 1938; s. Oscar and Muriel (Mullane) Van S.; m. Marilyn J. Noonan, May 31, 1981; children: William, Kathy, David, Susan, Jeffrey. BSMechE, U. Iowa, 1966, MSMechE, 1967. With Deere & Co., 1957-83; gen. mgr. Waterloo, Iowa, 1975-80; dir. Moline, Ill., 1980-81; v.p. Deere & Co., Moline, Ill., 1981-83; pres. Cessna Aircraft Co., Wichita, Kans., 1983-87, also bd. dirs.; pres., CEO Blount, Inc., Montgomery, Ala., 1987-91, also bd. dirs.; chmn. Lukens Steel Co., Coatsville, Pa., 1991—, also bd. dirs.; bd. dirs. NAM, Lukens Inc., Blount, Inc. Trustee Mfrs.'s Alliance for Productivity Innovation. Home: 1288 Farm Rd Berwyn PA 19312-2000

VAN SCHAACK, ERIC, art historian, educator; b. Evanston, Ill., June 10, 1931; s. Cornelius Peter and Sigrid (Schold) Van S.; m. Carol Fryling, June 16, 1965; children—Elizabeth M., Leslie A. AB, Dartmouth Coll., 1953; Ph.D., Columbia U., 1969. Lectr., rsch. asst. The Frick Collection, N.Y.C., 1960-62; asst. prof. fine arts, then full prof. visual arts Goucher Coll., Balt., 1964-77; prof. art and art history Colgate U., Hamilton, N.Y., 1977—, chmn. dept. art and art history, 1978-83; vis. prof. fine arts Md. Inst. Coll. Art Johns Hopkins U., Balt. Author: Master Drawings in Private Collections, 1962, Baroque Art in Italy, 1964; contbr. articles to profl. jours., encys. Served with U.S. Army, 1954-56. Grantee Fulbright/Italian Govt., 1962-63, Ford Found., 1972-73, Colgate U. faculty, 1979-80, 92-93, others. Mem. Coll. Art Assn., Am. Soc. Archtl. Historians, Nat. Trust Hist. Preservation. Club: Hamilton. Home: 28 W Pleasant St Hamilton NY 13346-1216 Office: Colgate U Dept Art & Art History Hamilton NY 13346-1398

VAN SCHILFGAARDE, JAN, agricultural engineer, government agricultural service administrator; b. The Hague, Netherlands, Feb. 7, 1929; came to U.S., 1946, naturalized, 1957; married; 3 children. B.S., Iowa State Coll. 1949, M.S., 1950, Ph.D. in Agrl. Engring. and Soil Physics, 1954. Instr., assoc. agrl. engr. Iowa State Coll., 1949-54; asst. prof. agrl. engring. N.C. State Coll., 1954-57, assoc. prof., 1957-62, prof.; 1962-64; drainage engr. Agrl. Rsch. Svc. USDA, Raleigh, N.C., 1954-64; chief water mgmt. engr. soil and water conservation rsch. div. USDA, Beltsville, Md., 1964-67; assoc. dir., 1967-71; dir. USDA, 1971-72; dir. Salinity Lab. USDA, Riverside, Calif., 1972-84; dir. Mountain States Area Agrl. Rsch. Svc. USDA, Ft. Collins, Colo., 1984-86, assoc. dir. no. plains area Agrl. Rsch. Svc., 1986-91; assoc. dep. administr. for natural resources Agrl. Rsch. Svc. USDA, Beltsville, Md., 1991—; vis. prof. Ohio State U., 1962. Mem. ASCE, NAE, Am. Soc. Agrl. Engrs., Soil Sci. Soc., Soil Conservation Soc. Am. Office: Agrl Rsch Svc Nat Program Staff Barc W # 005 Beltsville MD 20705

VANSELOW, NEAL ARTHUR, university administrator, physician; b. Milw., Mar. 18, 1932; s. Arthur Frederick and Mildred (Hoffmann) V.; m. Mary Ellen McKenzie, June 20, 1958; children: Julie Ann, Richard Arthur. AB, U. Mich., 1954, MD, 1958, MS, 1963. Diplomate: Am. Bd. Internal Medicine, Am. Bd. Allergy and Immunology. Intern Mpls. Gen. Hosp., 1958-59; resident Univ. Hosp., Ann Arbor, Mich., 1959-63; instr. medicine U. Mich., 1963-64, asst. prof., 1964-68, assoc. prof., 1968-72, prof.; chmn. dept. postgrad. medicine and health professions edn., 1972-74; dean Coll. Medicine U. Ariz., Tucson, 1974-77; chancellor med. ctr. U. Nebr., Omaha, 1977-82, v.p., 1977-82; v.p health scis. U. Minn., 1982-89, prof. internal medicine, 1982-89; chancellor Tulane U. Med. Ctr., New Orleans, 1989-94; prof. internal medicine, adj. prof. health sys. mgmt. Tulane U., New Orleans, 1989—; chmn. Joint Bd. Osteo. and Med. Examiners Ariz., 1974-77; chmn. council on Grad. Med. Edn., Dept. Health and Human Services, 1986-91; scholar in residence Inst. Medicine Nat. Acad. Scis., 1994—. Bd. dirs. Devel. Authority for Tucson's Economy, 1975-77, Minn. Coalition for Health Care Costs, 1983-87, La. Health Care Authority, 1989-90, United Way Greater N Orleans Area, 1992—; mem. exec. com. United Way Midlands, 1980-82, vice chmn. 1981 campaign; bd. dirs., mem. exec. com. Health Planning Coun. Midlands, Omaha, 1978-82, v.p., 1981-82; bd. dirs. Minn. High Tech. Coun., 1983-86; mem. commn. on Health Professions Pew Charitable Trusts, 1990-92; mem. Gov.'s Pan Am. Commn., La., 1991-92; mem. mktg. mgmt. governing coun. U. Hosp. Consortium, 1993—. Fellow ACP, Am. Acad. Allergy, Am. Coll. Physician Execs.; mem. Assn. Acad. Health Ctrs. (bd. dirs. 1983-89, chmn. bd. dirs. 1988), NAS/Inst. of Medicine (com. on educating dentists for future 1993-95, chairperson com. on future of primary care 1994—), Soc. Med. Adminstrs., Phi Beta Kappa, Sigma Xi, Alpha Omega Alpha, Beta Theta Pi, Nu Sigma Nu. Home: 1828 Palmer Ave New Orleans LA 70118-6216 Office: Tulane U 1430 Tulane Ave New Orleans LA 70112-2699

VAN SETERS, JOHN, biblical literature educator; b. Hamilton, Ont., Can., May 2, 1935; s. Hugo and Anne (Hubert) Van S.; m. Elizabeth Marie Malmberg, June 11, 1960; children: Peter John, Deborah Elizabeth. B.A., U. Toronto, 1958; M.A., Yale U., 1959, Ph.D., 1965; B.D., Princeton Theol. Sem., 1962. Asst. prof. dept. Near Eastern studies Waterloo Luth. U., 1965-67; assoc prof. Old Testament Andover Newton Theol. Sch., 1967-70; assoc. prof. dept. Near Eastern studies U. Toronto, 1970-76, prof., 1976-77; James A. Gray prof. Bibl. lit., dept. religion U.N.C., Chapel Hill, 1977—; chmn. dept. religious studies U. N.C., 1993-95. Author: The Hyksos: A New Investigation, 1966, Abraham in History and Tradition, 1975, In Search of History, 1983, Der Jahwist als Historiker, 1987, Prologue to History, 1992, The Life of Moses, 1994. Recipient James Henry Breasted prize Am. Hist. Assn., 1985, Book award Am. Acad. Religion, 1986; Woodrow Wilson fellow, 1958; J.J. Obermann fellow, 1962-64; Guggenheim fellow, 1979-80; NEH fellow, 1985-86, Am. Coun. Learned Socs. fellow, 1991-92. Mem. AAUP, Soc. Bibl. Lit., Am. Schs. Oriental Rsch., Soc. Study of Egyptian Antiquities, Am. Oriental Soc., Soc. for Old Testament Study, Cath. Bibl. Assn. Home: 104 Mullin Ct Chapel Hill NC 27514-2646 Office: U NC 101 Saunders Hall CB # 3225 Chapel Hill NC 27599

VAN SICKLE, BRUCE MARION, federal judge; b. Minot, N.D., Feb. 13, 1917; s. Guy Robin and Hilda Alice (Rosenquist) Van S.; m. Dorothy Alfreda Hermann, May 26, 1943; children: Susan Van Sickle Cooper, John Allan, Craig Bruce, David Max. B.S.L., U. Minn., 1941, J.D., 1941. Bar: Minn. 1941, N.D. 1946. Pvt. practice law, Minot, 1947-71; judge U.S. Dist. Ct. N.D., 1971-85, sr. judge, 1985—; mem. N.D. Ho. of Reps., 1957, 59. Served with USMCR, 1941-46. Mem. ABA, N.D. Bar Assn., N.W. Bar Assn., Ward County Bar Assn., Am. Trial Lawyers Assn., Am. Coll. Probate Counsel, Am. Judicature Soc., Bruce M. Van Sickle Inns of Ct. Masons, Shriners, Elks. Office: US Dist Ct 430 US Courthouse PO Box 670 Bismarck ND 58502-0670

VAN SICKLE, FREDERICK L., federal judge; b. 1943; m. Jane Bloomquist. BS, U. Wis., 1965; JD, U. Wash., 1968. Ptnr. Clark & Van Sickle, 1970-75; prosecuting atty. Douglas County, Waterville, Wash., 1971-75; judge State of Wash. Superior Ct., Grant and Douglas counties, 1975-79, Chelan and Douglas Counties, 1979-91; judge U.S. Dist. Ct. (ea. dist.) Wash., Spokane, 1991—; co-chair rural ct. com. Nat. Conf. State Trial Judges, 1987-91. 1st lt. U.S. Army, 1968-70. Mem. ABA (nat. conf. state trial judges jud. adminstrn.), Am. Adjudicature Soc., Wash. State Bar Assn., Masons (pres. badger mountain lodge 1982-84), Scottish Rite, Spokane Rotary. Office: US Dist Cts US Courthouse 920 W Riverside Ave Rm 914 Spokane WA 99201-1008

VAN SICKLE, PAUL BRUNTON, financial executive; b. Toronto, Ont., Can., Sept. 17, 1939; came to U.S., 1967; s. Percy Orton Van Sickle and Audrey Winefred (Dandie) Palmquist; m. Christine Cornfoot, Sept. 9, 1967 (div. July 1985); children: Giles, Kirsten. Grad. advanced mgmt. program, Harvard U., 1986. Canadian chartered acct. V.p. Fin. Rexcel, Ludlow, Mass., 1973-76, Specialty Products Sector, LaGrange, Ga., 1976-77; v.p.

Thompson Industries, Phoenix, 1977-79, exec. v.p., 1979-81; controller Home & comml. Products Group, Northbrook, Ill., 1981-82, Duracell, Inc., Danbury, Conn., 1982-83; sr. v.p. fin. Hobart Corp., Troy, Ohio, 1983-85; v.p., controller Dart & Kraft, Inc., Northbrook, Ill., 1986; v.p., controller Premark Internat., Deerfield, Ill., 1986-88, v.p. control and info. systems, 1988-89; v.p., chief fin. officer Tupperware, Orlando, Fla., 1989—. Avocations: golf, walking, sailing. Office: Premark Internat 1717 Deerfield Rd Deerfield IL 60015-3978 also: Tupperware Orlando FL

VANSINA, JAN MARIA JOZEF, historian, educator; b. Antwerp, Belgium, Sept. 14, 1929; came to the U.S., 1960; s. Dirk and Suzanne (Verellen) V.; m. Claudine Marie-Jeanne Herman, Mar. 26, 1933; 1 child, Bruno. PhD, Katolieke U. Leuven, 1957. Rsch. fellow Inst. for Scientific Rsch. Ctrl. Africa, 1952-60; prof. history and anthropology U. Wis., 1960—, Vilas rsch. prof., 1973-75; vis. prof. numerous univs., 1963—. Author 19 books, including Paths in the Rainforest Towards a History of Political Tradition in Equatorial Africa, 1990, Living with Africa, 1994; mem. editl. bd. 14 jours. in African studies; contbr. articles to profl. jours. Sgt. Belgian Army, 1954-56. J.D. MacArthur scholar, 1987; recipient Herskovits prize in African studies, 1967, Belgian Nat. Prize History, 1967, A. Von Humboldt prize, 1983; Guggenheim grantee, 1980. Mem. U.S. Acad. Arts and Scis., UNESCO Com. Gen. History Africa, Belgian Acad. Overseas, Brit. Acad. Avocations: oral history, oral tradition, African history, anthropology, African art history. Home: 2810 Ridge Rd Madison WI 53705-5224

VAN SINDEREN, ALFRED WHITE, former telephone company executive; b. Bklyn., June 20, 1924; s. Adrian and Jean (White) Van S.; m. Suzanne Petersen, Apr. 21, 1962; children: Alexander, David Cabot, Sylvia Van Sinderen Abbate, Jean Van Sinderen Vashaw, Katherine Van Sinderen Tucker. B.A., Yale U., 1945; M.B.A., Harvard U., 1947. With So. New Eng. Telephone Co., New Haven, 1947-85; v.p. So. New Eng. Telephone Co. (No. area), Hartford, Conn., 1962-65; v.p. pres. So. New Eng. Telephone Co., 1965-67, pres., 1967-82, chmn., chief exec. officer, 1982-84, chmn. bd., 1984-85; William H. Donaldson disting. faculty fellow Yale U. Sch. Mgmt., 1985-89. Past mem. adv. bd. Yale-U.S. Sch. Orgn. and Mgmt.; mem. Yale Libr. Assocs.; past co-chmn. Gov. Conf. Human Rights, 1967; past bd. dirs. Conn. Econ. Devel. Corp., Hartford; bd. dirs., past chmn. Shirley Frank Found.; pres Found. for New Haven Green, Inc., 1986-91. With USNR, 1943-46. Recipient Charter Oak Leadership medal Hartford, 1965; Conn. Man of Yr. New Eng. Council, 1976; Human Relations award NCCJ, 1981. Mem. Quinnipiack Club (New Haven). Home: 12 Highview Dr Woodbridge CT 06525-1934 Office: 227 Church St New Haven CT 06506

VANSITTART, PETER, novelist, lecturer, critic; b. Bedford, Eng., Aug. 27, 1920; s. Edward Morris and Mignon Therese V. Student, Worcester Coll., Oxford U., 1940-41. Author: I Am The World, 1942, Enemies, 1947, The Overseer, 1949, Broken Canes, 1951, A Verdict of Treason, 1953, A Little Madness, 1953, The Game and Ground, 1957, Orders of Chivalry, 1959, The Tournament, 1961, A Sort of Forgetting, 1961, Carolina, 1961, The Siege, 1962, Sources of Unrest, 1962, The Friends of God, 1963, The Lost Lands, 1964, The Dark Tower, 1965, The Shadow Land, 1967, Green Knights, Black Angels, 1967, The Storyteller, 1968, Pastimes of a Red Summer, 1969, Landlord, 1970, Vladivostock, 1972, Dictators, 1973, Worlds and Underworlds, 1974, Quintet, 1976, Lancelot, 1978, Flakes of History, 1978, The Death of Robin Hood, 1981, Harry, 1981, Voices from the Great War, 1981, Three, Six, Seven, 1983, Voices: 1870-1914, 1983, The Ancient Mariner and the Old Sailor, 1985, Paths from a White Horse, 1985, Aspects of Feeling, 1986; editor: John Masefield's Letters from the Front, 1985, Happy and Glorious, 1988, Parsifal, 1988, Voices From the Revolution, 1989, The Wall, 1990, A Choice of Murder, 1992, London, 1992, A Safe Conduct, 1995, In the Fifties, 1995. Address: care Anthony Sheil, 43 Doughty St, London England NW3 3AR

VAN SLYKE, ANDREW JAMES, professional baseball player; b. Utica, N.Y., Dec. 21, 1960; m. Lauri Van Slyke; children: Andrew, Jr., Scott, Jared. With St. Louis Cardinals, 1979-87; formerly with Pitts. Pirates, Balt. Orioles; now with Phila. Phillies; mem. Nat. League All-Star Team, 1988, 1992; Sporting News All-Star team, 1988, 92; recipient Gold Glove award, 1988-92, Silver Slugger award, 1988, 92, Sporting News Nat. League Player of the Yr. award, 1988. Office: Phila Phillies PO Box 7575 Philadelphia PA 19101*

VAN SLYKE, LYMAN PAGE, history educator; b. Duluth, Minn., Apr. 20, 1929; s. William R. and Frances (Baird) Van S.; m. Barbara Heaps, July 11, 1953; children: Peter Baird, John Porter, Elizabeth Munro. B.A., Carleton Coll., 1951; M.A., U. Calif.-Berkeley, 1958, Ph.D., 1964. Faculty Stanford U., 1963—, assoc. prof., 1968-78, prof. history, 1978—, exec. sec. Inter-Univ. Program for Chinese Lang. Studies in Taipei, 1963—. Author: Enemies and Friends, 1968, The Chinese Communist Movement, 1969, Marshall's Mission to China, 1976; contbr. to Cambridge History of China, Vol. 13, 1986, Ency. Brit., Chinese edit., 1985—, Ency. of Asian History, 1986. Served to lt. (j.g.) USN, 1951-55. Fulbright fellow, 1969; Social Sci. Research Council fellow, 1978-79. Mem. Assn. Asian Studies (dir. 1976-79). Office: Dept History Stanford Univ Stanford CA 94305

VAN SLYKE, PAUL CHRISTOPHER, lawyer; b. Dallas, Mar. 13, 1942; s. Anson Jr. and Winnell (Hill) Van S.; m. Lora Lynn Davis, July 18, 1964 (div. Apr. 1982); children: Christopher Paul, Scott Allen; m. Karen Lea Block, Aug. 24, 1990. BS in Elec. Engr., U. Tex., 1964; JD, So. Meth. U., 1968; diploma, Nat. Inst. for Trial Advocacy, 1980, postgrad., 1981; AA, White Dispute Resolution Inst., 1994. Patent engr. Mobil Oil Corp., Dallas, 1964-68, patent atty., 1968-69; assoc. Arnold, White & Durkee, Houston, 1969-72, mem., 1972-87; mem. Pravel, Hewitt, Kimball & Krieger, Houston, 1987—; lectr. So. Tex. Coll. of Law, 1970-76; mem. comml. panel of arbitration Am. Arbitration Assn., 1990—. Contbr. articles to profl. jours. Trustee So. Tex. Coll. Law, 1976-88, Gulf Coast Legal Found., 1994—; active St. Lukes United Meth. Ch. Fellow ABA, Tex. Bar Found., Houston Bar Found.; mem. Patent, Trademark and Copyright Soc. (chmn. divsn. on trademark & unfair competition), State Bar Tex., Houston Bar Assn., Houston Intellectual Property Law Assn. (pres. 1995—), U.S. Trademark Assn., Am. Intellectual Property Law Assn., Fed. Cir. Bar Assn. (chmn. trademark appeals com. 1990-91), Computer Law Assn., Assn. Computing Machinery. Republican. Avocations: snow skiing. Home: 4527 Ivanhoe St Houston TX 77027-4807 Office: Pravel Hewitt Kimball & Krieger 1177 West Loop S Ste 1010 Houston TX 77027-9007

VANSLYKE, ROBERT EMMETT, health care executive; b. Warsaw, N.Y., Oct. 26, 1943; s. Norman Beardsley and Grace Winona (Chandler) VanS.; m. Nancy Lynne Hartz, June 7, 1969; children: Keith Norman, Christopher Hartz. BS in Pharmacy, SUNY, Buffalo, 1967; MS, SW Tex. State U., 1977; MHA, Trinity U., 1978. Instr. pharmacy Med. Field Svc. Sch., Fort Sam Houston, Tex., 1968-70; staff pharmacist Camp Kue Army Hosp., Okinawa, Japan, 1970-71; community pharmacist Van Slyke's Pharmacies, Buffalo, 1971-72; staff pharmacist Luth. Gen. Hosp., San Antonio, 1972-74; staff pharmacist Audie Murphy VA Hosp., San Antonio, 1974-76, purchasing pharmacist, 1976; adminstrv. resident Bexar County Hosp. Dist., San Antonio, 1977-78, asst. adminstr., 1978-81, assoc. adminstr. profl. svcs., 1982; v.p. operational svcs. Meth. Hosp., Lubbock, Tex., 1982-86; v.p. Meth. Hosp. System, Lubbock, Tex., 1986-89, Bapt. Health Care, Pensacola, Fla., 1989—; part-time instr. Wayland Bapt. U., 1983; lectr. Tex. Tech U. Health Scis. Ctr., Lubbock, 1985-89. Mem. construction com. Agape Meth. Ch., 1984-85, chmn. ch. fin. com., 1985-87, lay leader, 1988; mem. employer's adv. com. Tex. Hosp. Assn., 1984—, chmn., 1985-86; mem. fin. com. adminstrv. bd. Gulf Breeze United Meth. Ch., active, 1989—; active Leadership Lubbock Alumni Group, United Way Allocation Com. With U.S. Army, 1968-71. Fellow ACHE; mem. Am. Hosp. Assn., Fla. Hosp. Assn. (mem. edn. com.), Tex. Hosp. Assn., Am. Heart Assn. (bd. dirs. West Fla. region 1990—, bd. dirs. pres.-elect Lubbock chpt. 1988-89, Lubbock campaign chmn. 1987-88), Gulf Breeze Rotary Club, Trinity U. HCA Alumni Assn., U. Buffalo Alumni Assn., Kappa Psi. Office: Bapt Health Care 1717 N E St Pensacola FL 32501-6339

VAN STAVOREN, WILLIAM DAVID, management consultant, retired government official; b. Lunenburg, Va., Mar. 14, 1930; s. James Eugene and Marion Estelle (Boyer) Van S.; m. Rosa Kouyoundijian, Dec. 29, 1962;

children: John, Christopher, Diane. B.S., Va. Poly. Inst., 1960, M.S., 1966. Budget analyst U.S. Treasury Dept., Washington, 1963-68; fin. mgr. AID, Washington, 1968-69; fin. mgr. U.S. Dept. Justice, Washington, 1969-74, dep. asst. atty. gen., 1977-84, dep. assoc. atty. gen., 1984-85; mgmt. cons., 1985—; mgmt. advisor Va. Commn. on State Govt. Mgmt., Richmond, 1974-76. Served with U.S. Army, 1954-56. Methodist. Office: 2526 E Meredith Dr Vienna VA 22181-4038

VAN STEKELENBURG, MARK, food service executive. Pres., CEO G.V.A., The Netherlands; pres., CEO, also bd. dirs. Rykoff-Sexton Inc., L.A. Office: Rykoff-Sexton Inc 761 Terminal St Los Angeles CA 90021-1112*

VANSTROM, MARILYN JUNE, retired elementary education educator; b. Mpls., June 10, 1924; d. Harry Clifford and Myrtle Agnes (Hagland) Christensen; m. Reginald Earl Vanstrom, Mar. 20, 1948; children: Gary Alan, Kathryn June Vanstrom Marinello. AA, U. Minn., 1943, BS, 1946. Cert. elem. tchr., N.Y., Ill. Tchr. Pub. Sch., St. Louis Park, Minn., 1946-47, Deephaven, Minn., 1947-50, Chicago Heights, Ill., 1950-52, Steger, Ill., 1964; substitute tchr. Pub. Sch., Dobbs Ferry, N.Y., 1965-72, Yonkers, N.Y., 1965-92. Mem. Ch. Women, Dobbs Ferry Luth. Ch.; election supr. Town of Greenburgh, Elmsford, N.Y.; vol. Children's Village, Dobbs Ferry. Mem. AAUW (life, pres. 1988-90, Ednl. Found. award 1990), Westchester County Fedn. Women's Clubs Inc., Past Pres.'s Club of Westchester, Yonkers Fedn. Tchrs., U. Minn. Alumni Assn. Democrat. Avocations: painting, sketching, choir, piano, travel. Home: 12300 Marion Ln W Apt 2105 Minnetonka MN 55305-1317

VAN TAMELEN, EUGENE EARLE, chemist, educator; b. Zeeland, Mich., July 20, 1925; s. Gerrit and Henrietta (Vanden Bosch) van T.; m. Mary Ruth Houtman, June 16, 1951; children: Jane Elizabeth, Carey Catherine, Peter Gerrit. A.B., Hope Coll., 1947, D.Sc., 1970; M.S., Harvard, 1949, Ph.D., 1950; D.Sc., Bucknell U., 1970. Instr. U. Wis., 1950-52, from asst. to asso. prof., 1952-59, prof., 1959-61, Homer Adkins prof. chemistry, 1961-62; prof. chemistry Stanford, 1962-87, prof. emeritus chemistry, 1987—, chmn. dept., 1974-78; Am.-Swiss Found. lectr., 1964. Mem. editorial bd.: Chem. and Engring. News, 1968-70, Synthesis, 1969-91, Accounts of Chem. Research, 1970-73; editor: Bioorganic Chemistry, 1971-82. Recipient A.T. Godfrey award, 1947; G. Haight traveling fellow, 1957; Guggenheim fellow, 1965, 73; Leo Hendrik Baekeland award, 1965; Prof. Extraordinarius Netherlands, 1967-73. Mem. NAS, Am. Chem. Soc. (Pure Chemistry award 1961, Creative Work in Synthetic Organic Chemistry award 1970), Am. Acad. Arts and Scis., English-Speaking Union (patron 1990—), Rolls Royce Owners Club, Churchill Club (bd. dirs. 1990-92, vice chmn. 1991-92), Los Altos Tomorrow (bd. dirs. 1991—). Home: 23570 Camino Hermosa Dr Los Altos CA 94024-6407 also: Moorings, PO Box 101, Castries Saint Lucia West Indies

VAN TASSEL, JAMES HENRY, retired electronics executive; b. LaCrosse, Wis., Feb. 15, 1929; s. John Henry and Agnes Cecilia (Anderson) Van T.; m. Mary Louise Carman, Dec. 23, 1961; children: John, James. B.S., U. Wis.-LaCrosse, 1951; M.S., Tex. Tech. Coll., 1957, Ph.D., 1959. Postdoctoral fellow Princeton U., N.J., 1959-60; rsch. tech. staff, mgr. Tex. Instruments Co., Dallas, 1960-80; v.p. microelectronics div. NCR Corp., Dayton, Ohio, 1980-91; ret., 1991. Contbr. articles to profl. jours.; patentee in field. Bd. dirs. Dayton Philharm. Orch., 1983-89. Recipient Florilege d'Or Am Ecia, Paris, 1976. Disting. Alumnus award U. Wis.-LaCrosse, 1979, Holley medal ASME, 1989. Episcopalian.

VAN TASSEL-BASKA, JOYCE LENORE, education educator; b. Toledo, July 28, 1944; d. Robert Rae and Eleanor Jane (Kenyon) Sloan; m. Thomas Harold Van Tassal, May 21, 1964 (div. 1975); m. Leland Karl Baska, July 25, 1980; 1 child, Ariel Sloan. BEd cum laude, U. Toledo, 1966, MA, MEd, 1969, EdD, 1981. Tchr. Toledo Pub. Schs., 1965-72, coord. gifted programs, 1973-76; dir. Ill. gifted program Ill. State Bd. Edn., Springfield, 1976-79; dir. area svc. ctr. Matteson (Ill.) Sch. Dist., 1979-82; dir. Ctr. for Talent Devel. Northwestern U., Evanston, Ill., 1982-87; Smith prof. edn. Coll. William and Mary, Williamsburg, Va., 1987—; dir. Ctr. for Gifted Edn. Coll. William and Mary, Williamsburg, 1988—; mem. Va. Adv. Bd. on Gifted and Talented, 1988—; mem. State Ohio Adv. Bd. Gifted and Talented, 1975-76; mem. edn. coun. Nat. Bus. Consortium, 1984-84. Mem. editorial bd. Roeper Rev., 1980-82; pub. Talent Devel. Quar., 1983-87; manuscript rev. editor Jour. Edn. of Gifted, 1981—; mem. editorial adv. bd. Critical Issues in Gifted Edn. series; mem. editorial bd. Gifted Child Quar., 1984—, Jour. Advanced Devel.; column editor Understanding the Gifted Newsletter author 6 books; contbr. chpts. and articles to profl. jours. Bd. trustees Lourdes High Sch., Chgo., 1985-86. Grantee U.S. Office Edn., 1977-78, 78-79, Ill. State Bd. Edn., 1979-82, 84-61, Richardson Found., 1986, 89, Fry Found., 1987-90, Va. State Coun. Highed Edn., 1987-89, 90-91, Bur. Indian Affairs, 1989, Hughes Found., 1989-94, Va. State Libr., 1989-90, Va. State Dept. Edn., 1990-93, Funding Agy. Dept. Edn., 1990-93; eminent scholar Coll. William and Mary, 1987—, Nat. Ednl. policy fellow U.S. Office Edn., 1979-80, Paul Witty fellow in gifted edn., 1979. Mem. Nat. Assn. Gifted Children (bd. dirs. 1984—), Coun. Exceptional Children Assn. for Gifted (pres. 1980-81), World Coun. on Gifted, ASCD, Am. Ednl. Rsch. Assn., Phi Delta Kappa (pres. Northwestern chpt. 1986-87). Avocations: photography, tennis, writing. Home: 225 Richard Burbydge Williamsburg VA 23185-5115 Office: Coll William and Mary Jones Hall Williamsburg VA 23185

VAN'T HOF, WILLIAM KEITH, lawyer; b. N.Y.C., Feb. 18, 1930; s. William and Nell (DeValois) Van't H.; m. Barbara Marie Rogers, Oct. 6, 1961; children: Sarah Lynn, David Edward. BA, Hope Coll., 1951; LLB, U. Mich., 1954. Bar: Mich. 1954, Conn. 1955, U.S. Dist. Ct. (we. dist.) Mich. 1956, U.S. Ct. Appeals (6th cir.) 1956. Assoc. Gumbart, Corbin, Tyler & Cooper, New Haven, 1954-56; ptnr. McCobb, Heaney & Van't Hof, Grand Rapids, Mich., 1959-72, Schmidt, Howlett, Van't Hof, Smell & Vana, Grand Rapids, 1972-82, Varnum, Riddering, Schmidt & Howlett, Grand Rapids, 1983—; mem. faculty Inst. Continuing Legal Edn., Ann Arbor, Mich., 1974—. Chmn. Mich. Heart Assn., 1973-75; pres. United Way Kent County, 1979-80, hon. life mem., 1986—; chmn. Am. Heart Assn., Dallas, 1989-90. Mem. ABA, State Bar Mich. (grievance and arbitration panel 1970-91, chmn. com. on coops. and condos. 1982-86), Grand Rapids Bar Assn. (trustee 1965-67), West Mich. Hort. Soc. (pres. 1992-93), Cascade Hills Country Club, Univ. Club. Home: 3160 Hall St SE Grand Rapids MI 49506-3171 Office: Varnum Riddering Schmidt & Howlett 333 Bridge St NW Grand Rapids MI 49504-5356

VAN'T HOFF, WINFRIED C. J., retired diversified manufacturing executive; b. The Hague, The Netherlands, Feb. 20, 1928; s. Johannes Adrianus Wilhelmus and Anna Frieda (Naegelin) van't H.; m. Maria Johanna Jacoba Popma, June 28, 1957; children: Ingeborg, Annelies, Caroline. BA in Bus. Law, U. Amsterdam, 1949, M of Law, 1952. Mktg. mgr. Philips Internat. B.V., Eindhoven, The Netherlands, 1955-60; mktg. mgr. Philips Chile, Santiago, 1960-62, pres., 1962-66; pres. Philips India, Bombay, 1966-70, Philips Internat. B.V., Eindhoven, 1970-83, Philips Norden AB, Stockholm, 1983-86; exec. v.p. N.Am. Philips Corp., N.Y.C., 1986-89, ret., 1989. Avocations: golf, sailing.

VAN TIL, WILLIAM, education educator, writer; b. Corona, N.Y., Jan. 8, 1911; s. William Joseph and Florence Alberta (MacLean) Van T.; m. Beatrice Barbara Blaha, Aug. 24, 1935; children: Jon, Barbara, Roy. B.A., Columbia, 1933; M.A., Tchrs. Coll., 1935; Ph.D., Ohio State U., 1946. Tchr. N.Y. State Tng. Sch. for Boys, 1933-34; instr. dept. univ. schs. Coll. Edn., Ohio State U., 1934-36, asst. prof., 1936-43, on leave, 1943-45; researchist, writer Consumer Edn. Study NEA, 1943-44; dir. learning materials Bur. Intercultural Edn., 1944-47; prof. edn. U. Ill., 1947-51; prof. edn., chmn. div. curriculum and teaching George Peabody Coll. Tchrs., Nashville, 1951-57; prof. edn., chmn. dept. secondary edn. N.Y. U., 1957-66, head div. secondary and higher edn., 1966-67; Coffman disting. prof. edn. Ind. State U., Terre Haute, 1967-77, prof. emeritus, 1977; dir. univ. workshops Writing for Profl. Publs., 1978—; founder Lake Lure Press, 1983. Author: The Danube Flows Through Fascism, Economic Roads for American Democracy, The Making of a Modern Educator, Modern Education for the Junior High School Years, The Year 2000: Teacher Education, One Way of Looking At It, Education: A Beginning, Another Way of Looking At It, Van Til on Education, Secondary Education: School and Community, Writing for Professional Publication, rev., 1986; autobiography My Way of Looking At It, 1983; Sketches, 1989;

editor: Forces Affecting American Education, Curriculum: Quest for Relevance, ASCD in Retrospect, 1986; co-editor: Democratic Human Relations, Intercultural Attitudes in the Making, Education in American Life; adv. editor Houghton Mifflin, 1964-70; interviewed in Social Education, 1989; contbr. to numerous other publs. including Saturday Rev., Woman's Day, Parents; author articles, reviews and editorials; columnist: Ednl. Leadership, Contemporary Edn., Kappan; adv. bd. Profl. Educator, 1984-95. Mem. Ill. Interracial Commn., 1949-51; moderator Nashville Sch. desegregation meetings, 1955-57; mem. adv. bd. Jour. Tchr. Edn., 1956-59; coorganizer Nashville Community Rels. Conf., 1956; cons. Phelps-Stokes Fund project, 1958-62; mem. staff P.R. Edn. Survey, 1958-59, Iran Tchr. Edn. Survey, 1962, V.I. Edn. Survey, 1964; lectr. abroad, 1974; mem. staff U. Ind. Phi Delta Kappa Inst., 1984-90; 1st Ann. Van Til lectr. Ind. State U., 1989. Recipient Centennial Achievement award, Ohio State U., 1970; awards N.J. Collegiate Press Assn., 1962; N.J. Assn. Tchrs. English, 1962; inducted into Edn. Hall of Fame, Ohio State U., 1989; Annual Van Til Lectr. Series, Ind. State U., est. 1989, est. Annual Van Til Writing award, 1989. Mem. John Dewey Soc. (v.p. 1957-60, acting pres. 1958-59, pres. 1964-66, award 1977, 86, Outstanding Achievement award 1991), Assn. Supervision and Curriculum Devel. (dir. 1951-54, 57-60, pres. 1961-62, chmn. rev. council 1972-73, resolutions com. 1982-85), United Educators (chmn. bd. educators 1969-77), Nat. Soc. Coll. Tchrs. Edn. (pres. 1967-68), Am. Edn. Studies Assn. (editorial bd. 1970-77), Asso. Orgn. Tchr. Edn. (adv. council 1967-73, chmn. issues tchr. edn. 1972-73), Nat. Soc. Study Edn. (editor Yearbook Issues in Secondary Edn. 1976), Kappa Delta Pi (laureate 1980—, chmn. book-of-yr. com. 1984-86). Office: 10200 E Spence Ave Terre Haute IN 47803-9712 Office: Ind State U IN State U Terre Haute IN 47809 *As an educator and writer, I believe that mankind's best hope is education which meets individual needs, illuminates social realities, fosters democratic values and utilizes relevant knowledge.*

VAN TILBURG, JOHANNES, architectural firm executive. Student, Coll. Arts and Architecture. Founder Johannes Van Tilburg & Ptnrs., Architects, Inc., 1971—. Prin. works include Seacliff on the Greens, La Florentine, Renaissance La Jolla, The 1993 New Am. Home for Nat. Assn. Home Builders, Crossroads Condominiums (Project of Yr. Nat. Assn. Home Builders and Builder Mag. 1990), Venice Renaissance (Citation AIA 1991), Janss Ct., Santa Monica. Fellow AIA. Office: Johannes Van Tiburg & Ptrn 225 Arizona Ave Ph Santa Monica CA 90401-1210

VAN TOL, WILLIAM, religious organization administrator. Dir. Christian Ref. World Missions. Office: Christian Ref Ch in N Am 2850 Kalamazoo Ave SE Grand Rapids MI 49560

VAN TREESE, JAMES BRYAN, book publishing and investment company executive; b. Dallaas, Dec. 23, 1946; s. James Braswell and Vivian Pauline (Bowdon) Van T.; m. Lynne Irma Erekson, Apr. 9, 1970; children: Jason Bryan, Annillicia, Madison Lynne. Sales mgr. Globe Life Ins. Co., Oklahoma City, 1962-63; owner, mgr. Van Treese Fin. Corp., Dallas, 1974-81, Rockwell One Inc., Dallas, 1979—, N.W. Pub. Inc., Salt Lake City, 1984—; designer, editor, pub. over 400 books, 1984—. Republican. Baptist. Home: 5419 South 900 East Salt Lake City UT 84117 Office: Northwest Pub Inc 5949 South 350 West Salt Lake City UT 84107

VAN UITERT, LEGRAND GERARD, chemist; b. Salt Lake City, May 6, 1922; s. Antone and Lambertha Maria (Groeneveld) Van U.; m. Marion Emma Woolley, June 8, 1945; children: Robert, Bonnie, Craig. B.S., George Washington U., 1949; M.S., Pa. State U., 1951, Ph.D., 1952. Union Carbide fellow Pa. State U., 1951-52; materials scientist Bell Telephone Labs., Murray Hill, N.J., 1952-89, ret., 1989. Served with USN, 1940-46. Corecipient W.R.G. Baker award IEEE, 1971, recipient Quantum Electronics award, 1992; recipient H.N. Potts award Franklin Inst., 1975, Indsl. Rsch. Inst. award, 1976, Am. Phys. Soc. internat. award for new materials, 1981, AT&T Patent award, 1993, R.W. Wood prize Optical Soc. Am., 1993. Mem. Nat. Acad. Engring., Am. Chem. Soc. (award for creative invention 1978), Sigma Xi. Research on microwave ferrites, lasers, bubble domain memory, electro, non-linear and acusto-optic materials, luminescence, optical fibers, crystal growth, passive displays, supercondr. dielectric films for processing and correlation of properties of matter. Home: 2 Terry Dr Morristown NJ 07960-4713*

VAN UMMERSEN, CLAIRE A(NN), university president, biologist, educator; b. Chelsea, Mass., July 28, 1935; d. George and Catherine (Courtovich); m. Frank Van Ummersen, June 7, 1958; children: Lynn, Scott. BS, Tufts U., 1957, MS, 1960, PhD, 1963; DSc (hon.), U. Mass., 1988, U. Maine, 1991. Rsch. asst. Tufts U., 1957-60, 60-67, grad. asst. in embryology, 1962, postdoctoral teaching asst., 1963-66, lectr. in biology, 1967-68; asst. prof. biology U. Mass., Boston, 1968-74; assoc. prof. U. Mass., 1974-86, assoc. dean acad. affairs, 1975-76, assoc. vice chancellor acad. affairs, 1976-78, chancellor, 1978-79, dir. Environ. Sci. Ctr., 1980-82; assoc. vice chancellor acad. affairs Mass. Bd. Regents for Higher Edn., 1982-85, vice chancellor for mgmt. systems and telecommunications, 1985-86; chancellor Univ. System N.H., Durham, 1986-92; sr. fellow New Eng. Bd. Higher Edn., 1992-93; sr. fellow New Eng. Resource Ctr. Higher Edn. U. Mass., 1992-93; pres. Cleve. (Ohio) State U., 1993—; cons. Mass. Bd. Regents, 1981-82, AGB, 1992; Kuwait U., 1992-93; asst. Lancaster Course in Ophthalmology, Mass. Eye. and Ear Infirmary, 1962-69, lectr., 1970-93, also coord.; reviewer HEW; mem. rsch. team which established safety stds. for exposure to microwave radiation, 1958-65; participant Leadership Am. program, 1992-93. Mem. N.H. Ct. Systems Rev. Task Force, 1989-90; mem. New Eng. Bd. Higher Edn., 1986-92, mem. exec. com., 1989-92, N.H. adv. coun., 1990-92; chair Rhodes Scholarship Selection Com., 1986-91; bd. dirs. N.H. Bus. and Industry Assn., 1987-90, 90-93; governing bd. N.H. Math. Coalition, 1991-92; exec. com. 21st Century Learning Community, 1992-93; state panelist N.H. Women in Higher Edn., 1986-93; bd. dirs. Urban League Greater Cleve., 1993—, Great Lakes Sci. & Tech. Mus., 1993—, Cleve. Playhouse, 1994—, Greater Cleve. Growth Assn., Sci. & Tech. Coun. Cleve. Tomorrow, Ohio Aerospace; mem. Leadership Am. Class '93, Leadership Cleve. Class '95. Recipient Disting. Svc. medal U. Mass., 1979, Am. Cancer Soc. grantee Tufts U., 1960. Mem. Am. Coun. on Edn. (com. on self-regulation 1987-91), State Higher Exec. Officers (fed. rels. com., cost accountability task force, exec. com. 1990-92), Nat. Assn. Sys. Heads (exec. com. 1990-92), Nat. Ctr. for Edn. Stats. (network adv. com. 1989-92, chair accreditation teams 1988—), New Eng. Assn. Schs. and Colls. (commn. on higher edn. 1990-93), Zoologists, Soc. Devel. Biology, Greater Cleve. Round Table (bd. dirs. 1993—), Greater Cleve. Growth Assn. (bd. dirs. 1993—), Leadership Am. Class of '95, Cleve. Playhouse (bd. trustees 1994—), United Way (bd. dirs. 1995—), Phi Beta Kappa, Sigma Xi. Office: Cleve State Univ Rhodes Tower Euclid Ave at E 24th St Cleveland OH 44115

VAN VALEN, LEIGH MAIORANA, biologist, educator; b. Albany, N.Y., Aug. 12, 1935; s. A Donald and Eleanor (Williams) Van V.; m. Phebe May Hoff, 1959; children: Katrina, Diana; m. Virginia C. Maiorana, 1974. B.A., Miami U., Ohio, 1956; M.A., Columbia U., 1957, Ph.D. 1961. Boese postdoctoral fellow Columbia U., N.Y.C., 1961-62; NATO and NIH fellow Univ. Coll. London, 1962-63; with Am. Mus. Natural History, N.Y.C., 1963-66; asst. prof. anatomy U. Chgo., 1967-71, assoc. prof. evolutionary biology & conceptual founds. sci., 1971-73, assoc. prof. biology & conceptual founds. of sci., 1973-76, prof. biology and conceptual founds. of sci., 1988—; research assoc. dept. geology Field Mus., Chgo., 1971—. Author: Deltatheridia, A New Order of Mammals, 1966, Paleocene Dinosaurs or Cretaceous Ungulates in South America?, 1988, The Origin of the Plesiadapid Primates and the Nature of Purgatorius, 1994; editor: Evolutionary Theory, 1973—, Evolutionary Monographs, 1977—; mem. editl. bd. Jour. Molecular Evolution, 1970-76, Evolución Biológica, 1988—; mem. editl. bd. commentators Behavioral and Brain Scis., 1978—; assoc. editor Evolution, 1969-71. Mem. nat. adv. bd. Voice of Reason, N.Y., 1981—. NIH Research Career Devel. awardee, 1967-72; NSF grantee, 1963-71; others. Mem. AAUP (pres. U. Chgo. chpt.), Soc. Study Evolution (v.p. 1973, 80), Am. Soc. Naturalists (v.p. 1974-75), Paleontol. Soc. (councillor 1980-82), Soc. Cryptozoology (bd. dirs.), Ecol. Soc. Am. Office: Univ Chgo Dept Ecology and Evolution 1101 E 57th St Chicago IL 60637-1503

VAN VALIN, CLYDE EMORY, bishop; b. Windham, N.Y., Nov. 24, 1929; s. Ernest Clyde and Josephine Louise (Howard) Van V.; m. Beatrice Mae Roushey, Aug. 25, 1950; children: Carolyn, Wendell, Martha, Luella, Loretta. A.B., Roberts Wesleyan Coll., North Chili, N.Y., 1951; B.D., Asbury Theol. Sem., Wilmore, Ky., 1954, D.D. (hon.), 1972. Ordained deacon Free Meth. Ch. N.Am., 1954, elder, 1955, consecrated bishop, 1976. Pastor Free Meth. Ch., Allentown, Pa., 1954-58; Eastern regional dir. Free Meth. youth, Winona Lake, Ind., 1958-60; dir., chaplain John Wesley Sem. Found., Wilmore, 1960-74, asst. dir., 1974-76; pastor Wilmore Free Meth. Ch., 1961-76, 92-94; bishop Free Meth. Ch. N.Am., Winona Lake, 1976-91; internat. quizmaster Free Meth. Youth, 1958-60; chmn. bd. dirs. Nat. Coalition Against Pornography, 1988-91; pres., bd. dirs. Free Meth. Ch., 1985-91, pres. bd. adminstrn., 1985-89; pres. Free Meth. World Fellowship, 1985-89; chmn. constl. counsel Free Meth. Ch., 1985-91, pres. bd. adminstrn., 1985, 89; chmn. Free Meth. Bd. of Bishops, 1989-90; chmn. study commn. on doctrine, Free Meth. Ch., 1979-85, 90-91. Author: Transforming Grace and Tithing, God's Plan for the Church, 1990; editor: Pastor's Handbook Free Methodist Church of North America, 1982. Trustee Asbury Theol. Sem., 1982-91. Named Today's Young Leader, Roberts Wesleyan Coll., 1959; recipient Disting. Service award Asbury Theol. Sem., 1973. Mem. Christian Holiness Assn. (exec. com., bd. adminstrn. 1989-94), Theta Phi. Methodist. Republican. Club: Nicholasville Rotary (Ky.) (hon. life).

VAN VALIN, JOHN ERNEST, publisher; b. Catskill, N.Y., Mar. 15, 1942; s. Ernest Clyde and Josephine Louise (Howard) Van V.; m. Elizabeth Ann Kennison, Aug. 10, 1968. BA, Roberts Wesleyan Coll., 1965; MDiv, Asbury Theol. Sem., 1969; DD, Western Evang. Sem., 1994. Ordained minister, 1969. Missionary Free Meth. Ch., Zaire, 1967; pastor Free Meth. Ch., Bedford, Ind., 1969-70, Danville, Ill., 1970-75, Indpls., 1975-83; conf. supt. Free Meth. Ch., McPherson, Kans., 1983-90; publisher Free Meth. Ch., Indpls., 1990—; mem. commn. in missions Free Meth. Ch., Winona Lake, Ind., 1983-89, chmn. bd. adminstrn., 1989-90; bd. trustees Ctrl. Coll., McPherson, 1983-90; chmn. Holiness Publishers Alliance, Kansas City, Mo., 1990-91; pub. Light and Life Press, 1990—. Mem. Rep. Nat. Com. Avocations: woodworking, gardening, reading, fishing, hunting. Office: Free Methodist Church of NA PO Box 5350002 Indianapolis IN 46253

VAN VALKENBURG, EDGAR WALTER, lawyer; b. Seattle, Jan. 8, 1953; s. Edgar Walter and Margaret Catherine (McKenna) Van V.; m. Turid L. Owren, Sept. 29, 1990; children: Ingrid Catherine, Andrew Owen. BA, U. Wash., 1975; JD summa cum laude, Willamette Coll. of Law, 1978; LLM, Columbia U., 1984. Bar: Oreg. 1978, U.S. Dist. Ct. Oreg. 1979, U.S. Ct. Appeals (9th cir.) 1980. Law clk. to assoc. justice Oreg. Supreme Ct., Salem, 1978-79; assoc. Stoel, Rives, Boley, Fraser & Wyse, Portland, Oreg., 1979-82, 84-86; ptnr. Stoel, Rives, Boley, Jones & Grey, Portland, Oreg., 1986—; instr. Columbia U., N.Y.C., 1982-84. Editor-in-chief: Williamette Law Jour. 1977-78. Mem. ACLU (pres. Oreg. chpt. 1991-93), Oreg. State Bar (chmn. antitrust sect. 1989-90). Office: Stoel Rives Boley Jones & Grey 900 SW 5th Ave Portland OR 97204-1235

VAN VALKENBURG, MAC ELWYN, electrical engineering educator; b. Union, Utah, Oct. 5, 1921; s. Charles Mac and Nora (Walker) Van V.; m. Evelyn J. Pate, Aug. 27, 1943; children: Charles Mac II, JoLynne, Kaye, David R., Nancy J., Susan L. B.S. in Elec. Engring. U. Utah, 1943; M.S., Mass. Inst. Tech., 1946; Ph.D., Stanford, 1952. With Radiation Lab., Mass. Inst. Tech., 1943-45, Research Lab. Electronics, 1945-46; mem. faculty U. Utah, 1946-55, U. Ill., 1955-66; prof. elec. engring. Princeton, 1966-74, chmn. dept., 1966-72; prof. elec. engring. U. Ill., Urbana, 1974—, acting dean Coll. Engring., 1984-85, dean Coll. Engring., 1985-88, dean emeritus, 1988—; vis. prof. Stanford, U. Colo., U. Calif., Berkeley, U. Hawaii, Manoa, 1978-79, U. Ariz., 1982-83. Author: Network Analysis, 3d edit, 1974, Introduction to Modern Network Synthesis, 1960, Introductory Signals and Circuits, 1967, Signals in Linear Circuits, 1974, Circuit Theory: Foundations and Classical Contributions, 1974, Linear Circuits, 1982, Analog Filter Design, 1982; editor-in-chief: IEEE Press, 1983-86. Recipient Disting. Alumni award U. Utah, 1991. Fellow IEEE (v.p., bd. dirs. 1969-73, editor transactions 1960-63, proc. 1966-69, Edn. medal 1972, Cirs. medal 1987), Am. Soc. Engring. Edn. (George Westinghouse award 1963, Benjamin Garver Lamme award 1978, Guillemin prize 1978, Hall of Fame 1993, Centennial Medallion 1993); mem. NAE, Sigma Xi, Tau Beta Pi, Phi Kappa Phi. Home: 2609 SW 64th Pl Portland OR 97225

VAN VARENBERG, JEAN-CLAUDE See VAN DAMME, JEAN-CLAUDE

VAN VINKENROYE DU WAYSAECK, FEDIA MAURICE GILLES, financial services executive; b. Brussels, Sept. 18, 1932; s. Maurice G. and Simone Barré, Van V.; m. Jutta (Stoltenberg); divorced; 1 child, Christophe. Student, Sorbonne U., 1948-49. Mgr. Editions and Publicité, Brussels, 1957-60; journalist Abpi, Brussels, 1961-68; asst. gen. mgr. Romanian Tourism Ministry, Brussels and Bucarest, 1963-73; asst. gen. mgr., chief exec. officer Cogeco-Alsaver, Brussels, 1973-78, Hotel and Tourism Engring., Brussels, 1979—; gen. mgr. Engring. Cy ICDK, Brussels, 1981-85; sr. v.p., chief exec. officer Gold Mining and Mktg., Nairobi, Kenya, 1985—, United Fin. Services, Santiago, Chile, 1985—; sr. v.p., chief exec. officer, Alpha Enterprises, Ltd., Rhodes, Greece, 1987—, Société Africaine de Pêche. Mag. editor: Diplomatic Courier, Ras Le Bol, Evasion, Semaine de Bruxelles. Sec. gen. Rassemblement de la Majorité-Rassemblement des Mécontents, Belgium, 1985—, Assn. Européene des Diabétiques, A.E.D.R.A, Assn. Européene des Rhumatisants et Arthrosiques, Association des Psoriasiques, Coopération et Coordination Internationale, Assistance au Monde Affamé Aide & Assistance. Decorated Presdl. Citation of U.S., Presdl. Citation of Republic of Korea, Comdr. De L'Ordre Du Christ. Mem. European Brokers Assn. (sec. 1981—). Lodge: K.T. (Osmer Du Christ Comdr.).

VAN VLACK, CHARLES W., lawyer, trade association executive; b. Auburn, N.Y., May 25, 1949; s. C.S. and Elisabeth (Lamade) Van V.; m. Marjorie Zoll, Aug. 10, 1974; children: Christian, Amelia. AB, Hamilton Coll., 1971; JD, Dickinson Sch. Law, 1974. Bar: Pa. 1974. Legis. counsel Pa. Gen. Assy., Harrisburg, 1974-81; mgr. state issues Chem. Mfrs. Assn., Washington, 1981-82, asst. dir. state affairs, 1982-84, corp. sec., 1984-86, v.p., sec., 1986-92, sr. v.p., sec., 1992—. Mem. ABA, Pa. Bar Assn., City Club Washington, Internat. Town and Country Club. Republican. Presbyterian. Office: Chem Mfrs Assn 2501 M St NW Washington DC 20037-1303

VAN VLEET, WILLIAM BENJAMIN, lawyer, life insurance company executive; b. Milw., Dec. 4, 1924; s. William Benjamin and Irene (Peppy) Van V.; m. Marilyn Nilles, Dec. 26, 1946; children: Terese Van Vleet Svetich, Susan Van Vleet Waldo, William Benjamin III, Monica Van Vleet McCarthy, Mark. Student, Marquette U., 1942-43, Lawrence Coll., Appleton, Wis., 1943-44; LLB, JD, Marquette U., 1948. Bar: Wis. 1948, Ill. 1950. Gen. counsel George Rogers Clark Mut. Casualty Co., Rockford, Ill., 1948-59; gen. counsel Pioneer Life Ins. Co. Ill., Rockford, 1950-68, 81—, v.p., 1959-68, v.p., gen. counsel, 1968-91, exec. v.p., 1981-94, also bd. dirs.; exec. v.p., gen. counsel Pioneer Fin. Svcs., Inc., Rockford, 1985—; pres., bd. dirs. Nat. Group Life Ins. Co. Rockford, 1992-93, exec. v.p., gen. counsel, 1993-94; pres. Western Life Ins. Co. Am., Rockford, 1981-82, Health & Life Ins. Co. Am., Rockford, 1984-92, exec. v.p., gen. counsel, 1993-94; pres. Manhattan Nat. Life Ins. Co., Cin., 1990-92, exec. v.p., gen. counsel, 1993-94, also bd. dirs.; exec. v.p., gen. counsel Continental Life and Accident Co., Boise, Idano, 1993-94, also bd. dirs.; bd. dirs. Nat. Health Svcs. Milw. Mem. adminstrn. Boylan Cen. Cath. H.S., Rockford, 1965-72; pres. Diocesan Bd. Edn., Rockford, 1970-78; v.p., pres. Nat. Assn. Bds. Edn., 1972-78; mem. bd. advisors Marion Coll., 1976-79; mem. adv. bd. St. Anthony's Hosp., Rockford, 1978-91; bd. dirs. Crimestoppers, Rockford, 1982-90; cochmn. United Cerebral Palsy Telethon, Rockford. Mem. ABA, Ill. Bar Assn., Winnebago County Bar Assn., Forest Hills Country Club, Masons. Office: Pioneer Life Ins Co Ill 304 N Main St Rockford IL 61101-1019 *Credibility is one of the few things we leave behind us.*

VAN VLIET, CAROLYNE MARINA, physicist, educator; b. Dordrecht, Netherlands, Dec. 27, 1929; emigrated to U.S., 1960, naturalized, 1967; d. Marinus and Jacoba (de Lange) Van V. B.S., Free U. Amsterdam, Netherlands, 1949, M.A., 1953, Ph.D. in Physics, 1956. Research fellow Free U. Amsterdam, 1950-54, research assoc., 1954-56, asst. dir., 1958-60; postdoctoral fellow U. Minn., Mpls., 1956-57; mem. faculty U. Minn., 1957-58, 60-70, prof. elec. engring. and physics, 1965-70; sr. research mem., prof.

Centre Recherches Math. U. Montreal, Que., 1969—; vis. prof. U. Fla., 1974, 4 months annually, 78-88; prof. elec. and computer engring. Fla. Internat. U., 1992—. Contbg. author: Fluctuation Phenomena in Solids, 1965; editor Proc. 9th Internat. Conf. Noise in Physical Systems, 1987; author numerous articles. Research grantee NSF; Research grantee Air Force OSR; Research grantee Nat. Sci. and Engring. Research Council, Ottawa. Fellow IEEE, Am. Sci. Affiliation; mem. Can. Phys. Soc., American Phys. Soc. Home: 920 Van Dyck Ave, Brossard, Montreal, PQ Canada J4W 2E6 *The purpose of life is to honor God and to serve mankind.*

VAN VLIET, CLAIRE, artist; b. Ottawa, Ont., Can., Aug. 9, 1933; d. Wilbur Dennison and Audrey Ilene (Wallace) Van V. A.B., San Diego State Coll., 1952; M.F.A., Claremont Grad. Sch., 1954; DFA (hon.), U. of the Arts, Phila., 1993. Instr. printmaking Phila. Coll. Art, 1959-65; owner The Janus Press, 1954—; vis. lectr. printmaking U. Wis.-Madison, 1965-66; mem. bd. advisors Hand Papermaking. one-man exhbns. include Print Club Phila., 1963, 66, 73, 77, Wiggin Gallery, Boston Pub. Libr., 1977, Rutgers U. Art Gallery, 1978, AAA Gallery, Phila., 1980, Dolan/Maxwell Gallery, Phila., 1984, 91, Mary Ryan Gallery, N.Y.C., 1986, Mills Coll., 1986, U. of the Arts, Phila., 1989, Victoria and Albert Mus., London, 1994, Ottawa Sch. Art Gallery, Can., 1994, Bates Coll. Mus. of Art, Lewiston, Maine, 1994, Bates Coll. Mus. Art, 1994, Victoria and Albert Mus., London, 1994; group exhbns. include. Bklyn. Nat. Phila. Arts Festival, Kunst zu Kafka, Germany, Paper as Medium, Smithsonian Instn., Washington, Paper Now, Cleve. Mus. Art, 1986, Boyle Arts Festival, Ireland, 1993; represented in permanent collections, Nat. Gallery Art, Phila. Mus. Art, Boston Pub. Libr., Libr. of Congress, Cleve. Mus. Art, Montreal Mus. Fine Arts, Victoria and Albert Mus. London. NEA grantee, 1976-80, Ingram-Merrill Found. grantee, 1989; MacArthur fellow, 1989. Mem. Soc. Printers Boston. Address: RR 1 West Burke VT 05871-9801

VAN VOGT, ALFRED ELTON, author; b. Man., Can., Apr. 26, 1912; came to U.S., 1944, naturalized, 1952; s. Henry and Agnes (Buhr) van V.; m. Edna Mayne Hill, May 9, 1939 (dec. Jan. 1975); m. Lydia I. Brayman, Oct. 6, 1979. Census clk. Ottawa, Ont., Can., 1931-32; rep. trade papers Maclean Pub. Co., Toronto, Ont., Can., 1935-39; mng. dir. Hubbard Dianetic Rsch. Found., L.A., 1950-53; co-owner Hubbard Dianetic Ctr., L.A., 1953-61. Contbr. short stories to MacFadden True Story Mag., 1932-36; author radio plays,Can., 1935-38; author numerous short stories, novels including Slan, 1946, The Book of Ptath, 1947, Out of the Unknown, 1948, Masters of Time, 1950, The Voyage of the Space Beagle, 1950, The House That Stood Still, 1950, The Mixed Men, 1952, Away and Beyond, 1952, Destination: Universe!, 1952, The Universe Maker, 1953, Planets for Sale, 1954, The Hypnotism Handbook, 1956, The Mind Cage, 1957, Siege of the Unseen, 1959, The War Against the Rull, 1959, Earth's Last Fortress, 1960, The Violent Man, 1962, The Beast, 1963, The Twisted Man, 1964, Monsters, 1965, The Winged Man, 1966, The Far-Out Worlds of A.E. Van Vogt, 1968, The Silkie, 1969, Quest for the Future, 1970, Children of Tomorrow, 1970, The Search for Certainty, 1970, The Battle of Forever, 1971, More than Superhuman, 1971, The Proxy Intelligence and Other Mind Benders, 1971, M-33 in Andromeda, 1971, The Book of Van Vogt, 1972, The Darkness on Diamondia, 1972, Future Glitter, 1973, The Money Personality, 1973, The Secret Galactics, 1974, The Man with a Thousand Names, 1974, The Best of A.E. Van Vogt, 1974, Reflections of A.E. Van Vogt: The Autobiography of a Science Fiction Giant, 1975, The Gryb, 1976, Supermind, 1977, The Anarchistic Colossus, 1977, Pendulum, 1978, Renaissance, 1979, The Cosmic Encounter, 1980, Computerworld, 1983; series include "Weapon Shop" series, "Gosseyn" series, "Clane Linn" series. Recipient Manuscripters Lit. award 1948, Anne Radcliffe Lit. award, 1968, Acad. Sci. Fiction, Fantasy, and Horror Films award, 1979, Jules Verne award, 1983; guest of honor 4th World Sci. Fiction Conv., 1946, European Sci. Fiction Conv., Brussels, 1978, Metz Festival, France, 1985. Mem. Calif. Assn. Dianetic Auditors (pres. 1958-70), Internat. Dianetic Soc. (pres. 1958—), Authors League Am., Sci. Fiction Writers Am., Soc. Gen. Semantics, Authors Guild, 200 Lang. Club (founder). Office: care Daw Books Inc 1633 Broadway New York NY 10019-6708 *A. E. van Vogt does everything by systems. Writes his stories in 800 word scenes, using fictional sentences. Dreams his story ideas by waking himself up 5 times a night, thinking about the story and going back to sleep, exercises using self-psychotherapy; has 12 rules for making money (The Money Personality), and has 5 other systems including 1, whereby he sets aside one day a week for reading and research.*

VAN VOROUS, TED, manufacturing company executive; b. Billings, Mont., Jan. 6, 1929; s. Benjamin and Gladys (Yaeger) Van V.; m. Mary Tuttle; children: David B., James L., Paul F., Peter D., Lisa J. BS in Chemistry, Mont. State Coll., MS in Chemistry. Chemist Dow Chem., Midland, Mich., 1956-69; chemist, mgr. research and devel. Dow Chem., Golden, Colo., 1959-69; pres. VTA, Inc., Boulder, Colo., 1969-75, VacTec Systems, Boulder, 1975-82, E-Line Systems, Inc., Boulder, 1983—, Vacuum, Inc., Boulder, 1982—; pres., cons. Van Vorous Cons., Boulder; bd. dirs. Everteeh, Ltd., Hong Kong, Universal Vacuum (U.K.), Ltd., Shrenik Vacuum Pvt. Ltd., Bombay, India. Served as sgt. USAF, 1946-49. Home: 992 Sycamore Ave Boulder CO 80303-2860 Office: Van Vorous Cons 5547 Central Ave Boulder CO 80301-2858

VAN VRANKEN, DAVID LEE, chemist; b. St. Charles, Mo., Jan. 9, 1965; s. James Frederick and Rebeca Y.M. (Choy) Van V. BS in Chemistry summa cum laude, U. Tex., 1987; postgrad. in organic chemistry, Stanford U., 1987—. Surface spectroscopy technician IBM, Austin, Tex., 1985-86; teaching and rsch. asst. Stanford (Calif.) U., 1987-94; prof. U. Calif., Irvine, 1994—. Scholar Robert A. Welch Found., 1983-87, CONOCO, 1983-85, White Family Meml. Found., 1983-87, U. Tex., 1983-87, Darryl Royal Endowed Presdl. scholar, 1985-86, Floy Agnew Endowed Presdl. scholar, 1986-87; NSF fellow, 1988-91; Chemistry grantee Camille and Henry Dreyfus Found., 1994. Mem. Am. Chem. Soc., AAAS, Golden Key, Phi Beta Kappa, Phi Kappa Phi, Alpha Lambda Delta, Phi Eta Sigma, Phi Lambda Upsilon. Republican. Avocations: chess, snow skiing. Office: U Calif Dept Chemistry Irvine CA 92717*

VAN VUGT, ERIC J., lawyer; b. Grand Rapids, Mich., Sept. 17, 1951; s. Ernest and Phyllis N. (Van Someren) Van V.; m. Wendy S. Yonker, June 3, 1972; children: Erin L., Heather J., Timothy D. BA, Calvin Coll., 1973; JD, Marquette Univ., 1976. Bar: Wis. 1976, U.S. Dist. Ct. (ea. and we. dist.) Wis. 1976, U.S. Dist. Ct. (we. dist.) Mich. 1993, U.S. Ct. Appeals (7th cir.) 1976, U.S. Ct. Appeals (fed. cir.) 1990, U.S. Supreme Ct. 1994. Assoc. Kluwin, Dunphy & Hankin, Milw., 1976-80; ptnr. Kluwin, Dunphy, Hankin & McNulty, Milw., 1980-85, Minahan & Peterson, Milw., 1985-91, Quarles & Brady, Milw., 1991—. Mem. ABA, State Bar Wis. Avocations: aviation, golf. Home: 14910 Hushing Brae Ct Brookfield WI 53005-2682 Office: Quarles & Brady 411 E Wisconsin Ave Milwaukee WI 53202-4409

VAN WACHEM, LODEWIJK CHRISTIAAN, petroleum company executive; b. Pangkalan Brandan, Indonesia, July 31, 1931; m. Elisabeth G. Cristofoli, June 10, 1958; 3 children. Degree Mech. Engring., Delft U., Delft, The Netherlands., 1953. With Bataafsche Petroleum Maatschappij, The Hague, The Netherlands, 1953; pres. Royal Dutch Petroleum Co., The Hague, The Netherlands, 1982-92; chmn. com. mng. dir. Royal Dutch/Shell Group, The Hague, The Netherlands, 1985-92; chmn. supr. bd. Royal Dutch Petroleum Co., The Hague, The Netherlands, 1992—; head prodn. divsn. Shell Internat. Petroleum Maatschappij, The Hague, 1971-72, coord. exploration and prodn., 1976-79; mng. dir. Royal Dutch Petroleum Co., until 1982, pres, 1982-92; mem. presidium bd. dirs. Shell Petroleum Co., Ltd., 1977-92; chmn. bd. dirs. Shell Oil Co. USA, 1982-92, De Nederlandsche Bank N.V., 1987-92; non-exec. dir. IBM, Armonk, 1992—, Credit Suisse Holding, Zurich, 1992—, Atco Ltd., Calgary, 1993—, Zurich Versicherungs Gesellschaft, 1993—; mem. supr. bd. AKZO, Arnhem, 1992—, Philips Electronics, Eindhoven, 1993—, BMW, Munich, 1994—; chmn. supervisory bd. Royal Dutch Petroleum Co., 1992—. Decorated C.B.E. (hon.), Knight Brit. Empire (hon.), Comdr. Order of Oranje Nassau, Knight Order Netherlands Lion. Office: Royal Dutch Petroleum Co, 30 Carel van Bylandtlaan, 2596 HR The Hague The Netherlands

VAN WAGNER, BRUCE, telecommunications equipment distribution company executive; b. 1925. Student, Harvard U.; AB, U. N.C., 1945, BS, 1947. Various positions to v.p. Anaconda Wire and Cable Co., 1947-64; v.p. Am. Enka Corp., 1964-68; v.p. ops. then exec. v.p. Anixter Bros. Inc.,

1968—, now chmn. exec. com. Served to lt. j.g. USN, 1942-46. Office: Anixter Bros Inc 4711 Golf Rd Skokie IL 60076-1224

VAN WAGNER, ELLEN, lawyer, educator; b. Chgo., Dec. 10, 1942; d. Paul David and Eleanor (Sullivan) Van W.; m. Burton Neal Genda, Mar. 27, 1964 (div.); children: Kevin Paul, Kelly Elan. BA, U. Ariz., 1964; MA, Calif. State U., L.A., 1971; JD, U. La Verne, 1984. Bar: Calif. 1984, U.S. Dist. Ct. (cen. dist.) Calif. 1985, U.S. Ct. Appeals (9th cir.) 1985. Tchr., administr. Baldwin Park (Calif.) Sch. Dist., 1965-81; ptnr. Rose, Klein & Marias, Pomona, Calif., 1985-94; prof. U. La Verne (Calif.) Coll. Law, 1987—. Writer, asst. editor U. La Verne Law Rev., 1981-83, editor-in-chief, 1983-84. Chmn. youth activities commn. City of Baldwin Park, 1971-81. Recipient Humanitarian and Svc. awards L.A. Human Rels. Commn., 1976, 77. Mem. Calif. Bar Assn., L.A. County Bar Assn., Ea. County Bar Assn., Phi Delta Theta. Avocations: traveling, sports. Home: PO Box 351 Blue Jay CA 92317-0351 Office: Law Offices Ellen Van Wagner 12490 Central Ave Ste 104 Chino CA 91710

VAN WAGONER, ROBERT LOUIS, lawyer; b. Lake Orion, Mich., June 4, 1936; s. Ray John and Gladys Elizabeth Van W.; m. Charlotte Robertson, June 10, 1968 (div. 1979); m. Mary Carlin Kaczor, Aug. 10, 1984. BS, Northwestern U., 1958; JD, Calif. We. U., 1966; cert., Nat. Jud. Coll., Reno, Nev., 1981. Bar: Nev. 1967, U.S. Dist. Ct. Nev. 1969, U.S. Supreme Ct. 1973. Commd. ensign USN, 1958; advanced through grades to lt., retired, 1963; asst. atty. City of Reno, 1967-69, city atty., 1971-78, 83-87; assoc. Law Offices Richard Fray, Reno, 1969-71; judge County of Washoe, Reno, 1979-82; pvt. practice Reno, 1987—; administrv. atty. Pub. Service Commn. Nev., 1988—, adminstrv. law judge, 1989—; judicial state leader Nat. Judicial Coll., 1992—. Author: Tort Liability for Firemen, 1986, (bulletin series) Reno Land Use Planning, 1983-87; editor: La Balanza Law Jour., 1963-66. Chmn. Dem. Com. County of Washoe, 1969-71; bd. dirs. Child Runaway Youth Svcs., Reno, 1987—, No. Nev. chpt. Multiple Sclerosis Soc., 1969- (citation of merit 1986); active on Nev. Crime Commn., Carson City, 1971-78; mem. Nat. Assn. of Transp. Practitioners, 1989—, Nat. Conf. State Trans. Specialists, 1990—, Nat. Assn. Administrv. Law Judges, 1992—, The Nat. Trust for Historic Preservation, 1994—; assoc. mem. Am. Mus. Nat. History, 1994—. Mem. ABA, Nev. Bar Assn., Am. Judicature Soc., U.S. Naval Inst., Elks, Masons, Prospectors, Jesters Reno Ct. (bd. dirs. 1984), Am. Legion, The Nat. Trust for Hist. Preservation, Am. Mus. of Nat. History, Nat. Assn. Transp. Practitioners, Nat. Jud. Coll. (state jud. leader 1992—), Nat. Assn. Administrv. Law Judges. Avocations: golf, fishing, home repair. Office: Robert Van Wagoner Offices 727 Fairview Dr Carson City NV 89701-5451

VAN WINKLE, WILLIAM, financial planner; b. Englewood, N.J., July 3, 1934; s. Marshall Jr. and Helen (Wescott) V.; m. Beverly Elsie Peterson, Sept. 9, 1956; children: Stuart Wilson, Ainsley Ann, Carrie Lee. BS in Mech. Engring. and Bus. Adminstrn., Lehigh U., 1957. Cert. fin. planner, CLU. Ops. mgr., plant engr. Procter and Gamble, N.Y., Ga., Kans., Calif., Ohio, 1957-67; ops. mgr. Sheffield Chem. div. Kraftco, Union, N.J., 1967-71; dir. mfg. USA C.R. Bard, Inc., Murray Hill, N.J., 1971-74; v.p. Estey Corp., Eatontown, N.J., 1974-79; pres. Van Winkle Assocs., Tinton Falls, N.J., 1979—. Host, prodr. (cable TV program) Financial Matters, 1980—; contbr. articles to profl. jours. Bd. dirs. Vis. Nurse Assn. Ctrl. Jersey, Red. Bank, N.J., 1985—; trustee Greater Red Bank (N.J.) YMCA, 1986-94; past pres., trustee Brookdale C.C. Found., Lincroft, N.J. Mem. Inst. CFPs, Internat. Assn. Fin. Planning (bd. dirs. ctrl. N.J. chpt. 1986-91), Nat. Assn. Life Underwriters (pres. 1982-83), Nat. Estate Planning Coun., Million Dollar Round Table (divsnl. v.p. 1994-95), Navesink Country Club, Holland Soc. (pres. Jersey Shore br. 1994—), N.Y. Club. Republican. Avocations: sailing, walking, reading. Home: 41 Breezy Pt Little Silver NJ 07739-1703 Office: Van Winkle Assocs 776 Shrewsbury Ave Tinton Falls NJ 07724-3001

VAN WYCK, GEORGE RICHARD, insurance company executive; b. Wilmington, Vt., Feb. 6, 1928; s. Harold Wait Van Wyck and Ruth Anna Learnard; m. Jeanne Mildred Andersen, Apr. 17, 1948; children: Diana Lee Van Wyck Jenkins, Beryl Jeanne. BS in Math. cum laude, St. Lawrence U., 1953. Actuarial clk. Aetna Life Ins. Co., Hartford, Conn., 1953-55; with Am. Bankers Ins. Group, Miami, Fla., 1955-91, sec., bd. dirs., 1983-89, ret., 1991. Bd. dirs. Jr. Achievement of Greater Miami, 1966-83, pres., 1975-76; bd. dirs., chmn. fin. com. Epworth Village Retirement Complex, Miami, 1966—; founding dir., pres. Brickel Children's Ctr., Miami, 1980-82; mem. pers. adv. bd., vice chmn. Dade County, Miami, 1987-89. With USAF, 1946-49. Fellow Life Office Mgmt. Inst.; mem. Coral Way Meth. Ch., Phi Beta Kappa. Democrat. Methodist. Avocations: photography, golf, bridge. Home: 8455 SW 44th St Miami FL 33155-4126

VAN WYK, JUDSON JOHN, endocrinologist, pediatric educator; b. Maurice, Iowa, June 10, 1921; s. John Cornelius and Amelia Susan (Menning) Van W.; m. Persis Ruth Parker, June 8, 1944; children: Judith Parker, Persis Allen, Peter Menning, Judson John. AB, Hope Coll., 1943, ScD (hon.), 1979; postgrad. in biochemistry, St. Louis U., 1943-44; MD, Johns Hopkins U., 1948. Diplomate Am. Bd. Pediatrics. Intern Johns Hopkins Hosp., 1948-49, resident in pediatrics, 1949-50, fellow in pediatric endocrinology, 1953-55; resident in pediatrics Cin. Children's Hosp., 1951-52; asst. prof. pediatrics U. N.C. Sch. Medicine, 1955-59, assoc. prof., 1959-62, prof., 1962-91, Kenan prof. pediatrics, 1975-91, prof. emeritus, 1992—, chief div. endocrinology, 1955-89, dir. tng. program in endocrinology and metabolism, 1962-89; mem. staff N.C. Meml. Hosp.; cons. Womack Army Hosp., Ft. Bragg, N.C., 1957-88; vis. scientist Karolinska Institutet, Stockholm, 1968-69; mem. dir. cell biology Lineberger Cancer Rsch. Ctr., 1976—; vis. prof. basic med. scis. Mich. State U., 1984. Editor Progress in Growth Factor Research, 1988—; mem. editorial bd. Jour. Clin. Endocrinology and Metabolism, 1956-71, editor, 1983-89; mem. editorial bd. Pediatrics, 1969-70; contbr. chpts. to books, articles to profl. jours. Mem. basic sci. adv. com. March Dimes, 1985-88. With USPHS, 1951-53. Recipient numerous fellowships and grants, Lauria honoris causa, U. Genoa, "To commemorate 500th Anniversary of Discovery of N. Am. by Christopher Columbus", 1992, O. Max Gardner award Bd. Govs. U. N.C., 1980. Fellow Am. Acad. Pediatrics; mem. NIH (endocrine study sect. 1968-72), Endocrine Soc. (mem. coun. 1975-79, Fred Conrad Koch medal 1989), Soc. Pediatric Rsch., Am. Pediatric Soc., Soc. Soc. Clin. Investigation, Am. Fedn. Clin. Rsch., Soc. Soc. Pediatric Rsch., Lawson Wilkins Pediatric Endocrine Soc. (pres. 1976-77), Internat. Endocrine Soc. (cen. com. 1988—), La Sociedad Peruana de Pediatria (hon.), Sociedad Pediatrica de Trujillo (hon.), European Soc. for Pediatric Endocrinology (corr.), Japanese Pediatric Endocrine Soc. (hon.). Presbyterian. Home: 1020 Highland Woods Rd Chapel Hill NC 27514-4410 Office: U NC Sch Medicine Dept Pediatrics CB 7220 509 Burnett-Womack Chapel Hill NC 27599-7220

VAN WYLEN, GORDON JOHN, former college president; b. Grant, Mich., Feb. 6, 1920; s. John and Effa (Bierema) Van W.; m. Margaret E. DeWitt, Dec. 29, 1951; children—Elizabeth Ann Van Wylen Rudenga, Stephen John, Ruth Margaret Van Wylen Jasperse, David Gordon, Emily Jane Van Wylen Overway. A.B., Calvin Coll., 1942; B.S.E., U. Mich., 1942, M.S., 1947; Sc.D., MIT, 1951. Indsl. engr. duPont Co., 1942-43; instr. mech. engring. Pa. State U., 1946-48; asst. prof. mech. engring. U. Mich., 1951-55, assoc. prof., 1955-57, prof., 1957-72, chmn. dept., 1958-65, dean Coll. Engring., 1965-72; pres. Hope Coll., Holland, Mich., 1972-87, pres. emeritus, 1987—. Author: Thermodynamics, 1959, (with R.E. Sonntag) Fundamentals of Classical Thermodynamics, 1965, 4th edit., 1994, Fundamentals of Statistical Thermodynamics, 1966, Introduction to Thermodynamics, 1971, 3d edit., 1991, Encounter at Dea, 1994; contbr. articles to profl. jours. Lt. USNR, 1943-46. Fellow ASME, AAAS; mem. Phi Beta Kappa (hon.), Sigma Xi, Tau Beta Pi, Phi Kappa Phi. Mem. Reform Ch. Am. Home: 817 Brook Village Dr Holland MI 49423-4641

VAN ZANTE, SHIRLEY M(AE), magazine editor; b. Elma, Iowa; d. Vernon E. and Georgene (Woodmansee) Borland; m. Dirk C. Van Zante. AA, Grandview Coll., 1950; BA, Drake U., 1952. Assoc. editor Mchts. Trade Jour., Des Moines, 1952-55; copywriter Meredith Pub. Co., Des Moines, 1955-60, book editor, 1960-67; home furnishings editor Better Homes and Gardens Spl. Interest Pubs., Meredith Corp., 1967-74; home furnishing and design editor Better Homes and Gardens mag., 1974-89;

writer, editl. cons., 1989—. Named Advt. Woman of Yr. in Des Moines, 1961; recipient Dorothy Dawe award, 1971, 73, 75, 76, 77, Dallas Market Ctr. award, 1983, So. Furniture Market Writer's award, 1984. Mem. Am. Soc. Interior Designers (press affiliate), Alpha Xi Delta. Address: 1905 74th St Des Moines IA 50322

VAN ZANTEN, FRANK VELDHUYZEN, library system director; b. Heemstede, The Netherlands, Oct. 21, 1932; came to U.S., 1946, naturalized, 1953; s. Adrian V. and Cornelia (Van Eesteren) Van Z.; m. Lois Ruth Holkeboer, June 17, 1961; children—Kiki Maria, Lili Roxanne, Amy Suzanne. A.B., Calvin Coll., Mich., 1959; postgrad., U. Wash., 1960; M.A. in L.S, U. Mich., 1961. Cataloger, extension project asst. Mich. State Library, Lansing, 1961-62; dir. Dickinson County (Mich.) Library, 1962-65, Mid-Peninsula Library Fedn., Iron Mountain, Mich., 1963-65, St. Clair County (Mich.) Library, 1965-68, Tucson Pub. Library, 1968-73; library cons. Ill. State Library, Springfield, 1973-75; asso. dir. for library devel. Ill. State Library, 1975-78; dir. Mid-Hudson Library System, Poughkeepsie, N.Y., 1978—. Served with AUS, 1953-55. Mem. Am., N.Y. library assns. Home: 138 Wilbur Blvd Poughkeepsie NY 12603-4635 Office: 103 Market St Poughkeepsie NY 12601-4029

VAN ZELST, THEODORE WILLIAM, civil engineer, natural resource exploration company executive; b. Chgo., May 11, 1923; s. Theodore Walter and Wilhelmina (Oomens) Van Z.; m. Louann Hurter, Dec. 29, 1951; children: Anne, Jean, David. B.S., U. Calif., Berkeley, 1944; BS in Naval Sci., Northwestern U., 1944, B.A.S., 1945, M.S. in Civil Engring., 1948. Registered profl. engr., Ill. Pres., Soil Testing Services, Inc., Chgo., 1948-52; pres. Soiltest, Inc., Chgo., 1948-78; chmn. bd. Soiltest, Inc., 1978-80; sec., dir. Exploration Data Cons., Inc., 1980-82; exec. v.p. Cenco Inc., Chgo., 1962-77; vice chmn. Cenco Inc., 1975-77, also dir., 1962-77; bd. dirs. Minann, Inc., Testing Sci. Inc., 26th St. Venture, Lunaré Ltd., Rsch Park, Inc., Northwestern U., 1992—; chmn. bd. dirs. Envirotech Svcs., Inc., 1983-85; sec., bd. dirs. Van Zelst Inc., Wadsworth, Ill., 1983—; pres., bd. dirs. Geneva-Pacific Corp., 1969-83, Geneva Resources, Inc., 1983-91. Treas. Internat. Road Fedn., 1961-64, sec., 1964-79; dir., 1973-88, vice chmn., 1980-87; pres. Internat. Road Edn. Found., 1978-80, 87-88, hon. life bd. dirs., 1988—; bd. dirs. Chgo. Acad. Scis., 1983-86, v.p., 1985-86, hon. dir., 1986—; bd. dirs. Pres.'s Assn., Chgo., 1985-86; mem. adv. bd. Mitchell Indian Mus., Kendall Coll., 1977-94. Lt. (j.g.) USNR, 1942-45. Recipient Service award Northwestern U., 1970, Merit award, 1974, Alumni medal, 1989, Svc. award U. Wis., 1971, La Sallian award, 1975. Mem. ASCE (Chgo. Civil Engr. of Yr., 1988), Nat. Soc. Profl. Engrs., Western Soc. Engrs., Evanston C. of C. (v.p. 1969-73), Ovid Esbach Soc. (pres. 1968-80), Northwestern U. Alumni Assn., Tau Beta Pi. Clubs: Economic, North Shore. Inventor engring. testing equipment for soil, rock concrete and asphalt. Home: 1213 Wagner Rd Glenview IL 60025-3219 Office: PO Box 126 Glenview IL 60025-0126

VAN ZYL, JACOBUS LODEWYK, advertising executive; b. Mossel Bay, Republic of South Africa, May 14, 1936; came to U.S., 1989; s. Jacobus Lodewyk and Sophia Magdalene (Erasmus) van Z.; m. Elise Deodata Cronje, Dec. 23, 1961; children: Tanya, Jan-Louis. B in Comml. Law and Econs., Rhodes U., Grahamstown, Republic of South Africa, 1959. Product mgr. Unilever, Durban, Republic of South Africa, 1960-64; account supr. J. Walter Thompson, Cape Town, Republic of South Africa, 1966-67; account supr. Lindsay Smithers/FCB, Johannesburg, Republic of South Africa, 1968-72, chief exec. officer, 1972-89; pres., chief exec. officer FCB/Lewis, Gilman & Kynett, Phila., 1989—; chmn. Assn. Ad Agys., Republic of South Africa, 1977-79, 88-89; vice chmn. Ad Standards Authority, Republic of South Africa, 1986-89. Recipient Protea award Soc. Marketers, Republic of South Africa, 1983. Mem. Union League Club (Phila.). Presbyterian. Avocation: music. Office: FCB/Lewis Gilman & Kynett Inc 200 S Broad St Philadelphia PA 19102-3803

VARAT, JONATHAN D., law educator; b. 1945. BA, U. Pa., Phila., 1967, JD, 1972. Law clk. to judge Walter Mansfield U.S. Ct. Appeals (2d cir.), N.Y.C., 1972-73; law clk. to justice Byron White U.S. Supreme Ct., Washington, 1973-74; asst. prof. law U. Pa., 1974-75; assoc. O'Melveny & Myers, Los Angeles, 1974-76; acting prof. UCLA, 1976-81, prof., 1981—; assoc. dean, 1982-83, 91-92. Office: U Calif Sch Law 405 Hilgard Ave Los Angeles CA 90095

VARCHMIN, THOMAS EDWARD, environmental health administrator; b. Chgo., Dec. 5, 1947; s. Arthur William and Laurie Eileen (Allen) V.; m. Beth Virginia Plank, Dec. 16, 1972; children: Jeffrey Thomas, Brian Arthur, Jennifer Beth, Matthew James. B.A., St. Mary's Coll., Winona, Minn., 1969; M.S., Western Ill. U., Macomb, 1977. Registered sanitarian, Wis. Virologist, microbiologist Chgo. Dept. Health, 1974-78; environ. health and safety mgr. Great Atlantic & Pacific Tea Co., Chgo., 1978-79; adminstr. occupational safety and environ. health Nat. Safety Council, Chgo., 1979-80; mgr. environ. health Lake County Health Dept., Waukegan, Ill., 1980-84, mgr. environ. health and pub. relations, 1984-87; mgr. environ. health Cook County Dept. Pub. Health, Oak Park, Ill., 1987-89, asst. dir. environ. health, mgr. intergovtl. rels., 1989—; environ. health cons. Editor: Food and Beverage Newsletter, Hospital and Health Care Newsletter, Trades and Services Newsletter, 1979-80. NSF grantee, 1968-69. Mem. Nat. Environ. Health Assn. (registered environ. health specialist), Ill. Environ. Health Assn. (registered environ. health practitioner), Nat. Safety Coun., Am. Soc. Microbiology, Anvil Club of Ill., Phi Mu Alpha, Delta Epsilon Sigma. Research on autumn food habits of game fish, behavioral and phys. devel. of barred owl nestlings in Ill. Office: Cook County Dept Pub Health 1010 Lake St Ste 300 Oak Park IL 60301-1144

VARDON, JAMES LEWES, bank executive; b. Aylesbury, Buckinghamshire, Eng., May 22, 1941; came to U.S., 1979; s. Sidney James and Veronica (Williams) V.; m. Gillian Spain, Sept. 9, 1965; children—Helen Antonia, Catherine Philippa, Emma Frances. M.A., Univ. Coll., Oxford, Eng., 1962. Chartered acct. Pub. acct., 1963-68; European treasury analyst Occidental Petroleum Corp., Geneva, Switzerland, 1969-71; controller European ops. Ashland Oil Inc., London, 1971-73; v.p. Marine Midland Bank,, London, 1973-77; sr. v.p., controller Security Pacific Nat. Bank, Los Angeles, 1977-82; exec. v.p., chief fin. officer Southeast Banking Corp., Miami, Fla., 1982-84, First Empire State Corp., Buffalo, 1984—; dir. M & T Capital Corp., Buffalo, 1984—. Bd. dirs. Zool. Soc. Buffalo Inc., 1984, Studio Arena Theatre, 1990, Daemen Coll., 1991. Fellow Inst. Chartered Accts. Eng. and Wales; mem. Inst. Taxation (assoc.), Fin. Execs. Inst. Brit. Conservative. Episcopalian. Clubs: Oxford, Cambridge (London); Oxford Union (Oxford). Avocations: tennis; theatre; baroque music. Office: 1st Empire State Corp 1 M & T Plz Buffalo NY 14203-2301

VARELLAS, SANDRA MOTTE, judge; b. Anderson, S.C., Oct. 17, 1946; d. James E. and Helen Lucille (Gilliam) Motte; m. James John Varellas, July 3, 1971; children: James John III, David Todd. BA, Winthrop Coll., 1968; MA, U. Ky., 1970, JD, 1975. Bar: Ky. 1975, Fla. 1976, U.S. Dist. Ct. (ea. dist.) Ky. 1975, U.S. Ct. Appeals (6th cir.) 1976, U.S. Supreme Ct. 1978. Instr. Midway Coll., Ky., 1970-72; adj. prof. U. Ky. Coll. Law, Lexington, 1976-78; instr. dept. bus. adminstrn. U. Ky., Lexington, 1976-78; atty. Varellas, Pratt & Cooley, Lexington, 1975-93; atty. Varellas & Pratt, Lexington, 1993—; Fayette County judge exec., Ky., 1980—; hearing officer Ky. Natural Resources and Environ. Protection Cabinet, Frankfort, 1984-88. Committeewoman Ky. Young Dems., Frankfort, 1977-80; pres. Fayette County Young Dems., Lexington, 1977; bd. dirs. Ky. Dem. Women's Club, Frankfort, 1980-84; grad. Leadership Lexington, 1981; chairwoman Profl. Women's Forum, Lexington, Ky., 1985-86, bd. dirs., 1984-92. Aquarama award com, 1989-92; mem. devel. coun. Midway Coll., 1990-92; co-chair Gift Club Com., 1992. Named Outstanding Young Dem. Woman, Ky. Young Dems., Frankfort, 1977, Outstanding Former Young Dem., Ky. Young Dems., 1983. Mem. Ky. Bar Assn. (legis. affairs com. 1988-89), Fla. Bar, Fayette County Bar Assn. (treas. 1977-78, bd. govs. 1978-80), LWV (nominating com 1984-85), Greater Lexington C. of C. (legis. affairs com 1994—), bd. dirs. coun. smaller enterprises 1992—, legis. affairs com. 1994—). Club: The Lexington Forum, Lexington Philharm. Guild (bd. dirs. 1979-81, 86—), Nat. Assn. Women Bus. Owners (chmn. community liaison/govtl. affairs com. 1992-93), Lexington Network (sec. 1994—). Office: Varellas & Pratt 167 W Main St Lexington KY 40507-1713

VARET, MICHAEL A., lawyer; b. N.Y.C., Mar. 9, 1942; s. Guster V. and Frances B. (Goldberg) V.; m. Esther Marie Pfister, June 3, 1973; 3 children. BS in Econs., U. Pa., 1962; LLB, Yale U., 1965. Bar: N.Y. 1966, U.S. Supreme Ct. 1975, U.S. Dist. Ct. (ea. and so. dists.) N.Y. 1975, U.S. Tax Ct. 1975, U.S. Claims Ct. 1975, U.S. Ct. Appeals (2d cir.) 1975. Mem., chmn. Varet & Fink P.C. (formerly Milgrim Thomajan & Lee), N.Y.C., 1982-95; ptnr. Piper & Marbury LLP, N.Y.C., 1995—. Trustee Montefiore Med. Ctr., Bronx, N.Y., 1980-92; bd. dirs. Sem. Libr. Corp. Jewish Theol. Sem., N.Y.C., 1983-87, United Jewish Appeal-Fedn. Jewish Philanthropies of Greater N.Y., Inc., 1979-86, Mosholu Preservation Corp., Bronx, 1982-88; bd. overseers Jewish Theol. Sem., 1982-90, Jewish Publ. Soc. of Am., 1986—, exec. com., 1989-94; mem. exec. com. Montefiore Med. Ctr., 1985-92, Yale Law Sch. Assn., 1990-93; mem. coun. of overseers United Jewish Appeal Fedn. of Jewish Philanthropies of Greater N.Y., Inc., 1986—. Mem. ABA, N.Y. State Bar Assn., Assn. of Bar of City of N.Y. (bd. dirs., exec. com. 1971-75), Internat. Fiscal Assn., Internat. Tax Planning Assn., Yale Club, (N.Y.C.), Lotos Club (N.Y.C.). Democrat. Office: Piper & Marbury LLP 53 Wall St New York NY 10005-2815

VARGA, RICHARD STEVEN, mathematics educator; b. Cleve., Oct. 9, 1928; s. Steven and Ella (Krejcs) V.; m. Esther Marie Pfister, Sept. 22, 1951; 1 dau., Gretchen Marie. BS, Case Inst. Tech. (merged with Case Western Res. U.), 1950; AM, Harvard U., 1951, PhD, 1954; hon. doctorate, U. Karlsruhe, 1991, U. Lille, 1993. With Bettis Atomic Power Lab., Westinghouse Electric Co., 1954-60, adv. mathematician, 1959-60; full prof. math. Case Inst. Tech. (now Case We. Res. U.), 1960-69; univ. prof. Kent (Ohio) State U., 1969—, dir. rsch. Inst. for Computational Math.; Cons. to govt. and industry. Author: Matrix Iterative Analysis, 1962, Functional Analysis and Approximation Theory in Numerical Analysis, 1971, Topics in Polynomial and Rational Interpolation and Approximation, 1982, Zeros of Sections of Power Series, 1983, Scientific Computation on Mathematical Problems and Conjectures, 1990; editor: Numerical Solution of Field Problems in Continuum Physics, 1970, Padé and Rational Approximations: Theory and Applications, 1977, Rational Approximations and Interpolation, 1984, Computational Methods and Function Theory, 1990, Numerical Linear Algebra, 1993; editor-in-chief. Numerische Math., Electronic Transactions Numerical Analysis; mem. editl. bd. Linear Algebra and Applications, Constructive Approximation, Computational Mathematics (China), Utilities Mathematica, Revue Française d'Automatique, Informatique, Recherche Opérationelle, Numerical Algorithms, Analysis. Recipient Rsch. award Sigma Xi, 1965, von Humboldt prize, 1982, Pres.' medal Kent State U., 1981; Guggenheim fellow, 1963; Fairchild scholar, 1974. Home: 7065 Arcadia Dr Cleveland OH 44129-6065 Office: Kent State U Inst Computational Mat Kent OH 44242

VARGAS, EDUARDO, advertising executive; b. Boston, June 3, 1944; s. Guillermo Vargas and Elvira (Gracia) de Vargas; m. Gladys Richard, Mar. 25, 1981; children: Eduardo, Erika. Student, Art Ctr. Coll. Design, 1963-66. Founder, pres. Atenas Publicidad, Bogota, Colombia, 1968—; assoc. agy. BBDO Worldwide, Bogota, 1978; chmn. BBDO/Latin Am. div. BBDO Worldwide, N.Y.C., 1980—; exec. v.p. BBDO Worldwide, 1980—, also bd. dirs. Mem. Colombian Kennel Club (pres. 1975-80). Republican. Roman Catholic. Home: Apartado Aereo #90154, Bogota 8, Colombia Office: BBDO Worldwide Inc 1285 Avenue Of The Americas New York NY 10019-6028

VARGHESE, MARY, secondary education educator; b. Mavelikara, Kerala, India, May 30, 1952; d. Joshua Puthenmadhom Zachariah and Kunjamma Joshua; m. Manalel Varghese, May 24, 1976; children: Renju Annu, Roger. BS, U. Kerala, 1973, BEd, 1975. Cert. secondary tchr. Tchr. St. John's High Sch., Kerala, 1977-81, Leulu Moega Fou Coll., Apia, AS, 1981-84, Leone (AS) High Sch., 1984—; sponsor, advisor Sci. Club, 1984—; chair com. judging Sci. Fair, 1989-90. Recipient Commendation award Internat. Sci. and Engring. Fair, Washington, 1990, recipient Excellence in Teaching Sci. award (U.S. Ter.), 1993. Mem. ASCD, Nat. Assn. Biology Tchrs. (Outstanding Tchr. 1990), Sci. Tchrs. Assn. AS., (recipient Presdl. award), 1992. Avocation: gardening. Home: PO Box 4740 Pago Pago AS 96799 Office: Leone High Sch Pago Pago AS 96799

VARGO, RONALD PAUL, oil company executive; b. Painesville, Ohio, Mar. 26, 1954; s. Anton M. and Ingrid E. (Olson) V.; m. Kathleen M. Martell, Nov. 20, 1976; children: Mary Christine, Kevin Matthew. BA in Econs., Dartmouth Coll., 1976; MBA, Stanford U., 1981. Various fin. positions GE, Stamford, Conn., 1976-79; various fin. positions Standard Oil Co., Cleve., 1981-87, dir. corp. fin., 1986-87; comml. mgr. BP Exploration, Houston, 1987-89; gen. mgr. crude oil trading BP Oil Supply Co., Cleve., 1989—. Office: BP Oil Supply Co 200 Public Sq Cleveland OH 44114-2209

VARIAN, HAL RONALD, economics educator; b. Wooster, Ohio, Mar. 18, 1947; s. Max Ronald and Elaine Catherine (Shultzman) V.; m. Carol Johnston, Nov. 1986. S.B., MIT, 1969; M.A., U. Calif.-Berkeley, 1973, Ph.D. (NSF fellow), 1973. Asst. prof. econs. MIT, 1973-77; prof. U. Mich., 1977—, prof. fin., 1983—; Reuben Kempf prof. econs., 1984—; Siena chair in econs., U. Siena, Italy, 1990. Author: Microeconomic Analysis, 1978, Intermediate Microeconomics, 1987; co-editor Am. Econ. Rev., 1987-90. Guggenheim fellow, 1979-80; Fulbright scholar, 1990. Fellow Econometric Soc.; mem. Am. Econ. Soc. Home: 2017 Vinewood Blvd Ann Arbor MI 48104-3613 Office: U Mich Dept Econs 240 Lorch Hall 1220 Ann Arbor MI 48109

VARIN, ROGER ROBERT, textile executive; b. Bern, Switzerland, Feb. 15, 1925; came to U.S., 1951; s. Robert Francois and Anna (Martz) V.; m. Annemarie Louis, May 24, 1951; children: Roger R.R., Edward C.H., Viviane A.H. BBA, Mcpl. Coll., Bern, 1944; PhD in Chemistry, U. Bern, 1951. Rsch. fellow Harvard U., Cambridge, Mass., 1951-52; rsch. assoc. E.I. DuPont De Nemours, Wilmington, Del., 1952-62; dir. rsch. Riegel Textile Corp., Ware Shoals, S.C., 1962-71; founder, chief exec. officer Varinit Corp., Greenville, S.C., 1971—; founder, chief exec. officer Varinit S.A., Geneva, 1974—. Pres. Greenville Sister City Internat., 1993. Mem. Am. Chem. Soc., Fiber Soc., Soc. Advanced Materials and Process Engring., Rotary (pres. Greenville chpt. 1979-80), Sigma Xi. Office: Varinit Corp PO Box 6602 Greenville SC 29606-6602

VARLACK, ADRIAN, church administrator. Administr. comm. mem. Ch. of God of Prphecy. Office: Ch God Prophecy Can PO Box 2910 Cleveland TN 37320

VARLEY, HERBERT PAUL, Japanese language and cultural history educator; b. Paterson, N.J., Feb. 8, 1931; s. Herbert Paul and Katharine L. (Norcross) V.; m. Betty Jane Geiskopf, Dec. 24, 1960. B.S., Lehigh U., 1952; M.A., Columbia U., 1961, Ph.D., 1964; DHL (hon.), Lehigh U., 1988. Asst. prof. U. Hawaii, Honolulu, 1964-65; asst. prof. dept. East Asian Langs. and Cultures Columbia U., N.Y.C., 1965-69, assoc. prof., 1975, prof. 1975-94, chmn. dept. East Asian Langs. and Cultures, 1983-89; Sen Soshitsu XV prof. Japanese Cultural History U. Hawaii, spring 1991-93, 94—. Author: The Onin War, 1967, The Samurai, 1970, Imperial Restoration in Medieval Japan, 1971, Japanese Culture, 1973, A Chronicle of Gods and Sovereigns, 1980, Tea in Japan: Essays on the History of Chanoyu, 1989, Warriors of Japan, As Portrayed in the War Tales, 1994. Bd. govs. Japanese Cultural Ctr. of Hawaii. Served with U.S. Army, 1952-54, Japan. Mem. Assn. Asian Studies, Japan Soc., Soc. Am. Magicians (pres. local chpt. 1983-84). Avocations: sleight of hand magic; piano. Home: Apt 15B 38 S Judd St Honolulu HI 96817 Office: U Hawaii History Dept Sakamaki Hall A 203 2530 Dole St Honolulu HI 96822

VARMA, ARVIND, chemical engineering educator, researcher; b. Ferozabad, India, Oct. 13, 1947; s. Hans Raj and Vijay L. (Jhanjhee) V.; m. Karen K. Guse, Aug. 7, 1971; children: Anita, Sophia. BS ChemE, Panjab U., 1966; MS ChemE, U. N.B., Fredericton, Can., 1968; PhD ChemE, U. Minn., 1972. Asst. prof. U. Minn., Mpls., 1972-73; sr. research engr. Union Carbide Corp., Tarrytown, N.Y., 1973-75; asst. prof. chem. engring. U. Notre Dame, Ind., 1975-77, assoc. prof., 1977-80, prof., 1980-88, Arthur J. Schmitt prof., 1988—, chmn. dept., 1983-88; vis. prof. U. Wis., Madison, fall 1981; Chevron vis. prof. Calif. Inst. Tech., Pasadena, spring 1982; vis. prof. Ind. Inst. Tech.-Kanpur, spring 1989, U. Cagliari, Italy, summer 1989, 92. Editor: (with others) The Mathematical Understanding of Chemical

Engineering Systems, 1980, Chemical reaction and Reactor Engineering, 1987; contbr. over 145 articles to profl. jours. Recipient Tchr. of Yr. award Coll. Engring. U. Notre Dame, 1991, Spl. Presdl. award 1992, R.H. Wilhelm award AIChE, 1993; Fulbright scholar; Indo-Am. fellow, 1988-89. Home: 52121 N Lakeshore Dr Granger IN 46530-7848 Office: Dept Chem Engring U Notre Dame Notre Dame IN 46556

VARMA, BAIDYA NATH, sociologist, broadcaster, poet; m. Savitri Devi. PhD, Columbia U., 1958. Radio broadcaster to India UN; Asian News Moderator Nat. Edn. TV Network, N.Y.C.; prof. emeritus sociology CUNY; prodr. radio dramas Voice of Am.; wrote, narrated over 200 documentary films, News of the Day; lectr. numerous univs. U.S., Can., Eng., India; chair Plenary Sessions World Congress of Sociology, Internat. Congress Anthrop. and Enthnological Scis; cons. Nat. Endowment Humanities, Ctr. Migration Studies, Dept. Energy, Wenner-Gren Found. Anthrop. Rsch. in U.S., Can. Coun., Indian Law Inst.; chair faculty seminars Columbia U.; presided Centenary Celebrations Indian Writers, N.Y.C.; vis. prof. Columbia U., other U.S., Indian Univs.; chair panel on religions and sexuality Parliament of World's Religions, 1993. Author: The Sociology and Politics of Development: A Theoretical Study, 1980, Social Science and Indian Society, 1985, New Directions in Theory and Methodology, 1993, Contemporary India (cert. of merit German Govt.), Love Feast, 1995, Spring of Civilization, 1995; author, editor others; contbr. articles Ency. Americana, profl. jours.; edit. adv. nat., internat. sociol. jours. Assoc. trustee Wordsworth Trust; trustee Taraknath Das Found.; bd. scholars Buddhist Cultural Inst., U.S.; judge Permanent People's Tribunal Indsl. and Environ. Hazards and Human Rights, Rome; established Varma Found.; founding mems. Lincoln Ctr. for Performing Arts, N.Y.C.; chmn. bd. trustees Soc. for Restoration of Ancient Vidyadhams of India; trustee Internat. Found. for Vedic Edn., U.S., U.S. Capitol Hist. Soc. Sr. faculty fellow Am. Inst. Indian Studies, 1964-65, 1984-85; elected to Am. Film Inst.; guest fellow Oxford U., The Sorbonne, Inst. Advanced Study; named hon. citizen Colonial Williamsburg; recipient cert. of merit Pres. City Coun. of Yonkers. Mem. N.Y. Acad. Scis., South Asian Sociols. (1st pres.), Soc. Indian Acads. in Am. (exec. com.), Global Orgn. People of Indian Origin (life), First World Conv. (pres. opening session, 1989). Home: 62 Belvedere Dr Yonkers NY 10705-2814

VARMUS, HAROLD ELIOT, government health institutes administrator; b. Oceanside, N.Y., Dec. 18, 1939; s. Frank and Beatrice (Barasch) V.; m. Constance Louise Casey, Oct. 25, 1969; children: Jacob Carey, Christopher Isaac. AB, Amherst Coll., 1961, DSc (hon.), 1984; MA, Literature, Harvard U., 1962; MD, Columbia U. Med. Sch., 1966. Lic. physician, Calif. Intern, resident Presbyterian Hosp., N.Y.C., 1966-68; clin. assoc. NIH, Bethesda, Md., 1968-70; lectr. dept. microbiology U. Calif.-San Francisco, 1970-72; asst. prof., depts. microbiology and immunology, biochemistry and biophysics U. Calif., San Francisco, 1972-74; assoc. prof. U. Calif., San Franisco, 1974-79; prof. U. Calif., San Francisco, 1979-83, Am. Cancer Soc. research prof., 1984-93; dir. NIH, Bethesda, Md., 1993—; chmn. bd. on biology NRC. Editor: Molecular Biology of Tumor Viruses, 1982, 85; Readings in Tumor Virology, 1983; assoc. editor Genes and Development Jour., Cell Jour.; mem. editorial bd. Cancer Surveys. Named Calif. Acad. Sci. Scientist of Yr., 1982; co-recipient Lasker Found. award, 1982, Passano Found. award, 1983, Armand Hammer Cancer prize, 1984, GM Alfred Sloan award 1984, Shubitz Cancer prize, 1985, Nobel Prize in Physiology or Medicine, 1989. Mem. AAAS, NAS, Inst. Medicine of NAS, Am. Soc. Virology, Am. Soc. Microbiology, Am. Acad. Arts and Scis. Democrat. Research (with J. Michael Bishop) on the replication of retroviruses. Office: NIH Bldg 1 Rm 126 1 Center Dr MSC 0148 Bethesda MD 20892-0148

VARN, RICHARD JAMES, university administrator, lawyer, consultant; b. Des Moines, May 31, 1958; s. Leonard Harold and Carolyn Cecelia (Balkus) V.; m. Julia Ellen Burton, June 9, 1984; children: Sarah, Emily. BA, U. Iowa, 1981, JD, 1988. Bar: Iowa 1988. Truckloader Colonial Bakery, Cedar Rapids, Iowa, 1976-85; adminstrv. asst. Iowa Senator Art Small, Des Moines, 1981-82; mem. Iowa Ho. of Reps., Des Moines, 1982-86; mem. Iowa Senate, Des Moines, 1986-94, majority whip, 1990-94, chmn. human svcs. appropriations com., 1992-94, chmn. comms. and info. policy com., 1992-94; dir. telecoms. U. No. Iowa, 1994—; labor-mgmt. cons. Cedar Rapids/Iowa City Labor Mgmt. Coun., 1988-93. Field staff Culver for Senate, Iowa City, 1980-81; precinct chmn. Johnson County Dems., 1980-88; mem. Solon (Iowa) Devel. Commn., 1984-88; steering com. Nagle for Congress, Iowa, 1986, Dukakis for Pres., Iowa, 1988; mem. panel on info. mgmt. Nat. Acad. Pub. Adminstrn., 1992—. Named Fairfall History scholar U. Iowa, 1979; recipient Civil Libertarian of Yr. award Iowa Civil Liberties Union, 1988, Fed. 100 award Fed. Computer Week, 1994. Mem. Nat. Conf. State Legislators, Iowa State Bar Assn., Optimist Club. Democrat. Roman Catholic.

VARNEDOE, HEETH, III, food products company executive; b. 1937; married. Grad., U. Ga., 1959. With Flowers Industries Inc., Thomasville, Ga., 1959—, pres. baked foods div., 1976-83, exec. v.p. ops., from 1983-86, now pres., chief oper. officer., 1986—; also dir. Flowers Industries Inc. Office: Flowers Industries Inc PO Box 1338 US Hwy 19 S Thomasville GA 31792

VARNEDOE, JOHN KIRK TRAIN, museum curator; b. Savannah, Ga., Jan. 18, 1946; s. Samuel Lamartine and Lilla (Train) V.; m. Elyn Zimmerman. BA with honors, Williams Coll., 1967, DFA (hon.), 1994; MA, Stanford U., 1970, PhD, 1972. Asst. instr. art history Williams Coll., 1967-68; asst. prof. art history Stamford (Calif.) U., 1973-74; assoc. prof. Columbia U., N.Y.C. 1974-80; assoc. prof. Inst. Fine Arts, NYU, N.Y.C., 1980-88; prof. fine arts Inst. Fine Arts, NYU, 1984-88; chief curator dept. painting and sculpture Mus. Modern Art, N.Y.C., 1989—; vis. lectr. in law Columbia U. Law Sch., 1980-81; adj. curator dept. painting and sculpture Mus. Modern Art, 1985-88; mem. adv. bd. J. Paul Getty Program for Art on Film, 1985-87, Ctr. for Advanced Study in Visual Arts, 1990-93; mem. selection panel J. Paul Getty Postdoctoral Fellowships, 1985-88, J. Paul Getty Sr. Fellowships, 1988-90; Slade prof. art history Oxford (Eng.) U., 1992; lectr. in field. Author: The Drawings of Auguste Rodin, 1971, Vienna 1900, 1986, Gustave Caillebotte, 1987, Northern Light, 1988 (Henry Allen Moe prize 1983), A Fine Disregard—What Makes Modern Art Modern, 1990, High and Low: Modern Art and Popular Culture, 1990, Cy Twombly: A Retrospective, 1994; mem. editl. bd. The Art Bull., 1985-90; contbr. articles and revs. to profl. jours. Decorated knight The Royal Order of Donnebroge (Denmark); David E. Finley fellow Nat. Gallery Art, 1970-73, NEH fellow, 1977-78, McArthur Found. fellow, 1984-89; Rsch. grantee Columbia U., 1975, Travel grantee Am. Coun. Learned Socs. Fellow Am. Acad. Arts & Scis., NYU Soc. Fellows. Office: Mus of Modern Art 11 W 53rd St New York NY 10019-5498

VARNER, BARTON DOUGLAS, lawyer; b. Ida Grove, Iowa, May 2, 1920; s. Charles R. and Mary E. (Whinery) V.; m. Frances Elaine Seaton, May 9, 1943; children: Charles R., John A. Student, U. Nebr., 1938-42; LL.B., U. Mo. at Kansas City, 1951. Bar: Mo. 1951. Since practiced in Kansas City and Lake Ozark, Mo., ret. 1985; of counsel Gage and Tucker, Kansas City and Lake Ozark, 1985—; partner firm Gage and Tucker (and predecessors), 1955-85. Bd. mgrs. Kansas City YMCA, 1958-80, chmn., 1962; pres. Miller County Hist. Soc., 1991-92, 94-95. With USNR, 1942-45. Mem. ABA, Mo. Bar Assn., Nebr. U. Alumni Assn. Kansas City (pres. 1958-60, bd. dirs., counsel), Kansas City Club, Delta Sigma Pi, Delta Theta Phi. Methodist (steward 1964-66, trustee 1968-69). Home: 8 Maple Tree Cir Lake Ozark MO 65049 Office: Mut Benefit Life Bldg Kansas City MO 64108 *Ralph Waldo Emerson best expressed the principle that has helped me the most in attaining what success that I have attained when he stated in his Essay on Self Reliance the following: "There is a time in every man's education when he arrives at the conviction that envy is ignorance; that imitation is suicide; that he must take himself for better or worse as his portion; that though the wide universe is full of good, no kernel of nourishing corn can come to him but through his toil bestowed on that plot of ground which is given him to till. The power which resides in him is new in nature and none but he knows what that is which he can do, nor does he know until he has tried."*

VARNER, CHARLEEN LAVERNE MCCLANAHAN (MRS. ROBERT B. VARNER), nutritionist, educator, administrator, dietitian; b. Alba, Mo., Aug. 28, 1931; d. Roy Calvin and Lela Ruhama (Smith) McClanahan; student Joplin (Mo.) Jr. Coll., 1949-51; B.S. in Edn., Kans. State Coll.

Pittsburg, 1953; M.S., U. Ark., 1958; Ph.D., Tex. Woman's U. 1966; postgrad. Mich. State U., summer, 1955, U. Mo., summer 1962; m. Robert Bernard Varner, July 4, 1953. Apprentice county home agt. U. Mo., summer 1952; tchr. Ferry Pass Sch., Escambia County, Fla., 1953-54; tchr. biology, home econs. Joplin Sr. High Sch., 1954-59; instr. home econs. Kans. State Coll., Pittsburg, 1959-63; lectr. foods, nutrition Coll. Household Arts and Scis., Tex. Woman's U., 1963-64, research asst. NASA grant, 1964-66; assoc. prof. home econs. Central Mo. State U., Warrensburg, 1966-70, adviser to Colhecon, 1966-70, adviser to Alpha Sigma Alpha, 1967-70, 72, mem. bd. advisers Honors Group, 1967-70; prof., head dept. home econs. Kans. State Tchrs. Coll., Emporia, 1970-73; prof., chmn. dept. home econs. Benedictine Coll., Atchison, Kans., 1973-74; prof., chmn. dept. home econs. Baker U., Baldwin City, Kans., 1974-75; owner, operator Diet-Con Dietary Cons. Enterprises, cons. dietitian, 1973—, Home-Con Cons. Enterprises. Mem. Joplin Little Theater, 1956-60. Mem. NEA, Mo., Kans. state tchrs. assns., AAUW, Am., Mo., Kans. dietetics assns., Am., Mo., Kans. home econs. assns., Mo. Acad. Scis., AAUP, U. Ark. Alumni Assn., Alumni Assn. Kans. State Coll. of Pittsburg, Am. Vocat. Assn., Assn. Edn. Young Children, Sigma Xi, Beta Sigma Phi, Beta Beta Beta, Alpha Sigma Alpha, Delta Kappa Gamma, Kappa Kappa Iota, Phi Upsilon Omicron, Theta Alpha Pi. Methodist (organist). Home: Main PO Box 1009 Topeka KS 66601

VARNER, CHILTON DAVIS, lawyer; b. Opelika, Ala., Mar. 12, 1943; s. William Cole and Frances (Thornton) Davis; m. K. Morgan Varner III, June 19, 1965; 1 child, Ashley Elizabeth. AB with distinction, Smith Coll., 1965; JD with distinction, Emory U., 1976. Assoc. King & Spalding, Atlanta, 1976-83, ptnr., 1983—. Author: Appellate Handbook for Georgia Lawyers, 1995. Mem. Leadership Atlanta, 1984-85; asst. clk., elder, bd. elders Trinity Presbyn. Ch., Atlanta, 1985-88; exec. com. Ate Arts Alliance, Atlanta, 1981-85; mem. Atlanta Symphony Chorus, 1970-74. Mem. ABA, Ga. Bar Assn., Atlanta Bar Assn., Bleckley Inn of Ct. (master), Order of Coif, Phi Beta Kappa. Office: King & Spalding 191 Peachtree St NE Atlanta GA 30303-1740

VARNER, DAVID EUGENE, lawyer, energy company executive; b. Dallas, Oct. 9, 1937; s. E.C. and D. Evelyn (Bauguss) V.; m. Joan Paula Oransky, Aug. 13, 1962; children: Michael A., Kevin E., Cheryl L. B.A., So. Meth. U., Dallas, 1958, J.D., 1961. Bar: Tex. 1961, Fla. 1974, Okla., 1977, U.S. Supreme Ct. 1978. Assoc. Eldridge, Goggans, Davidson & Silverberg, Dallas, 1962-65; atty., asst. sec. Redman Industries, Inc., Dallas, 1965-66; assoc. gen. atty. Tex. Instruments, Inc., Dallas, 1966-73; sr. atty., asst. sec. Fla. Gas Co., Winter Park, 1973-76; v.p., gen. counsel, sec. Facet Enterprises, Inc., Tulsa, 1976-78, Summa Corp., Las Vegas, Nev., 1978-82; sr. v.p., gen. counsel, sec. Transco Energy Co., Houston, 1982—. Mng. editor Southwestern Law Jour., 1960-61. Mem. ABA, Fed. Energy Bar Assn., Houston Bar Assn., Tex. Bar Assn., Okla. Bar, Fla. Bar., Am. Soc. Corp. Secs., Nat. Assn. Corp. Dirs. Office: Transco Energy Co 2800 Post Oak Blvd Houston TX 77056-6106

VARNER, DICKSON DREW, veterinarian; b. Tuscumbia, Mo., Sept. 20, 1953; s. Victor Irvin and Hope Carol (Kemnitz) V.; m. Tricia Anne Wilcox, Aug. 23, 1978; children: Victor, Zachary. BS, 1976, DVM, 1978; MS, Tex. A&M U., 1990. Resident Castleton Farm, Lexington, Ky., 1978-81; resident reprodn. U. Pa., Kennett Square, 1981-83, lectr. 1983-85; asst. prof. Tex. A&M U., College Station, 1986-91, assoc. prof., 1991—. Author: (textbook) Diseases and Management of Breeding Stallions, 1991; co-editor: (textbook) Stallion Management, 1992. Named Distng. Alumnus Sch. of Osage, 1989. Mem. AVMA, Am. Coll. Theriogenologists (sec. 1992—), Am. Soc. Andrology, Am. Assn. Equine Practitioners (chmn. reprodn. com. 1994—), Tex. Vet. Med. Assn. (chmn. reprodn. tech. com. 1992-93, Rsch. award 1990), Soc. Theriogenology, Rotary (dir. club svc 1992-93, dir. community svc. 1993-94). Republican. Lutheran. Avocations: horses, sports. Office: Dept Large Anim Med Surgery TX Vet Med Ctr Tex A & M U College Station TX 77843-4475

VARNER, JOSEPH ELMER, biology educator, researcher; b. Nashport, Ohio, Oct. 7, 1921; s. George Ezra and Inez Charlotte (Gladden) V.; m. Carol Roberta Dewey, June, 1945 (div. 1971); children—Lee, Lynn, Karen, Beth; m. Jane Elanor Burton, June, 1976. B.Sc., Ohio State U., 1942, M.Sc., 1943, Ph.D., 1949; Docteur Honoris Causa (hon.), Nancy U., France, 1977. Chemist Owens Corning, Newark, 1943-44; analytical chemist Battelle Meml. Inst., Columbus, Ohio, 1946-47; from asst. prof. to prof. biology Ohio State U., Columbus, Ohio, 1950-61; postdoctoral Calif. Inst. Tech., Pasadena, 1953-54; NSF fellow Cambridge U., Eng., 1959-60; research scientist Martin-Marietta, Balt., 1961-65; prof. biochemistry Mich. State U., East Lansing, 1965-73; NSF fellow U. Wash., Seattle, 1971-72; prof. biology Washington U., St. Louis, 1973—, Am. Cancer Soc. scholar, 1980-81. Author, editor: Plant Biochemistry, 1965, 2d edit., 1976; contbr. articles on plant biology to profl. jours. Fellow AAAS; mem. NAS, Am. Soc. Plant Physiologists (pres. 1969, Stephen Hales Prize 1990), Am. Soc. Developmental Biology (pres. 1986), Am. Acad. Arts and Sci. Avocation: soaring. Home: 7275 Kingsbury Blvd Saint Louis MO 63130-4141 Office: Washington U Dept Biology Saint Louis MO 63130

VARNER, ROBERT EDWARD, federal judge; b. Montgomery, Ala., June 11, 1921; s. William and Georgia (Thomas) V.; children: Robert Edward, Carolyn Stuart; m. Jane Dennis Hannah, Feb. 27, 1982. B.S., Auburn U., 1946; J.D., U. Ala., 1949. Bar: Ala. 1949. Atty. City of Tuskegee, 1951; asst. U.S. atty. Middle Dist. Ala., 1954-58; practice in Montgomery, 1958-71; partner firm Jones, Murray, Stewart & Varner, 1958-71; U.S. dist. judge Montgomery, 1971—; guest lectr. bus. law Huntingdon Coll. Pres. Montgomery Rotary Charity Found.; v.p. fin. chmn. Tukabatchee Area council Boy Scouts Am.; Mem. Macon County Bd. Edn., 1950-54. Served with USNR, 1942-46. Recipient Silver Beaver award Boy Scouts Am. Mem. ABA, Fed. Bar Assn., Montgomery Bar Assn. (pres. 1971), Macon County Bar Assn., Am. Trial Lawyers Assn., Jud. Conf. of U.S. (com. on operation of jury system), Phi Alpha Delta, Phi Delta Theta. Republican. Methodist. Club: Rotarian (pres. 1961). Office: US Dist Ct PO Box 2046 Montgomery AL 36102-2046

VARNER, STERLING VERL, retired oil company executive; b. Ranger, Tex., Dec. 20, 1919; s. George Virgle and Christina Ellen (Shafer) V.; m. Paula Jean Kennedy, Nov. 17, 1945; children: Jane Ann, Richard Alan. Student, Murray State Sch. Agr., 1940, Wichita State U., 1949. With Kerr-McGee, Inc., 1941-45; with Koch Industries, Inc., Wichita, Kans., 1945-90, pres., chief operating officer, 1974-86, vice chmn., 1987-90, chmn. bd. dirs., 1990, now bd. dirs.; ret.; owner Shadow Valley Ranch; bd. dirs. Koch Industries Inc. Trustee The Nature Conservancy; bd. dirs. YMCA, Maude Carpenter Children's Ctr. Mem. Wichita Club, Crestview Country Club. Mem. Ch. of Christ. Home: 1515 N Linden Ct Wichita KS 67206-3312 Office: Koch Industries Inc PO Box 2256 411 E 37th St N Wichita KS 67201-2256

VARNERIN, LAWRENCE JOHN, physicist; b. Boston, July 10, 1923; s. Lawrence John and Josephine Louise (Nangeroni) V.; m. Marie Elizabeth Hynes, Apr. 19, 1952; children—Melanie, Lawrence, Gregory, Sharon, Suzanne, Bruce, Carol, Jeffery. S.B. in Physics, MIT, 1947, Ph.D. in Physics, 1949. Supr., TR/ATR microwave tube Sylvania Electronics Div., Boston, 1949-52; acting mgr. physics dept. Westinghouse Research Labs., Pitts., 1952-57; head heterojunction IC and materials dept. AT&T Bell Labs., Murray Hill, N.J., 1957-86; Chandler-Weaver prof. elec. engring., elec. engring. computer sci. dept. Lehigh U., Bethlehem, Pa., 1986-92, Chandler-Weaver prof. emeritus, 1992—. Assoc. editor Jour. Magnetism and Magnetic Materials, 1973-94. Served with U.S. Army, 1943-46. Fellow IEEE, Am. Phys. Soc.; mem. Magnetics Soc. Roman Catholic. Home: PO Box 1107 Wolfeboro NH 03894-1107 Office: Lehigh U Packard Lab # 19 Bethlehem PA 18015

VARNEY, CARLETON BATES, JR., interior designer, columnist, educator, author; b. Lynn, Mass., Jan. 23, 1937; s. Carleton Bates and Julia (Raczkowskos) V.; divorced; children: Nicholas, Seamus, Sebastian. BA, Oberlin Coll., 1958; student, U. Madrid, 1957, MA, NYU, 1969; LHD (hon.), U. Charleston, 1987. Sch. tchr. 1958-59; asst. to pres. Dorothy Draper & Co., Inc., 1959-63, exec. v.p. 1963-66, pres. 1966—; dean Carleton Varney Sch. of Art & Design, U. Charleston, W.Va. Designer: chairs, decorative fabrics, dinnerware and china, crystal glassware, table and

bed linen, ready to wear resort collection Cruzanwear, 1987, mens' wear furnishings for Rawlinson & Marking, London, 1987; interior designer: Dromoland Castle, Ireland, 1963, 88, Westbury Hotel, Belgium, 1964, N.Y. World's Fair, 1965, Clare Inn, Ireland, 1968, Greenbrier Hotel, White Sulphur Springs, W.Va., 1968, Westbury Hotel, San Francisco, 1973, Copley Plaza Hotel, Boston, 1976, Amway Grand Plaza Hotel, Grand Rapids, Mich., 1980, The Grand Hotel, Mackinac Island, Mich., 1978, Equinox House, Manchester, Vt., 1984, Brazilian Ct. Hotel, Palm Beach, Fla., 1985, Waldorf Towers, N.Y.C., 1985, Dawn Beach Hotel, St. Maarten, 1985, Christian Broadcasting Conv. Ctr., 1986, Met. Opera House boutique, N.Y.C., 1985, (cruise ship) World Discoverer, 1984, Arrowwood Conv. Ctr., Purchase, N.Y., 1987, Boca Raton Hotel and Club, Fla., 1987, Speedway Club, Charlotte, N.C., 1987, Coccoloba Plantation, Anguilla, Brit. Virgin Islands, 1987, Villa Madeleine, St. Croix, V.I., 1987, Ashford Castle, Ireland, 1988, Adare Manor, Ireland, 1988, The Breakers, Palm Beach, Fla., 1989, Jackson Lake Lodge, Wyo., 1989, The Pub. Rms., V.P.'s Residence, Washington, 1989, Cormorant Cove, St. Croix, V.I., 1990, The Buccaneer Hotel, St. Croix, 1991, Dromoland Castle, Internat. Ctr., Ireland, 1991, West Village Golf Resort, Tokyo, 1993, Half Moon Bay Club, Jamaica, numerous others; designer: White House party for celebration Israel-Egypt Peace Treaty, 1979; Palm Beach Cares fashion benefit for Am. Found. for AIDS Research, 1988, log home for Pres. and Mrs. Carter, Ellijay, Ga., 1983; color cons. Carter Presdl. Library, 1986; trustee and curator: former presdl. yacht U.S.S. Sequoia, 1982; retail stores: Carleton Varney at the Greenbrier, White Sulphur Springs, W.Va., 1981, Carleton Varney at the Mill, Christiansted, St. Croix, 1988, Carleton Varney By-The Yard, Sarasota, Fla., 1990, Carleton Varney Rose Cottage, Newmarket-on-Fergus, Ireland, 1991; author: numerous books including You and Your Apartment, 1960, The Family Decorates a Home, 1962 Carleton Varney Decorates Windows, 1975, Be Your Own Decorator, 1979, There's No Place Like Home, 1980, Down Home, 1981, Carleton Varney's ABC's of Decorating, 1983, Staying in Shape: An Insider's Guide to the Great Spas, 1983, Room by Room Decorating, 1984, Color Magic, 1985, The Draper Touch, 1988, Kiss the Hibiscus Goodnight, 1992; syndicated columnist: Your Family Decorator, 1968—; contbg. editor Good Housekeeping Mag. Recipient Shelby Williams award for design achievement, 1967, Tommy design award for Covington's Heraldry collection, 1989, Interior Design Hall of Fame award, 1990. Mem. Indsl. Designers Soc. Am., N.Y. State Bd. for Interior Design. Clubs: N.Y. Athletic; Shannon Rowing (Ireland); Millbrook Golf and Tennis (N.Y.). Office: Dorothy Draper & Co Inc 60 E 56th St New York NY 10022-3204 also: Rose Cottage, NewMarket-on-Fergus, County Clare Ireland *My success, I believe, is due to an ability to understand and use vibrant color appropriately, and to strive for perfection of detail in all my designs as details separate the excellent from the ordinary.*

VARNEY, CHRISTINE A., federal official. Honors degree in Politics, Philosophy and Econs., Trinity Coll., Dublin, Ireland, 1975; BA in Polit. Sci. and History magna cum laude, SUNY, Albany, 1977; MPA in Policy Analysis, Legislation and Rsch. magna cum laude, Syracuse U., 1978; JD cum laude, Georgetown U., 1986. Legis. asst. N.Y. Senate, Albany, 1977; econ. analyst GAO, Washington, 1978; econ. devel. dir. El Centro, Calif., 1979; dir. Neighborhood Outreach Program, San Diego, 1980-82; assoc. Surry & Morse, Washington, 1984-86, Pierson, Semmes & Finley, Washington, 1986-88; counsel Hogan & Hartson, Washington, 1990-92; chief counsel Clinton for Pres. Primary Campaign, 1992, Clinton-Gore Campaign, 1992; gen. counsel Dem. Nat. Com., 1992, Presdl. Inauguration Com., 1993; dep. asst. to President U.S., sec. to Cabinet The White House, Washington, 1993—. Active Women's Legal Def. Fund. Mem. D.C. Bar Assn., N.Y. State Bar Assn., Nat. Lawyer's Coun. Office: The White House 1600 Pennsylvania Ave NW Washington DC 20500

VARNEY, RICHARD ALAN, medical office manager; b. Concord, N.H., July 8, 1950; s. John Berry and Hattie Elizabeth (Harrington) V.; m. Cheryl Suzanne Glaab, Dec. 31, 1983; stepchildren: Alysen Suzanne, Craig Judson. BS in Phys. Edn., U. N.H., 1972; MHA in Healthcare Adminstrn., Baylor U., 1984; diploma, Command and Gen. Staff Coll., 1986. Commd. 2d lt. U.S. Army, 1973, advanced through grades to lt. col., 1991; dep. asst. CEO Cutler Army Hosp., Ft. Devens, Mass., 1973-76, 15th Med. Battalion, Ft. Hood, Tex., 1979-81; adminstrv. resident Ireland Army Hosp., Ft. Knox, Ky., 1982-83; COO, exec. officer U.S. Army Dental Activity, Ft. Knox, 1983-86; grad. instr. Army-Baylor Healthcare Program, San Antonio, 1986-90; project mgr. Office of the Army Surgeon Gen., Washington, 1990-93; ret. U.S. Army, 1993; office mgr. Aebi, Ginty, Romaker & Sprouse MD's, Inc., Lancaster, Ohio, 1993—; mem. Source Selection Evaluation Bd.-Champus Reform, Arlington, Va., 1987. Adult leader Boy Scouts Am., Tex., Va. and Ohio, 1988—. Decorated Legion of Merit, Order of Mil. Med. Merit award; named to Hon. Order Ky. Cols., 1989. Fellow Am. Coll. Healthcare Execs. (examiner oral portion membership exam); mem. Ctrl. Ohio Health Adminstrs. Assn., Ohio Med. Group Mgmt. Assn., Mid-Ohio Med. Mgmt. Assn., Lancaster Area Soc. for Human Resource Mgmt., Am. Hosp. Assn. Avocations: home improvement, camping, hiking, music. Home: 1025 E 5th Ave Lancaster OH 43130 Office: Aebi Ginty Romaker Sprouse 1800 Granville Pike Lancaster OH 43130

VARNUM, JAMES WILLIAM, hospital administrator; b. Grand Rapids, Mich., May 29, 1941; s. Robert Otto and Jeannette (Badger) V.; m. Lucinda Hotchkiss, June 6, 1964; children: Kenneth James, Susan Lucinda. A.B., Dartmouth Coll., 1962; M.Hosp. Adminstrn. with honors, U. Mich., 1964. Adminstrv. asst. U. Wis. Hosps., Madison, 1963-64; asst. supt. U. Wis. Hosps., 1964-68, assoc. supt., 1968-69, supt., 1969-73; hosp. adminstr. U. Wash. Hosp., Seattle, 1973-78; pres. Mary Hitchcock Meml. Hosp., Lebanon, N.H., 1978—; prof. Med. Sch., Dartmouth Coll., 1978—. Mem. Am. Hosp. Assn. (bd. trustees 1994—), The Hitchcock Alliance (pres. 1983—). Home: 7 Woodcock Rd Etna NH 03750-4403 Office: Mary Hitchcock Meml Hosp 1 Medical Center Dr Lebanon NH 03756-0002

VARON, DAN, electrical engineer; b. Tel-Aviv, Israel, July 24, 1935; came to U.S., 1961; s. Reuven and Stephanie Varon; m. Judith Hilda Mansbach, Aug. 12, 1962; 2 children: BSEE, The Technion, Haifa, Israel, 1957, Diplom Ingenieur, 1960; MSc, Polytechnic U., Bklyn., 1963; D of Engring. Sci., NYU, 1965. Engr. Israeli Air Force, Israel, 1957-61; rsch. fellow Polytechnic U., Bklyn., 1961-63; teaching asst. NYU, N.Y.C., 1963-65; mem. tech. staff Bell Telephone Labs., Whippany, N.J., 1965-69; engr. Tymshare (Dial Data, Inc.), Newton, Mass., 1969-71; prin. engr. Raytheon Co., Marlborough, Mass., 1971—. Contbr. articles to Bell System Tech. Jour., IEEE, Radio Sci., Jour. Air Traffic Control Assn. Mem. IEEE (mem. tech. program com. 1970), N.Y. Acad. Scis., Assn. Computing Machinery.

VARONA, DANIEL ROBERT, lawyer, insurance company executive; b. Bklyn., Oct. 26, 1944; s. Theodore A. and Elsie Varona; m. Camille Mastronardi Feb. 14, 1986; children: David, Christopher, Julia. BS in Psychology, CCNY, 1971; JD, N.Y. Law Sch., 1977. Atty.office of gen. counsel N.Y. State Ins. Dept., N.Y.C., 1977-79; gen. coun., sec. Ideal Mut. Ins. Co. & Optimum Holding Corp., N.Y.C., 1979-85; sec. and counsel North Atlantic Life Ins. Co., Jerico, N.Y., 1985-87; gen. counsel, sec., chief adminstrv. officer Companion Life/Mut. Omaha Cos., Rye, N.Y., 1987—. With USN, 1964-68. N.Y. State Regents scholar, 1962-64, Vietnam War Svc. scholar N.Y. State, 1968-71. Mem. N.Y. State Bar Assn. (chmn. life, health & accident com., torts, ins. & compensation sect.), Westchester Bar Assn., Putnam Bar Assn. Avocations: gardening, martial arts. Office: Companion Life/Mut Omaha 401 Theodore Fremd Ave Rye NY 10580-1422

VARRO, BARBARA JOAN, editor; b. East Chicago, Ind., Jan. 25, 1938; d. Alexander R. and Lottie R. (Bess) V. B.A., Duquesne U., 1959. Feature reporter, asst. fashion editor Chgo. Sun-Times, 1959-64, fashion editor, 1964-76, feature writer, 1976-84; v.p. pub. rels. Daniel J. Edelman Inc., Chgo., 1984-85; v.p. PRB/Needham Porter Novelli, Chgo., 1985-86; editor Am. Hosp. Assn. News, Chgo., 1987-94; asst. editor spl. sects. Chgo. Tribune, 1995—. Recipient awards for feature writing Ill. AP, 1978, 79, 80. Mem. AAAS, Chgo. Council on Fgn. Relations. Office: Chgo Tribune 435 N Michigan Ave Chicago IL 60611

VARS, GORDON FORREST, education educator; b. Erie, Pa., Feb. 10, 1923; s. Ethan Wiard and Mildred Fredrica (Place) V.; m. Annis Tallentire, (div. 1975); m. Alice McVetty, Dec. 21, 1975; children: Christine McMahan, Lynn B. AB, Antioch Coll., 1948; MA, Ohio State U., 1949; EdD, George

Peabody Coll. for Tchrs, Nashville, 1958. Tchr. Bel Air Jr. Sr. High Sch., 1949-52, Peabody Demonstration Sch., Nashville, 1952-56; assoc. prof. edn. State U. Coll., Plattsburgh, N.Y., 1956-60, Cornell U., Ithaca, N.Y., 1960-66; prof. edn. Kent (Ohio) State U., 1966-93; cons. Various Depts. of Edn., Various Sch. Dists. Contbr. articles to profl. jours. Mem. Nat. Assn. for Core Curriculum (exec. sec.-treas.), Nat. Mid. Sch. Assn., Phi Delta Kappa (chpt. pres., v.p., sec. 1949-93). Avocations: choral singing, square dancing, hiking, camping, nature study. Home: 551 Fairchild Ave Kent OH 44240-2127 Office: Ste 5 1100 E Summit St Kent OH 44240-4094

VARSBERGS, VILIS, minister, former religious organization administrator; b. Prauliena, Latvia, June 1, 1929; s. Viktors and Marta (Barbans) V.; m. Biruta Grinbergs, July 2, 1960; children: Anita Valda, Krista Maija, Victor Andrew. BA magna cum laude, Midland Coll., 1954; MDiv, Luth. Sch. Theology, Chgo., 1957. Ordained to ministry United Luth. Ch., 1957. Mission developer, pastor Grace Luth. Ch., Albion, Mich., 1957-63; pastor Messiah Luth. Ch., Constantine, Mich., 1963-69; adminstr., dir. Latvian Ctr. Garezers, Inc., Three Rivers, Mich., 1969-72; pastor Zion Latvian Luth. Ch., Chgo., 1973—; pres. Latvian Evang. Luth. Ch. in Am., 1984-93; assembly del. Luth. World Fedn., Budapest, Hungary, 1984, Curitiba, Brazil, 1990. Sec. Helsinki Monitoring Com., Chgo., 1983-85; mem. adv. bd. Ill. Ethnic Cons., Chgo., 1986; bd. dirs. Luth. Immigration & Refugee Svc., N.Y.C., 1988—. Office: Zion Latvian Luth Ch 6551 W Montrose Ave Chicago IL 60634-1423

VARSHNI, YATENDRA PAL, physicist; b. Allahabad, India, May 21, 1932; emigrated to Can., 1960; s. Harpal and Bhagyawati V. B.Sc., U. Allahabad, 1950, M.Sc., 1952, Ph.D., 1956. Asst. prof. U. Allahabad, 1955-60; postdoctoral fellow NRC, Ottawa, Ont., Can., 1960-62; asst. prof. U. Ottawa, 1962-65, assoc. prof., 1965-69, prof., 1969—. Contbr. numerous articles to profl. jours. Fellow Am. Phys. Soc., Indian Phys. Soc., Royal Astron. Soc. (U.K.), Inst. Physics U.K.; mem. Royal Soc. Chemistry (U.K.) (assoc.), Am. Astron. Soc., Astron. Soc. of Pacific, Can. Astron. Soc., Can. Assn. Physicists, AAAS, Royal Astron. Soc. Can., Astron. Soc. India, Am. Assn. Physics Tchrs., European Phys. Soc. Office: Dept Physics, U Ottawa, Ottawa, ON Canada K1N 6N5

VARTANIAN, ARAM, French literature educator, researcher, writer; b. N.Y.C., Nov. 14, 1922; s. Vahan and Sirane (Casparian) V.; m. Irka Eitingon, Jan. 28, 1948 (div. 1961); 1 child, Michael; m. Anne Darrow, June 28, 1979 (div. 1984); m. Susanne Schroeder, June 28, 1990. B.A., Columbia U., 1944, M.A., 1947, Ph.D., 1951. Asst. prof. French Tulane U., 1951-52, Harvard U., 1952-57; assoc. prof. then prof. French U. Minn., Mpls., 1957-64; prof. French NYU, 1964-81; William R. Kenan prof. French lit. U. Va., Charlottesville, 1981-93; emeritus, 1993. Author: Diderot and Descartes, 1953, La Mettrie's L'Homme Machine, 1960, Critical Edition of Diderot's Les Bijoux Indiscrets, 1978; adv. editor Jour. History of Ideas, 1977, Continuum, 1987. Served with AUS, 1943-46. Recipient Gold medal City of Paris, 1988; fellow Ford Found., 1951-52, Fulbright rsch. fellow, 1962-63, Guggenheim Found. fellow, 1962-63. Mem. MLA, Am. Soc. 18th Century Studies (pres. 1990-91), Societe Francaise d'Etude du XVIIIe Siecle. Home: 49 Wynkoop Ln Rhinebeck NY 12572

VASIL, INDRA KUMAR, botanist; b. Basti, India, Aug. 31, 1932; arrived in U.S., 1962; s. Lal Chand and Puspa Lata (Abrol) V.; married, 1959; children: Kavita, Charu. BS, Banaras Hindu U., 1952; MS in Botany, U. Delhi, 1954, PhD in Botany, 1958. Lectr. in botany U. Delhi, 1959-63; postdoctoral rsch. assoc. U. Ill., Champaign-Urbana, 1962-63, U. Wis., Madison, 1963-65; scientist Coun. Sci. and Indsl. Rsch., New Delhi, 1966, Dept. Sci. and Indsl. Rsch., Palmerston North, New Zealand, 1974; assoc. prof. to prof. U. Fla., Gainesville, 1967-79, grad. rsch. prof., 1979—; vis. scientific expert Cath. U. Nijmegen, Netherlands, 1970; vis. prof. U. Hohenheim/Giessen, West Germany, 1975, 76; chmn. Biotechnology Action Coun. UNESCO, Paris, 1990—; svc. many internat. coms.; dir. numerous internat. tng. courses and workshops. Editor (20 vols.) Plant Cell Culture and Somatic Cell Genetics and Cellular and Molecular Biology of Plants, 1980—; editorial bd. six major internat. scientific jours. Fulbright fellowship U.S. Edn'l. Found., 1962, Climate Lab. fellowship Govt. of New Zealand, 1974; recipient Humboldt award Alexander von Humboldt Found. Mem. Internat. Cell Rsch. Orgn. (convenor of panel on plant cell biology and biotech.). Avocations: travel, reading, stamps, gardening. Home: 4901 NW 19th Pl Gainesville FL 32605 Office: U Fla 1143 Fifield Hall Gainesville FL 32611-0690

VASILACHI, GHEORGHE VASILE, priest, vicar; b. Idrici, Romania, Jan. 29, 1909; s. Gheorghe and Aglaia (Nestian) V. ThD, Universiti Iassy, Romania, 1938. Dir. Mitropolia, Iasi, 1935-39; secretar patriarchy Bucharest, 1939-42, preacher patriarchy, 1942-44; abbott Monastery Antim, Bucharest, 1943-48; igumen Pocrov, Romania, 1949-59; priest for prisons, 1959-64; priest Bobălna, 1965-69; priest Southbridge, Mass., 1969-79, Windsor, Can., 1979-84; priest St. Nicholas Parish, N.Y.C., 1984—; vicar Romanian Archdiocese Detroit, 1973. Author: Jesus Christ through the Ages, 1973, We Belong to Christ, 1980, Another World: Memories from Communist Prisons, 1987, The Supremacy of God--All in My Theology and Collection from the Word of Life, 1991; translator Holy Bible in Romanian lang.; pub. over 50 books in Romanian lang. Recipient Recognition award Commonwealth Mass., 1975. Republican. Office: The Romanian Orthodox Ch 45-03 48th Ave Flushing NY 11377

VASILE, GENNARO JAMES, health care executive; b. Auburn, N.Y., Jan. 16, 1946; s. Louis Joseph and Regina Elena (Santaniello) V.; m. Mary Ellen Dwyer, Aug. 10, 1968; children: Kevin, Colleen, Brian. B.A., St. John Fisher Coll., 1967; M.B.A., Xavier U., 1969; D.U. Iowa, 1973. Asst. adminstr. St. Elizabeth Hosp., Utica, N.Y., 1971-74; sr. cons. Booz-Allen & Hamilton, Inc., N.Y.C., 1974-75; asst. provost adminstrn. Med. Coll. Va., Commonwealth U., Richmond, 1975-78; dir. hosp. and health services mgmt. consulting Booz-Allen & Hamilton, Inc., Bethesda, Md., 1978-79; exec. dir. Strong Meml. Hosp. of U. Rochester, N.Y., 1979-84; pres. United Health Services Inc., Binghamton, N.Y., 1984-93; exec. v.p. Johns Hopkins Hosp., Balt., 1993—; asst. prof. U. Rochester, Med. Coll. Va.; assoc. prof. Johns Hopkins U.; vis. prof. U. Rochester Med. Ctr.; dir., pres. Med. Ctr. Ins. Co.; cons. health-related agencies. Author: Comprehensive Health Planning, 1971, 74. Bd. dirs. Rochester Soc. Prevention of Cruelty to Children, 1980, asst. treas., 1981; bd. dirs. Pittsford Vince Lombardi Youth Football, 1980, v.p., 1981; bd. dirs. St. Ann's Home, Voluntary Hosps. Am. Inc., Broome County C. of C., 1985, United Way, 1985; trustee St. John Fisher Coll. Recipient Dean's award for contbns. to Sch. Medicine Med. Coll. Va., 1978, Outstanding Contbn. to Mankind, 1993, Exec. of Yr., 1985, Preceptor of Yr. Xavier U., 1992. Fellow Am. Coll. Health Care Execs.; Am. Acad. Med. Care Adminstrs. (bd. dirs. 1988); mem. Am. Coll. Hosp. Adminstrs., Am. Hosp. Assn., Council Teaching Hosps., Assn. Am. Med. Colls. Roman Catholic. Home: 204 Lambeth Rd Baltimore MD 21218-1108 Office: Johns Hopkins Hosp 600 N Wolfe St # 101 Baltimore MD 21201 *The approach I have taken to my professional and personal life has been to seek out the world as it is, formulate a vision as to how it can be improved, and strive to bridge the resultant gaps. If I have been successful in bridging any gaps, it is only because of the substantial support I have received along the way.*

VASILOPOULOS, ATHANASIOS V., engineering educator; b. Mavranei, Grevena, Greece, May 25, 1937; came to U.S., 1955; s. Vasilios and Ekaterini Vasilopoulos; m. Paraskevi Tsiotas, Feb. 5, 1961; children: Basil John, Katherine, Pamela. BEE, NYU, 1962, MEE, 1965, PhD in Ops. Rsch., 1974. Computer technician Atomic Energy Commn., NYU, N.Y.C., 1957-59; asst. engr. Am. Electric Power Co., N.Y.C., 1959-62; staff engr. Grumman Aerospace, Bethpage, N.Y., 1962-78; assoc. prof. ops. rsch. St. John's U., Jamaica, N.Y., 1978—; adj. prof. math. SUNY at Farmingdale, 1974-78; vis. prof. U. Crete, Greece, 1980; cons. State of N.Y., Albany and Syracuse, summer 1982, AT&T, N.Y.C., summer 1985, Grumman Aerospace, 1980-91, Blue Bay Shipping, N.Y.C., 1983-84. Referee ASME Jour. Engring. for Industry, 1984, Jour. Collegiate Microcomputer, Terre Haute, Ind., 1984-87; contbr. articles to Jour. Quality Tech., Jour. Collegiate Microcomputer, Jour. Bus. Forecasting, others. Mem. coun. Boy Scouts Am., Commack, N.Y., 1970-75; soccer coach Huntington (N.Y.) Boys Club, 1974-75; v.p. St. Paraskevi Greek Orthodox Ch., Greenlawn, N.Y., 1976-78, chmn. edn. com., 1968-85. Recipient Patriarch Athenagoras medallion

Greek Orthodox Archdiocese N.Y.C., 1981. Mem. IEEE (sr.), N.Y. Acad. Scis., Ops. Rsch. Soc. Am., Inst. of Mgmt. Scis. Achievements include development of method for analyzing generalized quality control data, method for generating correlated random variables for quality control applications, use of extended input-output methodology for forecasting purposes; proposal of methodology to use computer to generate density functions for sums of independent random variables; use of computer to demonstrate validity of central limit theorem and law of large numbers in statistics. Office: St John's Univ Grand Central And Utop Jamaica NY 11439

VASLEF, IRENE, historian, librarian; b. Budapest, Hungary, Mar. 23, 1934; came to U.S., 1956, naturalized, 1960; d. Imre and Ilona (Selyebi-Kovats) Szabo; m. Nicholas P. Vaslef, Sept. 22, 1956; children—Suzanne, Steven. B.A., San Jose (Calif.) State U., 1960, M.S., Simmons Grad. Sch. Library Sci., Boston, 1963; postgrad., Columbia U., 1968, U. Colo., 1961-62, U. Munich, 1967-68; Ph.D., Catholic U. Am., 1984. Librarian Cambridge, Mass., 1962-64; librarian Colorado Springs (Colo.) Sch. System, 1964-67; head catalog librarian Colo. Coll., Colorado Springs, 1968-72; librarian Dumbarton Oaks Rsch. Libr., Trustees for Harvard U., 1972—. Editor/compiler Am. Byzantine Bibliography in Byzantine studies/Etudes Byzantines, 1979—, Classica et Mediaevalia, 1986, Leyden: Brill, 1986; contbr. articles to profl. jours. Mem. Spl. Libraries Assn., Art Libraries Assn. N.Am., Phi Gamma Mu. Home: 1405 Grady Randall Ct Mc Lean VA 22101-2512 Office: Harvard U Dumbarton Oaks Rsch Libr 1703 32nd St NW Washington DC 20007-2934

VASQUEZ, GADDI, county official; b. Carrizo Springs, Tex., Jan. 22, 1955; m. Elaine Vasquez; 1 child, Jason. AA in Criminal Justice, Rancho Santiago C.C., 1972; BA in Pub. Svc. Mgmt., U. Redlands, 1980. Police officer City of Orange, Calif., 1975-79; coord. community rels., mgr.'s office City of Riverside, Calif., 1979-81; exec. asst. Orange County Bd. Supervisors, 3d Dist., Calif., 1981-85; mem. Orange County Bd. Supervisers 3d Dist., Calif., 1987—; area mgr. So. Calif. Edison Co., 1985; hispanic liaison Office of Gov. George Deukmejian, Calif., 1985, from dep. appointments sec. to chief dep. appointments sec., 1985-87; Mem. Transp. Corridor Agys. Bd., 1987—, chmn. 1990-91; local agy. formation commn., 1988-93, chmn. 1990-91; mem. Calif. Film Commn., 1988-91, Calif. Coun. Criminal Justice, 1989—; founder, co-chair, Orange County Health Care Task Force, 1990—, with White House Fellowships Commn., 1990-91; co-chmn. Orange County Congestion Mgmt. Policy Task Force, 1990—; bd. dirs. Orange County Transp. Authority, 1991—, exec. com. 1992—, vice chmn. 1993—; regional advisory and planning coun., 1991—, vice chmn. 1992, chmn. 1993; official observer Armenian Independence elections, 1991. Bd. dirs. Future Leaders Am., Southwest Voter Rsch. Inst., calif. First Amendment Coalition, Orange County Boy Scout Coun., So. Area Foster Care Effort, Orange County Performing Arts Ctr., Opera Pacific; trustee Am. Coun. Young Polit. Leaders; adv. bd. Pediatric Cancer Rsch. Found, Orange County Juvenile Connection Project, Calif. Office Traffic Safety, The Salvation Army Orange County, Project AERO, Constitutional Rights Found. Orange County; community coun. Prentice Day Sch.; hon. adv. bd. Adam Walsh Ctr.; hon. bd. govs. Bower Mus.; leadership coun. Orange County Points Light. Named Officer of Yr., Am. Legion, 1977. Outstanding Young Man of Am. U.S. C.of C., 1985, One of 100 Most Influential Hispanics in U.S. Hispanic Bus. Mag., 1986-87, 88-89, 91-92, 92-93, Govt. Hispanic Bus. Advocate of Yr. U.S. Hispanic Champer Region I, 1991; recipient Alumni Achievement award, Santa Ana Coll., 1988, Alumni of Yr.award U. Redlands, 1989, Humanitarian award Nat. Conf. Christians and Jews, 1989, award State Child Devel. Adv. Com., 1990, Tree of Life award Jewish Nat. Fund, 1991, Ralph E. Hudson Open Space award Landscape Architects Found., 1992. Office: Orange County Bd of Supervisors 10 Civic Center Plz Santa Ana CA 92701-4017

VASQUEZ, WILLIAM LEROY, marketing professional, educator; b. Austin, Tex., Mar. 9, 1944; s. Eliseo M. and Janie (Garcia) V. BS with distinction, Nova U., 1983, MBA, 1985, DBA, 1992. Cert. Inst. Cert. Profl. Mgrs., 1990, Inst. Cert. Computing Profls., 1993. Svc. mgr. Data Gen. Corp., various, Latin Am., 1972-80; product mgr. Gould, Inc., Ft. Lauderdale, Fla., 1980-84, Tektronix Inc., Portland, Oreg., 1984-86, Racal-Milgo, Ft. Lauderdale, 1988-90, Citibank, N.A., Ft. Lauderdale, 1990—; instr. City U. Portland campus, 1987-88, Maryhurst Coll., 1985-88, Nova U. (domestic and internat.), 1988—, St. Thomas U., 1989—, Fla. Atlantic U., 1993—; mem. adv. com. Art Inst. of Ft. Lauderdale; freelance writer DataPro divsn. McGraw Hill, 1991—. Mem. mktg. com. Fla. Philharm. Orch., 1994. Served on USN nuclear submarines, 1961-70. Mem. IEEE, VFW, Am. Mktg. Assn. (pres.), Nat. Mgmt. Assn., Mensa. Republican. Presbyterian. Avocations: guitar, jogging, fine arts, reading. Home: 4090 NW 110th Ave Coral Springs FL 33065-7718 Office: Citibank NA 899 W Cypress Creek Rd Ste 701 Fort Lauderdale FL 33309-2064

VASS, JOAN, fashion designer; b. N.Y.C., May 19, 1925; d. Max S. and Rose L.; children by previous marriage: Richard, Sara, Jason. Student Vassar Coll., 1941; BA, U. Wis., 1946. Pres., Joan Vass Inc., N.Y.C., 1977—, Vass-Ludacer, N.Y.C., 1993—. Recipient Prix de Cachet, Prince Machiabelli, 1980, Coty award, 1979, Disting. Woman in Fashion award Smithsonian Instn., 1980. Office: Joan Vass Inc 117 E 29th St New York NY 10016-8022 also: 485 7th Ave Ste 510 New York NY 10018-6804

VASSAR, WILLIAM GERALD, gifted and talented education educator; b. Springfield, Mass., Oct. 5, 1925; s. William Walter and Mary Ellen (Burns) V.; m. Barbara Ellen Benhard, June 21, 1952; children: William G., James P., Richard G., Carol A. BA in History magna cum laude, Am. Internat. Coll., Springfield, 1950; MEd, Springfield Coll., 1951; cert. of advanced grad. study, U. Mass., 1967, postgrad., 1962-70. Elem. tchr. West Springfield (Mass.) Pub. Schs., 1950-53, jr. high tchr., 1953-55, secondary sch. prin., 1955-65, dir. program for gifted, 1955-65; sr. supr. academically talented Mass. State Dept. Edn., Boston, 1965-66; state dir. programs for gifted and talented Conn. State Dept. Edn., Hartford, 1966-86; coord. gifted edn., dept. spl. edn. Cen. Conn. State U., New Britain, 1986-88, asst. to dean Sch. Edn., 1986-88; spl. cons. advanced placement program The Coll. Bd., N.Y.C., 1986—; coord. White House Task Force Gifted and Talented, Washington, 1967-68, U.S. Dept. Edn. Congl. Study Gifted and Talented, Washington, 1969-71, Capitol Region Edn. Coun. Info. and Resource Ctr., Windsor, Conn., 1992—; cons. gifted and talented U.S. Dept. Edn., 1967-85, Nat. Assn. State Bds. Edn., 1978-84, George Washington U. Edn. Policy Fellowship Program, 1978-84; spl. cons. gifted and talented legislation Staff of Senated subcom. on Edn., 1967-85; vis. lectr. U. Conn., 1966-83, So. Conn. State U., 1970-84, Sacred Heart U., 1986—, others. Contbg. editor The Gifted Child Quar., Jour. Talented and Gifted; contbr. numerous articles to profl. jours. Mem. exec. bd. Mass. Commn. on Children and Youth, Boston, 1959-65, Nat. Commn. Orgn. and Children and Youth, Washington, 1964-68; mem. Conn. Commn. on Youth Svcs., Hartford, 1966-70; mem. Mass. Hwy. Safety Commn., Boston, 1957-63; baseball scout San Francisco Giants, 1957-70. With USN, 1943-46, PTO. Named Disting. Educator U.S. Dept. Edn. Office Gifted, Washington, 1971, Disting. Educator, Conn. State Legislature, Hartford, 1986; recipient Disting. Svc. award Mass. Commn. on Children and Youth, Boston, 1966. Mem. Internat. Coun. Exceptional Children (pres. Assn. Gifted div. 1970-71, chmn. regionals 1969-78, Disting. Svc. award 1976), Nat. Assn. Gifted Children (life, pres. 1965-68, bd. dirs. 1960-68, Disting. Svc. award 1970), Coun. State Dirs. Gifted (pres. 1977-80), Conn. Assn. Gifted, Conn. Assn. Pub. Sch. Supts., Nat. Football Hall of Fame Found., Eastern Assn. Intercollegiate Football Ofcls., Indian Hill Country Club, Eastern Coll. Athletic Conf., Phi Delta Kappa. Democrat. Roman Catholic. Avocations: reading, golf, football. Home: 47 Dowd St Newington CT 06111-2611

VASSBERG, DAVID ERLAND, history educator; b. Harlingen, Tex., Mar. 13, 1936; s. Sven and Evelyn (Redlund) V.; m. Liliane Mangold, Nov. 10, 1962; children: Mark Andrew, Alan Henry. BA, U. Tex., 1958, MA, 1966, PhD, 1971. Farmer Lyford, Tex., 1961-66; assoc. prof. history Pan Am. U., Edinburg, Tex., 1971-77; assoc. prof., 1977-83; prof., 1983—; vis. prof. U. Valladolid, Spain, 1991. Author: Land and Society in Golden Age Castile, 1984, others; contbr. articles to profl. jours. Fellow NDEA, 1967-70, Spanish Fgn. Ministry, 1969-70, 95, NEH, 1974-75, 93-94, U.S. and Spanish Govts., 1978-79, Sr. Nat. Rsch. fellow NIH, 1995—. Mem. Am. Hist. Assn., Soc. for Spanish and Portuguese Hist. Studies (exec. com. 1986-88), Tex. Assn. for Advancement of History, Lions (pres., v.p. local chpt. 1962-

65). Lutheran. Avocations: photography, music, numismatics. Home: 5000 N 5th St Mcallen TX 78504-2807 Office: U Tex Pan Am 1201 W University Dr Edinburg TX 78539-2909

VASSELL, GREGORY S., electric utility consultant; b. Moscow, Dec. 24, 1921; came to U.S., 1951, naturalized, 1957; s. Gregory M. and Eugenia M. Wasiljeff; m. Martha Elizabeth Williams, Apr. 26, 1957; children: Laura Kay, Thomas Gregory. Dipl. Ing. in Elec. Engring, Tech. U. Berlin, 1951; MBA in Corp. Fin., NYU, 1954. With Am. Electric Power Svc. Corp., Columbus, Ohio, 1951-88; v.p. system planning Am. Electric Power Svc. Corp., 1973-76, dir., 1973-88, sr. v.p. system planning, 1976-88; electric utility cons. Upper Arlington, Ohio, 1988—; bd. dirs. Columbus & Southern Ohio Electric Co., 1981-88, Cardinal Operating Co.; mem. tech. adv. com. transmission FPC, 1968-70, FERC Task Force on Power Pooling, 1980-81; mem. U.S. com. World Energy Coun. Contbr. articles to profl. jours. Fellow IEEE (life); mem. NAE, Internat. Conf. Large High Voltage Electric Systems, Columbus Athletic Club. Home and Office: 2247 Pinebrook Rd Columbus OH 43220-4327

VASSIL, PAMELA, graphic designer; b. N.Y.C., Nov. 29, 1943; d. George Peter and Lenora (Zabludofsky) Vassilopoulos; 1 child, Sadye Lee. B.S. in Art Edn., Hofstra U., 1965; M.A. in Art Edn., NYU, 1968. Designer Columbia Records, N.Y.C., 1970-72; assoc. art dir. Harper's Bazaar, N.Y.C., 1972-74; designer, mech. artist Album Graphics Inc., N.Y.C., 1974-75; free-lance designer, mech. artist; prodn. dir. Push Pin Studios, N.Y.C., 1975-77; art dir. op. editorial page N.Y. Times, N.Y.C., 1977-79; art dir. arts and leisure sect., 1982-87, art dir. living sect., 1987; free-lance designer/art dir./mech. artist, 1979-82; instr. production, graphic design and illustration Parsons Sch. Design, N.Y.C., 1974—; instr. illustration Sch. Visual Arts, 1981; features art dir. The Daily News, N.Y.C., 1987; sr. art dir. Wells, Rich, Greene Inc. N.Y.C., 1987-88; free-lance graphic designer/art dir., 1988-89; design dir. Roger Black Inc., N.Y.C., 1989-90; design dir. McCall's mag., N.Y.C., 1990-91, freelance art dir., 1991-92; dir., Continuing Edn Parson's Sch. Design, 1992—. Assoc. editor and designer: (book) Images of Labor, 1981.

VASTA, BRUNO MORREALE, information scientist, chemist; b. Washington, Apr. 1, 1933; s. John and Charlotte M. Vasta; m. Dorothy Delaney, Aug. 18, 1956; children: Karen, Vicki, Charlotte, Robert. BS, Georgetown U., 1954; MS, George Washington U., 1957. Rsch. assoc. Nat. Heart Inst., NIH, Bethesda, Md., 1955-57; rsch. biochemist NIH, Beltsville, Md., 1957-60; info. scientist FDA, 1963-70; chief toxicology info. svcs. Nat. Libr. Medicine, Bethesda, 1970-76, chief bibliog. svcs. div., 1976-77, adminstr. Toxicology Data Network, 1982—; dir. chem. info. div. Office Toxic Substances, EPA, 1977-80, sr. sci. advisor, 1980-82. Editor: Drug Interactions Bibliography, Vols. I and II, 1974-75. Mem. Am. Chem. Soc. (chmn. div. chem. info. 1976-76), Am. Soc. Info. Scis., Chesapeake Bay Found., Salt Water Sportsmens Club, Friends of Libr. Medicine. Home: 9111 Westerholme Way Vienna VA 22182-2144 Office: Nat Libr Medicine 8600 Rockville Pike Bethesda MD 20894-0001

VATIKIOTIS, MICHAEL RICHARD JOHN, journalist, writer; b. Indpls., July 30, 1957; s. Panayotis and Patricia (Mumford) V.; m. Janick Shirley Bhavon, July 21, 1984; children: Chloe Maeve, Stefan Alexandre. Student, Am. U. Cairo, 1976, London U., 1977-80; BA in History with 1st class honours, Oxford (Eng.) U., DPhil. Bur. chief Far Ea. Econ. Rev., Bangkok, 1994—; feature writer Bangkok Post, 1981-82; trainee, then with world svc. current affairs BBC, London, 1984-87; corr. BBC, Jakarta, Indonesia, 1987-88; Jakarta bur. chief Far Ea. Econ. Rev., 1988-91; Malaysia bur. chief, Asean corr. Far Ea. Econ. Rev., Jakarta, 1991-94. Greek Orthodox. Avocation: drawing. Office: Far Es Econ Review, GPO Box 160, Hong Kong Hong Kong

VATTER, PAUL AUGUST, business administration educator, dean; b. Boston, Sept. 14, 1924; s. August John and Elizabeth Emelia (Kunstler) V.; m. Josette Roman, July 23, 1966; children: Joel Paul, Katherine Alexandra. BA, Holy Cross Coll., 1944; MA, U. Pa., 1947, PhD, 1953; MA (hon.), Harvard U., 1970. Instr. U. Pa., Phila., 1945-53, asst. prof., 1953-58, vice dean of men, 1953-58; asst. dean Harvard U. Bus. Sch., Boston, 1958-62, assoc. prof. bus. adminstrn., 1962-70, prof., 1970—, Lawrence E. Fouraker prof. bus. adminstrn., sr. assoc. dean, 1989-91; bd. dirs. Hartford (Conn.) Steam Boiler Inspection & Ins. Co., Sbarro, Inc., L.I., N.Y. Author: Quantitative Methods in Management, 1978, The Structure of Retail Trade by Size of Store, 1979, also video tapes. Home: 244 Clifton St Belmont MA 02178-2647 Office: Harvard U Bus Sch Soldiers Fld Boston MA 02163

VAUGHAN, ALDEN TRUE, history educator; b. Providence, Jan. 23, 1929; s. Dana Prescott and Muriel Louise (True) V.; m. Lauraine A. Freethy, June 1, 1956 (div. 1981); children: Jeffrey Alden, Lynn Elizabeth; m. Virginia Mason Carr, July 16, 1983. BA, Amherst Coll., 1950; MEd, Columbia U., 1956, MA in History, 1958, PhD, 1964. Tchr. Hackley Sch., Tarrytown, N.Y., 1950-51, A.B. Davis High Sch., Mt. Vernon, N.Y., 1956-60; From history instr. to prof. Columbia U., N.Y.C., 1961—, prof. emeritus, 1994; editor Polit. Sci. Quar., N.Y., 1970-71; gen. editor Early Am. Indian Documents, Univ. Pubs. of Am., 1977—; assoc. editor Ency. of the N.Am. Colonies, Scribners, N.Y., 1993; vis. adj. prof. CUNY, Lehman Coll., N.Y.C., 1971; vis. prof. Clark U., Worcester, Mass., 1987. Author: New England Frontier, 1965, rev. edit., 1979, 3rd edit. 1995, American Genesis, 1975, Shakespeare's Caliban, 1991, Roots of American Racism, 1995; contbr. articles to Am. Heritage, Am. Hist. Rev., New Eng. Quar., and others. Lt. (j.g.) USNR, 1951-55. Recipient fellowship Guggenheim Found., 1973, Sr. fellowship Folger Shakespeare Libr., 1977, 89, Sr. fellowship Am. Antiquarian Soc., 1983. Mem. Am. Antiquarian Soc. (sr. fellowship), Am. Hist. Assn., Soc. Am. Historians (exec. sec., treas. 1965-70), Orgn. Am. Historians (program chmn. 1976), Inst. Early Am. History and Culture (coun. mem. 1985-87), Colonial Soc. Mass. Home: 50 Howland Ter Worcester MA 01602-2631

VAUGHAN, CLIFFORD JAMES, automotive manufacturing company executive; b. Cin., Apr. 2, 1934; s. Clifford James and Lela (Hoffman) V.; m. Elsie Verree Fisk, Nov. 3, 1956; children—Mark, Todd, James, Andrea, Scott, Sean. B.S. in Indsl. Engring., Gen. Motors Inst., 1956. Dir. reliability assembly div. Gen. Motors Corp., Warren, Mich., 1977-78, regional plant mgr. assembly div., 1978-79; dir. mfg. Adam Opel, Fed. Republic Germany, 1979-80, exec. dir. mfg., 1980-83; mng. dir. Gen. Motors DO Brasil, Sao Paulo, 1983-87; mng. dir. Chevrolet-Pontiac-Can. Group Gen. Motors Corp., Warren, Mich., 1987—. Avocation: golf. Office: GM Gen Motors Bldg 3044 W Grand Blvd Detroit MI 48202-3091

VAUGHAN, EDWIN DARRACOTT, JR., urologist, surgeon; b. Richmond, Va., May 13, 1939; s. Edwin Darracott and Blanche V. (Bashaw) V.; m. Virginia Ann Lloyd, June 30, 1962; children—Edwin Darracott, III, Barbara Anderson. B.S., Washington and Lee U., 1961; M.D., U. Va., 1965, M.S., 1969; D.Sc., Washington and Lee U., 1982. Diplomate Am. Bd. Urology (trustee, v.p. 1988, pres. 1989). Intern Vanderbilt U., 1965-66, asst. resident, 1966-67; chief resident in urology U. Va., 1970-71, asst. prof. urology, 1973-75, assoc. prof., 1975-78, prof., 1978; clin. research fellow Columbia U., 1971-72, research assoc. dept. medicine, 1972-73; James J. Colt prof. urology, chmn. dept. urology Cornell U. Med. Coll., N.Y.C. and; attending urologist-in-chief N.Y. Hosp., N.Y.C., 1978—; sr. assoc. dean clin. affairs Cornell U. Med. Coll., N.Y.C., 1993—; chmn. dept. urology, 1993—; mem. sci. adv. bd. Nat. Kidney Found., 1977; sec.-treas. Urology Council, 1977, chmn., 1980; mem. med. adv. bd. Council High Blood Pressure, 1977. Editor: Seminars in Urology; assoc. editor Investigative Urology, 1977-78, mem. editorial bd., 1978-94; editor Campbell's Urology; contbr. articles on obstructive uropathy, renal hemodynamics, hypertension to profl. jours. Recipient Research Career Devel. award NIH, 1976-78; NIH tng. grantee, 1967-68; USPHS grantee, 1971-73, 74-77; Am. Heart Assn. grantee, 1976-79. Mem. ACS, AAAS, N.Y. Acad. Scis., Soc. Univ. Urologists, Am. Urol. Assn. (chmn. research com. 1980-91, treas. N.Y. sect. 1985, v.p. N.Y. sect. 1986, pres. N.Y. sect. 1987, Golden Cystoscope award 1981, exec. com. 1992, Disting. Contbn. award 1992), Urol. Soc. Australasia (hon.), Soc. Exptl. Biology and Medicine, Soc. Univ. Surgeons, Société Internat. d'Urologie, Am. Found. Urol. Disease (pres. 1987-92), Nat. Kidney and Urol. Disease Adv. Bd. (dep. chmn.), Intersoc. for Kidney and Urol. Disease Research (chmn. 1987), Am. Assn. Genito-Urinary Surgeons, Am. Surg.

Assn. (AAGUS Barringen Metal, 1993), Sigma Xi, Alpha Omega Alpha (award 1976), Omicron Delta Kappa (award 1981). Home: 1165 Park Ave Apt 6A New York NY 10128-1210 Office: 525 E 68th St New York NY 10021-4873

VAUGHAN, EMMETT JOHN, academic dean, insurance educator; b. Omaha, Dec. 1, 1934; s. Leo William and Mary (Simones) V.; m. Lonne Kay Smith, July 2, 1955; children: Therese, Timothy, Mary, Joan, Thomas, Michael, Emmett (dec.). B.A. in Econs., Creighton U., 1960; MA in Econs. and Ins., U. Nebr., 1962, PhD in Econs. and Ins., 1964. Asst. prof. U. Iowa, Iowa City, 1963-65, assoc. prof., 1965-68, Partington Disting. prof. ins., 1968—, dean Div. Continuing Edn., 1986—. Author: Fundamentals of Risk and Insurance, 1972, 6th edit., 1992; contbr. numerous articles to profl. jours. Participated in assessment of war damages in Kuwait UN Commn. on Compensation, 1992. Capt. USAR, 1955-75. Mem. Japan Risk Mgmt. Soc. (hon.). Office: U Iowa 116 Internat Ctr Inst Ins Edn & Rsch Iowa City IA 52242

VAUGHAN, EUGENE H., investment company executive; b. Brownsville, Tenn., Oct. 5, 1933; s. Eugene H. Sr. and Margaret (Musgrave) V.; m. Susan Bolinger Westbrook, May 11, 1963; children: Margaret Corbin, Richard Bolinger. BA, Vanderbilt U., 1955; MBA, Harvard U., 1961. CFA, 1967. Security analyst Putnam Mgmt. Co., Boston, 1961-64; dir., dir. rsch. Underwood, Neuhaus & Co., Inc., Houston, 1964-70; pres., chief exec. officer Vaughan, Nelson & Boston, Inc., Houston, 1970-77, Vaughan, Nelson, Scarborough & McConnell, Inc., Houston, 1970—; bd. dirs. Founders Asset Mgmt. Co., Denver, 1970—. Chair Fin. Analyst Fedn., N.Y.C., 1973-74, bd. dirs., 1969-76; pres. Houston Soc. Fin. Analysts, 1967-68; founder Internat. Coordinating Com., 1974; bd. dirs., chmn. investment com. Presbyn. Bd. Pensions (USA), Phila., 1988—; mem. investment com. Tex. State Employees Retirement System, Austin, 1988-93; trustee Vanderbilt U., Nashville, 1972—, St. John's Sch., Houston, 1980-85, Goodwill Industries, Houston, 1978—; elder First Presbyn. Ch., 1976—; founding chmn., trustee Presbyn. Sch., Houston, 1986-90. Lt. USN, 1955-58. Recipient Disting. Svc. award Fin. Analyst Fedn., 1978, Humanitarian award Am. Jewish Com., 1993, Disting. Svc. award Houston Soc. Fin. Analysts, 1993. Mem. Inst. Chartered Fin. Analysts (trustee 1986-93, chmn. 1989), Assn. for Investment Mgmt. and Rsch. (founding chmn. 1990-91, gov. 1990-93), Greater Houston Partnership (bd. dirs. 1990—, exec. com. 1993—), Houston Club (pres. 1983-84, bd. dirs. 1979-85, chair centennial celebration, 1992-94), Houston Country Club, Forum Club Houston (pres. 1991-92, chmn. 1992-93), Harvard U. Bus. Sch. Club Houston (pres. 1968-69, bd. dirs. 1966-71, 86-90), Vanderbilt Club Houston (chmn. 1984—, pres. 1966-68, Disting. Svc. award 1994), Conferie des Chevaliers du Tastevin, Belle Meade Country Club (Nashville), Argyle Club (San Antonio). Republican. Avocations: traveling, sailing. Home: 3465 Inwood Dr Houston TX 77019-3129 Office: Vaughan Nelson Scarborough & McConnell 6300 Texas Commerce Towers Houston TX 77002

VAUGHAN, HERBERT WILEY, lawyer; b. Brookline, Mass., June 1, 1920; s. David D. and Elzie G. (Wiley) V.; m. Ann Graustein, June 28, 1941. Student, U. Chgo., 1937-38; SB cum laude, Harvard U., 1941, LLB, 1948. Bar: Mass. 1948. Assoc. Hale and Dorr, Boston, 1948-54, jr. ptnr., 1954-56, sr. ptnr., 1956-82, co-mng. ptnr., 1976-80; pres. Herbert W. Vaughan, P.C., sr. ptnr. Hale and Dorr, 1982-89, of counsel, 1990—. Sec. and mem. standing com., The Trustees of Reservations; mem. Com. of Fund for Preservation of Wildlife and Natural Areas; mem. bd. trustees, Am. Friends of New Coll. (Oxford Univ.); bd. dirs. Am. Friends Fund of Inst. of U.S. Studies of U. London. Fellow Am. Bar Found. (life); mem. ABA, Chesterton Soc. (internat. com.), Mass. Bar Assn., Boston Bar Assn., Internat. Bar Assn., Am. Law Inst., Am. Coll. Mortgage Attys., Am. Coll. Real Estate Lawyers, Bay Badminton and Tennis Club, Union Club (Boston), Boston Econ. Club, Longwood Cricket Club (Brookline, Mass.). Office: Hale & Dorr 60 State St Boston MA 02109-1803

VAUGHAN, JOHN CHARLES, III, horticultural products executive; b. N.Y.C., July 30, 1934; s. John Charles II and Lucille Grace (Dixon) V.; m. Ruth Darden MacLeod, Mar. 4, 1962; children: Elizabeth, John IV, George. AB in Econs., Cornell U., 1956; MBA, Northwestern U., 1962. Salesman Hall & Ellis, Chgo., 1959-62; br. mgr. Vaughan's Seed Co., Downers Grove, Ill., 1963-74, exec. v.p. 1974-76, pres., 1976-84, chmn. bd., 1985-93, ret., 1993; regional v.p. Am. Seed Trade Assn., Washington, 1985-88; pres. Atlantic Seedsmen's Assn., N.Y.C., 1968; dir. Nat. Seed Co., Ill. & N.J. Bd. dirs. George Williams Coll., Downers Grove, 1982-92. 1st Lt. USMCR, 1956-59. Mem. Downers Grove C. of C. (chmn. 1989).

VAUGHAN, JOHN THOMAS, veterinarian, educator, university dean; b. Tuskegee, Ala., Feb. 6, 1932; s. Henry Asa and Mary (Howard) V.; m. Ethel Evelyn Sell, July 7, 1956; children: John Thomas, Faythe, Michael Sell. D.V.M., Auburn U., 1955, M.S., 1963. Clin. resident U. Pa. Sch. Vet. Medicine, Phila., 1958; instr. Auburn U. Coll. Vet. Medicine, Ala., 1955-57; asst. prof. Auburn U. Coll. Vet. Medicine, 1959-65, assoc. prof., 1965-70, prof., head dept. large animal surgery and medicine, 1974-77, dean, 1977—; tenured prof. vet. surgery, dir. Large Animal Hosp. N.Y. State Vet. Coll., Cornell U., Ithaca, N.Y., 1970-74; bd. dirs. Compass Bank, Auburn. Co-author 2 textbooks; contbr. chpts. to books, articles to profl. jours. Chmn. ofcl. bd. Auburn Meth. Ch., 1968-69; pres. bd. dirs. United Fund, Auburn, 1968-69, Hughston Orthopaedic Rsch. Found., 1985—, So. Heart and Lung Inst., 1988-90; bd. dirs., exec. com. Diabetes Trust Fund, 1992—. Mem. AVMA, Am. Assn. Equine Practitioners (pres.), Am. Coll. Vet. Surgeons (pres., chmn. bd. regents), Assn. Am. Vet. Med. Colls. (coun. deans), Nat. Acads. Practice, Nat. Assn. State Univs. and Land Grant Colls. (chmn. bd. vet. medicine 1987, 91-94, chmn., bd. dirs. vet. medicine of commn. on food, environment and renewable resources 1991-94, exec. com. bd. on agriculture 1992-94), Ala. Vet. Med. Assn. (Vet. of Yr. 1985), Rotary. Office: Auburn U Coll Vet Medicine Auburn AL 36849 *Far from pursuing any manifest destiny, my efforts have been directed to the tasks at hand, some assigned, some assumed, whether great or small. This has been influenced by a lifestyle inclined to self-reliance with no requirements on extravagance. Aside from striving for a measure of competence in a specific field of endeavor, recognition and acceptance of one's principles and purposes depends much upon a positive attitude and the ability to associate agreeably with one's fellows.*

VAUGHAN, JOSEPH LEE, language educator; b. Lynchburg, Va., Jan. 26, 1905; s. Ellis Lee and Anna Margaret (Worley) V.; m. Ann Cleveland Doner, Aug. 3, 1938 (dec. Aug. 1992); children: Joseph Lee, Ann Sahlman. AB, U. Va., 1926, AM, 1927, PhD, 1940. Instr. English, U. Va., Charlottesville, 1930-32; instr. English dept. engring. U. Va., 1932-35, asst. prof., 1936-40, assoc. prof., 1940-45, prof., 1945—, Joseph L. Vaughan prof. humanities, chmn. dept., 1970—, provost, 1956-60, chancellor Community Colls., 1960-66, dir. studies Humanities Inst., 1968-70; lectr., cons. Inst. Textile Tech., Charlottesville, 1947-81, pres., 1951-53; assoc. dir. sch. for tchrs. of English in engring. colls. U. Mich., 1941; regional dir. Cen. Div. Jefferson Nat. Bank, Charlottesville; mem. info. council NSF; cons. Va.-Md. Bankers Assn., Fieldcrest Mills, State Farm Ins. Co., Va. Employment Commn. Author: (with W.O. Birk, H. Melvin, F. Holmes) Basic Principles of Writing, 1937, rev. edit., 1943; (sect.) 19th Century America; Good Reading, 1948, Oral Communications for the Layman, (with O.A. Giannini Jr.) Thomas Jefferson's Rotunda Restored, 1981, Rotunda Tales, 1991; editor: English Notes sect. Jour. Engring. Edn., 1936-40; contbr. articles to jours., 1940—; assoc. editor: Report on Instruction in English in Engineering Colleges in the U.S., 1940; assoc. editor and contbr.: A Guide to Good Reading, 1942-48; contbr. to prof. publs. Recipient Significant Sig award, 1969, Raven award, 1977, Disting. Prof. award, 1971, Mac Wade award 1975, Disting. Svc. award Va. Engring. Found., 1991, Vaughan House, U. Va. named in his honor, 1992. Mem. Albemarle Art Assn., Albemarle Hist. Assn., Va. Watercolor Soc. Ctrl. Va. Watercolor Guild, Phi Beta Kappa, Omicron Delta Kappa, Pi Delta Epsilon, Sigma Chi, Raven Soc. Presbyterian. Clubs: Colonnade, Farmington Country. Specialist in communication techniques. Home: The Colonnades 2600 Barracks Rd Charlottesville VA 22901-2100

VAUGHAN, JOSEPH LEE, JR., education educator, consultant; b. Charlottesville, Va., Dec. 31, 1942; s. Joseph Lee and Ann (Doner) V.; children: Leigh Ann, Kelley. BA, U. Va., 1964, MEd, 1968, EdD, 1974. Tchr. Madison (Va.) High Sch., 1965-67, Darlington Sch., Rome, Ga., 1967-69, Woodberry Forest (Va.) Sch., 1969-74; asst. prof. edn. U. Ariz., Tucson,

1974-80; prof. East Tex. State U., Commerce, 1980—; dir. programs in reading edn. East Tex. State U., 1980-86, 91-92; dir. Tex. Ctr. Learning Styles, 1989-95; bd. dirs. Nat. Learning Styles Network, 1991-95. Coauthor: Reading and Learning in Content Classrooms, 1978, 2d rev. edit., 1985, Reading and Reasoning Beyond The Primary Grades, 1986. Bd. govs. Sancta Sophia Sem., 1991—. Mem. ASCD, Nat. Reading Conf., Internat. Reading Assn., Internat. Inst. Integral Human Scis., Agni Yoga Soc. Universalist. Avocations: spiritual sci. studies, golf, travel, reading. Home: PO Box 280126 Dallas TX 75228 Office: East Tex State U 2600 Motley Dr Mesquite TX 75150

VAUGHAN, JOSEPH ROBERT, lawyer; b. Los Angeles, Jan. 28, 1916; s. Vincent B. and Lucile (Eichler) V.; m. Margaret Koetters, Jan. 20, 1940; children: Barbara (Sister Kieran, CSJ), Christine, Judith (Sister Judith Marie, CSJ). A.B., Loyola U., 1937, J.D., 1939. Bar: Calif. 1939. Mem. firm Vaughan, Brandlin, Robinson & Roemer, 1939-65; v.p. finance Knudsen Creamery Co. of Calif., Los Angeles, 1965; exec. v.p. Knudsen Creamery Co. of Calif., 1965-69; pres. Knudsen Corp., 1969-71, pres., chief exec. officer, 1971-77, chmn., pres., 1977-78, chmn. bd., 1979-80; bd. dirs. Dominguez Water Co., 1983-91, Fed. Res. Bank of San Francisco, 1973-84, chmn. L.A. br., 1974-77, Carson Estate Co., 1981-89. Bd. dirs. Los Angeles Beautiful, 1957-65, fin. chmn. 1980; trustee Pacific Legal Found., 1973-85; trustee Mt. St. Mary's Coll., 1979-83, regent, 1983—; bd. dirs. Daniel Freeman Hosp., 1955-65, sec., 1956-60, pres., 1963-65; bd. dirs. Nat. Dairy Coun., 1972-81, vice chmn., 1978-81; bd. visitors Loyola Law Sch., 1978-90, chmn., 1978-79; bd. regents Loyola Marymount U., 1973-79; bd. dirs. Tom and Valley Knudsen Found., 1954—, pres., 1971—; bd. dirs. Fritz B. Burns Found., 1986—, William H. Hannon Found., 1989—, Dominguez Hills Found., Calif. State U., 1990-94, Kirk Mayer, Inc., 1992-94. Mem. Calif. State Bar Assn., Inst. Corp. Counsel (gov. 1981-85), Los Angeles C. of C. (gov. 1971-73). Home: 404 Lorraine Blvd Los Angeles CA 90020-4730 Office: 1434 Hilton Ctr 900 Wilshire Blvd Los Angeles CA 90017-4701

VAUGHAN, KIRK WILLIAM, banker; b. St. Louis, Oct. 16, 1943; s. William Edward and Daisy Lenore (Coates) V.; m. Barbara Jean Aaron, Mar. 7, 1986; children: William Aaron, Michael Bartlett. BA, Baker U., 1966. Field sales mgr. Ford Motor Co., Richmond, Va., 1967-73; exec. v.p. United Mo. Bank of Kansas City, 1973—. Editor: The Best of Bill Vaughan, 1979. Republican. Roman Catholic. Home: 800 W 54th St Kansas City MO 64112-2330 Office: United Mo Bank Kansas City 1010 Grand Ave Kansas City MO 64106-2220

VAUGHAN, LINDA, publishing executive. Pub. Soap Opera Digest, N.Y.C. Office: Soap Opera Digest 888 7th Ave New York NY 10106*

VAUGHAN, MARTHA, biochemist; b. Dodgeville, Wis., Aug. 4, 1926; d. John Anthony and Luciel (Ellingen) V.; m. Jack Orloff, Aug. 4, 1951 (dec. Dec. 1988); children: Jonathan Michael, David Geoffrey, Gregory Joshua. Ph.B., U. Chgo., 1944; M.D., Yale U., 1949. Intern New Haven Hosp., Conn., 1950-51; research fellow U. Pa., Phila., 1951-52; research fellow Nat. Heart Inst., Bethesda, Md., 1952-54, mem. research staff, 1954-68; head metabolism sect. Nat. Heart and Lung Inst., Bethesda, 1968-74; acting chief molecular disease br. Nat. Heart, Lung and Blood Inst., Bethesda, 1974-76, chief cell metabolism lab., 1974-94; dep. chief pulmonary and critical care medicine br. Nat. Heart, Lung, and Blood Inst., Bethesda, 1994—; mem. metabolism study sect. NIH, 1965-68; mem. bd. sci. counselors Nat. Inst. Alcohol Abuse and Alcoholism, 1988-91. Mem. editl. bd.: Jour. Biol. Chemistry, 1971-76, 80-83, 88-90, assoc. editor, 1992—; editl. adv. bd.: Molecular Pharmacology, 1972-80, Biochemistry, 1989-94; ditor: Biochemistry and Biophysics Rsch. Comms., 1990-91; contbr. articles to profl. jours., chpts. to books. Bd. dirs. Found. Advanced Edn. in Scis., Inc., Bethesda, 1979-92, exec. com., 1980-92, treas., 1984-86, v.p., 1986-88, pres., 1988-90; mem. Yale U. Coun. com. med. affairs, New Haven, 1974-80. Recipient Meritorious Service medal HEW, 1974, Disting. Service medal HEW, 1979, Commd. Officer award USPHS, 1982. Mem. NAS, Am. Acad. Arts and Scis., Am. Soc. Biol. Chemists (chmn. pub. com. 1984-86), Assn. Am. Physicians, Am. Soc. Clin. Investigation. Home: 11608 W Hill Dr Rockville MD 20852-3751 Office: Nat Heart Lung & Blood Inst NIH Bldg 10 Rm 5N-307 Bethesda MD 20892

VAUGHAN, ODIE FRANK, oil company executive; b. Camden, Ark., Feb. 3, 1936; s. Odie Frank and Bernece (May) V.; m. Sandra Beard, Sept. 8, 1962; children: Christopher Michael, Laura Elizabeth. Student, So. State U. 1954-55; BS in Acctg., La. Tech. U., 1959. Acct. Peat, Marwick, Mitchell & Co., Dallas, 1959-61; asst. v.p., dir. tax Murphy Oil Corp., El Dorado, Ark., 1962-72, treas., 1972—; v.p., treas. Ocean Drilling and Exploration Co., New Orleans, 1973-91. Mem. AICPA, Am. Petroleum Inst. (gen. tax com.), Fin. Execs. Inst., Tax Execs. Inst. Baptist. Home: 1700 N Calion Rd El Dorado AR 71730-3420 Office: Murphy Oil Corp 200 Peach St El Dorado AR 71730

VAUGHAN, PETER HUGH, theater critic; b. Oxford, Eng., Dec. 12, 1937; children: Rachel V., Thomas Hugh, Jeremy P. BA, Yale U., 1959; LLB, London U., 1963. With Mpls. Star Tribune, 1965—, theater critic, 1974—. Mem. French-Am. Theatrical Friendship Soc. Montrichard (founding), John Falstaff Eating and Drinking Ensemble of Otisville. Avocations: travel, reading, tennis, cooking, gun control. Office: Star Tribune 425 Portland Ave Minneapolis MN 55488

VAUGHAN, ROLAND, church administrator. Dir. Ch. of God World Missions. Office: Ch of God World Missions PO Box 8016 Cleveland TN 37320-8016

VAUGHAN, SAMUEL SNELL, editor, author; b. Phila., Aug. 3, 1928; s. Joseph and Anna Catherine (Alexander) V.; m. Jo LoBiondo, Oct. 22, 1949; children: Jeffrey Marc, Leslie Jane, Dana Alexander, David Samuel. B.A., Pa. State U., 1951. Deskman King Features Syndicate, N.Y.C., 1951; asst. mgr. Doubleday Syndicate, 1952-54; advt. mgr. Doubleday & Co., Inc., N.Y.C., 1954-56; sales mgr., 1956-58, sr. editor, 1958-68; exec. editor Doubleday & Co., Inc., 1969-70, pub., pres. pub. div., 1970-82, v.p. parent co., 1970-86, editor in chief, 1982-86; sr. v.p., editor Random House, Inc., 1986-90; editor-at-large Random House, Inc., Wm. Morrow Co., 1990—; mem. faculty dept. English, Columbia U., 1978-88; lectr. Harvard U., Libr. Congress, U. Denver, Bowker meml. lectr. Author: (juvenile) Whoever Heard of Kangaroo Eggs? 1957, New Shoes, 1961, The Two-Thirty Bird, 1965, (history) The Little Church, 1969, Medium Rare: A Look at the Book and Its People, 1977, (humor) Little Red Hood, 1979; prin. author: The Accidental Profession, 1979, The Community of the Book, 1983, The State of the Heart, 1985; contbr. to N.Y. Times, Sunday Times of London, Daedalus, Am. Heritage, others. Served with USMC, 1946-48. Named Disting. Alumnus Pa. State U., 1977, Alumni fellow, 1981. Mem. Tenafly Tennis Club, Quantuck Beach Club (Westhampton, N.Y.), Century Assn. Episcopalian. Home: 23 Inness Rd Tenafly NJ 07670-2714 Office: c/o Random House 201 E 50th St New York NY 10022-7703

VAUGHAN, SUSAN CAROLE, psychiatrist, psychoanalyst; b. Houston, Dec. 22, 1963; d. Chester Austin and Norma Leigh (Hill) V. BA in Psychology magna cum laude, Harvard U., 1985; MD, Columbia U., 1989. Diplomate Nat. Bd. Med. Examiners. Transitional intern St. Vincent's Hosp., N.Y.C., 1989-90; resident in psychiatry N.Y. State Psychiat. Inst., Columbia-Presbyn. Hosp., N.Y.C., 1990-92, chief resident, 1992-93, Am. Psychiat. Assn.-Lilly rsch. fellow, 1993-94, psychiatrist homebound elderly program, 1992-93, instr. clin. psychiatry, asst. psychiatrist, 1993—, attending psychiatrist McKeen Behavioral and Allen pavilions, 1993—, attending psychiatrist psychiat. emergency room, 1993—; rsch. fellow in Affective and Anxiety Disorders NYSPI, N.Y.C., 1993—; candidate Columbia U. Ctr. for Psychoanalytic Tng. and Rsch., 1993—. mem. rsch. com., 1992—; staff psychiatrist Barnard Coll.; cons. psychiatry Hunter Coll., CUNY; presenter in field. Contbr. articles to profl. jours. Mem. Am. Psychiat. Assn. (dist. br. resident's com. 1990-92, area II bull. editl. bd. 1992—), Soc. for Psychotherapy Rsch., Am. Psychoanalytic Assn. (com. on homosexuality 1993—), Assn. for Psychoanalytic Medicine, Am. Assn. Med. Colls. (orgn. resident reps. 1991—, chmn. task force on residents at tchrs. 1992—). Avocations: rowing, bicycling, theater, reading, gardening. Office: 25 W 81st St Ste 1C New York NY 10024-6023

VAUGHAN, THOMAS JAMES GREGORY, historian; b. Seattle, Oct. 13, 1924; s. Daniel George and Kathryn Genevieve (Browne) V.; m. Elizabeth Ann Perpetua Crownhart, June 16, 1951; children: Meagan, Margot, Stephen, Cameron. BA, Yale U., 1948; MS, U. Wis., 1950, doctoral residence, 1951-53; LittD, Pacific U., 1969; LLD, Reed Coll., 1975. Exec. dir. Oreg. Hist. Soc., Portland, 1954-90; editor in chief Oreg. Hist. Quar., 1954-89; adj. prof. Portland State U., 1968—; chmn. bd. Salar Enterprises, Ltd.; bd. dirs. Am. Heritage Pub. Co., 1976-85; film producer, 1958-76; historian laureate State of Oreg., 1989. Author: A Century of Portland Architecture, 1967, Captain Cook, R.N, The Resolute Mariner: An International Record of Oceanic Discovery, 1974, Portland, A Historical Sketch and Guide, 1976, 2d edit., 1983, Voyage of Enlightenment: Malaspina on the Northwest Coast, 1977; editor: Space, Style and Structure: Building in Northwest America, 2 vols., 1974, The Western Shore, 1975, Ascent of the Athabasca Pass, 1978, Wheels of Fortune, High and Mighty, 1981, Soft Gold, 1982, 2d edit., 1990, To Siberia and Russian America, Vols. I, II and III, also others.; co-editor: Siberica, 1989; mem. adv. bd. Am. Heritage Mag., 1977-90; prodr. film The Crimean War, 1994. 1st chmn. Oreg. State Com. for Humanities, NEH, 1969—; 1st chmn. Gov.'s Adv. Com. on Historic Preservation Oreg., 1970-77; sec. Oreg. Geog. Names Bd., 1958-89; adviser 1000 Friends of Oreg., 1972—; lay mem. Oreg. State Bar Disciplinary Rev. Bd., 1975-82; vice chmn. adv. panel Nat. Endowment Arts, 1975—; mem. Nat. Hist. Publs. and Records Commn. Matrix, 1975-76; historian laureate State of Oreg., 1989. With USMC, 1942-45. Decorated comdr. Order Brit. Empire; recipient Aubrey Watzek award Lewis and Clark Coll., 1975;, Edith Knight Hill award, 1977, Disting. Svc. award U. Oreg.; grantee English Speaking Union, 1961; Columbia Maritime Mus. 1st rsch. fellow, 1992. Fellow Royal Geog. Soc.; mem. Am. Assn. State and Local History (bd. dirs. 1955-74, pres. 1976-78), Am. Assn. Mus. (coun., exec. com.), Nat. Trust Hist. Preservation (adv. coun.), Ctr. for Study Russian Am., Russian Acad. Scis., City Club (Portland, bd. govs.), Univ. Club (Portland, bd. govs.), The Arts Club (London). Home: 2135 SW Laurel St Portland OR 97201-2367

VAUGHAN, WILLIAM WALTON, atmospheric scientist; b. Clearwater, Fla., Sept. 7, 1930; s. William Walton and Ella Vermelle (Warr) V.; m. Wilma Geraldine Stapleton, Dec. 23, 1951; children: Stephen W., David A., William D., Robert T. BS with honors, U. Fla., 1951; grad. cert., USAF Inst. Tech./Fla. State U., 1952; PhD, U. Tenn., 1976. Sci. asst. Air Force Armament Center, Eglin AFB, Fla., 1955-58; Army Ballistic Missile Agy., Huntsville, Ala., 1958-60; chief aerospace environ. div. Marshall Space Flight Center, NASA, Huntsville, 1960-76; chief atmospheric scis. div. Marshall Space Flight Center, NASA, 1976-86; rsch. prof. atmospheric sci. U. Ala., Huntsville, 1986-94, dir. Rsch. Inst., 1986-94; retired, 1994; cons. atmospheric sci.; mem. adv. com. NASA. Contbr. articles to profl. jours. Served to capt. USAF, 1951-55. Recipient Exceptional Service medal NASA, 1971. Assoc. fellow AIAA (Losey Atmospheric Scis. award 1980); fellow Am. Meterol. Soc.; mem. AAAS, Am. Geophys. Union, Sigma Xi. Office: U Ala Atmospheric/Environ Sci Program Huntsville AL 35899

VAUGHAN, WORTH EDWARD, chemistry educator; b. N.Y.C., Feb. 1, 1936; s. Royal Worth and Sylvia Marie (Fernholz) V.; m. Diane Marilyn Mayer, Aug. 9, 1969; 1 child, Wayne John. B.A., Oberlin Coll., 1957; M.A., Princeton U., 1959, Ph.D., 1960. Asst. prof. chemistry U. Wis.-Madison, 1961-66, assoc. prof., 1967-76, prof., 1977—; mem. bd. advisors Am. Exchange Bank West Br., Madison, 1983-87. Author: Dielectric Properties and Molecular Behavior, 1969; editor: Digest of Literature on Dielectrics, 1974; translation editor: Dipole Moments of Organic Compounds, 1970; contbr. articles to profl. jours. Mem. Am. Chem. Soc. (pres. Wis. sect. 1968), Am. Phys. Soc., AAAS, Phi Beta Kappa, Sigma Xi, Alpha Chi Sigma. Avocations: canoeing, contract bridge. Home: 501 Ozark Trl Madison WI 53705-2538 Office: Univ Wis 1101 University Ave Madison WI 53706-1396

VAUGHN, DONALD CHARLES, international engineering and construction company executive; b. McPherson, Kans., Mar. 21, 1936; s. Vernon (dec.) and Ramona Vaughn; m. Moira Lynch Provan; children: James, Sandra Vaughn Cornwell, Connie Vaughn Ohman. BSCE, Va. Poly. Inst., 1958. Registered profl. engr., Tex. Field engr. The M.W. Kellogg Co., Houston, 1958-59, from constrn. supt. to pres., 1961-83; pres. M.W. Kellogg Co., Houston, 1983—; exec. v.p. ops. Rust Internat. Corp., Birmingham, Ala., 1982-83; pres. M.W. Kellogg Constructors, Inc., Houston, 1980-82; past chmn. adv. com. Eximbank, Export-Import Bank of the U.S.; bd. dirs. Cen. Houston, Inc. Mem. Bus. Arts Fund of Houston; mem. Va. Poly. Inst. Com. for Excellence. Mem. Tex. Engring. Soc., Turkish-U.S. Bus. Coun. (former chmn.), Greater Houston Partnership (sr. rep.), Tex. Research League (sr. rep.), U.S.C. of C. (internat. policy com.), 25 Yr. Club Petroleum Industry, Nat. Constructors Assn. (past mem. adv. bd., chmn., vice chmn.), Va. Polytech 100, Houston City Club, Heritage Club, Coronado Club, Houston Met. Club, Chi Epsilon. Office: M W Kellogg Co 601 Jefferson St Houston TX 77002-4557

VAUGHN, ELEANOR, state legislator; b. Troy, Idaho, Nov. 12, 1922; m. Benjamin Vaughn Sr.; 3 children. Grad., Kinman Bus. U. Mem. Mont. Senate. Democrat. Home: 251 Mahoney Rd PO Box 45 Libby MT 59923-2819 Office: Mont Senate State Capitol Helena MT 59620-0001

VAUGHN, GORDON E., bishop. Bishop of Western Pa. Ch. of God in Christ, Pitts. Office: Ch of God in Christ 6437 Stanton Ave Pittsburgh PA 15206-2248

VAUGHN, GREGORY LAMONT, professional baseball player; b. Sacramento, July 3, 1965. Student, Sacramento City Coll., Miami Coll. Player Milw. Brewers, 1986—; mem. Am. League All-Star Team, 1993. Named Midwest co-MVP, 1987, Am. Assn. MVP, 1989. Office: Milw Brewers Milw County Stadium PO Box 3099 Milwaukee WI 53215*

VAUGHN, JACKIE, III, state legislator. BA, Hillsdale (Mich.) Coll.; MA, Oberlin (Ohio) Coll.; LittB, Oxford U.; LLD (hon.) Marygrove Coll., Detroit, Shaw Coll., Detroit; HHD (hon.), Highland Park (Mich.) Community Coll. Tchr. U. Detroit, Wayne State U., Detroit, 1963-64; mem. Mich. Ho. of Reps., Lansing, 1966-78; mem. Mich. Senate, Lansing, 1978—, asst. pres. pro tem, 1978-82, pres. pro tem, 1982-86, assoc. pres. pro tem, 1986—; Past pres. Mich. Young Dems.; chmn. Mich. Dr. Martin Luther King Jr. Holiday commn.; exec. bd. dirs. Detroit NAACP. With USN. Fulbright fellow; recipient Frank J. Wieting Meml. Service award, 1977, Focus and Impact award Cotillion Club, 1980, Outstanding Achievement award Booker T. Washington Bus. Assn., Outstanding Community Service award Charles Stewart Mott Community Coll. and Urban Coalition of Greater Flint, Mich.; 1981; named Outstanding State Senator of Yr., Detroit Urban League Guild, 1983, Most Outstanding Legislator of Yr., Washburn-Ilene Block Club, 1983, numerous others. Mem. Am. Oxonian Assn., Fulbright Alumni Assn. Baptist. Home: 19930 Roslyn Rd Detroit MI 48221-1853 Office: Mich Senate PO Box 30036 Lansing MI 48909-7536

VAUGHN, JAMES T., former state police officer, state senator; b. Cheswold, Del., Apr. 12, 1925; s. Charles Townsend and Ada (Van Pelt) V.; m. Sylvia Harris, Nov. 12, 1947; children—James T., Robert G., Judith A. Student schs. Smyrna, Del. Policeman, Del. State Police, 1944-66; with Vaughn Law Office, Dover, Del., 1966-76; commr. Dept. Corrections, Del., 1976-79; chief probation dept. Smyrna, 1980; mem. Del. Senate, 1980—. Mgr., coach Smyrna-Clayton Little League, 1957-91; mem. Bd. Edn., Smyrna, 1966-81. Served with USMC, 1943-46. Mem. F.B.I. Nat. Acad., Del. Assn. Chiefs of Police, Am. Legion, VFW. Democrat. Methodist. Lodge: Masons. Office: Del State Senate Legis Hall Dover DE 19901

VAUGHN, JOHN ROLLAND, auditor; b. Iola, Kans., Aug. 4, 1938; s. Ralph H. and Aldie (Dille) V.; m. Doris K. Black; Sept. 4, 1960; children: Lisa Ann, Brian Douglas. BS in Bus, Emporia State U., 1960. Sr. auditor Arthur Andersen & Co., Kansas City, Mo., 1961-66; auditor First Nat. Bank Kansas City, 1966-69, Commerce Bancshares, Inc., 1969-73; sr. v.p. Adminstrv. Services div. Peoples Trust Bank, Ft. Wayne, Ind., 1973-77; dep. gen. auditor, v.p. Crocker Nat. Bank, San Francisco, 1978-79; v.p., gen. auditor S.W. Bancshares, Houston, 1980-83; v.p., gen. auditor MCorp., Houston, 1984-87, mng. dir., 1988-89; audit dir. Banc One Corp., Dallas, 1990-92; v.p., gen. auditor St. Paul Cos., St. Paul, 1992—. Treas. Overland Park (Kans.) Jr. C. of C., 1965-66; outside dir. Overland Park Credit Union; controller Fort Wayne Bicentennial Commn., 1974-77. Mem. Mo. Air N.G.,

1961-67. Mem. Inst. Internal Auditors (1st v.p. Kansas City 1969-70, pres. 1970-71, midwest regional v.p. 1971-72, Twin Cities chpt. gov. 1993-94, pres. 1994—), Fin. Execs. Inst. (dir. Ft. Wayne 1976-77), Risk and Ins. Mgmt. Soc., Hartsmen, Soc. Preservation and Encouragement Barber Shop Quartet Singing in Am., Vocal Majority Chorus, Gt. No. Union Chorus, Sigma Tau Gamma. Home: 8986 Hunters Trl Woodbury MN 55125-8667 Office: 385 Washington St Saint Paul MN 55102-1309

VAUGHN, JOHN VERNON, banker, industrialist; b. Grand Junction, Colo., June 24, 1909; s. John S. and Alice Ann (Baylis) V.; m. Dorothy May Pickrell, Oct. 12, 1934; children: Dorothy (Mrs. Richard H. Stone), John Spencer. AB, UCLA, 1932; LLD (hon.), Pepperdine U., 1974. Br. mgr. Nat. Lead Co., 1932-37; sales mgr. Sillers Paint & Varnish Co., 1937-46, pres., gen. mgr., dir., 1946-58; pres., chmn. Dartell Labs., Inc., 1959-70; vice chmn. bd. Crocker Nat. Bank and Crocker Nat. Corp., San Francisco, 1970-75; dir. Crocker Nat. Bank and Crocker Nat. Corp., 1969-85; hon. dir. Crocker Nat. Bank; cons. Coopers & Lybrand, 1975-85; chmn. bd. Recon Optical, Inc., 1979-90; bd. dirs. Trust Svcs. Am., Forest Lawn Corp., Am. Security & Fidelity Corp.; IT Corp. Chmn. San Marino Recreation Commn., 1956-58, La. Better Bus. Bur., 1959-61, Invest-in-Am., 1970-73; chmn. citizen's adv. Council Pub. Trans., 1965-67; commr. Los Angeles Coliseum Commn., 1971-74; trustee Calif. Mus. Found., 1968-79; bd. dirs. Orthopaedic Hosp., 1965-87, pres., 1974-78, chmn. bd., 1978-79; bd. dirs. YMCA, Los Angeles, 1965-77, Central City Assn., So. Calif. Visitors Council, 1970-76, NCCJ, Calif. Museum Sci. and Industry, United Way of Los Angeles, Am. Heart Assn.; mem. Los Angeles Adv. Bd., Friends of Claremont Coll., 1973-78, Los Angeles Beautiful, 1972-74; regent U. Calif., 1958-59; hon. trustee UCLA Found., 1967—, Forest Lawn Meml. Park, 1968—, Claremont Men's Coll., 1970-71, Pepperdine U., 1972—; regent, mem. bd. visitors Grad. Sch. Bus. Adminstrn. UCLA, 1971-85; mem. Chancellor's Assocs., Calif. State Univs. and Colls. Recipient Disting. Svc. award UCLA, 1965, Outstanding Community Svc. award UCLA, , 1970, Alumnus of Yr. UCLA award, 1971; Brotherhood award NCCJ, 1971; Los Angeles Jaycees award of merit, 1972; Most Disting. Citizen Los Angeles Realty Bd., 1972; other honors. Mem. Los Angeles Area C. of C. (bd. dirs. 1961, pres. 1969, chmn. 1970), World Affairs Coun. (chpt. v.p., treas. 1970-85, hon. dir. 1985—), Iranian-Am. Chamber Industry and Commerce (pres. 1971-79), Paint, Varnish and Lacquer Assn. (past nat. v.p., past chpt. pres.), Town Hall Calif. (dir. 1973-75), Young Pres.'s Orgn., Jonathan Club (pres. 1964), Los Angeles Country Club (bd. dirs. 1979-85), California Club, San Gabriel Country Club (bd. dirs. 1964-68), Valley Hunt Club, Pasadena Athletic Club, Bohemian Club of San Francisco, Internat. Order St. Hubertus, Masons, Beta Theta Pi (pres. 1960). Republican. Presbyterian. Avocations: fishing, hunting, golf. Home and Office: 454 S Orange Grove Blvd Pasadena CA 91105-1707

VAUGHN, KAREN IVERSEN, economics educator; b. N.Y.C., July 21, 1944; d. Willy and Cecelia (Douglas) Iversen; m. Garrett Alan Vaughn, Sept. 7, 1968; 1 child, Jessica Susan. BA, Queens Coll. CUNY, 1966; MA, Duke U., 1969, PhD, 1971. Asst. prof. U. Tenn., Knoxville, 1969-75; assoc. prof. George Mason U., Fairfax, Va., 1978-84, chmn. dept. econs., 1982-89, prof. econs., 1984—; sr. rsch. asssoc. Ctr. for Study Market Processes, 1981-92; adj. scholar CATO Inst., Washington, 1982-90. Author: John Locke: Economist and Social Scientist, 1980, Austrian Economics in America: The Migration of a Tradition, 1994; editor: Perspectives on the History of Economic Thought, vol. 10, 1994; mem. editorial bd. History of Polit. Economy Jour., 1984-88, Jour. of History of Economic Thought, 1993—; editor: HES Bull., 1978-84; contbr. articles to profl. jours. NDEA fellow, 1966-69. Mem. So. Econs. Assn. (exec. com. 1978-80, v.p. 1986-87, pres.-elect 1993-94, pres. 1994—), Am. Econs. Assn., History of Econs. Soc. (v.p. 1988-89, pres.-elect 1991-92, pres. 1992-93), Mont Pelerin Soc. Avocations: piano, choral singing. Office: George Mason U Dept Economics 4400 University Dr Fairfax VA 22030-4443

VAUGHN, MAURICE SAMUEL (MO VAUGHN), professional baseball player; b. Norwalk, Conn., Dec. 15, 1967. Student, Seton Hall U., 1987-89. Infielder Boston Red Sox, 1989—. Active cmty. svc. with youth groups, Boston. Office: Boston Red Sox 4 Yawkey Way Boston MA 02215*

VAUGHN, ROBERT (FRANCIS VAUGHN), actor; b. N.Y.C., Nov. 22, 1932; s. Walter and Marcella Vaughn; m. Linda Staab, 1974; children: Caitlin, Cassidy. BS in Theatre Arts, Los Angeles State Coll., MA in Theatre Arts, 1956; PhD in Communications, U. So. Calif., 1970. Appeared in local Calif. stage prodn. End as a Man, then small roles in several motion pictures; appeared as Napoleon Solo on TV series: The Man From U.N.C.L.E, 1964-67; star TV series Emerald Point NAS, 1983-84; appeared in motion pictures Hell's Crossroads, 1957, No Time to be Young, 1957, Unwed Mother, 1958, Good Day for a Hanging, 1959, The Young Philadelphians, 1959 (Acad. Motion Picture Arts and Scis. nomination 1960), The City Jungle, The Big Show, 1961, The Caretakers, 1963, To Trap a Spy, 1966, The Spy With My Face, 1966, One Spy Too Many, 1966, The Venetian Affair, 1967, How to Steal a Million, The Bridge at Remagen, 1969, If It's Tuesday, This Must Be Belgium, 1969, The Clay Pigeon, The Towering Inferno, 1974, Bullitt, 1968, The Mind of Mr. Soames, 1970, The Assassination of Julius Caesar, The Statue, 1971, The Magnificent 7, 1960, Brass Target, 1978, Battle Beyond the Stars, 1980, Virus, 1980, Cuba Crossing, 1980, Hangar 18, 1981, S.O.B, 1981, Superman III, 1983, The Delta Force, 1986, Black Moon Rising, 1986, Delta Force, 1986, Hour of the Assassin, 1987, River of Death, 1989, Nobody's Perfect, 1990, That's Adequate, 1990; appeared as Hamlet at Pasadena Playhouse, 1964; star one-man play F.D.R. 1978; portrayed Harry Truman in TV play: The Man From Independence, 1974; Woodrow Wilson in TV movie: Backstairs at the White House, 1979; appeared in TV mini-series Washington: Behind Closed Doors, 1977 (Emmy award), The Blue and the Gray, 1984, Evergreen, 1985, Centennial, 1978-79; TV movies include: The Greatest Heroes of the Bible, 1978, The Rebels, 1979, The Gossip Columnist, 1980, International Airport, 1985, Private Sessions, 1985; author: Only Victims, 1972. Former chmn. registration and Speaker's Bur., Calif. Democratic Com. Mem. Am. Acad. Polit. and Social Scis. Democrat. Roman Catholic. Address: care Agy for Performing Arts 9000 Sunset Blvd Ste 1200 Los Angeles CA 90069*

VAUGHN, ROBERT LOCKARD, aerospace and astronautics company executive; b. Rochester, N.Y., Sept. 19, 1922; s. Henry Clifford and Belva Blanche (Lockard) V.; m. Virginia Ethel Harness, June 19, 1943; children—Sandra Sue, Roberta Jean, Larry Lockard, Virginia Gail. B.S. in M.E, Iowa State U. Sci. and Tech., 1952; MS in Tech. Adminstrv. Mgmt., Calif. State U., Northridge, 1967. Registered profl. engr., Calif. Journeyman Washington Naval Gun Factory, 1940-49; lab. technician U.S. AEC, Ames (Iowa) Lab., 1949-52; with Lockheed Corp., 1953-88; corp. dir. productivity Lockheed Missiles & Space Co., Inc., Sunnyvale, Calif., 1977-88; pres. R.L. Vaughn & Assoc., Cons. Engrs., Ramona, Calif., 1988—. Contbr. over 140 articles to tech. jours. and other publications. With AUS, World War II, ETO. Recipient Calif. State Legis. Resolution award, 1982; various other awards. Fellow ASME (Internat. Gold Medal award 1969), Soc. Mfg. Engrs., Inst. Advancement of Engring., Instn. Prodn. Engrs.; mem. San Fernando Valley Engrs. Council (past pres., dir.), Calif. Soc. Profl. Engrs. (past pres., dir. San Fernando Valley chpt.; Outstanding Service award 1972, 73, 76), Nat. Mgmt. Assn. (Internat. award for mfg. excellence 1983, McGraw-Hill Am.), Am. Soc. Metals, Am. Assn. Engring. Socs. (bd. govs., dir.), Fedn. Materials Socs. (past trustee), Soc. Mfg. Engrs. (past pres., dir.). Patentee in field. Home: 23635 Barona Mesa Rd Ramona CA 92065-4339

VAUGHN, RUFUS MAHLON, psychiatrist; b. Ensley, Ala., Oct. 31, 1924; s. Rufus Samuel and Anna Martina (Fink) V.; children: Stephen Andrew, Alexander. Student, U. Mich., 1942-43, 46-47; AB, Birmingham So. Coll., 1949; MD, Med. Coll. ala., 1953. Diplomate Am. Bd. Psychiatry and Neurology, Am. Bd. Forensic Psychiatry. Intern USPHS Hosp., San Francisco, 1953-54; resident in psychiatry Ind. U. Hosp., Indpls., 1954-56, U. Calif. Hosp., L.A., 1956-57; dir. psychiatry Student Health Svc., U. Mass., Amherst, 1958-59; researcher Boston State Hosp., 1959-61; assoc. prof. psychiatry U. Fla., Gainesville, 1961-70; dir. Palm Beach County Mental Health Ctr., West Palm Beach, Fla., 1970-71; med. dir. Lake Hosp. and Clinic, Lake Worth, Fla., 1971-73; dir. tng., rsch. So. Fla. State Hosp., Hollywood, 1973-74, supt., 1974; chief Bur. Mental Hosp. Svcs., Fla. Div. Mental Health, Tallahassee, 1974-75; pvt. practice medicine specializing in forensic psychiatry West Palm Beach, 1975-87; sr. physician No. Fla. Evalu-

ation and Treatment Ctr., Gainesville, 1982-89; clin. prof. psychiatry U. Miami, 1973-75; med. dir. USPHS Res., 1980—; clin. assoc. prof. psychiatry U. Fla., 1983—; med. dir. Mental Health Svcs. Inc., Gainesville, Fla., 1989-94, cons., 1994—. With USNR, 1943-46. Home: 1205 NW 35th Ave Gainesville FL 32609-2112 Office: 4300 SW 13th St Gainesville FL 32608-4006

VAUGHN, WILLIAM PRESTON, historian, educator; b. East Chicago, Ind., May 28, 1933; s. James Carl and Georgiana (Preston) V.; m. Virginia Lee Meyer, June 10, 1961; 1 child, Rhonda Louise. AB, U. Mo., Columbia, 1955; MA, Ohio State U., 1956, PhD, 1961. Instr. in history U. So. Calif., 1961-62; asst. prof. history U. N. Tex., Denton, 1962-65, assoc. prof., 1965-69, prof., 1969-91; instr. Tex. Project, Malaysia, 1986, 88. Author: Schools for All: The Blacks and Public Education in the South, 1865-77, 1974, The Antimasonic Party in the United States, 1826-43, 1983; editor Transactions Tex. Lodge of Rsch., 1988—; contbr. numerous articles on black edn. masonry and polit. antimasonry to profl. jours. With arty. U.S. Army, 1956-57. Mem. SAR, So. Hist. Assn. (life), Historians Early Am. Republic, Kiwanis, Masons, Phi Beta Kappa, Phi Alpha Theta (Manuscript Competition winner 1972), Phi Delta Kappa, Phi Beta Delta. Republican. Episcopalian. Home: 908 Hilton Pl Denton TX 76201-8606

VAUGHN, WILLIAM WEAVER, lawyer; b. Los Angeles, Aug. 29, 1930; s. William Weaver and Josephine (Sweigert) V.; m. Claire Louise M'Closkey, June 2, 1962; children: Robert, Gregory, Elizabeth, Anthony, Christina, James. B.A., Stanford U., 1952; LL.B., UCLA, 1955. Bar: Calif. 1956. Mem. O'Melveny & Myers, L.A., 1955-56, 57—, ptnr., 1964—; mem. adv. group U.S. Dist. Ct. (ctrl. dist.) Calif. 1991-93, L.A. Area alt. dispute resolution panel Ctr. for Pub. Resources, 1988—. Served with U.S. Army, 1956-57. Recipient Learned Hand award Am. Jewish Com., 1991. Fellow Am. Coll. Trial Lawyers (bd. regents 1992-95); mem. L.A. County Bar Assn. (trustee 1976-78, 80-82), L.A. County Bar Found. (bd. dirs. 1991-95), Assn. Bus. Trial Lawyers (bd. govs. 1980-82), Order of Coif. Clubs: California (Los Angeles), Chancery (Los Angeles). Office: O'Melveny & Myers 400 S Hope St Los Angeles CA 90071

VAUSE, EDWIN HAMILTON, research foundation administrator; b. Chgo., Mar. 30, 1923; s. Harry Russell and Sylvia Clair (Webster) V.; m. Harriet Evelyn Oestmann, June 30, 1951; children—Karen L., Russell E., Kurt H., Dirk C., Luke E. B.S., U. Ill., 1947, M.S., 1948; M.B.A., U. Chgo., 1952; D.Sc. (hon.), U. Evansville, 1977. Registered profl. engr., Ill., Ind. Engr., research dept. Standard Oil Co., Ind., 1948-52; asst. gen. foreman mfg. dept. Standard Oil Co., 1952-57; dir. research adminstrn. Mead Johnson & Co., Evansville, Ind., 1957-60; v.p. Charles F. Kettering Found., Dayton, Ohio, 1960-66; v.p., adminstrn. dir. Charles F. Kettering Found., 1966-67, exec. v.p., 1967-71, v.p. for sci. and tech., 1971-88; trustee The Found. Center, 1967-73; mem. adv. com. Acad. Forum, Nat. Acad. Scis. Vice-pres. Washington Twp. Bd. Edn., 1963-67; mem. Centerville-Washington Twp. Joint Planning Commn., 1967-80; mem. adv. bd. Center for Students Rights, Dayton, 1966-70; active Boy Scouts Am. Mem. Am. Inst. Chem. Engrs. (past chmn. Chgo. sect.), N.Y. Acad. Scis., Agrl. Research Inst., Nat. Industry State Agrl. Research Council. Republican. Lutheran. Clubs: Elks, Kiwanis (past pres.), Masons. Home: 11834 Calle Parral San Diego CA 92128-4534

VAUX, HENRY JAMES, forest economist, educator; b. Bryn Mawr, Pa., Nov. 6, 1912; s. George and Mary (James) V.; m. Jean Macduff, Jan. 11, 1937; children: Henry J., Alice J. B.S., Haverford Coll., 1933, D.Sc. (hon.), 1985; M.S., U. Calif., 1935, Ph.D., 1948. Forest engr. Crown Willamette Paper Co., Portland, Oreg., 1936-37; instr. Sch. Forestry, Oreg. State Coll., Corvallis, 1937-42; assoc. economist La. Agrl. Expt. Sta., Baton Rouge, 1942-43; economist U.S. Forest Service, Berkeley, Calif. and Wash., 1946-48; lectr. Sch. Forestry, U. Calif.-Berkeley, 1948-50, assoc. prof., 1950-53, prof., 1953-78, prof. emeritus, 1978—, dean, 1955-65; asst. dir. Agrl. Expt. Sta. U. Calif., 1955-65, dir. Wildland Research Center, 1955-65; chmn. Calif. Bd. Forestry, 1976-83. Author tech. articles, bulls. Served from ensign to lt. (j.g.) USNR, 1943-46. Recipient Berkeley citation U. Calif., 1978, Disting. Service award Forestry Assn., 1986; hon. fellow Calif. Acad. Scis., 1986. Fellow AAAS, Soc. Am. Foresters (Gifford Pinchot medal 1983); mem. Forest History Soc. (dir. 1975), Sigma Xi, Xi Sigma Pi. Mem. Soc. of Friends. Home: 622 San Luis Rd Berkeley CA 94707-1726

VAVALA, DOMENIC ANTHONY, medical scientist, educator, retired air force officer; b. Providence, Feb. 1, 1925; s. Salvatore and Maria (Grenci) V. BA, Brown U., 1947; MS, U. R.I., 1950; MA, Trinity U., San Antonio, 1954; PhD in Physiology, Accademia di Studi Superiori "Minerva", Italy, 1957; MEd, U. Houston, 1958; DSc (hon.), Nobile Accademia di Santa Teodora Imperatrice, Rome, 1966, DMS (hon.), 1970; DPH (hon.), Nobile Accademia di Santa Teodora Imperatrice, 1983; D Pedagogy (hon.), Studiorum Universitas Constantiniana of Sovrano Ordine Constantiniano di San Giorgio, Rome, 1966; DEd (hon.); Imperiale Accademia di San Cirillo, Pomezia, Italy, 1977; LittD, Univ. Internazionale Sveva "Frederick II", Bergamo, Italy, 1979; D Health Scis. (hon.), Johnson & Wales U., 1993. Research asst. tumor research U. R.I., also asst. entomol. research, 1950; research asst. pharmacology Boston U. Sch. Medicine, 1950-51; commd. 2d lt. med. service USAF, 1951, advanced through grades to lt. col., 1968; physiologist cold injury research team Army Med. Research Lab., Osaka (Japan) Army Hosp., 1951-52; research aviation physiologist USAF Sch. Aviation Medicine, Randolph AFB, Tex., 1952-54, 3605th USAF Hosp., Ellington AFB, Tex., 1955-57; chief physiol. tng. 3605th USAF Hosp., 1957; cons. aviation physiology, film prodn. dept. U. Houston, 1956; research aviation physiologist, head acad. sect. dept. physiol. tng. USAF Hosp., Lackland AFB, Tex., 1957-58; vis. prof. physiology Incarnate Word Coll., San Antonio, 1958; research aviation physiologist, chief physiol. tng. comdr. 832d Physiol. Tng. Flight, 832d Tactical Hosp., Cannon AFB, N.Mex., 1958-65; adj. faculty mem. Eastern N.Mex. U., Portales, 1959-64; instr. adult edn. div. Clovis (N.Mex.) mcpl. schs., 1960; research aviation physiologist, comdr. 15th Physiol. Tng. Flight, 824th USAF Dispensary, Kadena Air Base, Okinawa, 1965-66; research scientist, directorate figh. tech., aerospace med. div. Brooks AFB, Tex., 1966-68; chief R & D support and interface div., dep. dir. for fgn. tech., 1968-70; adj. instr. Johnson & Wales U., Providence, 1973-74; instr. humanities Johnson and Wales U., Providence, 1974-75, asst. prof. humanities, 1975-77, prof. health scis., 1977-93, prof. emeritus, 1993—, coord. biomed. and behavioral scis. Day Coll. div., 1973-75, psychology coord. vets. div. Coll. Continuing Edn., 1974-76, assoc. dean adj. faculty, 1975, dean faculty, 1975-77, coord. acad. devel., 1977-78, dir. musical series, 1990—; curator Chapel Empress St. Theodora, 1992—; pres. corp., chmn. bd. Sovereign Constantinian Order of Saint George, Inc., R.I., 1986—. Writer, producer: (TV Series) Your Body in Flight, Sta. KUHT, Houston, 1956; (TV series) Highway to Health, Okinawa, 1965; editor-in-chief: NADUS Jour., 1963-85; compiled and edited: Fifty Years of Progress of Soviet Medicine, 1917-67; abstractor: Am. Chem. Soc., 1963-74. Contbr. articles to profl. jours. Trustee, Boy Scout Ctr. Rsch., Providence, 1979-85; mem. scholarship com. St. Sahag and St. Mesrob Armenian Apostolic Ch., Providence. Served with AUS, 1943-44. Recipient Disting. Service award Clovis, N.Mex. Jaycees, 1959, Academic Palms Gold medal Accademia di Studi Superiori "Minerva", 1960, citation from chief chaplains USAF, 1970, chief biomed. scientist insignia, biomed. scis. corps USAF Med. Service, 1970, spl. faculty citation Johnson and Wales Univ., 1981; academician div. scis. Accademia di Studi Superiori "Minerva", 1960; Minister Plenipotentiary for U.S. of Nobile Accademia di Santa Teodora Imperatrice, Rome, 1967, rector pro tempore, 1980, pres. R.I. corp., chmn. bd., 1988; decorated Air Force Commendation medal, 1970, Cert. of Achievement Dept. Army, 1966; decorated knight grand officer Merit Class, Sovereign Constantinian Order St. George, Rome, 1969, knight of Grand Cross with Constantinian neckchain, Justice class, Sovereign Constantinian Order of St. George, 1969, knight of Grand Cordon, Justice Class, Order of Teutonic Knights, Sao Paulo, Brazil, 1986, knigh Grand Cross Justice Class, Mil. Order St. Gereon, Sao Paulo, 1986, knight of Grand Cross, Justice Class, Mil. and Hospitaler Order St. Jean d'Acre and St. Thomas, Capua, Italy, 1987, knight Grand Cross, Justice Class, Mil. and Hospitalier Order St. Mary of Bethlehem, Capua, 1987; named Magnificent Rector and Pres. of The Constantinian Univ. (Studiorum Universitas Constantiniana), Italy, 1970. Fellow AAAS, Tex. Acad. Sci., Royal Soc. Health (London), Am. Inst. Chemists; mem. Assn. Mil. Surgeons U.S., Nat. Assn. Doctors U.S. (founder 1958, sec.-treas. 1958-85, exec. coun. 1958-85), Accademia di San Cirillo Italy (hon.), N.Y. Acad. Scis., Phi Sigma, Kappa Delta Pi, Phi Kappa

Phi, Alpha Beta Kappa (charter mem., pres. R.I. Alpha chpt. 1984-92). Home: 30 Oaklawn Ave Apt 219 Cranston RI 02920-9319 Office: Johnson and Wales Univ Providence RI 02903

VAWTER, WILLIAM SNYDER, computer software consultant; b. N.Y.C., Oct. 26, 1931; s. William Snyder and Flora Adeline (Woods) V.; m. June Elizabeth Lindahl Mahoney, June 22, 1957 (div. Sept. 1972); children: Jonathan, Timothy, Jamison; m. Donia Ibrahim Hamarneh, Dec. 26, 1976; 1 child, Rafic William. Ba, Rutgers U., 1953; postgrad., Harvard Divinity Sch., 1957-58. 1st lt. U.S. Army Signal Corps, Fort Devens, Mass., 1953-55; computer analyst B.F. Goodrich Co., Watertown, Mass., 1956, Traffic Exec. Assn., Eastern R.R., N.Y.C., 1959-60; systems analyst Mangels Stores, N.Y.C., 1961, Gimbels, N.Y.C., 1962-63; mgr. environ. data applications Computer Applications, Inc., N.Y.C., 1963-64; systems analyst Fire Ins. Rsch. & Actuarial Assn., N.Y.C., 1965; v.p. Mgmt. Datavision, Inc., N.Y.C., 1965; pres. Mgmt. Data, Inc., Dover, Del., 1965—; cons. in field; with computerized reapportionment plan for subcom. N.Y. State Legislature, 1965; data base adminstr. NASA, Houston, 1976; computer mgr. Saudi Arabia N.G., Riyadh, 1980-81; computer cons. U.S. AID-funded Afghan Relief Project, Quetta, Pakisatan, 1990-91; logistics and computer cons. U.S. AID-funded Family Planning Project for Ministry of Health, Dhaka, Bangladesh, 1991-92; mem. MIS needs assessment team for Ministry of Health and Family Welfare for World Bank & Who, Dhaka, 1993; computerized med. records IPGMR Hosp., Dhaka, 1994; established Devel. Plus, 1994; supportd computer conversion South Tex. Project Electric Generating Sta. nuc. info. sys. Patentee in field. Speaker Queens Village (N.Y.) Fair Housing Coun., 1967. Recipient Honor medal Freedoms Found., 1949, Tuition scholarship Rutgers U., 1949, N.Y. State Med. scholarship, 1955, Tuition scholarship, 1957. Mem. Assn. for Computing Machinery, Computer Soc. of IEEE, Royal Sch. Ch. Music, Am. Guild of Organists, Theta Chi Frat. Democrat. Episcopalian. Avocations: photography, yoga, teaching piano. Home: 4901 Misty Ln Apt 423 Bay City TX 77414-8455 also: PO Box 232, Madaba Jordan Office: Mgmt Data Inc 15 E North St PO Box 899 Dover DE 19903-0899 also: GPO Box 3135, Dhaka 1000, Bangladesh

VAYHINGER, JOHN MONROE, psychotherapist, minister; b. Upland, Ind., Jan. 27, 1916; s. Paul Johnson and Harriet Estelle (Palmer) V.; m. Ruth Imler, Sept. 19, 1939; children: John Earl, Karen Lynn Vayhinger Kuper Childs. AB, Taylor U., 1937; grad., Asbury Theol. Sem., Wilmore, Ky., 1937-39; BD, MA, Drew U., 1940, 51; MA, PhD, Columbia U., 1948, 56. Diplomate Am. Bd. Psychology; ordained Meth. Ch. as pastor. Pastor United Meth. Ch., Conn., Ind., N.Y., Colo., 1938-68, ret.68; assoc. prof., head dept. W.Va. Wesleyan U., Buckhannon, 1949-51; chief clin. psychologist Mental Health Clin., South Bend, Ind., 1951-58; lectr. Ind. U., South Bend, 1953-58; prof. psychology and pastoral counseling Garrett Theol. Sem. Northwestern U., Evanston, Ill., 1958-64; prof. psychology of religion and pastoral counseling Iliff Sch. Theology U. Denver, 1964-67; prof. psychology and pastoral counseling Anderson (Ind.) U. Sch. Theology, 1968-81, Asbury Theol. Sem., Wilmore, Ky., 1981-84, ret.84; pvt. practice Ky., Ind., Ill, Colo., 1958—, Colorado Springs, Colo., 1984—; dir. inst. ministries Ind. Coun. Chs., Indpls., 1968-81; chairperson Pastoral Counseling Inst., Atlanta, 1985—. Author: Before Divorce, 1972, (with Norman Cryer), Casebook of Pastoral Counseling, 1962; contbr. 12 chpts. edited books. Tchr. police schs., South Bend, Ind., Anderson, Ind., Denver. Capt. AUS, 1944-47, PTO. Fellow Am. Orthopsychiatric Assn., Am. Assn. Sci. Study of Religion, Christian Assn. Psychol. Studies, Am. Assn. Clin. Sexiologists, Am. Assn. Christian Counselors; mem. Am. Assn. Pastoral Counselors (diplomate), Soc. Psychol. in Pvt. Practice, Am. Psychol. Assn., AAUP, AAAS, Colo. Psychol. Assn., Ind. Psychol. Assn., Am. Assn. Marital and Family Therapists (clin.), Religious Rsch. Assn., Am. Assn. Sex Educators, Counselors and Therapists, Nat. Coun. Family Relations, Assn. Clin. Pastoral Edn., Nat. Congress Parents and Tchrs. (life), USN Inst., and more. Republican. Home: 119 Illini Dr Woodland Park CO 80863-8705 Office: 420 N Nevada Ave Colorado Springs CO 80903-1227

VAYO, DAVID JOSEPH, composer, music educator; b. New Haven, Mar. 28, 1957; s. Harold Edward and Joan Virginia (Cassidy) V.; m. Margot Ehrlich, May 16, 1981; children: Rebecca Lynne, Gordon Francis. BMus, Ind. U., 1980, MMus, 1982; AMusD, U. Mich., 1990. Prof. Nat. U., Heredia, Costa Rica, 1982-84, Nat. Symphony Youth Sch., San Jose, Costa Rica, 1982-84; asst. prof. music Conn. Coll., New London, 1988-91, Ill. Wesleyan U. Sch. Music, Bloomington, 1991—; resident artist Banff Ctr. for Arts, 1992, 94, Va. Ctr. for Creative Arts, 1994; participating composer Internat. Soc. Contemporary Music-World Music Days, Mexico City, 1993, Internat. Festival Contemporary Music, Bogota, Colombia, 1995. Composer chamber composition Poem, 1990 (wwinner Spectri Sonori Internat. Composition competition Tulane U. 1992), Symphony: Blossoms and Awakenings, 1990 (performer St. Louis Symphony, Leonard Slatkin condr. 1993), Wind Quintet, 1991 (winner Symposium Seven for New Woodwind Quinted Music, U. Ga. 1993), Eight Poems of William Carlos Williams for solo trombonist, 1994 (commd. by St. Louis Symphony); works pub. by MMB Music and Am. Percussion Publs. Charles E. Ives scholar Am. Acad. and Inst. Arts and Letters, 1988. Mem. ASCAP (awards 1988—), Am. Music Ctr. (copying assistance grantee 1992), Coll. Music Soc. (presenter nat. conf. 1990-94), Soc. for Electro-Acoustic Music in U.S. (presenter nat. conf. 1989), Soc. Composers (membership chmn. 1990—, presenter nat. conf. 1990-92), Nat. Assn. Composers USA, Minn. Composers Forum. Avocations: athletics, Latin American culture, travel. Office: Ill Wesleyan U Sch Music PO Box 2900 Bloomington IL 61701

VAZQUEZ, GILBERT FALCON, lawyer; b. Eagle Pass, Tex., Oct. 29, 1952; s. Catalina (Falcon) V. AB in Polit. Sci., Yale U., 1975; JD, Harvard U., 1978. Bar: Tex. 1978, U.S. Dist. Ct. (we. dist.) Tex. 1980, U.S. Ct. Appeals (5th and 11th cirs.) 1981. Ptnr. Matthews & Branscomb, San Antonio, Tex., 1978-85, Akin, Gump, Strauss, Hauer & Feld, L.L.P., San Antonio, 1985—. Co-chmn. issues com. H. Cisneros Mayoral Campaign, San Antonio, 1981; bd. dirs. Bexar County-San Antonio United Way, 1982-87, 91—, San Antonio World Affairs Coun., 1993—, San Antonio Mus. Assn., 1993-95, San Antonio Zool. Soc., 1988—, exec. com. mem.; exec. com. Mayor's Target 90 Commn., San Antonio, 1985-89, vice-chmn., 1987-89; chmn. City of San Antonio Charter Rev. Com., 1991-93, State of Tex. Pension Rev. Bd., 1991—, vice-chmn., chmn. 1995. Named Outstanding Young San Antonian, U.S. Jaycees, 1985, Outstanding Vol., J.C. Penny Co., 1984. Mem. ABA (internat. law sect., assoc. editor newsletter 1985-87), Nat. Assn. Bond Lawyers, Tex. Bar Assn. (governing coun. internat. law sect. 1985-88), San Antonio Bar Assn., San Antonio Young Lawyers Assn. (Outstanding Young Lawyer 1987), Hispanic Nat. Bar Assn. (regional pres. 1987-88, nat. sec. 1988-89, v.p. 1989-90), San Antonio World Trade Assn. (bd. dirs. 1987-90), Mexican C. of C. (bd. dirs. 1984-85), Greater San Antonio C. of C. (bd. dirs. 1992-95), Yale Club South Tex. (pres. 1982-85). Democrat. Roman Catholic. Avocations: community redevelopment, music, reading. Office: Akin Gump Strauss Hauer & Feld LLP 300 Convent St Ste 1500 San Antonio TX 78205-3716

VAZQUEZ, MARTHA ALICIA, judge; b. Santa Barbara, Calif., Feb. 21, 1953; d. Remigio and Consuelo (Mendez) V.; m. Frank Mathew, Aug. 7, 1976; children: Cristina Vazquez Matthew, Nicholas Vazquez Matthew, Nathan Vazquez Matthew. BA in Govt., U. Notre Dame, 1975, JD, 1978. Bar: N.Mex. 1979, U.S. Dist. Ct. (we. dist.) N.Mex. 1979. Atty. Pub. Defender's Office, Santa Fe, 1979-81; ptnr. Jones, Snead, Wertheim, Rodriguez & Wentworth, Santa Fe, 1981-93; judge U.S. District Ct., 10th Circuit, Santa Fe, 1993—. Chmn. City Santa Fe Grievance Bd. Mem. N.Mex. Bar Assn. (fee arbitration com., chmn. trial practice sect. 1984-85, mem. task force on minority involvement in bar activities), Santa Fe Bar Assn. (jud. liasion com.), Nat. Assn. Criminal Def. Lawyers, Assn. Trial Lawyers Am., N.Mex. Trial Lawyers Assn. Democrat. Roman Catholic. Office: US Courthouse PO Box 2710 Santa Fe NM 87504-2710

VEACH, ROBERT RAYMOND, JR., lawyer; b. Charleston, S.C., Nov. 28, 1950; s. Robert Raymond and Evelyn Ardell (Vegter) V.; m. Lori Sue Erickson, May 27, 1989. Student, St. Olaf Coll., 1968-70; BS in Acctg., Ariz. State U., 1972; JD, So. Meth. U., 1975. Bar: Tex. 1975, Nebr. 1975, U.S. Dist. Ct. Nebr. 1975, U.S. Dist. Ct. (no. dist.) Tex. 1975, Temporary Emergency Ct. Appeals 1975. Acctg. instr. Sch. Bus. So. Meth. U., Dallas, 1973-74; law clk. to Hon. Joe E. Estes, sr. judge U.S. Dist. Ct. (no. dist.)

Tex., and judge temporary emergency Ct. Appeals, Dallas, 1975-76; assoc. Locke Purnell Boren Laney & Neely, Dallas, 1976-80; v.p. The Lomas & Nettleton Co., Dallas, 1980-83, Rauscher Pierce Refsnes, Inc., Dallas, 1983-87; pres. RPR Mortgage Fin. Corp., Dallas, 1985-87; sr. shareholder Locke Purnell Rain Harrell, Dallas, 1987—; allied mem. N.Y. Stock Exch., 1985-87; lectr. securities and banking confs. Author legal articles. Dir. North Tex. affiliate Am. Diabetes Assn., Dallas, 1978-81; mem. Gov.'s Task Force Wash. State Housing Commn., 1982-83. Mem. ABA, State Bar of Tex., Nebr. State Bar Assn., Fed. Bar Assn., Dallas Bar Assn. Republican. Methodist. Avocations: golf, antique Am. firearms. Home: 4223 Brookview Dr Dallas TX 75220-3801 Office: Locke Purnell Rain Harrell 2200 Ross Ave Ste 2200 Dallas TX 75201-6766

VEACO, KRISTINA, lawyer; b. Sacramento, Calif., Mar. 4, 1948; d. Robert Glenn and Lelia (McCain) V.; m. William H. Heinemann, June 23, 1984 (div. Aug. 1991). BA, U. Calif., Davis, 1978; JD, Hastings Coll. of the Law, 1981. Legal adv. to commr. William T. Bagley Calif. Public Utilities Commn., San Francisco, Calif., 1981-86; sr. counsel Pacific Telesis Group, San Francisco, Calif., 1986-94; sr. counsel corp. and securities and pol. law Air Touch Comms., San Francisco, 1994—. Mem. ABA, Calif. Women Lawyers, San Francisco Bar Assn., Am. Soc. Corp. Secs., Phi Beta Kappa. Democrat. Episcopalian. Avocations: cooking, reading. Office: Air Touch Coms 1 California St Rm 2108 San Francisco CA 94111

VEALE, TINKHAM, II, former chemical company executive, engineer; b. Topeka, Dec. 26, 1914; s. George W. and Grace Elizabeth (Walworth) V.; m. Harriett Alice Ernst, Sept. 6, 1941; children: Harriett Elizabeth Veale Leedy, Tinkham III, Helen Ernst Veale Gelbach. BS in Mech. Engring., Case Inst. Tech., 1937; LLD, Kenyon Coll., 1981. Registered profl. engr. With Gen. Motors Corp., 1937-38, Avery Engring. Co., 1939, Reliance Electric Co., 1940-41; asst. to pres. Ohio Crankshaft Co., 1942-46; gen. mgr. Tocco Co., 1947-51; pres. Ric Wil Corp., 1952-53; pres. Alco Chem. Corp., 1954-56, dir., 1954-86; spl. ptnr. Ball Burge & Kraus, investment bankers, 1957-60; chmn. bd. V. and V. Cos., Inc. and subs., Cleve., 1960-65, Alco Standard Corp. and subs., Valley Forge, Pa., 1965-86, Horsehead Industries, Inc. and subs., N.Y.C., 1981—, HTV Industries Inc. and subs., Cleve., 1978—; ptnr. Fair Elm Farm, 1948—, Kennedy Veale Stable, 1954—. Trustee V. and V. Charitable Found., 1966—. Recipient Silver Bowl award Case Inst. Tech., 1980; recipient Gold Medal Case Inst. Tech., 1982. Mem. Cleve. Engring. Soc., Nat. Soc. Registered Profl. Engrs., Newcomen Soc., Phi Kappa Psi. Home: Fair Elm Gate Mills OH 44040 Office: HTV Industries Inc PO Box 295 Gates Mills OH 44040-0295

VEASEY, EUGENE NORMAN, lawyer; b. Wilmington, Del., Jan. 9, 1933; s. Eugene E. and Elizabeth B. (Norman) V.; m. Suzanne Johnson, Aug. 4, 1956; children: Andrew Scott, Douglas Ross, E. Norman Jr., Marian Elizabeth. AB, Dartmouth Coll., 1954; LLB, U. Pa., 1957. Bar: Del. 1958, U.S. Supreme Ct. 1963. Dep. atty. gen. State of Del., 1961-62, chief dep., 1962-63; ptnr. Richards, Layton & Finger, Wilmington, Del., 1963-92, chief justice, Del. Supreme Ct., 1992—. Contbr. articles to profl. jours. Bd. advisors U. Pa. Inst. for Law and Econs. Served to Capt. Del. Air N.G., 1957-63. Fellow Am. Bar Found., Am. Coll. Trial Lawyers, Am. Intellectual Property Law Assn; mem. Del. Bd. Bar Examiners (chmn. 1973-80), Del. Bar Assn. (pres. 1982-83, chmn. corp. law com. 1969-74, chmn. rules com. of Del. Supreme Ct. 1974-80), ABA (officer 1991—, coun. of bus. law sect. 1987—, com. corp. laws, chmn. program com., litigation sect.), Am. Law Inst. (lawyers adv. com. for 3rd cir. judicial conf.) Republican. Episcopalian. Office: Del Supreme Ct PO Box 1997 Wilmington DE 19899

VEATCH, JOHN WILLIAM, speech pathologist; b. Mitchell, S.D., Dec. 9, 1923; s. William Homer and Helen Gwendolyn (Lowther) V.; m. Doris Lavelle Guthrie (dec. 1978); children: Dean, Joan; m. Winnifred Ann Sawin, 1982 (div. 1992); m. Joy Sullivan, Aug. 21, 1993. BA in Speech, Wash. State U., 1946, BEd, 1951; MA in Speech, U. Wash., 1950; DEd, U. Idaho, 1970. Pvt. practice speech pathology Spokane, Wash., 1950-79; pvt. practice speech pathology and ednl. cons. Tacoma, 1980—; bus., ednl. dir. Sullivan Ctr., Puyallop, Wash., 1990—; lectr. in speech pathology Gonzaga U., Spokane, Wash., 1963-70; adj. prof. Wash. State U., 1972-77, Applied Psychology, Eastern Wash. U., 1977; chief exec. officer and dir. Amercan. Espial Inst., Tacoma, 1982-92; mem. home health adv. bd. Spokane County Health Dept., past. pres. Wash. State Health Dept. Crippled Children's Svc. Adv. Bd. Maxillofacial Defects; co-dir. Sullivan Ctr., dir. ednl. programs, 1992—; cons. in field. Author: (with D. Hughes) Teacher Qualities, 1947; (test profiles) Personal Stress Balance Profile, 1982, Info. Processing Style, 1984, The Deep Screening Profile of Tongue Thrusting Activity, 1985, The Tongue Thrust Screening Test, 1986, Learning Style Profile, 1986; writer, contbr. guides, workbooks, studies and films in field. Fellow Northwest Acad. Speech Pathology (pres. 1978-82, 86-91); mem. Am. Speech-Lang.-Hearing Assn. (pres. bd. Oakbridge U. 1989-90). Office: 2717 E Main Ave Puyallup WA 98372-3165

VEATCH, ROBERT MARLIN, philosophy educator, medical ethics researcher; b. Utica, N.Y., Jan. 22, 1939; s. Cecil Ross and Regina (Braddock) V.; m. Laurelyn Kay Lovett, June 17, 1961 (div. Oct. 1986); children: Paul Martin, Carlton Elliot; m. Ann Bender Pastore, May 23, 1987. BS, Purdue U., 1961; MS, U. Calif. at San Francisco, 1962; BD, Harvard U., 1964, MA, 1970, Ph.D., 1971. Teaching fellow Harvard U. 1968-70; research assoc. in medicine Columbia U. Physicians and Surgeons, Columbia U. 1971-72; assoc. for med. ethics Inst. of Society, Ethics and Life Scis., Hastings-on-Hudson, N.Y., 1970-75; sr. assoc. Inst. of Society, Ethics and Life Scis., 1975-79; prof. med. ethics Kennedy Inst. Ethics Georgetown U., 1979—, prof. philosophy, 1981—, dir., 1989—; adj. prof. depts. community and family medicine and ob/gyn, 1984—; mem. vis. faculty various colls. and univs.; mem. gov. bd. Washington Regional Transplant Consortium, 1988—; bd. dirs. Hospice Care D.C., 1989—, pres., 1993—; active United Network Organ Sharing Ethics Com., 1989—. Mem. Soc. Christian Ethics. Home: 11200 Richland Grove Dr Great Falls VA 22066-1104 Office: Georgetown U Kennedy Inst Of Ethics Washington DC 20057

VEAZEY, DORIS ANNE, field office administrator; b. Dawson Spring, Ky., Feb. 16, 1935; d. Bradley Basil and Lucy Mable (Hamby) Sisk; m. Herman Veazey Jr., Aug. 15, 1964 (dec. Sept. 1987); 1 child, Vickie Dianne Veazey Kicinski. Murray State U., 1952-54. Unemployment ins. examiner Dept. for Employment Svcs., Madisonville, Ky., 1954-73, unemployment ins. supr., 1973-85, field office mgr., 1985-95; bd. dirs., adv. bd. Region II Vocat. Tech. Schs. Madisonville, 1988-92. Mem. Mayor's Work Force Devel. Com., 1993—, Ky. Indsl. Devel. Com., 1992—; dept. dir. Adult III Sunday Sch., 1994—, ch. choir, 1990—. Mem. Internat. Assn. of Personnel in Employment Svcs., Southeastern Employment and Tng. Assn., Tenure, Order Ky. Cols., Greater Madisonville C. of C. (dir. leadership 1988-93). Baptist. Avocations: reading, T.V., travel, photography. Office: Dept Employment Svcs 56 Federal St # 1226 Madisonville KY 42431-1226

VEBLEN, THOMAS CLAYTON, management consultant; b. Hallock, Minn., Dec. 17, 1929; s. Edgar R. and Hattie (Lundgren) V.; m. Susan Alma Beaver, Sept. 1, 1950 (div. 1971); children: Kari Christen, Erik Rodli, Mark Andrew, Sara Catherine; m. Linda Joyce Eaton, Aug. 30, 1975; 1 child, Kristen Kirby. Student, U. Calif., Santa Barbara, 1950-51; BS, Calif. Poly. U., 1953; MS, Oreg. State U., 1955. Corp. v.p Cargill, Inc., Wayzata, Minn., 1955-75; spl. asst. Sec. Interior, Washington, 1965; dir. food and agr. SRI Internat., Menlo Park, Calif., 1975-80; pres. Food Sys. Assocs., Inc., Washington, 1980-94; also bd. dirs. Food System Assocs., Inc., Washington; chmn. Enterprise Cons., Inc., Washington, 1990—; dir. Georgetown Cons. Inc., 1993—; mem. CMC Inst. Mgmt. Cons., 1988—, pres. Washington chpt., 1991-93. Author: The U.S. Food System, 1978; (with M. Abel) Creating a Superior National Food System, 1992; editor Food System Update, 1986—. Treas., bd. dirs. White House Fellows Assn., Washington, 1985; trustee Freedom from Hunger Found., Davis, Calif., 1980—, chmn., 1986-89; bd. dirs. Patterson Sch., U. Ky., Lexington, Pax World Svc., Am. Near East Refugee Aid. Recipient Presdl. Appointment White House Fellows Commn., Washington, 1965. Mem. Coun. for Nat. Interest, Coun. on Fgn. Rels. Episcopalian. Avocations: canoeing, ice skating. Office: Enterprise Cons Inc 2806 36th Pl NW Washington DC 20007-1417

VECCHIO, ROBERT PETER, business management educator; b. Chgo., June 29, 1950; s. Dominick C. and Angeline V.; m. Betty Ann Vecchio; Aug.

21, 1974; children: Julie. Mark. BS summa cum laude, DePaul U., 1972; MA, U. Ill., 1974, PhD, 1976. Instr. U. Ill., Urbana, 1973-76; mem. faculty dept. mgmt. U. Notre Dame, 1976-86, dept. chmn., 1983-90, Franklin D. Schurz Prof. Mgmt., 1986—. Editor Jour. of Mgmt., 1995—. Mem. Acad. Mtm., Am. Psychol. Assn., Academy Assn. Consumer Rsch., Am. Inst. Decision Scis., Midwest Acad. Mgmt., Midwest Psychol. Assn., Phi Kappa Phi, Delta Epsilon Sigma, Phi Eta Sigma, Psi Chi. Home: 16856 Hampton Dr Granger IN 46530-6907 Office: U Notre Dame Dept Mgmt Notre Dame IN 46556

VECCHIONE, JOSEPH JOHN, newspaper editor; b. Jersey City, Jan. 9, 1937; s. Joseph and Jennie Marie V.; m. Elizabeth Marie Tobin, Oct. 10, 1964; children—Elissa, Andrea. B.S., St. Peter's Coll., Jersey City, 1959. Mem. staff N.Y. Times, 1960—, dep. editor nat. edit., 1980—, sports editor, 1980—; formerly adj. prof. journalism L.I. U. Mem. N.J. N.G., 1959-66. Mem. AP Sports Editors. Roman Catholic. Home: 711 Amsterdam Ave New York NY 10025 Office: NY Times Co 229 W 43rd St New York NY 10036-3913

VECCHIOTTI, ROBERT ANTHONY, management and organizational consultant; b. N.Y.C., May 21, 1941; s. R. Lucien and Louise Victoria V.; BS, St. Peter's Coll., 1962; MA, Fordham U., 1964; PhD, St. Louis U., 1973; m. Dorothea Irene Hoban, Oct. 12, 1963; children: John Robert, Rachel Irene, Sara Christine. Psychologist Testing and Advisement Ctr.NYU, Washington Sq. campus, 1964-65; group psychologist McDonnell Douglas, St. Louis, 1967-76, sr. bus. analyst, 1976-77, mgr. bus. systems planning, 1977-79; pres. Organizational Cons. Svcs., Inc., St. Louis, 1980—; adj. assoc. prof. mgmt. Maryville Coll., St. Louis, 1975-81. Bd. dirs. Cath. Charities of St. Louis, 1981-86, Cath. Family Svc., 1986—, Mental Health Assn. St. Louis, 1989—, Sta. KWMU-FM, 1989-94. With U.S. Army, 1965-67. Lic. psychologist, Mo. Mem. Am. Psychol. Assn., Planning Forum, Inst. Mgmt. Cons., Human Factors Soc. Club: Mo. Athletic. Lodge: Rotary (past pres.). Office: Organizational Consulting Svcs 230 S Bemiston Ave # 1107 Clayton MO 63105-1907

VECCI, RAYMOND JOSEPH, airline executive; b. N.Y.C., Jan. 22, 1943; s. Romeo John and Mary (Fabretti) V.; m. Helen Cecelia Clampett, Sept. 3, 1967; children: Brian John, Damon Jay. BBA, CCNY, 1965; MBA, NYU, 1967. Adminstrv. asst. Internat. Air Transport Assn., N.Y.C., 1961-66; econ. analyst United Airlines, Chgo., 1967-74; asst. v.p. planning and regulatory affairs Alaska Airlines Inc., Seattle, 1975-76, staff v.p. planning and regulatory affairs, 1976-79, staff v.p. planning, 1979, v.p. planning, 1979-85, exec. v.p., chief operating officer, 1986-90, pres., chief exec. officer, 1990—; chmn., dir. Alaska Airlines Inc., 1991—; also chmn., pres., chief exec. officer, dir. Alaska Air Group Inc. Served with U.S. Army, 1968-69, Vietnam. Decorated Bronze Star. Roman Catholic. Office: Alaska Airlines Inc PO Box 68900 19300 Pacific Hwy S Seattle WA 98168-5303*

VECELLIO, LEO ARTHUR, JR., construction company executive; b. Beckley, W.Va., Oct. 26, 1946; s. Leo Arthur and Evelyn (Pais) V.; m. Kathryn Grace Cottrill, Nov. 29, 1975; children: Christopher Scott, Michael Andrew. BCE, Va. Poly. Inst. and State U., 1968; MCE, Ga. Inst. Tech., 1969; LLD (hon.), Northwood U. Sr. v.p. Vecellio & Grogan, Inc., Beckley, 1973—; pres. Vecellio Contracting Corp. and subs. (Ranger Constrn. Industries, West Palm Beach, PAVEX Corp., Deerfield Beach, White Rock Quarries, Miami), Fla., 1982—; mng. ptnr. Vecellio Realty Co., Deerfield Property Assocs.; bd. dirs. United Nat. Bank-South, Beckley, Barnett Bank of Palm Beach County; founder, past dir. Gulf Nat. Bank, Sophia, W.Va.; founder, past dir. Nat. Bankers Trust, Beckley. Chmn. bd. dirs., mem. Econ. Coun. of Palm Beach County, Fla., 1985—, chmn.-elect 1987, chmn., 1989; gov. Northwood U., West Palm Beach, 1985—; organizer, trustee Beckley Family Found., 1985; v.p., trustee Vecellio Family Found., Beckley, 1972—; mem. Mini-Grace Commn., Fla. Coun. of 100, 1989—, vice chmn., 1991—; commn. dir., v.p. Criminal Justice Commn.; chmn. Budget Rev. Task Force, Budget Oversight Task Force; bd. dirs. Gulfstream coun. Boy Scouts Am., 1989-93, Floridians for Better Transp., Palm Beach County Cultural Coun. and Art Sch. Task Force; bd. dirs. Fla. Coun. 100; exec. com. Floridians for Better Transp. Capt. USAF, 1969-73. Recipient Free Enterprise medal Palm Beach Atlantic Coll., 1988. Mem. Flexible Pavements Assn. (found, bd. dirs. 1979—), Contractors Assn. W. (bd. dirs. 1979—). Republican. Roman Catholic. Clubs: Mayacoo Lakes Country (West Palm Beach), Adios Golf (Coconut Creek, Fla.), Jupiter Hills (Fla.). Lost Tree. Avocations: golf, boating, skiing. Home: 771 Village Rd North Palm Beach FL 33408-3331 Office: Vecellio Contracting Corp PO Box 15065 West Palm Beach FL 33416-5065

VECOLI, RUDOLPH JOHN, history educator; b. Wallingford, Conn., Mar. 2, 1927; s. Giovanni Battista and Settima Maria (Palmerini) V.; m. Jill Cherrington, June 27, 1959; children: Christopher, Lisa, Jeremy. BA, U. Conn., 1950; MA, U. Pa., 1951; PhD, U. Wis., 1963. Fgn. affairs officer Dept. State, 1951-54; instr. history Ohio State U., 1957-59, Pa. State U., 1960-61; asst. prof. Rutgers U., 1961-65; assoc. prof. U. Ill., Champaign, 1965-67; prof. history, dir. Immigration History Research Center, U. Minn., Mpls., 1967—; vis. prof. U. Uppsala, Sweden, 1970, U. Amsterdam, The Netherlands, 1988, Maria Curie-Sklodowsk U., Lublin, Poland, 1992; acad. specialist U.S. Info. Agy., Brazil, 1993. Author: The People of New Jersey, 1965, Foreword to Marie Hall Ets, Rosa: The Story of an Italian Immigrant, 1970, (with Joy Lintelman) A Century of American Immigration, 1884-1984, 1984, (with others) The Invention of Ethnicity, 1990; contbg. author: Gli italiani fuori d'Italia, 1983, They Chose Minnesota: A Survey of the State's Ethnic Groups, 1981, Pane e Lavoro: The Italian American Working Class, 1980, Perspectives in Italian Immigration and Ethnicity, 1977, Immigrants and Religion in Urban America, 1977, The State of American History, 1970, The Reinterpretation of American History and Culture, 1973, Failure of a Dream, Essays in the History of American Socialism, 1984; Italian Americans: New Perspectives, 1985, May Day Celebration, 1988, In the Shadow of the Statue of Liberty, 1988, From Melting Pot to Multiculturalism, 1990, Studi Sull' Emigrazione, 1991, The Lebanese in the World, 1992, Swedes in America: New Perspectives, 1993, The Statue of Liberty Revisited, 1994; editor, contbg. author: The Other Catholics, 1978, Italian Immigrants in Rural and Small Town America, 1987; mem. editorial bd.: Jour. Am. Ethnic History, Studi Emigrazione, America: History and Life, Mid-America, International Migration Review, Estudios Migratorios Latino Americanos, Altreitalie; co-editor (with Suzanne Sinke) A Century of European Migrations, 1830-1930, 1991; contbr. articles to profl. jours. Chair history com Statue of Liberty-Ellis Island Centennial Commn., 1983-90. With USNR, 1945-46. Decorated Knight Officer, Order of Merit (Italy); recipient Am. Philos. Soc. grantee, 1970; Newberry Libr. fellow, 1964, Am.-Scandinavian Found. fellow, 1970, NEH fellow, 1985-86; Fulbright-Hays sr. rsch. scholar Italy, 1973-74; Am. Coun. Learned Soc. grantee, 1974, 86, U.S. Dept. State Travel grantee, 1977, Acad. Specialist, U.S. Info. Agy., Brazil, 1993. Mem. Am. Italian Hist. Assn. (pres., mem. exec. council), Am. Hist. Assn., Orgn. Am. Historians, AAUP, Immigration History Soc. (pres., exec. council). Home: 610 E 58th St Minneapolis MN 55417-2426

VECSEY, GEORGE SPENCER, sports columnist; b. Jamaica, N.Y., July 4, 1939; s. George Stephen and May (Spencer) V.; m. Marianne Graham; children: Laura, Corinna, David. BA in English, Hofstra Coll., 1960; LHD (hon.), Hofstra U., 1991. Sports reporter Newsday, Garden City, N.Y., 1960-68; sports reporter N.Y. Times, N.Y.C., 1968-70, nat. corr., 1970-73, met., religion reporter, 1973-80, sports reporter, 1980-82, sports columnist, 1982—. Author: (with others) Naked Came the Stranger, 1969, Joy in Mudville: Being a Complete Account of the Unparalleled History of the New York Mets, 1970, One Sunset a Week: The Story of a Coal Miner, 1974, (with Loretta Lynn) Coal Miner's Daughter, 1976, (with Jacques Lowe) Kentucky: A Celebration of American Life, 1979, (with George C. Dade) Getting Off the Ground: The Pioneers of Aviation Speak for Themselves, 1978, (with Leonore Fleischer) Sweet Dreams, 1985, (with Martina Navratilova) Martina, 1985, (with Bob Welch) Five O'Clock Comes Early: A Young Man's Battle with Alcoholism, 1982, A Year in the Sun, 1989, (with Barbara Mandrell) Get to the Heart, 1991; author 8 children's books; editor: The Way It Was: Great Sports Events from the Past, 1974. Recipient Disting. Writing award Am. Soc. Newspaper Editors, 1995; named N.Y. State Sportswriter of Yr. Nat. Sportscasters and Sportswriters Assn., 1985-95. Mem. Kentuckians (bd. dirs. 1988—). Avocations: running, swimming, music, travel, languages. Office: NY Times 229 W 43rd St New York NY 10036-3913

VEDDER, BYRON CHARLES, newspaper executive; b. Adrian, Mich., Feb. 9, 1910; s. Adelbert and Adah (Dibble) V.; m. Kathleen Fry, June 20, 1936 (dec. 1960); children: Richard Kent, Robert Allen; m. Helen Cochrane, Dec. 16, 1976. A.B., U. Mich., 1933. Grad. mgr. student publs. U. Mich., Ann Arbor, 1933-34; with Champaign-Urbana (Ill.) Courier, 1934-64, pub., 1960-64; v.p. ops. Lindsay-Schaub Newspapers, Inc., 1964-75, v.p. planning, 1975-79; v.p. Sun Coast Media Inc., 1979—; sec. Pasco Pub. Inc., 1981-86; bd. dirs. Commi. Savs. & Loan Assn., Urbana, v.p., 1975-76, chmn., 1977-83; bd. dirs. Mut. Home and Savs., 1983-86. Mem. Arrowhead council exec. bd. Boy Scouts Am., 1951—, pres., 1960-64; mem. Pres.'s Com. Traffic Safety, 1954-58. Recipient Silver Beaver award Boy Scouts Am., 1959; named Boss of Year Champaign-Urbana chpt. Nat. Secs. Assn., 1958; Disting. Service to Journalism award U. Minn., 1979, Disting. Svc. award Inland Press Assn., 1991; James E. West fellow Boy Scouts of Am. award, 1995. Mem. Inland Daily Press Assn. (bd. dirs. 1950-53, pres. 1954, chmn. 1955, Disting. Svc. award 1991), Cen. States Circulation Mfrs. Assn. (pres. 1944-46), Ill. Daily Newspaper Markets Assn. (pres. 1962-63, chmn. 1963-64), Am. Newspaper Pubs. Assn. (com. chmn.), Urban Assn. Commerce (v.p. 1946), Campus Bus. Men's Assn. (bd. dirs.), Champaign C. of C. (bd. dirs. 1955-57, Internat. Circulation Mfrs. Assn. (hon.), U. Ill. Quarterback Club (hon. life). Presbyterian (trustee). Club: Urbana Country, Champaign Country. Lodge: Kiwanis (lt. gov. 1951, dir., Kiwanian of Year 1971, pres. 1978). Home: 3 Stanford Pl Champaign IL 61820-7620

VEDDER, EDDIE, singer; b. Evanston, Ill., Dec. 23, 1965; m. Beth Liebling, June 3, 1994. lead singer (band) Pearl Jam, 1991—; albums include Ten, 1991, Vs., 1993, Vitalogy, 1994; contbr. vocals (album) Temple of the Dog, 1991, Mother Love Bone, 1992, Bob Dylan Thirtieth-Anniversary Tribute, 1993, Sweet Reliee: A Tribute to Victoria Williams, 1993, Shame, 1993, Judgement Night Soundtrack, 1993; film appearances include Singles, 1992. Office: c/o Epic Records 550 Madison Ave New York NY 10022*

VEDROS, NEYLAN ANTHONY, microbiologist; b. New Orleans, Oct. 6, 1929; s. Phillip John and Solange Agnes (Melancon) V.; m. Elizabeth Corbett, Apr. 9, 1955; children: Sally Ann, Philippa Jane. B.S. in Chemistry, La. State U., 1951, M.S. in Microbiology, 1957; Ph.D., U. Colo., 1960. Postdoctoral fellow Nat. Inst. Allergy and Infectious Diseases, U. Oreg., Portland, 1960-62; microbiologist Naval Med. Research Inst., Bethesda, Md., 1962-66; research microbiologist Naval Biosci. Lab., Oakland, Calif., 1966-67; assoc. prof. med. microbiology and immunology U. Calif., Berkeley, 1967-72; prof. U. Calif., 1972-91, prof. emeritus, 1991—; dir. Naval Biosci. Lab., 1968-81; mem. expert panel on bacteriology WHO, 1972-91. Bd. trustees Alameda (Calif.) Library, 1973-78. Served to comdr. M.S.C. USNR, 1952-55, 62-67. Mem. Am. Assn. Immunologists, Am. Soc. Microbiology, Internat. Assn. Human and Animal Mycology, Internat. Assn. Microbiol. Sci., Internat. Assn. Aquatic Animal Medicine, Assn. Mil. Surgeons. Home: 2610 Evelyn Ct Alameda CA 94501-6333 Office: 239 Warren Hall U Calif Berkeley CA 94725

VEENKER, CLAUDE HAROLD, health education educator; b. George, Iowa, July 31, 1919; s. Ralph C. and Fannie (Casjens) V.; m. Elizabeth Louise Higgins, Jan. 1, 1944; children—Jo Lee, Vicki Susan. BA, U. No. Iowa, 1943; MA, U. No. Colo., 1953; D of Health and Safety, Ind. U., 1957. Tchr. Osage (Iowa) High Sch., 1946-47, Mason City (Iowa) Pub. Schs., 1947-55; teaching asst. Ind. U., 1955-56, vis. lectr., 1956-57; asst. prof. Purdue U., Lafayette, Ind., 1957-61, assoc. prof., 1961-66, prof., 1966-84, prof. emeritus, 1984—, chmn. health edn. sect., 1961-77; chmn. health edn. test project Ednl. Testing Svc., Princeton, 1965-74; cons. bur. rsch. coop. rsch. br. U.S. Office Edn., 1966-68; cons. healthful sch. environment AMA, NEA, Washington, 1969; mem. Ind. Coun. on Sch. Health, 1971-84, Ind. Adv. Com. on Drug Edn., 1969-74, Ind. Gov.'s Regional Com. on Mental Health, 1966-67. Editor, contbr. author: Synthesis of Research in Selected Areas of Health Instruction, 1963; mem. editorial bd.: Jour. Health, Phys. Edn. and Recreation, 1961-62, 64-66; Contbr. articles to profl. jours. Served to 1st lt. USMC, 1943-46. Decorated Purple Heart. Fellow Am. Sch. Health Assn., Am. Pub. Health Assn. (governing council 1974-76, mem. sch. health sect. council 1970-73); mem. Am. Alliance for Health, Phys. Edn. and Recreation (exec. council sch. health div. 1964-67, chmn. sch. health service sect. 1959-60), Mid-Am. Coll. Health Assn., Ind. Assn. Health Educators (pres. 1970), Phi Delta Kappa, Eta Sigma Gamma. Methodist. Club: Elks. Home: 224 Knox Dr West Lafayette IN 47906-2150 Office: Purdue U Lambert Bldg Lafayette IN 49707 *Life as a child during the Roaring 20's, as a young teen-ager during the Great Depression of the 30's, and as a young adult during World War II, was a great adventure. But the world is no easier now than it was then. It seems that living is a continual challenge: to seek, to find, to try, to conquer. To succeed, one must live with confidence and hope, fearing neither failure nor success. To live well is to live with self-discipline in the present, using the hard-learned lessons of the past to brighten one's prospects for the future.*

VEGA, FRANK J., newspaper publishing executive. Pres., CEO Detroit Newspapers. Office: 615 W Lafayette Blvd Detroit MI 48226*

VEGA, J. WILLIAM, aerospace engineering executive, consultant; b. Elizabeth, N.J., Jan. 30, 1931; s. John Charles and Margaret (Walker) V.; m. Carolyn Louise Burt, June 7, 1957 (div. 1976); children: Lynn Vega Membreño, Lore Vega Hynes, Susan; m. Pauline Anne Garner, Apr. 27, 1983. BSE, Princeton U., 1952, postgrad., 1955-56; MS, U.S. Internat. U., 1973. Sr. engr. Reaction Motors, Inc., Denville, N.J., 1956-58; sr. engr. Convair div. Gen. Dynamics, San Diego, 1958, project engr., sr. project engr., asst. chief engr., 1970-75, dir. advanced programs, 1975-83, v.p. advanced programs 1983-88, v.p. rsch. and engring., 1988-90; cons. aerospace mgmt., 1991—. Pres. bd. dirs. Durango (Colo.) Art Ctr. Lt. USN, 1952-55. Fellow AIAA (assoc.); mem. Phi Beta Kappa. Avocations: skiing, sailing, hiking, camping.

VEGA, MARIO, family practice physician; b. Encarnación, Itapua, Paraguay, Jan. 26, 1928; came to U.S., 1966; s. Manuel and Maria Clotilde (Perini) V.; m. Sady Diaz de Bedoya (dec. 1988); 1 child, Jennifer Alexandra. BS, Nat. Coll., Paraguay, 1949; MD, Nat. U. Asunción, Paraguay, 1954; postgrad., U. Miami, 1966-67. Diplomate Am. Bd. Family Practice. Resident Med. Sch. Nat. U. Asunción, 1955; Med. Sch. fellow Nat. U. Asunción, 1956; Polytech. Inst. Surgery fellow Britanic Hosp., Rosario, Argentina, 1957; pvt. practice Rosario, 1957-66; rotating intern Mt. Sinai Hosp., Miami Beach, Fla., 1967; pvt. practice Charles Town, W.Va., 1968-70; resident in anesthesiology Albert Einstein Coll. Medicine, Bronx, N.Y., 1971-72, Meml. Hosp. Cornell U., N.Y.C., 1972-73, Jackson Meml. Hosp. U. Miami, 1973; anesthesiology fellow Wilmington (Del.) Med. Ctr., 1973-74; pvt. practice Bradenton, Fla., 1975—; staff Charles Town Gen. Hosp., Ransom, W.Va., 1968-70; founder Non Invasive Vascular Lab., Tampa, Fla., 1981—. Fellow Am. Acad. Family Physicians; mem. Fla. Med. Assn., Orange County Med. Soc., Internat. Assn. Bilingual Physicians, Am. Assn. Residents and Interns, Royal Soc. Medicine (Eng., affiliate). Democrat. Adventist. Home: 4450 Cluster Dr Orlando FL 32808-5978 Office: Profl Med Ctr 503 Manatee Ave Ste E Bradenton Beach FL 34217

VEGA, MARYLOIS PURDY, journalist; b. Chgo., Nov. 4, 1914; d. William Thomas and Mary Helene (Buggy) Purdy; m. Carlos Juan Vega, Sept. 4, 1965. B.A., U. Wis., Madison, 1935. With Time mag., N.Y.C., 1942-84; chief Letters to the Editor, 1951-67, chief editl. rsch., 1967-76, assoc. editor 1976-84. Roman Catholic. Club: Overseas Press. Home: 140 West End Ave New York NY 10023-6131 also: Sand Hill Rd Gardiner NY 12525

VEGA, MATIAS ALFONSO, lawyer; b. Paris, Feb. 2, 1952; s. Matias Guillermo and Colette (Lafosse) V.; m. Carmella Margarita Kurczewski, Nov. 20, 1982; 1 child, Alexandra Leonie. AB, Yale U., 1974; JD, Harvard U., 1977. Bar: N.Y. 1978, U.S. Dist. Ct. (so. and ea. dists.) N.Y. 1979, U.S. Supreme Ct. 1984, U.S. Ct. Appeals (6th and 9th cirs.) 1985, U.S. Dist. Ct. (no. dist.) Calif. 1985. Assoc. Curtis, Mallet-Prevost, Colt & Mosle, N.Y.C., 1977-85, ptnr., 1986—. Contbr. articles to profl. jours. Mem. ABA, Am. Assn. Internat. Law, N.Y. State Bar Assn. (chmn. com. Latin Am. law, internat. law and practice) Republican. Roman Catholic. Home: 809 Long Hill Rd W Briarcliff Manor NY 10510-2124 Office: Curtis Mallet-Prevost Colt 101 Park Ave New York NY 10178-0061

VEGTER, WILLIAM CHARLES, wholesale supply executive; b. Kalamazoo; s. J. Robert and Rose Arleen (Brunsell) V.; m. Barbara Ann Siemers, June 26, 1971; children: William Charles, James Michael, Emily Ann. BBA, We. Mich. U., Kalamazoo, 1972, MBA, 1982-87. CPA, Mich. Staff acct. Herkner, Smits, Miskill & Johnson CPA's, Benton Harbor, Mich., 1972-74; acct. mgr. All Phase Electric Supply Co., Benton Harbor, Mich., 1974-76, asst. controller, 1976-79, controller, 1979-86, chief fin. officer, 1986—, v.p., fin., 1988—. Recipient Magna Cum Laude We. Mich. U., Kalamazoo 1972. Mem. AICPA, Mich. Assn. CPAs, Lions Club Benton Harbor Mich., pres. 1978-79). Republican. Methodist. Home: 5361 N Alpine Rdg Stevensville MI 49127-1354

VEIDENHEIMER, MALCOLM CHARLES, surgeon; b. Hamilton, Ont., Can., Oct. 6, 1928; came to U.S., 1960; s. Wilbur Charles and Violet Agnes (Joyce) V.; m. Sheila Colquhoun, June 12, 1956; children: Michael Brock, Robert Charles, Richard Ian, Paul Scott. MD, CM, Queens U., Kingston, Ont., 1954. Diplomate Am. Bd. Surgery, Am. Bd. Colon and Rectal Surgery. Intern Vancouver (B.C.) Gen. Hosp., 1954-55, resident, pathology, 1955-56; resident, gen. surgery Kingston Gen. Hosp. and Queens U., 1956-57, Walton Hosp., Liverpool, Eng., 1957; registrar in surgery Hammersmith Hosp., London, 1957-59; fellow in surgery Lahey Clinic Found., Burlington, Mass., 1960-61, surgeon, 1962, chief sect. colon and rectal surgery, 1970-87, chmn. dept. gen. surgery, 1983-87, staff, 1961-93. Pub. edn. com. Am. Cancer Soc., Boston, 1980—, profl. edn. com., 1986—. Named Physician of Yr. Nat. Found. for Ileitis and Colitis, 1986. Fellow ACS, Royal Coll. Surgeons, Am. Surg. Assn.; mem. Am. Bd. Colon & Rectal Surgery (pres. 1985-87), Am. Soc. Colon and Rectal Surgeons (sec. 1975-79, pres. 1980-81), Am. Bd. Surgery (bd. dirs. 1981-87), Royal Soc. Medicine (hon.), Proctologic Sect. Royal Australasian Coll. Surgeons (hon.), Brazilian Coll. of Surgeons (hon.), Ostomy Assn. Greater Boston, 1974—. Club: Wellesley Curling (Wayland, Mass.). Avocations: travel, photography, skiing, hiking. Office: Lahey Clinic Med Ctr 41 Mall Rd Burlington MA 01805-0001*

VEIGEL, JON MICHAEL, corporate professional; b. Mankato, Minn., Nov. 10, 1938; s. Walter Thomas and Thelma Geraldine (Lein) V.; m. Carol June Bradley, Aug. 10, 1962. BS, U. Washington, 1960; PhD, UCLA, 1965. Program mgr. Office of Tech. Assessment, U.S. Congress, Washington, 1974-75; div. mgr. Calif. Energy Commn., Sacramento, 1975-78; asst. dir. Solar Energy Rsch. Inst., Golden, Colo., 1978-81; pres. Alt. Energy Corp., Rsch. Triangle Park, N.C., 1981-88, Oak Ridge (Tenn.) Assoc. U., 1988—; bd. dirs. Am. Coun. Energy Efficient Economy, Washington, Pacific Internat. Ctr. for High Tech. Rsch., Honolulu; mem. bd. energy and environ. systems Nat. Rsch. Coun. Contbr. articles to jours. Bd. dirs. Oak Ridge Community Found., also chmn.; trustee Maryville Coll., Mendeleyev U., Moscow, Russia. 1st lt. USAF, 1965-68. Mem. AAAS. Avocations: photography, flying. Office: Oak Ridge Assoc Univs PO Box 117 Oak Ridge TN 37831-0117

VEINOTT, CYRIL GEORGE, electrical engineer, consultant; b. Somerville, Mass., Feb. 15, 1905; s. Jason A. and I. Laura (Fales) V.; m. Dorothy Helen Bassett, Nov. 28, 1936 (dec. Sept. 1988); 1 child, Richard A.; m. June Urlwin, Jan. 6, 1990. BSEE cum laude, U. Vt., 1926; EE, 1939; D in Engring. (hon.), 1951. Mgr. induction motor sect. Westinghouse, Lima, Ohio, 1926-52; chief engring. analyst Reliance Elec. Co., Cleve., 1953-70; invited prof. Laval U., Quebec City, Can., 1970-72; vol. exec. Internat. Exec. Svc. Corps, N.Y.C., 1972-79; pvt. practice as consultant in computer-aided design of electric motors, Sarasota, Fla., 1970—. Author: Fractional HP Electric Motors, 1939, 4th edit. 1986; Theory and Design Small Motors, 1959; How to Design a 1-ph Motor on a Personal Computer, 1989; How to Design a Metric 1-ph Motor on a PC, 1991; Computer-Aided Design Electric Machines, 1972. Patentee in field. Recipient Merit award Rsch. Inst. Rotating Machines Czechoslovakia, 1968; named to Hall of Fame Small Motors Mfg. Assn., 1985. Fellow IEEE (chmn. standards com. 1962-63, Tesla medal 1977, Centennial medal 1984), AIEE (v.p. 1949-51, chmn. rotating machines com. 1951-53, chmn. standards com. 1961-62); mem. Navy League U.S., Phi Beta Kappa, Eta Kappa Nu, Tau Beta Pi. Republican. Presbyterian. Club: High Twelve. Lodges: Masons, Shriners, Honorable Order Ky. Cols. Avocations: devel. of computer-aided design software for induction machines, home computers. Home: 4197 Oakhurst Cir W Sarasota FL 34233-1443

VEIT, FRITZ, librarian; b. Emmendingen, Baden, Germany, Sept. 17, 1907; came to U.S., 1935, naturalized, 1940; s. Samuel W. and Helene (Geismar) V.; m. Lucille Stearns, June 11, 1939; children: Joanne Grace, Mary Catherine (dec.). Student, U. Berlin, 1927, Heidelberg U., 1928; J.U.D., U. Freiburg, 1932; B.S. in Library Sci, Peabody Library Sch., Nashville, 1936; Ph.D., U. Chgo. Grad. Library Sch., 1941. Research asst. Inst. History Law, U. Freiburg, Germany, 1932-33; librarian U. Chgo. Grad. Library Sch., 1937-42, Social Sci. Reading Room, 1942; acting librarian Law Sch., 1943; librarian Chgo. City Jr. Coll. (Englewood evening br.), 1941-48; law librarian U.S.R.R. Retirement Bd., Chgo., 1943-49; supr. library John Marshall Law Sch., 1949-57; vis. prof. library sci. Rosary Coll., River Forest, Ill., 1950-78, Western Mich. U., summer 1959, Ariz. State U., summer 1964, 65, 67, 68, Emporia State U., summer 1977, Grad. Library Sch. U. Chgo., summer 1975, 78, fall 1977; dir. libraries Chgo. State U., 1949-73, also Kennedy-King Coll., 1949-72; chmn. adv. com. library tech. program Chgo. City Colls., 1968-74; mem. adv. council librarians U. Ill. Grad. Sch. Library Sci., 1971-74. Author: The Community College Library, 1975, Presidential Libraries and Collections, 1987; mem. editorial bd. Internat. Jour. Revs. in Libr. and Info. Sci., 1984-89, Third World Librs., 1990—; contbr. articles to profl. jours. Mem. ALA (sec., chmn. tchr. edn. libraries sect. ACRL 1959-61, assoc. editor monographs 1952-60, local chmn. ACRL 1963 Conf), Ill. Library Assn., Chgo. Library Club (pres. 1964-65), Pi Gamma Mu. Home: 1716 E 55th St Chicago IL 60615-5957

VEITCH, STEPHEN WILLIAM, investment counselor; b. Albuquerque, Aug. 19, 1927; s. Kenneth Easton and Edna (Miller) V.; B.A., U. N.Mex., 1949; LL.B., Stanford, 1957; student U. Nacional, Mex., 1949; m. Nancy Baker, June 28, 1951; children—Christopher Oxnard, Julia Blair. Bar: Calif., 1958. Probate adminstr. Wells Fargo Bank, San Francisco, 1957-59; sr. v.p. Van Strum & Towne, Inc., San Francisco, 1959-76, sr. v.p., 1976-82, pres., 1982-91, vice chmn, 1991—. Mem. Guardsman, San Francisco, 1960—. With USNR, 1945-46; 1st lt. USAF, 1950-54. Mem. Am., San Francisco bar assns., Delta Theta Phi, Sigma Chi. Republican. Episcopalian. Clubs: Commonwealth, Pacific Union (San Francisco); Menlo Circus (Atherton, Calif.). Home: 33 Spencer Ln Atherton CA 94027-4038 Office: 505 Sansome St Ste 1001 San Francisco CA 94111-3134

VEITH, ILZA, retired psychiatric history educator; b. Ludwigshafen, Germany, May 13, 1915; came to U.S., 1937, naturalized, 1945; m. Hans von Valentini Veith, Oct. 20, 1935 (dec. Mar. 1991). Student med. schs., Geneva and Vienna, Austria, 1934-36; M.A., Johns Hopkins, 1944, Ph.D., 1947; Igaku hakase (M.D., D.M.S.), Sch. Medicine, Juntendo U., Tokyo, 1975. Cons. Oriental medicine Armed Forces Med. Library, Washington, 1947-57; lectr. in history medicine U. Chgo., 1949-51; editorial bd. U. Chgo. Press, 1951-53; asst. prof. history medicine U. Chgo., 1953-57, assoc. prof., 1957-63; cons. in History of Medicine Nat. Inst. Health, 1959-64; vis. prof. Menninger Sch. Psychiatry, 1963; prof. history medicine, vice chmn. dept. U. Calif. at San Francisco Med. Center, 1964-79, prof. history psychiatry, 1967-79, prof. emeritus, 1979—; D.J. Davies Meml. lectr. U. Ill. Sch. Medicine, 1958; Sloan vis. prof. Menninger Found., 1963, 66; John Shaw Billings lectr. U. Ind. Sch. Medicine, Indpls., 1970; George W. Corner lectr. history medicine U. Rochester, N.Y., 1970; Logan Clendenning lectr. history of medicine U. Kans. Sch. Medicine, 1971; spl. lectr. VI World Congress Psychiatry, 1977; Hideyo Noguchi lectr. Johns Hopkins U., 1977. Author: Leverkusen, 1961, Medizin in Tibet, 1962, Hysteria: The History of a Disease, 1965, 3d edit., 1993, Yellow Emperor's Classic of Internal Medicine, 1966, Englishman or Samurai? The Story of Will Adams, 1981, Can You Hear the Clapping of One Hand? Learning to Live With a Stroke, 1988; co-author: Great Ideas in the History of Surgery, 3d edit., 1961, Acupuncture Therapy: Current Chinese Practice, 1973, 2d rev. and enlarged edit., 1976, Histoire de l' hystérie, 1974, Nei-Ching: Canone di Medicina Interna dell' Imperatore Giallo, 1976, Ishimpo The Essentials of Medicine in Ancient China and Japan, 1986; mem. editorial bd. Ency. Britannica; contbr. articles to profl. jours. Decorated officer's Cross of Merit Fed. Republic Germany, 1971; recipient Gold-Headed Cane award U. Kans. Sch. Medicine, 1976,

Disting. Service award for sci. achievement Med. Alumni Assn. of U. Chgo., 1983. Hon. fellow Am. Psychiat. Assn. (Benjamin Rush Meml. lectr. 1987); mem. Am. Assn. History of Medicine (council mem. 1958-62, 73-77), AAAS, Soc. History of Medicine Chgo. (pres. 1954-64), Soc. History Med. Scis. Los Angeles (hon.), History Sci. Soc., AMA (asso.), Marin Med. Soc. (hon.), Spanish Soc. History of Medicine (hon., corr. mem.), Bay Area Med. History Soc. (v.p. 1972), Johns Hopkins Alumni Assn. (past pres. Ill.), Royal Soc. Medicine (London), Vishwa Inst. of Oriental Medicine, Sri Lanka (hon.), German Soc. History Medicine, Sci. and Tech. (hon.), Sigma Xi. Home: 2235 Centro St E Belvedere Tiburon CA 94920-1947 Office: U Calif Med Ctr San Francisco CA 94143 also: Med Ctr, PO Box 70, Abidi Village Anambra State, Nigeria *In a long and severely handicapped life I have had to live with chronic illness and pain. Thanks to my husband's endless patience and helpfulness, I have learned to accept what cannot be changed, and to change what can be altered. I have had a successful and highly satisfactory academic career in spite of endless obstacles that lie in the way of a woman scholar. In short, I have had a difficult but eminently happy life.*

VEIZER, JÁN, geology educator; b. Pobedim, Slovakia, June 22, 1941; came to Can., 1973; s. Viktor and Brigita (Brandstetter) V.; m. Elena Ondrus, July 30, 1966; children: Robert, Andrew Douglas. Prom. Geol. Comenius U., Bratislava, Slovakia, 1964; RNDr, Comenius U. Bratislava, Slovak Republic, 1968; CSc, Slovak Acad. Sci. Bratislava, Slovakia, 1968; PhD, Australian Nat. U., Canberra, 1971. Asst. lectr. Comenius U., 1963-66; research scientist Slovak Acad. Sci., 1966-71; vis. asst. prof. UCLA, Los Angeles, 1972; vis. research scientist U. Göttingen, Fed. Republic Germany, 1972-73; research scientist U. Tübingen, Fed. Republic Germany, 1973; from asst. prof. to full prof. U. Ottawa (Can.), 1973—; prof. Ruhr U., Bochum, Fed. Republic of Germany, 1988—; cons. NASA, Houston, 1983-86; vis. prof. and scholar Northwestern U., Evanston, Ill., 1983-87; vis. fellow Australian Nat. U., 1979; vis. prof. U. Tübingen, 1974; Lady Davis professorship Hebrew U., Jerusalem, 1987. Contbr. articles to profl. jours., chpts. to books. Served to j.lt. Med., 1965-66, Czechoslovakia. Recipient W. Leibniz prize German Rsch. Found., 1992; named Rsch. Prof. Yr., 1987, Willet G. Miller Medal, 1991, Royal Soc. Can.; Humboldt fellow, 1980, Killam Research fellow Can. Council, 1986-88. Fellow Royal Soc. Can. (Willet G. Miller medal 1991), Geol. Assoc. Can. (Past-Pres. medal 1987, Logan medal 1995), Geol. Soc. Am.; mem. Geochem. Soc. Am. Roman Catholic. Club: Ski. Avocations: reading, hiking, skiing, history. Office: U Ottawa Dept Geology, Derry/Rust Rsch Group, Ottawa, ON Canada K1N 6N5 also: Ruhr U Inst Geologie, Lehrstuhl Sedimentgeologie, 44780 Bochum Federal Republic of Germany

VELA, DAVID, lawyer. Pub. defender Denver. Office: Pub Defender 110 16th St Ste 800 Denver CO 80202-5210

VELA, FILEMON B., federal judge; b. Harlingen, Tex., May 1, 1935; s. Roberto and Maria Luisa Cardenas V.; m. Blanca Sanchez, Jan. 28, 1962; children: Filemon, Rafael Eduardo, Sylvia Adriana. Student, Tex. Southmost Coll., 1954-56, U. Tex., 1956-57; JD, St. Mary's U., San Antonio, 1962. Bar: Tex. 1962. Mem. Vela & Vela, 1962-63; atty. Mexican-Am. Legal Def. Fund, 1962-75; pvt. practice law Brownsville, 1963-75; judge dist. 107, Tex. Dist. Ct., 1975-80; judge U.S. Dist. Ct. (so. dist.) Tex., Brownsville, 1980—; instr. Law Enforcement Coll. City commr., Brownsville, 1971-73. Served with U.S. Army, 1957-59. Mem. State Bar Tex. Democrat. Office: US Courthouse PO Box 1072 Brownsville TX 78520

VELARDO, JOSEPH THOMAS, molecular biology and endocrinology educator; b. Newark, Jan. 27, 1923; s. Michael Arthur and Antoinette (Iacullo) V.; m. Forresta M. Monica Power, Aug. 12, 1948 (dec. July 1976). AB, U. No. Colo., 1948; SM, Miami U., 1949; PhD, Harvard U., 1952. Rsch. fellow in biology and endocrinology Harvard U., Cambridge, Mass., 1952-53; rsch. assoc. in pathology, ob-gyn. and surgery Sch. Medicine Harvard U., Boston, 1953-55; asst. in surgery Peter Bent Brigham and Women's Hosp., Boston, 1954-55; asst. prof. anatomy and endocrinology Sch. Medicine, Yale U., New Haven, 1955-61; prof. anatomy, chmn. dept. N.Y. Med. Coll., N.Y.C., 1961-62; cons. N.Y. Fertility Inst., 1961-62; dir. Inst. for Study Human Reprodn., Cleve., 1962-67; prof. biology John Carroll U., Cleve., 1962-67; mem. rsch. and edn. divs. Saint Ann Obstetric and Gynecologic Hosp., Cleve., 1962-67; head dept. rsch. Saint Ann Hosp., Cleve., 1964-67; prof. anatomy Stritch Sch. Medicine Loyola U., Chgo., 1967-88, chmn. dept. anatomy Stritch Sch. of Medicine, 1967-73; pres. Internat. Basic and Biol.-Biomed. Curricula, Lombard, Ill., 1979—; course moderator laparoscopy Brazil-Israel Congress on Fertility and Sterility, and Brazil Soc. of Human Reproduction, Rio de Janeiro, 1973; organizer, chmn. symposia in field. Author, contbr. to: (with others) Annual Revs. Physiology, Reproduction, 1961, Histochemistry of Enzymes in the Female Genital System, 1963, The Ovary, 1963, The Ureter, 1967, rev. edit., 1981; editor, contbr. Endocrinology of Reproduction, 1958, Essentials of Human Reproduction, 1958; cons. editor, co-author: The Uterus, 1959; contbr. Progestational Substances, 1958, Trophoblast and Its Tumors, 1959, The Vagina, 1959, Hormonal Steroids, Biochemistry, Pharmacology and Therapeutics, 1964, Human Reproduction, 1973; co-editor, contbr.: Biology of Reproduction, Basic and Clinical Studies, 1973; co-author (movie) The Soft Anvil; appearances on several radio and TV networks; contbr. articles to profl. jours. Apptd. U.S. del. to Vatican, 1964; charter mem. U.S. Rep. Presdl. Task Force, 1988—; rep. U.S. Senate Inner Circle, 1988—, U.S. Rep. Senatorial Commn., 1991—. With USAAF, 1943-45. Decorated Presdl. Unit citation with 2 oak leaf clusters; award recipient Lederle Med. Faculty Awards Com., 1955-58; named hon. citizen City of Sao Paulo, Brazil, 1972; U.S. del. to Vatican, 1964. Fellow AAAS, N.Y. Acad. Scis. (co-organizer, chmn., consulting editor internat. symposium The Uterus), Gerontol. Soc., Pacific Coast Fertility Soc. (hon.); mem. Am. Assn. Anatomists, Am. Soc. Zoologists (organizer symposium The Uterus 1973), Am. Physiol. Soc. (vis. prof. 1962), Endocrine Soc., Soc. Endocrinology (Gt. Britain), Soc. Exptl. Biology and Medicine, Am. Soc. Study Sterility (Rubin award 1954), Internat. Fertility Assn., Pan Am. Assn. Anatomy (co-organizer symposium Reproduction 1972), Midwestern Soc. Anatomists (pres. 1973-74), Mexican Soc. Anatomy (hon.), Harvard Club, Sigma Xi, Kappa Delta Pi, Phi Sigma, Gamma Alpha, Alpha Epsilon Delta. Achievements include extensive original research and publications on the physiology and development of decidual tissue (experimental equivalent of the maternal portion of the placenta) in the rat; biological investigation of eighteen human adenohypophyses (anterior lobes of the human pituitary glands); induction of ovulation utilizing highly purified adenohypophyseal gonadotropic hormones in mammals; the pacemaker action of ovarian sex steroid hormones on reproductive processes; and the interaction of steroids in reproductive mechanisms. Office: 607 E Wilson Ave Lombard IL 60148-4062 *Personal philosophy: Success is best highlighted by the invincible instruments of truth, hard work, thinking, running the extra mile, leading or giving help where no other help seems forthcoming, recognizing the talents of our fellow man and lady, and above all, practicing of the Golden Rule.*

VELASCO, EUGENIO, advertising executive; b. Cananea, Sonora, Mex., Dec. 26, 1944; s. J. Ruben and Alma (Williams) V.; m. Norma Kirschner, June 5, 1971; children: Eugenio, Norma. BSC Mktg., U. Santa Clara, 1967. Brand mgr. Proctor & Gamble, Mexico City, Mexico, 1967-71; acct. supr. Doyle Dane Berbanch, Mexico City, Mexico, 1971-72; acct. dir. Arellano Nck., Mexico City, Mexico, 1972-75; v.p. mng. dir. Leo Burnett, Mexico City, Mexico, 1975-78, Madrid, 1978-79; pres. gen. mgr. Leo Burnett Columbiana, Bogota, Columbia, 1980-84, Foote Cone & Belding, Mexico City, Mex., 1984-86; exec. v.p. Publicidad Augusto Elias, Mexico City, Mex., 1986-88; pres., gen. mgr. Grey Mex., Mexico City, Mex., 1989—; bd. dirs. Assn. Mexicana de Agencias de Publicidad, Mexico City; v.p. Union Columbiana de Emprseas de Publicidad, Bogota, 1980-84. Mem. Univ. Club, Delta Sigma Pi (life), Club de Golf la Hacienda. Roman Catholic. Avocations: golf, reading. Home: Bosques de Reforma 1447 T4PB, Mexico City 11700, Mexico Office: Grey Mexico SA de CV, Horacio 1844, Mexico City 11550, Mexico

VELASQUEZ, JOE, labor union administrator; b. Taylor, Tex., Nov. 17, 1946; m. Mary Frances; children: Pilar, Casey. BS, Ind. State U., 1970. Staff mem. United Auto Workers, Detroit; spl. asst. to exec. sec. Labor for Occupational Safety and Health/Carter Adminstrn.; exec. dir. Workers' Inst. for Safety and Health; asst. dir. polit. dept. AFL-CIO; dir. dept. community svcs. AFL-CIO, Washington. Office: AFL-CIO Dept Community Svcs 815 16th St NW Washington DC 20006-4104

VELASQUEZ, JORGE LUIS, JR., jockey; b. Panama, Dec. 28, 1946; s. Jorge Luis and Francisca V.; m. Margaria Knipping, Nov. 13, 1969; children: Jorge, Michele, Monique. Jockey; rider horses Pleasant Colony, Alydar, Fort Marcy; Devona Dale (Triple Crown Winner for fillies), 1974; rider horses Hawaii, Fort Maray, Late Bloomer, Our Mims, Before Dawn, others. Mem. Jockeys Guild. Nat. leader in wins, 1967, in money won, 1969; 6 times leading rider in N.Y.; winner Ky. Derby and Preakness riding Pleasant Colony; winner richest thoroughbred match riding Chris Evert, 1973; winner Fla. Derby and Breeders' Cup riding Proud Truth, 1985; set N.Y. record for 6 wins out of 6 mounts, July 1981. Office: Jockey's Guild 20 E 46th St Rm 901 New York NY 10017-2417

VELAZQUEZ, NYDIA M., congresswoman; b. Yabucoa, P.R.. Grad. U. P.R.; MA, NYU, 1976. Mem. 103rd-104th Congress from 12th N.Y. dist., Washington, D.C., 1992—. Office: US Ho of Reps 132 Cannon Washington DC 20515*

VELDE, JOHN ERNEST, JR., business executive; b. Pekin, Ill., June 15, 1917; s. John Ernest and Alga (Anderson) V.; m. Shirley Margaret Walker, July 29, 1940 (dec. 1969); 1 dau., Drew; m. Gail Patrick, Sept. 28, 1974 (dec. July 1980); m. Gretchen Swanson Pullen, Nov. 7, 1981. A.B., U. Ill., 1938. Pres. Velde, Roelfs & Co., Pekin, 1955-60; dir. Herget Nat. Bank, 1948-75, Kroehler Mfg. Co., 1979-81; pres. Paisano Prodns., Inc., 1980-94, mng. ptnr., 1994—; mng. ptnr. The Gardner Partnership, 1994—. Trustee Pekin Pub. Library, 1948-69, Pekin Meml. Hosp., 1950-69, Everett McKinley Dirksen Rsch. Ctr., 1965-74, Am. Libr. Assn. Endowment, 1976-82, Joint Coun. Econ. Edn., 1977-83, Ctr. Am. Archeology, 1978-83, Western Heritage Mus., Omaha, 1994—; chmn. Am. Libr. Trustee Assn. Found., 1976; chmn. trustees, bd. dirs. Ctr. Ulcer Rsch. and Edn. Found., 1977-82; mem. bd. councilors Brain Rsch. Inst. UCLA, 1977-82; mem. Nat. Commn. on Libr. and Info. Sci., 1970-79; mem. adv. bd. on White House Conf. on Librs., 1976-80; bd. dirs. U. Ill. Found., 1977-83, Omaha Pub. Libr. Found., 1985-92, James Madison Coun. Libr. Congress, 1990—; vice chmn. U. Ill. Pres.' Coun., 1977-79, chmn., 1979-81, mem. fin. resources coun. steering com., 1976-78; mem. adv. coun. UCLA Grad. Sch. Libr. and Info. Sci., 1981-82; pres. Ill. Valley Library System, 1965-69; dir. Lakeview Ctr. for Arts and Scis., Peoria, Ill., 1962-73; mem. Nat. Book Com., 1969-74. Served as lt. (j.g.) USNR, World War II. Mem. Am. Libr. Trustee Assn. (regional v.p. 1970-72, chmn. internat. rels. com. 1973-76), Internat. Boy Scouts (Baden-Powell fellow 1987—), Kappa Sigma. Clubs: Chgo. Yacht, Internat. (Chgo.); California (Los Angeles); Outrigger Canoe (Honolulu); Thunderbird Country (Rancho Mirage, Calif.); Chaine des Rotisseurs, Chevaliers du Tastevin; Circumnavigators (N.Y.C.); Omaha, Omaha Country; Old Baldy (Saratoga, Wyo.), Eldorado Country (Indian Wells, Calif.). Home: 8405 Indian Hills Dr Omaha NE 68114-4067 also: 40-231 Club View Dr Rancho Mirage CA 92270 also: 123 Arapahoe Dr Saratoga WY 82331

VELIANOFF, GEORGE D., nursing administrator. Diploma, Bethesda Hosp. Sch. Nursing, Cin., 1979; BSN, Edgecliff Coll., 1981; PhD in Nursing Sci., Ind. U., Indpls., 1986. RN, Ohio, W.Va., Ind. Nurse Bethesda Hosp., Cin., 1979-81, chg. nurse emer. dept., 1981-82, nursing supr., 1982-85; asst. dir. med.-surg. nursing Univ. Hosps., Cleve., 1986-89; asst. adminstr. Heartland Hosps., St. Joseph, Mo., 1989-90; adminstr. for nursing Charleston (W.Va.) Area Med. Ctr., 1990—; clin. nurse to plastic and reconstructive surgeon in pvt. practice, Cin., 1980-85; asst. clin. prof. Frances Payne Bolton Sch. Nursing, Case Western Res. U., Cleve., 1986-89; mem. affiliate faculty U. Mo. Sch. Nursing, Kansas City, 1989-91; lectr. to profl. orgns. and confs.; adj. faculty Marshall U., 1991—. Editor: NurseNet, 1991; contbr. articles to profl. pubs. Mem. ANA, AACN, Nat. League Nursing, Sigma Theta Tau. Home: 23 Cedar Dr Hurricane WV 25526-9221 Office: Charleston Area Med Ctr 3101 Maccorkle Ave SE Charleston WV 25304-1217

VELICER, LELAND FRANK, veterinarian, microbiologist, virologist, educator; b. Kewaunee, Wis., Oct. 16, 1939; s. George Matthew and Elsie (Cherney) V.; m. Janet Francis Schafbuch, Aug. 17, 1963; children: Mark Allen, Gregory Jon, Daniel James. D.V.M., Iowa State U., 1964; Ph.D., U. Pa., 1969. Asst. prof. microbiology Mich. State U., 1969-74, asso. prof., 1974-79, prof., 1979—; vis. scientist Center for Cancer Research, MIT, 1977-78. Patentee in field. Served with U.S. Army, 1957. Recipient USPHS rsch. career devel. award Nat. Cancer Inst., 1974-79, SmithKline Beecham award for rsch. excellence, 1993. Mem. AAAS, AVMA, Am. Soc. Microbiology, Am. Soc. Virology, Am. Assn. Cancer Rsch., Conf. Rsch. Workers in Animal Diseases, Grayson-Jockey Club Rsch. Found. (sci. adv. com. 1976-92), Vet. Cancer Soc., Mich. Vet. Medicine Assn., Sigma Xi. Roman Catholic. Home: 2678 Blue Haven Ct East Lansing MI 48823-3804 Office: Dept Microbiology Mich State U East Lansing MI 48824-1101

VELICK, SIDNEY FREDERICK, research biochemist, educator; b. Detroit, May 3, 1913; s. Harry Alexander and Ella (Stocker) V.; m. Bernadette Stemler, Sept. 5, 1941; children: William Frederick, Martha Elizabeth. B.S., Wayne State U., 1935; Ph.D., U. Mich., 1938. Research fellow parasitology Johns Hopkins U., 1939-40; research asso. chemistry Yale U., 1941-45; mem. biol. chemistry dept. Washington U. Sch. Medicine, 1958-64; prof., head dept. biol. chemistry Washington U. Sch. Medicine, 1964-79, prof. emeritus, 1988—; mem. biochemistry study sect. NIH. Assoc. editor: Archives Biochemistry and Biophysics; editorial bd.: Jour. Biol. Chemistry; contbr. papers on enzyme chemistry to tech. lit. Co-founder, pres. Alliance for the Mentally Ill Utah, 1980-85. Mem. NAS, AAAS, Am. Soc. Biol. Chemists, Am. Chem. Soc., Sigma Xi. Home: 4183 Parkview Dr Salt Lake City UT 84124-3436

VELIE, LESTER, journalist; b. Kiev, Ukraine, 1907; came to U.S., 1912, naturalized, 1922; s. Samuel and Sarah (Spector) V.; m. Frances Rockmore, Oct. 29, 1932; children: Alan R., Franklin Bell. BA, U. Wis., 1929. Reporter AP, N.Y., 1931-32; suburban editor Bklyn. Eagle, 1932-35; assoc. editor Jour. Commerce, N.Y.C., 1937-46; radio analyst Sta. WQXR, N.Y.C., 1941-45; assoc. editor Collier's, 1945-52; roving editor Reader's Digest, 1953-85. Author: Labor U.S.A, 1959, Labor U.S.A Today, 1964, Countdown in the Holy Land, 1969, Desperate Bargain: Why Jimmy Hoffa had to Die, 1977, Murder Story: A Tragedy of Our Time, 1983; contbr. to Op Ed N.Y. Times; ABC TV series Target the Corrupters based on mag. articles. Recipient Disting. Svc. award for mag. journalism Sigma Delta Chi, 1949, Sch. Bell award for mag. journalism NEA, 1966, Silver Gavel award ABA, 1973; Ford Found. grantee, 1981-82. Home and Office: 32 Hemlock Dr Great Neck NY 11024-1234

VELIOTES, NICHOLAS ALEXANDER, professional association executive, former ambassador and assistant secretary of state; b. Oakland, Calif., Oct. 28, 1928; s. Alexander and Irene (Kiskaskis) V.; m. Patricia Jane Nolan, July 17, 1953; children: Christopher, Michael. BA, U. Calif.-Berkeley, 1952, MA, 1954; postgrad., Princeton U., 1969-70. Teaching asst. U. Calif.-Berkeley, 1952-54; commd. officer U.S. Fgn. Service, 1955; held various Fgn. Service posts Italy, India, Laos, Israel, Jordan, Egypt; Asst. Sec. of State Near East/South Asia, 1981-83; ambassador to Jordan, 1978-81, ambassador to Egypt, 1983-86; pres. Assn. Am. Pubs., 1986—. Bd. dirs. Fund for Free Expression, Amer. Acad. Diplomacy, Com. on Pres., Access and Amideast. Served with U.S. Army, 1946-48. Recipient Sec. of State and Presdl. Disting. Service awards. Mem. Council on Fgn. Relations, VFW. Office: Assn Am Pub 1718 Connecticut Ave NW Washington DC 20009-1148

VELLENGA, KATHLEEN OSBORNE, former state legislator; b. Alliance, Nebr., Aug. 5, 1938; d. Howard Benson and Marjorie (Menke) Osborne; m. James Alan Vellenga, Aug. 9, 1959; children: Thomas, Charlotte Vellenga Landreau, Carolyn. BA, Macalester Coll. 1959. Tchr. St. Paul Pub. Schs., 1959-60, Children's Ctr. Montessori, St. Paul, 1973-74, Children's House Montessori, St. Paul. 1974-79; mem. Minn. Ho. of Reps., St. Paul, 1980-94, mem. health and human svcs. com., 1981-92, mem. tax com., rules com., chmn. judiciary comm., 1991—; chmn. St. Paul del., 1985-89, chmn. criminal justice div., 1989-90, chmn. crime and family law div., 1987-88, mem. Dem. steering com., 1987-94; chmn. judiciary Minn. Ho. of Reps, 1991, 92, chmn. edn. fin., 1992-93, 93-94; mem. St. Paul Family Svcs. Bd., 1994-95; coord. St. Paul, Ramsey County Children's Initiative, 1994-95. Mem. steering com. Alliance for Sci., St. Paul, 1982-84; chmn. Healthstart, St. Paul, 1987-91;

mem. Children, Youth & Families Consortium, 1995—, St. Paul Pub. Safety Coun., 1995, Macalester Coll. Bd. Alumni, 1995—. Mem. LWV (v.p. St. Paul chpt. 1979), Minn. Women Elected Ofcls. (vice chair 1994). Democrat. Presbyterian. Office: A H Wilder 919 La Fond Saint Paul MN 55104

VELMANS, LOET ABRAHAM, retired public relations executive; b. Amsterdam, Netherlands, Mar. 18, 1923; s. Joseph and Anna (Cohen) V.; m. Pauline Edith Van Hessen; Mar. 29, 1949; children: Marianne and Hester (twins), Jessica. Grad., U. Amsterdam, 1947. Info. officer Dutch Govt. in Singapore, 1945-47; with Hill & Knowlton, Inc., 1953-86; v.p. Hill Knowlton Internat., Geneva, 1959-69; pres. Hill Knowlton Internat., 1960-74; vice chmn. Hill Knowlton Internat., London, 1969-76; pres. Hill Knowlton Internat., N.Y.C., 1976-86; chmn. bd., chief exec. officer Hill Knowlton Internat., 1980-86. Contbr. articles on multinat. corps. to profl. jours. Bd. dirs. Lincoln Ctr. Inst., Netherland Am. Found., Global Pub. Affairs Inst. NYU. Decorated Grande Ufficiale Order of Merit, Italy, 1989. Club: Mid-Atlantic of N.Y. Inc. (pres.). Home: PO Box 178 Sheffield MA 01257-0178

VELTMAN, MARTINUS J., physics educator. John D. MacArthur prof. physics U. Mich., Ann Arbor. Recipient High Energy and Particle Physics prize European Phys. Soc., 1993. Office: U Mich Dept Physics 500 E University Ave Ann Arbor MI 48108-1105*

VELZ, JOHN WILLIAM, literature educator; b. Englewood, N.J., Aug. 5, 1930; s. Clarence Joseph and Harriet Josephine (O'Brien) V.; m. Sarah Elizabeth Campbell, Oct. 18, 1967; children: Jody, Emily; 3 children from previous marriage. BA in English with high distinction and honors, U. Mich., 1953, MA in English and French, 1954; PhD in English and Classical Greek, U. Minn., 1963. Instr. Coll. St. Thomas, St. Paul, 1958-60; asst. prof. English Rice U., Houston, 1963-69; prof. U. Tex., Austin, 1969—; vis. prof. U. Paul Valery, Montpelier, France, 1977-78, Julius Maximillians U., Wuerzburg, West Germany, 1981-82, 85-86; asst. dir., lit. adv. Odessa Shakespeare Festival, 1977; faculty mem. Oreg. Shakespeare Festival, 1979; lectr. tour Cen. and Ea. Europe univs., 1993; dir. acad. prodns. of Shakespeare and medieval drama; mem. Acad. Adv. Coun. Globe Theatre Ctr., 1981—; mem. U.S. Com. for Shakespeare's Globe, 1990—. Author: Shakespeare and the Classical Tradition, 1968 (ALA citation, Assn. Coll. and Research Libraries citation); editor: Julius Caesar (Shakespeare): co-editor: Collected Papers of James G. McManaway, 1969, One Touch of Shakespeare: Letters of Joseph Crosby to Joseph Parker Norris 1875-1878, 1986, editor: Shakespeare's English Histories: A Quest for Form and Genre, 1995; contbr. numerous scholarly, interpretive articles, mainly on Shakespeare and on medieval drama, to profl. jours.; presenter numerous papers to learned socs.; mem. editorial bd. Shakespeare Quar., 1975—, Classical and Modern Lit., 1981-85, Tex. Studies in Lit. and Lang., 1969-92, Shakespeare and the Classroom, 1993—; editor (N.Am.) Cahiers Elisabethains, 1979-81; editorial adv. bd. Complete Works of Shakespeare, 3d edit., 1980, 4th edit., 1992; cons. editor South Cen. Rev., 1989-92; mem. cons. com. International Studies in Shakespeare and His Contemporaries, 1990—. Recipient Fulbright award, 1977-78, 81-82; recipient Oreon E. Scott award U. Mich., 1953; NEH fellow, 1967-68; Folger Library fellow, 1968. Mem. MLA, Internat. Shakespeare Assn. (charter), Shakespeare Assn. Am., Malone Soc., Renaissance English Text Soc., Medieval and Renaissance Drama Soc., Marlowe Soc. of Am., Soc. for Textual Scholarship, H.W. Fowler Soc. (charter), Phi Beta Kappa, Phi Kappa Phi, Phi Eta Sigma. Home: 809 W 32d St Austin TX 78705 Office: U Tex Dept English Austin TX 78712 *Academic life is predicated on the obligation to teach as generously as we have been taught, to serve others as we have been served. This sense of mutuality has been a rationale for my professional life, though it would be impossible to pay all I owe.*

VELZY, CHARLES O., mechanical engineer; b. Oak Park, Ill., Mar. 17, 1930; s. Charles R and Ethel B V.; m. Marilyn A. Gilman, Aug. 17, 1957; children: Charles Mark, Barbara Helen, Patricia Ethel. B.S.M.E., U. Ill., 1953, B.S. in Civil Engring., 1960, M.S. in San. Engring., 1959. Registered profl. engr., N.Y., 13 other states. Design engr., project engr. Nussbaumer, Clarke & Velzy, N.Y.C., 1959-66; sec.-treas., dir. Charles R Velzy Assos., Inc., Armonk, N.Y., 1966-76; pres. Charles R Velzy Assoc., Inc., 1976-92; v.p. Roy F. Weston Inc., 1987-92; pres. Charles O. Velzy, P.E., Lyndonville, Vt., 1992—. Contbr. articles to profl. jours. Mem. White Plains (N.Y.) Bldg. Code Appeals Bd., 1970-92. With U.S. Army, 1954-56. Fellow ASME (chmn. solid waste processing divsn. 1973, 74, mem. policy bd. Rsch. 1974-78, bd. govs. 1983-84, pres. 1989-90, Centennial medal 1980, Medal of Achievement 1981), Am. Cons. Engrs. Coun.; mem. ASTM, ASCE (life), NSPE, Am. Acad. Environ. Engrs. (trustee 1984-87, treas. 1993—), Am. Water Works Assn. (life), Water Environ. Fedn., Air Waste Mgmt. Assn. Methodist. *After deciding on what is needed in a specific situation, based on the facts, establish your objectives and goals and persist to a successful conclusion.*

VENA, DAVID HENRY, lawyer; b. Los Angeles, Dec. 21, 1938; s. David P. and Frances (Wilks) V.; m. Carolyn Willis, Jan. 20, 1961 (div. Dec. 1980); children: Gabrielle, Arianne; m. Carol A. Vena-Mondt, Sept. 30, 1984. AB, UCLA, 1961; LLB, Harvard U., 1964. Bar: Calif. 1965, U.S Dist. Ct. (so. dist.) Calif. 1965, U.S. Ct. Appeals (9th cir.) 1965. Assoc. Latham & Watkins, Los Angeles, ptnr.; legal cons. Concept Team Summa Corp., Marina del Ray, Calif., 1984—; bd. dirs The Becket Group, Santa Monica, Calif. Founder Mus. Contemporary Art, Los Angeles; trustee Friends of Photography, Carmel, Calif., 1983—; bd. dirs Otis/Parsons, Los Angeles, 1980—, Skystone Found. Inc., Flagstaff, Ariz., 1985—, UCLA Arts Council, 1986—. Mem. Los Angeles Bar Assn.. Club: Los Angeles Country. Avocations: collecting contemporary art, golf. Home: 929 E 2nd St #206 Los Angeles CA 90012 Office: Latham & Watkins 633 W 5th St Ste 4000 Los Angeles CA 90071-2005

VENDELA, model. With Ford Models, Inc., N.Y., 1986, Elizabeth Arden, 1988. appeared on cover of Sports Illustrated Swimsuit Edition, 1993. Office: Ford Models Inc 344 E 59th St New York NY 10022-1570

VENDLER, HELEN HENNESSY, literature educator, poetry critic; b. Boston, Mass., Apr. 30, 1933; d. George and Helen (Conway) Hennessy; 1 son, David. A.B., Emmanuel Coll., 1954; Ph.D., Harvard U., 1960; Ph.D. (hon.), U. Oslo; D.Litt. (hon.), Smith Coll., Kenyon Coll., U. Hartford, Union Coll., Columbia U., George Washington U., Marlboro Coll., St. Louis; DHL (hon.), Dartmouth Coll., U. Mass., Bates Coll., U. Toronto, Ont., Can., Trinity Coll., Dublin, Ireland. Instr. Cornell U., Ithaca, N.Y., 1960-63; lectr. Swarthmore (Pa.) Coll. and Haverford (Pa.) Coll., 1963-64; asst. prof. Smith Coll., Northampton, Mass., 1964-66; asso. prof. Boston U., 1966-68, prof., 1968-85; $D; Fulbright lectr. U. Bordeaux, France, 1968-69; vis. prof. Harvard U., 1981-85, Kenan prof., 1985—, Porter U. prof., 1990—, assoc. acad. dean, 1987-92, sr. fellow Harvard Soc. Fellows, 1981-93; poetry critic New Yorker, 1978—; mem. ednl. adv. bd. Guggenheim Found., 1991—, Pulitzer Prize Bd., 1991—. Author: Yeats' Vision and the Later Plays, 1963, On Extended Wings: Wallace Stevens' Longer Poems, 1969, The Poetry of George Herbert, 1975, Part of Nature, Part of Us, 1980, The Odes of John Keats, 1983, Wallace Stevens: Words Chosen Out of Desire, 1985, Harvard Book of Contemporary Am. Poetry, 1985; editor: Voices and Visions: The Poet in America, 1987, The Music of What Happens, 1988, Soul Says, 1995, The Given and the Made, 1995, The Breaking of Style, 1995. Fulbright fellow, 1954, AAUW fellow, 1959, Guggenheim fellow, 1971-72, Am. Coun. Learned Socs. fellow, 1971-72, NEH fellow, 1980, 85, 94, Overseas fellow Churchill Coll., Cambridge, 1980, Charles Stewart Parnell fellow Magdalene Coll., 1995; recipient Lowell prize 1969, Explicator prize, 1969, award Nat. Inst. Arts and Letters, 1975, Radcliffe Grad. Soc. medal, 1978, Nat. Book Critics award, 1980, Keats-Shelley Assn. award, 1994. Mem. MLA (exec. coun. 1972-75, pres. 1980), English Inst. (trustee 1977-85), Am. Acad. Arts and Scis (v.p. 1992—), Norwegian Acad. Letters and Sci., Nat. Humanities Ctr. (bd. dirs. 1989-93), Am. Acad. Arts and Letters, Am. Philos. Soc., Phi Beta Kappa. Home: 54 Trowbridge St # 2 Cambridge MA 02138 also: Harvard U Dept English 8 Prescott St Cambridge MA 02138

VENEGAS, ARTURO, JR., chief police; b. San Nicolas de Ibarra, Jalisco, Mexico, Dec. 22, 1948; m. Anna Marie Venegas; children: Angela, Adriana, Anthony, Andrew. BA, U. San Francisco, 1978; MS in Mgmt., Calif. Poly., Pomona, 1991. Police officer Fresno (Calif.) Police Dept., 1970-75, police specialist, 1975-79, sgt., field supr., 1979, 80-85, lt., 1985-90, lt., acting divsn.

comdr. adminstrv. svcs., 1990-92, dep. chief police investigations divsn., 1992-93; chief program devel., program mgr. State Office Criminal Justice Planning, Sacramento, Calif., 1979-80; chief police Sacramento Police Dept., 1993—. Mem. Calif. Atty. Gen.'s Policy Coun. on Violence Prevention; bd. dirs. Safety Ctr.; mem. exec. bd. Sacramento Safe Sts.; mem. adv. bd. Cath. Social Svcs. With U.S. Army, 1966-68. Mem. Internat. Assn. Chiefs of Police, Calif. Assn. Chiefs of Police, Calif. Peace Officers Assn. (chair law and legis. com.), Police Exec. Rsch. Forum, Ctrl. Sierra Police Chief's Assn., FBI Nat. Acad. Assocs., Latino Peace Officers Assn., Hispanic-Am. Command Officers Assn., Am. Legion, Footprinters Internat., KC, Point West Rotary. Office: Police Dept Hall of Justice 813 6th St Sacramento CA 95814-2403

VENEMAN, GERARD EARL, paper company executive; b. Wheeling, W.Va., June 30, 1920; s. F. Earl and Ethel Martha (Joyce) V.; m. Doris D. Alexander, Jan. 10, 1948; children: Stephanie Joyce, Dean Gerard, Leslie Ann, Nancy Ellen, Jill Edwards. Student, U. Detroit, Northwestern U. Sales mgr. Agar Packing Co., Chgo., 1945-49; with Nekoosa Papers Inc., Port Edwards, Wis., 1949-85; v.p., dir. sales Nekoosa Papers Inc., 1954-62, exec. v.p., dir. mktg., 1962-69, exec. v.p., 1969-70, pres., 1970-85; bd. dirs. Wood County Nat. Bank, Wisconsin Rapids, Wis., Franklin Electric, Bluffton, Ind., Sentry Ins. Co., Stevens Point, Wis. Pres., bd. dirs. Alexander Charitable Found.; bd. dirs., v.p. South Wood County YMCA, Port Edwards; bd. regents U. Wis. System, 1979-86. Served with AUS, World War II. Decorated Bronze Star. Mem. Sales Assn. Paper Industry (pres. 1960, gov. 1964—), Writing Paper Mfrs. Assn. (exec. and finance coms. 1954—, chmn. sulphite bond group 1960-62, v.p 1960-62, pres. 1963-65), Printing and Writing Assn. (chmn. 1975), Am. Paper Inst. (rep. bd. govs. 1963-65). Home: PO Box 70 Port Edwards WI 54409-0070

VENETSANOPOULOS, ANASTASIOS NICOLAOS, electrical engineer, educator; b. Athens, Greece, June 19, 1941; emigrated to Can., 1968; s. Nicolaos Anastasios and Elli (Papacondilis) V. Diploma, Athens Coll. 1960; diploma in elec. and mech. engring., Nat. Tech. U., Athens, 1965, hon. doctorate, 1994; MS, Yale U., 1966, MPhil, 1968, PhD, 1969. Registered profl. engr., Greece, Ont. Asst. in instrn. engring. and applied sci. Yale U., 1966-68, research asst., 1968-69; lectr. U. Toronto, Ont., Can., 1968-69; asst. prof. elec. engring. U. Toronto, 1970-73, assoc. prof., 1973-81, prof., 1981—, chmn. communications group dept. elec. engring., 1974-78, 81-86, assoc. chmn. elec. engring., 1978-79, mem. elec. engring. exec. com., 1974-78, 81-86, mem. elec. engring. curriculum com., 1972-79; acad. visitor Imperial Coll. Arts and Tech., U. London, 1979-80; vis. prof. Nat. Tech. U. Athens, spring 1979-80, Fed. U. of Technology of Lausanne, Switzerland, 1986-87, 93-94, U. Florence, Italy, summer 1987; cons. elec. engring. Consociates Ltd. Editor Can. Elec. Engring. Jour., 1981-83; contbr. over 480 articles to profl. jours; contbr. to 23 books. Mem. allocations and agy. relations com. United Community Fund, Toronto, 1971-74; pres. Hellenic-Can. Cultural Soc., 1972-75; sec. gen. Greek Community Met. Toronto, 1973-75. Fulbright travel grantee in U.S., 1965; Def. Research Bd. Can. grantee, 1972-75, UN grantee; NSF grantee; J.P. Bickell Found. grantee; Natural Scis. and Engring. Research Council of Can. Fellow IEEE (fin. chmn. internat. symposium on circuit theory 1973, tech. program chmn. internat. conf. communications 1978, 86, vice-chmn. Toronto sect. 1976-77, chmn. 1977-79, assoc. editor transactions on circuits and systems 1985-87, guest editor spl. issue Transactions on Circuits and Systems in Image Processing 1987), Engring. Inst. Can.; mem. Assn. Profl. Engrs. Ont., Assn. Profl. Elec. Engrs. Greece, Assn. Profl. Mech. Engrs. Greece, Can. Soc. Elec. Engring. (chmn. Toronto sect. 1975-77, nat. dir. 1976-88, pres. 1983-86), Yale Sci. and Engring. Assn., N.Y. Acad. Scis., Tech. Chamber Greece, Am.-Hellenic Ednl. Progress Assn. (v.p Toronto sect. 1979-75), Intercultural Council (chmn. ednl. com. 1971-80, sr. v.p 1977-80), Sigma Xi. Office: U Toronto, Dept Elec and Computer Engring, Toronto, ON Canada M5S 1A4

VENEZKY, RICHARD LAWRENCE, English educator; b. Pitts., Apr. 16, 1938; s. Bernard Jacob and Isabel (Zeisel) V.; m. Karen F. Gauz, Aug. 2, 1964; children: Dina Yael, Elie Michael. BEE, Cornell U., 1961, MA, 1962; postgrad., U. Calif.-Berkeley, 1962-63; PhD, Stanford U., 1965. Systems programmer, tech. writer Control Data Corp., Palo Alto, Calif., 1962-65; asst. prof. English and computer scis. U. Wis., Madison, 1965-69; assoc. prof. English, computer and info. scis. U. Del., Newark, 1977—; Benton fellow in literacy U. Chgo., 1994-95; vis. rsch. assoc. Tel Aviv U., 1969-70, rsch. fellow, 1973; cons. Oxford English Dictionary Supplement; dir. computing Dictionary of Old English, 1971— co-dir. for R&D Nat. Ctr. on Adult Literacy, 1990—. Author: The Structure of English Orthography, 1970, Testing in Reading, 1974, Random House Spelling Across the Curriculum, 1988; co-author: A Microfiche Concordance to Old English, 1981, Letter and Word Perception, 1980, PRS-Pre-Reading Skills Program, 1985, The Subtle Danger, 1987, World of Reading, 1989, The Intelligent Design of Computer-Assisted Instruction, 1991; co-editor: Orthography, Reading and Dyslexia, 1980, Toward Defining Literacy, 1990; contbr. articles to profl. jours., chpts. to books. Chmn. edin. commn Madison Jewish Community Coun., 1973-77; v.p. Jewish Fedn. Del., 1986-89; regional chmn. Am. Profs. for Peace in Mid. East, 1968-73. Named to Reading Hall of Fame, 1991; grantee Office of Edn., 1964-66, NSF, 1964-74, Nat. Inst. Edn., 1973-77, NEH, 1978-89, Office of Ednl. Rsch. and Improvement, Dept. Edn., 1990—. Mem. Am. Psychol. Soc., Am. Edn. Rsch. Assn., Internat. Reading Assn., Assn. Computing Machinery. Democrat. Jewish. Home: 206 Hullihen Dr Newark DE 19711-3651

VENKATA, SUBRAHMANYAM SARASWATI, electrical engineering educator, electri energy and power researcher; b. Nellore, Andhra Pradesh, India, June 28, 1942; came to U.S., 1968; s. Ramiah Saraswati and Lakshmi (Alladi) V.; m. Padma Subrahmanyam Mahadevan, Sept. 3, 1971; children: Sridevi Saraswati, Harish Saraswati. BSEE, Andhra U., Waltair, India, 1963; MSEE, Indian Inst. Tech., Madras, 1965; PhD, U.S.C., 1971. Registered profl. engr., W.Va., Wash. Lectr. in elec. engring. Coimbatore (India) Inst. Tech., 1965-66; planning engr. S.C. Elec. & Gas Co., Columbia, 1969-70; postdoctoral fellow U. S.C., Columbia, 1971; instr. elec. engring. U. Mass., Lowell, 1971-72; asst. prof. W.Va. U., Morgantown, 1972-75, assoc. prof., 1975-79; prof. U. Wash., Seattle, 1979—; cons. Puget Sound Power & Light, Bellevue, Wash., 1980—, GEC/Alsthom, N.Y.C., 1991—; series editor, bd. dirs. PWS Pub. Co., 1991—. Author: Introduction of Electrical Energy Devices, 1987; patentee adaptive var compensator. Advisor Explorers Club, Morgantown, 1976-78; sec. Hindu Temple and Cultural Ctr. Pacific N.W., Seattle, 1990, chmn., 1991, 95. Recipient W.Va. U. Assocs. award W.Va. U. Found., 1974, 78. Fellow IEEE (best paper award 1985, 88, 91); mem. Conf. Internat. des Grands Reseaux Electriques, Sigma Xi, Tau Beta Pi, Eta Kappa Nu. Democrat. Avocations: photography, tennis, table tennis. Home: 14520 183rd Ave NE Woodinville WA 98072-9377 Office: U Wash Dept Elec Engring Ft # 10 Seattle WA 98195

VENNAT, MICHEL, lawyer; b. Sept. 17, 1941; m. Marie-Anne Tawil; children: Catherine, Charles-Alexandre, Frédéric, Michèle Anne, Philippe-Olivier. B.A. magna cum laude, Coll. Jean-de-Brébeuf, Montreal, Que., Can., 1960; LL.L., U. Montreal, 1963; M.A., Oxford U., Eng., 1965. Bar: Que. 1966; apptd. Queen's Counsel 1983. Fgn. affairs officer Dept. External Affairs, Ottawa, Ont., Can., 1965; spl. asst. to Min. Fin., 1966-68; spl. asst. to Hon. Pierre E. Trudeau, Prime Min. of Can., 1968-70, spl. counsel, 1977; chmn. Can. Film Devel. Corp., Montreal, 1976-81; sr. ptnr. Stikeman, Elliott, Montreal, 1970-90; pres. Dumez Investments Inc., 1986-87, Westshore Internat. Industries Ltd., 1987; vice chmn. United Westburne Inc., 1990, vice chmn., CEO, 1991-93, chmn., CEO, 1993-94, also bd. dirs.; pres. Bastos du Canada Limitée, 1987—, also bd. dirs.; ptnr. Stikeman Elliot, Montreal, 1994—; lectr. in constl. law U. Montreal, 1970; bd. dirs. Nat. Bank of Greece (Can.), Meloche-Monnex Inc., Hewlett-Packard (Can.) Ltd., Acklands Ltd.; pres. bd. dirs. Maxi-Krisp Can., Inc. Rhodes scholar, 1963-65. Mem. Conf. Bd. Can., Bus. Coun., Barreau du Que., Can. C. of C., French C. of C. (Can., bd. dirs.), Montreal Barrinton and Squash Club, Mt. Bruno Country Club, Hillside Tennis Club, Mt. Royal Club, Hermitage Club. Avocations: squash, golf, tennis, skiing. Home: 22 Claude Champagne, Outremont, PQ Canada H2V 2X1 Office: Stikeman Elliott, 1155 René-Lévesque Blvd W, Montreal, PQ Canada H3B 3V2

VENNING, ROBERT STANLEY, lawyer; b. Boise, Idaho, July 24, 1943; s. William Lucas and Corey Elizabeth (Brown) V.; m. Sandra Macdonald, May

9, 1966 (div. 1976); 1 child, Rachel Elizabeth; m. Laura Siegel, Mar. 24, 1979; 1 child, Daniel Rockhill Siegel. AB, Harvard U., 1965; MA, U. Chgo., 1966; LLB, Yale U., 1970. Bar: Calif., U.S. Dist. Ct. (no. dist.) Calif. 1971, U.S. Dist. Ct. (cen. dist.) Calif. 1973, U.S. Ct. Appeals (9th cir.) 1977, U.S. Supreme Ct. 1977, U.S. Ct. Appeals (fed. cir.) 1986, U.S. Ct. Appeals (D.C. cir.) 1987. Assoc. Heller, Ehrman, White & McAuliffe, San Francisco, 1970-73, 73-76, ptnr., 1977—; exec. com., 1991—; vis. lectr. U. Wash., Seattle, 1973, Boalt Hall Sch. Law, U. Calif., Berkeley, 1982-85, 89, Sch. Bus., Stanford U., 1986-87. Editor Yale Law Jour., 1969-70. Early neutral evaluator U.S. Dist. Ct. (no. dist.) Calif., 1987—; mem. Natural Resources Def. Coun. Fellow Am. Bar Found.; mem. ABA, Am. Arbitration Assn. (mem. panel arbitrators), San Francisco Bar Assn., Commonwealth Club, Sierra Club. Office: Heller White & McAuliffe 333 Bush St San Francisco CA 94104-2806

VENTER, RONALD DANIEL, mechanical engineering educator, researcher, administrator; b. East London, Republic of South Africa, Jan. 3, 1944; came to Can., 1974; s. Daniel Frans and Myrtle (Quirk) V.; m. Beryl Venter, July 17, 1975 (dec.). BASc, U. Witwatersrand, Johannesburg, Republic of South Africa, 1966; M in Engring., McMaster U., Hamilton, Can., 1969, PhD, 1971. Head mechanics div. Indsl. Diamond div. DeBeers, Johanneburg, 1971-72, head high pressure systems Indsl. Diamonds div., 1972-74; asst. prof. dept. mech. engring. U. Toronto, 1975-78, prof., 1981—; assoc. chmn. dept. mech. engring., 1979-81, chmn., 1981-91, vice dean Faculty of Applied Sci. and Engring., 1993—, Wallace G. Chalmers prof. engring. design, 1993—; dir. Ont. Ctr. for Automotive Arts Tech., St. Catherine's, 1983-89, Ctr. for Hydrogen and Electrochem. Studies, Toronto, 1986—, Indsl. R&D Inst., Midland, Ont., 1992—, Ont. Ctr. Materials Rsch., 1993—, Info. Tech. Rsch. Ctr., 1993—. Co-author: Plane Strain Slip Line Fields, 1982; contbr. articles to profl. jours. Recipient Gold medal award Chamber of Mines South Africa, 1966. Fellow Can. Soc. Mech. Engrs.; mem. ASME, Soc. Mfg. Engrs., Assn. Profl. Engrs. Ont. Conservative. Roman Catholic. Home: 55 Thorncrest Rd, Islington, ON Canada W9A 1S8 Office: U of Toronto, 5 King's College Rd, Toronto, ON Canada M5S 1A4

VENTO, BRUCE FRANK, congressman; b. St. Paul, Oct. 7, 1940; s. Frank A. and Ann V. (Sauer) V.; children: Michael, Peter, John. A.A., U. Minn., 1961; B.A., Wis. State U., River Falls, 1965. Tchr. sci., social studies Mpls. Pub. Schs.; mem. Minn. Ho. of Reps., 1971-76; asst. majority leader, chmn. jud. com. 95th-103rd Congresses from 4th Minn. Dist., 1977—, mem. resources and banking and fin. svcs. com., ranking mem. subcom. fin. instns. and consumer credit. Mem. legis. rev. com. Minn. Commn. on Future Del.; Democratic Farm Labor party Central Com., 1972; chmn. Ramsey County Com., 1972. NSF grantee, 1967-68. Mem. Minn. Fedn. Tchrs., Beta Beta Beta, Kappa Delta Phi. Office: US House of Reps 2304 Rayburn House Office Bldg Washington DC 20515

VENTRE, FRANCIS THOMAS, environmental design and policy educator; b. Old Forge, Pa., Sept. 16, 1937; s. Thomas Anthony and Theresa Mary (Grippi) V.; m. Mary Alice Tibbals, Apr. 4, 1964; children—Antonina Alma, Emily Lucrezia. B.Arch., Pa. State U., 1961; M.C.P., U. Calif., Berkeley, 1966; Ph.D., M.I.T., 1973. City planner Louisville and Jefferson County (Ky.) Planning Commn., 1962-64; asst. prof. arch. and urban planning UCLA, 1966-68; research assoc. MIT-Harvard Joint Center Urban Studies, Cambridge, 1970-73; chief environ. design research div. Nat. Bur. Standards, Washington, 1973-83; prof. environ. design and policy, dir. Ctr. for Building Econs. and Industry Studies Va. Poly. Inst., Blacksburg, 1983-90, dir. Environ Systems Lab., 1983-87; prin. BuildingMeasure, cons. firm; mem. faculty U.Md., UCLA.; faculty mem. Va. Polytech. State U., 1983-93; faculty emeritus; mem. com. tech. advanced bldg. NAS, Nat. Acad. Engring., NRC, 1985-87; elected Consultative Coun. Nat. Inst. Bldg. Scis.; mem. Info. Com. co-founder, past assoc. editor, editorial adv. bd. Environ. and Behavior; mem. editorial bd. Jour. Archtl. and Planning Rsch., 1989-90; contbr. articles to profl. jours., chpts. to books. Mem. indsl. and profl. adv. coun. Pa. State Coll. Engring., 1979-84; del. State, Montgomery County, Va. Dem. Conv., 1989; libr. reader Nat. Gallery Art, 1989. With AUS, 1961-62. Mellon fellow in city planning, 1964-66; recipient award Pa. Soc. Architects, 1961; Stern Family Fund grantee, 1969; Catherine Bauer Wurster fellow, 1971-72; Nat. Endowment Arts grantee, 1984; NSF grantee, 1985, 87, Urban Land Inst. grantee, 1987. Mem. AIA (assoc.), Am. Inst. Cert. Planners, Am. Planning Assn., Environ. Design Rsch. Assn., ASTM, Internat. Facilities Mgmt. Assn., Archtl. Rsch. Ctrs. Consortium (founding sec., mem. panel on bldg. econs. and industry studies, 1984-90), AAUP (pres. Va. Poly. Inst. chpt.), Intelligent Bldgs. Inst. Found. (apptd. trustee), Va. Poly. Inst. Faculty Senate and Senate Cabinet, Montgomery County Stroke Club. Home: 4007 Rickover Rd Silver Spring MD 20902-2330

VENTRES, ROMEO JOHN, manufacturing company executive; b. Boston, Nov. 2, 1924; s. Christy and Marzia (Giammarco) V.; m. Norma Louise Chapman, July 10, 1948; children: Judith, Jane, Mary, Patricia, Katherine, Michael, Peter. BSchemE, Worcester Poly. Inst., 1948; DSc (hon.), Mercy Coll., 1989. Lic. profl. engr., Mass. Jr. engr. Atlantic Refining Co., Phila., 1948-55, group leader, 1955; oil indsl. engr. Govt. Refineries Adminstrn., Baghdad, Iraq, 1955-57; asst. chief engr. Borden Chem. Div. Borden Inc., Leominster, Mass., 1957, chief engr., 1958, ops. mgr., 1961, gen. mgr., 1966, div. v.p., 1968-72, group v.p., 1972-74; exec. v.p. Haven Industries, Phila., 1974-79; group v.p. Borden Chem. div. Borden Inc., Columbus, Ohio, 1979-83, div. pres., 1983-85; pres. Borden Inc., N.Y.C., 1985-90, chief exec. officer, 1986-91, chmn., 1987-92; chmn. exec. com. Borden, Inc., N.Y.C., 1992-93; bd. dirs. Bane One Corp., Marsh & McLennan Cos., Inc., Schering-Plough Corp. Trustee St. Clare's Hosp., N.Y.C. With USN, 1944-46, PTO. Republican. Roman Catholic. Office: Borden Inc 277 Park Ave New York NY 10172

VENTULETT, THOMAS WALKER, III, architect; b. Albany, Ga., Oct. 29, 1935; s. Thomas Walker, Jr. and Edith Mae (Poole) V.; B.S., Ga. Inst. Tech., 1957, B.Arch., 1958; M.Arch., U. Pa., 1961; m. Elizabeth Paulick, Dec. 29, 1956; children—Suzanne, Thomas, Jonathan. With archtl. firms in Ga. and Fla., 1959-67; v.p., prin. charge design Thompson, Ventulett & Stainback, Inc., Atlanta, 1968-76; v.p. dir. design Thompson, Ventulett, Stainback & Assocs., Inc. Atlanta, 1977—; mem. Auburn U. archtl. adv. coun., Ga. Inst. Tech. archtl. com., Cen. Atlanta Progress Bd., Holy Innocents Episcopal Sch. Bd.; chmn. bd. Phoenix Soc.; div. chmn. Atlanta United Way, 1974; exec. bd. Atlanta Area coun. Boy Scouts Am., 1977; bd. trustees Ga. Tech. Found. Capt. AUS, 1958. Recipient Kawneer prize Student Design competition, 1957, Leadership and Merit medal Alpha Rho Chi, 1958, Excellence award Ga. Assn., 1983, 84, 85, 87, Excellence award Am. Inst. Steel Constrn., 1973, 77, 87, Silver medal Atlanta chpt., 1984; Wade meml. scholar, 1961. Fellow AIA (pres. Atlanta 1976, mem. nat. coms. design and urban planning, various design awards juries; Honor award Ga. chpt. 1973, 76, 78, Nat. Bronze medal 1975, South Atlantic Region Conf. Honor award 1976, 78); mem. Midtown Alliance (bd. dirs.), Nat. Archtl. Accreditation Bd., Tau Sigma Delta (hon.). Democrat. Episcopalian. Prin. works include Omni Arena, Atlanta, 1972, CNN Ctr., 1975, Ga. World Congress Ctr., Atlanta, 1985, Pa. Conv. Ctr., Phila., Mobile Conv. Ctr., Buckhead Plaza, Atlanta, 1988, AT&T Promenade, Atlanta, 1989, Woodruff Arts Ctr., Atlanta, 1995. Home: 4234 Conway Valley Rd NW Atlanta GA 30327-3610 Office: Thompson Ventulett Stainback 1230 Peachtree St NE 2700 Atlanta GA 30303-2705

VENTURA, ROBIN MARK, professional baseball player; b. Santa Maria, Calif., July 14, 1967. Student, Oklahoma State U. Mem. U.S. Olympic Baseball Team, Seoul, South Korea, 1988; with Chgo. White Sox, 1988—. Recipient Golden Glove award, 1991-93, Golden Spikes award USA Baseball, 1988; named Sporting News Coll. Player of Yr., 1987-88, Third Basemen Sporting News All-Am. team, 1987-88; named to Am. League All-Star team, 1992. Office: Chgo White Sox 333 W 35th St Chicago IL 60616-3621*

VENTURI, ROBERT, architect; b. Phila., June 25, 1925; s. Robert C. and Vanna (Lanzetta) V.; m. Denise (Lakofski) Scott Brown, July 23, 1967; 1 child, James Charles. Grad., Episcopal Acad., 1943; A.B. summa cum laude, Princeton U., 1947, M.F.A., 1950, D.F.A. (hon.), 1983; D.F.A. (hon.), Oberlin Coll., 1977, Yale U., 1979, U. Pa., 1980, Phila. Coll. Art, 1985; LHD (hon.), N.J. Inst. Tech., 1984; Laurea Honoris Causa in Architecture,

U. Rome "La Sapienza", 1994. Designer firms of Oskar Stonorov, Eero Saarinen and Assos., Louis I. Kahn, 1950-58; partner firm Venturi, Cope & Lippincott, Phila., 1958-61, Venturi and Short, Phila., 1961-64, Venturi and Rauch, Phila., 1964-80; ptnr. firm Venturi, Rauch & Scott Brown, Phila., 1980-89, Venturi, Scott, Brown and Assocs., Inc., 1989—; from asst. to assoc. prof. architecture U. Pa., 1957-65; Charlotte Shepherd Davenport prof. architecture Yale, 1966-70. Author: Complexity and Contradiction in Architecture, 1966, 2d edit., 1977, (with Denise Scott Brown and Steven Izenour) Learning from Las Vegas, 1972, 2d edit., 1977, (with Denise Scott Brown) A View from the Campidoglio, Selected Essays, 1953-84, others, also articles; prin. works include Vanna Venturi House, Phila., 1961, Guild House, Phila., 1961, Humanities Bldg., SUNY, 1972, Franklin Ct., Phila., 1972, addition to Allen Meml. Art Mus., Oberlin Coll., 1973, Inst. for Sci. Info. Corp. Hdqrts., Phila., 1978, Gordon Wu Hall, Princeton U., 1980, Seattle Art Mus., 1984, The Nat. Gallery, Sainsbury Wing, London, 1986, Fisher and Bendheim Halls, Princeton U., 1986, Gordon and Virginia MacDonald Med. Rsch. Labs. (with Payette Assocs.), UCLA, 1986, Charles P. Stevenson Jr. Libr. Bard Coll., 1989, Regional Govt. Bldg., Toulouse, France, 1992, Kirifuri Resort Facilities, Nikko, Japan, 1992. Trustee Am. Acad. Rome, 1966-71. Recipient Nat. Medal of Arts, 1992, Pritzker Architecture prize, 1991, Benjamin Franklin medal The Royal Soc. for Encouragement of Arts, Mfrs. and Commerce, 1993; Rome Prize fellow Am. Acad. in Rome, 1954-56. Fellow AIA (awards 1974, 77, 78), Am. Acad. in Rome, Am. Acad. of Arts and Letters, Am. Acad. Arts and Scis., Royal Inst. of Brit. Architects (hon.), Royal Incorp. Architects of Scotland (hon.), Accademia Nazionale di San Luca; mem. Phi Beta Kappa. Office: 4236 Main St Philadelphia PA 19127-1696

VENZA, JAC, broadcast executive, cultural and arts program administrator; b. Chgo., Dec. 23, 1926. Student, Goodman Sch. Theater and Design, Chgo. Producer, assoc. producer, designer, CBS, N.Y.C., 1950-64, exec. producer, NET Playhouse (Peabody award 1968, Emmy award 1969), for cultural programs, NET, N.Y.C., 1964-69 (recipient Prix D'Italia 1966), for drama, 1969-73; dir.: Performance Programs, PBS WNET/13, N.Y.C., 1981; exec. producer: Dance In America, Nureyev and the Joffrey Ballet in Tribute to Nijinsky (Emmy award nomination), Adams Chronicles (Emmy award nomination 1976, Peabody award 1977), WNET's Great Performances; series including Dance in America (Emmy awards 1979, 87), Theater in America (Peabody award 1974), Fine Music (Emmy award 1975); spls. (TV Critics Circle awards 1976-77), Fred Astaire: Change Partners and Dance, 1980; organizer, dir., Mus. Modern Art's TV USA-13 season, 1976; condr.: workshop Creating Dramas for TV, Tarrytown, N.Y., 1976; exec. producer: Am. Masters, Broadway's Dreamers (Emmy award). Recipient Emmy award for opera Nixon in China, 1988, Capezio award, 1987. Mem. Nat. Acad. TV Arts and Scis. Office: Sta WNET-TV 356 W 58th St New York NY 10019-1804

VÉR, ISTVÁN LÁSZLÓ, acoustical consultant; b. Tápiószecső, Hungary, Dec. 22, 1934; came to U.S., 1965; s. István and Erzsebet G. (Darázs) V.; m. Elisabeth H. Waltering, Dec. 6, 1961; 1 child, Kristina M. BSEE, Tech. U., Budapest, 1956; MSEE, Tech. U., Aachen, Germany, 1960; PhD in Acoustics, Tech. U., Munich, 1963. R&d engr. Rohde and Schwarz, Munich, 1960-65; prin. cons. Bolt Beranek & Newman Inc., Cambridge, Mass., 1965—. Author, editor: Noise & Vibration Engineering, 1992; holder patents. Recipient U.S. Sr. Scientist award Alexander von Humboldt Found., Germany, 1978, Best Paper award Am. Soc. Heating and Refrigeration Engring., 1979. Fellow Acoustical Soc. Am.; mem. Inst. Noise Control Engring. USA (dir. 1976-77), German Acoustical Soc. Avocations: literature, philosophy, travel, tennis. Office: Bolt Beranek and Newman Inc 10 Moulton St Cambridge MA 02138-1119

VERANO, ANTHONY FRANK, retired banker; b. West Harrison, N.Y., Jan. 4, 1931; s. Frank and Rose (Viscome) V.; m. Clara Cosentino, July 8, 1951; children—Rosemarie, Diana Lynn. Student, Am. Inst. Banking, 1956-60, Bank Adminstrn. Inst., U. Wis., 1962-64, RCA Programmers Sch., 1965, Burroughs Programmers Sch., 1965, N.J. Bankers Data Processing Sch., 1966-68, others. With County Trust Co., White Plains, N.Y., 1949-61; sr. auditor County Trust Co., 1960-61; with State Nat. Bank Conn., Bridgeport, 1961—; auditor State Nat. Bank Conn., 1962-79, exec. auditor, 1979—; exec. auditor Conn. Bank & Trust Co., 1983—; v.p., auditor Gateway Bank, Newtown, Conn., 1987, first v.p., auditor, 1988-94, sr. v.p., auditor, 1989-94, ret., 1994; tchr. bank auditing Am. Inst. Banking, 1976-78. Mem. adv. bd. Norwalk Community Coll., 1968—. Served with USN, 1951-52. Mem. Bank Adminstrn. Inst. (dir. Stamford chpt. 1967-68, sec. Western Conn. chpt. 1968-69, treas. 1969-70, v.p. 1970-71, pres. 1971-72), Am. Accounting Assn., Inst. Internal Auditors (chartered bank auditor, cert. bank compliance officer). Home: 59 Bug Hill Rd Monroe CT 06468-1710 Office: Gateway Bank 191 S Main St Newtown CT 06470 *It is difficult to define the elements of success. There are those who say success is achieved through drive and ambition only. However, those who have achieved their goals in life using only these two principles have probably destroyed more than they have created. Success, I feel, is achieved when drive and ambition are tempered with honesty, fairness, and respect for others. An individual must have a sense of dedication not only to his work and for those with whom he works but, most importantly, for those who work for him. This has been my philosophy in achieving my success.*

VERBA, SIDNEY, political scientist, educator; b. Bklyn., May 26, 1932; s. Morris Harold and Recci (Salman) V.; m. E. Cynthia Winston, June 17, 1955; children—Margaret Lynn, Ericka Kim, Martina Claire. B.A., Harvard U., 1953; M.A., Princeton U., 1955, Ph.D., 1959. Asst. prof. polit. sci. Princeton U., 1960-63, asso. prof., 1963-64; prof. Stanford U., 1964-68, U. Chgo., 1968-72; prof. govt. Harvard U., 1972—; now Carl H. Pforzheimer prof., dir. univ. library, chmn. dept. govt., 1976-80, asso. dean Faculty Arts and Scis., 1981—; dir. Harvard U. Library; chmn. bd. dirs. Harvard U. Press, 1991—; chmn. policy com. Social Sci. Rsch. Coun., 1980-86; mem. Commn. on Behavioral and Social Scis., NRC, 1986-91; Commn. on Preservation and Access, chair com. on internat. conflict and cooperation, NRC, 1991-93; vis. com. MIT Polit. Sci. Dept., Stanford U. Libr. Author: Small Groups and Political Behavior, 1961, The Civic Culture, 1963, Caste, Race and Politics, 1969, Participation in America, 1972, Vietnam and the Silent Majority, 1972, The Changing American Voter, 1976, Participation and Political Equality, 1978, Injury to Insult, 1979, Introduction to American Government, 1983, Equality in America, 1985, Elites and the Idea of Equality, 1987, Designing Social Inquiry, 1994. Guggenheim fellow, 1980-81. Fellow Am. Acad. Arts and Scis.; mem. Am. Polit. Sci. Assn. (exec. coun. 1971-74, v.p. 1979-81, pres.-elect 1993-94, pres. 1994—, Gladys Kammerer award 1972, Woodrow Wilson Found. award 1976, James Madison award 1993), Nat. Acad. Scis., Internat. Studies Assn. (v.p. 1971-72). Jewish. Home: 142 Summit Ave Brookline MA 02146-2358 Office: Harvard U Harvard Univ Library Director Cambridge MA 02138

VERBEKE, FRANK GIRARD, JR., mechanical engineer; b. Detroit, Dec. 11, 1934; s. Frank Girard and Elizabeth Aurelia (Winter) V.; children: Kerri Lynn, Frank Girard III. BSME, U. Mich., 1958. Registered profl. engr., Calif. Devel. engr. Continental Aviation and Engring., Detroit, 1958-59, Curtiss Wright Corp., Santa Barbara, Calif., 1959-60; devel. engr. solar div. Internat. Harvester Co., San Diego, 1960-68; v.p. King-Knight Co., Emeryville, Calif., 1968-70; pres. Alturdyne, Inc., Altur-Service, Altuair, Verbeke & Assocs., Engring. Reps. Co., Emeryville, 1970—. Mem. ASME, IEEE, Soc. Automotive Engrs., Exptl. Aircraft Assn., San Diego C. of C., Mission Bay Yacht Club. Republican. Episcopalian. Office: 8050 Armour St San Diego CA 92111-3788

VERBRIDGE, GERALD, religious organization administrator. Pres. Bd. of Dir. of the Reformed Church in America, N.Y.C. Office: Reformed Church in Am 475 Riverside Dr Rm 1811 New York NY 10115-0001

VERBURG, EDWIN ARNOLD, federal agency administrator; b. Lakehurst, N.J., Oct. 6, 1945; s. Edwin Donald Verburg and Dorothy (Orrell) Hoodless; m. Joyce Elaine Majack, Sept. 14, 1968; children: Adelle Kristine, Wendi Elizabeth. BS, Calif. Polytech. U., 1968; M in City Planning, U. Calif., Berkeley, 1970; D in Pub. Adminstrn., George Washington U., 1975. Asst. planner City of Inglewood (Calif.), 1970-71; planner City of Glendale (Calif.), 1971-72; grad. assoc. U.S. Army Corps Engrs., Washington, 1974-75; mgr. fiscal analysis Met. Washington Council Govts., 1975-

77; sr. program analyst U.S. Fish and Wildlife Service, Washington, 1977-79, asst. div. chief, 1979-80, div. chief, 1980-82, asst. dir. planning and budget, 1982-86, dep. asst. dir. policy budget and adminstrn., 1986-87; dir. office of fin. U.S. Dept. Treas., Washington, 1987-88, dir. fin. svcs. directorate, 1988-91, dir. fin. svcs. directorate, dep. CFO, 1991—. Author: Local State and Federal Fiscal Flows, 5 Vols., 1976; contbr. articles to fed. jours. Recipient Disting. Pub. Svc. award George Washington U. Sch. of Bus. and Pub. Mgmt., 1994. Mem. Am. Inst. Cert. Planners, Am. Planning Assn. (Merit award Calif. chpt. 1973, First award Nat. Capital area chpt. 1980, Peer award for pub. svc. Dept. of Treasury 1990, sec.'s cert. appreciation 1991, Pres.'s Meritorious Svc. award 1991.). Home: 538 N Oakland St Arlington VA 22203-2219

VERBURG, KENNETH, political scientist, educator, writer; b. Feb. 13, 1933; s. Cornelius and Lucy VerB.; m. Esther Marie VerBurg, June 30, 1955; children: Kenneth M., Marilou, Craig Alan, Rachel Sue, Jeffrey R.C. AB in Pre-law, Calvin Coll., 1957; MA in Polit. Sci., Mich. State U., 1960. Asst. instr. inst. community devel. Mich. State U., East Lansing, 1957-59, community devel. specialist inst. community devel., 1959-60, from asst. to assoc. prof. inst. community devel., 1969-78, prof., 1978-83, prof. community devel. programs, 1985-90, prof. dept. resource devel., 1990—, acting assoc. dean lifelong edn. programs, 1983-85; exec. asst. Durabilt Homes Mfg., Inc., Kalamazoo, Mich., 1960-61; bus. mgr. Grand Valley State Coll., Allendale, Mich., 1961-67; supr. fiscal sect. bur. higher edn. Mich. Dept. Edn., 1967-69; com. counsel Senate labor com. Mich. State Senate, 1958-59; cons. Mich. Legislature, Mich. Mcpl. League, Mich. Twp. Assn., Mich. Assn. Counties, others. Author: (with others) Michigan Political Atlas, 1984, Guide To Michigan County Government, 2d edit., 1987, (with Gordon Thomas) Conducting Public Meetings, 2d edit., 1987, (with Charles Press) American Politicians and Journalists, 1988, (with William P. Browne) The Government of Michigan, 1991, numerous others. Chair, mem. Mich. State Boundary Commn., 1991—; v.p. River Ter. Christian Reformed Ch., 1992-94. Recipient Outstanding Contbn. award Mich. Twps. Assn., 1984, Spl. Recognition award United County Officers Assn., 1987, Spl. Appreciation award Mich. Assn. Assessors, 1988, Award for Innovation, Nat. Univ. Continuing Edn. Assn. and Am. Testing Svc., 1988. Office: Mich State U Dept Resource Devel 312A Natural Resources Bldg East Lansing MI 48824-1222

VERCAMMEN, KENNETH ALBERT, lawyer; b. Edison, N.J., Aug. 7, 1959; s. Albert Peter and Carol Ann (Rasche) V.; m. Cynthia Ann Bachenski, July 9, 1989. BS, U. Scranton, 1981; JD, U. Del., 1985. Bar: N.J., Pa. 1985, N.Y. 1986, D.C. 1987. Mng. atty. Metuchen, N.J., 1990—; adj. prof. Middlesex County Coll., Edison, 1990—. Contbr. articles to profl. jours. Mem. Am. Cancer Soc., Edison, 1989—; counselor Cen. Jersey Road Runners, 1987. Named a Top Young Profl. by Am. Cancer Soc., New Brunswick, 1988, 89. Mem. KC. Roman Catholic. Avocations: cross country running, skiing. Office: 407 Main St Metuchen NJ 08840

VERDECCHIA, GUILLERMO LUIS, playwright; b. Buenos Aires, Dec. 7, 1962; arrived in Can., 1969.; m. Tamsin Kelsey; 1 child, Anaïs Kelsey-Verdecchia. Author: (plays) Not Another Banana Republic, 1988, i.d., 1989, (Chalmers award Outstanding New Play 1990, Dora award Outstanding Prodn. 1990), Get Off the Stage, 1990, Final Decisions (WAR), 1991, (with Daniel Brooks) The Noam Chomsky Lectures, 1991, (Chalmers award Outstanding New Play 1992, Gov.-Gen.'s Literary award Shortlist), Fronteras Americanas, 1993 (Gov.-Gen.'s Literary award for drama 1993, Chalmers Can. Play award 1994), (with M. Youssef) A Line in the Sand, 1995; (screenplay) Crucero/Crossroads, 1993; (radio) Cancion en el Viento, Fronteras Americanas 1 & 2; (books) Fronteras Americanas, The Noam Chomsky Lectures.

VERDEJA, SAM, newspaper publishing executive. V.p. cmty. rels./mktg. svcs., v.p. mktg. and promotions The Miami Herald, Fla. Office: The Miami Herald One Herald Plz Miami FL 33132-1693*

VERDERBER, JOSEPH ANTHONY, capital equipment company executive; b. Cleve., Nov. 30, 1938; s. Joseph Arthur and Dorothy Louise (Buchta) V.; m. Anita Barto, Sept. 10, 1960; children: Joseph Anthony, Lisa C., Paul A. BS in Mech. Engring., MIT, 1960, MS in Mech. Engring., 1961. Registered profl. engr., Ohio. Mgr. sci. rsch. AM Internat., Cleve., 1964-70; dir. engring. Varityper div., East Hanover, N.J., 1971-73, product mgr., 1973-77; v.p. advanced bus. devel. multigraphics div., Mt. Prospect, Ill., 1977-81, gen. mgr. imaging systems group, Bedford, Mass., Chgo., 1981, pres. Varityper div., East Hanover, N.J., 1982-88; corp. v.p. bus. devel. AM Internat., Inc., Chgo., 1988-89; pres. Am. Splty. Products, Dayton, Ohio, 1989-90; pres. Barco Graphics, Inc., Dayton, 1990; pres. TLSI, Somerville, Mass., 1991—; lectr. Cleve. State U., 1962-67. Recipient Karl Taylor Compton prize MIT, 1960; NSF fellow, 1961; named Inventor of Yr., AM Internat., Chgo., 1980. Mem. ASME, Nat. Printing Equipment and Supply Assn. (bd. dirs. 1986-88, chmn. SEMI New Eng. Forum 1994—). Office: TLSI 32 Cobble Hill Rd Somerville MA 02143-4412

VERDERY, DAVID NORWOOD, broadcast programming executive; b. Waco, Tex., Dec. 12, 1943; s. David Paul and Ruthe (McCawley) V.; m. Randy Lee Mahan, June 6, 1968 (div. 1970); 1 child, David Roderick. Student, Baylor U., 1961-64. Announcer KEFC, Waco, 1962-64; announcer, producer KHFI, Austin, Tex., 1964-65; announcer, prodn. dir. KIXL, Dallas, 1965-66; program dir. KVIL, Dallas, 1967, KABL, San Francisco, 1968-69; nat. program coord. The McLendon Co., Dallas, 1969-73; v.p. programming TM Programming, Dallas, 1973-80, Bonneville Broadcasting System, Northbrook, Ill., 1980-86; music dir. KBIG, L.A., 1985—. Mem. Project Angel Food, L.A., 1992-94. Named Adult Contemporary Music Dir. of Yr., The Gavin Report, 1992, 93. Avocations: gourmet cooking, theater, travel, musical composing and arranging. Office: KBIG Radio 7755 W Sunset Blvd Los Angeles CA 90046-3911

VERDERY, KATHERINE MAUREEN, anthropologist, educator; b. Bangor, Maine, July 9, 1948; d. Francis Deluze and Beatrice (Hardy) V. BA, Reed Coll., Portland, Oreg., 1970; MA, PhD, Stanford U., 1977. Asst. prof. Johns Hopkins U., Balt., 1977-83, assoc. prof., 1983-87, prof., 1987—, chmn. anthropology dept., 1989—; asst. commr. Soviet-Am. Commn. on Ethnology, 1988—. Author: Transylvanian Villagers, 1983, Nat. Ideology Under Socialism, 1991; contbr. articles to profl. publs. Mem. Balt. Choral Arts Soc. Fellow Internat. Rsch. and Exchanges Bd., 1973-74, 79-80, 84-85, 87-88, Social Sci. Rsch. Coun., 1979-80, Woodrow Wilson Internat. Ctr., 1988. Fellow Am. Anthropol. Assn., Am. Ethnological Soc. (bd. dirs. 1987—); mem. Am. Assn. Advancement Slavic Studies (bd. dirs. 1991—, Am. Sociol. Assn., Soc. for Romanian Studies. Democrat. Office: Johns Hopkins U 34th and Charles Sts Baltimore MD 21218

VERDI, DAVID JOSEPH, broadcast news executive; b. Newark, Apr. 4, 1956; s. Joseph Peter and Georgina Alice (Meing) V.; m. Bernadette Rubino, June 26, 1982; children: Andriana Rubino, David Rubino. BA in Journalism, U. No. Colo., 1979. Desk asst. ABC News, N.Y.C., 1980-82, prodn. assoc. Nightline, 1982-84, assoc. prodr. World News Tonight, 1984-86; field prodr. ABC News, St. Louis, 1986-88; prodr. This Week with David Brinkley ABC News, Washington, 1988-90; exec. news dir. NBC News, N.Y.C., 1990—. Office: NBC News 30 Rockefeller Plz New York NY 10112-0001

VERDI, ROBERT WILLIAM, sports columnist; b. Bklyn., Aug. 31, 1946. BA in English, Lake Forest Coll., Ill., 1967. Reporter L.I. Press, Queens, N.Y., summers 1964, 65; sports columnist Chgo. Tribune, 1967—. Named Sportswriter of Yr. for Ill., Nat. Sportscasters and Sportswriters Assn., 1975-78, 80-82, 86-87, 89-90. Mem. Baseball Writers Assn. Am., Football Writers Assn. Am., Golf Writers Assn. Office: Chgo Tribune Sports Dept PO Box 25340 Chicago IL 60625-0340

VERDINE, GREGORY LAWRENCE, chemist, educator; b. Somers Point, N.J., June 10, 1959; s. Richard Daniel and Therese Mary (Delaney) V.; m. Kasumi Verdine, Dec. 1, 1987; children: Vanessa Kaori, Lauren Arika, Erika Rose. BS, St. Joseph's U., Phila., 1982; MA, Columbia U., 1983, PhD, 1986; AB (hon.), Harvard U., 1995. Postdoctoral fellow MIT, Cambridge, Mass., 1986, 87, Harvard Med. Sch., Boston, 1987, 8; asst. prof. chemistry Faculty Arts and Scis. Harvard U., Cambridge, 1988-92, Thomas D. Cabot

assoc. prof. chemistry, 1992-94, prof., 1994—; mem. sci. adv. bd. Ariad Pharms., Cambridge, 1992—, La Jolla (Calif.) Pharms., 1990—; cons. Hoffmann-LaRoche, Nutley, N.J., 1991—. Assoc. editor Chemistry and Biology, 1994—; contbr. numerous articles to profl. jours. Recipient Excellence in Chemistry award Zeneca Pharms., 1994; DuPont Young Faculty fellow, 1988, Searle schoalr, 1990, Eli Lilly grantee, 1990, Alfred P. Sloan fellow, 1991, NSF grantee, 1991, others. Mem. AAAS, Am. Chem. Soc. (Arthur C. Cope Scholar award 1994). Achievements include research in chemical genetics: the propagation, preservation and expression of genetic information. Office: Harvard U Dept Chemistry 12 Oxford St Cambridge MA 02138*

VERDOL, JOSEPH ARTHUR, chemist; b. Chgo., Oct. 30, 1927; s. Joseph and Molly (Fangerl) Vrdolak; m. Elaine C. Glenn, July 7, 1973; children: David A., Lori. BS in Chemistry cum laude, U. Ill., 1951; PhD in Chemistry, Cornell U., 1955. Dir. polymer rsch. Sinclair Rsch., Harvey, Ill., 1963-68; v.p. Sinclair Rsch., N.Y.C., 1968-69; sr. v.p. Arco Tech. Inc., Phila. 1970-86; v.p. Arco Chem. Asia Pacific, Tokyo, 1980-86; pres. Chem. Tech. Worldwide Cons., N.Y.C., 1986—; former lectr. East-West trade Harvard U. patentee in field of petrochemicals in Canada, Japan and Europe; Contbr. numerous articles to Ency. Polymer Sci. & Tech., Jour. Am. Chem. Soc., Oil & Gas Jour., Rubber Age, Rubber World, Harvard Revs. Lt. USMC, 1945-46, U.S. Army, 1950-51. Fellow Am. Inst. Chemists; mem. Am. Chem. Soc., AAAS. Roman Catholic. Achievements include patents in Petroleum, Polymer and Petrochemical fields, Methyl tertiarybutyl ether; invention of processes and new polymers which are used in petroleum refining, petrochemicals and chemical industry. Office: Chem Tech Worldwide 1641 3rd Ave Ste 16-he New York NY 10128-3623

VERDON, GWEN (GWYNETH EVELYN), actress, dancer, choreographer; b. L.A., Jan. 13, 1925; d. Joseph William and Gertrude (Standring) V.; m. James Henaghan, 1942 (div. June 1947); children: James O'Farrell; m. Robert Louis Fosse, Apr. 3, 1960; 1 child, Nicole. Ed. pub. schs., studied dance with E. Belcher, Carmelita Marrachi, Jack Cole. Bd. dirs. Postgrad. Center for Mental Health. Broadway debut in Alive and Kicking, 1950; appeared in musical plays including: Can Can (Tony award 1954), 1953-54, Damn Yankees (Tony award 1956), 1955-56, New Girl in Town (Tony award 1958), 1957, Red Head (Tony award 1959), 1959, Sweet Charity, 1966, (starring role) Chicago, 1975; staged 2d co.: musical Dancin; also acted as dance mistress; appeared in play Love Letters, L.A., 1990; motion pictures: On The Riviera, 1951, Meet Me After the Show, 1951, David and Bathsheba, 1952, Mississippi Gambler, 1953, Damn Yankees, 1958, Cotton Club, 1984, Cocoon, 1986, Nadine, 1987, Cocoon II, 1988, Alice, 1990; TV series appearances include: MASH, Fame, All is Forgiven, Trapper John M.D., The Equalizer, Magnum P.I. (Emmy award nominee), Webster, Dear John, HBO's Dream On (Emmy award nominee), Homicide (Emmy award nominee). Recipient Donaldson award for acting and dancing, Lambs Gambol award for acting, Grammy award, 1959, Silver Bowl award Dance Mag., 1961. Office: care Shapiro & Lobel 111 W 40th St New York NY 10018*

VERDUIN, CLAIRE LEONE, publishing company executive; b. Chgo., Mar. 23, 1932; d. David R. and Helen (Vande Velde) Ellman; m. J. Richard Verduin, Aug. 25, 1956 (Mar. 1979); children: Pamela A., Paul D., Beth L. Verduin Bacher. BBA, U. Wis., 1954. Editorial asst. Brooks/Cole Pub. Co., Pacific Grove and Monterey, Calif., 1973, project devel. editor, 1974-78, editor, 1978-85, mng. editor, 1985-91; pub., 1991—. Treas. Am. Field Service, Pacific Grove, 1978; mem. Pacific Grove Sch. Bd., 1983. Mem. ACA, AAUW, Nat. Assn. Human Svc. Educators, Nat. Assn. Devel. Edn., Coun. Social Work Edn., Audubon Soc. Office: Brooks/Cole Pub Co 511 Forest Ave Pacific Grove CA 93950-4202

VERDUIN, JACOB, botany educator; b. Orange City, Iowa, Nov. 19, 1913; s. Peter and Jennie (Lagestee) V.; m. Bethy Albertha Anderson, July 3, 1942; children: Lans, Jan, Charlotte, Leslie, Bethy. B.S., Iowa State Coll., 1939, M.S., 1941, Ph.D., 1947. Farmer, 1933-35; head botany dept. S.D. State U., 1946-48; asso. prof. hydrobiology F. T. Stone Lab., Ohio State U., 1948-54; head biology dept. Bowling Green State U., 1955-64; prof. botany So. Ill. U., Carbondale, 1964-84, prof. emeritus, 1984—; Cons. NIH, summer 1954; cons. water pollution control sect. TVA, summer 1957, Commonwealth Edison, 1972-86, EPA, 1975-79. Mem. editorial bd.: Ecology, 1954-57, Limnology and Oceanography, Ohio Jour. Sci, Trans. Am. Fisheries Soc. Served to ensign USNR, 1942-45. Fellow Ohio Acad. Sci. (exec. v.p. plant sci. sect. 1958), AAAS; mem. Am. Inst. Biol. Scis., Societas Internationalis Limnologiae, Ecol. Soc. Am., Am. Fisheries Soc., Am. Assn. Limnologists and Oceanographers, Sigma Xi, Phi Kappa Phi, Beta Beta Beta, Gamma Sigma Delta, Omicron Delta Kappa. Episcopalian. Home: 2999 Country Club Rd Carbondale IL 62901-9219 *As a scientist, I have always believed that objectivity and integrity were more important than prestige. As a teacher I have believed that understanding is the goal and memorization should never be a substitute for it. As a person I have believed that most misunderstandings result from inadequate communication.*

VEREB, MICHAEL JOSEPH, pharmaceutical and cosmetic executive; b. Leechburg, Pa., Apr. 1, 1931; s. Michael Andrew and Mary Elizabeth (Chernay) V.; m. Joanne Maria Helms, Oct. 9, 1955; children: Kenneth Michael, Wayne William. BS in Indsl. Mgmt., Carnegie Mellon U., 1953; postgrad., U. Pitts., 1955-56, U. So. Ill., 1959. Registered profl. engr., Calif. Methods engr. Schenley (Pa.) Distillers, 1955-57; cons. EnServCo, Pitts., 1957-58; sr. indsl. engr. Olin Industries, Alton, Ill., 1958-59; mgr. indsl. engr. Ormet Aluminum subs. Olin Industries, Bucks Bottom, Ohio, 1959-66; resource mgr. Olin Aluminum, N.Y.C., 1966-67; dir. engring. Squibb Corp., New Brunswick, N.J., 1967-78; dir. facilities planning Squibb Corp., Lawrenceville, N.J., 1978-84; v.p. facilities planning Charles of Ritz Group, Ltd. div. Squibb Corp., Holmdel, N.J., 1984-87; div. mgr. pharms. Fluor Daniel, Inc., Marlton, N.J., 1988—; cons. EnServCo, Pitts., 1957-58, Pitman Moore div. of IMC, Washington Crossing, N.J.; rsch. coord. Lehigh U., Bethlehem, Pa., 1984-86. Inventor disposable containers. Coord. fund drives Carnegie Mellon U., Lawrenceville, N.J., 1973-83; 1st v.p. Raritan Valley Regional Chpt. C. of C., 1976-78. With U.S. Army, 1953-55. Mem. Inst. Indsl. Engring., Assn. Info. and Image Mgmt., Soc. Mfg. Engrs., Elks (v.p. 1960-66), Pi Kappa Alpha (v.p. 1952-53). Home: 5 Arncliffe Rise Medford NJ 08055-3337

VER EECKE, WILFRIED CAMIEL, philosopher, educator; b. Tielt, Belgium, Aug. 22, 1938; came to U.S., 1966; s. Jerome and Maria (Declercq) Ver E.; license philosophy, Cath. U. Leuven (Belgium), 1962, Ph.D., 1966; postgrad. U. Freiburg, 1966, Harvard U., 1966-67; M.A. in Econs., Georgetown U., 1972; m. Josiane Berten, Sept. 4, 1967; children—Mieke, Stefaan, Renaat, Jan. High sch. tchr., Heule, Belgium, 1962-63, Kortrijk, 1963-65; NSF research fellow, Belgium, 1965-69; asst. prof. Georgetown U., Washington, 1967-72, assoc. prof., 1972-80, prof., 1980—, chmn. dept. philosophy, 1980-83. Alexander von Humboldt fellow, Ger., 1975-76, 78. Mem. Am. Philos. Assn., Am. Cath. Philos. Assn., Hegel Soc. Am., Soc. Phenomenology and Existential Philosophy, Public Choice, Washington Forum Psychiatry-Humanities. Roman Catholic. Author: Negativity and Subjectivity, 1977; translator: Schizophrenia (La psychose) (A de Waelhens), 1978; Saying No, 1984; contbr. articles to profl. jours. Home: 4100 Nebraska Ave NW Washington DC 20016-2794 Office: Dept Philosophy Georgetown U Washington DC 20057

VEREEN, BEN, actor, singer, dancer; b. Miami, Fla., Oct. 10, 1946; m. Nancy Vereen; children: Benjamin, Malakia, Naja, Kabara, Karon. Student, High Sch. of Performing Arts; LHD (hon.), Emerson Coll., 1977. Debut off-Broadway in The Prodigal Son, 1965; played Brother Ben in Sweet Charity, N.Y.C., Las Vegas, San Francisco, 1966, Daddy Brubeck in Can. tour, 1968, in Los Angeles co. of Hair, 1968, joined Broadway cast, 1969; played role of Judas in Jesus Christ Superstar, 1971 (Theatre World award); leading role in Pippin', 1972 (Tony award, Drama Desk award); appeared in Grind, 1985, Jelly's Last Jam, 1992; numerous theatrical appearances, including I'm Not Rappaport, San Francisco, 1989; appeared in TV movie Louis Armstrong-Chicago Style, 1976; created role of Chicken George in TV miniseries Roots, 1977 (TV Critics award); other TV miniseries include Ellis Island, 1984, A.D., 1985; appeared in TV spl. Ben Vereen-His Roots, 1978, Uptown-A Tribute to the Apollo Theatre; film appearances: Funny Lady, 1975, All That Jazz, 1979, Buy and Cell, 1989, Once Upon a Forrest, 1993 (voice only); TV series include: Tenspeed and Brown Shoe, 1980, Webster, J.J. Starbuck, 1988; also nightclub appearances. Chmn. Dance for Heart campaign Am. Heart Assn.; internat. chmn. Sudden Infant Death Syndrome; established Naja Vereen Meml. Scholarship Fund, 1988; founder, pres. Celebrities for a Drug-Free Am. Recipient George M. Cohan award Am. Guild Variety Artists, 1976, Image award NAACP, 1978, 79, Israel's Cultural award, 1978, Israel's Humanitarian award, 1979, Eleanor Roosevelt Humanitarian award, 1983. Mem. Actor's Equity Assn., Am. Guild Variety Artists, AFTRA, SAG. Office: care Writers and Artists Agy 924 Westwood Blvd 9th Fl Los Angeles CA 90024 *I am like the turtle--determined and will stick my neck out; turtles also teach me patience.*

VEREEN, ROBERT CHARLES, retired trade association executive; b. Stillwater, Minn., Sept. 8, 1924; s. George and Leona Lucille (Made) Wihren; m. Rose Catherine Blair, Nov. 5, 1945; children: Robin, Stacy, Kim. Grad. high sch. Mng. editor Comml. West Mag. Mpls., 1946-50, Bruce Pub. Co. St. Paul, 1950-53, Nat. Retail Hardware Assn., Indpls., 1953-59; mng. dir. Liberty Distbrs., Phila., 1959-63; editor Hardware Retailing, Indpls., 1963-80; assoc. pub., dir. communications Nat. Retail Hardware Assn., 1980-84, sr. v.p., 1984-87; Vereen & Assocs., Mgmt., Mktg. Cons., 1987--; lectr. mgmt. insts.; guest lectr. on distbn. pub.; co-founder Eurotrade Mktg. and U.S.A. Direct. Author: (with Paul M. Doane) Hunting for Profit, 1965, The Computer Age in Merchandising, 1968, Perpetuating the Family-Owned Business, 1970, The How-To of Merchandising, 1975, The How-To of Store Operations, 1976, A Guide to Financial Management, 1976, Productivity: A Crisis for Management, 1978, Hardlines Rep Report Newsletter, 1984--, Guidelines to Improve the Rep/Factory Relationships, 1992. Served with AUS, 1943-45. Mem. Am. Soc. Bus Press Editors (dir., v.p. 1966-70), Soc. Nat. Assn. Publs. (dir., pres. 1970-75, chmn. journalism edn. liaison com. 1976-79), Toastmasters (v.p., treas., sec. 1955-59), Am Hardware Mfrs. Assn. (co-founder, sec.-treas. Young Execs. Club 1958-59, 63-65), Hardware-Housewares Packaging Expn. (founder 1960, chmn. com. packaging 1960-62, chmn. judging com. Hardware-Packaging Expn. 1975-78), Packaging Inst., Household Consumer Products Export Council (chmn. 1981-83), World-Wide DIY Council (exec. sec. 1981--). Home and Office: 4560 Lincoln Rd Indianapolis IN 46208-6706

VEREEN, WILLIAM JEROME, uniform manufacturing company executive; b. Moultrie, Ga., Sept. 7, 1940; s. William Coachman and Mary Elizabeth (Bunn) V.; m. Lula Evelyn King, June 9, 1963; children: Elizabeth King, William Coachman. BS in Indsl. Mgmt, Ga. Inst. Tech., 1963. With Riverside Mfg. Co., Moultrie, 1967--; v.p., then exec. v.p Riverside Mfg. Co., 1970-77, pres., 1977-84, pres., treas., CEO, 1984--; also dir.; v.p., dir. Moultrie Cotton Mills, 1969--; exec. v.p. Riverside Industries, Inc., Moultrie, 1973-77; pres. Riverside Industries, Inc., 1977-84, CEO, 1984--, also dir.; v.p., bd. dirs. Riverside Uniform Rentals, Inc., Moultrie, 1971-80, pres., 1980-84, CEO, bd. dirs., 1984--; pres. Riverside Mfg. Co. (Ireland) Ltd., 1977--, Right Image Corp., Riverside Mfg. Co. GmbH, Germany, 1979--; also CEO, dir., 1984; pres., treas., CEO G.A. Rivers Corp., Riverside Mfg. Co. (U.K.) Ltd.; pres., treas., CEO, bd. dirs. Textile Clothing Tech. Corp.; chairholder Tyner eminent scholars, prof. coll. human scis. Fla. State U. 1993-94, mem. coll. human scis. devel. bd.; bd. dirs. Ga. Power Co., Gerber Sci., Inc., Blue Cross/Blue Shield Ga.; mem. trilateral commn. apparel labeling NAFTA; so. regional dir. Nations Bank of Ga., N.A.; advisor textile and apparel tariffs and quotas U.S. Dept. State Bd.; active Gov. Devel. Coun. With Gov. Devel. Coun. State of Ga.; bd. dirs. Moultrie-Colquitt County (Ga.) Devel. Authority, 1973--, Moultrie-Colquitt County United Givers, 1968-75, Moultrie YMCA, 1968--, Colquitt County Cancer Soc., 1969-73; trustee Community Welfare Assn. Moultrie, 1970, Pineland Sch., Moultrie, 1971--, Leadership Ga., 1972--, Ga. Coun. Econ. Edn.; trustee Am. Apparel Edn. Found.; adv. bd. Ga. Tech. sch. of textile and fiber engring.; elder 1st Presbyterian Ch.; exec. com. existing industry coun. State Ga. Capt. USMCR, 1963-67. Decorated Bronze Star, Purple Heart. Mem. Internat. Apparel Fedn. (2d v.p., 1st v.p., bd. dirs., exec. com., chmn. 1991-92), Am. Apparel Mfrs. Assn. (bd. dirs., exec. com., edn. found. com., 2d vice chmn., chmn. 1990-91), Nat. Assn. Uniform Mfrs. and Distbrs. (bd. dirs.), Young Pres. Orgn., Am. Apparel Edn. Found. (v.p., trustee), Capital City Club (Atlanta), Commerce Club (Atlanta), Sunset Country Club, Ga. C. of C. (vice chmn., bd. dirs., mem. exec. com., chmn. existing industry com.), Elks, Kiwanis, Sigma Alpha Epsilon. Home: 21 Dogwood Dr Moultrie GA 31768-6537 Office: PO Box 460 Moultrie GA 31776-0460

VERGARI, CARL ANTHONY, lawyer; b. Yonkers, N.Y., Dec. 7, 1921; s. Frank and Teresa (Molinari) V.; m. Genevieve Louise Lindermann, June 21, 1922; children--Bohn C., Jeanne Vergari Martinelli. Student Fordham U., 1938-40; LL.B., St. John's U., 1948; LL.M., N.Y.U., 1952. Bar: N.Y. 1948, U.S. Supreme Ct. asst. dist. atty. N.Y. County, 1948-58; chief counsel N.Y. State Commn. of Investigation, 1958-68; dist. atty. Westchester County, White Plains, N.Y., 1968--; mem. joint strike force council on organized crime U.S. Justice Dept., 1972--; mem. exec. working group for fed.-state prosecutorial relations, 1978--. Bd. dirs. Am. Com. on Italian Migration, 1976--; bd. dirs. Enrico Fermi Ednl. Fund of Yonkers, 1972--, pres., 1973-75, mem. adv. bd. Nat. Obscenity Law Center, 1976--; mem. Westchester County Youth Services Adv. Com., 1968--; Westchester County Exec.'s Adv. Com. on Narcotics, 1968--. Served to capt. USMCR, 1941-45. Mem. Nat. Dist. Attys. Assn. (v.p. 1968, chmn. commn. on victim/witness assistance 1973-77, chmn. task force on ofcl. corruption 1978-80), N.Y. State Dist. Attys. Assn. (exec. com. 1968, pres. 1973-74), ABA, Westchester Bar Assn., Guild Cath. Lawyers. Office: Courthouse 111 Grove St White Plains NY 10601-2509

VERGE, PIERRE, legal educator; b. Quebec City, Can., Jan. 9, 1936; s. Francis and Regina (Roy) V.; m. Colette Habel, June 29, 1963; children--Marc, Caroline, Louis. B.A., Laval U., 1956, LL.L., 1959, LL.D., 1971; M.A., McGill U., 1962, Cambridge U., 1977; LL.M., U. Toronto, 1968; 1971. Q.C. 1961, Queen's Counsel 1976. Pvt. practice law Quebec City, Can., 1961-66; mem. faculty Laval U. Faculty of Law, 1966--; dean Laval U. Faculty of Law (Faculty of Law), 1973-77. Commonwealth fellow St. John's Coll., Cambridge U., 1977-78. Mem. Assn. Can. Law Tchrs. (pres. 1972-73, chmn. conf. law deans 1975-76), Que. Bar, Canadian Bar, Royal Soc. Can. Home: 2542 de la Falaise, Sillery, PQ Canada G1T 1W3 Office: Cite Universitaire, Universite Laval, Quebec, PQ Canada

VERGER, MORRIS DAVID, architect, planner; b. Ft. Worth, Mar. 25, 1915; s. Joseph and Dora (Bunyan) V.; m. Florence Brown, June 21, 1939; children: Paul, Alice. B.Arch., U. Calif., Berkeley, 1943. Naval architect U.S. Navy Bur. Ships, San Pedro, Calif., 1943-45; draftsman various archtl. firms So. Calif., 1946-50; pvt. practice as architect and planner Los Angeles, 1951--; lectr. architecture UCLA Extension; vis. critic Calif. State U., San Luis Obispo; leader Seminar on Interactive Planning, San Francisco; cons. to legal profession, tech. witness. Works include program for City of Hope, Duarte, Calif., 1972, Terman Engring. Ctr., Stanford U., 1974, and design of Huntington Dr. Sch., L.A., 1975, Flax Artist Materials Bldg., L.A., 1976, Frank D. Lanterman H.S., L.A., 1978, exec. offices S.E. Rykoff & Co., L.A., 1982, condominiums, Stoneman Corp., L.A., 1988, 91; developed DiscoveryBased Planning, 1994. Recipient design awards Westwood C. of C., 1974, 75. Fellow AIA (pres. So. Calif. chpt. 1975, v.p. environ. affairs Calif. council 1979, v.p. Calif. council 1979-80, pres. Calif. council 1980). Inventor (with E.H. Porter) Interactive Planning, evolved to Connective Planning; developed method for computer design of Interstitial Space and computer-generated drawings for affordable housing using related dimensions and datum points to coordinate all trades. Home: 1362 Comstock Ave Los Angeles CA 90024-5315 Office: 10801 National Blvd Los Angeles CA 90064-4126

VERGES, ERNEST E., architectural firm executive. BS in Agrl. Engring., La. State U., 1954; student, USAF Inst. Tech., 1955, Harvard Grad. Sch. Design, 1983. Registered profl. arch., La., Ala., Miss., Fla. Commd. 2d lt. USAF, 1954, advanced through grades to maj.; with H.T. Underwood & Assocs., 1956-58, ptnr., 1958-63; ptnr.-in-charge design and document prodn. Underwood-Verges & Asso. (formerly H.T. Underwood & Asso.), 1963-66; prin. Ernest E. Verges & Asso. (formerly Underwood-Verges & Asso.), 1966-68; pres. Verges Associated Architects; prin., pres., CFO Morton Verges Archs. (merger Morton Assocs.), 1991--; mem. La. Bldg. Energy Conservation Adv. Bd. Mem. standing com. on arch. Luth. Ch., Mo. Synod; active mem. Internat. Luth. Laymen's League; past v.p., regional gov.; past pres., sec.

Gulf Dist. Luth. Laymen's League; past pres. New Orleans Zone Luth. Ch., La. State U. Alumni, Jefferson Parish, Concordia Sem. Regents Coun. Mem. AIA (practice mgmt. com., past pres. and various coms. New Orleans chpt., La. chpt.), La. Archs. Assn. (past pres., past v.p., bd. dirs., various coms), La. Inst. Bldg. Scis., Constrn. Industry Assn. (bd. dirs.), Constrn. Reps. Assn., IFRAA (regional dir.), Am. Arbitration Assn. (panel mem.); Mid City Kiwanis Club, Metairie Country Club, La. State U. "L" Club, La. State U. Alumni Fedn. Office: Verges Associates Architects 4640 South Carrollton Ave New Orleans LA 70119

VERGES, MARIANNE MURPHREE, writer; b. Oklahoma City, Apr. 19, 1939; d. Buren Thomas and Ellen Marie (Kanaly) Murphree; m. James Thomas Verges, Aug. 6, 1960; children: Keith, Philip, John, Stasi. BA, U. Okla., 1962; postgrad. U. Tex., 1980-84. Interior designer A.J. Bullard, Oklahoma City, 1962-64; owner, ptnr. Stuff Novelty Co., Westport, Conn., 1972-79; freelance writer Dallas, 1983--. Author: On Silver Wings, 1990; columnist Children's Pages, 1982--; contbr. articles to various regional publs. Bd. dirs. Westport Young Women's League, 1972-79, Youth Adult Council, 1975-76, Alcohol Guidance Ctr., 1975-77; mem. Republican Women, Dallas, 1980--; bd. dirs. Frontiers of Flight Mus., 1989--. Mem. Greater Dallas Writers. Roman Catholic. Avocations: community volunteer work, travel, dog breeding and training, distance walking, sewing. Home: 6904 La Manga Dr Dallas TX 75248-2908

VERGHESE, ABRAHAM CHEERAN, internist, writer, educator; b. Addis Ababa, Ethiopia, May 30, 1955; came to U.S., 1980; s. George and Mary Verghese; m. Rajani Chacko; children: Steven, Jacob. MD, Madras (India) U., 1979; intern Govt. Gen. Hosp., Madras Med. Coll., India, 1979-80; from. res. to chief res., E. Tenn. State U., Johnson City, 1980-83; MFA, U. Iowa, 1991. Diplomate Am. Bd. Internal Medicine, Am. Bd. Infectious Diseases, Geriat., and Pulmonary Medicine. Instr. in medicine E. Tenn. State U., Johnson City, 1982-83, asst. prof. medicine, 1985-88, assoc. prof. medicine, 1988-90; teaching asst. medicine Boston U., 1983-85; chief infectious diseases VA Med. Ctr., Johnson City, 1986-90, asst. chief medicine, 1988-90; vis. assoc. U. Iowa, Iowa City, 1990-91; prof. medicine Tex. Tech. U., El Paso, Tex., 1991--; chief infectious diseases Tex. Tech. Regional Acad. Health Ctr., El Paso, 1991--. Author: My Own Country: A Doctor's Story of a Town and Its People in the Age of AIDS, 1994, (with others) Great Lives from History, 1987, Infection in the Nursing Home, 1990. Mem. El Paso Mayor's Commn. on Primary Health Care, 1992-93. Named Tchr. of Yr. Internat. Medicine residents and Alpha Omega Alpha E. Tenn. State U., 1989; recipient James Michener fellowship to Writer's Workshop U. Iowa. Fellow ACP (publs. coms.), Royal Coll. Physicians Can., Infectious Diseases Soc. Am., Coll. Chest Physicians; mem. Am. Geriat. Soc., Am. Fedn. for Clin. Rsch., Am. Soc. Microbiology, Soc. for Exptl. Biology and Medicine. Office: Tex Tech U 4800 Alberta Ave El Paso TX 79905-2709

VER HAGEN, JAN KAROL, manufacturing company executive; b. Eau Claire, Wis., Nov. 11, 1937; s. Henry Joseph and Elsie Marie (Hagenstad) Ver H.; m. Kathryn Frances Fults; m. June 25, 1960; children: Mark A., David M. (dec.) Kathryn T. BSME, U. Wis., Madison, 1961. Capital goods mktg. Trane Co., La Crosse, Wis., 1961-69, group sales mgr., mng. dir. Trane Ltd., 1969-72, v.p., gen. mgr. process div. (heat transfer), 1972-73, v.p., gen. mgr. internat div., 1973-77; exec. v.p. internat., v.p. corp. projects A.B. Chance div. Emerson Electric, Centralia, Mo., 1977-78; v.p. internat. Emerson Electric Co., St. Louis, 1978; pres., group v.p. White-Rodgers div. Emerson Electric Co., St. Louis, 1978-84, exec. v.p., pres., 1984-85; exec. v.p. Emerson Electric Co., St. Louis 1985-86, exec. v.p. corp., chmn. electronics and space div., 1986-87, exec. v.p., corp. dir., 1987-88, vice chmn., dir., 1988-94; pres., COO United Dominion Industries, Ltd., Charlotte, N.C., 1994--; bd. dirs. Hon Industries, Univ. Wis. Found. Trustee Wis. Alumni Rsch. Found. Mem. Wis. Alumni Assn. (dir.), St. Louis Club, Bellerive Country Club, Boone Valley Club, Firestone Country Club, Long Cove, Quail Hollow Country Club, Charlotte City Club, Royal Dornoch Club (Scotland). Republican. Mem. Ch. Christ. Avocation: golf, skiing. Office: United Dominion Industries Ltd 2300 One First Union Ctr 301 S College St Charlotte NC 28202

VERHALEN, ROBERT DONALD, federal agency executive; b. Chgo., July 6, 1935; s. William Joseph and Pearl Evelyn (Anderson) V.; m. Phyllis Scandridge, Jan. 11, 1958; children: Elizabeth L., David S. BA, U. Iowa, 1963; MPH, U. N.C., 1965, DrPH, 1972. Expediter Fansteel Metall. Corp., North Chicago, Ill., 1957-58; tech. writer Collins Radio Co., Cedar Rapids, Iowa, 1958-59; rsch. aide Dept. Physics and Astronomy, Iowa City, 1960-63; sanitarian Lake County Health Dept., Waukegan, Ill., 1963-64; cons. safety mgmt. Ga. Dept. Pub. Health, Atlanta, 1965-68; instr. U. N.C., Chapel Hill, 1968-70; chief task force Pres.'s Commn. on Product Safety, Washington, 1969-70; asst. dir. Bur. Product Safety FDA, Washington, 1970-73; assoc. dir. U.S. Consumer Product Safety Commn., Washington, 1973--; guest lectr. Sch. Pub. Health U. N.C., Chapel Hill, 1975--, Walter Reed Army Med. Ctr., Washington, 1982--. Mem. editorial bd. Jour. Safety Rsch.; developer Nat. Electronic Injury Surveillance System; contbr. articles to profl. jours. Mem. adv. com. Nat. Ctr. Injury Prevention and Control; mem. interagy. exec. com. Tech. Transfer; mem. Conservative Network, Washington, 1985--. Sgt. USMC, 1953-57. Mem. Am. Coll. Epidemiology, Soc. Epidemiologic Rsch., Am. Pub. Health Assn., Am. Statis. Assn., Sr. Exec.'s Assn., Sr. Exec. Svc. Lutheran. Avocation: sailing. Home: 7209 Matthew Mills Rd Mc Lean VA 22101-2643 Office: Consumer Product Safety Commn Washington DC 20207-0002

VERHESEN, ANNA MARIA HUBERTINA, counselor; b. Heerenveen, Friesland, Netherland, Dec. 6, 1932; came to U.S., 1968; d. Hendrikus H. and Henrika C. (Kluessjen) V. BS, Mercy Coll. of Detroit, 1981; MA, Sienna Height, Adrian, Mich., 1992. Childcare worker Schiedam, Netherland, 1952-54; social worker Rotterdam Halfweg, Netherland, 1954-59; childcare worker Mt. St. Ann's Home, Worcester and Lawrence, Mass., 1968-70; chem. dependency social worker St. Vincent Med. Ctr., Toledo, Ohio, 1970-75; social worker St. Joseph Hosp., Nashua, N.H., 1975-78; vocation dir. Grey Nuns, Lexington, Mass., 1978-79; coord. community svcs. St. Vincents Med. Ctr., Toledo, 1981-91; pvt. practice clin. therapist Sylvania, Ohio, 1992--; alcohol/drug addiction/mental health counselor for ex-prisoners; founder St. Vincent Med. Ctr. Alcoholism Detox and Rehab. Unit, Toledo, 1970-75. Co-founder Transitional Residences for the Homeless, Toledo, 1981-90, Ohio Coalition for the Homeless, Columbus, 1982-89; co-founder of a home for persons with AIDS, co-chair City of Toledo Housing Policy, 1985-90; coord. Housing Now, Toledo, 1988-90. Recipient Woman of Achievement award Women in Communication, Toledo, 1986, Spirit of '87 award N.W. Ordinance and U.S. Constn. Bicentennial Commn., Toledo, 1987, Gov.'s Spl. Recognition award, 1988, Man for Others award St. John's High Sch., 1991; named Woman of Toledo St. Vincent Med. Ctr. Aux., 1988, Ohio Ho. of Reps., 1987; featured in various mags. Roman Catholic. Home: 219 Page St Toledo OH 43620-1400 Office: Elliott and Assocs Inc 5600 Monroe St Sylvania OH 43560

VERHEYEN, EGON, art historian, educator; b. Duisburg, Germany, Apr. 13, 1936; came to U.S., 1966; s. Franz and Klara (Läufer) V.; children: Peter David, Gero, Esther. Student, U. Mainz, Germany, 1956-58; Ph.D., U. Würzburg, Fed. Republic Germany, 1962. With German Nat. Museum, Nuremberg, 1961; Herodotos mem. Inst. for Advanced Study, Princeton, N.J., 1962-63, mem., 1983; research fellow Bayerische Staatsgemäldesammlungen, Munich, Fed. Republic Germany, 1965-66; asst. prof. history of art U. Mass., Amherst, 1966; asst. prof. U. Mich., Ann Arbor, 1967-70; assoc. prof. U. Mich., 1970-72; prof. dept history of art Johns Hopkins, 1972-87, chmn. dept., 1972-76; Clarence J. Robinson prof. humanities George Mason U., 1987--; research fellow Bibliotheca Hertziana, Rome, Italy, 1963-65; bd. dirs. Univ. Press Va. Author: Minoritenkirche Duisburg, 1959, Goldene Evangelienbuch von Echternach, 1963, Studiolo of Isabella d'Este, 1971, Palazzo del Te in Mantua, 1977; bd. editors: Emblemata, Architectura. Max Planck Gesellschaft grantee, 1963-65; Horace H. Rackham Found. grantee, 1968, 70; NEH grantee, 1972, 76, 77, 85, 90; Fritz Thyssen Gesellschaft grantee, 1965-66; U. Mich. travel grantee, 1971-72; Office Rsch. Administrn. grantee, 1971. Mem. Soc. Archtl. Historians (v.p. Latrobe chpt. 1990-91), Renaissance Soc. Am. (bd. 1984-86), Coll. Art Assn., Soc. for Emblem Studies. Office: MS1D6 George Mason U Fairfax VA 22030-4444

VERHOEK, SUSAN ELIZABETH, botany educator; b. Columbus, Ohio, 1942; m. S.E. Williams. Student, Carleton Coll., 1960-62; BA, Ohio Wesleyan U., 1964; MA, Ind. U., 1966; PhD, Cornell U., 1975. Herbarium supr. Mo. Bot. Garden, St. Louis, 1966-70; asst. prof. Lebanon Valley Coll., Annville, Pa., 1974-82, assoc. prof., 1982-85, prof., 1985--; vis. researcher Cornell U., Ithaca, N.Y., 1982-83; content cons. Merrill Pub. Co., 1987-89; vis. profl. Chgo. Bot. Garden, 1991. Author: How to Know the Spring Flowers, 1982; contbr. articles to profl. jours., newspapers, and bulls. Bd. trustees Lebanon Valley Coll., Annville, 1979-82, 84-90, 92-95. Named one of Outstanding Young Women of Am., 1976. Mem. Soc. for Econ. Botany (pres. 1985-86), Bot. Soc. Am., Am. Soc. Plant Taxonomists, Am. Assn. Bot. Gardens and Arboreta. Office: Lebanon Valley Coll Pa Annville PA 17003

VERHOEVEN, PAUL, film director; b. Amsterdam, Netherlands, July 18, 1938. PhD Mathematics, Physics, Univ. Leiden. Dir. Wat Zien Ik, 1971, Turkish Delight, 1973, Keetje Tippel, 1975, Spetters, 1981, The Fourth Man, 1983, Robocop, 1987, Total Recall, 1990, Basic Instinct, 1992; dir., co-screenwriter Soldier of Orange, 1979, Flesh and Blood, 1985. Office: care Marion Rosenberg 8428 Melrose Pl Ste C West Hollywood CA 90069-5371 also: Robert Brenner Brenner & Glassberg 2049 Century Park E Ste 950 Los Angeles CA 90067*

VERING, JOHN ALBERT, lawyer; b. Marysville, Kans., Feb. 6, 1951; s. John Albert and Bernadine E. (Kieffer) V.; m. Ann E. Arman, June 28, 1980; children: Julia Ann, Catherine Ann, Mary Ann. BA summa cum laude, Harvard U., 1973; JD, U. Va., 1976. Bar: Mo. 1976, U.S. Dist. Ct. (we. dist.) Mo. 1976, U.S. Ct. Appeals (8th cir.) 1977, U.S. Ct. Appeals (10th cir.) 1980, U.S. Ct. Appeals (4th cir.) 1987, Kans. 1990, U.S. Dist. Ct. Kans. 1990; cert. mediator, Mo., Kans. Assoc. Dietrich, Davis, Dicus, Rowlands, Schmitt & Gorman, Kansas City, Mo., 1976-81, ptnr., 1982--. Editor: U. Va. Law Rev., 1974-76. Bd. dirs. Greater Kansas City YMCA Southwest Dist., 1987. Mem. Harvard Club (schs. com. Kansas City 1977-95, v.p. 1981-82, 92-93, pres. 1994-95). Democrat. Roman Catholic. Home: 1210 W 68th Ter Kansas City MO 64113-1904 Office: Armstrong Teasdale Schlafy & Davis 1700 City Ctr S 1100 Main St Kansas City MO 64105

VERINK, ELLIS DANIEL, JR., metallurgical engineering educator, consultant; b. Peking, China, Feb. 9, 1920; s. Ellis Daniel and Phoebe Elizabeth (Smith) V.; m. Martha Eulala Owens, July 4, 1942; children: Barbara Ann, Wendy Susan. B.S., Purdue U., 1941; M.S., Ohio State U., 1963, Ph.D., 1965. Registered profl. engr., Fla., Pa., Calif. Mgr. chem. sect., sales devel. div. Alcoa, New Kensington, Pa., 1946-59; mgr. chem. and petroleum indsl. sales Alcoa, Pitts., 1959-62; assoc. prof. metall. engring. U. Fla., Gainesville, 1965-68, prof. materials sci. and engring., 1968--; disting. service prof. U. Fla., 1984--, chmn. dept. materials sci. and engring., 1973-86; pres. Materials Cons., Inc., 1970--; cons. Aluminum Assn., Washington, 1966-84; mem. U.S. nuclear waste tech. rev. bd., 1989--. Contbrs. articles to profl. jours.; editor: Methods of Materials Selections, 1968. Pres. Gainesville YMCA, 1977. Recipient Sam Tour award ASTM, 1979, Donald E. Marlowe award Am. Soc. Engring. Edn., 1991; recipient Disting. Alumnus award Ohio State U., 1982, Disting. Faculty award Fla. Blue Key, 1983; named Tchr.-Scholar of Year U. Fla., 1979. Fellow Metall. Soc.-AIME (pres. 1984, Educator of Yr. award 1988), NACE Internat.; mem. Nat. Assn. Corrosion Engrs. (bd. dirs. 1984-87, Willis Rodney Whitney award, fellow award 1992), Sigma Tau, Tau Beta Pi. Republican. Presbyterian. Lodges: Masons; Shriners; Kiwanis. Home: 4401 NW 18th Pl Gainesville FL 32605-3423 Office: U Fla Dept Materials Sci Eng Gainesville FL 32611

VERITY, GEORGE LUTHER, lawyer; b. Oklahoma City, Jan. 3, 1914; s. George H. and Mae (Tibbals) V.; m. Ellen Van Hoesen, Mar. 18, 1939; children: George Luther II, Grover Steven, David Webster, Mark Sidney. LLB, Okla. U., 1937; M of Theol. Studies, So. Meth. U., 1989. Bar: Okla. 1937, Tex. 1939, N.Mex. 1957. Practice in Shawnee, Okla., 1937-39, Wichita Falls, Tex., 1939-40, 46-48, Oklahoma City, 1948-57, Farmington, N.Mex., 1957-64, Oklahoma City, 1964--; ptnr. Verity, Brown & Verity (and predecessor), 1964-77; of counsel Bay, Hamilton, Lee, Spears & Verity, 1978--; chmn. bd., dir. Big D Industries; pres. dir. Okla. Mgmt. Co., Okla. Ind. Exploration Co.; former chmn. bd., dir. Progress Life & Accident Ins. Co. Author: The Modern Oil and Gas Lease, From Bataan to Victory, An Agnostic Finds God in Jananese Prison Camp. Trustee Rocky Mountain Mineral Law Found. Capt. USAAF, 1941-46, PTO; prisoner of war. Decorated Purple Heart. Mem. ABA, Okla. Bar Assn., State Bar N.Mex. (chmn. mineral sect.), State Bar Tex., Assn. Trial Lawyers Am., Okla. Trial Lawyers Assn., Acacia. Lodges: Masons; Elks. Home: Villa 55 3101 Castle Rock Rd Oklahoma City OK 73120-1899 Office: 5620 SW 29th St Oklahoma City OK 73148-7603 *In a Japanese prison camp during World War II the love of God came into my life in a magnificent and dramatic way. The expression of this love has brought to my life, health, happiness, and success.*

VERITY, MAURICE ANTHONY, pathologist, neuropathologist, educator, consultant; b. Bradford, Eng. Apr. 21, 1931; came to U.S., 1959; s. Arthur Maurice and Nora (Fox) V.; m. Valerie Ann Blake, June 15, 1957; children: Michael, Neil, Gail. BA, Denstone Coll., Eng., 1949, MA, 1950; MD, U. London, 1956. Intern St. Mary's Hosp., London, 1956-57; clin. pathologist United Bristol (Eng.) Hosp., 1958; asst. prof. pharmacology UCLA, 1959-61, resident in pathology, 1961-63, asst. prof. pathology, 1963-67, assoc. prof., 1968-74, prof., 1974-93, prof. emeritus, 1993--; mem. Brain Rsch. Inst. and Mental Retardation Ctr., 1968--; cons. neuropathology Kaiser Permanente Found.; dep. coroner L.A. County, 1986--; cons. neuro-pathologist Leeds U., Eng., 1982; mem. health sci. study sect. EPA, 1987-92. Author: A Sterotaxic Atlas of the Mongolian Gerbil Brain, 1974; author: (with others) Metabolic Conjugation and Hydrolysis, 1973, The Striated Muscle, 1973; assoc. editor Neurotoxicology, 1990; contbr. articles to profl. jours. NIH fellow Bristol U., 1968; numerous fed. and pvt. founds. grantee. Mem. Am. Soc. Exptl. Pathology, Am. Assn. Pathologists and Bacteriologists, Am. Neurochem. Soc., Histochem. Soc., Nat. Inst. Environ. Health Sci. (toxicology study sect. 1988-92), Brit. Pathology Soc., Am. Soc. Neuropathology, Am. Soc. Toxicology (diagnostic and experimental neuropathology, neuro-toxicology diagnostic muscle histo-chemistry and neuro chemistry coms.). Home: 9431 Texhoma Ave Northridge CA 91325-2332 Office: U Calif Ctr Health Scis Dept Pathology Los Angeles CA 90024

VERKUIL, PAUL ROBERT, corporate executive; b. S.I., N.Y., Dec. 4, 1939; s. Marinus and Elsie Dorothy (Pohlmann) V.; m. Frances H. Gibson, Aug. 31, 1963; children: Tara Aldridge, John Gibson. BA, Coll. William and Mary, 1961; LLB, U. Va., 1967; LLM, NYU, 1969, JSD, 1972; MA, New Sch. Social Rsch., 1971. Bar: N.Y. 1968, Va. 1988, D.C. 1990. Assoc. Cravath, Swaine & Moore, N.Y.C., 1967-69, Paul, Weiss, Rifkind, Wharton & Garrison, N.Y.C., 1969-71; asst. prof. U. N.C. Law Sch., Chapel Hill, 1971-74, assoc. prof., 1974-76, prof. 1976-78; dean and Jospeh Jones prof. Tulane Law Sch., New Orleans, 1978-85; pres., prof. law and govt. Coll. William and Mary, Williamsburg, Va., 1985-92; pres. CEO Am. Automobile Assn., 1992--; vis. prof. Duke U., 1973-74; cons. U.S. Dept. Energy, 1977-79; Kenan research prof., vis. scholar Columbia U., 1978; mem. Administrv. Conf. U.S., 1982--, spl. master U.S v. La., 1989. Co-author: Public Control of Business, 1977, Social Security Hearings and Appeals, 1978, Administrative Law and Process, 1985, 2nd edit., 1992, Economic Regulation of Business, 2d edit., 1985. Served with U.S. Army, 1962-64. Mem. ABA, (chmn. sect. on administrv. law and regulatory practice 1989-90), Raven Soc., Am. Law Inst., Maritime Law Assn., Order of Coif, U. N.Y.C., Univ. D.C. Home: Coll William & Mary President's House Williamsburg VA 23185

VERLINDE, HERMAN L., physics educator. Asst. prof. physics Princeton U., N.J. Recipient Packard Fellowship David & Lucile Packard Found., 1993. Office: Princeton U Dept Physics Jadwin Hall Princeton NJ 08544-1019*

VERMA, GHASI RAM, mathematics educator; b. Sigari, Rajasthan, India, Aug. 1, 1927; came to U.S., 1958; s. Lachhu Ram and Jiwani Devi (Punia) V.; children: Om Prakash, Subhash, Anand. BA, Birla Coll., Pilani, 1950; MA, Banaras U., 1954; PhD, Rajasthan U., Jaipur, 1957. Postdoctoral fellow Courant Inst. Math. Scis., N.Y.C., 1958-59; asst. prof. Fordham U., N.Y.C., 1959-61; reader Birla Inst. Tech., Pilani, India, 1961-64; assoc. prof. U. R.I., Kingston, 1964-80, prof., 1980--. Contbr. articles to profl. jours.

Home: 61 Paul Ave Wakefield RI 02879-1504 Office: U RI 214 Tyler Hall Kingston RI 02881

VERMA, KRISHNANAND, mathematics educator, researcher, administrator, consultant; b. Muzaffarpur, Bihar, India, Aug. 1, 1946; came to U.S., 1984; s. Raisaheb Brinda Prasad Varma and Ramjyoti (kuar) Varma; m. Sushma Verma, Feb. 25, 1975; children: Kaninika, Samarth. BS in Math. (hons.), Physics and Chemistry, U. Bihar, 1964, MS in Math, 1966, MA in Econs., 1971, PhD in Math., 1973; BA in Lit., Orisa Rashtra Bhasha Parisad, 1980; MA in Lit., Bombai Hindi Vidya Pith, Bombay, 1980. Hon. lectr. U. Bihar, 1966-68; asst. prof. M.I.T., Bihar, India, 1968-76; prof., coord. and planner rsch. divsn. Fed. U. Brazil, Joao Pessoa, 1976-78; sr. faculty mem. MIT, Bihar, India, 1978-84; dir., pres. S.V. Coll. India, 1980-84, founder mem. governing body, bd. regents, 1973-84; assoc. prof. U. Nevada, Las Vegas, 1984-87, U. Minn., Duluth, 1987-89; assoc. prof. U. Wis., Whitewater, 1989-92, prof., 1992—; specialist in field of numerical analysis, optimization techniques, math. modeling, biomechanics, algebra, econ. planning and devel., fed. fin., pub. fin. and Indian lit.; propounder, discoverer of numerical quadratures and a variety of math. postulates, theorems, formulae, and identities; supr. and examiner of PhD and MS theses; tech. adv. manuscript examiner for more than 25 grad. and undergrad. upper-divsn. textbooks; cons., tech. adv. biomed. human subject com. U. Nev.-Reno, 1987—, Neurol. Inst. Nev., Sparks, 1987—, Am. Med. Laser, Inc., Dallas, 1988—; dept. math. Aichi U. Edn., Japan, 1986—, Med. Intelcom., Inc., Las Vegas, 1987—; judge Internat. Sci. and Engring. Fair, U.S. Naval Rsch., 1991, 92; referee 7 math. jours.; invited speaker profl. instns. worldwide. Contbr. over 100 articles to profl. jours. Troup sgt. Nat. Cadet Corps, India, 1957-59; active numerous rsch. oriented comty. svc. projects, com. works at internat., nat., and local levels, and univs. Recipient Best Sportsman award, Excellence in Teaching and Rsch. award, nat. and merit scholarships for outstanding acad. results, variety of medals and prizes for best sportsman, debator, essay writer, musician. Mem. Am. Math. Soc., Math. Assn. Am., Can. Math Soc., Indian Math Soc. Avocations: traveling, photography, sports, music, writing. Home: 274 N Esterly Ave Whitewater WI 53190-1315 Office: U Wis 800 W Main St Whitewater WI 53190-1705

VERMA, SURJIT K., school system administrator; b. India, May 17, 1940; arrived in Canada 1966; s. Sohara Lal and Gian Devi V.; m. Raj Verma; 1 child, Soania. MEd, St. Francis Xavier U., N.S., 1975; postgrad., Dalhousie U., N.S., U. Ottawa, Ont., Can, 1979. Cert. tchr. Nova Scotia. Sci. dept. head Halifax County Bedford Dist. Sch. Bd., N.S., Canada, 1968-88, curriculum supr., 1988—; served on C.T.F. Project Overseas Can. Teams, W.I., Nigeria, 1976, 77; mem. provincial sci. task force, biology rev. com., elem. sci.; mem. Internat. Sci. Symposium, 1979; worksop presenter numerous sci. workshops. Contbr. to profl. jours. Chmn. First Metro Halifax Dartmouth Reg Sci. Fair, 1975; co-chmn. Canada Wide Sci Fair, 1984. U. Ottawa fellow, 1979, Dalhousie U. Grad. fellow, 1980, Math. Sci. Tech. Edn. fellow Royal Bank Queen's U., 1994; Dalhousie U. Rsch. Devel. grantee, 1979; N.S. Tchrs. Union scholar, 1979; recipient Sci. Teaching Achievement Recognition award US Nat. Sci. Tchrs. Assn. and Am. Gas Assn., 1993, Profl. Devel. award N.S. Tchrs. Union, Teaching Excellence in Sci., Tech. and Math. award Prime Minister Can., 1993, Sci. on Display award NASCO, 1993-94. Mem. Nat. Sci. Tchrs. Assn., Nova Scotia Assn. Sci. Tchrs., Nova Scotia Assn. Curriculum Suprs., Assn. for Suprs. and Curriculum Devel. (provincial sci. 10 task force and rev. com.). Avocations: jogging, yoga. Home: 49 Rosewood Ave, Timberlea, NS Canada B3T 1C6

VERMEER, MAUREEN DOROTHY, sales executive; b. Bronxville, N.Y., Mar. 21, 1945; d. Albert Casey and Helen (Valentine Casey) Vermeer; m. John R. Fassnacht, Feb. 11, 1966 (div. 1975); m. George M. Dallas Peltz IV, Oct. 26, 1985. Grad., NYU Real Estate Inst., 1976. Lic. real estate broker, notary pub., N.Y. With Douglas Elliman, N.Y.C., 1965-74, mgmt. supr., 1974-78, v.p., 1978-83; real estate broker Rachmani Corp., N.Y.C., 1983-84; v.p. sales and mktg. Carol Mgmt. Corp., N.Y.C., 1984-90; v.p. mktg. The Sunshine Group, N.Y.C., 1990; v.p., sec., bd. dirs. H.J. Kalikow & Co., N.Y.C., 1991—; bd. dirs. Ascot Owners, Inc., N.Y.C.; speaker in field. Mem. Real Estate Bd. N.Y., Assn. Real Estate Women. Republican. Presbyterian. Avocations: skiing, scuba diving. Home: 206 County Rd Demarest NJ 07627-2202 Office: H J Kalikow & Co 101 Park Ave New York NY 10178-0001

VERMETTE, RAYMOND EDWARD, clinical laboratories administrator; b. Lewiston, Maine, June 30, 1942; s. Edward Louis and Anna Lucy (Raymond) V.; m. Ernestine Pero, Dec. 28, 1963; children: Tamara, Gregory. BS in Bacteriology, U. Maine, 1964; MS in Biochemistry, U. Wis., 1966; cert. personnel mgmt. Va. Dept. Edn., Fairfax, 1969; MBA, Temple U., 1973; master tchrs.' cert., Cath. Diocese of Boston, 1981. Supr. animal toxicology Hazleton Labs., Vienna, Va., 1967-71; personnel mgr. Damon Clin. Lab., Phila., 1971-73, ops. mgr., 1973-75, gen. mgr., Needham, Heights, Mass., 1975-90; v.p. ops. Damon Corp., Needham Hts., 1983-87, corp. v.p., 1987-89, sr. v.p., 1990-93; sr. v.p., gen. mgr. Corning/MetPath, Westwood, Mass., 1994-95; ret. 1995; vis. lectr fin. mgmt. and bus. adminstrn. Framingham State Coll., 1978-84; instr. mgmt. Newbury Jr. Coll., Boston, 1976-79. Author: (with B. Kliman and E. Kolowrat) What You Should Know About Medical Lab Tests, 1979. V.p. fin. com. Framingham, Mass., 1982-84; mem. capital budget com., Town of Framingham, 1987; mem.-elect, Town Meeting, 1987—; chmn. bd. religious edn. Cath. Ch., Framingham, 1981-84, co-chmn. Pre-Marriage Preparation Council, 1981—, organist, 1979—. Democrat. Home: 11 Willowbrook Dr Framingham MA 01701-5515

VERMEULE, CORNELIUS CLARKSON, III, museum curator; b. Orange, N.J., Aug. 10, 1925; s. Cornelius Clarkson Jr. and Catherine Sayre (Comstock) V.; m. Emily Dickinson Townsend, Feb. 2, 1957; children—Emily D. Blake, Cornelius Adrian Comstock. Grad., Pomfret Sch., 1943; A.B., Harvard, 1949, M.A., 1951; Ph.D., U. London, Eng. 1953; DHL (hon.), Boston Coll., 1995. Instr. fine arts, then asst. prof. U. Mich., 1953-55; asst. prof. classical archaeology Bryn Mawr (Pa.) Coll., 1955-57; curator classical art Mus. Fine Arts, Boston, 1956—; acting dir. Mus. Fine Arts, 1972-73; assoc. curator coins Mass. Hist. Soc., 1965-71, curator, 1971—; lectr. fine arts Smith Coll., 1960-64, Boston U., Harvard, Wellesley Coll.; vis. prof. Yale, 1969-70, 72-73; Thomas Spencer Jerome lectr. U. Mich., 1975-76; vis. prof. Boston Coll., 1978—; vis. prof. U. Aberdeen, Scotland, 1993; pres. Internat. Com. to Save Jewish Catacombs of Italy, 1980-84, chmn.- Author: (with N. Jacobs) Japanese Coinage, 1948, 2d edit., 1972, Bibliography of Applied Numismatics, 1956, The Goddess Roma, 1959, 2d edit., 1974, Dal Pozzo-Albani Drawings, 1960, European Art and the Classical Past, 1964, Drawings at Windsor Castle, 1966, Roman Imperial Art in Greece and Asia Minor, 1968, Polykleitos, 1969, Numismatic Art in America, 1971, (with M. Comstock) Greek Etruscan and Roman Bronzes, 1972, (with N. Neuerburg) Catalogue of the Ancient Art in the J. Paul Getty Museum, 1973, Greek and Roman Sculpture in Gold and Silver, 1974, Greek and Roman Cyprus, 1976, (with M. Comstock) Sculpture in Stone, 1976, Greek Sculpture and Roman Taste, 1977, Roman Art: Early Republic to Late Empire, 1978, (with A Herrmann) The Ernest Brummer Collections, Vol. II, 1979, Greek Art: Socrates to Sulla, 1980, The Jewish Experience in Roman Art, 1981, Masterpieces of Greek and Roman Sculpture in America, 1982, Greek Art: Prehistoric to Perikles, 1982, Numismatic Studies, 1983, Alexander the Great Conquers Rome, 1985, The Cult Images of Imperial Rome, 1986, Numismatic Art of the Greek Imperial World, 1987, Philatelic Art in America, 1987, (with M. Comstock) Sculpture in Stone and Bronze, 1988, (with A. Brauer) Stone Sculptures, The Greek, Roman and Etruscan Collections of the Harvard University Art Museums, 1990, (with others) Le Sport dans la Grèce Antique, 1992, Du Jeu à la Compétition, 1992, (with others) El Deporte en la Grecia Antigua, La génesis del olimpismo, 1992-93, (with others) Vase-Painting in Italy, 1993. Trustee Cardinal Spellman Philatelic Mus., 1980-93. Served to 1st lt. AUS, 1943-47. Recipient Bicentennial medal Boston Coll., 1976; Fulbright fellow, 1951-53; Guggenheim fellow, 1968. Fellow AAAS, Am. Numis. Soc. (life), Royal Numis. Soc., Soc. Antiquaries; mem. Coll. Art Assn. (life), Archaeol. Inst. Am. (life) German Archaeol. Inst., Holland Soc. N.Y., Colonial Lords of Manors in Am., Mass. Hist. Soc. (hon.). Republican. Episcopalian. Club: Tavern (medalist 1986) (Boston). Home: 47 Coolidge Hill Rd Cambridge MA 02138-5509 Office: Mus Fine Arts 465 Huntington Ave Boston MA 02115-5519 *To teach, collect and record the past, as exemplar for the present, as prologue to the future, can there be any better use of a historian's and archaeologist's professional life?.*

VERMEULE, EMILY TOWNSEND (MRS. CORNELIUS C. VERMEULE, III), classicist, educator; b. N.Y.C., Aug. 11, 1928; d. Clinton Blake and Eleanor (Meneely) Townsend; m. Cornelius C. Vermeule III, Feb. 2, 1957; children: Emily Dickinson Blake, Cornelius Adrian Comstock. AB, Bryn Mawr Coll., 1950; student, Am. Sch. Classical Studies, Athens, 1950-51, St. Anne's Coll., Oxford U., 1953; MA, Harvard, 1954; PhD, Bryn Mawr Coll., 1956; DLitt, Douglass Coll.; D. Litt., Rutgers U., 1968, Tufts U., 1980, U. Pitts., 1983, Bates Coll., 1983, U. Miami, Oxford, Ohio, 1986; LL.D., Regis Coll., 1971; D. Fine Arts, U. Mass, Amherst, 1971; D.Litt., Smith Coll., 1972, Wheaton Coll., 1973, Trinity Coll., 1974; LHD, Emmanuel Coll., 1980, Princeton U., 1989, Bard Coll., 1994. Instr. Greek lang. Bryn Mawr Coll., 1956-57; instr. Wellesley (Mass.) Coll., 1957-58, prof. art and Greek, 1965-70, chmn. dept. art, 1966-67; asst. prof. classics Boston U., 1958-61, assoc. prof. classics, 1961-65; fellow for research Boston Mus. Fine Arts, 1965—; James C. Loeb vis. prof. classical philology Harvard, 1969; dir. univ. Cyprus expdn. Harvard U., 1971—; Samuel and Doris Zemurray Stone-Radcliffe prof., 1970-94; Sather prof. U. Calif., Berkeley, 1975; Geddes-Harrower prof. Greek art and archaeology U. Aberdeen, 1980-81; Bernhard vis. prof. Williams Coll., 1986; excavations in Greece, Turkey, Libya, Cyprus. Author: Euripides v. Electra, 1959, Greece in the Bronze Age, 1964, The Trojan War in Greek Art, 1964, Götterkult, 1974, Toumba tou Skourou, The Mound of Darkness, 1975, Death in Early Greek Art and Poetry, Mycenaean Pictorial Vase-Painting (with F.Z. Wolsky), 1990; contbr. articles to scholarly publs. Judge Nat. Book Award, 1977; bd. dirs. Humanities Rsch. Inst., U. Calif., 1988-91, bd. govs., 1989-90; trustee Isabella Stewart Gardner Mus., 1988—. Recipient Gold medal for disting. achievement Radcliffe Coll. Grad. Soc., 1968; Guggenheim fellow, 1964-65. Fellow Soc. Antiquaries, Brit. Acad. (corr.), German Archaeol. Inst. (corr.); mem. AAAS, Am. Inst. Archaeology, Am. Philos. Soc. (v.p. 1978-81), Am. Philol. Assn. (Charles J. Goodwin award 1980, pres.-elect 1994), Smithsonian Coun. (bd. scholars 1983-89), Hellenic Soc. Office: Harvard U Widener Libr 215 Cambridge MA 02138

VERMILYE, PETER HOAGLAND, banker; b. N.Y.C., Jan. 17, 1920; s. Herbert Noble and Elise Tace (Hillyer) V.; m. Lucy Shaw Mitchell, Oct. 14, 1950; children: Peter H., Dana R., Andrew R., Mary S. AB, Princeton U., 1940. V.p. pension investments J.P. Morgan & Co. and Morgan Guaranty Trust, 1940-64; ptnr. State St. Research & Mgmt., Boston, 1965-69; pres. Alliance Capital Mgmt., N.Y.C., 1970-77; sr. v.p., chief investment officer Citibank, N.Y.C., 1977-84; chmn. Baring Am. Asset Mgmt., Boston, 1984-89; sr. advisor Baring Asset Mgmt., 1990—; chmn. bd. dirs. Huntington Theatre' bd. dirs. Baring Puma Fund, Fosterlane Mgmt. Trustee Boston U. Clubs: Brook, Somerset, Myopia. Home: 157 School St Manchester MA 01944-1236 also: 107 Chestnut St Boston MA 02108 Office: Baring Asset Mgmt 125 High St Boston MA 02110-2723

VERMYLEN, PAUL ANTHONY, JR., oil company executive; b. N.Y.C., Dec. 5, 1946; s. Paul Anthony and Nancy Primrose (Barr) V.; m. Robin S. Collins, Jan. 24, 1970; children: Robert T.C., Nancy Barr, Sarah Morgan, Paul Anthony III. AB, Georgetown U., 1968; MBA, Columbia U., 1971. V.p. Citibank N.A., N.Y.C., 1971-78; treas. Commonwealth Oil Refining Co., San Antonio, 1978-81; v.p., chief fin. officer Commonwealth Oil Refining Co., 1981-82; v.p., chief fin. officer, dir. Meenan Oil Co., Inc., Syosset, N.Y., 1982-91, pres., 1992—; pres. Meenan Oil Co., L.P., 1992—; bd. dirs. Petroleum Industry Rsch. Found., 1992—. Bd. dirs. Huntington Arts Coun., N.Y., 1983-89, v.p., 1986-87, pres., 1987-89; bd. advisors Cold Spring Harbor Lab. DNA Learning Ctr., 1991—. Mem. Winter Club, Cold Spring Harbor Beach Club, Seawanhaka Corinthian Yacht Club. Office: 6900 Jericho Tpke Syosset NY 11791-4401

VERNBERG, FRANK JOHN, marine and biological sciences educator; b. Fenton, Mich., Nov. 6, 1925; s. Sigurd A. and Edna (Anderson) V.; m. Winona M. Bortz, Sept. 7, 1945; children—Marcia Lynn, Eric Morrison, Amy Louise. A.B., DePauw U., 1949, M.A., 1950; Ph.D., Purdue U., 1951. Prof. zoology Duke Marine Lab., Beaufort, N.C., 1951-69; Belle W. Baruch prof. marine ecology, dir. Bell W. Baruch Marine Biology and Coastal Rsch. Inst., Columbia, 1969—; interim dean Coll. Sci. and Math. Belle W. Baruch Coastal Research Inst., U.S.C., Columbia, 1993—; vis. prof. U. Coll. West Indies, Jamaica, 1957-58, U. Sao Paulo, Brazil, 1965; program dir. exptl. analytical biogeography of sea Internat. Biol. Program, 1967-69; mem. com. manned orbital research lab. Am. Inst. Biol. Scis.-NASA, 1966-68; pres. Estuarine Research Fedn., 1975-77. Contbr. articles to profl. jours.; spl. editor: Am. Zoologist, 1963; mem. editorial bd.: Biol. Bull., 1977-80; editor: Jour. Exptl. Marine Biology and Ecology, 1978—. Served with USNR, 1944-46. Recipient W.S. Proctor award Sigma Xi, award Drug Sci. Found., 1987; Guggenheim fellow, 1957-58; Fulbright-Hays fellow, 1965. Fellow AAAS, Am. Soc. Zoologists (sec.-treas. divsn. comparative physiologists 1959-61, sec.-treas. edn. com. 1960-62, mem. coun. 1965-67, pres. 1982), Southeastern Estuarine Rsch. Soc. (pres. 1974-76), So. Assn. Marine Labs. (pres. 1993), Estuarine Rsch. Fedn. (pres. 1975-77), S.C. Wildlife Fedn. (Conservationist of Yr. 1983). Office: U SC Belle W Baruch Coastal Rsch Inst Columbia SC 29208

VERNER, JAMES MELTON, lawyer; b. Selma, Ala., Sept. 19, 1915; s. Singleton Foster and Jennie (Harris) V.; m. Gretchen Gores, Aug. 12, 1939; children: Ann Verner Picardo, James Singleton, William Melton. Student, Biltmore Coll., 1932-34; A.B., U. N.C., 1936, LL.B., 1938. Bar: N.C. 1938, Tenn. 1947, D.C. 1950, Va., 1986. Assoc. firm Gover & Covington, Charlotte, N.C. 1938; law clk. atty. gen. N.C., 1938-40; atty. CAB, Washington, 1940-43; asst. gen. counsel Chgo. & So. Airlines, Memphis, 1946-47; atty. Air Transport Assn. Am., Washington, 1947-49; hearing examiner CAB, 1949-50, exec. asst. to chmn., 1950, exec. dir., 1950-53; atty. Turney & Turney, 1953-60, ptnr., 1954-60; ptnr. firm Verner, Liipfert, Bernhard, McPherson & Hand, Chartered (and predecessor firms), 1960-88, hon. mem. bd. dirs., 1988—; mem. policy adv. bd. Legal Counsel for the Elderly, Washington. Assoc. editor: N.C. Law Rev, 1937-38. Former mem., chmn. policy bd. Legal Counsel for Elderly, Washington. Served as lt. (j.g.) USNR, 1943-46; legal officer Naval Air Transport Svc., 1945-46. Mem. ABA, Order of Golden Fleece, Cosmos Club (Washington). Home: 3618 N Nelson St Arlington VA 22207-5319 Office: 901 15th St NW Washington DC 20005-2327 *My belief is that if you treat other people fairly and trust them, you will seldom be disappointed and will be the better for it.*

VERNIER, RICHARD, foreign language educator, author; b. Clermont-Ferrand, France, Feb. 1, 1929; came to U.S., 1951; s. Marcel Eugene Vernier and Marie José Guerra; m. Kathleen Manion, July 14, 1962; children: Matthew, John, Stephen. Student in pre-med., Université de Bordeaux, France, 1949; AB, U. Calif., Berkeley, 1958, PhD, 1965. Instr. Mills Coll., Oakland, Calif., 1961-62; lectr. CCNY, 1962-63; asst. prof. San Diego State Coll., 1963-66, U. Wash., Seattle, 1966-72; prof. French Wayne State U., Detroit, 1973-92, prof. emeritus, 1993—; cons. NEH, 1989. Author: Paul Eluard, 1971, Le Feu Parmi les Arbres, 1981, Yves Bonnefoy, 1985, La Patience, 1986, Parcours américain, 1991; mem. editorial bd. Swiss-French Studies, Wolfville, N.S., 1981-87. With U.S. Army, 1952-54, Korea. Decorated chevalier Palmes Académiques, Republic of France, 1981, officier, 1990. Mem. Am. Assn. Tchrs. French, Soc. for Creative Anachronism, Early Music Am. Avocations: long walks, ancient music. Home: 1326 Marion St Enumclaw WA 98022

VERNIER, ROBERT LAWRENCE, physician, educator; b. El Paso, Tex., July 29, 1924; s. William J. and Ada E. (McQuillen) V.; m. Molly Katherine Bennett, Apr. 31, 1945; children—Katherine (Mrs. David Peterson), Patricia (Mrs. Louis DeMartino), Janet, Richard, Christine. B.S., U. Dayton, 1948; M.D., U. Cin., 1952. Intern Univ. Hosp., Little Rock, 1952-53; resident U. Ark., 1952-54; resident U. Minn., 1954-58, asst. prof., 1959, asso. prof., 1963; prof. U. Calif., Los Angeles, 1964-68; prof. pediatrics U. Minn., Mpls., 1968-95; ret.; Nat. cons. USAF, 1970—; established investigator Am. Heart Assn., 1959-64, mem. research com., 1966-71, chmn., 1970; Pres. Kidney Found. Upper-Midwest, 1968-71; mem. sci. rev. com. NIH, 1961-66. Contbr. sci. articles to jours., chpts. to books. Served to 1st lt., mtt. AUS, 1943-46. Guggenheim fellow, 1960-61. Mem. Am. Soc. Clin. Investigation, Am. Soc. Nephrology (pres. 1980), Am. Soc. Pediatric Rsch. (Mead Johnson award for rsch. 1962), Am. Soc. Pediatric Nephrology (pres. 1977). Home: 5444 W Bavarian Pass Fridley MN 55432-6042

VERNON, CARL ATLEE, JR., retired wholesale food distributor executive; b. Topeka, Aug. 15, 1926; s. Carl Atlee and Capitola May (Jarboe) V.; m. Marion Leila Colton, May 7, 1950; children—Mary Catherine, Matthew Fowler, Susan Elizabeth. B.S., Yale U., 1947. Merchandising mgr. Fleming Cos., Topeka, 1957-61, dir. merchandising, 1961-66, dir. info. services, 1966-72, v.p. info. services, 1972-74, v.p. regional systems, 1974-79; sr. v.p. mktg. services Fleming Cos., Oklahoma City, 1979-88. Chmn. Shawnee County chpt. ARC, Topeka, Kans., 1957-58. Served to ensign USNR, 1944-46. Republican. Episcopalian. Avocations: golf; gardening; travel.

VERNON, DAVID HARVEY, lawyer, educator; b. Boston, Aug. 9, 1925; s. Bernard Nathan and Ida E. (Cohen) V.; m. Rhoda Louise Sterman, June 1, 1947; children: Amy Lynne, Charles Adam. AB, Harvard U., 1949, LLB, 1952; LLM, NYU, 1953, JSD, 1960; DCL (hon.), U. Durham, Eng., 1988. Bar: Mass. 1952, Iowa 1966. Instr. NYU, 1953-54; asst. prof. law U. Houston, 1954-55; from asst. prof. to prof. law U. N.Mex., Albuquerque, 1955-64; assoc. dean, prof. law U. Wash., Seattle, 1964-66; prof. law U. Iowa, 1966—, dean Coll. Law, 1966-71, A.D. Vestal prof. law, 1986—, acad. v.p., 1988-90; vis. prof. Sch. Law, Washington U., St. Louis, 1974-75, U. Durham (Eng.), fall 1980, Victoria U. Wellington, New Zealand, 1986; vis. scholar Sch. Law, Washington and Lee U., Lexington, Va., spring 1991, So. Tex. Coll. Law, spring 1993. Editor: (with Depew) General State Food and Drug Law, Annotated, 1955, Title XIV of the American Law of Mining, 1960, Conflict of Laws: Cases, Problems and Essays, 1973, supplement, 1979, Contracts: Theory and Practice, 1980, 2d edit., 1991, Conflict of Law: Theory and Practice, 1982, 2d edit., 1991, (with Weinberg, Reynolds and Richmond) Conflict of Law: Cases, Materials and Problems, 1991. Bd. dirs. Wash. State affiliate ACLU, 1964-66, Iowa Civil Liberties Union, 1966-72. With USNR, 1943-46. Fulbright travel awardee, New Zealand, 1986. Mem. ABA (ho. of dels. 1986-91, trustee law sch. admission coun. 1985-86), Iowa Bar Assn., Assn. Am. Law Schs. (mem. exec. com. 1978-80, pres. 1983, editor Jour. Legal Edn. 1987-92). Home: 327 Koser Ave Iowa City IA 52246-3036 Office: U Iowa Coll Law Iowa City IA 52242

VERNON, LILLIAN, mail order company executive; b. Leipzig, Germany; d. Herman and Erna Menasche; children: Fred, David. DCS (hon.), Mercy Coll., Dobbs Ferry, N.Y., 1984, Coll. New Rochelle, DSc in Bus. Adminstrn. (hon.), Bryant Coll., LLD (hon.), Baruch Coll., LHD (hon), Old Dominion U., DCS (hon.) Mercy Coll., DCS (hon.) Coll. New Rochelle; D in Bus. Adminstrn. (hon.) Bryant Coll., LLD (hon.) Baruch Coll. CEOLillian Vernon, New Rochelle, N.Y., 1951—; lectr. in field. Contbr. articles to profl. jours. Bd. dirs. Westchester County Assn., N.Y., Mental Health Assn. Westchester County, Ctr. Preventive Psychiatry, Va. Opera, Children's Mus. Arts, Retinitis Pigmentosa Found.; trustee Coll. Human Svcs., Bryant Coll.; mem. adv. bd. Giraffe Project, Girl Scout Coun. Tidewater, Women's News; mem. bd. overseers Columbia U. Bus. Sch., NYU; mem. adv. com. Citizen Amb. Program; mem. bus. com. Met. Mus. Art; bd. govs. The Forum; mem. nat. com. The Kennedy Ctr. for Performing Arts, Washington; active The Ellis Island Reopening Com., Women's News Bd. Advisors; bd. govs. The Forum. Recipient Dist. Achievement award Lab. Inst. Merchandising, Entrepreneural award Women's Bus. Owners of N.Y., 1983, Bravo award YWCA, Woman of Achievement award Woman's News, Nat. Hero award Big Bros./Big Sisters, Legend in Leadership award Emory U., A Woman Who Has Made A Difference award Inter. Womens Forum, medal of honor Ellis Island, Bus. Leadership award Gannett Newspapers, Outstanding Bus. Leader award Northwood Inst., Congl. Record Commendation award, Crystal award Coll. Human Svcs., City of Peace award Bonds of Israel, Svc. award Sr. Placement Bur., Excellence award Westchester Assn. Women Bus. Owners, Commendation in Congl. Record, Magnificent Seven award Bus. and Profl. Women, Woman of Distinction award Birmingham So. Coll.; named Va. Press Women Newsmaker of Yr., Woman of Yr., Women's Direct Response Group and Westchester County Fedn. Women's Clubs, Hampton Roads Woman of Yr., So. New England Entrepreneur Yr., Bravo award YWCA; named to Acad. Women Achievers, YWCA, Direct Mktg. Assn. Hall of Fame. Mem. Am. Bus. Conf. (dir.), Am. Stock Exch. (listed co. adv. com.), Com. of 200, Women's Forum, Nat. Retail Fedn. (bd. dirs.), Lotos Club. Office: Lillian Vernon Corp 543 Main St New Rochelle NY 10801

VERNON, RAYMOND, economist, educator; b. N.Y.C., Sept. 1, 1913; s. Hyman and Lillian (Sonnenberg) V.; m. Josephine Stone, Aug. 9, 1935; children: Heidi, Susan Patricia. A.B. cum laude, CCNY, 1933; Ph.D., Columbia U., 1941; M.A. (hon.), Harvard, 1959. Statistician SEC, 1935-42, asst. dir. trading and exchange div., 1942-46; asst. chief internat. resources div. Dept. State, 1946-48; became advisor on comml. policy, 1948; dep. dir. Office of Econ. Def. and Trade Policy, 1951, acting dir., 1954; staff mem. joint Presdl. Congl. Commn. on Fgn. Econ. policy, 1953-54; planning and control dir. Hawley and Hoops, Inc., 1954-56; dir. N.Y. Met. Region Study, 1956-59; prof. Harvard U. Bus. Sch., 1959-78, dir. Harvard Devel. Adv. Service, 1962-65, dir. Ctr. for Internat. Affairs, 1973-78, prof. internat. relations, 1978-83, prof. emeritus, 1983—; bd. dirs. Cambridge Energy Rsch. Assocs.; lectr. Am. U., 1946-48, Princeton U., 1954-55, Swarthmore Coll., 1955-56; adj. prof. Fletcher Sch. Law and Diplomacy., 1979-81; mem. Mission on Japanese Combines, Tokyo, 1946; mem. U.S. del. GATT, Geneva, 1950, Torquay, Eng., 1951, vice chmn. U.S. del. Geneva, 1952; spl. cons. to undersec. Dept. State, 1962, Dept. Treasury, 1978-79; participant UN Conf. on Regional Devel., Tokyo, 1958; vis. prof. World Bank, 1987. Author: Regulation of Stock Exchange Members, 1941, America's Trade Policy and GATT, 1954, Organizing for World Trade, 1956, (with Edgar M. Hoover) Anatomy of a Metropolis, 1959, Metropolis 1985, 1960, The Dilemma of Mexico's Development, 1963, Myth and Reality of Our Urban Problems, 1965, Manager in The International Economy, 1968, Sovereignty at Bay, 1971, Storm over the Multinationals, 1976, Two Hungry Giants, 1983, Exploring the Global Economy, 1985, (with D.L. Spar) Beyond Globalism, 1988; editor: Public Policy and Private Enterprise in Mexico, 1964, How Latin America Views the U.S. Investor, 1966, The Technology Factor in International Trade, 1970, Big Business and the State, 1974, The Oil Crisis, 1976, State-owned Enterprises in the Western Economies, 1980, The Promise of Privatization, 1988, (with D.L. Spar and Glenn Tobin) Iron Triangles and Revolving Doors, 1991, (with Ethan Kapstein) Defense and Dependence in a Global Economy, 1992; founding editor Jour. Policy Analysis and Mgmt., 1981-85; contbr. articles to profl. jours. Recipient Meritorious Svc. award Dept. State, 1951, Disting. Svc. award Harvard Bus. Sch., 1986; decorated Order of Rising Sun (Japan), 1986; named Eminent scholar Internat. Studies Assn., 1994. Fellow Am. Acad. Arts and Scis., Acad. Internat. Bus.; mem. Council on Fgn. Relations, U.S./UN Assn., Phi Beta Kappa. Home: 1 Dunstable Rd Cambridge MA 02138-3341 Office: Harvard U Kennedy Sch Govt 79 Kennedy St Cambridge MA 02138-3352

VERNON, SHIRLEY JANE, architect, educator; b. Mt. Kisco, N.Y., Dec. 9, 1930; d. J.H. and M.R. (Maher) V. B.Arch. cum laude, Pa. State U., 1953. Asso., coordinating architect for design, designer Vincent G. Kling and Assos., Phila., 1953-68; pvt. practice architecture Phila., 1968-74, 75—; mgr. archtl. design Ballinger Co., Phila., 1974-75; instr. architecture Drexel U., 1956-58, adj. asst. prof., 1959-64, adj. asso. prof., 1965-69, adj. prof., 1970-87; adv. advisor Phila. Coll. Art, 1980-81; prof. Moore Coll. Art and Design (formerly Moore Coll. Art), 1986—. Recipient 25 Yr. Service award Drexel U., 1982. Fellow AIA (chpt. dir. 1973, 79, chpt. v.p. 1975); mem. Art Alliance Phila., Assn. Collegiate Schs. Architecture, Print Club Phila., Tau Beta Pi. Office: 1704 Delancey St Philadelphia PA 19103-6715

VERNON, WESTON, III (WES VERNON), journalist; b. N.Y.C., Aug. 23, 1931; s. Weston, Jr. and Adelaide (Nielson) V.; m. Alida Steinvoort, Oct. 5, 1951; children: Rosanne, Weston IV, Diane, John Randall. Student, Utah State U., 1949-50, Brigham Young U., 1953-54. Reporter, producer KBUH, Brigham City, Utah, 1950-51, KVRS, Rock Springs, Wyo., 1952, KOVO, Provo, Utah, 1952-54, Intermountain Network, Salt Lake City, 1954, KLO, Ogden, Utah, 1954, KBMY, Billings, Mont., 1954-63; news dir.-polit. specialist KSL Radio-TV, Salt Lake City, 1963-68; bur. chief Bonneville Internat. Corp., Washington, 1968-72; corr. CBS Radio Stas. News Service, CBS Radio, Washington, 1972—; bd. dirs. Am. Zephyr, Inc. Columnist The High Green, The Timetable; contbr. to Passenger Train jour., Railfan and Railroad. Bd. dirs. Winding-Orchard Citizens Assn., Wheaton-Glenmont, Md., 1974-77, 86—, pres., 1975-76. Served with AUS, 1951-52. Recipient Journalism awards Mont. A.P. Press Stas., 1960, Journalism awards Utah Bar Assn., 1965, Journalism awards Utah Broadcasters Assn., 1965-66. Mem. Radio-TV Corrs. Assn., Am. Legion (comdr. Yellowstone Post 4 1962-63), Railroad Enthusiasts (pres. Chesapeake divsn. 1992-94), Nat.

Assn. Radio Talk Show Hosts. Office: CBS Radio Stas News Svc 2020 M St NW Washington DC 20036-3368

VERONIS, GEORGE, geophysics educator; b. New Brunswick, N.J., June 6, 1926; s. Nicholas Emmanuel and Angeliki (Efthimakis) V.; m. Anna Margareta Olsson, Nov. 8, 1963; m. Catherine Elizabeth, Jan. 29, 1949 (div. Nov. 1962); children—Melissa, Benjamin. A.B, Lafayette Coll., 1950; Ph.D., Brown U., 1954; M.A. (hon.), Yale U., 1966. Staff meteorologist Inst. Advanced Study, Princeton, 1953-56; staff mathematician Woods Hole Oceanographic Inst., Mass., 1956-64, mem. staff, dir. geophys. fluid dynamics summer program, 1959—, assoc. prof. MIT, Cambridge, 1961-64, research ocenographer, 1964-66; prof. geophysics and applied sci. Yale U., New Haven, 1966—, Henry Barnard Davis prof., 1985—, chmn. geology and geophysics, 1976-79, dir. applied math, 1979-93. Editor Jour. Marine Rsch., 1973—; contbr. articles to profl. jours. Served with USN, 1943-46. Fellow Am. Acad. Arts and Scis., Am. Geophys. Union; mem. NAS, Norwegian Acad. Scis. (Robert L. and Bettie P. Cody award 1989). Greek Orthodox.

VERONIS, PETER, publisher; b. New Brunswick, N.J., June 15, 1923; s. Nicholas M. and Angeliki (Efthemakis) V.; m. Dorothy E. White, Sept. 8, 1946; 1 dau., Judith Anne Veronis Rodgers. Student, Columbia U., 1951-54. Nat. advt. mgr. Springfield (Mass.) Newspapers, 1954-57; v.p., gen. sales mgr. Ridder Johns Co., N.Y.C., 1957-62; corp. exec. Curtis Pub. Co., N.Y.C., 1963-64; assoc. sales mgr. Look mag., 1964-68; v.p., advt. dir. Psychology Today mag. 1968-71; v.p. advt. Saturday Rev., N.Y.C., 1971-73; pub. Book Digest, N.Y.C., 1973-80; pres. PV Pub. Inc., N.Y.C., 1980-81, Conn., 1980—; v.p., dir. CBS Mag. Network, N.Y.C., 1981-85, pres., 1985-87; pres. Diamandis Mag. Network, 1987-88. Served with USN, 1941-51. Home: 42 Thornwood Rd Stamford CT 06903-2613

VEROSUB, KENNETH LEE, geology educator, researcher; b. N.Y.C., July 10, 1944; s. Bernard B. and Vera (Lipman) V.; m. Evelyn Kay Falkenstein, June 15, 1967; children: Abra Laurie, Ellis Marshall. BA, U. Mich., 1966; MS, Stanford U., 1971, PhD, 1973. Asst. prof. Amherst (Mass.) Coll., 1972-75; asst. prof. U. Calif., Davis, 1975-79, assoc. prof., 1979-84, prof., 1984—, chmn. grad. group in earth scis. and resources, 1980-87, faculty asst. to provost, 1992-93; vis. researcher Centre des Faibles Radioactivities, Gif-Sur-Yvette, France, 1982-83; vis. researcher Centre de Geologie et Geophysique, Montpellier, France, 1989-90; vis. prof. Universite des Science et Technique du Languedoc, Montpellier, France, 1989-90. Contbr. articles, abstracts to profl. jours. Bd. dirs. Davis Sci. Ctr., 1983-85. Fellow NSF, 1966, Danforth Found., 1966, Woodrow Wilson Found., 1966; recipient Disting. Teaching award U. Calif.-Davis, 1988; Fulbright fellow, France, 1989-90. Mem. Am. Geophys. Union, Geol. Soc. Am., AAAS, Earthquake Engring. Research Inst. Avocations: photography, traveling. Office: Univ of Calif Davis Dept Of Geology Davis CA 95616

VERPLANCK, WILLIAM SAMUEL, psychologist, educator; b. Plainfield, N.J., Jan. 6, 1916; s. William Samuel and Kathryn (Tracy) V. B.S., U. Va., 1937, M.A., 1938; Ph.D., Brown U., 1941. Asst. prof. Ind. U., 1946-50; asst. prof. Harvard, 1950-55, acting asso. prof., 1955-56; research asso. Stanford U., 1956-57; asso. prof. Hunter Coll., 1957-59; prof. U. Md., 1958-62; prof. psychology U. Tenn., 1963-81, head dept., 1963-73; founder, chmn. Resource Assocs., Inc., 1980-82; bd. dirs. Cambridge Ctr. for Behavioral Sci. Author: (with others) Modern Learning Theory, 1953. Served to lt. USNR, 1943-46. Recipient travel grant Am. Philos. Assn., 1953. Fellow APA, Am. Psychol. Soc., Assn. Study Animal Behavior, AAAS; mem. Ea. Psychol. Assn., Psychonomic Soc. (founder, past sec.-treas., bd. govs.), Sigma Xi, Sigma Alpha Epsilon. *The history of psychology is largely constituted of a succession of fads overlying the continuity given by a few plausible technological methods which have been progressively misapplied, with little critical concern for their social, political or scientific consequences. Can any person, working over a period of fifty years, make a difference?.*

VERRECCHIA, ALFRED J., toy company executive; b. 1943. Asst. controller Hasbro Inc., 1965-70, controller, 1970-74, treas., 1974—, v.p., 1980—, then sr. v.p. fin., then exec. v.p. fin. and adminstrn., pres. mfg. svcs. div., exec. v.p., 1989—, chief oper. officer, 1989—. Office: Hasbro Inc 1027 Newport Ave Pawtucket RI 02861-2539

VERRET, JOHN CYRIL, advertising executive; b. Burlington, Vt., Oct. 21, 1945; s. Albert A. and Barbara (Cote) V.; m. Margaret Simisky, Feb. 20, 1971; children: Michael John, Justin Thomas. BS in Econ., St. Michael's Coll., 1968. Account exec. Quinn and Johnson, Boston, 1969-75; account supr. Hill Holliday Connors Cosmopulus, Boston, 1975-76; v.p. account supr. Pearson and MacDonald, Boston, 1976-78; v.p. mgmt. supr. Ingalls Assoc., Boston, 1978-87; exec. v.p. Arnold and Co., Boston, 1987-88, pres., 1988-89; pres. New Eng. Broadcasting, 1988—; 1st v.p. New Eastland Broadcasting Assn., Boston, 1990—. Mem. Boston Ad Club, Exec. Club. Roman Catholic,. Avocations: coaching, basketball, carpentry, reading, squashing.

VERRICO, ERNEST JOSEPH, banker; b. Stamford, Conn., May 21, 1955; s. Leo Andrew and Carmella Maria (Mallozzi) V.; m. Madeline C. Lombardo, Sept. 14, 1985. BBA in Acctg. cum laude, Iona Coll., 1977. Sr. supr. Price Warehouse and Co., N.Y. and Conn., 1977-82; v.p. comptroller, treas. Union Trust Co. Stamford, 1982—, Union Capital Services Corp., Stamford, 1983—; dir. Am. Inst. Banking, Stamford, Conn. Corp. solicitor United Way Stamford. 1985—. Mem. West Side Bus. Assn. (v.p., bd. dirs. 1985—), Fin. Exec. Inst., Nat. Assn. Acctg., Am. Inst. Banking, Bank Adminstrn. Inst. Republican. Roman Catholic. Avocations: snow skiing, tennis, softball, jogging, traveling. Office: Union Trust Co PO Box 700 300 Main St Stamford CT 06904

VERRILL, CHARLES OWEN, JR., lawyer; b. Biddeford, Maine, Sept. 30, 1937; s. Charles Owen and Elizabeth (Handy) V.; m. Mary Ann Blanchard, Aug. 13, 1960 (dec.); children: Martha Anne, Edward Blanchard, Ethan Christopher, Elizabeth Handy, Matthew Lawton, Peter Goldthwait; m. Diana Baber, Dec. 11, 1993. AB, Tufts U., 1959; LLB, Duke U., 1962. Bar: D.C. 1962. Assoc. Weaver & Glassie, 1962-64; assoc. Barco, Cook, Patton & Blow, 1964-66, ptnr.; 1967; ptnr. Patton, Boggs & Blow, 1967-84, Wiley, Rein & Fielding, Washington, 1984—; adj. prof. internat. trade law Georgetown U. Law Ctr., Washington, 1978—, Charles Fahy Disting. adj. prof., 1993; conf. chmn. The Future of the Internat. Steel Industry, Bellagio, Italy, 1984, The U.S Agenda for the Uruguay Round, Airlie House, Warrenton, Va., 1986, The Polish Joint Venture Law, Cracow, Poland, 1987, Internat. Steel Industry II, Bellagio, 1987, Bulgaria and the GATT, Washington, 1988. lectr. law sch. Duke U., 1970-73; conf. chmn. The Future of the Internat. Steel Industry, Bellagio, Italy, 1984, The U.S. Agenda for the Uruguay Round, Airlie House, Warrenton, Va., 1986, The Polish Joint Venture Law, Cracow, Poland, 1987, Internat. Steel Industry II, Bellagio, 1987, Bulgaria and the GATT, Washington, 1988. Local dir. Tufts U. Ann. Fund, 1965-69; mem. Duke Law Alumni Coun., 1972-75; trustee Internat. Law Inst., 1981—, chmn. bd. trustees, 1983-87; trustee Bulgarian Am. Friendship Soc., 1992—; Christ Ch., Dark Harbor, Maine. Local dir. Tufts U. Ann. Fund, 1965-69; mem. Duke Law Alumni Coun., 1972-75; trustee Internat. Law Inst., 1981—, chmn. bd. trustees, 1983-87; trustee Bulgarian Am. Friendship Soc., 1992—; Christ Ch., Dark Harbor, Maine; chair Protection of Intellectual Property from Theft and Piracy Abroad, Southwestern Legal Found. Gen. Symposium, 1995. Mem. ABA, Internat. Bar Assn., D.C. Bar Assn., Order of Coif, Theta Delta Chi, Phi Delta Phi, Met. Club (Washington), Chevy Chase Club (Md.), Tarratine Club (Dark Harbor, Maine). Home: 3000 Q St NW Washington DC 20007-3080 Office: 1776 K St NW Washington DC 20006-2304

VERRILL, F. GLENN, advertising executive; b. N.Y.C., Dec. 17, 1923; s. Ralph Francis and Rose (Verner) V.; m. Jean Demar, Aug. 25, 1946; children: Gary, Joan. A.B., Adelphi Coll., 1949; A.M., Harvard U., 1950. With Batten, Barton, Durstine & Osborn, Inc., 1952—, v.p., 1964; creative dir. Batten, Barton, Durstine & Osborn, Inc. (Burke Dowling Adams div.), Atlanta, 1965-70, exec. v.p., gen. mgr., 1970-71, pres., 1971-88, chmn., 1988—, also dir. parent co. Author: Advertising Procedure, 1983, rev. edit., 1986, 88. Mem. adv. bd. U. Ga.; vice chmn. bd. overseers Coll. Bus. Adminstrn., Ga. State U.; bd. dirs. Atlanta Humane Soc., pres., 1980-81; chmn. Advanced Advt. Inst. Atlanta, 1981; mem. Peabody award com., 1984—; bd. dirs Atlanta Coll. of Art, 1990. With USAAF, 1943-46. Mem.

Am. Assn. Advt. Agys. (nat. dir. 1973—). Episcopalian. Clubs: Atlanta Athletic, Cherokee, Harvard (Atlanta). Home: 2600 W Wesley Rd NW Atlanta GA 30327-2036 Office: 3414 Peachtree Rd NE Atlanta GA 30326-1113

VERRILL, KATHLEEN WILLS, special education educator; b. Tucson, Jan. 4, 1938; d. William Oscar Wills and Helen Louise (Boswell) Perry; m. Thomas Anthony Verrill, July 30, 1966; 1 child, Nathan Anthony. AA, Monterey Peninsula Coll., 1958; BA, San Francisco State U., 1963, MA, 1965. Tchr. educable mentally retarded Albany (Calif.) Unified Schs., 1963-70, Sch. Dist. # 49, Fairfield, Maine, 1970-73; resource tchr. Indpls. Schs., 1973-75; tchr. learning handicapped Phila. Sch. Dist., 1975-77, ednl. evaluator, 1977-79, instructional advisor, 1979-81; resource specialist San Francisco Unified Schs., 1981-82, Alameda (Calif.) Unified Sch. Dist., 1982—. Author Food Centered Curriculum for Learning Disabled, 1965. Rep. Sch. Dist. Affirmative Action com., Alameda, 1988-90. Recipient PTA Calif. Hon. Svc. award Lum Sch., 1991; named Tchr. of Yr. Alameda Sch. Dist., 1986; Crown Zellerbach Found. fellowship, 1964, edn. grant Alameda County Schs., 1964. Mem. NEA, Coun. Exceptional Children, Alameda Edn. Assn. (rep. 1989-90), Calif. Tchrs. Assn., Delta Kappa Gamma (chmn. rsch. 1988-89, pres. Delta Zeta chpt. 1992-94, exec. bd. 1994—). Avocations: travel, classical music, reading, cooking, study of artists. Home: 1006 Rock Way Pittsburg CA 94565-4347 Office: Alameda Unified Sch Dist 1801 Sandcreek Way Alameda CA 94501-6024

VERRILLO, RONALD THOMAS, neuroscience educator, researcher; b. Hartford, Conn., July 31, 1927; s. Francesco Paul and Angela (Forte) V.; m. Violet Silverstein, June 3, 1950; children—Erica, Dan, Thomas. B.A., Syracuse U., 1952; Ph.D., U. Rochester, 1958. Asst. prof. Syracuse U., 1957-62, research assoc., 1959-63, research fellow, 1963-67, assoc. prof., 1967-74, prof., 1974-94, prof. emeritus, 1995, assoc. dir. Inst. Sensory Research, 1980-84, dir., 1984-93, dir. grad. neurosci. program, 1984-93; advisor com. on hearing, bioacoustics and biomechanics NRC. Author: Adjustment to Visual Disability, 1961 (award 1962). Contbr. many chpts. to books, articles to profl. jours. Served with USN, 1945-46. Fellow Am. Found. for Blind, 1956, NATO, 1970, grantee NSF, 1969-72, 84-87, NIH, 1972—. Fellow Acoustical Soc. Am.; mem. Psychonomic Soc., Soc. for Neurosci. N.Y. Acad. Scis., Sigma Xi (research award 1982). Home: 312 Berkeley Dr Syracuse NY 13210-3031 Office: Syracuse U Inst Sensory Rsch Merrill Ln Syracuse NY 13244

VERRONE, PATRIC MILLER, lawyer, writer; b. Glendale, N.Y.C., Sept. 29, 1959; s. Pat and Edna (Miller) V.; m. Margaret Maiya Williams, 1989; 1 child, Patric Carroll Williams. BA, Harvard U., 1981; JD, Boston Coll., 1984. Bar: Fla. 1984, U.S. Dist. Ct. (mid. dist.) Fla. 1984, Calif. 1988. Assoc. Allen, Knudsen, Swartz, DeBoest, Rhoads & Edwards, Ft. Myers, Fla., 1984-86; writer The Tonight Show, Burbank, Calif., 1987-90; temp. judge L.A. Mcpl. Ct., 1995—; temp. judge L.A. Mcpl. Ct. Dir., producer, writer The Civil War-The Lost Episode, 1991; writer The Larry Sanders Show, 1992-94, The Critic, 1995—; editor Harvard Lampoon, 1978-84, Boston Coll. Law Rev., 1983-84, Fla. Bar Jour., 1987-88, L.A. Lawyer, 1994—; contbr. articles to profl. jours. Bd. dirs. Calif. Confedn. of Arts, Mus. Contemporary Art. Mem. ABA (vice chair arts, entertainment & sports law com.), Calif. Bar, Calif. Lawyers for Arts, L.A. County Bar Assn. (sec. barristers exec. com., chair artists and the law com., mem. steering com. homeless shelter project, mem. intellectual property and entertainment law sect., mem. legis. activity com.), Fla. Bar Assn., Writers Guild of Am. West (contract com. animation writers caucus), Harvard Club Lee County (v.p. 1985-86), Harvard Club of So. Calif. Republican. Roman Catholic. Avocations: filmmaking, video, baseball. Home and Office: 6466 Odin St Los Angeles CA 90068-2730

VERROT, PASCAL, conductor, educator. Degree, l'Université de Paris, Sorbonne, The Paris Conservatoire; studies with Franco Ferrara, Jean-Sebastien Béreau, Accademia Musicale Chigiana; studies with Franco. Asst. condr. Boston Symphony Orch., 1986-90. Condr. Boston Chmaber Players, l'Orchestre de Paris, l'Orchestre Nat. de Lyon,and Orchestre de Radio France; debut appearances with major orchs. in Can. and the U.S.; toured Japan as a condr. Recipient 1st prize Paris Conseratory, 1985, 3d prize Min-on competition, Tokyo. Office: care Boston Symphony Orchestra Symphony Hall Boston MA 02115 Office: New England Conservatory 290 Huntington Ave Boston MA 02115-5000

VERSACE, GIANNI, fashion designer; b. Reggion Calabria, Italy, Dec. 2, 1946; s. Antonio and Francesca Versace. Student, pub. sch., Italy. Designer: Complice, Genny and Callaghan, Milan, Italy, 1972-78; 1st signature women's wear collection, Milan, Italy, 1978—; menswear collection; founder 1st of 80 exclusive boutiques, Milan, 1979—; developer namesake fragrance, Italy, France, Switzerland, Austria and U.S.A., 1981—; costume designer for ballets Leib und Leid, Josephlegende, Dyonisos, for opera Don Pasquale (La Scala), 1984; collaborator South Beach Stories, 1992; author: Designs, 1994. Recipient Golden Eye award for best fashion designer of women's wear for fall-winter, 1982-84, Cutty Sark award, 1983, International award, CFDA, 1992. Home: Via Gesu 12, 20121 Milan Italy Office: Gianni Versace Boutique 816 Madison Ave New York NY 10021-4904

VERSCHOOR, CURTIS CARL, business educator, consultant; b. Grand Rapids, Mich., June 7, 1931; s. Peter and Leonene (Dahlstrom) V.; m. Marie Emilie Kritschgau, June 18, 1952; children—Katherine Anne, Carolyn Marie, John Peter, Carla Michelle. BBA with distinction, U. Mich., 1951, MBA, 1952; PhD, No. Ill. U., 1977. CPA; cert. mgmt. acctg., cert. fin. planner, cert. fraud examiner, cert. internal auditor; chartered fin. cons. Pub. accountant Touche, Ross, Bailey & Smart (C.P.A.'s), 1955-63; with Singer Co., 1963-68, asst. controller, 1965-68; controller Colgate-Palmolive Co., 1968-69; asst. controller bus. products group Xerox Corp., 1969-72; controller Baxter Internat., 1972-73; v.p. finance Altair Corp., Chgo., 1973-74; prof. DePaul U., Chgo., 1974-94, ledger and quill alumni rsch. prof., 1994—; pres. C.C. Verschoor & Assocs., Inc., 1981—; part-time instr. Wayne State U., 1955-60. Contbg. editor: Jour. Accountancy, 1961-62, Jour. Internal Auditing, 1985—. Served with AUS, 1953-55. Recipient Elijah Watts Sells award Am. Inst. C.P.A.'s, 1953. Mem. AICPA, Ill. Soc. CPAs, Fin. Execs. Inst., Am. Acctg. Assn., Inst. Mgmt. Accts., Inst. Internal Auditors, Nat. Assn. Corp. Dirs., Beta Gamma Sigma, Beta Alpha Psi, Delta Pi Epsilon, Phi Kappa Phi, Phi Eta Sigma. Home: 231 Wyngate Dr Barrington IL 60010-4840 Office: DePaul Univ One E Jackson Blvd Chicago IL 60604-2287

VERSFELT, DAVID SCOTT, lawyer; b. Mineola, N.Y., Feb. 17, 1951; s. William H. and Ruth (Gerland) V.; m. Mary Deborah Garber, Aug. 31, 1974; children: Christopher L., William S., Kathryn H. AB, Princeton U., 1973; JD, Columbia U., 1976. Bar: N.Y. 1977, U.S. Dist. Ct. (so. and ea. dists.) N.Y. 1977, U.S. Ct. Appeals (D.C. cir.) 1979, U.S. Ct. Appeals (2d and 7th cirs.) 1980, U.S. Supreme Ct. 1980, U.S. Ct. Appeals (9th cir.) 1981, U.S. Ct. Appeals (3d cir.) 1982, Ct. Internat. Trade 1990, U.S. Ct. Appeals (fed. cir.) 1994. Mem. Coun. of Community Law Office; vol. div. Legal Aid Soc., N.Y.C., 1985-88; dir. Partnership for a Drug-Free Am., 1989—. Mem. ABA, Assn. Bar City N.Y. (com. on state legislation 1983-85). Office: Donovan Leisure Newton & Irvine 30 Rockefeller Plz New York NY 10112-0001

VERSHBOW, ARTHUR EMMANUEL, mechanical engineer; b. Boston, Mar. 22, 1922; m. Charlotte Zimmerman; children: Alexander, Ann. BS, MIT, 1943, MS, 1946. Mech. engr., ptnr., v.p., dir. labor rels. Modern Die & Machine Co., Boston, 1946—; chmn. mgmt. trustees Internat. Assn. Machinists Dist. 38 Health and Welfare Fund. Contbr. articles to profl. jours. Trustee, chmn. Newton Free Libr.; trustee Buckingham Browne & Nichols Sch., 1966-75; ; trustee Boston Athenaeum, 1977—, pres., 1982—; trustee Mus. Fine Arts, 1982—, vice chmn. overseers, 1990-93; vis. com. philosophy dept., libr. MIT, Harvard U. Libr., 1963-90, libr., print dept., decor, arts Mus. Fine Arts, hon. curator illustrated books Harvard Coll. Libr. Recipient Cardinal Cushing ann. award for excellence in labor rels., 1981. Mem. Club of Odd Vols. (pres. 1977, 78, 79), Grolier Club (N.Y.C.), St. Botolph Club (Boston). Avocations: old prints and books. Office: Boston Athenaeum 10 1/2 Beacon St Boston MA 02108-3777

VERSTANDIG, TONI GRANT, federal agency administrator; b. Pitts., Jan. 15, 1953; d. Louis A. and Ruth M. (O'Block) Grant; m. Lee L. Verstandig, Feb. 20, 1982; 1 stepchild, Scott B.; 1 child, Grant L. BA, Boston U., 1974;

AD, Stephens Coll., 1972. Legis. asst. subcom. on agrl. labor House Com. on Edn. and Labor, 1976-77; staff dir. subcom. on accts. House Adminstrn. Com., 1977-78; mem. profl. staff subcom. on internat. security/sci. affairs House Com. on Fgn. Affairs, 1978-86; mem. profl. staff Com. on Fgn. Affairs, 1986-93; dep. asst. sec. of state Near Ea. affairs U.S. Dept. of State, Washington, 1993—; cons. to com. on fgn. affairs U.S. Ho. of Reps., 1978-93, staff dir. subcom. accts., com. on house adminstrn., prin. legis. asst. to Congressman John N. Dent. Vol. cons. on fgn. policy and nat. security Clinton-Gore Presdl. Campaign, 1992. Recipient Spl. Merit of Honor commendation Mayor Kevin White. Office: Dept of State Near Eastern Affairs 2201 C St NW Washington DC 20520-6243

VER STEEG, CLARENCE LESTER, historian, educator; b. Orange City, Iowa, Dec. 28, 1922; s. John A. and Annie (Vischer) Ver S.; m. Dorothy Ann De Vries, Dec. 24, 1943; 1 child, John Charles. AB, Morningside Coll., Sioux City, Iowa, 1943; MA, Columbia U., 1946, PhD, 1950; LHD, Morningside Coll., 1988. Lectr., then instr. history Columbia U., N.Y.C., 1946-50; mem. faculty Northwestern U., Evanston, Ill., 1950—, prof. history, 1959—, dean grad. sch., 1975-86; vis. lectr. Harvard U., 1959-60; mem. council Inst. Early Am. History and Culture, Williamsburg, Va., 1961-64, 68-72, chmn. exec. com., 1972-73; vis. mem. Inst. Advanced Study, Princeton, N.J., 1967-68; chmn. faculty com. to recommend Master Plan Higher Edn. in Ill., 1962-64; mem. Grad. Record Exam. Bd., 1981-86, chmn., 1984-86; bd. dirs. Ctr. for Research Libraries, 1980-85, Council Grad. Schs. in U.S., 1983-87; pres. Assn. Grad. Schs., 1984-85; mem. steering com. Grad. Research Project, Consortium on Financing Higher Edn., 1981-85; mem. working group on talent Nat. Acad. Scis., 1984-87; mem. Higher Edn. Policy Adv. Com. to OCLC, Online Computer Library Ctr., 1984-87. Author: Robert Morris, Revolutionary Financier, 1954, A True and Historical Narrative of the Colony of Georgia, 1960, The American People: Their History, 1961, The Formative Years, 1607-1763, 1964, (Brit. edit.), 1965, The Story of Our Country, 1965, (with others) Investigating Man's World, 6 vols., 1970, A People and a Nation, 1971, The Origins of a Southern Mosaic: Studies of Early Carolina and Georgia, 1975, World Cultures, 1977, American Spirit, 1982, rev. edit., 1990; sr. author: Heath Social Studies, 7 Vols., 1991, Planning at Northwestern University in the 1960s, 1993; editor: Great Issues in American History, From Settlement to Revolution 1584-1776, 1969; editorial cons.: Papers of Robert Morris, vols. I-VII, 1973—; contbr. articles to profl. jours. Served with USAAF, 1942-45. Decorated Air medal with 3 oak leaf clusters; 5 Battle Stars; Social Sci. Research Council fellow, 1948-49, George A. and Eliza Gardner Howard Found. fellow, 1954-55, Huntington Library research fellow, 1955, Am. Council Learned Socs. sr. fellow, 1958-59, Guggenheim fellow, 1964-65, NEH sr. fellow, 1973. Mem. AAUP, Am. Hist. Assn. (nominating com. 1965-68, chmn. 1967-68, Albert J. Beveridge prize 1952, hon. mention 1991 Eugene Asher Disting. Teaching award), Orgn. Am. Historians (editorial bd. Jour. Am. History 1968-72), So. Hist. Assn. (nominating com. 1970-72). Presbyterian. Home: 2619 Ridge Ave Evanston IL 60201-1717 Office: Northwestern U Evanston IL 60208

VERU, THEODORE, advertising agency executive. Formerly exec. v.p., chief operating officer, then pres., chief operating officer Lois Pitts Gershon Pon/GGK (now Lois/GGK) N.Y.C. Office: Lois USA Inc 40 W 57th St New York NY 10019-4001

VERVILLE, ELIZABETH GIAVANI, federal official; b. N.Y.C., July 13, 1940; d. Joseph and Gertrude (Levy) Giavani. BA, Duke U., 1961; LLB, Columbia U., 1964. Bar: Mass. 1965, U.S. Supreme Ct. 1970, D.C. 1980. Assoc. Snow Motley & Holt, successor Gaston Snow & Ely Bartlett, Boston, 1965-67; asst. atty. gen. Commonwealth of Mass., Boston, 1967-69; atty. advisor for African affairs U.S. Dept. State, Washington, 1979-72, asst. legal advisor for East Asian and Pacific affairs, 1972-80, dep. legal adviser, 1980-89; dep. asst. sec. state Bur. Politico-Mil. Affairs Bur. Politico-Mil. Affairs, Washington, 1989-92; sr. coord. Bur. Politico-Mil. Affairs, 1992—. Recipient presdl. rank of meritorious exec., 1985, 90, presdl. rank disting. exec., 1988. Mem. Am. Soc. Internat. Law, Coun. on Fgn. Rels. Home: 3012 Dumbarton Ave NW Washington DC 20007-3305 Office: Dept of State Bur Polit Mil Affairs 2201 C St NW Washington DC 20520-0001

VERWOERDT, ADRIAAN, psychiatrist; b. Voorburg, The Netherlands, July 5, 1927; came to U.S., 1953, naturalized, 1958; s. Christopher and Juliana Margaretha (Busch) V.; children: Christopher Earl, Mark Adrian. M.D., Med. Sch. of Amsterdam, 1952. Diplomate: Pan Am. Med. Assn. Rotating intern Touro Infirmary, New Orleans, 1953-54; resident in psychiatry Duke U. Med. Center, Durham, N.C., 1954-55, 58-60; fellow in psychiat. research Duke U. Med. Center, 1960-61, asst. prof. psychiatry, 1963-67, assoc. prof., 1967-71, prof., 1971—, dir. geriatric psychiatry tng. program, 1966-78; dir. psychiat. residency tng. John Umstead Hosp., Butner, N.C., 1968-80; dir. Geropsychiatry Inst. (John Umstead Hosp.), Butner, N.C., 1980-86; cons. N.C. Dept. Human Resources, 1989—. Author: Communication with the Fatally Ill, 1966, Clinical Geropsychiatry, 1976, 1st rev. edit., 1981, 2d rev. edit., 1987; contbr. articles to profl. jours. Served as capt. M.C. U.S. Army, 1955-57. NIMH Career Tchr. Tng. grantee, 1964-66. Fellow Am. Psychiat. Assn.; mem. Am. Assn. for Geriatric Psychiatry, Am. Psychoanalytic Assn.

VESCOVI, SELVI, pharmaceutical company executive; b. N.Y.C., June 14, 1930; s. Antonio and Desolina V.; BS, Coll. William and Mary, 1951; m. Elma Pasquinelli, Oct. 16, 1954; children: Mark, James, Anne. Salesman, Upjohn Co., N.Y.C., 1954-59, sales supr.,1959-62, product mgr. U.S. domestic pharm. dir., 1962-65, mgr. mktg. planning internat. div., 1965-71, v.p. Europe, 1971-74, group v.p. Europe, 1975-77, exec. v.p. Upjohn Internat., Inc., Kalamazoo, Mich., 1978-85, pres., gen. mgr., 1975-88, v.p. parent co., 1978-88; adj. prof. mgmt. Western Mich. U., Kalamazoo, 1988-92; chmn. bd. Carrington Labs; bd. dirs. Cytrx Pharms. Corp. 2d lt. M.C., U.S. Army, 1951-53. Mem. Internat. Pharm. Mfrs. Assn., Park Club (Kalamazoo), NYAC (N.Y.). Republican. Roman Catholic. Office: Upjon Internat Co 7000 Portage Rd Kalamazoo MI 49001-0102

VESECKY, JOHN F., science educator, electrical engineering educator, researcher; b. Dallas, June 20, 1940; s. Stephen and Mary Emily (Baum) V.; m. Carol Ruth Benedict, Dec. 20, 1966 (div. July 1990); children: Stephen, Holly; m. Cynthia Ann Noble, July 17, 1991. BA in Elec. Engring., Rice U., 1962, BS in Elec. Engring., 1963; MS in Elec. Engring., Stanford U., 1965, PhD in Elec. Engring.. 1967. Rsch. asst. radiosci. lab. Stanford (Calif.) U., 1963-67; rsch. fellow astronomy U. Leicester, Eng., 1967-69, assoc. prof. astronomy, 1971-76; rsch. assoc. Ctr. Radar Astronomy, Radiosci. Lab. Elec. Engring. Dept. Stanford U., 1969-73, sr. rsch. assoc. Ctr. Radar Astronomy, STAR Lab., Elec. Engring. Dept., 1976-82, prof. elec. engring., 1990-93; prof. atmospheric, oceanic and space sci. U. Mich., Ann Arbor, 1990—; rsch. engr., cons. SRI Internat., Menlo Park, Calif., 1965—; vis. prof. U. Coll. London, 1982-83; cons. Environ. Task Force, Washington, 1992—, Dept. Energy Tech. Oversight, Washington, 1991—, NAS/NRC STAR Com., Washington 1989-91, JASON, San Diego, 1974—; bd. vis., mem. tech. adv. group for remote sensing Office of Naval Rsch., 1988-91; mem. ERS-1 Product Support Group Brit. Nat. Ctr. for Remote Sensing, 1982-87; mem. NRC Polar Rsch. Bd. ad hoc panel on remote sensing of ice 1985-89; mem. NASA Task Force Sci. Uses of Space Sta., 1986-87; mem. Brit. Nat. Com. Space Rsch. Solar Physics Working Group, 1974-76; cons. MITRE Corp., Mc Lean, Va., 1982—, Environ. Rsch. Inst., Mich., 1985—, SAIC, San Diego, 1991-95, ESL, Inc., Sunnyvale, Calif., 1985-90; participant Aspen Global Change Inst., 1990, 91; mem. tech. program com. Oceans '83 Conf., San Francisco, 1983. Author: Radar Remote Sensing from Spacecraft, 1990, (with others) Long Term Impacts of Increasing Atmospheric Carbon Dioxide Levels, 1982; co-editor: Wave Scattering from Statistically Rough Surfaces, 1979; contbr. articles to profl. jours., book chpts. Head coach Am. Youth Soccer Orgn., Palo Alto, Calif., 1977-87, Stanford Area Youth Basketball, 1980-86. Rackham Rsch. Ptnrs. fellow, 1992-93, NASA fellow Stanford U., 1966-67. Fellow Royal Astron. Soc.; mem. IEEE, Am. Astron. Soc., Am. Geophys. Union, Oceanography Soc., Internat. Astron. Union, Internat. Sci. Radio Union, IEEE Geosci. and Remote Sensing Soc. (chmn. Santa Clara Valley sect. 1989-90). Episcopalian. Avocations: basketball, music, ancient astronomy. Office: U Mich Space Physics Rsch Lab 2455 Hayward Ann Arbor MI 48109-2143

VESELL, ELLIOT SAUL, pharmacologist, educator; b. N.Y.C., Dec. 24, 1933; s. Harry and Evelyn (Jaffe) V.; m. Kristen Paige Peery, Mar. 24, 1968;

children: Liane Clark, Hilary Peery. AB, Harvard U., 1955, MD, 1959; DSc (hon.), Phila. Coll. Pharmacy & Sci., 1988; PhD, Philipps U., Marburg, Germany, 1991. Intern, children's med. svc. Mass. Gen. Hosp., Boston, 1959-60; rsch. assoc. Rockefeller U., N.Y.C., 1960-62; resident in medicine Peter Bent Brigham Hosp., Boston, 1962-63; clin. assoc. Nat. Inst. Arthritis and Metabolic Diseases, NIH, Bethesda, Md., 1963-65; head sect. pharmacogenetics Nat. Heart Inst., NIH, Bethesda, 1965-68; Evan Pugh prof. pharmacology, chmn. dept. Pa. State U., Hershey, 1968—, asst. dean grad. edn., 1973—; Frohlich vis. prof. Royal Medicine, 1985, Pfizer vis. prof., Burroughs Wellcome vis. prof. Editor: The Life and Works of Thomas Cole, 1964, Progress in Basic and Clinical Pharmacology, 1990, numerous others; contbr. more than 290 articles to profl. jours. Recipient Von Humboldt award, 1988. Fellow AAAS, Royal Soc. of Medicine; mem. Assn. Am. Physicians, Am. Soc. for Clin. Investigation, Am. Soc. Pharmacology and Exptl. Therapeutics (sec.-treas. 1995-98, Exptl. Therapeutics award 1971, Harry Gold award in clin. pharmacology, 1985), Am. Coll. Clin. Pharmacology (pres. 1980-82), Am. Soc. Clin. Pharmacology and Therapeutics (Oscar B. Hunter Meml. award 1991). Office: Pa State U Coll Medicine Dept Pharmacology PO Box 850 Hershey PA 17033-0850

VESELY, ALEXANDER, civil engineer; b. Ladmovce, Czechoslovakia, Dec. 7, 1926; came to U.S., 1949; s. Joseph and Margaret (Lefkovitz) V.; m. Harriet Lee Roth, Aug. 11, 1957; 1 child, David Seth. BSCE, Carnegie Mellon U., 1952; postgrad. John Marshall Law Sch., 1955, MSCE, Ill. Inst. Tech., 1957. Registered profl. engr., Ind., Mass.; registered land surveyor, Ind. Staff engr., Amoco Oil Co., Whiting, Ind., 1952-62; mgr. engring. Borg Warner Chem. Co., Washington, W.Va., 1962-77; assoc. engr. Mobil Rsch. & Devel. Corp., Princeton, N.J., 1977-83; cons. engr. D.G. Peterson & Assocs. Inc., Greenfield, Mass., 1983-87; prin. Alexander Vesely & Assocs., 1987—; assoc. prof. Community Coll., Parkersburg, W.Va., 1965-67; chmn. Engrs. Week Com., Parkersburg, 1973. Pres. B'nai Israel Congregation, Parkersburg, 1976; bd. dirs. Bros. of Israel Congregation, Trenton, N.J., 1978-83. Served with U.S. Army, 1952-54. Carnegie Mellon U. scholar, 1950-52. Mem. Nat. Soc. Profl. Engrs. (pres. Parkersburg chpt. 1973-74), Am. Inst. Plant Engrs., ASCE, Scrabble Club, Chess Club, Bridge Club, Tau Beta Pi (life). Republican. Jewish. Avocations: ping-pong, tennis, swimming. Home and Office: 48 Hillcrest Dr Northampton MA 01060-1362

VESPA, NED ANGELO, photographer; b. Streator, Ill., May 31, 1942; s. Ned James and Evelyn Blanche (Flanigan) V.; m. Carol DeMasters, Sept. 11, 1976; 1 child, Nicole Marie; 1 son by previous marriage, James Paul. B.S., So. Ill. U., 1965. Photographer Milw. Jour. Co., 1965-95, Milw. Sentinel, 1965-95; ret., 1995, freelance, 1995—. Mem. Nat. Press Photographers Assn., Wis. News Photographers Assn. (past pres.), Milw. Press Photographers. Home: 38309 Genesee Lake Rd Oconomowoc WI 53066-8614 Office: 333 W State St Milwaukee WI 53203-1305

VESPER, CAROLYN F., newspaper publishing executive. Sr. v.p. and assoc. publisher USA TODAY, Arlington, Va. Office: USA Today 1000 Wilson Blvd Arlington VA 22229

VESPER, KARL HAMPTON, business and mechanical engineering educator; b. San Marino, Calif., Aug. 12, 1932; s. Karl Conrad and Roxie (Armstrong) V.; m. Joan Frantz, June, 1964; children—Karen, Linda, Holly, Nancy. B.S. in Mech. Engring. Stanford U., 1955; M.S. in Mech. Engring, 1965, Ph.D., 1969; M.B.A., Harvard U., 1960. Casewriter Harvard Bus. Sch., 1960-61; bus. mgr., mech. engr. Marine Advisers, 1961-62; cons. Dept. State, summer, 1963; dir. Hosmer Machine Co., Contoock, N.H., 1966-67; dir. summer insts. Stanford U., 1966, 67, dir. case devel., research assoc., lectr. mech. engring., 1963-69, research asso., NASA faculty fellow in air pollution research design project, summer 1970; editor mech. engring. series McGraw Hill Book Co., N.Y.C., 1966-74; prof. bus. adminstrn., mech. engring. and marine studies U. Wash., Seattle, 1969—; Paul T. Babson prof. Babson Coll., 1980-81. Author: How To Write Engineering Cases, 1966, 73, Engineers at Work, 1975, The Entrepreneurial Function, 1977, Entrepreneurship Education, 1985, New Venture Strategies, 1980, rev. edition, 1990, Frontiers of Entrepreneurship Research, 1981-91, Entrepreneurship and National Policy, 1983, New Venture Mechanics, 1993, (with Paul Larson) Washington Entrepreneur's Guide, 1993, New Venture Experience, 1993; contbr. articles to profl. jours., chpts. to books. Served with USAF, 1955-57. Mem. Am. Inst. for Decision Scis., Acad. Mgmt., Sigma Xi. Home: 3721 47th Pl NE Seattle WA 98105-5224 Office: U Wash Sch Business Adminstrn Seattle WA 98195

VESSOT, ROBERT FREDERICK CHARLES, physicist; b. Montreal, Que., Can., Apr. 16, 1930; s. Robert Charles Ulysses and Marguerite Yvonne (Giauque) V.; m. Norma Newman Wight, Apr. 18, 1959; children: Judith Norma, Margaret Anne, Nancy Elizabeth. B.A., McGill U., 1951, B.Sc., 1954, Ph.D., 1956. Mem. research staff MIT, 1956-60; mgr. Maser Research and Devel., Varian Assos., Hewlett Packard, Beverly, Mass., 1960-69; sr. physicist Harvard-Smithsonian Center for Astrophysics, Cambridge, Mass., 1969—. Contbr. articles to profl. jours. Served with RCAF, 1951-53. Recipient medal for outstanding sci. achievement NASA, 1978, I.I. Rabi award IEEE, 1993. Fellow Am. Phys. Soc.; mem. Eastern Yacht Club. Patentee in field. Office: 60 Garden St Cambridge MA 02138-1596

VEST, CHARLES MARSTILLER, university president; b. Morgantown, W.Va., Sept. 9, 1941; s. Marvin Lewis and Winifred Louise (Buzzard) V.; m. Rebecca Ann McCue, June 8, 1963; children: Ann Kemper, John Andrew. BSME, W.Va. U., 1963; MSME, U. Mich., 1964, PhD, 1967; DEng (hon.), Mich. Tech. U., 1992, W.Va. U., 1994. Asst. prof., then assoc. prof. U. Mich., Ann Arbor, 1968-77, prof. mech. engring., 1977-90, assoc. dean acad. affairs Coll. Engring., 1981-86, dean Coll. Engring., 1986-89, provost, v.p. acad. affairs, 1989-90; pres. MIT, Cambridge, 1990—; bd. dirs. E.I. du Pont de Nemours and Co., IBM; vis. assoc. prof. Stanford (Calif.) U., 1974-75. Author: Holographic Interferometry, 1979; assoc. editor Jour. Optical Soc. Am., 1982-83; contbr. articles to profl. jours. Trustee Wellesley Coll., Woods Hole Oceanog. Inst., New England Aquarium, WGBH Ednl. Found.; adv. trustee Environ. Rsch. Inst. Mich. Recipient Excellence in Rsch. award U. Mich., 1980, Disting. Svc. award, 1972, Disting. Visitor award U. La Plata, Argentina, 1979, Centennial medal Am Soc. Engring. Edn., 1993. Fellow AAAS, Am. Acad. Arts and Scis., Optical Soc. Am.; mem. ASME, NAE, Sigma Xi, Tau Beta Pi, Pi Tau Sigma. Presbyterian. Office: MIT 77 Massachusetts Ave Cambridge MA 02139-4307

VEST, FRANK HARRIS, JR., bishop; b. Salem, Va., Jan. 5, 1936; s. Frank Harris and Viola Gray (Woodson) V.; m. Ann Jarvis, June 14, 1961; children: Nina Woodson, Frank Harris III, Robert Alexander. BA, Roanoke Coll., 1959; MDiv, Va. Theol. Sem., 1962, DD, 1985; DD (hon.), U. of South, 1987; LHD (hon.), St. Paul's Coll., 1991. Ordained to ministry Episcopal Ch. as deacon, 1962, as priest 1963. Curate St. John's Episcopal Ch., Roanoke, Va., 1962-64; rector Grace Episcopal Ch., Radford, Va., 1964-68; rector Christ Episcopal Ch., Roanoke, 1968-73, Charlotte, N.C., 1973-85; suffragan bishop Diocese of N.C., Raleigh, 1985-89; bishop coadjutor Diocese of So. Va., Norfolk, 1989-91, bishop, 1991—. Chmn. exec. com. Thompsons Children's Home, Charlotte, 1976-79; pres. Crisis Assistance Ministry, Charlotte, 1983-85; trustee Va. Theol. Sem., Alexandria, 1968-73, 91—, U. of South, Sewanee, Tenn., 1985-89, Episc. Radio TV Found., Atlanta, 1976-82. Democrat. Avocations: tennis, reading, walking, golf, fly-fishing. Office: Diocese of So Va 600 Talbot Hall Rd Norfolk VA 23505-4393

VEST, GAYLE SOUTHWORTH, obstetrician and gynecologist; b. Duluth, Minn., Apr. 7, 1948; d. Russell Eugene and Brandon (Young) Southworth; m. Steven Lee Vest, Nov. 27, 1971; 1 child, Matthew Steven. BS, U. Mich. 1970. Diplomate Am. Bd. Ob-Gyn. Intern in ob-gyn. Milw. County Gen. Hosp., 1974-75, So. Ill. U. Sch. Medicine, 1975-78; pvt. practice Chapel Hill (N.C.) Ob-Gyn., 1978-80; asst. attending physician dept. ob-gyn. U. N.C. Sch. Medicine, Chapel Hill, 1978-80; clin. assoc. dept. ob-gyn. Duke U. Med. Ctr., Durham, N.C., 1978-80; pvt. practice Big Stone Gap (Va.) Clinic, 1980-88, Norwise Ob-Gyn. Assocs., Norton, Va., 1988—. Fellow Am. Coll. Obstetricians and Gynecologists; mem. Am. Fertility Soc., Va. Ob-Gyn. Soc., Va. Perinatal Assn., Med. Soc. Va., Wise County Med. Soc. Avocations: skiing, kayaking, travel. Office: Norwise Ob-Gyn Assocs Med Arts Bldg 3 100 15th St NW Norton VA 24273

VEST, GEORGE SOUTHALL, diplomat; b. Columbia, Va., Dec. 25, 1918; s. George Southall and Nancy Margaret (Robertson) V.; m. Emily Barber Clemons, June 21, 1947; children—Jeannie, George, Henry. B.A., U. Va., 1941, M.A., 1947. Fgn. service duty SHAPE and NATO, Quito, Ottawa, Paris; dir. bur. polit. mil. affairs Dept. State; asst. sec. of state for European affairs Dept. State, Washington, 1977-81; ambassador to European Communities Brussels, 1981-85; dir. gen. Fgn. Svc. Dept. State, Washington, 1985-89; career amb. Dept. State, 1987-89, ret., 1989; cons. Akin, Gump, Strauss, Hauer and Feld, Washington, 1989—. Served to capt. U.S. Army, 1941-46, ETO. Mem. Phi Beta Kappa. Episcopalian. Avocations: bicycling; hiking; gardening. Home: 5307 Iroquois Rd Bethesda MD 20816-3104

VEST, HYRUM GRANT, JR., horticultural sciences educator; b. Salt Lake City, Sept. 23, 1935; s. Hyrum and Josephine Gwendolyn (Lund) V.; m. Gayle Pixton, Sept. 18, 1958; children: Kelly, Lani, Kari, Kamille, Kyle. B.S., Utah State U., 1960, M.S., 1964; Ph.D., U. Minn., 1967. Pathologist, agronomist U.S. Dept. Agr., Beltsville, Md., 1967-70; vegetable breeder Mich. State U., East Lansing, 1970-76; dept. head dept. hort. and landscape architecture Okla. State U., Stillwater, 1976-83; head dept. hort. scis. Tex A & M U., College Station, 1983-89; head dept. plants, soils and biometeorology Utah State U., 1989—; mem. Nat. Plant Genetics Resource Bd., Washington, 1982-88. Served to 1st lt. U.S. Army, 1960-63. Utah research fellow Utah State U., 1963-64. Fellow Am. Soc. Hort. Sci. Republican. Ch. Jesus Christ of Latter-day Saints. Lodge: Rotary. Home: 368 Spring Creek Rd Providence UT 84332-9432 Office: Utah State U Dept Plants Soils/Biometeorology Logan UT 84322-4820

VEST, MARVIN LEWIS, mathematical educator; b. Elkins, W.Va., May 17, 1906; s. Marvin Johnson and Margaret (Kley) V.; m. Winifred Louise Buzzerd, Aug. 3, 1930; children: Marvin Lewis, Charles Marstiller. BS, Davis and Elkins Coll., 1927, ScD (hon.), 1970; MS, W.Va. U., 1932; AM, U. Mich., 1942, PhD in Math., 1948. Prin. Franklin (W.Va.) High Sch., 1927-28; instr. Elkins High Sch., 1928-31, 33-35; assoc. prof. math. Davis and Elkins Coll., 1935-38; mem. faculty W.Va. U., Morgantown, 1931-33, 38—, prof. math., 1955-73, emeritus, 1973—; cons. U.S. Bur. Mines, 1952-57. Mem. Am. Math. Soc., Math. Assn. Am., W.Va. Acad. Scis. (sec. 1934-37, pres. 1950-51), Sigma Xi, Pi Mu Epsilon. Republican. Presbyterian (elder). Lodge: Mason. Home: 417 Elm St Morgantown WV 26505-6507

VEST, R. LAMAR, church administrator. Dir. Ch. of God Media Ministries. Office: Ch of God PO Box 2430 Cleveland TN 37320-2430

VEST, ROBERT WILSON, ceramic engineering educator; b. Lawrenceburg, Ind., Oct. 17, 1930; s. Wilson Purlee and Mildred Emily (Baker) V.; m. Ariel Maxine Huffman, June 7, 1952 (dec. Oct. 1981); children: Gary Wilson, Gregory Robert, Scott Alden.; m. Geraldine Marie (O'Neill) Deputy, June 26, 1982. B.S., Purdue U., 1952; Ph.D., Iowa State U., 1957. Chemist Nat. Lead Co., Fernald, Ohio, 1952-53; research asst. Inst. Atomic Research, Ames, Iowa, 1953-57; research chemist Monsanto Corp., Dayton, Ohio, 1957-61; sr. scientist Systems Research Labs., Dayton, 1961-66; Turner prof. engring. Purdue U., West Lafayette, Ind., 1966—; cons. in field. Contbr. articles to profl. publs. Fellow Am. Ceramic Soc. (Ross Coffin Purdy award 1969); mem. Nat. Inst. Ceramic Engrs., Ceramic Edn. Council, Internat. Soc. Hybrid Microelectronics, Am. Soc. Metals, Tau Beta Pi (Eminent Engr. award 1981). Office: Purdue U MSEE Bldg Turner Lab West Lafayette IN 47907 My goal has always been to do the best possible job on all endeavors, both personal and professional. The most effective method for me to approach this goal has been to always have a number of activities underway at any time, and not to force results on any of them.

VESTAL, JEANNE MARIE GOODSPEED, book publishing company executive; b. Ithaca, N.Y., Oct. 30, 1930; d. Alvin Francis and Margaret Josephine (Stoddart) Goodspeed; m. Fred Lowe Vestal, July 17, 1959. BA, Nazareth Coll., 1952. Sec. G.P. Putnam's Sons, N.Y.C., 1953-56; asst. editor Alfred A. Knopf, N.Y.C., 1956-60; editor-in-chief Dial Press, Inc., N.Y.C., 1960-63; v.p., editor-in-chief J.B. Lippincott, Inc., N.Y.C., 1963-73; sr. v.p., editorial dir. Franklin Watts, N.Y.C., 1975-91; pub. 21st Century Books divsn. Henry Holts & Co., N.Y.C., 1991—. Mem. Children's Book Council (pres. 1966-67). Home: 1161 York Ave New York NY 10021-7940 Office: Twenty First Century Books Div of Henry Holts & Co Inc 115 W 18th St New York NY 10011

VESTAL, LUCIAN LAROE, financier; b. Whitewright, Tex., Aug. 10, 1925; s. Rolla C. and Lora A. (Robinson) V.; m. Ezetalee Kranz Banzhaf, Nov. 8, 1994; 1 child, Denise Millington. Student, Baylor U., 1942-43; B.S. U. Pitts., 1947; postgrad., N.Y.U., 1948-50, Ill. Inst. Tech., 1960. Security analyst Lionel D. Edie & Co., N.Y.C., 1947-54; asst. dir. finance Champion Papers, Inc., Hamilton, Ohio, 1954-55; dir. research Rotan, Mosle & Co., Houston, 1955-58; dir. planning Pure Oil Co., Palatine, Ill., 1958-63; dir. planning and fin. services Weyerhaeuser Co., Tacoma, 1963-65; treas. Sunray DX Oil Co., Tulsa, 1965-68; asst. treas. Sun Oil Co., Tulsa, 1968-69; group v.p. Tesoro Petroleum Corp., San Antonio, 1969-72; sr. v.p. affiliate banking Palmer Bank Corp., Sarasota, Fla., 1973-75; trustee Citizens Growth Properties, 1969-78; chmn., dir. Palmer banks of Siesta Key, Village Plaza, N.A., Gulf Gate, Sarasota, Palmer Bank of Bradenton (N.A.), Fla., Palmer Bank & Trust Co. Naples (N.A.), Fla., Palmer Bank & Trust Co. Ft. Myers (N.A.), Fla.; pres., dir. Point Palma Sola, Inc., 1975-78, Cortez Yachts, Inc., 1975-78, So. Yachts, Inc., 1978-90; ceo, chmn., dir. Advantage Nat. Charge System, Sarasota, 1990; dir. Seaman Corp., Ohio; chmn. Trident Environ. Sys., Inc., Citizens Growth Properties. Served to 1st lt., inf. USMCR, 1943-45, So.Pacific. Decorated Navy Cross, Purple Heart. Mem. N.Y. Soc. Security Analysts, Retired Officers Club, U.S. Power Squadron, Sarasota Yacht Club (mem., dir.), Delta Tau Delta. Republican. Baptist. Home: 1648 Pine Harrier Cir Sarasota FL 34231

VESTAL, TOMMY RAY, lawyer; b. Shreveport, La., Sept. 19, 1939; s. Louie Wallace and Margaret (Golden) V.; m. Patricia Marie Blackwell, Jan. 24, 1981; children: Virginia Ann Hollingsworth, John Wallace Vestal, Douglas William Yancy. BSME, U. Houston, 1967, JD, 1970. Bar: Tex. 1970, U.S. Patent Office 1972, U.S. Ct. Appeals (D.C. cir.) 1975. Patent atty. Am. Enka Corp., Asheville, N.C., 1970-71, Akzona Inc., Asheville, 1971-84, Akzo Am., Inc., Asheville, 1985-86; sr. patent atty. Fibers div. BASF Corp., Enka, N.C., 1986-87, div. patent counsel, 1987-89, sr. patent counsel, 1989-90; pvt. practice law, 1990-91; dir. Geary Glast & Middleton, Dallas, 1992; ptnr. Falk, Vestal & Fish, Dallas, 1992—. Mem. ABA, State Bar Tex., Am. Intellectual Property Law Assn., Carolina Patent, Trademark and Copyright Law Assn. (bd. dirs 1983-85, 2d v.p. 1985-86, 1st v.p. 1986-87, pres. 1987-88), Dallas Bar Assn. (mem. com. law in schs. and comm., schs. and the community bd.), DFW Patent Law Assn., Asheville C. of C. (chmn. legal affairs com.), Phi Alpha Delta. Republican. Lutheran. Lodge: Kiwanis (pres. 1982). Avocations: golf, fishing, hiking. Home: 3109 Squireswood Dr Carrollton TX 75006 Office: 700 N Pearl Dallas TX 75201

VETACK, RICHARD S., textiles executive; b. 1937; married. BS, Rutgers U. With Cone Mills Corp., Greensboro, N.C., 1962-80, 82—, v.p. mktg., 1984-85, v.p., group exec. v.p. mktg., 1985-86, pres. textile products divsn., 1986-87, sr. v.p., 1987—; with Cropmton & Knowles Corp., Stamford, Conn., 1980-82. Office: Cone Mills Corp 1201 Maple St Greensboro NC 27405-6939

VETOG, EDWIN JOSEPH, retired gas utility executive; b. N.Y.C., Apr. 7, 1921; s. Lester and Lucy V.; m. Elizabeth Ann Long, July 18, 1942; children: Judith Ann Vetog Ciafone, Victoria Ann Vetog Thode. B.B.A., CCNY, 1949; M.B.A., NYU, 1953. With Bklyn. Union Gas Co., 1941-86, various positions, 1941-67, comptroller, 1967-69, v.p., 1969-75, sr. v.p., chief fin. officer, 1975-81, adminstrv. v.p., chief fin. officer, 1981-84, exec. v.p., chief fin. officer, 1984-86; trustee Ridgewood Savs. Bank, L.I., 1980—; adv. bd. Mfrs. Hanover Trust Co., Bklyn., 1979-86; chmn. Delaware Valley Propane Co., Woodstown, N.J., 1981-86. Pres. Indsl. Home for the Blind, L.I., 1976-85. Served to capt. C.E., U.S. Army, 1942-46. Decorated Bronze Star; decorated medal of Metz (France). Mem. Am. Gas Assn., Fin. Execs. Inst. Lutheran. Club: Brooklyn. Home: 5 View Rd E Setauket NY 11733

VETTER, HERBERT, physician, educator; b. Vienna, Austria, Aug. 24, 1920; m. Eleonore von Hacklaender, July 6, 1946 (div. 1969); 1 child, Barbara Weber; m. Brigitte Frei, Dec. 20, 1973 (div. 1993). M.D., U. Vienna, 1948. Physician, Allgemeines Krankenhaus, Vienna, Austria, 1948-60; Brit. Council research fellow, 1951; research fellow Sloan-Kettering Inst. Cancer Research, N.Y.C., 1954; head radioisotopes lab. 2d Med. Univ. Clinic, Vienna, 1951-60; asso. prof. medicine U. Vienna, 1959-67, prof., 1967—; sr. officer IAEA, 1958-81; chmn. sci. adv. council Austrian Soc. Energy Affairs, 1979—; v.p. Austrian Nuclear Tech. Soc., 1980—; bd. dirs. Austrian sect. Internat. Physicians for Prevention of Nuclear War, 1983-86; chmn. planning bd. IB, Internat. Commn. Radiation Units and Measurements, 1962-69, cons., 1969-89. Author: (with N. Veall) Radioisotope Techniques in Clinical Research and Diagnosis, 1958, Zwickmnühle Zwentendorf, 1983; editor: Radioaktive Isotope in Klinik und Forschung, Vols. I-III, 1955-58, (with E.H. Belcher) Radioisotopes in Medical Diagnosis, 1971, Jour. Nuclear Medicine, 1959—, Internat. Jour. Biomed. Engring., 1971-89. Recipient prize for art and sci. Republic of Austria, 1956, award of distinction Philippine Soc. Nuclear Medicine; Paul Harris fellow, 1983. Affiliate Royal Soc. Medicine; mem. Gesellschaft der Aerzte, Gesellschaft für Innere Medizin, Österreichische Roentgengesellschaft, Österreichische Gesellschaft für Nuklearmedizin (hon.). Club: Rotarian (pres. Vienna 1975-76). Home: Am Hausberg 1, 2344 Maria Enzersdorf Austria

VETTER, JAMES GEORGE, JR., lawyer; b. Omaha, Apr. 8, 1934; s. James George and Helen Louise (Adams) V.; m. Mary Ellen Froelich, June 25, 1960; 1 child, James G. III. BS, Georgetown U., 1954; JD, Creighton U., 1960. Bar: Nebr. 1960, Tex. 1967. Counsel IRS, Washington, 1960-64, Dallas, 1964-67; practiced in Dallas, 1967—; sr. ptnr. Vetter, Bates, Tibbals, Lee & DeBusk P.C., 1979-89; mem. Godwin & Carlton P.C., 1989—, mng. dir., 1994—; lectr. taxation seminars; bd. dirs. Pilgrim's Pride Corp., AFV Energy, Inc., VLSI Packaging Corp. Contbr. articles to profl. jours. Asst. sgt.-at-arms Tex. Dem. Conv., 1968; advisor selection com. Georgetown U., 1970-85; scoutmaster Boy Scouts Am., 1974-75. With USAF, 1954-57; capt. USAFR, ret. Mem. Nebr. Bar Assn., State Bar Tex. (cert. tax law 1983—), Coll. State Bar Tex., Dallas Bar Assn. (chmn. fee disputes com. 1985, chmn. publs. com. 1988), Real Estate Fin. Execs. Assn. (pres. 1982-83), Cash Alliance (pres. 1987-88), Creighton U. Alumni Assn. (pres. Dallas-Ft. Worth 1969-70), Ctrl. Dallas Assn. (dir. 1994—), Park Cities Club, City Club, Delta Theta Phi. Roman Catholic. Home: 11023 Rosser Rd Dallas TX 75229-3915 Office: Godwin & Carlton 3300 Nations Bank Plz Dallas TX 75202

VETTER, JAMES LOUIS, food research association administrator; b. St. Louis, Jan. 26, 1933; s. Charles W. and Dorothy (Smith) V.; m. Rose Marie Gentille, Aug. 21, 1954; children: Douglas John, Debra Dianne. AB, Washington U., St. Louis, 1954; MS, U. Ill., 1955, PhD, 1958. Food technologist Monsanto Co., St. Louis, 1958-63; dir. rsch. Keebler Co., Elmhurst, Ill., 1963-72; v.p. tech. dir. div. Standard Brands, Fraklin Park, Ill., 1972-75; pres. West Tex. Milling, Amarillo, 1975-77; v.p. Am. Inst. Baking, Manhattan, Kans., 1977—; adj. prof. Kans. State U., Manhattan, 1977—; tech. cons. Author: Food Labeling-Requirements for FDA Regulated Products, 1992; editor: Adding Nutrients to Foods, 1982; Dairy Products for Cereal Processing, 1984. Contbr. articles to profl. jours. Patentee in field. Bd. dirs., pres. Wharton Manor Nursing Home, Inc., Manhattan, 1980-81. Fellow Inst. Food Technologists; mem. Am. Assn. Cereal Chemists (sec. 1983-85, pres. 1986-87), Kiwanis (bd. dirs.), Phi Tau Sigma. Avocations: photography; golf. Home: 1947 Bluestem Ter Manhattan KS 66502-4530 Office: Am Inst Baking 1213 Bakers Way Manhattan KS 66502-4576

VETTER, JAN, legal educator; b. 1934. B.A., UCLA, 1956, LL.B., 1962. Bar: Calif. 1963. Assoc. Gibson, Dunn & Crutcher, Los Angeles, 1962-67; now. assoc. dean academic affairs, prof. law U. Calif.-Berkeley; vis. prof. Harvard U. Sch. Law, 1975-76. Former editor-in-chief UCLA Law Rev. Office: U Calif Law Sch 225 Boalt Hall Berkeley CA 94720

VETTRUS, RICHARD JAMES, minister; b. Superior, Wis., Oct. 23, 1938; s. Ole K. and Clara (Olson) V. BA, Pasadena Coll., 1964; MDiv, Luth. Brethren Sem., 1967; MS in Edn., Wagner Coll., 1975. Ordained to ministry Luth. Ch., 1971. Youth worker 59th St. Luth. Brethren Ch., Bklyn., 1958-60; nat. pres. Luth. Brethren Youth Fellowship, Fergus Falls, Minn., 1965-69; pastor Elim Luth. Ch., Floral Park, N.Y., 1967-69, Nanuet (N.Y.) Luth. Brethren Ch., 1971-74, 59th St Luth. Brethren Ch., 1975-79, Immanuel Luth. Ch., Pasadena, Calif., 1979-82, Bethany Luth. Ch., West Union, Iowa, 1982—; youth page editor Luth. Brethren Youth, Fergus Falls, 1958-90; studnet coun. rep. Fuller Theol. Sem., Pasadena, 1964-66; tour dir. to Israel, Jordan and Greece, Bklyn., 1979, to Israel, Jordan, Egypt and Greece, Pasadena, 1981. Dist. pres. Ch. Luth. Brethren, Ea. Dist., 1978-79, synodical sec., 1986—; bd. dirs. Tuscarora Inn Conf. Ctr., Mt. Bethel, Pa., 1978-79. Luth. Brotherhood scholar, Mpls., 1967. Republican. Avocations: photography, travel, skiing, antique cars, reading. Home: 707 Crestview Dr West Union IA 52175-1004 Office: Church The Lutheran Brethen Am 707 Crestview Dr West Union IA 52175-1004

VEVIER, CHARLES, historian, educator, consultant, university administrator; b. N.Y.C., June 15, 1924; s. Max and Sarah (Kramer) V.; m. Marcia Gold, Sept. 7, 1952; children: Ann, Ellen, John. B.A., U. Wis., 1948, M.A., 1949, Ph.D., 1953. Instr. U. Wis. Extension at Wausau, 1951-52, Rutgers U., 1952-54; asst. prof. U. Rochester, 1954-59; prof. U. Wis., Milw., 1959—, vice chancellor, 1963-69; pres. Adelphi U., 1969-71; exec. v.p. Univ. Medicine and Dentistry N.J.-N.J. Med. Sch., 1971-83, prof. div. social and behavioral sci., dept. psychiatry, 1972—; faculty cons. Thomas Edison Coll.; cons. Urban Affairs Com. Action, 1968; vis. adj. prof. Rutgers U. and Essex County Coll. Author: United States and China, 1906-16; also articles; editor: A Voyage Down the Amur, 1969-71, Flexner—75 Years Later. Trustee Mt. St. Paul Coll., Lexington Sch. for Deaf, North Shore Hosp., 1967-70; bd. dirs. Coun. Higher Edn. in Newark, N.J. Assn. for Children with Hearing Impairments, WBGO-FM, Newark. With USAAF, 1943-45. Decorated Air medal. Mem. Am. Hist. Assn., Orgn. Am. Historians, Soc. History Am. Fgn. Rels., Med. History Soc. N.J., AAUP. Home: 9 Peter Lynas Ct Tenafly NJ 07670-1115 Office: U Medicine and Dentistry NJ NJ Med Sch 185 S Orange Ave Newark NJ 07103-2714

VEYSEY, ARTHUR ERNEST, reporter, administrator, biographer; b. Boulder, Colo., Sept. 28, 1914; s. Ernest Charles and Lillian (Larson) V.; m. Florence Jones, 1937 (dec. 1940); 1 dau., Priscilla Joan; m. Gwendolyn Morgan, 1946. B.A., U. Colo., 1935; L.H.D., Ill. Benedictine Coll., 1986. Reporter Denver Post, 1935-37, Scottsbluff (Neb.) Star-Herald, 1937-41, Omaha World-Herald, 1941-43; war corr. Southwest Pacific, Chgo. Tribune, 1943- 45, fgn. corr., 1946-50, chief London bur., 1950-75; gen. mgr. Cantigny Trust, 1975-86. Author: Death in the Jungle, 1966, (with Gwen Morgan) Halas by Halas, 1979, (with Gwen Morgan) Poor Little Rich Boy, Biography of Col. R.R. McCormick. Bd. dirs. The Forest Found. Recipient Norlin award U. Colo., 1986, Margaret Landon award, 1986. Address: 3 Cobham Ct, PO Box 232, Kerikeri Bay of Islands New Zealand

VEZIROGLU, TURHAN NEJAT, mechanical engineering educator, energy researcher; b. Istanbul, Turkey, Jan. 24, 1924; came to U.S., 1962; s. Abdul Kadir and Ferruh (Bürün) V.; m. Bengi Isikli, Mar. 17, 1961; children: Emre Alp, Oya Sureyya. A.C.G.I., City and Guilds Coll., London, 1946; B.Sc. with honors, U. London, 1947; D.I.C., Imperial Coll., London, 1948; Ph.D., U. London, 1951. Engring. apprentice Alfred Herbert Ltd., Coventry, U.K., 1945; project engr. Office of Soil Products, Ankara, Turkey, 1953-56; tech. dir. M.K.V. Constrn. Co, Istanbul, 1957-61; assoc. prof. mech. engring. U. Miami, Coral Gables, Fla., 1962-65; prof. U. Miami, Coral Fables, Fla., 1966—; dir. grad. studies mech. engring. U. Miami, Coral Gables, Fla., 1965-71, chmn. dept. mech. engring. 1971-75, assoc. dean research Coll. Engring., 1975-79, dir. Clean Energy Research Inst., 1974—; UNESCO cons., Paris; vis. prof. Middle East Tech. U., Ankara, 1969. Editor-in-chief: Internat. Jour. Hydrogen Energy, 1976—. Pres. Learning Disabilities Found. Miami, 1972-73, advisor, 1974-80. Recipient Turkish Presdl. sci. award Turkish Sci. and Tech. Research Found., 1975; named hon. prof. Xian Jiaotong U., China, 1982. Fellow AAAS, ASME, Instn. Mech. Engrs.; mem. Internat. Assn. Hydrogen Energy (pres. 1975), AIAA, Assn. Energy Engrs., Am. Nuclear Soc., Am. Soc. Engring. Edn., AAUP, Internat. Soc. Solar Energy, Systems Engring. Soc., Sigma Xi. Home: 4910 Biltmore Dr Miami FL 33146-1724 Office: U Miami Clean Energy Rsch Inst PO Box 248294 Miami FL 33124-8294 Hydrogen energy system will provide the *world with clean and abundant energy, while doing away with pollution, acid rains and the greenhouse effect. It is a noble and worthwhile goal to strive for.*

VIALARDI, ENZO JOSEPH, publishing company executive; b. N.Y.C., Nov. 22, 1936; s. Ottavio and Maria (Bertagnolio) V.; m. Barbette Joyce Pollack, Aug. 10, 1969; children: Robert, Suzanne. BBA, Iona Coll., 1959. CPA, N.Y. Acct. Deloitte, Haskins & Sells, N.Y.C., 1959-66; div. v.p., controller PepsiCo Inc., Purchase, N.Y., 1966-72; v.p., treas. Revlon Inc., N.Y.C., 1972-84; exec. v.p., chief operating officer Simon & Schuster, N.Y.C., 1984—. Served with USAR, 1959-65. Office: Simon & Schuster Inc 1230 Ave Of The Americas New York NY 10020-1513

VIALL, J(OHN) THOMAS, non-profit organization executive, fundraiser; b. Ft. Hood, Tex., Aug. 15, 1948; s. Otis DePry and Margaret Helen (Cowie) V.; m. Susan Jane Bright, Aug. 25, 1973 (div. Dec. 1980); m. Barbra Jill Baken, Oct. 17, 1982; children: Larissa Rachel, Alessandra Lauren. BA, Fairleigh Dickinson U., 1970, MA magna cum laude, 1972; postgrad., Columbia U., 1972-74; Tchg. Cert., Montclair State Coll., 1975. Tutor ED/ LD Bd. of Edn., Bogota and Ridgefield Par, N.J., 1975-77; dir. devel. The Vail-Deane Sch., Elizabeth, N.J., 1977-83; dir. corp. devel. Save the Children, Westport, Conn., 1983-86, Thirteen/WNET, N.Y.C., 1986-87; exec. dir. Sister City Program of City of N.Y., Office of Mayor, 1987-91; dir. devel. Sister Cities Internat., Alexandria, Va., 1991-93; exec. dir. Internat. Coll. Surgeons, Chgo., 1993—; editor: N.Y.-Beijing Directory, 1987; project coord.: Hard Choices-Portraits of Poverty and Hunger in America, 1983. Recipient Key to City, Mayorof Owensboro, Ky., 1992. Mem. U.S. Golf Assn. Achievements include negotiation of loan of 2 giant pandas from Beijing Zoo to N.Y. Zool. Soc. Avocations: golf, tennis, computer technology. Home: 2905 Keystone Rd Northbrook IL 60062 Office: Internat Coll Surgeons 1516 N Lake Shore Dr Chicago IL 60610

VIANI, JAMES L., lawyer; b. Kincaid, Ill., Dec. 24, 1932; s. Frank Jerome and Alfonsina V.; m. Virginia Lee Wilson, Dec. 27, 1958; children: Theresa, Diana, Deborah. BS, Millikin U., 1954; LLB, Wash. U., St. Louis, 1957. Bar: Ill. 1957, Mo. 1957. Assoc. Blackmar, Swanson, Midgley, Jones & Eager, Kansas City, Mo., 1958-59, Stinson, Mag & Fizzell, Kansas City, 1960-62; ptnr. Stinson, Mag & Fizzel, Kansas City, 1962-87, chmn. corp. dept., 1979-85, cons. ptnr., 1988-92. Br. bd. chmn. YMCA, Kansas City, 1979-81. With U.S. Army, 1957-63. Mem. ABA, Phi Kappa Phi, Order of the Coif. Republican. Avocations: hiking, reading, farming. Home: 11106 Belleview Ave Kansas City MO 64114-5115 Office: Stinson Mag & Fizzell PO box 419251 1201 Walnut St Kansas City MO 64141-6251

VIANO, DAVID CHARLES, automotive safety research scientist; b. San Mateo, Calif., May 7, 1946; s. James Louis and Dorothy Marie (Clark) V.; m. Sharon Lynne Henderson, Dec. 7, 1975. BSEE, U. Santa Clara, 1968; MS in Applied Mechanics, Calif. Inst. Tech., 1969, PhD in Applied Mechanics, 1972; postdoctoral degree in biomed. sci., Swiss Inst. Tech., Zurich, 1974. Sr. rsch. engr. biomed. scis. dept., GM Rsch. Labs., Warren, Mich., 1974-76, staff rsch. engr., 1976-78, asst. dept. head, 1978-87, prin. rsch. scientist, leader safety rsch. program, 1987-92; mgr. global R&D programs, 1992—; tech. sec. med. com. for automotive safety biomed. scis. dept., GM Rsch. Labs., Warren, Mich., 1984—, mem. accident avoidance tech. com., 1989-93; adj. asst. prof. dept. mech. engring., Wayne State U., Detroit, 1981-86, adj. assoc. prof., 1986-89, adj. prof., 1989—, vis. prof., Chalmers U., Sweden, 1992—; chmn. indsl. adv. com. Bioengring. Ctr., Wayne State U., 1984—; mem. injury rsch. grant rev. com., Ctrs. for Disease Control, HHS, Atlanta, 1986-88, mem. adv. com. for injury prevention and control, 1989-92; mem. indsl. adv. com. bioengring. div. U. Pa., Phila, 1988—; mem. com. on fed. trauma rsch., NRC, NAS, 1984-85; mem. com. sch. bus safety , 1987-89, com. on occupant restraint rsch. needs, 1988-92; Transp. Rsch. Bd., NRC; com. to rev. Ctr. Disease Control injury control program progress, NRC, 1988; mem. engring. directorate rev. panel bioengring., NSF, 1987. Assoc. editor Jour. Biomech. Engring., 1982-88, Accident Analysis and Prevention, 1988—; editl. cons. Jour. Trauma, 1988-92; emeritus, 1992—; tech. reviewer Handbook of Bioengineering, 1985, Protecting Your Bank From Injury, 1985. Mem. property tax assessment bd. rev. City of Bloomfield Hills, Mich., 1986—; bd. dirs., mem.-at-large Mich. Head Injury Alliance chpt. Nat. Head Injury Found., 1987-89, exec. com., bd. dirs. nat. orgn., Southborough, Mass., 1987-91, treas., chmn. fin. com., 1988-91; trustee Del Harder Rehab. Fund Bd., 1987-89, pres., 1989, Rehab. Inst. Found., Detroit; bd. dirs. Rehab. Inst. Wayne State U., 1989—. Recipient Safety Engring. Excellence award Nat. Hwy. Traffic Safety Adminstrn., Dept. Transp., 1989, Best Paper award 30th Stapp Car Crash Conf., 1988, Bertil Aldman award IRCOBI, 1992. Fellow ASME (mem. transp. safety com. 1982-92, bioengring. honors com. 1982—, govt. rels. contact bioengring. div. 1980-92, program chmn. editor symposium, 1981), Soc. Automotive Engrs. (chmn. Stapp car crash adv. com., 1976-90, passenger protection com. 1980—, safety adv. com. 1985—, Ralph Isbrandt automotive safety engring. awards bd. 1987-89, organizer, editor 18 symposia 1982-86, mem. other coms., Isbrandt medals 1981, 85, 86, Forest R. McFarland Ousttanding Svc. award 1982, Arch T. Colwell awards 1982, (3) 1988, (2) 1989), Assn. Advancement Automotive Medicine (chmn. ad hoc com. for impairment scaling, 1985—, mem. exec. bd. 1986-91, pres.-elect 1988, pres. 1989); mem. Am. Trauma Soc. (bd. dirs. 1989—), Motor Vehicle Mfrs. Assn. (mem. biomechanics task group 1976-84), U.S. Nat. Com. on Biomechanics (Soc. Automotive Engrs. del. 1982-89), Internat. Standards Orgn. (impact safety group 1976—), Am. Soc. Biomechanics, ACS (com. on truama and burns conjoint coun. surg. rsch. 1986—), Biomed. Engring. Soc. (sr.), AAAS. Republican. Home: 62 Barden Ct Bloomfield Hills MI 48304 Office: Gen Motors Rsch and Devel Ctr Warren MI 48090-9055

VIAULT, BIRDSALL SCRYMSER, history educator; b. Mineola, N.Y., Sept. 20, 1932; s. Joseph Choate and Helen Lee (Scrymser) V.; m. Sarah Reed Underhill, May 9, 1970. BS, Adelphi U., 1955, MA, 1956; MA, Duke U., 1957, PhD, 1963. Instr. history Adelphi U., Garden City, N.Y., 1959-63, asst. prof. history, 1963-68; assoc. prof. historry Winthrop U., Rock Hill, S.C., 1968-72, prof. history, 1972—, chmn. dept. history, 1979-89; vis. assoc. prof. Duke U., Durham, N.C., 1970; leader ann. tours to Europe, 1977—. Author: World History in the 20th Century, 1969, American History Since 1865, 1989, rev. edit., 1993, Western Civilization Since 1600, 1990, Modern European History, 1990, English History, 1992; author weekly column, 1979-87; contbr. articles and revs. to profl. jours. Mem. Nassau County (N.Y.) Dem. Com., 1961-68, S.C. Commn. for Archives and History, 1979-89, S.C. Bd. Rev. for Nat. Register of Hist. Places, 1988—; del. S.C. State Dem. Conv., 1972, 74, 94; leader ann. tours to Europe, 1977—. Ford Found. Coop. Program for Humanities Postdoctoral fellow U. N.C., Duke U., 1969-70. Mem. So. Hist. Assn., Am. Cath. Hist. Assn., Soc. Historians of Am. Fgn. Rels., S.C. Hist. Assn., Kiwanis Club Rock Hill, Phi Kappa Phi, Phi Alpha Theta, Zeta Beta Tau. Roman Catholic. Avocations: travel, photography, cooking. Home: 2186 Wentworth Dr Rock Hill SC 29732-1242 Office: Winthrop U Dept History Rock Hill SC 29733

VICARY, DUANE S., chamber of commerce executive. Pres. Lincoln C. of C., Lincoln, Neb. Office: Lincoln C of C 1221 N St Suite 606 Lincoln NE 68508

VICCELLIO, HENRY, JR., career military officer. Gen. USAF; dir., commdr. Joint Chief of Staff. Office: USAF Air Material Command Write-Patterson AFB Dayton OH 45433

VICE, JON EARL, hospital executive; b. Fairfield, Ala., July 1, 1947; s. Jon Walker Vice and Martha Ann (Lee) Cain; m. Sara Rose Romano Marino, July 26, 1967 (div. Feb. 1975); children: Jon E. Jr., Lisa Ann; m. Joanne Katherine Richter, June 28, 1975; children: Jeffrey Walker, Jessica Lynn. BS, U. Ala., Tuscaloosa, 1970; MS, U. Ala., Birmingham, 1974. Asst. to adminstr. Children's Hosp. Ala., Birmingham, 1971-72, adminstr., chief operating officer, 1977-79; assoc. adminstr. Children's Hosp. Med. Ctr., Cin., 1972-76; exec. v.p., chief operating officer Children's Hosp. Wis., Milw. 1979-84, pres., chief exec. officer, 1984—; mem. exec. com. & dirs. Milw. Regional Med. Ctr., Milw., 1985—; bd. dirs. Child Health Corp. Am., Kansas City, Mo.; pres., bd. dirs. Total Care Health Plan (HMO), Milw., 1985-87. Named Outstandng Alumnus Grad. Program in Health Adminstrn., U. Ala-Birmingham Alumni Assn., 1987. Mem. Am. Coll. Healthcare Execs., Nat. Assn. Childrens Hosps. (exec. coun., bd. dirs

1986—, chmn. 1989—), Westmoor Country Club, Univ. Club. Presbyterian. Avocations: golf, skiing. Office: Children's Hosp Wis PO Box 1997 Milwaukee WI 53201-1997

VICK, COLUMBUS EDWIN, JR., civil engineering design firm executive; b. Jacksonville, Fla., Nov. 8, 1934; s. Columbus Edwin Sr. and Lucretia (Dean) V.; m. Laura Anne McGowan, Mar. 20, 1964; children: Jennifer, Carolyn, Elizabeth. BSCE, N.C. State U., 1956, MSCE, 1960. Registered profl. engr., 15 states. Research asst. N.C. State Civil Engring. Dept., Raleigh, 1958-60; transp. planning engr. Harland Bartholomew & Assocs., Memphis, 1960-64; office and project mgr. Harland Bartholomew & Assocs., Raleigh, 1964-67; prin., co-founder Kimley-Horn and Assocs. Inc., Raleigh, 1967-72, pres., 1972-92; chmn., 1992—. Co-author: North Carolina Atlas; contbr. numerous research and tech. publs. in fields of transp. engring. planning and traffic engring. Bd. dirs. N.C. State U. Engring. Found.; past pres. bd. assocs. Meredith Coll.; past dir. N.C. State U. Alumni Assn.; 2d v.p. Bapt. State Conv. of N.C.; bd. dirs. Associated Bapt. Press, Biblical Recorder. Named Disting. Engring. alumnus N.C. State U. Engring. Found., 1991. Fellow ASCE (Outstanding Young Engr. award ea. br. N.C. sect. 1966), Inst. Transp. Engrs. (Outstanding Individual Activity award so. sect. 1978, Disting. Svc. award so. sect. 1981, Lifetime Svc. award N.C. sect. 1994); mem. NSPE, Am. Cons. Engrs. Coun., Am. Inst. Cert. Planners (PSMA pres. 1994), Phi Kappa Phi (Outstanding Engring. Achievement award N.C. sect. 1992). Baptist. Home: 2205 Nancy Ann Dr Raleigh NC 27607-3318 Office: Kimley-Horn and Assocs Inc 3001 Weston Pky Cary NC 27513

VICK, FRANCES BRANNEN, publishing executive; b. Trinity, Tex., Aug. 14, 1935; d. Carl Andrew and Bess (courtney) B.; m. Ross William Vick Jr., June 23, 1956; children: Karen Lynn, Ross William III, Patrick Brannen. BA, U. Tex., 1958; MA, Stephen F. Austin State U., 1968. Teaching fellow Stephen F. Austin State U., Nacogdoches, Tex., 1966-68, lectr., 1968-69; lectr. Angelina Coll., Lufkin, Tex., 1969-71, Baylor U., Waco, Tex., 1974-75, 77-78; vice prin. Vanguard Sch., Waco, 1975-77; pres. E-Heart Press, Inc., Dallas, 1979—; co-dir. UNT Press U. North Tex., Denton, 1987-89, dir., 1989—. Publisher 107 books; editor 40 books. Leadership coun. Ann Richards Com., Austin, 1990-94; amb. Inst. Texan Cultures; mem. Tex. Commn. on Arts, Lit., 1991. Mem. AAUW, Book Pubs. Tex. (v.p. 1990—), Tex. Folklore Soc. (councillor 1991-93), Tex. Humanities Resource Ctr. (bd. dirs. 1990-91), Conf. Coll. Tchrs. English, Western Lit. Assn., Western Writers Am., Philos. Soc. Tex., Pen Ctr. U.S.A. West, Tex. State Hist. Assn. (life), East Tex. Hist. Assn., Western Writers Am., Western Lit. Assn., Soc. Scholarly Pub., Women in Scholarly Pub., Rocky Mountain Book Pubs. Assn., Leadership Tex., Leadership Am., Tex. Humanities Alliance, UNT League Profl. Women. Democrat. Episcopalian. Home: 3700 Mockingbird Ln Dallas TX 75205-2125 Office: U North Tex PO Box 13856 Denton TX 76203-6856

VICK, JAMES ALBERT, publishing executive, consultant; b. Norwalk, Conn., Feb. 5, 1945; s. James Albert and Madeline (Mayhew) V.; m. Deborah M. Ashley, Dec. 23, 1964 (div. Oct. 1974); children: James Ashley, Guy Robert; m. Susan Jane Collins, May 14, 1977; 1 child, Jonathan Scott. BS, Boston U., 1967. Dist. mgr. McGraw Hill Pub. Co., N.Y.C., 1969-75, Cahners Pub. Co., N.Y.C., 1975-79; mgr. advt. ASCE, N.Y.C. 1979-82; v.p. mktg. Bill Communications, N.Y.C., 1982-85; pub. Thomas Pub. Co., N.Y.C., 1985—; cons. Carvajal, Calle, Columbia, 1984, McLarens, London, 1987. Capt. USAR, 1967-70, Vietnam. Mem. Bus. Mktg. Assn. (cert. bus. communicator), Am. Bus. Press (pubs. com.), Soc. Plastics Engrs., Pharm Ad Club, Instrument Soc. Am., Indsl. Computing Soc., Princeton Club, Beacon Hill Country Club, Port Royal Golf Club, Elks. Episcopalian. Avocations: golf, sailing, antique restoration. Home: 17 Sailers Way Rumson NJ 07760-1242 Office: Thomas Pub 5 Penn Plz New York NY 10001-1810

VICK, MARIE, retired health science educator; b. Saltillo, Tex., Jan. 22, 1922; d. Alphy Edgar and Mollie (Cowser) Pitts; m. Joe Edward Vick, Apr. 5, 1942; children: Mona Marie, Rex Edward. BS, Tex. Woman's U., Denton, 1942, MA, 1949. Tchr. Coahoma (Tex.) High Sch., 1942-43, Santa Rita Elem. Sch., San Angelo, Tex., 1943-45, Crozier Tech. High Sch., Dallas, 1946-47, Monroe Jr. High Sch., Omaha, 1947-48; instr. Tex. Woman's U., Denton, 1948-50; tchr. San Angelo (Tex.) Jr. High Sch., 1957-58, San Angelo (Tex.) Sr. High Sch., 1957-58, Harlingen Bonham Elem. Sch., 1958-59, Harlingen (Tex.) High Sch., 1959-62; prof. health sci. Coll. Edn. U. Houston, 1962-80. Author: A Collection of Dances for Children, 1970; Health Science in the Elementary School, 1979; contbr. articles to profl. jours.; artist in oil, watercolor and acrylic. Mem. exec. bd. Health Care Task Force of Walker County. Recipient Cert. of Achievement, Tex. Commn. Intercollegiate Athletics for Women, 1972, Research Service award Tex. Cancer Control Program, 1978-79, Plaudit award Nat. Dance Assn., 1982, Disting. Service award Pan Am. U., 1983, Service citation Am. Cancer Soc., Cert. of Appreciation, Tex. div. Am. Cancer Soc., 1980; Favorite Prof. honoree Cap and Gown Mortar Bd., U. Houston, 1974. Mem. AAHPERD (dance editor 1971-74), NEA, Am. Sch. Health Assn., Am. Assn. Health, Phys. Edn. Coll. Women (sec. dance sect. 1970-73), Tex. State Tchrs. Assn. (sect. chmn. 1964-65), Tex. Assn. Health, Phys. Edn. and Recreation (chmn. dance sect. 1968-69), Tex. Assn. Coll. Tchrs., Tex. Women's U. Nat. Alumnae Assn. (life), Tex. Women's Pioneer Club, Am. Assn. Ret. Persons (chmn. legis. com. Huntsville chpt. 1988-90, bd. dirs., liaison person Walker County commrs. 1989-90, chmn. community svc. project Walker County Unpaved Rd. Survey 1989, mem. exec. bd. 1992—), Nat. Ret. Tchrs. Assn. (legis. chmn. 1988-89), Tex. Assn. Ret. Tchrs., Property Owners Assn. (organizer, past pres.), U. Houston Assn. Ret. Profs., U. Houston 20 Yr. Club. Democrat. Methodist. Home: RR 6 Box 681A Huntsville TX 77340-9806

VICKER, RAY, writer; b. Wis., Aug. 27, 1917; s. Joseph John and Mary (Young) V.; m. Margaret Ella Leach, Feb. 23, 1944. Student, Wis. State U., Stevens Point, 1934, Los Angeles City Coll., 1940-41, U.S. Mcht. Marine Officers' Sch., 1944, Northwestern U., 1947. With Chgo. Jour. Commerce, 1946-50, automobile editor, 1947-50; mem. staff Wall St. Jour., 1950-83; European editor Wall St. Jour., London, Eng., 1960-75. Author: How an Election Was Won, 1962, Those Swiss Money Men, 1973, Kingdom of Oil, 1974, Realms of Gold, 1975, This Hungry World, 1976, Dow Jones Guide to Retirement Planning, 1985, The Informed Investor, 1990; also numerous articles. Served with U.S. Merchant Marine, 1942-46. Recipient Outstanding Reporting Abroad award Chgo. Newspaper Guild, 1959; Best Bus. Reporting Abroad award E. W. Fairchild, 1963, 67; hon. mention, 1965; Bob Considine award, 1979; ICMA Journalism award, 1983. Mem. Soc. Profl. Journalists, Authors Guild. Roman Catholic. Clubs: Overseas Press (Reporting award 1963, 67) (N.Y.C.); Press (Chgo.). Home and Office: 4131 E Pontatoc Canyon Dr Tucson AZ 85718-5227

VICKERS, JAMES HUDSON, veterinarian, research pathologist; b. Columbus, Ohio, Apr. 21, 1930; s. Carl James and Olga Elizabeth (Schaer) V.; m. Valerie Janet May, Apr. 5, 1964; 1 child, Dana Carlton. BS, Ohio State U., 1952, DVM, 1958; MS, U. Conn., 1966. Diplomate Am. Coll. Vet. Pathologists. Veterinarian Columbus Mcpl. Zoo, 1958-60; dir. pathology dept. Lederle Labs., Pearl River, N.Y., 1960-70; v.p., dir. rsch. Primelabs. Inc., Farmingdale, N.J., 1970-72; dir. spl. studies Johnson & Johnson, Washington Crossing, N.J., 1972-73; dir. pathology and primatology br. FDA, Bethesda, Md., 1973-92 dir. div. vet. svcs., 1992—; rep. interagy. rsch. animal commn. FDA, Bethesda, 1974-89; cons. Gov. Arab Republic Egypt, Cairo, 1976-84, Paul Erlich Inst., Frankfurt, Fed. Republic Germany, 1977-78; chmn. com. on animalcare Ctr. for Biologics, Bethesda. Contbr. chpts. to books. Spokesman Urbana (Md.) Civic Assn., 1987. Capt. U.S. Army, 1952-54. Recipient Presdl. citation Pres. James Carter, 1980, Alumni Svc. award Ohio St. Coll. Vet. Medicine, 1987, FDA Commr.'s spl. citation, 1988. Mem. Am. Vet. Med. Assn., Soc. Toxicology, Internat. Acad. Pathology, Ohio State Vet. Med. Assn., Zane Grey's West Soc. (pres. 1987—), Westerners Internat. Avocations: fine arts, books. Office: Ctr for Biologics Rsch 8800 Rockville Pike Bethesda MD 20892-0001

VICKERS, ROGER SPENCER, physicist, program director; b. Hitchin, Hertfordshire, Eng., Nov. 13, 1937; came to U.S. 1963, naturalized, 1974; s. John Hector and Corona (McCarthy) V.; m. Solvi Loken, May 18, 1968; children—Michelle, Jacqueline, Kevin. B.Sc. with honors, Southampton U., Eng., 1959, Ph.D., 1963. Physicist Ill. Inst. Tech. Research Inst., Chgo.,

1963-66; research asso. Stanford U., 1966-68; v.p. sci. and applications E.R.A., Inc., Houston, 1969-70; asso. prof. elec. engring. Colo. State U., 1970-73; dir. advanced radar program SRI Internat., Menlo Park, Calif., 1973—; cons. NSF. Mem. Soc. Exploration Geophysicists, IEEE. Home: 1143 Los Altos Ave Los Altos CA 94022-1021 Office: Bldg G Stanford Research Inst Menlo Park CA 94025

VICKERY, ANN MORGAN, lawyer; b. Anderson, S.C., June 25, 1944; d. Joseph Harold and Doris (Rogers) Morgan; m. Raymond Ezekiel Vickery, Jr., June 23, 1979; children: Raymond Morgan, Philip Dickens. AB History, Mary Baldwin Coll., 1965; JD, Georgetown U., 1978. Bar: D.C. 1978. Elem. sch. tchr. Chesterfield County, Va., 1965-66; legal publs. specialist Nat. Archives and Record Svc., Washington, 1966-69; speech writing staff to Pres., rsch. asst., chief rschr., staff asst. The White House, Washington, 1969-74; summer clerk Graham & James, Washington, 1975; various positions Dept. Treasury, Washington, 1975-78; atty. Hogan & Hartson, Washington, 1978—; health group dir. Hogan and Hartson, Washington, 1991—, exec. com., 1992-95; gen. counsel Nat. Hospice Orgn., 1982— (named Woman of the Yr. 1986); spkr. in field. Contbr. articles to profl. jours. Dir. Hospice No Va., Arlington, 1987-93. Mem. ABA, Nat. Health Lawyers Assn., D.C. Bar, Health on Wednesday, Phi Alpha Theta. Office: Hogan & Hartson Columbia Square 555 13th St NW Washington DC 20004-1109

VICKERY, ROBERT BRUCE, oil industry executive, consultant; b. Shreveport, La., Aug. 25, 1938; s. Wilbur Claude and Clara Louise (Powell) V.; m. Margaret Lynn Gray, April 6, 1961; children: Joy Lynn, Andrew Gray, William Charles. Degree in Petroleum Engring., Colo. Sch. Mines, 1962; degree in Arctic Engring., U. Alaska, 1974. Petroleum engr. Pan Am. Petroleum Corp., Worland, Wyo., 1962-64; v.p. ops. Vickery Drilling Co., Inc., Evansville, Ind., 1964-73; mgr. drilling BP Alaska, Inc., Sohio-BP, Sohio Petroleum Corp., Anchorage, 1973-80; chmn. Artic Alaska Drilling Co., Inc., Anchorage, 1980-85; pres. Walker Energy Ptnrs., Houston, 1986-87; pres. Refuge Exploration, Inc., Houston, Tex., 1988—, Owensboro, Ky., 1988—. Author: World Oil, 1982. Pres. Boys Club of Alaska, 1978-80; trustee Boys Clubs Am. 1980-87; Alaska fin. chmn. Re-election of Pres. Reagan Com., 1980. Recipient Alaska Engr. of the Year award SPE of AIME, 1982. Mem. Soc. Petroleum Engrs., Ky. Oil and Gas Assn. (dir.). Office: Refuge Exploration Co Inc 734 Carlton Dr Owensboro KY 42303

VICKERY, TRAMMELL EUGENE, lawyer; b. Dalton, Ga., Sept. 6, 1932; s. James Edmond and Eva Mae (Houston) V.; m. Mae Gohley, Feb. 11, 1955; children—Trammell Eugene, David Ray, Alan Scott. B.A., Emory U., 1953, LL.B., 1956. Bar: Ga. 1955. Assoc. Jones, Bird & Howell, Atlanta, 1955-75; assoc. Hansell & Post, Atlanta, 1975-89; ptnr. Troutman Sanders, Atlanta, 1989—; chmn. NCBE, Chgo., 1977-78; chmn. State Bd. Bar Examiners Ga., 1971-74; faculty mem. Emory U. Sch. of Law, Atlanta, 1968-70; lectr. Legal Edn. Ga. Contbr. articles to Bus. Law jours., Ency. Ga. Law. Mem. ABA, Atlanta Bar Assn., Am. Coll. Trial Lawyers. Office: Troutman Sanders 5200 Nationsbank Plz 600 Peachtree St NE Atlanta GA 30308-2216

VICKREY, ROBERT EDWARD, JR., petroleum engineer; b. Cooper, Ky., Nov. 20, 1912; s. Robert Edward and Idell (Wade) V.; m. Ruth LaVerne Chambers, Nov. 30, 1935 (div. 1965); children: Jeanie, Paul; m. Dixie Doyle Richards, June 5, 1971. BS, Okla. State U., 1934; postgrad., U. Dallas, 1971. Registered petroleum engr., Tex. Prodn. engr. Sun Oil Co., Tulsa, 1934-41; natural gas engr. Sun Oil Co., Dallas, 1942-46; prodn. supt. Sun Oil Co., Carthage, Tex., 1947-49; mgr. gas measurement Sun Oil Co., Dallas, 1950-71; advisor pipeline ops. Nat. Iranian Gas Co., Tehran, 1972-74; cons. Sun Exploration & Prodn. Co., Dallas, 1975-85; pres. Vickrey Engring., Inc., Dallas, 1986—; part-time instr. U. Okla., Norman, 1956—, U. Tex. Extension, Kilgore, 1955-82; supr. Dept. of Energy/U. Okla. Petroleum Data System, Dallas, 1977-82; chmn. working groups Measurement Standards, Am. Petroleum Inst., 1982-92. Contbr. articles to profl. jours.; chmn. working groups Measurement Standards, 1982-95. Presdl. commn. Nat. Rep. Senatorial Com., Washington, 1992. Recipient Citation for Svc. Am. Petroleum Inst., 1975, 92, Presdl. Order of Merit Nat. Rep. Senatorial Com., 1991. Mem. Soc. Petroleum Engrs. (North Tex. chmn. 1961-62), Soc. of Petroleum Evaluation Engrs., Dallas Geol. Soc., Petroleum Engrs. Club of Dallas (pres. 1960-61, Permian Pot award 1982), Instrument Soc. Am. (North Tex. pres. 1955-56), Nat. Soc. Profl. Engrs., Tex. Soc. Profl. Engrs., North Tex. Measurement Soc. (pres. 1968-69), Exchange Club of Oak Cliff (pres. 1958). Republican. Ch. of Christ. Avocations: computers, gardening, golf, hunting.

VICKREY, ROBERT REMSEN, artist; b. N.Y.C., Aug. 20, 1926; s. Claude Claire and Caroline (McKim) V.; m. Marjorie Elizabeth Alexander, Sept. 18, 1950; children: Remsen Scott, Elizabeth Nicole, Wendy Caroline, Alexander Sean. Studied with Victoria Huntley; B.A., Yale U., 1947, B.F.A., 1950; student, Art Students League. Co-author: New Techniques in Egg Tempera, 1973; author: Robert Vickrey-Artist at Work, The Affable Curmudgeon, 1979; one-man shows, Midtown Galleries, N.Y.C., 1954-58, 65, 69, 70, 72, Columbia (S.C.) Mus. Art, 1959, Davison Art Ctr., Wesleyan U., 1966, Va. Mus. Fine Arts, 1965, retrospective, U. Ariz. Mus. Art, 1973, San Diego Fine Arts Gallery, 1973; exhibited in nat. group shows; represented in permanent collections, Whitney Mus., Corcoran Gallery of Art, Washington, Lakeland (Fla.) Mus., Mus. Modern Art, Rio de Janeiro, Brazil, Sara Roby Found., Parrish Art Mus., Southampton, Isaac Delgado Mus., Dallas Mus., Munson-Williams-Proctor Inst., Utica, N.Y., Met. Mus. Art, NAD, Butler Inst. Am. Art, New Britain Mus. Am. Art, Gallery of Modern Art, Birmingham Mus., Spelman Coll., Newark Mus., many others; illustrator mag. covers, books. Recipient award Edward Austin Abbey mural competition, 1949, top prize Fla. Internat. Art Exhbn., 1952, 2d prize Internat. Hallmark competition, 1955, Am. Artist mag. citation, 1956, Winsor and Newton award Am. Water Color Soc., 1956, S.J. Wallace Truman prize Nat. Acad. ann., 1958, Salmagundi Club award Audubon Artists, 1971, spl. prize Internat. Biennial of Sport in Fine Arts, Mus. Contemporary Art, Madrid, 1973, Gold Medal NAD, numerous others. Mem. Audubon Artists, Am. Water Color Soc., Nat. Acad. Office: Harmon-Meek Gallery Naples FL

VICKREY, WILLIAM SPENCER, economist, emeritus educator; b. Victoria, B.C., Can., June 21, 1914; came to U.S. 1914; s. Charles Vernon and Ada Eliza (Spencer) V.; m. Cecile Montez Thompson, July 21, 1951. B.A. in Math. with high honors (scholar), Yale, 1935; M.A., Columbia, 1937, Ph.D., 1947; D.H.L., U. Chgo., 1979; Social Sci. Research Council predoctoral field fellow, 1938-39. Jr. economist Nat. Resources Com., Washington, 1937-38; research asst. 20th Century Fund, 1939-40; economist OPA, 1940-41; sr. economist, div. tax research Treasury Dept., 1941-43; civilian pub. service assignee, 1943- 46, tax cons. to gov. P.R., 1946; mem. faculty Columbia U., N.Y.C., 1946-81; prof. econs. Columbia U., 1958-81; chmn. dept. Columbia, 1964-67, McVickar prof. polit. economy, 1971-81, prof. emeritus, 1981—; Cons. to govt. and industry, 1949—; participant numerous coms., seminars; Ford research prof. Columbia, 1958-59; instr. IBM Systems Research Inst., 1964; vis. lectr. Monash U., Melbourne, Australia, 1971; inter-regional adviser UN, 1974-75. Author: Agenda for Progressive Taxation, 1947, Microstatics: Metastatics and Macroeconomics, 1964, Public Economics, 1994. Clk. Scarsdale (N.Y.) Friends Meeting, 1959-62. Fellow Inst. Advanced Study Behavioral Scis., Stanford, 1967-68. Fellow Am. Econ. Assn. (pres. 1992), Econometric Soc., Nat. Tax Assn., Am. Statis. Assn., Royal Econ. Soc., Ea. Econ. Assn., Atlantic Econ. Soc. (pres. 1992-93). Home: 162 Warburton Ave Hastings On Hudson NY 10706-3706 Office: Econ Dept Columbia Univ New York NY 10027 *Having been born with considerable talent in an environment that encouraged its development and provided a modicum of recognition for its exercise, I can claim no special virtue for what this has enabled me to achieve. Indeed I have left undone many things that I ought to have done and can only hope that there is enough health left in me to make good some of the deficiency.*

VICKS, JOANN, biology educator; b. Starkville, Miss., Nov. 3, 1938; d. Adolphus and Ella (Perkins) V. BS, Tougaloo Coll., 1961; MA, Ind. U., 1967; edn. specialist, Miss. State U., 1976, D in edn. 1979. Ordained minister. Sci. tchr. Moor High Sch., Crawford, Miss., 1961-63, John Hay High Sch., Cleve., 1963-69; prof. biology Mary Holmes Coll., West Point, Miss., 1970—; instr. Miss. State U. for Women, Columbus, Miss., summer 1993; dir. CASET, West Point, 1989-91, NSF Instrumentation, West Point, 1989-91. Contbr. articles to profl. jours. Recipient Faculty Fellowship award Nat Sci. Found., 1965, 76. Mem. AAAS, Am. Biology Tchrs. Assn., Phi Delta Kappa. Avocations: pianist, vocal choral music, artistic painting. Home: P O Box 404 Starkville MS 39759 Office: Mary Holmes Coll PO Drawer 1257 West Point MS 39773

VICTOR, A. PAUL, lawyer; b. N.Y.C., Nov. 6, 1938; s. Samuel L. and Sophie (Ostrow) V.; m. Ellen Grabois, Aug. 30, 1959; children: Stephanie, Rebecca, Diana. BBA, U. Mich., 1960, JD with distinction, 1963. Bar: N.Y. 1964, D.C. 1964. Atty. antitrust div. U.S. Dept. Justice, Washington, 1963-66; assoc. Kirkland, Ellis & Rowe, Washington, 1966-68; assoc. Weil, Gotshal & Manges, N.Y.C., 1968-72, ptnr., 1972—; adj. prof. law Fordham U., N.Y.C., 1983—; mem. adv. bd. Southwestern Legal Found., Dallas, 1984—; bd. dirs. Toray Industries (Am.) Inc., N.Y.C., 1987—. Contbr. numerous articles to law revs., other legal publs. regarding U.S. internat. antitrust and trade law. Mem. visitors com. U. Mich. Law Sch., 1980—; trustee Mass. Sch. of Law, Andover, 1989—; mem. pub. affairs adv. com. Japan Soc., 1987-89. Mem. ABA (vice-chair 1994-95, coun. mem. sect. on antitrust law 1983-86, 91-94, chmn. internat. antitrust com. 1982-85, 87-90), Internat. Bar Assn., N.Y. State Bar Assn. Jewish. Avocations: golf, travel, swimming. Office: Weil Gotshal & Manges 767 5th Ave New York NY 10153-0002

VICTOR, MICHAEL GARY, physician, lawyer; b. Detroit, Sept. 20, 1945; s. Simon H. and Helen (Litsky) V.; m. Karen Sue Hutson, July 20, 1975; children: Elise Nicole, Sara Lisabeth. Bars: Ill. 1980, U.S. Dist. Ct. (no. dist.) Ill. 1980, U.S. Ct. Appeals (7th cir.) 1981; diplomate Am. Bd. Legal Medicine. Pres., Advocate Adv. Assocs., Chgo., 1982—; asst. prof. medicine Northwestern U. Med. Sch., Chgo., 1982—; pvt. practice law, Barrington, Ill., 1982—; dir. emergency medicine Loretto Hosp., Chgo., 1980-85 , chief. sect. of emergency medicine St. Josephs Hosp., Chgo., 1985-87; v.p. Med. Emergency Svcs. Assocs., Buffalo Grove, Ill., 1989; v.p. MESA Mgmt. Corp.; of counsel Bollinger, Ruberry & Garvey, Chgo. Author: Informed Consent, 1980; Brain Death, 1980; (with others) Due Process for Physicians, 1984, A Physicians Guide to the Illinois Living Will Act, The Choice is Ours!, 1989. Recipient Service awards Am. Coll. Emergency Medicine, 1973-83. Fellow Am. Coll. Legal Medicine, Chgo. Acad. Legal Medicine; mem. Am. Coll. Emergency Physicians (pres. Ill. chpt. 1980, med.-legal-ins. council 1980-81, 83-84), ABA, Ill. State Bar Assn., Am. Soc. Law and Medicine, Chgo. Bar Assn. (med.-legal council 1981-83), AMA, Ill. State Med. Soc. (med-legal council 1980-86, 88), Chgo. Med. Soc. Jewish. Home and Office: 1609 Guthrie Cir Barrington IL 60010-5721

VICTOR, ROBERT EUGENE, real estate corporation executive, lawyer; b. N.Y.C., Dec. 17, 1929; s. Louis and Rebecca (Teitelbaum) V.; m. Dorothy Saffir, Oct. 14, 1951; children—Priscilla Saffir Victor Faubel, Pandora Saffir. LL.B., St. John's U., 1953, J.D., 1968. Bar: N.Y. bar 1953, Calif. bar 1965. With firm Szold and Brandwen, N.Y.C., 1953-54; atty. Dept. Army, Phila., 1955-56; with Hughes Aircraft Co., Culver City, Calif., 1956-62; v.p., gen. counsel Packard Bell Electronics Corp., Los Angeles, 1962-70; sr. v.p., gen. counsel Cordon Internat. Corp., Los Angeles, 1970-78; also dir.; gen. counsel Am. Harp Soc., 1969-85; pres. Vanowen Realty Corp., 1978-93, also dir. Mem. Los Angeles County Bar Assn. Club: Masons. Office: 722 Walden Dr Beverly Hills CA 90210-3125

VICTOR, WILLIAM WEIR, retired telephone company executive, consultant; b. Marshall, Ill., Apr. 16, 1924; s. Sturges L. and Esther (Weir) V.; m. Patricia Kelly, Sept. 7, 1946; children: William K., Jill Victor Buelsing, D. Gregory. Student, U. Okla., 1943-44; E.E. U. Cin., 1948, U. Ill., 1949. Various positions Cin. Bell Telephone, Ohio, 1947-69, v.p., 1972-85, sr. v.p., 1986-87; v.p. 195 Corp., N.Y., 1969-72; bd. dirs. Skidmore Sales and Distbn. Co. Trustee Goodwill Industries, Cin., 1973-91, WCET Ednl. TV Found., Cin., 1972-86, Bethesda Hosp., Cin., 1978, Herman Schneider Found., Cin., 1983, Armstrong Chapel Found., 1992; trustee, v.p. Millcreek Valley Conservancy Dist., 1990—. Sgt. USAR, 1943-45, ETO, lt. col. USAR, ret. Mem. IEEE, Engring. Soc. Cin., Cin. Country Club. Home: 5440 Windridge Ct Cincinnati OH 45243-2967

VICTORIN, HIS EMINENCE THE MOST REVEREND ARCHBISHOP See URSACHE, VICTORIN

VIDAL, GORE, writer; b. West Point, N.Y., Oct. 3, 1925; s. Eugene L. and Nina (Gore) V. Grad., Phillips Exeter Acad., 1943. Author, 1946—. Author: (novels) Williwaw, 1946, In a Yellow Wood, 1947, The City and the Pillar, 1948, The Season of Comfort, 1949, A Search for the King, 1950, Dark Green, Bright Red, 1950, The Judgment of Paris, 1952, Messiah, 1954, , Julian, 1964, Washington, D.C, 1967, Myra Breckinridge, 1968, Two Sisters, 1970, Burr, 1973, Myron, 1974, Kalki, 1978, Creation, 1981 (Prix Deauville 1983), Duluth, 1983, Lincoln, 1984, Empire, 1987, Hollywood/ Live From Golgotha, 1990, (under name Edgar Box) Death in the Fifth Position, 1952, Death Before Bedtime, 1953, Death Likes It Hot, 1954, (short stories) A Thirsty Evil, 1956; (play) Visit to a Small Planet, 1957, (TV and Broadway prodns.) The Best Man, 1960, Romulus, 1962, Weekend, 1968, An Evening with Richard Nixon, 1972, (essays) Rocking the Boat, 1962, Sex, Death, and Money, 1968, Reflections upon a Sinking Ship, 1969, Homage to Daniel Shays, 1973, Matters of Fact and of Fiction, 1977, The Second American Revolution, 1982 (Nat. Book Critics Circle award for criticism 1982), Armageddon?, 1987 (London), United States: Essays 1952-1992, 1993 (Nat. Book award for nonfiction 1993), Live from Golgotha: The Gospel According to Gore Vidal, 1993; (films) The Catered Affair, 1956, I Accuse, 1958, The Left-Handed Gun, 1958, The Scapegoat, 1959, Suddenly Last Summer, 1959, The Best Man, 1964 (Cannes Critics prize 1964), Is Paris Burning?, 1966, The Last of the Mobile Hotshots, 1970; (teleplays) Barn Burning, 1954, Dark Possession, 1954, Smoke, 1954, Visit to a Small Planet, 1955, Dr. Jekyll and Mr. Hyde, 1955, A Sense of Justice, 1955, Summer Pavilion, 1955, The Turn of the Screw, 1955, Stage Door, 1955, A Farewell to Arms, 1955, The Death of Billy the Kid, 1955, Honor, 1956, The Indestructible Mr. Gore, 1959, Dear Arthur, 1960, Dress Gray, 1986, Billy the Kid, 1989; actor: Fellini Roma, 1978, Bob Roberts, 1992, With Honors, 1994, (memoire) Screening History, 1992. Mem. Pres.'s Adv. Com. on Arts, 1961-63; Dem.-Liberal candidate for U.S. Congress, 1960, candidate for Dem. nomination from Calif., 1982; co-chmn. The New Party, 1970-71. Served with AUS, 1943-46. Recipient Edgar Allan Poe award TV drama Mystery Writers of Am., 1955; named hon. citizen Ravello, Italy, 1983.

VIDALE, JOHN EMILIO, geologist; b. Phila., Mar. 15, 1959; s. Guido Levi and Rosemary (Jacobson) V.; 1 child, Laura. BS, Yale U., 1981; PhD, Calif. Inst. Tech., 1986. Scientist U. Calif., Santa Cruz, 1987-90, U.S. Geol. Survey, Menlo Park, Calif., 1991—. Editor Bulletin Seismology Soc. Am., 1988-93; contbr. articles to profl. jours. Gilbert fellow U.S. Geol. survey, 1994-95. Fellow Am. Geophys. Union (Macelwane medal 1994). Home: 156 Archer Dr Santa Cruz CA 95060 Office: US Geol Survey Mail Stop 977 345 Middlefield Rd Menlo Park CA 94025

VIDAS, VINCENT GEORGE, engineering executive; b. Phila., May 25, 1931; s. Joseph and Blanche (Misch) V.; m. Judith Weber, Oct. 15 1955; children: Lisa Louise, Jeffrey Vincent, Kristen Judith. BSEE, Drexel U., 1959, MSEE, 1964. Systems engr. RCA, Moorestown, N.J., 1959-65, Sci. Mgmt. Assn., Haddonfield, N.J., 1965-67; chief exec. officer, owner SEMCOR, Inc., Mt. Laurel, N.J., 1967—; also bd. dirs.; chmn., owner, bd. dirs. Edn. Mgmt. Corp., Cherry Hill, N.J., 1991-93. Staff Sgt. USAF, 1949-53. Mem. IEEE. Avocations: chess, tennis, photography, music. Office: SEMCOR Inc 815 E Gate Dr Mount Laurel NJ 08054-1240

VIDRICKSEN, BEN EUGENE, food service executive, state legislator; b. Salina, Kans., June 11, 1927; s. Henry and Ruby Mae Vidricksen; m. Lola Mae Nienke, Jan. 20, 1950; children: Nancy, Janice, Ben, Penelope, Jeffery. AB, Kans. Wesleyan U., 1951. Field supt. Harding Creamery div. Nat. Dairy Products, Kearney, Kans., 1951-52; plant mgr. Kraft divsn. Nat. Dairy Products, O'Neill, Nebr., 1952-59; owner Vidricksen's Food Service, Salina, 1959—; cons. in field; mem. Kansas Senate, 1979—, asst. majority leader; chmn. joint bldg. constrn. com., legis. and congressional apportionment com., legis. post audit,econ. devel., transp. and utilities, pub. health and welfare, fed.and state affairs, govtl. orgn., spl. interim com. on efficiency in state govt., 1983, del. White House conf. small bus., 1995; mem. Hennessy/ USAF Worldwide Food Service Evaluation Team, 1978, 79. Mem. Salina Airport Authority, 1972-84, chmn., 1976-77; chmn. Republican Central

Com., County of Saline, Kans., 1974-79; adv. council SBA, 1982—, chmn. adv. coun. small bus. devel. ctr.; mem. adv. bd. Salvation Army; past chmn. Salina Convention and Tourism Bur.; Served with USN, 1945-46. Recipient Salut au Restaurateur award Fla. State U., 1974, Gov.'s Spl. award Kans. Assn. Broadcasters, Guardian award Nat. Fedn. Indep. Bus., 1989, Promotion of Tourism and Travel award Travel Ind. Assn. Kans., 1989, Support of Kans. Nat. Guard award Kans. Adjutant Gen., 1990, Good Citizenship award Kans. Engring. Soc., 1991, 92, Freedom award NRA, 1994; named Nat. Rep. Legislator of Yr., Nat. Rep. Legislators Assn., 1991, Assoc. of Yr., Am. Womens Bus. Assn., 1992. Mem. USAF Assn., U.S. Army, Nat. Rep. Legislators Assn., Am. Legis Exch. Coun., Pan Am. Hwy. Assn. (Internat. Achievement award 1992), North Salina Bus. Assn. (past pres.), Kans. Restaurant Assn. (past pres., Restauranteur of Yr. 1973), Kans. Tourism and Travel Commn., Kans. Film Commn., Nat. Restaurant Assn. (dir. 1977—), Travel Industry Assn. Kans. (dir.) VFW (life), Salina C. of C. (past bd. dirs.), Am. Legion, Optimists, North Salina Lions Club, Elks, Moose, Eagles, Masons (knight commdr. Scottish rite, 1994), Shriners. Office: State Senate State Capitol Topeka KS 66612

VIE, RICHARD CARL, insurance company executive; b. St. Louis, Sept. 26, 1937; s. George William and Geraldine (Bell) V.; m. Joan Kay Wilschetz, June 4, 1960; children: Laura, Mark, Todd, Amy, Paul, Sarah. Student, St. Louis U., U. Mo. With Reliable Life Ins. Co., St. Louis, 1962-79; pres. Commonwealth Life Ins. Co., St. Louis, 1979-82; pres., chmn. bd. dirs. United Ins. Co. Am., Chgo., 1983—; sr. v.p., bd. dirs Unitrin, Inc., 1990-92, pres., CEO, 1992—; chmn. Life Insurers Conf., 1994; trustee Life Underwriters Tng. Coun., 1990-94; mem. exec. com. (home svc.) Life Ins. Mktg. and Rsch. Assn., 1990-92. Bd. dirs. Concordia U. Found., 1985-94, Valparaiso U., 1995—; trustee Luth. Assn. Higher Edn., St. Louis, 1979-82. Lt. USN, 1958-62. Mem. The Racquet Club St. Louis. Home: 6286 Timberview Dr Lisle IL 60532-3272 Office: Unitrin Inc 1 E Wacker Dr Chicago IL 60601-1800

VIEHL, MARJORIE ALICE, nursing educator; b. Peoria, Ill., Jan. 1, 1932; d. Oscar Frederick and Margaret Ellen (Parr) Petzing; m. Donald Harvey Viehl, Oct. 3, 1953; children: Warren Arthur, Brian Mark. BSN, Marquette U., 1962, MSN, 1964; PhD, U. Wis., 1984. Instr., asst. prof. Marquette U., Milw., 1964-81; assoc. prof. Concordia U. Wis., Mequon, 1982-90, Bellin Coll. Nursing, Green Bay, Wis., 1990-91; prof. Hope-Calvin Dept. Nursing, Grand Rapids, Mich., 1991—; bd. dirs. Christian Community Living Systems, Watertown, Wis., 1980-82. Mem. ANA, Nat. League Nursing, Mich. Nurses Assn.,Mich. League for Nursing, Christian Nurse Educators. Lutheran. Avocations: reading, traveling, music concerts. Office: Hope Calvin Dept Nursing 3201 Burton St SE Grand Rapids MI 49546

VIELE, GEORGE BROOKINS, library executive; b. Flint, Mich., Apr. 20, 1932; s. Roy Millard and Mable Anna (Brookins) V.; m. Shirley Louise Larzelere, Aug. 29, 1955; 1 child, Sara (dec.). B.S., Central Mich. U., 1960, M.A., 1965; M.S.L.S., U. N.C., 1969; postgrad. Wayne State U. Cert. pub. librarian; cert. adminstrv. mgr. Asst. dir. Wake County Pub. Library, Raleigh, N.C., 1968-71; dir. Greensboro Pub. Library, N.C., 1971—; instr. library sch. U. N.C.-Greensboro, 1977-79. Contbr. articles to profl. jours. Bd. dirs. Lawndale Community Club, Greensboro, 1976-78, Guilford County Pub. Sch. Student Enrichment Found., 1992—; councilman Twining Town Council, Mich., 1963-65; mem. fin. com., chmn. edn. com. Fellowship Presbyn. Ch., Greensboro, 1978-80, elder, 1989-92; mem. Habitat for Humanity. Served to cpl. U.S. Army, 1953-55. Mem. N.C. Library Assn. (stats. com. Pub. Library sect., chmn. 1977-79, devel. com. 1977-79), Triad Management Assn. (pres. 1992-94). Republican. Lodges: Torch, Lions, Rotary. Avocations: bridge, photography, gardening. Office: Greensboro Pub Libr 201 N Greene St Greensboro NC 27401-2410

VIEMEISTER, TUCKER L., industrial designer; b. Dayton, Ohio, Aug. 14, 1948; s. Read and Beverly (Lipsett) V. B Indsl. Design, Pratt Inst., 1974. Jr. designer Vie Design Studios, Yellow Springs, Ohio, 1969; owner, mgr. Ohio Silver, Yellow Springs, 1971-73; designer Wyman & Cannon, N.Y.C., 1974-77; ptnr. Ted Muehling, N.Y.C., 1977-79; v.p. Smart Design Inc., N.Y.C., 1979—; juror Annu. ID Design Rev., Backpacker mag., Convenience Store Merchandiser, 1991 IDEA awards, design e7e 89, Nagoya, Japan; lectr. Form One Conf., 1986, Pratt Inst., 1985, 86, RISD, 1986, Cranbrook Acad. Art, 1986, Axis in Tokyo, 1989; faculty Parsons Sch. Design, 1986; workshop condr.; del. Internat. Coun. Socs. Indsl. Design Congress, Amsterdam, Holland, 1987. Contbr. articles to profl. publs. and confs.; represented in permanent collections Cooper-Hewitt Mus., Smithsonian Instn., N.Y.C., Staatliches Mus. fur Angewandte Kunst, Munich-Mus. Modern Art, N.Y.C., work reviewed in numerous publs. Trustee Rowena Reed Kostellow Fund, Pratt Inst., 1989—. Recipient Presdl. Design Achievement award, 1984, best symbol award Archtl. League, 1986, award Neste, Finland, 1988, also others. Mem. Indsl. Designer Soc. Am. (co-chmn. N.Y. chpt. 1986-87, dir.-at-large 1991-92), Am. Inst. Graphic Designers. Office: Smart Design Inc 7 West 18th St New York NY 10011

VIENER, JOHN D., lawyer; b. Richmond, Va., Oct. 18, 1939; s. Reuben and Thelma (Kurtz) V.; m. Karin Erika Bauer, Apr. 7, 1969; children: John D. Jr., Katherine Bauer. BA, Yale U., 1961; JD, Harvard U., 1964. Bar: N.Y. State 1965, U.S. Supreme Ct. 1970, U.S. Dist. Ct. (so. dist.) N.Y. 1974, U.S. Tax Ct. 1975. Assoc. Satterlee, Warfield & Stephens, N.Y.C., 1964-69; sole practice N.Y.C., 1969-76; founder, bd. dirs., gen. counsel Foxfire Fund Inc., 1968-88; sr. ptnr. Christy & Viener, N.Y.C., 1976—; gen. counsel, bd. dirs. Landmark Communities, Inc., 1970—, NF&M Internat., Inc., 1976—, Singer Fund, Inc., 1979—; gen. counsel Nat. Cancer Found. Cancer Care, 1982-85, Am. Continental Properties Group, 1978—, Troster, Singer & Co., 1970-77; bd. dirs. Gen. Financiere Immob. et Commer. S.A., 1985-89; spl. counsel fin. instns., investment banking and securities concerns; real estate and tax advisor to fgn. instns. Mem. Meeker Brook Sporting Assn., Manursing Island Club, Washington Club. Home: 45 E 62nd St New York NY 10021-8025 also: The Parsonage Washington CT 06793 Office: Christy & Viener 620 Fifth Ave New York NY 10020-2457

VIENNE, DOROTHY TITUS, school principal; b. Buffalo, May 8, 1939; d. Robert Paul and Bertha (Wissman) Titus; m. Richard Paul Vienne, Aug. 27, 1960; children: Richard Paul Jr., Kerstina Elaine. BS in Elem. Edn., SUNY, Brockport, 1960; MS in Elem. Edn., SUNY, Buffalo, 1964; postgrad., U. Buffalo, 1968-76, Canisius Coll., 1978. Cert. elem. tchr., N.Y. Elem. tchr. Lancaster (N.Y.) Cen. Schs., 1960-62, reading tchr., 1962-68, reading specialist, 1968-76; program supr. Kenmore-Town of Tonawanda, Kenmore, N.Y., 1976-79, 81-86; coordinator pupil personnel services Assn. for Retarded Children, Buffalo, 1980-81; prin. Thomas Edison Sch., Kenmore-Tonawanda Union Free Sch. Dist., Kenmore, 1986—; speaker Summer Inst. for Prins., 1987—; 1st Internat. Forum on Total Quality, Brazil, 1993; trainer 4MAT learning styles; author, presenter on total quality mgmt. in schs.; ednl. cons. U.S. Info. Svcs., Brazil, 1994. Named N.Y. State Disting. Elem. Prin., 1991. Mem. ASCD, Sch. Adminstrs. N.Y. State, Western N.Y. Women in Adminstrn. (bd. dirs., Woman Adminstr. of Yr. award 1990), Phi Delta Kappa (officer). Republican. Methodist. Avocations: skiing, travel, bridge. Home: 50 Gaylord Ct Elma NY 14059-9450 Office: Thomas Edison Elem Sch 236 Grayton Kenmore NY 14150-9999

VIENS, HARRY HENRY, JR., communications executive; b. Waterbury, Conn., Mar. 28, 1950; s. Harry Henry Sr. and Madeline (Botti) V.; m. Kathleen Emerson, Oct. 18, 1975; children: Christopher, Jill. BA, Georgetown U., 1972; postgrad., Universitat Salzburg, Austria, 1971; MBA, U. Conn., 1986. Copywriter Arnold & Co., Boston, 1973; dir. creative svcs. Spencer, Bennett & Nowak, Providence, 1974; account exec. O'Neal & Prelle, Hartford, Conn., 1975-78, Mintz & Hoke, Avon, Conn., 1978-80, Flair Communications, N.Y.C., 1981, Creamer, Inc., Hartford, 1982; v.p. account svc. Mason & Madison, New Haven, 1983-86, exec. v.p., 1986—. Bd. dirs. New Hartford (Conn.) Bd. of Edn., 1988—. Mem. Am. Mktg. Assn. (EFFIE award 1979), Bus. and Profl. Advt. Assn., Hartford Advt. Club, Conn. Art Dirs. Club (bd. dirs. 1975, 76), Hartford Club, Quinnipiac Game Assn. Avocations: fishing, hunting, Karate. Office: Mason & Madison Inc 23 Amity Rd Bethany CT 06524-3433

VIERA, JAMES JOSEPH, financial executive; b. Erie, Pa., June 14, 1940; s. Joseph C. and Margaret (Kelly) V.; m. Cheryl Batchelder, Dec. 9, 1967; children: Robert, James Jay. BS, Rensselaer Poly. Inst., 1962; MBA,

Columbia U., 1970. Fin. analyst Ford Motor Co., Dearborn, Mich., 1970-75; asst. compt. Pullman, Inc., Chgo., 1975-76; div. compt. The Pillsbury Co., Mpls., 1976-80; pres., chief fin. officer Jefferson Co., Mpls., 1980-87; chief fin. officer Cowles Media Co., Mpls., 1987—. Bd. dirs. Edina (Minn.) Hockey Assn., 1985-87, Edina Baseball Assn., 1985-87, MApls. C. of C., 1992—, Cowles Media Found.; trustee Sci. Mus. Minn., 1990—. Mem. Rotary. Avocations: jogging, skiing. Home: 7131 Gleason Rd Minneapolis MN 55439-1610 Office: Cowles Media Co 329 Portland Ave Minneapolis MN 55415-1112

VIERCK, CHARLES JOHN, JR., neuroscience educator, scientist; b. Columbus, Ohio, July 6, 1936; s. Charles John and Esther (Amadon) V.; m. Cheryl Stogner; children: Kenneth Christopher, Karl Frederick. B.Sc., U. Fla., 1959, M.Sc., 1961, Ph.D., 1963. Postdoctoral fellow U. Pa. Phila., 1963-65; asst. prof. U. Fla., Gainesville, 1965-71, assoc. prof., 1971-77, prof., 1977—; adj. prof. U. N.C., Chapel Hill, 1977—; dir. Ctr. Neurobiol. Scis. U. Fla., Gainesville. Editor: (textbook) Basics of Neuroscience, 1974; contbr. articles to profl. jours., also chpts. to books; mem. editorial bd. Somatosensory Motor Research, Am. Pain Soc. Jour. Grantee NIH, NIMH, NSF, VA, 1966—. Mem. Soc. Neurosci., Internat. Assn. Study Pain. Democrat. Avocations: jazz, golf. Home: 9331 NW 15th Pl Gainesville FL 32606 Office: U Fla Ctr Neurobiol Scis Med Scis Bldg M 344 Gainesville FL 32610-0244

VIERECK, PETER, poet, historian, educator; b. N.Y.C., Aug. 5, 1916; s. George S. and Margaret (Hein) V.; m. Anya de Markov, June 1945 (div. May 1970); children: John-Alexis, Valerie Edwina (Mrs. John Gibbs); m. Betty Martin Falkenberg, Aug. 30, 1972. B.S. summa cum laude, Harvard, 1937, M.A., 1939, Ph.D., 1942; Henry fellow, Christ Ch., Oxford U., Eng., 1937-38; L.H.D. (hon.), Olivet Coll., 1959. Teaching asst. Harvard, 1941-42, instr. German lit., tutor history and lit. dept., 1946-47; instr. history U.S. Army U., Florence, Italy, 1945; asst. prof. history Smith Coll., 1947-48, vis. lectr. Russian history, 1948-49; assoc. prof. Modern European, Russian history Mt. Holyoke Coll., 1948-55, prof., 1955—; vis. lectr. Am. Culture Oxford U., 1953; Whittal lectr. in poetry Library of Congress, 1954, 63, 79; Fulbright prof. Am. poetry and civilization U. Florence, Italy, 1954-56; Elliston chair poetry lectr. U. Cin., 1956; vis. lectr. U. Calif. at, Berkeley, 1957; Disting. William R. Kenan prof. Mt. Holyoke Coll., 1979—; Charter mem. Council Basic Edn.; vis. poet Russian-Am. cultural exchange program Dept. State, USSR, 1961; vis. research scholar 20th Century Fund, USSR, 1962-63; vis. scholar Rockefeller Study Center at Bellagio, Italy, 1967-68; artist and scholar Am. Acad. in, Rome, 1949-50, 78; dir. poetry workshop N.Y. Writers Conf., 1965-67; research fellow Huntington Library, San Marino, Calif., 1978. Author: Metapolitics—From the Romantics to Hitler, 1941 (Swedish edit., 1942, Italian, 1948), Terror and Decorum, poems, 1948, reprinted, 1972, Who Killed the Universe, novelette included in anthology New Directions Ten, 1948, Conservatism Revisited-The Revolt Against Revolt 1815-1949, 1949 (English edit, 1950), Strike Through the Mask, New Lyrical Poems, 1950, reprinted, 1972, The First Morning: New Poems, 1952, reprinted, 1972, Shame and Glory of the Intellectuals, 1953, rev. edit., 1965, reprinted 1978, Dream and Responsibility, The Tension Between Poetry and Society, 1953, The Unadjusted Man; a New Hero for Americans, 1956, reprinted, 1973, Conservatism: From John Adams to Churchill, 1956, reprinted, 1978, The Persimmon Tree, poems, 1956, Inner Liberty, The Stubborn Grit in the Machine, 1957, The Tree Witch: A Verse Drama, 1961, reprinted, 1973, Meta-politics, The Roots of the Nazi Mind, 1961, rev. expanded edit. 1965, Conservatism Revisited and The New Conservatives: What Went Wrong; rev. paperback edits., 1962, 65, reprinted hardcover, 1978, New and Selected Poems, 1932-67, 1967, Archer in the Marrow: The Applewood Poetry Cycles of 1967-87, 1987, Tide & Continuities: Last & First Poems, 1995; also author of selections in symposium books Towards a World Community, 1951, Midcentury American Poets, 1950, Arts in Renewal, 1951, The New American Right, 1955, Education in a Free Society, 1958, The Radical Right, 1962, Soviet Policy Making, 1967, Outside Looking In, 1972, A Question of Quality, 1976, The Southern California Anthology, 1987, rev. edits., 1987, 89, Decade: New Letters Anthology of the 80s, 1990; contbr. essays, poems to popular mags., and profl. jours.; monograph on Conservatism in Ency. Brit., 1974. Sgt. U.S Army, 1943-45, Africa and Italy. Decorated 2 battle stars; awarded Tietjens prize for poetry, 1948, Pulitzer prize for poetry, 1949; recipient Most Disting. Alumnus award Horace Mann School for Boys, 1958, Poetry Translation award Translation Center, Columbia U., 1978, Sadin poetry prize N.Y. Quar., 1977, Golden Rose award New Eng. Poetry Club, 1981, Varoujan prize, 1983; Guggenheim fellow Rome, 1949-50; Rockefeller Found. researcher in history Germany, summer 1955; NEH sr. rsch. fellow USSR, 1969; Mass. Artists Found. fellow, 1978. Mem. Am. Hist. Assn., Oxford Soc., Poetry Soc. Am., P.E.N., Phi Beta Kappa. Clubs: Harvard (N.Y.C. and London); Bryce (Oxford, Eng.). Home: 12 Silver St South Hadley MA 01075-1616 After 78 years of books, scars, and sugar plums, my rock-bottom thought on life is a line of Vachel Lindsay: "Courage and sleep are the principal things."

VIEREGG, ROBERT TODD, lawyer; b. Woodstock, Ill., Oct. 3, 1934; s. Robert and Mae (Todd) V.; m. Darla Jean Ax, Dec. 12, 1959 (div. Oct. 1983); children: Dorian Jean Griffin, Robert Todd II; m. Carilane Newman Awalt, May 25, 1985. Student, U. Ill., 1952-53; BA, Mich. State U., 1955; postgrad., U. Chgo., 1968-69; JD cum laude, Northwestern u., 1970. Bar: Ill. 1970, U.S. Dist. Ct. (no. dist.) Ill. 1970. From assoc. to ptnr. Sidley & Austin, Chgo., 1970—. With USN, 1956-59. Mem. ABA, Ill. Bar Assn. Chgo. Bar Assn., Law Club Chgo., Union League (bd. dirs. 1987-88), Glen View Country Club. Republican. Office: Sidley & Austin 1 First Nat Plz Chicago IL 60603

VIERMETZ, KURT F., banker; b. Augsburg, Bavaria, Germany, Apr. 27, 1939; came to U.S., 1985; s. Alfons and Clare (Bruck) V.; m. Felicitas Kempe, May, 1966; 1 child, Maximilian. Grad., Heilig Kreuz Coll., Germany, 1957. With Morgan Guaranty Trust Co. of N.Y., Frankfurt, Fed. Republic Germany, 1966-69; asst. v.p. Morgan Guaranty Trust Co. of N.Y., Frankfurt, 1969-71; v.p. Morgan Guaranty Trust Co. of N.Y., Paris, 1971-82; sr. v.p. for Central Europe Morgan Guaranty Trust Co. of N.Y., N.Y.C., 1982-85; vice chmn. Morgan Guaranty Trust Co. N.Y., 1990—; also bd. dirs. Morgan Guaranty Trust Co. of N.Y., N.Y.C.; vice chmn. J.P. Morgan & Co., Inc., 1990—; gen. mgr. Saudi Internat. Bank, London, 1975-77. Author books and articles on internat. fin. to profl. publs. Mem. Am. C. of C in Germany. Roman Catholic. Home: 30 Island Dr Rye NY 10580-4306 Office: Morgan Guaranty Trust Co NY 23 Wall St New York NY 10005-1915

VIERRA, FRED A., communications executive; b. 1932. With Adolph Coors Co., Golden, CO, 1972-77, Daniels & Assoc., Denver, CO, 1978-81; pres. United Cable TV Corp., Denver, CO, 1982-88; pres., COO United Artists Entertainment Co., Englewood, CO, 1988—. Office: United Artists Entertainment Co 9110 E Nichols Ave Englewood CO 80112*

VIERTEL, JACK, theatrical producer, writer; b. Stamford, Conn., Feb. 7, 1949; s. Joseph Maurice and Janet (Man) V.; m. Linda Gilmore, July 31, 1973; children: Joshua Louis, Anna Daisy. AB, Harvard Coll., 1971. Theater critic L.A. Reader, 1977-80; theater critic L.A. Herald Examiner, 1980-85, arts editor, 1984-85; dramaturg Mark Taper Forum Theater, L.A., 1986-87; creative dir. Jujamcyn Theaters, N.Y.C., 1987—. Co-author: (nonfiction) Becoming Parents, 1978; adaptor (play) Ghetto, 1986. Cert. judge Memphis-in-May Barbecue Contest Circuit, 1992—. Mem. League Am. Theaters and Producers. Democrat. Jewish. Avocation: guitar. Office: Jujamcyn Theatres 246 W 44th St New York NY 10036

VIESSMAN, WARREN, JR., academic dean, civil engineering educator, researcher; b. Balt., Nov. 9, 1930; s. Warren and Helen Adair (Berlinckee) V.; m. Gloria Marie Scheiner, May 11, 1953 (div. Apr. 1975); children: Wendy, Stephen, Suzanne, Michael, Thomas, Sandra; m. Elizabeth Gertrude Rothe, Aug. 8, 1980; children: Heather, Joshua. B in Engring., Johns Hopkins U., 1952, MS in Engring., 1958, DEng, 1961. Registered profl. engr., Md. Engr. W. H. Primrose & Assocs., Towson, Md., 1955-57; principal engr. Johns Hopkins U., Balt., 1957-61; from asst. to assoc. prof. N.Mex. State U., Las Cruces, 1961-66; prof. U. Maine, Orono, 1966-68, U. Nebr., Lincoln, 1968-75; sr. specialist Libr. Congress, Washington, 1975-83; prof. chmn. U. Fla., Gainesville, 1983-90, assoc. dean for rsch. and grad. study, 1990-91, assoc. dean for acad. programs, 1991—; vis. scientist Am. Geophys.

Union, 1970-71; Maurice Kremer lectr. U. Nebr., 1985; lectr. Harvard U. Water Policy Seminar, 1988, Wayne S. Nichols Meml. Fund Ohio State U., 1990; mem. steering com. on groundwater and energy U.S. Dept. Energy, 1979-80; mem. task group on fed. water rsch. U.S. Geol. Survey, 1985-87; mem. com. of the water sci. and tech. bd. NAS, 1986-90; mem. water resources working group Nat. Coun. on Pub. Works Improvement, 1987; chmn., chief of engrs. Environ. Adv. Bd., Washington, 1991-93; chmn. solid and hazardous waste mgmt. adv. bd. State U. System Fla. Co-author: Water Supply and Pollution Control, 1993, Water Management: Technology and Institutions, 1984, Introduction to Hydrology, 1988; contbr. over 145 articles to profl. jours. Mem. Water Mgmt. Com., Gainesville, 1983-88, Fla. Environ. Efficiency Study Commn., 1986-88. 1st lt. U.S. Army C.E., 1952-54, Korea. Fellow ASCE (Julian Hinds award 1989), Am. Water Resources Assn. (nat. pres. 1990, Icko Iben award 1983), Univs. Coun. on Water Resources (pres. 1987, Warren A. Hall medal 1994), Sigma Xi, Tau Beta Pi. Avocations: scuba diving, woodworking. Office: U Fla Coll Engring PO Box 116550 Gainesville FL 32611-6550

VIEST, IVAN M(IROSLAV), consulting structural engineer; b. Bratislava, Czechoslovakia, Oct. 10, 1922; came to U.S., 1947, naturalized, 1955; s. Ivan and Maria (Zacharova) V.; m. Barbara K. Stevenson, May 23, 1953. Ing., Slovak Tech. U., Bratislava, 1946; M.S., Ga. Inst. Tech., 1948; Ph.D., U. Ill., 1951. Registered profl. engr., Pa. Research asst. U. Ill., Urbana, 1948-50; research assoc. U. Ill., 1950-51, research asst. prof., 1951-55, research assoc. prof., 1955-57; bridge research engr. Am. Assn. State Hwy. Ofcls.; rd. test Nat. Acad. Scis., Ottawa, Ill., 1957-61; structural engr. Bethlehem Steel Corp., Pa. 1961-67; sr. structural cons. Bethlehem Steel Corp., 1967-70, asst. mgr. sales engring. div., 1970-82; pvt. cons. structural engr. IMV Cons., 1983—; lectr. in field. Author: Composite Construction, 1958, History of Engineering Foundation, 1991. Recipient Constrn. award Engring. News Record, 1972. Fellow AAAS, Am. Concrete Inst. (Wason Rsch. medal 1956); mem. NAE, ASCE (hon., v.p. 1973-75, Rsch. prize, Ernest E. Howard award 1991), Internat. Assn. Bridge and Structural Engring., Transp. Rsch. Bd., Czechoslovak Soc. Arts and Scis. (exec. v.p. 1992-93), Earthquake Engring. Rsch. Inst., Saucon Valley Country Club (Bethlehem). Research, numerous pubs. on various steel and concrete structures, especially bridges and bldgs., to profl. jours. Office: PO Box 1428 Bethlehem PA 18016

VIETH, G. DUANE, lawyer; b. Omaha, Sept. 20, 1923; s. Walter E. and Irene E. (Horn) V.; m. Jane G. Richardson, Feb. 16, 1952; children: Peter D., Robert R., Jane G. BA, U. Iowa, 1947, JD, 1949. Bar: Iowa 1949, D.C. 1949, U.S. Dist. Ct. Iowa 1953, U.S. Dist. Ct. Md. 1955, U.S. Ct. Claims 1958, U.S. Ct. Appeals (3d cir.) 1960, U.S. Dist. Ct. (ea. dist.) Wis. 1965, U.S. Supreme Ct. 1966, U.S. Ct. Appeals (2d cir.) 1970, U.S. Ct. Appeals (7th cir.) 1971. Ptnr. Arnold & Porter, Washington, 1949—; mem. D.C. Commn. on Budget and Financial Priorities, 1989-90. Trustee Iowa Law Sch. Found., Iowa City, 1971-88, Fed. City Council, Washington, 1972—. With USAAF, 1942-45, ETO. Mem. ABA, D.C. Bar Assn., Iowa State Bar Assn., Columbia Country Club, Burning Tree Club, Met. Club. Lutheran. Avocation: golf. Home: 3717 Cardiff Rd Bethesda MD 20815-5943 Office: Arnold & Porter Ste 955 555 12th St NW Washington DC 20004-1202

VIETH, WOLF RANDOLPH, chemical engineering educator; b. St. Louis, May 5, 1934; s. Hans W. and Hedy (Fahrig) V.; m. Peggy Schira, July 6, 1957; children—Jane, Linda, Christopher, Mark. S.B. in Chem. Engring. Mass. Inst. Tech., 1956, Sc.D. 1961; M. Sc., Ohio State U., 1958. Registered profl. engr., N.J. From asst. prof. to assoc. prof. chem. engring. MIT, Cambridge, 1961-68, dir. Sch. Chem. Engring. Practice, 1965-68; prof. chem. and biochem. engring. Rutgers U., New Brunswick, N.J., 1968—, chmn. dept., 1968-78; cons. to govt. and industry; chmn. Gordon Research Conf. on Separation and Purification, 1975, Engring. Conf. on Biochem. Engring. 1978. Mem. econ. study subcom., planning bd. Montgomery (N.J.) Twp., 1970—. Served to 1st lt. AUS, 1961. Recipient DuPont Co. Invention award, 1960, St. Albert the Great medal for sci. Aquinas Coll., 1952; Vis. Fgn. Scientist award Japan Soc. for Promotion Sci., 1975; Ford postdoctoral fellow, 1961. Fellow Am. Inst. Chemists, N.Y. Acad. Scis.; mem. Am. Inst. Chem. Engrs., Am. Chem. Soc., Am. Soc. Engring. Edn., Sigma Xi, Phi Lambda Upsilon. Research on applied molecular biology, semipermeable membranes, polymers. Home: RR 2 Belle Mead NJ 08502-9803 Office: Rutgers Univ Heights Campus New Brunswick NJ 08903

VIETOR, HAROLD DUANE, federal judge; b. Parkersburg, Iowa, Dec. 29, 1931; s. Harold Howard and Alma Johanna (Kreimeyer) V.; m. Dalia Artemisa Zamarripa Cadena, Mar. 24, 1973; children: Christine Elizabeth, John Richard, Greta Maria. BA, U. Iowa, 1955, JD, 1958. Bar: Iowa 1958. Law clk. U.S. Ct. Appeals 8th Circuit, 1958-59; ptnr. Bleakley Law Offices, Cedar Rapids, Iowa, 1959-65; judge Iowa Dist. Ct., Cedar Rapids, 1965-79, chief judge, 1970-79; U.S. dist. judge So. Dist. Iowa, Des Moines, 1979—, chief judge, 1985-92; lectr. at law schs., legal seminars U.S. and Japan. Contbr. articles to profl. jours. in U.S. and Japan. Served with USN, 1952-54. Mem. ABA, Iowa Bar Assn. (pres. jr. sect. 1966-67), Iowa Judges Assn. (pres. 1975-76), 8th Cir. Dist. Judges Assn. (pres. 1986-88). Office: US Dist Ct 221 US Courthouse E 1st & Walnut Sts Des Moines IA 50309-2038

VIETS, HERMANN, college president, consultant; b. Quedlinburg, Fed. Republic Germany, Jan. 28, 1943; came to U.S., 1949, naturalized, 1961; s. Hans and Herta (Heik) V.; m. Pamela Deane, June 30, 1968; children: Danielle, Deane, Hans, Hillary. BS, Polytech. U., 1965, MS, 1966, PhD, 1970. Postdoctoral fellow von Karman Inst., Brussels, 1969-70; group leader Wright-Patterson AFB, Dayton, Ohio, 1970-76; prof. Wright State U., Dayton, Ohio, 1976-81; assoc. dean W.Va. U., Morgantown, 1981-83; dean U. R.I., Kingston, 1983-91; pres. Milw. Sch. Engring., 1991—; chmn. bd., dir. Precision Stampings, Inc., Beaumont, Calif.; bd. dirs. Astro-Med, Inc., West Warwick, R.I., Promptus Comm. Inc., Portsmouth, R.I., 1989-95; cons. USAF Aero Propulsion Lab., Dayton, 1976-80, Covington & Burling, Washington, 1976-77; cons. several cos. and govt. agys. Patentee in aero. field; contbr. numerous articles to tech. publs. Mem. Gov. Regional H.S. of Excellence Co., Gov. Coun. Sci. and Tech.; mem. Sch. to Work Task Force; mem. Gov.'s Commn. on Export Strategy, Greater Milw. Com., Greater Milw. County Econ. Trust, Competitive Wis.; trustee Pub. Policy Forum; dir. Japan-Am. Soc. Recipient Tech. Achievement award USAF, 1974, Sci. Achievement award, 1975, Gov.'s Sci. and Tech. award State of R.I., 1987, Goodrich Pub. Svc. award 1990, Citation R.I. Legislature, 1987, 90, 91, Outstanding Alumnus award aerospace engring. dept. Polytechnic U., 1994, Disting. Alumnus, 1995; postdoctoral fellow NATO, 1969-70, NASA, 1965-69. Fellow AIAA (assoc., Best Tech. Paper award Aeronautical-Pitts. sect. 1982); mem. Deutsche Gesellschaft für Luft und Raumfahrt, Am. Soc. Engring. Edn., Japan-Am. Soc. (bd. dirs.), Soc. Mfg. Engrs., Rotary, Sigma Xi, Phi Kappa Phi, Tau Beta Pi, Sigma Gamma Tau. Avocations: antique automobiles; beer steins. Home: 4216 N Lake Dr Shorewood WI 53211 Office: Milw Sch Engring 1025 N Broadway Milwaukee WI 53202-3109

VIETS, ROBERT O., utilities executive; b. Girard, Kans., Dec. 8, 1943; s. Willard O. and Caroline L. (Bollwinkel) V.; m. Karen M. Kreiter, June 13, 1980. BA in Econs., Washburn U., 1965; JD, Washington U., 1969. Bar: Kans. 1966, Mo. 1969, Ill. 1975; CPA, Kans. Auditor Arthur Andersen & Co., St. Louis, 1969-73; mgr. spl. studies Cen. Ill. Light Co., Peoria, 1973-76, mgr. rates and regulatory affairs 1976-80, asst. v.p., regulatory affairs, 1980-81, v.p. fin. services, 1981-83, v.p. fin. group, 1983-86, sr. v.p., 1988—; sr. v.p. Cilcorp, Inc., Peoria, 1988-88; pres., chief exec. officer, chmn. bd. Cilcorp, Inc. and Cen. Ill. Light Co., Peoria, 1988—; bd. dirs. First of Am. Bank, N.A., Ill., Lincoln Office Supply, Inc., RLI Corp., Environ. Sci. and Engring., Inc., Peoria. Bd. dirs. Heart of Ill. United Way, Meth. Health Svcs., Inc.; trustee Bradley U. Mem. ABA, Ill. Bar Assn., Peoria County Bar Assn., AICPA, Ill. Soc. CPAs. Republican. Lutheran. Lodge: Rotary (bd. dirs. 1985—, pres. 1986-87). Avocation: golf. Home: 11305 N Pawnee Rd Peoria IL 61615-9796 Office: Cilcorp Inc Hamilton Blvd Peoria IL 61602

VIG, VERNON EDWARD, lawyer; b. St. Cloud, Minn., June 19, 1937; s. Edward Enoch and Salley Johanna (Johnson) V.; m. Susan Jane Rosenow, June 10, 1961; 1 child, Elizabeth Karen. BA, Carleton Coll., 1959; LLB, NYU, 1962, LLM, 1963; postdoctoral Université de Paris, Faculté de Droit, 1964. Bar: N.Y. 1962, Avocat (France) 1992. Assoc. Cleary, Gottlieb, Steen & Hamilton, Paris, 1964-65; assoc. Donovan, Leisure, Newton & Irvine, N.Y.C. and Paris, 1965-72, ptnr., 1972-86; ptnr. LeBoeuf, Lamb, Greene &

MacRae, N.Y.C., 1986—. Sr. warden Grace Ch., Bklyn., 1986—. George F. Baker scholar, Fullbright scholar, 1963-64, Ford Found. scholar, 1963-64. Mem. ABA (internat. trade com.), N.Y. State Bar Assn. (chmn. antitrust 1987-88), Assn. of Bar of City of N.Y., Internat. Bar Assn., Union Internationale des Avocats. Episcopalian. Clubs: Heights Casino (Bklyn.); Merriewold (Forestburgh, N.Y., bd. dirs. 1985-91). Office: LeBoeuf Lamb Greene & MacRae 125 W 55th St New York NY 10019

VIGEN, KATHRYN L. VOSS, nursing administrator, educator; b. Lakefield, Minn., Sept. 24, 1934; d. Edward Stanley and Bertha C. (Richter) Voss; m. David C. Vigen, June 23, 1956 (div. 1977); children: Eric. E., Amy Vigen Hemstad, Aana Marie. BS in Nursing magna cum laude, St. Olaf Coll., 1956; MEd, S.D. State U., 1975; MS, Rush U., 1980; PhD, U. Minn., 1987. RN. Staff nurse various hosps., Mpls, Boston, Chgo., 1956-68; nursing instr. S.E.A. Sch. Practical Nursing, Sioux Falls, S.D., 1969-74; statewide coord. upward mobility in nursing Augustana Coll., Sioux Falls, S.D., 1974-78; cons./researcher S.D. Commn. Higher Edn., 1974-79; gov. appointed bd. mem. S.D. Bd. Nursing, 1975-79; RN upward mobility project dir., chair/dir. div. of nursing Huron Coll. S.D. State U., 1978-79, mobility project dir., 1980-84; head dept. nursing, assoc. prof. Luther Coll., Decorah, Iowa, 1984-94; prof. nursing Graceland Coll., Independence, Mo., 1994—; cons. in field; governing bd. mem. Midwest Alliance in Nursing, 1984-92; founder Soc. for Advancement of Nursing, Malta, 1992; developer Health Care in the Mediterranean study abroad program, Greece and Malta, 1994; developer summer internship for Maltese nursing students Mayo Med. Ctr. and Luther Coll. Author: Role of a Dean in a Private Liberal Arts College, 1992; devel. and initiated 3 nursing programs in S.D., 1974-84 (named Women of Yr., 1982). Lobbyist Nursing Schs. in S.D., 1974-79; task force mem. Sen. Tom Harkin's Nurse's Adv. Com., 1986-94. Fellow to rep. U.S.A. ANA cand. in internat. coun. nursing 3M, St. Paul, 1978; recipient Leadership award Bush Found., St. Paul, 1979; tenure Luther Coll., 1986; Faculty fellow Minn. Area Geriatric Edn. Ctr. U. Minn., 1990-91; recipient Fulbright award Malta Coun. 1994. Internat. Exch. of Scholars, Washington, 1992—. Mem. AAUW, ANA, Am. Assn. Colls. Nursing (exec. devel. subcom. 1990—), Internat. Assn. Human Caring, Iowa Nurse's Assn. (bd. dirs. 1989-92, mem. nursing edn. com. 1989—, co-pres. 1989—), Midwest Alliance in Nursing (gov. bd. rep. Iowa 1989-92, chair membership com. 1989-92, S.D. gov. bd. rep. 1984-86, Rozella Schlotfeldt Leadership award 1993), Iowa Acad. Sci., Iowa Assn. Colls. Nursing Soc., Gerontol. Soc. Am., Rotary, Sigma Theta Tau. Democrat. Lutheran. Avocations: singing, travel and other cultures, meeting people, sailing, reading. Home: 4316 Northern Ave # 2633 Kansas City MO 64133-7249 Office: Graceland Coll Divsn Nursing 221 W Lexington Independence MO 64050-3720

VIGIER, FRANÇOIS CLAUDE DENIS, city planning educator; b. Geneva, Oct. 14, 1931; s. Eugene Henri Rene and Françoise (Dupuy) V. BArch, MIT, 1955; M in City Planning, Harvard U., 1959, PhD, 1967. Architect UN Relief and Works Agy., Jordan, 1955-57; designer Town Planning Cons., Cambridge, Mass., 1957-58; mem. faculty Harvard Grad. Sch. Design, Cambridge, 1960—, prof. city planning and urban design, 1968-85, Charles Dyer Norton prof. regional planning, 1985—, dir. unit for housing and urbanization, 1987—, chmn. spl. programs, 1982-86; chmn. dept. urban planning and design, 1992—; vis. lectr. art Dartmouth Coll., 1962, 64; vis. critic urban design U. N.C., 1963; cons. Ford Found. Latin Am. program, 1964-65, Ednl. Svcs., Inc., 1966; dir. Harvard Ctr. Environ. Design Studies, 1967-69; pres. Nash-Vigier Inc., Cambridge, 1965-91. Author: Change and Apathy: Liverpool and Manchester During the Industrial Revolution, 1970, Housing in Tunis, 1987; contbr. articles to various periodicals. Mem. Am. Inst. Cert. Planners, Am. Planning Assn. Home: 27 Fayerweather St Cambridge MA 02138-3329

VIGIL, CHARLES S., lawyer; b. Trinidad, Colo., June 9, 1912; s. J.U. and Andreita (Maes) V.; m. Kathleen A. Liebert, Jan. 2, 1943; children: David Charles Edward, Marcia Kathleen. LL.B., U. Colo., 1936. Bar: Colo. 1936. Dep. dist. atty. 3d Jud. Dist. Colo., 1937-42, asst. dist. atty., 1946-51; U.S. atty. Dist. Colo., 1951-53; pvt. practice law Denver.; Dir., sec. Las Animas Co. (Colo); ARC. Author: Saga of Casimiro Barela. Bd. dirs. Family and Children's Svc. Denver, Colo. Humane Soc., Animal Rescue Soc., Auraria Community Ctr.; mem. Bishop's com. on housing; Dem. candidate for U.S. Congress, 1988. Lt. USCG, 1942-46. Recipient award of civil merit Spain, 1960, award of civil merit Colo. Centennial Expn. Bd., 1976; award Colo. Chicano Bar Assn., 1979. Mem. Internat. Law Assn., ABA, Fed. Bar Assn., Colo. Bar Assn. (bd. govs.), So. Colo. Bar Assn., Hispanic Bar Colo. (bd. dirs.), Am. Judicature Soc., Internat. Bar Assn., Inter-Am. Bar, V.F.W. (comdr.), Am. Legion (comdr.), Nat. Assn. Def. Lawyers, Assn. Trial Lawyers Am., Lambda Chi Alpha, Elks, Eagles, Cootie. Home: 1085 Sherman St Denver CO 80203-2880 Office: 1715 Colo State Bank 1600 Broadway Denver CO 80202-4927 *Desire to serve and achieve in all matters related to public good as promoted and espoused by thoughts of father and mother-and family-brothers and sisters.*

VIGILANTE, JOSEPH LOUIS, social worker, social policy educator; b. Phila., June 21, 1925; m. Florence W. Vigilante; children: Amy, Grace, Theodore. A.B., Temple U., 1950; M.S., Columbia U., 1951, D.S.W., 1968. Cert. social worker, N.Y. Child welfare worker Div. Children and Youth Wis. Dept. Welfare, 1951-53; caseworker, student supr. VA Hosp. Northport, N.Y., 1953-55; part-time caseworker, case supr., chief social worker Mid-Nassau Community Guidance Clinic, Hicksville, N.Y., 1955-60; dir. field work, asst. prof. Sch. Social Work, Adelphi U., Garden City, N.Y., 1955-60, asst. prof., asst. dean, 1960-62, assoc. prof., acting dean, 1962, prof., dean, 1962-87, Univ. prof. social policy, 1987—, exec. v.p. Inst. for Child Mental Health, 1976-89; prof. part-time New Sch. for Social Rsch., N.Y.C., 1972-75, Florence Hollis Prof. Social Policy, summer 1988, Smith Coll., Northampton, Mass., 1987—; vis. prof. Rutgers U., 1987, Yeshiva U., 1988; cons. South Oaks Hosp., L.I., 1987-92, ICMH, N.Y., 1989—; ptnr. Balaban Assocs.; performer, dir. Adelphi Film Co.; cons. and speaker in field. Editor: (with others) Social Service Delivery Systems: An International Annual; Sophie Moses Robison; Twentieth Century Women, 1982; editor in chief Ency. of Social Work; mem. editorial bd. Smith Coll. Studies in Social Work, 1989—; contbr. articles to profl. jours. Bd. dirs. Nassau County Health and Welfare Coun., Huntington Hosp., N.Y., 1982, Community Advs., Great Neck, N.Y., Community Coun. of Greater N.Y., Young Adult Inst., 1982—; chair Joint Task Force on Labor Force Needs, NASW/Coun. Social Work Edn. Mem. AAUP, N.Y. State Assn. Deans of Schs. Social Work (pres. 1975), Nat. Assn. Social Workers, Acad. Cert. Social Workers, Acad. Polit. Sci., Council Social Work Edn., Phi Gamma Mu. Office: Adelphi U Earle Hall Rm 106 Garden City NY 11530

VIGNELLI, MASSIMO, architecture and design executive; b. Milan, Italy, Jan. 10, 1931; came to U.S., 1965; s. Ettore and Noemi (Guazzoni) V.; m. Lella Elena Valle, Sept. 15, 1957; children: Luca, Valentina. Student, Brera Acad. Art, Milan, 1948-50, Politecnico di Milano, 1950-53, U. Venice, 1953-57; DFA (hon.), Parsons Sch. Design, 1983, Pratt Inst., 1987, R.I. Sch. Design, 1988, Istituto Universitario di Architettura, Venice, 1994, Corcoran Sch. Art, 1994. Prin. Lella & Massimo Vignelli Office Design and Architecture, Milan, 1960-64; dir., sr. v.p. design Unimark Internat., Milan and N.Y.C., 1965-71; pres. Vignelli Assocs., N.Y.C., 1971—; chmn. Vignelli Designs, Inc., N.Y.C., 1978—. Retrospective shows include: Parsons Sch. Design, N.Y.C., 1980, Padiglione d'Arte Moderna, Milan, 1980, Acad. of Art USSR, Moscow and Leningrad, 1989, Helsinki, 1989, London, 1990, Budapest, Barcelona, 1991, Copenhagen, Munich, 1992, Prague, Paris, 1992-93; represented in permanent collections: Mus. Modern Art, N.Y.C., Cooper-Hewitt Mus., N.Y., Met. Mus. Art, N.Y., Die Neue Sammlung, Munich, Musée des Arts Décoratifs, Montreal, Tel Aviv Mus. Modern Art; designer: Heller stacking dinnerware, 1964, Heller glass bakeware, 1975, furniture for Sunar, 1979, Rosenthal, 1980, tableware for Sasaki Crystal, 1985, furniture for Knoll, 1985, furniture for Poltrona Frau, 1988, glassware for Steuben, 1993; interiors St. Peter's Ch., Citicorp Ctr., N.Y.C., 1975, Inst. Fine Arts, Mpls., 1974; corp. image Knoll Internat., 1966, Lancia, 1978, Ciga Hotels, 1979, Solomon R. Guggenheim Mus., 1992—, Am. Ctr. in Paris, 1994, COSMIT, Milan, 1994, Benetton Worldwide, 1995—; graphics Am. Airlines, 1967, Bloomingdales, 1972, books for Rizzoli Internat., 1980—; author: Knoll Design, 1981 (Am. Inst. Graphic Arts award 1982). Recipient Indsl. Arts medal AIA, 1973, Presdl. design award, 1985, Gold medal for design Nat. Arts Club, 1991, Fellowship of Excellence Interior Product Designers, 1992; named to Hall of Fame N.Y. Art Dirs. Club, 1982, Compasso d'Oro, 1964, Interior Design Hall of Fame, 1988. Mem. Am. Inst. Graphic Arts

(pres. 1976-77 Gold medal 1983), Indsl. Designers Soc. Am., Alliance Graphique Internationale (past pres.), Archtl. League N.Y. (v.p.). Office: Vignelli Assocs 475 10th Ave New York NY 10018-1120

VIGNIERI, CHARLES JOSEPH, meat packing co. exec.; b. Chgo., Oct. 7, 1924; s. Frank and Rosario (Saporito) V.; student pub. schs., Kenosha, Wis.; m. Lorraine Vander Warn, June 29, 1946; children—Allan, Susan, Dennis, Richard, Patricia, Joseph, Thomas, Daniel, Mark. With Frank Vignieri & Sons, Kenosha, 1936-54; with Kenosha Packing Co., 1954—, pres., 1960—; pres. Birchwood Meat & Provision, Inc., Kenosha, 1960—; dir. Kenosha Savs. & Loan Assn.; sec. Milw. Meat Council, 1965-67; guest lectr. Carthage Coll., Kenosha, 1970-75, bd. assos., 1970—. Co-chmn. March of Dimes Campaign, Kenosha, 1964; chmn. Paris-Kenosha County Plan Commn., 1965; co-founder, chmn. Kenosha Youth, Inc., 1968-70; bd. dirs. United Way, Kenosha, 1966-68, 72-75, campaign gen. chmn., 1972, pres., 1973-74; mem. adv. bd. Dominican Sisters of Bethany, Kenosha, 1963-71. Served with AUS, 1943-46; PTO. Mem. Kenosha C. of C. (dir. 1965-68), Nat. Meat Assn. (dir. 1965-77, v.p. central div. 1974-77, 1st v.p. 1978, chmn. 1980-82). Roman Catholic (trustee, treas. 1952-66, parish chmn. archbishops fund appeal 1952-66). Clubs: Elks, Rotary (dir. 1965-70, pres. 1967-68). Contbr. articles to profl. jours. Home: 4001 5th Pl Kenosha WI 53144-1032 Office: Kenosha Beef Internat Ltd 3111 152nd Ave Kenosha WI 53144

VIGNOLA, LEONARD ROBERT, foundation executive; b. S.I., N.Y., Oct. 12, 1937; s. Joseph and Aurora B. Vignola; m. Nancy Anne D'Aigle, Aug. 26, 1961; 1 child, Valerie. BS in Fin. and Acctg., Rutgers U., New Brunswick, N.J., 1962. CPA, N.J. Mgr. Price Waterhouse, N.Y.C., 1962-69; pres., CEO Leonard R. Vignola, C.P.A. Profl. Assn., N.Y.C., 1969-83; exec. v.p., treas./sec. Nat. Arts Stabilization Fund, N.Y.C., 1983-91, pres., CEO, 1991—; instr. MFA program Yale Sch. Drama, New Haven, 1979—. Mem. AICPAs, N.J. State Soc. CPAs, Morris/Sussex/Warren Chpt. of CPAs (pres. 1967-69). Episcopalian. Avocation: wines. Office: Natl. Arts Stabilization Fund 220 East 42 St Ste 1310 New York NY 10017

VIGNOLA, WILLIAM J., communications executive; b. N.Y.C., Feb. 12, 1943; s. Anthony J. and Anne R. (Ranno) V.; m. Christine Marie Cannata, July 10, 1965; children: William Jr., Michael, Richard. Diploma, H.F. Carey high sch., Franklin So. N.Y., 1961; BS in Maths, St. John's U., Jamaica, N.Y., 1965. Asst. prodns. mgr. Advt. Distbrs. Am., Hicksville, N.Y., 1965-68; prodns. mgr. Blair Mail Mktg., Farmingdale, N.Y., 1970-77; v.p. gen. mgr. Mailmen Inc., Hauppauge, N.Y., 1977—; chmn. L.I. P.C.C., N.Y., 1979—; dir. MASA N.Y. 1980—, MASA Internat., Bethesda Md. Chmn. Long Island Postal Customer Council 1984-85. With Army 1968-70. Mem. Mail Advt. Svc. Assn. N.Y. (dir. 1982—, 1st v.p. 1988—), Mail Advt. Svc. Assn. Internat. (dir. 1980—). Roman Catholic. Avocations: fishing, golf. Office: Mailmen Inc 15 Enter Ln Hauppauge NY 11788-4811

VIGNOLO, BIAGIO NICKOLAS, JR., chemical company executive; b. New Brunswick, N.J., June 15, 1947; s. Biagio and Helen (Carleo) V.; m. Olga Tkachuk, Mar. 23, 1974; children: Adam, John. BS in Acctg., Rider Coll., 1970. Mgr. acctg. staff Peat, Marwick & Mitchell Co., Trenton, N.J., 1969-77; controller Revlon Inc., N.Y.C., 1977-83; v.p., controller Am. Bakeries Co., N.Y.C., 1983-88; v.p. fin. Sun Chem. Corp., Ft. Lee, N.J., 1989—. Fellow Am. Inst. CPA's, N.J. Soc. CPA's. Republican. Roman Catholic. Office: Sun Chem Corp 222 Brg Plz S Fort Lee NJ 07024

VIGNONE, RONALD JOHN, advertising agency executive; b. Jersey City, Apr. 28, 1941; s. Ettore and Jeanette (Verga) V.; m. Ellen Marie Donelan, June 22, 1963; children: Susan, Ronald J. Jr.. BS, St. Peter's Coll., Jersey City, 1963. Copywriter Bamberger's, Newark, 1965-66, Ciba Pharm. Co., Summit, N.J., 1966-68; copywriter, supr. Robert A. Becker, Inc., N.Y.C., 1968-71; copy supr. William Douglas McAdams, Inc., N.Y.C., 1972-73, v.p. copy, 1973-74, v.p., account supr., 1976-78, sr. v.p., 1978-86, exec. v.p., 1986—. 1st lt. with U.S. Army, 1963-65. Mem. Pharm Advt. Coun. (bd. dirs.). Avocations: golf, classical music, opera, sports cars, computers. Office: William Douglas McAdams Inc 1740 Broadway New York NY 10019-4315

VIGTEL, GUDMUND, museum director emeritus; b. Jerusalem, July 9, 1925; came to U.S., 1948, naturalized, 1966; s. Arne Jonsen and Elisabeth (Petri) V.; m. Solveig Lund, 1951 (div. 1964); 1 child, Elisabeth; m. Carolyn Gates Smith, July 18, 1964; 1 child, Catherine Higdon. BFA, U. Ga., 1952, MFA, 1953; DFA (hon.), Atlanta Coll. Art, 1991. Adminstrv. asst. Corcoran Gallery Art, Washington, 1954-61, asst. dir., 1961-63; dir. High Mus. Art, Atlanta, 1963-91, dir. emeritus, 1991—. Contbr. articles and essays to profl. publs. Served with Royal Norwegian Air Force, 1944-45. Decorated Chevalier des Arts et Lettres, Minister of Culture (France); recipient Order of Merit First Class Fed. Republic Germany, 1989. Home: 2082 Golf View Dr NW Atlanta GA 30309-1210

VIJH, ASHOK KUMAR, chemistry educator, researcher; b. Multan, India (now Pakistan), Mar. 15, 1938; s. Bishamber Nath and Prem Lata (Bahl) V.; m. Danielle Blais (div.); 1 child, Aldous Ian. BSc with honors, Panjab U., India, 1960, MSc with honors, 1961; PhD, Ottawa U., 1966; LLD (hon.), Concordia U., 1988; DSc (hon.), Waterloo U., 1993. Group leader Inst. Research Hydro-Quebec, 1969-74, program leader, 1975-81, maitre-de-research, 1973—; vis. prof., thesis dir. INRS-Energie, U. Que., 1970—; Xerox lectr. U. Montreal, 1991. Author: Electrochemistry of Metals and Semiconductors, 1973; editor: Oxides and Oxide Films; mem. editorial bd. Applied Physics Communications, Internat. Jour. Hydrogen Energy, Materials Chemistry and Physics, also several other jours.; contbr. over 250 articles to profl. jours. Decorated officer Order of Can.; chevalier de Ordre Nationale de Quebec; knight Order of Malta; recipient Urgel Archambault medal Assn. Canadienne pour Advancement Scis., 1984, Commemorative medal 125th Anniversary Confederation Can., 1992. Fellow IEEE, Royal Soc. Chemistry, Chem. Inst. Can. (Noranda lectr. 1979, Palladium medal 1990), Inst. Physics (U.K.), Royal Soc. Can. (dir. applied scis. and engring. div. 1990, Acad. Sci., dir. math. and phys. sci. 1994—, Thomas W. Eadie medal 1989), Am. Phys. Soc., Third World Acad. Scis., Nat. Acad. Scis. India, Acad. Francophone d'Ingenieus (France; founding fellow 1993), Indian Nat. Sci. Acad. (fgn.); mem. European Acad. Arts, Scis. and Humanities (academician), Electrochem. Soc. (Lash Miller award 1973), Can. Com. Scientists and Scholars (exec. 1994), Can. Coun. (mem. Killam Awards com. 1994—, Izaak Walton Killam Meml. prize 1987), Materials Rsch. Soc. India (hon.). Office: Hydro-Quebec Research Inst, 1800 Montee Ste Julie, Varennes, PQ Canada J3X 1S1

VIKAN, GARY KENT, art museum administrator; b. Fosston, Minn., Nov. 30, 1946; s. Franklin and Wilma (Johnson) V.; m. Elana Klausner, Sept. 12, 1971; children: Nicole, Sonia. BA, Carleton U., 1967; MA, Princeton U., 1970, PhD, 1976. Art mus. administr., curator Byzantine art Dumbarton Oaks, Washington, 1975-84, Harvard U., 1985—. Woodrow Wilson Found. fellow, 1967-68. mem. Byzantine Studies Conf. (governing bd. 1989—), U.S. Nat. Com. for Byzantine Studies (exec. com. 1988-92. Office: Walters Art Gallery 6000 N Charles St Baltimore MD 21212

VIKEN, LINDA LEA MARGARET, lawyer; b. Sioux Falls, S.D., Oct. 27, 1945; d. Carl Thomas and Eleanor Bertha (Zehnpfennig) Crampton; m. Jerry Lee Miller, June 10, 1967 (div. 1975); m. Jeffrey Lynn Viken, Feb. 2, 1980. BS in Bus. Edn., U. S.D., 1967, JD in Law, 1977. Bar: S.D. 1978, U.S. Dist. Ct. S.D. 1978, U.S. Ct. Appeals (8th cir.) 1981. Tchr. Yankton (S.D.) High Sch., 1967-69, Edison Jr. High Sch., Sioux Falls, 1969-75; pvt. practice law Sioux Falls, 1978; ptnr. Finch, Viken, Viken, & Pechota, Rapid City, S.D., 1978-92, Viken, Viken, Pechota, Leach & Dewell, Rapid City, 1992—; part-time instr. Nat. Coll., Rapid City, 1978-80; magistrate judge Seventh Jud. Cir., Rapid City, 1983-84; chair S.D. Commn. on Child Support, 1985, 88; mem. S.D. Bd. of Bar Examiners, 1987-88. Contbr. articles to profl. jours. State rep. D.S. Legislature Minnehaha County, 1973-76, Pennington County, 1988-92; state party vice chair D.S. Dem. Party, 1978-80, 92-94; chair Pennington County Dem. Party, Rapid City, 1985-87. Named Woman Atty. of Yr. Law Sch. Women, 1987. Fellow Am. Acad. of Matrimonial Lawyers; mem. ABA, S.D. Assn., S.D. Trial Lawyers Assn. Democrat. Roman Catholic. Avocations: poetry, skiing. Home: 4760 Trout Ct Rapid City SD 57702-4751 Office: Viken Viken Pechota Leach and Dewell 1617 Sheridan Lake Rd Rapid City SD 57702-3483

VIKIS-FREIBERGS, VAIRA, psychologist, educator; b. Riga, Latvia, Dec. 1, 1937; d. Karlis and Annemarie (Rankis) V.; m. Imants F. Freibergs, July 16, 1960; children: Karlis Roberts, Indra Karoline. B.A., U. Toronto, 1958, M.A., 1960; Ph.D., McGill U., 1965; LLD, Queen's U., 1991. Clin. psychologist Toronto (Ont.) Psychiat. Hosp., 1960-61; asst. prof. dept. psychology U. Montreal, Que., Can., 1967-72; asso. prof. U. Montreal, 1972-77, prof., 1977—; pres. Social Sci. Fedn. Can., 1980; chmn. NATO (spl. program panel on human factors), 1980; dir. Latvian Youth Ethnic Heritage Seminars Divreizdivi, 1979; mem. Sci. Council Can., 1980-89, vice chmn., 1984-89. Author: Le Fréquence Lexicale au Quebec, 1974, The Amber Mountain, 1989, Against the Current, 1993; co-author: Latvian Sun Songs, 1988; editor: Linguistics and Poetics of Latvian Folk Songs, 1989; contbr. articles to profl. jours. Recipient Prof. A. Abele Meml. prize, 1979, Disting. Contbn. prize Montreal Free Latvians, 1989, Order of the Three Star, Republic of Latvia, 1995; Can. Coun. leave fellow, 1974-75; Killam Rsch. fellow Can. Coun., 1993-95. Fellow Can. Psychol. Assn. (pres. 1980), Royal Soc. Can. (Pierre Chauveau medal for disting. wk. in the humanities 1995); mem. Acad. Sci. Latvia (fgn.), Assn. Advancement Baltic Studies (pres. 1984-86), Assn. Canadienne Francaise pour l'Avancement des Scis. (Marcel-Vincent prize and medal 1992), Sigma Xi. Lutheran. Home: 444 Grenfell Ave, Town of Mount Royal, PQ Canada H3R 1G5 Office: U Montreal Dept Psych CP 6128, Succursale Centre-ville, Montreal, PQ Canada H3C 3J7

VIKLUND, WILLIAM EDWIN, banker; b. Bklyn., June 12, 1940; s. Edvin Oscar and Anna Ingegard (Kvarnstrom) V.; m. Joyce Eleanor Larson, Apr. 14, 1962; children—Mark William, David Andrew, Andrea Lynn. B.A., L.I. U., Bklyn., 1960. Vice-pres. Anchor Savs. Bank, Bklyn., 1966-72; sr. v.p. Bankers Trust Co., N.Y.C., 1972-80; pres. L.I. Savs. Bank, Melville, N.Y., 1980—. Contbr. articles to profl. jours. Bd. overseers Tilles Ctr., L.I. U., 1987—. Mem. N.Y. Real Estate Bd. Lutheran. Club: Westhampton (N.Y.) Country. Office: The Long Island Savs Bank 201 Old Country Rd Melville NY 11747-2725

VILA, ADIS MARIA, corporate executive, former government official, lawyer; b. Cuba, Aug. 1, 1953; came to U.S., 1962; d. Calixto Vila and Adis C. Fernandez. BA with distinction, Rollins Coll., 1974; JD with honors, U. Fla., 1978; LLM with high honors, Institut Universitaire de Hautes Estudes Internationales, Geneva, 1981. Bar: Fla. 1979, D.C. 1984. Assoc. Paul & Thomson, 1979-82; White House fellow Office Pub. Liaison, Washington, 1982-83; spl. asst. to sec. state for inter-Am. affairs Dept. State, Washington, 1983-86; dir. Office of Mex. and Caribbean Basin, Dept. Commerce, Washington, 1986-87; sec. Dept. Adminstrn., State of Fla., 1987-89; asst. sec. for adminstrn. USDA, Washington, 1989-91; vis. asst., prof. Fla. Internat. U., 1993-94; vis. fellow Nat. Def. U., Washington, 1992-93; v.p. internat. devel. The Vigoro Corp., Chgo., 1994—; trustee So. Center for Internat. Studies, 1987—. Bd. dirs. Rollings Coll. Alumni Coun., Winter Park, Fla., 1979—. Named one of 100 Most Influential Hispanics, 1988, Paul Harris fellow Rotary Internat., 1983, U.S.-Japan Leadership fellow, 1991-92, Eisenhower Exch. fellow, Beca Fiore, Argentina, 1992. Mem. Dade County Bar Assn. (bd. dirs. young and lawyers sect. 1979-87), Coun. Fgn. Rels., 1993— (term mem. 1987-92), Am. Coun. Young Polit. Leaders (bd. dirs. 1984—), Women Execs. in State Govt. (bd. dirs. 1987-89). Republican. Roman Catholic. Avocations: tennis, skiing, golf, theater, arts.

VILA, ROBERT JOSEPH, television host, designer, real estate developer; b. Miami, Fla., June 20, 1946; s. Roberto and Esperanza (Robles) V.; m. Diana Barrett, Oct. 3, 1975; children: Christopher, Monica, Susannah. AA in Architecture, Miami Dade Jr. Coll., 1966; BS in Journalism, U. Fla., 1969. Editor English Lang. Cons., Stuttgart, Fed. Republic of Germany, 1971; stagehand Wurttemburg State Theatre, Stuttgart, 1972; project mgr. Barrett Assocs., Boston, 1973-74; pres. R.J. Vila, Inc., Boston, 1975-85; host This Old House Sta. WGBH-TV, Boston, 1978-89; host Bob Vila's Home Again, Cape Cod and Chgo., 1990; host Plymouth, Mass., Naples, Fla., 1991—; host Martha's Vineyard and Naples, Malibu, Calif., 1991-92. Author: This Old House, 1980, Bob Vila's This Old House, 1982, Guide to Building Materials, 1986, Guide to Buying Your Dream House, 1990, Bob Vila's Tool Box, 1993, Bob Vila's Guide to Historic Homes of New England, 1993, Bob Vila's Guide to Historic Homes of the South, 1993, Bob Vila's Guide to Historic Homes of the Mid-Atlantic, 1993, Bob Vila's Workshop, 1994. Bd. dirs. Plimouth Plantation, Plymouth, Mass., Nat. Alliance to End Homelessness, Washington. Emmy award New England Region, 1979, Nat., 1985. Mem. Am. Fedn. TV Radio Artists, Screen Actors Guild, Oyster Harbors Club (Osterville, Mass.). Roman Catholic. Avocations: sailing, fishing, cycling, gardening, woodworking. Home: PO Box 749 Marstons Mills MA 02648-0749 Office: BVTV PO Box 749 Marstons Mills MA 02648-0749

VILARDEBO, ANGIE MARIE, management consultant, parochial school educator; b. Tampa, Fla., July 15, 1938; d. Vincent and Antonina (Fazio) Noto; m. Charles Kenneth Vilardebo, June 26, 1960; children: Charles, Kenneth, Michele, Melanie. B.A., Notre Dame Md., 1960; postgrad., Rollins Coll., 1960. Cert. tchr., Fla. Tchr. Sea Park Elem. Sch., Satellite Beach, Fla., 1960-61; office mgr. Computer Systems Enterprises, Satellite Beach, 1973-76; artist Satellite Beach, 1976-79; employment counselor Career Cons., Melbourne, Fla., 1979-80; tchr. Our Lady of Lourdes Parochial Sch., Melbourne 1980-89; pres. Consol. Ventures, Inc., Satellite Beach, 1989—. Versatile Suppliers, Inc., Satellite Beach, 1989—; prin. search com. Diocese of Orlando, Fla., 1989-90. Patentee personal grading machine. V.p. Jaycees, Satellite Beach, 1976-77, pres., 1977-78. Recipient 1st Place Art award Fla. Fedn. Woman's Clubs, 1978, 2nd Place Art award, 1979, Honorable Mention, 1980. Mem. Satellite Beach Woman's Club, Paper Chaser's Investment Club, Brevard Arts Ctr. & Mus., Space Coast Art League (social chmn. 1987—). Roman Catholic. Avocations: bridge, writing, reading, oil painting, entrepreneurship. Home: 606 Barcelona Ct Satellite Beach FL 32937

VILCEK, JAN TOMAS, medical educator; b. Bratislava, Czechoslovakia, June 17, 1933; came to U.S., 1965, naturalized, 1970.; s. Julius and Friderika (Fischer) V.; m. Marica F. Gerhath, July 28, 1962. MD, Comenius U., Bratislava, 1957; CSc (PhD), Czechoslovak Acad. Sci., Bratislava, 1962. Fellow Inst. Virology, Bratislava, 1957-62, head of lab., 1962-64; asst. prof. microbiology NYU Med. Ctr., N.Y.C., 1965-68, assoc. prof., 1968-73, prof., 1973—, head biol. response modifiers, 1983—; lectr. Chinese Acad. Med. Sci., Beijing, 1981, 83, Osaka U., 1987-88; chmn. nomenclature com. WHO, 1981-86, cons. biol. standardization com., 1982-88; mem. adv. com. Cancer Soc., 1981-87, chmn., 1983; expert French Ministry Health, 1983-88; mem. sci. adv. bd. Max Planck Inst., Munich, 1987—. Author: Interferon, 1969; editor in chief Jour. Archives of Virology, 1975-86; editor: Interferons and the Immune Systems, 1984, Tumor Necrosis Factor: Structure, Function and Mechanism of Action, 1991; mem. editorial bd. Virology, 1979-81, Archives of Virology, 1986-92, Infection and Immunity, 1983-85, Antiviral Research, 1984-88, Jour. Inteferon Rsch. 1980—, Jour. Immunological Methods, 1986—, Natural Immunity and Cell Growth Regulation, 1986-92, Jour. Immunology, 1987-89, Lymphokine Rsch., 1987—, Jour. Biol. Chemistry, 1988-90, ISI Atlas Sci. Immunology, 1988-89, Jour. Cellular Physiology, 1989—, Cytokine, 1989—, Biologicals, 1989—, Acta Virologica, 1991—, Internat. Archives of Allergy and Immunology, 1992—, Folia Biologica, 1993—, Cellular Immunology, 1993—, Circulatory Shock, 1994—; contbr. articles to profl. jours. Mem. rev. panel Israel Cancer Rsch. Fund, 1993—; mem. fellowship rev. com. Am. Heart Assn., 1992—. Recipient Rsch. Career Devel. award USPHS, 1968-73, Recognition award Japanese Inflammation Soc., 1989, Outstanding Investigator award Nat. Cancer Inst., NIH, 1991—; grantee USPHS, numerous other orgns. Mem. AAAS, Soc. Gen. Microbiology, Am. Soc. Microbiology, Am. Assn. Immunologists, Internat. Soc. Interferon Rsch., Czech Immunology Soc., Internat. Cytokine Soc., Czechoslovak Soc. for Microbiology. Office: NYU Med Ctr 550 1st Ave New York NY 10016-6497

VILIM, NANCY CATHERINE, advertising agency executive; b. Quincy, Mass., Jan. 15, 1952; d. John Robert and Rosemary (Malpede) V.; m. Geoffrey S. Horner, Feb. 16, 1992; children: Matthew Edward Cajda, Megan Catherine Cajda, Margaret Horner. Student, Miami U., Oxford, Ohio, 1970-72. Media asst. Draper Daniels, Inc., Chgo., 1972-74; asst. buyer Campbell Mithun, Chgo., 1974-75; buyer Tatham, Laird & Kudner, Chgo., 1975-77; media buyer Adcom, Inc. div. Quaker Oats Co., Chgo., 1977-79; media supr. G.M. Feldman, Chgo., 1979-81; v.p. media dir. Media Mgmt., 1981-83; v.p. broadcast dir. Bozell, Jacobs, Kenyon & Eckhardt, Chgo., 1983-88; v.p.,

media mgr. McCann-Erickson, Inc., 1989—; judge 27th Internat. Broadcast Awards, Chgo., 1987. mem. Berwyn (Ill.) Parents Assn., Inc., 1988. Recipient Media All Star awards Sound Mgmt. Mag., N.Y.C., 1987. Mem. Broadcast Advt. Club Chgo., Mus. Broadcast Communications, NAFE. Office: McCann-Erickson Inc 625 N Michigan Ave Chicago IL 60611-3110

VILLA, JACQUELINE I., newspaper editor; b. N.Y.C., Oct. 30, 1917; d. Thomas Charles and Ada Louise (Clementi) V. BA, Hofstra U. Reporter Newsday, Hempstead, N.Y., 1942, editor, 1942-47; editor L.I. Press, Jamaica, N.Y., 1951-58, night city editor, 1958-67, editl. editor, 1967-77; travel and food editor The Ariz. Daily Star, Tucson, 1977—. Mem. Ariz. Press Women (bd. dirs., sec., chairwoman So. chpt.). Office: The Ariz Daily Star PO Box 26807 4850 S Park Ave Tucson AZ 85726-6807

VILLABLANCA, JAIME ROLANDO, medical scientist, educator; b. Chillàn, Chile, Feb. 29, 1929; came to U.S., 1971; naturalized, 1985; s. Ernesto and Teresa (Hernàndez) V.; m. Guillermina Nieto, Dec. 3, 1955; children: Amparo C., Jaime G., Pablo J., Francis X., Claudio I. Bachelor in Biology, Nat. Inst. Chile, 1946; licentiate medicine, U. Chile, 1953, MD, 1954. Cert. neurophysiology. Rockefeller Found. postdoctoral fellow in physiology John Hopkins and Harvard Med. Schs., 1959-61; Fogarty internat. rsch. fellow in anatomy UCLA, 1966-68, assoc. research anatomist and psychiatrist, 1971-72, assoc. prof. psychiatry and biobehavioral scis., 1972-76, prof. psychiatry and biobehavioral scis., 1976—, prof. anatomy and cell biology, 1977—; mem. faculty U. Chile Sch. Medicine, 1954-71, prof. exptl. medicine, 1970-71; vis. prof. neurobiology Cath. U. Chile Sch. Medicine, 1974; cons. in field. Author over 200 rsch. papers, book chpts., abstracts; chief regional editor Developmental Brain Dysfunction, 1988—. Decorated Order Francisco de Miranda (Venezuela); recipient Premio Reina Sofia, Madrid, 1990; fellow Rockefeller Found., 1959-61, Fogarty Internat. Rsch. fellow NIH, 1966-68; grantee USAF Office Sci. Rsch., 1962-65, found. Fund Rsch. Psychiatry, 1969-72, USPHS-Nat. Inst. Child Human Devel., 1972—, USPHS-Nat. Inst. Drug Abuse, 1981-85, USPHS-Nat. Inst. Neurol. Disorders and Stroke, 1988-92. Mem. AAAS, AAUP, AVEPANE (internat. sic. com., Caracas, Venezuela), Am. Assn. Anatomists, Mental Retardation Rsch. Ctr., Brain Rsch. Inst., Internat. Brain Rsch. Orgn., Am. Physiol. Soc., Soc. Neurosci., Assn. Venezolana Padres de Niños Exepcionales, Sci. Coun. Internat. Inst. Rsch. and Advice in Mental Deficiency (Madrid), Sigma Xi. Home: 200 Surfview Dr Pacific Palisades CA 90272-2911 Office: UCLA Dept Psychiatry & Biobehavioral Scis. Los Angeles CA 90024

VILLAFRANCA, JOSEPH J., biochemistry educator; b. Silver Creek, N.Y., Mar. 23, 1944; s. Joseph Nicholas and Mildred (Dolce) C.; children: Jennifer, June. BS, SUNY, Fredonia, 1965; PhD, Purdue U., 1969. From asst. prof. to prof. Pa. State U., University Park, 1971-76, Evan Pugh prof. chemistry, 1986—; cons. Monsanto Corp., St. Louis, 1985-89, Eastman Kodak Co., Rochester, N.Y., 1985-87. Author 132 sci. pubis. Mem. Am. Chem. Soc. (councilor 1986-89), Am. Soc. for Biochemistry and Molecular Biology, Biophysical Soc. Avocation: skiing. Office: Bristol-Myers Squibb Pharm Res Inst PO Box 4000 Princeton NJ 08543*

VILLALOBOS, REYNALDO, cinematographers. Cinematographer: (films) Nine to Five, 1980, Urban Cowboy, 1980, The Ballad of Gregorio Cortez, 1983, Mike's Murder, 1984, Windy City, 1984, Blame It on Rio, 1984, Grandview, U.S.A., 1984, Saving Grace, 1986, Band of the Hand, 1986, Desert Bloom, 1986, Lucas, 1986, Punchline, 1988, Major League, 1989, Sibling Rivalry, 1990, Coupe de Ville, 1990, American Me, 1992, A Bronx Tale, 1992, PCU, 1993; dir.: (TV movies) Louis L'Amour's Conagher, 1991. Office: Am Soc of Cinematographers PO Box 2230 Los Angeles CA 90078*

VILLALOBOS PADILLA, FRANCISCO, bishop; b. Guadalajara, Mexico, Feb. 1, 1921. Ordained priest Roman Cath. Ch., 1949; named titular bishop of Colonnata, 1971; now bishop of Saltillo Mexico, 1975—. Office: Bishop's Residence, Obispado Apartado 25, Saltillo Coahuila, Mexico also: Hidalgo Sur 166, Apartado 25 CP25000, Saltillo Mexico Coahuila

VILLANI, KEVIN EMIL, banker; b. Boston, Apr. 16, 1948; s. Edmund Vincent and Alice Louise (Maloof) V.; m. Jane Elizabeth Flynn, Dec. 23, 1967; children: David, Brian, Patrick. BS in Math., U. Mass., 1970; MA in Econs., Purdue U., 1971, PhD in Econs. and Fin., 1974. Dep. asst. sec., chief economist HUD, Washington, 1979-82; sr. v.p., chief economist Fed. Home Loan Mortgage Corp., Washington, 1982-85; fin. officer Imperial Corp. Am., San Diego, 1985— Author approx. 100 books and articles; editor-in-chief (mag.) Secondary Mortgage Markets, 1983-85; co-editor (mag.) Housing Fin. Rev. Recipient service awards, HUD, 1979-82. Mem. Am. Real Estate & Urban Econs. Assn. (program chmn. 198-84, 1st v.p. 1985, pres-elect, bd. dirs. 1985,), Am. Econ. Assn., Am. Fin. Assn., Krannert Alumni Assn. Avocations: water and snow skiing. Office: Imperial Corp Am 8787 Complex Dr San Diego CA 92123-1401

VILLAREAL, DEWEY R., lawyer; b. Atlanta, June 9, 1926; s. Dewey R. and Cadie Belle (Adams) V.; m. Jean Bates; children: Warren, Holly. Student, USCG Acad., 1944-46; JD, U. Fla., 1957. Bar: Fla., U.S Ct. Appeals (5th, 6th and 11th cirs.), U.S. Supreme Ct. Assoc. Fowler, White, Gillen, Boggs, Villareal & Banker, P.A., Tampa, Fla., 1957—, chmn. bd. dirs., 1987-92; towing safety adv. com. Hdqs. USCG, 1990-92; adj. instr. maritime law Stetson Coll., St. Petersburg, Fla., 1981—. Contbr. articles to profl. jours. Lt. USN, 1951-53. Mem. Maritime Law Assn. of U.S. (bills of lading com. 1962—, vice chmn. 1977-82, chmn. 1982-84, exec. com. 1973-76, chmn. maritime products liability com. 1988-92). Office: Fowler White Gillen Boggs Villareal & Banker PA 501 E Kennedy Blvd Fl 1700 Tampa FL 33602-4988

VILLARONGA, RAUL G., mayor, realtor; b. Ponce, Puerto Rico, Apr. 1, 1938; s. Raul Gil and Maria M. (Martinez) V.; m. Julia M. Bush, Dec. 25, 1958; children: Raul, Rafael, Robert. BS in Indsl. Engring., Tex. A&M Coll., 1959; MS in Indsl. Engring., Tex. Tech U., 1973. Cert. realtor, logistician. Officer U.S. Army, 1959-85; mgr. Office Tex. Atty. Gen., Austin, 1989-94; realtor Realty World-Hill Country, Killeen, Tex., 1994—; cons. Brown & Root, Houston, 1987-89; hon. chmn. Sister Cities-Killeen, 1993—. Author: Evaluation of ILS Programs, 1983, City of Killeen Tax Abatement Policy, 1991. Active NAACP, Killeen, 1989, League United Latin Am. Citizens, Killeen, 1993—; mem. coun. City of Killeen, 1989-91, mayor, 1992—. Decorated Silver Star, Bronze Star, Air medal, Legion of Merit; named Vet. of Yr., Ft. Hood Area Vets. Com., 1992. Mem. VFW, DAV (life), Am. Legion, Ft. Hood Area Bd. Realtors, Ret. Officers Assn., Mil. Affairs Com., Assn. U.S. Army, KC. Roman Catholic. Avocations: personal computers, desk-top publishing. Home: 602 Trout Cove Killeen TX 76542 Office: Office of the Mayor PO Box 1329 Killeen TX 76540-1329

VILLAR-PALASI, CARLOS, pharmacology educator; b. Valencia, Spain, Mar. 3, 1928; came to U.S., 1963; s. Vicente Villar Bolinaga and Teresa (Palasi-Pinazo); m. Amparo Gosalvez-Sobrino, Aug. 17, 1957 (dec. July 1978); children: Victor, Carlos, Juan Jose, María Amparo. MS in Chemistry, U. Valencia, Spain, 1951; PhD in Biochemistry, U. Madrid, Spain, 1955; MS in Pharmacy, U. Barcelona, Spain, 1962. Rsch. fellow med. sch. U. Hamburg, Fed. Republic of Germany, 1953-54, Spanish Rsch. Coun., Madrid, 1954-57, Case Western Res. U., Cleve., 1960-63; rsch. assoc. Spanish Rsch. Coun., Madrid, 1960-63, Case Western Res. U., Cleve., 1963-64; rsch. assoc. U. Minn., Mpls., 1964-65, asst. prof., 1965-69; assoc. prof. U. Va., Charlottesville, 1969-72 prof., 1972—; invited speaker Fedn. European Biochem. Soc., 1969. March Found. fellow, 1957; recipient Rsch. award Cleve. Diabetes Found., 1960, NIH, 1967-69. Mem. AAAS (Rsch. award 1960-62), Am. Soc. Pharmacology, Am. Soc. Biol. Chemistry. Roman Catholic. Avocations: horse riding, camping. Home: PO Box 101 Ivy VA 22945-0101 Office: U Va Med Sch Dept Pharmacology 1300 Jefferson Park Ave Charlottesville VA 22908-0001

VILLARREAL, CARLOS CASTANEDA, engineering executive; b. Brownsville, Tex., Nov. 9, 1924; s. Jesus Jose and Elisa L. (Castaneda) V.; m. Doris Ann Akers, Sept. 10, 1948; children: Timothy Hill, David Akers. BA, U.S. Naval Acad., 1948; MS, U.S. Navy Postgrad. Sch., 1950; LLD (hon.), St. Mary's U., 1972. Registered profl. engr. Commd. ensign U.S. Navy, 1948, advanced through grades to lt., 1956; comdg. officer U.S.S. Rhea, 1951, U.S.S Osprey, 1952; comdr. Mine Div. 31, 1953; resigned, 1956; mgr. marine

and indsl. operation Gen. Electric Co., 1956-66; v.p. mktg. and adminstrn. Marquardt Corp., 1966-69; head Urban Mass Transit Adminstrn., Dept. Transp., Washington, 1969-73; commr. Postal Rate Commn., 1973-79, vice chmn., 1975-79; v.p. Washington ops. Wilbur Smith and Assocs., 1979-84, sr. v.p., 1984-86, exec. v.p., 1987—, also bd. dirs.; lectr. in field; mem. industry sector adv. com. Dept. Commerce; mem. sect. 13 adv. com. Dept. Transp., 1983-86. Contbr. to profl. jours. Mem. devel. com. Wolftrap Farm Park for the Performing Arts, 1973-78; mem. council St. Elizabeth Ch., 1982-86, chmn. fin. com.; mem. bd. elin. St. Elizabeth Sch.; bd. dirs. Assoc. Catholic Charities, 1983-86; mem. fin. com. Cath. Charities, U.S.A. Decorated knight Sovereign Mil. Hospitaller Order St. John of Jerusalem of Rhodes and Malta, 1981; recipient award outstanding achievement Dept. Transp. Fellow ASCE, Am. Cons. Engrs. Coun. (vice chmn. internat. com.); mem. IEEE, NSPE (pres. D.C. soc. 1986-87, bd. dirs. 1988-91), Am. Pub. Transit Assn., Soc. Naval Architects and Marine Engrs., Soc. Am. Mil. Engrs., Am. Rds. and Transp. Builders Assn. (chmn. pub. transp. adv. coun.), Transp. Rsch. Bd., Washington Soc. Engrs., Internat. Bridge, Tunnel and Turnpike Assn., Inst. Traffic Engrs., Intelligent Transp. Soc. Am. (chmn. fin. com., bd. dirs.), Univ. Club, Army-Navy Club. Republican. Roman Catholic. Office: Wilbur Smith Assocs 2921 Telestar Ct Falls Church VA 22042

VILLARREAL, HOMERO ATENÓGENES, human resources executive; b. McAllen, Tex., June 13, 1946; s. Atenógenes Alejandro and Estella Marie (Lopez) V.; m. Lynne Carol Kastrup, Sept. 20, 1980; children: Alissa Lynne, Ashley Cameron, Ana Victoria. BBA, U. Houston, 1969. Asst. mgr. manpower internat. div. Mobil Corp., N.Y.C., 1974-77; dir. adminstrn. CBS Inc., 1977-80; mgr. internat. human resources AT&T Inc., Basking Ridge, N.J., 1981-89; v.p. HR Cadbury-Schweppes Inc., Stamford, Conn., 1989—; v.p. AIESEC-Houston, 1967-69. Served with U.S. Army, 1969-72. Mem. Am. Compensation Assn., Soc. Human Resources Mgmt. Republican. Presbyterian. Office: Cadbury-Schweppes Inc 6 High Ridge Park Stamford CT 06905-1327

VILLARS, FELIX MARC HERMANN, physicist, educator; b. Biel, Switzerland, Jan. 6, 1921; came to U.S., 1949, naturalized, 1955; s. Jean Felix and Alma (Engel) V.; m. Jacqueline Dubois, June 25, 1949; children: J. Frederic, Cecile, Monique, Philippe. Diplome, Swiss Fed. Inst. Tech., Zurich, 1945, D.Sc.Nat., 1946. Research asst. Swiss Fed. Inst. Tech., 1946-49; vis. mem. Inst. Advanced Study at Princeton, 1949-50; research assoc. MIT, 1950-52, asst. prof. physics, 1952-55, assoc. prof., 1955-60, prof., 1960-91, prof. emeritus, sr. lectr., 1991—; lectr. biophysics Harvard Med. Sch., 1974—. Served with Swiss Army, 1940-45. Fellow Am. Acad. Arts and Scis., AAAS; mem. Am. Phys. Soc., N.Y. Acad. Sci. Home: 55 Orchard St Belmont MA 02178-3008 Office: Ctr for Theoretical Physics MIT 77 Massachusetts Ave Cambridge MA 02139-4307

VILLAVASO, STEPHEN DONALD, urban planner, lawyer; b. New Orleans, July 12, 1949; s. Donald Philip and Jacklyn (Tully) V.; m. Regina Smith, Apr. 17, 1971; children: Christine Regina, Stephen Warner. BS in Econs., U. New Orleans, 1971, M in Urban and Regional Planning, 1976; JD, Loyola U., New Orleans, 1981. Bar: La. 1982; recognized ct. expert in land use, planning and zoning. Urban and regional planner Barnard & Thomas, New Orleans, 1976-78; dir. analysis and planning City of New Orleans, 1978-81, counsel for planning and devel., 1983-84; dir. planning and environ. affairs Tecon Realty, New Orleans, 1981-83; v.p. for planning and project mgmt. Morphy, Makofsky, Mumphrey & Masson, New Orleans, 1984-89; project devel. mgr. Waste Mgmt. N.Am., Inc., New Orleans, 1989—; bd. dirs. Regional Loan Corp.; guest lectr., adj. prof. Coll. of Urban and Pub. Affairs, U. New Orleans, 1976—; spl. instr. grad. studies in urban planning So. U. New Orleans, 1987—. Bd. dirs. New Orleans Traffic and Transp. Bur., 1981-86, Riverfront Awareness, New Orleans, 1984-86, Vols. Am. Greater New Orleans, 1987—, vice chmn., 1990, chmn. bd., 1992. With USN, 1971-74. Named one of Outstanding Young Men of Am., 1980, 82. Mem. ABA, Am. Inst. of Cert. Planners, Am. Planning Assn. (pres. La. div. 1980-84, disting. svc. award 1985), Urban Land Inst., La. Bar Assn., U. New Orleans Alumni Assn. (bd. dirs. 1990—), Phi Kappa Phi, Delta Sigma Pi (pres. 1971), Omicron Delta Kappa. Democrat. Roman Catholic. Avocations: philately, camping, travel, road racing. Home: 6304 Beauregard Ave New Orleans LA 70124-4502

VILLEE, CLAUDE ALVIN, JR., biochemistry educator; b. Lancaster, Pa., Feb. 9, 1917; s. Claude Alvin and Mary Elizabeth (Nestel) V.; m. Dorothy Theresa Balzer, Jan. 21, 1952; children: Claude Alvin III, Stephen Eric Fortney, Suzanne Villee, Charles Andrew. BS, Franklin and Marshall Coll., 1937; PhD, U. Calif.-Berkeley, 1941; AM (hon.), Harvard U., 1957; ScD (hon.), Franklin and Marshall Coll., 1991. Research fellow U. Calif. at Berkeley, 1941-42; asst. prof. U. N.C., 1942-45; mem. faculty Harvard, 1946—, prof. biol. chemistry, 1962-63, Andelot prof. biol. chemistry, 1964—; fellow Winthrop House, 1957—; tech. aide Nat. Acad. Scis., 1946-87; research assoc. Boston Lying in Hosp., 1950-66; dir. lab. reproductive biology Boston Hosp., 1966—; disting. vis. prof. U. Belgrade, Yugoslavia, 1974, 77; vis. prof. Mahidol U., Bangkok, Thailand, 1974; cons. NSF, Ford Found., Nat. Found./March of Dimes; mem. nat. adv. child health and human devel. council NIH; pres. Internat. Symposium Foeto-Placental unit, Milan, 1968. Author: Biology, 10th edit, 1993, General Zoology, 6th edit, 1984, Fallout from the Population Explosion, 1986, Metabolism, 1985, Introduction to Animal Biology, 1979, Control of Ovulation, 1961, Mechanism of Action of Steroid Hormones, 1960, The Placenta and Fetal Membranes, 1960, Gestation, Vols. 2-5, 1955-58, Respiratory Distress Syndrome, 1973, Biological Principles and Processes, 1976, The Placenta: A Neglected Experimental Animal, 1979, Human Reproduction, 1981, PDQ Biochemistry, 1986; mem. editorial bd. Paragon House Pus., 1984—; contbr. articles to profl. jours. Trustee Forsythe Dental Center, Boston, Winsor Sch.; trustee, v.p. Internat. Found. for Biochem. Endocrinology, 1980—; bd. dirs. Moors Assn., Falmouth, Mass. Lalor fellow, 1946-47; Guggenheim fellow, 1949-50; recipient Ciba award, 1956, Rubin award, 1957. Fellow Am. Acad. Arts and Scis., Am. Gynecol. Soc. (hon.), Am. Coll. Obstetrics and Gynecology (hon.), Soc. for Gynecol. Investigation (hon.), Serbian Acad. Arts and Scis. (hon.); mem. Moors Assn. Falmouth (pres.), Am. Soc. Biol. Chemists, Endocrine Soc. Am., Biochem. Soc. (Eng.), Am. Chem. Soc., Soc. Devel. Biology, Marine Biol. Lab. (Woods Hole, Mass.). Home: 485 Elm Rd Falmouth MA 02540-2414 Office: 25 Shattuck St Boston MA 02115-6092

VILLELLA, EDWARD JOSEPH, ballet dancer, choreographer, artistic director; b. L.I., N.Y., Oct. 1, 1936; s. Joseph and Mildred (DeGiovanni) V.; m. Janet Greschler (div. Nov. 1980); 1 child, Roddy; m. Linda Carbonetta, Apr. 1981; children: Christa Francesca, Lauren. BS in Marine Transp., N.Y. State Maritime Coll., 1957; LHD (hon.), Boston Conservatory, 1985; hon. degree, Skidmore Coll., Fordham U., Nazareth Coll., Siena Coll., Union Coll., Schenectady, N.Y., 1991. Mem. N.Y.C. Ballet, 1957, soloist, 1958-60, prin. soloist, 1960-83; artistic dir. Ballet Okla., Oklahoma City, 1983-86; founding artistic dir. Miami (Fla.) City Ballet, 1985—; Heritage chair in arts and cultural criticism George Mason U., Fairfax, Va., 1992-93, 93-94; vis. artist U.S. Mil. Acad. at West Point, 1981-82; vis. prof. dance U. Iowa, 1981; Heritage Chair Arts and Cultural Criticism, George Mason U., 1992-94; lectr. in field. Performed dances in Symphony C, Scotch Symphony, Western Symphony, Donizetti Variations, Swan Lake, La Source, The Nutcraker, Agon, Stars and Stripes, The Prodigal Son; premiered in Balanchine works including The Figure in the Carpet, 1960, Electronics, 1961, A Midsummer Night's Dream, 1962, Bugaku, 1963, Tarantella, 1964, Harlequinade, 1965, The Brahms-Schoenberg Quartet, 1966, Jewels, 1967, Symphony in Three Movements, 1972, Schéhérazade, 1975; choreography includes Narkissas, 1966, Shostakovitch Ballet Suite, 1972, Gayane Pas de Deux, 1972, Salute to Cole, 1973, Sea Chanties, 1974, Prelude, Riffs and Fugues, 1980; TV appearances include The Ed Sullivan Show, Bell Telephone Hour, Mike Douglas Show, (TV spl.) Harlequin, 1975 (Emmy award), summer theaters, festivals, U.S. and abroad, 1957—; co-author: (autobiography) Prodigal Son, 1991. Mem. Nat. Coun. of Arts, 1968-74; chmn. Commn. for Cultural Affairs City N.Y., 1978; bd. visitors N.C Sch. for the Arts; mem. dance adv. panel Nat. Endowment for Arts; trustee Wolf Trap Found. for the Arts. Recipient Dance Mag. award, 1964, Lions of the Performing Arts award N.Y. Pub. Libr., 1987, Capezio Dance award, 1989, Gold medal Nat. Soc. Arts and Letters, 1990, William G. Anderson Merit Award, Am. Alliance for Health, Physical Educ., Recreation, and Dance, 1991.

VILLENEUVE, DONALD AVILA, biology educator; b. Ventura, Calif., Oct. 25, 1930; s. Victor Fredrick V.; and Florence Ann (Pelletier) Goodin; m. Marylyn Yvonne Peoples, Jan. 7, 1950; children: Debra Lynn, Theresa Dianne, Karen Elaine, Kathryn Anne. BS, U. Idaho, 1958; MS, Univ. of Pacific, 1960; MA, U. Colo., 1967; PhD, UCLA, 1976. Cert. tchr., Calif., cert. community coll. tchr., adminstr. Biology tchr. Glendora (Calif.) High Sch., 1960-61; prof. biology and environ. sci. Ventura Coll., 1961-76; dir. div. math. and sci. Moorpark (Calif.) Coll., 1976-78; asst. prof. biol. sci. Calif. Poly. U., San Luis Obispo, Calif., 1978; prof. biology and environ. sci. Ventura Coll., 1978-92 (ret.); pres. acad. senate Ventura Coll., 1985-87; bd. dirs. Calif. Acad. Partnership Program, Long Beach, 1985-88; curriculum cons. Calif. State Dept. Edn., Sacramento, 1986-87; mem. sci. tchr. preparatory panel Calif. Commn. on Tchr. Credentialing, Sacramento, 1988-93. Mem. City Coun. City of San Buenaventura, Ventura, 1987-91; mem. Calif. Coastal Commn., Santa Barbara, 1977-81; mem. planning commn. City of San Buenaventura, 1975-77, parks and recreation commn., 1974-75; v.p. Ventura County Symphony Assn., 1969-71; bd. dirs. Beach Erosion Authority, 1987-91, League for Coastal Protection, 1985—, League Calif. Cities, 1987-91; mem. Ventura County Ctr. Planned Parenthood Adv. Coun., 1991-94; treas. Cambria Dem. Club; mem. San Luis Obispo County Dem. Ctrl. Com.; co-chmn. Cambria Friends of the Ranchland. Sgt. U.S. Army, 1950-53. NIMH grantee, 1971-72. Mem. Faculty Assn. Calif. Community Colls., Calif. Fedn. Tchrs. (bd. dirs. 1985-87), Lincoln Continental Owners Club, Volvo Sports Am. Avocations: fishing, camping, hiking, boating, collecting antique automobiles. Home: 394 Orlando Dr Cambria CA 93428

VILLENEUVE, JEAN-PIERRE, science association director, educator; b. Roberval, Que., Can., May 19, 1938; s. Pascal and Simone (Duval) V.; m. Céline Laroche, Feb. 9, 1962 (div.); children: Isabelle, Elise; m. Christiane Marcoux, Oct. 9, 1979. BScA in Civil Engring., U. Laval, Que., 1963; DES in Hydrodynamics, U. Toulouse, France, 1964, PhD in Hydraulics, 1966. Project engr. Natural Resources Can., Que., 1967; jr. lectr. U. Sherbrooke, Can., 1968-69, U. Que. è Chicoutimi, 1969-70; prof. U. Laval, 1966-70; prof. INRS-Eau, Ste. Foy, Que., 1970—, dir., 1990; pres. bd. dirs. Revue des Scis. de l'Eau, Que. and France, 1995, sci. dir., 1988-94. Contbr. numerous articles to profl. publs. Recipient prize for sci. excellence SNC Lavallin-AQTE, 1994. Mem. Am. Geophys. Union (mem. network design com. 1976-87), Club Tennis Montcalm (pres. 1984—). Achievements include development of software in field. Office: INRS-Eau, 2800 rue Einstein Ste 020, Quebec, PQ Canada G1X 4N8

VILLERS, PHILIPPE, mechanical engineer; b. Paris, June 20, 1935; came to U.S., 1940, naturalized, 1946; s. Raymond and Garda (Schmidt) V.; m. Annie Louise Young, July 13, 1957 (div. 1973); children: Jocelyn Anne (dec.), Renata Jane; m. Katherine Stephan, 1973; children: Noel Stephan, Carolyn Grace. AB in Applied Scis. cum laude, Harvard U., 1955; SM in Mech. Engring. Mass. Inst. Tech., 1960. Mem. mfg. tng. program Gen. Electric Co., 1955-58; project engr. Perkin-Elmer Corp., Wilton, Conn., 1959-62; project engr. Apollo Antenna pointings sensor Barnes Engring. Co., Stamford, Conn., 1962-65; project mgr. Advanced Products Center, Link Group, Gen. Precision, Inc., Binghamton, N.Y., 1965-67; mgr. advanced products Concord Control, Inc., Boston, 1967-69; co-founder, sr. v.p., dir. Computervision Corp., Bedford, Mass., 1969-80; founder, pres., dir. Automatix, Inc., Billerica, Mass., 1980-84; chmn. bd. Automatix Inc., Billerica, Mass., 1984-86; founder, pres., dir. Cognition Inc., 1985-88; bd. dirs. Xyvision, Inc., Wakefield, Mass., 1992-94; bd. dirs. Conflict Mgmt. Group, Cambridge, Mass., Energia Global, Wakefield. Patentee process welding aluminum liners to steel surfaces, horizon sensor for visible wavelength, infrared roughness testing instrument, improved thermopile constrn. thermal die marker; pioneer design and feasibility solar sail applications for interplanetary probe propulsion and stblzn. Mem. Dem. Town Com., Wilton, Conn., 1963, Concord, Mass., 1978—, chmn., 1984—; mem. Harvard Com. on Univ. Resources, 1982-92; mem. various vis. coms. MIT, 1981-91; mem. vis. com. Nat. Bur. Standards, 1981-84; trustee U. Lowell, 1985-91; founder, pres. Families U.S.A. Founds. (formerly Villers Found.), Washington, 1981—, Bay State Retiree Vol. Coun., Concord, 1989-92; del. Dem. Nat. Conv., 1988, 92. NSF grad. fellow, 1959-60. Mem. IEEE, ASME, Amnesty Internat. (bd. dirs. 1990—), ombudsman 1992-94, exec. com. 1994—), Soc. Mfg. Engrs., ACLU (pres. com. 1981—), bd. dirs. Physicians for Human Rights 1991-94), Unitarian-Universalist Assn. (pres. coun. 1982-86), Sigma Xi. Home: 20 Whits End Rd Concord MA 01742-5411 Office: 97 Lowell Rd Ste 11-4 Concord MA 01742-1700

VILLFORTH, JOHN CARL, health physicist; b. Reading, Pa., Dec. 28, 1930; s. Carl and Grace L. (Fichthorn) V.; m. Joanne E. Heine, Sept. 12, 1953; children: Mary Jane Smith, Elaine, Jennifer. B.S. in San. Engring., Pa. State U., 1952, M.S., 1954; M.S. in Physics, Vanderbilt U., 1958. Cert. Am. Bd. Health Physics. With USPHS, 1961-90; dir. Ctr. for Devices and Radiol. Health, 1969-90, asst. surgeon gen., 1972-90, chief engr., 1985-89; pres. Food and Drug Law Inst., Washington, 1990—. Served to capt. USAF, 1954-61. Recipient Meritorious Svc. medal USPHS, 1974, D.S.M., 1980, 84, Outstanding Svc. medal, 1986. Mem. Health Physics Soc. (pres. 1976-77, Elda Anderson award 1970), Am. Soc. Quality Control, AAAS, Internat. Radiation Protection Assn., Regulatory Affairs Profl. Soc., Commd. Officers Assn. Office: 1000 Vermont Ave NW Washington DC 20005-4903

VILLINSKI, PAUL STEPHEN, artist; b. York, Maine, May 28, 1960; s. Paul Bernard and Jacqueline L. (Whalen) V. Student, Mass. Coll. Art, 1980-82; BFA, Cooper Union, 1984. adj. lectr. art history LaGuardia C.C., CUNY, L.I. City, 1990-93. Solo exhbns. include St. Peter's Ch. at Citicorp Ctr., N.Y.C., 1987, Midtown Payson Galleries, N.Y.C., 1989, Queens Mus. Art at Bulova Corp. Ctr., Jackson Heights, N.Y., 1990; group shows include Ridge St. Gallery, N.Y.C., 1986, 87, Queens Mus. Art, Flushing, N.Y., 1987, Studio K Gallery, L.I., N.Y., 1987, 88, Midtown Payson Galleries 1988, 89, The Barn Gallery, Ogunquit, Maine, 1990, PS Gallery, Ogunquit, 1991, 92, DMB&B, N.Y.C., 1991, Cooper Union, N.Y.C., 1992, Nat. Acad. Design, N.Y.C., 1992, Paine Webber Art Gallery, N.Y.C., 1992, Fuel Gallery, Seattle, 1992, Herron Test-Site, Blkyn., 1992, Jamaica (N.Y.) Arts Ctr., 1992, 80 Washington Square Galleries, N.Y.C., NYU, 1993, Blkyn. Union Gas Co. Cmty. Galleries, 1993, PDG Gallery, 1993, Flushing Coun. on Culture and Arts Town Hall, 1994; represented in permanent collections. Resident Millay Colony for Arts, Austerlitz, N.Y., 1987; grantee Nat. Endowment Arts, 1987; Agnes Bourne fellow in painting Djerassi Found., Woodside, Calif., 1988, fellow Montalvo Ctr. for the Arts, Saratoga, Calif., 1991, fellow Ucross Found., 1992. Home: 9-01 44th Dr Long Island City NY 11101

VILNROTTER, VICTOR ALPÁR, research engineer; b. Kunhegyes, Hungary, Nov. 8, 1944; came to U.S., 1957; s. Nicholas and Aranka (Vidovits) V.; m. Felicia D'Auria, Jan. 20, 1974; children: Katherine, Brian. BSEE, NYU, 1971; MS, MIT, 1974; PhD in EE, U. So. Calif., L.A., 1978. Teaching asst. MIT, Cambridge, Mass., 1972-74; rsch. engr. Jet Propulsion Lab., Pasadena, Calif., 1979—. Contbr. articles to profl. jours.; patentee in field. Mem. IEEE (referee in communications soc. 1980—), N.Y. Acad. Scis., Sigma Xi, Eta Kappa Nu. Achievements include development and demonstration of real-time array-feed antenna compensation system for future deep-space missions. Avocations: astronomy, chess, hiking, backpacking, music. Home: 1334 Greenbriar Rd Glendale CA 91207-1254

VILTER, RICHARD WILLIAM, physician, educator; b. Cin., Mar. 21, 1911; s. William Frederick and Clara (Bieler) V.; m. Sue Potter, Aug. 17, 1935; 1 son, Richard William. A.B., Harvard U., 1933, M.D., 1937. Diplomate: Am. Bd. Internal Medicine. Intern, resident internal medicine Cin. Gen. Hosp., 1937-42, founding dir. divsn. hematology/oncology, 1945-56, asst. dir. dept. internal medicine, 1953-56, dir., 1956-78; assoc. prof. medicine U. Cin. Coll. Medicine, 1948-56, Gordon and Helen Hughes Taylor prof., 1956-78, prof. medicine on spl. assignment 1978-81, prof. medicine emeritus, 1981—, asst. dean, 1945-51; cons. VA, 1947—; cons. hematology Good Samaritan Hosp., Cin.; cons. physician Christ, Drake hosps., Cin.; mem. sci adv. bd. Nat. Vitamin Found, 1953-56; spl. cons. nutrition and anemias in Egypt WHO, 1954; cons. Pan Am. Sanitary Bur. Anemias of Kashiorkor in Guatemala and Panama, 1955; mem. Am. Cancer Soc. Com. on Investigation and Therapy of Cancer, 1960-64, chmn. 1964; chmn. hematology sect. NIH, 1965-69, nat. adv. com. anemia malnutrition Rsch. Ctr. Chiengmai, Thailand, 1967-75. Assoc. editor Jour. Clin. Investigation 1951-52; contbr. to profl. publs. Recipient Joseph Goldberger award AMA,

1960, Daniel Drake medal U. Cin., 1985, Golden Apple award U. Cin., 1985, award for excellence U. Cin., 1990, Daniel Drake Humanitarian award Acad. Medicine, Cin., 1991. Master ACP (past gov. Ohio bd. regents, sec. gen. 1973-78, pres.-elect 1978-79, pres. 1979-80, pres. emeritus 1984); mem. Federated Coun. for Internal Medicine (chmn. 1979-80), Clin. and Climatol. Assn. (v.p. 1982-83), Assn. Am. Physicians, Am. Soc. Clin. Nutrition (pres. 1960-61), Am. Soc. Clin. Investigation, Ctrl. Soc. Clin. Rsch. (coun. mem. 1957-60), Am. Soc. Hematology, Am. Bd. Nutrition, Internat. Soc. Hematology, Cin. Lit. Club (pres. 1990-91), Phi Beta Kappa, Alpha Omega Alpha, Nu Sigma Nu. Home: 5 Annwood Ln Cincinnati OH 45206-1419 Office: U Cin Med Center Cincinnati OH 45267-0562

VINCE, CLINTON ANDREW, lawyer; b. Bklyn., May 31, 1949; s. Tibor Andrew and Priscilla (Ward) V.; m. Pamela Anne McHale, May 17, 1980; children: Matthew McHale, Jennifer Anne. AB, Trinity Coll., 1971; JD, Georgetown U., 1974. Bar: N.Y. 1975, U.S. Dist. Ct. (so. and ea. dists.) N.Y. 1975, U.S. Ct. Appeals (2nd cir.) 1975, D.C. 1976, U.S. Dist. Ct. D.C. 1976, U.S. Ct. Appeals (D.C. and 8th cirs.) 1976, U.S. Supreme Ct. 1979, U.S. Ct. Appeals (4th and 11th cirs.) 1984, U.S. Ct. Appeals (5th cir.) 1985, U.S. Ct. Appeals (10th cir.) 1988. Ptnr. Verner, Liipfert, Bernhard, McPherson & Hand, Washington, 1984—, also bd. dirs., exec. com.; chief energy cons. City of New Orleans 1983—; gen. counsel Southeastern Power Resources Com., Tucker, Ga., 1986—. Contbr. articles to profl. jours. Bd. dirs. McLean Sch. Md., Inc., Fed. City Coun., Keystone Energy Trustees; bd. dirs., treas. Writer's Ctr.; chmn. Found. Energy Law Jour. Mem. ABA, ATLA, Fed. Energy Bar Assn., D.C. Bar Assn., Econ. Club Washington, City Tavern Club, Cosmos Club. Avocations: sailing, skiing, tennis, literature, writing. Office: Verner Liipfert Bernhard McPherson & Hand 901 15th St NW Washington DC 20005-2327

VINCENT, CHARLES EAGAR, JR., sports columnist; b. Beaumont, Tex., Mar. 24, 1940; s. Charles Eagar and Hazel Ruth (Balston) V.; m. Mary Jacquelyn Bertman, Aug. 8, 1959 (div. Jan. 1977); children: Lisa Marie, Dixie Ann, Charles Joseph, John Patrick; m. Patricia Revue des Skinner, Mar. 28, 1970 (div. Apr. 1985); 1 child, Susanna Lee; m. Karen Judith Peterson, Aug. 17, 1985. Student, Victoria Coll., 1958-59. Reporter Victoria (Tex.) Mirror, 1958-59, Taylor (Tex.) Daily Press, 1959-60; sports writer Beaumont (Tex.) Jour., 1960-62; sports editor Galveston (Tex.) Tribune, 1962-63; sports writer San Antonio Express-News, 1963-69, Sandusky (Ohio) Register, 1969-70; sports writer Detroit Free Press, 1970-85, sports columnist, 1985—. Author: Welcome to My World, 1994. Recipient 4th Pl. award Nat. AP Sports Editors, 1981, 5th Pl., 1989, 92, Sister Mary Leila Meml. award, 1991, Mich. Columnist of Yr. award, 1991; Afro-Am. Night honoree, 1991. Mem. Baseball Writers Assn. Am. Avocations: traveling, cooking, geneology. Office: Detroit Free Press 321 W Lafayette Blvd Detroit MI 48226-2703

VINCENT, DAVID RIDGELY, management consulting executive; b. Detroit, Aug. 9, 1941; s. Charles Ridgely and Charlotte Jane (McCarroll) V.; m. Margaret Helen Anderson, Aug. 25, 1962 (div. 1973); children: Sandra Lee, Cheryl Ann; m. Judith Ann Gomez, July 2, 1978; 1 child, Amber; stepchildren: Michael Jr., Jesse Joseph Flores. BS, BA, Calif. State U.-Sacramento, 1964; MBA, Calif. State U.-Sacramento, 1971; PhD Somerset U, 1991. Cert. Mgmt. Cons. 1994. Sr. ops. analyst Aerojet Gen. Corp., Sacramento, 1960-66; contr. Hexcel Corp., Dublin, Calif., 1966-70; mng. dir. Memorex, Austria, 1970-74; sales mgr. Ampex World Ops., Switzerland, 1974-76; dir. product mgmt. NCR, Sunnyvale, Calif., 1976-79; v.p Boole & Babbage Inc., gen. mgr. Inst. Info. Mgmt., Sunnyvale, Calif., 1979-85; pres. The Info. Group, Inc., Santa Clara, Calif., 1985—. Deacon Union Ch., Cupertino, Calif.; USSF soccer referee. Author: Perspectives in Information Management, Information Economics, 1983, Handbook of Information Resource Management, 1987, The Information-Based Corporation: stakeholder economics and the technology investment, 1990, Reengineering Fundamentals: Business Processes and the Global Economy, 1994; contbr. monographs and papers to profl. jours. Home: 2803 Kalliam Dr Santa Clara CA 95051-6838 Office: PO Box Q Santa Clara CA 95055-3756

VINCENT, EDWARD See BRACKEN, EDDIE

VINCENT, HAL WELLMAN, marine corps officer, investor; b. Pontiac, Mich., Sept. 27, 1927; s. Harold and Glenda (Wellman) V.; m. Virginia Bayler, June 9, 1951; children: David B., Dale W., Deborah K. Vincent Minder. Student, Navy V-5 program Western Mich. Coll./Colgate U., 1945; BS, U.S. Naval Acad., 1950; postgrad., Marine Officers Basic Sch., 1950, Flight Sch., 1952, Test Pilot Sch., 1955, Navy Fleet Air Gunnery Sch., 1958, Air Force Fighter Weapons Sch., 1959, Marine Corps Command and Staff Coll., 1964, Indsl. Coll., 1969, Marine Air Weapons Tng. Unit, 1972. Cert. flight and instrument instr. Commd. 2d lt. U.S. Marine Corps, 1950, advanced through grades to maj. gen., 1974; rifle and machinegun platoon comdr. Camp Lejeune, N.C., 1951; fighter pilot El Toro, Calif. and Korea, 1953-54; test pilot Flight Test Div., Patuxent River, Md., 1955-57; ops. officer, squadron asst. and fighter pilot El Toro, 1958-59; conventional weapons project test pilot Naval Air Weapons Test Ctr., China Lake, Calif., 1960-62; squadron ops. and exec. officer El Toro and Japan, 1962-64; aviation specialist Marine Corps amphibious warfare presentation team and staff officer Quantico, Va., 1965-66; comdg. officer 2d Marine Aircraft Wing fighter-attack squadron, Beaufort, S.C., 1967-68; exec. officer Marine Aircraft Group, Vietnam, 1969; logistics staff officer Fleet Marine Force Pacific, Hawaii, 1970-72; comdg. officer Marine Aircraft Group, Yuma, Ariz., 1972-73; chief of staff 3d Marine Aircraft Wing, El Toro, 1973-76; dep. chief. of staff plans and policy to Comdr. in Chief Atlantic, Norfolk, Va., 1976-78; comdg. gen. 2d Marine Aircraft Wing, Cherry Point, N.C., 1978-80; dep. comdg. gen. Fleet Marine Force Atlantic, Norfolk, 1980-81; ret., 1981, pvt. investor, 1981—; flight test pilot; preliminary pilot, evaluator new mil. aircraft. Contbr. numerous articles on tactics and conventional weapons delivery, flight test stability and control to various mil. publs. Decorated Legion of Merit with 2 gold stars, D.F.C., Bronze Star with combat V, Air medal with star and numeral 14, Joint Svcs. Commendation medal U.S.; Honor medal 1st class; Cross of Gallantry with gold star (Republic of Vietnam). Mem. SAR, Soc. Exptl. Test Pilots, Marine Corps Assn., Early Pioneer Naval Aviators, Marine Corps Aviation Assn., Mach 2 Club, Marbella Country Club. Invented Triple Ejector Rack for delivery of conventional bombs, 1961; devel. fighter tactics in F8 and F4 aircraft, 1958-69; flew 165 models of fgn. and U.S. mil. aircraft; flew 8 models of fixed wing and helicopters on 242 combat missions; first Marine to fly MACH-2. *In all 36 years in the service I am convinced that war is bad, and little is accomplished in the long term by warfare. However when National policy dictates a war, then we must not limit what can be done. We must win! My thought then remains: "Winning isn't everything, it's the only thing!" When I must go to battle I want to be allowed to "fight to win."*

VINCENT, JAMES LOUIS, biotechnology company executive; b. Johnstown, Pa., Dec. 15, 1939; s. Robert Clyde and Marietta Lucille (Kennedy) V.; m. Elizabth M. Matthews, Aug. 19, 1961; children: Aimee Archelle, Christopher James. BSME, Duke U., 1961; MBA in Indsl. Mgmt., U. Pa., 1963. Mgr. Far East div. Tex. Instruments, Inc., Tokyo, 1970-72; pres. Tex. Instrument Asia, Ltd., Tokyo, 1970-72; v.p. diagnostic ops., pres. diagnostics div. Abbott Labs., North Chgo., Ill., 1972-74, group v.p., bd. dirs., 1974-81, exec. v.p., COO, bd. dirs., 1979-81; corp. group v.p., pres. Allied Health and Sci. Products Co. Allied Corp., Morristown, N.J., 1982-85; CEO Biogen, Inc., 1985—; also bd. dirs. Bd. trustees Duke U., U. Pa.; bd. dirs. Found. for the Nat. Tech., U. Pa. Health System; bd. overseers Wharton Grad. Bus. Sch. U. Pa. Recipient Young Exec. Achievement Young Execs. Club, Chgo., 1976, Disting. Alumni award Duke U., 1988. Mem. Biotech. Industry Orgn. (bd. dirs.), Econ. Club Chgo., Shoreacres Country Club, Algonquin Club, Boston Club, Chgo. Club, The Links (N.Y.C.). Republican. Presbyterian. Office: Biogen Inc 14 Cambridge Ctr Cambridge MA 02142-1481

VINCENT, JEFF, labor studies educator; b. Regensberg, Germany, Mar. 18, 1956; came to U.S., 1956; s. John J. and Norma J. (Trindle) V.; m. Patti Ann E. Knoff, Aug. 18, 1978; children: Natalie and Nicole (twins). BS in Ednl. Studies, U. Wis., Milw., 1978, MS in Indsl. Rels., 1984. Rsch. assoc. Inst. for Study Labor in Society Ind. U., Bloomington, 1985—; mem. review panel Ind. Econ. Devel. Coun., Indpls., 1993; mem. bur. labor mgmt. rels. and coop. programs U.S. Dept. Labor, Constrn. Ind. Svc. Corp., Madison Area Labor Mgmt. Com., Nat. Labor Mgmt. Com. Custom Woodowrking

Industry, Operation Top-Notch, So. Ind. Constrn. Industry Labor Mgmt. Com.; tchr., cons. labor mgmt. coms. in Colo., Fla., Ill., Mich., Ohio. Contbr. articles to profl. jours. Active Southwest Ill. Leadership Coun. Mem. AFL-CIO, United Food and Comml. Workers Union (shop steward local # 1444 1978-81), Am. Fedn. Tchrs. (treas, local # 2254, 1987-88, 91—), Internat. Brotherhood Elec. Workers (region 6, local # 481), Nat. Elec. Contractors Assn. (dist. IV), Univ. and Coll. Labor Edn. Assn., Workers. Edn. (local 189), Constrn. Industry Labor-Mgmt. Network, Ind. State Bldg. and Constrn. Trades Coun., Ohio State Bldg. and Constrn. Trades Coun., Workers Rights Inst. (pres. bd. dirs. 1980-83). Home: 3261 Carowinds Ct Bloomington IN 47401 Office: Ind Univ Divsn Labor Studies Poplars 628 Bloomington IN 47405

VINCENT, JOHN GRAHAM, administrator; b. Rustington, Sussex, England, Sept. 17, 1935; came to U.S.; 1965; s. Leroy Michael and Ethel Maude (Pascoe) V. BA in Bldg., Worthing Coll., 1957; MA in Archtl. Design, Brighton Coll., 1960. Asst. mng. dir. Vincent Bros., England, 1959-61; mktg. dir. Mktg. Assocs. Internat., England, 1960-62; trade show officer Am. Embassy Depts. Agrl. and Commerce, England, 1962-65; acct. exec. United Expn. Svcs., Chgo., 1965-71; resort owner Casa Grand, Portugal, 1971-76; v.p., dir. nat. sales Greyhound Corp., San Francisco, 1976-81, Washington, 1976-81; gen. mgr. Freeman Decoration Co., Atlanta, 1981-83; dir. trade shows Nat. Assn. Music Mchts., Carlsbad, Calif., 1984—. Mem. Internat. Assn. Expn. Mgmt. (bd. dirs. So. Calif. chpt. 1984-94, pres. 1991). Avocations: skiing, kayaking, scuba diving, competitive track and field. Home: 2623 Abedul St Carlsbad CA 92009-5308 Office: Nat Assn Music Merchants 438-4051 Avenida Encinas Carlsbad CA 92008

VINCENT, JON STEPHEN, foreign language educator; b. Denver, Feb. 28, 1938; s. Joseph William and Lillian (Diamond) V.; m. Maria Louise Girard, June 13, 1962; children—Sean David, Tanya Maria. B.A., U. N.Mex., 1961, Ph.D., 1970. Instr. U. N.Mex., Albuquerque, 1963-64; asst. prof. U. Kans., Lawrence, 1974-78, assoc. prof., 1979-82; prof., 1979—, assoc. chmn. dept. Spanish, 1974-78, chmn., 1978-82; vis. prof. U. Costa Rica, San Jose, 1972; co-dir. Latin Am. Studies, 1982-89, dir., 1989-92. Author: Joao Guimaraes Rosa, 1978; assoc. editor Hispania, 1984-90, Brasil/Brazil, 1989—; asst. editor Latin Am. Theatre Rev., 1969—; mem. rev. staff World Lit. Today, 1983—. Served with U.S. Army, 1953-56. Mem. MLA (chmn. Luso-Brazilian div. 1982), Am. Assn. Tchrs. Spanish and Portuguese, Latin Am. Studies Assn., Fulbright Am. Republics, Kans. Fgn. Lang. Assn., Am. Republics Adv. Com. Democrat. Avocations: Fishing; hunting. Home: 1104 Centennial Dr Lawrence KS 66049-2700 Office: U Kans Dept Spanish and Portu Lawrence KS 66045

VINCENT, NORMAN FULLER, broadcasting executive; b. Boston, Oct. 5, 1930; s. Norman Harrison and Marian Bernice (Fuller) V.; m. Karen Ann Walter, June 21, 1969. B.A., Denison U., 1953. Sales mgr. Sta. WMBR, Jacksonville, Fla., 1956-62; gen. mgr. Sta. WZOK, Jacksonville, 1962-66; owner, pres. Norm Vincent Sound Recording Studios, Inc., Jacksonville, 1966-75; dir. radio ops. Sta. WJCT, Jacksonville, 1975-91; announcer, narrator radio, TV film and video, talking books, 1991—. Producer, host (radio): Swing Time with Norm Vincent, 1992—. Served with USN, 1953-56; to comdr. USNR, 1958-80. Mem. Navy League, Advt. Fedn. Am., Jacksonville C. of C. (armed services com.), Exchange Club. Republican. Episcopalian. Home: 2110 The Woods Dr Jacksonville FL 32246

VINCENT, NORMAN L., insurance company executive; b. Milw., July 21, 1933; s. Victor V. Vincent and Hilda I. (Boedecker) Vincent Patlow; m. Arlene Page, Jan. 31, 1953 (div. 1978); children: J. Todd, Meg; m. Donna Jean Doll, Aug. 8, 1980. B.S., U. Wis., 1957; M.S., Purdue U., 1958, Ph.D., 1960. Diplomate Am. Bd. Profl. Psychology; registered psychologist., Ill., C.P.C.U., C.L.U. Supr. agy. research State Farm Ins. Cos., Bloomington, Ill., 1960-63, dir. agy. research, 1963-66, asst. v.p. agy., 1966-69, asst. v.p. exec., 1969-70, v.p. data processing, 1970-94; systems v.p., 1994—. Pres. Bloomington Bd. Edn., 1974-77; bd. dirs. YMCA, Bloomington, 1971-85. Served with M.I. U.S. Army, 1953-55. Mem. AAAS. Home: 304 Perrin Ave Bloomington IL 61701-4238 Office: State Farm Mut Automobile Ins Co 1 State Farm Pla Bloomington IL 61710

VINCENT, THOMAS JAMES, retired manufacturing company executive; b. Balt., Mar. 17, 1934; s. Thomas Alonzo and Helen Geraldine (Cloman) V.; divorced; children: Wayne S., Robin K. MS, MIT, 1968. Div. gen. mgr. Fairchild Industries, St. Augustine, Fla., 1969-72; pres. T.J. Vincent Properties Ltd., St. Augustine, 1972-75, Pacific Concrete & Rock Co., Honolulu, 1975-77, Ramsey Engring. Co., St. Paul, 1977-80, Kobe Inc., Los Angeles, 1980-84, Milchem Inc., Houston, 1984-85; pres. York (Pa.) Internat. Corp., 1985-88, also bd. dirs., cons.; chmn., CEO Hawaii Seafood Growers, Inc., Kahuku, 1990-92. Author: Fairplan, 1962. Founder, pres. Thomas J. Vincent Found. Inc. Casselberry, Fla., 1990—. Named one of Outstanding Young Men in Am., Jaycees, 1965; Alfred P. Sloan fellow MIT, 1967; recipient Research for Progress Achievement award, 1972. Avocations: deep sea fishing, orchid growing. Home and Office: 225 Overbrook Dr Casselberry FL 32707-4343

VINCENT, TONY, cable television/radio executive and personality; b. Newark, June 18, 1946; s. James Michael and Jennie Anna (Grieco) Petrillo. DD (hon.), Kingway Bible Coll., Des Moines, 1986. Pres. WAVP Cable Radio, Bloomfield, N.J., 1980-83, Tony Vincent Prodns., Bloomfield, 1983—; pres., chief exec. officer WJEN Cable TV and Radio, Bloomfield, 1983—; liaison N.J. Motion Picture and TV Commn., 1986—; chmn. Bloomfield Cable TV Commn., 1983-93. Chaplain Northward First Aid Squad, Newark, 1970—; active Bloomfield Bd. Edn., Essex County Ednl. Svcs. Commn. Recipient Citation of Merit, Muscular Dystrophy Assn., 1966, 87, Humanitarian award United Cerebral Palsy, 1980, Citations, Joint Meml. Com., Bloomfield, 1984, Bloomfield PBA Local 32, 1987. Mem. Am. Fedn. Radio and TV Artists, Am. Guild Variety Artists, N.J. Ednl. Assn. Republican. Pentecostal. Avocation: soccer. Home: 33 Park Ave Bloomfield NJ 07003-2609 Office: WJEN Cable PO Box 55 Bloomfield NJ 07003-0055

VINCENTI, WALTER GUIDO, aeronautical engineer, emeritus educator; b. Balt., Apr. 20, 1917; s. Guido A. and Agnes (Nicolini) V.; m. Joyce H. Weaver, Sept. 6, 1947; children—Margaret Anna, Marc Guido. A.B., Stanford U., 1938, Aero. Engr., 1940. Aero. research scientist NACA, 1940-57; prof. aero. and astronautics and history of tech. Stanford U., 1957-83, prof. emeritus, 1983—; cons to industry, 1964—; mem. adv. panel engring. sec. NSF, 1960-63. Author: (with Charles H. Kruger, Jr.) Introduction to Physical Gas Dynamics, 1965, (with Nathan Rosenberg) The Britannia Bridge, 1978, What Engineers Know and How They Know It, 1990; also papers.; co-editor (with Milton Van Dyke) Annual Review of Fluid Mechanics, 1970-72. Served with USN, 1945-46. Recipient Gold medal Pi Tau Sigma, 1948; Rockefeller Pub. Service award, 1956; Guggenheim fellow, 1963. Fellow AIAA; mem. Internat. Acad. Astronautics (corr.), History of Sci. Soc., Soc. History Tech. (Usher prize 1984), Nat. Acad. Engring., Newcomen Soc., Phi Beta Kappa, Sigma Xi, Tau Beta Pi. Home: 13200 E Sunset Dr Los Altos CA 94022-3427 Office: Stanford U Stanford CA 94305

VINCENTI-BROWN, CRISPIN RUFUS WILLIAM, engineering executive; b. Epsom, Surrey, England, Sept. 20, 1951; came to U.S., 1989; s. Douglas Hector and Joan Margaret Patricia (Lowe) Brown; m. Terry Doreen Bennett, May 20, 1978 (dec. Oct. 1992); children: Genevieve Louise, Juliette Alexandra; m. Margaret Anna Vincenti, Feb. 13, 1993. BSc in Engring. Prodn., U. Birmingham, 1974. Mgr. Soc. M.O.M. Engrs, France, 1975; prin. cons. Ingersoll Engrs. Inc., Rugby, England, 1975-79; pres. dir. Ingersoll Engrs. SA, Annecy, France, 1979-89; sr. ptnr. Ingersoll Engrs. Inc., Los Altos, Calif., 1989—; v.p. Groupe de Talloires, Geneva, 1987-89; bd. dirs. Ops. Mgmt. Assn., Waco, Tex. Fellow Inst. Elec. Engrs. (chartered engr.). Avocation: fixed wing and helicopter pilot. Home: 1098 Eastwood Ct Los Altos CA 94024 Office: Ingersoll Engrs 5100 E State St # 4 Rockford IL 61108

VINCI, JOHN NICHOLAS, architect, educator; b. Chgo., Feb. 6, 1937; s. Nicholas and Nicolina (Camiola) V. B.Arch., Ill. Inst. Tech., 1960. Registered architect, Ill.; Mich. Draftsman Skidmore, Owings, Merrill, Chgo., 1960-61; with City of Chgo., 1961; stencil restorer Crombie Taylor, Chgo., 1961-62; designer Brenner, Danforth, Rockwell, Chgo., 1962-68; architect

Vinci, Inc., Chgo., 1977—; lectr. Roosevelt U., Chgo., 1969-72, Ill. Inst. Tech., Chgo., 1972-90. Author: (booklet) Trading Room-Art Inst. Chgo., 1977; contr. articles to profl. jours. Bd. dirs. Music of Baroque, Chgo., 1976-87, Campbell Ctr. Found.; mem. adv. com. Commn. on Chgo. Archtl. and Hist. Landmarks, 1971-83; exec. sec. Richard Nickel Com, Chgo., 1972—; chmn. Howard Van Doren Shaw Soc., 1994—; vice chmn. Van Allen Found., Clinton, Iowa, 1993—; internat. arts adv. coun. Wexner Ctr. for the Arts, 1994—. Fellow AIA; mem. Soc. Archtl. Historians, Frank Lloyd Wright Home and Studio Found., Art Inst. Chgo., The Corp. of YADDO, Chgo. Hist. Soc. Roman Catholic. Home: 3152 N Cambridge Ave Chicago IL 60657-4613 Office: Office of John Vinci Inc 1147 W Ohio St Chicago IL 60622-5874

VINCIGUERRA, JEAN-LOUIS, finance company executive; b. Casablanca, Morocco, Mar. 31, 1944; s. Jacques and Etiennette (Bonetti) V.; m. Catherine Quitard, May 6, 1965; children: Nathalie, Marc. Diploma, Sch. Polit. Sci., Paris, 1968; PhD in Econ., Paris U., 1969; PMD in Bus., Harvard U., 1976. From exec. to v.p. fin. and treas. Pechiney Ugine Kuhlmann, Paris, 1971-83; chief fin. officer Pechiney, Paris, 1983-89, exec. v.p., 1989—; chmn. bd. Am. Nat. Can Co., Chgo. Mem. Racing Club de France. Avocation: tennis. Home: 23 Boulevard Lannes, 75116 Paris France Office: Pechiney, 1 Place des Vosges, 92048 Paris la Defense, France

VINCIGUERRA, SALVATORE JOSEPH, scientific instrument company executive; b. Methuen, Mass., Jan. 21, 1938; s. Joseph Frederick and Erminia (Bonnacorsi) V.; m. Grace Stevens, Apr. 20, 1963; children: Elizabeth, Catherine, Joseph, Suzanne. BSE, Princeton U., 1959; MBA, Harvard U., 1968. Systems analyst GE, Phoenix, 1962-63; cons. Arthur D. Little, Inc., Cambridge, Mass., 1964-66; with Instron Corp., 1968—; contr. Canton, Mass., 1968-71; treas. Canton, 1971-76; gen. mgr. Asia/Pacific Ops. Toyko, 1976-81; v.p., gen. mgr. Western Hemisphere Ops. Canton, 1981-85, pres., 1985—; dir. Lytron Inc., Woburn, Mass. Dir. Japan Soc. Boston, 1986—; corp. mem. Children's Mus. Boston, 1984—. Mem. High Tech. Council, Internat. Bus. Ctr. Clubs: Harvard (Boston); Harvard of Japan (Toyko) (treas. 1978-81). Office: Staveley Inc 401 Merritt 7 Norwalk CT 06851

VINCZE, L. STEPHAN, lawyer; b. Boston, Sept. 25, 1957; s. Laszlo Otto and Marianne (Szent-Ivanyi Magyar) V.; m. Laura Anne Scruggs, Dec. 17, 1988. AB, Columbia U., 1982; JD, So. Meth. U., 1988; postgrad., Georgetown. Bar: Tex. 1989. Commd. lt. USMC, 1982, advanced through grades to capt., 1993; artillery officer USMC, Camp Pendleton, Calif., 1983-85; staff civil law, environ. counsel JAG USMC, Parris Island, S.C., 1988-90; asst. dep. Office Sec. Def. USMC, Washington, 1990-93; Rep. staff com. on govt. pos. U.S. House Reps., Washington, 1993—. Mem. ABA (internat. environ. and litigation sects.), Tex. State Bar Assn., Tex. State Soc., Andover Alumni Assn. (Washington chpt.), Phi Alpha Delta, Delta Psi (pres. alpha chpt. 1980-81). Methodist. Avocations: sailing, fitness, theatre, music, reading. Office: House Govt Ops Com Rep Staff Rm B350A Rayburn House Ofc Bld Washington DC 20515-0003

VINEBURGH, JAMES HOLLANDER, banking executive; b. Hartford, Conn., July 17, 1943; s. Lawrence Harold and Dorothy Helen (Brandvein) V.; m. Nancy Cynthia Taylor; children: James Hollander Jr., Philip Lawrence Taylor. AB, Tufts U., 1966. CLU. Mgmt. trainee Conn. Gen. Life Ins. Co., Boston, 1966-68, asst. mgr., 1968-72; asst. sec. Conn. Gen. Life Ins. Co., Hartford, 1973-75; mgr. Conn. Gen. Life Ins. Co., Oakland, Calif., 1975-76; dir. br. mktg. Conn. Gen. Life Ins. Co., Hartford, 1977, regional v.p., 1978-81, v.p., 1981-84; sr. v.p employee benefits & fin. services group CIGNA Corp., Hartford, 1984, sr. v.p individual fin. group, 1985-88; exec. v.p. Conn. Bank and Trust Co., N.A, Hartford, 1989-91; chmn., dir. Bank of New Eng. Trust Co., Palm Beach, Fla., 1989-91; exec. v.p. Fleet Bank, N.A., Hartford, Conn., 1991-93; sr. v.p. The Pvt. Bank, Bank of Boston, 1994—. Class sec. The Hill Sch., Pottstown, Pa., 1986—; bd. dirs. Big Bros. Assn. Greater Boston, 1995—; bd. dirs. Boston Olympics Organizing Com., 1995—; pres. parent's com. Middlesex Sch., Concord, Mass., 1995—; past chmn., bd. dirs. Child and Family Svcs., Hartford, 1983-93; past pres., bd. dirs. West Hartford Youth Baseball League, 1981-90; bd. dirs., exec. com. Riverfront Recapture, Hartford, 1986-94; adv. bd. WALKS Found., Simsbury, Conn., 1983-94; bd. dirs. March of Dimes, 1991-92; trustee Bushnell Meml. Hall, Hartford, 1992-94. Mem. Leadership Greater Hartford. Avocations: golf, politics, squash. Office: Bank of Boston 100 Federal St Boston MA 02110

VINES, CHARLES JERRY, minister; b. Carroll County, Ga., Sept. 22, 1937; s. Charles Clarence and Ruby Johnson V.; m. Janet Denney, Dec. 17, 1960; children: Joy Vines Williams, Jim, Jodi, Jon. BA, Mercer U., 1959; BD, New Orleans Bapt. Sem., 1966; ThD, Luther Rice Sem., Jacksonville, Fla., 1974; DD (hon.), Criswell Coll., 1991, Liberty U., 1991. Pastor West Rome Bapt. Ch., Rome, Ga., 1968-74, 79-81, Dauphin Way Bapt. Ch., Moblie, Ala., 1974-79, 1st Bapt. ch., Jacksonville, Fla., 1981—. Author: Practical Guide to Sermon Preparation, An Effective Guide to Sermon Delivery, Great Events in the Life of Christ, I Shall Return - Jesus, Family Fellowship, Great Interviews of Jesus, God Speaks Today, Exploring the Epistles of John, Exploring Daniel, Exploring Mark, Wanted: Soul Winners, Wanted: Church Growers, Basic Sermons on the Ten Commandments. Pres. So. Bapt. Conv., 1988-89. Office: First Bapt Ch 124 W Ashley St Jacksonville FL 32202-3104

VINH, BINH, architect; b. Hue, Vietnam, Oct. 23, 1945; came to U.S., 1975; s. Tri and Chinh H. (Nguyen) Buu; m. Hang T. Nguyen, Jan. 22, 1975; 1 child, Michael. MArch and Urban Planning, U. Saigon, 1973; MArch, U. Pa., 1977; postgrad., Harvard U., 1991. Registered arch., Pa., N.J., N.C., S.C., Ala., Tenn., N.Y., Ark. Prin. BV Architects, Saigon, 1974-75; designer Berger Assocs., Harrisburg, Pa., 1975-77; project architect, designer Kling Partnership, Phila., 1977-89; ptnr., design prin. Kling Lindquist Partnership, Phila., 1989—; assoc. prof. Thu Duc (Vietnam) Poly. Inst., 1974-75; vis. critic U. Pa.; speaker and presenter in field. Prin. works include Ethyl Corp. Hdqs., Richmond, Va.; Chester County Libr., Exton, Pa., C.C. Phila. First Place Silver medal AIA Phila. chpt.), Radnor/Plymouth Meeting (Pa.) Exec. Campus, SOHIO Corp. Rsch. Ctr., Cleve., Prudential Ins. Co., Roseland, N.J., Greyhound Terminal, Phila., E.I. du Pont de Nemours & Co., Inc. Life Scis. Complex, Wilmington, Del., Boehringer Ingelheim, Ltd., Danbury and Ridgefield, Conn., NIH Bldg 29B, Bethesda, Md., Kennametal, Inc. Corp. Tech. Ctr., Latrobe, Pa. (Best Bld. in Westmoreland County, Latrobe C. of C.), Am. Cyanamid Co. Greenhouse Support Facility, Princeton, N.J., Ciba-Geigy Corp. Prodn. Facility, Suffern, N.Y., FAA Continuous Airworthiness Rsch. Facility, Jet Propulsion Testing and Fuels Rsch. Lab., Atlantic City (N.J.) Internat. Airport, Nat. Cancer Inst. Monoclonal Antibodies and Recombinant Protein Facility, Frederick, Md., Allied-Signal Corp. Charles W. Nichols, Jr. Tech. Ctr., Morristown, N.J. (High Honors award Rsch. and Devel. Mag.), Glaxo Inc. Rsch. and Devel. Facilities, Rsch. Triangle Park, N.C. (Triangle Devel. award 1992, Design Excellence award Archtl. Precast Assn. 1993, Best Mixed Use Project award Precast/Prestressed Concrete Inst. 1993), Miles, Inc. Pharm. Rsch. and Devel. Hdqs., West Haven, Conn., Glaxo Group Rsch. Ltd. Rsch. and Devel. Hdqs., Stevenage, Hertfordshire, Eng.; contr. articles to, works featured in numerous profl. and popular jours. Bd. dirs. Harrisburg chpt. ARC; active Phila. Fellowship Commn. Mem. AIA (regional liaison Pa., coms. on design, environ. and internat. practice), Precast/Prestressed Concrete Inst., Union Internat. Archs., Fedn. Pan Am. Assn. Archs., L'Ordre Archs. D'lle de France, Pa. Soc. Archs., Phila. Solar Energy Assn., Phila. Philos. Consortium. Avocations: tennis, golf, music, travel, painting. Office: Kling-Lindquist Partnership 2301 Chestnut St Philadelphia PA 19103-3035

VINH, NGUYEN XUAN, aerospace engineer, educator; b. Yenbay, Vietnam, Jan. 3, 1930; married, 1955; 4 children. BS, Air Inst., France, 1953; MS, U. Marseille, 1954, U. Colo., 1962; PhD in Aerospace, U. Colo., 1965; DSc in Math., U. Paris, 1972. Asst. prof. aerospace engring. U. Colo. 1965-68; assoc. prof., 1968-72; prof. aerospace engring U. Mich., Ann Arbor, 1972—; vis. lectr. U. Calif., Berkeley, 1967; vis. prof. ecol. nat. sup aero., France, 1974; chair prof. Nat Tsing Hua U., Taiwan, 1982. Assoc. editor Acta Astronautica, 1979—. Recipient Mechanics and Control of Flight award Am. Inst. Aeronautics & Astronautics, 1994. Mem. Math. Assn. Am., Internat. Acad. Astronauts, French Nat. Acad. Air & Space. Research in ordinary differential equations; astrodynamics and optimization of space flight trajectories; theory of non-linear oscillations. Office: U

Michigan Dept Aerospace Engring 2508 Patterson Ann Arbor MI 48104-2127*

VINIK, H(YMIE) RONALD, anesthesiologist, physician; b. Johannesburg, Transvaal, Republic of South Africa, Aug. 27, 1932; came to U.S., 1976, naturalized, 1986; s. Joseph and Fanny (Shain) V.; m. Sandra Lois Kirkel, Mar. 26, 1967; children—Dion, Grant, Russell. Nat. Sr. Cert., Regis Coll., Johannesburg, 1955; M.B., U. Witwatersrand, Johannesburg, 1961. Resident Coll. of Medicine, South Africa, 1972-75; prin. anesthesiologist Baragwanath Hosp., Johannesburg, South Africa, 1975-76; assoc. prof. anesthesiology U. Ala., Birmingham, 1977-89, prof., 1989—; dir. pain ctr. U. Ala., 1977—; dir. anesthesia svcs. Eye Found. Hosp., Birmingham, 1989—; mem. faculty Merck, Sharp & Dohme, Phila., 1982—. Mem. editorial bd. Ala. Jour. Med. Scis., Birmingham, 1985; contbr. articles on pain and anesthesia to profl. jours. Merit scholar U. Witwatersrand. Mem. AMA, Internat. Assn. for Study of Pain, Am. Soc. Anesthesiology (chmn. com. for pain therapy 1986). Avocations: golf; sailing. Home: 3128 Warrington Rd Birmingham AL 35223-2754 Office: U Ala 1920 7th Ave S Birmingham AL 35294-0001

VINIK, JEFFREY, investment portfolio manager. Portfolio mgr., Growth & Income Fund Fidelity Investments, Boston, 1992, portfolio mgr., Magellan Fund, 1992—. Office: Fidelity Magellan Fund 82 Devonshire St Boston MA 02109-3614

VINING, ELIZABETH GRAY, author; b. Phila., Oct. 6, 1902; d. John Gordon and Anne (Iszard) Gray; m. Morgan Fisher Vining, Jan 31, 1929 (dec. 1933). A.B. Bryn Mawr Coll., 1923; M.S. in L.S, Drexel Inst. Tech., 1926, Litt.D., 1951; Litt.D., Tufts Coll., 1952, Douglas Coll., 1953, Women's Med. Coll. Phila., 1953, Lafayette Coll., 1956, U. N.C.-Greensboro, 1968; L.H.D., Russell Sage Coll., 1952, Haverford Coll., 1958, Western Coll. Women, 1959, Cedar Crest Coll., 1959, Moravian Coll., 1961, Wilmington Coll., 1962, Internat. Christian U., Tokyo, Japan, 1966; D.Ed., R.I. Coll. Edn., 1956. Tutor to Crown Prince of Japan, 1946-50; vice pres. bd. trustees Bryn Mawr Coll., 1952-71, vice chmn. bd. dirs., 1952-71. Author: Windows for the Crown Prince, 1952, The World in Tune, 1954, The Virginia Exiles, 1955, Friend of Life, The Biography of Rufus M. Jones, 1958, Return to Japan, 1960, Take Heed of Loving Me, 1964, Flora: A Biography, 1966, also I. Roberta, 1969, Quiet Pilgrimage, 1970, The Taken Girl, 1973, Mr. Whittier, 1974, Being Seventy: The Measure of a Year, 1978; also 14 juveniles under name Elizabeth Janet Gray, including Penn, 1938; Adam of the Road, 1942 (John Newbery medal 1943), The Cheerful Heart, 1959. Decorated 3d Order Sacred Crown Japan, 1950; recipient Skinner award Women's Nat. Book Assn., 1954. Address: Kendal at Longwood Box 256 Kennett Square PA 19348

VINING, GLEN W., JR., insurance company executive. With Farmers New World Life Ins., Mercer Island, Washington, 1961, now pres. Office: Farmers New World Life Ins 3003 77th Ave SE Mercer Island WA 98040-2890

VINING, (GEORGE) JOSEPH, law educator; b. Fulton, Mo., Mar. 3, 1938; s. D. Rutledge and Margaret (McClanahan) V.; m. Alice Marshall Williams, Sept. 18, 1965; children: George Joseph IV, Spencer Carter. BA, Yale U., 1959, Cambridge U., 1961; MA, Cambridge U., 1970; JD, Harvard U., 1964. Bar: D.C. 1965. Atty. Office Dep. Atty. Gen., Dept. Justice, Washington, 1965; asst. to exec. dir. Nat. Crime Commn., 1966; assoc. Covington and Burling, Washington, 1966-69; asst. prof. law U. Mich., 1969-72, assoc. prof., 1972-74, prof., 1974-85, Hutchins prof., 1985—. Author: Legal Identity, 1978, The Authoritative and the Authoritarian, 1986, From Newton's Sleep, 1995. Bd. dirs. Am. Friends of Cambridge U. NEH sr. fellow, 1982-83. Mem. ABA, D.C. Bar Assn., Am. Law Inst., Century Assn. Office: U Mich 432 Hutchins Hall Ann Arbor MI 48109-1215

VINING, ROBERT LUKE, JR., federal judge; b. Chatsworth, Ga., Mar. 30, 1931; m. Martha Sue Cates; 1 child, Laura. B.A., J.D., U. Ga., 1959. With Mitchell & Mitchell, 1958-60; ptnr. McCamy, Miner & Vining, Dalton, 1960-69; solicitor gen. Conasauga Judicial Cir., 1963-68; judge Whitfield County Superior Ct., Dalton, 1969-79, U.S. Dist. Ct. (no. dist.) Ga., 1979-95; chief judge, 1995—. Served to staff sgt. USAF, 1951-59. Office: US Dist Ct 600 E First St Rome GA 30162

VINKEN, PIERRE JACQUES, publishing executive, neurosurgeon; b. Heerlen, The Netherlands, Nov. 25, 1927; M.D., U. Utrecht, 1955, postgrad. in psychiatry, neurology and neurosurgery, U. Amsterdam, 1957-63; hon. Dr., U. Paris, 1981. Staff neurosurgeon Univ. Clinic, Amsterdam, 1964-69; cons. neurosurgeon Boerhaave Clinic, Amsterdam, 1964-72; pres., chief editor Excerpta Medica Found., Amsterdam and Princeton, N.J., 1962-88; mng. dir. Elsevier Pub. Co., Amsterdam, 1972-78; chmn. Elsevier Pub. Co., Amsterdam, 1979-95; chmn. bd. dirs. Reed Elsevier, London, 1993-95; bd. dirs. Wereldhave Investment Co., The Hague, Mees Pierson, Amsterdam, Logica, London, Halder Holdings, The Hague, The Lancet, London, Aalberts Industries, Driebergen; chmn. Basis Fdn. Hosp. Info. System, Leyden, prof. med.database informatics U. Leyden, 1975-93; mem. Nat. Sci. Policy Council, The Hague, 1983-90; chmn. Netherlands del. Intergovtl. Unisist Conf., Paris, 1970; mem.Netherlands Unisist Commn., 1971-79. Chmn. Netherlands Commn. Bibliography andDocumentation, 1972-81; pres. Internat. Congress Patient Counselling, 1976-79. Mem. European Pubs. Coun. (dep. chmn.), Neurol. Soc. India (hon.), French Neurol. Soc. (hon.), European Info. Providers Assn. (pres. 1980-83), Amsterdam Neurol. Soc. (hon.), Peruvian Soc. Psychiat. Neurology and Neurosurgey (hon.). Founder, editor-in-chief Handbook of Clinical Neurology, 77 vols.; editor sci. books; contbr. articles to profl. jours. Home: 142 Bentveldsweg, 2111 EE Aerdenhout The Netherlands

VINOCUR, M. RICHARD, publisher; b. Columbus, Ohio, Nov. 16, 1934; s. Louis O. and Edith (Solomon) V.; m. Carol S. Lennard, Oct. 26, 1957; children: Michael Drew, Lesle Jane. B.A. in Journalism, Ohio State U., 1956. Asso. editor R.H. Donnelley, 1956-59; v.p., pub. Vance Pub., N.Y.C., 1959-79; pub. Graphic Arts Monthly, N.Y.C., 1979-87, group pub. Fire Engring.; pres. Footprint Communications, Inc., N.Y.C., 1987—; pub. Footprints (twice monthly newsletter for printing industry execs.), Vue/Point:The Hard Copy Mag., Web Offset: The Hard Copy; columnist Am. Printer Mag., 1988—; organizing mgr., founder Vue/Point 90, 1990—; lectr. N.Y.U.; cons. CSV Found. Author: How to Win Occasionally, 1980. Pres. Greentree Assn.; sec. S. Harris Fund. Named Pub. of Yr., Hopkins Found., 1980, Internat. Assn. Printers and Craftsmen; recipient citizenship award Newcomb Club, 1979, Gutenberg media award Printing Industries, 1995. Mem. Graphic Arts Tech. Found., Sigma Delta Chi. Republican. Jewish. Club: Bonat BG. Home: 9 Greentree Ter Tenafly NJ 07670-2405 Office: Footprint Communications Inc PO Box 255 Tenafly NJ 07670-0255 also: Footprint Communications Inc 2400 Lemoine Ave Fort Lee NJ 07024-6204

VINROOT, RICHARD ALLEN, lawyer, mayor; b. Charlotte, N.C., Apr. 14, 1941; s. Gustav Edgar and Vera Frances (Pickett) V.; m. Judith Lee Allen, Dec. 29, 1964; children: Richard A., Laura Tabor, Kathryn Pickett. BS in BA, U. N.C., 1963, JD, 1966. Bar: N.C. 1966, U.S. Dist. Ct. (ea., mid. and we. dists.) N.C. 1969, U.S. Ct. Appeals (4th cir.) 1969. Ptnr. Robinson, Bradshaw & Hinson, P.A., Charlotte, 1969—; mayor City of Charlotte, N.C., 1991—. Mem. Charlotte City Coun., 1983-91. Mem. ABA, N.C. Bar Assn., Mecklenburg County Bar Assn. (sec. 1976). Republican. Presbyterian. Office: Office of the Mayor Charlotte-Mecklenburg Govt Ctr 600 E 4th St Charlotte NC 28202-2870

VINSON, C. ROGER, federal judge; b. Cadiz, Ky., Feb. 19, 1940; m. Ellen Watson; children: Matt, Todd, Cate, Patrick, Joey. BS, U.S. Naval Acad., 1962; JD, Vanderbilt U., 1971. Commd. ensign USN, 1962, advanced through grades to lt., 1963, naval aviator, until 1968, resigned, 1968; assoc. to ptnr. Beggs & Lane, Pensacola, Fla., 1971-83; judge U.S. Dist. Ct. (no. dist.) Fla., Pensacola, 1983—. Office: US Courthouse 100 N Palafox St Pensacola FL 32501-4839

VINSON, JAMES SPANGLER, university president; b. Chambersburg, Pa., May 17, 1941; s. Wilbur S. and Anna M. (Spangler) V.; m. Susan Alexander, Apr. 8, 1967; children: Suzannah, Elizabeth. B.A., Gettysburg Coll., 1963; M.S. U. Va., 1965, Ph.D., 1967. Asst. prof. physics MacMurray

Coll., Jacksonville, Ill., 1967-71; asso. prof. physics U. N.C., Asheville, 1971-78; prof. physics U. N.C., 1974-78, chmn. dept. physics, dir. acad. computing, 1974-78; prof. physics, dean Coll. Arts and Scis. U. Hartford (Conn.), 1978-83; v.p. acad. affairs Trinity U., San Antonio, 1983-87; pres. U. Evansville, Ind., 1987—; computer cons. Contbr. articles to profl. jours. Mem. Am. Phys. Soc., World Future Soc., AAAS, Am. Assn. for Advancement of Humanities, Am. Assn. for Higher Edn., Am. Assn. Physics Tchrs., Phi Beta Kappa, Sigma Xi, Phi Sigma Kappa. Methodist. Office: U Evansville 1800 Lincoln Ave Evansville IN 47722-0001

VINSON, LAURENCE DUNCAN, JR., lawyer; b. Gadsden, Ala., Mar. 17, 1947. BS with hons., U. Ala., Tuscaloosa, 1969; JD, U. Ala., 1973. Bar: Ala., U.S. Dist. Ct. (no., mid. and so. dists.) Ala., U.S. Ct. Appeals (11th cir.), U.S. Supreme Ct. Assoc. Bradley, Arant, Rose & White, Birmingham, Ala., 1973-79; ptnr. Bradley, Arant, Rose & White, 1979—. Bar: Ala. 1973, U.S. Dist. Ct. (no. dist.) Ala. 1973, U.S. Supreme Ct. 1977, U.S. Ct. Appeals (11th cir.) 1981, U.S. Dist. Ct. (so. dist.) Ala. 1989, U.S. Dist. Ct. (mid. dist.) Ala. 1991. Chmn. Ala. Uniform Comml. Code Revisions Coms., Arts 3, 4, and 4A. Mem. ABA, Birmingham Bar Assn., Ala. State Bar, Ala. Law Inst., Order of Coif, Phi Beta Kappa, Omicron Delta Kappa. Office: Bradley Arant Rose & White PO Box 830709 2001 Park Pl Ste 1400 Birmingham AL 35283-0709

VINSON, MORTY CONRAD (MORTY VINSON), oil company executive, rancher; b. Mertzon, Tex. Dec. 12, 1921; s. Albert Frank and May Victoria (Miller) V.; m. Anna Louise Rowan, Sep. 25, 1947; children: Bryan, Wayne, Wade David. BS in Geology, U. Tex., 1951. Registered petroleum geologist. Subsurface geologist Magnolia Petroleum Co., Oklahoma City, Okla., 1951-55; area geologist Magnolia Petroleum Co., Midland, Tex., 1955-59, dist. geologist, 1959-60; dist. geologist Mobil Oil Corp., Midland, Tex., 1960-62, div. geologist, 1962-66; v.p. Sams Oil Corp., Midland, 1966-68; gen. mgr. N.Am. Royalties Inc., Midland, 1968-70; pres. Tejas Energy Exploartiaon Inc., Midland, 1970-72, Vinson Exploration Inc., Midland, 1972—; pres. Vinson Operating Co., Midland, 1991—, Concho Creek Corp., Midland, 1992—; finder Brown-Bassett Gas Field, 1959, Frances Hill, Companero Gas Fields, 1971; joint finder Coynosa, Rojo Cabollos Gas Field, 1960-61. Supporter ARC, Salvation Army, 1955—, Republican Party, 1975—, Stewarts of the Range, 1992—. Sgt. USMC, 1942-46. Mem. Am. Assn. Petroleum Geologists, Nat. Cattlemen's Assn., West Tex. Geol. Soc. (hon. life mem., pres. 1964-65), Permian Basin Petroleum Assn., Soc. Ind. Profl. Earth Scis., Southwest Tex. Cattlemen's Assn. Republican. Avocations: ranching, cattle, horses, wildlife. Home: 1505 Douglas Midland TX 79701 Office: Vinson Exploration Inc 507 N Marienfeld Ste 201 Midland TX 79701

VINSON, WILLIAM C., architectural firm executive. BArch, U. Tenn., 1973. Lic. architect, Fla.; cert. Nat. Coun. Archtl. Registration Bds. With Community Tectonics, Inc., 1973—, office dir., sec., v.p., prodn. dir. Deacon, dir. royal amb. program Ctrl. Bapt. Ch. Bearden; active Knoxville Mus. Art, Knoxville Zoo. Mem. AIA (East Tenn. chpt.), Tenn. Soc. Architects, Tenn. Heritage Alliance, Knoxville Heritage, So. Bldg. Code Congress. Office: Community Tectonics Inc 105 North Concord 200 Knoxville TN 37919

VINTON, SAMUEL R., JR., religious organization administrator, Adj. prof. Grace Bible Coll., Grand Rapids, Mich.; exec. dir. Grace Ministries Internat., Grand Rapids, Mich. Office: Grace Ministries Internat PO Box 9405 Grand Rapids MI 49509

VINZ, FRANK LOUIS, electrical engineer; b. Laredo, Tex., Jan. 5, 1932; s. Louis and Margaret Reeves (Schaer) V.; m. Mary Marguerite Harlow, June 24, 1956; children: Laura Lee, Susan Elizabeth, Bradley Louis. BSEE, Tex. A&M U., 1953; MSEE, USAF Inst. Tech., 1963; postgrad. in Elec. Engring., U. Tenn., 1967. Cert. FAA flight instr., 1975—. Officer USAF, 1953-58; project officer Air Force Armament Ctr., 1955-58; electronic engr. Army Ballistic Missile Agy., Redstone Arsenal, Ala., 1958-60; engring. supr. Marshall Space Flight Ctr. NASA, Huntsville, Ala., 1960-89; prin. engr. BDM Internat., Inc., Huntsville, 1989-91; sr. engr. Loral AeroSys divsn., Huntsville, 1991-94; ret., 1994; participant Apollo/Saturn, space shuttle, space sta. programs NASA. Contbr. articles to Jour. Navigation, SPIE Symposium on Intelligent Robots. Pres. Huntsville Assn. Tech. Socs., 1995-96; trustee, chmn. Presbyn. Ch., Huntsville, 1974-76, elder, 1959-63, 78-81, 83-85. Grad. sch. scholarship NASA-MSFC, U. Tenn., 1966-67. Mem. NSS, AIAA (com. for flight simulation), Tau Beta Pi Engring. Honor Soc. Home: 1006 San Ramon Ave SE Huntsville AL 35802

VIOLA, FRANK JOHN, JR., professional baseball player; b. East Meadow, N.Y., Apr. 19, 1960; m. Kathy Daltas; children: Frank III, Brittany Ann, Kaley Marie. Student, St. John's U. Pitcher Minnesota Twins, Mpls., 1981-89, N.Y. Mets, 1989-92, Boston Red Sox, 1992-94, Toronto Blue Jays, 1994—; mem. Am. League All-Star Team, 1988; mem. Nat. League All-Star Team, 1990-91; World Series champions, 1987; Nat. League Innings Pitched Leader, 1990. Recipient Am. League Cy Young award, 1988; named to Sporting News All-Star Team, 1988, Sporting News Nat. League All-Star Team, 1990; named Sporting News Am. League Pitcher of Yr., 1988. Office: Toronto Blue Jays, One Blue Jay Way Ste 3200, Toronto, ON Canada M5V 1J1*

VIOLA, HERMAN JOSEPH, museum director; b. Chgo., Feb. 24, 1938; s. Joseph and Mary (Incollingo) V.; m. Susan Patricia Bennett, June 13, 1964; children—Joseph, Paul, Peter. B.A. Marquette U., 1960, M.A., 1964; Ph.D., Ind. U., 1970. Founding editor Prologue: Jour. of Nat. Archives, 1969-72; dir. Nat. Anthrop. Archives, 1972-86; dir. quincentenary programs Mus. Natural History Smithsonian Inst., Washington, 1986-94; curator emeritus Smithsonian Instn., Washington, 1994—. Author: Thomas L. McKenney, Architect of America's Early Indian Policy, 1816-1830, 1974, The Indian Legacy of Charles Bird King, 1976, Diplomats in Buckskins: A History of Indian Delegations in Washington City, 1981, The National Archives of the United States, 1984, Magnificent Voyagers: The U.S. Exploring Expedition, 1938-42, 1985, Exploring the West: A Smithsonian Book, 1987, After Columbus: America's Indians Since 1492, 1990, Seeds of Change: Five Hundred Years Since Columbus, 1991, Ben Nighthorse Campbell: An American Warrior, 1993. Served with USNR, 1960-62. Mem. Orgn. Am. Historians, Western History Assn., Am. Hist. Assn., Soc. Am. Archivists (program chmn. 1972). Home: 7307 Pinewood St Falls Church VA 22046-2725 Office: Mus Natural History Smithsonian Instn Washington DC 20560

VIOLENUS, AGNES A., school system administrator; b. N.Y.C., May 17, 1931; d. Antonio and Constance Violenus. BA, Hunter Coll., 1952; MA, Columbia U., 1958; EdD, Nova U., 1990. Tchr. N.Y. State Day Care, N.Y.C., 1952-53, N.Y.C. Bd. Edn., 1953-66; asst. prin. N.Y.C. Elem. and Jr. High Sch., 1966-91; adj. instr. computer dept. continuing edn. div. York Coll., N.Y.C., 1985-88; adj. instr. tchr. mentor program grad. edn. div. CCNY, 1990-91; reviewer ednl. and instructional films. Avocation: LOGO: K-12, 1980; contbr. articles to profl. jours. Life mem. Girl Scouts U.S., N.Y.C.; mem. N.Y.C. Sch. Vol. Program, 1991—. Recipient Dedicated Svc. award Coun. Suprs. and Adminstrs. Mem. N.Y. Acad. Scis., Nat. Assn. Negro Bus. and Profl. Women's Clubs (scholarship com. 1989—), Nat. Black Child Devel. Inst. (bd. dir. 1991—, pub. policy com. 1991—), Pub. Edn. Assn. (mem. good schs. exch. com.), Schomburg Ctr. Rsch. in Black Culture (bd. trustee, co-chair corp. task force on African-Am. in math., sci., and tech. 1992—). Doctorate Assn. N.Y. Educators, N.Y. Alliance Black Sch. Educators, Hunter Coll. Alumni Assn. (bd. dirs. 1993—), Bank St. Alumni Coun. Greater N.Y. (asst. sec. 1991—), Wistarians Alumni Hunter Coll. (pres. 1990—). Democrat. Roman Catholic. Avocations: science, music, collecting black edn. memorabilia, instructing survival strategies and techniques for women and children. Office: 626 Riverside Dr Apt 24P New York NY 10031-7238

VIORST, JUDITH STAHL, author; b. Newark, Feb. 2, 1931; d. Martin Leonard and Ruth June (Ehrenkranz) Stahl; m. Milton Viorst, Jan. 30, 1960; children: Anthony Jacob, Nicholas Nathan, Alexander Noah. BA, Rutgers U., 1952; grad., Washington Psychoanalytic Inst., 1981. Author: (children's books) Sunday Morning, 1968, I'll Fix Anthony, 1969, Try It Again Sam, 1970, The Tenth Good Thing About Barney, 1971 (Silver Pencil award 1973), Alexander and the Terrible Horrible No Good Very Bad Day, 1972, My Mama Says There Aren't Any Zombies, Ghosts, Vampires, Creatures,

Demons, Monsters, Fiends, Goblins or Things, 1973, Rosie and Michael, 1974, Alexander, Who Used to Be Rich Last Sunday, 1978, The Good-Bye Book, 1988, Earrings!, 1990, The Alphabet from Z to A (with Much Confusion on the Way, 1994, Alexander, Who's Not (Do You Hear Me? I Mean It!) Going to Move, 1995; (poetry) The Village Square, 1965-66, It's Hard to Be Hip Over Thirty and Other Tragedies of Married Life, 1968, People and Other Aggravations, 1971, How Did I Get to Be Forty and Other Atrocities, 1976, If I Were in Charge of the World and Other Worries, 1981, When Did I Stop Being Twenty and Other Injustices, 1987, Forever Fifty and Other Negotiations, 1989, Sad Underwear and Other Complications, 1995; (with Milton Viorst) The Washington Underground Gourmet, 1970, Yes Married, 1972, A Visit From St. Nicholas (To a Liberated Household), 1977, Love and Guild and the Meaning of Life, Etc., 1979, Necessary Losses, 1986, Murdering Mr. Monti, 1994; columnist Redbook mag. (Penney-Mo. award 1974, Am. Acad. Pediatrics award 1977, AAUW 1980). Jewish. Home: 3432 Ashley Ter NW Washington DC 20008-3238

VIORST, MILTON, writer; b. Paterson, N.J., Feb. 18, 1930; s. Louis and Betty (LeVine) V.; m. Judith Stahl, Jan. 30, 1960; children—Anthony, Nicholas, Alexander. B.A. summa cum laude, Rutgers U., 1951; student (Fulbright scholar), U. Lyon, France, 1952; M.A., Harvard U., 1955; M.S., Columbia U., 1956. Reporter Bergen (N.J.) Record, 1955-56, Newark StarLedger, 1956-57, Washington Post, 1957-61; Washington corr. N.Y. Post, 1961-64; syndicated columnist Washington Evening Star, 1971-75; staff writer The New Yorker, N.Y.C., 1987-93; Fervis prof. journalism Princeton (N.J.) U.,1995-96; lectr. in field. Author: Hostile Allies: FDR and deGaulle, 1965, Great Documents of Western Civilization, 1965, Fall from Grace: The Republican Party and the Puritan Ethic, 1968, Hustlers and Heroes, 1971, Fire in the Streets: America in the 1960's, 1980, Making a Difference: The Peace Corps at Twenty-five, 1986, Sands of Sorrow: Israel's Journey from Independence, 1987, Reaching for the Olive Branch: UNRWA and Peace in the Middle East, 1990, Sandcastles: The Arabs in Search of the Modern World, 1994; also articles.; contbg. editor Tikkun. Chmn. Fund for Investigative Journalism, 1969-78; bd. dirs. Georgetown Day Sch., 1977-80. Served as officer USAF, 1952-54. Recipient Columbia Journalism Alumni award, 1992; Woodrow Wilson sr. fellow, 1973-79, Alicia Patterson fellow, 1979; Middle East Inst. sr. scholar. Mem. PEN, Soc. Profl. Journalists, Author's Guild, Coun. on Fgn. Rels., Am. Peace Now (bd. dirs.), Phi Beta Kappa.

VIRGO, JOHN MICHAEL, economist, researcher, educator; b. Pressburry, Eng., Mar. 11, 1943; s. John Joseph and Muriel Agnes (Franks) V.; m. Katherine Sue Ulmrich, Sept. 6, 1980 (div. 1979); 1 child, Debra Marie. BA, Calif. State U., Fullerton, 1967, MA, 1969; MA, Claremont Grad. Sch., 1971, PhD, 1972. Instr. econs. Whittier (Calif.) Coll., 1970-71, Calif. State U., Fullerton and Long Beach, 1971-72, Claremont (Calif.) Grad. Sch., 1971-72; asst. prof. econs. Va. Commonwealth U., Richmond, 1972-74; assoc. prof. mgmt. So. Ill. U., Edwardsville, 1975-83, prof., 1984—; bd. dirs., founder Internat. Health Econ. & Mgmt. Inst., Edwardsville, 1983-87. Author: Legal & Illegal California Farmworkers, 1974; author, editor: Health Care: An International Perspective, 1984, Exploring New Vistas in Health Care, 1985, Restructuring Health Policy, 1986; founder, editor-in-chief Internat. Advances in Econ. Rsch. Served with USN, 1965-68. Mem. Internat. Hosp. Fedn., Am. Econ. Assn. Am. Hosp. Assn., Am. Soc. Assn. Execs., Royal Econ. Soc. Atlantic Econ. Soc. (founder, exec. v.p., mng. editor jour. 1973—), Allied Social Scis. Assn. (chmn. exec. confs. 1982-84), AMA, So. Econs. Assn., Sunset Hills Club (Edwardsville). Democrat. Roman Catholic. Avocations: tennis, skiing. Home: 5277 Lindell Blvd Saint Louis MO 63108 Office: So Ill U Atlantic Econ Soc PO Box 1101 Edwardsville IL 62026

VIRGO, JULIE ANNE CARROLL, management consultant; b. Adelaide, South Australia, Australia, June 14, 1944; came to U.S., 1966; d. Archibald Henry and Norma Mae (Gillett) Noolan; m. Daniel Thuering Carroll, Aug. 20, 1977. M.A., U. Chgo., 1968, Ph.D., 1974, Exec. M.B.A., 1983. With State Library of South Australia, 1962-63, Repatriation Dept. South Australia, 1962-66; asst. librarian U. Chgo. Libraries, 1966-68; dir. edn. Med. Library Assn., Chgo., 1972-77; exec. dir. Assn. Coll. and Research Libraries, Chgo., 1977-84; exec. v.p., COO Carroll Group, Inc., 1984—; mem. faculty U. Chgo., 1968-89. Author: Libraries and Accreditation in Higher Education; contbr. articles to jours. U. Chgo. fellow, 1967-68, Higher Edn. Act fellow, 1969-72; Nat. Library of Medicine grantee, 1967-69; named Outstanding Young U.S. Leader 1985 Coun. on the U.S...; Mem. ALA, Am. Soc. Assn. Execs., Am. Mgmt. Assn., Spol. Librs. Assn., Am. Soc. for Info. Scis. (past pres., doctoral award), ASTD, Nat. Tng. Labs. (bd. dirs. 1990—), Orgn. Devel. Network, Internat. Assn. Neuro-Linguistic Programming (bd. dirs. 1990-93), Internat. Bd. for Plant Genetic Resources (Rome, bd. dirs. 1991—), Internat. Ctr. Agrl. Rsch. in Dry Areas (Syris, bd. dirs. 1992—), Planning Forum, Beta Phi Mu.

VIRGO, MURIEL AGNES, swimming school owner; b. Liverpool, Cheshire, Eng., Apr. 3, 1924; d. Harold Thornhill and Susan Ann (Duff) Franks; m. John Virgo, Aug. 13, 1942; children: John Michael, Angela Victoria, Barbara Ann, Collin Anthony, Donna Marie. Grad. parochial schs. Co-owner Virgo Swim Sch., Garden Grove, Calif., 1967—. Mem. Ancient Mystical Order Rosae Crucis, Traditional Martinist Order. Republican. Roman Catholic. Avocation: ballroom dancing. Home: 12751 Crestwood Cir Garden Grove CA 92641-5250 Office: Virgo Swim Sch 12851 Brookhurst Way Garden Grove CA 92641-5205

VIRKHAUS, TAAVO, symphony orchestra conductor; b. Tartu, Estonia, June 29, 1934; came to U.S., 1949; s. Adalbert August and Helene Marie (Sild) V.; m. Nancy Ellen Herman, Mar. 29, 1969. MusB U. Miami, 1955; MusM Eastman Sch. of Music, Rochester, 1957, DMA, 1967. Dir. music U. Rochester (N.Y.), also assoc. prof. Eastman Sch., Rochester, 1967-77; music dir., condr. Duluth (Minn.) Superior Symphony Orch., 1977-94; guest condr. Rochester Philharm., Minn. Orch., Balt. Symphony, Vancouver Symphony and others, 1972—; music dir., condr. Hunstville (Ala.) Symphony Orch., 1989—; guest condr. at Tallinn, Estonia, 1978, 88, 90, 92, 93, 94; lectr. U. Minn.-Duluth, U. of Wis.-Superior. With U.S. Army, 1957-58, USAR, 1957-61. Recipient Howard Hanson Composition award, 1966, Am. Heritage award JFK Libr. for Minorities, 1974; Fulbright scholar, Musickhochschule, Cologne, 1963. Mem. Am. Symphony Orch. League, Condrs. Guild, Am. Fedn. of Musicians. Composer: Violin Concerto, 1966, Symphony No. 1, 1976, Symphony No. 2, 1979, Symphony No. 3, 1984, Symphony No. 4, 1989, Symphony No. 5, 1994. Republican. Lutheran.

VIRKLER, DENNIS M., film editor. Editor: (films) Burnt Offerings, 1976, Xanadu, 1980, Continental Divide, 1981, Airplane II: The Sequel, 1982, Gorky Park, 1983, Independence Day, 1983, The River Rat, 1984, Secret Admirer, 1985, Nobody's Fool, 1986, (with William M. Anderson and Sheldon Kahn) Big Shots, 1987, Distant Thunder, 1988, (with John Wright) The Hunt for Red October, 1990 (Academy award nomination best film editing 1990), (with Don Brochu, Robert A. Ferretti, and Dov Hoenig) Under Siege, 1992, (with David Finfer) The Fugitive, 1993 (Academy award nomination best film editing 1993), Batman Forever, 1995. Office: Broder Kurland Webb Uffner Agency 9242 Beverly Blvd Beverly Hills CA 90210*

VIS, MARY A. MURGA, elementary education educator; b. East Chicago, Ind., Nov. 25, 1932; d. John and Rose (Cheranko) Murga; m. Ira Vis, Sept. 5, 1970; 1 child, Douglas. Diploma, Nat. Inst. Practical Nursing, Chgo., 1955; BS cum laude, St. Joseph's Coll., East Chicago, 1968; MS, Purdue U., Hammond, Ind., 1974, reading specialist endorsement, 1991. Elem. tchr. Gary Sch. Diocese, Hammond, 1968-70; tchr. spl. edn. Hammond Sch. System, 1986-87; elem. tchr. East Chicago Sch. System, 1987—. Author: East Chicago My Hometown, 1993. Mem. Hammond Area Reading Coun., AAUW, Delta Epsilon Sigma. Office: 2400 Cardinal Dr East Chicago IN 46312-3185

VISCHER, HAROLD HARRY, manufacturing company executive; b. Toledo, Oct. 17, 1914; s. Harry Philip and Hazel May (Patterson) V.; m. DeNell Meyers, Feb. 18, 1938; children: Harold Harry, Robert P., Michael L. B.B.A., U. Toledo, 1937. With Ohio Bell Telephone Co., 1937-38; with Firestone Tire & Rubber Co., Toledo, 1948-61; nat. passenger tire sales mgr. Firestone Tire & Rubber Co., 1953-57, dist. mgr., 1957-61; with Bandag Inc., Muscatine, Iowa, 1961-80; exec. v.p., pres. Bandag Inc. (Rubber and Equipment Sales group), 1975-80; also dir.; pres., gen. mgr. Hardline International., Inc., Jackson, Mich.. 1980-82; chmn. Tred-X Corp., 1982—. Mem. City Council, Muscatine, 1964-76; chmn., mem. Dist. Export Council Iowa, 1964-81; chmn. Muscatine United Way, 1969-70; mem. adv. bd. Engring. Coll. Iowa State U., 1970-81; mem. Muscatine Light & Water Bd., 1979-80. Elected to Nat. Tire Dealers and Retreaders Assn. Hall of Fame, 1988, to Internat. Tire Retreading and Repairing Hall of Fame, 1990. Mem. Nat. Tire and Retreaders Suppliers Group Assn. (chmn. 1979-80, exec. com. 1977-80), Tire Retread Info. Bur. (exec. com. 1974-81), Am. Retreading Assn. (adv. bd. 1970-72), Retreading Industry Assn., Industry Man of Yr. 1979), Christian Business men's Com., Gideons, Rotary. Republican. Baptist. Home: 13500 Vischer Rd Brooklyn MI 49230-9022 Office: 116 Frost St Jackson MI 49202-2310

VISCLOSKY, PETER JOHN, congressman, lawyer; b. Gary, Ind., Aug. 13, 1949; s. John and Helen (Kauzlaric) V. B.S. in Acctg., Ind. U.-Indpls., 1970; J.D., U. Notre Dame, 1973; LL.M. in Internat. and Comparative Law, Georgetown U., 1983. Bar: Ind., D.C., U.S. Supreme Court. Legal asst. Dist. Atty.'s Office, N.Y.C., 1972; assoc. Benjamin, Greco & Gouveia, Merrillville, Ind., 1973-76, Greco, Gouveia, Miller, Pera & Bishop, Merrillville, Ind., 1982-84; assoc. staff appropriations com. U.S. Ho. of Reps., Washington, 1976-80, assoc. staff budget com., 1980-82; mem. 99th-104th Congresses from 1st dist. Ind., 1985—; mem. Appropriations com., subcoms. treasury, postal svc., gen. govt. and military constrn. Democrat. Roman Catholic. Office: US House of Reps 2464 Rayburn Washington DC 20515*

VISE, DAVID ALLAN, journalist; b. Nashville, Tenn., June 16, 1960; s. Harry and Doris Bertha (Oppenheim) V.; m. Lori Silverman, July 14, 1984; children: Lisa Michelle, Allison Sarah. BS in Econs. magna cum Laude, U Pa., Phila., 1982; MBA, U Pa., 1983. Investment banker Goldman, Sachs & Co., N.Y.C., 1983-84; business reporter The Washington Post, 1984-90, 1993—, local business editor, 1990-91, deputy business editor, 1991-92. Author: Eagle On The Street, 1991; contbr. to World Book Encyclopedia. Vol. Children's Hosp. Wash., 1984-87, Martha's Table Shelter, 1991—; bd. dirs. Wash. Hebrew Congregation, 1989—. Recipient Pulitzer Prize for explanatory journalism, 1990, Gerald Loeb award for disting. bus. and fin. journalism, UCLA bus. sch., 1990. Jewish. Avocations: Tennis, basketball, swimming, travel, reading. Office: Washington Post 1150 15th St NW Washington DC 20071-0002*

VISEK, ALBERT JAMES, computer engineer; b. Phila., July 7, 1934; s. Albert John and Rose (Schlacta) V.; m. Patricia Ann Mullen, Aug. 25, 1962; children: Patrick Albert, Kelly Ann. BS in Physics and Electronics, LaSalle Coll., 1968; MBA, Temple U., 1978. Project engring. mgr., test dir. spl. projects GE Co., Phila.. 1961-73; mgr. EMI/EMC Group Sperry Corp. Hdqtrs., Blue Bell, Pa., 1973-88; program coord. Tempest Def. Systems Div., Great Valley, Pa., 1986-87; mgr. product engring. and environ. support Info. Systems Group, Exton, Pa.. 1987-89; OEM product quality staff engr. Personal Workstation Div., Flemington, N.J., 1990-92; staff engr. Power Supply Engring. Group Computer Systems Group, Tredyffrin, Pa., 1992—; with Unisys Corp., Blue Bell, 1973—; co-founder, dir. engring., cons. Computer Room Specialists, Bethlehem, Pa., 1989-92; co. rep., vice-chmn. CBEMA trade assn.; presenter tech. papers in field, seminars and confs. in field. With USN, 1957-59. Mem. IEEE (presenter paper symposium 1986), Nat. Assn. Radio and Telecomm. Engrs. (cert. electromagnetic compatibility engr.). Roman Catholic. Avocations: fishing, boating, travel, cooking, reading. Home: 1306 Hartrantf Ave Fort Washington PA 19034 Office: Unisy 2476 Swedesford Rd Paoli PA 19301

VISEK, WILLARD JAMES, nutritionist, animal scientist, physician, educator; b. Sargent, Nebr., Sept. 19, 1922; s. James and Anna S. (Dworak) V.; m. Priscilla Flagg, Dec. 28, 1949; children: Dianna, Madeleine, Clayton Paul. B.Sc. with honors (Carl R. Gray scholar), U. Nebr., 1947; MSc (Smith fellow in agr.), Cornell U., 1949, Ph.D., 1951; M.D. (Peter Yost Fund scholar), U. Chgo., 1957; DSc (hon.), U. Nebr., 1980. Diplomate Nat. Bd. Med. Examiners, 1960. Grad. asst., lab. animal nutrition Cornell U., 1947-51; AEC postdoctoral fellow Oak Ridge, 1951-52; research assoc., 1952-53; research asst. pharmacology U. Chgo., 1953-57, asst. prof., 1957-61, assoc. prof., 1961-64; rotating med. intern U. Chgo. Clinics, 1957-58, 58-59, 59; prof. nutrition and comparative metabolism, dept. animal sci. Cornell U., Ithaca, N.Y., 1964-75; prof. clin. sci. (nutrition and metabolism) Coll. Medicine and dept. food sci. U. Ill. Coll. Agr., Urbana-Champaign, 1975—; prof. dept. internal medicine U. Ill. Coll. Medicine, Urbana-Champaign, 1986-93, prof. emeritus, 1993—; bd. dirs. Coun. Agriculture, Sci. and Tech., 1994—; bd. sci. advisors Coun. Sci. and Health, 1994—; Brittingham vis. prof. U Wis., Madison, 1982-83; Hogan meml. lectr. U. Mo.., 1987; mem. subcom. dog nutrition, com. animal nutrition NRC-Nat. Acad. Sci., 1965-71; adv. council Inst. Lab. Animal Resources, NRC-Nat. Acad. Sci., 1966-69; sub-com. animal care facilities Survey Inst. Lab. Animal Resources, 1967-70; cons., lectr. in field; mem. sci. adv. com. diet and nutrition cancer program Nat. Cancer Inst., 1976—; mem. nutrition study sect. NIH, 1980-84; chmn. membership com. Am. Inst. Nutrition-Am. Soc. Clin. Nutrition, 1978-79, 80-83, 85; cons. VA, NSF, indsl. orgns.; Wellcome vis. prof. in basic med. scis. Oreg. State U., 1991-92; bd. sci. counselors USDA, 1989—. Mem. editorial bd. Jour. Nutrition, 1980-84, editor, 1990—; contbr. articles to profl. jours. Active local Boy Scouts Am. Served with AUS, 1943-46. Nat. Cancer Inst. spl. fellow M.I.T., research fellow Mass. Gen. Hosp., 1970-71; recipient Alumni award Neb. 4-H, 1967, Osborne and Mendel award, 1985, U. Ill. Coll. Medicine faculty merit award, 1988; sr. scholar U. Ill., 1988. Fellow AAAS, Am. Inst. Nutrition, Am. Soc. Animal Sci. (Am. subcom. antimicrobials, mem. regulatory agency com. 1973-78); mem. Soc. Pharmacology and Exptl. Therapeutics, Am. Inst. Nutrition (council 1980-83, 85-86), Soc. Exptl. Biology and Medicine, Am. Soc. Clin. Nutrition, Am. Therapeutic Soc., Am. Gastroenterol. Assn., Am. Bd. Clin. Nutrition, Innocents Soc., Fedn. Am. Socs. Exptl. Biology (sci. steering group life scis. rsch. office, adv. com. 1986-92), Am. Bd. Nutrition (bd. dirs.), Nat. Dairy Coun. (rsch. adv. com. 1987-91, vis. prof. nutrition program 1981-92), Gamma Alpha (pres. 1948-49), Phi Kappa Phi (pres. 1981-82), Alpha Gamma Rho (pres. 1946-47), Gamma Sigma Delta. Presbyterian (elder). Lodge: Masons. Home: 1405 W William St Champaign IL 61821-4406 Office: U Ill 190 Med Sci Bldg 506 S Mathews Ave Urbana IL 61801-3618

VISHNEVSKAYA, GALINA PAVLOVNA, soprano, opera company director; b. Leningrad, USSR, Oct. 25, 1926; m. Mstislav Rostropovich; children: Olga, Elena. Soprano, Bolshoi Opera, Moscow, to 1974; appeared throughout Europe, U.S., S.Am., including Covent Garden, Paris Opera, Met. Opera; appeared as Tatiana in Eugene Onegin, Paris 1982, Leonora in Fidelio, Aida, Kupava in Snow Maiden, Lisa in Queen of Spades, Chio-Chio San in Madame Butterfly, Margaret in Faust, Natasha in War and Peace, Cherubino in Marriage of Figaro. Author: Galina (autobiography), 1985. Decorated officier Legion of Honor (France); recipient People's Artist of USSR prize, Lenin prize. Mem. Sigma Alpha Iota. Russian Orthodox. Office: care Victor Hochhauser, 4 Holland Park Ave, London W11 3QU, England*

VISKANTA, RAYMOND, mechanical engineering educator; b. Lithuania, July 16, 1931; came to U.S., 1949, naturalized, 1955; s. Vincas and Genovaite (Vinickas) V.; m. Birute Barbara Barpsys, Oct. 13, 1956; children: Renata, Vitas, Tadas. BSME, U. Ill., 1955; MSME, Purdue U., 1956, PhD, 1960; DEng (hon.), Tech. U. Munich, 1994. Registered profl. engr., Ill. Asst. mech. engr. Argonne (Ill.) Nat. Lab., 1956-59, student rsch. assoc., 1959-60, assoc. mech. engr., 1960-62; assoc. prof. mech. engring. Purdue U., West Lafayette, Ind., 1962-66, prof. mech. engring., 1966-86, Gross disting. prof. engring., 1986—; guest prof. Tech. U. Munich, 1976-77, U. Karlsruhe, Germany, 1987; vis. prof. Tohoku Inst. Tech., 1983. Contbr. over 400 tech. articles to profl. jours. Recipient Sr. U.S. Scientist award Alexander von Humboldt Found., 1975, Sr. Rsch. award Am. Soc. Engring. Edn., 1984, Nusselt-Reynolds prize, 1991; Japan Soc. for Promotion Sci. fellow, 1983. Fellow ASME (Heat Transfer Meml. award 1976, Max Jakob Meml. award 1986, Melville medal 1988), AIAA (Thermophysics award 1979); mem. AAUP, AAAS, NAE, Sigma Xi, Pi Tau Sigma, Tau Beta Pi. Home: 3631 Chancellor Way West Lafayette IN 47906-8809 Office: Purdue Univ 1288 Mechanical Engring Bui West Lafayette IN 47907

VISOCKI, NANCY GAYLE, infosystems design consultant; b. Dumont, N.J., May 13, 1952; d. Thomas and Gloria (Valle) V. BA in Maths., Manhattanville Coll.. 1974; MS in Ops. Rsch. and Stats., Rensselaer Poly. Inst., 1977. Rsch. asst. Coll. Physicians and Surgeons Columbia U., N.Y.C., 1974-75; programmer analyst R. Shriver Assocs., Parsippany, N.J., 1977-79; sr. tech. rep. GE Info. Svcs. Co., East Orange, N.J., 1979-81; mgr. project office GE Info. Svcs. Co., Morristown, N.J., 1981-83, tech. dir., 1983-87, tech. mgr., 1988-89; area mgr. system devel. and consulting GE Info. Svcs. Co., Parsippany, 1989-92; area tech. mgr. system devel. and cons., Fin. Info. Systems GE Info. Svcs. Co., Parsippany, N.J., 1992-93, sr. cons. electronic commerce info. svcs., 1993—. Active Western Hills Christian Ch., Tranquility, N.J., 1986—; vol. Women's Ctr., Hackettstown, N.J., 1989-93; class fundraising and gift chmn. Rensselaer Poly. Inst., 1991-95; vol. Elfun Soc. Manhattanville Coll. grantee, Purchase, N.Y., 1970-71; tuition fellow Rensselaer Poly. Inst., Troy, N.Y., 1975-77. Mem. NAFE, Women of Accomplishment. Avocations: skiing, needlepoint, walking, bicycling, reading. Home: 140 E Linden Ave Dumont NJ 07628-1916 Office: GE Info Svcs Co 20 Waterview Blvd Parsippany NJ 07054-1219

VISSER, JOHN EVERT, university president emeritus, historian; b. Orange City, Iowa, Apr. 24, 1920; s. Arthur J. and Frances (TePaske) V.; m. Virginia Jean Schuyler, May 29, 1946; children: Betty Jean, Mary Frances, Nancy Ann, Martha Ellen. BA, Hope Coll., 1942, LittD (hon.), 1995; MA, U. Iowa, 1947, PhD, 1957; D honoris causa, Indsl. U. Santander, Bucaramanga, Colombia, 1968. Asst. prof. history Hope Coll., Holland, Mich., 1949-56; asst. registrar Western Mich. U., 1956-57; asst. dean Ball State U., 1957-58, exec. asst. to pres., prof. history, 1962-67; dean Grand Rapids (Mich.) Jr. Coll., 1958- 62; pres. Emporia (Kans.) State U., 1967-84; cons. U. Alaska, 1985-86; interim chancellor U. Alaska, Juneau, 1986-87; interim vice chancellor, U. Wis., Green Bay, 1987-88. Served to capt. inf. AUS, 1942-46. Inducted into Infantry OCS Hall of Fame, 1982. Mem. Nat. Assn. Intercollegiate Athletics (pres., mem. exec. com.), Am. Assn. State Colls. and Univs. (treas. 1971-75), Kans. Assn. Colls. and Univs. (pres. 1972-73), Blue Key, Phi Delta Kappa, Phi Alpha Theta. Presbyn. Club: Rotarian. Home: RR 1 Box 52 Vassar KS 66543-9716

VISSER, VALYA ELIZABETH, physician; b. Chgo., Oct. 2, 1947; d. Roy Warren and Tania Eugenia (Morozoff) Nelson; children: Kira Elizabeth Visser, Michael Philip Visser. BS, Iowa State U., 1968; MD, U. Iowa, 1973. Diplomate Am. Bd. Pediatrics, Sub-Bd. Neonatal-Perinatal Medicine. Resident pediatrics U. Iowa Hosps. and Clinics, Iowa City, 1976; fellow neonatology Children's Mercy Hosp., Kansas City, 1978; asst. prof. pediatrics U. Kans. Sch. Medicine, Kansas City, 1978-81; staff pediatrician U.S. Army Med. Corps., Ft. Bragg, N.C., 1981-83; attending neonatologist Carolinas Med. Ctr., Charlotte, 1983—; acting chair dept. pediatrics Carolinas Med. Ctr., Charlotte, 1992-94; conf. chair Extracorporeal Life Support Orgn., Ann Arbor, Mich., 1993—. Major Med. Corps., 1981-83. Fellow Am. Acad. Pediatrics; mem. Soc. for Critical Care Medicine. Mem. Unitarian-Universalist Ch. Avocations: parenting, music. Office: Carolinas Med Ctr Dept Pediatrics PO Box 32861 Charlotte NC 28232-2861

VISWANATH, DABIR SRIKANTIAH, chemical engineer; b. Bangalore, India, Aug. 5, 1934; s. Srikantiah and Kamalamma Viswanath; m. Pramila Viswanath, Jan. 5, 1967; 1 child, Arvind. BS, Mysore U., Bangalore, 1953; DIIS, Indian Inst. of Sci., Bangalore, 1956; MS, U. Rochester, 1960, PhD, 1962. Chemist Essen & Co. Bangalore, 1953-54; chem. engr. Sarabhai Chems., Bangalore, 1956-57; asst. prof. to prof., chmn. Indian Inst. of Sci., Barda, 1965-78; vis. prof. Tex. A&M, College Station, 1978-79; prof. U. Mo., Columbia, 1979-90, prof., chmn., 1990—. Co-author: Data Book on Viscosity of Liquids, 1989; contbr. articles to profl. jours. Pari Hargovandas fellowship Indian Inst. of Sci., Lever Bros. fellowship U. Rochester; recipient Halliburton Travel awards, Mo; grantee NSF, 1985, 1990-91, U. Wis., 1982-83, IBM Corp., 1988-91, USEPA-Kans. State, 1988-91, Waste Mgmt. of N.Am., 1992-93. Fellow Am. Inst. of Chemists; mem. AAAS, Am. Inst. of Chem. Engrs., Am. Chem. Soc., Columbia Rotary Club, Indian Inst. of Chem. Engrs., Catalyst Soc. of India. Achievements include rsch. in the chemistry of ordorant components, generalized thermodynamic properties of real gases-generalized compressibility charts, thermodynamic properties of CC14, supercritical extraction, hydrocarbon oxidation, thermophysical properties of gases, liquids and polymer composites. Home: 507 Onofrio Ct Columbia MO 65203-0318 Office: U Mo Dept Chem Engring Columbia MO 65211

VITALE, ALBERTO ALDO, publishing company executive; b. Vercelli, Italy, Dec. 22, 1933; came to U.S., 1960; s. Sergio and Elena (Segre) V.; m. Gemma G. Calori, Oct. 11, 1961; children:—Raffaele Robert, Alessandro David. Dr. Econs. and Bus. Adminstrn., U. Turin, Italy, 1956, postgrad., 1956-57; postgrad. (Fulbright scholar), Wharton Sch. Finance, U. Pa., 1957-58. With Olivetti Corp. Am., 1959-72; dir. corp. planning Olivetti Corp. Am., N.Y.C., 1965-69; v.p. adminstrn. Olivetti Corp. Am., 1969-70; v.p. adminstrn., treas. Olivetti Corp. Am., N.Y.C., 1970-72; prin. officer IFI, Torino, 1972-75; exec. v.p., chief operating officer, dir. Bantam Books, Inc., N.Y.C., 1975-85, pres., 1985-87, co-chief exec. officer, 1985-86, chief exec. officer, 1986-87; pres., chief exec. officer Bantam, Doubleday, Dell Publishing Group, from 1987; now chmn. bd., pres., chief exec. officer Random House, N.Y.C.; bd. dirs. Transworld Pubs. Ltd. Mem. Assn. Am. Pubs. (dir. 1979, 86). Home: 505 Alda Rd Mamaroneck NY 10543-4002 Office: Random House Inc 201 E 50th St New York NY 10022-7703

VITALE, DICK, color commentator, sports writer; b. Garfield, N.J.; m. Lorraine Vitale; children: Terri, Sherri. Basketball coach East Rutherford (N.J.) High Sch., 1965-71; asst. basketball coach Rutgers U., New Brunswick, N.J., 1972; coll. basketball coach U. Detroit, 1973-77, athletic dir., 1978; pro basketball coach Detroit Pistons, Auburn Hills, Mich., 1978-79; TV color commentator ESPN Sports, 1979—, ABC Sports, 1987—; sports radio commentator ABC Radio Network, 1987—; sports columnist Basketball Times, 1979—, Ea. Basketball, 1979—; radio commentator The J. P. McCarthy Show, Detroit; guest spkr., lectr. Co-author: (with Curay Kirk Patrick) Vitale: Just Your Average, Bald, One-Eyed Basketball Wacko Who Beat the Ziggy and Became a PTP'er, 1989, (with Dick Weiss) Time Out, Baby!, 1992, (with Mike Douchant) Tourney Time, It's Awesome Baby, 1994; co-author various computer games; appeared in TV commls. for Adidas, Taco Bell. Named Sports Personality of Yr., Am. Sportscasters Assn., 1989. Roman Catholic. Earned 5 sectional and 2 consecutive state championships as high sch. basketball coach. Office: IMG Peter Goldberg 22 E 71st St New York NY 10021

VITALIANO, CHARLES J(OSEPH), geologist, educator; b. N.Y.C., Apr. 2, 1910; s. Joseph and Catherine (deBarberi) V.; m. Dorothy A. Brauneck, Oct. 19, 1940; children: Judith E., Peter W. B.S., CCNY, 1936; A.M., Columbia U., 1938, Ph.D. (James Furman Kemp fellow), 1944. Instr. extension div. Columbia U., 1938-40; instr. ceramics dept. Rutgers U., 1940-42; geologist U.S. Geol. Survey, 1942-47; assoc. prof. geology Ind. U., Bloomington, 1947-57; prof. Ind. U., 1957-80, prof. emeritus, 1980—; prof. field geology Ind. U. Field Sta. in Mont., summers, 1948-50, 58-74; mem. sci. adv. com. Ind. U., 1979-81; chmn. Ind. U. Credit Union, 1967-68, bd. dirs., 1966-84; prof. field geology U.S. Geol. Survey, Nev. and N.Mex., summers 1950-58; cons. Earth Resources Tech. Satellite project, U. Mont., summer 1973; geol. cons. archaeol. projects, Greece, summers, 1971, 74, 78, 79. Contbr. articles to profl. jours. Fulbright sr. research fellow N.Z., 1954-55; Fulbright lectr. Australia, 1955; NSF grantee, 1957-61, 66-72; recipient Outstanding Teaching award Ind. U., 1982. Fellow Geol. Soc. Am. (chmn. archaeol. geology div. 1985—), AAAS, Mineral. Soc. Am.; mem. Geochem. Soc., Soc. Econ. Geologists. Unitarian. Office: Indiana U Dept Geology Bloomington IN 47405

VITALIANO, ERIC NICHOLAS, state legislator, lawyer; b. S.I., N.Y., Feb. 27, 1948; m. Helen M. Fleming, Sept. 9, 1983; children: Michael, Emma. AB, Fordham Coll., 1969; JD cum laude, NYU, 1971; postgrad., U. Colo., 1977. Bar: N.Y. 1971. Law clk. to Mark A Constantino, U.S. Dist. Ct. for Ea. Dist. N.Y., N.Y.C., 1971-72; assoc. Simpson Thacher & Bartlett, N.Y.C., 1972-79; chief staff to Congressman John M. Murphy U.S. Ho. of Reps., 1979-80; mem. Russo, Silverman & Vitaliano, 1981-82; 86, N.Y. Assembly, Albany, 1982—. Rsch. editor NYU Law Rev., 1970-71. Co-founder Citizens Against Bus Exhaust; co-founder Bodine Creek Civic Assn.; former parish chmn. Cardinal's Archdiocesan Appeal; mem. Dem. Com. Richmond County, N.Y.; pres. N.Y. Conf. Italian-Am. State Legislators; past adv. Assumption Coun. Recipient Stella Falletta Meml. award Clifton Homeowners and Tenants Assn., S.I., 1986, Aldo R. Benedetto Outstanding Citizen award Am. Legion, 1994; named Dem. of Yr., Young Dems. Richmond County, 1980, Friend of Edn., Susan E. Wanger H.S., S.I., 1983, Legislator of Yr., N.Y. State Clks. Assn., 1987, Friend of Italian-Am. Inst., CUNY, 1990, Man of Yr., Italian Club S.I., 1991, Outstanding Citizen, Am. Legion, Richmond County, 1994. Mem. ABA, KC, Order of Coif. Home: 130 Chapin Ave Staten Island NY 10304 Office: NY State Assembly 839 Legislative Office Bldg Albany NY 12248

VITE, FRANK ANTHONY, realtor; b. Aurora, Ill., Feb. 9, 1930; s. Frank A. and Rose (Cosentino) V.; grad. Marmion Mil. Acad., 1948; student Sch. Mgmt., U. Notre Dame, 1958; D.B.A. (hon.), Hillsdale Coll., 1972; m. Barbara Ann Decio, Oct. 23, 1954; children: Bradley Scott, Mark Steven, Michael Lee, Leslie Ann, Lisa Ann. Plant engr. Lyon Metal Products, Aurora, 1951-52, purchasing agt., 1953-54; became sales mgr., exec. v.p., owner, dir. Skyline Homes, Inc., Elkhart, Ind., 1954; pres., owner B&F Realty, Inc., No. Ind. Appraisal Co., Golden Falcon Homes, Inc.; real estate broker; dir. 1st Nat. Bank, Elkhart, Ind. Trustee Hillsdale (Mich.) Coll., Holy Cross Coll., South Bend, Ind.; bd. dirs. Ind. Commn. Higher Edn. Served with AUS, 1952-53, Korea. Mem. Elkhart Bd. Realtors, Nat. Sales Execs. Assn., Ind. Real Estate Assn., Nat. Inst. Real Estate Brokers, Holy Name Soc. Republican. Clubs: K.C. (4 deg.), Knight of Malta, Elks. Home: 23236 Shorelane Elkhart IN 46514-4560 Office: 1300 Cassopolis St Elkhart IN 46514-3248

VITEK, VACLAV, materials scientist; b. Olomouc, Czechoslovakia, Sept. 10, 1940; came to U.S., 1978; s. Josef and Ruzena V.; m. Ludovita Stankovicova, Aug. 5, 1972; children: Adrian Joseph, Clementine Mary. BSc in Physics, Charles U., Prague, 1962; PhD in Physics, Czechoslovakian Acad. Scis., Prague, 1966. Research assoc. dept. metall. materials sci. and research fellow Wolfson Coll., Oxford (Eng.) U., 1967-75; research officer Central Elec. Research Labs., Central Elec. Generating Bd., Leatherhead, Eng., 1975-78; prof. materials sci. and engring. U. Pa., 1978—; vis. prf. U. Groningen, The Netherlands, 1985-86. Recipient Humboldt award for sr. scientists, Germany, 1992-93. Fellow Inst. Physics (London), Am. Soc. Metals Internat.; mem. Am. Phys. Soc., Materials Rsch. Soc. Research on atomistic models of lattice defects, interfaces and amorphous structures, fracture processes and mechanisms, plastic deformation, intermetallic compounds. Office: U Pa Dept Materials Sci and Engring 3231 Walnut St Philadelphia PA 19104-6202

VITERBI, ANDREW JAMES, electrical engineering and computer science educator, business executive; b. Bergamo, Italy, Mar. 9, 1935; came to U.S., 1939, naturalized, 1945; s. Achille and Maria (Luria) V.; m. Erna Finci, June 15, 1958; children: Audrey, Alan, Alexander. SB, MIT, 1957, SM, 1957; PhD, U. So. Calif., 1962; DEng (honoris causa), U. Waterloo, 1990. Research group supr. C.I.T. Jet Propulsion Lab., 1957-63; mem. faculty Sch. Engring. and Applied Sci., UCLA, 1963-73, assoc. prof., 1965-69, prof., 1969-73; exec. v.p. Linkabit Corp., 1973-82; pres. M/A-Com Linkabit, Inc., 1982-84; chief scientist, sr. v.p. M/A-Com. Inc., 1985; prof. elec. engring. and computer sci. U. Calif., San Diego, 1985-94; vice chmn., chief tech. officer Qualcomm Inc., 1985—; chmn. U.S. Commn. C, URSI, 1982-85; vis. com. dept. elec. engring. and computer sci. MIT, 1984—. Author: Principles of Coherent Communication, 1966, (with J.K. Omura) Principles of Digital Communication and Coding, 1979; bd. editors: Proc. IEEE, 1968-77; mem. bd. editors: Information and Control, 1967, Transactions on Info. Theory, 1972-75. Recipient award for valuable contbns. to telemetry, space electonics and telemetry group IRE, 1962, best original paper award Nat. Electronics Conf., 1963, outstanding papers award, info. theory group IEEE, 1968, Christopher Columbus Internat. Comms. award, 1975, Aerospace Comm. award AIAA, 1980, Outstanding Engring. Grad. award U. So. Calif., 1986; co-recipient NEC Corp. C and C Found. award, 1992, S.O. Rice award, 1994, Edward Rhein Found. award, 1994; Marconi Internat. fellow, 1990. Fellow IEEE (Alexander Graham Bell medal 1984, Shannon lectr. internat. symposium on info. theory 1991); mem. NAE. Office: Qualcomm Inc 6455 Lusk Blvd San Diego CA 92121

VITITOE, WILLIAM PAUL, natural gas company executive; b. Evansville, Ind., Sept. 19, 1938; s. Paul Revere and Mariam Elizabeth V.; m. Susan Hoover, July 16, 1960; children: Laura, Stephanie. BS, Ind. U., 1960. With Ind. Bell Telephone Co., 1961-71, 73-77, gen. mgr. North area, 1977; traffic ops. mgr. AT&T, N.Y.C., 1971-73; asst. v.p. bus. svcs. implementation AT&T, 1981-82; v.p. fin., comptroller Mich. Bell Telephone Co., Detroit, 1977-80, v.p. bus., 1980-81, pres., 1983-89; pres. Ameritech Enterprise Group, Chgo., 1989-90; pres., chief exec. officer ANR Pipeline Co., Detroit, 1990—; bd. dirs. Amerisure, Inc., Comerica Inc., Comerica Bank-Detroit, Cross & Trecker Corp. Bd. dirs. Detroit Symphony Orch., 1983—, St. John Hosp., Detroit, 1983—, United Found.; trustee Interlochen Ctr. for Arts, Safety Council S.E. Mich.; mem.-at-large Detroit Area council Boy Scouts Am.; vice chmn. Detroit Renaissance,Inc.; trustee Community Found. for S.E. Mich.; chmn. Mich. Opera Theatre, Partnerships for Edn. Task Force; mem. Conference Bd. Served with USAR, 1960-61. Mem. Fin. Execs. Inst., Detroit Econ. Club (chmn. bd. 1985—), NAACP (life mem.), Founders Soc. Detroit Inst. Arts, Detroit Artists Market, Country of Detroit Club, Detroit Athletic Club, Renaissance Club, Chgo. Club, Grosse Pointe Club, Tournament Players Club. Office: ANR Pipeline Co 500 Renaissance Ctr Detroit MI 48243-1902

VITKOWSKY, VINCENT JOSEPH, lawyer; b. Newark, Oct. 3, 1955; s. Boniface and Rosemary (Ofack) V.; m. Mary Gunzburg, May 16, 1981; children: Vincent Jr., Victoria. BA, Northwestern U., 1977; JD, Cornell U., 1980. Bar: N.Y. 1981. Assoc. Hart and Hume, N.Y.C., 1980-84, Kroll & Tract, N.Y.C., 1984-87; of counsel Nixon, Hargrave, Devans & Doyle, N.Y.C., 1988-89; ptnr. Buchalter, Nemer, Fields & Younger, N.Y.C., 1990—; lectr. industry and bar groups. Contbr. articles to profl. jours. Mem. ABA (com. chmn.), Assn. Bar City of N.Y., Internat. Bar Assn. (com. officer), Am. Arbitration Assn., Bus. Execs. for Nat. Security, Empower Am., Federalist Soc., Cornell Club. Republican. Home: 16 Weed St New Canaan CT 06840 Office: Buchalter Nemer Fields & Younger 237 Park Ave New York NY 10017

VITT, DAVID AARON, medical manufacturing company executive; b. Phila., Aug. 3, 1938; s. Nathan and Flora B.; m. Renee Lee Salkever, Oct. 20, 1963; children: Nadine Lori, Jeffrey Richard. BS, Temple U., 1961. Sales engr. Picker X-Ray Corp., Phila., 1961-65; sales engr. Midwest Am., Chgo., 1965-67, product mgr., 1967-68, product mgr. regional sales, 1968-70; dir. mktg. Valtronic & Living Wills, Bronx, N.Y., 1970-74; v.p. Siemens Med. Systems Inc., gen. mgr. dental div., Iselin, N.J., 1974-86, past corp. v.p.; chief exec. officer, pres. Pelton & Crane, Charlotte, N.C., 1986-89; v.p. govt. sales Siemens Med. Systems Corp. Officers, ret., 1994; founder, pres., CEO D.A.V., Inc., 1995—; industry rep. to Am. Nat. Standards Inst.; co. rep. U.S.-USSR Trade and Econ. Coun.; mem. exec. com. Jr. Achievement, Charlotte. Bd. dirs. Am. Fund for Dental Health; apptd. mem. Charlotte Mecklenburg Community Relations Com.; mem. bd. visitors, bd. vis. U. N.C., Charlotte; Jr. Achievement exec com., officer. Served in USAR, 1961-68. Mem. Am. Mgmt. Assn. (bd. dirs. N.J. chpt.), Am. Mktg. Assn., Am. Dental Trade Assn. (bd. dirs.), Dental Mfrs. Am. (past pres.), Am. Acad. Dental Radiology, Charlotte C. of C. (bd. advisors), Acad. Gen. Dentists (bd. mem. found.), Masons (32 deg.), Shriners. Republican. Office: Siemens Med Systems Inc 186 Wood Ave Iselin NJ 08830-1527

VITT, SAM BRADSHAW, communications media services executive; b. Greensboro, N.C., Oct. 23, 1926; s. Bruno Caesar and Gray (Bradshaw) V.; m. Marie Foster, Oct. 30, 1955; children: Joanne Louise, Michael Bradshaw, Mark Thomas. A.B., Dartmouth Coll., 1950. Exec. asst. TV film CBS, N.Y.C., 1950-52; broadcast media buyer Benton & Bowles, Inc., N.Y.C., 1952-54; broadcast media buyer Biow Co., N.Y.C., 1954-55, assoc. account exec., 1955-56; advt. dir. Banking Law Jour., 1955-69; broadcast media buyer Doherty, Clifford, Steers & Shenfield, Inc., N.Y.C., 1956-57, media supr., 1958-59, v.p., media supr., 1960, v.p., assoc. media dir., 1960, v.p., media dir., 1960-63, v.p. in charge media and broadcast programming, 1963-64; v.p., exec. dir. media-program dept. Ted Bates & Co., Inc., N.Y.C., 1964-65; sr. v.p., exec. dir. media-program dept., 1966-69; dir. Advt. Info. Services, Inc., 1964-65; founder, pres. Vitt Media Internat., Inc., N.Y.C., 1969-81, chmn., CEO, 1982-91, chmn. emeritus, 1991—; lectr. in field, 1967—; lectr. advt. media NYU, 1973, 74, Am. Mgmt. Assn., 1974, 75, Assn. Nat. Advertisers, 1967, 69, 70, Advt. Age Media Workshop, 1975. Media

columnist Madison Ave, 1963-68; editorial cons. Media/Scope, 1968-69; contbr. Advertising Procedure, 1969, rev. edit., 1973, 5th, 6th, 7th edits., 1977, Exploring Advertising, 1970; contbg. editor Handbook of Advertising Management, 1970; contbg. editor Nation's Bus., Broadcasting, Variety, Anny, TV/Radio Age, Sponsor, Printer's Ink; producer rec. album The Body in the Seine; cover story guest editor Media Decisions, 1967. Chmn. radio-TV reps. divsn. Greater N.Y. Fund, 1962, chmn. consumer pub. divsn., 1963; mem. Nat. UN Day Com., 1973, vice chmn., 1974, assoc. chmn. 1975, co-chmn., 1976-77; bd. dirs. UN Assn. Am., 1977; bd. dirs., chmn. Rsch. Inst. Hearing and Balance Disorders Ltd., 1979—; mem. advt. adv. com. The Acting Com., 1984; mem. Pres. Reagan's Joint Presdl. Congl. Steering Com., 1982, Bush Presdl. Roundtable, 1990—. Served to Lt. (j.g.) USN, 1944-46. Recipient Media awards Sta. WRAP, Norfolk, Va., 1962, award of Merit Greater N.Y. Fund, 1963, Gold Key Advt. Leadership award Sta. Reps. Assn., 1967, ann. honors Ad Daily, 1967, Cert. Merit Media/Scope, 1967, 69, Creative Pub. Statement Concerning Advt. award, Cert. of Appreciation, U.S. Congress, 1993, Rep. Congl. Order Liberty, Nat. Rep. Congl. Com., 1993, Order of Merit, Nat. Rep. Senatorial Com., 1994, Rep. Presdl. award Pres. Ronald Reagan and Rep. Senate Leadership, 1994, (with wife) Rep. Senatorial Medal of Freedom, 1994; named one of 10 Best Dressed Men in Advt. Cmty., Gentlemen's Quar., 1979; honoree (with wife) New Rochelle Hosp. Med. Ctr. Centennial Waldorf-Astoria Gala, 1992. Mem. Am. Assn. Advt. Agys. (broadcast media com. dir. com. 1958-63, media operating com. on consumer mags. 1964-65), Internat. Radio and TV Soc. (time-buying and selling seminar com. dir. 1961-62), Internat. Radio and TV Found. (faculty seminar 1974), Nat. Acad. Arts Sci. (mem. com. dir.), Media Dirs. Coun., Sigma Alpha Epsilon, Manor Park Beach Club, N.Y. Athletic Club, Roxbury Run Club (N.Y., Denver). Presbyterian. Avocations: tennis, skiing, golf, swimming, chess. Home: 3 Roosevelt Ave Larchmont NY 10538-2912 Office: Vitt Media Internat Inc 1114 Avenue Of The Americas New York NY 10036-7701

VITTADINI, ADRIENNE, fashion designer; b. Gyor, Hungary; came to U.S., 1957; d. Alexander and Aranka (Langhiel) Toth; m. Gian Luigi Maria Vittadini, 1972; 1 stepchild, Emanuele. Ed., Moore Coll. Art, Phila. Designer Rosanna-Warneco, N.Y.C., 1970-76; v.p. for design Kimberly Knitwear-Gen. Mills, N.Y.C., 1976-78; chmn. bd. Adrienne Vittadini Inc., N.Y.C., 1979—. Recipient Design award Retail Fashion Authorities Am., 1979, Outstanding Phila. Fashion Designer award Council for Labor and Industry, Phila., 1984, Coty Am. Fashion Critics award, 1984. Avocations: tennis; skiing; sailing; swimming. Office: Adrienne Vittadini Inc 575 7th Ave 29th fl New York NY 10018-1805*

VITTER, JEFFREY SCOTT, computer science educator, consultant; b. New Orleans, Nov. 13, 1955; s. Albert Leopold Jr. and Audrey Malvina (St. Raymond) V.; m. Sharon Louise Weaver, Aug. 14, 1982; children: Jillian St. Raymond, J. Scott Jr., Audrey Louise. BS in Math. with highest honors, U. Notre Dame, 1977; PhD in Computer Sci., Stanford U., 1980; AM (hon.), Brown U., 1986. Teaching fellow Stanford (Calif.) U., 1979; asst. prof. Brown U., Providence, 1980-85, assoc. prof., 1985-88, prof., 1988-93; Gilbert, Louis and Edward Lehrman prof. computer sci. Duke U., Durham, N.C., 1993—, chmn. dept., 1993—; cons. IBM, 1981-86, Inst. for Def. Analyses, 1986-86, Supercomputing Rsch. Ctr., 1992—; mem. rsch. staff Math. Scis. Rsch. Inst., Berkeley, 1986, Inst. Recherche en Informatique et en Automatique, Roquencourt, France, 1986-87; vis. prof. Ecole Normale Superieure, Paris, 1986-89; vis. and adj. prof. Tulane U., 1990—; lectr. Asian Sch. on Computer Sci., Bangkok, 1987; assoc. mem. Ctr. Excellence in Space Data and Info. Scis. Author: The Design and Analysis of Coalesced Hashing, 1987; editor Algorithmica, 1988—, guest editor, 1994; editor Math. Sys. Theory: Internat. Jour. on Math. Computing Theory, 1991—, Soc. for Indsl. and Applied Math. Jour. on Computing, 1989—; contbr. articles to profl. jours.; patentee in field. Recipient Faculty Devel. award IBM, 1984, NSF Presdl. Young Investigator award, 1985; NSF grad. fellow, 1977-80; Guggenheim fellow, N.Y.C., 1986-87. Fellow IEEE (editor Trans. on Computers, 1985, 87-91); mem. Assn. for Computing Machinery (editor Communications 1988—), ACM Spl. Interest Group on Automata and Computability Theory (mem. at large 1987-91, vice chair 1991—), Phi Beta Kappa, Sigma Xi. Avocations: reading, golf, basketball, baseball, football. Office: Duke U Dept Computer Sci Durham NC 27708-0129

VITTETOE, MARIE CLARE, retired medical technology educator; b. Keota, Iowa, May 19, 1927; d. Edward Daniel and Marcella Matilda (Peiffer) V. BS, Marycrest Coll., 1950; MS, W.Va. U., 1971, EdD, 1973. Staff technician St. Joseph Hosp., Ottumwa, Iowa, 1950-70; instr. Ottumwa Hosp. Sch. Med. Tech., 1957-70, St. Joseph Hosp. Sch. Nursing, Ottumwa, 1950-70; asst. prof. U. Ill., Champaign-Urbana, 1973-78; prof. clin. lab. scis., med. tech. U. Ky., Lexington, 1978-94. Contbr. articles to profl. jours. Recipient Kingston award for Creative Teaching; Recognition award for svc. to edn. Commonwealth of Ky. Coun. on Higher Edn.; named Ky. Col. Mem. Am. Soc. for Med. Tech. (chmn. 1986-89, Profl. Achievement award 1991, Ky. Mem. of Yr. award 1994), Am. Soc. Clin. Lab. Scis., Alpha Mu Tau, Phi Delta Kappa, Alpha Eta. Avocation: bicycling. Office: 122 Medical Center Anx # 2 Lexington KY 40536

VITTONE, JOHN MICHAEL, federal judge; b. Masontown, Pa., Apr. 29, 1942; s. August and Sarah (Rao) V.; m. Karen Talbott, May 2, 1964; children: John Michael, Anthony Fauster. BA, U. Richmond, 1964; JD, U. Ky., 1967. Bar: Ky. 1967, D.C. 1973, U.S. Supreme Ct. 1978. Atty. FTC, Washington, 1967-68, 70-72; trade regulation counsel G.A. Saxton & Co., Washington, 1972-74; atty. antitrust div. U.S. Dept. Justice, Washington, 1974-80; adminstrv. law judge CAB, Washington, 1980-84, U.S. Dept. Transp., Washington, 1985-87; dep. chief judge U.S. Dept. Labor, Washington, 1987—. Capt. U.S. Army, 1968-70. Mem. ABA (chmn. nat. com. adminstrv. law judges). Roman Catholic. Office: US Dept Labor 1111 20th St NW Suite 700 Washington DC 20036

VITTORIA, JOSEPH V., car rental company executive; b. 1935; married; 4 children. B.S., Yale U., 1957; M.B.A., Columbia U., 1959. With Hertz Corp., 1961-65, 77-82, former pres., chief exec. officer; with Avis Inc., Garden City, N.Y., 1965-77, 82—, regional mgr., 1965-69, v.p. ops., 1969-71, v.p., gen. mgr., 1971-73, sr. v.p., gen. mgr., 1973-77, exec. v.p. sales and mktg., 1982-83, pres., chief operating officer, 1983-87, chmn., chief exec. officer, 1987—, also dir. Mem. bd. regents Georgetown U.; mem. devel. bd. Yale U., bd. dirs. Columbia U. Grad. Sch. of Bus., Nat. Coun. Crime Prevention Coun., Nat. Ctr. for Disability Svcs. Office: Avis Inc 900 Old Country Rd Garden City NY 11530-2128*

VITTORINI, CARLO, publishing company executive; b. Phila., Feb. 28, 1929; s. Domenico and Helen (Whitney) V.; m. Alice Hellerman, Oct. 10, 1953 (div. Dec. 1993); children: Carolyn, Stephen Whitney; m. Nancy Braddock, Dec. 19, 1993. B.A., U. Pa., 1950. Promotion assoc. Chilton Co., Phila., 1950-51; merchandising mgr. Farm-Jour., Inc., Phila., 1951-53; advt. sales rep. Saturday Evening Post, Phila., 1953-61; assoc. advt. mgr. Look Mag., N.Y.C., 1961-65; publisher Redbook Mag., N.Y.C., 1965-75; pres. Charter Publishing, N.Y.C., 1975-78, Harlequin Publishing, N.Y.C., 1978—; chmn. pub., chief exec. officer Parade Publications pubs. Advance Pubs. Inc., N.Y.C., 1979—. Trustee The Jackson Lab., Bar Harbor, Maine, 1973—; former mem. vestry St. Matthew's Ch., Bedford, N.Y. Served with USAR, 1950-57. Judge Advt. Hall of Fame, Am. Advt. Fedn. Mem. Advt. Coun. N.Y.C. (dir.-at-large 1977—), Mag. Pubs. Assn. (bd. dirs 1970-79), Am. Advt. Fedn. (chmn. 1992-93), The Sky Club. Avocations: outdoor activities; tennis. Home: 40 Durenberry Rd Bronxville NY 10708 Office: Parade Publications Inc 711 3d Ave New York NY 10017-4014

VITTUM, DANIEL WEEKS, JR., lawyer; b. Lynch, Ky., Feb. 10, 1939; s. Daniel W. and Kathryn Margaret (Jones) V.; m. Stephanie Ann Empkie, Aug. 18, 1962 (div. July 1987); children: Daniel W. III, Stephen F.; m. Christine L. Jacobek, Nov. 17, 1990. BS, U. Ill., 1961; JD, U. Mich. 1964. Bar: Ill. 1964, U.S Dist. Ct. (no. dist.) Ill. 1965, U.S. Supreme Ct. 1977, U.S. Ct. Appeals (7th cir.) 1976, U.S. Ct. Appeals (4th cir.) 1982, U.S. Ct. Appeals (9th cir.) 1978, U.S. Ct. Appeals (fed.) 1982, U.S. Ct. Appeals (6th cir.) 1992. Assoc. Kirkland & Ellis, Chgo., 1964-69, ptnr., 1970—. Bd. dirs., pres. Northwestern U. Settlement Assn.; mem. vis. com. U. Mich. Law Sch. Mem. ABA, Am. Intellectual Property Assn., Intellectual Property Law Assn. Chgo., Order of Coif, Phi Beta Kappa. Clubs: Mid-Am., East

Bank (Chgo.), Chgo. Yacht Club. Office: Kirkland & Ellis 200 E Randolph Dr Chicago IL 60601-6401

VITULLI, WILLIAM FRANCIS, psychology educator; b. Bklyn., July 17, 1936; s. William S. and Sadie Rosaria (Stallone) V.; m. Betty Jean Sheubrooks, June 15, 1961; children: Paige Vitulli Baggett, Quinn Anthony, Sherik Denise. BA, U. Miami, 1961, MS, 1963, PhD, 1966. Lic. psychologist, Ala. Grad. asst. U. Miami, Coral Gables, Fla., 1961-65; asst. prof. psychology U. South Ala., Mobile, 1965-69, assoc. prof., 1969-75, prof., 1975—; v.p. Ala. Bd. Examiners in Psychology, Montgomery, 1982-84; rsch. cons. Drug Edn. Coun., Mobile, 1988-94. Mem. editorial bd. Jour. Sport Behavior, 1978—; contbr. articles to profl. jours. Mem. adv. bd. Contact Mobile, 1987-92. Named Prof. of Quar., Alpha Lambda Delta, Faculty Mem. of Yr., 1993-94; recipient Outstanding Prof. award Alumni Assn. 1994. Mem. APA, Southeastern Psychol. Assn., Ala. Psychol. Assn. (pres. 1975), Italian-Am. Cultural Soc. South Ala. (chair hist.-cultural com. 1982), Sigma Xi, Psi Chi (faculty adviser U. South Ala. chpt. 1972-80). Roman Catholic. Avocations: jogging, athletics research and analysis, fishing. Home: 2025 Maryknoll Ct Mobile AL 36695-3829 Office: U South Ala 307 University Blvd N Mobile AL 36688

VITUNAC, ANN E., judge; b. 1949. BS, Univ. of Fla., 1970; JD, Stetson Coll. of Law, 1972. Chief trial atty. Fla. State Attorney's Office, West Palm Beach, 1973-85; magistrate judge U.S. Dist. Ct. (Fla. so. dist.), 11th circuit, West Palm Beach, 1985—. Recipient Moot Court award Stetson Coll. of Law, 1972, Robert Sykes award Stetson Coll. of Law, 1973. Mem. Phi Delta Phi Legal Frat., Palm Beach County Bar Assn. Office: US Courthouse 701 Clematis St Rm 423 West Palm Beach FL 33401-5101

VITZ, PAUL CLAYTON, psychologist, educator; b. Toledo, Aug. 27, 1935; m. Evelyn Birge; 6 children. BA high honors in Psychology, U. Mich., 1953; PhD, Stanford U., 1962. Instr. psychology Pomona (Calif.) Coll., 1962-64; asst. prof. NYU, 1965-70, assoc. prof., 1970-85, dir. psychology dept. undergrad. program, 1973-79, prof., 1985—, acting dir. master's program, 1988-89, 90-91, acting dir. grad. program, 1989-90; adj. prof. John Paul II Inst. on Marriage and Family, Washington, 1990?, Internat. Acad. Philosophy, 1994—; lectr. in field. Author: Psychology as Religion: The Cult of Self-Worship, 1977, 2d edit., 1994, (with A.B. Glimeher) Modern Art and Modern Science: The Parallel Analysis of Vision, 1984, Censorship: Evidence of Bias in Our Children's Textbooks, 1986 ,Sigmund Greud's Christian Inconscious, 1988; author chpts. to books; contbr. articles to profl. jours. Rsch. grantee Nat. Inst. Mental Health, 1963-64, 64-66, 66-67, Nat. Inst. Neurol. Diseases and Blindness grantee, 1970-73, 73-74, Shalom Found. grantee, 1974-78, Nat. Inst. Edn. grantee, 1983, 84-85, Dept. Edn. grantee, 1986-87. Office: NYU Dept Psychology New York NY 10003

VIVIAN, JOHNSON EDWARD, retired chemical engineering educator; b. Montreal, Que., Can., July 6, 1913; came to U.S., 1936, naturalized, 1942; s. Edgar John and Mary Meade (McMahon) V.; m. Florence Evelyn Frye, Feb. 10, 1940; children: John Edward, David James, Ann. B. Chem. Engring., McGill U., 1936; S.M., Mass. Inst. Tech., 1939, Sc.D., 1945. Research engr. Canadian Pulp and Paper Assn., 1936; teaching asst. MIT, Cambridge, 1937-38; asst. dir. Bangor chem. engring. practice sch. MIT, 1938-41, dir. Buffalo chem. engring. practice sch. sta., 1941-43, research engr. govt. project, 1943-46, assoc. prof. chem. engring., 1946-56, prof., 1956-80, sr. lectr., 1980-85, prof. emeritus, 1980—, dir. chem. engring. practice sch., 1946-57, 72-80, dir. Oak Ridge E.P.S., 1948-57; Cons. chem. engring., 1946—; vis. prof. Birla Inst. Tech. and Sci., Pilani, Rajasthan, India, 1972—; exec. officer dept. chem. engring., 1974-79. Fellow Am. Inst. Chem. Engrs. (Colburn award 1948); mem. TAPPI, Am. Chem. Soc., AAAS, Am. Soc. Engring. Edn., Sigma Xi. Home: Ledgewood E #203 80 Austin Dr Burlington VT 05401-5448 Office: Mass Inst Tech Dept Chem Engring Cambridge MA 02139

VIVIANO, SAM JOSEPH, illustrator; b. Detroit, Mar. 13, 1953; s. Thomas John Viviano and Prudy Katherine (DiGiuseppe) LaMendola; m. Diane E. Bloomfield, Sept. 3, 1988; 1 child, Alicia Catherine Viviano. BFA, U. Mich., 1975. Textile designer Manes Fabric Co., N.Y.C., 1976-77; freelance illustrator N.Y.C., 1976—; art instr. Sch. Visual Arts, N.Y.C., 1981-93, Pratt Manhattan Sch. Art, 1992—. Mem. Graphic Artists Guild (chmn. N.Y.C. chpt. 1981-87, treas. 1987-89). Office: 25 W 13th St New York NY 10011

VIZARD, FRANK JOSEPH, journalist; b. N.Y.C., July 7, 1955; s. Matthew Joseph and Anne (Tierney) V.; m. Mary McAleer, Apr. 28, 1984. BA, NYU, 1977. News editor Paper Trade Jour., N.Y.C., 1977-78; mng. editor Paperboard Packaging, N.Y.C., 1978-80; editor Autosound & Communications, N.Y.C., 1980-84; freelance writer N.Y.C., 1984-90; electronics and photography editor Popular Mechanics mag., N.Y.C., 1990—. Avocations: basketball, Irish affairs, sports science. Office: Popular Mechanics Mag 224 W 57th St New York NY 10019-3212

VIZCAINO, HENRY P., mining engineer, consultant; b. Hurley, N.Mex., Aug. 28, 1918; s. Emilio D. and Petra (Perea) V.; m. Esther B. Lopez, Sept. 16, 1941; children: Maria Elena, Rick, Arthur, Carlos. BS in Engring., Nat. U., Mexico City, 1941; geology student, U. N.Mex., 1951-54. Registered profl. engr. With Financiera Minera S.A. Mexico City, 1942-47; gen. mgr. Minas Mexicanas S.A., Torreon, Mex., 1947-51; exploration engr. Kerr McGee Corp., Okla., 1955-69; cons. Albuquerque, 1969-75, 84—; regional geologist Bendix Field Engring., Austin, Tex., 1976-79; staff geo-scientist Bendix Field Engring., Grand Junction, Colo., 1979-81; sr. geologist Hunt Oil Co., Dallas, 1981-84. Contbr. articles to profl. publs. Mem. AIME, Internat. Platform Assn., Aircraft Owners and Pilots Assn., Rotary, Elks. Republican. Congregationalist. Home and Office: 20 Canoncito Vista Rd Tijeras NM 87059-7833

VIZZA, ROBERT FRANCIS, hospital executive, former university administrator, marketing educator; b. N.Y.C., Apr. 2, 1933; s. Saverio and Agatha (Costanzo) V.; m. Joan Kilday, Dec. 11, 1954; children: Lorraine, Mary, Cathy, Robert. BBA, Pace Coll., 1954; MBA, CUNY, 1959; PhD, NYU, 1967; LLD (hon.), LaSalle Coll., 1978. Account exec. Diebold Inc. N.Y.C., 1954-61; asst. prof. mktg. St. John's U., 1962-66; assoc. prof. mktg., chmn. dept. bus. adminstrn. C.W. Post Coll., 1966-67; dean Sch. Bus., prof. mktg. Manhattan Coll., 1967-85; pres., chief exec. officer St. Francis Hosp., Roslyn, N.Y., 1985—; cons. to industry; dir. Air Freight Corp.; bd. dirs. Am., Assembly Collegiate Schs. Bus.; Home Life Ins., The Green Point Savs. Bank. Author: Improving Salesmen's Use of Time, 1962, Measuring the Value of the Field Sales Force, Training and Developing the Field Sales Manager, 1965, Basic Facts in Marketing, 1966, Adoption of the Marketing Concept, 1967, New Handbook of Sales Training, 1967, Time and Territory Management, 1972, Time and Territorial Management-A Programmed Learning Course, 1975, 2d edit., 1979; contbr. articles to profl. jours. Pres. bd. St. Mary's Sch.; bd. dirs. Pace U., Sch. of the Holy Child. Ford Found. fellow; recipient Jerome Levy Found. award. Fellow Internat. Acad. Mgmt.; mem. Middle Atlantic Assn. Colls. of Bus., Adminstrn. (v.p. 1970-71, pres. 1972-73, exec. com. 1969—), Sales Execs. Club N.Y. (bd. dirs.), Am. Mktg. Assn., Delta Sigma Pi, Delta Mu Delta, Pi Sigma Epsilon. Home: 3 Maria Ln Glen Head NY 11545-2507 Office: St Francis Hosp 100 Port Washington Blvd Roslyn NY 11576

VLACH, JIRI, electrical engineering educator, researcher; b. Prague, Czechoslovakia, Oct. 5, 1922; emigrated to Can., 1969; s. Frantisek and Bozena (Papouskova) V.; m. Dagmar Gutova, 32, 1949; 1 son, Martin. Dipl.eng., Tech. U. Prague, 1947, C.Sc., 1957. With Research Inst. for Radio Communications, Prague, 1948-67; head math. dept. Research Inst. for Radio Communications, until 1967; vis. prof. U. Ill., Urbana, 1967-69; prof. elec. engring. U. Waterloo (Ont., Can.), 1969—. Author: Computerized Approximation and Synthesis of Linear Networks, 1969, (with others) Computer Methods for Circuit Analysis and Design, 1983, 2nd edit., 1994, Basic Network Theory with Computer Applications, 1992; assoc. editor IEEE Trans. on Circuits and Systems, 1979-80. Fellow IEEE; mem. Eta Kappa Nu. Home: 355 Craigleith Dr, Waterloo, ON Canada N2L 5B5 Office: University Waterloo 200 University Ave West, Waterloo, ON Canada N2L 3G1

VLASIC, ROBERT JOSEPH, food company executive; b. Detroit, Mar. 9, 1926; m. Nancy Rita Reuter; children: James, William, Richard, Michael, Paul. BS, U. Mich., 1949. Chmn. Vlasic Foods, Inc., West Bloomfield, Mich., 1963-88, chmn. emeritus, 1988—; chmn. Campbell Soup Co., Camden, N.J., 1988-93, chmn. emeritus, 1993—; bd. dirs. Reynolds Metals Co., Richmond, Va. Vice chmn. bd. trustees Henry Ford Health System, Detroit, 1977; vice chmn. bd. trustees Cranbrook Ednl. Community, Bloomfield Hills, 1979. Home: 1910 Rathmor Rd Bloomfield Hills MI 48304-2149 Office: 710 North Woodward Bloomfield Hills MI 48304-2851

VLAZNY, JOHN GEORGE, bishop; b. Chgo., Feb. 22, 1937; s. John George and Marie Hattie (Brezina) V. BA, St. Mary of the Lake Coll., Mundelein, Ill., 1958; STL, Pontifical Gregorian U., Rome, 1962; MA in Classics, U. Mich., 1967; MEd, Loyola U., 1972. Ordained priest Roman Catholic Church, 1961, consecrated bishop, 1983. Assoc. pastor St. Paul of the Cross Ch., Park Ridge, Ill., 1962-63; assoc. pastor St. Clement Ch., Chgo., 1963-68; assoc. pastor St. Aloysius Ch., Chgo., 1968-72, pastor, 1979-81; assoc. pastor St. Sylvester Ch., Chgo., 1972-74, Precious Blood Ch., Chgo., 1974-79; faculty Quigley Prep., North Chgo., 1963-79; dean of studies Quigley Prep., 1969-79; rector Niles Coll., Chgo., 1981-83; aux. bishop Archdiocese of Chgo., 1983-87; Episcopal vicar Vicariate I, Chgo., 1983-87; bishop Episc. Ch., Winona, Minn., 1987—; pres. Presbyteral Senate, Chgo., 1976-77; mem. Diocesan Clergy Personnel Bd., Chgo., 1981-84, chmn., 1983-84. Bd. dirs. NED, Latino Tng. Ctr., Chgo., 1980-81, Sacred Heart Sch. Theology, Hales Corners, Wis., 1986—, St. Mary's Coll., Winona, 1987—. Mem. Nat. Communications Found. (bd. dirs. 1990—), Nat. Conf. Cath. Bishops (various coms. 1983—). Roman Catholic. Avocations: music; running. Office: Chancery Office PO Box 588 55 W Sanborn Winona MN 55987-0588*

VLCEK, DONALD JOSEPH, JR., food distribution company executive; b. Chgo., Oct. 30, 1949; s. Donald Joseph and Rosemarie (Krizek) V.; m. Claudia Germain Meyer, July 22, 1978 (div. 1983); 1 child, Suzanne Mae; m. Valeria Olive Russell, Nov. 11, 1989; children: James Donald, Victoria Rose. BBA, U. Mich., 1971. Gen. mgr. Popps, Inc., Hamtramck, Mich., 1969-76; pres. Domino's Pizza Distbn. Corp., Ann Arbor, Mich., 1978-93, chmn., 1993-94, also bd. dirs.; pres. Don Vlcek & Assocs., Ltd., Plymouth, Mich., 1994—; trustee Domino's Pizza Ptnrs. Found.; bd. dirs. RPM Pizza Inc., Gulfport, Miss., Dimango Corp., South Lyon, Mich.; sr. v.p. distbn. and tech. Domino's Ohio Commissary, Zanesville; pres. Morel Mountain Corp.; judge 1994 Duck Stamp contest, U.S. Dept. Interior, Jr. Fed. Duck Stamp Contest, 1995. Author: The Domino Effect, 1991 (Best of Bus. award ALA 1992, Soundview's Top 30 Business books of 1993); contbr. articles to profl. jours. Bd. dirs. Men's Hockey League of Oak Park, Mich., 1973-78. Named Person of Yr. Bd. Franchises, Boston, 1981; recipient Teal award Ducks Unltd., 1992, State Major Gifts Chmn. award, 1992, 93, State Chmn.'s award, 1992, State Major Gifts award, 1994. Mem. Mich. Steelheaders Assn. (life), Ducks Unltd. (life, Domino's Pizza chpt. treas., sponsor, chmn. 1988—, Mich. state bd. dirs., life sponsor, chmn. 1989, 91-92, major gifts chmn. 1993—, state trustee 1992—, chmn. exec. com. 1992-94, chmn. strategic devel. com., 1994—, sponsor in perpetuity Grand Slam Life), Mich. United Conservation Club (life), Whitetails Unltd. (life), Pheasants Forever (life), Midstates Masters Bowling Assn. (bd. dirs. 1976-85), Barton Hills Country Club, U. Mich. Alumni Club (life), Domino's Lodge/Drummond Island Wildlife Habitat Found. (pres., chmn. bd.), Vlcek Family Wildlife Found. (pres., chmn. bd.), Elks (life), Die Hard Cubs Fan Club. Republican. Roman Catholic. Avocations: hunting, fishing, hockey, collecting wildlife art, coins, and sports cards and memorabilia. Home: 9251 N Beck Rd Plymouth MI 48170-3332 Office: Don Vlcek & Assoc Ltd PO Box 701353 Plymouth MI 48170-0963

VLCEK, JAN BENES, lawyer; b. Chgo., Nov. 16, 1943; s. Anton John and Alice (Benes) V.; m. Ann Lewis, Aug. 23, 1973; children: Elizabeth, Katharine. A.B., Princeton U., 1965; J.D., U. Pa., 1968; M.B.A., George Washington U., 1975. Bar: Fla. 1968, D.C. 1969. Trial atty. CAB, Washington, 1968-69; atty.-advisor Office of Legis., EPA, Washington, 1971-73; assoc. minority counsel Commerce Com. Ho. of Reps., Washington, 1973-76, regulatory programs counsel Energy Com., 1977-78; assoc., then ptnr. Gardner, Carton & Douglas, Washington, 1978-81; with Reagan Energy Transition Team, Washington, 1980-81; ptnr. Sutherland, Asbill & Brennan, Washington, 1981-91; with Bush Transition Team, Washington, 1989; ptnr. Wunder, Diefenderfer, Ryan, Cannon & Thelan (now Wunder, Diefenderfer, Cannon & Thelen, Washington, 1991—; bd. dirs. Nat. Energy Resources Orgn.; with Bush Transition Team, Washington, 1989; fed. rep. Western Interstate Energy Bd., 1990—. Sgt. U.S. Army, 1969-71. Mem. ABA (coun. natural resources, energy and environ. law), Fed. Energy Bar Assn., Capitol Hill Club. Office: Wunder Diefenderfer 1615 L St NW Ste 650 Washington DC 20036-5611

VLIET, GARY CLARK, mechanical engineering educator; b. Bassano, Alta., Can., June 3, 1933. BS in Chem. Engring, U. Alta., 1955; M.S. in Mech. Engring, Stanford U., 1957, Ph.D., 1962. With Lockheed Research Labs., Palo Alto, Calif., 1961-71; mem. faculty U. Tex., Austin, 1971—; prof. mech. engring. U. Tex., 1979—, W. R. Woolrich prof. engring., 1985—. Contbr. articles to profl. jours. Mem. Austin Renewable Energy Commn., 1979-83. Recipient awards and fellowships. Fellow ASME (Best HEat Transfer Paper award 1970); mem. ASRAE, Am. Solar Energy Soc., Tex. Solar Energy Soc. (founder, bd. dirs. 1976—, pres. 1980, 94). Research areas include heat and mass transfer, solar energy. Office: U Tex Dept Mech Engr ETC 5.160 Austin TX 78712

VOBACH, WILLIAM H., state senator. Mem. Ind. State Senate from Dist. 31, 1983-90; pvt. practice law, Indpls. Chmn. State Senate Com. on Environ. Consumer Affairs; co-chmn. Ind. State Environ. Policy Commn., 1990. Republican. Office: 1000 Capitol Ctr S 201 N Illinois St Indianapolis IN 46204-1904

VODREY, ROSEMARY, province attorney general. Elected to legis. Manitoba Legislative Assembly, Can., 1990; Min. Edn. and Tng. Man. Legislative Assembly, Winnipeg, Can., 1992; now Min. and Atty. Gen. Ministry of Justice, Man., Winnipeg, Can. Office: Rm 168 Legis Bldg, Winnipeg, MB Canada R3C 0V8*

VOEGELI, VICTOR JACQUE, history educator, dean; b. Jackson, Tenn., Dec. 21, 1934; s. Victor Jacque and Winnie Lou (Lassiter) V.; m. Anna Jean King, Oct. 14, 1956; children: Victor Jacque, Charles Lassiter. B.S., Murray State Coll., 1956; M.A., Tulane U., 1961, Ph.D., 1965. Instr. history Tulane U., 1963-65, asst. prof., 1965-67; asst. prof. history Vanderbilt U., 1967-69, assoc. prof., 1969-73; prof. history, 1973—, chmn. history dept., 1973-76, dean Coll. Arts and Sci., 1976-92. Author: Free But Not Equal: The Midwest and the Negro During the Civil War, 1967. Served with U.S. Army, 1956-58. Nat. Endowment Humanities grantee, 1969-70, 72. Mem. So. Hist. Assn. Presbyterian. Home: 3704D Estes Rd Nashville TN 37215-1729 Office: Vanderbilt U Nashville TN 37240

VOELKER, CHARLES ROBERT, archbishop, academic dean; b. Cleve., June 12, 1944; s. Charles Christ and Bertha Elizabeth (Zak) V. BA, Nat. Coll. Edn., 1968; STL, Holy Trinity Sem., 1989; PhD, Internat. Sem., 1989. Ordained to ministry Orthodox Ch. as priest, 1974, as bishop, 1984. Parish priest Am. Orthodox Ch., Cleve., 1974-84; bishop Am. Orthodox Ch., Deltona, Fla., 1984—; tchr., adminstr. Ashtubula County Schs., 1971-76; acad. dean Internat. Sem., Plymouth, Fla., 1990—; pres., rector Holy Trinity Sem., Deltona, 1985—; dir. human svcs. New London (Ohio) Hosp., 1981-84; pres. Eagles Fitness Ctr., Middleburg Heights, Ohio, 1977-84; tchr. Polaris Vocat. Ctr., Middleburg Heights, 1981-83. Chaplain maj. Air Force Aux., CPA, 1993—. Mem. Order of St. Gregory the Illuminator (comdr. 1989—), Order of St. George (comdr. 1989—), Order St. John of Jerusalem. Home: 1088 Eastbrook Ave Deltona FL 32738-6925 Office: Internat Sem PO Box 1208 Plymouth FL 32768-1208 *To feed God's people you must first feed yourself.*

VOELL, RICHARD ALLEN, real estate services company executive; b. Chgo., Dec. 29, 1933; s. John Herman and Esther Frances (Anderson) V.; m. Virginia Charlotte Broderick, Dec. 20, 1958; children: David Broderick, Gregory Jon, Jeffrey Scott. B.A., U. Ill., 1956; M.B.A., U. Hawaii, 1960. With Beatrice Foods Co., Chgo., 1958-79, group mgr. recreational products

group, 1971-73, corp. v.p., 1973-75, vice chmn., 1975-79; pres., chief operating officer Penn Central Corp., Greenwich, Conn., 1979-81, chief exec. officer, 1981; pres., chief exec. officer The Rockefeller Group, N.Y.C., 1982—; bd. dirs. Lehndorff USA Group of Cos., Ltd., Fiat S.p.A., Ifint, USA, Club Med, Inc., Rockefeller Ctr. Properties, Con Edison. Chmn. com. for pub. issues N.Y.C. Partnership; mem. nominating com. Wildlife Conservation Soc. Served to 1st lt. AUS, 1956-58. Mem. Chief Execs. Orgn., Coun. on Fgn. Rels., Econ. Club N.Y. (past chmn.), Rockefeller Ctr. Club, Greenwich (Conn.) Country Club, Riverside (Conn.) Yacht Club, Chgo. Club, U. Ill. Founders Club. Home: 25 Pilot Rock Ln Riverside CT 06878-2615 Office: Rockefeller Group 1230 Avenue of the Americas New York NY 10020

VOET, PAUL C., specialty chemical company executive; b. Cin., July 7, 1946; s. Leo C. and Claire G. (Burdick) V.; m. Judy A. Gates, Aug. 24, 1968; children—Jeffrey, Jeannette, Jamie, Jodie. B.A., U. Cin., 1968; M.B.A., U. Pa., 1970. Asst. to pres. KDI Corp., Cin., 1970; asst. to pres. Chemed Corp., 1970-72; v.p. Vestal Labs. div. Chemed, St. Louis, 1972-74, exec. v.p., 1974-76, pres., 1976-80; exec. v.p., chief operating officer Chemed Corp., Cin., 1986-88, exec. v.p., 1988—; pres., CEO Nat. Sanitary Supply Co. Mem. Pres.'s adv. council St. Louis U., 1979. Mem. Am. Mgmt. Assn. (president's coun.), Young Pres. Assn., Phi Beta Kappa, Beta Gamma Sigma (dir.'s table), Omicron Delta Epsilon, Phi Alpha Theta, Phi Eta Sigma. Avocations: scuba diving, photography, personal computers. Home: 8180 Graves Rd Cincinnati OH 45243-3631 Office: Chemed Corp 2900 Chemed Ctr 255 E 5th St Cincinnati OH 45202-4700 Also: Nat San Supply Co 255 E 5th St Cincinnati OH 45202-4700

VOGEL, ARTHUR ANTON, clergyman; b. Milw., Feb. 24, 1924; s. Arthur Louis and Gladys Eirene (Larson) V.; m. Katharine Louise Nunn, Dec. 29, 1947; children: John Nunn, Arthur Anton, Katharine Ann. Student, U. of South, 1942-43, Carroll Coll., 1943-44; B.D., Nashotah House Theol. Sem., 1946; M.A., U. Chgo., 1948; Ph.D., Harvard, 1952; S.T.D., Gen. Theol. Sem., 1969; D.C.L., Nashotah House, 1969; D.D., U. of South, 1971. Ordained deacon Episcopal Ch., 1946, priest, 1948; teaching asst. philosophy Harvard, Cambridge, Mass., 1949-50; instr. Trinity Coll., Hartford, Conn., 1950-52; mem. faculty Nashotah House Theol. Sem., Nashotah, Wis., 1952-71; asso. prof. Nashotah House Theol. Sem., 1954-56, William Adams prof. philosophical and systematic theology, 1956-71, sub-dean Sem., 1964-71; bishop coadjutor Diocese of West Mo., Kansas City, 1971-72; bishop Diocese of West Mo., 1972-89; rector Ch. St. John Chrysostom, Delafield, Wis., 1952-56; dir Anglican Theol. Rev., Evanston, Ill., 1964-69; mem. Internat. Anglican-Roman Cath. Consultation, 1970-90; mem. Nat. Anglican-Roman Catholic Consultation, 1965-84, Anglican chmn., 1973-84; mem. Standing Commn. on Ecumenical Relations of Episcopal Ch., 1957-79; mem. gen. bd. examining chaplains Episcopal Ch., 1971-72; del. Episcopal Ch., 4th Assembly World Council Chruches, Uppsala, Sweden, 1968, and others. Author: Reality, Reason and Religion, 1957, The Gift of Grace, 1958, The Christian Person, 1963, The Next Christian Epoch, 1966, Is the Last Supper Finished?, 1968, Body Theology, 1973, The Power of His Resurrection, 1976, Proclamation 2: Easter, 1980, The Jesus Prayer for Today, 1982, I Know God Better Than I Know Myself, 1989, Christ in His Time and Ours, 1982, God, Prayer and Healing, 1995; editor: Theology in Anglicanism, 1985; contbr. articles to profl. jours. Vice chmn. bd. dirs. St. Luke's Hosp., Kansas City, Mo., 1971, chmn., 1973-89. Research fellow Harvard, 1950. Mem. Am. Philos. Assn., Metaphys. Soc. Am., Soc. Existential and Phenomenological Philosophy, Catholic Theol. Soc. Am. Home: 524 W 119th Ter Kansas City MO 64145

VOGEL, CHARLES STIMMEL, lawyer; b. L.A., Aug. 26, 1932; s. Charles Paul and Thurza Mae V.; m. Miriam Friedfeld, May 11, 1979; children by previous marriage: Steven, Beverly. B.A., Pomona Coll., 1955; LL.B., UCLA, 1959. Bar: Calif. 1959, U.S. Dist. Ct. (so. dist.) Calif. 1959. Partner firm Allard, Shelton & O'Connor, Pomona, Calif., 1959-69; judge Mepl. Ct., Pomona Jud. Dist., 1969-70, Los Angeles Superior Ct., 1970-77; partner firm Nossaman, Krueger & Marsh, Los Angeles, 1977-81, Sidley & Austin, Los Angeles, 1981-93; assoc. justice Calif. Ct. Appeals (2d dist.), L.A., 1993—. Served with USN, 1955-56. Fellow Am. Bar Found., Am. Coll. Trial Lawyers; mem. Los Angeles County Bar Assn. (trustee 1980-82, pres. 1985-86), UCLA Law Alumni Assn. (pres. 1977), Assn. Bus. Trial Lawyers (pres. 1984-85), State Bar Calif. (bd. govs. 1987—, pres. 1990-91). Office: Calif Ct Appeals 300 S Spring St Los Angeles CA 90013

VOGEL, DAVID JAY, business educator; b. N.Y.C., Apr. 14, 1947; s. Harry Jacob and Charlotte (Rab) V.; m. Virginia Sue Ellen Glickler, Oct. 2, 1977; children: Philip Joel, Barbara Joy. BA, Queens Coll., CUNY, 1967; PhD, Princeton U., 1974. Asst. prof. U. Calif., Berkeley, 1973-79, assoc. prof., 1979-84, prof., 1984—; vis. prof. Stanford U., Palo Alto, Calif., 1979, London Bus. Sch., 1981; cons. Council on Fgn. Relations, N.Y.C., 1976, Aspen (Colo.) Inst., 1977, Hastings Ctr., Hastings-on-Hudson, N.Y., 1978-80. Author: Lobbying the Corporation, 1978, National Styles of Regulation, 1986, Fluctuating Fortunes: The Political Power of Business in America, 1989; co-author: Ethics and Profits, 1976, Ethics in the Education of Business Managers, 1980; editor Calif. Mgmt. Rev., 1982—; mem. editorial bd. Jour. Bus. Ethics, 1980—, Jour. Policy History, 1990—; co-editor: Corporations and Their Critics, 1980; contbr. articles to profl. jours. Chair consumer product panel Pacific Bell, San Francisco, 1987-90. Grantee Aspen Inst., 1979-80, Columbia U. Ctr. for Law and Econ. Studies, 1980-82, Inst. for Internat. Studies, 1984-86, Social Sci. Research Council, 1987-89. Mem. NAS (com. on human dimensions global change 1989-90), Am. Polit. Sci. Assn., Acad. Mgmt. Jewish. Office: Univ of Calif 350 Barrows Hall Berkeley CA 94720

VOGEL, DONALD STANLEY, gallery executive, artist; b. Milw., Oct. 20, 1917; s. Walter Frederick and Francis Osborne (Talmadge) V.; m. Margaret Katherine Mayer, Oct. 14, 1947 (dec. June 1974); children—Eric Stefan, Kevin Eliot, Katherine Barley; m. Erika Kjar Farkac, Oct. 4, 1980. Student Chgo. Art Inst., 1936. With WPA Easel Project, Chgo., 1940; tech. dir. Dallas Little Theatre, 1942-43; dir. Betty McLean Gallery, Dallas, 1951-54; dir., owner Valley House Gallery, Dallas, 1954—; dir., ptnr. Main Place Gallery, Dallas, 1968-70. Author: (with Margaret Mayer) Aunt Clara: The Paintings of Clara McDonald Williamson, 1966, Charcoal and Cadmium Red, 1989, Not for Revenge, 1991, King of the Hill, 1991, Transcendent Collector, 1992, Drawing for Paintings, 1992, The Untold Studio Secret, A Fantasy, 1992, The Boardinghouse, 1995; also essays and catalogues. Mem. Art Dealers Assn. Am. Inc. Avocations: travel; swimming. Office: Valley House Gallery 6616 Spring Valley Rd Dallas TX 75240-8635

VOGEL, EUGENE L., lawyer; b. Balt., May 2, 1931; s. Phillip and Dorothy (Shor) V.; m. Sara Altman, Aug. 22, 1958; children—Jennifer L., Amanda J. B.S., U. Md., 1953; J.D. magna cum laude, Harvard U., 1958. C.P.A., Md. Bar: N.Y. Assoc. atty. Rosenman and Colin, N.Y.C., 1958-67, tax ptnr., 1967-77, sr. tax ptnr., 1977—; adj. prof. law NYU, 1977-88. Co-author: (with Ness): Taxation of the Closely-Held Corp., 5th edit. 1991; contbr. articles to profl. jours. Bd. dirs. The Appleseed Found., Washington; bd. dirs., treas. N.Y. Lawyers For Pub. Interest, N.Y.C., 1984-87; lectr. Practicing Law Inst. Served to 1st Lt. USAF, 1953-55. Mem. ABA, N.Y. State Bar Assn. (exec. com. tax sect.), Assn. of Bar of City of N.Y. (chmn. com. on personal income taxation 1991-94, coun. on taxation 1990—). Home: 245 E 50th St New York NY 10022-7752 Office: Rosenman & Colin 575 Madison Ave New York NY 10022-2511

VOGEL, EZRA F., sociology educator; b. Delaware, Ohio, July 11, 1930; s. Joseph H. and Edith (Nachman) V.; m. Suzanne Hall, July 5, 1953; children: David, Steven, Eva; m. Charlotte Ikels, Nov. 3, 1979. BA, Ohio Wesleyan U., 1950; MA, Bowling Green State U., 1951; PhD, Harvard U., 1958; LittD (hon.), Kwansai Gakuin, 1980, Wittenberg Coll., 1981, Bowling Green State U., 1982, U. Md., 1983, Albion Coll., 1988, Chinese U., Hong Kong, 1992. Research fellow Harvard (for work in Japan), 1958-60; asst. prof. Yale U., 1960-61; research assoc., lectr. Harvard U., 1961-67, prof., 1967—, Henry Ford II prof. social scis., 1990—, assoc. dir. East Asian Research Ctr., 1967-73, dir. 1977-73; chmn. council East Asian studies, 1977-80, dir. program on U.S.-Japan relations, 1980-87, hon. chmn. program on U.S.-Japan rels., 1988—, mem. faculty council, 1981-84; nat. intelligence officer for East Asia Nat. Intelligence Coun., 1993-95, dir. Fairbank Ctr. East Asian Studies, 1995—; Mem. Joint Com. on Contemporary China,

1968-75, Com. on Scholarly Communication with Peoples Republic China, 1973-75, Joint Com. Japanese Studies, 1977-79. Author: Japan's New Middle Class, 1963, Canton Under Communism, 1969, Japan As Number One, 1979, Comeback, 1985, The Impact of Japan on a Changing World, 1987, One Step Ahead in China, 1989, The Four Little Dragons, 1991; editor: (with Norman W. Bell) A Modern Introduction to the Family, 1960, Modern Japanese Organization and Decision-Making, 1975, (with George Lodge) Ideology and National Competitiveness. Trustee Ohio Wesleyan U., 1970-75, 80-94. Served with AUS, 1951-53. Recipient Harvard faculty prize for book of year, 1970; Guggenheim fellow, 1972. Mem. Assn. Asian Studies (bd. dirs. 1970-72), Am. Sociol. Assn., Am. Acad. Arts and Scis. Home: 14 Sumner Rd Cambridge MA 02138-3018

VOGEL, FREDERICK JOHN, diplomat; b. Annapolis, Md., July 11, 1943; s. Raymond William Vogel and Clair Patricia (O'Neill) Foley; m. Donsiri Kamak, Dec. 26, 1983; children: Chantharaphon M., Jenchira Erin, Thinarom Clair. BS in Engring., US Naval Acad., 1965; postgrad, Purdue U., 1961; cert. in Lao lang., Def. Lang. Inst., 1970; cert. in Thai lang., Union Lang. Sch., Bangkok, 1975; cert. Korean lang., Fgn. Svc. Inst., 1979. Lic. pvt. pilot, lic. tae kwon do instr., 2d Dan, lic. D parachutist, lic. 2d class diver. Commd. 2nd lt. USMC, 1965, advanced through grades to col., 1986; fgn. svc. officer on assignment to Pentagon Bangkok, London,, Washington, 1972-88; dept. of state rep. to conf. on disarmament Geneva, 1988-90; dep. chief of mission Am. Embassy, Vientiane, Laos, 1991-93, charge d' affaires, 1993; asst. dir. of fgn. mil. rights affairs, office of the Sec. of Def. The Pentagon, 1994—; embassy rep. Thai-Am. Edn. Found., Bangkok, 1976-78; sec. martial arts com. Royal Bangkok Sports Club, 1984-86; chmn. Vientiane Internat. Sch. Bd., 1991-93. Active Am. Community Supprt Assn., Bangkok, 1984-85. Mem. Am. Fgn. Svc. Assn., Marine Corps Assn., U.S. Naval Acad. Alumni Assn., Force Recon Assn. Roman Catholic. Avocations: martial arts, parachuting, private flying, traveling, languages. Home: 1332 Cassia St Herndon VA 22070

VOGEL, HENRY ELLIOTT, retired university dean and physics educator; b. Greenville, S.C., Sept. 16, 1925; s. Henry Lamprecht and Alice (Cousins) V.; m. Barbara Argyle Gladden, Aug. 16, 1953; children: Alisabeth, Henry L. II, Barbara Alice, Susan Marie. BS, Furman U., 1948; MS, U. N.C., 1950, PhD, 1962. Instr. dept. physics Clemson (S.C.) U., 1950-52, asst. prof. physics, 1952-59, assoc. prof., 1959-65, prof., 1965-67, prof., head physics dept., 1967-71; prof., dean Clemson (S.C.) U. Coll. Scis., 1971-87, prof. physics, 1987-90, dean emeritus, prof. emeritus dept. physics and astronomy, 1990—; mem. S.C. ad hoc com. for NSF exptl. program to stimulate competitive research, 1978-87; mem. tech. adv. bd. S.C. Research Authority, 1984-87. Served with AUS, 1943-45. Decorated Purple Heart. Mem. Am. Phys. Soc., Am. Assn. Physics Tchrs., Sigma Xi, Sigma Pi, Alpha Epsilon Delta. Address: 222 Wyatt Ave Clemson SC 29631-3003

VOGEL, HOWARD H., lawyer; b. Paris, Tenn., Sept. 4, 1949; s. Herman Lentz and Caroline Powell (Carothers) V.; m. Kathryn Lynn Massey, Sept. 14, 1974; children: Caroline Carothers, Patrick Alexander, Anna Kathryn. BA, Vanderbilt U., 1971; JD, U. Tenn., 1974. Assoc. atty. O'Neil, Parker & Williamson, Knoxville, Tenn., 1976-77; ptnr. O'Neil, Parker & Williamson, 1977—. Pres. Dogwood Arts festival Inc., Knoxville, 1990-92. Fellow Tenn. Bar Found., Am. Bar Found.; mem. ABA (bd. govs. 1985-88, chmn. standing com. on meetings and travel 1990-92, chair 1993-94), Tenn. Young Lawyers Conf. (pres. 1980-81), Knoxville Bar Assn. (pres.-elect 1990-92, pres. 1993), Tenn. Bar Assn. (v.p. 1993-94, pres.-elect 1994—). Office: PO Box 217 Knoxville TN 37901-0217 also: 416 Cumberland Ave Knoxville TN 37902-2301

VOGEL, JOSEPH OTTO, archaeologist, educator, museologist; b. N.Y.C., Aug. 8, 1936; s. Albert William and Grace Ethel (McLaughlin) V.; m. Jean Eleanor Solomon, Dec. 20, 1959; 1 child, Amber. B.A., Hunter Coll., CCNY, 1958; D.Phil., Balliol Coll., Oxford U., Eng., 1974. Research assoc. Ill. State Mus., 1961-64; staff archaeologist Fortress of Louisbourg, N.S., Can., 1964-66; keeper of prehistory Nat. Mus. of Zambia, Livingstone, 1966-75; asst. prof. No. Ill. U., DeKalb, 1975-77; prof. anthropology U. Ala., Tuscaloosa, 1977—; dir. Ala. Mus. Nat. History, Tuscaloosa, 1978-83. Cons. film documentary Kansanshe, 1973; cons., writer film documentary Lost in Time (Golden Eagle award 1984), 1984; author numerous sci. articles and books. Mem. Tuscaloosa County Republican Com., 1979-86. Inducted into Hunter Coll. Athletic Hall of Fame, 1990; rsch. grantee Nat. Geog. Soc., 1976. Fellow Explorer's Club. Episcopalian. Avocation: military modelling. Home: 109 Country Club Apts Mimosa Park Rd Tuscaloosa AL 35405 Office: U Ala Dept Anthropology PO Box 6135 Tuscaloosa AL 35486-6135

VOGEL, JULIUS, consulting actuary, former insurance company executive; b. N.Y.C., Jan. 22, 1924; s. Max and Bertha V.; m. Corinne Iskowitz, Mar. 11, 1947; children: Robert, Charles. B.A., Bklyn. Coll., 1943. With Prudential Ins. Co. Am., Newark, 1946-82; sr. v.p., chief actuary Prudential Ins. Co. Am., 1977-82; chmn. Pruco Services Inc., 1979-82, Prudential's Gibraltar Fund, 1980-82. Served with U.S. Army, 1944-46. Recipient Disting. Public Service award Dept. Navy, 1976. Fellow Soc. Actuaries (pres. 1979-80); mem. Am. Acad. Actuaries. Office: 72 Colt Rd Summit NJ 07901-3041

VOGEL, MICHAEL N., journalist, writer, historian; b. Buffalo, May 26, 1947; s. Ralph John and Florence Helen (Pohlmann) V.; m. Stasia Zoladz, Aug. 28, 1971; children: Charity Ann, Rebecca Marie, Alex Christian. BA in English, Canisius Coll., 1969; MA in English, So. Ill. U., 1970. Journalist Buffalo News, 1970—; assoc. prof. journalism Buffalo State U. Coll., 1979-80. Author: Maritime Buffalo, 1990, Echoes in the Mist, 1991, America's Crossroads, 1993. Pres. Buffalo Lighthouse Assn., Inc., 1985—; co-founder St. Michael's Sch. at Greycliff, Derby, N.Y., 1987; pres. Buffalo Newspaper Guild, 1994—; bd. dirs. Landmark Soc. Niagara Frontier, 1990-91. 1st lt. U.S. Army, 1971-73. Recipient numerous awards including One to One Media award, 1978, 79, Newspaper Editorial Workshop award, 1979-80, N.Y. State AP award, 1982-90, Am. Planning Assn. award, 1987. Mem. AAAS, U.S. Lighthouse Soc., Nat. Assn. Sci. Writers, Gt. Lakes Hist. Soc., Buffalo & Erie County Hist. Soc. (Augsburger award 1989, Niederlander award 1990), Buffalo Mus. Sci. Roman Catholic. Avocations: sailing, photography, reading. Home: 6540 Lake Shore Rd Derby NY 14047 Office: Buffalo News PO Box 100 1 News Plz Buffalo NY 14240

VOGEL, NELSON J., JR., lawyer; b. South Bend, Ind., Oct. 13, 1946; s. Nelson J. and Carolyn B. (Drzewiecki) V.; m. Sandra L. Cudney, May 17, 1969; children: Ryan C., Justin M., Nathan J., Lindsey M. BS cum laude, Miami U., Oxford, Ohio, 1968; JD cum laude, U. Notre Dame, 1971. Bar: Ind. 1971, Mich. 1971, U.S. Ct. (no. dist.) Ind. 1971, Fla. 1972, U.S. Tax Ct. 1972, U.S. Ct. Appeals (5th cir.) 1975, U.S. Ct. Claims 1980. Acct. Coopers & Lybrand, South Bend, 1969-71; assoc. Barnes & Thornburg, South Bend, 1971-76, ptnr., 1977—; lectr. U. Notre Dame, South Bend, 1971, 74-80; instr. Ind. U., South Bend., 1971-74. Pres. Big Bros., Big Sisters, South Bend, 1978-79; bd. pres. South Bend Regional Mus. Art, 1984-86; mem. ethics com. Meml. Hosp., South Bend, 1986-94. Mem. Nat. Employee Stock Ownership Plan Assn. (sec.-treas. Ind. chpt.), Am. Assn. Atty.-CPAs, Nat. Assn. State Bar Tax Sect. (exec. com. 1982-84), Ind. State Bar Assn. (Citation of Merit 1979, chmn. taxation sect. 1981-82), Mich. Bar Assn. (tax sect.), Fla. Bar Assn., Michiana World Affairs Coun. (bd. dirs. 1992—), Michiana World Trade Club (bd. dirs. 1992—), Goshen Coll. Family Bus. Program (bd. advisors 1994—), Family Firm Inst. Home: 1146 E Dunrobbin South Bend IN 46614 Office: Barnes & Thornburg 600 1st Source Bank 100 N Michigan South Bend IN 46601

VOGEL, PHILLIP T., manufacturing executive. Sr. v.p. diagnostic divsn. Abbott Labs.; pres. Ares-Serono Diagnostics, Polaroid-Behringwerke Diagnostic System Inc., Fisher Sci. Co., Inc., Hampton, N.H., 1992—. Office: Fisher Scientific Co Liberty Lane Hampton NH 03842

VOGEL, ROBERT, lawyer, educator; b. Coleharbor, N.D., Dec. 6, 1918; s. Frank A. and Louella (Larsen) V.; m. Elsa Mork, May 29, 1942; children: Mary Lou, Sarah May, Frank, Robert. B.S., U. N.D., 1939; LL.B., Mpls. Coll. Law, 1942. Bar: N.D. 1943. Practiced in Garrison, 1943-54; state's atty. McLean County, 1948-54; U.S. atty. Fargo, 1954-61; mem. Vogel, Bair & Brown, Mandan, N.D., 1961-73; judge N.D. Supreme Ct., 1973-78; prof.

U. N.D. Law Sch., Grand Forks, 1978—. Democratic candidate for U.S. Ho. of Reps., 2d Dist. N.D., 1962; mem., sec. Nonpartisan League State Exec. Com., 1952; mem. N.D. Parole Bd., 1966-73. Fellow Am. Bar Found.; mem. Am. Coll. Trial Lawyers, Am. Law Inst. Home 524 Harvard St Grand Forks ND 58203-2845 Office: 108 N 3d St Grand Forks ND 58206

VOGEL, ROBERT LEE, college administrator, clergyman; b. Phillipsburg, Kans., Sept. 27, 1934; s. Howard and Marie V.; m. Sally M. Johnson, June 3, 1956; children—Susan, Kirk. B.A., Wartburg Coll., 1956; B.D., M.Div., Wartburg Theol. Sem., 1960, D.D. (hon.), 1976. Ordained to ministry Am. Lutheran Ch., 1960. Organizing pastor Faith Luth. Ch., Golden, Colo., 1960-65; regional dir. div. youth activity Am. Luth. Ch., Chgo., 1965-67; dir. parish resources, div. youth activity Am. Luth. Ch., Mpls., 1967-69; sr. pastor Our Savior's Luth. Ch., Denver, 1969-73; exec. asst. to pres. Am. Luth. Ch., Mpls., 1973-80; pres. Wartburg Coll., Waverly, Iowa, 1980—; v.p. Internat. Luther League, Am. Luth. Ch., 1953-58, pres., 1958-60; ofcl. observer Luth. World Fedn. Assembly, 1957; mem. com. on laity Am. Luth. Ch., 1964-67. Recipient Alumni citation Wartburg Coll., 1978. Mem. Coun. Ind. Colls., Iowa Assn. Ind. Colls. and Univs. (chmn. bd. 1987-88), Luth. Ednl. Conf. N. Am. (pres. 1988-89), Nat. Assn. Ind. Colls. and Univs. (commn. mem.). Lodge: Rotary. Office: Wartburg Coll 222 9th St NW Waverly IA 50677-2215

VOGEL, RONALD BRUCE, food products executive; b. Vancouver, Wash., Feb. 16, 1934; s. Joseph John and Thelma Mae (Karker) V.; m. Donita Dawn Schneider, Aug. 8, 1970 (dec. June 1974); 1 child, Cynthia Dawn; m. Karen Vogel, Feb. 14, 1992. BS in Chemistry, U. Wash., 1959. Glass maker Peuberthy Instrument Co., Seattle, 1959-60; lab. technician Gt. Western Malting Co., Vancouver, 1960-62, chief chemist, 1962-67, mgr. corp. quality control, 1967-72, mgr. customer svcs., 1972-77, v.p. customer svcs., 1977-79, v.p. sales, 1979-84, gen. mgr., 1984-89, pres., CEO, 1989—; chmn. bd. dirs. R&K Bus. Mgmt. Cons., Vancouver. Contbr. articles to profl. jours. Chmn. bd. dirs. Columbia Empire Jr. Achievement, Portland, Oreg., 1991-92. With U.S. Army, 1954-56. Recipient numerous awards. Mem. Master Brewers Assn. Am. Home: 30103 SE Shepherd Rd Washougal WA 98671

VOGEL, SARAH, state agency administrator, lawyer; b. Bismarck, N.D., May 3, 1946; d. Robert and Elsa Marie (Mork) V.; 1 child, Andrew. BA, U. N.D., 1967; JD, NYU, 1970. Bar: N.D., 1982. Commr. N.D. Agrl. Dept., Bismarck, N.D. Office: ND Agrl Dept 600 East Blvd Bismarck ND 58505

VOGEL, STEPHEN EUGENE, systems analyst; b. N.Y.C., Dec. 10, 1952; s. Robert Benedict Vogel and Gertrude Elizabeth (Bahlinger) Schubert; m. Melissa Gay Wintermote, Feb. 20, 1982; 1 child, Veronica. BA, Herbert H. Lehman Coll., 1975. Lic. tchr. secondary edn., N.Y. Instr. English Monroe Bus. Inst., Bronx, N.Y., 1976-77; customer service rep. Bowne Time Sharing, N.Y.C., 1977-78; border patrol agt. U.S. Immigration and Naturalization Service, Calexico, Calif., 1978-79; sales rep. N.Y. Telephone Co., N.Y.C., 1980-81, computer ops. supr., 1981-83, asst. mgr., 1983-86; systems analyst NYNEX Service Co., N.Y.C., 1986—; cons. Advance Cons., Bronx, 1983-85. Recipient citation Commr. Immigration and Naturalization Service, 1976. Democrat. Roman Catholic. Avocation: magic tricks. Home: 65 Flagler St East Brunswick NJ 08816-3929 Office: Synergy Group Inc 175 Price Pky New York NY 11735

VOGEL, SUSAN MULLIN, museum director. BS in French and English Literature, Georgetown U., 1964; MA, NYU, 1971, cert. mus. tng., 1977, PhD in Art History, 1977. Libr. asst. USIS Libr., Abidjan, 1964-65; libr. asst. Mus. Primitive Art, N.Y.C., 1966-67, asst. registrar, 1967-68, asst. curator, 1971-74; assoc. curator Met. Mus. Art, N.Y.C., 1975-82, sr. cons. African Art, 1982-84; exec. dir. The Ctr. for African Art, N.Y.C., 1983-1994; dir. Yale U Art Gallery, 1995—; lectr. in field. Arranged exhbns. including The Art of Black Africa: Nigeria and Cameroon, Met. Mus. Art, 1971, The Sculpture of Black Africa: Upper Volta, Mus. Primitive Art, 1972, Faces (Africa only), Mus. Primitive Art, 1973, Gods of Fortune: The Cult of the Hand in Nigeria, Mus. Primitive Art, 1974, Primitive Art Masterworks (Africa only), Met. Mus. Art, 1975, Patterns of Collecting (Africa only), Met. Mus. Art, 1975, Treasures of Ancient Nigeria (N.Y. installation and presentation), Met. Mus. Art, 1980, Rapacious Birds and Severed Heads: Early Bronze Rings from Nigeria, Art Inst. Chgo., 1979, The Buli Master: An African Artist of the 19th Century, Met. Mus. Art, 1980, For Spirit and Kings: African Art from the Paul and Ruth Tishman Collection, Met. Mus. Art, 1981, Michael C. Rockefeller Meml. Wing permanent installation of African art, Met. Mus. Art, 1982, African Masterpieces from the Musee de l'Homme Paris, Ctr. for African Art, 1984, African Aesthetics: The Carlo Monzino Collection, Ctr. for African Art, 1986, African Masterpieces from the Staatliches Mus. fur Volkerkunde Munich, Ctr. for African Art, 1987, Perspectives: Angles on African Art, Ctr. for African Art, 1987, Art/Artifact, Ctr. for African Art, 1988, The Art of Collecting African Art, Ctr. for African Art, 1988, Closeup: Lessons in the Art of Seeing African Art, Ctr. for African Art, 1990, Africa Explores: 20th Century African Art, Ctr. for African Art and New Mus. Contemporary Art, 1991, Home and the World: Archtl. Sculpture of two contemporary African Art, 1993, Fusion: West African Artist and the Venice Bienniale, Italy Mus. for African Art, 1993, Exhibition-ism: Mus. and African Art, Mus. for African Art, 1994; author exhbn. catalogues Ctr. for African Art: African Masterpieces from the Musee de l'Homme, 1985, African Aesthetics: The Carlo Monzino Collection, 1986, Africa Explores: 20th Century African Art, 1991, Closeup: Lessons in the Art of Seeing African Art, 1990; editor For Spirits and Kings, Met. Mus. Art; editor chpts. of books; contbr. articles to profl. jours. and many books in field. Office: Yale U Art Gallery PO Box 208271 New Haven CT 06520-8271

VOGEL, WILLIAM CHARLES, advertising executive; b. New York, N.Y., Aug. 16, 1941; s. Samuel and Pearl (Lefkowitz) V.; m. Nicole Lund, Sept. 30, 1968; children: David Roswell, Peter Samuel, (div. 1977); m. Joan Baeder, May 19, 1985. BA, NYU, 1964. Asst. account exec. Doyle Dane Bernbach, New York, 1965-68; account exec. McCann-Erickson, San Francisco, 1968-70; account dir. Foote, Cone and Belding, L.A., 1970-77; sr. v.p. Hall and Levine Advt., L.A., 1977-79; sr. v.p., gen. mgr. Cunningham and Walsh, L.A., 1979-85; prin. Liebowitz, Olshever, Vogel and Baruch, 1985-86; exec. v.p., mng. ptnr. Abert, Newhoff and Burr, L.A., 1986-87; pres. The Vogel Communications Group, Los Angeles, 1987-92; sr. v.p. DDB Needham Worldwide, 1992-94; mktg. cons. Vogel Internat. Mktg., 1994—; v.p. Western States Advt. Agencies Assoc., Los Angeles, 1977-78. Mem. Citizens Adv. Commn., L.A. Olympic Orgn. Com., 1983-84, bd. dir. L.A. Art Fair. With M.I. U.S. Army, 1964-65. Recipient Dare award, City Long Beach, Calif., 1987, Recognition award, L.A.Olympic Orgn. Commn., 1984, Dallas Advt. League, 1985, Diplome D' Excellence, UTA French Airlines, Paris, 1981. Mem. L.A. Advt. Club, The Aero Club, Riviera Tennis Club, St. James Club. Avocations: art collecting, horticulture, tennis. Home: 2187 Mcnell Rd Ojai CA 93023-9318 Office: Vogel Internat Mktg The Queen Mary 1126 Queens Hwy Long Beach CA 90802

VOGELEY, CLYDE EICHER, JR., engineering educator, artist, consultant; b. Pitts., Oct. 19, 1917; s. Clyde Eicher and Eva May (Reynolds) V.; m. Blanche Wormington Peters, Dec. 15, 1947; children: Eva Anne, Susan Elizabeth Steele. BFA in Art Edn., Carnegie Mellon U., 1940; BS in Engring. Physics, U. Pitts., 1944, PhD in Math., 1949. Rsch. asst. Westinghouse Rsch. Labs., East Pitts., Pa., 1944-54; adj. prof. math. U. Pitts., 1954-64; sr. scientist Bettis Atomic Power Lab., W. Mifflin, Pa., 1956-59; supr. tech. tng. Bettis Atomic Power Lab., W. Mifflin, 1959-71; mgr. Bettis Reactor Engring. Sch., W. Mifflin, 1971-77, dir., 1977-92; cons. U.S. Dept. Energy, Washington, 1992—; cons. Bettis Atomic Power Lab., W. Mifflin, 1954-56; U.S. Navy Nuclear Power Schs., Mare Island, Calif., Bainbridge, Md., 1959-69. Author: (grad. sch. course) Non-linear Differential Equations, 1954; (rev. text) Ordinary Differential Equations, Rev. edit. 5, Shock and Vibration Problems, Rev. Edit. 6, 1991; rsch. report distributed to Brit., Can. and U.S. Govts. for use in design of airborne radar systems, 1944; oil painting represented in permanent Latrobe collection; acrylics, water colors and Christmas card designs in several pvt. collections. Pres., trustee Whitehall (Pa.) Pub. Libr., 1985. Recipient USN commendation, Naval Reactors Br., 1992. Mem. IEEE (life), Am. Phys. Soc., Associated Artists of Pitts., Pitts. Watercolor Soc., Sigma Pi Sigma, Sigma Tau, Sigma Xi. Presbyterian. Achievements include patents for Automatic Continuous Wave Radar

Tracking System, Modulating Signals Passing Along Ridged Waveguides, Ridged Waveguide Matching Device, Method for Joining Several Ridged Waveguides, Antenna Feed Modulation Unit, others. Home: 185 Peach Dr Pittsburgh PA 15236

VOGELMAN, JOSEPH HERBERT, scientific engineering company executive; b. N.Y.C., Aug. 18, 1920; s. Jacob and Sabina (Weingarten) V.; m. Norma Schneider, Dec. 8, 1946; children: Jeffrey Allan, Leslie Sue, Linda Leigh. B.S., CCNY, 1940; M.E.E., Poly. Inst. Bklyn., 1948, D.Elec. Engring., 1957. Registered profl. engr., N.Y., N.J. Project engr. Signal Corps Engr. Labs., Belmar, N.J., 1943-45; chief devel. br. Watson Labs., Eatontown, N.J., 1945-50; chief scientist Rome Air Devel. Center, Griffiss AFB, N.Y., 1951-52; chief electronic warfare lab. Rome Air Devel. Center, 1953-56, dir. communications, 1956-59; v.p., dir. Capehart Corp., N.Y.C., 1959-64; dir. electronics Chromalloy Am. Corp., N.Y.C., 1964-67; gen. mgr. pocket fone div. Chromalloy Am. Corp., 1966-67, v.p., 1967-73; v.p., dir. Cro-Med Bionics Corp., 1968-73; vice chmn. bd., dir. Laser Link Corp., 1968-73; chief scientist, dir. Orentreich Found. for Advancement Sci., 1973—; pres. Vogelman Devel. Corp., 1973—; chmn. tech. adv. com. Compupix, Inc., 1984-86. Contbr. articles to profl. jours. and encys.; patentee in field. Served with AUS, 1942-43. Recipient Outstanding Performance award USAF, 1957. Fellow AAAS, IEEE; mem. Titulaire, Societe Francaise de Electroniciens et des Radio Electriciens, N.Y. Acad. Scis., Sigma Xi, Eta Kappa Nu. Home: 48 Green Dr Roslyn NY 11576-3221 Office: 910 5th Ave New York NY 10021-4155

VOGELSANG, JOHN MARTIN, financial executive; b. Parkersburg, W.Va., May 16, 1940; s. Martin Albert and Vlasta Florence (Unger) V.; m. Sharon Diana Linder, Sept. 27, 1986. BS, U.S. Air Force Acad., 1963; MBA, Ohio State U., 1971. Divisional contr. Rockwell Internat., 1971-87; v.p. fin. Fairchild Industries, Germantown, Md., 1987-90; CFO space and def. Hi-Shear Industries, North Hills, N.Y., 1990-92; CFO So. Rsch. Inst., Birmingham, Ala., 1992—; bd. dirs. SRT Electro-Optics, Inc., Birmingham, Met. Devel. Bd. Capt. USAF, 1963-69. Office: So Rsch Inst 2000 9th Ave S Birmingham AL 35205-2708

VOGELSTEIN, BERT, oncology educator. BS, U. Pa., 1970; MD, Johns Hopkins U. Rsch. assoc. Nat. Cancer Inst., 1976-78; prof. dept. oncology Johns Hopkins U. Sch. Medicine, Balt., 1978—; advisor Nat. Insts. Health Scientific Review Groups, Nat. Cancer Inst. Assoc. editor Genes, Chromosomes and Cancer; mem bd. reviewing editors Science Magazine; contbr. article to profl. jours. Recipient Anne & Jason Farber Lecture award Am. Acad. Neurology, 1991, Gairdner Found. Internat. award Gairdner Found., 1992, ACS Medal Honor Am. Cancer Soc., 1992, Richard Lounsbery award Nat. Acad. Scis., 1993, Baxter Rsch. award Assn. Am. Med. Coll., 1994. Mem. NAS, Am. Acad. Arts Scis. Achievements include revolutionizing our understanding of complex genetic mutations that occur when an normal bowel epithelial cell is transformed into a malignant cell. Office: Johns Hopkins U Sch Med Dept Oncology 720 Rutland Ave Baltimore MD 21205-2109*

VOGL, OTTO, polymer science and engineering educator; b. Traiskirchen, Austria, Nov. 6, 1927; came to U.S., 1953, naturalized, 1959; s. Franz and Leopoldine (Scholz) V.; m. Jane Cunningham, June 10, 1955; children: Eric, Yvonne. Ph.D., U. Vienna, 1950; Dr. rer. nat. h.c., U. Jena, 1983; Dr h.c., Poly. Inst., Iasi, Romania, 1992. Instr. U. Vienna, 1948-55; research asso. U. Mich., 1953-55; Princeton U., 1955-56; scientist E.I. Du Pont de Nemours & Co., Wilmington, Del., 1956-70; prof. polymer sci. and engring. U. Mass., 1970-83, prof. emeritus, 1983—; Herman F. Mark prof. polymer sci. Poly. U., Bklyn., 1983—; guest prof. Kyoto U., 1968, 80, Osaka U., 1968, Royal Inst. Stockholm, 1971, 87, U. Freiburg, Germany, 1973, U. Berlin, 1977, Strasbourg U., 1976, Tech. U. Dresden, 1982; guest Soviet Acad. Sci., 1973, Polish Acad. Sci., 1973, 75, Acad. Sci. Rumania, 1974, 76; cons. in field. Chmn. com. on macromolecular chemistry Nat. Acad. Sci. Author: Polyaldehydes, 1967, (with Furukawa) Polymerization of Heterocyclics, 1973, Ionic Polymerization, 1976, (with Simionescu) Radical Co and Graftpolymerization, 1978, (with Donaruma) Polymeric Drugs, 1978, (with Donaruma and Ottenbrite) Polymers in Biology and Medicine, 1980, (with Goldberg and Donaruma) Targeted Drugs, 1983, (with Immergut) Polymer Science in the Next Decade, 1987; contbr. articles to profl. jours. Recipient Fulbright award, 1976, Humboldt prize, 1977, Chemistry Pioneer award, 1985, Gold medal City of Vienna, Austria, 1986, Exner medal, 1987, Mark medal, 1989, Honor Ring, City of Traiskirchen, 1989; Japan Soc. Promotion of Sci. sr. fellow, 1980. Mem. Am. Chem. Soc. (chmn. div. polymer chemistry 1974, chmn. Conn. Valley sect. 1974, award applied polymer chemistry 1990), Am. Inst. Chemistry, AAAS, Austrian Chem. Soc., Japanese Soc. Polymer Sci. (award 1991), Sigma Xi, N.Y. Acad. Sci., Austrian Acad. Sci., The Royal Swedish Acad. Sci., Pacific Polymer Fedn. (pres.), Slovak Chem. Soc. (hon. mem.), Soc. Polymer Sci. Japan. Home: 349 Oxford Rd New Rochelle NY 10804-3324 Office: Poly Univ Six MetroTech Ctr Brooklyn NY 11201-2990

VOGLER, DIANE CLARK, elementary school principal; b. McGehee, Ark., Jan. 11, 1945; d. Stuart Emerson and Mamye Tompye (Campbell) Clark; m. Richard Joseph Vogler, June 16, 1968 (dec. Nov. 1979); children: Amy Diane, Jodi Leigh. BSE, Ark. A&M Coll., 1966; MSE, U. Ark., 1975, EdS, 1983. Cert. elem. adminstr., Ark. Tchr. 6th grade McGehee Pub. Schs., 1966-67; tchr. 5th grade North Little Rock (Ark.) Schs., 1967-68, tchr. 6th grade, 1970-73, tchr. math. grades 1-6, 1975-80; tchr. 6th grade Manhattan (Kans.) Pub. Schs., 1968-70; tchr. 1st grade Pulaski County Spl. Schs., North Little Rock, 1980-85, prin., 1985—; prin. Sylvan Hills Elem., Pulaski County Special Sch. Dist., Sherwood, Ark., 1990—. Mem., v.p. United Meth. Women of United Meth. Ch., North Little Rock, 1980—; del. Ark. Democratic Party, Little Rock, 1988; active Sylvan Hills Elem. PTA. Recipient Tchr. of Yr. award Ark. PTA Coun., 1985, Ednl. Excellence award Greater Little Rock C of C., 1985; named Elem. Prin. of Yr. Pulaski County Spl. Sch. Dist. Mem. ASCD, Internat. Reading Assn., Nat. Assn. Elem. Sch. Prins., Ctrl. Ark. Reading Coun., Ark. Assn. Elem. Prins. (zone dir. 1990-93), Pulaski County Adminstrs. Assn. (pres. 1989-90), Pulaski County Elem. Prins.' Forum (pres. 1993-94), Sherwood Rotary Club, Delta Kappa Gamma (pres. 1981-82), Phi Delta Kappa. Democrat. Avocations: music, needlework, travel. Office: Pulaski County Spl Sch Dist 402 Dee Jay Hudson Dr North Little Rock AR 72120-2302

VOGLER, FREDERICK WRIGHT, French language educator; b. Burlington, Vt., May 27, 1931; s. Curtis Linville and Marion (Wright) V.; m. Mary Frances Angle, Aug. 27, 1965; 1 child, Robert. B.A., U. N.C.-Chapel Hill, 1953, M.A., 1955, Ph.D., 1961; postgrad, U. Strasbourg, France, 1953-54. Instr. U. N.C, Chapel Hill, 1961-62, asst. prof., 1963-66, assoc. prof., 1966-78, prof. French, 1978—, assoc. dean arts and scis., 1976-87, dir. undergrad. studies French and Italian, 1989—; asst. prof. U. Iowa, Iowa City, 1962-63; cons. Ednl. Testing Service, Princeton, N.J., 1967-70. Author: Vital d'Audiguier and the Early 17th Century French Novel, 1964; editor: Moliere Mocked: Three Contemporary Hostile Comedies, 1973; contbr. articles on French lit. and cultural history to profl. jours. Served to 1st lt. U.S. Army, 1955-57. Fulbright Commn. scholar, Washington, Paris, 1953; So. Fellowship Bd. fellow, Chapel Hill, 1955. Mem. Am. Assn. Tchrs. French, Swiss Am. Hist. Soc. Episcopalian. Home: 1010 Dawes St Chapel Hill NC 27516-3010 Office: Dept Romance Langs U NC CB #3170 Chapel Hill NC 27599-3170

VOGLER, JAMES R., lawyer; b. St. Louis, Oct. 4, 1952. BA magna cum laude, Harvard U., 1974; JD, So. Ill. U., 1977. Bar: Ill. 1977, U.S. Dist. Ct. (no. dist.) Ill. 1977, U.S. Ct. Appeals (7th cir.) Ill. 1979, U.S. Dist. Ct. (no. dist. trial bar) Ill. 1983, U.S. Supreme Ct. 1984. Ptnr. Winston & Strawn, Chgo. Mem. Ill. State Bar Assn., Chgo. Bar Assn. (mem. evaluation of jud. candidates 1980-83). Office: Winston & Strawn 35 W Wacker Dr Chicago IL 60601-1614

VOGT, CARL WILLIAM, lawyer; b. Houston, Apr. 20, 1936; s. Carl Wilhelm and Myrtle Jesse (Jones) V.; m. Margrit Wulff, July 27, 1968; children—Erika, Bianca. B.A., Williams Coll., 1958; LL.B., U. Tex., 1965. Bar: Tex. 1965, U.S. Dist. Dist. (so. dist.) Tex. 1966, U.S. Dist. Ct. D.C., U.S. Ct. Appeals (5th cir. 1968, U.S. Ct. Appeals (D.C. cir.), U.S. Ct. Appeals (4th cir.), U.S. Ct. Appeals (3d cir.), U.S. Supreme Ct. 1980. Assoc., Fulbright, Crooker, Freeman, Bates & Jaworski, Houston, 1966-68; assoc.,

ptnr. Thompson, Ogletree, Deakins & Vogt, Atlanta and Washington, 1968-72; assoc., ptnr. Fulbright & Jaworski, Washington, 1972—; presdl. appointee, bd. dirs. Nat. Passenger Ry. Corp. (Amtrak), 1991-92, Nat. Transportation Safety Bd., 1992-94, chmn. 1992-94. Chmn., bd. dirs. Chinquapin Sch., Highlands, Tex., 1968-73; mem., hon. mem. bd. trustees Boy and Girls Club of Washington, 1978—; Served to capt. USMC, 1958-62. Fellow Am. Bar Found., Royal Aeronautical Soc.; mem. ABA (mem. adminstn. law sect., chmn. equal employment opportunity com. 1976-80, chmn. mgmt. com. 1984, mem. labor and employment law sect., mem. litigation sect.), Nat. Assn. Coll. and Univ. Attys. (chmn. nat. office com. 1978-81, mem. exec. bd. 1981—), State Bar Tex., Bar D.C., Flight Safety Found. (bd. gov., 1994), Republican. Club: Metropolitan (Washington). Office: Fulbright & Jaworski Ste 500 801 Pennsylvania Ave NW Washington DC 20004

VOGT, ERICH WOLFGANG, physicist, academic administrator; b. Steinbach, Man., Can., Nov. 12, 1929; s. Peter Andrew and Susanna (Reimer) V.; m. Barbara Mary Greenfield, Aug. 27, 1952; children: Edith Susan, Elizabeth Mary, David Eric, Jonathan Michael, Robert Jeremy. B.S., U. Man., 1951, M.S., 1952; Ph.D., Princeton U., 1955; D.Sc. (hon.), U. Man., 1982, Queen's U., 1984, Carleton U., 1988; LL.D. (hon.), U. Regina, 1986. Rsch. officer Chalk River (Ont.) Nuclear Labs., 1956-65; prof. physics U. B.C., Vancouver, 1965-95, prof. emeritus, 1995—, assoc. dir. TRIUMF Project, 1968-73, dir. TRIUMF Project, 1981-94, v.p. univ., 1975-81; chmn. Sci. Council B.C., 1978-80. Co-editor: Advances in Nuclear Physics, 1968—; Contbr. articles to profl. jours. Decorated officer Order of Can.; recipient Centennial medal of Can., 1967. Fellow Royal Soc. Can., Am. Phys. Soc.; mem. Can. Assn. Physicists (past pres., gold medal for achievement in physics 1988). Office: Triumf, 4004 Wesbrook Mall, Vancouver, BC Canada V6T 2A3

VOGT, EVON ZARTMAN, JR., anthropologist; b. Gallup, N.Mex., Aug. 20, 1918; s. Evon and Shirley (Bergman) V.; m. Catherine Christine Hiller, Sept. 4, 1941; children—Shirley Naneen (Mrs. Geza Teleki), Evon Zartman III, Eric Edwards, Charles Anthony. A.B., U. Chgo., 1941, M.A., 1946, Ph.D., 1948. Instr. Harvard U., 1948-50, asst. prof., 1950-55, assoc. prof., 1955-59, prof. anthropology, 1959-89, prof. emeritus, 1989—, dir. Harvard Chiapas project, 1957—, chmn. dept. anthropology, 1969-73, master Kirkland House, 1974-82; asst. curator Am. ethnology Harvard (Peabody Mus.), 1950-59, curator Middle Am. ethnology, 1960-89, hon. curator Middle Am. ethnology, 1990—; vis. prof. U. Hawaii, 1972; Mem. div. anthropology and psychology NRC, 1955-57. Author: Navaho Veterans, 1951, Modern Homesteaders, 1955, (with W.A. Lessa) Reader in Comparative Religion, 1958, (with Ray Hyman) Water Witching U.S.A., 1959, 2nd edit., 1970, Zinacantan: A Maya Community in The Highlands of Chiapas, 1969 (Harvard Press Faculty prize Sahagun prize 1969), The Zinacantecos of Mexico: A Modern Maya Way of Life, 1970, 2d edit. 1990, Tortillas for the Gods: A Symbolic Analysis of Zinacanteco Rituals, 1976, 2d edit., 1993, Fieldwork Among the Maya: Reflections on The Harvard Chiapas Project, 1994; editor: Desarrollo Cultural de Los Mayas, 1964, Los Zinacantecos, 1966, People of Rimrock, 1966, Handbook of Middle American Indians, vols. 7 and 8, 1969, Aerial Photography in Anthropological Field Research, 1974, (with Richard M. Leventhal) Prehistoric Settlement Patterns, 1983. Served from ensign to lt. USNR, 1942-46. Decorated Order Aztec Eagle Mexico; fellow Center for Advanced Study in Behavioral Sci., 1956-57. Fellow Am. Acad. Arts and Scis. (councilor 1974-78), Am. Anthrop. Assn. (exec. bd. 1958-60); mem. Nat. Acad. Scis. (chmn. anthropology sect. 1981-84, class V behavioral and social scis. 1986-89), Soc. Am. Archaeology, Royal Anthrop. Inst. Gt. Britain and Ireland, Am. Ethonological Soc. Clubs: Harvard (Boston), Tavern (Boston). Home: 14 Chauncy St Cambridge MA 02138-2528

VOGT, JOHN HENRY, corporate executive; b. Ft. Madison, Iowa, Dec. 31, 1918; s. John Andrew and Edith Elizabeth (Cramer) V.; m. Jean Hilleary, Aug. 4, 1942; children: John Hilleary, Linda Jean, Lisa Louise. B.S.C., Iowa U., 1940. Retail exec. trainee Sears Roebuck & Co., 1940-41; mgmt. trainee, then chief standards engr. Nat. Pressure Cooker Co., Eau Claire, Wis., 1946; sr. indsl. engr. Continental Can Co., 1950-51; with aircraft engine div. Ford Motor Co., Chgo., 1951-57; asst. to gen. mgr. Ford Motor Co., 1956-57; exec. adminstr. Lions Internat., Chgo., 1957-71; exec. v.p. Dairy and Food Industries Supply Assn., Washington, 1971-73; pres. Nat. Eye Research Found., Chgo., 1973-79; exec. dir. North Bus. and Indsl. Council Chgo., 1979-80; exec. dir. Nat. Assn. Corp. Real Estate Execs., West Palm Beach, Fla., 1980-85, sr. mgmt. advisor, 1985-90. Mem. at large nat. coun. Boy Scouts Am.; bd. dirs. Nat. Eye Rsch. Found., 1973-79. Capt. USAAF, 1941-46. Mem. Am. Soc. Assn. Execs. (life), Internat. Assn. Attys. and Execs. in Corp. Real Estate (founder, exec. v.p. 1990—), Toastmasters (past pres. Chgo. chpt.), Lions, Execs. Club Chgo. Home and Office: 2103 Collett Ln Flossmoor IL 60422-1306

VOGT, ROCHUS EUGEN, physicist, educator; b. Neckarelz, Germany, Dec. 21, 1929; came to U.S., 1953; s. Heinrich and Paula (Schaefer) V.; m. Micheline Alice Yvonne Bauduin, Sept. 6, 1958; children: Michele, Nicole. Student, U. Karlsruhe, Germany, 1950-52, U. Heidelberg, Germany, 1952-53; S.M., U. Chgo., 1957, Ph.D., 1961. Asst. prof. physics Calif. Inst. Tech., Pasadena, 1962-65, assoc. prof., 1965-70, prof., 1970—, R. Stanton Avery Disting. Service prof., 1982—, chmn. faculty, 1975-77, chief scientist Jet Propulsion Lab., 1977-78, chmn. div. physics, math. and astronomy, 1978-83; acting dir. Owens Valley Radio Obs., 1980-81; v.p. and provost Calif. Inst. Tech., Pasadena, 1983-87; vis. prof. physics MIT, 1988-94; dir. Caltech/MIT Laser Interferometer Gravitational Wave Observatory Project, 1987-94. Author: Cosmic Rays (in World Book Ency.), 1978, (with R.B. Leighton) Exercises in Introductory Physics, 1969; contbr. articles to profl. jours. Fulbright fellow, 1953-54; recipient Exceptional Sci. Achievement medal NASA, 1981, Profl. Achievement award U. Chgo. Alumni Assn., 1981. Fellow AAAS, A. Phys. Soc. Achievements include research in astrophysics and gravitation. Office: Calif Inst Tech # 102-33 Pasadena CA 91125

VOHRA, RANBIR, political scientist, educator; b. Lyallpur, Punjab, Pakistan, Mar. 5, 1928; came to U.S., 1964; s. Dualatram and Gurandevi V.; m. Meena Vincent, Jan. 14, 1954. B.A. with honours, Govt. Coll., Lahore, 1946; diploma in Chinese, Peking (China) U., 1959; M.A. (Ford Found. fellow 1964-68, teaching fellow 1965-67, 68-69), Harvard U., 1965, Ph.D., 1969. Program exec. All India Radio, 1947-64, head Chinese unit external services, 1959-64; instr., then lectr. history Harvard U., 1969-71; asso. prof. U. Calgary, Alta., Can., 1971-73; mem. faculty Trinity Coll., Hartford, Conn., 1973—; Charles A. Dana prof. polit. sci. Trinity Coll., 1975—, chmn. dept., 1973-85, 93—; tutor Dudley House, Harvard U., 1966-71, vis. univ. prof., summer 1972; vis. prof. Amherst Coll., spring 1974; vis. scholar Harvard Ctr. for East Asian Rsch., 1989-90. Author: Lao She and the Chinese Revolution, 1974, China's Path to Modernization, 1987, 2d edit., 1992, China: The Search for Social Justice and Democracy, 1990; editor: The Chinese Revolution 1900-1950, 1974. Mem. Assn. Asian Studies, Internat. Polit. Sci. Assn., India Internat. Center. Home: 4 Shepard Rd Hartford CT 06110 Office: Trinity Coll Hartford CT 06106

VOHS, JAMES ARTHUR, health care program executive; b. Idaho Falls, Idaho, Sept. 26, 1928; s. John Dale and Cliff Lucille (Packer) V.; m. Janice Hughes, Sept. 19, 1953; children: Lorraine, Carol, Nancy, Sharla. B.A., U. Calif., Berkeley, 1952; postgrad., Harvard Bus. Sch., 1966. Employed by various Kaiser affiliated orgns., 1952-92; chmn., pres., CEO Kaiser Found. Hosps. and Kaiser Found. Health Plan, INc., Oakland, Calif. 1975-92, chmn. emeritus; chmn. bd. dirs. Holy Names Coll., 1981-92; chmn. Marcus Foster Inst., 1981—; bd. dirs. Clorox Co.; dep. chmn. Fed. Res. Bank San Francisco, chmn. 1991-94. Bd. dirs. Oakland-Alameda County Coliseum Complex, Bay Area Coun., 1985-94, chmn.; 1985-94, mem. Oakland Bd. Port Commrs. With AUS, 1946-48. Mem. NAS, Inst. Medicine. Office: Kaiser Center Ordway Bldg Oakland CA 94612

VOIGHT, ELIZABETH ANNE, lawyer; b. Sapulpa, Okla., Aug. 6, 1944; d. Robert Guy and Garnetta Ruth (Bell) Voight; m. Bodo Barske, Feb. 22, 1985; children: Anne Katharine, Ruth Caroline. BA, U. Ark.-Fayetteville, 1967, MA, 1969; postgrad. U. Hamburg (W.Ger.), 1966-67; J.D., Georgetown U., 1978. Bar: N.Y. 1979. Lectr. German, Oral Roberts U., Tulsa, 1968-69; tchr. German, D.C. pub. schs., 1971-73; instr. German, Georgetown U., Washington, 1973-74, adminstrv. asst. to dean Sch. Fgn. Svc., 1974-77;

law clk. Cole & Corette, Washington, 1977-78; atty. Walter, Conston, Alexander & Green, P.C., N.Y.C., 1978-88, Munich, 1990—. Translator articles for profl. jours. Chmn. regional screening Am. Field Svc., N.Y.C., 1981-86. German Acad. Exchange Program fellow, 1966-67. Mem. Assn. Bar City N.Y., ABA, Internat. Fiscal Assn., Internat. Bar Assn., Am. C. of C. in Germany, Phi Beta Kappa, Kappa Kappa Gamma.

VOIGHT, JON, actor; b. Yonkers, N.Y., Dec. 29, 1938; s. Elmer and Barbara (Camp) V.; m. Lauri Peters, 1962 (div. 1967); m. Marcheline Bertrand, Dec. 12, 1971 (div.); children: James Haven, Angelina Jolie. BFA, Cath. U., 1960; studied with, Sanford Meisner and Samantha Harper, N.Y.C. Stage appearances include O Oysters Revue, 1961, The Sound of Music, 1961, A View from the Bridge, 1965, Romeo and Juliet, 1966, The Tempest, 1966, Two Gentlemen of Verona, 1966, That Summer-That Fall, 1967 (Theatre World award 1967), A Streetcar Named Desire, 1973, The Hashish Club, 1975, Hamlet, 1976, The Seagull, 1992; TV appearances include Cimarron Strip, Gunsmoke; films include Fearless Frank, 1967, Hour of the Gun, 1967, Out of It, 1969, Midnight Cowboy, 1969 (Best Actor Acad. award nominee 1969, N.Y. Critics Circle award 1969, L.A. Film Critics Best Actor award 1969, Brit. Acad. Most Promising Newcomer to Leading Film Role award 1969), Catch-22, 1970, The Revolutionary, 1970, Deliverance, 1972, The All American Boy, 1973, Conrack, 1974, The Odessa File, 1974, End of the Game, 1976, Coming Home, 1978 (Best Actor Acad. award 1978, Golden Globe award 1978, Cannes Internat. Film festival award 1978, N.Y. Film Critics Best Actor award 1978, L.A. Film Critics Best Actor award 1978), The Champ, 1979 (Golden Globe award 1979), Runaway Train, 1985 (Acad. award nominee 1986, London Film Critics award nominee 1986), Desert Bloom, 1986, Eternity, 1990; TV films include Chernobyl: The Final Warning, 1991, The Last of His Tribe, 1992; actor, prodr., co-writer film Lookin' To Get Out, 1982; actor, prodr. film Table for Five, 1983. Winner Best Actor awards for Midnight Cowboy and Coming Home, Cannes Internat. Film Festival, Golden Globe award for Best Actor, Coming Home and The Champ, Acad. award for Best Actor, Coming Home 1979, N.Y. Film Critics award, Los Angeles Film Critics award for Best Actor, Midnight Cowboy, Coming Home. Office: care CAA 9830 Wilshire Blvd Beverly Hills CA 90212*

VOIGT, CYNTHIA, author; b. Boston, Feb. 25, 1942; d. Frederick C. and Elise (Keeney) Irving; married, 1964 (div. 1972); m. Walter Voigt, Aug. 30, 1974; children: Jessica, Peter. BA, Smith Coll., 1963. High sch. tchr. English Glen Burnie, Md., 1965-67; tchr. English Key Sch., Annapolis, Md., 1968-69, dept. chmn., 1971-79, tchr., dept. chmn., 1981-88. Author: Homecoming, 1981, Tell Me If the Lovers Are Losers, 1982, Dicey's Song, 1982 (John Newbery medal 1983), The Callender Papers, 1983 (Edgar award 1984), A Solitary Blue, 1983, Building Blocks, 1984, Jackeroo, 1985, The Runner, 1985 (Silver Pencil award 1988, Deutscher Jugend Literator Preis 1989, ALAN award 1989), Come a Stranger, 1986, Izzy, Willy Nilly, 1986 (Calif. Young Reader's award 1990), Stories About Rosie, 1986, Sons From Afar, 1987, Tree by Leaf, 1988, Seventeen Against the Dealer, 1989, On Fortune's Wheel, 1990, The Vandemark Mummy, 1991, Orfe, 1992, Glass Mountain, 1991, David and Jonathan, 1992, The Wings of a Falcon, 1993, When She Hollers, 1994. *

VOIGT, JOHN JACOB, telecommunications executive, international investment banker; b. Atlantic City, Apr. 2, 1942; s. Jacob Joseph and Mary Margret (Camp) V.; grad. Lawrenceville Sch., 1960; student U. Pitts., 1960-61; BS in Econs., U. Pa., 1963, postgrad., 1964; m. Glenna Fitzsimons, Sept. 22, 1961; children: Bridget Glenna, John Jacob Jr. Pres., Nat. Accessories Co., Phila., 1970—; chmn. ICCI, ICCI Europe Ltd., Brussels, The Dynoptics Corp., Lausanne, Switzerland, 1984—, also bd. dirs.; pres., treas., dir. The Inteleplex Corp.; pres. Howard Butcher Trading Corp., Phila., 1976—; chmn. IMS Corp., Geneva, Switzerland, 1987—; dir. Atlantic Metal Finishing Co., Butcher Foods Inc., Cont. Quality Industries, IHESA, San Pedro Sula, Honduras, Sterling Group Ltd., London, Torreya Fin. Corp., Palm Beach, Fla., Metea Trading & Fin. Internat., Geneva, Switzerland, Euro-Am. Money Fund, Sea Consult Ltd., Pan Am. Casuality & Liability Ins. Co.; cons. Compagnie Generale d'Electricite, Paris, Matra Group, Paris; bd. dirs. Howell, Dreyden & Dolan. Bd. govs. Betty Bacharach Hosp., 1976—; mem. vestry, sr. warden Ch. of Epiphany, Ventnor, N.J., 1975—. Republican. Mem. European Econ. Inst. (bd. dirs., Liechtenstein). Clubs: Union League Phila., Princeton N.Y.C., Atlantic City Country, Seaview Country, Ocean City Yacht, U. Pa. (N.Y.C.), Phi Gamma Delta. Lodges: Order of St. John Jerusalem, Knights of Malta. Home: 2215 Burroughs Ave Linwood NJ 08221-1330

VOIGT, PAUL WARREN, research geneticist; b. Ann Arbor, Mich., Mar. 20, 1940; s. Melvin John and Susie (Warkentin) V.; m. Josephine Bergeret, Aug. 24, 1963; children: Valorie Christine, Suzanna Jo, Peter Charles. BS, Iowa State U., 1962; MS, U. Wis., 1964, PhD, 1967. Rsch. geneticist Agrl. Rsch. Svc., USDA, Woodward, Okla., 1967-74, Temple, Tex., 1978; rsch. geneticist, rsch. leader Grassland Soil & Water Rsch. Lab., Temple, Tex., 1978-93; rsch. geneticist Appalachian Soil and Water Conservation Rsch. Lab., 1993—; v.p. Grass Breeder's Work Planning Conf., 1971-73, pres., 1973-75; mem. Nat. Cert. Grass Variety Rev. Bd., 1976-78, 84-87, Grass Crop Adv. Com., 1982-93. Author: (with others) The Science of Grassland Agriculture, 1985; contbr. numerous articles to profl. jours. Mem. Temple Civic Chorus, 1979-90. Fellow Am. Soc. Agronomy, Crop Sci. Soc. Am. (assoc. editor jour. 1980-82, tech. editor 1985-87); mem. Am. Forage and Grassland Coun., Soc. for Range Mgmt., Soil and Water Conservation Soc., Sigma Xi. Avocations: music, gardening, swimming, camping, photography. Office: Appalachian Soil & Water Conservation Rsch Lab Airport Rd Beckley WV 25802-0867

VOIGT, RICHARD, lawyer; b. Oskaloosa, Iowa, Jan. 20, 1946; s. Franz Otto Wilhelm and Minni (Heilbrunn) V.; m. Annemarie H. Riemer, Oct. 2, 1976; children: Samuel, Nicholas. BA, Conn. Wesleyan U., 1968; JD, U. Va., 1974. Bar: Va. 1974, U.S. Dist. Ct. (ea. dist.) Va. 1979, Conn. 1981, U.S. Dist. Ct. Conn. 1982, U.S. Ct. Claims 1982, U.S. Ct. Appeals (4th cir.) 1982. Assoc. counsel regional litigation Solicitor's Office Osha Div., 1978-80; staff atty. U.S. Dept. Labor, Washington, 1977-78; prin. Siegel, O'Connor, Schiff, Zangari & Kainen, P.C., 1981-88, 87-88; ptnr. Cummings & Lockwood, Hartford, 1988—. Contbg. author: ABA Treatise on Occupational Safety and Health Law, 1988; contbr. articles to profl. jours. Bd. dirs. Urban League Greater Hartford, 1984-88, Isnt. for Non-Profit Tng. and Devel., 1991—, Hartford Proud and Beautiful, 1995—. Mem. ABA (labor and employment law sect., OSHA com., litigation sect.), Conn. Bar Assn. (labor employment law sect., employment discrimination com., com. on alternative dispute resolution). Avocations: acrylic design, military history, sports. Office: 36th Floor Cityplace I Hartford CT 06103

VOIGT, ROBERT GARY, numerical analyst; b. Olney, Ill., Dec. 21, 1939; s. Donald E. and Jean C. (Fishel) V.; m. Susan J. Strand, Aug. 25, 1962; children: Christine, Jennifer. BA, Wabash Coll., 1961; MS, Purdue U., 1963; PhD, U. Md., 1969. Mathematician Naval Ship R & D Ctr., Washington, 1962-69, 71-72; vis. prof. U. Md., College Park, 1969-71; asst. dir. Inst. for Computer Application in Sci. and Engring., Hampton, Va., 1973-83, assoc. dir., 1983-86, dir., 1986-91; program dir. NSF, Arlington, Va., 1992-94; high performance computing and comm. coord. NSF, Arlington, 1994—; mem. tech. adv. bd. NSF, NASA, Dept. of Energy, and others. Co-author: Solution of Partial Differential Equations on Parallel and Vector Computers, 1985; co-editor 7 books; editor numerous jours.; contbr. 21 articles to profl. jours. Recipient Pub. Svc. award NASA, 1989. Mem. IEEE, Am. Math. Soc., Assn. for Computing Machinery, Soc. for Indsl. and Applied Math. (sec. 1987-91). Office: NSF Rm 1105 4201 Wilson Blvd Arlington VA 22230

VOINOVICH, GEORGE V., governor; b. Cleve., July 15, 1936; m. Janet Voinovich; 3 children. B.A., Ohio U., 1958; J.D., Ohio State U., 1961; LL.D. (hon.), Ohio U., 1981. Bar: Ohio 1961, U.S. Supreme Ct. 1968. Asst. atty. gen. State of Ohio, 1963-64; mem. Ohio Ho. of Reps., 1967-71; auditor Cuyahoga County, Ohio, 1971-76; commr., 1976-78; lt. gov. State of Ohio, 1979; mayor City of Cleve., 1979-90; gov. State of Ohio, 1991—; 1st v.p. Nat. League Cities, 1984-85, pres., 1985; trustee U.S. Conf. Mayors; chmn. Midwestern Govs. Conf., 1991-92, Coun. Gt. Lakes Govs., 1992-94. Recipient cert. of Merit award Ohio U., Humanitarian award NCCJ, 1988, named one of Outstanding Young Men in Ohio Ohio Jaycees, 1970; one of Outstanding Young Men in Greater Cleve. Cleve. Jaycees; Disting. Urban

Mayor award Nat. Urban Coalition, 1987; named to All-Pro City Mgmt. team City & State Mag., 1987. Mem. Rep. Govs. Assn. (vice chmn. 1991-92, chmn. 1992-93), Nat. Govs. Assn. (chmn. edn. action team on sch. readiness 1991, chmn. child support enforcement work group 1991-92, mem. strategic planning task force 1991-92, mem. human resources com. 1991—, co-chmn. task force on edn. 1992-93, mem. exec. com. 1993—, co-lead gov. on fed. mandates 1993—), Omicron Delta Kappa, Phi Alpha Theta, Phi Delta Phi. Republican. Office: Office of Governor 77 S High St 30th fl Columbus OH 43215*

VOITLE, ROBERT ALLEN, college dean, physiologist; b. Parkersburg, W.Va., May 12, 1938; s. Ray Christian and Ruby Virginia (Hannaman) V.; m. Linda Ellen Loveday, Dec. 5, 1975; children: Robert Allen, Elizabeth Anne, Christian Blair, Vanessa Virginia. BS, W.Va. U., 1962; M.S., W.Va., 1965; Ph.D., U. Tenn., 1969. Asst. in poultry U. Tenn., Knoxville, 1965-69; asst. prof. physiology U. Fla., Gainesville, 1969-75, assoc. prof., 1975-79; prof., head dept. poultry Calif. Poly. State U., San Luis Obispo, 1979-81; assoc. dean Coll. Agr., Auburn U., Ala., 1981—; cons. Columbia Bank for Coops., S.C., 1972. Contbr. articles to sci. jours. Pres., other offices Alachua County Fair Assn., Gainesville, 1969-79. Recipient Pub. Service award Alachua County Commn., 1975; recipient Tchr. of Yr. award U. Fla., 1977, Golden Feather award Calif. Poly. Inst., 1982. Mem. Poultry Sci. Assn., So. Poultry Sci. Assn., Gainesville Jaycees (JCI senatorship), Sigma Xi, Gamma Sigma Delta. Episcopalian. Club: Elks. Home: 2247 Longwood Dr Auburn AL 36830-7105 Office: Auburn U Coll Agr Auburn AL 36849

VOKETAITIS, ARNOLD MATHEW, bass-baritone, educator; b. East Haven, Conn., May 11, 1930; s. Mathew Joseph and Agnes Mary (Pilvelis) V.; m. Marion Lee Dever, June 1959 (div. 1967); children: Arnold Mathew Jr., Paul Stanley; m. Nijole Lipciute, Sept. 6, 1968. B.S. in Bus. Adminstrn, Quinnipiac Coll., 1954; postgrad., Yale U. Dir. opera program De Paul U., Chgo., 1987-89; lectr. on singing, acting Northwestern U., Evanston, Ill. 1986; mem. adv. panels in music and ethnic affairs Ill. Arts Coun.; mem. panel for opera and mus. theatre NEA; faculty mem. Brevard (N.C.) Summer Music Ctr., 1987, 88; artist-in-residence for opera Auburn U., Ala., 1990-93. Condr. master classes in singing; Operatic Debut with, N.Y.C. Opera, 1958, European debut at, Liceo, Barcelona, Spain, 1968; mem., Met. Opera Nat. Co., appeared with maj. operatic and symphony orchs. in U.S., Can., Mex., Cen. Am., S.Am., Lyric Opera of Chgo., 1966-84, 89, rec. artist for, Desto, Vox, Columbia, RCA, Turnabout; recitalist appearances on Pay-TV; classical soloist, U.S. Army Band, Washington. Served as sgt. U.S. Army, 1954-56. Recipient 1st place award Conn. Opera Assn. auditions, 1957, Rockefeller Found. award, 1964, Lithuanian Man of Yr. award, 1990, Disting. Alumni award Quinnipiac Coll., 1991. Mem. AFTRA, Am. Guild Mus. Artists (life), Actors Equity. Avocations: golfing, fishing, theater. I have felt very strongly over the years that opera was written to be enjoyed, not revered, and that it cried out to be acted as well as sung. With television's influence on the viewer, necessity became reality and my hopes are being realized.

VOLBERG, HERMAN WILLIAM, electronic engineer, consultant; b. Hilo, Hawaii, Apr. 6, 1925; s. Fred Joseph and Kathryn Thelma (Ludloff) V.; m. Louise Ethel Potter, Apr. 26, 1968; children: Michael, Lori. BSEE, U. Calif., Berkeley, 1949. Project engr. Naval Electronics Lab., San Diego, 1950-56; head solid state rsch. S.C. div. Gen. Dynamics, San Diego, 1956-60; founder Solidyne Solid State Instruments, La Jolla, Calif., 1958-60; founder, v.p. electronics divsn. Ametek/Straza, El Cajon, Calif., 1960-66; founder, cons. H.V. Cons., San Diego, 1966-69; sr. scientist Naval Ocean Systems Ctr., Oahu, Hawaii, 1970-77; chief scientist Integrated Scis. Corp., Santa Monica, Calif., 1978-80; founder, pres. Acoustic Sys. Inc., Goleta, Calif., 1980-84; founder, pres. Invotron, Inc., Lafayette, Calif., Murray, Utah, 1984—; tech. dir. Reson, Inc., Santa Barbara, Calif., 1992—; cons. U. Utah Ctr. for Engring. Design, 1991; cons. on autonomous underwater vehicle sonar systems Mitsui/U. Tokyo, 1992; lectr. solid state course UCLA and IBM, 1956-62; instr. Applied Tech. Inst., Columbia, Md., 1988—; contbr. to undersea acoustical rsch. and devel. programs European Union, 1990—. Contbr. articles to IRE Bull., IEEE Ocean Electronics Symposium. Mem. adv. panels for advanced sonar systems and for high resolution sonars UCLA, 1970-77. 1st lt. U.S. Army, 1944-47, ETO. Recipient award of merit Dept. Navy, 1973, 94. Mem. IEEE, AAAS, NRA, Acoustical Soc. Am., N.Y. Acad. Scis., Marine Tech. Soc., U.S. Naval Inst., Planetary Assn., Old Crows, Masons, Elks. Achievements include patents for device for detecting and displaying the response of tissue to stimuli, high rate neutralizer (HIRAN), crane high-voltage sensing system. Home and Office: 41 W 6830 S Murray UT 84107-7124

VOLBORTH, ALEXIS, geochemistry and geological engineering educator; b. Viipuri, Finland, July 11, 1924; came to U.S., naturalized; m. Nadia Hasso, 1947; children: Tatyana, Swetlana, Maria, Gregory, Anna, Nicholaus H.W., Elisabeth. PhC, U. Helsinki, 1950, PhLic and PhD in Geology-Mineralogy, 1954. Mineralogist, rsch. assoc., assoc. prof., prof. U. Nev., Reno, 1956-68; Killam vis. prof. geology, Killam rsch. prof. Dalhhousie U. Can., 1968-72; vis. prof. NASA Lunar Sci. Inst., U. Houston, 1972-73; vis. rsch. chemist U. Calif., Irvine, 1973-76; prof. geology and chemistry N.D. State U., 1975-78; prof. geology, scientist Nucleaar Radiation Ctr., Wash. State U., Pullman, 1978-79; prof. geochemistry and chemistry Mont. Coll. Mineral Sci. and Tech., Butte, 1979-94, prof. geol. engring., 1987-92, dir. accelerator lab., 1983-86, sr. radiation safety officer, 1983-86, prof. emeritus, 1995—; prin. investigator Stoichiometry Study Lunar Rocks, NASA, 1972-73; cons. AEC, 1961-63, NASA, 1965-73, Anaconda Co., 1968, Atomic Energy Orgn. Iran, 1975, Johns Manville Corp., Chevron, 1980-83, Pegasus Gold Inc., 1987, Placer Dome Inc., Echo Bay, Inc., 1990; U.S. rep., del. 2d Conf. on Natural Reactors, IAEC, Paris, 1977; U.S. rep. Internat. Geol. Correlation Program, 1990—; interpreter, Russian translator in Soviet Siberia for U.S. and Can. mining cos., 1990—. Contbr. articles to profl. jours. Traveling rsch. fellow Outokumpu Found., U. Vienna, U. Heidelberg, 1954-55, Hoover fellow Calif. Inst. Tech., 1955-56, sr. fellow Australian Acad. Sci., 1965, fellow Guggenheim Found., 1965-66. Fellow Mineral. Soc. Am., Am. Inst. Chemists; mem. Am. Chem. Soc., Am. Nuclear Soc., Soc. Econ. Geologists, Internat. Precious Metals Inst. Home: PO Box 80 Dayton MT 59914 Office: Mont Coll Mineral Sci-Tech U Mont Dept Chemistry-Geochem Butte MT 59701

VOLCKER, PAUL A., economist; b. Cape May, N.J., Sept. 5, 1927; s. Paul A. and Alma Louise (Klippel) V.; m. Barbara Marie Bahnson, Sept. 11, 1954; children: Janice, James. AB summa cum laude, Princeton U., 1949, LLD (hon.), 1982; MA, Harvard U., 1951, LLD (hon.), 1985. Economist Fed. Res. Bank N.Y., 1952-57; pres. Fed. Res. Bank of N.Y., 1975-79; economist Chase Manhattan Bank, N.Y.C., 1957-61, v.p., dir. planning, 1965-68; with Dept. Treasury, Washington, 1961-65, 69-74, dep. under sec. monetary affairs, 1963-65, under sec., 1969-74; chmn. bd. govs. Fed. Res. Bd., Washington, 1979-87; chmn. James D. Wolfensohn Inc., N.Y.C., 1988—; prof. internat. Econ. Policy, Princeton U., 1988; chmn. Nat. Commn. on the Pub. Svc., 1987-90, Trilateral Commn., Group of Thirty; chmn., adv. bd. Ctr. for Strategic and Internat. Studies. Sr. fellow Woodrow Wilson Sch. Pub. and Internat. Affairs, 1974-75.

VOLCKHAUSEN, WILLIAM ALEXANDER, lawyer, banker; b. N.Y.C., Mar. 13, 1937; s. William Louis and Jessie (Rankin) V.; m. Grace Lyu, Aug. 2, 1968; children: Sharon, Alexander. AB, Princeton U., 1959; AM, U. Calif., Berkeley, 1963; JD, Harvard U., 1966. Bar: N.Y. 1967. Program officer Asia Found., N.Y.C. and San Francisco, 1966-69; mng. atty. Moblzn. for Youth Legal Svcs., N.Y.C., 1969-73; dep. suprt., gen. counsel N.Y. State Banking Dept., N.Y.C., 1973-79; spl. counsel Hughes Hubbard & Reed, N.Y.C., 1979-80; exec. v.p., counsel, sec. The Dime Savs. Bank of N.Y. Fed. Savs. Bank, N.Y.C., 1980-89, sr. counsel, pub. affairs exec., 1989—; adj. prof. Cardozo Sch. Law Yeshiva U., N.Y.C., 1980—. Bd. dirs. N.Y. Tech. Coll., Asian-Am. Fedn. of N.Y., 100 Yr. Assn. Mem. ABA, Assn. of Bar of City of N.Y., N.Y. County Bar Assn., Princton Club (N.Y.C.). Democrat. Avocations: swimming, skiing, gardening, reading, travel. Home: 262 President St Brooklyn NY 11231-4346 Office: Dime Savs Bank 589 Fifth Ave 2d Fl New York NY 10017

VOLES, LORRAINE ANN, government administrator; b. N.Y.C., Jan. 15, 1959; d. Joseph and Marie Voles; m. Daniel E. Smith. BA, George Washington U. Press sec. Mondale for Pres. campaign, Des Moines, Iowa, 1984,

Sen. Tom Harkin campaign, Washington, 1990-93, Harkin for Pres. campaign, Washington, 1992; dir. comms. Nat. Hospice Orgn., 1985-87; dep. press sec. Dukakis for Pres. campaign, Boston, 1987-88, Exec. Office of Pres., Washington, 1993; nat. coord. Mothers & Others, Washington, 1991; dir. comms. Office of the V.P., Washington, 1993—; membership coord. Employee Relocation Coun., Washington, 1981-84. Contbr. articles to Mobility Mag. Mem. Iowa Dem. Party. Roman Catholic. Office: Office of the VP Old Exec Office Bldg Washington DC 20501

VOLGENAU, DOUGLAS, career officer; b. Buffalo, Nov. 13, 1937; s. Elmer Porter and Dorothy (Coleman) V.; m. Susan Steadman Graham, Aug. 27, 1961; children: Gretchen, Douglas Jr., Andrea. BS in Engring., U.S. Naval Acad., 1959; MS in Oceanography, U.S. Naval Post. Sch., Monterey, Calif., 1970. Commd. ensign USN, 1959, advanced through grades to rear adm., 1987; jr. officer billets USS Mitscher (DL-2) USN, Newport, Charleston, R.I., S.C., 1959-61; student U.S. Naval Submarine Sch. USN, New London, Conn., 1961-62, billet officer USS Seawolf (SSN-575), 1962-65, engr. officer USS Francis Scott Key (SSBN657), 1965-68, exec. officer USS Skate (SSN578), 1970-72; comdg. officer US Naval Nuclear Power Sch. USN, Mare Island, Calif., 1972-75; comdg. officer USS Billfish (SSN676) USN, New London, Conn., 1976-79, dep. squadron comdr. Submarine Devel. Squadron, 1979-81; sr. insp. nuclear property exam. bd. CINCPACFLt USN, Pearl Harbor, Hawaii, 1981-83; squadron comdr. Submarine Squadron Ten New London, Conn., 1983-85; comdr. Naval Underwater Systems Ctr. Newport, R.I., 1985-87; program exec. officer, Asst. Sec. Navy (rsch., devel., acquisition) Washington, 1987-91; pvt. cons. firm specializing tech., energy, mgmt. svcs. Arlington, Va. Decorated Legion of Merit with three gold stars, Navy Meritorious Svc. medal with one gold star, Navy Commendation medal, Navy Unit Commendation medal with two gold stars, Navy Achievement medal. Mem. U.S. Naval Acad. Alumni Assn., U.S. Naval Inst. Republican. Mem. Protestant Episcopal Ch. Avocations: golf, racquetball, fishing, hunting, reading. Home and Office: 1130 20th St S Arlington VA 22202-2100 Each person should, in his or her own way, work hard to improve society for the benefit of all.

VOLGY, THOMAS JOHN, political science educator, organization official; b. Budapest, Hungary, Mar. 19, 1946; m. Susan Dubow, Feb. 1987. BA magna cum laude, Oakland U., 1967; MA, U. Minn., 1969, PhD, 1972. Assoc. prof. polit. sci. U. Ariz., Tucson; dir. Univ. Teaching Ctr.; mayor City of Tucson, 1987-91; exec. dir. Internat. Studies Assn.; exec. dir. Internat. Studies Assn., 1995—; chmn. telecom. com. U. Conf. Mayors, 1988—; cons. H.S. curriculum project Ind. U.; bd. dirs. Nat. League of Cities, 1989-91. Co-author: The Forgotten Americans, 1992; editor: Exploring Relationships Between Mass Media and Political Culture: The Impact of Television and Music on American Society, 1976; contbr. numerous articles to profl. jours.; producer two TV documentaries for PBS affiliate. Mem. Nat. Women's Polit. Caucus Conv., 1983, U.S. Senate Fin. Com., 1985, U.S. Ho. of Reps. Telecommunications Com., 1988—, Polit. Sci. Adminstrn. Com., 1986, Gov.'s Task Force on Women and Poverty, 1986, United Way, 1985-87; bd. dirs. Honors Program, 1981—, U. Teaching Ctr., 1988—, Tucson Urban League, 1981, Ododo Theatre, 1984, So. Ariz. Mental Health Care Ctr., 1987, Nat. Fedn. Local Cable TV Programmers; chmn. Internat. Rels. Caucus, 1981, 86—, Transp. and Telecommunications Com. Nat. League Cities, 1986, 88, 89-91. Recipient NDEA scholarship, 1964-76, NDEA fellowship, 1967-70, Oasis award for outstanding prodn. of local affairs TV programming; named Outstanding Young Am., 1981, Outstanding Naturalized Citizen of Yr., 1980; faculty research grantee U. Ariz., 1972-73, 73-74, 74-75, 77-78. Mem. Pima Assn. Govts., Nat. Fedn. Local Cable Programmers. Democrat. Jewish. Office: U Ariz Polit Dept Sci Tucson AZ 85721

VOLICER, LADISLAV, physician, educator; b. Prague, Czechoslovakia, May 21, 1935; came to U.S., 1969, naturalized, 1977; s. Ladislav and Vilma (Molnarova) V.; m. Olga Holeckova, July 14, 1959 (div. 1970); children: Irena, Katerina; m. Beverly J. Beers, May 20, 1972; children: Zuzka, Marika, Nadine. MD, Charles U., Prague, 1959; PhD in Pharmacology, Czechoslovak Acad. Scis., Prague, 1964. Research assoc. Czechoslovak Acad. Sci., Prague, 1966-68; research asst. prof. U. Munich, Fed. Republic Germany, 1968-69; from asst. to assoc. prof. pharmacology Boston U. Sch. Medicine, 1969-77, asst. prof. medicine, 1975—, prof. pharmacology, 1977—, prof. psychiatry, 1985—, mem. inst. rev. bd., 1975-78; clin. pharmacologist E.N. Rogers Meml. Vets. Hosp., Bedford, Mass., 1982—; dep. dir. Geriatric Research Edn. Clin. Ctr., 1987-92, clin. dir., 1992—; mem. drug formulary com. State Mass., Boston, 1977-83; mem. inst. rev. bd. McLean Hosp., Belmont, Mass., 1980—. Editor: Clinical Aspects of Cyclic Nucleotides, 1977, Clinical Management of Alzheimer's Disease, 1988; contbr. papers to profl. publs. Grantee Nat. Inst. Aging, 1986—, Nat. Inst. Alcoholism and Alcohol Abuse, 1972-79, Nat. Inst. Drug Abuse, 1973-78, Merck, Sharp & Dohme, 1971; recipient Alcoholism Research award VA, 1979-85. Mem. Soc. for Neurosci., Am. Soc. Pharmacology Exptl. Therapeutics, Gerontol. Soc. Democrat. Unitarian. Home: 11 Beverly Rd Bedford MA 01730-1136 Office: EN Rogers Meml Vets Hosp 200 Springs Rd Bedford MA 01730-1114

VOLK, JAN, professional sports team executive; b. Davenport, Iowa; m. Lissa Volk; children: Shari, Matthew. Grad., Colby Coll., Maine, 1968; J.D., Columbia U., 1971. With Boston Celtics, 1971—; dir. ticket sales, mgr. equipment purchases, travel arrangements, bus. mgr., legal counsel, 1974-76, v.p., 1976-83, gen. mgr., 1983—, now also v.p. Office: Boston Celtics 151 Merrimac St Boston MA 02114*

VOLK, KENNETH HOHNE, lawyer; b. Hackensack, N.J., Nov. 8, 1922; s. Henry L. and Constance (Brady) V.; m. Joyce Geary, May 11, 1954; children: Christopher H., Cynthia. BS, U.S. Naval Acad., 1946; LLB, Yale U., 1953. Ptnr. Burlingham, Underwood, N.Y.C., 1955-92; of counsel McLane, Graf, Raulerson & Middleton, Portsmouth, N.H., 1992—; speaker various symposia and confs. on maritime law. Contbr. articles to profl. jours. Pres. Maritime Assocs., N.Y.C., 1967-68; chmn. bd. dirs. Seamen's House YMCA, N.Y.C., 1971-76; sec., bd. dirs. Seamen's Ch. Inst., N.Y.C., 1977-92; bd. dirs. Strawbery Banke Mus., Portsmouth, N.H.; mem. adv. bd. Tulane Admiralty Law Inst.. Fellow Am. Bar Found., Am. Coll. Trial Lawyers; mem. ABA, Assn. Bar of City of N.Y., Maritime Law Assn. U.S. (exec. com. 1977-80, pres. 1990-92), Comite Maritime Internat. (titulary mem.), Quaker Hill Country Club (pres. 1976-78). Republican. Espicopalian. Avocations: reading, hiking, swimming. Office: McLane Graf Raulerson 30 Penhallow St Portsmouth NH 03801-4017

VOLK, NORMAN HANS, financial executive; b. N.Y.C., Jan. 10, 1935; s. Hans and Mary (Zurl) V.; m. Karlyn Schram, Aug. 17, 1959; children: Kari, Heidi, Jenny. BA, Valparaiso (Ind.) U., 1957; MA, Marquette U., Milw., 1959. Dir. pub. rels. Wagner Coll., N.Y.C., 1961-62; asst. to owner Alan M. Wood, N.Y.C., 1962-72; sr. v.p. Bessemer Trust Co., N.Y.C., 1972-85; pres. Chamberlain & Steward, N.Y.C., 1985—. Trustee John Hartford Found., N.Y.C., 1979—. With U.S. Army, 1959-61. Mem. Univ. Club, Univ. Glee Club of N.Y.C., Doubles Club. Lutheran. Home: 445 Walton Rd Maplewood NJ 07040-1119 Office: 400 Park Ave New York NY 10022-4406

VOLK, ROBERT HARKINS, aviations company executive; b. East Orange, N.J., Nov. 27, 1932; s. Harry Joseph and Marion (Waters) V.; m. Barbara June Klant, Sept. 10, 1954; children: Christopher G., William V., Laura L., Elisabeth M. BA, Stanford U., 1954, LLB, 1958. Bar: Calif. 1959. Assoc. Adams Duque & Hazeltine, L.A., 1959-62; ptnr. Adams Duque & Hazelyine, L.A., 1962-67; commr. of corps. State of Calif., Sacramento, 1967-69; pres. Union Bancorp, L.A., 1969-73; pres., chmn. Union Am., L.A., 1973-79; owner, chief exec. officer Martin Aviation Inc., Santa Ana, Calif., 1980-90, Media Aviation L.P. Burbank, 1994—. Sgt. USAF, 1955-57. Mem. Calif. Bar Assn. Republican. Episcopalian. Avocations: skiing, golf, tennis. Home: 332 Conway Ave Los Angeles CA 90024-2604 Office: Media Aviation LP 3000 N Clybourn Ave Burbank CA 91505-1012

VOLK, STEPHEN RICHARD, lawyer; b. Boston, Apr. 22, 1936; s. Ralph and Miriam (Rose) V.; m. Veronica J. Brown, June 19, 1959 (dec. Feb. 1989); children: Jeffrey A., Andrew M., Michael J.; m. Diane Kemelman, Apr. 22, 1990; 1 child, Anne. Student, Dartmouth Coll., 1957; JD, Harvard U., 1960. Bar: N.Y. 1961. Assoc. Sherman & Sterling, N.Y., 1960-68, ptnr., 1968—; dep. sr. ptnr., 1988-91, sr. ptnr., 1991—. Trustee St. Luke's/Roosevelt Hosp., N.Y.C., 1990; ptnr. N.Y.C. Partnership, 1991. Mem. ABA (com. on securities regulation 1974), Am. Law Inst., Assn. Bar City N.Y., Coun. on Fgn. Rels., Univ. Club, Phi Beta Kappa. Office: 599 Lexington Ave New York NY 10022-6030

VOLKER, DALE MARTIN, state senator, lawyer; b. Lancaster, N.Y., Aug. 2, 1940; s. Julius J. and Loretta (O'Neill) V.; m. Carol A. Suchyna, Nov. 28, 1970; children: Martin Andrew, Mark Dale, Meredith Ann. BA, Canisius Coll., 1963; JD, SUNY-Buffalo, 1966. Bar: N.Y. 1967. Police officer Village of Depew, N.Y., 1966-72; assemblyman State Assembly, Albany, N.Y., 1972-74; mem. N.Y. State Senate, Albany, 1975-; sole practice law, Lancaster. Mem. Erie County Bar Assn., Elks, Moose, Eagles. Republican. Roman Catholic. Home: 92 Center Dr Depew NY 14043-1706 Office: 708 Legislative Office Bldg Albany NY 12247

VOLKHARDT, JOHN MALCOLM, food company executive; b. Chester, Pa., Apr. 13, 1917; s. George Thomas and Evelyn (Mitchell) V.; m. Linda J. Volkhardt; children—Jacqueline, Janet, Dana. A.B. cum laude, Brown U., 1939. Product mgr. Vick Chem. Co., N.Y.C., 1939-48; gen. mgr. Northam Warren Co., Stamford, Conn., 1948-56, Rit div. Best Foods Co., N.Y.C., 1956-58; with Best Foods div. CPC Internat. Inc., Englewood Cliffs, N.J., 1958-78, exec. v.p., 1968-71, pres., 1971-78; pres. North Am. div. CPC Internat. and exec. v.p. CPC Internat., 1978-82, group v.p., 1979; v.p. CPC, 1971-78, dir., 1977-82; pres., chmn. Full Circle Corp., Moss Creek, 1985-91; pres. Water Oak Utility, 1985-91. Chmn. bd. Keep Am. Beautiful, Inc., 1979-82, chmn. bd. trustees, 1982. Recipient Herbert Hoover award Nat. Assn. Wholesale Grocers Am.; honoree Nat. Jewish Hosp., 1976. Mem. Phi Beta Kappa.

VOLKMAN, BEATRICE KRAMER, special education educator; b. New Hampton, Iowa, May 7, 1940; d. Pinkey and Bernice Beatrice (Babcock) K.; m. Dale Volkman, Feb. 10, 1961; children: Valarie Volkman Bane, Todd Kramer, Jason Dale. BS, Drake U., 1962; MS, U. South Ala., 1976, cert., 1989. Tchr. 1st grade Kelly (Iowa) Elem. Sch., 1962-63; tchr. Holy Cross Kindergarten, Mobile, Ala., 1967-76; tchr. visually impaired S.W. Regional Sch. for Deaf/Blind, Mobile, 1976-77; reading specialist St. Paul's Episc. Sch., Mobile, 1977-80; dir. learning disabled IDEALS Sch., Mobile, 1980-82; spl. edn. resource tchr. Semmes Elem. Sch., Mobile, 1984-90; arts facilitator Magnet Schs. for Creative and Performing Arts, Mobile, 1990—; cons. South Ala. Rsch. and Insvc. Ctr., Mobile, 1988—. Bd. dirs. Children's Theatre, Pixie Playhouse, Mobile, Children's Mus., Exploreum, Mobile. Named Tchr. of Yr., Mobile County, 1986-87, Ala. Tchr. of Yr. State Dept. Edn., 1990-91, Nat. Tchr. of Yr. Washington OCSSO, 1990-91; Mobile Arts Coun. grantee, 1985, 86, Mobile Jr. League grantee, 1987, 88, 90. Mem. ASCD (program presenter), Internat. Reading Assn., Mobile Reading Assn., Ala. Reading Assn. (program presenter), Mobile County Edn. Assn., Ala. Edn. Assn. (program presenter). Republican. Lutheran. Office: Old Shell Road Elem Sch 1706 Old Shell Rd Mobile AL 36604-1324

VOLKMANN, DANIEL GEORGE, JR., architect; b. San Francisco, June 3, 1924; s. Daniel George and Beatrice (Simpson) V.; m. Marvin Johnson, Sept. 1, 1949 (dec. 1991); children: Daniel G., William R., David R., Wendy. BA, Yale U., 1945, U. Calif., Berkeley, 1950; MA, U. Calif. Berkeley, 1951. Practice architecture San Francisco, 1952—; prin. emeritus Bull, Volkmann, Stockwell, Architects, 1969-91; ltd. ptnr. Dean Witter & Co., San Francisco, 1967-69; bd. dirs. St. Francis Hosp Found., Gleeson Libr. Assoc., San Francisco Libr. Found. Mem. coun. Friends Bancroft Libr. U. Calif., Berkeley, 1976-82; trustee San Francisco Mus. Art, 1970-81, Marin Country Day Sch., 1972-77, San Francisco Conservatory Music, 1982-90, Cypress Lawn Cemetery, 1979—; pres., bd. dirs Cypress Lawn Cemetery, 1993—; mem. Art Commn. City and County San Francisco, 1975—; bd. dirs. Pacific Enterprises, 1967-93. With USNR, 1944-46. Mem. AIA (numerous awards in design), San Francisco Planning and Urban Renewal Assn., Cow Hollow Improvement Assn. (bd. dirs., pres. 1970), Bohemian Club, Olympic Club, McCloud Fly Fishing Club, Pacific Union (San Francisco), Grolier Club (N.Y.C.). Home: 2616 Union St San Francisco CA 94123-3817

VOLKMANN, FRANCES COOPER, psychologist, educator; b. Harlingen, Tex., May 4, 1935; d. Edward O. and Elizabeth (Bass) C.; m. John Volkmann, Nov. 1, 1958 (dec.); children: Stephen Edward, Thomas Frederick. A.B. magna cum laude, Mt. Holyoke Coll., 1957; M.A., Brown U., 1959, Ph.D., 1961; DSci., Mt. Holyoke Coll., 1987. Research assoc. Mt. Holyoke Coll., South Hadley, Mass., 1964-65; lectr. U. Mass., Amherst, 1964-65, Smith Coll., Northampton, Mass., 1966-67; asst. prof. Smith Coll., 1967-72, assoc. prof., 1972-78, prof. psychology, 1978—, dean faculty, 1983-88, Harold E. Israel and Elsa M. Siipola prof. psychology, 1988—, acting pres., 1991; vis. assoc. prof. Brown U., Providence, 1974, vis. prof., 1978-82; vis. scholar U. Wash., Seattle, summer 1977. Contbr. articles to profl. jours. Trustee Chatham Coll., 1987—. USPHS fellow, 1961-62; NSF grantee, 1974-78; Nat. Eye Inst. grantee, 1978-82. Fellow APA, AAAS, Optical Soc. Am.; mem. Ea. Psychol. Assn., Soc. Neurosci. Psychonomic Soc., Assn. Rsch. in Vision and Ophthalmology, New Eng. Assn. Schs. and Colls. (vice chair commn. instns. higher edn. 1991-93, chair 1993—). Home: 40 Arlington St Northampton MA 01060-2003 Office: Smith Coll Northampton MA 01063

VOLKMER, HAROLD L., congressman; b. Jefferson City, Mo., Apr. 4, 1931; m. Shirley Ruth Braskett; children: Jerry Wayne, John Paul, Elizabeth Ann. Student, Jefferson City Jr. Coll., 1949-51, St. Louis U. Sch. Commerce and Finance, 1951-52; LL.B., U. Mo., 1955. Bar: Mo. 1955. Individual practice law Hannibal, 1958—; asst. atty. gen. Mo., 1955; pros. atty. Marion County, 1960-66; mem. Mo. Ho. of Reps., 1966-76; chmn. judiciary com., mem. revenue and econs. com.; mem. 95th-104th Congresses from 9th Mo. Dist., 1977—; ranking minority mem. agr. subcom. livestock, dairy, & poultry. Served with U.S. Army, 1955-57. Recipient award for meritorious pub. service in Gen. Assembly St. Louis Globe-Democrat, 1972-74. Mem. Mo., 10th Jud. Circuit bar assns. Roman Catholic. Clubs: KC, Hannibal Lions. Office: US House of Reps 2409 Rayburn House Bldg Washington DC 20515*

VOLKOFF, GEORGE MICHAEL, educational administrator, former physics educator; b. Moscow, Feb. 23, 1914; came to Can., 1924; s. Mikhail Mikhailovich and Elizabeth Pavlovna (Titova) V., m. Olga Okulitch, June 22, 1940; children—Elizabeth Volkoff Bell, Alexandra, Olga Volkoff Richardson. B.A., U.B.C., Vancouver, Can., 1934, M.A., 1936, D.Sc. (hon.), 1945; Ph.D., U. Calif.-Berkeley, 1940. Asst. prof. physics U. B.C., Vancouver, 1940-46, prof., 1946-79, head dept. physics, 1961-71, dean Faculty of Sci., 1972-79, prof. emeritus, 1979—; research physicist NRC, Montreal, 1943-45; head theoretical physics br. div. atomic energy NRC, Chalk River, Ont., 1945-46; vis. lectr. McGill U., spring 1946, Purdue U., spring 1948, U. Wash., spring 1949, UCLA, summer 1950, 5l, 52, U. Calif.-Berkeley; cons. in field. Translator 2 books, author numerous articles. Mem. Univ. Hill Sch. Bd., Vancouver, 1959-61; trustee Vancouver Gen. Hosp., 1980-86, chmn. bd. trustees, 1984-85. Decorated mem. Order Brit.Empire, officer Order of Can.; recipient Centennial medal Govt. of Can., 1967. Fellow Royal Soc. Can., Am. Phys. Soc., AAAS; mem. Can. Assn. Physicists (pres. 1962-63). Club; Round Table (Vancouver). Avocations: hiking; listening to music. Home: 1776 Western Pkwy, Vancouver, BC Canada V6T 1V3

VOLL, JOHN OBERT, history educator; b. Hudson, Wis., Apr. 20, 1936; s. Obert Frank and Ruth Olivia (Seaberg) V.; m. Sarah Lynne Potts, June 12, 1965; children: Sarah Layla, Michael Obert. A.B. summa cum laude, Dartmouth Coll., 1958, Ph.D. (Ford Found. fellow), 1969; A.M. (Danforth fellow), Harvard U., 1960. Instr. history U. N.H., Durham, 1965-69, asst. prof., 1969-74, assoc. prof., 1974-82, prof., 1982-95, chair dept., 1988-91; prof. history Georgetown U., Washington, 1995—; mem. history and social scis. adv. com. Coll. Bd. 1983-86, chmn. European history and world cultures achievement test com., 1985-88; teaching fellow Harvard U., 1969; del. Am. Coun. Learned Socs., 1989—, also del. exec. com., 1989-92. Author: Historical Dictionary of the Sudan, 1978, Islam Continuity and Change in the Modern World, 2d edit., 1994, (with others) The Sudan: Unity and Diversity, 1985, Eighteenth Century Renewal and Reform in Islam, 1987, Sudan: State and Society in Crisis, 1991; contbr. articles to profl. jours. Mem. bd. Ecumenical Ministry U. N.H., 1974-78, pres., 1975-77; (chmn. social action Durham Community Ch., 1974-75, mem. ch. council, 1977-78, deacon, 1986—. Sheldon traveling fellow, 1960-61, U. N.H. summer fellow,

1969, 89, NEH fellow, 1971-72, Fulbright faculty rsch. abroad fellow, 1978-79, Inst. Advanced Studies fellow Hebrew U., 1984-85; recipient Egyptian Presdl. medal, 1991. Mem. Am. Coun. Learned Socs. (del. exec. com. 1989-92, bd. dirs. 1990-92), New Eng. Hist. Assn. (sec. 1975-78, v.p. 1981, pres. 1982), Sudan Studies Assn. (bd. dirs. 1981-82, co-exec. dir. 1990-94), N.H. Coun. on World Affairs (bd. dirs. 1989—), Am. Hist. Assn., Middle East Studies Assn. (bd. dirs. 1987-89, pres. 1992-93), Am. Coun. for Study of Islamic Socs. (bd. dirs. 1989—, v.p. 1989-91), N.H. Humanities Coun. (bd. dirs. 1991-95). Mem. United Ch. of Christ. Home: 4 Croghan Ln Durham NH 03824-3027 Office: U NH Dept History Durham NH 03824

VOLLAND, ROBERT STEPHEN, financial executive; b. N.Y.C., Mar. 9, 1941; s. William M. and Margaret E. (Farrell) V.; m. Patricia Joan Lane, June 17, 1967. BS, Fairleigh Dickinson U., 1964; MBA, Loyola Coll., 1979. Acct. exec. Merrill Lynch, N.Y.C., 1968-73; regional mgr. treasury Comml. Credit Co., Balt., 1973-79, v.p. dept. mgr., 1980-85, v.p., treas., 1986-89; v.p. corp. assets Primerica Corp., N.Y.C., 1989-91; pvt. practice N.Y.C., 1991—; v.p. adminstr. Air & Water Techs. Sgt. U.S. Army, 1962-66, Vietnam. Mem. Am. Fin. Svcs. Assn. (chmn.). Republican. Home: PO Box 4014 17 Sandpiper Point Rd Old Lyme CT 06371-1640

VOLLEN, ROBERT JAY, lawyer; b. Chgo., Jan. 23, 1940; s. Ben N. and Rose (Belonsky) V.; m. Judith Paula Spector, Aug. 12, 1961; children: Steven, Neil, Jennifer. A.B., U. Mich., 1961; J.D., U. Chgo., 1964. Bar: Ill. 1964, D.C. 1965, U.S. Supreme Ct. 1975. Atty. appellate sect. Civil Div., U.S. Dept. Justice, Washington, 1964-65; asso. firm Schiff Hardin & Waite, Chgo., 1965-70; partner firm Schiff Hardin & Waite, 1971-72; gen. counsel BPI (Bus. and Profl. People for Pub. Interest), Chgo., 1972-83; ptnr. Schwartz & Freeman, Chgo., 1983-87. Mem. com. U. Chgo. Law Sch., 1978-81. Mem. Chgo. Council Lawyers (gov. 1972-76, 79-81), ABA (ho. of dels. 1974-76). Home: 2 Kingswood Ln Deerfield IL 60015-1912

VOLLHARDT, KURT PETER CHRISTIAN, chemistry educator; b. Madrid, Mar. 7, 1946; came to U.S., 1972; Vordiplom, U. Munich, 1967; PhD, U. Coll., London, 1972. Postdoctoral fellow Calif. Inst. Tech., Pasadena, 1972-74; asst. prof. chemistry U. Calif., Berkeley, 1974-78, assoc. prof., 1978-82, prof., 1982—; prin. investigator Lawrence Berkeley Lab., 1975—; cons. Monsanto Corp., St. Louis, Exxon Corp., Annandale, N.J., Maruzen Corp., Tokyo; vis. prof. U. Paris-Orsay, 1979, U. Bordeaux, 1985, U. Lyon, 1987, U. Rennes, 1991, U. Paris VI, 1992, Tech. U. Munich, 1992. Author: Organic Chemistry, 1987, 2d edit., 1994; co-author: Aromatizität, 1972; assoc. editor: Synthesis, 1984-89; editor Synlett, 1989; contbr. articles to profl. jours.; patentee in field. Sloan fellow, 1976-90; Camille and Henry Dreyfus scholar, 1978-83; recipient Adolf Windaus medal, 1983, Humboldt Sr. Scientist award, 1985, 92, Otto Bayer prize, 1990, A.C. Cope Scholar award, 1991; named one of Am.'s 100 Brightest Scientists Under 40, Sci. Digest, 1984. Mem. Am. Chem. Soc. (Organometallic Chemistry award 1987), German Chem. Soc., Chem. Soc. of London, Internat. Union Pure & Applied Chemistry (organic chemistry div. com.). Office: U Calif Berkeley Dept of Chemistry Berkeley CA 94720

VOLLMANN, JOHN JACOB, JR., cosmetic packaging executive; b. Elizabeth, N.J., Apr. 10, 1938; s. John Jacob and Marie Louise (Sirois) V.; m. Marian Ethel Snetsinger, May 29, 1976; children: Andrea Leah, John Jacob III. BA, Queen's U., Kingston, Ont., 1973, BA with honor, 1976; postgrad., Rutgers U., 1977; PhD, Walden U., Naples, Fla., 1991. Cert. hypnotherapist; criminal justice instr., Fla. V.p. No. Trading Co., Inc., Madawaska, Maine, 1976—, also bd. dirs.; instr. Sch. of Justice and Safety Adminstrn., Miami-Dade Community Coll., 1978—; bd. dirs. Edward Sagarin Inst. for Study of Deviance and Social Issues. Contbr. articles to profl. jours. Vice chmn. Police & Fire Pension Bd., Dania, Fla., 1984; chmn. Unsafe Structures Bd., Dania, 1984; code Enforcement Bd., Dania, 1984; adv. dep. Broward County Sheriff, Ft. Lauderdale, Fla., 1986-92; maj. Fla. Sheriff's Adv. Coun., 1992—. Recipient Richard A. McGhee award Am. Justice Inst., 1992. Mem. NRA, Am. Correctional Assn., Am. Soc. Criminology (life), Acad. Criminal Justice Scis. (life), Am. Jail Assn., Am. Probation and Parole Assn., Northeastern Criminal Justice Assn. (life), Fla. Criminal Justice Educators (pres. 1984-88), So. Assn. Criminal Justice (bd. dirs. 1981-90), Internat. Assn. for Study Organized Crime, N.Am. Assn. Wardens and Supts., Optimists (lt. gov. South Fla. dist. 1994). Avocations: hunting, fishing. Home: 411 SE 3d Pl Dania FL 33004 Office: No Trading Co Inc 190-202 E Main St Madawaska ME 04756-1510

VOLLMAR, JOHN RAYMOND, electrical engineer; b. Phila., Nov. 8, 1929; s. William Gustav and Pauline Marie (Jesanker) V.; m. Sara Lois Jacob, Feb. 1, 1964; children—Paul Gary, Virginia Ann, Pamela Jean, Barbara Gayle, Thomas Edward, Timothy Morris. B.E.E., Drexel U., Phila., 1952. Registered profl. engr., Pa. Sales and application engr. Gen. Electric Co., Erie, Pa., 1955-59; rail transit and equipment engr. Louis T. Klauder & Assocs., Phila., 1959-65; ptnr. in charge r.r. and transit equipment engring. Louis T. Klauder & Assocs., 1965-84; v.p. LTK Engring. Svcs., Phila. 1985-92, sr. v.p., 1993-94; cons. emeritus, 1995—. Served with C.E. AUS, 1952-54. Decorated Army Commendation ribbon. Mem. Nat., Pa. socs. profl. engrs., IEEE, Am. Pub. Transit Assn. Methodist. Clubs: Union League (Phila.). Home: 727 Gregory Dr Horsham PA 19044 Office: 2 Valley Sq Ste 300 Blue Bell PA 19422-2705

VOLLMER, JAMES E., consulting company executive; b. Phila., Apr. 19, 1924; s. Edward L. and Elizabeth (MacMichael) V.; m. Mary Campolieto, Nov. 16, 1946 (dec. July 1992); children: Jamie, Kurt, Kimarie; m. Avalon E. Kolar, Jan. 27, 1994. B.S., Union Coll., Schenectady, 1945; M.A., Temple U., Phila., 1951, Ph.D., 1956; grad. Advanced Mgmt. Program, Harvard U. Bus. Sch., 1971. Instr. physics Temple U., 1946-51; research supr. Honeywell Corp., Phila., 1952-59 with RCA, 1959—; dir. Advanced Tech. Labs., Camden, N.J., 1959-72; div. v.p., gen. mgr. Govt. Systems Group, RCA, Moorestown, N.J., 1972-79; corp. group v.p. Govt. Systems Div., Comml. Communications Div. and Picture Tube Div. RCA, Cherry Hill, N.J., 1979-83; corp. sr. v.p. RCA, Princeton, N.J., 1983-84; pres. James Vollmer Assocs. Inc., Jupiter Inlet Colony, Fla., 1984-89; disting. lectr. Am. Soc. Engring. Edn., 1972. Author; patentee in field. Vice pres. Palm Beach County (Fla.) United Way, 1974-75; exec. adv. council Fla. Atlantic U., Boca Raton, Fla., 1974-75; vice chmn. campaign Camden County (N.J.) United Way, 1980; bd. dirs. W. Jersey Hosp., Camden, 1980; bd. govs. Franklin Inst., Phila. 1980; chmn. bd. Bartol Rsch. Found., 1980-87. With USNR, 1943-45. Fellow IEEE, AAAS; mem. Am. Phys. Soc., Nat. Security Indsl. Assn. (nat. trustee, past pres. Phila. chpt.), World Affairs Coun. Phila. (bd. dirs. 1982-85), Navy League (life), N. Jersey C. of C. (dir. 1975-77), Northland C. of C., Tequesta Country Club, Phi Beta Kappa, Sigma Xi, Sigma Pi Sigma, Eta Kappa Nu. Home: 212 Turtle Creek Dr Tequesta FL 33469-1545

VOLLMER, RICHARD HENRY, federal agency administrator; b. St. Marys, Pa., Jan. 10, 1931; s. John Edwin and Eileen (Simons) V.; m. Sarah Pauline Lavin, June 6, 1953; children: Sarah Pauline, Richard Henry Jr., John Charles. BS, U. Notre Dame, 1952. Sr. physicist DuPont Savannah River, Aiken, S.C., 1952-57, AMF Atomics, Greenwich, Conn., 1957-58; mgr. physics and tests Allis Chalmers Mfg. Co., Greendale, Wis., 1958-62; mgr. physics Atomics Internat., Canoga Park, Calif., 1962-68; dept. dir. U.S. NRC, Bethesda, Md., 1968-87, dir. policy planning, 1992—; sr. v.p. Tenera, L.P., Bethesda, 1987-92; nuclear ops. cons. Atomics Internat., 1965-68; pvt. practice nuclear mgmt. cons., Rockville, Md., 1992—; prin. lectr. Structural Mechanics in Realtor Tech., 1985; vis. fgn. lectr. on reactor safety Rsch. Assns., Tokyo, 1986. Republican. Roman Catholic. Home: 4804 Flower Valley Dr Rockville MD 20853 Office: US NRC 11155 Rockville Pike Rockville MD 20852

VOLMAN, DAVID HERSCHEL, chemistry educator; b. Los Angeles, July 10, 1916; s. Carl Herman and Blanche (Taylor) V.; m. Ruth Clare Jackson,

Sept. 15, 1944; children: Thomas Peter, Susan Frances, Daniel Henry. B.A., UCLA, 1937; M.S., 1938; Ph.D. (Standard Oil Co. fellow), Stanford U., 1940. Mem. faculty U. Calif.-Davis 1940-41, 46—, prof. chemistry, 1956-87, emeritus prof. chemistry, 1987—, chmn. dept., 1974-81, chmn. Acad. Senate, 1971-72; research chemist OSRD, 1941-46; research fellow Harvard U. 1949-50; Vis. prof. U. Wash. 1958. Editor: Advances in Photochemistry, 1983; mem. editorial bd. Jour. Photochemistry and Photobiology, 1972; contbr. articles to profl. jours. Grantee Research Corp. Am.; Grantee NIH; Grantee U.S. Army Research Office; Grantee NSF; Guggenheim fellow, 1949-50. Mem. Am. Chem. Soc., AAUP, Inter-Am. Photochem. Soc., Assn. Harvard Chemists, Sigma Xi. Office: U Calif-Davis Dept Chemistry Davis CA 95616

VOLNEY, TAYLOR, financial executive; b. Portsmouth, Ohio, Dec. 6, 1939; s. Lafayette and Martha Louise (Frederick) T.; m. Kathleen Ann MacMahon, May 17, 1969; children: Lafayette, Lloyd MacMahon, Kerry Erin, Frederick Daly. BS in Indsl. Engring., Ohio State U., 1962; MBA, Harvard U., 1966. Assoc. McKinsey & Co., N.Y.C., 1966-72; exec. v.p. Funk & Wagnalls, N.Y.C., 1972-74; v.p. fin. Holland Publs. N.Y.C., 1974-76; dir. corp. planning Dun & Bradstreet Corp., N.Y.C., 1976, v.p. corp. planning, 1977-78; gen. mgr. Transp. Guides div., Ofcl. Airline Guides div. Dun & Bradstreet Corp., Oak Brook, Ill., 1978; corp. v.p. Dun & Bradstreet Corp., N.Y.C., 1979-80, sr. v.p., 1980-8l, exec. v.p., 1982—, also bd. dirs. Lt. (j.g.) USNR, 1962-64. Office: Dun & Bradstreet Corp 299 Park Ave New York NY 10171-0001

VOLPE, ANGELO ANTHONY, university administrator, chemistry educator; b. N.Y.C., Nov. 8, 1938; s. Bernard Charles and Serafina (Martorana) V.; m. Jennette Murray, May 15, 1965. B.S., Bklyn. Coll., 1959; M.S., U. Md., 1962, Ph.D., 1966; M.Engring. (hons.), Stevens Inst. 1975. Rsch. chemist USN Ordnance Lab., Silver Spring, Md., 1961-66; asst. prof. to prof. chemistry Stevens Inst. Tech., Hoboken, N.J., 1966-77; chmn. dept. chemistry East Carolina U., Greenville, N.C., 1977-80, dean. coll. arts and scis., 1980-83, vice chancellor for acad. affairs, 1983-87; pres. Tenn. Tech. U., 1987—; adj. prof. textile chem. N.C. State U., Raleigh, 1978-82; guest lect. Plastics Inst. Am., Hoboken, 1967-82. Contbr. articles to profl. jours. Recipient Ednl. Svc. award Plastics Inst. Am., 1973; named Freygang Outstanding Tchr., Stevens Inst. Tech., 1975. Mem. Am. Chem. Soc., Tenn. Acad. of Scis., Sigma Xi, Phi Kappa Phi. Democrat. Roman Catholic. Avocations: golf; reading. Home: Tenn Tech U Walton House Box 5007 Cookeville TN 38505 Office: Tenn Tech U Office of President Cookeville TN 38505

VOLPE, EDMOND L(ORIS), college president; b. New Haven, Nov. 16, 1922; s. Joseph D. and Rose (Maisano) V.; m. Rose Conte, May 20, 1950; children: Rosalind, Lisa. A.B., U. Mich., 1943; M.A., Columbia U., 1947, Ph.D., 1954. Instr. N.Y. U., 1949-54; mem. faculty City Coll. N.Y., 1954-74, prof. English, 1968-74, chmn. dept., 1964-70; pres. Richmond Coll., 1974-76, Coll. S.I., 1976-94; Fulbright prof. Am. lit., France, 1960-61. Author: A Reader's Guide to William Faulkner, 1964; also anthologies and coll. text books.; Co-editor: Eleven Modern Short Novels; other books. Staten Island United Way, 1975—, S.I. council Boy Scouts Am., 1977-84, S.I. Doctors Hosp., 1977-78, Snug Harbor Cultural Ctr., 1978-83, St. Vincent's Hosp., 1979—; mem. N.Y.C. Mayor's Commn. on Bias, 1986-88. With AUS, 1943-46. Recipient Community Service award Italian Club Staten Island, Humanitarian award Staten Island Jewish Found. Sch., Mills G. Skinner award Staten Island branch N. Y. Urban League, Christopher Columbus award Columbian Assn. Bd. Edn., Disting. Community Service award YMCA, Community Service award Staten Island women's division Am. Com. on Italian Migration, Outstanding Acheivement award Guisepe Mazzini Lodge of the Sons of Italy; named Educator Yr., Am. Legion Richmond County. Mem. MLA, Am. Studies Assn., Assn. Dept. English (exec. com. 1969-71), Am. Assn. State Colls. and Univs. (task force ednl. opportunites for the aging, research and liason com., com. internat. programs, health affairs com.), Am. Assn. Higher Edn., Am. Assn. Colls. for Tchr. Edn., Am. Assn. Univ. Profs., Am. Council Edn., Am. Studies Assn., Assn. Colls. and Univs N.Y., Assn. Depts. of English (nat. exec. com.), Coll. English Assn. (nat. bd. dirs.), Consortium Internat. Programs, Inst. Internat. Edn., Inc., Middle States Assn. Colls. and Schs. Club: Andiron N.Y. (pres. 1972-75).

VOLPE, ERMINIO PETER, biologist, educator; b. N.Y.C., Apr. 7, 1927; s. Rocco and Rose (Ciano) V.; m. 1991; children: Laura Elizabeth, Lisa Lawton, John Peter. B.S., City Coll. N.Y., 1948; M.A., Columbia, 1949, Ph.D. (Newberry award 1952), 1952. Asst. zoologist Columbia U., N.Y.C., 1948-51; instr. biology CCNY, N.Y.C., 1951-52; asst. prof. zoology Newcomb Coll., Tulane Uu., 1952-81, chmn. dept. zoology, 1954-64, 64-66, 69-79; W.R. Irby disting. prof. biology Tulane U., 1979-81, asso dean grad. sch., 1967-69; prof. basic med. scis. (genetics) Mercer U. Sch. Medicine, Macon, Ga., 1981—; cons. Nat. Commn. Undergrad. Edn. in Biol. Scis., 1964-71; mem. steering com. Biol. Scis. Curriculum Study, 1966-70; panelist NRC, 1967-70; mem. U.S. Nat. Commn. for UNESCO, 1968-72; regional lectr. Sigma Xi, 1970-72; lectr. Elderhostel, 1988—; chmn. Advanced Placement Test in Biology, Ednl. Testing Service, 1975-80. Author: (textbook) Understanding Evolution, 1985, Human Heredity and Birth Defects, 1971, Patterns and Experiments in Developmental Biology, 1973, Man, Nature, and Society, 1975, The Amphibian Embryo in Transplantation Immunity, 1980, Biology and Human Concerns, 1993, Patient in the Womb, 1984, Test-Tube Conception: A Blend of Love and Science, 1987; mem. editorial bd. jour. Copeia, 1962-63; asso. editor Jour. Exptl. Zoology, 1968-76, 84-85; editor (jour.) Am. Zoologist, 1975-80; contbr. articles to profl. jours. Served with USNR, 1945-46. Fellow AAAS; mem. Genetics Soc. Am., Am. Soc. Zoologists (pres. 1981), Am. Soc. Naturalists, Soc. Devel. Biology, Soc. Study Evolution, Am. Soc. for Cell Biology, Am. Soc. Human Genetics, Phi Beta Kappa (v.p. Tulane U. chpt. 1962), Sigma Xi (pres. Tulane U. chpt. 1964, faculty award 1972.). Office: Mercer Univ Sch Medicine PO Box 134 Macon GA 31207-0002*

VOLPE, JOSEPH, opera company administrator. Gen. mgr. Met. Opera Assn., N.Y.C. Office: Met Opera Lincoln Ctr New York NY 10023

VOLPE, JOSEPH JOHN, pediatric neurologist, educator; b. Salem, Mass., Dec. 17, 1938; s. John Rosario and Anne Eleanor (Femino) V.; m. Sara Lee Solov, June 2, 1980; children from previous marriage: Joanna Marie, Joseph Anthony, John Matthew. BA, Bowdoin Coll., 1960; MD, Harvard U., 1964. Diplomate Am. Bd. Pediatrics, Am. Bd. Neurology and Psychiatry with spl. competence in child neurology. Pediatric intern Mass. Gen. Hosp., Boston, 1964-65, pediatric resident, 1965-66, neurology and pediatric resident, 1968-71; rsch. assoc. Nat. Inst. Child Health and Human Devel., Bethesda, Md., 1966-68; asst. prof. pediatrics and neurology Washington U. Med. Sch., St. Louis, 1971-76, assoc. prof. pediatrics and neurology, 1976-79, prof. pediatrics and neurology, 1979—, prof. biol. chemistry, 1980-90, dir. div. pediatric neurology, 1984-90; Bronson Crothers prof. neurology Harvard Med. Sch., Boston, 1990—; neurologist in chief Children's Hosp., Boston, 1990—. Author: Neurology of the Newborn, 1981, 2d edit., 1987, 3d edit., 1995; contbr. over 240 articles to profl. jours. Active United Cerebral Palsy Found., 1992—; Capt. USPHS, 1966-68. Recipient Weinstein-Goldensohn award United Cerebral Palsy Assn., 1985; rsch. grantee NIH, 1973—, 85—, March of Dimes Nat. Found., 1985-87. Democrat. Unitarian. Office: Children's Hosp 300 Longwood Ave Boston MA 02115-5737

VOLPE, PETER ANTHONY, surgeon; b. Columbus, Ohio, Dec. 17, 1936; s. Peter Anthony and Jeanette Katherine (Volz) V.; m. Suzanne Stephens, Sept. 5, 1959 (div. 1977); children: John David, Michael Charles; m. Kathleen Ann Townsend, Mar. 28, 1978; 1 child, Mark Christopher. BA cum laude, Ohio State U., 1958, MD summa cum laude, 1961. Diplomate Am. Bd. Surgery, Am. Bd. Colon and Rectal Surgery (pres. 1988). Pvt. practice San Francisco, 1969-86; sr. ptnr. Volpe, Russell, Chiu, Abel, MD's, San Francisco, 1987—; asst. clin. prof. surgery U. Calif., San Francisco, 1972—; chmn. dept. surgery St. Mary's Hosp. and Med. Ctr., San Francisco, 1978-90. Contbr. articles to profl. jours. Lt. USN, 1962-64. Fellow ACS (bd. govs. 1988-94), Am. Soc. Colon and Rectal Surgeons (treas. 1985-89, pres. 1990); mem. Am. Thoracic Surg. Soc., San Francisco Med. Soc. Republican. Roman Catholic. Office: Volpe Russell Chiu Abel 3838 California St San Francisco CA 94118-1522

VOLPE, RALPH PASQUALE, insurance company executive; b. Souderton, Pa., Sept. 20, 1936; s. Pasquale S. and Katie M. (Hartzell) V.; m. Marie F. Romano, Feb. 6, 1965; children: William, Anthony, Lynda. BA in Polit. Sci., Pa. State U., University Park, 1963. Claim cons. Aetna Life & Casualty Co., King of Prussia, 1964—. Mem. Upper Merion Twp. Bd. Suprs., 1974-79, 82-87, 94—, chmn., 1984, 86, 87, vice chmn., 1985; 2d v.p. Montgomery County Assn. Twp. Ofcls., 1995—; mem. Upper Merion Govt. Study Commn., 1974: chmn. Upper Merion Dems., 1980-81; chmn. Montgomery County Dem. Campaign, 1975. With U.S. Army, 1959-61. Recipient Good Govt. award Upper Merion Jaycees, 1977. Mem. Chapel Four Chaplains, Legion Hon. Mem., Optimists, Valley Forge Order Sons of Italy in Am. #1776. Republican. Roman Catholic. Home: 240 Strawberry Ln King Of Prussia PA 19406

VOLPÉ, ROBERT, endocrinologist; b. Toronto, Ont., Can., Mar. 6, 1926; s. Aaron G. and Esther (Shulman) V.; m. Ruth Vera Pullan, Sept. 5, 1949; children: Catherine, Elizabeth, Peter, Edward, Rose Ellen. MD, U. Toronto, 1950. Intern U. Toronto, 1950-51, resident in medicine, 1951-52, 53-55, fellow in endocrinology, 1952-53, 55-57, sr. rsch. fellow dept. medicine, 1957-62, McPhedran fellow, 1957-65, asst. prof., 1962-68, assoc. prof., 1968-72, prof., 1972-92, prof. emeritus, 1992—, dir. div. endocrinology and metabolism, 1987-92, chmn. Centennial Com. 1987-88; attending staff St. Joseph's Hosp., Toronto, 1957-66; active staff Wellesley Hosp., Toronto, 1966—; dir. endocrinology rsch. lab. Wellesley Hosp., 1968—, physician-in-chief, 1974-87; trans-Atlantic vis. prof. Caledonia Endocrine Soc., 1985; Hashimoto Meml. lectr. Kyushu U., Fukuoka, Japan, 1992; K.J.R. Wightman vis. prof. Royal Coll. Physicians, Can., 1994. Author: Systematic Endocrinology, 1973, 2d edit., 1979, Thyrotoxicosis, 1978, Auto-immunity in the Endocrine System, 1981, Auto-immunity and Endocrine Disease, 1985, Thyroid Function and Disease, 1987, Autoimmunity in Endocrine Disease, 1990; also over 300 rsch. articles mostly on immunology of thyroid disease; past editl. bd. Jour. Clin. Endocrinology and Metabolism, Clin. Medicine, Clin. Endocrinology, Annals Internal Medicine, Endocrine Pathology; editl. bd.: Am. Jour. Physiology, Opinions in Endocrinology Metabolism, Thyroid. Served with Royal Can. Naval Vol. Res., 1943-45. Recipient Goldie medal for med. rsch. U. Toronto, 1971, Novo-Nordisk prize Irish Endocrine Soc., 1990; Med. Rsch. Coun. Can. grantee, 1955—. Fellow Royal Coll. Physicians Can. (coun. 1988—, chmn. annual meetings com. 1988-94, sci. program com. 1988-94, chmn. rsch. com. 1990—, v.p. medicine 1994—), Royal Coll. Physicians Edinburgh, Royal Coll. Physicians London, Royal Soc. Medicine, ACP (gov. for Ont. 1978-83); mem. AAAS, Can. Soc. Endocrinology and Metabolism (past pres., Sandoz prize lectr. 1985, disting. svc. award 1990), Toronto Soc. Clin. Rsch. (Baxter prize lectr. 1984), Can. Soc. Clin. Investigation, Am. Thyroid Assn. (pres. 1980-81, disting. scientist award 1991), Assn. Am. Physicians, Endocrine Soc., Am. Fedn. Clin. Rsch., Can. Soc. Nuclear Medicine (Jamieson prize lectr. 1980), Can. Inst. Acad. Medicine, N.Y. Acad. Sci., European Thyroid Assn. (corr.), Latin Am. Thyroid Assn. (corr.), Soc. Endocrinology and Metabolism of Chile (hon.), Japan Endocrine Soc. (hon., gold medal 1986), Donalda Club, Alpine Ski Club (bd. dirs. 1987-89), U. Toronto Faculty Club. Home: 3 Daleberry Pl, Don Mills, ON Canada M3B 2A5 Office: Wellesley Hosp, Toronto, ON Canada M4Y 1J3 *Rigid adherence to high standards and integrity is essential. Do what is worth doing now, not tomorrow.*

VOLPE, THOMAS J., advertising executive; b. Bklyn., Dec. 22, 1935; s. John G. and Josephine (Fontana) V.; m. Anita Mazzei, Nov. 24, 1957; children: Lisa, Lori, John. BS in Econs., Bklyn. Coll., 1957; MBA, CCNY, 1965. Mgr. Deloitte Haskins & Sells, N.Y.C., 1957-70; v.p., treas. Colgate Palmolive Co., N.Y.C., 1970-85; sr. v.p., fin. ops. Interpublic Group of Cos., N.Y.C., 1986—. Trustee St. Francis Coll., Bklyn., 1971—; bd. dirs., treas. Multiple Sclerosis Soc., N.Y.C. chpt., 1979—. Mem. Fin. Execs. Inst. (com. chmn.), N.Y. State Soc. of CPA's (com. chmn.). Office: The Interpub Group Cos Inc 1271 Ave Of The Americas New York NY 10020-1300

VOLPERT, RICHARD SIDNEY, lawyer; b. Cambridge, Mass., Feb. 16, 1935; s. Samuel Abbot and Julia (Fogel) V.; m. Marcia Flaster, June 11, 1958; children: Barry, Sandy, Linda, Nancy. B.A., Amherst Coll., 1956; LL.B. (Stone scholar), Columbia U., 1959. Bar: Calif. bar 1960. Atty. firm O'Melveny & Myers, Los Angeles, 1959-86; ptnr. O'Melveny & Myers, 1967-86, Skadden, Arps, Slate, Meagher & Flom, Los Angeles, 1986—; pub. Jewish Jour. of Los Angeles. 1985-87 . Editor, chmn.: Los Angeles Bar Jour, 1965, 66, 67, Calif. State Bar Jour, 1972-73. Chmn. community relations com. Jewish Fedn.-Council Los Angeles, 1977-80; bd. dirs. Jewish Fedn.-Council Greater Los Angeles, 1976—, v.p., 1978-81; pres. Los Angeles County Natural History Mus. Found., 1978-84, trustee, 1974—, chair bd. dirs., 1992—; chmn. bd. councilors U. So. Calif. Law Center, 1979-85; vice chmn. Nat. Jewish Community Relations Adv. Council, 1981-84, mem. exec. com., 1978-85; bd. dirs. U. Judaism, 1973-89, bd. govs., 1973-89; bd. dirs. Valley Beth Shalom, Encino, Calif., 1964-88; mem. capital program major gifts com. Amherst Coll., 1978-86; bd. dirs., mem. exec. com. Los Angeles Wholesale Produce Market Devel. Corp., 1978-95, v.p. 1981-93, pres. 1993-95; mem. exec. bd. Los Angeles chpt. Am. Jewish Com., 1967—; vice-chmn. Los Angeles County Econ. Devel. Council, 1978-81; bd. dirs. Jewish Community Fund, 1981—; mem. Pacific S.W. regional bd. Anti Defamation League B'nai B'rith, 1964—. Named Man of Year, 1978. Fellow Am. Bar Found.; mem. ABA, Am. Soc. Planning Ofcls., Urban Land Inst., Los Angeles County Bar Assn. (trustee 1968-70, chmn. real property sect. 1974-75), Los Angeles County Bar Found. (trustee 1977-80), Calif. Bar Assn. (com. on adminstrn. justice 1973-76), Am. Coll. Real Estate Lawyers, Anglo-Am. Real Property Inst., Amherst Club of So. Calif. (dir. 1968-85, pres. 1972-73), City Club (L.A.). Jewish. Home: 4001 Stansbury Ave Sherman Oaks CA 91423-4619 Office: Skadden Arps Slate Meagher& Flom 300 S Grand Ave Los Angeles CA 90071-3165

VOLPICELLI, STEPHEN L., lawyer; b. Norristown, Pa., Jan. 5, 1945; s. Dominic Joseph and Mary (Lesinicchia) V.; m. Margaret M. Pipala, Dec. 4, 1971; 1 child, Regina A. BA, Albright Coll., Reading, Pa., 1966; JD, Dickinson Sch. Law, 1969. Bar: Pa. 1970, U.S. Dist. Ct. (ea. dist.) Pa. 1970, U.S. Ct. Appeals (3d cir.) 1970, U.S. Supreme Ct. 1976, N.Y. 1986. Asst. counsel Fidelity Mut. Life Ins. Co., Phila., 1971-72; ptnr. Garfinkel & Volpicelli, Phila., 1972-86, Mesirov, Gelman, Jaffe, Cramer & Jamieson, Phila., 1986-88, Dechert, Price & Rhoads, Phila., 1988—; lectr. grad. legal div. Temple U., Phila., 1976—, Pa. Bar Inst., 1988—; lectr., course planner Nat. Bus. Inst., Phila., 1992—. Mem. ABA, Pa. Bar Assn., Phila. Bar Assn. Roman Catholic. Office: Dechert Price & Rhoads 4000 Bell Atlantic Tower 1717 Arch St Philadelphia PA 19103-2713

VOLTZ, JEANNE APPLETON, author b. Collinsville, Ala.; d. James Lamar and Marie (Sewell) Appleton; m. Luther Manship Voltz, July 31, 1943 (dec. Aug. 1977); children: Luther Manship, Jeanne Marie; m. Frank B. MacKnight, Aug. 6, 1988 (div. Sept. 1994). AB, U. Montevallo, Ala., 1942. Corr., The Birmingham (Ala.) News, 1939-42; reporter The Press-Register, Mobile, Ala., 1942-45; reporter, feature writer The Miami Herald, 1947-53, food editor, 1953-60; food editor Los Angeles Times, 1960-73, Woman's Day, N.Y.C., 1973-84; free-lance writer, food cons., N.Y.C., 1984-88, Chapel Hill, N.C., 1988—; instr. wine and food in civilization UCLA, 1972-73; expert witness Senate Com. on Nutrition and Health, Ft. Lauderdale, Fla., 1980; adj. prof. Dept. Nutrition Hotel Mgmt. NYU, 1986—, Home Econs. Hotel Mgmt., 1987—; judge Hardee's Willow Creek Rib Cook-Off, Raleigh, N.C., 1993, 94, 95; Blue Ridge Barbecue and Rib Festival, Tryon, N.C., 1994, 95. Author: The California Cookbook, 1970 (Tastemaker award 1970), The Los Angeles Times Natural Foods Cookbook, 1974, The Flavor of the South, 1976 (Tastemaker award 1976), An Apple A Day, 1983, Barbecued Ribs and Other Great Feeds, 1985 (Tastemaker award 1985), Community Suppers, 1987, Barbecued Ribs, Smoked Butts and Other Great Feeds, 1991; author: (with Burks Hamner) The L.A. Gourmet, 1971, (with Elayne Kleeman) How to Turn a Passion for Food into Profit, 1979, (with Caroline Stuart) The Florida Cookbooks, 1993. Mem. N.C. Mus. Art, Raleigh. Mem. adv. bd. James Beard Found., N.Y. Recipient Vesta award Am. Meat Inst., 1962-72; Alumna of Yr. award U. Montevallo, 1981. Mem. Les Dames d'Escoffier (dir. 1976, pres. 1985-86, internat. pres. 1986-87), Inst. Food Technologists, Women in Communications, Soc. Women Geographers, Internat. Assn. Culinary Profls., The Authors' Guild N.Y., Am. Inst. Wine and Food (chairperson Piedmont chpt.), Culinary Historians N.Y., Phi Tau Sigma. Democrat. Methodist.

VOLUSE, CHARLES RODGER, III, education educator; b. Balt., Oct. 14, 1943; s. Charles Rodger Jr. and Beulah (Gisriel) V.; children: Steven Michael, Andrew Craig. BS in Edn., Southwestern U., Georgetown, Tex., 1965; MEd, Boston U., 1968; EdD, U. Va., 1973. Prof. grad. reading edn. SUNY, Potsdam, 1973-77, Xavier U., Cin., 1977-80; cons. Hamilton County Office Edn., Cin., 1980—; assoc. dir. grad. reading program Xavier U., Cin., 1976-83; cons. Hamilton County Bd. of Mental Retardation, Cin., 1983-85, gifted and talented programs Hamilton County Office Edn., 1985—; dir. Curriculum Devel. Assocs., Cin., 1982—. Author: Adult Subvocalization Behaviors, 1973, Experiences in Language for the Learning Handicapped, 1985; creator editl. programs. Mem. Internat. Reading Assn., Nat. Council Tchrs. of English, Nat. Council Tchrs. of Math, Ohio Valley Assn for the Talented and Gifted. Home: 6573 Rollymeade Ave Cincinnati OH 45243-3002 Office: Hamilton County Office Edn 11083 Hamilton Ave Cincinnati OH 45231-1409

VOLZ, CHARLES HARVIE, JR., lawyer; b. Richmond, Va., Sept. 15, 1925; s. Charles Harvie and Mary V. (Mallory) V.; m. Constance A. Lewis, July 30, 1976; children: Charles Harvie III, Judith C. BS, U. Ala., 1950, JD, 1951. Bar: Ala. 1951. Spl. agt. FBI, 1951; claim mgr. Allstate Ins. Co., 1952-54; claims atty. State Farm Ins. Co., 1954-57; sole practice, 1957-63, Montgomery, 1959—; asst. dir. Dept. Indsl. Relations, State of Ala., 1959-62; pntr. Volz, Capouano, Wampold & Prestwood, 1963-84, Volz & Volz, 1984-95, Volz, Prestwood, Hanan & Sizemore, 1995—. Note editor Ala. Law Rev, 1950-51. Campaign dir. March of Dimes, 1958, Am. Cancer Soc., 1967; exec. sec. Gov.'s Com. on Employment Physically Handicapped, 1959-62; mem. Pres.'s Com. on Employment Physically Handicapped, 1959-62; pres., bd. dirs. Montgomery chpt. Am. Cancer Soc. Served to 2d lt. USAAF, 1943-45. Recipient Outstanding Service award Am. Cancer Soc., 1967. Mem. Am. Arbitration Assn. (mem. nat. panel), ABA, Ala. Bar Assn., Assn. Trial Lawyers Am. (state committeeman 1973-75), Ala. Trial Lawyers Assn. (bd. govs.), Phi Alpha Delta. Methodist. Lodges: Masons, Kiwanis. Home: 1638 Cobblestone Ct Montgomery AL 36117-1713 Office: 350 Adams Ave Montgomery AL 36104

VOLZ, MARLIN MILTON, legal educator; b. Cecil, Wis., Sept. 3, 1917; s. Edward A. and Mae C. (Winter) V.; m. Esther R. Krug, Aug. 23, 1941; children: Marlin M., Karen D., Thomas A. BA, U. Wis., 1938, JD, 1940, SJD, 1945; LLD (hon.), San Juan (P.R.) Law Sch., 1957. Bar: Wis. 1940, Mo. 1951, Ky. 1958. Asst. prof. law sch. faculty U. Wis., 1946-50; prof., dean sch. law U. Kansas City (now U. Mo. in Kansas City), 1950-58; dean sch. law U. Louisville, 1958-65, prof. sch. law, 1965-87, ret., 1987; county judge pro tem, probate judge Jefferson County, Ky., 1970-74; chmn. Ky. Pub. Svc. Commn., Frankfort, 1981-82; mem. panel labor arbitrators Fed. Mediation and Conciliation Svc., Am. Arbitration Assn.; reporter on legal draftsmanship Am. Law Inst.; adviser San Juan (P.R.) Sch. Law; mem. Nat. Coun. Legal Clinics, Chgo., 1960-67; mem. Louisville Labor Mgmt. Com. Co-author: Drafting Partnership Agreements, 7th edit., 1984, 86, Wisconsin Practice Methods, 1949, Missouri Practice Methods, 1953, Iowa Practice Methods, 1954, Kansas Practice Methods, 1957; co-author, gen. editor rev. edit. West's Federal practice Manual; co-author, gen. editor Kentucky Legal Forms, vol. 3 and 4, 1965, co-author, vol. 5 and 6, gen. editor revision, 1985; co-author, gen. editor Caldwell's Kentucky Form Book; editor: Cases and Materials, Civil Procedure, 1975, 83. Chmn. Ky. Com. Correctional Rsch., Frankfort, 1962-65, Louisville Human Rels. Commn., 1962-65; candidate for mayor, Louisville, 1965. Sgt. U.S. Army, 1943-46. Recipient Teaching and Major Svc. awards. Mem. ABA (co-chair arbitration com. 1986-89), Fed. Bar Assn., Ky. Bar Assn., Wis. Bar Assn., Am. Judicature Soc. (bd. dir. 1976-80), Nat. Orgn. Legal Problems Edn. (nat. pres. 1963), Nat. Acad. Arbitrators (com. chmn. 1987-88, bd. govs. 1989-92), Rotary. Democrat. Methodist. Home: 1819 Woodfill Way Louisville KY 40205-2433 Office: U Louisville Sch Law Louisville KY 40292

VOLZ, WILLIAM HARRY, legal educator, administrator; b. Sandusky, Mich., Dec. 28, 1946; s. Harry Bender and Belva Geneva (Riehl) V. B.A., Mich. State U., 1968; A.M., U. Mich., 1972; J.D., Wayne State U., 1975; M.B.A., Harvard U., 1978. Bar: Mich. 1975. Sole practice, Detroit, 1975-77; mgmt. analyst Office of Gen. Counsel, HEW, Woodlawn, Md., 1977; asst., then assoc. prof. bus. law Wayne State U., Detroit, 1978-85, interim dean sch. Bus. Adminstrn., 1985, now prof. bus. law, dean; cons. Merrill, Lynch, Pierce, Fenner & Smith, N.Y.C., 1980—, City of Detroit law dept., 1982, Mich. Supreme Ct., Detroit, 1981; ptnr. Mich. C.P.A. Rev., Southfield, 1983-85. Author: Managing a Trial, 1982; contbr. articles to legal jours.; editorial bds. of bus. and law jours, AACSB visitation com.; internat. adv. bd., Inst. of Mgmt., Univ. of L'viv, Ukraine, Legal counsel Free Legal Aid Clinic, Inc., Detroit, 1976—, Shared Ministries, Detroit, 1981, Sino-Am. Tech. Exchange Council, People's Republic of China, 1982; chair advt. rev. panel Better Bus. Bur. Detroit, 1988-90; bd. dirs. Greater Detroit Alliance Bus., Olde Custodian Fund. Recipient Disting. Faculty award Wayne State Sch. Bus. Adminstrn., 1982. Mem. ABA, Am. Bus. Law Assn., Amateur Mendicant Soc. (commissionaire 1981-85), Players, Golden Key, Alpha Kappa Psi, Beta Alpha Psi. Mem. Reorganized Ch. Latter Day Saints. Clubs: Detroit Athletic Club, Econ. of Detroit, Harvard Bus. Sch. of Detroit. Home: 3846 Wedgewood Dr Bloomfield Hills MI 48301 Office: Wayne State U Sch Bus Adminstrn Cass Ave Detroit MI 48202

VONA, CARMINE, banker; b. Quindici, Italy, April 6, 1938; came to U.S., 1966, naturalized, 1972; s. Salvatore and Luisa (Volino) V.; m. Carmela Josephine Pacia, July 22, 1967; children—Salvatore, Joseph C. Doctorate in Physics, U. Naples, Italy, 1962. Asst. prof. physics U. Naples, 1962-63; computer analyst Italsider, Genova, Italy, 1963-66; prof. physics U. Natal, Brazil, 1966; sr. cons. Computer Usage Co., N.Y.C., 1967-69; sr. v.p. Bankers Trust Co., N.Y.C., 1969—. Editor: Automation in the Bank of the Future, 1980. Office: Bankers Trust Co 280 Park Ave New York NY 10017-1216

VON ARX, DOLPH WILLIAM, food products executive; b. St. Louis, Aug. 30, 1934; s. Adolph William and Margaret Louise (Linderer) von A.; m. Sharon Joy Landolt, Dec. 21, 1957; children: Vanessa von Arx Gilvarg, Eric S., Valerie L. BSBA, Washington U., St. Louis, 1961; LHD, St. Augustine Coll., 1988. Account exec. Compton Advt., N.Y.C., 1961-64; v.p. mktg. Ralston Purina Co., St. Louis, 1964-69; exec. v.p. mktg. Gillette Personal Care Div., Chgo., 1969-72; exec. v.p. gen. mgmt. group T.J. Lipton Inc., Englewood Cliffs, N.J., 1973-87; pres., chief exec. officer R.J. Reynold Tobacco Co., Winston-Salem, N.C. 1987-88; chmn., chief exec. officer Planters LifeSavers Co., Winston-Salem, 1988-91; bd. dirs. Carolina Medicorp, Winston-Salem, Wachovia Bank & Trust Co., Winston Salem, 1988-92, Morrison Restaurants Inc. Mobile, Ala., Care Rsch. Inc., Durham, N.C. Bd. visitors U. N.C., 1988-92; chmn. bd. trustees Wake Forest U. Grad. Sch. Mgmt., 1988—; pres. bd. trustees N.C. Dance Theater, Winston-Salem, 1989-90; bd. dirs. Forsyth Meml. Hosp., Naples Conservancy, Naples Philharmonic Ctr. for Arts, Wheeling Thunderbirds Hockey, Inc., Reynolda Mus. Am. Art, Naples Cmty. Hosp., Women's Legis. Lobby. Unitarian. Avocation: theater. Home: 1300 Sinnissippi Rd Sterling IL 61081

VON BERGEN WESSELS, PENNIE LEA, state legislator; b. Sterling, Ill., Mar. 19, 1949; d. Donald LeRoy and Mary Lou (Hammere) von Bergen; m. Michael J. Wessels, Aug. 23, 1969. AA, Sauk Valley Coll., 1969; BSEd in English and Theater, No. Ill. U., 1971; postgrad., So. Ill. U., 1972-73; JD magna cum laude, U. Ill., 1983. Bar: Ill., 1983; cert. tchr., Ill. English and theater tchr. various schs., Ill., 1971-80; pvt. practice law Morrison, Ill., 1984-85; mem. Whiteside County Bd., Morrison, 1984-88, Ill. Gen. Assembly, Springfield, 1993-95. Bd. dirs. Ill. Citizens Utility Bd., 1989-92; mem. Save Our Kids Schs., various other orgns.; del. candidate Dem. Nat. Convention, 1980, 92. Named Outstanding Working Woman of Ill. Ill. Bus. and Profl. Women, 1988; recipient Mounders Pride award Mt. Morris Sch. Dist., 1993, Friend of Agr. award Farm Bus. Educator Assn., 1994, Outstanding Freshman Legislator award Ill. Edn. Assn., 1994. Mem. ABA, Ill. Bar Assn., Ill. Women in Govt., Women's Legis. Lobby. Unitarian. Avocation: theater. Home: 1300 Sinnissippi Rd Sterling IL 61081

VON BERNUTH, CARL W., diversified corporation executive, lawyer. BA, Yale U., 1966, LLB, 1969. Bar: N.Y. 1970, Pa. 1990. Corp. atty. White & Case, 1969-80; assoc. gen. counsel Union Pacific Corp., Bethlehem, Pa., 1980-83, dep. gen. counsel fin. and adminstrn., 1984-88, v.p., gen. counsel, 1988-91, sr. v.p., gen. counsel, 1991—. Office: Union Pacific Corp 8th & Eaton Aves Bethlehem PA 18018

VON BERNUTH, ROBERT DEAN, agricultural engineering educator, consultant; b. Del Norte, Colo., Apr. 14, 1946; s. John Daniel and Bernice H. (Dunlap) von B.; m. Judy M. Wehrman, Dec. 27, 1969; children: Jeanie, Suzie. BSE, Colo. State U., 1968; MS, U. Idaho, 1970; MBA, Claremont (Calif.) Grad. Sch., 1980; PhD in Engring., U. Nebr., 1982. Registered profl. engr., Calif., Nebr. Agrl. product mgr. Rain Bird Sprinkler Mfg., Glendora, Calif., 1974-80; instr. agrl. engring. U. Nebr., Lincoln, 1980-82; from assoc. prof. to prof. U. Tenn., Knoxville, 1982-90; prof., chmn. Mich. State U., East Lansing, 1990—; v.p. Von-Sol Cons., Lincoln, 1980-82; prin. Von Bernuth Agrl. cons., Knoxville, East Lansing, 1982—. Patentee in field. With USNR, 1970-92, Vietnam. Decorated DFC (2); recipient Disting. Naval Grad. award USN Flight Program, Pensacola, Fla., 1970. Mem. ASCE, Am. Soc. Agrl. Engrs. (chair irrigation group), Irrigation Assn. (chair awards com., person of yr. 1994), Naval Reserve Assn. Avocations: flying, skiing, antique tractors. Office: Mich State U Agrl Engring 215 Farrall Hall East Lansing MI 48824

VON BRANDENSTEIN, PATRIZIA, production designer. Prodn. designer films including Girlfriends, 1978, Heartland, 1979, Breaking Away, 1979, Ragtime, 1981 (Academy Award nomination best art direction 1981), Silkwood, 1983, Amadeus, 1984 (Academy Award best art direction 1984), Beat Street, 1984, A Chorus Line, 1985, The Money Pit, 1986, No Mercy, 1987, The Untouchables, 1987 (Academy Award nomination best art direction 1987), Betrayed, 1988, Working Girl, 1988, The Lemon Sisters, 1990, Postcards From the Edge, 1990, State of Grace, 1990, Billy Bathgate, 1992, Sneakers, 1992, Leap of Faith, 1993, Six Degrees of Separation, 1993, The Quick and the Dead, 1995, Just Cause, 1995; costume designer films including Between the Lines, 1977, Saturday Night Fever, 1977, A Little Sex, 1982. Address: 161 W 15th St Apt 7B New York NY 10011-6768 Office: care Lawrence Mirisch The Mirisch Agency 10100 Santa Monica Blvd Ste 700 Los Angeles CA 90067

VON BRAUN, PETER CARL MOORE STEWART, company executive; b. Greenwich, Conn., June 24, 1940; s. Carl Conrad and Martha Irwin (Moore) von B.; m. Elisabeth Esser, July 1, 1967 (div. Dec. 1980); m. Denene Jensen, Sept. 26, 1987; children: Christina Stewart, Alexander Stewart. BA with high honors, Yale U., 1964; PhD summa cum laude, U. Cologne, 1966. Assoc. McKinsey & Co., Inc., N.Y.C., 1966-72, prin., 1972-77; chief internat. programme devel. Order of St. John, London, 1977-80; exec. dir. The Sight Programme, London and Sultanate of Oman, 1977-84; chmn., CEO Am. Microtrace Corp., Virginia Beach, Va., 1987—; RusPetrol (USA), Inc., 1989—; chmn., CEO CLEW, LLC, Austin, 1995—. Author: Die Verteidigung Indiens, 1968, How to Save An Eye, 1981; contbr. articles to profl. jours.; producer (film) How to Save a Life, 1977. Chmn. Battle Harbour Found., Greenwich, 1972—; vestryman Trinity Parish, N.Y.C., 1977-84; chmn. Anglican Service Tng. & Relief Orgn., London, 1986—; bd. dirs. Presiding Bishop's Fund, N.Y.C., 1977-81; mem. Internat. Adv. Bd. Yale U., 1989—. Served with USN, 1956-58, U.S. Army, 1958-64. Decorated knight of grace and knight of justice Order of St. John, companion with star Order of Merit (Cyprus); Fulbright scholar, 1964-66. Republican. Episcopalian. Clubs: Cavalry, Guards Polo (London); N.Y. Yacht (N.Y.C.), Indian Harbor Yacht (Greenwich, Conn.), Battle Harbour Yacht (Newfoundland, Can.), Commodore. Avocations: sailing, military history, cooking. Home: 36 Zaccheus Meades Ln Greenwich CT 06831 Office: Am Micro Trace Inc 569 Central Dr Virginia Beach VA 23454-5228

VON BUEDINGEN, RICHARD PAUL, urologist; b. Rochester, N.Y., Sept. 14, 1938; s. Wilmer Edward and Clara Elma von B.; BS, U. Wis., 1960, MA in Philosophy, 1961, MD, 1965; m. Bari Luwe Solesky, Nov. 26, 1966 (dec. 1992); children: Kirsten Karla, Christian Karl. Commd. ensign U.S. Navy, 1964, advanced through grades to capt., 1975, intern, U.S. Naval Hosp., St. Albans, N.Y., 1965-66, resident in internal medicine, in plastic and thoracic surgery, in urology affiliate programs Naval Regional Med. Ctr., Oakland, Calif., and U.S. Hosp., Oakland, U. Calif. San Francisco, Stanford U., 1969-73, resident in pediatric urology, 1973, scientist astronaut trainee Naval Aerospace Med. Inst., Pensacola, Fla., 1966-67, group flight surgeon Marine Corp Air Sta., Beaufort, S.C., 1967-69, chief urology Naval Regional Med. Ctr., Long Beach, Calif., 1973-75, asst. clin. prof. urology U. Calif., Irvine, 1973-75, resigned, 1975; pvt. practice urology, Aiken, S.C., 1975—; bd. trustees, chief of surgery HCA Aiken Regional Med. Ctrs., 1985—. Fellow Internat. Coll. Surgeons, ACS; mem. AMA, Am. Urol. Assn., S.C. Med. Assn. (com. on continuing edn. 1981-83), S.C. Urol. Assn. So. Med. Assn., Soc. Govt. Urologists, Aiken County Med. Soc., Am. Cancer Soc. (chmn. com. profl. edn. in S.C. 1980-82, nat. award for contbns. to profl. edn. 1982), Am. Diabetes Assn. (state bd. dirs., med. edn. com.), Am. Fertility Soc., Am. Lithotripsy Soc. Club: Edisto River Hounds (Master of Foxhounds). Contbr. articles to profl. publs. Home: 1500 Huntsman Dr Aiken SC 29803-5236 Office: 210 University Pky Ste 2300 Aiken SC 29801-6808

VON DER HEYDEN, KARL INGOLF MUELLER, manufacturing company executive; b. Berlin, July 18, 1936; came to U.S., 1957, naturalized, 1967; s. Werner and Erika (Mueller) von der H.; m. Mary Ellen Terrell, Aug. 17, 1963; children: Ellen, Eric. Student, Free U., Berlin, 1959-61; B.A., Duke, 1962; M.B.A., Wharton Sch. U.Pa., 1964. C.P.A., Pa. Mgmt. trainee Berliner Bank, Berlin, 1955-57; sr. staff accountant Coopers & Lybrand, Phila., 1963-66; asst. comptroller, corporate comptroller Pitney-Bowes, Inc., Stamford, Conn., 1966-74; v.p., controller PepsiCo., Inc., Purchase, N.Y., 1974-77; v.p. finance Pepsi-Cola Co., 1977-79, v.p. mfg., 1979-80; v.p. fin., treas. H.J. Heinz Co., Pitts., 1980-83, sr. v.p. fin, chief fin. officer; also bd. dirs., 1983-89; exec. v.p., chief fin. officer RJR Nabisco Inc., N.Y.C., 1989-93, co-chmn., CEO, 1993; pres., CEO Metallgesellschaft Corp., N.Y.C., 1993-94; sr. advisor The Clipper Group, 1994—; bd. dirs. Federated Dept. Stores, Inc., Trizec Corp. Ltd. Bd. trustees Duke U.; vice chmn. YMCA Greater N.Y. Mem. AICPA, Univ. Club (Greenwich), Field Club (Greenwich, Conn.). Home: 15 Khakum Wood Rd Greenwich CT 06831-3728 Office: The Clipper Group 12 E 49th St 30th Fl New York NY 10017

VON DER HEYDT, JAMES ARNOLD, federal judge; lawyer; b. Miles City, Mont., July 15, 1919; s. Harry Karl and Alice S. (Arnold) von der H.; m. Verna E. Johnson, May 21, 1952. A.B., Albion (Mich.) Coll., 1942; J.D., Northwestern, 1951. Bar: Alaska 1951. Pvt. law practice Nome, 1953-59; judge superior ct. Juneau, Alaska, 1959-66; U.S. dist. judge Alaska, 1966—; U.S. commr. Nome, Alaska, 1951—; U.S. atty. div. 2 Dist. Alaska, 1951-53; mem. Alaska Ho. of Reps., 1957-59. Pres. Anchorage Fine Arts Mus. Assn. Mem. Alaska Bar Assn. (mem. bd. govs. 1955-59, pres. 1959-60), Wilson Ornithologists Soc., Am. Judicature Soc., Sigma Nu, Phi Delta Phi. Club: Mason (32 deg.), Shriner. Avocation: research. Aretic bird life. Office: US Dist Ct 510 L St Ste 100 Anchorage AK 99501-1946

VON DER MEHDEN, FRED R., political science educator; b. San Francisco, Dec. 1, 1927; s. Fred G. and Margaret (de Valasco) von der M.; m. Audrey Eleanor Whitehead, Dec. 27, 1954; children—Laura Davis, Victoria Margaret. B.A., U. of Pacific, 1948; M.A., Claremont Grad. Sch., 1950; Ph.D., U. Calif. Berkeley, 1957. Mem. faculty U. Wis. Madison, 1957-68; chmn. East Asian studies U. Wis.-Madison, 1963-65, 67-68; Albert Thomas prof. polit. sci. Rice U., 1968—; dir. Center for Research, 1969-70, chmn. dept., 1975-78, dir. program devel. studies, 1978-83; editor Rice U. Press, 1982-95; cons. AID, 1967-78. Author: Politics of the Developing Nations, 1964, 2d edit., 1969, Religion and Nationalism in Southeast Asia, 1963, Comparative Political Violence, 1973; co-author: Issues of Political Development, 1967, The Military and Politics of Five Developing Nations, 1970, Southeast Asia 1930-1970, 1974, Religion and Modernization in 1970, Southeast Asia, 1986, Two Worlds of Islam, 1993; editor: (with R. Soligo) Issues on Income Distribution, 1975, Ethnic Groups of Houston, 1984. Mem. Mid-West Conf. Asian Affairs (pres. 1968-69), Assn. Asian Studies, Am. Polit. Sci. Assn., S.W. Conf. Asian Affairs (pres. 1976-77). Home: 12530 Mossycup Dr Houston TX 77024-4937

VON DOHNÁNYI, CHRISTOPH, musician, conductor; b. Berlin, Sept. 8, 1929; s. Hans and Christina (Bonhoeffer) von D.; m. Anja Silja, Apr. 21,

1979; children: Julia, Benedikt, Olga. Student, Sch. Law, Munich, Musikhochschule, Germany, Fla. State U., Berkshire Music Ctr.; doctorate (hon.), Oberlin Coll., Cleve. Inst. Music, Case Western Res. U. Coach, condr. Frankfurt (Germany) Opera, 1952-57, gen. music dir., artistic dir., 1968-77; gen. music dir. Lubeck, Kassel, Germany, 1957-63; dir. West German Radio Symphony Cologne, 1964-70; artistic dir., prin. condr. Hamburg (Germany) State Opera, 1977-84; artistic dir. designate Cleve. Orch., 1982-84, music dir., 1984—; prin. guest condr. London Philharmonia, 1994—; guest condr. in U.S. and Europe; prin. guest condr. London Philharmonia, 1994—. Numerous recordings including 5 symphonies of Mendelssohn with Vienna Philharm., opera Lulu, Petrouchka Suite, Wozzeck, symphonies of Beethoven, Brahms, Schumann, Dvorak, Mahler, Mozart, Schubert and Bruckner with Cleve. Orch. Recipient Richard Strauss prize, Munich, 1951, Bartok prize, Hungary, 1982, Goethe-Plaket award City of Frankfurt, 1979, Comdr. of Yr. award Mus. Am., 1992; Domrd. d'ordre des arts et des lettres, Republic of France, 1988, Cross of the Order of Merit, Fed. Republic Germany, 1989, Comdr.'s Cross of Republic of Austria, 1992. Office: Cleve Orch 11001 Euclid Ave Cleveland OH 44106-1713

VONDRACEK, BETTY SUE, interior designer, remodeling contractor, real estate agent; b. Tulsa, Aug. 27, 1938; d. John Carson and Susan Elizabeth (Nall) Bumgarner; m. Rudy J. Vondracek, Feb. 4, 1961 (dec. Sept. 1990); children: Richard, John, Vikki. BFA, U. Kans., 1960. Lic. interior designer; lic. real estate agt. Comml. artist Hall & Floyd Advt., Tulsa, 1960-62; freelance artist El Dorado, Ark., 1962-67, Chgo., 1967-69; interior designer Jeanette Interiors, Dallas, 1974-76; owner, designer, contractor Bee Vee Studio, Dallas, 1976—; real estate agt. Mahoney Realty Svcs., Dallas, 1992—; mem. grievance com. Greater Dallas Bd. Realtors, 1992—; mem. Dallas Supts. Adv. Com. Designer Scottish Rite Hosp. Parade of Homes, 1984, March of Dimes Holiday Tour of Homes, 1985-86, Christmas at DeGolyer, 1988-90, Dallas Symphony Showhouse, 1985, 87, 89, 92. Elected ofcl. Dallas Ind. Sch. Dist., 1986-92; pres. West-Lake Rep. Women, Dallas, 1975-77, 92-94; chmn. bd. dirs. Am. Heart Assn., Dallas, 1990-91, Tex. chpt. bd. dirs. 1990—, chmn. capital campaign, chmn. pub. affairs); mem. edn. com. Womens Coun. Dallas County; chmn.-elect Tex. affiliate Am. Heart Assn. Recipient Dwight D. Eisenhower award Am. Heart Assn., 1993, Douglas S. Perry Vol. of Yr., Am. Heart Assn., 1990, Key Communicator award Tex. Sch. Pub. Rels., 1984, Disting. Svc. award Nat. Com. for Citizens in Edn., 1984. Mem. Am. Soc. Interior Designers. Roman Catholic. Avocations: painting, gardening, cooking, skiing. Office: Bee Vee Studio 6215 Chesley Ln Dallas TX 75214-2118

VON DREHLE, RAMON ARNOLD, lawyer; b. St. Louis, Mar. 12, 1930; s. Arnold Henry and Sylvia E. (Ahrens) Von D.; m. Gillian Margaret Turner, Sept. 13, 1980; children by previous marriage: Carin L., Lisa A., Courtney A. B.S., Washington U., St. Louis, 1952; LL.B., U. Tex., Austin, 1957; postgrad. Parker Sch. Internat. Law, Columbia U., 1965. Bar: Tex. 1956, Mich. 1957, U.S. Supreme Ct. 1981. Sr. atty. Ford Motor Co., Dearborn, Mich., 1957-67; assoc., asst. gen. counsel Ford of Europe, Inc., Brentwood, Essex, Eng., 1967-75; v.p., gen. counsel Ford of Europe, Inc., 1975-79; v.p. legal Ford Motor Credit Co., Dearborn, 1979-87; v.p., gen. counsel Am. Road Ins. Co., Dearborn, 1979-87; exec. dir. legal affairs Ford Fin. Services Group, Dearborn, 1987-91; leader in residence Walsh Coll., Mich., 1992; panelist large complex case program Am. Arbitration Assn., 1993—; advisor to Czech Republic Ministry of Privatization, Prague, 1993-94; advisor Russian Def. Conversion Project, 1995; lectr. in Ea. Europe, 1995. Article editor: Tex. Law Rev, 1956-57. Trustee Birmingham Unitarian Ch., 1966-67. Served to 1st lt. AUS, 1952-54, Korea. Mem. ABA, Mich. Bar Assn., Tex. Bar Assn., Internat. Bar Assn., Am. Fin. Svcs. Assn. (chmn. 1990-91, bd. dirs. 1981-91), Fin. Svcs. Coun. (bd. dirs. 1987-91), Washington U. Alumni Club Detroit (past pres.), Order of Coif, Renaissance Club (Detroit) Les Ambassadeur (London), Confrérie des Chevliers du Tastevin (France), Capitol Hill Club (Washington), Royal Automobile Club (London), Tau Beta Pi, Omicron Delta Kappa. Mem. Christ Ch. Home and Office: 6894 McLean Province Cir Falls Church VA 22043-9999

VON ECKARDT, WOLF, design critic, educator; b. Berlin, Germany, Mar. 6, 1918; came to U.S., 1936, naturalized, 1943; s. Hans Felix and Gertrude (Lederer) E.; m. Marianne Horney, June 28, 1941 (div.); children: Barbara, Marina Von Eckardt Gilman; m. Nina ffrench-frazier, Feb. 14, 1987. Student, New Sch. Social Research, 1936-38; L.H.D. (hon.), The Md. Inst., 1983. Info. officer Dept. State, Washington, 1949-53; free-lance pub. info. specialist Washington, 1953-59; dir. pub. info. AIA, 1959-63; architecture critic Washington Post, 1963-81; design critic Time mag., 1981-85; guest prof. dept. city and regional planning Cornell U., Ithaca, N.Y., 1986; Albert A. Levin prof. urban studies and pub. service Coll. Urban Affairs, Cleve. State U., 1978-80; lectr. Harvard U., 1966, MIT, 1967. Graphic artist, book designer, N.Y.C., 1936-41; Author: Eric Mendelsohn, 1960, The Challenge of Megalopolis, 1964, A Place to Live-The Crisis of the Cities, 1968, (with Sander Gilman) Bertolt Brecht's Berlin, 1975, Back to the Drawing Board! Planning Livable Cities, 1979, (with Sander Gilman) Oscar Wilde's London, 1987, Please Write, How To Improve Your Handwriting for Business and Pleasure in Ten Quick and Easy Lessons, 1988; also articles. Served with AUS, World War II. Hon. mem. AIA; mem. Am. Inst. Graphic Arts (pres. Washington chpt. 1962-65), Soc. Archtl. Historians. Home: 87 Bryant Rd Jaffrey NH 03452-1635

VON ESCHEN, ROBERT LEROY, electrical engineer, consultant; b. Glasgow, Mont., Oct. 3, 1936; s. Leroy and Lillian Victoria (Eliason) Von E.; m. Carolyn Kay Frampton, Dec. 14, 1965; children: Eric Leroy, Marc Alfred. BSEE, Mont. State U., 1961; postgrad. U. Idaho, Lakeland C.C., Glendale C.C. Registered profl. engr., Pa. Hydro constrn. engr. U.S. Army Corps of Engrs., Mont. and S.D., 1961-62; hdqrs. chief engr. Eagle Constrn. Co., Colo., 1962; resident elec. engr. transmission and distbn. divs. Stanley Cons., Inc., West Africa, 1962-63; cons. engr. fossil div. Stanley Cons., Inc., Ky. and Colo., 1963-65; constrn. startup/hydro engr. Stanley Cons., Inc., West Africa, 1965-66; cons. engr. fossil div. Gilbert Assocs., Inc., 1968-72, cons. engr. nuclear div., 1972-74, 77-84, project site mgr., 1974-77; cons. engr. nuclear div. United Energy Svcs. Corp., 1984-86; safety systems functional insp. nuclear div. United Energy Svcs. Corp., Marietta, Ga., 1986-91, mgmt. assessment, 1992; mgmt. assessment Mason & Hanger-Silas Mason Co., Inc., Amarillo, Tex., 1992-93, maintenance planning mgr., 1993—; tech. cons. World Bank, Monrovia, 1963; engring. cons. USN, Manila, 1967. Founder, dir. Madison (Ohio) Computer Soc., 1983-85; v.p., bd. dirs. N.E. coun. Boy Scouts Am., Painesville, 1983-85. Recipient Silver Beaver award Boy Scouts Am., 1981, 84. Mem. IEEE, NRA, NPSE, Nat. Assn. Ret. Persons, Soc. Am. Mil. Engrs., Am. Def. Preparedness Assn., Tex. Profl. Engrs. Soc., Ohio Profl. Engrs. Soc., Masons (life), Elks, Scottish Rite (life), Shriners. Avocations: target and skeet shooting, constrn. design, computers, electronics. Home: 3445 Gladstone Ln Amarillo TX 79121-1925 Office: Mason & Hanger-Silas Mason Co Inc PO Box 30020 Amarillo TX 79177-0001

VON FRAUNHOFER-KOSINSKI, KATHERINA, bank executive; b. N.Y.C.; m. Jerzy Kosinski, Feb. 15, 1987 (dec. May 3, 1991). Student, St. Joseph's Convent, London, Clark's Coll., London. Various positions Robert W. Orr & Assocs., N.Y.C., 1954-55; with traffic dept. Compton Advt., Inc., N.Y.C., 1956-63; acct. exec. J. Walter Thompson Co., N.Y.C., 1963-69; product mgr. Natural Wonder line Revlon Co., N.Y., 1969-71; pres. Scientia Factum, Inc., N.Y.C., 1971—; co-founder Polish Am. Resources Corp., N.Y.C., 1988—, pres., CEO, 1992—; founder, CEO, pres. Polish Am. Techs., L.P., N.Y.C., 1992—; chmn. bd. dirs. AmerBank, Warsaw, 1991—. Co-founder Westchester Sports Club. Avocations: skiing, horse/polo, swimming, photography. Home: 60 W 57th St New York NY 10019

VON FURSTENBERG, BETSY, actress, writer; b. Neiheim Heusen, Germany, Aug. 16, 1931; d. Count Franz-Egon and Elizabeth (Johnson) von F.; m. Guy Vincent de la Maisoneuve (div.); 2 children.; m. John J. Reynolds, Mar. 26, 1984. Attended Miss Hewitt's Classes, N.Y. Tutoring Sch.; prepared for stage with Sanford Meisner at Neighborhood Playhouse. Made Broadway stage debut in Second Threshold, N.Y., 1951; appeared in Dear Barbarians, 1952, Oh Men Oh Women, 1954, The Chalk Garden, 1955, Child of Fortune, 1956, Nature's Way, 1957, Much Ado About Nothing, 1959, Mary Mary, 1963, Paisley Convertible, 1967, Avanti, 1968, The Gingerbread Lady, 1970 (toured 1971), Absurd Person Singular, 1976; off Broadway appearances include For Love or Money, 1951; toured in Petrified

Forest, Jason and Second Man, 1952; appeared in Josephine, 1953; subsequently toured, 1955; What Every Woman Knows, 1955, The Making of Moo, 1958 (toured 1958), Say Darling, 1959, Wonderful Town, 1959, Season of Choice, 1959, Beyond Desire, 1967, Private Lives, 1968, Does Anyone Here Do the Peabody, 1976; appeared in Along Came a Spider, Theatre in the Park, N.Y.C., 1985; appeared in film Women Without Names, 1950; TV appearances include Robert Montgomery Show, Ed Sullivan Show, Alfred Hitchcock Presents, One Step Beyond, The Mike Wallace Show, Johnny Carson Show, Omnibus, Theatre of the Week, The Secret Storm, As the World Turns, Movie of the Week, Your Money or Your Wife, Another World; writer syndicated column More Than Beauty; contbr. articles to newspapers and mags. including N.Y. Times Sunday Arts and Leisure, Saturday Rev. of Literature, People, Good Housekeeping, Art News, Pan Am Travel; co-author: (novel) Mirror, Mirror, 1988. Avocations: tennis, painting, photography. Office: care Don Buchwald 10 E 44th St New York NY 10017-3606

VON FURSTENBERG, DIANE SIMONE MICHELLE, fashion designer; b. Brussels, Belgium, Dec. 31, 1946; came to U.S., 1969; d. Leon L. and Liliane L. (Nahmias) Halfin; m. Eduard Egon von Furstenberg, July 16, 1969 (div.); children: Alexandre, Tatiana. Student, U. Madrid, 1965-66, U. Geneva, 1966-68. Founder, pres. Diane von Furstenberg Studio, N.Y.C., 1970—; pres. Diane Von Furstenberg Ltd., N.Y.C. Author: Diane Von Furstenberg's Book of Beauty and Beds, The Bath; contbg. editor Vanity Fair. Recipient Ellis Island Medal of Honor, 1986. Office: Diane Von Furstenberg Studio 745 5th Ave Fl 24 New York NY 10151-0127 *Honesty in all ways—honest products, honest and straight approach to needs.**

VON FURSTENBERG, GEORGE MICHAEL, economics educator, researcher; b. Germany, Dec. 3, 1941; came to U.S., 1961; s. Kaspar Freiherr and Elisabeth Freifrau (von Boeselager) von F.; m. Gabrielle M. Freiin Koblitz von Willmburg, June 9, 1967; 1 child, Philip G. Ph.D., Princeton U., 1967. Asst. prof. econs. Cornell U., Ithaca, N.Y., 1966-70; assoc. prof. econs. Ind. U., Bloomington, 1970-73, prof., 1976-78, Rudy prof. econs., 1983—; sr. staff economist Council Econ. Advisors, Washington, 1973-76; div. chief research dept. IMF, Washington, 1978-83; project dir. Am. Coun. Life Ins., Washington, 1976-78; sr. advisor Brookings Instn., Washington, 1978-90; vis. sr. economist planning and analysis staff Dept. State, Washington 1989-90; Bissell-Fulbright vis. prof. Can.-Am. rels. U. Toronto, 1994-95. Contbg. author; editor: The Government and Capital Formation, 1980, Capital, Efficiency and Growth, 1980, Acting Under Uncertainty: Multidisciplinary Conceptions, 1990; editor: International Money and Credit: The Policy Roles, 1983; assoc. editor Rev. of Econs. and Stats., 1987-92; contbr. articles to profl. jours. Fulbright grantee to Poland, 1991-92. Mem. Am. Econ. Assn., Am. Fin. Assn. Roman Catholic. Avocations: tennis, sailing. Office: Ind U Dept Econs Bloomington IN 47405

VON GIERKE, HENNING EDGAR, biomedical science educator, former government official, researcher; b. Karlsruhe, Germany, May 22, 1917; came to U.S., 1947, naturalized, 1977; s. Edgar and Julie (Braun) Von G.; married; 2 children. Dipl. Ing., Karlsruhe Tech., 1943, Dr. Engr., 1944. Asst. in acoustics Karlsruhe Tech., 1944-47, lectr. 1946; cons. Aerospace Med. Research Labs, Wright-Patterson AFB, Ohio, 1947-54; chief bioacoustics br. Aerospace Med. Research Labs, 1954-63, dir. biodynamics and bionics div., 1963-88; assoc. prof. Ohio State U., 1963-88; clin. prof. Wright State U., 1980—; mem. com. hearing bioacoustics and biomechanics NRC, 1953-93, chmn. 1990-93, bio-astronaut com., 1959-61; mem. adv. com., flight medicine and biology NASA, 1960-61. Author over 160 tech. publs., book chpts.; patentee in field. Recipient Dept. Def. Disting. Civilian Svc. award, 1963, Hubertus Strughold medal, 1980, Meritorious and Disting. Exec. Presdl. rank Pres. of U.S., 1980, 81, H.R. Lissner award ASME, 1983, Lord Rayleigh medal, 1988. Fellow Acoustical Soc. Am. (pres. 1979-80, Silver medal 1981), Aerospace Med. Assn. (v.p. 1966-67, E. Liljenkrantz award 1966, A.D. Tuttle award 1974), Inst. Environ. Scis. (hon.), Internat. Acad. Aviation and Space Medicine; mem. NAE, Inst. Noise Control Engring., Biomed. Engring. Soc., Internat. Acad. Astronautics. Researcher in bioacoustics, acoustics, biomechanics and bioengring. Home: 1325 Meadow Ln Yellow Springs OH 45387-1219 Office: Armstrong Aerospace Med Rsch Lab Dayton OH 45433

VON GLAHN, KEITH G., lawyer; b. Passaic, N.J., May 4, 1952. BA, St. Peter's Coll., 1974; JD, Vermont Law Sch., 1977. Bar: N.J. 1978, U.S. Tax Ct. 1982, U.S. Dist. Ct. N.J., U.S. Supreme Ct. 1983, N.Y. 1988, U.S. Dist. Ct. N.Y. Law clk. to hon. William Arwold, 1977-78; asst. prosecutor Paterson, N.J., 1987-81; ptnr. Wilson, Elser, Moskowitz, Edelman and Dicker, Newark, N.J., 1983—. Mem. ABA, N.J. Bar Assn., Essex County Bar Assn., William Brennan Inn of Ct. (master). Office: Wilson Elser Moskowitz Edelman & Dicker Gateway # 1600 Newark NJ 07102

VON GUNTEN, DAVID, church administrator. Svc. dir. Missionary Church, Fort Wayne, Ind. Office: The Missionary Church PO Box 9127 3811 Vanguard Dr Fort Wayne IN 46809-3304

VON HAKE, MARGARET JOAN, librarian; b. Santa Monica, Calif., Oct. 27, 1933; d. Carl August and Inez Garnet (Johnson) von Hake;. BA, La Sierra U., 1955; MS in Library Sci., U. So. Calif., 1963. Tchr., librarian Newbury Park (Calif.) Acad., 1955-60; librarian Columbia Union Coll., Takoma Park, Md., 1962-67, library dir., 1967—. Mem. ALA, Md. Libr. Assn., Congress of Acad. Libr. Dirs. of Md., Md. Ind. Coll. and Univ. Assn. Libr. Dir.'s Roundtable, Assn. Seventh Day Adventist Librs. (newsletter editor 1982, 83, pres. 1989-90), Paul Hill Chorale. Republican. Office: Columbia Union Coll 7600 Flower Ave Silver Spring MD 20912-7794

VON HERZEN, RICHARD PIERRE, research scientist, consultant; b. L.A., May 21, 1930; s. Constantine Pierre Von Herzen and Elizabeth Martha (Hevener) Hough; m. Janice Elaine Rutter, Mar. 8, 1958; children—Brian P., Carol E. B.S., Calif. Inst. Tech., 1952; M.A., Harvard U., 1956; Ph.D., UCLA, 1960. Asst. researcher Scripps Inst. Oceanography, LaJolla, Calif., 1960-64, vis. investigator, lectr., 1974-75; dep. dir. office oceanography UNESCO, Paris, 1964-66; assoc. to sr. scientist Woods Hole Oceano. Inst., Mass., 1966—, chmn. dept. geology and geophysics, 1982-85. Author/co-author 125 sci. articles. Served with U.S. Army, 1953-55. Fellow Am. Geophys. Union (pres. Tectonics sect. 1986-88, assoc. editor Jour. Geophys. Research 1969-71). Avocations: sports; sailing; hiking. Home: PO Box 271 Woods Hole MA 02543-0271 Office: Woods Hole Oceanog Inst Woods Hole MA 02543

VON HIPPEL, FRANK NIELS, public and international affairs educator; b. Cambridge, Mass., Dec. 26, 1937; s. Arthur Robert and Dagmar (Franck) Von H.; m. Patricia Bardi, June, 1987; 1 child from previous marriage, Paul Thomas. S.B., MIT, 1959; Ph.D., Oxford U., 1962. Research assoc. U. Chgo., 1962-64; research assoc. Cornell U., Ithaca, N.Y., 1964-66; asst. prof. Stanford U., Calif., 1966-69; assoc. physicist Argonne Nat. Lab., Ill., 1970-73; research physicist Princeton U., N.J., 1974-83, prof. pub. and internat. affairs, 1983-93, 95—; asst. dir. for nat. security Pres.'s Office of Sci. and Tech. Policy, Washington, N.J., 1993-94; bd. dirs. Bull. of Atomic Scientists, Chgo., 1983-86, chmn. editorial bd., 1991-93. Author: Advice and Dissent, 1974, Citizen Scientist, 1991; chmn. editl. bd. Sci. and Global Security, 1989—; contbr. articles to profl. jours. Rhodes scholar, 1959-62; McArthur Found. Prize fellow, 1993-98. Fellow AAAS (bd. dirs. 1987-88); mem. Fedn. Am. Scientists (chmn. 1979-84, Pub. Svc. award 1989), Fedn. Am. Scientists Fund (chmn. 1986-93). Home: 3 University Way Princeton Junction NJ 08550-1617 Office: Ctr for Energy & Environ Studies Princeton University Princeton NJ 08544

VON HIPPEL, PETER HANS, chemistry educator; b. Goettingen, Germany, Mar. 13, 1931; came to U.S., 1937, naturalized, 1942; s. Arthur Robert and Dagmar (franck) von H.; m. Josephine Baron Raskind, June 20, 1954; children: David F., James A., Benjamin J. B.S., MIT, 1952, M.S., 1953, Ph.D., 1955. Phys. biochemist Naval Med. Research Inst., Bethesda, Md., 1956-59; from asst. prof. to assoc. prof. biochemistry Dartmouth Coll., 1959-67; prof. chemistry, mem. Inst. Molecular Biology U. Oreg., 1967-79, dir. Inst. Molcdular Biology, 1969-80, chmn. dept. chemistry, 1980-87; rsch. prof. chemistry Am. Cancer Soc., 1989—; chmn. biopolymers Gordon Conf., 1968; mem. trustees' vis. com. biology dept. MIT, 1973-76; mem. bd. sci. counsellors Nat. Inst. Arthritis, Metabolic and Digestive Diseases NIH,

1974-78, mem. coun. Nat. Inst. Gen. Med. Scis., 1982-86, mem. dir.'s adv. com., 1987-92; mem. Sci. and Tech. Ctrs. Adv. Com. NSF, 1987-89; mem. Fedn. Am. Socs. for Exptl. Biology Exec. Bd., 1994—. Mem. editorial bd. Jour. Biol. Chemistry, 1967-73, 76-82, Biochem. Biophys. Acta, 1965-70, Physiol. Revs., 1972-77, Biochemistry, 1977-80, Trends in Biochem. Sci., 1987—, Protein Sci., 1990—; editor Jour. Molecular Biology, 1986-94; contbr. articles to profl. jours., chpts. to books. Lt. M.S.C. USNR, 1956-59. NSF predoctoral fellow, 1953-55; NIH postdoctoral fellow, 1955-56; NIH sr. fellow, 1959-67; Guggenheim fellow, 1973-74. Fellow Am. Acad. Arts and Scis.; mem. AAAS, Am. Chem. Soc., Am. Soc. Biol. Chemists, Biophys. Soc. (mem. council 1970-73, pres. 1973-74), Nat. Acad. Scis., Fedn. Am. Scientists, Sigma Xi. Home: 1900 Crest Dr Eugene OR 97405-1753

VON HOFFMAN, NICHOLAS, writer, former journalist; b. N.Y.C., Oct. 16, 1929; s. Carl and Anna (Bruenn) von H.; m. Ann Byrne, 1950 (div.); children: Alexander, Aristodemos, Constantine; m. Patricia Bennett, 1979 (div.). Grad., Fordham Prep. Sch., 1948. Assoc. dir. Indsl. Area Found., Chgo., 1954-63; mem. staff Chgo. Daily News, 1963-66, Washington Post, 1966-76. Author: Mississippi Notebook, 1964, Multiversity, 1966, We Are The People Our Parents Warned Us Against, 1968, Two, Three, Many More, 1969, Left at The Post, 1970, (with Garry Trudeau) Fireside Watergate, 1973, Tales From the Margaret Mead Taproom, 1976, Make-Believe Presidents: Illusions of Power from McKinley to Carter, 1978, Organized Crimes, 1984, Citizen Cohn, 1988, Capitalist Fools, 1992; also articles.

VON HOLDEN, MARTIN HARVEY, psychologist; b. Bronx, N.Y., May 29, 1942; s. Leon and Gertrude (Fishbein) Von H.; m. Virginia T. Brown, Dec. 17, 1971; 1 child, Mark Walter; children by previous marriage: Sandi Gwen Bitton, David Lawrence; 1 stepchild, Theresa Ann Brilli-Rogers. B.A., NYU, 1964; M.A., U. Toledo, 1965; D.P.A., NYU, 1981. Sr. psychologist N.Y. State Dept. Mental Hygiene, Rockland State Hosp., Orangeberg, 1966-67, team leader, 1970-71, dir. interdisciplinary tng. team, 1971-73; chief of service Metro Unit Harlem Valley Psychiat. Ctr., Wingdale, N.Y., 1973-74, dep. dir. programs, 1974-75; dep. dir. treatment services Pilgrim Psychiat. Ctr., West Brentwood, N.Y., 1975-76; dir. Matteawan State Hosp., Beacon, N.Y., 1977, Central N.Y. Psychiat. Ctr., Marcy, N.Y., 1977-82; exec. dir. Rochester Psychiat. Ctr., Rochester, N.Y., 1982—; assoc. dir. Inst. for Motivation Rsch., Croton-on-Hudson, N.Y., 1965-73; dir. Martin H. Von Holden Assocs., motivation rsch., Fairlawn, N.J., 1970-74; cons. psychologist, group therapist Green Haven Correctional Facility, Stormville, N.Y., 1970-77; cons. psychologist, group therapist Auburn Correctional Facility, N.Y., 1977-94, Butler Correctional Facility, 1994—; clin. assoc. prof. dept. psychiatry Sch. Medicine, U. Rochester, 1983—; speaker nat. and internat. profl. confs. including 2d World Congress on Prison Health Care, 1983. Contbr. articles to profl. jours. Mem. adv. coun. N.Y. State Commn. Quality Care to Mentally Disabled, 1989—. Capt. MSC, U.S. Army, 1967-70. Recipient James Gordon Bennett prize NYU, 1964, Outstanding Achievement award United Way of N.Y. State, 1994. Fellow Am. Assn. Mental Health Adminstrs. (cert. mental health adminstr.); mem. Am. Psychol. Assn., Am. Correctional Assn., Am. Correctional Psychologists, Assn. Facility Dirs. N.Y. State Office Mental Health (pres. 1984-85), Order of Arrow, Psi Chi. Independent. Jewish. Home: 15 Waterbury Ln Rochester NY 14625-1361

VONK, HANS, conductor; b. Amsterdam, The Netherlands, June 18, 1942; s. Frans Vonk; m. Jessie Folkerts. Degree in Music, Ignatius Coll., Amsterdam; Degree in Law, City U., Amsterdam, 1964; trained with Franco Ferrara, 1964-66. Condr. Nat. Ballet, Amsterdam, 1966-69; asst. condr. Concertgebouw Orch., Amsterdam, 1969-73; condr. Radio Philharm. Orch., Hilversom, The Netherlands, 1973-79; chief condr. Netherlands Opera, Amsterdam, 1976-85, Residentie Orkestra, Ben Haag, 1980-91, Staatskapelle, Dresden, Germany, 1985-90, Radio Symphonie Orch., Cologne, Germany, 1991—; assoc. condr. Royal Philharmonie, London, 1976-79; music dir., condr.-elect St. Louis Symphony, 1995—; prin. guest condr. Netherlands Radio Philharm.; guest condr. l'Orchestre Nat. de France, Oslo Philharmonic, London Symphony, Norddeutsche Rendfunk, London Philharmonic, English Chamber Orch., Phila. Orch., Minn. Orch., Nat. Symphony Orch., Detroit Orch., Montreal Orch., Dallas Orch., Seattle Orch., Cleve. Orch., Boston Symphony Orch., Pitts. Orch., San Francisco Orch., Houston Orch., Balt. Orch., Mostly Mozart Festival Orch.; opera condr. La Scala, Rome, 1980, 88, Netherlands Opera, Dresden State Opera. Recs.: (with Christian Zacharias) 5 Beethoven piano concertos, Mozart overtures, The Nutcracker (Tchaikovsky), Der Rosenkavalier, Schumann symphonies and concertos, Bruckner Symphonies 4 and 6. Office: St Louis Symphony Orch Powell Symphony Hall 718 North Grand Blvd Saint Louis MO 63103

VON KALINOWSKI, JULIAN ONESIME, lawyer; b. St. Louis, May 19, 1916; s. Walter E. and Maybelle (Michaud) von K.; m. Penelope Jayne Dyer, June 29, 1980; children by previous marriage: Julian Onesime, Wendy Jean von Kalinowski. BA, Miss. Coll., 1937; JD with honors, U. Va., 1940. Bar: Va. 1940, Calif. 1946. Assoc. Gibson, Dunn and Crutcher, L.A., 1946-52, ptnr., 1953-62, mem. exec. com., 1962-82, adv. ptnr., 1985—; CEO, chmn. Litigation Scis., Inc., Culver City, Calif., 1991-94, chmn. emeritus, 1994—; bd. dirs., mem. exec. com. W.M. Keck Found.; mem. faculty Practising Law Inst., 1971, 76, 78, 79, 80; instr. in spl. course on antitrust litigation Columbia U. Law Sch., N.Y.C., 1981; mem. lawyers dels. com. to 9th Cir. Jud. Conf., 1953-73; UN expert Mission to People's Republic China, 1982. Contbr. articles to legal jours.; author: Antitrust Laws and Trade Regulation, 1969, desk edit., 1981; gen. editor: World Law of Competition, 1978, Antitrust Counseling and Litigation Techniques, 1984. With USN, 1941-46, capt. Res. ret. Fellow Am. Bar Found., Am. Coll. Trial Lawyers (chmn. complex litigation com. 1984-87); mem. ABA (mem. ho. dels. 1970, chmn. antitrust law sect. 1972-73), State Bar of Calif., L.A. Bar Assn., U. Va. Law Sch. Alumni Assn., Calif. Club, L.A. Country Club, La Jolla Beach and Tennis Club, N.Y. Athletic Club, Regency Club, The Sky Club (N.Y.C.), Phi Kappa Psi, Phi Alpha Delta. Republican. Episcopalian. Home: 12320 Ridge Cir Los Angeles CA 90049-1151 Office: Litigation Scis Inc 200 Corporate Pointe Ste 300 Culver City CA 90230-7633

VON KANN, CLIFTON FERDINAND, aviation and space executive, software executive; b. Boston, Oct. 14, 1915; s. Alfred and Lyllian (Kaufman) von K.; m. Sallie Emery Flint, Oct. 6, 1938 (div. May 1965); children: Curtis Emery, Lisa Christine; m. Kathryn Heyne, July 18, 1965. AB cum laude, Harvard U., 1937, MBA, 1948, D in Aero. Sc. (hon.), 1984; grad., Arty. Sch., 1942, Command and Gen. Staff Sch., 1945, Armed Forces Staff Coll., 1954, Nat. War Coll., 1957. Commd. 2d lt., F.A. U.S. Army, 1938, advanced through grades to maj. gen., 1962; various assignments, North Africa, Sicily and Italy, 1937-45; mem. War Dept. gen. staff, 1945-46, with Office Compt., Dept. of Army, 1948-51, with CIA, 1951-53, comdg. officer 7th Inf. Div. Arty., 8th Army, 1954; with Korean Mil. Adv. Group Korea, 1954-55; with Hdqrs. Army Forces Far East and 8th Army, Japan, 1955-56; asst. div. comdr. 82d Airborne Div. Ft. Bragg, N.C., 1957-59; dir. army aviation Dept. Army, 1959-61; J-3 U.S. Strike Command, Tampa, Fla., 1961-62; comdg. gen. 1st cavalry div. Korea, 1962-63; comdg. gen. U.S. Army Aviation Ctr. Ft. Rucker, Ala., 1963-65; ret., 1965; v.p. ops. and engring. Air Transport Assn., 1965-70, sr. v.p. ops. and engring. 1970-80; pres. Nat. Aeron. Assn., 1980-89; chmn. bd. Nat. Aeronautic Assn., 1989-90, chmn. emeritus, 1992—; bd. dirs. The AVEMCO Corp., Frederick, Md.; chmn. bd. dirs. Traverse Techs., Inc., 1994—. Decorated Silver Star, Legion of Merit; Cross of Mil. Vaolr (Italy); recipient Charles Edwin Webb Meml. medal Pa. Mil. Coll., 1964, mil. rev. award Command and Gen. Staff Coll., 1964, Clifford W. Henderson award for achievement, 1990, Dept. Transp./FAA award for disting. svc., 1990. Mem. Am. Helicopter Soc. (chmn. bd. 1962-63, pres. 1961-62), World Aerospace Edn. Assn. (bd. dirs. 1987-93, pres. 1990-91), Fedn. Aeronautique Internat. (v.p. 1980-88, pres. 1988-90), Harvard Varsity Club (Cambridge, Mass.), Met. Club (Washington), Nat. Aviation Club (Washington, pres. 1974-75), Black Tie Club (Washington, pres. 1978-79), Aero Club (Washington, pres. 1974-75). Clubs: Harvard Varsity (Cambridge); Metropolitan, Nat. Aviation (pres. 1974-75). Home and Office: 4311 Torchlight Cir Bethesda MD 20816-1846

VON KAPPELHOFF, DORIS See DAY, DORIS

VON KLEMPERER, KLEMENS, historian, educator; b. Berlin, Nov. 2, 1916; came to U.S., 1938; s. Herbert O. and Frieda (Kuffner) Von K.; m.

Elizabeth Lee Gallaher, Dec. 19, 1953; children—Catharine Lee, James Alfred. Abitur, Französisches Gymnasium, Berlin, 1934; M.A., Harvard U., 1940, Ph.D., 1949; MA, Cambridge U., 1974. Vis. prof. Stanford U., Palo Alto, Calif., 1960; prof. history Bonn U., Fed. Republic Germany, 1963-64; L. Clark Seelye prof. history Smith Coll., Northampton, Mass., 1960-87, prof. emeritus, 1987—; vis. prof. Amherst (Mass.) Coll., 1989, 91; vis. fellow Trinity Coll., Oxford, Eng., 1982. Author: Germany's New Conservatism, 1957, Mandate for Resistance, 1969, Ignaz Seipel: Christian Statesman, 1972, German Resistance Against Hitler: The Search for Allied Abroad 1938-1945, 1992; editor: A Noble Combat. The Letters of Shiela Grant Duff and Adam von Trott, 1988, "Fur Deutschland" Die Manner des 20, 1994; contbr. articles to profl. jours. Served with AUS, 1943-46, ETO. Guggenheim Found. fellow, 1957-58; Fulbright fellow, 1957-58, 63-64; Overseas fellow Churchill Coll., Cambridge, Eng., 1973-74; Inst. for Advanced Study fellow, Berlin, 1986; Am. Philos. Soc. grantee, 1977-78, Am. Council of Learned Socs. grantee, 1978-79. Mem. Am. Hist. Soc. (chmn. conf. group for central European history 1982-83). Club: Century (N.Y.C.). Avocations: playing recorder; mountaineering; hiking. Home: 23 Washington Ave Northampton MA 01060-2822 Office: Smith Coll Northampton MA 01063

VON KNORRING, HENRIK JOHAN, publisher; b. Lisbon, Portugal, Dec. 20, 1943; came to U.S., 1978; s. Helge and Denise (Halla) von K.; m. Robin Ellis Evans, Oct. 1966; children: Katharina Elizabeth, Helena Alexandra. MA, Oxford U., Eng., 1963. Joint mng. dir. Chapman and Hall Ltd., London, 1973-78; group mktg. dir. Associated Book Pub. Ltd., London, 1977-78; pres. Routledge Inc. N.Y.C., 1978—. Office: Routledge 29 W 35th St New York NY 10001-2291

VON LAUE, THEODORE HERMAN, historian, educator; b. Frankfurt Main, Germany, June 22, 1916; came to U.S., 1937, naturalized, 1945; s. Max Felix and Magda (Milkau) Von L.; m. Hildegarde Hunt, Oct. 23, 1943 (div. 1976); children: Christopher (dec.), Madeleine, Esther; m. Angela Turner, Nov. 13, 1976. A.B., Princeton U., 1939, Ph.D., 1944; cert. Russian Inst., Columbia U., 1948. Asst. prof. history U. Pa., Phila., 1948-49, Swarthmore Coll., (Pa.) 1949-51; lectr. Bryn Mawr Coll. and Swarthmore Coll., 1952-54; asst. prof. history U. Calif.-Riverside, 1955-59, assoc. prof., 1959-60, prof., 1960-64; prof. Washington U., St. Louis, 1964-70; Frances and Jacob Hiatt prof. history Clark U., 1970-82, Frances and Jacob Hiatt prof. history emeritus, 1983—; fgn. expert Shaanxi Tchrs. U., Xian, People's Republic of China, 1989-90. Author: Leopold Ranke, The Formative Years, 1950, Sergei Witte and the Industrialization of Russia, 1963, Why Lenin? Why Stalin?, 1964, The Global City, 1969, The World Revolution of Westernization: The Twentieth Century in Global Perspective, 1987, Why Lenin? Why Stalin? Why Gorbachev?, 1993. Columbia U. Russian Inst. sr. fellow, 1951-52; Fulbright research fellow Finland, 1954-55; Guggenheim fellow, 1961-62, 74-75; Social Sci. Research Council grantee, 1951-52,58. Mem. Am. Hist. Assn., Am. Assn. Advancement Slavic Studies (dir. 1968-71), World History Assn. (coun. 1991-94, pres. New Eng. affiliate 1993-94). Quaker. Office: Clark U Dept History Worcester MA 01610

VON MEHREN, ARTHUR TAYLOR, lawyer, educator; b. Albert Lea, Minn., Aug. 10, 1922; s. Sigurd Anders and Eulalia Marion (Anderson) von M.; m. Joan Elizabeth Moore, Oct. 11, 1947; children—George Moore, Peter Anders, Philip Taylor. S.B., Harvard U., 1942, LL.B., 1945, Ph.D., 1946; Faculty of Law, U. Zurich, 1946-47; Faculte de Droit, U. Paris, 1948-49; Doctor iuris (h.c.), Katholeke U., Leuven, 1985. Bar: Mass. 1950, U.S. Dist. Ct. Mass. 1980. Law clk. U.S. Ct. Appeals (1st cir.), 1945-46; asst. prof. law Harvard U., 1946-53, prof., 1953-76, Story prof., 1976-93, prof. emeritus, 1993—, dir. East Asian legal studies program, 1981-83; acting chief legislation br., legal div. Occupation Mil. Govt. U.S.,Germany, 1947-48, cons. legal div., 1949; tchr. Salzburg Seminar in Am. Studies, summers 1953, 54; Fulbright research prof. U. Tokyo, Japan, 1956-57, Rome, Italy, 1968-69; cons. legal studies Ford Found., New Delhi, 1962-63; vis. prof. U Frankfurt, summer 1967; Ford vis. prof. Inst Advanced Legal Studies, U. London, 1976; assoc. prof. U. Paris, 1977; Goodhart prof. legal sci. U Cambridge, 1983-84, fellow Downing Coll., 1983-84, hon. fellow, 1984—; fellow Wissenschaftskolleg zu Berlin, 1990-91. Author: The Civil Law System, 1957, 2d edit. (with J. Gordley), 1977, Law in the United States: A General and Comparative View, 1988; co-author: The Law of Multistate Problems, 1965; bd. editors Am. Jour. Comparative Law, 1952-86; contbr. articles to profl. jours.; editor: Law in Japan-The Legal Order in a Changing Soc., 1963; mem. editorial com. Internat. Ency. Comparative Law, 1969—; mem. adv. bd. Internat. Ctr. for Settlement of Investment Disputes Rev.-Fgn. Investment Law Jour., 1985—. Mem. U.S. Del. Hague Conf. pvt. internat. law, 1966, 68, 76, 80, 85, 93. Named to Order of the Rising Sun, golden rays Japanese Govt., 1989; Guggenheim fellow, 1968-69; inst. fellow Sackler Inst. Advanced Studies, 1986-87. Mem. ABA, Am. Acad. Arts and Scis., Am. Fgn. Law Assn., Internat. Acad. Comparative Law, Institut de Droit Internat., Japanese Am. Soc. Legal Studies, Am. Arbitration Assn. (comml. panel), Am. Soc. Comparative Law (bd. dirs., pres.), Am. Soc. Polit. and Legal Philosophy, Internat. C. of C., Inst. Internat. Bus. Law and Practice (acad. coun.), Institut Grand-Duchal (corr.), Phi Beta Kappa. Office: Harvard Law Sch Cambridge MA 02138

VON MEHREN, GEORGE M., lawyer; b. Boston, Nov. 2, 1950; s. Arthur Taylor and Joan Elizabeth (Moore) von M.; m. Laurie Beth Markworth, July 25, 1987; children: Paige Elizabeth, Reed Carl. AB, Harvard U., 1972, JD, 1977; Ba, Cambridge U., Eng., 1974, MA, 1985. Bar: Ohio 1977. Assoc. Squire, Sanders & Dempsey, Cleve., 1977-86, ptnr., 1986—, mem. mgmt. com., 1990-93; mem. adv. com. U.S. Dist. Ct. (no. dist.) Ohio, 1991-95. Mem. ABA, Ohio State Bar Assn. Cleve. Bar Assn. Office: Squire Sanders & Dempsey 127 Public Sq Cleveland OH 44114

VON MEHREN, JANE, editor; b. N.Y.C., Feb. 12, 1963; d. Robert Brandt and Mary Katharine (Kelly) von M. B, Vassar Coll., 1985. Editorial asst. Crown Publs., Inc., N.Y.C., 1984-85, asst. editor, 1985-87, assoc. editor, 1987-89, editor, 1989-90; sr. editor Ticknor & Fields, N.Y.C., 1990-93; exec. editor Viking Penguin Books, N.Y.C., 1994—; adj. lectr. NYU Sch. Continuing Edn., N.Y.C., 1990-94. Author: Editors on Editing, 1993, My Forst Year in Publishing, 1994. mem. alumnae bd. Nightingale Bamford Sch., N.Y.C., 1984-86. Editorial fellow Internat. Bookfair, N.Y., 1993; Tory Godwin Meml. award, 1989. Mem. Women's Media Group)programming com. 1995—), Women in Publ. (treas. 1988-90), PEN. Office: Viking Penguin 375 Hudson St New York NY 10014

VON MEHREN, ROBERT BRANDT, lawyer; b. Albert Lea, Minn., Aug. 10, 1922; s. Sigurd Anders and Eulalia Marion (Anderson) von M.; m. Mary Katharine Kelly, June 26, 1948 (dec. Mar. 1985); children: Carl S., John M., Katharine, Jane, Margaret; m. Susan Heller Anderson, Apr. 2, 1988. BA summa cum laude with philosophical oration, Yale U., 1943; LLB magna cum laude, Harvard U., 1946. Bar: N.Y. 1946, U.S. Supreme Ct. 1954. Law clk. to Judge Learned Hand U.S. Ct. Appeals (2d cir.), 1946-47; law clk. to Assoc. Justice Stanley Reed U.S. Supreme Ct., 1947-48; assoc. Debevoise & Plimpton, N.Y.C., 1946, 48-57; ptnr. Debevoise & Plimpton, N.Y.C., 1957-93, of counsel, 1994—; sr. lectr. in law Wharton Sch. U. Pa., Phila., 1985-86; legal counsel Preparatory Commn. for Internat. Atomic Energy Agy., N.Y.C., 1956-57; trustee Practising Law Inst., N.Y.C., 1972—, pres., 1979-86, chmn. bd., 1986—. Bd. editors Harvard Law Rev., 1944-46, Am. Jour. Internat. Law, 1981-89, hon. editor, 1990—; contbr. articles to profl. jours. Trustee Axe Houghton Found., N.Y.C., 1965—; bd. dirs. Legal Aid Soc., N.Y.C., 1966-70; pres. Harvard Law Sch. Assn. N.Y., 1982-83. Mem. Assn. Bar City N.Y., Internat. Law Assn. (vice chmn. 1989—, pres. Am. br. 1978-86, chmn. exec. com. 1986-92), Coun. on Fgn. Rels., Univ. Club, Century Assn. N.Y.C. Home: 925 Park Ave New York NY 10028-0210 Office: Debevoise & Plimpton 875 3rd Ave New York NY 10022-6225

VON MERING, OTTO OSWALD, anthropology educator; b. Berlin, Germany, Oct. 21, 1922; came to Switzerland, 1933, to U.S., 1939, naturalized, 1954; s. Otto O. and Henriette (Troeger) von M.; m. Shirley Ruth Brook, Sept. 11, 1954; children: Gretchen, Karin, Gregory. Grad., Belmont Hill Sch., 1940; BA in History, Williams Coll., 1944; PhD in Social Anthropology, Harvard U., 1956. Instr. Belmont Hill Sch., Belmont, Mass., 1945-47, Boston U., 1947-48, Cambridge Jr. Coll., 1948-49; tech. asst. lab. social rels. Harvard U., 1950-51, Boston Psychopathic Hosp., 1951-53; Russell Sage Found. fellow N.Y.C., 1953-55; asst. prof. social anthropology U. Pitts. Coll. Medicine, 1955-60, assoc. prof., 1960-65; prof. social anthropology

---

1965-71; prof. child devel. and child care U. Pitts. Coll. Allied Health Professions, 1969-71; prof. anthropology and family medicine U. Fla., 1971-76, prof. anthropology in ob-gyn, 1979-84, prof. anthropology and gerontology, 1984—, joint prof. dept. medicine, coll. medicine, 1994—; lectr. Sigmund Freud Inst., Frankfurt, Germany, 1962-64, Pitts. Psychoanalytical Inst., 1960-71, Interuniversity Forum, 1967-71; tech. adviser Maurice Falk Med. Fund; Fulbright vis. lectr., 1962-63; Richard-Merton guest prof. Heidelberg U., Germany, 1962-63; vis. prof. Dartmouth, 1970-71; vis. lectr. continuing edn. Med. Coll. Pa., 1990-92; bd. dirs Tech. Assistance Resource Assos., U. Fla., 1979-84; supvr. grad. study program Ctr. Gerontological Studies, U. Fla., 1983-85, assoc. dir., 1985-86, dir., 1986—; mem. coordinating com. Geriatric Edn. Ctr., Coll. of Medicine, U. Fla.; mem. nat. tech. expert panel on long-term care Health Care Financing Adminstrn., Washington; chair, mem. adv. bd. Internat. Exch. Ctr. on Gerontology State U. System of Fla., 1987-92; adv. bd. Second Season Broadcasting Network, Palm Beach, Fla., 1989-92, Fla. Policy Exch. Ctr. on Aging, State U. System Fla., 1991—, Assoc. Health Industries of Fla., Inc., Nat. Shared Housing Resource Ctr., Balt.; cons. mental hosps. Author: Remotivating the Mental Patient, 1957, A Grammar of Human Values, 1961, (with Mitscherlich and Brocher) Der Kranke in der Modernen Gesellschaft, 1967, (with Kasdan) Anthropology in the Behavioral and Health Sciences, 1970, (with R. Binstock and L. Cluff) The Future of Long Term Care, 1995; also articles; commentary editor: Human Organization, 1974-76; corr. editor Jour. Geriatric Psychiatry; mem. editl. bd. Med. Anthropology, 1976-84, Ednl. Gerontology, 1990—. Mem. nat. adv. bd. Nat. Shared Housing Resource Ctr., 1994—. Recipient Fulbright-Hayes Travel award, 1962-63; grantee Wenner-Gren Found., N.Y., 1962-63; Maurice Falk Med. Fund, 1970-71, HHS, 1979-83, Walter Reed Army Inst. Rsch., 1987-91, AOA/FIDOEA, 1993-94; spl. fellow NIMH, 1971-72. Fellow AAAS, Am. Anthrop. Assn. (mem. James Mooney award com. 1978-81, vis. lectr. 1961,-62, 71-74, 91-92), Am. Gerontol. Soc., Royal Soc. Health, Acad. Psychosomatic Medicine, Am. Ethnological Soc., Soc. Applied Anthropology, Royal Anthrop. Inst.; mem. Assn. Am. Med. Colls., Assn. Anthrop. Gerontol. (pres.-elect 1991-92, pres. 1992-93), Am. Fedn. Clin. Research, Am. Public Health Assn., Canadian Assn. Gerontology, British Soc. Gerontology, Med. Group Mgmt. Assn., World Fedn. Mental Health, Internat. Assn. Social Psychiatry (regional counselor), Internat. Hosp. Fedn., Help Age Internat. (London). Office: U Fla Ctr for Gerontol Studies 3355 Turlington Hall Gainesville FL 32611 *Three guides to conduct I value most: always search for the best fit of fact, argument, and experience. Every first remedy must be amended quickly. When the past disturbs the present, more work on the future is needed.*

VON MINCKWITZ, BERNHARD, publishing company executive; b. Göttingen, Germany, Aug. 11, 1944; s. Erasmus and Mary (von Lilienfeld) von M.; m. Cornelia Böhning; children: Alexis, Vanessa, Nicolas. Diploma, U. Berlin, 1971. Bd. dirs. Bertelsmann AG, Gütersloh, Fed. Republic Germany, Verband Bayerische Zeitschriftenverlage. Office: Bertelsmann Fachinformation, Neumarkter Strasse 18 PF 802020, 81673 Munich Germany also: Bertelsmann Profl Info 1540 Broadway New York NY 10036-4039

VONNEGUT, KURT, JR., writer; b. Indpls., Nov. 11, 1922; s. Kurt and Edith (Lieber) V.; m. Jane Marie Cox, Sept. 1, 1945 (div. 1979); children: Mark, Edith, Nanette; adopted nephews: James, Steven and Kurt Adams; m. Jill Krementz, 1979, 1 child, Lily. Student, Cornell U., 1940-42, U. Chgo., 1945-47; MA in Anthropology, U. Chgo., 1971. Reporter Chgo. City News Bur., 1946; pub. relations with Gen. Electric Co., 1947-50; free-lance writer N.Y.C., 1950-65, 74—; lectr. writers workshop U. Iowa, Iowa City, 1965-67; lectr. in English Harvard U., Cambridge, Mass., 1970; disting. prof. CCNY, 1973-74. Author: (novels) Player Piano, 1951, Sirens of Titan, 1959, Mother Night, 1961, Cat's Cradle, 1963, God Bless You, Mr. Rosewater, 1964, Slaughterhouse-Five, 1969, Breakfast of Champions, 1973, Slapstick, or Lonesome No More, 1976, Jailbird, 1979, Deadeye Dick, 1982, Galápagos, 1985, Bluebeard, 1987, Hocus Pocus, 1990, (collected stories) Welcome to the Monkey House, 1968; (play) Happy Birthday, Wanda June, 1970; (TV Script) Between Time and Timbuktu or Prometheus-5, 1972; (essays) Wampeters, Foma and Granfalloons, 1974; (Christmas Story with illustrations by Ivan Chermayeff) Sun Moon Star, 1980; (autobiographical collage) Palm Sunday, 1981, (collection of speeches and essays) Fates Worse Than Death, 1991; also short stories, articles, revs. Served with inf. AUS, 1942-45. Guggenheim fellow, 1967-68. Mem. Nat. Inst. Arts and Letters (recipient Lit. award 1970). Office: care Donald C Farber 99 Park Ave New York NY 10016-1503

VON OHAIN, HANS JOACHIM P., aerospace scientist; b. Dessau, Fed. Republic of Germany, Dec. 14, 1911; came to U.S., 1947; s. Wolf and Katherine L. (Nagel) von O.; m. Hanny Lemke, Nov. 26, 1949; children: Stephen, Christopher, Catherine, Stephanie. PhD in physics and aerodyn., U. Goettingen, Fed. Republic of Germany, 1935; DSc (hon.), U. W.Va., 1982. Head jet proplusion devel. div. Heinkel Aircraft Corp., Rostock, Fed. Republic of Germany, 1935-45; cons. U.S. Navy, Stuttgart, Fed. Republic of Germany, 1945-46; chief scientist USAF, Dayton, Ohio, 1947-79, aircraft aerospace Research Lab., 1963-75 with Propulsion Lab., 1975-79; now aerospace research cons. U. Dayton Research Inst. Multiple patents in field; contbr. article to profl. jours. Recipient R. Tom Sawyer award ASME, 1990, Godfrey L. Cabot award Aero Club New Eng., 1993. Fellow AIAA (hon., Goddard prize 1966, Daniel Guggenheim Medal award 1991); mem. NAE (Charles Stark Draper prize 1991). Club: Wings (N.Y.C.). Home and office: 3305 Nan Pablo Dr Melbourne FL 32934*

VON PAGENHARDT, ROBERT, policy sciences educator, diplomat; b. St. Louis, Aug. 21, 1923; s. Maximilian Hugo and Marie Dupuy (Adams) von P.; m. Hope Allen, 1946 (div. 1954); m. Heidi Elizabeth Schwitzer, June 25, 1962; children: Alexandra, Tania, stepchildren: Christian Fischbacher, Chasper Fischbacher, Joy Fischbacher Law. BA summa cum laude, Stanford U., 1948, MA in Internat. Rels., 1954, PhD, 1970. With U.S. Army, 1942-46; teaching asst., Polit. Sci. Stanford Univ., 1948-49, 51-54; staff asst. to sec. gen. UN, N.Y.C., 1949; Fulbright scholar U. Bordeaux and U. Paris, 1949-51; dep. exec. dir. World Affairs Coun. of No. Calif., San Francisco, 1951-52; instr. Univ. of Santa Clara, Calif., 1953-54; foreign svc. officer, Bur. Internat. Affairs Dept. of State, 1957-59, U.S. Embassy to Pakistan, 1959-61, U.S. Missions to UNESCO, NATO, Paris, 1962-67; prin. sec. Eight Nation Multilateral Force Working Group, Paris, 1963-67; prof. scis., diplomatic advisor to supt. Naval Postgrad. Sch. and Def. Resources Mgmt. Inst., Monterey, Calif., 1967—; pres. Monterey Inst. Internat. Studies, 1977. Author: (with others) To Unite Our Strength, 1992. Chmn. adv. bd. Salvation Army, Monterye Peninsula, 1980-82, vin. chmn. 1978— With U.S. Army, 1942-46, PTO. Mem. Higher Edn. Assn. Monterey Bay (exec. sec. 1976—), Am. Fgn. Svc. Assn., Internat. Studies Assn., Internat. Inst. Strategic Studies, Mil. Ops. Rsch. Soc., Inst. Mgmt. Scis., World Futures Studies Fedn., UN Assn. of U.S. (pres. Monterey Bay chpt. 1975-77, No. Calif. div. 1977-79), U.S. Assn. for Club of Rome (vice chmn. 1990-92), SAR (v.p. Calif. chpt. 1990-94, pres. 1994-95, 1994—, Silver Citizenship medal 1992, Meritorious Svc. medal 1991, Patriot medal 1995), Monterey Peninsula Yacht Club (commodore 1972), Old Capital Club Monterey, Rotary (Paul Harris fellow), Nat. Soc. Democrat. Episcopalian. Avocations: computer sciences, skiing, swimming, reading, walking. Home: 60 Encina Dr Carmel Valley CA 93924 Office: Defense Resources Mgmt Inst Naval Postgrad Sch Monterey CA 93943

VON PIERER, HEINRICH, manufacturing executive; b. 1941. With legal dept. Siemens, Minich, 1969-77; dir. power plant divsn. KWU Power Sta. Unit, Siemens, 1977-88, comml. dir., 1988-89; mem. adminstrv. bd. Siemens AG, Munich, 1989-91, dep. chief exec., 1991-92, pres., chief exec., 1992—. Avocation: tennis. Office: Siemens AG, Wittelsbacherplatz 2, 80333 Munich Germany also: Siemens KWU Inc 1301 Ave of the Americas New York NY 10019

VON RAFFLER-ENGEL, WALBURGA, linguist, lecturer, writer; b. Munich, Germany, Sept. 25, 1920; came to U.S., 1949, naturalized, 1955; d. Friedrich J. and Gertrud E. (Kiefer) von M. A Ferdinand Engel, June 2, 1957; children: Lea Maxine, Eric Robert von Raffler. DLitt, U. Turin, Italy, 1947; MS, Columbia U., 1951; PhD, Ind. U., 1953. Free-lance journalist, 1949-58; mem. faculty Bennett Coll., Greensboro, N.C., 1953-55, U. Charleston (formerly Morris Harvey Coll.), W.Va., 1955-57, Adelphi U.,

---

CUNY, 1957-58, NYU, 1958-59, U. Florence, Italy, 1959-60, Istituto Postuniversitario Organizzazione Aziendale, Turin, 1960-61, Bologna Center of Johns Hopkins U., 1964; assoc. prof. linguistics Vanderbilt U., Nashville, 1965-77, prof. linguistics, 1977-85, prof. emerita, sr. rsch. assoc. Inst. Pub. Policy Studies, 1985—; dir. linguistics program Vanderbilt U. 1978-86; chmn. com. on linguistics Nashville U. Ctr., 1974-79; Italian NSF prof. Psychol. Inst. U. Florence, Italy, 1986-87; prof. NATO Advanced Study Inst., Cortona, Italy, 1988; pres. Kinesics Internat., 1988—; vis. prof. linguistics Shanxi U., Peoples Republic China, 1985; vis. prof. U. Ottawa, Ont., Can., 1971-72, Lang. Scis. Inst., Tokyo, 1976; grant evaluator NEH, NSF, Can. Coun.; manuscript reader Ind. U. Press, U. Ill. Press, Prentice-Hall; advisor Trinity U., Simon Frazer U.; lectr. in field. Author: Il prelinguaggio infantile, 1964, The Perception of Nonverbal Behavior in the Career Interview, 1983, The Perception of the Unborn Across the Cultures of the World, Japanese edit., 1993, English edit., 1994 (transl. into Chinese); co-author: Language Intervention Programs, 1960-74, 75; editor, co-editor 12 books; author films and videotape; contbr. over 300 articles to scholarly jours., over 200 to profl. and popular publs. in various countries. Grantee Am. Coun. Learned Socs., NSF, Can. Coun., Ford Found., Kenan Venture Fund, Japanese Ministry Edn., NATO, UNESCO, Finnish Acad., Meharry Med. Coll., Internat. Sociol. Assn., Internat. Coun. Linguists, Tex. A&M U. Vanderbilt U., others. Mem. AAUP, Internat. Linguistic Assn., Linguistic Soc. Am. (chmn. Golden Anniversary film com. 1974, emerita 1985—), Internat. Assn. for Applied Linguistics (com. on discourse analyses, sessions chmn. 1978), Lang. Origins Soc. (exec. com. 1985—, chmn. internat. congress, 1987), Internat. Sociol. Assn. (rsch. com. for sociolinguistics, session co-chmn. internat. conf. 1983, session chmn. profl. conf. 1983), Internat. Assn. for Study of Child Lang. (v.p. 1975-78, chmn. internat. conf. 1972), Inst. for Nonverbal Communication Research (workshop leader 1981), Southeastern Conf. on Linguistics, 1980— (hon. mem. 1985—), Semiotic Soc. Am. (organizing com. Internat. Semiotics Inst. 1981), Sietar Internat., Kinesics Internat. (pres. 1988—). Home and Office: 116 Brighton Close Nashville TN 37205-2501 *In the social sciences theories come and theories go. Carefully collected and objectively analyzed data are useful for generations and the cleanest research design in the lab does not equal a moderately neat design in the naturalistic setting.*

VON RECUM, ANDREAS F., bioengineer; b. Bavaria, Germany, July 5, 1939; came to U.S., 1971; s. Bogdan Freiherr and Ilse Freifrau (von Rosenberg) von R.; m. Grudrun F. Bredenbröker-Hardt, Oct. 2, 1965; children: Derik F., Vera F., Uta F., Horst F., Thomas F., Elsa F. BS, U. Giessen, 1965; DVM, Free U. Berlin, 1968, PhD, 1969; PhD in Vet. Surgery, Colo. State U., 1974. Practitioner farm animal medicine and surgery Meitingen, Germany, 1968-69; clin. staff small animal clinic Free U. Berlin (Germany), Coll. Vet. Medicine, 1969-72; rsch. asst. surg. lab. Colo. State U., Coll. Vet. Medicine, Ft. Collins, 1972-74; dir. surg. rsch. lab. Sinai Hosp. Detroit, 1975-77; prof. dept. bioengring. Clemson (S.C.) U., 1978-93, head dept. bioengring., 1982-93; chmn. bioengring. alliance S.C. Coll. Engring., Clemson U., 1984-88; scientific staff Shriners Hosp., Greenville, S.C., 1989—; prof. Hunter endowed chair bioengring. Clemson U. Coll. Engring., 1993—; adj. assoc. prof. comparative surgery Wayne State U. Sch. Medicine, Dept. Comparative Medicine, 1975-77; adj. prof. surgery U. S.C. Sch. Medicine, 1984—, Med. U. S.C., 1987—; adj. prof. biomaterials Coll. Dentistry U. Nijmegen, 1993—; cons. in field. Editor Jour. Investigative Surg.; patentee in field. Recipient Fulbright Scientist award, 1990-91, Alexander von Humboldt Sr. Scientist award, 1990-91. Mem. AVMA, Am. Soc. Lab. Animal Practitioners (governing body), Coll. Vet. Medicine (elected), Blue Ridge Vet. Med. Assn. (pres. 1984), Soc. Biomaterials (asst. editor 1986—, editl. bd. 1983, program chmn. 1990, sec.-treas. 1990-92, pres. 1993-94), Internat. Soc. Artificial Internal Organs, Am. Soc. Artificial Organs, Am. Heart Assn., Acad. Surg. Rsch. (founder 1982, pres. 1982-83, newsletter editor 1982-85), Biomed. Engring. Soc., Am. Soc. Engring. Edn., Assn. Advancement Med. Instrumentation. Presbyterian. Office: Clemson Univ Dept of Bioengineering Clemson SC 29631

VON RHEIN, JOHN RICHARD, music critic, editor; b. Pasadena, Calif., Sept. 10, 1945; s. Hans Walter and Elsa Maryon (Brossmann) von R. AA, Pasadena City Coll., 1965; BA in Eng., UCLA, 1967; BA in Music, Calif. State U., Los Angeles, 1970. Music reviewer Hollywood (Calif.) Citizen-News, 1968-70; music editor and critic, dance critic Akron (Ohio) Beacon Jour., 1971-77; music critic Chgo. Tribune, 1977—; prof. music appreciation Rio Hondo Jr. Coll., Calif., 1970-71; lectr., TV host, rec. annotator. Author: (with Andrew Porter) Bravi; contbr. revs., articles to World Book Ency. 1995 Yr. Book, Opera News, High Fidelity/Mus. Am. Ovation, L.A. Times, Boston Globe, Vanity Fair, Fanfare, Am. Record Guild, others. Music Critics Assn.-Kennedy Center for Performing Arts fellow, 1972, 75. Mem. Music Critics Assn. (edn. com., dir. 1988), Ravinia Critics Inst. (dir. 1988). Office: Chgo Tribune Co PO Box 25340 Chicago IL 60625-0340

VON RINGELHEIM, PAUL HELMUT, sculptor; b. Vienna; s. Henry and Rosita (Altschuler) Von R. BS, Bklyn. Coll., 1956; MA, Fairleigh Dickinson U., 1958; postgrad., Art Students League, N.Y.C., 1958-59, grad. prof. Arts, Munich, 1960-61. Tchr. printmaking Bklyn. Mus. Sch., 1957-58; prof. sculpture Sch. Visual Arts, N.Y.C., 1967-71. One-man shows include Niveau Art Gallery, N.Y.C., 1958, Am. House, Berlin, Munich and Hamburg, 1960-61, Rose Fried Gallery, N.Y.C., 1964, 67, Fairleigh Dickinson U., 1964, New Vision Galleries, London, Paris, N.Y. Cultural Center, 1975, O.K. Harris Gallery, N.Y.C., 1971-73, 76, 78, 80, 82, Mitzi Landau Gallery, Los Angeles, 1974, Amarillo Mus. of Art, 1987, Amarillo Art Ctr., Tex., 1987, Robert Berman Gallery, Los Angeles, 1988; exhibited in group shows at Bklyn. Mus., 1958, Whitney Mus., 1963, 65, Mus. Modern Art, N.Y.C., 1964, 67, 69, O.K. Harris Gallery, Providence, 1964, Ben Uri Gallery, London, 1965, Jewish Mus., N.Y.C., 1966, 68, Cleve. Mus., 1966, Obelisk Gallery, Boston, 1967, Albright-Knox Gallery, Buffalo, 1967, Rose Art Mus., Brandeis U., 1967, Am. Embassy, Brussels, 1967, Meml. Hall, Boston, 1968, Finch Coll., N.Y.C., 1968, Frick Mus., Pitts., 1968, also in Rotterdam and Daensstadt, and numerous other galleries and museums; represented in permanent collections at Welton Becket Assos., Broadway Maintenance Corp., CBS, N.Y.C., Fairleigh Dickinson U., Martin Found., Mus. Modern Art, N.Y.C., Mus. Modern Art, Tel Aviv, Mus. Modern Art, Tokyo, Whitney Mus. Am. Art, Time and Life collections, N.Y.C., others; archtl. commns. include World Peace Monument, U.S. Pavilion, World's Fair, 1964; Tangential 32 at Park Ave. and 55th St., N.Y.C., 1969; Variance inflatable at Internat. Sculpture Festival, Govt. Center, Boston, 1971; Fulcrum at Westinghouse Nuclear Center, Pitts., 1972; Vortex in Red for Main St. Ann. Art Festival, Houston, 1975, Nebr. Interstate 80 Bicentennial Sculpture Project, Houston Center, Tex. Eastern Corp.; also sculptures Columbia (N.C.) Mall, Taubman Corp., Century City, Los Angeles, Diamond Shamrock, Dallas, Exec. Hdqrs. Becket Group, Los Angeles; also Endless Force for former Pres. Gerald R. Ford, Equinox for Diamond Shamrock Corp., fountain Exec. Hdqrs. Becket Group, Los Angeles, Freeflight Lincoln Properties Co., San Jose, Ca. Recipient Outstanding Young Man of Yr. award N.Y. World's Fair, 1964; Fulbright scholar, 1974-75. Mem. Archtl. League City N.Y., Lambs Club (hon.), Explorers Club. Home: 9 Great Jones St New York NY 10012-1128

VON RYDINGSVARD, URSULA KAROLISZYN, sculptor; b. Deensen, Germany, July 26, 1942; came to U.S., 1951; d. Ignacy and Koneganda (Sternal) Karoliszyn; m. Pual Greengard. BA, MA, U. Miami, Coral Gables, Fla., 1965; postgrad., U. Calif., Berkeley, 1969-70; MFA, Columbia U., 1975; PhD (hon.), Md. Inst. Inst., 1994. With Sch. Visual Arts, N.Y.C., 1978-82; assoc. prof. Yale U., New Haven, 1982-86; prof. grad. div. Sch. Visual Arts, N.Y.C., 1986—. One-woman shows include Rosa Esman Gallery, 1981, 82, Studio Bassanese, Trieste, 1985, Laumeier Sculpture Gallery, St. Louis, 1988, Capp St. Project San Francisco, 1990, Lorence-Monk Gallery, N.Y.C., 1990, 91, Zamek Ujazdowski Contemporary Art Ctr., Warsaw, Poland, 1992, Storm King Art Ctr., Mountainville, N.Y., 1992-94, Galerie Lelong, N.Y.C., 1994; exhibited in group shows at Lowe Art Mus., Coral Gables, Fla., 1975, Aldrich Mus. Contemporary Art, Ridgefield, Conn., 1976, 55 Mercer Gallery, N.Y.C., 1983, Pratt Inst., Bklyn., 1985, Contemporary Arts Ctr., Cin., 1987, Krygier/Landau Contemporary Art Gallery, Santa Monica, Calif., 1989, Damon Brandt Gallery, N.Y.C., 1989, Met. Mus. Art, N.Y.C., 1989-93, Whitney Mus. Contemporary Art, 1990, Cultural Ctr., Chgo., 1991, Ctrl. Bur. Art Exhbns., Warsaw and Krakow, Poland, 1991, The Cultural Space/Exit Art, N.Y.C., 1992, Galerie Lelong, N.Y.C., 1993, Denver Art Mus. and Columbus Art Mus., 1994—; others; outdoor exhbns. include Pelham Bay Park, Bronx, N.Y., 1978, Neuberger

Mus., Purchase, N.Y., 1979, Artpark, Lewiston, N.Y., 1979, Laumeier Sculpture Park, St. Louis, 1989-94, Walker Art Ctr., Mpls., 1990-93, Oliver Ranch, Geyserville, Calif., Storm King Art Ctr., Mountainville, N.Y., 1992-93. contbr. articles to profl. jours. Fulbright Hays travel grantee, 1975; grantee N.Y. State Coun. Arts, Am. the Beautiful Fund, Nat. Endowment for Arts, Creative Artists Program Svc.; Griswald traveling grantee Yale U., 1985; Guggenheim fellow, 1983-84; Nat. Endowment for Arts individual artists grantee, 1986-87. Office: 429 S 5th St Brooklyn NY 11211

VON SCHACK, WESLEY W., energy holding company executive; b. N.Y., 1944; married. AB, Fordham U., 1965; MBA, St. John's U., Jamaica, N.Y., 1971; doctorate, Pace U., 1990. V.p. fin. Duquesne Light Co., Pitts., 1984-86, pres., CEO, 1986—, chmn., CEO, 1987—; chmn., CEO, pres. Duquesne Light Co., 1989—; chmn., CEO DQE, 1989; also bd. dirs. Duquesne Light Co., Pitts.; bd. dirs. DQE, Mellon Bank Corp., Mellon Bank, N.A., RMI Titanium Co., Pitts. br. Fed. Res. Bank Cleve., Pitts. br. Office: DQE 301 Grant St Pittsburgh PA 15279-0001

VON STADE, FREDERICA, mezzo-soprano; b. Somerville, N.J., June 1, 1945; m. Peter Elkus, 1973 (div.); children: Jennie, Lisa; m. Michael G. Gorman, Jan. 1991. Student, Mannes Coll. Music, N.Y.C., Ecole Mozart, Paris; DMus (hon.), Yale U., 1985. Former nanny, salesgirl; sec. Am. Shakespeare Festival. Debut in Die Zauberfloete with Met. Opera, 1970, later resident mem., Covent Garden debut, 1975; appeared with opera cos. including Paris Opera, San Francisco Opera, Salzburg Festival, London Royal Opera, Spoleto Festival, Boston Opera Co., Santa Fe Opera, Houston Grand Opera, La Scala; recital artist, soloist with symphony orchs.; appeared in operas The Marriage of Figaro, Faust, The Magic Flute, Don Giovanni, Tales of Hoffman, Rigoletto, Der Rosenkavalier, The Seagull, Werther, The Barber of Seville, The Dangerous Liasons, Le Nozze di Figaro; albums Frederica Von Stade Sings Mozart-Rossini Opera Arias, French Opera Arias, Pelleas and Melisande, Idomeneo, La Sonnambula, Simple Gifts with Mormon Tabernacle Choir, Songs of the Cat with Garrison Keillor; created roles of Nina in the Seagull (Pastieri), 1974, Tina in the Aspern Papers (Arganto), 1988; starred in Dominick Argento's Casa Guidi, 1985, Carnegie Hall, N.Y.C.; rec. artist EMI. Mem. Am. Guild Mus. Artists. Roman Catholic. Avocations: tennis, skiing, dancing. Office: Columbia Artists Mgt Inc Arbib/Treuhaft Div 167 W 57th St New York NY 10019*

VON SYDOW, MAX (CARL ADOLF VON SYDOW), actor; b. Lund, Sweden, Apr. 10, 1929; s. Carl Wilhelm and Greta (Rappe) von S.; m. Christina Olin, Aug. 1, 1951; children: Clas Wilhelm, Per Henrik. Student, Royal Dramatic Theatre Acad. Stockholm, 1948-51. Appearances with Mcpl. Theatre of Norrköping-Linköping, 1951-53, Mcpl. Theatre of Hälsingborg, 1953-55, Mcpl. Theatre of Malmö, 1955-60, Royal Dramatic Theatre Stockholm, 1960-74, 1988; appeared in plays including: Peer Gynt, Henry IV, The Tempest, Le misanthrope, Faust, Ett Dromspel, La valse des toreadors, Les sequestres d'Altona, After the Fall, The Wild Duck, The Night of the Tribades, 1977, Duet for One, 1981, The Tempest, 1988; films include: Bara en mor, 1949, Miss Julie, 1950, Det sjunde inseglet, 1957, Ansiktet (The Face), 1958, The Seventh Seal, 1956, The Magician, 1958, The Virgin Spring, 1959, The Wedding Day, 1960, Through a Glass Darkly, 1961, The Mistress, 1962, The Wonderful Adventures of Nils, 1962, Winter Light, 1963, 4 X 4, 1965, The Hour of the Wolf, 1968, The Shame, 1969, A Passion, 1968, The Greatest Story Ever Told, 1963, Hawaii, 1965, The Reward, 1965, The Quiller Memorandum, 1966, The Kremlin Letter, 1971, Night Visitor, 1971, The Emigrants, 1972, The Exorcist, 1973, The New Land, 1973, Steppenwolf, 1973, Heart of a Dog, 1975, Three Days of the Condor, 1975, CadaveriEccelenti, 1976, Voyage of the Damned, 1976, The Desert of the Tartars, 1976, Flash Gordon, 1980, Death Watch, 1980, Victory, 1980, The Flight of the Eagle, 1981, Conan the Barbarian, 1982, She Dances Alone, 1982, Le Cercle des Passions, 1982, Never Say Never Again, 1983, Dune, 1984, Dreamscape, 1984, Emerald, 1985, Hannah and her Sisters, 1986, The Second Victory, 1986, Oviri, 1986, Duet for One,1986, Pelle the Conqueror, 1987 (Acad. award for Best Fgn. Film 1989), The Wolfat the Door, 1987, The Second Victory, Dr. Grassler, Awakenings, Until the End ofthe World, A Kiss Before Dying, The Bachelor, 1991, Needful Things, 1993, Judge Dredd, 1995; TV appearances include: Diary of Anne Frank, 1967, The Last Civilian, 1983, Samson and Delilah, 1984, The Belarus File, 1984, Christopher Columbus, 1985, The Last Place on Earth, 1985, The Wisdom and the Dream, 1989, Citizen X, 1995; dir. Katinka, 1988. Served with Swedish Quartermaster Corps, 1947-48. Recipient Royal Found. Cultural award, 1954. Office: UTA 9560 Wilshire Blvd 5th Fl Beverly Hills CA 90212*

VON TERSCH, LAWRENCE WAYNE, electrical engineering educator, university dean; b. Waverly, Iowa, Mar. 17, 1923; s. Alfred and Martha (Emerson) Von T.; m. LaValle Sills, Dec. 17, 1948; 1 son, Richard George. B.S., Iowa State U., 1943, M.S., 1948, Ph.D., 1953. From instr. to prof. elec. engring. Iowa State U., 1946-56; dir. computer lab. Mich. State U., 1956-83, prof. elec. engring., chmn. dept., 1958-65, assoc. dean engring., 1965-68, dean, 1968-89, dean emeritus, 1989—. Author: (with A. W. Swago) Recurrent Electrical Transients, 1953. Mem. IEEE; mem. Sigma Xi, Tau Beta Pi, Eta Kappa Nu, Phi Kappa Phi, Pi Mu Epsilon. Home: 4282 Tacoma Blvd Okemos MI 48864-2734 Office: Michigan State U Coll Engring East Lansing MI 48823

VON TUNGELN, GEORGE ROBERT, retired university administrator, economics consultant; b. Golconda, Ill., July 18, 1931; s. Cecil Ernest and Rachel Elizabeth (Wright) von T.; m. Marilyn Ruth Burris, Nov. 6, 1955; children—Stuart, Cheryl, Brenda, Sonya, Eric. B.S., So. Ill. U., 1951, M.S., 1956; Ph.D., U. Ga., 1974. Asst. mgr. exptl. farms So. Ill. U., Carbondale, 1951-52; instr., research asst. Pa. State U., 1955-58; asst. to prof. agrl. sci. Clemson (S.C.) U., 1958-85, asst. to dean internat. programs, 1977-85; cons. econs. and internat. econ. devel. El Paso, 1985—; Pres. P.T.O., 1973. Contbr. articles to profl. jours. Served with AUS, 1952-54. Mem. Assn. U.S. Univ. Dirs. Internat. Agrl. Programs, Partners of Americas, West Tex. Football Officials Assn., Phi Kappa Phi, Gamma Sigma Delta. Republican. Baptist. Clubs: S.C. Football Ofcls. Assn., Sertoma (chmn. bd. 1972). Home and Office: 547 Cocula Ave El Paso TX 79932-2731

VONTUR, RUTH POTH, elementary physical education educator; b. Beeville, Tex., Sept. 10, 1944; d. Robert Bennal and Ruth (Matejek) Poth; m. Robert F. Vontur, Aug. 8, 1964; children: Catherine Anne, Craig Robert, Cynthia Anne. BS in Edn., Southwest Tex. State U., 1966. Cert. health and phys. edn. tchr., biology tchr. Tex. Teachng asst. Blessed Sacrament Confraternity Christian Doctrine, Poth, Tex., 1958-64; phys. edn. tchr. Judson Ind. Sch. Dist., Converse, Tex., 1966-68; substitute tchr. St. Monica's Confraternity Christian Doctrine, Converse, 1971—; substitute tchr. Judson Ind. Sch. Dist., Converse, 1972-75, phys. edn. tchr., 1981—; county adv. bd. Am. Heart Assn., San Antonio, Tex., 1985-88, jump rope for heart coord., 1984—, heart ptnr., 1992—. Pres. St. Monica's Coun. Cath. Women, Converse, 1975; sponsor Young Astronauts, 1993—. Mem. NEA, AAHPERD, Alamo Area Tex. Assn. Health, Phys. Edn., Recreation and Dance, Tex. Assn. Health, Phys. Edn., Recreation and Dance, Judson Tchrs. Assn. (exec. dir. 1993—), Tex. State Tchrs. Assn., Judson Athletic Booster Club. Roman Catholic. Avocations: oil painting, tee shirt painting, sewing. Home: 105 Norris Dr W Converse TX 78109-1905 Office: Judson Ind Sch Dist Converse Elem Sch 102 School St Converse TX 78109

VON ZERNECK, FRANK ERNEST, television producer; b. N.Y.C., Nov. 3, 1940; s. Peter and Beatrice (Francis) von Z.; m. Julie Hawthorne Mannix, Jan. 15, 1965; children: Danielle, Frank. BA in Speech and Drama, Hofstra Coll., 1962. Gen. mgr. JuJamcyn Theatres, N.Y.C., 1965-70, Ctr. Theatre Group, Los Angeles, 1970-74; ptnr. Moonlight Prodns., Hollywood, Calif. 1974-84; prin. Frank von Zerneck Films, Studio City, Calif., 1984—; cons. Found. for the Extension and Devel. of Am. Profl. Theatre, N.Y.C., 1970-77; v.p. League of Resident Theatres, N.Y.C. 1970-75; sec. Portrait of A Bookstore, North Hollywood, 1985—. Producer numerous movies including: The Desperate Miles, 1975, 21 Hours at Munich, 1976, Sharon: Portrait of a Mistress, 1977, Portrait of a Stripper, 1979, Texas Rangers, 1980, Love Canal, 1982, Policewoman Centerfold, 1983, Summer Fantasy, 1984, Hostage Flight, 1985; (TV miniseries) Dress Gray, 1985, Queenie, 1987, To Heal a Nation, 1988, Billy the Kid, 1989, The Great Los Angeles Earthquake, 1990, Survive the Savage Sea, 1991, Too Young To Die, 1992, Jackie Collins' Lady Boss, 1992, The Broken Chain, 1994, Robin Cook's Mortal Fear, 1994,

Take Me Home Again, 1994, The West Side Waltz, 1995. Bd. dirs. Oakhill Sch., Los Angeles, 1984— Recipient award of merit Nat. Cath. Broadcasters, N.Y.C., 1982, silver gavel award ABA, Washington, 1983, TV Prodr. of Yr. AFI, 1994. Mem. Caucus of Writers, Producers and Dirs., Producers Guild Am., League N.Y. Theatres and Prodns., Calif. Theatre Coun. (chmn. 1973-74), League Resident Theatres (v.p. 1972-73), ACI (bd. dirs. 1990-95). Home: 4355 Forman Ave Toluca Lake CA 91602-2909 Office: Frank von Zerneck Films 12001 Ventura Pl Ste 400 Studio City CA 91604-2629

VOOK, FREDERICK LUDWIG, physicist; b. Milw., Jan. 17, 1931; s. Fred Ludwig and Hedwig Anna (Werner) V.; m. Frederica Jean Sandin, Aug. 16, 1958; children: Eric Robert, Dietrich Werner. BA with honors, U. Chgo., 1951, BS, 1952; MS, U. Ill., 1954, PhD in Physics, 1958. With Sandia Labs., Kirtland AFB East, N.Mex., 1958—; div. supr., 1962-71, mgr. dept. research, 1971-78, dir. research, 1978—. Editor: Radiation Effects in Semiconductors, 1968; co-editor: Applications of Ion Beams to Metals, 1974. Mem. coll. engring. adv. bd. U. Ill.; mem. policy bd. Nat. Nanofabrication Facility Cornell U. U. Chgo. and U. Ill. scholar and fellow. Fellow Am. Phys. Soc.; mem. IEEE (sr. mem.), Böhmische Physikalische Gesellschaft, Phi Beta Kappa, Sigma Xi. Office: Sandia Nat Labs Orgn 1100 Ms # 0335 Albuquerque NM 87185

VOOK, RICHARD WERNER, physics educator; b. Milw., Aug. 2, 1929; s. Fred Ludwig and Hedwig Anna (Werner) V.; m. Julia Deskins, Sept. 7, 1957; children: Katherine, Elizabeth, Richard S., Frederick W. BA, Carleton Coll., 1951; MS, U. Ill., 1952, PhD, 1957. Staff physicist IBM Rsch. Lab., Yorktown Heights, N.Y., 1957-61; sr. rsch. physicist Franklin Inst. Rsch. Labs., Phila., 1961-65; assoc. prof. of metallurgy Syracuse (N.Y.) U., 1965-70, prof. of materials sci., 1970-84, prof. of physics, 1984-93, prof. emeritus, 1993—, dir. solid state sci. and tech., 1984-87, 90-91; physicist/chemist U. Calif., Lawrence Livermore Nat. Lab., summers 1977-81; summer faculty mem. Sandia Nat. Lab., Albuquerque, 1983, 84; bd. editors Thin Solid Films, 1985—. Contbr. articles to profl. publs., chpts. to books. Recipient L. B. Pfeil medal and prize Metals Soc. of Great Britain, 1983. Mem. Am. Vacuum Soc., Electron Microscope Soc. Am., Phi Beta Kappa, Sigma Xi, Pi Mu Epsilon. Lutheran. Achievements include discovery of Auger R-factor characterization of thin film growth; development of theory of substrate-induced differential thermal expansion strains in thin films; first observation of Stranski-Krastanov growth mode in vapor deposited thin films, first use of flash evaporation to form high Tc superconducting thin films. Office: Syracuse U 201 Physics Bldg Syracuse NY 13244-1130

VOORHEES, JAMES DAYTON, JR., lawyer; b. Haverford, Pa., Nov. 14, 1917; s. James Dayton Voorhees and Elsa Denison Jameson; m. Mary Margaret Fuller, Sept. 5, 1942 (dec. Apr. 1991); children: J. Dayton III, Susan F. Voorhees-Maxfield, Jane Voorhees Kiss. BA, Yale U., 1940; JD, Harvard U., 1943. Bar: N.H. 1947, Colo. 1948, U.S. Dist. Ct. Colo. 1948, U.S. Ct. Appeals (10th cir.) 1949, U.S. Ct. Appeals (5th cir.) 1956, U.S. Supreme Ct. 1960. Assoc. Johnson & Robertson, Denver, 1947-50; atty. Conoco Inc., Denver, 1950-56; ptnr. Moran, Reidy & Voorhees, Denver, 1956-78, Kutak, Rock & Huie, Denver, 1978-80; ptnr., counsel Davis, Graham & Stubbs, Denver, 1980—; bd. dirs. Japex (U.S.) Corp., Houston, Mercury Internat. Techs., Tulsa. Mem. Denver Bd. Edn., 1965-71, pres. 1967-69. Lt. comdr. USNR, 1941-46, ATO, PTO. Mem. ABA, Colo. Bar Assn., Denver Bar Assn., Fed. Energy Bar Assn., Denver Country Club, University Club. Republican. Avocations: golf, skiing.

VOORHEES, JOHN HENRY, military officer; b. New Brunswick, N.J., Aug. 12, 1936; s. John H. Voorhees and Mabel (DeMunn) Nicholson; m. Jeanine Carter, June 15, 1963; children: Melanie Shemyne, John Carter. BS in Chemistry, Rutgers U., 1958; MS in Mgmt., U. So. Calif., 1967. Commd. USAF, 1958, advanced through grades to maj. gen., 1986; navigator 432d Tactical Reconnaissance Wing, Thailand, 1968-69; chief test spt. div. Space and Missiles Systems Orgn., Los Angeles, 1969-72; research and devel. planner Orgn. of Joint Chiefs of Staff, Washington, 1973-76; chief strategic planning hdqrs. Air Force Logistics Command, Dayton, Ohio, 1976-79; chief B-52 div. Air Logistics Ctr., Oklahoma City, 1979-81; dir. material mgmt. Air Logistics Ctr., Sacramento, 1981-82; comdr. Def. Contract Adminstrv. Services Region, Los Angeles, 1982-84; dep. dir. logistics Hdqrs. European Command, Stuttgart, Fed. Republic Germany, 1984-86; comdr. Def. Personnel Support Ctr., Phila., 1986—; mem. Fed. Exec. Bd., Los Angeles, 1982-84, Phila., 1986—; chmn. Combined Fed. Campaign, Phila., 1987-88. Bd. dirs. YMCA, Phila., 1986-89, United Way S.E. Pa., Phila., 1986-89. Sr. exec. fellow JFK Sch. Govt., Harvard U., 1981. Mem. Nat. Def. Transp. Assn., Air Force Assn., Tuskegee Airmen. Baptist. Avocations: oil painting, photography. Home: 3648 E Kent Dr Phoenix AZ 85044

VOORHEES, JOHN JAMES, dermatologist. B.S., Bowling Green U., 1959; M.D., U. Mich., 1963. Intern U. Mich., 1963-64; resident in dermatology, 1966-69; asso. prof. dermatology U. Mich., Ann Arbor, 1972-74; prof. U. Mich., 1974—; chief dermatology service Univ. Hosp., Ann Arbor, 1975; chmn. dept. dermatology U. Mich., 1975—. Contbr. articles to profl. jours., chpts. in books. Recipient Taub Internat. Meml. award for psoriasis research, 1973, 86, Henry Russel award U. Mich., 1973; Herzog fellow Am. Dermatol. Assn., 1968-70. Mem. Am. Soc. Clin. Investigation, Am. Soc. Pharmacology and Exptl. Therapeutics, Am. Assn. Pathologists, Central Soc. Clin. Research, Soc. Investigative Dermatology, Dermatology Found., Skin Pharmacol. Soc., Assn. Profs. Dermatology, Am. Soc. Cell Biology, Am. Acad. Dermatology, Am. Dermatol. Assn., Alpha Omega Alpha. Office: U Mich Med Ctr Dept Dermatology 1910 Taubman Health Care Ctr Ann Arbor MI 48109

VOORHEES, JOHN LLOYD, columnist; b. DeWitt, Iowa, Aug. 30, 1925; s. Lloyd William and Elsie Irene (Bousselot) V. BA in History, U. Iowa, 1951; BA in Journalism, U. Wash., 1953. Tchr. Oelwein (Iowa) High Sch., 1951-52; columnist Seattle Post-Intelligencer, 1953-71; columnist, critic Seattle Times, 1971—. With U.S. Army, 1946-48. Democrat. Office: The Seattle Times Fairview Ave N & John St Seattle WA 98111

VOORHEES, JOHN SCHENCK, lawyer; b. Bklyn., Apr. 28, 1923; s. Tracy Stebbins and Josephine (Palmer) V.; m. Virginia Taylor, July 24, 1948; children—Virginia Taylor Voorhees Wilcox, Susan Palmer Voorhees Murphy, Katrina Ludlow Voorhees Ogilby, John Schenck Jr. B.A., Yale U., 1947; J.D., Columbia U., 1950. Bar: N.Y. 1951, D.C. 1958. Assoc. Dorr, Hand & Dawson, N.Y.C., 1950-52; asst. gen. counsel Mut. Security Program, Paris, 1952-53; asst. gen. counsel USIA, Washington, 1953-54, spl. asst. to dir., 1954-58; assoc. Howrey & Simon, Washington, 1958-60, ptnr., 1960-89. Served to lt. (naval aviator) USNR, 1942-45. Mem. ABA, Fed. Bar Assn., D.C. Bar Assn., Metropolitan Club (Washington) (bd. govs., pres. 1988-89), Belle Haven Country Club (Alexandria, Va.), Chevy Chase Club (Md.), Profile Golf Club (Franconia, N.H.), De Anza Country Club (Borrego Springs, Calif.). Republican.

VOORHEES, LEE R., JR., lawyer; b. St. Joseph, Mo., Oct. 28, 1937; s. Lee R. and Nora Wilkinson (Bell) V.; m. Sandra Louise Day, Nov. 1965 (div.); children: Philip David, Alexandra Elizabeth; m. Joan Lind Heublein, Sept., 1992. AB, Yale U., 1959, JD, 1962. Bar: Wash. 1962, U.S. Supreme Ct. 1984. Assoc. Roberts & Shefelman, Seattle, 1966-71, ptnr., 1972-88; ptnr. Foster Pepper & Shefelman, Seattle, 1988—. Author: Taxable and Tax-Exempt Financing of Health Care Facilities. 1981. Lt. USNR, 1962-66. Mem. ABA, Wash. State Bar Assn., King County Bar Assn., Am. Acad. Hosp. Attys. (pres. 1987-88), Wash. State Soc. Hosp. Attys. (pres. 1979-80), Nat. Assn. Bond Lawyers, Wash. Coun. Sch. Attys., Wash. State Assn. Mcpl. Attys., Yale Alumni Assn. Western Wash. (pres. 1971-72), Yale Law Sch. Assn. (exec. com. 1981—), Rainier Club, Yale Club (N.Y.C.). Republican. Episcopalian. Avocations: skiing, boating. Home: 5211 W Mercer Pl Mercer Island WA 98040 Office: Foster Pepper & Shefelman 34th Fl 1111 3rd Ave Seattle WA 98101

VOORHEES, RICHARD LESLEY, federal judge; b. Syracuse, N.Y., June 5, 1941; s. Henry Austin and Catherine Adeline (Fait) V.; m. Barbara Holway Humphries, 1968; children: Martha Northrop, Steven Coerte. BA, Davidson Coll., 1963; JD, U. N.C., Chapel Hill, 1968. Bar: N.C. 1968, U.S. Dist. Ct. (we. dist.) N.C. 1969, U.S. Tax Ct. 1969, U.S. Ct. Appeals (4th cir.) 1978, U.S. Dist. Ct. (mid. dist.) N.C. 1981. Mem., ptnr. Garland, Alala, Bradley & Gray, Gastonia, N.C., 1968-80; pvt. practice Gastonia, N.C.,

1980-88; judge U.S. Dist. Ct., Asheville, N.C., 1988—, chief judge, 1991—. Mem. N.C. State Rep. Exec. Com., Gaston County Rep. Com., chmn., 1979-83, U.S. Jud. Conf. Com., 1993— case mgmt. and ct. adminstrn. com., 4th Cir. Ct. Appeals Jud. Coun., 1992-93; chmn. Gaston County Bd. Elections, Gastonia, 1985-86; alt. del. Rep. Nat. Conv., Kansas City, Kans., 1976. 1st lt. U.S. Army, 1963-65. Mem. N.C. Bar Assn., Fed. Judges Assn., Dist. Judges Assn., Buncombe County Bar Assn. Avocation: boating. Office: US Courthouse 100 Otis St Rm 241 Asheville NC 28801-2611

VOORHESS, MARY LOUISE, pediatric endocrinologist; b. Livingston Manor, N.Y., June 2, 1926; d. Harry William and Helen Grace (Schwartz) V. BA in Zoology, U. Tex., 1952; MD, Baylor Coll., Houston, 1956. Diplomate Am. Bd. Pediatrics and Pediatric Endocrinology. Rotating intern Albany (N.Y.) Med. Ctr., 1956-57, asst. resident pediatrics, 1957-58, chief resident pediatrics, 1958-59; rsch. fellow pediatric endocrinology and genetics SUNY Health Sci. Ctr., Syracuse, 1959-61, asst. prof. pediatrics, 1961-65, assoc. prof. pediatrics, 1965-70, prof. pediatrics, 1970-76; prof. pediatrics SUNY Sch. Medicine and Biomed. Scis., Buffalo, 1976-91, prof. pediatrics emeritus, 1991—; co-chief div. endocrinology Children's Hosp. Buffalo, 1976-91; ad hoc reviewer Jour. Pediatrics, Pediatrics, Am. Jour. Diseases Children, other. Contbr. sci. articles to profl. jours., chpts. to books. Mem. adv. bd. Med. Pers. Pool Buffalo, 1991—; mem. clinical investor Children's Hosp. Buffalo Found., 1991—; med. dir. Children's Growth Found., Buffalo, 1976—; community advisor Assn. for Rsch. Childhood Cancer, Buffalo, 1990—. Recipient rsch. career devel. award Nat. Caneer Inst., 1961-71, Dean's award SUNY Sch. Medicine and Biomed. Scis., 1991. Fellow Am. Acad. Pediatrics, AAAS; mem. Soc. Pediatric Rsch., Am. Pediatric Soc., Endocrine Soc., Lawson Wilkins Pediatric Endocrine Soc., Buffalo Pediatric Soc., Zonta Internat., Phi Beta Kappa, Alpha Omega Alpha. Presbyterian. Home: 325 Lincoln Pky Buffalo NY 14216-3120 Office: Children Hosp 219 Bryant St Buffalo NY 14222-2006

VOORSANGER, BARTHOLOMEW, architect; b. Detroit, Mar. 23, 1937; s. Jacob H. and Ethel A. (Arnstein) V.; m. Lisa Livingston, 1964; m. Catherine Hoover, Sept. 10, 1983; children—Roxanna Virginia (dec.), Matthew Ansley. A.B. cum laude, Princeton U., 1960; diplome, Fontainebleau, 1960; M.Arch., Harvard U., 1964. Assoc. Vincent Ponte, Montreal, Que., Can., 1964-67, I.M. Pei & Ptnrs., 1968-78; dir. I.M. Pei & Ptnrs., Iran, 1975-78; co-chmn. Voorsanger & Mills (Architects), N.Y.C., 1978-90; founder, prin. Voorsanger & Assocs., Architects, N.Y.C., 1990—; founder Taylor/Voorsanger Urban Designers, 1991; lectr. Bennington (Vt.) Coll., U. Pa., Columbia U. Harvard U.; guest critic, lectr. Yale U., Pratt Inst., CUNY, R.I. Sch. Design, U. Cin., Syracuse U., U. Tex., Arlington; mem. adv. bd. Parson Sch. Architecture; mem. archtl. rev. panel Port Authority of N.Y. & N.J.; advisor to Samsung Corp., Korea. Exhbns. include: NYU, Archtl. Assn., London, Harvard Grad. Sch. Design, Vacant Lots Housing Study, N.Y., Deutsches Architeckur Mus., Frankfurt, Mus. Finnish Architecture, Avery Lib.Centennial Exhbn. Columbia Univ., Helsinki, Bklyn. Mus.; major projects include: Le Cygne Restaurant, Neiman houseboat, NYU Midtown Ctr., NYU Bus. Sch. Library, La Grandeur housing, NYU dormitories, Hostos Community Coll., N.Y.; finalist Bklyn. Mus. masterplan internat. competition, expansion and master plan Pierpont Morgan Libr., R. Krasnow Apt., N.Y.C.; fellow J. Pierpont Morgan Libr., N.Y. Mem. vis. com. R.I. Sch. Design, U. Tex.-Arlington; mem. N.Y. Hist. Soc., mem. arch. cir. steering com.; chmn. bd. advisors Temple Hoyne Buell Ctr. Study Am. Arch., Columbia U., N.Y.C., 1989—; mem. adv. bd. Parsons Sch. Arch.; chair arch. rev. panel Port Authority N.Y. and N.J. 1st lt. U.S. Army, 1960-61. Recipient awards N.Y.C. chpt. AIA, AIA/Better Homes, Bard City Club, Interiors mag., Stone Inst., AIA/Libr., Lumen, Pratt Inst., NYU, N.Y.C. Art Commn. Fellow AIA (bd. dirs. N.Y.C. chpt. 1979-81, v.p. 1987, chmn. Brunner award com. 1978-80, Bard award pres.-elect N.Y.C. chpt. 1984, Nat. Honor award, N.Y. State award); mem. Archtl. League N.Y.C. (bd. dirs.), Sir John Soane Mus. Found., N.Y. Found. for Arch. (bd. dirs.), Century Assn., River Club, Thursday Evening Club, Wadawanuck Club, Alumni Coun. Grad. Sch. Design Harvard. Home: 350 E 52nd St Apt 9G New York NY 10022-6739 Office: 246 W 38th St Fl 14 New York NY 10018-5805 Home: 83 Main St Stonington CT 06378-1221

VOORTMAN, JOHN J., lawyer; b. Kanawha, Iowa, Dec. 27, 1931; s. John Marinus and Anna (DeVries) V.; m. Bettylou Vandermeulen, Oct. 3, 1959; children: John Mark, Timothy John, Jane Ellen, Matthew Allen, Jennifer Ann. BA, Mich. State U., 1956; JD, U. Chgo., 1959. Bar: D.C. 1959, Ill. 1965, U.S. Ct. Appeals (7th cir.) 1973. Asst. U.S. Dept. Justice, Washington, 1959-61; assoc. Bergson & Borkland, Washington, 1961-65; ptnr. McDermott, Will & Emory, Chgo., 1965-71; assoc. Freeman, Freeman & Salzman, Chgo., 1971-73; ptnr. Schiff Hardin & Waite, Chgo., 1973—. Assoc. editor U. Chgo. Law Rev., 1957-59. Nat. Merit scholar U. Chgo., 1956-57. Mem. ABA (vice chmn. com. on intellectual property 1985), Chgo. Bar Assn. (chmn. antitrust-patent law subcom.), Patent Law Assn. Chgo., Am. Arbitration Assn. (panel arbitrators 1983—). Republican. Mem. Christian Reformed Ch. Avocation: sailing. Home: 448 S Spring Ave La Grange IL 60525-2747 Office: Schiff Hardin & Waite 7200 Sears Towers Chicago IL 60606

VORA, ASHOK, financial economist; b. Bombay, India, July 19, 1947; came to U.S., 1970; s. Kevalchand and Laxmi (Mehta) V.; m. Rama Kata, Dec. 12, 1982; children: Anjali Serena, Amit Raunak. B.Sc., U. Bombay, 1967; M.B.A., Indian Inst. Mgmt., 1970; Ph.D., Northwestern U., 1973. Asst. to chmn. Vora Automotives Ltd., Bombay, 1963-67, dir., 1967-70; asst. prof. fin. CUNY, 1973-80; vis. asst. prof. fin. U. Wis., Madison, 1977; vis. assoc. prof. fin. Northwestern U., Evanston, Ill., 1979-80; assoc. prof. fin. CUNY, 1980-84, prof. fin., 1984—; dir. fin. rsch. Fed. Home Loan Mortgage Corp., Reston, Va., 1987-88; vis. prof. fin. Hofstra U., Hempstead, N.Y., 1990-91; cons. in field. Contbr. articles to profl. jours. Mem. Am. Econ. Assn., Am. Fin. Assn., Fin. Mgmt. Assn., So. Fin. Assn., S.W. Fin. Assn., Western Fin. Assn., Mensa, Nat. Wildlife Fedn., Beta Gamma Sigma. Office: CUNY Box E0621 17 Lexington Ave New York NY 10010-5585

VORA, MANU KISHANDAS, chemical engineer, quality consultant; b. Bombay, India, Oct. 31, 1945; s. Kishandas Narandas and Shantaben K. (Valia) V.; m. Nila Narotamdas Kothari, June 16, 1974; children: Ashish, Anand. BSChemE, Banaras (India) Hindu U., 1968; MSChemE, Ill. Inst. Tech., Chgo., 1970, PhD in ChemE, 1975; MBA, Keller Grad. Sch. Mgmt., Chgo., 1985. Grad. asst. Ill. Inst. Tech. 1969-74; rsch. assoc. Inst. Gas Tech., Chgo., 1976-77, chem. engr., 1977-79, engring. supr., 1979-82; mem. tech. staff AT&T Bell Labs., Holmdel, N.J., 1983-84, Naperville, Ill., 1984—; customer satisfaction mgr., Naperville, 1990—, Milw., 1990—; speaker in field. Invited editor Internat. Petroleum Encyclopedia, 1980. Chmn. Save the Children Holiday Fund Drive, 1986—; trustee Avery Coonley Sch., Downers Grove, Ill., 1987-91; pres., dir. Blind Found. for India, Naperville, 1989—; dir. Nat. Edol. Quality Initiatives, Inc., Milw., 1991—, fellow, 1992. Recipient Non-Supervisory AA award Affirmative Actions Adv. Com., 1987, Outstanding Contbn. award Asian Am. for Affirmative Actions, 1989, Disting. Svc. award Save The Children, 1990. Mem. Am. Soc. Quality Control (cert., standing rev. bd. 1988—, editl. rev. bd. 1989, tech. media com. 1989, mixed media rev. bd. 1994, nat. quality month regional planning com. 1989—, nat. cert. com. 1989-94, chmn. cert. process improvements subcom. 1990-94, Chgo. sect. exec. bd., sr. mem., vice chair sect. affairs 1993-94, sect. chair 1994-95, Spl. award 1991, Century Club award 1992, Founders' award Chgo. Sect. 1993, Joe Lisy Quality award Chgo. Sect. 1994), Chgo. Assn. Tech. Socs. (Ann. Merit award 1992, Ill. Team Excellence award, chief judge 1993—, steering com., 1993—). Hindu. Avocations: reading, photography, travel, philanthropic activities. Home: 1256 Hamilton Ln Naperville IL 60540 Office: AT&T Bell Labs 2000 N Naperville Rd Naperville IL 60563-1443

VORAN, JAMES F., principal. Prin Sealey Elem. Sch. Recipient Elem. Sch. Recognition award U.S. Dept. Edn., 1989-90. Office: Sealey Elem Sch 2815 Allen Rd Tallahassee FL 32312-2614

VORBRICH, LYNN KARL, lawyer, utility executive; b. Iowa City, Feb. 12, 1939; s. William August and Anna Margaretha (Seibert) V.; m. Jody Nolan; children: Sally, Andrew, Peter, David. BS Indsl. Adminstrn., Iowa State U., 1960; JD, U. Iowa, 1962. Bar: Iowa 1962, Ill. 1962. Assoc. Seyfarth, Shaw, Fairweather & Geraldson, Chgo., 1962-64; assoc., ptnr. Dickinson, Throckmorton, Parker, et al, Des Moines, 1964-69; asst. counsel The

Bankers Life Co., Des Moines, 1969-73; assoc. counsel Iowa Power, Des Moines, 1973-76, assoc. gen. counsel, 1976-78, sec., assoc. gen. counsel, 1978-79, sr. v.p., 1985, exec. v.p., 1986-89, pres., 1989-92; exec. v.p. Midwest Power Systems, Inc., Des Moines, 1992—; bd. dirs. Bankers Trust Co., Des Moines, 1986—, Preferred Risk Ins. Group, 1993—. Mem. adv. com. Iowa State Boys Tng. Sch., Eldora, Iowa, 1987-95, legis. study com. on juvenile justice, 1989-90; dean's adv. coun. Iowa State U. Coll. Bus. Adminstrn., Ames, 1987-90; pres. bd. Polk County Legal Aid Soc., 1970, Iowa Children's and Family Svcs., 1970, 78, Planned Parenthood of Mid-Iowa, 1983, Des Moines Area C.C. Found., 1986-87; chmn. Des Moines Human Rights Commn., 1970; bd. dirs. Golden Circle Incubator bd., Golden Circle Labor-Mgmt. Commn., Ankeny, Iowa, 1988—, Civic Music Assn., Des Moines, 1986-87; mem. Bur. Econ. Devel. Coun. of the Greater Des Moines C. of C., 1989—. Named Outstanding Young Alumnus Iowa State U., 1973. Mem. ABA, Iowa Bar Assn., Des Moines Club (trustee 1982-88). United Church of Christ. Office: Midwest Power Systems Inc PO Box 657 Des Moines IA 50303

VORE, MARY EDITH, pharmacology educator, researcher; b. Guatemala City, Guatemala, June 27, 1947; came to U.S., 1962; d. Charles Schrater and Sammye (Smith) V.; m. Edgar Tadasu Iwamoto, Dec. 27, 1976; children: Kenneth Edgar, Daniel Vore. BA, Asbury Coll., Wilmore, Ky., 1968; PhD, Vanderbilt U., Nashville, Tenn., 1972. Postdoctoral fellow Hoffman-LaRoche, Nutley, N.J., 1972-74; asst. prof. U. Calif., San Francisco, 1974-78; asst. prof. pharmacology U. Ky., Lexington, 1978-81, assoc. prof., 1981-86, prof., 1986—, vice chmn. dept., 1983-94, dir. grad. ctr. for toxicology, 1994—; cons. NIH, Bethesda, Md., 1983-87. Contbr. numerous articles to profl. jours., chpts. to books. USPHS grantee, 1979—. Mem. Soc. Toxicology, Am. Assn. Study of Liver Disease, Am. Soc. Pharmacology and Exptl. Therapeutics (sec., treas. 1986-89), Nat. Adv. Environ. Health Scis. Coun. Office: U Ky Coll Medicine 800 Rose St Lexington KY 40536-0001

VORENBERG, JAMES, lawyer, educator, university dean; b. Boston, Jan. 10, 1928; s. F. Frank and Ida (Muhlfelder) V.; m. Dorothy Greeley, Oct. 25, 1952; children: Jill, Amy, Eliza; m. Elizabeth Weiner Troubh, June 20, 1970. A.B., Harvard U., 1948, LL.B., 1951. Law clk. to Justice Frankfurter, 1953-54; with firm Ropes & Gray, 1954-62, partner, 1960-62; prof. law Harvard U., Cambridge, Mass., 1962—, Roscoe Pound prof. law, 1981—; dean Law Sch. Harvard U., 1981-89; dir. Office of Criminal Justice, 1964-65; exec. dir. Pres.'s Commn. on Law Enforcement and Adminstrn Justice, 1965-67; assoc. spl. prosecutor Watergate Spl. Prosecution Force, 1973-75. Trustee Legal Def. Fund, NAACP; chmn. Mass. Ethics Commn., 1978-83. With USAF, 1951-53. Home: 9 Willard St Cambridge MA 02138-4836 Office: Law Sch Harvard U Cambridge MA 02138

VORHIES, MAHLON WESLEY, veterinary pathologist, educator; b. Fairfield, Iowa, June 26, 1937; s. Harold Wesley and Edith Mae (Bender) V.; m. Ilene Lanore Hoffman, Aug. 29, 1959; children—Susan Rae, Robert Wesley. D.V.M., Iowa State U., 1962; M.S., Mich. State U., 1967. Veterinarian in pvt. practice Riverside, Iowa, 1962-64; clin. instr. Mich. State U., East Lansing, 1964-67; vet. pathologist Iowa State U., Ames, 1962-72; vet. pathologist, dir., dept. head S.D. State U., Brookings, 1972-86; dir., dept. head Kans. State U. Coll. Vet. Medicine, Manhattan, 1986-95, dept. head, diagonostic medicine patho biology, 1995—; cons. NIH, Commonwealth Pa., Winrock Internat. Hdqrs., U.S. Dept. Agr., FAO-Fundagro/MIAC, LIFE, Quito, Ecuador, 1991. Contbr. articles to profl. jours. Trustee Brookings United Presbyn. Ch., 1975-78, elder, 1981-84; mem. adv. com. Pipestone Area Vocat. Tech. Inst., 1984. Mem. AVMA, Assn. Am. Vet. Med. Colls., S.D. Vet. Med. Assn. (Vet. of Yr. award 1979), Kans. Vet. Med. Assn., Am. Assn. Avian Pathologists, U.S. Animal Health Assn., Am. Assn. Vet. Lab. Diagnosticians (E.P. Pope award 1984, pres. 1977), North Central Conf. Vet. Lab. Diagnosticians (chmn. 1984, 94), Commn. Vet Medicine, Phi Zeta, Gamma Sigma Delta. Clubs: Brookings Country (dir. 1983-86). Lodge: Shrine (chmn. 1984-85). Home: 2035 Rockhill Cir Manhattan KS 66502-3952 Office: Coll Vet Medicine Kans State U Manhattan KS 66506

VORHOLT, JEFFREY JOSEPH, lawyer, telecommunications company executive; b. Cin., Feb. 20, 1953; s. Edward C. and Rita L. (Kinross) V.; m. Marcia Anne Meyer, Apr. 30, 1976; children: Kimberly Anne, Gregory Michael, Karen Michelle. BBA cum laude, U. Cin., 1976; MBA, Xavier U., Cin., 1978; JD, Chase Law Sch., 1983. Bar: Ohio, 1983; CPA, Ohio. Sec., treas. Cin. Bell Info. Systems, Inc., 1983-84, v.p., chief fin. officer, 1984-88, also bd. dirs.; v.p. controller Cin. Bell, Inc., 1988-89; sr. v.p. Cin. Bell Info. Systems, Inc., 1989-91, Cin. Bell Telephone Co., 1991-93; CFO Structural Dynamics Rsch. Corp., Milford, Ohio, 1994—. Voting mem. Cin. Playhouse, 1986—; mem. fin. planning com. ARC, Cin., 1986-89; trustee U. Health Maintenance Orgn., Inc., St. Joseph Infant and Maternity Home Inc. Mem. ABA, AICPAs, Ohio Bar Assn., Aircraft Owners and Pilots Assn., Cin. Hist. Soc., Bankers Club of Cin. (bd. govs. 1990—). Avocations: golf, tennis, hiking, photography. Office: Structural Dynamics Rsch Corp 2000 Eastman Dr Milford OH 45150-2789

VORIS, WILLIAM, educational administrator; b. Neoga, Ill., Mar. 20, 1924; s. Louis K. and Faye (Hancock) V.; m. Mavis Marie Myre, Mar. 20, 1949; children: Charles William II, Michael K. BS, U. So. Calif., 1947, MBA, 1948; PhD, Ohio State U., 1951; LLD, Sung Kyun Kwan U. (Korea), 1972, Eastern Ill. U. 1976. Teaching asst. Ohio State U., Columbus, 1948-50; prof. mgmt. Wash. State U., Pullman, 1950-52; prof., head dept. mgmt. Los Angeles State Coll., 1952-58, 60-63; dean Coll. Bus. and Pub. Adminstrn., U. Ariz., Tucson, 1963-71; pres. Am. Grad. Sch. Internat. Mgmt., Glendale, Ariz., 1971-89, pres. emeritus, 1989—, adj. prof., 1994—; Ford Found. research grantee Los Angeles State Coll., 1956; prof. U. Tehran (Iran), 1958-59; Ford Found. fellow Carnegie Inst. Tech., Pitts., 1961; prof. Am. U., Beirut, Lebanon, 1961, 62; cons. Hughes Aircraft Co., Los Angeles, Rheem Mfg. Co., Los Angeles, Northrop Aircraft Co., Palmdale, Calif., Harwood Co., Alhambra, Calif., ICA, Govt. Iran. Served with USNR, 1942-45. Fellow Acad. Mgmt.; mem. Ariz. Acad., Beta Gamma Sigma, Alpha Kappa Psi, Phi Delta Theta. Author: Production Control, Text and Cases, 1956, 3d edit., 1966; Management of Production, 1960. Research in indsl. future of Iran, mgmt. devel. in Middle East. Home: Thunderbird Campus Glendale AZ 85306

VORSANGER, FRED S., university administrator; b. Calumet City, Ill., Apr. 20, 1928; s. Fred and Hannah (Steifel) V.; m. Doreen D. Carter, Apr. 24, 1965; children: Diana, Bruce, Bob; B.S. in Bus. Adminstrn., Ind. U., 1951; M.B.A., George Washington U., 1970; postgrad., U. Ark., 1971. Acct. Ernst & Ernst, Chgo., 1951-53; internal auditor Purdue U., Lafayette, Ind., 1953-59; treas., bus. mgr. Am. Council on Edn., Washington, 1959-68; v.p. U. Ark., Fayetteville, 1968—; mgr. Walton Arena U. Ark.; exec. dir. U. Ark. Found., Inc., 1985-88, v.p. emeritus, 1988—; lectr. U. Ky. Mgmt. Inst., 1976—, U. Calif. Mgmt. Inst., 1976-85; adj. prof. Coll. Bus. Adminstrn., 1985—; trustee Common Fund, N.Y.C., chmn., 1982-85; bd. dirs. Tyson Foods, Inc., United Educators Ins. Risk Retention Co., McIlroy Bank and Trust,Ozark Guidance Ctr.; spl. cons. Meridian House Found., Washington, 1960-68; examiner North Central Commn. on Accrediting, 1971—. Author: (with Julian H. Levi) Patterns of Giving to Higher Education, 1968; contbr. articles to profl. jours.; mem. editorial adv. bd. Commerce Clearing House, Inc, 1963-68; mem. editorial adv. com. Coll. and Univ. Bus. Mag. Pres. Washington County unit Am. Cancer Soc., 1971-72; bd. dirs. Nationwide Edn. Conf. Centers, N.W. Ark. Regional Planning Commn., Ark. Regional Med. Program, U. Ark. Found., Fayetteville Community Concert Assn., Northwest Ark. Film Commn., 1983—; city dir. N.W. Ark. Econ. Devel. Dist., alderman, 1993—; mayor, 1991, Fayetteville, Ark. Served with U.S. Army, 1945-47. Mem. Nat. Assn. Land Grant Colls. and State Univs. (dir.), Nat. Assn. Ednl. Buyers (treas., dir.), Nat. Assn. Coll. and Univ. Bus. Officers (dir., pres. 1984-85, Disting. Bus. Officer award 1991), So. Assn. Coll. and Univ. Bus. Officers (pres.), Am. Council Edn., Fayetteville C. of C. (dir., 2d v.p.), Blue Key, Fayetteville Country Club, Capitol Club, Rotary, Delta Sigma Pi, Sigma Phi Epsilon. Home: 1315 E Ridgeway Dr Fayetteville AR 72701-2616 From standing in a public welfare relief line to being listed in Who's Who; Thank God for America.

VORYS, ARTHUR ISAIAH, lawyer; b. Columbus, Ohio, June 16, 1923; s. Webb Isaiah and Adeline (Werner) V.; m. Lucia Rogers, July 16, 1949 (div. 1980); children: Caroline S., Adeline Vorys Cranson, Lucy Vorys Noll, Webb I.; m. Ann Harris, Dec. 13, 1980. BA, Williams Coll., 1945; LLB, JD, Ohio

State U., 1949. Bar: Ohio 1949. From assoc. to ptnr. Vorys, Sater, Seymour & Pease, Columbus, 1949-82, sr. ptnr., 1982-93, of counsel, 1993—; supt. ins. State of Ohio, 1957-59; bd. dirs Vorys Bros., Inc., others. Trustee, past Children's Hosp., Greenlawn Cemetery Found.; trustee, former chmn. Ohio State U. Hosps.; regent Capital U.; del. Rep. Nat. Conv., 1968, 72. Lt. USMCR, World War II. Decorated Purple Heart. Fellow Ohio State Bar, Columbus Bar Assn.; mem. ABA, Am. Judicature Soc., Rocky Fork Headley Hunt Club, Rocky Fork Hunt and Country Club, Capital Club, Phi Delta Phi, Chi Psi. Home: 5826 Havens Corners Rd Columbus OH 43230-3142 Office: Vorys Sater Seymour & Pease PO Box 1008 52 E Gay St Columbus OH 43215-3161

VOS, FRANK, advertising and marketing executive; b. N.Y.C., Dec. 1, 1919; s. George W. and Anna (Lewis) V.; m. Mary C. Dempsey, June 24, 1951; children: George Andrew, Julia Elizabeth. Student, MIT, 1936-37; BA magna cum laude, Columbia U., 1982, MA, 1984, M of Philosophy, 1989. Copywriter firm Schwab & Beatty, N.Y.C., 1941-42, 46-48; sales promotion mgr. Doubleday & Co., N.Y.C., 1948-52; group head Kleppner Co., N.Y.C., 1952-57; founder, chmn. Vos & Co., N.Y.C., 1957, Vos & Co. (became Vos & Reichberg, 1965), Altman, Vos & Reichberg, Inc., 1970-76, Vos & White, Inc., 1976-79, Frank Vos Co. Inc., 1979-85; vis. lectr. NYU, 1961, 73, 75; chmn. Direct Mktg. Day, N.Y., 1972; spl. cons. dean Columbia U., 1983; instr. U. Conn., Stamford, 1986. Author: The Ency. of N.Y.C. Bd. dirs. Stamford (Conn.) Symphony Soc., 1981-89. 1st lt. inf. AUS, World War II, ETO. Decorated Bronze Star U.S.; Knight's Cross Crown of Italy; recipient Silver Apple award N.Y.C. Direct Mktg. Club, 1985. Mem. Am. Hist. Assn., Orgn. Am. Historians, Urban History Soc., Lotos Club of N.Y.C. (chmn. lit. com. 1965-73, dir. 1971-79, admissions com. 1985—, Medal of Merit 1993), Stamford (Conn.) Yacht Club, Silvermine Golf Club (Conn.), Phi Beta Kappa. Home: Windermere Ln Stamford CT 06902

VOS, MORRIS, foreign languages educator, language services consultant; b. Mahaska County, Iowa, Dec. 10, 1944; s. Peter G. and Edith (De Vries) V.; m. Mary Elizabeth Posthuma, Aug. 16, 1966; children: Jeremy, Allison. AB in English and German, Calvin Coll., Grand Rapids, Mich., 1962-66; MA in German, Ind. U., 1968, PhD in German, 1975. Cert. oral proficiency tester in German. Assoc. instr. Ind. U., Bloomington, 1970-71; asst. prof. Western Ill. U., Macomb, 1971-79, assoc. prof., 1979-91, prof. German, 1991—; cons. Ill. State Bd. Edn., Springfield, 1984-87; mem. adv. coun. Cen. States Conf. on Teaching Fgn. Langs., 1980—. Editor: Essays in Literature, 1986-93; contbr. articles to profl. jours. Adult leader Boy Scouts Am., Macomb, 1985-87. Grantee NEH, DAAD, Goethe Inst.; recipient Lt. Gov.'s award State of Ill. for enhancement of profession, 1993. Mem. Am. Assn. Tchrs. German, Ill. Coun. on the Tchg. Fgn. Langs. (charter), Presbytery No. Ill. (treas. 1985—). Presbyterian. Avocation: aerobic fitness activities. Home: 456 S Edwards St Macomb IL 61455-3015 Office: Western Ill U Fgn Langs And Lits Macomb IL 61455

VOSBECK, ROBERT RANDALL, architect; b. Mankato, Minn., May 18, 1930; s. William Frederick and Gladys (Anderson) V.; m. Phoebe Macklin, June 21, 1953; children: Gretchen, Randy, Heidi, Macklin. BArch, U. Minn., 1954. Various archtl. positions, 1956-62; ptnr. Vosbeck-Vosbeck & Assocs., Alexandria, Va., 1962-66, VVKR Partnership, Alexandria, Va., exec. v.p. VVKR Inc., 1979-82, pres., 1982-88; prin. Vosbeck/DMJM, Washington and Alexandria, Va., 1989-94; archtl. cons., 1994—; mem. Nat. Capital Planning Commn., 1976-81, U.S./USSR Joint Group on Bldg. Design and Constrn., 1974-79; mem. Nat. Park System Adv. Bd., 1983-88. Archtl. works include Pub. Safety Ctr., Alexandria, Va., 1987, Yorktown (Va.) Visitors Ctr, 1976, Frank Reeves Mcpl. Office Bldg., Washington, 1986, Fed. Bldg., NOrfolk, Va., 1979, Jeff Davis Assocs. Office Complex, Arlington, Va., 1991, Westminster Continued Care Retirement Community, Lake Ridge, Va., 1993. Served as engr. officer USMC, 1954-56. Recipient Plaque of Honor Fedn. Colegios Architects (Republic of Mexico); named Acadamecian, Internt. Acad. Architecture, hon. fellow Royal Architects of Can., Soc. Architects of Mexico; recipient hons. Collegios Architects Spain, Union Bulgarian Architects. Fellow AIA (bd. dirs. 1976-78, v.p. 1979-80, pres. 1981); mem. Internat. Union Architects (coun. 1981-87), Nat. Trust Hist. Preservation, Alexandria C. of C. (pres. 1974-75). Presbyterian. Home and Office: Unit A 770 Potato Patch Dr Vail CO 81657

VOSBURG, NOBLE E., fur company executive; b. Omaha, Aug. 5, 1941; s. N.P. and Dena Vosburg; m. Susan E. Vosburg, Jan. 2, 1965; children—Victoria, Sally, Lindsay. B.S., Iowa State U., 1963; M.A., U. Nebr., 1965. Vice pres. U.S. Nat. Bank, Omaha, 1967-77; sr. v.p. Norwest Bank Great Falls, Mont., 1977-78, dir., 1983—; pres. Pacific Hide & Fur Depot, Great Falls, 1978—; dir. Hardrock Oil Co., Great Falls. Bd. dirs. Mont. Internat. Trade Commn., Helena, 1982—, Deaconess Hosp., Great Falls, 1981-83; ambassador State of Mont., Helena, 1984. Served to 1st lt. U.S. Army, 1963-65; Korea. Mem. Mont. C. of C. (bd. dirs. 1984—). Lodge: Rotary.

VOSBURGH, FREDERICK GEORGE, writer, editor; b. Johnstown, N.Y., Sept. 16, 1904; s. John Ross and Alice (Baker) V.; m. Doris Kennedy, Jan. 2, 1929 (div. 1948); children: Richard Kennedy, Alan Frederick; m. Valerie Paterson, May 28, 1949. A.B., Syracuse U., 1925; postgrad., George Washington U., 1938-39. Reporter, Syracuse (N.Y.) Jour., 1922-24; Reporter Syracuse Post-Standard, 1925-26, AP, N.Y.C. and Washington, 1927-33; joined editorial staff Nat. Geog. Mag., 1933, asst. editor, 1951-56, sr. asst. editor, 1956, asso. editor, 1957-67, editor, 1967-70. Author numerous articles in various fields. Served to lt. col. USAAF, 1942-45, overseas. Recipient Bronze Star, Air Medal. Mem. Nat. Geog. Soc. (v.p. 1958-70, trustee 1962-79, trustee emeritus 1979—), Phi Beta Kappa. Club: Nat. Press. Home: 8500 W Howell Rd Bethesda MD 20817-6827

VOSBURGH, MARGARET MURPHY, nurse administrator; b. Aug. 29, 1948; d. John Joseph and Rita (Ryan) Murphy. Diploma, St. Clare's Hosp., 1971; BSN, Mount Saint Mary Coll., 1976; MS in Nursing, Russell Sage Coll., 1979; MBA, U. So. Calif., 1989. Dir. nursing Albany (N.Y.) Med. Ctr. Hosp., 1981-86; dir. nursing svc. Cedars-Sinai Med. Ctr., L.A., 1986-89; v.p. nursing svcs. Hoag Meml. Hosp., Newport Beach, Calif., 1989-92; v.p. patient care svcs. Hosp. of Good Samaritan, L.A., 1992-93; assoc. exec. dir. Swedish Health Sys., Seattle, 1993—. Recipient Wharton Fellow, 1983, Fed. Traineeship award for Grad. Studies in Nursing; named to Sigma Theta Tau. Mem. Am. Orgn. Nurse Execs., Orgn. Nurse Execs. Calif., ANA.

VOSE, ROBERT CHURCHILL, JR., former art gallery executive; b. Boston, Mar. 30, 1911; s. Robert Churchill and Sarah Helen (Williams) V.; m. Ann Peterson, Mar. 8, 1941; children: Robert Churchill III, Abbot Williams. Student, Harvard, 1930-32. With Vose Galleries of Boston, Inc., 1932-85, treas., 1953-85, pres., 1976-80, chmn., 1980-85; ret., 1985; mem. Friends of Art, Boston U., 1957-59, Friends of Art, Colby Coll., 1959-89. Contbr. articles to profl. jours. Chmn. Community Fund drive, Dedham, Mass., 1952. Fellow Pilgrim Soc. (life); mem. Copley Soc. (dir. 1950-53, Copley medal 1987), Back Bay Assn.; v.p. (since 1958, dir. 1964-66), New Eng. Hist. Geneal. Soc. (coun. 1958-77, pres. 1971-74, trustee emeritus 1985—), Dedham Hist. Soc. (corr. sec. 1958), Boston Mus. Fine Arts, Bostonian Soc. (life), Albany Inst. History and Art, Conn. Hist. Soc., Duxbury Rural and Hist. Soc. (exec. com.), N.Y. State Hist. Assn., Mass. Hist. Soc. (chmn. house com., chmn. art com.), Colonial Soc. Mass., Back Bay Coun., Pilgrim Soc. (trustee 1992—), Neighbourhood Assn. Back Bay (dir. 1964-66), Plimouth Plantation, Harvard Club (Boston), Algonquin Club (Boston), Somerset Club (Boston). Republican. Unitarian (chmn. parish com. 1941). Address: 394 King Caesar Rd Duxbury MA 02332

VOSS, CARL HERMANN, clergyman, humanities educator, author; b. Pitts., Dec. 8, 1910; s. Carl August and Lucy (Wilms) V.; m. Dorothy Katherine Grote, Nov. 25, 1940 (div. 1957); 1 dau., Carlyn Grote (Mrs. Harold Iuzzolino); m. Phyllis MacKenzie Gierlotka, May 9, 1959; 1 dau., Christina Elisabeth Gierlotka (Mrs. Russell P. Wynings Jr.). AB, U. Pitts., 1931, PhD, 1942; student, Internat. People's Coll., Elsinore, Denmark, U. Geneva, Switzerland, 1931, Chgo. Theol. Sem., 1932; M.Div., Union Theol. Sem., N.Y.C., 1935; postgrad. Yale Div. Sch., 1938-40; postgrad. in Hebrew studies, Oxford U., 1977 postgrad., Ecumenical Inst. Bossey, World Council Chs., Geneva, 1980-81; L.H.D., Hebrew Union Coll.-Jewish Inst. Religion, N.Y.C., 1981. Minister United Ch. (Congl.-Christian-Friends), Raleigh, N.C., 1935-38; chaplain Cheshire (Conn.) Acad., 1938-40;

assoc. minister Smithfield United Ch., Pitts., 1940-43; extension sec. Ch. Peace Union and World Alliance for Internat. Friendship Through the Chs., 1943-49; editor World Alliance News Letter, 1944-49; exec. sec. Christian Council on Palestine, 1943-46; chmn. exec. council Am. Christian Palestine Com., 1946-57; minister Flatbush Unitarian Ch., Bklyn., 1953-57, N.E. Congl. Ch., Saratoga Springs, N.Y., 1957-64; Merrill research assoc. Brandeis U., 1965-67; lectr. New Sch. for Soc. Research, 1948-56; lectr. dept. philosophy and religion Skidmore College, Saratoga Springs, 1960-61, 65-66; vis. prof. theology and history religions Theol. Sch. St. Lawrence U., Canton, N.Y., 1964-65; prof. humanities Edward Waters Coll., Jacksonville, Fla., 1973-76; chmn. humanities div. Edward Waters Coll., 1974-76; NCCJ ecumenical-scholar-in-residence; resident scholar Ecumenical Inst. Advanced Theol. Studies, Tantur, Jerusalem, 1976-77; Centre Postgrad. Hebrew Studies Oxford U., 1977, 79; conducted European tours, 1930, 31, 35, (Arab countries and Israel), 1949, 51, 53, 55, 58, 63, 66, 70, 73, 75, 79; (lectr. tour) Rhodesia, South Africa under auspices Good Will Council S.Africa, 1947. Author: The Palestine Problem Today, 1953, (with Theodore Huebner) This Is Israel, 1956, Rabbi and Minister: The Friendship of Stephen S. Wise and John Haynes Holmes, 1964, In Search of Meaning: Living Religions of the World, 1968, Stephen S. Wise: Servant of The People-Selected Letters, 1969, A Summons unto Men: An Anthology of the Writings of John Haynes Holmes, 1971, Living Religions of the World: Our Search for Meaning, 1977, (with David A. Rausch) Protestantism: Its Modern Meaning, 1987; editor: The Universal God: An Interfaith Anthology, 1953, Excalibur Books, 1964—, Quotations of Courage and Vision: A Source Book for Speaking, Writing and Meditation, 1972, (with David A. Rausch) World Religions: Our Quest for Meaning, 1989; contbr. to mags. and religious jours. Recipient Nat. Brotherhood award NCCJ, 1978; hon. fellow Hebrew U., Jerusalem, 1990; Carl Hermann Voss scholarship named in honor by Ctr. for Hebrew Studies Oxford U., Eng., 1990. Mem. United Ch. of Christ. Home: Baymeadows 7783 Point Vicente Ct Jacksonville FL 32256

VOSS, EDWARD WILLIAM, JR., immunologist, educator; b. Chgo., Dec. 2, 1933; s. Edward William and Lois Wilma (Graham) V.; m. Virginia Hellman, June 15, 1974; children: Cathleen, Valerie. A.B., Cornell Coll., Iowa, 1955; M.S., Ind. U., 1964, Ph.D., 1966. Asst. prof. microbiology U. Ill., Urbana, 1967-71; assoc. prof. U. Ill., 1971-74, prof., 1974—; dir. cell sci. ctr., 1988—, LAS Jubilee prof., 1990; mem. rev. panel USDA on molecular biology/gene structure, Washington, 1985, 86, U.S. Dept. of Energy Rsch., 1994; panel mem. in biol. scis. NSF Minority Grad. Fellowships, Washington, 1986, 87, 88; mem. sci. adv. bd. Biotech. Rsch. and Devel. Corp., 1989—. Author: editor: Fluorescein Hapten: An Immunological Probe, 1984, Anti-DNA Antibodies in SLE, 1988; adv. editor: Immunochemistry, 1975-78, Molecular Immunology, 1980—; mem. editorial bd.: Applied and Environ. Microbiology, 1979—; contbr. articles to profl. jours. Served with U.S. Army, 1956-58. NIH fellow, 1966-67, NSF fellow, 1975-77; NIH grantee, 1967—, NSF grantee, 1967—; recipient Disting. Lectr. award U. Ill., 1983; named 1st James R. Martin Univ. scholar, 1994. Fellow Am. Inst. Chemists; mem. AAAS, Fedn. Am. Scientists, Am. Assn. Immunologists, Am. Assn. Biol. Chemists, Reticuloendothelial Soc., Am. Lupus Soc. (hon. bd. dirs. Cen. Ill. chpt. 1986—, named to Nat. Lupus Hall of Fame 1988), N.Y. Acad. Scis., U.S. Pharmacopeial Conv., Inc., Nat. Geog. Soc., Am. Chem. Soc. (tour speaker 1984-87), Protein Soc., Sigma Xi. Home: 2207 Boudreau Cir Urbana IL 61801-6601 Office: U Ill Dept Microbiology 131 Burrill Hall Urbana IL 61801 Perserverance, determination and sacrifice only when coupled to appropriate goals in basic research and teaching yield results that justify the effort and commitment.

VOSS, JACK DONALD, international business consultant, lawyer; b. Stoughton, Wis., Sept. 24, 1921; s. George C. and Grace (Tusler) V.; m. Mary Josephine Edgarton, May 7, 1955; children: Julia, Jennifer, Andrew, Charles. Ph.B., U. Wis., 1943; J.D., Harvard U., 1948. Bar: Ill. 1949, Ohio 1963. From assoc. to ptnr. Sidney & Austin predecessor firm, Chgo., 1948-62; gen. counsel Anchor Hocking Corp., Lancaster, Ohio, 1962-67, v.p., gen. counsel, 1967-72, gen. mgr. internat., 1970-86; pres. Anchor Hocking Internat. Corp., Lancaster, 1972-86; mng. ptnr. Voss Internat., Lancaster, 1986—; chmn. Internat. Coun. Conf. bd., 1985-87. Mem. Fairfield County Rep. Ctrl. and Exec. Com.; pres. Fairfield Heritage Assn., 1966-69; v.p. Lancaster Community Concert Assn., 1965-73; trustee, chmn. Ohio Info. Com. With USNR, 1943-46, ATO, MTO, PTO. Mem. ABA (internat. law & practice and bus. law sects.), Ohio Bar Assn. (chmn. corp. counsel sect. 1966), Columbus Bar Assn., Chgo. Bar Assn., Fairfield County Bar Assn., Licensing Execs. Soc., Am. Arbitration Assn. (panel mem.), Ctr. for Internat. Comml. Arbitration (panel mem.), Harvard Law Sch. Assn., Ohio Mfrs. Assn. (trustee, v.p. 1970-72), Symposiatch, Alpha Chi Rho. Lutheran. Clubs: Rotary (pres. Lancaster 1968), Racquet (Chgo.); Landsdowne (London). Home: 3375 Cincinnati-Zane Rd Lancaster OH 43130 Office: Voss Internat 212 S Broad St Lancaster OH 43130-4305

VOSS, JAMES FREDERICK, psychologist, educator; b. Chgo., Dec. 5, 1930; s. Leo Carl and Lydia (Isreal) V.; m. Marilyn Luzia Timm, June 20, 1953 (dec. Oct. 1982); children: Barbara Lynn, Katherine Ann, Mark Frederick, Carol Jean, David James; m. Deborah Jane Steinbach, Oct. 8, 1988; 1 child, Regina Lynn. B.A., Valparaiso (Ind.) U., 1952; M.S., U. Wis., 1954, Ph.D., 1956. Instr., asst. prof. Wis. State Coll., Eau Claire, 1956-58; asst. prof., asso. prof. Coll. of Wooster, Ohio, 1958-63; asso. prof. U. Pitts., 1963-66, prof., 1966—, chmn. dept. psychology, 1968-70, assoc. dir. Learning Rsch. and Devel. Ctr., 1985-92; prin. investigator Nat. Inst. Child Health and Human Devel., 1956-58, 59-70; Fulbright Disting. prof., lectr., USSR, 1979; NSF fellow Ind. U., 1960; vis. prof. U. Wis., 1964; vis. prof. NIMH spl. fellow U. Calif., Irvine, 1970—; vis. prof. Mershon Ctr., Ohio State U., 1989. Author: Psychology as a Behavioral Science, 1974; editor: Approaches to Thought, 1969, Topics in Human Performance, 1972, Informal Reasoning and Education, 1990; cons. editor: Jour. Exptl. Psychology, 1975-80, Jour. Verbal Learning and Verbal Behavior, 1981-87. Recipient Disting. Alumni award Valparaiso U., 1979. Fellow Am. Psychol. Assn., AAAS; mem. Midwestern, Eastern psychol. assns., AAAS, N.Y. Acad. Sci., Psychonomic Soc. (sec.-treas. 1978-80), Am. Diabetes Assn. (chmn. bd. Western Pa. affiliate 1974-77, 173-75), Internat. Soc. Political Psychology, Sigma Xi. Home: 115 Glen David Dr Pittsburgh PA 15238-1513

VOSS, JAMES LEO, veterinarian; b. Grand Junction, Colo., Apr. 17, 1934; s. Edward John and Ruth I. (Michele) V.; m. Kathleen Alice Claxton, Dec. 19, 1954; children: Edward Duane, William David, Laura Jean. DVM, Colo. State U., 1958, MS, 1965. Instr. Colo. State U., Ft. Collins, 1958-60, asst. prof., 1960-66, assoc. prof., 1966-72, prof., 1972—, dept. head of clin. scis., 1974-86, dean coll. vet. medicine, biomedical scis., 1986—; cons. various horse breeding farms nationally and internationally, 1958—. Mem. AVMA (ho. of dels. 1986-89), Am. Assn. Equine Practioner (v.p. 1987, pres. 1989), Colo. Vet. Med. Assn. (pres. 1971), Nat. Swine Repopulation Assn. (bd. dirs. 1983-87), Am. Soc. Animal Sci. (editorial bd. 1983-87). Republican. Avocations: hunting, fishing. Home: 1217 Southridge Dr Fort Collins CO 80521-4432 Office: Colo State U Coll Vet Med & Biomed Scis Office of the Dean Fort Collins CO 80523

VOSS, JERROLD RICHARD, city planner, educator, university official; b. Chgo., Nov. 4, 1932; s. Peter Walter and Annis Lorraine (Hayes) V.; m. Jean Evelyn Peterson, Aug. 21, 1954; children—Cynthia Jean, Tania Hayes. B.Arch., Cornell U., 1955; M. City Planning, Harvard U., 1959; Ph.D. (Bus. History fellow, Univ. fellow, IBM fellow), 1971. Asst. prof. U. Calif., 1960-61; asst. prof., assoc. prof. U. Ill., 1961-69; assoc. prof. Harvard U., 1969-71; prof. city and regional planning Ohio State U., Columbus, 1971—; chmn. dept. city and regional planning Ohio State U., 1971-79; dir. Ohio State U. (Knowlton Sch. Architecture), 1981—; UN advisor to Govt. Indonesia, 1964-65; social affairs officer UN Secretariat, 1971-77; project mgr. UN Task Force on Human Environment, Thailand, 1975-76; dir. rsch. and devel. UN Ctr. for Human Settlements (Habitat), 1979-81; cons. Ill. Dept. Devel., J.S. Bolles & Assocs., UN Office Tech. Cooperation, UN Devel. Program, AID, Bechtel Nat. Inc., other pvt. and pub. orgns.; mem. external examiners team United Arab U., 1992—. Author: Human Settlements: Problems and Priorities; Contbr. articles to profl. jours. Mem. pub. policy com. Smithsonian Instn., 1970-73; bd. dirs. Champaign County United Community Council, 1966-69, Columbus Theatre Ballet Assn., 1972-75. Served to 1st lt. U.S. Army, 1955-57. Mem. Acad. for Contemporary Problems (asso.), Am. Am. Inst. Planners, Am. Soc. Engring. Edn., Internat.

Center for Urban Land Policy (London). Office: 190 W 17th Ave Columbus OH 43210-1320

VOSS, JOHN, retired association executive; b. Albany, Oreg., July 7, 1917; s. Enoch George and Lulu (Porter) V.; m. Barbara Fischer, Sept. 8, 1945; children: Christopher, Caroline. A.B., Willamette U., 1942. Instr. history Tufts U., 1946-47, M.I.T., 1949-54; mgr. spl. projects Arthur D. Little, Inc., Cambridge, Mass., 1954-64; exec. officer Am. Acad. Arts and Scis., Boston, 1964-86; pres. ICIPE Found., 1985-90; mem. corp. Internat. Centre Insect Physiology and Ecology, Nairobi, Kenya, 1968—; trustee ICIPE Found., Stockholm, Sweden, 1977-90; mem. U.S. Pugwash Com., 1966-85. Editor: Confrontation and Learned Societies, 1970, (with others) When Values Conflict, 1976, (with A. Oleson) Organization of Knowledge in Modern America, 1860-1920, 1979. Trustee, mem. exec. com., sec.-treas. Nat. Humanities Center, Research Triangle Park, N.C., 1975-92, trustee emeritus, 1992—; sec. Commn. on Yr. 2000, 1965-68. Fellow AAAS, Am. Acad. Arts and Scis. Democrat. Unitarian. Clubs: St. Botolph, Century, Appalachian Mountain, Mass. Audubon Soc. Home: 187 Garfield Rd Concord MA 01742-4905 Office: 136 Irving St Norton's Woods Cambridge MA 02138

VOSS, OMER GERALD, truck company executive; b. Downs, Kans., Sept. 14, 1916; s. John and Grace (Bohlen) V.; m. Annabelle Katherine Lutz, June 20, 1940; children—Jerrol Ann, Omer Gerald. A.B., Ft. Hays (Kans.) State Coll., 1937; J.D., U. Kans., 1939. Bar: Kans. bar 1939. With Internat. Harvester Co., 1936-79, v.p. farm equipment div., 1962-66, exec. v.p., dir., 1966—, vice chmn., 1977-79. Served with USAAF, 1943-46. Clubs: Chicago, Commercial, Westmoreland Country.

VOSS, REGIS DALE, agronomist, educator; b. Cedar Rapids, Iowa, Jan. 4, 1931; s. Francis Joseph and Mary Valeria (Womichil) V.; m. Margaret Anne Mitchell, Nov. 24, 1956; children: Lori Anne, John Patrick, David James. BS, Iowa State U., 1952, PhD, 1962. cert. profl. agronomist. Agriculturist Tenn. Valley Authority, Muscle Shoals, Ala., 1962-64; prof. Iowa State U., Ames, 1964—; bd. dirs. fertilizer adv. Farmland Industries, Kansas City, Mo. Co-author: (chpt.) Sulfur in Agriculture, 1986, Organic Farming, 1984; assoc. editor Jour. Prodn. Agr., 1988-92. Pres. FarmHouse Frat. Alumni Assn. Bd., Ames, 1990. 1st lt. USAF, 1952-56, Korea. Recipient Agronomic Extension Edn. award Am. Soc. Agronomy, 1984, Agronomic Achievement award Am. Soc. Agronomy, 1989, Werner L. Nelson award Am. Soc. Agronomy, 1992, Burlington No. Found. award Iowa State U., 1990, Faculty Citation Iowa State U., 1992. Fellow AAAS, Am. Soc. Agronomy (bd. dirs. 1976-78), Soil Sci. Soc. Am. (bd. dirs. 1980-83). Republican. Roman Catholic. Achievements include development of field laboratory for training of crop advisors on diagnosis of crop problems; research on effects of soil amendments on chemical indices and crop yields and economic analysis of crop yield response to soil amendments. Office: Iowa State Univ Agronomy Hall Ames IA 50011

VOSS, WILLIAM CHARLES, retired oil company executive; b. Buffalo, Sept. 22, 1937; s. William T. and Dorathea S. (Grotke) V.; m. Marilyn Erickson, Sept. 6, 1958; children: William, John, Douglas. AB with honors, Harvard U., 1959, MBA with honors, 1961. With Northwestern Refining Co., St. Paul Park, 1961-70; v.p. adminstrn. Northwestern Refining Co., 1969-71; with Ashland Oil Inc., Ky., 1971-89, v.p., 1973-79, adminstrv. v.p., 1979-80, sr. v.p., group operating officer, 1980-89; pres. Ashland-Warren Inc., 1979-83, APAC, Inc., 1980-82, 83-86. Mem. Am. Petroleum Inst., Ind. Petroleum Assn., Am. Chem. Soc. Republican. Home: Park Pl Apt 24-B 2660 Peachtree Rd NW Atlanta GA 30305-3679

VOSS, WILLIAM R., poultry feed company executive; b. 1951. BBA, Univ. Tex.; MBA, Stanford U. CPA. V.p. merchandising Compco Computer Ctrs.; with Booz Allen & Hamilton Inc., Dallas; pres., chief oper. officer Pilgrims Pride Corp., 1988—. Office: Pilgrims Pride Corp 110 S Texas St Pittsburg TX 75686-1532

VOTAW, CHARLES LESLEY, academic dean; b. Chgo., Oct. 11, 1929; m. May Louise Korteling; children: John Ralph, Diana Lynn, Paul Charles. BA, Hope Coll., 1951; MD, U. Mich., 1955, PhD, 1959. Intern St. Joseph Mercy Hosp., Ann Arbor, Mich., 1955-56; instr. in anatomy U. Mich. Med. Sch., Ann Arbor, 1956-60, asst. prof., 1960-64, assoc. prof., 1964-70, prof., 1970-77, asst. dean for curriculum, 1971-75, assoc. dean, 1975-77; prof. James H. Quillen Coll. Medicine, East Tenn. State U., Johnson City, 1977—, assoc. dean clin affairs, 1977-80, assoc. dean acad. affairs, 1980-85, exec. assoc. dean acad. affairs, 1985—; cons. dept. neurology VA Hosp., Ann Arbor, 1968-76; chmn. accreditation task force James H. Quillen Coll. Medicine, 1992—, accreditation site visitor, 1991, dir. space mgmt. and capital expansion program, 1989—. Author: (with E. W. Lauer) A Laboratory Guide to Neuroanatomy, 1963; contbr. articles to profl. jours. Local chmn. bd., pres. and treas coun. PTO, Ann Arbor; chmn. election proposals com., mem. ad hoc fin. com. Ann Arbor Pub. Schs.; active Family Life Health Edn. Com., Ann Arbor, local Little League organ.; mem. adv. com. Glaxo Pharmacy Program, 1986-91. Lederle Found. fellow, 1954, UCLA fellow, 1962-63. Mem. AAAS, Am. Assn. Anatomy, Am. Assn. Med. Colls. (chmn. so. region group on ednl. affairs 1989-91, mem. nat. steering com. group on ednl. affairs 1989-91), Am. Acad. Neurology (assoc.), Am. Soc. Zoologists, Soc. for Neurosci., Blue Key, Cajal Club, Sigma Xi, Phi Kappa Phi, Alpha Omega Alpha, Phi Chi. Presbyterian. Home: 3603 Honeywood Dr Johnson City TN 37604-1480 Office: East Tenn U James H Quillen Coll Medicine Office of Academic Affairs PO Box 70571 Johnson City TN 37614-0571

VOTOLATO, ARTHUR NICHOLAS, JR., judge; b. Providence, Aug. 20, 1930; s. Arthur N. and Mary (Tavani) V.; children: Dacia Lorraine, Hera Lisbeth; m. Janice Greene. BA, U. R.I., 1953; LLB, Boston U., 1956. Bar: R.I. 1956, U.S. Dist. Ct. R.I. 1956. Ptnr. Votolato & Votolato, Providence, 1956-62; chief spl. counsel R.I. Dept. Pub. Works, Providence, 1962-68; judge U.S. Bankruptcy Ct., Dist. R.I., Providence, 1968—; chief judge First Cir. Bankruptcy Appellate Panel, Mass. Panel; mem. Adv. Com. to Adminstrv. Office of U.S. Cts., 1988—; mem. faculty Roger Williams Coll., N.E. Bankruptcy Law Inst.; program speaker Bankruptcy Litigation and Practice Seminar. Republican candidate for R.I. Atty. Gen., 1962; bd. dirs. Urban League R.I., 1975-80, Ocean State Marathon Com., 1979-83; trustee U. R.I. Found., 1984-92. With USAF, 1951-52. Fellow Am. Coll. Bankruptcy; mem. R.I. Bar Assn., Fed. Bar Assn., Nat. Conf. Bankruptcy Judges (liason com., fed. cts. study com, gov. 1st cir.), Boston U. Alumni Assn., Aircraft Owners and Pilots Assn. Digest editor Am. Bankruptcy Law Jour., 1977-83, mem. editorial adv. bd., 1977-89; digest editor Bankruptcy Law Jour. Office: US Bankruptcy Ct 380 Westminster Mall The Federal Ctr Rm 619 Providence RI 02903

VOULKOS, PETER, artist; b. Bozeman, Mont., Jan. 29, 1924. B.S., Mont. State U., hon. doctorate, 1968; M.F.A., Calif. Coll. Arts and Crafts, hon. doctorate, 1972; hon. doctorate, Otis Inst. of Parsons Sch. Design, 1980, San Francisco Art Inst., 1982. Tchr. Archie Bray Found., Helena, Mont., Black Mountain Coll., Los Angeles County Art Inst., Mont. State U., Greenwich House Pottery, N.Y.C., Columbia U. Tchrs. Coll., U. Calif.-Berkeley, ret. 1985. One man shows include Gump's Gallery, San Francisco, U. Fla., Hist. Soc. Mont., Felix Landau Gallery, Chgo. Art Inst., Bonniers, Inc., N.Y.C., Fresno State Coll. Scripps Coll., U. So. Calif., Pasadena Art Mus. (purchase prize), Scripps Coll., Nat. Ceramic Exhbn., U. Tenn., Brussels World's Fair, 1958, de Young Mus., Seattle World's Fair, 1962, Whitney Mus. Art, Denver Art Mus. (purchase prize), Smithsonian Instn. (purchase prize), Los Angeles County Mus. Art (purchase prize), Okun-Thomas Gallery, St. Louis, 1980, Morgan Gallery, Kansas City, Kans., 1980, Exhibit A, Chgo., 1976, 79, 81, Braunstein Gallery, San Francisco, 1968, 75, 78, 82, 86, 87, 91, 93, Cowles Gallery, N.Y.C., 1981, 83, 90, Thomas Segal Gallery, Boston, 1981, 88, Twining Gallery, N.Y.C., 1988, 89, Point View, Tokyo, 1983, Hordaland Kunstnersentrum, Bergan, Norway, 1993, travelling retrospective show, San Francisco Mus. Modern Art, 1978-79, Contemporary Arts Mus., Houston, Mus. Contemporary Craft, N.Y.C., Milw. Art Ctr.; exhibited in group shows, including Whitney Mus., N.Y.C., 1981, San Francisco Mus. Modern Art, 1981, Los Angeles County Mus. Art, Kunst Industri Museet, Oslo, Norway, 1993; represented in permanent collections Balt. Mus. Art, Denver Art Mus., Univs. Calif., Colo., Fla., Ill., Mich., Utah, Wis., Ind., Mont. State U., Ariz. State U., Bemidji State U., Fresno State U., Iowa State U., Tokyo

Folk Art Mus., Los Angeles County Art Mus., Mus. Contemporary Crafts, N.Y.C., Oakland Art Mus., Pasadena Mus. Art, San Francisco Mus. Modern Art, Smithsonian Instn., Boston Mus. Fine Arts, Corcoran Gallery, Washington, Den Permanente, Copenhagen, Fed. Bldg., Honolulu, Everson Mus., Syracuse, N.Y., Long Beach (Calif.) Mus. Art, Milw. Art Mus., Minn. Mus. Art, Mus. Boymans van Beuningen, Netherlands, Mus. Modern Art, N.Y.C., Portland Art Mus., Whitney Mus., N.Y.C., Stedelijk Mus., Amsterdam and Eindhoven, Netherlands, Nelson Atkins Mus., Kansas City. Recipient first prize RAC, Nat. Decorative Art Show, Wichita, award N.W. Craft Show, award Pacific Coast Ceramic Show, purchase prize Cranbrook Art Mus., award Los Angeles County Fair, Ford. Found., Silver medal Internat. Ceramic Exhbn., Ostend, Belgium, 1954, Gold medal Cannes, France, award I Paris Biennial, 1959, Rodin Mus. prize in sculpture, citation for disting. contbns. to visual arts Nat. Assn. Schs. Art, 1980, award of honor San Francisco Art Commn., 1981, Creative Arts Awards medal for sculpture Brandeis U., 1982, Gold medal Am. Craft Council, 1986; Nat. Endowment for Arts sr. fellow, 1976 and grantee, 1986; Guggenheim fellow, 1984. Mem. Soc. Centennial Alumni Mont. State U. Address: 1306 3rd St Berkeley CA 94710

VOWELL, JACK C., former state legislator, investor; b. May 9, 1927; s. Jack C. and Daurice (McDaniel) V.; m. Mary Johnson, Apr. 19, 1957; 1 child, Janice Vowell Alexander. BS in Fgn. Svc., Georgetown U., 1948, MS in Fgn. Svc., 1952; MA in History, Tex. Western Coll., 1952; postgrad., Harvard U., 1953-55. Mem. faculty Sch. Fgn. Svcs. Georgetown U., Washington, 1948-49, U. Tex., El Paso, 1955-60; exec. v.p. Vowell Constrn. Co., El Paso, 1962-69, pres., chmn. bd., 1969-73; rep. Tex. Ho. of Reps., Austin, 1980-95, mem. numerous coms. 68th to 73rd legis., 1980-95; personal investor, 1973—; chmn. Tex. sunset commn., 1987-89. Pres. Yucca Coun., Boy Scouts Am., 1972-74, mem. adv. bd., 1987-92, adv. bd. we. region, 1993—; bd. dirs. South Ctrl. region, 1993-86, mem. adv. bd., 1987—, nat. coun., 1971-87; mem. adv. bd. Hotel Dieu Hosp., 1974-87; adv. dir. Tex. Art Alliance, 1981-83; bd. dirs. Goodwill Industries of El Paso, 1973-77, El Paso Indsl. Devel. Corp., 1962-82; pres. El Paso Hist. Soc., 1957-59, assoc. editor Password, 1962-64; chmn. pers. com. El Paso Pub. Libr. Sys., 1969-74, bd. dirs., 1969-74; adminstrv. adv. bd. City of El Paso, 1973-74; coun. state policy and planning agencies, 1989-92; adv. comm., 1985-89; Tex. coun. on disabilities, 1984-85; state coun. on child abuse, 1984-85. With U.S. Army, 1946-47. Recipient City of El Paso Conquistador award, 1967, 73, Goodwill Industries of El Paso Outstanding Svc. award to Handicapped Workers, 1972, Disting. Eagle award Boy Scouts Am., 1972, Silver Beaver award, 1973, Silver Antelope award, 1983, Tex. Assn. for Marriage and Family Therapy Recognition cert., 1982, U. Tex. El Paso Coll of Edn. Clin. Programs Assistance award, 1985, award for Commitment to Reshaping and Improvement of Svcs. MHMR, 1985, Texans for Children Support for Needy Children, 1985, U. Tex. El Paso Spl. Edn. commendation for Spl. Achievement Autism Program, 1985, Coalition of Texas with Disabilities Pub. Servant of Yr. award, 1985, Anti-Defamation League of El Paso Torch of Liberty award, 1985, Tex. Network of Youth Svcs. Outstanding Youth award, 1987, Nat. Coun. of State Human Svcs. Adminstrs. Nat. commendation, 1987, Disting. Svc. Award Tex. Assn. Deaf, 1987, Am. Public Welfare Assn. Nat. Recognition of Statesmanship in Tex. Ho. Reps., 1987, Better Life award Tex. Health Care Assn., 1987, Legis. Excellence award Tex. Health Care Assn., 1987, United Way of El Paso vol. of the year award, 1988, Am. Coll. of Health Care Adminstrs. Tex. chpt. award, 1988, award for contbn. developmentally delayed and at risk infants, 1988, 94, Tex. Head Injury Legislative award, 1991, Legis. award Tex. Rehab. Assn., 1991, Rio Grande Coun. Govt. Legislative Leadership in Human Svcs. award, 1992, Helen Farabee Leadership award Tex. Perinatal Assn., 1992, Friend of Child award Tex. Coalition Juvenile Justice, 1993, Alviane NO-AD, Public Svc. award, 1993, Unite El Paso Appreciation award, 1993, Gran Paseño award U. Tex. El Paso, 1994, Good Hands award Tex. Dept. Transp., 1994. Mem. El Paso C. of C. (bd. dirs. 1962-69), Rotary (bd. dirs. 1967-68, pres. 1968, Disting. Svc. award 1988). Republican. Episcopalian.

VOWLES, RICHARD BECKMAN, language educator, foreign language; b. Fargo, N.D., Oct. 5, 1917; s. Guy Richard and Ella (Beckman) V.; m. Ellen Noah Hudson, Aug. 1, 1942 (div. 1969); children: Elizabeth Ellen, Richard Hudson. B.S., Davidson Coll., 1938; postgrad., U. N.C., 1938-39, U. Stockholm, 1939-40; M.A., Yale U., 1942, Ph.D., 1950. Engr. Hercules Powder Co., Wilmington, Chattanooga, 1941-43; chemist Rohm & Haas, Knoxville, Tenn., 1943-44; econ. cons. War Dept., 1944; Am. vice consul Gothenburg, Sweden, 1944-46; asst. prof. English Southwestern U., Memphis, 1948-50, Queens U., N.Y.C., 1950-51; assoc. prof. English U. Fla., 1951-60; prof. Scandinavian and comparative lit. U. Wis., Madison, 1960-85; prof. emeritus U. Wis., 1985—, chmn. comparative lit., 1962-63, 64-67, 71-72, chmn. Scandinavian studies, 1977-80; Am. specialist in Scandinavia Dept. State, summer 1963; vis. prof. N.Y.U., summer 1964, U. Helsinki, Finland, spring 1968, Stockholm, 1969; lectr., Sydney, Australia, 1975, Paris, 1975; master ceremonies Santa Fe Scandinavian Film Festival, 1984. Editor: Eternal Smile, 1954, Dramatic Theory, 1956, Comparatists at Work, 1968; Adv. editor: Nordic Council Series, 1965-70, Herder Ency. of World Lit; contbr. articles to profl. jours. Am.-Scandinavian Found. fellow Stockholm, 1939-40, Lassen fellow Am. Scandinavian Found., 1986; Fulbright fellow Copenhagen, 1955-56; Strindberg fellow Stockholm, 1973; Swedish govt. research award, 1978; Norwegian Govt. fellow, summer 1978. Mem. Modern Lang. Assn., Soc. Advancement Scandinavian Study (mem. exec. com.), Internat. Comparative Lit. Assn., Am. Comparative Lit. Assn. (adv. bd.), Strindberg Soc., Phi Beta Kappa. Home: 1115 Oak Way Madison WI 53705-1420

VRABLE, JOHN BERNARD, retired oil corrosion engineer, consultant; b. Greensburg, Pa., Sept. 24, 1929; s. John Joseph and Elizabeth Dorothy (Zubach) V.; m. Marjorie Ann Peters, Jan. 29, 1950 (div. 1990); children: John, Kathleen, Elizabeth Michael, David; m. Rose Marie Wilkins, Aug. 16, 1990. BS in Petroleum Engring., U. Pitts., 1957. Engr. N.Y. State Natural Gas Co., Pitts., 1951-61; regional engr. Cathodic Protection Svc., Houston, 1961-63; rsch. cons. U.S. Steel Corp., Monroeville, Pa., 1963-86; sr. cons. engr. Harco Corp., Medina, Ohio, 1986-87; mgr. standards, quality assurance CNG Transmission Corp., Clarksburg, W.Va., 1987-94; ret., 1994; prin. investigator Nat. Coop Hwy. Rsch. Program, Monroeville, 1977-80; adv. bridge corr. Fed. Hwy. Adminstrn., Washington, 1978-80; cons. USS Engrs. and Cons., Pitts., 1980-86; mem. pipeline rsch. com. Am. Gas Assn., Washington, 1989—. 3 patents in field; contbr. articles to profl. jours. and chpts. to books. Recipient Rsch. Achievement award U.S. Steel Rsch., 1972, Spl. Recognition award Steel Tank Inst., Chgo., 1980, Appalachian Underground Corrosion Short Course Col. George C. Cox Outstanding award, 1995. Mem. NSPE, Nat. Assn. Corrosion Engrs. (chmn. Pitts. sect. 1960), Am. Gas Assn., So. Gas Assn., Pa. Gas Assn., Elks, Am. Assn. Ret. Persons. Republican. Roman Catholic. Home: 14031 W Horizon Dr Sun City West AZ 85375

VRABLIK, EDWARD ROBERT, import/export company executive; b. Chgo., June 8, 1932; s. Steven Martin and Meri (Korbel) V.; m. Bernice G. Germer, Jan. 25, 1958; children: Edward Robert II, Scott S. B.S. in Chem. Engring., Northwestern U., 1956; M.B.A., U. Chgo., 1961; postgrad., MIT, 1970. Registered profl. engr., Ill. Dir. indsl. mktg. Eimco Corp., 1956-61; dir. indsl. mktg. and planning Swift & Co., Chgo., 1961-68; v.p., gen. mgr. Swift Chem. Co., Chgo., 1968-73; pres., chief exec. officer Estech Gen. Chems. Corp., Chgo., 1973-86; pres. Kare Internat. Inc., Chgo., 1986—; pres. Julius and Associates, Inc., Kare Internat., Inc.; bd dirs. Potash Phosphate Inst., Consol. Fertilizers, Ltd.; mem. mgmt. com. Esmark Inc., Korbel, Inc., Mister Lawn Care, Inc. Author. Bd. dirs., v.p. Northwestern U. Tech. Inst.; trustee Future Farmers Am. Mem. Internat. Superphosphate Mfrs. Assn. (dir.), Am. Inst. Chem. Engrs., Fertilizer Inst. (dir.). Lutheran. Clubs: Butler Nat. (Oak Brook, Ill.). Patentee in field. Home: 631 Thompsons Way Palatine IL 60067-4653 Office: 141 W Jackson Blvd Chicago IL 60604-2904

VRADENBURG, GEORGE, III, lawyer, corporate executive. AB cum laude, Oberlin Coll., 1964; LLB cum laude, Harvard U., 1967. Bar: N.Y. 1968. Former sr. v.p., gen. counsel, sec. CBS Inc., N.Y.C.; now exec. v.p. Fox, Inc., L.A. Mem. Phi Beta Kappa. Office: Fox Inc 10201 W Pico Blvd Bldg 88 Los Angeles CA 90064-2606

VRANA, VERLON KENNETH, professional society administrator, conservationist; b. Seward, Nebr., June 25, 1925; s. Anton and Florence

(Walker) V.; m. Elaine Janet Flowerday, June 5, 1949; children: Verlon Rodney, Timothy James, Carolyn Elaine, Jon David. Student, U. Nebr., 1959-62; BBA, George Washington U., 1967, MBA, 1970; mgmt. course, Harvard U., 1979. Field technician Soil Conservation Svc., USDA, Seward, 1948-58; watershed planner, cons. Soil Conservation Svc., USDA, Lincoln, Nebr., 1958-62; mem. pers. staff Soil Conservation Svc., USDA, Washington, 1962-72, dir. pers. div., 1972-76, asst. adminstr. for mgmt., 1976-79, assoc. dep. chief for adminstrn., 1979-80; chief planning div. Nebr. Natural Resources Com., Lincoln, 1980-88; owner-farmer Blue Ridge Farm, Seward, 1980-89; exec. v.p. Soil and Water Conservation Soc., Ankeny, Iowa, 1989-91; pres. Vrana Assocs., Seward, Nebr., 1992—; bd. dirs. sec. N.E. Natural Resources Dist., York, Nebr., 1988-89; bd. dirs. Watershed Coalition, Denver, Groundwater Policy Edn. Project, Mpls., Cattle Nat. Bank, Seward; alt. dir. Renewable Natural Resources Foun., Washington, 1989-91. Contbr. articles to jours. in field. Mem. Com. on Ministry Presbyn. Ch. U.S.A., 1986-89, elder, 1970—; vice moderator Homestead Presbytery, 1989; treas. Nebr. Soil and Water Conservation Found., 1992—. Recipient N.E. Centennial Grass Seeding award N.E. Centennial Commn., Lincoln, 1967, N.E. Soil Steward award N.E. Natural Resources Commn., Lincoln, 1986. Fellow Soil and Water Conservation Soc. (pres. N.E. Coun. 1986, Presdl. citation 1989), Isaac Walton League (dir. Seward chpt. 1984-89), Nat. Wildlife Fedn. (soil conservationist of yr. award 1987), Seward Grange (officer 1984-89), Shriner. Home and Office: Vrana Assocs 131 N 1st St Seward NE 68434-2130

VRANCKEN, ROBERT DANLOY, facilities management educator; b. Charleston, W.Va., June 28, 1936; s. Roger Joseph and Kathryn Elizabeth (Toben) V.; children: Robert, Brett, Paige, Mark. BFA, U. Notre Dame, 1958, MBA, 1984; PhD in Facilities Mgmt., Union Inst., 1992. Cert. facilities mgr. Designer Stone & Thomas, Wheeling, W.Va., 1962-63; pvt. practice in designing Wheeling, W.Va., 1962-63; asst. to pres. Lederman Elevator Co., Detroit, 1963-66; mgr. facilities planning and design Sperry Univac, Blue Bell, Pa., 1966-82; assoc. prof. mgmt. Grand Valley State U., Grand Rapids, Mich., 1982—; cons. space planning facilities design and mgmt., W.Va., Mich., Pa., 1963—; active Ops. Mgmt. Edn. Rsch. Found. Mem. Internat. Facilities Mgmt. Assn. (Educator of Yr. 1986), Nat. Assn. Corp. Real Estate Execs., Work Place Environment Group, Indsl. Devel. Rsch. Coun., Notre Dame Club. Roman Catholic. Avocations: sailing, carpentry, tennis, singing. Office: Grand Valley State U 301 W Fulton St Grand Rapids MI 49504-6430

VRATIL, KATHRYN HOEFER, federal judge; b. Manhattan, Kans., Apr. 21, 1949; d. John J. and Kathryn Ruth (Fryer) Hoefer; children: Alison K., John A., Ashley A. BA, U. Kans., 1971, JD, 1975; postgrad., Exeter U., 1971-72. Bar: Kans. 1975, U.S. Dist. Ct. Kans. 1975, Mo. 1978, U.S. Dist. Ct. (we. dist.) Mo. 1978, U.S. Ct. Appeals (8th cir.) 1978, U.S. Ct. Appeals (10th cir.) 1980, U.S. Ct. Appeals (11th cir.) 1983, U.S. Dist. Ct. (ea. dist.) Mo. 1985. Law clk. U.S. Dist. Ct., Kansas City, Kans., 1975-78; assoc. Lathrop Koontz & Norquist, Kansas City, Mo., 1978-83; ptnr. Lathrop & Norquist, Kansas City, 1984-92; judge City of Prairie Village, Kans., 1991-92; bd. dirs. Kans. Legal Svcs. Bd. editors Kans. Law Rev., 1974-75, Jour. Kans. Bar Assn., 1992—. Mem. Kansas City Tomorrow (XIV); bd. trustees, shepherd-deacon Village Presbyn. Ch.; nat. adv. bd. U. Kans. Ctr. for Environ. Edn. and Tng., 1993—. Fellow Kans. Bar Found., Am. Bar Found.; mem. ABA, Am. Judicature Soc., Nat. Assn. Judges, Fed. Judges Assn., Kans. Bar Assn., Mo. Bar Assn., Kansas City Met. Area Bar Assn., Wyandotte County Bar Assn., Johnson County Bar Assn., Assn. Women Lawyers, Lawyers Assn. Kansas City, Supreme Ct. Hist. Soc., Kans. State Hist. Soc., U. Kans. Law Soc. (bd. govs. 1978-81), Kans. U. Alumni Assn. (mem. devel. com. 1985—, mem. Kansas City chpt. alumni bd. 1990-92, nat. bd. dirs. 1991—, bd. govs. Adams alumni ctr. 1992—, mem. learned club 1992—, mem. chancellor's club 1993—, mem. Williams ednl. fund 1993—, mem. Jayhawks for higher edn. 1993—), Homestead Country Club Prairie Village (pres.), Sons and Daus. of Kans. (life), Rotary, Jr. League Wyandotte and Johnson Counties, Kans. State Hist. Soc., Supreme Ct. Hist. Soc., Order of Coif, Kans. Inn. of Ct. (master 1993—), Overland Park Rotary, Univ. Club, Phi Kappa Phi. Republican. Presbyterian. Avocations: cycling, sailing. Office: 511 US Courthouse 500 State Ave Kansas City KS 66101

VRECHEK, GEORGE GERALD, architectural firm executive; b. Chgo., May 21, 1945. BBA, U. Mich., 1967, MBA, 1968. CPA. Small bus. audit mgr. Arthur Andersen & Co., Chgo., 1967-77; v.p., treas. Harry Weese Assocs., Chgo., 1977-92, prin., 1992—. Prin. works include West Millbrook, Millbrook, Ill., River Cottages, Chgo., Donohue Bldg./Printing House Row, Chgo., Mt. Carmel High Sch., Chgo., St. Viator High Sch., St. Francis Xavier, Wilmette, Ill., Dominican Conf. Ctr., River Forest, Ill., Fenwick High Sch., Oak Park, Ill., Holy Name Cathedral Sch./Old St. Patrick's Sch., Chgo., others. Bd. trustees Fenwick High Sch., Oak Park, Ill., 1979—, chmn., 1985-87, chmn. fin. com., 1978-84, chmn. facilities com., 1989—; bd. dirs. Frank Lloyd Wright Home and Studio Found., Oak Park, 1980-82, Evans Scholarship Found. Alumni, 1989—; vice chmn. Oak Park Police Pension Bd., 1975-82; mem. finance com. St. Giles Parish, Oak Park, 1989—, Cath. Charities, 1994—; past pres. Unity Temple Restoration Found., Oak Park, 1991-93. Mem. AIA (Chgo. chpt.), Profl. Svcs. Mgmt. Assn. (meeting chmn. 1992—), Lambda Alpha Internat. Office: Harry Weese Assoc Arch Inc 10 W Hubbard Chicago IL 60610

VREDENBURG, DWIGHT CHARLES, retired supermarket chain executive; b. Lamoni, Iowa, Jan. 17, 1914; s. David Milton and Kate Emelyn (Putnam) V.; m. Ruth Irene Taylor, Apr. 25, 1937; children: John, Martha Vredenburg Kraklow, Charles. Student, Graceland Coll., 1931-34, LLD, 1988; BS in Commerce, U. Iowa, 1935. Store mgr. Hy-Vee Food Stores Inc., Chariton, Iowa, 1935-38, pres., from 1938, chief exec. officer, 1978-89; chmn. Hy-Vee Food Stores Inc., Chariton, Iowa, 1978-89; pres. Chariton Storage Co.; pres., dir. Iamo Realty Co. Served with USCGR, 1942-44. Named Citizen of Yr., 1965-66. Mem. Masons, Shriners, Des Moines Club. Home: RR 5 Box 217 Chariton IA 50049-9804

VREDEVOE, DONNA LOU, research immunologist, microbiologist, educator; b. Ann Arbor, Mich., Jan. 11, 1938; d. Lawrence E. and Verna (Brower) V.; m. John Porter, Aug. 22, 1962; 1 child, Verna. B.A. in Bacteriology, UCLA, 1959, Ph.D. in Microbiology (Univ. fellow, USPHS fellow), 1963. USPHS postdoctoral fellow Stanford U., 1963-64; instr. bacteriology UCLA, 1963, postgrad. research immunologist dept. surgery Center Health Scis., 1964-65, asst. research immunologist dept. surgery Center Health Scis., 1964-67; asst. prof. Sch. Nursing, Center Health Scis., 1967-70, assoc. prof., 1970-76, prof., 1976—, assoc. dean Sch. Nursing, 1976-78, acting assoc. dean Sch. Nursing., 1985-86, asst. dir. space planning Cancer Center, 1976-78, dir. space planning, 1978-90, cons. to lab. nuclear medicine and radiation biology, 1967-80; acting dean Sch. Nursing Center Health Scis., 1995—. Contbr. articles to profl. publs. Postdoctoral fellow USPHS, 1963-64; Mabel Wilson Richards scholar UCLA, 1960-61; research grantee including Am. Cancer Soc.; Calif. Inst. Cancer Research; Calif. div. Am. Cancer Soc.; USPHS; Am. Nurses Found.; Cancer Research Coordinating Com. U. Calif.; Dept. Energy. Mem. Am. Soc. Microbiology, Am. Assn. Immunologists, Am. Assn. Cancer Research, Nat. League Nursing (2d v.p. 1979-81), Sigma Xi, Alpha Gamma Sigma, Sigma Theta Tau (nat. hon. mem.). Home: 355 21st Pl Santa Monica CA 90402-2503 Office: U Calif Sch Nursing Los Angeles CA 90024-6918

VREE, ROGER ALLEN, lawyer; b. Chgo., Oct. 2, 1943; s. Louis Gerard and Ruby June (Boersma) V.; m. Lauren Trumbull Gartside, Mar. 29, 1969; children: Jonathan Todd, Matthew David. BA, Wheaton Coll., 1965; MA, Stanford U., 1966, JD, 1969. Bar: Ill. 1969, U.S. Dist. Ct. (no. dist.) Ill. 1969. Assoc. Sidley & Austin, Chgo., 1969-75, ptnr., 1975—. Mem. ABA, Ill. Bar Assn., Chgo. Bar Assn., Law Club, Legal Club. Club: Caxton Club (Chgo.); University (Chgo.). Office: Sidley & Austin 1 First Nat Plz Chicago IL 60603

VROOM, VICTOR HAROLD, management consultant, educator; b. Montreal, Que., Can., Aug. 9, 1932; s. Harold Heard and Avice May (Brown) V.; m. Ann Louise Workman, June 12, 1956 (div. June 3, 1989); children: Derek Alan, Jeffrey James; m. Julia Ann Francis, Dec. 27, 1989; children: Tristan, Alexander. B.Sc., McGill U. Montreal, 1953, M.Sc., 1955; Ph.D., U. Mich., 1958; M.A. (hon.), Yale, 1972. Lectr., study dir. U. Mich., Ann Arbor, 1958-60; asst. prof. psychology U. Pa., Phila., 1960-63; asso. prof.

psychology and indsl. adminstrn. Carnegie-Mellon U., Pitts., 1963-66; prof. Carnegie-Mellon U., 1966-72; John G. Searle prof. orgn. and mgmt. Yale U., 1972—. Author: Work and Motivation, 1964, Leadership and Decision-Making, 1973, The New Leadership, 1988. Recipient Ford Found. Doctoral Dissertation award, 1958-59; McKinsey Found. research design award, 1967; Fulbright lectr. U.K., 1967-68. Fellow APA (James McKeen Cattell award 1970), APS Acad. Mgmt. Office: Yale U PO Box 1A New Haven CT 06520-8200

VUCANOVICH, BARBARA FARRELL, congresswoman; b. Fort Dix, N.J., June 22, 1921; d. Thomas F. and Ynez (White) Farrell; m. Ken Dillon, Mar. 8, 1950 (div. 1964); children: Patty Dillon Cafferata, Mike, Ken, Tom, Susan Dillon Stoddard; m. George Vucanovich, June 19, 1965. Student, Manhattanville Coll. of Sacred Heart, 1938-39. Owner, operator Welcome Aboard Travel, Reno, 1968-74; Nev. rep. for Senator Paul Laxalt, 1974-82; mem. 98th-104th Congresses from 2d Nev. dist., 1983—; chmn. appropriations subcom. on military construction. Pres. Nev. Fedn. Republican Women, Reno, 1955-56; former pres. St. Mary's Hosp. Guild, Lawyer's Wives. Roman Catholic. Club: Hidden Valley Country (Reno). Office: 2202 Rayburn House of Representatives Washington DC 20515*

VUCKOVICH, DRAGOMIR MICHAEL, neurologist, educator; b. Bileca, Herzegovina, Yugoslavia, Oct. 27, 1927; came to U.S., 1957; s. Alexander John and Anka Mia (Ivanisevich) V.; m. Brenda Mary Luther, Aug. 23, 1958; children: John, Nicholas, Adrian. M.D., U. Birmingham, Eng., 1953. Diplomate Am. Bd. Psychiatry and Neurology, Am. Bd. Pediatrics. Intern United Birmingham Hosps., Eng., 1953-54, resident in pediatrics, 1954-55; resident med. officer Princess Beatrice Hosp., London, 1955; sr. resident Hosp. for Sick Children, London, 1955; sr. resident in neurology Atkinson Morley br. St. George's Hosp., London, 1955-56; resident in neurology Nat. Hosp. Queens Sq., London, 1956-57, VA Hosp., Chgo., 1958-59; resident in psychiatry Wesley Meml. Hosp., Chgo., 1959-60; fellow in neurology Northwestern U. Med. Sch., Chgo., 1960; resident in pediatrics Children's Meml. Hosp., Chgo., 1961; asst. prof. neurology, psychiatry and pediatrics Northwestern U. Med. Ctr., Chgo., 1967-70; assoc. clin. prof. neurology and pediatrics Stritch Sch. Medicine, Chgo., 1970-77, clin. prof. neurology and pediatrics, 1977-93; chmn. Columbus Hosp., Chgo., 1981-88; chief of neurology svc. N. Chgo. VAMC, 1992-94; prof. neurology and pediatrics Finch U. Health Sch. Chgo. Med. Sch., 1994—; dir. EEG Lab. Columbus Hosp., Chgo., 1969-89, chief neurology and psychiatry, 1971-81; chief of child neurology Loyola U., Maywood, Ill., 1970-79; cons. Trinity House, 1988-92; acting chmn. neurology FUHS/CMS, 1993—; program dir. neurology residency program FUHS/CMS affiliated hosp., 1993—. Coauthor: Psychoanalysis and the Two Cerebral Hemispheres, 1983; contbr., co-author: articles in field to profl. jours. Lt. col. MC, USAR, 1983-87. Decorated Army Achievement medal, Army Commendation medal, 1986; recipient Physician Recognition award AMA, 1971; named Best Attending Physician Med. House Staff, Columbus Hosp., 1979. Fellow Am. Acad. Pediatrics, Am. Acad. Neurology, Royal Soc. Health Eng.; mem. Am. Med. Electroencephalographic Assn., Profs. of Child Neurology, Cen. Neuropsychiat. Assn. Republican. Serbian Orthodox. Clubs: Beefeaters (N.Y.C.); Les Gourmet's (Chgo.). Avocations: music, reading, writing, tennis, swimming. Office: Neurosci Ctr Ste C8 825 S Waukegan Rd Lake Forest IL 60045

VUILLEUMIER, FRANCOIS, curator; b. Berne, Switzerland, Nov. 26, 1938; came to U.S., 1961; s. Willy Georges and Denise Geneviève (Privat) V.; m. Bonita Rae Johnson, 1972 (div. 1981); children: Alexis Brendan, Claire Anne; m. Rebecca Branch Finnell, Feb. 26, 1983; 1 child, Isabelle Finnell. Licence es sciences, U. Geneva, Switzerland, 1961; PhD, Harvard U., 1967. Instr. U Mass., Boston, 1966-67, asst. prof., 1967-70, assoc. prof., 1971; prof. U. Lausanne, Switzerland, 1971-72; sr. researcher Marine Biol. Sta., Roscoff, France, 1972-73; assoc. curator Am. Mus. Natural History, N.Y.C., 1974-79, curator, 1979—; dir. Inst. Animal Ecology, U. Lausanne, 1971-72; vis. prof. U. Paris, 1973-74, U. of the Andes, Mérida, Venezuela, 1981; chmn. Dept. Ornithology, Chapman Fund, Am. Mus. Natural History, 1987-92. Author: High Altitude Tropical Biogeography, 1986; contbr. 185 articles to jours. in field. Chapman fellow Am. Mus., 1967-68. Fellow Am. Ornithologists Union; mem. French Ornithol. Soc. (hon.), Soc. for Study of Evolution. Avocations: painting, reading, foreign languages, cooking. Office: Am Mus Natural History Central Pk West at 79th St W New York NY 10024

VUITTON, HENRY-LOUIS, designer; b. Asnieres, Seine, France, Aug. 10, 1911; s. Gaston-Louis and Renee (Versillé) V.; m. Josette Rateau, Oct. 15, 1935; children: Colette (Mrs. Jacques Novatin), Philippe-Louis (dec.), Daniele (Mrs. Philippe Masson). Student, Cours Saint-Louis, Paris. Comml. dir. Vuitton et Vuitton, Paris, 1945-75, pres. bd. mgrs., 1975-77; pres. bd. insps. Louis Vuitton (S.A.). Author: La Malle aux Souvenirs. Decorated officer Order Nat. of Merit France; Grande Medaille d'Or du Travail; recipient Silver medal City of Paris. Office: 54 Ave Montaigue, 75008 Paris France

VULGAMORE, MELVIN L., college president; b. Springfield, Ohio, July 19, 1935; s. Leo Beeman and Della Marie (McCoy) V.; m. Ethelanne Oyer, Feb. 17, 1957; children: Allison Beth, Sarah Faith Vulgamore Evans. B.A. with honors, Ohio Wesleyan U., 1957; B.D., Harvard U., 1960; Ph.D., Boston U., 1963. Chmn., prof. religion Ohio Wesleyan U., Delaware, 1962-78, assoc. dean faculty, 1972-73, dean acad. affairs, 1973-78; v.p., provost U. Richmond, Va., 1978-83; pres. Albion Coll., Mich., 1983—; vis. prof. Am. U. Beirut, 1971-72; dir. Chem. Bank. Contbr. articles to profl. jours. Trustee Howe Mil. Sch., Ind., 1984—; mem. Mich. Coun. for Humanities, 1985-89. Mem. Am. Acad. Religion, Tillich Soc. N.Am., Phi Beta Kappa, Omicron Delta Kappa, Delta Sigma Rho, Pi Sigma Alpha. Club: Detroit Athletic. Lodge: Rotary. Avocations: bicycling, classical music, antique collecting and refinishing. Home: 1620 Van Wert Rd Albion MI 49224-9743 Office: Albion Coll Office of Pres Albion MI 49224

VUONO, CARL E., army officer; b. Monongahela, Pa., Oct. 18, 1934. BS in Engring., U. S. Mil. Acad., 1957; MS in Pub. Adminstrn., Shippensburg State Coll., 1973. Commd. 2d lt. U.S. Army, 1957, advanced through grades to gen. Roman Catholic. Home: 5796 Westchester St Alexandria VA 22310-1146

VYAS, CHAND BHAOURBHAI, coal company executive; b. Bombay, India, Oct. 2, 1944; s. Bhanubbhai and Dolar (Bhatt) V.; m. Debra Elaine Dellget, Apr. 6, 1974; children: Aaron, Christin. B of Commerce, Bombay U., 1966; MBA in Fin., Atlanta U., 1969. Div. contr. Consolidation Coal Co., 1974-75, regional contr., 1976-81; treas. Zeigler Coal Co., Des Plaines, Ill., 1982-84; sr. v.p. fin., adminstrn. Zeigler Coal Co., Fairview Heights, Ill., 1985—, sr. v.p., 1988—; bd. dirs. Zeigler Coal Holding Co., Fairview Heights, 1985—, Zeigler Coal Co., Fairview Heights, 1985—, Jefferson Oil and Gas Co., Fairview Heights, Ill.,1985—;mem. exec. com. Zeigler Coal Co., Fairview Heights, 1985—. Contbr. articles to profl. jours. Mem. Ill. Coal Assn. (tax com.), Nat. Coal Assn., Nat. Assn. of Accts., Ind. Exec. Program (dir. adv. bd.). Avocations: golf, gardening, tennis. Office: Zeigler Coal Co 50 Jerome Ln Fairview Heights IL 62208

VYAS, GIRISH NARMADASHANKAR, virologist, immunohematologist; b. Aglod, India, June 11, 1933; came to U.S., 1965, naturalized, 1973; s. Narmadashankar P. and Rukshmani A. (Joshi) V.; m. Devi Ratilal Trivedi, Apr. 3, 1962; children: Jay, Shrikrishna. B.Sc., U. Bombay, 1954, M.Sc., 1956, Ph.D., 1964. Postdoctoral fellow Western Res. U., 1965-66; mem. faculty U. Calif., San Francisco, 1967—, chief blood bank, 1969-88; prof. lab. medicine U. Calif., 1977—; dir. transfusion rsch. program, 1985—; WHO cons., S.E. Asia, 1980; cons. in field; mem. com. viral hepatitis NRC, 1974-76; mem. task force blood processing Nat. Heart and Lung Inst., 1972-73; sci. program com. Am. Assn. Blood Banks, 1971-76; com. immunoglobulin allotypes WHO, 1974—; mem. U.S. del. immunologists to Romania and Hungary, 1980; mem. FDA com. on blood and blood products, 1987-92; cons. to VA on med. rsch., 1985, UN Devel. Program in India, 1986; and others; chmn. Transmed Biotech Inc., South San Francisco, 1989-95. Author: Hepatitis and Blood Transfusion, 1972, Laboratory Diagnosis of Immunological Disorders, 1975, Membrane Structure and Function of Human Blood Cells, 1976, Viral Hepatitis, 1978, Viral Hepatitis and Liver Disease, 1984, Use and Standardization of Chemically Defined Antigens,

1986; also research papers. Recipient Julliard prize Internat. Soc. Blood Transfusion, 1969; named Outstanding Immigrant in Bay Area Communities Mayor of Oakland, Calif., 1969; Fulbright scholar France, 1980. Mem. AAAS, Am. Soc. Hematology (chmn. com. on transfusion medicine 1989-90), Am. Assn. Immunologists, Am. Soc. Clin. Pathologists, Internat. Assn. for Biol. Standarization (coun. 1992—). Democrat. Hindu. Office: U Calif Lab Med S-555 San Francisco CA 94143-0134 *Truth alone wins. Truth in our actions manifests beauty in character. Beauty in character brings harmony into the home. Harmony in the home produces order in our society. Order in our society leads to peace in the nation. And peace in the nation can win for us universal prosperity and happiness for mankind, only if individuals practice truth in their actions.*

VYKUKAL, EUGENE LAWRENCE, wholesale drug company executive; b. Caldwell, Tex., June 26, 1929; s. Henry J. and Anna P. (Polansky) V.; m. Judith Anderson, Jan. 1, 1977; children—Anna K., Mark Roman, Laura Roman, Gene. B.S. in Pharmacy, U. Tex., Austin, 1952. Pharmacist Scarborough's Pharmacy, Baytown, Tex., 1952-53; pharmacist Gene Vykukal's Pharmacy, Clifton, Tex., 1953-57; with Southwestern Drug Corp. (name now Bergen Brunswig Drug Co.), 1957-86; gen. sales mgr. Southwestern Drug Corp., Dallas, 1966-67; v.p., dir. sales Southwestern Drug Corp., 1967-75, exec. v.p., dir. sales, 1975-81, exec. v.p., 1980-81, pres., chief exec. officer, 1981-86, vice chmn., 1985-86, dir., 1966-86; asst. dean for devel., lectr. Coll. Pharmacy U. Tex., Austin, 1991—, mem. adv. coun. Pharm. Found., chmn., 1978—; sr. v.p. profl. affairs Bergen Brunswig Corp., Bergen Brunswig Drug Co., 1986—. Mem. centennial endowment com. U. Tex., 1980—; bd. dirs. Baylor U. Med. Center Found., Dallas; mem. indsl. adv. coun. Coll. Pharmacy, U. Ky., 1990—. Recipient Disting. Alumni award U. Tex. Coll. Pharmacy, 1979, William J. Sheffield Disting. Alumni award U. Tex. at Austin Coll. Pharmacy, 1987. Mem. Nat. Wholesale Druggists Assn. (chmn. sales mgmt. com. 1972-73, dir. 1980—, chmn. bd. 1985-86, 1st vice chmn. 1983—, chmn. exec. com. 1987—, Timothy Barry award 1990), Am. Pharm. Assn., Tex. Pharm. Assn. (long range planning com. 1983—), Wholesale Druggist Assn. Tex. (pres. 1978-79), Drug Travelers Assn. Tex. (pres. 1977-78), Sales and Mktg. Execs. Dallas (dir. 1971-72). Roman Catholic. Office: U Tex Coll Pharmacy Pharmacy Bldg Austin TX 78712-1074 *The quality of life in our great country has been enhanced by the tremendous strides made in our health care delivery system over the past three decades. To have served in the pharmaceutical segment has been very rewarding.*

WAAGE, MERVIN BERNARD, lawyer; b. Spirit Lake, Iowa, May 12, 1944; s. Bernard and Pearl Peterson W.; m. Eileen Barbara Waage, Feb. 17, 1947; children: Love Lee, Mark Warren. BA, Northwestern Coll., Roseville Minn., 1966; MDiv, Southwestern Sem., 1969; JD, So. Methodist U., 1974. Bar: Tex., 1974, U.S. Dist Ct. (no. dist.) Tex. 1974, U.S. Dist. Ct. (ea. dist.) Tex. 1976, U.S. Supreme Ct. 1977, U.S. Tax Ct. 1978, U.S. Ct. Claims, 1978, U.S. Dist. Ct. (we. dist) Tex. 1988, U.S. Ct. Appeals (5th cir.) 1989. Asst. dist. atty. Denton County (Tex.) Atty.'s Office, 1974-76; pvt. practice law Denton, Tex., 1977—; bankruptcy trustee, 1980-87. Mem. Tex. Bar Assn., Tex. State Bar (bankruptcy com.), Tex. Bd. Legal Specialization (cert. in consumer bankruptcy 1986, cert. in bus. bankruptcy 1988). Republican. Baptist. Avocations: singing, jogging, camping. Home: 107 Lexington Ln Denton TX 76205-5473 Office: Waage & Waage LLP 8350 S Stemmons St Denton TX 76205-2402

WAALAND, IRVING THEODORE, retired aerospace engineer; b. Bklyn., July 2, 1927; s. Trygve and Marie Waaland; m. Helen Rita Katz, Apr. 7, 1961; children: Theodore, Neil, Elizabeth, Scott, Diane. B of Aero. Engring. magna cum laude, NYU, 1953. Project engr. Grumman Corp., Bethpage, N.Y., 1953-74; v.p., chief designer Northrop Corp., Pico Rivera, Calif., 1974-93. Patentee in field. With USAF, 1946-48. Fellow AIAA (Aircraft Design award 1989, Aircraft Design cert. merit 1989, Wright Bros. lectr. in Aeronautics 1991); mem. NAE, Am. Def. Preparedness Assn. (Leslie E Simon award 1990), SAE (Aerospace Engring. Leadership award 1993). Home: 65 Rollingwood Dr Palos Verdes Peninsula CA 90274-2425

WAAS, LES, advertising executive; b. Phila., May 18, 1931; s. Lester Leonard and Alice (Maybaum) W.; m. Sylvia Wasserman; children: Sherri, Murray. Dir. advt. M&H Sport Stores, Phila., 1947-49; creative dir. J. Cunningham Cox, Phila., 1950-52, J. Dugan Agy., Phila., 1952-55; pres. Waas Inc., Phila., 1956—; owner New Sounds, Huntingdon Valley, Pa., 1958—; chief exec. officer Mother's Whistler, Huntingdon Valley, Pa., 1975—. Contbr. articles on procrastination to mags.; appeared on numerous TV shows. Pres., v.p., bd. dirs. Muscular Dystrophy Assn., Phila., 1949-85; candidate for Pa. State House, Montgomery/Bucks Counties, Pa., 1980. Served to 1st lt. USAF, 1942-46. Recipient awards TV/Radio Advt. Club, 1985—, ADDY award Phila. Club Advt. Women, 1986; One Show award The One Club, 1987. Mem. Broadcast Pioneers (pres. 1972-73, Pioneer award 1986), Procrastinators' Club Am. (pres. 1956—). Avocations: flying, jogging, art, music. Office: 1111 Broad Locust Bldg Philadelphia PA 19102

WABLER, ROBERT CHARLES, II, retail and distribution executive; b. Dayton, Ohio, Dec. 14, 1948; s. Robert Charles Sr. and Eileen Marie (Langen) W.; m. Linda Adele Rayburn; 1 child, Robert Charles III. BS in Acctg. cum laude, U. Dayton, 1971; MS in Acctg. magna cum laude, U. Ga., 1976. Sr. auditor Touche Ross and Co., Dayton, 1971-73; internal auditor So. Company Services, Atlanta, 1974-75; acctg. mgr. Rich's div. Federated Dept. Stores, Atlanta, 1976-77; dir. auditing Munford, Inc., Atlanta, 1977-81, v.p., controller, 1982-83, v.p. fin. analyses, 1983-86; sr. v.p. adminstrn. World Bazaar div. Munford, Inc., Atlanta, 1981-82, sr. v.p. fin., 1986-89; sr. v.p. fin. and adminstrn., sec. The Athlete's Foot Group, Inc., Atlanta, 1989-93; exec. v.p., CFO, treas. Just for Feet Inc., Birmingham, Ala., 1993—. Author: The Minimum Expenses Needed Technique, 1985. Mem. AICPA, Ga. Soc. CPAs, Inst. Internal Auditors, Assn. Systems Mgmt., EDP Auditor Assn. (bd. dirs. 1978-79). Home: 1541 Fairway View Dr Hoover AL 35244 Office: Just For Feet Inc 3000 Riverchase Galleria Ste 990 Birmingham AL 35244

WACHAL, ROBERT STANLEY, linguistics educator, consultant; b. Omaha, Mar. 13, 1929; s. Stanley William and Marie Frances (Rokusek) W.; m. Jane McCune, Sept. 15, 1968. B.A., U. Minn., 1952; M.S., U. Wis., 1959, Ph.D., 1966. Tchr. Mound Sch. Dist., Minn., 1955-59; faculty mem. U. Iowa, Iowa City, 1964—; prof. linguistics, 1975—, chmn. dept., 1975-81; cons. Am. Coll. Testing Program, Iowa City, 1981—, NSF, Washington, 1975—, Can. Council, Ottawa, Ont., 1975—, Nat. Endowment for Humanities, N.Y.C., 1978; mem. editorial advisory com. American Speech, 1988—. Fulbright prof. Athens, Greece, 1966-67; research grantee U.S. Office Naval Research, 1969-72, Can. Med. Research Council Victoria, B.C., 1967-74. Fellow Acad. Aphasia; mem. Linguistics Soc. Am., Am. Dialect Soc., Am. Assn. Applied Linguistics, Dictionary Soc. of N.Am. Home: 8 Woodland Heights NE Iowa City IA 52240-9136 Office: U Iowa Linguistics Dept Iowa City IA 52242

WACHENFELD, TIMOTHY H., aeronautical engineering executive. Gen. mgr. Gen. Electric Aircraft Engines, Cin. Recipient Leadership in Quality Mgmt. award AIAA, 1994. Office: BE Aircraft Engines 1 Neumann Way PO Box 156301 J101 Cincinnati OH 45215-6301*

WACHENFELD, WILLIAM THOMAS, lawyer, foundation executive; b. Orange, N.J., Feb. 9, 1926; s. William A. and Ann (Weir) W.; children: William S., Robin A., John C. A.B., Tufts U., 1947; LL.B., Duke U., 1950. Bar: N.J. 1949. Since practiced in Newark; mem. firm Lum, Biunno & Tompkins, 1957-58; pres. Charles Hayden Found., N.Y.C., 1956—; prof. law Jersey City div. Rutgers U., 1954-56; v.p., assoc. gen. counsel Prudential Ins. Co. Am., 1965-84; of counsel Tompkins, McGuire & Wachenfeld, Newark, 1984—. Pres. Essex County Park Commn., 1960-65, Newark Acad., 1972-80; commr. pub. affairs, Orange, 1956-58; mem. N.J. Econ. Devel. Coun., 1980-88, 91-94; bd. govs. N.J. Hist. Soc., 1983; mem. adv. bd. N.Y. Zool. Soc., 1983-93; trustee Liberty Sci. Ctr., 1988-93. Fellow Am. Bar Found.; mem. ABA, N.J. Bar Assn., Essex County Bar Assn., N.Y. Regional Assn. Grantmakers (bd. dirs. 1992—), Eastward Ho Country Club, HC Yacht Club (commodore 1992—). Home: 40 Windsor Pl Essex Fells NJ 07021-1711 Office: Tompkins McGuire & Wachenfeld 4 Gateway Ctr 100 Mulberry St Newark NJ 07102-4004

WACHMAN, MARVIN, university chancellor; b. Milw., Mar. 24, 1917; s. Alex and Ida (Epstein) W.; m. Adeline Lillian Schpok, Apr. 12, 1942; children: Kathleen M., Lynn A. B.S., Northwestern U., 1939, M.A., 1940; Ph.D., U. Ill., 1942; LLD (hon.), Pa. U., 1964, Lincoln (Pa.) U., 1970, Del. Valley Coll. Sci. and Agr., 1973, Med. Coll. Pa., 1982, Bloomfield Coll., 1987, Albright Coll., 1991; DHL (hon.), Gratz Coll., 1973; LittD (hon.), Jewish Theol. Sem., 1974, Drexel U., 1980; LHD (hon.), Colgate U., 1975, Widener U., 1976 (hon.), Thomas Jefferson U., 1980. Asst. in history U. Ill., 1940-42; instr. Biarritz Am. U., Biarritz, France, 1945-46; vis. asst. prof. San Diego State Coll., summer 1948, U. Minn., 1950; assoc. prof. history U. Md. in Europe, 1952-53; from instr. to prof. Colgate U., 1946-61, dir. upper class core program, 1956-61; pres. Lincoln (Pa.) U., 1961-70; v.p. acad. affairs Temple U., 1970-73, pres., 1973-82, chancellor, 1982—, Dir. Salzburg Seminar in Am. Studies, 1958-60, pres. Pa. Higher Edn. Assistance Agy., 1989; acting pres. Phila. Coll. of Textiles & Scis., 1991; pres. Albright Coll., 1991-92; past chmn. Nat. Ctr. for Higher Edn. Mgmt. Sys.; specialist in Africa for State Dept., 1965, 68; mem. adv. coun. World Learning, Inc.; mem. Colgate Nat. Coun., Phila. Com. Fgn. Rels.; dir., chair Tech. Specialists; dir. emeritus Germantown Ins. Co. Author: History of Social-Democratic Party of Milwaukee, 1897-1910, 1945; contbr. articles to profl. jours. and newspapers, also chpts. in books. Mem. bd. overseers Coll. V.I.; hon. trustee Albright Coll.; hon. life trustee Temple U.; trustee Cheyney U.; trustee, chmn. Phila. Coll. Textiles and Sci.; vice chair Fgn. Policy Rsch. Inst.; trustee emeritus Balch Inst. Ethnic Studies; mem. adv. coun. Greater Phila. Urban Affairs Coalition, World Affairs Coun.; mem. bd. mgrs. Phila. Found.; bd. dirs. Fund for Open Soc., Operation Understanding; hon. dir. Phila. Contributorship; alumni regent Phila. area Northwestern U. With AUS, 1942-46. Mem. NAACP, Am. Studies Assn. (past mem. exec. com.), AAUP (past pres. Colgate U. chpt.), Am. Hist. Assn., ACLU, Pa. Assn. Colls. and Univs. (past chmn., pres. 1993), Phi Beta Kappa. Office: Temple U Philadelphia PA 19122

WACHNER, LINDA JOY, apparel marketing and manufacturing executive; b. N.Y.C., Feb. 3, 1946; d. Herman and Shirley W.; m. Seymour Applebaum, Dec. 21, 1973 (dec. 1983). BS in Econs. and Bus., U. Buffalo, 1966. Buyer Foley's Federated Dept. Store, Houston, 1968-69; sr. buyer R.H. Macy's, N.Y.C., 1969-74; v.p. Warner divsn. Warnaco, Bridgeport, Conn., 1974-77; v.p. corp. mktg. Caron Internat., N.Y.C., 1977-79; chief exec. officer U.S. divsn. Max Factor & Co., Hollywood, Calif., 1979-82, pres., chief exec. officer, 1982-83; pres., chief exec. officer Max Factor & Co. Worldwide, 1983-84; mng. dir. Adler & Shaykin, N.Y.C., 1985-86; owner, pres., CEO, chmn. Warnaco Inc., N.Y.C., 1986—; chmn., CEO Authentic Fitness Corp., 1991—; bd. dirs. The Travellers, Inc., Castle & Cooke Homes, Inc. Presdl. appointee Adv. Com. for Trade, Policy, Negotiations; trustee U. Buffalo Found., Carnegie Hall, Aspen Inst. Recipient Silver Achievement award L.A. YWCA; named Outstanding Woman in Bus. Women's Equity Action League, 1980, Woman of Yr., MS. Mag., 1986, one of the Yr.'s Most Fascinating Bus. People, Fortune Mag., 1986, one of 10 Most Powerful Women in Corp. Am., Savvy Woman Mag., 1989, 90, Am.'s Most Successful Bus. Woman, Fortune Mag., 1992, Queen of Cash Flow, Chief Exec. Mag., 1994. Mem. Young Pres.'s Orgn., Am. Mgmt. Assn., Am. Apparel Mktg. Assn. (bd. dirs.), Bus. Roundtable. Republican. Jewish. Office: Warnaco Inc/Authentic Fitness Corp 90 Park Ave New York NY 10016-1302

WACHS, DAVID V., apparel executive; b. Phila. Attended, U Penn Wharton, 1948. With Charming Shoppes Inc., 1950—, C.E.O., 1988—. Office: Charming Shoppes Inc 450 Winks Ln Bensalem PA 19020-5993

WACHS, MARTIN, urban planning educator, author, consultant; b. N.Y.C., June 8, 1941; s. Robert and Doris (Margolis) W.; m. Helen Pollner, Aug. 18, 1963; children: Faye Linda, Steven Brett. B.C.E., CUNY, 1963; M.S., Northwestern U., 1965, Ph.D., 1967. Asst. prof. U. Ill.-Chgo., 1967-69, Northwestern U., Evanston, Ill., 1969-71; assoc. prof. urban planning UCLA, 1971-76, prof., 1976—; dir. UCLA Inst. Tranp. Studies, 1993—; vis. disting. prof. Rutgers U., New Brunswick, N.J., 1983-84. Author: Transportation for the Elderly: Changing Lifestyles, Changing Needs, 1979, The Clean Air Act in Court: New Demands on Transportation Planning, 1995; also numerous articles; editor: Ethics in Planning, 1984, The Car and the City, 1992. Mem. steering com. Los Angeles Parking Mgmt. Study, 1976-78; bd. dirs. Los Angeles Commuter Computer, 1978—. Served to capt. Ordnance Corps, U.S. Army, 1967-69. Recipient Pike Johnson award Transp. Research Bd., 1976, Disting. Teaching award UCLA Alumni Assn., 1986, Disting. Planning Educator award Calif. Planners Found., 1986, vis. fellow Oxford U. (Eng.), 1976-77; Guggenheim fellow, 1977; Rockefeller Found. humanities fellow, 1980. Fellow Am. Coun. Edn.; mem. Am. Planning Assn., Am. Inst. Cert. Planners, Architects, Designers, Planners for Social Responsibility. Jewish. Home: 1088 N Kenter Ave Los Angeles CA 90049-1336 Office: UCLA Dept Urban Planning 1118A Perloff Hall Los Angeles CA 90024

WACHSMAN, HARVEY FREDERICK, lawyer, neurosurgeon; b. Bklyn., June 13, 1936; s. Ben and Mollie (Kugel) W.; m. Kathryn M. D'Agostino, Jan. 31, 1976; children: Dara Nicole, David Winston, Jacqueline Victoria, Lauren Elizabeth, Derek Charles, Ashley Max, Marea Lane, Melissa Roseanne. B.A., Tulane U., 1958; M.D., Chgo. Med. Sch., 1962; J.D., Bklyn. Law Sch., 1976. Bar: Conn. 1976, N.Y. 1977, Fla. 1977, D.C. 1978, U.S. Supreme Ct. 1980, Pa. 1984, Md. 1986, Tex. 1987. Diplomate Nat. Bd. Med. Examiners; cert. Am. Bd. Legal Medicine, Am. Bd. Profl. Liability Attys. (pres.); cert. civil trial advocate Nat. Bd. Trial Advocacy (trustee). Intern surgery Kings County Hosp. Ctr., Bklyn., 1962-63; resident in surgery Kingsbrook Med. Ctr., Bklyn., 1964-65; resident in neurol. surgery Emory U. Hosp., Atlanta, 1965-69; practice medicine specializing in neurosurgery Bridgeport, Conn., 1972-74; ptnr. firm Wachsman & Wachsman, Great Neck, 1976—, Pegalis & Wachsman, Great Neck, N.Y., 1977—; adj. prof. neurosurgery SUNY, Stony Brook; adj. prof. law St. John's Sch. Law, U. South Fla. Coll. Medicine. Author: American Law of Medical Malpractice, Vol. I, 1980, 2d edit., 1992, American Law of Medical Malpractice, Vol. II, 1981, American Law of Medical Malpractice, Vol. III, 1982, Cumulative Supplement to American Law of Medical Malpractice, 1981, 82, 83, 84, 85, American Law of Medical Malpractice, 2d edit., Vols. I, II, and III, Lethal Medicine, 1993; mem. editl. bd. Legal Aspects of Med. Practice, 1978-82. Fellow Am. Coll. Legal Medicine (mem. bd. govs. 1986, chmn. edn. com. 1983—, chmn. 1985 nat. meeting, New Orleans, chmn. 1988 nat. meeting, Va., bd. dirs. ACLM Found.), Am. Acad. Forensic Scis., Royal Soc. Medicine, Royal Soc. Arts (London), Royal Soc. Medicine (London), Roscoe Pound Found. of Assn. Trial Lawyers Am.; mem. ABA, Am. Soc. Law and Medicine, Congress Neurol. Surgeons, Assn. Trial Lawyers Am., Soc. Med. Jurisprudence (trustee), N.Y. Bar Assn., Conn. Bar Assn., Fla. Bar Assn., D.C. Bar Assn., N.Y. Acad. Scis., Assn. Trial Lawyers Am. (bd. govs.), N.Y. Trial Lawyers Assn., Conn. Trial Lawyers Assn., Fla. Acad. Trial Lawyers, Md. Trial Lawyers Assn., Tex. Trial Lawyers Assn., Pa. Trial Lawyers Assn., Nat. Bar Assn. (mem. com. on South Africa), Nassau County Bar Assn., Fairfield County Med. Soc., Nassau-Suffolk Trial Lawyers Assn. Club: Cosmos (Washington). Home: 55 Mill River Rd Oyster Bay NY 11771-2711 Office: 175 E Shore Rd Great Neck NY 11023-2430 *In my pursuit of knowledge and excellence in the fields of neurosurgery and the law, I Have found that arming oneself with the power of knowledge is truly the key to helping others. Let one's goal in life be to help others, and he shall always find fulfillment, challenge and hope.*

WACHSMAN, PHYLLIS GERI, advertising executive; b. N.Y.C., Feb. 2, 1947; d. Benjamin Gilbert and Leonora (Kleidman) Brown. BA, New Sch. for Social Research, N.Y., 1978; MHA, New Sch. for Social Research, 1980. RN, N.Y., N.J. Staff nurse Mt. Sinai Hosp., N.Y.C., 1968-70; supr. Hackensack (N.J.) Hosp., 1970-75; dir. of community psychiatry program Hackensack (N.J.) Hosp., Hackensack, 1975-80; sr. writer Kallir, Phillips, Ross Inc., N.Y.C., 1980-81, copy supr. 1981-84, v.p. copy supr. 1984-85, sr. v.p. assoc. creative dir. 1985-86, sr. v.p. copy supr. Smithouse, Torre & Ferrante, Rutherford, N.J., 1985-86, sr. v.p., creative dir. copy, 1986-90; exec. v.p., creative dir. Kallir, Philips, Ross Inc., N.Y.C., 1990-93, exec. v.p., dir. strategic planning, 1993—; judge Clio awards, 1986, Triangle awards, 1987. Mem. Mental Health Assn. N.J. Recipient Jacob Javits award, 1980, Starch award MD. Mag., 1985, 86, Triangle awards Modern Medicine, 1984, 85, award Rx Club, 1988, 89. Mem. Am. Contract Bridge League. Avocations: travel, dance, reading, tournament bridge. Office: Kallir Phillips Ross Inc 333 E 38th St New York NY 10016-2745

WACHSTETER, GEORGE, illustrator; b. Hartford, Conn., Mar. 12, 1911; s. Josef and Therese (Weiss) W.; m. Thelma Altshuler, July 29, 1939 (dec. 1991). Ed. pub. schs., Hartford. Illustrator Major Advt. Agys, Theatre and Motion Picture Prodns., 1936—; CBS, NBC, ABC Radio and TV Networks, 1937—; weekly illustrator and caricature to drama pages N.Y. Herald Tribune, 1941-50; contbr. illustration and caricature to drama and polit. pages N.Y. Times, 1938-50; caricaturist Theatre Guild On The Air, U.S. Steel, 1945-63; artist TV section N.Y. Times, 1950-51; featured drama artist N.Y. Jour. Am., 1956-63, artist TV mag. covers, 1958-63; artist TV mag. covers Hearst Syndicate, 1963-65; drama artist N.Y. World Telegram, 1964-66; syndicated feature illustrator Hallmark TV Drama Series, 1964-69. Illustrator, caricaturist (book) NBC Book of Stars, 1957; portrait Taft Meml. Fund Campaign, 1956; numerous work in pub. and pvt. collections. Jewish. Home: 85-05 Elmhurst Ave Elmhurst NY 11373

WACHTEL, HARRY H., lawyer, chain store executive; b. N.Y.C., Mar. 26, 1917; s. Samuel and Minnie (Herzhaft) W.; m. Leonora Golden, July 30, 1939; children: Alan B., Susan M., William B. B.S. in Social Sci, CCNY, 1938; LL.B., Columbia U., 1940. Bar: N.Y. bar 1940. Since practiced in N.Y.C.; sr. partner firm Rubin, Wachtel, Baum & Levin, until 1975; counsel Gold and Wachtel, N.Y.C., 1985—; exec. v.p., gen. counsel, dir. McCrory Corp., 1959-75, exec. asst. to pres., 1975-83; vice chmn., exec. v.p. Rapid Am. Corp., 1960-65; gen. counsel, dir. Lerner Stores Corp., 1961-75; Vis. prof. polit. sci. Hofstra U., 1967-71; adj. prof. polit. sci. Columbia, 1973-85; fellow Urban Center, 1972-80; dir. Vanguard Nat. Bank, Hempstead, N.Y., 1972-74. Mem. exec. com. N.Y. State Com. Am. Vets. Com., 1947; bd. dirs. North Shore Cmty. Arts Ctr., Roslyn, N.Y., 1960-72; v.p., counsel Martin Luther King Jr. Ctr. for Nonviolent Social Change, 1969-82, bd. dirs. 1969-92, mem. bd. advisors, 1992—; exec. v.p., counsel Am. Found. Nonviolence, 1964-72; trustee SCLC, 1970-72; past mem. coun. Hofstra U. With AUS, 1942-45. Decorated Bronze Star medal. Mem. Phi Beta Kappa. Home: 24 Clover Ln Roslyn Heights NY 11577-2724 Office: Gold and Wachtel 110 E 59th St New York NY 10022-1304

WACHTEL, NORMAN JAY, lawyer; b. N.Y.C., June 1, 1941; s. A. Allen and Lillian (Rolnik) W.; m. C. Robin Fixler, June 12, 1969; children: Jonathan, Charles. AB, U. Pa., 1963, LLB, 1966; LLM, Boston U., 1967. Bar: N.Y. 1967. Assoc. Demov, Morris & Hammerling, N.Y.C., 1966-78, ptnr., 1978-87; ptnr. Rogers & Wells, N.Y.C., 1987—; bd. advisors 1st Am. Title Ins. Co. N.Y., 1982—. Author: (chpt.) Real Estate Titles, 1984. Office: Rogers & Wells 200 Park Ave Ste 5200 New York NY 10166-0153

WACHTER, MICHAEL L., economics educator; b. N.Y.C., Mar. 12, 1943; s. Abraham and Florence W.; m. Susan M. Jaffe, June 23, 1968; children: Jessica, Jonathan. B.S., Cornell U., 1964; M.A., Harvard U., 1967, Ph.D. 1970. Asst. prof. econs. U. Pa., Phila., 1969-73, assoc. prof., 1973-76, prof. econs., law and mgmt., 1976—, dir. Inst. for Law and Econs., 1984—; sr. advisor Brookings Instn., Washington, 1976-90; mem. Minimum Wage Study Commn., Washington, 1978-81; cons. U.S. Postal Svc., 1980—. Editor: Removing Obstacles to Economic Growth, 1984, Toward a New U.S. Industrial Policy, 1982; contbr. articles to profl. jours. NIH grantee, 1981-83; NSF grantee, 1974-77; 20th Century Fund grantee, 1978-82; Gen. Electric Found. grantee, 1980-83. Mem. Am. Econ. Assn., Econometric Soc., Indsl. Relations Research Assn. Office: U Pa Law Sch Inst Law & Econs 3400 Chestnut St Philadelphia PA 19104-6204

WACHTMEISTER, COUNT WILHELM H. F., diplomat; b. Vanas, Sweden, Apr. 29, 1923; s. Gustaf and Margaretha (Trolle) W.; m. Ulla Leuhusen, 1947; children: Anna, Erik. LLD, U. Stockholm, Sweden, 1946. Attache Swedish Ministry for Fgn. Affairs, 1946-47; attache Swedish Embassy, Vienna, Madrid and Lisbon, 1947-50; 2d sec. Swedish Ministry Fgn. Affairs, Stockholm, Sweden, 1950-55; 1st sec. Swedish Embassy, Moscow, 1955-58; personal asst. to UN Gen. Sec., 1958-61; head UN sect. Fgn. Ministry, Stockholm, 1962-65, dep. under-sec. polit. affairs, 1965-66; ambassador to Algeria Swedish Embassy, 1966-67; under-sec. for polit. affairs Swedish Ministry Fgn. Affairs, Stockholm, 1968-74; Swedish ambassador to U.S. Swedish Embassy, Washington, 1974-89; dean diplomatic corps in Washington, 1986-89; sr. advisor to chmn. AB Volvo, 1989-94. Mem. Soc. Cin. (France), Swedish-Am. C. of C. (chmn.), Met. Club (Washingotn), Sallskapet Club (Stockholm). Avocation: tennis. Home: 4202 48th Pl NW Washington DC 20016-2338

WACK, THOMAS E., lawyer; b. Mo., 1944. AB, Georgetown U., 1966; JD, Northwestern U., 1969. Bar: Mo. 1969. Ptnr. Bryan Cave, St. Louis; program dir. Fed. Practice Com. U.S. Dist. Ct. (Mo. dist.). Fellow Am. Coll. Trial Lawyers; mem. ABA, Mo. Bar Assn. (mem. bus. torts com., mem. unfair competition com. 1990-92). Office: Bryan Cave 1 Met Sq Saint Louis MO 63102-2750

WACKENHUT, GEORGE RUSSELL, security services executive; b. Phila., Sept. 3, 1919; s. William Henry and Frances (Hogan) W.; m. Ruth Johann Bell, Apr. 8, 1944; children: Janis Lynn Wackenhut Ward, Richard Russell. Student, U. Pa. Wharton Evening Sch., 1937-38, State Tchrs. Coll., West Chester, Pa., 1938-41; B.S., U. Hawaii, 1943; postgrad., Temple U., 1946; M.Ed., Johns Hopkins U., 1949. Ops. edn. profl. program tchrs. Ing. Johns Hopkins U., 1946-50; civilian cons. recreational sports br. Office Spl. Svcs. U.S. Army, Washington, 1950-51; spl. agt. FBI, 1951-54; dir. pers., security and safety Giffin Industries, Inc., Miami, Fla., 1954; pres., chmn. bd. Spl. Agt. Investigators, Inc., Spl. Agts. Security Guards, Inc., Security Svcs. Corp. (all Miami), 1954-58; chmn. bd., dir. Wackenhut Corp., Coral Gables, Fla., 1958-86, chmn. bd., CEO, 1986—; chmn. bd. dirs. Wackenhut Airlines Svcs., Am. Guard and Alert, Inc., Wackenhut Internat., Inc., Wackenhut of Alaska, Inc., Wackenhut Svcs., Inc., Wackenhut of Can., Ltd., Wackenhut Corrections Corp., Wackenhut Edn. Svcs., Inc., Wackenhut Properties, Inc., Wackenhut Sports Security Inc., Wackenhut U.K. Ltd., Wackenhut Dominicana (S.A.), Wackenhut del Ecuador (S.A.); chmn. bd. dirs. CEO Titania Ins. Co. Am.; chmn., bd. dirs., pres. Titania Advt., Inc.; mem. Dean's Adv. Bd., U. Miami Sch. Bus.; bd. dirs. Plexus Healthcare Devel. Corp.; mem. bd. dirs. SSJ Med. Devel. Co., Inc., 1987-94. Mem. law enforcement coun. Nat. Coun. Crime and Delinquency, 1971-73; bd. dirs. Heart Assn. of Greater Miami, 1965-66, Gov.'s War on Crime, Fla., 1967-70; bd. visitors U.S. Army M.P. Sch., 1972-74; mem. Small Bus. Administrn. Region IV, Miami Adv. Coun., 1983—, Nat. Coun. Trustees Freedoms Found. at Valley Forge, 1989—; mem. nat. bd. dirs. Nat. Soccer Hall of Fame, 1993—. With U.S. Army, 1941-45. Recipient Vigilant Patrior award All Ams. Conf. to Combat Communism, Labor Order of Merit 1st Class, Gold award Govt. Venezuela, 1990, CEO of Yr., Bronze award Fin. World Mag., 1987, Disting. Alumni U. Hawaii, West Chester U., 1979. Mem. Soc. Former Spl. Agts. FBI, Inc., Am. Soc. for Indsl. Security, Cert. Protection Profl., AIM (pres. coun. 1964-66), Freedoms Found. at Valley Forge (George Washington Honor medal, trustee), Ocean Reef Club (Key Largo, Fla.), 200 Club Greater Miami. Christian Scientist. Home: Gables Estates 20 Casuarina Concourse Coral Gables FL 33143-6502 Office: Wackenhut Corp 1500 San Remo Ave Miami FL 33146-3036

WACKENHUT, RICHARD RUSSELL, security company executive; b. Balt., Nov. 11, 1947; s. George Russell and Ruth Johann (Bell) W.; m. Mariane Hutson Ball, Mar. 13, 1971; children: Jennifer Anne, Lisa Renee, Ashley Elizabeth, Lauren Hutson. BA in Polit. Sci., The Citadel Mil. Coll., 1969; grad. bus. sch. advanced mgmt. program, Harvard U., 1987. With Wackenhut Corp., Coral Gables, Fla. and Columbia, S.C., 1973—; v.p. ops. Wackenhut Corp., Coral Gables, 1981-82, sr. v.p. domestic ops., 1982-83, sr. v.p. ops., 1983-86, pres., chief operating officer, 1986—, also bd. dirs. Wackenhut Corp., Coral Gables, Fla.; dir. Assoc. Industries of Fla. Mem. exec. com. St. Thomas U. Mem. Internat. Assn. Chiefs Police, Internat. Security Mgmt. Assn., Am. Soc. Indsl. Security, Ocean Reef Club, Seabrook Island Club, Biltmore Club. Republican. Christian Scientist. Avocations: racquetball, jogging, boating. Office: Wackenhut Corp 1500 San Remo Ave Miami FL 33146-3036

WACKER, FREDERICK GLADE, JR., manufacturing company executive; b. Chgo., July 10, 1918; s. Frederick Glade Wacker and Grace Cook Anderson; m. Ursula Comandatore, Apr. 26, 1958; children: Frederick Glade III, Wendy, Joseph Comandatore. BA, Yale U., 1940; student, Gen. Motors Inst. Tech., 1940-42; LLD (hon.), Northwood U., 1989. Efficiency engr. AC Spark Plug divsn. Gen. Motors Corp., 1940-43; with Ammco Tools, Inc.,

North Chicago, Ill., 1947-87, pres., 1948-87, chmn. bd., 1948-87; founder, pres. Liquid Controls Corp., North Chicago, 1954-87, chmn. bd., 1954—; chmn. bd. Liquid Controls Europe, Zurich, Switzerland, 1985-87; ltd. ptnr. Francis I. DuPont & Co., N.Y.C., 1954-70; mem. exec. coun. Conf. Bd., 1971-92, chmn., 1977. Condr. Freddie Wacker and His Orch., 1955-69, orch. has appeared on TV and radio, recs. for Dolphin and Cadet records. Bd. govs. United Rep. Fund Ill., Art Inst. Chgo., 1984—; trustee Lake Forest Acad., 1956-71, life trustee, 1992—; trustee Warren Wilson Coll., 1973-81, Chgo. chpt. Multiple Sclerosis Soc. bd. govs. Lyric Opera Chgo., 1963-66; bd. advisers Nat. Schs. Com., 1988-86; adv. coun. Trinity Evang. Div. Sch., 1977-87; adv. bd. Internat. Coun. Biblical Inerrancy, 1981-88; bd. dirs., vice chmn. Rockford Inst., 1983-91; bd. govs. GMI Engring. and Mgmt. Inst., 1983-91; bd. regents Milw. Sch. Engring., 1981-91; mem. pres.'s coun. Ligonier Ministries, 1989—. Lt. (j.g.) USNR, 1943-45, PTO. Recipient Outstanding Bus. Leader award, Northwood, 1994; named to Hall of Fame Lake Forest Acad., 1987. Mem. Chief Execs. Forum, Young Pres. Orgn. (chmn. Chgo. chpt. 1965-66), Sports Car Club Am. (pres. 1952-53), Ill. Mfrs. Assn. (bd. dirs. 1966-91, chmn. bd. 1975), Chgo. Pres. Orgn. (pres. 1972-73), Automotive Hall of Fame (life, dir. 1976-88, v.p. 1980-81, sec. 1981-88, Chief Exec. Forum 1967-89, Disting. Svc. Citation 1989), Soc. Automotive Engrs., World Bus. Coun., Waukegan C. of C. (dir. 1965-68), Art Inst. Chgo. (gov.), Chgo. Fedn. Musicians (life), Am. Motorcycle Assn. (life), Racquet Club (pres. 1960-61), Shoreacres Club, Onwentsia Club, Vintage Club (Indian Wells, Calif.), Conway Farms Golf Club, The Quarry (La Quinta, Calif.). Presbyterian. Home: 1600 Green Bay Rd Lake Bluff IL 60044-2306 Office: Liquid Controls Corp 105 Albrecht Dr Lake Bluff IL 60044-2242

WACKER, JOHN LEE, landscape architect; b. Lancaster, Ohio, Sept. 10, 1934; s. Norbert Pierce and Phyllis (Sharp) W.; m. Margaret Marie Bielawski, June 23, 1957; children—John Lee, Michelle Marie. Student, Heidelberg Coll., Tiffin, Ohio, 1952-54; B.S.L.A., Mich. State U., 1957; M.L.A., Harvard Grad. Sch. Design, 1958. Lic. landscape architect, Ohio, Mich., Mass., R.I., Conn., Miss. Draftsman Mich. State U., East Lansing, 1956-57; landscape architect Milton Baron, Hazlett, Mich., 1956-57, Walter Chambers, Cambridge, Mass., 1958; sr. assoc. Hugh Stubbins & Assocs., Inc., Cambridge, 1958-71; pres. John Wacker & Assocs., Inc., Weston, Mass., 1971—; vis. critic, lectr. dept. archtl. planning MIT, U. Mich., Harvard Grad. Sch. Design, Mich. State U.; assoc. prof. Great Masters Atelier in Landscape Arch., Tex. A&M U., 1983, 84; clk., dir. Hubbard Ednl. Trust, Inc. for L.A. Edn., 1975—; dir. Landscape Architecture Found., 1980-84. Chmn. Traffic Safety Com., Weston, Mass., 1975-78, com. mem., 1968-78; bd. dirs., v.p. Boston Environment, Inc., 1969-79. Recipient Cert. of Merit Am. Assn. Nurserymen, 1969; Disting. Alumni award Mich. State U., 1981. Fellow Am. Soc. Landscape Architects (trustee 1974-81, v.p. 1983-84); mem. Boston Soc. Landscape Architects (pres. 1966-70), Mass. Hort. Soc. (trustee 1970-76). Democrat. Lodge: Rotary. Home: 699 Boston Post Rd Weston MA 02193-1543 Office: John Wacker & Assocs Inc 99 School St PO Box 157 Weston MA 02193

WACKER, WARREN ERNEST CLYDE, physician, educator; b. Bklyn., Feb. 29, 1924; s. John Frederick and Kitty Dora (Morrissey) W.; m. Ann Romeyn MacMillan, May 22, 1948; children: Margaret Morrissey, John Frederick. Student, Georgetown U., 1946-47; M.D., George Washington U., 1951; M.A. (hon.), Harvard, 1968. Intern George Washington U. Hosp., 1951-52, resident, 1952-53; resident Peter Bent Brigham Hosp., Boston, 1953-55; Nat. Found. Infantile Paralysis fellow, 1955-57; investigator Howard Hughes Med. Inst., Boston, 1957-68; mem. faculty Harvard Med. Sch., Boston, 1955—; assoc. prof. medicine Harvard Med. Sch., 1968-71, Henry K. Oliver prof. hygiene, 1971-89, prof. hygiene, 1989—; dir. univ. health services, 1971-89; acting master Mather House, 1974-75, acting master Kirkland House, 1975-76, master Cabot House, 1978-84; sr. med. cons. Risk Mgmt. Found. of the Harvard Med. Instns., Cambridge, 1992—; vis. scholar St. Mary's Hosp. Med. Sch., 1964; vis. prof. U. Tel Aviv, 1987; dir. Applied Mgmt. Systems, Burlington, Mass., Millipore Corp., Bedford, Mass., 1971-94. Author: Magnesium and Man, 1981; sec., editorial adv. bd.: Biochemistry, 1962-76; assoc. editor: Magnesium; contbr. articles to med. and sci. jours. Vestryman St. Paul's Episc. Ch., Brookline, Mass., 1965-68, 76-79, 91-94; bd. dirs. Harvard Community Health Plan, Boston, 1973-84; mem. fin. com., 1984-86, mem. corp., 1986—; bd. dirs. Bishop Rhinelander Found., Cambridge, 1973-76, 78-84, Controlled Risk Ins. Co., 1976-78; pres. bd. overseers Peter Bent Brigham Hosp., Boston, 1979-84; trustee Brigham and Women's Hosp., Boston, 1984-89, Risk Mgmt. Found., 1979-92; mem. mgmt. bd., med. bd. MIT, 1985—; mem. corp. Mt. Auburn Hosp., Cambridge, 1986—; mem. adv. bd. hospitality program Episc. Diocese Mass., 1989—. Served to 1st lt. USAAF, 1942-45. Decorated Air medal, D.F.C., Liberation medal (Greece); named Disting. Alumnus, George Washington U., 1963; recipient Cert. of Merit, Soc. Magnesium Research, 1985. Mem. Am. Chem. Soc., Am. Soc. Biol. Chemistry, Am. Soc. Clin. Investigation, AMA, Mass. Med. Soc., A.C.P., Am. Coll. Health Assn. (pres. 1981, Boynton award 1986), Biochemistry Soc. (London), Am. Coll. Nutrition, Sigma Xi, Alpha Omega Alpha. Democrat. Episcopalian. Clubs: Harvard (Boston); Cosmos (Washington). Home: 91 Glen Rd Brookline MA 02146-7764 Office: Risk Mgmt Found 840 Memorial Dr Cambridge MA 02139

WACKERLE, FREDERICK WILLIAM, management consultant; b. Chgo., June 25, 1939; s. Fred and Babette (Buck) W.; m. Elaine Gately, Apr. 28, 1962 (div.); children: Jennifer, Ruth; m. Barbara L. Provus, Mar. 29, 1985. BA, Monmouth (Ill.) Coll., 1961. Prin. A.T. Kearney & Co., Chgo., 1964-66; v.p. Berry Henderson & Aberlin, Chgo., 1966-68, R.M. Schmitz & Co., Chgo. 1968-70; ptnr. McFeely-Wackerle-Shulman, Chgo., 1970—; dir. Rehab. Inst. Chgo. Trustee Monmouth Coll. Served with USAF, 1957-62. Mem. Assn. Exec. Search Cons. (bd. dirs., exec. v.p.), Tau Kappa Epsilon. Home: 3750 N Lake Shore Dr Apt 17F Chicago IL 60613-4234 Office: McFeely-Wackerle-Shulman 20 N Wacker Dr Ste 3110 Chicago IL 60606-3101

WADA, HARRY NOBUYOSHI, training company executive; b. North Platte, Nebr., Nov. 29, 1919; s. Gosaku and Hina (Arakawa) W.; m. Carol Tanaka, July 30, 1950; children: Sharon, Leslie, Gregg. B.S., Ill. Inst. Tech., 1954, M.S., 1956. Owner Palace Cafe, North Platte, 1950-58; mgr. purchases IIT Research Inst., Chgo., 1954-65; materials mgr. IIT Research Inst., 1965-76; dir. continuing edn. Nat. Assn. Purchasing Mgmt., 1976-83; pres. H. N. Wada & Assocs., 1983—; instr. Ill. Inst. Tech., Roosevelt U. Editor chpt. from George Aljians Handbook, 1973; contbr. articles to profl. jours. Mem. Bd. Standardization Cook County, Health and Hosps. Governing Commn. Served with AUS, 1942-46. Recipient J. Shipman Gold medal, 1976. Mem. Purchasing Mgmt. Assn. Chgo. (pres. 1969), Nat. Assn. Purchasing Mgmt. (chmn. dist. III profl. devel. 1970-71, program chmn. Internat. Conf. 1971, pres. 1974—, Brueggemann award 1974), Ill. C. of C., Ill. Inst. Tech. Alumni (bd. dirs.), Phi Eta Sigma, Sigma Iota Epsilon. Home and Office: 3128 Tarpon Dr #104 Las Vegas NV 89120

WADA, SADAMI (CHRIS), manufacturing executive; b. Tokyo, Oct. 1, 1932; came to U.S., 1961; s. Shigeru and Kiyoko (Urabe) W.; m. Reiko Niizu, Nov. 3, 1962. BA, Internat. Christian U., Tokyo, 1960; MBA in Mktg., NYU, N.Y.C., 1972. Simultaneous interpreter ICA, Dept. of State, Washington, 1961-62; asst. mgr., mgr., gen. mgr. Sony Corp. of Am., N.Y.C., 1962-78, asst. v.p. import/export, govt. relations, 1978-82, v.p. govt. affairs, 1982-87, sr. v.p. govt. affairs, 1988-95; pres. Chris Wada & Assocs., Greenwich, Conn., 1995—; bd. advisors Karl F. Landegger Program in Internat. Bus. Diplomacy, Sch. Fgn. Service, Georgetown U.; US councilor to Keidanren's (Japan's Fedn. Econ. Orgns.) Coun. for Better Corp. Citizenship; lectr. for pub. radio, TV and pub. hearing audiences on US-Japan related issues. Trustee Ctr. for Excellence in Edn., McLean, Va.; pres. Alumni Assn. Ams., Internat. Christian U.; mem. adv. bd. Japan Soc. Boston, inc. Recipient Chmns. award on unitary tax repeal SONAM, 1986, Gold Key award Pub. Rels. News, 1989, U.S.-Japan rels. award Japanese Cultural & Community Ctr. of No. Calif., 1993. Avocations: skiing, scuba diving, hiking. Office: Chris Wada & Assocs 9 Winterset Rd Greenwich CT 06830

WADDELL, ALFRED MOORE, JR., investment company executive; b. Chattanooga, Tenn., Jan. 30, 1939; s. Alfred Moore and Harriet Belseth Aplin W.; m. Clara Teresa Saxon, Jan. 3, 1961; children—Virginia Martin, Alfred Moore III, David Sewall. B.A. in Econs, U. of South, 1961; M.B.A.,

Harvard U., 1968. Various positions IBM, Tenn., Ark., Mass., 1962-68; pres. UC Leasing, Memphis, 1968-71; v.p. fin. Gable Industries Inc., Atlanta, 1971-74; chmn. bd. Gable Industries Inc., 1974-76, also dir.; sr. v.p. Flintkote Co., Stamford, Conn., 1976-78; also dir. Flintkote Co.; pres., chmn., chief exec. officer Hajoca Corp. (formerly Gable Industries), Ardmore, Pa., 1978-83; pres., chief exec. officer Waddell & Assocs., Delray Beach, Fla., then Memphis, 1985—. Pub. Sane Investing for the Non Financial, 1995. Home and Office: 4921 William Arnold Rd Memphis TN 38117-4238

WADDELL, HARRY LEE, editor, publisher; b. Monarch, Wyo., June 19, 1912; s. Edward Lee and Naomi (Epstein) W.; m. Eleanor Hazeltine, 1937 (dec.); children: Nancy, Caroline, Jessica; m. Helene Jamieson, Apr. 6, 1968 (dec.). A.B., Ohio U., 1933. Reporter, fin. editor, asst. city editor, news editor Buffalo Evening News, 1933-46; asst. mng. editor Bus. Week, McGraw-Hill, N.Y.C., 1946-49; editor Factory, 1949-53, pub. oil industry group, 1953-57, sr. v.p. mag. div., 1957-59, corp. exec. v.p., 1959-65; gen. exec. Doubleday & Co., N.Y.C., 1966-69; with Simmons-Boardman Pub. Corp., N.Y.C., 1969—; chief editor Am. Bankers Assn. Banking Jour., 1971-82, editor emeritus, 1982—, chmn. bd., 1972-82, vice chmn., 1982—; lectr. Am. Press Inst., Columbia U., 1946-59; Mem. Ednl. Adv. Bd., Garden City, N.Y., 1955-58, chmn., 1957-58. Trustee Orange County Citizens Found., 1983—, v.p. 1987-93. Mem. Am. Bus. Press (dir. 1977-83), Phi Beta Kappa, Sigma Delta Chi, Beta Theta Pi. Republican. Presbyterian. Office: 345 Hudson St New York NY 10014-4502

WADDELL, JOHN COMER, electronics distribution company executive; b. Bridgeport, Conn., Sept. 10, 1937; s. John and Dorothy Margot (Comer) W. B.A., Yale U., 1959; M.B.A., Harvard U., 1965. Assoc. R.W. Pressprich & Co., N.Y.C., 1965-68; ptnr. Glenn, Green & Waddell, N.Y.C., 1968-80; exec. v.p. Arrow Electronics, Inc., Melville, N.Y., 1969-80; chmn. bd. Arrow Electronics, Inc., 1980—. Served with U.S. Navy, 1960-63. Home: 375 Park Ave New York NY 10152-0002

WADDELL, OLIVER W., banker; b. Covington, Ky., Dec. 27, 1930; s. Frank and Ida Mae Waddell; m. Virgilee Casey; children—Jeffrey, Gregory, Michelle. BA, Duke U., 1954; JD, U. Ky., 1957; grad., Stonier Grad. Sch. Banking, Rutgers U., 1969. Mgmt. trainee First Nat. Bank of Cin., 1957-64, asst. cashier, 1964-65, asst. v.p., 1965-71, v.p., 1971-76, sr. v.p., 1976-80, pres., dir., 1980-82, pres., chief exec. officer, 1982-83; chmn. First Nat. Bank of Cin. (became Star Bank N.A., Cin., 1988), 1983—; bd. dirs. Myers Y. Cooper Co., Cin., Nat. Life Ins. Co., Cin. Gas & Electric Co., Star Banc Corp; adv. bd. Greater Cin./No. Ky. Internat. Airport; with Cin. Bus. Co. Trustee Christ Hosp.; bd. dirs. Cin. Hist. Soc. Mem. Greater Cin. C. of C., Comml. Club, Cin. Country Club, Queen City Club. Republican. Methodist. Office: Star Bank NA 425 Walnut St Cincinnati OH 45202-3912

WADDELL, R. EUGENE, minister; b. Wayne County, N.C., Feb. 7, 1932; s. Robert Lee and Rena (Holland) W.; m. Elva Leah Nichols, July 22, 1954 (dec. Apr. 1962); children: Rhonda Waddell Sagraves, Robert, Paul, Marcia Waddell Thompson; m. Genevieve Johnson, July 4, 1963; children: Michael, John. BA, Free Will Bapt. Bible Coll., Nashville, 1954; MA, Columbia (S.C.) Bibl. Sem., 1966. Ordained to ministry Free Will Bapt. Ch., 1952. Pastor Bay Branch Free Will Bapt. Ch., Timmonsville, S.C., 1954-56, 1st Free Will Bapt. Ch., Portsmouth, Va., 1956-60, Garner (N.C.) Free Will Bapt. Ch., 1960-64, Cofer's Chapel Free Will Bapt. Ch., Nashville, 1964-81; assoc. dir. Free Will Bapt. Fgn. Missions Dept., Nashville, 1981-86, gen. dir., 1986—; bd. dirs. Free Will Bapt. Fgn. Missions, Nashville, 1959-78, bd. sec., 1971-78; founder, editor Free Will Bapt. Witness, Garner, 1962-63. Office: Free Will Bapt Fgn Missions 5233 Mount View Rd Antioch TN 37013-2306

WADDELL, WILLIAM JOSEPH, pharmacologist, toxicologist; b. Commerce, Ga., Mar. 16, 1929; s. John Daniel and Lillian Marie (Vollrath) W.; m. Grace Carolyn Marlowe, Oct. 19, 1974; children: William Joseph, James Glenn, Martin Christie, Amy Alison. A.B. in Chemistry, U. N.C., 1951, M.D., 1955. Postdoctoral research fellow U. N.C. Sch. Medicine, 1955-58, asst. prof. pharmacology, 1958-62, asso. prof., 1962-72; assoc. prof. oral biology U. N.C. Sch. Medicine (Dental Research Center), 1967-69, prof., 1969-72, assoc. dir., 1968-72; prof. pharmacology U. Ky. Coll. Medicine, Lexington, 1972-77; prof., chmn. dept. pharmacology and toxicology U. Louisville, 1977—; Centennial Alumni Disting. vis. prof. U. N.C. Sch. Medicine, 1979. Contbr. articles to profl. jours. Fellow Acad. Toxicological Scis.; mem. Am. Soc. for Pharmacology and Exptl. Therapeutics, Am. Physiol. Soc., Am. Teratology Soc., Internat. Soc. for Study Xenobiotics, Soc. for Exptl. Biology and Medicine, Soc. Toxicology, Sigma Xi. Home: 14300 Rose Wycombe Rd Prospect KY 40059-9024 Office: U Louisville Dept Pharmacology Louisville KY 40292

WADDEN, RICHARD ALBERT, environmental science educator, consultant, researcher; b. Sioux City, Iowa, Oct. 3, 1936; s. Sylvester Francis and Hermina Lillian (Costello) W.; m. Angela Louise Trabert, Aug. 9, 1975; children—Angela Terese, Noah Albert, Nuiko Clare. Student, St. John's U., Collegeville, Minn., 1954-56; B.S. in Chem. Engring., Iowa State U., 1959; M.S. in Chem. Engring, N.C. State U., 1962; Ph.D. in Chem. and Environ. Engring., Northwestern U., 1972. Registered profl. engr., Ill.; cert. indsl. hygienist. Engr. Linde Co., Tonnawanda, N.Y., 1959-60, Humble Oil Co., Houston, 1962-65; instr. engring. Pahlavi U. Peace Corps, Shiraz, Iran, 1965-67; tech. adviser Ill. Pollution Control Bd., Chgo., 1971-72; asst. dir. Environ. Health Resource Ctr. Ill., Chgo., 1972-74; asst. prof. environ. and occupational health scis. Sch. Pub. Health U. Ill.-Chgo., 1972-75, assoc. prof., 1975-79, prof., 1979—, dir., 1984-86, 88-92; dir. Office Tech. Transfer U. Ill. Ctr. for Solid Waste Mgmt. and Resch., 1987-92; dir. indsl. hygiene program Ednl. Resource Ctr. Occupational Safety and Health U. Ill.-Chgo.; vis. scientist Nat. Inst. Environ. Studies, Japan, 1978-79, invited scientist, 1983, 84, 88; cons. air pollution control, health implications of energy devel., indoor air pollution. Author: Energy Utilization and Environmental Health, 1978, (with P.A. Scheff) Indoor Air Pollution, 1983, Engineering Design for Control of Workplace Hazards, 1987; contbr. numerous articles to profl. publs. Sr. Internat. fellow Fogarty Internat. Ctr.-NIH, 1978-79, 83; WHO fellow, 1984. Mem. AIChE, Am. Chem. Soc., Am. Acad. Environ. Engrs. (diplomate), Am. Acad. Indsl. Hygiene (diplomate), Air and Waste Mgmt. Assn., Am. Indsl. Hygiene, Am. Conf. Govtl. Indsl. Hygienists. Office: U Ill m/c 922 2121 W Taylor St Chicago IL 60612-7260

WADDEN, THOMAS ANTONY, psychologist, educator; b. Richmond, Va., Sept. 3, 1952; s. Thomas Antony Jr. and Mary Lloyd (Cradock) W.; m. Jan Robin Linowitz, Nov. 11, 1984; children: David Joseph, Michael James, Steven Zachary. AB magna cum laude, Brown U., 1975; PhD, U. N.C., 1981. Psychology intern Boston VA Med. Ctr., 1980-81; instr. in psychology U. Pa. Sch. Medicine, Phila., 1981-82, asst. prof. psychology, 1982-87, assoc. prof. psychology, 1987-91, prof. psychology, 1994—; prof. psychology, dir. clin. tng. Syracuse (N.Y.) U., 1992-93; clin. dir. Obesity Rsch. Group, U. Pa., Phila., 1983-91, dir. Weight and Eating Disorders Program, 1994—; dir. Ctr. for Health and Behavior, Syracuse U., 1992-93. Assoc. editor Annals of Behavior Medicine, 1990-93, mem. editorial bd. Behavior Therapy, Obesity Rsch., Jour. Consulting and Clin. Psychology; editor: (with T.B. VanItallie) Treatment of the Seriously Obese Patient, 1992, (with A.J. Stunkard) Obesity: Theory and Therapy, 1993; contb. chpts. to books; writer numerous sci. papers. Recipient Nat. Rsch. Svc. award NIMH, 1983-85, Rsch. Scientist Devel. award, 1987-91, 94—. Mem. APA, Soc. Behavioral Medicine (bd. dirs. 1987-90), Assn. for Advancement of Behavior Therapy (New Rschr. award 1986), Acad. Behavioral Medicine, N.Y. Acad. Scis., Phi Beta Kappa, Sigma Xi. Democrat. Avocations: tennis, squash, symphonic music, guitar. Home: 433 Bolsover Rd Wynnewood PA 19096-1301 Office: U Pa 3600 Market St Fl 738 Philadelphia PA 19104-2648

WADDICK, SHERYL F. BAIKY, lawyer; b. Portland, Maine, Feb. 10, 1959; d. Burton Dodge and Faith Elaine (Poulin) B.; m. Robert J. Waddick, June 29, 1991. BA, U. Maine, 1981; JD, Suffolk U., 1989. Bar: Mass. 1989, Maine 1989. Corp. paralegal Choate, Hall & Stewart, Boston, 1982-86; paralegal Cullinet Software, Inc., Westwood, Mass., 1986-87, Cabot Corp., Waltham, Mass., 1987-89; atty. Cabot Corp., Boston, 1989—. Mem. ABA, Boston Bar Assn., Mass. Bar Assn. Office: Cabot Corp 75 State St Boston MA 02109-1807

WADDILL, GRAHAM WALKER, retail executive; b. Phila., Aug. 25, 1931; s. Graham W. and Elsie C. (Weigmann) W.; m. Marian J. Hatcher, Nov. 20, 1949; children: M. Lynn, Graham W. III, Karen L. BS in Bus. Adminstrn., Temple U., 1960; MA in Bus. Sci., Anna Maria Coll., 1977. Cert. adminstrv. mgr. Gen. auditor Phila. Gas Works, 1955-61; v.p.: sec - treas. Genetti's Markets Et Al, Hazelton, Pa., 1961-69; v.p., treas. Iandoli's Markets Et Al, Worcester, Pa., 1969-83; fin. v.p. Nat. Office Supply, Providence, 1984; v.p., corp. controller Mott's Super Markets Inc., E. Hartford, Conn., 1984-87; fin. v.p. Lloyd's Shopping Ctrs., Middletown, N.Y., 1987—. Served with USN, 1948-52. Fellow Cert. Adminstrv. Acad., mem. Adminstrv. Mgmt. Soc. Office: Lloyd's Shopping Ctrs 330 Route 211 E Middletown NY 10940-2804

WADDINGHAM, JOHN ALFRED, artist, journalist; b. London, Eng., July 9, 1915; came to U.S., 1927, naturalized, 1943; s. Charles Alfred and Mary Elizabeth (Coles) W.; m. Joan Lee Larson, May 3, 1952; children: Mary Kathryn, Thomas Richard. Student, Coronado (Calif.) Sch. Fine Arts, 1953-54, Portland Art Mus., 1940-65, U. Portland, 1946-47; pupil, Rex Brandt, Eliot Ohara, George Post. Promotion art dir. Oreg. Jour., Portland, 1946-59; with The Oregonian, Portland, 1959-81; editorial art dir. The Oregonian, 1959-81; tchr. watercolor Ore. Soc. Artists, 1954-56; tchr. art Oreg. Sch. Arts and Crafts, 1981—. Portland Community Coll.; represented by several galleries, Oreg. and Wash. One man show includes Art in the Gov.'s Office Ore State Capitol, 1991; rep. mus. rental collections, Portland Art Mus., Bush House, Salem, Ore., U. Oreg. Mus., Vincent Price collection, Ford Times collection, also, Am. Watercolor Soc. Travelling Show; judge art events, 1946—, over 50 one-man shows; ofcl. artist, Kiwanis Internat. Conv., 1966; designed, dir. constrn. cast: concrete mural Genesis, St. Barnabas Episcopal Ch., Portland, 1960; spl. work drawings old Portland landmarks and houses; propr. John Waddingham Hand Prints, fine arts serigraphs and silk screen drawings, 1965—; featured artist: Am. Artist mag., May 1967, June 1990, published in numerous mags. Served with USAAF, 1942-46. Recipient gold medal Salone Internazionale dell' Umorismo, Italy, 1974, 76, 80; honored with a 45 yr. retrospective Assignment: The Artist as Journalist Oreg. Hist. Soc., 1991. Artist mem. Portland Art Mus.; mem. Portland Art Dirs. Club (past pres.), N.W. Watercolor Soc., Watercolor Soc. Oreg., Oreg. Soc. Artists (watercolor tchr.), Multnomah Athletic Club, Jewish Community Ctr., Univ. Oreg. Med. Sch., Art in the Mounts., Oreg. Old Time Fiddlers, Clan Macleay Bagpipe Band. Home and Studio: 955 SW Westwood Dr Portland OR 97201-2744

WADDINGTON, RAYMOND BRUCE, JR., English language educator; b. Santa Barbara, Calif., Sept. 27, 1935; s. Raymond Bruce and Marjorie Gladys (Waddell) W.; m. Linda Gayle Jones, Sept. 7, 1957 (div.); children: Raymond Bruce, Edward Jackson; m. Kathleen Martha Ward, Oct. 11, 1985. B.A., Stanford U., 1957; Ph.D., Rice U., 1963; postdoctoral (Univ. fellow in Humanities), Johns Hopkins U., 1965-66. Instr. English U. Houston, 1961-62; instr. U. Kans., 1962-63; asst. prof., 1963-65; asst. prof. English lit. U. Wis. Madison, 1966-68; asso. prof. U. Wis., 1968-74, prof., 1974-82; prof. English lit. U. Calif., Davis, 1982—. Author: The Mind's Empire, 1974; co-editor: The Rhetoric of Renaissance Poetry, 1974, The Age of Milton, 1980, The Expulsion of the Jews, 1994; mem. editl. bd. The Medal, 1991; sr. editor: Sixteenth Century Jour.; editor: Garland Studies in the Renaissance. Huntington Library fellow, 1967, 75; Inst. Research in Humanities fellow, 1971-72; Guggenheim fellow, 1972-73; NEH fellow, 1977, 83; Newberry Library fellow, 1978; Am. Philos. Soc. grantee, 1965. Mem. Renaissance Soc. Am., Milton Soc. Am., 16th Century Studies Conf. (pres. 1985). Club: Logos. Home: 39 Pershing Ave Woodland CA 95695-2845 Office: U Calif Dept English Davis CA 95616

WADDLE, JOHN FREDERICK, former retail chain executive; b. Somerset, Ky., July 1, 1927; s. Lewis Everett and Anna Hail (Prather) W.; m. Catherine Joan Osborn, June 3, 1977; children: Lewis Victor, Joan Catherine, John Frederick. B.S., U. Ky., 1949; M.S., NYU, 1952. With Sears, Roebuck and Co., Chgo., 1949-85; nat. mgr. toys Sears, Roebuck and Co., 1969-72, asst. to sr. exec. v.p. merchandising, 1972-76, group nat. merchandising mgr., 1977-78, v.p. children's apparel, 1978-82; mng. dir., exec. v.p. Sears World Trade, Inc., Chgo., 1982-85. Served with USN, 1945-46. Republican. Presbyterian.

WADE, BEN FRANK, college administrator; b. Roanoke, Va., July 20, 1935; s. Frank Hart and Clyde Temple (Weaver) W.; m. Janice Marie Wine, June 14, 1958; children—Andrea Marie, Laurel Faye. B.A., Bridgewater Coll., 1957; M.Div. cum laude, United Theol. Sem., 1960; S.T.M., Boston U., 1961; M.S., Columbia U., 1966; Ph.D., Hartford Sem. Found., 1966. Prof. Shenandoah Coll., Winchester, Va., 1963-65, United Theol. Sem., Dayton, Ohio, 1965-69, James Madison U., Harrisonburg, Va., 1969-71; acad. dean Brevard Coll., N.C., 1971-73, Fla. So. Coll., Lakeland, Fla., 1973-77; pres. Westmar Coll., LeMars, Iowa, 1977-79; provost Bridgewater Coll., Va., 1979-85; v.p., acad. dean Fla. So. Coll., Lakeland, Fla., 1985—; mem., chmn. accreditation visit teams So. Assn. Colls. and Schs., State Council Higher Edn. Va.; vis. lectr. Contbr. articles to profl. jours. Div. chmn. YMCA Capital Funds Campaign, Lakeland, Fla., 1975. Named Disting. Alumnus, Bridgewater Coll., 1994; Hartzler fellow Hartford Sem. Found., 1961-62, 62-63. Mem. AAUP, Theta Chi Beta, Phi Eta Sigma, Omicron Delta Kappa. Mem. Ch. of Brethren. Avocations: breadmaking; saddle horses; music. Home: 947 Hollingsworth Rd Lakeland FL 33801-5821 Office: Fla So Coll Lakeland FL 33801

WADE, BENNY BERNAR, educational administrator; b. Crisp County, Ga., Oct. 3, 1939; s. Julius D. and Eleanor Eugenia (Boulware) W.; m. Merle Bailey Wade, Nov. 11, 1957; children: Noel, Tara. BS in Edn., Ga. So. Coll., 1964; MEd, U. Ga., 1968, Specialist Edn., 1973, EdD, 1977. Lic. reading specialist gifted, adminstrn. and supervision. Tchr., coach Turner County Bd. Edn., Ashburn, Ga., 1964-67; acad. skills coord. Ga. Southwestern Coll., Americus, 1968-71, asst. prof., 1978; curriculum dir. Dooly County Bd. Edn., Vienna, Ga., 1971-78; dir. edn. svcs. agy. Heart of Ga. Coop. Ednl. Svcs. Agy./Regional Ednl. Svcs. Agy., Eastman, 1979-94; exec. dir. RANREB Learning Enhancement Svcs., Inc., Eastman, Ga., 1994—; cons. parent edn., Eastman, 1977—; mem. Regional Ednl. Svcs. Agy. stds. task force Ga. Dept. Edn., Atlanta, 1988-91; mentor, coach So. Regional Ednl. Bd., 1993-94. Author: Benny's Book of Peruvian Proverbs, 1983; editor newsletter Ga. RESA Dirs., 1992. Organizer Four Dimensional Wellness Club, Eastman, 1991; activist Environ. Concers Agy., Eastman, 1989—. Exp. tchr. fellow U. Ga., Athens, 1967; recipient Alumni award for ednl. leadership Ga. Southwestern Coll., Americus, 1980. Mem. Internat. Reading Assn. (local leadership chairperson 1992-93), Ga. Regional Ednl. Svcs. Agy. Dirs. (pres. 1984-85), Ga. Assn. Ednl. Leaders, Eastman Rotary (pres. 1985-86), Phi Delta Kappa. Democrat. Methodist. Avocations: reading, writing, running, ruminating, renewing. Home: PO Box 774 Eastman GA 31023 Office: RANREB Learning Enhancement Svcs Inc PO Box 334 Cordele GA 31015

WADE, CHERYL H., church official. Counselor, tchr. Latin Sch. of Chgo.; assoc. pastor North Shore Bapt. Ch., Chgo., 1980-83; mem. staff Ministers and Missionaries Benefit Bd., 1984—, asst. treas., 1987-90, treas., 1990-92; assoc. gen. sec., treas. Am Bapt. Chs., Valley Forge, Pa., 1993—. Office: American Baptist Churches in USA PO Box 851 Valley Forge PA 19482

WADE, EDGAR L., church administrator. Sec. Christian Meth. Episcopal Ch. Annual Conf., Memphis. Address: Chirstian Meth Episcopal Ch PO Box 3403 Memphis TN 38103

WADE, EDWIN LEE, writer, lawyer; b. Yonkers, N.Y., Jan. 26, 1932; s. James and Helen Pierce (Kinne) W.; m. Nancy Lou Sells, Mar. 23, 1957; children: James Lee, Jeffrey K. BS, Columbia U., 1954; MA, U. Chgo., 1956; JD, Georgetown U., 1965. Bar: Ill. 1965; fgn. svc. officer U.S. Dept. State, 1956-57; mktg. analyst Chrysler Internat., S.A., Switzerland, 1957-61; intelligence officer CIA, 1961-63; industry analyst U.S. Internat. Trade Commn., 1963-65; gen. atty. Universal Oil Products Co., Des Plaines, Ill., 1965-72; atty. Amsted Industries, Inc., Chgo., 1972-73; chief counsel dept. gen. svcs. State of Ill., Springfield, 1973-75; sr. atty. U.S. Gypsum Co., Chgo., 1975-84; gen. atty., USG Corp., 1985, corp. counsel, 1986, asst. gen. counsel, 1987, corp. counsel, 1987-90, corp. sec., asst. gen. counsel, 1990-93; prin. Edwin L. Wade, 1993-95; editor, pub. Let's Talk Sense, A Public Affairs Newsletter, 1995—. Fellow Chgo. Bar Assn. (life); mem. ABA, Ill. Bar Assn., Union League Club Chgo., Am. Philatelic Soc., Royal Philatelic Soc. Can., Toastmasters Internat. Democrat. Episcopalian. Home: 434 Mary Ln Crystal Lake IL 60014-7257 Office: Let's Talk Sense PO Box 6716 Chicago IL 60680-6716

WADE, GEORGE JOSEPH, lawyer; b. N.Y.C., Mar. 3, 1938; s. George J. and Catherine V. (Sweeney) W.; m. Gwendolen Belmont Livermore, June 27, 1964; children: Barbara Caroline, George J. A.B., Fordham Coll., 1959; LL.B., Harvard U., 1962. Bar: N.Y. 1963, U.S. Supreme Ct., U.S. Dist. Ct. (so. and ea. dists.) N.Y., U.S. Dist. Ct. (we. and no. dists.) Tex., U.S. Ct. Appeals (2d, 3d, 5th, 6th, 11th cir.). Assoc. Cravath, Swaine & Moore, N.Y.C., 1963-70; assoc. Shearman & Sterling, N.Y.C., 1970-72, ptnr., 1972—. Vestryman St. James Episcopal Ch., N.Y.C., 1984-90; chancellor Episcopal Diocese of N.Y., 1992—; bd. dirs. The Big Apple Circus, Ltd., 1977-94, pres., 1987-90; bd. dirs. Lamb's Theatre Co., N.Y.C., 1984-87. Mem. ABA, N.Y. State Bar Assn., Assn. of Bar of City of N.Y., Union Club, West Side Tennis (gov. 1982-92). Democrat. Office: Shearman & Sterling 599 Lexington Ave Fl 2C New York NY 10022-6030

WADE, GLEN, electrical engineer, educator; b. Ogden, Utah, Mar. 19, 1921; s. Lester Andrew and Nellie (Vanderwerff) W.; m. LaRee Bailey, Mar. 20, 1945; children: Kathleen Ann, RaLee, Lisa Jean, Mary Sue. B.S. in Elec. Engring, U. Utah, 1948, M.S., 1949; Ph.D., Stanford U., 1954. Research group leader, asso. prof. elec. engring. Stanford U., 1955-60; asso. dir. engring., microwave and power tube div. Raytheon Co., 1960-61, asst gen. mgr. research div., 1961-63; dir. Sch. Elec. Engring., Cornell U., 1963-66, J.P. Levis prof. engring., 1963-66; prof. engring. U. Calif. at Santa Barbara, 1966—; indsl. adviser U. R.I., 1961-63; vis. lectr. Harvard, 1963; cons. to industry, 1956—; vis. prof. Tokyo. U., 1971; Fulbright-Hays lectr., Spain, 1972-73; cons. mem. Dept. Def. Adv. Group Electron Devices, 1966-73; Spl. Chair prof. Nat. Taiwan U., 1980-81; UN vis. prof., Nanjing Inst. Tech., 1986; internationally renowned fgn. scholar lectureship, Nat. Taiwan U., 1988, UN vis. prof. Southeast U., People's Republic China, 1989, Comité Nacional de Ciencia y Tecnologia vis. prof. Universidad de Guanajuato, Mex., 1994; elected mem. The Electromagnetics Acad., 1990. Editor: Transactions on Electron Devices, 1961-71, IEEE Jour. Quantum Electronics, 1965-68; series editor: Harcourt Brace Jovanovich, 1964—; contbr. articles to profl. jours. U.S. del. Tech. Cooperation Program internat. meeting, 1970. Served with USNR, 1944-46. Recipient ann. award Nat. Electronics Conf., 1959, Outstanding Teaching award Acad. Senate, U. Calif., Santa Barbara, 1977, Prof. of Yr. award U. Calif. at Santa Barbara Mortar Bd. Sr. Honor Soc., 1988, Hon. Chairmanship award Twentieth Acoustical Imaging, 1992. Fellow IEEE (life) (mem. adminstrv. com. profl. group election devices 1960-71, mem. publs. bd., chmn. info. processing com., mem. exec. com. 1971-72, dir. 1971-72, chmn. ednl. activities bd. 1971-72, editor proc. 1977-80, Centennial award 1984); mem. Am. Phys. Soc., Phi Kappa Phi, Tau Beta Pi, Sigma Xi, Eta Kappa Nu (Outstanding Young Elec. Engr. award 1955). Home: 1098 Golf Rd Santa Barbara CA 93108-2411

WADE, JAMES MICHAEL, treasurer; b. Fremont, Ohio, July 30, 1943; s. William M. and Jeanne (Freeh) W.; m. Jacqueline Quatman, Oct. 31, 1964; children: Wendy, Amy, James. BA in Fin., St. Joseph's U., Rensselaer, Ind., 1965. Mktg. rep. IBM Corp., Lima, Ohio, 1965-67; systems analyst Johnson Controls, Inc., Milw., 1967-73, mgr. fin. planning, 1973-76, contr., 1976-83, treas., 1983-87, v.p., chief fin. officer, 1987-91; chmn. Portico Mut. Funds, 1988—. Treas., bd. dirs. Wis. chpt. Arthritis Found., 1984-91. Home: 2802 Wind Bluff Cir Wilmington NC 28409-2046

WADE, JAMES O'SHEA, publisher; b. Atlanta, June 17, 1940; s. Richard J. and Mary Clare (O'Shea) W.; m. Linda Norman, June 19, 1971; 1 child, Christopher Scott. AB magna cum laude, Harvard U., 1962. Editor Blaisdell Pub. Co., N.Y.C., 1963-65; asst. to pres., sr. editor Macmillan Co., 1966-69; editor-in-chief World Pub. Co., 1969-71; v.p., editorial dir. David McKay Co., 1971-74; founder, pres. Wade Pub. Co., Inc., N.Y.C., 1975-78; exec. v.p. Rawson, Wade Pubs., Inc., N.Y.C., 1978-82; sr. editor Crown Pubs., Inc., N.Y.C., 1982-85, exec. editor, 1985—, v.p., 1988—. Mem. Century Club (N.Y.C.), Iroquois/D.U. Club (Harvard), Hasty-Pudding Inst. 1770 (Harvard U.). Democrat. Clubs: Harvard (N.Y.C.); Iroquois/D.U. (Harvard); Hasty-Pudding Inst. 1770 (Harvard U.). Home: 1565 Baptist Church Rd Yorktown Heights NY 10598 Office: Crown Pubs Inc 201 E 50th St New York NY 10022-7703

WADE, LEWIS V., mineral research director. Dir. Twin Cites Research Ctr., Minneapolis, Minn. Office: Twin Cities Rsch Ctr US Bur of Mines 5629 Minnehaha Ave Minneapolis MN 55417-3029*

WADE, MICHAEL JOHN, ecology and evolution educator, researcher; b. Evanston, Ill., Oct. 21, 1949; s. John Francis and Mary Loretta (Sweeney) W.; m. Debra Lynn, Sept. 4, 1987; children: Catherine, Megan, Travis. BA, Boston Coll., 1971; PhD, U. Chgo., 1975. Asst. prof. dept. biology U. Chgo., 1975-81, assoc. prof., 1981-86, prof. dept. ecology and evolution, 1986—, chmn. dept., 1991—; mem. predoctoral panel NSF, 1979-84, population biology panel, 1986-88, genetics study sect. NIH, 1988-91. Mem. Soc. for Study Evolution (v.p. 1985). Office: U Chgo Prizker Sch of Medicine 5841 S Maryland Ave Chicago IL 60637-1503

WADE, NICHOLAS MICHAEL LANDON, journalist; b. Aylesbury, Buckinghamshire, U.K., May 17, 1942; came to U.S., 1971; s. Michael Rubens and Laurien (Beesley) W.; m. Mary Veronica Scallan; children: Jessica, Alexander. Student, Eton (Eng.) Coll., 1955-59; BA, Cambridge (Eng.) U., 1960, MA, 1963. Journalist Nature mag., London, 1967-71, Science mag., Washington, 1972-82; editorial writer N.Y. Times, 1982-90, editor sci. sect., 1990—. Author: The Ultimate Experiment, 1977, The Nobel Duel, 1981, A World Beyond Healing, 1987; co-author: Betrayers of the Truth, 1983. Office: New York Times 229 W 43rd St New York NY 10036-3959

WADE, ROBERT HIRSCH BEARD, international consultant, former government and educational association official; b. Tamaqua, Pa., Oct. 5, 1916; s. Edgar Gerber and Florence Annabelle (Hirsch) W.; m. Eleanor Marguerite Borden, Sept. 14, 1946; 1 son, Gregory Borden. A.B. magna cum laude, Lafayette Coll., 1937; diplome d'etudes universitaires, Bordeaux U., 1938; Ph.D., Yale U., 1942. Instr. French Yale U., 1939-42; chief Far Eastern analyst Office Naval Intelligence, 1944-54; asst. Office Nat. Security Coun. Affairs, Dept. Def., Washington, 1954-56, dir., 1956-61; spl. asst. to asst. sec. state for ednl. and cultural affairs, 1962; dir. multilateral and spl. activities Bur. Ednl. and Cultural Affairs, Dept. State, 1962-64; U.S. permanent rep. to UNESCO, with rank of minister, 1964-69; asst. dir. U.S. Arms Control & Disarmament Agy., Washington, 1969-73; exec. dir. Fgn. Student Service Council, Washington, 1974-77; dir. Washington office Am. Assembly Collegiate Schs. Bus., 1977-85; internat. cons., 1986—; Mem. U.S. del. to UNESCO Gen. Confs., 1962, 1964, 1966, 68; dep. U.S. mem. exec. bd. UNESCO, 1964-69; mem. U.S. Nat. Commn. for UNESCO, 1977-83, vice chmn., 1978-79. Author; editor: Management for XXI Century, 1982. Trustee Am. Coll. in Paris, 1967-78, chmn. bd., 1967-69. Served to lt. USNR, 1942-46, PTO. Recipient Merit Citation award Nat. Civil Service League. Fellow Acad. Internat. Bus.; mem. Am. Fgn. Svc. Assn., Friends of Vieilles Maisons Francaises, Phi Beta Kappa, Kappa Delta Rho (Ordo Honorium 1991). Republican. Christian Scientist. Clubs: Union Interallie (Paris), Racing (Paris); Chevy Chase (Washington). Avocations: tennis, swimming, piano. Home and Office: 3049 W Lane Ky NW Washington DC 20007-3057

WADE, ROBERT PAUL, lawyer; b. Atlantic City, Aug. 22, 1936; s. John Joseph and Irene Madeline (Saxon) W.; m. Jeanne Krohn, Aug. 5, 1979; children: Elliott Saxon, Kellyn Deirdre. AB, George Washington U., 1963, JD, 1968. Bar: D.C. 1968, Md. 1990. Assoc. Denning and Wohlstetter, Washington, 1968-69; atty. Office Compt. Gen. U.S., Washington, 1969-72; gen. counsel Nat. Endowment for the Arts, Washington, 1972-83; ptnr. Lowe, Bressler & Wade, Washington, 1983-86, Silverberg and Wade, Washington, 1986-94, Duncan & Wade Assocs., 1994—; vis. lectr. in intellectual property and employment law Stanford U., NYU, George Washington U. With U.S. Army, 1955-58. Mem. Phi Sigma Tau, Nat. Honor Soc. (philosophy). Home: RR 1 Box 467 Bluemont VA 22012-9510 Office: Ste 600 1625 Massachusetts Ave NW Washington DC 20036-2212

WADE, RODGER GRANT, financial systems analyst; b. Littlefield, Tex., June 25, 1945; s. George and Jimmie Frank (Grant) W.; m. Karla Kay Morrison, Dec. 18, 1966 (div. 1974); children: Eric Shawn, Shannon Annelle, Shelby Elaine; m. Carol Ruth Manning, Mar. 28, 1981. BA in Sociology, Tex. Tech. U., 1971. Programmer First Nat. Bank, Lubbock, Tex., 1971-73, Nat. Sharedata Corp., Odessa, Tex., 1973; asst. dir. computing ctr. Odessa Community Coll., 1973-74; programmer/analyst Med. Sci. Ctr., Tex. Tech U., Lubbock, 1974-76; sys. mgr. Hosp. Info. Sys., Addison, Tex., 1976-78; programmer, analyst Harris Corp., Grapevine, Tex., 1978-80, Joy Petroleum, Waxahachie, Tex., 1980-82; owner R&C Bus. Sys./Requerdos de Santa Fe, N.Mex., 1982-84; fin. sys. analyst Los Alamos (N.Mex.) Tech. Assocs., 1984—; owner El Rancho Herbs, Santa Fe, 1988-91, Wade Gallery, Santa Fe, 1990-91, Wade Systems, Santa Fe, 1992—. Vol. programmer Los Alamos Arts Coun., 1987-88; mem. regulations task force N.Mex. Gov.'s Health Policy Adv. Com.; vol. systems support Amigos Unidos de Taos, 1990—. Republican. Avocation: photography. Home: 3336 La Avenida de San Marcos Santa Fe NM 87505 Office: Los Alamos Tech Assocs 1650 Trinity Dr Los Alamos NM 87544-3065

WADE, THOMAS EDWARD, electrical engineering educator, university research administrator; b. Jacksonville, Fla., Sept. 14, 1943; s. Wilton Fred and Alice Lucyle (Hedge) W.; m. Ann Elizabeth Chitty, Aug. 6, 1966; children: Amy Renee, Nathan Thomas, Laura Ann. BSEE, U. Fla.-Gainesville, 1966, MSEE, 1968, PhD, 1974. Cert. Rsch. Adminstr., 1992—. Interim asst. prof. U. Fla.-Gainesville, 1974-76; prof. elec. engring. Miss. State U., Starkville, 1976-85, state-wide dir. microelectronics rsch. lab., Miss., 1978-85, assoc. dean., prof. electrical engring. U. South Fla., Tampa, 1985—, dir. Engring. Indsl. Experiment Sta., 1986-93, exec. dir. Ctrs. for Engring. Devel. and Rsch., 1985-90, mem. presdl. faculty adv. com. for rsch. and tech. devel., 1986-88, mem. fed. demonstration project com. for contracts and grants, 1986-88; mem. adv. bd. USF Exec. Fellows Program, 1987-91; chmn. evaluation task force applied rsch. grants program High Tech. and Industry Coun. State of Fla., 1988-90, vice chmn. microelectronics and materials subcom. 1987-93, mem. telecom. subcom., 1988-89, chmn. legis. report com. FHTIC, 1989-90; vice chmn. subcom. on microelectronics and materials Enterprise Fla. Innovation Partnership, 1993-94; mem. Tampa Bay Internat. Super Task Force, 1986-92, vice chmn. edn. com. 1988; dir. Fla. Ctr. for Microelectronics Design and Test, 1986-88; bd. dirs. NASA Ctr. Comml. Devel. of Space Comm. Ctr., Fla., 1990-93; rev. panel govt.-univ.-industry rsch. round table for fed. demonstration project, NAS, 1988; solid state circuit specialist Applied Micro-Circuits Corp., San Diego, 1981-82; sr. scientist NASA Marshall Space Flight Ctr., Huntsville, Ala., 1983; scientist Trilogy Semiconductor Corp., Santa Clara, Calif., 1984; organizer, chmn. Very Large Scale Integrated/Ultra Large Scale Integrated Multilevel Interconnection Conf., Seminar and Exhbn., editor proceedings, 1991—; organizer, gen. chmn. Dielectrics Ultra Large Scale Integrated Multilevel Interconnection Conf., 1995; cons. in field. Author: Polyimides for Very Large Scale Integrated Applications, 1984, (U.S. Army handbook) Modern Very Large Scale Integrated Circuit Fabrication Processess, 1984, Photosensitive Polyimides for Very Large Scale Integrated Applications, 1986, Very Large Scale Multilevel Interconnection State-of-the-Art Seminar, 1989—; contbr. to encys.; contbr. 120 articles to profl. jours. Treas. Tampa Palms Civic Assn., 1994—; vol., United Fund, Miss. State U., 1983-85. Recipient Outstanding Engring. Teaching award Coll. Engring. U. Fla., 1976, Cert. of Recognition NASA (5 times), 1981-88, Outstanding Rsch. award Sigma Xi, 1984, Outstanding Contbn. to Sci. and Tech award Fla. Gov., 1989, 90. Mem. AAAS, NSPE, IEEE (sr. mem., guest editor periodical 1982, gen. chmn. Internat. Very Large Scale Integrated Multilevel Interconnection Conf. annually 1984-90, editor conf. proceedings 1984-90, chmn. acad. affairs com. CHMT Soc. 1984-86, gen. chmn. univ./govt./industry microelectronics symposium, 1981, tech. program commn., 1991, bd. dirs. workshop on tungsten and other refractory metals 1987-90), Am. Soc. Engring. Edn. (gen. chmn. engring. research counc. ann. meeting 1987, chmn. engring. rsch. coun. adminstrv. com. 1987-90, chmn. coun., 1990-92, session chmn. ann. meeting 1990, 92, bd. dirs. 1990-92, mem. Nominations Com. 1992-94, mem. Long Range Planning Com. 1992-95, recipient ASEE Centennial Cert. 1992, 2d Century Cert. 1993), World Future Soc., Internat. Soc. Hybrid Microelectronics, Assn. U.S. Army (bd. dirs. Suncoast chpt. 1991-93), Soc. Photo Optical Instrumentation Engring., Univ. Faculty Senate Assn. of Miss. (organizer 1985), Am. Vacuum Soc., Am. Phys. Soc., Am. Electronics Assn., Am. Inst. Physics, Nat. Coun. Univ. Rsch. Adminstrn., Soc. Rsch. Adminstrs. (external rels. com. for SRA 1988-91), Fla. Engring. Soc. (v.p. edn. com. 1987-92, pres. 1989-90, bd. dirs. 1989-90, Fla. engring. found. trustee 1989-90, ann. meeting steering com. 1989-90, Outstanding Svc. to the Professiord 1992), Soc. Am. Mil. Engring., Order of Engrs., 1991, Sigma Xi (v.p. 1985), Tau Beta Pi (Fla. Alpha chpt. pres. 1969, 71, nat. outstanding chpt. award 1969, 71, faculty advisor Miss. Alpha chpt. 1977-85, faculty advisor Fla. Gamma chpt. 1986—, recipient outstanding hon. soc. advisor award, 1994), Eta Kappa Nu (pres. 1968), Sigma Tau, Omicron Delta Kappa, Soc. Am. Inventors, Fla. Blue Key (v.p. 1972, sec., 1971), Epsilon Lambda Chi (founder 1970, pres. 1971). Club: Rotary (Paul Harris Fellow 1987, perfect attendance award 1986—, chmn. com. on environ. issues 1990). Active First Bapt. Ch., Temple Terrace, Fla., vice-chmn. bd. deacons 1989-90, chmn. bd. deacons, 1990-91, 93-94, chmn. pastor search com. 1990-91, vice chmn. long range plannning com., 1989-91, vice chmn. pastor search com., 1994-95, chmn. adult coed III Sunday sch. dept. 1993-94; ch. coun. 1994-95. Avocations: collecting antique furniture, carpentry, restoring antique sports cars, basketball. Home: 5316 Witham Ct E Tampa FL 33647-1026

WADE, WILLIAM EDWARD, JR., oil company executive; b. Memphis, Aug. 3, 1942; s. William Edward and Martha (Moulder) W.; m. Noel Lynn Galloway; 1 child, William Galen. BS in Chem. Engring., U. Tenn., Knoxville, 1965; MS, MIT, 1968. Mgr. resource planning Atlantic Richfield, Los Angeles, 1975-76, mgr. Anaconda planning, 1976-79; mgr. oil, gas planning Atlantic Richfield, Dallas, 1979-81, v.p. fin. Arco Exploration, 1981-82, v.p. land acquisitions, mgmt. Arco Exploration, 1982-85; v.p. corp. planning Atlantic Richfield, Los Angeles, 1985-87, now sr. v.p.; pres. ARCO Alaska, Inc., Anchorage, 1987—. Bd. dirs. Los Angeles Theater Ctr. of the Arts, 1985—. Avocations: squash, tennis. Office: ARCO Alaska Inc Anchorage Tower 700 G St Anchorage AK 99501-3446 Other: Atlantic Richfield Co 515 S Flower St Los Angeles CA 90071

WADKINS, LANNY, professional golfer; b. Richmond, Va., Dec. 5, 1949; s. Jerry Lanston and Francis Ann (Burnett) W.; m. Rachel Irene Strong, Jan. 2, 1971; 1 child, Jessica. Student, Wake Forest U. Winner Sahara Invitational, 1972, PGA, 1977, World Series of Golf, 1977, Can. PGA, 1978, Tournament Players' Championship, 1979, 82, 83, Los Angeles Open, 1979, Phoenix Open, 1982, Greater Greensboro, 1983, Bob Hope Desert Classic, 1985, Doral Ryder, 1987, Hawaiian Open, 1988, Colonial Open, 1988, Anheuser Busch Classic, 1990, Hawaiian Open, 1991, Greater Hartford Open, 1992; mem. Ryder Cup Team, 1993. Office: care PGA Tour 112 TPC Blvd Ponte Vedra Beach FL 32082*

WADLER, ARNOLD L., lawyer; b. Bklyn., Aug. 15, 1943; s. Samuel and Anne (Lowenthal) W.; m. Elissa I. Devor, Sept. 17, 1967; children: Craig A., Todd J. BA, Bklyn. Coll., 1964; JD, NYU, 1967. Bar: N.Y. 1968, N.J. 1974. Asst. gen. counsel Metromedia, Inc., N.Y.C., 1968-82; assoc. gen. counsel, Los Angeles, 1982-85, v.p., gen. counsel, Secaucus, N.J., 1985-86; sr. v.p., sec. and gen. counsel Metromedia Co., East Rutherford, 1986—; pres., S&A Restaurant Corp., East Rutherford, 1992; bd. dirs. Orion Pictures Corp. Mem. Zoning Bd. Adjustment, Marlboro Twp., N.J., 1980-82; exec. v.p. Marlboro Jewish Ctr., 1980-82. Mem. ABA, N.Y. Bar Assn. Lodge: KP (asst. sec. 1961-63). Office: Metromedia Co Met Exec Towers 1 Meadowland Plz 6th Fl East Rutherford NJ 07073

WADLEY, M. RICHARD, consumer products executive; b. Lehi, Utah; s. Merlyn R. and Verla Ann (Ball); m. Nancy Zwiers; children: Lisa Kathleen, Staci Lin, Eric Richard. BS, Brigham Young U., 1967; MBA, Northwestern U., 1968. Brand asst. packaged soap and detergent div. Procter & Gamble Co., Cin., 1968-69, asst. brand mgr. packaged soap and detergent div., 1970-71, brand mgr. Dawn detergent, 1972-73, copy supr. packaged soap and detergent div., 1974-75, brand mgr. Tide detergent, 1975-77, assoc. advt. mgr. packaged soap and detergent div., 1977-81; corp. product dir. Hallmark Cards, Inc. Kansas City, Mo., 1982-83, corp. product dir. Ambassador Cards div., 1983-85; v.p., gen. mgr. feminine protection div. Tambrands Inc., Lake Success, N.Y., 1986-88; sr. v.p. Bongrain, Inc., N.Y.C., 1988-89; pres., CEO Alta-Dena Inc., Divsn. of Bongrain, Inc., 1989-91; pres. The Summit

Group, 1991—; chmn., CEO T-Chem Products Inc., 1993—, also bd. dirs.; mgmt. bd. Bongrain N.A., 1988-91; bd. dirs. Calif. Dairy Inst., 1989-90, Nat. Milk Assn., 1990-91, Alta Dena, Inc., 1989-91, Creative Nail Design, 1992—. Bd. dirs. Long Beach Opera, 1991-95, L.I. Friends of the Arts, 1986-88; mem. adv. bd. Bus. Sch. Calif. State U., Long Beach, 1991-93. Avocations: Civil War history, tennis, travel.

WADLEY, SUSAN SNOW, anthropologist; b. Baltimore, Nov. 18, 1943; d. Chester Page and Ellen Snow (Foster) W.; m. Bruce Woods Derr, Dec. 28, 1971 (div. July 1989); children: Shona Snow, Laura Woods; m. Richard Olanoff, July 4, 1992. BA, Carleton Coll., Northfield, 1965; MA, U. Chgo., 1967, PhD, 1973. Instr. Syracuse U., 1970-73, asst. prof., 1973-76; dir. Fgn. and Comparative Studies Program, Syracuse, 1978-83; prof. Syracuse U., 1982; dir. So. Asia Ctr. Syracuse U., 1985—; chair anthropology dept. Syracuse U., 1990-95; trustee Am. Inst. Indian Studies, Chgo., 1984—, exec. com., 1991-94; mem. joint com. South Asia Social Sci. Rsch. Coun., 1982-89. Author: Shakti: Power in the Conceptual Struture of Krimpur Women, 1975, Women in India: Two Perspectives, 1978, revised, 1989, 95, Struggling with Destiny in Karimpur, 1925-84, 1994; editor: Power of Tamil Women, 1980, Oral Epics in India, 1989, Media and the Transformation of Religion in South Asia, 1995. Pres. Edward Smith Parent Tchr. Orgn., Syracuse, 1988-89. Grantee NSF, 1967-69, U.S. Dept. Edn., 1983-84, Smithsonian Inst., 1983-84, Am. Inst. Indian Studies, 1989, NEH, 1995; recipient Marc Perry Galler prize for best doctroal dissertation in social scis. U. Chgo., 1974. Mem. Am. Anthropological Soc., Am. Folklore Soc., Soc. for Ethnomusicology, Assn. for Asian Studies. Home: 302 Carlton Dr Syracuse NY 13214-1906 Office: Syracuse U Maxwell Sch Syracuse NY 13244

WADLINGTON, WALTER JAMES, law educator; b. Biloxi, Miss., Jan. 17, 1931; s. Walter and Bernice (Taylor) W.; m. Ruth Miller Hardie, Aug. 20, 1955; children: Claire Hardie, Charlotte Taylor Griffith, Susan Miller, Derek Alan. A.B., Duke U., 1951; LL.B., Tulane U., 1954. Bar: La. 1954, Va. 1965. Pvt. practice New Orleans, 1954-55, 58-59; asst. prof. Tulane U., 1960-62; mem. faculty U. Va., 1962—, prof law, 1964—, James Madison prof., 1970—, prof. legal medicine, 1979—, Harrison Found. rsch. prof., 1990-92; tutor civil law U. Edinburgh, Scotland, 1959-60; vis. Tazewell Taylor prof. law Coll. William and Mary, spring 1986; program dir. Robert Wood Johnson Med. Malpractice Program, 1985-91; mem. adv. bd. clin. scholars program, 1989—. Author: Cases and Materials on Domestic Relations, 1970, 3d edit., 1994, Cases and Materials on Law and Medicine, 1980, (with Whitebread and Davis) Children in the Legal System, 1983; editor-in-chief Tulane U. Law Rev., 1953-54. Served to capt. AUS, 1955-58. Mem. Va. Bar Assn., Am. Law Inst., Inst. Medicine of NAS, Order of Coif. Home: 1620 Keith Valley Rd Charlottesville VA 22901-3018 Office: U Va Sch Law Charlottesville VA 22903

WADLINGTON, WARWICK PAUL, English language educator; b. New Orleans, May 2, 1938; s. Robert Lee and Della Frances (Guerin) W.; m. Elizabeth Bernard, Dec. 26, 1963 (div. 1988); children: Laura, Mark, Paul; m. Elizabeth H. Harris, Feb. 18, 1995. BS, US. Mil. Acad., 1961; MA, Tulane U., 1966, PhD, 1967. Asst. prof. English U. Tex., Austin, 1967-72, assoc. prof., 1972-78, prof., 1978—, Joan Negley Kelleher Centennial prof., 1987—. Author: The Confidence Game in American Literature, 1975, Reading Faulknerian Tragedy, 1987, As I Lay Dying: Stories Out of Stories, 1992; contbr. articles to profl. jours. With U.S. Army, 1961-64. Decorated Air medal. Mem. MLA, Faulkner Soc., Am. Studies Assn. Office: U Tex Dept English Austin TX 78712

WADLOW, JOAN KRUEGER, university chancellor; b. LeMars, Iowa, Aug. 21, 1932; d. R. John and Norma I. (IhLe) Krueger; m. Richard R. Wadlow, July 27, 1958; children: Dawn, Kit. B.A., U. Nebr., Lincoln, 1953; M.A. (Seacrest Journalism fellow 1953-54), Fletcher Sch. Law and Diplomacy, 1956; Ph.D. (Rotary fellow 1956-57), U. Nebr., Lincoln, 1963; cert., Grad. Inst. Internat. Studies, Geneva, 1957. Mem. faculty U. Nebr., Lincoln, 1966-79; prof. polit. scis. U. Nebr., 1964-79, assoc. dean Coll. Arts and Scis., 1972-79; prof. polit. scis., dean Coll. Arts and Scis., U. Wyo., Laramie, 1979-84, v.p. acad. affairs, 1984-86; prof. polit. sci., provost U. Okla., Norman, 1986-91; chancellor U. Alaska, Fairbanks, 1991—; cons. on fed. grants; bd. dirs. Key Bank Alaska; mem. Commn. Colls. N.W. Assn. Author articles in field. Bd. dirs. Nat. Merit Scholarship Corp., Lincoln United Way, 1976-77, Bryan Hosp., Lincoln, 1978-79, Washington Ctr., 1986—, Key Bank of Alaska; v.p., exec. commr. North Cen. Assn., pres., 1991; pres. adv. bd. Lincoln YWCA, 1970-71; mem. def. adv. com. Women in the Svcs., 1987-89; mem. community adv. bd. Alaska Airlines. Recipient Mortar Board Teaching award, 1976, Disting. Teaching award U. Nebr., Lincoln, 1979; fellow Conf. Coop. Man, Lund, Sweden, 1956. Mem. Internat. Studies Assn. (co-editor Internat. Studies Notes 1978-91), Nat. Assn. State Univs. and Land-Grant Colls. (exec. com. coun. acad. affairs 1989-91), Western Assn. Africanists (pres. 1980-82), Assn. Western Univs. (pres.-elect 1993—), Coun. Colls. Arts and Scis. (pres. 1983-84), Greater Fairbanks C. of C., Gamma Phi Beta. Republican. Congregationalist. Home and Office: PO Box 900147 Fairbanks AK 99775

WADLOW, R. CLARK, lawyer; b. Providence, Nov. 30, 1946. AB, Dartmouth Coll., 1968; JD, Harvard U., 1971. Bar: Alaska 1971, D.C. 1972, U.S. Supreme Ct. 1974. Law clk. to Hon. George F. Boney Alaska Supreme Ct., 1971-72; ptnr. Sidley & Austin, Washington; adj. prof. law Cath. U. Am., Washington, 1982-87. Mem. ABA (bd. govs. 1978-81, chmn. forum com. on comm. law 1987-89, chmn. standing com. on forum coms. 1990-92, chmn. standing com. on continuing edn. of the bar 1993—, chmn. com. on scope and correlation of work 1993-94), Fed. Bar Assn. (mem. exec. com. 1989-92). Office: Sidley & Austin 1722 I St NW Fl 4 Washington DC 20006-3705

WADSWORTH, CHARLES WILLIAM, pianist; b. Barnesville, Ga., May 21, 1929; s. Charles and Ethel (Capps) W.; m. Susan Popkin, June 5, 1966; 1 dau., Rebecca; children from previous marriage—David, Beryl. Student, U. Ga., 1946-48; BS, Juilliard Sch. Music, 1951, MS, 1952. Found. and artistic dir. Chamber Music Concerts of Spoleto (Italy) Festival, 1960-77; founder Chamber Music Concerts of the Spoleto Festival, Charleston, S.C., 1977; founder, artistic dir. pianist Chamber Music Soc. of Lincoln Ctr., N.Y.C., 1969-89; pianist in recitals with Beverly Sills, Hermann Prey, Jennie Tourel, Shirley Verrett, Pinchas Zukerman, Dietrich Fischer-Dieskau. Decorated Cavaliere Ufficiale nel Ordine di Merito dalla Repubblica Italiana, 1975, Chevalier in the Order of Arts and Letters, France, 1986; recipient Mayors award for excellence in the arts N.Y.C., 1979, Handel medallion of City of N.Y. Mayor Edward Koch, 1989. Office: Chamber Music Soc 1941 Broadway 225 E 79th St New York NY 10021 Office: c/o Judith Kurz Enterprises 215 W 91st St/Ste 32 New York NY 10024*

WADSWORTH, CHRISTOPHER, headmaster; b. Boston, June 18, 1940; s. Philip Pearson and Elizabeth (Shaffer) W.; m. Lori Dingman, July 27, 1963; children: Benjamin, Thomas Pearson. BA cum laude, Harvard U., 1962, MA, 1965, MA in Teaching, 1969. Adminstr. Harvard Coll., Cambridge, Mass., 1963-69; headmaster Nichols Sch., Buffalo, 1969-79, Belmont (Mass.) Hill Sch., 1979-93; head Robert Coll. of Istanbul, Turkey, 1993—. Trustee White Mountain Sch., Littleton, N.H., 1989-93, Winsor Sch., Boston, 1990-93, Istanbul Internat. Cmty. Sch.; mem. com. N.E. area coun. YMCA, 1968-74, 80-87; trustee, v.p. N.Y. State Assn. Ind. Schs., 1971-79. Mem. Country Day Sch. Headmasters Assn. (v.p. 1989-90), Headmasters Assn. (sec. 1990-92), Phi Delta Kappa. Avocations: fly fishing, jazz, banjo, racquet sports. Home: Robert Coll of Istanbul, PK 1 Arnavurkoy, 80820 Istanbul Turkey Office: 850 3rd Ave New York NY 10022-6222

WADSWORTH, DYER SEYMOUR, lawyer; b. N.Y.C., June 16, 1936; s. Seymour and Phoebe Armistead (Helmer) W.; m. Beverley Allen Dunn Barringer, Feb. 2, 1963; children: Sophia, Jennifer. B.A., Yale U., 1959; J.D., Harvard U., 1962. Bar: N.Y. 1963, Pa. 1979. Assoc. Humes, Andrews & Botzow, N.Y.C., 1962-64; with Inco Ltd. and subs., N.Y.C., 1964—; asst. gen. counsel Inco Ltd., N.Y.C.; pres. Inco U.S., Inc., N.Y.C., 1993—; v.p., chief legal officer, sec., bd. dirs. Internat. Nickel Inc., Saddle Brook, N.J.; chief legal officer, sec., bd. dirs. Inco Alloys Internat., Inc., Huntington, W.Va.; v.p., asst. sec., bd. dirs. Inco Securities Corp., N.Y.C., Western Aggregates, Inc., Boulder, Colo.; v.p., sec., bd. dirs. Internat. Metals Reclamation Co., Inc., Ellwood City, Pa., Inco Engineered Products, Inc., Springfield, Mass., Novamet Splty. Products Corp., Wyckoff, N.J.; sec., bd.

dirs. LaQue Ctr. Corrosion Tech. Inc., Wrightsville Beach, N.C.; bd. dirs. Inco Alloys Pte Ltd., Singapore, Explorations y Explotaciones Mineras Isabel S.A., Guatemala City, Guatemala; v.p., gen. coun., bd. dirs. Barringer Crater Co., Flagstaff, Ariz.; pres., treas., dir. Cass County Iron Co., Atlanta, Tex. Gen. counsel The Sailors Snug Harbor, Sea Level, N.C., 1987—; pres., bd. dirs. Amsterdam Nursing Home Corp., N.Y.C., 1986—; trustee, past treas. Isaac Tuttle Fund for the Aged, N.Y.C.; bd. dirs. N.Y. Health Care Network, Inc., N.Y.C. Named Trustee of Yr. N.Y. Assn. Homes and Svcs. for the Aging, 1995. Mem. ABA, Assn. of Bar of City of N.Y., Meteoritical Soc., Fgn. Policy Assn. (bd. dirs.), Bus. Coun. Internat. Understanding (bd. dirs.), The Conf. Bd. Clubs: Down Town Assn., Union, Pilgrims (N.Y.C.). Home: 215 E 48th St New York NY 10017-1538 Office: Inco US Inc I New York Plz New York NY 10004-1902

WADSWORTH, FRANK WHITTEMORE, foundation executive, literature educator; b. N.Y.C., June 14, 1919; s. Prescott Kingsley and Elizabeth (Whittemore) W.; m. Roxalene Harriet Nevin, Oct. 22, 1943 (dec. 1979); Susan, Roxalene; m. Deborah Yohalem, Dec. 22, 1980. A.B., Princeton U., 1946, Ph.D., 1951. Instr. English Princeton (N.J.) U., 1949-50; instr. to assoc. prof. English UCLA, 1950-61; prof. English, dean div. humanities U. Pitts., 1962-67; acad. v.p. SUNY-Purchase, 1967-78, prof. lit., 1967-89, emeritus, 1989—; nat. rep. Woodrow Wilson Nat. Fellowship Found., 1958-61, trustee, 1973—; vice-chmn. bd. trustees, 1992—; trustee Wenner-Gren Found., N.Y.C., 1970—, chmn. bd. trustees, 1977-87. Author: The Poacher from Stratford, 1958; contbr. articles to publs. Trustee Rye Country Day Sch., N.Y. Served to lt. (j.g.) USNR, 1942-45. Woodrow Wilson fellow, 1946-47; Scribner fellow, 1948-49; Folger Shakespeare Library fellow, 1961; Guggenheim fellow, 1961-62. Mem. MLA, Am. Soc. Theatre Research, Malone Soc., Phi Beta Kappa. Clubs: Princeton; Conanicut Yacht (R.I.). Home: Sterling Rd Harrison NY 10528-1404

WADSWORTH, HAROLD WAYNE, lawyer; b. Logan, Utah, Oct. 12, 1930; s. Harold Maughan and Nellie Grace (Grosjean) W.; m. Laila Anita Ingebrigtsen, Dec. 27, 1957; children: Warren, Kenneth, Jeffrey, Theresa, Erik. BS, Utah State U., 1952; JD with honor, George Washington U., 1959. Bar: D.C. 1959, Utah 1961, U.S. Dist. Ct. Utah 1961, U.S. Ct. Appeals (10th cir.) 1962, U.S. Ct. Appeals (9th cir.) 1978, U.S. Supreme Ct. 1972. Spl. agt. FBI, Atlanta and Macon, 1959-60; assoc. atty., ptnr. Hanson, Wadsworth & Russon, Salt Lake City, 1961-77; ptnr. Watkiss & Campbell, Salt Lake City, 1978-89, Watkiss & Saperstein, Salt Lake City, 1990-91, Ballard, Spahr, Andrews & Ingersoll, Salt Lake City, 1992—. 1st lt. U.S. Army, 1952-54. Republican. Mem. LDS Ch. Avocations: horsemanship, hunting, fishing, opera, Shakespeare. Office: Ballard Spahr Andrews & Ingersoll 201 S Main St Ste 1200 Salt Lake City UT 84111-2210

WADSWORTH, MICHAEL A., ambassador, director of athletics, former professional football player; b. Toronto, ON, Canada, 1943. Professional football player Toronto Argonauts, CFL, 1966-70; lawyer, 1971-81; ambassador to Ireland Canadian Foreign Min., 1989-94; athletic dir. U. Notre Dame, 1995—. Office: U. Notre Dame Dir Athletics Dept Athletics Notre Dame IN 46556

WADSWORTH, ROBERT DAVID, advertising agency executive; b. Prestbury, Cheshire, Eng., May 20, 1942; came to U.S., 1978; s. Eric and Irene (Thorpe) W.; m. Kathleen O'Meara, Dec. 13, 1968; children: Tracey, Charles Robert. B.A., U. Natal, S. Africa, 1963. With Lever Bros. S. Africa, 1960-66, sr. brand mgr., 1964-66; sr. brand mgr. Gen. Foods S. Africa, 1967; account exec. London Press Exch., S. Africa, 1968, Grant Advt., S. Africa, 1969; dir., then mng. dir. Cen. Advt., Johannesburg, S. Africa, 1970-73; dir. new bus. coord. McCann-Erickson, South Africa, 1973-78; sr. v.p., mng. rep., new bus. coord. McCann-Erickson, Inc., N.Y.C., 1978-82; client dir., exec. v.p. Lintas, N.Y.C., 1983-90; dir. corp. strategy, regional dir. So. Africa Lintas Worldwide, N.Y.C., 1991—. Home: 20 Hobson St Stamford CT 06902-8114 Office: Lintas Worldwide 1 Dag Hammarskjold Plz New York NY 10017-2201

WAECHTER, ARTHUR JOSEPH, JR., lawyer; b. New Orleans, Nov. 20, 1913; s. Arthur Joseph and Elinor (Reckner) W.; m. Peggy Weaver, Feb. 20, 1939; children: Susan Porter Waechter McClellan, Sally Ann Waechter McGehee, Robert. AB, Tulane U., 1934, LLB, 1936. Bar: La. 1936. Since practiced in New Orleans; ptnr. Jones, Walker, Waechter, Poitevent, Carrere & Denegre, 1942—; prof. law Sch. Law Tulane U., 1947-68, prof. emeritus, 1968—; bd. dirs. Canal Barge Co., Inc. Mem. bd. visitors Tulane U., 1959-64; mem. bd. advisors to editors Tulane Law Rev. Assn., 1960—; mem. bd. adminstrs. Tulane Ednl. Fund, 1968-83, mem. emeritus, 1983—. Lt. (j.g.) USNR, 1943-46. Mem. ABA, La. Bar Assn. (gov. 1968-70), New Orleans Bar Assn. (pres. 1961-62), Internat. Assn. Def. Counsel, Tulane U. Alumni Assn. (pres. 1962-63), Maritime Law Assn. U.S., Am. Law Inst., Am. Judicature Soc., Am. Coll. Real Estate Lawyers (gov. 1983-86), Order of Coif, Pickwick Club, Boston Club, stratford Club, So. Yacht Club, Plimsol Club (New Orleans), Phi Kappa Sigma, Phi Beta Pi. Home: 1210 Webster St New Orleans LA 70118-6031 Office: Jones Walker Waechter Poitevent Carrere & Denegre 201 Saint Charles Ave New Orleans LA 70170-1000

WAELSCH, SALOME GLUECKSOHN, geneticist, educator; b. Danzig, Germany, Oct. 6, 1907; came to U.S., 1933, naturalized, 1938; d. Ilya and Nadia Gluecksohn; m. Heinrich B. Waelsch, Jan. 8, 1943; children: Naomi Barbara, Peter Benedict. Student, U. Konigsberg, Germany, U. Berlin, 1927-28; PhD, U. Freiburg, Germany, 1932; D of Sci. (hon.), Columbia U., 1995. Rsch. assoc. in genetics Columbia U., 1936-55; assoc. prof. anatomy Albert Einstein Coll. Medicine, 1955-58, prof., 1958-63, prof. molecular genetics, 1963—, chmn. dept. genetics, 1963-76; mem. study sects. NIH. Contbr. numerous articles on devel. genetics. Recipient Nat. Medal of Sci., Pres. Clinton, 1993. Fellow AAAS, Am. Acad. Arts and Scis.; mem. NAS, N.Y. Acad. Scis. (hon. life), Am. Soc. Zoologists, Am. Assn. Anatomists, Genetics Soc., Soc. Devel. Biology, Am. Soc. Naturalists, Am. Soc. Human Genetics, Sigma Xi. Office: Albert Einstein Coll Med Dept Molecular Genetics 1300 Morris Park Ave Bronx NY 10461-1975

WAETJEN, HERMAN CHARLES, theologian, educator; b. Bremen, Germany, June 16, 1929; Arrived in U.S., Sept., 1931.; s. Henry and Anna (Rischmeyer) W.; m. Mary Suzanne Struyk, July 15, 1960; children: Thomas (dec.), Thembisa, Elaine, David. BA, Concordia Sem., St. Louis, 1950, BD, 1953; Dr. Theol., Tuebingen U., Fed. Republic Germany, 1958; postgrad., Hebrew U., Jerusalem, 1955. Instr. Concordia Sem., 1957; asst. prof. U. So. Calif., L.A., 1959-62; assoc. prof. San Francisco Theol. Sem., San Anselmo, Calif., 1962-70, prof., 1970-74, Robert S. Dollar prof. of New Testament, 1974—; vis. prof. U. Nairobi, Kenya, 1973-74, Fed. Theol. Sem., Republic South Africa, 1979-80, U. Zimbabwe, 1986-87, U. Namibia, 1993-94. Author: Origin and Destiny of Humanness, 1976, 78, A Reordering of Power, 1989, (with others) Reading from this Place: Social Location and Biblical Interpretation; contbr. chpts. to texts. mem. Soc. Biblical Lit., Pacific Coast Theol. Soc., Pacific Coast Theol. Soc. Democrat. Presbyterian. Avocations: backpacking, photography, travel. Home: 83 Jordan Ave San Francisco CA 94960-2351 Office: San Francisco Theol Sem 2 Kensington Rd San Anselmo CA 94960-2997

WAETJEN, WALTER BERNHARD, university president emeritus; b. Phila., Oct. 16, 1920; s. Walter E. and Marguerite D. (Dettmann) W.; m. Betty Walls, Sept. 28, 1945; children: Walter Bernhard, Kristi Waetjen Jenkins, Daniel G. BS, U Pa., Millersville, 1942; MS, U. Pa., 1947; EdD, U. Md., 1951; LittD (hon.), Hanyang U., Seoul, Korea, 1980; LLD (hon.), Gama Filho U., Brazil, 1980; LHD (hon.), Cleveland State U., 1992, Ashland U., 1993. Profl. football player Detroit Lions and Phila. Eagles, 1942-45; tchr. Sch. Dist. Phila., 1945-48; rsch. fellow U. Md., 1948-50, mem. faculty, 1950-73, prof. ednl. psychology, 1957-65; dir. Bur. Ednl. Rsch. and Field Svcs., 1962-65; gen. dir. Interprofl. Rsch. Commn. Pupil Pers. Svcs., 1963-65, v.p adminstrv. affairs, 1965-70, v.p. gen. adminstrn., 1970-73; pres. Cleve. State U., 1973-88; vis. prof. Cambridge U., 1988-89; sr. fellow Internat. Tech. Edn. Assn., 1989; interim pres. Ashland Ohio) U., 1992-93; vis. rsch. fellow U. Edinburgh, Scotland, 1991; Patty Hill Smith Meml. lectr. U. Louisville, 1964; psychol. cons. to sch. systems, 1951-62. Mem. Overseas Capital Corp.; mem. governing bd. St. Vincent Quadrangle, Inc.; chmn., bd. dirs. Talbot Philanthropies, Inc., 1994; mem. pys's commn. NCAA, 1984-88; chmn. Internat. Tech. Edn. Adc. Coun.; Nat. Coun. on Sci. and Tech., 1991—. Co-author in field.; contbr. articles to ednl. jours. Trustee Wood-

ruff Found.; mem. governing bd. St. Vincent Charity Hosp. and Health Ctr. Corp. Recipient Disting. Alumni award Pa. State Coll., 1972, Commdr's. Cross of Order of Merit award, Fed. Republic Germany, 1986, Order Yugoslav Flag Govt. of Yugoslavia, 1988. Mem. ASCD, AAAS (mem. nat. coun. on sci. and tech. edn. 1990—), Assn. Mid-Continent Univs. (pres. 1983), Soc. Rsch. Child Devel., Assn. Urban Univs. (chmn. 1984—), Am. Edn. Rsch. Assn., Aesculapian Soc., Blue Key, Iota Lambda Sigma, Phi Delta Kappa, Phi Kappa Phi, 50 Club, Union Club, Masons. Home and Office: 4790 Sailors Retreat Rd Oxford MD 21654

WAGEMAN, LYNETTE MENA, librarian; b. Trinidad, West Indies, Aug. 18, 1934; came to U.S., 1955.; d. Hubert and Alma (Sampath) Jagbandhansingh. BA in Modern Fgn. Langs., Park Coll., Parkville, Mo., 1959; MLS, U. Hawaii, 1966, MA in Asian Studies, 1976. Serials asst. East-West Ctr. Libr., Honolulu, 1962-66; catalog libr. U. Hawaii, Honolulu, 1966-71, South Asia specialist, 1971-93, acting head Asia collection, 1991-93, head, 1993—, collection devel. mgr. Asia collection, 1991—; exec. com. Ctr. South Asian Studies, 1973-75, 77-79, 81-83, 85-86, 87-90, acting dir., 1988, 90, 92. Mem. Hawaii Libr. Assn. (mem. bd. 1990-92, co-editor newsletter 1990-92), Assn. Asian Studies (exec. bd. com. on South Asian Librs. and Documentation 1983-85, 90—, chairperson 1992—, exec. com. Asian Libr. Liaison com. 1991—, adv. com. Bibliography Asian Studies 1992—), Internat. Assn. Orientalist Librs., South Asian Lit. Assn., Com. on Women in Asian Studies. Avocation: cultivating Bromeliads and other exotic plants. Office: U Hawaii Asia Collection Hamilton Libr 2550 The Mall Honolulu HI 96822 Office: Hamilton Libr Asia Collection 2550 The Mall Honolulu HI 96822

WAGENER, HOBART D., retired architect; b. Sioux Falls, S.D., May 10, 1921; s. Frank Samuel and Beatrice (Hobart) W.; m. Violet LaVaughn, Dec. 16, 1944; children: Diane Kay Wagener Welch, Jeffrey Scott, Shaw Bradley. BArch, U. Mich., 1944. Registered architect, Colo. Draftsman Eggers & Higgins, Architects, N.Y.C., 1946-47, Pietro Belluschi, Architect, Portland, Oreg., 1947-50; designer James Hunter, Architect, Boulder, Colo., 1950-53; prin. Hobart D. Wagener Assocs., Boulder, 1953-77; prin. ptnr. Wagener VanderVorste, Architects, Boulder, 1977-86; ret., 1986; mem. selection com. Colo. Supreme Ct., Denver, 1968-72. Co-author: The School Library, 1962; work pub. in Archtl. Record, Sunset mag., N.Y. Times, House Beautiful, 25 Years of Record Houses. Chmn. Boulder Planning Commn., 1966; pres. Boulder C. of C., 1971. Lt. (j.g.) USN, 1944-46, PTO. Named Outstanding Designer for past 50 yrs. Hist. Boulder, 1983; also numerous nat. and regional design awards. Fellow AIA (pres. Colo. 1973, Colo. Architect of Yr. award 1985), Lions (pres. Boulder 1965). Avocations: travel, golf. Address: 1730 Ave del Mundo #1607 Coronado CA 92118

WAGENER, JAMES WILBUR, social science educator; b. Edgewood, Tex., Mar. 18, 1930; s. James W. and Ima (Crump) W.; m. Ruth Elaine Hoffman, May 31, 1952; children: LuAnn Wagener Powers, Laurie Kay Wagener Ulman. Ba, So. Methodist U., 1951, BD, 1954; MA, U. Tex., Austin, 1967, PhD (Ellis fellow 1967-68), 1968. Instr. edn. U. Tex., Austin, 1967-68, asst. prof., 1970-74; asst. prof. U. Tenn., Knoxville, 1968-70; asst. to chancellor acad. affairs U. Tex. System, 1974; assoc. prof. U. Tex., San Antonio, 1974-78, acting pres., 1978, pres., 1978-89, prof. div. edn. Coll. Social and Behavioral Scis., 1978—; asst. to pres., then exec. asst. to pres. U. Tex. Health Sci. Center, San Antonio, 1974-78, acting dean Dental Sch., 1976-78. Author articles, book revs. in field. Bd. govs. Southwest Found. Research and Edn., San Antonio, 1978-89; bd. dirs., trustee Southwest Research Inst., 1978-89. Office: U Tex at San Antonio San Antonio TX 78249-0654

WAGENIUS, JEAN, state representative; b. 1941; m. Dwight Wagenius; children: Peter, Stuart. BA, George Washington U., 1963; JD, William Mitchell Coll., 1983. State rep. State of Minn., St. Paul, 1987—. Named Environmentalist of Yr., Sierra Club (North Star chpt.), 1992. Office: State of Minn Minn State House Rm 439 Saint Paul MN 55155

WAGENKNECHT, EDWARD, author; b. Chgo., Mar. 28, 1900; s. Henry E. and Mary (Erichsen) W.; m. Dorothy Arnold, Aug. 3, 1932; children: Robert Edward, David Arnold, Walter Chappell. PhB, U. Chgo., 1923, MA, 1924; PhD, U. Wash., 1932. Prof. of English Boston U., 1947-65, prof. emeritus, 1965—; editor Boston U. Studies in English, 1954-57; Lowell lectr., 1958. Author: many critical and biog. works, including The Man Charles Dickens, 1929, rev. edit., 1966, Mark Twain, The Man and His Work, 1935, rev., 1961, 67, Cavalcade of the English Novel, 1943, rev. edit., 1954, Cavalcade of the American Novel, 1952, A Preface to Literature, 1954, Longfellow, A Full Length Portrait, 1955, The Seven Worlds of Theodore Roosevelt, 1958, Nathaniel Hawthorne, Man and Writer, 1961, Washington Irving: Moderation Displayed, 1962, The Movies in the Age of Innocence, 1962, Edgar Allan Poe: The Man Behind the Legend, 1963, Chicago, 1964, Seven Daughters of the Theater, 1964, Harriet Beecher Stowe, The Known and The Unknown, 1965, Dickens and the Scandalmongers, 1965, Merely Players, 1966, Henry Wadsworth Longfellow: Portrait of an American Humanist, 1966, John Greenleaf Whittier: A Portrait in Paradox, 1967, The Personality of Chaucer, 1968, As Far As Yesterday: Memories and Reflections, 1968, William Dean Howells: The Friendly Eye, 1969, The Personality of Milton, 1970, James Russell Lowell: Portrait of a Many-Sided Man, 1971, Ambassadors for Christ: Seven American Preachers, 1972, The Personality of Shakespeare, 1972, Ralph Waldo Emerson: Portrait of a Balanced Soul, 1974; Nine Before Fotheringhay: A Novel about Mary Queen of Scots (under pseud. Julian Forrest), 1966, The Glory of The Lilies, A Novel about Joan of Arc (under pseud. Julian Forrest), 1969; (with Anthony Slide) The Films of D.W. Griffith, 1975, A Pictorial History of New England, 1976, Eve and Henry James: Portraits of Women and Girls in His Fiction, 1978; (with Anthony Slide) Fifty Great American Silent Films, 1912-20, 1980, Henry David Thoreau: What Manner of Man?, 1981, American Profile, 1900-1909, 1982, Gamaliel Bradford, 1982, The Novels of Henry James, 1983, Daughters of the Covenant, 1983, The Tales of Henry James, 1984, Henry Wadsworth Longfellow: His Poetry and Prose, 1986, Stars of the Silents, 1987, Nathaniel Hawthorne, The Man, His Tales and Romances, 1989, Sir Walter Scott, 1991, Seven Masters of Supernatural Fiction, 1991, Willa Cather, 1994; editor: Mrs. Longfellow: Selected Letters and Journals, 1956, The Supernaturalism of New England (John Greenleaf Whittier), 1969, The Letters of James Branch Cabell, 1974; also numerous anthologies including The Fireside Book of Christmas Stories, 1945, The Collected Tales of Walter de la Mare, 1950, An Introduction to Dickens, 1952, Chaucer: Modern Essays in Criticism, 1959, Stories of Christ and Christmas, 1963, The Stories and Fables of Ambrose Bierce, 1977, Washington Irving's Tales of the Supernatural, 1982. Home: 177 Leo Dr Gardner MA 01440

WAGER, BARBARA, principal. Prin. James P.B. Duffy Sch. No. 12, Rochester, N.Y. Recipient Elem. Sch. Recognition award U.S. Dept. Edn., 1989-90. Office: James P B Duffy Sch No 12 999 South Ave Rochester NY 14620

WAGER, DOUGLAS CHARLES, artistic director; b. Gloversville, N.Y., June 11, 1949; s. George Robert and Jane Margaret (Upright) W.; m. Cary Anne Spear, June 20, 1981 (div. Nov. 23, 1993). BA in English Lit. and Theater, SUNY, Albany, 1971; MFA in Directing, Boston U., 1974. Intern Arena Stage, Washington, 1974, asst. stage mgr., 1974-75, stage mgr., 1975-76, asst. prodn. coord., 1976-77, lit. mgr., 1977-80, assoc. dir., 1980-83, assoc. producing dir., 1983-91, artistic dir., 1991—; assoc. prof. drama Colo. Coll., Colorado Springs, 1981, 84, guest artist summer theatre inst., 1985, 86. Dir. (stage prodns.) Madmen, 1975, Singers, Scooping, 1976, Gemini Trappers, 1977, The Course of the Starving Class, 1978, The Past, 1978, Conjuring an Event, 1978, You Can't Take It With You, 1979, The Man Who Came to Dinner, 1980, 89, The Child, 1980, A Lesson from Aloes, 1981, Tomfoolery, 1981, 83, Animal Crackers, 1981, On the Razzle, 1982, Candide, 1982, As You Like It, 1983, Accidental Death of an Anarchist, 1983, 84, Man and Superman, 1984, Execution of Justice, 1984 (Helen Hayes awards for Outstanding Direction and Outstanding Resident Prodn.), Women and Water, 1985, The Philadelphia Story, 1985, The Taming of the Shrew, 1985, Measure for Measure, 1986, Glengary Glen Ross, 1986, Don Pasquale, 1986, All the King's Men, 1987, The Rivers and Ravines, 1987, The Cocoanuts, 1987 (Helen Hayes award for Outstanding Resident Musical), L'Amico Fritz, 1987, A Lie of the Mind, 1988, On the Town, 1988, Merrily We Roll Along, 1989, Our Town, 1990, Pygmalion, 1990, The Seagull, 1990, A

Wonderful Life, 1991, The Father, 1991, The Visit, 1991, Of Thee I Sing, 1992, The Skin of Our Teeth, 1992, Twelfth Night, 1993, The Revengers' Comedies, 1994, The Odyssey, 1994, Long Day's Journey Into Night, 1995. Recipient Creative Achievement in Theatre award Boston U. Sch. Arts Alumni Assn., 1989. Avocations: wine collection, tennis. Office: Arena Stage 6th And Maine Ave SW Washington DC 20024

WAGER, WALTER HERMAN, author, communications director; b. N.Y.C., Sept. 4, 1924; s. Max Louis and Jessie (Smith) W.; m. Sylvia Liebowitz Leonard, May 6, 1951 (div. May 1975); 1 child, Lisa Wendy; m. Winifred McIvor, Aug. 4, 1975. BA, Columbia U., 1943; LLB, Harvard U., 1946; LLM, Northwestern U., 1949. Bar: N.Y. 1946. Spl. asst to Israel dir. Civil Aviation, 1951-52; freelance writer N.Y.C., 1952-54; sr. editor UN, N.Y.C., 1954-56; freelance TV and mag. writer N.Y.C., 1956-63; editor-in-chief Playbill mag., N.Y.C., 1963-66; editor Show mag., N.Y.C., 1965; cons. pub. rels. and editorial dept. ASCAP, N.Y.C., 1966-72, dir. pub. relations, 1972-78; cons. pub. relations Nat. Music Pub. Assn., N.Y.C., 1978-84; dir. communications Juilliard Sch., N.Y.C., 1985-86; counsel pub. relations Mann Music Ctr., Phila., 1986-87, Eugene O'Neill Theater Ctr., N.Y.C., 1987-89; dir. pub. info. U. Bridgeport, 1991-93; tchr. Northwestern U., 1949, Columbia U., 1955-56; spl. asst. to atty. gen. N.Y. State investigation hate lit. in elections, 1962; bd. dirs. Jazz Hall of Fame, 1975-77. Author: Death Hits the Jackpot, 1954, Operation Intrigue, 1956, I Spy, 1965, Masterstroke, 1966, Superkill, 1966, Wipeout, 1967, Countertrap, 1967, Death Twist, 1968, The Girl Who Split, 1969, Sledgehammer, 1970, Viper Three, 1971 (filmed as Twilights's Last Gleaming 1977), Swap, 1972, Telefon, 1975 (filmed in 1977), My Side-By King Kong, 1976, Time of Reckoning, 1977, Blue Leader, 1979, Blue Moon, 1980, Blue Murder, 1981, Designated Hitter, 1982, Otto's Boy, 1984, 58 Minutes, 1987 (filmed as Die Hard 2, 1990); (non-fiction) Camp Century, 1962, Playwrights Speak, 1967, (with Mel Tillis) Stutterin' Boy, 1984. Pres. Columbia Coll., class 1944. Fulbright fellow Sorbonne, Paris, 1949-50, Northwestern U. Law Sch. fellow, 1948-49. Mem. Writers Guild Am., Mystery Writers Am. (bd. dirs. 1988-94), Authors League, Nat. Acad. Popular Music (bd. dirs. 1975-92). Democrat. Jewish. Avocation: traveling. Home and Office: 200 W 79th St New York NY 10024

WAGERS, ROBERT SHELBY, entrepreneur; b. Covington, Ky., Jan. 25, 1943; s. Isaac Shelby and Hazel Marguerite (Eissner) W.; m. Judy Anne Hipke, Aug. 16, 1969. BSEE, Ariz. State U., 1966, MSEE, 1967; PhD, Stanford U., 1972; MBA, So. Meth. U., 1988. Mem. tech. staff Tex. Instruments, Dallas, 1972-76, rsch. mgr., 1977-85; dir. tech. Fisher Controls, Austin, Tex., 1985-86; owner Medallion Custom Castings, Richardson, Tex., 1986—; dir. engring. Andrew SciComm, Garland, Tex., 1992-94; asst. prof. Princeton (N.J.) U., 1976-77. Contbr. book chpts., articles to profl. jours.; holder 11 patents. Rhodes scholar, 1966. Fellow IEEE (best paper award Sonics and Ultrasonics Soc. 1976, assoc. editor jour. 1979-84). Home: 921 Forreston Dr Richardson TX 75080-4002

WAGGENER, RONALD EDGAR, radiologist; b. Green River, Wyo., Oct. 6, 1926; s. Edgar Fleetwood and Mary Harlene (Hutton) W.; m. Everina Ann Stalker, Aug. 1, 1948; children: Marta, Nancy, Paul, Daphne. Student, Colo. A&M U., 1944; student, Oreg. State U., 1945; BS, U. Nebr., 1949, MS, 1952, PhD, 1957, MD cum laude, 1954, postgrad., 1955-58; postgrad., St. Bartholomew's, London, 1956-57. Diplomate Am. Bd. Radiology. Intern U. Nebr. Hosp., 1954-55, resident, 1955-56, 57-58; radiation therapist Nebr. Meth. Hosp., Omaha, 1965-70, chmn. cancer com., 1964-89, dir. cancer and radiation therapy, 1964-89, dir. dept. radiology, 1970-89, dir. cancer fellow-ship program, 1977-89; instr. radiology U. Nebr., Omaha, 1958, asst. prof., 1959-61, radiation therapist, 1959-65, assoc. prof., 1962-80, clin. assoc. prof., 1981—; pres. Highland Assocs. Ltd., Omaha, 1977-89; mem. cancer com. Children's Meml. Hosp., Omaha, 1970-89. Contbr. articles to profl. jours. With C.E., U.S. Army, 1944-46. Fellow AEC, 1952-53, Am. Cancer Soc., 1956-57. Fellow Am. Coll. Radiologists; mem. Nebr. Radiology Soc. (pres. 1963-64), Sigma Xi, Alpha Omega Alpha, Phi Nu. Home: 1227 S 109th St Omaha NE 68144-1813 Office: 13304 W Center Rd Omaha NE 68144

WAGGENER, SUSAN LEE, lawyer; b. Riverside, Calif., Oct. 21, 1951; d. Lee Richard and Alice Lillian (Fritch) W.; m. Steven Carl McCracken, July 29, 1979; children: Casey James McCracken, Scott Kevin McCracken. BA magna cum laude, U. So. Calif., 1973; JD magna cum laude, U. San Diego, 1976. Bar: Calif. 1977, Hawaii 1977. Law clk. to hon. Samuel P. King, Jr. U.S. Dist. Ct. Hawaii, Honolulu, 1976-77; assoc. Gibson, Dunn & Crutcher, Newport Beach, Calif., 1978-86; ptnr. Gibson, Dunn & Crutcher, Newport Beach, 1986—. Exec. editor U. San Diego Law Rev., 1975-76. V.p. 552 Club Hoag Hosp., Newport Beach, 1982-85. Mem. ABA, Orange County Bar Assn. Avocations: hiking, tennis, skiing, real estate law. Office: Gibson Dunn & Crutcher Jamboree Ctr 4 Park Plz Irvine CA 92714-8560

WAGGONER, JAMES CLYDE, lawyer; b. Nashville, May 7, 1946; s. Charles Franklin and Alpha (Noah) W.; m. Diane Dusenbery, Aug. 17, 1968; children: Benjamin, Elizabeth. BA, Reed Coll., 1968; JD, U. Oreg., 1974. Bar: Oreg. 1974, U.S. Dist. Ct. Oreg. 1975, U.S. Ct. Appeals (9th cir.) 1980, U.S. Tax Ct. 1979, U.S. Supreme Ct. 1979. Clerk to presiding justice Oreg. Supreme Ct., Salem, 1974-75; assoc. Martin, Bischoff & Templeton, Salem, 1975-78; ptnr. Martin, Bischoff & Templeton, Portland, 1978-82, Waggoner, Farleigh, Wada, Georgeff & Witt, Portland, 1982-89, Davis Wright Tremaine, Portland, 1990—. Contbr. articles to profl. jours. Fulbright scholar U. London, 1968-69. Mem. ABA, Oreg. Bar Assn., Multnomah Bar Assn., Reed Coll. Alumni Assn. (v.p. 1988, pres. 1989, bd. mgmt.), Alzheirmer's Assn. of Columbus-Willowmeth (v.p. 1992, pres., 1993), Order Coif, Phi Beta Kappa. Democrat. Avocations: wood turning, calligraphy. Office: Davis Wright Tremaine 1300 SW 5th Ave Ste 2300 Portland OR 97201-5630

WAGGONER, JAMES VIRGIL, chemicals company executive; b. Judsonia, Ark., Oct. 29, 1927; s. Loren Dye and Vera (Meacham) W.; m. M.E. June Howell; children: Liz Waggoner Quisenberry, Jay. BS in Chemistry and Math., Ouachita Bapt. U., 1948, DSc (hon.), 1990; MS in Organic Chemistry and Math., U. Tex., 1950. Successively rsch. chemist, sales asst., asst. sales mgr., sales mgr. Monsanto, Texas City, Tex., 1950-57; dir. sales Monsanto, Springfield, Mass., 1957-59; product adminstr. Monsanto, St. Louis, 1959-61, dir. sales, 1961-63, dir. mktg., 1963-67, bus. dir., 1967-68, gen. mgr. petrochems. div., 1972-76, gen. mgr. cycle-safe div., 1976, corp. v.p., mng. dir. Plastics & Resins Co., 1977, group v.p., 1978-80; pres. petrochem. and plastics unit El Paso Co., Odessa, Tex., 1980-83; cons. to petrochem. industry Houston, 1984-85; pres., chief exec. officer Sterling Chems., Inc., Houston, 1986—; mem. adv. bd. 1st Comml. Bank, N.A., Little Rock; bd. dirs. Kirby Corp., Houston, Mail-Well Holdings, Inc., Englewood, Colo. Chmn. adv. coun. Coll. Natural Scis., U. Tex., Austin; mem. devel. coun. Ouachita Bapt. U.; bd. dirs Tex. Rsch. League; bd. dirs., chmn. Good Samaritan Found., 1993-94; supporter, patron Star of Hope Mission; corp. leader, contbr. United Way, Texas City, LaMarque Area, Houston; mem. chmn.'s adv. bd. Nat. Conv. Mem. Nat. Petroleum Refiners Assn. (v.p., bd. dirs., exec. com.), Tex. Assn. Taxpayers (bd. dirs.) Avocations: golf, art collecting. Home: 11 Shadder Way Houston TX 77019 Office: 1200 Smith St Ste 1900 Houston TX 77002-4312 *In my opinion, the greatest single character trait that separates those who excel and achieve from those who don't is their constant committment to excellence and to strive for continuing improvement.*

WAGGONER, LAWRENCE WILLIAM, legal educator; b. Sidney, Ohio, July 2, 1937; s. William J. and Gladys L. Waggoner; m. Lynne S. Applebaum, Aug. 27, 1963; children: Ellen, Diane. BBA, U. Cin., 1960; JD, U. Mich., 1963; PhD, Oxford U. (England), 1966. Assoc. Cravath, Swaine & Moore, N.Y.C., 1963; prof. law U. Ill., Champaign, 1968-72; prof. law U.

Va., Charlottesville, 1972-74; prof. law U. Mich., Ann Arbor, 1974-84, James V. Campbell prof. law, 1984-87; Lewis M. Simes prof. law, 1987—; dir. rsch., chief reporter joint editorial bd. for Uniform Probate Code, 1986-94; dir. rsch., 1994—; adviser restatement (2d) of property, 1987-90; reporter restatement (3d) of property, 1990—. Served to capt. U.S. Army, 1966-68. Fulbright scholar Oxford U., 1963-65. Mem. Am. Law Inst., Am. Coll. Trust and Estates Counsel, Internat. Acad. Estate and Trust Law. Author: Estates in Land and Future Interests in a Nutshell, 1981, 2nd edit., 1993, Federal Taxation of Gifts, Trusts, and Estates (2d edit.), 1982, Family Property Law: Wills, Trusts, and Future Interests, 1991. Office: U Mich Law Sch 625 S State St Ann Arbor MI 48109-1215

WAGGONER, LELAND TATE, insurance company executive; b. Greensboro, Ga., Feb. 5, 1916; s. Andrew B. and Blanche (Proffitt) W.; m. Florence Adelaide Gee, Feb. 15, 1942; children: Frederick Charles, Leonora Blanche. AB, Maryville Coll., 1938; MBA with honors, NYU, 1972; CLU, 1941; LLD (hon.), Maryville Coll., 1987. Mgr. Mut. of N.Y., Boston, 1946-54; v.p. Western sect. Mut. of N.Y., San Francisco, 1954-57; v.p. sales Life Ins. Co. N.Am., Phila., 1957-63, Home Life Ins. Co., N.Y.C., 1963-69; sr. v.p., dir. Home Life Ins. Co., 1969-81; pres. Home Life Equity Sales Corp., 1970-81, Creative Mktg., Inc., 1981—; chmn. Va. Life Ins. Co. of N.Y., 1983—, chmn. emeritus; dir. Warring & Assocs. Internat. Cons., 1983—; instr. Stanford Grad. Sch. Bus. Adminstrn., 1957; exec. vis. prof. Ga. State U., 1981—; past mem. bd. CLU Inst.; mem. agy. officers round table Life Ins. Mktg. and Research Assn.; life ins. pub. relations council Inst. Life Ins.; adv. bd. N.Y. State Ins. Dept.; past mem. agy. officers roundtable. Author: You Can See the World in Forty Days!; contbg. author: other booklets. Life Ins. Sales Mgmt. Handbook; Sr. editor: CLU Jour, 1946—; co-editor: The Life Insurance Policy Contract; cons. editor, contbg. author: Life and Health Insurance Handbook; interviewed for: Am. Coll.'s Oral History of Life Ins. Bd. dirs. and exec. com. Am. Bible Soc.; past bd. dirs. Maryville Coll., U. Tampa, Foster Parents Plan. Served to lt. comdr. USNR, 1942-45. Recipient Leland T. Waggoner distinguished lecture series in life and health ins. established at Ga. State U.; L. T. Waggoner room of Am. Colls. Grad. Center named for him.; N.J. Room of Am. Coll. Grad. Center named in his honor. Mem. Internat. Ins. Soc. (bd. govs.), Tenn Soc., Baltusrol Golf Club. Episcopalian. Home: 83 Slope Dr Short Hills NJ 07078-1953 Office: 1 Gatehall Plz Parsippany NJ 07054-4514

WAGGONER, PAUL EDWARD, agricultural scientist; b. Appanoose County, Iowa, Mar. 29, 1923; s. Walter Loyal and Kathryn (Maring) W.; m. Barbara Ann Lockerbie, Nov. 3, 1945; children—Von Lockerbie, Daniel Maring. S.B., U. Chgo., 1946; M.S., Iowa State Coll., 1949, Ph.D., 1951. From asst. to chief scientist Conn. Agrl. Expt. Sta., New Haven, 1951-71; vice dir. Conn. Agrl. Expt. Sta., 1969-71, dir., 1972-87, disting. scientist, 1987—; lectr. Yale Forestry Sch., New Haven, 1962—; mem. panels on policy implications of global warming NAS, 1989-91. Contbr. articles to profl. jours. Served to capt. USAAF, 1943-46. Guggenheim fellow, 1963. Fellow AAAS (chmn. climate changes and water resources com. 1986-89), Am. Phytopath. Soc.; mem. NAS, Am. Meteorol. Soc. (Outstanding Achievement in Biometerology award 1967), Conn. Acad. Sci. and Engring. (v.p. 1976—), Grads Club. Achievements include mathematical simulation of plant disease epidemics; hydrologic role of foliar pores; impact of climate change on agriculture and water resources; how much ten billion can spare for nature. Home: 314 Vineyard Point Rd Guilford CT 06437-3255 Office: Conn Agrl Expt Sta PO Box 1106 New Haven CT 06504-1106

WAGGONER, RAYMOND WALTER, neuropsychiatrist; b. Carson City, Mich., Aug. 2, 1901; s. Charles W. and Anna J. (Herrick) W.; m. Marion Donnelly, Apr. 12, 1930; children: Raymond Walter, Karen. Student, Highland Park (Mich.) Jr. Coll., 1918-19, U. Mich., 1919-20; M.D., U. Mich., 1924; Sc.D., U. Pa. Grad. Sch. Medicine, 1930. Intern Harper Hosp., Detroit, 1924-25; resident Phila. Orthopedic Hosp., and Infirmary for Nervous Diseases, 1925-26; lab. intern Pa. Hosp., Phila., 1926; asso. with grad. course Pa. Hosp. for Nervous and Mental Diseases, 1927-28; Commonwealth Fund fellow, 1926-29; with U. Mich., 1929—; asst. prof. of neurology and asst. neurologist U. Mich. (Univ. Hosp.), 1929-32, asso. prof. and neurologist, 1932-36, prof. psychiatry, 1937—; dir. U. Mich. (Neuropsychiat. Inst.), 1937-70, chmn. dept. psychiatry, 1937-70, prof. emeritus, 1970—; pvt. practice psychiatry, 1970—; cons. Reproductive Biology Research Found. (name now Masters and Johnson Inst.), St. Louis, 1970—; disting. vis. prof. psychiatry U. Louisville Med. Sch., 1974-86, disting. vis. prof. emeritus, 1986—; co-founder Mental Health Research Inst., U. Mich., 1955; chmn. liaison com. Am. Psychiat. Assn. and Am. Hosp. Assn., 1957-67; U.S. com. World Fedn. for Mental Health, 1959; cons. surg. gen. U.S. Army, 1948-58; adv. to dir. SSS, 1943-48; mem. commn. Mich. Dept. Mental Health, 1945-49, sr. clin. cons., 1974-81; Bd. dirs. Masters and Johnson Inst., 1970—, Behavioral Sci. Found., 1978—. Contbr. sect. to: comprehensive textbook Medicine; contbr. articles to profl. jours. Recipient Disting. Faculty Achievement award U. Mich., 1968, Med. Alumni award, 1974; Golden Deeds award Ann Arbor Exch. Club, 1992. Fellow AAAS, Am. Psychiat. Assn. (mem. council 1943-47, 1954-57, pres. 1969-70, Disting. Svc. award 1988, spl. presdl. commendation 1991), Australia and N.Z. Coll. Psychiatrists (hon.); mem. Am. Neurol. Assn., Soc. for Biol. Psychiatry, Central Neuropsychiat. Assn. (pres. 1951-52), So. Psychiat. Soc. (hon.), W.I. Psychol. Assn. (hon.), Group for Advancement of Psychiatry, Assn. Research in Nervous and Mental Diseases, AMA, Am. Psychopath. Assn. (councillor 1946), Acad. Psychoanalysis, Mich. Soc. for Pastoral Care (dir. 1945, v.p. 1947-49), Washtenaw County Med. Soc. (mem. council 1987—), Mich. Med. Soc. (mental hygiene com.), World Med. Assn., Mich. Soc. Neurology and Psychiatry (pres. 1941-42), Mich. Acad. Sci., Mental Health Soc. Mich. (hon. dir., Vol. Friendship award 1988), Am. Coll. Psychiatrists (pres. 1966-67, E.B. Bowis award 1968), Am. Assn. Chairmen Depts. Psychiatry (1st pres.), N.Y. Acad. Scis.; hon. mem. So. Psychiat. Soc., Sociedad Colombiana de Psiquiatría (hon.). Club: Cosmos. Home: 3333 Geddes Rd Ann Arbor MI 48105-2518 Office: Univ Hosp Ann Arbor MI 48104

WAGGONNER, JOSEPH DAVID, III, architect; b. Shreveport, La., Feb. 27, 1949; s. Joseph David Jr. and Mary Ruth (Carter) W. B.A., Duke U., 1971; M. Arch., Yale U., 1975. Draftsman, Architect of the Capitol, Washington, 1974; archtl. designer Bechtel Corp., San Francisco, 1976-78; staff architect DMJM Curtis & Davis, New Orleans, 1978-80; assoc. Labouisse, Graeber Ltd., New Orleans, 1980-82; prin. Labouisse & Waggonner, New Orleans, 1982-89, Waggonner & Ball Architects, New Orleans, 1989—; vis. critic Tulane U., New Orleans, 1980—; design prof., 1983-84; Architect: 400 Lafayette St. (Gambit Best Comml. Renovation award 1984), 1981-84, 430 Notre Dame St (LAA Honor award 1984), 1982-84, Mignon Faget Canal Place (New Orleans chpt. AIA honor award 1987), Dominican H.S. (Gulf Stated region AIA honor award, 1995). NEA grantee, 1983, 85. Mem. AIA (Honor award, 1987), La. Architects Assn. (Design Festival Presentation 1984, chmn. 1986), Hist. Faubourg St. Mary Corp. (archtl. rev. com.), Soc. Architectural Historians, Assn. Preservation Tech., Nat. Trust Hist. Preservation, Preservation Resource Ctr. (archt. rev. com., bd. dirs.), La. Preservation Alliance (archtl. rev. com.). Democrat. Methodist. Office: Waggonner & Ball Architects APC 2200 Prytania St New Orleans LA 70130-5804

WAGLE, SUSAN, state legislator, small business owner; b. Allentown, Pa., Sept. 27, 1953; m. John Thomas Wagle, Apr. 3, 1980; children: Julia Marie, Andrea Elizabeth, John Timothy, Paul Thomas. BA in Elem. Edn. cum laude, Wichita State U., 1979, post grad., 1979-82. Tchr. Chisholm Trail Elem., Kans., 1979-80; tchr. emotionally disturbed, special edn. Price Elem., Kans., 1980-82; real estate investor Kans., 1980—; prin. Wichita Bus. Inc., Kans., 1983—; mem. Kansas Ho. Reps., 1990, 92, 94—, speaker pro tem, 1994—. Mem. Am. Legis. Exchange Coun. (Outstanding Legis. of the Yr. 1994), Farm Bur., Nat. Fedn. Ind. Bus., Nat. Restaurant Assn., Wichita Ind. Bus. Assn. Home: 14 N Sandalwood St Wichita KS 67230-6612 Office: Kans Ho of Reps Rm 330 N State Capitol Topeka KS 66612-1504

WAGMAN, DAVID S., computer company executive; b. 1951. BBA, Armstrong State Coll., 1973. With Nixdorf Computer, 1973-75, Computer Software Inc., 1975-79, Transaction Tech. Inc., 1979-80; with Merisel Internat., 1980—, chmn. bd., from 1980, co-chmn. bd., 1985—. Office: Merisel Internat 200 Continental Blvd El Segundo CA 90245-4510

WAGMAN, FREDERICK HERBERT, librarian, educator; b. Springfield, Mass., Oct. 12, 1912; s. Robert and Rebecca (Gaberman) W.; m. Ruth Jeannette Wagman, Nov. 21, 1941; children: Elizabeth I. Gaidos, William G. A.B. summa cum laude, Amherst Coll., 1933; A.M., Columbia U., 1934, Ph.D., 1942; L.H.D., Amherst Coll., 1958; LL.D. (hon.), Alderson Broaddus Coll., 1967; Litt.D., Luther Coll., 1969. Instr., Columbia Extension, 1933-35; Ottendorfer Meml. fellow NYU, 1935-36; teaching fellow Amherst Coll., 1936-37; instr. U. Minn., 1937-42; head planning unit postal div. U.S. Office Censorship, Washington, 1942-43; head regulations and trg. sect. postal div. U.S. Office Censorship, 1943-45, regulations officer, 1945; successively acting dir. personnel and acting dir. adminstrv. services Library of Congress, 1945-46, asst. dir. reference dept., 1946-47, dir. processing dept., 1947-51, dep. chief asst. librarian, 1951- 52, dir. adminstrn., 1952-53; dir. U. Mich. Library, Ann Arbor, 1953-78; prof. library sci. U. Mich. library, 1953-82; librarian Mich. Acad. Arts, Sci. and Letters, 1953-78; vice chmn. com. mgmt. Wm. L. Clements Library, 1953-78; exec. com. Mich. Hist. Collections, 1953-78; cons. UN Library, 1959-62, Hebrew U. Jerusalem, 1969, various other univs.; mem. exec. com. Nat. Book Com., 1963-64; vice chmn. Nat. Commn. Obscenity and Pornography, 1968-70; pres. Midwest Region Library Network, 1975-76; bd. dirs. Council Library Resources, 1956-91; bd. regents Nat. Library of Medicine, 1967-71. Author: Magic and Natural Science in German Baroque Literature, 1942. Named Hon. Alumnus, U. Mich. Sch. Library Sci. Mem. ALA (pres. 1963-64), Mich. Library Assn. (pres. 1960, hon. mem. 1978), Phi Beta Kappa, Phi Kappa Phi. Democrat. Home: 3840 Wynnstone Dr Ann Arbor MI 48105-2879

WAGMAN, GERALD HOWARD, library administrator; b. Newark, Mar. 4, 1926; s. David and Sophie (Milinsky) W.; B.S., Lehigh U., 1946; M.S., Va. Poly. Inst. and State U., 1947; m. Rhoda Kirschner, Dec. 9, 1948; children: Jan Donald, Neil Mark. Tech. research asst. Squibb Inst. for Med. Research, New Brunswick, N.J., 1947-49, research asst., 1954-57; mgr. Yankee Radio Corp., N.Y.C., 1950-54; assoc. biochemist Schering Corp. (now Schering-Plough Rsch. Inst.), Kenilworth, N.J., 1957-58, biochemist, 1958-65, sr. biochemist, 1966-68, sect. leader, 1969-70, mgr. antibiotics dept., 1970-74, assoc. dir. microbiol. scis.-antibiotics, 1974-76, assoc. dir. microbiol. scis. and head screening lab., 1977-78, dir. microbiol. strain lab., 1979-84, antibiotics isolation, 1984-85, dir. microbial products chem. screening, 1985-87, prin. scientist, 1987-89, mgr. libr. info. ctr., 1989-93; ret., 1993; freelance tech. writing , editor, cons. 1993—; mem. adv. bd. Nat. Cent. Commn. in Chemistry and Chem. Engring., 1985-88. Coun. mem. Troop 23 Boy Scouts Am., 1964-66; communications officer East Brunswick Civil Def. and Disaster Control, 1966-71; mem. sci. adv. com. East Brunswick Bd. Edn., 1960-68; bd. dirs. Tamarack N. Homeowners Assn., 1983-84, 89—, pres., 1989-93, treas. 1994—. Recipient Public Svc. award Am. Radio Relay League, 1965. Chartered chemist, Gt. Britain. Fellow Am. Inst. Chemists; mem. AAAS, ALA, Spl. Libns. Assn., Am. Chem. Soc., Am. Soc. Microbiology, Am. Inst. Biol. Scis., Soc. Indsl. Microbiology, Soc. Applied Bacteriology (Gt. Britain), Royal Soc. Chemistry, Sigma Xi, Tau Delta Phi. Author: Chromatography of Antibiotics, 1973, rev. edit., 1984; mem. editorial bd. Antimicrobial Agents and Chemotherapy, 1971-74; co-editor: Isolation, Separation and Purification of Antibiotics, 1978, Natural Products Isolation, 1989; contbr. articles to profl. jours. and books. Patentee in field. Home and Office: 17 Crommelin Ct East Brunswick NJ 08816-2406

WAGMAN, ROBERT JOHN, journalist, author; b. Chgo., Nov. 11, 1942; s. Albert Alan and Rosamond (Horner) W.; m. Carol Ann Mueller, Jan. 30, 1965; children: Jennifer, Robert, Patricia, Marilyn. A.B., St. Louis U., 1966, M.A., 1968, J.D., 1971. Analyst Dun & Bradstreet, 1965-67; with CBS News, 1967-71, 74-77; asst. to dean St. Louis U. Sch. Law, 1971-74; Washington bur. chief N.Am. Newspaper Alliance, 1977-80, Ind. News Alliance, 1980-82; columnist Newspaper Enterprise Assn., 1980—. Author, co-author: Hubert Humphrey, The Man and His Dream, 1978, Citizens Guide to the Tax Revolt, 1979, Asbestos: The Silent Killer, 1982, Lord's Justice, 1985, Instant Millionaires, 1986, The Nazi Hunters, 1988, The First Amendment Book, 1991, World Almanac Guide to the Supreme Court, 1993, Blood Oath, 1994; editor: World Almanac of U.S. Politics, 1988—; Washington editor Mobile Office mag., 1993—. Recipient Thomas Stokes award in journalism.

WAGNER, ALAN BURTON, entrepreneur; b. Balt., June 8, 1938; s. Robert Ellsworth and Anna Margaret (Schnitzlein) W.; B.Engring. Sci. (scholastic leadership award) Johns Hopkins, 1960; M.M.E., Case-Western Res. U., 1962, Ph.D. in Bus. Mgmt., 1965; m. Lynn Felton Wynant, June 26, 1964; children: Brian Alan, David Scott, Elizabeth Lynn. Mgr. orgn. planning and devel. Internat. Minerals & Chem. Corp., Libertyville, Ill., 1964-67, dir., 1967-70, dir. v.p., 1970-73, corp. v.p., 1973-78; pres., dir. Taylor Tot Products, Inc., Frankfort, Ky., 1979-80, Fed. Mining Co., 1980-82, Wagner Mgmt. Corp., 1982—; prin., pres. Hilliard-Lyons, Wagner Assoc., 1982-92, Ky. Metals, Inc., Carolina Metal, Inc., Fla. Metals, Inc., Tex. Almet, Inc., Control Machine, Inc., FM Properties; lectr. in field. Trustee, Union Coll., Furman U. Fellow Alfred P. Sloan Nat. Found.; mem. Chgo. Assn. Commerce and Industry, Chem. Industries Council of Midwest, ASME, Am. Mgmt. Assn., ASHRAE, (Homer Addams award), AAAS, Ky. Coal Assn. (dir.), Sigma Xi, Omicron Delta Kappa. Clubs: Knollwood (Lake Forest, Ill); Greenbrier, Lafayette (Lexington). Home: 1523 Lakewood Ct Lexington KY 40502-2567 Office: 651 Perimeter Dr Ste 600 Lexington KY 40517

WAGNER, ALAN CYRIL, television and film producer; b. N.Y.C., Oct. 1, 1931; s. Joseph and Isabelle (Chanson) W.; m. Martha Celia Dreyfus, Mar. 11, 1956; children: David Mark, Susan Jill, Elizabeth Celia. BA, Columbia U., 1951, MA in English, 1952. Mgr. network programs Benton & Bowles, Inc., N.Y.C., 1957-61; dir. program devel. CBS, N.Y.C., 1961-68; v.p. program devel. CBS, Hollywood, Calif., 1968-73; v.p. program planning and devel. CBS, N.Y.C., 1973-75 v.p. nighttime programs, 1975-78, v.p. programs, 1978-82; pres., chief exec. officer The Disney Channel, N.Y.C., 1982-83, Alan Wagner Prodns., Inc., N.Y.C., 1983—; exec. v.p. feature and TV devel. and prodn. Grosso-Jacobson Entertainment Corp., N.Y.C., 1985-90; pres. Boardwalk Entertainment, N.Y.C., 1990—; adj. assoc. prof. visual arts NYU, 1993—. Producer, dir., host: program Living Opera, Stas. WNYC/WNYC-FM, N.Y.C., 1958-68; host radio broadcasts, N.Y.C. Opera Co., 1978-80; exec. producer (film) Reunion at Fairborough, 1985; producer (TV pilot) We're Puttin' on the Ritz, 1986; author: Prima Donnas and Other Wild Beasts, 1961; exec. cons. The Gunfighters, Diamonds; supervising producer Cop Talk: Behind the Shield, 1988, 89, True Blue, TV movie and series, 1989, A Family for Joe, TV movie and series, 1989-90, TV series Counterstrike, 1990-93, Top Cops, 1990—; exec. producer TV movies Spenser: Ceremony, Spenser: Pale Kings and Princes, 1993, Spenser: The Judas Goat, Spenser: A Savage Place, 1994, Wounded Heart, 1995, (TV series) The Marriage Counselor, 1994— Lt. (j.g.) USNR, 1953-57. Recipient Evelyn Burkey Meml. award Writers Guild Am., 1983. Mem. Am. Arbitration Assn., Internat. Radio and TV Soc., Acad. of Cable Programming, Columbia U. Grad. Sch. Alumni Assn., Columbia Coll. Grad. Faculty Alumni Assn. Avocations: opera, other music, sound reproduction, baseball, other sports. Office: Boardwalk Entertainment 210 E 39th St New York NY 10016-0911 *A decent and abiding respect for the opinions and talents of the creative community on one hand, and the consuming community on the other, has always served as the necessary framework for any decision making in both my professional and personal life. The doers and the thinkers are crucially important, but no more so than those for whom they do and think. If I can serve as an effective middle man, a good part of my life's objective is realizable.*

WAGNER, ALLAN RAY, psychology educator, experimental psychologist; b. Springfield, Ill., Jan. 6, 1934; s. Raymond August and Grace (Johnson) W.; m. Barbara Rae Meland, Nov. 21, 1959, (dec. Nov. 1994); children: Krystn Rae, Kathryn Rae. B.A., U. Iowa, 1956, M.A., 1958, Ph.D., 1959; M.A. hon., Yale U., 1970. Asst. prof. psychology Yale U., New Haven, 1959-64, assoc. prof., 1964-69, prof., 1970-89, chmn. psychology dept., 1983-89, James Rowland Angell prof. psychology, 1990—, chmn. philosophy dept., 1991-93, dir., divsn. of the soc. sci., 1992—; cons. NIMH, 1968-71; mem. Pres. Biomed. Research Panel, 1975-76; adv. bd. Cambridge Ctr. Behavioral Studies, 1982—; mem. psychobiology panel NSF, 1984-85, com. on basic research in behavioral and social scis. NRC, 1984-87. Author: Reward and Punishment, 1965; assoc. editor: Learning and Motivation, 1969-74, Animal Learning and Behavior, 1972-74; editor: Jour. Exptl. Psychology, 1974-81, Quantitative Analyses of Behavior, Vol. 3, 1982, Vol. 4, 1983, Vol. 7, 1988. Fellow NSF, 1958 (grantee 1960—), NIMH, 1963.

Fellow APA, AAAS (mem. coun. 1988-91), Soc. Exptl. Psychologists (Howard Crosby Warren medal 1991), Am. Psychol. Soc.; mem. NAS, Psychonomic Soc., So. Quantitative Analysis of Behavior (sec. 1983-92), Ea. Psychol. Assn. (bd. dirs. 1985-88), Sigma Xi, New Haven Law Club. Home: 1405 Ridge Rd North Haven CT 06473-3051 Office: Yale U Dept Psychology PO Box 208205 New Haven CT 06520-8205

WAGNER, ALVIN LOUIS, JR., real estate appraiser, consultant; b. Chgo., Dec. 19, 1939; s. Alvin Louis and Esther Jane (Wheeler) W.; m. Susan Carole Fahey, Aug. 14, 1965; children: Alvin Louis III, Robert Percy. Student, U. Ill., 1958-59; BA, Drake U., 1962; postgrad., Real Estate Inst., Chgo. 1960-65. Asst. appraiser Oak Park (Ill.) Fed. Savings & Loan Co., 1955-60; v.p. real estate sales A. L. Wagner & Co., Flossmoor, Ill., 1961-63; real estate loan officer, chief appraiser Beverly Bank, Chgo., 1963-67; assoc. real estate appraiser C. A. Bruckner & Assocs., 1967-70; founder, profl. real estate appraiser, cons. A. L. Wagner & Co., Flossmoor, 1970—; mem. faculty Am. Inst. Real Estate Appraisers, Chgo., 1974—; instr. real estate appraising Prairie State Coll., Chicago Heights, Ill., 1970—; mem. adv. com. Real Estate Sch., 1972—; community prof. Gov.'s State U., 1977—. Author: The Relocation Appraisal Guide Book; mem. editorial bd. Appraisal Jour., 1975—; contbr. articles to real estate jours., also Mobility mag., Mcpl. Econ. Devel. Founding mem. real estate adv. bd. Gov.'s State U.; mem. Rich Township (Ill.) Personal Svcs. Commn., 1973—; v.p., drive chmn. Flossmoor Community Chest, Crusade of Mercy, 1974-75, pres., 1975-76; auditor Rich Township, 1973-77; mem. governing bd. Glenwood (Ill.) Sch. for Boys, 1973—; chmn. bus. edn. occupational adv. com. Homewood-Flossmoor High Sch., 1977; pres. South Suburban Focus Coun.; mem. South Suburban Mayors and Mgrs. Bus. and Industry Adv. Coun., Flossmoor Econ. Devel. Commn.; bd. dirs. Prairie State Coll. Found., 1985—; treas. U.S. Dept. Housing & Urban Devel. South Suburban Community Housing Resources Bd., 1981—; assoc. mem. Employee Relocation Coun. Recipient Profl. Recognition award, 1989, 92, Pres.'s award, 1989. Mem. Relocation Appraisers Consortium (founding v.p. 1991), Am. Inst. Real Estate Appraisers (mem. governing coun. 1974-75, Profl. Recognition award 1977), Soc. Real Estate Appraisers (nat. pub. rels. com., vice chmn. 1985—), Real Estate Educators Assn., South Suburban Assn. Commerce and Industry, Chgo. Assn. Commerce and Industry, Chgo. Real Estate Bd., Homewood-Flossmoor Real Estate Bd., Nat. Assn. Realtors, Ill. Assn. Realtors, Appraisal Inst., Homewood-Flossmoor Jaycees, Flossmoor Country Club, Variety Club, Rotary, Masons, Phi Delta Theta (pres. chpt. 1960), Chgo. Phi Delta Theta Alumni Club (pres.), Omega Tau Rho, Lambda Alpha. Home: 927 Park Dr Flossmoor IL 60422-1122 Office: 2709 Flossmoor Rd Flossmoor IL 60422-1141

WAGNER, ARTHUR WARD, JR., lawyer; b. Birmingham, Ala., Aug. 13, 1930; s. Arthur Ward and Lucille (Lockheart) W.; m. Ruth Shingler, May 11, 1957; children: Celia Wagner Minter, Julia Ann Wagner, Helen Wagner McAfee. BSBA, U. Fla., 1954, JD, 1957. Bar: Fla. 1957, U.S. Dist. Ct. (so. dist.) Fla. 1957, U.S. Dist. Ct. (mid. dist.) Fla. 1975. Ptnr. Wagner, Nugent, Johnson, & McAfee, P.A., West Palm Beach, Fla., 1959—; lectr. in field. Author: Art of Advocacy: Jury Selection, 1981; co-author: Anatomy of Personal Injury Lawsuit I & II, 1968 and 1981. Mem. 15th Jud. Nominating Com., Palm Beach City, 1979-82, 4th Dist. Nominating Commn., Palm Beach City, 1982-86; mem. pres.'s coun. U. Fla.; vestry, chancellor Holy Trinity Parish. Fellow Internat. Acad. Trial Lawyers, Am. Coll. Trial Lawyers, Internat. Soc. Barristers, Am. Bd. Trial Advs.; mem. Assn. Trial Lawyers Am. (pres. 1975-76, hon. life trustee Roscoe Pound Found.), So. Trial Lawyers Assn. (pres. 1991), U. Fla. Law Coll. Alumni (mem. bd. govs.). Democrat. Episcopalian. Office: Wagner Nugent Johnson & McAfee PA 1818 S Australian Ave West Palm Beach FL 33409-6487

WAGNER, BETTY VALIREE, medical organization executive; b. Chgo., Sept. 27, 1923; d. Frank Oliver and Valiree Pearl (Jones) Redmond; m. Robert Arnet Wagner, Oct. 17, 1942 (dec. Sept. 1975); children: Gail Wagner Gratzianna, Robert, Wayne (dec.), Mary Wagner Wright, Margaret Wagner Dowd, Dorothea Wagner Rasmussen, Helen Wagner Huntley; m. Paul Spandikow, Nov. 6, 1993. Co-founder La Leche League Internat., Franklin Park, Ill., 1956, exec. dir., 1972-92, exec. dir. emeritus, 1992—; speaker LaLeche League Internat. Confs., Eng., Ireland, N.J., Can., Fed. Rep. Ger., France, Switzerland, S. Africa, Zimbabwe, U.S.; speaker to med. community U.S., S. Africa. Co-author: The Womanly Art of Breastfeeding, 1963, 4th edit. 1987; contbr. to La Leche League News,. Office: La Leche League Internat 1400 N Meacham Rd Schaumburg IL 60176

WAGNER, BRUCE STANLEY, marketing communications executive; b. San Diego, Aug. 1, 1943; s. Robert Sheldon and Janet (Lowther) W.; m. Elizabeth Pearsall Winslow, Oct. 4, 1975; children: Sage Elizabeth, Alexander Winslow. BA, Dartmouth Coll., 1965; MBA, U. Pa., 1984. Sr. v.p. Grey Advt., Inc., N.Y.C., 1967-81; exec. v.p., chief operating officer Campaign '76 Media Communications, Inc., Washington, 1975-76; exec. v.p., bd. dirs. Ross Roy, Inc., Bloomfield Hills, Mich., 1981-91, Ross Roy Group, Inc., Bloomfield Hills, Mich., 1991-94; v.p. comm. ITT Automotive Inc., Auburn Hills, Mich., 1995—. Mem. Am. Mgmt. Assn. Advt. Agys. (bd. govs. ctrl region 1988-94, chmn., bd. govs. Mich. coun. 1985-86), Wharton Alumni Assn. (chmn. 1983-85), Wharton Club of Mich. (bd. dirs. 1985—), Detroit Athletic Club, Orchard Lakes Country Club, Birmingham Athletic Club. Home: 975 Arlington Rd Birmingham MI 48009-1684 Office: ITT Automotive Inc 3000 University Dr Auburn Hills MI 48326

WAGNER, BURTON ALLAN, lawyer; b. Milw., June 13, 1941; s. Irwin and Jennie (Oxman) W.; m. Georgia Olchoff, Aug. 29, 1964; children: Andrew, Laura. B.B.A. in Acctg, U. Wis., 1963, J.D., 1966, M.A. in Health Services Adminstrn, 1966. Bar: Wis. 1966. Assoc. legal counsel U. Wis., 1968-74; asst. to vice chancellor, legal counselor U. Wis. Hosps., 1974-77; asst. sec. Wis. Dept. Health and Social Services, 1977-83, adminstr. div. community services, 1979-83; clin. assoc. prof. health adminstrn. U. Wis.; ptnr. Thomas Harnisch & Wagner, Madison, 1983-85, Whyte & Hirschboeck, Madison, 1985-90; ptnr. (of counsel) Katten Muchin and Zavis, Madison, 1990-93; ptnr. Reinhart Boerner Van Deuren Nouvis & Rieselbach, Madison, 1993—. Chmn. personnel com. Dane County chpt. ARC, 1977-90. Served with USAR, 1966-68, Vietnam. Decorated Bronze Star. Mem. Soc. Law and Medicine, Wis. Bar Assn., Dane County Bar Assn. Jewish. Office: 44 E Mifflin St Ste 404 Madison WI 53703-2800

WAGNER, CARRUTH JOHN, physician; b. Omaha, Sept. 4, 1916; s. Emil Conrad and Mabel May (Knapp) W. A.B., Omaha U., 1938; B.Sc., U. Nebr., 1938, M.D., 1941, D.Sc., 1966. Diplomate: Am. Bd. Sugery, Am. Bd. Orthopaedic Surgery. Intern U.S. Marine Hosp., Seattle, 1941-42; resident gen. surgery and orthopaedic surgery USPHS hosps., Shriners Hosp., Phila., 1943-46; med. dir. USPHS, 1952-62; chief orthopaedic service USPHS Hosp., San Francisco, 1946-51, S.I., N.Y., 1951-55; health mblzn. USPHS Hosp., 1959-62; asst. surgeon gen. chief div. hosps. UPHS, 1957-59; chief div. USPHS, 1962-65, USPHS (Indian Health), 1962-65; dir. Bur. Health Services, 1965-68; Washington rep. AMA, 1968-72; health services cons., 1972-79; dept. health services State of Calif., 1979—. Contbr. articles to med. jours. Served with USCGR, World War II. Recipient Pfizer award, 1962; Meritorious award Am. Acad. Gen. Practice, 1965; Distinguished Service medal, 1968, Calif. Pub. Health recognitionaward, 1995. Fellow A.C.S. (bd. govs.), Am. Soc. Surgery Hand, Am. Assn. Surgery Trauma, Am. Geriatrics Soc., Am. Acad. Orthopaedic Surgeons; mem. Nat. Assn. Sanitarians, Am. Pub. Health Assn. Sanitarians, Am. Pub. Health Assn., Washington Orthopaedic Club, Am. Legion, Alpha Omega Alpha. Lutheran. Club: Mason (Shriner). Home: 6234 Silverton Way Carmichael CA 95608-0757 Office: PO Box 638 Carmichael CA 95609-0638 *My success can best be summarized as the result of efforts of other people. First my family, particularly my mother, then my teachers and preceptors, and finally my associates. Throughout my life there has been a key individual who created an environment where I could exercise my maximum capabilities. Later in life when it became possible for me to provide similar opportunities for associates I found the benefits I derived far exceeded anything I could have achieved on my own. In summary, success means getting things done, getting planned things done, and getting planned things done largely through other people.*

WAGNER, CHARLES LEONARD, electrical engineer, consultant; b. Pitts., Nov. 23, 1925; s. Charles Fredrick and Ada Sophia (Hanna) W.; m. Rachel

Mae Arbogast, Nov. 15, 1952 (dec. Mar. 1978); children: Charles John, Virginia Ann, Robert Alan. BSEE, Bucknell U., 1945; MSEE, U. Pitts., 1949. Registered profl. engr., Pa. Engr. Westinghouse Elec. Corp., Pitts., 1946-50, sponsor engr., 1950-67, mgr. transmission engring., 1967-76, cons. engr., 1976-85; pvt. cons. Export, Pa., 1985—; adj. instr. U. Pitts., Carnegie-Mellon U., 1952-85. Contbr. articles to profl. jours. Lt. (j.g.) USN, 1943-46. Fellow IEEE (C.P. Steinmetz award, Standards medallion, Centennial medal, Switchgear Com. Dist. Svc. award 1982, Relay Com. Dist. Svc. award 1985, Tech. Coun. Meritorious Svc. award 1990); mem. Internat. Conf. Large High Voltage Electric Systems (Attwood Assoc. award), Power Engring. Soc. of IEEE (chmn. tech. coun. 19771-81, v.p. 1981-83, pres. 1984-85, Meritorious Svc. award 1989, Paper prizes 1970, 90), Tau Beta Pi, Pi Mu Sigma. Presbyterian. Avocations: golf, woodworking, computing. Home and Office: 4933 Simmons Dr Export PA 15632-9330

WAGNER, CHRISTIAN NIKOLAUS JOHANN, materials engineering educator; b. Saarbrucken-Dudweiler, Germany, Mar. 6, 1927; came to U.S., 1959, naturalized, 1969; s. Christian Jakob and Regina (Bungert) W.; m. Rosemarie Anna Mayer, Apr. 5, 1952; children—Thomas Martin, Karla Regine, Petra Susanne. Student, U. Poitiers, France, 1948-49; Licence es Sci., U. Saar, Ger., 1951, Diplom-Ingenieur, 1954, Dr.rer.nat., 1957. Research asst. Inst. fur Metallforschung, Saarbrucken, 1953-54; vis. fellow M.I.T., 1955-56; research asso. Inst. fur Metallforschung, 1957-58; teaching, research asst. U. Saarbrucken, 1959; asst. prof. Yale U., New Haven, Conn., 1959-62; assoc. prof. Yale U., 1962-70; prof. dept. materials engring. UCLA, 1970-91, prof. emeritus, 1991—, chmn. dept., 1974-79, asst. dean undergrad. studies Sch. Engring. and Applied Sci., 1982-85, acting chmn., 1990-91; vis. prof. Tech. U., Berlin, 1969, U. Saarbrücken, 1979-80. Contbr. articles to profl. jours. Recipient U.S. Sci. Humboldt award U. Saarbrucken, 1989-90, 92. Fellow Am. Soc. Metals Internat.; mem. Am. Phys. Soc., Am. Crystallographic Assn., Minerals, Metals and Materials Soc., Materials Rsch. Soc., Sigma Xi. Home: 20407 Seaboard Rd Malibu CA 90265-5349 Office: UCLA 5731 Boelter Hall Los Angeles CA 90024-1595

WAGNER, CHRISTINA BREUER, media company executive; b. N.Y.C., Sept. 29, 1954; d. Wesley Allen and Ingrid (Reichhold) W. BA, Princeton U., 1976; MBA, Columbia U., 1983. Asst. mgr. Chemical Bank, Seoul, Korea and N.Y.C., 1977-80; corp. fin. assoc. Morgan Guaranty Trust, N.Y.C., 1983-84; dir. planning Macmillan, Inc., N.Y.C., 1985-88; v.p. fin. sch. div. Macmillan Pub. Co., N.Y.C., 1988-89; v.p. ops. Macmillan, Inc., N.Y.C., 1989-90; CFO Macmillan Pub. Co., N.Y.C., 1990-91; CFO K-III Mags. Inc., N.Y.C., 1991-94, v.p., 1994-95; CEO Stagebill, Inc., N.Y.C., 1994-95; group v.p. K-III Media, N.Y.C., 1995—. Office: K-III Comms Inc 745 5th Ave New York NY 10151

WAGNER, CLARENCE, historian. Historian National Baptist Conv. USA Inc., Gainesville, Ga. Office: Nat Baptist Conv USA Inc 500 Myrtle St Gainesville GA 30501

WAGNER, CURTIS LEE, JR., judge; b. Kingsport, Tenn., Nov. 8, 1928; m. Jeanne E. Allen; children: Curtis L. III, Rex A. Student Tenn. Poly. Inst., 1947-49; LLB, U. Tenn., 1951. Bar: Tenn. 1952. Assoc. Kramer, Dye, McNabb and Greenwood, Knoxville, Tenn., 1951-54; atty.-adv. gen. crimes and fraud sect. Criminal Div., Dept. Justice, Washington, 1954-56, trial atty. Dept. Justice, 1954-60, assigned to Ct. of Claims sect. Civil Div., 1956-60; spl. asst. to JAG for communications, transp. and utilities, Office JAG, Dept. Army, Washington, 1960-64, chief Regulatory Law Div., 1964-74, mem. civilian lawyer career com., 1960-74, chmn. JAG incentive awards com. 1960-74, mem. Army Staff Awards Bd., 1964-74, mem. Army Environ. Policy Council, 1972-74. Adminstrv. law judge FERC, Washington, 1974-79, chief adminstrv. law judge, 1979—. Dist. commr. Nat. Capital Area council Boy Scouts Am., 1967-69. Decorated Meritorious Civilian Service award, Exceptional Civilian Service award; recipient citation for outstanding performance Dept. Army, 1961-74; Scouter's Tng. award Boy Scouts Am., 1965, Scoutmaster's Key, 1966, Commr.'s Key, 1968, Commr.'s Arrowhead Honor, 1966, Silver Beaver award, 1969. Mem. Order of Arrow. Methodist. Clubs: Annapolis Yacht (parliamentarian). Office: Fed Energy Regulatory Commn 810 1st St NE Washington DC 20426

WAGNER, CYRIL, JR., metals manufacturing company executive; b. 1935. Independent Oil Producer, 1952-84; partner Wagner & Brown, 1962—; Ch Bd, dir Insilco Corp, 1988—; Mgr, INR partners, Midland, 1988—. Office: Insilco Corp 300 N. Marienfield/400 Midland TX 79701

WAGNER, D. WILLIAM, lawyer; b. Dixon, Ill., Jan. 14, 1943; s. Earl L. and Lois Mae (Schrock) W.; m. Barbara J. Bogott, June 11, 1966; children: Peter Alan, Nicholas William. BA, Northwestern U., 1965, JD, 1968. Bar: Ill. 1968, U.S. Dist. Ct. (no. dist.) Ill. 1969, U.S. Ct. Appeals (7th cir.) 1971, Calif. 1982. Ptnr. firm Sidley & Austin, Chgo. and L.A., 1969—. Dir. Housing Options for People to Excell, Inc., 1992—. Co-author: Illinois Municipal Law: Subdivisions and Subdivisions in Controls, 1978, 81. Mem. Los Angeles County Bar Assn., ABA, Ill. State Bar Assn., Chgo. Bar Assn. (chmn. real property land use com. 1980-81), Beverly Hills Bar Assn. (chmn. real estate sect. 1986-87). Presbyterian. Clubs: Legal (Chgo.); Beach (Santa Monica). Home: 20 Ocean Park Blvd Apt 25 Santa Monica CA 90405-3557 Office: Sidley & Austin 555 W 5th St Ste 4000 Los Angeles CA 90013-3018

WAGNER, DAVID JAMES, banker; b. Cin., Mar. 15, 1954; s. George A. and Mary (Tyssowski) W.; m. Kay A. Ambrosius, Dec. 27, 1975. BA, Ind. U., 1975, MBA, 1976. Chmn., pres., chief exec. officer Old Kent Bank of Grand Haven (Mich.), 1983-85; exec. v.p. Old Kent Bank and Trust Co., Grand Rapids, Mich., 1983-85, pres., 1986—. Office: Old Kent Fin Corp 1 Vandenberg Pl SE Grand Rapids MI 49506

WAGNER, DONALD BERT, health care consultant; b. York, Pa., July 27, 1930; s. Bert Daniel and Mary Elizabeth (Roelke) W.; m. Janet Louise Bankert, July 12, 1952; children: Kimberly, Susan, David, John. Student, Franklin & Marshall, 1948-50; BS in Phys. Therapy, Columbia U., 1952; MHA, Baylor U., 1960. Commd. 2d lt. USAF, 1952, advanced through grades to brig. gen., 1981; physical therapist Randolph AFB, San Antonio, 1952-55; asst. adminstr. USAF/RAF S. Ruislip, London; adminstr. USAF/RAF Bentwaters, Ipswich, Eng., 1955-58; various adminstrv. roles USAF Hosps. and Commands, Europe and U.S., 1958-73; dep. comdr. USAF Sch. Health Care Sci., Wichita Falls, Tex., 1973-75; adminstr. Wilford Hall Med. Ctr., San Antonio, 1975-79; chief med. svc. corps Office Surgeon Gen. USAF, San Antonio, 1979-82; dep. surgeon gen. USAF Med. Svc. Ctr., San Antonio, 1981-82, ret., 1982; adminstr., assoc. v.p. M. D. Anderson/U. Tex. Cancer Ctr., Houston, 1982-85; chief exec. officer Meml. Southwest Hosp., Houston, 1985-91; v.p. Meml. Hosp. System, Houston, 1985-91, cons., 1992—; dir. residency edn., grad. program in healthcare adminstrn. U. Houston, Clear Lake; adj. prof. Baylor and Trinity U., San Antonio, 1975-82; assoc. prof. U. Houston, St. Louis U., 1982-88. Bd. dirs. Hospice at the Med. Ctr., Child Advocates, Houston, 1985-89, Kidney Found., Houston, 1985-88, Westland YMCA, Houston, 1985-88, 90-94, Greater Houston Hosp. Coun., 1983-87, Sam Houston area Alzheimer's Assn. 1990-94; chmn. external adv. bd. Sch. Allied Health, U. Tex. Med. Br. Named Disting. Alumnus Baylor U. Program in Healthcare Adminstrn., 1993. Fellow Am. Coll. Healthcare Execs. (edn. com.), Royal Soc. Health; mem. Am. Hosp. Assn. (bd. dirs. hosp. rsch. and edn. found. 1990—), Tex. Hosp. Assn., Assn. Mil. Surgeons U.S. (Ray E. Brown award 1982, Outstanding Sr. Level Healthcare Exec. Ache Regents award 1991), Am. Mgmt. Soc. Republican. Methodist. Avocation: music. Home: 1746 Carriage Way Sugar Land TX 77478-4201 Office: Meml Healthcare System 7737 Southwest Fwy Houston TX 77074-1815

WAGNER, DOUGLAS WALKER ELLYSON, journal editor; b. Orange, N.J., Nov. 5, 1938; s. Norman Raphael and Virginia (Taylor) W. B.A., Yale U., 1960. Editorial coordinator Med. World News, N.Y.C., 1965-69, assoc. editor, 1969-70; writer, assoc. editor Emergency Medicine, N.Y.C., 1970-76, sr. editor, 1976-81, editor-in-chief, 1981-87; editor, pub. Pediatric Primary Care (formerly Pediatric Therapeutics and Toxicology, Jersey City, 1987—; editor Pediatric Emergency and Critical Care (formerly Pediatric Trauma and Acute Care, 1988—; editor-in-chief Transition: Medicine and the Aging Process, N.Y.C., 1983. Mem. Nat. Assn. Sci. Writers, Am. Med. Writers Assn., Soc. for Acad. Emergency Medicine (assoc.), Soc. Pediatric Emergency Medicine, Am. Acad. Clin. Toxicology. Home: PO Box 23 72

Sussex St Jersey City NJ 07303-0023 Office: Riverpress Inc PO Box 23 Jersey City NJ 07303-0023

WAGNER, DURRETT, former publisher, picture service executive; b. El Paso, Tex., Feb. 27, 1929; s. Francis and Florence (Durrett) W.; m. Betty Jane Brown, June 7, 1951; children—Gordon, Velma, Kendra. B.A., Baylor U., 1950; M.Div., Yale, 1954; postgrad., U. Chgo., 1954-59. Chmn. social sci. div. Kendall Coll., Evanston, Ill., 1959-63; dean Kendall Coll., 1963-67; partner v.p.; Swallow Press Inc., Chgo., 1967-92; owner, partner, pres. Hist. Pictures Service, Inc., Chgo., 1975-92; now pres. Bookworks, Inc., Chgo. Home and Office: 614 Ingleside Pl Evanston IL 60201-1742

WAGNER, EDWARD FREDERICK, JR., investment management company executive; b. Columbus, Ohio, Nov. 26, 1938; s. Edward Frederick and Margaret Ann (List) W.; m. Diana Beth Pietraszewski, Jan. 14, 1989; 1 child, Edward Frederick III. BS, Xavier U., Cin., 1960; MBA, Miami U., Oxford, Ohio, 1965. Registered prin. and ops. rep. N.Y. Stock Exch., Am. Stock Exch.; registered rep. Nat. Assn. Securities Dealers. Investment analyst The Equitable Life Assurance Soc. U.S., N.Y.C., 1965-68; security analyst H.C. Wainwright & Co., N.Y.C., 1968-71; v.p. William D. Witter, Inc., N.Y.C., 1971-76, Wainwright Securities, Inc., N.Y.C., 1976-78, Blyth Eastman Dillon & Co., Inc., N.Y.C., 1978-79, Salomon Bros., Inc., N.Y.C., 1979-81, Lehman Bros., Kuhn Loeb & Co., Inc., N.Y.C., 1981-84; sr. v.p. Gabelli & Co., Inc., Rye, N.Y., 1984—; GAMCO Investors, Inc., Rye, 1984—. 1st lt. U.S. Army, 1961-63. Mem. N.Y. Soc. Security Analysts Inc., Assn. for Investment Mgrs. and Rsch., Racquet and Tennis Club (N.Y.C.), The Leash (N.Y.C.), The Rockaway Hunting Club (Cedarhurst, N.Y.), Southampton (N.Y.) Club. Avocations: squash racquets, golf, billiards, gun dogs, ornithology. Home: 225 E 73d St New York NY 10021 Office: Gamco Investors Inc Corp Ctr at Rye Rye NY 10580-1430

WAGNER, EDWARD KURT, publishing company executive; b. N.Y.C., Sept. 29, 1936; s. Kurt Henry and Julia Marie (Selesky) W.; m. Ann Marie Philbin, Jan. 31, 1959; children: Denise, Steven, Kenneth, Jeanne. B.B.A., St. Francis Coll., 1961. With Pitman Pub. Corp., N.Y.C., 1952-75, v.p., treas., 1968-71, exec. v.p., 1971-75; financial mgr. Dun-Donnelley Pub. Corp., N.Y.C., 1975-76, contr. general bk. div., 1976-77; sr. mgr. contr.'s dept. Dun & Bradstreet, Inc., N.Y.C., 1977-78, asst. contr., 1978-83, contr., 1983-88, v.p., contr., 1989—. Home: 1660 Goldspire Rd Toms River NJ 08755 Office: 1 Diamond Hill Rd Murray Hill NJ 07974

WAGNER, FREDERIC HAMILTON, biology educator, dean, research ecologist; b. Corpus Christi, Sept. 26, 1926; married, 1949; 2 children. BS, So. Meth. U., 1949; MS, U. Wis., 1953, PhD in Wildlife Mgmt. and Zoology, 1961. Refuge asst. U.S. Fish & Wildlife Svc., 1945; asst. zoology and botany So. Meth. U., 1946-49; asst. wildlife mgmt. U. Wis., 1949-51; rsch. fellow Wildlife Mgmt. Inst., 1951; rsch. biologist Wis. Conservation Dept., 1952-58; asst. prof. wildlife resources Utah State U., 1958-59; rsch. biologist Wis. Conservation Dept., 1959-61; assoc. prof. Utah State U., 1961-66, prof. wildlife resources, 1966—; assoc. dean Coll. Natural Resources, 1970—; dir. desert biomedicine U.S.-Internat. Biol. Program, 1971-74; mem. U.S. exec. com. Internat. Biol. Program, 1971-74; mem. com. predator control Pres.'s Coun. Environ. Quality, 1971. Mem. Ecol. Soc. Am., Am. Soc. Mammal, Am. Inst. Biol. Sci., Wildlife Soc. (award 1968), Cooper Ornith. Soc., Sigma Xi. Achievements include research on vertebrate population ecology, especially population dynamics, limiting factors and homeostatic mechanisms, wildlife management, conservation of natural resources, and systems ecology. Office: Utah State U Coll Natural Resources UMC 5200 Logan UT 84322-5200*

WAGNER, FREDERICK BALTHAS, JR., historian, retired surgery educator; b. Phila., Jan. 18, 1916; s. Frederick Balthas and Gertrude Louise (Mattes) W.; m. Jean Lockwood, June 30, 1945; children: Frederick B. III, Theodore Walter. AB, U. Pa., 1937; MD, Thomas Jefferson U., 1941. Diplomate: Am. Bd. Surgery. Clin. prof. surgery Jefferson Med. Coll. Thomas Jefferson U., Phila., 1954-78, Grace Revere Osler prof. surgery, 1978-84, historian, 1984—. Author: Twilight Years of Lady Osler, 1985; editor: Thomas Jefferson University: Tradition and Heritage, 1989. Recipient Alumni Achievement award Jefferson Med. Coll., 1987. Fellow Phila. Acad. Surgery (pres. 1985-86), Coll. Physicians Phila.; mem. Meigs Med. Assn. (pres. 1989-91), Jefferson Alumni Assn. (pres. 1975), Union League Phila. Republican. Methodist. Home: 800 Chauncey Rd Narberth PA 19072-1304

WAGNER, FREDERICK REESE, language professional; b. Phila., Apr. 15, 1928; s. Fred Reese and Mildred Wagner; m. Barbara Alexander Brady, May 9, 1959 (div. 1968); 1 child, Christopher A. BA summa cum laude, Duke U., 1948, MA, 1949, PhD, 1971. Advt mgr. Prentice-Hall, Inc. N.Y.C., 1955-57; promotion mgr. Harper & Row, N.Y.C., 1957-65; instr. English Duke U., Durham, N.C., 1967-69; asst. prof. Hamilton Coll, Clinton, N.Y., 1969-73, assoc. prof., 1973-78, prof. English, chmn. dept., 1978-90; prof. English Hamilton Coll, Clinton, 1990-95. Author: Famous Underwater Adventurers, 1962; Submarine Fighter of the American Revolution, 1963; Patriot's Choice: The Story of John Hancock, 1964; Robert Morris, Audacious Patriot, 1976. Mem. Thoreau Soc. (pres. 1984-86), Hawthorne Soc., MLA, Phi Beta Kappa. Home: 28 Dwight Ave Clinton NY 13323-1630

WAGNER, FREDERICK WILLIAM (BILL WAGNER), lawyer; b. Daytona Beach, Fla., Apr. 13, 1933; s. Adam A. and Nella (Schroeder) W.; m. Ruth Whetstone; children: Alan Frederick, Darryl William, Thomas Adam. BA, U. Fla., 1955, LLB with honors, 1960. Bar: Fla. 1960, U.S. Supreme Ct. 1967, D.C. 1989. Pvt. practice law Miami, Fla., 1960-63, Orlando, Fla., 1963-65, Tampa, Fla., 1965—; ptnr. law firm Nichols, Gaither, Beckham, Colson, Spence & Hicks, Tampa, Fla., 1965-67; partner law firm Wagner, Vaughan & McLaughlin (P.A. and predecessor names), 1967-87; mem. Gov.'s Judicial Nominations Commn., 1971-72, Constnl. Judicial Nominations Commn., 1972-75; mem. Fla. Bd. Bar Examiners, 1974-77; chmn. Civil Procedure Rules com. Fla. Bar, 1977-78; bd. govs. Fla. Bar, 1978-83; trustee Roscoe Pound Found, 1984—. Contbr. articles to profl. jours. Capt. USAF, 1955-57. Fellow Am. Bar Found., Am. Coll. Trial Lawyers, Internat. Acad. Trial Lawyers; mem. Assn. Trial Lawyers Am. (bd. govs. 1973-80, 84-89, chmn. pub. affairs dept. 1984-89, treas. 1982-84, v.p. 1986-87, pres.-elect 1987-88, pres. 1988-89), Acad. Fla. Trial Lawyers (bd. dirs. 1965—, pres. 1972-73), Bay Area Trial Lawyers Assn. (v.p. 1966-68), Am. Law Inst. (coun. 1993—), Lawyer-Pilots Bar Assn., Fla. Bar Found., U. Fla. Alumni Assn., Nat. Bd. Trial Advocacy (cert. civil). Democrat. Methodist. Home: 78 Martinique Ave Tampa FL 33606-4053 Office: Wagner Vaughn & McLaughlin 601 Bayshore Blvd Ste 910 Tampa FL 33606

WAGNER, GEORGE FRANCIS ADOLF, naval officer; b. S.I., N.Y., Mar. 24, 1941; s. George and Cornelia F. (Cosmen) W.; m. Sarah Elizabeth Lilly, June 6, 1962; children: Kristine, Gregory, Karin. BS, U.S. Naval Acad. 1962; MS, MIT, 1968, Naval Engr., 1968. Commd. ensign USN, 1962, advanced through grades to rear adm., 1991; staff fleet introduction officer Naval Sea Systems Command, Washington, 1977-79; instr. Sr. Officer Materiel Readiness Course, Idaho Falls, Idaho, 1979-81; comdg. officer USS John Rodgers (DD-983), Charleston, S.C., 1981-83; program mgr. Cruise Missiles Project, Washington, 1983-87; dep. and asst. Chief of Naval Rsch., Washington, 1987-89; mem. policy staff Bur. Naval Pers., Washington, 1989-90; warfare system engr. Space and Naval Warfare System Command, Washington, 1990-91; program exec. officer cruise missiles projects and unmanned aerial vehicle joint project Washington, 1991-95; comdr. Space and Naval Warfare Sys. Command, Washington, 1995—. Decorated Legion of Merit with oak leaf cluster. Episcopalian. Office: Comspawarsyscom 2451 Crystal Dr Arlington VA 22245-5200

WAGNER, GÜNTER PAUL, biologist educator; b. Vienna, Austria, May 28, 1954; came to U.S., 1991; s. Otto Karl and Kathe Auguste (Birke) W.; m. Herta Ruttner Brinckmann, Dec. 31, 1978 (div. 1985); 1 child, Susanne Karoline; m. Michaela Sabine Hauser, July 19, 1985; 1 child, Veronika Eszter. PhD, U. Vienna, 1979; MA (hon.), Yale U., 1992. Asst. prof. U. Vienna, Austria, 1985-90; assoc. prof. U. Vienna, 1990-91; prof. Yale U., New Haven, 1991—; bd. dirs. Orgn. for Tropical Studies; vis. prof. Northwestern U., Evanston, Ill., 1987-88, U. Basel, Switzerland, 1991;

Gompertz lectr. U. Calif., Berkeley, 1993; disting. lectr. U. Leiden, Netherlands, 1995. Publ. com. mem. Yale U. Press, New Haven, 1992—; contbr. articles to profl. jours. Bd. dirs. Ctr. Computational Ecology, New Haven. Recipient MacArthur prize MacArthur Found., 1992. Mem. AAAS, European Soc. Evolutionary Biology (editorial bd. 1988-92), Soc. for Study of Evolution (assoc. editor 1994—), Soc. Systematic Biology, German Zool. Soc., Internat Inst. for Applied Syss. Analysis. Lutheran. Avocations: sailing, horseback riding, literature, music. Office: Yale Univ 165 Prospect St New Haven CT 06511

WAGNER, HAROLD A., industrial gas and chemical company executive; b. Oakland, Calif., Nov. 12, 1935; s. Harold A. and Lurline Frances (Madsen) W.; m. Marcia Kenaston, July 14, 1956; children: Sandra Wagner Boyce, Kristi Wagner, Schwiering, Tracey, Erik. BS in Mech. Engring., Stanford U., 1958, SEP, 1982; MBA, Harvard U., 1963. Regional sales mgr. ind. gases U.S. Air Products & Chems., Allentown, Pa., 1963-70; mgr. GM ind. gases U.K.Air Products & Chems., 1970-76; regional sales mgr. GM Ind. Gases Continental Europe, 1976-80, GM Ind. Gases U.S., 1980-81; v.p. sales ind. gases div. FM, 1981-82; v.p. corp. planning Air Products & Chems., 1982-87, v.p. bus. div. chems., 1987-88; pres. AP Europe, 1988-90, exec. v.p. 1990-91, pres., COO, 1991-92, past chmn. pres., CEO; now chmn., pres., CEO, dir. Air Products and Chems. 1st Lt. USAF, 1958-61. Avocations: squash, photography. Home: 1306 Prospect Ave Bethlehem PA 18018-4917 Office: Air Prods & Chems Inc 7201 Hamilton Blvd Allentown PA 18195

WAGNER, HARVEY ALAN, finance executive; b. Detroit, Feb. 11, 1941; s. Max and Anne (Levine) W.; m. Arlene F. Tasman, Jan. 26, 1963 (dec. June 1988); children: Brooke D., Jennifer D; m. Arlene L. Rittenberg-Gelb, June, 1992. BBA in Acctg., U. Miami, 1963. Sr. acct. Hoch, Frey and Zugman, Ft. Lauderdale, Fla., 1963-67; contr. Canaveral Internat. Corp., Miami, Fla., 1967-68, Systems Engring. Lab., Ft. Lauderdale, 1968-70; dir. fin. and adminstrn., western area Arcata Comms., Inc., Menlo Park, Calif., 1971-73; sec., treas., contr. Commodore Bus. Machines Inc., Palo Alto, Calif., 1973-75; group contr. Fairchild Camera and Instrument Corp., Mountainview, Calif., 1975-83; v.p. contr. internat. GTE Corp., Phoenix, 1983-86; v.p. fin., sec., CFO Am. Microsystems, Inc., Santa Clara, Calif., 1986-89; v.p. fin., CFO Datapoint Corp., San Antonio, 1989, Computervision Corp., Bedford, Mass., 1989-94; v.p. fin., CFO, treas. Scientific-Atlanta Inc., 1994—. Chmn. bd. Tech. Fed. Credit Union, San Jose, Calif., 1980-82, chmn. supervisory com., 1986-88, 78-80; v.p., founding dir. The Wellness Comty., Atlanta; mem. pres.'s adv. bd. U. Miami, 1995—; mem. Wharton Exec. Edn. Adv. Bd., 1995—. With USAR, 1959-67. Mem. Inst. Mgmt. Accts., Fin. Exec. Inst. (bd. dirs.), Assn. for Corp. Growth, Buckhead Club (bd. govs. 1995). Republican. Jewish. Avocations: golf, travel, art collecting. Office: Scientific-Atlanta Inc 1 Technology Pky S Norcross GA 30092

WAGNER, HARVEY ARTHUR, nuclear engineer; b. Ann Arbor, Mich., Jan. 2, 1905; s. Emanuel M. and Emma (Kiebler) W.; m. Eleanor Mary Bond, July 6, 1929. B.S. in Mech. Engring., U. Mich., 1927; D.Eng. Lawrence Inst. Tech., 1969. With Proctor & Gamble Co., 1927-28; with Detroit Edison Co., 1928-70, exec. v.p., 1969-70; cons. engr., 1970—; chmn., dir. Overseas Adv. Assocs., Inc., 1974—; Mem. Detroit Bd. Water Commrs., 1952-60; Trustee Nat. Sanitation Found., 1965-82. Author papers in field. Recipient Disting. Alumnus award U. Mich. Coll. Engring., 1953, Outstanding Alumni Achievement award, 1989; Sesquicentennial award as outstanding exec. and nuclear power cons. U. Mich., 1967; cert. pub. service Fed. Power Commn., 1964. Fellow ASME, Am. Nuclear Soc., Engring. Soc. Detroit (pres. 1968-69); mem. Nat. Acad. Engring., Tau Beta Pi, Phi Kappa Phi. Home: 932 Trombley Rd Grosse Pointe MI 48230-1860 Office: 3000 Book Bldg Detroit MI 48226

WAGNER, HENRY CARRH, III, health care executive; b. Charleston, W.Va., Oct. 30, 1942; s. Henry C. and Marguerite (Halstead) W.; m. Elisabeth Anne Tibbott, Sept. 12, 1964; children: Stephanie, Jeffrey, Alex. B.S., W.Va. U., 1966; M.H.A., Duke U., 1966. Assoc. dir. Univ. Hosp., Cleve., 1968-73; exec. v.p. Jewish Hosp., Louisville, Ky., 1973-82, pres., 1981—; pres. Hosp. Council Met. Louisville, 1979, Ohio Valley Hosp. Dist., Louisville, 1980; mem. editorial adv. bd. Healthweek; bd. dirs. Mid-Am. Bankcorp, Inc., Lumex, Inc. Bd. dirs. Louisville Orch., 1983-85, Met. United Way, Louisville, 1984-90, Spalding U., 1985-87; alumnus Leadership Louisville, 1983—, Louisville C. of C., 1986-88; bd. dirs. Louisville Fund for Arts, 1986—, campaign chmn., 1992; chmn. Nat. Black Achievers Banquet, 1992; awardee Conf. of Christians and Jews, 1992, 93; mem. bd. overseers U. Louisville, 1989—; bd. dirs., 1990—; bd. dirs. Downtown Devel. Corp., 1990—, Leadership Louisville, 1990—; campaign chmn. Met. United Way, Louisville, 1987. Served to 1st lt. U.S. Army, 1966-68. Named Person of Vision, 1993, Entrepreneur of Year-Healthcare, 1993. Fellow Am. Coll. Healthcare Execs.; mem. Ky. Hosp. Assn. (bd. dirs. 1979-84), Premier Hosps. Alliance (treas. 1984—, vice-chmn. 1988-90), Harmony Landing Country Club, Jefferson Club (bd. dirs. 1990—), Masons, Rotary. Republican. Methodist. Office: Jewish Hosp 217 E Chestnut St Louisville KY 40202-1886

WAGNER, HENRY NICHOLAS, JR., physician; b. Balt., May 12, 1927; s. Henry N. and Gertrude Loane W.; m. Anne Barrett Wagner, Feb., 1951; children—Henry N., Mary Randall, John Mark, Anne Elizabeth. A.B., Johns Hopkins U., 1948, M.D., 1952; D.Sc. (hon.), Washington Coll., Chestertown, Md., 1972, Free U., Brussels, 1985; M.D. (hon.), U. Gottingen, 1988. Chief med. resident Osler Med. Service, Johns Hopkins Hosp., Balt., 1958-59; asst. prof. medicine, radiology Johns Hopkins Med. Instns., 1959-64, asso. prof., 1964-65, prof., dir. divs. nuclear medicine and radiation health sci., 1965—. Author numerous books in field.; contbr. articles to med. jours. Served with USPHS, 1955-57. Recipient Georg von Hevesey medal, 1976. Fellow ACP; mem. Inst. Medicine of NAS, AMA (coun. sci. affairs, Sci. Achievement award 1991), Balt. City Med. Soc. (past pres.), World Fedn. Nuclear Medicine and Biology (past pres.), Am. Bd. Nuclear Medicine (founding mem.), Soc. Nuclear Medicine (past pres.), Am. Fedn. Clin. Research (past pres.), Research Socs. Council (past pres.), Assn. Am. Physicians, Am. Soc. Clin. Investigation, Phi Beta Kappa. Home: 5607 Wildwood Ln Baltimore MD 21209-4520 Office: 615 N Wolfe St Baltimore MD 21205-2103

WAGNER, JOHN GARNET, pharmacy educator; b. Weston, Ont., Can., Mar. 28, 1921; came to U.S., 1949; naturalized, 1993; s. Herbert William and Coral (Cates) W.; m. Eunice Winona Kelsey, July 4, 1946; children: Wendie Lynn, Linda Beth. Pharm.B., U. Toronto, Ont., 1947; B.S. in Pharmacy, U. Sask., Can., 1948, B.A., 1949; Ph.D., Ohio State U., 1952, D.Sc. (hon.), 1980. Asst. prof. pharm. chemistry Ohio State U., 1952-53; with Upjohn Co., Kalamazoo, 1953-68; head pharmacy research sect. Upjohn Co., 1956-63, sr. research scientist research div., 1963-68; prof. pharmacy Coll. Pharmacy U. Mich., Ann Arbor, 1968-81, Albert B. Prescott prof. pharmaceutics, 1982-86, John G. Searle prof. pharmaceutics, 1986-91, John G. Searle prof. emeritus, 1991—; prof. pharmacology sch. medicine, 1986-91, prof. pharmacology emeritus, 1991—; asst. dir. R. and D. Pharmacy Service, Univ. Hosp., 1968-72; mem. staff Upjohn Center for Clin. Pharmacology, 1973-91; cons. Bur. of Drugs, FDA, Washington, 1971-73, Upjohn Co., 1968-90, Key Pharms., Miami, Fla., 1980-91, Warner-Lambert, Ann Arbor, Mich., 1983-84. Author: Biopharmaceutics and Relevant Pharmacokinetics, 1971, Fundamentals of Clinical Pharmacokinetics, 1975, Pharmacokinetics for the Pharmaceutical Scientist, 1993; also numerous articles.; mem. editorial bd.: Internat. Jour. Clin. Pharmacology, 1967-91, Clin. Pharmacol. Therapeutics, 1973-91, Biopharmaceutics and Drug Disposition; cons. editor: Jour. Pharmacokinetics and Biopharmaceutics. Served with RCAF, 1941-45. Recipient L. George R. Parke Meml. scholarship and silver medal, 1946, John Roberts Gold medal for pharmacy and chemistry U. Toronto, 1947, Dr. William E. Upjohn award, 1960, Centennial Achievement award Ohio State U., 1970, Høst Madsen medal Fédération Internationale Pharmaceutique, 1972, Volwiler award Am. Assn. Colls. of Pharmacy, 1983, Rsch. Achievement award in pharmaceutics, pharmacodynamics, drug metabolism, 1992; fellow Am. Found. Pharm. Edn., 1949-51; FDA grantee, 1969-76, Am. Assn. Pharm. Sci. fellow, 1986. Fellow AAAS, Am. Coll. Clin. Pharmacology and Chemotherapy, Acad. Pharm. Sci. (Stimulation of Rsch. award 1983, Pharmaceutics award 1984, Rsch. Achievement award 1984); mem. Am. Soc. Clin. Pharmacology and Therapeutics (bd. regents 1968-72, v.p. 1972, vice chmn. on pharmacokinetics 1970-74), Am. Pharm. Assn. (Ebert prize 1961, Rsch. award 1983, 84, Takeru Higuchi prize 19920, N.Y.

Acad. Scis., Sigma Xi, Phi Lambda Upsilon, Rho Chi. Home: 908 Ivanhoe Dr Florence SC 29505-3614

WAGNER, JOHN LEO, federal judge, lawyer; b. Ithaca, N.Y., Mar. 12, 1954; s. Paul Francis and Doris Elizabeth (Hoffschneider) W.; m. Marilyn Modin, June 18, 1987. Student, U. Nebr., 1973-74; BA, U. Okla., 1976, JD, 1979. Bar: Okla. 1980, U.S. Dist. Ct. (we. dist.) Okla. 1980, U.S. Dist. Ct. (no. and ea. dists.) Okla. 1981, U.S. Ct. Appeals (10th cir.) 1982. Assoc. Franklin, Harmon & Satterfield Inc., Oklahoma City, 1980-82; ptnr. Franklin, Harmon & Satterfield, Inc., Oklahoma City, 1982; assoc Kornfeld, Franklin & Phillips, Oklahoma City, 1982-85, ptnr., 1985; magistrate judge U.S. Dist. Ct. for No. Dist. Okla., Tulsa, 1985—. Pres. U. Okla. Coll. Law Assn., 1991-92. Mem. ABA, Fed. Magistrate Judge's Assn. (dir. 10th cir. 1987-89), 10th Cir. Edn. Com., Okla. Bar Assn., Robert D. Hudson Am. Inn of Cts. (pres. 1992-93), Jud. Conf. U.S. (com. ct. adminstrn. and case mgmt. 1992—). Republican. Office: US Magistrate Judge 333 W 4th St Rm 3355 Tulsa OK 74103-3819

WAGNER, JOSEPH EDWARD, veterinarian, educator; b. Dubuque, Iowa, July 29, 1938; s. Jacob Edward and Leona (Callahan) W.; m. Kay Rose (div. Apr. 1983); children: Lucinda, Pamela, Jennifer, Douglas. DVM, Iowa State U., 1963; MPH, Tulane U., 1964; PhD, U. Ill., 1967. Asst. prof. U. Kans. Med. Ctr., Kansas City, 1967-69; assoc. prof. U. Mo. Coll. Vet. Medicine, Columbia, 1969-72, prof. vet. medicine, 1972—, Curator's prof., 1989—; cons. Harlan Sprague Dawley, Indpls., 1984—. Author: The Biology and Medicine of Rabbits and Rodents, 1989. Recipient award of excellence in lab. animal medicine Charles River Found., Wilmington, Mass., 1986. Mem. AMVA, Am. Coll. Lab. Animal Medicine (pres. 1985-86), Am. Assn. Lab. Animal Scis. (pres. 1980-81). Office: U Mo-Coll of Veterinary Medicine Dept of Vet Pathology 1600 W Rollins Rd Columbia MO 65211-0001

WAGNER, JOSEPH M., church administrator. Exec dir. Division for Ministry of the Evangelical Lutheran Church in America, Chgo. Office: Evangelical Lutheran Church Am 8765 W Higgins Rd Chicago IL 60631-4101

WAGNER, JUDITH BUCK, investment firm executive; b. Altoona, Pa. Sept. 25, 1943; d. Harry Bud and Mary Elizabeth (Rhodes) B.; m. Joseph E. Wagner, Mar. 15, 1980; 1 child, Elizabeth. BA in History, U. Wash., 1965; grad. N.Y. Inst. Fin., 1968. Registered Am. Stock Exchange; registered N.Y. Stock Exchange; registered investment advisor. Security analyst Morgan, Olmstead, Kennedy & Gardner, L.A., 1968-71; security analyst Boettcher & Co., Denver, 1972-75; pres. Wagner Investment Mgmt., 1975—; chmn., bd. dirs. The Women's Bank, N.A., Denver, 1977-94, organizational group pres., 1975-77; chmn. Equitable Bankshares Colo., Inc., Denver, 1980-94; bd. dirs. Equitable Bank of Littleton, 1983-88, pres., 1985; bd. dirs. Colo. Growth Capital, 1979-82; lectr. Denver U., Metro State, 1975-80. Author: Woman and Money series Colo. Woman Mag., 1976; moderator 'Catch 2' Sta. KWGN-TV, 1978-79. Pres. Big Sisters Colo., Denver, 1977-82, bd. dirs., 1973-83; bd. fellows U. Denver, 1985—; bd. dirs. Red Cross, 1980, Assn. Children's Hosp., 1985, Colo. Health Facilities Authority, 1978-84, Jr. League Community Adv. Com., 1979-92, Brother's Redevel., Inc., 1979-80; mem. Hist. Paramount Found., 1984, Denver Pub. Sch. Career Edn. Project, 1972; mem. investment com. YWCA, 1976-88; mem. adv. com. Girl Scouts U.S.; mem. agy. rels. com. Mile High United Way, 1978-81, chmn. United Way Venture Grant com., 1980-81; fin. chmn. Schoettler for State Treas., 1986; bd. dirs. Downtown Denver Inc., 1988—; bd. dirs., v.p., treas. The Women's Found. Colo., 1987-91; treas., trustee, v.p., Graland Country Day Sch., 1990—, pres. 1994—; trustee Denver Rotary Found., 1990-95; trustee Hunt Alternatives Fund, 1992—. Recipient Making It award Cosmopolitan Mag., 1977, Women on the Go award, Savvy mag., 1983, Minouri Yasoui award, 1986, Salute Spl. Honoree award, Big Sisters, 1987; named one of the Outstanding Young Women in Am., 1979; recipient Woman Who Makes A Difference award Internat. Women's Forum, 1987. Fellow Assn. Investment Mgmt. and Rsch.; mem. Women's Forum of Colo. (pres. 1979), Women's Found. Colo., Inc. (bd. dirs. 1986-91), Denver Soc. Security Analysts (bd. dirs. 1976-83, v.p. 1980-81, pres. 1981-82), Colo. Investment Advisors Assn., Rotary (treas. Denver chpt. found., 1993-94), Leadership Denver (Outstanding Alumna award 1987), Pi Beta Phi (pres. U. Wash. chpt. 1964-65). Office: Wagner Investment Mgmt Inc Ste 240 3200 Cherry Creek S Dr Denver CO 80209

WAGNER, JULIA A(NNE), retired editor; b. Alexandria, Va., Feb. 15, 1924; d. Luigi and Domenica (Di Giammarino) Coppa; Widowed. B.A., George Washington U., 1948, M.A., 1950. With U.S. Govt., Washington 1941-55, publs. editor, 1951-55; editorial asst. Dell Pub. Co., N.Y.C., 1956-59, mng. editor, 1959-72, editor-in-chief, 1973-87. Mem. Am. Fedn. Astrologers. Democrat. Roman Catholic.

WAGNER, LAWRENCE M., diversified financial services company executive. Exec. v.p., chief oper. offices The Hillman Co., Pitts. Office: The Hillman Company 1900 Grant Bldg Pittsburgh PA 15219

WAGNER, LINDSAY J., actress; b. L.A., June 22, 1949; d. Bill Nowels and Marilyn Louise (Thrasher) W.; m. Alan Rider (div.); m. Michael Brandon, Dec. 1976 (div.); m. Henry Kingi, 1981 (div.); m. Lawrence Mortorff, 1990; children: Dorian Henry, Alex Nathan. Student, U. Oreg., 1967. Tchr. acting children Founders Sch. Los Angeles, 1975. Actress numerous TV shows Universal Studios, Universal City, Calif., 1971-74; motion picture picture appearances include: Two People, 1972, The Paper Chase, 1973, Second Wind, 1976, Nighthawks, 1981, Martin's Day, 1984, Ricochet, 1991; TV series include The Bionic Woman, 1976-78, Jessie, 1984, Peaceable Kingdom, 1989; appeared in TV miniseries Scruples, 1980, Princess Daisy, 1983, The Dead of the Night, 1989, Voices of the Heart, 1990, To Be the Best, 1991; TV films include: The Two Worlds of Jennie Logan, 1979, The Incredible Journey of Dr. Meg Laurel, 1979, I Want to Live, 1983, Two Kinds of Love, 1983, Callie and Son, 1983, Passion, 1984, This Child is Mine, 1985, The Other Lover, 1985, Nightmare at Bitter Creek, 1988, The Taking of Flight 847, 1988, Shattered Dreams, 1990, Babies, 1990, A Message from Holly, 1992, Once in a Lifetime, 1994; author video film: (with others) Lindsay Wagner's New Beauty: The Acupressure Facelift. Office: care Jim Wyatt Internat Creative Mgmt 8942 Wilshire Blvd Beverly Hills CA 90211*

WAGNER, LOUIS CARSON, JR., retired army officer; b. Jackson, Mo., Jan. 24, 1932; s. Louis Carson and Margaret Marie (Macke) W.; m. Judith Gifford, Sept. 24, 1955; children: Susan, Amy. B.S., U.S. Mil. Acad., 1954; M.S. in Applied Mechanics, U. Ill., 1961; grad., U.S. Naval War Coll., 1971. Commd. 2d lt. U.S. Army, 1954, advanced through grades to gen., 1987; served in Vietnam, Germany, Alaska; dep. dir. material plans and programs Office Dept. Chief Staff Research, Devel. and Acquisition, Washington, 1976-78; dir. combat support systems, 1978-80; comdg. gen. Armor Ctr., Ft. Knox, 1980-83; asst. dep. chief of staff for ops. and plans ODCSOPS, USA, Washington, 1983-84, dep. chief of staff for research, devel. and acquisition, 1984-87; comdg. gen. Materiel Command, Alexandria, Va., 1987-89, retired, 1989; fellow Inst. of Land Warfare Assn. of U.S. Army, Arlington, Va., 1990—. Decorated D.S.C., D.S.M. with oak leaf cluster, Silver Star, Legion of Merit with oak leaf cluster, Bronze Star, Air medal with oak leaf cluster, Purple Heart, Meritorious Service medal, Army Commendation medal with 2 clusters, Combat Inf. badge. Mem. Assn. Grads. U.S. Mil. Acad., Armor Assn., Assn. U.S. Army, The Retired Officer's Assn. (chmn. bd. dirs.), Am. Def. Prearedness Assn., Army Aviation Assn. Am., Nat. Eagle Scout Assn. (bd. regents), S.C. Rsch. Authority (bd. dirs.). Office: 6309 Chaucer Ln Alexandria VA 22304

WAGNER, MARY KATHRYN, sociology educator, former state legislator; b. Madison, S.D., June 19, 1932; d. Irving Macaulay and Mary Browning (Wines) Mumford; m. Robert Todd Wagner, June 23, 1954; children: Christopher John, Andrea Browning. BA, U. SD., 1954; MEd, S.D. State U., 1974, PhD, 1978. Sec. R.A. Burleigh & Assocs., Evanston, Ill., 1954-57; dir. resource ctr. Watertown (S.D.) Sr. High Sch., 1969-71, Brookings (S.D.) High Sch., 1971-90; asst. prof. rural sociology S.D. State U., 1990—; mem. S.D. Ho. of Reps., 1981-88, S.D. Senate, 1988-92. Mem., pres. Brookings Sch. Bd., 1975-81; chair fund dr. Brookings United Way, 1985; bd. dirs. Brookings Chamber music Soc., 1981—, Advance and Career Learning Ctr. Named

Woman of Yr., Bus. and Profl. Women, 1981, Legislator Conservationist of Yr., Nat. and S.D. Wildlife Fedn., 1988. Mem. Population Assn. Am., Midwest Sociol. Soc., Rural Sociol. Soc., Brookings C. of C. (mem. indsl. devel. com. 1988—), PEO, Rotary. Republican. Avocations: reading, gardening, music, golf, bridge. Home: 929 Harvey Dunn St Brookings SD 57006-1347

WAGNER, MARY MARGARET, library and information science educator; b. Mpls., Feb. 4, 1946; d. Harvey F.J. and Yvonne M. (Brettner) W.; m. William Moore, June 16, 1988; children: Lebohang Y.C., Nora M. BA, Coll. St. Catherine, St. Paul, 1969; MLS, U. Wash., 1973. Asst. libr. St. Margarets Acad., Mpls., 1969-70; libr. Derham Hall High Sch., St. Paul, 1970-71; youth worker The Bridge for Runaways, Mpls., 1971-72; libr. Guthrie Theater Reference and Rsch. Libr., Mpls., 1973-75; asst. br. libr. St. Paul Pub. Libr., 1975; assoc. prof. dept. info. mgmt. Coll. St. Catherine, St. Paul, 1975—; del. Minn. Gov.'s Pre-White House Conf. on Librs. and Info. Svcs., 1990; mem. Minn. Pre-White House Conf. Program Com., 1989-90, Continuing Libr. Info. and Media Edn. com. Minn. Dept. Edn., Libr. Devel. and Svcs., 1980-83, 87-94; mem. cmty. faculty Met. State U., St. Paul, 1980—; mem. core revision com. Coll. St. Catherine, 1992-93, faculty budget adv. com., 1992—, faculty pers. com., 1989-92. Contbr. articles to profl. jours. Bd. dirs. Christian Sharing Fund, 1976-80, chair, 1977-78. Grantee: U.S. Embassy, Maseru, Lesotho, Africa, Brit. Consulate, Maseru, various founds.; Upper Midwest Assn. for Intercultural Edn. travel grantee Assoc. Colls. Twin Cities. Mem ALA (libr. book fellows program 1990-91), Am. Soc. Info. Sci., Am. Soc. Indexers, Spl. Libr. Assn., Minn. Libr. Assn. (pres. 1981-82, chair continuing edn. com. 1987-90, steering com. Readers Adv. Roundtable, 1989-91), Minn. Ednl. Media Orgn., Twin Cities Women in Computing. Office: Coll St Catherine Dept Info Mgmt 2004 Randolph Saint Paul MN 55105

WAGNER, MICHAEL DICKMAN, state representative, small business owner; b. Omaha, Sept. 24, 1957; s. Loyd R. and Donna (Dickman) W.; m. Paula Spriggs, Oct. 11, 1975; children: Jeremiah, Stephanie, Joshua. AAS in Bus. Mgmt., Kilian C.C., Sioux Falls, S.D., 1984, cert. computer programming, 1984; postgrad., Harvard U., 1995—. From mouldings worker to inventory database coord. Jordan Millwork Co., 1975-84; from dir. ops. info. systems to mgr. Austad's, 1984-93; owner grocery store, entertainment arcade, cons. svc., 1993-94; mayor Baltic S.D., 1986-92; state rep. State of S.D., Pierre, 1988—, asst. majority leader, 1993-94, mem. legis. exec. bd., 1994—; instr. Kilian C.C., Sioux Falls, 1984-86. Delegation leader Am. Coun. Young Polit. Leaders 1992 Exch. to China, del. 1990 Exch. to Japan; exec. dir. Habitat for Humanity, 1994—. Bus. Leadership fellow, 1995. Mem. Nat. League of Cities (Sm. Cities Coun., Community and Econ. Devel. Policy com.), S.D. Mcpl. League (1st and 2d v.p. 1987-89, state exec. bd. trustee 1984-87, dist. chmn. Southeast S.D. 1984, legis. policy com., chmn. Mcpl. Computerization Task Force), Nat. Conf. State Legislatures (vice chair fiscal oversight and intergovtl. affairs com.), S.Ea. Coun. Govts. (exec. bd.), Rotary Internat., Minnehaha County Rural Mayors Assn., Minnehaha County Centennial Commn., Baltic Area Cub Scouts (past chmn.), Baltic Area Jaycees, Baltic Community Club, Baltic Athletic Assn. Home: PO Box 308 Baltic SD 57003-0308

WAGNER, NORMAN ERNEST, former energy company executive, former university president; b. Edenwold, Sask., Can., Mar. 29, 1935; s. Robert Eric and Gertrude Margaret (Brandt) W.; m. Catherine Hack, May 16, 1957; children: Marjorie Dianne, Richard Roger, Janet Marie. B.A., U. Sask., 1958, M.Div., 1958; M.A., U. Toronto, Ont., Can., 1960, Ph.D. in Near Eastern Studies, 1965; LL.D. (hon.), Wilfrid Laurier U., 1984. Asst. prof. Near Eastern studies Wilfrid Laurier U., Waterloo, Ont., 1962-65, assoc. prof., 1965-69, prof., 1970-78, dean grad. studies and rsch., 1974-78; pres. U. Calgary, Alta., Can., 1978-88; chmn. bd. Alta. Natural Gas Co., Ltd., 1988—; pres. emeritus U. Calgary, Can.; officer Order of Can., 1989; bd. dirs. CFCN Comm. Ltd., Alta., Terry Fox Humanitarian award Program. Author: (with others) The Moyer Site: A Prehistoric Village in Waterloo County, 1974. Mem. Adv. Coun. on Adjustment, OCO '88, Alta. Heritage Found. for Med. Rsch., Nat. Adv. Bd. Sci. and Tech., Internat. Task Force Found. for Med. Rsch., Nat. Adv. Bd. Sci. and Tech., Internat. Task Force Comm. Lutheran. Home: Box 5 Site 33 RR # 12, Calgary, AB Canada T3E 6W3 Office: Alta Natural Gas Co Ltd, 2900 240 Fourth Ave SW, Calgary, AB Canada T2P 4L7

WAGNER, PATRICIA H., lawyer; b. Gastonia, N.C., Feb. 1, 1936; d. Luther Boyd and Mildred Ruth (Wheeler) Hamm; married; children: David Marion, Michael Marion, Laura Marion. AB summa cum laude, Wittenberg U., 1958; JD with distinction, Duke U., 1974. Bar: N.C. 1974, Wash. 1984. Asst. univ. counsel Duke U., Durham, N.C., 1974-75, assoc. univ. counsel health affairs, 1977-80; atty. N.C. Meml. Hosp., 1975-77; assoc. N.C. Atty. Gen. Office, 1975-77; prin. Powe, Porter and Alphin, P.A., Durham, 1980-83; assoc. Williams, Kastner & Gibbs, 1984-86, Wickwire, Goldmark & Schorr, 1986-88; spl. counsel Heller, Ehrman, White & McAuliffe, 1988-90, ptnr., 1990—; arbitrator Am. Arbitration Assn., 1978—; arbitrator, pro tem judge King County Superior Ct., 1986—; instr. in field. Mem. bd. visitors Law Sch. Duke U., 1992—; bd. dirs. Seattle Edn. Ctr., 1990-91, Metroctr. YMCA, 1991-94, Cmty. Psychiat. Clinic, Seattle, 1984-88, bd. dirs., sec.-treas. N.C. Found. Alternative Health Programs, Inc., 1982-84; bd. dirs. sec-treas. N.C. Ctr. Pub. Policy Rsch., 1976-83, vice chmn., 1977-80; mem. task force on committment law N.C. Dept. Human Resources, 1978; active Def. Rsch. Inst., 1982-84; bd. dirs. Law Fund, 1992—, v.p., 1993—. Fellow Am. Bar Found.; mem. ABA (mem. ho. dels. Seattle-King County Bar Assn. 1991-94, mem. litigation sect.), Am. Soc. Hosp. Attys., Wash. State Bar Assn. (mem. domestic rels. task force 1991-93), Seattle-King Bar Assn. (mem. bd. trustees 1990-93, sec. bd. 1989-90, chair judiciary and cts. com. 1987-89, mem. King County Superior Ct. delay reduction task force 1987-89, mem. gender bias com. 1990-94, chair 1990-91), Wash. Def. Trial Lawyers (chmn. ct. rules and procedures com. 1987, co-editor newsletter 1985-86), Wash. Stat. Soc. Hosp. Attys., Wash. Women Lawyers (treas. 1986, 87). Office: Heller Ehrman White & McAuliffe 6100 Columbia Ctr 701 5th Ave Seattle WA 98104-7016

WAGNER, PAUL ANTHONY, JR., education educator; b. Pitts., Aug. 28, 1947; s. Paul A. and Mary K. Wagner; m. Nancy C. Wright; children: Nicole S., Eric P., Jason G. BS, N.E. Mo. State U., 1969; MEd, U. Mo., 1972; MA in Philosophy, 1976, PhD in Philosophy of Edn., 1978. Internal expeditor electromotive div. GM, La Grange, Ill., 1970-71; instr. Moberly (Mo.) Jr. Coll., 1972-73; instr. U. Mo., Columbia, 1973-78, dir. univ. self-study, acting dir. instl. rsch. and planning, 1990-92; instr. Mo. Mil. Acad., 1978-79; prof. edn. and philosophy U. Houston-Clear Lake, 1979—, Atrium Cir. Disting. Rsch. Prof., 1980, Chancellor's Disting. Svc. Prof., 1985; dir. Inst. Logical and Cognitive Studies, 1980—; co-dir. Project in Profl. Ethics, 1992—; chmn. dept. edn. U. Houston-Clear Lake, 1989-92; pres. Wagner & Assocs. Ednl. Consulting, 1988-93; dir. Tex. Ctr. for Study Profl. Ethics in Teaching, 1988—; rsch. assoc. Ctr. for Moral Devel., Harvard U., 1985-86; vis. scholar Stanford U., Palo Alto, Calif., 1981; cons. to various sch. dists., 1979—; cons. in total quality mgmt. Golden Gate U., 1992-93, M.D. Anderson Cancer Ctr. & Hosp., 1992-93, U. Houston-Victoria, 1993; chair So. Accreditation of Colls. and Schs. steering com., U. Houston-Clear Lake, 1990-93; chair univ. planning com., 1993-94; mem. faculty Senate exec. com., 1993-95; mem. bd. dirs. chair planning and budgeting com. Houston Tenneco Marathon, 1992—; mem. steering com. Trilateral Conf. and Supershow Greater Human Partnership, 1994-95. Author: (with F. Kierstead) The Ethical Legal and Multicultural Founds. of Teaching, 1992; contbr. articles on sci. edn. and philosophy of edn. to profl. jours. Mem. editorial bd. Jour. of Thought, 1981—, Focus on Learning, 1982-85; editorial cons. Instrnl. Scis., 1981-83; editorial assoc. Brain and Behavioral Scis., 1986—. mem. Human Rights Commn., Columbia, Mo., 1976-79, vice chmn., 1978-79; Sunday sch. tchr. Mary Queen Cath. Ch., Friendswood, Tex., 1979—; founding bd. mem. Bay Area Symphony Soc., 1983-85; capital campaign com. Soc. Prevention Cruelty to Animals, 1989-91; publicity com. Am. Cancer Soc., Houston chpt., 1989-92; mem. Houston-Tenneco Marathon bd., 1989—, chair steering com. for strategic planning, 1993, chair planning and budgeting com., 1993—; cons. in strategic planning to M.D. Anderson Cancer Ctr. vol. divsn. Sgt. Mo. N.G., 1970-76; mem. steering com. City of Houston Emerging Bus. Conf., 1994-95, Trilatereral Conf., Greater Houston Partnership, 1994-95, active Houston Bus. Promise, 1995—. Recipient Cert. of Appreciation, City of Columbia, 1978; K.E. Graessle scholar, 1968, Mo. Peace Studies Inst. grantee, 1971. Mem. Am. Philos. Assn., Assn. Philosophers in Edn. (exec. bd., v.p.), Philosophy of Edn. Soc. (exec.sec.-

treas.), Am. Ednl. Studies Assn., Brit. Soc. for Philosophy of Sci., Philosophy of Sci. Assn., S.W. Philosophy of Edn. Soc., Tex. Network for Tchr. Tng. in Philosophy for Children (bd. dirs. 1983-90), Tex. Ctr. for Ethics in Edn. (bd. dirs.1988—), Tex. Ednl. Found. Soc. (pres. 1986—), Tex. Assn. Coll. Tchrs., So. Assn. Colls. Coord., Houston Bar Assn. (mem. steering com NAFTA Conf. 1993-94), Informal Logic Assn., Greater Houston Partnership (steering com.Tri-lateral Conf. 1994-95, mem. bus. promise com. 1995—), Clearlake Circle Club (chair 1979-85), Phi Delta Kappa, Kappa Delta Pi. Roman Catholic. Avocations: running, racquetball, reading, opera, ballet. Address: RR 4 Box 217 Navasota TX 77868 Office: U Houston 2700 Bay Area Blvd # 338 Houston TX 77058-1098

WAGNER, PETER EWING, physics and electrical engineering educator; b. Ann Arbor, Mich., July 4, 1929; s. Paul Clark and Charlotta Josephine (Ewing) W.; m. Caryl Jean Veon, June 23, 1951; children: Ann Frances, Stephen Charles. Student, Occidental Coll., 1946-48; AB with honors, U. Calif., Berkeley, 1950, PhD, 1956. Teaching rsch. asst. U. Calif., 1950-56; rsch. physicist Westinghouse Rsch. Labs., Pitts., 1956-59; assoc. prof. elec. engring. Johns Hopkins, 1960-65, prof., 1965-73; dir. Ctr. for Environ. and Estuarine Studies U. Md., 1973-80, prof., 1973-81; vis. prof. physics U. Ala., Huntsville, 1980-81, prof., 1981; vice chancellor for acad. affairs, prof. physics U. Miss., 1981-84; provost, prof. physics and elec. engring. Utah State U., 1984-89; v.p. acad. affars and provost SUNY, Binghamton, 1989-92, prof. physics and elec. engring., 1989—; spl. projects engr. State of Md., 1971-72; mem. Gov's Sci. Adv. Coun., 1973-77, Md. Power Plant Siting Adv. Com., 1972-80; cons. in field. Contbr. articles to profl. jours.; patentee in field. Trustee Chesapeake Rsch. Consortium, 1974-80, chmn. bd. trustees, 1979-80. Guggenheim fellow Oxford U., 1966-67. Mem. Nat. Assn. State Univs. and Land Grant Colls. (mem. coun. acad. affairs, mem. affirmative action com. 1986-89, chmn. nominating com. 1988-89, chmn. libr. commn. 1989-92), Ctr. Rsch. Librs. (bd. dirs. 1991—, mem. budget and fin. com. 1991-93, vice chairperson 1992-93, chairperson 1993-94, chair nominating com. 1994-95), Cosmos Club, Blue Key, Gold Key, Phi Beta Kappa, Phi Beta Kappa Assocs. (life), Sigma Xi (life), Phi Kappa Phi. Home: 2748 Grandview Pl Endwell NY 13760-7043

WAGNER, RICHARD, business executive, former baseball team executive; b. Central City, Nebr., Oct. 19, 1927; s. John Howard and Esther Marie (Wolken) W.; m. Gloria Jean Larsen, May 10, 1950; children—Randolph G., Cynthia Kaye. Student, pub. schs., Central City. Gen. mgr. Lincoln (Nebr.) Baseball Club, 1955-58; mgr. Pershing Mcpl. Auditorium, Lincoln, 1958-61; exec. staff Ice Capades, Inc., Hollywood, Calif., 1961-63; gen. mgr. Dix KSAL, Salina, Kans., 1963-65; dir. promotion and sales St. Louis Nat. Baseball Club, 1965-66; gen. mgr. Forum, Inglewood, Calif., 1966-67; asst. to exec. v.p. Cin. Reds, 1967-70, asst. to pres., 1970-74, v.p. adminstrn., 1975, exec. v.p., 1975-78, gen. mgr. 1977-83, pres., 1978-83; pres. Houston Astros Baseball Club, 1985-87; spl. asst. Office of Baseball Commr., 1988-93; asst. to chmn. Major League Exec. Coun., 1993-94; pres. RGW Enterprises, Inc., Phoenix, 1978—. Served with USNR, 1945-47, 50-52. Named Exec. of Yr., Minor League Baseball, Sporting News, 1958. Mem. Internat. Assn. Auditorium Mgrs. Republican. Methodist.

WAGNER, ROBERT, actor; b. Detroit, Feb. 10, 1930; m. Natalie Wood, 1957 (div. 1962); m. Marion Marshall Donen; 1 child, Kate; remarried Natalie Wood, 1972 (dec. 1981); 1 child, Courtney. Films include: Halls of Montezuma, The Frogmen, Let's Make It Legal, With a Song in My Heart, What Price Glory?, Stars and Stripes Forever, The Silver Whip, Titanic, Star of Tomorrow, Beneath the 12-Mile Reef, Prince Valiant, Broken Lance, White Feather, A Kiss Before Dying, The Mountain, The True Story of Jesse James, Stopover Tokyo, In Love and War, Say One For Me, Between Heaven and Hell, The Hunters, All the Fine Young Cannibals, Sail a Crooked Ship, The Longest Day, The War Lover, The Condemned of Altona, Harper, Banning, The Biggest Bundle of Them All, The Pink Panther, The Curse of the Pink Panther, Winning, The Affair, The Towering Inferno, Critical List, Dragon: The Bruce Lee Story; starred in TV series It Takes a Thief, Switch!, Hart to Hart, Lime St.; produced, starred in TV series Madame Sin; formed Robert Wagner Prodns.; other TV appearances include: Streets of San Francisco, The Ox-Bow Incident, Gun In His Hand, And Man Created Vanity, The Enemy on the Beach, Runaway Bay, How I Spent My Summer Vacation, Name of the Game, City Beneath the Sea, Cable Car Mystery, To Catch a King, Cat on a Hot Tin Roof, Indiscreet, 1988; Movies of the Week There Must Be a Pony, Love Amongst Thieves, This Gun for Hire. Address: care William Morris Agy 151 El Camino Beverly Hills CA 90212*

WAGNER, ROBERT DAVID, JR., banker; b. Bklyn., Jan. 17, 1942; s. Robert D. and Grace (Panitz) W.; m. Patricia M. Nicholson, Dec. 19, 1964; children: Lisa M., Christopher R., Kimberly A. A.B. in History, Holy Cross Coll., 1963; M.B.A., NYU, 1971. Asst. treas. Bankers Trust Co., N.Y.C., 1966-69, asst. v.p., 1969-71, v.p., 1971-78; v.p. First City Nat. Bank, Houston, 1978-80, sr. v.p., 1980-81, exec. v.p., 1981-86; assoc. dir. Bear Stearns & Co., N.Y.C. and Dallas, 1986—. Served to capt. USMC, 1963-66. Mem. Ind. Petroleum Assn. Am.

WAGNER, ROBERT EARL, agronomist; b. Garden City, Kans., Mar. 6, 1921; s. Fay Arthur and Margaret (Longbottom) W.; m. Bernice Bittner, Aug. 7, 1948; children—Robert Earl, James Warren, Douglas Alan. B.S., Kans. State Coll., 1942; M.S., U. Wis., 1943, Ph.D, 1950. Forage crops specialist Ft. Hays Expt. Sta., Hays, Kans., 1943-45; asso. agronomist Plant Industry Sta., U.S. Dept. Agr., Beltsville, Md., 1945-48; research agronomist, asst. project leader pasture and range project Plant Industry Sta., U.S. Dept. Agr., 1951-54, research agronomist, project leader western pasture and range project, 1954-56; prof., head dept. agronomy U. Md., 1956-59; regional dir. American Potash Inst., 1959-66, also Found. for Internat. Potash Research, v.p. both orgns., 1966-67; dir. Coop. Extension Service, U. Md., 1967-75; pres., bd. dirs. Potash Inst., 1975-77; pres., bd. dirs. Potash and Phosphate Inst., 1977-88, pres. emeritus, 1988—; chmn., bd. dirs. Potash & Phosphate Inst. Can., 1975-88; pres., bd. dirs. Found. for Agronomic Rsch., 1980-87; owner Wagner Performance Cattle, Norcross, Ga.; bd. dirs., mem. exec. com. Internat. Fertilizer Devel. Ctr., 1975—; bd. dirs. African Ctr. for Fertilizer Devel., 1988—; chmn. Nat. Ext. Com. on Orgn. and Policy; mem. U.S. del. 7th Internat. Grassland Congress, New Zealand. Author tech., popular publs.; Editor: Proc. Sixth Internat. Grassland Congress. Recipient Medallion award Am. Forage and Grassland Coun., Disting. Grasslander award, 1994; award Md. Farm Bur.; Disting. Svc. award in agr. Kansas State U., 1985, Disting. Alumnus award, 1990; Cert. of Disting. Citizenship, State of Md.; Robert E. Wagner Efficient Agr. award established in his honor; Disting. Grasslander award Am. Forages Md. Grassland Coun., 1994. Fellow AAAS, Am. Soc. Agronomy (chmn. grassland com., mem. exec. com., bd. dirs., pres. N.E. br.), Crops Sci. Soc. Am., Soil Sci. Soc. Am.; mem. Grassland Coun. (pres.), Am. Soc. Range Mgmt., Cosmos Club (Washington), Atlanta Athletic Club, Sigma Xi, Alpha Zeta, Gamma Sigma Delta, Phi Kappa Phi. Presbyterian. Home: 1934 Mountain Creek Dr Stone Mountain GA 30087-1016 Office: 655 Engineering Dr Norcross GA 30092-2821

WAGNER, ROBERT OWEN, association executive; b. Evansville, Ind., Aug. 15, 1935; s. Blount R. and Dorothy (Osborn) W.; m. Marilyn Gay Clark, May 12, 1964; children—Robert Owen, Lori Ann, Marilyn Clark. Student, Purdue U., 1962-63. Keeper, head keeper, asst. dir. Mesker Zoo, Evansville, 1956-59; dir. Washington Park Zoo, Michigan City, Ind., 1959-64, Jackson (Miss.) Zool. Park, 1964-75; exec. dir. Am. Assn. Zool. Parks and Aquariums, Wheeling, W.Va., 1975—. Instr. Boy Scouts Am., 1964-68; v.p. Provine High Sch. Band Parents Club, 1972-73. Recipient Order of Arrow Boy Scouts, 1972, Boss of Yr. award Am. Profl. Bus. Women's Assn., Jackson, 1974, Outstanding Service resolution City of Jackson, 1975. Fellow Am. Assn. Zool. Parks and Aquariums (dir., v.p., treas., com. chmn.); mem. Am. Assn. Museums (asso.), Nat. Audubon Soc., Nat. Wildlife Fedn., Internat. Wildlife Fedn., N.Y. Zool. Soc., Smithsonian Instn. Republican. Club: Masons. Office: Am Assn Zool Parks & Aquariums Rt 88 Oglebay Park Wheeling WV 26003

WAGNER, ROBERT RODERICK, microbiologist, oncology educator; b. N.Y.C., Jan. 5, 1923; s. Nathan and Mary (Mendelsohn) W.; m. Mary Elizabeth Burke, Mar. 23, 1967. A.B., Columbia U., 1943; M.D., Yale U., 1946. Intern, asst. resident physician Yale-New Haven Med. Center, 1946-

47, 49-50; research fellow Nat. Inst. Med. Research, London, Eng., 1950-51; instr., then asst. prof. medicine Yale U., 1951-55; asst., then assoc. prof. medicine Johns Hopkins U., Balt., 1956-59, assoc. prof. microbiology, 1959-64, asst., then assoc. dean med. faculty, 1957-63, prof. microbiology, 1964-67; vis. fellow, mem. Common Room All Souls Coll. Oxford U., 1967, 76; prof. microbiology U. Va., 1967—; chmn. dept. microbiology, 1967-94; Marion McNulty Weaver and Malvin C. Weaver prof. oncology U. Va., 1984—; dir. Cancer Ctr., 1984-94; vis. scientist Chinese Acad. Med. Scis., 1982; vis. prof. Univs. Giessen and Wuerzburg (W. Ger.), 1983; Cons. Am. Cancer Soc. Mem. coms.; USPHS, NSF, Assn. Am. Med. Colls., AMA, Nat. Bd. Med. Examiners.; bd. dirs. W. Alton Jones Cell Sci. Center, Lake Placid, N.Y., 1982—. Editor-in-chief: Jour. Virology, 1966-82. Served to lt. USNR, 1947-49. Rockefeller Found. resident scholar Villa Serbelloni, Bellagio, Italy, 1976; Macy Found. Faculty scholar Oxford U., 1976; recipient Disting. U.S. Scientist award Alexander von Humboldt Found., 1983. Fellow AAAS (councillor); mem. Assn. Am. Physicians, Am. Soc. Clin. Investigation, Am. Soc. Biol. Chemists, Am. Assn. Immunologists, Am. Soc. for Microbiology (councillor), Assn. Med. Sch. Microbiology Chmn. (pres. 1974), Am. Soc. Virology (pres. 1984). Office: Univ of Va Dept Microbiology Box 441 Charlottesville VA 22908

WAGNER, ROBERT TODD, university president, sociology educator; b. Sioux Falls, S.D., Oct. 30, 1932; s. Hans Herman and Helen Emilie (Castle) W.; m. Mary Kathryn Mumford, June 23, 1954; children: Christopher, Andrea. BA, Augustana Coll., Sioux Falls, 1954; MDiv, Seabury Western Theol. Sem., 1957, STM, 1970; PhD, S.D. State U., 1972; DHL, Augustana Coll., 1994. Ordained to ministry Episc. Ch., 1957. Staff analyst AMA, Chgo., 1954-57; vicar Ch. of Holy Apostles, Sioux Falls, 1957-64; chaplain All Saints Sch., Sioux Falls, 1962-64; rector Trinity Episcopal Ch., Watertown, S.D., 1964-69; prof. sociology S.D. State U., Brookings, 1971—, acting head dept. sociology, 1978, asst. to v.p. for acad. affairs, 1980-84, pres., 1985—; v.p. Dakota State U., Madison, S.D., 1984-85; cons. sociologist Devel. Planning and Research, Manhattan, Kans., 1976-85; bd. dirs. Deuel County Nat. Bank, Clear Lake, S.D., Found. Seed Stock. Bd. dirs. Karl Mundt Found.; Prairie Repertory Theatre, REACH, S.D. 4-H Found., S.D. State U. Found., SA Found., Griffith Charitable Trust, F.O. Butler Found., Christian Edn. Camp and Conf. of Episcopal Dioceses of S.D. Arthur Vinning Davis Found. fellow, 1969-70, Episcopal Ch. Found. fellow, 1969-71, Augustana Coll. fellow, 1977. Mem. Nat. Assn. State Univs. and Land Grant Colls., Brookings C. of C., Phi Kappa Phi, Phi Kappa Delta, Pi Gamma Mu, Alpha Kappa Delta, Alpha Lambda Delta, Sigma Gamma Delta. Republican. Lodges: Elks, Rotary. Avocations: railroading, gardening, cooking. Home: 929 Harvey Dunn St Brookings SD 57006-1347 Office: SD State U Adminstrn Bldg 222 Office of Pres Brookings SD 57007-2298

WAGNER, ROBIN SAMUEL ANTON, stage and set designer; b. San Francisco, Aug. 31, 1933; s. Jens Otto and Phyllis Edna (Smith-Spurgeon) W.; children: Kurt, Leslie, Christie. Student, Calif. Sch. Fine Arts, 1953-54. Pres. Scarab Prodns., Inc., 1975—; prof. theatre arts Columbia U., 1988—; sr. v.p. The Design Edge, 1989—. Designer on Broadway, including Death Defying Acts, Victor/Victoria, Angels in America, Millenium Approaches Perestroika, Crazy for You, Jelly's Last Jam, City of Angels, Jerome Robbins's Broadway, Teddy and Alice, Chess, Song and Dance, Merlin, Dreamgirls, 42nd Street, A Chorus Line, On the Twentieth Century, Ballroom, Mack and Mabel, Seesaw, Sugar, Jesus Christ Superstar, The Great White Hope, Promises, Promises, Lenny, Inner City, Hair; designer off Broadway, including: Putting It Together, Hamlet 90, In White America, View from the Bridge, Mahogony, The Prodigal, Between Two Thieves, Cages; designer regional theatres including Joseph Papp Pub. Theatre, Arena Stage, Washington, Actor's Workshop, San Francisco, Met Opera, San Francisco Ballet, Am. Ballet Theatre, Am. Shakespeare Festival, Eliot Feld Ballet, N.Y. Shakespeare Festival, Ensemble Studio Theater N.Y., N.Y.C. Ballet, Vienna State Opera, Hamburg State Opera, Royal Opera at Covent Garden, Rolling Stones Tour of Ams., 1975, (London prodns.) Crazy For You, City of Angels, Chess, 42d Street, A Chorus Line, Promises, Promises, Hair, (Tokyo prodns.) A Chorus Line, Dream Girls, 42nd St., City of Angels, Crazy for You. Mem. adv. bd. Nat. Corp. Theatre Fund, Theatre Adv. Coun. for City of N.Y.; mem. art adv. com. N.Y. Internat. Festival of the Arts; bd. trustees N.Y. Shakespeare Festival. Recipient Antoinette Perry (Tony) award for On the Twentieth Century, 1978, City of Angels, 1990, also numerous nominations; Drama Desk award, 1971, 78, 82, 90, Theatre World award, 1975, Outer Circle Critics award, 1978, 90, 92, Maharam award, 1973, 75, 82, Lumen award, 1975, Dramalogue award, 1980, Boston Critics Circle award, 1983, L.A. Drama Critics Circle award, 1974, 92, award for excellence in theatre Ensemble Studio Theatre, 1990. Mem. United Scenic Artists. Office: Robin Wagner Studio 890 Broadway New York NY 10003-1211

WAGNER, ROD, library director; b. Oakland, Nebr., Sept. 14, 1948; s. Francis Lynn and Doris Jean (Egbers) W.; m. M. Diane Kennedy, June 14, 1969; children: Jennifer, Brian, James. BA Social Sci. Edn., Wayne (Nebr.) State Coll., 1970; MA Polit. Sci., U. Nebr. Lincoln, 1971; MA Libr. Sci., U. Mo., 1981. Rsch. coord. Nebr. Libr. Commn., Lincoln, 1972, planning, evaluation, rsch. coord., 1972-73, adminstrv. asst., 1973-74, dep. dir., 1974-87, dir., 1988—; bd. dirs. Nebr. Ctr. for the Book, Nebr. Devel. Network. With U.S. Army Nat. Guard, 1970-77. Mem. ALA (contbr. awardbook 1981-84), Nat. Mgmt. Assn., Mountain Plains Libr. Assn., Nebr. Libr. Assn. (pres.-elect 1993-94, pres. 1994-95), Chief Officers State Libr. Agencies, Western Coun. State Librs. (pres. 1992-93). Presbyterian. Home: 3205 W Pershing Rd Lincoln NE 68502 Office: NE Libr Commn 1200 N St Ste 120 Lincoln NE 68508

WAGNER, ROGER PHILIP, hotel executive; b. Billings, Mont., July 13, 1947; s. Joseph Philip and Rosa Wilhelmena (Eisenman) W.; m. Patricia Ann Dively, Dec. 29, 1973 (div. Mar. 1979); m. Catherine Jean Brooks, Nov. 28, 1980; children: Michelle, Jeffrey, Joseph. Student, U. Idaho; BS in Hotel Adminstrn., U. Nev., Las Vegas. Asst. hotel mgr. Sands Hotel & Casino, Las Vegas, 1970-73, asst. gen. mgr., 1976-77, exec. v.p., 1978-81; hotel mgr. Dunes Hotel & Casino, Las Vegas, 1973-74, Frontier Hotel & Casino, Las Vegas, 1974-76; exec. v.p. MGM Grand Hotel, Reno, Nev., 1977-78; v.p., gen. mgr. Edgewater Hotel & Casino, Laughlin, Nev., 1981-83; pres. Claridge Hotel & Casino Corp., Atlantic City, N.J., 1983—, also bd. dirs. Campaign dir. Atlantic County chpt. United Way, Atlantic City, 1986-87; hon. trustee So. Jersey Regional Theater, Sommers Point, N.J., 1986-87; trustee So. Jersey Conf. Christians and Jews, Atlantic City, 1987—. Mem. Hotel Sales and Mgmt. Assn., MGM Employees Credit Union (founder, v.p. 1977-78), SYMMA Employees Credit Union (founder, v.p., sec. 1975-77), Elks. Republican. Methodist. Avocations: water skiing, tennis. Office: Claridge Hotel & Casino Boardwalk At Park Pl Atlantic City NJ 08401 also: Trump's Castle Assoc Huron Ave Brigantine Blvd Atlantic City NJ 08401

WAGNER, ROY, anthropology educator, researcher; b. Cleve., Oct. 2, 1938; s. Richard Robert and Florence Helen (Mueller) W.; m. Brenda Sue Geilhausen, June 14, 1968 (div. 1994); children: Erika Susan, Jonathan Richard. AB, Harvard U., 1961; AM, U. Chgo., 1962, PhD, 1966. Asst. prof. anthropology So. Ill. U., Carbondale, 1966-68; assoc. prof. Northwestern U., Evanston, Ill., 1969-74; prof. U. Va., Charlottesville, 1974—, chmn. dept., 1974-79; mem. cultural anthropology panel NSF, Washington, 1981-82. Author: Habu, 1972, The Invention of Culture, 1975, Lethal Speech, 1978, Symbols That Stand for Themselves, 1986. Social Sci. Research Council faculty research grantee, 1968; NSF postdoctoral research grantee, 1979. Fellow Am. Anthropol. Assn. Avocation: student hot-air balloon pilot. Home: 726 Cargil Ln Charlottesville VA 22902 Office: U Va Dept Anthropology University Station Charlottesville VA 22906

WAGNER, SAMUEL ALBIN MAR, records management executive, educator; b. Brighton, Colo., Feb. 23, 1942; s. Jacob Doer and Leota Garnet (Wilson) W.; m. Donna Dee Person, Mar. 20, 1987; children: Andrea, Kurt, Autumn, Jan, Arthur. BA in History, U. Colo., 1964, MA in History, 1965; STB (MTS) in History of World Religions, Harvard U., 1968; cert. in archival adminstrn., U. Denver, 1978. cert. records mgr., 1993, cert. archivist, 1994. Archival asst. Harvard U. & Harvard Bus. Sch., 1965-68; asst. curator we. hist. collections U. Colo.; sr. asst. archivist Cornell U., Ithaca, N.Y., 1971-73; editor Brighton Blade, Ft. Lupton Press, Colo., 1973-77; city archivist City of Providence, 1978-80; state records analyst Wyo.

State Archives, Cheyenne, 1979-83; records mgr. Ft. Collins (Colo.) Police Dept., 1984-87; pres. Records Mgmt. Cons. Internat., 1984—; pub. records adminstr. State R.I., Providence, 1987-90; asst. prof. Master Archival Studies program U. B.C., Vancouver, Can., 1990-93; editor Mo. State Archives, Jefferson City, 1994—; prodr. community access Sta. JCTV, Jefferson City; instr. Chapman, U., 1981-87, Colo. State U., 1985-87, Lincoln U., 1994—; pres. Records Mgmt. Cons., 1981—; speaker at nat. & internat. confs. Author: Brighton Reflections, 1976, Adams County: Crossroads of the West, 1977, Directory of Automated Records Management Systems, 1987, 88, 89, 90, 91, Crossroads of the West: A History of Brighton and the Platte Valley, 1987; editor: The Fort Lupton Story, 1987; contbr. numerous articles to profl. jours. Officer, bd. dirs. Adams County Hist. Soc., 1973-77; county historian Adams County, Brighton, 1976-77; mem. Brighton Human Rels. Commn., 1977-78; bd. dirs. Brighton Bicentennial Com., 1975-76, Ft. Lupton Bicentennial Com., 1975-76, R.I. RSVP, 1978-80, R.I. Pub. Records Adv. Coun., 1987-90, R.I. Hist. Records Adv. Bd., 1987-90; chair info. profls. legis. task force Freedom of Info. and Privacy Assn., 1991-93. Recipient Hist. Preservation award Adams County Hist. Soc., 1978, award Freedom of Info. and Privacy Assn., 1993; Ethnic Heritage Project grantee Colo. Humanities Council, 1977, Humanities and Social Scis. grantee U. B.C.; Ford Found. fellow, 1964. Mem. Assn. Records Mgrs. and Adminstrs. (pres. No. Colo. chpt. 1984-85, v.p. ocean state chpt. 1987-90, bd. dirs., editor Vancouver chpt. 1991, chmn. various coms., Mem. Yr. 1985), Microcomputer/PC Industry Action Com. (chmn. 1984-86, editor Software Dir. 1985-91, dir. Automated Records Sys. 1986-91, co-chmn. tech. applications com. 1989-90), Inst. Cert. Records Mgrs. (regional coord., exam proctor, grader 1982—, cert. records mgr. 1993), Soc. Am. Archivists (com. automated records and techniques 1990-94, select com. task force on automated records and techniques 1994—, chair microMARC users group 1994—), Nat. Assn. Govt. Archivists an Records Adminstrs., Archives Assn. B.C. (freedom of info. and privacy legis. com. 1990-93), Assn. Can. Archivists (electronic records select com. 1991-93, Acad. Cert. Archivists (cert. 1994). Democrat. Unitarian. Avocations: local historian, art, photography, film and TV production, hiking. Home: 231 Hobbs Ave Cheyenne WY 82009

WAGNER, SIGURD, electrical engineering educator, researcher; came to U.S., 1968; naturalized in 1990; s. Richard A. and Pauli (Steiner) W.; m. Erika Freiberger, 1968; children: Matthias, Wolfgang. PhD, U. Vienna, Austria, 1968. Univ. postdoctoral fellow Ohio State U., 1969-70; mem. tech. staff Bell Labs., Murray Hill, N.J., 1970-73, Holmdel, N.J., 1973-78; chief photovoltaic research br. Solar Energy Research Inst., Golden, Colo., 1978-80; prof. elec. engring. Princeton U., N.J., 1980—. Contbr. articles on electronic materials and devices to profl. jours.; assoc. editorial bd. Materials Letters, 1982—; patentee electronic materials and devices. Fellow Am. Phys. Soc.; mem. IEEE, Electrochem. Soc., Am. Chem. Soc., Materials Rsch. Soc.

WAGNER, SUE ELLEN, state official; b. Portland, Maine, Jan. 6, 1940; d. Raymond A. and Kathryn (Hooper) Pooler; m. Peter B. Wagner, 1964 (dec.); children: Kirk, Kristina. B.A. in Polit. Sci., U. Ariz., 1962; M.A. in History, Northwestern U., 1964. Asst. dean women Ohio State U., 1963-64; tchr. history and Am. govt. Catalina High Sch., Tucson, 1964-65; reporter Tucson Daily Citizen, 1965-68; mem. Nev. Assembly, 1975-83; mem. Nev. Senate from 3d dist.; elected lt. gov. of Nev., 1990-94. Author: Diary of a Candidate, On People and Things, 1974. Mem. Reno Mayor's Adv. Com., 1973-84; chmn. Blue Ribbon Task Force on Housing, 1974-75; mem. Washoe County Republican Central Com., 1974-84, Nev. State Rep. Central Com., 1975-84; mem. Nev. Legis. Commn., 1976-77; del. social service com. Council State Govts.; v.p. Am. Field Service, 1973, family liaison, 1974, mem.-at-large, 1975. Kappa Alpha Theta Nat. Grad. scholar, also Phelps-Dodge postgrad. fellow, 1962; named Outstanding Legislator, Nev. Young Republicans, 1976. Mem. AAUW (legis. chmn. 1974), Bus. and Profl. Women, Kappa Alpha Theta. Episcopalian. Home: 845 Tamarack Dr Reno NV 89509-3640 Office: Office of Lt Governor Capitol Complex Carson City NV 89710*

WAGNER, THOMAS JOSEPH, lawyer, insurance company executive; b. Jackson, Mich., June 29, 1939; s. O. Walter and Dorothy Ann (Hollinger) W.; m. Judith Louise Bogardus, Jan. 15, 1961; children—Ann Louise, Mark Robert, Rachel Miriam. B.A., Earlham Coll., 1957; J.D., U. Chgo., 1965. Bar: Ill. 1968, U.S. Supreme Ct. 1975. Asst. to gov. State of Ill., Springfield, 1966-67, legal counsel, adminstrv. asst. to treas., 1967-70; adminstrv. asst. to U.S. senator Adlai E. Stevenson, Washington, 1970-77; sr. v.p. govt. affairs div. Am. Ins. Assn., Washington, 1977-80; staff v.p. Ina Corp., 1980-82; v.p., chief counsel Property Casualty Group, CIGNA Corp., Phila., 1982-86, v.p., assoc. gen. counsel, 1986-88, sr. v.p., corp. sec., 1988-91, exec. v.p., gen. counsel, 1992—; trustee Eisenhower Exchange Fellowships, Inc.; v.p. fin. U.S.-PECC; bd. dir. Inst. Law and Econs., U. Penn. Past chmn. Phila. Crime Commn. Africa-Asia Pub. Svc. fellow Syracuse U., 1965-66. Mem. ABA (bus. law com.), Am. Corp. Counsel Assn. Office: Cigna Corp PO Box 7716 1 Liberty Place 55th Fl Philadelphia PA 19192-1550

WAGNER, WARREN HERBERT, JR., botanist, educator; b. Washington, Aug. 29, 1920; s. Warren Herbert and Harriet Lavinia (Claflin) W.; m. Florence Signaigo, July 16, 1948; children: Warren Charles, Margaret Frances. A.B., U. Pa., 1942; Ph.D., U. Calif. at Berkeley, 1950; spl. student, Harvard, 1950-51. Instr. Harvard, summer 1951; vis. prof., 1991; faculty U. Mich. at Ann Arbor, 1951—; prof. botany, 1962-91, prof. emeritus, 1991—, curator pteridophytes, 1961—; dir. Bot. Gardens, 1966-71, chmn. dept. botany, 1971-77; spl. rsch. higher plants, origin and evolution ferns, groundplan/divergence methods accurate deduction phylogenetic relationships fossil and living plants, pteridophytes of Hawaii, 1962-65; prin. investigator project evolutionary characters ferns NSF, 1960—, monograph grapeferns, 1980—, pteridophytes of Hawaii, 1991—; chmn. Mich. Natural Areas Coun., 1958-59; mem. Smithsonian Coun., 1966-72, hon. mem., 1972—; cons. mem. Survival Svc. Commn., Internat. Union for Conservation of Nature and Natural Resources, 1971—; mem. nat. hist. bd. Nat. Mus. 1989—. Trustee Cranbrook Inst. Scis. Recipient Distinguished Faculty Achievement award U. Mich., 1975, Amoco Outstanding Tchr. award, 1980, Disting. Sr. Lectr. award U. Mich., 1986. Fellow AAAS (sec. sect. bot. scis., v.p. sect. 1968), Am. Acad. Arts and Scis.; mem. NAS, Am. Fern Soc. (sec. 1952-54, curator, librarian 1957-77, pres. 1970, 71, hon. mem. 1978), Am. Soc. Plant Taxonomists (coun. 1958-65, pres. 1966, Asa Gray award 1990), Soc. for Study Evolution (v.p. 1965-66, coun. mem. 1967-69, pres. 1972), Am. Soc. Naturalists, Internat. Assn. Pteridologists (v.p. 1981-87, pres. 1987-93), Bot. Soc. Am. (pres. 1977, Merit award 1978, Henry Allan Gleason award, 1992, N.Y. Bot. Garden award, 1992), Mich. Bot. Club (pres. 1976-71), Torrey Bot. Club, New Eng. Bot. Club, Internat. Soc. Plant Morphologists, Internat. Assn. Plant Taxonomy, Sigma Xi, Phi Beta Kappa, Phi Kappa Tau. Home: 2111 Melrose Ave Ann Arbor MI 48104-4067

WAGNER, WILLIAM BRADLEY, lawyer; b. Memphis, Dec. 30, 1949; s. William G. and Wilmeth (Norman) W. BS in Econs., U. Fla., 1971; JD, U. Va., 1974. Bar: U.S. Ct. Appeals (5th and 11th cirs.) 1981, Tex. 1989, U.S. Dist. Ct. (ea., fed. and so. dists.) Tex. 1989, U.S. Tax Ct. Ptnr. Fulbright & Jaworski, Austin, Tex., 1974—. Contbg. author: (handbook) Natural Gas Regulation. Home: 1600 Westlake Dr Austin TX 78746 Office: Fulbright & Jaworski 600 Congress Ave Ste 2400 Austin TX 78701-3271

WAGNER, WILLIAM BURDETTE, business educator; b. Oswego, N.Y., Apr. 27, 1941; s. Guy Wesley and Gladys M. (Redlinger) W.; divorced; 1 child, Geoffrey D. BA with highest honors, Mich. State U., 1963; MBA, Ohio State U., 1965, PhD, 1967. Research and teaching asst. Ohio State U., Columbus, 1966-68; prof. mktg. and logistics U. Mo., Columbia, 1969—; guest prof. mktg. U. Nanjing, Peoples Republic of China, 1985-87, Prince of Songkla U., Hat Yai, Thailand, 1990, 92; expert witness petroleum industry, 1989—; adv. U. Mo. State Bank, St. Louis, 1981—. Contbr. articles to profl. jours. Univ. coordinator book procurement program for minorities McDonnell Douglas, St. Louis, 1972—; mem. St. Louis-Nanjing Sister City Com., 1985—; faculty ambassador U. Mo. Alumni Assn., 1987—; mem. speakers bur.; high sch. liaison team U. Mo., 1987—; Mizzou Outreach prof. 1987—; bd. dirs. Cen. Mo. Sheltered Enterprises for Handicapped, Columbia, 1985-92. Recipient Civic Svc. award McDonnell Douglas, 1977, Educator of Yr. award Jaycees, 1983, 1st Ann. Bus. Prof. of Yr. award, 1987, Golden Key Honor Soc. Faculty Mem. of Yr. award, 1987, Faculty Mem. of Yr. Beta Theta Pi, 1990, Prof. of Yr. award Kans. City Alumni Assn., 1990;

named Mktg. Prof. of Yr. U. Mo., 1987-88, 89-91; rsch. grantee SBA, Econ. Devel. Adminstrn., U. Mo., NDEA fellow Ohio State U., 1963-66, William T. Kemper Teaching fellow, 1991; Fulbright scholar, Korea, 1992. Mem. Nat. Assn. Purchasing Mgmt., St. Louis Purchasing Mgmt. Assn., Coun. Logistics Mgmt., Nat. Fulbright Assn., Nat. Eagle Scout Assn.; Am. Soc. Transp. and Logistics (pres. Mo. chpt. 1974-75, bd. govs. 1970-74, 75-82), Delta Sigma Pi, Beta Gamma Simga, Omicron Delta Epsilon, Rotary Internat. Methodist. Clubs: Mo. Athletic (St. Louis); Country of Mo. (Columbia). Avocations: stamp and coin collecting, bridge, golf, swimming, jogging. Home: 2401 Bluff Blvd Columbia MO 65201-8613 Office: Univ Mo 324 Middlebush Hall Columbia MO 65211

WAGNER, WILLIAM CHARLES, veterinarian; b. Elma, N.Y., Nov. 12, 1932; s. Frederick George and Doris Edna (Newton) W.; m. Donna Ann McNeill, Aug. 14, 1954 (div. May 1993); children: William Charles, Elizabeth Ann, Victoria Mary, Kathryn Farrington. D.V.M., Cornell U., 1956, Ph.D., 1968. Gen. practice vet. medicine Interlaken, N.Y., 1956-57; research veterinarian Cornell U., 1957-65, NIH postdoctoral fellow dept. animal sci., 1965-68; asst. prof. vet. medicine Vet. Med. Research Inst., Iowa State U., Ames, 1968-69; assoc. prof. Vet. Med. Research Inst., Iowa State U., 1969-74, prof., 1974-77; prof. physiology, head dept. vet. bioscis. U. Ill., Urbana, 1977-90, assoc. dean for rsch. and grad. studies Coll. Vet. Medicine, 1990—; gen. sec. Internat. Congress on Animal Reprodn., urbana, 1984, pres. standing com., 1988—; v.p. Conf. Rsch. Workers in Animal Disease, 1987-88, pres., 1988-89; prin. vet. scientist USDA-Coop. State Rsch. Svcs., Washington, 1990-91. Pres. Ames Community Theater, 1972-73, 76-77. Recipient Alexander von Humboldt U.S. Scientist award Humboldt Stiftung, Freising-Weihenstephan, W. Ger., 1973-74; Fulbright prof., W. Ger., 1984-85. Mem. Am. Coll. Theriogenologists (diplomate), AVMA (mem. coun. on edn. 1987-), Physiol. Soc., Am. Soc. Animal Sci., Soc. Study Reprodn., Soc. Study Fertility, N.Y. Acad. Scis., Sigma Xi, Phi Kappa Phi, Phi Zeta, Gamma Sigma Delta, Alpha Zeta. Lutheran. Home: 2315 S 1st St Apt 203 Champaign IL 61820-7421 Office: U Ill Coll Vet Medicine 2001 S Lincoln St Urbana IL 61801 *I believe that it is important to be friendly to others, to try to understand the other person's position or feelings and deal with colleagues and subordinates in an impartial and fair manner. One should always remember that talents are a gift to be used wisely and to the fullest extent possible.*

WAGNER, WILLIAM GERARD, university dean, physicist, consultant, information scientist, investment manager; b. St. Cloud, Minn., Aug. 22, 1936; s. Gerard C. and Mary V. (Cloone) W.; m. Janet Agatha Rowe, Jan. 30, 1968 (div. 1978); children: Mary, Robert, David, Anne; m. Christiane LeGuen, Feb. 21, 1985 (div. 1989). B.S., Calif. Inst. Tech., 1958, Ph.D. (NSF fellow, Howard Hughes fellow), 1962. Cons. Rand Corp., Santa Monica, Calif., 1960-65; sr. staff physicist Hughes Research Lab., Malibu, Calif., 1960-69; lectr. physics Calif. Inst. Tech., Pasadena, 1963-65; asst. prof. physics U. Calif. at Irvine, 1965-66; assoc. prof. physics and elec. engring. U. So. Calif., L.A., 1966-69, prof. depts. physics and elec. engring., 1969—, dean div. natural scis. and math. Coll. Letters, Arts and Scis., 1973-84, dean interdisciplinary studies and developmental activities, 1987-89, spl. asst. automated record services, 1975-81; founder program in neural, informational & behavioral scis., 1982—; chmn. bd. Malibu Securities Corp., L.A. 1971—; cons. Janus Mgmt. Corp., L.A., 1970-71, Croesus Capital Corp. L.A., 1971-74, Fin. Horizons Inc., Beverly Hills, Calif., 1974—; allied mem. Pacific Stock Exch., 1974-82; fin. and computer cons. Hollywood Reporter, 1979-81; mem. adv. coun. for emerging engring. techs. NSF, 1987—. Contbr. articles on physics to sci. publs. Richard Chase Tolman postdoctoral fellow, 1962-65. Mem. Am. Phys. Soc., Nat. Assn. Security Dealers, Sigma Xi. Home: 2828 Patricia Ave Los Angeles CA 90064-4425 Office: U So Calif Hedco Neurosci Bldg Los Angeles CA 90089

WAGNON, JOAN, former state legislator, association executive; b. Texarkana, Ark., Oct. 17, 1940; d. Jack and Louise (Lucas) D.; m. William O. Wagnon Jr., June 4, 1964; chidlren: Jack, William O. III. BA in Biology, Hendrix Coll., Conway, Ark., 1962; MEd in Guidance and Counseling, U. Mo., 1968. Sr. research technician U. Ark. Med. Sch., Little Rock, 1962-64; sr. research asst. U. Ark. Med. Sch., Columbia, Mo., 1964-68; tchr. No. Hills Jr. High Sch., Topeka, 1968-69, J.S. Kendall Sch., Boston, 1970-71; counselor Neighborhood Youth Corps, Topeka, 1973-74; exec. dir. Topeka YWCA, 1977-93; mem. Kans. Legislature, 1983-94. Mem. Health Planning Rev. Commn., Topeka, 1984-85. Recipient Service to Edn. award, Topeka NEA, 1979, Outstanding Achievement award, Kans. Home Econs. Assn., 1985; named Woman of Yr. Mayors Council Status of Women, 1983; named one of Top Ten Legislators Kans. Mag., Wichita, 1986. Mem. Topeka Assn. Human Svc. Execs. (pres. 1981-83), Topekans for Ednl. Involvement (pres. 1979-82), Women's Polit. Caucus (state chair). Democrat. Methodist. Lodge: Rotary. Avocations: music, swimming, boating. Home: 1606 SW Boswell Ave Topeka KS 66604-2729 Office: Kans Families for Kids 2209 SW 29th St Topeka KS 66611

WAGNON, WILLIAM ODELL, JR., history educator; b. Camden, Ark., Jan. 24, 1939; s. William Odell Sr. and Ernestine (Wilson) W.; m. Joan Davis, June 4, 1964; children: John Peter, William Odell III. AB, Hendrix Coll., 1962; MA, U. Mo., 1964, PhD, 1970. Asst. prof. history Washburn U., Topeka, 1968-76, assoc. prof., 1976-83, dir. internat. ctr., 1980-87, prof., 1983—, chmn. dept. history, 1991—; mem. Kans. Com. for the Humanities, Topeka, 1983-85; cons. NEH, Washington, 1981-83; distbn. officer DIS-Study, Copenhagen, 1981-87; dir. Inst. Cmty. Partnerships, 1993-95, Ctr. for Kans. Studies, 1995—. Contbr. articles to profl. jours. Assoc. Truman Inst. Independence, Mo., 1968—; bd. dirs. Kans. State Hist. Soc., Topeka, 1980—, pres., 1990, treas., 1992—; treas., bd. dirs. Hist. Topeka, Inc., 1984-87; gov.'s legis. edn. liaison, Topeka, 1991. Harvard-Newcomen fellow, 1970-71. Mem. Orgn. of Am. Historians, Bus. History Assn., AAUP (chpt. conf. pres. 1973-76), Saturday Night Lit. (pres. 1986), Masons. Democrat. Methodist. Avocations: gardening, sailing, camping. Office: Washburn U Topeka KS 66621

WAGONER, DAVID EVERETT, lawyer; b. Pottstown, Pa., May 16, 1928; s. Claude Brower and Mary Kathryn (Groff) W.; children: Paul R., Colin H., Elon D., Peter B.; m. Jean Morton Saunders; children: Dana F., Constance A., Jennifer L., Melissa J. B.A., Yale U., 1950; LL.B., U. Pa., 1953. Bar: D.C. 1953, Pa. 1953, Wash. 1953. Law clk. U.S. Ct. Appeals (3d cir.), Pa., 1955-56; law clk. U.S. Supreme Ct., Washington, 1956-57; ptnr. Perkins & Coie, Seattle, 1957—; panel mem. of arbitration forum worldwide including Republic of China, British Columnia Internat. Comml. Arbitration Ctr., Asian/Pacific Ctr. for Resolution of Internat. Bus. Disputes and the Ctr. fir Internat. Dispute Resolution for Asian/Pacific Region. Mem. sch. com. Mcpl. League Seattle and King County, 1958—, chmn., 1962-65; mem. Seattle schs. citizens coms. on equal edn. opportunity and adult vocat. edn., 1963-64; mem. Nat. Com. Support Pub. Schs.; mem. adv. com. on community colls., to 1965, legislature interim com. on edn., 1964-65; mem. community coll. adv. com. to state supt. pub. instrn., 1965; chmn. edn. com. Forward Thrust, 1968; mem. Univ. Congl. Ch. Council Seattle, 1968-70; bd. dirs. Met. YMCA Seattle, 1968; bd. dirs. Seattle Pub. Schs., 1965-73, v.p., 1966-67, 72-73, pres., 1968, 73; trustee Evergreen State Coll. Found., chmn. 1986-87, capitol campaign planning chmn.; trustee Pacific NW Ballet, v.p. 1986. Served to 1st lt. M.C., AUS, 1953-55. Fellow Am. Coll. Trial Lawyers (mem. ethics com., legal ethics com.); mem. ABA (mem. standing com. fed. judicial imprisonment, chmn. appellate advocacy com.), Wash. State Bar Assn., Seattle-King County Bar Assn., Chartered Inst. Arbitrators, Singapore Inst. Arbitrators, British Acad. Experts, Swiss Arbitration Assn., Comml. Bar Assn. London, Nat. Sch. Bds. Assn. (bd. dirs., chmn. coun. Big City bds. edn. 1971-72), English-Speaking Union (v.p. Seattle chpt. 1961-62), Chi Phi. Office: Perkins Coie 1201 3rd Ave Fl 40 Seattle WA 98101-3000

WAGONER, DAVID RUSSELL, author, educator; b. Massillon, Ohio, June 5, 1926; s. Walter Siffert and Ruth (Banyard) W.; m. Patricia Lee Parrott, July 8, 1961 (div. June 1982); m. Robin Heather Seyfried, July 24, 1982; children: Alexandra Dawn, Adrienne Campbell. B.A. in English, Pa. State U., 1947; M.A. in English, Ind. U., 1949. Instr. English DePauw U., 1949-50; instr. Pa. State U., 1950-53; asst. prof. U. Wash., 1954-57, assoc. prof., 1958-66, prof.; mem.—; Elliston lectr. U. Cin., 1968; editor Poetry NW, 1966—; poetry editor Princeton U. Press, 1977-81, Mo. Press, 1983—. Author: poetry books Dry Sun, Dry Wind, 1953, A Place to Stand, 1958, The Nesting Ground, 1963, Staying Alive, 1966, New and Selected Poems,

1969, Working Against Time, 1970, Riverbed, 1972, Sleeping in the Woods, 1974, Collected Poems, 1976, Who Shall Be the Sun?, 1978, In Broken Country, 1979, Landfall, 1981, First Light, 1983, Through the Forest, 1987; novels The Man in the Middle, 1954, Money, Money Money, 1955, Rock, 1958, The Escape Artist (also film 1982), 1965, Baby, Come on Inside, 1968, Where Is My Wandering Boy Tonight?, 1970, The Road To Many A Wonder, 1974, Tracker, 1975, Whole Hog, 1976, The Hanging Garden, 1980; editor: Straw for the Fire: From the Notebooks of Theodore Roethke, 1943-63, 1972. Recipient Morton Dauwen Zabel prize Poetry mag., 1967, Blumenthal-Leviton-Blonder prize, 1974, 2 Fels prizes Coordinating Coun. Lit. Mags., 1975, Tietjens prize, 1977, English-Speaking Union prize, 1980, Sherwood Anderson award, 1980, Ruth Lilly Poetry prize, 1991, Levinson prize, 1994; Guggenheim fellow, 1956, Ford fellow, 1964, Nat. Inst. Arts and Letters grantee, 1967, Nat. Endowment for Arts grantee, 1969. Mem. Acad. Am. Poets (chancellor 1978—), Soc. Am. Magicians, Nat. Assn. Blackfeet Indians (asso.). Home: 5416 154th Pl SW Edmonds WA 98026-4348 Office: U Wash 4045 Brooklyn Ave NE Seattle WA 98105-6261

WAGONER, JENNINGS LEE, JR., history educator; b. Winston-Salem, N.C., July 26, 1938; s. Jennings Lee and Carolyn Nelme (Phifer) W.; m. Shirley Canady, Aug. 12, 1962; children: David Carroll, Brian Jennings. BA, Wake Forest U., 1960; MATeaching, Duke U., 1961; PhD, Ohio State U., 1968. Tchr. High Point Pub. Schs., N.C., 1960-62; instr. Wake Forest U., 1962-65; teaching assoc. Ohio State U., 1965-68; from asst. prof. to prof. history of edn. U. Va., Charlottesville, 1968—, dir. Ctr. for Study Higher Edn., 1975-85, chmn. leadership and policy studies, 1985-87, disting. prof. Curry Sch. Edn. U. Va., 1987, William C. Parrish Jr. Endowed prof., 1994—; vis. research scholar Harvard U., 1972, U. Calif., Berkeley, 1984; vis. prof. Monash U., Melbourne, Australia, 1992. Author: Thomas Jefferson and the Education of a New Nation, 1976; co-author: A History of American Education, 1995; contbr. articles to profl. jours.; co-editor: Changing Politics of Education, 1978; editorial bd. History of Edn. Quar., Ednl. Studies jour. Sesquicentennial fellow U. Va., 1972, 84, 90. Mem. History of Edn. Soc. (pres. 1983-85, bd. dirs. 1979-81), Am. Ednl. Research Assn. (v.p. div. F 1981-83), Orgn. Am. Historians, Am. Ednl. Studies Assn. (bd. dirs.), Assn. Study Higher Edn., Raven Soc., Sierra Club, Outward Bound, Kappa Delta Pi, Phi Delta Kappa, Omicron Delta Kappa (faculty advisor), Golden Key Nat. Honor Soc. Avocations: hiking, fishing, canoeing. Home: 100 Juniper Ln Charlottesville VA 22901 Office: U Va 405 Emmet St Charlottesville VA 22903-2495

WAGONER, LYNDA JO, pediatrics nurse; b. Decator, Ind., Oct. 17, 1963; d. David C. and Carol A. (Mundell) Shoemaker; m. Scott A. Wagoner, July 26, 1985; 1 child, Erin M. BS in Nursing, Ball State U., 1986. Pediatric staff RN, charge nurse Ball Meml. Hosp., Muncie, Ind., 1987-88; med. surg. and obstetrics staff RN Randolph County Hosp., Winchester, Ind., 1986-87; pediatric RN office Anne Eliadas MD & Barbara P. Huss MD, Muncie, 1988—. Mem. Sigma Theta Tau.

WAGONER, PORTER, country music singer, composer; b. nr. West Plains, Mo., Aug. 12, 1927; s. Charles and Bertha W.; children: Richard, Denise, Debra. Former clerk, butcher. Singer, composer, radio and TV personality, 1950—, rec. artist, RCA Record Co., MCA/DOT Records, 1986—, radio and TV appearances include radio, KWPM, West Plains, Mo., 1950, KWTO, Springfield, Mo., 1951, Jubilee, U.S.A, ABC-TV, 1955, radio, WSM Grand Ole Opry, Nashville, Tenn., 1957—, Porter Wagoner TV Show; Records include A Satisfied Mind, Heartwarming Songs, Porter Wagoner Today, Best of Porter Wagoner, Porter & Dolly, Two of a Kind; composer songs including (with Gary Walker) Trade Mark, 1953, (with Michael Pearson) Bottom of the Fifth, 1982. Recipient (with Dolly Parton) Vocal Group of Yr. award, Vocal Duo of Yr. award Country Music Assn., 1970, 71. Address: World Class Talent Prod 48 Music Sq E Nashville TN 37203-4323*

WAGONER, RALPH HOWARD, academic administrator, educator; b. Pitts., May 30, 1938; s. Richard Henry and Charlotte (Stevenson) W.; m. Wilma Jo Staup, Dec. 21, 1961; children: Amanda Jane, Joseph Ryan. AB in Biology, Gettysburg Coll., 1960; MS in Ednl. Adminstrn., Westminster Coll., 1963; PhD, Kent State U., 1967; postgrad., MIT, 1973, Dartmouth Coll., 1979. Tchr., tchr. coach Williamsfield (Ohio) Elem. and Jr. High Sch., 1960-62; dir. elem. edn. Pymatuning Valley (Ohio) Local Schs., 1962-64, asst. supt. instrn., 1964-65; acad. counselor, asst. to dean coll. edn. Kent (Ohio) State U., 1965-66, instr. edn., 1966-67; asst. prof. Drake U., Des Moines, Iowa, 1967-70, assoc. prof., 1970-71, chmn. dept. elem. edn., 1968-70, chmn. dept. tchr. edn., 1970-71, acad. adminstrn. intern Am. Council Edn., Office of Pres., 1971-72, asst. to pres., 1972-77, dir. devel., 1975-77; v.p. pub. affairs and devel., prof. Western Ill. U., Macomb, 1977-87, pres., 1987-93; pres. Augustana Coll., Sioux Falls, S.D., 1993—; adj. prof. San Francisco Theol. Sem., 1971; mem. senate Drake U., 1968-77; sponsor interhall council Western Ill. U., 197893, mem. BOG/UPI task force on incentives for faculty excellence, co-chmn., faculty mentor, 1985-93; cons. in field. Co-author: (with L. Wayne Bryan) Societal Crises and Educational Response: A Book of Readings, 1969, (with Robert L. Evans) The Emerging Teacher, 1970, (with William R. Abell) The Instructional Module Package System, 1971, Writing Behavioral Objectives or How Do I Know When He Knows, 1971; contbr. articles to profl. jours. Chmn. Mid-Ill. Computer Consortium, 1980, 85, Western Ill. Corridor of Opportunity, 1987-93; mem. Pres.' Regional Adv. Coun., 1977-87; mem. investments com. McDonough County YMCA; mem. exec. com. Macomb Area Indsl. Corp.; trustee Robert Morris Coll., 1983-88, Chgo. and Carthage, Ill., 1983-88; bd. dirs. Ill. Coun. Econ. Edn., 1987-93, McDonough County United Way Dr., 1980-82. Recipient Man of Yr. award Andover Rotary Club, 1964, Quax Honor award, 1969-70, Disting. Alumni award Gettysburg (Pa.) Coll., 1991; named McDonough County Citizen of Yr., Elks, 1982. Fellow Am. Coun. Edn. (cons. fund raising 1984-87); mem. Am. Assn. State Colls. and Univs. (mem. econ. devel. com. on athletics 1987), Ednl. Computing Network (chmn. policy bd. 1985-87), Assn. Midcontinent Univs. (coun. dels. 1987-93), Gateway Conf. (coun. dels. 1987-93), Coun. for Advancement and Support of Edn. (discussion leader, speaker, 1975, 77, 80, 84, 86, Citation award 1981, 83, Grand award 1982, Bronze award 1985, Silver award 1986), Macomb C. of C. (exec. com., bd. dirs.), Ill. Chamber Econ. Devel. Policy Task Force, Blue Key (hon.), Omicron Delta Kappa, Phi Eta Sigma (hon.), Phi Mu Alpha. Lutheran. Lodge: Rotary. Home: 2817 S Grange Ave Sioux Falls SD 57105-4616 Office: Augustana Coll 29th and Summit Sioux Falls SD 57197

WAGONER, ROBERT VERNON, astrophysicist, educator; b. Teaneck, N.J., Aug. 6, 1938; s. Robert Vernon and Marie Theresa (Clifford) W.; m. Lynne Ray Moses, Sept. 2, 1963 (div. Feb. 1986); children: Alexa Frances, Shannon Stephanie; m. Stephanie Nightingale, June 27, 1987. B.M.E., Cornell U., 1961; M.S., Stanford U., 1962, Ph.D., 1965. Research fellow in physics Calif. Inst. Tech., 1965-68, Sherman Fairchild Disting. scholar, 1976; asst. prof. astronomy Cornell U., 1968-71, asso. prof., 1971-73; asso. prof. physics Stanford U., 1973-77, prof., 1977—; George Ellery Hale disting. vis. prof. U. Chgo., 1978; mem. Com. on Space Astronomy and Astrophysics, 1979-82, theory study panel Space Sci. Bd., 1980-82, physics survey com. NRC, 1983-84; grant selection com. NSERC (Can.), 1990-93. Contbr. articles on theoretical astrophysics and gravitation to profl. publs., mags.; co-author Cosmic Horizons. Sloan Found. fellow, 1969-71; Guggenheim Meml. fellow, 1979; grantee NSF, 1973-90, NASA, 1982—. Fellow Am. Phys. Soc.; mem. Am. Astron. Soc., Internat. Astron. Union, Tau Beta Pi, Phi Kappa Phi. Patentee. Office: Stanford U Dept Physics Stanford CA 94305

WAGONER, WILLIAM HAMPTON, university chancellor; b. Washington, N.C., May 12, 1927; s. William Gotha and Lossie Bell (Barrington) W.; June 3, 1952; children: William Michael, David Robin, Mark Hampton. BS cum laude, Wake Forest U., 1949, LLD, 1981; MA, East Carolina U., 1953; PhD in Ednl. Adminstrn. and Polit. Sci, U. N.C., Chapel Hill, 1958. Tchr. Washington (N.C.) High Sch., 1950-53; asst. prin. Elizabeth City (N.C.) High Sch., 1953-55; prin. Hattie Harney Elementary Sch., Elizabeth City, 1956; instr. U. N.C., 1957; asso. exec. N.C. State Sch. Bds. Assn., 1958-59; supt. Elizabeth City Schs., 1959-61, Wilmington-New Hanover County Schs., 1961-68; pres. Wilmington Coll., 1968; chancellor U. N.C. Wilmington, 1969-90, chancellor emeritus, 1990—; Speaker before various profl. groups at confs., convs. Pres. N.C. Div. Supts., 1967-68; chmn. bd. govs. N.C. Advancement Sch., 1967; mem. Gov.'s Tech. Coordinating Com. for Marine Sci. Council; pres. N.C. Assn. Colls. and

Univs., 1981. Trustee Cape Fear Meml. Hosp. With USNR, 1945-46. Recipient East Carolina Alumni award as Univ.'s Outstanding Alumni Award Winner, 1968. Mem. N.E.A. (life). Democrat. Episcopalian. Home: 2202 Marlwood Dr Wilmington NC 28403-6030 Office: U NC Wilmington 601 S College Rd Wilmington NC 28403-3201

WAGONSELLER, JAMES MYRL, real estate executive; b. Zanesville, Ohio, July 29, 1920; s. Myrl H. and Florence L. (Pfeiffer) W.; m. Mary J. McCauley, Nov. 16, 1943; children—Thomas James, John Myrl, Anne Elizabeth Wagonseller Bauswein. Grad. high sch. Draftsman apprentice machinist Hermann Mfg. Co., Lancaster, Ohio, 1945-47; advt. sales Lancaster (Ohio) Eagle-Gazette, 1947-50, classified mgr., 1950-52, dir. advt. sales, 1952-54; real estate salesman Larkin Durdin (Realtor), Lancaster, 1954-60; ptnr. Lancaster Realty Co., 1960-65, Simons & Wagonseller (Realtors), Lancaster, 1965-77; prin. James M. Wagonseller, Appraiser; Pres. Lancaster Bd. Realtors, 1965; mem. Bd. Zoning Appeals Lancaster, 1972-74. Pres. Community Service Council, 1944, United Appeal, 1968; Mem. central, exec. coms. Fairfield County Democratic Com., 1960-70, mem. exec. com., 1976—. Served with USAF, 1941-45. Decorated D.F.C., air medal with 3 clusters. Mem. Lancaster C. of C. (pres. 1970), Nat. Assn. Real Estate Brokers, Ohio Assn. Real Estate Brokers, Am. Assn. Cert. Appraisers, Am. Legion (nat. comdr. 1974-75). Democrat. Roman Catholic. Lodges: Kiwanis (pres.), Elk (Ann. Citizen award 1975). Home and Office: 1973 Coldspring Dr Lancaster OH 43130-1458

WAGSCHAL, KATHLEEN, education educator; b. Woburn, Mass., May 30, 1947; d. John Kenneth and Elizabeth (Ginivan) Lanpher; m. Peter Henry Wagschal, July 17, 1971; 1 child, Adam Colin. MEd, U. Mass., 1972, U. Mass., 1975. Cert. secondary tchr., Calif. Adminstrv. dir. lab. sch. Greenfield (Mass.) Community Coll., 1978-83; adj. faculty mem. Sch. Edn. Nat. U., San Diego, 1985-87, dir. student tchr. program, 1987-88, chair tchr. edn. program, 1987—, dean Sch. Edn., 1988—; cons., co-dir. Futures Unltd., N.Y. and Mass., 1972-85. Grantee Mass. Dept. Social Svcs., Mass. Dept. Edn., Bur. Nutrition and Edn., 1981-84. Mem. Calif. Assn. Colls Tchr. Edn., Calif. Coun. Edn. of Tchrs. Avocations: reading, pool. Office: Nat U 4141 Camino Del Rio S San Diego CA 92108-4103

WAHBA, GRACE, statistician, educator; b. Washington; d. Harry and Anne Goldsmith; 1 child, Jeffrey A. BA, Cornell U.; MA, U. Md.; PhD, Stanford U. Prof. statistics U. Wis., Madison, 1967-87, Bascom prof. 1987—; fellow Weizmann Inst., Israel, St. Cross Coll., Oxford (Eng.) U.; Lady Davis fellow Technion, Israel, Australian Nat. U., Canberra; Clare Booth Luce vis. prof. Yale U.; cons. to industry and govt. Author: Spline Models for Observational Data, 1990; assoc. editor; SIAM Jour. Sci. Computing, 1985—; adv. bd. Jour. Computational Graphical Stats., 1990—. Recipient Emanuel and Carol Parzen prize for Statis. Innovation, 1994, NSF Creativity award, 1994. Fellow AAAS, Inst. Math. Statis. (Neyman lectr. nat. meeting 1994), Am. Statis. Assn., Internat. Statis. Inst.; mem. Soc. Indsl. and Applied Math. (plenary speaker nat. meeting 1994), Bernoulli Soc., Am. Math. Soc., Am. Meteorol. Soc. Achievements include development of new statistical methods in biology and meteorology, of new methods for multivariate response function estimation, of analysis of variance in function spaces, of approximate solution of ill posed explicit and implicit inverse problems with noisy data, and of the assimilation of data from heterogenous sources. Office: U Wis Dept Stats 1210 W Dayton St Madison WI 53706-1685

WAHL, ARTHUR CHARLES, retired chemistry educator; b. Des Moines, Sept. 8, 1917; s. Arthur C. and Mabel (Mussetter) W.; m. Mary Elizabeth McCauley, Dec. 1, 1943; 1 child, Nancy Wahl Miegel. BS, Iowa State Coll., 1939; PhD, U. Calif., Berkeley, 1942. Group leader Los Alamos (N.Mex.) Nat. Lab., 1943-46; assoc. prof. chemistry Washington U., St. Louis, 1946-53, Farr prof. of radiochemistry, 1953-83, prof. emeritus, 1983—; cons. Los Alamos Nat. Lab., 1950—. Author, editor: Radioactivity Applied to Chemistry, 1951; contbr. articles to profl. jours. NSF fellow, 1967; recipient Sr. Vis. Scientist Humboldt award Humboldt Found., 1977. Mem. Am. Chem. Soc. (counselor for nuclear chem. divsn. 1946—). Office: Los Alamos Nat Lab MS # 514 Los Alamos NM 87545

WAHL, FLOYD MICHAEL, geologist; b. Hebron, Ind., July 7, 1931; s. Floyd Milford and Ann Pearl (DeCook) W.; m. Dorothy W. Daniel, July 4, 1953; children: Timothy, David, Jeffrey, Kathryn. A.B., DePauw U., 1953; M.S., U. Ill., 1957, Ph.D., 1958. Cert. profl. geologist. Prof. geology U. Fla., Gainesville, 1969-82, assoc. dean Grad. Sch., 1974-80, acting dean, 1980-81; exec. dir. Geol Soc Am., Boulder, Colo., 1982-94. Contbr. articles to profl. jours. Served to cpl. U.S. Army, 1953-55. Recipient Outstanding Tchr. award U. Ill., 1967. Fellow Geol. Soc. Am.; mem. Mineral Soc. Am., Am. Inst. Profl. Geologists (chpt. pres.), Sigma Xi. Office: Geol Soc Am PO Box 9140 3300 Penrose Pl Boulder CO 80301-1806

WAHL, HOWARD WAYNE, retired construction company executive, engineer; b. Hitterdal, Minn., Jan. 17, 1935; s. Milo Ormenzo and Esther Marie (Sorenson) W.; m. Carroll May Pollock, Aug. 16, 1958; children: Jeffrey David, Michael Edward, Nancy Elizabeth. BCE, U. Washington, 1957. Registered engr., Calif., N.Y., Mich., Ohio, Md. Structural engr. Bechtel Corp., San Francisco, 1956-69; project engr. Bechtel Corp., Gaithersburg, Md., 1969-72; chief civil engr. Bechter Power Corp., San Francisco, 1972-74; mgr. engring. and constrn. Bechter Power Corp., 1975-78; v.p., mgr. Andover Power Div.-Bechtel, Mich., 1978-84; dir. Bechtel Group, Inc., 1982-92; pres. Bechtel Ea. Power Corp., Gaithersburg, 1984-88; mng. dir. Bechtel Power Corp., San Francisco, 1988-89; pres. European region Bechtel Corp., Paris, 1989-91; ret., 1991; dir. Ann Arbor Bank-1st Am., 1978-84. Contbr. articles to profl. jours. Campaign chmn. Washtenaw County United Way, Ann Arbor, 1982; chmn. Turkish-U.S. Bus. Coun., Washington, 1988-90; mem. exec. coun. Boy Scouts Am., Ann Arbor, 1978-84; mem. devel. coun. U Wash. Coll. Engring.; trustee Desert Rsch. Inst. U. Nev., Reno. Mem. ASCE, Am. Concrete Inst., U. Mich. Pres. Club and Victors Club, U. Washington Pres. Club, Olympic Club (San Francisco). Republican. Presbyterian. Avocations: woodworking, gardening, cooking, boating, hiking. Home: PO Box 7601 Incline Village NV 89452-7601

WAHL, JONATHAN MICHAEL, mathematics educator; b. Washington, Jan. 29, 1945; s. Marvin C. and Blanche (Genauer) W.; m. Deborah R. Sody, Dec. 27, 1970; 1 child, Elizabeth Rachel. BS, MA, Yale U., 1965; PhD, Harvard U., 1971. Instr. U. Calif., Berkeley, 1970-72; asst. prof. U. N.C., Chapel Hill, 1973-75, assoc. prof., 1975-80, prof., 1980—. Office: U NC Dept Math Chapel Hill NC 27599-3250

WAHL, RICHARD LEO, radiology educator, nuclear medicine cancer researcher; b. Iowa, July 13, 1952; s. Max Henry and Josephine Elizabeth (Hogan) W.; m. Sandra K. Moeller, June 28, 1975; children: Daniel, Matthew, Peter, Katherine. BA in Chemistry, Wartburg Coll., 1974; MD, Washington U., St. Louis, 1974-78. Intern U. Calif., San Diego, 1978-79; resident in Radiology Mallinckrodt Inst. Washington U., 1979-82; fellow in nuclear medicine and immunology Washington U., St. Louis, 1982-83; asst. prof. U. Mich. Med. Ctr., Ann Arbor, 1983-87, assoc. prof., 1987-90, prof., 1990—; contbr. immunology study sect.NIH, Bethesda, Md., 1990—. Contbr. 100 articles to profl. jours., chpts. to books. Rsch. grantee NIH, ACS, 1985—; recipient Jerome W. Conn award U. Mich., 1987. Mem. AMA, Soc. Nuclear Medicine (Marc Tetalman award, 1986, Berson & Yalow award 1992, Hounsfield award 1992), Radiol. Soc. N.Am., Am. Soc. for Clin. Investigation, Am. Assn. for Cancer Rsch., Am. Coll. Nuclear Physicians. Avocations: reading, sports. Office: U Mich Med Ctr 1500 E Med Ctr Dr Ann Arbor MI 48109-0001

WAHL, ROSALIE E., state supreme court justice; b. Gordon, Kans., Aug. 27, 1924; children: Christopher Roswell, Sara Emilie, Timothy Eldon, Mark Patterson, Jenny Caroline. B.A., U. Kans., 1946; J.D., William Mitchell Coll. Law, 1967. Bar: Minn. 1967. Asst. state pub. defender Mpls., 1967-73; clin. prof. law William Mitchell Coll. Law, 1973-77; assoc. justice Minn. Supreme Ct., St. Paul, 1977-94. Fellow Am. Bar Foundl; mem. ABA (legal edn. and bar admissions, sect. jud. adminstrn., criminal justice sect., individual rights and responsibility sect.), Minn. State Bar Assn., Am. Judicature Soc., Nat. Assn. Women Judges, Minn. Women Lawyers Assn.

WAHLBERG, PHILIP LAWRENCE, former bishop, legislative liaison; b. Houston, Jan. 18, 1924; s. Philip Lawrence and Ella Alieda (Swenson) W.; m. Rachel Conrad, June 1, 1946; children: David, Christopher, Pauli, Sharon. AA, Tex. Luth. Coll., 1942, DD (hon.), 1963; BA, Lenoir Rhyne Coll., Hickory, N.C., 1944; MDiv, Luth. Theol. Sem., Columbia, S.C., 1946. Ordained to ministry United Luth. Ch. in Am., 1946. Pastor St. Luke Luth. Ch., Thunderbolt, Ga., 1946-50, Redeemer Luth. Ch., Wilmington Island, Ga., 1946-50, St. Mark Luth. Ch., Corpus Christi, Tex., 1950-59; pres. Tex.-La. Synod, United Luth. Ch. Am., Austin, Tex., 1959-62; bishop Tex.-La. Synod, Luth. Ch. Am., Austin, 1963-87; acting dir. devel. Lutheran Outdoor and Retreat Ministries Southwest, 1987-88; legis. liaison Tex. Impact, Austin, 1989-91; interim coord. Regional Ctr. for Mission Evang. Luth. Ch. in Am., Dallas, 1991-92; acting dir. devel. Luth. Sem. Program of Southwest, 1992—; mem. com. on appeals, also chmn. Evang. Luth. Ch. in Am., 1988—; also mem. exec. coun. Luth. Ch. in Am., N.Y.C., 1980-87, chmn. com. on legal matters, 1984-87; mem. mgmt. com. Div. for Mission in N.Am., N.Y.C., 1972-80, chmn., 1972-76; bd. dirs. Bd. Am. Missions, N.Y.C., 1963-72, chmn., 1968-72; bd. dirs. Luth. Sch. Theology, Chgo., 1967-87. Author articles in religious jours., sermons; author theol. cassette, 1973. Named Disting. churchman Tex. Luth. Coll., 1978; Disting. Alumnus, Lenoir Rhyne Coll., 1962; named Man of Year, Thunderbolt, Ga. C. of C., 1950. Mem. Interfaith Impact. Democrat. Avocations: winemaking, golf, choral singing. Office: 5804 Cary Dr Austin TX 78757-3108

WAHLEN, EDWIN ALFRED, lawyer; b. Gary, Ind., Mar. 12, 1919; s. Alfred and Ethel (Pearson) W.; m. Alice Elizabeth Condit, Apr. 24, 1943 (div. 1983); children: Edwin Alfred, Virginia Elizabeth, Martha Anne; m. Elizabeth L. Corey, Nov. 23, 1984. Student, U. Ala., 1936-38; A.B., U. Chgo., 1942, J.D., 1948. Bar: Ill. 1948. Practiced in Chgo., 1948—; mem. firm Haight, Goldstein & Haight, 1948-55; ptnr. Goldstein & Wahlen, 1956-59, Arvey, Hodes, Costello & Burman (and predecessor), 1959-91, Wildman, Harrold, Allen & Dixon, 1992—. Author: Soldiers and Sailors Wills: A Proposal For Federal Legislation, 1948. Served to 2d lt. AUS, 1942-46. Decorated Silver Star medal, Bronze Star medal. Mem. ABA, Ill. Bar Assn., Chgo. Bar Assn., Order of Coif, Phi Beta Kappa, Phi Alpha Delta. Home: 3750 N Lake Shore Dr Chicago IL 60613-4238 Office: 225 E Wacker Dr Chicago IL 60601-5103

WAHLEN, EDWIN ALFRED, JR., venture capitalist; b. Gary, Ind., Nov. 17, 1947; s. Edwin Alfred and Alice Elizabeth (Condit) W.; m. Catherine Frances Willard, Jan. 7, 1978. BS in Indsl. Mgmt., Ga. Inst. Tech., 1970; MBA, U. N.C., Chapel Hill, 1972. CFA. Assoc. investment banking Interstate Securities Corp., Charlotte, N.C., 1972-73; loan officer First Nat. Bank Chgo., Atlanta, 1973-77; sr. v.p. investment banking Dean Witter Reynolds, Inc., Atlanta, 1977-85; mng. dir. Cravey, Green & Wahlen Inc. Atlanta, 1985—, CGW S.W. Ptnrs., Atlanta, 1991—; bd. dirs. CGW Holdings, Inc., Atlanta, Intelimedia Corp., Atlanta, Ashley Aluminum, Inc., Tampa, Fla., Summit Cons., Inc., Lakeland, Fla.; chmn. bd. dirs. Rehrig Internat., Inc., Richmond, Va., Visionworks Holdings, Inc., Clearwater, Fla., Medaes Inc., Norcross, Ga. Chmn. bd. dirs. Met. Atlanta chpt. Am. Diabetes Assn., 1990, sec. bd. dirs. Ga. affiliate. Fellow Soc. Internat. Bus. Fellows; mem. Atlanta Venture Forum, U. N.C. Bus. Sch. Club Atlanta (pres. 1982-83), Ravinia Club, Burge Plantation Hunting Club, Lake Toxaway Country Club.

WAHLERT, ROBERT HENRY, food company executive; b. Dubuque, Iowa, Jan. 19, 1939; s. Robert Charles and Celeste Joan (Canepa) W.; m. Donna Jane Allendorf, June 3, 1961; children: Robert C., Amy, Kathleen, Marni, Mark. B.Sc., U. Iowa, 1963. Sales trainee Dubuque Packing Co., 1961-63, advt. mgr., 1963-65, gen. sales mgr., 1965-69, v.p. sales, 1969-73, exec. v.p., 1973-77, chmn. bd., chief exec. officer, 1977-82; founder, pres., chief exec. officer FDL Foods, Inc., Dubuque, 1982; dir., founder Key City Bank, Dubuque; dir. Rigid-Pak Corp., San Juan, P.R., Edelcar Corp., San Juan, Hawkeye Bank of Dubuque, Hawkeye Banks (parent co.); v.p. Dubuque Symphony Orch., 1967-74. Bd. dirs., treas. Wahlert Found.; v.p. Dubuque Symphony Orch., 1967-74. Republican. Roman Catholic. Club: Dubuque Golf and Country (past pres.). Home: 600 Sunset Rdg Dubuque IA 52003-7763 Office: FDL Foods Inc 701 E 16th St Dubuque IA 52001-4948

WAHLKE, JOHN CHARLES, political science educator; b. Cin., Oct. 29, 1917; s. Albert B.C. and Clara J. (Ernst) W.; m. Virginia Joan Higgins, Dec. 1, 1943; children: Janet Parmely, Dale. A.B., Harvard U., 1939, M.A., 1947, Ph.D., 1952. Instr., asst. prof. polit. sci. Amherst (Mass.) Coll., 1949-53; assoc. prof. polit. sci. Vanderbilt U., Nashville, Tenn., 1953-63; prof. polit. sci. SUNY, Buffalo, 1963-66, U. Iowa, 1966-71, SUNY, Stony Brook, 1971-72, U. Iowa, Iowa City, 1972-79; prof. polit. sci. U. Ariz., Tucson, 1979-87, prof. emeritus, 1987—. Author: (with others) The Legislative System, 1962, Government and Politics, 1966, The Politics of Representation, 1978; editor: Causes of the American Revolution, 1950, Loyalty in a Democratic State, 1952; co-editor: Legislative Behavior, 1959, The American Political System, 1967, Comparative Legislative Behavior, 1973. Served to capt., F.A. AUS, 1942-46. Decorated Air medal with 2 oak leaf clusters. Mem. AAAS, Am. Polit. Sci. Assn. (past pres.), Internat. Polit. Sci. Assn., So. Polit. Sci. Assn., Midwest Polit. Sci. Assn. (past pres.), Western Polit. Sci. Assn., Southwestern Polit. Sci. Assn., Assn. Politics and the Life Scis. Home: 5462 N Entrada Catorce Tucson AZ 85718-4851 Office: U Ariz Dept Polit Sci Tucson AZ 85721

WAHOSKE, MICHAEL JAMES, lawyer; b. Ripon, Wis., June 4, 1953; m. Marcia Wilson; children: Jennifer, John. BA with highest honors, U. Notre Dame, 1975, JD summa cum laude, 1978. Bar: Minn. 1978, U.S. Dist. Ct. Minn. 1979, U.S. Ct. Appeals (7th cir.) 1979, U.S. Ct. Appeals (8th and 9th cirs.) 1980, U.S. Ct. Appeals (10th cir.) 1982, U.S. Supreme Ct. 1982, U.S. Ct. Appeals (6th cir.) 1988, U.S. Ct. Appeals (fed. cir.) 1989, U.S. Ct. Appeals (D.C. cir.) 1992, U.S. Ct. Appeals (4th cir.) 1994. Law clk. to judge Luther M. Swygert U.S. Ct. Appeals (7th cir.), Chgo., 1978-79; law clk. to chief justice Warren E. Burger U.S. Supreme Ct., Washington, 1979-80; assoc. Dorsey & Whitney, Mpls., 1980-85, ptnr., 1986—; adj. prof. law U. Minn., Mpls., 1981-83. Exec. editor U. Notre Dame Law Rev., 1977-78; co-editor: Freedom & Education: Pierce v. Society of Sisters Reconsidered, 1978. Recipient Vol. Recognition award Nat. Assn. Attys. Gen., 1993, Supreme Ct. Reception honors State and Local Legal Ctr., 1991, 92, 93. Mem. ABA, Fed. Bar Assn., Minn. Bar Assn., Hennepin County Bar Assn., Phi Beta Kappa. Office: Dorsey & Whitney PLLP 220 S 6th St Minneapolis MN 55402-4500

WAILAND, GEORGE, lawyer; b. Munich, Fed. Republic Germany, Mar. 14, 1947; came to U.S., 1951; s. Max and Bella (Grylak) W.; m. Adele M. Rosen, Aug. 20, 1972; children: J. Zachary, William J. BS, NYU, 1969, JD, 1972. Bar: N.Y. 1973, U.S. Supreme Ct. 1976, U.S. Dist. Ct. (ea. dists.) N.Y. 1973, U.S. Dist. Ct. (no. dist.) N.Y. 1981, U.S. Claims Ct. 1979, U.S. Tax Ct., 1979, U.S. Ct. Appeals (2d cir.) 1973, U.S. Ct. Appeals (fed. cir.) 1982, U.S. Ct. Appeals (4th cir. and 9th cir.) 1986, U.S. Ct. Appeals (7th cir.) 1987. Assoc. Cahill Gordon & Reindel, N.Y.C., 1972-80, ptnr., 1980—. John Norton Pomeroy scholar NYU, 1970. Mem. ABA, Fed. Bar Council. Home: 1050 Park Ave New York NY 10028-1031 Office: Cahill Gordon & Reindel 80 Pine St New York NY 10005-1702

WAINBERG, ALAN, footwear company executive; b. Zelechow, Poland, June 25, 1937; came to U.S., 1949; s. Jaime M. and Pearl (Boruchowicz) W.; m. Karen Sue Schneider, July 31, 1966; children: David, Laura, Daniel. BS in Indsl. Engring., U. Miami, 1964; MS in Ops. Rsch., NYU, 1965. Indsl. engr. U.S. Naval Propellant Plant, Indian Head, Md., 1964; sr. cons., mgr. Arthur Andersen & Co., N.Y.C., 1965-70; sr. cons. Alexander Grant & Co., Miami, 1970-71; sr. v.p., sec., treas., dir. Suave Shoe Corp., Miami, 1971-75, 78-84; group v.p. G.H. Bass & Co., Falmouth, Maine, 1984-86, pres., 1986-88; pres. Alan Wainberg & Assocs., Cumberland Center, Maine, 1988; v.p. Internat. New Balance Athletic Shoes Inc., Boston, 1991—; owner, cons., pres. Mgmt. Cons. Services, Miami, 1975-77; dir., pres. Damaron Investment Services, Miami, 1975; vis. com. Coll. Engring. U. Miami. Mem. Footwear Industries Am. (mem. tech. steering com., chmn. new tech. com., 1981, bd. dirs. 1986—), U. Miami Coll. Engring. Alumni Assn. (bd. dirs., officer). Office: New Balance Athletic Shoes 61 Bencon St Boston MA 02134

WAINERDI, RICHARD ELLIOTT, medical center executive; b. N.Y.C., Nov. 27, 1931; s. Harold Roule and Margaret (Greenhut) W.; m. Angela Lampone, June 2, 1956; children: Thomas Joseph, James Cooper. B.S. in Petroleum Engring, Okla. U., 1952; M.S., Pa. State U., 1955, Ph.D., 1958. Registered profl. engr., Tex. Research asst. fellow petroleum engring. Pa. State U. 1953-55; mem. faculty Tex. A. and M. U., College Station, 1957-77; prof. chem. engring. Tex. A. and M. U., 1961-77, assoc. v.p. acad. affairs, 1974-77, also founder, head activation analysis lab., 1957-77; sr. v.p. 3D/Internat., Houston, 1977-82; coord. nuclear activities Dresser Industries Inc., Dallas, 1956-57; head Nuclear Sci. Ctr. Tex. Engring. Expt. Sta., 1957-59; pres. Gulf Research & Devel. Co. div. Gulf Oil Corp., Houston, 1982-84; pres., chief exec. officer Tex. Med. Ctr., Houston, 1984—. Author: Modern Methods of Geochemical Analysis, 1971; regional editor: Internat. Jour. Radioanalytical Chemistry; contbg. editor: Producers Monthly, 1957-69; assoc. editor: Radiochemical and Radioanalytical Letters; mem. editorial adv. bd. Talanta jour., 1969; contbr. to profl. jours. Served with USAF, 1952-53. Recipient 1st pl. presentation award Am. Inst. Chem. Engrs. and Chem. Inst. Can., 1961, faculty disting. rsch. award Tex. A. and M. U., 1962, George Hevesy medal, 1977, others. Mem. Am. Nuclear Soc. (chmn. isotopes and radiation divsn. 1964), Internat. Union Pure and Aplied Chemistry (chmn. com. on analytical radiochemistry), Am. Chem. Soc., River Oaks Country Club, Ramada Club, Sigma Xi, Tau Beta Pi, Phi Kappa Phi, Sigma Tau, Pi Epsilon Tau, Phi Eta Sigma. Office: Tex Med Ctr 406 Jesse H Jones Libr Bldg Houston TX 77030

WAINMAN, BARBARA WALDEN, legislative staff member; b. Washington, May 16, 1956; d. Charles Burwell and Dorothy Belle (Drinkard) Walden; m. Garth Michael Wainman, Aug. 2, 1980; children: Laura Channing Wainman, Matthew Nench Wainman. BA, Smith Coll., 1978. Reporter South Shore News Day, Rockland, Mass., 1978; legis. analyst Ho. Rep. Conf., Washington, 1979-81; legis. asst. appropriations com., Rep. Ralph Regula U.S. Ho. Reps., Washington, 1981—. Recipient Cert. Extraordinary Conservation Achievement Wilderness Soc., 1988. Republican. Episcopalian. Home: 4244 Brittany Ct Woodbridge VA 22192 Office: Rep Ralph Regula R-Ohio 2309 Rayburn House Office Bldg Washington DC 20515

WAINTROOB, ANDREA RUTH, lawyer; b. Chgo., Dec. 23, 1952; d. David Samuel and Lees (Carson) W. AB, Brown U., 1975; JD, U. Chgo., 1978. Bar: Ill. 1978, U.S. Dist. Ct. (no. dist.) Ill. 1978, U.S. Ct. Appeals (7th cir.) 1982. Assoc. Vedder, Price, Kaufman and Kammholz, Chgo., 1978-84; ptnr. Vedder, Price, Kaufman, Chgo., 1984-94, Franczek, Sullivan, Mann, Crement, Hein, Relias, P.C., Chgo., 1994—; lectr. indsl. relations Grad. Sch. Bus. U. Chgo. Mem. Chgo. Bar Assn., Nat. Coun. Sch. Attys. Home: 1345 E 54th St Chicago IL 60615-5318 Office: Franczek Sullivan et al 300 S Wacker Dr Ste 3400 Chicago IL 60606-6703

WAINWRIGHT, CARROLL LIVINGSTON, JR., lawyer; b. N.Y.C., Dec. 28, 1925; s. Carroll Livingston and Edith Katherine (Gould) W.; m. Nina Walker, July 2, 1948; children: Delos Walker, Mark Livingston. A.B., Yale U., 1949; LL.B., Harvard U., 1952. Bar: N.Y. 1953. With Milbank, Tweed, Hadley & McCloy (and predecessor), N.Y.C., 1952-58, 60-62, ptnr., 1963—; asst. counsel Gov. N.Y., 1959-60; mem. State Commn. Jud. Conduct, 1974-83; dir. U.S Trust Corp.; trustee U.S. Trust Co. N.Y.; adj. prof. law Washington and Lee U. Sch. Law, 1991—; mem. governing bd. N.Y. Community Trust, 1991—. Trustee Am. Mus. Natural History, Edward John Noble Found., Boys' Club N.Y., 1966—, pres., 1986-94; vice-chmn. Cooper Union Advancement Sci. and Art, 1988—, also trustee; trustee Ch. Pension Fund and Affiliates, 1974-91, treas., 1974-78; mem. univ. council Yale U., 1983-87; mem. vestry Trinity Ch., N.Y.C., 1983-90. Served with USMCR, 1943-46. Mem. ABA, N.Y. State Bar Assn., Assn. Bar City N.Y. (treas. 1970-73, v.p. 1975-76), Union Club, Down Town Assn. (pres. 1985-92), Maidstone Club (pres. 1970-73). Home: 825 Fifth Ave New York NY 10021-7268 Office: Milbank Tweed Hadley & McCloy 1 Chase Manhattan Plz New York NY 10005-1401

WAINWRIGHT, CHARLES ANTHONY, advertising company executive; b. Los Angeles, Sept. 14, 1933; m. Mary Beth Halbmeier, Jan. 1975; children: Colleen, Elizabeth. BA, U. Colo., 1955. Copywriter Leo Burnett, Chgo., 1958-60; v.p. Grey, Chgo., 1963-65, Tathan, Laird & Kudner, Chgo., 1965-69; pres. Wainwright, Smyth & Wright, Chgo., 1969-78; exec. v.p. Marschalk Co., N.Y.C., 1978-80; pres. Bloom Corp., Dallas and N.Y.C. 1980-89; vice chmn., ceo Campbell, Mithun, Esty, Inc., N.Y.C., 1989—; also bd. dirs. Campbell, Mithun, Esty, Inc., Mpls. and N.Y.C.; bd. dirs. Horn & Hardart, N.Y.C., G. Johansen Designs, Dallas, Roma Corp., Attention Med. Corp., Am. Woodmark Corp., Gibson Greetings, Del Webb Corp. Author: Television Commercials, 1965 (Venice Festival award 1967), Successful Management of New Products, 1969; Moment of Truth, 1970; co-author: Managing New Products, 1968; columnist Advertising Age; author (motion picture): Together For Days, 1972. Bd. dirs. U. Ga. MBA Program, Athens, 1983, North Tex. State U., Denton, 1983, Sacred Heart Coll., 1990, Cotton Bowl Festival, Dallas, 1984, Econ. Devel. Com. Tex., Austin, 1985, Baylor Hosp., Boy's Hope.; legatur N.Y., Cath. Found., Dallas; mem. Mayor's Med. Task Force, 1989, NFL Alumni Commn., 1988. With USN, 1956-58. Recipient Internat. Broadcast award IBA, 1967, Clio award Comml. Festival, 1968. Mem. Am. Assn. Advt. Agys. (regional bd. dirs., sec.), Pelham Country Club. Roman Catholic. Office: CME KHBB Advt 222 S 9th St Minneapolis MN 55402-3389

WAINWRIGHT, DAVID STANLEY, intellectual property professional; b. New Haven, May 23, 1955; s. Stanley Dunstan and Lillian (Karelitz) W.;m. Catherine Demetra Kefalas, Aug. 11, 1984; children: Maxwell Stanley Hector, Eric George Alexander. BSc with 1st class honors in Physics, Dalhousie U., Halifax, N.S., 1976; MSc in Physics, U. B.C., Vancouver, 1979. Registered patent agt., U.S., Can. Model plant supr., scientist, technician Moli Energy Ltd., Maple Ridge, B.C., Can., 1978-84, project leader cell devel., 1984-88, cell devel. mgr., 1988-90; cell devel. mgr. Moli Energy (1990) Ltd., Maple Ridge, 1990-92, mgr. intellectual property, 1992—. Contbr. articles to profl. jours. Mem. Am. Soc. Materials, Can. Assn. Physicists. Home: 2585 W 1st Ave, Vancouver, BC Canada V6K 1G8 Office: Moli Energy Ltd Maple Ridge, 20000 Stewart Crescent, Maple Ridge, BC Canada V2X 9E7

WAINWRIGHT, PAUL EDWARD BLECH, construction company executive; b. Annapolis, Md., Jan. 28, 1917; s. Richard and Alice Sorrel (Blech) W.; m. Helen Mae Rogers, July 10, 1941; children—Richard, Paul Edward Blech, John. B.S. in Civil Engring. Va. Mil. Inst., 1938. Cost engr. Turner Constrn. Co., N.Y.C. 1938-40; cost engr. asst. supt. Turner Constrn. Co., 1945-46; cost. engr. for contractors Pacific Naval Air Bases, Honolulu, 1940-42; with Dillingham Corp., Honolulu, 1946-82; asst. v.p., then v.p. Dillingham Corp., 1961-69, group v.p. constrn., 1969-82; cons. constrn. Honolulu, 1982—. Bd. dirs. Hawaii Visitors Bur., 1967, Goodwill Industries Hawaii, 1965-70; pres. Citizens Adminstrn. of Justice Found., 1968, Hawaii Epilepsy Soc., 1975. Served with AUS, 1942-45. Decorated Legion of Merit, Bronze Star, Air medal. Mem. Am. Soc. Mil. Engrs., Beavers, Gen. Contractors Assn. Hawaii (pres. 1966), Hawaii C. of C. (dir. 1964-65). Republican. Episcopalian. Clubs: Waikiki Yacht, Outrigger Canoe. Home: 4301 Providence Point Pl SE Issaquah WA 98027

WAINWRIGHT, STEPHEN A., zoology educator, design consultant; b. Indpls., Oct. 9, 1931; s. Guy A. and Jeannette (Harvey) W.; m. M. Ruth Palmer, July 25, 1956; children: Peter C., Ian P., Archer T., Jennifer S. BS in Zoology, Duke U., 1953; BA in Zoology, Cambridge U., England, 1958; PhD, U. Calif., Berkeley, 1962; MA, Cambridge U., 1963. Assoc. prof. zoology Duke U., Durham, N.C., 1964-76, prof., 1976-85, J.B. Duke prof., 1985—; adj. prof. design sch. N.C. State U., Raleigh, 1983—. Author: (with others) Mechanical Design in Organisms, 1976, Axis and Circumference, 1988. Served as cpl. U.S. Army, 1953-55. NSF postdoctoral fellow, 1962-64. Fellow AAAS; mem. Marine Biol. Assn. United Kingdom, Am. Soc. Zoologists (pres. 1988), Am. Soc. Biomechanics (pres. 1981). Avocation: sculpture. Office: Duke U Dept Zoology Durham NC 27706*

WAINWRIGHT, STUYVESANT, II, lawyer; b. N.Y.C., Mar. 16, 1921; s. Carroll L. and Edith Catherine (Gould) W.; m. Janet Parsons, June 12, 1941; children: Stuyvesant III, Jonathan Mayhew, Janet Snowden Kirby-Smith, Laura Livingston. LLB, Yale U., 1947. Bar: N.Y. 1948. With Satterlee,

Warfield & Stephens, N.Y.C., 1947-49; ptnr. Evarts, Balzell, Wainwright & Baker, N.Y.C., 1949-52, Wainwright & Matthews, Huntington, N.Y., 1953-64, Walker, Beale, Wainwright & Wolf, N.Y.C., 1965-70, Battle, Fowler, Lidstone, Jaffin, Pierce & Kheel, N.Y.C., 1970-75; pvt. practice law Wainscott, N.Y., 1975—; chmn. bd. Miltope Corp., Plainview, N.Y., 1975-79; Authur T. Vanderbilt prof. polit. sci. Rutgers, 1961-62; mem. 83d-86th Congresses, 1st Dist N.Y.; spl. congl. mission to Far East, 1953. Bd. dirs. Southampton Hosp., N.Y., 1980-86, Guild Hall, East Hampton, N.Y., 1980-86; vestry St. Luke's Ch. of East Hampton; mem. Soc. for Preservation L.I. Antiquities, 1987-90. With OSS, U.S. Army, 1942-45. Mem. Masons, Union Club, Maidstone Club, Cruising Club Am., Phi Delta Phi. Spl. mission to Vietnam with Lt. Gen. James Gavin, 1967. Home: PO Box 199 Wainscott NY 11975-0199

WAIT, CAROL GRACE COX, organization administrator; b. L.A., Dec. 20, 1942; d. Earl George Atkinson Sr. and Virginia Rose (Clanton) Boggs; m. David L. Edwards (div. 1974); children: Nicole Rose Smith, Alexandra Edwards; m. Gary G. Cox, Jan. 25, 1975 (div. 1982); m. Robert Atwood Wait, July 4, 1991. AA in Pre Law, Cerritos Coll., 1966; AB in History, Whittier Coll., 1969. Probation counselor Los Angeles County Probation Dept., Downey, Calif., 1967-69; corp. sec., mgr. Dennis and Dennis Personnel, Santa Ana, Calif., 1969-71; owner, pres. Cox Edwards & Assocs., Santa Ana, 1971-73; adminstrv. services officer County of Santa Cruz (Calif.), 1973-74; cons. State of Calif., Sacramento, 1974-75; project dir. Nat. Assn. Counties, Washington, 1975-77; legis. dir. U.S. Senate Com. on the Budget, Washington, 1977-81; pres. Com. for a Responsible Budget, Washington, 1981—, Carol Cox & Assocs., Washington, 1984—; bd. dirs. Cigna Corp.; cons. to bus. and other orgns. on the fed. budget, the budget process and other econ. issues; writer and speaker on the budget and budget process. Am. participant USIS/Brazilian Senate Symposium on Budget Process, Brazilia, Brazil, 1985—, Ampart speaker on 1990 budget agreement France, Ger., 1990. Named one of 150 Who Make a Difference Nat. Jour., 1986; recipient Nat. Disting. Svc. award Am. Assn. Budget and Program Analysis. Mem. Washington Women's Forum, Internat. Women's Forum (pres.). Republican. Episcopalian. Avocations: party bridge, wing shooting, tennis. Office: Com Responsible Fed Budget 220 1/2 E St NE Washington DC 20002-4923

WAIT, JAMES RICHARD, electrical engineering educator, scientist; b. Ottawa, Ont., Can., Jan. 23, 1924; came to U.S., 1955, naturalized, 1960; s. George Enoch and Doris Lillian (Browne) W.; m. Gertrude Laura Harriet, June 16, 1951; children: Laura, George. BASc, U. Toronto, Ont., 1948, MASc, 1949, PhD, 1951. Research engr. Newmont Exploration, Ltd., Jerome, Ariz., 1949-52; sect. leader Def. Research Telecommunications Establishment, Ottawa, 1952-55; scientist U.S. Dept. Commerce Labs., Boulder, Colo., 1955-80; adj. prof. elec. engring. U. Colo., Boulder, 1961-80; prof. elec. engring., geosci. U. Ariz., Tucson, 1980-88, Regents prof., 1988-90, emeritus Regents prof., 1990—; prin. Geo-Em Cons., Tucson, 1990—; fellow Coop. Inst. Rsch. Environ. Scis., 1968-80; sr. scientist Office of Dir. Environ. Rsch. Labs., Boulder, 1967-70, 72-80; vis. rsch. fellow lab. electromagnetic theory U. Denmark, Copenhagen, 1961; vis. prof. Harvard, 1966-67, Catholic U., Rio de Janeiro, 1971; vis. prof. elec. engring. U. B.C., Vancouver, Can., 1987; mem.-at-large U.S. nat. com. Internat. Sci. Radio Union, 1963-65, 69-72, del. gen. assemblies, Boulder, 1957, London, 1690, Tokyo, 1963, Ottawa, 1969, Warsaw, Poland, 1972, Lima, Peru, 1975, Helsinki, Finland, 1978; sec. U.S. nat. com., 1976-78; Lansdowne lectr. U. Victoria, B.C., Can., 1992.; adj. prof. in mining and geol. engring. U. Ariz., Tucson, 1995—. Founder Jour. Radio Sci, 1959, editor, 1959-68; assoc. editor: Pure and Applied Geophysics, 1964-75, Geoexploration, Ludea, Sweden, 1983-91; co-editor internat. series monographs on electromagnetic waves Pergamon Press, 1961-73, Instn. Elec. Engrs, London, 1974—. Served with Canadian Army, 1942-45. Recipient Gold medal Dept. Commerce, 1958; Samuel Wesley Stratton award Nat. Bur. Standards, 1962; Arthur S. Flemming award Washington C. of C., 1964; Outstanding Publ. award Office Telecommunications, Washington, 1972; Rsch. and Achievement award Nat. Oceanic and Atmospheric Adminstrn., 1973; Van der Pol gold medal, 1978; Evans fellow Otago U., New Zealand, 1990. Fellow IEEE (mem. adminstrv. com. on antennas and propagation 1966-73, Harry Diamond award 1964, Centennial medal 1984, Disting. Achievement award geosci. and remote sensing 1985, Disting. Achievement award antennas and propagation soc. 1990, Heinrich Hertz medal 1992), AAAS, Instn. Elec. Engrs. (G.B.), Sci. Rsch. Soc. Am. (Boulder Scientist award 1960); mem. NAE, Soc. Exploration Geophysicists (hon. mem.), Internat. Union of Radio Sci. (assoc. editor Radio Scientist Bull., 1995—). Home and Office: 2210 E Waverly St Tucson AZ 85719-3848

WAIT, SAMUEL CHARLES, JR., academic administrator, educator; b. Albany, N.Y., Jan. 26, 1932; s. Samuel C. and Isabel M. (Cassedy) W.; m. Carol D. Petrie, June 6, 1957; children: Robert J., Alison R. BS in Chemistry, Rensselaer Polytechnic Inst., 1953, MS in Physical Chemistry, 1955, PhD in Physical Chemistry, 1956. Postdoc. teaching fellow U. Minn., 1958-59; visiting asst. prof. Carnegie Inst. Tech., 1959-60; instr. Nat. Bur. Standards, 1960-61; from asst. prof. to prof. of chemistry Rensselaer Poly. Inst., Troy, N.Y., 1961—, from asst. dean of sci. to assoc. dean of sci., 1974—, acting dean of sci., 1978-80, 88-89; dir. Cooperative Coll. Sci. Improvement Program, Troy, 1972-73, Rsch. Participation for High Sch. Tchrs., Troy, 1962-67; asst. dir., prof. M of Sci. in Natural Scis. Program, Troy, 1962-74. Author: Scattering of Laser Radiation, 1971; contbr. articles to profl. jours. Pres. dist. 2 Niskayuna (N.Y.) Fire Co., 1970-72; mem. Niskayuna Bd. Fire Commrs., 1978-83; v.p., trustee Dudley Obs., 1990-91, pres., 1991—; mem. math., sci. and tech. adv. com. Schenectady County C.C., 1976—, 1977-78; vice chmn. Schenectady County Fire Adv. Bd., 1978-79; mem. Schenectady County Hazardous Materials Team, 1991—. Recipient Disting Faculty award Rensselaer Alumni Assn., 1988, Alumni Key award, 1994, Rensselaer Alumni Admission award of excellence, 1993; named fellow Rsch. Corp., 1954-55, Eastman Kodak Co., 1955-56; Fulbright scholar, 1956-58. Mem. Am. Chem. Soc., Optical Soc. Am., Coblentz Soc., Rensselaer Premed. Soc., Sigma Xi, Alpha Epsilon Delta, Phi Theta Kappa. Office: Rensselaer Poly Inst 1C 05 Sci Ctr Troy NY 12180-3590

WAITE, CHARLES MORRISON, food company executive; b. Chgo. Oct. 1, 1932; s. Norman and Lavinia M. (Fyke) W.; m. Barbara Chowning Wham, Aug. 21, 1954; children: Susan R., Charles M., John B., David T. B.A., Yale, 1954; M.B.A., Harvard, 1958. Mgr. planning and analysis Standard Fruit & Steamship Co., New Orleans, 1958-62; v.p., exec. v.p. Standard Fruit & Steamship Co., 1969-72, dir., 1972-76; div. mgr. Standard Fruit Co., La Ceiba, Honduras, 1962-69; dir. Standard Fruit Tropical Charities, Inc., 1970-76; sr. v.p. Castle & Cooke, Inc., Honolulu, 1972-76; exec. v.p. Castle & Cooke Foods, San Francisco, 1974-76; pres. United Fruit Co., Boston, 1976-77; sr. v.p. United Brands Co., Boston, 1976-77; pres. Genoa Packing Co., Boston, 1977-78, Catelli Foods, Inc., 1979-90; pres. Howard Foods Inc., Danvers, Mass., 1990—, also bd. dirs.; bd. dirs. Rock of Ages Corp., Barre, Vt., Swenson Granite Co., Concord, N.H. Served to 1st lt. USAF, 1955-57. Mem. Zeta Psi. Republican. Episcopalian. Club: Harvard (Boston). Home: 520 Cherry Valley Rd Oxford NH 03246-7841 Office: Howard Foods Inc 5 Ray St Danvers MA 01923-3531

WAITE, DANIEL ELMER, retired oral surgeon; b. Grand Rapids, Mich., Feb. 19, 1926; s. Charles Austin and Phoebe Isabel (Smith) W.; m. Alice Darlene Carlile, June 20, 1948; children—Christine Ann, Thomas Charles, Peter Daniel, Julie Marilyn, Stuart David. AA, Graceland Coll., 1948; DDS, State U. Ia., 1953, MS Grad. Coll., 1955. Diplomate: Am. Bd. Oral Surgery. Resident oral surgery State U. Ia. Hosps., 1953-55; instr. oral surgery State U. Ia. Coll. Dentistry, 1955-56, asst. prof., 1956-57, assoc. prof., acting head dept. oral surgery, 1957-59, prof. head dept., 1959-63; mem. staff Mayo Clinic, Mayo Grad. Sch. Medicine, Rochester, Minn., 1963-68; prof., also chmn. div. oral surgery U. Minn., 1968-84; chmn. dept. oral and maxillofacial surgery, asst. dean for hosp. affairs Baylor Coll. Dentistry, Dallas, 1984-90, prof. emeritus, 1990—, asst. dean emeritus, 1990—; clin. prof. U. Mo. Dental Sch., Kans. City, 1993—; vis. prof. U. Adelaide, Australia, 1980, U. Jinan, Guangzhou, China, 1987, U. Costa Rica, 1988; mem. Health Mission Team, Bolivia, 1991, Honduras, 1992. Author: Textbook of Practical Oral Surgery, 1972, 3d edit., 1986; contbr. over 100 articles to sci. jours.,author of 7 book chpts. Active People to People Found.; with Project HOPE, Peru, 1962, Sri Lanka, 1969, Egypt, 1975; trustee Graceland Coll., Lamoni, Iowa, 1960-78, Park Coll., Parkville, Mo., 1972-78, 90—. Outreach Internat., 1990—; bd. dirs. Hennepin County unit Am. Cancer Soc., 1970-73; evangelist Reorganized LDS Ch.; pres. med. and dental assn. health missions, Bolivia, 1990, Honduras, 1991, 92, 93. With USAAF, 1944-46; sr. dental surgeon USPHS Res. Recipient Novice award Internat. Assn. Dental Rsch., 1955, Disting. Alumni award Graceland Coll., 1989; named Man of Yr. U. Minn. Sch. Dentistry Century Club, 1980, Hon. Fellow Sch. Dentistry, U. Minn., 1990; Daniel E. Waite Lectureship established in his honor U. Minn., 1991—. Fellow Am. Coll. Dentists, Am. Soc. Oral Surgeons; mem. Christian Med. Soc., Midwestern Soc. Oral Surgeons, Ia. Soc. Oral Surgeons (sec. 1958-61, pres. 1962), Minn. Soc. Oral Surgeons (pres. 1974), Am. Dental Assn., Internat. Assn. Dental Research (sec. Ia. sect. 1957-62), Tex. Soc. of Oral & Maxillofacial Surgeons, Southwestern Soc. of Oral and Maxillofacial Surgeons, Kans. City Soc. of Oral and Maxillofacial Surgeons, Sigma Xi, Omicron Kappa Upsilon. Home: 319 NW Blue Beech Pt Lees Summit MO 64064

WAITE, DENNIS VERNON, investor relations consultant; b. Chgo., Aug. 26, 1938; s. Vernon George and Marie G. Waite; m. Christine Rene Hibbs; 1 child, Kip Anthony. BA, U. Ill., 1968; MS in Journalism, Northwestern U., 1969. Fin reporter, columnist Chgo. Sun-Times, Chgo., 1969-76; asst. prof. Northwestern U., Evanston, Ill., 1978-79; assoc. prof. Mich. State U., East Lansing, 1979-82; ptnr. Fin. Rels. Bd., Inc., Chgo., 1982-90. sr. ptnr., 1991—; reporter, producer econ. affairs Sta. WTTW-TV, Sta. WBBM-TV, Chgo., 1973-76. Mem. editorial adv. bd. alumni relations U. Ill., Chgo., 1980-84, 90-94. With USAF, 1956-60, PTO. Rutgers U. fellow, 1972. Mem. Medill Alumni Assn. (bd. dirs. 1989-92). Avocations: reading, tennis, fishing. Office: Financial Relations Bd John Hancock Ctr 875 N Michigan Ave Chicago IL 60611-1779

WAITE, ELLEN JANE, vice president; b. Oshkosh, Wis., Feb. 17, 1951; d. Earl Vincent and Margaret (Luft) W.; m. Thomas H. Dollar, Aug. 19, 1977 (div. July 1984); m. Kent Hendrickson, Mar. 26, 1994. BA, U. Wis., Oshkosh, 1973; MLS U. Wis., Milw., 1977. Head of cataloging Marquette U., Milw., 1977-82; head catalog librarian U. Ariz., Tucson, 1983-85; assoc. dir. libraries Loyola U., Chgo., 1985-86, acting dir. libraries, 1986-87, dir. libraries, 1987-94, v.p. acad. svcs., 1994—; cons. Loyola U., Chgo., 1984, Boston Coll., 1986, U. San Francisco, 1989; bd. trustees Online Computer Lib. Ctr., Dublin, Ohio, 1994—. Contbg. author: Research Libraries and Their Implementation of AACR2, 1985; author: (with others) Women in LC's Terms: A Thesaurus of Subject Headings Related to Women, 1988. Mem. ALA. Avocation: photography. Office: Loyola U 25 E Pearson St Chicago IL 60626

WAITE, MARGUERITE FRANCES, hospital administrator; b. Waterbury, Conn., Apr. 18, 1938; d. Frank Howard and Ruth Elizabeth (Johnson) W. BA, St. Joseph Coll., 1965; MHA, St. Louis U., 1972. Joined Congregation of Sisters of St. Joseph, Roman Cath. Ch., 1960. Nursing supr. St. Francis Hosp. and Med. Ctr., Hartford, Conn., 1965-70; adminstrv. resident Sacred Heart Med. Ctr., Spokane, 1971-72; asst. adminstr. St. Joseph Med. Ctr., Stamford, Conn., 1972-76; assoc. adminstr. St. Mary's Hosp., Waterbury, 1976-86, pres. chief exec. officer, 1986—; bd. dirs., sec. Slocum Corp., Waterbury, N.E. Hosp. Network, Hartford; bd. dirs. St. Mary's Hosp. Corp., Webster Fin. Corp., Waterbury, First Fed. Savs., Waterbury. Bd. dirs., vice chmn. United Way Can. Naugatuck Valley, Waterbury, 1988—; bd. dirs. Sacred Heart High Sch., Waterbury, 1989—. Named Woman of Yr., Greater Waterbury YWCA, 1991; recipient Community Svc. award Mattatuck Community Coll., 1991. Fellow Am. Coll. Health Care Execs.; mem. Conn. Hosp. Assn. (bd. dirs. 1987-89), New Eng. Conf. Cath. Health Care Assn., Cath. Health Care Assn. U.S., Greater Waterbury C. of C. (bd. dirs. 1990—), St. Louis U. Alumni Assn., Waterbury Club. Avocations: fly, stream and deep sea fishing, walking, photography. Office: St Mary's Hosp. 56 Franklin St Waterbury CT 06706-1200

WAITE, NORMAN, JR., lawyer; b. Chgo., Mar. 16, 1936; s. Norman and Lavinia (Fyke) W.; m. Jaqueline A. Hurlbutt; children: Leslie Catherine, Lindsay H., Norman III. BA, Yale U., 1958; LLB, Harvard U., 1963. Bar: Ill. 1963. Assoc. Winston & Strawn, Chgo., 1963-69, ptnr., 1969-78, capital ptnr., 1978—, exec. com., 1978-95, vice chmn., 1989—. Bd. dirs. United Charities, Jr. Achievement Chgo., Steadman/Hawkins Sports Medicine Found. Lt. (j.g.) USN, 1958-60. Mem. ABA, Ill. Bar Assn., Chgo. Bar Assn., Univ. Club of Chgo., The Tavern Club of Chgo., Indian Hill Club (Winnetka, Ill.), Econ. Club (Chgo.). Republican. Home: 1710 N Burling St Chicago IL 60614-5102 Office: Winston & Strawn 35 W Wacker Dr Chicago IL 60601-1614

WAITE, RALPH, actor; b. White Plains, N.Y., June 22, 1929; s. Ralph H. and Esther (Mitchell) W.; m. Kerry Shear, 1972 (div. 1980); children: Kathleen, Suzanne, Liam; m. Linda East, 1982. B.A., Bucknell U.; B.D., Yale U. Social worker Westchester County, N.Y.; Presbyterian minister Garden City, N.Y.; publicity dir. and asst. religious books editor Harper & Row Pub. Co., N.Y.C.; founder Los Angeles Actors Theatre, 1975, artistic dir., from 1975. Stage appearances include Hogan's Goat, 1965, Watering Place, 1969, The Trial of Lee Harvey Oswald, 1967, Blues for Mr. Charlie, The Father, 1981, The Balcony, 1981, Buried Child, South Coast Repertory, Costa Mesa, Calif., 1986, All My Sons, Long Wharf Theatre, New Haven, Conn., 1986-87 season, Half Deserted Streets, off Broadway, 1988, Bunker Reveries, Roundabout Theatre, N.Y.C., 1987; films include A Lovely Way to Die, 1968, Five Easy Pieces, 1970, Lawman, 1971, The Grissom Gang, 1971, The Sporting Club, 1971, The Stone Killer, 1973, On the Nickel, 1980, The Bodyguard, 1992, Cliffhanger, 1993; regular TV series The Waltons, 1972-80, The Mississippi, 1983, also appeared in TV movies A Wedding on Waltons Mountain, 1982, Mother's Day on Waltons Mountain, 1982, A Day for Thanks on Waltons Mountain; on ltd. dramatic series Roots, 1977; TV films include The Secret Life of John Chapman, Red Alert, Ohms, Angel City, The Gentleman Bandit, A Good Sport. Office: Care Andy Freedman 20 Ironside St #18 Marina Del Rey CA 90292*

WAITE, RIC, cinematographer; b. Sheboygan, Wis., July 10, 1933; s. Howard Pierce and Bertha Ann (Pippert) W.; m. Judy Lescher, Apr. 24, 1965; children: Richard R., Burgandy B. Student, U. Colo. Cinematographer: (films) Adventures in Babysitting, 1988, Cobra, 1988, Great Outdoors, 1989, Marked for Death, 1990, Price of Our Blood, 1990, 48 Hours, Uncommon Valor, Rep Dawn, Long Riders, The Border, Tex, Class, Volunteers, On Deadly Ground. 1st lt. USAF, 1951-56. Recipient Emmy award, 1976. Mem. Am. Soc. Cinematographers. Avocations: sailing, flying. Home: PO Box 1322 Friday Harbor WA 98250-1322 Office: 1216 Roulac Ln Friday Harbor WA 98250 also: The Gersh Agency 232 N Canon Dr Beverly Hills CA 90210

WAITE, ROBERT GEORGE LEESON, history educator; b. Cartwright, Manitoba, Can., Feb. 18, 1919; came to U.S., 1929; s. George Lloyd and Alice (Carter) W.; m. Anne Barnett, Sept. 8, 1943; children: Geoffrey, Peter. AB, Macalester Coll., 1941; MA, U. Minn., 1946, Harvard U., 1947; PhD, Harvard U., 1949; postgrad., U. Munich, 1953-54. Teaching asst. Macalester Coll., 1941; Emerton fellow history Harvard U., Cambridge, Mass., 1947, teaching fellow, 1947-49; asst. prof. history Williams Coll., 1949-53, assoc. prof., 1953-58, prof., 1958-88, Brown prof., 1960-88, chmn. dept., 1967-72; dir. History Insts., 1968, 69; vis. prof. U. Minn., summer 1957, U. Tex., Austin, 1974; sr. assoc. mem. St. Antony's Coll. Oxford U., 1978, 82; sr. fellow Inst. Humanities, Williams Coll., 1989-91. Author: Vanguard of Nazism: The Free Corps Movement in Postwar Germany, 1918-23, 1952, 69, The Psychopathic God: Adolf Hitler, 1977, rev. 1993; Editor, contbr. Hitler and Nazi Germany, 1965, 69; mem. editorial bd. Jour. Modern History, 1957-60; contbr. World Book, 1958, Collier's Ency, 1961, Afterword to the Mind of Adolf Hitler, 1972, Human Responses to the Holocaust, 1981, Genocide and the Modern Age, 1987, War: The Psychological Dimension, 1990; co-translator: (Erich Eyck) A History of the Weimar Republic, 2 vols., 1962, 70; cons. History of Third Reich Time-Life Mag., 1989-91. Guggenheim fellow, 1953-54; sr. Fulbright research fellow Germany, 1953-54; Am. Council Learned Socs. grantee, 1967, 82; grantee Social Sci. Research Council, 1967. Mem. Am. Hist. Assn., Central European Study Group (sec.-treas. 1970-72). Conglist. (bd. deacons). Home: PO Box 451 Williamstown MA 01267-0451

WAITE, STEPHEN HOLDEN, lawyer; b. Rochester, N.Y., Dec. 5, 1936; s. Richard Holden and Judith H. (Lapp) W.; m. Sarah T. Caswell, Aug. 20, 1960; children: Sarah T., Richard H. B.A., Amherst Coll., 1958; J.D., Yale U., 1961. Bar: N.Y. 1961. Mem. firm Nixon, Hargrave, Devans & Doyle

Rochester, N.Y., 1961-69; v.p., counsel Lincoln First Banks Inc., Rochester, 1969-73, sr. v.p., 1973-77, exec. v.p., 1978-81; chief fin. officer Lincoln First Banks Inc., 1973-81; sr. v.p. Schlegel Corp., 1981-82; mem. firm Harris, Beach, Wilcox, Rubin & Levey, Rochester, 1982-88, Underberg & Kessler, Rochester, 1988—; bd. dirs. Inst. for Rsch. and Reform in Edn., Inc. Past chmn. Rochester Area Hosp. Assn.; past bd. dirs. Highland Hosp., Monroe County Long Term Care, Inc., Rochester Regional Rsch. Libr. Coun., Hosp. Assn. N.Y. State, Health Futures for Rochester, Harley Sch., Hearing and Speech Ctr. Rochester; mem. strategic planning commn. Monroe Cmty. Hosp.; bd. dirs., treas. Hosp. Trustees N.Y. State; bd. dirs., past chmn. Ctr. for Govtl. Rsch. With U.S. Army, 1962. Mem. ABA, N.Y. State Bar Assn., Monroe County Bar Assn., Country Club Rochester. Home: 115 Pelham Rd Rochester NY 14610-2522 Office: 1800 Lincoln First Sq Rochester NY 14604

WAITER, SERGE-ALBERT, retired scientist, consultant; b. Paris, Feb. 8, 1930; came to U.S., 1959, naturalized, 1965; s. Bernard and Anny Waiter; 1 child, Thomas Bernard. Bachelor is Sciences Mathematiques, Lycée Voltaire, Paris, 1946; Licence ès Sciences, Facultes des Sciences de Lille and Paris, 1948-53; Doctorat, Faculté des Sciences de Paris, Sorbonne, 1954. Engr. math. dept. Onera, Chatillon, France, 1949-51; flight test engr. Fouga Aircraft, Aire S/Adour, France, 1951-53; mgr. Sud Aviation, Paris, 1953-59; rsch. scientist U. So. Calif., 1959-62; staff scientist hypersonic gasdynamics and plasma physics, mem. Apollo and space shuttle team in charge support analysis and flight testing Space div. Rockwell Internat., 1962-88, ret., 1988; sci. attaché avions Marcel Dassault/Breguet Aviation, St. Cloud, France, 1988-92; ret., 1992. Contbr. numerous articles to profl. jours. Decorated Knight of Beaujolais; recipient 114 NASA awards for tech. devel. Fellow AIAA (assoc.); mem. Société des Ingénieurs Civils de France, Research Soc. Am. Home: 801 S Crest Vista Dr Monterey Park CA 91754-3749

WAITES, CANDY YAGHJIAN, former state official; b. N.Y.C., Feb. 21, 1943; d. Edmund Kirken and Dorothy Joanne (Candy) Yaghjian; children: Jennifer Lisa, Robin Shelley. B.A., Wheaton Coll., Mass., 1965. Elected county councilwoman Richland County, S.C., 1976-88, mem. S.C. Ho., 1988-94; dir. external programs The Leadership Inst., Columbia Coll., 1993—; vice chmn. Adv. Commn. on Intergovtl. Relations, S.C., 1977-87; bd. dirs. Interagy. Council on Pub. Transp., S.C., 1977-85, Central Midlands Regional Planning Council, Columbia, S.C., 1977-84; dir. Wachovia Bank. Vice pres. bd. dirs. United Way of Midlands, 1977-89; trustee Columbia Mus. Art, 1982-88; bd. dirs. Rape Crisis Network, 1984-87; chmn. County Coun. Coalition; mem. C. of C. Leadership Forum, S.C. Fedn. of the Blind; mem. adv. bd. U. S.C. Hunanities and Social Scis. Coll., Family Shelter, Nurturing Ctr.; pres Trinity Housing Corp.; found. bd. Richland Meml. Hosp., 1995. Named Outstanding Young Career Woman, Columbia YWCA, 1980, YWCA Hall of Fame, 1993, Outstanding Young Woman of Yr., Columbia Jaycees, 1975, Pub. Citizen of Yr. Nat. Assn. Social Workers, nom. mem. Mortar Bd. Soc., 1994; recipient Ann. Legis. award Common Cause S.C., 1990, 91, Legis. Yr. award by S.C. Assn. Counties, 1992. Mem. S.C. Women in Govt. (vice chmn. 1984-86), S.C. Assn. Counties (bd. dirs. 1982-88 , Pres's award 1983), Network Female Execs., LWV (pres. 1973-76), Omicron Delta Kappa. Democrat. Episcopalian. Club: Univ. Assocs. (Columbia). Avocations: exercising, drawing, gardening, walking. Home: 3419 Duncan St Columbia SC 29205-2705 Office: Columbia Coll Leadership Inst 1301 Cola Coll Dr Columbia SC 29203

WAITS, JOHN A., lawyer; b. Greenville, Miss., June 6, 1947. BA summa cum laude, U. Miss., 1969; MA with honors, U. Va., 1973; JD, NYU, 1977. Bar: N.Y. 1978, U.S. Dist. Ct. (ea. and so. dists.) N.Y. 1978, D.C. 1988. Counsel to Ho. Agrl. Subcom. U.S. Ho. of Reps., Washington, 1979-80, asst. to Congressman David R. Bowen, 1980-82; ptnr. Winston & Strawn, Washington. Fulbright scholar. Mem. Assn. Bar City N.Y. Office: Winston & Strawn 1400 L St NW Washington DC 20051

WAITS, THOMAS ALAN, composer, actor, singer; b. Pomona, Calif., Dec. 7, 1949; s. Frank W. and Alma (Johnson) McMurray; m. Kathleen Patricia Brennan, Aug. 10, 1980; children: Kellesimone Wylder, Casey Xavier, Sullivan Blake. Composer 14 albums including Closing Time, 1973, The Heart of Saturday Nite, 1974, Nighthawks at the Diner, 1975, Small Change, 1976, Foreign Affairs, 1978, Heartattack and Vine, 1980, Swordfishtrombones, 1983, Rain Dogs, 1985, Anthology, 1985, Frank's Wild Years, 1987, Big Time, 1988, Bone Machine, 1992, The Black Rider, 1993; composer (film scores) One from the Heart, 1983, Streetwise, 1985, Night on Earth, 1991; co-author music and songs (with Kathleen Brennan) for Night on Earth, 1991, film American Heart; composer songs and music for The Black Rider opera, Hamburg, Germany, 1990, Alice in Wonderland opera, Hamburg, 1992; actor (musical) Frank's Wild Years, 1986, (stage play) Demon Wine, 1989; appeared in films Paradise Alley, 1978, The Outsiders, 1983, Rumble Fish, 1983, The Cotton Club, 1984, Down by Law, 1986, Ironweed, 1987, Candy Mountain, 1987, Big Time, 1988, Cold Feet, 1989, The Bearskin, 1991, Queen's Logic, 1991, At Play in the Fields of the Lord, 1991, Bram Stoker's Dracula, 1992, Short Cuts, 1993. Recipient Acad. Award nomination Best Song Score for One from the Heart, 1983; Grammy award for best alternative album Bone Machine, 1992. Mem. ASCAP, Musicians Union Local 47, SAG, AFTRA, Motion Picture Acad. Office: care Howard Grossman 10960 Wilishire Blvd #2210 Los Angeles CA 90024

WAITT, TED W., computer company executive. CEO Gateway 2000, 1992—, chmn., pres. Office: Gateway 2000 610 Gateway Dr North Sioux City SD 57049*

WAITZKIN, HOWARD BRUCE, physician, sociologist, educator; b. Akron, Ohio, Sept. 6, 1945; s. Edward and Dorothy (Lederman) W.; m. Stephany Borges, Mar. 13, 1983; 1 stepchild, Daren; 1 child, Sofia. BA summa cum laude, Harvard U., 1966, MA, 1969, MD, PhD, 1972. Diplomate Am. Bd. Internal Medicine, Am. Bd. Geriatric Medicine. Resident in medicine Stanford (Calif.) U. Med. Ctr., 1972-75, Robert Wood Johnson clin. scholar depts. sociology-medicine, 1973-75; sr. resident in medicine Mass. Gen. Hosp., Boston, 1977-78; assoc. prof. sociology, clin. asst. prof. medicine U. Vt., Burlington, 1975-77; vis. assoc. prof. health and med. scis. U. Calif., Berkeley, 1978-82; clin. asst. prof. medicine U. Calif., San Francisco, 1978-82; internist La Clínica de la Raza, Oakland, Calif., 1978-82; prof. medicine and social scis. U. Calif., Irvine, 1982—, chief div. gen. internal medicine and primary care, 1982-90; med. dir. U. Calif.-Irvine-North Orange County Community Clinic, Anaheim, 1982-90; regional rep., nat. sec. bd. dirs. Physicians for Nat. Health Program, Cambridge, Mass., 1989-91; cons. documentary Health Care Across the Border, Nat. Pub. TV, N.Y.C., 1989-90, documentary on U.S. health care system Nat. TV Austria, 1991; cons. BBC, 1992, Pew Health Professions Commn., 1992-94, Assn. Am. Med. Colls., 1992-93, Robert Wood Johnson Found., 1992, Rsch. and Tng. Group in Social Medicine, Santiago, Chile, 1990—; lectr. med. sociology U. Amsterdam, The Netherlands, 1977. Co-author: The Exploitation of Illness in Capitalist Society, 1974; author: The Second Sickness: Contradictions of Capitalist Health Care, 1983, paperback edit., 1986, The Politics of Medical Encounters: How Patients and Doctors Deal with Social Problems, 1991, paperback edit., 1993. Cons. on health policy Jesse Jackson Presdl. Campaign, 1988; bd. dirs., mem. com. on litigation Orange County Pub. Law Ctr., 1990—. Fellow in ind. study & rsch. NEH, 1984-85, Fulbright fellow, 1983, 88-90, 93-94, sr. fellow NIA, 1989-91, Fogarty Internat. Ctr., NIH, 1994—. Fellow ACP; mem. APHA, Am. Sociol. Assn. (nat. coun.-at-large med. sociology sect. 1989-92, coord. resolution process concerning nat. health program 1990-91), Soc. Gen. Internal Medicine, Phi Beta Kappa. Avocations: music, athletics, gardening, mountain hiking. Office: U Calif at Irvine Health Policy and Rsch 320 Berkeley Pl Irvine CA 92717

WAIXEL, VIVIAN, journalist; b. Norfolk, Va., July 22, 1946; d. Julius and Julia (Heimann) W.; m. Steven E. Scharbach, Aug. 24, 1969. BS in Communication, Simmons Coll., 1967; MA in Communication, U. Wis., 1971. Teaching asst. U. Wis., Madison, 1967-69; reporter Wis. State Jour., Madison, 1969-72, The Record, Hackensack, N.J., 1972-74; bus. editor The Record, Hackensack, 1974-76, assignment editor, 1976-86, sports editor 1986-88, chief news editor, 1988-92, mng. editor, 1992—. Recipient Tribute to Women and Industry award, YWCA, 1976. Avocations: snorkeling, fitness walking, music, reading. Office: The Record 150 River St Hackensack NJ 07601-7110

WAJDA, TADEUSZ, engineer; b. Korczyna, Poland, July 12, 1939; came to U.S., 1989; s. Wladyslaw and Janina (Kudla) W.; m. Krystyna Zawada, July 12, 1970; children: Martin, Anna. MS and Engirng., Tech. U., 1966, PhD in Engring., 1976. Asst. Inst. Soil Mechanics, Kracow, Poland, 1967-70, sr. asst., 1970-77; researcher, inventor, writer pvt. practice, Yorktown Heights, N.Y., 1989—; adj. Tech. U., 1977. Author: Na Rezydencji, 1993; freelance writer Polish Daily News; inventor, patentee in field. Recipient award Polish Assn. Higher Learning. Home: 2097 Saw Mill River Rd Yorktown Heights NY 10598-4109

WAJENBERG, ARNOLD SHERMAN, retired librarian, educator; b. Indpls., Apr. 11, 1929; s. Henry and Hazel L. (Johnson) W.; m. Joyce E. Dunham, Sept. 6, 1952; 1 child, Earl S. B.A., Butler U., Indpls., 1951, M.A., 1953; M.A., U. Chgo., 1955. Cataloger U. Chgo. Library, 1953-69; catalog librarian U. Ill., Chgo., 1969-74; asst. catalog librarian U. Ill., Champaign-Urbana, 1974-78, prin. cataloguer, 1979-94; retired, 1994; prof. library adminstrn. U. Ill., Champaign-Urbana; prin. educator, Ill. Tng. Program for Implementation of Anglo-Am. Cataloguing Rules, 2d edit., 1979-80; mem. editorial policy com. Dewey Decimal, 1981-92; Ill. rep. cataloging adv. com., Online Computer Libr. Ctr. 1979-82, cataloging and database svcs. adv. com., 1989-92. Author: FLC FEDLINK AACR 2 Cataloging Manual for Federal Libraries, 1981; contbr. articles to profl. jours. Mem. ALA (com. on cataloging: description and access 1981-86, mem.-at-large exec. com. cataloging and classification sect. 1982-86). Avocations: walking, science fiction. Home: 1702 Sheridan Rd Champaign IL 61821-4811

WAJER, RONALD EDWARD, management consultant; b. Chgo, Aug. 31, 1943; s. Edward Joseph and Gertrude Catherine (Rytelny) W.; m. Mary Earlene Hagan, July 5, 1969; children: Catherine, Michael. BSIE, Northwestern U., 1966; MBA, Loyola U., Chgo., 1970. Cert. mgmt. cons. Project engring. mgr. Procter & Gamble, Chgo., 1966-67; indsl. engring. mgr. Johnson & Johnson, Bedford Park, Ill., 1967-71; project mgr. Jewel Cos., Franklin Park, Ill., 1971-73; div. engring. mgr. Abbott Labs., North Chicago, Ill., 1973-79; pres. Bus. Engring. div. R.E. Wajer & Assocs., Northbrook, Ill., 1979—. Contbr. articles to profl. jours. Sec. Downtown Redevel. Commn., Mt. Prospect, Ill., 1977-78; fundraising vol. Maryville Acad., Des Plaines, 1985—; bd. dirs. Lattof YMCA, Des Plaines, 1994—. Recipient Community Svc. award Chgo. Lighthouse for the Bliknd, 1989, Cert. of Merit Village of Mt. Prospect, 1978. Mem. Inst. Indsl. Engrs. (community svc. chmn. 1984), Inst. Mgmt. Cons. (exec. v.p., bd. dirs. 1987-94), Assn. Mgmt. Cons. (ctrl. regional v.p. 1985-87), Midwest Soc. Profl. Cons., Northwestern Club Chgo. Roman Catholic. Office: Bus Engring 5 Revere Dr #200 Northbrook IL 60062

WAJNERT, THOMAS C., leasing company executive; b. Evergreen Park, Ill., May 9, 1943; s. Chester J. and Gabriella M. (Postanowicz) W.; m. Marianne Amanda Kienly, Sept. 9, 1967 (dec. 1981); m. Theresa Irene Altmix, Jan. 2. 1982; children—Melissa, Rachel, Sophia, Drew. B.S., Ill. Inst. Tech., Chgo., 1965; M.B.A., So. Methodist U., Dallas, 1966. Exec. v.p U.S. Leasing Corp., San Francisco, 1968-81; pres. U.S Portfolio Leasing, San Francisco, 1981-83, U.S. Instrument & Rentals, San Mateo, Calif., 1983-84; pres., chief exec. officer AT&T Credit Corp., Whippany, N.J., 1984-89, AT&T Capital Corp., Morristown, N.J., 1990—. Home: Young Rd Bernardsville NJ 07924 Office: AT&T Capital Corp 44 Whippany Rd Morristown NJ 07960-4558

WAKE, DAVID BURTON, biology educator, researcher; b. Webster, S.D., June 8, 1936; s. Thomas B. and Ina H. (Solem) W.; m. Marvalee Hendricks, June 23, 1962; 1 child, Thomas Andrew. BA, Pacific Luth. U., 1958; MS, U. So. Calif., 1960, PhD, 1964. Instr. anatomy and biology U. Chgo., 1964-66, asst. prof. anatomy and biology, 1966-69; assoc. prof. zoology U. Calif. Berkeley, 1969-72, prof., 1972-89, prof. integrative biology, 1989-91, John and Margaret Gompertz prof., 1991—; dir. Mus. Vertebrate Zoology U. Calif., Berkeley, 1971—. Author: Biology, 1979; co-editor: Functional Vertebrate Morphology, 1985, Complex Organismal Functions: Integration and Evolution in the Vertebrates, 1989. Mem. nat. bd. Nat. Mus. Natural History. Recipient Quantrell Teaching award U. Chgo., 1967, Outstanding Alumnus award Pacific Luth. U., 1979; grantee NSF, 1965—; Guggenheim fellow, 1982. Fellow AAAS, NRC (bd. biology 1986-92); mem. Internat. Union for Conservation of Nature and Natural Resources (chair task force on declining amphibian populations 1990-92), Am. Soc. Zoologists (pres. 1992), Am. Soc. Naturalists (pres. 1989), Am. Soc. Ichthyologists and Herpetologists (bd. govs.), Soc. Study Evolution (pres. 1983, editor 1979-81), Soc. Systematic Biology (coun. 1980-84), Herpetologist's League (Disting. Herpetologist 1984). Home: 999 Middlefield Rd Berkeley CA 94708-1509

WAKE, MARVALEE HENDRICKS, biology educator; b. Orange, Calif., July 31, 1939; d. Marvin Carlton and Velvalee (Borter) H.; m. David B. Wake, June 23, 1962; 1 child, Thomas A. BA, U. So. Calif., 1961, MS, 1964, PhD, 1968. Teaching asst./instr. U. Ill., Chgo., 1964-68, asst. prof., 1968-69; lectr. U. Calif., Berkeley, 1969-73, asst. prof., 1973-76, assoc. prof., 1976-80, prof. zoology, 1980-89, chmn. dept. zoology, 1985-89, chmn. dept. integrative biology, 1989-91, assoc. dean Coll. Letters and Sci., 1975-78, prof. integrative biology, 1989—. Editor, co-author: Hyman's Comparative Vertebrate Anatomy, 1979; co-author: Biology, 1978; contbr. articles to profl. jours. NSF grantee, 1978-94; Guggenheim fellow, 1988-89. Fellow AAAS, Calif. Acad. Sci. (trustee 1992—); mem. Am. Soc. Ichthyology and Herpetology (pres. 1984, bd. govs. 1978—), Internat. Union Biol. Scis. (U.S. Nat. Com. 1986-95, chair 1992-95, sec. gen. 1994—). Home: 999 Middlefield Rd Berkeley CA 94708-1509 Office: U Calif Dept Integrative Biology Berkeley CA 94720

WAKE, WILLIAM S., wholesale distribution executive; b. 1926. MBA, U. Mich., 1948. With Aurora (Ill.) EBy-Brown Co., Inc., 1948-56, chmn. bd., CEO, 1956. With USN, 1944-46. Office: Eby-Brown Co 280 Shuman Blvd Ste 280 Naperville IL 60563*

WAKEFIELD, BENTON MCMILLIN, JR., banker; b. Monroe, La., Apr. 8, 1920; s. Benton McMillin and Adele (Rhodes) W.; m. Cindy Walton, May 19, 1951; children: Benton McMillin, III, Will Walton. BS in Commerce summa cum laude, Washington and Lee U., 1941; postgrad., Grad. Sch. Banking, U. Wis., 1949-51. Asst. v.p. First Nat. Bank Memphis, 1946-52; v.p. Ouachita Nat. Bank, Monroe, La., 1952-63; pres., CEO, bd. dirs. Merc. Nat. Bank Ind., Hammond, 1963-72; pres., CEO 1st Bank and Trust Co., South Bend, Ind., 1972-79, FBT Bancorp., 1972-79; chmn., CEO First Nat. Bank of Jefferson Parish, 1979-84; chmn., pres., CEO First Fin. Bank, New Orleans, 1984-88; prin. Bank and Thrift Cons. Group, New Orleans, 1988—; cons., including trial expert testimony Fin. Litigation Support, 1988; bd. dirs. 10 banks, Mich. and Ind., 1972-79, Carpetland U.S.A, Chgo.; vice chmn. Jefferson Steering Com. on Edn.; mem. fin. adv. coun. Fed. Res. Bank Atlanta; mem. visitors com. Loyola U. Bus. Sch.; Chpt. 11 bankruptcy trustee Kirk Mfg. Inc. Bd. dirs. Econ. Devel. Com. New Orleans, Bur. Govt. Research, United Way. Served to lt. comdr. USNR, 1941-46. Mem. Am. Bankers Assn. (econ. policy com.), U.S. C. of C. (fin. com.), New Orleans Country Club, Bienville Club, Phi Beta Kappa, Sigma Alpha Epsilon, Omicron Delta Kappa, Beta Gamma Sigma, Rotary, Royal Soc. St. George, Huguenot Soc. Methodist. Home: 5301 Marcia Ave New Orleans LA 70124-1050 Office: 5301 Marcia Ave New Orleans LA 70124

WAKEFIELD, DAN, author, screenwriter; b. Indpls., May 21, 1932; s. Benjamin H. and Brucie (Ridge) W. B.A., Columbia U., 1955; Nieman fellow, Harvard U., 1963-64. News editor Princeton (N.J.) Packet, 1955; staff writer Nation mag. 1956-59; free lance writer, 1959—; contbg. editor The Atlantic Monthly, 1968-80; staff Bread Loaf Writers Conf., 1964, 66, 68, 70, 86; contbn. writer GQ mag., 1992—; vis. lectr. U. Mass., Boston, 1965-66; vis. lectr. journalism U. Ill., 1968; wrtiter-in-residence Emerson Coll., 1989-92; Disting. vis. writer Fla. Internat. U., 1995. Creator, story cons. TV show James at 15, 1977-78, Heartbeat, 1988; author: Island in the City: The World of Spanish Harlem, 1959, Revolt in the South, 1961, ananthology, 1963, Between the Lines, 1966, Suprenation at Peace and War, 1968, Going All the Way, 1970, (Nat. Book Award nomination), Starting Over, 1973, All Her Children, 1976, Home Free, 1977, Under the Apple Tree, 1982, Selling Out, 1985, Returning: A Spiritual Journey, 1988, The Story of Your Life: Writing a Spiritual Autobiography, 1990, New York in the Fifties, 1992, Expect A Miracle, 1995; editor: The Addict: An Anthology, 1963; (teleplay) the Innocents Abroad (Mark Twain) for PBS, 1983; writer, co-producer TV movie The Seduction of Miss Leona, 1980; contbg. editor: Atlantic Monthly, 1969-80 . Bernard DeVoto fellow Bread Loaf Writers Conf., 1957, Rockefeller Grant in Creative Writing, 1968; short story prize, Nat. Council of Arts, 1968. Mem. Authors Guild Am., Writers Guild Am., Nat. Writers Union, Vestry of King's Chapel. Address: care King's Chapel 64 Beacon St Boston MA 02108-3531

WAKEFIELD, RICHARD ALAN, energy consulting firm executive; b. Exeter, N.H., June 22, 1947; s. Frederick Irving and Helen (Smith) W.; m. Priscilla Jean Warnock, Aug. 16, 1969; 1 child, Laura Katherine. BSEE magna cum laude, U. N.H., 1969; MSEE, U. Ill., 1970; PhD in Elec. Engring., U. Wash., 1975. Project engr. Air Force Avionics Lab., Wright-Patterson AFB, Ohio, 1973-77; sr. engr., project mgr. Mathtec, Inc., Arlington, Va., 1977-81; v.p. CSA Energy Cons., Arlington, 1981-88, sr. v.p., 1988-90, pres., 1991—. Bd. dirs Arlington Community Residences, Inc., 1983-88, chmn., 1988-89; bd. dirs Arlington Community Svcs., 1989—. Capt. USAF, 1973-77. Recipient Nat. Capital award D.C. Coun. Engring. and Archtl. Socs., Washington, 1982, Perske award Assn. for Mentally Retarded, Arlington, 1983. Mem. IEEE (sr., mem. demand-side mgmt. subcom. Power Engring. Soc. 1983—, mem. system planning subcom. Power Engring. Soc. 1985—, chmn. energy policy com. 1992—), AAAS. Democrat. Roman Catholic. Avocations: tennis, fly fishing. Office: CSA Energy Cons 1901 N Fort Myer Dr Ste 503 Arlington VA 22209

WAKEFIELD, SAMUEL NORRIS, army officer; b. Abbeville County, S.C., May 24, 1938; s. Samuel J. and Mary (McAdams) W.; m. Linda J. Bowen, June 25, 1961; children: Richard B., Milton N. BA in Polit. Sci., The Citadel, 1960; MBA in Bus., U. Pa., 1969. Commd. 2d lt. U.S. Army, 1961, advanced through grades to lt. gen., 1992; transp. staff officer Mil. Assistance Command, Vietnam, 1967; student Command and Gen. Staff Coll., Ft. Leavenworth, Kans., 1970-71; exec. officer 10th Bn., 27th Bn., Vietnam, 1971-72; comdr. 24th Bn., 7th Transp. Group, Ft. Eustis, Va., 1975-77; student Navy War Coll., Newport, R.I., 1977-78; div. chief force structure and sustainability DCSLOG, Washington, 1977-81; comdr. 29th Area Support Group, U.S. Army Europe, Fed. Republic Germany, 1981-83; dir. logistics J-4 U.S. Readiness Command, MacDill AFB, 1983-86, U.S. Forces Command, Ft. McPherson, Ga., 1986-88; comdr., comdt. U.S. Army Transp. Ctr./Sch., Ft. Eustis, Va., 1988-92; comdr. U.S. Army Combined Arms Support Ctr., Ft. Lee, Va., 1992—; team mem. Study of Army Logistics, Washington, 1981. Bd. dirs United Way, Newport News, Va., 1991-92. Decorated D.S.M., Legion of Merit, Bronze Star with 2 oak leaf clusters, Def. Superior Svc. medal. Mem. Nat. Def. Transp. Assn. (regtl. chpt.), Assn. U.S. Army, Peninsula C. of C., Williamsburg C. of C., SAR (bd. dirs Williamsburg, Va. chpt. 1990—), One Ninety One Club (Atlanta). Baptist. Home: 396 Lexington Dr Fort Lee VA 23801-1323 Office: Combined Arms Support Command Office Of Cmdr Fort Lee VA 23801

WAKEFIELD, STEPHEN ALAN, lawyer; b. Olney, Ill., Oct. 18, 1940; s. George William and Blanche Lucille (Sheesley) W.; children from previous marraige: Melissa Cox, Tracy Lanz, Stephen Jr.; m. Patricia Ann McGuire, Nov. 29, 1980; 1 child, Mark. LLB, U. Tex., Austin, 1965. Bar: Tex. 1965. Assoc. Baker & Botts, Houston, 1965-70, ptnr., 1974-84, sr. ptnr., chmn. energy dept., 1986-89; atty. Federal Power Commn., Washington, 1970-72; dep. asst. sec. energy programs Dept. Interior, Washington, 1972-73, asst. sec. energy and minerals, 1973-74; asst. administr. Fed. Energy Office, Washington, 1973-74; vice chmn., gen. counsel United Energy Resources, Inc., Houston, 1985-86; pres. United Gas Pipe Line Co., Houston, 1985-86; exec. v.p. MidCon Corp., 1985-86; gen. coun. Dept. Energy, Washington, 1989-91; ptnr. Akin, Gump, Strauss, Hauer & Feld, L.L.P., 1991—. Bd. dirs. Houston Advanced Rsch. Ctr.; bd. visitors M.D. Anderson Cancer Ctr. Mem. ABA, Tex. Bar Assn., Fed. Energy Bar Assn. Clubs: River Oaks Country, Ramada (Houston). Home: 16 West Lane Houston TX 77019 Office: Akin Gump Strauss Hauer & Feld LLP 711 Louisiana Ste 1900 Houston TX 77002

WAKEFIELD, WESLEY HALPENNY, church official; b. Vancouver, B.C., Can., Aug. 22, 1929; s. William James Elijah and Jane mitchell (Halpenny) W.; m. Mildred June Shouldice, Oct. 24,1959. Ed. pub. schs., 1936-45, student tech. inst., 1945-47, student theology, 1947-51. Ordained to ministry The Bible Holiness Movement, 1951. Pastor Penticton, B.C., 1949-56; itinerant evangelist, 1956-59; internat. leader, bishop-gen. The Bible Holiness Movement, Vancouver, 1949—; mission to native Indians in Alta., Can., 1960-65, to Nigeria and Liberia, 1966, to drug culture youth in Pacific N.W., 1969—, among alcoholics, 1956-59, 64-66, 73; guest speaker, dir. Bible Broadcast, 1952-56, Freedom Broadcast, 1984-85; sec.-treas. Penticton Ministerial Assn., 1956; mgr. Evang. Book Svc., 1964—, Liberty Press, 1964—; presented opening prayer Fall legis. session, B.C., 1972; lectr. in field. Author: Bible Doctrine, 1951, Bible Basis of Christian Security, 1956, Jesus Is Lord, 1976, How to Incorporate a Nonprofit Society, 1976, Foundations of Freedom, 1978, Fire from Heaven, 1987, Bringing Back the Ark, 1987, John Wesley: The Burning Heart, 1988, Like Lightning, 1990, Antinominianism: The Curse of the Ages, 1990; legis. rsch. submissions: Effects of Marijuana and Youth, 1969, Labour Legislation Clauses, 1973, Religious Liberty in the Constitution, 1978, Alternatives to Electro-shock Therapy, 1988, 90, Present Day Slavery, 1973, 90; editor Hallelujah mag. (formerly Truth on Fire!), 1949—, Christian Social Vanguard, 196-61, Canadian Church and State, 1977-90, Hallelujah Songbook, 1981-83, Wesleyan Annotated Edition of the Bible, 1980—, Miniature Railways (quar.), 1988—. Chmn. Christians Concerned for Racial Equality, 1975—; v.p. Can. United for Separation of Ch. and State, 1977-90; chmn. Religious Freedom Coun. of Christian Minorities, 1978—; rsch. dir. United Citizens for Integrity, 1979—; v.p. Can. Coun. Japan Evang. Band, 1988—; chmn. Religious Info. Ctr., 1978—; Western Can. rep. Can. for the Protection of Religious Liberty, 1979—. Recipient Internat. Community Svc. award Gt. Britain, 1976, 79, Religious Liberty Advocacy award Religious Freedom Crusade, 1986, 87. Mem. NAACP, Anti-Slavery Soc., Can. Bible Soc., Bible Sci. Assn., Christian Holiness Assn. (com. mem.), Nat. Black Evang. Assn. (denomination rep. 1980-86), Wesley Study Bible (reference com. 1988-90), Evangs. for Social Action, Internat. Platform Assn., Salvation Army Hist. Soc. Avocation: miniature railways. Office: Bible Holiness Movement, PO Box 223 Postal Sta A, Vancouver, BC Canada V6C 2M3 *The real Christian is one who has exchanged the love of life for a life of love and desires the whole will of God—nothing else, nothing less, and nothing more. This consistency of service is the jewel of life and holiness its crowning glory.*

WAKEHAM, HELMUT RICHARD RAE, chemist, consulting company executive; b. Hamburg, Germany, Apr. 15, 1916; s. Rae G. and Augusta (Beiss) W.; m. Kathleen Ferguson, June 22, 1939; children: Stuart, Susan, Rosemary. BA, U. Nebr., 1936, MA, 1937; PhD, U. Calif.-Berkeley, 1939. Research chemist Standard Oil Co. Calif., 1939-41, So. Regional Research Lab., U.S. Dept. Agr., 1941-47; research assoc. Inst. Textile Tech., Charlottesville, Va., 1947-49; project head chem.-physics sect. Textile Research Inst., also research dir., 1949-56; dir. Ahmedabad (India) Textile Industries Research Assn., 1956-58; staff asst. for research to v.p. Philip Morris, Inc., 1958-59, dir. research and devel., 1959-61, v.p., dir. research and devel., 1961-65, v.p corporate research and devel., 1965-75, v.p. sci. and tech., 1975-80, v.p world tobacco tech. group, 1980-82; pres. HRW Tech. Assocs. Inc., 1983-92; chmn. MEGG Assocs., Inc., 1984—; pres. Vigor Corp., 1985-87; mem. Sci. Commn. of CORESTA (internat. tobacco research orgn.), 1966-72; gen. chmn. CORESTA/TCRC Conf., Williamsburg, Va., 1972; chmn. Nat. Conf. Adminstrn. Research, 1970; mem. gen. adv. com. Textile Research Inst., 1961-65; mem. tobacco working group Nat. Cancer Inst., 1967-76; session chmn. Nat. Cancer Plan Workshop, 1971. Pres. Robert E. Lee council Boy Scouts Am., 1972-75; pres. Sci. Mus. of Va. Found., 1974-77, Va. Ctr. for Performing Arts, 1980-85; chmn. Carpenter Ct. for Performing Arts; exec. v.p. Richmond Symphony, 1976-79, pres., 1979-81, chmn., 1981-83. Cultural Laureate in sci. and tech. State of Va., 1977; Angel award Internat. Soc. Performing Arts Adminstrs., 1985. Fellow Am. Inst. Chemists, Textile Inst. (Great Britain), Va. Acad. Sci., AAAS; mem. Am. Chem. Soc. (chmn. local program sect. 1943-45, Disting. Chemist award Va. sect. 1982), Fiber Soc. (program chmn., councilor 1950-55), Am. Inst. Physics. Home: 8905 Norwick Rd Richmond VA 23229-7715 Office: 2716 Enterprise Pky Richmond VA 23294

WAKEMAN, FREDERIC EVANS, JR., historian; b. Kansas City, Kans., Dec. 12, 1937; s. Frederic Evans and Margaret Ruth (Keyes) W.; divorced; children: Frederic Evans III, Matthew Clark, Sarah Elizabeth. B.A., Harvard Coll., 1959; postgrad., Institut d'Etudes Politiques, U. Paris, 1959-60; M.A., U. Calif., Berkeley, 1962, Ph.D., 1965. Asst. prof. history U. Calif., Berkeley, 1965-67, assoc. prof., 1968-70, prof., 1970-89, Haas prof. Asian Studies, 1989—, dir. Ctr. Chinese Studies, 1972-79; humanities research prof., vis. scholar Corpus Christi Coll., U. Cambridge, Eng., 1976-77, Beijing U., 1980-81, 85; acad. adviser U.S. Ednl. Del. for Study in China; chmn. Joint Com. Chinese Studies Am. Coun. Learned Socs./Social Sci. Rsch. Coun.; sr. adviser Beijing office Nat. Acad. Scis.; pres. Social Sci. Rsch. Coun., 1986-89; dir. Inst. of EAst Asian Studies, Berkeley, 1990—. Author: Strangers at the Gate, 1966, History and Will, 1973, The Fall of Imperial China, 1975, Conflict and Control in Late Imperial China, 1976, Ming and Qing Historical Studies in the People's Republic of China, 1981, The Great Enterprise, 1986, Shanghai Sojourners, 1992, Policing Shanghai, 1995. Harvard Nat. scholar, 1955-59; Tower fellow, 1959-60; Fgn. Area fellow, 1963-65; Am. Coun. Learned Socs. fellow, 1967-68; Guggenheim fellow, 1973-74; NRC fellow, 1985. Mem. Am. Acad. Arts and Scis., Coun. on Fgn. Rels., Am. Hist. Assn. (pres.). Home: 702 Gonzalez Dr San Francisco CA 94132-2234 Office: University of California Inst East Asian Studies Berkeley CA 94720

WAKEMAN, RICK, musician, composer; b. Middlesex, Eng., May 18, 1949; s. Cyril and Mildred W.; m. Nina Carter, 1983; children: Jemma, Oscar; children from previous marriages: Oliver, Adam, Benjamin. Educated, Royal Coll. Music, London. Keyboard and composition tng. Royal Coll. Music, 1968. Performed with group Strawbs, 1970-71; with Yes, 1971-72, 77-79, 91; with Anderson Bruford Wakeman Howe, 1989; formed own group, 1973—; rec. artist A & M Records, 1971-80, Charisma Records, from 1980, others; composed film score based on works of Liszt for film Lisztomania, 1975; original film scores White Rock, 1976, The Burning, 1982, G'Olé, 1983, Crimes of Passion, 1984; albums include Journey to the Centre of the Earth, 1974, Six Wives of Henry VIII, 1974, Myths and Legends of King Arthur, 1975, No Earthly Connection, 1976, Criminal Record, 1977, Best Known Works, 1978, 81, 84, Rhapsodies, 1979, Silent Nights, 1985, Live at Hammersmith, 1985, The Family Album, 1987, (with Tony Fernandez) Zodiaque, 1988, A Suite of Gods, 1988, Time Machine, 1988, Black Knights in the Court of Ferdinand IV, 1990, Phantom Power, 1990, Aspirant Sunset, 1990, Aspirant Sunrise, 1990, Softsword, King John & the Magna Carta, 1991, Greater Hits, 1994, numerous others; toured U.S. with Nat. Philharm. Orch. and Chorus, 1974, with own group, 1975, with Yes, 1977, 78, 79, 91, with Anderson Bruford Wakeman Howe, 1989. Address: Bajonor Ltd, Bajonor House, 2 Bridge St, Peel Isle of Man*

WAKIL, SALIH JAWAD, biochemistry educator; b. Kerballa, Iraq, Aug. 16, 1927; s. Jawad and Milook (Attraqchi) W.; m. Fawzia Bahrani, Nov. 30, 1952; children: Sonya, Aida, Adil, Youssef. B.Sc., Am. U., Beirut, 1948; Ph.D., U. Wash., 1952. Research fellow U. Wash., 1949-52; research fellow U. Wis., Madison, 1952-56, asst. prof., 1956-59; asst. prof. Duke U., 1959-60, assoc. prof., 1960-65, prof., 1965-71; prof. biochemistry, chmn. dept. Baylor Coll. Medicine, Houston, 1971—, Lodwick T. Bolin prof., chmn. dept. biochemistry, 1984—, prof. biotechnology, 1986—, Disting. Svc. prof., 1990—. Recipient Paul Lewis award in enzyme chemistry Am. Chem. Soc., 1967, Disting. Duke Med. Alumnus award, 1973, Chilton award U. Tex., Health Sci. Ctr., Dallas, 1985, Kuwait prize Kuwait Found. Advancement Sci., 1988, Disting. Svc. award Arab Am. Med. Assn., 1990, Supelco Rsch. award Am. Oil Chemists' Soc., 1993; John Simon Guggenheim fellow, 1968-69. Fellow Am. Acad. Microbiology; mem. NAS, Assn. Med. and Grad. Depts. Biochemistry (pres. 1988-89). Office: Baylor Coll Medicine Biochemistry Dept 1 Baylor Plz Houston TX 77030

WAKLEY, JAMES TURNER, manufacturing company executive; b. Springfield, Ohio, Feb. 17, 1921; s. James Henry and Edith Lynn (Welsh) W.; m. Mary Pennell, May 18, 1945; children: Ruth Nadine, Gary James, Martin Pennell. Student, pub. schs., Springfield. Regional sales mgr. Nat. Supply Co., 1947-54; exec. v.p. Kanawha Sand Co., 1956-60; pres. Ohio River Sand & Gravel Co., Parkersburg, W.Va., 1960-77; v.p., bd. dirs. McDonough Co., Parkersburg, 1960-81; pres. McDonough Found., 1981—; chmn. bd. dirs. Marmac Corp., Parkersburg, 1981—. Chmn. Parkersburg Urban Renewal Authority, 1968-75; trustee Ohio Valley Improvement Assn., Marietta Coll., W.Va. Found. Ind. Colls. Decorated DFC, Air medal. Mem. Nat. Sand and Gravel Assn. (bd. dirs. 1976-79). Lutheran. Home: 1906 Washington Ave Parkersburg WV 26101-3608 Office: PO Box 1825 Parkersburg WV 26102-1825

WAKOSKI, DIANE, poet; b. Whittier, Calif., Aug. 3, 1937; d. John Joseph and Marie Elvira (Mengel) W. BA in English, U. Calif., Berkeley, 1960. Writer-in-residence Mich. State U., East Lansing, 1976—, Univ. Disting. prof., 1990—; vis. writer Calif. Inst. Tech., 1972, U. Va., 1972-73, Wilamette U., 1973, Lake Forest Coll., 1974, Colo. Coll., 1974, U. Calif., Irvine, 1974, Macalester Coll., 1975, U. Wis., 1975, Hollins Coll., 1974, U. Wash., 1978, Whitman Coll., 1976, Emory U., 1980-81, U. Hawaii, 1978. Author: books Coins and Coffins, 1962, Discrepancies and Apparitions, 1966, Inside The Blood Factory, 1968, The George Washington Poems, 1967, The Magellanic Clouds, 1969, The Motorcycle Betrayal Poems, 1971, Smudging, 1972, Dancing On The Grave of A Son Of A Bitch, 1973, Trilogy, 1974, Virtuoso Literature For Two and Four Hands, 1976, Waiting For the King of Spain, 1977, The Man Who Shook Hands, 1978, Cap of Darkness, 1980, The Magician's Feastletters, 1982, The Collected Greed: Parts I-XIII, 1984, The Rings of Saturn, 1986, Emerald Ice: Selected Poems 1962-87, 1988 (William Carlos Williams prize 1989), Medea The Sorceress, 1991, Jason the Sailor, 1993, The Emerald City of Las Vegas, 1995. Cassandra Found. grantee, 1970; N.Y. State Cultural Council grantee, 1971-72; Nat. Endowment for Arts grantee, 1973-74; Guggenheim grantee, 1972-73; Fulbright grantee, 1984; Mich. Arts Coun. grantee, 1988; recipient Mich. Arts Found. award, 1989, Disting. Faculty award Mich. State U., 1989, Univ. Disting. Prof., 1990. Office: Mich State U 207 Morrill Hall East Lansing MI 48824-1036

WAKS, JAY WARREN, lawyer; b. Newark, Dec. 6, 1946; s. Isadore and Miriam Waks; m. Harriet S. Siedman, July 27, 1969; children: Jonathan Warren, Allison Lindsay. BS, Cornell U., 1968, JD, 1971. Bar: N.Y. 1972, U.S. Ct. Appeals (2d cir.) 1972, U.S. Dist. Ct. (no. dist.) N.Y. 1972, U.S Dist. Ct. (so. dist. & ea. dists.) N.Y. 1973, U.S. Ct. Appeals (3d cir.) 1983, U.S. Dist. Ct. D.C. 1985, U.S. Supreme Ct. 1991. Law clk. to Hon. Inzer B. Wyatt U.S. Dist. Ct. So. Dist. N.Y., 1971-72; assoc. Kaye, Scholer, Fierman, Hays & Handler, N.Y., 1972-80, ptnr., 1981—, assoc co-chmn. labor and employment law dept., chmn. health care law practice group and ADR practice group; gen. counsel, sec. to bd. dirs Work in Am. Inst., Inc., Scarsdale, N.Y., 1989—; mem., chmn. faculty numerous employment and labor law confs., 1982—; participant NYU Nat. Conf. on Labor, 1987, 90; speaker Nat. Law Jours.'s Gen. Counsel Conf., 1988—; mem. dean's spl. leadership com. Cornell U. Law Sch. Bus. watch columnist Nat. Law Jour., 1990—; contbg. author numerous articles to profl. jours. Mem. employment disputes com. Ctr. for Pub. Resources, Inc., 1988—, chair, 1991—; chmn. 20th reunion campaign Cornell Law Sch., Ithaca, N.Y., 1991. Named among Nation's Best Litigators in Employment Law, Nat. Law Jour., 1992, Best Lawyers in N.Y., N.Y. Mag., 1995. Mem. Assn. of Bar of City of N.Y. (chmn. labor and employment law com. 1990-93), N.Y. C. of C. and Industry (chmn. adv. panel on employment litigation 1986—). Avocations: swimming, tennis, skiing, bicycling, rollerblading. Home: 44 Eton Rd Larchmont NY 10538-1424 Office: Kaye Scholer Fierman Hays & Handler 425 Park Ave New York NY 10022-3506

WAKSMAN, BYRON HALSTED, neuroimmunologist, experimental pathologist, educator, medical association administrator; b. N.Y.C., Sept. 15, 1919; s. Selman A. and Bertha (Mitnik) W.; m. Joyce Ann Robertroy, Aug. 11, 1944; children: Nan, Peter. BS, Swarthmore Coll., 1940; MD, U. Pa., 1943. Intern Michael Reese Hosp., Chgo., 1944; fellow Mayo Found., 1946-48; NIH fellow Columbia U. Med. Sch., 1948-49; assoc., then asst. prof. bacteriology and immunology Harvard Med. Sch., 1949-63; research fellow, then assoc. bacteriologist (neurology) Mass. Gen. Hosp., 1949-63; prof. microbiology Yale U., 1963-74, prof. pathology, 1974-78, chmn. dept., 1964-70, 72-74, prof. pathology and biology, 1979-89; v.p. rsch. programs Nat. Multiple Sclerosis Soc., N.Y.C., 1979-87; v.p. research and med. programs Nat. Multiple Sclerosis Soc., N.Y.C., 1987-89; adj. prof. pathology NYU,

1979—; vis. scientist in neurology Harvard U., 1990—; mem. expert panel immunology WHO, 1962—; adv. panel and study sect. mem. NIH, 1961—; bd. trustees Biosis, 1987-95; dir. sci. writing fellowships program Marine Biol. Lab., Woods Hole, Mass., 1990-95; Humboldt prof. Max Planck Inst., Munich, 1991-92; dir. European Initiative for Communicators Sci., 1992-95. Author numerous articles on thymus, cell-mediated immunity, tolerance, lymphokines, lymphocyte stimulation mechanisms, autoimmunity; editor: Progress in Allergy/Chemical Immunology, 1962—; editorial adv. bd.: Cellular Immunology, 1970—, Immunol. Communications, 1972—, Annales d'Immunologie, 1973—, Pathologie et Biologie, 1975—, Inflammation, 1975—; assoc. editor: Bacteriological Revs, 1963-67, Jour. Immunology, 1962-66, Internat. Archives Allergy and Applied Immunology, 1962—. Served as psychiatrist AUS, 1944-46. Mem. Am. Assn. Immunologists (councillor 1965-70, pres. 1970-71), British Soc. Immunology, Am. Soc. Microbiology (councillor 1967-69). Home: 300 E 54th St New York NY 10022-5018 Office: NYU Med Ctr Dept Pathology 550 1st Ave New York NY 10016-6402

WAKSMAN, TED STEWART, lawyer; b. N.Y.C., July 4, 1949; s. Alfred and Helen (Greenberger) W.; m. Lois J. Lichter, Dec. 26, 1970; children: Scott, Michael. BS, Cornell U., 1970; JD, NYU, 1973. Bar: N.Y. 1974. Ptnr. Weil, Gotshal & Manges, N.Y.C., 1973—. Mem., assoc. editor NYU Law Rev., 1971-73. Mem. ABA (comml. fin. services com.). N.Y. State Bar Assn. Office: Weil Gotshal & Manges 767 5th Ave New York NY 10153-0001

WALASEK, OTTO FRANK, chemical engineer, biochemist, photographer; b. Park Falls, Wis., Mar. 11, 1919; s. Frank Otto and Mary (Swoboda) W.; m. Annie May Stockton (div. Nov. 1959); 1 child, Richard A.; m. Joan Constance Ashton, Sept. 18, 1965; children: Arthur, Carl. BS in Chem. Engring., U. Wis., 1946; MS in Biochemistry, U. Ill., 1968; postgrad., Loyola U., 1968-72. Penicillin processing product engr. I Abbott Labs., North Chgo., Ill., 1946-49; antibiotic process rsch. and devel. Abbott Labs., North Chgo., 1950-55, biochemical rsch., 1956-68, sr. biochemist, 1968-77, staff Leukemia project, 1978-80; pvt. photographer Sonora, Calif., 1981—. Patentee in field; contbr. articles to profl. jours. Recipient Excellence award Fedn. Internat. of Art Photographic, Switzerland, 1972; named Hon. Master of Profl. Photography, Profl. Photographic Assns., Taiwan, 1990. Mem. Photographic Soc. Am. (associateship), Royal Photographic Soc., Nat. Stereoscopic Soc., Internat. Stereoscopic Union. Democrat. Avocations: nature, wilderness, canoeing adventures, travel. Office: 10165 Hwy 49 Sonora CA 95370

WALASZEK, EDWARD JOSEPH, pharmacology educator; b. Chgo., July 4, 1927; married; two children. BS, U. Ill., 1949; PhD in Pharmacology, U. Chgo., 1953; MD honoris causa, U. Helsinki, 1990. Rsch. fellow U. Edinburgh, 1953-55; asst. prof. neurophysiology and biochemistry U. Ill., 1955-56; asst. prof. pharmacology U. Kans. Sch. Medicine, Kansas City, 1957-59; assoc. prof. U. Kans. Sch. Medicine, 1959-62, prof., 1962—, chmn. dept., 1964-92; USPHS spl. rsch. fellow, 1956-61; mem. health study sect. med. chemistry NIH, 1962-66, mem. health study sect. on rsch. career devel. award, 1966-70, mem. health study sect. on pharmacologyg-toxicology, 1974-78, rsch. career award, 1963; mem. com. teaching of sci. Internat. Coun. Sci. Unions; mem. adv. coun. Internat. Union Pharmacology, 1972-81, chmn. sect. teaching, 1975-85; chmn. bd. Computer Assisted Teaching Systems Consortium. Editorial bd.: Med. Biology, 1974-84, Arch. int. Pharmacodyn, 1977. Recipient vice-chancellor's award U. Kans., 1974, Rector's medal U. Helsinki, 1975, Recognition medal Vanderbilt U., 1991, Arstiteaduskond medal Tartu U., Estonia, 1993. Fellow Am. Coll. Clin. Pharmacologists, AAAS, Am. Chem. Soc., Soc. Pharmacology, Soc. Neurosci.; mem. Finnish Acad. Sci. and Letters (fgn.), Finnish Pharm. Soc. (hon.), Hungarian Pharm. Soc. (hon.), Sigma Xi, Alpha Omega Alpha, Rho Chi. Office: U Kans Sch Medicine Dept Pharmacology Kansas City KS 66160

WALBERG, HERBERT JOHN, psychologist, educator, consultant; b. Chgo., Dec. 27, 1937; s. Herbert J. and Helen (Bauer) W.; m. Madoka Bessho, Aug. 20, 1965; 1 child, Herbert J. III. BE in Edn. and Psychology, Chgo. State U., 1959; ME in Counseling, U. Ill., 1960; PhD in Ednl. Psychology, U. Chgo., 1964. Instr. psychology Chgo. State U., 1962-63, asst. prof., 1964-65; lectr. edn. Rutgers U., New Brunswick, N.J., 1965-66; asst. prof. edn. Harvard U., Cambridge, Mass., 1966-69; assoc. prof. edn. U. Ill., Chgo., 1970-71, prof., 1971-84, rsch. prof., 1984—; external examiner, 1981; ednl. cons. numerous orgns.; external examiner Monash U., 1974, 76, Australian Nat. U., 1977; speaker in field; former coord. worldwide radio broadcasts on Am. edn. Voice of Am., USIA, Office Pres. U.S. Author, editor 35 books; chmn. editorial bd. Internat. Jour. Ednl. Rsch., 1985—; contbr. over 350 articles to profl. jours., chpts. to books. Mem. Chgo. United Edn. Com., also other civic groups, 1971-86; bd. dirs Family Study Inst., 1987. Nat. Inst. Edn. rsch. grantee, 1973, NSF rsch. grantee, 1974, March of Dimes rsch. grantee, 1976, numerous others. Fellow AAAS, Am. Psychol. Assn., Royal Statis. Soc.; mem. Internat. Acad. Edn. (founding), Am. Ednl. Rsch. Assn., Assn. for Supervision and Curriculum Devel., Brit. Ednl. Rsch. Assn., Nat. Soc. for Study Edn., Evaluation Rsch. Soc., Internat. Acad. Scis., Phi Delta Kappa (Disting. Rsch. award U. Chgo. chpt. 1971, cert. of recognition 1985), Phi Kappa Phi (hon.). Lutheran. Avocation: travel. Home: 522 N Euclid Ave Oak Park IL 60302-1618 Office: U Ill PO Box 4348 Chicago IL 60680-4348

WALBORSKY, HARRY M., chemistry educator, consultant; b. Lodz, Poland, Dec. 15, 1923; came to U.S., 1929; s. Israel and Sarah (Miedowicz) Wolborski; m. Paula Levitt, Nov. 28, 1970; children: Edwin, Eric, Lisa, Irene. BS, CCNY, 1945; PhD, Ohio State U., 1949. Rsch. assoc. Calif. Inst. Tech., Pasadena, 1948; rsch. assoc. UCLA Med. Sch., 1949-50, rsch. assoc. chemistry dept. UCLA, 1950; instr. Fla. State U., Tallahassee, 1950-51, asst. prof. chemistry, 1951-54, assoc. prof., 1954-59, prof., 1959—, Disting. prof., 1980—; cons. Dow Chem. Co., Midland, Mich., 1956-72. Contbr. over 150 articles to profl. jours., 1949—. Recipient Sr. Scientist award von Humboldt Soc., Federal Republic of Germany, 1987; USPHI fellow, 1951, Japanese Soc. for Promotion Sci. fellow, 1977. Mem. Am. Chem. Soc. (award Fla. chpt. 1978), N.Y. Acad. Sci., Chem. Soc. London, Sigma Xi, Phi Lambda Upsilon. Avocations: tennis, bridge. Office: Fla State U Dept Chemistry Tallahassee FL 32306

WALBRIDGE, WILLARD EUGENE, broadcasting executive; b. Republic, Pa., Mar. 11, 1913; s. Peter D. and Anna (Higbee) W.; m. Marietta H. Arner, Nov. 15, 1941; 1 child, Peter F. A.B., U. Mich., 1936. Salesman, Sta. WWJ, Detroit, 1939-43; mgr. Sta. WWJ-TV, Detroit, 1946-53; exec. v.p., gen. mgr. Sta. WJIM AM-TV, Lansing, Mich., 1953-54, Sta. KTRK-TV, Houston, 1954-70; sr. v.p. corp. affairs Capital Cities Communications, Inc., 1970-78, cons., 1978-81; dir. Houston Lighting & Power Co., Houston Industries, Inc., 1975-83, Internat. Systems & Controls, Inc., Tex. Commerce Med. Bank. Pres., Greater Houston Community Found.; bd. dirs. Salvation Army, Houston Area council Boy Scouts Am., Houston Grand Opera Assn.; mem. nat. bd. govs. ARC, 1974-80, also bd. dirs. Houston chpt., 1965-83, chmn. Houston chpt., 1972-75; chmn. bd. TV Info. Office, N.Y.C., 1965-70; trustee Mus. Broadcasting, 1978-82. Served from ensign to lt. USNR, 1943-46. Decorated Silver Star. Mem. Maximum Service Telecasters (dir. 1971-81), Houston Assn. Community TV (dir. 1972-82), Internat. Radio and TV Fedn. (dir. 1969-76), Nat. Assn. Broadcasters (dir. 1965-70, chmn. bd. 1970-71), U.S.C. of C. (dir. 1975-81), Houston C. of C. (dir. 1971-83, chmn. bd. 1975-76), Houston Council Fgn. Relations (chmn. 1977-78). Home: 2828 Bammel Ln Apt 1203 Houston TX 77098-1132 Office: 1 Greenway Plz E Ste 716 Houston TX 77046 also: Hill & Knowlton Innc 1111 Bagby St Ste 2125 Houston TX 77002-2546

WALBURN, JOHN CLIFFORD, mental health services professional; b. Marion, Ind., Apr. 6, 1945; s. Rex Raymond and Norma Jane (Clifford) W.; m. Linda Sue Spall, Sept. 21, 1968 (div. Dec. 1987); 1 child, Geoffrey Jacob; m. Mitzi Lynn Johnson, June 20, 1992; 1 child, Abigail Rae. BS, Ball State U., 1969, MA, 1975; JD, I.U., Indpls., 1991. Bar: Ind. 1992. Planner Metro. Planning Commn., Muncie, Ind., 1970-72; dir. adult svcs. Del. County Assn. for Retarded, Muncie, Ind., 1972-76; exec. dir. Fayette-Union Assn. for Retarded, Connersville, Ind., 1976-83; cons. Ind. Protection and Advocacy, Indpls., 1984-86; case mgr. Ind. Dept. Mental Health, Indpls., 1986-87; v.p. Cardinal Svc. Mgmt., New Castle, Ind., 1987—; ofcl. Ind. Spl. Olympics, 1973—; chmn. Ind. Residential Mgmt. Com., 1991—; cons. DLG

Cons. and Mktg. Svc., Ind., 1992. Co-author: Feldman/Walburn Habilitation System, 1988; phote, drawing artist, 1978—. With USN, 1965-67. Named Ky. Col., Commonwealth of Ky., 1978. Mem. Am. Assn. Mental Retardation (bd. dirs. 1991—). Avocations: sports, playing/listening to music, movies, art, reading fiction. Home: 1121 Indiana Ave New Castle IN 47362-4616 Office: Cardinal Svc Mgmt Inc PO Box 505 New Castle IN 47362-0505

WALCH, PETER SANBORN, museum director, publisher; b. Portland, Maine, Oct. 10, 1940; s. J. Weston and Ruth Dyer (Sanborn) W.; m. Margaret S. Segal, June 29, 1962 (div. 1983); children: Maximilian F.S., Abigail M.; m. Linda P. Tyler, Aug. 3, 1990. BA, Swarthmore Coll., 1962; MFA, Princeton U., 1964, PhD, 1968. Asst. prof. fine arts Pomona Coll., Claremont, Calif., 1966-68, Vassar Coll., Poughkeepsie, N.Y., 1968-69, Yale U., New Haven, 1969-71; assoc. prof. U. N.Mex., Albuquerque, 1971-85, dir. Art Mus., 1985—; chmn., bd. dirs. J. Weston Walch, Pub., Portland, 1990—. Author: (exhbn. catalog) French Eighteenth-Century Oil Sketches, 1980; editor New Mexico Studies in the Fine Arts jour., 1978-86. Mem. Contemporary Art Soc. Home: 1520 Columbia Dr NE Albuquerque NM 87106-2635 Office: Univ NMex Art Mus Fine Arts Ctr Albuquerque NM 87131

WALCH, TIMOTHY GEORGE, library administrator; b. Detroit, Dec. 6, 1947; s. George Louis Walch and Margaret Mary (Shields) DeSchryver; m. Victoria Irons, June 24, 1978; children: Thomas Emmet, Brian Edward. BA, U. Notre Dame, 1970; PhD, Northwestern U., 1975. Assoc. dir. Soc. Am. Archivists, Chgo., 1975-79; grants analyst Nat. Hist. Publ. Commn., Washington, 1979-81; budget analyst Nat. Archives, Washington, 1981-82, editor Prologue, 1982-88; asst. dir. Hoover Presdl. Libr., West Branch, Iowa, 1988-93, acting dir., 1993—. Author: Catholicism in America, 1989, Pope John Paul II, 1989, Parish School, 1995, others; editor: Fairwell to the Chief, 1990, Herbert Hoover & Harry S. Truman, 1992, Immigrant America, 1994, and others; assoc. editor: U.S. Cath. Hist., 1983—; mem. editl. bd. Soc. Am. Archivists, 1982-86; series editor: Garland Pub. Co., 1988-92; contbr. articles to profl. jours. Recipient Journalism awards U.S. Cath. Press Assn., 1986-91, 1st place publ. award Nat. Assn. Govt. Communicators, 1988. Mem. Soc. Am. Archivists, Orgn. Am. Historians, U.S. Cath. Hist. Soc. Home: 65 N Westminster St Iowa City IA 52245-3833 Office: Hoover Presdl Libr PO Box 488 West Branch IA 52358-0488

WALCH, W. STANLEY, lawyer; b. Sedalia, Mo., Mar. 23, 1934; s. Harry W. and Martha (Inge) W.; m. Valerie Marvin, Apr. 9, 1957; children: Gretchen, Charles, John. AB cum laude with honors, Kenyon Coll., 1956; JD with distinction, U. Mich., 1959. Bar: Mo. 1959, U.S. Dist. Ct. (ea. dist) Mo. 1959, U.S. Dist. Ct. (so. dist.) Ill. 1962, U.S. Ct. Appeals (8th cir.) 1963, U.S. Supreme Ct., 1983. Assoc. Thompson & Mitchell, St. Louis, 1959-65; ptnr. Thompson & Mitchell, 1965-69; exec. v.p., gen. counsel, bd. dirs. Chrom Alloy Am. Corp., St. Louis, 1969-76; ptnr. Thompson & Mitchell, St. Louis, 1976—; mng. ptnr. Thompson & Mitchell, 1988-90; bd. dirs. Cen. States Diversified Corp., St. Louis, Orion Capital Corp., St. Louis, Precision Stainless Co., Alnwright-Wrightmann Supply Co. Assoc. editor Mich. Law Rev., 58-59. Vestryman Emmanuel Episcopal Ch., St. Louis, 1983-86, pres. Found., 1978-82; adv. trustee Ettie Jordan Charitable Trust, St. Louis, 1987—; mem. campaign com. United Way, St. Louis; bd. dirs. Downtown St. Louis, Inc. Mem. ABA (com. mem.), Am. Law Inst. (com. mem.), Mo. Bar Assn. (com. mem.), St. Louis Bar Assn. (com. mem.), Algonquin C. of C. (St. Louis), Noonday Club.

WALCHER, ALAN ERNEST, lawyer; b. Chgo., Oct. 2, 1949; s. Chester R. and Dorothy E. (Kullgren) W.; m. Penny Marie Walcher; children: Dustin Alan, Michael Alan, Christopher Ray; 1 stepchild, Ronald Edwin Culver. BS, U. Utah, 1971, cert. in internat. rels., 1971, JD, 1974. Bar: Utah 1974, U.S. Dist. Ct. Utah 1974, U.S. Ct. Appeals (10th cir.) 1977, Calif. 1979, U.S. Dist. Ct. (cen. dist.) Calif. 1979, U.S. Ct. Appeals (9th cir.) 1983, U.S. Dist. Ct. (ea., no., and so. dists.) Calif. 1994. Sole practice, Salt Lake City, 1974-79; ptnr. Costello & Walcher, L.A., 1979-85, Walcher & Scheuer, 1985-88, Ford & Harrison, 1988-91, Epstein Becker & Green, 1991—; judge pro tem Los Angeles Mcpl. Ct., 1986-91; dir. Citronia, Inc., Los Angeles, 1979-81. Trial counsel Utah chpt. Common Cause, Salt Lake City, 1978-79. Robert Mukai scholar U. Utah, 1971. Mem. Soc. Bar and Gavel (v.p. 1975-77), ABA, Los Angeles County Bar Assn., Century City Bar Assn., Assn. Bus. Trial Lawyers, Phi Delta Phi, Owl and Key. Club: Woodland Hills Country (Los Angeles). Home: 17933 Sunburst St Northridge CA 91325-2848 Office: Epstein Becker & Green 1875 Century Pk E Ste 500 Los Angeles CA 90067-2501

WALCOTT, CHARLES, neurobiology and behvior educator; b. Boston, July 19, 1934; s. Charles Folsom and Susan (Cabot) W.; m. Jane Clayton Taylor, Aug. 27, 1976; children: Thomas Stewart, Samuel Cabot. AB, Harvard U., 1956; PhD, Cornell U., 1959. Asst. prof. div. engring. and applied physics Harvard U., Cambridge, Mass., 1961-65; asst. prof. biology Tufts U., Medford, Mass., 1965-67; assoc. prof. dept. biology SUNY, Stony Brook, 1967-74, prof. dept. biology, 1974-81; prof., exec. dir. Cornell Lab. of Ornithology, Ithaca, N.Y., 1981-93, Louis Agassiz Fuertes dir., 1992-95; prof. neurobiology and behavior Cornell U., 1995—; cons., dir. Elem. Sci. Study, Watertown, Mass., 1961-67; dir. 3-2-1- Contact, Children's TV Workshop, N.Y.C., 1978—; dir. L.A. Fuertes. Contbr. many rsch. papers to sci. jours. Dir. sci. TV, Mass. Audubon, Lincoln, 1959-61. Avocations: gardening, sailing, photography. Home: 84 Besemer Hill Rd Ithaca NY 14850-9636 Office: Cornell U Sect Neurobiol & Behavior Seeley G Mudd Hall Ithaca NY 14853

WALCOTT, DEREK ALTON, poet, playwright; b. Castries, St. Lucia, Jan. 23, 1930; s. Warwick and Alix W.; m. Fay Moston, 1954 (div. 1959); 1 son; m. Margaret Ruth Maillard, 1962 (div.); 2 daus.; m. Norline Metivier (div.). BA, U. West Indies, Kingston-Jamaica, 1953, DLitt, 1972. Former tchr. St. Lucia, Grenada, Jamaica; poet-in-residence Hollins Coll., Roanoke, VA, 1980; prof. English Boston U.; founding dir. Trinidad Theatre Workshop, 1959—; lectr. Rutgers U., Yale U.; vis. prof. Columbia U., 1981, Harvard U., 1982, Boston U., 1985. Author: (poetry) Twenty-Five Poems, 1948, Epitath for the Young: A Poem in XII Cantos, 1949, Poems, 1953, In A Green Night: Poems, 1948-1960, 1962, Selected Poems, 1964, The Castaway and Other Poems, 1965 (Heinemann award Royal Soc. Lit. 1966), The Gulf and Other Poems, 1969 (Cholmondeley award 1969), Another Life, 1973 (Jock Campbell/New Statesman prize 1974), Sea Grapes, 1976, Selected Verse, 1976, The Star-Apple Kingdom, 1979, The Fortunate Traveller, 1981 (Heinemann award Royal Soc. Lit. 1983), Selected Poetry, 1981, Midsummer, 1984, Collected Poems, 1948-1984, 1986 (L.A. Times Book Rev. prize 1986), The Arkansas Testament, 1987, Omeros, 1990 (W.H. Smith Literary award 1991), Selected Poetry, 1993, Antiles: Fragments of Epic Memory, 1993; (plays) Henry Christophe: A Chronicle in Seven Scenes, 1950, Henry Dernier, 1951, Wine of the Country, 1953, The Sea at Dauphin: A Play in One Act, 1953, Ione: A Play with Music, 1957, Drums and Colours: An Epic Drama, 1958 (Jamaica Drama Festival prize 1958), Ti-Jean and His Brothers, 1958, Malcochon; or, Six in the Rain, 1959, Dream on Monkey Mountain, 1967 (Obie award 1971), In a Fine Castle, 1970, The Joker of Seville, 1974, The Charlatan, 1974, O Babylon!, 1976, Remembrance, 1977, Pantomine, 1978, The Isle Is Full of Noises, 1982, The Last Carnival, 1986, Beef, No Chicken, 1986, A Branch of the Blue Nile, 1986, The Odyssey, 1992. Recipient Guinness award, 1961, Nat. Writer's Coun. prize Welsh Arts Coun., 1979, Queen Elizabeth II Gold Medal for poetry, 1988, Nobel Prize for Lit., 1992; Rockefeller Found. fellow, 1957, 58; Eugene O'Neill Found.-Wesleyan U. fellow, 1969; MacArthur Found. grantee, 1981; decorated Order of the Hummingbird, Trinidad and Tobago, 1969. Founded Trinidad Theater workshop. Home: 71 St Mary's St Boston MA 02215 Office: Boston U Dept Eng 236 Bay St Rd Boston MA 02215 also: care Farrar Straus & Giroux 19 Union Sq W New York NY 10003-3304*

WALCOTT, JOHN L., journalist; b. Paterson, N.J., Aug. 29, 1949; s. Henry Richards Jr. and Katharine McCauley (Fearing) W.; m. Nancy Bittles, Aug. 11, 1973; children: Jennifer James, Allison Tierney, Elizabeth Bittles. BA, Williams Coll., Williamstown, Mass., 1971. Reporter The Ridgewood (N.J.) News, 1972, The Bergen Record, Hackensack, N.J., 1972-75; Washington correspondent The Bergen Record, Washington, 1975-77; Washington correspondent Newsweek Mag., Washington, 1977-81, chief diplomatic correspondent, 1981-86; nat. security correspondent The Wall Street Journal, Washington, 1986-89; fgn. editor U.S. News & World Report,

Washington, 1989-94, nat. editor, 1994—; U.S. Rep. U.N. Conf. on Media, Igls, Austria, 1983; mem. Georgetown U. Sch. Fgn. Svc. Leadership Seminar, Washington, 1985. Co-author: (with David C. Martin) Best Laid Plans: The Inside Story of America's War Against Terrorism, 1988. Named Disting. Friend, Georgetown U. Sch. Fgn. Svc., 1985—; recipient Edward Weintal prize Georgetown U., 1988, Edwin M. Hood award Nat. Press Club, 1983, Freedom of the Press award, 1995, Overseas Press Club award, 1983, 84, Newspaper Guild of N.Y. award, 1985. Mem. Overseas Writers Club (pres. 1986-88), White House Correspondents Assn., Sigma Delta Chi. Presbyterian. Office: US News & World Report 2400 N St NW Washington DC 20037-1153

WALCOTT, ROBERT, healthcare executive, priest; b. Boston, July 31, 1942; s. Robert and Rosamond (Pratt) W.; m. Diane Palmer, Sept. 1, 1966; 1 child, Sara. BA, Coll. of Wooster, 1964; MDiv, Ch. Div. Sch., Berkeley, Calif., 1967; M Healthcare Adminstrn., Ohio State U., 1972. Lic. nursing home adminstr., Ohio; ordained priest Episcopal Ch. Planning specialist Health Planning and Devel. Coun., Wooster, Ohio, 1972-73, asst. dir., 1974-75; asst. dir. St. Joseph Hosp., Lorain, Ohio, 1975-78, assoc. dir., 1978-81; CEO, Lakeside Meml. Hosp., Brockport, N.Y., 1981-85; adminstr. Dent Neurologic Inst., Buffalo, 1986-87, Oak Hills Nursing Ctr., Lorain, 1994; pastor Ch. of Transfiguration, Buffalo, 1988-91, St. Michael and All Angels Ch., Uniontown, Ohio, 1991-93; adminstr.-in-tng. Chapel Hill Cmty., Canal Fulton, Ohio, 1993; interim adminstr. Regina Health Ctr., Richfield, Ohio, 1994-95; adminstr. Echoing Lake Residential Home for Devel. Disabled, Lorain, 1995—. Mem. planning com. Tremont Devel. Corp., Cleve., 1994—; mem. steering com. Habitat for Humanity, Cleve., 1994—. Fellow Am. Coll. Healthcare Execs.; mem. Am. Coll. Health Care Adminstrs. Democrat. Avocations: travel, reading. Home: 2672 W 14th St Cleveland OH 44113 Office: Echoing Lake Residential Homes 3295 Leavitt Rd Lorain OH 44053

WALD, BERNARD JOSEPH, lawyer; b. Bklyn., Sept. 14, 1932; s. Max and Ruth (Mencher) W.; m. Francine Joy Weintraub, Feb. 2, 1964; children—David Evan, Kevin Mitchell. B.B.A. magna cum laude, CCNY; J.D. cum laude, NYU, 1955. Bar: N.Y. 1955, U.S. Dist. Ct. (so. dist.) N.Y. 1960, U.S. Dist. Ct. (ea. dist.) N.Y. 1960, U.S. Ct. Appeals (2d cir.) 1960, U.S. Supreme Ct. 1971. Mem. Herzfeld & Rubin, P.C. and predecessor firms, N.Y.C., 1955—. Mem. ABA, N.Y. State Bar Assn., Bar Assn. City N.Y., N.Y. County Lawyers Assn. Office: Herzfeld & Rubin PC 40 Wall St New York NY 10005-1302

WALD, DONNA GENE, advertising executive, media specialist; b. Peekskill, N.Y., July 24, 1947; d. David and Blossom (Karlin) W. BA, Rider Coll., 1969; MA, Hunter Coll., 1974. Broadcast traffic rep. SSC&B Inc., N.Y.C., 1969-74; broadcast buyer J. Walter Thompson, N.Y.C., 1974-78, regional broadcast supr., v.p., Dallas, 1978-81; v.p., regional broadcast supr., Los Angeles, 1981-85; prof. UCLA, 1984; sr. v.p., account dir. Western Internat. Media, Calif. Mem. Advt. Industry Emergency Fund, Hollywood Radio and TV Soc., Assn. Broadcast Execs. of Tex. (bd. dirs. 1979-80, sec. 1980-81). Home: 14844 Dickens St Apt 106 Sherman Oaks CA 91403-3655 Office: Western Internat Media Corp 8544 W Sunset Blvd West Hollywood CA 90069-2387

WALD, GEORGE, biochemist, educator; b. N.Y.C., N.Y., Nov. 18, 1906; s. Isaac and Ernestine (Rosenmann) W.; m. Frances Kingsley, May 15, 1931 (div.); children: Michael, David; m. Ruth Hubbard, 1958; children: Elijah, Deborah. BS, NYU, 1927, D.Sc. (hon.), 1965; M.A., Columbia U., 1928, Ph.D., 1932; M.D. (hon.), U. Berne, 1957, U. Leon, Nicaragua, 1984; D.Sc. (hon.), Yale U., 1958, Wesleyan U., 1962, McGill U., 1966, Amherst Coll., 1968, U. Rennes, 1970, U. Utah, 1971, Gustavus Adolphus U., 1972, Hamline U., 1977, Columbia U., 1990; D.H.L. (hon.), Kalamazoo Coll., 1984. NRC fellow at Kaiser Wilhelm Inst. Berlin and Heidelberg, U. Zurich, U. Chgo., 1932-34; tutor biochem. scis. Harvard U., 1934-35, instr. biology, 1935-39, faculty instr., 1939-44, assoc. prof. biology, 1944-48, prof., 1948-77, Higgins prof. biology, 1968-77, prof. emeritus, 1977—; vis. prof. biochemistry U. Calif., Berkeley, summer 1956; Nat. Sigma Xi lectr., 1952; chmn. divisional com. biology and med. scis. NSF, 1954-56; Guggenheim fellow, 1963-64; Overseas fellow Churchill Coll., Cambridge U., 1963-64; participant U.S.-Japan Eminent Scholar Exchange, 1973; guest China Assn. Friendship with Fgn. Peoples, 1972; v.p. Permanent Peoples' Tribunal, Rome, 1980—. Co-author: General Education in a Free Society, 1945, Twenty Six Afternoons of Biology, 1962, 66, also sci. papers on vision and biochem. evolution. Recipient Eli Lilly prize Am. Chem. Soc., 1939, Lasker award Am. Pub. Health Assn., 1953, Proctor medal Assn. Rsch. in Opthalmology, 1955, Rumford medal Am. Acad. Arts and Scis., 1959, Ives medal Optical Soc. Am., 1966, Paul Karrer medal in chemistry U. Zurich, 1967, T. Duckett Jones award Helen Hay Whitney Found., 1967, Bradford Washburn medal Boston Mus. Sci., 1968, Max Berg award, 1969, Priestley medal Dickinson Coll., 1970, Columbia U. award for Disting. Achievement, 1991; co-recipient Nobel prize for physiology or medicine, 1967. Fellow NAS, Am. Acad. Arts and Scis.; mem. Am. Philos. Soc.; mem. Optical Soc. Am. (hon.). Home: 21 Lakeview Ave Cambridge MA 02138-3325 Office: Harvard U Dept Biology Cambridge MA 02138 "A scientist lives with all reality. There is nothing better. To know reality is to accept it, and eventually to love it. A scientist is in a sense a learned child. There is something of the scientist in every child. Others must outgrow it. Scientists can stay that way all their lives." (Remarks on receiving the Nobel Prize, Stockholm, 1967.)

WALD, MARTIN, lawyer; b. Roxbury, Mass., May 4, 1934; s. Hyman and Eva (Krock) W.; m. Barbara Frankel, Aug. 3, 1958; children: Leah, Marcie, Adam. AB, Harvard Coll., 1955; MBA, U. Chgo., 1957, JD, 1964; postgrad. labor law program, Temple U., 1978-83. Ptnr. Schnader, Harrison, Segal & Lewis, Phila., 1967—; lectr. St. Joseph's Coll. Comey Inst. Indsl. Relations, 1970, Temple U., Phila. Co-editor: (with David E Kenty) Erisa: A Comprehensive Guide, 1991. Mem. ABA, Fed. Bar Assn., Pa. Bar Assn. (chmn. labor employment law sect. 1986-88), Indsl. Rels. Rsch. Assn., U. Chgo. Alumni Club (pres. Phila. area 1981-86). Avocation: tennis. Home: 508 Waldron Ter Merion Station PA 19066 Office: Schnader Harrison Segal & Lewis 1600 Market St Suite 3600 Philadelphia PA 19103

WALD, MICHAEL S., legal educator; b. 1941. A.B., Cornell U., 1963; LL.B., Yale U., 1967, M.A., 1967. Bar: Calif. 1970, D.C. 1970. Atty. Ctr. Law and Social Policy, D.C., 1970-71, Pub. Defender Service, Washington, 1970-71, Youth Law Ctr., San Francisco, 1971-72, nat. adv. commn. standards and goals LEAA, 1975-76; prof. law Stanford (Calif.) U.; reporter juvenile justice standards project Inst. Jud. Adminstrn., 1971-77. Chmn. Calif. adv. com. on child abuse, 1977—. Mem. Soc. Research in Child Devel., Order of Coif. Office: Stanford U Sch Law Nathan Abbott Way Stanford CA 94305

WALD, NIEL, medical educator; b. N.Y.C., Oct. 1, 1925; s. Albert and Rose (Fischel) W.; m. Lucienne Hill, May 24, 1953; children: David, Phillip. A.B., Columbia U., 1945; M.D., NYU, 1948. Sr. hematologist Atomic Bomb Casualty Commn., Hiroshima, Japan, 1954-57; head biologist health physics div. Oak Ridge Nat. Lab., 1957-58; med. rsch. and teaching specializing in radiation medicine and cytogenetics Pitts., 1958—; mem. faculty U. Pitts. Grad. Sch. Pub. Health and Med. Sch., 1958—, prof. radiation health, 1962-91, prof. environ. and occupational health, 1991—, prof. radiology, 1965—; prof. human genetics U. Pitts., 1991—; chmn. dept. radiation health U. Pitts. Grad. Sch. Pub. Health and Med. Sch., 1969-76, 77-89, chmn. dept. occupational health, 1973-76, chmn. dept. indsl. environ. health scis., 1976-77; dir. radiation medicine dept. Presbyn.-Univ. Hosp., 1966—; med. dir. Clin. Cytogenetics Lab. U. Pitts., 1982—; cons. U.S. Nuclear Regulatory Commn. Office of Nuclear Materials Safety and Safeguards, mem. adv. panel for decontamination of Three Mile Island Nuclear Power Sta. Unit 2, 1981-93, cons. adv. com. on reactor safeguards, 1989-94; mem. U.S. working group on health effects, U.S.-USSR Joint Coordinating Com. for Civilian Nuclear Reactor Safety, 1989-92; cons. U.S. Navy, nuclear industries and utilities; chmn. radiol. health study sect. USPHS, 1967-71; mem. Nat. Coun. Radiation Protection and Measurements, 1969-81, consociate mem., 1981—; mem. Gov. Pa. Adv. Com. Atomic Energy Devel. and Radiation Control, 1966-84, chmn., 1974-76; mem. Pa. Dept. Environ. Resources adv. com. on low level radioactive waste disposal, 1985—. Contbr. numerous articles to sci. and med. publs. Served to capt. M.C. USAF, 1952-54. Recipient Health Physics Faculty Rsch. award U.S. Dept. Energy, 1992-95. Mem. Health

Physics Soc. (pres. 1973-74), Am. Pub. Health Assn. (governing council 1971-73, program devel. bd. 1973-74), Radiation Rsch. Soc. (assoc. editor jour. 1965-68), Soc. Nuclear Medicine (assoc. editor jour. 1959-69), Am. Soc. Human Genetics, Am. Coll. Occupational & Environ. Medicine, AAAS, AMA, Internat. Soc. Hematology. Achievements include research in the diagnosis and treatment of accidental human radiation injury, in human radiation dosimetry by automatic image analysis of radiation-induced chromosome aberrations, and in the cytogenetics of murine radiation induced leukemia. Office: U Pitts Grad Sch Pub Health A-744 Crabtree Hall Pittsburgh PA 15261

WALD, PATRICIA MCGOWAN, federal judge; b. Torrington, Conn., Sept. 16, 1928; d. Joseph F. and Margaret (O'Keefe) McGowan; m. Robert L. Wald, June 22, 1952; children—Sarah, Douglas, Johanna, Frederica, Thomas. BA, Conn. Coll., 1948; LLB, Yale U., 1951; HHD (hon.), Mt. Vernon Jr. Coll., 1980; LLD (hon.), George Washington Law Sch., 1983, CUNY, 1984, Notre Dame U., John Jay Sch. Criminal Justice, Mt. Holyoke Coll., 1985, Georgetown U., 1987, Villanova U. Law Sch., Amherst Coll., N.Y. Law Sch., 1988, Colgate U., 1989, Hofstra Law Sch., 1991, New Eng. Coll., 1991, Hoffstra U., 1991. Bar: D.C. 1952. Clk. to judge Jerome Frank U.S. Ct. Appeals, 1951-52; asso. firm Arnold, Fortas & Porter, Washington, 1952-53; mem. D.C. Crime Commn., 1964-65; atty. Office of Criminal Justice, 1967-68, Neighborhood Legal Svc., Washington, 1968-70; co-dir. Ford Found. Project on Drug Abuse, 1970, Ctr. for Law and Social Policy, 1971-72, Mental Health Law Project, 1972-77; asst. atty. gen. for legis. affairs U.S. Dept. Justice, Washington, 1977-79; judge U.S. Ct. Appeals (D.C. cir.), 1979—, chief judge, 1986-91. Author: Law and Poverty, 1965; co-author: Bail in the United States, 1964, Dealing with Drug Abuse, 1973; contbr. articles on legal topics. Trustee Ford Found., 1972-77, Phillips Exeter Acad., 1975-77, Agnes Meyer Found., 1976-77, Conn. Coll., 1976-77; mem. Carnegie Council on Children, 1972-77. Mem. ABA (bd. editors ABA Jour. 1978-84), Am. Law Inst. (coun. 1979—, exec. com. 1985—, 2d v.p. 1988-93, 1st v.p. 1993—), Inst. Medicine, Am. Acad. Arts and Scis., Phi Beta Kappa. Office: US Ct Appeals US Courthouse 3rd & Constitution Ave NW Washington DC 20001

WALD, SYLVIA, artist; b. Phila., Oct. 30, 1915. Ed., Moore Inst. Art, Sci. and industry. One-woman shows include U. Louisville, 1945, 49, Kent State Coll., 1945, Nat. Serigraph Soc., 1946, Grand Central Moderns, N.Y.C. 1957, Devorah Sherman Gallery, Chgo., 1960, New Sch., 1967, Book Gallery, White Plains, N.Y., 1968, Benson Gallery, Bridgehampton, L.I., 1977, Knoll Internat., Munich, Germany, 1979, Amerika Havs, Munich, 1979, Aaron Berman Gallery, N.Y.C., 1981, Hirschtladler Gallery, 1994, New Britain (Conn.) Mus., 1994, Dongah Art Gallery, Seoul, Korea, 1995, Hanlim Art Gallery, Daejun, 1995; group shows include Nat. Sculpture Soc., 1940, Sculpture Internat., Phila., 1940, Chgo. Art Inst., 1941, Bklyn. Mus., 1975, Library of Congress, 1943, 52, 58, Smithsonian Instn., 1954, Internat. Print Exhbn., Salzburg and Vienna, 1952, 2d Sao Paulo Biennial, 1953, N.Y. Cultural Center, 1973, Mus. Modern Art, N.Y.C., 1975, Benson Gallery, Bridgehampton, L.I., 1982, Dumon-Landis Gallery, New Brunswick, N.J., 1982-83, Suzuki Gallery, N.Y.C., 1982, Sid Deutch Gallery, N.Y.C., 1983, Aaron Berman Gallery, N.Y.C., 1983, Full House Gallery, Kingston, N.J., 1984, Worcester Mus., 1991, Boston Mus. Fine Arts, 1991, Hirschl & Adler Gallery, N.Y.C., 1993, others; represented in permanent collections Aetna Oil Co., Am. Assn. U. Women, Ball State Tchrs. Coll., Bibliotheque Nationale, Paris, Bklyn. Mus., Howard U., State U. Iowa, Library of Congress, U. Louisville, Nat. Gallery, Mus. Modern Art, Phila. Mus., N.C. Mus., Rose Mus. Art at Brandeis U., Whitney Mus., N.Y.C., Finch Coll. Mus., N.Y.C., U. Nebr., Ohio U., U. Okla., Princeton, Victoria and Albert Mus., Walker Gallery, Worcester (Mass.) Art Mus., Guggenheim Mus., N.Y.C., Grunewald Mus., U.Calif. Los Angeles, Rutgers Mus., N.J., Aschenbach Collection Mus., San Francisco, Grunewald Coll. Mus. UCLA; Contbr. to profl. publs. Address: 417 Lafayette St New York NY 10003

WALDBAUER, GILBERT PETER, entomologist, educator; b. Bridgeport, Conn., Apr. 18, 1928; s. George Henry and Hedwig Martha (Gribisch) W.; m. Stephanie Margot Stiefel, Jan. 2, 1955; children: Gwen Ruth, Susan Martha. Student, U. Conn., 1949-50; BS, U. Mass., 1953; MS, U. Ill., Urbana, 1956, PhD, 1960. Instr. entomology U. Ill., 1958-60, asst. prof., 1960-65, assoc. prof., 1965-71, prof., 1971—; prof. agrl. entomology U. Ill. (Coll. Agr.), 1971—; sr. scientist Ill. Natural History Survey; vis. scientist ICA, Palmira, Colombia, 1971; vis. sr. scientist Internat. Rice Rsch. Inst., 1978-79; cons. AID, 1985; vis. prof. U. Philippines, 1978-79. Contbg. author: Insect and Mite Nutrition, 1972, Introduction to Insect Pest Management, 1975, Evolution of Insect Migration and Diapause, 1978, Sampling Methods in Soybean Entomology, 1980, Evolutionary Biology, 1988, Mimicry and the Evolutionary Process, 1988, Ann. Rev. Entomology 1991; contbr. numerous articles to profl. jours. Served with AUS, 1946-47, PTO. Grantee Agrl. Rsch. Svc. USDA, 1966-71, 83-90, Nat. Geog. Soc., 1972-74, NSF, 1976-79, 82-90. Mem. AAAS, Entomol. Soc. Am., Entomol. Soc. Washington, Soc. for Study of Evolution, Mich. Entomol. Soc., Sigma Xi, Phi Kappa Phi. Home: 807A Ramblewood Ct Savoy IL 61874 Office: U Ill Dept Entomology 320 Morrill Hall Urbana IL 61801

WALDBAUM, MAXIM HOWARD, lawyer; b. Paterson, N.J., Aug. 14, 1942; s. Albert and Mary (Mandelkorn) W.; m. Christine Mastrorilli, Dec. 9, 1983; children: Thomas, Franny, Alexander. BSEE, Rutgers U., 1964; MS in Engring., U. Pa., 1966; JD, NYU, 1970. Bar: N.Y. 1971, U.S. Dist. Ct. (so. and ea. dists.) N.Y. 1972, U.S. Dist. Ct. (ea. dist.) Mich., 1984, U.S. Supreme Ct. 1981, U.S. Ct. Appeals (2d, 3d and fed. cirs.) 1982, U.S. Dist. Ct. (we. dist.) N.Y. 1992. Assoc./ptnr. Watson Leavenworth Kelton & Taggart, N.Y.C., 1970-81; ptnr./managing ptnr. Darby & Darby, N.Y.C., 1981-89; ptnr. Jones Day Reavis & Pogue, N.Y.C., 1989-93, Fried, Frank, Harris, Shriver & Jacobson, N.Y.C., 1993—; mem. coun. Fedn Internationale Counseil Propriete Industrielle Group, N.Y.C., 1984-92, sec., treas. 1991-94, pres. 1994—; head Intellectual Property Group. Contbr. articles to profl. jours. Mem. Internat. Trademark Assn. (chmn. trade barrier task force 1991-94, group head Enforcement Group 1995—). Avocations: tennis, golf. Office: Fried Frank Harris Shriver & Jacobson One New York Plz New York NY 10004

WALDECK, JOHN WALTER, JR., lawyer; b. Cleve., Sept. 10, 1949; s. John Walter Sr. and Marjorie Ruth (Palenschat) W.; m. Cheryl Gene Cutter, Sept. 10, 1977; children: John III, Matthew, Rebecca. BS, John Carroll U., 1973; JD, Cleve. State U., 1977. Bar: Ohio 1977. Product applications chemist Synthetic Products Co., Cleve., 1969-76; assoc. Arter & Hadden, Cleve., 1977-85, ptnr., 1986-88; ptnr. Porter, Wright, Morris and Arthur, Cleve., 1988-90, ptnr. in charge, 1990—. Chmn. Bainbridge Twp. Bd. Zoning Appeals, Chagrin Falls, Ohio, 1981-94; trustee Greater Cleve. chpt. Lupus Found., Am., 1978-91, sec., 1979-86; trustee LeBlond Housing Corp., Cleve., 1990—, Univ. Circle, Inc., 1993—, Fairmount Ctr. for Performing and Fine Arts, Novelty, Ohio, 1993—, sec. 1994—; bd. dirs. Geauga County Mental Health Alcohol and Drug Addiction Svc. Bd., Chardon, Ohio, 1988—, treas., 1991-93, vice chmn., 1993—; mem. bd. advisors Palliative Care Svc., Cleve. Clinic Cancer Ctr., 1989-91. Mem. ABA (real property sect. bd. govs. 1992), Greater Cleve. Bar Assn. (real property, corp. banking sect., co-chair real estate law inst. 1990), Chagrin Valley Athletic Club. Democrat. Roman Catholic. Avocations: beekeeping, gardening, jogging. Home: 18814 Rivers Edge Dr W Chagrin Falls OH 44023-4968 Office: Porter Wright Morris & Arthur 925 Euclid Ave Cleveland OH 44115-1408

WALDEN, AMELIA ELIZABETH (MRS. JOHN WILLIAM HARMON), author; b. N.Y.C.; d. William A. and Elizabeth (Wanner) W.; m. John William Harmon, Feb. 9, 1946 (dec. 1950). B.S., Columbia U., 1934; cert., Am. Acad. Dramatic Arts. Author: Gateway, 1946, Waverly, 1947, Sunnycove, 1948, Skymountain, 1950, A Girl Called Hank, 1951, Marsha, On-Stage, 1952, Victory for Jill, 1953, All My Love, 1954, Daystar, 1955, Three Loves Has Sandy, 1955, The Bradford Story, 1956, I Found My Love, 1956, My Sister Mike, 1956, Palomino Girl, 1957, Flight Into Morning, 1957, Today is Mine, 1958, Queen of the Courts, 1959; duo of novels An American Teacher: Where Is My Heart?, 1960; How Bright the Dawn, 1962, A Boy to Remember, 1960, Shadow on Devils Peak, 1961; trilogy The American Shakespeare Festival: When Love Speaks, 1961; So Near the Heart, 1962, My World's the Stage, 1964, My Dreams Ride High, 1963, To Catch A Spy, 1964, The Spy on Danger Island, 1965, Race the Wild Wind, 1965, The Spy with Five Faces, 1966, In Search of Ophelia,

1966, A Spy Called Michel-E, 1967, A Name for Himself, 1967, The Spy Who Talked Too Much, 1968, Walk In A Tall Shadow, 1968, A Spycase Built For Two, 1969, Same Scene, Different Place, 1969, The Case of the Diamond Eye, 1969, Basketball Girl of the Year, 1970, What Happened to Candy Carmichael?, 1970, Valerie Valentine is Missing, 1971, Stay to Win, 1971, Play Ball, McGill, 1972, Where was Everyone when Sabrina Screamed?, 1973, Go, Phillips, Go, 1974, Escape on Skis, 1975, Heartbreak Tennis, 1977; Amelia Walden collection personal, profl. papers, original manuscripts, research data established at U. Oreg., Eugene, 1982; pioneer young adult novel. Home: 89 Compo Rd N Westport CT 06880-2507 *Cultivate staying power. Persistence serves one better than talent or genius. Finish everything you begin. Even if the result is not what you had hoped it would be (when is it ever!), what really counts is the fact that you have done it. Above all, cultivate laughter. Laughter is a weapon against a legion of foes, including frustration and discouragement. Laughter is contagious, and thus blesses our friends, and possibly our enemies too. But more even than this, laughter is a medicine for the mind.*

WALDEN, DANIEL, humanities and social sciences educator; b. Phila., Aug. 1, 1922; s. Benjamin and Reba (Freedman) Weinroth; m. Beatrice Schulman, Oct. 12, 1957; children: Moss Carl, Ruth E. Walden Turek. BA, CCNY, 1959; MA, Columbia U. 1961; PhD, NYU, 1964. Lectr. Queens Coll., N.Y.C., 1960-63; asst. prof. Mich. State U., East Lansing, 1963-66; prof. Pa. State U., University Park, 1966—. Co-editor: On Being Black, 1970, W.E.B. DuBois, The Crisis Writings, 1972, On Being Jewish, 1974, Twentieth Century American Jewish Fiction Writers, 1984, The World of Chaim Potok, 1985, The World of Cynthia Ozick, 1987, Bernard Malamud: in Memoriam, 1988, American Jewish Poets: The Roots and the Stems, 1990, Herbert Gold and Beyond, 1991, Jewish Identity: From Midrash to Modernity, 1991, American Jewish Women Writers, 1992, The Changing Mosaic: Cahan to Malamud and Ozick, 1993, New Voices in an Old Tradition, 1994, Bernard Malamud at Century's End: A Reexamination, 1995. Mem. ALA, MLA (MELUS pres. 1977-78, Disting. MELUS award 1993), N.E. MLA (pres. 1991-92), Soc. Am. Jewish Lit. (pres. 1991-92, Disting. Svc. award 1992), Am. Studies Assn. Am. Culture Assn., Soc. for Utopian Studies. Democrat. Jewish. Avocations: reading, music, photography. Office: Dept English/Am Studies Pa State U University Park PA 16802

WALDEN, JAMES WILLIAM, accountant, educator; b. Jellico, Tenn., Mar. 5, 1936; s. William Evert and Bertha L. (Faulkner) W.; m. Eva June Selvia, Jan. 16, 1957 (dec. Aug. 1988); 1 child, James William; m. Hattie Nan Lamb, Jan. 6, 1990 (div. June 1992); m. Janet Faulkner, Aug. 12, 1993. BS, Miami U., Oxford, Ohio, 1963; MBA, Xavier U., Cin., 1966. CPA, Ohio. Tchr. math. Middletown (Ohio) City Sch. Dist., 1963-67, Fairfield (Ohio) High Sch., 1967-69; instr. accounting Sinclair Community Coll., Dayton, Ohio, 1969-72, asst. prof., 1972-75, assoc. prof., 1975-78, prof., 1978-89, prof. emeritus, 1991—; cons., public acct. Group comdr. Ohio Wing, CAP. Served with USAF, 1954-59. Mem. Butler County Torch Club, Pub. Accts. Soc. Ohio (pres. S.W. chpt. 1985-86), Inst. Mgmt. Accts., Nat. Soc. Pub. Accts., Greater Hamilton Estate Planning Coun., Ohio Soc. CPAs, Beta Alpha Psi. Home: 265 N Main St Springboro OH 45066-0469 Office: Sinclair C C 444 W 3rd St Dayton OH 45402-1421

WALDEN, LINDA L., lawyer; b. Dallas, Aug. 16, 1951; d. Leslie LaFayette Jr. and Neva Irene (McBee) W.; m. David Lee Finney, June 9, 1984. BA, Tex. Women's U., 1972; JD, St. Mary's U., 1975. Asst. city atty. City of Amarillo, Tex., 1976-77; asst. dist. atty. 84th Judicial Dist., Forger, Tex., 1977-79; asst. atty. gen. Office Atty. Gen. Austin, 1979-84; litigation atty. Friedman & Ginsberg, Dallas, 1984-86, Bradford & Snyder, Dallas, 1986-88; corp. counsel Occidental Chem. Co., Dallas, 1988—. Home: 2209 Greenview Dr Carrollton TX 75010 Office: Occidental Chem Corp 5005 LBJ Freeway Dallas TX 75244

WALDEN, PHILIP MICHAEL, recording company executive, publishing company executive; b. Greenville, S.C., Jan. 11, 1940; s. Clemiel Barton and Carolyn Hayes (McClendon) W.; m. Peggy Hackett, Sept. 13, 1969; children: Philip Michael, Amantha Starr. A.B. in Econs., Mercer U., 1962. Pres. Phil Walden & Assocs., 1961, Capricorn Records, Inc., 1969—. Campaign chmn. Macon Muscular Dystrophy Assn., 1975; chmn. Macon Heritage Found.; mem. In-Town Macon Neighborhood Assn.; Mem. nat. finance com. Jimmy Carter for Pres.; mem. Com. for Preservation of the White House; mem. nat. adv. bd. NORML; bd. dirs. Brandywine Conservancy; mem. Presdl. Inaugural Com., 1977; trustee Ga. Trust for Historic Preservation; founder Otis Redding Scholarship Fund, Mercer U., Phil Walden scholarship. Served to 1st lt. Adj. Gen. Corps AUS, 1963-65. Recipient Gold and Platinum Record awards, pub. awards; Big Bear award Mercer U., 1975; Martin Luther King, Jr. Humanitarian award, 1977; Human Relations award Am. Jewish Com., 1978. Mem. Common Cause, Middle Ga. Hist. Soc., Nat. Assn. Rec. Arts and Scis., Rec. Industry Assn. Am. (dir.), Nat. Assn. Rec. Merchandisers, Phi Delta Theta Alumni Assn. Home: 3925 Woodlawn Dr Nashville TN 37205-1933

WALDEN, ROBERT THOMAS, physicist educator, consultant; b. Paducah, Ky., Mar. 25, 1939; s. Charles Robert and Anna Catherine (Robertson) W.; m. Nellie Sue Clayton, June 9, 1962; children: Clayton Thomas, Alan Keith. BS, Murray State U., 1961, MS, 1968; PhD, Miss. State U., 1973. Tchr. math. Dongola (Ill.) High Sch., 1962-63; instr. physics Paducah C.C., 1963-68; asst. prof. Ky. Wesleyan Coll., Owensboro, 1968-70; chair sci. Miss. Gulf Coast C.C., Perkinston, 1973-87; staff scientist Nat. Ctr. Phys. Acoustics, U. Miss., University, 1987-91; prof. physics, dean gen. edn. Mid-Continent Coll., Mayfield, Ky., 1990—; cons. Walden Assocs., Paducah, 1990—; vis. prof. U. Miss., University, 1986-87; cons. Paducah Gaseous Diffusion Plant, 1992—; organizer, chair 1st nat. symposium on agroacoustics; organizer, chair Miss. Alliance Sci. Advancement. Contbr. articles to Jour. Molecular Spectroscopy, Jour. Miss. Acad. Sci. Dir., founder Stone County Jr. Basketball League, Wiggins, Miss., 1979-82; vice-chmn. Stone Coutny Hosp. Bd., Wiggins, 1983-85. Mem. Acoustical Soc. Am., Rotary (Rotarian of Yr. Wiggins unit 1981), Sigma Pi Sigma, Phi Kappa Phi. Baptist. Achievements include initiation of acoustic remote sensing of bark beetles. Home: 420 Hutchinson Ave Paducah KY 42003-5726 Office: Walden Assocs 453 Hutchinson Ave Paducah KY 42003-5725

WALDEN, STANLEY EUGENE, composer, clarinetist; b. Bklyn., 1932. BA in Music with honors, Queens Coll.; studied composition with Ben Weber, clarinet with David Weber. Faculty C.W. Post Coll.; guest lectr. U. Wis., Yale Drama Sch.; mem. dance faculty (music) Juilliard Sch., N.Y.C., 1965-71; faculty Sarah Lawrence Coll., 1973-75, SUNY, Purchase, 1973-78; chmn. musical/show dept. H.D.K. Berlin, 1990. Guest composer: So. Meth. U., 1984, Eastman Sch., 1985; pianist for Martha Graham, Anna Sokolow; music dir. Tamaris-Nagrin Dance Co., Horseman, Pass By, 1967, Am. Dance Festival, 1984; solo clarinetist Contemporary Chamber Ensemble, Bennington Composers Conf., Penn Contemporary Players; guest artist N.Y. Woodwind Quintet.; commns. include Dance Sonata for Daniel Nagrin, Stretti for Group for Contemporary Music Columbia, Image for Harkness Ballet, (with Anna Sokolow) Manhattan Festival Ballet, Invisible Cities for Phila. Orch., 1985, 3 Ladies for Jan De Gaetani and Gilbert Kalish, Songs and Dances for Joel Krosnick and Gilbert Kalish, 1986; composer incidental music Off-Broadway prodn. Scuba Duba, 1967; mem. Open Theater (The Serpent, Mutation Show) 1968-72; music for Pinkville, Am. Place Theater, 1970, The Kid, 1972, Sigmunds Freude, Bremen Stadt Theater, 1975, Weewis for Joffrey Ballet, 1971; film The Crazy American Girl, Paris, 1975, Desperado City, 1980 (winner Camera d'Or at Cannes 1981), Frohes Fest (winner 1st Prize Mannheim Festival), The Open Window Trio; solo recitals, albums for Vanguard, Three Views; commd. and recorded (as mem.) Louisville Orch., 1969; music and lyrics Oh! Calcutta!, 1969; new score The Caucasian Chalk Circle, Arena Theater, Washington, 1978, musical Back Country, 1978, Shylock, 1978, My Mother's Courage, 1979, Untergang der Titanic, 1980, Hamlet, 1980; dir. We Each Got a Reason for Being Here Tonight, Vienna Festival, 1981, Der Voyeur; actor Berlin Festival, 1982, Jubiläum for Bochum Schauspielhaus, 1983, opera Doctor Faustus Lights the Lights (G. Stein), Cologne Schauspielhaus, 1983, Peepshow (G. Tabori), Bochum, 1984, The Beggars Opera, Renaissance Theater, Berlin, 1984, Claire, Bochum, 1985, U Ber Die Städte, Burg Theater, Vienna, 1986, Mein Kampf (G. Tabori) Burg Theater, 1987; co-dir. Der Tod Dankt Ab, 1987, Sigmunds Freude, 1987; Pour La Seconde Fois (J.C. Carrière) actor/composer-Der Kreis, Vienna, 1988; musical Bahn Frei!

for Hochschule der Künste, Berlin, 1989, Lear's Schatten, Bregenz Festival, 1989, Othello-Burg Theater, 1990, Miami Lights-Coconut Grove Playhouse, 1990, Faust-Bad Hersfeld Festspiele, 1990, Endangered Species, 1990, BAM Nextwave Fest, Babylon Blues, 1991, Goldberg Variationen at Burg Theater, Vienna, 1991, Miami Lights at Theater Works, Palo Alto, Calif., 1991, Kasimir and Karoline, Schloss Park Theater, Berlin, 1991, Abendwind and Mrozek, Schlosspark Theater, Berlin, 1992, Der Grossinquisitor (Tabori), Seville, 1992, Munich Residenz Theater, Potsdam; condr. Cividale Mittelfest, 1992, Pottsdam, 1993, Requiem Fur Einen Spion (Tabori) Burg Theatre, 1993, Memini Mortuarum, Eastman and Potsdam, 1993, Brandenburg Philharmonic, 1993, Die 25te Stunde (Tabori), Burg Theater, 1994; recitals with Hanna Schygulla, Hebbel Theater, Berlin, 1994, Delirium (Enzensberger) Thalia Theatre, Hamburg, 1994, Liebster Vater, Chamber Opera after Kafka, Stadttheatre, Bremen. Address: 60 Miller Hill Rd Hopewell Junction NY 12533-6829

WALDERA, WAYNE EUGENE, crisis management specialist; b. Cayuga, N.D., Mar. 23, 1930; s. Bernard Cyril and Eleanor Nee (Kugler) W.; m. Eva Jenzene Personius, Jan. 13, 1958; children: Anthony, Lori, Mia, Shauna. BSBA, N.D. State U., 1952. With Gamble-Skogmo, 1954-88; pres. Gamble div. Gamble-Skogmo, Mpls., 1972-88; pres., CEO Retail Resource Co., Mpls., 1988-89; pres., CEO Amdura Corp., Denver, 1989-92, also bd. dirs.; chmn. Sullivan Waldera, Inc., Mpls., 1992-93; prin., CEO Waldera & Co. Inc., Mpls., 1993—. Home: 12125 62nd St Waconia MN 55387-9411 Office: Waldera & Co Inc 15500 Wayzata Blvd Ste 604-208 Minneapolis MN 55391

WALDFOGEL, MORTON SUMNER, prefabricated housing/plywood company executive; b. Somerville, Mass., Nov. 5, 1922; s. Benjamin and Gertrude (Levins) W.; m. Lillian Thelma Gouse, June 14, 1949; children: Peter Douglas, Jane Leslie. AB, Harvard U., 1944; MBA, Boston U., 1948. Assoc. prof. math. econs. Boston U., 1947-48; mgr. Roddis Plywood Co., Cambridge, Mass., 1948-51; partner East Coast Mill Sales, 1951—; chmn. bd., chief exec. officer Allied Industries Inc., Charlestown, Mass., 1954-89; chmn., chief exec. officer Gilwal Industries, Charlestown, Mass., 1982—; pres. United Internat. Inc., Boston, 1990—. Served with USNR, 1942-47. Decorated Letter of Commendation. Jewish. Home: 16 Brown Rd Swampscott MA 01907-1608 Office: Gilwal Industries PO Box 580 Charlestown MA 02129-0001

WALDHAUER, FRED DONALD, health care executive; b. Bklyn., Dec. 6, 1927; s. Fred G. and Elsie L. (Haybach) W.; B.E.E., Cornell U., 1948; M.S.E.E., Columbia U., 1960; m. Ruth Irene Waina, Feb. 12, 1955; children—Neil, Amy, Ann, Alice, Kim. Engr. RCA, Camden, N.J., 1948-55, patent agt., Princeton, N.J., 1953-55; mem. tech. staff Bell Telephone Labs., Holmdel, N.J., 1956-87; supr. transmission tech. lab., 1963-87; with venture start-up in health care Resound Corp., Redwood City, Calif. 1987—; sec., dir. Expts. in Art and Tech., Inc. Fellow IEEE (mem. solid state circuits council 1974-78, mem. lightwave tech. 1982); mem. Audio Engring. Soc. Author: Feedback, 1982. Patentee in field; contbr. articles to profl. jours. Home: 22296 Skyline Blvd La Honda CA 94020

WALDHAUSEN, JOHN ANTON, surgeon, educator; b. N.Y.C., May 22, 1929; s. Max H. and Agnes H. (Stettner) W.; m. Marian Trescher, June 4, 1957; children: John H., Robert Rodney, Anthony Gordon Scarlett. B.S. magna cum laude, Coll. Great Falls, 1950; M.D., St. Louis U., 1954. Diplomate Am. Bd. Surgery (bd. dirs. 1985-88), Am. Bd. Thoracic Surgery (bd. dirs. 1989—). Intern Johns Hopkins Hosp., 1954-55, resident, 1955-57; clin. asst. Nat. Heart and Lung Inst., NIH, 1957-59; resident Hosp. U. Pa., 1959, Ind. U. Med. Center, 1960-62; practice medicine specializing in cardiothoracic surgery Indpls., 1962-66, Phila., 1966-70; mem. staff Milton S. Hershey (Pa.) Med. Ctr., 1970—, Milton S. Hershey Med. Ctr., Hershey, Pa., 1970—; from instr. to asst. prof. Ind. U. Med. Ctr., 1962-66; assoc. prof. surgery U. Pa., Phila., 1966-70; prof. surgery Pa. State U. Coll. Medicine, Milton S. Hershey Med. Ctr., Hershey, 1970-83, 94—; J.W. Oswald prof., 1983-94, assoc. dean and dir. Univ. Physicians, 1993—, sr. mem. grad. faculty, 1970—, chmn. dept. surgery, 1969-94, vice chmn. med. policy bd., 1971-72, interim provost, dean, 1972-73, assoc. dean health care, 1973-75. Mem. editl. bd. Jour. Cardiovascular Surgery, 1985-93; Jour. Pediatric Surgery, 1972-78; Jour. Thoracic and Cardiovascular Surgery, 1982, editor, 1995—; cons. editor Archives of Surgery, 1972-74; contbr. chpts. to books and articles to med. jours. Served with USPHS, 1957-59. Recipient Career Devel. award USPHS, 1964. Mem. AMA, Assn. ACS (chpt. pres. 1974-75, gov. 1979-85, chmn. adv. coun. Conn. surgery 1992—), Am. Acad. Pediatrics, Am. Assn. Surgery of Trauma, Am. Coll. Cardiology (sec. 1981-82, trustee 1984-89, mem. editorial bd. jour. 1983, assoc. editor 1986-89), Am. Fedn. Clin. Rsch., Am. Heart Assn., Am. Physiol. Soc., Am. Soc. Artificial Internal Organs, Am. Assn. Thoracic Surgery (1st v.p. 1990-91, pres., 1991-92), Am. Surg. Assn. (1st v.p. 1984-85), Central Surg. Assn., Internat. Cardiovascular Soc. (chpt. recorder 1969-74), Pa. Assn. Thoracic Surgery (pres. 1977-78), Thoracic Surgery Dirs. Assn. (pres. 1977-79), Societe Internat. de Chirurgie (membership chmn. 1987-92, treas. 1992—), Soc. Clin. Surgery (treas. 1971-80, v.p. 1981-82, Pres. 1982-83), Soc. Surg. Chairmen, Soc. Thoracic Surgeons, Soc. Univ. Surgeons, Soc. Vascular Surgery, So. Surg. Assn., Sigma Xi, Alpha Omega Alpha. Home: RR 1 Box 158G Annville PA 17003-9704 Office: Pa State U Coll Med MS Hershey Med Ctr PO Box 850 Hershey PA 17033-0850

WALDHAUSER, CATHY HOWARD, financial services executive; b. St. Paul, Oct. 18, 1949; d. Jack Roger and Lois (Johnson) Howard; m. Stanley Jay Waldhauser, Feb. 3, 1973. BA in Math. and Econs., Gustavus Adolphus Coll., 1971. Various actuarial positions IDS Life Ins. Co., Mpls., 1971-81; v.p. IDS Life Ins. Co., 1981-91; chief acctg. officer IDS Fin. Svcs., 1991-93; dir. Fin. Instns. Group, 1993—. Trustee Gustavus Adolphus Coll., 1993—, mem. alumni bd. dirs., 1984-90; active Golden Valley (Minn.) LWV, 1986-89; sec., treas. Calvary Luth. Ch., Golden Valley, 1988-89; allocations vol. United Way, Mpls., 1988-90; mem. family selection com. Habitat for Humanity, 1993—. Fellow Soc. Actuaries (product devel. sect. coun. and rsch. com. 1985-88, edn. and exam. com. 1980-81, 83, panelist, lectr. 1980, 87-90), Am. Acad. Actuaries, Minn. Life and Health Guarantee Assn. (bd. dirs. 1984-92), Life Office Mgmt. Assn. (mgmt. rsch. com. 1987-90), Twin Cities Actuarial Club.

WALDHOF, SHARKA EVA, lawyer; b. Prague, Czech Republic, Aug. 8, 1962; came to U.S., 1966; d. Martin and Libuse Kral; m. Kenneth James Waldhof; children: Kevin, Brian. BA, L.I.U., 1985; JD, St. John's U., 1988. Bar: N.Y. 1989, Conn. 1989. Atty. European Am. Bank, Uniondale, N.Y., 1989-90, asst. counsel, 1990-92, sr. atty., 1992—; bd. dirs. First Class at EAB, Inc., Uniondale. Active First Class Child Care Parent Adv. Coun., Uniondale, 1992—. Mem. ABA, N.Y. State Bar Assn., Nassau County Bar Assn. Avocations: skiing, swimming. Office: European Am Bank 1 EAB Plz Uniondale NY 11555-2722

WALDHOLTZ, ENID GREENE, congresswoman; b. San Rafael, Calif., Oct. 5, 1958; m. Joe Waldholtz. BS in Pol. Sci., U. Utah, 1980; JD, Brigham Young U., 1983. Caseworker, asst. to U.S. Rep. Dan Marriott, R., 1982; atty. Ray, Quinney & Nebeker, 1983-90; dep. chief of staff Gov. Norman H. Bangerter, 1990-92; corp. counsel Novell, Inc., 1993-94. Office: US House Reps 515 Cannon House Office Bldg Washington DC 20515-4402

WALDMAN, ANNE LESLEY, poet, performer, editor, publisher, educational administrator; b. Millville, N.J., Apr. 2, 1945; d. John Marvin and Frances (Le Fevre) W.; m. Reed Eyre Bye; 1 son, Ambrose. B.A., Bennington Coll., 1966. Dir. The Poetry Project, St. Marks Ch. In-the-Bowery, N.Y.C., 1968-78; co-dir. Jack Kerouac Sch. of Disembodied Poetics at Naropa Inst., Boulder, Colo., 1974—; adj. faculty Inst. Am. Indian Arts, Santa Fe; bd. dirs. Com. for Internat. Poetry, Eye and Ear Theatre, N.Y.C.; poet-in-residence with Bob Dylan's Rolling Thunder Rev. Author: (poetry) On the Wing, 1968, O My Life, 1969, Baby Breakdown, 1970, Giant Night, 1970, No Hassles, 1971, Life Notes, 1973, Fast Speaking Woman, 1975, Journals and Dreams, 1976, Shaman, 1977, Countries, 1980, Cabin, 1981, First Baby Poems, 1982, Makeup on Empty Space, 1983, Invention, 1986, Skin Meat Bones, 1986, The Romance Thing, 1987, Blue Mosque, 1988, Helping the Dreamer: New and Selected Poems, 1989, Not a Male Pseudonym, 1990, Lokapala, 1991, Troubairitz, 1993, Iovis: All is Full of Jove, 1993, Kill or Cure, 1994; editor: Nice To See You: Homage to Ted

Berrigan, 1991, (anthologies) The World Anthology, 1969, Another World, 1972, Talking Poetics From Naropa Institute vol. 1, 1978, vol. 2, 1979, Out of This World, 1991, (with Andrew Schelling) Disembodied Poetics: Annals of the Jack Kerowac School, 1994; publisher: anthologies Angel Hair Books, N.Y.C., Full Ct. Press, N.Y.C.; recordings: The Dial-a-Poem Poets Disconnected, Anne Waldman/John Giorno, Fast Speaking Woman, The Nova Convention, Big Ego, Uh-oh Plutonium!, 1982, Crack in My World, 1986, Assorted Singles, 1990; performance videos include Eyes in All Heads, 1990, Live at Naropa, 1991, Battle of the Bards, 1991; featured on nat. pub. radio show All Things Considered, also featured in the poetry documentary Poetry In Motion. Dir. summer writing program Naropa; organizer Surrealist, Objectivist, Feminist, Pan Am. Ecology, Performance Confs., and The Robert Creeley Symposium. Recipient Dylan Thomas Meml. award New Sch., N.Y.C., 1967, Blue Ribbon Am. Film Festival, Nat. Literary Anthology award, 1970; named Heavyweight Champion Poet, 1989, 90; Cultural Artists Program grantee, 1976-77; Nat. Endowment for Arts grantee, 1979-80. Mem. PEN Club, Amnesty Internat. Office: care Naropa Inst 2130 Arapahoe Ave Boulder CO 80302-6602

WALDMAN, DIANE, museum deputy director; b. N.Y.C., Feb. 24, 1936; m. Paul Waldman, 1957. B.F.A., Hunter Coll., 1956; M.A., Inst. Fine Arts, NYU, 1965, postgrad. With Solomon R. Guggenheim Mus., N.Y.C., 1965—, asst. curator, 1967-69, assoc. curator, 1969-71, curator exhbns., 1971-81, dir. exhbns., 1981-82, dep. dir., 1982—; Mem. adv. bd. Skowhegan Sch. Painting and Sculpture. Author: monographs Roy Lichtenstein, 1971, Ellsworth Kelly: Drawings, Collages and Prints, 1971, Joseph Cornell, 1977, Anthony Caro, 1982, Willem de Koonig, 1988; contr. articles to profl. jours. Am. commr. to Biennale Sydney, 1988; mem. adv. bd. Ctr. Internat. Am. Relations, Am. Soc.; mem. com. internat. Musee d'Art Moderne; mem. N.Y. State Gov.'s Task Force on Asbestos, 1987—. Mem. Am. Assn. Mus. (mus. accreditation com.), Internat. Council Mus., Internat. Com. for Mus. and Collections Modern Art, Internat. Adv. Bd. ROSC, Ireland, Louis Comfort Tiffany Found. (trustee), Am. Soc. Safety Engrs. Office: Solomon R Guggenheim Mus 1071 5th Ave New York NY 10128-0173

WALDMAN, JAY CARL, judge; b. Pitts., Nov. 16, 1944; s. Milton and Dorothy (Florence) W.; m. Roberta Tex Landy, Aug. 28, 1969. B.S., U. Wis., 1966; J.D., U. Pa., 1969. Bar: Pa. 1970, D.C. 1976, U.S. Supreme Ct. 1976. Assoc., Rose, Schmidt, Dixon & Hasley, Pitts., 1970-71; asst. U.S. atty. western dist. Pa., Pitts., 1971-75; dep. asst. U.S. Atty. Gen., Washington, 1977-79; counsel Gov. of Pa., Harrisburg, 1978-86; sr. ptnr., Dilworth, Paxson, Kalish & Kauffman, Phila., 1986-88; judge U.S. Dist. Ct. (ea. dist.) Pa., 1988—. Dir. Thornburgh for Gov. campaign., Pa., 1977-78; commr. Pa. Convention Ctr. Authority, 1986-88. Fellow Am. Bar Found.; mem. ABA, Fed. Bar Assn., Union League Phila. Republican. Office: US Dist Ct Pa 9613 US Courthouse 601 Market St Philadelphia PA 96136

WALDMANN, THOMAS ALEXANDER, medical research scientist, physician; b. N.Y.C., Sept. 21, 1930; s. Charles Elizabeth (Sipos) W.; m. Katharine Emory Spreng, Mar. 29, 1958; children—Richard Allen, Robert James, Carol Ann. A.B., U. Chgo., 1951; M.D., Harvard U., 1955; PhD (hon.), U. Med. Sch., Debrecin, Hungary, 1991. Diplomate Am. Bd. Allergy and Immunology. Intern Mass. Gen. Hosp., Boston, 1955-56; clin. assoc. Nat. Cancer Inst. NIH, Bethesda, Md., 1956-58, sr. investigator, 1958-68, head immunophysiology sect., 1968-73, chief metabolism br., 1971—; cons. WHO, 1975, 78; bd. dirs., v.p. Found. for Advanced Edn. in Scis., Bethesda, 1980—, treas., 1988-90, v.p., 1990—; William Dameshek vis. prof. Tufts U., 1983; Burroughs Welcome vis. prof. U. Calif., Irvine, 1984; mem. med. adv. bd. Howard Hughes Med. Inst., 1987-93; vis. com. mem. Harvard Med. Sch., Boston, 1988-94; scientific adv. com., chmn. Mass. Gen. Hosp., 1992-94; const. HealthCare Investment Corp., Edison, N.J., 1986—. Author: Plasma Protein Metabolism, 1970; contbr. over 570 articles to profl. jours. With USPHS, 1956-58, 59-63, 75-94. Recipient Henry M. Stratton medal Am. Hemotology Soc., 1977; named Man of Yr. Am. Leukemia Soc., 1980; recipient G. Burroughs Mider award NIH, 1980; Disting. Service medal Dept. Health and Human Services, 1983. Fellow Am. Acad. Allergy (Bela Schick award 1974, John M. Shelton award 1984, Lila Gruber prize 1986, Simon Shubitz prize 1987, CIBA-GEIGY Drew award 1987, Milken Family Med. Found. Disting. Basic Scientist prize, Artois Latour Internat. Rsch. prize 1991, Bristol-Myers Cancer prize 1992); mem. NAS (chmn. 1985—), Am. Acad. Arts and Scis., Inst. Medicine, Nat. Acad. Scis., Assn. Am. Physicians, Am. Soc. Clin. Investigation (mem. editorial bd. 1978-80, 83-88), Clin. Immunology Soc. (pres. 1988). Achievements include the defining of structure of multisubunit IL-2 receptor; identifying novel cytokine IL-T; introduction of different forms of IL-2R-directed therapy using alpha- and beta-emitting radionuclide chelate versions of humanized monoclonal antibodies for treatment of cancer; introduction of analysis of immunoglobulin gene rearrangements to define clonality and classify human lymphoid neoplasia; discovered intestinal lymphangecstasia and allergic gastroenteropathy. Avocation: photography. Office: Nat Inst Health Metabolism Br/NCI Bldg 10 9000 Rockville Pike Bethesda MD 20892-1374

WALDMEIR, PETER NIELSEN, journalist; b. Detroit, Jan. 16, 1931; s. Joseph John and Helen Sarah (Nielsen) W.; m. Marilyn C. Choma; children—Peter William, Patti Ann, Lindsey Marilyn, Christopher Norman. Student, Wayne State U., 1949-58. With Detroit News, 1949—, sports columnist, 1962-72, gen. columnist, 1972—. Trustee, Cleary Coll., Ypsilanti, Mich., 1985—; pres. Old Newsboys Goodfellow Fund, Detroit, 1988. Served with USMC, 1951-53. Recipient Headliners award Nat. Headliners Club, 1971; named Mich. Sports Writer of Yr., Nat. Sportscasters and Sportswriters, 1967, 69, 71; Heart award Variety Club Internat., 1985. Mem. Sigma Delta Chi. Roman Catholic. Office: Detroit News 615 W Lafayette Blvd Detroit MI 48226-3197

WALDMEIR, PETER WILLIAM, lawyer; b. Bethlehem, Pa., Sept. 18, 1953; s. Pete and Dorothy Grace (Bastianelli) W.; m. Renee Zamboni, Feb. 28, 1986; children: Sara Grace, Charlotte. BA summa cum laude, U. Mich. 1975; JD, George Washington U., 1978. Bar: D.C. 1979, Mich. 1987, U.S. Dist. Ct. (ea. dist.) Mich., U.S. Ct. Appeals (6th cir.). Law clk. President's Commn. on Rev. Nat. Policy toward Gambling, Washington, 1975-76; Duncan, Allen & Mitchell, Washington, 1976-77, Vinson & Elkins, Washington, 1977-78; jud. clk. to chief judge 6th Jud. Ct., Detroit, 1977; jud. clk. to assoc. justice Mich. Supreme Ct., Detroit, 1978-80; trial atty. civil div. fed. programs br. U.S. Dept. Justice, Washington, 1980-84; assoc. Miller, Canfield, Paddock and Stone, Detroit, 1984-87, sr. ptnr., 1987—; bd. dirs. Grosse Point Cable; instr. legal rsch. writing Detroit Coll. Law, 1978-80. Councilman-elect Grosse Pointe City Coun., 1989-93. Mem. ABA, Mich. Bar Assn., D.C. Bar Assn., Fed. Bar Assn., Goodfellows. Roman Catholic. Office: Miller Canfield Paddock & Stone 150 W Jefferson Ave Ste 2500 Detroit MI 48226-4415

WALDNER, GEORGE WITTMAN, university administrator; b. Phila., May 12, 1946; s. Robert Emil and Margaret (Wittman) W.; m. Judith Trimble, July 21, 1973; 1 child, Lizanne. AB, Cornell U., 1968; MA, Princeton U., 1973, PhD, 1975. Mem. polit. sci. faculty Oglethorpe U., Atlanta, 1973-87, provost, 1982-87; v.p. acad. affairs Wilkes U., Wilkes-Barre, Pa., 1987-91; pres. York Coll. U., Pa., 1991—. Editor: Japan in the 1980's, 1979. Mem. Japan-Am. Soc. Ga., Atlanta, 1979-87, Wyo. Sem. Sch., Kingston, Pa., 1989-93. Mem. Rotary, Hist. Soc. York County (pres. bd. dirs.). Lutheran. Home: 134 W Springetsbury Ave York PA 17403-2262 Office: York Coll Pa York PA 17405

WALDO, BURTON CORLETT, lawyer; b. Seattle, Aug. 11, 1920; s. William Earl and Ruth Ernestine (Corlett) W.; m. Margaret Jane Hoar, Aug. 24, 1946; children: James Chandler, Bruce Corlett. BA, U. Wash., 1941, JD, 1948. Bar: Wash. 1949. Assoc. Vedova, Horswill & Yeomans, Seattle, 1949-50, Kahin, Carmody & Horswill, 1950-54; ptnr. Keller Rohrback & predecessor firms, Seattle, 1954-86; mng. ptnr. Keller Rohrback & predecessor firms, 1978-83, sr. ptnr., 1983—. Mem. Seattle Bd. Theater Suprs., 1958-61, Mcpl. League of Seattle/King County, 1949—. Capt. U.S. Army, 1942-46; ETO. Mem. ABA, Internat. Assn. Def. Counsel, Fedn. Ins. and Corp. Counsel, Wash. Bar Assn., Wash. Def. Trial Lawyers Assn., Seattle-King County Bar Assn. (trustee 1965-68), Fedn. Fly Fishers (life), S.R., Puget Sound Civil War Roundtable, Rainier Club, Wash. Athletic Club, The Steamboaters, Flyfishers Club Oreg., Hope Island King-50 Club, Delta Tau Delta, Phi Delta Phi, Alpha Kappa Psi. Avocation: fly fishing.

WALDO, (CLIFFORD) DWIGHT, political science educator; b. DeWitt, Nebr., Sept. 28, 1913; s. Cliff Ford and Grace Gertrude (Lindley) W.; m. Gwendolyn Payne, Sept. 17, 1937; children: Mary Grace, Martha Gwen, Margret Ann. B.A., Nebr. State Tchrs. Coll., Peru, 1935; M.A., U. Nebr., 1937; Ph.D., Yale U., 1942. Instr. polit. sci. Yale U., 1941-42; price analyst OPA, 1942-44; adminstrv. analyst Exec. Office Pres., 1944-46; mem. faculty U. Calif. at Berkeley, 1946-67, prof. polit. sci., 1953-67, dir. Inst. Govt. Studies, 1958-67; Albert Schweitzer prof. humanities Syracuse U., 1967-79, emeritus prof., 1979—; Carl Hatch prof. law and pub. adminstrn. U. N.Mex., 1984-85; vis. disting. prof. Fla. Internat. U., 1989; resident fellow Woodrow Wilson Internat. Center for Scholars, Smithsonian Instn., Washington, 1979-81. Author: The Administrative State, 1948, The Study of Public Administration, 1955, Perspectives on Administration, 1956, Political Science in the U.S.A, 1956; Editor: Public Administration in a Time of Turbulence, 1972, others; editor-in-chief: Pub. Adminstrn. Rev, 1966-77. Mem. Am. Polit. Sci. Assn. (v.p. 1961-62), Am. Soc. Pub. Adminstrn., (v.p. 1985-86), Internat. City Mgmt. Assn. (hon. life), Nat. Assn. Schs. Pub. Affairs and Adminstrn. (v.p. 1976-77, pres. 1977-78), Nat. Acad. Pub. Adminstrn. Home: Apt 1411W 3713 S George Mason Dr Falls Church VA 22041-3738

WALDO, KATITA, ballet dancer; b. Madrid. Student, Escuela de Danza Classica, San Francisco Ballet Sch. Apprentice San Francisco Ballet, 1987-88, mem. Corps de Ballet, 1988-90, soloist, 1990-94, prin. dancer, 1994—; tchr. summer programs Ithaca (N.Y.) Ballet, Modesto Ballet, 1993. Appeared in ballets The Sleeping Beauty, Swan Lake, Concerto in d: Poulenc, Ballet d'Isoline, Guiliani: Variations on a Theme, Beads of Memory, Aurora Polaris, Handel- a Celebration, Menuetto, Bugaku, The Four Temperaments, Who Cares?, Theme and Variations, Stars and Stripes, Agon, Ballo della Regina, Serenade, La Pavane Rouge, Calcium Light Night, The Concert, Interplay, Rodin, Dark Elegies, Tagore, Nutcracker, Romeo and Juliet, La Sylphide, In the middle, somewhat elevated, Pulcinella, In Perpetuum, Job, The Sons of Horus, The "Wanderer" Fantasy, Dreams of Harmony, The Comfort Zone, Scarlatti Portfolio, Vivaldi Concerto Grosso, Variations de Ballet, La Fill mal gardee. Office: San Francisco Ballet 455 Franklin St San Francisco CA 94102-4471*

WALDO, ROBERT LELAND, retired insurance company executive; b. Pittsville, Wis., Sept. 1, 1923; s. Elmer Harley and Edith Viola (Senter) W.; m. Elaine Anne Jossie, June 4, 1947; children: Daniel Robert, Thomas Parker, Susan Jeanne. B.A., U. Wis., 1949, JD, 1951. Assoc. atty. Foley & Lardner, Milw., 1951-59; asst. sec., asst. gen. counsel Wis. Gas Co., Milw., 1959-69; v.p., gen. counsel Verex Corp. and Subss., Madison, Wis., 1969-72; exec. v.p., sec. Verex Corp. and subs., Madison, Wis., 1972-78, pres., chief operating officer, 1978-82, pres., chief exec. officer, 1982-85, chmn., chief exec. officer, 1985-86. Served as sgt. U.S. Army, 1943-46, ETO. Mem. Wis. Bar Assn., Dane County Bar Assn., Mortgage Ins. Co.'s Am. (pres. 1980-82), Maple Bluff Country Club. Republican. Methodist. Avocations: travel, golf. Home: 818 Charing Cross Rd Madison WI 53704-6010

WALDON, GRACE ROBERTA, insurance agent; b. Surry County, N.C., July 8, 1941; d. Brady Warren and Kathleen (Riggs) Felts; m. Jesse James Waldon Jr., May 17, 1958; children: James, Forrest. BS in Econs., U. N.C. 1981, postgrad., 1983-84. Registered rep. NML Investment Svcs., Inc. Real estate agt. Rob Ramby Real Estate, Abilene, Tex., 1982-84; asst. to v.p. Life Ins. Svcs., Charlotte, N.C., 1984-85; v.p. James R. Worrell Gen. Agy., N.W. Mut. Life., Charlotte, 1985—; investment officer Robert W. Baird & Co. Inc. Officer Symphony Guild, Abilene, 1972, Internat. Mgmt. Coun., Charlotte, 1989; chmn. faculty wives La. Tech. Inst., Ruston, 1966. Named Outstanding Mem. St. Paul's Meth. Ch., 1973. Mem. CLU, Chartered Fin. Cons., Charlotte Sales and Mktg. Execs. Republican. Avocations: snow skiing, weight training, music. Office: NW Mut Life 1900 Rexford Rd Ste 120 Charlotte NC 28211-3481

WALDRON, ACIE CHANDLER, agronomy and entomology educator; b. Malad, Idaho, Feb. 4, 1930; s. Nathaniel Acie and Leah Mary (Chandler) W.; m. Catherine Venonne Moore, Aug. 20, 1957; children: Deborah Waldron Noorda, Michael Acie, Joel Moore, Laurie Waldron Phister, Susan. Student, Idaho State Coll., 1948-50; BS in Agronomy, Brigham Young U., 1957; MSc in Agronomy, Ohio State U., 1959, PhD in Agronomy, 1961. Rsch. asst. Ohio Agrl. Experiment Sta., Columbus, 1957-60; analytical chemist Am. Cyanamid Co., Princeton, N.J., 1961-66; extension specialist, pesticide safety Ohio Coop. Extension Svc., Columbus, 1966-77, 88—, pesticide coord., 1969-77, 89—, pesticide applicator tng. coord., 1989—; from asst. prof. to prof. agronomy and entomology Ohio State U., Columbus, 1966—; coord. North Cen. Region Pesticide Impact Assessment Program Ohio State U., 1977—; Ohio state liaison IR-4, 1973—; chmn. pest control panel Agrl. Rsch. Inst., Washington, 1987—; mem. Nat. Commn. for Pub./Pvt. Sector Initiative on Pesticide Application Tng. Contbr. articles to sci. and tech. publs. With U.S. Army, 1953-56, with res., 1956-60. Mem. Am. Soc. Agronomy, Soil Sci. Soc. Am., Am. Chem. Soc., Entomol. Soc. Am., North Cen. Weed Sci. Soc., Ohio Fertilizer and Pesticide Assn. (co-pres. 1979), AAAS, Sigma Xi, Gamma Sigma Delta, Epsilon Sigma Phi. Democrat. Mormon. Avocations: gardening, athletics. Home: 4220 Lyon Dr Columbus OH 43220-4430 Office: Ohio State U 1991 Kenny Rd Columbus OH 43210-1000

WALDRON, ELLIS LEIGH, retired political science educator; b. Denver, Feb. 21, 1915; s. Grover C. and Maud M. (Dolbeer) W.; m. Phyllis Schwoegler, May 16, 1941; child, Jean Madelene. BA, Ohio State U. 1936; MA, U. Wis., 1939, PhD, 1952; student, Duke, 1939-40. Staff polit. corr. U.P., Columbus, Ohio, 1941-44; instr. polit. sci. extension div. U. Wis., 1946-49, fellow polit. sci., 1949-50; faculty dept. polit. sci. U. Mont., 1950—, prof. polit. sci., 1957—; dean U. Mont. (Grad. Sch.), 1957-61, emeritus, 1980—; fellow law and polit. sci. Harvard Law Sch., 1963-64. Author: Montana Legislators 1864-1979: Profiles and Biographical Directory, Mont. Politics Since 1864, An Atlas of Elections, 1958; (with Paul B. Wilson) Atlas of Montana Elections 1889-1976, 1978, Social and Economic Dimensions of Popular Vote on 110 State Ballot Issues in Montana, 1926-86, 1990-91. Mem. Mont. Constl. Conv. Commn., 1971-72. Served with AUS, 1944-46. Mem. Am. Polit. Sci. Assn. (coun. 1969-71), Phi Beta Kappa, Kappa Sigma, Phi Kappa Phi. Home: 53 Oak Creek Trl Madison WI 53717-1509

WALDRON, INGRID LORE, biology educator; b. Nyack, N.Y., Dec. 8, 1939; d. Paul Henry and Esther Hildegard (Sachs) W.; m. Joseph Eyer (div.); children: Jessie Eyer, Katie Rebecca Eyer. AB summa cum laude, Radcliffe Coll., 1961; PhD, U. Calif., Berkeley, 1967. Asst. prof. biology U. Pa., Phila., 1968-72, assoc. prof., 1972-90, prof., 1990—. Co-author: Population and Environment—Problems and Solutions, 1973; contbr. articles to various publs., 1964—. Organizer workshops and support Reevaluation Counsellors, Phila., 1985—; vol. tchr. Upattinas Sch., Glenmoore, Pa., 1989-90, Phila. Schs. Collaborative, 1992—. Mem. Population Assn. Am., Phi Beta Kappa. Office: Univ Pa Dept Biology Philadelphia PA 19104-6018

WALDRON, JEREMY JAMES, law educator; b. Invercargill, Southland, New Zealand, Oct. 13, 1953; s. Francis Herbert and Joyce Annette (Ainge) W.; m. Helen McGimpsey, Jan. 26, 1974 (div. Oct. 1989); 1 child, Samuel James. BA with honors, U. Otago, New Zealand, 1974, LLB with honors, 1978; DPhil, Oxford U., 1986. Bar: New Zealand 1978. Asst. lectr. philosophy U. Otago, 1975-78; fellow in polit. theory Lincoln Coll., Oxford, Eng., 1980-82; lectr. in polit. theory U. Edinburgh, Scotland, 1982-87; prof. law U. Calif., Berkeley, 1987—. Editor: collection of essays Theories of Rights, 1984, Nonsense Upon Stilts, 1987; author: (textbook) The Law, 1990, (monograph) The Right to Private Property, 1988; contbr. articles to profl. jours. Avocations: romance, music, travel. Home: 1061 Keith Ave Berkeley CA 94708-1604 Office: U Calif Sch Law Boalt Hall Berkeley CA 94720

WALDRON, ROBERT LEROY, II, physician; b. Carbondale, Ill., Feb. 6, 1936; s. Robert Leroy and Violet Mae (Thompson) W.; m. Sandra Sellers; children: Richard, Robert Leroy III, Ryan, Burton Johnson. AB, Princeton U., 1958; MD, Harvard U., 1962. Diplomate Am. Bd. Radiology. Intern, Mass. Gen. Hosp., Boston, 1962-63; resident in radiology Columbia-Presbyn. Med. Center, N.Y.C., 1965-68; instr. radiology Coll. Physicians and Surgeons, Columbia U. and spl. fellow in neuroradiology Neurol. Inst., N.Y.C., 1968-69; clin. asst. in radiology Harvard Med. Sch., asst. radiologist

Mt. Auburn Hosp. and MIT, Cambridge, 1969-71; assoc. prof. clin. radiology Coll. Physicians and Surgeons, 1971-73; dir. radiology French Hosp. and French Med. Clinic, San Luis Obispo, 1973-80, v.p., dir., 1976-77; assoc. clin. prof. radiology Loma Linda U. Sch. Medicine, 1977-80; dir. radiology Richland Meml. Hosp., Columbia, S.C., 1980-90; chief radiology svcs. Richland Meml. Hosp., 1982-90, trustee, 1990—; prof. radiology U.S.C. Sch. Medicine, Columbia, 1985—; mng. ptnr. Richland Radiol. Assn., Columbia, 1988-90; founder Chilean N.Am. Hosp. Corp., 1989; pres. MedBill; Bd. dirs. Am. Cancer Soc., San Luis Obispo. With USPHS, 1963-65. Recipient grants James Picker Found., Am. Cancer Soc., NRC, Nat. Acad. Scis., Nat. Cancer Inst. Fellow Am. Coll. Radiology, Soc. Internat. Med. Sci. Cooperation; mem. AMA, Am. Roentgen Ray Soc., Radiol. Soc. N.Am., Am. Soc. Neuroradiology, Western Neuroradiol. Soc., Southeastern Neuroradiol. Soc., S.C. Med. Assn., San Luis Obispo County Med. Soc. (pres. 1979), Columbia Med. Soc., Sierra-Cascade Trauma Soc. (pres. 1983-84), S.C. Radiol. Soc. (pres. 1992-93). Republican. Methodist. Clubs: Ivy of Princeton; Wildewood, Capital City (Columbia). Contbr. articles to profl. jours. Home: 1420 Adger Rd Columbia SC 29205-1406 Office: 1814 Bull St Columbia SC 29201-2506

WALDROP, BERNARD KEITH, English educator; b. Emporia, Kans., Dec. 11, 1932; s. Arthur and Opal Irene (Mohler) W.; m. Rosmarie Sebald, Jan. 22, 1959. B.A., Kans. State Tchrs. Coll., Emporia, 1955; M.A., U. Mich., Ann Arbor, 1958, Ph.D., 1964. Mem. faculty Brown U., Providence, 1968, prof. English, 1980—; editor Burning Deck Press, Providence, 1961—. Author: (poems) A Windmill Near Calvary, 1968, The Garden of Efford, 1977, The Ruins of Providence, 1984, A Ceremony Somewhere Else, 1984, Selected Poems, 1990, Shipwreck in Haven, 1992; (prose) Hegel's Family, 1989, Light While There is Light, 1993. Served with U.S. Army, 1953-55. Mem. PEN Am. Ctr. Home: 71 Elmgrove Ave Providence RI 02906-4132 Office: Brown U English Dept 79 Waterman St Providence RI 02912-9079

WALDROP, FRANCIS NEIL, physician; b. Asheville, N.C., Oct. 5, 1926; s. Troy Lester and Emma Louise (Ballard) W.; m. Eleanor Dorothy Wickes, June 10, 1950; children—Mark Lester, Barbara Louise. A.B., U. Minn., 1946; M.D., George Washington U., 1950. Intern George Washington U. Hosp., Washington, 1950-51; resident St. Elizabeth's Hosp., Washington, 1951-54; med. officer St. Elizabeth's Hosp., 1951-71; dir. manpower and tng. programs NIMH, Rockville, Md., 1972-75; dep. adminstr. Alcohol, Drug Abuse and Mental Health Adminstrn., HEW, Rockville, 1975-79; ret., 1979; clin. prof. psychiatry George Washington U. Recipient Superior Service award HEW, 1962, Disting. Service award, 1964. Fellow Am. Psychiat. Assn. (Vestermark award 1980). Research, publs. in field. Home: 1775 Elton Rd Silver Spring MD 20903-1726

WALDROP, GIDEON WILLIAM, composer, conductor, former president music school; b. Haskell County, Tex., Sept. 2, 1919; s. Gideon William and Margaret (Pierson) W. MusB, Baylor U., 1940; Mus M, U. Rochester, 1941, PhD, 1952. Asso. prof. music Baylor U., Waco, Tex., 1946-51; condr. Waco-Baylor Symphony Orch., 1946-51; editor Rev. Recorded Music, N.Y.C. 1952-54, Musical Courier, N.Y.C., 1953-58; cons. div. arts and humanities Ford Found., N.Y.C., 1958-61; asst. to pres. Juilliard Sch. Music, N.Y.C., 1961-63, dean, 1963-86, acting pres., 1983-84; pres. Manhattan Sch. Music, N.Y.C., 1986-89; mem. adv. com. Toscanini Archives; cons. to Minister Edn., Israel, summers 1972-74, Portugal, summer 1979, Fundacion Isaac Albeniz, Madrid, Spain, 1989—. Condr. Shreveport Symphony, 1941-42; composer (symphony overture) Prelude and Fugue for Orchestra, chamber music, choral works and songs.; commd. by, San Antonio Symphony Soc., 1958, 63. Served to maj. USAAF, 1942-46, ETO. Decorated Bronze Star. Mem. ASCAP, Phi Beta Kappa, Phi Mu Alpha. Democrat. Clubs: Players, Bohemians, N.Y. Athletic, Century (N.Y.C.).

WALDROP, LINDA M., medical administrator; b. Jefferson County, Ala., Oct. 24, 1942; d. Luther Grady Jr. and Anna Katherine (Gray) McGill; m. Bennie Lee Waldrop Jr., Mar. 14, 1961; children: Tracy L., Terry L. AS, Jefferson State Jr. Coll., 1971; BSN, Samford U., 1985; MA, U. Ala., Birmingham, 1989. Head nurse open heart ICU Bapt. Med. Ctr.-Montclair, Birmingham, 1976-82, head nurse telemetry unit, 1985-87, head nurse med. unit, 1983-85, head nurse oncology unit, 1987-90, adm. coord.; internal auditor Bapt. Med. Ctr.-Montclair, 1991; dir. med.-surg. telemetry nursing Shelby Med. Ctr., Alabaster, Ala., 1991—, dir. gastroenterol. svcs., 1993—, dir. women's svcs., nursing internal auditor, 1993—. Mem. ANA (cert. nursing adminstrn.), Oncology Nursing Soc., AACN, Nat. Mgmt. Assn.

WALDROP, WILLIAM THOMAS, executive; b. Jackson, Tenn., Dec. 1, 1929; s. Homer Hampton and Nelle (Hundley) W.; m. Doris Ebersole, Nov. 8, 1957; children: Robert Buxton, John Winfield. BS, U.S. Mil. Acad., 1952; M of Theol. Studies, Gordon-Conwell Theol. Sem., 1974. Ordained to ministry, Bapt. Ch. Commd. 2d lt. USAF, 1952, advanced through grades to lt. col., retired, 1972; sr. pastor Grace Evang. Ch., Atlanta, 1975-85; min.-at-large Advancing Chs. in Mission Commitment, Atlanta, 1985-88; pres. ACMC, Inc., Carol Stream, Ill., 1988—. Contbr. articles to profl. jours. Decorated Air medal, Disting. Flying Cross, Meriterious Svc. medal. Avocations: reading, hiking, bird-watching. Office: ACMC Inc 135 E St Charles Carol Stream IL 60188

WALDSCHUTZ, GERHARD, corporate executive; b. Vienna, Austria, June 4, 1939; came to U.S., 1961; s. Hans Georg and Ilse (Haar) W. BSChemE, U. Munich, 1960; MBA, U. Miami, 1963. Commr. Austrian Trade Del., Hong Kong, 1965-67; trade commr. Austrian Trade Del., Tokyo, 1968, Los Angeles, 1969-72; pres. Optyl Corp., Norwood, N.J., 1972—, Argo Advt. Agy., Norwood, N.J.; dir. Austrian Tourist Office, Los Angeles, 1969-72; consul Fgn. Service, Hong Kong, 1966-67.

WALDSTEIN, SHELDON SAUL, physician, educator; b. Chgo., June 23, 1924; s. Herman S. and Sophia (Klapper) W.; m. Jacqueline Sheila Denbo, Apr. 2, 1952; children: Sara Jean, Peter Denbo, David John. Student, Harvard U., 1941-43; M.D., Northwestern U., 1947. Diplomate: Am. Bd. Internal Medicine. Intern Cook County Hosp., 1947-48, resident in internal medicine, 1948-51; chief Northwestern Med. Service, 1954-62, exec. dir. dept. medicine, 1964-64, chmn. dept. medicine, 1964-69; exec. dir. North Suburban Assn. Health Resources, 1969-72; mem. faculty Northwestern U. Med. Sch., 1954-61, assoc. prof. medicine, 1961-66, prof. medicine, 1966—, assoc. dean health services, dir. Northwestern U. Med. Assos., 1974-77; exec. v.p. Nat. Ctr. for Advanced Med. Edn., Chgo., 1977-91; pres. Nat. Ctr. Advanced Med. Edn., Chgo., 1991—. Served to capt. M.C., AUS, 1952-54. Fellow Am. Coll. Physicians, Am. Coll. Endocrinology; mem. AMA, Chgo. Med. Soc., Cen. Soc. Clin. Rsch., Endocrine Soc., Am. Assn. Clin. Endocrinology, Am. Fedn. Clin. Rsch., Chgo. Soc. Internal Medicine, Alpha Omega Alpha. Home: 813 Moseley Rd Highland Park IL 60035-4635 Office: 541 N Fairbanks Ct Chicago IL 60611-3319

WALEN, HARRY LEONARD, historian, lecturer, author; b. Winchester, Mass., June 26, 1915; s. Harry Leonard and Alice (Garland) W.; m. Elizabeth Rowe Benson, June 26, 1939; children: Harry Benson, Kimball Frederick, Robert Leonard. AB cum laude, Harvard U., 1937, AM, 1942. Tchr. Los Alamos (N.M.) Ranch Sch., 1937-42, head English dept., 1939-42; tchr. English Groton (Mass.) Sch., 1942-46; instr. English, faculty marshal Newton Jr. Coll., 1946-51; tchr. English and journalism Newton High Sch., Newtonville, Mass., 1946-51, adminstr., 1951-55; directing editor secondary sch. English textbooks Ginn and Co., Boston, 1955-61; prin. Needham (Mass.) High Sch., 1961-72, career and post secondary guidance counselor, 1972-79; Mem. Regional Interviewing Com. for Overseas Grants and Fellowships, 1961-84; mem. planning com. Task Force on High Sch. Graduation Requirements, Mass Dept. Edn., 1976-80. Author: (books) The Family Travel-Camper, 1955, (with E. Gordon and others) Types of Literature, American Literature, English Literature, 1964, The Memory Book of the New England Association of Teachers of English, 1981, The Sons of the American Revolution 1962-82: An Historical Anthology, 1984; (monographs) English Learning Environments, 1972, History of the Order of Founders and Patriots of America, 1982; co-author Alluring Rockport, rev. edit. 1986; editor The English Leaflet, 1947-54; cons. editor on career edn. New Voices Series, 1978; contbr. chpts., articles, poems to books, profl. jours. and periodicals. Alderman City of Newton, Mass., 1961-72; corp. mem. USS Mass Meml. Com., Inc., 1972—; bd. dirs., 1984-91, honorary

dir., 1995—; chmn. edn. com. N.E. Conf. NCCJ, 1972-82, mem. study mission to Israel, 1974; vice chmn. New Eng. Conf. on Quality of Life, Boston, 1973; mem. Newton Regional Adv. Manpower Planning Bd., 1973-77; pres. counseling svcs. YMCA, Greater Boston, 1976-7; chmn. Newton Highlands Bd. Christian Edn., 1974-75; pres. bd. trustees weekday ch. sch. 1st Congl. Ch., Rockport, Mass., ch. historian, 1982—; del. Mass. Conf. United Ch. Christ, 1989-94. John Hay fellow, 1965, Mass. Dept. Edn. Commonwealth fellow, 1971; recipient citation U.S. Commr. Edn., 1971, citation New Eng. Assn. Schs. and Colls., 1984, cert. of Appreciation, City of Newton, 1971, Service award, YMCA, 1978. Mem. Nat. Council Tchrs. English (assoc. chmn. nat. conv. 1965, chmn., co-founder Emeritus Assembly 1979-83, various other coms. and offices, Citation 1969), Nat. Assn. Secondary Sch. Prins., Headmasters Assn. (life), New Eng. Assn. Tchrs. English (life, past pres., chmn. am. C. S. Thomas award com. 1975—, historian 1978—, Thomas award 1978), Mass. Secondary Sch. Prins. Assn. (diploma standards com. 1973-78, Bronze plaque 1974), Mass. Council Tchrs. English (co-founder), Mass. Schoolmasters Club (past pres., hon. life), Mensa, Friends of Jackson Homestead, Newton Hist. Soc. (life, past pres.), Los Alamos (N.Mex.) Hist. Soc. (life), Sandy Bay Hist. Soc. (pres. 1983-86), Essex County Geneal. Soc., Greater Boston Guidance Club (hon.), Nat. Gavel Soc., New Eng. Hist. and Geneal. Soc., SAR (pres. state 1979-81, nat. trustee 1981-83, historian gen. 1983-86, sec. Mus. Bd. 1982-88, Minuteman award 1985), Gen. Soc. Mayflower Descs. (mem. nat. exec. com. 1990-93), Mass. Soc. Mayflower Descs. (gov. 1985-88, dep. gov. gen. 1988-93), Pilgrim John Howland Soc. (pres. 1987—, led pilgrimage to Eng., 1989), Mass. Huguenot Soc. (pres. 1990-92, nat. del. 1983-92), Descs. Colonial Clergy, Soc. Colonial Wars, Navy League U.S. (life), Sons and Daus. of 1st Settlers of Newbury (pres. 1982-84), Piscataqua Pioneers (pres. 1990-91), Order of Crown of Charlemagne, Order Founders and Patriots (nat. treas. 1978-81, dep. gov. gen. 1981-84, exec. com. 1992-94, councillor gen. Mass. 1984—, N.H., 1987-90, 93—, gov. 1992-93, 94—, councillor gen. 1993—), Boston Athenaeum, Harvard Club, Authors Club (v.p 1992—), Coll. Club, English Lunch Club (pres. 1975-82), Friday Evening Club (most venerable 1979-Bay Yacht Club, Masons (32d degree, 50-Yr. award). Home: Penzance Rd Rockport MA 01966

WALENTIK, CORINNE ANNE, pediatrician; b. Rockville Centre, N.Y., Nov. 24, 1949; d. Edward Robert and Evelyn Mary (Brinskele) Finno; m. David Stephen Walentik, June 24, 1972; children: Anne, Stephen, Kristine. AB with honors, St. Louis U., 1970, MD, 1974, MPH, 1992. Diplomate Am. Bd. Pediatrics, Am. Bd. Neonatal and Perinatal Medicine. Resident in pediatrics St. Louis U. Group Hosps., 1974-76, fellow in neonatalogy, 1976-78; neonatalogist St. Mary's Health Ctr., St. Louis, 1978-79; co-dir. neonatal unit St. Louis City Hosps., 1979-83, dir. neonatal unit, 1983-85; dir. neonatalogy St. Louis Regional Med. Ctr., 1985—; asst. prof. pediatrics St. Louis U., 1980-94, assoc. clin. prof., 1994—; supr. nursery follow up program Cardinal Glennon Children's Hosp., 1979—. Contbr. articles to profl. jours. Mem. adv. com. Mo. Perinatal Program, 1983-86. Fellow Am. Acad. Pediatrics; mem. Mo. Perinatal Assn. (pres. 1983), Nat. Perinatal Assn. (coun. 1984-87), Mo. State Med. Assn., St. Louis Met. Med. Soc. Roman Catholic. Avocations: bridge, baseball, sports. Home: 7234 Princeton Ave Saint Louis MO 63130-3027 Office: St Louis Regional Med Ctr 5535 Delmar Blvd Saint Louis MO 63112-3005

WALES, GWYNNE HUNTINGTON, lawyer; b. Evanston, Ill., Apr. 18, 1933; s. Robert Willett and Solace (Huntington) W.; m. Janet McCobb, Feb. 8, 1957; children—Thomas Gwynne, Catherine Anne, Louise Carrie. A.B., Princeton U., 1954; J.D., Harvard U., 1961. Bar: N.Y. 1962. Asso. White & Case, N.Y.C., 1961-69; partner White & Case, 1969—; resident partner White & Case, Brussels, 1969-75. Served with USN, 1954-58. Mem. ABA, N.Y. State Bar Assn., Am. Law Inst., Union Internat. des Avocats. Club: Round Hill (Greenwich, Conn.). Home: 16 Oakwood Ln Greenwich CT 06830-3909 Office: White & Case 1155 Ave Of The Americas New York NY 10036-2711

WALES, HAROLD WEBSTER, lawyer; b. Seattle, June 23, 1928; s. John Harold and Clara (Webster) W.; m. Dorothy C. Kotthoff, July 15, 1955; children—Elizabeth Marie, Mary Celine. B.C.S. cum laude, Seattle U., 1950; J.D., U. San Francisco, 1958. Bar: Calif. 1959, Ariz. 1959. Pvt. practice, Phoenix, 1959—; pres. Central Ariz. Estate Planning Council, 1964-65; lectr. Tax Inst., Ariz. State U., 1962, 64, Nat. Automobile Dealers Assn., 1975-76; lectr., income tax Scottsdale (Ariz.) Community Coll., 1971—. Pres. Cath. Social Svc., Phoenix, 1964; Ariz. chmn. Nat. Found. March of Dimes, 1969; bd. dirs. Camelback Hosp., 1984-90, ARC, Maricopa County, Cath. Family and Cmty. Svcs., 1960-86; mem. exec. com. Friends of Orphans, 1990. With USAF, 1950-54. Mem. ABA, Maricopa County bar assns., State Bar Calif., State Bar Ariz. (chmn. taxation sect. 1966-67), Am. Coll. Trust and Estate Counsel, Ariz. Acad., Order of Malta, We. Assn., Alpha Sigma Nu. Republican. Club: Serra of Phoenix (pres. 1964-65, 86-87). Lodge: Rotary of Scottsdale. Home: 3106 E Vermont Ave Phoenix AZ 85016-3717 Office: 3101 N Central Ave Ste 1500 Phoenix AZ 85012-2644

WALES, HUGH GREGORY, marketing educator, business executive; b. Topeka, Feb. 28, 1910; s. Raymond Otis and Nola V. (Chestnut) W.; m. Alice Fulkerson, June 11, 1938. A.B., Washburn Coll., 1932; M.B.A., Harvard U., 1934; Ph.D., Northwestern U., 1944; D.Sc., Washburn Municipal U., 1968. Dean men W. Mo. State Tchrs. Coll., 1935-38, dean students, head dept. econs., 1938-39; dean students, dir. summer sch., vets. bur., head dept. econs. Washburn U., 1939-46; assoc. prof. marketing U. Ill., 1946-53, prof., 1953-70, prof. emeritus, dir. micro-precision projects, 1970—; prof. marketing and mgmt., head dept. Roosevelt U., 1970-75; pres. Decisions, Evaluations & Learning, Internat. Assocs.; vis. prof. marketing U. South Africa, Pretoria, 1962; lectr. U. Stellenbosch, South Africa, 1973, 75, 76; cons. South African Govt., Pretoria, 1974; participant internat. confs.; bus., marketing research cons.; internat. pres. Micro-precision Miniaturization Inst., 1970—, dir., program chmn., Chgo., 1970—. Author: Changing Perspectives in Marketing, 1951, Marketing Research, 1952, 4th edit., 1974, Marketing Research-Selected Literature, 1952, Cases and Problems in Marketing Research, 1953, (with Robert Ferber) Basic Bibliography in Marketing Research, 1956, 3d edit., 1974, Motivation and Market Behavior, (with Ferber), 1958, Advertising Copy, Layout, and Typography, (with Gentry and M. Wales), 1958, (with R. Ferber) The Champaign-Urbana Metropolitan Area, (with Engel and Warshaw) Promotional Strategy, 1967, 3d edit., 1975, (with Dik Twedt and Lyndon Dawson) Personality Theory in Marketing Research: A Basic Bibliography, 1976, (with Sharon Abrams) English as a Second Language in Business, 1978, (with Luck, Taylor and Rubin) Marketing Research, 1978; numerous others, works transl. several langs.; contbr. (with Luck, Taylor and Rubin) articles to profl. jours. Pres. Civic Symphony Soc., 1964-65. Mem. Am. Econ. Assn., Am. Marketing Assn. (sec., acad. v.p.), Am. Watchmakers Inst. (dir. research and edn. 1963-66), Nat. Assn. Watch and Clock Collectors (chpt. pres. 1981, 83), Arizonans for Nat. Watch (chmn. visual aids com. 1979—), Internat. Alliance Theatrical Stage Employees and Moving Picture Machine Operators, Internat. Platform Assn., Internat. TV Assn., Assn. Edn. Internat. Bus., Soc. Internat. Devel., Am. Statis. Assn., Nat. Assn. for Mgmt. Educators., Acad. Mgmt. Home: 2625 E Southern Ave 208C Tempe AZ 85282-7631

WALES, SISTER PATRICE, school system administrator; b. Washington, Sept. 9, 1935; d. Robert Corning and Bernardette Mary (Dyer) W. BA, Dunbarton Coll. of Holy Cross, 1957; MTS, Cath. U. Am., 1978; PhD, U. Md., 1993. Cert. tchr., Md. Tchr. mid. sch. St. Marys, Laurel, Md., 1960-61; tchr. high sch. St. Vincent Pallotti High Sch., Laurel, Md., 1962-65; instr. nursing sch. St. Mary's Sch. Nursing, Huntington, W.Va., 1965-66; tchr. St. Vincent Pallotti High Sch., Laurel, 1967-76, adminstr., 1976—, chair sci. dept., 1962-80, dean students, 1976-87, sponsorship dir., 1988—; bd. dirs. St. Vincent Pallotti High Sch., Laurel, 1988—; dir. German Exch. Program, Laurel, Ahlen, Germany, 1976—. Senator Sisters Senate Archdiocese of Washington, 1993—. NSF grantee, 1967, 69, 71. Mem. ASCD, Nat. Cath. Edn. Assn. Roman Catholic. Avocations: choir singing, walking, hiking, biking. Home: 404 8th St Laurel MD 20707-4032 Office: St Vincent Pallotti High Sch 113 8th St Laurel MD 20707-4025

WALES, ROSS ELLIOT, lawyer; b. Youngstown, Ohio, Oct. 17, 1947; s. Craig C. and Beverly (Bromley) W.; m. Juliana Fraser, Sept. 16, 1972; children: Dod Elliot, James Craig. AB, Princeton U., 1969; JD, U. Va., 1974. Bar: Ohio 1974, U.S. Dist. Ct. (so. dist.) Ohio 1974, U.S. Ct. Appeals

(5th cir.) 1979. Assoc. Taft, Stettinius & Hollister, Cin., 1974-81, ptnr., 1981—; pres. U.S. Swimming, Inc., Colorado Springs, 1979-84, U.S. Aquatic Sports, Inc., Colorado Springs, 1984-88, 94—. Pres. Cin. Active to Support Edn., 1987-88; chair sch. tax levy campaign, Cin., 1987; trustee The Children's Home of Cin., 1987—, Cin. State Tech. and C.C., 1995—. With U.S. Army, 1970-72. Mem. ABA, Ohio Bar Assn., Cin. Bar Assn., Internat. Swimming Fed. (sec. 1988-92, v. p. 1992—). Presbyterian. Office: Taft Stettinius & Hollister 1800 Star Bank Ctr 425 Walnut St Cincinnati OH 45202

WALES, WALTER D., physicist, educator; b. Oneonta, N.Y., Aug. 2, 1933; s. Walter D. and Anna Laura (Brockway) W.; m. Margaret Irene Keiter, June 19, 1955; children: Stephen Dirk, Carolyn Sue. B.A., Carleton Coll., 1954; M.S., Calif. Inst. Tech., 1955, Ph.D., 1960. Instr. physics U. Pa., Phila., 1959-62, asst. prof., 1962-64, assoc. prof., 1964-72, prof., 1972—, chmn. dept. physics, 1973-82, assoc. dean, 1982-87, acting dean, 1987-88; assoc. dean U. Pa., 1988-92, dep. provost, 1992—; assoc. dir. Princeton-Pa. Accelerator, Princeton, N.J., 1968-71; staff physicist AEC, 1972-73. Fellow Am. Phys. Soc.; mem. Am. Assn. Physics Tchrs. Research in exptl. particle physics. Home: 404 Drew Ave Swarthmore PA 19081-2406 Office: 209 S 33rd St Philadelphia PA 19104

WALGREEN, CHARLES RUDOLPH, III, retail store executive; b. Chgo., Nov. 11, 1935; s. Charles Rudolph and Mary Ann (Leslie) W.; m. Kathleen Bonsignore Allen, Jan. 23, 1977; children: Charles Richard, Tad Alexander, Kevin Patrick, Leslie Ray, Chris Patrick; stepchildren—Carleton A. Allen Jr., Jorie L. Allen Grassie. B.S. in Pharmacy, U. Mich., 1958. With Walgreen Co., Chgo., 1952—, adminstrv. asst. to v.p. store ops., 1963-65, 65-66, dist. mgr., 1966-69, regional dir., 1968-69, v.p., pres., 1969-71, chief exec. officer, 1971-76, chmn., chief exec. officer, 1976—. Mem. bus. adv. coun. Chgo. Urban League.; bd. dirs. Jr. Achievement Chgo. Mem. Nat. Assn. Chain Drug Stores (bd. dirs.), Ill. Retail Mchts. Assn. (bd. dirs. 1966—), Am. Pharm. Assn., Ill. Pharm. Assn., Comml. Club of Chgo., Great Lakes Cruising Club, Exmoor Country Club (Highland Park, Ill.), Key Largo (Fla.) Anglers Club, Sailfish Point Club (Stuart, Fla.), Delta Sigma Phi. Office: Walgreen Co 200 Wilmot Rd Deerfield IL 60015-4620

WALHOUT, JUSTINE SIMON, chemistry educator; b. Aberdeen, S.D., Dec. 11, 1930; d. Otto August and Mabel Ida (Tews) W.; m. Donald Walhout, Feb. 1, 1958; children: Mark, Timothy, Lynne, Peter. BS, Wheaton Coll., 1952; PhD, Northwestern U., 1956. Instr. Wright City Community Coll., Chgo., 1955-56; asst. prof. Rockford (Ill.) Coll., 1956-59, assoc. prof., 1959-66, 81-89, prof., 1989—, dept. chmn., 1987—; cons. Pierce Chem. Co., Rockford, 1968-69; trustee Rockford (Ill.) Coll., 1987-91. Contbr. articles to profl. jours. Mem. Ill. Bd. Edn., 1974-81. Mem. Am. Chem. Soc., AAUW (Ill. bd. mem. 1985-87), Rockford LWV (bd. dirs. 1983-85), Sigma Xi. Presbyterian. Home: 320 N Rockford Ave Rockford IL 61107 Office: Rockford Coll 5050 E State St Rockford IL 61108-2393

WALI, MOHAN KISHEN, environmental science and natural resources educator; b. Kashmir, India, Mar. 1, 1937; came to U.S., 1969, naturalized, 1975; s. Jagan Nath and Somavati (Wattal) W.; m. Sarla Safaya, Sept. 25, 1960; children: Pamela, Promod. BS, U. Jammu and Kashmir, 1957; MS, U. Allahabad, India, 1960; PhD, U. B.C., Can., 1970. Lectr. S.P. Coll., Srinagar, Kashmir, 1963-65; rsch. fellow U. Copenhagen, 1965-66; grad. fellow U. B.C., 1967-69; asst. prof. biology U. N.D., Grand Forks, 1969-73, assoc. prof., 1973-79, prof., 1979-83, Hill rsch. prof., 1983, dir. Forest River Biology Area Field Sta., 1970-79, Project Reclamation, 1975-83, spl. asst. to univ. pres., 1977-82; staff ecologist Grand Forks Energy Rsch. Lab., U.S. Dept. Interior, 1974-75; prof. Coll. Environ. Sci. and Forestry, SUNY, Syracuse, 1983-89, dir. grad. program environ. sci., 1983-85; prof. Sch. Natural Resources, 1990—; dir. A. Sch. Nat. Resources, assoc. dean, Coll. Agr., 1990-93; vice chmn. N.D. Air Pollution Adv. Council, 1981-83; co-chair IV Internat. Congress on Ecology, 1986. Editor: Some Environmental Aspects of Strip-Mining in North Dakota, 1973, Prairie: A Multiple View, 1975, Practices and Problems of Land Reclamation in Western North America, 1975, Ecology and Coal Resource Development, 1979, Ecosystem Rehabilitation-Preamble to Sustainable Development, 1992; co-editor Agriculture and the Environment, 1993; sr. editor Reclamation Rev., 1976-80, chief editor, 1980-81; chief editor Reclamation and Revegetation Rsch., 1982-87; contbr. articles to profl. jours. Recipient B.C. Gamble Disting. Teaching and Svc. award, 1977. Fellow AAAS, Nat. Acad. Sci. India; mem. Ecol. Soc. Am. (chmn. sect. internat. activities 1980-84), Brit. Ecol. Soc., Can. Bot. Assn. (dir. ecology sect. 1976-79, v.p. 1982-83), Ohio Acad. Sci., Torrey Bot. Club, Am. Soc. Agronomy, Am. Inst. Biol. Sci. (gen. chmn. 34th ann. meeting), Internat. Assn. Ecology (co-chmn. IV Internat. Congress Ecology), Internat. Soc. Soil Sci., N.D. Acad. Sci. (chmn. editorial com. 1979-81), Sigma Xi (nat. lectr. 1983-85, pres. Ohio State chpt. 1993-94, pres. Syracuse chpt. 1985-88, Outstanding Rsch. award U. N.D. chpt. 1975). Office: Ohio State U Sch Natural Resources 2021 Coffey Rd Columbus OH 43210-1044

WALICKI, ANDRZEJ STANISLAW, history educator; b. Warsaw, Poland, May 15, 1930; came to U.S., 1986, naturalized 1993.; s. Michal Walicki and Anna (Szlachcinska) Chmielewska; m. Janina Derks, Mar. 10, 1953 (div. June 1970); m. Maria Wodzynska, June 17, 1972 (div. May 1985); children: Malgorzata, Adam; m. Marzena Balicka, July 27, 1985. MA, Warsaw U., 1953; PhD, Polish Acad. Scis., 1957. Asst. prof. Warsaw U., 1958-60; asst. prof. Polish Acad. Scis., Warsaw, 1960-64, assoc. prof., 1964-72, prof., head dept. Inst. Philosophy, 1972-81; sr. rsch. fellow Australian Nat. U., Canberra, 1981-86; O'Neill prof. history U. Notre Dame, Ind., 1986—; vis. Kratter prof. history Stanford U., 1976; vice chmn. Com. on Social Thought, Polish Hist. Assn., 1973-81. Author: The Slavophile Controversy, 1975, A History of Russian Thought, 1979, Philosophy and Romantic Nationalism, 1982, Legal Philosophies of Russian Liberalism, 1987, Marxism and the Leap to the Kingdom of Freedom: The Rise and Fall of the Communist Utopia, 1995; also 13 others. Recipient award A. Jurzykowski Found., N.Y.C., 1983; Rsch. grantee Ford Found., N.Y.C., 1960, vis. fellow All Souls Coll., U. Oxford, 1966-67, 73, Guggenheim fellow J.S. Guggenheim Meml. Found. 1991. Mem. Am. Hist. Assn., Am. Assn. for Advancement Slavic Studies, Polish Acad. Scis. Roman Catholic. Office: U Notre Dame Dept History Notre Dame IN 46556

WALINSKI, NICHOLAS JOSEPH, federal judge; b. Toledo, Nov. 29, 1920; s. Nicholas Joseph and Helen Barbara (Morkowski) W.; m. Vivian Melotti, June 26, 1954 (dec.); children: Marcianne, Barbara, Deanna and Donna (twins), Nicholas Joseph III (dec.). BS in Engring., U. Toledo, 1949, LLB, 1951. Bar: Ohio 1951. Law dir. Toledo, 1953; police prosecutor, 1953-58, mcpl. ct. judge, 1958-64, common pleas ct. judge, 1964-70; judge No. dist. Ohio Western div. U.S. Dist. Ct., Toledo, 1970—; sr. judge, 1985—. Capt. USNR, 1942-48. Recipient Disting. Alumnus award U. Toledo Coll. of Law, 1989, Disting. Alumnus award U. Toledo Law Alumni Assn. Mem. Toledo Bar Assn., Lucas County Bar Assn., Am. Legion, VFW, Cath. War Vets, Toledo Jr. Bar Assn. (Order of Heel 1970). Office: US Dist Ct 203 US Courthouse 1716 Spielbusch Ave Toledo OH 43624-1332

WALINSKY, LOUIS JOSEPH, economic consultant, author; b. London, Apr. 19, 1908; came to U.S., 1912; s. Ossip Joseph and Rose (Newman) W.; m. Michele Benson, 1936 (div. 1947); 1 child, Adam; m. Dorothy Monie; children—Marian, Louisa. B.A. in Econs. with honors, Cornell U., 1929; postgrad., U. Berlin, CCNY, New Sch. Social Research. Tchr. econs. N.Y.C. Bd. Edn., 1930-43; econ. cons. War Prodn. Bd., Washington, 1943-47; fin. dir. dir. Germany-Austria ops., sec.-gen. World ORT Union, N.Y.C., 1947-49; v.p. Robert Nathan Assocs., Washington, 1950-63; econ. cons. Washington and Cohasset, Mass., 1963—; exec. sec. combined pulp and paper com. Combined Raw Materials Bd., 1944-45; dir. office of econ. rev. and analysis Civilian Prodn. Adminstrn., 1946-47; mem. and/or leader econ. missions to Korea, Afghanistan, El Salvador, Brazil, East Africa, Israel, Iran, India, Bolivia, Venezuela, Newfoundland, Papua-New Guinea and P.R.; chief resident econ. advisor Govt. Burma, 1953-58; spl. advisor Asia Dept. World Bank, 1971-72; cons. OECD, 1978. Author: Heil Hitler!, 1936, (dramatization) Brave New World, 1939, Economic Development in Burma, 1962, Planning and Execution of Economic Development, 1963, (with others) Planning Economic Development, 1963, Man, State and Society in Contemporary Southeast Asia, 1969, Issues Facing World Jewry, 1981, Coherent Defense Strategy, 1982; editor: Unfinished Business of Land

Reform, 1977; contbr. articles to profl. jours., encyclopedias, jours. of opinion. Mem. nat. bd. Ams. for Dem. Action, Washington, 1950-51; dir. internat. commn. World Jewish Congress, N.Y.C., 1979-80; vice chmn. Am. Friends Democracy in Burma, 1991—. Avocations: golf; music; reading. Home and Office: 4000 Massachusetts Ave NW Washington DC 20016-5105

WALK, FRANK HUMPHREY, consulting engineer; b. Decatur, Ala., Aug. 30, 1920; s. Francis Albert and Laura Adeline (Humphrey) W.; m. Consuelo Faust, Sept. 6, 1947; children: Wendelyn, Karen, Frank Humphrey, Edmond Wade, Wesley Albert. B.S. in M.E., La. State U., 1942. Vice pres., chief engr. Dunham-Wilson Mfg. Co., Baton Rouge, 1946-52; mng. assoc. Wayne & Assos., New Orleans, 1953-58; pres. Walk, Haydel & Assocs., Inc., New Orleans, 1959—, also bd. dirs., now chmn. bd., chief exec. officer; bd. dirs. Walk-Haydel Devel. Co. Vice pres. Met. Area Council, 1976-78; chmn. New Orleans Image Devel. Com., 1979—, U. New Orleans Engring. Devel. Fund; chmn. bd. Econ. Devel. Council New Orleans Area, 1974-76, award of appreciation, 1976; mem. La. State Bd. Commerce and Industry, 1981-84, Mississippi River Commn., exec. com. Internat. Trade Mart of New Orleans, 1980, World Trade Ctr.; pres. The Chamber, New Orleans and River Region, 1980; mem. industry sect. Adv. Commn. Services for Trade Policy Matters for the U.S.; co-chmn. Met. Forum for Econ. Action, 1975—. Served as officer with C.E. U.S. Army, 1942-47. Fellow ASME (chmn. New Orleans sect. 1965, chmn. petroleum div. 1977-78), ASCE; mem. La. Engring. Soc. (Lockett award for pub. service 1977, Paterson award for mgmt. 1986), Soc. Am. Mil. Engrs. (Outstanding Service award 1972, Nat. Service award 1974, Morris award 1983, pres. La. post 1967, regional v.p. 1977-79), Am. Cons. Engrs. Council, Nat., Miss. socs. profl. engrs., Am. Petroleum Inst., Miss. Valley Coal Exporters Council (bd. dirs.), Cons. Engrs. Council La. (pres. 1974), C. of C. of New Orleans and the River Region (pres. 1980). Republican. Roman Catholic. Clubs: Boston, Plimsoll , City, Petroleum, Internat. House, Lakeshore, New Orleans Lawn Tennis, New Orleans Serra (pres. 1967) (New Orleans); Baton Rouge City, Camelot (Baton Rouge). Home: 1579 Henry Clay Ave New Orleans LA 70118-6151 Office: Walk Haydel & Assocs 600 Carondelet St New Orleans LA 70130-3511 *God has been on my side throughout my life. Any success that I have attained is attributed to Him and to the wonderful wife He gave me.**

WALK, RICHARD DAVID, retired psychology educator; b. Camp Dix, N.J., Sept. 25, 1920; s. Arthur Richard and Elsie (Roberts) W.; m. Lois MacDonald, Apr. 1, 1950; children: Joan MacDonald Scharf, Elizabeth Walk Robbins, Richard David Jr. AB, Princeton U., 1942; MA, U. Iowa, 1947; PhD, Harvard U., 1951. Research assoc. Human Resource Research Office, George Washington U., Washington, 1952-53, from assoc. prof. to prof., 1959-91; asst. prof. Cornell U., Ithaca, N.Y., 1953-59, prof. emeritus, 1991—; vis. prof. MIT, Cambridge, 1965-66, London Sch. Econs., U. London, 1981. Author: Perceptual Development, 1981; editor: (with H.L. Pick Jr.) Perception and Experience, 1978, Chinese edit., 1987, Intersensory Perception and Sensory Integration, 1981; contbr. articles to profl. jours., chpts. to books. Served to 1st lt. U.S. Army, 1942-45, ETO, 1951-52. Fellow AAAS, Am. Psychol. Soc.; mem. Am. Psychol. Assn., Soc. for Rsch. in Child Devel., Psychonomic Soc., Brit. Psychol. Assn. (fgn. assoc.), Sigma Xi, Vet. OSS. Democrat. Episcopalian. Club: Princeton Terrace (N.J.); Princeton, Harvard (Washington). Home: 7100 Oakridge Ave Chevy Chase MD 20815-5170

WALK, RONALD DOUGLAS, retail grocery chain executive; b. LaGrande, Oreg., June 8, 1943; s. Ronald Darrel and Elizabeth (Carter) W.; m. Sandra Anne Shields, June 5, 1966; children: Richard M., Julia M. B.S. in Social Sci., Eastern Oreg. State Coll., 1967; Exec. Program, Stanford U., 1987. Clk. Super Mart, LaGrande, 1960-61; with Albertson's Inc., 1962—; now sr. v.p., regional mgr. Albertson's Inc., Boise, Idaho. Home: 1283 E Braemere Rd Boise ID 83702-1853 Office: Albertson's Inc PO Box 20 Boise ID 83706

WALKE, DAVID MICHAEL, public relations executive; b. Mt. Vernon, N.Y., Dec. 30, 1954; s. Charles Philip and Elinor Mae (Denner) W.; m. Linda Susan Berkover, Nov. 26, 1978; children: Evan Matthew, Hilary Rose. BS in Acctg., Syracuse U., 1976. Account exec. Ecom Cons., Inc., N.Y.C., 1976-79, Anametrics, Inc., N.Y.C., 1979-81, Ruder, Finn & Rotman, Inc., N.Y.C., 1981-82; prin. Morgen-Walke Assocs., Inc., N.Y.C., 1982—. Mem. Nat. Investor Rels. Inst. Office: Morgen-Walke Assocs Inc 380 Lexington Ave New York NY 10168-0002

WALKEN, CHRISTOPHER, actor; b. Astoria, N.Y., Mar. 31, 1943; s. Paul W. Attended Hofstra U., studied with Wynn Handman, Actors Studio. Stage appearances include Broadway, off-Broadway and regional theatres throughout U.S. and Can.; Broadway debut in J.B. 1959; other stage appearances include Best Foot Forward, West Side Story, Macbeth, The Lion in Winter (Clarence Derwent award 1966), Hamlet, The Rose Tatoo (Theatre World's Most Promising Personality 1966-67), Romeo and Juliet, The Seagull, The Night Thoreau Spent in Jail (Joseph Jefferson award 1970-71), Kid Champion (Obie award 1975), Miss Julie, Sweet Bird of Youth, Hurlyburly, 1984, Cinders, 1984, A Bill of Divorcement, 1985, Coriolanus, 1988, Othello, 1992, (also playwright) Him, 1995; films include The Anderson Tapes, 1971, Next Stop Greenwich Village, The Sentinel, 1977, Roseland, 1977, Annie Hall, 1977, The Deer Hunter, 1978 (N.Y. Film Critics Best Supporting Actor award 1978, Acad. award best supporting actor 1979), Last Embrace, 1979, Dogs of War, 1981, Heavens Gate, 1980, Pennies From Heaven, 1981, The Happiness Cage, 1982, The Dead Zone, 1983, Brainstorm, 1983, A View to a Kill, 1984, At Close Range, 1986, Deadline, 1987, Puss in Boots, 1988, The Milagro Beanfield War, 1988, Biloxi Blues, 1988, Communion, 1989, King of New York, 1990, Homeboy, 1991, The Comfort of Strangers, 1991, McBain, 1991, All American Murder, 1992, Batman Returns, 1992, True Romance, 1993, A Business Affair, 1994, Wayne's World II, 1994, Pulp Fiction, 1994, Search and Destroy, 1995; TV films include Sarah, Plain and Tall, 1991, Skylark, 1993, Scam, 1993. Office: William Morris Agy 151 S El Camino Dr Beverly Hills CA 90212-2704*

WALKENBACH, RONALD JOSEPH, foundation executive, pharmacology educator; b. Hermann, Mo., Mar. 15, 1948; s. Walter Bernard and Lillian Ann (Ochsner) W.; m. Mary McLean Hodge, June 21, 1975 (div. July 1981); m. DeAnna Marie Roemer, Oct. 3, 1984. B.S. in Chemistry, Quincy Coll., Ill., 1970; Ph.D. in Pharmacology, U. Mo., Columbia, 1975. Postdoctoral fellow U. Va., Charlottesville, 1975-77; postdoctoral fellow U. Mo., Columbia, 1977-78; lab. investigator Eye Research Found., Columbia, 1978-81, exec. dir., 1981—. Contbr. research articles to profl. jours. Troop coordinator Boy Scouts Am., Columbia, 1985. Research grantee Nat. Eye Inst., NIH, 1978—. Mem. AAAS, Assn. Research in Vision and Ophthalmology. Roman Catholic. Lodge: Lions (2d v.p. 1985). Avocations: hunting, fishing, skiing, hiking, woodworking. Office: Eye Research Found Mo Inc 404 Portland St Columbia MO 65201-6506

WALKER, A. HARRIS, lawyer, manufacturing executive; b. Lincoln, Ill., Feb. 7, 1935; s. Arthur M. and Margaret (Harris) W.; m. Ann Pontious, Aug. 27, 1960; children: Christine, Stuart, Melinda. BA, Northwestern U., 1956; JD, U. Mich., 1963; MBA, U. Chgo., 1969. Bar: Ill. 1963, U.S. Dist. Ct. (no. dist.) Ill. 1964, U.S. Ct. Appeals (7th cir.) 1963. Assoc. Peterson, Lowry, Rall, Barber & Ross, Chgo., 1963-66; atty. Am. Hosp. Supply Co., Evanston, Ill., 1966-71; sr. atty. A.B. Dick Co., Chgo., 1971-74, asst. gen. counsel, 1974-86, v.p., gen. counsel, sec., 1986—, also bd. dirs., officer of various subs. Presbyterian. Office: AB Dick Co 5700 W Touhy Ave Niles IL 60714-4628

WALKER, ALICE MALSENIOR, author; b. Eatonton, Ga., Feb. 9, 1944; d. Willie Lee and Minnie (Grant) W.; m. Melvyn R. Leventhal, Mar. 17, 1967 (div. 1976); 1 dau., Rebecca Walker Leventhal. BA, Sarah Lawrence Coll., 1966; PhD (hon.), Russell Sage U., 1972; DHL (hon.), U. Mass., 1983. Co-founder, pub. Wild Trees Pr., Navarro, Calif., 1984-88; writer in residence, tchr. black studies Jackson State Coll., 1968-69, Tougaloo Coll., 1970-71; lectr. literature Wellesley Coll., 1972-73, U. Mass., Boston, 1972-73; disting. writer Afro-American studies dept. U. Calif., Berkeley, 1982; Fannie Hurst Prof. of Literature Brandeis U., Waltham, Mass., 1982; cons. Friends of the Children of Miss., 1967. Author: Once, 1968, The Third Life of Grange Copeland, 1970, Five Poems, 1972, Revolutionary Petunias and Other Poems, 1973 (Nat. Book award nomination 1973, Lillian Smith award So. Regional Coun. 1973), In Love and Trouble, 1973 (Richard and Hinda Rosenthal Found. award Am. Acad. and Inst. of Arts and Letters 1974)

Langston Hughes: American Poet, 1973, Meridian, 1976, Goodnight, Willie Lee, I'll See You in the Morning, 1979, You Can't Keep a Good Woman Down, 1981, The Color Purple, 1982 (Nat. Book Critics Circle award nomination 1982, Pulitzer Prize for fiction 1983, Am. Book award 1983), In Search of Our Mothers' Gardens, 1983, Horses Make a Landscape Look More Beautiful, 1984, To Hell With Dying, 1988, Living By the Word: Selected Writings, 1973-1987, 1988, The Temple of My Familiar, 1989, Her Blue Body Everything We Know: Earthling Poems, 1965-1990, 1991, Finding the Green Stone, 1991, Possessing the Secret of Joy, 1992, (with Pratibha Parmar) Warrior Marks, 1993, (with others) Double Stitch: Black Women Write about Mothers & Daughters, 1993, Everyday Use, 1994; editor: I Love Myself When I'm Laughing... And Then Again When I'm Looking Mean and Impressive, 1979. Recipient first prize Am. Scholar essay contest, 1967, O. Henry award for "Kindred Spirits", 1986, Nora Astorga Leadership award, 1989, Fred Cody award for lifetime achievement Bay Area Book Reviewers Assn., 1990, Freedom to Write award PEN Ctr. USA West, 1990; Bread Loaf Writer's Conf. scholar, 1966; Merrill writing fellowship, 1967; McDowell Colony fellowship, 1967, 77-78; National Endowment for the Arts grantee, 1969, 77; Radcliffe Inst. fellowship, 1971-73; Guggenheim fellow, 1977-78. Address: care Harcourt Brace 111 Fifth Ave New York NY 10003*

WALKER, ARTHUR LONZO, religious organization administrator; b. Birmingham, Ala., Apr. 10, 1926; s. Arthur Lonzo and Nannie Agnes (Bynum) W.; m. Gladys Evelyn Walker, Aug. 4, 1949; children: Marcia Lea Hamby, Gregory Arthur. BA, Samford U., 1949; MDiv, So. Bapt. Theol. Sem., 1952; ThD, New Orleans Bapt. Theol. Sem., 1956; LHD (hon.), Campbell U., 1984; HHD (hon.), Houston Bapt. U., 1985. Prof. theology Samford U., Birmingham, 1956-76, v.p. student affairs, 1965-68, v.p. adminstrv. affairs, 1968-73; v.p. student affairs So. Bapt. Theol. Sem., Louisville, 1976-78; exec. dir. edn. commn. So. Bapt. Conv., Nashville, 1978—; sec.-treas. So. Bapt. Commn. Am. Bapt. Theol. Sem., Nashville, 1978—; mem. adv. bd. Ctr. for Constl. Studies, Macon, Ga., 1978-90; mem. nat. adv. coun. J.M. Dawson Inst. of Ch. State Studies, Waco, Tex., 1990—. Author: By Their Fruits, 1982; editor: Educating For Christian Missions, 1981, Directory of Southern Baptist Colleges, 1986; (jour.) The Southern Baptist Educator, 1978—. Pres. Birmingham Council of Christian Edn., 1970-71. Served as sgt. U.S. Army, 1944-46, PTO. Mem. Nat. Assn. Ind. Colls. and Univs. (bd. dirs. 1987-91). Office: Assn So Baptist Colls 901 Commerce St Ste 750 Nashville TN 37203-3629

WALKER, BAILUS, JR., environmental scientist, dean, health facility administrator. MPH, U. Mich., 1959, PhD in Occupl. and Environ. Health, 1975. Environ. health scientist, adminstr. Environ. Health Svc., Washington, 1972-79; dir. occupl. health standard U.S. Dept. Labor, 1979-81; commr. pub. health Commonwealth Mass., 1983-87; toxicologist Sch. Pub. Health SUNY, Albany, 1987-90; prof. dept. occupl. and environ. health, dean coll. pub. health U. Okla. Health Sci. Ctr., 1990—; head U.S. Exch. Mission to Japan, collaborator U.S.-Japanese efforts in occupl. medicine, 1980; mem Physicians Human Rights Mission, South Korea, 1987, Mozambique Health Assessment Mission, 1988, Sec.'s Coun. Health Prom & Dis Prev U.S. Dept. Health & Human Svc., Commn. Study Future Pub. Health U.S. NAS. Fellow Royal Soc. Health; mem. Inst. Medicine NAS. Research in physical, chemical, and biological hazards in macroenvironments. Office: College of Public Health U of OK Health Sciences Center PO Box 26901 # U Oklahoma City OK 73190*

WALKER, BETSY ELLEN, computer products and services company executive; b. Atlanta, Sept. 14, 1953; d. John Franklin and Betty Louise (Brown) W. BA summa cum laude, Duke U., 1974; MBA, Harvard U., 1978. Mgmt. trainee, First Atlanta, 1974, officer, 1975-76; analyst Coca Cola, Atlanta, 1977; bus. analyst Am. Mgmt. Systems Inc., N.Y.C., 1978-80, prin., 1981, v.p., 1982—, dir. fin. svcs. group, 1982-90, IBM Svcs. sector group, 1990-92, fin. strategic initiatives group, 1993, fin. industry Strategic Alliance Group, 1994—; mem. mgmt. policy com. Am. Mgmt. Systems, 1988—, mem. corporate operating group. J. Spenser Love fellow Harvard U., 1976-78. Mem. Alexandria North Ridge Citizens Assn. (exec. bd.), Phi Beta Kappa, Pi Mu Epsilon (treas. 1990-91, bd. mgrs. Madison Green 1990-91), Harvard Bus. Sch. Club, Downtown Athletic Club (N.Y.C.). Office: Am Mgmt Systems Inc 4050 Legato Rd Fairfax VA 22033-4003

WALKER, BILLY KENNETH, computer science educator, academic administrator; b. Canyon, Tex., June 17, 1946; m. Anita Marie Ransdell, Mar. 8, 1980. BS in Math., West Tex. State U., 1968, postgrad., 1974, 77; postgrad., U. Utah, 1969; MS in Math., Tex. Tech U., 1970, PhD in Math., 1974. Teaching fellow in math. U. Utah, Salt Lake City, 1968-69; teaching asst. in math. Tex. Tech U., Lubbock, 1969-70, part-time instr. math., 1970-74, adj. prof. elec. engring., 1979-83; instr. sci., physics and math. Carver Learning Ctr., Amarillo, Tex., 1974-76; instr. computer info. systems West Tex. State U., Canyon, 1976-77, acting head dept. computer info. system, 1977; asst. prof. computer info. system Amarillo Coll., 1977-79; asst. prof. elec. engring. and computer sci. U. Okla., Norman, 1979-83; assoc. prof. computer sci. East Okla. State U., Ada, 1983-87; prof. and chmn. dept. computer sci. East Cen. U., Ada, 1983—; mem. engring. computer network user's com. computer sci. U. Okla., Ada, chmn. convocation com. Coll. Engring.; cons. Amstar Corp., Dimmit, Tex., Silverman and Silverman, Attys. at Law, Hutchinson County Mus., City of Amarillo, City of Cushing, Okla., Southwestern Bell Telephone Co., U.S. Armu Corps Engrs.; researcher in field. Author: A Structured Approach to Pascal, 1983, Essentials of Pascal, 1984, Modula-2 Programming with Data Structures, 1986; editorial reviewer Math. Revs., Ann ARbor, Mich., Apple Edn. Found., Cupertino, Calif., Army; contbr. numerous articles to profl. jours. NSF fellow U. Utah, 1969. Mem. IEEE (sr.), Am. Math. Soc., Assn. for Computing Machinery, Math. Assn. Am., Am. Indian Sci. and Engring. Soc., Okla. Acad. Sci. (vice-chmn. computer sci. section 1987, 89, chmn. computer sci. section 1988, mem. exec. com. 1987-88-89), Am. Radio Relay League, Comanche War Dance Soc., Comanche Gourd Clan, Lone Star War Dance Soc., Masons, Order Eastern Star, Pi Mu Epsilon, Kappa Mu Epsilon, Alpha Chi. Home: PO Box 2107 Ada OK 74821-2107 Office: East Cen U Dept Computer Sci Ada OK 74820-6899

WALKER, BRADFORD C., architect. BS in Architecture, U. Va., 1982; MArch, Harvard U., 1985. Registered arch., Mass.; cert. Nat. Coun. Archtl. Registration Bd. Sr. assoc. Peter Forbes & Assocs., Inc., Boston, 1985—; mem. design studio faculty Boston Archtl. Ctr., 1984, 85, 86, mem. design theory faculty, 1987; mem. faculty architecture Roger Williams Coll., Bristol, R.I., 1988; mem. design studio faculty RISD, Providence, 1989; critic core curriculum Harvard U., Cambridge, Mass., 1992. Contbr. articles to profl. jours. Recipient Spl. award for unbuilt architecture Boston Soc. Archs., 1991, Interior Architecture Excellence award, 1992, Sustainable Design award, 1993, Silver award Indsl. Designers Soc. Am., 1993. Mem. AIA (Design award New Eng. Regional Coun. 1991, Excellence Interior Architecture award 1993). Office: Peter Forbes & Assoc Inc 69 Union St Newton Center MA 02159-2224

WALKER, BRIGITTE MARIA, translator, linguistic consultant; b. Stolp, Germany, Sept. 20, 1934; came to U.S., 1957; d. Joseph Karl and Ursula Maria Margot Ehrler; m. John V. Walker (div.); 1 child, John V. Jr.; m. Edward D. Walker, July 3, 1977. Grad., Erlangen Translator's Sch., Germany, 1956; grad. fgn. corres., Berlitz Sch., Germany, 1956. Bilingual sec., translator Spencer Patent Law Office, Washington, 1959-62; office mgr., translator I. William Millen, Millen and White, Patent Law, Washington, 1962-67; prin. Tech. Translating Bur., Washington, 1967-68, St. Petersburg Beach, Fla., 1968—; cons. for patent law offices, Washington, 1962—; ofcl. expert for ct. Paul M. Craig, Patent Atty., Rockford, Ill., 1981; cons. to sci. editor Merriam-Webster, Inc., Springfield, Mass., 1987—. Author: German-English/English-German Last-Resort Dictionary for Technical Translators, 1991, (poetry) The Other Side of the Mirror, 1992 (Poetry award Nat. League Am. Pen Women 1994); co-translator: The Many Faces of Research, 1980; holder of trademark in field. Evaluator fgn. textbooks Pinellas County Sch. Bd., St. Petersburg, 1987, German judge, 1988. Recognized for support of pub. edn. Pinellas County Sch. Bd., 1988; recipient Mentions Public Svc. award City of St. Petersburg Beach, 1987, Poetry award Nat. Leage Am. Pen Women, 1994. Mem. Mensa. Democrat. Lutheran. Avocations: swimming, aerobics, piano, painting. Home and Office: 7150 Sunset Way Apt 1007 Saint Petersburg FL 33706-3650

WALKER, BRUCE EDWARD, anatomy educator; b. Montreal, Que., Can., June 17, 1926; s. Robinson Clarence and Dorothea Winston (Brown) W.; m. Lois Catherine McCuaig, June 26, 1948; children—Brian Ross, Dianne Heather, Donald Robert, Susan Lois. B.S., McGill U., 1947, M.S., 1952, Ph.D., 1954; M.D., U. Tex. at Galveston, 1966. Instr. anatomy McGill U., 1955-57; asst. prof. anatomy U. Tex. Med. Br., 1957-61, assoc. prof. anatomy, 1961-67; prof. Mich. State U., East Lansing, 1967—; chmn. dept., 1967-75. Contbr. articles to profl. jours. Mem. Am. Assn. Anatomists, Teratology Soc., Am. Assn. for Cancer Research. Office: Mich State U Anatomy Dept East Lansing MI 48824

WALKER, CHARLES ALLEN, chemical engineer, educator; b. Wise County, Tex., June 18, 1914; s. Jackson Lamar and Eula (Hamilton) W.; m. Bernice Rolf, Dec. 24, 1942; children: Allen Rolf, John Lamar, Laurence Gordon. BS, U. Tex., 1938, MS, 1940; DEng, Yale U., 1948. Mem. faculty Yale U., New Haven, 1942-84, prof. chem. engring., 1956-84, master Berkeley Coll., 1959-69, chmn. dept. engring. and applied sci., 1974-76, Raymond John Wean prof., 1979-84, prof. emeritus, 1984—, chmn. dept. chem. engring., 1981-84; mem. staff Yale Inst. for Social and Policy Studies, 1970-84; cons. chem. engr., 1942—. Bd. dirs. Conn. Fund for the Environ., 1978-86. Fellow AAAS; mem. AICE, Sci. Rsch. Soc. Am. (past nat. dir., treas. 1968-73), Am. Chem. Soc. (petroleum rsch. fund adv. bd. 1976-80, chmn. 1972-81), Am. Soc. Engring. Edn., Conn. Acad. Sci. and Engring., Conn. Acad. Arts and Scis., Yale Club, Phi Beta Kappa (hon.), Sigma Xi (bd. dirs. 1976-78), Tau Beta Pi, Phi Lambda Upsilon. Home: 1155 Whitney Ave Hamden CT 06517-3434

WALKER, CHARLES B., chemicals company executive; b. 1939. Attended, Univ. of Richmond, Richmond, VA, 1961. With Southern States Co-Op, Inc., 1961-64, Albemarle Paper Mfg. Co., 1965-68; pres. Spotless Stores, Richmond, Va., 1969-74; with State Comp. State of Va., 1974-81, sec. adminstrn. and fin., 1978; v.p. Ethyl Corp., Richmond, 1981—; now CFO, vice chmn., tng. dir. Ethyl Corp, Richmond. Office: Ethyl Corp 330 S 4th St Richmond VA 23219-4304

WALKER, CHARLES DODSLEY, conductor, organist; b. N.Y.C., Mar. 16, 1920; s. Marshall Starr and Maude Graham (Marriott) W.; m. Janet Elizabeth Hayes, May 30, 1949; children: Peter Hayes, Susan Starr. BS, Trinity Coll., 1940; AM, Harvard U., 1947. Organist, choirmaster Am. Cathedral, Paris, 1948-50, Ch. of the Heavenly Rest, N.Y.C., 1951-88; music dir. Blue Hill Troupe, Ltd., N.Y.C., 1955-90, The Chapin Sch., N.Y.C., 1961-85; mem. organ faculty Union Theol. Sem., N.Y.C., 1962-73, NYU, 1968-80; dean, music dir. Berkshire Choral Inst., Sheffield, Mass., 1982-91; organist, choirmaster Trinity Episcopal Ch., Southport, Conn., 1988—. Contbr. articles to profl. jours. Lt. comdr. USNR, 1942-46. Recipient Disting. Alumnus award Cathedral Choir Sch., 1988. Fellow Am. Guild of Organists (nat. pres. 1971-75); mem. Am. Fedn. of Musicians, Canterbury Choral Soc. (founder, conductor 1952—), Saint Wilfrid Club, The Bohemians. Avocations: travel, photography. Home: 160 W 96th St Apt 15N New York NY 10025-9212 Office: Trinity Episcopal Ch 651 Pequot Ave Southport CT 06490-1416

WALKER, CHARLES MONTGOMERY, lawyer; b. St. Louis, Sept. 30, 1915; s. Charles J. and Gertrude (Zoll) W.; m. Gertrude E. Acton, Apr. 30, 1943. A.B., U. Mo., 1937, LL.B., 1939. Bar: Mo. 1939, Calif. 1941, D.C. 1977. Practiced law Los Angeles, 1941—; mem. Brady, Nossaman & Walker, 1941-62; partner Paul, Hastings, Janofsky & Walker, 1962-75, 77-81, counsel, 1981—; asst. sec. treasury for tax policy Washington, 1975-77. Served with AUS, 1942-46. Decorated Bronze Star. Fellow Am. Bar Found., Am. Coll. Tax Counsel (bd. regents 1987-93), Am. Bar Retirement Assn. (bd. dirs.,pres. 1986), Am. Tax Policy Inst. (trustee, pres. 1990-93); mem. ABA (chmn. taxation sect. 1979-80, coms.), L.A. Bar Assn., Am. Law Inst., Am. Judicature Soc., State Bar Calif., Order of Coif, L.A. Country Club, Chevy Chase Club, Metropolitan Club, Sigma Chi. Home: 9255 Doheny Rd West Hollywood CA 90069-3201 Office: 1299 Ocean Ave Santa Monica CA 90401-1038

WALKER, CHARLES NORMAN, retired insurance company executive; b. Buchanan, Mich., Mar. 8, 1923; s. Leland Seymour and Beatrice (Fairchild) W.; m. Rosemary McElwee, Aug. 21, 1919 (dec.); children: James Charles, Christopher Hugh. Student, Western Mich. U., 1939-41; B.S., U. Mich., 1945, M.A., 1947. With Lincoln Nat. Life Ins. Co., Ft. Wayne, Ind., 1947-75; asst. v.p., mgr. accident and sickness Lincoln Nat. Life Ins. Co., 1957-60, 2d v.p., 1960-64, v.p., 1964-75; v.p. selection and issue New Eng. Mut. Life Ins. Co., Boston, 1975-83. Served to 1st lt. USAF, 1943-46. Fellow Soc. Actuaries; mem. Am. Acad. Actuaries. Episcopalian. Home: 506 Mill Rd Woodstock VA 22664

WALKER, CHARLES R., III, lawyer; b. Concord, N.H., Mar. 16, 1930; s. Charles R. and Adelaide (George) W.; children—Charlotte, Matthew, Timothy. BA, Yale U., 1951, LLB, 1954. Bar: N.Y. 1956. Mem. firm Lord Day & Lord, Barrett Smith, N.Y.C., 1956-94, Rogan, Lewis & Bockius, N.Y.C., 1994—. Served with U.S. Army, 1954-56. Mem. ABA, N.Y. State Bar Assn., Assn. of Bar of City of N.Y. Office: Morgan Lewis & Bockius 101 Park Ave New York NY 10178

WALKER, CHARLES THOMAS, physicist, educator; b. Chgo., Sept. 5, 1932; s. Charles William and Velma Rose (Reich) W.; m. Alice Ann Pawlak, Dec. 26, 1953 (div. 1973); children: David John, Valerie Anne, Carolyn Marie; m. Carrie Anna Ramsey, Sept. 14, 1973. A.B. in Math., U. Louisville, 1956, M.S. in Physics, 1958; PH.D. in Physics, Brown U., 1961. Research assoc Cornell U., Ithaca, N.Y., 1961-63; asst. prof. Northwestern U., Evanston, Ill., 1963-67, assoc. prof., 1967-71; prof. physics Ariz. State U., Tempe, 1971-85, chmn. dept., 1981-85; corp. scientist 3M Co./Photonics Rsch. Lab., St. Paul, 1985—; cons. U.S. Dept. Def., Washington, 1966-71, Coronet Films, Chgo., 1969-71, Motorola, Inc., Phoenix, 1974-78. Contbr. articles to profl. jours. Served to sgt. U.S. Army, 1953-55. Guggenheim Found. fellow, 1967-68; Alexander von Humboldt Found. sr. U.S. scientist, 1978-79. Fellow Am. Phys. Soc.; mem. AAAS, Optical Soc. Am. Home: 163 Riverview Acres Rd Hudson WI 54016-6753 Office: 3M Co/Photonics Rsch Lab Corp Rsch Lab 3M Center 201-2S-05 Saint Paul MN 55144-1000

WALKER, CHARLES URMSTON, retired university president; b. Bolivar, Pa., June 20, 1931; s. Charles William and Frances May (Urmston) W.; m. Cherie Hall Duckworth, Aug. 7, 1959; children: Douglas Leland, Christy Lynn. BA, U. Pitts., 1953; MA, Columbia U., 1958; PhD, Stanford U., 1964; LLD (hon.), Kanto Gakuin U., 1979; LHD (hon.), Linfield Coll., 1992. Asst. prof. English Rockford (Ill.) Coll., 1958-61; dept. head, residence dir. Menlo Coll., Menlo Park, Calif., 1961-64; v.p., dean Hamline U., St. Paul, 1964-70; pres. Russell Sage Coll., Troy, N.Y., 1970-75; pres. Linfield Coll., McMinnville, Oreg., 1975-92, pres. emeritus, 1992—; ednl. cons., 1992—; dir. Ford scholar program Ford Family Found., Roseburg, Oreg., 1994—; bd. dirs. 1st Fed. Savs. & Loan, McMinnville, Wespro Ins. Co., Oreg. Mut. Ins. Co.; mem. Univ. Pres. Initiative, IIE/USIA/NATO, Brussels, 1991. Mem. men's com. Internat. Christian U. Found., Japan; bd. overseers World Affairs Coun. Oreg.; bd. dirs., pres. Hillside Manor, McMinnville, 1990; bd. dirs. South Tillamook County Libr., 1994, McMinnville Indsl. Promotions, 1993, Oreg. Bapt. Found., Portland Oreg., Oregon Trail chpt. ARC, Portland, Coll. and Univ. Partnership Program, Memphis; pres. Neskowin (Oreg.) Chamber Music. Warg scholar U. Pitts., 1949-51; Univ. fellow Stanford U., 1963-64; Hill Found. grantee, St. Paul, 1970; Paul Harris fellow Rotary Internat., 1987; recipient Community Svc. award Troy, N.Y., 1975, First Citizen award McMinnville, Oreg., 1989; named Man of Yr., Troy C. of C., 1975. Mem. Rotary Club (Portland), Rotary (past pres. McMinnville). Home: 1324 Gilorr St Mcminnville OR 97128-6617

WALKER, CHARLS EDWARD, economist, consultant; b. Graham, Tex., Dec. 24, 1923; s. Pinkney Clay and Sammye D. (McCombs) W.; m. Harmolyn Hart, June 24, 1949; children: Carolyn, Charls Edward. B.B.A., U. Tex., 1947, M.B.A., 1948; Ph.D. in Econs, U. Pa., 1955. Instr. finance U. Tex., 1947-48, asst., then assoc. prof., 1950-54; instr. finance U. Pa. Wharton Sch., 1948-50; fin. economist Fed. Res. Bank Phila., 1953; with Fed. Res. Bank Dallas, 1954-61, v.p., econ. adviser, 1958-61; economist Republic Nat. Bank Dallas, 1955-56; asst. to sec. treasury, 1959-61; exec. v.p. Am. Bankers Assn., N.Y.C., 1961-69; under sec. treasury, 1969-72, dep. sec., 1972-73;

chmn. Walker/Potter Assocs., Washington, 1973—; adj. prof. fin. and pub. affairs U. Tex., Austin, 1986—; bd. dirs. Enron Corp., Potomac Electric Power Co., Washington Campus. Co-editor: The Bankers Handbook, New Directions in Federal Tax Policy, The Consumption Tax: A Better Alternative, 1987, Intellectual Property Rights and Capital Formation, 1988, The U.S. Savings Challenge, 1990; contbr. articles to profl. jours. and newspapers, chpts. to books. Founder and chmn. Am. Coun. for Capital Formation; co-founder Com. on the Present Danger, chmn. Pres.'s adv. coun. on minority enterprise, 1973-75; co-founder and co-chmn. Presdl. Debates, 1976; co-chmn. Bretton Woods Com.; chmn. Ronald Reagan's Task Force on Tax Policy, 1980. Recipient Alexander Hamilton award U.S. Treasury Dept., award Urban League; named Disting. Alumnus U. Tex., 1994. Mem. Coun. Fgn. Rels., Burning Tree Club, Congressional Club (Bethesda, Md.), The Hills of Lakeway Club (Austin, Tex.). Home: 10120 Chapel Rd Potomac MD 20854-4143 Office: Walker/Potter Assocs 1730 Pennsylvania Ave NW Washington DC 20006-4706 *What's good for the public interest ultimately is good for every person, business, or other group in the nation. This, combined with modern application of the Golden Rule, about sums it up.*

WALKER, CLARENCE EUGENE, psychology educator; b. Monongahela, Pa., Jan. 8, 1939; s. Lewis G. Walker and Olga T. Brioli; divorced; children: Chad Eugene, Kyle Lewis, Cass Emanuel. BS in Psychology summa cum laude, Geneva Coll., 1960; MS in Clin. Psychology, Purdue U., 1963, PhD in Clin. Psychology, 1965. Lic. psychologist, Okla. Asst. prof. Westmont Coll., 1964-68; from asst. prof. to assoc. prof. Baylor U., 1968-74; pvt. practice clin. psychology Waco, Tex., 1970-74; assoc. prof. med. sch. U. Okla., Oklahoma City, 1974-80; chief pediatric psychology svc. Okla. Children's Meml. Hosp., 1974-80, dir. out-patient pediatric psychology clinic, 1974-80; prof. med. sch., dir. pediatric psychology tng. program U. Okla., Oklahoma City, 1980—; assoc. chief mental health svcs. Children's Hosp. Okla., 1980—; intern clin. psychology Riley Children's Hosp., West 10th St. VA Hosp., Indpls., 1963-64; psychology trainee West 10th St. VA Hosp., Indpls., 1963; cons. Head Start Program, Waco, 1968-70, VA Hosp., Waco, 1969-74, VA Ctr., Temple, Tex., 1969-74, Region XII Ednl. Svc. Ctr., Waco, 1971-74, Rusk (Tex.) State Hosp., 1972-74, Bapt. Children's Home, Oklahoma City, 1975-79; rsch. cons. Los Alamos (N.Mex.) Pub. Schs., 1975-79; chmn. div. ednl. and psychology Westmont Coll., 1966-68. Author: Learn to Relax, 1975, 2d edit., 1991, (with P. Clement, A. Hedberg, L. Wright) Clinical Procedures for Behavior Therapy, 1981, (with B.L. Bonner, K. Kaurman) The Physically and Sexually Abused Child, 1988, others; editor: The History of Clinical Psychology in Autobiography, Vol. I, 1992, Vol. II, 1993, (with M.C. Roberts) Handbook of Clinical Child Psychology, 1992; contbr. articles to profl. jours. Pres. Okla. Psychol. Assn., 1983, Soc. Pediatric Psychology, 1986, Cen. Tex. Psychol. Assn., 1973. Fellow APA; mem. AAAS, Southwestern Psychol. Assn. (pres. 1977), Okla. Psychol. Assn., Sigma Xi. Avocations: reading, wine tasting, travel. Office: U Okla Med Sch Po Box 26901 920 S L Young Blvd Oklahoma City OK 73190

WALKER, CLARENCE WESLEY, lawyer; b. Durham, N.C., July 19, 1931; s. Ernie Franklin and Mollie Elizabeth (Cole) W.; m. Ann-Heath Harris, June 5, 1954; children: Clare Ann, Wesley Gregg. A.B., Duke U., 1953, LL.B. 1955. Bar: N.C. 1955. Assoc Mudge Stern Baldwin & Todd, 1955-59; ptnr. Kennedy, Covington, Loddell & Hickman, Charlotte, N.C., 1959—; bd. dirs. Lawyers Mut. Liability Ins. Co., Legal Services Corp. N.C., Oakwood Home Corp. Glendale Hosiery Co.; lectr. N.C. Bar Found. Continuing Legal Edn. Insts., N.C. Jud. Planning Com., 1978-79; pres. Pvt. Adjudication Found. Chmn. bd. mgrs. Charlotte Meml. Hosp. and Med. Ctr., 1981-87; trustee N.C. Central U., 1979-83; vice-chmn. Charlotte-Mecklenburg Hosp. Authority; adv. bd. Central Piedmont Paralegal Sch.; trustee Charlotte Country Day Sch., 1977-81; state chmn. Nat. Found. March of Dimes, 1968-70; chmn. Charlotte Park and Recreation Commn., 1970-73; bd. dirs. Charlotte Symphony, 1965-71, Bethlehem Ctr., 1975-77, N.C. Recreators Found., 1973-75; adv. bd. Charlotte Children's Theater, 1972; bd. dirs. Charlotte C. of C., 1970-72; bd. visitors Duke U. Law Sch.; dir., gen. campaign chmn. United Way Cen. Carolinas, 1985. Fellow Am. Bar Found.; mem. N.C. Bar Assn. (pres. 1978-79, gov. 1971-75), ABA (state del. 1980-89), assembly del. 26th Jud. Dist. Bar Assn., 1989—; Mecklenburg Bar Found. (trustee), Am. Law Inst., Order of Coif, Phi Eta Sigma, Phi Beta Kappa. Democrat. Methodist. Home: 1047 Ardsley Rd Charlotte NC 28207-1815 Office: Kennedy Covington Lobdell & Hickman NationsBank Ctr 100 N Tryon St Ste 4200 Charlotte NC 28201-4006

WALKER, CLAUD LADALE, SR., state representative; b. Pell City, Ala., May 11, 1934; s. Leilus Law and Ruby Lucille (Goodwin) W.; m. Cecelia Louise Thompson, Mar. 17, 1956; children: Claud LaDale Jr., Cecelia Jene Walker, Cheri Louise, Christi Denise. Student, Jacksonville State Tchrs. Coll., 1954-55, Bob Jones U., 1955-56. Sales rep. Courtesy Ford, Montgomery, Ala., 1957-61; franchised dealer Saladmaster Corp., Dallas, 1962-65, v.p. sales, 1966-80; authorized regional dist. sales rep. Saladmaster Corp., 1989—; mem. ho. of reps. State of Ala., Montgomery, 1986—. Tchr. Sunday sch.; scout leader Boy Scouts Am.; mem. Vol. Fire Dept. Cattlemen's Assn. Democrat. Baptist. Home: 8080 Butler Mill Rd Montgomery AL 36105-3612 Office: Salad Distrs PO Box 250477 Montgomery AL 36125-0477

WALKER, CRAIG MICHAEL, lawyer; b. Vt., Mar. 16, 1947; m. Patricia A. Magruder; three children. BA, Williams Coll., 1969; JD, Cornell U., 1972. Bar: N.Y. 1973, U.S. Dist. Ct. (so. dist.) N.Y. 1975, U.S. Ct. Appeals (2d cir) 1975, U.S. Supreme Ct 1976. Assoc. Alexander & Green, N.Y.C., 1972-80, ptnr., 1980-86, chmn. litigation dept., 1985-86; ptnr. Walter, Conston, Alexander & Green P.C., N.Y.C., 1987-89, Rogers & Wells, N.Y.C., 1990—. Contbr. author: New York Forms of Jury Instruction, 1992; contbr. articles to profl. jours. Fellow Am. Bar Found.; mem. ABA, N.Y. State Bar Assn., Def. Rsch. Inst., Fed. Bar Coun. (sustaining mem.). Democrat.

WALKER, DALE RUSH, banker; b. High Point, N.C., Jan. 14, 1943; s. Raymond Lowe and Virginia (Rush) W.; m. Linda Gates, 1990; children by previous marriage: Virginia Ashley, Whitney Beaumont. BS in Math., Wake Forest U., 1965; MBA, U. N.C., 1967. Asst. cashier Citibank, N.Y.C., 1967-70; sr. v.p. Union Bank, San Francisco, 1970-75, regional v.p., 1975-78; regional v.p. Union Bank, Oakland, Calif., 1978-80; chief mktg. officer Wells Fargo Leasing, San Francisco, 1980-81, chmn. bd., CEO, 1986-89; exec. v.p. and group head real estate group Wells Fargo Bank, San Francisco, 1981-92; exec. v.p. chief credit officer ITT Fin. Corp., St. Louis, 1993—; chmn., pres., CEO ITT Lyndon Ins. Cos., St. Louis, 1993—. Chmn. Pacific Vision Found., 1989-93. Mem. Urban Land Inst., Univ. Club (San Francisco, v.p. 1977-78). Democrat. Presbyterian. Avocations: skiing, windsurfing, piano, golf. Home: 19 Upper Price Rd Saint Louis MO 63132-4470 Office: ITT Fin Corp 645 Maryville Center Dr Saint Louis MO 63141

WALKER, DAVID A(LAN), finance educator; b. York, Pa., Jan. 5, 1941; s. Arthur Benjamin and Alva (Strasbourger) W. B.A., Pa. State U., 1962; M.S., Iowa State U., 1964, Ph.D., 1968. Asst. prof. Pa. State U., 1968-70; economist FDIC, 1970-76, 78-80; vis. assoc. prof. Northwestern U., 1976-77; dir. rsch. Office Compt. Currency, 1977-78; assoc. prof. fin. Georgetown U., 1980-82, prof., 1982-92, assoc. dean, 1985-87, John A. Largay Scholar, 1992—; dir. Ctr. for Bus. and Govt. Rels.; advisor U.S. Dept. Treas., U.S. SBA; cons. in field. Co-author textbooks; editor Jour. Fin. Rsch., 1981-87; co-editor Jour. Small Bus. Fin., 1992—; mem. editorial bds. Jour. Fin. Rsch., Fin. Mgmt., J.F.Q.A., Fin. Rev., Quarterly Rev. Econs. and Fin.; contbr. articles to profl. jours. NDEA fellow, 1964—. Mem. Am. Econ. Assn., Fin. Mgmt. Assn. (pres. 1994—), So. Fin. Assn. (bd. dirs.), Ea. Fin. Assn. (bd. dirs.), Fin. Mgmt. Assn. (v.p. 1990-91, pres.-elect 1993-94, pres. 1994—). Republican. Home: 4845 Loughboro Rd NW Washington DC 20016-3454 Office: Georgetown U Sch Bus Washington DC 20057

WALKER, DAVID BRADSTREET, political science educator; b. Salem, Mass., May 7, 1927; s. George Lincoln and Mildred (Bradstreet) W.; m. Jeanne Hallahan, Sept. 1955; children: Melissa J., Stephen B., Justin D. BA, Boston U., 1949, MA, 1950; PhD, Brown U., 1956. Instr. in govt. Bowdoin Coll., Brunswick, Maine, 1956-57; ass.t prof. in govt. Bowdoin Coll., 1957-63; staff dir. subcom. on intergovt. relations U.S. Senate, Washington, 1963-66; assat. dir. for govt. structure & function Adv. Commn. on Intergovt. Relations, Washington, 1966-84; prof. polit. sci. U. Conn., Storrs, 1984—; dir. Inst. Pub. & Urban Affairs, U. Conn., Storrs, 1986-90; publ. and urban

affairs keynote speaker ann. meetings of nat. orgns.; speaker at polit. sci. and govtl. orgns.; Fulbright prof. U. Göttingen, Germany, 1990-91. Author: Toward a Functioning Federalism, 1981, (with others) Managing Public Programs, 1989, (with others) The Great Society and its Legacy, 1986, The Rebirth of Federalism, 1995; contbr. articles to profl. jours. Citizen mem. Conn. Adv. Commn. on Intergovt. Rels., Hartford, 1985, chmn., 1986-90; bd. dirs. Nat. Civic League, Denver. With U.S. Army, 1945-47. Recipient Disting. Citizen award Nat. Mcpl. League, 1984, Donald C. Stone award for Significant Contbn. to Intergovt. Mgmt. in Acad./Rsch. Areas Membership, NAt. Acad. Pub. Adminstrn., Bosworth Meml. award Conn. chpt. Mem. Am. Soc. for Public Adminstrn., Am. Polit. Sci. Assn., Phi Alpha Alpha, Phi Beta Kappa. Democrat. Episcopalian. Avocations: swimming, gardening, white water rafting, fishing. Home: 31 Edgewood Lane Ext Mansfield Center CT 06250-1210 Office: Inst Pub and Urban Affairs U 106 421 Whitney Rd Storrs CT 06268

WALKER, DAVID ELLIS, JR., dean, educator, minister, consultant; b. Richmond, Va., Oct. 5, 1938; s. David Ellis and Laura Eloise (Vaughan) W.; m. Sandra Barnes, Feb. 3, 1964; children: David Ellis III, Virginia Suzanne Walker Frizzell, Cindy Poole Key, Michelle Poole. BA, David Lipscomb U., 1960; MA, U. Fla., 1961, PhD, 1969. Ordained to ministry Ch. Christ, 1954. Instr. Jacksonville (Fla.) U., 1963-65; min. Ch. of Christ, 1954—; prof. Middle Tenn. State U., Murfreesboro, 1965—; dean Theol. U. of Am., New Orleans, 1989—; cons. 1981—; acting chmn. dept. speech Middle Tenn. State U., summer 1984, fall 1990, dir. debate, 1965-70, pres. faculty senate, 1983-84. Author: Aletheia, 1991; editor Jour. of NonTraditional Education, 1992—; contbr. articles to profl. jours. and Ency. of U.S.A. Grad. fellow U. Fla., 1961-63; grantee Mid. Tenn. State U., 1967, 72, 77, 78, 88, 89, 90, 92, 93, 94, David Walker scholarship Mid. Tenn. State U., 1993—. Mem. Tenn. State Communication Assn. (v.p. 1973-74, pres. 1974-75, editor Jour. Tenn. Speech Communication Assn. 1977-85), Tenn. Intercollegiate Forensic Assn. (pres. 1966-67, exec. sec. 1967-68), Popular Culture Assn., Popular Culture Assn. of South, So. Speech Communication Assn., Fla. Communication Assn., Speech Communication Assn., Pi Kappa Delta (gov. province of S.E. 1966-68), Phi Kappa Phi (chpt. treas. 1989-90). Democrat. Avocations: reading, walking. Home: 2644 E Compton Rd Murfreesboro TN 37130-6848 Office: Mid Tenn State U Murfreesboro TN 37132

WALKER, DAVID MICHAEL, compensation and benefits consultant, accountant; b. Birmingham, Ala., Oct. 2, 1951; s. David Sellers and Dorothy Ann (West) W.; m. Mary Carmel Etheredge, June 12, 1971; children: Carol Marie, James Andrew. BS in Acctg., Jacksonville U., 1973; Sr. Exec. Govt. Cert., Harvard U., 1986. CPA, Fla., Tex., Ga. Sr. auditor Price Waterhouse & Co. and Coopers & Lybrand, Jacksonville, Fla., 1973-76; dir. personnel Coopers & Lybrand, Atlanta and Houston, 1976-79; Ea. regional mgr. Source Services Corp., Washington, 1979-83; acting exec. dir. and dep. exec. dir. Pension Benefit Guaranty Corp., Washington, 1983-85; dep. asst. sec. U.S. Dept. of Labor, Washington, 1985-87, asst. sec., 1987-89; ptnr., worldwide mng. ptnr. compensation & benefits practice Arthur Andersen LLP, Atlanta, 1989—; speaker in field. Contbr. articles, editorial adv. bd. several profl. jours. Asst. Pvt. Pension and Welfare Plans; dir., former chmn. Investment and Acctg. Issues Com.; former vice-chmn. chair legis. affairs com. So. Employee Benefits Inst.; sec. of labor Erisa Adv. Coun.; former trustee Social Security and Medicare Trust Funds. Recipient numerous industry and achievement awards for outstanding svc. and contbns. Mem. AICPA (chmn. employee benefit plans com.), Fla. Inst. CPAs, Ga. Soc. CPAs, Nat. Acad. Social Ins., ESOP Assn. and Internat. Found. of Employee Benefit Plans. Republican. Methodist. Home: 997 Peachtree Battle Ave NW Atlanta GA 30327 Office: Arthur Andersen & Co 133 Peachtree St Atlanta GA 30303

WALKER, DECKER FANNIN, education educator; b. Catlettsburg, Ky., Jan. 14, 1942; s. Robert Farrel Walker and Ruby Opal (Cyrus) Stotts; m. Joanne Edith Bakunas, 1962 (div. 1975); children: Glenn, David; m. Mary Ellen Bock, June 12, 1981; 1 child, Decker Jr. BS in Physics, Carnegie-Mellon U., 1963, MA in Natural Sci., 1966; EdD, Stanford U., 1971. Sci. tchr. Taylor Anderdice High Sch., Pitts., 1963-67; asst. prof. Sch. Edn. Stanford U., Palo Alto, Calif., 1971—; assoc. prof. U. Ill., Urbana, 1973-74; program officer NSF, Washington, 1988-89; cons. AAAS, Washington, 1988, Getty Found., L.A., 1984—. Author: Fundamentals of Curriculum, 1989; co-author: Curriculum and Aims, 1987. Recipient Young Scholar award Spencer Found., 1975. Mem. Am. Ednl. Rsch. Assn. (v.p. div. B 1975), Assn. for Supervision and Curriculum Devel., Computer Using Educators. Democrat.

WALKER, DELOSS, advertising agency executive; b. Okean, Ark., Aug. 14, 1931; s. Lonnie G. and Dora G. (Rickey) W.; children: Curtis Blake, Carla Alane; m. Ceil Ann Thomas, Dec. 30, 1979; children: Deloss Thomas, Cecelia Lona. Student, Williams Bapt. Coll., Walnut Ridege, Ark., 1952-56. Announcer Sta. KPOC Radio, Pocahantas, Ark., 1951-52, Sta. KRLW Radio, Walnut Ridge, Ark., 1954-55; sales mgr. Sta. KNEA, Jonesboro, Ark., 1956-58, gen. mgr., 1958-60; sales mgr. Sta. WMC Radio, Memphis, 1960-65; pres., founder Walker & Assoc., Inc., Memphis, 1965—; pres. Memphis Radio Fedn., 1973-74. Mgr. numerous polit. campaigns, 1965-90; chmn. Memphis Heart Assn., 1971-73; bd. dirs. Goodwill Industries, Memphis, 1972-73, So. Bapt. Coll., 1989—, Memphis Ronald McDonald House, 1990—; trustee Pink Palace Mus., Memphis, 1973-75. With U.S. Army, 1952-54. Decorated Bronze Star U.S. Army, 1953; named Man of Yr. Jaycees, 1963. Mem. Mid-South Advt. Agy. Assn. (charter), Racquet Club, Chickasaw Country Club, Crescent Club (bd. govs.). Democrat. Presbyterian. Office: Walker & Assoc, Inc 50 N Front St 1100 Morgan Keegan Tower Memphis TN 38193

WALKER, DEWARD EDGAR, JR., anthropologist, educator; b. Johnson City, Tenn., Aug. 3, 1935; s. Deward Edgar and Matilda Jane (Clark) W.; m. Candace A. Walker; children: Alice, Deward Edgar III, Mary Jane, Sarah, Daniel, Joseph Benjamin. Student, Ea. Oreg. Coll., 1953-54, 56-58, Mexico City Coll., 1958; BA in Anthropology with honors, U. Oreg., 1960-61, PhD in Anthropology, 1964; postgrad., Wash. State U., 1962. Asst. prof. anthropology George Washington U., Washington, 1964-65; asst. prof. anthropology Wash. State U., Pullman, 1965-67, research collaborator, 1967-69; assoc. prof., chmn. dept. Sociology/Anthropology, asst. dir. U. Idaho, Moscow, 1967-69; prof. U. Colo., Boulder, 1969—; research assoc. in population processes program of inst. behavioral sci., 1969-73, assoc. dean Grad. Sch., 1973-76; affiliate faculty U. Idaho, 1971—; presenter in field. Founder, co-editor Northwest Anthropol. Rsch. Notes, 1966—; editor, Plateau Vol.: Handbook of North American Indians, 1971—; author, co-author of fifteen books, 125 conf. reports on the Northern Plains; contbr. articles to profl. jours. Mem. tech/ steering panel Hanford Environ. Dose Reconstrn. Project; advisor on Native Am. affairs Smithsonian Inst. With U.S. Army, 1954-62. Fellow NSF, 1961, NDEA, 1961-64. Fellow Am. Anthropol. Assn. (assoc. editor Am. Anthropologist 1973-74), Soc. Applied Anthropology (hon. life, exec. com. 1970-79, treas. 1976-79, chmn. 1980-95, cons., expert witness tribes of N.W., editor Human Orgn. 1970-76, rsch. over 65 separate projects); mem. AAAS, Am. Acad. Polit. Social Scis., Northwest Anthropol. Conf. Avocations: geology, mining. Home: PO Box 4147 Boulder CO 80306-4147 Office: U Colo PO Box 233 Boulder CO 80309-0233

WALKER, DONALD ANTHONY, economist, educator; b. Mar. 6, 1934; s. Timothy Anthony and Helen (Walker) W.; m. Patricia Ann McKeage, Feb. 14, 1961; 1 dau., Valerie Alana. A.B., S.W. Tex. State U., 1952, M.A., U. Tex., 1956; Ph.D., Harvard U., 1961. Asst. prof. econs. Miami U., Oxford, Ohio, 1961-67; assoc. prof. econs. Miami U., 1967-69; prof. econs. Indiana U. Pa., 1969-88, chmn. dept., 1969—, Univ. prof., 1988—. Author books; editor: Jour. of the History of Economic Thought; contbr. articles to profl. jours. Recipient Commonwealth of Pa. Distinguished Acad. Service award, 1974, Ind.-U. Pa. Disting. Research Award, 1984; Harvard fellow, 1956-57, 57-58; Henry Lee Meml. fellow, 1957-58. Mem. History of Econs. Soc. (pres. 1986-87). Home: 48 Shady Dr Indiana PA 15701-3245 Office: Indiana U of Pennsylvania Dept Econs Keith Hall Indiana PA 15705-1087

WALKER, DONALD EZZELL, retired academic administrator; b. Springfield, Mo., July 13, 1921; s. Edward Everett and Cecilia (Ezzell) W.; m. Ann Lathrop, Dec. 17, 1943; 1 son, Craig Lathrop. A.B., U. So. Calif., 1943, M.Th., 1947; Ph.D., Stanford U., 1954; L.H.D. (hon.), Southeastern

Mass. U., 1973. Recreational dir. club work All Nations Found., Los Angeles, 1941-42, Wilshire Meth. Ch., Los Angeles, 1942-43; asst. minister Vincent Meth. Ch., Los Angeles, 1943-44; minister Encinitas Meth. Ch., 1945-47; teaching asst. Stanford U., 1947-49; instr. sociology San Diego State Coll., 1949-51, asst. prof. sociology, 1951-54, assoc. dean students, counseling, 1954-56, dean counseling, 1956-58, v.p. acad. affairs, 1968-71, acting pres., 1971-72; dean of students San Fernando Valley State Coll., Northridge, Calif., 1958-60; pres. Idaho State U., 1960-64; dean of students Sonoma State Coll., Rohnert Park, Calif., 1964-66; vice chancellor student affairs U. Calif., Irvine, 1966-68, sr. lectr. Grad. Sch. Administrn., 1967-68, fellow Univ. Coll., 1967-68; pres. Southeastern Mass. State U., N. Dartmouth, 1972-83; chancellor Grossmont-Cuyamaca Community Coll. Dist., El Cajon, Calif., 1983-92; ret., 1992. Author: (with others) Readings in American Public Opinion; The Effective Administrator: A Practical Approach to Problem-Solving, Decision-Making, and Campus Leadership, 1979; contbr. (with others) articles to profl. jours. Home: 8661 Lake Murray Blvd Apt 19 San Diego CA 92119-2837

WALKER, DOUGLAS, computer developement company executive. Graduate, Vanderbilt U., 1976. With Western Data Corp., Seattle, 1976-80; with Walker, Richer & Quinn, Inc., Seattle, 1980—, now pres., 1989—. Office: Walker Richer & Quinn Inc 1500 Dexter Ave N Seattle WA 98109*

WALKER, DOUGLAS CRAIG, publishing company executive; b. Kansas City, Mo., May 7, 1944; s. Garnet Cleveland Walker and Mary Frances (Schuette) Bivins. BS, U. Mo., 1966, MA, 1968. Editorial mgr. Hallmark Cards, Kansas City, Mo., 1974-81; editorial dir. Hippocrene/Lee Publs. Group, N.Y.C., 1981-82; book club dir. Scholastic Inc., N.Y.C., 1984-91; pub., v.p. Putnam/Grosset & Dunlap, N.Y.C., 1991-94; editl. dir. Scholastic paperbacks Scholastic Inc., N.Y.C., 1994—. Editor, creator children's sci. book series The Magic Schoolbus, 1990— (Boston Globe Hornbook award for nonfiction 1990). With U.S. Army, 1968-70. Democrat. Lutheran. Home: 175 E 96th St New York NY 10128 Office: Scholastic Inc 555 Broadway New York NY 10012

WALKER, DOUGLASS WILLEY, retired pediatrician-medical center administrator; b. Thomaston, Maine, Aug. 3, 1913; s. Lee Wilson and Eliza Ann (Willey) W.; m. Janet Franklin Stockbridge, Mar. 21, 1942; children: Barbara, Elizabeth, Ann. BS, Bowdoin Coll., 1935, ScD (hon.), 1977; MD, Yale U., 1939. Diplomate Am. Bd. Pediatrics. Resident in pediatrics Yale Med. Sch.-New Haven Hosp., 1939-41, 46; pvt. practice, Laconia, N.H., 1946-63; pres. Laconia Clinic, 1963; asst. prof., asst. dean Johns Hopkins U. Med. Sch., Balt., 1963-67, assoc. prof., assoc. dean, 1967-70; med. dir. Maine Med. Ctr., Portland, 1970-75, v.p. med. affairs, 1975-78, corporator, 1970—; ret., 1978; assoc. clin. prof. Tufts U. Med. Sch., Boston, 1970-78; trustee Penobscot Bay Med. Ctr., Rockport, Maine, 1985-91; incorporator N.E. Health, Camden, Maine, 1985—. Mem. editl. bd. History of Preventive Medicine, World War II, 8 vols., 1955-76. Chmn. child health com. N.H. White House Conf., 1960; mem. adv. bd. So. Maine Vocat. Tech. Inst., South Portland, 1978-84; bd. mgrs. Park Danforth Home, Portland, 1980-82; sec., past pres. Martin Point Improvement Assn. Lt col. M.C., AUS, 1941-46. Decorated Legion of Merit. Mem. New Eng. Pediatric Soc. (past pres.). Republican. Methodist. Avocations: sailing, gardening, bridge. Home: PO Box 40 Friendship ME 04547

WALKER, DUARD LEE, medical educator; b. Bishop, Calif., June 2, 1921; s. Fred H. and Anna Lee (Shumate) W.; m. Dorothea Virginia McHenry, Aug. 11, 1945; children: Douglas Keith, Donna Judith, David Cameron, Diane Susan. A.B., U. Calif.-Berkeley, 1943, M.A., 1947; M.D., U. Calif.-San Francisco, 1945. Diplomate Am. Bd. Microbiology. Intern, U.S. Naval Hosp., Shoemaker, Cal., 1945-46; asst. resident internal medicine Stanford U. Service San Francisco Hosp., 1950-52; assoc. prof. med. microbiology and preventive medicine U. Wis., Madison, 1952-59; prof. med. microbiology U. Wis., 1959-88, prof., chmn. med. microbiology, 1970-76, 81-88, Paul F. Clark prof. med. microbiology, 1977-88, prof. emeritus, 1988—; cons. Naval Med. Rsch. Unit, Gt. Lakes, Ill., 1958-74; mem. microbiology tng. com. Nat. Inst. Gen. Med. Scis., 1966-70; mem. nat. adv. Allergy and Infectious Diseases Coun., 1970-74; mem. adv. com. on blood program rsch. ARC, 1978-79; mem. study group on paovaviridae Internat. Com. on Taxonomy of Viruses, 1976-90; mem. vaccines and related biol. products adv. com. FDA, 1985-89. Mem. editorial bd. Infection and Immunity, 1975-83, Archives of Virology, 1981-83, Microbial Pathogenesis, 1985-90. Served to lt. comdr. USNR, 1943-46, 53-55. NRC postdoctoral fellow virology Rockefeller Inst. Med. Research, N.Y.C., 1947-49; USPHS fellow immunology George Williams Hooper Found., U. Calif.-San Francisco, 1949-50. Fellow Am. Pub. Health Assn., Am. Acad. Microbiology, Infectious Diseases Soc. Am.; mem. NAS, Am. Assn. Immunologists, Am. Soc. Microbiology, AAAS, Soc. Exptl. Biology and Medicine (editorial bd. Procs.), Reticuloendothelial Soc. AAUP, Am. Soc. Virology, Wis. Acad. Scis., Arts and Letters. Home: 618 Odell St Madison WI 53711-1435 Office: U Wis Med Sch 1300 University Ave Madison WI 53706

WALKER, E. JERRY, retired clergyman; b. Seattle, May 31, 1918; s. Septimus and Mae Ruth (Roys) W.; m. Holly Rae Harding, Nov. 10, 1941; children: Jerrianne, Dale Harding, Barbara Rae. AB, Seattle Pacific U., 1940; MDiv, Garrett Theol. Sch., 1945; DD, Wiley Coll., 1958, Northland Coll., 1971. Ordained to ministry United Meth. Ch. Teaching fellow State Coll. Wash., 1940-41; dir. edn. Prairie Farmer Sta. WLS, Chgo., 1942-45; dir. radio Internat. Coun. Religious Edn., 1945-48; freelance writer, dir. radio and TV Sta. WBKB-TV, Chgo., 1948-53; pastor St James Meth. Ch., Chgo., 1953-62, First United Meth. Ch., Duluth, 1962-74; freelance daily commentary Sta. KDAL-TV, Duluth, Minn., 1964-76; exec. dir. Ctr. for Family Studies, Duluth, 1972-82; ptnr. SoundVideo Prodns., Tahuya, Wash., 1987—; cons. environ. grants, 1987—; project dir. Hood Canal Wetlands Interp Ctr., 1988—; bd. dirs. Pacific N.W. WRiters Conf., Wash., 1983-88; mem. gen. bd. Nat. Coun. Chs., 1954-66. Author: Five Minute Stories from the Bible, 1948, Stories from the Bible, 1955, Seeking a Faith of Your Own, 1961, Sinner's Parish, 1963, (plays) Checkerboard, Kyrie, The Unpainted Wall; also numerous articles. Bd. dirs. Chgo. chpt. NCCJ, 1955-62, nat. bd. trustees, 1974-76; mem. Kenwood-Ellis Cmty. Renewal Commn., 1957-62, Gov. Ill.'s Adv. Commn. on Aged, 1958-62, S.E. Chgo. Commn., 1958-62, United Fund Survey Com., 1968-70; co-chmn. Duluth Citizens Com. Secondary Edn., 1963-64; bd. dirs. Mary E. Theler Cmty. Ctr., Belfair, Wash., 1988-91; cons. Mason County United Way, 1990-94, co-chmn. needs assessment com., 1992-94; cons. Bremerton Hist. Ships Assn., 1994—. Recipient Human Rels. award Chgo. Commn. Human Rels., 1954, Friend of Youth award Southside Community Com., 1955, Disting. Citizen award Com. of One Hundred, 1962, Achievement award Freedom Found., 1963-65, Broadcast Journalism award Minn. Coun. Chs., 1971, Appreciation award North Mason Sch. Dist., 1990, Environ. Pride award Pacific Northwest Mag., 1992; named Chicagoan of Yr. Chgo. Jaycees, 1962. Mem. Internat. Platform Assn., Seattle Free Lances, Kiwanis. Democrat. Avocation: boating. Home: 18341 E State Highway 106 Belfair WA 98528-9588 Office: North Mason Sch Dist PO Box 167 Belfair WA 98528-0167

WALKER, EARL E., manufacturing executive; b. St. Louis, Mo., Feb. 12, 1921; s. Thomas T. and Ella Mary (Steggerman) W.; m. Myrtle Agnew, Sept. 27, 1942; children: Mary, Tom, Nancy, Peggy. Grad., Ranken Tech. Sch., 1941. Welder Curtis-Wright Aircraft Co., St. Louis, 1941-49; welder McDonnell-Douglas Aircraft Co., St. Louis, 1949-51, foreman, 1951-53; pres. S.N.W. Welding, St. Louis, 1952-53, Coeur Lane Mfg. Co., St. Louis, 1953-55, Carr Lane Mfg. Co., St. Louis, 1955—; bd. dirs. All Am. Products Co., Los Angeles, Am. Assn. Indsl. Mgmt. Com. Educ. Edn. Program, Scottish Rite Clinic for Childhood Lang. Disorders, U. Tex. Sch. Nursing; sec. of interior, Jefferson Nat. Meml. Commn., 1986—. Named Subcontractor of Yr. Small Bus. Adminstrn., Midwest Region VII, 1987; recipient Silver Platter award, Scottish Rite, Mo. Valley. Mem. Soc. Mfg. Engrs. (internat. dir., chmn. nat. exposition com., Nat. Businessman of Yr. 1975, Mgmt. Achievement award, Eli Whitney award 1991, Edn. Found. award for individual achievement 1991, Fellows award 1993), Masons (33 degree). Avocation: golf. Office: Carr Lane Mgf Co 4200 Carr Lane Ct Saint Louis MO 63119-2129

WALKER, EDWARD KEITH, JR., business executive, retired naval officer; b. Annapolis, Md., Jan. 23, 1933; s. Edward Keith and Miriam (Whitmore) W.; m. Carol Ann Turner, June 12, 1954; children: Lynn Walker Streett,

Wendy Louise. BS, U.S. Naval Acad., 1954; postgrad., Armed Forces Staff Coll., 1966; MBA in Fin. Mgmt., George Washington U., 1970. Commd. ensign U.S. Navy, 1954, advanced through grades to rear admiral, 1981; force supply officer COMSUBLANT Norfolk, Va., 1975-78; exec. officer SPCC Mechanicsburg, Pa., 1978-80; comdr. Naval Supply Ctr., Puget Sound, Bremerton, Wash., 1980-81; Atlantic Fleet supply officer CINCLANTFLT Norfolk, 1981-83; asst. comptroller Navy Dept., Washington, 1983-84; comdr. Naval Supply Systems Command and 35th chief supply corps Washington, 1984-88; v.p. adminstrn. and corp. strategy Resource Cons. Inc., Vienna, Va., 1989—. Decorated D.S.M., Legion of Merit (3 awards); recipient Def. Superior Service medal, 1983. Mem. Vinson Hall Corp. (bd. dirs.), Naval Acad. Found. (trustee), U.S. Navy Meml. Found. (bd. dirs., treas.), Supply Corps Found. (past pres.), Supply Corps Assn. (past pres.), Am. Soc. Mil. Comptrs., U.S. Naval Inst., Am. Soc. Naval Engrs., Soc. Logistics Engrs., Nat. Security Indsl. Assn., Naval Submarine League, Naval Order U.S., Navy League U.S., Am. Def. Preparedness Assn., N.Y. Yacht Club, Chesapeake Yacht Club. Republican. Episcopalian. Home: 3520 Saylor Pl Alexandria VA 22304-1831 Office: Resource Cons Inc 1960 Gallows Rd Vienna VA 22182-3824

WALKER, EDWARD S., JR., diplomat; b. Abington, Pa., June 13, 1940; s. Edward Stanley and Rosabel Dunlop (Gould) W.; m. Wendy Jane Griffiths, Apr. 7, 1973; children: Kathryn Erica, Christopher James. BA, Hamilton Coll., 1963; MA, Boston U., 1965. Joined Fgn. Svc., Dept. State, Washington, 1967; polit. officer Am. Embassy, Tel Aviv, 1969-73; staff asst. Nr. Ea. affairs Fgn. Svc., Dept. State, Washington, 1974-75; Arabic lang. trainee Fgn. Svc. Inst., Lebanon, Tunis, Egypt, 1975-77; polit. officer Am. Embassy, Damascus, Syria, 1977-79; spl. asst. Pres.'s personal rep., Washington, 1980-82; exec. dir. Office of Dep. Sec. State, Washington, 1982-84; mem. Royal Coll. Def. Studies, London, 1984-85; dep. chief of mission Am. Embassy, Riyadh, Saudi Arabia, 1985-88; dep. asst. sec. Dept. State, 1988-89; U.S. amb. to United Arab Emirates Abu Dhabi, 1989-92; dept. permanent rep. to UN, N.Y.C., 1993-94; U.S. amb. to Egypt Cairo, 1994—. With U.S. Army, 1962-65. Recipient Superior Honor award Dept. State, 1975, Meritorious Honor award, 1976, Abu Dhabi, Order of Independence, 1992. Mem. Internat. Inst. Strategic Studies. Episcopalian. Office: US Embassy AMB Unit 64900 Box 1 APO AE 09839-4900

WALKER, ELJANA M. DU VALL, civic worker; b. France, Jan. 18, 1924; came to U.S., 1948; naturalized, 1954; student Med. Inst., U. Paris, 1942-47; m. John S. Walker, Jr., Dec. 31, 1947; children—John, Peter, Barbara. Pres., Loyola Sch. PTA, 1958-59; bd. dirs. Santa Claus shop, 1959-73; treas. Archdiocese Denver Catholic Women, 1962-64; rep. Cath. Parent-Tchr League, 1962-65; pres. Aux. Denver Gen. Hosp., 1966-69; precinct committeewoman Arapahoe County Republican Women's Com., 1973-74; mem. re-election com. Arapahoe County Rep. Party, 1973-78, Reagan election com., 1980; block worker Arapahoe County March of Dimes, Heart Assn., Hemophilia Drive, Muscular Dystrophy and Multiple Sclerosis Drive, 1978-81; cen. city asst. Guild Debutante Charities, Inc. Recipient Distinguished Service award Am.-by-choice, 1966; named to Honor Roll, ARC, 1971. Mem. Cherry Hills Symphony, Lyric Opera Guild, Alliance Franciase (life mem.), ARC, Civic Ballet Guild (life mem.), Needlework Guild Am. (v.p. 1980-82), Kidney Found. (life), Denver Art Mus., U. Denver Art and Conservation Assns. (chmn. 1980-82), U. Denver Women's Library Assn., Chancellors Soc, Passage Inc., Friends of the Fine Arts Found. (life). Roman Catholic. Clubs: Union (Chgo.); Denver Athletic, 26 (Denver); Welcome to Colo. Internat. Address: 2301 Green Oaks Dr Greenwood Village CO 80121

WALKER, ELVA MAE DAWSON, health consultant; b. Everett, Mass. June 29, 1914; d. Charles Edward and Mary Elizabeth (Livingston) Dawson; m. John J. Spillane Jr. R.N., Peter Bent Brigham Hosp., Boston, 1937; student Simmons Coll., 1935, U. Minn., 1945-48; m. Walter Willard Walker, Dec. 16, 1939 (div. 1969). Supr. nursery Wesson Maternity Hosp., Springfield, Mass., 1937-38; asst. supr. out-patient dept. Peter Bent Brigham Hosp., Boston, 1938-40; supr. surgery and out-patient dept. Univ. Hosps., Mpls., 1945. Chmn. Gov.'s Citizens Coun. on Aging, Minn., 1960-68, acting dir., 1962-66, Econ. Opportunity Com. Hennepin County, 1964-69; v.p., treas. Nat. Purity Soap & Chem. Co., 1968-69, pres., 1969-76, chmn. bd., 1976—, co. exec. officer, 1993—; cons. on aging to Minn. Dept. Pub. Welfare, 1962-67; mem. nat. adv. Coun. for Nurse Tng. Act, 1965-69, Com. Status on Women in Armed Svcs., 1967-70; dir. Nat. Coun. on the Aging, 1963-67, sec., 1965-67, 1986-88, chairperson, 1988-91; chmn. Minn. Bd. on Aging, 1982-91, Nat. Retiree Vol. Ctr., 1982-89; dir. Planning Agy. for Hosps. of Met. Mpls., 1963-67, United Hosp. Fund of Hennepin County, 1955-60, Nat. Coun. Social Work Edn., 1966-68; vice chmn. Hennepin County Gen. Hosp. Adv. Bd., 1965-68; sec. Hennepin County Health Coalition, 1973; chmn. bd. dirs. Am. Rehab. Found., 1962-68, vice chmn., 1968-70, chmn. Minn. Bd. On Aging, 1988-91, Sr. Resources, 1985-87; pres. bd. trustees Northwestern Hosp., 1956-59, Children's Hosp. Mpls., 1961-65; dir. Twin Cities Internat. Program for Youth Leaders and Social Workers, Inc., 1965-67; mem. community adv. coun. United Community Funds and Coun. Am., Inc., 1968, Nat. Assembly Social Policy and Devel., Inc., 1968-74, Minn. Action for Children Commn., 1989—, mem., 1991—; mem. priorities determination com. United Fund Mpls., 1971; vice chmn. govt. specifications com. Soap and Detergent Assn., 1972-76, vice-chmn. indsl. and instn. com., 1974-76, chmn., 1976-78, bd. dirs., 1974—; candidate for Congress, 3d Minn. Dist., 1966; trustee Macalester Coll., Archie D. and Bertha H. Walker Found.; chmn. St. Mary's Jr. Coll. Bd., 1970-74, 78-80; pres. U. Minn. Sch. Nursing Found., 1958-70; pres. Minn. Gerontological Soc., 1994-95; sec. Metro Area Agy. Aging Minn., 1995—. Mem. Am. Pub. Welfare Assn., Minn. Gerontol. Soc. (pres. 1994—), Mpls. Med. Research Found., Minn. League Nursing (pres. 1971-73), Jr. League Minn. Democrat. Presbyterian. Home: 3655 Northome Rd Wayzata MN 55391-3020 Office: Nat Purity Soap & Chem Co 434 Lakeside Ave Minneapolis MN 55405-1529

WALKER, ERIC ARTHUR, consulting engineer, institute executive; b. Long Eaton, Eng., Apr. 29, 1910; came to U.S., 1923, naturalized, 1937; s. Arthur and Violet Elizabeth (Haywood) W.; m. L. Josephine Schmeiser, Dec. 20, 1937; children: Gail (Mrs. Peter Hearn), Brian. B.S., Harvard U., 1932, M.S., 1933, Sc.D., 1935; LL.D., Temple U., 1957, Lehigh U., 1957, Hofstra Coll., 1960, Lafayette Coll., 1960, U. Pa., 1960, U. R.I., 1962; L.H.D., Elizabethtown Coll., 1958; D.Litt., Jefferson Med. Coll., 1960; D.Sc., Wayne State U., 1965, Thiel Coll., 1966, U. Notre Dame, 1968, U. Pitts., 1970. Registered profl. engr., Pa. Instr. math. Tufts Coll., 1933-34, asst. prof., assoc. prof. elec. engring., 1935-38, head elec. engring. dept., 1935-40; head elec. engring dept. U. Conn., 1940-43; assoc. dir. Harvard U. Underwater Sound Lab., 1942-45; dir. Ordnance Research Lab., Pa. State U., 1945-52, head elec. engring. dept., 1945-51; dean Sch. Engring. Pa. State U., 1951-56, v.p. univ., 1956, pres., 1956-70; v.p. sci. and tech. Aluminum Co. Am., 1970-76; mem. and past chmn. bd. Inst. for Def. Analysis, 1978-85; exec. sec. Rsch. and Devel. Bd., 1950-51; cons. NRC, 1949-50; mem. and past chmn. com. on undersea warfare; chmn. Pres.'s Com. on Tech. and Distbn. Research for Benefit of Small Bus., 1957; mem. nat. sci. bd. NSF, 1962-68, chmn. nat. sci. bd., 1966-68; chmn. Naval Research Adv. Com., 1963-65, 71-73, Army Sci. Adv. Panel, 1956-58; vice chmn. Pres.'s Com. Scientists and Engrs., 1956-58; adv. panel on engring. and tech. manpower Pres.'s Sci. Adv. Com.; mem. Gov.'s Com. of 100 for Better Edn., 1960-61; bd. dirs. Engring. Found. Contbr. to tech. mags. United bd. visitors U.S. Naval Acad., 1958-60, U.S. Mil. Acad., 1962-64. Recipient Horatio Alger award, 1959, Tasker H. Bliss award Am. Soc. Mil. Engrs., 1959; Golden Omega award Am. Inst. E.E and Nat. Elec. Mfg. Assn., 1962; DoD Pub. Service medal, 1970; Presdl. citation, 1970. Fellow IEEE, Am. Acoustical Soc., Am. Inst. E.E., Am. Phys. Soc.; mem. Am. Inst. Physics Am. Soc. Engring. Edn. (Lamme award 1965, pres. 1956-57), Pa. Assn. Colls. and Univs. (pres. 1950- 60), Middle States Assn. Colls. and Secondary Schs. (commn. higher edn. 1958-61), Engrs. Joint Council (pres. 1962-63), Nat. Assn. State Univs. and Land-Grant Colls. (exec. com. 1958-62), Nat. Acad. Engring. (pres. 1966-70), Am. Acad. Arts and Scis. Newcomen Soc., Royal Soc. Arts, Duquesne Club, Cosmos Club, Sigma Xi, Tau Beta Pi, Phi Kappa Phi. Home: 222 Haymaker Circle State College PA 16801 Office: Penn State U 222 A Hammond Bldg University Park PA 16802

WALKER, ESPER LAFAYETTE, JR., retired civil engineer; b. Decatur, Tex., Sept. 22, 1930; s. Esper Lafayette and Ruth (Mauldin) W.; B.S., Tex. A&M U., 1953; B.H.T., Yale U., 1958; m. Sara Lynn Dunlap, Oct. 2, 1955; children: William David, Annette Ruth. Design engr. Tex. Hwy. Dept.,

WALKER, EVELYN, retired educational television executive; b. Birmingham, Ala.; d. Preston Lucas and Mattie (Williams) W.; AB, Huntingdon Coll., 1927; student Cornell U., 1927-28; MA, U. Ala., 1963; LHD, Huntingdon Coll., 1974. Speech instr. Phillips High Sch., Birmingham, 1930-34; head speech dept. Ramsay High Sch., Birmingham, 1934-52; chmn. radio and TV, Birmingham Pub. Schs., 1944-75, head instructional TV programming svcs., 1969-75; mem. summer faculty extension div. U. Va., 1965, 66, 67; former regional cons. ednl. TV broadcasting; Miss Ann, broadcaster children's daily radio program, Birmingham, 1946-57; prodr. Our Am. Heritage radio series, 1944-54; TV staff prodr. programs shown daily Ala. Pub. TV Network, 1954-75; past cons. Gov.'s Ednl. TV Legis. Study Com., 1953; nat. del. Asian-Am. Women Broadcasters Conf., 1966; former regional cons. Ednl. TV Broadcasting. Mem. emerita Nat. Def. Adv. Com. on Women in Svcs.; past TV-radio co-chmn. Gov.'s Adv. Bd. Safety Com.; past chmn. creative TV-radio writing competition Festival of Arts; past audio-visual chmn. Ala. Congress, also past mem. Birmingham coun. PTA; media chmn. Gov.'s Commn. on Yr. of the Child; bd. dirs. Women's Army Corps Mus., Fort MiCllellen, 1960-93. Recipient Alumnae Achievement award Huntingdon Coll., 1958; Tops in Our Town award Birmingham News, 1957; Air Force Recruiting plaque, 1961; Spl. Bowl award for promoting arts through Ednl. TV. Birmingham Festival of Arts, 1962; citation 4th Army Corps., 1962; cert. of appreciation Ala. Multiple Sclerosis Soc., 1962; Freedoms Found. at Valley Forge Educator's medal award, 1963; Top TV award ARC, 1964; Ala. Woman of Achievement award, 1964; Bronze plaque Ala. Dist. Exch. Clubs, 1969; cert. of appreciation Birmingham Bd. Edn., 1975; Obelisk award Children's Theatre, 1976; 20-Yr. Svc. award Ala. Ednl. TV Commn.; key to city of Birmingham, 1966; named Woman of Yr., Birmingham, 1965; named Ala. Woman of Yr. Progressive Farmer mag., 1966; hon. col. Ala. Militia. Mem. Am. Assn. Ret. Persons, Ala. Assn. Ret. Tchrs., Huntingdon Coll. Alumnae Assn. (former internat. pres.), Former Am. Women in Radio and TV, Arlington Hist. Assn. (dir., pres. 1981-83), Magna Charta Dames (past state sec.-treas.), DAR (former pub. rels. com. Ala., TV chmn., state program chmn. 1979-85, state chmn. Seimes Microfilm com. 1985-88, state chmn. Motion Picture, Radio TV com 1988-94, tricom. chmn. 1988-94), Colonial Dames 17th Century, U.S. Daus. 1812 (past state TV chmn.), Daus. Am. Colonists (past 2d v.p. local chpt., past state TV and radio chmn.), Ams. Royal Descent, Royal Order Garter, Plantagenets Soc. Am., Salvation Army Women's Aux., Symphony Aux., Humane Soc. Aux., Eagle Forum, Nat. League Am. Pen Women, Womens's Com. 100 for Birmingham (bd. dirs.), Royal Order Crown, Women in Communications (past local pres., nat. headliner 1965), Birmingham-Jefferson Hist. Soc., Delta Delta Delta (mem. Golden Circle), Ladies Golf Assn., Birmingham Country Club, The.Club. Methodist. Home: Mountain Brook 744 Euclid Ave Birmingham AL 35213-2538

WALKER, FERGUS JOSEPH, JR., manufacturing company executive; b. Hannibal, Mo., Aug. 19, 1934; s. Fergus Joseph and Helen Barbara (Herl) W.; m. Nancy Beatrice Turner, Apr. 28, 1962; children—Patrick F., Gregory T., Julia C. B.S. in Commerce, St. Louis U., 1956. C.P.A. Tex., Mo. Audit mgr. Ernst & Whinney, St. Louis, Ft. Worth, 1959-66; controller Tex. Industries Inc., Dallas, 1967-69, v.p., controller, 1969-71, v.p. fin., 1971-76, sr. v.p., 1976-81, exec. v.p., chief operating officer, 1981-88, cons., 1988—; exec. v.p. Redman Industries, Dallas, 1989—. Bd. dirs. Ctr. for Non-profit Mgmt., Dallas, Non-profit Loan Fund, 1983—; mem. fin. com. St. Rita Roman Cath. Ch., Dallas, 1975-77, 83—; sch. bd. Urusline Acad. for Girls, Dallas. With U.S. Army, 1957-59. Mem. Fin. Execs. Inst., Am. Inst. C.P.A.s, Tex. Soc. C.P.A.s. Republican. Office: Redman Industries Inc 2550 Walnut Hill Ln Ste 200 Dallas TX 75229-5634

WALKER, FLORENCE ANN, preschool educator, insurance underwriter; b. Magnolia, Miss., Nov. 23, 1939; d. Albert E. and Florence (Hunnicutt) Pardue; m. Charles Hickman Walker, June 24, 1961; children: Charles David (dec.), John Dwayne, Paul Douglas. BA, La. Coll., 1961. Cert. elem. tchr., La. Tchr. Cen. Elem., Baton Rouge, 1961, North Bayou Rapides Elem., Alexandria, La., 1961-64; tchr., asst. dir. Southside Bapt. Preschool, Baton Rouge, 1972-86, dir., 1986—; chief underwriter/adminstr. Starmount Life Ins. Co., Baton Rouge, 1986—. Mem. Parkview Eagle Backers, 1983-87, Parent, Tchr. and Friends, Baton Rouge. Mem. Assn. Life Ins. Underwriters, La. Assn. Educators, La. Assn. for Children Under Six, Nat. Assn. for Edn. of Young Children, So. Early Childhood Assn., Optimist Internat. Republican. Baptist. Avocations: aerobics, walking, weights. Office: Southside Bapt Presch 1700 Lee Dr Baton Rouge LA 70808-3831

WALKER, FLOYD LEE, lawyer; b. Kiefer, Okla., Mar. 27, 1919; s. Willis and Sarah Josephine (McFarl) W.; children by previous marriage: Mary Lea Walker Byrd, Cheryl Sue Walker Newman, James M.; m. Virginia Gifford Raines, Oct. 8, 1971. LLB, Tulsa U., 1949. Bar: Okla. 1949. Claims atty. Standard Ins. Co., Tulsa, 1949-53; pvt. practice Tulsa, 1953—. 1st lt. USAAF, 1942-45. Decorated DFC, Air medal with 3 oak leaf clusters. Fellow Am. Coll. Trial Lawyers; mem. ABA, Okla. Bar Assn. (bd. govs. 1979—), Tulsa County Bar Assn. (pres. 1979-80), Am. Bd. Trial Lawyers, Assn. Trial Lawyers Am. Home: 1502 S Boulder Ave Apt 7B Tulsa OK 74119-4022 Office: 900 Oneok Plz Tulsa OK 74103

WALKER, FRANK BANGHART, pathologist; b. Detroit, June 14, 1931; s. Roger Venning and Helen Frances (Reade) W.; m. Phyllis Childs; children: Nancy Anne, David Carl, Roger Osborne, Mark Andrew. B.S., Union Coll., N.Y., 1951; M.D., Wayne State U., 1955, M.S., 1962. Diplomate Am. Bd. Pathology. Intern Detroit Meml. Hosp., 1955-56; resident Wayne State U. and affiliated hosps., Detroit, 1958-62; pathologist, 1962-93; dir. labs. Detroit Meml. Hosp., 1984-87, Cottage Hosp., Grosse Pointe, Mich., 1984-93; pathologist, dir. labs. Macomb Hosp Ctr. (formerly South Macomb Hosp.), Warren, Mich., 1966-93, Jennings Meml. Hosp., Detroit, 1971-79, Alexander Blain Hosp., Detroit, 1971-85; ptnr. Langston, Walker & Assocs., P.C, Grosse Pointe, 1968-93; instr. pathology Wayne State U. Med. Sch., Detroit, 1962-72, asst. clin. prof., 1972-94, assoc. clin. prof., 1994—. Pres. Mich. Assn. Blood Banks, 1969-70; mem. med. adv. com. ARC, 1972-83; mem. Mich. Higher Edn. Assistance Authority, 1975-77; trustee Alexander Blain Meml. Hosp., Detroit, 1974-83, Detroit-Macomb Hosp. Corp., 1974-93; bd. dirs. Wayne State Found, 1971-83. Capt. M.C., AUS, 1956-58. Recipient Disting. Svc. award Wayne State U. Med. Sch., 1990. Fellow Detroit Acad. Medicine; mem. AMA (coun. on long-range planning and devel. 1982-88, vice chmn. 1985-87, chmn. 1987-88, trustee 1988—), Am. Bd. Pathology (trustee 1982—, treas. 1984-91, v.p. 1991-92, pres. 1993-94), Coll. Am. Pathologists (disting. svc. award 1983), Am. Soc. Clin. Pathologists (sec. 1971-77, pres. 1979-80, disting. svc. award 1989), Mich. Soc. Pathologists (pres. 1980-81), Wayne County Med. Soc. (pres. 1984-85, trustee 1986-91, chmn. 1990-91), Mich. Med. Soc. (bd. dirs. 1981-90, vice chmn. 1986-88, chmn. 1988-90), Am. Assn. Blood Banks, Mich. Assn. Blood Banks, Wayne State U. Alumni Assn. (bd. govs. 1968-71). Wayne State U. Med. Alumni Assn. (pres. 1969, trustee 1970-85, Disting. Alumni award 1994), Econ. Club Detroit, Detroit Athletic Club, Lochmoor Club, Mid-Am. Club, Phi Gamma Delta, Nu Sigma Nu, Alpha Omega Alpha. Republican. Episcopalian. Home and Office: 14004 Harbor Place Dr Saint Clair Shores MI 48080-1528

WALKER, FRANK DILLING, market research executive; b. Indpls., Dec. 31, 1934; s. Frank D. and Dorothy Mae (Cole) W.; m. Jane Tatman, Aug. 25, 1979; children—Steven F., Leah R. B.A., DePauw U. 1957. Chmn., chief exec. officer Walker Group, Indpls., 1960—, Walker Clin. Evaluations,

Inc., Indpls., 1986—; bd. dirs. Am. United Life Ins. Co., NBD Ind. Nat. Bank, State Life Ins. Co.; frequent speaker on market rsch. to various groups. Contbr. articles trade publs. Past mem. Indpls. Hist. Preservation Commn.; bd. dirs. Ind. Repertory Theatre, Meth. Hosp., United Way of Greater Indpls.; adv. council Indpls. Mus. Art, Buchanan Counseling Center; former chmn. Central Ind. Better Bus. Bur.; former chmn. Indpls. Econ. Devel. Corp.; trustee Children's Mus. Indpls., Univ. Indpls.; former bd. dirs. Jr. Achievement Central Ind., mem. adv. council; trustee The Children's Mus., YMCA Found.; bd. dirs. Citizens Gas and Coke Utility. With USAF, 1958-60. Mem. Council Am. Survey Research Orgns. (past chmn. bd.), Am. Mktg. Assn. (past pres. Ind. chpt.), Indpls. Sales and Mktg. Execs. Assn. (past pres.), Indpls. C. of C. (past chmn.), Mktg. Rsch. Assn. (hon. life), Sigma Chi. Republican. Methodist. Office: Walker Group 3939 Priority Way South Dr Indianapolis IN 46240-1438

WALKER, FRANK HOUSTON, JR., minister; b. Jennersville, Pa., Nov. 27, 1960; s. Frank H. Sr. and Betty J. (Daughton) W.; m. Christine D. Cretsinger, June 23, 1979; children: Sharon, Bethann, Cathryn, Tarilyn, Jonathan. BA, Covenant Coll., 1985; MDiv, Reformed Episcopal Sem., 1985. Ordained minister Reformed Episcopal Ch., 1986. Pastor Trinity Reformed Ch., Cin., 1987-89, Peace Reformed Ch., Napoleon, Ohio, 1989—; stated clk. Reformed Ch. in the U.S., Eureka, S.D., 1991—. Republican. Avocations: research, writing, computers. Office: Peace Reformed Ch 638 Huddle Rd Napoleon OH 43545-9134

WALKER, FRED ELMER, broadcasting executive; b. Trenton, N.J., May 31, 1931; s. Elmer and Adele F. (Decker) W.; m. Catharine Middleton Sullivan, Nov. 26, 1952; children: Catharine Walker Bergstrom, Elizabeth Walker Phillips, Frederick Christopher. Student, Trenton State Coll., 1952, NYU, 1953. Dir. pub. relations Sta. WPTZ-TV, Phila., 1953; v.p., gen. mgr. Sta. WTTM-AM, Trenton, 1956-59; gen. sales mgr. Sta. KYW-AM, Cleve., 1959-62; v.p., gen. mgr. Sta. KDKA-AM, Pitts., 1962-65, Sta. KYW-TV, Phila., 1965-67, Sta. KPIX-TV, San Francisco, 1967-69, Sta. WLWT-TV, Cin., 1969-71; pres. Broad St. Communications Corp., New Haven, 1971-85; v.p. radio group Westinghouse Broadcasting, N.Y.C., 1985-88; exec. v.p. Broad St. Ventures, N.Y.C., 1988—; pres. Broad St. TV Corp., 1988—, Broad. St. Mgmt. Corp., 1988—; bd. dirs. Broadcast Music, Inc., 1984-87, Call for Action, Washington, 1993—. Bd. dirs. Long Wharf Theatre, New Haven; chmn. Long Wharf Theatre Future Fund campaign, 1983-85, chmn. devel., 1986-90. chmn. and pres., 1990—; mem. Pres.'s Coun. Albertus Magnus Coll.; trustee Hamden Hall Country Day Sch., chmn. devel. com.; chmn. 250th fund dr. United Ch. Christ, 1987—. Recipient Alfred P. Sloan award, 1954, Ohio State Ednl. award, 1953; fellow Berkeley Coll. Yale U., 1976. Mem. Radio Advt. Bur. (dir.), TV Bur. Advt., Nat. Assn. Broadcasters, New Haven C. of C. (vice chmn.), New Haven Lawn Club, Quinnipiac Club. Republican. Office: Sturbridge Commons North Haven CT 06473 also: Long Wharf Theatre 222 Sargent Dr New Haven CT 06511-5955

WALKER, GEORGE HERBERT, III, investment banking company executive, lawyer; b. St. Louis, Mar. 16, 1931; s. George H. and Mary (Carter) W.; m. Sandra E. Canning, Dec. 23, 1955 (div. Oct. 1962); children: Mary Elizabeth, Wendy, Isabelle; m. Kimberly Gedge, July 27, 1968 (div. Jan. 1977); children: George H. IV, Carter; m. Carol Banta, Feb. 21, 1987. B.A., Yale U., 1953; LL.B., Harvard U., 1956. Bar: Conn. 1956. Gen. ptnr. G.H. Walker & Co. (later G.H. Walker, Laird Inc.), 1961-74; sr. v.p. White, Weld & Co. Inc., 1974-75, also bd. dirs.; chmn. bd. dirs. G.H. Walker & Co., 1973-74; exec. v.p. Stifel Nicolaus & Co., 1976-78, pres., CEO, 1978-92, chmn., 1982—, also bd. dirs.; civilian aide to sec. U.S. Army for Ea. Mo., 1973-80; bd. dirs. Laidlaw Corp., Lacledc Steel Co., Eck-Adams Corp.; bd. govs. Midwest Stock Exch., 1982-88. Bd. dirs. Downtown St. Louis Inc., 1975-90, chmn. 1984-86; bd. dirs. Webster U., chmn. bd., 1987-92; trustee Mo. Hist. Soc., St. Louis Children's Hosp., 1972-92, Jefferson Nat. Expansion Meml. Assn., 1992; vestryman St. Ann's Ch., Kennebunkport, Maine; mem. Mo. Rep. Ctrl. Com., 1983—; adv. bd. St. Louis Area coun. Boy Scouts Am., 1989—; trustee investment trust Episcopal Diocese of Mo.; hon. bd. dirs. Anti-Drug Abuse Edn. Fund, Inc., 1990—; bd. dirs. St. Louis Zoo, 1992. With USAF, 1956-58. Mem. Rotary (St. Louis club). Home: 136 S Price Rd Saint Louis MO 63124-1858 Office: Stifel Fin Corp 500 N Broadway Saint Louis MO 63102-2110

WALKER, GEORGE KONTZ, law educator; b. Tuscaloosa, Ala., July 8, 1938; s. Joseph Henry and Catherine Louise (Indorf) W.; m. Phyllis Ann Sherman, July 30, 1966; children: Charles Edward, Mary Neel. BA, U. Ala., 1959; LLB, Vanderbilt U., 1966; AM, Duke U., 1968; LLM, U. Va., 1972; postgrad. (Sterling fellow), Law Sch. Yale U., 1975-76. Bar: Va. 1967, N.C. 1976. Law clk. U.S. Dist. Ct., Richmond, Va., 1966-67; assoc. Hunton, Williams, Gay, Powell & Gibson, Richmond, 1967-70; pvt. practice Charlottesville, Va., 1970-71; asst. prof. Law Sch. Wake Forest U., Winston-Salem, N.C., 1972-73, assoc. prof. Law Sch., 1974-77, prof. Law Sch., 1977—, dir. grad. studies in law, 1994—; mem. bd. advisors Divinity Sch. Wake Forest U., 1991—; dir. grad. studies in law Wake Forest U., Winston-Salem, N.C., 1994—; Charles H. Stockton prof. internat. law U.S. Naval War Coll., 1992-93; vis. prof. Marshall-Wythe Sch. Law, Coll. William and Mary, Williamsburg, Va., 1979-80, U. Ala. Law Sch., 1985; cons. Naval War Coll., 1976—, Nat. Def. Exec. Res., 1991—, Naval War Coll., Operational Law Adv. Bd., 1993—. Author: International Law for the Naval Commander, 1985; contbr. articles to profl. jours. With USN, 1959-62, capt. USNR, ret. Woodrow Wilson fellow, 1962-63; recipient Joseph Branch Alumni Svc. award, Wake Forest, 1988; named Hon. Atty. Gen. N.C., 1986. Mem. ABA, Va. Bar Assn., N.C. Bar Assn., Am. Soc. Internat. Law (exec. coun. 1988-91), Internat. Law Assn., Am. Judicature Soc., Am. Law Inst., Maritime Law Assn., Order of Barristers, Piedmont Club, Phi Beta Kappa, Sigma Alpha Epsilon, Phi Delta Phi. Democrat. Episcopalian. Home: 3321 Pennington Ln Winston Salem NC 27106-5439 Office: Wake Forest U Sch Law PO Box 7206 # U Winston Salem NC 27109

WALKER, GEORGE THEOPHILUS, JR., composer, pianist, music educator; b. Washington, June 27, 1922; s. George Theophilus Sr. and Rosa (King) W.; m. Helen Siemens; children: Gregory, Ian. MusB, Oberlin Coll., 1941; student of, Rudolf Serkin, Rosario Scalero; Artist Diploma, Curtis Inst. music, 1945; student, Nadia Boulanger; D of Mus. Arts, U. Rochester, 1957; DFA (hon.), Lafayette Coll., 1982; MusD (hon.), Oberlin Coll., 1983; student of, Nadia Boulanger. Instr. Dillard U., New Orleans, 1953-54; instr. Dalcroze Sch. Music, N.Y.C., 1960-61, New Sch. Social Research, N.Y.C. 1961; instr. to assoc. prof. Smith Coll., Northampton, Mass., 1961-68; assoc. prof. U. Colo., Boulder, 1968-69; disting. prof. Rutgers U., Newark, 1976-92, prof. emeritus, 1992; concert pianist Nat. Concert Artists, N.Y.C., 1950-53, Columbia Artists, N.Y.C., 1959-60; adj. prof. Peabody Inst. Johns Hopkins U., Balt., 1973-76; disting. prof. U. Del., Newark, 1975-76. Composer: Sonata for 2 Pianos (Harvey Gaul prize 1963), numerous sonatas, cantatas and concertos, Concerto for Cello and Orch., 1982, Sinfonias for Orch. Bd. dirs. Am. Bach Found., 1988. Recipient award Am. Acad. and Inst. Arts and Letters, 1982, Koussevitsky award, 1988; grantee Smith Coll., U. Colo., Rutgers U. Rsch. Coun., NEA, N.J. State Coun. for Arts; Fulbright fellow, 1957; John Hay Whitney fellow, 1958; Guggenheim fellow, 1971, 75. Mem. ASCAP, Am. Bach Found. (bd. dirs. 1988), Am. Symphony League. Democrat. Avocations: tennis, photography, audio. Home: 323 Grove St Montclair NJ 07042-4223

WALKER, GEORGE W., bishop. Bishop, treas. Bd. Bishops AME Zion Ch., flossmoor, Il. Office: AME Zion Church 3654 Poplar Rd Flossmoor IL 60422

WALKER, GORDON DAVIES, former government official, writer, lecturer, consultant; b. Logan, Utah, July 10, 1944; s. Rudger Harper and Fawn Lucile (Davies) W.; m. Carlene Martin, June 5, 1968; children—Kimberly Anne, Kelly Anne, Gordon Davies Jr., Bradford Martin. A.B., Brigham Young U., 1968; M.B.A., Harvard U., 1971. Project dir. Becker Research Co., Boston, 1969-71; dir. mktg. Am. Nat. Enterprises, Salt Lake City, 1971-72; v.p., dir. Sweetwater Properties, Salt Lake City, 1972-76; gen. ptnr. Covecrest Properties, Salt Lake City, 1976—; spl. asst. to sec. HUD, Washington, 1981-82; dep. under sec. HUD, 1983-86; cons. real estate, fin. Commerce Cons., Washington, 1986-87; pres., chief exec. officer Deseret Fed. Savs. and Loan, Salt Lake City, 1987-88; pres. U.S. Resources, Inc., Phoenix, 1988-92, also bd. dirs.; pres. Energy Lock Inc., Salt Lake City, 1992—. Author: Finance Your Own Way to Success, 1980; Develop Your Road to

Success, 1981; Hottest New Ideas of the 1980's, 1982. Rep. state del., Salt Lake City, 1974; del. Rep. Nat. Conv., 1988. Mem. Nat. Assn. Realtors. Mem. LDS Ch.

WALKER, GORDON T., lawyer; b. June 12, 1942; M. Nancy Geary; children: Angus, Gwendolyn. AB, Tufts U., 1964; LLB, Harvard U., 1967. Bar: Mass. 1968, U.S. Dist. Ct. Mass., U.S. Ct. Appeals (1st cir.), U.S. Supreme Ct. Assoc., then ptnr. Hale and Dorr, Boston, 1968-82; ptnr. Finnegan, Stanzler, Nadeau & Walker, Boston, 1982-84; ptnr., head litigation dept. McDermott, Will & Emery, Boston, 1984—. Mem. ABA (co-chmn. litigation sect. alternative dispute resolution com. 1986-91, vice chmn. 1993—), Am. Arbitration Assn., Boston Bar Assn. (chair com. internat. dispute resolution 1992—). Office: McDermott Will & Emery 75 State St Ste 1700 Boston MA 02109-1812

WALKER, GRAHAM CHARLES, biology educator; b. Boston, Feb. 8, 1948; s. Charles Bertram and Margaret Elizabeth (Biehn) W.; m. Janet Elizabeth Haliburton, May 30, 1970; 1 child, Gordon Andrew. BSc with honors, Carleton U., Ottawa, Ont., Can., 1970; PhD, U. Ill., 1974. Asst. prof. biology MIT, Cambridge, Mass., 1976-80, assoc. prof. biology, 1980-86; prof. biology MIT, Cambridge, 1986—. Editor-in-chief Jour. Bacteriology, 1991—, editor, 1985-91; editorial bd. Mutation Rsch. Amsterdam, Netherlands, 1982—; contbr. articles to Procs. NAS USA, Cell, Microbiology Rev. Housemaster McCormick Hall, MIT, Cambridge, 1986-92. Margaret MacVicar Faculty fellow MIT, 1992-2002, John Simon Guggenheim Meml. fellow, 1984, Woodrow Wilson fellow, 1970; recipient Rita Allen Career Devel. award, 1978-83. Mem. Am. Soc. for Microbiology, Genetics Soc. Am., Am. Chem. Soc., Environ. Mutagen Soc. Achievements include discovery of umuDC analogs on plasmid pKM101; demonstration of repetoire of SOS genes; demonstrated critical role of exopolysaccharide in nodule invation by Rhizobium meliloti; cloning and analysis of roles of UmuDC in UV mutagenesis; demonstrated RecA-mediated cleavage activates UmuD, second symbiotically active exopolysaccharide in R. meliloti, DnaK as a molecular thermometer, differential transcriptional activation by Ada protein. Office: MIT Biology Dept 77 Massachusetts Ave Cambridge MA 02139

WALKER, H. LAWSON, lawyer; b. Cin., Feb. 10, 1949; s. H. Lawson and Lucille (Kerr) W.; m. Peggy L. Walker, June 1, 1974; children: Erin, Jonathan. BBA, U. Coll. of Bus., Cin., 1972; JD, U. Cin. Coll. of Law, Cin., 1975. Bar: 6th cir. 1975, U.S. Dist. Ct. (Ohio dist.) 1975, ED Ky. 1975, Ohio 1975, Ky. 1976. Assoc. Riggs & Riggs, Erlanger, Ky., 1975-80; ptnr. Riggs, Riggs & Walker, Erlanger, Ky., 1980-87, Dinsmore & Shohl, Florence, Ky., 1987—; dir. Liberty Nat. Bank of No. Ky. State rep. Ky. Legislature, Frankfort, Ky., 1987; chmn. Rep. Party, Kenton County, Ky., 1980, 85; chmn. No. Ky. Legis. Caucus, 1991—; dir., U. Cin. Alumni Assn., 1988; deacon Lakeside Christian Ch., Ft. Mitchell, Ky., 1983—; dir. No. Ky. Easter Seals, Covington, Ky., 1982—. Recipient Leadership award, Ky. C. of C., Frankfort, 1988. Mem. No. Ky. Bar Assn., Ohio Bar Ass., Ky. Bar Assn., Ky. Sch. Bd. Atty. Assn., Ky. Acad. Trial Attys. Republican. Christian. Home: 28A Linden Hill Dr Covington KY 41017-1308 Office: Dinsmore & Shohl 7300 Turfway Rd Ste 430 Florence KY 41042-1397

WALKER, HAROLD BLAKE, minister; b. Denver, May 7, 1904; s. Herbert R. and Ethel G. (Blake) W.; m. Mary Alice Corder, Feb. 1, 1930; children—Herbert Elwood, Howard Deane, Timothy Blake. AB, U. Denver, 1925, DD, 1952; AM, Boston U., 1927; BD, McCormick Theol. Sem., 1932; postgrad., U. Chgo., 1933-34; DD, Emporia Coll., 1944, Hamilton Coll., 1949, U. Denver, 1952, Rocky Mountain Coll., 1971; LHD, Lake Forest U., 1959, Nat. Coll. Edn., 1970; STD, Northwestern U., 1970. Editor, writer A.P., Kansas City, 1927-30; ordained to ministry Presbyn. Ch., 1932; minister Fullerton-Covenant Ch., Chgo., 1932-36; minister First Ch., Utica, N.Y., 1936-42, Oklahoma City, 1942-47; minister 1st Presbyn. Ch., Evanston, Ill., 1947-69; columnist Splty. Syndicate mag., 1954-67, Chgo. Tribune-N.Y. News syndicated columnist, 1954-81; lectr. homiletics McCormick Theol. Sem.; lectr. bd. dirs. Harold Blake Walker chair pastoral theology; cons. W. Clement Stone Enterprises, 1970-74; sem. v.p. Bd. Fgn. Missions Presbyn. Ch. U.S.A.; Nat. Commn. Evangelism, 1946-47; dir. Presbyn. Tribune, 1943-55; mem. Presbyn. Commn. on Consolidation, 1957-58, Commn. on Ecumenical Mission Relations, 1958-61. Author: Going God's Way, 1946, Ladder of Light, 1951, Upper Room on Main Street, 1954, Power to Manage Yourself, 1955, (with wife) Venture of Faith, 1959, Heart of the Christian Year, 1962, Faith for Times of Tension, 1963, Thoughts to Live By, 1965, To Conquer Loneliness, 1966, Prayers to Live By, 1966, Memories to Live By, 1968, Inspirational Thoughts for Everyday, 1970, Days Demanding Courage, 1978, History of St. John's of Red Cross of Constantine, 1985, Caring Community, 1986; contbr. to religious publs. Bd. dirs. Nat. Presbyn. Ch. and Ctr., Washington; bd. dirs. McCormick Theol. Sem., pres., 1953-55, 57-71; bd. dirs. Ill. Masonic Med. Center, Chgo., Lake Forest Coll.; trustee Maryville Coll. Recipient DeMolay Legion of Honor; Freedoms Found. sermon prize, 1950, 55, 77; citations Protestant Fund. Greater Chgo., 1970; Chgo. Inst. Medicine Citizens fellow, 1987; citations Chgo. Friends of Lit., 1971, 79; Disting. Alumnus award McCormick Theol. Sem., 1979. Mem. Utica Council Chs. (pres. 1940), Am. Theol. Soc. Chgo. Cleric, Pi Kappa Alpha. Clubs: Univ. (Chgo.). Lodge: Masons (Chgo., Evanston) (Shriner, 33 deg. grand chaplain N.Y. 1940-41). Home: 422 Davis St Evanston IL 60201-4688

WALKER, HAROLD OSMONDE, newspaper and cable television executive; b. Bronxville, N.Y., Aug. 1, 1928; s. Harold Osmonde and Marie Louise (Clinch) Walker; m. Dorothy Jean Tollifson, Aug. 21, 1954; children: Pamela Gardner, Richard Talbot. AB, Harvard U., 1953, MBA, 1962. Asst. contr. Copley Press, Inc., La Jolla, Calif., 1962-66, dir. corp. planning, 1974-76, v.p., 1976-78, v.p. mktg., planning and rsch., 1978-90; sec. Copley Internat. Corp., La Jolla, Calif., 1965-66, treas., 1967-69, v.p.s., 1969-86, 71-74; v.p. Copley/Colony (Cablevision) Inc., Providence, 1984-90; pres., treas. Emerald Baseball, Inc., Eugene, Oreg., 1979-82; asst. sec. Ivac Corp., San Diego, 1968-70, v.p. 1968, exec. v.p. 1969-70; sec. Spasors Electronics Corp., San Diego, 1964-65, treas. 1964-68, v.p. 1965-68. Contbr. articles to profl. jours. Sgt. U.S Army, 1946-49; capt. USAF, 1953-60. Mem. Internat. Newspaper Fin. Execs., Nat. Assn. Bus. Economists, Harvard Bus. Sch. Assn. of San Diego (pres. 1965-66), San Diego Press Club, Harvard Club of San Diego, La Jolla Beach and Tennis Club. Republican. Home: 5528 Via Callado La Jolla CA 92037-7835

WALKER, HARRY GREY, retired state supreme court justice; b. Ovett, Miss., Sept. 30, 1924; s. Chester A. and Ina (Mangum) W.; m. Carrie Thorne Lang, Apr. 4, 1953; 1 child, Harry Grey. LLB, U. Miss., 1952. Bar: Miss. 1952. Pvt. practice law Gulfport, Miss., 1952-64; judge Harrison County (Miss.) Ct., 1964-68; cir. judge Harrison, Hancock and Stone Counties, Miss., 1968-73; justice Miss. Supreme Ct., 1973-82; presiding justice Miss. Supreme Ct., Jackson, 1982-86, chief justice, 1986-87. Mem. Miss. Ho. of Reps., 1964. Served with USCG, 1942-44. Mem. Am. Judicature Soc., Miss. Bar, DAV, Paralyzed Vets. Am., Am. Legion, Rotary, Elks, Magnolia Hunting Club, Phi Alpha Delta, Kappa Alpha. Democrat. Methodist. Home: 23 53rd St Gulfport MS 39507-4551

WALKER, HENRY GILBERT, health care executive, consultant; b. Gowanda, N.Y., Feb. 16, 1947; s. Henry George and Grace Dayton (Moore) W.; m. Elaine Ruth Darbee, July 18, 1970 (div. Dec. 1979); 1 child, Matthew Case; m. Patricia Ann Andrade, May 14, 1983; children: Michael David, Christopher John. B.S. in Indsl. Engring., Cornell U., 1969; M.B.A., U. Chgo., 1975. Evening adminstr. Rush-Presbyn. St.-Luke's Med. Ctr., Chgo., 1973-75; mgmt. cons. Booz, Allen & Hamilton, Chgo., 1975-79; regional adminstr., v.p. S.W. Community Health Service, Albuquerque, 1979-83; adminstr., v.p. S.W. Community Health Service, 1983-86, v.p., Exec. v.p. Presbyn. Healthcare Services, Albuquerque, 1986-92; pres., CEO Tucson Med. Ctr., 1992—. Campaign mgr. United Fund, Newport, R.I., 1971, 72; bd. dirs. Park Dist., Elmhurst, Ill., 1978, 79; mem. Dist. III Community Action Com., Albuquerque, 1985; div. chmn. United Way of Albuquerque, 1985, 88. Recipient Hosp. Survey award U. Chgo., 1975, Bachmeyer award U. Chgo., 1975, Outstanding Midshipman award Cornell U., 1969; named one of Emerging Healthcare Leaders, Hosp. Forum Mag., 1985, 86, Healthcares Up and Comers, Modern Healthcare Mag., 1987. Mem. Am. Coll. Healthcare Execs., Healthcare Fin. Mgmt. Assn., Am. Hosp. Assn., N.Mex. Hosp. Assn. (chmn. bd. dirs. 1983-85, treas. 1991—), Healthcare Forum (bd.

dirs., chmn. elect). Democrat. Presbyterian. Avocations: reading; hiking; skiing; tennis.

WALKER, H(ERBERT) LESLIE, JR., architect; b. Wilmington, N.C., July 6, 1918; s. Herbert Leslie and May Bell (Sellers) W.; m. Elnita Frances Sellers, June 18, 1939 (dec.); children: Judy S., Robert L.; m. Ernie Katherine Watson, July 20, 1973. Student, N.C. State Coll., Raleigh, 1939-40, Duke U., 1948-49. Apprentice architect H. Raymond Weeks, architect, Durham, N.C., 1946-56; ptnr. Walker & Jackson, architects and engrs., Tampa, Fla., 1959-61; prin. H. Leslie Walker & Assocs., architects, Tampa, 1961-65, 66-71; ptnr. Walker & Weilage, Tampa, 1965-66, Walker & McLane, Architects, Engrs. & Planners Inc., Tampa, 1972-75; pres. H. Leslie Walker, Architect Inc., Tampa, 1975—. Fellow AIA (dir. Fla. region 1973-75, chmn. govtl. affairs commn. 1975, chmn. architect-engr. com. fedn. constrn. 1975, chmn. fed. agencies com. 1976-77, pres. Fla. Cen. chpt. 1962-63; Pullara Meml. award Fla. Cen. chpt. 1973, medal of honor 1974, pres. Fla. assn. 1969; Design Competition Honor award Fla. assn. 1965, Design Competition award merit 1966). Democrat. Clubs: Palma Ceia Golf and Country, Tampa Commerce (pres. 1964). Lodges: Masons (32 degree), Shriners. Home: 4645 Bay Crest Dr Tampa FL 33615-4901 Office: H Leslie Walker Architect Inc 7926 W Hillsborough Ave Ste D Tampa FL 33615-4600

WALKER, HERSCHEL, professional football player; b. Wrightsville, Ga., Mar. 3, 1962; m. Cindi Di Angelis. BS in Criminal Justice, U. Ga., 1984. Football player N.J. Generals, 1983-85, Dallas Cowboys, 1986-89, Minn. Vikings, 1989-91, Phila. Eagles, 1992-95, N.Y. Giants, 1995—. Named to Sporting News coll. All-Am. team, 1980-82, United States Football League All-Star team, 1983, 85, Pro Bowl, 1987, 88; recipient Heisman trophy, 1982; named Sporting News Coll. Football Player of Yr., 1982, Sporting News United States Football League Player of Yr., 1985. Office: NY Giants Giants Stadium East Rutherford NJ 07073*

WALKER, HOWARD ERNEST, lawyer; b. Mobile, Ala., Mar. 3, 1944; s. Ernest W. and Denise (Kearney) W.; m. Michelle Ann Pinsonneault, June 20, 1992. BA, U. Ill., 1966; JD, Boston U., 1974. Bar: R.I. 1974. Assoc. Hinckley, Allen & Snyder, Providence, R.I., 1974-80, ptnr., 1980—. Trustee Providence Pub. Libr., 1978—, pres. 1988-92; trustee R.I. Civic Chorale & Orchestra, 1988—. Lt. USNR, 1967-71. Mem. ABA, R.I. Bar Assn. (chmn. superior ct. bench/bar com. 1990-93, 94—), Maritime Law Assn. of U.S., Nat. Assn. R.R. Trial Counsel, Def. Rsch. Inst., Phi Kappa Phi, Phi Beta Kappa. Avocations: Western Americana, nat. hist. Home: 39A Berrie Ln PO Box 118 Rockville RI 02873-0118 Office: Hinckley Allen & Snyder 1500 Fleet Ctr Providence RI 02903

WALKER, HOWARD KENT, diplomat; b. Newport News, Va., Dec. 3, 1935; s. William Roscoe and Jean Marie (King) W.; m. Terry Berkley Taylor, Sept. 10, 1960; children: Gregory, Wendy. BA, U. Mich., 1957, MA, 1958; PhD, Boston U., 1968. Joined Fgn. Svc., Dept. State, 1970; polit. officer Am. Embassy, Lagos, Nigeria, 1970-71; prin. officer Am. Consulate, Kaduna, Nigeria, 1971-73; internat. rels. officer Dept. State, Washington, 1973-75; polit. counselor Am. Embassy, Amman, Jordan, 1975-77; dep. chief of mission Am. Embassy, Tanzania, 1977-79, Republic of South Africa, 1979-82; amb. to Togo Lome, 1982-84; dir. affairs fellow Ctr. for Study Fgn. Affairs, 1984-85; dir. Office of West Africa Dept. State, Washington, 1985-87, sr. inspector Office Inspector Gen., 1987-89; amb. to Madagascar and The Comoros Islands Antananarivo, 1989—. 1st lt. USAF, 1962-65. Office: Am Embassy Antananrivo Dept State Washington DC 20521-2040

WALKER, IRVING EDWARD, lawyer; b. Balt., Jan. 31, 1952; s. Bertram and Mildred (Shapiro) W.; m. Laura Sachs, May 21, 1978; children: Brandon Harris, Aaron Seth, Emily Celeste. BA, Duke U., 1973; JD, U. Md., 1978. Bar: Md. 1978, U.S. Dist. Ct. Md. 1978, U.S. Ct. Appeals (4th cir.) 1980. Assoc. Frank, Bernstein, Conaway & Goldman, Balt., 1978-85, ptnr., 1986-91; ptnr. Miles & Stockbridge, Balt., 1991—; chair Bankruptcy & Creditors Rights Group, 1991—. Contbg. author: Bankruptcy Deskbook, 1986. Legal advisor Balt. chpt. The Holiday Project, San Francisco, 1982—; bd. dirs. Jewish Community Ctr. Greater Balt., 1986-88. Mem. ABA (mem. chpt. 11 subcom. 1993, co-chairperson task force 3rd, 4th and D.C. cirs.), Md. Bar Assn., Bar Assn. Balt. City (chmn. bankruptcy and bus. law com. 1989-90), Am. Bankruptcy Inst., Bankruptcy Assn. Dist. Md. (pres. 1992-93, chmn. Balt. chpt. 1989-91), Order of Coif. Avocation: sports. Office: Miles & Stockbridge 10 Light St Baltimore MD 21202-1435

WALKER, JAMES ELLIOT CABOT, physician; b. Bryn Mawr, Pa., Sept. 28, 1926; s. Arthur Meeker and Sylvia (Cabot) W.; m. Audrey Crowder Wakeman, July 11, 1965; children—Holly Barnwell, James Elliot Cabot. B.A., Williams Coll., 1949; M.D., U. Pa., 1953; M.S. in Hygiene, Harvard U., 1966. Intern and resident in medicine U. Wis., 1953, U. Mich., 1954-55, Peter Bent Brigham Hosp., 1958-60; assoc. dir., sr. assoc. dept. medicine Peter Bent Brigham Hosp., Boston; also research asst., lectr. Harvard U. Med. Sch., 1959-65; chmn. dept. community medicine U. Conn. Med. Sch., Farmington, 1966-86, prof. medicine, 1966—; vis. prof. St. Thomas' Hosp., London, 1975-76, Harvard Med. Sch., Cambridge, Mass. 1986-87; pres. Northeast Can./Am. Health Coun., 1978-87; dir. Ctr. for Internat. Cmty. Health Studies, 1981-86; assoc. dir. Traveler's Ctr. on Aging, 1987—; chmn. Alzheimers Coalition of Conn., 1992-94; med. dir. Avery Heights Retirement Cmty., 1992—. Author articles, monograph in field. Served with Am. Field Service, 1945; to capt. M.C. U.S. Army, 1955-58. Fellow ACP, AGS. Home: 111 Westmont St West Hartford CT 06117-2929 Office: U Conn Health Center Farmington CT 06032

WALKER, JAMES KENNETH, judge; b. Decatur, Tex., Jan. 10, 1936; s. James Bluford and Elmer Vernice (Clark) W.; m. Mary Frank Garrett, July 9, 1960 (dec. Nov. 1976); children—James Garrett, Steven Wade; m. Jo Beth Robertson, July 28, 1978; 1 child, Ann Elizabeth. LLB, Baylor U., 1960. Bar: Tex. 1960. Practice law Lubbock, Tex., 1960-63, Morton, Tex., 1963-84; judge 286th Dist. Ct., 1984-91; Cochran County atty., 1965-73, 79-84. Bd. dirs. Morton Indsl. Found. Mem. ABA, Tex. Bar Assn. Methodist. Club: Lion. Home: 218 Sandalwood Ln Levelland TX 79336-6816

WALKER, JAMES ROY, microbiologist; b. Chestnut, La., Nov. 8, 1937; s. Clint Cortez and Annie Mae (Holland) W.; m. Barbara Ann Fess, Aug. 8, 1959; children: James Bryan, Melinda Lee. BS, Northwestern State U., 1960; PhD, U. Tex., 1963. Asst. prof. U. Tex., Austin, 1967-71, assoc. prof., 1971-78, prof., 1978—, chmn. dept. microbiology, 1981-93. Contbr. articles to profl. jours. Served to capt. U.S. Army, 1963-65. Fellow NIH, 1965-67, Rosalie B. Hite U. Tex., 1960-63; grantee NIH, 1967-91, NSF, 1978-84, 91—, Am. Cancer Soc., 1976-91. Mem. Am. Soc. Microbiology (vis. professorship at Fed. U. Rio de Janeiro 1977). Home: 8504 Greenflint Ln Austin TX 78759-8131 Office: U Tex Dept Microbiology Austin TX 78712-1095

WALKER, JAMES SILAS, college president; b. LaFollette, Tenn., Aug. 21, 1933; s. John Charles and Ruth Constance (Yeagle) W.; m. Nadine Leas Mortenson, May 28, 1954; children: Steven J., David K., Bradley P., Scott C. BA, U. Ariz., 1954; BDiv, McCormick Theol. Sem., 1956; postgrad. U. Basel, Switzerland, 1956-57; PhD, Claremont Coll., 1963. Ordained to ministry Presbyn. Ch., 1956. Asst. pastor Central Presbyn. Ch., Denver, 1957-60; prof. Huron Coll., S.D., 1960-65, dean, 1960-67; prof. Hastings (Nebr.) Coll., 1966-75, dir. devel., 1975-79, dean, 1979-83; pres. Jamestown Coll., N.D., 1983—; adj. faculty mem. Luther Northwestern Theol. Sem., St. Paul, 1984—. Author: Theology of Karl Barth, 1963. Bd. dirs. Salvation Army, Rotary Internat. Found. fellow, 1956-57; Nat. Def. Title IV grantee, 1960-63. Mem. Assn. Presbyn. Colls. and Univs., Presbytery of No. Plains (coun.), Jamestown C. of C. (pres.), Rotary (dist. 563 gov. 1978-79). Republican. Avocations: travel, hunting, photography. Office: Jamestown Coll Office of Pres # 6080 Jamestown ND 58405

WALKER, JAMES WILLIAM, JR., lawyer; b. Birmingham, Ala., Aug. 19, 1927; s. James William and Eva Victoria (Harris) W.; m. Eileen Newton, Apr. 30, 1949; children: James William III, Michael, Lee, Helen, Caroline. AB, Birmingham So. Coll., 1949; JD, Emory U., 1953. Bar: Ga. 1954, D.C. 1966. With Merrill Lynch, Fenner & Smith, N.Y.C., 1954-67; exec. v.p. Am. Stock Exchange, N.Y.C., 1967-74, Securities Industry Assn. Washington, 1974-77; exec. v.p. gen. counsel INA Corp., Phila., 1977-82; exec. v.p., gen. counsel CIGNA Corp., Phila., 1982-92, ret., 1992. Mem.

Emory U. Law Sch. Coun.; trustee Phila. Mus. Art. Capt. U.S. Army, 1946-48, Res. 1948-57. Mem. ABA, Am. Law Inst., Union League Phila.

WALKER, JERALD CARTER, university administrator, minister; b. Bixby, Okla., May 22, 1938; s. Joseph Carter and Trula Tosh (Jackson) W.; m. Virginia Canfield, Apr. 14, 1963; children: Elisabeth Katherine, Anne Carter. BA in Sociology, Oklahoma City U., 1960; BD, U. Chgo., 1964; D of Religion, Sch. Theology at Claremont, 1966. Ordained to ministry Meth. Ch., 1964. Dir., campus minister Campus Christian Assn., Chgo., 1961-64; minister of outreach Temple Meth. Ch., San Francisco, 1965-66; chaplain, asst. prof. religion Nebr. Wesleyan U., Lincoln, 1966-69; pres. John J. Pershing Coll., Beatrice, Nebr., 1969-70; v/p. univ. rels., assoc. prof. Southwestern U., Georgetown, Tex., 1970-74; pres. Baker U., Baldwin, Kans., 1974-79, Oklahoma City U., 1979—; ednl. adv. to bd. dirs. Tianjin U. Commerce, People's Republic of China; participant Okla. Ann. Conf. of United Meth. Ch. Co-author: The State of Sequoyah: An Impressionistic View of Eastern Oklahoma, 1985; contbr. chpt. book, articles to profl. jours. Bd. dirs., past chmn. Okla. Ind. Coll. Found. Recipient Alumni Recognition award Nebr. 4H Club, 1970, Okla. 4H Club, Disting. Alumnis award Oklahoma City U., 1974, Outstanding Citizen award Dist. 575 Rotary Internat., 1990, Award for Excellence Asia Soc. Okla., 1990, Humanitarian award for Okla/Ark. region NCCJ, 1992, Nat. Police Adminstrn. award for promotion or peace and order Rep. of China, 1992, Francis Asbury award for fostering United Meth. Ministries in Higher Edn., 1994. Mem. Nat. Assn. Schs. and Colls. of United Meth. Ch. (past pres.), Nat. Assn. Colls. and Univs. (bd. dirs.). Office: Oklahoma City U 2501 N Blackwelder Ave Oklahoma City OK 73106-1493

WALKER, JERRY VANZANT, lawyer; b. Casa Grande, Ariz., Dec. 12, 1925; s. Gerald Lee and Mildred (McMeans) W.; m. Virginia Lee Ridenhower, Dec. 18, 1948; children: Jerry Vanzant, Lucinda Lee. B.S., Tex. A&M U., 1949; LL.B., U. Tex., 1952. Bar: Tex. 1952. Since practiced in Houston; ptnr. Fulbright & Jaworski, 1952-86; vis. prof. med. jurisprudence Baylor Coll. Medicine; pres. Houston Jr. Bar Assn., 1960. Served with AUS, 1944-46. Fellow Am. Coll. Trial Lawyers; mem. ABA (com. admiralty and maritime law 1979-82, commn. med. profl. liability 1975-80, vice chmn. sect. ins., negligence and compensation 1976-79, vice chmn. sect. litigation 1979-80), State Bar Tex. (chmn. tort and compenation sect. 1966-67), Houston Bar Assn. (chmn. inter-profession relations with physicians com. 1970-74), Houston Assn. Def. Counsel (1st v.p. 1971), Tex. Assn. Def. Counsel, State Bar Tex. (dir. 1960-61), Internat. Assn. Ins. Counsel (pres. 1975-76), Def. Research Inst. (exec. com., dir. 1974-77, vice chmn. com. to improve adminstrn. civil justice 1976-77), Am. Bar Found., Tex. Bar Found., Houston Bar Found., Maritime Law Assn. U.S. (com. maritime internat. 1978-82), Houston C. of C. (life). Republican. Presbyterian. Clubs: Houston Country. Home: 101 Westcott St 1706 Houston TX 77007 Office: Houston Nat Bank Bldg 5757 Memorial Dr Ste 210 Houston TX 77007-8000

WALKER, JIMMIE KENT, mechanical engineer; b. Lawton, Okla., May 1, 1940; s. James K. and Ruth L. (Fleming) W.; m. Carol T. Walker, Mar. 22, 1962; (div. Aug. 1979); children: Mollie Walker Freeman, Keith M.; m. Joan F. Koeth, Feb. 11, 1983; 1 stepson, Raymond Van Buskirk. BSME, Okla. U., 1963; MBA, U.S.D., 1991. Design engr. Cessna Aircraft, Hutchinson, Kans., 1965-68, 72-75; chief engr. Lyons (Kans.) Mfg. Corp., 1968-72; sales engr. Prince Mfg. Co., Sioux City, Iowa, 1975-79, mfg. mgr., 1979-83, dir. engring., 1983—. Treas. Hutchinson Jaycees, 1968; pres. Lyons Jaycees, 1970; mem. adv. bd. adult edn. Western Iowa Tech., Sioux City, 1980-90, Cosmo, 1992-93; judge Physics Olympics, 1992-94; bd. dirs. Jr. Achievement Sioux City, 1993-94. Maj. U.S. Army, 1972. Mem. Am. Welding Soc., Am. Soc. Metals, Soc. Profl. Engrs., Tau Beta Pi, Sigma Tau, Beta Gamma Sigma. Roman Catholic. Achievements include patents for square wire, internal piston lock for hydraulic cylinders, design of high efficiency, square wire lock for telescopic hydraulic cylinder stop rings, low speed tractor pto pump, design of durable series/rephase implement carrier wheel cylinders, unique zero leakage telescopic, constant speed telescopic cylinder. Home: 4816 Royal Ct Sioux City IA 51104-1128 Office: Prince Mfg Co PO Box 537 Sioux City IA 51102-0537

WALKER, JOAN H., public relations executive. With N.J. State Govt., 1973-80; pres. Richmann & Ptnrs. Ltd., 1980-88; exec. v.p. office chmn. Saatchi & Saatchi Worldwide, 1988-89; mng. dir. mktg. comm. Nynex, 1990-92; pres. Bozell Pub. Rels., N.Y.C., 1993—. Office: Bozell Pub Rels 75 Rockefeller Plz New York NY 10019-6908

WALKER, JOHN ANDREW, mechanical engineer, educator; b. Hagerstown, Md., June 20, 1939; s. William Andrew and Harriet Marion (Raabe) W. B.S.M.E., U. Del., 1961; Ph.D., U. Tex., 1964. Teaching asst. U. Tex., Austin, 1961-64; mem. faculty dept. mech. engring. Northwestern U., Evanston, Ill., 1964—; prof. Northwestern U., 1975—. Author: Dynamical Systems and Evolution Equations, 1980; contbr. articles to profl. jours. Ford Found. fellow, 1961-64. Mem. Am. Math. Soc. Office: Northwestern Univ Mech Engring Dept Evanston IL 60201

WALKER, JOHN DENLEY, foundation director, former government official; b. Petersburg, Va., July 15, 1921; s. John Otey and Evelyn Mildred (Denley) W.; m. Diana Taylor, Apr. 30, 1949 (div. 1980); children—Walker Diana, John Denley, Joseph Warren; m. Helen Hoogerwerff, Mar. 15, 1984; step children—Saskia Roskam, Hugo, Frederick. B.A., U. N.C.-Chapel Hill, 1944; postgrad., U. Pa., 1950-51. Superintendant N.J. Bell, 1946-48; asst. dir. labor div. ECA, Paris, France, 1948-50; mgmt. cons., 1951-53; fgn. service res. officer U.S. Govt., Paris, Malta, Israel, Australia, 1953-77; exec. dir. English Speaking Union of U.S., N.Y.C., 1978-87. Contbr. articles to profl. jours. Bd. dirs. Am. Student Ctr., Paris, 1953-57; v.p. Ctr. for Security Studies, 1988—. Lt. USN, 1942-45. Episcopalian. Clubs: Pilgrims, Standrews (N.Y.C.); Univ. (Washington); Chevy Chase (Md.). Lodges: Legion of Valor, Soc. Cin., Order of St. Johns of Jerusalem. Home: 3271 P St NW Washington DC 20007-2756

WALKER, JOHN LOCKWOOD, lawyer; b. Atlanta, Sept. 3, 1952; s. James William and Doris (Camp) W.; m. Caroline Asher Walker, Jan. 16, 1952; children: Ann Caroline, John Lockwood Jr., Elizabeth Davis, Lindsay Eleise. BA, Duke U., 1974, JD, 1977. Atty. legal div. bd. govs. FRS, Washington, 1977-79; assoc. Simpson Thacher & Bartlett, N.Y.C. 1979-84; ptnr. Simpson, Thacher & Bartlett, N.Y.C., 1984—. Mem. Fin. Svcs. Vol. Corps (dir.), Coun. on Fgn. Rels., Met. Club of Washington, Univ. Club (N.Y.C.), Chevy Chase (Md.) Club, Bedford (N.Y.) Golf and Tennis Club. Democrat. Episcopalian. Office: Simpson Thacher & Bartlett 425 Lexington Ave New York NY 10017-3903

WALKER, JOHN MERCER, JR., federal judge; b. N.Y.C., Dec. 26, 1940; s. John Mercer and Louise (Mead) W.; m. Cristy West, June 20, 1980 (div. Apr. 1983); m. Katharine Kirkland, Feb. 14, 1987. BA, Yale U., 1962; JD, U. Mich., 1966. Bar: N.Y. 1969, U.S. Dist. Ct. (so. dist.) N.Y. 1971, U.S. Ct. Appeals (2d cir.) 1972, U.S. Supreme Ct. 1977, U.S. Ct. Appeals (D.C. cir.) 1982. Maxwell Sch. Pub. Adminstrn. fellow, state counsel Republic of Botswana, Africa, 1966-68; assoc. Davis, Polk and Warwell, N.Y.C., 1969-70; asst. U.S. atty. U.S. Dist. Ct. (so. dist.) N.Y., N.Y.C., 1971-75; assoc. to ptnr. Carter, Ledyard and Milburn, N.Y.C., 1975-81; asst. sec. enforcement ops. Dept. Treasury, Washington, 1981-85; judge U.S. Dist. Ct. (so. dist.) N.Y., 1985-89, U.S. Ct. Appeals (2nd cir.), 1989—; gen. counsel Nat. Coun. on Crime and Deliquency, N.Y.C., 1977-81; chmn. Fed. Law Enforcement Tng. Ctr., Washington, 1981-85; spl. counsel Adminstrv. Conf. of U.S., Washington, 1986-92; mem. budget com. of judicial conf., 1992—; dir. Inst. Judicial Adminstrn., 1992—. Del. Rep. Nat. Conv., Detroit, 1980. With USMCR, 1963-67. Recipient Alexander Hamilton award Sec. of Treas., Washington, 1985, Secret Service Honor award, 1985. Mem. ABA, D.C. Bar Assn., Assn. Bar City of N.Y., Fed. Judges Assn. (pres. 1993—), Heights Casino Club (Bklyn.). Republican. Episcopalian. Office: US Cir Ct US Courthouse 40 Foley Sq New York NY 10007-1551

WALKER, JOHN MICHAEL, environmental hydrogeologist, consultant; b. New Orleans, Apr. 9, 1947; s. William Jefferson and Frances Juanita (Nummy) W.; m. Terry Ann Leff, Aug. 22, 1969; children: Juli Christine, Erik Michael, Ariel Lindsey. BS in Geology, Old Dominion U., 1973; postgrad., Colo. State U., 1980. Cert. profl. geologist. Constrn. inspector U.S. Corps of Engrs., Arlington, Va., 1963-68; geologist U.S. Corps of Engrs.,

Norfolk, Va., 1970-73; field project engring. geologist U.S. Dept. Interior Bur. of Reclamation, Denver, 1974-78; project design engring. geologist U.S. Corps of Engrs., Savannah, Ga., 1978-81; sr. consulting engr. E.I. du Pont de Nemours & Co., Beaumont, Tex., 1981-91; ret., 1991; pres. Sci. Environ. Tng., Inc., Beaumont, Tex., 1989—; tng. com. Dupont Well Operators Network, 1988-89; cons. in field. Producer edn. films Geology, Injection Wells, 1989, Environ. Regulations, 1990. Planning com. Hazardous and Solid Waste Inst. U. Tex. Sch. of Law, Austin, 1988-89; mem. Environ. Health & Safety Law, 1990. Sgt. U.S. Army, 1968-70. Recipient Accomplishment award E.I. Dupont de Nemours & Co., Tenn., 1988, Bronze award for engring. excellence, Tex., 1990, Safety award Dept. of Interior, 1979, TELLY award for tng. film excellence, 1990, Environ. Excellence award Dupont Chems., 1992. Mem. Assn. Engring. Geology, Assn. Groundwater Scientists and Engrs., Underground Injection Practices Coun., The Platform Soc., MENSA. Republican. Episcopalian. Achievements include patent pending on "Dilithium Crystals," 1993; copyright on "Gifts of the Magi," 1993. Home and Office: SETI Inc 6795 Knollwood Dr Beaumont TX 77706-5408

WALKER, JOHN NEAL, agricultural engineering educator; b. Erie, Pa., Feb. 19, 1930; s. Gordon Durwood and Marie Katherine (Beck) W.; m. Betty Jane Bloeser, Aug. 14, 1954; children: David Thomas, Janet Ann. B.S. in Agrl. Engring, Pa. State U., M.S., 1958; Ph.D., Purdue U., 1961. Registered profl. engr., cons., Ky. Extension agrl. engr. Pa. State U., 1954-58; mem. faculty U. Ky., 1960—; prof. agrl. engring., 1966-74, chmn. dept., 1974-81, acting dir. Inst. Mining and Minerals Research, 1981-82, assoc. dean Coll. Agr., 1982-88, assoc. dean Coll. Engring., 1989—, dir. Ctr. for Robotics and Mfg. Systems, 1991—; Duggar lectr. Auburn (Ala.) U., 1976. Author articles in field, chpts. in books. Officer USNR, 1951-77. Named Gt. Tchr. U. Ky. Alumni Assn., 1974. Fellow Am. Soc. Agrl. Engrs. (exec. coun. 1984-87, 88-91, v.p. adminstrv. coun. 1984-87, pres. 1989-90, MBMA award 1974); mem. Order Ky. Cols. Office: U Ky 177 Anderson Hall Lexington KY 40506

WALKER, JOHN PATRICK, theater director, actor; b. Elgin, Ill., Apr. 21, 1956; s. John Patrick and Ruth Ellen (Borror) W.; m. Pamela Jean Gay, Dec. 5, 1981; children: Miranda, Caitlin. BA, Notre Dame U., 1978; cert., Am. Conservatory Theatre, San Francisco, 1980. Actor Peninsula Players, Door County, Wis., 1978-84, gen. mgr., 1984-86; house mgr. Civil Ctr. Performing Arts, Chgo., 1984-86; gen. mgr. Royal George Theater, Chgo., 1986-89, Cullen, Henaghan, Platt, Chgo., 1989-91; mng. dir. Victory Gardens Theater, Chgo., 1991—; imm. mktg. com., bd. dirs. League of Chgo. Theaters. Avocations: fly fishing, skiing. Office: Victory Gardens Theater 2257 N Lincoln Ave Chicago IL 60614-3717

WALKER, JOHN SUMPTER, JR., lawyer; b. Richmond, Ark., Oct. 13, 1921; s. John Sumpter, Martha (Wilson) W.; m. Eljana M. duVall, Dec. 31, 1947; children: John Stephen, Barbara Monika Ann, Peter Mark Gregory. BA, Tulane U., 1942; MS, U. Denver, 1952, JD, 1960; diploma Nat. Def. U., 1981. Bar: Colo. 1960, U.S. Dist. Ct. Colo. 1960, U.S. Supreme Ct., 1968, U.S. Ct. Appeals (10th cir.) 1960, U.S. Tax. Ct., 1981. With Denver & Rio Grande Western R.R. Co., 1951-61, gen. solicitor, 1961-89; pres. Denver Union Terminal Ry. Co. Apptd. gen. counsel Moffat Tunnel Commn., 1991. With U.S. Army, 1942-46. Decorated Bronze Star. Mem. Colo. Bar Assn., Arapahoe County Bar Assn., Alliance Francaise (life), Order of St. Ives, U. Denver Chancellors' Soc., Cath. Lawyers Guild. Republican. Roman Catholic. Club: Denver Athletic.

WALKER, JOSEPH, retired research executive; b. Rockford, Ill., Dec. 28, 1922; s. Joseph H. and Elizabeth (McEachran) W.; m. June Farley Enerson, Jan. 22, 1944; children—Joseph A., Amy E., Richard H., Jeanne A. B.S. with high honors, Beloit Coll., 1943; M.S., U. Wis., 1948, Ph.D., 1950. Sr. research chemist Pure Oil Co. Research Center, Crystal Lake, Ill., 1950-51; project technologist Pure Oil Co. Research Center, 1952-54, sect. supr., 1954-58, div. dir. analytical research and service div., 1958-64, research coordinator, 1964, dir. research, 1965; assoc. dir. research Union Oil Co. of Calif., Research Center, Brea, Calif., 1965-68; v.p. chem. research Union Oil Co. of Calif., Research Center, 1979-85. Pres. Sch. Bd., Crystal Lake, 1963-65. Served to lt. (j.g.) USNR, 1943-46. Mem. Am. Chem. Soc., Am. Petroleum Inst., Phi Beta Kappa, Sigma Xi, Phi Lambda Upsilon, Sigma Alpha Epsilon. Home: 406A Pasadena Ct San Clemente CA 92672-5479

WALKER, K. GRAHAME, manufacturing company executive; b. West Bridgford, Nottinghamshire, Eng., June 19, 1937; came to U.S., 1979; s. John P. and Lilian (Wright) W.; m. Robina Mary Bendell, Aug. 20, 1959 (div. 1979); children: Belinda Sharon, Victoria Jane; m. Shirley Dean Allison, Dec. 6, 1980. Student, Merchant Taylors' Sch., 1948-55; grad., Britannia Royal Naval Coll., 1955-57, Royal Naval Engring Coll., 1959-62. Mktg. exec. Rank Orgn., Eng., 1962-65; mng. dir. Hysol Sterling Ltd., Eng., 1965-74, Dexter GmbH, Fed. Republic Germany, 1974-79; pres. Hysol div. The Dexter Corp., Industry, Calif., 1979-85; pres. specialty chems. and services group The Dexter Corp., Windsor Locks, Conn., 1985-88; pres., chief operating officer Dexter Corp., Windsor Locks, Conn., 1988-89, pres., chief exec. officer, dir., 1989-93; chmn., pres., CEO The Dexter Corp., Windsor Locks, Conn., 1993—, also bd. dirs.; bd. dirs. Life Techs., Inc. (subs. Dexter Corp.). Bd. dirs. Greater Hartford chpt. ARC, 1988-89, chmn., 1990-92; bd. dirs. Barnes Group Inc., Bristol, 1988—, New Eng. Air Mus., Windsor Locks, 1988—; trustee Hartford U., 1992—; corporator St. Francis Hosp., 1994—, Hartford Hosp., 1990. Lt. Royal Navy, 1955-62. Mem. Conn. Bus. and Industry Assn. (bd. dirs. 1990, chmn. 1994), Hartford Club. Avocations: skiing, gardening, literature. Office: The Dexter Corp 1 Elm St Windsor Locks CT 06096-2334

WALKER, KENNETH DALE, automotive parts company executive; b. Ft. Worth, Feb. 25, 1948; s. Billy Glenn and Jo Ann (Prestridge) W.; m. Cheri Lee Propp, Feb. 28, 1969 (div. Aug. 1980); children: Joel Glenn, Corbett Dale; m. Vickie Lynn Franklin, Sept. 27, 1980. BBA, U. Tex., 1970. CPA, Tex. Mgr. Arthur Young & Co., Ft. Worth, 1970-76; controller, v.p. fin. Big 4 Automotive, Ft. Worth, 1976-80, v.p. ops West Tex., 1980-82, v.p. retail, 1982-84; chief fin. officer southwest region AI Automotive Corp., Ft. Worth, 1984-86, v.p. fin. ops., chief operating officer southwest region, 1986—. Instr. project bus. Jr. Achievement, Ft. Worth, 1981; bd. dirs. All Pro Program, Inc., Andolusia, Ala., 1978-84. Bumper to Bumper Program, Ft. Worth, 1987—. Recipient Automotive Replacement Edn. award Northwood Inst. 1987. Mem. Inst. Internal Auditors (v.p. 1975-76, pres. 1976), Automotive Warehouse Distbr. Assn. (chmn. fin. stats. com. 1984-87, chmn. univ. facalty 1986-87, bd. govs. 1986—, Pursuit of Excellence award 1986). Methodist. Clubs: Ridglea Country, Ft. Worth. Avocations: golf, skiing.

WALKER, KENNETH HENRY, architect; b. N.Y.C., June 11, 1940; s. Matthew and Lillian (Goldfarb) W. B.A., Brown U., 1962; M.Arch., Harvard U., 1966. Founder, pres. Walker Grad, 1973-76; founder, pres. Walker Group, N.Y.C., 1976-85, WalkerGroup/CNI, N.Y.C., 1985-93; pres. Retail Options, Inc., N.Y.C., 1993—; lectr. on design. Prin. works include Isetan Dept. Store, Tokyo, Saks 5th Ave., N.Y.C., John Wanamaker, Phila., Bloomingdales, Boca Raton, Fla., FAO Schwarz, N.Y.C., Citibank (nationally), Galeries Lafayette, France; contbr. articles to Time mag., Fortune, Interior Design, Archtl. Record, others; exhibited indsl. designs at Whitney Mus. Past pres. Art Adv. Com., Brown U. Providence, 1979-83; mem. architecture and design commn. Mus. Modern Art, N.Y.C., 1976-93; trustee Village of Dering Harbor, Shelter Island, N.Y., 1982-87; pres. alumni coun. Harvard U. Grad. Sch. Design, 1985-88. Named to Interior Design Hall of Fame, Interior Design mag., 1985. Fellow AIA (over 20 design awards); mem. Young Pres.'s Orgn., Inst. Store Planners, Harvard U. Alumni Assn. Office: Retail Options Inc 15 E 26th St New York NY 10010-1501

WALKER, KENT, lawyer; b. Geneva, Ill., Oct. 4, 1944; s. Robert and Jean (McCullough) W.; m. Helene Feinberg, Sept. 14, 1984; children: Forrest, Lowell, Molly. BA, Wheaton Coll., 1966; JD, Northwestern U., Evanston, Ill., 1969. Bar: Ill. 1969, Del. 1970, Pa. 1984; U.S. Dist. Ct. Del. 1971, U.S. Dist. Ct. D.C. 1973, U.S. Dist. Ct. (ea. dist.) Pa. 1984; U.S. Ct. Appeals (3rd cir.) 1972, U.S. Ct. Appeals D.C. 1972, U.S. Tax Ct. 1975. Dep. atty. gen. Del. Dept. Justice, Wilmington, 1971-72, state solicitor and chief, 1972-74; acting U.S. atty. U.S. Dept. Justice, Wilmington, 1977, 1st asst. U.S. atty., 1975-78; assoc. Garfinkel & Volpicelli, Phila., 1984-86; assoc., ptnr. Mesirov, Gelman, Jaffe, Cramer & Jamieson, Phila., 1986-89; ptnr. Ballard, Spahr,

Andrews & Ingersoll, Phila., 1989—. Mem. ABA, Pa. Bar Assn., Phila. Bar Assn., Del. State Bar Assn. Republican. Episcopalian. Office: Ballard Spahr Andrews 1735 Market St Philadelphia PA 19103-7501

WALKER, L. T., bishop. Bishop of Ark. ch. of God in Christ, Little Rock. Office: Ch of God in Christ 2315 S Chester St Little Rock AR 72206-2021

WALKER, LANNON, foreign service officer; b. Los Angeles, Jan. 17, 1936; s. James Orville and Esther W.; m. Arlette Daguet, July 14, 1954; children: Rachelle, Anne. B.S., Georgetown U., 1961. Fgn. service officer Dept. State, 71961; polit. officer Dept. State, Rabat, Morocco, 1962-64; prin. officer Dept. State, Constantine, Algeria, 1964-66; assigned Exec. Secretariat Dept. State, 1966-69; econ. counselor Dept. State, Tripoli, Libya, 1969-70; dep. chief mission Dept. State, Yaounde, Cameroon, 1971-73; adminstrv. counselor Dept. State, Saigon, Viet Nam, 1973-74; dep. chief mission Dept. State, Kinshasa, Zaire, 1974-77; dep. asst. sec. African Affairs Dept. State, Washington, 1977-82; spl. adviser African affairs Dept. State, 1983-84, dep. insp. gen., 1984-85, ambassador to Senegal, 1985-88, amb. to Nigeria, 1989-92; employed in pvt. sector, 1982-83; sr. assoc. Carnegie Endowment, 1988-89. Served with USAF, 1953-58. Mem. Am. Fgn. Service Assn. (chmn. 1966-69). Roman Catholic. Home: 5911 Overlea Rd Bethesda MD 20816-2455

WALKER, LELAND JASPER, civil engineer; b. Fallon, Nev., Apr. 18, 1923; s. Albert Willard and Grayce (Wilkinson) W.; m. Margaret Frances Noble, Jan. 21, 1946; children: Thomas, Margaret, Timothy. B.S. in Civil Engring, Iowa State U., 1944; D. Eng. (hon.), Mont. State U., 1983. Engr. with various govtl. depts., 1946-51, 53-55; v.p. Wenzel & Co. (cons. engrs.), Great Falls, Mont., 1955-58; pres., chmn. bd. No. Engring and Testing, Inc., Great Falls, 1958-88; pres. Ind. Labs. Assurance Co., 1977-79; bd. dirs. Mont. Power Co., Entech Inc., 1982-92, Lewis and Clark Biologicals, Inc., 1989-92, Applied Tech., Inc. Pres., trustee Endowment and Rsch. Found. Mont. State U., 1969-82, Mont. Deaconess Hosp., Great Falls, 1959-67, McLaughlin Rsch. Inst. Biol. Scis., 1989-92, Mont. Sch. Deaf and Blind Found., 1984—; trustee Rocky Mountain Coll., 1977-80, Dufresne Found., 1979-87; chmn., bd. dirs. Mont. Tech. Svcs. Adv. Coun. adv. coun. Engring. Coll. Mont. State U.; bd. dirs. Mont. State Fair, Engring. Socs. Commn. on Energy, 1977-79, Mont. Bd. Sci. and Tech., 1983-88, Great Falls Chamber Found., 1989-91. Fellow ASCE (pres. 1976-77), AAAS, Cons. Engrs. Coun. (pres. Mont. 1971), Accrediting Bd. Engring. and Tech. (v.p. 1978-79, pres. 1980-83); mem. Nat. Acad. Engring., Am. Coun. Ind. Labs. (hon. sec. 1973-76), Meadowlark Country Club, Pachyderm Club (bd. dirs., v.p. 1992—), Chi Epsilon (nat. hon.), Tau Beta Pi (hon.). Republican. Methodist. Home: 2819 8th Ave S Great Falls MT 59405-3219 Office: PO Box 7425 Great Falls MT 59406-7425

WALKER, LEROY, Olympic official; b. 1918. BS, Benedict Coll.; MS, Columbia U., PhD. Former athletic coach N.C. Ctrl., former chancellor; former coach Olympic teams for Israel, Jamaica, Kenya and Ethiopia; coach U.S. Olympic Team, 1976; pres. The Athletic Congress; treas. U.S. Olympic Com.; pres. U.S. Olympic Com., Colorado Springs, Colo., 1992—. Office: US Olympic Com 1750 E Boulder St Colorado Springs CO 80909-5746

WALKER, LEROY TASHREAU, university chancellor, coach; b. Atlanta, June 14, 1918; s. Willie and Mary Elizabeth (Thomas) W.; m. Katherine McDowell, Dec. 31, 1938 (dec.); children—LeRoy, Carolyn. BS, Benedict Coll., 1940, PhD (hon.); MA, Columbia U., 1941; PhD, NYU, 1957; PhD (hon.), Defiance Coll.; D of Sports Sci., U.S. Sports Acad.; LLD (hon.), Ea. Ky. U. and N.C. Cen. U., Wake Forest U., 1993, Morehouse U., 1993; DHL (hon.), Tuskegee U., 1993. Chmn. dept. phys. edn., coach basketball, football, track and field Benedict Coll., Columbia, S.C., 1941-42; chmn. dept. phys. edn., coach basketball, football, track and field Bishop Coll., Marshall, Tex., 1942-43, Prairie View State U., 1943-45; chmn. dept. phys. edn. and recreation, coach basketball, football, track and field N.C. Cen. U., Durham, 1945-73; vice-chancellor for univ. relations N.C. Cen. U., 1974-83, chancellor, 1983-86, chancellor emeritus, 1986—; ednl. specialist Cultural Exchange Program, Dept. State, 1959, 60, 62; dir. program, planning and tng. Peace Corps, Africa, 1966-68; coach Ethiopian and Israeli teams Olympic Games, Rome, 1960; adviser track and field teams throughout world; mem. U.S. Collegiate Sports Coun., 1971; chmn. Coll. Commrs. Assn., 1971-74; chmn. track and field com. Athletic Union U.S.A., 1973-75; head coach U.S. track and field team Olympic Games, Montreal, 1976; chmn. bd. dirs. U.S. Olympic Festival, 1987—; mem. exec. bd., treas. U.S. Olympic Com.; chef de mission for 1992 Barcelona Olympic Games, 1991—; sr. v.p. sports Atlanta Com. for the Olympic Games 1996, 1991—. Author: Manual of Adapted Physical Education, 1960; Physical Education for the Exceptional Student, 1965; Championship Techniques in Track and Field, 1969, Track and Field for Boys and Girls, 1983; also articles. Bd. dirs. U.S.A.-China Rels. Com.; bd. trustees U.S. Olympic Com.; pres. Athletic Congress, U.S. Olympic Com., 1992—. Recipient James E. Shepard Outstanding Tchr. award Hamilton Watch Co., 1964, U. N.C. Systems Bd. Govs. award, 1989; Achievement award Cen. Intercollegiate Athletic Assn. 1967; Disting. Alumnus award Benedict Coll., 1968, Disting. Service award Kiwanis Internat., 1971, City of Durham, 1971, Durham C. of C., 1973, Gov.'s Ambassador of Goodwill award, 1974; O. Max Gardner award, 1976; N.C. Disting. Citizen award, 1977; Achievement in Life award Ency. Brit., 1977, Achievement award Sertoma; Heritage award YMCA, 1988, Robert Giegengack award The Athletics Congress, 1990, Amb. award Pres.' Coun. on Phys. Fitness and Sports, 1991, Disting. Alumni award NYU, 1993, Jim Corbett award Nat. Assn. Coll. Athletic Dirs., 1993; named to N.C. Hall of Fame, 1975, S.C. Hall of Fame, 1977, Nat. Assn. Sport and Phys. Edn. Hall of Fame, 1977, N.C. Cen. U. Hall of Fame, 1984, U.S. Olympic Hall of Fame, 1987, Ga. Hall of Fame, 1988, Benedict Coll. Hall of Fame. Mem. Am. Alliance Health, Phys. Edn., Recreation, and Dance (nat. pres.; Honor award 1972, Gulick award), NEA, U.S. Track Coaches Assn. (Nat. Track Coach of Yr. 1972), N.C. Assn. Health, Phys. Edn., Recreation and Dance (Honor award 1971; v.p. div., dir.), Internat. Assn. Athletic Fedns. (U.S. rep. 1976—), Sigma Delta Psi, Alpha Phi Omega, Omega Psi Phi. Episcopalian.

WALKER, LESLEY, film editor. Editor: (films) Portrait of an Artist as a Young Man, 1979, The Tempest, 1980, Eagle's Wing, 1980, Richard's Things, 1981, Ill Fares the Land, 1982, Meantime, 1983, Winter's Flight, 1984, Letter to Brezhnev, 1985, Mona Lisa, 1986, Cry Freedom, 1987, Buster, 1988, Shirley Valentine, 1989, The Fisher King, 1991, Waterland, 1992, Born Yesterday, 1993, Shadowlands, 1993, (TV movies) Winston Churchill: The Wilderness Years, 1983, The Secret Life of Ian Fleming, 1990. Office: Sandra Marsh Mgt 9150 Wilshire Blvd Ste 220 Beverly Hills CA 90210*

WALKER, LOREN HAINES, electrical engineer; b. Bartow, Fla., Sept. 25, 1936; s. Robert Ellsworth and Vera May (Williams) W.; m. Barbara Gray Doss, Aug. 26, 1961; children: Linda Gray, Katherine Leigh, Virginia Kent. BEE, U. Fla., 1958; SM, MIT, 1961. Registered profl. engr., Va. Program engr. GE Corp., 1958-59; sr. design engr. specialty control dept. GE Corp., Waynesboro, Va., 1959-70; elec. engr. R & D GE Corp., Schenctady, N.Y., 1972-76; cons. engr. drive systems GE Corp., Salem, Va., 1976—; sr. devel. engr. Exide Power Systems div. ESB, Raleigh, N.C., 1970-72. Inventor 53 patents in field. Active Presbyn. Ch. Recipient IR-100 award Indsl. Rsch., 1974. Fellow IEEE (1st prize conf. papers 1979, 2d prize 1989). Office: GE Drive Systems 1501 Roanoke Blvd Salem VA 24153-6422

WALKER, M. LUCIUS, JR., mechanical engineer; b. Washington, Dec. 16, 1936; s. M. Lucius and Inez L. Walker; m. Oswaldene E. Cocking, Feb. 13, 1961; children: Mark, Monique. Student, Morehouse Coll., 1952-54; BSME summa cum laude, Howard U., 1957; MSME, Carnegie Inst. Tech., 1958, PhD, 1966. Registered profl. engr., Washington. Instr. Howard U., Washington, 1958-63, asst. prof., 1963-67, assoc. prof., 1967—; prof. mech. engring., 1970—, assoc. dean, 1965-66, chmn. dept., 1966, 68-73, assoc. dean, 1973-74, acting dean, 1977-78, dean, 1978-95; vis. prof. U. Mass., 1978; vis. sr. staff mem. Internat. Rsch. and Tech. Corp., 1969-70; mem. engring. manpower commn. Engrs.' Coun. Profl. Devel.; exec. dir. Engring. Coalitions Schs. Excellence and Leadership in Edn., 1990—; reviewer NRC Postdoctoral Fellowship Evaluation Panels; mem. biotech. resources rev. com. NIH; exec. dir. NSF-funded Engring. Coalition Schs. for Excellence in Edn. and Leadership, 1990—; bd. dirs. Ctr. for Naval Analysis, 1991-94; cons. in field. Contr. articles to profl. jours., chpts. to books. Trustee

Carnegie-Mellon U., 1980-88. Recipient Ralph R. Teetor award Soc. Automotive Engrs.; named U.S. Black Engr. of Yr., Career Comm. Group, U.S. Black Engr. mag. 1988; Ford teaching fellow; Ford faculty-in-engring. resident, 1969-70. Mem. ASME, Am. Soc. Engring. Edn., Sigma Xi, Tau Beta Pi, Pi Mu Epsilon, Kappa Alpha Psi. Episcopalian. Home: 703 Twin Holly Lane Silver Spring MD 20904 Office: 2300 6th St NW Washington DC 20059-0001

WALKER, MACK, historian, educator; b. Springfield, Mass., June 6, 1929; s. Gilbert Creighton and Lavinia Pillsbury (Mack) W.; m. Irma Julianne Wiesinger, 1954; children: Barbara B., Gilbert C., Benjamin F. AB, Bowdoin Coll., 1950; PhD, Harvard U., 1959. Instr. R.I. Sch. of Design, Providence, 1957-59; instr., asst. prof. Harvard U., Cambridge, Mass., 1959-66; assoc. prof., Cornell U., Ithaca, N.Y., 1966-74; prof. Johns Hopkins U., Balt., 1974—, dept. chmn., 1979-82. Author: Germany and the Emigration, 1964, German Home Towns, 1971, Johann Jakob Moser, 1981, The Salzburg Transaction, 1993; editor: Metternich's Europe, 1968, Plombières, 1968. Sgt. U.S. Army, 1951-53. Fellow Inst. for Advanced Study, Princeton, 1977, Wissenschaftskolleg zu Berlin, 1982-83, Max-Planck-Inst. für Geschichte, Göttingen, 1987-88; recipient Forschungspreis Alexander von Humboldt Found., 1989. Fellow Am. Acad. Arts and Scis. Office: Dept History Johns Hopkins U Baltimore MD 21218

WALKER, MALLORY, real estate executive; b. Washington, Apr. 13, 1939; s. Oliver Mallory and Elizabeth Powell (Dunlop) W.; m. Diana Hardin Walker; children—Taylor Scott Walker, William Mallory. Ed., U. Va., 1958-63. Joined Walker & Dunlop, 1963, v.p., 1968-71, dir., 1969—, exec. v.p., 1971-76, pres., 1976—; cons. and lectr. in field; bd. dirs. Atlantic Trust Co., 1993-94, Charles E. Smith Residential Realty Inc., 1994—, Fed. Nat. Mortgage Assn., 1981-94, Fannie Mae Found.; trustee Group Hospitalization and Med. Svcs., Inc., 1989-93. Trustee Fed. City Coun., 1977—, Greater Washington Rsch. Ctr., 1977—, Eugene and Agnes E. Meyer Found., 1977-89, vice chmn. 1981-83, chmn. 1983-89. Mem. Am. Soc. Real Estate Counselors, Urban Land Inst., Mortgage Bankers Assn. Am. (bd. govs. 1986-90, exec. com. 1986-87). Office: Walker & Dunlop 7500 Old Georgetown Rd Ste 800 Bethesda MD 20814-6133

WALKER, MALLORY ELTON, tenor; b. New Orleans, May 22, 1935; s. James Hugh and Edith Mamie (Gilmore) W.; m. Carolyn Pryor, Dec. 21, 1956; children: Maria Vanessa, Anthony Hugh, Jamie Eugene. BA, Occidental Coll., 1957. Vocal instr. Boston Conservatory of Music, 1974-77. Prin. artist Met. Opera, N.Y.C., 1978-89; appeared with Dallas Opera, Cologne Opera, Stuttgart Opera, Miami Opera, L.A. Music Ctr. Opera; soloist Robert Shaw Chorale, 1960, also with L.A. Philharm., Cleve. Symphony, Boston Symphony, Phila. Orch., Chgo. Symphony. With U.S. Army, 1957-60. Rockefeller Found. grantee, 1962-63; Ford Found. grantee, 1963. Mem. Am. Guild Mus. Artists, AFTRA, SAG. Home: 1400 S Citrus Ave Apt 4 Fullerton CA 92633-4750

WALKER, MARK A., lawyer; b. N.Y.C., June 24, 1941; s. Joseph and Eleanor (Junger) W.; m. Tania Khodjamirian; children: Marie, Andrew. BA, Stanford U., 1963; LLB, Yale U., 1966. Bar: N.Y. 1967, U.S. Dist. Ct. (so. dist.) N.Y. 1977. Assoc. Cleary, Gottlieb, Steen & Hamilton, Paris, Brussels and N.Y., 1966-75; ptnr. Cleary, Gottlieb, Steen & Hamilton, N.Y.C., 1975—. Mem. Assn. Bar City N.Y. Office: 1 Liberty Plz New York NY 10006-1401

WALKER, MARTIN DEAN, specialty chemical company executive; b. 1932; married. BS, GM Inst.; MBA, Mich. State U. With GM, Detroit, 1954-70; v.p. Am. Motors Corp., Detroit, 1970-72; exec. v.p. Rockwell Internat. Corp., Pitts., 1972-86; chmn., chief exec. officer M.A. Hanna Co., Cleve., 1986—. Office: M A Hanna Co 200 Public Sq Ste 36-5000 Cleveland OH 44114-2304

WALKER, MARY ANN, lawyer; b. Anderson, S.C., Aug. 21, 1953; d. Ernest McCreary and Virginia (Selman) Glymph; m. Thomas M. Walker, Aug. 28, 1976. BS, U. Va., 1975; JD, U. Richmond, 1979. Bar: Va. 1979, U.S. Dist. Ct. (ea. dist.) Va. 1980, U.S. Ct. Appeals (4th cir.) 1980, U.S. Ct. Appeals (5th, 7th and D.C. cirs.) 1984, U.S. Ct. Appeals (10th cir.) 1987, U.S. Supreme Ct. 1987, D.C. 1988. Assoc. Wickwire, Gavin & Gibbs, P.C., Washington and Vienna, Va., 1980-86; ptnr. Wickwire, Gavin & Gibbs, P.C., Washington, 1986-89, Pepper, Hamilton & Scheetz, Washington, 1989-91, Shaw, Pittman, Potts & Trowbridge, Washington, 1992-94, Mudge Rose Guthrie Alexander & Ferdon, Washington, 1994—; bus. mgr. Energy Law Jour., Washington, 1986-88; sec. Cogeneration Coalition Am. Inc., Washington, 1985-87. Contbr. articles to profl. jours. Named Outstanding Atty. in Va. Met. Women's Bar Assn., Va. Womens Attys. Assn., 1986. Mem. ABA (chair ratemaking com. sect. of adminstrv. law and regulatory practice), Va. Bar Assn., Fairfax Bar Assn., Fed. Bar Assn., Fed. Energy Bar Assn. (vice chmn. practice and procedures com. 1985-86, vice chmn. phys. facilities com. 1987-88), Midwest Gas Assn. (exec. bd. legal affairs sect.). Presbyterian. Avocations: sailing, gardening, traveling. Office: Mudge Rose Guthrie 2121 K St NW Ste 700 Washington DC 20037

WALKER, MARY L., lawyer; b. Dayton, Ohio, Dec. 1, 1948; d. William Willard and Lady D. Walker; 1 child, Winston Samuel. Student, U. Calif., Irvine, 1966-68; BA in Biology/Ecology, U. Calif., Berkeley, 1970; postgrad., UCLA, 1972-73; JD, Boston U., 1973. Bar: Calif. 1973, U.S. Supreme Ct. 1979. Atty. So. Pacific Co., San Francisco, 1973-76; from assoc. to ptnr. Richards, Watson, & Gershon, L.A., 1976-82; dep. asst. atty. gen. lands div. U.S. Dept. Justice, Washington, 1982-84; dep. solicitor U.S. Dept. Interior, Washington, 1984-85; asst. sec. for environment, safety and health U.S. Dept. Energy, Washington, 1985-88; spl. cons. to chmn. bd. Law Engring., Atlanta, 1988-89; v.p., West Coast and the Pacific Law Environ., Inc., San Francisco, 1989; ptnr., head environ. law dept. Richards, Watson & Gershon, San Francisco, 1989-91; ptnr. Luce, Forward, Hamilton & Scripps, San Diego, 1991-94; ptnr. and head San Diego Environ. Practice Group Brobeck, Phleger & Harrison, San Diego, 1994—; U.S. commr. InterAm. Tropical Tuna Commn., 1989-95. Bd. dirs. Endowment for Community Leadership, 1987—; adv. coun. Adam Smith Inst., 1993—. Mem. Calif. Bar Assn., San Diego Bar Assn., San Diego BioCommerce Assn. (bd. dirs. 1991—, pres. 1994), World Affairs Coun., Renaissance Women. Republican.

WALKER, MICHAEL CHARLES, SR., retirement services executive; b. Rochester, N.Y., Mar. 4, 1940; s. Charles Boyle and Evelyn Esther (Young) W.; m. Patricia Ann Camelio, Feb. 2, 1963; children: Michael Charles Jr., Lyn, Lea, Matthew. BA, U. Colo., 1962; MBA, Columbia Pacific U., 1982, DBA, 1984. Adminstrv. trainee Lincoln Rochester (N.Y.) Trust Co., 1962-64, mktg. officer, 1964-68; asst. v.p. Lincoln First Bank of Rochester, 1968-72, v.p., 1972-77; pres. M.C. Walker Co., Inc., Spencerport, N.Y., 1977-80; exec. dir. The Valley Manor, Rochester, 1980-85; pres., chief exec. officer Presbyn. Residence Ctr. Corp., Rochester, 1985—; lectr. SUNY, Brockport, 1982-89; v.p., dir. Kilian and Caroline Schmitt Found., Rochester, 1985—; mem. adv. bd. Chase Lincoln 1st Bank, Rochester, 1989-92; trustee Rochester Hearing and Speech Ctr., 1989-95, chmn., 1993-94; bd. dirs. Genesee Region Home Care Assn., Rochester, 1990—, chmn., 1995—; trustee Greater Rochester Metro C. of C., 1981-89. Author: Introduction to Bank Marketing Research, 1969, rev. edit., 1972, Practical Handbook of Marketing Definitions, 1970; contbr. articles to profl. jours. Leader task force Spencerport Ctrl. Schs. Bd. Edn., 1977, 80-81, 85; chmn. Monroe County Svs. Bond Com., Rochester, 1972—; mem. United Way Evaluation Team, 1990-94; mem. bus. adv. bd. SUNY, Brockport, 1993—; mem. N.Y. State Bd. Profl. Med. Conduct, 1993—; mem. health adv. com. Self Help for Hard of Hearing, 1994—. Recipient Pres.'s Geneseekers award Rochester Area C. of C., 1979, Innovation of Yr. award NYAHSA 1989. Mem. Am. Assn. Homes for Aging (various coms.), Am. Mktg. Assn. (pres. Rochester chpt. 1969-70), N.Y. State Bankers Assn. (pres. residential mortgage com. 1975-76), N.Y. Assn. Homes and Svcs. for Aging (various coms.), Ridgemont Country Club, Rochester Rotary. Episcopalian. Avocations: golf, reading, travel, physical fitness. Home: Spencerport NY 14559 Office: Presbyn Residence Ctr Corp 1570 East Ave Rochester NY 14610-1610

WALKER, MICHAEL CLAUDE, finance educator; b. Sherman, Tex., June 8, 1940; s. Andrew Jackson and Alice Lorene (Curry) W.; m. Martha Ellen Hindman, Sept. 10, 1966; children: Stephanie Elizabeth, Rebecca Elaine, Priscilla Eileen. BA, Austin Coll., 1965; MA, Ohio State U., 1966; PhD, U.

Houston, 1971. Instr. U. Houston, 1969-70; asst. prof. Ga. State U., Atlanta, 1971-75; assoc. prof. U. Okla., Norman, 1975-78; prof., head dept. fin., ins. and real estate North Tex. State U., Denton, 1978-88; prof. U. Cin., 1985-88, dept. head, 1985—, Virgil M. Schwarm prof. fin. and investments, 1988—. Co-editor: Cases in Financial Institutions, 1979; contbr. articles to profl. jours. Served with AUS, 1958-61. Recipient Leonard P. Ayers fellowship award, 1973. Mem. Am. Fin. Assn., Fin. Execs. Inst., Fin. Mgmt. Assn., So. Fin. Assn. (bd. dirs. 1983-85, sec.-treas. 1986-88, v.p. 1988-89, pres. 1989-90), Southwestern Fin. Assn. (bd. dirs. 1986-88), Ea. Fin. Assn., Midwest Fin. Assn., Beta Gamma Sigma, Omicron Delta Epsilon. Methodist. Office: U Cin Fin Dept Mail Location 195 Cincinnati OH 45221-0195

WALKER, MORT, cartoonist; b. El Dorado, Kans., Sept. 3, 1923; s. Robin A. and Carolyn (Richards) W.; m. Catherine Prentice, Aug. 24, 1985; children: Greg, Brian, Polly, Morgan, Marjorie, Neal, Roger, Whitney, Cathy, Jr., Priscilla. Student, Kansas City Jr. Coll., 1941-42, Washington U., St. Louis, 1943-44; B.A., U. Mo., 1948; LL.D., William Penn Coll., 1981. Designer Hallmark Greeting Cards, 1941; editor Dell Pub. Co., 1948-49; free lance cartoonist Saturday Evening Post, other popular mags., 1948-50; scholar in residence Mo. U., 1992. Comic strip artist King Features, 1950—; creator Beetle Bailey, 1950, Hi and Lois, 1954, Sam's Strip, 1961, Boner's Ark, 1968, Sam and Silo, 1977, The Evermores, 1982, Betty Boop and Felix, 1984, (for United Features) Gamin and Patches, 1987; author: Most, 1971, Land of Lost Things, 1973, Backstage at the Strips, 1975, The Lexicon of Comicana, 1981, The Best of Beetle Bailey, 1984; contbr. to numerous anthologies and textbooks. Mem. Pres.'s Com. to Hire Handicapped, People to People Com. Exhbn. touring group show Met. Mus. Art, N.Y.C., 1951; chmn. Internat. Mus. Cartoon Art. Served to 1st lt. AUS, 1943-46, ETO. Recipient Outstanding Cartoonist award The Banshees, 1955, Il Secolo XIX award (Italy), 1972, Adamson award (Sweden), 1975, 88, Segar award, 1977, 4th Estate award Am. Legion, The Jester, 1979, Fourth Estate award, 1978, Power of Printing, 1977; named Man of Yr. NCCJ, 1988. Mem. Nat. Cartoonists Soc. (pres. 1959-60, Reuben award 1953, award for best humor strip of 1966, 69, Mus. Cartoon Art Hall of Fame 1989), Artists and Writers, Newspaper Features Coun. Authors Guild, Soc. Illustrators, Silvermine Club (Norwalk, Conn.), Greenwich Country Club, Quechee Club (Vt.), Boca Raton Resort and Club (Fla.), Kappa Sigma (Man of Yr. 1988). Office: care King Features Syndicate 235 E 45th St New York NY 10017-3305 If I enjoy my own life that's one life enjoyed. But if I can help others enjoy their lives more, many lives are made more enjoyable.

WALKER, OLENE S., lieutenant governor; b. Ogden, Utah, Nov. 15, 1930; d. Thomas Ole and Nina Hadley (Smith) W.; m. J. Myron Walker, 1957; children: Stephen Brett, David Walden, Bryan Jesse, Lori, Mylene, Nina, Thomas Myron. BA, Brigham Young U., 1954; MA, Stanford U., 1954; PhD, U. Utah, 1986. V.p. Country Crisp Foods; mem. Utah Ho. of Reps. Dist. 24; lt. gov. State of Utah, 1993—. Mem. Salt Lake Edn. Found. bd. dirs. 1983-90; dir. community econ. devel.; mem. Ballet West, Sch. Vol. United Way, Commn. on Youth, Girls Village, Salt Lake Conv. and Tourism Bd. Mormon. Office: 203 State Capitol Salt Lake City UT 84114

WALKER, PHILIP CHAMBERLAIN, II, health care executive; b. Big Spring, Tex., July 7, 1944; s. Philip Chamberlain and Mary Catherine (St. John) W.; m. Linda Jane Holsclaw, Jan. 21, 1978; children: Shannon M., Meghan M. BA, Cen. Wash. State Coll., 1970; MS, U. Idaho, 1971. Exec. dir. Multnomah Found. for Med. Care, Portland, Oreg., 1972-81; chief exec. officer Peer Rev. Orgn. for Wash. State, Seattle, 1981-84; dir. Preferred Provider Orgn. devel. Provident Life and Accident, Chattanooga, 1984-88; v.p. Maxicare Health Plans, L.A., 1988-91; v.p., gen. mgr. Maxicare Health Plans Midwest, Chgo., 1991-92; pres. Health Plus, Peoria, Ill., 1992—; CEO, chmn. bd. Kepple & Co., Peoria, 1992—; v.p. Health Care Horizons, Albuquerque, 1992—; bd. dirs. RMR Group; cons. to numerous orgns. Contbr. articles to profl. jours. With USAF, 1961-66, Vietnam. Office: 209 W 5th St East Peoria IL 61651

WALKER, PHILLIP R., agricultural products supplier. Pres. Tenn. Farmers Coop., La Vergne, Tenn., Dyer Lauderdale Farmers Inc., Dyersburg, Tenn. Office: Tenn Farmers Coop PO Box 3003 200 Waldron Rd La Vergne TN 37086 also: Dyer Lauderdale Farmers Inc Dyersburg TN 38024*

WALKER, RALPH CLIFFORD, lawyer; b. Bradenton, Fla., Apr. 30, 1938; s. Julius Clifford and Dorothy (Hefner) W.; m. Sarah Mildred Walker, Sept. 9, 1959 (div. Sept. 1971), 1 child, Laura Elizabeth; m. Katherine Marie Christensen, Oct. 10, 1971; children: Mark Clifford, Tyler Lanier. BA cum laude, Vanderbilt U., 1959; LLB, U. Calif., Berkeley, 1965. Bar: Calif. Ptnr. Orrick Herrington & Sutcliffe, San Francisco, 1965—. Town councilman Town of Ross, Calif., 1970-72. Lt. (j.g.) USN, 1959-62. Mem. ABA, State Bar Calif., San Francisco Bar Assn., University Club (San Francisco, dir. 1986-88, counsel 1983—), Meadow Club (Fairfax, Calif.), Order of Coif. Republican. Presbyterian. Avocations: golf, wine, youth sports. Office: Orrick Herrington & Sutcliffe 400 Sansome St San Francisco CA 94111

WALKER, RICHARD HAROLD, pathologist, educator; b. Cleve., Dec. 2, 1928; s. Harold Deford and Bernice Margaret (Wright) W.; m. Carolyn Franklin, Sept. 28, 1954; children: Bruce, Lynn, Cara, Leah. BS, Emory U., 1950, MD, 1953. Intern City Memphis Hosps., 1953-54; resident in pathology U. Tenn. Coll. Medicine, Memphis, 1954-55, 57-59; Am. Cancer Soc. clin. fellow U. Tenn. Coll. Medicine, 1957-59; med. dir. blood bank and transfusion service City of Memphis Hosps., 1961-70; prof. pathology Coll. Medicine, U. Tenn., Memphis, 1966-70; chief of blood bank and transfusion service William Beaumont Hosp., Royal Oak, Mich., 1970—; med. dir. Sch. Med. Tech. William Beaumont Hosp., 1970-91; clin. prof. pathology Wayne State U. Sch. Medicine, Detroit, 1982—. Contbr. articles on blood transfusion, blood group genetics and transfusion medicine to med. jours. With USNR, 1955-76. Recipient Murray Thelin Humanitarian award Memphis chpt. Nat. Hemophilia Found., 1968. Mem. AMA, Coll. Am. Pathologists, Am. Soc. Clin. Pathologists (Disting. Svc. award 1977, Ward Burdick award 1992), Am. Assn. Blood Banks (pres. 1976-77, John Elliott Meml. award 1986), Tenn. Assn. Blood Banks (L.W. Diggs award 1986), Internat. Soc. Blood Transfusion, Am. Soc. for Histocompatibility and Immunogenetics. Republican. Presbyterian. Home: 22301 Nottingham Dr Beverly Hills MI 48025-3518 Office: William Beaumont Hosp Blood Bank Royal Oak MI 48073

WALKER, RICHARD K., lawyer; b. Knoxville, Tenn., Oct. 21, 1948. BA with honors, U. Kans., 1970, JD, 1975; student, U. Bonn, Germany. Bar: Ariz. 1975, D.C. 1977, U.S. Supreme Ct. 1977. Asst. prof. law U. S.C. 1977-81, assoc. prof. law, 1981-82; ptnr. Winston & Strawn, Washington; dir. Streich Lang, Phoenix, 1993—. Fulbright scholar. Mem. ABA (mem. equal employment opportunity law com. 1979—). Office: Streich Lang Renaissance One 2 N Central Ave Phoenix AZ 85004-2391

WALKER, RICHARD LOUIS, former ambassador, educator, author; b. Bellefonte, Pa., Apr. 13, 1922; s. Robert Shortlidge and Genevieve (Bible) W.; m. Celeno Claypole Kenly, Mar. 29, 1945; children: Geoffrey Kenly, Dorothy Anne, Stephen Bradley. BA, Drew U., 1944; cert. Chinese lang. and area, U. Pa., 1944; MA, Yale U., 1947, PhD, 1950; LLD (hon.), Coll. of Charleston, 1985, Drew U., 1986, The Citadel, 1990; D of Polit. Sci. (hon.), Seoul Nat. U., 1982; D. Pub. Svc., U. S.C., 1991. Asst. prof. history Yale U., 1950-57; prof. internat. studies U. S.C., 1957—, James F. Byrnes prof. internat. relations, 1959—, prof. emeritus, 1972—; U.S. amb. to Republic of Korea, 1981-86; vis. assoc. prof. Nat. Taiwan U., Taipei, China, 1954-55; vis. prof. U. Wash., 1959, 65; prof. polit. affairs Nat. War Coll., 1960-61; spl. rsch. internat. rels., Far East; lectr. coms. U.S. Govt., 1953—, Dept. Def., 1969—; rep. U.S. Dept. State, USIS, 1973-74; lectr. numerous confs., major U.S. govt. svc. schs. and univs. in Asia, Australia and Europe. Author: Western Language Periodicals on China, 1949, Multi-State System of Ancient China, 1954, China Under Communism, 1955, China and the West, 1956, The Continuing Struggle, 1958, Democracy Confronts Communism in World Affairs, 1965, Edward R. Stettmius, Jr, 1965, The China Danger, 1966, Ancient China, 1969, Prospects in the Pacific 1972, Asia in Perspective, 1974, Ancient Japan, 1975; contbr. articles to various symposium vols., learned jours. Bd. dirs. Nat. Com. U.S.-China Rels., 1968-94, U.S. Strategic Inst., 1977—; U. S.C. Ednl. Found., 1958—, Conf. on European Problems, 1967—. With AUS, 1942-46, PTO. Recipient Alumni Achievement award

in arts Drew U., 1958; Disting. Service award Air U., 1970; Fgn. Service Inst. award, 1971; Armed Forces Staff Coll. award, 1978; Fulbright-Social Sci. Research Council research scholar Academia Sinica Republic China, 1965-66. Mem. Assn. Asian Studies, Pi Gamma Mu, Omicron Delta Kappa, Aurelian Honor Soc. Episcopalian. Clubs: Forest Lake, Torch. Home: 700 Spring Lake Rd Columbia SC 29206-2111

WALKER, ROBERT DIXON, III, surgeon, urologist, educator; b. Rochester, N.Y., July 22, 1936; s. Robert Dixon, Jr. and Virginia (Weir) W.; m. Joyce Ann Copeland, June 23, 1961; children—Sherri Lynn, Lisa Marie, Jeffrey Alan. B.A., B.S., Carson-Newman Coll., 1959; M.D., U. Miami, Fla., 1963. Intern Wake Forest U., 1964; resident in surgery U. Fla., 1968, asst. prof., 1970-74, assoc. prof., 1974-76, prof. surgery, 1976—, dir. admissions Coll. Medicine, 1976-79; instr. U. Tenn., 1969-70; chief of staff Shands Teaching Hosp., 1976. Assoc. editor: Jour. Urology. Served to comdr. USNR, 1968-70. Fellow ACS (gov.); mem. Assn. Univ. Urologists, Am. Urol. Assn. (editorial bd. Update Series), Am. Assn. Genitourinary Surgeons, Soc. Pediatric Rsch., Soc. Pediatric Urology (exec. com., sec., pres.), Am. Acad. Pediatrics (sec., chmn. urology sect.), Fla. Urologic Soc. (sec., pres.). Home: 6322 SW 37th Way Gainesville FL 32608-5105 Office: Div of Urology Box J 247 JHM Health Center Gainesville FL 32610

WALKER, ROBERT GILES, JR., architect; b. Chgo., Feb. 4, 1939; s. Robert Giles and Jane (McMurray) W.; m. Coralyn Eleanor Ingersoll, Aug. 19, 1961; children: Robert I., Scott M., Jeffrey S. AB, Princeton U., 1961; BArch, U. Mich., 1963. Registered arch., Ill., Ind., Wis., Mich., Fla., Colo., Ky. Archtl. draftsman Perkins & Will, Chgo., 1966-70; archtl. designer Otis Assocs., Northbrook, Ill., 1970-73, exec. v.p., 1973-79, pres., 1979-86, vice chmn., 1986-90, chmn., 1990—; commr., pres. Archtl. Commn., Northfield, Ill., 1973-83. Commr., pres. Northfield (Ill.) Park Dept., 1979-85; gov. Winnetka (Ill.) Cmty. House, 1993—; commr. Zoning Bd. Appeal, Northfield, Ill., 1993—. Mem. AIA, Nat. Coun. Archtl. Registration Bd., Econ. Clun Chgo., Chgo. Commonwealth Club (bd. dirs.), Sunset Ridge Country Club (bd. dirs. 1975-79, 93-94). Republican. Presbyterian. Avocations: golf, fishing, gardening, youth sports. Home: 2355 Pebblefork Ln Northfield IL 60093 Office: Otis Assocs Inc 1450 American Ln Ste 1300 Schaumburg IL 60173

WALKER, ROBERT HARRIS, historian, author, editor; b. Cin., Mar. 15, 1924; m. Grace Burtt; children: Amy, Rachel, Matthew. BS, Northwestern U., 1945; MA, Columbia U., 1950; PhD, U. Pa., 1955. Edn. specialist U.S. Mil. Govt., Japan, 1946-47; instr. Carnegie Inst. Tech., 1950-51, U. Pa., 1953-54; asst. prof. Am. studies U. Wyo., 1955-59; asso. prof. George Washington U., 1959-63, prof. Am. civilization, 1963-94, dir. Am. studies program, 1959-66, 68-70; first dir. edn. and pub. programs NEH, 1966-68; fellow Woodrow Wilson Internat. Ctr., 1972-73, Rockefeller Rsch. Ctr., 1979, Hoover Instn., Huntington Libr., 1980; specialist grants to Japan, Germany, Thailand, Iran, Greece, Israel, Brazil, China, People's Republic of Korea, Hong Kong, 1964-91; Fulbright lectr., Australia, New Zealand, Philippines, 1971, Sweden, France, West Germany, Norway, all 1987; Am. Coun. Learned Socs. alt. del. UNESCO Gen. Info. Program, 1978—; cofounder Algonquin Books, 1982. Author: Poet and Gilded Age, 1963, Life in the Age of Enterprise, 1967, American Society, 1981, Reform in America (nominated for Pulitzer prize in history), 1985, (with R.H. Gabriel) Course of American Democratic Thought, 3d edit., 1986, Cincinnati and the Big Red Machine, 1988; editor, compiler: American Studies in the U.S., 1958, American Studies Abroad, 1975, Reform Spirit in America, 1976, 85, American Studies: Topics and Sources, 1976; editor: Am. Quar, 1953-54; sr. editor: Am. Studies Internat, 1970-80, Am. studies series for Greenwood Press, 1972—. Founding mem. Japan-U.S. Friendship Commn., 1977-89; pres. Friends of Raoul Wallenberg Found., 1989—. With USNR, 1943-46, 50. Mem. Am. Studies Assn. (nat. pres. 1970-71), Cosmos Club, Phi Beta Kappa. Office: 915 26th St NW Washington DC 20037

WALKER, ROBERT MOWBRAY, physicist, educator; b. Phila., Feb. 6, 1929; s. Robert and Margaret (Seivwright) W.; m. Alice J. Agedal, Sept. 2, 1951 (div. 1973); children: Eric, Mark; m. Ghislaine Crozaz, Aug. 24, 1973. B.S. in Physics, Union Coll., 1950, D.Sc., 1967; M.S., Yale U., 1951, Ph.D., 1954; Dr honoris causa, Université de Clermont-Ferrand, 1975. Physicist Gen. Electric Research Lab., Schenectady, 1954-62, 63-66; McDonnell prof. physics Washington U., St. Louis, 1966—; dir. McDonnell Center for Space Scis., 1975—; vis. prof. U. Paris, 1962-63; adj. prof. metallurgy Rensselaer Poly. Inst., 1958, adj. prof. physics 1965-66; vis. prof. physics and geology Calif. Inst. Tech., 1972, Phys. Research Lab., Ahmedabad, India, 1981, Institut d'Astrophysique, Paris, 1981; nat. lectr. Sigma Xi, 1984-85; pres. Vols. for Internat. Tech. Assistance, 1960-62, 65-66, founder, 1960, bd. dirs., 1961—; mem. Lunar Sample Analysis Planning Team, 1968-70, Lunar Sample Rev. Bd., 1970-72; adv. com. Lunar Sci. Inst., 1972-75; mem. temporary nominating group in planetary scis. Nat. Acad. Scis., 1973-75, bd. on sci. and tech. for internat. devel., 1974-76, com. planetary and lunar exploration, 1977-80, mem. space sci. bd., 1979-82; bd. dirs. Univs. Space Research Assn., 1969-71; mem. organizing com. Com. on Space Research-Internat. Astron. Union, Marseille, France, 1984; mem. task force on sci. uses of space sta. Solar System Exploration Com., 1985-86; mem. Antarctic Meteorite Working Group, 1985-92; mem. NASA Planetary Geosci. Strategy Com., 1986-88; mem. European Sci. Found. Sci. Orgn. Com., Workshop on Analysis of Samples from Solar System Bodies, 1990; chmn. Antarctic Meteorite Working Group, 1990-92. Decorated officer de l'Ordre des Palmes Academiques (France); recipient Disting. Svc. award Am. Nuclear Soc., 1966; E.O. Lawrence award AEC, 1971; Antarctic Svc. medal NSF, 1985; NSF fellow, 1962-63. Fellow AAAS, Am. Phys. Soc., Meteoritical Soc. (Leonard medal 1993), Am. Geophys. Union; mem. NAS (mem. polar rsch. bd. com. 1995, J. Lawrence Smith medal 1991), Am. Astron. Soc. Achievements include research and publs. on cosmic rays, nuclear physics, geophysics, radiation effects in solids, particularly devel. solid state track detectors and their application to geophysics and nuclear physics problems; discovery of fossil particle tracks in terrestrial and extraterrestrial materials and fission track method of dating; application of phys. scis. to art and archaeology; lab. studies of interplanetary dust and interstellar grains in primitive meteorites. Home: 3 Romany Park Ln Saint Louis MO 63132-4211

WALKER, ROBERT SMITH, congressman; b. Bradford, Pa., Dec. 23, 1942; s. Joseph Eddman and Rachael Viola (Smith) W.; m. Sue Ellen Albertson, Apr. 13, 1968. BS, Millersville (Pa.) U., 1964; MA in Polit. Sci, U. Del., 1968. Tchr. Penn Manor High Sch., Lancaster, Pa., 1964-67; legis. asst. to Congressman Edwin D. Eshleman, 1967-74, adminstrv. asst., 1974-76; mem. 95th-104th Congresses from 16th Pa. dist., Washington, D.C., 1977—; chmn. House Com. Sci. Co-author: Congress-The Pennsylvania Dutch Representatives, 1774-1974. Can You Afford This House, 1978, House of Ill Repute, 1987; contbr. articles to profl. jours. Served with Pa. NG, 1967-73. Republican. Office: US House of Reps 2369 Rayburn House Office Bldg Washington DC 20515 When you decide to seek public office, you accept a trust. The responsibilities of that trust involve not only your talents, your wisdom and your energies, but also your integrity, your character and your commitment to a better tomorrow.

WALKER, ROGER GEOFFREY, geology educator, consultant; b. London, Mar. 26, 1939; s. Reginald Noel and Edith Annie (Wells) W.; m. Gay Parsons, Sept. 18, 1965; children—David John, Susan Elizabeth. B.A., Oxford U., Eng., 1961; D.Phil., Oxford U., 1964. NATO postdoctoral fellow Johns Hopkins U., Balt., 1964-66; geology faculty McMaster U., Hamilton, Ont., Can., 1966—; prof. McMaster U., 1973—; vis. scientist Marathon Oil Research Ctr., Littleton, Colo., 1973-74, Amoco Can., Calgary, Alta., 1982; vis. prof. Australian Nat. U., Canberra, 1981; tchr. 80 profl. short courses on various aspects of oil exploration in clastic reservoirs, Can., U.S., Brazil, Australia, Japan; mem. grant selection com. earth scis. sect. Nat. Scis. and Engring. Rsch. Coun. Can., 1981-84. Editor: Facies Models, 1979, 2d edit., 1984, 3d edit., 1992; contbr. over 130 articles to profl. jours. Recipient operating and strategic grants Nat. Scis. and Engring. Rsch. Coun. Can., 1966—. Fellow Royal Soc. Can.; mem. Geol. Assn. Can. (assoc. editor 1977-80, Past President's medal 1975, Disting. Svc. award 1994), Can. Soc. Petroleum Geologists (Link award 1983, R.J.W. Douglas Meml. medal 1990), Am. Assn. Petroleum Geologists (Disting. lectr. 1979-80), Soc. Econ.

Paleontologists and Mineralogists (pres. eastern sect. 1975-76, coun. for mineralogy 1979-80, hon. mem. 1991, assoc. editor 1970-78), Can. Assn. Univ. Tchrs., Internat. Assn. Sedimentologists. Avocations: skiing, classical music, photography, model railroading. Home: 71 Robin Hood Dr, Dundas, ON Canada L9H 4G2 Office: McMaster U Dept Geology, 1280 Main St W, Hamilton, ON Canada L8S 4M1

WALKER, RONALD C., oil company executive. BSc in Engring., Queen's U., Kingston, Ont., Can., 1964; LLB, McGill U., Montreal, Que., Can., 1973. V.p. gen. counsel Imperial Oil Ltd., Toronto, Ont. Office: Imperial Oil Ltd, 111 St Clair Ave W, Toronto, ON Canada M5W 1K3

WALKER, RONALD C., magazine publisher; m. Lou Ann Walker; two children. BA, U. Nebr. Market rsch. mgr. Lane Pub., Menlo Park, Calif., 1967-69, marketing dir., 1969-74, v.p., circulation dir., 1974-84, v.p., gen. mgr. Sunset mag., 1984-90; pub. Smithsonian mag., D.C., 1991—, Air & Space/Smithsonian mag., D.C., 1991—. Office: Smithsonian Mag 900 Jefferson Dr SW Washington DC 20560

WALKER, RONALD EDWARD, psychologist, educator; b. East St. Louis, Ill., Jan. 23, 1935; s. George Edward and Marnella (Altmeyer) W.; m. Aldona M. Mogenis, Oct. 4, 1958; children: Regina, Mark, Paula, Alexis. B.S., St. Louis U., 1957; M.A., Northwestern U., 1959, Ph.D., 1961. Lectr. psychology Northwestern U., 1959-61; faculty dept. psychology Loyola U., Chgo., 1961—; asst. then asso. prof. Loyola U., 1961-68, prof., chmn. dept., 1965—; acting dean Loyola U. (Coll. Arts and Scis.), 1973-74, dean, 1974-80, academic v.p., 1980-81, sr. v.p., dean faculties, 1981-89, exec. v.p., 1989—; Cons. VA, Chgo., 1965-74; Am. Psychol. Assn.-NIMH; vis. cons., 1969; vis. scientist Am. Psychol. Assn. NSF, 1968; Cook County (Ill.) rep. from Ill. Psychol. Assn., 1969-72; cons.-evaluator North Cen. Assn., 1986—. Contbr. articles to profl. jours. Trustee St. Francis Hosp., Evanston, Ill., 1986-92, Chgo. Archdiocesan Sems., 1985—, Loyola Acad., Wilmette, Ill., 1987-93, St. Louis U., 1988—. Mem. Am. Psychol. Assn. (council rep. 1970-72, Ill. Psychol. Assn. (chmn. student devel. com. 1965-67, chmn. acad. sec. 1966-67, disting. psychologist of yr. award 1986), AAAS, Sigma Xi, Psi Chi. Home: 2712 Park Pl Evanston IL 60201-1337 Office: 820 N Michigan Ave Chicago IL 60611-2103

WALKER, RONALD F., corporate executive; b. Cin., Apr. 9, 1938; married. BBA, U. Cin., 1961. V.p. Kroger Co., Cin., 1962-72; with Am. Fin. Corp., Cin., 1972—, exec. v.p., 1978-84, pres., COO, bd. dirs., 1984-95; exec. v.p. Gt. Am. Ins., Cin., 1972-80, pres., 1980-87, vice chmn., 1987—; pres., COO Penn Cen. Corp., 1987-92, COO, 1987-92; pres., CEO Gen. Cable Corp., 1992-94; also bd. dirs.; bd. dirs. Chiquita Brands Internat., Cin., Am. Fin. Enterprises, Cin., Am. Annuity Gruop, Inc., Tejas Gas Corp. Office: Gt Am Ins Co 580 Walnut St Cincinnati OH 45202 also: Am Fin Corp 1 E 4th St Cincinnati OH 45202

WALKER, RONALD HUGH, executive search company executive; b. Bryan, Tex., July 25, 1937; s. Walter Hugh and Maxine (Tarver) W.; m. Anne Lucille Collins, Aug. 8, 1959; children: Lisa, Marjorie, Lynne. BA, U. Ariz., 1960. With Allstate Ins. Co., Pasadena, Calif., 1964-67, Hudson Co., 1967-69; asst. to sec. interior, 1969-70; founder, 1st dir., staff asst. to Pres. U.S. White House Advance Office, 1970-72; spl. asst. to Pres., 1972-73; dir. Nat. Park Service, 1973-75; cons. Saudi Arabia, 1975; assoc. dir. World Championship Tennis, 1975-77; pres. Ron Walker & Assocs., Inc., Dallas, 1977-79; sr. officer, mng. dir. Korn/Ferry Internat., Washington, 1979—. vid. Nixon/Agnew Campaign, 1968, transition and inauguration, 1969; founder, chmn. emeritus Order of Raft, 1972; mem. spl. presdl. del. to Prime Min. Indira Gandhi's funeral, New Delhi, 1984, Games of XXIV Olympiad, Seoul, 1988; trustee Nat. Outdoor Leadership Sch., Nat. Fitness Found., Pres.'s Coun. on Phys. Fitness and Sports, 1981-85; vice chmn., mem. Pres.'s Commn. on Bicentennial U.S. Constn., 1985—; mem. U.S. Olympic Com., 1989-93; bd. dirs., mem. exec. com. NCAA Found.; bd. dirs. Meridian Internat.; mem. Ctr. for Study of Presidency, 1988—, Coun. for Excellence in Govt., 1988—; chmn. Freedom Found. at Valley Forge, 1989—; trustee Ford's Theater, Washington; men's chair Project Hope Ann. Ball, 1989, 90, 91; chmn. ann. dinner Boys and Girls Clubs Am., 1993; chmn. 50th Presdl. Inauguration, Dedication Richard Nixon Libr., Birthplace, 1990, bd. dirs., 1990—; mgr. 1984 Rep. Nat. Conv.; sr. advisor Rep. Nat. Conv., 1988, 92, Bush/Quayle Presdl. Campaign, 1988; nat. chair Celebrities & Sports for Bush/Quayle; mem. oversite com. U.S. Rowing, 1993; active Commn. for Preservation of White House, 1973-75, Nat. Park adv. bd., 1973-75, Nat. Park Found., 1973-75, John F. Kennedy Ctr. for Performing Arts, 1973-75, Friends of Nancy Hanks Ctr., Meridian House Internat. Bd. Trustees, 1992—, USA Gymnasium Found., 1993— Capt. U.S. Army, 1961-64. Recipient Disting. Citizen award U. Ariz., 1973, Outstanding Svc. award Dept. Interior, 1975, Centennial Medallion award U. Ariz., 1989, Ellis Island Congl. medal of honor, 1992. Mem. NCAA (bd. dirs. 1992—, exec. com. 1992—), Econs. Club of Washington, Met. Club of Washington, Congl. Country Club, Georgetown Club, City Club of Washington, Univ. Club. of N.Y., Burning Tree Club, Phi Delta Theta (named to Hall of Fame, 1991). Republican. Methodist. Office: Presidential Pla 900 19th St NW Washington DC 20006-2100

WALKER, RUTH ANN, journalist; b. Elmhurst, Ill., June 22, 1954; d. Robert F. and Jeanne (Carsman) W. AB, Oberlin (Ohio) Coll., 1976. Staff reporter Aiken (S.C.) Standard, 1977-78; various editing and writing positions Christian Sci. Monitor, Boston, 1978-83, bus. corr., 1983-85, editorial writer, 1985-88, asst. editor editorial page, 1988, asst. mng. editor, 1988-90, dep. editor, 1990-94, assoc. editor, 1994-95, sr. correspondent Europe, 1995—. Recipient Exceptional Merit Media award Nat. Women's Polit. Caucus, 1987. Christian Scientist. Home: 26 Waverly St #402 Brighton MA 02135

WALKER, SALLY BARBARA, retired glass company executive; b. Bellerose, N.Y., Nov. 21, 1921; d. Lambert Roger and Edith Demerest (Parkhouse) W. Diploma Cathedral Sch. St. Mary, 1939; AA, Finch Jr. Coll., 1941. Tchr. interior design Finch Coll., 1941-42; draftsman AT&T, 1942-43; with Steuben Glass Co., N.Y.C., 1943—, exec. v.p., 1959-62, exec. v.p. ops., 1962-78, exec. v.p. ops. and sales, 1978-83, exec. v.p., 1983-88, ret. 1988. Pres. 116 E. 66th St. Corp. Mem. Fifth Ave. Assn. Republican. Episcopalian. Clubs: Rockaway Hunting, Lawrence Beach, U.S. Lawn Tennis, Colony, English-Speaking Union. Home: 116 E 66th St New York NY 10021-6547

WALKER, SALLY WARDEN, state legislator; b. Wilmette, Ill., Feb. 5, 1929; d. Sydney C. and Florence (Collins) Warden; m. O.B. Walker, Dec. 28, 1948; children: Richard, Christine, Nancy, Catherine, Sara. Student, William Jewell Coll., 1947-48. Commr., chmn. Univ. Pl. Parks and Recreation Bd., Tacoma, 1979-85; mem. Wash. Ho. of Reps., 1985—, environ. affairs, edn., and commerce and labor coms., transp. com. Formerly vol. dir. Pierce County Rep. Party, del. Pierce County Conv., precinct committeewoman 28th dist., 1978—; past bd. dirs. Town Hall Lecture Series; former dir. Christian Edn., mem. vestry St. Mary's Episc. Ch. Recipient Woman of Community award Inter-Chpt. Council Am. Bus. Women's Assn., 1986, Achievement award Puget Sound Inter-Chpt., Golden Acorn award PTA. Mem. Tacoma/Pierce County C. of C., Lakewood C. of C., LWV. Clubs: 28th Dist. Rep., Lakewood Rep. Women's. Home: 4617 Bellview St W Tacoma WA 98466-1013 Office: Office County Coun County-City Bldg Rm 1046 930 Tacoma Ave S Tacoma WA 98402-2176

WALKER, SANDRA, mezzo-soprano; b. Richmond, Va., Oct. 1, 1946; d. Phillip Loth and Mary Jane W.; m. Melvin Brown, May 17, 1975; 1 child, Noel Christian Brown. MusB, U. N.C. 1969; postgrad., Manhattan Sch. Music, 1971-72. Artist-in-residence Ky. Opera Assn. 1980. Recorded Ned Rorem's song cycle King Midas on Desto Records, 1974; debut San Francisco Opera, 1972, re-engaged 1988, Chgo. Lyric Opera, 1973, 88, re-engaged 1988, Washington Opera Soc., 1973, Phila. Lyric Opera, 1973, Teatro Communale, Florence, Italy, 1985, Met. Opera, N.Y.C., 1986, re-engaged 1989, Opernhaus Zurich, 1987, Stadt Theater Wiesbaden, 1987, Rigoletto, Eugene-Onegin, Met. Opera. 1989, Netherlands Opera, 1989, Orlands Furioso, San Francisco Opera, 1989, Ring Cycle, 1990; leading mezzo soprano N.Y.C. Opera, 1974—; Stadt Theater, Würzburg, Germany, 1980-82, Stadt Theater Gelsenkirchen, Fed. Republic Germany, 1983-85, Stadt Theater Essen, Fed. Republic Germany, 1984, Frankfurt Opera, Fed. Republic Germany, 1985; soloist Orchestra Santa Cecilia Academia, Rome,

1987, New Orch. Paris, 1988; singer in major U.S. and European music festivals Tanglewood, Caramoor, Spoleto-U.S.A. and Spoleto Festival of Two Worlds in, Italy; soloist, Am. Symphony, San Francisco Symphony, 1980; appeared in: PBS nat. telecasts Manon, The Ballad of Baby Doe, Saint of Bleeker Street, 1981, on Great Performances: in The Consul and Eugene Onegin, 1986; Met. Opera nat. broadcast Samson, 1986, Eugene Onegin, 1989; orchestral appearances with Nat. Symphony, Washington, St. Louis Symphony, Chgo. Symphony, Richmond (Va.) Symphony, Houston Symphony, San Francisco Symphony, Charlotte Symphony, Cleve. Orch.; comml. video prodns. Eugene Onegin, Manon, Orlando Furioso; opera appearances include Falstaff, Calgary Opera, 1991, Mephistofiles, Chgo. Lyric Opera, 1991, Barber of Seville, Phila. Lyric Opera, 1991, Theatre De Capitole Toulouse France, 1992, Paris Opera, 1993, Blossom Festival Clev. Opera, 1993, Met. Opera, 1994, Met. Opera, 1995, Recording Die Walkuere with Cleve. Orch. Recipient Nat. Endowment for Arts Affiliate Artist grant sponsored by Va. Opera Assn. and Sears Roebuck Co., 1978. Office: care Columbia Artists Mgmt Inc 165 W 57th St New York NY 10019-2201

WALKER, STANLEY P., publishing executive; b. Arkham, Mass., May 23, 1955; s. Gerald Jeffrey and Rebecca (Chamberlain) W.; m. Faith Darwin, Aug. 17, 1977; children: Erin, Emily, Amy. BA in English, Oberlin Coll. 1977; MFA in Creative Writing, Western Mich. U., 1979; MA in English Lit., Columbia U., 1982, PhD in English Lit., 1983. Sr. editor Farrar Straus Giroux, N.Y.C., 1980-83; assoc. prof. creative writing, early English lit. Columbia U., N.Y.C., 1983-87; pres., editor-in-chief Walker Press, N.Y.C., 1987-90; pres. Walker/Sturgeon Publs., New Providence, N.J., 1990—; vis. assoc. prof. Grinnell (Iowa) Coll., 1985-86; adj. prof. CUNY, 1987-90; cons. Farrar Straus Giroux, N.Y.C., 1990—. Author: (short story collections) The Rudeness of Youth, 1989, Life in the Sour Patch, 1991; co-author: (with L.Q. Sturgeon) Succeeding in Small-Scale Publishing, 1991; book reviewer numerous publs., N.Y.C., 1987—; contbr. articles to profl. jours. Trustee Grinnell Coll., 1990—; soccer coach, referee Am. Youth Soccer League, New Providence, 1990—. Mem. Writers Guild, Mensa, Ragnarok Lumberjacks, Phi Beta Kappa. Avocations: Old and Middle English writings, linguistics, music criticism, soccer, poker. Office: Reed Reference Publishing 121 Chanlon Rd New Providence NJ 07974-1541

WALKER, TENNYSON A., corporation executive; b. Moncton, N.B., Can., July 22, 1927; s. Trueman H. and Viola (Graves) W.; m. Hilda Hoar Thorne; 1 child, William T. Graduate, Success Bus. Coll., 1945. With Lounsbury Co. Ltd., Moncton, 1945-94, v.p. fin., 1976-79, pres., 1979-94, now shareholder and bd. dirs. Mem. Gideons Internat., Rotary. Mem. Conservative Party. Baptist. Office: Lounsbury Co Ltd, 1655 Mountain Rd, Moncton, NB Canada E1C 8H7

WALKER, THEODORE DELBERT, landscape architect; b. Tremonton, Utah, Feb. 17, 1933; s. Delbert Stevenson and Geneve (Cutler) W.; m. Doris Jenkins, June 1, 1957; children: Steven, Alan, Dahn, Jayne. BS, Utah State U., 1957; M Landscape Architecture, U. Ill., 1967. Registered landscape architect, Ariz. Assoc. landscape architect Office of Leon Frehner, Salt Lake City, 1957-60; site planner Brigham Young U., Provo, Utah, 1960-66; prof. Purdue U., West Lafayette, Ind., 1967-82; pres. Walker Harris Assocs. Inc., West Lafayette and Mesa, Ariz., 1973-84, PDA Pubs. Corp., West Lafayette, Ind. and Mesa, Ariz., 1971-88; adj. prof. Ariz. State U., Tempe, 1985—; pres. The Walker Design Group, Mesa, 1988—; cons. Browning Day Mullins Dierdorf, Indpls., 1969—, Van Nostrand Reinhold, N.Y.C., 1988—. Author 9 books including Plan Graphics, 3d edit., 1985, Site Design and Construction Detailing, 3d edit., 1991, Perspective Sketches, 5th edit., 1989, Plan Graphics, 4th edit., 1990. Mem. Design Rev. Advisory Bd., City of Mesa, Ariz., 1986-88. Recipient cert. of special recognition for contbns. to landscape archtl. edn. Coun. Educators in Landscape Architecture, 1980. Fellow Am. Soc. Landscape Architects (trustee 1972-80). Mem. LDS Ch. Avocations: playing cello, computers, photography, gardening. Office: Arizona State U Dept Planning Tempe AZ 85287

WALKER, THOMAS COLE, telephone company executive; b. Indpls., Sept. 14, 1929; s. Frank Dilling and Dorothy Mae (Cole) W.; m. Dorothy Henson, June 15, 1952; children: David, Karen, Michael, Linda. B.A. in Econs., DePauw U., 1951. Various ops. positions Ind. Bell Telephone Co., Indpls., 1951-74, v.p mktg., rates and revenue requirements, 1974-78, v.p bus., 1978-80, v.p., chief fin. officer, 1980-83, exec. v.p., chief fin. officer, 1983-90, exec. v.p. fin., adminstrn., 1990—; bd. dirs. Associated Ins. Cos. (formerly Blue Cross-Blue Shield), Indpls., Bison Money Market Fund, Indpls. Bd. dirs. 500 Festival Assocs. Mem. Fin. Execs. Inst., Econ. Club Indpls., Indpls. C. of C., Salvation Army (adv. bd). Methodist. Clubs: Indpls. Athletic, Columbia, Skyline. Lodge: Rotary. Office: Ind Bell Tel Co Inc 240 N Meridian St Indianapolis IN 46204-1915

WALKER, TIM, printing company executive. Chmn. bd. dirs. Clarke Am. Checks Inc., San Antonio. Office: Clarke Am Checks Inc 10931 Laureate Dr San Antonio TX 78249*

WALKER, TIMOTHY BLAKE, lawyer, educator; b. Utica, N.Y., May 21, 1940; s. Harold Blake and Mary Alice (Corder) W.; m. Sandra Blake; children: Kimberlee Corder, Tyler Blake, Kelley Loren. AB magna cum laude, Princeton U., 1962; JD magna cum laude, U. Denver, 1967, MA in Sociology, 1969. Bar: Colo. 1968, Calif. 1969, Ind. 1971. Asst. prof. law U. Pacific, 1968-69; vis. assoc. prof. U. Toledo, 1969-70; assoc. prof. Indpls. Law Sch., Ind. U., 1970-71; assoc. prof. U. Denver, 1971-75, prof., 1975—; dir. adminstrn. of justice program, 1971-78; sole practice law Denver, 1972-79; of counsel Robert T. Hinds, Jr. & Assocs. (P.C.), Littleton, Colo., 1980-85; ptnr., of counsel Cox, Mustain-Wood & Walker, Littleton, 1985—; cons. in field; rsch. on lay representation in adminstrv. agys., Colo., 1975-76. Contbr. articles to profl. publs.; lectr., symposium editor: Denver Law Jour., 1966-67; editor-in-chief: Family Law Quar., 1983-92. Mem. Ind. Child Support Commn., 1970-71; pres. Shawnee (Colo.) Water Consumers Assn., 1975-84; del. Colo. Republican Conv., 1978. Colo. Bar Assn. grantee, 1975-76. Fellow Am. Sociol. Assn., Am. Acad. Matrimonial Lawyers, Internat. Acad. Matrimonial Lawyers; mem. ABA (vice chmn. child custody subcom., sec. sect. family law 1992-93, vice chairperson, sec. family law 1993-94, chairperson sect. family law 1995-96, mem. child custody task force, chmn. alimony maintenance and support com.), Calif. Bar Assn., Colo. Bar Assn., Ind. Bar Assn., Colo. Trial Lawyers Assn. (cons.). Presbyterian. Home: 10162 E Exposition Ave Denver CO 80231-1918 Office: Univ Denver Coll of Law 1900 Olive St Denver CO 80220-1879 also: 6601 S University Blvd Littleton CO 80121 *Law and justice require the combination of intellectual self-discipline and an awareness of human dignity. The path of the law is often twisted and circuitous, and my goal has been to leave the trail better than I found it.*

WALKER, VAUGHN R., federal judge; b. Watseka, Ill., Feb. 27, 1944; s. Vaughn Rosenworth and Catharine (Miles) W. AB, U. Mich., 1966; JD, Stanford U., 1970. Intern economist SEC, Washington, 1966, 68; law clk. to the Hon. Robert J. Kelleher U.S. Dist. Ct. Calif., L.A., 1971-72; assoc. atty. Pillsbury Madison & Sutro, San Francisco, 1972-77, ptnr., 1978-90; judge U.S. Dist. Ct. (no. dist.) Calif., San Francisco, 1990—; mem. Calif. Law Revision Commn., Palo Alto, 1986-89. Dir. Jr. Achievement of Bay Area, San Francisco, 1979-83, St. Francis Found., San Francisco, 1991—, Woodrow Wilson Found. fellow U. Calif., Berkeley, 1966-67. Fellow Am. Bar Found.; mem. ABA (jud. rep., antitrust sect. 1991—), Lawyers' Club (pres. 1985-86), Am. Law Inst., Am. Saddlebred Horse Assn., San Francisco Mus. Modern Art, Bokemian Club. Office: US Dist Ct 16700 Valley View Ave Ste 300 La Mirada CA 90638-5841

WALKER, WALDO SYLVESTER, academic administrator; b. Fayette, Iowa, June 12, 1931; s. Waldo S. and Mildred (Littelle) W.; m. Marie J. Olsen, July 27, 1952 (div.); children: Martha Lynn, Gayle Ann; m. Rita K. White, June 16, 1984. BS cum laude, Upper Iowa U., Fayette, 1953; MS, U. Iowa, 1957, PhD, 1959. Mem. faculty Grinnell (Iowa) Coll., 1958, assoc. dean coll., 1963-65, chmn. div. Natural Scis., 1968-69, dean of adminstrn., 1969-73, exec. v.p., 1973-77, dean coll., 1973-80, provost, 1977-80, exec. v.p., 1980-90, exec. v.p. and treas., 1988-90, v.p. for coll. svcs., 1991—; research assoc. U. B.C. Dept. of Botany, 1966-67. Author articles on plant physiology, ultrastructural cytology. Served with U.S. Army, 1953-55. Fellow NSF Sci. Faculty, 1966-67; recipient NSF research grants, 1960-63, 68. Mem. Am. Assn. Colls., Am. Conf. Acad. Deans (nat. chmn. 1977-78), Am.

Assn. Higher Edn., Sigma Xi. Home: 1920 Country Club Dr Grinnell IA 50112-1130 Office: Grinnell Coll PO Box 805 Grinnell IA 50112-0813

WALKER, WALTER GRAY, JR., small business owner, program statistician; b. Newport News, Va., June 6, 1931; s. Walter Gray and Verna Elizabeth (Haughton) W.; divorced; children: James Gray, Thomas Shelton, Martha Anne Crute. AB, William and Mary Coll., 1956; AAS magna cum laude, No. Va. Community, 1983; D of Noetic Scis. (hon.), Fergle U., 1987. Broadcast engr. Sta. WGH, Hampton, Va., 1957-58; instr. Chesterfield Sch. Bd., Va., 1958-63; asst. coord. Va. Mental Health Study Commn., Richmond, Va., 1964; asst. dir. Community Action Agency, Hampton, Va., 1965; statistician U.S. Govt., Washington, 1966-78; pres. Diversified Svcs. Co., Arlington, Va., 1980—; automotive tech. instr. No. Va. Community Coll., Alexandria, Va., 1983; radio electronics officer Vulcan Carriers, Inc., N.Y.C., 1991; real estate broker Va. Real Estate Commn., Richmond, Va., 1962; bd. dir. Chesterfield Hosp. Corp., Va., 1963-64. Author: Public Housing Review, 1973, Automotive Technical Document Study of Northern Virginia Community College, 1983. Treas. 1st Congregational Ch., Washington, 1972; del. Arlington (Va.) Dem. Party, 1992; active mem. Common Cause, Washington, 1968—; Am. for Dem. Action, Washington, 1993—; active The Unitarian Universalist Ch. of Arlington, Va. With USNR, 1949-53, Korea, 1950-52. Mem. Am. Radio Assn., World Federalist Assn., Vets. for Peace, Chesterfield Jaycees (external affairs rep. 1962-63, Arlington Radio Club (treas. 1988-89), Oxford Club. Democrat. Home: 2915 N Nottingham St Arlington VA 22207-1252 Office: Diversified Svcs Co PO Box 5315 Arlington VA 22205-5315

WALKER, WARREN STANLEY, English educator; b. Bklyn., Mar. 19, 1921; s. Harold Stanley and Althea (Luscher) W.; m. Barbara Jeanne Kerlin, Dec. 9, 1943; children—Brian, Theresa. BA, SUNY-Albany, 1947, MA, 1948; PhD, Cornell U., 1951; LittD (hon.), Selcuk U., 1989. Prof., chmn. dept. English Blackburn Coll., Carlinville, Ill., 1951-59; prof., dean arts and scis. Parsons Coll., Fairfield, Iowa, 1959-64; Fulbright lectr. Am. lit. Ankara (Turkey) U., 1961-62; prof. English Tex. Tech U., Lubbock, 1964-86; Horn prof. Tex. Tech U., 1972-86; dir. Archive Turkish Oral Narrative, 1971; adv. council Tex. Cultural Alliance, 1975. Author: Nigerian Folktales, 1961, Twentieth-Century Short Story Explication, 14 vols., 1961-93, James Fenimore Cooper, 1962, Leatherstocking and the Critics, 1965, Tales Alive in Turkey, 1966, Archive of Turkish Oral Narrative: Catalogue 1, 1975, Plots and Characters in the Fiction of J.F. Cooper, 1978, A Bibliography of American Scholarship on Turkish Folklore and Ethnography, 1982, Turkish Games for Health and Recreation, 1983, Archive of Turkish Oral Narrative: Catalogue 2, 1988, Catalogue 3, 1994, The Book of Dede Korkut-A Turkish Epic, 1991, More Tales Alive in Turkey, 1992; mem. editorial bd. Definitive Edit. Works of James Fenimore Cooper, 1968; bibliographer Studies in Short Fiction, 1973. Served with USAAF, 1943-45. Recipient Tex. Writers award, 1967; citation Turkish Ministry Edn., 1967, Turkish Ministry State, 1973; research grantee Am. Council Learned Socs., 1973, 79; Am. Philos. Soc., 1974, Tex. Tech U., 1971-74, 76, 83, Republic of Turkey, 1983, Inst. Turkish Studies, 1984. Mem. MLA, Am. Folklore Soc., Nat. Coun. Tchrs. English, Internat. Soc. Folk Narrative Rsch., Middle East Studies Assn., Tex. Assn. Middle East Scholars (exec. coun.), Turkish Studies Assn., Atatürk Supreme Coun. on Turkish Culture (hon.). Home: 3703 66th St Lubbock TX 79413-5325 Office: Tex Tech U Archive Turkish Oral N Lubbock TX 79409

WALKER, WESLEY M., lawyer; b. Union, S.C., Jan. 28, 1915; s. John Frost and Cornelia (Greer) W.; m. Martha Bratton, Nov. 8, 1941; children—Martha Bratton, Wesley M., Nancy F. A.B., U.S.C., 1936, LL.B., 1938. Bar: S.C. 1938. Now partner firm Leatherwood, Walker, Todd & Mann, Greenville, S.C.; city atty. Greenville, 1949-51; spl. circuit judge York County, 6th Jud. Circuit, 1962. Served to lt. USNR, 1941-45. Fellow Am. Bar Found. (50 Yr. award 1994); mem. ABA (ho. of dels. 1952-54, 72-86, mem. com. law lists 1955-68, chmn. 1965-68, bd. govs. 1976-79), S.C. Bar Assn. (state del. 1973-77), Greenville Bar Assn. (pres. 1973), Am. Law Inst., Am. Coll. Trust and Estate Counsel, Phi Delta Phi. Home: 233 Camille Ave Greenville SC 29605-1703 Office: 100 E Coffee St Greenville SC 29601-2753

WALKER, WILLARD BREWER, anthropology educator, linguist; b. Boston, July 29, 1926; s. William Henry Clowes and Helen (Brewer) W.; m. C. Pearline Large, Oct. 18, 1952; children: Christopher William, Andrew Francis. AB, Harvard U., 1950; MA, U. Ariz., 1953; PhD, Cornell U., 1964. Teaching fellow dept. modern langs. Cornell U., Ithaca, N.Y., 1960-61; rsch. asst. comparative study codes and models Cornell U., Nat. Inst. Mental Health, Ithaca, N.Y., 1963; rsch. assoc. dept. anthropology U. Chicago, Tahlequah, Okla., 1964-66; asst. prof. anthropology Wesleyan U., Middletown, Conn., 1966-70, assoc. prof., 1970-77, prof., 1977-89, prof. emeritus, 1989—, chmn. anthropology dept., 1971, 74-77, chmn. linguistics program, 1986-89. Author: Cherokee Primer, 1965; co-author: Cherokee Stories, 1966, A History of World's End, 1973, 1984; co-editor: Hopis, Tewas, & the American Road, 1983, 1986; contbr. numerous articles to profl. jours. Fellow Am. Anthrop. Assn.; mem. Am. Ethnological Soc., Linguistic Soc. Am., Am. Soc. Ethnohistory, Soc. for the Study of Indigenous Langs. of the Americas. Democrat. Avocation: forestry. Address: Rte 2 Box 3310 Canaan ME 04924

WALKER, WILLIAM BOND, retired librarian; b. Brownsville, Tenn., Apr. 15, 1930; s. Marshall Francis and Mary Louise (Taylor) W. B.A., State U. Iowa, 1953; M.L.S., Rutgers U., 1958. Librarian-trainee Donnell br. N.Y. Public Library, N.Y.C., 1955-57; reference librarian/cataloger Met. Mus. Art, N.Y.C., 1957-59; chief librarian Bklyn. Mus., 1959-64; supervisory librarian Library of Nat. Collection Fine Arts and Nat. Portrait Gallery, Smithsonian Instn., Washington, 1964-80; Arthur K. Watson chief librarian Thomas J. Watson Library, Met. Mus. Art, N.Y.C., 1980-94; ret., 1994; adj. lectr. Columbia U. Sch. Library Service, 1987-88. Author: annotated bibliography American Sculpture, 18th-20th Century, 1979. Mem. ALA, Art Libra. Soc. N.Am (pres. 1975, Disting. Svc. award), Geneal. and Biog. Soc. (corr.), Phi Beta Kappa. Home: Queechy Lake Dr PO Box 237 Canaan NY 12029

WALKER, WILLIAM EASTON, surgeon, educator, lawyer; b. Glasgow, Scotland, Aug. 7, 1945; came to U.S. 1969; s. William Telfer and Josephine Blair (Easton) W.; m. Mary Fraley Cooley, June 23, 1973; children—Sarah Cooley, Blair Easton, Denton Arthur Cooley, William Easton, II. M.D., Glasgow U., Scotland, 1968; Ph.D., Johns Hopkins U., 1975; JD, South Tex. Coll Law, 1993. Diplomate Am. Bd. Surgery, Am. Bd. Thoracic Surgery, Am. Bd. Vascular Surgery. Intern, resident Johns Hopkins U., Balt., 1969-75; resident Vanderbilt U., Nashville, 1976-79; assoc. prof., div. dir. thoracic and cardiovascular surgery U. Tex. Med. Sch., Houston, 1979—; cons. M.D. Anderson Hosp., Houston, 1979—. Recipient Harwell Wilson award Vanderbilt U., Nashville, 1979. Fellow So. Surg. Assn., ACS, Royal Coll. Surgeons, Am. Coll. Cardiology; mem. Am. Assn. Thoracic Surgery, Coun. Fgn. Rels., Confrérie de la Chaine de Rôtisseurs, Houston Country Club, Belle Meade Country Club, Cosmos Club (Washington), Phi Beta Kappa, Sigma Xi. Republican. Presbyterian. Avocations: law, golf, flying, backgammon, bridge. Home and office: 2831 Sackett St Houston TX 77098-1125

WALKER, WILLIAM GRAHAM, ambassador; b. Kearney, N.J., June 1, 1935; s. Walter and Elizabeth (Graham) W.; m. Aldeize Nery de Sousa, May 17, 1977; children: Gordon G., Gillian E., Douglas G., Christopher A. Student, U. So. Calif., 1953-58; BA in Polit. Sci., UCLA, 1960, postgrad., 1968-9. Joined Fgn. Svc., Dept. State, 1961; officer Am. Embassy, Lima, Peru, 1962-63, Arequipa, Peru, 1963-64, Tokyo and Okinawa, Japan, 1964-67; polit. officer Am. Embassy, Rio de Janeiro, 1969-72; polit. counsellor Am. Embassy, San Salvador, El Salvador, 1974-77; dep. chief mission Am. Embassy, Tegulcigalpa, Honduras, 1980-82, La Paz, Bolivia, 1982-85; amb. to El Salvador, Am. Embassy, San Salvador, 1988—; EPA rep. on secretariat Fed. Regional Coun., San Francisco, 1972-74; inspector Fgn. Svc. Dept. State, Washington, 1978-80, dep. asst. sec., 1985-88. With U.S. Army, 1957-58. Dept. State fellow, 1977-78. Home and Office: Am Embassy APO AA 34023

WALKER, WILLIAM OLIVER, JR., religion educator; b. Sweetwater, Tex., Dec. 6, 1930; s. William Oliver and Frances Baker (White) W.; m. Mary Scott Daugherty, Dec. 22, 1955 (div. Dec. 1978); children: William Scott, Mary Evan, Michael Neal. Ba, Austin Coll., 1953; MDiv, Austin Presbyterian Sem., 1957; MA, U. Tex., 1958; PhD, Duke U., 1962. Instr.

religion Austin Coll., Sherman, Tex., 1954-55, Duke U., 1960-62; from asst. to prof. religion Trinity U., San Antonio, 1962—, chair dept., 1980-88, acting dean div. Humanities and Arts, 1988-89, dean, 1989—. Contbr. articles and book reviews to profl. jours. Editor: The Relationships, 1978, The Harper Collins Bible Pronunciation Guide, 1994; assoc. editor Harper's Bible Dictionary, 1985. Mem. Studiorum Novi Testamenti Soc., Soc. Bibl. Lit. (regional sec.-treas. 1980-86), Am. Acad. Religion (regional pres. 1966-67), Soc. Sci. Study Religion, Cath. Bibl. Assn. Am., Coll. Theology Soc. Democrat. Presbyterian. Avocations: tennis, traveling, photography. Home: 315 Cloverleaf Ave San Antonio TX 78209-3822 Office: Trinity U Office Dean Humanities & Arts 715 Stadium Dr San Antonio TX 78212-7212

WALKER, WILLIAM R., manufacturing executive, light; b. 1941. BS in Econs., U. Wis.; MBA, U. Md. CPA. With Exxon Corp., N.Y.C., 1964-84, Zilog, Inc., Campbell, Calif., 1984—; now sr. v.p. fin. and admnistrn., CFO Zilog, Inc., Campbell. Office: Zilog Inc 210 E Hacienda Ave Campbell CA 95008*

WALKER, WILLIAM RAY, broadcasting executive; b. Madison, Wis., Aug. 28, 1923; s. William E. and Edna (Blied) W.; m. Eleanor Bauhs, Jan. 17, 1953; children: Diana (dec.), Thomas, Robert. BBA, U. Wis., 1947, MS, 1963, PhD, 1964. Advt. agy. account exec. Arthur Towell Inc and Scott Inc., 1947-50; radio advt. salesman Sta. WMAM, Marinette, Wis., Sta. WBEV, Beaver Dam, others, 1950-54; mgr. Sta WMBV-TV, Green Bay and Marinette, Wis., 1954-56, Sta. WRRR, Rockford, Ill., 1956-59, Sta. WISM-AM-FM, Madison, 1959-82; pres., dir. Midwest Family Radio Stas., Madison, Oshkosh, Eau Claire and LaCrosse, Wis., 1955—, Escanaba, Saginaw, and St. Joseph, Mich., 1955—, Springfield, Ill., 1955—, Springfield, Mo., 1992—. Past pres. adv. bd. St. Mary's Hosp. and Med. Ctr., Madison; past pres., bd. dirs. United Way Dane County; past pres. United Madison Community Found. Capt. AUS, 1943-46. Named knight of St. Gregory, 1975. Mem. Rotary, Serra Club (past pres., dist. gov.), Alpha Delta Phi. Roman Catholic. Office: PO Box 2058 Madison WI 53701-2058

WALKER, WILLIAM ROSS, accountant; b. Winnipeg, Man., Can., Apr. 15, 1934; s. Edwin and Mary Margaret (MacCharles) W.; m. Audrey Erickson, Nov. 20, 1959; children—Jayne, Karen, Graham, Douglas. B.Comm., U. Alta., 1956. With KPMG, Toronto, Ont., Can., 1956-93, ptnr., 1964, mng. ptnr., 1972-84, sr. ptnr., chief exec., 1984-89; chmn., chief exec. KPMG Peat Marwick Thorne, Toronto, Ont., Can., 1989-93, internat. exec. com. and bd., 1989—; international. exec. ptnr. KPMG, Amsterdam, Netherlands, 1993—; past mem. panel sr. advisors to auditor gen. of Can.; past vice-chmn., bd. dirs. Can. Comprehensive Auditing Found.; past chmn. U. Waterloo Acctg. Adv. Coun. Past chmn. bd. trustees Clarke Inst. Psychiatry; past. chmn. Ottawa Gen. Hosp. Decorated Queen's Jubilee medal. Fellow Inst. Chartered Accts. Ont., Alta. (coun. 1982-89, pres. 1988-89); mem. National, York, Rosedale Golf and Toronto Clubs. Clubs: National; York; Rosedale Golf; Toronto. Avocations: skiing, travel. Office: KPMG Internat Headquarters, PO Box 74111, 1070 BC Amsterdam The Netherlands

WALKER, WILLIAM TIDD, JR., investment banker; b. Detroit, Sept. 5, 1931; s. William Tidd and Irene (Rhode) W.; m. Patricia Louise Frazier, Sept. 10, 1953; children—Donna Louise, Carol Ann, Sally Lynn, Alyssa Jane. Student, Stanford, 1950. Rep. William R. Staats & Co., Los Angeles, 1952-57; sales mgr. William R. Staats & Co., 1957-58, syndicate partner, 1958-65; sr. v.p. Glore Forgan, William R. Staats Inc., N.Y.C., 1965-68; partner, exec. com. Lester, Ryons & Co., Los Angeles, 1968; exec. v.p. Bateman Eichler, Hill Richards Inc., Los Angeles, 1969-85; past pres., bd. dirs. Delhi Co., L.A.; pres., bd. dirs. Kingo Farms Inc., L.A.; chmn., pres., CEO, WTW Inc.; chmn., CEO Walker Assocs.; bd. dirs. Ameriquest Techs., Inc., Go-Video, Inc., Aquajet Corp., Fortune Petroleum Corp.; adv. mem. Am. Stock Exch., 1981—. With USAF, 1949-52. With USAF, 1949-52. Mem. Securities Industry Assn. (dir. nat. syndicate com., chmn. Calif. Dist. 10), Pacific Coast Stock Exch. (bd. govs. 1971-72), Investment Bankers Assn. (nat. pub. rels. com. 1966—), Bond Club L.A. (pres. 1973—), Calif. Yacht Club, Newport Harbor Yacht Club. Office: Walker Assocs PO Box 10684 Beverly Hills CA 90213-3684

WALKER, WILLIAM W, III, wholesale distribution executive. Ptnr. Walker Drug Co., Pelham, Ala. Office: Walker Drug Co 172 Cahaba Valley Pky Pelham AL 35124*

WALKER, WINSTON WAKEFIELD, JR., insurance company executive; b. Traverse City, Mich., Oct. 19, 1943; s. Winston W. and Ann (Bridges) W.; m. Mary Martin, Sept. 11, 1965; children: Alan, Ross. BA, Tulane U., 1965; PhD, U. Ga., 1969. Asst. prof. Wake Forest U., Winston Salem, N.C., 1970-73; asst. actuary Provident Life & Accident Ins. Co., Chattanooga, 1974, exec. v.p. 1985-86, exec. v.p., CFO 1986-87, pres., COO 1987-88, pres., CEO, 1988—; also bd. dirs.; acutary Provident Nat. Assurance Co., Des Moines, 1975-78; v.p. admnstrn. Provident Nat. Assurance Co., Chattanooga, 1978-80, pres., 1980-85; pres. Provident Gen. Ins. Co., Chattanooga, 1984-85, pres., COO, 1987—; also pres., CEO; also pres., CEO Provident Life and Accident Ins. Co. Am.; bd. dirs. Am. Nat. Bank, Chattanooga. Mem. bd. dirs. exec. com. Greater Chattanooga United Way, 1986—. Fellow Am. Soc. Actuaries; mem. Southeastern Actuaries Club, Rotary, Mountain City Club, Lookout Mountain Fairyland Club. Office: Provident Life & Accident 1 Fountain Sq Chattanooga TN 37402-1330

WALKLET, JOHN JAMES, JR., publishing executive; b. Trenton, N.J., June 14, 1922; s. John James and Katherine Helen (Slamin) W.; m. Gretchen Crowell, Aug. 21, 1948; children: John III, Philip, Deborah, Preston, Richard, Colin, Keith, Christopher, Megan. BL in Journalism, Rutgers U., 1943. Reporter Montclair (N.J.) Times, 1943; prodn. editor Macmillan Pub. Co., N.Y.C., 1946-52, dir. mfg. sch. div., 1969-88, asst. v.p., 1982, v.p., 1983-88, cons., 1989, ret.; tech. writer Shell Chem. Corp., N.Y.C., 1952-54; dir. publs. Colonial Williamsburg, Williamsburg Va., 1954-69; cons. book prodn. U. Press of Va., Charlottesville, 1963-69. Author: designer: Adventure in Williamsburg, 1960 (So. Books Competition award), A Window on Williamsburg, 1966 (So. Books Competition award); designer: The Journal of John Harrower, 1963 (One of 50 Books of Yr. award Am. Inst. Graphic Arts). Pres. Kiwanis Club of Williamsburg, 1969; cons. Va. Travel Coun., Richmond, 1960-69. Sgt. U.S. Army, 1943-46. Mem. Assn. Am. Pubs. (mfg. com. rep. Adv. Commn. Textbook Specifications 1980-84, vice chmn. mfg. com. 1984-86, chmn. mfg. com. 1986-88), Williamsburg Stirrup Club (bd. dirs. 1965-69), James Iredell Assn. (bd. dirs. Edenton soc. 1989—). Republican. Roman Catholic. Avocations: reading, piano and organ, golf, fishing, spectator sports. Home: 1222 Sound Shore Dr Edenton NC 27932-9804

WALKLEY, BARBARA ANN, public relations executive; b. Mt. Kisco, N.Y., June 24, 1945; d. Salvatore Samuel and Teresa Elizabeth (Amuso) Intrieri; m. Arthur H. Walkley IV, Oct. 15, 1966; children: Arthur V, Kimberly. AB, Berkeley Coll., 1964. Notary public N.Y. Admnstrv. asst. Hill & Knowlton Inc., N.Y.C., 1977-86, asst. corp. sec., 1986-88, corp. sec., 1988-90, corp. v.p , sec., 1990—; dir. Bus. Coun. Internat. Understanding, N.Y.C., 1991; trustee John W. Hill and Knowlton, 1989; sec., exec. com. Hill and Knowlton, 1991; admnstrt. Hill and Knowlton Coll., N.Y.C., 1990; sec. Hill and Knowlton Retirement Trust, N.Y.C., 1987; corp. sec. Carl Byoir & Assocs., 1992. Co-pres. Bedford Hills (N.Y.) Elem. Sch. Parents Assn., 1980; sec. Bedford Rem. Town Com., 1977. Recipient Alumni of Yr. award Berkeley Coll., White Plains, N.Y., 1988. Roman Catholic. Avocations: hiking, canoeing, cross country skiing. Office: Hill & Knowlton Inc 420 Lexington Ave New York NY 10170-0001

WALKOWIAK, VINCENT STEVEN, lawyer, educator; b. Chgo., Apr. 22, 1946; s. Vincent Albert and Elizabeth (Modla) W.; m. Linda Kae Schweigert, Aug., 1968; children—Jenifer, Steven. B.A., U. Ill., 1968, J.D., 1971. Bar: Ill. 1971, Tex. 1981, U.S. Ct. Appeals (8th cir.) 1971, U.S. Ct. Appeals (5th cir.) 1982, U.S. Dist. Ct. (so. and no. dists. Tex.) 1982. Assoc. Dorsey, Marquart, Windhorst, West & Halladay, Mpls., 1971-74; ptnr. Fulbright & Jaworski, Houston, 1982—; prof. Fla. State U., Tallahassee, 1974-76, So. Meth. U., Dallas, 1976-84. Editor: Uniform Product Liability Act, 1980; Trial of a Product Liability Case, vol. 1, 1981, vol. 2, 1982; Preparation and Presentation of Product Liability, 1983. Office: Fulbright & Jaworski 2200 Ross Ave Ste 2800 Dallas TX 75201-2784

WALKOWITZ, DANIEL J., historian, filmmaker, educator; b. Paterson, N.J., Nov. 25, 1942; s. Sol and Selda (Margel) W.; m. Judith Rosenberg, Dec. 26, 1965; 1 child, Rebecca Lara. AB, U. Rochester, 1964, PhD, 1972; postgrad., U. Grenoble, France, 1965. Lectr. in history U. Rochester, N.Y., 1967-69; instr. history Rensselaer Poly. Inst., Troy, N.Y., 1969-71; asst. prof. history Rutgers U., New Brunswick, N.J., 1971-78, NYU, N.Y.C., 1978-81; assoc. prof. NYU, 1981-88, co-dir. pub. history program, 1981-89, prof., 1988—, dir. met. studies, 1989—; ptnr., film producer PastTimes Prodns., N.Y.C., 1982—; vis. prof. Johns Hopkins U., 1991-92, U. Calif. Irvine, 1982; editorial sec. Radical History Rev., N.Y.C., 1985-89; bd. dirs. N.Y. Marxist Sch., 1987-90. Author: Worker City, Company Town, 1978; co-author: Workers of the Donbass Speak, 1995; film project dir. The Molders of Troy, 1980; co-editor: Workers in the Industrial Revolution, 1974, Working-Class America, 1984; video dir., co-prodr.: Perestroika From Below, 1990; co-prodr., writer Public History Today. Grantee, Nat. Endowment Humanities, 1976, 78, 82. Mem. Nat. Coun. Pub. History (bd. dirs. 1986-89), Am. Hist. Assn., Orgn. Am. Historians, Oral History Assn. Avocation: international folk dance. Office: Met Studies Program NYU New York NY 10003

WALKUP, JOHN FRANK, electrical engineer, educator; b. Oakland, Calif, Feb. 7, 1941; s. Francis Milton and Mabel Doreen (Lishman) W.; m. Patricia Ann Hagbom, June 26, 1965; children: Mary Kathleen, Amy Christine, Rebecca Joy. BA magna cum laude, Dartmouth Coll., 1962, BEE, 1963; MS, Stanford U., 1965, Engr., 1969, PhD, 1971. Registered profl. engr.; Tex. Rsch asst. Stanford Electronics Labs., Stanford U., 1963-71; asst. prof. elec. engring. Tex. Tech. U., Lubbock, 1971-76, assoc. prof., 1976-81, prof., 1981-85, P.W. Horn prof., 1985—, assoc. dean engring., 1982-83; chmn. Gordon Rsch. Conf. on Holography and Optical Info. Processing, 1991; Nat. Rsch. Coun. sen. assoc., NASA Am. Rsch. Ctr., 1992-93; vis. scholar Univ. Ariz. 1982, vis. prof. Stanford U., 1992-93; cons. in field. Contbr. articles to jours. and chpts. to books. Faculty affiliate Christian Leadership Ministries, faculty sponsor Inter-Varsity Christian Fellowship, 1972-92; mem. bd. dirs. Found. for Thought and Ethics. Recipient Goodrich prize Dartmouth Coll., 1963, Halliburton award for excellence in teaching Tex. Tech U., 1980, Pres.'s award for excellence in teaching, 1981, AT&T Found. award for teaching, 1985, Rushing Faculty Rsch. award, 1986, Pres.'s Acad. Achievement award, 1994, El Paso Natural Gas found. award, 1995. Fellow IEEE, Optical Soc. Am. (chmn. edn. coun. 1987-88, bd. dirs. 1987-88, topical editor jour. 1992-94); mem. Internat. Soc. Optical Engring., Phi Beta Kappa, Sigma Xi, Eta Kappa Nu, Tau Beta Pi.

WALL, BARBARA WARTELLE, lawyer; b. New Orleans, Sept. 30, 1954; d. Richard Cole and Ruth Druhan (Power) W.; m. Christopher Read Wall, June 21, 1980; children: Christopher, Louisa. BA, U. Va., 1976, JD, 1979. Bar: N.Y. 1980, U.S. Dist. Ct. (so. and ea. dists.) N.Y. 1980. Assoc. Satterlee & Stephens, N.Y.C., 1979-85; asst. gen. counsel Gannett Co., Inc., Arlington, Va., 1985-90, sr. legal counsel, 1990-93, v.p., sr. legal counsel, 1993—. Mem. ABA (co-chair first amendment and media litigation com. of sect. litigation, mem. gov. bd. forum on comm. law), N.Y. State Bar Assn., Assn. of Bar of City of N.Y. Republican. Roman Catholic. Home: 5026 Tilden St NW Washington DC 20016-2334 Office: Gannett Co Inc 1100 Wilson Blvd Arlington VA 22209-2297

WALL, BENNETT HARRISON, history educator; b. Raleigh, N.C., Dec. 7, 1914; s. Bennett Louis and Evie David (Harrison) W.; m. Neva White Armstrong, Sept. 7, 1968; children by previous marriage: Maie (Mrs. John E. Clark) (dec.), Diana (Mrs. John Freckman), Ann Bennett. AB, Wake Forest Coll., 1933; MA, U. N.C., 1941, PhD, 1947. Instr. N.C. State U., 1942-43; instr. U. N.C., 1943-44; instr. U. Ky., 1944-46, asst. prof., 1946-52, assoc. prof., 1952-64; prof. history dept. Tulane U., New Orleans, 1965-80; head dept. Tulane U., 1968-73; dir. Tulane Center Bus. History Studies, 1974-79; lectr. U. Ga., 1980-85. Author: Growth in a Changing Environment: History of Standard Oil Company New Jersey, 1950-1972, Exxon Corporation 1972-75, 1988; co-author Teagle of Jersey Standard, 1974; contbr. numerous articles to profl. jours. Fellow La. History Assn. (pres. 1974-75, McGinty award 1991); mem. Orgn. Am. Historians, Agrl. History Soc., Bus. History Soc., Econ. History Soc., So. History Assn. (sec., treas. 1952-85, v.p. 1986-87, pres. 1987-88), N.C. History Soc., A.C.T. Hist. Soc., Ga. History Soc., Omicron Delta Kappa, Phi Alpha Theta. Home: 150 Ashton Dr Athens GA 30606-1618

WALL, BRIAN ARTHUR, sculptor; b. London, Sept. 5, 1931; s. Arthur Francis and Dorothy (Seymour) W.; m. Sylvia Brown, Oct. 27, 1973; children—Nathaniel, Gideon. Student, Luton (Eng.) Coll. Art, 1951. First asst. to Dame Barbara Hepworth, St. Ives, Cornwall, Eng., 1954-59; instr. Ealing Coll. Art, Middlesex, Eng., 1961-62; prin. lectr. Central Sch. Art and Design, London, 1962-72; head dept. sculpture Central Sch. Art and Design, 1962-72; vis. lectr. U. Calif., Berkeley, 1969-73; lectr. U. Calif., 1973-75, asst. prof., 1975-77, asso. prof. art, 1977-81, prof., 1981-93; prof. emeritus, 1993—. Exhibited in one-man shows U. Nev., Las Vegas, 1976, Braunstein Gallery, San Francisco, 1974, 76, 78, Sculpture Now, N.Y.C., 1977, 78, Max Hutchinson Gallery, Houston, 1979, May Hutchinson Gallery, N.Y.C., 1981, Seattle Art Mus., 1982, San Francisco Mus. Modern Art, 1983, John Berggruen Gallery, San Francisco, 1983, Lowinsky Gallery, N.Y.C., 1987, Francis Graham-Dixon Gallery, London, 1992, Sheldon Meml. Art Gallery, U. Nebr., 1995; group shows include Mus. Modern Art, Paris, 1961, U. Tex., Dallas, 1976, Crocker Art Mus., Sacramento, 1979, Tate Gallery, London, 1985, others; works represented in collections at Tate Gallery, London, Mus. Art, Dublin, Art Gallery of NSW, Australia, Univ. Art Mus., Berkeley, Calif., U. Houston, Sheldon Meml. Art Gallery U. Nebr., Seattle Art Mus., Towson State U., Balt., Oakland Mus.; works include Thornaby, 1968, Ali, 1978. Mem. Arts Council Gt. Brit., 1969-72; trustee San Francisco Art Inst., 1974-77; mem. San Francisco Twin Bicentennial Arts Com., 1975-76. Served with RAF, 1950-52. U. Calif. at Berkeley Humanities Rsch. Fellowship Program grantee, 1978-79; recipient prize BART Sculpture Competition, 1975. Subject of numerous profl. articles. Home: 306 Lombard St San Francisco CA 94133-2415

WALL, CARROLL EDWARD, librarian, publisher; b. Cherokee, Iowa, Mar. 3, 1942; s. Clifford R. and Mabel B. (Tjossem) W.; m. Mary Ellen Stratton, Sept. 1, 1962; children: Annette, Jannette, Heather, Christopher. B.A. with distinction, U. Iowa, 1964; postgrad. in Chinese mil. history, U. Mich., 1964-65, M.A. in L.S, 1966. Reference librarian U. Mich., Dearborn, 1966-67; head librarian U. Mich., 1967-84; founder, pub. Pierian Press. (pub. reference books), Ann Arbor, Mich., 1968—; speaker, cons. in field. Editor: books, the most recent being Author Index to Public Affairs Information Service, 1965-69, 1971; author: books, the most recent being Index to A.L.A.'s Index to General Literature, 1972; contbr. articles to profl. jours.; editor Media Rev. Digest, 1970—, Reference Services Rev., 1972—, Consumers Index, 1972—, Serials Rev., 1975—, Index to Free Periodicals, 1976—, Libr. Hi Tech, 1983—, Libr. Hi Tech News, 1985—, Libr. Hi Tech. Bibliography, 1986—, Computer and Office Product Evaluations, 1989—. Mem. exec. com. Mich. region Am. Friends Service Com., 1968-73, Dearborn Hist. Commn., 1971-73; vice chmn., chmn. Fairlane Music Guild, 1971-73; trustee Pittsfield Charter Twp., 1982-89. Recipient Loleta Fyan award Mich. Library Assn., 1971; Ford Found. scholar, 1963. Mem. ALA, Mich. Library Assn. (chmn. acad. div. nominating com. 1971), Assn. Ednl. Communications and Tech., Ednl. Film Library Assn., Phi Beta Kappa, Beta Phi Mu. Office: The Pierian Press Box 1808 Ann Arbor MI 48106

WALL, CLARENCE VINSON, congressman; b. Athens, Ga., Oct. 17, 1947; s. Clarence Jacob and Fannie Lucile (Clark) W.; m. Linda Gail Mason, Dec. 6, 1964 (div. 1980); 1 child, Jeffrey Vinson. Grad. high sch. Lawrenceville, Ga., 1965. Rep. Ga. Ho. of Reps., Lawrenceville, 1973-82, 85—. Staff sgt. Ga. ANG, 1967-73. Republican. Baptist. Home: 164 E Oak St Lawrenceville GA 30245-4900

WALL, DONALD ARTHUR, lawyer; b. Lafayette, Ind., Mar. 17, 1946; s. Dwight Arthur and Myra Virgina (Peavey) W.; m. Cheryn Lynn Heinen, Aug. 29, 1970; children: Sarah Lynn, Michael Donald. BA, Butler U., 1968; JD, Northwestern U., 1971. Bar: Ohio 1971, U.S. Dist. Ct. (no. dist.) Ohio 1973, U.S. Ct. Appeals (6th cir.) 1982, U.S. Supreme Ct. 1980, Ariz. 1982, U.S. Dist. Ct. (no. dist.) W.Va. 1982, U.S. Dist. Ct. Ariz. 1983, U.S. Ct. Appeals (9th and 10th cir.) 1984, U.S. Ct. Appeals (5th cir.) 1988. Assoc. Squire, Sanders & Dempsey, Cleve., 1971-80, ptnr., 1980-82, Phoenix, 1983—; speaker at profl. meetings; program moderator. Contbr. articles to

profl. jours. Mem. admnstrv. bd. Ch. of Saviour, Cleve. Heights, Ohio, 1980-83; trustee Ch. of the Saviour Day Center, Cleve. Heights, 1979-82; fin. com. Paradise Valley (Ariz.) United Meth. Ch., 1986-87; bd. dirs., div. commr. North Scottsdale (Ariz.) Little League, 1983-92; bd. dirs. Epilepsy Found. N.E. Ohio, 1976-82, pres., 1981-82, N.E. Cmty. Basketball Assn., 1993-94. Mem. ABA (torts and ins. practice and litigation sect., past chmn. r.r. law com., litigation sect.), Def. Research Inst., Ariz. Bar Assn. (labor and trial practice sects.), Maricopa County Bar Assn., Am. Judicature Soc., Ariz. Assn Def. Counsel. Methodist. Office: Squire Sanders & Dempsey 40 N Central Ave Phoenix AZ 85004-4441

WALL, ERVING HENRY, JR., sales agency executive, state senator; b. Plymouth, Mass., Sept. 27, 1934; s. Erving Henry Sr. and Madeline Blanche (Northrup) W.; m. Harriett Florence Marr, July 6, 1959; children: Deborah, Carol, Harriett, Susan. Grad. high sch., Plymouth. Lic. real estate broker, Mass. Electronics technician Raytheon, Waltham, North Dighton, and Quincy, Mass., 1957-65; tech. rep. Mt. Hope Machinery, Taunton, Mass., 1965-68, Beckman Instruments, Palo Alto, Calif., 1968-70; sales rep. Louis Batson Co., Greenville, S.C., 1970-73, Marshall & Williams Co., Providence, 1973-76, W.R. Grace and Co., Lexington, Mass., 1976-78; owner, operator Wall Machinery Inc., Taunton, 1978—; mem. Mass. State Senate, 1991—. Mem. Mass. Rep. Senate Com., Corp. Morton Hosp. Chief petty officer USN, 1953-57, with USNR, 1964-82. Mem. Am. Assn. Textile Colorists, Nat. Rep. Legis. Assn., Mass. Archeol. Soc., Inc., Korean War Vets., Tin Can Sailors, Segregansett Country Club. Baptist. Avocation: sports. Home: 128 Winthrop St Taunton MA 02780-4124 Office: MA State Senate State House Rm 314 Boston MA 02133

WALL, FRED WILLARD, agricultural products supplier; b. 1923. With Porterville (Calif.) Drug Co., 1946-49; with Walco Internat. Inc., 1950—, now pres., chmn. bd., CEO. With USN, 1946. Office: Walco Internat Inc 15 W Putnam Ave Fl 2 Porterville CA 93257*

WALL, FREDERICK THEODORE, chemistry educator; b. Chisholm, Minn., Dec. 14, 1912; s. Peter and Fanny Maria (Rauhala) W.; m. Clara Elizabeth Vivian, June 5, 1940; children: Elizabeth Wall Ralston, Jane Vivian Wall-Meinke. B.Chemistry, U. Minn., 1933, Ph.D., 1937. Mem. faculty chemistry dept. U. Ill., 1937-64, dean grad. coll., 1955-63; prof., chmn. dept. chemistry U. Calif., Santa Barbara, 1964-66, vice chancellor rsch., 1965-66; vice chancellor grad. studies and research, prof. chemistry U. Calif. at San Diego, 1966-69; exec. dir. Am. Chem. Soc., Washington, 1969-72; prof. chemistry Rice U., Houston, 1972-78; Pres. Assn. Grad. Schs., 1961; trustee Inst. Def. Analyses, 1962-64; mem. governing bd. Nat. Acad. Scis.-NRC, 1963- 67. Author: Chemical Thermodynamics, 1958; editor: Jour. Phys. Chemistry, 1965-69; contbr. articles on quantum mechanics and statis. mechanics to sci. jours. Mem. Am. Chem. Soc. (Pure Chemistry award 1945, dir. 1962-64), Finnish Chem. Soc. (corr.), Am. Acad. Arts and Scis., Nat. Acad. Scis. Achievements include early work on Monte Carlo computer simulation of macromolecular configurations and of basic reaction probabilities. Home: 2468 Via Viesta La Jolla CA 92037-3935

WALL, JAMES EDWARD, petroleum, pharmaceutical executive; b. Santa Barbara, Calif., Nov. 24, 1947; s. Charles Caswell II and Lydia (Sinn) W.; m. Judith Ann Hochman, Aug. 1, 1976. AA, Bakersfield Coll., 1967; BS, Calif. State U., Los Angeles, 1969; MBA, UCLA, 1970; D of Profl. Studies, Pace U., 1985; PMD, Harvard U. Sch. Bus., 1987. CPA, Calif. Agt. IRS, Los Angeles, 1971-74; agt. service office internat. ops. IRS, Washington, 1974-76; mgr. fin. forecasts Ultramar, Ltd., Mt. Kisco, N.Y., 1976-80, treas., 1980-85, v.p., treas., 1985-91; exec. dir. fin. and admnstrn. Ultramar Exploration, London, 1991; v.p., treas. Ultramar Corp., Greenwich, Conn., 1992-94; v.p., corp. treas. ICN Pharms., Costa Mesa, Calif., 1994—; chief fin. officer Enstar Corp., Indonesia; mem. bd. mgmt. Unimar Co., 1985-91. Recipient award in acctg. UCLA, 1972, award in gen. bus. mgmt., 1973. Mem. AICPA, Fin. Execs. Inst., Nat. Assn. Corp. Treas., UCLA Grad. Sch. Alumni Assn., Harvard U. Bus. Sch. Alumni Assn. Office: ICN Pharms 3300 Hyland Ave Costa Mesa CA 92626

WALL, JAMES McKENDREE, minister, editor; b. Monroe, Ga., Oct. 27, 1928; s. Louie David and Lida (Day) W.; m. Mary Eleanor Kidder, Sept. 11, 1953; children: David McKendree, Robert Kidder, Richard James. Student, Ga. Inst. Tech., 1945-47; BA, Emory U., 1949, BD, 1955, LHD (hon.), 1985; MA, U. Chgo., 1960; LittD (hon.), Ohio No. U., 1969; DHL (hon.), Willamette Coll., 1978; DD (hon.), MacMurray, 1981; DHL (hon.), Coe Coll. 1987. Ordained to ministry United Meth. Ch, 1954. Staff writer, sports dept. Atlanta Jour., 1948-50; asst. minister East Lake Meth. Ch., Atlanta, 1953; asst. to dean students Emory U., Atlanta, 1954-55; pastor North Ga. Conf. Moreland, Luthersville Meth. Chs., Ga., 1955-57, Bethel United Meth. Ch., Chgo., 1957-59; mng. editor Christian Adv. mag., Park Ridge, Ill., 1959-63, editor, 1963-72; editor Christian Century mag., Chgo., 1972—. Author: Church and Cinema, 1971, Three European Directors, 1973, Winning the War, Losing Our Soul, 1991; author, editor: Theologians in Transition, 1981, A Century of the Century, 1987, How My Mind Has Changed, 1991. Del. Dem. Nat. Conv., 1972, 76, 80, 92; mem. Dem. Nat. Com., 1976-80, Dem. State Cen. Com., 1974-86, Pres. Commn. White House Fellowships, 1976-80. Served to 1st lt. USAF, 1950-52. Mem. Alpha Tau Omega, Omicron Delta Kappa, Sigma Delta Chi. Home: 451 S Kenilworth Ave Elmhurst IL 60126-3928 Office: Christian Century 407 S Dearborn St Ste 1405 Chicago IL 60605-1150

WALL, JERRY LEON, management educator, university administrator; b. Minot, N.D., Sept. 30, 1942; s. Claude Leon and Beulah Dollie (Widney) W.; m. Katharine Hoffmann, Sept. 4, 1965; children: Christopher, Stephan, Alison. BA, Okla. State U., 1964; MBA, East Carolina U., 1968; PhD, U. Mo., 1974; cert., Army War Coll., Carlisle Barracks, Pa., 1989. Cert. sr. profl. human resources; accredited pers. diplomate. From asst. to full prof. mgmt. Western Ill. U., Macomb, 1972-81, prof. mgmt., 1982; prof. mgmt. scis. U. Iowa, Iowa City, 1981-82; dir. ctr. for bus. and econ. rsch. N.E. La. U., Monroe, 1983—; pres., chmn. JKW Assocs., West Monroe, 1972—; adj. prof. law enforcement Western Ill. U., Macomb, 1979-81. Editor Jour. of Behavioral Economics, 1975-81, Northeast La. Bus. Rev., 1983-89, Delta Bus. Rev., 1989-91; contbr. over 100 articles to profl. jours., papers and books. Mem. joint legis. com. on alt. econ. strategy for La., Baton Rouge, 1986-87; grad. Leadership La. Col. USAR. Mem. Assn. for U. Bus. and Econ. Rsch. (bd. dirs.), Midwest Soc. for Human Resources/Indsl. Rels. (pres. 1986-87), S.W. Decision Scis. Inst. (adv. coun., area chmn. 1984-86), Am. Arbitration Assn. (panel mem. 1973-90), Arm. Nat. Bus. Hall of Fame (bd. dirs. 1983—), Ill. Bus. Hall of Fame (bd. dirs. 1978-83), Small Bus. Inst. (dir. 1976-81), Beta Gamma Sigma. Republican. Presbyterian. Lodge: Rotary. Avocations: scuba diving, magic, racquet sports. Office: NE La U Ctr Bus Econ Rsch Monroe LA 71209-0101

WALL, JOHN W., trust company executive; b. New Haven, Conn., 1925. With Bank of Boston Corp., 1949-89, retired, 1989-90; chmn., pres. Rhode Island Hosp. Tr. Nat. Bank, Providence, 1990-92; vice chmn. Rhode Island Hosp. Tr. Nat. Bank, 1992—. Office: Rhode Island Hosp Tr Nat Bk 1 Hosp Trust Plz Providence RI 02903*

WALL, JOSEPH FRAZIER, historian, educator; b. Des Moines, July 10, 1920; s. Joseph Frazier and Minnie Ellen (Patton) W.; m. Beatrice Mills, Apr. 16, 1944; children—April Ane, Joseph Frazier, Julia Mills. B.A., Grinnell Coll., 1941, LL.D. (hon.), 1978; M.A., Harvard U., 1942; Ph.D. Columbia U., 1951; LL.D. (hon.), Simpson Coll., 1978, Luther Coll. 1982. Faculty Grinnell (Iowa) Coll., 1947-78, 80-90, prof. history, 1957-78, James Morton Roberts honor prof., 1960-61, Parker prof., 1961-78, Earl Strong Disting. prof., 1972-78, chmn. dept. history, 1954-57, 58-60, chmn. div. social studies, 1956-57, 59-60, chmn. div. history, philosophy and math., 1965-66, chmn. faculty, 1966-69, dean coll., 1969-73, Rosenfield prof. pub. affairs, 1980-85; profl. history, chmn. dept. SUNY, Albany, 1978-80; prof. emeritus, 1990—; spl. assignment to asst. oral history project Columbia, 1957; sr. research Fulbright scholar U. Edinburgh, Scotland, 1957-58; Fulbright prof. U. Gothenburg, Sweden, 1964-65, U. Salzburg, Austria, 1987-88. Author: (with Robert Parks) Freedoms, 1955 (ann. Iowa Civil Liberties Union award 1956), Henry Watterson: Reconstructed Rebel, 1956 (hon. mention John A. Dunning prize 1956), Andrew Carnegie, 1970 (Bancroft prize 1971), Iowa, 1978, Policies and People, 1979, Skibo, 1985, Alfred I. du Pont, 1990 (Pulitzer prize finalist 1991), Andrew Carnegie Reader, 1992.

Served to lt. USNR, 1942-46. Mem. AAUP, Iowa Assn. Univ. Profs. (chmn. 1955-56), Am. Hist. Assn., Orgn. Am. Historians (exec. bd. 1974-77), Soc. Am. Historians, Phi Beta Kappa (senator-at-large 1988-94), Sigma Delta Chi. Democrat. Home: 2000 Country Club Dr Grinnell IA 50112-1132

WALL, JULIA ANN WILHITE, educational administrator, consultant; b. Eros, La., Aug. 6, 1942; d. Walter Elder and Myrtle Lee (Aswell) Wilhite; children: Julia Ann, Lee Barclay, Whitney Leane. BA, Northeast La. State U., Monroe, 1965; MA, La. Tech. U., Ruston, 1969; Adminstr. Cert., Stephen F. Austin U., 1981. Tchr. profoundly handicapped G. B. Cooley Hosp., West Monroe, La., 1966-68; speech pathologist Ouachita Parish Schs., Monroe, La., 1969-71, various independent sch. dists., Tex., 1971-75; coord. lang., speech, hearing Longview (Tex.) Independent Sch. Dist., 1975-79; asst. prin. Longview (Tex.) High Sch., 1979-80; prin. Hudson Prep Sch., Longview, Tex., 1980-83; head of sch. Trinity Sch. Tex., Longview, 1983--; Bd. dirs. Tex. Assn. Non-Public Schs., Austin, 1988--. Bd. dirs. Zonta Internat., Longview, Tex., 1983-86, Am. Heart Assn., Longview, 1982-86, Vol. Action Coun. Longview, 1982-85; bd. dirs. Palmer Drug Abuse Program, Lonview, 1988, pres., 1988, 89; vestry mem. Trinity Episc. Ch., Longview, 1980-83; mem. Teen Coalition Longview, 1990--; sustainer Jr. League Longview; bd. dirs. Gregg County Children's Assn., 1991--, Longview Opera Repertory Co., 1992--. Recipient First Lady of Longview award Beta Sigma Phi, 1982, Premier Principal award Tex. PTA, Ft. Worth, Tex., 1983. Mem. Tex. Assn. Gifted and Talented, Tex. ASCD, LeTourneau Univ. Assocs., Rotary, Phi Delta Kappa. Republican. Episcopalian. Avocations: gardening, reading, sewing, music, drama. Home: 1908 Warwick Cir W Longview TX 75601-3139

WALL, LEONARD J., bishop; b. Windsor, Ont., Can., Sept. 27, 1924; Ordained Roman Catholic priest, June 11, 1949; ordained titular bishop of Leptiminus and aux. bishop of Toronto, 1979-92; archbishop of Winnipeg Archdiocese of Winnipeg, 1992--. Office: Archdiocese of Winnipeg, 1495 Pembina Hwy, Winnipeg, MB Canada R3T 2C6

WALL, M. DANNY, financial services consultant. BArch, N.D. State U., 1963. Exec. dir. Urban Renewal Agy., Fargo, N.D., 1964-71, Salt Lake City Redevel. Agy., 1971-75; dir. legis. Office U.S. Senator Jake Garn, Washington, 1975-78; minority staff dir. Senate Com. for Banking, Housing and Urban Affairs, Washington, 1979-80, staff dir., 1980-86, Rep. staff dir., 1987; chmn. Fed. Home Loan Bank Bd./Fed. Home Loan Mortgage Corp., Washington, 1987-89; dir. Office Thrift Supervision (formerly Fed. Home Loan Bank Bd.), 1989-90.

WALL, ROBERT ANTHONY, JR., lawyer; b. Hartford, Conn., Mar. 3, 1945; s. Robert Anthony and Eileen (Fitzgerald) W.; divorced; children: Andrea, Melanie, Victoria, Robert, Natalie. BA, Georgetown U., Washington, 1968; JD, Am. U., Washington, 1973. Bar: Conn. 1974, U.S. Ct. Appeals (D.C. cir.) 1974, U.S. Dist. Ct. Conn. 1974, U.S. Supreme Ct. 1977. Ptnr. Wall, Wall & Frauenhofer, Torrington, Conn., 1974-87; pvt. practice Torrington, 1987--. Mem. State of Conn. Rep. Ctrl. Com., 1976-79. Mem. Conn. Trial Lawyers Assn. (bd. govs. 1984-86), Ct. Washington #67 Foresters of Am. (trustee 1988--). Roman Catholic. Home: 55 Quail Run Torrington CT 06790 Office: 8 Church St Torrington CT 06790-5247

WALL, ROBERT EMMET, educational administrator, novelist; b. N.Y.C., Apr. 29, 1937; s. Robert Emmet and Sabina (Daly) W.; m. Regina Palasek, Aug. 1, 1959; children—Elizabeth, Nina, Amy, Christopher, Craig. BA, Holy Cross Coll., 1960; MA, Yale U., 1961, PhD, 1965. Asst. in instrn. Yale U., New Haven, 1963; instr. history Duke U., Durham, N.C., 1963-65; asst. prof. Mich. State U., East Lansing, 1965-69, asso. prof. history, 1970; asso. prof. Concordia U. (Sir George Williams U.), Montreal, Que., Can., 1971-72, prof., 1972-80, chmn. dept., 1972-77, dean, 1977-80; provost, acting v.p. Fairleigh Dickinson U., Rutherford, N.J., 1980-85; v.p. academic affairs Gannon U., Erie, Pa., 1986-92; acad. v.p. Fairfield (Conn.) U., 1992—. Author: Massachusetts Bay, The Crucial Decade, 1640-1650, 1972, The Canadians, Vol. I (Blackrobe), 1981, Vol. II (Bloodbrothers), 1981, Vol. III (Birthright), 1982, Vol. IV (The Patriots), 1982, Vol. V (The Inherators), 1983, Vol. VI (Dominion), 1984, Vol. VII (Brotherhood), 1985, The Acadians, 1984, Sierre Gold, 1987, The Massachusetts Bay General Court, 1630-1686, 1990, The Cat and The Rat, 1991. Home: 1232 Windward Rd Milford CT 06460-6667

WALL, ROBERT F., lawyer; b. Chgo., Jan. 7, 1952. BA with distinction, Northwestern U., 1973; JD summa cum laude, U. Santa Clara, 1977. Bar: Ill. 1977, U.S. Dist. Ct. (no. dist.) Ill. 1977. Ptnr. Winston & Strawn, Chgo. Mem. editorial bd. M&A and Corp. Control Law Reporter, 1988—. Mem. ABA. Office: Winston & Strawn 35 W Wacker Dr Chicago IL 60601-1614

WALL, ROBERT WILSON, JR., former utility executive; b. Monticello, Ark., June 11, 1916; s. Robert Wilson and Thursa (Cotham) W.; m. Joyce Esther Hoffman, Sept. 27, 1943; children: Mary Lynn Wall Sykes, Kathy Ann Wall Theros. B.A., U. Miss., 1938, J.D., 1940; grad. exec. program bus. adminstrn., Columbia U., 1974. Bar: Miss. bar 1940. With FBI, 1940-41, 47-53, spl. agt. in charge Miami (Fla.) office, 1951-53; with U.S. Fgn. Service, 1941-46; legal attache embassy U.S. Fgn. Service, Mexico City, 1944-46; personnel dir. Phillips Petroleum Co., Caracas, Venezuela, 1946-47; with Fla. Power & Light Co., Miami, 1953-81; v.p. Fla. Power & Light Co., 1963-73, sr. v.p., 1973-81; asst. chmn. Nat. Alliance Businessmen, 1966-70; bd. dirs. Southeastern Legal Found.; adv. bd. U. Miami Sch. Bus. Adminstrn. Div. chmn. United Fund Dade County, 1964-67; bd. dirs. Miami Better Bus. Bur., 1955-62, Goodwill Industries Miami, 1964-66, Miami council Girl Scouts Am., 1971-72. Mem. Am. Bar Assn., Am. Soc. Corp. Secs., Am. Arbitration Assn. (panel 1987), Soc. Former Spl. Agts. FBI, Miss. Bar Assn., Greater Miami C. of C. (dir. 1963, exec. com. 1964), Blue Key, Phi Delta Theta, Phi Delta Phi, Omicron Delta Kappa. Republican. Home: 16 Kituhwa Trl Brevard NC 28712-9438

WALL, SIDNEY SMITH RODERICK, JR., architectural firm executive, architect, consultant; b. Springfield, Ill., Jan. 6, 1942; s. Sidney Smith and Augusta Maine (Roderick) W.; m. Judith Ann O'Neill, June 13, 1964; children: Lisa Janelle, Christian Matthew. Student, U. Idaho, 1961; diploma in Art and Archtl. Studies, Am. Ctr. Students and Artists, Paris, 1964; BA in Art and Printmaking, So. Ill. U., 1965; postgrad., U. Mo., 1966; BA in Architecture, Iowa State U., 1972. Registered architect, Nebr., S.D., Wis., Ill., Va., Tex., Iowa; registered interior designer, Tex.; Nat. Coun. Archtl. Registration Bds. cert. Land surveyor, architect's office So. Ill. U., Carbondale, 1964-65; cockpit instrumentation designer, flight test divsn. McDonnell Douglas Corp., St. Louis, 1965-67, tech. artist, illustrator, product support divsn., 1966-67; engring. designer Gemini and Apollo space flight programs McDonnell Douglass Corp., St. Louis, 1967-69; archtl. and engring. designer Iowa State Hwy. Commn., Ames, 1969; archtl.and engring. designer Norval H. Curry,P.E. Consulting Engring., Ames, 1970-73; architect, project mgr. Henningson, Durham and Richardson, Inc., A.E.P., Omaha, 1973-84; hosp. architect, project mgr. Henningson, Durham and Richardson, Inc., A.E.P., Dallas, 1984-88, v.p., project mgr., healthcare consulting architect, 1988-89, v.p., sr. project mgr.; healthcare consulting architect, 1990--; bldg. advisor Mercy High Sch. Bldg. Program, Omaha, 1981-84; cons. Los Rios Homeowner's Assn., Plano, Tex., 1990-91; design review bd. Milcare Inc./Herman Miller, Zeeland, Mich., 1991—; lectr. in field. Illustrator: Voles, Moles and Other Vertebrates, 1964; exhibited in several midwest art shows; contbr. articles to profl. publs. Active religious edn. commn. Mary Our Queen Sch., Omaha, 1976-82. Mem. AIA (nat. and state chpts. 1974-84, edn. chmn. 1974, Nat. Svc. award 1974, Svc. award 1975), C.S.I. (nat. and state chpts.), Am. Arbitration Assn., Nat. Assn. Children's Hosps. and Related Instns., Elks, KC. Republican. Roman Catholic. Avocations: travel, hunting, camping, woodwork, sci. engring. and medicine. Home: 2304 San Gabriel Dr Plano TX 75074-3463 Office: Henningson Durham and Richardson Inc AEP 12700 Hillcrest Rd Ste 125 Dallas TX 75230-2009

WALL, STEPHEN JAMES, senior executive consultant; b. Wallasy, U.K., Aug. 25, 1947; came to U.S., 1955, naturalized, 1966; s. John and Margaret M. (Dixon) W.; B.A., SUNY, 1969; M.A. in Psychology, U. Akron, 1971; M.A. in Indsl./Organizational Psychology, N.Y. U., 1980; m. Shannon Rye, Feb. 24, 1989; 1 child, Alissa Gabrielle. With Human Resources Lab., AT&T, N.Y.C., 1972-73; pers. supr., mgmt. selection and devel. research,

1973-75; profl. devel. assoc. Union Carbide Corp., N.Y.C., 1975-76, mgr. profl. devel., 1976-77, dir. corp. mgmt. devel., 1977-82, dir. employee rels. and adminstrn., 1983-84; pres., chief exec. officer Manus, N.Y.C., 1985—. Mem. Ctr. Creative Leadership (editorial rev. bd.), Instl. Systems Assn. (exec.v.p.) Contbr. articles to profl. jours. Home: 1201 Foxboro Dr Norwalk CT 06851-1160 Office: Manus Associates 100 Prospect St Stamford CT 06901-1640

WALL, WILLIAM E., lawyer, former utility executive; b. 1928. BS, U. Wash., 1951, LLB, 1954. Asst. atty. gen. State of Wash., 1956-59; chief examiner Pub. Svc. Commn., 1959; sec., house counsel Cascade Natural Gas Corp., 1959-64; pres. United Cities Gas Co., 1964-65; exec. v.p. Cascade Natural Gas Corp., 1965-67; spl. asst. to chmn. bd. Consol. Edison Co., N.Y.C., 1967-68, v.p., 1968-70, sr. v.p. gas ops., 1970-71, exec. v.p. div. ops., 1971-73; gen. mgr. pub. affairs Standard Oil Co., 1973-74; exec. v.p. Kans. Power and Light Co., Topeka, 1974-75, pres., 1975-85, chief exec. officer, 1976-88, chmn., 1979-88; of counsel Siderius, Lonergan & Crowley, Seattle, 1988—. Served with AUS, 1954-56. Office: Siderius Lonergan & Crowley 847 Logan Bldg Seattle WA 98101

WALLACE, ANDREW GROVER, physician; b. Columbus, Ohio, Mar. 22, 1935; s. Richard Homes and Eleanor Bradley (Grover) W.; m. Kathleen Barrick Altvater, June 22, 1957; children: Stephen Andrew, Michael Bradley, Kathleen Claude. BS, Duke, 1958, MD, 1959. Diplomate Am. Bd. Internal Medicine. Intern medicine Duke U., Durham, N.C., 1959-60, asst. resident, 1960-61; fellow NIH, 1961-63; chief resident medicine Duke U., Durham, 1963-64, asst. prof., 1965-67, assoc. prof., 1967-71, chief, div. cardiology, 1970, prof. medicine, 1971, Walter Kempner prof. medicine, 1973; vice chancellor health affairs, chief exec. officer Duke U. Hosp., Durham, 1981; v.p. Duke U., 1987; dean Dartmouth Med. Sch., Hanover, N.H., 1990—; v.p. for health affairs Dartmouth Coll., 1990; cons. program project com., cardiology adv. com. and pharmacology study sect. Nat. Heart and Lung Inst., cardiovascular merit rev. bd. VA. Mem. editorial bd. Am. Jour. of Physiology, 1965-70, Jour. of Pharmacology and Exptl. Therapeutics, 1966-71, Jour. of Molecular and Cellular Cardiology, 1970-75, Jour. of Clin. Investigation, 1973-78. Pres. Durham YMCA Swim Assn., 1975-77. Markle scholar, 1965-70. Mem. Am. Fedn. for Clin. Research, Am. Soc. Clin. Investigation, Am. Heart Assn. (council on clin. cardiology), Am. Physiol. Soc., Biomedical Engring. Soc., Assn. U. Cardiologists, Am. Assn. Physicians, Soc. Med. Adminstrs. Home: 62 Oak Ridge Rd West Lebanon NH 03784-3113 Office: Dartmouth Coll Med Sch Office of Dean Hanover NH 03755-3833

WALLACE, ANTHONY FRANCIS CLARKE, anthropologist, educator; b. Toronto, Ont., Can., Apr. 15, 1923; s. Paul A.W. and Dorothy Eleanor (Clarke) W.; m. Betty Louise Shillott, Dec. 1, 1942; children: Anthony, Daniel, Sun Ai, Samuel, Cheryl, Joseph. B.A., U. Pa., 1948, M.A., 1949, Ph.D., 1950; L.H.D. (hon.), U. Chgo., 1983. Instr. anthropology Bryn Mawr Coll., 1948-50; asst. instr. anthropology U. Pa., research sec. Behavioral Research Council, 1951-55; research asst. prof. U. Pa., 1952-55, vis. assoc. prof., 1955-61, prof., 1955-61, —chmn. dept., 1961-71, Geraldine R. Segal prof. Am. social thought, 1980-83, Univ. prof. anthropology, 1983-88, prof. emeritus, 1988—; sr. research assoc. anthropology Eastern Pa. Psychiat. Inst., 1955-60, dir. clin. research, 1960-61, med. research scientist III, 1961-80; mem. tech. adv. com. N.J. Psychiat. Inst., 1958; cons. disaster studies NRC, 1956-57; cons. Phila. Housing Authority, 1952; mem. research adv. com. Commonwealth Mental Health Research Found., 1960-61, U.S. Office Edn., 1965-68; mem. behavioral scis. study sect. NIMH, 1964-68; mem. NRC, 1963-66; mem. various adv. coms. NIMH, 1962—; mem. social sci. adv. council NSF, 1969-72. Author: King of the Delawares: Teedyuscung, 1700-1763, 1949, Culture and Personality, 1961, rev. edit., 1970, Religion: An Anthropological View, 1966, Death and Rebirth of the Seneca, 1970, Rockdale: The Growth of an American Village in the Early Industrial Revolution, 1978, Social Context of Innovation, 1983, St. Clair, 1987, The Long, Bitter Trail, 1993. Bd. mgrs. Founds. Fund for Research in Psychiatry, 1969-71. Served AUS, 1942-45. Recipient Bancroft prize in Am. History, 1979, Dexter prize in History of Technology, 1989; Guggenheim fellow, 1978-79. Fellow Am. Anthrop. Assn. (pres. 1971-72),; mem. Nat. Acad. Scis., Am. Philos. Soc., Am. Acad. Arts and Scis. Office: Univ PA Dept Anthropology 33rd and Spruce Sts Philadelphia PA 19174

WALLACE, ARTHUR, agricultural educator; b. Bear River City, Utah, Jan. 4, 1919; s. James Newton and Clara Caroline (Mackay) W.; m. Elna Kemp, Apr. 16, 1943; children: Garn, Loretta, Marlin, Scott. BS, Utah State U., 1943; PhD, Rutgers U., 1949. Asst. prof. biomed. and environ. scis. UCLA, 1949-56, assoc. prof., 1956-62, prof., 1962-89, prof. emeritus, 1989—; co-owner Wallace Labs., Internat. Contbr. numerous articles to profl. jours. Served to sgt. U.S. Army, 1943-46. Fellow Am. Soc. Agronomy, Soil Sci. Soc. Am., Crop Sci. Soc. Am.; mem. Am. Soc. Hort. Sci. Mormon. Home: 10215 Clematis Ct Los Angeles CA 90077-2107 Office: 365 Coral Cir El Segundo CA 90245

WALLACE, ARTHUR, JR., college dean; b. Muskogee, Okla., June 12, 1939; s. Arthur and Edna (Collins) W.; m. Claudina Young, Oct. 4, 1969; children: Dwayne, Jon, Charles. BS, Langston U., 1960; MS, Okla. State U., Stillwater, 1962, PhD, 1964. Dir. commodity rsch. Gen. Foods Corp., White Plains, N.Y., 1964-67; v.p. sr. economist Merrill Lynch & Lionel D. Edie & Co., N.Y.C., 1968-71; econ. cons. Wall St. fin. instns. Group IV Econs., N.Y.C., 1972-76; mgr. U.S. and Can. econs. Internat. Paper Co. N.Y.C., 1976-78, chief economist, 1978-82, dir. corp. affairs and policy analysis, 1982-83; corp. sec. Internat. Paper Co., Purchase, N.Y., 1983-87; v.p., corp. sec. Internat. Paper Co., 1987-93; pres. Internat. Paper Co. Found., 1983-93; dean coll. bus. San Francisco State U., 1993—. Home: 1085 Greenwich St #1 San Francisco CA 94133 Office: San Francisco State U School of Business 1600 Holloway Ave San Francisco CA 94132-1722

WALLACE, BARBARA BROOKS, writer; b. Soochow, China, Dec. 3, 1922; came to U.S., 1938; d. Otis Frank and Nicia Brooks; m. James Wallace Jr., Feb. 27, 1954; 1 child, James V. BA, UCLA, 1945. Script sec. Foote, Cone & Belding, Hollywood, Calif., 1946-49; tchr. Wright MacMahon Secretarial Sch., Beverly Hills, Calif., 1949-50; head fund drive Commerce and Industry Divsn. ARC, San Francisco, 1950-52. Author: Claudia, 1969 (Nat. League of Am. Pen Women Juvenile Book award 1970), Andrew the Big Deal, 1970, The Trouble with Miss Switch, 1971, Victoria, 1973, Can Do, Missy Charlie, 1974, The Secret Summer of L.E.B. (Nat. League of Am. Pen Women Juvenile Book award 1974), Julia and the Third Bad Thing, 1975, Palmer Patch, 1976, Hawkins, 1977, Peppermints in the Parlor, 1980 (William Allen White award 1983), The Contest Kid Strikes Again, 1980, Hawkins and the Soccer Solution, 1981, Miss Switch to the Rescue, 1981, Hello, Claudia, 1982, Claudia and Duffy, 1982, The Barrel in the Basement, 1985, Argyle, 1987, 92, Perfect Acres, Inc., 1988, The Twin in the Tavern, 1993 (Edgar award Mystery Writers Am. 1994). Mem. Children's Book Guild of Washington, Alpha Phi. Episcopalian. Home and Office: 2708 George Mason Pl Alexandria VA 22305

WALLACE, CHRISTOPHER, broadcast television correspondent; b. Chgo., Oct. 12, 1947; s. Mike and Norma (Kaphan) W.; m. Elizabeth Farrell, May 12, 1973; children: Peter Farrell, Margaret Coleman, Andrew Farrell, Catherine Farrell. BA, Harvard U., 1969. Nat. reporter Boston Globe, 1969-73; polit. reporter Sta. WBBM-TV, Chgo., 1973-75; investigative reporter Sta. WNBC-TV, N.Y.C., 1975-78; polit. reporter NBC News, Washington, 1978-81; anchor Today Show, 1981-82; corr. White House, 1982-89, Prime Time Live, ABC-TV, 1989—. Reporter, writer: documentaries NBC The Migrants, 1980, Protection For Sale: The Insurance Industry, 1981, Nancy Reagan, The First Lady, 1985. Recipient Peabody award U. Ga., 1977, Emmy award NATAS, 1981, 90, award Overseas Press Club, 1981, Humanitas Found. award, 1981, Investigative Reporters and Editors award U. Mo., 1990, 95, George Polk award, 1992. Office: PrimeTime Live 1717 DeSales St NW Washington DC 20036

WALLACE, CLIFFORD NOBLE, III, public assembly facility management executive; b. Greenville, S.C., Mar. 3, 1947; s. Clifford Noble and Hilda (Rosser) W.; m. Susan Eujania Safrit, Aug. 2, 1969; children: Elizabeth Hope, Carrie Rosser, Leslie Miller. BA, Erskine Coll., 1968. With Lockheed-Ga. Co., Marietta, 1968-72; asst. mgr. Greenville Meml. Auditorium, 1972-75; dir. Von Braun Civic Ctr., Huntsville, Ala., 1975-80;

exec. v.p., gen. mgr. La. Superdome, New Orleans, 1980-83, pres., gen. mgr., 1983-86; pres., CEO Leisure Mgmt. Internat., Houston, 1986-93; pres. Leisure Mgmt. Nashville Inc., 1993—, Facility Mgmt. Group, Inc., Atlanta, 1993—; pres. Leisure Mgmt. Miami, Inc., La. Leisure Mgmt. Inc., Leisure Mgmt. Memphis Inc., Leisure Mgmt. North Ga., Inc., Palm Springs Leisure Mgmt., Inc., Leisure Mgmt. Europe, 1988-93. Trustee IAAM Found., 1983-85; mem. bd. counselors Erskine Coll., 1988-91, bd. trustees, 1991—; vice chair SugarLand Airport Adv. Bd., 1991-93. Mem. Internat. Assn. Auditorium Mgrs. (bd. dirs. 1978-86, 2d v.p. 1982-83, 1st v.p. 1983-84, pres. 1984-85), Aircraft Owners and Pilots Assn. Presbyterian. Home: 2864 Tynewick Dr Roswell GA 30075 Office: Facility Mgmt Group 2233 Lake Park Dr Smyrna GA 30080-8899

WALLACE, DAVID ALEXANDER, architect, educator; b. Chgo., Aug. 30, 1917; s. David A. and Grace (Eaton) W.; m. Joan Heatly Dulles, Oct. 23, 1954; 1 stepchild, Robert N. Cunningham III. B.Arch., U. Pa., 1940, M.Arch., 1941; M.City Planning, Harvard, 1950, Ph.D., 1953. With various archtl. offices, 1941, 46-48; supervising planner Chgo. Housing Authority, 1951; asst. dir. Marshall Field Found. Study of Housing of Low Income Groups, 1952; asst. prof. U. Chgo., 1952; dir. planning Phila. Redevel. Authority, 1953-57, Council Greater Balt. Com., 1957-61; prof. city planning U. Pa. Sch. Fine Arts, Phila., 1961-72; adj. prof. U. Pa. Sch. Fine Arts, 1972-76; ptnr. Wallace, McHarg, Roberts & Todd, Phila., 1963-79, Wallace Roberts & Todd, Phila., 1980-92. Served to maj. AUS, 1941-46. Fellow AIA; mem. Am. Planning Assn. (bd. govs. 1961-63). Home: 7316 Elbow Ln Philadelphia PA 19119-2809 Office: Wallace Roberts Todd 260 S Broad St Philadelphia PA 19102-5023

WALLACE, DAVID DUNSMORE, architect, planner, urban designer; b. Haverhill, Mass., Oct. 26, 1928; s. Henry Arthur and Doris Stanley (Conley) W.; m. June A. Feuer, June 7, 1953; children—Susan, Andrew, Gordon. B.A., Middlebury Coll., 1950; B.Arch., M.I.T., 1952, M. Arch., 1956. Registered architect, Mass., Tex., N.H., Nat. Council Archtl. Registration Bds. Prin. architect Geometrics, Inc., Cambridge, Mass., 1961-70, Wallace, Floyd, Ellenzweig, Moore, Inc., Cambridge, 1970-81, Wallace, Floyd, Assocs. Inc., Boston, 1981—. Prin. archtl. works include univ. bldgs., pub. housing renovation, mass transit stations. Trustee Schwamb Mill Preservation Trust, Arlington, 1970—; mem. town Meeting, Arlington, 1965-72, Conservation Commn., Arlington, 1967-72; incorporator Cambridge Sch. of Weston, Mass., 1979-85. Voorhis, Walker, Smith & Smith research fellow MIT, 1955-56; Fulbright research grantee, 1960. Mem. Am. Planning Assn., Am. Water Works Assn. Avocations: watercolor painting; photography; tennis. Office: Wallace Floyd Assocs Inc 286 Congress St Boston MA 02210-1009

WALLACE, DON, JR., law educator; b. Vienna, Austria, Apr. 23, 1932; s. Don and Julie (Baer) W. (parents Am. citizens); m. Daphne Mary Wickham, 1963; children: Alexandra Jane, Sarah Anne, Benjamin James. B.A. with high honors, Yale U., 1953; LL.B. cum laude, Harvard U., 1957. Bar: N.Y. 1957, D.C. 1978. Assoc. Fleischmann, Jaeckle, Stokes and Hitchcock, N.Y.C., 1959-60, Paul, Weiss, Rifkind, Wharton and Garrison, N.Y.C., 1957-58, 60-62; rsch. asst. to faculty mem. Harvard Law Sch., Cambridge, Mass., 1958-59; regional legal adv. Middle East AID, Dept. State, 1963-65, dep. asst. gen. counsel, 1965-66; assoc. prof. law Georgetown U. Law Ctr., Washington, 1966-71, prof., 1971—; chmn. Internat. Law Inst., Washington, 1969—; cons. AID, 1966-70, UN Centre on Transnat. Corps., 1977-78; counsel Wald, Harkrader & Ross, Washington, 1978-86, Arnold & Porter, 1986-89, Shearman & Sterling, 1989—; legal advisor State of Qatar, 1979-82; chmn. adv. com. on tech. and world trade Office of Tech. Assessment, U.S. Congress, 1976-79; mem. Sec. of State's Adv. Com. on Pvt. Internat. Law, 1979—; mem. U.S. del. UN Conf. on State Succession in Respect of Treaties, Vienna, 1978; mem. U.S. del. new internat. econ. order working group UN Commn. Internat. Trade Law, Vienna, 1981—. Co-author: Internat. Business and Economics: Law and Policy; author: International Regulation of Multinational Corporations, 1976, Dear Mr. President: The Needed Turnaround in America's International Economic Affairs, 1984; editor: A Lawyer's Guide to International Business Transactions, 1977-87; contbr. numerous articles on internat. trade and law to profl. jours., books revs. on law and bus. to profl. jours. Coord. Anne Arundel County (Md.) Dem. Nat. Com., 1972-79; sec. Chesapeake Found., 1972-73; nat. chmn. Law Profs. for Bush and Quayle, 1988, 92. Fulbright fellow, 1967, Eisenhower Exch. fellow, 1976. Mem. ABA (chmn. sect. internat. law 1978-79), Ho. of Dels. 1982-84), Am. Law Inst., Internat. Law Assn., Shaybani Soc. of Internat. Law (v.p.), Ctrl. and Ea. European Law Initiative (mem. adv. bd.), Cosmos Club, Met. Club. Home: 2800 35th St NW Washington DC 20007-1411 Office: Georgetown U Law Ctr 600 New Jersey Ave NW Washington DC 20001-2022

WALLACE, DONALD QUERK, architect, civil engineer; b. Harlan, Ky., July 29, 1931; s. Harry E. and Nell May (Wilson) W.; m. Geraldine Royse, May 10, 1958; children: Donald Querk Jr., Jon Paul. BSCE, U. Ky., 1959. Registered architect and profl. engr., Ky. Architect Brock & Johnson, Lexington, Ky., 1959-60; architect, owner D.Q. Wallace, Lexington, 1960-62, Affiliated Architects, 1962-63, CMW, Inc., 1963-83, D.Q.W. Inc. & Assocs., Lexington, 1983-92, ARCH II, Inc. & Assoc., Lexington, 1992—; design critic U. Ky., 1961-72; dir. Ky. Archtl. Registration Bd., 1983-92; vice chmn. Ky. Dept. Housing, Bldg. and Constrn., 1978-85. Bd. dirs. U. Ky. Nat. Alumni Bd., 1980-86; vice chmn. Lexington Econ. Devel. Commn., 1984-96, Lexington Home Builders Scholarship Found., 1979-84; chmn. bd. dirs. Lexington Convention and Visitors Bur., 1986-91. Fellow AIA; mem. Ky. Soc. Architects, Greater Lexington C. of C., Lexington Club (bd. govs. 1982-). Democrat. Baptist. Home: 543 Laketower Dr Unit 135 Lexington KY 40502-2676

WALLACE, DOROTHY ALENE, special education administrator; b. Wright County, Mo., Sept. 11, 1942; d. Stephen Foster and Lois Alene (Breman) Dudley; widowed; children: Michael Dean Huckaby, David Lee. BS in Edn., Drury Coll., 1975, MS in Edn., 1978; Specialist in Ednl. Adminstrn., Southwest Mo. State U., 1988. Cert. tchr. and adminstr., Mo. Tchr. 3rd grade Mansfield (Mo.) R-IV Schs., 1975-78, tchr. 1st grade, 1978-85, tchr. learning disabled, 1985-89, adminstr. spl. edn., 1989-92, adminstr. spl. svcs., 1992—; active sch. coms. on curriculum and nutrition Mansfield R-IV Schs., mem. sch./cmty. adv. coun., 1992—. Mem. Am. Salers Assn., Mo. State Tchrs. Assn., Mo. Coun. Adminstrs. of Spl. Edn., Coun. for Exceptional Children, Coun. Adminstrs. of Spl. Edn., Local Adminstrs. of Spl. Edn., Cmty. Tchrs. Assn. Avocations: raising beef cattle, writing, collecting antiques. Home: 202 N Ash Ave Mansfield MO 65704

WALLACE, F. BLAKE, aerospace executive, mechanical engineer; b. Phoenix, Ariz., Jan. 10, 1933. BMechE, Calif. Inst. Tech., 1955; MS in Engring., Ariz. State U., 1963, PhD in Engring., 1967. Preliminary design engr. Pratt & Whitney, East Hartford, Conn., 1955-59; chief engr. advanced tech. Garrett Corp., Phoenix, 1959-80; mgr. advanced plans and programs Aircraft Engine Group GE, Evendale, Ohio, 1981-83; gen. mgr. Allison div. GM, Indpls., 1983-93; v.p. GM, 1987-93; chmn. & CEO Allison Engine Co., Indpls., 1993—; mem. aero. adv. com. NASA, 1985-92. Author numerous tech. papers. Fellow AIAA (chmn. air breathing propulsion tech. com. 1977-78, Air Breathing Propulsion award 1991), U.S. Advanced Ceramic Assn. (chmn. 1987-89). Office: Allison Engine Co 2001 S Tibbs Ave #420 Indianapolis IN 46241-4893

WALLACE, FRANKLIN SHERWOOD, lawyer; b. Bklyn., Nov. 24, 1927; s. Abraham Charles and Jennie (Erlin) Wolowitz; student U. Wis., 1943-45; BS cum laude, U.S. Mcht. Marine Acad., 1950; LLB, JD, U. Mich., 1953; m. Eleanor Ruth Pope, Aug. 23, 1953; children: Julia Diane, Charles Andrew. Bar: 1954. Practiced in Rock Island; ptnr. firm Winstein, Kavensky & Wallace; asst. state's atty. Rock Island County, 1967-68; local counsel UAW at John Deere-J.I. Case Plants. Former bd. dirs. Tri City Jewish Ctr.; former trustee United Jewish Charities of Quad Cities; bd. dirs. Blackhawk Coll. Found. Mem. ABA, Ill. Bar Assn. (chmn. jud. adv. polls com. 1979-84), Rock Island County Bar Assn., Am. Trial Lawyers Assn., Ill. Trial Lawyers Assn., Nat. Assn. Criminal Def. Lawyers, Ill. Appellate Lawyers Assn., Am. Orthopsychiat. Assn., Am. Judicature Soc., Blackhawk Coll. Found. Democrat. Jewish. Home: 3405 20th Street Ct Rock Island IL 61201-6201 Office: Rock Island Bank Bldg Rock Island IL 61201

WALLACE, HAROLD JAMES, JR., physician; b. South Hadley Falls, Mass., Aug. 15, 1930; s. Harold James and Evelyn (Mason) W.; m. Dorothy Ann Green, July 4, 1959; children—Harold James III, Elizabeth Marie, John Hill. BA, U. Vt., 1954, MD cum laude, 1958. Intern Mary Fletcher Hosp., Burlington, Vt., 1958-59; resident Mary Fletcher Hosp. 1959-62; practice medicine specializing in oncology Buffalo, 1970-79, Rutland, Vt., 1979—; assoc. chief dept. medicine Roswell Pk. Meml. Inst., Buffalo, 1970-75; dir. Cancer Control Rehab. and Adolescent Program, 1976-79; oncologist Rutland Hosp., 1979—; dir. Cmty. Cancer Ctr., Rutland Regional Med. Ctr., 1989—; rsch. prof. medicine Dartmouth Med. Sch.; exec. officer Cancer and Leukemia Group B, 1992-95. Mem. Am. Cancer Soc. (pres. Vt. div. 1983-84, Nat. div. award 1969), Am. Assn. for Cancer Research, Am. Soc. Clin. Oncology, Green Mountain Oncology Group (chmn. 1983—), Alpha Omega Alpha. Congregationalist. Office: Cancer & Leukemia Group B 444 Mount Support Rd Lebanon NH 03766-2809

WALLACE, HAROLD LEW, historian, educator; b. Montgomery, Ind., Nov. 9, 1932; s. Lewis Alfred and Winifred Maria (Summers) W.; m. Janice June Inman, June 22, 1957; children: Stefanie Ann, Stacy Elizabeth, Jason Lew. A.B., Ind. U., 1961, M.A. (Univ. grantee), 1964, Ph.D., 1970. Tchr. history and English Mooresville (Ind.) High Sch., 1961-63; teaching asst. Ind. U., 1963-64, univ. fellow, 1964-65; asst. prof., then assoc. prof. history Murray (Ky.) State U., 1965-71; prof. history, head social sci. div. No. Ky. U., Highland Heights, Ky., 1971—, dir. oral history program, 1980—; mem. continuing seminar community edn. Ball State U. and Mott Found., 1973—; mem. adv. bd. Ky. Oral History Commn., 1981—; vis. prof. Ky. Inst. for European Studies, Bregenz, Austria, summer 1987, Andhra U., Visakhapatnam, India, spring 1989. Author: Coal in Kentucky, 1975; Contbr. articles to profl. jours.; Editorial bd.: U. Ky. Press, 1971—; cons., reviewer: Oceana Press, Inc, 1973—. Mem. advisory com. pub. documents, State of Ky.; Bd. dirs. Coll. Programs for No. Ky. Sr. Citizens; faculty regent No. Ky. Bd. Regents, 1985-91, pres. Ky. Conf. State AAUP, 1991—. Served with USNR, 1952-56. Recipient Svc. award State of Ind., 1957, Univ. Teaching award Andhra Univ., India, 1992; Eli Lilly fellow, 1962, 63, Smithsonian fellow, 1982; Harry S. Truman Rsch. scholar, 1965, 71; Murray State U. grantee, 1967, 71, No. Ky. State U. grantee, 1973, 76, 78, 90, Ky. Humanities Coun. grantee, 1988, 90, Ky. Oral History Commn. grantee, 1988; Fulbright grant lectr. Andhra U., India, 1992; Art Coll. Gold medal Andhra Univ., India, 1992. Mem. AAUP (pres. Ky. chpt. 1991—), Disting. Svc. award 1992), Am., So. hist. assns., Orgn. Am. Historians, Polit. Sci. Acad., AAUP, Center Study Democratic Instrn., Mensa, Intertel, Sierra Club, Alpha Epsilon Delta, Phi Delta Kappa, Phi Alpha Theta. Home: 22 Orchard Ter Newport KY 41076-1532 Office: No Ky State U Highland Heights KY 41076

WALLACE, HARRY LELAND, lawyer; b. San Francisco, June 26, 1927; s. Leon Harry and Anna Ruth (Haworth) W.; m. Mary Lue Eckels, Apr. 16, 1951; 1 dau., Mary Ann Wallace Frantz. A.B. in Govt.; B.S. in Bus, Ind. U., 1949; J.D., Harvard U., 1952. Bar: Wis. 1953. Law clk. U.S. Supreme Ct. Justice Sherman Minton, Washington, 1952-53; assoc. firm Foley & Lardner, Milw., 1953-61; partner Foley & Lardner, 1961—; counselor adv. dir. various corps.; Treas. Mequon-Thiensville Sch. Bds., 1966-67, 71-73, pres., 1965-66, 67-71, 73-75; bd. dirs. Milwaukee County Assn. for Mental Health, 1970-76, Milw. Mental Health Found., 1983—; chmn. financing policies com. Gov.'s Commn. on Edn., 1969-70; mem. Gov.'s Task Force on Sch. Financing and Property Tax Reform, 1972-73; chmn. Gov.'s Commn. on State-Local Relations and Fin. Policies, 1975-76; trustee Pub. Policy Forum, 1976—, sec., 1984-86, pres., 1986-88. Served with USN, 1945-46. Mem. Am., Wis., Milw. bar assns., Am. Law Inst., Phi Beta Kappa, Beta Gamma Sigma, Beta Tau Delta. Methodist. Club: Milwaukee. Home: 2104 W Quincy Ct Thiensville WI 53092-5415 Office: Foley & Lardner 777 E Wisconsin Ave Milwaukee WI 53202-5367

WALLACE, HELEN MARGARET, physician, educator; b. Hoosick Falls, N.Y., Feb. 18, 1913; d. Jonas and Ray (Schweizer) W. AB, Wellesley Coll., 1933; MD, Columbia U., 1937; MPH cum laude, Harvard U., 1943. Diplomate Am. Bd. Pediatrics, Am. Bd. Preventive Medicine. Intern Bellevue Hosp., N.Y.C., 1938-40; child hygiene physician Conn. Health Dept., 1941-42; successively jr. health officer, health officer, chief maternity and new born div., dir. bur. for handicapped children N.Y.C. Health Dept., 1943-55; prof., dir. dept. pub. health N.Y. Med. Coll., 1955-56; prof. maternal and child health U. Minn. Sch. Pub. Health, 1956-59; chief profl. tng. U.S. Children's Bur., 1959-60, chief child health studies, 1961-62; prof. maternal and child health U. Calif. Sch. Pub. Health, Berkeley, 1962-80; prof., head divsn. maternal and child health Sch. Pub. Health San Diego State U., 1980—; Univ. Research lectr. San Diego State U., 1985—; cons. WHO numerous locations, including Uganda, The Philippines, Turkey, India, Geneva, Iran, Burma, Sri Lanka, East Africa, Australia, Indonesia, China, Taiwan, 1961—, traveling fellow, 1989—; cons. Hahnemann U., Phila., 1993, Ford Found., Colombia, 1971; UN cons. to Health Bur., Beijing, China, 1987; fellow Aiiku Inst. on Maternal and Child Health, Tokyo, and NIH Inst. Child Health and Human Devel., 1994; dir. Family Planning Project, Zimbabwe, 1984-87. Author; editor 10 textbooks; contbr. 325 articles to profl. jours. Mem. coun. on Disabled Children to Media, 1991; dir. San Diego County Infant Mortality Study, 1989—; San Diego Study of Prenatal Care, 1991. Recipient Alumnae Achievement award Wellesley Coll., 1982, U. Minn. award, 1985; Ford Found. study grantee, 1986, 87, 88; fellow World Rehab. Fund, India, 1991-92, Fulbright Found., 1992—, NIH Inst. Child Health and Human Devel., 1994, Aiiku Inst. of Maternal-Child Health, Tokyo, 1994. Fellow APHA (officer sect., Martha May Eliot award 1978), Am. Acad. Pediatrics (Job Smith award 1980, award 1989); mem. AMA, Assn. Tchrs. Maternal and Child Health, Am. Acad. Cerebral Palsy, Ambulatory Pediatric Assn., Am. Sch. Preventive Medicine. Home: 850 State St San Diego CA 92101-6046

WALLACE, HERBERT WILLIAM, physician, surgery educator, researcher; b. Bklyn., Dec. 11, 1930; s. Philip and Jean (Brand) W.; m. Rosalie Sandra Becker, Dec. 18, 1954; children: Ira, Ellen, Lisa. AB, Harvard U., 1952; MD, Tufts U., 1956, MS, 1960; MBA, U. Pa., 1981, MA (hon.), 1973. Diplomate Am. Bd. Surgery, Am. Bd. Thoracic Surgery. Resident in gen. surgery Tufts U.-New Eng. Med. Ctr., Boston, 1956-61; thoracic and cardiovascular surg. resident Mt. Sinai Hosp., N.Y.C., 1963-65; assoc. in surgery and physiology U. Pa., Phila., 1966-70, asst. prof. surgery, 1970-72, assoc. prof. surgery, physiology and bioengring., 1972-76, prof., 1976—; chief div. thoracic and cardiovascular surgery Grad. Hosp. U. Pa., 1976-79; assoc. in univ. seminar on biomaterials Columbia U., N.Y.C., 1972—. Contbr. over 100 articles to profl. jours. Rsch. grantee NIH, 1965—. Fellow Am. Coll. Surgeons, Am. Heart Assn.; mem. Am. Assn. Cancer Rsch., Am. Assn. Thoracic Surgery, Am. Thoracic Soc., Biomedical Engring. Soc., Soc. Thoracic Surgeons, others. Avocations: computers, squash, sailing, skiing. Home: 255 Harrogate Rd Wynnewood PA 19096-3131 Office: U Pa Dept Surgery One Graduate Pla Philadelphia PA 19146

WALLACE, J. CLIFFORD, federal judge; b. San Diego, Dec. 11, 1928; s. John Franklin and Lillie Isabel (Overing) W.; m. Virginia Lee Schlosser, Apr. 8, 1957; children: Paige, Laurie, Teri, John. B.A., San Diego State U., 1952; LL.B., U. Calif., Berkeley, 1955. Bar: Calif. 1955. With firm Gray, Cary, Ames & Frye, San Diego, 1955-70; judge U.S. Dist. Ct. (so. dist.) Calif., 1970-72; judge U.S. Ct. Appeals (9th cir.), 1972-91, chief judge, 1991—. Contbr. articles to profl. jours. Served with USN, 1946-49. Mem. Am. Bd. Trial Advocates, Inst. Jud. Adminstrn. Mem. LDS Ch. (stake pres. San Diego East 1967-74, 77-79). Office: US Ct Appeals 9th Cir 940 Front St Ste 4192 San Diego CA 92101-8918 *My principles, ideals and goals and my standard of conduct are embodied in the Gospel of Jesus Christ. They come to fruition in family life, service, industry and integrity and in an attempt, in some small way, to make my community a better place within which to live.*

WALLACE, JAMES HAROLD, JR., lawyer; b. Atlanta, Feb. 8, 1941; s. James Harold Sr. and Ruth (Cocking) W. BSEE, U.S.C., 1963; JD, Georgetown U., 1966. Bar: D.C. 1967. Patent examiner U.S. Patent & Trademark Office, Washington, 1966-67; trial atty. antitrust div. U.S. Dept. Justice, Washington, 1967-70; from assoc. to ptnr. Kirkland & Ellis, Washington, 1970-83; ptnr. Wiley, Rein & Fielding, Washington, 1983—; mem. adv. bd. BNA Patent, Trademark & Copyright Jour., Washington, 1971—. Contbr. articles to profl. jours. Mem. ABA. Home: 3029 Cambridge Pl

NW Washington DC 20007-2914 Office: Wiley Rein & Fielding 1776 K St NW Washington DC 20006-2304

WALLACE, JAMES WENDELL, lawyer; b. Clinton, Tenn., July 13, 1930; s. John Nelson and Rose Ella (Carden) W.; m. Jeanne Mary Ellen Newlin; children: Karen Wallace Young, Michael James. Student, Syracuse U., 1952-53; BS, U. Tenn., Knoxville, 1959, JD, 1958. Bar: Calif. 1959, U.S. Dist. Ct. (cen. dist.) Calif. 1959, U.S. Ct. Appeals (9th cir.) 1977, U.S. Supreme Ct. 1964. Sec., legal counsel Guidance Tech., Inc., Santa Monica, Calif., 1958-65; sr. atty., asst. sec. Varian Assocs., Palo Alto, Calif., 1965-67; gen. counsel, asst. sec. Electronic Splty. Co., Pasadena, Calif., 1967-69; asst. gen. counsel, asst. sec. The Times Mirror Co., L.A., 1969-75, assoc. gen. counsel, asst. sec., 1976-85, assoc. gen. counsel, sec., 1985-89; dir., v.p. and sec. Flintridge Asset Mgmt. Co., San Marino, Calif., 1990—. Mem. editorial bd. Tenn. Law Rev., 1956-58. Mem. Town Hall of Calif. World Affairs Coun., L.A. Served with USAF, 1951-55. Mem. ABA, L.A. County Bar Assn., Am. Soc. Corp. Secs. (bd. dirs. 1979-82), Jonathan Club, Phi Delta Phi, Phi Kappa Phi. Home: 5822 Briartree Dr La Canada Flintridge CA 91011-1825

WALLACE, JEANNETTE OWENS, state legislator; b. Scottsdale, Ariz., Jan. 16, 1934; d. Albert and Velma (Whinery) Owens; m. Terry Charles Wallace Sr., May 21, 1955; children: Terry C. Jr., Randall J., Timothy A., Sheryl L., Janice M. BS, Ariz. State U., 1955. Mem. Los Alamos (N.Mex.) County Coun., 1981-82; cons. County of Los Alamos, 1983-84; chmn., vice chmn. Los Alamos County Coun., 1985-88; cons. County of Los Alamos, Los Alamos Schs., 1989-90; rep. N.Mex. State Legislature, 1991—; mem. appropriations & fin. govt. and urban affairs, N.Mex., 1991—, legis. fin. com., Indian affairs; co-chmn. Los Alamos County's Dept. Energy Negotiating Com., 1987-88; mem. legis. policy com. Mcpl. League, N.Mex., 1986-88. Bd. dirs. Tri-Area Econ. Devel., Pojoaque, N.Mex., 1987-92, Los Alamos Econ. Devel., 1988-94, Crime Stoppers, Los Alamos, 1988-92, Los Alamos Citizens Against Substance Abuse, 1989-94; mem. N.Mex. First, Albuquerque, 1989-93; legis. chmn. LWV, 1990; mem. Los Alamos Rep. Women, pres. 1989-90. Mem. Los Alamos Bus. & Profl. Women (legis. chmn. 1990), Los Alamos C. of C., Mana del Norte, Kiwanis. Methodist. Avocations: tennis, needlework, reading. Home: 146 Monte Rey Dr S Los Alamos NM 87544-3826

WALLACE, JESSE WYATT, pharmaceutical company executive; b. Canton, Ga., Jan. 24, 1925; s. Jesse Washington and Lula (Wyatt) W.; m. Myra Brown, Jan. 1, 1949; children: Karin, Kimberly, Stephen, David. BBA magna cum laude, U. Ga., 1954; MS, Ga. Inst. Tech., 1960. Chmn. svc. groups Ga. Tech, Atlanta, 1953-57; adminstrv. mgr. Am. Viscose Corp., Marcus Hook, Pa., 1957-61; various exec. positions FMC Corp., Phila., 1961-85; pres. Wallco Internat. Corp., Wilmington, Del., 1985-89; v.p., sec. Pharm. Svc. and Tech., Inc., Woodbury, N.J., 1989—, also bd. dirs.; bd. dirs. Wallco Internat. Corp., Artist Alive, Inc., Pharm. Svc. and Tech., Inc.; adv. bd. Pharm. Tech. Conf., 1986—. Editor: Controlled Release Systems, 1988; contbr. Encyclopedia, 1989; contbr. articles to profl. jours; author (manual) Problem Solver, 1980. Vice chmn. Ch. Deacons, Wilmington; v.p., pres. Wilmington Gideons, 1969-71; v.p. ACA Acad., 1971-73; vice chmn. Del. Family Found., 1990—. Lt. USN, 1943-46, 50-53. Fellow Acad. Pharm. Scis., Am. Assn. Pharm. Scientists, Pharm. Tech. (Pub. award, 1989); mem. Internat. Platform Assn., Controlled Release Soc., La. Fedn. Internat. Pharm., Am. Mgmt. Assn., Mensa, Delta Sigma Pi (life), Delta Mu Delta. Republican. Avocations: reading, golf, racquet ball, travel, family. Home: 1106 Grinnell Rd Wilmington DE 19803-5126 Office: Pharm Svc and Tech Inc 15 E Centre St Ste 201 Woodbury NJ 08096-2415

WALLACE, JOAN SCOTT, psychologist, social worker, international consultant; b. Chgo., Nov. 8, 1930; d. William Edouard and Esther (Fulks) Scott; m. John Wallace, June 12, 1954 (div. Mar. 1976); children—Mark, Eric, Victor; m. Maurice A. Dawkins, Oct. 14, 1979. A.B., Bradley U., 1952; M.S.W., Columbia U., 1954; postgrad., U. Chgo., 1965; Ph.D., Northwestern U., 1973; H.H.D (hon.), U. Md., 1979; L.H.D. (hon.), Bowie State Coll., 1981; LLD (hon.), Ala. A&M U., 1990. Lic. social psychologist, social worker. Asst. prof., then assoc. prof. U. Ill.-Chgo., 1967-73; assoc. dean, prof. Howard U., Washington, 1973-76; v.p.-programs Nat. Urban League, N.Y.C., 1975-76; v.p. adminstrn. Morgan State U., Balt., 1976-77; asst. sec. adminstrn. USDA, Washington, 1977-81, adminstr. Office Internat. Cooperation and Devel., 1981-89; rep. to Trinidad and Tobago Inter Am. Inst. for Cooperation in Agr., USDA, 1989; internat. cons. U.S Partnerships Internat., Ft. Lauderdale, 1993—; speaker in field. Contbr. articles, chpts. to profl. publs. Chair Binat. Agrl. Research and Devel. Fund, 1987. Recipient Disting. Alumni award Bradley U., 1978, Meritorious award Delta Sigma Theta, 1978, award for leadership Lambda Kappa Mu, 1978, award for outstanding achievement and svc. to nation Capital Hill Kiwanis Club, 1978, Links Achievement award, 1979, Presdl. Rank for Meritorious Exec., 1980, NAFEO award, 1989, Community Svc. award Alpha Phi Alpha, 1987, Pres.' award for outstanding pub. svc. Fla. A&M U., 1990. Mem. APA, NASW, AAAS, Am. Consortium for Internat. Pub. Adminstrn. (exec. com., governing bd. 1987), Soc. Internat. Devel. (Washington chpt.), Sr. Exec. Assn., Soc. for Internat. Devel., White House Com. on Internat. Sci., Engring. and Tech., Internat. Sci. and Edn. Coun. (chmn. 1981-89), Am. Evaluation Assn., Consortium Internat. Higher Edn. (adv. com.), Caribbean Studies Soc., Caribbean Assn. of Agriculture Economists, Assn. Polit. Psychologists, Pi Gamma Mu. Presbyterian. Avocations: crafts, painting, collecting international art. Home: 6010 S Falls Circle Dr Fort Lauderdale FL 33319-6900 Office: Joan Wallace and Assocs 5557 W Oakland Park Blvd Fort Lauderdale FL 33313-1411

WALLACE, JOHN, investment company executive; b. Boston, Sept. 11, 1909; s. John and Wilhelmina (Hay) W.; m. Amelie Margaret Alexanderson, Aug. 25, 1934 (dec. 1980); children—John David (dec.), Amelie Wallace Porter, James Hay. B.A., Harvard U., 1930. Security analyst E.H. Rollins and Sons, N.Y.C., 1930-41; ptnr. Hallgarten and Co., N.Y.C., 1945-64, First Manhattan Co., N.Y.C., 1964—; dir. Earth Satellite Corp., Washington, Voice Identification Inc., Somerville, N.J. Trustee Village of Garden City, N.Y., 1967-70, Roxbury Latin Sch., Boston, 1961—. Served to lt. commdr. USNR, 1941-45. Mem. N.Y. Soc. Security Analysts, Am. Water Works Assn. Republican. Episcopalian. Clubs: Cherry Valley Country (Garden City); Lake George (Diamond Point); Harvard (N.Y.C.) Avocations: skiing, sailing. Home: care Willows 1 Lyman St # 431-M Westborough MA 01581-1437 Office: Nova Biomedical Corp 200 Prospect St Waltham MA 02154

WALLACE, JOHN DUNCAN, banker; b. Princeton, N.J., Feb. 12, 1933; s. John H. and Margaret (Cook) W.; m. Marjorie Goebel, Sept. 12, 1959; children: John (dec.), Christian, Marjorie. BA, Princeton U., 1955. With fgn. dept. Hanover Bank, N.Y.C., 1959-62, Morgan Stanley Investment Bankers, N.Y.C., 1962-65; with N.J. Nat. Bank, Trenton, 1965—; sr. v.p. N.J. Nat. Bank, 1972-74, exec. v.p., 1974-76, pres., 1976—, chief exec. officer, 1987, chmn., 1992—. Mem. Princeton Twp. Com., 1966-72; mayor Princeton, 1969, 70-72; trustee Princeton Day Sch., 1977-87, Trinity Counseling, Princeton Community Found., Med. Ctr. at Princeton; exec. com. Coun. Princeton Univ. Community, 1978-81; vice chmn. Rider Coll., Diocesan Investment Trust. Mem. Bedens Brook Club (pres.), Mercer C. of C. (v.p.), Nassau Club, Cap and Gown Club. Republican. Episcopalian. Office: # Cn-1 Pennington NJ 08603

WALLACE, JOHN EDWIN, retired meteorologist, consultant; b. Holton, Kans., Dec. 22, 1913; s. Verne P. Wallace and Clara E. Lott; m. Elizabeth Ann Johnson, June 24, 1944; 1 son, David A. BSME, Rice U., 1937; MS in Meteorology, Calif. Inst. Tech., 1942. Indsl. salesman Gulf Oil Corp., Houston, 1937-39; rsch. cons. MIT, Cambridge, 1946-47; pres., founder, chief exec. officer Weather Svcs. Corp., Bedford, Mass., 1947-93; pres. Coun. Indsl. Meteorologists, Denver, also bd. dirs. Contbr. articles on meteorology to various trade jours. Major AC, U.S. Army, 1939-45, PTO. Recipient Outstanding Svc. award N.J. Turnpike Authority, 1986. Fellow Am. Meteorol. Soc. (award for pioneering pvt. meteorology 1974). Belmont Hill Club (bd. dirs. 1972-74). Avocations: fishing, tennis, travel, golf. Home: 8 Glen Rd Lexington MA 02173-3614

WALLACE, JOHN LOYS, aviation services executive; b. Decatur, Tex., July 31, 1941; s. John K. and Flora Viola (Lumsden) Montgomery W.; m. Linda M. Jackson, May 18, 1962; children—John, Amy Lynn, Katherine

Lea, Elizabeth D'Ann. Student, U. Tex.-Arlington, 1961-65, North Tex. State U., Denton, 1960-61. V.p. acctg. svcs. Cooper Airmotive, Dallas, 1975-77, v.p. fin., 1977-80, exec. v.p., gen. mgr. Gen. Aviation div., 1980-82; exec. v.p. fin., adminstrn. Aviall, Dallas, 1982-85; exec. v.p., chief oper. officer Aviall, Inc., Dallas, 1985-89, pres. Gen. Aviation Svcs. div., 1989-93; pres. Ryder Aviall Inc., ret. 1993. Mem. Fin. Execs. Inst., N. Dallas C. of C., U.S./Mex. C. of C. (bd. dirs.), Chief Exec.'s Round Table, Delta Sigma Phi. Republican. Presbyterian. Clubs: Univ., Cotton Creek Club. Avocation: gardening, fishing, golf. Home: 3651 Pinehurst Cir Gulf Shores AL 36542-9052

WALLACE, JOHN MICHAEL, meteorology educator; b. Flushing, N.Y., Oct. 28, 1940; 3 children. BS, Webb Inst. Naval Architecture, 1962; PhD, MIT, 1966. From asst. to assoc. prof. U. Wash., Seattle, 1966-67, prof. atmos. sci., 1977—; dir. Joint Inst. Study Atmosphere and Ocean, 1980—. Mem. Am. Meteorol. Soc. (Meisinger award 1975, Carl-Gustav Rossby Rsch. medal 1993), Am. Geophys. Union (Macelwane award 1972). Achievements include rsch. in gen. circulation; tropical meteorology. Office: U Wash Dept Atmos Scis # Ak-40 Seattle WA 98195

WALLACE, JOHN ROBERT, county administrator; b. Princeton, Ind., Mar. 24, 1939; s. Robert Floyd and Marjorie Eloise (Steele) W.; m. Karen Sue Katilius, June 18, 1967 (div. Mar. 1985). BS in Engring. with honors, USCG Acad., 1961; BS in Civil Engring. with honors, U. Ill., 1967. Commd. ensign USCG, 1961, advanced through grades to capt., 1982; facilities engr. Coast Guard Res. Tng. Ctr., Yorktown, Va., 1975-77; chief engr. Coast Guard Activities Europe, Am. Embassy, London, 1977-80; mem. planning/plans evaluation staff USCG Chief of Staff, Washington, 1980-82; dep. chief office USCG Office Engring., Washington, 1982-83; chief dep. chief office USCG Office Rsch. and Devel., Washington, 1983-86; commanding officer, sr. engr. USCG Facilities Design and Constrn. Ctr., Norfolk, Va., 1986-89; asst. county adminstr. planning and community devel. Pittsylvania County, Chatham, Va.; county adminstr. County of Amelia, Va., 1992—. Recipient Man of Yr. award Optimists, 1982, Spl. award Kennedy Found., 1984, Haskel Small USO Vol. awards, Washington, 1985, 86. Fellow Soc. Am. Mil. Engrs.; mem. VFW, Am. Def. Preparedness Assn., U.S. Lighthouse Soc., Naval Airship Assn., Royal Nat. Lifeboat Instn. Eng., Scottish Soc. Tidewater, St. Andrews Soc. Tidewater, Clan Wallace Soc., Nat. Rifle Assn. (life), Scottish-Am. Mil. Soc., Am. Legion, Retired Officers Assn., Am. Planning Assn., Va. Citizen's Planning Assn., Am. Soc. Pub. Adminstrn., Va. Econ. Developers Assn., Va. Assn. County Ofcls., Coast Guard Combat Vets. Assn., Va.-Carolina Scottish Soc., Lions. Office: County of Amelia PO Box A Amelia Court House VA 23002

WALLACE, JULIA DIANE, newspaper editor; b. Davenport, Iowa, Dec. 3, 1956; d. Franklin Sherwood and Eleanor Ruth (Pope) W.; m. Doniver Dean Campbell, Aug. 23, 1986; children: Emmaline Livingston Campbell, Eden Jennifer Campbell. BS in Journalism, Northwestern U., 1978. Reporter Norfolk (Va.) Ledger-Star, 1978-80, Dallas Times Herald, 1980-82; reporter, editor News sect. USA Today, Arlington, Va., 1982-89, mng. editor spl. projects, 1989-92; mng. editor Chgo. Sun-Times, 1992—. Mem. Am. Soc. Newspaper Editors. Office: Chgo Sun-Times 401 N Wabash Ave Chicago IL 60611-3532

WALLACE, KEITH ALTON, legislator, dairy farmer; b. Waterbury, Vt., Feb. 26, 1908; s. James Moses and Florence Ida (Richardson) W.; m. Gladys Helen Pike, Jan. 26, 1942 (dec. May 1985); children: Roaine, Rosina, Kay Alan. BS in Agr., Syracuse U., 1932. mem. State Grange Agr. Com.; pres. Mt. Mansfield Coop. Creamery, Vt. Coop. Coun.; trustee Ea. States Exposition. Pres. Vt. State Sch. Bd. Assn., Vt. Ch. Coun.; auditor Town of Waterbury; sch. dir., town moderator, Harwood Union moderator; mem. Vt. Devel. Commn.; mem. State Senate, 1975-78, Vt. House, 1949-50, 81-95; vice chmn. agr. com. Senate and House; lay leader Meth. Ch.; Vt. storyteller. Recipient Citizenship award Vt. State C. of C., 1975, Vt. Edn. Assn. award, 1975, Sen. George Aiken Agriculturist award, 1989, Award of Recognition Svc. to Vt. Rehab. Corp., 1994; recognized for 59 years of pub. svc. as elected ofcl. to Town of Waterbury; named Future Farmer of Am., 1965; Paul Harris fellow Rotary Internat., 1991. Master Waterbury Grange, Harmony Pomona Grange; mem. Washington County Farm Bur. (pres. 1943-44), Vt. State Farm Bur. (pres., CEO 1953-74), Am. Farm Bur. Fedn. (bd. dirs. 1960-69, chmn. dairy com. 1968-69, Disting. Svc. award 1992). Republican. Methodist.

WALLACE, KEN, magazine publisher. BBA, St. John's U. With Reader's Digest mag., 1967-1981; v.p. advt. Sylvia Porter's Personal Finance mag.; v.p., advt. dir. Parade mag.; now pub. Prevention mag., Emmaus, Pa. Office: Prevention 733 Third Ave 15th Fl New York NY 10017 also: Prevention 33 East Minor St Emmaus PA 18098

WALLACE, KENNETH DONALD, lawyer; b. Spokane, Wash., Oct. 2, 1918; s. Donald and Adillah (Mason) W.; m. Ida H. Harvey, June 6, 1946 (div. 1965); children: Ann H. Jane B.; m. Betty Casey Major, July 31, 1965. AB summa cum laude, Wash. State U., 1940; LLB, Columbia U., 1946. Bar: N.Y. 1947, Conn. 1971. Pvt. practice law N.Y.C. and Conn., 1947—; with Cahill, Gordon, Reindel & Ohl, 1946-60; gen. counsel, sec. Bigelow-Sanford, Inc., 1960-70; v.p., dir. Oconee Realty Corp.; dir. JAI Press, Inc.; of counsel Philip E. Silberberg, N.Y.C.; gen. counsel Johnson Assocs., Inc., JAI Press, Inc., Alpen Pantry, Inc. Editor: Columbia Law Review, 1946. Trustee Bigelow-Charitable Trust. Served to 1st lt. USAAF, 1942-46. Decorated D.F.C. with oak leaf cluster, Air medal with oak leaf cluster; recipient Presdl. citation, medal; pilot's wings, Republic of China. Mem. ABA, Am. Acad. Polit. Sci. (life), Fed. Bar Coun., N.Y. State Bar Assn., Conn. Bar Assn., Assn. Bar City N.Y., Stamford/Darien Bar Assn., Am. Soc. Corp. Secs., Hump Pilot's Assn. (life), Phi Beta Kappa, Phi Sigma Kappa. Home and Office: PO Box 843 Smith Ridge Rd New Canaan CT 06840-0843

WALLACE, LINDA SUZAN, journalist; b. Chgo., Dec. 1, 1954; d. Henry Bronlow and Adelaide (Hawkins) W.; m. Karanja Ajanaku, Jan., 1978. B in Journalism, U. Mo., 1976. Reporter St. Louis Post-Dispatch, 1976-77; edn. reporter Memphis Comml. Appeal, 1977-85, Dallas Times-Herald, 1985-87; bus. reporter Phila. Inquirer, 1987-89; nat. corr. Phila. Inquirer, Houston, 1989-92; copy editor Phila. Inquirer, 1992, real estate editor, 1992—; instr. Am. Press Inst., Washington, 1988, 89; organizer journalism workshop for high sch. students, Memphis, 1984. Active Big Sisters, Phila., 1992—; dist. organizer Girl Scouts, Memphis, 1984-85. Fellow Inst. for Ednl. Leadership, 1984, Multicultural Edn. Seminar U. Mo., 1988. Mem. Phila. Assn. Black Journalists. Avocations: reading, exercise. Office: Phila Inquirer 400 N Broad St Philadelphia PA 19130

WALLACE, MALCOLM VINCENT TIMOTHY, classics educator; b. Pittsfield, Mass., Oct. 3, 1915; s. Robert Emmett and Rachel Mary (Mooney) W.; m. Kathryn Teresa Meyer, June 5, 1943; children—Michael William, Edmund Anthony, Mary Clare. A.B., St. Bonaventure Coll., 1936, postgrad., 1936-37; postgrad., U. Notre Dame, 1938-39; Ed.M., U. Buffalo, 1947; A.M., Harvard U., 1949, postgrad., 1949-50, Ph.D., 1955. Clk. Liberty Bank of Buffalo, 1937-38; cashier's office Buffalo Gen. Hosp., 1939-42; instr. St. Bonaventure U., N.Y., 1950-51; prof. classics St. Bonaventure U., 1951-81, prof. emeritus, 1981—, Univ. archivist, 1981—; Vis. prof. classics U. Iowa summer 1974. Founding editor Cithara: Essays in the Judaeo-Christian Tradition, 1960-63; mng. editor, 1966-78. Served with AUS, 1942-45, ETO. Named Man of Year Buffalo Council Catholic Men, 1960. Mem. Allegany Meml. Library Assn. (pres. 1962), AAUP, Am. Philol. Assn. Classical Assn. Atlantic States, Vergilian Soc., Vergil Soc. (Eng.). Democrat. Roman Catholic. Club: K.C. Home: 107 Jefferson Ave Allegany NY 14706-1147 Office: PO Box 61 Saint Bonaventure NY 14778-0061

WALLACE, MARK ALLEN, hospital executive; b. Oklahoma City, Apr. 24, 1953; s. William Howell and Mollie Marie (Godsby) W.; m. AnneMarie, May 14, 1976; children: Emily, Benjamin. BS, Okla. Bapt. U., 1975; MS, Washington U., St. Louis, 1978. Adminstrv. asst. Bapt. Med. Ctr.,

Oklahoma City, 1975-77; administry. resident Meth. Hosp., Houston, 1977-78; asst. v.p. Tex. Meth. Hosp., Houston, 1978-80, v.p.; 1980-83, sr. v.p., 1983-89; exec. dir., chief exec. officer Tex. Children's Hosp., Houston, 1989—; adj. instr. Washington U., 1984—; adj. asst. prof. Tex. Womans U., Houston, 1983—; bd. dirs., chmn. fin. com., treas. Greater Houston Hosp. Svc. Corp., 1986-90. Contbr. articles to profl. jours. Chmn. campaign drives United Way, Houston, 1984, 86; class chmn. alumni vision for excellence and growth for future campaigns Okla. Bapt. U., 1982; bd. dirs. Tex. Gulf Coast chpt. March of Dimes Birth Defects Found., 1985-91. Recipient Emerging Leaders in Health Care award Healthcare Forum Mag. and Korn/Ferry Internat., 1987, Robert S. Hudgens Meml. award, 1992. Fellow Am. Coll. Healthcare Execs. (com. on membership, subcom. on recruitment 1990—, Young Healthcare Exec. of Yr.), mem. Am. Heart Assn. (med. adv. com. 1990-91), Healthcare Forum (pres. emerging leaders alumni group 1988-91), Am. Hosp. Assn., Tex. Hosp. Assn. (bd. dirs., bd. dirs. polit. action com. 1988—), Greater Houston Hosp. Coun. (bd. dirs. 1991—), Houston Area Health Care Coalition, Childrens Hosp. Assn. Tex. (pres. 1992—), Tex. Gulf Coast Arthritis Found. (bd. dirs. 1990-91). Republican. Baptist. Office: Tex Children's Hosp PO Box 300630 Houston TX 77230-0630

WALLACE, MARY ELAINE, opera director, author; m. Robert House. BFA cum laude, U. Nebr., Kearney, 1940; MusM, U. Ill., 1954; postgrad., Music Acad. West, Santa Barbara, Calif., 1955, Eastman Sch. Music, 1960, Fla. State U., 1962. Prof. voice, dir. opera La. Tech. U., Ruston, 1959-62, SUNY-Fredonia, 1962-69, So. Ill. U.-Carbondale, 1969-79; dir. Marjorie Lawrence Opera Theatre, Opera on Wheels; adminstrv. adviser Summer Playhouse, Carbondale; stage mgr. Chautauqua Opera Co., N.Y., 1963; asst. mus. dir., condr. Asolo Festival, Sarasota, Fla., 1961; music editor, critic The Chautauquan Daily; adjudicator Met. Opera auditions; exec. sec. Nat. Opera Assn., 1981-91. Co-author: Opera Scenes for Class and Stage, 1979, (with Robert Wallace) More Opera Scenes for Class and Stage, 1990, Upstage Downstage, 1992. Mem. Nat. Opera Assn. (pres. 1974, 75), Music Tchrs. Nat. Assn., Nat. Assn. Tchrs. Singing, AAUP, AAUW, Met. Opera Guild, Mortar Bd., Sigma Tau Delta, Pi Kappa Lambda, Phi Beta, Alpha Psi Omega, Delta Kappa Gamma. Address: 3106 Lakeside Rockwall TX 75087

WALLACE, MIKE, television interviewer and reporter; b. Brookline, Mass., May 9, 1918; s. Frank and Zina (Sharfman) W.; m. Lorraine Perigord (dec.); children: Peter (dec.) Christopher, Pauline; m. Mary Yates, June 28, 1986. AB, U. Mich., 1935-39, hon. degree, 1987; hon. degree, U. Mass., 1978, U. Pa., 1989. Associated with radio, 1939—, TV, 1946—; commentator, CBS-TV, 1951-54, TV interviewer, reporter, 1951—; CBS news corr., 1963—; co-editor: 60 Minutes, CBS; Author: Mike Wallace Asks, 1958, Close Encounters, 1984. Recipient Robert Sherwood award, 18 ATVAS Emmy awards, George Foster Peabody awards, 1963-71, DuPont Columbia Journalism award, 1972, 83, Carr Van Anda award, 1977, Thomas Hart Benton award, 1978. Mem. Century Assocs., Sigma Delta Chi. Office: CBS News 60 Minutes 555 W 57th St New York NY 10019-2925

WALLACE, PATRICIA JEAN, artist, educator, writer; b. Sacramento, Jan. 3, 1945; d. Millard Edward Rogers and Katherine Lottie (Crabtree) Briggs; m. Feb. 23, 1964 (div. July 1992); children: Raabe, Brian, Marni. Student, Calif. Bapt. Coll., 1962-63, Am. River Coll., 1976-77, Tahoe Community Coll., 1991-92. Art, music tchr. Sunrise Elem. Sch., Citrus Heights, Calif., 1977-80; art restorer Arcade Antiques, North Sacramento, 1977-79; artist P.J.'s Illustration, North Sacramento, 1982—; instr. adult arts and crafts Community of Fair Oaks, Calif., 1982-84; instr., artist Laughing Cir. Gallery, Colo., Tex., N.Mex., 1984-92; writer On the Wing mag., No. Calif., 1988-92; artist ArtWorks Gallery, Fair Oaks, 1989—, Sacramento, 1988-91; artist S.W. Gallery, Fair Oaks and San Antonio, 1988—; set artist Fair Oaks Shakespeare Theatre, 1990. Illustrator numerous books, 1982—; contbr. articles to profl. mags. Pres. Sacramento Women's Club, 1984-85; city coun. rep. South Lake Tahoe Women's Ctr., 1978-79; amb. C. of C., Citrus Heights, 1985-89; rep. Historic Assn., Citrus Heights, 1987-88; adv. Bus. and the Arts, Sacramento County, 1987-89, C. of C., Sacramento, 1987-89; mem., guest artist KVIE-Channel 6, Sacramento, 1986-88; contbr. AIDS Found., Sacramento, 1990, Process Theatre Prodns., 1988. Mem. Tallac Historic Assn., Citrus Heights Art Assn. (pres., bd. dirs. 1985-89), Crocker Art Mus. Avocations: photography, cultural events, poetry, hiking, travel. Address: c/o M. Gates 3313 Eisenhower Dr Sacramento CA 95826-4510

WALLACE, PAUL F., real estate company officer. Chmn. bd. dirs., pres. Broadstone Group Inc. Office: Broadstone Group Inc 888 7th Ste 3400 New York NY 10106*

WALLACE, PEGGY MARIE, state commissioner; b. Barbourville, Ky., Jan. 3, 1950; d. Chester and Katherine (White) W. BS, Union Coll., 1971; MSSW, U. Louisville, 1977. Eligibility worker Dept. Econ. Security, State of Ky., Barbourville, 1972-74; social worker Dept. Social Svcs., Barbourville, 1974-76; social svcs. trainer, cons. Dept. Social Svcs., Frankfort, 1977-78, budget analyst, 1978-80, adminstrv. asst., 1980-81, adminstrv. supr., 1981, exec. asst., 1981-85, prin. asst., 1985-88, dep. commr., 1988-92, commr., 1992—; mem. Ky. Atty. Gen's. Task Force on Child Sexual Abuse, Ky. Child Labor Task Force, Ky. Multi-Disciplinary Commn. on Child Sexual Abuse, Ky. Crime Commn. (mem. juvenile justice adv. com.), Ky. Children's Justice Act Task Force, Ky. Family Resource and Youth Svcs. Ctr. Task Force, Ky. Child Care Policy Coun., Ky. Adv. Coun. on the Homeless, Ky. Early Intervention System Interagy. Coord. Coun., Ky. Gender Fairness Standing Com. (mem. subcom. on domestic violence), Ky. Birth Surveillance Adv. Com., Ky. Long Range Juvenile Detention Planning Com., Ky. State Interagy. Coun. for Children and Youth; chair Am. Pub. Welfare Assn's. Children, Families and Adult Svcs. Com. Mem. NASW (mem. bluegrass chpt.), Nat. Forum for Black Pub. Adminstrs. Baptist. Avocations: antiques, reading, old movies. Office: Social Svcs Dept 275 E Main St Frankfort KY 40601

WALLACE, PHILIP RUSSELL, retired physics educator; b. Toronto, Ont., Can., Apr. 19, 1915; s. George Russell and Mildred (Stillwaugh) W.; m. Jean Elizabeth Young, Aug. 15, 1940; children—Michael David, Kathryn Joan, Robert Philip. B.A., U. Toronto, 1937, M.A., 1938, Ph.D., 1940. Lectr. U. Cin., 1940-42; lectr. MIT, Cambridge, 1942; assoc. research physicist Atomic Energy of Can., Montreal and Chalk River, Que., 1943-46; assoc. prof. dept. math. McGill U., Montreal, Que., 1946-50, prof. math., 1950-60, prof. physics, 1961-81, MacDonald prof., 1972-81, prof. emeritus, 1981—; prin. Sci. Coll. Concordia U., Montreal, 1984-87; vis. prof. U. Paul Sabatier, Toulouse, France, 1972-73, 81-82. Author: Mathematical Analysis of Physical Problems, 1972-84, Physics: Imagination and Reality, 1991; contbd. over 90 scientific articles on relativity, nuclear physics, radar meterology, solid state physics, intense magnetic field effects; editor: Superconductivity, 1968, New Developments in Semiconductors, 1972, Can. Jour. Physics, 1972-80. Fellow Royal Soc. Can., Nat. Acad. Sci. (hon., India); mem. Am. Phys. Soc., Can. Assn. Physicists (pres. theoretical physics div. 1957-58), Am. Assn. Physics Tchrs. Club: McGill Faculty (pres. 1960-61). Avocations: medieval history, art and architecture. Home: 104-1039 Linden Ave, Victoria, BC Canada V8V 4H3 Office: McGill University Dept Physics, 3600 University St, Montreal, PQ Canada H3A 2T8

WALLACE, R. BYRON, lawyer; b. Seattle, Dec. 19, 1945. AB, Harvard U., 1967; JD, Case Western Reserve U., 1974. Bar: Ohio 1974. Ptnr. Baker & Hostetler, Cleve. Office: Baker & Hostetler 3200 Nat City Ctr 1900 E 9th St Cleveland OH 44114-3303

WALLACE, RALPH, superintendent; b. Halifax, Nova Scotia; s. Ralph and Alberta (Warren) W.; m. Haunani Wallace, Aug. 1, 1980; children: Lianne, Travis. BEd, U. British Columbia, 1968, MEd, 1976; postgrad., U. Conn., 1986; CAGS, Boston U., 1987, EdD, 1992. Cert. supt., adminstr., Conn. Asst. supt. West Vancouver (B.C.) Bd. Edn., 1967-83; prin. Farmington (Conn.) Bd. Edn., 1983-85; prin. Granby (Conn.) Bd. Edn., 1985-88, supt., 1988-92; supt. Cheshire (Conn.) Bd. Edn., 1992—; apptd. Pres. Nat. Excellence Panel. Contbr. articles to profl. jours. Dir. Gov.'s Sch., Conn. State U. Recipient Nat. Excellence award U.S. Dept. Edn.; named Conn. Supt. of Yr., 1992. Mem. ASCD, SDE (Conn. tech. com.), PDK, Am. Assn. Sch. Adminstrn., Conn. Assn. Pub. Sch. Supts. (legis), Am. Edn. Rsch. Assn., Edn. Rsch. Svc., Conn. Transp. Commn. (hon.), Conn. Tech. Commn.

Home: 40 Dorset Ln Farmington CT 06032-2330 Office: Cheshire Pub Schs 29 Main St Cheshire CT 06410-2405

WALLACE, RALPH HOWES, retired engineering company executive; b. Williamsburg, Iowa, Feb. 25, 1916; s. John Rea and Lois Mary (Howes) W.; m. Dorothea Lee Dexheimer, Dec. 28, 1941 (div. 1976); children: John F., Mary Helene; m. Muriel W. Nangle, 1976; adopted child, Lori Ann. BS, Iowa State U., 1946. Registered profl. engr., Iowa, Minn. Engr. bldgs and grounds Iowa State U., 1946; project engr. L.W. Mahone (cons. engrs.), Clear Lake, Iowa, 1946-48; cons. engr. Mason City, Iowa, 1948-56; partner Wallace & Holland (cons. engrs.), Mason City, Iowa, 1956-64, Wallace Holland Kastler & Schmitz (cons. engrs.), Mason City, 1964-69; pres. Wallace Holland Kastler Schmitz & Co., Mason City, 1969-81; mem. Iowa State Bd. Regents, 1967-73, Iowa Bd. Engring. Examiners, 1958-67, chmn., 1962, 63, 67; bd. dirs. Nat. Council State Bds. Engring. Examiners, 1965-67. Mem. Mason City Ind. sch. Bd., 1952-64, pres., 1964; mem. adv. bd. Center Indsl. Research and Service, Iowa State U., 1965-66; mem. adv. bd. Engring. Coll. U. Iowa, 1973-77, 84-88; mem. adv. council Engring. Coll., Iowa State U. 1973—; bd. dirs. Iowa Ednl. Radio and TV Facility, 1972-76; dir. Iowa Good Roads Assn., 1967-84, pres., 1976-77; bd. dirs. North Iowa Med. Center, 1980-93, Prairie Ridge Addiction Treatment Svcs., 1990—; mem. Mason City Human Rights Commn., 1985-92, chmn., 1988-92. Capt. AUS 1941-46. Decorated Bronze Star, Croix de Guerre with Etoile d'Argent; recipient Outstanding Boss award Mason City Jaycees, 1958, Svc. to Mankind award Sertoma Club, 1971, Silver Beaver award Boy Scouts Am., 1974, Anson Marston medal Iowa State U., 1988. Fellow ASCE (dir. 1970-72, v.p. 1976, 77), Am. Cons. Engrs. Council; mem. NSPE, Iowa Engring. Soc. (Disting. Svc. award 1969, Profl. Achievement citation 1982, hon. life mem. 1987), AAAS (life), VFW, Rotary Internat. (Paul Harris fellow 1988, hon. mem. 1989), Tau Beta Pi, Scabbard and Blade. Republican. Mem. United Ch. Christ. Home: 718 E State St Mason City IA 50401-4144

WALLACE, RICHARD, editor, writer; b. Bronxville, N.Y., May 25, 1947; m. Elisabeth Wallace; 1 child, Eric B. BA, Columbia U., 1974. Reporter, editor, contbr. varius industry and bus. pubs., Electronic News, EE Times, 1976-92; editor-in-chief Electronic Engring Times, Manhasset, N.Y., 1992—. Mem. Internat. Platform Assn. Democrat. Avocations: running, writing, reading, orchardist. Office: CMP Pubs Inc Electronic Engring Times 600 Community Dr Manhasset NY 11030

WALLACE, RICHARD CHRISTOPHER, JR., school system administrator, educator; b. Haverhill, Mass., Jan. 3, 1931; s. Richard C. and Anna Catharine (Rogan) W.; m. Rita Wallace, June 18, 1957; children: Monica, Margaret, Mona. BS in Edn., Gorham State Coll., Maine, 1953; MEd, Boston Coll., 1960, EdD, 1966; postgrad., Stanford U., 1968-69. Dir. Eastern Regional Inst. Edn., Syracuse, N.Y., 1969-70, 1970-71; deputy dir. program planning and evaluation U. Tex., Austin, 1971-73; supt. Fitchburg (Mass.) Pub. Schs., 1973-80, Pitts. Pub. Schs., 1980-92; prof. U. Pitts., 1993—; chmn. nat. adv. panel ctr. sch. restructuring U. Wis., 1990—; rsch. assoc. Learning Rsch. and Devel. Ctr. U. Pitts., 1983—; chmn. nat. adv. panel Ctr. Effective Secondary Schs., U. Wis., Madison, 1986-90; mem. Coun. of Great City Schs. Exec. Com., 1980-92, Coun. of Great City Schs. Bylaws and Personnel Policies Com., 1986-87. Contbr. articles to profl. jours. Trustee Chatham Coll., 1984—; bd. dirs. Urban League Pitts, 1985-92, Sta. WQED-TV, Pitts., 1987, Carnegie Found. for Advancement of Teaching, 1990. Named Man of Yr. Edn. Vectors, Pitts., 1981; recipient Shaw medal Boston Coll., Chestnut Hill, Mass., 1985, Leadership for Learning award Am. Assn. Sch. Adminstrs., Washington, 1987, Harold W. McGraw Jr. prize, 1990. Mem. Am. Assn. Sch. Adminstrs., Am. Ednl. Research Assn., Assn. Supervision Curriculum Devel. Democrat. Roman Catholic. Lodge: Rotary (chmn. youth com. 1980) (Pitts.). Office: U Pitts 5034 Forbes Quad Pittsburgh PA 15260

WALLACE, RICHARD K., editor, journalist; b. Bronxville, N.Y., May 25, 1947; s. J. Roger and Edith (Tiffany) W.; m. Elisabeth H. Beeftink, May 24, 1969; 1 child, Eric J. BA, Columbia U., 1974, postgrad., 1976; postgrad., N.Y. Sch. Visual Arts, 1983. Mktg. mgr. Litton Systems, Mt. Vernon, N.Y., 1974-76; mng. editor Electronic News Fairchild Pubs., N.Y.C.; design automation editor Electronic Engring Times, CMP Pubs, Manhasset, N.Y., 1987-92, news editor, 1990-92, mng. editor, 1990-92, editor, 1992-93, editor-in-chief, 1993—; media cons. polit. candidates. Contbr. articles to profl. jours. Vice chmn. White Plains (N.Y.) Dem. City Com., 1987-90. Served with U.S. Army, 1969-71. Avocations: woodworking, hiking, travel. Home: 50 Concord Ave White Plains NY 10606-2213 Office: Electronic Eng Times 600 Community Dr Manhasset NY 11030-3847

WALLACE, ROBERT BRUCE, surgeon; b. Washington, Apr. 12, 1931; s. William B. and Anne E. W.; m. Betty Jean Newel, Aug. 28, 1955; children: Robert B., Anne E., Barbara N. B.A., Columbia U., 1953, M.D., 1957. Diplomate: Am. Bd. Surgery, Am. Bd. Thoracic Surgery. Chmn. / prof. dept. surgery Mayo Clinic and Mayo Med. Sch., Rochester, Minn.; bd. govs. Mayo Clinic, 1968-79; chmn., prof. dept. surgery Georgetown U. Sch. Medicine, 1980—, surgeon and chief univ. hosp. Trustee Mayo Found., 1970-78. Mem. ACS (bd. govs. 1975-79), Am. Surg. Assn., Soc. Clin. Surgery, Am. Assn. Thoracic Surgery (pres. 1994-95), Internat. Cardiovascular Soc., Soc. Vascular Surgery. Home: 1322 Darnall Dr Mc Lean VA 22101-3009 Office: Dept Surgery Georgetown U Hosp 3800 Reservoir Rd NW Washington DC 20007-2196

WALLACE, ROBERT BRUCE, lawyer, educator; b. Washington, Apr. 23, 1944; s. Thomas Edward and Mary (Beeler) W.; m. Jane Susan Johnson, Sept. 13, 1969; children: Mead Alison, Jared Corwin. BA in Econs., George Washington U., 1966, JD, 1970. Bar: Va. 1970, U.S. Ct. Appeals (6th cir.) 1970, D.C. 1971, U.S. Dist. Ct. D.C. 1971, U.S. Ct. Appeals (10th and D.C. cirs.) 1971, U.S. Ct. Appeals (4th cir.) 1975, U.S. Supreme Ct. 1975, U.S. Dist. Ct. (ea. dist.) Va. 1974, U.S. Dist. Ct. (we. dist.) Va. 1975, U.S. Ct. Appeals (5th cir.) 1979. Atty. Office of Gen. Counsel, EEOC, Washington, 1970-71; atty., project dir. Washington Lawyers Com. for Civil Rights Under Law, 1971-74, atty., nat. coordinator, 1974-77, mem. exec. com., 1982—; assoc. Surrey & Morse, Washington, 1977-80, ptnr., 1980-86; ptnr. Wilson, Elser, Moskowitz, Edelman & Dicker, Washington, 1986-89, regional mng. ptnr., 1990—; adj. prof. law Cath. U., Washington, 1974-77, Howard U., 1975-76; guest lectr. George Washington U. Sch. Law, 1976, U. Va. Sch. Law, 1970. Author: (chpt.) Conflict of Law-Reinsurance IBA, 1988; contbr. articles to profl. jours. 1st lt. USAR, 1966-72. Mem. ABA, Internat. Bar Assn., Va. Bar Assn., D.C. Bar Assn., Am. Soc. Internat. Law, Washington Bd. Trade, Belle Haven Country Club. Democrat. Roman Catholic. Avocations: tennis, golf, sailing. Home: 1113 Prince St Alexandria VA 22314-2934 Office: Wilson Elser Moskowitz Edelman & Dicker The Colorado Bldg 5th Fl 1341 G St NW Washington DC 20025

WALLACE, ROBERT EARL, geologist; b. N.Y.C., July 16, 1916; s. Clarence Earl and Harriet (Wheeler) W.; m. Gertrude Kivela, Mar. 19, 1945; 1 child: Alan R. BS, Northwestern U., 1938; MS, Calif. Inst. Tech., 1940, PhD, 1946. Registered geologist, Calif. engring. geologist, Calif. Geologist U.S. Geol. Survey, various locations, 1942—; regional geologist U.S. Geol. Survey, Menlo Park, Calif., 1970-74; chief scientist Office of Earthquakes, Volcanoes and Engring. U.S. Geol. Survey, Menlo Park, 1974-87, emeritus, 1987—; asst. and assoc. prof. Wash. State Coll., Pullman, Wash., 1946-51; mem. adv. panel Nat. Earthquake Prediction Evaluation Coun., 1980-90, Stanford U. Sch. Earth Sci., 1972-82; mem. engring. criteria rev. bd. San Francisco Bay Conservation and Devel. Commn. Contbr. articles to profl. jours. Recipient Meritorious Service award U.S. Dept. Interior, 1978, Disting. Service award U.S. Dept. Interior, 1978; Japanese Indsl. Tech. Assn. fellow, 1984. Fellow AAAS, Geol. Soc. Am. (chair cordillidan sect. 1967-68), Earthquake Engring. Research Inst., mem. Seismol. Soc. Am. (medalist 1989). Avocations: bird watching, ham radio, water color painting. Office: US Geol Survey MS-977 345 Middlefield Rd Menlo Park CA 94025-3591

WALLACE, ROBERT FERGUS, banker; b. Bklyn., Oct. 5, 1934; s. Fergus F. and Isabelle (Wilson) W.; m. Florence Faminow, Dec. 18, 1959; children: Douglas, Barbara. BA, Colgate U., 1956. Comml. loan officer Chem. Bank, N.Y.C., 1956-68; chmn. First Interstate Bank, Portland, Oreg., 1968-81; pres. Nat. Westminster Bank U.S.A., N.Y.C., 1982—; now chmn. bd. dirs. Nat. Westminster Bancorp, N.Y.C. Bd. dirs. N.Y.C. Opera Co., 1986—; Served to lt. USN, 1957-60. Mem. Assn. Res. City Banks, Downtown-

Lower Manhattan Assn. (treas. 1988). Republican. Presbyterian. Club: Econ. of N.Y. Office: Nat Westminster Bank USA 175 Water St New York NY 10038-4918

WALLACE, ROBERT GEORGE, retired construction company executive, civil engineer; b. Flagstaff, Ariz., Apr. 30, 1928; s. William Robert Francis and Maeclaire (Wright) W.; m. Gloria Mae Reid, Oct. 29, 1960. B.S.C.E., U. Ariz., Tucson, 1953. Registered profl. civil engr. Pres. Wallace & Royden Equipment Co., Phoenix, 1956-67; v.p. Royden Constrn. Co., Phoenix, 1953-67; v.p. The Tanner Cos., Phoenix, 1967-81, exec. v.p., 1971-82, pres., 1982-88, also dir.; nat. bd. dirs. Scripps Rsch. Inst., Kasler Holding Co., The Fenton Cos. Bd. dirs. Assn. Gen. Contractors, 1973-80, The Road Information Rrogram 1978-82, The Beavers, 1982-88, Western Force, 1972-78. Served with USN, 1946-48; PTO. Recipient award of Disting. Service Ariz. Assoc. Gen. Contractors, 1967; Disting. Citizen award U. Ariz. Engring. Coll., 1983. Mem. Univ. Club of San Diego, Masons (32d degree). Republican. Episcopalian. Home: 1001 Genter St Apt 8F La Jolla CA 92037-5526

WALLACE, SAMUEL TAYLOR, hospital administrator; b. Blytheville, Ark., Sept. 2, 1943; s. Samuel Edward and Minnie (Taylor) W.; m. Sara Billow, Apr. 30, 1992. B.S., U. Mo., 1965; M.H.A., Washington U., St. Louis, 1970. Asst. adminstr. Hillcrest Med. Ctr., Tulsa, 1969-75; adminstr. St. Luke's Meth. Hosp., Cedar Rapids, Iowa, 1975-81, pres., 1981—. Bd. dirs. Vol. Hosp. Am., Dallas, 1982-94; Cedar Rapids Symphony, 1993—; chmn. bd. dirs. Vol. Hosp. Iowa, Cedar Rapids, 1983—; bd. dirs. Cedar Rapids Pub. Libr., 1983; pres. bd. Cedar Rapids Community Theatre, 1983, Cedar Rapids coun. Boy Scouts Am., 1983. Served to capt. M.S.C. U.S. Amry, 1965-68, Vietnam. Recipient Silver Beaver award Boy Scouts Am., 1979, Silver Antelope award, 1992. Fellow Am. Coll. Healthcare Execs. (Iowa bd. regents 1982-85, 88—); mem. Iowa Hosp. Assn. (dir. 1982-85). Republican. Methodist. Lodge: Rotary (pres.-elect Cedar Rapids 1985, pres. 1986—). Office: St Luke's Meth Hosp 1026 A Ave NE Cedar Rapids IA 52402-5036

WALLACE, SPENCER MILLER, JR., hotel executive; b. Portland, Maine, Aug. 17, 1923; s. Spencer M. and Caroline (Clark) W.; m. Margaret Keeler, May 12, 1956; 1 son, Daniel Walker. With Hotels Statler, 1944-54, Hilton Hotels Corp., 1954-57, Hilton Hotels, Internat., 1957-61; exec. v.p., dir. Hotel Syracuse Corp., N.Y., 1961-80; chmn. Onondaga County Tourism and Conv. Com.; mem. N.Y. State Tourism Adv. Council. Trustee Milton J. Rubenstein Mus. Sci. and Tech. Mem. N.Y. State Hotel Assn., Am. Hotel and Motel Assn. (past dir.), N.Y. State Hotel and Motel Assn. (past pres.), Am. Diabetes Assn. (bd. dirs. N.Y. state affiliate), N.Y. Srs. Golf Assn., Rotary (Syracuse Club). Episcopalian. Clubs: Mason (Shriner, Jester), Onondaga Golf and Country (bd. dirs.). Home: 11 Wheeler Ave Fayetteville NY 13066-2530 Office: 6875 E Genesee St Fayetteville NY 13066-1096

WALLACE, TED, wholesale goods distribution executive; b. 1948. BA, Muskingum Coll., 1971. Store mgr. Fazio Foods, 1971-77; warehouse mgr. Price Co., San Diego, 1977-82, sr. warehouse mgr., 1982-83, v.p. ops., 1983-84, exec. v.p. ops., 1984—. Office: Price Co 4649 Morena Blvd San Diego CA 92117-3650

WALLACE, THOMAS C(HRISTOPHER), editor, literary agent; b. Vienna, Austria, Dec. 13, 1933; came to U.S., 1938; s. Don and Julia (Baer) W.; m. Lois Kahn, July 19, 1962; 1 son, George Baer. Grad., Peddie Sch., 1951; BA, Yale U., 1955, MA in History, 1957. Editor G.P. Putnam Sons, N.Y.C., 1959-63; with Holt, Rinehart & Winston, N.Y.C., 1963-81, editor-in-chief gen. books div., 1968-81; v.p., sr. editor Simon and Schuster, N.Y.C., 1981; editor W.W. Norton, N.Y.C., 1982-87; v.p. Wallace Lit. Agy., N.Y.C., 1987—; bd. dirs. Roger Klein Found. Mem. PEN, Yale Club, Century Assn. (N.Y.C.), Pound Ridge (N.Y.) Tennis Club. Home: 45 E 82d St New York NY 10028 Office: Wallace Lit Agy 177 E 70th St New York NY 10021-5109

WALLACE, THOMAS J., magazine editor-in-chief. Editor-in-chief Conde Nast Traveler, N.Y.C. Office: Conde Nast Traveler 360 Madison Ave New York NY 10017

WALLACE, THOMAS PATRICK, university administrator; b. Washington, Apr. 11, 1935; 4 children. BS, SUNY, Potsdam, 1958; MS, Syracuse U., 1961, St. Lawrence U., 1964; PhD in Physical Chemistry, Clarkson U., 1968. Asst. prof. chemistry SUNY, Potsdam, 1961-67; Mellon Inst. fellow Carnegie-Mellon Inst., 1967-68; mem. faculty Rochester (N.Y.) Inst. Tech., 1968-78, assoc. prof., 1970-78, head dept. chemistry, 1970-72, assoc. dean, 1972-73, dean, 1973-78; prof. chem. scis. Old Dominion U., Norfolk, Va., 1978-86, dean sci. and health professions, 1978-83, v.p. acad. affairs, 1983-86; chancellor Ind. U.-Purdue U., Ft. Wayne, 1986-88; pres. Ill. State U., Normal, 1988—. Contbr. articles to profl. jours. Mem. Am. Chem. Soc. Office: Ill State U Office of Pres Normal IL 61761

WALLACE, THOMAS ROBERT, public relations executive; b. Glen Ridge, N.J., Apr. 27, 1954; s. John Henry and Roseann Elizabeth (Pantoliano) W.; m. Catherine Marshall Rollman, June 25, 1983; children: Katherine, Jennifer, Alexander. BA magna cum laude, Emory U., 1976; MA, U. Va., 1978. Account exec. Makovsky & Co., N.Y.C., 1979-81, exec. v.p., 1984—; v.p. Hill & Knowlton, N.Y.C., 1981-84. Congregationalist. Office: Makovsky & Co 245 5th Ave New York NY 10016-8728

WALLACE, VICTOR L., II, lawyer; b. Shawnee, Okla., Jan. 14, 1938. BS, U. Okla., 1961, JD, 1967. Bar: Colo. 1967, Tex. 1991. Ptnr. Baker & Hostetler, Denver. Capt. USMC, 1961-64. Fellow Am. Coll. Mortgage Attys. (bd. regents 1984—, pres., 1989-90), Am. Coll. Real Estate Lawyers; mem. ABA, Colo. Bar Assn., Denver Bar Assn., State Bar Tex., Phi Delta Phi. Office: Baker & Hostetler 303 E 17th St Ste 1100 Denver CO 80203-1264

WALLACE, WALTER C., lawyer, government official; b. N.Y.C., Mar. 25, 1924; m. Frances Helm, Apr. 5, 1963; 1 dau., Laura. BA magna cum laude, St. John's U., Hillsdale, N.Y., 1948; LLB with distinction, Cornell U., 1951. Bar: N.Y. 1952, Calif. 1954, D.C. 1975, U.S. Dist. Ct. (no. dist.) Calif. 1954, U.S. Ct. Appeals (9th cir.) 1954, D.C. 1975, U.S. Dist. Ct. D.C. 1975, U.S. Ct. Appeals (D.C. cir.) 1975. Assoc. Cahill, Gordan & Reindel, N.Y.C., 1951-54; exec. asst. sec. of labor Dept. of Labor, Washington, 1955-60, asst. sec. of labor, 1960-61; gen. counsel Presdl. R.R. Commn., Washington, 1961; v.p. labor rels. Hudson Pulp & Paper Corp., N.Y.C., 1963-73; pres. Bituminous Coal Operators Assn., Washington, 1974-75; ptnr. Ables & Wallace, Washington, 1977-80; prin. Law Offices Walter C. Wallace, N.Y.C., 1981-82; mem. Nat. Mediation Bd., Washington, 1982—, chmn., 1983, 85, 88; U.S. del. Internat. Labor Orgn. Conf. on Labor Rels. in Timber Industry, Geneva, 1958. Mem. bd. editors Cornell Law Quar., 1950-51. Bd. dirs. Nat. Safety Coun., Washington, 1974-75; asst. to chmn. United Givers Fund, Washington, 1956, mem. admission and allocations com., 1957-58. Staff sgt. U.S. Army, 1943-45, ETO. Decorated Bronze Star; recipient Presdl. commendation Pres. Eisenhower, Washington, 1961, Disting. Svc. award United Givers Fund, 1956. Mem. Calif. Bar Assn., N.Y. State Bar Assn., D.C. Bar Assn., Order of Coif. Republican. Roman Catholic. Home: 55 Central Park W New York NY 10023-6003

WALLACE, WALTER L., sociologist, educator; b. Washington, Aug. 21, 1927; s. Walter L. and Rosa Belle (Boisseau) W.; children: Jeffrey Richard, Robin Claire, Jennifer Rose. B.A., Columbia U., 1954; M.A., Atlanta U., 1955; Ph.D., U. Chgo., 1963. Instr. Spelman Coll., Atlanta U., 1955-57; from lectr. to prof. sociology Northwestern U., Evanston, Ill., 1963-71; prof. sociology Princeton, 1971—; staff sociologist Russell Sage Found., N.Y.C., 1969-77, vis. scholar, 1968; fellow Ctr. for Advanced Study in Behavioral Scis., Stanford, Calif., 1974-75. Author: Student Culture, 1966, Logic of Science in Sociology, 1971, (with James E. Conyers) Black Elected Officials, 1975, Principles of Scientific Sociology, 1983, A Weberian Theory of Human Society, 1994; editor, author: Sociological Theory, 1969; mem. social scis. adv. com. World Book, 1977-94, editorial bd. Social Forces, 1984-87, The Am. Sociologist, 1988-91, Sociol. Quar., 1989-92. Mem. council Found. for Child Devel., N.Y.C. Served with AUS, 1950-52. Mem. Am. Sociol. Assn.

(council 1971-74, theory sect. 1988—), Sociol. Rsch. Assn. Office: Princeton U Dept Sociology Princeton NJ 08544

WALLACE, WILLIAM, III, engineering executive; b. Bklyn., June 7, 1926; s. William and Ruth (Fitch) W.; m. Dorothy Ann Reimann, Aug. 2, 1969 (dec.); 1 child, Andrew William. B.E.E., Union Coll., 1947. Registered prof. engr., 22 states. Test engr. Gen. Electric Co., Schenectady, 1947; engr. Ebasco Services Inc., N.Y.C., 1948-67, chief elec. engr., 1967-70, mgr. projects, 1970-73; v.p. Atlanta office Ebasco Services Inc., Norcross, Ga., 1973-76; exec. v.p. Ebasco Services Inc., N.Y.C., 1976-80, dir., pres., chief exec. officer, 1980-82, chmn., chief exec. officer, 1982-86, also bd. dirs.; cons., 1986—; bd. dirs. McNab Corp. Chmn. bd. advisors Sch. engring., N.C. State U., 1986-89; mem. adv. bd. trustees Union Coll.; trustee Poly. Prep. Country Day Sch.; v.p. Saddle River Day Sch.; deacon West Side Presbyn. Ch., Ridgewood, N.J., 1988-90, elder, 1990-93. Mem. IEEE (sr.), NSPE, N.J. State Soc. Profl. Engrs., World Rehab. Fund (bd. dirs.), N.Y.C. C. of C. and Industry (bd. dirs 1980-88), Delta Upsilon (vice chmn. Ednl. Found.). Republican. Home and Office: 84 Buckhaven Hl Upper Saddle River NJ 07458

WALLACE, WILLIAM AUGUSTINE, philosophy and history educator; b. N.Y.C., May 11, 1918; s. William Augustine and Louise Cecilia (Teufel) W. BEE, Manhattan Coll., 1940, LHD (hon.), 1975; MS in Physics, Cath. U. Am., 1952; PhD in Philosophy, U. Freiburg, Switzerland, 1959, STD, 1962; Lector of Sacred Theology, Dominican House of Studies, Washington, 1954, M of Sacred Theology, 1967; DSc (hon.), Providence Coll., 1973; DLitt (hon.), Molloy Coll.; 1974; LHD (hon.), Fairfield U., 1986. Entered Dominican Order, 1946; ordained priest Roman Cath. Ch., 1953. Elec. engr. Consol. Edison, N.Y.C., 1940-41; rsch. engr. Naval Ordnance Lab., Washington, 1941-43; lector philosophy Dominican House of Philosophy, Dover, Mass., 1954-62; philosophy editor New Cath. Ency., Washington, 1962-65; rsch. assoc. Harvard U., Cambridge, Mass., 1965-67; regent of studies Dominican House of Studies, Washington, 1967-70; prof. philosophy and history Cath. U. Am., Washington, 1970-88, prof. emeritus, 1988—; prof. philosophy U. Md., College Park, 1988—; mem. Inst. for Advanced Study, Princeton, 1976-77; fellow Woodrow Wilson Ctr. for Scholars, Washington, 1983-84; dir. gen. Leonine Commn., Washington, 1976-87. Author: The Scientific Methodology of Theodoric of Freiberg, 1959, The Role of Demonstration in Moral Theology, 1963, Causality and Scientific Explanation, vol. 1, 1972, vol. 2, 1974, The Elements of Philosophy, 1977, From a Realist Point of View, 1979 2d edit. 1983, Prelude to Galileo, 1981, Galileo and His Sources, 1984, Galileo, the Jesuits, and the Medieval Aristotle, 1991, Galileo's Logic of Discovery and Proof, 1992; editor, translator: Thomas Aquinas: Cosmogony, 1967, Galileo's Early Notebooks: the Physical Questions, 1977; editor: Reinterpreting Galileo, 1986; co-editor: Galileo Galilei: De praecognitionibus and De demonstratione, 1988, editor, translator: Galileo's Logical Treatises, 1992; mem. editorial bd. Rev. of Metaphysics, The Thomist; contbr. over 300 articles to jours., encys. and books. Lt. Comdr. USN, 1941-46, PTO. Decorated Legion of Merit; recipient Alumni Achievement award Manhattan Coll., 1967, Alumni Achievement award Cath. U. Am., 1986; grantee NSF, 1965-84, NEH, 1981-89. Mem. Am. Cath. Philos. Assn. (pres. 1969-70, Aquinas medal 1983), History of Sci. Soc. (mem. coun. 1974-77, 88-91), Philosophy of Sci. Assn., Phi Beta Kappa, Sigma Xi. Democrat.

WALLACE, WILLIAM C., airline executive; b. Pittsburg, Tex., July 12, 1941; m. Joyce Johnson, Apr. 22, 1978; children: Kristin, Kari, Michael. BBA, U. Tex., Arlington, 1965. Various positions Am. Airlines, Dallas, Ft. Worth, 1967-79, mgr. passenger svcs., 1979-82; div. mgr. reservations Am. Airlines, L.A., 1982-84; mgr. airport terminal svcs. Am. Airlines, Dallas, Ft. Worth, 1984-85, dir. idea systems, 1985-87; regional mgr. Am. Airlines, Nashville, 1987-88, v.p. field svc., 1990—; exec. v.p. Nashville Eagle (Am. Eagle), 1988-89, pres., 1989-90. Exec. bd. Nashville Symphony, 1990-93; adv. bd. Girl Scouts Am., Nashville. Bd. dirs. Mid. Tenn. coun. Boy Scouts Am., 1991-93. Capt. U.S. Army, 1965-70. Mem. Nashville C. of C. (bd. govs. 1991-93). Republican. Episcopalian. Avocations: photography, gardening. Office: Am Airlines Inc PO Box MD 5452 619616 Dallas TX 75261

WALLACE, WILLIAM EDWARD, engineering educator,scientist; b. Fayette, Miss., Mar. 11, 1917; s. James D. and Mattie (Rogers) W.; m. Helen Meyer, June 21, 1947; children: Richard Glen, Donald Alan, Marcia Louise. BS, Miss. Coll., 1936; PhD, U. Pitts., 1940. Teaching asst. U. Pitts., 1936-40, rsch. assoc. chemistry, 1941-45, mem. faculty, 1945-83, prof. chemistry, chmn. dept., 1963-77, prof. materials and metall. engring., 1973-83, prof. chem. engring., 1977-83; prof. applied sci. and engring. Carnegie-Mellon U., Pitts., 1983—; rsch. assoc. manhattan project Ohio State U., 1945; cons. Wright-Patterson AFB, 1962—, Du Pont, 1977—, Gen. Motors, 1974—, Amoco, 1977—; Union Oil Co., 1979—; mem. Pa. Gov.'s Sci. Com., Pa. Sci. and Engring. Found.; fellow Carnegie Instn., Washington, 1940-42; pres. Advanced Materials Corp., 1986-93. Recipient Frank Spedding award 1978, Morley award, 1983; Buhl fellow, 1942-44; Guggenheim fellow, 1954-55. Fellow AAAS; mem. Am. Chem. Soc., Phi Beta Kappa (hon.), Sigma Xi, Phi Lambda Upsilon. Research on metals and intermetallics, hydrogen as a fuel, magnetic materials. Home: 201 Pinecrest Dr Pittsburgh PA 15237-3652

WALLACE, WILLIAM HALL, economic and financial consultant; b. Senatobia, Miss., Aug. 8, 1933; s. Woodard Harvey and Cellie (Carter) W.; m. Margaret Jaeger, Mar. 7, 1964 (dec. 1978); children—Amy Margaret, William Douglas, John Richard Bruce; m. Virginia Wilson, Aug. 25, 1979. B.B.A., U. Miss., 1955, M.B.A., 1956; Ph.D., U. Ill., 1962. Asst. prof. econs. Duke U., Durham, N.C., 1962-67; v.p. Fed. Res. Bank Richmond, Va., 1967-73; prof. econs. N.C. State U., Raleigh, 1973-74; staff dir. Fed. Res. Bd., Washington, 1974-80; 1st v.p., chief oper. officer Fed. Res. Bank Dallas, 1981-91; prof. fin. place coll. Bus. and Pub. Adminstrn. Old Dominion U., Norfolk, Va., 1991-94; rett. 1994; pres. Wallace Cons., Inc., 1994—; co-dir. Eurasia Found. Program in Banking & Fin. Markets for Russia and CIS, 1994-95. Trustee Dallas Hist. Soc.; mem. Dallas Com. Fgn. Rels. Served to 1st lt. U.S. Army, 1956-58. Mem. Am. Econs. Assn., Am. Statis. Assn., Cen. Dallas Assn. (exec. com.), Greater Dallas C. of C. (edn. com. 1984-88, chmn. edn. com. 1989-90), Rotary. Methodist. Home: 6 Mansilla Way Hot Springs AR 71909-4312 Office: Wallace Consultants Inc Hot Springs National Park AR 71909

WALLACE, WILLIAM RAY, fabricated steel manufacturing company executive; b. Shreveport, La., Mar. 25, 1923; s. Jason Mohoney and Mattie Evelyn (Adair) W.; m. Minyone Milligan Rose, Oct. 5, 1966; children: Jayne Cecile Rose McDearman, Susan Rose O'Brien, H. Robert Rose; children by previous marriage: Patrick Scott, Michael B., Timothy R., Shelly W. Taetz. BS in Engring., La. Tech., 1944. Field engr. Austin Bridge Co., Dallas, 1944-45; core analyst Core Labs., Bakersfield, Calif., 1945-46; chief engr., then sec.-treas., exec. v.p. Trinity Industries, Inc., Dallas, 1946-58, pres., CEO, 1958—, also bd. dirs.; bd. dirs. Lomas Fin. Corp., Trinity Industries, ENSERCH Corp. Trustee Dallas Meth. Hosps. Found. Methodist. Office: Trinity Industries Inc 2525 N Stemmons Fwy Dallas TX 75207-2400

WALLACH, ALAN, art historian, educator; b. Bklyn., June 8, 1942; s. Israel and Vivian (Esner) W.; m. Phyllis Rosenzweig, Jan. 3, 1988. BA, Columbia U., 1963, MA, 1965, PhD, 1973. Assoc. prof. Kean Coll., Union, N.J., 1974-89; Ralph H. Wark prof. fine arts Coll. William and Mary, Williamsburg, Va., 1989—; vis. prof. UCLA, 1982-83, Stanford (Calif.) U., 1987, CUNY, 1988, U. Mich., 1989; co-curator Nat. Mus. Am. Art, Washington, 1991-94. Author: (with William Truettner) Thomas Cole: Landscape into History, 1994; contbr. to profl. jours. Sr. Postdoctorate Rsch. award Smithsonian Inst., 1985-86. Mem. Am. Studies Assn., Coll. Art Assn., Assn. Art Historians. Home: 2009 Belmont Rd NW Washington DC 20009 Office: Coll William and Mary Dept Art and Art History Williamsburg VA 23187-8795

WALLACH, ALLAN HENRY, former senior critic; b. N.Y.C., Oct. 23, 1927; s. Julius and Beatrice (Markowitz) W.; m. Shirley Meyrowitz, Nov. 26, 1953; children: Jonathan, Mark, Paul. B.A. magna cum laude, Syracuse U., 1951. Tech. writer H.L. Yoh Co., Phila., 1951-53; reporter Patchogue (N.Y.) Advance, 1953-54; reporter, copy editor New Haven Register, 1954-56; suc-

cessively reporter, copy editor, asst. night city editor, news feature editor, entertainment editor Newsday, Melville, N.Y., 1957-71; chief drama critic Newsday, 1972-88; sr. critic N.Y. Newsday, N.Y.C., 1988-92; bd. dirs. Lucille Lortel Co. Served with USNR, 1946-47. Mem. Drama Desk. Home: 315 W 70th St Apt 4J New York NY 10023-3507

WALLACH, ANNE JACKSON See **JACKSON, ANNE**

WALLACH, EDWARD ELIOT, physician, educator; b. N.Y.C., Oct. 8, 1933; s. David Abraham and Madeleine (Spiro) W.; m. Joanne Levey, June 24, 1956; children: Paul, Julie. B.A., Swarthmore Coll., 1954; M.D., Cornell U., 1958; M.A. (hon.), U. Pa., 1970. Diplomate Am. Bd. Obstetrics and Gynecology. (bd. dirs.), subcert. in reproductive endocrinology. Intern 2d med. div. Bellevue Hosp., N.Y.C., 1958-59; resident obstetrics and gynecology Kings County Hosp., Bklyn., 1959-63; asst. instr. State U. N.Y. Downstate Med. Center, Bklyn., 1962-63; mem. faculty U. Pa. Sch. Medicine, 1965-84, prof. obstetrics and gynecology, 1971-84, chief endocrinology sect., div. human reprodn., dept. obstetrics and gynecology, 1968-71, mem. admissions com., 1970-73, mem. community health com., 1966-71, mem. student adv. com., 1968-84, mem. com. for appointments and promotions, 1972-77, chmn., 1974-77; dir. dept. obstetrics and gynecology Pa. Hosp., 1971-84, sec., treas. profl. staff, 1972-75; prof., chmn. dept. ob-gyn. Johns Hopkins U. Sch. Medicine, 1984-94, chmn. med. staff, 1991-94, prof., 1984-94; vis. prof. obstetrics and gynecology U. Kyoto Sch. Medicine, 1981; vis. prof. Keio U. Sch. of Medicine, 1987;. Assoc. editor: Fertility and Sterility, 1974—; co-editor: Modern Trends in Infertility and Conception Control; editor-in-chief Postgrad. Obstetrics and Gynecology, 1980—; mem. editorial bd. Fertility and Sterility, 1970—, Obstetrics and Gynecology, 1976-79, Contemporary Obstetrics and Gynecology, 1976—, Biology of Reproduction, 1978-84; editor-in-chief Current Opinion in Obstetrics and Gynecology, 1989-93; contbr. to med. jours. Trustee Marriage Council Phila., 1970-78; chmn. finance com. Phila. Coordinating Council for Family Planning, 1972-73, chmn. med. adv. com., 1973-76; trustee Balt. Chamber Orch., 1989—. Served as surgeon USPHS, 1963-65. Trainee NIH, 1961-62; recipient Lindback Found. Disting. Teaching award U. Pa., 1971. Fellow Am. Coll. Obstetricians and Gynecologists, Am. Fertility Soc. (dir. 1977-81, pres. 1985-86); mem. AAAS, Am. Gynecol. and Obstet. Soc. (v.p. 1983-84), FDA Fertility and Maternal Health Drugs Adv. Com., 1992-96, Endocrine Soc., Soc. Gynecol. Investigation (pres. 1986-87), Am. Bd. Ob-Gyn (bd. dirs. 1989—, dir. div. reproductive endocrinology 1989—), Phila. Endocrine Soc., Obstet. Soc. Phila. (program chmn. 1969-70, 70-71, 71-72, mem. coun. 1972-83, v.p. 1976-77, pres. 1979-80), Soc. Study Reprodn., Alpha Omega Alpha. Office: Johns Hopkins Med Instn Dept Gyne & Ob 600 N Wolfe St Baltimore MD 21287-1201

WALLACH, ELI, actor; b. Bklyn., Dec. 7, 1915; s. Abraham and Bertha (Schorr) W.; m. Anne Jackson, Mar. 5, 1948; children: Peter Douglas, Roberta Lee, Katherine Beatrice. AB, U. Tex., 1936; MS in Edn, CCNY, 1938; student, Neighborhood Playhouse Sch. of Theatre, 1940; hon. doctorate, Emerson Coll., Boston, Sch. for Visual Arts, 1991. Corp. mem., dir. Neighborhood Playhouse Sch. Theatre. Actor, 1945—; Broadway plays include Antony and Cleopatra, 1948, Mr. Roberts, 1949-50, Rose Tatoo, 1950-52, Camino Real, 1953, Mademoiselle Colombe, 1953, Teahouse of the August Moon, 1954-55, London prodn., 1954, Twice Around the Park, 1983, Major Barbara, 1956, Rhinoceros, 1961, Luv, 1964, Promenade All, 1972, Opera Comique, Kennedy Ctr. Performing Arts, 1987, The Flowering Peach, Fla., 1987, Broadway, 1994, Cafe Crown, 1989; appeared off-Broadway prodn. Typists and the Tiger, 1962-63, London prodn., 1964, Saturday, Sunday, Monday, 1974, (with wife and 2 daus.) Diary of Anne Frank, 1977-78; appeared in: nat. tour co. Waltz of the Toreadors, 1973-74; appeared in TV film Murder By Reason of Insanity, 1985, TV series Our Family Honor, 1985, TV miniseries Christopher Columbus, 1985, Executioner's Song, 1986; motion pictures include Baby Doll, 1955, The Misfits, 1960, The Victors, 1962, Lord Jim, 1964, How To Steal a Million, The Good, the Bad and the Ugly, The Tiger Makes Out, Band of Gold, Zig-Zag, Cinderella Liberty, 1973, Crazy Joe, 1973, Movie, Movie, 1976, Sam's Son, 1985, Tough Guys, 1986, Rocket to the Moon,1986, Nuts, 1987, The Impossible Spy, 1987, Godfather III, 1990, The Two Jakes, 1990, Article 99, Mistress, 1991, Night and the City, 1991, Honey, Sweet Love, 1993, Two Much Film, 1995. Served to capt. Med. Adminstrn. Corps AUS, World War II. Recipient Donaldson, Theatre World, Variety, Antoinette Perry, Drama League awards, Brit. Film Acad. award, 1956, Disting. Alumnus award U. Tex., 1989. Original mem. Actors Studio.

WALLACH, ERIC JEAN, lawyer; b. N.Y.C., June 11, 1947; s. Milton Harold and Jacqueline (Goldschmidt) W.; m. Miriam Grunberger, Mar. 21, 1976; children: Katherine, Emily, Peter. BA, Harvard U., 1968, JD, 1972. Bar: N.Y. 1973, U.S. Dist. Ct. (so. and ea. dists.) N.Y. 1973, U.S. Dist. Ct. (no. dist.) N.Y. 1989, U.S. Ct. Appeals (2nd cir.) 1973, U.S. Tax Ct. 1976. Assoc. Webster & Sheffield, N.Y.C., 1972-77; assoc. Rosenman & Colin, N.Y.C., 1977-80, ptnr., 1981—, mem. mgmt com., 1993—. Mem. editorial bd. You and the Law, 1992—; contbr. articles to profl. jours. Sec., treas. Art Dealers Assn. Am., Inc., N.Y.C., 1985—; trustee C.G. Jung Found. for Analytical Psychology; trustee Am. Jewish World Svc., Inc., N.Y.C., 1989—, chmn., 1995—. Mem. Harvard Club N.Y.C. (admissions com. 1992-94), Sunningdale Country Club, Poughkeepsie Tennis Club. Democrat. Avocations: sports, travel, reading. Home: 20 W 64th St New York NY 10023-7129 Office: Rosenman & Colin 575 Madison Ave New York NY 10022-2511 Home: 16 Buttonwood Ln Rhinebeck NY 12572-2402

WALLACH, IRA, writer; b. N.Y.C., Jan. 22, 1913; s. Morris David and Rose (Sims) W.; m. Devera Sievers, Jan. 25, 1941; 1 dau., Leah B.S.; m. Lillian Opatoshu, June 4, 1970. Student, Cornell. Author: The Horn and the Roses, 1947, How to be Deliriously Happy, 1949, Hopalong-Freud, 1951, Hopalong-Freud Rides Again, 1950, Gutenberg's Folly, 1954, How to Pick a Wedlock, 1956, Muscle Beach, 1959, The Absence of a Cello, 1960, Horatio, 1954, Phoenix 55, 1955, (with A.S. Ginnes) Drink To Me Only, 1958; (anthology) The Courage to Grow Old, 1989; (play) Smiling, the Boy Fell Dead, 1961, The Eye of the Beholder, 1993; (screenplay) Boys' Night Out, 1962, (with George Goodman) The Wheeler-Dealers, (with Peter Ustinov) Absence of a Cello, 1964, Hot Millions (Motion Picture Acad. nomination 1968, Writers Guild of Gt. Britain Best Brit. Comedy Screenplay award, 1968), Five Thousand Years of Foreplay, 1976; (musical) Sweet Mistress, 1976. Mem. Authors Guild Am., Dramatists Guild, Writer's Guild Am. Aircraft Owners and Pilots Assn., P.E.N. Home: 345 W 58th St New York NY 10019-1145

WALLACH, IRA DAVID, lawyer, business executive; b. N.Y.C., June 3, 1909; s. Joseph and Della (Kahn) W.; m. Miriam Gottesman, Dec. 25, 1938. AB, Columbia U., 1929, JD, 1931, LLD (hon.), 1983; LLD (hon.), U. Maine, 1983. Bar: N.Y. 1932. Practiced in N.Y.C., 1932-41; exec. v.p. Gottesman & Co., Inc. (name changed to Central Nat.-Gottesman Inc. 1984), N.Y.C., 1952-56; pres., CEO Gottesman & Co., Inc. (name changed to Central Nat.-Gottesman Inc. 1984), 1956-74, chmn., CEO, 1974-79, chmn., 1979—, dir., 1947—; exec. v.p. Ctrl. Nat. Corp., N.Y.C., 1952-56, pres., CEO, 1956-74, chmn., CEO, 1974-79, chmn., 1979—, dir., 1948—; exec. v.p. Eastern Corp., Bangor, Maine, 1951-52, dir., 1947-58; dir., pres. Sejak Corp., N.Y.C., dir., exec. v.p. Cenro Corp., N.Y.C.; bd. dirs. Stora Kopparberg Sales Co., Inc., N.Y.C. Pres. D.S. and R. H. Gottesman Found., 1956—; bd. dirs., 1941—; chmn., dir. Miriam and Ira D. Wallach Found., 1956—; bd. dirs. Inst. for EastWest Studies, N.Y.C., Internat. Peace Acad., People for the Am. Way. Served to lt. USNR, 1943-46. Mem. Am. Bar Assn., assn. of Bar of City of N.Y., N.Y.C. Lawyers Assn. Home: 5 Sherbrooke Rd Scarsdale NY 10583-4429 Office: 3 Manhattanville Rd Purchase NY 10577-2110

WALLACH, JOHN PAUL, foundation administrator, author; b. N.Y.C., Jan. 18, 1943; s. Paul and Edith (Putzel) W.; m. Janet Lee Weil, June 9, 1974; children: David, Michael. BA, Middlebury Coll., 1964; MA, New Sch. for Social Research, 1966. Corr. state dept. Hearst Newspapers, Washington, 1968-74, corr. white house, 1974-76; fgn. editor, 1976-95; founding editor WE, Russian-Am. newspaper, 1992-94; founder Seeds Peace Found., 1993—; exec. dir. Elie Wiesel Found. for Humanity, N.Y.C., 1995—. Author: Still Small Voices: The Human Story Benind the Intifada, 1989, Arafat: In the Eyes of the Beholder, 1990, The New Palestinians, 1993; contbg. editor Washingtonian mag., 1984-89. Dir. Chautauqua (N.Y.) Conf.

U.S.-Soviet Rels., 1983-87; founder Seeds of Peace Found., 1993—; mem. nat. adv. bd. Am. U., Washington. Recipient Raymond Clapper award Standing Com. Corrs., 1979, Edward Weintal prize Georgetown U., 1980, Overseas Press Club award, 1980, 83; named Adj. Prof. of Yr. Am. U., 1985; recipient Edwin Hood award Nat. Press Club, 1989. Mem. Overseas Writers Club (pres. 1991-92). Office: Elie Wiesel Found Humanity 1177 Ave of Americas New York NY 10036

WALLACH, JOHN S(IDNEY), library administrator; b. Toronto, Ohio, Jan. 6, 1939; s. Arthur M. and Alice I. (Smith) W.; children: John Michael, Wendy Anne, Bethany Lynne, Kristen Michele; m. Joyce Bapst. B.S. in Edn, Kent State U., 1963; M.L.S. U. R.I., 1968; M.P.A., U. Dayton, 1977. Dir. Mercer County (Ohio) Library, 1968-70, Greene County (Ohio) Library, 1970-77; asso. dir. Dayton and Montgomery County (Ohio) Library, 1978, dir., 1979—. Bd. dirs. Dayton Mus. Natrual History, Family Svc. Assn., Dayton, Technology Resource Ctr. Served with USN, 1963-68, capt. ret. Mem. ALA, Ohio Libr. Assn. Office: Dayton & Montgomery County Pub Libr 215 E 3rd St Dayton OH 45402-2135

WALLACH, LESLIE ROTHAUS, architect; b. Pitts., Feb. 4, 1944; s. Albert and Sara F. (Rothaus) W.; m. Susan Rose Berger, June 15, 1969; 1 child, Aaron. BS in Mining Engring., U. Ariz., 1967, BArch, 1974. Registered architect, Ariz.; registered contractor, Ariz. Prin. Line and Space, Tucson, 1978—. Representative projects include Ariz. Sonora Desert Mus. Restaurant Complex, Tucson Ariz., Elgin Elem. Sch., Ariz., Hillel Student Ctr. U. Ariz., Tucson, Boyce Thompson Southwestern Arboretum Vis. Ctr., Superior, Ariz., San Pedro Riparian Ctr., Sierra Vista, Ariz.; contbr. to Sunset Mag., Architecture Mag. and Fine Homebuilding; exhibited at U. Ariz., AIA Nat. Convention, Wash., D.C. Bd. dirs Tucson Regional Plan, Inc. Recipient Roy P. Drachman Design award, 1982, 85, 93, Electric League Ariz. Design award, 1987, 88, Gov. Solar Energy award, 1989, Desert Living awards Citation, 1991, Ariz. Architect's medal, 1989. Fellow AIA (Ariz. Honor award 1989, 92, AIA/ACSA Nat. Design award 1991, Western Mountain region Design award 1992, CA AIA/Phoenix Homes and Gardens Home of the Yr. Honor award 1992); mem. SAC AIA (past pres., Design award 1988, 88, 90). Office: Line and Space 627 E Speedway Blvd Tucson AZ 85705-7433

WALLACH, MARK IRWIN, lawyer; b. Cleve., May 19, 1949; s. Ivan A. and Janice (Grossman) W.; m. Harriet Kinney, Aug. 11, 1974; children: Kerry Melissa, Philip Alexander. BA magna cum laude, Wesleyan U., 1971; JD cum laude, Harvard U., 1974. Bar: Ohio 1974, U.S. dist. ct. (no. dist.) Ohio 1974, U.S. Ct. Appeals (6th cir.) 1985, U.S. Supreme Ct. 1985. Law clk. U.S. Dist. Ct., Cleve., 1974-75; assoc. Baker & Hostetler, Cleve., 1975-79; chief trial counsel City of Cleve., 1979-81; assoc. Calfee, Halter & Griswold, Cleve., 1981-82, ptnr., 1982—; mem. fed. ct. adv. com. U.S. Dist. Ct. (no. dist.) Ohio, 1991-95. Author: Christopher Morley, 1976. Chmn. bd. trustees Ohio Group Against Smoking Pollution, 1986-90; trustee Cleve. chpt. Am. Jewish Com., 1986—, sec. 1989-91, v.p., 1991—; bd. trustees Citizens League of Greater Cleve., 1978-79, 87-92; pres. Wesleyan Alumni Club Cleve., 1983-87, 1992—; trustee Lyric Opera, Cleve., 1995—, Ratner Schs., 1994—. Mem. ABA, Ohio Bar Assn., Fed. Bar Assn., Cuyahoga County Law Dirs. Assn., Greater Cleve. Bar Assn., The Club at Soc. Ctr. Republican. Avocations: reading, space exploration, politics. Home: 23538 Duffield Rd Cleveland OH 44122-3105 Office: Calfee Halter & Griswold 800 Superior Ave E Ste 1800 Cleveland OH 44114

WALLACH, PHILIP C(HARLES), financial, public relations consultant; b. N.Y.C., Nov. 17, 1912; s. Edgar Smith and Rix Wallach; m. Magdalena Charlotta Falkenberg, Mar. 5, 1950. Student, NYU, 1930-33. Editor, writer Hearst Publs., N.Y.C., 1935-42; editor Shell Oil Co., N.Y.C., 1943-46; editor, dir. pub. relations W.R. Grace & Co., N.Y.C., 1946-54; dir. pub. relations and advt. H.K. Porter & Co., N.Y.C., 1954-58; pres. Wallach Assocs., Inc., N.Y.C., 1958-85; officer and v.p. investor rels. Occidental Petroleum Co., L.A., 1985-91; v.p. Occidental Internat. Corp., N.Y.C., 1987-91, cons., 1991-92. Pres. St. Paul Guild, N.Y.C., 1959-68, bd. dirs., 1964-72; pres. Cath. Inst. Press, N.Y.C., 1959-75; co-founder Air Force Assn., Washington, 1946; nat. committeeman Rep. Party, N.Y., 1945-60; mem. Rep. Nat. Com., Greenwich, Conn., 1982-91; bd. dirs., mem. exec. com. U.S. Pakistan Econ. Coun. With USAF, 1942-43. Mem. Overseas Press Club. Home: 126 W Lyon Farm Dr Greenwich CT 06831-4352

WALLACH, STANLEY, medical educator, consultant, administrator; b. Bklyn., Dec. 10, 1928; s. Abraham and Ida Helen (Pevin) W.; m. Pearl Small, 1973; children: Sara Lynn, Rhonda, Peter, Francine, Shellie, Allen, Corinne, Mara. AB, Cornell U., 1948; MA in Phys. Chemistry, Columbia U., 1949; MD, SUNY Downstate Med. Ctr., 1953. Diplomate Am. Bd. Internal Medicine, Am. Bd. Endocrinology and Metabolism. Intern Kings County Hosp., Bklyn., 1953-54; resident in internal medicine VA Hosp./Salt Lake Gen. Hosp., Salt Lake City, 1954-56; fellow in endocrinology and metabolism Mass. Gen. Hosp., Boston, 1956-57; attending physician Kings County Hosp., Bklyn., 1957-73, SUNY Hosp., Bklyn., 1966-73, Albany (N.Y.) Med. Ctr., 1973-83; chief of med. svc. VA Med. Ctr., Albany, 1973-83, Bay Pines, Fla., 1983-90; cons. VA Med. Ctr., Tampa, Fla., 1991-92; attending physician Tampa Gen. Hosp., 1991—, Moffitt Cancer Ctr., 1991-92; dir. med. edn. Cath. Med. Ctr., Jamaica, N.Y., 1992-93; dir. endocrinology and metabolic bone disease ctr. Hosp. for Joint Diseases, N.Y.C., 1993—; instr. in medicine SUNY Downstate Med. Ctr., 1957-58, from asst. prof. to assoc. prof., 1960-71, prof., 1971-73; prof., asst. chmn. dept. medicine Albany Med. Coll., 1973-77, prof., assoc. chmn. dept. medicine, 1977-83; prof. internal medicine Coll. Medicine U. South Fla., 1983-92, assoc. chmn. dept. internal medicine, 1988-92; exec. dir. Am. Coll. Nutrition, 1993—; career scientist Health Rsch. Coun., City of N.Y., 1967-71; program dir. USPHS Clin. Rsch. Ctr., SUNY Downstate Med. Ctr., 1966-73; rsch. collaborator Brookhaven Nat. Lab., Upton, N.Y., 1970-82; vice-chmn. Gordon Rsch. Conf. on Magnesium in Biochem. Processes and Medicine, 1987, chmn., 1990; cons. NIH, NSF, USDA, Nat. Osteoporosis Found., Nat. Arthritis Found., U.S. Pharmacopeial Conv. Mem. editorial bd. Jour. Am. Coll. of Nutrition, 1981—, Magnesium and Trace Elements, 1982—, Jour. Trace Elements in Exptl. Medicine, 1987—; reviewer Am. Jour. Medicine, Annals of Internal Medicine, Archives of Internal Medicine, Jour. Clin. Endocrinology and Metabolism, Endocrinology, Metabolism, Calcified Tissue Internat., Jour. Bone and Mineral Rsch., Proceedings of Soc. Exptl. Biology and Medicine, Jour. Nutritional Biochemistry; contbr. numerous articles to profl. jours. Capt. USNR, 1957-88. Co-recipient Hektoen Silver award AMA Conv., 1959, John B. Johnson award Paget's Disease Found., 1989. Fellow ACP (emeritus), Am. Coll. Clin. Pharmacology, Am. Coll. Nutrition (bd. dirs. 1982—, v.p. 1983-85, pres. elect 1985-87, pres. 1987-89, sec.-treas. 1991—); mem. Assn. Am. Physicians, Am. Soc. for Clin. Investigation (emeritus), Am. Fedn. Clin. Rsch. (emeritus), Am. Soc. for Magnesium Rsch., Am. Soc. Bone and Mineral Rsch., Am. Soc. for Clin. Nutrition, Am. Inst. of Nutrition, Am. Assn. Clin. Endocrinology, Endocrine Soc., Confedn. of Nutrition Socs., European Calcified Tissue Soc., Paget's Disease Found. (bd. dirs. med. adv. panel), Internat. Conf. on Calcium Regulating Hormones, Internat. Soc. Trace Element Rsch. in Humans, Nat. Orgn. Rare Disorders, Harvey Soc. (emeritus), Sigma Xi. Office: Hosp for Joint Diseases 301 E 17 St New York NY 10003

WALLACK, STANLEY S., healthcare administrator. PhD in Econs., Washington U. Educator U. Ill., Champaign; dept. asst. dir. Congl. Budget Office for Health Income Assistance, Washington; dir. divsn. health resources U.S. Office Asst. Sec. for Planning and Evaluation, HEW; dir. Inst. for Health Policy Brandeis U., Waltham, Mass., mem. faculty; chmn. bd. dirs., CEO LifePlans, Inc.; developer Social Health Maintenca Orgn.; prin. investigator Health Policy Rsch. Consirtium/HCFA; dir. Pew Doctoral Program; co-dir. Kaiser Found. Ctr. for State Svcs.; co-prin. investigator NIDA Ctr. for Drug Abuse Svcs. Rsch. Contbr. articles to profl. publs. Office: Brandeis U Bigel Inst for Health Policy 415 South St Waltham MA 02254-9110

WALLACK-ROSELLI, RINA EVELYN, lawyer; b. Pitts.; d. Erwin Norman and Gloria A. (Schacher). AD in Nursing, Delta Coll., 1973; BS cum laude in Psychology, Eastern Mich. U., 1980; JD cum laude, Wayne State U., 1983. Registered nurse Mich.; bar: Calif. 1983. Psychiat. head nurse Ypsilanti (Mich.) State Hosp., 1973-77, instr., nursing educator, 1977-80; teaching asst. contracts Wayne State U., Detroit, 1981-83; legal asst.

Wayne County Prosecutor's Office, 1982-83; atty. NLRB, L.A., 1983-86, dir. employee rels. legal svcs. Paramount Pictures Corp., L.A., 1986-89, v.p., 1989—. Contbr. articles to profl. jours. Instr. ARC, Mich., 1978-80. Recipient Am. Jurisprudence Book award, 1983. Mem. ABA, L.A. County Bar Assn., Am. Trial Lawyers Assn., Mich. Bar Assn., Calif. Bar Assn., Order of Coif. Avocations: shooting, movies, dancing, reading, photography.

WALLANCE, GREGORY J., lawyer; b. Washington, Oct. 24, 1948; s. Donald Aaron Wallance and Shula Cohen; m. Elizabeth Van Veen, Jan. 4, 1981; children: Daniel, Carina, Lisanne. BA, Grinnell Coll., 1970; JD, Bklyn. Law Sch., 1976. Bar: N.Y. 1977, U.S. Dist. Ct. (ea. dist.) N.Y. 1977, U.S. Dist. Ct. (so. dist.) N.Y. 1978, U.S. Ct. Appeals (2d cir.) 1980, U.S. Dist. Ct. (no. dist.) 1989. Clk. to Hon. Jacob Mishler N.Y.C., 1976-77; assoc. Paul, Weiss, Rifkind, Wharton & Garrison, N.Y.C., 1977-79; asst. U.S. atty., U.S. Atty's. Office, N.Y.C., 1979-85; assoc. Kaye Scholer Fierman Hays & Handler, N.Y.C., 1985-88; ptnr. Kaye, Scholer, Fierman, Hays & Handler, 1988—. Author: Papa's Game, 1981; assoc. prodr. (HBO) Sakharov, 1981; columnist Nat. Law Jour., 1993—; contbr. articles to profl. jours. Vol. VISTA, N.Y.C., 1970-72. Mem. ABA. Assn. for Bar of City of N.Y. Office: Kaye Scholer Fierman Hays & Handler 425 Park Ave New York NY 10022-3506

WALLCRAFT, MARY JANE LOUISE, religious organization executive, songwriter, author; b. Deloraine, Man., Can., Nov. 2, 1933; d. Norman Zephaniah and Mary Jane (McKinney) Sexton; m. James Orval Wallcraft, Oct. 13, 1956; children: Angela Mae, Ronald Clarke. Assoc. in piano, Royal Conservatory Toronto, Brandon, Man., 1952; AA, Victor Valley Coll., 1973. Tchr. piano Souris, Man., 1963-67; church organist St. George's Anglican, Brandon, 1960-63, St. Lukes Anglican, Souris, Man., 1963-67, Victorville (Calif.) United Meth. Ch., 1970-74; tchr. piano Hines House of Music, Victorville, 1969-72; ch. sec. Fredericksburg (Va.) United Meth. Ch., 1977-79; med. transcriptionist Mary Washington Hosp., Fredericksburg, 1985-87, Shady Grove Adventist, Rockville, Md., 1987-89; founder, pres. Make Me a Blessing Ministries, Inc., Zellwood, Fla., 1992—; hostess, narrator Make Me a Blessing Family Worship program Sta. WTLN, Apopka, Fla., 1993-94. Author: Make Me a Blessing, 1991, Sing Your Way to Victory, A Modern Day Psalter, Shadows, Symbols, and Strategies, 1994; songwriter albums Make Me a Blessing, 1992, Grandkid's Praise, 1993, A Word of Encouragement from Make Me a Blessing, 1995. Republican. Avocations: writing and compiling daily devotional book and putting the scriptures to music. Home and Office: 4162 Greenbluff Ct Zellwood FL 32798-9005

WALLEIGH, ROBERT SHULER, consultant; b. Washington, Mar. 31, 1915; s. Charles Henry and Martha (McDaniel) W.; m. Catherine Richarde Coulon, Feb. 22, 1938; children—Margaret Coulon (Mrs. Shaffer), Catherine Richarde (Mrs. Carnevale). B.S. in Elec. Engring, George Washington U., 1936. Test engr. Gen. Electric Co., 1936-38; rating examiner Civil Service Commn., 1938-39; adminstrv. asst. Pub. Roads Adminstrn., Washington, 1939-42; elec. engr. to dep. asst. dir. for adminstrn. Nat. Bur. Standards, 1943-53, assoc. dir for adminstrn., 1955-75, acting dep. dir., 1975-79, sr. adv. internat. affairs, 1978-79; asst. for adminstrn. Diamond Ordnance Fuze labs. Dept. Army, 1953-55; cons. IEEE, Washington, 1979—. Recipient Naval Ordnance Devel. award, 1945; Exceptional Service award with gold medal Dept. Commerce, 1967; Engr. Alumni Achievement award George Washington U., 1975; others. Methodist. Home: 5701 Springfield Dr Bethesda MD 20816-1237

WALLEN, VERA S., school superintendent; b. Ft. Knox, Ky., Sept. 24, 1941; d. Glen Lockwood and Mary Elizabeth (DeMoulin) Foote; m. Gary Leon Stone, Apr. 13, 1968 (div. May 1975); m. Jack Allen Wallen, Oct. 23, 1982. BA in English and History, U. Calif., Berkeley, 1963, PhD in Edn. Leadership, 1979, postgrad, 1964; MA in Ednl. Administration, Calif. State U., San Francisco, 1974. Tchr. Oakland (Calif.) Sch. Dist., 1964-69, Weston (Mass.) Pub. Schs., 1969-72; asst. dir. spl. edn. Vallejo (Calif.) Sch. Dist., 1972-75; prin. Santa Clara County Schs., Gilroy, Calif., 1975-79; supt., prin. Oak Valley Sch. Dist., Tulare, Calif., 1979-82; supt. of schs. Richland Sch. Dist., Shafter, Calif., 1982-87, Rosemead Sch. Dist., Rosemead, Calif., 1987-88; supt., prin. Cayucos (Calif.) Elem. Sch. Dist., 1988-89; supt. of schs. Coast, Cambria, Cayucos (Calif.) Sch. Dists., 1989—; bilingual instrn. researcher Richland Schs.; curriculum developer Oak Valley, Springville, Richland Sch. Dists., 1981-88, facilities builder and reconstruction, 1983-88. Active Nat. and Calif. PTA, 1964—. Mem. AAUW (career workshop coordinator), Assn. Calif. Sch. Adminstrs., Aircraft Owners and Pilots Assn., 99's, Cambria Univ. Women's, Lioness Club of Cayucos, Rotary, Phi Delta Kappa. Democrat. Avocations: traveling, reading, ballet, flying. Home: 1285 S Ocean Ave Cayucos CA 93430-1343 Office: 2950 Santa Rosa Creek Rd Cambria CA 93428-3506

WALLENBORN, JANICE RAE, elementary education educator; b. Chgo., Jan. 22, 1938; d. Ramon Joseph and Anne Joan (Seaquist) W. BEd, Beloit Coll., 1960; MEd, The George Washington U., 1966; postgrad., George Mason U., 1987-88, U. Va., 1965-85; Degree in Theol. Edn., U. of South, 1989. Cert. tchr. Va. Tchr. Quantico (Va.) Marine Base, 1960-62; elem. tchr. Pearl Harbor Elem. Sch., Honolulu, 1962-64, Quantico Dependents Sch. System, 1964—. Counselor Diet Ctr., Springfield, Va., 1979-89. Mem. NEA (life), Quantico Edn. Assn. (treas. 1968-72), Va. Edn. Assn., Pi Lambda Theta (life), Kappa Alpha Theta (treas. 1979-81, pres. North Va. chpt. 1981-85, alumni dist. pres. 1989—). Republican. Episcopalian. Avocations: sewing, crafts, cooking, yardwork, lay Eucharistic minister. Home: 8576 Gwynedd Way Springfield VA 22153-3422 Office: Quantico Dependents Sch Sys WW Burrows 3308 John Quick Rd Quantico VA 22134-1702

WALLENDER, MICHAEL TODD, lawyer; b. Schenectady, N.Y., Apr. 8, 1950; s. Kenneth Clark and Martha Lee (Getty) W.; m. Joyce Ann Mushaw, June 3, 1978; children: Kristina Lee, Michael David. BA, Colgate U., 1972; JD, Harvard U., 1975. Law assst. N.Y. State Supreme Ct. Appellate Div., Albany, 1975-76; assoc. DeGraff, Foy, Conway, Holt-Harris & Mealey, Albany, 1976-80, ptnr., 1981-90; counsel N.Y. State Assn. Realtors, Albany, 1981—, Albany County Bd. Realtors, 1985-92, Capital Regional Multiple Listing Svc., Albany, 1986—, Greater Capitol Assn. Realtors, 1992—. Author: Realtors and the Law of Agency, 1988. counsel Tercentenary Fund, Schenectady, 1978, Step 6 Citizens Against Child Sexual Abuse, Schenectady, 1985. Mem. Am. Trial Lawyers Assn., ABA, N.Y. State Bar Assn., Albany County Bar Assn., Ft. Orange Club, Mohawk Golf Club, Colgate Club (capital dist. chpt., Albany), Saratoga Reading Rm. Avocation: thoroughbred horse racing. Home: 28 Cheshire Pl Niskayuna NY 12309-4939 Office: 100 State St Ste 800 Albany NY 12207-1809

WALLENSTEIN, JAMES HARRY, lawyer; b. N.Y.C., Oct. 28, 1942; s. Ira Jerome and Jane Irene (Hoffman) W.; m. Marcia Faye Michaelson, July 9, 1967; children: Julie, Debbie. BA cum laude, Washington and Lee U., 1964; LLB cum laude, So. Meth. U., 1967. Bar: Tex. 1967, U.S. Ct. Appeals (5th cir.) 1967. Law clk. to justice U.S. Ct. Appeals (5th cir.), Dallas, 1967-68; assoc. Johnson, Bromberg & Leeds, Dallas, 1970-73; pvt. practice law Dallas, 1973-78; ptnr. Wallenstein & St. Claire, Dallas, 1978-81, Jenkens & Gilchrist, Dallas, 1981-88, Jenkens & Gilchrist, P.C., Dallas, 1988—; adj. prof. So. Meth. U. Law Sch., 1978-91; lectr. numerous orgns. including U. Tex., So. Meth. U. Law Sch., State Bar Tex., N.W. Ctr. for Profl. Edn., 1974—. Editor in chief S.W. Law Jour., 1966-67; contbr. articles to profl. jours. Capt. U.S. Army, 1969-70, Vietnam. Mem. ABA (vice chmn. opinion letter com. real property, probate and trust law sect. 1985-89), Tex. Bar Assn. (lectr., coun. sect. on real estate, probate and trust law 1976-84, 86-89, chair sect. 1988-89, chair opinion letter com. 1983—, chair subcom. legal fees paid by title cos. 1985-89, editor newsletter 1981-84), Dallas Bar Assn. (lectr., chair real property sect. 1980-81), Am. Coll. Real Estate Lawyers (lectr.), Dallas Area Real Estate Lawyers' Discussion Group (founder, chair 1976—), Order of Coif, Barristers. Democrat. Jewish. Avocations: reading, swimming. Office: Jenkens & Gilchrist PC Ste 3200 1445 Ross Ave Dallas TX 75202-2799

WALLENTINE, MARY KATHRYN, secondary educator; b. Moscow, Idaho, Dec. 27, 1943; d. Elwood Vernon and Mary Berenice (Hillard) White; m. William Edward Wallentine, Dec. 29, 1977; 1 child, Nicki. BA, Whitman Coll., 1966. Tchr. math. and art Mt. Rainier High Sch., Des Moines, Wash., 1966-85; pres. Highline Edn. Assn., Seattle, 1985-88; tchr. math., dept. head

Tyee High Sch., SeaTac, Wash., 1988—; tchr. leadership cadre Highline Sch. Dist., 1988-92, co-chair dist. site-based decision making com., 1989-92. Precinct committeeperson Dem. Cen. Com., King County, Wash., 1980-92, state committeewoman, 1982-88, del. nat. conv., 1980. Mem. NEA (PULSE dir. 1992—, resolutions com. 1987-92, nat. del. 1980-92), Nat. Coun. Tchrs. Math. (speaker), Wash. Edn. Assn., Highline Edn. Assn. (pres. 1986-89). Episcopalian. Avocations: gardening, politics, visual arts, community service. Home: 860 100th Ave NE # 34 Bellevue WA 98004

WALLER, AARON BRET, III, museum director; b. Liberal, Kans., Dec. 7, 1935; s. Aaron Bret and Juanita M. (Slawson) W.; m. Mary Lou Dooley, Sept. 3, 1959; children: Bret, Mary Elizabeth. BFA, Kansas City Art Inst., 1957; MFA, U. Kans., 1958, postgrad., 1964-67; postgrad. (Fulbright grantee), U. Oslo, 1963-64. Grad. asst. U. Kans., 1957-58; dir. The Citadel Mus., Mil. Coll. S.C., 1957-58, Mus. Art, U. Kans., 1964-71; dept. head public edn. and higher edn. Met. Mus. Art, N.Y.C., 1971-73; dir. Museum Art, U. Mich., Ann Arbor, 1973-80, Meml. Art Gallery, U. Rochester, N.Y., 1980-85; adj. assoc. prof. fine arts dept. Meml. Art Gallery, U. Rochester, 1980-85; assoc. dir. for edn. and pub. affairs J. Paul Getty Mus., Malibu, Calif., 1985-90; dir Indpls. Mus. Art, 1990—; assoc. prof. U. Mich., 1973-80; coordinator museum studies program Inst. Fine Arts, NYU, 1971-73; tchr. City Coll. N.Y., 1971-73. Mem. Assn. Art Mus. Dirs. (treas. 1980-81, trustee 1992-94), Intermuseum Conservation Assn. (pres. 1977-78), Am. Assn. Museums (nat. com. on mus. tng 1976-78, counselor-at-large 1986-89, treas. standing com. on edn. 1990-92), Coll. Art Assn. Office: Indpls Mus Art 1200 W 38th St Indianapolis IN 46208-4196

WALLER, BURTON WOODROW, JR., health care executive; b. Jackson, Tenn., Nov. 30, 1949; s. Burton Woodrow and Jeanne Elizabeth (Russell) W.; m. Sandra Desbien, Mar. 22, 1970; children—Craig, Catherine. B.S. cum laude, U. Tenn., 1971; M.H.A., Washington U., St. Louis, 1974. Asst. adminstr. Methodist Hosp. Dallas, 1975-78, v.p., 1978-82, sr. v.p., adminstr., 1982-85; v.p., gen. mgr. Cigna Healthplan of Tex., 1985—; dir. Dallas-Ft. Worth Hosp. Council. Mem. Am. Coll. Hosp. Adminstrs. (chmn. Dallas chpt. 1984—), Tex. Hosp. Assn. Democrat. Baptist. Office: Regional Med Ctr Memphis 877 Jefferson Ave Memphis TN 38103

WALLER, FRANK S., engineering company executive; b. 1937. With Woodward-Clyde Group Inc., Denver, 1962—, chmn. bd. dirs. Office: Woodward-Clyde Group Inc 4582 S Ulster St Ste 600 Denver CO 80237-2635*

WALLER, GARY FREDRIC, English language educator, poet; b. Auckland, N.Z., Jan. 3, 1944; came to U.S., 1983; s. Fred and Joan Elsie (Smythe) W.; m. Jennifer Robyn Denham, July 2, 1966 (div. 1980); children: Michael, Andrew; m. Kathleen Ann McCormick, Nov. 12, 1988; one child, Philip. BA, U. Auckland, 1965, MA, 1966; PhD, Cambridge U., Eng., 1970. Prof. English and interdisciplinary studies, dean arts and scis. U. Hartford, Conn. Author: The Strong Necessity of Time, 1976, The Triumph of Death, 1977, Pamphilia to Amphilanthus, 1977, Dreaming America, 1979, Mary Sidney Countess of Pembroke, 1979, Sir Philip Sidney and the Interpretation of Renaissance Culture, 1984, Sixteenth Century Poetry, 1986, 2d edit., 1993, Reading Texts, 1986, Lexington Introduction to Literature, 1987, Shakespeare's Comedies, 1991, Reading Mary Wroth, 1991, The Sidney Family Romance, 1993, Edmund Spenser: A Literary Life, 1994; (poems) Other Flights, Always, 1991, Impossible Futures Indelible Pasts, 1983.

WALLER, GEORGE MACGREGOR, historian, educator; b. Detroit, June 7, 1919; s. George and Marguerite (Rowl) W.; m. Martha Huntington Stifler, Oct. 16, 1943; children: Susan, Marguerite, Elizabeth, Donald, Richard. Grad., Deerfield Acad., 1937; AB, Amherst Coll., 1941; MA, Columbia U., 1947, PhD, 1953. Comml. rep. Detroit Edison Co., 1941-42; lectr. Hunter Coll., 1946-47; instr. Amherst Coll., 1948-52; chief Am. history research center Wis. Hist. Soc., 1952-54; prof., head dept. history and polit. sci. Butler U., Indpls., 1954-84, McGregor prof. history, 1987-89, McGregor prof. history emeritus, 1989—; Fulbright sr. scholar U. Southampton, Eng., 1961-62; vis. prof. U. Ill., 1967-69. Author: Samuel Vetch. Colonial Enterpriser, 1960, The American Revolution in the West, 1976; Editor: Puritanism in Early America, 1950, rev. 1973, Pearl Harbor, Roosevelt and the Coming War, 1953, 65, 3d edit., 1976; contbr. to: Ency. Southern History, World Book Ency., Dictionary of Canadian Biography, Vol. I. Mem. Ind. Am. Revolution Bicentennial Commn., 1971-82. Served to lt. comdr. USNR, 1943-46. Recipient Holcomb award, 1960, Daus. of Founders and Patriots of Am. award, 1977, Disting. Hoosier award, 1989, Sugarmore of the Wabash award, 1990. Mem. Orgn. Am. Historians, Ind. Acad.Social Scis. (pres. 1983), English Speaking Union, Ind. Mus. Soc. (past pres.), Internat. Platform Assn., Phi Beta Kappa (past pres. Ind. chtp.), Phi Kappa Phi, Phi Alpha Theta. Home: 740 Broad Ave S Naples FL 33940-7330

WALLER, HAROLD MYRON, political science educator; b. Detroit, Oct. 12, 1940; s. Allan L. and Lillian R. (LeVine) W.; m. Diane Carol Goodman, June 28, 1966; children: Sharon, Dahvi, Jeffrey. SB, MIT, 1962; MS, Northwestern U., 1966; PhD, Georgetown U., 1968. Asst. prof. McGill U., Montreal, 1967-71, assoc. prof., 1971-93, prof., 1993—, chmn. polit. sci. dept., 1969-74, 89-90, acting chmn., 1980-81, 86-87, assoc. dean (acad.) faculty arts, 1991-94, acting dean faculty arts, 1994—; pres. McGill Assn. Univ. Tchrs., Montreal, 1978-79; fellow Jerusalem Ctr. Pub. Affairs, 1980—; dir. Can. Ctr. Jewish Community Studies, Montreal, 1980—. Co-author: Maintaining Consensus: The Canadian Jewish Polity in the Postwar World, 1990; co-editor: Canadian Federalism: From Crisis to Constitution; contbg. editor: Middle East Focus; mem. editorial bd. Jewish Political Studies, Patterns of Prejudice; chmn. editorial bd. Viewpoints; contbr. numerous articles to profl. jours. and books in field. Com. chmn. Can. Jewish Congress, Montreal, 1971-74; chair, nat. exec. Can. Profs. for Peace in Middle East, Toronto, 1975-85; pres. Akiva Sch., Montreal, 1984-85; com. chmn. Jewish Edn. Council, Montreal, 1986-88. Recipient Nat. Jewish Book award Jewish Book Coun., N.Y.C., 1991; Grad. fellowship NSF, Washington, 1965-66; leave fellowship Social Sci. Humanities Rsch. Council, Ottawa, 1981-82. Mem. Am. Polit. Sci. Assn., Can. Polit. Sci. Assn., Assn. Jewish Studies, Assn. Sociol. Study of Jewry, Assn. Israel Studies, Sigma Xi, Pi Sigma Alpha. Jewish. Club: MIT Hillel (Cambridge, Mass.) (pres. 1961-62). Avocations: travel, athletics, reading, politics. Office: McGill U Dept Polit Sci, 855 Sherbrooke St W, Montreal, PQ Canada H3A 2T7

WALLER, JOEL N., consumer products executive; b. 1939. Pvt. practice L.A., 1963-75; with Bermans Leather Experts, Mpls., 1975-83; with Wilsons House of Suede, Mpls., 1983—, officer, 1983—, pres., 1984—. Served U.S. Army, 1962-63. Office: Rosedale Wilsons Inc 400 Highway 169 S Ste 600 Minneapolis MN 55426-1114

WALLER, JOHN LOUIS, anesthesiology educator; b. Loma Linda, Calif., Dec. 1, 1944; s. Louis Clinton and Sue (Bruce) W.; m. Jo Lynn Marie Haas, Aug. 4, 1968; children: Kristina, Karla, David. BA, So. Coll., Collegedale, Tenn., 1967; MD, Loma Linda U., 1971. Diplomate Am. Bd. Anesthesiology. Intern Hartford (Conn.) Hosp., 1971-72; resident in anesthesiology Harvard U. Med. Sch.-Mass. Gen. Hosp., Boston, 1972-74, fellow, 1974-75; asst. prof. anesthesiology Emory U. Sch. Medicine, Atlanta, 1977-80, assoc. prof., 1980-86, prof., chmn. dept., 1986-94; svc. chief anesthesiology Emory Univ. Hosp., Atlanta, 1986-94, med. dir., 1993—; cons. Arrow Internat., Inc., Reading, Pa., 1988—; bd. dirs. Clifton Casualty Co., Colo.; mem. adv. com. on anesthetic and life support drugs FDA, Washington, 1986-92; numerous vis. professorships and lectures. Contbr. articles to med. jours. Maj. M.C., USAF, 1975-77. Recipient cert. of appreciation Office Sec. Def., 1983. Fellow Am. Coll. Anesthesiologists, Am. Coll. Chest Physicians; mem. AMA, Am. Soc. Anesthesiologists, Soc. Cardiovascular Anesthesiologists (pres. 1991-93), Internat. Anesthesia Rsch. Soc. (trustee 1984—, sec. 1993—), Assn. Univ. Anesthetists, Soc. Acad. Anesthesia Chairmen (councillor 1990—), Assn. Cardiac Anesthesiologists. Avocations: tennis, sailing, swimming. Office: Emory U Hosp Dept Anes 1364 Clifton Rd NE Atlanta GA 30322-1102

WALLER, JOHN OSCAR, English language educator; b. L.A., Oct. 29, 1916; s. David Oscar and Susan Veva (Williams) W.; m. Elaine Louise Johnson, Jan. 6, 1946. B.A., San Diego State Coll., 1941; M.A., U. So. Calif., 1949; Ph.D., 1954. Instr. San Diego State Coll., 1946-48; dir. publs. Oxnard (Calif.) Union High Sch., 1951-52; mem. faculty Walla Walla Coll.,

College Place, Wash., 1952-60; prof. English Andrews U., Berrien Springs, Mich., 1960-88, chmn. dept., 1963-79. Author: A Circle of Friends: The Tennysons and the Lushingtons of Park House; author articles on lit. history; mem. editorial bd.: Abstracts of English Studies, 1967-80, contbr., 1988—. Served with USNR, 1941-45. Mem. Seventh Day Adventist Ch. Home: 8886 George Ave Berrien Springs MI 49103-1406

WALLER, PATRICIA FOSSUM, transportation executive, researcher, psychologist; b. Winnipeg, Man., Can., Oct. 12, 1932; d. Magnus Samuel and Diana Isabel (Briggs) Fossum; m. Marcus Bishop Waller, Feb. 27, 1957; children: Anna Estelle, Justin Magnus, Martha Wilkinson, Benjamin Earl. AB in Psychology cum laude, U. Miami, Coral Gables, 1953, MS in Psychology, 1955; PhD in Psychology, U. N.C., 1959. Lic. psychologist, N.C. Psychology intern VA Hosp., Salem, Va., 1956; psychology instr. Med. Sch. U. N.C., Chapel Hill, 1957; USPHS postdoctoral fellow R.B. Jackson Lab., Bar Harbor, Maine, 1958-60; psychologist VA Hosp., Brockton, Mass., 1961-62; psychology lectr. U. N.C., Chapel Hill, Greensboro, 1962-67; assoc. dir. driver studies Hwy. Safety Rsch. Ctr. U. N.C., Chapel Hill, 1967-89, dir. Injury Prevention Rsch. Ctr., 1987-89; dir. Transp. Rsch. Inst. U. Mich., Ann Arbor, 1989—; bd. dirs. Intelligent Transp. Soc. Am., Washington, 1991—, Traffic Safety Assn. Mich., Lansing, 1991—; bd. advisors Eno Transp. Found., Inc., Landsdowne, Va., 1994—; chair group 5 coun. Transp. Rsch. Bd. of NRC, Washington, 1992-95, chmn. Task Force Operator Regulations, 1974-76, mem. study com. devel. ranking rail safety R&D projects, 1980-82, chmn. group 3 coun. operation, safety and maintenance transp. facilities, 1980-83, mem. IVHS-IDEA tech. rev. panel, 1993—, chair workshop human factors rsch. in hwy. safety, 1992, chair ad hoc com. environ. activies, 1992, mem. task force on elderly drivers, 1990-93, mem. com. vehicle user characteristics, 1983-86, mem. com. planning and adminstrn. of transp. safety, 1986-92, mem. com. alcohol, other drugs and transp., 1986—; numerous other coms., mem. spl. coms. including Inst. Medicine Dana Award com., 1986-90, com. of 55MPH nat. maximum speed limit, 1983-84; mem. motor vehicle safety rsch. adv. com. Dept. Transp., Washington, 1991—; reviewer JAMA, Jour. Studies on Alcohol, Jour. of Gerontology, Am. Jour. Pub. Health; apptd. Pres. Coun. Spinal Cord Injury, 1981; apptd. advisor Nat. Hwy. Safety Adv. Com. to Sec. U.S. Dept. Transp., 1979-80, 80-83; author numerous reports on transp. to govtl. coms. and univs. Author: (with Paul G. Shinkman) Instructor's Manual for Mogan and King: Introduction to Psychology, 1971; author: (with others) Psychological Concepts in the Classroom, 1974, Drinking: Alcohol in American Society—Issues and Current Research, 1978, The American Handbook of Alcoholism, 1982, The Role of the Civil Engineer in Highway Safety, 1983, Aging and Public Health, 1985, Young Driver Accidents: In Search of Solutions, 1985, Alcohol, Accidents and Injuries, 1986, Transportation in an Aging Society: Improving the Mobility and Safety for Older Persons, 1988, Young Drivers Impaired by Alcohol and Drugs, 1988; mem. editorial bd. Jour. Safety Rsch., 1979—; assoc. guest editor Health Edn. Quar., 1989; assoc. editor Accident, Analysis, and Prevention, 1978-84, mem. editorial bd., 1976-87; contbr. articles to profl. jours. Grantee HHS, 1992, NIH. Mem. AAAS, APA (Harold M. Hildreth award 1993), APHA (injury control and emergency health svcs. sect., Disting. Career award 1994, transp. rsch. bd., Roy W. Crum award for rsch. contbns. 1995), Assn. for the Advancement of Automotive Medicine (chmn. human factors sect. 1978-80, bd. dirs. 1979-82, pres. 1981-82), Coun. Univ. Transp. Ctrs. (exec. com. 1991—), Transp. Rsch. Bd., Ea. Psychol. Assn., Sigma Xi. Democrat. Avocations: gardening, reading. Office: U Mich Transp Rsch Inst 2901 Baxter Rd Ann Arbor MI 48109-2150

WALLER, ROBERT JAMES, writer; b. Aug. 1, 1939; s. Robert Sr. and Ruth W.; m. Georgia Ann Wiedemeier; 1 child, Rachel. Student, U. Iowa, 1957-58, U. No. Iowa, 1958; PhD, Ind. U., 1968. Prof. mgmt. U. No. Iowa, Cedar Falls, 1968-91, dean bus. sch., 1979-85. Author: Just Beyond the Firelight: Stories & Essays, 1988, One Good Road is Enough: Essays, 1990, The Bridges of Madison County, 1992, Slow Waltz in Cedar Bend, 1993, Old Songs in a New Cafe: Selected Essays, 1994, Border Music, 1995; recorded album The Ballads of Madison County, 1993. Recipient Literary Lion award New York Public Library, 1993. Office: care Aaron Priest Literary Agy 708 3rd Ave 23rd Fl New York NY 10017*

WALLER, ROBERT REX, ophthalmologist, educator, foundation executive; b. N.Y.C., Feb. 19, 1937; s. Madison Rex and Sally Elizabeth (Pearce) W.; m. Sarah Elizabeth Pickens, Dec. 27, 1963; children: Elizabeth, Katherine, Robert Jr. BA, Duke U., 1958; MD, U. Tenn., 1963. Diplomate Am. Bd. Ophthalmology (dir. 1982—, vice chmn. 1988-89, chmn. 1989—). Intern City of Memphis Hosps., 1963-64; resident internal medicine Mayo Grad. Sch. Medicine, Rochester, Minn., 1966-67, resident in ophthalmology, 1967-70, mem. faculty, 1970—; assoc. prof. ophthalmology Mayo Clinic, Rochester, Minn., 1974-78, prof., 1978—; chmn. dept. ophthalmology Mayo Med. Sch., Rochester, Minn., 1974-84, cons., 1970—, mem. bd. govs., 1978-93, chmn., 1988-93; trustee Mayo Found., Rochester, 1978—, pres., chief exec. officer, 1988—. Contbr. chpts. to books, articles to profl. jours. Elder 1st Presbyn. Ch., Rochester, 1975-78; mem. Rochester Task Force on Pub. Assembly Facilities, 1983-84. Sr. asst. surgeon USPHS, 1964-66. Oculastic surgery fellow U. Calif. San Francisco, 1973. Mem. AMA, Minn. State Med. Assn., Zumbro Valley Med. Assn., Am. Acad. Ophthalmology, Am. Ophthalmol. Soc., Am. Soc. Plastic and Reconstructive Surgery, Orbital Soc., Am. Soc. Ophthalmic Plastic and Reconstructive Surgery, Minn. Acad. Ophthalmology and Otolaryngology, Rochester Golf and Country Club, Augusta Nat. Golf Club, Alpha Omega Alpha, Delta Tau Delta. Presbyterian. Avocations: golf, travel, photography, dogs. Home: 800 12th Ave SW Rochester MN 55902-2071

WALLER, STEPHEN, air transportation executive; b. 1949. Student, New Zealand U., 1970-74. Courier, country mgr., european mktg. mgr. DHL Airways, Inc., London, 1975-80, Tehran, Iran, 1975-80; sr. v.p. DHL Airways, Inc. Redwood City, Calif., 1981—. Office: DHL Airways Inc 333 Twin Dolphin Dr Redwood City CA 94065

WALLER, WILHELMINE KIRBY (MRS. THOMAS MERCER WALLER), civic worker, organization official; b. N.Y.C., Jan. 19, 1914; d. Gustavus Town and Wilhelmine (Claflin) Kirby; m. Thomas Mercer Waller, Apr. 7, 1942. Ed., Chapin Sch., N.Y.C. Conservation chmn. Garden Club Am., 1959-61, pres., 1965-68, chmn. nat. affairs, 1968-74, dir., 1969-71; mem. adv. com. N.Y. State Conservation Commn., 1959-70; mem. Nat. Adv. Com. Hwy. Beautification, 1965-68; trustee Mianus River Gorge Conservation Com. of Nature Conservancy, 1955—; Arthur W. Butler Meml. Sanctuary, 1955-79; dir. Westchester County Soil and Water Conservation Dist., 1967-74; adviser N.Y. Gov.'s Study Commn. Future of Adirondacks, 1968-70; adv. com. N.Y. State Parks and Recreation Commn., 1971-72; adv. com. to sec. state UN Conf. Human Environment, 1971-72; mem. Pres.'s Citizens Adv. Com. on Environ. Quality, 1974-78. Mem. planning bd., Bedford, 1953-57; mem. Conservation adv. coun., Bedford, N.Y., 1968-70, Westchester County Planning Bd., 1970-88; bd. govs. Nature Conservancy, 1970-78; Mem. Lyndhurst council Nat. Trust for Historic Preservation, 1965-74; bd. dirs. Scenic Hudson, Inc., 1985-88. Recipient Frances K. Hutchinson medal Garden Club Am., 1971, Holiday mag. award for beautiful Am., 1971, Conservation award Am. Motors Corp., 1975, Oak Leaf award Nature Conservancy, 1988. Mem. Nat. Soc. Colonial Dames, Huguenot Soc. Am., Daus. of Cincinnati. Address: Tanrackin Farm Bedford Hills NY 10507

WALLERICH, PETER KENNETH, banker; b. Tacoma, Mar. 4, 1931; s. Clarence W. and Ellen (Hansen) W.; m. Marylu Ann Oakland, July 9, 1954; children—Karen, Kristen, Karla, Kaari. B.A.A., U. Wash., 1953. Investment officer N.Pacific Bank, Tacoma, 1956-59, exec. v.p., 1959-71, chmn. bd., 1971-73, pres., 1973—; gen. mgr. Soutn Tacoma Motor Co., 1959-68, pres., 1968-71; dir. North Pacific Bank, Western Div. Co., Mountain View Devel. Co. Pres. Design for Progress, 1970-71; bd. dirs Goodwill Industries, Wash. Research Council; trustee, treas. U. Puget Sound; chmn. bd. trustees Mary Bridge Children's Hosp; trustee Lakewood Gen. Hosp.; bd. visitors Sch. Law U. Puget Soun; gen. chmn. Tacoma Pierce County United Way, 1981. Mem. Wash. Bankers Assn. (dir., treas.), Am. Bankers Assn. (nat. exec. planning com.), C. of C. (dir.), Mensa, Beta Gamma Sigma (chpt. award 1980). Home: 12111 Gravelly Lake Dr SW Tacoma WA 98499-1415 Office: N Pacific Bank 5448 S Tacoma Way Tacoma WA 98409-4398

WALLERSTEIN, GEORGE, astronomy educator; b. N.Y.C., Jan. 13, 1930; s. Leo and Dorothy (Calman) W. B.A., Brown U., 1951; M.S., Calif. Inst. Tech., 1954, Ph.D., 1958. Research asso. Calif. Inst. Tech., Pasadena, 1957-58; instr. U. Calif., Berkeley, 1958-60; asst. prof. U. Calif., 1960-64, asso. prof., 1964-65; prof., chmn. astronomy U. Wash., Seattle, 1965-80; prof. astronomy U. Wash., 1980—. Trustee Brown U., Providence, 1975-80. Served with U.S. Navy, 1951-53. Mem. Am. Astron. Soc., Astron. Soc. Pacific, AAAS, Arctic Inst. N. Am. Home: 2309 NE 77th St Seattle WA 98115 Office: U Wash Astronomy Seattle WA 98195 *It is not sufficient "to follow knowledge like a sinking star, beyond the utmost bounds of human thought." One must endeavor to create knowledge, and beyond that to create understanding.*

WALLERSTEIN, LEIBERT BENET, economist; b. Bklyn., July 5, 1922; s. William Mark and Ray Leah (Goldberg) W.; m. Alice Stehle, Oct. 10, 1929; stepchildren: Nora Odendahl, Steven Odendahl. BA in Econs., U. N.Mex., 1950; MA in Econs., U. Minn., 1951; PhD in Econs., Social Scis., Columbia Pacific U., 1988. With U.S. Corps of Engrs. and Army Air Corps Matl. Command, Washington, 1943-46; Merchant Marine; with AUS, 1944-47, U.S. Navy Bur. ORD, 1954-55, U.S. Dept. Labor, 1956-67, HUD, 1967-69, U.S. DOT, 1961-80; with U.S. Merchant Marine Acad., Kings Point, 1977; faculty U. Minn., U. Md., U. N. Mex., Pentagon, Georgetown U., Ben Franklin U., Montgomery Coll., La Salle U., Momtgomery County Adult Edn. Ctr.; cons. economist, 1980—; v.p. Reano Co., L.A. Contbr. articles to profl. jours. Vol. Shepard's Table, Washington, 1985—, Jewish Community Ctr. D.C. Area, Chevy Chase (Md.) grade schs., 1986, polit. pres. campaigns, 1980, 84, 92; v.p. Univ. Young Dems., U. N.Mex., Albuquerque, 1947-50, NAACP, 1947-50. Mem. Atlantic Econ. Soc., Am. Econ. Assn., Economists Club Washington (charter), Soc. Govt. Economists, Sr. Club (chmn. 1983), Disabled Am. Vets., Am. Legion. Jewish. Avocations: fishing, hiking, reading, swimming, fgn. travel. Home and Office: 3505 Thornapple St Chevy Chase MD 20815-4014

WALLERSTEIN, MITCHEL BRUCE, government official; b. N.Y.C., Mar. 8, 1949; s. Melvin Julian and Rita Helen (Nomburg) W.; m. Susan Elyse Perlik, June 29, 1974; children: Matthew, Leah. AB, Dartmouth Coll., 1971; MPA, Syracuse U., 1972; MS, MIT, 1977, PhD, 1978. Assoc. dir. Internat. Food Policy Program MIT, Cambridge, Mass., 1978-83, lectr. dept. polit. sci., 1978-83; asst. prof. dept. polit. sci. Holy Cross Coll., Worcester, Mass., 1979-81; assoc. exec. dir. Office Internat. Affairs NAS, Washington, 1983-89, dep. exec. officer, 1989-93; dep. asst. sec. for counterproliferation policy U.S. Dept. Def., Washington, 1993—; adj. prof. Sch. Advanced Internat. Studies, Johns Hopkins U., Washington, 1992—; adj. prof. Sch. Fgn. Svc., Georgetown U., Washington, 1989—. Author: Food for War - Food for Peace: The Politics of U.S. Food Aid, 1979; author, dir. reports in field including multiple NAS reports on tech. transfer and nat. security. Mem. Internat. Inst. Strategic Studies, Coun. Fgn. Rels. Democrat. Avocations: backpacking, skiing, classical music, house restoration, reading. Office: US Dept Def Rm 1E 443 The Pentagon Washington DC 20301-2600

WALLERSTEIN, RALPH OLIVER, physician; b. Dusseldorf, Germany, Mar. 7, 1922; came to U.S., 1938, naturalized, 1944; s. Otto R. and Ilse (Hollander) W.; m. Betty Ane Christensen, June 21, 1952; children: Ralph Jr., Richard, Ann. A.B., U. Calif., Berkeley, 1943; M.D., U. Calif., San Francisco, 1945. Diplomate: Am. Bd. Internal Medicine. Intern San Francisco Hosp., 1945-46, resident, 1948-49; resident U. Calif. Hosp., San Francisco, 1949-50; research fellow Thorndike Meml. Lab., Boston City Hosp., 1950-52; chief clin. hematology San Francisco Gen. Hosp., 1953-87; faculty U. Calif., San Francisco, 1952—; clin. prof. medicine U. Calif., 1969—. Served to capt. M.C. AUS, 1946-48. Mem. AMA, ACP (gov. 1977-87, chmn. bd. govs. 1980-81, regent 1981-87, pres. 1988-89), Am. Soc. Hematology (pres. 1978), San Francisco Med. Soc., Am. Clin. and Climatol. Assn., Am. Fedn. Clin. Rsch., Am. Soc. Internal Medicine, Am. Bd. Internal Medicine (bd. govs. 1975-83, chmn. 1982-83), Am. Assn. Blood Banks, Inst. Medicine, Calif. Acad. Medicine, Internat. Soc. Hematology, Western Soc. Clin. Rsch., Western Assn. Physicians, Gold Headed Cane Soc. Republican. Home: 3447 Clay St San Francisco CA 94118-2008 Office: 3838 California St Rm 707 San Francisco CA 94118-1509

WALLERSTEIN, ROBERT SOLOMON, psychiatrist; b. Berlin, Jan. 28, 1921; s. Lazar and Sarah (Guensberg) W.; m. Judith Hannah Saretsky, Jan. 26, 1947; children—Michael Jonathan, Nina Beth, Amy Lisa. B.A., Columbia, 1941, M.D., 1944; postgrad., Topeka Inst. Psychoanalysis, 1951-58. Assoc. dir., then dir. rsch. Menninger Found., Topeka, 1954-66; chief psychiatry Mt. Zion Hosp., San Francisco, 1966-78; tng. and supervising analyst San Francisco Psychoanalytic Inst., 1966—; clin. prof. U. Calif. Sch. Medicine, Langley-Porter Neuropsychiat. Inst., 1967-75, prof., chmn. dept. psychiatry, also dir. inst., 1975-85, prof. dept. psychiatry, 1985-91, prof. emeritus, 1991—; vis. prof. psychiatry La. State U. Sch. Medicine, also New Orleans Psychoanalytic Inst., 1972-73, Pahlavi U., Shiraz, Iran, 1977, Fed. U. Rio Grande do Sul, Porto Alegre, Brasil, 1980; mem., chmn. rsch. scientist career devel. com. NIMH, 1966-70; fellow Ctr. Advanced Study Behavioral Scis., Stanford, Calif., 1964-65, 81-82, Rockefeller Found. Study Ctr., Bellagio, Italy, 1992. Author 14 books and monographs; mem. editl. bd. 19 profl. jours; contbr. over 200 articles to profl. jours. Served with AUS, 1946-48. Recipient Heinz Hartmann award N.Y. Psychoanalytic Inst., 1968, Disting. Alumnus award Menninger Sch. Psychiatry, 1972, J. Elliott Royer award U. Calif., San Francisco, 1973, Outstanding Achievement award No. Calif. Psychiat. Soc., 1987, Mt. Airy gold medal, 1990, Mary Singleton Sigourney award, 1991. Fellow ACP, Am. Psychiat. Assn., Am. Orthopsychiat. Assn.; mem. Am. Psychoanlytic Assn. (pres. 1971-72), Internat. Psychoanalytic Assn. (v.p. 1977-85, pres. 1985-89), Group for Advancement Psychiatry, Brit. Psycho-Analytical Soc. (hon.), Phi Beta Kappa, Alpha Omega Alpha. Home: 290 Beach Rd Belvedere Tiburon CA 94920-2472 Office: 655 Redwood Hwy Ste 261 Mill Valley CA 94941-3011

WALLEY, BYRON See CARD, ORSON SCOTT

WALLFESH, HENRY MAURICE, business communications company executive, editor, writer; b. N.Y.C., June 15, 1937; s. David Shibe and Rose (Silk) W.; m. Suzanne Krakowitch, Dec. 26, 1960; children: Saundra Kay, Gerald Bruce. Grad. indsl. and labor rels., Cornell U., 1958. Editor, co-pub. Indsl. Rels. News, N.Y.C. and Stamford, Conn., 1960-67; pres., chief exec. officer RAI div. Hearst Bus. Communications, N.Y.C., 1968-91, sr. v.p., editor at large, 1991—; pres. Whale Communications, Inc., Stamford, Conn., 1992—; pres. Indsl. Rels. Inst., Stamford, 1964-67; founder, bd. dirs. Internat. Soc. Pre-Retirement Planners, 1975-88; bd. dirs. VSOP Mktg., Boston. Author: Implications of the Age Discrimination in Employment, 1977, When a CEO Retires, 1978. Bd. dirs. Aging in Am., N.Y.C. 1985-90, N.Y.C. Anti-Defamation League, 1987-89. Capt. inf. USAR, 1958-67. Recipient Corp. Achievement award Nat. Assn. for Sr. Living Industries, 1990; inducted into Internat. Soc. Pre-Retirement Planners Hall of Fame, 1988. Mem. Roxbury Swim and Tennis Club (bd. dirs. 1975-78), Cornell Club. Jewish. Avocations: tennis, theatre, writing. Home and Office: 1616 Long Ridge Rd Stamford CT 06903

WALLIN, FRANKLIN WHITTELSEY, educational consultant, former college president; b. Grand Rapids, Mich., Jan. 22, 1925; s. Franklin Whittelsey and Agnes (Sarles) W.; m. Florence Gilbert Evans, Feb. 21, 1948; children: Susan Q. (Mrs. Ray Michael Hively), Thomas E., Elizabeth M. (Mme. Henri Sirot), Franklin B. B.S., U. Wis., 1948; M.A., U. Calif. at Berkeley, 1950, Ph.D., 1953; DHL (hon.), Haverford Coll., 1983, Earlham Coll., 1987. Trustee in to assoc. prof. history Wayne State U., 1953-68, asst. to pres., 1958-60; provost, dean faculty Colgate U., 1968-73, acting pres., 1969; pres. Inst. for World Order (now World Policy Inst.), 1973-74, bd. dirs., 1972-90; pres. Earlham Coll., Richmond, Ind., 1974-83; resident scholar Inter-Univ. Centre, Dubrovnik, Yugoslavia, 1983-84; pres. Asheville (N.C.) Art Mus., 1993—; planning cons. Franklin Coll., Lugano, Switzerland, 1985; co-dir. Nat. Commn. Global Edn., 1986-87; vis. prof. Earlham Coll., 1987; prof. Coll. for Srs., adj. prof. dept. humanities U. N.C., Asheville. Bd. dirs. Friends Sch., Detroit, 1962-68, chmn., 1962-64, 67-68; bd. dirs. Global Perspectives in Edn. (now Am. Forum), 1976—; Joyce Mertz-Gilmore Found., 1982—, Asheville Art Mus., 1992—, Community Arts Coun., Asheville, 1990—. With USN, 1942-46. Mem. Am. Coun. on Edn. (dir. 1978-81), Nat. Assn. Ind. Colls. and Univs. (dir. 1981-83). Home:

1 Lady Slipper Weaverville NC 28787 Office: Asheville Art Mus 2 S Pack Sq Asheville NC 28801

WALLIN, JACK ROBB, research plant pathology educator; b. Omaha, Nov. 21, 1915; s. Carl O.A. (Wallin) and Elizabeth Josephine (Smith) W.; m. Janet Mary Melhus, Sept. 25, 1937; children: Jack I.M., Robb M. B.S., Iowa State U., 1939, Ph.D., 1944. Rsch. asst. prof. Iowa State U., Ames, 1944-47; rsch. prof., rsch. plant pathologist Agr. Rsch. Svc. USDA/Iowa State U., 1947-75; prof. plant pathology, researcher Agrl. Rsch. Svc. USDA/ U. Mo., Columbia, 1975-87; ret., 1986; disaster assistance employee region 7 Fed. Emergency Mgmt. Agy., Kansas City, 1989—; U.S. rep. World Meteorol. Orgn., Geneva, 1959-61; mem. aeriobiology com. Nat. Acad. Sci., NRC, Washington, 1976-80. Patentee (in field). Recipient 1st Peterson award Internat. Soc. Biometeorology, 1966. Mem. Internat. Assn. Aerobiology, Am. Phytopathol. Soc. (sec. treas. N. Central div. 1964-65), Internat. Soc. Plant Pathology, Nat. Acad. Sci. (chmn. agrl. div. 1976-81). Republican. Presbyterian. Lodge: Rotary. Home: 4036 Fletcher Blvd Ames IA 50010 *My genetic constitution must be basically responsible for those talents and abilities that have been expressed in any success that I have attained. Along with reasonable intelligence, I have been endowed with determination, tenacity and loyalty in the desire to achieve set goals. A sense of humor has enabled me to survive mistakes and failures. An agricultural scientist father-in-law inspired me to make a useful contribution to mankind. A supportive wife provided encouragement along the way.*

WALLIN, WINSTON ROGER, manufacturing company executive; b. Mpls., Mar. 6, 1926; s. Carl A. and Theresa (Hegge) W.; m. Maxine Houghton, Sept. 10, 1949; children: Rebecca, Brooks, Lance, Bradford. BBA, U. Minn., 1948. With Pillsbury Co., Mpls., 1948-85, v.p. commodity ops., 1971-76, exec. v.p., 1976, pres., chief oper. officer, 1977-84, vice chmn. bd., 1984-85; with Medtronic, Inc., Mpls., 1985-91, chmn. bd., CEO, chmn. bd., 1991—; bd. dirs. Bemis Co., McGlynn Bakeries, Super Valu, Cargill, Inc. Chmn. bd. trustees Carleton Coll.; bd. overseers U. Minn. Bus. Sch. With USN, 1944-46. Mem. Mpls. Club (bd. govs.), Minikahda Club, Interlachen Club. Home: 7022 Tupa Cir Minneapolis MN 55439-1640 Office: Medtronic Inc 7000 Central Ave NE Minneapolis MN 55432-3576

WALLING, CHEVES THOMSON, chemistry educator; b. Evanston, Ill., Feb. 28, 1916; s. Willoughby George and Frederika Christina (Haskell) W.; m. Jane Ann Wilson, Sept. 17, 1940; children—Hazel, Rosalind, Cheves, Janie, Barbara. A.B., Harvard, 1937; P.h.D., U. Chgo., 1939. Rsch. chemist E.I. duPont de Nemours, 1939-43, U.S Rubber Co., 1943-49; tech. aide Office Sci. Research, Washington, 1945; sr. rsch. assoc. Lever Bros. Co., 1949-52; prof. chemistry Columbia U., N.Y.C., 1952-69; Disting. prof. chemistry U. Utah, Salt Lake City, 1970-91, prof. chemistry emeritus, 1991—. Author: Free Radicals in Solution, 1957; also numerous articles. Fellow AAAS; mem. Nat. Acad. Scis., Am. Acad. Arts and Scis., Am. Chem. Soc. (editor jour. 1975-81, James Flack Norris award 1970, Lubrizol award 1984). Home: PO Box 537 Jaffrey NH 03452-0537

WALLINGFORD, JOHN RUFUS, lawyer; b. Artesia, N.Y., Apr. 6, 1940; s. Joseph Keevil and Ellen (Williams) W.; m. Katharine Tapers, July 22, 1966; children: Halley Martha, John Beckett. BA, U. of the South, 1962; LLB, So. Meth. U., 1965. Bar: Tex. 1965. Sr. ptnr. Fulbright & Jaworski, Houston, 1967-93; sr. v.p., gen. counsel Browning Ferris Industries, Houston, 1994—. Bd. dirs. St. Luke's Episcopal Hosp., Houston, 1986—; The Children's Mus., Houston, 1994—. Fellow Am. Coll. Trial Lawyers; mem. Internat. Soc. of Barristers, Am. Bd. Trial Advocates. Office: Browning Ferris Industries 757 N Eldridge Houston TX 77079

WALLIS, CARLTON LAMAR, librarian; b. Blue Springs, Miss., Oct. 15, 1915; s. William Ralph and Tellie (Jones) W.; m. Mary Elizabeth Cooper, Feb. 22, 1944; 1 child, Carlton Lamar. B.A. with spl. distinction, Miss. Coll., 1936; M.A., Tulane U., 1946; B.L.S., U. Chgo., 1947; L.H.D., Rhodes Coll., Memphis, 1980. English tchr., coach Miss. Pub. Schs., 1936-41; teaching fellow Miss. Coll. and Tulane U., 1941-42; chief librarian Rosenberg Library, Galveston, Tex., 1947-55; city librarian Richmond, Va., 1955-58; dir. Memphis Pub. Library, 1958-80, ret., 1980. Author: Libraries in the Golden Triangle, 1966; contbr. articles to library jours. Trustee Belhaven Coll., 1978-82, Nat. Ornamental Metal Mus., 1989—. Served as chief warrant officer AUS, 1942-46. Decorated Bronze Star. Mem. ALA (chmn. library mgmt. sect. 1969-71), Pub. Library Assn. (dir. 1973-77), Tex. Library Assn. (pres. 1952-53), Va. Library Assn., Southwestern Library Assn. (exec. bd. 1950-55), Southeastern Library Assn. (chmn. pub. library sect. 1960-62), Tenn. Library Assn. (pres. 1969-70, Distinguished Service award 1979). Presbyterian (elder). Club: Egyptian (pres. 1973-74). Home: 365 Kenilworth Pl Memphis TN 38112-5405

WALLIS, DIANA LYNN, artistic director; b. Windsor, Eng., Dec. 11, 1946; d. Dennis Blackwell and Joan Williamson (Gatcombe) W. Grad., Royal Ballet Sch., Eng., 1962-65. Dancer Royal Ballet Touring Co., London, 1965-68; ballet mistress Royal Ballet Sch., London, 1969-81, dep. ballet prin., 1981-84; artistic coord. Nat. Ballet of Can., Toronto, 1984-86, assoc. artistic dir., 1986-87, co-artistic dir., 1987-89; free-lance prod., tchr. London; dep. artistic dir. English Nat. Ballet, London, 1990-94; artistic dir. Royal Acad. Dancing, 1994—. Fellow Imperial Soc. Tchrs. Dancing. Home: 41 Musard Rd, London W68NR, England

WALLIS, DONALD WILLS, lawyer; b. Wilkes-Barre, Pa., Aug. 22, 1950; s. Donald and Hazel (Jansen) W.; m. Kathryn Macon Waggoner, Aug. 28, 1971; children: Neill Jansen, Kathryn Spencer. AB, Duke U., 1971, JD, 1974. Bar: Fla. 1974, U.S. Tax Ct. 1975, U.S. Dist. Ct. (mid. dist.) Fla. 1977, U.S. Ct. Appeals (5th cir.) 1978, U.S. Claims Ct. 1978, U.S. Supreme Ct. 1979. Assoc. Mahoney, Hadlow, Chambers & Adams, Jacksonville, Fla., 1974-78; mem. firm Fisher, Tousey & Wallis, P.A., Jacksonville, Fla., 1978-89; ptnr. Holland & Knight, Jacksonville, Fla., 1989—. Co-author: (book) Bank Holding Companies: A Practical Guide to Bank Acquisitions and Mergers, 1978; tax notes editor: (book) The Forida Probate System, 1977; contbg. editor: Journal of Partnership Taxation, 1989—. Chmn. Duke U. Alumni Admissions Adv. Com., Jacksonville, 1986—; chmn. Beaches Fine Arts Series, Inc., Jacksonville Beach, Fla., 1990—. Mem. ABA (taxation sect.), Fla. Bar (tax sect., bd. cert. tax atty.), Jacksonville Bar Assn. (tax sect.), Duke U. Alumni assn. (admissions com 1986—), Selva Marina Country Club, Inc. (bd. govs. 1987-89). Episcopalian. Avocations: Jacksonville symphony chorus, sailing, scuba diving, backpacking, cycling. Office: Holland & Knight 50 N Laura St Ste 3900 Jacksonville FL 32202-3622

WALLIS, GRAHAM BLAIR, engineer, educator; b. Rugby, Warwickshire, Eng., Apr. 1, 1936; came to U.S., 1957; s. Alfred Stanley and Dora (Fleming) W.; m. Suzanne Harriet White, Sept. 12, 1959; children: Iain, Tasha, Peter, Jeremy. B.A., Cambridge U., Eng., 1957; Ph.D., Cambrige U., Eng., 1961; M.S., MIT, 1959. Registered profl. engr., N.H. Asst. prof. Dartmouth Coll., Hanover, N.H., 1962-65, assoc. prof., 1966-72, prof., 1972—, assoc. dean, 1989-93; prof. engring. Sherman Fairchild, 1991—; interim dean engring., 1994—; cons. Creare Inc., Hanover, 1964—. Author: One-Dimensional Two-Phase Flow, 1959. Recipient Inst. Mech. Engring. Ludwig Mond prize, 1962. Mem. ASME (Moody award 1971, Centennial award and medal 1980, Fluids Engring. award 1994). Home: Blood Rd Norwich VT 05055 Office: Dartmouth Coll Thayer Sch Engring Hanover NH 03755

WALLIS, JOHN JAMES (JIMMY WALLIS), entertainer, ventriloquist, video production executive; b. Searcy, Ark., Mar. 21, 1939; s. Prentiss Bascom and Maxine (James) W.; children: Lori Diana Wallis Waterman, Shauna Kathleen. Grad., Okla. U., 1960. advisor Am. Acad. for Entertainment at U.S. Vets. Hosps., N.Y.C., 1988—. Nat. TV debut Art Linkletter's Hollywood Talent Scouts, 1966; entertained troops in S.E. Asia, 1967-70; performed with Ann Murray, Lou Rawls, Lola Falana, Ben Vereen, Al Hirt, Debbie Reynolds, Rip Taylor, Suzanne Somers, others; performed in numerous clubs including Tropicana, Las Vegas, The Sahara, Las Vegas, The Flamingo, Las Vegas, Chauteau Champlain, Montreal, The Cave, Vancouver, The Paradise Island Casino, The Bahamas, The Superstar Theater, Atlantic City, Riviera, Las Vegas, Harrah's, Reno, The Reno Hilton, Las Vegas Hilton, Flamingo Hilton; featured in Royal Carribean Cruise Lines, Premier's Disney Theme Cruises, Norwegian Cruise Lines, Holland America and Celebrity Cruise Lines. Named Okla.'s Top Comedian, Okla. Ho. of

Reps.; recipient Am. Legion medal. Mem. Nat. Park and Conservation Assn., Planetary Soc., Smithsonian. Presbyterian. Avocations: photography, scuba diving, computers, tennis, target shooting. Office: PO Box 276100 Boca Raton FL 33427-6100

WALLIS, RICHARD FISHER, physicist, educator; b. Washington, May 14, 1924; s. William F. and Alberta (Sigelen) W.; m. Mary Camilla Williams, Aug. 20, 1955; children: Maria Fisher, Sylvia Camilla. BS, George Washington U., 1945, MS, 1948; PhD, Cath. U. Am., 1952. Postdoctoral fellow (U. Md.), College Park, 1951-53; chemist Applied Physics Lab. Johns Hopkins U., Silver Spring, Md., 1953-56; physicist Naval Rsch. Lab., Washington, 1956-66, 67-69, head semiconductors br., 1958-66, 67-69; prof. physics U. Calif., Irvine, 1966-67, 69—; prof. emeritus, 1993—; chmn. dept. physics U. Calif., Irvine, 1972-75, 80-83; cons. Gen. Motors, Naval Rsch. Lab.; vis. prof. U. Paris, 1975-76, 79, 85. Author: (with Maradudin and Dobrzynski) Handbook of Surfaces and Interfaces, 1980, (with Balkanski) Many-Body Aspects of Solid State Spectroscopy, 1986; editor: Lattice Dynamics, 1965, Localized Excitations in Solids, 1968 (with Stegeman) Electromagnetic Surface Excitations, 1986, (with Birman and Sebenne) Elementary Excitations in Solids, 1992; contbr. articles to profl. jours. Served with U.S. Army, 1945-46. Recipient Pure Sci. award Naval Rsch. Lab., 1964, Disting. Alumni Achievement award George Washington U., 1991. Fellow Am. Phys. Soc., AAAS; mem. Philos. Soc. Washington, Phi Beta Kappa, Sigma Xi. Home: 2635 Alta Vista Dr Newport Beach CA 92660-4102 Office: U Calif Dept Physics Irvine CA 92717

WALLIS, RICHARD JAMES, lawyer; b. Hagerstown, Md., June 24, 1954; s. O. Lee and Teresa Marie (Rigley) W.; m. Cheri Wallis; children: Rory Evan, Rebecca Erin. BA magna cum laude, Duquesne U., 1976; JD magna cum laude, U. Pitts., 1979. Bar: Wash. 1979, U.S. Dist. Ct. (we. dist.) Wash. 1979, U.S. Ct. Appeals (9th cir.) 1982, U.S. Supreme Ct. 1985. Assoc. Bogle & Gates, Seattle, 1979-86, ptnr., 1987—. Author: (with others) Antitrust Counselling and Litigation Techniques, 1984; editor Washington Antitrust Law Developments, 1985 and Washington Antitrust Law Developments, 2d edit. 1988. Mem. Fed. Bar Assn. (pres. 1990-91), Wash. State Bar ASsn. (exec. com. 1987—, chmn. antitrust sect. 1989-90). Democrat. Roman Catholic. Clubs: Tyee (Knight Inlet, B.C.), Columbia Tower (Seattle), Washington Athletic. Avocations: hiking, climbing, fishing. Office: Bogle & Gates Two Union Sq 601 Union St Seattle WA 98101-2322

WALLIS, ROBERT RAY, psychologist, entrepreneur; b. Hardwood, Okla., Sept. 1, 1927; s. Walter William and Osie Oma (Luckett) W.; m. Joan Elaine Martino, Sept. 10, 1955; children: Rosalie, Glenn, Damon, Gina, Darren. Student, Southwestern Inst. Tech., 1945; B.A., U. Okla., 1951, Ed.M., 1960, Ph.D., 1963. Lic. psychologist, Pa., N.J. From psychology intern to dir. div. psychology Greater Kansas City Mental Health Found., 1962-71; from fellow to chief psychologist Western Mo. Mental Health Center, Kansas City, 1965-71; from program dir. to exec. dir. Horizon House Inc., Phila., 1971-79; chief exec. officer Ancora Psychiat. Hosp., Hammonton, N.J., 1979-81; individual practice clin. and cons. psychology, Medford, N.J., 1981—; propr. Wallis Printing Ctr., Phila., 1984-91; clin. supr. Alcoholism and Psychotherapy Assocs., Cranbury, N.J., 1985-89; from asst. prof. to chmn. div. psychology dept. psychiatry, U. Mo., Kansas City Sch. Medicine, 1965-71. Contbr. articles to profl. jours. Served with USNR, 1945-46. Mem. Am. Psychol. Assn. Home and Office: 32 School House Dr Medford NJ 08055-9209 *Treat each person with respect and dignity, without regard to rank or power.*

WALLIS, W(ILSON) ALLEN, economist, educator, statistician; b. Phila., Nov. 5, 1912; s. Wilson Dallam and Grace Steele (Allen) W.; m. Anne Armstrong, Oct. 5, 1935; children: Nancy Wallis Ingling, Virginia Wallis Cates. AB, U. Minn., 1932, postgrad., 1932-33; postgrad. fellow, U. Chgo., 1933-35, Columbia U., 1935-36; DSc, Hobart and William Smith Colls., 1973; LLD, Roberts Wesleyan Coll., 1973, U. Rochester, 1984; LHD, Grove City Coll., 1975; D of Social Scis., Francisco Marroquin U., Guatemala, 1992. Economist Nat. Resources Com., 1935-37; instr. econs. Yale U., 1937-38; asst. to assoc. prof. econs. Stanford U., 1938-46; Carnegie rsch. assoc. Nat. Bur. Econ. Rsch., 1939-40, 41; dir. war rsch. Statis. Rsch. Group Columbia U., 1942-46; prof. stats. and econs. U. Chgo., 1946-62, chmn. dept. stats., 1949-57, dean Grad. Sch. Bus., 1956-62; pres. (title later chancellor) U. Rochester, N.Y., 1962-82; under sec. for econ. affairs U.S. Dept. State, Washington, 1982-89; resident scholar Am. Enterprise Inst., Washington, 1989—; staff Ford Found., 1953-54; fellow Ctr. for Advanced Study in Behavioral Scis., 1956-57. mem. math. div. NRC, 1958-60; bd. dir. Nat. Bur. Econ. Rsch., 1953-74; spl. asst. Pres. Eisenhower, 1959-61; pres. Nat. Commn. Study of Nursing and Nursing Edn., 1967-70; chmn. Commn. Presdl. Scholars, 1969-78; mem. Pres.'s Commn. on All-Vol. Armed Force, 1969-70; chmn. Pres.'s Commn. Fed. Stats., 1970-71; mem. Nat. Coun. Ednl. Rsch., 1973-75; chmn. Adv. Coun. Social Security, 1974-75; bd. dirs. Corp. Pub. Broadcasting, 1975-78, chmn., 1977-78. Author: (with others) Consumer Expenditures in the United States, 1939, A Significance Test for Time Series and Other Ordered Observations, 1941, Sequential Analysis of Statistical Data: Applications, 1945, Techniques of Statistical Analysis, 1947, Sampling Inspection, 1948, Acceptance Sampling, 1950, Statistics: A New Approach, 1956, The Nature of Statistics, 1962, Welfare Programs: An Economic Appraisal, 1968; An Overgoverned Society, 1976; co-compiler: The Ethics of Competition and Other Essays by Frank H. Knight, 1935; chmn. editorial adv. bd.: Internat. Ency. Social Scis., 1960-68; contbr. articles to profl. jours. Trustee Tax Found., 1961-82, chmn. bd., 1972-75, chmn. exec. com., 1975-78; bd. overseers Hoover Instn. War, Revolution and Peace, 1972-78; trustee Eisenhower Coll., 1969-79, Nat. Opinion Rsch. Ctr., 1957-62, 64-68, Com. Econ. Devel., 1965-71, Colgate Rochester Div. Sch., 1963-82, Ctr. Govtl. Rsch., Inc., 1962-82, Internat. Mus. Photography at George Eastman House, 1963-82, Robert A. Taft Inst. Govt., 1973-77, Ethics and Pub. Policy Ctr., 1980-82, 89—; mem. Com. on the Present Danger, 1980-82, 1989—; chmn. bd. overseers Ctr. Naval Analyses, 1967-82. Recipient Sec.'s Disting. Svc. award Dept. of State, Washington, 1988. Fellow Am. Stat. Assn. (pres. 1965, Wilks medal 1980), Am. Acad. Arts and Scis.; mem. Am. Econ. Assn. (exec. com. 1962-64), Rochester C. of C. (trustee 1963-68, 70-75), Mont Pelerin Soc. (treas. 1949-54), Washington Inst. Fgn. Affairs, Cosmos Club (Washington), Bohemian Club (San Francisco), Phi Beta Kappa, Chi Phi, Beta Gamma Sigma. Office: Am Enterprise Inst 1150 17th St NW Washington DC 20036-4603

WALLISON, FRIEDA K., lawyer; b. N.Y.C., Jan. 15, 1943; d. Ruvin H. and Edith (Landes) Koslow; m. Peter J. Wallison, Nov. 24, 1966; children: Ethan S., Jeremy L., Rebecca K. AB, Smith Coll., 1963; LLB, Harvard U., 1966. Bar: N.Y. 1967, DC 1982. Assoc. Carter, Ledyard & Milburn, N.Y.C., 1966-75; spl. counsel, div. market regulation Securities & Exchange Commn., Washington, 1975; exec. dir., gen. counsel Mcpl. Securities Rulemaking Bd., Washington, 1975-78; ptnr. Rogers & Wells, N.Y.C. and Washington, 1978-83; ptnr. Jones, Day, Reavis & Pogue, N.Y.C., and Washington, 1983—; mem. Govtl. Acctg. Standards Adv. Council, Washington, 1984-90, Nat. Council on Pub. Works Improvement, Washington, 1985-88; mem. environ. fin. adv. bd. EPA. Fellow Am. Bar Found. (vice chair 1988-93); mem. Nat. Assn. Bond Lawyers, N.Y.C. Bar Assn. Contbr. articles to profl. jours. Office: Jones Day Reavis & Pogue Ste 600 1450 G St NW Washington DC 20005-2088

WALLMAN, GEORGE, hospital and food services administrator; b. N.Y.C., Apr. 10, 1917; s. Joseph and Celia (Kascawal) W.; m. Benita B. Kaufman, June 11, 1941. Student public schs., N.Y.C. Dir. food and banquet services Normandy Hotel, Hollywood, Calif., 1945-47; dir. food services Med. Center, N.Y.C., 1947-64; menucologist and cons. to hosps., 1964-67; dir. food services Montefiore Hosp., Pitts., 1967—; cons. public schs., homes and hosps. for aged, 1947—, cons. new food products various cos., 1967—; mem. Cancer Rehab. Project, U. Pitts., 1973—; lectr. on food to various profl. orgns., 1947—. Lectr.: program Exercise is Not Enough, Sta. NBC-TV, 1976; narrator, CBS Evening News; show Hosp. Gourmet, 1974; Contbg. editor, feature writer: Today's Chef, 1978—. Mem. Nat. Restaurant Assn., Pitts. Restaurant Assn., Am. Fedn. Musicians. Home: 1420 Centre Ave Pittsburgh PA 15219-3517 Office: Montefiore Hosp Fifth Ave Pittsburgh PA 15213 *My goals are to continue to maintain the ultimate in high level quality food service enhanced with the very best of culinary skill. Ten years ago I wrote an article in a national food trade magazine titled 'The*

Great Captive Audience in White'. I stated that hospitals should serve a beautiful orchestrated food tray to romanticize the pleasure of fine food, rather than the usual adequate meal that is merely nutritionally sufficient. It would mean so much to the patients. Let each dinner be serendipity, each dinner a dining event not just eating.

WALLMAN, STEVEN MARK HARTE, lawyer; b. N.Y.C., Nov. 14, 1953; s. Eugene and Doris (Lee) W.; m. Kathleen M. Harte, May 5, 1985. BS, MIT, 1975, MS, 1976; postgrad., Harvard U. 1976-77; JD, Columbia U. 1978. Bar: D.C. 1978, Va. 1986. Assoc. Covington & Burling, Washington, 1978-86, ptnr., 1986-94; commr. SEC, Washington, 1994—. Home: 9332 Ramey Ln Great Falls VA 22066-2025 Office: SEC 450 Fifth St NW Washington DC 20549

WALLOT, JEAN-PIERRE, archivist, historian; b. Valleyfield, Que., Can., May 22, 1935; s. Albert and Adrienne (Thibodeau) W.; m. Denyse Caron; children: Normand, Robert, Sylvie. B.A., Coll. Valleyfield, 1954; lic. es lettres, U. Montreal, 1957, M.A. in History, 1957, Ph.D. in History, 1965; D (hon.), U. Rennes, France, 1987. Reporter Le Progres de Valleyfield, 1954-61; lectr. U. Montreal, 1961-65, asst. prof., 1965-66, prof. dept. history, 1973-85, chmn. dept., 1973-75, vice dean studies faculty arts and scis., 1975-78, vice dean research Faculty Arts and Scis, 1979-82, academic v.p., 1982-85; nat. archivist, Can., 1985—; historian Nat. Mus. Man, Ottawa, Ont., 1966-69, assoc. prof. U. Toronto, 1969-71; prof. Concordia U., Montreal, Que., 1971-73; dir. Etude Associé Ecole Pratique des Hautes Etudes en Sciences Sociales, Paris, 1975, 79, 81, 83, 85, 87, 89, 94. Author: Intrigues françaises et americaines au Canada, 1965, (with John Hare) Les Imprimés dans le Bas-Canada, 1967, Confrontations, 1971, (with G. Paquet) Patronage et Pouvoir dans le Bas-Canada, 1973, Un Quebec qui bougeait, 1973; Editor: (with R. Girard) Memoires de J.E. McComber, bourgeois de Montréal, 1981; (with J. Goy) Evolution et eclatement du monde rural, 1986. Decorated officer Order Arts et Lettres (France), 1987; officer Order of Can., 1991; recipient Marie Tremaine medal, 1973, Tyrrell medal, 1982, Royal Soc. Centenary medal, 1994. Fellow Royal Soc. Can. (sect. pres. 1985-87); mem. Am. Antiquarian Soc., Acad. des Lettres du Quebec, Inst. d'Histoire l'Amerique Francaise (pres. 1973-77), Can. Hist. Assn. (pres. 1982), Assn. Can.-Francaise l'Avancement Scis. (pres. 1981-83), Assn. Archivists Que., Assn. Can. Archivists, Internat. Coun. on Archives (v.p. 1988-92, pres. 1992—). Roman Catholic. Office: Nat Archives, 395 Wellington St, Ottawa, ON Canada K1A 0N3

WALLRAFF, BARBARA JEAN, magazine editor, writer; b. Tucson, Mar. 1, 1953; d. Charles Frederick and Evelyn Pauline (Bartels) W.; m. Julian Hart Fisher, Apr. 25, 1992. BA in Polit. Sci. and Philosophy, Antioch Coll., 1972. Sect. editor Boston Phoenix, 1979-83; assoc. editor The Atlantic Monthly, Boston, 1983-89, sr. editor, 1989—; freelance writer 1978—. Columnist Word Court, 1995—. Office: Atlantic Monthly 745 Boylston St Boston MA 02116-2636

WALLS, CARL EDWARD, JR., communications company official; b. Magnolia, Ark., Sept. 9, 1948; s. Carl E. and Melba Rene (Garrard) W.; m. Doris Duhart, Aug. 1, 1970; children: Carl Edward, Forrest Allen. Student San Antonio Coll. 1966-68. Div. mgr. Sears Roebuck & Co., San Antonio, 1967-73, area sales mgr., 1973-78; service cons. Southwestern Bell, 1978-79, account exec., 1979-82; account exec., industry cons. AT&T Info. Systems, 1983-88, account mgr., 1988-89; gen. mgr. Tex. State Govt., 1989—. Mem. citizens advisory com. Tex. Senate, 1975-81; legis. aide Tex. Ho. of Reps., 1981-85; commr. Alamo Area council Boy Scouts Am., 1979-79, Capitol Area council, 1980—, nat. jamboree staff, 1973, 77, 81, 85, 89, 93; mem. Republican Nat. Com., 1980—, Rep. Presdl. Task Force, 1980—, Rep. Senatorial Club, 1981—. Recipient Patriotic Service award U.S. Treasury Dept., 1975-76; Scouters Key and Commrs. award Boy Scout Am., Dist. Merit award Boy Scouts Am., 1978. Mem. Scouting Collectors Assn. (pres. South Central region 1979-80, v.p. region 1980-81, sec. 1983-86), U. Ark. Alumni Assn. (life), Am. Legion. Baptist. Home: 11712 D K Ranch Rd Austin TX 78759-3770 Office: 1624 Headway Ct Austin TX 78754

WALLS, CARMAGE, newspaper publisher; b. Crisp County, Ga., Oct. 28, 1908; s. Benjamin Gaff and Anna (Byrd) W.; m. Odessa Dobbs (div.); children: Carmage Lee, Ronald Eugene (dec.), Mark Thomas (dec.), Dinah Jean Gareich; m. Martha Ann Williams, Jan. 2, 1954; children: Byrd Cooper, Lissa Walls Vahldiek. Ed. pub. schs., Fla. Bus. mgr. Orlando (Fla.) Newspaper, Inc., 1934-40; pub. Macon (Ga.) Telegraph News, 1940-47; pres. Gen. Newspapers, Inc., Gadsden, Ala., 1945-59, So. Newspapers, Inc., Montgomery, Ala., 1951-69; also dir.; pub. Montgomery (Ala.) Advt.-Jour., 1963-69; chmn. bd., dir. Galveston Newspapers, Inc., Tex.; owner Walls Investment Co., Houston.; bd. dirs. Tex. City Newspapers, Inc. Pres. Macon Area Devel. Commn., 1943-44, Macon C. of C., 1945; trustee Birmingham-So. Coll., 1971-7. Mem. So. Newspaper Pubs. Assn., Soc. Profl. Journalists, The Houstonian. Episcopalian. Home: 623 Shartle Cir Houston TX 77024-5521 Office: 1050 Wilcrest Dr Houston TX 77042-1608

WALLS, JOHN WILLIAM, association executive; b. Knightstown, Ind., Mar. 25, 1927; s. Otto and Ruth (Miller) W.; m. Phyllis Hardin, June 20, 1948; children—Ann, Kathryn, Elizabeth, Timothy. B.A., Ind. U., 1949; M.P.A., Wayne State U., 1955. Various positions with assns. and state and local govt., 1949-62; dep. planning dir. City Planning Dept., Pitts., 1962-65; exec. dir. Greater Indpls. Progress Com., 1965-68; sr. dep. mayor City of Indpls., 1968-73, v.p. govt. and community affairs Mchts. Nat. Bank, Indpls., 1973-78; pres. Ind. State C. of C., Indpls., 1978-93; mem. Ind. Job Tng. Coordinating Council, Indpls., 1983; chmn. Council of State Chambers of Commerce, Washington, 1984-86. Served as sgt. USAAF, 1944-46. Recipient Good Govt. award Indpls. Jaycees, 1970, Brotherhood award NCCJ, 1972, Disting. Alumni award, Ind. U., 1986. Republican. Mem. Soc. Friends. Clubs: Meridian Hills Country, Columbia (Indpls.). Home: 5465 Far Hill Rd Indianapolis IN 46226-1537 Office: Ind State C of C 1 N Capitol Ave Ste 200 Indianapolis IN 46204-2248 *Personal philosophy: There are no absolutes. When in doubt, go ahead.*

WALLS, MARTHA ANN WILLIAMS (MRS. B. CARMAGE WALLS), newspaper executive; b. Gadsden, Ala., Apr. 21, 1927; d. Aubrey Joseph and Inez (Cooper) Williams; m. B. Carmage Walls, Jan. 2, 1954; children: Byrd Cooper, Lissa Walls Vahldiek. Student pub. schs., Gadsden. Pres., dir. Walls Newspapers, Inc., 1969-70; sec., treas., dir. Summer Camps, Inc., Guntersville, Ala., 1954-93; CEO, pres., dir. So. Newspapers, Inc., Houston, 1970—; v.p., dir. Scottsboro (Ala.) Newspapers, Angleton (Tex.) Times, Ft. Payne (Ala.) Newspapers, Inc., sec.-treas., dir. Portales (N.M.) News Tribune Publ. Co., Quay County Sun Newspaper, Inc., Tucumcari, N.M.; v.p., dir. Bay City (Tex.) Newspapers, Inc.; bd. dirs. Liberal (Kans.) Newspapers, Inc., Monroe (Ga.) Newspapers, Inc., Moore Newspapers, Inc., Dumas, Tex., Jefferson Pilot Corp., Greensboro, N.C., Jefferson-Pilot Life Ins. Co., Jefferson Pilot Communications. Bd. dirs. Montgomery Acad., 1970-74. Mem. Soc. Profl. Journalists, The Houstonian. Episcopalian. Office: So Newspapers Inc 1050 Wilcrest Dr Houston TX 77042-1608

WALLS, WILLIAM WALTON, JR., helicopter company executive; b. Phila., Oct. 3, 1932; s. William Walton and Mary Crown (Elliott) W.; m. Nina Catherine deAngeli, July 1, 1961; 1 child, Deborah. BSME, Swarthmore Coll., 1959. With Boeing Helicopters, Phila., 1959—, v.p. light helicopter joint venture, 1989-91, v.p. devel. programs, 1991-92, v.p. rsch. and engring., 1992—; cons. in field. Chmn. Pa. State Aerospace adv. Coun. State Coll., 1974-79; advisor NATO Indsl. Advisors Group, 1988—; mem., bd. advisors Rotorcraft Ctr. Excellence, Rensselaer Polytech. Inst., 1982-84. Mem. Am. Helicopter Soc. (pres. 1988-89, chmn. 1989-90). Republican. Avocations: skiing, racquetball, jogging. Home: 502 Harrison St Ridley Park PA 19078-3208 Office: Boeing Helicopter PO Box 16858 Philadelphia PA 19142-0858

WALLWORK, WILLIAM WILSON, III, leasing company executive; b. Fargo, N.D., Mar. 8, 1961; s. William Wilson Jr.; m. Shannon Brodshaug, July 12, 1991. AA in Automotive Mktg., Northwood Inst., 1981; student, San Diego State U., Moorhead State U. Lease rep. Wallwork Lease and Rental, 1984-86; sales mgr. W.W. Wallwork, Inc., Fargo, N.D., 1986-87, v.p., 1987-91, pres., 1991—; v.p. Valley Imports Inc, Fargo, N.D., 1986-91; pres. Valley Imports Inc., Fargo, N.D., 1991—. Mem. Fargo-Moorhead

Automobile Dealers Assn. (v.p. 1986-88, pres. 1988-90). Avocation: skiing. Office: W W Wallwork Inc 4001 Main Ave Fargo ND 58107-1819

WALMER, EDWIN FITCH, lawyer; b. Chgo., Mar. 24, 1930; s. Hillard Wentz and Anna C. (Fitch) W.; m. Florence Poling, June 17, 1952; children: Linda Diane Walmer Dennis, Fred Fitch. BS with distinction, Ind. U., 1952, JD with high distinction, 1957. Bar: Wis. 1957, U.S. Dist. Ct. (ea. dist.) Wis. 1957. Assoc. Foley & Lardner, Milw., 1957-65, ptnr., 1965-90, ret., 1990. Served to 1st lt. U.S. Army, 1952-54. Recipient Cal. C. Chambers award Culver (Ind.) Mil. Acad., 1948. Fellow Am. Coll. Trust and Estate Counsel; mem. Order of Coif, Tripoli Golf Club (Milw.), Dairymen's Country Club (Boulder Junction, Wis.), Vineyards Country Club (Naples, Fla.), Phi Eta Sigma, Beta Gamma Sigma. Republican. Congregationalist. Avocations: golf, fishing. Office: Foley & Lardner 777 E Wisconsin Ave Milwaukee WI 53202-5367

WALMSLEY, ARTHUR EDWARD, bishop; b. New Bedford, Mass., May 4, 1928; s. Harry Barlow and Elizabeth Doris (Clegg) W.; m. Roberta Brownell Chapin, Dec. 29, 1954; children: Elizabeth Trent, John Barlow. B.A., Trinity Coll., Hartford, Conn., 1948; D.D. (hon.), Trinity Coll., 1982; M.Div., Episcopal Theol. Sch., Cambridge, Mass., 1951; Hum.D. (hon.), New Eng. Sch. Law, Boston, 1970; D.D. (hon.), Berkeley Div. Sch., New Haven, 1980. Ordained to ministry Episcopal Ch., 1952, consecrated bishop, 1979. Asst., then rector Ch. of Holy Apostles, St. Louis, 1951-53; rector Trinity Ch., St. Louis, 1953-58; staff office exec. council Episcopal Ch., N.Y.C., 1958-68; dir. Mass. Council Chs., Boston, 1969-72; dep. to rector Trinity Ch., N.Y.C., 1972-73; rector St. Paul's Ch., New Haven, 1974-79; bishop Diocese of Conn., Hartford, 1979-93. Editor: The Church in a Society of Abundance, 1963. Trustee Berkeley Divsn. Sch., 1979-92, Trinity Coll., 1982-92. Sr. fellow Am. Leadership Forum; mem. Phi Beta Kappa, Pi Gamma Mu. Home: RD # 1 Box 224 Hillsboro NH 03244

WALNER, ROBERT JOEL, lawyer; b. Chgo., Dec. 22, 1946; s. Wallace and Elsie W.; m. Charlene Walner; children: Marci, Lisa. BA, U. Ill., 1968; JD, De Paul U., 1972; M in Mgmt. with distinction, Northwestern U., 1991. Bar: Ill. 1972, U.S. Dist. Ct. (no. dist.) Ill. 1972, U.S. Ct. Appeals (7th cir.) 1972, Fla. 1973. Atty. SEC, Chgo., 1972-73; pvt. practice Chgo., 1973—; adminstrv. law judge Ill. Commerce Commn., Chgo., 1973-76; atty. Allied Van Lines, Inc., Broadview, Ill., 1976-79; sr. v.p. gen. counsel, sec. The Balcor Co., Skokie, Ill., 1979-92; prin. fin. ops Balcor Securities divsn. The Balcor Co., Skokie, 1984-92, pres., 1989-92; of counsel Lawrence, Walner & Assocs., Ltd., Chgo., 1992-93; sr. v.p., gen. counsel, sec. Grubb & Ellis Co., San Francisco, 1994—; mem. securities adv. com. to Ill. Sec. of State; mem. editorial bd. Real Estate Securities Jour., Real Estate Securities & Capital Markets; program chmn. Regulators and You seminar. Contbr. chpts. to books, articles on real estate and securities law to profl. jours.; assoc. editor De Paul U. Law Rev. Mem. Kellogg Career Devel. Com., 1992—, Kellogg Bus. Adv. Com., 1992—; mem. enterprise forum MIT, 1992—, mem. exec. com., 1993-94. With USAR, 1968-73. Mem. ABA, Ill. Bar Assn., Chgo. Bar Assn., Am. Real Estate Com. (pres. com. 1985-90), Real Estate Syndication Com. (chmn. 1982-85), Ill. Inst. Continuing Legal Edn., N.Am. Securities Adminstrs. Assn. Inc. (industry adv. com. to real estate com., 1987-89), Real Estate Securities and Syndication Inst. of Nat. Assn. Realtors (chmn. regulatory and legis. com., 1984, 87, specialist, real estate investment, group v.p., 1987, exec. com. 1987-90), Nat. Real Estate Investment Forum (chmn. 1985, 88), Real Estate Investment Assn. (founder, exec. com. 1990-92), Beta Gamma Sigma.

WALPIN, GERALD, lawyer; b. N.Y.C., Sept. 1, 1931; s. Michael and Mary (Gordon) W.; m. Sheila Kainer, Apr. 13, 1957; children: Amanda Eve, Edward Andrew, Jennifer Hope. BA, CCNY, 1952; LLB cum laude, Yale Law Sch., 1955. Bar: N.Y. 1955, U.S. Supreme Ct. 1965, U.S. Ct. Appeals (2d cir.) 1960, (6th cir.) 1969, (3d cir.) 1976, (8th cir.) 1982, (9th cir.) 1983, (11th cir.) 1983, (7th cir.) 1984, U.S. Ct. Claims 1984. Law clk. to Hon. Justice E.J. Dimock U.S. Dist. Ct. (so. dist.) N.Y., N.Y.C.; law clk. to Hon. F.P. Bryan U.S. Dist. Judge (so. dist.) N.Y., N.Y.C., 1955-57; asst. U.S. atty., chief spl. prosecutions U.S. Atty. Office, N.Y.C., 1960-65; sr. ptnr. Rosenman & Colin and predecessor firm, N.Y.C., 1965—; chmn. litigation dept., 1985—; mem. adv. com. Fed. Ct. So. Dist. N.Y., 1991—; co-chmn. Lawyers div. Anti-Defamation League, N.Y. Editor Yale Law Jour., 1953-54, mng. editor, 1954-55; contbr. articles to profl. jours. Pres., trustee Parker Jewish Geriatric Inst., New Hyde Park, N.Y., 1979-87, chmn., trustee, 1987—; bd. dirs. Fund for Modern Cts., N.Y.C., 1985-91; mem. law com. Am. Jewish Com., 1980—; mem. Com. for Free World, N.Y.C., 1983-91; trustee, mem. exec. com. United Jewish Appeal-Fedn. Jewish Philanthropies, N.Y.C., 1984—; mem. Nassau County Crime Commn., 1970; pres. Kensington Civic Orgn., Gt. Neck, N.Y., 1972-73. Recipient Quality of Life award United Jewish Appeal Fedn., 1978, Human Rels. award Am. Jewish Com., 1982, Gift of Life award Jewish Inst. Geriatric Care, 1987, Learned Hand award Am. Jewish Com., 1990. Mem. ABA, Assn. of Bar of City of N.Y., Fed. Bar Coun. (v.p. 1991—, chmn. admissions com. 1989—, chmn. bench/bar liaison com 1994—), Univ. Club, Yale Club. Republican. Jewish. Home: 875 Park Ave New York NY 10021-0341 Office: Rosenman & Colin 575 Madison Ave New York NY 10022-2511

WALPOLE, ROBERT, heavy manufacturing executive. BA, Principia Coll., 1962; MBA, Washington U., 1964. Distbn. sales office, planning and distbn. mgr. Ford Motor Co., Atlanta, 1964-70; officer Walbro Corp., Cass City, Mich., 1970—; now v.p. Walbro Corp., Cass City; pres. Walbro Engine Mgmt. Corp., 1991—. Office: Walbro Corp 6242 Garfield Ave Cass City MI 48726-1342*

WALRATH, PATRICIA A., state legislator; b. Brainerd, Minn., Aug. 11, 1941; d. Joseph James and Pansey Patricia (Drake) McCarvill; m. Robert Eugene Walrath, Sept. 1, 1961; children: Karen, Susan, David, Julie. BS, Bemidji State U., 1962; MS, SUNY, Oswego, 1975. Cert. secondary math. tchr., N.Y., Mass. Programmer analyst Control Data Corp., Mpls., 1962-65; crewleader dept. commerce U.S. Census, Middlesex County, Mass., 1979-80; selectman Town of Stow, Mass., 1980-85; tchr. math. Hale Jr. High Sch., Stow, 1981-82; instr. math. Johnson & Wale Coll. Hanscom AFB, Bedford, Mass., 1983-84; test examiner Hanscom AFB, Bedford, 1983-84; state rep. 3d Middlesex dist. State of Mass., Boston, 1985—; mem. House ways and means com., 1987-92, joint coms. on local affairs, 1993-95, pub. svc., 1993—, election law, 1995—. Chmn. Mass. Indoor Air Pollution Commn., Boston, 1987-88; mem. Stow Dem. Com., 1988—; merit badge counselor Boy Scouts Am., Stow and Hudson, Mass., 1990—; bd. dirs. Hudson Arts Alliance, 1991—. Recipient Disting. Svc. award Auburn N.Y. Jaycees, 1976. Mem. LWV (pres. 1973-76, dir. fin. 1977-78), Am. Legis. Exch. Coun., Mass. Legislators' Assn., Mass. Dem. Leadership Coun. (v.p. 1991-92, co-chmn. 1993-94), Mass. Women's Legis. Caucus (chair 1986). Roman Catholic. Avocations: gardening, stamp collecting, travel. Home: 20 Middlemost Way Stow MA 01775-1363 Office: State Capital RM 275 Boston MA 02133

WALRAVEN, JOSEPH WILLIAM (BILL WALRAVEN), writer, publisher; b. Dallas, July 1, 1925; s. Orange Daniel Sr. and Valerie (Garrison) W.; m. Marjorie Kathryn Yeager, May 28, 1950; children: Valerie Ruth, Wilson Frederick, Joseph William Jr. BA, Tex. A&I U., 1950; postgrad. sch. profl. writing, U. Okla., 1950-51. Copy editor San Antonio Light, 1951-52; reporter Corpus Christi (Tex.) Caller-Times, 1952-68, daily columnist, 1968-89; pub. Sandcrab Press, Corpus Christi, 1983—, Javelina Press, Corpus Christi, 1989—; freelance writer Corpus Christi, 1989—; pub. Javelina Press, Corpus Christi, 1995—. Author, pub.: Real Texans Don't Drink Scotch in Their Dr. Pepper, 1983; author: Corpus Christi, History of a TexasSeaport, 1983, Wairaven's World or Star Boater (and other) Wars, 1985, El Rincon, A History of Corpus Christi Beach, 1990, (with Marjorie Kathryn Walraven) The Magnificent Barbarians, Little-Told Tales of the Texas Revolution, 1993, All I Know Is What's On TV, 1995. V.p. South Tex. Hist. Soc., 1978 (active Tex. State Hist. Assn. With USN, 1943-45, PTO. Recipient 1st pl. gen. interest column Harte-Hanks Newspapers, 1979, 2nd prize, 1987; recipient 2nd pl. news story Tex. AP, 1954, 1st pl. features, 1958; recipient 2nd prize series Animal Def. League Tex., 1987; award recipient Corpus Christi Police Officers Assn., 1967, ARC, 1970, Tex. Hist. Commn. and Tex. Hist. Found., 1980, 81, Corpus Christi Landmark Commn., 1987, Nueces County Hist. Commn., 1989; named Civic Salesman of Yr., Sales and Mktg. Execs. Corpus Christi, 1984. Mem. Nat. Soc. Newspaper Columnists, Corpus Christi Press Club (v.p. 1964, pres. 1965,

many awards). Democrat. Methodist. Avocations: reading, travel, flounder fishing. Home: 4609 Wilma Corpus Christi TX 78412 Office: Sandcrab Press PO Box 1479 Corpus Christi TX 78403

WALROD, DAVID JAMES, retail grocery chain executive; b. Toledo, Dec. 9, 1946; s. Maynard Elmer and Isabella (Soldwish) W.; m. Judith Kay Stevens, Aug. 17, 1968; children—David, Bryant, Marc. Student, Michael Owens Coll.; student in food distbn. mgmt. mktg., Toledo U., 1968. With Seaway Food Town, Inc., Maumee, Ohio, 1963—, grocery merchandiser, 1971-74, v.p. supermarket ops., 1974-77, corp. v.p. ops., 1977-80, sr. v.p. ops., 1980-88, exec. v.p., chief oper. officer, 1988—; bd. dirs. Ohio Grocers Assn. Bd. dirs. Toledo Mud Hens, Riverside Hosp., St. Francis Desales H.S., Toledo, Corp. for Effective Govt., Junior Achievement, Toledo City Parks Commn., Labor Mgmt. Coun., Bishop's Edn. Coun. Cath. Diocese of Toledo. Mem. Brandywine Country Club. Office: Seaway Food Town Inc 1020 Ford St Maumee OH 43537-1898

WALSER, MACKENZIE, physician, educator; b. N.Y.C., Sept. 19, 1924; s. Kenneth Eastwood and Jean (Mackenzie) W.; m. Elizabeth C. Gearon, Sept. 17, 1988; children from previous marriage: Karen D., Jennifer McK., Cameron M., Eric H. Grad., Phillips Exeter Acad., 1941; A.B., Yale, 1944; M.D., Columbia, 1948. Diplomate: Am. Bd. Internal Medicine. Intern Mass. Gen. Hosp., Boston, 1948-49; asst. resident in medicine Mass. Gen. Hosp., 1949-50; resident Parkland Hosp., Dallas, 1950-52; staff mem. Johns Hopkins Hosp., Balt., 1957—; instr. U. Tex. at Dallas, 1950-51, asst. prof., 1951-52; investigator Nat. Heart Inst., Bethesda, Md., 1954-57; asst. prof. pharmacology Johns Hopkins Med. Sch., 1957-61, assoc. prof., 1961-70, prof., 1970—, asst. prof. medicine, 1957-64, assoc. prof., 1964-74, prof., 1974—; Med. dir. USPHS, 1970—, pharmacology study sect., 1968-72. Co-author: Mineral Metabolism, 2d edit, 1969, Handbook of Physiology, 1973, The Kidney, 1976, 3d edit., 1986, also articles; co-editor: Branched-Chain Amino and Ketoacids, 1981, Nutritional Management, 1984. Served with USNR, 1942-45; to lt. M.C. USNR, 1952-54. Recipient Research Career Devel. award USPHS, 1959-69. Mem. AAAS, AAUP (pres. Johns Hopkins 1970), Am. Soc. Clin. Investigation, Assn. Am. Physicians, Am. Fedn. Clin. Rsch., Am. Physiol. Soc., Biophys. Soc., Am. Soc. Pharmacology and Exptl. Therapeutics (Exptl. Therapeutics award 1975), Am. Soc. Nephrology, Am. Inst. Nutrition, Am. Soc. Clin. Nutrition (Hermann award 1988), Internat. Soc. Nutrition and Metabolism in Renal Disease (Addis award 1994), Century Assn. Club. Home: 7513 Club Rd Baltimore MD 21204-6418 Office: Johns Hopkins U Sch Medicine Baltimore MD 21205

WALSH, ARTHUR CAMPBELL, psychiatrist; b. Vancouver, B.C., Can., Dec. 21, 1919; came to U.S., 1964; s. William Charles and Kathleen (Patterson) W.; m. Bernice Martha Hessom, Dec. 26, 1944; children: Kathleen, David, Thomas. MD, U. Alta., Edmonton, 1943. Intern Vancouver Gen. Hosp., B.C., 1943; pvt. practice Vancouver, B.C., 1964-67; resident psychiatry U. Pitts., 1967, clin. assoc. prof. psychiatry, 1968-69; pvt. practice Pitts., 1968—; pres. Ctr. Senility Studies Alzheimer Treatment Rsch. Ctr., Pitts., 1969—; psychiat. cons. VA, Pitts., 1969-89, Woodville State Hosp., Pitts., 1969-86. Author: Conquering Senility; co-author: Mental Capacity Medical Legal Aspects of Aging, 1975, 2d edit. 1994. Mem. AMA, Am. Psychiat. Assn., Am. Assn. Geriatric Psychiatry, Pa. Med. Soc. Home: 307 S Dithridge St Apt 202 Pittsburgh PA 15213-3514 Office: Alzheimer Treatment Rsch Ctr Ctr Senility Studies 161 N Dithridge St Pittsburgh PA 15213-2646

WALSH, BRYAN OLIVER, social services administrator, priest; b. PortArlington, Ireland, June 19, 1930; came to U.S., 1950; s. Richard and Kathleen Rose (Cummins) W. STB, St. Mary's U., Balt., 1952, STL, 1954; MA, U. North Colo., 1974; ThD, Cath. U. P.R., 1979. Ordained priest Roman Cath. Ch., 1954. Asst. pastor St. Joseph's Ch., Lakeland, Fla., 1954-55; exec. dir. Cath. Cmty. Svcs., Miami, Fla., 1955—; chmn. working group on refugees Caritas Internat., Vatican City, 1987—. Chmn. Dade County (Fla.) Pub. Health Trust, 1978-80; founder Operation Pedro Pan. Mem. Knights of Malta, Knights of Holy Sepulcure. Avocations: sailing, flying, travel, cycling. Office: Cath Cmty Svcs 9401 Biscayne Blvd Miami FL 33138

WALSH, CHARLES RICHARD, banker; b. Bklyn., Jan. 30, 1939; s. Charles John and Anna Ellen Walsh; m. Marie Anne Goulden, June 24, 1961; children: Kevin C., Brian R., Gregory M. BS, Fordham U., 1960; MBA, St. John's U., 1966, D of Comml. Scis. (hon.), 1985. V.p. Mfrs. Hanover Trust Co., Hicksville, N.Y., 1974-80, sr. v.p. 1980-86, exec. v.p., 1986-90, group exec., mem. mgmt. com., 1990-92; exec. v.p., group exec. Chem. Banking Corp., Hicksville, N.Y., 1992—; bd. dirs. Mastercard Internat; bd. dirs., former chmn. Eastern States Monetary Svcs., Lake Success, N.Y., 1978-88; former pres., CEO, bd. dirs. The Bankcard Assn., Hicksville, 1988-91. Sustaining mem. Rep. Nat. Com., 1978—; vice chmn. adv. bd. St. John's U., 1982—. With USAR, 1960, 61-62. Mem. N.Y. State Bankers Assn. (former bd. dirs., mem. gov. coun., chmn. consumer banking divsn.), Am. Bankers Assn. (mem. govt. rels. coun., chmn. bank card divsn., mem. exec. com., former mem. comms. coun. and chmn. edn. com.), Am. Mgmt. Assn., N.Y. Credit and Fin. Mgmt. Assn., Soc. Cert. Consumer Credit Execs. (cert.), Beta Gamma Sigma, Omicron Delta Epsilon, North Hempstead Country Club, Gov.'s Club Kiawah Island (S.C.). Republican. Home: 9 Blueberry Ln Oyster Bay NY 11771-3901 also: 121 Turnberry Dr Johns Island SC 29455-5726 Office: 100 Duffy Ave Hicksville NY 11801-3639

WALSH, CHRISTOPHER THOMAS, biochemist, department chairman; b. Boston, Feb. 16, 1944; married; 1 child. BA, Harvard U., 1965; PhD in Life Sci., Rockefeller U., 1970. Helen Hay Whitney Found. fellow Brandeis U., 1970-72; from asst. prof. to prof. chemistry and biology MIT, 1972-87, assoc. dir. Whitaker Coll. Mgmt., 1979-82, Uncas and Helen Whitaker prof., 1980-85, Karl Taylor Compton prof., 1985-87, chmn. chemistry dept., 1982-87; David Wesley Gaiser prof. Harvard U., 1987-91, chmn. dept. biol. chemistry and molecular pharmacology Med. Sch., 1987—, Hamilton Kuhn prof., 1991—; pres. Dana-Farber Cancer Inst., Boston, 1992—; cons. Merck, Sharp & Dohme Rsch. Labs., 1975-81, Monsanto Corp. Res. Labs., 1980-81, Johnson & Johnson, 1982-83, Hoffman LaRoche, 1982—, Genzyme & Bioinfo Assocs., 1983—, Firmenich, S A, 1986-90, Enzymatics, 1988—, Biotage, 1989—; mem. panel rsch. grants study NSF, 1977-79, panel study sect. biochemistry NIH, 1978-82, gen. med. coun., NIH, 1983-85, Chemal Rsch. Group, WHO, 1984-86; co-chmn. Gordon Rsch. Conf. Enzymes, Coenzymes & Molecular Biology, 1978, Conf. Methanogenesis, 1984; chmn. study sect. biochemistry NIH, 1982—; lectr. in field. Alfred P. Sloan Found. fellow, 1975-77, Camille and Henry Dreyfus Tchr.-Scholar grantee, 1976-80; recipient Eli Lilly award, 1979. Mem. NAS, Inst. Medicine-NAS, Am. Acad. Arts & Sci., Am. Soc. Biol. Chemists, Am. Chem. Soc., Am. Soc. Microbiology. Achievements include research in enzymatic reation mechanisms, phosphoryl and pyrophosphoryl transfers, flavin-dependent enzymes, membrane biochemistry and mechanism of active transport. Office: Dana Farber Cancer Inst 44 Binney St Ste B 1828 Boston MA 02215-5328

WALSH, CORNELIUS STEPHEN, leasing company executive; b. N.Y.C., Dec. 27, 1907; s. William Francis and Frances (Murphy) W.; m. Edwyna Lois Senter, May 1, 1930; children: Jane Linda (Mrs. Walsh Weed), Richard Stephen, Suzanne Patricia. Student, Eastman-Gaines Sch., 1924-25. Assoc. with Dyson Shipping Co., Inc., 1925-27, Interocean Steamship Corp., 1928-30; sec. States Marine Corp., 1931-38, v.p., 1938-53, pres., 1953-65, dir., 1950-65; pres. dir. States Marine Corp. Del., 1946-65; chmn. Waterman Steamship Corp., N.Y.C., 1965-89, Waterman Industries Corp., 1965-89, Hammond Leasing Corp., 1987—; dir. Oliver Corp. Mem. Far East-Am. Coun. Commerce and Industry (bd. dirs.), Soc. Naval Architects and Marine Engrs. (assoc.), Soc. of Four Arts (Palm Beach, Fla.), Japan Soc. (hon. bd. dirs.), Am. Bur. Shipping, Yacht Club (N.Y.C.), Seawanhaka Corinthian Yacht Club (Oyster Bay, L.I., N.Y.), N.Am. Sta. Royal Scandinavian Yacht Club, Pine Valley Golf Club (Clementon, N.J.), Everglades Club (Palm Beach), Bath and Tennis Club (Palm Beach), Sailfish of Fla. Club (Palm Beach). Home: 220 El Bravo Way Palm Beach FL 33480-4722

WALSH, DANIEL FRANCIS, bishop; b. San Francisco, Oct. 2, 1937. Grad., St. Joseph Sem., St. Patrick Sem., Catholic U. Am. Ordained priest, Roman Catholic Ch., 1963. Ordained titular bishop of Tigia, 1981; aux. bishop of San Francisco, 1981-87, bishop of Reno-Las Vegas, 1987—. Home: 2809 Cameo Cir Las Vegas NV 89107-3213 Office: Diocese of Reno-Las Vegas Office of Bishop PO Box 18316 Las Vegas NV 89114-8316*

WALSH, DAVID GRAVES, lawyer; b. Madison, Wis., Jan. 7, 1943; s. John J. and Audrey B. Walsh; married; children: Michael, Kathrine, Mary Ellen, John. BBA, U. Wis., 1965; JD, Harvard U., 1970. Bar: Wis. Law clk. Wis. Supreme Ct., Madison, 1970-71; ptnr. Walsh, Walsh, Sweeney & Whitney, Madison, 1971-86; ptnr.-in-charge Foley & Lardner, Madison, 1986—; bd. dirs. Nat. Guardian Life, Madison, 1981—; lectr. U. Wis., Madison, 1974-75, 77-78. Chmn. State of Wis. Elections Bd., Madison, 1978. Lt. USN, 1965-67, Vietnam. Maple Bluff Country Club (Madison) (pres. 1987). Roman Catholic. Avocations: tennis, golf, fishing. Home: 41 Fuller Dr Madison WI 53704-5962 Office: Foley & Lardner 1st Wisconsin Pla 1 S Pinckney St PO Box 1497 Madison WI 53701-1497

WALSH, DENNY JAY, reporter; b. Omaha, Nov. 23, 1935; s. Gerald Jerome and Muriel (Morton) W.; m. Peggy Marie Moore, Feb. 12, 1966; children by previous marriage—Catherine Camille, Colleen Cecile; 1 son, Sean Joseph. B.J., U. Mo., 1962. Staff writer St. Louis Globe-Democrat, 1961-68; asst. editor Life mag., N.Y.C., 1968-70; assoc. editor Life mag., 1970-73; reporter N.Y. Times, 1973-74, Sacramento Bee, 1974—. Served with USMC, 1954-58. Recipient Con Lee Kelliher award St. Louis chpt. Sigma Delta Chi, 1962; award Am. Polit. Sci. Assn., 1963; award Sigma Delta Chi, 1968; Pulitzer prize spl. local reporting, 1969; 1st prize San Francisco Press Club, 1977. Office: Sacramento Bee 21st and Q Sts Sacramento CA 95813

WALSH, DIANA CHAPMAN, academic administrator, social and behavioral sciences educator; b. Phila., July 30, 1944; d. Robert Francis and Gwen (Jenkins) Chapman; m. Christopher Thomas Walsh, June 18, 1966; 1 child, Allison Chapman Walsh. BA, Wellesley Coll., 1966; MS, Boston U. Sch. of Pub. Comm., 1971; PhD, Boston U., 1983; LHD (hon.), Boston U., 1994; LHD, Amer. Coll. of Greece, Athens, 1995. Mgr. spl. events Barnard Coll., N.Y.C., 1967-70; dir. info., edn. Planned Parenthood League, Newton, Mass., 1971-74; sr. program assoc. Dept Pub. Health, Boston, 1974-76; dir. program evaluations Boston U. Health Policy Inst., 1976-85; asst. prof. Sch. Pub. Health, Sch. Medicine, Boston U., 1982-84, assoc. prof., 1984-87, prof., 1987-93, assoc. dir. Health Policy Inst., 1985-93; pres. Wellesley Coll., 1993—; editorial bd. dirs. Bus. and Health; C.O. Sappington lectr. Am. Occupational Med. Assn. Nat. Conv., Phila., 1987. Author: (book) Corporate Physicians, 1987; editor: Women, Work, and Health: Challenges to Corporate Policy, 1980, (book series) Industry and Health Care, 1977-80; contbr. articles to profl. jours. Bd. dirs. Planned Parenthood League of Mass., 1974-79, 1981-85, bd. of overseers 1993—; trustee Occupational Physicians Scholarship Fund, 1987—; trustee WGBH Educational Found., 1993—. Kellogg Nat. fellow, 1987-90. Mem. AM. Pub. Health Assn., Am. Sociol. Assn., Soc. for Study of Social Problems, Health Affairs Editorial Bd., Jour. of Pub. Health Policy, Amer. Academy of Arts & Scis. Intersts include: gender and health, leadership studies, social policy, the craft of writing, skiing. Office: Wellesley Coll Office of the Pres Wellesley MA 02181

WALSH, DON, marine consultant, executive; b. Berkeley, Calif., Nov. 2, 1931; s. J. Don and Marguerite Grace (Van Auker) W.; m. Joan A. Betzmer, Aug. 18, 1962; children—Kelly Drennan, Elizabeth McDonough. B.S., U.S. Naval Acad., 1954; MS, Tex. A&M U., 1967, Ph.D., 1968; M.A., San Diego State Coll., 1968. Commd. ensign USN, 1954, advanced through grades to capt., 1974; officer-in-charge Bathyscaph Trieste USN, Trieste, 1959-62; comdr. in USS Bashaw USN, 1968-69; dir. Inst. Marine and Coastal Studies, prof. ocean engring. U. So. Calif., Los Angeles, 1975-83; pres., chief exec. officer Internat. Maritime, Inc., Los Angeles, 1976—; mng. dir. Deep Ocean Engring., Inc., 1990—, also bd. dirs.; dir. Ctr. for Marine Transp. Studies, U. So. Calif., 1980-83, Coastal Resources Ctr., 1990-94; trustee USN Mus. Found., 1989—; mem. Nat. Adv. Com. on Oceans and Atmosphere, 1979-85; bd. govs. Calif. Maritime Acad., 1985-95; pres. Parker Diving, 1989-94. Author: Law of the Sea: Issues in Ocean Resource Management, 1977, Energy and Resources Development of Continental Margins, 1980, Energy and Sea Power: Challenge for the Decade, 1981, Waste Disposal in the Oceans: Minimizing Impact, Maximizing Benefits, 1983; editor Jour. Marine Tech. Soc., 1975-80; mem. editorial bd. U.S. Naval Inst., 1974-75. Decorated Legion of Merit (2), Meritorious Service medal (2); Woodrow Wilson Internat. Ctr. for Scholars fellow, 1973-74. Fellow Marine Tech. Soc. (hon. life), Acad. Underwater Arts and Scis., Explorers Club (hon. life, bd. dirs. 1994—); mem. AAAS, Soc. Naval Archs. and Marine Engrs., Am. Soc. Naval Engrs., Am. Geophys. Union, Navy League, Navy Inst. Office: Internat Maritime Inc HC-86 Box 101 Myrtle Point OR 97458-0101

WALSH, DONALD PETER, retired oil company executive, lawyer; b. Flushing, N.Y., Apr. 2, 1930; s. Harold S. and Geraldine V. (Shannon) W.; m. Joyce Marie Curtin, June 29, 1957; children: Donald Peter, Michael T., Patricia A., Richard T. BS in Econs., Georgetown U., 1952, LLB, 1957. Bar: D.C. 1957, N.Y. 1957, Tex. 1971, Pa. 1981. Atty., Shell Oil Co., Houston, 1957-70, gen. atty., 1970-77, asst. gen. counsel, 1977-80; asst. gen. counsel Sun Co., Inc., Radnor, Pa., 1980, sr. v.p., gen. counsel, 1980-92. 1st lt. U.S. Army, 1952-54. Mem. ABA (chair com. on corp. law depts. bus. law sect.), Pa. Bar Assn., Tex. Bar Assn., D.C. Bar Assn., Am. Corp. Counsel Assn. (bd. dirs.). Aronimink Golf Club (Newtown Square, Pa.). Roman Catholic. Office: Sun Co Inc 1801 Market St Philadelphia PA 19103-1699

WALSH, DONNIE, sports club executive; married; 5 children. Grad., U. N.C.; attended, N.C. Law Sch. Bar: 1977. Assoc. head coach U. N.C.; staff coach Denver Nuggets, head coach, 1979-81; asst. coach Ind. Pacers, 1984-86, exec. v.p., gen. mgr., 1986-92, pres., 1992—. Office: Ind Pacers Market Sq Arena 300 E Market St Indianapolis IN 36104

WALSH, EDWARD JOSEPH, toiletries and food company executive; b. Mt. Vernon, N.Y., Mar. 18, 1932; s. Edward Aloysius and Charlotte Cecilia (Borup) W.; m. Patricia Ann Farrell, Sept. 16, 1961; children: Edward Joseph, Megan Simpson, John, Robert. BBA, Iona Coll., 1953; MBA, NYU, 1958. Sales rep. M & R Dietetic Labs., Columbus, Ohio, 1955-60; with Armour & Co., 1961-71, Greyhound Corp., 1971-87; v.p. toiletries div. Armour Dial Co., Phoenix, 1973-74; exec. v.p. Armour Dial Co., 1975-77; pres. Armour Internat. Co., Phoenix, 1978-84; pres. The Dial Corp. (formerly Armour-Dial Co.), Phoenix, 1984-87, chief exec. officer, 1984-87; pres., chief exec. officer Purex Corp., 1985; chmn., chief exec. officer The Sparta Group Ltd., Scottsdale, Ariz., 1988—; bd. dirs. Phillips Ramsey Advt., San Diego, Phoenix, Guest Supply Inc., New Brunswick, N.J., WD-40 Co., San Diego, Nortrust Ariz. Holding Corp., Phoenix, Ariz., No. Trust Bank of Ariz., N.A., Executive Services Corps. of Ariz., Inc. Bd. trustees Scottsdale Meml. Health Found.; pres. Mt. Vernon Fire Dept. Mems. Assn., 1960-61. Served with U.S. Army, 1953-55, Germany. Mem. Am. Mgmt. Assn., Nat. Meat Canner Assn. (pres. 1971-72), Cosmetic, Toiletries and Fragrance Assn. (bd. dirs. 1985—), Nat. Food Processors Assn. (bd. dirs.). Republican. Roman Catholic. Office: The Sparta Group Ltd 6623 N Scottsdale Rd Scottsdale AZ 85250-4421

WALSH, EDWARD PATRICK, federal agency administrator; b. N.Y.C., Nov. 21, 1937; s. Edward P. and Marion B. (Burnich) W.; m. Kathleen F. Ringrose, Nov. 25, 1967; children: Megan, Brendan. BS in Econs., Villanova U., 1959. Patrol inspector U.S. Border Patrol Immigration and Naturalization Svc., Harlingen, Tex., 1959-65; spl. agt. U.S. Secret Svc., 1965-86; dep. asst. dir. U.S. Secret Svc., Washington, 1986; dir. Bur. Investigations FMC, Washington, 1986, mng. dir., 1986—. Trustee, assoc. Villanova U., 1990—. With U.S. Army, 1959-61, Korea. Recipient Presdl. Rank award, 1989. Mem. Internat. Assn. Chiefs of Police, Assn. Former Secret Svc. Agts., Fed. Exec. Inst. Alumni Assn., Sr. Exec. Assn. Office: FMC Office of Chmn 800 N Capitol St NW Washington DC 20573-0001

WALSH, ERIC, food products executive. Pres. Klondike Ice Cream Inc., Green Bay. Office: Good Humor Corp 909 Packerland Dr Green Bay WI 54303*

WALSH, FRANCIS RICHARD, law educator; b. Newark, Jan. 1, 1924; s. Loretta Anne (Norton) W.; m. Ethel Anne Walsh, Mar. 12, 1944; 1 child, Jeffrey R. BSBA, Seton Hall U., 1943; JD, Georgetown U., 1948. Prof. Law Sch. Georgetown U., Washington, 1949-51; law clk. to presiding justice U.S. Ct. Appeals (9th cir.), San Francisco, 1948-49; chief broadcast bur. FCC, Washington, 1970-71; pvt. practice San Francisco, 1954-70; prof. law U. San Francisco, 1951-54, 71-74, dean, prof. law, 1957-70; prof. law Hast-

ings Coll. of Law, U. Calif., San Francisco, 1974—. Lt. USNR, 1934-46, PTO. Avocations: golf, travel. Home: 28 Spring Rd San Rafael CA 94904-2625 Office: Hastings Coll Law 200 Mcallister St San Francisco CA 94102-4976

WALSH, GARY L., consumer products company executive; b. 1942. Sr. mgmt. Sara Lee Corp. and Sysco Foods, 1966-77; CEO Miller Cascade Foodsvc. of Am., 1077-90; Core-Mark Internat., Inc., South San Francisco, 1990—. Office: Core-Mark International Inc 395 Oyster Point Blvd South San Francisco CA 94080 also: Core Mark Interrlated Cos 311 Reed Cir Corona CA 91719*

WALSH, GEORGE WILLIAM, engineering executive; b. Teton County, Idaho, Mar. 22, 1923; s. Raymond Eugene and Maude Ethel (Brack) W.; m. Catherine Mary Yunker, July 1, 1950; children: Dwight, Maureen, John. BSEE, U. Idaho, 1947; MEE, Rensselaer Poly. Inst., 1960. Registered profl. engr., N.Y. With GE, 1947-94; test engr. GE, Cleve. and Schenectady, N.Y., 1947-49; design engr. GE, Pittsfield, Mass., 1949-50; power system engr. GE, Schenectady, 1950-66, mgr. power system engring., 1966-85, mgr. power system cons. engring., 1985-93, cons., 1993-94; profl. cons. engr., 1994—. Contbr. numerous papers and articles relating to electric power system engring. to profl. publs. Recipient GE Power Systems Engring. awards for Outstanding Tech. Contbn., 1986, and Outstanding Profl. and Social Svcs., 1991. Fellow IEEE (life, Centennial medal 1984, Richard Harold Kaufmann field award for outstanding contbn. to indsl. engring. 1993); mem. IEEE Industry Applications Soc. (pres., mem. exec. bd., adminstrv. and tech. coms., Power Systems Achievement award 1980, Outstanding Achievement award 1990), IEEE Power Engring. Soc. Home and Office: 26 St Stephens Ln E Schenectady NY 12302-4221

WALSH, GEORGE WILLIAM, publishing company executive, editor; b. N.Y.C., Jan. 16, 1931; s. William Francis and Madeline (Maass) W.; m. Joan Mary Dunn, May 20, 1961; children—Grail, Simon. B.S., Fordham U., 1952; M.S., Columbia U. Sch. Journalism, 1953. Copy editor, reporter Cape Cod Standard-Times, Hyannis, Mass., 1955; communications specialist IBM, N.Y.C., 1955-58; editorial trainee Time, Inc., 1958-59; writer-reporter Sports Illus., N.Y.C., 1959-62; book editor Cosmopolitan, N.Y.C., 1962-65; mng. editor Cosmopolitan, 1965-74; editor-in-chief, v.p. Ballantine Books div. Random House, N.Y.C., 1974-79, Macmillan Pub. Co., N.Y.C., 1979-85; pub. cons., 1985—. Author: Gentleman Jimmy Walker, 1974, Public Enemies, 1980. Served with AUS, 1953-55. Mem. Authors Am. Pubs. Roman Catholic. Clubs: Univ. (N.Y.C.); Pamet Harbor Yacht and Tennis (Truro, Mass.). Home: 35 Prospect Park West Brooklyn NY 11215-3008

WALSH, JAMES HAMILTON, lawyer; b. Astoria, N.Y., May 20, 1947; s. Edward James and Helen Smith (Hamilton) W.; m. Janice Ausherman, Aug. 3, 1968; children: Tracy, Courtney, Eric. B.A. in Psychology, Bridgewater Coll., 1968; J.D., U. Va., 1975. Bar: Va. 1975, U.S. Dist. Ct. (ea. and we. dists.) Va. 1975, U.S. Ct. Appeals (4th cir.) 1976, U.S. Supreme Ct. 1982. Assoc. McGuire, Woods, Battle & Boothe (and predecessor firms), Richmond, Va., 1975-82, ptnr., 1982—; instr. Nat. Inst. Trial Adv.; adj. prof. U. Richmond, 1992, 93; spl. prosecutor U.S. Dist. Ct. (ea. dist.) Va., 1979, 84. Trustee Bridgewater (Va.) Coll.; mem. staff Va. Law Rev. With U.S. Army, 1969-72. Mem. ABA (mem. antitrust sect. health care com., litigation sect.), Va. State Bar (bd. govs. antitrust sect. 1984-90, chmn. 1986), Va. Bar Assn. (vice chmn. criminal law sect.), Richmond Bar Assn., Order Coif, Phi Delta Phi. Episcopalian. Clubs: Willow Oaks. Contbr. articles to profl. jours. Home: 113 Adingham Ct Richmond VA 23229-7761 Office: McGuire Woods Battle & Boothe 1 James Ctr 910 E Cary St Richmond VA 23219

WALSH, JAMES JEROME, philosophy educator; b. Seattle, May 23, 1924; s. John Jerome and Agnes (Counihan) W.; m. Carol Jean Paton, Sept. 16, 1946; children—John Jerome II, James Paton. B.A., Reed Coll., 1949, Oxford (Eng.) U., 1951; M.A., Oxford (Eng.) U., 1956; Ph.D., Columbia U., 1960. Mem. faculty Columbia U., 1954-90, prof. philosophy, 1966-90, prof. emeritus, 1990—, dir. grad. studies philosophy dept., 1963-66, 73-88, chmn. dept., 1967-71, acting chmn. dept., 1982-83; vis. instr. U. Calif.-Berkeley, 1958; cons. TV series G.E. Coll. Bowl, 1965-70. Author: Aristotle's Conception of Moral Weakness, 1963, Philosophy in the Middle Ages, 1967, 2d edit., 1983; Editor Jour. Philosophy, 1965-90. Mem. Rockland County Democratic Com., 1960-63. Served with AUS, 1943-45. Decorated Purple Heart.; Rhodes scholar, 1949; Ford Found. fellow, 1958; Am. Coun. Learned Socs. fellow, 1962; Guggenheim fellow, 1966. Mem. Soc. Medieval and Renaissance Philosophy. Home: 300 Haverstraw Rd Suffern NY 10901-3137

WALSH, JAMES JOSEPH, lawyer; b. Kansas City, Mo., Nov. 11, 1930; s. James J. and Kathryn J. (Pierce) W.; m. Lavern Snellen, Oct. 4, 1952; children: Michelle, Kelley. BJ, U. Mo., Columbia, 1951; LLB, U. Mo., Kansas City, 1961. Bar: Calif. 1963. Atty. Dept. Justice, Washington, 1961-62; assoc. Pillsbury, Madison & Suto, San Francisco, 1962-71, ptnr., 1971—. With USN, 1953-55. Mem. ABA, Calif. Bar Assn., Bar Assn. San Francisco. Home: 60 Rowley Cir Belvedere Tiburon CA 94920-1427 Office: Pillsbury Madison & Sutro 225 Bush St San Francisco CA 94104-4207

WALSH, JAMES PATRICK, lawyer; b. North Bend, Oreg., Dec. 28, 1944; s. William P. And Ethel A. (Smith) W.; m. Cynthia J. Raffel, Aug. 3, 1968; children: Nicholas, Faye, Robinson. AB, Stanford U., 1967; JD, U. Wash., 1970, LLM, 1971. Bar: Wash. 1970, D.C. 1976. Asst. atty. gen. State of Wash., Olympia, 1971-72; staff counsel com. on commerce U.S. Senate, Washington, 1972-76, gen. counsel, 1977-78; dep. administr. NOAA, Washington, 1978-81; of counsel Davis Wright Jones, Washington, 1983-84; ptnr. Davis Wright Tremaine, Washington, 1985—. Lt. USAR, 1970-76. Home: 4403 Klingle St NW Washington DC 20016-3578 Office: Davis Wright Tremaine 1155 Connecticut Ave NW ste 700 Washington DC 20036

WALSH, JAMES THOMAS, congressman; b. Syracuse, N.Y., June 19, 1947. BA, St. Bonaventure U., 1970. Agrl. extension agt. Peace Corps, 1970-72; mktg. exec. telecommunications co. 1974-88; exec.-in-residence telecommunications inst. Coll. Tech. SUNY, Utica, Rome, N.Y., 1986-87; common councilor City of Syracuse, 1977-85, pres. common coun., 1986-88; mem. 101st-103rd Congresses from 27th (now 25th) N.Y. dist., Washington, D.C., 1989—. Republican. Office: US House of Reps 1330 Longworth House Washington DC 20515 also: 1269 Federal Bldg 45 Church St Cortland NY 13045-2743 also: One Lincoln St Auburn NY 13021

WALSH, JOANNE ELIZABETH, art educator, librarian; b. Chgo., Nov. 25, 1942; d. Joseph Frank and Elizabeth Margaret (Gretz) Fiali; m. John Kerwin Walsh, July 17, 1976; 1 child, Kevin Joseph. BA in English, Mundelein Coll., Chgo., 1965; MEd Ednl. Adminstrn. and Supervision, Loyola U., Chgo., 1969. Tchr. Chgo. Pub. Schs., 1965-83, prin., 1983-89; tchr. libr. Burbank (Ill.) Dist III, 1990-93; tchr. art Tate Sch. of Discovery, Knoxville, Tenn., 1994—. Vol. Palos Community Hosp., Palos Park, Ill., 1990, Palos Heights Libr., 1993; Rainbow facilitator, 1992, 93; mem. St. John Neumann Cath. Ch. Recipient Tchr. of Yr. award McCord Sch., 1992-93. Mem. Retired Chgo. Prins. Club, Aquin Guild, Knoxville Welcome Wagon Club, Knoxville Newcomers Club. Avocations: reading, boating, gardening, crafts, golf. Home: 12301 Butternut Circle Knoxville TN 37922

WALSH, JOHN, JR., museum director; b. Mason City, Wash., Dec. 9, 1937; s. John J. and Eleanor (Wilson) W.; m. Virginia Alys Galston, Feb. 17, 1962; children: Peter Wilson, Anne Galston, Frederick Matthiessen. B.A., Yale U., 1961; postgrad., U. Leyden, Netherlands, 1965-66; MA, Columbia U., 1965, PhD, 1971. Lectr., rsch. asst. Frick Collection, N.Y.C., 1966-68; assoc. higher edn. Met. Mus. Art, N.Y.C., 1968-71; assoc. curator European paintings Met. Mus. Art, 1970-72, curator dept. European paintings, 1972-74, vice-chmn., 1973-77; adj. assoc. prof. art history Columbia U., N.Y.C., 1969-72; adj. prof. Columbia U., 1972-75; prof. art history Barnard Coll. Columbia U., N.Y.C., 1975-77; Mrs. Russell W. Baker curator paintings Mus. Fine Arts, Boston, 1977-83; dir. J. Paul Getty Mus., Malibu, Calif., 1983—; vis. prof. fine arts Harvard U., 1979; mem. governing bd. Yale U. Art Gallery, 1975—, Smithsonian Coun., 1990—. Contbr. articles to profl. jours. Mem. Dem. County Com., N.Y.C., 1968-71; mem. vis. com. Fogg Mus., Harvard U., 1982-87; bd. fellows Claremont U. Ctr. and Grad. Sch., Calif. With USNR, 1957-63. Fulbright grad. fellow The Netherlands, 1988—. With USNR, 1957-63. Fulbright grad. fellow The Netherlands,

1965-66. Mem. Coll. Art Assn., Am. Assn. Mus., Archaeol. Inst. Am., Am. Antiquarian Soc., Assn. Art Mus. Dirs. (trustee 1986—, pres. 1989-90), Century Assn. N.Y.C. Office: J Paul Getty Museum PO Box 2112 Santa Monica CA 90406*

WALSH, JOHN BREFFNI, aerospace consultant; b. Bklyn., Aug. 20, 1927; s. George and Margaret Mary (Rigney) W.; m. Marie Louise Leclerc, June 18, 1955; children: George Breffni, John Leclerc, Darina Louise. B.E.E., Manhattan Coll., 1948; M.S., Columbia U., 1950; postgrad., NYU, 1954-62. Asst., instr. Columbia U., N.Y.C., 1948-51, asst. prof., asst. dir. Electronics Research Labs., 1953-66; various positions through tech. dir. Intelligence and Reconnaissance Div., Rome Air Devel. Center, N.Y., 1951-53; dep. for research to asst. sec. Air Force, 1966-71; sr. staff mem. Nat. Security Council, 1971-72, asst. to Pres.'s sci. advisor, 1971-72; dep. dir. Def. Research and Engring., 1972-77; asst. sec. gen. for def. support NATO, 1977-80; holder chair in systems acquisition mgmt., dean exec. inst. Def. Systems Mgmt. Coll., Ft. Belvoir, Va., 1981-82; prof. emeritus Def. Systems Mgmt. Coll., Ft. Belvoir, Va.; v.p., chief scientist Boeing Mil. Airplane Co., Wichita, Kans., 1982-89; v.p. rsch. and engring. programs Boeing Aerospace and Electronics div., Seattle, 1990-92; v.p. strategic analysis Boeing Defense and Space Group, Seattle, 1992-93; prin. John B. Walsh Assocs., 1993—; mem. aeros. adv. com. NASA; mem. Congl. Adv. Com. on Aeros., 1984-85; assoc. Def. Sci. Bd.; mem. indsl. adv. bd. Wichita State U. Coll. Engring., adj. prof. elec. engring., 1989-90; chmn. tech. working group Defense Trade Adv. Group Dept. State, 1992—. Author: Electromagnetic Theory and Engineering Applications, 1960, (with K.S. Miller) Introductory Electric Circuits, 1960, Elementary and Advanced Trigonometry, 1961, Advanced Trigonometry, 1977; contbr. tech. papers to publs.; 2 patents. Mem. planning bd., Cresskill, N.J., 1964-66; commr. Kans. Advanced Tech. Commn., 1985-86; bd. dirs. Kans. Inc., 1986-90; mem. math. scis. edn. bd. NRC, 1989-92. Served with U.S. Army, 1946-47. Recipient Air Force Exceptional Civilian Service award, 1969; recipient Dept. Def. Meritorious Civilian Service award, 1971, Disting. Civilian Service award, 1977, Air Force Assn. citation of honor as outstanding Air Force civilian employee of year, 1971, Theodore von Karman award Air Force Assn., 1977. Fellow IEEE (life), AIAA (v.p. tech. 1987-89); mem. N.Y. Acad. Scis., GPS Internat. Assn., Electromagnetics Acad., Sigma Xi, Eta Kappa Nu. Roman Catholic. Office: John B Walsh Assocs 13822 NE 37th Pl Bellevue WA 98005-1420

WALSH, JOHN CHARLES, metallurgical company executive; b. Indpls., Sept. 8, 1924; s. John Charles and Nell (O'Neil) W.; m. Mary Louise Dreiss, Feb. 5, 1949; children: Michael S., Carolyn Ann, Anne D. B.S., Notre Dame U., 1949. Auditor Herdrich Boggs & Co., Indpls., 1949-50; with P.R. Mallory & Co., Inc., 1949-80; pres. Walgang Co. Inc., Indpls., 1980—; v.p., treas. P.R. Mallory & Co., 1971. Served with USMCR, 1943-45. Mem. Fin. Execs. Inst., Indpls. C. of C., Ind. Hist. Soc., Econ. Club, Notre Dame Club, Rotary. Home: 7365 Huntington Rd Indianapolis IN 46240-3657 Office: 6100 Bldg 6100 N Keystone Ave Indianapolis IN 46220-2452

WALSH, JOHN E., JR., business educator, consultant; b. St. Louis, Apr. 28, 1927; s. John E. and Ann M. (Narkewicz) W. B.S., U.S. Naval Acad., 1950; M.B.A., Washington U., St. Louis, 1957; D.B.A., Harvard U., 1960. Asst. prof. Washington U., St. Louis, 1959-60; assoc. prof. Washington U., 1960-68, prof., 1968—; vis. assoc. prof. Stanford U., 1964-65; vis. prof. INSEAD, Fontainebleau, France, 1970. Author: Preparing Feasibility Studies in Asia, 1971, Guidelines for Management Consultants in Asia, 1973, Planning New Ventures in International Business, 1976, (with others) Strategies in Business, 1978, Management Tactics, 1980, International Business Case Studies: For the Multicultural Market Place, 1994. Served to 1st lt. USAF, 1950-54. Zurn Found. fellow, 1958. Mem. St. Louis Com. on Fgn. Rels., Harvard Club N.Y.C. Home: 5471 Charglow Dr Saint Louis MO 63129-3564 Office: Washington U Grad Sch Bus PO Box 1133 1 Brookings Dr Saint Louis MO 63130-4889

WALSH, JOHN HARLEY, medical educator; b. Jackson, Miss., Aug. 22, 1938; s. John Howard and Aimee Nugent (Shands) W.; m. Courtney Kathleen McFadden, June 12, 1963 (div. 1979); children: Courtney Shands (Mrs. Peter Phleger), John Harley Jr.; m. Mary Carol Territo, Feb. 4, 1989. BA, Vanderbilt U., 1959, MD, 1963. Diplomate Am. Bd. Internal Medicine, Am. Bd. Gastroenterology. Intern N.Y. Hosp., N.Y.C., 1963-64; resident N.Y. Hosp. Cornell Med. Ctr., N.Y.C., 1964-67; rsch. assoc. Bronx VA Hosp., N.Y., 1969-70; fellow gastroenterology Wadsworth, Va., LA, 1970-71; clin. investigator Wadsworth VA Hosp., L.A., 1971-73; asst. to assoc. prof. UCLA, 1970-78, prof. medicine, 1978—, dir. Integrated Gastroenterology Tng. Program, 1983-89, dir. Div. Gastroenterology, 1988—; Dorothy and Leonard Straus prof., 1989—; dep. dir. Ctr. Ulcer Rsch. and Edn., L.A., 1974-80, assoc. dir., 1980-87, dir. 1987—; adv. coun. mem. NIH, Bethesda, Md., 1982-85; mem. Nat. Digestive Disease Adv. Bd., 1987—. Assoc. editor: Gastroenterology Jour., 1976-86; mem. editorial bd. Am. Jour. Physiology, Jour. Clin. Endocrinology and Metabolism, Peptides Jour.; contbr. articles to profl. jours. Served with USPHS, 1967-69. Recipient Rorer award So. Calif. Soc. Gastroenterology, 1972, Western Gastroent. Rsch. prize Western Gut Club, 1983, Merit award NIH, 1987. Mem. Am. Gastroent. Assn., Am. Soc. Clin. Investigation, Assn. Am. Physicians, Endocrine Soc., Western Soc. Clin. Investigation (counselor 1978-81). Episcopalian. Avocations: tennis, golf, ballet, modern fiction. Home: 266 Dolores St San Francisco CA 94103-2203 Office: UCLA Sch Medicine Ctr for Health Scis Rm 44-146 10833 Le Conte Ave Los Angeles CA 90024-1372*

WALSH, JOHN JOSEPH, medical school administrator, physician; b. N.Y.C., July 31, 1924; s. Patrick Joseph and Elizabeth (Lawless) W.; m. Gloria Paolini (dec. 1971); children: Maureen Walsh Garland, John Joseph Jr., Kathleen Walsh Saer; m. Dorothy B. Ray, 1989. Student, Fordham U., 1941-43, Cornell U., 1943-44; MD, L.I. Coll. Medicine, 1948; postdoctoral, Tulane U., 1957-58; ScD (hon.), SUNY, 1989. Diplomate Am. Bd. Internal Medicine. Commd. USPHS, 1948, advanced through grades to rear admiral, 1966; intern USPHS Hosp., Staten Island, N.Y., 1948-49; resident USPHS Hosp., Seattle, 1951-54; asst. chief medicine USPHS Hosp., New Orleans, 1954-56, dep. chief, 1956-57, chief research activities, 1958-64, chief med. service, 1963-64, med. dir., med. officer in charge, 1964-66; asst. surgeon gen., dir. div. direct health services USPHS, 1966-68, ret., 1968; instr. Tulane U. Sch. Medicine, New Orleans, 1957-58, asst. prof., 1958-60, assoc. prof., 1960-67, prof. medicine emeritus, 1989—, dean, 1968-69; dean, coordinator health sci. and programs Tulane U. Med. Ctr., New Orleans, 1968-69, v.p. health affairs, 1969-78, chancellor, 1973-89; chancellor emeritus Tulane U. Med. Ctr., 1989—; acting dean sch. pub. health and tropical medicine Tulane U. Med. Ctr., New Orleans, 1974, Jack R. Aron prof. in adminstrv. medicine, 1978-89; adj. prof. Tulane U. Sch. Pub. Health and Tropical Medicine, 1978-89; pres., CEO Mahorner Clinic, Kenner, La., 1989-92; cons. VA Hosp., New Orleans, 1969-89, VA Hosp., Alexandria, La., 1969-89, USPHS Hosp., New Orleans, 1968-89; vis. physician Charity Hosp., New Orleans, 1957-66, sr. vis. physician, 1966-89, chief service Tulane div., 1968-69, acting chief service Tulane div., 1972; instr. La. State U. Sch. Medicine, New Orleans, 1956-57; mem. bd. cons. to comdr. Naval Med. Command Dept. Navy, Washington, 1983-86; mem. adv. com. to dir. NIH, 1983-85. Contbr. articles to profl. jours. Mem. planning com. Touro Infirmary, New Orleans; bd. dirs., mem. exec. com. Am. Cancer Soc., Internat. House, 1978-82, 83-84; mem. New Orleans Area Health Planning Council, 1968-70, task force in health manpower; trustee La. Sci. Ctr., 1983-85, La. Regional Med. Programs, 1969; bd. dirs. Friends of Charity Inc., 1986-89, Blue Cross, Washington, 1966-68, New Orleans Area/Bayou-River Health Systems Agy., 1978-82, Tuberculosis Assn. Greater New Orleans, 1968—, Flint-Goodridge Hosp., New Orleans, 1978-82. Fellow Tulane U. Sch. Medicine, 1957-58; recipient Outstanding Alumni award Downstate Med. Ctr., 1973. Fellow ACP, Am. Coll. Cardiology, Am. Coll. Chest Physicians, Am. Coll. Clin. Pharmacology and Chemotherapy; mem. AMA (com. on emergency health service), Am. Thoracic Soc. (councilor), La. Thoracic Soc. (pres. 1964), Nat. Adv. Rsch. Resources Coun. (mem. health care tech. study sect. 1970-74, chmn. 1972-74), Am. Lung Assn. La. (hon. life), Delta Omega, Kappa Delta Phi, Alpha Epsilon Delta, Omicron Delta Kappa, Alpha Omega Alpha. Roman Catholic. Office: Tulane Univ Office Chancellor New Orleans LA 70118

WALSH, JOSEPH A., JR., lawyer; b. Teaneck, N.J., July 19, 1949. BA magna cum laude, Ind. U., 1971, JD magna cum laude, 1974. Bar: Ill. 1974, Fla. 1988, U.S. Dist. Ct. (no. dist. Ill.) 1988. Ptnr. Winston & Strawn, Chgo. Mem. ABA, Fla. Bar. Office: Winston & Strawn 35 W Wacker Dr Chicago IL 60601-1614

WALSH, JOSEPH FIDLER, recording artist, record producer; b. Wichita, Kans., Nov. 20, 1947; s. George William and Helen Alice (Bowen) W. Student, Kent (Ohio) State U. Recording artist with James Gang to 1971, Barnstorm, 1971-74, Eagles, 1976-81; also solo artist; songs include Walk Away, Funk #49, In the City, Life's Been Good; solo albums include You Can't Argue With a Sick Mind, But Seriously Folks, There Goes the Neighborhood, The Smoker You Drink The Player You Get, So What, You Bought It, You Name It, Ordinary Average Guy, 1991, Songs For A Dying Planet, 1992, The Confessor, Got Any Gum?; other albums include (with The James Gang) The James Gang, The James Gang Rides Again, (with Barnstorm) Barnstorm Featuring Joe Walsh, (with The Eagles) Hotel California, The Eagles Live, The Long Run, Hell Freezes Over; disc jockey WXRK, N.Y., 1990; mem. Ringo Starr's All Star Band, 1990. Mem. Amateur Radio Relay League. Research electronic music synthesizers. *

WALSH, JOSEPH MICHAEL, magazine distribution executive; b. N.Y.C., Jan. 19, 1943; s. John Redmond and Bridget Judith (Donovan) W.; m. Theresa Rose Vericker, Oct. 3, 1964; children—Joseph, Matthew, Teresa Ann, John, James. B.B.A. in Acctg., Iona Coll., 1964. With Peat, Marwick, Mitchell & Co., C.P.A.s, N.Y.C., 1964-70, audit supr., until 1970; asst. to chmn. bd. and pres. Cadence Industries Corp., West Caldwell, N.J., 1970-71, v.p.; 1971-74, exec. v.p., 1974-87; pres. subs. Curtis Circulation Co., 1972-74, chmn., chief exec. officer, 1982—; pres. Data Services for Health, 1976-77, U.S. Pencil and Stationery Co., 1977-79, Perfect Subscription Co. (merger Perfect Sch. Plans, Perfect Telephone Plan, Moore Cottrell and Keystone Readers Service), 1980-83. Mem. AICPA, N.J. State Soc. CPAs, K.C. Home: 9 Pond Rd Woodcliff Lake NJ 07675-7706 Office: Curtis Circulation Co 433 Hackensack Ave Hackensack NJ 07601-6319

WALSH, JOSEPH THOMAS, state supreme court justice; b. Wilmington, Del., May 18, 1930; s. Joseph Patrick and Mary Agnes (Bolton) W.; m. Madeline Maria Lamb, Oct. 6, 1955; children: Kevin, Lois, Patrick, Daniel, Thomas, Nancy. BA, LaSalle Coll., 1952; LLB, Georgetown U., 1955. Bar: D.C. 1955, Del. 1955. Atty. Ho. of Reps., Dover, Del., 1961-62; chief counsel Pub. Svc. Commn., Dover, 1964-72; judge Del. Superior Ct., Wilmington, 1972-84; vice chancellor Ct. of Chancery, Wilmington, 1984-85; justice Del. Supreme Ct., Wilmington, 1985—. Capt. U.S. Army, 1955-58. Democrat. Roman Catholic. Office: Del Supreme Ct PO Box 1997 Wilmington DE 19899-1997

WALSH, KATHERINE HERALD, state legislator; b. Pitts., May 1, 1944; m. James L. Walsh; children: Elizabeth, Sara. BA, U. Pitts., 1966; student, U. London, England, 1972-73; JD magna cum laude, Cleve. State U., 1976. Staff atty. Lorain County Legal Aid Soc., 1976-77; pvt. practice Oberlin, Ohio, 1977-91; mem. Ohio Legislature, 1989—; chmn. ethics and standards com Ohio Legis. Mem. exec. com. March of Dimes. Recipient award of Merit Ohio Probate Judge's Assn. for Legis. Action on Probate Legis., award of Distinction Ohio Assn. County Bds. Mental Retardation and Devel. Disabilities, Govtl. Leaders Against Drunk Driving award MADD (Ohio chpt.); named Outstanding Legislator of the Yr. Ohio Acad. Trial Lawyers, 1990. Home: 365 Edison Dr Vermilion OH 44089 also: 15 Hawthorne Dr Oberlin OH 44074 Office: Ohio House of Reps State House Columbus OH 43215

WALSH, KENNETH ALBERT, chemist; b. Yankton, S.D., May 23, 1922; s. Albert Lawrence and Edna (Slear) W.; m. Dorothy Jeanne Thompson, Dec. 22, 1944; children: Jeanne K., Kenneth Albert, David Bruce, Rhonda Jean, Leslie Gay. BA, Yankton Coll., 1942; PhD, Iowa State U., 1950. Asst. prof. chemistry Iowa State U., Ames, 1950-51; staff mem. Los Alamos Sci. Lab., 1951-57; supr. Internat. Minerals & Chem. Corp., Mulberry, Fla., 1957-60; mgr. Brush Beryllium Co., Elmore, Ohio, 1960-72; assoc. dir. tech. Brush Wellman Inc., Elmore, 1972-86; cons., patentee in field. Democratic precinct chmn., Los Alamos, 1956, Fremont, Ohio, 1980. Mem. AIME, Am. Chem. Soc. (sect. treas. 1956), ASM Internat., Toastmasters Internat., Theta Xi, Phi Lambda Upsilon. Methodist.

WALSH, KEVIN A., lawyer; b. Davenport, Iowa, Nov. 28, 1950; s. Thomas Joseph and Ann (Liddle) W.; m. Kathleen Mocciola, Feb. 27, 1982; children: Kelly, Regan, Mallory. BA, Tulane U., 1973; JD, St. Johns Law Sch., 1978; LLM in Taxation, NYU, 1979. Bar: Conn. 1978, N.Y. 1979. Assoc. Hall, McNicol, Hamilton & Clark, N.Y.C., 1979-83, ptnr., 1983-92; ptnr. Keck Mahin & Cate, N.Y.C., 1992—. Pres. bd. dirs. YMCA, Darien, Conn., 1993. Mem. ABA, Conn. Bar Assn., Union League Club. Home: 10 Settlers Trl Darien CT 06820-5531 Office: Keck Mahin & Cate 220 E 42nd St New York NY 10017-5806

WALSH, LAWRENCE EDWARD, lawyer; b. Port Maitland, N.S., Can., Jan. 8, 1912; came to U.S. 1914, naturalized, 1922; s. Cornelius Edward and Lila May (Sanders) W.; m. Mary Alma Porter; children: Barbara Marie, Janet Maxine (Mrs. Alan Larson), Sara Porter, Dale Edward, Elizabeth Porter (Mrs. Joseph Wells). A.B., Columbia, 1932, LL.B., 1935; LL.D., Union U., 1959, St. John's U., 1975, Suffolk U., 1976, Waynesburg Coll., 1976, Vt. Law Sch., 1976. Bar: N.Y. 1936, D.C. 1981, Okla. 1981, U.S. Supreme Ct. 1951. Spl. asst. atty. gen. Drukman Investigation, 1936-38; dep. asst. dist. atty. N.Y. County, 1938-41; assoc. Davis Polk Wardwell Sunderland & Kiendl, 1941-43; asst. counsel to gov. N.Y., 1943-49, counsel to gov., 1950-51; counsel Pub. Service Commn., 1951-53; gen. counsel, exec. dir. Waterfront Commn. of N.Y. Harbor, 1953-54; U.S. judge So. Dist. N.Y., 1954-57; U.S. dep. atty. gen., 1957-60; partner Davis, Polk & Wardwell, 1961-81; counsel firm Crowe & Dunlevy, Oklahoma City, 1981—; ind. counsel Iran/Contra investigation, 1986-93; chmn. N.Y. State Moreland Commn. Alcoholic Beverage Control Law, 1963-64; pres. Columbia Alumni Fedn., 1968-69; dep. head with rank of amb. U.S. del. meetings on Vietnam, Paris, 1969; counsel to N.Y. State Ct. on Judiciary, 1971-72; 2d crct. mem. U.S. Crct. Judge Nominating Commn., 1978-80. Trustee emeritus Columbia U., Mut. Life Ins. Co., N.Y.; trustee William Nelson Cromwell Found. Recipient medal for excellence Columbia U., 1959, Law Sch., Columbia U., 1980, John Jay award Columbia Coll., 1989. Fellow Am. Bar Found., Am. Coll. Trial Lawyers; mem. Am. Law Inst. (coun.), ABA (pres. 1975-76), N.Y. State Bar Assn. (pres. 1966-67), Oklahoma County Bar Assn., Okla. State Bar Assn., Internat. Bar Assn., Assn. of Bar of City of New York, N.Y. County Lawyers Assn., Fed. Bar Coun.; hon. mem. Law Soc. Eng. and Wales, Can. Bar Assn., Mexican Bar Assn., Beta Theta Pi. Presbyterian. Clubs: N.Y. India House, The Century, Oklahoma City Golf and Country; Petroleum (Oklahoma City), Beacon (Oklahoma City). Home: 1902 Bedford Dr Oklahoma City OK 73116-5306 Office: 1800 Mid Am Towers Oklahoma City OK 73102

WALSH, MARTIN R., computer company executive; b. Roca, N.Y., Oct. 2, 1952; s. John M. and Anne R. (Ryan) W.; m. Karen Marie Kolmer, Dec. 30, 1977; children: Ryan, Collin, Shane, Rory, Devlyn. BS in Mktg., U. Colo., 1974; MBA in Fin., U. Rochester, 1977. Fin. analyst Eastman Kodak, Windsor, Colo., 1975, Am. Airlines, N.Y.C., 1977-78; regional mktg. mgr. Comdisco Inc., Rosemont, Ill., 1978-81; v.p. trading Comdisco Inc., Rosemont, 1981-86, sr. v.p. trading, 1986—. Office: Comdisco Inc 6111 N River Rd Rosemont IL 60018-5159

WALSH, MASON, retired newspaperman; b. Dallas, Nov. 27, 1912; s. Herbert C. and Margaret (Hayes) W.; m. Margaret Anne Calhoun, Mar. 7, 1947; children: Margaret Anne (Mrs. James G. Dunn), Timothy Mason, Kevin Calhoun. B.A. in Polit. Sci., So. Meth. U., 1934. Staff Dallas Evening Jour., 1929-37; staff Dallas Dispatch-Jour. (later Dallas Jour.), 1938-42; editor Austin (Tex.) Tribune, 1942; dir. employee relations N.Am. Aviation, Dallas, 1942-45; with Dallas Times-Herald, 1945-60, mng. editor, 1952-60; mng. editor Phoenix Gazette, 1960-66; gen. mgr. Phoenix Newspapers, Inc., 1966-75, asst. pub., 1975-78; pub. Ariz. Republic and Phoenix Gazette, 1978-80, pub. emeritus, 1980—. Profl. musician 1929-33. Chmn. Ariz. Dept. Econ. Planning and Devel. Bd., 1968-71; bd. dirs., v.p. Goodwill Industries Central Ariz., 1978-84, v.p., 1982-83; bd. dirs. Western Newspaper Found., 1974-81; trustee Desert Found., Scottsdale, 1982-85; mem. Nat. Def. Exec. Res., 1964-80. Mem. A.P. Mng. Editors Assn. (dir. 1956-63, pres.

1963), A.P. Assn. Calif., Ariz., Hawaii and Nev. (pres. 1976-77), Ariz. Acad. (dir. 1973-81, v.p. 1980-81), Valley Forward Assn. (dir. 1970-87), Newcomen Soc., Phoenix 40, Sigma Delta Chi. Episcopalian. Clubs: University, Arizona. Home: 4102 N 64th Pl Scottsdale AZ 85251-3110

WALSH, MAURICE DAVID, JR., former librarian, business executive; b. N.Y.C., Dec. 24, 1924; s. Maurice David and Helen Merlyn (Flynn) W.; m. Alice Louise Flynn, Oct. 18, 1952; children—Maud Maureen, Michael Sean, James Liam, Douglas Padraic. B.J., U. Mo., 1949; M.S. in Library Sci, La. State U., 1963; grad., U.S. Army Command and Gen. Staff Coll., 1967. With Jefferson Parish Library, Metairie, La., 1959-80; head librarian Jefferson Parish Library, 1963-80; ret., 1980; area dir. Housing Authority New Orleans, 1980-85; exec. v.p. GTF Enterprises, Inc., 1985—. Contbr. articles to mil. and libr. publs. and Encyclopedia Americana; vol. broadcaster Radio for the Blind and Print Handicapped, WRBH-FM Radio, New Orleans; co-author (film) The Jefferson Parish Story. Past pres. Pontchartrain Shores Civic Assn.; former bd. dirs. East Jefferson Parish ARC, Vets. Blvd. Bus. Assn. With AUS, 1943-45, 50-52; ret. col. Army Res. Mem. Le Petit Theatre du Vieux Carré, Jefferson Performing Arts Soc., Assn. U.S. Army, First Cav. Div. Assn., 11th Armored Div. Assn. (past v.p.). La. State U. Alumni Assn. (past pres. Greater New Orleans chpt.), Elks, Rotary (Paul Harris fellow), Alpha Delta Sigma. Republican. Roman Catholic. Home: 4536 Folse Dr Metairie LA 70006-1261

WALSH, MICHAEL FRANCIS, advertising executive; b. Pitts., June 22, 1956; s. Peter Paul and Joan Brooks (Murdoch) W.; m. Lisa Ann Ruscillo, May 14, 1983; children: Megan, Allison. BA, Duquesne U., 1978; MBA, U. Pitts., 1990. Asst. media planner Ketchum Advt./Pitts., 1978-79, media planner 1979-82, media supr., 1982-84, v.p., assoc. media dir., 1984-86, dir. media ops., 1986-87, media dir., 1987-88, sr. v.p., media dir., 1988-92, dir. ops. and fin., 1993—; part-time mem. faculty U. Pitts., 1990—; adj. faculty Point Park Coll., 1992—. Contbr. articles to advt. jours. Mem. Pitts. Advt. Club (bd. dirs. 1991—), Pitts. Radio and TV Club (bd. dirs. 1988-91, pres. info. tech. media adv. coun. 1995—), Bus. and Profl. Advt. Internat., Inc. (bd. dirs., exec. com. 1991—). Office: Ketchum Communications Inc 6 PPG Pl Pittsburgh PA 15222-5406

WALSH, MICHAEL J., lawyer; b. Portland, Oreg., Sept. 4, 1932; s. Frank M.J. and Elisemary (Derbes) W.; m. June Griffin, Nov. 28, 1959; children: Molly, Erin, Kathryn (dec.), Anne. BA, U. Portland, 1954; JD, Georgetown U., 1959. Bar: D.C. 1959, Oreg. 1959, U.S. Ct. Appeals (fed. and 9th cirs.) 1959, U.S. Tax Ct. 1959, U.S. Supreme Ct. 1968. Law ck. to presiding justice Oreg. Supreme Ct., Salem, 1959-60; mng. ptnr. Rankin, Walsh, Ragen and Roberts, Portland, 1960-75; sole practice Portland, 1976-81; ptnr. Walsh and Conolly, Portland, 1982-83; of counsel McEwen, Hanna, Gisvold and Rankin, Portland, 1983-85, Bullivant, Houser, Bailey, Pendergrass, & Hoffman, Washington, 1985—; chmn. Employees Compensation Appeals Bd. U.S. Dept. Labor, Washington, 1985—; legal counsel to Reagan-Bush '84, Nat. Hdqtrs., Washington, 1983-84. Chmn. legal dev. March of Dimes, 1967; chmn. admissions Georgetown U., Oreg., 1972-83; trustee Christie Sch., 1974-78; trustee Cath. Charities Oreg., 1966-72, pres. 1971; trustee Parry Ctr. for Children, 1967-73, v.p. 1970-71; trustee Portland Tennis Ctr. Assn., 1972-83, pres. 1976-82; bd. dirs. Portland Traffic Safety Commn., 1981-83. Served with JAGC, USAF, capt. res. Mem. Am. Judicature Soc., Am. Trial Lawyers Assn., Nat. Assn. Coll. and Uiv. Attys., Am. Arbitration Assn., D.C. Bar Assn., Oreg. Bar Assn. (mem. various coms.), Multnomah County Bar Assn., Portland C. of C. (bd. dirs. 1975-78, chmn. legis. coun. 1975). Club: Georgetown Univ. (Oreg.) (pres. 1966). Home: 3273 Sutton Pl NW # B Washington DC 20016-3537 Office: Dept of Labor Employee Compensation Appeals Bd 300 7th St SW Washington DC 20210-0001

WALSH, NICOLAS EUGENE, rehabilitation medicine physician, educator; b. Mpls., July 1, 1947; s. Leonard Cyril and June Alice (Otte) W.; m. Wendy Sarah Allnutt, June 1, 1973; children: Meghan, Rorey, Katlin, Alaine. BS, USAF Acad., 1969; MS, Marquette U., 1974; MD, U. Colo., 1979. Asst. prof. naval sci. Marquette U., Milw., 1972-74; from asst. prof. to assoc. prof. rehab. medicine U. Tex. Health Sci. Ctr., San Antonio, 1982-89, prof., chmn. rehab. medicine, 1989—; med. dir. U. Health Sys., San Antonio, 1992—; mem. devel. bd., 1991—; dir. Am. Bd. Phys. Medicine and Rehab., Rochester, Minn., 1994—. Author: (book chpts.) CIBA Collection of Medical Illustrations, 1993, Management of Cancer Pain, 1993, Low Back Pain, 1994; editor: Rehabilitation of Chronic Pain, 1991; editor-in-chief Archives of Physical Medicine and Rehabilitation, Oreg., 1994—. Bd. dirs. Goodwill Industries, San Antonio, 1991—; mem. prof. adv. com. Our Lady of the Lake U., San Antonio, 1992—; mem. devel. bd. Incarnate Word Coll., San Antonio, 1991-93. Recipient Excellence in Rsch. award Am. Jour. Phys. Medicine & Rehab., 1991; named Health Care Profl. of Yr., Gov.'s Com. for Disabled Persons, 1989. Fellow Am. bd. Pain Medicine (v.p. 1993—), Am. Acad. Phys. Medicine and Rehab. (Richard and Hinda Rosenthal Found. award 1991); mem. Assn. Acad. Physiatrists (v.p. 1993—), Phys. Medicine & Rehab. Edn. and Rsch. Found. (mem. 1991—), Excellence in Rsch. award 1991). Office: Rehab Medicine Dept UTHSC-SA 7703 Floyd Curl Dr San Antonio TX 78284

WALSH, PATRICK CRAIG, urologist; b. Akron, Ohio, Feb. 13, 1938; s. Raymond Michael and Catherine N. (Rodden) W.; m. Margaret Campbell, May 23, 1964; children—Christopher, Jonathan, Alexander. A.B., Case Western Res. U., 1960, M.D., 1964. Intern in surgery Peter Bent Brigham Hosp., Boston, 1964-65; asst. resident in surgery Peter Bent Brigham Hosp., 1965-66; asst. resident in pediatric surgery Children's Hosp. Med. Center, Boston, 1966-67; resident in urology U. Calif.-Los Angeles Med. Center, 1967-71; dir. Brady Urol. Inst., urologist-in-chief Johns Hopkins Hosp., Balt., 1974—; prof., dir. dept. urology Johns Hopkins U. Sch. Medicine, 1974—. Contbr. articles to med. jours. Served to comdr. M.C. USN, 1971-73. Mem. Soc. Univ. Surgeons, Am. Assn. Genito-Urinary Surgeons, Clin. Soc. Genito-Urinary Surgeons, Am. Urol. Assn., Endocrine Soc., Am. Surg. Assn., Alpha Omega Alpha. Roman Catholic. Home: 13910 Cuba Rd Baltimore MD 21287 Office: Johns Hopkins Med Insts 600 N Wolfe St Baltimore MD 21287-0001

WALSH, PATRICK J., medical products executive; b. 1928. Registered indsl. acct. With A V Roe Ltd., Can., 1951-56, Ford Motor Co. of Can., 1956-59, Packard Bell Co., Ltd., Can., 1959-70; sr. v.p. Spacelabs Med. Inc., Redmond, Wash., 1970—. Office: Spacelabs Med Inc 15220 NE 40th St Redmond WA 98052*

WALSH, PAUL S., food products executive. CEO Pillsbury Co., Mpls. Office: Pillsbury Co 200 S 6th St Minneapolis MN 55402-1464

WALSH, PETER JOSEPH, physics educator; b. N.Y.C., Aug. 21, 1929; s. Peter and Mary Ellen (Kelly) W.; m. Rosemarie Imundo, May 13, 1952; children: Kathleen, Mary Ellen, Susan, Carole, Karen. B.S., Fordham U., 1951; M.S., N.Y.U., 1953, Ph.D., 1960. Research physicist Westinghouse Elec. Co., Bloomfield, N.J., 1951-60; supervisory physicist Am. Standard, Piscattaway, N.J., 1960-62; prof. Fairleigh Dickinson U., 1962-93; prof. emeritus, 1993—; vis. rsch. scientist MIT, 1977; vis. prof. electronics and elec. engring. U. Sheffield, 1978-79; NASA fellow U. Santa Clara, 1980; Am. Soc. Engring. Edn. Navy fellow Naval Rsch. Labs., 1981, 82, 86, NASA Langley, 1987, Air Force fellow Hanscom AFB, 1988, Kirtland AFB, 1990; vis. prof. U. Genoa, 1984; vis. scholar Stanford U., 1984-85; chmn. bd. trustees EMS Corp., 1991—; cons. physics to 20 labs., 1963—. Author: Dark Side of Knowledge, articles in field. Mem. Am. Phys. Soc., AAAS, N.J. Acad. Sci., Sigma Xi (sec. 1969). Patentee in field. Home: 40 St Josephs Dr Stirling NJ 07980-1224 Office: Fairleigh Dickinson U Teaneck NJ 07666

WALSH, PHILIP CORNELIUS, mining consultant; b. Harrison, N.J., May 23, 1921; s. Philip Cornelius and Frances Walsh (Prendergast) W.; m. Alexandra Somerville Tuck, May 19, 1945 (dec. Sept. 1993); children: Eugenie Philbin Flaherty, Philip C.C., Frances Cornelia Cummings, Alexander Tuck, Nicholas Holladay, Elizabeth Lovering. BA, Yale U., 1944. With W.R. Grace & Co., Lima, Peru and N.Y.C., 1946-71; v.p. parent co., chief operating officer Latin Am. group, 1961-71; group exec. corp. adminstrv. group, 1970-71; v.p. Cerro Corp., 1972-74, Newmont Mining Corp., 1974-80; chmn. bd. Foote Mineral Co., Exton, Pa., 1979-80; vice chmn. St. Joe Minerals Corp., 1980-85; chmn. bd. Chilean Lithium Corp. Ltd.,

1980-94; dir. Cyprus Minerals Co., 1985-93; bd. dirs. T. Rowe Price Assocs., Inc.; mem. Nat. Strategic Minerals and Metals Program Adv. Commn. Mem. Harding Twp. Bd. Edn., N.J., 1960-66; mem. Harding Twp. Com., 1966-72, police commr., 1966-72; trustee Morristown Meml. Hosp., 1969-79; vis. com. Colo. Sch. Mines, Global Systems and Cultures. 1st lt. F.A., U.S. Army, 1943-46. Decorated Silver Star, Purple Heart. Mem. AIME (Saunders gold medal 1992. Disting. Mem. award 1993), Pan Am. Soc. U.S. (past vice chmn.), Am. Soc. (hon. dir.), Am. Assn. Order of Malta (chancellor, bd. chancellors), Racquet and Tennis Club, Edgartown Yacht Club (commodore), Edgartown Golf Club, Phi Beta Kappa, Sigma Xi. Republican. Roman Catholic. Home: Caleb Pond Rd Edgartown MA 02539

WALSH, RICHARD GEORGE, agricultural economist; b. Seward, Nebr., Aug. 16, 1930; s. Thomas George and Francis Kathryn (Pape) W.; m. Patricia Burke Bard, 1976; children by previous marriage: Cathryn M., Susan E., Thomas R., Robert J. B.S., U. Nebr., 1952, M.A., 1955; Ph.D., U. Wis., 1961. From asst. prof. to prof. agrl. econs. U. Nebr., 1958-68; prof. dept. agrl. and resource econs. Colo. State U., Ft. Collins, 1968—; intergovt. exchange EPA, 1973-74; cons. FTC, 1965-66, 72, 78-79, U. P.R., 1967, Justice Dept., 1971, U.S. Forest Service, 1972, 82, 86, Bur. Land Mgmt., 1973, 85, Nat. Park Service, 1975-79; vis. prof. U. Md., 1965, Stanford Research Inst., 1971, U. Newcastle upon Tyne, 1991. Author: Economics of the Baking Industry, 1963, Market Structure of the Agricultural Industries, 1966, The Structure of Food Manufacturing, 1966, Organization and Competition in Food Retailing, 1966, Wilderness Resource Economics, 1982, Wild and Scenic River Economics, 1985, Recreation Economic Decisions: Comparing Benefits and Costs, 1986, Long-Run Forecasts of Participation in Fishing, Hunting and Nonconsumptive Wildlife Recreation, 1987, Economic Demand Studies with Nonmarket Benefit Estimates, 1988, Recreation Value of Ranch Open Space, 1994; contbr. articles to profl. jours. Bd. dirs. North Ft. Collins Sanitation Dist., 1971-73. Served to lt. (j.g.) USNR, 1952-54. Mem. Am. Agrl. Econs. Assn. (Outstanding Published Research award 1964), Assn. Environ. & Resource Econs., Western Agrl. Econs. Assn., European Assn. Environ. & Resource Econs., Internat. Soc. Ecological Economics. Office: Colo State U Dept Agrl Resource Eco Fort Collins CO 80523

WALSH, ROBERT, publishing executive. Pres. Directoriesamerica, Inc., Shawnee Mission, Kas., 1989—. Office: Directoriesamerica Inc 7015 College Blvd Ste 400 Shawnee Mission KS 66211*

WALSH, ROBERT CHARLES, chemical company executive; b. Boston, Aug. 13, 1938; m. Joan E. Kelley, Aug. 26, 1961; children: Joseph, Michael, Robert. B in Commerce, St. Francis Xavier U., 1960; MBA, U. Detroit, 1962. Fin. analyst Dewey and Almy Chem. div. W.R. Grace & Co., Lexington, Mass., 1962-66, mgr. fin. planner, analyst, 1966-67, treas., 1967-69, v.p. fin., 1969-72, v.p. fin. and adminstrn., 1972-77, v.p. ops., 1977-79, v.p., gen. mgr., 1979-82; exec. v.p. constrn. products div. W.R. Grace & Co.-Conn., Cambridge, Mass., 1982-86, pres., 1986-89; sr. v.p. W.R. Grace; exec. v.p. Grace Spl. Chems., Boca Raton, Fla., 1989—; bd. dirs. Grace-Sierra Hort. Products Co., Milpitas, Calif. Office: W R Grace & Co 1 Town Ctr Boca Raton FL 33486

WALSH, ROBERT FRANCIS, oil company executive; b. N.Y.C., Sept. 8, 1930; s. Robert F. and Marie R. (Schultz) W.; m. Carol A. Teston; children: Robert F., Brian D., Michael K., Maureen A., Christopher D., Julie M., Kathy M. BS ChemE, MIT, 1952, MS ChemE, 1953. Refinery planner ea. div. Chevron Oil, Perth Amboy, N.J., 1955-63, econ. analyst ea. div., 1963-66; supply coordinator Standard Oil Co. Calif. (later Chevron), San Francisco, 1966-71; traffic mgr. Chevron Shipping Co., San Francisco, 1971-74; v.p. Standard Oil div. Chevron Oil, Louisville, 1974-76; v.p. supply Chevron U.S.A. Inc., San Francisco, 1977-86; pres. Chevron Internat. Oil Co. Inc., San Francisco, 1986—. Served to lt. U.S. Army, 1953-55. Club: World Trade (San Francisco). Office: Chevron Industries Inc PO Box 7643 San Francisco CA 94104

WALSH, RODGER JOHN, lawyer; b. Kansas City, Mo., Apr. 20, 1924; s. John Joseph and Margaret Mary (Halloran) W.; m. Patricia Ann O'Brien, Nov. 18, 1950; children—Regina, Martin, Eileen, Daniel, Veronica, Bernard, Kathleen. B.S., Rockhurst Coll., 1947; J.D., Georgetown U., 1950. Bar: Mo. 1950, D.C. 1950, U.S. Ct. Appeals (8th cir.) 1955, U.S. Supreme Ct. 1960. Spl. agt. FBI, Washington, 1950-53; ptnr. Linde-Thomson Van Dyke Fairchild, Kansas City, Mo., 1953-63, Biersmith & Walsh, 1963-69; v.p., asst. gen. counsel Riss Internat., 1969-83, exec. v.p., gen. counsel, 1983-87; pvt. practice law Independence, Mo., 1987—; bd. dir. Grandview Bank & Trust Co., Mo., chmn., mem. Mo. State Personnel Adv. Bd., Jefferson City, 1979-84; mem. Mo. State Environ. Improvement Authority, 1977-83. Bd. dirs. Mo. Bus and Truck Assn., Jefferson City, 1983-87, Democracy Inc., Kansas City, Mo., 1960—; hon. dir. Rockhurst Coll., 1960—. With U.S. Army, 1942-45; ETO. Decorated Air Medal with 5 oak leaf clusters. Mem. Mo. Bar Assn., Fed. Bar Assn., Kansas City Bar Assn., Am. Legion, Soc. Former FBI Agts. Democrat. Roman Catholic. Home: 10512 Mersington Ave Kansas City MO 64137-1626 Office: Po Box 1078 115 W Lexington Independence MO 64051-0578

WALSH, SEMMES GUEST, retired insurance company executive; b. Annapolis, Md., June 15, 1926; m. Annette Hunt Cromwell, Aug. 23, 1952; children: Semmes. G. Jr., Annette T., Marion H., Jacquelyn C. BE, Yale U., 1946; MBA, Harvard U., 1950. Gen. ptnr. Baker, Watts & Co., Balt., 1962-74, mng. ptnr., 1974-80; exec. v.p., chief fin. officer Monumental Corp., Balt., 1980-89, ret., 1989. Bd. dirs. Wm. G. Baker Meml. Fund, Jas. L. Kernan Hosp. Found. Lt. (j.g.) USNR, 1943-46. Republican. Episcopalian. Avocations: tennis, golf. Home: 230 Hopkins Ln Owings Mills MD 21117-4327

WALSH, THOMAS A., production designer. Prodn. designer: (IMAX films) Flyers, 1980, Speed, 1984, The Discoverers, 1993, (TV movies) Miss Lonely Hearts, 1981, A Gathering of Old Men, 1986 (Emmy award nomination outstanding art direction 1987), Eugene O'Neill, 1986, War Story: Vietnam, 1988, Without Warning: The James Brady Story, 1990 (Emmy award nomination outstanding art direction 1991), Blindspot, 1992, In Search of Dr. Seuss, 1994, (documentaries) John Huston, 1988, MGM: When the Lion Roars, 1992 (Emmy award outstanding art direction 1993), (feature films) The Handmaid's Tale, 1990, Prayer of the Rollerboys, 1990. Office: Doug Apatow Agency 10559 Blythe Ave Los Angeles CA 90064*

WALSH, THOMAS CHARLES, lawyer; b. Mpls., July 6, 1940; s. William G. and Kathryne M. Walsh; m. Joyce Williams, Sept. 7, 1968; children: Brian Christopher, Timothy Daniel, Laura Elizabeth. BS in Commerce magna cum laude, St. Louis U., 1962, LLB cum laude, 1964. Bar: Mo. 1964, U.S. Supreme Ct. 1971, U.S. Dist. Ct. (ea. dist.) Mo. 1964, U.S. Ct. Appeals (8th cir.) 1968, U.S. Ct. Appeals (6th cir.) 1972, U.S. Ct. Appeals (5th cir.) 1974, U.S. Ct. Appeals (D.C. cir.) 1980, U.S. Ct. Appeals (7th cir.) 1982, U.S. Ct. Appeals (9th cir.) 1987, U.S. Ct. Appeals (4th cir.) 1989, U.S. Ct. Appeals (11th and Fed. cirs.) 1992, U.S. Ct. Appeals (2d and 10th cirs.) 1993. Jr. ptnr. Bryan, Cave, McPheeters & McRoberts, St. Louis, 1964-73, ptnr. Bryan Cave, 1974—, exec. com., 1980—; mem. 8th Cir. Adv. Com., 1983-84. Served with U.S. Louis Symphony Soc., 1983— Served with U.S. Army, 1965-66, to lt. USNR, 1966-71. Fellow Am. Coll. Trial Lawyers, Am. Acad. Appellate Lawyers; mem. ABA, Mo. Bar, St. Louis Bar Assn., Am. Law Inst., Mo. Athletic Club, Noonday Club, Bellerive Country Club. Roman Catholic. Office: Bryan Cave 1 Metropolitan Sq 211 N Broadway Saint Louis MO 63102

WALSH, THOMAS GERARD, actuary; b. N.Y.C., Jan. 14, 1942; s. Martin Joseph and Margaret Ellen (Moyles) W.; children: Brian, Kristen, Meghan, Jacqueline. B.S., Manhattan Coll. Exec. v.p. Tchrs. Ins. & Annuity Am./CREF, N.Y.C. Fellow Soc. Actuaries. Office: Tchrs Ins & Annuity Assn Am 730 3rd Ave New York NY 10017-3206

WALSH, THOMAS JAMES, state senator; b. Chgo., July 4, 1960; s. William Dowdle and Barbara Ann (Kennedy) W. BBA, Loras Coll., 1982. Lic. real estate salesperson. From sales rep. to pub. rels. mgr. Binks Mfg. Co., Franklin Park, Ill., 1982—; state rep. State of Ill., Springfield, 1992—; state senator, 1994—. Commr. Met. Water Reclamation Dist. of Greater

Chgo., 1988-90, chmn. Engring. com., Health and Pub. Welfare com.; active LaGrange Park Caucus, LaGrange Park Libr., St. Francis Xavier Ch., LaGrange. Mem. Irish Fellowship Club Chgo., Phoenix Soc. of Community Family Svc. and Mental Health Assn., LaGrange Kiwanis, Loras Coll. Alumni Club Chgo. Office: State of Ill 10544 Cermak Rd Westchester IL 60154

WALSH, THOMAS JOSEPH, neuro-ophthalmologist; b. N.Y.C., Sept. 18, 1931; s. Thomas Joseph and Virginia (Hughes) W.; m. Sally Ann Maust, June 21, 1958; children—Thomas Raymond, Sara Ann, Mary Kelly, Kathleen Meghan. BA, Coll. Fordham, 1954; MD, Bowman Gray Med. Sch., 1958. Intern St. Vincent's Hosp., N.Y.C., 1958-59; resident ophthalmology Bowman Gray Med. Sch., Winston-Salem, N.C., 1961-64; fellow neuro-ophthalmology Bascom Palmer Eye Inst., Miami, Fla., 1964-65; practice medicine specializing in neuro-ophthalmology Stamford, Conn., 1965—; dir. neuro-ophthalmology service, asst. prof. ophthalmology and neurology Yale Sch. Medicine, New Haven, 1965-74; assoc. prof. Yale Sch. Medicine, 1974-79, prof., 1979—, also bd. permanent officers; dir. ophthalmology Stamford Hosp., 1978-83; mem. staff St. Joseph Hosp., Yale New Haven Hosp.; cons. to surgeon gen. army in neuro-ophthalmology Walter Reed Hosp., Washington, 1966—, VA Hosp., West Haven, 1965—, Silver Hill Found., New Canaan, Conn., 1974—; frequent lectr. various univs. Contbr. articles to various publs. Mem. adv. bd. Stamford Salvation Army, 1972-92; mem. med. bd. Darien Nurses Assn., Conn., 1972—; surgeon Darien Fire Dept., 1969—. With AUS, 1959-61. Decorated Knight of Malta, 1983; Centennial fellow Johns Hopkins, 1976. Mem. AMA, Conn., Fairfield County med. socs., Acad. Ophthalmology, Oxford Ophthal. Congress, Acad. Neurology, Am. Assn. Neurol. Surgeons, Internat. Neuro-Ophthalmology Soc., Soc. Med. Cons. to Armed Forces, Cosmos Club (Washington), Darien County Club, Yale Club (N.Y.C.), Lions, Army-Navy Club. Office: 1100 Bedford St Stamford CT 06905-5301

WALSH, W. TERENCE, lawyer; b. Toledo, Ohio, Nov. 18, 1943; s. Walter James and Ann (Gifford) W.; m. Patricia Jane Walker, Dec. 17, 1966; children: Christopher O'Brien, Ryan Kerrick, Ann Elisabeth. AB, Brown U., 1965; JD, Emory U., 1970. Bar: Ga., 1971, U.S. Dist. Ct. (no. dist.) Ga., 1971, U.S. Ct. Appeals (11th cir.), 1971. Assoc. Alston, Miller & Gaines, Atlanta, 1970-76, ptnr., 1976-83; ptnr. Alston & Bird, Atlanta, 1983—; lectr. various seminars on appellate procedure, juvenile law, ethics, and professionalism. Contbr. articles to profl. jours. Bd. dirs. Georgians for Children, Atlanta, The Bridge, Atlanta; bd. dirs. Atlanta Legal Aid Soc., 1987-88; bd. dirs. Capital Area Mosai, Atlanta, chmn., 1994-95; chmn. sch. bd. Christ the King Sch., Atlanta, 1982-84; alumni trustee Brown U., 1994—. Fellow Ga. Bar Found.; Mem. ABA, State Bar Ga. (bd. govs. 1979—, pres. young lawyers sect. 1980-81, H. Sol Clark award 1987), Atlanta Bar Assn. (bd. dirs. 1987-93, pres. 1991-92, Charles E. Watkins award 1994), Gate City Bar Assn. Avocations: sports, gardening, reading. Office: Alston & Bird 1201 W Peachtree St NW Atlanta GA 30309-3400

WALSH, WILLIAM, former football coach; b. Los Angeles, Nov. 30, 1931. Student, San Mateo Jr. Coll.; BA, San Jose State U., 1954, MA in Edn., 1959. Asst. coach Monterey Peninsula Coll., 1955, San Jose State U., 1956; head coach Washington Union High Sch., Fremont, Calif., 1957-59; asst. coach U. Calif., Berkeley, 1960-62, Stanford U., 1963-65, Oakland Raiders, Am. Football League, 1966-67, Cin. Bengals, 1968-75, San Diego Chargers, Nat. Football League, 1976; head coach Stanford U., 1977-78; head coach, gen. mgr. San Francisco 49ers, NFL, 1979-89, exec. v.p., 1989; broadcaster NBC Sports, 1989-91; head coach Stanford U., 1992-95. Named NFL Coach of Yr., Sporting News, 1981; coached Stanford U. winning team Sun Bowl, 1977, Bluebonnet Bowl, 1978, Blockbuster Bowl, 1993, San Francisco 49ers to Super Bowl championships, 1981, 84, 88; elected to Pro Football Hall of Fame, 1993. Office: c/o Stanford U Gary Migdol Sports Info Office Dept Athletics Stanford CA 94305-1684*

WALSH, WILLIAM ALBERT, management consultant, former naval officer; b. Gilman, Ill., Aug. 15, 1933; s. Lawrence Eugene and Myrtle R. (Mulder) W.; m. Joan Elizabeth Kennedy, Dec. 28, 1957; children: Kathryn, Michael, Julie. B.S. in Commerce, U. Notre Dame, 1955; M.S. in Mgmt. with distinction, U.S. Naval Postgrad. Sch., Monterey, Calif., 1962; M.S. in Internat. Affairs with honors, George Washington U., 1972. Commd. ensign U.S. Navy, 1955, advanced through grades to rear adm., 1981; exec. asst. to dep. chief naval ops. (Surface Warfare), Washington, 1974-76; comdg. officer USS Juneau, San Diego, 1976-78; comdr. Amphibious Squadron Three, San Diego, 1978-79; head plans and policy div., comdr. rapid deployment naval forces Comdr. in Chief U.S. Pacific Fleet, Honolulu, 1979-81; comdr. Amphibious Group Eastern Pacific, San Diego, 1981-82; dir. surface warfare div. Office Chief Naval Ops., Pentagon, Washington, 1983-85; ret., 1985; pres. Air/Space Am., San Diego, 1986-89, W.A. Walsh Enterprises, 1990—. Decorated Legion of Merit with 2 gold stars, Bronze Star, Navy Commendation medal U.S.; Disting. Service Order 2d Class Vietnam.

WALSH, WILLIAM ARTHUR, JR., lawyer; b. Washington, Mar. 17, 1949; children: Jesse Creighton, Patrick McKay. BS in Econs. and Fin., U. Md., 1972; JD, U. Richmond, 1977. Bar: Va. Ptnr. Hunton & Williams, Richmond, Va.; mem. adv. bd. for law rev. U. Richmond. Mem. adv. bd. Boys' and Girls' Club Richmond chpt. Salvation Army, 1993. Mem. Va. Bar Assn. (chmn. real estate legal opinions com.), Richmond Bar Assn., Ctrl. Richmond Assn. (mem. bd. dirs.), Omicron Delta Kappa. Home: 4705 Leonard Pky Richmond VA 23226-1337 Office: Hunton & Williams Riverfront Pla East Tower 951 E Byrd St Richmond VA 23219-4040

WALSH, WILLIAM DESMOND, investor; b. N.Y.C., Aug. 4, 1930; s. William J. and Catherine Grace (Desmond) W.; m. Mary Jane Gordon, Apr. 5, 1951; children: Deborah, Caroline, Michael, Suzanne, Tara Jane, Peter. JD, Fordham U., 1951; LL.B., Harvard, 1955. Bar: N.Y. state bar 1955. Asst. U.S. atty. So. dist. N.Y., N.Y.C., 1955-58; counsel N.Y. Commn. Investigation, N.Y.C., 1958-61; mgmt. cons. McKinsey & Co., N.Y.C., 1961-67; sr. v.p. Arcata Corp., Menlo Park, Calif., 1967-82; gen. ptnr. Sequoia Assocs., 1982—; pres., chief exec. officer Atacra Liquidating Trust, 1982-88; chmn. bd. dirs. Deanco, Inc., Ithaca, N.Y., Newell Indsl. Crop., Lowell, Mich., Champion Rd. Machinery Ltd., Goderick, Ont.; bd. dirs. URS Inc., San Francisco, Newcourt Credit Group, Inc., Basic Vegetable Products, King City, Calif., Consolidated Freightways, Inc., Palo Alto, Calif., Nat. Edn. Corp. of Irvine, Calif., Mike Yurosek & Sons, L.P., Lamont, Calif. Mem. bd. visitors Sch. Bus. U. So. Calif., Harvard Law Sch.; trustee Fordham U. Mem. N.Y. State Bar Assn., Harvard Club (N.Y.C. and San Francisco), Knights of Malta. Home: 279 Park Ln Menlo Park CA 94027-5448 Office: 3000 Sand Hill Rd Bldg 2 Ste 140 Menlo Park CA 94025-7116

WALSH, WILLIAM EGAN, JR., electronics executive; b. Springfield, Mass., Dec. 2, 1948; s. William Egan and Veronica (Maroney) W.; m. Terese Anne Sullivan, Oct. 25, 1952; children: Brian, Kathleen, John, Kevin. BA in Physics, Holy Cross, 1970; MS in Physical Oceanography, U.S. Naval Sch., Monterey, Calif., 1971; MBA, U. North Fla., 1975. Oceanographer Sippican, Inc., Marion, Mass., 1975-77, mktg. mgr., 1977-80, from v.p. to sr. v.p., 1980-90; pres., dir. Sippican Inc., Marion, Mass., 1990—; also bd. dirs. Sippican, Inc., Marion. Lt. USN, 1970-75, lt. comdr. USNR, 1976-80. Mem. Marine Tech. Soc. Roman Catholic. Avocations: boating, jogging, racquetball, photography. Office: Sippican Inc 7 Barnabas Rd Marion MA 02738-1421

WALSH, WILLIAM H., JR., statistical research director. Dir. National Highway Traffic Safety Administration National ctr for Statistics and Analysis, Washington, D.C. Office: Nat Hwy Traffic Safety Adminstrn NRD-30 400 7th St SW Washington DC 20590

WALSHE, AUBREY PETER, political science educator; b. Johannesburg, South Africa, Jan. 12, 1934; s. Aubrey John and Joan Kathleen (Evans) W.; m. Catherine Ann Pettifer, Jan. 28, 1957; children: Sally, Jane, Dominic, Emma. BA, Wadham Coll., Oxford, Eng., 1956, MA, 1959; PhD, St. Antony's Coll., Oxford, 1968. Vis. asst. prof. U. Notre Dame, Ind., 1962-63, asst. prof. dept. govt. and internat. studies, 1971-77, dir. African studies, 1971-77, assoc. prof., 1971-77, prof., 1977—; sr. assoc. fellow St. Antony's Coll., Oxford, 1972-73; dir. ann. Missionary Inst. on Sub-Saharan Africa, U.Notre Dame, 1989—; lectr. and cons. in field; found. mem. So. African

Rsch. Archival Project;l mem. N.Am. Support Com., Ecumenical Dialogue of Third World Theologians. Contbr. articles to profl. jours.; author: The Rise of African Nationalism in South Africa, 1971, 2d edit. 1988, Black Nationalism in South Africa: A Short History, 1975, Church Versus State in South Africa, 1983; contbr. revs. to numerous jours.; occasional reader: U. Calif. Press, U. Notre Dame Press, Rev. of Politics, Social Scis. and Humanities Rsch. Coun. of Can., Ottawa, Ind. U. African Studies Pubs. Com., Cath. Inst. for Internat. Rels., London, U. Queensland, Australia. Mem. edn. com. cath. Inst. for Internat. Rels., London; adv. bd. Storypoint Ctr., Presbyn. Ch. U.S.A., N.Y.C.; cons. Nat. Coun. of Chs. of Christ, Convocation of the Kairos Document: Challenge to the Ch. in South Africa. Walsh-Price fellow Ctr. for Mission Studies, Maryknoll, N.Y., 1980-81, Helen Kellogg Inst. for Internat. Studies fellow, 1983, Inst. for Internat. Peace Studies fellow, 1987; MacArthur Found. grantee, 1989-90. Ecumenical Christian. Home: 914 N Niles Ave South Bend IN 46617-1248 Office: Univ Notre Dame Dept Govt Notre Dame IN 46556

WALSKE, M(AX) CARL, JR., physicist; b. Seattle, June 2, 1922; s. Max Carl and Margaret Ella (Fowler) W.; m. Elsa Marjorie Nelson, Dec. 28, 1946; children: C. Susan, Steven C., Carol A. B.S. in Math. cum laude, U. Wash., 1944; Ph.D. in Theoretical Physics, Cornell U., 1951. Staff mem., then asst. theoretical div. leader Los Alamos Sci. Lab., 1951-56; dep. research dir. Atomics Internat., Canoga Park, Calif., 1956-59; sci. rep. AEC in U.K., London, Eng., 1961-62; theoretical physicist RAND Corp., 1962-63; sci. attache U.S. missions to NATO and OECD, Paris, France, 1963-65; staff mem. Los Alamos Sci. Lab., 1965-66; asst. to sec. def. (atomic energy), 1966-73; pres., chief operating officer Atomic Indsl. Forum, Inc., Washington, 1973-87; chmn. Dept. Def. Mil. Liaison Com. to U.S. AEC, 1966-73; mem. U.S. del. Conf. Suspension Nuclear Tests, Geneva, 1959-61; chair reunion com. U. Wash., 1994-95; chair Upper Hood Canal Watershed Mgmt. Com., 1994-95; comdr. Agate Pass Power Squadron, 1995; mem. fin. com. Ctrl. Kitsap Sch. Dist., 1994-95. Served to lt. (j.g.) USNR, 1943-46. Recipient Disting. Civilian Service medal Dept. Def. Fellow Explorers Club, Am. Phys. Soc.; mem. Am. Nuclear Soc., U.S. Power Squadrons, Poulsbo Yacht Club, Phi Beta Kappa, Sigma Xi. Home: PO Box 370 Silverdale WA 98383-0370 *To seek out positions which appeared the most challenging and personally satisfying; to gain my reward through self-respect rather than public recognition; to expend extra effort as an offset to my limitations.*

WALSKE, STEVEN C., computer software company executive; b. 1952. Grad., Harvard U., 1978. With venture capital divsn. Paine Webber, Boston, 1978-83; pres., CEO Multiplication Software, Cambridge, Mass., 1983-85; CFO Computer Corp. of Am., Cambridge, 1985-86; pres., CEO Parametric Tech. Corp., Waltham, Mass., 1986—. Office: Parametric Technology Corp 128 Technology Dr Waltham MA 02154-8938*

WALSTON, RAY, actor; b. Laurel, Miss., Nov. 2, 1924; s. Harry Norman and Mittie (Kimbrell) W.; m. Ruth Calvert, Nov. 3, 1943; 1 dau., Katharine Ann. Grad. high sch., New Orleans. Appeared at Margo Jones Theatre, Houston, 1938-43, Cleve. Playhouse, 1943-45; Broadway appearances include GI Hamlet, 1945, Front Page, 1946, The Survivors, 1947, The Insect Comedy, 1948, Richard III, 1949, Summer and Smoke, 1949 (Clarence Derwent award 1949), The Rat Race, 1949, South Pacific, 1950, Me and Juliet, 1953, House of Flowers, 1954, Damn Yankees, 1955 (Tony award 1955); films include Kiss Them for Me, 1957, South Pacific, 1957, Damn Yankees, 1958, Tall Story, 1958, The Apartment, 1959, Portrait in Black, 1960, Wives & Lovers, 1963, Kiss Me Stupid, 1964, Paint Your Wagon, 1968, Who's Minding the Store, Caprice, The Sting, 1973, The Silver Streak, 1976, Popeye, 1980, Fast Times at Ridgemont High, 1982, Johnny Dangerously, 1984, From the Hip, 1986, Fine Gold, 1987, A Man of Passion, 1988, Popcorn, 1989, Ski Patrol, 1989, Of Mice and Men, 1991; dir.: Broadway musical Damn Yankees, 1974; TV series My Favorite Martian, 1963-66, Picket Fences, 1993— (Emmy nomination, Supporting Actor - Drama Series, 1994); TV movies include: The Stand, 1994. Mem. Actors Studio, Players Club. *Regarding success in any field, two of the most important words in the English language, or any language for that matter, are persistence and determination. They are all-powerful; nothing can match them.*

WALSTON, RODERICK EUGENE, state attorney general; b. Gooding, Idaho, Dec. 15, 1935; s. Loren R. and Iva M. (Boyer) W.; m. Margaret D. Grandey; children: Gregory Scott W., Valerie Lynne W. A.A., Boise Jr. Coll., 1956; B.A. cum laude, Columbia Coll., 1958; LL.B. scholar, Stanford U., 1961. Bar: Calif. 1961, U.S. Supreme Ct. 1973. Law clk to judge U.S. Ct. Appeals 9th Cir., 1961-62; dep. atty. gen State of Calif., San Francisco, 1963-91, head natural resources sect, 1969-91, chief asst. atty. gen. pub. rights div., 1991—; spl. dep counsel Kings County, Calif., 1975-76; mem. environ. and natural resources adv. coun. Stanford (Calif.) Law Sch. Contbr. articles to profl. jours.; bd. editors: Stanford Law Rev., 1959-61, Western Natural Resources Litigation Digest, Calif. Water Law and Policy Reporter; spl. editor Jour. of the West. Co-chmn. Idaho campaign against Right-to-Work initiative, 1958; Calif. rep. Western States Water Coun., 1986—; environ. and natural resources adv. coun., Stanford Law Sch. Nat. Essay Contest winner Nat. Assn. Internat. Rels. Clubs, 1956, Stanford Law Rev. prize, 1961; Astor Found. scholar, 1956-58. Mem. ABA (chmn. water resources com., 1988-90, vice chmn. and conf. chmn., 1985-88, 90—), Contra Costa County Bar Assn., U.S. Supreme Ct. Hist. Soc., World Affairs Coun. No. Calif. Office: Calif Atty Gen's Office 1515 K St Fl 6 Sacramento CA 95814-4017

WALT, ALEXANDER JEFFREY, surgeon, educator; b. Cape Town, South Africa, June 13, 1923; came to U.S., 1961, naturalized, 1966; s. Isaac and Lea (Garb) W.; m. Irene Lapping, Dec. 21, 1947; children: John R., Steven D., Lindsay J. MB, ChB, U. Cape Town, 1948; MS, U. Minn., 1956. Diplomate: Am. Bd. Surgery (bd. dirs. 1976-85, vice chmn. 1983-85). Intern Groote Schuur Hosp. U. Cape Town, 1949-50; resident in surgery Mayo Clinic, Rochester, Minn., 1952-56; surg. registrar St. Martin's Hosp., Bath, Eng., 1956-57; asst. surgeon Groote Schuur Hosp., Cape Town, 1957-61; asst. chief surgery VA Hosp., Dearborn, Mich., 1961-62; chmn. dept. surgery Wayne State U., Detroit, 1966-88; chief of surgery Detroit Receiving Hosp., 1965-80, Harper-Grace Hosps., Detroit, 1972-88; prof. surgery Wayne State U., 1966-90, disting. prof. surgery, 1990—. Author: (with R.F. Wilson) Management of Trauma: Pitfalls and Practice, 1975; editor: Early Care of the Injured, 1982. Served with South Africa Armed Forces, 1943-45. Fellow Royal Coll. Surgeons (Can.), Royal Coll. Surgeons (Eng., Hunterian prof. 1969, Moynihan lectr. 1989) ACS (bd. govs. 1975-81, bd. regents 1984-93, chmn. 1991-93, pres. elect 1993-94, pres. 1994-95, scudder orator 1978), Coll. Surgeons of South Africa (hon.), Royal Coll. Surgeons of Edinburgh (hon.); mem. Am. Surg. Assn. (1st v.p. 1990), Cen. Surg. Assn. (pres. 1977-78), Western Surg. Assn. (pres. 1986-87), Soc. Surgery of Alimentary Tract (founder's lectr. 1977, v.p. 1992-93), Am. Assn. Surgery of Trauma (pres. 1976-77), Am. Bd. Med. Specialists (exec. com. 1983-89, treas. 1985-89, v.p.), Internat. Soc. Surgery, Am. Bd. Med. Specialties (pres. 1992-94), Asian Surg. Assn. (hon.), Royal Australasian Coll. Surgeons (hon.), Alpha Omega Alpha. Office: 6-C Univ Health Ctr 4201 St Antoine St Detroit MI 48201-2194

WALT, HAROLD RICHARD, rancher; b. Berkeley, Calif., Jan. 30, 1923; s. Ralph Sidney and Frances Kathryn (Leahy) W.; m. Kathleen Dorothy O'Connell, Dec. 20, 1947; children: Michael Lowney, Timothy Gordon, Kimberly Ann, Patrick Randolph, Jennifer Joan, Carolyn Marie. B.S. in Forestry, U. Calif.-Berkeley, 1948, B.S. in Bus. Adminstrn., 1950, M.B.A. in Corp. Fin., 1953. Vice chancellor fin., lectr. bus. adminstrn. U. Calif., Berkeley, 1964-68; asst. budget dir. Kaiser Industries Corp., Oakland, Calif., 1961-64; dep. dir. fin. State of Calif., 1965-66; dir. civil systems Aerojet-Gen. Corp., El Monte, Calif., 1967-68; exec. v.p. SysteMed Corp., Newport Beach, Calif., 1969-71; pres. William L. Pereira Assos., Los Angeles, 1972-74; dean Coll. Bus. Adminstrn., U. San Francisco, 1978-89; prof. mgmt., 1989; rancher, co-owner, mgt. Box D Ranch, Ashland, Oreg., 1989—; vis. prof. fin. San Francisco State U., 1978; chmn. bd. Fidelity Savs. & Loan Assn., 1982; bd. dirs. Homestead Savs.vis. scholar, 1981; bd. dirs Eureka Savs. & Loan; adv. com. Fed. Home Loan Mortgage Corp., Washington, 1980-83; vis. scholar Coll. Natural Resources, U. Calif., 1984; S.J. Hall lectr. in indsl. forestry U. Calif., Berkeley, 1986; vis. prof. forest policy U. Calif., 1987, 88. Contbr. over 50 articles related to bus. and forestry. Mem. Calif. Gov.'s Commn. Ocean Resources, 1965-66, Gov.'s Com. Econ. Devel., 1965-66;

chmn. Calif. State Bd. Forestry, 1983-90; chmn. bd. Children's Hosp., Stanford, Calif. 1974-80; bd. dirs. Calif. Dept. Forestry, 1990-91, Nat. Forest Found., 1992-94. Served with USMCR, 1942-47. Fellow Fund Adult Edn., 1958; named Calif. Forester of Yr., Calif. Assn. Resource Conservation Dists., 1986. Mem. Soc. Am. Foresters, Am. Forestry Assn. (bd. dirs.), Fin. Execs. Inst., Bay Area Pub. Affairs Council, Acad. Mgmt., Security Analysts Soc., Town Hall of Calif. (bd. dirs. 1972-74), Beta Gamma Sigma, Pi Sigma Alpha, Alpha Zeta, Xi Sigma Pi, Theta Delta Chi, Delta Sigma Pi, Beta Alpha Psi. Republican. Roman Catholic. Clubs: Bohemian (San Francisco); Sutter (Sacramento). Home: PO Box 1267 Ashland OR 97520

WALT, MARTIN, physicist, consulting educator; b. West Plains, Mo., June 1, 1926; s. Martin and Dorothy (Mantz) W.; m. Mary Estelle Thompson, Aug. 16, 1950; children: Susan Mary, Stephen Martin, Anne Elizabeth, Patricia Ruth. B.S., Calif. Inst. Tech., 1950; M.S., U. Wis., 1951, Ph.D., 1953. Staff mem. Los Alamos Sci. Lab., 1953-56; research scientist, mgr. physics Lockheed Missiles and Space Co., Palo Alto (Calif.) Rsch. Lab., 1956-71, dir. phys. scis., 1971-86, dir. research, 1986-93; cons. prof. Stanford U., 1986—; mem. adv. com. NRC, NASA, Dept. Def., U. Calif. Lawrence Berkeley Lab. Contbr. articles to sci. jours. Served with USNR, 1944-46. Wis. Research Found. fellow, 1950-51; AEC fellow, 1951-53. Fellow Am. Geophys. Union, Am. Phys. Soc.; mem. Am. Inst. Physics (bd. govs.), Bd. Overseers for Superconducting Supercollider, Fremont Hills Country Club. Home: 12650 Viscaino Ct Los Altos Hills CA 94022 Office: Stanford U Starlab Durand 317 Stanford CA 94305

WALTER, ALAN STUART, crop insurance industry association executive; b. Ottawa, Ill., May 21, 1945; s. Arthur L. and Edna L. (Schober) W.; m. M. Kathleen Yednock, Aug. 26, 1967; children: Aaron, Bryce. BS in Agrl. Econs., U. Ill., 1967; MS in Agrl. Econs., Cornell U., 1969; PhD in Agrl. Econs., Wash. State U., 1974. Agrl. economist Econ. Rsch. Svc., Washington, 1974-77; br. chief Structures br. Econ. Rsch. Svc., Washington, 1978-79; staff economist Fed. Crop Ins. Corp., Kansas City, Mo., 1980-81, dir. reins., 1981-84; dir. multiple peril svcs. Crop Hail Ins. Actuarial Assn., Overland Park, Kans., 1984-87, v.p. actuarial svcs., 1987-89; pres. Nat. Crop Ins. Svcs., Overland Park, Kans., 1990—; adv. com. Midwest Climate Ctr., Champaign, Ill., 1989—. Cubmaster Boy Scouts Am., Overland Park, 1987; bd. dirs., umpire Little League Baseball, Overland Park, 1985-90. With U.S. Army, 1969-71. Decorated Bronze Star. Mem. Nat. Assn. Bus. Economists, Overland Park C. of C., Am. Agrl. Econ. Assn. (Disting. Policy Contbn. 1978). Avocations: reading, travel. Office: Nat Crop Ins Svcs 7301 College Blvd Ste 170 Overland Park KS 66210-1895

WALTER, DONALD ELLSWORTH, federal judge; b. Jennings, La., Mar. 15, 1936; s. Robert R. and Ada (Lafleur) D'Aquin; m. Charlotte Sevier Donald, Jan. 5, 1942; children: Laura Ney, Robert Ellsworth, Susannah Brooks. BA, La. State U., 1961, JD, 1964. Bar: La. 1964, U.S. Supreme Ct. 1969. Assoc. Cavanaugh, Brame, Holt & Woodley, 1964-66, Holt & Woodley, Lake Charles, La., 1966-69; U.S. atty. U.S. Dept. Justice, Shreveport, La., 1969-77; lawyer Hargrove, Guyton, Ramey & Barlow, Shreveport, La., 1977-85; judge U.S. Dist. Ct. (west. dist.) La., Monroe, 1985-92, Shreveport, La., 1993—. Served with AUS, 1957-58. Office: 300 Fannin St Ste 4200 Shreveport LA 71101-3059

WALTER, DOUGLAS HANSON, lawyer; b. Chgo., Sept. 13, 1941; m. Priscilla Ann McConnell, Sept. 6, 1964; children: Kristin L., Nicholas D. BA magna cum laude, Harvard U., 1963, JD, 1966. Bar: Ill. 1966. Office: Jones Day Reavis & Pogue 77 W Wacker Dr Chicago IL 60601-1629

WALTER, FRANK SHERMAN, retired health care corporation executive; b. Denver, June 23, 1926; s. Frank J. and Nancy (Sherman) W.; m. Carolyn May Cox, July 29, 1949; children: Douglas, Steven, Nancy. Student, U. Colo., 1944; B.S., U. Ore., 1950; M.B.A., U. Chgo., 1951. Adminstrv. resident Grad. Hosp. U. Pa., 1950-51, adminstrv. asst., 1951-52, asst. dir., 1952-55; adminstr. Meth. Hosp., Phila., 1955-63, St. Barnabas Hosp., Mpls., 1963-70; pres. Met. Med. Center, Mpls., 1970-83; exec. v.p. Health One Corp., 1983-85; clin. preceptor U. Minn., 1965-85; trustee Blue Cross/Blue Shield of Minn., 1977-85. Bd. dirs. Mpls. War Meml. Blood Bank, 1964-70, Health Manpower Mgmt., 1972-77; vestryman Episc. Ch., Mpls., 1966-69. With USAAF, 1944-46. Fellow Am. Coll. Hosp. Adminstrs.; mem. Twin City Hosp. Assn. (dir., pres. 1970-71), Minn. Hosp. Assn. (trustee 1970-77, treas. 1973-74, pres. 1975-76), Am. Hosp. Assn., Upper Midwest Hosp. Conf. (dir. 1977-85), Downtown Council (dir. 1977-85). Home: 6809 Dovre Dr Minneapolis MN 55436-1714

WALTER, HELEN JOY, executive director, teacher; b. Bronx, May 22, 1938; d. David and Frieda (Halpern) Presby; m. Wolfgang Walter, Feb. 4, 1962; children: Cheryl, Rochelle, Laurie. BA, Yeshiva U., 1961; MEd, Northeastern U., Boston, 1979. Tchr. Maimonides Day Sch., Brookline, Mass., N.Y.C. Pub. Schs.; counselor Northeastern U.; exec. dir. Brookline C. of C., 1979—. Office: Brookline C of C 1330 Beacon St Brookline MA 02146-3202

WALTER, INGO, economics educator; b. Kiel, Fed. Republic of Germany, Apr. 11, 1940; s. Hellmuth and Ingeborg (Moeller) W.; m. Jutta Ragnhild Dobernecker, June 24, 1963; children: Carsten Erik, Inga Maria. AB summa cum laude, Lehigh U., 1962, MS, 1963; PhD, NYU, 1966. Asst. prof. econs. U. Mo., St. Louis, 1965-67, assoc. prof., chmn. dept., 1967-70; prof. econs. and fin. Stern Sch. Bus. Adminstrn. NYU, N.Y.C., 1970—, assoc. dean academic affairs, 1970-79, chmn. internat. bus. and fin. depts., 1980-85, Dean Abraham L. Gitlow chair, 1987-90; Charles Simon chair, dir. NYU Salomon Ctr., 1990—; Swiss Bank Corp. prof. internat. mgmt. (joint appointment) INSEAD, Fontainebleau, France, 1985—; cons. in field. Author: editor 22 books including Secret Money, 1985, 2d edit., 1989, Global Financial Services, 1990, Universal Banking in the United States, 1994; contbr. articles to profl. jours. Recipient Bernhard Harms medal, 1992; Ford Found. fellow, 1974-76, Rockefeller Found. fellow, 1977-78. Mem. Am. Econ. Assn., Am. Fin. Assn., Acad. Internat. Bus., Royal Econ. Soc., So. Econ. Assn., Phi Beta Kappa, Beta Gamma Sigma, Omicron Delta Epsilon. Home: 77 Club Rd Montclair NJ 07043-2528 Office: NYU Stern Sch Bus 44 W 4th St New York NY 10012-1126

WALTER, J. JACKSON, consultant; b. Abington, Pa., Nov. 6, 1940; s. Joseph Horace and Edith Wilson (Jackson) W.; m. Susan Draude, Feb. 3, 1978; 1 child. Allison K. Mabe. A.B., Amherst Coll., Mass., 1962; LL.B., Yale U., New Haven, 1966. Sr. Fla. Dept. Bus. Regulation, Tallahassee, 1976-79; dir. U.S. Office Govt. Ethics, Washington, 1979-82; pres. Nat. Acad. Pub. Adminstrn., Washington, 1982-84, Nat. Trust Historic Preservation, Washington, 1984-92; cons. in field. Co-author: America's Unelected Government, 1983. Contbr. articles to profl. jours. Bd. dirs. Sabre Found., Boston, 1983—; mem. Am. Alliance for Rights and Responsibilities, Washington. Mem. Nat. Acad. Pub. Adminstrn., ABA, Yale (N.Y.C.) Club, Met. (Washington) Club.

WALTER, JAMES W., diversified manufacturing executive; b. Lewes, Del., 1922; m. Monica Saraw, 1946 (wid. 1982); children: James W., Robert; m. Constance Spoto, 1983. Ptnr. Walter Constrn. Co., 1948-55; chmn. bd., dir. Walter Industries Inc. (formerly Jim Walter Corp.), Tampa, Fla., 1955—; bd. dirs. Gen. Telephone & Electronics Co., Contel Cellular, Inc., Anchor Glass Container Corp. With USN, 1942-46. *

WALTER, JOHN, newspaper editor. Mng. editor Atlanta Jour. and Constn. Office: Journal-Constitution PO Box 4689 72 Marietta St NW Atlanta GA 30303-2804

WALTER, JOHN ROBERT, printing company executive; b. Pitts., Jan. 20, 1947; s. Jack and Helen (Sech) W.; m. Carol Ann Kost, Sept. 6, 1969; children: Lindsay, Ashley. BBA, Miami U., Oxford, Ohio, 1969. With R.R. Donnelley & Sons Co., Chgo., 1969—, various sales positions, 1969-77, v.p. sales, 1977-81, sr. v.p. sales, 1981-83, dir. mfg. div., 1983-85, group pres., 1985-86, exec. v.p., 1986-87, pres., 1987-89, pres., chmn., CEO, 1989, chmn., CEO, 1990—; bd. dirs. Abbott Labs., Deere & Co., Dayton Hudson Corp.; mem. bus. adv. com. Miami U., 1987—. Trustee Chgo. Symphony Orch.; mem. univ. assocs. bd. Northwestern U.; CEO bd. advisors U. So. Calif.; bd. dirs. Evanston (Ill.) Hosp., Steppenwolf Theatre Co. Mem. Am. Soc. Corp.

Execs., Internat. Adv. Coun. of Singapore Econ. Devel. Bd., Bus. Coun., Bus. Round Table (policy com.), Comml. Club Chgo., Chgo. Commonwealth Club, Exec. Club (bd. dirs.), Links Club (N.Y.), River Club (N.Y.), Chgo. Club, Econ. Club Chgo., Historic Georgetown Club. Republican. Lutheran. Avocations: golfing, tennis, sailing.

WALTER, JUDITH ANNE, government executive; b. Ames, Iowa, Feb. 13, 1941; d. Gordon Escher and Eileen Anna (Womeldorff) Walter; m. Irvin B. Nathan; stepchildren: Daniel Nathan, Jonathan Nathan. BA, U. Wis., 1964; MA, U. Calif., Berkeley, 1968, MBA, 1976. Intelligence analyst Nat. Security Agy., Ft. Meade, Md., 1964-66; asst. v.p. internat. Wells Fargo Bank, San Francisco, 1969-75; spl. asst. to under sec. State Dept., Washington, 1975-76; exec. asst. to pres. Am. U., Washington, 1976-77; v.p. corp. banking Wells Fargo Bank, San Francisco, 1977-79; dep. dir. strategic analysis Office of the Comptroller of the Currency, Washington, 1979-82, dir. strategic planning, 1982-85, dep. comptroller ops., 1985-86, sr. dep. comptroller adminstrn., 1986—. Bd. dirs., chmn. governance com. Girl Scout Coun. of Nation's Capital, Washington. Mem. White House Fellows Assn. (pres.), Women in Housing and Fin. Office: Office of the Comptroller of the Currency 250 E St SW Washington DC 20219

WALTER, KENNETH LUVERNE, agricultural facility director; b. Buffalo Lake, Minn., June 20, 1936; s. Clarence Andrew and Ruth (Schafer) W.; m. Nancy Lee Woolard, Jan. 30, 1959; children: Katrina Lynn Walter Eggers, Matthew Thomas (dec.), Janelle Mae. BS in Agr., U. Minn., St. Paul, 1963. Sales and tech. rep. Midland Coops. Inc., Mpls., 1963-68; asst. to supt. Agr. Experiment Sta. U. Minn., Rosemount, 1968-90, acting supt. Agr. Experiment Sta., 1990-93, dir. ops. Agr. Experiment Sta., 1993—. With USN, 1955-59. Mem. Am. Soc. Agrl. Engrs. Office: U Minn Agrl Experiment Sta 1605 160th St W Rosemount MN 55068-6053

WALTER, LLOYD GUY, JR., architect; b. Tampa, Fla., June 19, 1934; s. Lloyd Guy and Frances (Davant) W.; m. Shirley Hollis, June 7, 1957 (div. 1977); children: David Lloyd, Sharon Naomi Walter Yuenger, April Frances Walter Anderson; m. Gwendolyn Chapman, July 12, 1986. BArch., N.C. State Coll., 1960. Intern architect A.G. Odell & Assocs., Charlotte, N.C., 1961-64, architect, 1964-65; architect, firm prin. Colvin, Hammill & Walter Assocs., Winston-Salem, N.C., 1965-70, Hammill-Walter Assocs., Winston-Salem, N.C., 1970-88, Walter, Robbs, Callahan & Pierce Architects P.A., Winston-Salem, N.C., 1988—; chmn. Hist. Dists. Commn., Winston-Salem, 1977-81; bd. dirs., sec. Enterprise Nat. Bank of the Piedmont, Winston-Salem, City-County Planning Bd., Winston-Salem, 1983-91. Prin. works include Greek Orthodox Ch., Winston-Salem, 1967, U.S. Courthouse and Fed. Office Bldgs., Winston-Salem, 1976, First Ctr. Bldg., Winston-Salem, 1972 (Pre-cast Concrete Inst. award 1974), Reynolds Plaza Complex, Winston-Salem, 1981, N.C. State Univ. Coll. of Textiles, 1990. 1st v.p., mem. Piedmont Craftsmen, Winston-Salem, 1986-89; bd. dirs., program chmn. Leadership Winston-Salem, 1984-91; bd. dirs. Civic Ventures, Winston-Salem, 1984, 90; participant pilot project Triad Leadership Network, 1991. Recipient student design award N.C. chpt., AIA, Raleigh, 1960, Lloyd Warren fellowship, Nat. Inst. for Archtl. Edn., N.Y.C., 1960. Mem. AIA (N.C. chpt.: sec. 1988, pres.-elect 1989, pres. 1990, immediate past pres. 1991), Winston-Salem C. of C. (pres. 1985, named Small Bus. Advocate of Yr. 1988), Old Town Club, Piedmont Club, Stratford Rotary Club. Democrat. Moravian. Avocation: sailing. Office: Walter Robbs Callahan PO Box 11032 723 Coliseum Dr Winston Salem NC 27106-5312

WALTER, MARTIN EDWARD, mathematician, educator; b. Lone Pine, Calif., Jan. 26, 1945; s. Karl Emil and Clare Marie (Larsen) W.; m. Elaine I. Austin, June 24, 1967 (div. Nov. 85); 1 child, Liv Muir. BS, U. Redlands, 1966; MS, PhD, U. Calif., Irvine, 1971. Functional analysis yr. fellow UCLA, 1970-71; research assoc. Queen's U., Kingston, Ont., Can., 1971-73; asst. prof. math. U. Colo., Boulder, 1973-77, assoc. prof. math., 1977-84, prof. math., 1984—; cons. Rocky Mountain chpt. Sierra Club, 1973—. Contbr. articles to profl. jours. Fellow Alfred P. Sloan Found., 1976-78, Woodrow Wilson Found., 1966, NSF, 1966-70. Mem. Am. Math. Soc., AAAS, Sierra Club, Colo. Mountain Club (rock climbing instr.). Avocations: mountain and rock climbing, karate, guitar, scuba diving, farming.

WALTER, ORRIS G., JR., health facilities adminstrator. Pres. Episcopal Health Svcs. Inc., Uniondale, N.Y. Office: Episcopal Health Svcs Inc 333 Earle Ovington Blvd Uniondale NY 11553*

WALTER, PAUL HERMANN LAWRENCE, chemistry educator; b. Jersey City, N.Y., Sept. 22, 1934; s. Helmuth Justus and Adelaide C. J. (Twardy) W.; m. Grace Louise Carpenter, Aug. 25, 1956; children: Katherine Elizabeth Walter Bousquet, Marjorie Allison Walter Moran. BS, MIT, 1956; PhD, U. Kans., 1960. Rsch. scientist DuPont Cen. Rsch. Dept., Wilmington, Del., 1960-67; prof. chem. Skidmore Coll., Saratoga Springs, N.Y., 1967—, chair chemistry and physics, 1975-85. Translator: (book) Foundations of Crystal Chemistry, 1968; contbr. articles to sci. publs. Fellow Chem. Inst. Can.; mem. AAAS, AAUP (pres. 1984-86), Am. Chem. Soc. (bd. dirs. 1991—, chmn. 1993—), Sociedad Quimica de Mexico (hon.). Democrat. Presbyterian. Achievements include patents in field. Home: 9 Walter Dr Saratoga Springs NY 12866-9233 Office: Skidmore Coll Dept Chemistry and Physics N Broadway Saratoga Springs NY 12866-1632

WALTER, PRISCILLA ANNE, lawyer; b. Chgo., Feb. 9, 1943; d. William M. and Anne (Rogers) McConnell; m. Douglas H. Walter, Sept. 6, 1964; children: Kristin Lynn, Nicholas D. BA, Wellesley Coll., 1965; MSc, London Sch. Econ., 1967; JD magna cum laude, Northwestern U., 1978. Bar: Chgo. 1978. Law clk. to presiding justice 7th Cir. Ct. Appeals, Chgo., 1978-79; ptnr. Gardner, Carton & Douglas, Chgo., 1979—. Pres. Bd. trustees The Latin Sch. of Chgo., 1988-90; bd. govs. Met. Planning Coun.; co-pres. Field Mus. of Nat. Hist. Founder's Coun. Mem. ABA, Info. Industry Assn. (proprietary rights com.), Chgo. Bar Assn., Computer Law Assn., Am. Bar Found. Office: Gardner Carton & Douglas 321 N Clark St Ste 3400 Chicago IL 60610-4795

WALTER, RICHARD LAWRENCE, physicist, educator; b. Chgo., Nov. 1, 1933; s. Lawrence Barnabas and Marie Ann (Boehmer) W.; m. Carol Elizabeth Goethals, Dec. 27, 1958; children—Timothy, Susan, Matthew. BS., St. Procopius Coll., 1955; Ph.D., Notre Dame U., 1960. Teaching asst., research asst. Notre Dame U., 1955-59; research asso. dept. physics U. Wis., 1960-61, instr., 1961-62; asst. prof. physics Duke U., Durham, N.C., 1962-67; asso. prof. Duke U., 1967-74, prof., 1974—; vis. staff mem. Los Alamos Sci. Lab., 1964, 70, 75; vis. prof. Max Planck Inst. fur Kernphysik, Heidelberg, Germany, 1970, 75; Fudan U., Shanghai and Tsinghua U., Beijing, People's Republic of China, 1985, 88, 91, 94, 95; staff mem. Traingle Univs. Nuclear Lab., 1970—. Contbr. articles to profl. jours. Fulbright scholar, 1970-71. Mem. Am. Phys. Soc., Environ. Metals Group (council 1973-76), Sigma Xi, Sigma Pi Sigma (nat. council 1964-68). Home: 2818 McDowell Rd Durham NC 27705-5621 Office: Duke Univ Dept Physics PO Box 90305 Durham NC 27708-0305

WALTER, ROBERT, think-tank executive, career officer. Commdg. officer Naval Med. Rsch. Inst., Bethesda, Md. Office: Naval Med Rsch Inst 8901 Wisconsin Ave Bldg 17 Bethesda MD 20889

WALTER, ROBERT D., wholesale pharmaceutical distribution executive; b. 1945. BMechE, Ohio U., 1967; MBA, Harvard U., 1970. With Cardinal Foods Inc. (acquired by Roundy's Inc. 1988), Dublin, Ohio, 1971-88; CEO, chmn. bd. Cardinal Health, Inc., Dublin, 1979—. Office: Cardinal Health Inc 655 Metro Pl S Dublin OH 43017-3313*

WALTER, ROBERT IRVING, chemistry educator, chemist; b. Johnstown, Pa., Mar. 12, 1920; s. Charles Weller and Frances (Riethmiller) W.; m. Farideh Asghari, Oct. 17, 1973. AB, Swarthmore Coll., 1941; MA, Johns Hopkins U., 1942; PhD, U. Chgo., 1949. Instr. U. Colo. 1949-51, U. Conn., 1953-55; rsch. assoc. Rutgers U., 1951-53; assoc. physicist Brookhaven Nat. Lab., 1955-56; mem. faculty Haverford Coll., 1956-68, prof. chemistry, 1963-68; prof. U. Ill., Chgo., 1968—, prof. emeritus, 1990—; vis. lectr. Stanford (Calif.) U., winter 1967; acad. guest U. Zurich, 1976; U.S. NAS exch. visitor to Romania, 1982, 88. Mem. Adv. Council Coll. Chemistry, 1976-70. Served with USNR, 1944-46. Grantee U.S. Army Signal Research and Devel. Lab.,

NIH, NSF, Dept. Energy; NSF fellow, 1960-61. Fellow AAAS; mem. Am. Chem. Soc. (vis. scientist div. chem. edn. 1964-73), Sigma Xi. Achievments include special research preparation, proof of structure, chemical and physical properties of stable aromatic free radicals, C1 reactions and mechanisms in heterogeneous catalysis, reactions of porphyrin bases. Home: 987 Inverleith Ter Lake Forest IL 60045

WALTER, VIRGINIA LEE, psychologist, educator; b. Temple, Tex., Oct. 30, 1937; d. Luther Patterson and Virginia Lafayette (Wilkins) W.; m. Glen Ellis, 1958 (div.); children: Glen Edward, David Walter; m. Robert Reinehr, 1963 (div.); 1 son, Charles Allen; m. Robert Bruininks, 1975 (div.). B.S., U. Tex.-Austin, 1959, M.Edn., 1967; postgrad. internship program in spl. Edn. Adminstrn., 1970; Ed.D., U. Houston, 1973. Tchr. elem. sch. Austin Ind. Sch. Dist., 1959-60, Houston Ind. Sch. Dist, 1965; teaching asst. and research asst. dept. ednl. psychology U. Tex.-Austin, 1965-66; intern Austin State Hosp., 1967; curriculum specialist Spl. Ednl. Instructional Materials Ctr. U. Tex., 1967-68; dir. field activities Edn. Personnel Devel., Austin, 1969-70; parent trainer-communication coordinator Edn. Service Ctr., Austin, 1970-71; grad. asst. U. Houston, 1971-72, teaching fellow, summer 1972, evaluator lab. experiences Tchrs. Inst. Program, 1972-73, grad. asst., advisor in curriculum and instrn. student services ctr., 1972-73, teaching fellow dept. curriculum and instrn., 1973; prof. ednl. psychology dept. ednl. psychology U. Minn., Mpls., 1973-85; pres. Sch. Resource Ctr., Austin, Tex., 1985-90; tchr. Llano Pub. Schs., 1988—; chmn. State Adv. Council for Inservice Tng. Regular Classroom Tchrs., 1977-79; cons. spl. ednl. various sch. dists., state depts. and agys.; Editorial cons.: Jour. Ednl. Psychology, 1979, Reading Research Quar., 1982; assoc. editor: Exceptional Children, 1979-84; assoc. editor Teaching Exceptional Children, 1985-89; contbr. articles to profl. jours., papers to profl. confs. Named Minn. Spl. Educator of Yr., 1978; recipient Service award Internat. Council Exceptional Children, 1978; HEW Office of Human Devel. Services grantee, 1976-80; Dept. Edn. contractee, 1980-83. Mem. Council for Exceptional Children, Nat. Assn. Children with Learning Disabilities (dir. Minn. chpt. 1978-80), Nat. Assn. Retarded Citizens, AAUP, Assn. Supervision and Curriculum Devel. Home and Office: PO Box 493 Llano TX 78643

WALTER, WILLIAM ARNOLD, JR., physician; b. Pitts., May 17, 1922; s. William Arnold and Theresa Elizabeth (Schank) W.; m. Carol Patricia Turner, June 22, 1946; children—Kathleen Ann, Elizabeth Louise. A.B., Ind. U., 1943, M.D., 1945; M.P.H., Johns Hopkins U., 1951. Intern St. Ann's Hosp., Chgo., 1945-46; med. officer in charge Ky. Treatment Centers, Ky. Bd. Health, Louisville, 1948-50; dir. div. venereal disease control Fla. State Bd. Health, Jacksonville, 1951-53; asso. dir. Bur. Preventable Diseases, 1953-55; mem. staff epidemiology sect. Nat. Cancer Inst., 1955-57; med. officer in charge Houston Pulmonary Cytology Project, U. Tex.; M.D. Anderson Hosp. and Tumor Inst., 1957-59; med. officer in charge Phila. Cytology Project, Women's Med. Coll. Pa., 1959-60; program dir. research grants br. Nat. Cancer Inst., Bethesda, Md., 1960-65; dep. dir. extramural activities Nat. Cancer Inst., 1969-72, dep. dir. div. cancer grants, 1972-74, dep. dir. div. cancer research resources and centers, 1974-80, acting dir. centers and treatment program, 1976-77, acting dir. div. extramural activities, 1980—, assoc. dir. rev. activities, 1983—; pvt. cons. med. research and rev., 1984—. Served to capt AUS, 1946-48. Recipient Commendation medal USPHS, 1969, 74. Mem. Am. Venereal Disease Assn., Am. Social Hygiene Assn., Soc. Epidemiologic Research, Assn. Mil. Surgeons U.S., Am. Public Health Assn., AMA, Commd. Officers Assn. USPHS. Roman Catholic. Office: 6310 Wilson Ln Bethesda MD 20817-5534

WALTER-ROBINSON, CAROL SUE, investment executive; b. Joliet, Ill., Dec. 24, 1942; d. Loren John Sr. and Myrtle F. (Sistler) Walter; adopted d. Lillian M. Winnett; m. Patrick Allen Robinson, Apr. 17, 1991; adopted children: Teresa, Christopher, Ellen, Melissa, Catrina, Elizabeth, Sherlene. Student, Waubonsee Jr. Coll., Aurora, Ill., 1963-65, Aurora Coll., 1967-71, Hypnosis Motivation Inst., 1992, U. Metaphysics, 1992. Lic. cosmetologist, paralegal; cert. hypnotherapist. Office mgr., bookkeeper Edward M. Kyser Appraiser, Aurora, 1961-66; legal sec., aide Hon. Paul Schnake, Aurora, 1961-66; pers. mgr. H.W. Gossard Co., Batavia, Ill., 1966-68; pers. recruiter Dresser Industries, Franklin Park, Ill., 1968-71; exec. sec. pres. Am. Picture Co., Anaheim, Calif., 1972-75; contract mgr. state operators incorp. divsn. Mobil Oil Corp., Orange County, Calif., 1975-81; owner Inland Tele-Sec., Riverside, Calif., 1982-84; pvt. practice investment mgr. Riverside, 1984—; sec. Legal Sec.-Fox Valley, Aurora, 1964-66. Author: Capital Punishment—Pro and Con, 1970; editor (newsletter) Humane News, 1964-68. Pres./founder The Fosterkids Alliance, Riverside, 1988-91; exec. sec. Fox Valley Animal Welfare, Aurora, 1963-68; historian Am. Cancer Soc., Aurora, 1964; exec. sec. pub. rels. Humane Soc. U.S., Garden Grove, Calif., 1972; community liaison El Centro Hispano Americano, Aurora, 1970; coord. No. Ill. Pers. Assn., Chgo., 1966-68; com. chair-advisor Employee Personnel Testing, Melrose Park, Ill., 1965; arbitration moderator I.G.W.U., Chgo., 1969. Democrat. Unity. Avocations: researching paranormal psychology, genealogy, music, metaphysics. Home: 845 Spruce St Riverside CA 92507-2525 Office: TFA PO Box 52092 Riverside CA 92517-3092

WALTERS, ALAN STANLEY, distribution company executive; b. Balt., Feb. 20, 1941; s. David and Rebbeca (Keyser) W.; m. JoAnn Burkhart, Apr. 16, 1966; children: Scott, Tracy. BA, U. N.C., 1962; MBA, Harvard U., 1977. Cons. A.T. Kearney, Dusseldorf, West Germany, 1968-75; asst. to mng. dir. Gen. Motors Ltd., Dunstable, Eng., 1977-78; dir. fin. and adminstrn. Gen. Motors Europe, Antwerp, Belgium, 1978-79; chief fin. officer Electrowatt Holdings, Quincy, Mass., 1980-83; pres. The Gamewell Corp., Medway, Mass., 1983-86; prin. The Lek Partnership, Boston, 1986-89; mng. ptnr. Siar Bossard, Cambridge, Mass., 1989-94; exec. v.p. L. Knife & Son, Inc., Kingston, Mass., 1994—. Lt. USNR, 1963-66. Baker scholar Harvard Bus. Sch., 1977. Mem. Soc. Am. Baseball Rsch., Wellesley Country Club, Fortunes Rocks Assn. Office: L Knife & Son Inc Elder Ave Ext Rte 3 PO Box K Kingston MA 02364-0510

WALTERS, ARTHUR SCOTT, neurologist, educator, clinical research scientist; b. Balt., Feb. 20, 1943; s. Charles Henry and Jean Vivian (Scott) W.; m. Bokyun Kim, May 18, 1985 (div. Oct. 1992); m. Lesley J. Gill, Dec. 19, 1992. BA, Kalamazoo Coll., 1965; MS, Northwestern U., 1967; MD, Wayne State U., 1972. Diplomate Am. Bd. Psychiatry and Neurology. Intern Oakwood Hosp., Dearborn, Mich., 1972-73; resident in neurology SUNY Downstate Med. Ctr., Bklyn., 1976-79; movement disorder fellow Neurol. Inst., N.Y.C., 1982-84; asst. prof. neurology Robert Wood Johnson Med. Sch., U. Medicine & Dentistry N.J., New Brunswick, 1984-91, assoc. prof. neurology, 1991—; asst. chief divsn. neurology Lyons (N.J.) VA Med. ctr., 1985-89, neurology cons., 1984—; nat. chmn. med. adv. bd. Restless Legs Syndrome Found., 1992—; organizer Internat. Restless Legs Study Group, 1992—; head Restless Legs Syndrome and Periodic Limb Movement coun. Nat. Sleep Found., 1994—; neurology cons. Coney Island Hosp., Bklyn., Bklyn. Jewish Hosp., 1980-83; organizer contb. Contbr. articles, abstracts, to profl. publs., chpts. to books. Grantee UMDNJ, 1984-86, VA RAG, 1985-86, Sandoz Corp., 1985-88, VA Merit Rev., 1989—, Clemente Found., 1994—. Fellow Am. Acad. Neurology; mem. N.Y. Acad. Scis., Assn. Profl. Sleep Socs., Sleep Rsch. Soc., Am. Sleep Disorders Assn., Movement Disorder Soc. Home: 207 S Adelaide Ave Highland Park NJ 08904 Office: Robert Wood Johnson Med & Dentistry NJ Neurology Dept Robert Wood Johnson Med Sch CN 19 1 Robert Wood Johnson Pl New Brunswick NJ 08903-0019

WALTERS, BARBARA, television journalist; b. Sept. 25, 1931; d. Lou and Dena (Selett) W.; 1 child, Jacqueline. Grad., Sarah Lawrence Coll., 1953; LHD (hon.), Ohio State U., Marymount Coll., Tarrytown, N.Y., 1975, Wheaton Coll., 1983. Former writer-producer WNBC-TV; then with Stars. WPIX and CBS-TV; joined Today Show, 1961, regular panel mem., 1964-74, co-host, 1974-76; moderator syndicated program Not For Women Only, 1974-76; newscaster ABC Evening News (now ABC World News Tonight), 1976-78; host The Barbara Walters Specials, 1976—; co-host ABC TV news show 20/20, 1979—. Contbr. to ABC programs Issues and Answers. Author: How To Talk With Practically Anybody About Practically Anything, 1970; contbr. to Reader's Digest, Good Housekeeping, Family Weekly. Recipient award of yr. Nat. Assn. TV Program Execs., 1975, Emmy award Nat. Acad. TV Arts and Scis., 1975, Mass Media award Am. Jewish Com. Inst. Human Relations, 1975, Hubert H. Humphrey Freedom

prize Anti-Defamation League-B'nai B'rith, 1978, Matrix award N.Y. Women in Communications, 1977, Barbara Walters' Coll. Scholarship in Broadcast Journalism established in her honor Ill. Broadcasters Assn., 1975, Pres.'s award Overseas Press Club, 1988, Lowell Thomas award Marist Coll., 1990, Lifetime Achievement award Internat. Women's Media Found., 1992; named to 100 Women Accomplishment Harper's Bazaar, 1967, 71, One of Am.'s 75 Most Important Women Ladies' Home Jour., 1970, One of 10 Women of Decade Ladies' Home Jour., 1979, One of Am.'s 100 Most Important Women Ladies' Home Jour., 1983, Woman of Year in Communications, 1974, Woman of Year Theta Sigma Phi, Broadcaster of Yr. Internat. Radio and TV Soc., 1975, One of 200 Leaders of Future Time Mag., 1974, One of Most Important Women of 1979 Roper Report, One of Women Most Admired by Am. People Gallup Poll, 1982, 84, to Hall of Fame Acad. TV Arts and Scis., 1990. Office: 20/20 147 Columbus Ave Fl 10 New York NY 10023-5900 also: Barwall Productions The Barbara Walters Specials 825 7th Ave Fl 3 New York NY 10019-6014*

WALTERS, BILL, state senator, lawyer; b. Paris, Ark., Apr. 17, 1943; s. Peter Louis and Elizabeth Cecelia (Wilhelm) W.; m. Joyce Leslie Garrett Moore, Jan. 9, 1964 (div. 1970); children: Jamie, Sherry Ann; m. Shirley Ann Dixon, Aug. 20, 1971; 1 child, Sandra. BS, U. Ark., 1966, JD, 1971. Bar: Ark. 1971, U.S. Dist. Ct. Ark. 1971. Asst. prosecuting atty. 12th Jud. Dist. Ark., Ft. Smith, 1971-74; pvt. practice Greenwood, Ark., 1975—; mem. Ark. Senate, Little Rock, 1982—; bd. dirs. 1st Ark. Title Co., Pine Bluff; bd. dirs., sec.-treas. Mineral Owners Collective Assn. Inc., Greenwood; v.p., bd. dirs. Sebastian County Abstract & Title Ins. Co., Greenwood; mem. Ark. Real Estate Commn., Ark. Abstract and Title Commn. Committeeman Rep. Ctrl. Com. Ark., Ft. Smith, 1980; search pilot CAP, Ft. Smith. Decorated Silver Medal of Valor; recipient Cert. of Honor Justice for Crime's Victims, 1983. Mem. Ark. Bar Assn., South Sebastian County Bar Assn. (pres. 1991-94), Profl. Landmen's Assn. Roman Catholic. Home: PO Box 280 Greenwood AR 72936-0280 Office: 44 Town Square St Greenwood AR 72936-4019

WALTERS, CHRISTOPHER KENT, lawyer; b. Bryn Mawr, Pa., Oct. 10, 1942; s. Lester K. and Margaret (Becker) W.; m. Teri R. Simon, Nov. 23, 1980. AB, Princeton U., 1964; JD, U. Mich., 1967. Bar: Pa. 1967, U.S. Supreme Ct. 1980. Ptnr. Reed Smith Shaw & McClay, Phila., 1980—; Capt. U.S. Army, 1968-70, Vietnam. Office: Reed Smith Shaw & McClay 2500 One Liberty Pl Philadelphia PA 19103

WALTERS, DANIEL RAYMOND, political columnist; b. Hutchinson, Kans., Oct. 10, 1943; s. Howard Duke and Glenna Lucille (Hesse) W.; m. Diana Lee Flack, July 8, 1963 (div.); children: Danielle, Staci. Mng. editor Hanford (Calif.) Sentinel, 1966-69, Herald News, Klamath Falls, Oreg., 1969-71, Times-Standard, Eureka, Calif., 1971-73; polit. writer and columnist Sacramento (Calif.) Union, 1973-84; polit. columnist Sacramento Bee, 1984—. Author: The New California: Facing the 21st Century, 1986; founding editor Calif. Polit. Almanac, 1989. Office: The Sacramento Bee 925 L St Ste 1404 Sacramento CA 95814

WALTERS, DAVID MCLEAN, lawyer; b. Cleve., Apr. 4, 1917; s. William L. and Marguerite (McLean) W.; m. Betty J. Latimer, Mar. 25, 1939 (dec. 1983); 1 child, Susan Patricia (Mrs. James Edward Smith); m. Rebecca Brewer, Feb. 14, 1991. BA, Baldwin-Wallace Coll., 1938, LHD (hon.); LLB, Cleve. Sch. Law, 1943; JD, U. Miami, 1950; LHD (hon.), St. Thomas of Villanova U. Bar: D.C. 1950, Fla. 1950, Fed. 1950. Judge adminstrv. practices U.S. Dept. Justice, Washington, 1940-50; sr. law ptnr. firm Walters & Costanzo, Miami, Fla., 1950-80; of counsel firm Walters, Costanzo, Russell, Zyne, 1980-85; amb. to Vatican, 1976-78; fellow internat. medicine, bd. advisors Med. Sch., Boston U., 1985. Chmn. Fla. Harbor Pilot Commn., 1952-54, City of Miami Seaport Commn., 1953-54, Nat. Leukemia Soc., 1965-66, Archbishops Charities Dr., 1975-76; spl. bond counsel Dade County, 1957-58; gen. counsel Dade County Port Authority, 1957-58; vice-chmn. Nat. Dem. Fin. Coun., 1966-77; mem. Gov.'s Adv. Bd. on Health and Rehabilitative Svc., 1976-77; sec.-treas. Inter-Am. Ctr. Authority, 1960-74; bd. advisor St. Thomas Law Sch., 1985-88; personal rep. Pres. Reagan F.D.R. Meml. Commn., 1985; bd. dirs. Barry U.; chmn. bd. trustees Variety Children's Hosp.; pres. Miami Children's Hosp. Found., 1980—; trustee Gregorian Inst. Found., Rome. Served with Counter Intelligence Corps., U.S. Army, 1943-46. Decorated Bronze Star medal., Knight St. Gregory the Great; recipient Silver medallion NCCJ, Resolution of Commendation award for civic contbn. Fla. Legislature, 1988. Mem. Am., Fla., Fed., D.C., Interam. bar assns., Am. Assn. Knights of Malta (v.p.), Serra Club, Sovereign Mil. Order Malta (master knight 1975—, exec. com. papal visit to U.S. 1987), Omicron Delta Kappa, Lambda Chi Alpha. Democrat. Roman Catholic. Home: 9202 SW 78th Pl Miami FL 33156-7515 Home (summer): 5 St Helens, Marine Parade Sandycove, Dublin Ireland Office: 3000 SW 62d Ave Miami FL 33155

WALTERS, DORIS LAVONNE, pastoral counselor; b. Peachland, N.C., Feb. 24, 1931; d. H. Lloyd and Mary Lou (Helms) W. BA cum laude, Carson-Newman Coll., 1961; MRE, Southwestern Bapt. Theol. Sem., 1963; MA in Pastoral Counseling, Wake Forest U., 1982; DMIn in Pastoral Counseling, Southeastern Bapt. Theol. Sem., 1988. Min. of edn. and youth First Bapt. Ch., Orange, Tex., 1963-66; assoc. prof. Seinan Jo Gakuin Jr. Coll., Japan, 1968-72; dir. Fukuoka (Japan) Friendship House, 1972-88, pastoral counselor, chaplain, 1983-86; Tokyo lifeline referral counselor (in English) Hiroshima-South, Fukuoka, 1983-86; supr. Japanese and Am. staff Fukuoka Friendship House, 1972-86; with chaplaincy Med. Coll. Va., Richmond, 1976; resident chaplain N.C. Bapt. Hosp., Winston-Salem, 1981-82, counselor-in-tng. pastoral care dept., 1986-88; dir. missionary counseling and support svcs. Pastoral Care Found. N.C. Bapt. Hosp., Winston-Salem, 1989-93; dir. Missionary Family Counseling Svcs., Inc., Winston-Salem, 1993—; mem. Japan Bapt. Mission Exec. Com., Tokyo, 1973-76. Author: An Assessment of the Reentry Issues of the Children of Missionaries, 1991; translator: The Story of the Craft Dogs, 1983. J.M. Price scholar Southwestern Bapt. Theol. Sem., 1962; First Bapt. Ch. Blackwell grantee Southeastern Sem., 1986-88. Mem. Assn. for Clin. Pastoral Counselors (assoc.), Am. Assn. Pastoral Counselors (pastoral affiliate). Democrat. Avocations: photography, travel, reading, classical music, concerts. Home: 208 Oakwood Sq Winston Salem NC 27103-1914 Office: Missionary Family Counseling Svcs Inc Stratford Oaks Bldg Ste 420 514 S Stratford Rd Winston Salem NC 27103

WALTERS, EVERETT, retired university official, author; b. Bethlehem, Pa., Apr. 4, 1915; s. Raymond and Elsie (Rosenberg) W.; m. Jane C. Schrader, Apr. 23, 1938; children: Diane Colley (Mrs. Patrick B. Hearne), Everett Garrison. A.B., U. Cin., 1936; M.A., Columbia U., 1940, Ph.D., 1947. Instr. Finch Jr. Coll., 1940-43; rep. U.S. Civil Service Commn., 1943-44; instr. history Ohio State U., 1946-48, asst. prof., 1948-54, assoc. prof., 1954-63, asst. dean Grad. Sch., 1954-55, acting dean Grad. Sch., 1956-57, dean Grad. Sch., 1957-63, chmn. editorial bd. Ohio State U. Press; Vis. prof. Whittier Coll., summer 1950; dir. grad. fellowship program U.S. Office Edn., 1962-63; v.p. acad. affairs Boston U., 1963-69, sr. v.p., dean faculties, 1969-71; dean faculties U. Mo.-St. Louis, 1971-75, vice chancellor community affairs, 1975-79, prof., 1979-80, interim chancellor, 1972-73; Chmn. Grad. Conf. on Grad. Study and Research, 1961-62. Author: Joseph Benson Foraker; An Uncompromising Republican, 1948; Editor, contbr: Graduate Education Today, 1965; Contbr. articles to hist., ednl. jours. Bd. dirs. Sta. KETC-TV, St. Louis, 1973-80, chmn., 1979-80; chmn. bd. dirs. St. Louis Bach Soc., 1977-78. Served as lt. USNR, 1944-46; Naval Officers Candidate Sch. 1950-52, Newport, R.I. Recipient Centennial Achievement award Ohio State U., 1970. Mem. Am. Hist. Assn., Ohio Hist. Soc. (trustee 1961-63, 82-87), Ohio Hist. Found. (trustee, sec. 1987-91), Assn. Grad. Schs. (sec.-treas. 1960-61, editor Procs. Jour. 1959-63), St. Louis Council World Affairs (chmn. bd.), Columbus Met. Club, University Club (Columbus), Phi Delta Theta. Episcopalian. Home: 2872 Pickwick Dr Columbus OH 43221-2920

WALTERS, FARAH M., hospital administrator; b. Feb. 10, 1945. BS, Ohio State U., 1968; MS, Case Western Res. U., 1975, MBA, 1984. Sr. dir. gen. mgr. Univs. Hosps. Cleve., 1987-89, exec. v.p., 1989-91, exec. dir. 1991-92, pres., CEO, 1992—. Office: Univ Hosps Cleve 11100 Euclid Ave Cleveland OH 44106

WALTERS, GEOFFREY KING, physicist, educator; b. Baton Rouge, Aug. 23, 1931; s. Robert King and Harriett (Fuller) W.; m. Jeanette Long, June

17, 1954; children—Terry, Jeffrey, Gina. B.A., Rice U., 1953; Ph.D., Duke, 1956. Research asso. Duke, 1956-57; mem. tech. staff Tex. Instruments, Inc., Dallas, 1957-62; corporate research asso. Tex. Instruments, Inc., 1962-63; prof. physics and space sci. Rice U., Houston, 1963—; chmn. physics dept. Rice U., 1973-77, dean natural scis., 1980-87; acting chief fire tech. divsn. Nat. Bur. Standards, Gaithersburg, Md., 1971-72; dir. Rsch. Corp., 1977—. Rsch. Corp. Techs., 1987—; Guggenheim fellow Stanford U., 1977-78; vis. prof. Collège de France, Paris, 1987; vis. com. Nat. Bur. Standards, 1980-82, 92-94, chmn. vis. com., 1982. Contbr. articles on low temperature, solid state, atomic collision, nuclear physics, solar-terrestrial relationships, radio astronomy to profl. jours. Recipient Disting. Alumnus award Rice U., 1990. Fellow AAAS, Am. Phys. Soc. (chmn. div. electron and atomic physics 1972-73, councillor 1974-79, 89, chmn. Nominating Com. 1989); mem. Am. Geophys. Union. Home: 5102 Jackwood St Houston TX 77096-1416 Office: Rice University PO Box 1892 6100 South Main Houston TX 77251

WALTERS, GLEN ROBERT, banker; b. Mpls., Sept. 11, 1943; s. Sterling Thomas and Mildred Eunice (Parkinson) W.; m. Gail Elvira Engelsen, June 11, 1966; children—Nicole Marie, Brent Aaron, Hillary Renee. B.A., U. Minn., Mpls., 1965, postgrad., 1965-67; banking degree, Stonier Grad. Sch. Banking, Rutgers U., New Brunswick, N.J., 1982. Comml. banker 1st Nat. Bank, Mpls., 1967-83, sr. v.p. human resources, 1983-90; sr. v.p. Firstar Bank Minn., Mpls., 1990—. Served to sgt. USNG, 1967-73. Republican. Presbyterian. Office: Firstar Bank 1550 E 79th St Minneapolis MN 55425-1139

WALTERS, JAY B., banker; b. Bourbonnais, Ill, Jan. 13, 1946; s. Jack B. and Elaine V. (Frette) W.; m. Monique P. Pagano, Jan. 31, 1970; children: Danielle, Aaron, Anique. B.A., U. Ill., Champaign, 1968; M.B.A. U. Mo., Columbia, 1970. With Harris Bank & Trust, Chgo., 1970-81, mgr. cons. group, 1980-81; investment banker E.F. Hutton & Co., Chgo., 1981; exec. v.p. Sears Bank & Trust, Chgo., 1981-83; pres., chief exec. officer First Bank Milw., 1983-86; exec. v.p. First Bank System, 1987-88; pres. corp. banking First Bank Nat. Assn., 1988; pres. comml. and investment banking First Bank System, 1989—; mem. Marquette U. Sch. Bus. Adv. Coun., 1984—; lectr. Fed. Res. Bd. Sr. Examiner Tng., 1980—. Mem. Bank Adminstrn. Inst., Assn. Res. City Bankers, Greater Mpls. C. of C. Office: 1st Bank System Inc 300 First Bank Pl E Minneapolis MN 55402

WALTERS, JEFFERSON BROOKS, musician, retired real estate broker; b. Dayton, Ohio, Jan. 20, 1922; s. Jefferson Brooks and Mildred Frances (Smith) W.; m. Mary Elizabeth Espey, Apr. 6, 1963 (dec. July 22, 1983); children: Dinah Christine Basson, Jefferson Brooks; m. Carol Elaine Clayton Gillette, Feb. 19, 1984. Student, U. Dayton, 1947. Composer, cornetist Dayton, 1934—, real estate broker, 1948-88; ret., 1988. Condr., composer choral, solo voice settings of psalms and poetry Alfred Lord Tennyson; composer Crossing the Bar (meml. performances U.S. Navy band), 1961; composer The Yorktown Grand March (Good Citizenship medal SAR, 1988). Founder Am. Psalm Choir, 1965; apptd. deferred giving officer Kettering (Ohio) Med. Ctr., 1982-85. Served with USCGR, 1942-45, PTO, ETO. Mem. SAR, Greater Dayton Antique Study Club (past pres.), Dayton Art Inst., Montgomery County Hist. Soc., Masons (32d deg.). Brethren Ch. Home: 4113 Roman Dr Dayton OH 45415-2423

WALTERS, JOHN LINTON, electronics engineer, consultant; b. Washington, Mar. 8, 1924; s. Francis Marion Jr. and Roma (Crow) W.; m. Grace Elizabeth Piper, June 19, 1948; children: Richard Miller, Gretchen Elizabeth, Christopher Linton, John Michael, Kim Anne. BS, U.S. Naval Acad., 1944; SM, Harvard U., 1949; DrEng, Johns Hopkins U., 1959. Staff mem. Los Alamos (N.Mex.) Sci. Lab, 1949-52; rsch. assoc. Johns Hopkins U., Balt., 1952-59; assoc. elec. engr. Brookhaven Nat. Lab., Upton, N.Y., 1959-62; rsch. scientist Johns Hopkins U., Balt., 1962-70; electronics engr. Naval Rsch. Lab., Washington, 1970—; sci. advisor Comdr. 6th Fleet, Gaeta, Italy, 1979-80; lectr. dept. elec. engring. Johns Hopkins U., 1964-65. Lt. (j.g.) USN, 1944-47, PTO. Recipient commendation Dir. of Navy Labs., 1979. Mem. IEEE, Sigma Xi. Achievements include research on theoretical evaluations of electronic countermeasures, refinements to measurement techniques used in particle accelerators, radar data collection, analysis of radar and jamming phenomena. Home: 212 Winchester Beach Dr Annapolis MD 21401-5856 Office: Radar Divsn Naval Rsch Lab Washington DC 20375

WALTERS, JOHN SHERWOOD, retired newspaperman; b. Junction City, Ark., May 15, 1917; s. John Thomas and Cora (McBride) W.; m. Claire Dailey, June 1, 1941; children: Elizabeth Claire, Mary Dailey (dec.). B.A., La. Tech. Inst., 1939; M.A., La. State U., 1941. Editor Ruston (La.) Daily Leader, 1940; reporter Baton Rouge Morning Adv., 1941; rating examiner Jacksonville Naval Air Sta., 1941-42; reporter Fla. Times-Union, Jacksonville, 1943, 44-53; city editor Fla. Times-Union, 1953-60; exec. editor Times-Union and Jacksonville Jour., 1960-78, assn. pub. 1978-82, ret., 1982; asst. prof. journalism La. Tech. Inst., 1943-44; mem. jud. Nominating Commn., 1st Dist. Ct. Appeals of Fla. Bd. dirs. Duval County chpt. A.R.C., chmn., 1966-67; charter trustee U. North Fla. Found., Inc., pres., 1973-75; chmn. council advisers U. North Fla., 1975; bd. dirs. Health Planning Council, N.E. Fla. Cancer Program, Jacksonville Blood Bank. Mem. Am. Soc. Newspaper Editors, Fla. Soc. Newspaper Editors (pres. 1971-72), Alpha Lambda Tau, Sigma Delta Chi. Democrat. Methodist. Clubs: Rotarian (Jacksonville) (sec. 1970-71, pres. 1971-72); Timuquana Country, River. Home: 1750 Dogwood Pl Jacksonville FL 32210-2202

WALTERS, JOHNNIE MCKEIVER, lawyer; b. nr. Hartsville, S.C., Dec. 20, 1919; s. Tommie Ellis and Lizzie Lee (Grantham) W.; m. Donna Lucile Hall, Sept. 1, 1947; children: Donna Dianne Walters Gent, Lizbeth Kathern Walters Kukorowski, Hilton Horace, John Roy. AB, Furman U., 1942, LLD, 1973; LLB, U. Mich., 1948. Bar: Mich. 1948, N.Y. 1955, S.C. 1961, D.C. 1973. Atty. office chief counsel IRS, Washington, 1949-53; asst. mgr. tax div. law dept. Texaco, Inc., N.Y.C., 1953-61; ptnr. firm Geer, Walters, & Demo, Greenville, S.C., 1961-69; asst. atty. gen. tax div. Dept. Justice, Washington, 1969-71; commr. IRS, 1971-73; ptnr. firm Hunton & Williams, Washington, 1973-79; Leatherwood Walker Todd & Mann, P.C., Greenville 1979-94; bd. dirs. Textile Hall Corp., Greenville, Santee Cooper, Moncks Corner, S.C. Mem. S.C. Coun. on Competitiveness, 1987-91; bd. dirs. Greenville Hosp. System Found., S.C. State Mus. Found. With USAAF, 1942-45. Fellow Am. Coll. Tax Counsel (founding regent), Am. Coll. Trust and Estate Counsel, Am. Bar Found., S.C. Bar Found. (bd. dirs. 1988-92); mem. ABA (taxation sect.), S.C. Bar (chmn. taxation sect. 1983-84), Rotary (pres. local club 1968-69). Republican. Baptist. Home: 1804 N Main St Greenville SC 29609-4729 Office: PO Box 87 100 E Coffee St Greenville SC 29602

WALTERS, JUDITH RICHMOND, neuropharmacologist; b. Concord, N.H., June 20, 1944; d. Samuel Smith and Hazel Albertina (Stewart) Richmond; m. James Wilson Walters, Aug. 23, 1969 (div. 1992); children: James Richmond, Gregory Stewart, Douglas Powers. BA, Mt. Holyoke Coll., 1966; PhD, Yale U., 1972. Postdoctoral fellow dept. psychiatry Yale U. Med. Sch., New Haven, rsch. assoc. dept. pharmacology, asst. prof. dept. psychiatry; unit chief neurophysiol. pharmacology sect. expt. therapeutics br. Nat. Inst. Neurol. Disease and Stroke, Bethesda, Md., 1976-81, sect. chief physiol. neuropharmacology sect. expt. therapeutics br.; mem. sci. adv. bd. Hereditary Disease Found., L.A., 1977-80, 82-86, Tourette Syndrome Assn., 1992—; mem. bd. sci. counselors Nat. Inst. on Alcohol Abuse and Alcoholism, 1992—. Contbr. more than 100 articles on neuropharmacology and neurophysiology to profl. jours. Recipient NIH Dir.'s award, 1994. Mem. Am. Soc. Pharmacology and Exptl. Therapeutics, Soc. for Neuroscience. Home: 3615 Littledale Rd Kensington MD 20895-3435 Office: NIH Bldg 10 Rm 5C106 Bethesda MD 20892

WALTERS, KIRK W., financial services holding company executive; b. 1955. Student, U. So. Calif., 1978. Audit supr. Coopers & Lybrand, L.A., 1978-81; corp. fin. Atlantic Richfield Co., L.A., 1981-84; sr. v.p., controller Calif. Fed. Savings & Loan Assn., 1984-89; pres., CEO, chmn. bd., CFO NE Fed. Corp., Hartford, Conn., 1990—. Office: NE Fed Corp 50 State House SQ Hartford CT 06103*

WALTERS, MILTON JAMES, investment banker; b. Hornell, N.Y., May 21, 1942; s. James Henry and Frances Eleanor (Simmons) W.; m. Caroline Houck, May 24, 1963; children: Melissa Ann, Gregory Thomas, Timothy

Allen. BA, Hamilton Coll., 1964. Trainee Mfrs. Hanover, 1964-65; with A.G. Becker Paribas Inc. N.Y.C., 1965-84, v.p., 1969-78, mng. dir., 1978-84; sr. v.p. corp. fin., mng. dir. Smith Barney, N.Y.C., 1984-88; pres. Tri-River Capital Group, 1988—; trustee Hamilton Coll., Clinton, N.Y., 1983-88, Friends Acad., Locust Valley, N.Y., 1981-91. Mem. Econ. Club N.Y., Am. Bankers Assn., Seawanhaka Corinthian Yacht Club, Mill River Club. Republican. Presbyterian. Office: Tri River Capital Group Inc 689 5th Ave New York NY 10022

WALTERS, PHILIP RAYMOND, foundation executive; b. Frankfort, Ind., Jan. 26, 1938; s. Raymond and Ruth Edna (Grimes) W.; m. Sharon Pearl Wilfong, May 31, 1958 (div. Nov. 1992); children: Raymond (dec.), Robert, Sharon Ruth; m. Candace Gina Oden, Jan. 29, 1994. BSBA, Olivet Nazarene Coll., 1959; JD, Ind. U., Indpls., 1969; postgrad., NYU, 1969-70. Bar: Ind. 1969, U.S. Dist. Ct. (so. dist.) Ind. 1969; CLU; CPCU; cert. fund raising exec.; lic. real estate broker, Fla., Ind.; lic. in life, health and variable annuities, Fla., N.C., property and casualty ins., Fla., others. Co-corp. counsel Ind. Farm Bur. Ins. Indpls., 1975-79; dir. gift & estate planning Orlando (Fla.) Regional Healthcare Found.; dep. atty. gen. State of Ind., Indpls.; planned giving officer Wheaton (Ill.) Coll.; campaign dir. Ketchum, Inc., Pitts.,; dir. planned giving Presbyn. Sch. Christian Edn., Richmond, Va.; presenter in field. Contbr. articles to profl. jours. Mem. 1st Presbyn. Ch., Orlando. Mem. Am. Soc. CLU and ChFC, Nat. Soc. Fund Raising Execs. (bd. dirs. Ctrl. Fla. chpt.), Ind. State Bar Assn., Ctrl. Fla. Estate Planning Coun., Planned Giving Coun. Ctrl. Fla., Estate Planning Discussion Group, Rotary Club. Republican. Avocation: running. Home: 897 Cutler Rd Longwood FL 32779

WALTERS, RAYMOND, JR., newspaper editor, author; b. Bethlehem, Pa., Aug. 23, 1912; s. Raymond and Elsie (Rosenberg) W. A.B., Swarthmore Coll., 1933; postgrad., Princeton U., 1933-35; M.A., Columbia U., 1937, Ph.D., 1942. Editorial staff Current History mag., 1937-39; editorial staff Saturday Rev., 1946-58, book rev. editor, 1948-58; editor Encore mag., 1946-48; editor, columnist N.Y. Times Book Rev., 1958—; Mem. fiction jury Pulitzer Prize adv. bd., 1968. Author: Alexander James Dallas: Lawyer, Politician, Financier, 1943, Albert Gallatin: Jeffersonian Financier and Diplomat, 1957 (named One of Notable Books of Year, ALA), The Virginia Dynasty, 1965, Paperback Talk, 1985; Contbr. articles to profl. jours. Served with USAAF, 1942-46; hist. office hdqrs. USAAF, 1943-46. Mem. Am. Hist. Assn., Soc. Am. Historians (v.p.), P.E.N., Authors Guild. Episcopalian. Home: 315 E 68th St New York NY 10021-5692

WALTERS, RONALD OGDEN, finance company executive; b. Holcombe, Wis., July 13, 1939; s. Ogden Eugene and Josephine Ann (Hennekens) W.; m. Margaret Ellen Weisheipl, July 14, 1962; children—Laurie, Cheryl, Michael, Patrick. Student, U. Wis. Mgr. Thorp Fin., LaCrosse, Wis., 1962-65; regional mgr. Thorp Fin., Milw., 1965-69, ITT Consumer Fin. Corp. Milw., 1969-74; sr. v.p. ITT Consumer Fin. Corp., Brookfield, Wis., 1974—, exec. v.p. adminstrn., 1991—. Mem. Wis. Fin. Services Assn. (pres. 1980). Republican. Roman Catholic. Avocations: boating; fishing; hunting. Home: N62w15763 Skyline Dr Menomonee Falls WI 53051-5748

WALTERS, STEPHEN SCOTT, lawyer; b. Chgo., Mar. 20, 1945; s. Harold Stephen Walters and Thelma Rae (Scott) Carlyle; m. Mabel Barnett, Aug. 29, 1967; children: Sarah Elizabeth, Rebecca Strong. BS, Stanford U., 1967, JD, 1972. Bar: Calif. 1972, U.S. Dist. Ct. (no. dist.) Calif. 1972, U.S. Dist. Ct. (ea. dist.) Calif. 1978, U.S. Dist. Ct. Oreg. 1980, U.S. Ct. Appeals (9th cir.) 1980, U.S. Ct. Appeals (10th cir.) 1986, U.S. Supreme Ct. 1988. Law clk. to judge U.S. Ct. Appeals (9th cir.), San Francisco, 1972-73; assoc. Steinhart et al, San Francisco, 1973-74, 75-76; law clk. to chief justice U.S. Supreme Ct., Washington, 1974-75; dep. gen. counsel Legal Services Corp., Washington, 1976-79; assoc. Stoel, Rives, Boley, Jones & Grey, Portland, Oreg., 1979-81, ptnr., 1981—; instr. law U Pa., Phila., 1978-79; chmn. MBA com. Legal Services, Portland, 1986—. Editor Stanford Law Rev. Cooperating atty. ACLU, Portland, 1980—; bd. dirs. Oreg. Law Found., 1990—, Oreg. Racing Commn., 1991—. Nat. Merit scholar, 1963; recipient Hilmer Oehlman Jr, prize Stanford U., 1968. Mem. ABA, Oreg. Bar Assn., Calif. Bar Assn., Multnomah County Bar Assn. Democrat. Avocations: horse racing, fishing, music. Home: 7324 NW Penridge Rd Portland OR 97229 Office: Stoel Rives Boley Jones & Grey 900 SW 5th Ave Portland OR 97204-1235

WALTERS, VERNON ANTHONY, ambassador; b. N.Y.C., Jan. 3, 1917; s. Frederick J. and Laura (O'Connor) W. Student, St. Louis Gonzaga U., Paris, 1927-28, Stonyhurst Coll., Eng., 1928-34. Commd. 2d lt. U.S. Army, 1941, advanced through grades to lt. gen., ret., 1976; served in N. Africa, Italy, World War II; mil. attache Brazil, 1945-48; asst. to Gov. Harriman in Korea, 1950; accompanied to Paris, 1951; asst. dep. chief staff SHAPE, Paris, 1951-56; staff asst. Pres. Eisenhower, 1956-60; mem. NATO standing group, Washington, 1956, 60; served in Vietnam, 1967; aide V.P. Nixon to S. Am., 1958; accompanied Pres. Nixon to Europe, 1969, 70; def. attache Am. Embassy, Paris, 1967-72; dep. dir. CIA, 1972-76; bus. cons., lectr., 1977-81; sr. advisor to sec. state Dept. State, Washington, 1981, ambassador-at-large, 1981-85; U.S. permanent rep. to UN, 1985-89; ambassador to Fed. Republic Germany Bonn, 1989-91; interpreter Pres. Roosevelt, Truman, Eisenhower, Nixon; participant IX Pan Am. Conf., Bogota, Colombia, 1948, Geneva, 1953, Bermuda, 1955, summit meetings. Author: Silent Missions. Decorated D.S.M. with 2 oak leaf clusters, U.S. Disting. Intelligence medal, Legion of Merit with oak leaf cluster, Bronze Star, Air medal; Legion of Honor, Croix de Guerre (France); Combat cross (Brazil): Bronze medal valor (Italy); recipient 3 Freedom Found. awards. Mem. VFW, Nat. Mil. Intelligence Assn. (pres.). Roman Catholic.

WALTERS, VICTOR, holding company executive. Treas. One UP Enterprises Inc., Falls Church, Va. Office: One UP Enterprises Inc 7777 Leesburg Pike 406N Falls Church VA 22043*

WALTERS, WILLIAM LEROY, physics educator; b. Racine, Wis., Mar. 30, 1932; s. Robert N. and Elsie (Ahrens) W.; m. Darlene A. Kessenich, Feb. 5, 1955; children: Judy, Sandra, Robert, James. BS, U. Wis., 1954, MS, 1958, PhD, 1961. Assoc. dean scis. Coll. Letters and Sci. U. Wis., Milw. 1965-67, spl. asst. to chancellor, 1967-68, exec. asst. chancellor, 1968-69, asst. chancellor, acting dean Coll. Applied Sci. and Engring., 1969-70, vice chancellor univ., 1971-81, prof. physics, 1981—; sci. edn. grant administr. Contbr. articles to physics jours. With U.S. Army, 1954-56. Mem. AAAS, Am. Assn. Physics Tchrs., Am. Phys. Soc., Nat. Assn. State Univs. and Land Grant Colls. (mem., chmn. exec. com. coun. acad. affairs 1978), Physics Club Milw. (dir. 1964-67, 82-92). Home: 2100 E Jarvis St Milwaukee WI 53211-2003

WALTHALL, DAVID N., advertising executive; b. 1945. Grad., U. Kans. 1967; MBA, Drake U., 1971. With Iowa Des Moines Nat. Bank, 1969-74; Hawkeye Capital Bank & Trust, Des Moines, 1974-85; officer Heritage Comm., Inc., Des Moines, 1985-87; pres., CEO Heritage Media Corp., Dallas, 1987—; bd. dirs. Equitable Bank, Equitable Bankshares. Office: Heritage Media Corp 13355 Noel Rd Dallas TX 75240-6601*

WALTHALL, LEE WADE, artistic director, dancer; b. Houston, Nov. 12, 1953; s. L.W. and Martha Virginia (Tacker) W. Student, Sch. of Am. Ballet, N.Y.C., 1974-75; BA cum laude, U. Wash., 1994. Prin. dancer Dutch Nat. Ballet, Amsterdam, 1975-82, Pacific N.W. Ballet, Seattle, 1982-90; dancer, ballet master Ballet Austin, Tex., 1990-91; artistic dir. Eastside Dance Theatre, Seattle, 1993—, The Evergreen City Ballet, 1994—; dir. Evergreen City Ballet Acad., 1995—; artist in residence Hong Kong Ballet, 1991; guest artist Nureyev Internat. Ballet Festival, Kazan, Russia, 1994. Guest appearances throughout Europe and U.S.; starring role in Nutcracker-The Movie, 1986. Study grantee U. Wash. Dept. Dance, 1991-94.

WALTHER, JOHN HENRY, banker; b. Hartford, Conn., June 13, 1935; m. Pamela Ball; children: John, Jerome, Joshua. BA in Econs., Wesleyan U., 1957. Pres. N.J. Nat. Bank, Pennington, 1972-76, chief exec. officer, 1976-87, chmn., 1976-92; chmn., CEO BMJ Fin. Corp., Bordentown, N.J., 1992—; bd. dirs. N.J. Bankers Assn., Princeton, 1980-81; bd. dirs. Am. Bankers Assn., Washington, 1983-84, Fed. Reserve Bank Phila., 1984-

86; bd. dirs., mem. exec. com. Assn. Bank Holding Cos., 1985-87. Office: BMJ Fin Corp 243 Rt 130 Bordentown NJ 08505

WALTHER, ROBERT R., physician, educator; b. Bayshore, N.Y., Aug. 19, 1947; s. Raymond Edward and Adeline Ann (Haas) W.; m. Virgina Anne Newland, Sept. 15, 1973; 1 child, Robert John. AB in Chemistry, Cornell U., 1969; MD, U. N.C., 1973. Diplomate Am. Bd. Internal Medicine, Am. Bd. Dermatology, Am. Bd. Med. Examiners; lic. physician, N.Y., Fla. Intern U. Miami Affiliated Hosp., 1973-74, resident in medicine, 1974-75; resident in dermatology Columbia Presbyn. Med. Ctr., N.Y.C., 1975-77; rsch. fellow dept. metabolism and pharmacology Rockefeller U. Hosp., N.Y.C., 1978; from asst. prof. to assoc. prof. dermatology Columbia U., N.Y.C., 1978-89, clin. prof., 1989—, vice chair dept. dermatology, 1994—; attending dermatologist Presbyn. Hosp., N.Y.C., 1989—, dir. clin. svcs., 1994—. Contbr. numerous articles to med. jours. USPHS vis. fellow to Yugoslavia, 1972. Fellow ACP, N.Y. Acad. Medicine (chmn. sect. on dermatology 1993-94); mem. AMA, Soc. for Investigative Dermatology, N.Y. County Med. Soc., Internat. Soc. Tropical Dermatology, Dermatology Found., Assn. Profs. Dermatology. Greater N.Y. Episcopalian. Home: 1070 Park Ave Apt 14D New York NY 10128 Office: Columbia Presbyn Med Ctr Col of Physicians & Surgeons New York NY 10032

WALTI, RANDAL FRED, management consultant; b. Chgo., Apr. 10, 1939; s. Fred Henry and Alice Ann (Steger) W.; m. Judith Ann Hodson, Jan. 31, 1960; children: Lee, Rod, Lynn. BSME, Purdue U., 1961. Program mgr. Aerojet Gen., El Monte, Calif., 1961-66; applications mgr. TRW Systems, Redondo Beach, Calif., 1966-70; br. mgr. A.B. Dick Co., Long Beach, Calif., 1970-71; pres. Randal Data Systems, Inc., Torrance, Calif., 1971-79, The Oaktree Consulting Group, Torrance, Calif., 1980—; chmn. chief exec. officer Oaktree Publ. Inc., Torrance, Calif., 1993—; founder, bd. dirs. Software Coun. So. Calif., Torrance; bd. dirs. Silver Cloud Travel, Inc., Torrance; chmn. The Exec. Com., La Jolla, Calif., 1986-88. Chmn. So. Calif. Leadership Coun., Christian Businessmen's Com., Santa Ana, Calif., 1994—. Republican. Mem. Covenant Ch. Home: 1806 Mount Shasta Dr San Pedro CA 90732-1527 Office: Oaktree Consulting Group 21041 S Western Ave Ste 160 Torrance CA 90501-1727

WALTNER, JOHN RANDOLPH, bank executive; b. San Diego, Dec. 11, 1938; s. Glenn H. and Pauline B. (Hoffman) W.; m. Janice L. McNamara, Nov. 23, 1963; children: Mary E., Ann L. BSBA, U. S.D., 1961, MBA, 1989. Trainee 1st Nat. Bank, Freeman, S.D., 1961-62, v.p., cashier and bd. dirs., 1968-87, pres., CEO and bd. dirs., 1988—; ops. officer Wells Fargo Bank, Monterey, Calif., 1964-67; bd. dirs. S.D. Blue Shield; mem. faculty U. S.D., Vermillion, 1990—, bus. adv. coun. Sch. of Bus., 1985—, chmn., 1992; mem. S.D. Investment Coun., 1994—. Mem. Freeman (S.D.) Community Devel. Corp. (past pres.), 1967—; past pres. Freeman Sch. Bd., 1981-84; past treas. City of Freeman, 1961-62. With U.S. Army, 1962-64. Mem. S.D. Bankers Assn. (bd. dirs., v.p. 1991, pres.-elect 1992, pres. 1993-94), Freeman C. of C. (past sec.-treas.), Beta Gamma Sigma. Republican. Mennonite. Avocations: pub. speaking, community theater, amateur radio, astronomy, chess. Home: 541 S Poplar St PO Box 566 Freeman SD 57029 Office: 1st Nat Bank PO Box H Freeman SD 57029-0090

WALTON, ALAN, oceanographer; b. Consett, County Durham, England, May 29, 1932; s. Albert and Mary Walton; m. Dorothy Foreman, Aug. 18, 1956; children: Deborah Anne, Karen Elizabeth, Susan Caryl. BS with honors, U. Durham, Eng., 1953, PhD, 1956; DSc, U. Glasgow, Scotland, 1971. Asst. sci. dir. Isotopes Inc., Westwood, N.J., 1959-64; sr. lectr. U. Glasgow, Scotland, 1965-70; head chem. oceanography Bedford Inst., Halifax, N.S., Can., 1970-78; dir. Internat. Lab. of Marine Radioactivity, Monaco, 1979-82, 86-90; spl. advisor Fisheries and Oceans, Ottawa, Ont., Can., 1982-84; dir. gen. Bayfield Lab., Burlington, Ont., 1984-85; dir. Ctr. Océanographique, Rimouski, P.Q., Can., 1990—; chmn. marine standards program N.R.C., Ottawa, 1972-80; vice-chmn. UN Expert Group Standards, Paris, 1992—. Contbr. over 100 articles on environ. sci. to jours. including Nature, Jour. Environ. Radioactivity, Radiocarbon. Fellow Royal Soc. Chem. (U.K.). Home: 65 Wrenwood Cres, Nepean, ON Canada K2G 5V5 Office: Univ du Quebec, 310 Alleé des Ursulines, Rimouski, PQ Canada G5L 3A1

WALTON, ALAN GEORGE, venture capitalist; b. Birmingham, Eng., Apr. 3, 1936; s. Thomas George and Hilda (Glover) W.; m. Jasmin Yvonne Christensen, Sept. 1, 1958 (dec. Nov. 1970); children: Kimm A., Keir D.A.; m. Elenor Jean McElliott, Aug. 6, 1977; children: Kristin M., Sherri L. Ph.D., U. Nottingham, Eng., 1960, D.Sc., 1973. Research assoc. Ind. U., Bloomington, 1960-62; asst. prof. chemistry Case Western Res. U., Cleve., 1962-66, assoc. prof., 1966-69, assoc. prof. macromolecular sci., 1969-71, prof., 1971-81, dir. Lab. for Biol. Macromolecules, 1972-81; pres., chief exec. officer Univ. Genetics Co., 1981-86, chmn., 1986-87; ptnr. Oxford Ptnrs., Stamford, Conn., 1987—; chmn. Oxford Biosci. Corp., 1992—; vis. lectr. biol. chemistry Harvard Med. Sch., 1971; mem. Pres. Carter's Task Force on Sci. and Tech.; U.S. project officer Rudjer Boskovic Inst., Zagreb, Yugoslavia, 1967-75; bd. dirs. Sphinx Pharms., Inc., Genetic Therapy Inc., Martek Biosci. Corp., Genica Pharms., Inc., Human Genome Sci. Inc., Collaborative Clin. Rsch. Inc.; chmn. AVID Corp., Exelixis Inc.; chmn., CEO Senatics Corp. Author: Formation and Properties of Precipitates, 1967, Biopolymers, 1973, Structure and Properties of Amorphous Polymers, 1980, Polypeptide and Protein Structure, 1981, Recombinant DNA, 1981, Yearbook of Genetic Engineering and Biotechnology, 1983, 85, 88. Recipient Israel State medal, 1972, Case Inst. Centennial Scholar medal, 1981. Mem. Nat. Venture Capital Assn., Conn. Venture Group, Sigma Xi (Research award 1973), Pi Kappa Alpha. Home: 17 Walnut Ln Weston CT 06883-1417 Office: Oxford Venture Corp/ Oxford Biosci Corp 215 Post Rd W Westport CT 06880

WALTON, ANTHONY JOHN (TONY WALTON), theater and film designer, book illustrator; b. Walton on Thames, Eng., Oct. 24, 1934; s. Lancelot Henry Frederick and Hilda Betty (Drew) W.; m. Julie Andrews, May 10, 1959 (div. 1968); 1 child, Emma Kate; m. Genevieve LeRoy, Sept. 12, 1991; 1 stepchild, Bridget. Student, Oxford Sch. Tech. Art and Commerce, 1949-52, Slade Sch. Fine Art, London, 1954-55. Designer settings, costumes for theater prodns., London, off-Broadway, 1957-60, Broadway, 1961—; Broadway prodns. include Pippin, 1972 (Tony award 1972-73, Drama Desk award 1972-73), Sophisticated Ladies, 1981, The Real Thing, 1984, Hurlyburly, 1984, I'm Not Rappaport, 1985, House of Blue Leaves, 1986 (Tony award 1985-86, Drama Desk award 1985-86), Front Page, 1986, Social Security, 1986 (Drama Desk award 1985-86), Anything Goes, 1987, Grand Hotel, 1989, Six Degrees of Separation, 1990, The Will Rogers Follies, 1991, Death and the Maiden, 1992, Conversations with My Father, 1992, Four Baboons Adoring the Sun, 1992, Guys and Dolls, 1992 (Tony award 1991-92, Drama Desk award 1991-92), Tommy Tune Tonight, 1992, She Loves Me, 1993, A Grand Night for Singing, 1993, Laughter on the 23rd Floor, 1993, Picnic, 1994, A Christmas Carol, N.Y.C. 1994; ballets, principally San Francisco Ballet Co., Am. Ballet Theatre; films include Mary Poppins, A Funny Thing Happened on the Way to the Forum, Murder on the Orient Express, The Wiz, All That Jazz (Acad. award with Philip Rosenberg 1980), Prince of the City, Star 80, The Glass Menagerie, 1987, Regarding Henry, 1991; operas in London, 1963-68, Spoleto, Italy, 1965, Santa Fe, 1975, San Francisco, 1992, Chgo., 1993; Author: Adelie Penguin in Wonders, 1981; illustrator: Wonders, 1981, The Importance of Being Earnest, 1973, Lady Windemere's Fan, 1973, Popcorn, 1972, God Is a Good Friend, 1969, Popcorn, 1972, God Is a Good Friend, 1969, Witches Holiday, 1971, others. Served with RAF, 1952-54. Recipient Drama Desk award Shelter, 1972-73, Emmy award Death of a Salesman, 1986; named to Theatre Hall of Fame, 1991; elected to Interior Design Hall of Fame, 1993. Mem. United Scenic Artists, Costume Designers Guild Calif. Acad. Motion Picture Arts and Scis. Office: care Martino ICM 40 W 57th St New York NY 10019-4001

WALTON, ARTHUR L., state education official. Dep. commr. Elem., Mid., Secondary Edn. Office, Albany, N.Y. Office: Elem Middle Secondary Edn Ofc Edn Bldg Annex Hawk & Elk Sts Rm 875 Albany NY 12234

WALTON, BILL (WILLIAM THEODORE WALTON, III), sportscaster, former professional basketball player; b. La Mesa, Calif., Nov. 5, 1952; s.

Theodore and Gloria W.; m. Susan Walton; children: Adam, Nathan, Luke. Grad., UCLA, 1974. Team center Portland Trail Blazers, 1974-79, capt., 1976-77; with Los Angeles Clippers (formerly San Diego Clippers), 1979-85, Boston Celtics, 1985-87; sportscaster NBC Sports, 1993—; mem. NCAA Divisional Championship Team, 1972-73, NBA Championship Teams, 1977, 86. Recipient James E. Sullivan Meml. award, 1974, James Naismith award, 1972, 73, 74, Adolph Rupp trophy, 1972, 73, 74, NBA Sixth Man award, 1986; named NBA Most Valuable Player, 1978. Office: care Boston Celtics Boston Garden Boston MA 02114-1310*

WALTON, BRIAN, lawyer, union negotiator; b. London, Dec. 24, 1947; came to U.S., 1966; s. Frank William and Irene Mary (Thornton) W.; m. Pamela Abegg Nemelka (div.); children: Robert, Sarah. BA with honors, Brigham Young U., 1969, MA in Polit. Sci., 1971; JD, U. Utah, 1974. Bar: Calif. 1974, U.S. Dist. Ct. (ctrl., so. and no. dists.) Calif. 1974. Law clk. to Hon. J. Allan Crockett Utah Supreme Ct., 1974; assoc. Reavis & McGrath and predecessor firms, L.A., 1974-82; ptnr. Selvin and Weiner, L.A., 1982-85; exec. dir. Writers Guild Am., West, Inc., L.A., 1985—; teaching asst. Coll. Law, Utah U., 1973, asst. to v.p. of spl. projects, 1971-73, rsch. asst. Coll. Law, 1972-74, tchr., dir. legal skills seminar Coll. Law, 1974. Contbr. articles to law jours. Edwin S. Hinckley scholar. Mem. ABA (antitrust sect.), L.A. County Bar Assn. (antitrust sect., intellectual property and unfair competition sect.), Assn. Bus. Trial Lawyers, Internation Assn. des Avocats du Droit d'Auteur. Office: Writers Guild Am West Inc 8955 Beverly Blvd West Hollywood CA 90048

WALTON, CHARLES MICHAEL, civil engineering educator; b. Hickory, N.C., July 28, 1941; s. Charles O. and Virginia Ruth (Hart) W.; m. Betty Grey Hughes; children: Susan, Camila, Michael, Gantt. BS, Va. Mil. Inst., 1963; MCE, N.C. State U., 1969, PhD, 1971. Research asst. N.C. State U., Raleigh, 1967-71; transp. planning engr. N.C. Hwy. Commn., Raleigh, 1970-71; asst. prof. civil engring. U. Tex., Austin, 1971-76, assoc. prof., 1976-83, prof., 1983—; Bess Harris Jones Centennial prof. natural resource policy studies, 1987-91, Paul D. and Betty Robertson Meek Centennial prof. engring., 1991-93, Ernest H. Cockrell Centennial chair engring., 1993—; chmn. dept. civil engring., 1988—; transp. cons., 1970—; assoc. dir. Ctr. for Transp. Rsch., U. Tex., 1980-88; chmn., exec. com. NRC, 1991, Transp. Rsch. Bd., Disting. Lectr., 1994. Contbr. articles to profl. jours. Past chmn. Urban Transp. Commn., Austin. Fellow ASCE (Harland Bartholomew urban planning award 1987, Frank M. Masters transp. engring. award 1987, James Laurie prize 1992), Inst. Transp. Engrs.; mem. NSPE, NAE, Intelligent Transp. Soc. of Am. (vice chair tech. coord. coun., immediate past chair tech. com. Comml. Vehicle Ops.), Soc. Automotive Engrs., Urban Land Inst., Soc. Am. Mil. Engrs., Urban Land Inst., Soc. Am. Mil. Engrs., Inst. for Ops. Rsch. and Mgmt. Scis., Internat. Rd. Fedn. (bd. dirs.), Austin C. of C. (Leadership Austin Program). Democrat. Methodist. Home: 3404 River Rd Austin TX 78703-1031 Office: U Tex Dept Civil Engring ECJ Hall Ste 4.200 Austin TX 78712

WALTON, CLARENCE, political science and history educator; b. Scranton, Pa., June 22, 1915; s. Leo and Mary (Southard) W.; m. Elizabeth Kennedy, June 1, 1946; children: Thomas Michael, Mary Elizabeth. B.A., U. Scranton, 1937; M.A., Syracuse U., 1938; Ph.D., Cath. U., 1951. Social sci. instr. Duquesne U., 1940-42; prof., chmn. dept. history and polit. sci. U. Scranton, 1946-53; dean Duquesne U. (Sch. Bus. Adminstrn.), 1953-58; assoc. dean, prof. Cath. Sch. Bus. Columbia U., 1958-64, dean Sch. Gen. Studies, 1964-69, prof. Grad. Sch. Bus., 1978-80; pres. Cath. U. Am., 1969-78; Charles Lamont Post disting. prof. Am. Coll., 1980-85, now prof. emeritus, 1985—; Penfield fellow Inst. Advanced Internat. Studies, Geneva, Switzerland, 1951-52; vis. prof. U. Helsinki, Finland, summer 1959, U. Buenos Aires, summer 1961, U. Calif., Berkeley, 1963-64, Oreg. State U., 1969, Villanova U., 1984-93, Santa Clara U., 1986-87; Kukin Disting. vis. prof. Yeshiva U., 1993. Author: Corporate Social Responsibilities, Big Government and Big Business, 1968, Ethos and the Executive, 1969; editor: Ethics of Corporate Conduct, 1977, Inflation and National Survival, 1979, (with others) Disorder in Higher Education, 1979, Management's Rights and Prerogatives, 1986, The Moral Manager, 1988, Enriching Business Ethics, 1990, Corporate Encounters: Ethics and Law in the Business Environment, 1992; Intellectual Elites: Subversifying of Basic Institutions; contbr. articles to profl. jours. Mem. Scranton Sch. Bd., 1948-52; chmn. Gov.'s Commn. on Pa. Housing, 1956-57, Pres.'s Panel on Non-Public Edn., 1975-76; bd. dirs. emeritus Am. Assembly; trustee emeritus Rosemont Coll. Served as lt. USNR, 1942-46. Home: 1336 Montgomery Ave Bryn Mawr PA 19010-1629

WALTON, DEWITT TALMAGE, JR., dentist; b. Macon, Ga., May 25, 1937; s. DeWitt T. Sr. and Jimmie (Braswell) W.; m. Joan Robinson, June 11, 1960; children: Jimmie Walton Paschall, Gwen N., Gayle N., Joy A. BS, Howard U., 1960, DDS, 1961. Pvt. practice Macon, 1963—; chmn. dental adv. com. Ga. Dept. Med. Assistance; dental svcs. adv. com. Dept. Physical Health, Ga. Dept. Human Resources. Fin. chmn. Boy Scouts Am., Piedmont/Creek Dist., 1978-80, exec. bd. 1978-82, v.p. exec. com., 1983-84; appointed Bibb County Bd. Edn., 1969-73, vice chmn. MAcon-Bibb County Transit Authority, 1981-87; dir. exec. com. Devel. Corp. Middle Ga., 1984-91; sec./treas. Urban Devel. Authority, Macon-Bibb County, 1984-87; trustee Macon Heritage Found., 1983-87; bd. dirs. Cen. Ga. Speech and Hearing Ctr., 1984-87, Boys' Club Macon, Inc., 1986, 87, 88, The Grand Opera House, 1988, 89, 90; mem. oversight com. Minority Bus. Assistance Program, 1984-91; active Bibb County Commn. on Excellence in Edn., 1984; trustee United Way Macon-Bibb County, 1985, 86, 87; deacon, elder, treas. Washington Ave. Presbyn. Ch.; active Downtown Coun., Coalition for Polit. Awareness, So. Poverty Law Ctr., Booker T. Washington Ctr., Macon Heritage Found., NAACP. Served with U.S. Army, 1961-63. Recipient Cert. of Appreciation State Bar of Ga., Citizenship award Bibb County Voter's Registration League, Inc., 1977, Community Svc. award NAACP, 1982, Community Svc. award Alpha Kappa Alpha Sorority, 1982, Meritorious Svc. award United Negro Co. Fund, 1983, Comml. Bldg. of Yr. award Macon Heritage Found., 1983, Faithful Svc. award Bibb County Dept. Family and Children's Svcs., 1983-90, citation Macon-Bibb County Beautification Clean Community Comm., 1983-84, Cert. appreciation Macon-Bibb County Econ. Opportunity Coun., 1984, Outstanding Svc. award So. Poverty Law Ctr., 1984, Proclamation Mayor George Israel Svc. on Macon-Bibb County Transit Authority, 1984, Outstanding Alumni award Coll. Dentistry Howard U., 1985, award for Outstanding Svc. Macon-Bibb County Urban Devel. Authority, 1987, award for Outstanding Svc. Macon-Bibb County Transit Authority, 1987, cert. Appreciation Close-Up Found., 1988, cert. Appreciation Ga. Dental Edn. Found., 1988, Community Svc. award United Way Macon-Bibb County, 1988, cert. Disting. Svc. Devel. Corp. Middle Ga., 1990, Continuous Corp. Support award Entrepreneurship and Black Youth Program U. Ga., 1990, cert. Recognition Outstanding Svc. So. Poverty Law Ctr., 1990, cert. Appreciation Keep Macon-Bibb Beautiful Commn. and Cherry Blossom Festival, 1990, James E. Carter award Ga. Dental Soc., 1993. Fellow Acad. Gen. Dentistry (Membership award 1983-85), Acad. Dentistry Internat., Am. Coll. Dentists, Ga. Dental Assn. (hon.), Internat. Coll. Dentists, Pierre Fauchard Acad.; mem. AAAS, ADA (alt. del. Ga. 1986-91), Am. Analgesic Soc., Am. Endodontic Soc., Am. Fund Dental Health, Am. Sch. Health Assn., Am. Soc. Dentistry for Children, Nat. Dental Assn., Nat. Rehab. Assn., Ga. Dental Soc. (pres., 1978, Citizenship award 1979-80, Humanitarian award 1981-82, James E. Carter Jr. award 1993), North Ga. Dental Soc. (pres. 1978-79), Cen. Dist. Dental Soc. (peer rev. com., legis. com., alt. del. to Ga. Dental Assn. 1982, 83, 84, del. 1984, 85, 86, 87), Bibb County Dental Soc. (charter), Acad. Continuing Edn., Fed. Dentaire Internat. (life), Pres.' Club Howard U. (life), Am. Running and Fitness Assn. (life), Greater Macon C. of C. (bd. dirs. 1995—), Macon Tracks, Sigma Pi Phi, Omega Psi Phi (life). Presbyterian. Avocations: walking, jogging, aerobics, coin collecting, real estate. Home: 2988 Malibu Dr Macon GA 31211-2609 Office: DeWitt T Walton Jr DDS 591 Cotton Ave Macon GA 31201-7504

WALTON, EILEEN ROWAN, lawyer; b. Bklyn., Jan. 29, 1948; d. Charles Thomas and Helen Bridget (McCormick) Rowan; m. David Richard Walton, Oct. 14, 1978; 1 child, Megan Bridget. BA, Hofstra U., 1969; JD, Fordham U., 1976. Bar: N.Y. Atty. Pfizer, Inc., N.Y.C., 1977-88, corp. counsel, 1988-91, corp. coun., asst. sec., 1991—. Office: Pfizer Inc 235 E 42d St New York NY 10017

WALTON, EMMA, artistic director; b. London, Nov. 27, 1962; arrived in U.S., 1964; d. Tony Walton and Julie Andrews Edwards; m. Stephen Paul Hamilton, May 11, 1991. Student, Brown U., 1980-81. Mem. tchg. faculty Ensemble Studio Theatre, N.Y.C., 1989-92; actress, dir. in theater, film and TV, 1981-89; founder, artistic dir. Bay Street Theatre Festival, Sag Harbor, N.Y., 1991—; resident dir. Spectrum Stage; co-dir. Ensemble Studio Theatre Summer Conf., Tannersville, N.Y., 1989-90. Mem. AEA, SAG, AFTRA, Lit. Mgrs. & Dramaturgs Am. Office: Bay Street Theatre Festival PO Box 810 Sag Harbor NY 11963-0022

WALTON, GERALD WAYNE, English educator, university officiala; b. Union, Miss., Sept. 11, 1934; s. Willie Jay and Ruby Elizabeth (Williamson) W.; m. Juliet Katherine Hart, Aug. 26, 1960; children: Katherine Hart, Dorothy Elizabeth, Margaret Stevens. A.A., East Central Jr. Coll., 1954; B.S., U. So. Miss., 1956; M.A., U. Miss., 1959, Ph.D., 1967. Tchr. asst. U. Miss., 1956-59, instr. English, 1959-62, asst. prof., 1962-67, assoc. prof., 1967-70, prof., 1970—, assoc. dean Coll. Liberal Arts, 1970-76, dean, 1976-82, assoc. vice chancellor for acad. affairs, 1982—. Contbr. articles to profl. jours. Vice-pres. Oxford Human Rels. Coun., 1968; mem. adminstrv. bd. Oxford U. Meth. Ch., chmn. bd. trustees, 1971-72; bd. dirs. Yoknapatawpha Arts Coun., 1980-81; sec.-treas. So. Lit. Festival, 1965. Tri-Univ. fellow in linguistics U. Nebr., 1969-70. Mem. MLA, Am. Dialect Soc., Miss. Folklore Soc., Friends of Arts in Miss., Miss. Assn. English Tchrs. (sec. 1968), Miss. Inst. Arts and Letters (sec. 1979-80), Nat. Coun. Tchrs. English, William Faulkner Soc., Miss. Hist. Soc., Rotary, Golden Key, Phi Kappa Phi, Sigma Tau Delta, Omicron Delta Kappa. Home: 106 Ole Miss Dr Oxford MS 38655-2615 Office: U Miss Vice Chancellor Acad Affairs University MS 38677

WALTON, HAROLD VINCENT, former agricultural engineering educator, academic administrator; b. Christiana, Pa., June 17, 1921; s. Howard King and Alice Lauretta (Kirk) W.; m. Velma Purvis Braun, June 24, 1946; children: H. Richard, Marilyn J. Walton Friedersdorf, Carol A. BS in Agrl. Engring., Pa. State U., 1942, M.S. in Agrl. Engring., 1950; PhD in Agrl. Engring., Purdue U., 1961. Licensed profl. engr., Mo. Test engr. Gen. Electric Co., Schenectady, 1943-45; instr. Pa. State U., 1947-50, asst. prof. agrl. engring., 1950-52, assoc. prof., 1952-61, prof., 1961, 76-85, head dept. agrl. engring., 1976-85, ret., 1985; prof., chmn. dept. agrl. engring. U. Mo.-Columbia, 1962-69; chief of party U. Mo.-Columbia, Bhubaneswar, India, 1969-71; prof. U. Mo.-Columbia, 1971-76; cons. OAS, Trinidad and Tobago, 1980, Ptnrs. of Ams., Brazil, 1984. Served with U.S. Army, 1945-46. Fulbright scholar, Cyprus, 1989-90. Fellow Am. Soc. Agrl. Engrs. (bd. dirs. 1967-69, 85-87). Republican.

WALTON, JAMES M., investment company executive; b. Pitts., Dec. 18, 1930; m. Ellen Carroll; 4 children. B.A., Yale U.; M.B.A., Harvard U. With Gulf Oil Corp., Phila., Houston, Pitts., Tokyo, Rome, 1958-67; pres. Carnegie Inst., Pitts., 1968-84, Carnegie Mus. Natural History and Mus. of Art, Pitts., 1968-84, Carnegie Library, Pitts., 1968-84; life trustee, pres. Carnegie Inst. and Carnegie Library, Pitts., 1984—; vice chmn. bd. dirs. MMC Group Inc.; bd. dirs. Irish Investment Fund, Inc. Mem. sponsoring com. Penn's Southwest Assn.; life trustee Carnegie-Mellon U.; treas. Carnegie Hero Fund Commn.; dir. World Affairs Coun. of Pitts., One Hundred Friends of Pitts. Art; trustee Sarah Scaife Found. Inc., Scaife Family Found., Matthew T. Mellon Found.; chmn. Vira I. Heinz Endowment; mem. Cultural Dist. Devel. Com. Lt. U.S. Army, 1954-56. Office: 525 William Penn Pl Rm 3902 Pittsburgh PA 15219-1710

WALTON, JOAN See FROHOCK, JOAN

WALTON, JON DAVID, lawyer; b. Clairton, Pa., Sept. 18, 1942; s. Thomas Edward and Matilda Lucy (Sunday) W.; m. Carol Jeanne Rowland, Sept. 15, 1964; children: David Edward, Diane Elizabeth. BS, Purdue U., 1964; JD, Valparaiso U., 1969. Bar: Pa. 1969. Atty. U.S. Steel Corp. (now USX Corp.), Pitts., 1969-73; asst. gen. counsel Harbison-Walker Refractories, Pitts., 1973-75; gen. counsel Harbison-Walker Refractories, 1975-81, v.p., gen. counsel, 1981-83; regional gen. counsel Dresser Industries., Inc., Pitts., 1983-86; gen. counsel, sec. Allegheny Ludlum Corp., Pitts., 1986-90, v.p., gen. counsel, sec., 1990—. 1st v.p., bd. dirs. Music for Mt. Lebanon; chmn. bd. dirs. Pitts. Youth Golf Found., 1991—. Mem. ABA, Pa. Bar Assn., Allegheny County Bar Assn., Licensing Exec. Soc., Am. Soc. Corp. Secs. (past pres. regional group) Pa. Chamber Bus. and Industry (bd. dirs., exec. com.), Am. Corp. Counsel Assn., Am. Arbitration Assn. (panel of arbitrators), Duquesne Club, Valley Brook Country Club. Home: 137 Hoodridge Dr Pittsburgh PA 15228-1803 Office: Allegheny Ludlum Corp 1000 Six PPG Pl Pittsburgh PA 15222-5479

WALTON, JONATHAN TAYLOR, banker; b. Evanston, Ill., Mar. 28, 1930; s. Howard Roberts and Louise (Ryther) W.; m. Salome Edgeworth, Nov. 27, 1954; children: Jonathan Taylor, Katherine Edgeworth Walton Day, Lucy Downes Walton Mooney, Andrew Roberts. B.A., Dartmouth Coll., 1952, M.B.A., 1953. Analyst trainee Nat. Bank of Detroit, 1956-59, asst. cashier, 1959-62, asst. v.p., 1962-64, v.p., 1964-72, sr. v.p., 1972-79, exec. v.p., 1979—; exec. v.p. NBD Bancorp, Inc., 1982—; bd. dirs. The Depository Trust Co., N.Y.C. Trustee W.K. Kellogg Found., Battle Creek, Mich., 1980, Community Found. Southeastern Mich., Detroit, 1988; chmn. Mich. exec. com. United Negro Coll. Fund, 1990. Mem. Assn. Res. City Bankers. Home: 40 Oldbrook Ln Grosse Pointe MI 48236-3010 Office: NBD Bancorp Inc 611 Woodward Ave Detroit MI 48226-3497

WALTON, KATHLEEN ENDRES, librarian; b. Columbus, Ohio, Mar. 24, 1961; d. Kenneth Raymond and Mary Margaret (Brown) Endres; m. Thomas Walton, Dec. 7, 1985; children: Tristan James, Arden Siobhan. BA, U. Md., 1982; MLS, Cath. U. Am., 1985. Head engring./architecture/math libr. Cath. U. Am. Libr., Washington, 1985-87; libr. Congl. Quarterly Inc., Washington, 1987-90, head libr., 1991-92, libr. dir., 1992—. Mem. ALA, Am. Assn. Law Librs., D.C. Libr. Assn., Spl. Librs. Assn. Roman Catholic. Office: Congl Quarterly Inc 1414 22nd St NW Washington DC 20037

WALTON, MATT SAVAGE, geologist, educator; b. Lexington, Ky., Sept. 16, 1915; m. Kathryn Ralston, Dec. 6, 1939 (div.); m. Nalda Robison, May 22, 1969 (dec.); m. Kay Ann Thorson, June 21, 1970; children: Matt Savage III, Kate Johns, Lisa Baar, Anne Elizabeth, Owen Hardwick. B.A., U. Chgo., 1936; M.A. (James Furman Kemp fellow), Columbia U., 1947, Ph.D., 1951. Geologist U.S. Geol. Survey, 1942-46; assoc. prof. Yale U., New Haven, 1948-65; geologist N.Y. State Geol. Survey, summers, 1947-57; cons. geologist, 1947-73; regents lectr. environ. sci. and engring. UCLA, 1970-71; dir. Minn. Geol. Survey, U. Minn., 1973-86, prof. geology and geophysics, 1973-86, prof. emeritus, 1986—; dir. Deep Observation and Sampling of the Earth's Continental Crust, Inc., 1984-86; mem. exec. com. Great Lakes Internat. Project. Contbr. articles on engring. geology to sci. jours. Pres. Old Town Restorations, Inc., St. Paul, 1974-79; bd. dirs. Summit Hill Assn., 1974-79. Fellow Geol. Soc. Am.; mem. Assn. Am. State Geologists. Home: 30 Crocus Pl Saint Paul MN 55102-2810

WALTON, MORGAN LAUCK, III, lawyer; b. Woodstock, Va., July 30, 1932; s. Morgan Lauck Jr. and Frances (Allen) W.; m. Jeannette Freeman Minor, Mar. 4, 1961; children: Morgan Lauck IV, Charles Lancelot Minor, Christopher Allen, Laura Cathlyn. BA, Randolph-Macon Coll., 1953; LLB, U. Va., 1959. Bar: Va. 1959, N.Y. 1959, U.S. Ct. Appeals (2d cir.) 1959, U.S. Dist. Ct. (ea. and so. dists.) N.Y. 1960, U.S. Dist. Ct. (we. dist.) Va. 1988. Assoc. Donovan Leisure Newton & Irvine, N.Y.C., 1959-68; ptnr. Donovan, Leisure, Newton & Irvine, N.Y.C., 1968-84; counsel FDIC, Washington, 1989-91, asst. gen. counsel, 1990—. Contbr. articles to legal jours. Trustee Randolph-Macon Acad., Front Royal, Va., 1987-92, Unitarian Ch. Shenandoah Valley, Stephens City, Va., 1987—; mem. coun. Law Sch. U. Va., 1989-92; treas. Shenandoah Valley Music Festival, Woodstock, 1986-87; chmn. bd. All Souls Ch., N.Y.C., 1974-76. With U.S. Army, 1953-56. Mem. ABA (co-chmn. long term planning com. govt. lawyers divsn. 1993-94, chmn. Clayton Act com. antitrust sect. 1976-78), Assn. of Bar of City of N.Y., Univ. Club, Collectors Club, Order of Coif, Phi Beta Kappa. Democrat. Home: 908 Kern Springs Rd Woodstock VA 22664-9554 Office: FDIC 550 17th St NW H6018 Washington DC 20429-0001

WALTON, ORTIZ MONTAIGNE, musician, sociologist; b. Chgo.; m. Kara Dozier. Student, Hartt Sch. Music, 1951-54, Mannes Sch. Music, 1954-55; BS in Psychol., Roosevelt U., 1966; MA in Sociol., U. Calif., Berkeley, 1970, PhD in Socio., 1973. Musician Hartford, New Haven, Springfield, Bridgeport Symphony Orchestras, 1951-54, Buffalo Philharmonic Orchestra, 1954-57, Boston Symphony Orchestra, 1957-63; program coord. Chgo. Assn. Retarded Children, 1964-66; musician Cairo (Egypt) Symphony, 1963-64; prin. investigator Soc. Survey of Alcohol and Drug Use among Adolescents and Young Adults Nat. Inst. Alcohol Abuse and Alcoholism, 1977-79; asst. dir. Chgo. Fedn. Settlement Houses, 1964-66; instr. Dept. African-Am. Studies U. Calif. Berkeley, 1974-76; faculty Wright Inst. of Berkeley Grad. Sch., 1974-75; mem. bd. of studies in sociology U. Calif. Santa Cruz, 1975; career and guidance counseling Opportunities Industrialization, Oakland, Calif., 1967-68; cons. alcohol. drugs and youth criminal justics Merritt Coll., Oakland, 1979, curriculum devel., 1973; program devel., talent recruitment Today's Artists, Berkeley, 1979. Solo recitals (contrabass) include U. Buffalo, 1956, Merkin Concert Hall, N.Y.C., 1987, Weil Recital Hall at Carnegie Hall, N.Y.C., 1987, Bklyn. Acad. Music, 1988, YMCA Harlem Branch, 1988, Rutgers U., New Brunswick, N.J., 1989, Lehman Coll., N.Y.C., 1989, Cheyney, U. Pa., 1990, Chgo. State U., 1993; composer: Fantasy to Duke Ellington for solo contrabass, 1968, Scale Method for contrabass, 1981, Resonance for contrabass and piano, 1983, Sonata for contrabass and piano, 1985; recordings: (with Ishmael Reed) Black Box, Nat. Philharmonic Orchestra, The Walton Statement for Contrabass and Orch. (by Arthur Cunningham), 1987, Art of the Bass Viol: Music of the Baroque Era, 1991; author: Music: Black, White and Blue, 1972, others. Active mayoral campaign Harold Washington, Chgo., 1983. U. Calif. Berkeley Grad. fellow, 1968-72; Nat. Inst. Mental Health fellow, 1968-72; Ford Found. dissertation grant 1970-71; Inst. Community and Race Relations grant U. Calif. Berkeley, 1970-71. Mem. Am. Sociol. Assn., Internat. Soc. Bassists, Chamber Music Am. Home: 1129 Bancroft Way Berkeley CA 94702-1849 Home: 242 W 123rd St New York NY 10027-5428

WALTON, RALPH ERVIN, community mental health services administrator; b. Council Bluffs, Iowa, Aug. 9, 1903; s. Willard Ervin and Maude Jesse (Crow) W.; m. Norma Ruth Needham, Mar. 4, 1944 (dec. Apr. 1980); children: Lawrence, Dennis, Patrick, Carol. LLB, U. Omaha, 1927, AB in Psychology, 1933, MA in Psychology, 1935; MA in Edn., U. Chgo., 1941. Bar: Nebr. 1927. Asst. to dean of men U. Omaha, Nebr., 1935-37; counselor Huron (S.D.) Coll., 1939-40; part time stats. worker U. Chgo., Ill., 1940-42; counselor N.Y. State Tng. Sch. for Boys, Warwick, 1943-45; psychologist Mich. Dept. Mental Health, Detroit, 1945-47; adminstr. div. mental hygiene Mich. Dept. Mental Health, Lansing, 1947-73; ret., 1973; adminstr. State Mental Health Statutes Rev. Commn.; dept. rep. State Commn. on Aging. Adult leader 4-H Youth Movement, Mason, Mich., 1960's; bd. mem. State Employee Retirees Assn., 1974-78, Sr. Ctr., Florence, Oreg., 1983-85; bd. mem., pres. Unitarian Ch., Lansing, 1976-78; pres. Neighborhood Assn., Florence, 1979-80, Tenant's Assn., Willamette Oaks Retirement Community, Eugene, Oreg., 1991-93. Democrat. Unitarian. Avocations: gardening, traveling, reading, walking, crossword puzzles. Home: 4372 Forsythia Dr Springfield OR 97478

WALTON, RALPH GERALD, psychiatrist, educator; b. Darlington, Eng., Aug. 18, 1942; came to U.S., 1950; s. Kenneth and Paula (Weissman) W.; m. Ellen Paula Liebling, Feb. 15, 1970 (div. 1980); children: Deborah, Rachel; m. Mary Elaine Hultburg, Sept. 27, 1981; children: Lisa, Jonathan. AB, U. Rochester, 1963; MD, SUNY, Syracuse, 1967. Diplomate Am. Bd. Psychiatry and Neurology. Intern Strong Meml. Hosp., Rochester, N.Y., 1967-68, resident in psychiatry, 1968-71; asst. prof. psychiatry St. Medicine U. Rochester, N.Y., 1973-76; chief psychiatry Jamestown (N.Y.) Gen. Hosp., 1976-88; community mental health Chautauqua County, Jamestown, 1985-88; chmn. dept. psychiatry Western Res. Care System, Youngstown, Ohio, 1988—; prof. psychiatry N.E. Ohio Univs. Coll. of Medicine, Rootstown, Ohio, 1988—; med. dir. Profl. Recovery Plus Alcoholic Clinic, Youngstown, 1992—. Contbr. chpt. to: Dietary Phenylalanine and Brain Function, 1988; contbr. foreword to: Katherine It's Time, 1989; contbr. articles to profl. jours., 1972—. Maj. U.S. Army, 1971-73, Panama. Fellow Am. Psychiat. Assn. Jewish. Office: Ste L-2 725 Boardman-Canfield Rd Youngstown OH 44512

WALTON, RICHARD EUGENE, business educator; b. Pulaski, Iowa, Apr. 15, 1931; s. Lee Richard and Florence (King) W.; m. Sharon Claire Doty, Apr. 13, 1952; children—John, Elizabeth, Margaret, Andrew. B.S., Purdue U., 1953, M.S. 1954; postgrad., Victoria U., New Zealand, 1953; D.B.A., Harvard, 1959. Faculty Harvard Bus. Sch., 1968—, Edsel Bryant Ford prof. bus., 1970-76, dir. rsch. div., 1970-76, now Wallace Brett Donham prof. bus.; cons. various indsl. firms, govt. agys. including Dept. State; bd. dirs. Champion Internat. Corp. Author: A Behavioral Theory of Labor Negotiations: An Analysis of a Social Interaction System, 1965, (with R.B. McKersie) The Impact of the Professional Engineering Union, 1961, (with M. Beer and others) Human Assets, 1984, (with P. Lawrence) Human Resource Management Trends and Challenges, 1985, Managing Conflict, 1987, Innovating to Compete, 1987, Up and Running, 1989, (with Joel Cutcher-Gershenfeld and Robert B. McKersie) Strategic Negotiations: A Theory of Change in Labor-Management Relations, 1994. Served with AUS, 1954-56. Ford Found. faculty grantee U. Mich., 1962-63. Home: 109 Beaver Rd Weston MA 02193-1035 Office: Harvard Bus Sch Boston MA 02163

WALTON, RODNEY EARL, lawyer; b. Corvallis, Oreg., Apr. 28, 1947; s. Ray Daniel Jr. and Carolyn Jane (Smith) W. BA, Coll. of Wooster, 1969; JD, Cornell U., 1976. Bar: Fla. 1976, U.S. Dist. Ct. (so. dist.) Fla. 1976, U.S. Dist. Ct. (mid. dist.) Fla. 1977, U.S. Supreme Ct. 1980, U.S. Ct. Appeals (11th cir.) 1981. Assoc. to jr. ptnr. Smathers & Thompson, Miami, Fla., 1976-87; ptnr. Kelley, Drye and Warren, Miami, 1987-93; of counsel Heinrich Gordon Hargrove & Weihe, P.A., Ft. Lauderdale, 1994—. Sec. bd. dirs. Kings Creek Condominium Assn., Miami, 1984-89, treas., 1984, pres., 1990-91. 1st lt. U.S. Army, 1969-73, Vietnam. Decorated Bronze Star. Mem. ABA, Fla. Bar Assn., Broward County Bar Assn., Maritime Law Assn. Republican. Methodist. Club: Bankers (Miami). Avocations: travel, reading, sports. Home: 2331 NW 33rd St Apt 301 Fort Lauderdale FL 33309-6444 Office: Heinrich Gordon PA 500 E Broward Blvd Ste 1000 Fort Lauderdale FL 33394

WALTON, ROGER ALAN, public relations executive, mediator, writer; b. Denver, June 25, 1941; s. Lyle R. and Velda V. (Nicholson) W.; m. Helen Anderson. Attended, U. Colo., 1960-63. Govt. rep. Continental Airlines, Denver, 1964-72; dir. pub. affairs Regional Transp. Dist., Denver, 1972-77; pub. affairs cons. Denver, 1977—; res. pub. info. officer Fed. Emergency Mgmt. Agy., 1995—; pres. Colo. Times Pub. Co.; res. pub. info officer FEMA, 1995. Author: Colorado-A Practical Guide to its Government and Politics, 1973, 6th rev. edit., 1990, Colorado Gambling - A Guide, 1991; columnist The Denver Post newspaper, 1983—, The Rocky Mountain Jour., 1977-81. Mem. U.S. Presdl. Electoral Coll., Washington, 1968; commr. U.S. Bicentennial Revolution Commn., Colo., 1972-76, U.S. Commn. on the Bicentennial of U.S. Constn., Denver, 1985-90; pres.; trustee Arapahoe County (Colo.) Libr. Bd., 1982-86; chmn. lobbyist ethics com. Colo. Gen. Assembly, 1990-91. Republican. Avocations: reading, fishing, photography. Home and Office: 12550 W 2nd Dr Lakewood CO 80228

WALTON, RONALD ELWOOD, retired school superintendent; b. Elkhart, Ind., May 5, 1932; s. Marvin Glenn and Faye (Beisel) W.; m. Bernita Jo Yunker, June 3, 1956; 1 child, Ronald Yunker. BS, Manchester Coll., 1953; MS, Ind. U., 1958, EdD, 1962. Vocal and instrumental music and speech tchr. Berne (Ind.)-French Twp. Schs., 1953-56; instrumental music tchr. John Adams High Sch., South Bend, Ind., 1956-58; supervising prin. Galveston (Ind.) Sch., 1958-60; adminstrv. asst. MSD of Perry Twp. Indpls., 1962-63; supt. of Schs. Southeastern Sch. Corp., Cass County, Ind., 1963-64, Jeffersonville (Ind.) City Schs., 1964-66, Monroe County Com. Schs., Bloomington, Ind., 1966-84, Fayette County Pub. Schs., Lexington, Ky., 1984-94; ret., 1994; bd. dirs. Ky. Coun. of Econ. Edn., Louisville, Bluegrass Coun. Goodwill Industries, Jr. Achievement Bluegrass Inc., Friends of Music-Univ. Ky. Contbr. articles to profl. jours. Adv. mem. Acad. Sweet Sixteen, Lexington, 1985—; mem. Lexington Race Rels. Com., 1988-94, Fighting Back Task Force, 1989-94. Recipient St. Adminstr. award Kennedy Ctr./Alliance for Arts, 1988, Sch. Adminstr. Yr. award Ky. Assn. of Ednl. Office Pers., 1989, Top 100 Exec. Educators award The Exec. Educator, 1987, 93,

Roundtable Educator award George Peabody coll. 1987, Ky. Assn. Sch. Supt. of Yr. award, 1990-91, Nat. Art Edn. Assn. Disting. Svc. award, 1990-91. Mem. Am. Assn. Sch. Adminstrs. (adv. coun. 1986-89, chmn. and suburban supt. planning com. 1986-89), Nat. Acad. Sch. Exec. (bd. dirs. 1989-92), Mid-Am. Assn. Sch. Supt., Network U. Com. Sch. Dist., Ky. Assn. Sch. Adminstrs. (conf. planning com. 1989-90), Ky. Assn. Sch. Supts. (bd. dirs. 1984—; sec. treas. 1989-90, pres. 1990-91), Ky. Ednl. Leadership Inst. (bd. dirs. 1985-94), Ky. Congress of PTA (Supt. Yr award 1988), Cen. Ky. Assn. Sch. Supt., Nat. Assn. Ednl. Office Pers. (Adminstr. of Yr. 1990), Greater Lexington C. of C., Lexington Rotary. Republican. Methodist. Avocations: music, gardening.

WALTON, RUSSELL SPAREY, foundation administrator; b. Trenton, N.J., Nov. 28, 1921; s. Lewis Kirk and Edna Russell (Sparey) W.; m. Ila E. Lappe, Aug. 23, 1969. Student, King's Coll., 1938-39, DHL (hon.), 1991; student, Temple U., 1940-41. Mgr. publs. and pub. rels. Rexall Drug Co., L.A., 1946-49; mgr. advt. and pub. rels. Gladding McBean & Co., Glendale, Calif., 1949-51; editor, pub. San Bruno (Calif.) Herald, 1951-52; dir. pub. affairs West Divsn. Nat. Assn. Mfgrs., Palo Alto, Calif., 1952-62; exec. dir. United Rep. Calif., Los Altos, 1962-66; sec. program devel. Gov. Calif. Sacramento, 1967-71; columnist, radio commentator newspapers in Calif. and Midwest, 1971-74; mng. editor Third Century Pub., Washington, 1974-76; exec. dir. Plymouth Rock Found., Marlborough, N.H., 1976—. Author: One Nation Under God, 1978, Fundamentals for American Christians, 1979, Biblical Solutions to Continuing Problems, 1984. Capt. U.S. Army Air Corps, 1941-46. Baptist. Office: Plymouth Rock Found Fisk Mill on Water St Marlborough NH 03455

WALTON, S. ROBSON, discount department store chain executive; b. 1945; s. Sam Moore W.; married. Grad., Columbia U., 1969. Formerly with Conner, Winters, Ballaine, Barry & McGowen; with Wal-Mart Stores Inc., Bentonville, Ark., 1969—, sr. v.p., 1978-82, also bd. dirs. vice chmn. bd., 1982-92, chmn. 1992—. Office: Wal-Mart Stores Inc 702 SW 8th St Bentonville AR 72716-0001*

WALTON, STANLEY ANTHONY, III, lawyer; b. Chgo., Dec. 10, 1939; s. Stanley Anthony and Emily Ann (Pouzar) W.; m. Karen Kayser, Aug. 10, 1963; children: Katherine, Anne, Alex. BA, Washington and Lee U., 1962, LLB, 1965. Bar: Ill. 1965, U.S. Dist. Ct. (no. dist.) Ill. 1966, U.S. Ct. Appeals (7th cir.) 1966. With Winston & Strawn, Chgo. 1965-89; ptnr. Sayfarth Shaw Fairweather, Chgo. Trustee Village of Hinsdale (Ill.), 1985-89; bd. dirs. Washington and Lee Law Sch., Lexington, Va., 1975-78, bd. dirs. univ. alumni, 1983-85, pres. 1986-87; bd. dirs. UNICEF, Chgo., 1983; pres. Hinsdale Hist. Soc., 1979-81, St. Isaac Jogues PTA, 1980. Mem. ABA, Phi Alpha Delta. Republican. Roman Catholic. Club: Hinsdale Golf. Home: 321 S Elm St Hinsdale IL 60521-4620 Office: Sayfarth Shaw Fairweather 55 E Monroe St Fl 42 Chicago IL 60603

WALTRIP, DARRELL LEE, professional stock car driver; b. Owensboro, Ky., Feb. 5, 1947; s. Leroy and Margaret Jean (Evans) W.; m. Stephanie Hamilton Rader, Aug. 15, 1969; 1 child, Jessica Leigh. Student, Ky. Wesleyan Coll. Driver for Junior Johnson & Assocs., Rick Hendrick Motor Sports. Named Driver of Yr., Nat. Motorsports Press Assn., 1977, Olsonite Driver of Yr., 1979; winner Winston Cup, 1982, Nat. Assn. Stock Car Auto Racing Championship, 1985, Winston Cup Championship, 1981, 82, 85, numerous auto races including Coca Cola 600, 1985, 88, 89, Wrangler 500, 1985, Busch 500, 1986, Budweiser 400, 1986, Holly Farms 400, 1986, Goody's 500, 1987, 88, 89, Motorcraft 500, 1989, Daytona 500, 1989, Champion Spark Plug 500, 1991. Mem. Nat. Assn. Stock Car Auto Racing. Republican. Presbyterian. Top Motor Sport money winner worldwide with more than 7.5 million dollars.*

WALTRIP, ROBERT L., environmentalist; b. Austin, TX, 1931. BBA in Mgmt., U. Houston, 1954. With Heights Funeral Home, 1954-62; founder, chmn. bd. dirs., chief exec. officer Service Corp. Internat., Houston, 1962—; founder, chmn. bd. dirs. Waltrip Enterprises Inc., Houston, 1982—; with Tanknology Corp. Internat., Houston, 1988—, Tanknology Environ. Inc., Houston, 1989—. Office: Service Corp International 1929 Allen Pky Houston TX 77019-2506 Office: Tanknology Environ Inc 5225 Hollister St Houston TX 77040

WALTZ, JON RICHARD, lawyer, educator, author; b. Napoleon, Ohio, Oct. 11, 1929; s. Richard R. and Lenore (Tharp) W. B.A. with honors in Polit. Sci, Coll. Wooster, 1951; J.D., Yale U., 1954. Bar: Ohio 1954, Ill. 1965. Assoc. Squire, Sanders & Dempsey, Cleve., 1954-64; chief prosecutor City of Willowick (Ohio), 1958-64; assoc. prof. law Northwestern U. Sch. Law, Chgo., 1964-65; prof. law Northwestern U. Sch. Law, 1965-78, Edna B. and Ednyfed H. Williams prof. law, 1978—; instr. med. jurisprudence Northwestern Med. Sch., 1969—; book critic Washington Post, Chgo. Tribune, others; Disting. vis. prof. law Ill. Inst. Tech.-Chgo.-Kent Coll. Law, 1974; lectr. Co-author: The Trial of Jack Ruby, 1965, Cases and Materials on Evidence, 1968, Principles of Evidence and Proof, 1968, Medical Jurisprudence, 1971, Cases and Materials on Law and Medicine, 1980, Evidence: Making the Record, 1981; author: The Federal Rules of Evidence-An Analysis, 1973, Criminal Evidence, 1975, Evidence: A Summary Analysis, 1976, Introduction to Criminal Evidence, 1991, Chinese lang. edit., 1993; note and comment editor: Yale Law Jour., 1953-54; mem. editorial adv. bd., Harcourt Brace Jovanovich Law Group, 1978—; contbr. numerous articles to profl. jours. Mem. Ill. adv. com. U.S. Commn. on Civil Rights, 1971-74; mem. Ill. Criminal Justice System Policy and Planning Com., 1973-74, Ill. Jud. Inquiry Bd., 1980-88; mem. com. med. edn. AMA, 1982-83; mem. Gov.'s Task Force on Med. Malpractice, 1985; Rep. candidate Ill. Appellate Ct., 1978. Capt. AUS, 1955-58. Decorated Commendation medal; recipient Disting. Svc. award Soc. Midland Authors, 1972, Disting. Alumni award Coll. Wooster, 1987. Mem. Am. Arbitration Assn., Assn. Am. Law Schs., Judge Advs. Assn., Nat. Assn. Def. Lawyers in Criminal Cases, Bar Assn. 7th Jud. Circuit, ABA, Chgo. Bar Assn., Chgo. Council Lawyers, Law-Medicine Soc., Soc. Am. Law Tchrs., Order of Coif, Phi Alpha Delta, Pi Sigma Alpha. Presbyterian. Home: 421 W Melrose St Chicago IL 60657-3848 also: 4005 Lakeridge Dr Holland MI 49424-2263 Office: Northwestern U Sch Law 357 E Chicago Ave Chicago IL 60611-3008

WALTZ, JOSEPH MCKENDREE, neurosurgeon, educator; b. Detroit, July 23, 1931; s. Ralph McKinley and Bertha (Seeley) W.; m. Janet Maureen Journey, June 26, 1954; children: Jeffrey McKinley, Mary Elaine, David Seelye, Stephen McKendree; m. Marilyn Liska, June 5, 1967; 1 child, Tristana McKendree. Student, U. Mich., 1950; B.S., U. Oreg., 1954, M.D., 1956. Diplomate Am. Bd. Neurol. Surgery. Surg. intern U. Mich. Hosp., 1956-57, gen. surg. resident, 1957-58, clin. instr. neurosurgery, 1960-63; neurosurg. assoc. St. Barnabas Hosp., N.Y.C., 1963—; assoc. dir. Inst. Neurosci., 1974—; dir. dept. neurol. surgery, 1977—; assoc. cons. in neurosurgery Englewood (N.J.) Hosp., 1964—; assoc. prof. neurosurgery NYU Med. Ctr., 1974—; asst. prof. dept. surgery (neurosurgery) N.Y. Coll. Osteo. Medicine, 1989—; bd. dirs. Neurol. Surgery Rsch. Found., 1978. Author papers on functional neurosurg. treatment of abnormal movement disorders cerebral palsy, others; cryothalamectomy-cryopulvinectomy and implantation brain pacemakers; chpt. in book on cryogenic surgery; contbr. chpts. to Cryogenic Surgery, Neurology, 1982, Advances in Neurology, 1983. Patentee 4-electrode quadrapolar computerized spinal cord stimulator. Mem. sci. adv. bd. Dystonia Med. Research Found., 1980—; trustee St. Barnabas Hosp., 1980—. Served to capt. M.C. AUS, 1958-60. Recipient bronze award Am. Congress Rehab. Medicine, 1967, World Community Svc. award Rotary. Mem. AMA, Am. Paralysis Assn., World Soc. Stereotactic and Functional Neurosurgery, Congress Neurol. Surgeons, Math. Assn. Am., Internat. Neural Network Soc., Soc. for Cryobiology, N.Y. State Med. Soc., Bronx County Med. Soc., N.Y. State Neurosurg Soc., Nat. Sci Patrol, Phi Beta Pi. Achievements include spl. rsch. on neurophysiology and treatment of epilepsy, basal ganglia disorders, abnormal movement disorders, cerebral palsy, also neurosurg. application stereotactic thalamic surgery and spinal cord stimulation. Home: Four B Island South 720 Milton Rd Rye NY 10580-3258 Office: St Barnabas Hosp 222 Bedford Park Blvd Apt 1G Bronx NY 10458-2513

WALTZ, KENNETH NEAL, political science educator; b. Ann Arbor, Mich., June 8, 1924; s. Christian Benjamin and Luella (Braun) W.; m. Helen Elizabeth Lindsley, June 4, 1949; children: Kenneth L., Thomas E. (dec.),

Daniel E. A.B., Oberlin Coll., 1948; M.A., Columbia U., 1950, Ph.D., 1954. Instr., then asst. prof. Columbia U., 1953-57; from assoc. prof. to prof. politics Swarthmore Coll., 1957-66; research assoc. Center Internat. Affairs, Harvard, 1963-64, 68-69, 72; prof. politics Brandeis U., Waltham, Mass., 1966-71, Adlai E. Stevenson prof. internat. politics, 1967-71; Ford prof. polit. sci. U. Calif., Berkeley, 1971-94, Ford prof. emeritus, 1994—; vis. sr. research assoc. King's Coll., U. London, 1986-87; Cons. govt. agys.; vis. scholar dept. of philosophy, The London Sch. of Econ., 1976-77, rsch. sch. of Pacific studies, Australian Nat. U., 1978, dept. of Internat. politics, Peking U., 1982, 91, dept. of Internat. Politics, Fudan U., Shang ai, 1991, USAF Acad., 1991-92. Author: Man, The State and War, 1959, Foreign Policy and Democratic Politics, 1967, Theory of International Politics, 1979, The Spread of Nuclear Weapons, 1981; co-author: The Spread of Nuclear Weapons: A Debate, 1995: co-author, co-editor: Conflict in World Politics, 1971, The Use of Force, 1971, 4th edit.; mem. edtl. bd. Jour. Strategic Studies, ABC Polit. Sci. Served to 1st lt. AUS, 1944-46, 51-52. NSF grantee, 1968-71; Guggenheim fellow, 1976-77; fellow Woodrow Wilson Center, Internat. Center for Scholars, 1979-80; Heinz Eulau award for best article in the Am. Polit. Sci. Rev., 1990. Fellow Am. Acad. Arts and Scis.; mem. Am. Polit. Sci. Assn. (sec. 1966-67, pres. 1987-88), Internat. Studies Assn. (pres. New Eng. sect. 1966-67), Coun. Fgn. Rels., Phi Beta Kappa. Office: Polit Sci Dept U Calif at Berkeley Berkeley CA 94720-1950

WALVOORD, JOHN FLIPSE, seminary president, chancellor, theologian; b. Sheboygan, Wis., May 1, 1910; s. John Garrett and Mary (Flipse) W.; m. Geraldine Lundgren, June 28, 1939; children: John Edward, James Randall, Timothy, Paul. A.B., Wheaton Coll., 1931, D.D., 1960; B.Th., Dallas Theol. Sem., 1934, M.Th., 1934, D.Th., 1936; A.M., Tex. Christian U., 1945; D.Litt. (hon.), Liberty Bapt. Sem. Registrar Dallas Theol. Sem., 1935-45, prof. systematic theology, 1936-52, prof., 1952-85, regent, 1940-86, asst. to pres., 1945-52, pres., 1952-86, chancellor, 1986—; editor Sem. Bull., 1940-53; pastor Ft. Worth, 1935-50; editor Bibliotheca Sacra, 1952-85. Author: The Doctrine of the Holy Spirit, 1943, The Holy Spirit, 1954, The Return of the Lord, 1955, The Thessalonian Epistles, 1956, The Rapture Question, 1957, The Millennial Kingdom, 1959, To Live Is Christ, 1961, Israel in Prophecy, 1962, The Church in Prophecy, 1964, The Revelation of Jesus Christ, 1966, The Nations in Prophecy, 1967, Jesus Christ Our Lord, 1969, Philippians, 1971, Daniel, 1971, The Holy Spirit at Work Today, 1973, Major Bible Themes, 1974, Armageddon, Oil and the Middle East Crisis, 1974, 2d edit., 1990, Matthew: Thy Kingdom Come, 1975, The Blessed Hope and the Tribulation, 1976, Prophecy Knowledge Handbook, 1990, What We Believe: Discovering the Truths of Scripture, 1990, Major Bible Prophecies, 1991; contbr. to: Four Views of Hell, 1992, Prophecy: 14 Essential Keys to Understanding the Final Drama, 1993; editor: Inspiration and Interpretation, 1957, Truth for Today, 1963; co-editor: The Bib Sac Reader, 1983, The Bible Knowledge Commentary, N.T. edit., 1983, Old Testament edit., 1985; editor: Lewis Sperry Chafer Systematic Theology, abridged edit., 1988. Named Alumnus of Yr. Wheaton Coll., 1981. Mem. Evang. Theol. Soc., Wheaton Coll. Scholastic Honor Soc. Home: 1302 El Patio Dr Dallas TX 75218-3209

WALWER, FRANK KURT, dean, legal educator; b. 1930; s. Kurt and Beatrice (Ahlert) W.; m. Maryann Pancake, Apr. 15, 1961; 1 child, Gregory F. AB, Columbia U., 1952, LLB, 1956. Bar: N.Y. 1959. Assoc. dean Columbia U., 1972-80; dean, prof. U. Tulsa, 1980-91, trustee's prof. law, 1991-94, dean, prof. Tex. Wesleyan U. Law Sch., 1994—, chmn. Grad. and Profl. Sch. Fin. Aid Svc., 1976-78, pres. Law Sch. Admission Coun., 1983-84; bd. dirs. The Coun. on Postsecondary Accreditation, 1989-92. Mem. Assn. Am. Law Schs. (chmn. sect. econs. of legal edn. 1974-76), ABA (accreditation com. 1976-94, chair legal edn and bar admissions sect. 1986-87, lawyer competency com. 1986-92, standards rev. com. 1986-94, AALS/ABA commn. on financing), Am. Bar Fellows, Am. Inns of Court. Office: 2535 E Grauwyler Irving TX 75061

WALWORTH, ARTHUR, author; b. Newton, Mass., July 9, 1903; s. Arthur Clarence and Ruth Richardson (Lippincott) W. Grad., Phillips Andover Acad., 1921; B.A., Yale U., 1925. Ednl. dept. Houghton Mifflin Co., 1927-43; staff OWI, 1943; staff Medomak Camp, Washington, Maine, summers 1943-63. Author: School Histories at War, 1938, Black Ships Off Japan, 1946, Cape Breton, 1948, The Medomak Way, 1953, Woodrow Wilson, 2 vols, 1958, 1 vol., 1967, 78, America's Moment: 1918, 1977, Wilson and his Peacemakers, 1986. Recipient Pulitzer prize in biography, 1958. Clubs: Cosmos; Graduates (New Haven). Home: North Hill 865 Central Ave Apt C201 Needham MA 02192-1338

WALZ, BRUCE JAMES, radiation oncologist; b. Waterloo, Ill., Sept. 18, 1940; s. George Frederick and Alberta Emma (Heyl) W.; m. Renata T. Jaeger, Mar. 8, 1970; children: Jennifer Mara Walz Kuhn, Rachel Elizabeth. A.B., Washington U., 1962, M.D., 1966. Diplomate Am. Bd. Radiology Therapy. Intern, St. Luke's Hosp., St. Louis, 1966-67; resident Washington U. St. Louis, 1969-72; instr. Harvard Med. Sch., Boston, 1972-74; asst. prof. Washington U., 1974-82, assoc. prof., 1982-86, clin. assoc. prof., 1986—; dir. radiation therapy St. Anthony's Med. Ctr., St. Louis. 1986—. Contbr. articles to profl. jours. Active med. adv. com. Medicare, 1992—. Served to lt. comdr. USNR, 1967-69, Vietnam. Harvard Med. Sch. fellow, 1972-73. Fellow Am. Coll. Radiology; mem. AMA, Am. Cancer Soc. (bd. dirs. Mo. divsn. 1992—), Mo. Med. Soc. (ho. of dels. 1975—), Mo. State Radiol. Soc. (bd. dirs. 1982-87, secs.-treas. 1987-90, v.p 1990-91, pres. 1991-92, ACR counselor 1995—), St. Louis Metro Med. Assn. (councilor 1987-89), Greater St. Louis Soc. Radiologists (chair therapy sect. 1985, sec.-treas. 1988-89, pres. elect 1989-90, pres. 1990-91), Am. Soc. Therapeutic Radiologists and Oncologists, Am. Coll. Radiology, Am. Soc. Clin. Oncologists, Arab-Am. Med. Soc. Presbyterian. Clubs: Whittemore House (Clayton, Mo.). Avocations: gardening, travelling, scuba diving. Office: St Anthony's Med Ctr Div Radiation Therapy Saint Louis MO 63128

WALZ, JACK, advertising executive; b. 1938. Grad., Ga. Inst. Tech., 1960. With IBM, 1960; various positions BBDO, Atlanta, 1963—, now exec. v.p., worldwide account dir. With USAF, 1961-63. Office: BBDO Atlanta 3414 Peachtree Rd NE Atlanta GA 30326-1113*

WALZER, JUDITH BORODOVKO, university administrator, educator; b. N.Y.C., May 27, 1935; d. Isidore and Ida (Gins) Borodovko; m. Michael L. Walzer, June 17, 1956; children:—Sarah, Rebecca. B.A., Brandeis U., 1958, M.A., 1960, Ph.D., 1967. Dir. office women's edn. Radcliffe Coll., Cambridge, Mass., 1974-77, assoc. dean., 1976-77; Allston Burr sr. tutor, asst. dean for co-edn. Harvard Coll., Cambridge, Mass., 1977-80; asst. to the pres. Princeton U., N.J., 1980-85; provost New Sch. for Social Research, N.Y.C., 1985—. Mem. alumni fund com. Brandeis U., Waltham, Mass., 1983—; mem. adv. com. Overseas Sch., Hebrew U. in Jerusalem, 1989—; bd. dirs. Woodrow Wilson Found., Princeton U., 1991—. Democrat. Jewish. Office: New Sch for Social Rsch 66 W 12th St New York NY 10011-8603

WALZER, MICHAEL LABAN, political science educator; b. N.Y.C., Mar. 3, 1935; s. Joseph P. and Sally (Hochman) W.; m. Judith Borodovko, June 17, 1956; children: Sarah, Rebecca. B.A., Brandeis U., 1956; Ph.D. Harvard U., 1961. Fulbright fellow Cambridge (Eng.) U., 1956-57; asst. prof. Princeton U., 1962-66; faculty Harvard U., 1966-80, prof. govt., 1968-80; prof. Sch. Social Scis., Inst. Advanced Study, Princeton, N.J., 1980—. Author: The Revolution of the Saints, 1965, Obligations: Essays on Disobedience, War and Citizenship, 1970, Political Action, 1971, Regicide and Revolution, 1974, Just and Unjust Wars, 1977, Radical Principles: Reflections of an Unreconstructed Democrat, 1980, Spheres of Justice: A Defense of Pluralism and Equality, 1983, Exodus and Revolution, 1985, Interpretation and Social Criticism, 1987, The Company of Critics: Social Criticism and Political Commitment in the Twentieth Century, 1988, What It Means To Be an American, 1993, Thick and Thin: Moral Argument at Home and Abroad, 1994, (with David Miller) Pluralism, Justice, and Equality, 1995; mem. edtl. bd. Dissent mag., 1960—; contbg. editor New Republic, 1974-. Bd. govs. Hebrew U., Jerusalem, 1975—; trustee Brandeis U., 1983-88 ; chmn. faculty adv. cabinet United Jewish Appeal, 1977-81. Home: 103 Linwood Cir Princeton NJ 08540-3625

WALZER, NORMAN CHARLES, economics educator; b. Mendota, Ill., Mar. 17, 1943; s. Elmer J. and Anna L. (Johnston) W.; m. Dona Lee Maurer, Aug. 22, 1970; children: Steven, Mark. BS, Ill. State U., Normal, 1966; MA, U. Ill., 1969, PhD, 1970. Rsch. dir. Cities and Villages Mcpl.

Problems Com., Springfield, Ill., 1974-84; vis. prof. U. Ill., Urbana, 1977-78; prof. econs. Western Ill. U., Macomb, 1978—, chmn. dept. econs., 1980-89, dir. Ill. Inst. Rural Affairs, 1988—, interim dean coll. bus. and tech., 1993-94. Author: Cities, Suburbs and Property Tax, 1981; Government Structure and Public Finance, 1984; editor: Financing State and Local Governments, 1981, Rural Community Economic Development, 1991; co-editor: Financing Local Infrastructure in Non Metro Areas, 1986, Financing Economic Development in The 1980s, 1986, Financing Rural Health Care, 1988, Rural Health Care, 1992, Rural Community Economic Development, 1992, International Local Economic Development: Trends and Practices, 1995. Mem. Am. Econs. Assn., Ill. Econs. Assn. (pres. 1979-80), Mid-Continent Regional Sci. Assn. (pres. 1985-86). Lodge: K.C. Home: 727 Auburn Dr Macomb IL 61455-3002 Office: Western Ill U Ill Inst Rural Affairs 518 Stipes Hall Macomb IL 61455

WALZER, WILLIAM CHARLES, church official, interdenominational religious publishing agency executive; b. Rochester, N.Y., July 20, 1912; s. William Frederick and Mable Beatrice (McElroy) W.; m. Dorothy Mae Kramer, Aug. 28, 1938; children—Carolyn Walzer Dennis, Lorraine Walzer Harbaugh, William T. B.A., U. Rochester, 1935; M.A., 1937; B.D., Colgate-Rochester Div. Sch., 1941; Ph.D., U. Chgo., 1944; postgrad., Syracuse U. Sch. Journalism, 1951. Ordained to ministry United Meth. Ch., 1941, United Ch. of Christ, 1985, Christian Ch. (Disciples of Christ), 1986. Tchr. high sch., 1935-38; pastor Stafford (N.Y.) Meth. Ch., 1938-41; asst. pastor Hyde Park Meth. Ch., Chgo., 1941-43; asst. prof. Garrett Theol. Sem., Evanston, Ill., 1943-45; prof. Scarritt Coll. for Christian Workers and Vanderbilt U. Div. Sch., Nashville, 1945-51; mem. staff Bd. Missions, Presbyn. Ch. in U.S.A., N.Y.C., 1951-54; exec. dir. dept. edn. for mission Nat. Council Chs., N.Y.C., 1954-77; exec. dir. Friendship Press, N.Y.C., 1954-77; interim pastor Westminster Presbyn. Ch., N.Y.C., 1955-59, 66-68, 75-77; minister Community Ch. of Great Neck, N.Y., 1979-85; treas. Eastern Ecumenical Conf. Christian World Mission, 1985-92; interim minister Fairfax (Va.) Christian Ch., 1987-88, 92-93; cons. div. world mission and ecumenism Luth. Ch. in Am., N.Y.C., 1978-79; chmn. Eastern Ecumenical Conf. on World Mission, Silver Bay, N.Y., 1978-80; pres. Religious Pub. Relations Council, 1959-61; bd. dirs. Religion in Am. Life, 1965-68; del. World Council Christian Edn., Tokyo, 1958, Lima, Peru, 1971; cons. Pacific Council of Chs., Suva, Fiji, Joint Bd. Christian Edn., Australia and N.Z., 1972; staff World Council Chs. Assembly, New Delhi, 1961, Uppsala, Sweden, 1968. Author: American Denominations, 1953, Your World, Your Mission, 1963, Great Protestant Leaders, 1965. Mem. U.S. Nat. Commn. for UNESCO, 1972-78; chmn. Potomac assn. stewardship and mission com. United Ch. of Christ, 1991-92. Mem. Am. Soc. Ch. History, Internat. Soc. Missiology, Gray Panthers, Phi Beta Kappa, Phi Sigma Iota. Home: 1901 Villaridge Dr # A Reston VA 22091-4820 *I am committed to educating people for interracial, intercultural and international understanding and concern. To that end a major goal has been a better educated church and community, leading to social justice, world peace and human mutual helpfulness, all of which I feel are demands of my religious heritage.Died Feb. 21, 1995.*

WALZOG, NANCY LEE, film and television executive; b. Balt., Feb. 12, 1963; d. William Richard and Barbara Jane (Lombardi) W. BFA, NYU, 1983; MBA, Pace U., 1991. Dir. TV sales and mktg. Internat. Film Exch., N.Y.C., 1984-86; producer ABC Entertainment, N.Y.C., 1984; comml. producer Nancy Walzog Film and TV, Ltd., N.Y.C., 1982-84; v.p. Tapestry Internat., Ltd., N.Y.C., 1986-94, pres., 1994—. Recipient Emmy award, Acad. TV Arts and Scis., N.Y.C., 1987, Emmy nominiation, 1990, ACE award, Nat. Acad. Cable TV Programming, Washington, 1987, Gold award San Francisco Internat. Film Festival, 1987, Hugo award Chgo. Internat. Film Festival, 1988. Office: Tapestry Internat 920 Broadway 16th Fl New York NY 10010-6007

WAMBAUGH, JOSEPH, author; b. East Pittsburgh, Pa., Jan. 22, 1937; s. Joseph Aloysius and Anne (Malloy) W; m. Dee Allsup, Nov. 26, 1955; children: Mark, David, Jeannette. BA, Calif. State Coll., Los Angeles, 1960, MA, 1968. Police officer Los Angeles, 1960-74. Creator, cons.: (TV series) Police Story, 1973-77, The Blue Knight, 1975; author: The New Centurions, 1971, The Blue Knight, 1972, The Onion Field, 1973 (Edgar Allan Poe award Mystery Writers Am. 1974), The Choirboys, 1975, The Black Marble, 1978, The Glitter Dome, 1981, The Delta Star, 1983, Lines and Shadows, 1984 (Rodolfo Walsh prize Internat. Assn. Crime Writers 1989), The Secrets of Harry Bright, 1985, Echoes in the Darkness, 1987, The Blooding, 1989, The Golden Orange, 1990, Fugitive Nights, 1992, Finnegan's Week, 1993; screenwriter: (films) The Onion Field, 1979, The Black Marble, 1980 (Edgar Allan Poe award Mystery Writers Am. 1981), (TV movies) The Glitter Dome, 1984, Echoes in the Darkness, 1987, Fugitive Knights, 1993. Served with USMC, 1954-57. *

WAMBOLD, JUDSON J., lawyer; b. Columbus, Ohio, 1952. BS magna cum laude, U. Pa., 1974; JD, Cornell U., 1978. Bar: Pa. 1978. Ptnr. Dechert Price & Rhoads, Phila. Office: Dechert Price & Rhoads 4000 Bell Atlantic 1717 Arch St Philadelphia PA 19103-2793

WAMBOLT, RONALD RALPH, electronics company executive; b. Halifax, N.S., Can., Aug. 15, 1934; came to U.S., 1974; s. Norman Holland M. (Slaunwhite) W.; m. Shirley Marie Burgess, June 22, 1957; children: Cathy, David, Robert, Ronald, Deborah. Grad. high sch., Halifax, 1952. Field service engr. Sperry Gyroscope Can. Ltd., 1960-65; field engr. Tektronix, Inc., Can., 1965-69, advt. program mgr.; 1969-71; internat. sales mgr. Tektronix, Inc., Beaverton, Oreg., 1974-77, gen. mgr. Americas/Pacific, 1977-79; asst. sales mgr. Tektronix Can. Ltd., 1971-72, v.p., gen. mgr., 1972-74; mgr. internat. ops. John Fluke Mfg. Co., Inc., Everett, Wash., 1979-82, dir. internat. ops., 1982-84, v.p. dir. internat. ops., 1984-87, sr. v.p. dir. worldwide sales, 1987-91, sr. v.p. dir. worldwide sales and svc., 1991—; mem. adv. bd. World Trade Council, Seattle, 1984-87, Wash. export council internat. trade, Dept. Commerce, Seattle, 1986—; trustee Wash. State Taiwan Trade Assn., Seattle, 1987; bd. dirs. Wash. Coun. on Internat. Trade, 1991—. Adv. bd. Global Reach Consortium, 1986-87. Served with RCAF, 1952-55. Mem. Machinery and Allied Products Inst. Roman Catholic. Office: John Fluke Mfg Co Inc 6920 Seaway Blvd PO Box 9090 Everett WA 98206

WAMP, ZACH P., congressman; b. Ft. Benning, Ga., Oct. 28, 1957; m. Kim Wamp; 2 children. Student, U. N.C., U. Tenn. Chmn. Hamilton County Rep. Party, 1987; regional dir. Tenn. Rep. Party, 1989; v.p. Charter Real Estate Co., 1989-92; real estate broker Fletcher Bright Co., 1992-94; mem. 104th Congress from 3d Tenn. dist., 1995—. Office: US House Reps 423 Cannon House Office Bldg Washington DC 20515-4203

WAMPLER, LLOYD CHARLES, retired lawyer; b. Spencer, Ind., Nov. 4, 1920; s. Charles and Vivian (Hawkins) W.; m. Joyce Ann Hoppenrath, Sept. 28, 1950 (dec. 1954); 1 child, Natalie Gay (dec.); m. Mary E. Shumaker, Sept. 16, 1982. AB, Ind. U., 1942, JD, 1947. Bar: Ind. 1947, U.S. Supreme Ct. 1971. Instr. bus. law U. Kans., 1947-49; dep. atty. gen. Ind., 1949-50; mem. legal com. Interstate Oil Compact Commn., 1950; asst. pub. counselor Ind., 1950-53; mem. Stevens, Wampler, Travis & Fortin, Plymouth, 1953-83; claim counsel Am. Family Ins. Group, Indpls., 1983-88; ret., 1988. Mem. Ind. Rehab. Services Bd., 1978-86; Dem. nominee for judge Ind. Supreme Ct., 1956. With USNR, 1942-46. Mem. ABA, Am. Judicature Soc., Ind. Bar Assn. (bd. mgrs. 1975-77), Indpls. Bar Assn., Ind. Acad. Sci., Ind. Def. Lawyers Assn. (bd. dirs. 1967-72, v.p. 1970, pres. 1971-72), Ind. Hist. Soc., Marshall County Hist. Soc. (bd. dirs. 1969-75), Sagamore of the Wabash, Am. Legion, Phi Delta Phi. Home: 4000 N Meridian St Indianapolis IN 46208-4034

WAMPOLD, CHARLES HENRY, JR., lawyer; b. Montgomery, Ala., Oct. 21, 1925; s. Charles Henry and Selma (Manasse) W.; m. Babette Levy, Mar. 14, 1954; children: Jerre Lynn, Carolyn M., Charles Henry III. B.A., U. Ala., 1946, LL.B., 1948, J.D., 1950. Bar: Ala. 1948. Practice in Montgomery, 1949—; mem. Capouano, Wampold, Prestwood & Sansone, 1960-83, of counsel, 1983—. Bd. dirs. Griel Meml. Hosp., Mus. Fine Arts, Montgomery Community Council. Mem. ABA, Ala. Bar Assn., Montgomery Area Mental Health Assn., Zeta Beta Tau. Jewish. Club: Lions. Home: 3113 Jasmine Rd Montgomery AL 36111-1114 Office:

Capouano Wampold Prestwood & Sansone 350 Adams Ave Montgomery AL 36104-6108

WAMSLEY, BARBARA SIMBORSKI, federal agency administrator; b. Holden, W.Va., July 6, 1945; d. Joseph and Katie (Stepson) Simborski; m. Dennis Edward Wamsley, Dec. 27, 1969. MPA, Harvard U., 1985. Analyst U.S. Govt. Dept. HEW, Washington, 1963-67; deputy asst. sec. U.S. Govt. Dept. Health & Human Svcs., Washington, 1982-86, sr. policy/mgmt. position, 1986-88; dep. dir. fed. programs Nat. Acad. Pub. Adminstrn., Washington, 1988-93, sr. advisor to dep. sec., 1993-95; fellow Syracuse Maxwell Ctr. for Advanced Pub. Adminstrn., 1995—; spkr. in field. Author, editor: Modernizing Federal Classification, 1991, Leading People in Change, 1993; contbr. articles to profl. jours. Labauch tutor Literacy Coun., Charles County, 1992. Littauer fellow Harvard U., Cambridge, 1985. Fellow Am. Soc. Polit. Sci.; mem. Am. Soc. Pub. Adminstrn., Nat. Acad. Pub. Adminstrn. (assoc.). Avocations: flying, water coloring, col. work, history. Home: Pomonkey Landing 2900 Creedon Dr Indian Head MD 20640

WAMSLEY, JAMES LAWRENCE, III, lawyer; b. Cleve., June 18, 1950; s. James Lawrence Jr. and Dorothy Mae (Auberger) W.; m. Christine Lou Anderson, July 29, 1972; children: Bryan Douglas, Katherine Anne. BS in Electrical Engring., U. Va., 1972; JD, U. Mich., 1975. Bar: Ohio 1975, U.S. Patent and Trademark Office 1984, U.S. Ct. Appeals (6th cir.) 1976, U.S. Ct. Appeals (Fed. cir.) 1984. Assoc. Jones, Day, Reavis & Pogue, Cleve., 1975-84, ptnr., 1985—. Mem. Am. Intellectual Property Law Assn., Cleve. Intellectual Property Law Assn. Avocations: reading, theater, golf, skiing. Office: Jones Day Reavis & Pogue 901 Lakeside Ave Cleveland OH 44114

WAN, FREDERIC YUI-MING, mathematician, educator; b. Shanghai, Jan. 7, 1936; s. Wai-Nam and Olga Pearl (Jung) W.; m. Julia Y.S. Chang, Sept. 10, 1960. SB, MIT, 1959, SM, 1963, PhD, 1965. Mem. staff MIT Lincoln Lab., Lexington, 1959-65; instr. math. MIT, Cambridge, 1965-67, asst. prof., 1967-69, assoc. prof., 1969-74; prof. math., dir. Inst. Applied Math. and Stats. U. B.C., Vancouver, 1974-83; prof. applied math. and math. U. Wash., Seattle, 1983-95, chmn. Dept. Applied Math., 1984-88, assoc. dean scis. coll. arts and scis., 1988-92; vice chancellor rsch., dean grad. studies U. Calif., Irvine, 1995—; program dir. Divsn. Math. Sci. NSF, 1986-87, divsn. dir., 1993-94; cons. indsl. firms and govt. agys.; mem. MIT Ednl. Coun. for B.C. Area of Can., 1974-83. Assoc. editor Jour. Applied Mechanics, 1991-95, Can. Applied Math. Quar., Studies in Applied Math., Jour. of Dynamics of Continuous Discrete and Impulse Systems; contbr. articles to profl. jours. Sloan Found. award, 1973, Killam sr. fellow, 1979. Fellow AAAS, ASME, Am. Acad. Mechanics (sec. fellows 1984-90, pres.-elect 1992-93, pres. 1993-94), Soc. Indsl. and Applied Math., Can. Applied Math. Soc. (coun. 1980-83, pres. 1983-85, Arthur Beaumont Disting. Svc. award 1991), Am. Math. Soc., Math. Assn. Am., Sigma Xi. Home: 58 Whitman St Irvine CA 92715 Office: U Calif Irvine Office Rsch & Grad Studies 155 Administration Irvine CA 92717-3175

WAN, WEIYING, library curator; b. Tientsin, China, May 21, 1932; s. Hsin-chuan and Mei-Hsuan (Hu) W.; m. Ching Chao, Feb. 5, 1955; children: Bertram H.C., Julian H.C. BA, Nat. Taiwan Normal U., 1952; MALS, U Minn., 1957; MA, Wayne State U., 1959. Lectr. Tamkaing Coll., Taipei, Taiwan, 1953-55; dir. acquisition Nat. Ctr. Libr., Taipei, 1959-62; assoc. prof. Nat. Taiwan U., Taipei, 1962-64; curator Chinese collection U. Mich. Libr., Ann Arbor, 1964-66; curator East Asian collection Yale U. Libr., New Haven, 1966-69; head of Asia Libr. U. Mich. Libr., Ann Arbor, 1969—. Mem. Assn. for Asian Studies (chair com. on East Asian libraries 1964-70), Ctr. for Chinese Rsch. Materials (dir. 1985). Office: Asia Libr U Mich North University Ann Arbor MI 48109-1205

WANAMAKER, ROBERT JOSEPH, advertising company executive; b. Oak Park, Ill., Nov. 24, 1924; s. Daniel John and Mabel (Maloney) W.; m. Carol Anne George, Apr. 20, 1968; children: Stacey Lynne, Bethanne. Ed., Northwestern U., 1949. Vice pres., copy dir. Edward H. Weiss & Co., Chgo., 1957-62; sr. v.p., U.S. creative dir. Clinton E. Frank, Inc., Chgo., 1962-72; sr. v.p., creative dir. Grey-North, Inc., Chgo., 1972-76; sr. v.p., dir. creative services Y & R/Buchen, Reincke, Chgo., 1976-79; v.p. creative services Pollenex, Chgo., 1979-86; pres. Robert Wanamaker Inc. "Getting Thru" Mktg. Communications, River Forest, Ill., 1987—. Served with AUS, 1943. Named one of 100 top advt. creative people in U.S.A. Ad Daily U.S.A., 1975. Home and Office: 7225 Division St River Forest IL 60305-1267 One of the biggest problems with success in worldly things is keeping your sense of values in proper perspective. Affluence can dull your sensitivity to the needs and aspirations of those less fortunate. You can become obsessed with building your own financial assets. The misguided fear of losing your status, your luxuries, your comforts can be abnormally painful. Every once in awhile you have to chasten your thinking and remind yourself that the only three riches in life are love, health, and being at peace with yourself and your God.

WAND, PATRICIA ANN, librarian; b. Portland, Oreg., Mar. 28, 1942; d. Ignatius Bernard and Alice Ruth (Suhr) W.; m. Francis Dean Silvernail, Dec. 20, 1966 (div. Jan. 19, 1986); children: Marjorie Lynn Silvernail, Kirk Dean Silvernail. BA, Seattle U., 1963; MAT, Antioch Grad. Sch., 1967; AMLS, U. Mich., 1972. Vol. Peace Corps, Colombia, S.Am., 1963-65; secondary tchr. Langley Jr. High Sch., Washington, 1965-66; asst. libr. Wittenberg U. Libr., Springfield, Ohio, 1967-69; secondary tchr. Caro (Mich.) High Sch., 1969-70; assoc. libr. Coll. of S.I. (N.Y.) Libr., 1972-77; head, access svcs. Columbia U. Libr., N.Y.C., 1977-82; asst. univ. libr. U. Oreg., Eugene, 1982-89; univ. libr. The Am. U., Washington, 1989—; cons. Bloomsburg (Pa.) U. Libr., 1990. Contbr. articles to profl. jours. Pres. West Cascade Returned Peace Corps Vols., Eugene, 1985-88; v.p. Friends of Colombia, Washington, 1990—; speaker on Peace Corps, 1965—, libr. and info. svcs., 1979—. Honors Program scholarship Seattle U., 1960-62, Peace Corps scholarship Antioch U., 1965-66; recipient Beyond War award, 1987, Fulbright Sr. Lectr. award Fulbright, 1989, Disting. Alumnus award Sch. of Info. and Libr. Studies, U. Mich., 1992. Mem. ALA, Assn. Coll. and Rsch. Librs. (chair budge and fin. bd. dirs. 1987-89; chair WHCLIS task force 1989-92, On-line Computer Libr. Ctr. Adv. com. on Coll. and Univ. Librs. 1991—), D.C. Libr. Assn. (bd. dirs. 1993—). Home: 4854 Bayard Blvd Bethesda MD 20816-1785 Office: Am Univ Libr 4400 Massachusetts Ave NW Washington DC 20016-8046

WAND, RICHARD WALTON, paper company executive; b. Shelbyville, Ind., Sept. 20, 1939; s. J. Harold and Josephine Katharine (Harvey) W.; m. Sharon Brierly, June 21, 1964; children: Brian James, Katharine. BS in Mech. Engring., Purdue U., 1961; MBA, Ind. U., 1964. Project engr. Combustion Engring., Inc., 1961-63; mgr. tech. ops. Aerospace Research Applications Ctr., Ind. U., 1963-65; with Bergstrom Paper Co., Neenah, Wis., 1965-80, adminstrv. v.p., 1972-79, exec. v.p. ops., 1979-80; v.p. adminstrn. P.H. Glatfelter Co., Spring Grove, Pa., 1980—; bd. dirs. Ecusta Australia Ltd. Contbg. editor: Infosystems Mag., 1972-73. Bd. dirs. Jr. Achievement York County, Pa., York Found., Strand Capitol Performing Arts Ctr.; mem. Citizens Adv. Coun. Pa. Dept. Environ. Resources. Mem. Am. Paper Inst. (dir. pulp consumers bd.), Syracuse Pulp and Paper Found. (dir., pres.), Beta Theta Pi. Republican. Presbyterian. Home: 391 Tri-Hill Rd York PA 17403-3854 Office: PH Glatfelter Co 228 S Main St Spring Grove PA 17362-1000

WANDEL, THADDEUS, ophthalmologist; b. Boston, Feb. 10, 1945; s. Barney and Jean (Scryoner) W.; children: Holly, Erika. AB, Harvard U., 1961; MD, Harvard U., Boston, 1965. Diplomate Am. Bd. Ophthalmology. Pvt. practice, Croton-on-Hudson, N.Y.; co-dir. glaucoma Albert Einstein Coll. Medicine, Bronx, N.Y., 1985-87; dir. glaucoma svc. N.Y. Med. Coll., Valhalla, 1987—. Capt. M.C., USAF, 1967-69. Fellow Am. Acad. Ophthalmology, Am. Soc. for Laser Medicine and Surgery; mem. Assn. for Rsch. in Vision and Ophthalmology. Office: 136 Old Post Rd N Croton On Hudson NY 10520

WANDER, HERBERT STANTON, lawyer; b. Cin., Mar. 17, 1935; s. Louis Marvin and Pauline (Schuster) W.; m. Ruth Cele Fell, Aug. 7, 1960; children: Daniel Jerome, Susan Gail, Lois Marlene. AB, U. Mich., 1957; LLB, Yale U., 1960. Bar: Ohio 1960, Ill. 1960. Law clk. to judge U.S. Dist. Ct. (no. dist.) Ill., 1960-61; ptnr. Pope Ballard Shepard & Fowle, Chgo., 1961-78, Katten Muchin & Zavis, Chgo., 1978—; trustee Michael Reese Found.,

1991—; bd. dirs. Tel. & Data Systems, Chgo., 1968—, Advance Ross Corp., 1991—; mem. legal adv. com. to the bd. govs. N.Y. Stock Exch., 1989-92. Contbr. numerous articles to profl. jours. Bd. dirs. Jewish Fedn. Met. Chgo., 1972—, pres., 1981-83; bd. dirs. Jewish United Fund, 1972—, pres., 1981-83, chmn. pub. affairs com., 1984-87, gen. campaign chmn., 1993; former regional chmn. nat. young leadership cabinet United Jewish Appeal; vice chmn. large city budgeting com. Council Jewish Fedns., 1979-82, bd. dirs., 1980—, exec. com., 1983-84. Editor (jour.) Bus. Law Today, 1992-93; editor-in-chief (jour.) The Bus. Lawyer, 1993-94. Mem. ABA (sec. bus. law sect. 1992-93, vice-chair 1993-94, chair-elect 1994—), Chgo. Bar Assn., Ill. State Bar Assn., Yale Law Sch. Assn. (exec. com. 1982-86), Phi Beta Kappa. Clubs: Standard, Econ. (Chgo.); Northmoor Country (Highland Park, Ill.). Home: 2023 Linden Ave Highland Park IL 60035-2513 Office: Katten Muchin & Zavis Ste 1600 525 W Monroe St Chicago IL 60661-3693

WANDERS, HANS WALTER, banker; b. Aachen, Germany, Apr. 3, 1925; came to U.S., 1929, naturalized, 1943; s. Herbert and Anna Maria (Kusters) W.; m. Elizabeth Knox Kimball, Apr. 2, 1949; children: Crayton Kimball, David Gillette. BS, Yale, 1947; postgrad., Rutgers U. Grad Sch. Banking, 1961-64. With Gen. Electric Co., 1947-48, Libbey-Owens-Ford Glass Co., 1948-53, Allied Chem. Co., 1953-55, McKinsey & Co., Inc., 1955-57; from asst. cashier to v.p. No. Trust Co., Chgo., 1957-65; v.p. Nat. Blvd. Bank, Chgo., 1965-66, pres., 1966-70; exec. v.p. Wachovia Bank & Trust Co., N.A., Winston-Salem, N.C., 1970-74, chmn., 1977-85, vice chmn., 1985-88, also bd. dirs.; pres. Wachovia Corp., Winston-Salem, 1974-76, 85-87, chmn., 1977-85, vice chmn., 1987-88, also bd. dirs.; pres., chief exec. officer 1st Wachovia Corp. Services, Inc., Winston-Salem, 1986-88, ret., 1988; dir. Exxon Supply Co., 1989-94, Goody's Pharmaceuticals, 1989-94; dir. Gulf USA, Inc., 1989-92. Chmn. Winston-Salem Found. Com., 1981-82; bd. dirs. N.C. Textile Found., N.C. Engring. Found., Inc., 1971-88; trustee, mem. exec. com. Salem Coll. and Acad., 1986-91, Tax. Found., 1982—, vice chmn., 1984-86, chmn., 1986-88, chmn. exec. com., 1989; bd. visitors Fuqua Sch. Bus., Duke U., 1978-89; mem. nat. corps. com. United Negro Coll. Fund; mem., chmn. N.C. Bd. Econ. Devel., 1989-93. Lt. USNR, 1943-46, 51-53. Mem. Am. Bankers Assn. (chmn. mktg. divsn. 1979-80, dir. 1971-73), Assn. Res. City Bankers, Conf. Bd. (So. regional adv. coun.), Assn. Bank Holding Cos. (bd. dirs., exec. com. 1981-83), Chgo. Club, Commonwealth Club Chgo., Piedmont Club, Old Town Club Winston-Salem, Roaring Gap Club N.C. Home: 10 Graylyn Pl Winston Salem NC 27106 Office: Wachovia Corp PO Box 3099 Winston Salem NC 27102-3099

WANDLER, LESLIE ROY, financial executive; b. Cleve., Dec. 7, 1945; s. Paul R. and Laverne (Melvin) W.; m. Jean Leslie Ostrow, Dec. 21, 1967 (div. June 1985); 1 child, Lisa; m. Susan A. Simpson, Feb. 6, 1988; 1 child, Andrew. AB, Columbia U., 1967; MBA, Old Dominion U., 1971. Salesman Goldman Sachs, St. Louis, 1971-73; asst. treas. CIT Fin. Corp., N.Y.C., 1973-76; treasury supr. Texaco, N.Y.C., 1976-77; dep. dir. corp. fin. Mfrs. Hanover, N.Y.C., 1977-83; treas. S.E. Banking Corp., Miami, Fla., 1983-87; chief fin. officer, treas. Home Shopping Network, Clearwater, Fla., 1987—; bd. dirs. Nat. Registry Inc., Silver King Comm. Served to lt. USN, 1967-70, Vietnam. Mem. Nat. Assn. Corp. Treas., Fin. Execs. Inst., N.E. Racquet Club. Avocations: golf, sailing, tennis. Office: Home Shopping Network 2501 118th Ave N Saint Petersburg FL 33716

WANDLING, MARILYN ELIZABETH BRANSON, artist, art educator; b. Alton, Ill., May 16, 1932; d. Ralph Marion and Mary Mildred (Branson) W.; children: Jeffrey W., Douglas H., Pamela. Student, Monticello Coll., Godfrey, Ill, 1950-51, U. Ill. U-C Sch. Fine Arts, 1951-53; BA in Art, Webster U., St. Louis, 1968; MA Edn. in Art Edn., Washington U., St. Louis, 1975. Cert. tchr. at Kindergarten-Grade 12, Mo. 4th grade tchr. Alton (Ill.) Pub. Schs., 1961-62; art tchr. mid. sch. Lindbergh Sch. Dist., St. Louis, 1962-63; art tchr. mid. sch. Lindbergh Sch. Dist., St. Louis, 1968-75; cons., designer V.P. Fair, Inc., St. Louis, 1982; adminstrv. asst. to headmaster, coll. counseling dept. John Burroughs Sch., St. Louis, 1979-82; dir. pub. rels. and advt. Dance St. Louis, 1983-85; freelance art and design St. Louis, 1970—; art tchr. mid. sch. St. Louis Pub. Schs., 1987-90, art tchr. Elem. Magnet Sch. for Visual & Performing Arts, 1990—; tchr. drawing and painting Summer Arts Inst., St. Louis Pub. Schs., 1992, graphic arts designer, cons. comty. affairs divsn., 1985—, sch. vol. divsn., 1990-92, Webster Groves (Mo.) Sch. Dist., 1989-90, Pub. Sch. Retirement Sys., St. Louis, 1991; implementer classroom multi-cultural art edn. projects, 1987—; summer participant Improving Visual Arts Edn., Getty Ctr. for Edn. in Arts, 1990; book illustrator-McGraw Hill Inter-Americana de Mexico, Mexico City, 1994-95. Designer Centennial Logo for St. Louis Pub. Schs. Sesquicentennial, 1988; painter, designer murals for Ctrl. Presbyn. Ch. Nursery, 1978-79, St. Nicholas Greek Orthodox Ch., 1980; designer two outdoor villages VP Fair, Arch Grounds, St. Louis, 1982. Recipient merit and honor awards Nat. Sch. Pub. Rels. Assn., 1990, 91, 92, 93, Mo. Sch. Pub. Rels. Assn., 1989-90, 91, 92, 93. Mem. Nat. Art Edn. Assn., St. Louis Art Mus., PEO Sisterhood, Nat. Soc. DAR, Chi Omega Alumnae. Avocations: Native American arts and culture, paintings, drawings, portraits. Office: Ames Magnet Elem Sch Adminstrv Office 2900 Hadley St Saint Louis MO 63107-3911

WANDYCZ, PIOTR STEFAN, history educator; b. Krakow, Poland, Sept. 20, 1923; s. Damian Stanislaw and Stefania (Dunikowska) W.; m. Maria Teresa Chrzaszcz, Aug. 13, 1963; children: Anna, Joanna, Antoni. B.A., Cambridge U., 1948, M.A., 1952; Ph.D., London U., 1951; M.A. (hon.), Yale U., 1968; PhD (hon.), Wroclaw U., Poland, 1993. Instr. to assoc. prof. history Ind. U., 1954-66; fellow Harvard's Russian Research Center, 1963-65; assoc. prof. history Yale U., 1966-68, prof., 1968-89, chmn. Russian and East European council, 1974-76, 81-83, Bradford Durfee prof., 1989—; vis. prof. history Columbia U., 1967, 69, 74. Author: Czechoslovak-Polish Confederation and Great Powers, 1956, France and Her Eastern Allies, 1962, Soviet-Polish Relations, 1969, The Lands of Partitioned Poland, 1974, United States and Poland, 1980, August Zaleski, 1980, Polska i Zagranica, 1986, The Twilight of French Eastern Alliances, 1988, Z Dziejow dyplomacji, 1988, Polish Diplomacy 1914-1945, 1988, The Price of Freedom, 1992, Die Freiheit und ihr Preis, 1993, Pod zaborami, 1994, Cena wolnosci, 1995; contbr. articles to profl. jours.; mem. editl. bd. Slavic Rev., Internat. History Rev., Polish Rev., Polin., East European Politics and Soc. Served as 2d lt. Polish Army, 1942-45. Recipient Alfred Jurzykowski Found. award in history, 1977; Guggenheim Found. fellow, Ford Found. fellow, Rockefeller Found. fellow, Am. Philos. Soc. fellow, Am. Council Learned Socs. fellow, Social Sci. Research Council fellow, Internat. Research and Exchanges Bd. fellow. Mem. AAAS (Wayne Vucinich prize 1989), Am. Hist. Assn. (George Louis Beer prize 1962, 89), Polish Hist. Assn. (hon.), Polish Acad. Arts and Scis., Polish Acad. Scis., Polish Inst. Arts and Scis. Abroad (A. Lenkszewicz prize 1991), Czechoslovak Acad. of Scis. (Hlavka medal 1992), Czechoslovak Soc. Arts and Scis. Home: 27 Spring Gardens St Hamden CT 06517-1913 Office: Yale University New Haven CT 06520

WANEK, RONALD G., manufacturing executive; b. 1941. With Winona (Minn.) Industries, Inc., 1961-63, Red Wing (Minn.) Industries, Inc., 1963-70; chmn. bd., CEO Ashley Furniture Industries, Arcadia, Wis., 1970—. Office: Ashley Furniture Industries 1 Ashley Way Arcadia WI 54612*

WANEK, STEPHEN J., electronics executive. V.p. ops. divsn. Rosemount Inc., Hopkins, Minn., 1973-90; exec. v.p. Interactive Tech., Inc., Saint Paul, Minn., 1990—. Office: Interactive Tech Inc 2266 2nd St N Saint Paul MN 55109*

WANEK, WILLIAM CHARLES, public relations executive; b. Ridgewood, N.Y., Oct. 21, 1932; s. William John and Anna (Benes) W.; m. Robbie Gene Fairbanks, Feb. 14, 1974; children: William Robert, Jennifer Leigh. BA in English, CCNY, 1954; MA in Psychology, The New Sch. Social Rsch., N.Y.C., 1982. Asst. editor Soap Chem. Spltys. Mag., N.Y.C., 1956-58; editor in chief Maintenance Supplies Mag., N.Y.C., 1958-60; acct. exec. O.S. Tyson & Co. Inc., N.Y.C., 1960-62; dir. advt. and pub. rels. Pa. Glass Sand Corp., N.Y.C., 1962-64; sr. acct. exec. McCann-Erickson Inc., N.Y.C., 1964-66; acct. supr. Burson-Marsteller Assocs., N.Y.C., 1966-71; exec. v.p. Gibbs & Soell Inc., N.Y.C., 1971—. With U.S. Army, 1954-56. Mem. Am. Agrl. Editors Assn., Nat. Agri-Mktg. Assn. (bd. dirs. ea chpt. 1974-76), Nat. Assn. Farm Broadcasters. Presbyterian. Avocations: horticulture, classical music, theater, reading, swimming. Office: Gibbs & Soell Inc 600 3rd Ave New York NY 10016

WANG, ALAN PING-I, mathematics educator; b. Shanghai, Republic of China, May 1, 1930; came to U.S., 1950; s. Jun Liang Wang and Jan Yan Pan; m. Cecilia Y. Wang, Aug. 30, 1957; children: Geoffrey, James, Eugene. BS, Wash. State U., 1954; MS, U. So. Calif., 1957; PhD, UCLA, 1962. Sr. research engr. Northrop Corp., Los Angeles, 1957-62; sr. staff mem. Hughes Aircraft, Los Angeles, 1962-69; sr. cons. Hughes /aircraft, IBM Corp., Los Angeles, 1969-74; prof. Ariz. State U., Tempe, 1970—. Contbr. articles to profl. jours. Mem. Am. Math Soc., Soc. Applied Math., Internat. Radiative Soc., Sigma Xi. Office: Ariz State U Tempe AZ 85281

WANG, ALBERT JAMES, violinist, educator; b. Ann Arbor, Mich., Nov. 19, 1958; s. James and Lydia (Ebenoch) W.; m. Bridget Renee Becker, June 30, 1987; children: Ona Lenore, Kevin Lewis. BM, Ind. U., 1979; MM, U. Mich., 1981; DMA, Am. Conservatory, 1993. Prin. second violin Baton Rouge Symphony Orch., 1981-82; first violin Valcour String Quartet, Baton Rouge, 1981-82, Loyola String Quartet, 1982-83; mem. Lyric Opera Chgo. Orch., 1982—; mem. Orch. Ill., Chgo., 1982-88; prin. 2d violin Internat. Symphony Orch., Port Huron, Mich., 1984; 1st violin Internat. String Quartet, Port Huron, 1984; concertmaster, soloist Chgo. Chamber Orch., 1985-88, Chgo. Philharm., 1985—; mem. Grant Park Symphony Orch., Chgo., 1986-87; concertmaster, soloist Birch Creek Music Festival, Wis. Woodstock (Ill.) Mozart Festival Orch., 1988-90; concertmaster Rockford (Ill.) Symphony Orch., 1990-91, Northwestern Music Festival Orch., 1994; soloist, concertmaster Pro Musica Orch. of Mauritius, 1992-93; soloist, concertmaster China tour Classical Symphony Orch., 1994; music dir. Baroque Masterplayers, 1994—; artist-in-residence St. Clair Coll., Port Huron, 1984, Elgin C.C., 1994—; lectr. Am. Conservatory Music, Chgo., 1989-92; Fulbright lectr. Francois Mitterand Conservatory of Music, Quatre Bornes, Mauritius, 1992-93; asst. prof. violin Roosevelt U., 1993—. Numerous solo, recital and chamber music appearances and master classes throughout U.S., Can. and Mauritius; recs. and broadcasts by Mauritian Nat. Radio and WFMT Chgo. Fine Arts Radio, PBS and Nat. Pub. Radio; numerous world premiers; contbr. articles and revs. to profl. jours. Vol. ARC, Literacy Vols. Am., Chgo. Pub. Librs., United Way; bd. advisors Prism Music Festival, 1984—, Chgo. Chamber Symphony, 1985, Symphony II, 1993-94. Fulbright grantee, 1992-93; recipient 1st prize Ann Arbor (Mich.) Symphony Competition, 1976, Soc. Am. Musicians Competition, Chgo., 1984, Internat. Concerts Atlantique Competition, N.Y.C., 1989, Chgo. Park Dist. Competition, 1991, 2nd prize Biennial Adult Artist Competition, 1992; selected to Arts Am. Touring Artist Roster, 1993; finalist Lilly Fellows Program in Humanities and the Arts, Valparaiso U., 1994; recipient Leo Sowerby medal, 1994. Mem. Am. Fedn. Musicians, Am. String Tchrs. Assn., Coll. Music Soc., Chamber Music Am., Am. Music Ctr. Avocations: powerlifting, fishing, travel, woodworking. Office: Roosevelt U 430 S Michigan Ave Chicago IL 60605 also: Lyric Opera Chgo 20 N Wacker Dr Chicago IL 60606 also: Elgin CC 1700 Spartin Dr Elgin IL 60123 also: Baroque Masterplayers 5528 S Hyde Park # 1002 Chicago IL 60637

WANG, ALLAN ZUWU, cell biologist; b. Shanghai, China, June 1, 1939; came to U.S., 1982; m. Qin-Yu Chen, Mar. 30, 1968; 1 child, George Qi. MD, Shanghai Med. U., 1962; PhD, Chinese Acad. Scis., 1966. Rsch. assoc. Chinese Acad. Sci., Shanghai, 1966-80; postdoctoral rsch. fellow Imperial Cancer Rsch. Fund, London, 1980-82; assoc. rsch. scientist U. Tex. System Cancer Ctr., Houston, 1982-83; assoc. prof. Chinese Acad. Scis., 1983-85; Stanley Reimann rsch. scientist Fox Chase Cancer Ctr., Phila., 1987-90; acting scientific dir. Western Pa. Hosp. Found. Rsch. Inst., Pitts., 1990-91, dir. rsch. dept. medicine, sr. faculty scientist, 1990—; vis. assoc. prof. Med. Coll. Pa., 1986-87; mem. rsch. bd. advisors Am. Biophys. Inst., N.C., 1989—, Internat. Biophys. Ctr., Cambridge, Eng., 1989—; com. mem. Instnl. Animal Care & Use Com., Western Pa. Found., 1990—. Contbr. articles to 105 profl. jours. Mem. AAAS, Am. Soc. Cell Biology, Am. Assn. Cancer Rsch., British Soc. Cell Biology, British Assn. Cancer Rsch. Achievements include mechanisms of cell adhesion, migration and interactions between cell-cell and cell-matrix; pharmacological study of anti-cancer drug Methoxyl Sarcolysin; application of image processing in SEM investigation of experimental tumor matastasis, synoviocyte chemotaxis migration and invasion, renal epithelial membrane polarity and electrolyte transport. Office: Western Pa Hosp Found 4800 Friendship Ave Pittsburgh PA 15224-1722

WANG, ARTHUR C., lawyer, educator; b. Boston, Feb. 4, 1949; s. Kung Shou and Lucy (Chow) W.; m. Wendy F. Hamai, May 22, 1976 (div. 1981); m. Nancy J. Norton, Sept. 1, 1985; children: Alexander Xinglin, Sierra Xinan. BA, Franconia Coll., 1970; JD, U. Puget Sound, 1984. Bar: Wash. 1984. Printer Carmel Valley (Calif.) Outlook, 1970-73; project coord. Tacoma (Wash.) Community House, 1973-76; rsch. analyst Wash. Ho. of Reps., Olympia, Wash., 1977-80. mem., 1981-94; of counsel Davies Pearson, P.C., Tacoma, 1984-94; adj. prof. U. Puget Sound Law Sch., Tacoma, 1987-93, Seattle U. Law Sch., Tacoma, 1995—; chmn House Capital Budget Com., 1993-94, Revenue Com., 1989-92, Commerce and Labor Com., 1985-88; mem. Wash. Pers. Appeals Bd., Olympia, 1994—. Assoc. editor U. Puget Sound Law Review, 1983-84. Vista vol. Tacoma Urban League, 1973-74; del. Dem. Nat. Conv., 1976. Named Chinese Am. Man of Yr., Seattle Chinese Post, 1991, Legislator of Yr., Wash. Health Care Assn., 1992. Democrat. Avocation: birding. Home: 3319 N Union Ave Tacoma WA 98407-6043 Office: Wash Pers Appt Bd PO Box 40911 Olympia WA 98504

WANG, ARTHUR WOODS, publisher; b. Port Chester, N.Y., Oct. 7, 1918; s. Israel and Madolin (Woods) W.; m. Mary Ellen Mackay, Aug. 13, 1955; 1 son, Michael Anthony. B.S., Bowdoin Coll., 1940; postgrad., Columbia U., 1949-51. Advt. research McCann-Erickson, Inc., 1940-41; editor Doubleday & Co., 1942-43, Alfred A. Knopf, Inc., 1943, T.Y. Crowell (Pub.), 1943-47; with E.M. Hale & Co., Eau Claire, Wis., 1947-52; editor A.A. Wyn, Inc., 1952-56; co-founder, pres., editor-in-chief Hill & Wang, Inc., 1956-71; pub., editor-in-chief Hill & Wang div. Farrar, Straus & Giroux, Inc., N.Y.C., 1971-87; sr. editor Hill and Wang div. Farrar, Straus & Giroux, Inc., 1988—; also v.p. Hill & Wang div. Farrar, Straus & Giroux, Inc.;. Mem. Am. Book Pubs. Coun. (bd. dirs. 1968-70). Home: 150 E 69th St New York NY 10021 Office: Hill & Wang 19 Union Sq W New York NY 10003-3304

WANG, CHAO-CHENG, mathematician, engineer; b. Peoples Republic of China, July 20, 1938; came to U.S., 1961; s. N.S. and Y.T. Wang; m. Sophia C.L. Wang; children: Ferdinand, Edward. BS, Nat. Taiwan U., 1959; PhD, Johns Hopkins U., 1965. Registered profl. engr., Tex. Asst. prof. Johns Hopkins U., Balt., 1966-68, assoc. prof., 1968-69; prof. Rice U., Houston, 1968-79, Noah Harding prof., 1979—, chmn. math. sci. dept.,, 1983-89, chmn. mech. engring. and materials sci., 1991-94. Author numerous books in field; contbr. articles to profl. jours. Named Disting. Young Scientist Md. Acad. Sci., 1968. Mem. ASME, Soc. Natural Philosophy (treas. 1985-86), Am. Acad. Mechs. Office: Rice Univ Dept Mech Engring Materials Sci Houston TX 77251

WANG, CHARLES B., computer software company executive; b. Shanghai, Rep. China, Aug. 19, 1944. BS, Queens Coll. 1967. Chmn., CEO Computer Assocs., Islandia, N.Y., 1976—. Office: Computer Assocs Internat Inc 1 Computer Assocs Plz Islandia NY 11788-7000*

WANG, CHARLES PEI, social service administrator; b. Ta Lien, People's Republic of China, Nov. 20, 1939; came to U.S., 1965; s. Chia Ming and Sue Yen (Hsing) W.; m. Rita Yen, Dec. 25, 1965; 1 child, Angelina. BA, Nat. Chengchi U., 1964; MA, St. John's U., 1967. Case worker Riverdale Children's Assn., N.Y.C., 1967; child care worker Childville, Inc., Bklyn., 1968; community orgn. coordinator Chinatown Planning Council, N.Y.C., 1968-72, asst. exec. dir., 1972-78, mng. dir., 1978-82, exec. dir., 1982-84; U.S. Commn. on Civil Rights, N.Y.C., 1972-73; mem. selection com. NIMH Dr. Fellowship, Washington, 1972-76; panel cons. N.Y. State Council on Arts, N.Y.C., 1973-76; mem. Asian task panel Pres.'s Commn. Mental Health, Washington, 1978-79. Mem. N.Y.C. Youth Bur., 1984—; sec. Health System Agy. of N.Y.C., 1985-87; chmn.asian/pacific islander adv. bd., U.S. Census Bur., Washington, 1987.Served with Chinese Army in Taiwan, 1964-65. Recipient Dynamic Achiever award Orgn. Chinese Ams., 1982, Man of Yr., 1985, Liberty award Staten Island Borough Pres., 1986, Leadership award Gettysburg Coll., 1987. Mem. Am. Mgmt. Assn., Am. Planning Assn., Assn. Chinese Studies. Democrat. Baptist. Avocations: music, basketball. Office: Chinese-Am Planning Council 480 Broadway New York NY 10013-2639

WANG, CHIA PING, physicist, educator; came to U.S., 1963, naturalized; (parents Chinese citizens).; s. Guan Can and Tah (Lin) W. BS, U. London, 1950; MS, U. Malaya (now U. Singapore), 1951; PhD in Physics, U. Malaya (now U. Singapore) and U. Cambridge, 1953; DSc in Physics, U. Singapore, 1972. Asst. lectr. U. Malaya, 1951-53; mem. faculty Nankai U., Tientsin, 1954-58, prof. physics, 1956-58, head electron physics div., 1955-58, mem. steering com. nuclear physics div., 1956-58; head electron physics Lanchow Atomic Project, 1958; mem. faculty Hong Kong U.; mem. faculty Chinese U., Hong Kong, 1958-63, prof. physics, 1959-63, acting head physics, math. depts., 1959; rsch. assoc. lab. nuclear studies Cornell U, Ithaca, N.Y., 1963-64; assoc. prof. space sci. and applied physics Cath. U. Am., Washington, 1964-68; prof. physics Case Inst. Tech. Case Western Res. U., Cleve., 1966-70; vis. scientist, vis. prof. U. Cambridge (Eng.), U. Leuven (Belgium), U.S. Naval Rsch. Labs., U. Md., MIT, 1970-75; rsch. physicist radiation lab. U.S. Army Natick (Mass.) R & D Command, 1975—, mem. steering com. sci. and tech. directorate, 1993—; pioneer in fields of nuclear sub-structure (now often referred to as parton), nucleon sub-unit structure, multiparticle prodn., cosmic radiation, picosecond time to pulse-height conversion, thermal physics, lasers, microwaves. Contbg. author: Atomic Structure and Interactions of Ionizing Radiations with Matter in Preservation of Food by Ionizing Radiation, 1982; contbr. numerous articles to profl. jours. Recipient Outstanding Performance award Dept. Army, 1980, Quality Increase award, 1980. Mem. Am. Phys. Soc., Inst. Physics London, N.Y. Acad. Scis., AAAS, Sigma Xi. Home: 28 Hallett Hill Rd Weston MA 02193-1753 Office: US Army Natick Rsch And Devel Ctr Natick MA 01760

WANG, CHIH CHUN, material scientist, business executive; b. Beijing, Oct. 9, 1932; came to U.S., 1958; s. H.W. and Hilda (Yang) W.; m. Lena Y. Liu, Dec. 1959 (dec. Dec. 1967); 1 child, Joyce; m. Betty R. Tung, Mar. 29, 1969; children: Francis, Bessie. BS in Chem. Engring., Nat. Taiwan U., 1955; MS in Chem. Engring., Kans. State U., 1959; PhD in Phys. Chemistry, Colo. State U., 1962; postdoctoral assoc. U. Kans., 1963. Postdoctoral assoc. U. Kans., 1963; mem. tech staff RCA Labs. div. RCA Corp., Princeton, N.J., 1963-67, rsch. leader, 1967-73, fellow, 1973-88; v.p. Am. Lumi Corp., Cranbury, N.J., 1989-91, pres., 1991—; cons. NASA, Washington, 1978-79, Gen. Elec. Co., Milw., 1989-90; hon. prof. Jilin (China) U., 1985-90; joint mng. dir. Phosphor Tech. Ltd., Essex, Eng., 1989-90. Author, editor: Heteroepitaxial Semiconductor Devices, 1978; author: Characterization of Semiconductors, 1979; contbr. numerous articles to profl. jours.; inventor, patentee more than 20 U.S. patents. Mem. ACS, Electrochem. Soc. for Info. Display (div. editor Jour. 1978-91), Am. Assn. in Crystal Growth, Sigma Pi Sigma, Sigma Xi, Phi Lambda Upsilon. Home: 41 Maple Stream Rd East Windsor NJ 08520-1812 Office: Am Lumi Corp 2525 Rt 130 Bldg B Cranbury NJ 08512

WANG, CHUN-JUAN KAO, mycology educator; b. Shenyang, Liaoning, People's Republic of China, Jan. 10, 1928; came to U.S., 1950; d. Si-Ping and Chung-Huang (Tang) Kao; m. Stephen S. Wang, July 30, 1955; children: Effie, Vivian, Andrew. BS, Nat. Taiwan U., Taipei, 1950; student, Nat. Tsing-Hua U., Reiping, Hopei, People's Republic of China, 1946-48; MS, Vassar Coll., 1952; PhD, U. Iowa, 1955. Med. mycology rsch. assoc. Jewish Hosp. Clin. Lab., Cin., 1955-58; instr. med. mycology dept. dermatology Sch. Medicine, U. Cin., 1956-58; rsch. assoc. Coll. Forestry SUNY, Syracuse, 1959-60, from instr. to assoc. prof. Coll. Environ. Sci. and Forestry, 1961, prof. Author: Fungi of Pulp and Paper in New York, 1965; author, co-editor: Identification Manual for Fungi from Utility Poles in Eastern United States, 1990; contbr. articles to profl. jours. Named one of Women of Distinction in Fields of Sci., Medicine and Nursing, Women's div. N.Y. State Fair, 1984; named Woman of Achievement for Sci., Fed. Wom'n's Clubs and Syracuse Post-Standard, 1988. Mem. Mycol. Soc. Am. (chairperson am. lectr. com. 1982, William H. Weston Jr. Award for Excellence in Teaching 1990), Assn. Women in Sci. (organizer Syracuse chpt. 1988), Brit. Mycol. Soc., Sigma Xi. Office: SUNYS Coll Environ Sci Forestry Dr Syracuse NY 13210-2788

WANG, FRANKLIN FU YEN, materials scientist, educator; b. Macau, China, Sept. 19, 1928; s. Kwan Hsien and Shu Tsiang (Hsiang) W.; m. Katharine Wang, Sept. 8, 1956; children—Jennifer, Alexander. B.A., Pomona Coll., 1951; M.S., U. Toledo, 1953; Ph.D., U. Ill., 1956. Dir. research Glascote Products, Cleve., 1956-58; research scientist A.O. Smith Corp., Milw., 1958-61; research staff mem. Sperry Rand Research Center, Sudbury, Mass., 1961-66; asso. prof. dept. materials sci. SUNY, Stony Brook, 1966-72; prof. SUNY, 1972—, chmn., 1971-74. Author: Introduction to Solid State Electronics, 1980; editor: Materials Processing: Theory and Practices, 1980; prin. editor: Materials Letters, 1982. Fellow Am. Inst. Chemists, Am. Ceramic Soc.; mem. IEEE, Am. Soc. Engring. Edn., Am. Chem. Soc., Assn. Crystal Growth, Am. Phys. Soc., Engring. Soc., Materials Research Soc. Office: NSF Math & Phys Scis 1800 G St NW Washington DC 20550-0001

WANG, FRANNY, electronics executive; b. 1946. Grad., Nat. Taiwan U., 1969; MBA, Temple U., 1970. Acct. PMI, Santa Clara, Calif., 1970-73; sec.-treas. Pantronix Corp., San Jose, Calif., 1974—. Office: Pantronix Corp 145 Rio Robles San Jose CA 95134*

WANG, GUNG H., management consultant; b. Ningpo, Zhejiang, China, Feb. 3, 1909; s. Cheng V. and Zhao S. (Zhu) W.; m. Gladys Chen Wang, Sept. 10, 1938; children: Edward, Jo-Ann, Nancy, James. BA, U. Shanghai, China, 1928; MA, Tulane U., New Orleans, 1952; LLD (hon.), Loyola U., Chgo., 1989. Staff officer Mil. Fgn. Affairs, Nanking, China, 1928-30; vice cons. Consulate Gen. China, Chgo., 1930-38; cons. Consulate of China, New Orleans, 1938-50; exec. dir. Chinese Am. Civic Council, Chgo.; mng. dir. Chinatown Devel. Inc., Chgo., 1960-64; asst. dir. Chgo. Dwellings Assn., 1964-69; housing specialist Model Cities Program, Chgo., 1969-73; dir. Neighborhood Housing Services, Dept. Human Services, 1973-76; owner G.H. Wang Assocs., Chgo., 1976—; cons. Chinese Del. UN Gen. Assembly, Lake Success, N.Y., 1946-47; alt. del. UN Temporary Commn. on Korea, Seoul and Paris, 1948; pres. Neighborhood Redevel. Assn. Inc., Chgo., 1972—; exec. dir. South Side Planning Bd., 1977; administr. fund for intercultural edn. NRAI, 1989—. Author: The Chinese Mind 1946, Kinsiskt Tankande, 1948; contbr. articles to profl. jours. 1948-51. Mem. Nat. Assn. Housing and Redevel. Officials, Am. Planning Assn., Met. Coalition on Aging, Rotary Club Chgo., Pi Sigma Alpha Nat. Pol. Sci. Honor Soc. Presbyterian. Avocation: writing. Home: 8200 S Indiana Ave Chicago IL 60619-4725

WANG, HENRY Y., chemical engineering educator; b. Shanghai, July 22, 1951; came to U.S., 1969; s. T. C. and Aurza Wang; m. Evangeline Yap Cesar, 1983; 1 child, Stephanie. BS, Iowa State U., 1972; MS, MIT, 1974, PhD, 1977. Rsch. asst. MIT, Cambridge, 1972-77; engring. assoc. Merckle & Co., Rahway, N.J., 1977; sr. scientist Schering-Plough, Union, N.J., 1978-79; from asst. prof. to assoc. prof. U. Mich., Ann Arbor, 1978-84, prof., 1989—; disting. sr. scientist Mich. Biotech. Inst., Lansing, 1984—; cons. Hong Kong U. of Sci. and Tech., 1993—. Internat. editor: Jour. Ferm. Biotech., 1991—. Mem. AIChE, Am. Chem. Soc. (councilor 1984-86), Am. Soc. Microbiology, Soc. Indsl. Microbiology. Home: 1215 Bradstown Trail Ann Arbor MI 48105 Office: U Mich Dept Chem Engring Ann Arbor MI 48109

WANG, HERBERT FAN, geophysics educator; b. Shanghai, China, Sept. 14, 1946; came to U.S., 1948; s. Chu-Kia and Wei-Woh (Sun) W.; m. Rosemary Jane Dugan, June 3, 1968; children: Michelle Q., Melissa Y., Michael Benjamin, Matthew Alexander. BA, U. Wis., 1966; AM, Harvard U., 1968; PhD, MIT, 1973. Asst. prof. geophysics U. Wis., Madison, 1972-77, assoc. prof., 1977-82, prof., 1982—; program scientist Dept. Energy, Germantown, Md., 1980-81; vis. scientist Lawrence Livermore (Calif.) Nat. Lab., 1986-87; vis. prof. SUNY, Albany, 1989-90. Author: Introduction to Groundwater Modeling, 1982; also numerous articles. Mem. Am. Geophys. Union. Home: 5118 Juneau Rd Madison WI 53705-4744 Office: U Wis 1215 W Dayton St Madison WI 53706-1692

WANG, I-TUNG, atmospheric scientist; b. Peking, People's Republic of China, Feb. 16, 1933; came to U.S., 1958; s. Shen and Wei-Yun (Wen) W.; m. Amy Hung Kong; children: Cynthia P., Clifford T. BS in Physics, Nat. Taiwan U., 1955; MA in Physics, U. Toronto, 1957; PhD in Physics, Columbia U., 1965. Rsch. physicist Carnegie-Mellon U., Pitts., 1965-67,

asst. prof., 1967-70; environ. systems engr. Argonne (Ill.) Nat. Lab., 1970-76; mem. tech. staff Environ. Monitoring and Svcs. Ctr. Rockwell Internat. Creve Coeur, Mo., 1976-80, Newbury Park, Calif., 1980-84; sr. scientist, combustion engr. Environ. Monitoring and Svcs. Inc., Newbury Park, Camarillo, 1984-88; sr. scientist ENSR Corp (formerly ERT), 1988; pres. EMA Co., Thosand Oaks, Calif., 1989—; tech. advisor Bur. of Environ. Protection, Republic of China, 1985; environ. cons. ABB Environ., 1989-92, ARCO, 1990-91, Du Pont (SAFER Systems Divsn.), 1992-93, So. Calif. Edison, 1993—. Contbr. papers to profl jours. First violin Conejo Symphony Orch., Thousand Oaks, Calif., 1981-83. Grantee Bureau of Environ. Protection, Taiwan, 1985. Mem. N.Y. Acad. of Scis., Air and Waste Mgmt. Assn., Sigma Xi. Avocations: violin and chamber music. Office: EMA Co Ste 435 2219 E Thousand Oaks Blvd Thousand Oaks CA 91362-2921 *Personal philosophy: The pursuit of science is much like the pursuit of art. It requires one's complete involvement and devotion.*

WANG, JAMES CHIA-FANG, political science educator; b. Nanling, China, Apr. 4, 1926; came to U.S., 1946, naturalized, 1962; s. Chien-Yu and Lilian W.; m. Sarah Cutter, May 7, 1960; children—Sarah, Eric. BA in Polit. Sci., Oberlin Coll., 1950; postgrad., N.Y. U., 1951; PhD in Polit. Sci, U. Hawaii, 1971. Rsch. asst., internat. study group Brookings Instn., 1951-53; adminstrv. and tng. officer UN Secretariat, N.Y.C., 1953-57; editor-in-charge UN Documents Edit., Readex Corp., N.Y.C., 1957-60; lectr. far eastern politics NYU, N.Y.C., 1957-60; instr. Asian history and econs. Punahou Sch., Honolulu, 1960-64; program officer Inst. Student Interchange, East-West Ctr., Honolulu, 1964-69, acting dir. participant svcs., 1970, adminstrv. officer admissions, 1969-71; dir. freshmen integrated program Hilo (Hawaii) Coll., 1971-72; asst. prof. polit. sci. and internat. studies U. Hawaii, Hilo, 1971-72, assoc. prof., 1973-76, prof., 1976—; mem. U. Hawaii Contemporary China Study Group), Hilo, 1971—; chmn. dept. polit. sci. U. Hawaii, Hilo, 1973-75, 84—; profl. assoc. East-West Communications Inst., Honolulu, 1978, East-West Communications Inst. (Resource System Inst.), 1980-81; adviser to AAUW, Hawaii, 1978-79; cons. World Polit. Risk Forecast, Frost & Sullivan, Inc., N.Y.C., 1980-81. Author: The Cultural Revolution in China: An Annotated Bibliography, 1976, Contemporary Chinese Politics: An Introduction, 1980, rev. edit., 1985, 89, 92, 95, Hawaii State and Local Politics, 1982, Study Guide for Power in Hawaii, 1982, Ocean Law and Politics, 1992 (selected One of 1993 Outstanding Acad. Books ALA), Comparative Asian Politics, 1994; contbr. articles to profl. jours. Mem. Hawaii County Bicentennial Com., 1988-89; vice chmn. Dem. Party, County of Hawaii, 1972-76, chmn., 1982-84; mem. Dem. State Ctrl. Com., 1982-84, chmn., 1994—; chmn. univ. adv. com. to Hawaii County Coun.; mem. coordinating com. Hawaii Polit. Studies Assn., 1986—; mem. Hawaii State Campaign Spending Commn., 1990—, chmn., 1994—. U. Hawaii Rsch. Found. grantee, 1972-78. Mem. Assn. Asian Studies, Internat. Studies Assn., Coun. Ocean Law and the Law of the Sea Inst., Big Island Press Club. Home: PO Box 13 Hilo HI 96721-0013 Office: U Hawaii Dept Polit Sci Hilo HI 96720

WANG, JAMES CHUO, biochemistry and molecular biology educator; b. Kiangsu, China, Nov. 18, 1936; came to U.S., 1960; s. Chin and H.-L. (Shih) W.; m. Sophia Shu-lan Hwang, Dec. 23, 1961; children: Janice S., Jessica A. BS, Nat. Taiwan U., 1959; MA, U. S.D., 1961; PhD, U. Mo. Coll. Arts and Sci., 1964. Asst. instr. Nat. Taiwan U., Taipei, 1959-60; rsch. fellow in chemistry Calif. Inst. Tech., Pasadena, 1964-66; asst. prof. chemistry U. Calif. at Berkeley, 1966-69, assoc. prof., 1969-74, prof., 1974-77; prof. biochemistry and molecular biology Harvard U., Cambridge, Mass., 1977-88, Mallinckrodt prof. biochemistry and molecular biology, 1988—; Chiron lectr. U. Calif., Berkeley, 1994; Chancellor's Disting. lectr. U. Calif., Berkeley, 1984; mem. molecular biology study sect. NIH, 1988-91, chair, 1990-91; disting. faculty lectr. U. Tex., M.D. Anderson Cancer Ctr., 1989. Mem. editl. bd. Quar. Rev. Biophysics, 1988-94. Guggenheim fellow Guggenheim Found., 1986-87; recipient Disting. Alumnus award U. Mo. Coll. Arts and Scis., 1991. Fellow Am. Acad. Arts and Scis.; mem. NAS (molecular biology award 1983), Third World Acad. Scis., Academia Sinica (Taipei). Office: Harvard University Dept Molecular/Cellular Biology 7 Divinity Ave Cambridge MA 02138-2092

WANG, JAMES T., public planning executive; b. Shon-Tan, Hunan, China, Aug. 17, 1938; came to U.S. 1969; s. En-Hua and Sue (Lu) W.; m. Keifun Chan; 1 child, Amity. MA, Western Mich. U., 1970; M in Urban Planning, Mich. State U., 1972. Urban planner UN Devel. Project, Far East, 1967-69; site planner Robert O'Boyle Assocs., Kalamazoo, Mich., 1970-72; city-county planner Dalton-Whitfield County Planning Commn., Dalton, Ga., 1972-75; planning dir. City Planning Dept., Lexington, Ky., 1975-80; exec. dir. Greater Bridgeport Regional Planning Agy., Bridgeport, Conn., 1980—; adv. in city planning & housing devel. Housing & Real Estate Administrv. Bur., City of Tianjin, China, 1986—. Author: Urban Service Area Concept, Lexington's Experience, 1982. Mem. Govs.' Task Force on Solid Waste Mgmt., Conn., 1985-86, State Bd. of Examiners for Profl. Engrs. and Land Surveyors, Conn., 1989—; trustee Acad. of Our Lady of Mercy Lauralton Hall, Milford, Conn., 1992-94. Recipient Spl. Design award Newtown Devl., State of Ga., 1974, Spl. Achievement award City of Lexington. Mem. Am. Instit. of Cert. Planners, AIA. Lodge: Rotary.

WANG, JAW-KAI, agricultural engineering educator; b. Nanjing, Jiangsu, People's Republic of China, Mar. 4, 1932; came to U.S., 1952; s. Shuling and Hsi-Ying (Lo) W.; m. Kwang Mei Chow, Sept. 7, 1957 (div. Oct. 1989); children: Angela C.C., Dora C.C., Lawrence C.Y. BS, Nat. Taiwan U., 1953; MS in Agri. Engring., Mich. State U., 1956, PhD, 1958. Registered profl. engr., Hawaii. Faculty agrl. engring. dept. U. Hawaii, Honolulu, 1959-93; assoc. prof., chmn. dept. U. Hawaii, 1964-68, prof., 1968—, chmn. dept. agrl. engring., 1968-75; dir. Aquaculture Program, 1990—; prof. biosystems engring. dept. U. Hawaii-Manoa, Honolulu, 1994—; pres. Wang & Assocs., 1979—; spl. asst., Internat. Rsch. Dept., Office of Internat. Cooperation and Devel. U.S. Dept. Agr., 1988; pres. Aquaculture Tech., Inc., 1990—; co-dir. internat. sci. and ednl. coun. USDA; vis. assoc. dir. internat. programs and studies office Nat. Assn. State Univs. and Land-Grant Colls., 1979; vis. prof. Nat. Taiwan U., 1965, U. Calif., Davis, 1980; cons. U.S. Army Civilian Adminstrn., Ryukus, Okinawa, 1966, Internat. Rice Rsch. Inst., The Philippines, 1971, Pacific Concrete and Rock Co. Ltd., 1974, AID, 1974, Universe Tankships, Inc., 1980-81, World Bank, 1981, 81, ABA Internat., 1981-85, Internat. Found. for Agrl. Devel./World Bank, 1981, Rockefeller Found., 1980, Orizaba, Inc., 1983, Agrisys./FAO, 1983, Info. Processing Assocs., 1984, County of Maui, 1984, 85, Alexander and Baldwin, 1986; mem. expert panel on agrl. mechanization FAO/UN, 1984-90; sr. fellow East-West Ctr. Food Inst., 1973-74; dir. Info. Sys. and Svcs. Internat., Inc., 1986-90; mem. Am. Soc. Agrl. Cons. Internat. Dept. of State, 1985. Author: Irrigated Rice Production Systems, 1980; editor: Taro—A Review of Colocasia Esculenta and its Potentials, 1983; mem. editorial bd. Aquacultural Engring., 1982—; assoc. editor Am. Soc. of Aquacultural Engrs., 1988—. Recipient Exemplary State Employee award State of Hawaii, 1986, State of Hawaii Employee of Yr. award Office of Gov., 1990. Fellow Am. Soc. Agrl. Engrs. (chmn. Hawaii sect. 1962-63, chmn. grad. instrn. com. 1971-73, chmn. aquacultural engring. com. 1977-79, assoc. editor Trans. 1975-76, Emerging Tech. Task Force Engr. of Yr. 1976, Tech. Paper award 1978, Kishida internat. award 1991), Am. Inst. Med. and Biol. Engring.; mem. Chinese Soc. Agrl. Engrs., Nat. Acad. Engring., Aquaculture Engring. Soc. (pres. 1993-95), Sigma Xi, Gamma Sigma Delta (pres. Hawaii chpt. 1974-75), Pi Mu Epsilon. Office: U Hawaii Biosystems Engring Dept 3050 Maile Way Honolulu HI 96822-2271 *To be allowed a continuing search for truth even when you are doubting its existence, is to be blessed.*

WANG, JIAN-SHENG, materials scientist; b. Taihe, Jiangxi, China, July 7, 1941; came to U.S., 1980; s. Shuo-Ru and Feng-Zi (Liu) W.; m. Hui-Jian Liu, Aug. 17, 1963; children: Yi-Bin, Yi-Min. MS, Northwestern Poly. U., China, 1963; PhD, Stanford U., 1985. Rsch. engr. Iron and Steel Rsch. Inst., Beijing, 1963-80; rsch. asst. Stanford (Calif.) U., 1982-85; sr. rsch. assoc. Harvard U., Cambridge, Mass., 1985—; vis. scholar Stanford U., 1980-82; vis. scientist Max-Planck Inst. fü Eisenforschung, Düsseldorf, Germany, 1989-90; hon. prof. Northwestern Poly. U. China, 1994. Contbr. articles to profl. jours., proceedings and treatises; keynote speaker nat. and internat. confs. Recipient Nat. Prize sci. and technol. innovation China Nat. Com. Sci. and Tech., Beijing, 1981, various awards All China Sci. Cong., Beijing, 1978. Mem. Materials Rsch. Soc., Am. Soc. Metals, Am. Physics Soc. Achievements include patents for heat-resistant steels; notable findings in micromechanics and chemistry of interfacial fracture and brittle versus

ductile transition; mechanisms of creep and creep rupture; the alloying principle and phase transformation in low-alloying steels. Home: 52 Albion St Somerville MA 02143-1103 Office: Harvard Univ 29 Oxford St Cambridge MA 02138-2901

WANG, JOHN CHENG HWAI, communications engineer; b. Beijing, Feb. 12, 1934; s. Hwa Lung and Shu Shiang (Shia) W.; m. Rosa Jenny Chu, Sept. 9, 1967; children: Sophia, Maria, Nina, Amy. BS, U. Md., 1959; MS, U. Pitts., 1968. Engr. Chesapeake Instrument Corp., Shadyside, Md., 1959-64; rsch. scientist Rsch. Ctr. U.S. Steel Corp., Monroeville, Pa., 1964-67; asst. prof. Pa. State U., New Kensington, 1967-69; rsch. engr. FCC, Washington, 1969—; chmn. working party medium wave propagation Internat. Radio Consultative Com., Geneva, 1983—. Contbr. articles to profl. jours. Fellow IEEE. Avocations: astronomy, bridge, Chinese history. Office: FCC 1919 M St NW Washington DC 20554-0002

WANG, JONAS CHIA-TSUNG, pharmaceutical executive; b. Canton, People's Republic of China, July 21, 1944; came to U.S., 1977; s. Gin-Han and Gin (Lai) W.; m. Huey-Wen An, Nov. 15, 1969; children: Jeremy, Joseph, JoAnn. BS in Pharmacy, Nat. Def. Med. Ctr., Taipei, Republic of China, 1967; PhD in Phys. Pharmacy, U. Iowa, 1982. Registered pharmacist, Republic of China. Instr. in pharm. chemistry Nat. Def. Med. Ctr., 1968-77; chief quality control dept. Ret. Serviceman's Pharm. Plant, Taipei, 1968-77; teaching asst. U. Iowa, Iowa City, 1977-81; assoc. dir. R & D Bristol-Myers Squibb, Buffalo, 1981-88; dir. R & D Johnson & Johnson Consumer Products, Inc., Skillman, N.J., 1988-94, v.p. Applied Rsch. and Tech. Rsch. Ctr., 1994—; adj. prof. cosmetic sci. program Coll. Pharmacy, U. Cin., 1985—; mem. coun. biology dept. Canisius Coll., Buffalo, 1984-88; reviewer Pharm. Rsch., 1986-94; mem. faculty spl. seminar IV Internat. Symposium on Psoriasis, Stanford U., 1986; tech. cons. Western N.Y. Tech. Transfer Com., 1984-88; lectr., presenter in field; vis. prof. Sch. Pharmacy Nat. Def. Med. Ctr., 1986. Contbr. articles to profl. publs.patentee in field. Maj. Rep. of China armed forces, 1965-67. Mem. Acad. Pharm. Sci., Soc. Cosmetic Chemists (mem. Merit award com. 1991), Am. Assn. Pharm. Scientists, Am. Acad. Dermatology, Nat. Def. Med. Ctr. Alumni Assn. (pres. N.Y. chpt. 1991-93), Chinese Pharm. Soc., Asian Pharm. Assn. Avocations: tennis, skiing, ballroom dancing, swimming. Home: 23 Ellsworth Dr Robbinsville NJ 08691-9006 Office: Johnson & Johnson Consumer Products Inc Grandview Rd Skillman NJ 08558

WANG, JUI HSIN, biochemistry educator; b. Peking, Republic of China, Mar. 16, 1921; s. Lieh and Sun Li (Sun) W.; m. Yen Chan Yang, Apr. 2, 1949; children: Jane, Nancy. BS, Nat. SW Assoc. U., Kunming, Republic of China, 1945; PhD, Washington U., St. Louis, 1949; MA (hon.), Yale U., 1960. Postdoctoral fellow radiochemistry Washington U., 1949-51; mem. faculty Yale U., New Haven, Conn., 1951—, prof. chemistry, 1960-62, Eugene Higgins prof. chemistry, 1962-65, Eugene Higgins prof. chemistry and molecular biophysics, 1965-72; Einstein prof. sci. SUNY, Buffalo, 1972—; rschr. molecular structure and biochem. activity, superconductivity. Contbr. articles to profl. jours., chapters in books. Guggenheim fellow Cambridge U., 1960-61. Fellow AAAS, Am. Acad. Arts and Scis.; mem. Am. Chem. Soc., Chem. Soc. London, Yale Chemists Assn., Am. Soc. for Biochemistry and Molecular Biology, Am. Phys. Soc., Biophys. Soc., Academia Sinica, Am. Soc. Photobiology, Electrochem. Soc., Materials Rsch. Soc., Sigma Xi. Home: 477 Lebrun Rd Buffalo NY 14226-4218 Office: SUNY Dept Chemistry Buffalo NY 14260

WANG, JULIE CAROLINE, public relations executive; b. Petersfield, Hampshire, Eng., June 17, 1947; came to U.S., 1972; d. Raymond Garnier and Molly Eileen (Travers-Drapes) Dreyer; m. Paul Wang, Jan. 6, 1969 (div. Apr. 1981); children: Timothy, Katharine; m. Bronson Binger, June 26, 1982; 1 child, Walter. BA, McGill U., Montreal, Can., 1967. Journalist Montreal Gazette, 1968-72; asst. dir. Univ. Hosp. Pa., Phila., 1972-74; editor Sci. and Medicine, N.Y.C., 1974-79; v.p. Manning Selvage and Lee, N.Y.C., 1979-82, Burson-Marsteller, N.Y.C., 1982-83; chmn., CEO Wang Assocs., N.Y.C., 1983—; adj. prof. NYU, 1989—. Author: Phobia Free and Flying High, 1979, Everything You Wanted to Know About Phobias but Were Afraid to Ask, 1981. Mem. Nat. Assn. Sci. Writers, Am. Soc. Journalists and Authors, N.Y. Acad. Scis., Heights Casino club. Episcopalian. Avocations: gardening, sailing, tennis, skiing. Home: 142 Dean St Brooklyn NY 11217-2212 Office: Wang Assoc Health Comm 373 Park Ave S New York NY 10016

WANG, KUO-KING, manufacturing engineer, educator. BSME, Nat. Ctrl. U., China, 1947; MSME, U. Wis., 1962, PhD in Mech. Engring., 1968. Sibley prof. mech. engring. Cornell U., Ithaca, N.Y.; founder, dir. Cornell Injection Molding Program, 1974—; cofounder Cornell Mfg. Engring. and Productivity Program, Advanced CAE Tech., Inc. Recipient Disting. Svc. citation U. Wis., 1990. Fellow ASME (Blackall Machine Tool and Gage award 1968, William T. Ennor Mfg. Tech. award 1991), Soc. Mfg. Engrs. (Frederick W. Taylor Rsch. medal 1987); mem. CIRP, ASM Internat., Nat. Acad. Engring., Am. Welding Soc. (Adams Meml. Membership award 1976), Soc. Plastic Engrs., Polymer Processing Soc. Achievements include pioneering research in injection molding, friction welding and applications of solid modeling to CAD/CAM. Office: Cornell Univ Dept Mech/Aero Engring Upson Hall Ithaca NY 14853

WANG, L. EDWIN, church official; b. Medford, Oreg., Nov. 2, 1919; s. Lorang Edwin and Laura (Thomas) W.; m. Astrid H. Wikander, Sept. 4, 1942; children: David M., Linnea M., Judith L. Extension student, U. Calif., 1947-48, U. Minn., 1956-65; LHD, Midland Luth. Coll., 1970. CLU. Field underwriter, then asst. mgr. Mut. of N.Y., 1943-51; mgr. Standard Ins. Co., Oakland, Calif., 1951-56; exec. sec. Augustana Pension & Aid Fund, Mpls., 1956-62; pres. bd. pensions Luth Ch. Am., 1962-87; acting ins. commr., Minn., 1967; part-time ins. instr. Oakland Jr. Coll., Contra Costa Jr. Coll. 1954-56; pres. Oakland-East Bay Life Underwriters Assn., 1951, Oakland Mgrs. and Gen. Agts. Assn., 1955; pres. Ch. Pensions Conf., 1967; mem. pension research council U. Pa. Wharton Sch. Fin., 1971-92. Bd. dirs. Nat. Found. for Philanthropy, 1981—; pres. Lewis and Clark Trail Heritage Found. Inc., 1985-86; pres. Luth. Ch. Libr. Assn. 1988-90, bd. dirs., 1988—. Recipient Outstanding Service award Gov. Minn. Mem. Am. Risk and Ins. Assn., Am. Soc. CLU's (bd. dirs. 1980-84), Mpls. Chpt. CLU's (pres. 1973-74). Home: 6013 St Johns Ave Minneapolis MN 55424-1834

WANG, SHIH-HO, electrical engineer, educator; b. Kiangsu, China, June 29, 1944; came to U.S., 1968; s. C.C. Wang and Man Shih. BEE, Nat. Taiwan U., Taipei, 1967; MEE, U. Calif., Berkeley, 1970, PhD in Elec. Engring., 1971. Asst. prof. elec. engring. U. Colo., Colo. Springs, 1973-76, Boulder, 1976-77; asst. prof. electrical engring. U. Md., College Park, 1977-78, assoc. prof., 1978-84; prof. U. Calif., Davis, 1984—; cons. Lawrence Livermore (Calif.) Nat. Lab., 1986—; scientific officer Office Naval Research, Arlington, Va., 1983-84. Assoc. editor Internat. Jour. Robotics and Automation, 1986—. Served to 2d lt. China Air Force, Taiwan, 1967-68. Mem. IEEE (hon. mention award control systems soc. 1975). Office: Univ Calif Dept Elec/Computer Engring Davis CA 95616

WANG, STANLEY, electronics executive; b. 1943. MBA, Temple U. Mgr. Philco-Ford, Sunnyvale, Calif., 1964-71; materials mgr., mktg. rep. Intersil Corp., Cupertino, Calif., 1971-73; with Pantronix Corp., San Jose, Calif. 1974—, pres. Office: Pantronix Corp 145 Rio Robles San Jose CA 95134-1808*

WANG, TAYLOR GUNJIN, science administrator, astronaut, educator; b. Shanghai, China, June 16, 1940; came to U.S., 1963; s. Beverly Fung, 1966; children: Kenneth, Eric. BS, UCLA, 1967, MS, 1968, PhD, 1971. Mgr. microgravity sci. and applications program Jet Propulsion Lab., Pasadena, Calif., 1972-88, cons., 1987-89; Space Shuttle astronaut-scientist NASA, 1983-85; Centennial prof., dir. Ctr. for Microgravity Rsch. and Applications Vanderbilt U., Nashville, 1988—. Contbr. over 170 articles to profl. jours.; inventor living cellls encapsulation tech. as cure of hormone deficiency states in humans; over 20 patents in field. Bd. dirs. Com. of 100. Fellow Acoustical Soc. Am.; mem. AIAA, Am. Phys. Soc., Assn. Space Explorers-USA (pres. 1988), Sigma Xi. Office: Vanderbilt U Sta B Box 6079 Nashville TN 37235

WANG, TIMOTHY C., gastroenterologist; b. Allentown, Pa., 1957. MD, Columbia Coll. Physicians and Surgeons, 1983. Diplomate Am. Bd. Internal Medicine, Am. Bd. Gastroenterology. Intern Barnes Hosp., St. Louis, 1983-84, resident in internal medicine, 1984-86; fellow in gastroenterology Mass. Gen. Hosp., Boston, 1986-89, mem. staff; asst. prof. med. sch. Harvard U. R. Robert and Sally D. Funderburg Rsch. Scholar awards Am. Gastroent. Assn. Found., 1993, 94. Mem. AMA, ABIM, Am. Gastroent. Assn. Office: MA General Hospital GI Unit GRJ 706 32 Fruit St Boston MA 02114*

WANG, VERA, fashion designer; b. 1950; d. Cheng Ching Wang; m. Arthur Becker; children: Cecilia, Josephine. Grad., Sarah Lawrence Coll., New York. Sr. fashion editor Vogue, N.Y.C.; design dir. Ralph Lauren Women's Wear, N.Y.C., 1987-89; prin. Vera Wang Bridal House Ltd., N.Y.C., 1990—. Office: Vera Wang Bridal House Ltd 980 Madison Ave New York NY 10021

WANG, WALTER, chemicals executive; b. 1947. Sec. asst. to pres. Formosa Plaztic Group, 1985-90; pres. J M Mfg Co, Livingston, N.J., 1990—. Office: J M Mfg Co 9 Peach Tree Hill Rd Livingston NJ 07039*

WANG, WILLIAM KAI-SHENG, legal educator; b. N.Y.C., Feb. 28, 1946; s. Yuan-Chao and Julia Ying-Ru (Li) W.; m. Kwan Kwan Tan, July 29, 1972; 1 child, Karen You-Chuan. B.A., Amherst Coll., 1967; J.D., Yale U., 1971. Bar: Calif. 1972. Asst. to mng. partner Gruss & Co., N.Y.C., 1971-72; asst. prof. law U. San Diego, 1972-74, assoc. prof., 1974-77, prof., 1977-81; prof. Hastings Coll. Law, U. Calif. San Francisco, 1981—; vis. prof. law U. Calif., Davis, 1975-76, U. Calif. L.A., 1990; cons. to White House Domestic Policy Staff, Washington, 1979; vis. prof. Hastings Coll. Law, U. Calif., 1980. Contbr. articles to newspapers, mags., scholarly jours. Mem. State Bar Calif., Am. Law Inst., Phi Beta Kappa. Home: 455 39th Ave San Francisco CA 94121-1507 Office: U Calif Hastings Coll Law 200 Mcallister St San Francisco CA 94102-4978

WANG, WILLIAM SHI-YUAN, linguistics educator; b. Shanghai, China, Aug. 14, 1933; came to U.S., 1948, naturalized, 1960; s. Harper and Lily W.; children: Eugene, Yulun, Yumei, Yusi. A.B., Columbia U., 1955; M.A., U. Mich., Ph.D., 1960. Assoc. prof., chmn. dept. linguistics Ohio State U., Columbus, 1963-65; prof. linguistics U. Calif., Berkeley, 1966—, dir. Project on Linguistic Analysis, 1966—; prof. grad. sch., 1994—; lectr. Center Advanced Studies in Behavioral Scis., 1969-70, 83-84; sr. Fulbright lectr. in Sweden, 1972, India, 1979. Author: Explorations in Language, 1991; editor: The Lexicon in Phonological Change, 1977, Human Communication, 1982, Language Writing and the Computer, 1986; co-editor: Individual Differences in Language Ability and Language Behavior, 1979; assoc. editor Language, 1967-73; founding editor Jour. Chinese Linguistics, 1973—; contbr. numerous articles to profl. jours. Guggenheim Found. fellow, 1978-79. Mem. Linguistic Soc. Am., Acoustical Soc. Am., Academia Sinica, Internat. Assn. Chinese Linguistics (pres. 1992-93). Office: U Calif 2222 Piedmont Ave Berkeley CA 94720-2170 Because language penetrates so many aspects of life, my attempt to understand its nature has frequently led me into anthropology, biology, etc. These forays into neighboring fields have enhanced my awareness of the unity of knowledge, and of the importance of a broad perspective in any serious intellectual venture.

WANG, Y. C., chemicals executive; b. 1916. Lumberman Taiwan, 1937-58; with Formosa Plastic Group, Taipei, Taiwan, 1958-79, chmn. bd. dirs., 1979—. Office: Formosa Plastics Corp USA 9 Peach Tree Hill Rd Livingston NJ 07039-5701*

WANGER, OLIVER WINSTON, federal judge, educator; b. L.A., Nov. 27, 1940; m. Lorrie A. Reinhart; children: Guy A., Christopher L., Andrew G., W. Derek, Oliver Winston II. Student, Colo. Sch. Mines, 1958-60; BS, U. So. Calif., 1963; LLB, U. Calif., Berkeley, 1966. Bar: Calif. 1967, U.S. Dist. Ct. (ea. dist.) Calif. 1969, U.S. Tax Ct. 1969, U.S. Dist. Ct. (cen. dist.) Calif. 1975, U.S. Dist. Ct. (so. dist.) Calif. 1977, U.S. Dist. Ct. (no. dist.) Calif. 1989, U.S. Ct. Appeals (9th cir.) 1989. Dep. dist. atty. Fresno (Calif.) County Dist. Atty., 1967-69; ptnr. Gallagher, Baker & Manock, Fresno, 1969-74; sr. ptnr. McCormick, Barstow, Sheppard, Wayte & Carruth, Fresno, 1974-91; judge U.S. Dist. Ct. (ea. dist.) Calif., Fresno, 1991—; adj. prof. law Humphreys Coll. Law, Fresno, 1968-70; adj. prof. law San Joaquin Coll. Law, Fresno, 1970-94, dean Law Sch., 1980-82, pres., chmn. bd. dirs., 1982-94. Fellow Am. Coll. Trial Lawyers, Internat. Acad. Trial Lawyers; mem. Am. Bd. Trial Advs. (pres. San Joaquin Valley chpt. 1987-89, nat. bd. dirs. 1989-91), Am. Bd. Profl. Liability Attys. (founder, diplomate), Calif. State Bar (mem. exec. com. litigation sect. 1989-92, mem. com. on fed. cts. 1989-90), San Joaquin Valley Am. Inn of Ct. (pres. 1992-93), Beta Gamma Sigma. Office: US Dist Ct 5104 US Courthouse 1130 O St Fresno CA 93721-2201

WANGLER, WILLIAM CLARENCE, retired insurance company executive; b. Buffalo, Dec. 7, 1929; s. Emil A. and Viola M. (Roesser) W.; m. Carol B. Sullivan, Aug. 17, 1957; children: Jeffrey W., Eric J. BS, SUNY, Cortland, 1951. Claims adjuster Liberty Mut. Ins. Co., Buffalo, 1954-60; claims supr. Liberty Mut. Ins. Co., Miami, Fla., 1960-65; home office examiner Liberty Mut. Ins. Co., Boston, 1965-68; asst. claims mgr. Liberty Mut. Ins. Co., Cleve., 1968-69; claims mgr. Liberty Mut. Ins. Co., Cleve, 1969-73; div. claims service mgr. Liberty Mut. Ins. Co., Pitts., 1973-79, div. claims mgr., 1979-86; v.p. asst. gen. claims mgr. adminstrn. Liberty Mut. Ins. Co., Boston, 1986-94; ret., 1994; pres. Claims Mgrs. Counsel, Cleve., 1970; chmn. Nationwide Intercompany Arbitration, Cleve., 1969-70. Loaned exec. Mass. Bay United Way, Boston, 1964; account exec. Pitts. United Way, 1985-86. Served to capt. USMC, 1951-54. Republican. Roman Catholic. Home: 64 Trout Farm Ln Duxbury MA 02332-4609

WANK, GERALD SIDNEY, periodontist; b. Bklyn., Jan. 20, 1925; s. Joseph and Sadie (Ikowitz) W.; m. Gloria Baum, June 4, 1949; children: David, Stephen, Daniel. B.A., NYU, 1945, D.D.S. 1949; cert. in orthodontia, Columbia U., 1951, cert. in periodontia, 1956. Intern in oral surgery Bellevue Hosp., 1949-50; practice dentistry specializing in oral rehab. and periodontal prosthetics N.Y.C., Great Neck, N.Y., 1949—; instr. dept. periodontia and oral medicine NYU Dental Sch., 1956-63, asst. clin. prof. dept. periodontia, 1963-67, asst. prof. periodontia, oral medicine, former postgrad. dir. periodontal-prosthesis dept. fixed partial prosthesis, 1970—, clin. assoc. prof. periodontia and oral medicine, 1970-77, clin. prof., 1977—, postgrad. dir. periodontia, 1968-71; staff lectr. periodontology Harvard U. Sch. Dental Medicine, 1973-74; vis. lectr. Albert Einstein Coll. Medicine, N.Y.C. Community Coll. Sch. Dental Hygiene; sr. asst. attending staff North Shore Univ. Hosp., 1974-77, sr. asst. attending div. surgery, 1977—; cons. orthodontic panel N.Y. State, N.Y.C. depts. health; cons. periodontal prosthesis, Goldwater Meml. Hosp., N.Y.C.; former postgrad. instr. 1st Dist. Dental Soc. Postgrad. Sch.; lectr. various socs. N.Y. U.; mem. com. admissions N.Y. U. Coll. Dentistry, 1975—, chmn. fund raising, 1976—. Contbr. to: Practice of Periodontia, 1960, Dental Clinics of North America, 1972, 81, Manual of Clinical Periodontics, 1973; contbr. articles to profl. jours. Served to capt. USAF, 1953-55. Recipient Alumni Meritorious Service award N.Y. U., 1981, Coll. Dentistry Alumni Achievement award N.Y. U., 1983. Fellow Acad. Gen. Dentistry, N.Y. Acad. Dentistry, Internat. Coll. Dentists, Am. Coll. Dentists, Am. Acad. Oral Medicine (pres. N.Y. sect. 1971-72), Am. Pub. Health Assn.; mem. N.Y. Coll. Dentists (dir.), ADA, Dental Soc. N.Y.C. (dir. 1st dist., chmn. ethics com. 1985-86), Fedn. Dentaire Internat., Am. Assn. Dental Schs., N.Y. State Pub. Health Assn., AAUP, Pan Am Med. Assn. (life), AAAS, ADA, Am. Acad. Periodontology, Sci. Rsch. Soc. Am., Northeastern Soc. Periodontia, Am. Acad. Dental Medicine, Acad. Gen. Dentistry, Internat. Acad. Orthodontia, Am. Acad. Endodontia (life), Am. Acad. Periodontia (life), Am. Acad. Oral Medicine (life), NYU Coll. Dentistry Alumni Assn. (dir., sec. 1973-74, v.p 1974-75, pres. 1976-77), Am. Soc. Anesthesiology, Am. Assn. Endodontists, NYU Coll. Dentistry Dental Assocs. (charter), Acad. Oral Rehab. (hon.), First Dist Dental Soc. (program chmn. 1984, chmn. continuing edn. 1983, sec., 1985, v.p. Eastern Dental Soc. bd. 1986, pres.-elect 1987, pres. bd. 1988, bd. dirs.), First Dist. Dental Soc. (bd. dirs. 1989—), Am. Acad. Osseointegration, NYU Gallatin Assos., Alumni Fedn. N.Y. U. (dir. 1976-81), Omicron Kappa Upsilon, Alpha Omega. Jewish. Clubs: Fresh Meadow Country (Great Neck, N.Y.); N.Y. U. (charter N.Y. U. Coll. Dentistry), Century (charter N.Y. U. Coll. Dentistry); Masons. Home and Office: 40 Bayview Ave Great Neck NY 11021-2819 Office: 310 Madison Ave New York NY 10017-6006

WANKAT, PHILLIP CHARLES, chemical engineering educator; b. Oak Park, Ill., July 11, 1944; s. Charles and Grace Leona (Pryor) W.; m. Dorothy Nel Richardson, Dec. 13, 1980; children: Charles, Jennifer. BS in Chem. Engring., Purdue U., 1966, MS in Edn., 1982; PhD, Princeton U., 1970. From asst. prof. to prof. chem. engring. Purdue U., West Lafayette, Ind., 1970—, head freshman engring., 1987—; cons. Pharmaceutical Firm, 1985—. Author: Large Scale Ads and Chromatog, 1986, Equil Staged Separations, 1988, Rate Controlled Separations, 1990, Teaching Engineering, 1993; patentee in field. With AUS, 1962-64. Mem. AIChE, Am. Soc. Engring. Edn., Am. Chem. Soc. Avocations: fishing, canoeing, camping. Office: Purdue U Dept Freshman Engring West Lafayette IN 47907-1286

WANKE, RONALD LEE, lawyer; b. Chgo., June 22, 1941; s. William F. and Lucille (Kleinwachter) W.; m. Rose Klonowski, Oct. 23, 1987. BSEE, Northwestern U., 1964; JD, DePaul U., 1968. Bar: Ill. 1968. Assoc. Wood, Dalton, Phillips, Mason & Rowe, Chgo., 1968-71, ptnr., 1971-84; ptnr. Jenner & Block, Chgo., 1984–; lectr. John Marshall Law Sch., Chgo., 1985-94. Contbr. article to Software Law Jour., 1987. Mem. ABA, Chgo. Bar Assn. (lectr. 1985-87, chmn. computer law com. 1987-88), Computer Law Assn., Intellectual Property Law Assn. Chgo. (chmn. inventor svcs. com. 1976, chmn. fed. rules com. 1981). Home: 1806 N Sedgwick St Chicago IL 60614-5306 Office: Jenner & Block 1 E IBM Plz Chicago IL 60611-3608

WANKEL, ROBERT E., financial executive; b. Bklyn., Dec. 5, 1946; s. Ellery E. and Rose J. (Falco) W.; m. Helen Pfeiffer, Aug. 2, 1969; 1 child, Virginia. BBA, St. John's U., Jamaica, N.Y., 1968. CPA, N.Y. Acct. Laventhol & Horwath, N.Y.C., 1968-75; contr., v.p. fin. The Shubert Orgn., Inc., N.Y.C., 1975—. Office: The Shubert Orgn Inc 234 W 44th St New York NY 10036

WANNER, ERIC, foundation executive, researcher, writer, editor; b. Wilmington, Del., Mar. 14, 1942; s. Edwin and Isabel Smith (Speakman) W.; m. Patricia Attix, June 13, 1964 (div. 1976); children: Noel Edwin, Erin Cole; m. Carla Francesca Seal, June 18, 1983. BA, Amherst Coll., 1963; PhD, Harvard U., 1969. Asst. to assoc. prof. Harvard U., Cambridge, Mass., 1968-76; behavioral sci. editor Harvard U. Press, Cambridge, Mass., 1976-82; program officer Alfred P. Sloan Found., N.Y.C., 1982-84; v.p., 1984-86; pres. Russell Sage Found., N.Y.C., 1986—; adv. bd. mem. NSF Edn. Directorate, 1984-85, Harvard Ctr. Health and Human Resources Policy, 1988—; vis. com. dept. psychology Harvard U., 1989; mem. adv. com. on spl. projects Ctr. for Advanced Study in Behavioral Scis., 1986—. Author: Remembering, Forgetting and Understanding Sentences, 1974; editor: Language Acquisition: the State of the Art, 1982; contbr. articles to profl. jours. Fulbright fellowship Sussex U., Brighton, Eng., 1979, fellow N.Y. Inst. for Humanities, NYU, 1985—. Mem. Am. Psychol. Assn., Cognitive Sci. Soc., N.Y. Acad. Sci., Sigma Xi, Harvard Club. Office: Russell Sage Found 112 E 64th St New York NY 10021-7332

WANNSTEDT, DAVID RAYMOND, professional football team coach; b. Pitts., May 21, 1952; m. Jan Wannstedt; children: Keri, Jami. Student, U. Pitts. Player Green Bay Packers, 1974; asst. coach U. Pitts., 1975-79, Okla. State U., 1979-82, U. So. Calif., 1983-85; def. coord. U. Miami, 1986-89, Dallas Cowboys, 1989-93; head coach Chgo. Bears, 1993—. Named to NCAA 2nd team All-East; inducted into Western Pa. Hall of Fame, 1990. Office: Chgo Bears Halas Hall 250 Washington Rd Lake Forest IL 60045-2471*

WANTLAND, WILLIAM CHARLES, bishop, lawyer; b. Edmond, Okla., Apr. 14, 1934; s. William Lindsay and Edna Louise (Yost) W. BA, U. Hawaii, 1957; JD, Okla. City U., 1967; D in Religion, Geneva Theol. Coll., Knoxville, Tenn., 1996; DD (hon.), Nashotah House, Wis., 1983, Seabury-Western Sem., Evanston, Ill., 1983. With FBI, various locations, 1954-59, Ins. Co. of N.Am., Oklahoma City, 1960-62; law clk.-atty. Bishop & Wantland, Seminole, Okla., 1962-77; vicar St. Mark's Ch., Seminole, 1963-77, St. Paul's Ch., Holdenville, Okla., 1974-77; presiding judge Seminole Mcpl. Ct., 1970-77; atty. gen. Seminole Nation of Okla., 1969-72, 75-77; exec. dir. Okla. Indian Rights Assn., Norman, 1972-73; rector St. John's Ch., Oklahoma City, 1977-80; bishop Episcopal Diocese of Eau Claire, Wis., 1980—; interim bishop of Navajoland, 1993-94; adj. prof. Cath. U. Okla., Norman, 1970-78; instr. canon law Nashotah House, 1983—; mem. nat. coun. Evang. & Cath. Mission, Chgo., 1977-90; co-chmn. Luth.-Anglican Roman Cath. Commn. of Wis., 1987-95; mem. Episcopal Commn. on Racism, 1990-92, Episcopal Coun. Indian Ministries, 1990-95, Standing Commn. on Constitution and Canons, 1992-95. Author: Foundations of the Faith, 1983, Canon Law of the Episcopal Church, 1984, The Prayer Book nd the Catholic Faith, 1994; co-author: Oklahoma Probate Forms, 1971; contbr. articles to profl. jours. Pres. Okla. Conf. Mcpl. Judges, 1973; v.p. South African Ch. Union, 1985-95; trustee Nashotah House, Wis., 1981—, chmn. 1992—; bd. dirs. SPEAK, Eureka Springs, Ark., 1983-89; mem. Wis. adv. com. U.S. Civil Rights Commn., 1990-91; mem. support com. Native Am. Rights Fund, 1990—; co-chmn. Lutheran-Anglican-Roman Catholic Commn. of Wis., 1989-95. Recipient Most Outstanding Contbn. to Law and Order award Okla. Supreme Ct., 1975, Outstanding Alumnus award Okla. City U., 1980, Wis. Equal Rights Coun. award, 1986, Manitou Ikwe award Indian Alcoholism Coun., 1988. Mem. Okla. Bar Assn., Okla. Indian Bar Assn., Living Ch. Found., Oklahoma City Law Sch. Alumni Assn. (pres. 1968), Wis. Conf. Chs. (pres. 1985-86). Democrat. Episcopalian. Avocations: canoeing, skin-diving, cross-country skiing. Home: 145 Marston Ave Eau Claire WI 54701-3911 Office: Diocese of Eau Claire 510 S Farwell St Eau Claire WI 54701-3723 If we truly believe that God reigns, we will so order our lives that such a belief is clearly reflected in all that we do and say; further, such a belief will shape our relations, not only with all other people, but all of God's created order.

WAPENHANS, WILLI ADOLF, banking executive; b. Kusey, Altmark, Germany, Aug. 12, 1931; came to U.S., 1961; s. Willi and Frieda Luise (Streese) W.; m. Rosemarie Ingrid Schneider, Dec. 30, 1958; children: Heike, Kai-Uwe, Kerstin, Henner. Agr. Enginier, Friedrich Aereboe Sch., Michelstadt, Fed. Republic Germany, 1953; Diploma in Agronomy, Justus Liebig U., Giessen, Fed. Republic Germany, 1956; D in Agrl. Econs. summa cum laude, Justus Lichig Universitat, Giessen, Fed. Republic Germany, 1958, Habilitation Econs., 1960. Adminstr. Agrl. Estate, Wiesbaden, Fed. Republic Germany, 1951-52; researcher Inst. for kontinental Agronomy and Econs. Rsch., Giessen, Fed. Republic Germany, 1956-58; researcher Inst. for Econs. and Fiscal Scis., Giessen, Fed. Republic Germany, 1958-60, asst. prof. (docent), 1960-91; from agrl. economist to sr. v.p. external affairs, pers. and adminstrn. World Bank Devel. Fin. Inst., Washington, 1991-92; v.p., spl. advisor to pres. World Bank, Washington, 1991-92, chmn. task force project implementation; ret.; chmn. Assn. Researchers Justus Liebig U., 1958; sr. adivosr Republic of Belaris, 1992-94; sec. devel. com. Task Force on the Role of Multilateral Devel. Banks, 1994. Author books, monographs; contbr. articles to profl. jours. Chmn. Student Assn. Justus Liebig U., 1955-56; vice chmn. German Sch. Assn., Washington, 1968-74. Recipient Order of Merit 1st Class, Fed. Republic Germany, 1992; German Rsch. Found. grantee, 1958-59, Brit. Coun. grantee, 1959-60. Mem. List Gesellschaft. Lutheran. Service is the source of true satisfaction.

WAPIENNIK, CARL FRANCIS, manufacturing firm executive, planetarium and science institute executive; b. Donora, Pa., Oct. 10, 1926; s. Karl and Rose (Kidzinski) W.; m. Elva Louise Bartron, Nov. 27, 1953; children: Carl Eric, Ellen Louise. B.S., U. Pitts., 1953. Prodn. supr. RCA, Canonsburg, Pa., 1953-54; staff physicist Buhl Planetarium and Inst. Popular Sci., Pitts., 1954-64; exec. dir. Buhl Planetarium and Inst. Popular Sci., 1964-82; owner, operator Work-o-Art Miniatures (small mfg. firm), 1983—. Mem. Rostraver Twp. Planning Commn., 1965-67; mem. adv. bd. Allegheny C. of C. (formerly North Side Pitts. C. of C.), 1966-67; dir., 1968-73, pres., 1970; mem. adv. coun. Salvation Army, 1978-82; bd. dirs. Bapt. Home, Pitts., 1982-94; chmn. Rostraver Twp. Mcpl. Water Authority, 1970-94. With USNR, 1945-46. Recipient Man of Yr. award in sci. Pitts. Jaycees, 1969. Mem. Service Core Ret. Execs., Pitts. Bapt. Assn. (bd. dirs. 1976-82), Phi Beta Kappa, Sigma Pi Sigma. Patentee means for controlling liquid flow. Home: Salem Church Rd RR 4 Box 227 Belle Vernon PA 15012-9457 Office: Work-o-Art Miniatures RR 4 Box 227 Belle Vernon PA 15012-9457

WAPLES, ERIC SNOWDEN, headmaster; b. Lafayette, Ind., Oct. 16, 1944; s. Eliot Otto and Margaret (Miller) W.; m. Carolyn M., June 11, 1968; children: Jacob Snowden, Megan Elizabeth. AB in History, Dartmouth Coll., 1966; MAT in History, Colo. Coll., 1972; postgrad., Trinity Coll., 1967. History tchr. The Loomis Sch., Windsor, Conn., 1966-68; staff trust dept. First Nat. Bank & Trust, Evanston, Ill., 1970-71; tchr. history Fountain Valley Sch., Colorado Springs, Colo., 1972-80, acad. dean, 1980-83, asst. headmaster, 1983-87, headmaster, 1987—. Bd. dirs. Found. for Dist. #11, Colorado Springs, 1991—; co-pres. Pikes Peak Squash Assn., Colorado Springs, 1982-86; del. Colo. State Dem. Conv., 1976. Ballantine fellow Fountain Valley Sch., 1978. Mem. Assn. of Colo. Ind. Schs. (sec. 1988-89, treas. 1989—), Nat. Assn. of Exptl. Edn., VFW, Am. Hist. Assn., U.S. Squash Racquets Assn., Wilderness Soc., Outward Bound, Sierra Club. Methodist. Avocations: mountaineering, photography, film, competitive sports. Office: Fountain Valley Sch 6155 Fountain Valley School Rd Colorado Springs CO 80911-2297

WAPNER, SEYMOUR, psychologist, educator, administrator; b. Bklyn., Nov. 20, 1917; s. Hyman and Rose S. (Liese) W.; m. Lorraine E. Gallant, June 4, 1946; children: Jeffrey Gallant, Amy Beth. A.B., NYU, 1939; A.M., U. Mich., 1940, Ph.D., 1943. Instr., dir. U. Rochester Office Com. Selection and Tng. Aircraft Pilots, NRC, N.Y., 1943-46, 45-46; asst. prof. Bklyn. Coll., 1946-48, acting chmn. psychology dept., 1947-48; assoc. prof. dept. psychology Clark U., Worcester, Mass., 1948-56, prof., 1956-63, chmn. dept., 1960-86, G. Stanley Hall prof. genetic psychology, 1963-88; prof. emeritus Clark U., 1988—; chmn. exec. com. H. Werner Inst. Devel. Analysis, 1957—; mem. exec. bd. Council Grad. Depts. of Psychology, 1981-84; mem. U.S. Nat. Com. for Man and the Biosphere Directorate, 1975-86. Author: (with H.A. Watkin, et al) Personality Throuth Perception, 1954, (with H. Werner) Perceptual Development, 1957; editor: The Body Percept, 1965, (with W.A. Koelsch) Freud In Our Time, 1988, (with S.B. Cohen, B. Kaplan) Experiencing the Environment, 1976, (with B. Kaplan) Toward a Holistic Developmental Psychology, 1983, Perspectives in Psychological Theory, 1960, (with M. Bertini and L. Pizzamiglio) Field Dependence in Psychological Theory, Research and Application, 1986, (with L. Cirillo) Value Presuppositions in Theories of Human Development, 1986, (with L. Cirillo and B. Kaplan) Emotions in Ideal Human Development, 1989, (with J. Demick) Field Dependence-Independence, 1991, (with T. Yamamoto) Developmental Psychology of Life Transitions, 1992, Relations Between Psychology and Allied Fields, 1995. Fellow APA, AAAS; mem. AAUP, Soc. Rsch. in Child Devel., Eastern Psychol. Assn. (dir. 1968-70, 71-74, 85-88, 93—, pres. 1979-80), New Eng. Psychol. Assn. (pres. 1979-80), Mass. Psychol. Assn., Phi Beta Kappa, Sigma Xi. Office: Clark U Werner Inst for Devel Analysis 950 Main St Worcester MA 01610-1473

WARBURTON, (NATHANIEL) CALVIN, JR., state legislator, retired clergyman; b. Lynn, Mass., May 28, 1910; s. Nathaniel Calvin and Susan Blanche (Dillihunt) W.; m. Janice Orene Fitch, Sept. 18, 1935 (dec. 1991); children: David Calvin, Natalie Rae Warburton Sable, Mary Susan Warburton Ward, Ellen Orena Warburton Levesque, Edward James. BS, Boston U., 1932, STB, 1935; postgrad., U. N.H., 1946-47; ThM, Sch. Theology, Colorado Springs, Colo., 1960. Ordained elder Meth. Ch., 1937. Pastor Fremont (N.H.) Meth. Episcopal Ch., 1935-36, Moultonville (N.H.) and Tuftonboro Meth. Episcopal Ch., 1936-38, 1st Meth. Ch., Hampton, N.H., 1938-42, Pleasant Street Meth. Ch., Salem, N.H., 1945-48, 1st Meth. Ch., Bushton, Kans., 1957-63, Trinity Heights Meth. Ch., Newton, Kans., 1963-65, Contoocook and Bow Mills United Meth. Ch., Penacook, N.H., 1965-71, Grace United Meth. Ch., Haverhill, Mass., 1971-75; ret., 1975; rep. N.H. Gen. Ct., Concord, 1978-94; sec. bd. Christian edn. Ctrl. Kans. Conf. Meth. Chs., 1960-65; treas., trustee bd. hosp. and homes, 1963-65; chmn. bd. pensions N.H. Ann. Conf., 1971-75, exec. bd. treas. N.H. Preacher's Aid Soc., 1984-93. Mem. Gt. Bend (N.Y.) Sch. Bd., 1953. Lt. col. U.S. Army, 1942-45, 48-57; chaplain Kans. Army N.G., 1958-64, mem. USAR ret. Mem. VFW (surgeon), Am. Legion, Heroes of '76 (comdr. 1990-91), Sojourners (pres. 1989-90, 94-95), Masons, Kiwanis, Demolay (master councillor 1930, Legion of Honor 1995). Libertarian. Home: PO Box 365 Raymond NH 03077-0365

WARBURTON, RALPH JOSEPH, architect, engineer, planner, educator; b. Kansas City, Mo., Sept. 5, 1935; s. Ralph Gray and Emma Frieda (Niemann) W.; m. Carol Ruth Hychka, June 14, 1958; children: John Geoffrey, Joy Frances. B.Arch., MIT, 1958; M.Arch., Yale U., 1959, M.C.P., 1960. Registered architect, Colo., Fla., Ill., La., N.J., Md., N.Y., Va., D.C.; registered profl. engr., Fla., N.J., N.Y.; registered cmty. planner, Mich., N.J. With various archtl. planning and engring. firms Kansas City, Mo., 1952-55, Boston, 1956-58, N.Y.C., 1959-62, Chgo., 1962-64; chief planning Skidmore, Owings & Merrill, Chgo., 1964-66; spl. asst. for urban design HUD, Washington, 1966-72, cons., 1972-77; prof. architecture, archtl. engring. and planning U. Miami, Coral Gables, Fla., 1972—, chmn. dept. architecture, archtl. engring. and planning, 1972-75, assoc. dean engring. and environ. design, 1973-74; dir. grad. urban and regional planning program, 1973-75, 81, 87-93; advisor govt. Iran, 1970; advisor govt. France, 1973, govt. Ecuador, 1974, govt. Saudi Arabia, 1985; cons. in field, 1972—, lectr., critic design juror in field, 1965—; mem. chmn. Coral Gables Bd. Architects, 1980-82; mem. archtl. portfolio jury Am. Sch. and U., 1993. Assoc. author: Man-Made America: Chaos or Control, 1963; editor: New Concepts in Urban Transportation, 1968, Housing Systems Proposals for Operation Breakthrough, 1970, Focus on Furniture, 1971, National Community Art Competition, 1971, Defining Critical Environmental Areas, 1974; contbg. editor: Progressive Architecture, 1974-84; editorial adv. bd.: Jour. Am. Planning Assn., 1983-88, Planning for Higher Edn., 1986—, Urban Design and Preservation Quarterly, 1987—; contbr. over 100 articles to profl. jours.; mem. adv. panel Industrialization Forum Quar., 1969-79, archtl. portfolio jury Am. Sch. and Univ., 1993. Mem. Met. Housing and Planning Council, Chgo., 1965-67; mem. exec. com. Yale U. Arts Assn., 1965-70; pres. Yale U. Planning Alumni Assn., 1983—; mem. ednl. adv. com. Fla. Bd. Architecture 1975. Recipient W.E Parsons medal Yale U., 1960; recipient Spl. Achievement award HUD, 1972, commendation Fla. Bd. Architecture, 1974, Fla. Trust Historic Preservation award, 1983, Group Achievement award NASA, 1976; Skidmore, Owings & Merrill traveling fellow MIT, 1958; vis. fellow Inst. Architecture and Urban Studies, N.Y.C., 1972-74; NSF grantee, 1980-82. Fellow AIA (nat. housing com. 1968-72, nat. regional devel. and natural resources com. 1974-75, nat. systems devel. com. 1972-73, nat. urban design com. 1968-73, bd. dirs. Fla. S. chpt. 1974-75), ASCE, Fla. Engring. Soc.; mem. Am. Inst. Cert. Planners (exec. com. dept. environ. planning 1973-74), Am. Soc. Engring. Edn. (chmn. archtl. engring. div. 1975-76), Nat. Soc. Archtl. Engrs. (founding profl.), Nat. Soc. Sculpture Soc. (allied profl. mem.), Nat. Trust Hist. Preservation (principles and guidelines com. 1967), Am. Soc. Landscape Architects (hon., chmn. design awards jury 1971, 1972), Am. Planning Assn. (Fla. chpt. award excellence 1983), Am. Soc. Interior Designers (hon.), Urban Land Inst., Omicron Delta Kappa, Sigma Xi, Tau Beta Pi. Club: Cosmos (Washington). Home: 6910 Veronese St Coral Gables FL 33146-3846 Office: 420 S Dixie Hwy Coral Gables FL 33146 also: U Miami Sch Architecture Coral Gables FL 33124-5010 My contribution to society is made through comprehensive determination, design and development activity leading to habitats most suited to the optimum continuing progress of mankind.

WARBURTON, RICHARD JOHN, financial executive; b. Wallington, Eng., May 30, 1935; came to U.S. in 1978; s. Eric John and Louise Rachel (Martin) W.; m. Barbara Rosemary Cribb, July 26, 1958; children: Fiona, Helen, Alison, Charles, Clare. M in Econs. with honors, Cambridge U., 1958. Div. contr. Power & Indsl. div. Gen. Motors Corp., Wellingborough, Eng., 1961-65; div. contr., mktg. mgr. Pirelli Gen. PLC, Eastleigh, Eng., 1966-70; div. mgr. Gen. Cable div. Pirelli Gen. PLC, Southampton, Eng., 1971-78; contr. Cable Sector, Pirelli SpA, Basel, Switzerland, 1982-85; CFO Pirelli Cables Inc., St. Jean, Que., Can., 1985-93, Pirelli Cable Corp., Florham Park, N.J., 1978-93; prin. RJW Assocs., N.J., 1993—. Sr. warden Grace Ch., Madison, N.J. Mem. Morristown Club. Episcopalian. Avocations: gardening, sailing, French culture, classical music and opera. *

WARCH, RICHARD, university president; b. Hackensack, N.J., Aug. 4, 1939; s. George William and Helen Anna (Hansen) W.; m. Margot Lynn Moses, Sept. 8, 1962; children: Stephen Knud, David Preston, Karin Joy. B.A., Williams Coll., 1961; B.D., Yale Div. Sch., 1964; Ph.D., Yale U., 1969; postgrad., U. Edinburgh, 1962-63; H.H.D., Ripon Coll., 1980. Asst. prof. history and Am. studies Yale U., 1968-73, assoc. prof., 1973-77; assoc. dean Yale Coll.; dir. summer plans Yale U., 1976-77; assoc. dir. Nat. Humanities Inst., New Haven, 1975-76; v.p. acad. affairs Lawrence U., Appleton, Wis., 1977-79; pres. Lawrence U., 1979—; cons. Nat. Humanities Faculty; ordained to ministry United Presbyn. Ch. in U.S.A., 1968; dir. Bank One of Appleton. Author: School of the Prophets, Yale College, 1701-1740, 1973; editor: John Brown, 1973. Rockefeller Bros. Theol. fellow, 1961-62. Mem. Am. Studies Assn., Soc. for Values in Higher Edn., Winnebago Presbytery. Club: Rotary. Home: 229 N Park Ave Appleton WI 54911-5414 Office: Lawrence U Box 599 Appleton WI 54912

WARCHOL, RICHARD JAMES, physician; b. Lawrence, Mass., July 21, 1945; s. Michael Frank and Julia Alice (Malek) W. AB, Millikin U., 1967; MD, George Washigton U., 1972. Diplomate Am. Bd. Internal Medicine, Am. Acad. Pain Mgmt. Intern straight medicine George Washington U. Hosp., Washington, 1972-73, resident internatl medicine, 1973-74; resident internatl medicine Howard U. D.C. Gen. Hosp., Washington, 1974-75; fellow in endocrinology George Washington U. Hosp./Washington VA Hosp., 1977-79; staff physician Washington D.C. VA Med. Ctr., 1977-79, chief pain control sect., 1979—. Mem. Am. Coll. Physicians, Am. Acad. Pain Mgmt., Nat. Assn. VA Physicians and Dentists. Roman Catholic. Avocations: gardening, collectors' plates, stamp collecting, woodworking. Office: Washington DC VA Med Ctr 50 Irving St NW Washington DC 20422

WARD, ALAN L., architectural landscape designer. Design principal Sasaki Assocs., Watertown, Mass.; lecturer, architecture Ball State U., Harvard U., Graduate Sch. Design, Cambridge, Mass.; Jury member P/A awards. Recipient Citation in Urban Design, P/A Awards, 1990, 93. Office: Sasaki Assoc 64 Pleasant St Watertown MA 02172-2391

WARD, ALAN S., lawyer; b. Wilmington, Del., Jan. 1, 1931; s. Gilbert Hughes and Sarah Anna (Sparks) W.; m. Mariette S. Schneider, Apr. 4, 1959; children: Kathryn Ann Ward Koch, Guy Gilbert, Carolyn Alice. A.B., Wesleyan U., 1952; J.D., U. Chgo., 1955. Bar: Del. 1955, U.S. Supreme Ct. 1959, N.Y. 1962, D.C. 1964. Law clk. to judge U.S. Dist. Ct., Wilmington, 1955-56; trial atty. Antitrust div. Dept. Justice, Washington, 1956-61, asst. chief spl. litigation sect., 1960-61; assoc. Breed, Abbott & Morgan, N.Y.C., 1961-63; ptnr. Hollabaugh & Jacobs, Washington, 1963-70; dir. Bur. Competition, FTC, Washington, 1970-73; ptnr. Baker & Hostetler, Washington, 1973—; mem. mng. com., 1977-87; lectr. law George Washington U., 1967-70; lectr. profl. assns. Mem. bd. trustees Wesleyan U., 1986-89. Mem. ABA, (chmn. ABA's Antitrust Com. Litigation Section, 1986 and 1987), Assn. of Bar of City of N.Y., Bar Assn. D.C., Del. Bar Assn., Wesleyan U. Alumni Assn. (chmn. 1983-86). Republican. Methodist. Clubs: Univ. (Washington); Union (N.Y.C.); Union (Cleve.); Columbia Country (Chevy Chase, Md.). Avocations: squash, tennis, sailing. Home: 5804 Cedar Pky Bethesda MD 20815-4252 Office: Baker & Hostetler 1050 Connecticut Ave NW Washington DC 20036-5303

WARD, BETHEA, artist, small business owner; b. Montgomery, Ala., July 6, 1924; d. Charles E. and Lucy (Walter) W. BFA, Syracuse U., 1946; postgrad., Trinity U., San Antonio, 1965, 66, 68, San Antonio Art Inst., 1967, Houston Mus. Fine Arts Sch., 1973-75. Interior designer Davison-Paxon, Atlanta, 1946-47; assoc. prof. interior design U. Tex., Austin, 1947-51; interior designer Heminways-Bundrick, Shreveport, La., 1951-55; draftsman, supr. Ark. Fuel subs. Cities Service Co., Shreveport, 1955-60, Cities Svc. Co. Midland, San Antonio, 1961-82; visual artist, owner Tex. Notables Studio-Gallerie, Houston, 1983—. Juried shows include (watercolor paintings) Midland (Tex.) Art Fest. (2d place award, 1962), 35th Ann. Local Artist Exhbn., San Antonio (Wofford award 1965), Wichita, Kas. Centennial Nat. Exhbn. (inclusion award 1970), Cen. Tex. Hist. on Canvas Exhbn. (1st place award TFAA 1972), Laguna Gloria, Austin; group exhibits include U. Houston, 1986; contbr. ink drawing to Southwestern Hist. Quarterly, 1977; commns. include drawing for Moody Found. of Galveston; one person shows include Star of the Republic Mus., Houston Pub. Libr., Harris County Heritage Soc., San Antonio Pub. Libr. Recipient Award of Distinction Juried Art Fair, Houston Internat. Festival, 1987, numerous awards for watercolor paintings. Mem. Hoover Watercolor Soc. (founding mem. 1952), Watercolor Art Soc. Houston (chmn bd. social chmn., sec., co-founder), Art League Houston, Cultural Arts Council Houston, Coppini Acad. Fine Arts (life), Tex. Arts Alliance, Tex. Commn. on the Arts, Southwestern Watercolor Soc. (founding mem., pub. chmn.), Tex. State Hist. Assn., Tex. Hist. Found., Cultural Arts Council of Houston. Presbyterian. Avocations: classical music, ballet, Tex. history, exploring unknown streets and roads. Home and Studio: Tex Notables Studio-Gallerie 9614 Valverde St Houston TX 77063

WARD, C. BRUCE, entrepreneur; b. 1953. Graduate, U. Calif.; MBA, Stanford U., 1969. From sales mgr. to divsn. pres. Gunderson Bros. Engring. divsn. of FMC Corp., Portland, 1985-89, chmn., 1989—; regional v.p. Midwest ops. FMC Corp., Chgo., 1974-78; v.p. American Steel, Portland, 1978-80; pres. Western Acquisitions Group, Portland, 1980-84, American Guaranty Fin. Corp., Portland, 1984-85; bd. dirs. Stimson Lumber Co., Portland, Greenbrier Cos., Inc., Oswego, Or. Office: Gunderson Inc 4350 NW Front Ave Portland OR 97210*

WARD, CALVIN H., academic director, environmental science educator, federal agency administrator; b. Strawberry, Ark., Mar. 1, 1933; married; 3 children. BS in Biology, N.Mex. State U., 1955; MS in Plant Pathology-Genetics, Cornell U., 1958, PhD in Plant Pathology-Physiology, 1960; MPH in Environ. Health, U. Tex., 1978. Rsch. scientist Sch. Aerospace Medicine USAF, San Antonio, 1960-63, physiologist, dir. bioregenerative life support systems rsch. Sch. Aerospace Medicine, 1963-66; assoc. prof. dept. chem. engring. Rice U., Houston, 1966-68, assoc. prof. environ. sci. and engring. program, 1968-70, prof., chair dept. biology, 1970-88, prof., chair dept. environ. sci. and engring., 1970-92, prof. environ. sci./engring., ecology, evolutionary biology, 1970—; Foyt Family chair engring. Rice U., 1993—; dir. Energy and Environ. Systems Inst., Rice U., Houston, 1992—; vis. prof. environ. health U. Tex. Sch. Pub. Health, 1973-74; dir. Nat. Ctr. Ground Water Rsch., Rice U., U.S. EPA Exploratory Rsch. Ctr. for Excellence, 1981—; dir. Superfund Univ. Tng. Inst., Rice U., U.S. EPA Office Solid Wastes and Emergency Response, 1989—; co-dir. Hazardous Substances Rsch.Ctr.-South and S.W., La. State U., Rice U., Gas. Tech., U.S. EPA Superfund Rsch. Ctr., 1991—; dir. Advanced Applied Tech. Demonstration Facility, U.S. Dept. Def., 1993—; mem. profl. sci. adv. coms.; cons. Mem. editorial bd. Houston Engr., 1979-83; assoc. editor SIM News, 1979-90; editor-in-chief Environ. Toxicology and Chemistry, 1981—; sr. editor Jour. Indsl. Microbiology, 1985-91; co-editor 10 books; contbr. more than 200 articles to peer-reviewed jours., chpts. to books, provs. of confs., symposia, others. Mem. SW Ctr. Urban Rsch., 1969-82, treas., 1974-75, chmn., bd. dirs., 1977-79. Roger Boles scholar 1951; Shell Found. grad. fellow 1957-59; Regents grad. fellow 1957-59; recipient Bausch and Lomb award in Sci., 1951, Achievement award Nat. Aeronautics and Space Adminstrn., 1981, Controlled Ecol. Life Support Systems award, 1993; named Corr. in Gravitational Physiology, Internat. Union Physiol. Scis., 1985. Fellow Soc. Indsl. Microbiology (sec. 1979-82, bd. dirs. 1982-85, pres. 1983-84, Charles Porter award 1986), Am. Acad. Microbiology; mem. AAAS, Am. Soc. Microbiology, Am. Inst. Biol. Scis. (gov. bd. mem.-at-large 1977-82, exec. com. 1982-86, pres. 1984-85), Am. Soc. Plant Physiologists, Am. Phytopathological Soc., Internat. Water Resources Assn. (v.p. U.S. nat. com. 1977—), Soc. Environ. Toxicology and Chemistry (founder, bd. dirs. 1979-82, Disting. Svc. award 1990), Assn. Ground Water Scientists and Engrs., Assn. Environ. Engring. Profs. Office: Rice U 260 Mech Lab 6100 S Main Houston TX 77005

WARD, CARL EDWARD, research chemist; b. Albuquerque, Oct. 16, 1948; s. Joe E. and Loris E. (Wenk) W.; m. Bertha R. Schloer, June 9, 1970. BS in Chemistry, N.Mex. Inst. Mining and Tech., 1970; MS in Chemistry, Oreg. Grad. Ctr., 1972; PhD in Chemistry, Stanford U., 1977. Research chemist Union Carbide Corp., Charleston, W.Va., 1977-79, Dynapol Corp., Palo Alto, Calif., 1979-80; research chemist Chevron Chem. Co., Richmond, Calif., 1980-85, sr. research chemist, 1986-88; apptd. supr. chemical synthesis Chevron Chem. Co., Richmond, 1988-90; Sr. rsch. assoc. Chevron Rsch. & Tech. Co., Richmond, 1990-91, staff scientist, 1991—. Referee Jour. Organic Chemistry, 1983—; patentee in field; contbr. articles to profl. jours. Recipient NSF traineeship, Stanford U., 1972-73; Upjohn fellow, Stanford U., 1976-77. Mem. AAAS, Soc. Tribologists and Lubrication Engrs., Am.

Chem. Soc., Calif. Acad. Sci., N.Mex. Inst. Mining and Tech. Pres. Club (Socorro), Stanford Alumni Assn. Democrat. Avocations: gardening, camping, fishing. Home: 1355 Nisich Dr San Jose CA 95122-3061 Office: Chevron Rsch & Tech Co PO Box 1627 Richmond CA 94802-1792

WARD, CHARLES RICHARD, extension and research entomologist, educator; b. Tahoka, Tex., Mar. 25, 1940; s. James Henry and Bertrice Opha (Moore) W.; m. Norma Faye Martin, Aug. 25, 1960; children: Beverly Jan, Charles Edward. AA, South Plains Coll., 1960; BS, Tex. Tech U., 1962, MS, 1964; PhD, Cornell U., 1968. Entomology specialist N.Mex. State U., Santa Cruz, Bolivia, 1976-78; rsch. assoc., assoc. prof. entomology N.Mex. State U., Las Cruces, 1978-80; pest mgmt. specialist N.Mex. State U. Artesia, 1980-82, 1984-85; chief party, entomologist N.Mex. State U., San Pedro Sula, Honduras, 1983-84; supt. agrl. sci. ctr., prof. entomology N.Mex. State U., Alcalde, N.Mex., 1985-86; extension and rsch. entomologist, prof. N.Mex. State U., Albuquerque, 1986—; cons. entomologist Internat. Irrigation Ctr., Logan, Utah, 1985-86, Consortium for Internat. Crop Protection, College Park, Md., 1986-93, Cornell U., Ithaca, N.Y., 1993—, Tropical Rsch. and Devel., Gainesville, Fla., 1989—. Contbr. numerous articles to profl. jours. Mem. Bd. Cert. Entomologists (Outstanding Contbrn. award 1981), Entomol. Soc. Am. (sec. subsect. ea. 1992-93), Southwestern Entomol. Soc. (pres. 1993-94), Extension Specialists Assn., N.Mex. Acad. Sci. Avocations: insect collecting, hunting, fishing. Home: 12105 El Dorado Pl NE Albuquerque NM 87111-4059 Office: NMex State U Ste B495 9301 Indian School Rd NE Albuquerque NM 87112-2884

WARD, CHESTER LAWRENCE, physician, county health official, retired military officer; b. Woodland, Yolo, Calif., June 8, 1932; s. Benjamin Briggs and Nora Elizabeth (Cash) W.; m. Sally Diane McCloud, Dec. 10, 1960; children: Katharine, Lynda. BA, U. Calif., Santa Barbara, 1955; MD, U. So. Calif., 1962; MPH, U. Calif., Berkeley, 1966; grad., Indsl. Coll. Armed Forces, 1978. Commd. 2d lt., inf. U.S. Army, 1954; advanced through grades to brig. gen., 1980; chief aviation medicine, preventive medicine and aeromed. consultation service Ft. Rucker, Ala., 1967-68; surgeon Aviation Brigade and USA Vietnam Aviation Medicine Cons., 1968-69; flight surgeon Office of U.S. Army Surgeon Gen., 1970-71; physician The White House, Washington, 1971-75, 76; dir. environ. quality research U.S. Army Med. Research and Devel. Commd., 1975-76; comdr. Womack Community Hosp.; surgeon XVIII Airborne Corps, Ft. Bragg, N.C., 1978-80; comdr. William Beaumont Army Med. Center, El Paso, Tex., 1980-82; med. dir. Union Oil Co., Schaumburg, Ill., 1982-83; dir. domestic medicine Union Oil Co., Los Angeles, 1983-84; exec. dir. continuing med. edn. and clin. prof. emergency medicine U. So. Calif. Sch. Medicine, Los Angeles, 1984-85; dir., health officer Dept. Health, Butte County, Calif., 1985—. Apptd. by Gov. Wilson Calif. Commn. Emergency Med. Svcs. Decorated D.S.M., Legion of Merit (2), Bronze Star, Air medal (2). Fellow Am. Coll. Preventive Medicine, Aerospace Med. Assn.; mem. Calif. Council Local Health Officers (rep. Calif. vector control adv. com.), Health Officers Assn. Calif., Butte-Glenn County Med. Soc. (past pres.), Calif. Med. Assn. (del.), Calif. Commn. Emergency Med. Svcs., No. Calif. Emergency Med. Svcs. Calif. Home: 4 Lemon Hill Ct Oroville CA 95966-3700 Office: Butte County Dept Health 18B County Center Dr Oroville CA 95965-3335

WARD, DANIEL PATRICK, lawyer; b. Chgo., Aug. 30, 1918; s. Patrick and Jane (Convery) W.; m. Marilyn Corleto, June 23, 1951; children—Mary Jane, John, Susan Elizabeth. Student, St. Viator Coll., 1936-38; J.D. DePaul U., 1941, L.H.D., 1976; LL.D., John Marshall Law Sch., 1972. Bar: Ill. bar 1941. Asst. prof. law Southeastern U., 1941-42; pvt. practice, 1945-48; asst. U.S. atty. No. Dist. Ill., 1948- 54, chief criminal div., 1951-54; with Eardley & Ward, Chgo., 1954-55; dean DePaul U. Coll. Law, 1955-60, adj. prof. law, 1979-85; states atty. Cook County, Ill., 1960-66; judge Supreme Ct. Ill., 1966-90, chief justice, 1976-79; chmn. Ill. Cts. Commn., 1969-73; lawyer Bell, Boyd & Lloyd, Chgo., 1991—. Served with AUS, 1942-45. Mem. ABA, Ill. Bar Assn., Chgo. Bar Assn. Office: Bell Boyd & Lloyd Three First National Pla 70 W Madison St Chicago IL 60602-4284

WARD, DANIEL THOMAS, bishop; b. Umri, Yavatmal, India, Apr. 8, 1942; s. Thomas Tuckker and Sudina Thomas (Suhasini) W.; m. Suhasini Daniel, Nov. 27, 1968; children: Vandan, Prerana. BA, Amolakchand Coll., Yavatmal, 1964; BD, Union Bibl. Sem., Yavatmal, 1967; ThM, Fuller Sem., Pasadena, Calif., 1982. Bishop Free Meth. Ch. of N.Am. Indpls.; deacon, minister Free Meth. Ch., Yavatmal, 1969-71, elder, 1971-91, dist. supt., 1986-87, bishop, 1989—; mem. hosp. bd. Free Meth. Ch., Yavatmal, 1989, mem. sem. faculty, 1983, registrar, 1984, bishop on U.S. bd., 1989—, Editor, author (newsletter) Christ-Jyot, 1974, (monthly publ.) Ankur, 1985, (quar. publ.) The New Day, 1989. Speaker All Religions Platform Meeting Lions Club, Yavatmal, 1986, Nat. Integrity, 1987. Avocations: soccer, badminton, cricket, basketball, volleyball. Home: Bishop House Maharashtra, PO Box 27 Vanjari Rd Rd, 445001 Yavatmal Maharashtra India Office: Free Meth Ch N Am, PO Box 27, Bishop House, 445001 Yavatmal Maharashtra, India Office: PO Box 535002 Indianapolis IN 46253

WARD, DAVID, academic administrator, educator; b. Manchester, Eng., July 8, 1938; came to U.S., 1960; s. Horace and Alice (Harwood) W.; m. Judith B. Freifeld, June 11, 1964; children: Michael J.H., Peter F.B. BA, U. Leeds, Eng., 1959; MA, U. Leeds, 1961; MS, U. Wis., 1961, PhD, 1963; LittD, U. Leeds, 1992. Lectr. Carleton U. Ottawa, Ont., Can., 1963-64; asst. prof. Univ. B.C., Vancouver, Can., 1964-66; asst. prof. U. Wis., Madison, 1966-67, assoc. prof., 1967-70, prof., 1970—, chmn. geography dept., 1974-77; assoc. dean Grad. Sch., 1980-88, provost and vice chancellor acad. affairs, Andrew Clark prof. geography, 1989—; now chancellor U. Wis. Madison; mem. exec. com. Argonne (Ill.) Nat. Lab. 1990-93; dir.-at-large Social Sci. Rsch. Coun., 1991-93. Author: Cities and Immigrants, 1970, Geographic Perspectives on Americas Past, 1978, Poverty Ethnicity and the American City, 1989, Landscape of Modernity, 1992; contbr. articles to profl. jours. Guggenheim fellow, 1970, Einstein fellow Hebrew U., 1980, Fulbright fellow, 1979. Mem. Assn. Am. Geographers (pres. 1989). Office: U Wis-Madison 161 Bascom Hall 500 Lincoln Dr Madison WI 53706-1380

WARD, DAVID ALLEN, sociology educator; b. Dedham, Mass., June 21, 1933; s. Theodore Allen and Jessie Miller (Ketchum) W.; m. Carol Jane Barton, June 10, 1957 (div. 1964); children: Douglas Allen, Andrew Barton; m. Reneé Ellen Light, Mar. 10, 1967. BA, Colby Coll., 1955; PhD, U. Ill. 1960. Asst. prof. Wash. State U., Pullman, 1960-61; asst. research sociologist UCLA, 1961-64; assoc. prof. U. Minn., Mpls., 1965-68, prof., 1968—, chmn. dept. sociology, 1984-88, 92—; chmn. Salzburg (Austria) Seminar in Am. Studies, 1977; mem. research adv. com. Fed. Bur. Prisons, Washington, 1983—; cons. jud. com. U.S. Ho. Reps., Washington, 1984. Co-author: Women's Prison, 1965, Prison Treatment, 1971; co-editor: Delinquency, Crime and Social Process, 1969, Confinement in Maximum Custody, 1981; editorial cons. Jour. Criminal Law and Criminology, 1969—. Liberal Arts fellow Harvard U. Law Sch., 1968-69; Fulbright research fellow, 1971-72; research fellow Norwegian Fgn. Office, Oslo, 1976. Mem. Am. Sociol. Assn. (chmn. sect. criminology 1976-77), Law and Soc. Assn., Am. Soc. Criminology, Internat. Criminological Soc. Office: Univ of Minn Dept of Sociology 909 Social Sci Bldg Minneapolis MN 55455

WARD, DAVID SCHAD, screenwriter, film director; b. Providence, Oct. 24, 1947; s. Robert McCollum and Miriam (Schad) W.; children: Joaquin Atwood, Sylvana Soto. B.A., Pomona Coll., 1967; M.F.A., UCLA, 1970. Scriptwriter: films include Steelyard Blues, 1971, The Sting, 1973 (Acad. award best original screenplay 1973), The Milagro Beanfield War, 1988, (with Nora Ephron and Jeff Arch) Sleepless in Seattle, 1993 (Academy award nominee Best Original Screenplay 1993); writer, dir. films include Cannery Row, 1981, Major League, 1989, King Ralph, 1991, The Program, 1993. Mem. Dirs. Guild Am., Acad. Motion Picture Arts and Scis. Office: care CAA/Ken Stovitz 9830 Wilshire Blvd Beverly Hills CA 90212-1804

WARD, DUANE, professional baseball player; b. Parkview, N.M., May 28, 1964. With Atlanta Braves, 1982-86, Toronto Blue Jays, 1986—; player Am. League All-Star Team, 1993. Office: Toronto Blue Jays, 300 Bremner Blvd, Toronto, ON Canada M5V 3B3*

WARD, ELAINE, artist; b. Boston, June 4, 1927; d. Robert and Gertrude (Toibb) Winston; m. William Ward (dec.); 1 child, Heather; m. Arthur Lee Dann. BA, Ecole des Beaux Arts, Paris, 1958; student, Art Students League, N.Y.C.; hon. degree, Ecole des Beaux Arts, Cannes, France. Mem. Phoenix Gallery, N.Y.C., 8 yrs. Solo show at Phoenix Gallery, 1989; group shows include Lever House, N.Y.C., 1987-89, 93, 95, Guild Hall, Easthampton N.Y., 1988, 95, Phoenix Gallery, N.Y.C., 1992-94, C.W. Post Coll., 1993, Agora Gallery, N.Y.C., 1994, Elaine Benson Gallery, Bridgehampton, N.Y., 1992, Linda Woodward Gallery, Palmas Del Mar, P.R., 1993, Gallery 400, N.Y.C., 1995, Meadowlands Ctr. for Arts, N.J., 1995, Marcella Geltman Gallery, N.J., 1995; represented in collections at Coastal Steel Co., Carteret, N.H., Pandora and Co., Conway, N.H., Ardan Assocs. Ltd., N.Y.C.; subject of articles. Mem. Nat. Arts Club, Nat. Assn. Women Artists, Guild Hall Mus., Parrish Mus.

WARD, ERICA ANNE, lawyer, educator; b. Okiyama, Japan, Oct. 20, 1950; d. Robert Edward and Constance Regina (Barnett) W.; m. Ralph Joseph Gerson, May 20, 1979; 1 child, Stephanie Claire. B.A., Stanford U., 1972; J.D., U. Mich., 1975. Bar: Calif. 1975, D.C. 1976, U.S. Ct. Appeals (5th and D.C. cirs.) 1977, Temporary Emergency Ct. Appeals 1983, Mich. 1989. Assoc. Wilmer, Cutler & Pickering, Washington, 1975-77; staff counsel U.S. Senate Ethics Com., Washington, 1977-78; exec. asst. gen. counsel Dept. Energy, Washington, 1978-79, counsellor to dep. sec., 1980; assoc. dir. energy and natural resources, domestic policy staff White House, Washington, 1980-81; of counsel Skadden, Arps, Slate, Meagher & Flom, Washington, 1981-87, ptnr., 1987—; adj. prof. law U. Mich., Ann Arbor, 1984-85. Editor Mich. Law Rev., 1975. Commr. Mackinac Island (Mich.) State Park Commn., 1989—; mem. adv. bd. Ctr. Edn. of Women U. Mich., Ann Arbor, 1989—; bd. trustees Cranbrook Ednl. Cmty., 1993—; mem. visitors com. U. Mich. Law Sch. Recipient Outstanding Svc. medal Dept. Energy, 1981. Mem. ABA, Fed. Energy Bar Assn., Women's Bar Assn. D.C. Democrat. Jewish. Office: Skadden Arps Slate Meagher Flom 1440 New York Ave NW Washington DC 20005-2111

WARD, FRANK JAY, banker; b. Bklyn., Nov. 18, 1934; s. Frank Jay and May (Waugh) W.; m. Gail Martin Bruce, June 6, 1964; children: Stacy Ann, Fraser Preston, Richard Bruce. Student, Johns Hopkins U., 1952-55; grad. Sch. Banking Rutgers U., 1964. Mktg. mgr. IBM Corp., N.Y.C., 1955-68; project dir. Automation Engring. Labs., Norwalk, Conn., 1968-70; industry dir. Leasco Info. Systems, Lake Success, N.Y., 1970-71; v.p. Security Nat. Bank, Huntington, N.Y., 1971-75; pres. Western Bancorp Data Processing Co., Los Angeles, 1975-79; v.p. ops. Fin. Industry Systems, Hartford, Conn., 1979-81; dir. industry mktg. TRW-Fujitsu, Farmington, Conn., 1981-82; exec. v.p. KeyCorp, Albany, N.Y., 1982—; pres. Key Services Corp., Albany, 1983—. Tech. asst. Albany Inst. History and Art, 1986-87; pres. Combined Health Appeal, Albany, 1986—. Served with U.S. Army, 1957, 61-62. Club: Schuyler Meadows (Loudonville, N.Y.). Avocations: flying, sailing, woodworking, electronics. Office: Keycorp 17 Corporate Woods Blvd Albany NY 12211

WARD, FRED, actor; b. 1943. Film appearances include Escape From Alcatraz, 1979, Tilt, 1979, Carny, 1980, Southern Comfort, 1981, Timerider: The Adventures of Lyle Swann, 1982, Silkwood, 1983, Uncommon Valor, 1983, The Right Stuff, 1984, Swing Shift, 1984, Secret Admirer, 1985, UFOria, 1985, Remo Wiliaims: The Adventure Begins..., 1985, Train of Dreams, 1987, The Prince of Pennsylvania, 1988, Big Business, 1988, Off Limits, 1988, Tremors, 1990, Henry and June, 1990, Backtrack, 1990, Miami Blues, 1990 (also co-exec. prodr.), Thunderheart, 1992, The Player, 1992, Bob Roberts, 1992, Equinox, 1993, Short Cuts, 1993, The Naked Gun 33 1/3: The Final Insult, 1994; TV appearances (movies) Belle Star, 1980, Florida Straights, 1986, Cast A Deadly Spell, 1991, Four Eyes and Six Guns, 1992, (spls.) Noon Wine, 1985. Office: Paradigm Talent Agy 10100 Santa Monica Blvd 25th Fl Los Angeles CA 90067

WARD, GEOFFREY CHAMPION, author, editor; b. Newark, Ohio, Nov. 30, 1940; s. Frederick Champion and Duira Rachel (Baldinger) W.; m. Diane Raines; children—Nathan, Kelly; 1 stepchild, Garrett Keim. BA, Oberlin Coll., 1962. Sr. picture editor Ency. Britannica, Chgo., 1964-68; co-founder, editor Audience mag., Boston, 1969-73; mng. editor Am. Heritage Mag., N.Y.C., 1976-78; editor Am. Heritage Mag., 1978-82. Author: Lincoln's Though and the Present, 1978, Treasures of the Maharajas, 1983, Before the Trumpet: Young Franklin Roosevelt, 1992-1905, 1985, A First-Class Temperament: The Emergenceof Franklin Roosevelt, 1989 (Nat. Book Critics Cir. award, Francis Parkman prize Soc. am. Historians, L.A. Times biography prize, Ohioana award), The Civil War: An Ullustrated History, 1990, American Originals: The Provate Worlds of Some Singular Men and Women, 1991, Tiger Wahhahs, 1993 (with Diane Raines Ward) Encounters Wth the Men Who Tried to Save the Greatest Cats, Vaseball: An Illustrated History, 1994, Closets Champanion: The Unkown Story of the Intimate Friendship Between Franklin Roosevelt and Margaret Suckley, 1995; (TV documentary) Huey Long, 1985, Thomas Hart Benton, 1989, Lindbergh, 1990, Nixon, 1990 (Writers Guild Am. award), The Civil War, 1990 (Emmy award), Reminiscing in Tempo, 1991, Empire of the Air, 1992, The Kennedys, 1992 (Emmy award), George Marshall and the American Century, 1993, Baseball, 1994; regular columnist: The Life and Times for Am. Heritage; contbr. articles to mags., jours. Recipient Christopher awards for The Statue of Liberty, The Christophers, The Civil War, New England Booksellers Assn. award Am. Booksellers award, Lila Achesonson Wallace Readers Digest writers award. Mem. Soc. Am. Historians, Writers Guild Am., East Inc., Century Assn. Home: 17 C 290 W End Ave New York NY 10023-8106 Office: Brandt & Brandt care Carl Brandt 1501 Broadway New York NY 10036-5502

WARD, GEORGE FRANK, JR., foreign service officer; b. Jamaica, N.Y., Apr. 9, 1945; s. George Frank and Hildegard Louisa (Evans) W.; m. Peggy Elizabeth Coote, June 12, 1965; 1 child, Pamela Ward Priester. BA, U. Rochester, 1965; MPA, Harvard U., 1980. U.S. vice consul Am. Consulate, Hamburg, Germany, 1970-72; ops. officer Office Sec. State, Washington, 1972-74; U.S. consul Am. Consulate Gen., Genoa, Italy, 1974-76; polit. officer Am. Embassy, Rome, 1976-77, exec. asst., 1977-79; polit. officer Am. Embassy, Bonn, Germany, 1984-85, dep. chief mission, 1989-92; polit.-military officer U.S. Dept. State, Washington, 1980-84, deputy dir. European Security and Polit. Affairs, 1985-88, prin. dep. asst. sec. Bur. Internat. Orgns., 1992—. Capt. USMC, 1965-69. Decorated Vietnamese Cross Gallantry (Vietnam); Naval Commendation medal; recipient Presdl. Meritorious Svc. awards, 1992, 94. Mem. Am. Fgn. Svc. Assn., Phi Beta Kappa. Episcopalian. Avocations: classical music, running, skiing, tennis. Home: 6407 Recreation Ln Falls Church VA 22041 Office: Dept of State 2201 C St NW Washington DC 20520

WARD, GEORGE TRUMAN, architect; b. Washington, July 24, 1927; s. Truman and Gladys Anna (Nutt) W.; m. Margaret Ann Hall, Sept. 10, 1949; children: Carol Ann Ward Dickson, Donna Lynne Ward Solomon, George Truman, Robert Stephen. BS, Va. Poly. Inst., 1951, MS, 1952; postgrad., George Washington U., 1966. Registered profl. architect, Va., Md., D.C., W.Va., Ohio, N.J., Del., N.C. Archtl. draftsman Charles A. Pearson, Radford, Va., 1950; head archtl. sect. Hayes, Seay, Mattern & Mattern, Radford and Roanoke, 1951-52; with Joseph Saunders & Assos., Alexandria, Va., 1952-57, assoc. architect, 1955-57; ptnr. Vosbeck-Ward & Assos. Alexandria, 1957-64, Ward/Hall Assocs., Fairfax, Va., 1964—; dir. Crestar Bank/Greater Washington Region. Pres. PTA Burke (Va.) Sch., 1970-71; mem. bd. mgrs. Fairfax (Va.) County YMCA, 1964-76; chmn. adv. com. Coll. Architecture, Va. Poly. Inst., 1984-90; bd. dirs., mem. investment com. Va. Tech. Found., Inc. 1986-91, 93—; pres. Springfield Rotary Found., 1978-79; chmn. county adv. bd. Salvation Army, 1978-79, 86-87, co-chmn. Fairfax County Salvation Army Capital Campaign, 1991-94; mem. Gen. Bd. Va. Bapts., deacon, moderator; mem. bd. visitors Va. Poly. Inst. & State U., 1984-87; trustee Fairfax County Pub. Schs. Edn. Found., Inc. With AUS, 1946-47. Paul Harris fellow; recipient Disting. Svc. award Va. Tech. Alumni Assn., 1988. Fellow Coll. AIA, mem. AIA (corp., charter design Svc. award 1989), Va. Soc. AIA (chmn. polit. action com. 1991—, Disting. Svc. award 1990, treas. Va. soc. 1994—), Rowe Fellowship (charter mem. 1988), Alumni Assn. Va. Poly. Inst. & State U. (bd. dirs., v.p. 1992, pres. 1994), Interfaith Forum on Religion, Art and Architecture, Va. Found. for Architecture (trustee), Va. Assn. Professions, Va. C. of C., No. Va. Angus Assn. (pres. 1987-88), Masons, Shriners, KT, Rotary (charter mem., pres. Springfield 1973-74), Tau Sigma Delta, Omicron Delta Kappa, Phi Kappa Phi, Pi Delta Epsilon, Ut Prosim. Baptist. Home: Glenara Farm 10239 Glenara Ln Marshall VA

22115-9601 Office: Ward Hall Assoc AIA 12011 Lee Jackson Hwy Fairfax VA 22033-3310

WARD, HAROLD ROY, chemist, educator; b. Mt. Vernon, Ill., Nov. 3, 1935; s. Arthur G. and Gladys J. (Thomas) W.; m. Cynthia Van Lente, Mar. 17, 1956 (div.); children—Kenneth, Cynthia Ann. A.B., So. Ill. U., 1957; Ph.D., M.I.T., 1961; J.D., Harvard U., 1975. Bar: R.I. bar 1975. NSF postdoctoral fellow U. Calif., Berkeley, 1961-62; NATO postdoctoral fellow Oxford U., Eng., 1962-63; asst. prof. Brown U., Providence, 1963-68; assoc. prof. Brown U., 1968-71, prof. chemistry, 1971—; dir. Brown U. (Center Environ. Studies), 1978—; com. priority mechanisms NRC, 1981-84. Chmn. Conservation Law Found. R.I., 1975-79; mem. Nat. Commn. Air Conservation of Am. Lung Assn., 1978-79; pres. Ecology Action of R.I., 1972-74; mem. Citizens Com. Hazardous Waste, 1980-82, Gov.'s Hazardous Waste Facilities Planning Com., 1980-82; Pesticide Relief Adv. Com., 1986—. Alfred P. Sloan research fellow, 1969-71; NATO sr. postdoctoral fellow, 1970; EPA spl. fellow, 1972-75; Andrew W. Mellon Found. grantee, 1980-83, 84; Dept. Energy grantee, 1980; Richard King Mellon grantee, 1981; Jessie Smith Noyes Found. grantee, 1980-81; grantee Charles Stewart Mott Found., Edward John Noble Found. Home: 286 Doyle Ave Providence RI 02906-3355 Office: Brown U PO Box 1943 Providence RI 02912-1943

WARD, HARRY PFEFFER, physician, university chancellor; b. Pueblo, Colo., June 6, 1933; s. Lester L. and Alysmai (Pfeffer) W.; m. Betty Jo Stewart, Aug. 20, 1955; children—Stewart, Leslie, Elizabeth, Mary Alice, Amy. A.B., Princeton U., 1955; M.D., U. Colo., 1959; M.S., U. Minn., 1963. Intern Bellevue Hosp., N.Y.C., 1959; resident Mayo Clinic, Rochester, Minn., 1960-63; practice medicine specializing in hematology; chief medicine Denver VA hosp., 1968-72; dean, assoc. v.p. U. Colo. Sch. Medicine, 1972-78, prof. medicine, 1972; chancellor U. Ark. Med. Sci., Little Rock, 1979—; clin. investigator Va, 1964-67. Chmn. Assn. Acad. Health Ctr., 1993-94. Mem. ACP, AMA, Am. Fedn. Clin. Research, Central Soc. Clin. Investigation, Am. Soc. Hematology, Internat. Soc. Hematology, Western Soc. Clin. Research. Home: 369 Valley Club Cir Little Rock AR 72212-2900 Office: U Ark Med Scis 4301 W Markham St Little Rock AR 72205-7101

WARD, HILEY HENRY, journalist, educator; b. Lafayette, Ind., July 30, 1929; s. Hiley Lemen and Agnes (Fuller) W.; m. Charlotte Burns, May 28, 1951 (div. 1971); children: Dianne, Carolee, Marceline, Laurel; m. Joan Bastel, Aug. 20, 1977. BA, William Jewell Coll., 1951; MA, Berkeley (Calif.) Bapt. Div. Sch., 1953; MDiv, McCormick Theol. Sem., Chgo., 1955; summer, evening student, Northwestern U., 1948, 54, 56-57; PhD, U. Minn., 1977. News asst. Christian Advocate, 1953-55; editor jr. publs. David C. Cook Pub. Co., 1956-59; editor Record, Buchanan, Mich., 1960; religion editor Detroit Free Press, 1960-73; asst. prof. journalism Mankato (Minn.) State U., 1974-76; assoc. prof. journalism Wichita (Kans.) State U., 1976; prof. journalism Temple U., Phila., 1977—; dir. news-editorial sequence, journalism dept., 1977-80, chmn. dept., 1978-80; instr. journalism Oakland U., Rochester, Mich., evenings 1963-66. Author: Creative Giving, 1958, Space-age Sunday, 1960, Documents of Dialogue, 1966, God and Marx Today, 1968, Ecumania, 1968, Rock 2000, 1969, Prophet of the Black Nation, 1969, The Far-out Saints of the Jesus Communes, 1972, Religion 2101 A.D., 1975, Feeling Good About Myself, 1983, Professional Newswriting, 1985, My Friend's Beliefs: A Young Reader's Guide to World Religions, 1988, Reporting in Depth, 1991, Magazine and Feature Writing, 1993; editor: Media History Digest, 1979-94; exec. editor: Kidbits, 1981-82; book editor: Editor and Publisher, 1989—; contbr. articles to profl. jours., feature articles to newspapers and mags.; also short stories and poems. Religious Pub. Rels. Coun. fellow, 1970; recipient citation Religious Heritage Am., 1962, Leidt award Epsic. Ch., 1969, citation U.S. Am. Revolution Bicentennial Adminstrn., 1976. Mem. Religion Newswriters Assn. (sec.-treas. 1970-72), Am. Soc. Mag. Editors, Am. Soc. Journalists and Authors, Am. Journalism Historians Assn. (bd. dirs.), Overseas Press Club. Home: PO Box 399 1263 Folly Rd Warrington PA 18976-1422 Office: Temple U Dept Journalism Philadelphia PA 19122

WARD, HIRAM HAMILTON, federal judge; b. Thomasville, N.C., Apr. 29, 1923; s. O.L. and Margaret A. W.; m. Evelyn M. McDaniel, June 1, 1947; children: William McDaniel, James Randolph. Student, Wake Forest Coll., 1945-47; J.D., Wake Forest U., 1950. Bar: N.C. bar 1950. Practiced law Denton, N.C., 1950-51; staff atty. Nat. Prodn. Authority, Washington, 1951-52; partner firm DeLapp, Ward & Hedrick, Lexington, N.C., 1952-72; U.S. dist. judge Mid. Dist. N.C., 1972—; chief judge, 1982-88, sr. judge, 1988—; mem. com. on Codes of Conduct of Jud. Conf., U.S., 1990—; mem. Fourth Cir. Jud. Coun., 1984-87. Contbr.: legal opinions to Fed. Reporter System, 1972—. Bd. visitors Wake Forest U. Sch. Law, 1973—; Mem. N.C. Bd. Elections, 1964-72; trustee Wingate Coll., 1969-72. Served with USAAF, 1940-45. Decorated Air medal, Purple Heart; recipient Liberty Bell award N.C. Bar Assn., 1994. Mem. ABA, N.C. Bar Assn., Am. Judicature Soc., N.C. State Bar, Masons, Lions, Phi Alpha Delta (hon. life). Republican. Baptist. Home: Forest Park Dr Denton NC 27239 Office: US Courthouse 246 Fed Bldg 251 N Main St Winston Salem NC 27101

WARD, HORACE TALIAFERRO, federal judge; b. LaGrange, Ga., July 29, 1927; m. Ruth LeFlore (dec.); 1 son. AB, Morehouse Coll., 1949; MA, Atlanta U., 1950; JD, Northwestern U., 1959. Bar: Ga. 1960. Instr. polit. sci. Ark. A.M. and N. Coll., 1950-51, Ala. State Coll., 1951-53, 55-56; claims authorizer U.S. Social Security Adminstrn., 1959-60; assoc. firm Hollowell Ward Moore & Alexander (and successors), Atlanta, 1960-69; individual practice law Atlanta, 1971-74; judge Civil Ct. Fulton County, 1974-77, Fulton Superior Ct., 1977-79; U.S. Dist. Ct. judge No. Dist. Ga., Atlanta, 1979—; lectr. bus. and sch. law Atlanta U., 1965-70; dep. city atty., Atlanta, 1969-70, asst. county atty., Fulton County, 1971-74. Former Trustee Friendship Baptist Ch., Atlanta; mem. Ga. adv. com. U.S. Civil Rights Commn., 1963-65; assisting lawyer NAACP Legal Def. and Edn. Fund, Inc., 1960-70; mem. Jud. Selection Commn., Atlanta, 1972-74, Charter Commn., 1971-72; mem. Ga. Senate, 1964-74, jud. com., rules com., county and urban affairs com.; mem. State Democratic Exec. com., 1966-74; former bd. dirs. Atlanta Legal Aid Soc.; bd. dirs. Atlanta Urban League, Fed. Defender Program, No. Dist. Ga.; trustee Met. Atlanta Commn. on Crime and Delinquency, Atlanta U., Fledgling Found. Mem. Am. Bar Assn., Nat. Bar Assn. (chmn. jud. council 1978-79), State Bar Ga., Atlanta Bar Assn., Gate City Bar Assn. (pres. 1972-74), Atlanta Lawyers Club, Phi Beta Kappa, Alpha Phi Alpha, Phi Alpha Delta, Sigma Pi Phi. Office: US Dist Court 2388 US Courthouse 75 Spring St SW Atlanta GA 30303

WARD, JACKIE M., computer company executive. Student, Ga. State U., Ariz. State U.; completed internat. bus. fellows program, Ga. State U., The London Bus. Sch. With data processing dept. J.P. Stevens Co.; with UNIVAC div. Sperry Rand Corp.; founder, chief exec. officer Computer Generation, Inc., Atlanta, v.p., then pres., 1970. Vice chmn.-elect bd. regents Univ. System Ga., 1987—; commr. Edn. Commn. of States; pres., bd. dirs. Internat. Claim Services Ltd.; mem. Com. of 200. Office: Computer Generation Inc 3855 Presidential Pky Atlanta GA 30340-3713

WARD, JACQUELINE ANN BEAS, nurse, healthcare administrator; b. Somerset, Pa., Oct. 23, 1945; d. Donald C. and Thelma R. (Wable) Beas; divorced; children: Charles L. Jr., Shawn M. BS in Nursing, U. Pitts., 1966; MA in Counseling and Guidance, W.va. Coll. Grad. Studies, 1976; MBA, Columbus Coll., 1983. Cert. in advanced nursing adminstrn. Staff nurse W.Va. U. Hosp., Morgantown, 1966-67; staff nurse, head nurse Meml. Hosp. Charleston, W.Va., 1967-69; staff nurse Santa Rosa Hosp., San Antonio, 1969; staff nurse, supr. Bexar County Hosp., San Antonio, 1970; charge, staff nurse Rocky Mountain Osteo. Hosp., Denver, 1971; staff nurse Charleston Area Med. Ctr., 1971-74; asst. dir. nursing, 1974-82; dir. nursing H.D. Cobb Meml. Hosp., Phenix City, Ala.; clin. nurse Chattahoochie Valley C.C., Phenix City, 1984-92, v.p. nursing Venice (Fla.) Hosp., 1984-90, v.p. ops., 1990-94, exec. dir., pres. Life Counseling Ctr., Osprey, Fla., 1994—. Mem. Am. Coll. Healthcare Exec., Fla. Hosp. Assn., Nat. League Nursing, Articulation Council of Sarasota and Manatee Counties, Am. Orgn. of Nurse Execs. (pres. region II south Fla. 1985-86, 90-94), Fla. Orgn. Nurse Execs., Fla. Commn. on Nursing. Office: Venice Hosp Life Counseling Ctr 873 S Tamiami Trl Osprey FL 34229

WARD, JAMES D., bank executive building material executive. V. chmn. Citizens Bancorp., Laurel, Md. Office: Citizens Bank Maryland 14401 Sweitzer Lane Laurel MD 20707*

WARD, JAMES FRANK, pension fund administrator; b. Chgo., May 29, 1938; s. Frank William and Josephine (Calderone) W.; m. Judith Evelyn Drake, Nov. 22, 1957 (dec. Sept. 1981); children: Jeffrey Thomas, Jason Banning. BEd in Acctg., Ill. State U.; MBA, DePaul U., 1967. Chartered fin. analyst. Asst. traffic mgr. Witco Chem. Co., Stickney, Ill., 1958-59; office mgr. R.E. Chatterton Indsl. Diamonds, Chgo., 1960-62; acctg. tchr. Chgo. Bd. Edn., 1963-66; asst. exec. dir. Chgo. Tchrs. Pension Fund, 1967-76, exec. dir., 1977—. Author, editor numerous newsletters, bulletins. Speaker on pension topics various civic & tchr. orgns. Mem. Nat. Coun. on Tchr. Retirement, Nat. Conf. Pub. Employee Retirement Systems, Govt. Fin. Officers Assn. U.S. & Canada (cert. of excellence in achievement for fin. acctg. & disclosures 1989, 90), Investment Analysts Soc. Chgo., Assn. for Investment Mgmt. & Rsch. Avocations: instrumental music, tennis, skiing. Home: 300 N State St Apt 5233 Chicago IL 60610-4808 Office: Chgo Tchrs Pension Fund 205 W Wacker Dr Chicago IL 60606-1216

WARD, JAMES HUBERT, social work educator, university dean, researcher, consultant; b. Lawndale, N.C., Apr. 8, 1937; s. Frank A. and Helen (Wray) W.; m. Jacqueline Ferman Ward, Dec. 29, 1966; children—Dawn Alese, Audran Maria, James H., Christopher F. B.S., N.C A&T State U., 1960; M.S.W., U. Md., 1968; Ph.D., Ohio State U., 1974. Tchr., counselor Ohio Youth Commn., Columbus, 1962-66, dep. dir., 1971-73; adj. instr. social work dept. sociology and anthropology, U. Dayton (Ohio), 1968-69; exec. dir. Montgomery County Community Action Agy., Dayton, 1969-71; asst. prof. sociology and anthropology, Central State U., Wilberforce, Ohio, 1973; asst. prof., sr. research assoc. Sch. Applied Social Scis., Case Western Res. U., Cleve., 1975-76, asst. prof., assoc. dean, 1976-79, assoc. prof., assoc. dean, 1979-81; dean, prof. Sch. Social Work, U. Ala., Tuscaloosa, 1981-88; prof., dean, Grad. Sch. Social Work, Portland State U., Portland, Oreg., 1988—; cons. in field; mem. Ala. Juvenile Justice Adv. Com., 1983—; mem. adv. council on social work edn. Ala. Commn. on Higher Edn., 1982—; mem. ho. of dels. Council on Social Work Edn., 1981-87; mem. Coun. Social Work Edn. Accreditation Commn., 1987-93; mem. annual program planning com. Council on Social Work Edn., 1984-85; chmn. bd. dirs. United Way of Columbia-Willamette, 1988—; mem. rels. com., mem. community orgn. and planning com., chair agency rels. com., mem. strategic planning com.; bd. dirs. Urban League, Portland, 1988-89; bd. dirs. Mt. Hood Community Mental Health Ctr., 1988-91; mem. govs. panel on ecclesia, 1988-89; mem. adv. coun. mental health edn. planning Dept. Human Resources, Mental Health Divsn., Salem, Oreg., 1988-91; mem. Portland City Club, 1988—; mem. task force on licensing for social work practice, Ala. State Bd. Social Work Examiners, 1985; mem.local human resources bd. Tuscaloosa County Dept. Pensions and Security, 1982-87, mem. external central adminstrv. rev. panel, 1985. Bd. dirs. Greater Tuscaloosa chpt. ARC, 1982-87; pres. Eastwood Middle Sch. PTA, Tuscaloosa Bd. Edn., 1983-84; hon. mem. bd. Parents Anonymous of Ala. State Bd., 1982; mem. W. Ala. Nat. Issues Forum, 1984-86; bd. dirs., chmn. fin. com. Tuscaloosa County Mental Health Assn., 1984-87. Served to capt. U.S. Army, 1960-68. Recipient Pace Setters award for disting. achievement Coll. Adminstrv. Sci. Ohio State U., 1974; named Outstanding Profl. in Human Services, Acad. Human Services, 1974. Mem. Acad. Cert. Social Workers (cert), Council on Social Work Edn., Internat. Assn. Schs. Social Work, Internat. Council on Social Welfare, Nat. Assn. Social Workers (mem.-at-large, bd. dirs. Ala. Chpt. 1985, v.p. Oreg. chpt. 1991—, edit. bd. jour. Social Work 1990-93), Am. Assn. Deans and Dirs. of Grad. Schs. of Social Work (chair deans group S.E. region 1985-87), Ala. Conf. of Social Work (chmn. program com.), Greater Tuscaloosa of C. of C. Contbr. numerous articles to various profl. jours., also chpts. to books. Office: Portland State Univ Grad Sch Social Work PO Box 751 Portland OR 97207-0751

WARD, JAMES THERON, protective services official; b. July 15, 1942; s. Cecil S. and Gerterude (Craig) W.; m. Kathryn Ward; children: Scott, Brian. Grad. high sch., Hollywood, Fla., 1960. Cert. paramedic, Fla. Firefighter Hollywood Fire Dept., 1963-69, driver engr., 1969-73, paramedic lt., 1973-76, capt. fire suppression, 1976-77, chief tng. divsn., 1977-78, with 1978-82, chief, 1982—; initial chmn. Fla. State Emergency Med. Svc. Adv. Coun.; chmn. planning com. Broward Emergency Med. Svc. Coun., Broward County, Fla.; chmn. Broward County Fire Adminstr.'s Emergency Med. Svc. Com. With USAF, 1961-63. Recipient Larry S. Jordon Emergency Med. Svc. Hall of Fame award HRS, 1993; named Emergency Med. Svc. Provider of Yr., Fla. Emergency Med. Svc. Adminstrn., 1994. Mem. Fla. Emergency Med. Svc. Providers Assn. (pres., Al Ridgway award 1989), Fla. Fire Chiefs Assn., Broward County Profl. Fire Chiefs Assn., Internat. Assn. Fire Chiefs, Hollywood Com. of 100, Rotary. Avocations: fishing, scuba diving, photography. Home: 844 Johnson St Hollywood FL 33019 Office: Hollywood Fire Rescue 3401 Hollywood Blvd Hollywood FL 33021

WARD, JANET LYNN, magazine editor, sports wire reporter; b. Albany, Ga., Feb. 20, 1955; d. Andrew Johnson and Dorothy Iris (Pepera) W.; m. William Thomas Hankins III, Apr. 25, 1981 (div. Feb. 1990); m. Jack Wilkinson, May 22, 1993. AB in Journalism, U. Ga., 1977; JD, Woodrow Wilson Coll. Law, 1984. Sports editor Marietta (Ga.) Daily Jour., 1977-79, North Fulton extra-Atlanta Jour. Constitution, 1979-80; asst. editor In town extra-Atlanta Jour. Constitution, 1980-84; lawyer Atlanta, 1984-89; editor Am. City & County Mag., Atlanta, 1989—. Democrat. Roman Catholic. Avocations: sports, reading. Home: 372 Oakdale Rd NE Atlanta GA 30307-2070 Office: Am City & County Ste 1200 6151 Powers Ferry Rd NW Atlanta GA 30339-2943

WARD, JASPER DUDLEY, III, architect; b. Flemington, N.J., Oct. 8, 1921; s. Jasper Dudley and Constance Fargis (Allen) W.; m. Lucretia Baldwin; children: Lucretia B., James R., Michael D., Alexander A., Abigail B. B.Arch., M.I.T., 1948. Designer Skidmore, Owings & Merrill, N.Y.C., 1948-50; partner Ward-Knight, N.Y.C., 1950; architect Kelly & Gruzen, N.Y.C., Knappen, Tippetts, Abbott & McCarthy, N.Y.C., Gen. Electric Co., Reynolds Metals Co., Louisville, 1951-58; pvt. practice architecture Louisville, 1958-93; chief architect Hazelet * Erdal Consulting Engrs. & Architects, various, 1993—; Vis. critic archtl. design Pratt Inst., 1954-56, Columbia U., 1955, U. Ky., 1960-71; lectr. U. Louisville, 1983-86. Prin. works include: Neighborhood House, 1964 (award), Portland Sch. 1968 (award), Ky. Sch. for Blind, Recital Hall and Music Bldg., 1977 (award), Alice Lloyd Coll. Sci. Bldg., 1977 (award), St. Francis Sch, Goshen, Ky., 1000 Car Fed. Parking Garage, Louisville, Alice Lloyd Coll. Boy's and Girl's dormitory, Pippa Passes, Ky., John F. Kennedy Library, West Liberty, Ky., U. Louisville Radiation Center, Jefferson County Elementary Sch, Okolona, Ky., Ballard Mills Silo Apts. and Redevel. of Big 4 Bridge, U. Louisville Student Activities Ctr., 6th and Main Sts. Parking Garage, 1988 (award), Louisville Gardens Parking Garage, 1990 (award). Served to 1st Lt. C.E. AUS, M41943-46. Recipient AIA award of merit for Swain House, Watching, N.Y. 1956, 1st Honor awards Ky. Soc. Architects for CIT Bldg., 1961; White Cement award of excellence for Drs. Office Bldg., Louisville, Portland Cement Assn. 1971; City Blue Print Co. Louisville in Archtl. Collection, Mus. of Modern Art. Home: 6601 Mayfair Dr Prospect KY 40059-9614 Office: 325 W Main St Ste 1200 Louisville KY 40202-4251

WARD, JEANNETTE POOLE, psychologist, educator; b. Honolulu, June 19, 1932; d. Russell Masterton and Bessie Naomi (Hammett) Poole; children: John Russell Ward, Lisa Joy Ward. BA, Birmingham (Ala.) So. Coll., 1963; PhD in Psychology, Vanderbilt U., 1969. NSF summer rsch. asst. U. Iowa, Iowa City, 1962; NSF summer rsch. asst. Vanderbilt U., Nashville, 1963, NASA fellow, 1963-66, NIH postdoctoral fellow, 1966-67; spl. rsch. fellow Duke U., Durham, N.C., 1970-71; asst. prof. psychology Memphis State U., 1967-72, assoc. prof. psychology, 1972-77, prof. psychology, 1977—. Editor: Current Research in Primate Laterality, 1990, Primate Laterality, 1992; mem. editorial bd. Jour. Comparative Psychology, 1988—; contbr. chpts. to books and articles to profl. jours. Fellow Am. Psychol. Soc.; mem. Psychonomic Soc., Animal Behavior Soc., Am. Psychol. Assn., Am. Primatology Soc., Southeastern Psychol. Assn., Soc. for Neuroscis., Internat. Soc. for Comparative Psychology (treas. 1989-90), Sigma Xi (pres. Memphis State U. chpt. 1989-90, rsch. award 1985). Democrat. Avocations: dogs, reading, art, music. Office: Univ of Memphis Dept Psychology Memphis TN 38152

WARD, JENNIFER C., diplomat; b. Worcester, Eng., Jan. 29, 1944; 1 child. BA, Vassar Coll., 1965; MA, PhD, UCLA. Asst. to v.p. for acad. affairs, lectr. in social sci., Medgar Evers Coll. CUNY, 1971-73; dir. grad. admissions, lectr. in pub. and internat. affairs Princeton U., 1975-78; staff dir. House Fgn. Affairs Com., subcom. on Africa U.S. Congress, 1978-79; cons. Office of Asst. Sec. of Def. for Internat. Security Affairs for Africa, 1979; dep. dir. office of Inter-African affairs Bur. African Affairs, 1979-81; counselor for polit. affairs U.S. Embassy, Kinshasa, Zaire, 1981-83; sr. watch officer ops. ctr. U.S. Dept. State, 1983-84, dep. dir. office security assistance and sales, bur. politico-military affairs, 1984-86; dep. chief of mission U.S. Embassy, Dakar, Senegal, 1986-89; counselor for polit affairs U.S. Embassy, Kingston, Jamaica, 1989-91; U.S. amb. Niger, 1991-93; special asst. to the pres./sr. dir. for African affairs Nat. Security Council, Washington, D.C., 1993—. Office: Dept of State Niamey Embassy Washington DC 20521-2420*

WARD, JOHN MILTON, music educator; b. Oakland, Calif., July 6, 1917; s. John Milton and Maud (Van Alstyne) W.; m. Ruth Marie Neils, Jan. 9, 1945. B.A., San Francisco State Coll., 1941; M.Mus., U. Wash., 1942; Ph.D., NYU, 1953; A.M. (hon.), Harvard U., 1955. Instr. lit. and fine arts Mich. State U., 1947-53; asst., later assoc. prof. music U. Ill., 1953-55; assoc. prof. music Harvard U., 1955-58, prof., chmn. dept., 1958-62, William Powell Mason prof., 1961-85, William Powell Mason prof. emeritus, 1985—. Author: The Dublin Virginal Manuscript, 1954, 3d edit., 1983, A Dowland Miscellany, 1977, Sprightly and Cheerful Musick, 1981, Music for Elizabethan Lutes, 1992, The Lute Music of John Johnson, 1994; editor series Pantomime, Dance, and Ballet; contbr. articles to profl. jours. Chmn. bd. dirs. Laura Boulton Found.; mem. adv. bd. London Entertainment, 1660-1800; hon. curator music and dance Harvard Theatre Collection. Mem. Am. Acad. Arts and Scis., Am. Musicol. Soc. (hon.), Internat. Musicological Soc., Internat. Coun. for Traditional Music, Soc. Ethnomusicology, Royal Mus. Assn. (hon. fgn. mem.), Lute Soc. (hon.). Home: 20 Follen St Cambridge MA 02138-3503

WARD, JOHN ROBERT, physician, educator; b. Salt Lake City, Nov. 23, 1923; s. John I. and Clara (Elzi) W.; m. Norma Harris, Nov. 5, 1948; children: John Harris, Pamela Lyn, Robert Scott, James Alan. BS, U. Utah, 1944, MD, 1946; MPH, U. Calif., Berkeley, 1967; Masters, Am. Coll. of Rheumatology, 1990. Diplomate Am. Bd. Internal Medicine. Intern Salt Lake County Gen. Hosp., 1947-48, asst. resident, 1949-50, resident physician internal medicine, 1950-51, asst. physician, 1957-58, assoc. physician, 1958-69; clin. fellow medicine Harvard U., Boston, 1955-57; instr. medicine U. Utah Med. Sch., Salt Lake City, 1954-58, asst. prof., 1958-63, assoc. prof., 1963, prof., 1966-93, chmn. dept. preventive medicine, 1966-70, emeritus prof. internal medicine, 1993—, chief div. rheumatology, 1957-88; prof. internal medicine emeritus U. Utah. Med. Sch., Salt Lake City, 1994—; attending physician internal medicine Salt Lake City VA Hosp., 1957-70; Nora Eccles Harrison prof. medicine, Am. Coll. Rheumatology. Served as capt. M.C. AUS, 1951-53. Master Am. Coll. Rheumatology; fellow ACP; mem. Am. Coll. Rheumatology (Disting. rheumatologist award 1994), Utah State Med. Assn. (hon. pres. 1994-95). Home: 1249 E 3770 S Salt Lake City UT 84106-2446 Office: U Utah Health Scis Ctr 50 N Medical Dr Salt Lake City UT 84132

WARD, JOHN WESLEY, retired pharmacologist; b. Martin, Tenn., Apr. 8, 1925; s. Charles Wesley and Sara Elizabeth (Little) W.; m. Martha Isabelle Hendley, Dec. 7, 1947; children: Judith Carol, Charles Wesley, Richard Little. A.A., George Washington U., 1948, B.S., 1950, M.S., 1955; Ph.D., Georgetown U., 1959. Research assoc. in pharmacology Hazleton Labs., Falls Church, Va., 1950-55; head dept. pharmacology Hazleton Labs., 1955-58, chief depts. biochemistry and pharmacology, 1958-59; with A. H. Robins Co., Richmond, Va., 1959-90, dir. biol. research, 1978-80, dir. research, 1980-82, v.p. research, 1982-89, v.p., gen. mgr. R & D div., 1989-90; ret., 1990; lectr. in pharmacology Med. Coll. Va., 1960-64, adj. assoc. prof. pharmacology, 1982-90; guest lectr. Seminar on Good Lab. Practices, FDA, Washington, 1979, Chgo., 1979, San Francisco, 1979; apptd. expert pharmacologue toxicologue, France, 1986. Contbr. articles on pharmacology, toxicology and medicinal chemistry to profl. pubs. Served with USMC, 1943; Served with USN, 1944-46; Served with U.S. Army, 1944. Mem. AAAS, N.Y. Acad. Sci., Va. Acad. Sci., Am. Chem. Soc., Soc. Toxicology (charter), Soc. Pharmacology and Exptl. Therapeutics, Internat. Soc. Regulatory Toxicology and Pharmacology (charter), Pharm. Mfrs. Assn. (chmn. animal care and use com. 1971-88), Am. Assn. for Accreditation Lab. Animal Care (chmn. bd. trustees 1976-80), Sigma Xi. Clubs: Willow Oaks (Richmond); Cosmos (Washington), Masons (Washington). Achievements include patents in field. Home: 10275 Cherokee Rd Richmond VA 23235-1107 *An appreciation of the responsibility we have to society has set the standards by which I live. These responsibilities are as important as the rights to be gained from society. Those who are unwilling to assume responsibility should have no rights.*

WARD, LESLIE ALLYSON, journalist, editor; b. L.A., June 3, 1946; d. Harold Gordon and Marilyn Lucille (Dahlstead) W.; m. Robert L. Biggs, 1971 (div. 1977); m. Colman Robert Andrews, May 26, 1979 (div. 1988). AA, Coll. San Mateo, 1966; BA, UCLA, 1968, MJ, 1971. Reporter, researcher L.A. Bur. Life mag., 1971-72; reporter, news asst. L.A. bur. N.Y. Times, 1973-76; sr. editor New West mag., L.A., 1976-78, 79-80; L.A. bur. chief US mag., 1978-79; Sunday style editor L.A. Herald Examiner, 1981-82, editor-in-chief Sunday mags., 1982-83, Olympics editor, 1984, sports editor, 1985-86, sr. writer, 1986; sr. editor L.A. Times Mag., 1988-90; travel editor L.A. Times, 1990—. Democrat. Office: LA Times Times Mirror Sq Los Angeles CA 90053

WARD, LLEWELLYN O(RCUTT), III, oil company executive; b. Oklahoma City, July 24, 1930; s. Llewellyn Orcutt II and Addie (Reisdorph) W.; m. Myra Beth Gungoll, Oct. 29, 1955: children: Casidy Ann, William Carlton. Student, Okla. Mil. Acad. Jr. Coll., 1948-50; BS, Okla. U., 1953; postgrad. Harvard U., 1986. Registered profl. engr., Okla. Dist. engr. Delhi-Taylor Oil Corp., Tulsa, 1955-56; ptnr. Ward-Gungoll Oil Investments, Enid, Okla., 1956—; owner L.O. Ward Oil Ops., Enid, 1963—; v.p. 1420 Lahoma Rd Inc., Enid, 1967—; also bd. dirs.; mem. Okla. Gov.'s Adv. Coun. on Energy; rep. to Interstate Oil Compact Commn.; bd. dirs. Community Bank and Trust Co. Enid. Chmn. Indsl. Devel. Commn., Enid, 1968—; active YMCA; mem. bd. visitors Coll. Engring., U. Okla.; mem. adv. coun. Sch. Bus. trustee Phillips U., Enid, Univ. Bd., Pepperdine, Calif.; Okla. chmn. U.S. Olympic Com., 1986—; chmn. bd. Okla. Polit. Action Com., 1974—; Bass Hosp.; Rep. chmn. Garfield County, 1967-69; Rep. nat. committeeman from Okla.; bd. dirs. Enid Indsl. Devel. Found. Served with C.E., U.S. Army, 1953-55. Named to Order of Ky. Cols. Mem. Am. Inst. Mining and Metall. Engrs., Ind. Petroleum Assn. Am. (area v.p., bd. dirs.), Okla. Ind. Petroleum Assn. (pres., bd. dirs.), Nat. Petroleum Council, Enid C. of C. (v.p., then pres.), Alpha Tau Omega. Methodist. Clubs: Toastmasters (pres. Enid chpt. 1966), Am. Bus. (pres. 1964). Lodges: Masons, Shriners, Rotary (pres. Enid 1990-91). Home: 900 Brookside Dr Enid OK 73703-6941 Office: 502 S Fillmore St Enid OK 73703-5703

WARD, LOUIS EMMERSON, retired physician; b. Mt. Vernon, Ill., Jan. 19, 1918; s. Henry Ben Pope and Aline (Emmerson) W.; m. Nan Talbot, June 5, 1942; children—Nancy, Louis, Robert, Mark; m. Marian Mansfield, Jan. 27, 1979. A.B., U. Ill., 1939; M.D., Harvard, 1943; M.S. in Medicine, U. Minn., 1949. Intern Ill. Research and Ednl. Hosp., Chgo., 1943; fellow medicine Mayo Found., 1946-76; cons. medicine, rheumatology Mayo Clinic, 1950-83, chmn. bd. govs., 1964-75. Contbr. articles to profl. jours. Vice chmn. bd. trustees Mayo Found., 1964-76; past bd. dirs. Fund for Republic, Ctr. for Study Democratic Instns., Arthritis Found.; mem. Nat. Council Health Planning and Devel., 1976-83. Recipient U. Ill. Alumni Achievement award, 1968; recipient disting. alumnus award Mayo Found., 1983. Master Am. Coll. Rheumatology (pres. 1969-70); mem. AMA, Nat. Soc. Clin. Rheumatologists (pres. 1967-69), Ctrl. Soc. Clin. Rsch., Minn. Med. Soc., Zumbro Valley Med. Soc., So. Minn. Med. Assn., Phi Beta Kappa, Sigma Xi, Alpha Omega Alpha, Phi Delta Theta. Home: 30 Raeburn Ct Port Ludlow WA 98365-9796

WARD, LOUIS LARRICK, candy company executive; b. Kansas City, Mo., Nov. 18, 1919; s. Carter William and Fern Alpha (Larrick) W.; m. Adelaide Selby Cobb, Dec. 17, 1955; children—Scott Hardman, Thomas Selby, Linda

Larrick. Student, U. Kans., 1937-38; B.S. in Chem. Engring. Stanford, 1941. With Drexel, Harriman & Co., 1946-47, Spencer Chem. Co., 1947-50, Ward Paper Box Co., 1950-60; pres., chmn. bd. Russell Stover Candies, Inc. Kansas City, Mo., 1960-93, bd. dirs. emeritus, 1993—; retired, 1993; dir. First Nat Bank, Ward Paper Box Co., all Kansas City, Mo. Served with USNR, 1941-46. Mem. Kappa Sigma. Clubs: Kansas City Country (Kansas City, Mo.), River (Kansas City, Mo.), University (Kansas City, Mo.). Home: 1240 W 57th Ter Kansas City MO 64113-1172

WARD, MARVIN MARTIN, retired state senator; b. Newport News, Va., Feb. 10, 1914; s. Charles Tilden and Nora Belle (Martin) W.; m. Mary June Darden, Aug. 23, 1941; children: Elizabeth Darden Ward Cone, Marvin Thomas. BS, Appalachian U., 1934; MA, U. N.C., 1940. Tchr. Bethel Sch., Midland, N.C., 1934-37, Reynolds High Sch., Winston-Salem, N.C., 1937-46; prin. Granville Elem. Sch., Winston-Salem, N.C., 1946-49; asst. supt. Winston-Salem City Schs., 1949-62, supt., 1962-63; supt. Winston-Salem/Forsyth County Schs., 1963-76; mem. N.C. State Senate, Raleigh, 1979-94; mem. ret., 1994; mem. exec. com. N.C. Pub. Sch. Forum, Raleigh, 1986—; mem. edn. com. Nat. Cong. State Legis., Denver, 1985—. Sunday sch. tchr. Centenary Meth. Ch., Winston-Salem, 1941—; mem. Forsyth County Emergency Planning Com., Winston-Salem, 1987—. Recipient Valand award Mental Health Assocs. Inc., Raleigh, 1982, Leadership award N.C. Assn. Educators, 1985; named Disting. Alumni Appalachian State U., 1986, The Educator A. Phillip Randolph Inst., 1989, Legis. of Yr. N.C. Nurses Assn., 1989. Mem. Winston-Salem C. of C., Lions, Ardmore Community Club (pres. 1950). Democrat. Avocations: golf, fishing, travel, photography, wood carving. Home: 641 Yorkshire Rd Winston Salem NC 27106

WARD, MICHAEL DELAVAN, congressman, former state legislator; b. Jan. 7, 1951; s. Jasper Dudley III and Lucretia (Baldwin) W.; m. Christina Heavrin, July 18, 1975; children: Jasper Dudley IV, Kevin Michael. BS, U. Louisville, 1975. Salesperson Matthew Bender & Co., Louisville, 1979-83; owner Campaign Svcs., Polit. Cons. Louisville, 1983—; campaign mgr. Ron Mazzoli for Congress, Louisville, 1984; salesman Sta. WAVG, Louisville, 1984-85; spl. asst. Jefferson County, Louisville, 1985-88; state rep. Ky. Gen. Assembly, Frankfort, 1988-93; mem. 3rd congl. dist. U.S. Ho Reps., 1994—. State chair Common Cause/Ky. Louisville, 1975-77, 79-80; treas. Jefferson County Dem. Com., Louisville, 1984-91; bd. dirs. Ohio Valley March of Dimes, 1987-88. Mem. Kentuckiana Hemophilia Soc. (bd. dirs. 1987—), Action League for Physically Handicapped Adults (bd. dirs. 1987—). Home: 1905 Deer Park Ave Louisville KY 40205-1201 Office: US Capital Washington DC 20015

WARD, MILTON HAWKINS, mining company executive; b. Bessemer, Ala., Aug. 1, 1932; s. William Howard and Mae Ivy (Smith) W.; m. Sylvia Adele Randle, June 30, 1951; children: Jeffrey Randle, Lisa Adele. BS in Mining Engring., U. Ala., 1955, MS in Engring., 1981; MBA, U. N.Mex., 1974; DEng (hon.), Colo. Sch. of Mines, 1994. Registered profl. engr., Tex., Ala. Supr., engr. San Manuel (Ariz.) Copper Corp., 1955-60; mine supt., divsn. supt., gen. supt. of mines, divsn. mgr. Kerr-McGee Corp., Oklahoma City and Grants, N.Mex., 1960-66; gen. mgr. Homestake Mining Co. Grants, 1966-70; v.p. ops. Ranchers Exploration & Devel. Corp., Albuquerque, 1970-74; pres., bd. dirs. Freeport Minerals Co., 1974-85; pres., COO Freeport-McMoRan, Inc., New Orleans, 1985-92, also bd. dirs.; co-chmn., pres., CEO Cyprus Amax Minerals Co., Englewood, Colo., 1992—; bd. dirs. Mineral Info. Inst., Inc., Internat. Copper Assn. Contbr. articles to profl. jours. Former trustee, former pres. New Orleans Mus. Art; trustee Children's Hosp., New Orleans, Denver Art Mus.; dir. Smithsonian Nat. Mus. Natural History, Nat. Mining Hall of Fame and Mus.; mem. adv. bd. bus. coun. Tulane U. Sch. Bus.; disting. engring. CIL Inc.; also mem. mining engring. adv. coun., mem. pres.'s cabinet. Recipient Daniel C. Jackling award and Saunders Gold medal Soc. Mining, Metallurgy and Exploration, 1992; inductee Am. Mining Hall of Fame. Fellow Inst. Mining & Metallurgy (London); mem. NAE, AIME (former sect. chmn., Disting. Mem. award), Am. Mining Congress (chmn., dir. 1989-92), Am. Australian Assn., Mining and Metall. Soc. Am. (pres. 1981-83, mem. exec. com.), Can. Inst. Mining and Metall., NAM (mem. natural resource com.), N.Mex. Mining Assn. (former chmn. dir.), Internat. Copper Assn. (bd. dirs.), Copper Club, Mining Club (v.p., gov. 1979—), Cherry Hills Country Club (Englewood), Met. Club (Washington), Met. Club (Englewood). Republican. Presbyterian. Avocations: tennis, enology, flying. Office: Cyprus Amax Minerals Co 9100 E Mineral Circle Englewood CO 80112

WARD, PATRICIA ANN, dean; b. Warren, Pa., Aug. 26, 1940; d. H. Blair and M. Edwinna (Wilson) Ward. BA, Ea. Nazarene Coll., Quincy, Mass., 1962; MA, U. Wis., 1964, PhD, 1968. Asst. prof. SUNY, Albany, 1968-72; asst., assoc. and full prof. Pa. State U., University Park, 1972-84; dean arts and scis. Wheaton (Ill.) Coll., 1984—; cons. evaluator N. Cen. Assn. Commn. on Instns. of Higher Edn., 1988—; adv. bd. Am. Comparative Lit. Assn., 1986-89; v.p. Conf. on Christianity and Lit., 1978-80. Humanities editor Christian Scholar's Rev., 1981-86; editorial bd. Christianity and Lit., 1989—; author: The Medievalism of Victor Hugo, 1975, Joseph Joubert and the Critical Tradition, 1983, Christian Women at Work, 1981; contbr. articles to profl. jours. Fulbright fellow, Paris, 1966-67; Pa. State U. Rsch. grantee, 1974-75; Midwest Faculty Seminar/U. Chgo. fellow, 1988-89, 91, others. Fellow Soc. for Values in Higher Edn.; mem. Am. Assn. Higher Edn., Am. Conf. Acad. Deans, MLA, Am. Comparative Lit. Assn., Conf. on Christianity and Lit., Am. Assn. Tchrs. French, Pi Kappa Delta, Phi Delta Lambda. Office: Wheaton Coll Dean of Arts and Scis Wheaton IL 60187

WARD, PATRICK J., oil industry executive; b. 1931. With Caltex Petroleum Corp., Irving, Tex., 1955—, now chmn. bd., CEO. Office: Caltex Petroleum Corp 125 E John Carpenter Fwy Irving TX 75062

WARD, PETER ALLAN, pathologist, educator; b. Winsted, Conn., Nov. 1, 1934; s. Parker J. and Mary Alice (McEvoy) W. B.S., U. Mich., Ann Arbor, 1958, M.D., 1960. Diplomate: Am. Bd. Anat. Pathology, Am. Bd. Immunopathology. Intern Bellevue Hosp., 1960-61; resident U. Mich. Hosp., Ann Arbor, 1961-63; postdoctoral fellow Scripps Clinic, La Jolla, Calif., 1963-65; chief immunobiology br. Armed Forces Inst. Pathology, Washington, 1967-71; prof. dept. pathology, chmn. dept. U. Conn. Health Center, Farmington, 1971-80; prof., chmn. dept. pathology U. Mich., Ann Arbor, 1980—; interim dean U. Mich. Med. Sch., 1982-85, 1st Godfrey D. Stobbe prof. pathology, 1987; Disting. faculty lectr. U. Mich. Biomed. Rsch. Coun., 1989; cons. VA Hosp., 1980—; mem. rsch. rev. com. Nat. Heart, Lung, Blood Inst., NIH, Bethesda, Md., 1978-82, Inst. Medicine, 1990—, NAS; trustee Am. Bd. Pathology, 1988—, v.p., 1995; bd. dirs. Univ. Association for Rsch. and Edn. in Pathology, Inc., 1978—, pres. bd. dirs., 1988-90; chmn., bd. mem. sci. adv. bd. Armed Forces Inst. Pathology, Washington, 1981-83; mem. Pathology A study sect. NIH, 1972-76, chmn., 1976-78; pres.-elect U.S./Can. Acad. Pathology, 1991-92, pres., 1992-93, past. pres., 1993-94. Served to capt. M.C. U.S. Army, 1965-67. Capt., M.C. U.S. Army, 1965-67. Recipient Borden Research award U. Mich. Med. Sch., Ann Arbor, 1960; recipient Research and Devel. award U.S. Army, 1969, Meritorious Civilian Service award Dept. Army, 1970, Parke-Davis award Am. Soc. Exptl. Pathology, 1971. Mem. Am. Assn. Pathologists (pres. 1978-79), Am. Soc. Clin. Investigation, Am. Assn. Immunologists, U.S./Can. Acad. Pathologists (past pres. 1993-94), Assn. Pathology Chmn., Mich. Soc. Pathologists. Office: U Mich Med Sci I PO Box 0602 1301 Catherine Rd #M5240 Ann Arbor MI 48109-0602

WARD, R. J., bishop. Bishop of Ea. Md. Ch. of God in Christ, St. Louis. Office: Ch of God in Christ 4724 Palm St Saint Louis MO 63115-2017

WARD, RICHARD C., advertising executive; b. 1933. With Kenyon & Eckhardt, Dearborn, Mich., 1954-73, Monroe (Mich.) Auto Equipment, 1973-78; with Ross Roy, Inc., Bloomfield Hills, Mich., 1978-94, former pres., vice chmn. Ross Roy Comm., Inc., 1994—. Office: Ross Roy Comm Inc 100 Bloomfield Hills Pky Bloomfield Hills MI 48304-2906

WARD, RICHARD C., lawyer; b. Hyden, Ky., Sept. 6, 1937; s. Donald A. and Hazel M. (Fox) W.; m. Karen Gallegly, July 24, 1960; children: John Richard, Jeff Michael. BS in Commerce, Georgetown Coll., 1960; JD, U. Ky., 1964. Bar: Ky., U.S. Dist. Ct. (ea. dist.) Ky., U.S. Ct. Appeals (6th cir.). Ptnr. Craft, Barret, Haynes & Ward, Hazard, Ky., 1964-80, Wyatt Tarrant & Combs, Lexington, Ky., 1980—; trustee Ea. Mineral Law Found.,

Morgantown, 1987—. Mem. editorial bd. Jour. Mineral Law and Policy, 1985—; editor: Kentucky Mineral Law, 1986; contbr. chpts. to books. Bd. dirs. Ea. Ky. Leadership Found., Hindman, 1986—; mem. adv. bd. Republic Savs. Bank, Lexington, 1986—; devel. chmn. Am. Heart Assn., 1988—. Mem. ABA (vice-chair coal com. 1989—), Ky. Bar Assn., Assn. Trial Lawyers Am., Rotary. Republican. Baptist. Avocation: golf. Office: Wyatt Tarrant & Combs 1700 Lexington Fin Ctr 250 W Main St Lexington KY 40507-1714

WARD, RICHARD JOSEPH, university official, educator, author; b. Beverly, Mass., Nov. 7, 1921; s. Ralph Woodbury and Margaret (Lyons) W.; m. Cecilia Butler, Sept. 1, 1951; children: Timothy, Mary, Richard, Christopher. BS, Harvard U., 1946; MA, U. Mich., 1948, PhD, 1958. Dir. planning U.S. Aid Mission to Jordan, 1961-63; chmn. econ. dept. C.W. Post Coll., L.I. U., 1960-61, 63-65; chief planning Bur. for Near East, S. Asia, U.S. Agy. for Internat. Devel., 1965-69; mgr. internat. cons. Peat, Marwick, Mitchell & Co., Washington, 1969-75; dean U. Mass. Coll. Bus., Dartmouth, 1975-87, dean dir. rsch., prof., 1990—; dir. U.S. Internat. U. Sch. Bus., London, 1988-89; cons. in field. Author: Principles of Economics, 1967, Development Problems, 1973, The Palestine State, 1978, Development Horizon, '80, 1980; editor: The Challenge of Development, 1967; also numerous articles. Bd. dirs. Indsl. Found., 1976-82, New Bedford Symphony, 1982-85; bd. dirs. Jr. Achievement, 1977—, also past pres.; mem. exec. com. World Congress on Violence and Human Co-existence. Lt. USN, 1943-46, PTO. Recipient Disting. Svc. award AID, Jordan Mission, 1963, Univ. Svc. award U. Mass. Alumni Assn., 1983; fellow Ford Found., 1957. Mem. Assn. Social Econs. (pres. 1970-71), Ea. Econ. Assn. (exec. com.), Am. Econ. Assn., Harvard Club (pres. 1984-87, regional bd. dirs. Mass. and R.I. 1989-92), U.S. Signatory/Found. for Human Co-Existence. Home: 20 Pleasant St South Dartmouth MA 02748

WARD, RICHARD STORER, child psychiatrist, educator emeritus; b. Beirut, Lebanon, Oct. 9, 1920; came to U.S., 1931; s. Edwin St. John and Charlotte Edwards (Allen) W.; m. Adele Marie Zangara, Sept. 2, 1960; children: Steven Henry, Charlotte Canham, Richard Zangara. BA, Amherst Coll., 1942; MD, Columbia U., 1945, postgrad., 1957. Diplomate Am. Bd. Psychiatry and Neurology (child psychiatry cert. com. 1972-80). Intern Babies Hosp., N.Y.C., 1945; resident in psychiatry Stony Lodge, Ossining, N.Y., 1950-51, Psychiat. Inst., N.Y.C., 1951-52; clin. dir. Child Guidance Clinic, Jewish Child Care Assn., Newark, 1952-56, M.B. Child Guidance Inst., Jewish Bd. Guardians, N.Y.C., 1956-60; prof. clinical psychiatry Emory U., Atlanta, 1960-86, prof. emeritus, 1986—; dir. child unit Parkwood Hosp., Altanta, 1976-90; pvt. practice psychiatry Atlanta, 1986—. Fellow Am. Psychiat. Assn., Am. Acad. Child Psychiatry, Am. Psychoanalytic Assn.; mem. Am. Orthopsychiat. Assn., Am. Coll. Psychoanalysts. Democrat. Mem. United Ch. of Christ. Home: 868 Castle Falls Dr NE Atlanta GA 30329-4114 Office: 27 Lenox Pt NE Atlanta GA 30324-3172

WARD, RICHARD VANCE, JR., management executive; b. Montreal, Que., Can., June 19, 1929; s. Richard Vance Ward and Isobel Eugene Moseley; m. Elizabeth Anne Gareau, Aug. 15, 1953; children: Carolyn, Jennifer, Philip, Karen, Katherine. BSc, McGill U., Montreal, 1951; diploma in bus. adminstrn., U. Western Ont., London, Can., 1952. Indsl. engr. CIL Inc., Montreal, 1952-63, prodn. mgr., 1963-65; prodn. dir. ICI Am. Inc., Stamford, 1965-73; prodn. dir. CIL Inc., Montreal, 1973-76, v.p., 1976-84; pres. CIL Corp. of Am., Stamford, Conn., 1984-89, Ward Assocs. Mgmt. Cons., 1989—; bd. dirs. Cornwall Chems. Inc., CIL Corp. Am., Cansco Chems. Inc., Can.; bd. dirs. Chlorine Inst., Washington, exec. com., 1984-86, Friends of McGill, Inc., N.Y.C. Mem. Chem. Mfrs. Assn. Avocations: sailing, hiking, curling, skiing. Home: 45 Brushy Ridge Rd New Canaan CT 06840-4207

WARD, ROBERT, composer, conductor, educator; b. Cleve., Sept. 13, 1917; s. Albert E. and Carrie (Mollenkopf) W.; m. Mary Raymond Benedict, June 19, 1944; children: Melinda, Johanna, Jonathon, Mark, Timothy. B.Mus., Eastman Sch. Music, 1939; cert., Juilliard Grad. Sch. Music, 1946; student composition with, Bernard Rogers, Howard Hanson, Frederick Jacobi, Aaron Copland; conducting with, Albert Stoessel, Edgar Schenkman; D.F.A., Duke, 1972; Mus.D., Peabody Inst., 1975; D.F.A., U. N.C., Greensboro, 1992. Tchr. Juilliard Sch. Music, 1946-56; mng. editor, mem. bd. Galaxy Music Corp., until 1967, dir., 1967—; exec. v.p. Highgate Press, 1967; pres. N.C. Sch. Arts, Winston-Salem, 1967-74; tchr. composition N.C. Sch. Arts, 1974-79; prof. composition Duke U., Durham, N.C., 1978-87, Mary Duke Biddle prof. music, 1978-87; chmn. bd. Triangle Music Theater Assocs. Composer: 1st Symphony, 1942, Hush'd Be the Camps Today, 1943, Second Symphony, 1947, Third Symphony, 1951, Fourth Symphony, 1958, Divertimento for Orchestra, 1961, Earth Shall Be Fair, 1960, He Who Gets Slapped (Pantaloon) (opera in 3 acts); opera in 4 acts The Crucible, 1962 (Pulitzer Prize in music); Hymn and Celebration (for orch.), 1962; for orch. Invocation and Toccata, 1963; opera in 2 acts The Lady From Colorado, 1964; Let the Word Go Forth, 1965; cantata Sweet Freedom's Song, 1965, Hymn To The Night, 1966; First String Quartet, 1966, Concerto for Piano and Orchestra, 1968; opera Claudia Legare, 1974; Fifth Symphony-Canticles for America, 1976, Sonic Structure (for orch.), 1980; opera Abelard and Heloise, 1981, Minutes Till Midnight, 1982, Dialogues for Violin, Cello and Orchestra, 1983, Concerto for Saxophone and Orchestra, 1984, Raleigh Divertimento for Wind Quintet, 1986, Festival Triptych, 1987, Sixth Symphony, 1988, First Symphonic Set for the New South, 1988, Fanfare, 1988, Second Symphonic Set, 1988, Appalachian Ditties and Dances, 1988, 5x5, 1989, Images of God, 1989, Ballet Music on The Scarlet Letter, 1990, Second Sonata for Violin and Piano, 1990, Bath County Rhapsody, 1991, Serenade for Mallarmé, 1991, one act opera Roman Fever, 1993. Bd. dirs. Martha Baird Rockefeller Fund for Music, 1971-82, Am. Symphony Orch. League, 1977-89, Nat. Inst. Music Theatre, 1977-85; mem. music com. Henry St. Settlement; bd. dirs. Durham Arts Coun. Served with AUS, 1942-46. Decorated Bronze Star; MacDowell Colony fellow, 1938; recipient Juilliard Pub. award, 1942, Fine Arts award State of N.C., 1975, Gold Baton award Am. Symphony Orch. League, 1991, Disting. Faculty Alumnus award U. N.C., 1992, A.I. DuPont award of Del. Symphony, 1995; Alice M. Ditson fellow Columbia U., 1944, Guggenheim fellow, 1950, 52, 66-67; Am. Acad. Arts and Letters grantee, 1946. Mem. Nat. Acad. Arts and Letters. Home: The Forest at Duke # 4029 2701 Pickett Rd Durham NC 27705-5654

WARD, ROBERT, property manager; b. 1926. BA, Colgate U., 1951. Exec. v.p. Arcade Bldg. Maintenance, Inc., 1971-92, pres., 1973-92; exec. v.p., pres. Northeast/Midwest Group Internat. Svcs. Sys., N.Y.C., 1992—. Office: Internat Svc Sys Inc 375 Hudson St New York NY 10014*

WARD, ROBERT ALLEN, textile company executive; b. Greensboro, N.C., Aug. 2, 1940; m. Margaret Cude; children: David, Robert Jr. BSBA, East Carolina U., 1962; cert. for postgrad. exec. program, U. N.C., 1976. CPA, N.C. Staff acct. A.M. Pullen & Co., Raleigh, N.C., 1962-65; acctg. mgr. Stedman Mfg. Co., Asheboro, N.C., 1965-67; v.p., treas. Universal Textured Yarns, Mebane, N.C., 1967-71; exec. v.p. fin. and adminstrn. Unifi Inc., Greensboro, 1971—, also bd. dirs. Mem. bd. visitors Elon (N.C.) Coll., 1987—; fellow bus. adv. coun. sch. bus. East Carolina U., Greenville, N.C.; mem. ecec. com. Pirate Club, bd. dirs. Named Disting. Alumni East Carolina U., 1988. Mem. AICPA, Fin. Execs. Inst. (pres. 1987-88), N.C. Assn. CPAs, Rotary (fellow). Office: Unifi Spun Yarns Inc 1921 Boone Trail Rd Sanford NC 27330

WARD, ROBERT ALLEN, JR., advertising executive; b. Summit, N.J., Sept. 25, 1937; s. Robert Allen and Edith Allen (Edith) Seiberling; m. Nancy Prescott, Oct. 3, 1964; children: Victoria, Jennifer, Robert. BA, Yale U., 1959. Account exec. U.S. Trust Co., N.Y.C., 1959-62; v.p., dir. Progressive Mktg. Svcs., N.Y.C., 1962-63, Coin Depot Corp., Elizabeth, N.J., 1963-68; pres. J.S. Riley Co., Wayne, N.J., 1964-70, C.G.W. Enterprises, Butler, N.J., 1970-78; v.p. R.L. Carelli, Glynn & Ward Advt. Co.; pres., dir. All Hours Answering Svc., Pompton Lakes, N.J., 1969-93; v.p., dir. N.J. Exchange, 1969-93, v.p. direct Anserve Inc., 1993—; pres., dir. B.E.K., Inc., real estate mgmt. co., Wayne, N.J., Litho Four Printers, 1970-88; dir. Devon Pubs., Butler, N.J., 1977-78. Pres., Kinnelon PTA, N.J., 1972-73; councilman Kinnelon Borough Coun., 1978-83; police commr., Kinnelon, 1978-83; mem. Kinnelon Drug Adv. Coun., 1978-83; vestry St. David Episc. Ch., Kinnelon, 1969-72, 78-87, 9-93, sr. warden, 1978-87; bd. dirs. Morris Area Coun. Girl Scouts U.S.A., 1977-80; dir. Inner City Ensemble, 1983-90, Willing Hands, 1989—; mem.

sports awards dinner com. North Jersey March of Dimes, 1986-90; chmn. Yale Alumni Schs. commn., 1984—. Served with USMC, 1959-60; served to capt. USAR, 1960-72. Mem. No. N.J. Advt. Club (bd. dirs. 1970-72), Commerce and Industry Assn. of N.J. (Penpac bd. dirs. 1982-90), Bank Mktg. Assn., Inner City Ensemble/N.J. Dance Troupe (bd. dirs. 1983-89). Republican. Clubs: Yale (trustee, v.p. 1981—, pres. 1993—, Montclair); Nippon (N.Y.C.); Smoke Rise (Kinnelon), Smoke Rise Paddle Tennis (pres. 1988—). Home: 393 Ski Trail Kinnelon NJ 07405 Office: CGW Enterprises 1250 State Route 23 Butler NJ 07405-2026

WARD, ROBERT CLEVELAND, research mathematician, science administrator; b. Sparta, Tenn., Dec. 7, 1944; s. James C. and Mary E. (Pharris) W.; m. C. Gayle Gillen, Sept. 3, 1965; children: Kimberly M. Ward Smith, Jonathan R. BS in Math., Tenn. Tech. U., 1966; MS in Math., Coll. of William and Mary, 1969; PhD in Applied Math., U. Va., 1974. Mathematician NASA Langley Rsch. Ctr., Hampton, Va., 1966-74; rschr. Oak Ridge (Tenn.) Nat. Lab., 1974-77, head math rsch. sect., 1977-82, head math. sci., 1982-90, dir. engring. physics and math., 1990—; prof., head computer sci. dept. U. Tenn., Knoxville, 1995—. Fellow AAAS; mem. IEEE Computer Soc., Soc. Indsl. and Applied Math. (various offices 1974—), Assn. for Computing Machinery, Sigma Xi. Achievements include devel., analysis and improvement numerical techniques in areas of numerical linear algebra and scientific computing. Office: Math Sci Oak Ridge Nat Lab P O Box X Bldg 6025 Oak Ridge TN 37831-6359*

WARD, ROBERT EDWARD, retired political science educator and university administrator; b. San Francisco, Jan. 29, 1916; s. Edward Butler and Claire Catherine (Unger) W.; m. Constance Regina Barnett, Oct. 31, 1942; children: Erica Anne, Katherine Elizabeth. B.A., Stanford U., 1936; M.A., U. Calif.-Berkeley, 1938, Ph.D., 1948. Instr. in polit. sci. U. Mich., 1948-50, asst. prof. polit. sci., 1950-54, assoc. prof., 1954-58, prof., 1958-73; prof. Stanford U., 1973-87, dir. Center for Research in Internat. Studies, 1973-87; cons. in field; advisor Center for Strategic and Internat. Studies, Washington, 1968-87. Author: Modern Political Systems: Asia, 1963, Political Modernization in Japan and Turkey, 1964. Mem. nat. council Nat. Endowment for Humanities, Washington, 1968-73; mem. Pres.'s Commn. on Fgn. Lang.-Internat. Studies, 1978-79; chmn. Japan-U.S. Friendship Commn., 1980-83; mem. Dept. Def. Univ. Forum, 1982-87. Served to lt. (j.g.) USN, 1942-45. Recipient Japan Found. award Tokyo, 1976; recipient Order of Sacred Treasure 2d class (Japan), 1983. Fellow Am. Acad. Arts and Scis.; mem. Am. Polit. Sci. Assn. (pres. 1972-73), Assn. Asian Studies (pres. 1972-73), Social Sci. Research Council (chmn. 1969-71), Am. Philos. Soc. Home: Box 8129 501 Portola Rd Portola Valley CA 94028

WARD, ROBERT JOSEPH, federal judge; b. N.Y.C., Jan. 31, 1926; s. Joseph G. and Honor V. (Hess) W.; m. Florence C. Maisel, Apr. 15, 1951 (dec. Mar. 1994); children: Laura Alice, Carolyn. S.B., Harvard, 1945, LL.B., 1949. Bar: N.Y. State bar 1949. Practiced in N.Y.C., 1949-51, 61-72; asst. atty. N.Y. County, 1951-55; asst. U.S. atty. So. Dist. N.Y., 1956-61; judge U.S. Dist. Ct. (so. dist.) N.Y., 1972—. Served with USNR, 1944-46. Mem. Am. N.Y. State bar assns., Assn. of the Bar of City of N.Y. Office: US Dist Ct US Courthouse Foley Sq New York NY 10007-1501

WARD, ROBERTSON, JR., architect; b. Boston, Sept. 7, 1922; s. Robertson and Sylvia (Whiting) W.; m. Sara Weeks, June 2, 1948 (div. 1953); 1 child, Robin Regina. A.B. cum laude, Harvard Coll., 1944, M.Arch., 1951. Mem. faculty dept. advanced bldg. research III. Inst. Tech., Chgo., 1951-52; research designer Arnold Rosner, Chgo., 1952; architect Skidmore, Owings & Merrill, Tokyo, 1953, Breuer, Nervi and Zehrfuss, UNESCO, Paris, 1953-54; head dept. design research Skidmore, Owings & Merrill, Chgo., 1954-60; pvt. practice architecture, bldg. systems, research Chgo., from 1960; rep., cons. UNESCO archtl. environ. info. system, 1976-79, U.S. Nat. Com./Coun. Internat. Bldg. Rsch., 1973-78; rep. from U.S. Econ. Commn. for Europe, 1972; mem. Chgo. Urban Renewal Rev. Commn., 1965; mem. tech. adv. bd. U.S. Dept. Commerce, 1967; dir. ARCC/NSF Office Environ. Rsch., 1984—, AIA/R.W. Johnson Found./Health Facilities Rsch. Program on Oper. Costs., 1992—, others. Archtl. works include Sci., Visual and Performing Arts Centers, Bennington Coll., Exptl. Theater, Vassar Coll., Sci. Center, Deerfield Acad. Served with USNR, 1944-46. Recipient Gov. of Calif.'s Design award, 1966; Graham Found. fellow, 1963, 75; NSF grantee 1984, 89. Fellow AIA, 1970; mem. Illuminating Engring. Soc., U.S. Inst. Theater Tech., Environ. Design Research Assn. Clubs: Harvard (N.Y.C.), Tavern. Home: 17 Brimmer St Boston MA 02108-1041 Office: MIT Architecture/Bldg Tech Group Rm 4-209 Cambridge MA 02139

WARD, RODMAN, JR., lawyer; b. Wilmington, Del., Apr. 3, 1934; s. Rodman and Dorcas (Andrews) W.; m. Susan Speakman Hill, Oct. 10, 1959; children: Margery Ward Garnett, Emily Ward Neilson, Rodman III, Jennifer Ward Oppenheimer. BA, Williams Coll., 1956; LLB, Harvard U., 1959. Bar: Del. 1959, D.C. 1959. Partner Prickett, Ward, Burt & Sanders, Wilmington, 1967-79, Skadden, Arps, Slate, Meagher & Flom, Wilmington, 1979—; bd. dirs. WMB Holdings, Inc. Author: (with Folk and Welch) Folk on the Delaware General Corporation Law, 1987; contbr. articles to profl. jours. Trustee, mem. fin. com. Med. Ctr. of Del. Served to capt. USAF, 1960-63. Fellow Am. Coll. Trial Lawyers; mem. ABA, Am. Law Inst., Del. State Bar Assn. (pres. 1989-90), D.C. Bar Assn., Assn. of Bar of City of N.Y., Am. Judicature Soc., Wilmington Club, Wilmington Country Club, Vicmead Hunt Club. Home: 52 Selborne Dr Wilmington DE 19807-1216 Office: PO Box 636 Wilmington DE 19899-0636

WARD, ROGER COURSEN, lawyer; b. Newark, June 19, 1922; s. Waldron Merry and Aline Toppin (Coursen) W.; m. Katharine More Stevens, Oct. 22, 1949; children: James Olney, Alexander More. Grad., Phillips Exeter Acad., 1940; A.B., Princeton U., 1943; LL.B., Columbia U., 1949. Bar: N.J. 1949. Law clk. to justice N.J. Supreme Ct., 1951; since practiced in Newark, Morristown, Montclair, N.J.; ptnr. Hardin, Kipp & Szuch, 1959-91, counsel, 1991-92; counsel Schwartz, Tobia & Stanziale, 1993—; bd. advisors Am. Inst. Law Tng. Within Office, Phila. 1986-88, Law Hiring and Tng. Report, Chgo., 1983-88. Bd. dirs. United Hosps. Newark, 1965-78, pres., 1973; trustee, v.p. Newark Mus. Assn., 1969-92; bd. dirs. Better Bus. Bur. Greater Newark, 1970-84; mem. Summit Zoning Bd. Adjustment, 1966-70; trustee Eye Inst. N.J., 1973, Pingry Sch., 1966-68, Summit YMCA, 1960-62, Newark Council Social Agys., 1956-60; vice chmn. Newark Mayor's Commn. on Youth, 1958-60. Served to lt. (j.g.) USNR, 1943-46, PTO, ETO. Harlan Fiske Stone scholar Columbia U., 1949. Mem. N.J. State Bar Assn., Essex County Bar Assn., Princeton Club N.Y., Short Hills (N.J.) Club, Phi Beta Kappa. Office: Schwartz Tobia & Stanziale 22 Crestmont Rd Montclair NJ 07042

WARD, ROSCOE FREDRICK, engineering educator; b. Boise, Idaho, Dec. 5, 1930; s. Roscoe C. W. and Alice E. (Ward) W.; m. Julia Duffy, June 8, 1963; children: Eric R., David C. Student, U. Oreg., 1949-50; B.A., Coll. of Idaho, 1953; postgrad., U. Wash., 1955-57; B.S., Oreg. State U., 1959; M.S., Wash. State U., 1961; Sc.D., Washington U., St. Louis, 1964. Registered profl. engr., Ohio. Asst. prof. civil engring. U. Mo., Columbia, 1963-65, Robert Coll., Istanbul, Turkey, 1965-67; assoc. prof. civil engring. Asian Inst. Tech., Bangkok, Thailand, 1967-68; assoc. prof. civil engring., assoc. dean Sch. Engring. U. Mass., Amherst, 1968-75; prof. Bogazici U., Istanbul, 1974-75; br. chief biomass energy Dept. Energy, Washington, 1975-79; interregional advisor UN/World Bank, N.Y.C., 1979-83; dean Sch. Applied Scis. Miami U., Oxford, Ohio, 1983-88; prof. paper sci. and engring. Sch. Applied Scis. Miami U., Oxford, 1983—; vis. scientist Csir, Republic of South Africa, 1990-91. Contbr. chpts. to books, articles to profl. jours. Fellow ASCE. Home: 4818 Bonham Rd Oxford OH 45056-1423 Office: Miami U Oxford OH 45056

WARD, SELA, actress; b. Meridian, Miss.; d. Granberry Holland and Annie Kate Ward. BA, U. Ala. Appearances include: (TV series) Emerald Point, N.A.S., 1983-84, Sisters, 1991— (Emmy award for Lead Actress in Drama Series 1994), (TV movies) Rainbow Drive, 1990, Double Jeopardy, 1993, (films) Nothing in Common, 1986, Hello Again, 1987, Rustler's Rhapsody, 1985, The Fugitive, 1993. Office: Somers Teitelbaum David 1925 Century Park E # 2320 Los Angeles CA 90067

WARD, SHARON POLK, nursing administrator; b. Huntsville, Ala., Sept. 20, 1957; d. Marvin Leroy and Ruth Carolyn (Hughes) Polk; m. Ernest Scott

Ward, Mar. 27, 1981; 1 child, Derrick Scott. BSN, U, Ala., Huntsville, 1979; postgrad., Nova U., 1991—. Nurse technician Humana Hosp., Huntsville, 1978-79, nurse exec. specialist, 1986-87; assoc. exec. DON. Humana Hosp., Muscle Shoals, Ala., 1987-88, Walton Beach, Fla., 1988-91; assoc. exec. DON. Humana Hosp.-Lucerne, Orlando, Fla., 1991—; staff nurse Hunstville Hosp., 1979-81; rehab. nurse dir. Ariz. Bridgeto Independent Living, Phoenix, 1981-83; DON Ariz. State U., Tempe, 1983-85; dir. patient svcs. Parkview Health Care Ctr., Huntsville, 1986; advisor Valencia Community Coll., Orlando, 1992; cons. in field. Mem. Fla. Orgn. for Nurse Execs. (mktg. com. 1991-92). Republican. Methodist. Home: 708 Beverly Dr Muscle Shoals AL 35661-1977 Office: Humana Hosp-Lucerne 818 Main Ln Orlando FL 32801-3727

WARD, SUE ELLEANORE FRYER, social worker, state agency administrator; b. Albuquerque, Oct. 28, 1935; d. E. Reeseman and Florence Ione (Pierce) F.; m. Archibald Floyd Ward, Nov. 3, 1959; children: Beth Ione, Lucille Elleanore. BA, Coll. William and Mary, 1957; MSW, U. Utah, 1961; postgrad., Am. U., Beirut, McGill U., Montreal, Can. Cert. social worker; diplomate in clin. social work Am. Bd. Examiners in Clin. Social Work. Social worker, clin. social worker State Hosp. South, Blackfoot, Idaho, 1959-61; social worker Children's Convalescent Hosp., Washington, 1961-62; caseworker Children's Home Soc. N.C., Greensboro, 1967-68; social worker Mental Health Study Ctr., NIMH, Adelphi, Md., 1968-70; therapist in pvt. practice Annapolis, Md., 1970-74, Clinton, Md., 1973-77; dir. Charles County Children's Aid Soc., La Plata, Md., 1977; project coord. Regional Direction Ctr. for Handicapped, Upper Marlboro, Md., 1980; dir. spl. projects Viacom Cablevision of Md., Rockville, 1981-82; dir. Prince George's County Dept. Aging, Hyattsville, Md., 1982-91, dir. dept. family svcs., 1991-95; dir. Md. Office on Aging, Balt., 1995—; mem. faculty and adv. bd. U. Md. Leisure and Aging, Therapeutic Recreation Mgmt. Sch., 1984-89; chmn. Elder Abuse and Neglect Project Oversight Com. Prince George's County; mem. Md. Gov.'s Task Force on Delivery Svcs. to Elderly, 1990. Contbr. articles to profl. jours. Mem., treas., chmn. bd. Hospice of Prince George's County, Md., 1983—; chmn. profl. adv. com. Prince George's Mental Health Assn., 1983-90; Dem. nominee from 4th Congl. dist., Md., 1978; bd. dirs. Md. Congress Parents and Tchrs., 1974-82; sec. Older Women's League, Prince George's County, 1988-90; pres. Women's Polit. Caucus, Prince George's County, 1986. Recipient Gladys Noon Spellman award for excellence in pub. svc., 1994; certs. for pub. svc. and awards. Mem. NASW, Acad. Cert. Social Workers, Nat. Assn. Area Agys. on Aging (bd. dirs., 2d v.p., pres. 1988-92), Md. Assn. Area Agys. on Aging (chmn. 1989-92). Avocations: reading, cooking, travel, multi-cultural activities. Home: 6109 Buckler Rd Clinton MD 20735-3417

WARD, SUSAN MARIE, cultural organization administrator; b. Detroit, Jan. 29, 1954; d. Richard Guerin and Helen Marie (Stone) W. BA in Art History, Wayne State U., 1983; MA in Decorative Arts, Parsons Sch. Design/Cooper-Hewitt Mus., 1985. Intern Met. Mus. Art, N.Y.C., 1985; asst. curator Biltmore Estate, Asheville, N.C., 1985-86, curator, 1987-92; exec. dir. Travellers Rest, Nashville, 1992-94; founder, dir. Heritage Comm., Brentwood, Tenn., 1994—; sec. Biltmore Village Hist. Mus., Asheville, 1989-91; adj. prof. O'More Coll. Design, Franklin, Tenn., 1995—. Author: The Gilded Age at Biltmore Estate, 1990. Vol. Big Bros. and Sisters, Asheville, 1988-92; com. mem. Bele Cher, Asheville, 1989; bd. dirs. Asheville Art Mus.; vol. cons. Jr. Achievement, 1994. Mem. Am. Assn. State and Local History (state membership chmn. 1989), N.C. Mus. Coun. (chmn. computers and museums com.), Southeast Museums Conf. (chmn. intern staff devel. com.), Asheville Mus. of Art (bd. dirs. 1991-92).

WARD, SYLVAN DONALD, music conductor, educator; b. Rock Springs, Wyo., July 7, 1909; s. Samuel and Hannah (Davis) W.; m. Beatrice Dorrell Stackhouse, June 27, 1936; children—Dorrell Deen (Mrs. Gordon H. Williams), Susan Diane (Mrs. William D. Johnston), Jill Dawn (Mrs. George L. Manderino), Jack Donald, Nancy Deborah (Mrs. Dennis P. Orgill). B.Mus., Chgo. Mus. Coll., 1931, M.Mus., 1932; M.S. in Edn Northwestern U., 1934, M.Edn., 1946; D.Mus. Edn., Chgo. Mus. Coll., 1954; student violin, John Brueggemann, Leon Sametini. Advt. mgr. Edn. Music mag., Chgo., 1931-36; asso. editor edn. Edn. Music mag., 1937-43; asst. gen. mgr. edn. Music Bur., 1936-37; tchr. instrumental, vocal music Farragut High Sch., Chgo., 1936-49; instr. music Chgo. Mus. Coll., 1946-51, Chgo. Tchrs. Coll., 1949-58, Wilson Jr. Coll., part-time 1951-63, Crane Jr. Coll., Loop Jr. Coll., 1965; vis. prof. U. Ill., summers 1959-61; prof. music Chgo. State U., 1958-77, chmn. dept., 1958-71; tchr. Vandercook Coll. Music, 1975-81. Dir., Chgo. Regional Mormon Choir, 1935-91, condr., mus. dir., Chgo. Bus. Men's Orch., 1963-68, 77-82, Chgo. Met. Symphony Orch., 1982-84, mem., Chgo. State Coll. String Quartet, 1952-77, stage orch., Chgo. Lyric Opera Co., 1960-69; author: Instrumental Director's Handbook, Methods for Viola, Cello and String Bass; contbr. articles to profl. jours. Bishop Ch. of Jesus Christ of Latter-day Saints, 1963-72; mem. high council Chgo. Heights Stake, 1973, music chmn., 1973-91. Served with USAAF, 1943-45. Mem. NEA (life), Music Educators Nat. Conf., Ill. Music Educators Assn. (life), Am. Fedn. Musicians (life), Am. String Tchrs. Assn. (pres. Ill. unit 1959-63, editor Scroll 1961-63), Phi Mu Alpha (life). Home: 6264 Brynwood Dr Rockford IL 61114-7802

WARD, THOMAS JEROME, lawyer; b. New Kensington, Pa., May 6, 1936; s. Richard Thomas and Renatha Ann (Hruscienski) W.; m. Lindley Ann Bennett, Aug. 20, 1960; children: Christine Lester, Janice Nolte, Thomas, James, Jeffrey, Matthew. BS, Duquesne U., 1958; JD, Villanova U., 1961. Tax atty. Westinghouse Electric Corp., Pitts., 1961-65; successively atty., sr. atty., asst. gen. atty. Rockwell Mfg. Co., Pitts., 1965-71, mgr. corp. devel., 1971-73; v.p., gen. counsel, sec. Disston Inc., Pitts., 1973-78; ptnr. Meyer, Darragh, Buckler, Bebenek & Eck, Pitts., 1978-84; v.p. fin. and law, gen. counsel, sec. Dravo Corp., Pitts., 1984-87, sr. v.p. fin. and adminstrn., 1987-88, exec. v.p., 1988-90; sr. atty. Buchanan Ingersoll. PC, Pitts.; dir. Buchanan Ingersoll (Europa), Frankfurt, Fed. Republic Germany, 1990-91; sr. v.p., asst. gen. counsel Federated Investors, Pitts., 1991—. Editor Villanova Law Rev., 1960-61. Bd. dirs., past pres. Cath. Charities of Pitts.; past bd. advisors Duquesne U. Sch. Bus. and Adminstrn., Pitts. Mem. ABA, Pa. Bar Assn., Allegheny County Bar Assn., Am. Soc. Corp. Secs., Century Club Disting. Alumni, Duquesne U. Democrat. Roman Catholic. Club: Duquesne. Office: Federated Investors Tower Pittsburgh PA 15222

WARD, THOMAS LEON, engineering educator; b. Norfolk, Va., May 12, 1930; s. Thomas Leon and Emma Anna (Meyer) W. B.S. in Physics, U. Tex., 1953; M.S. in Systems Engring., West Coast U., 1969; M.S. in Indsl. and Systems Engring., U. So. Calif., 1972, Ph.D. in Engring., 1975. Registered profl. engr., Ky., Calif. Engr. Glenn L. Martin Co., Balt., 1953-55, Convair, Edwards AFB, Calif., 1955-58; prin. engr. Rep. Aviation Corp., Edwards AFB, 1958-59; group engr. Giannini Controls Corp., Pasadena, Calif., 1959-62; chief engr. Parsons Electronics, Pasadena, 1962-63; engr. Delta Semicondrs., Inc., Newport Beach, Calif., 1963-64; sr. engr. Electro-Optical Systems, Pasadena, 1964-65, 67-68; group engr. Hycon Mfg. Co., Morovia, Calif., 1965-66; mem. engring. staff Truesdail Labs., Los Angeles, 1966-67, 70-76; engring. specialist Aerojet-Gen. Corp., Azusa, Calif., 1968-69; chief engr. Giannini-Voltex, Whittier, Calif., 1969-70; lectr. indsl. and systems engring. U. So. Calif., 1972-75, asst. prof., 1975-78; prof., chmn. indsl. and mfg. engring. Calif. State Poly. U., Pomona, 1978-80; mem. tech. staff Jet Propulsion Lab., Calif. Inst. Tech., 1980-81; prof., chmn. dept. indsl. engring. Speed Sci. Sch., U. Louisville, 1981-86, prof., 1986—; dir. Instn. for Fuzzy Systems and Intelligent Control. Sr. mem. Am. Inst. Indsl. Engrs., IEEE, Soc. Mfg. Engrs.; mem. AAAS, ASME, Sigma Xi, Alpha Pi Mu, Omega Rho., Tau Beta Pi. Democrat. Office: Speed Sci Sch Louisville KY 40292

WARD, WALLACE DIXON, medical educator; b. Pierre, S.D., June 30, 1924; s. Edmund Dixon and Thelma Marie (Hill) W.; m. Edith Marion Bystrom, Dec. 27,1949; children: Edith Marion IV, Laurie Elizabeth, Kathryn Christine, Holly Lydene. BS in Physics, S.D. Sch. Mines and Tech., 1944, DSc, 1971; PhD in Exptl. Psychology, Harvard U., 1953. Research engr. Baldwin Piano Co., Cin., 1953-54; research assoc. Cen. Inst. for Deaf, St. Louis, 1954-57; assoc. dir. research Noise Research Ctr., Am. Acad. Ophthalmology and Otolaryngology, Los Angeles, 1957-62; prof., depts. communication disorders, otolaryngology, pub. health and psychology U. Minn., Mpls., 1962—; mem. com. on hearing bioacoustics and biomechanics NRC, 1960-92, mem. exec. coun., 1970-75, chmn., 1971-73;

mem. communicative scis. study sect. div. rsch. grants NIH, 1969-73; sci. adviser Callier Hearing and Speech Ctr., Dallas, 1968-86; cons. U.S. Army, 1972-88, EPA Office Noise Abatement and Control, 1973; mem., co-chmn. Internat. Sci. Noise Teams, 1973—. Editor: Noise as a Public Health Hazard, 1969, Noise as a Public Health Problem, 1974, Noise and Hearing Conservation Manual, 1986; contbr. articles to tech. jours. Served with USNR, 1944-46. Recipient Research Career Devel. award NIH, 1962. Fellow Acoustical Soc. Am. (mem. exec. coun. 1978-81, pres. 1988), Am. Speech and Hearing Assn.; mem. AAAS, Am. Audiology Soc. (v.p 1973-75, pres. 1976), Internat. Soc. Audiology (governing bd., pres. 1978-80), Am. Otol. Soc., Am. Indsl. Hygiene Assn., Mensa, Triangle, Soc. for Music Perception and Cognition (v.p. 1992), Sigma Xi, Sigma Tau. Libertarian. Home: 1666 Coffman St Apt 315 Falcon Heights MN 55108 Office: U Minn Med Sch Dept Otolaryngology 2001 6th St SE Minneapolis MN 55455-3007

WARD, WILLIAM BINNINGTON, agricultural communicator; b. Idaho Falls, Ida., July 16, 1917; s. William A. and Daisy (Binnington) W.; m. Thora Bracken, Sept. 12, 1939; children—Ann Lyn, William Bracken, Cristen Lee, Alan Miller. B.S., Utah State Agrl. Coll., 1940; M.S., U. Wis., 1941. With editorial dept. Post Register (daily newspaper), Idaho Falls, 1935-36; asst. to extension editor Utah State Agrl. Coll., Logan, 1937-40; corr. A.P. and Rocky Mountain newspapers, 1938-40; asst. to extension editor, grad. instr. agrl. journalism U. Wis., 1940-41; information specialist dairy marketing, handling pub. relations on milk marketing agreements and orders U.S. Dept. Agr., 1941-42; chief information sect. Agrl. Marketing Adminstrn., then Food Distbn. Adminstrn., 1943-44; prof., head dept. communication arts, editor, chief of publs. N.Y. State Coll. Agr. Life Scis. and Human Ecology, Cornell U., Ithaca, N.Y., 1945-72; prof. N.Y. State Coll. Agr. Life Scis., Cornell U., 1973-88, prof. emeritus, 1988—; chmn. nat. adv. com. on information U.S. Dept. Agr., 1953-55; agr. com. adviser U. Philippines, 1956-57, 65; communcations adviser Argentine Govt., 1961-62; agr. communications cons. Ford Found., India, 1968-69, 70; communication adviser, chief of party U. Tenn./U.S. AID India Agrl. Programs, 1972; cons. ICRISAT, India, 1973, World Bank, Bangladesh, 1977, 78-89, 92—; cons. Boyce Thompson Inst. Plant Research, 1981-82; communications cons., Indonesia, 1978-81, 87, Internat. Center Argrl. Rsch. in Dry Areas, 1981-86; cons., mem. adv. bd. Acad. Ednl. Devel., 1985-88. Author: Agricultural News in the Daily Press, 1941, Reporting Agriculture, 2d edit, 1959, Science and Rice in Indonesia, 1985; contbr. articles to internat., nat., regional agrl. publs. Mem. Am. Assn. Agrl. Coll. Editors (pres.), Agrl. Communicators in Edn., Rotarian Club, Blue Key, Sigma Delta Chi. Home: 1825 Mooringline Dr Vero Beach FL 32963-2961

WARD, WILLIAM FRANCIS, JR., real estate investment banker; b. Everett, Mass., Aug. 23, 1928; s. William Francis and Helen (Schriber) W.; m. Elaine L. Wilson, June 11, 1950 (dec. Oct. 1993); children: Jeffrey W., Gary T., Michelle A., Gregory W., Suzanne M. B.S., U.S. Mil. Acad., 1950; M.B.A., Harvard U., 1956; LLB, La Salle U., 1966. Econ. analyst E.I. duPont de Nemours & Co., Inc., Wilmington, Del., 1956-58; sec. N.Y. State Bridge Authority, Poughkeepsie, 1958-60; div. controller, dir. marketing services GAF Corp., N.Y.C., 1960-63; asst. to pres. Grosset & Dunlap, Inc., 1963-65, v.p., 1965-67; controller Dun & Bradstreet, 1967-71, v.p., 1968-71; chmn. bd., pres. Dun-Donnelley Pub. Corp., 1971-77; v.p., treas. Gestam, Inc., 1981-83, pres., 1983-86; chief Army Res., 1986-91; chmn., pres. Realicam, 1985—; bd. dirs. Quotron Electronics, Inc., Empire Nat. Bank, Eastern Savs. Bank, Apple Bank for Savs., Greater N.Y. Bank for Savs.; trustee All-City Funds; faculty N.Y. U. Sch. Commerce, 1960-64. Pres. Ramapo Central Sch. Dist., 1966-72, 1982-87; mem. facilities and planning bd. Good Samaritan Hosp., 1980-85; County chmn. Citizen for Kennedy and Johnson, 1960; Dem. candidate for Ho. of Reps., 1962; chmn. Young Citizens for Johnson and Humphrey, 55 counties N.Y., 1964; exec. v.p. Am. Cancer Soc., 1976-81; bd. dirs. N.Y.C. div. Aerospace Edn. Found., U.S. Army War Coll. Found., West Point Fund, 1979, Franciscan Sisters of the Poor Found., 1980-92; trustee N.Y. Mil. Acad., 1982-86, 91—, Assn. Grads. U.S. Military Acad., 1993—; Hist. Soc. Rockland County, 1993—. Served to capt. AUS, 1950-54; maj. gen. U.S. Army Res. Decorated D.S.M. with 1 oak leaf cluster, Legion of Merit, Meritorious Service medal with oak leaf cluster, Air medal with 3 oak leaf clusters, Army Commendation medal with oak leaf cluster, Purple Heart. Mem. West Point Soc. (Washington chpt., Space Coast chpt., N.Y. chpt., pres. 1974-76), Antrim Players, Soc. Harvard Engrs. and Scientists, Fin. Execs. Inst., Newcomen Soc., Res. Officers Assn., Am. Friends of Viet Nam (nat. chmn.), VFW, Am. Legion, Disabled Am. Vets., Pilgrim Soc., Army and Navy Club, Squadron "A" Club, Univ. Club (N.Y.), Harvard Club (Washington), Nat. Press Club, KC. Roman Catholic. Home: Summit View Farm RJ17A PO Box 150 Goshen NY 10924 also: 1271 Continental Ave Melbourne FL 32940

WARD, WILLIAM REED, composer, educator; b. Norton, Kans., May 20, 1918; s. Joseph Aloysius and Maude (Jones) W.; m. Elizabeth Jane Adam, Aug. 8, 1943; children—Claudia Christine, Joseph Andrew, John David. Mus.B., Mus.Edn.B., U. Kans., 1941; Mus.M., Eastman Sch. Music, 1942, Ph.D., 1954; student, Charles S. Skilton, L.E. Anderson, Robert Palmer, Bernard Rogers, Howard Hanson. Instr. music Colo. State U., 1942-44; asst. prof. music, head composition and theory curriculum Lawrence U., 1944-47; faculty San Francisco State U., 1947—, head music dept., 1954-69, prof. music, 1959—; asso. dean San Francisco State U. (Sch. Creative Arts), 1977-80; Lectr. panelist music Idyllwild Inst. Arts; Lectr. panelist music Cal. Music Tchrs. Assn., Choral Condrs. Guild Calif., Am. Guild Organists, Music Educators Nat. Conf., Music Tchrs. Nat. Assn. Choir dir., First Christian Ch., Ft. Collins, Colo., 1942-44, Meml. Presbyn. Ch., Appleton, Wis., 1944-47, First Bapt. Ch., Burlingame, Calif., 1949-63, United Meth. Ch., 1967—; dir., Asian Arts Acad. and Music of Whole Earth Festival, San Francisco, 1978, World Arts Acad., San Francisco, 1979; compositions performed by Eastman-Rochester, Indpls., Oklahoma City, San Francisco symphony orchs., numerous others. Recipient Nat. Arrangers contest award 1947; composer: Lullaby for a Pinto Colt, 1941, A Vision of the World, 1955, Psalm 136, 1959, Fray Junipero Serra, The Great Walker; dramatic oratorio, 1960, Symphony 1, 1938, 2, 1947, 3, 1954, Variations on a Western Tune, 1948, Suite for Woodwind Quintet, 1954, A Psalm of Praise, 1964, The Crucufixion, 1971, Fun, Love, Joy, Trains, 1971, In Town Again, 1973, Arcs, 1973, O For A Thousand Tongues, 1973, They Shall Mount Up With Wings, 1980, Four Old American Songs of Merriment, 1994, others.; Author: Examples for the Study of Musical Style, rev. edit, 1970, American Bicentennial Song Book, 2 vols, 1975. Mem. City of Burlingame Beautification Commn., 1988—; mem. artistic adv. com. Music at Kohl Mansion, 1987—. Mem. Assn. Univ. Composers, ASCAP, Music Tchrs. Nat. Assn., Music Educators Nat. Conf., Choral Condrs. Guild, AAUP. Home: 120 Occidental Ave Burlingame CA 94010-5268

WARD, WILLIAM T., insurance company executive; b. 1939. BS, Drexel U., 1961. Mgr. Smith, Kline & French, Phila., 1963-67; v.p. Cambridge Computer Corp., Saddlebrook, N.J., 1968-71; sr. v.p. Health Application Systems, Inc., Burlingame, Calif., 1972-76; pres. Deltanet, Inc., San Francisco, Calif., 1977-80, Delta Dental Plan of Calif., San Francisco, 1980—. Office: Delta Dental Plan of Calif 100 1st St San Francisco CA 94105

WARD, YVETTE HENNIG, advertising executive; b. St. Paul, June 15, 1910; d. Leo J. and Adele (Hennig) Borer; m. Charles Saunders, Nov. 30, 1931 (div.); 1 child, Charlene; m. Charles Allen Ward, Feb. 29, 1940 (dec. May 1959); children—Allen, Vida, Herbert. Publisher Hudson (Wis.) Star-Observer, 1952-58; with Brown & Bigelow, 1942—, pres., 1959—. Profl. dancer, 1918-28, free-lance interior decorator, 25 yrs; Author: Russia Through Women's Eyes, 1956, Around the World in 32 Days, 1958. Chmn. fine arts and jewelry funding Compas 11, Phoenix.; Chmn. bd. Hudson Meml. Hosp.; bd. dirs. Heard Mus., Phoenix, Barrows Neurol. Inst., trustee; trustee Harrington Arthritis Research Ctr., St. Luke's Hosp., Phoenix Art Mus.; bd. dirs. Florence Crittenton Home.; bd. dirs. Western Arts. The Nat. Livestock show honors Yvette Ward as a Pioneer Stockman and mem. of the Ariz. Living-Stockman Hall of Fame, 1991. Mem. Phoenix Zoo Aux., Phoenix Symphony Aux., Costume Design Inst. Club: Phoenix Country. Office: Brown & Bigelow 106 E San Miguel Ave Phoenix AZ 85012-1339

WARDELL, JAY HOWARD, association executive; b. Greeley, Colo., May 8, 1943; W. Jerrold Jay and Anna Elizabeth (Harper) W.; m. Laura Susan

Nisiewicz, July 20, 1989; children: Jason Harper, Jared Roy. BS, Colo. State U., 1966. Industry rels. specialist Nat. Live Stock and Meat Bd., Chgo., 1969-70; promotion mgr. Beef Industry Coun. Beef Industry Coun. Nat. Live Stock and Mead Bd., Chgo., 1970-78; mgr. Nat. Life Stock and Meat Bd., Chgo., 1978-80, chief staff officer, 1980—, sr. v.p., 1986-88, exec. v.p., chief staff officer, 1988—. Mem. Westmont (Ill.) Planning Commn., 1977-79; chmn. adminstrv. coun. Granville Meth. Ch., Chgo., 1986—. 1st lt. U.S. Army, 1966-69, Vietnam. Mem. Am. Mgmt. Assn., Am. Soc. Assn. Execs., Nat. Agri-Mktg. Assn. Home: 5403 N Lakewood Ave Chicago IL 60640-1302 Office: Nat Live Stock and Meat Bd Beef Industry Coun 444 N Michigan Ave Chicago IL 60611-3903

WARDELL, JOE RUSSELL, JR., pharmacologist; b. Omaha, Nov. 11, 1929; s. Joe Russell and Marie Hamilton (Waugh) W.; m. Leta Harris, July 14, 1952 (div. Oct. 1981); children: Michael R., Susan E., John D.; m. Doris Erway, Aug. 27, 1983. BS in Pharmacy, Creighton U., 1951; MS in Pharmacology, U. Nebr., Omaha, 1959, PhD in Pharmacology, 1962. Lic. pharmacist Nebr. Pharmacist Osco Drug, Waterloo, Iowa, 1953-56; grad. asst. Coll. of Medicine U. Nebr., Omaha, 1956-62; sr. pharmacologist Smith Kline & French Labs., Phila., 1962-64, advanced to assoc. dir. biol. rsch., 1974-78; dir. R & D compound acquisitions R&D, 1978-86; pres. Wardell Assocs., Park City, Utah, 1986—. Author: more than 40 articles in profl. pubs.; inventor/co-inventor 4 patents respiratory and cardiovascular drugs. Asst. scoutmaster, Boy Scouts of Am., N.J., 1969-75. Recipient Merck Award Creighton U., 1951. Mem. Soc. of Parmacology & Experiemental Therapeutics, Am. Acad. of Pharmaceutical Scis., Am. Chem. Soc., Licensing Exec. Soc., Exptl. Aircraft Assn. Avocations: recreational flying, skiing, fly fishing. Home and Office: Wardell Assocs 55 Thaynes Canyon Dr Park City UT 84060

WARDELL, KEVIN STUART, hospital administrator; b. L.A., May 19, 1951; married. Bachelors degree, U. Calif., 1972, masters degree, 1975; masters degree, Duke U., 1976. Adminstrv. asst. Hoag Meml. Hosp. Presbyn., Newport Beach, Calif., 1974-75; asst. adminstr. Utah Valley Regional Med. Ctr., Provo, 1976-79; dir. shared svcs. Associated Hosp. System, Salt Lake City, 1979-80; asst. adminstr. McKay-Dee Hosp. Ctr., Ogden, Utah, 1980-82; sr. v.p., COO Miami Valley Hosp., Dayton, Ohio, 1983-88; exec. v.p., COO Luth. Gen. Hosp.-Lincoln Park, Park Ridge, Ill., 1988-89; pres. Luth. Gen. Hosp., Park Ridge, 1991-93; exec. v.p., COO Luth. Gen. Health System, Park Ridge, 1991-94; exec. v.p regional ops. south Advocate Health Care, Oak Brook, Ill., 1995—. Contbr. articles to profl. jours. Home: 965 North Ave Deerfield IL 60015 Office: Advocate Health Care 2025 Windsor Dr Oak Brook IL 60521

WARDELL, WILLIAM MICHAEL, drug development executive; b. New Zealand, Nov. 15, 1938; came to U.S., 1971; m. Dorothy Rile; children: Michael, Steven. MA in Physiology, U. Oxford, Eng., 1961, DPhil in Pharmacology, 1964, MD, 1967. Diplomate Am. Bd. Clin. Pharmacology. Faculty U. Otago (New Zealand) Med. Sch., 1967-71; also rsch. officer New Zealand Med. Rsch. Coun.; assoc. prof. pharmacology and medicine Med. Ctr., U. Rochester, N.Y., 1971-83; v.p. med. dir. Boehringer Ingelheim Pharms., Inc., Ridgefield, Conn., 1983-91; sr. v.p. drug devel., pharm. rsch. div. Parke-Davis Pharm., Ann Arbor, Mich., 1991-92; pres. Protein Engring. Corp., Cambridge, Mass., 1993—. Author: Regulation and Drug Development, 1975, Systems for Controlling Drug Utilization: An International Comparison, 1978. Mem. AMA (coun. sect. on clin. pharmacology and therapeutics), Pharm. Mfrs. Assn. (steering com. med. sect.), Am. Soc. for Clin. Pharmacology and Therapeutics (former chmn. govt. affairs com.), Conn. Acad. Scis. and Engring. Home: 1225 Fair Oaks Pky Ann Arbor MI 48104-3628 also: 49 Hill Rd # 21 Belmont MA 02178 Office: Protein Engring Corp 765 Concord Ave Cambridge MA 02138-1044

WARDEN, GAIL LEE, health care executive; b. Clarinda, Iowa, May 11, 1938; s. Lee Roy and Juanita (Haley) W.; m. Lois Jean Johnson, Oct. 9, 1965; children: Jay Christopher, Janna Lynn, Jena Marie. B.A., Dartmouth Coll., 1960; M.H.A., U. Mich., 1962. Adminstrv. asst. Blodgett Meml. Hosp., Grand Rapids, Mich., 1962; adj. Dewitt Hosp., Ft. Belvoir, Va., 1963-65; adminstrv. asst. Presbyn.-St. Luke's Hosp., Chgo., 1965-68, asst. to pres., 1968, v.p. adminstrn., 1968-69; exec. v.p. Rush-Presbyn.-St. Luke's Med. Center, Chgo., 1970-76, Am. Hosp. Assn., Chgo., 1976-81; pres., CEO Group Health Coop. Puget Sound, Seattle, 1981-88, Henry Ford Health System, Detroit, 1988—; chmn. Am. Hosp. Assn.; vice chmn. Hosp. Rsch. and Ednl. Trust; bd. dirs. Medicus Systems Corp., Evanston, Ill., Comerica Bank; bd. overseers Dartmouth Med. Schs.; vice chmn., bd. dirs. Matthew Thornton Health Plan; mem., governing coun. Inst. Medicine of NAS; mem. Pew Health Professions Commn. Contbr. articles to profl. jours. Served to capt. AUS, 1965. Named one of Ten Outstanding Young Men in Chgo., Jr. Assn. Commerce and Industry, 1968, Nat. Health Care award B'nai B'rith Internat., 1992, CEO award Am. Hosp. Assn.'s Soc. for Healthcare Planning and Mktg., 1993. Mem. NAS, Am. Coll. Hosp. Adminstrs. (named Young Adminstr. of Yr. 1972), Am. Pub. Health Assn., Am. Healthcare Systems, Alpha Chi Rho. Office: Henry Ford Health System 1 Ford Pl Detroit MI 48202-3450

WARDEN, GLENN DONALD, burn surgeon; b. Palo Alto, Calif., Jan. 25, 1943; s. John and Thelma Warden; m. Nori Katherine Bartschi, Mar. 30, 1971; children: Glenn David, Nori Lei, Emilie Nicole, Lianna Katherine. Student, U. Ariz., 1961-64; MD, U. Utah, 1968. Diplomate Am. Bd. Surgery; qualifications in surg. critical care; lic., Utah, Tex., Ohio. Intern in surgery dept. surgery U. Utah Med. Ctr., Salt Lake City, 1968-69, resident in gen. surgery dept. surgery, 1969-71, 74-76; fellow in renal transplantation - nephrology dept. medicine divsn. nephrology VA Hosp., Salt Lake City, 1970-71; dir. Intermountain Burn Ctr. U. Utah Sch. Medicine, Salt Lake City, 1977-85, dir. trauma divsn. dept. surgery, 1978-85, co-dir. surg. ICU, 1983-84, from instr. to asst. prof. to assoc. prof. dept. surgery, 1976-85, prof. dept. surgery, 1985; prof. dept. surgery, dir. divsn. burn surgery U. Cin. Med. Ctr., 1985—; chief of staff Shriners Burn Inst., Cin., 1985—; mem. exec. com. dept. surgery U. Cin. Med. Ctr., 1985, com. on reappointment, promotion and tenure, 1985—, chmn., 1991, dir. search com. oral surgery, 1991, adv. com. dept. phys. medicine & rehab., 1985-87, dir. search com., 1985-87, med. scis. scholars com., 1985-87, faculty forum exec. com., 1987-89, operating rm. subcom., 1985—, equipment control com., 1986—, trauma com., 1985—, spl. care units com., 1988—; critical care unit coms. emergency med. svcs. Salt Lake City Dept. Health, 1977-85, bd. dirs. emergency trng. coun., 1982-85, curriculum com., 1984-85; burn coms. Handicapped Children's Svcs., Utah State Dept. Health, 1981-85; mem. univ. senate U. Utah, 1984-85; chmn. I.V. subcom. U. Utah Med. Ctr., 1976-80, 82-85, oper. rm. exec. com., 1979-85, pharmacy and therapeutics com., 1979-85, infection ctrl. com., 1979-85, med. dir. disaster com., 1981-85, ambulatory svcs. com., 1982-85, emergency med. svcs. com., 1983-85, critical care com., 1985-85; contbr. (with others) various exhibits and posters ACS, U.S. Army Inst. Surg. Rsch., Brooke Army Med. Ctr., Am. Burn Assn.; lectures, presentations, symposiums ACS, Internat. Transplantation Soc., Am. Assn. Surgery of Trauma, Western Surg. Assn., Brooke Army Med. Ctr., Am. Burn Assn., Internat. Soc. for Burn Injuries, Assn. Acad. Surgery, Inst. Surg. Rsch., Intermountain Pediatric Soc., Nat. Inst. Gen. Med. Sci., Soc. Univ. Surgeons, Marion Labs., U. Cal., U. Texas S.W. Med. Ctr., Ky. Surg. Soc., Ohio Respiratory Care Soc., Ohio Burn Team Soc., Am. Soc. Parenteral and Enteral Nutrition, Grady Meml. Hosp., Atlanta, U. Iowa Hosps., Miami Valley Hosp., Christ Hosp., Cin., Internat. Soc. Surgery, Ohio State U., Fedn. Am. Socs. for Exptl. Biology, Am. Assn. Tissue Banks, U.S. Army Inst. Surg. Rsch., Am. Soc. Plastic & Reconstructive Surg. Nurses, others. Mem. editorial bd. Jour. Burn Care and Rehab., 1982—; contbr. numerous chpts. to books including Burns of the Upper Extremities, 1976, Surgery of the Ambulatory Patient, 1980, Management of the Burned Patient, 1987, Manual of Excision, 1988, Immune Consequences of Trauma, Shock and Sepsis, 1989, Total Parenteral Nutrition, 1991, The Critical Care of the Burned Patient, 1992, Host Defense Dysfunction in Trauma, Shock and Sepsis, 1993; contbr. numerous articles to profl. jours. Maj. U.S. Army, 1971-74. Named Internat. Hon. prof. surgery Third Mil. Med. Coll., People's Republic of China; Mel Ott scholar U. Ariz., 1962, Paul Spaulding scholar U. Ariz., 1963, Gen. Resident scholar U. Ariz., 1963, Martha Bamburger scholar U. Utah Sch. Medicine, 1965. Fellow ACS (Utah chpt. 1980, sec.-treas. 1984); mem. Internat. Soc. for Burn Injuries, Internat. Soc. of Surgery, Internat. Burn Found. of U.S. (bd. dirs. 1992), Pan-Pacific Surg. Assn., Pan-Am. Med. Assn., Am. Burn Assn. (com. on organ. and delivery of burn care 1976-80, com. edn. 1986, chmn. 1986-87, sec. 1987-90, 1st v.p.

1990-91, pres.-elect 1991-92, pres. 1992-93, bd. trustees 1993), Transplantation Soc., Soc. for Leukocyte Biology (formerly Reticuloendothelial ssn. for Acad. Surgery, Utah Med. Assn. (del. 1979-81), Am. Assn. Tissue Banks (inter-regional exch. com. 1977-79, skin coun. 1989-91), Western Transplant Assns., Am. Soc. Transplant Surgeons, Am. Soc. Parenteral and Enteral Nutrition (edn. com. 1981—), Southwestern Surg. Congress, Salt Lake Surg. Soc., Utah Soc. Certified Surgeons (treas. 1981, pres. 1982), Am. Assn. Surgery of Trauma, Univ. Surg. Soc., Surg. Infection Soc. (chmn. fellowship com. 1986-88), Soc. Univ. Surgeons, Western Surg. Assn., Soc. Critical Care Medicine, Acad. Medicine Cin., Ohio State Med. Assn., Cin. Surg. Soc., Surg. Biology Club III, Ohio Burn Team Soc., U. Cin. Grad. Surg. Soc., Eastern Great Lakes Burn Study Group, Am. Surg. Assn., Ctrl. Surg. Assn., Wound Healing Soc., Am. Trauma Soc. (liaison bd. 1990-91). Office: Shriners Burn Inst 3229 Burnet Ave Cincinnati OH 45229-3095•

WARDEN, HERBERT EDGAR, surgeon, educator; b. Cleve., Aug. 30, 1920; s. Fred Edgar and Eva Alethea (Powers) W.; m. Audrey Eleanor Flaten, June 14, 1958; children: Karen Eleanor, Bradford Edgar, Douglas Edward, Suzanne Elise. BS, Washington and Jefferson Coll., 1942; MD, U. Chgo., 1946. Diplomate Am. Bd. Surgery, Am. Bd. Thoracic Surgery. Intern U. Chgo. Clinics, 1946-47; med. officer U.S. Naval Hosp., Mare Island, Calif., 1947-49; surgeon USAF Hosp., Travis AFB, Calif., 1949-50; asst. resident in surgery U. Minn., Mpls., 1951-56, rsch. asst. cardio vascular surgery, 1953-56, chief resident, 1956-57, instr., 1957-60; assoc. prof. surgery W.Va. U., Morgantown, 1960-62, head cardiovascular surgery, 1960-82, prof., 1962—, vice chmn. dept. surgery, 1968-76; cons. Louis A. Johnson VA Hosp., Clarksburg, W.Va., 1962—; bd. dirs. W.Va. U. Med. Corp., Morgantown, 1987—; physician football team W.Va. U., bd. dirs. First Nat. Bank, Morgantown. Contbr. articles to profl. jours. Trustee Drummond Chapel, Morgantown, 1974-78, Washington and Jefferson Coll., Washington, Pa., 1974—; bd. dirs. Am. Heart Assn., 1968-73. Lt. M.C., USNR, 1947-49. Recipient Albert Lasker award Am. Pub. Health Assn., 1955, Disting. Svc. awards W.Va. Heart Assn., 1973, W.Va. U., 1976; named Disting. Alumnus Washington and Jefferson Coll., 1968; named to Shaker Hgt. Hall of Fame, 1992. Fellow ACS (gov. 1988—), Am. Coll. Cardiology (gov. 1982-85), Southeastern Surg. Congress; mem. AMA (Hektoen Gold medal 1957), Am. Surg. Assn., Am. Assn. Thoracic Surgery, Soc. Univ. Surgeons, Soc. Thoracic Sugeons (founder, chair program com. 1983-84, Chamberlin award 1985), So. Thoracic Surg. Assn., Halsted Soc., Lillehei Surg. Soc. (pres. 1988), Alpha Kappa Alpha, Alpha Omega Alpha, Sigma Xi. Republican. Methodist. Avocations: golfing, fishing, gardening, reading. Home: 616 Schubert Pl Morgantown WV 26505-2330 Office: Health Scis Ctr N W Va U Morgantown WV 26505

WARDEN, JACK, actor; b. Newark, Sept. 18, 1920; s. Jack Warden and Laura M. (Costello) Lebzelter; m. W. Dupree, 1958; 1 son, Christopher. Student, pub. schs., Newark; acting classes, N.Y.C. Appeared in repertory Margo Jones Theatre, Dallas, 1947-51; appeared in numerous dramatic TV shows including Playhouse 90, Kraft Television Theater, Goodyear Television Playhouse; Broadway play The Man in The Glass Booth, 1969; motion pictures include From Here to Eternity, 1953, Donovan's Reef, 1962, Shampoo, 1975, Heaven Can Wait, 1978, The Great Muppet Caper, 1981, Carbon Copy, So Fine, 1981, The Verdict, 1982, September, 1987, The Presidio, 1988, Everybody Wins, 1990, Problem Child, 1990, Problem Child 2, 1991, Passed Away, 1992, Night and the City, 1992, Toys, 1992, Guilty as Sin, 1993, Beyond Innocence, 1993, Bullets Over Broadway, 1994, While You Were Sleeping, 1995; appeared in TV series Mr. Peepers, 1952-55, Norby, 1955, The Asphalt Jungle, 1961, The Wackiest Ship in the Army, 1965-66, N.Y.P.D., 1967-69, Jigsaw John, 1976, The Bad News Bears, 1979-80, Crazy Like a Fox, 1984-86, TV motion picture A Memory of Two Mondays, Nat. Ednl. TV, Topper, 1979, Bad News Bears; (recipient Obie award 1963, Emmy award 1972). Served with USN, 1938-41, U.S. Maritime Service, 1941-42, USA Army, 1942-46, ETO. Mem. Screen Actors Guild, AFTRA, Actors Equity. Democrat. Office: care Agy for Performing Arts 888 7th Ave New York NY 10106-0001•

WARDEN, JOHN L., lawyer; b. Evansville, Ind., Sept. 22, 1941; s. Walter Wilson and Juanita (Veatch) W.; m. Phillis Ann Rodgers, Oct. 27, 1960; children: Anne W. Clark, John L. W Carson. AB, Harvard U., 1962; LLB, U. Va., 1965. Bar: N.Y. 1966, U.S. C. Appeals (2d cir.) 1966, U.S. Dist. Ct. (so. and ea. dists.) N.Y. 1967, U.S. Ct. Appeals (10th cir.) 1971, U.S. Supreme Ct. 1972, U.S. Ct. Appeals (D.C. cir.) 1980. Assoc. Sullivan & Cromwell, N.Y.C., 1965-73, ptnr., 1973—. Trustee U.Va. Law Sch. Found.; Am. Ballet Theatre; dir. Lower Manhattan Cultural Coun. Fellow Am. Coll. Trial Lawyers; mem. ABA, Am. Law Inst., N.Y. State Bar Assn., Assn. of Bar of City of N.Y., N.Y. County Lawyers Assn., Knickerbocker Club, Down Town Assn. Club, Bedford Golf and Tennis Club, Lyford Cay Club. Republican. Episcopalian. Editor-in-chief Va. Law Review, 1964-65. Office: Sullivan & Cromwell 125 Broad St New York NY 10004

WARDEN, RICHARD DANA, government labor union official; b. Great Falls, Mont., Dec. 10, 1931; s. Robert Dickinson and Helen (Leach) W.; m. Barbara Freeman; children: Denise, Michael, Joseph, Jerome. B.A., Mont. State U., 1957, M.A., 1958. Reporter, then state editor Gt. Falls (Mont.) Tribune, 1959-61; legis. asst. to U.S. Senator Lee Metcalf of Mont., 1962-63; adminstrv. asst. to U.S. Congressman James G. O'Hara of Mich., 1963-67; dep. dir. Office Civil Rights, HEW, 1967-68; legis. rep. AFL-CIO, 1969-70; dir. Washington Research Project Action Council, 1970-72; legis. rep. UAW, 1972-75, legis. dir., 1975-77, 79-91, 1991; asst. sec. legis. HEW, 1977-79. Served with USN, 1951-54. Congressional fellow, 1961-62; recipient Pub. Affairs Reporting award Am. Polit. Sci. Assn., 1960. Home: 4700 Connecticut Ave NW Apt 50 Washington DC 20008-5629

WARDER, RICHARD CURREY, JR., mechanical aerospace engineering educator; b. Nitro, W.Va., Sept. 30, 1936; s. Richard Currey and Edith Irene (Moser) W.; m. Carolyn Strickler, Mar. 7, 1964 (div. Dec. 1978); children: Jennifer, Jeffrey W.; m. Marjorie Dianne Forney, Jan. 10, 1981. B.S., S.D. Sch. Mines, 1958; M.S., Northwestern U., 1959, Ph.D., 1963. Registered profl. engr., Mo., Tenn. Asst. prof. Northwestern U., Evanston, Ill., 1963-65; mgr. energy processes research Litton Industries, Beverly Hills, Calif., 1965-68; assoc. prof. mech. and aerospace engring. U. Mo., Columbia, 1968-72, prof., 1972—; James C. Dowell prof., 1989-94, chmn. mech. aerospace engring., 1988-94; dean Herff Coll. of Engring. U. Memphis, Tenn., 1994—; program mgr., head resources sect. NSF, Washington, 1974-76; cons. to industry U.S. govt. Bd. dirs. Columbia Montessori Soc., 1971-73; bd. dirs. Columbia Soccer Club, 1976-80, pres., 1978-80; referee Maj. Indoor Soccer League, 1979-83. Fellow AIAA (assoc.); mem. AAAS, Am. Phys. Soc., ASME, Am. Soc. Engring. Edn., Am. Assn. for Aerosol Research, Am. Soc. Heating, Refrigerating and Air Conditioning Engrs. Methodist.

WARDLAW, FRANK PATTERSON, foreign service officer; b. Columbia, S.C., Apr. 16, 1944; s. Frank Harper and Jane Wallace (Williamson) W.; m. Eva Janebo, Aug. 26, 1978. BA, U. Tex., 1968. Consul gen. U.S. Consulate, Shanghai, Republic of China, 1989-92, Frankfurt, Germany, 1993-; diplomat-in-residence U. Tex., Austin, 1992-93. With U.S. Army, 1968-70, Vietnam. Office: US Consulate Gen PSC 115 APO AE 09213 AE 09213

WARD-PRESSON, KATHRYN M., health facility administrator; b. St. Petersburg, Fla., Dec. 4, 1951; d. Eugene R. Ward, Sr. and Sarah Marie Dillon; m. David Michael Presson, Oct. 29, 1988. BSN summa cum laude, Barry Coll., 1973; MSN, U. Ala., 1978. CCRN. Staff, charge nurse USN Nat. Naval Med. Ctr., Bethesda, Md.; ambulatory care coord. VA Med. Ctr., Houston; head nurse, SICU Meth. Hosp., Houston mgr. OR nurses and PACU nurses; asst. administr. Southside Cmty. Hosp./Bay Area Med. Ctr., Corpus Christi, Tex., 1992-94; v.p. patient svcs. Faucett Meml. Hosp., Punta Gorda, Fla., 1994—; Mem. audit and care plan coms., Nat. Naval Med. Ctr., 1973-77, various profl. coms. including several at VA Med. Ctr., Houston and Meth. Hosp., Houston, others; adj. faculty appt. UTHSC; presenter workshops in field. Contbr. articles to profl. jours. Mem. Am. Coll. Health Care Execs. (nominee), Lambda Sigma, Delta Epsilon Sigma, Sigma Theta Tau. Office: Fawcett Meml Hosp Mail Sta D394 Port Charlotte FL 33952

WARDROPPER, BRUCE WEAR, language educator; b. Edinburgh, Scotland, Feb. 2, 1919; came to U.S., 1945; s. Joseph Blair and Edna (Bruce) W.; m. Joyce Vaz, Dec. 15, 1942 (dec. Mar. 1959); 1 son, Ian Bruce;

---

m. Nancy Hélène Palmer, July 19, 1960. Student, King Edward's Sch., Birmingham, Eng., 1932-36; B.A., U. Cambridge, 1939, M.A., 1942; Ph.D., U. Pa., 1949. Head modern lang. dept. Wolmer's Sch., Kingston, Jamaica, 1940-45; instr. U. Pa., 1945-49; asst. prof. Johns Hopkins U., 1949-53, asso. prof., 1953-55, chmn. dept. Romance langs., 1954-55, prof. Spanish, 1959-62; William H. Wannamaker prof. Romance langs. Duke U., 1962-89, William H. Wannamaker prof. Romance studies emeritus, 1989—; prof. Spanish, Ohio State U., 1955-59; vis. Andrew Mellon prof. Romance langs. U. Pitts., 1965; vis. prof. U. N.C., 1967-68; cons. bd. overseers U. Louisville, 1976-78; NEH Fellowships in Residence Program, 1977-78; seminar dir. NEHSummer Seminars for Coll. Tchrs., 1975, 76, 81; mem. ednl. adv. bd. John Simon Guggenheim Meml. Found., 1978-82. Author: Introducción al teatro religioso, 1953, Historia de la poesía lírica a lo divino, 1958, Critical Essays on the Theatre of Calderón, 1965, Poesía elegíaca española, 1967, Teatro español del Siglo de Oro, 1970, Spanish Poetry of the Golden Age, 1971; co-author: Teoría de la comedia: La comedia española del Siglo de Oro, 1978; mem. editorial bd., PMLA (MLA), 1962-69, 73-75; assoc. editor: Purdue U. Monographs in Romance Langs., 1978-90; editor, translator: (Calderon) El Magico Prodigioso, 1982; editor Historia y Crítica de la Literatura Española, vol. 3: Barroco, 1983. Guggenheim fellow, 1952, 59; Recipient award Am. Philos. Soc., 1957, award Am. Council Learned Socs., 1959, fellow, 1969. Mem. MLA (editorial bd. PMLA 1973-75), Internat. Assn. Hispanists (exec. com. 1971-77), Renaissance Soc. Am., South Atlantic MLA, Acad. Lit. Studies (membership com. 1973-78), Assn. Hispanists Gt. Britain and Ireland, Modern Humanities Research Assn. (Am. com. 1976-80), Cervantes Soc. Am. (v.p 1980-83, pres. 1983-85, Am. com. 1976-90). Home: 3443 Rugby Rd Hope Valley Durham NC 27707

WARDROPPER, IAN BRUCE, museum curator, educator; b. Balt., May 11, 1951; s. Bruce Wear and Joyce (Vaz) W.; stepmother: Nancy Hélène (Palmer) W.; m. Laurel Ellen Bradley, May 22, 1982; 1 child, Chloe Bradley. BA, Brown U., 1973; MA, NYU, 1976, PhD, 1985. Asst. curator European sculpture Art Inst. Chgo., 1982-85, assoc. curator European decorative arts and sculpture, 1985-89, Eloise W. Martin curator European decorative arts and sculpture, and classical art, 1989—; adj. instr. Drew U., N.J., 1982; vis. asst. prof. Northwestern U., Evanston, Ill., 1986, Sch. of Art Inst: Chgo., 1988; guest scholar J. Paul Getty Mus., Malibu, Calif., 1995. Co-author: European Decorative Arts in the Art Institute of Chicago, 1991, Austrian Architecture and Design beyond Tradition in the 1990s, 1991, News from a Radiant Future: Soviet Porcelain from the Collection of Craig H. and Kay A. Tuber, 1992, Chiseled with a Brush: Italian Sculpture, 1860-1925, from The Gilgore Collections, 1994; contbr. articles to profl. jours. Mem. sculpture and garden ornament com. Chgo. Bot. Garden, Glencoe, Ill., 1988—. NEA fellow, 1976-77, Chester Dale fellow Met. Mus. Art, 1978-79; Kress Found. rsch. grantee, Paris, 1979-81, Am. Philos. Soc. grantee, 1991. Mem. Phi Beta Kappa. Office: The Art Inst Chgo 111 S Michigan Ave Chicago IL 60603-6110

WARDRUP, LEO C., JR., state legislator; married; 3 children. AB in English, U. N.C., 1958; MBA in Fin., George Wash. U., 1972; disting. grad., U.S. Naval War Coll., 1976. Capt. USN, ret., 1986, mil. asst. to sec. defense, 1968-70, comptroller Air Sta. Oceana, 1972-74, comptroller air forces Atlantic Fleet, 1976-78, comptroller Norfolk Naval Shipyard, 1979-83, commdg. officer Atlantic Fleet acctg. and disbursing ctr., 1983-86; dir. fin. and devel. Tidewater Consultants, Inc., 1986-90; cost and fin. analyst Virginia Beach, 1990—; rep. Commonwealth of Va. Ho. of Dels., Virginia Beach, 1991—; asst. prof. English and Lit., U.S. Naval Acad., 1960-63; sr. adj. prof. in econs. and fin. Golden Gate U., 1973-90; mem. econs. faculty Tidewater C.C. and St. Leo's, 1975-86; adj. prof. econs. Old Dominion U., 1992. Bd. dirs. Samaritan House; Heart Found., Prevention of Child Abuse; commr. econ. devel., Va. Beach, 1990-91; vice-chmn. Econ. Devel. Authority, Va. Beach, 1991. Mem. Disabled Am. Vets., Am. Legion, Fleet Res. Assn., Ret. Officers Assn., Phi Beta Kappa. Home: 2208 Sunvista Dr Virginia Beach VA 23455 Office: PO Box 5266 Virginia Beach VA 23455

WARD-STEINMAN, DAVID, composer, music educator; b. Alexandria, La., Nov. 6, 1936; s. Irving Steinman and Daisy Leila (Ward) W.-S.; m. Susan Diana Lucas, Dec. 28, 1956; children: Jenna, Matthew. MusB cum laude, Fla. State U., 1957; MusM, U. Ill., 1958, DMA, 1961; studies with Nadia Boulanger, Paris, 1958-59; postdoctoral vis. fellow, Princeton U., 1970. Grad. instr. U. Ill., 1957-58; mem. faculty San Diego State U., 1961—; prof. music, 1968—; dir. comprehensive musicianship program, 1972—; composer in residence, 1961—, univ. research lectr., 1986-87; mem. summer faculty Eastman Sch. Music Workshop, 1969; Ford Found. composer in residence Tampa Bay (Fla.) Area, 1970-72; acad. cons. U. North Sumatra (Indonesia), 1982; concert and lecture tour U.S. Info. Agy., Indonesia, 1982; mem. faculty Coll. Music Soc. Nat. Inst. for Music in Gen. Studies, U. Colo., 1983, 84, Calif. State Summer Sch. for the Arts, Loyola Marymount U., 1988; composer-in-residence Brevard Music Ctr., N.C., summer 1986. Composer: Symphony, 1959, Prelude & Toccata for orch., 1962, Concerto No. 2 for chamber orch., 1962, ballet Western Orpheus, 1964, Cello Concerto, 1966, These Three ballet, 1966, The Tale of Issoumbochi chamber opera, 1968, Rituals for Dancers and Musicians, 1971, Antares, 1971, Arcturus, 1972, The Tracker, 1976, Brancusi's Brass Beds, 1977; oratorio Song of Moses, 1964; Jazz Tangents, 1967, Childs Play, 1968; 3-act opera Tamar, 1977; Golden Apples, 1981; choral suite Of Wind and Water, 1982; Christmas cantata And In These Times, 1982; Moiré for piano and chamber ensemble, 1983, And Waken Green, song cycle on poems by Douglas Worth, 1983, Olympics Overture for orchestra, 1984, Children's Corner Revisited, song cycle, 1984, Summer Suite for oboe and piano, 1984, Quintessence for double quintet and percussion, 1985, Chroma concerto for multiple keyboards, percussion and chamber orch., 1985, Winging It for chamber orchestra, 1986, Elegy for Astronauts, for orchestra, 1986, What's Left for piano, 1987, Gemini for 2 guitars, 1988, Intersections II Borobudur, Under Capricorn, 1989, 1989 Voices from the Gallery, 1990, Cinnabar for viola and piano, 1991, Seasons Fantastic for chorus and harp, 1992, Cinnabar Concerto for Viola and Chamber Orchestra, 1993, Night Winds Quintet # 2 for woodwinds, 1993, Double Concerto for Two Violins and Orchestra, 1995; recs. include Fragments from Sappho, 1969; Duo for cello and piano, 1974, Childs Play for bassoon and piano, 1974, The Tracker, 1989, Brancusi's Brass Beds, 1984, concert suite from Western Orpheus, 1987, Sonata for Piano Fortified, 1987, Moiré, 1987, 3 Songs for Clarinet and Piano, 1987, Concerto #2 for Chamber Orchestra, 1990; commd. by Chgo. Symphony, Joffrey Ballet, numerous others; author: (with Susan L. Ward-Steinman) Comparative Anthology of Musical Forms, 2 vols, 1976, Toward a Comparative Structural Theory of the Arts, 1989. Recipient Joseph H. Bearns prize in Music Columbia U., 1961, SAI Am. Music award, 1962, Dohnanyi award Fla. State U., 1965, ann. BMI awards, 1970—; Broadcast Music prize, 1954, 55, 60, 61; named Outstanding Prof., Calif. State Univs. and Colls., 1968, Outstanding Alumnus of Yr., Fla. State U., 1976; Fulbright sr. scholar La Trobe U. and Victorian Coll. Arts, Victorian Arts Ctr., Melbourne, Australia, 1989-90. Mem. Coll. Music Soc. (nat. bd. for composition 1991-93), BMI, SCI, NACUSA. Presbyterian. Club: Golden State Flying. Office: San Diego State U Dept Music San Diego CA 92182

WARD-STEINMAN, IRVING, lawyer; b. N.Y.C., Mar. 26, 1905; s. Avram Mosha ben Yahuda and Michilena (Ihjmanovich) Labe; m. Daisy Ward-Steinman (dec. Nov. 1986); children: David, Judy Karst. DD, Coll. Divinitatas Metaphysica, 1925; B Oriental Lit., Oriental Inst., 1926; cert., Vanderbilt U. Sch. Religion, 1928, 30; AB, La. Coll., 1930; AM, La. State U., 1931; PhD, Meml. Christian Coll. and Sem., 1970, Baptist Christian U., 1975; ThD, Baptist Christian U., 1975; D of Worldly Wisdom (hon.), Loyola U., Boswell, Que. Inst. Culture. Sole practice La. Contbr. over 1000 articles on lit. to profl. jours. Chmn. Indigent Defender Bd., 9th Jud. Dist., Rapides Parish, La.; dir. Civil Def. Rapides Parish and Alexandria; lay pastor Polk Meml. Episcopal Ch., Leesville, La.; pres., bd. chmn. Cen. La Japan Soc. Inc.; pres., bd. chmn. Confederate States of Am., Inc.; instr. adult Bible class St. James Episcopal Ch., Alexandria. Col. USACL, 1936. Mem. ABA, La. Bar Assn., Alexandria Bar Assn., Moose (life). Avocations: art, lecturing. Office: 11309-th St Alexandria LA 71301

WARDWELL, ALLEN, art historian; b. N.Y.C., Jan. 18, 1935; s. Edward Rogers and Lelia (Morgan) W.; m. Sarah Williams Tilghman, June 29, 1957; children: William Thomas, Lelia Morgan, Alexander Tilghman. Grad. Groton Sch., 1953; BA, Yale, 1957; MA, NYU, 1960. Asst. curator primitive art dept. Art Inst. Chgo. 1960-62, curator, 1962-73, acting curator decorative arts dept., 1963-70, asst. dir. mus. svcs., 1969-72; dir. Gallery Asia

---

Soc., N.Y.C., 1974-84, Isamu Noguchi Garden Mus., 1985-90; sr. cons. on tribal art Christie's, N.Y.C., 1992—; vis. prof. art history Princeton (N.J.) U., 1994-95. Trustee Yale Art Gallery; adv. coun. U. Notre Dame Art Gallery, 1970-84; mem. mus. panel Indo-U.S. Subcommn. Edn. and Culture, 1975-84; mem. vis. com. Asian Art Met. Mus. Art, 1977—. Mem. Coll. Art Assn., Am. Mus. Assn. Office: 88 Central Park W New York NY 10023-5209

WARE, BRENDAN JOHN, electrical engineer, electric utility company executive; b. Dublin, Ireland, Aug. 27, 1932; came to U.S., 1959, naturalized, 1967; s. Michael and Rose Anna (Ryan) W.; m. Jane Mills Orth, Oct. 7, 1961; children—Michael, Henry, Frieda. B.E. with honors, Nat. U. Ireland, Dublin, 1954; M.E.E., Newark Coll. Engring., 1967. Various engring. positions Am. Elec. Power Service Corp., N.Y.C., 1960-76; mgr. elec. research and tech. svcs. Am. Elec. Power Service Corp., Columbus, Ohio, 1976—. Contbr. articles to profl. jours. Fellow IEEE; mem. Conf. Internat. de Grand Reseau. Roman Catholic. Home: 2478 Bryden Rd Columbus OH 43209-2132 Office: Am Elec Power Service Corp 1 Riverside Plz Columbus OH 43215-2355

WARE, CARL, bottling company executive; b. Newnan, Ga., Sept. 30, 1943; s. U.B. and Lois (Wimberly) W.; m. Mary Clark, Jan. 1 1966; 1 son, Timothy Alexander. B.A., Clark Coll., 1965; M.P.A., U. Pitts., 1968; postgrad., Carnegie Mellon U., 1965-66. Dir. Atlanta Housing Authority, 1970-73; pres. city council City of Atlanta, 1974-79; v.p The Coca-Cola Co., Atlanta, 1974-86, sr. v.p., 1986—; dir. Ga. Power Co. Mem. adv. council U.S. Civil Rights Commn., 1983; bd. dirs. Nat. Council Black Agencies, 1983—, United Way of Met. Atlanta, 1983—; trustee Clark Coll. Mem. Gammon Theol. Sem. (trustee), Ga. State U. Found. (trustee), Sigma Pi Phi. Democrat. Methodist. Office: The Coca-Cola Co PO Box 1734 Atlanta GA 30301-1734

WARE, D. CLIFTON, singer, educator; b. Newton, Miss., Mar. 15, 1937; s. Durward Clifton and Emma Edna (Blount) W.; m. Elizabeth Jean Oldham, June 20, 1958; children: Jon Clifton, David Michael, Stephen Alan. B.A., Millsaps Coll., 1959; MusM, U. So. Miss., 1962; MusD, Northwestern U., 1970. Voice instr. U. So. Miss., Hattiesburg, Miss., 1964-69; coord. voice instrn., chmn. Roy A. Schuessler Vocal Arts Ctr. U. Minn., Mpls., 1970—; clinician, cons., adjudicator. Author: (book, song collection and video) Voice Adventures, 1988, (text, song collection, audio cassette) Adventures in Singing, 1995; made recs. St. Nicolas, 1977, Paul Bunyan, 1988; tenor soloist opera, oratorio, recitals. Mem. Nat. Assn. Tchrs. Singing (pres. Minn. chpt. 1972-73, 81-82), Nat. Opera Assn. (pres. 1978-79), Pi Kappa Lambda, Phi Kappa Delta, Phi Mu Alpha Sinfonia, Pi Kappa Alpha. Avocations: travel, hiking, cycling. Home: 1923 NW 3d St New Brighton MN 55112 Office: U Minn Sch Music 100 Ferguson Minneapolis MN 55455

WARE, JAMES EDWIN, retired international company executive; b. Athens, Ga., Jan. 27, 1925; s. James Edwin and Marguerite (McCue) W.; m. Petronella J. Knoors, Dec. 13, 1952; children Marguerite Linda, Jennifer Ellen. Student, St. Petersburg Jr. Coll., Fla., 1942-43, Rutgers U., 1943-44; M.E., Stevens Inst. Tech., 1948. Salesman Chgo. Pneumatic Tool Co., N.Y.C., N.Y., 1948-61; gen. sales mgr. Hoke, Inc., Cresskill, N.J., 1961-63; mgr. instrument systems sales McKiernan Terry div. Litton Industries, Clifton, N.J., 1963-66; dir. marketing, mining and constrn. div. Joy Mfg. Co., Claremont, N.H., 1966-67; v.p., gen. mgr. Picker X-Ray Co., White Plains, N.Y., 1967-70; pres., gen. mgr. Northrop Archtl. Systems, City of Industry, Calif., 1971-82; v.p Northrop Corp., 1971-82, dir. comml. internat. offset trade program, 1982-84; dir. Shinko-Northrop, Japan, dir. Société d'Etudes et de Prefabrication, France., dir. Industry Mfrs. Council, City of Industry, Calif., 1971-74. Served with inf. AUS, World War II, ETO. Decorated Bronze Star. Home: 10952 Cherry Hill Dr Santa Ana CA 92705-2442

WARE, JAMES W., federal judge; b. 1946. BA, Calif. Luth. U., 1969; JD, Stanford U., 1972. Assoc. Blase, Valentine & Klein, Palo Alto, Calif., 1972-77, ptnr., 1977; judge Santa Clara County Superior Ct., U.S. Dist. Ct. (no. dist.) Calif., 1990—; pro bono East Palo Alto Law Project. Active Am. Leadership Forum; mem. bd. visitors Stanford Law Sch.; active Martin Luther King Papers Project. 2nd lt. USAR, 1969-86. Office: US Dist Cts 280 S 1st St Rm 2112 San Jose CA 95113-3008

WARE, LUCILE MAHIEU, child psychiatrist, educator, researcher; b. Kansas City, Mo., Feb. 23, 1929; d. Robert Georges and Lucile (Bailey) Mahieu; m. Jean Andre Demonchaux, Sept. 4, 1958; children: Elisabeth (dec.), Catherine, Theodore. AB cum laude, Bryn Mawr Coll., 1949; MD, Columbia U., 1953. Diplomate Am. Bd. Psychiatry and Neurology, Am. Bd. Child Psychiatry. Staff psychiatrist, Children's Div. Menninger Clinic, Topeka, 1968—; dir. Presch. Day Treatment Ctr., 1972—; dir. admissions and diagnosis Children's Div. Menninger Clinic, 1974-75,77,78; cons. No. Topeka Head Start, 1979—, co-principle investigator, DHHS-NIMH (CPR) MH#39895, 1982-87; mem. faculty Karl Menninger Sch. of Psychiatry, Topeka, 1969—, Topeka Inst. for Psychoanalysis, 1974—; cons. C.F. Menninger Hosp. and Children's Hosp., Topeka, 1975—. Contbr. articles to profl. jours. Assoc. leader Campfire Girls, Topeka, 1968-72; bd. dirs. Dance Arts of Topeka, 1974-77; bd. dirs., founder Ballet Midwest, 1977-88. Fellow Albert Einstein Coll. Med. N.Y.C., 1957-58, Seeley Fellow Menninger Found. Children's Div.; named Kenworthy Prof. Menninger Found., 1983-84. Fellow Am. Assn. Child and Adolescent Psychiatry, Am. Psychiatric Assn.; mem. AMA. Club: Alliance Francaise (Topeka). Home: 1925 SW Wayne Ave Topeka KS 66604-3138 Office: Menninger Clinic Children's Div PO Box 829 Topeka KS 66601-0829

WARE, MARCUS JOHN, lawyer; b. Yakima, Wash., Mar. 17, 1904; s. Marcus Clark and Ruby Marie (Cross) W.; m. Helen Gorton, June 6, 1933; children: Robert Gorton, Donald Frank (dec.), Barbara Jean (Mrs. Wray W. Featherstone, Jr.), Mary Elizabeth (Mrs. James H. Rathlesberger). LL.B., U. Idaho, 1927. Bar: Idaho 1927. Since practiced in Lewiston; with firm Ware, O'Connell & Creason, and predecessors, 1927-87, sr. ptnr., 1955-87; ret., 1987; pros. atty. Nez Perce County, Idaho, 1943, 44. Chmn. Lewis-Clark Sesquicentennial Celebration, Lewiston, also Clarkston, Wash., 1955-56; chmn. Lewiston Centennial Celebration, 1961; former vice chmn. Lewis and Clark Trail Commn.; mem. Idaho Hist. Sites Rev. Bd., 1969-91, Idaho Bicentennial Commn., 1972-76, Lewiston Bicentennial Commn., 1973-76, Idaho TV History series adv. bd., 1988-91; mem. nat. adv. coun. on ethnic heritage studies Office Edn., HEW, 1975-76; bd. dirs. Pacific N.W. Nat. Parks Assn., 1976-82, Pacific N.W. Nat. Parks and Forests Assn., 1985-91; past dir. Lewis and Clark Trail Heritage Found. Recipient award of merit Am. Assn. State and Local History, 1961, citation Idaho Recreation and Park Soc., 1973, Disting. Service award Lewis and Clark Trail Heritage Found., 1983. Mem. ABA, Idaho State Bar Assn. (commr. 1959-62, pres. 1961-62, Outstanding Svc. award 1988, Idaho Disting. Lawyer award Idaho State Bar 1991), Clearwater Bar Assn., Am. Coll. Trial Lawyers, SAR (past state pres.), Soc. Mayflower Descendants (past gov. Idaho soc., past dep. gov. gen.), Nez Perce County Hist. Soc. (past pres.), James Willard Schultz Soc., Scottish Gaelic Texts Soc., Gaelic Soc. Inverness, An Comunn Gaidhealach, Mont. Hist. Soc., Nev. HIst. Soc., Idaho State Hist. Soc. (trustee 1971-91), The Nature Conservancy, Outlook Club (Lewiston), Ind. Order Odd Fellows, Masons (33 deg., Blue Lodge, Nez Perce #10 , grand master Idaho 1945-46), Scottish Rite, 33d Degree, York Rite, Red Cross Constantine, Shrine, Elks, Kiwanis (past pres.). Home: 308 Prospect Blvd Lewiston ID 83501-2153 Office: 1219 Idaho St Lewiston ID 83501-1940

WARE, RICHARD ANDERSON, foundation executive; b. N.Y.C., Nov. 7, 1919; s. John Sayers and Mabelle (Anderson) W.; m. Lucille Henney, Mar. 20, 1942 (div. 1972); children: Alexander W., Janet M., Bradley J., Patricia E.; m. Beverly G. Mytinger, Dec. 22, 1972. BA, Lehigh U., 1941; M in Pub. Adminstrn., Wayne State U., 1943; D in Social Sci. (honoris causa), Francisco Marroquin U., Guatemala, 1988. Research asst. Detroit Bur. Govt. Research, 1941-42; personnel technician Lend-Lease Adminstrn., Washington, 1942-43; research asso. to asst. dir. Citizens Research Council, Detroit, 1946-56; sec. Earhart and Relm Founds., Ann Arbor, Mich., 1956-70; trustee, pres. Earhart and Relm Founds., 1970-84, trustee, pres. emeritus, 1985—; prin. dep. asst. sec. Def. for internat. security affairs Washington, 1969-70; cons. Office Asst. Sec. Def., 1970-73; dir. Citizens Trust Co., 1970-87. Vice pres. Ann Arbor United Fund and Community Svcs., 1968, pres., 1969; asst. dir. Mich. Joint Legis. Com. on State Reorgn., 1950-52; sec.

Gov.'s Com. to Study Prisons, 1952-53; com. to chmn. Ann Arbor City Planning Commn., 1958-67; mem. Detroit Com. on Fgn. Rels., 1971-87; mem. coun. Woodrow Wilson Internat. Center for Scholars, 1977-85; vis. com. div. social scis. U. Chgo., 1977-85; mem. adv. com. The Citadel, 1977-85; mem. adv. coun. internat. studies program Fletcher Sch., Tufts U., 1979-85; trustee Greenhills Sch., 1973-80, Ann Arbor Area Found., 1977-83, Inst. Fgn. Policy Analysis, 1985—, Inst. Polit. Economy, 1985—, Ctr. for Study Social and Polit. Change Smith Coll., 1988—, Pequawket Found., 1989—; polit. analyst Republican Nat. Com., Washington, 1964; bd. dirs. The Liberty Fund, Inc., Indpls., 1980—, Bd. Fgn. Scholarships, 1984-90, chmn., 1987-89. With USAAF, 1943-46. Recipient Civilian Meritorious Service medal Dept. Def., 1970. Mem. Govtl. Research Assoc. (trustee, v.p. 1955-56), Am. Polit. Sci. Assn., Mont Pelerin Soc., Phi Beta Kappa, Phi Alpha Theta. Congregationalist. Clubs: Ann Arbor; North Conway Country, Cosmos (Washington). Home: PO Box 310 Intervale NH 03845-0310 Office: 2200 Green Rd Ste H Ann Arbor MI 48105-2948

WARE, ROGER B., insurance company executive; b. 1934. With Reliance Ins. Co., Phila., 1967-83, Guaranty Nat. Ins. Co., Englewood, Colo., Landmark Am. Ins. Co., Englewood, Colo.; pres., CEO Guaranty Nat. Ins. Co. Office: Guaranty Nat Corp 100 Inverness Ter E Englewood CO 80112*

WARE, THADDEUS VAN, government official; b. High Point, N.C., Mar. 31, 1935; s. Elsec and Irene (Myers) W.; m. Doretha Ardella Lee, June 18, 1960; children—Kimberly Melissa, Chrystal Lynn. B.A. cum laude, Va. Union U., 1957; J.D., Howard U., 1960. Bar: Va. bar 1961, D.C. bar 1970, U.S. Supreme Ct. bar 1970. Gen. atty. Office of Solicitor, Dept. Labor, 1961-66; trial counsel Chief Counsel's Office, Fed. Hwy. Adminstrn., 1966-69; staff asst. to Pres. Richard M. Nixon, 1969-70; chief adminstrv. judge, chmn. Bd. Contract Appeals, Dept. Transp., 1987—. Served with AUS, 1960-61. Mem. Va., D.C., U.S. Supreme Ct., Fed. Bar Assns., Urban League, NAACP, Bd. Contract Appeals Judges Assn. (pres. 1988-89), Alpha Phi Alpha, Sigma Delta Tau, Alpha Kappa Mu. Home: 2213 Parallel Ln Silver Spring MD 20904-5446 Office: 400 7th St SW Washington DC 20590-0002

WARE, THOMAS EARLE, building consultant; b. Cleve., Apr. 13, 1931; s. Orval Bertele and Dorothy Lillian (Brammar) W.; m. Ann Sanborn Gilkey, Dec. 21, 1955 (div. Dec. 1960); 1 child, Thomas Earle Jr.; m. Gillian May Arnold, June 8, 1968 (div. Dec. 1983); 1 child, Elizabeth. BArch, Cornell U., 1955. Assoc. ptnr. Kelly and Kress and Assocs., Architects and Planners, Cleve., 1955-59; project architect J. Gordon Lorimer, F.A.I.A., N.Y.C., 1959; gen. mgr., ptnr. Project Design, Inc., Cleve., 1960-64; project architect, mgr. Cleve. dist. and hdqrs. The Austin Co., 1961-68; project architect, mgr., asst. and acting chief bldg. systems sect., bldg. rsch. divsn. Inst. Applied Tech., Nat. Bur. Standards U.S. Dept. Commerce, Washington, 1968-71; sr. program specialist, Office of the Sec., Office of Asst. Sec. for Sci. and Tech., Office of Dep. Asst. Sec. for Environ. Affairs U.S. Dept. Commerce, 1971-72; with Bldg. Cons., Reston, Va., 1972-73; v.p., dir. Bldg. Tech., Inc., Silver Spring, Md., 1973—, TCSB, Inc., Silver Spring, Md., Tehran and Shiraz, Iran, 1974-82; instr. continuing engring. edn. program, Sch. Engring. and Applied Sci., George Washington U., 1969-71; lectr. dept. architecture The Cath. U. Am., 1969-71; lectr., discussion leader U. Wis.-Ext., 1980-83; presenter in field. Contbr. articles to profl. jours. Named Architect of Yr., D.C. Coun. Engring. and Archtl. Socs., 1971; recipient Sci. and Tech. fellowship U.S. Dept. Commerce, 1971. Mem. Nat. Inst. Bldg. Scis., Soc. Am. Mil. Engrs., Constrn. Specifications Inst. Home: 11478 Links Dr Reston VA 22090-4814 Office: Bldg Tech Inc 1109 Spring St Silver Spring MD 20910-4002

WARE, WILLIAM LEVI, physical education educator, researcher; b. Greenwood, Miss., May 15, 1934; s. Leslie and Catherine (Bowden) W.; m. Lottie Herger, Apr. 26, 1958; children: Felicia Rogene, Trevor Lesleo, Melvinia Simone. BS, Mississippi Valley State U., 1957; MA, Calif. State U., L.A., 1969; PhD, U. So. Calif., 1978. Tchr., coach Greenwood Pub. Schs., 1957-63; Bellflower (Calif.) Unified Sch. Dist., 1963-72; teaching asst. U. So. Calif., L.A., 1972-73; asst. prof. Calif. State U., Northridge, 1973-79; assoc. prof. Miss. State U., Starkville, 1979-90; prof. phys. edn., chmn. dept. Mississippi Valley State U., Itta Bena, 1990—; presenter in field; chmn. Delta Algebra Project Planning & Coordinating Group, 1991-93. Advisor Affirmative Action Coun., Whittier, Calif., 1977-78; bd. dirs. United Way, Starkville, 1983-86. Recipient Outstanding Svc. award Kiwanis Internat., 1985, Outstanding Educator award Greenwood Cultural Club, 1986, Presdl. citation Nat. Assn. for Equal Opportunity in Higher Edn., 1989; Inducted into Southwestern Athletic Conference Hall of Fame, 1993. Mem. Phi Delta Kappa (svc. award 1989), Greenwood/Leflore C. of C. (chmn. Leadership Tomorrow 1992-93). Avocations: racquetball, jogging. Office: Miss Valley State U PO Box 620 Itta Bena MS 38941-1499

WARE, WILLIS HOWARD, computer scientist; b. Atlantic City, Aug. 31, 1920; s. Willis and Ethel (Rossworth) W.; m. Floy Hoffer, Oct. 10, 1943; children—Deborah Susanne Ware Pinson, David Willis, Alison Floy Ware Manoli. B.S.E.E., U. Pa., 1941; M.S.E.E., MIT, 1942; Ph.D. in Elec. Engring, Princeton U., 1951. Research engr. Hazeltine Electronics Corp., Little Neck, N.Y., 1942-46; mem. research staff Inst. Advanced Study, Princeton, N.J., 1946-51, North Am. Aviation, Downey, Calif., 1951-52; mem. corp. research staff Rand Corp., Santa Monica, Calif., 1952—; adj. prof. UCLA Extension Service, 1955-68; first chmn. Am. Fedn. Info. Processing Socs., 1961, 62; chmn. HEW sec.'s Adv. Com. on Automated Personal Data Systems, 1971-73; mem. Privacy Protection Study Commn., 1975-77, vice chmn., 1975-77; mem. numerous other adv. groups, spl. coms. for fed. govt., 1959—. Author: Digital Computer Technology and Design, vols. I and II, 1963. Recipient Computers Scis. Man of Yr. award Data Processing Mgmt. Assn., 1975, Exceptional Civilian Svc. medal USAF, 1979, Disting. Svc. award Am. Fedn. Info. Processing Socs., 1986, Nat. Computer Sys. Security award Nat. Computer Sys. Lab./Nat. Computer Security Ctr., 1989, Computer Pioneer award IEEE Computer Soc., 1993, Pioneer award Electronic Frontier Found., 1995; named one of Fed. 100 of 1994, Fed. Computer Week. Fellow IEEE (Centennial medal 1984), AAAS, Assn. for Computing Machinery; mem. NAE, AIAA, Sigma Xi, Eta Kappa Nu, Pi Mu Epsilon, Tau Beta Pi. Office: The Rand Corp 1700 Main St Santa Monica CA 90401-3208

WAREHAM, JAMES LYMAN, steel company executive; b. Clinton, Iowa, Oct. 8, 1939; s. Lyman Hugh and Ulainee Maria (Pitts) W.; m. Patricia Josephine Wrubel, June 18, 1966; children: Lisa Jo, Tara Lynn. BSEE, U. Notre Dame, 1961. Various mgmt. positions U.S. Steel-Gary Works, Ind., 1961-69, div. mgr., 1976-79; various mgmt. positions U.S. Steel-Tex. Works, Baytown, 1969-72; various mgmt. positions U.S. Steel-South Works, Chgo., 1972-76, gen. plant mgr., 1979-84; v.p. engring. U.S. Steel, Pitts., 1984-86; pres., CEO Bliss Salem, Inc., Ohio, 1986-89; pres., COO Wheeling-Pitts. Steel Corp., W.Va., 1989-92, chmn., pres., CEO, 1992—; pres., bd. dirs. Wheeling-Pitts. Corp.; bd. dirs. Bliss-Salem Inc., Wesbanco, Am. Iron and Steel Inst. Area coord. Thompson for Gov., Homewood, Ill., 1978; div. chmn. United Way, Gary, Ind., 1976; gen. chmn. United Way Wheeling, W.Va., 1990; bd. dirs. United Way of Upper Ohio Valley, Wheeling Jesuit Coll., 1989—, Wheeling Hosp., 1990—. Named Small Businessman of Yr. Salem C. of C., 1988, Entrepreneur of Yr. Ernst & Young, Pitts., 1989. Mem. Assn. Iron & Steel Engrs., Inst. Mining & Metall. Engrs., Ohio Steel Industry Adv. Commn., W.Va. Mfg. Assn., Wheeling C. of C. Home: 234 Greenwood Dr Canonsburg PA 15317-5211 Office: 1134 Market St Wheeling WV 26003-2906

WAREHAM, RAYMOND NOBLE, investment banker; b. Rochester, N.Y., Nov. 20, 1948; s. Simon Harold and Barbara (Snell) W.; m. Cornelia Lee Clifford, June 28, 1975; children: Ellinor Park, Laura Stewart, Cornelia Ashley. BS in Indsl. Engring., Northwestern U., 1970; MBA, Harvard U., 1975. V.p. J.P. Morgan & Co., N.Y., 1975-80; head-corp. fin. J.P. Morgan & Co. Tokyo, 1980-85; exec. dir. J.P. Morgan Securities Ltd., London, 1986-87; mngr. dir., head banking industry group J.P. Morgan & Co., N.Y., 1988-92; mng. dir., co-head J.P. Morgan Securities, N.Y.C., 1992—. Pres. bd. trustees Spence Sch., N.Y.C.; trustee Am. Sch., Tokyo, 1982-85; elder Brick Presbyn. Ch., N.Y.C., 1989-92; bd. dirs. Brick Church Day Sch., 1989-92. Mem. DERU (Northwestern hon.), Union Club (N.Y.), Duxbury Yacht Club, Century Club (Harvard Bus. hon.). Republican. Avocations: athletics, Japanese antique furniture, secondary school education. Home:

1148 Fifth Ave New York NY 10128-0807 Office: JP Morgan Securities Inc 60 Wall St New York NY 10260

WAREHIME, JOHN A., food products executive. Student, Pa. State U. With Hanover (Pa.) Brands Inc., 1959-1968, Hanover (Pa.) Guest Quality Foods Corp., 1968-74, Food Svc. East Inc., Hanover, Pa., 1974—; chmn. Hanover (Pa.) Foods Corp., 1989—. Office: Hanover Foods Corp 1486 York St Hanover PA 17331*

WAREN, STANLEY A., university administrator, theatre and arts center administrator, director; b. N.Y.C., Mar. 22, 1919; s. Maurice and Minnie (Rosen) W.; m. Florence Rigal, Nov. 21, 1949; 1 child, Mark. B.S.S., CCNY, 1938; M.A., Columbia U., 1939, Ph.D., 1953. Exec. producer, dir. theatre U.S. and abroad, 1953-70; prof., chmn. dept. speech and theatre CCNY, 1967-72; prof., exec. officer Ph.D. program theatre CUNY, 1972-81, v.p.; provost, dep. pres. Grad. Sch., 1981-84; dir. Ctr. for Advanced Study in Theatre Arts, N.Y.C., 1979-82, 84-86; reviewer NEH, 1978-91; advisor humanities com. Bklyn. Acad. Music, N.Y.C., 1980-81; spl. edn. cons. Double Image Theatre, N.Y.C., 1982-90; mem. adv. council Roundabout Theatre, N.Y.C., 1985—; Fulbright-Hayes vis. prof. Nat. Taiwan U., 1986-87; vis. prof. Shanghai Drama Inst., 1988. Dir. musical The Chess King (Taiwan) 1987, Old B Hanging on the Wall (Shanghai), 1988, Judas, Mexico (N.Y.), 1989. Bd. dirs. Women's Inter. Art Ctr., N.Y.C., 1978-82; mem. grants panel N.Y.C. Dept. Cultural Affairs, 1979; bd. dirs. Frank Silvera Workshops for Writers, N.Y.C., 1979-81. Served to capt. USAF, 1942-46. Grantee Herman Goldman Found., 1980-82, NEH, 1980-81, N.Y. Coun. Humanities, USIA/Arts Am., Singapore, 1990. Mem. AAUP, Soc. Stage Dirs. and Choreographers, Profl. Staff Congress CUNY. Democrat. Club: The Century Assn. (resident 1984—). Avocations: arts; tennis; swimming. Home: 465 W End Ave New York NY 10024-4926 Office: CUNY Grad Sch 33 West 42d St New York NY 10036

WARFEL, JOHN HIATT, medical educator, retired; b. Marion, Ind., Mar. 3, 1916; s. Robert A. and Mary (Hiatt) W.; m. Marjorie Jane Wolfe, Oct. 28, 1942; children: Barbara, Susan, David. BS, Capital U., 1938; MS, Ohio State U., 1941; PhD, Case Western Res. U., 1948. Assoc. prof. anatomy SUNY, Buffalo, 1949-86. Author: The Extremities, 6th edit., 1993, The Head, Neck and Trunk, 6th edit., 1993. Lt. (s.g.) USNR, 1942-46. Mem. Am. Assn. Anatomists, Mason, Sigma Xi. Methodist.

WARFIELD, GERALD ALEXANDER, composer, writer; b. Ft. Worth, Feb. 23, 1940; s. George Alexander and Geraldine (Spencer) W. Student, Tex. Christian U., 1958-61; B.A., North Tex. State U., 1963, M.Mus., 1965; M.F.A., Princeton U., 1967; postgrad., Tanglewood, summers 1963-64. Instr. Princeton, 1968-71; asso. dir. Index of New Mus. Notation, N.Y.C., 1971-75; lectr. contemporary music notation. Mem. conf. com. Internat. Conf. on New Mus. Notation, Belgium, 1974; chmn. program com. 2d Nat. Conf. Music Theory, 1977. Author: A Beginner's Manual of Music 4B, 1967, Layer Analysis: a Primer of Elementary Tonal Structures, 1976, Writings on Contemporary Music Notations, 1977, How to Write Music Manuscript, 1977, (with others) Layer Dictation, 1978, The Investor's Guide to Stock Quotations, 1982, How To Buy Foreign Stocks and Bonds, 1984, How to Read the Financial News, 1986; (with others) Export-Import Financing, 1986; No Nonesence Guides to the Stock Market, Mutual Funds, Tax-Free Bonds, 1991, Managing Your Stock Portfolio, Money Market Funds, 1993; composer: Variations and Metamorphoses, 1973 (1st prize Ariz. Cello Soc.); filmstrip Introduction to Musical Notation, 1976; Fantasy Quintet, 1978 (2d prize New Music for Young Ensembles); contbr.: Grove's Dictionary of Music and Musicians, 1976; editor: Longman Music Series, 1976-85; contbr. articles to profl. jours. Mem. Am. Soc. Univ. Composers (chmn. exec. com. 1972-74, conf. chmn. 9th Ann. Conf. 1974, founding editor Jour. of Music Scores), Am. Composers Alliance (treas. 1979—), Coll. Music Soc. (council, conf. chmn. 1981), Broadcast Music Inc. Home: 205 West 22d St New York NY 10011

WARFIELD, JOHN NELSON, engineering educator, consultant; b. Sullivan, Mo., Nov. 21, 1925; s. John Daniel and Flora Alice (Land) W.; m. Rosamond Arline Howe, Feb. 2, 1948; children: Daniel, Nancy, Thomas. BA, U. Mo., 1948, BSEE, 1948, MSEE, 1949; PhD, Purdue U., 1952. Assoc. prof. Pa. State U., University Park, 1949-55, U. Ill.-Urbana, 1955-57, Purdue U., West Lafayette, Ind., 1957-58; prof. elec. engring U. Kans., Lawrence, 1958-66; sr. research leader Battelle Meml. Inst., Columbus, Ohio, 1966-74; prof. elec. engring. U. Va., Charlottesville, 1974-83; sr. mgr. Burroughs Corp., 1983-84; dir. Inst. for Info. Tech. George Mason U., Fairfax, Va., 1984-87, dir. Inst. for Advanced Study in Integrative Scis., 1987—; cons. IBM, Armonk, N.Y., 1979-82, Saudi Arabian Nat. Ctr. Sci. and Tech., Riyadh, 1978-82, Ghana Tech. Transfer Ctr., Accra, 1989—, Niagara-Mohawk Power Co., 1989, Ford Motor Co., 1990—, Defense Systems Mgmt. Coll., 1990—. Author: Societal Systems, 1976, A Science of Generic Design, 1990, A Handbook of Interactive Management, 1994; inventor interpretive structural modeling, 1973; editor: IEEE Transactions on Systems, Man, and Cybernetics, 1968-73, Systems Research, 1981-90. Recipient Excellence in Intrm. award Western Electric Co., 1966. Fellow IEEE (life, outstanding contbn. award 1977, Centennial medal 1984); mem. Systems, Man and Cybernetics Soc. (pres. 1972), Soc. Gen. Systems Research (pres. 1982-83), Assn. for Integrative Studies, Internat. Soc. Panetics. Home: 4308 Wakefield Dr Annandale VA 22003-3611 Office: George Mason U Fairfax VA 22030

WARFIELD, WILLIAM CAESAR, singer, actor, educator; b. West Helena, Ark., Jan. 22, 1920; s. Robert Elza and Bertha (McCamery) W.; m. Leontyne Price, Aug. 31, 1952 (div. Dec. 1972). MusB, Eastman Sch. Music, 1942; LL.D. (hon.), U. Ark., 1972; MusD (hon.), Lafayette Coll., 1978. Prof. music dept. U. Ill., Champaign, 1974—; Bd. dirs. N.Y. Coll. Music; also trustee; trustee Berkshire Boys Choir, 1966-70, Nat. Assn. Negro Musicians. Actor nat. co. Call Me Mister, 1946-47; Broadway plays include Regina, 1948-49; Town Hall debut, 1950, tour of, Australia, 1950; motion picture Showboat, 1951; toured with: govt. sponsored European prodn. Porgy and Bess; singing role of Porgy govt. sponsored European prodn., 1952, concerts, radio and TV appearances; Symphony soloist recitals, 1950—, concert tour for, Dept. State; as soloist with Phila. Orch. for its continental debut, 1955, tour, Africa, Nr. East, Europe, 1956, Asia, Australia, 1958, Cuba, 1959, Europe, 1966, recital, Brussels Fair, 1958; starred as De Lawd in: Green Pastures, NBC-TV, 1957, 59; star: N.Y.C. Opera revival Porgy and Bess, 1961, 64; also Vienna prodn., 1965-72; featured soloist, Casals Festival, P.R. and N.Y.C., 1962-63, Athens Festival, Greece, 1966; starred in: Richard Rodgers' prodn. Show Boat for, Music Theater of Lincoln Center, 1966; German lang. Show Boat for Vienna Volksoper, 1971-72; soloist (with Pablo Casals) German lang., Geneva, Switzerland, Pacem in Terris II Convocation, 1967; title role in: German lang. Mendelssohn's Elijah, 1969; presented by Central City Opera (Colo.) as: star prodn. Puccini opera Gianni Schicchi, 1972; performed concert, Carnegie Hall, 1975. Recipient hon. citation Eastman Sch. Music, 1954, Grammy award Nat. Acad. Rec. Arts and Scis., 1984. Mem. Actors Equity, Am. Guild Mus. Artists, Screen Actors Guild, AFTRA, NAACP (life), Phi Mu Alpha Sinfonia (life). Office: U Ill Dept Music 2136 Music Urbana IL 61801*

WARGA, JACK, mathematician, educator; b. Warsaw, Poland, Dec. 5, 1922; came to U.S., 1943, naturalized, 1944; s. Herman and Czarna (Lichtenstein) W.; m. Faye Kleinman, Feb. 27, 1949; children—Charna Ruth, Arthur David. Student, Brussels (Belgium) U., 1939-40; BA, Carleton Coll., 1944; PhD, NYU, 1951. Assoc. mathematician Reeves Instrument Corp., N.Y.C., 1951-52; Chief engring. computing sect. Republic Aviation Corp., Farmingdale, N.Y., 1952-53; head math dept. Burroughs Corp., Pasadena, Cal., 1954-56; mgr., math dept. Avco Research and Devel., Wilmington, Mass., 1957-66; prof. math. Northeastern U., Boston, 1966-93, prof. emeritus, 1993—. Author: Optimal Control of Differential and Functional Equations, 1972, expanded Russian transl., 1977; contbr. articles to profl. jours. Served with AUS, 1944-46. Weizmann Meml. fellow, 1956-57. Fellow AAAS; mem. Am. Math. Soc., Soc. Indsl. and Applied Math. (editor Jour. on Control and Optimization 1963-89). Home: 233 Clark Rd Brookline MA 02146-5847 Office: Northeastern U Dept Math Boston MA 02115

WARGA, JOHN, construction company executive; b. 1942. BS in Acctg., LaSalle U., 1969. CPA. With Dynalectric Co., McLean, Va., 1973—, treas.,

sr. v.p., 1988—. Office: Dynalectric Co 1420 Spring Hill Rd 500 Mc Lean VA 22102*

WARGO, TOM, professional golfer; b. Mayville, Mich., 1943; m. Irene Wargo; 1 child, Michelle. Previous occupations include dairy farmer, salmon fisherman, GM assembly-line worker, iron worker; apprentice Carlyle Golf Club, to 1982; co-owner Colonial Inn, Sandoval, Ill., 1972-82; co-owner, club pro Greenview Golf Club, Centralia, Ill., 1982—. Recipient Club Profl. of Yr. award, 1992. Winner PGA Srs. Championship, 1993. Office: Greenview Golf Club Centralia IL 62801*

WARHAFTIG, SOLOMON L., lawyer; b. N.Y.C., Apr. 11, 1938; s. Paul and Sara (Raskin) W.; m. Toby Bremen, Dec. 25, 1965 (div. 1977); children: Jeremy Paul, Daniel Ethan; m. Susan Klein, July 4, 1984. BS, Columbia U., 1959; JD, Harvard U., 1964. Atty. U.S. Dept. Justice, Washington, 1964-67; ptnr. Kaye, Scholer, Fierman, Hays & Handler, N.Y.C., 1967-79, Gelbert & Abrams, N.Y.C., 1979-87, Proskauer, Rose, Goetz & Mendelsohn, N.Y.C., 1987—. Lt. USNR, 1959-61. Office: Proskauer Rose 1585 Broadway New York NY 10036-8200

WARHOVER, STEPHEN HUNT, food company executive; b. Denver, Mar. 9, 1944; s. Robert E. and Leslie (Robinson) W.; m. Anne Tate, June 17, 1967; children: Julie, Jeffrey, Susan. A.B., Dartmouth Coll., 1966; M.B.A., Northwestern U., 1968. Mem. mktg. staff Gen. Mills, Mpls., 1968-80, v.p., gen. mgr., 1980-86; pres. Gorton Group, 1986—. Chmn. bd. dirs. Mpls. unit Am. Cancer Soc., 1982-83; bd. dirs. Minnetonka Little League, 1982-83, Bank of New England, 1987—, Assoc. Industries of Mass., 1987—. Recipient Disting. Scholar award Northwestern U. Grad. Sch. Mgmt., 1967. Office: Gorton Group PO Box 361 Gloucester MA 01931-0361 also: Gen Mills Inc 1 General Mills Blvd Minneapolis MN 55426

WARING, JOHN ALFRED, former research writer, lecturer, consultant; b. San Francisco, Dec. 30, 1913; s. John A. and Mary (Wheeler) W. Student pub. schs. Yachting, marine editor Chgo. Tribune, 1934-47; editor Kellogg Messenger, Kellogg Switchboard & Supply Co., Chgo., 1945-49; rsch. cons. Baxter Internat. Econ. Rsch. Bur., Inc., investment counselling, N.Y.C., 1951-52; rsch. asst. mktg. rsch. dept. Fuller, Smith & Ross, Inc., advt., N.Y.C., 1953; rsch. writer, cons. Twentieth Century Fund, N.Y.C., 1953-54; rsch. cons. Ford Motor Co., Dearborn, Mich., 1955; chief rschr. Internat. Fact Finding Inst., Lawrence Orgn., pub. rels. cons., N.Y.C., Washington, 1957-58; lectr. on energy, tech. and history World Power Conf., Montreal, 1958, First Energy Inst., Am. U., Washington, 1960, Nat. Archives, Washington, 1962, Smithsonian Mus. History and Tech., Washington, 1968; guest lectr. social responsibility in sci. U. Md., 1972, guest lectr. sci. and environment, 1974; lectr. Internat. Conf. on Energy and Humanity, Queen Mary Coll., U. London, 1972, World Energy Conf., Detroit, 1974, History of Sci. Soc., Norwalk, Conn., 1974; rsch. cons. PARM Project, Nat. Planning Assn., Washington, 1961-62; cons. Sci., Tech. and Fgn. Affairs Seminar, Fgn. Svc. Inst., Dept. State, 1965; vis. lectr. social implications of sci. for N. Am. U. Alta., Edmonton (Can.), 1981; lectr. Carnahan Conf. Harmonizing Tech. with Soc., U. Ky., Lexington, 1987; del. U.S. commn. UNESCO Conf., San Francisco, 1969; inaugural lectr. Future of Sci. and Soc. in Am. Seminar U.S. Civil Svc. Commn., Washington, 1970; editorial cons. Nat. Acad. Engring., Washington, 1971; rsch. cons., analyst Seminar Sch., Indsl. Coll. Armed Forces, Ft. Lesley J. McNair, Washington, 1958-74; researcher Office Plans and Programs, U.S. Army Med. Dept., Washington, 1975-76; asst. editor Def. Systems Mgmt. Rev. mag. Def. Systems Mgmt. Coll., Ft. Belvoir, Va., 1977-78; ret., 1978. Contbr. chpts. to books; compiler statis. tabulations. Mem. AAAS, Soc. History of Tech. (charter), History Sci. Soc., Technocracy, Washington Acad. Scis., Washington Sci. Engrs. (sec. 1977), Internat. Soc. Gen. Semantics, N.Y. Acad. Sci., D.C. Area Phi Beta Kappa Assn. Home: 1320 S George Mason Dr Arlington VA 22204-3851

WARING, WALTER WEYLER, English language educator; b. Sterling, Kans., May 13, 1917; s. Walter Wray and Bonnie Laura (Weyler) W.; m. Mary Esther Griffith, Feb. 8, 1946; children: Mary Laura, Helen Ruth, Elizabeth Anne, Claire Joyce. B.A., Kans. Wesleyan U., 1939; M.A., U. Colo., 1946; Ph.D., Cornell U., 1949. Tchr., English and chemistry Belleville (Kan.) High Sch., 1939-41; instr. U. Colo., Boulder, 1941-42, 46-47; mem. faculty Kalamazoo Coll., 1949—, prof. English, 1955-85, prof. emeritus, 1985—, chmn. dept., 1953-78, dir. humanities, 1978-83; Ednl. TV lectr.; vis. prof. Kenyon Coll., 1984-86, 90-91. Painter watercolors.; author: Thomas Carlyle, 1978, also articles. Served to 1st lt. AUS, World War II, PTO. Decorated Legion of Merit. Mem. Phi Beta Kappa. Home: 156 Monroe St Kalamazoo MI 49006-4475

WARING, WILLIAM WINBURN, pediatric pulmonologist, educator; b. Savannah, Ga., July 20, 1923; s. Antonio Johnston and Sue Cole (Winburn) W.; m. Nell Pape Williams, July 19, 1952; children—William Winburn, Benjamin Joseph, Antonio Johnston, Peter Ayraud, Patrick Houstoun. Grad., Hotchkiss Sch., Lakeville, Conn., 1942; student, Yale U., 1942-43; M.D., Harvard U., 1947. Diplomate Am. Bd. Pediatrics (subdd. of pediatric pulmonology 1985-89). Intern Children's Hosp., Boston, 1947-48; intern, then resident Johns Hopkins Hosp., Balt., 1948-52; practice medicine specializing in pediatrics Jacksonville, Fla., 1955-57; instr. dept. pediatrics Sch. Medicine, Tulane U., New Orleans, 1957-58, asst. prof., 1958-61, assoc. prof., 1961-66, prof., 1966—; Jane B. Aron Prof. Pediatrics, 1987—; dir. Pediatric Pulmonary Ctr., New Orleans, 1969-88, Cystic Fibrosis Ctr., Tulane U., New Orleans, 1963-88; chmn. pediatric profl. tng. com. Cystic Fibrosis Found., 1978-86; cons. La. State Handicapped Children's Assn., 1963—; mem. pulmonary diseases adv. com. NIH, 1978-80. Co-author, editor: Practical Manual of Pediatrics, 1975, 2d edit., 1982; editor: Harriet Lane Handbook: A Manual for Pediatric House Officers, 1952, Hospital Pediatric Manual, 1958; contbg. author books on pediatric pulmonary disease, also articles in field; assoc. editor Am. Jour. Diseases of Children, 1989-91; mem. editl. bd. Pediatric Pulmonology, 1985-94. Served to capt. M.C., U.S. Army, 1952-54. Recipient Research Career Devel. award NIH, 1970-72. Fellow Am. Acad. Pediatrics (exec. com. 1966-71), Am. Coll. Chest Physicians; mem. Am. Pediatric Soc., Am. Thoracic Soc. (v.p. 1977). Republican. Roman Catholic. Clubs: Boston, So. Yacht, Wyvern (New Orleans). Avocations: fly fishing; running; computing. Home: 123 Walnut St Suite 9A New Orleans LA 70118 Office: Tulane U Sch of Medicine Dept of Pediatrics 1430 Tulane Ave New Orleans LA 70112

WARIS, MICHAEL, JR., lawyer; b. Phila., July 3, 1921; s. Michael and Esther (March) W.; m. Mary Luschyk, June 2, 1956. B.S. in Econs., U. Pa., 1942, J.D. cum laude, 1944. Bar: Pa., D.C. Law clk. to judge U.S. Tax Ct., Washington, 1946-48; trial counsel IRS, Washington, 1948-52; legis. atty. Legislation and Regulations div. IRS Washington, 1952-55; assoc. tax legis. counsel U.S. Treasury Dept., Washington, 1955-62; ptnr. Baker & McKenzie, Washington, 1962-88, of counsel, 1988—; adj. prof. Georgetown U. Law Sch., Washington, 1963-73. Bd. dirs. United Service Orgn. Nat. Capital Area, 1978-79; mem. adv. group to U.S Commr. of IRS, Washington, 1979-80. Named Master of the Bench, J. Edgar Murdock Am. Inn of Ct., 1988. Fellow ABA; mem. Fed. Bar Assn., Bar Assn. D.C., Ukrainian-Am. Bar Assn. (past chmn. bd. govs.), Cosmos Club, Met. Club, Beta Gamma Sigma. Ukrainian Catholic. Home: 6707 Tusculum Rd Bethesda MD 20817-1521 Office: Baker & McKenzie 815 Connecticut Ave NW Washington DC 20006-4004

WARK, ROBERT RODGER, art curator; b. Edmonton, Can., Oct. 7, 1924; came to U.S., 1948, naturalized, 1970; s. Joseph Henry and Louise (Rodger) W. B.A., U. Alta., 1944, M.A., 1946, LLD (hon.), 1986; A.M., Harvard, 1949, Ph.D., 1952. Asst. instr. art history art Yale U., 1954-56; curator art Henry E. Huntington Library and Art Gallery, San Marino, Calif., 1956-90; lectr. at Calif. Inst. Tech., 1960-91, UCLA, 1966-80. Author: Sculpture in the Huntington Collection, 1959, French Decorative Art in the Huntington Collection, 1961, Rowlandson's Drawings for a Tour in a Post Chaise, 1963, Rowlandson's Drawings for the English Dance of Death, 1966, Isaac Cruikshank's Drawings for Drolls, 1968, Early British Drawings in the Huntington Collection 1600-1750, 1969, Drawings by John Flaxman, 1970, Ten British Pictures 1740-1840, 1971, Meet the Ladies: Personalities in Huntington Portraits, 1972, Drawings from the Turner Shakespeare, 1973, Drawings by Thomas Rowlandson in the Huntington Collection, 1975, British Silver in the Huntington Collection, 1978; editor: Sir Joshua Reynolds: Discourses on Art, 1959. Served with RCAF, 1944-45;

Served with RCNVR, 1945. Mem. Coll. Art Assn. Home: 1330 Lombardy Rd Pasadena CA 91106-4120 Office: Huntington Library San Marino CA 91108

WARLICK, ROBERT PATTERSON, investment management company executive; b. Durham, N.C., July 25, 1924; s. Louis F. and Katie Alene (Maynard) W.; m. Margaret-Anne Buchanan, Oct. 22, 1960; children: Elizabeth Baetjer, Peter Maynard. A.B. cum laude, Brown U., 1948; M.B.A., Harvard U., 1950. Gen. investment mgr. Prudential Ins. Co., 1960-68; chmn. bd. First Morris Bank, Morristown, N.J., 1968-69; dir. First Morris Bank, 1969-87; ptnr. Lord, Abbett & Co., N.Y.C., 1969-82; ptnr. charge investment div. Lord, Abbett & Co., 1972-82; pres., dir. portfolio mgr. Lord Abbett Bond-Debenture Fund, 1974-82; chmn. Warlick & Baker, Inc., Morristown, N.J., 1983-87, Mitchell Hutchins Inst. Investors Inc., N.Y.C., 1988-89; pres. Warlick Capital Mgmt. Inc., Morristown, N.J., 1989—. Mem. planning bd., Chester Twp., N.J., 1975—, councilman, 1976-78, mayor, 1978-80; past vestryman Episcopal Ch. of St. John on Mountain, Bernardsville, N.J. Served with USAAF, 1943-46. Decorated Bronze Star. Mem. N.Y. Soc. Security Analysts, Harvard Bus. Sch. N.Y.C. Republican. Clubs: Somerset Hills (N.J.) Country, Morristown, Harvard (N.Y.C.). Home: Three Brook Farm 500 Old Chester Rd Chester NJ 07930 Office: Warlick Capital Mgmt Inc 10 Park Pl Morristown NJ 07960

WARLICK, ROGER KINNEY, history educator, assistant dean; b. San Diego, Oct. 1, 1930; s. John Portland and Bernice Catherine (Johnson) W.; m. Claudette Evans, Aug. 22, 1953 (div. 1972); m. Lorraine Vanden Bout, Dec. 13, 1973; children: David, Andrea, Kathryn, Dawn, Elizabeth, Sarah, Amy. BA, Ariz. State U., 1957; PhD, Boston U., 1965. Asst. to assoc. prof. history Bentley Coll., Boston and Waltham, Mass., 1963-70; prof., head history dept. Armstrong State Coll., Savannah, Ga., 1970-93, asst. dean Arts and Scis., 1993-94, prof. emeritus, 1994—; asst. program dir. Brit. studies U. Ga. system, London, 1982, 83, program dir., 1988, 89, 90, 92, 93, 94. Author: As Grain Once Scattered, 1988; contbr. articles to profl. jours. Bd. dirs. Hist. Savannah Found., 1980-86, Savannah Park and Tree Commn., 1976-87, vice chmn. 1983-87; gov. appointed mem. Ga. Hist. Records Adv. Bd., 1993—. Staff sgt. USAF, 1951-55. Cokesbury, resident fellow Boston U., 1961-63. Mem. Ga. Hist. Soc. (pres. 1990-94), Ga. Trust for Hist. Preservation, Nat. Trust for Hist. Preservation, Ga. Assn. Historians (various coms. 1978—), Savannah Symphony Soc. (bd. dirs. 1983-86).

WARMBROD, JAMES ROBERT, agriculture educator, university administrator; b. Belvidere, Tenn., Dec. 13, 1929; s. George Victor and Anna Sophia (Zimmerman) W.; m. Catharine P. Phelps, Jan. 30, 1965. B.S., U. Tenn., 1952, M.S., 1954; Ed.D. (Univ. fellow), U. Ill., 1962. Instr. edn. U. Tenn., Knoxville, 1956-57; tchr. high sch. Winchester, Tenn., 1957-59; asst. prof. U. Ill., Urbana, 1961-66; assoc. prof. U. Ill., 1966-67; prof. agrl. edn. Ohio State U., Columbus, 1968—, Presdl. prof., 1989, Presdl. prof. emeritus, 1995, chmn. dept., 1978-86, acting assoc. dean Coll. Agr., 1989, acting v.p. agrl. adminstrn., dean Coll. Agr., 1989-91; vis. prof. Pa. State U., 1970, U. Minn., 1971, Iowa State U., 1974, La. State U., 1986; vis. scholar Va. Poly. Inst. and State U., 1976, Univ. Coun. Vocat. Edn., 1988-89; mem. com. on agr. in secondary schs. Nat. Acad. Scis., 1985-87. Author: Review and Synthesis of Research on the Economics of Vocational Education, 1968, The Liberalization of Vocat. Education, 1974, (with others) Methods of Teaching Agriculture, 1986, 2d edit. 1993; editor: Agrl. Edn. mag., 1968-71. Served with USAF, 1954-56. Recipient Disting. Teaching award Ohio State U., 1972, 95, Teaching award Ohio State U. Chpt. Gamma Sigma Delta, 1977. Fellow Am. Assn. Agrl. Edn.; mem. Am. Vocat. Assn. (v.p. 1976-79, Outstanding Svc. award 1987), Am. Ednl. Rsch. Assn., Am. Vocat. Edn. Rsch. Assn. (pres. 1976), Am. Assn. Tchr. Educators in Agr. (Disting. Svc. award 1974, Disting. lectr. 1974). Home: 3853 Surrey Hill Pl Columbus OH 43220-4778 Office: 2120 Fyffe Rd Columbus OH 43210-1067

WARMENHOVEN, DANIEL JOHN, communications equipment executive; b. Jersey City, Nov. 27, 1950; s. Peter F. and Roseann E. (Fedkenheuer) W.; m. Charmaine C. Andre, June 16, 1973; children: Eric A., Laura A. BS in Elec. Engring., Princeton U., 1972. Program mgr. communication products div. IBM Corp., Research Triangle Park, N.C., 1972-85; gen. mgr. Info. Networks Group Hewlett-Packard Co., Cupertino, Calif., 1985-89; chmn., pres., chief exec. officer Network Equipment Techs., Redwood City, Calif., 1989—. Avocations: golf, amatuer photography. Office: Network Equipment Tech Inc 800 Saginaw Dr Redwood City CA 94063-4740

WARMER, RICHARD CRAIG, lawyer; b. Los Angeles, Aug. 12, 1936; s. George A. and Marian L. (Paine) W.; children: Craig McEchron, Alexander Richard. AB, Occidental Coll., 1958; MA, Tufts U., 1959; LLB, NYU, 1962. Bar: Calif. 1963, D.C. 1976. Assoc. O'Melveny & Myers, Los Angeles, 1962-69, ptnr., 1970-75; mng. ptnr. O'Melveny & Myers, Washington, 1976-92, mem. mgmt. com., 1986-92; with O'Melveny & Myers, San Francisco, 1994—; speaker in field. Contbr. articles to profl. jours. Trustee Law Ctr. Found. NYU, 1981—. Mem. ABA, D.C. Bar, State Bar Calif., Order of Coif, Phi Beta Kappa, Cosmos Club. Home: 550 Davis St Apt 26 San Francisco CA 94111-1953 Office: O'Melveny & Myers Embarcadero Ctr W 275 Battery St San Francisco CA 94111-3305

WARNATH, MAXINE AMMER, organizational psychologist, mediator; b. N.Y.C., Dec. 3, 1928; d. Philip and Jeanette Ammer; m. Charles Frederick Warnath, Aug. 20, 1952; children: Stephen Charles, Cindy Ruth. B.A., Bklyn. Coll., 1949; M.A., Columbia U., 1951, Ed.D., 1982. Lic. psychologist, Oreg. Various profl. positions Hunter Coll., U. Minn., U. Nebr., U. Oreg., 1951-62; assoc. prof. psychology Oreg. Coll. Edn., Monmouth, 1962-77; assoc. prof. psychology, chmn. dept. psychology and spl. edn. Western Oreg. St. Coll., Monmouth, 1978-83, prof. 1986—; dir. organizational psychology program 1983—; pres. Profl. Perspectives Internat., Salem, Oreg., 1987—; cons., dir. Orgn. Rsch. and Devel., Salem, Oreg., 1983-87, seminar leader Endeavors for Excellence program. Author: Power Dynamism, 1987. Mem. APA (com. pre-coll. psychology 1970-74), ASTD, N.Y. Acad. Sci., Oreg. Acad. Sci., Oreg. Psychol. Assn. (pres. 1980-81, pres.-elect 1979-80, legis. liaison 1977-78), Western Psychol. Assn. Office: Profl Perspectives Internat PO Box 2265 Salem OR 97308-2265

WARNE, RONSON JOSEPH, mathematics educator; b. East Orange, N.J., June 14, 1930; s. Ronson Joseph and Mildred (Morton) W.; m. Gloria Jean La France, Oct. 24, 1950. BA, Columbia U., 1953; MS, NYU, 1955; PhD, U. Tenn., 1959. Teaching asst., instr. U. Tenn., Knoxville, 1955-59; asst. prof. Math. La. State U., New Orleans, 1959-63; assoc. prof. Math. Va. Polytech. Inst., Blacksburg, 1963-64; prof. Math. W.Va. U., Morgantown, 1964-70, U. Ala., Birmingham, 1970-89, King Fahd U. of Petroleum and Minerals, Dhahran, Saudi Arabia, 1989—. Contbr. articles to profl. jours. Oak Ridge Nat. Lab. fellow, 1960, Dryser fellow, U. Tenn., 1957; vis. rsch. scholar U. Calif., Berkeley, 1982. Mem. Am. Math. Soc. Avocations: body building, weightlifting, running. Office: KFUPM # 1564, Dhahran 31261, Saudi Arabia

WARNE, WILLIAM ELMO, irrigationist; b. nr. Seafield, Ind., Sept. 2, 1905; s. William Rufus and Nettie Jane (Williams) W.; m. Edith Margaret Peterson, July 19, 1929; children: Jane Ingrid (Mrs. David C. Beeder), William Robert, Margaret Edith (Mrs. John W. Monroe). AB, U. Calif., 1927; DEcons (hon.), Yonsei U., Seoul, 1959; LLD, Seoul Nat. U., 1959. Reporter San Francisco Bull. and Oakland (Calif.) Post-Enquirer, 1925-27; news editor Brawley (Calif.) News, 1927, Calexico (Calif.) Chronicle, 1927-28; editor, night mgr. L.A. AP, 1928-31, corr. San Diego bur., 1931-33, Washington corr., 1933-35; editor, bur. reclamation Dept. Interior, 1935-37; on staff Third World Power Conf., 1936; assoc. to reviewing com. Nat. Resources Com. on preparation Drainage Basin Problems and Programs, 1936, mem. editorial com. for revision, 1937; chief of information Bur. Reclamation, 1937-42; co-dir. (with Harlan H. Barrows) Columbia Basin Joint Investigations, 1939-42; chief of staff, war prodn. drive WPB, 1942; asst. dir. div. power Dept. Interior, 1942-43, dept. dir. information, 1943; asst. commr. Bur. Reclamation, 1943-47; apptd. asst. sec. Dept. Interior, 1947, asst. sec. Water and Power Devel., 1950-51; U.S. minister charge tech. cooperation Iran, 1951-55, Brazil, 1955-56; U.S. minister and econ. coord. for Korea, 1956-59; dir. Cal. Dept. Fish and Game, 1959-60, Dept. Agr., 1960-61, Dept. Water Resources, 1961-67; v.p. water resources Devel. and Resources Corp., 1967-69; resources cons., 1969—; pres. Warne & Blanton Pubs. Inc., 1985-90, Warne Walnut Wrancho, Inc., 1979—; Disting. Practi-

tioner in Residence Sch. Pub. Adminstrn., U. So. Calif. at Sacramento, 1976-78; adminstr. Resources Agy. of Calif., 1961-63; Chmn. Pres.'s Com. on San Diego Water Supply, 1944-46; chmn. Fed. Inter-Agy. River Basin Com., 1948, Fed. Com. on Alaskan Devel., 1948; pres. Group Health Assn., Inc., 1947-51; chmn. U.S. delegation 2d Inter-Am. Conf. Indian Life, Cuzco, Peru, 1949; U.S. del. 4th World Power Conf., London, Eng., 1950; mem. Calif. Water Pollution Control Bd., 1959-67; vice chmn. 1960-62; mem. water pollution control adv. bd. Dept. Health, Edn. and Welfare, 1962-65, cons., 1966-67; chmn. Calif. delegation Western States Water Council, 1965-67. Author: Mission for Peace-Point 4 in Iran, 1956, The Bureau of Reclamation, 1973, How the Colorado River Was Spent, 1975, The Need to Institutionalize Desalting, 1978; prin. author: The California Experience with Mass Transfers of Water over Long Distances, 1978; editor Geothermal Report, 1985-90. Served as 2d lt. O.R.C., 1927-37. Recipient Disting. Svc. award Dept. Interior, 1951, Disting. Pub. Svc. Honor award FOA, 1955, Order of Crown Shah of Iran, 1955, Outstanding Svc. citation UN Command Korea, 1959, Order of Indsl. Sv. Merit Bronze Star, Korea, 1991. Fellow Nat. Acad. Pub. Adminstrn. (sr., chmn. standing com. on environ. and resources mgmt. 1971-78); mem. Nat. Water Supply Improvement Assn. (pres. 1978-80, Lifetime Achievement award 1984), Internat. Desalination Assn. (founding mem., Lifetime Disting. Service award 1991), Soc. Profl. Journalists, Sutter Club, Nat. Press Club (Washington), Lambda Chi Alpha. Home and Office: 1570 Madrono Ave Palo Alto CA 94306-1015

WARNE, WILLIAM ROBERT, economist; b. Washington, Nov. 30, 1937. BA, Princeton U., 1960; MA, Johns Hopkins U., 1974. Provincial advisor U.S. Mission, Vinh Binh, Vinh Long, Vietnam, 1962-64; officer in charge trade, devel. and fin. policy U.S. Mission to European Communities, Brussels, 1974-77; dep. dir. East Asian Econ. Policy, 1977-79; dir. Caribbean affairs U.S. Dept. State, Kingston, Jamaica, 1979-81, charge d'affaires, dep. chief mission, 1981-84; dir. Latin Am. Econ. Policy U.S. Dept. State, Washington, 1984-86; counselor for trade, energy, social affairs and agr. U.S. Delegation OECD, Paris, 1986-88; v.p. Midwest Ctr. Exec. Coun. on Fgn. Diplomats, Indpls., 1988-89; pres. Korea Econ. Inst. Am., Washington, 1990—. With U.S. Army, 1960-62. Office: Korea Econ Inst Am 1101 Vermont Ave NW Ste 401 Washington DC 20005

WARNECKE, MICHAEL O., lawyer; b. Chgo., June 28, 1941. BS, ME, Purdue U., 1963; JD, George Washington U., 1967. Bar: Ill. 1967. Ptnr. Keck, Mahin & Cate, Chgo.; lectr. in field. Mem. ABA, Am. Arbitration Assn. (mem. panel arbitrators), Am. Intellectual Property Law Assn., Chgo. Bar Assn., Bar Assn. 7th Cir., Intellectual Property Law Assn. Chgo., Internat. Patent and Trademark Assn. Office: Keck Mahin & Cate 77 W Wacker Dr Ste 4900 Chicago IL 60601-1693

WARNECKE, RICHARD BASLEY, social epidemiology and medical sociology researcher and educator; b. Bklyn., Aug. 23, 1937; s. Robert I. and Althea (Reynolds) W.; m. Barbara Billings, Aug. 24, 1963; children—Mark, Elizabeth. B.S. in Indsl. Relations, Cornell U., 1959; M.A., Colgate U., 1963; Ph.D. in Sociology, Duke U., 1966. Asst. prof. sociology SUNY-Buffalo, 1967-74; assoc. prof. U. Ill.-Chgo., 1974-82; prof. sociology and epidemiology, 1982—; assoc. dir. Survey Research Lab., 1974-82, dir. Survey Research Lab., 1982—; assoc. dir. Ill. Cancer Council, Chgo., 1976-82, dep. dir. Ill. Cancer Coun., 1983-86; cons. Nat. Cancer Inst., Bethesda, Md., 1979—. Contbr. articles to profl. publs. Nat. Cancer Inst. grantee, 1977—. Mem. Soc. Epidemiol. Research, Am. Assn. Pub. Opinion Research, Am. Statis. Assn., Am. Soc. Preventive Oncology. Office: U Ill Survey Research Lab Ste 500 910 W Van Buren M/C 336 Chicago IL 60607

WARNEMUNDE, BRADLEY LEE, insurance company executive; b. Norfolk, Nebr., Mar. 21, 1933; s. Erwin Theodore and Frances Irene (Render) W.; m. Mary Fauneil Carhart, Aug. 3, 1952 (div. Nov. 1981); children—Jon B., Ralph E., Brian C., Clay S. Student, Kans. State Coll., 1950-51, U. Nebr., 1952-53. With Ohio Nat. Life Ins. Co., 1954—; from agt. to exec. v.p. mktg. Ohio Nat. Life Ins. Co., Cin., 1969-84, pres., 1984-93, chmn., CEO, 1985-94, chmn. emeritus, 1994—, also bd. dirs.; mem. bd. advisers U. Cin. Coll. Bus. Adminstrn., 1978-79. Grad. Leadership Cin. Program, 1985, chmn. Leadership Cin. steering com., 1989-90; chmn. corp. div. Cin. Fine Arts Fund, 1990; bd. dirs. LOMA/Life Mgmt. Inst. Atlanta, 1988-92. Mem. Life Ins. Mktg. and Rsch. Assn. Hartford (past mem., bd. dirs.), Am. Coun. Life Ins. (bd. dirs. 1993—), Assn. Ohio Life Cos. (pres. 1990), Cin. C. of C., Eastern Hills Tennis Club, Queen City Club, Comml. Club, Masons, Shriners. Republican. Lutheran. Avocations: tennis; fishing; gardening. Home: 7081 Salem Rd Cincinnati OH 45230-2946 Office: Ohio Nat Life Ins Co Ste 205 250 William Howard Taft Rd Cincinnati OH 45219-2662

WARNER, BARRY GREGORY, geographer; b. Cambridge, Ont., Can., July 20, 1955; s. Gregory O. and Alma (Jansen) W. B in Environ. Studies, U. Waterloo, 1978, MS, 1980; PhD, Simon Fraser U., Burnaby, Can., 1984. Rsch. asst. prof. U. Waterloo, Ont., 1985-89, rsch. assoc. prof., 1989-91, assoc. prof. geography, 1991—; interim dir. Wetlands Rsch. Inst., 1991—; U. Neuchatel; vis. prof. U. Neuchatel, 1993; chair Can. Nat. Wetlands Working Group, 1993—. Editor: Methods in Quaternary Ecolgy, 1990; contbr. articles to profl. jours. Postdoctoral fellow Natural Scis. and Engring. Rsch. Coun. of Can., 1984-85, rsch. fellow, 1985-90; fellow Suisse Nat. Res. Fond, 1993. Fellow Geol. Assn. Can. Office: Univ of Waterloo, Dept Geography, Waterloo, ON Canada N2L 3G1

WARNER, BART C., retail executive; b. 1953. Grad., U. Utah. Pres. BCW Enterprises, Inc., Salt Lake City, 1979—. Office: BCW Enterprises Inc 310 W 1370 S Salt Lake City UT 84115*

WARNER, CECIL RANDOLPH, JR., lawyer; b. Ft. Smith, Ark., Jan. 13, 1929; s. Cecil Randolph and Reba (Cheeves) W.; m. Susan Curry, Dec. 10, 1955 (div. 1982); children: Susan Rutledge, Rebecca Jane, Cecil Randolph III, Matthew Holmes Preston, Katherine Mary; m. Barbara Ragsdale, May 26, 1983. B.A. magna cum laude, U. Ark., 1950; LL.B. magna cum laude, Harvard U., 1953, Sheldon fellow, 1953-54. Bar: Ark. 1953. Ptnr. Warner & Smith and predecessor firm, 1954-89; pres., CEO, Fairfield Communities Inc., Little Rock, 1973-81; chmn., CEO Fairfield Communities Inc., 1981-85, chmn., pres., CEO, 1985-91; chmn., pres., CEO Environ. Systems Co., Little Rock, 1991-93; cons., 1993—; chmn. bd. Wortz Co., Poteau, Okla., 1993—; instr. U. Ark. Sch. Law, 1954, 56; vice chmn. Ark. Constl. Revision Study Commn., 1967; v.p. 7th Ark. Constl. Conv., 1969-70. Scoutmaster troop 23 Boy Scouts Am., Fort Smith, 1955-58; commr. Ark. State Police Commn., 1970; bd. dirs. St. Vincent Infirmary Found., Ctrs. for Youth and Family. Fellow Am. Bar Found., Ark. Bar Found.; mem. ABA, Ark. Bar Assn. (past chmn. exec. com., past chmn. young lawyers sect.), Pulaski County Bar Assn., Am. Law Inst., Fifty for the Future, Phi Beta Kappa, Phi Eta Sigma, Omicron Delta Kappa, Sigma Alpha Epsilon. Methodist. Office: PO Box 7462 Little Rock AR 72217-7462

WARNER, CHARLES COLLINS, lawyer; b. Cambridge, Mass., June 19, 1942; s. Noel Landon and Charlotte (Collins) W.; m. Elizabeth Denny, Aug. 24, 1964; children: Peter, Andrew, Elizabeth. BA, Yale U., 1964; JD cum laude, Ohio State U., 1970. Bar: Ohio 1970. Assoc. Porter, Wright, Morris & Arthur and predecessor, Columbus, 1970-76, ptnr., 1976—, also mgr. labor and employment law dept., 1988-92. Pres. Peace Corps Svc. Coun., Columbus, 1974-76, Old Worthington (Ohio) Assn., 1976-78, Alliance for Quality Edn. Worthington, 1987-89, Worthington Ednl. Found., 1994—; chmn. lawyers sect. United Way, Columbus, 1983-84. Mem. ABA (subcom. chmn. EEO com. 1986-89, exec. com. Met. Bar Caucus 1992-94), Ohio State Bar Assn. (coun. of dels. 1993—, chmn. fed. cts. com. 1992-94), Ohio Met. Bar Assn. (pres. 1991-92), Columbus Bar Assn. (pres. 1991-92, bd. govs. 1982-87, 88-93), FBA, Ohio Assn. Civil Trial Attys. (exec. bd. 1988—), Nat. Coun. Ohio State U. Law Alumni Assn., Capital Club, Univ. Club, Yale Club (pres. 1979-81). Avocations: clarinet, singing, tennis. Home: 145 E South St Columbus OH 43085-4129 Office: Porter Wright Morris & Arthur 41 S High St Columbus OH 43215-6101

WARNER, DARRELL G., petroleum company executive. Pres. Exxon Pipeline Co., Houston. Office: Exxon Pipeline Co PO Box 2220 Houston TX 77252-2220

WARNER, DENNIS ALLAN, psychology educator; b. Idaho Falls, Idaho, Apr. 27, 1940; s. Perry and Marcia E. (Finlayson) W.; m. Charyl Ann DeHart, Dec. 12, 1962; children: Lisa Rae, Sara Michelle, David Perry, Matthew Arie. BS, Brigham Young U., 1964; MS with honors, U. Oreg., 1966, PhD, 1968. Asst. prof. edn. Wash. State U., Pullman, 1968-72, assoc. prof. edn., 1972-78, prof. edn., 1978-85, dir. tchr. edn., 1983-85, prof., chmn. ednl. counseling psychology, 1985-93, interim dir. Partnership Ctr., 1993-94; prof. edn. leadership and counseling psychology Wash. State U., Pullman, 1994—; vis. asst. prof. psychology U. Idaho, Moscow, 1971. Author: Interpreting and Improving Student Test Performance, 1982; contbr. articles to profl. jours. Postdoctoral research assoc. U. Kans., 1976-77. Mem. Am. Psychol. Assn., Council for Exceptional Children, Phi Delta Kappa. Mem. LDS Ch. Home: 645 SW Mies St Pullman WA 99163-2057 Office: Wash State Univ Dept Ednl and Counsel Psych Rm 371 Cleveland Hall Pullman WA 99164-2131

WARNER, DON LEE, dean emeritus; b. Norfolk, N.B., Jan. 4, 1934; s. Donald A. and Cleo V. (Slagel) W.; m. Patricia Ann Walker, Feb. 24, 1957; children: Mark J., Scott Lee. BS in Geol. Engring., Colo. Sch. Mines, 1956, MSc in Geol. Engring., 1961; PhD in Engring. Sci., U. Calif., Berkeley, 1964. Registered profl. engr., Mo. Geol. engr. Gulf Oil Corp., Casper, Wyo., 1956, Calif. Exploration Co., Guatemala, 1957-58; civil engr. U.S. Forest Svc., Gunnison, Colo., 1958-59; teaching asst. Colo. Sch. Mines, Golden, 1959-61; rsch. asst. U. Calif., Berkeley, 1962-64; rsch. geologist and engr. U.S. Pub. Health Svc., Cin., 1964-67; chief, earth scis. Ohio Basin Region Fed. Water Pollution Control Adminstrn., 1967-69; prof. geol. engring. U. Mo., Rolla, 1969-92, prof. emeritus geol. engring., 1992—, dean emeritus Sch. Mines and Metallurgy, 1992—, chmn., geol. engring., 1980-81, dean Sch. Mines and Metallurgy, 1981-93; bd. dirs. Underground Injection Practices Coun., 1985-89; mem. adv. com. to Sec. of Interior for Mineral Resources Rsch., 1985-92. Author: Subsurface Wastewater Injection, 1977. Special award scholarship Colo. Sch. Mines, 1951-56, grad. fellowship Colo. Sch. Mines, 1959-61, rsch. fellowship U. Calif., 1962-64; recipient Best Paper award Am. Water Works Assn., 1971. Mem. AIME, Am. Assn. Petroleum Geologists, Am. Inst. Profl. Geologists (cert.), Assn. Engring. Geologists, Am. Assn. Univ. Profs., Nat. Ground Water Assn. (sci.award 1984, disting. lectr., 1986), NSPE, Mo. Soc. Profl. Engrs., Rolla C. of C., Blue Key, Soc. Petroleum Engrs., Scabbard and Blade, Theta Tau, Tau Beta Pi. Avocations: fishing, boating, tennis, golf. Office: U Mo-Rolla Sch Mines and Metallurgy Rolla MO 65401-0249

WARNER, DOUGLAS ALEXANDER, III, banker; b. Cin., June 9, 1946; s. Douglas Alexander Jr. and Eleanor (Wright) W.; m. Patricia Grant, May 13, 1977; children: Alexander, Katherine, Michael. BA, Yale U., 1968. Officer's asst. Morgan Guaranty Trust Co., N.Y.C., 1968-70, asst. treas., 1970-72, asst. v.p., 1972-75, v.p., 1975-85; sr. v.p. Morgan Guaranty Trust Co., London, 1983-87; exec. v.p. Morgan Guaranty Trust Co., N.Y.C., 1987-89, mng. dir., 1989-90, pres., 1990-95, chmn., pres., CEO, 1995—, also bd. dirs.; bd. counselors Bechtel Group, Inc.; bd. dirs. Gen. Electric Co., Anheuser-Busch Cos., Inc.; mem. bd. overseers Meml. Sloan-Kettering Cancer Ctr., N.Y.C.; active The Bus. Coun. Trustee Pierpont Morgan Libr., Cold Spring Harbor Lab. Mem. Bankers Roundtable, Links Club, River Club, Meadowbrook Club (L.I.). Avocations: golf, skiing, shooting. Home: PO Box 914 New York NY 10268-0914 Office: Morgan Guaranty Trust Co of NY 60 Wall St New York NY 10260-0001

WARNER, E. JOHN, manufacturing financial executive; b. Chgo., Sept. 28, 1942; s. Eugene John and Kathryn (Jones) W.; m. Nan Shipley, Aug. 21, 1965; children: John Warner, Thomas Shipley. BSBA, Ohio State U., 1965; MCS, Harvard U., 1978; PEE, Carnegie Mellon U., 1981. Mgmt. trainee GM, Flint, Mich., 1965-68; asst. prodn. mgr. Diebold Inc., Canton, Ohio, 1968-70, prodn. mgr., 1970-77, gen. mgr. Wooster (Ohio) divsn., 1977-85, dir. strategic planning, 1985-88; pres. W.L. Jenkins Co., Canton, 1988—; guest lectr. Harvard U. Bus. Sch., Boston, 1979. Bd. dirs. United Way, Canton, 1987—, gen. campaign chmn., 1987; bd. dirs. Jr. Achievement, Wooster, 1985-89, YMCA, Wooster, 1980-85. Mem. Canton City Club, Glemoor Country Club. Episcopalian. Avocations: tennis, swimming, sailing, fishing, golf. Home: 3304 Croydon Dr NW Canton OH 44718-3220 Office: WL Jenkins Co 1445 Whipple Ave SW Canton OH 44710-1321

WARNER, EDWARD WAIDE, JR., lawyer; b. St. Louis, Oct. 17, 1951; s. Edward Waide Sr. and Barbara (Hardy) W.; m. Cecilia Tso, Oct. 1, 1983; children: Edward Waide Tso, Sarah Liang, Rebecca Li, Genevieve An Hardy. AB magna cum laude, Boston Coll., 1973; JD, Rutgers U., 1977; postgrad., U. Chgo., 1974. Bar: Mo. 1978, N.Y. 1980. Law clk. to sr. cir. judge U.S. Ct. Appeals (8th cir.), St. Louis, 1977-78; assoc. Davis, Polk & Wardwell, N.Y.C., 1978-85, ptnr., 1986—; bd. advisors Morin Ctr. Banking Law Studies, Boston U. Sch. Law. Trustee Episcopal Sch., N.Y.C., 1994. Mem. ABA, Internat. Bar Assn., Assn. of Bar of City of N.Y., Mo. Bar Assn., Knickerbocker Club, Appawamis Club, Manursing Island Club, Phi Beta Kappa. Home: 151 E 74th St New York NY 10021 Office: Davis Polk & Wardwell 450 Lexington Ave New York NY 10017

WARNER, FRANK WILSON, III, mathematics educator; b. Pittsfield, Mass., Mar. 2, 1938; s. Frank Wilson Jr. and Charlotte (Walton) W.; m. Ada Woodward, June 6, 1958; children: Bruce Woodward, Clifford Powell. BS, Pa. State U., 1959; PhD, MIT, 1963. Instr. MIT, Cambridge, 1963-64; acting asst. prof. U. Calif., Berkeley, 1964-65, asst. prof., 1965-68; assoc. prof. U. Pa., Phila., 1968-73, prof. math., 1973—, assoc. dean Sch of Arts and Scis., 1992—. Author: Foundations of Differentiable Manifolds and Lie Groups, 1971; contbr. articles to scholarly jours. Fellow Guggenheim Found., 1976. Mem. AAAS, Am. Math. Soc., Math. Assn. Am., Sigma Xi. Achievements include research on the conjugate locus of a Riemannian manifold, on existence and conformal deformation of metrics with prescribed gaussian and scalar curvatures, on great circle fibrations of spheres. Office: U Pa Dept Math Philadelphia PA 19104-6395

WARNER, HAROLD CLAY, JR., banker, investment management executive; b. Knoxville, Tenn., Feb. 24, 1939; s. Harold Clay and Mary Frances (Waters) W.; m. Patricia Alice Rethorst, Sept. 1, 1961; children—Martha Lee, Carol Frances. B.S. in Econs, U. Tenn., 1961, Ph.D., 1965. Asst. to pres. Third Fed. Savs., Savannah, Ga., 1965-67; v.p. and economist No. Trust Co., Chgo., 1967-73; sr. v.p. and chief economist Crocker Nat. Bank, San Francisco, 1974-79; sr. v.p. liability mgmt. Crocker Nat. Bank, 1979-82; exec. v.p., dir. fixed income mgmt. BA Investment Mgmt. Corp., 1982-84, dir., pres., chief operating officer, 1984-86; dir., pres. Montgomery St. Income Securities, Inc., 1984-86; sr. v.p. Bank of Am., San Francisco, 1982-86; chmn. BA Investment Mgmt. Internat., Ltd., 1985-86; pres. Arthur D. Gimbel, Inc., San Mateo, Calif., 1986-87; exec. v.p., chief investment officer Riggs Nat. Bank Washington, 1987-88; chmn. Riggs Investment Mgmt. Corp., 1988-89; sr. v.p., chief economist Bank of Calif., San Francisco, 1989-93; pres., chief investment officer MERUS Capital Mgmt., San Francisco, 1989-93; pres. Govett Asset Mgmt. Co., 1993—, Govett Fin. Svcs. Ltd., 1993—; lectr. dept. econs. U. Tenn., 1962-63, Grad. Sch. Bus., Loyola U., Chgo., 1969-73; lectr. Pacific Coast Banking Sch., U. Wash., 1978-79. NDEA fellow, 1961-64. Mem. Chgo. Commons Assn. (bd. dirs. 1973-74), Burlingame Country Club, Phi Gamma Delta, Phi Eta Sigma, Beta Gamma Sigma, Omicron Delta Kappa, Phi Kappa Phi. Home: 2419 Vallejo St San Francisco CA 94123-4638 Office: 650 California St San Francisco CA 94108-2702

WARNER, HARRY BACKER, JR., retired journalist, freelance writer; b. Chambersburg, Pa., Dec. 19, 1922; s. Harry Backer, Sr. and Margaret Caroline (Klipp) W. Student pub. schs., Hagerstown, Md. Reporter, editor, columnist Herald-Mail Co., Hagerstown, 1942-82. Author: All Our Yesterdays, 1969, A Wealth of Fable, 1976; editor, author (amateur jour.) Horizons, 1939—. Com. mem. Community Action Coun., Hagerstown, Civic Music Assn., Hagerstown, Washington County Adult Edn., Hagerstown; mem. publicity com. Washington County United Fund, Hagerstown. Recipient Hugo award World Sci. Fiction Convs., 1968, 72, 93, Hist. Preservation award Washington County Commrs., 1980. Mem. Spectator Amateur Press Soc. (v.p. 1982-95), So. Fandom Pubs. Alliance. Republican. Lutheran. Avocations: science fiction fandom, classical music. Home: 423 Summit Ave Hagerstown MD 21740

WARNER, HARRY HATHAWAY, financial consultant; b. Staunton, Va., Nov. 30, 1935; s. Morris Thompson and Virginia Drury (Worthington) W.; m. Mary Elizabeth Patrick, Sept. 24, 1960; children—Harry Hathaway, Cabell Worthington, Ann Morris, Morris Patrick. B.A., U. Va. Mil. Inst., 1957; grad., U. Va. Sch. Bank Mgmt., 1963, Stonier Grad. Sch. Banking, 1969. With Met. Nat. Bank, Richmond, Va., 1965-71; exec. v.p. Met. Nat. Bank, 1969-71; pres., dir. Transohio Fin. Corp., Cleve., 1971-78; exec. v.p. VMI Found., Lexington, Va., 1978-90; cons. in field; bd. dirs. Chesapeake Corp., Pulaski Furniture Corp. Va., Am. Filtrona Corp. Served as 2d lt. AUS, 1957. Recipient Distinguished Service award Richmond Jaycees, 1969. Episcopalian. Clubs: Country of Va, Commonwealth. Address: PO Box 1577 Lexington VA 24450

WARNER, JACK, JR., motion picture and television producer, writer; b. San Francisco, Mar. 27, 1916; s. Jack Leonard and Irma Warner Rogell; m. Barbara Ann Richman, May 30, 1948; children—Elizabeth Susan, Sally Jo (dec.), Deborah. A.B. cum laude, U. So. Calif., 1938. Formerly with home office Warner Bros. Pictures, Inc. (distbn. and exhbn. of films), U.S., Can.; former exec. television div. Warner Bros. Pictures, Inc., past v.p. charge TV commls. and indsl. films div.; prodr. short subject films Warner Bros. Studios, Burbank, Calif., in theatre dept. and distbn., 1946-49; prodr. Warner Bros. Studios, London, 1948-49; other exec. positions, until 1959; organizer own co. Jack M. Warner Prodns., Inc., 1949. Author: (novels) Bijou Dream, 1983, The Dream Factory, 1986; co-author: (nonfiction) Hollywood Be Thy Name, 1994. Past pres. Los Angeles County Assn. Mental Health; v.p. Mental Health Found. Served as 2d lt. Signal Corps Photog. Co.; advanced through grades to col. photo officer ETO, World War II; col. Res. ret. Mem. Acad. Motion Picture Arts and Scis. (asso.), Assn. U.S. Army, 12th Army Group Assn., Zeta Beta Tau, Pi Sigma Alpha. Democrat. Jewish.

WARNER, JAMES JOHN, small business owner; b. Paw Paw, Mich., Feb. 22, 1942; s. James Kelley and Arleta Alice (Turner) W.; m. Lynne Ann McGuire, June 19, 1965 (div. Apr. 4, 1994); children: Todd M., Kirk T., Beth K. BA, Mich. State U., 1965; postgrad., Western Mich. U., 1968-72. Sales rep. Warner Vineyards, Paw Paw, 1965-70, gen. mgr., 1970-73, v.p., 1973-75, pres., 1976—, also bd. dirs.; bd. dirs. Insularian Products Co., Lansing, Mich., 1975—. Chmn. Lakeview Found., Paw Paw, Mich., 1978, Van Buren County Econ. Devel. Corp., Paw Paw, 1977; dir. Van Buren Emergency Med. Svcs., Paw Paw, 1982, Hospice of Van Buren and Kalamazoo, 1988. With U.S. Army, 1966-68, Vietnam. Decorated Bronze Star. Mem. Am. Mktg. Assn. (Man of Yr. 1978), Am. Assn. Vintners (dir. 1981—), Young Pres.' Orgn. (chmn. 1982-83), Mich. Grape and Wine Industry Coun. Episcopalian. Avocations: reading, walking, sailing, gardening, swimming. Home: 304 S Kalamazoo St Paw Paw MI 49079 Office: Warner Vineyards 706 S Kalamazoo St Paw Paw MI 49079-0269

WARNER, JEFFREY F., banker; b. Casper, Wyo., Apr. 3, 1941; s. Daniel Louis and Lorence (Jamison) W.; m. Jennifer Forest, May 9, 1966; children: Paul, Jared, Denise. BS in Econs., U. So. Calif., 1964. Teller Casper Fed. Savs., 1966-68, loan officer, 1968-72, dir. new accounts, 1972-78, v.p. loan dept., 1978-84; sr. v.p. N.Y. State Bank, Syracuse, 1984-89, pres., CEO, 1989. Mem. Am. Banking Inst. (regional officer 1988—). Office: NY State Bank Werrik Plz 1072 James St # B-10 Syracuse NY 13203-2701

WARNER, JOHN ANDREW, foundry executive; b. Kansas City, Mo., Jan. 1, 1924; s. Richard G. and Margaret (Falconer) W.; m. Patricia Pooley, Feb. 25, 1950; children: Katherine, Amanda. Sec. Warner Oil Co., Oklahoma City, 1948-50; pres., chief exec. officer Tyler Pipe Industries, Tex., 1950-89; ret., 1989; bd. dirs. Tex. Power & Light Co., Dallas. Past chmn. East Tex. Hosp. Found.; trustee Tex. Chest Found.; former mem. Tex. Gov.'s Commn. on Phys. Fitness. Served with USCGR, 1942-46. Named Tyler's Most Outstanding Citizen, 1973. Mem. Tyler C. of C. (dir., past pres.), Cast Iron Soil Pipe Inst. (dir., past pres.), Am. Foundrymen's Soc. Tex. Assn. Bus. (dir., past state chmn.), Hollytree C. of C., Willow Brook Country Club (dir., past pres. Tyler), Masons, Shriners, Sigma Alpha Epsilon. Presbyterian. Home: 608 Rosemont Pl Tyler TX 75701-8643

WARNER, JOHN EDWARD, advertising executive; b. Troy, N.Y., Mar. 26, 1936; s. George Edward and Ann Frances (Teson) W.; m. Anne Elizabeth Hibbard, Sept. 19, 1959; children—Matthew J., Barbara A., Peter J., Christopher J. B.S. in Chemistry and Philosophy, Coll. Holy Cross, 1957. Promotion mgr. Union Carbide Corp., N.Y.C., 1957-62; account exec. McCann-Erickson, Inc., N.Y.C., 1962-64; pres. Warner, Bicking & Fenwick, Inc., N.Y.C., 1964-84; chmn. Warner, Bicking, Morris & Ptnrs. Inc., 1984—; Pres. Transworld Advt. Agy. Network, 1987—; speaker confs. advt. mktg. assns. Columnist advt. and mktg. publs. Home: 706 Hillcrest Rd Ridgewood NJ 07450-1110 Office: 866 UN Pla New York NY 10017

WARNER, JOHN HILLIARD, JR., technical services, military and commercial systems and software company executive; b. Santa Monica, Calif., Mar. 2, 1941; s. John Hilliard and Irene Anne (Oliva) W.; m. Helga Magdalena Farrington, Sept. 4, 1961; children: Tania Renee, James Michael. BS in Engring. with honors, UCLA, 1963, MS in Engring., 1965, PhD in Engring., 1967. Mem. staff Marquardt Corp., Van Nuys, Calif., 1963; mem. faculty West Coast U., Los Angeles, 1966-72; mem. staff TRW Systems Group, Redondo Beach, Calif., 1967-70; asst. mgr., 1970-73; mem. staff Sci. Applications Internat. Corp., San Diego, 1973-75, asst. v.p., 1975-77, v.p., 1977-80, corp. v.p., 1980-81, sr. v.p., 1981-87, sector v.p., 1987-89; exec. v.p. Sci. Applications Internat Corp., San Diego, 1989—, bd. dirs., 1988—; cons. Rand Corp., Santa Monica, 1964-66. Contbr. articles to profl. jours. AEC fellow, 1963, 66, NSF fellow, 1964, 65. Mem. AIAA, Assn. U.S. Army, Air Force Assn. Am. Def. Preparedness Assn., Am. Security Coun., Armed Forces Communications and Electronics Assn., Navy League U.S., La Jolla Chamber Music Soc. (bd. dirs. 1990—), Sigma Nu, Tau Beta Pi. Methodist. Avocations: bicycling, fishing, water skiing, music. Office: SAIC 10260 Campus Point Dr San Diego CA 92121-1522

WARNER, JOHN WILLIAM, lawyer; b. Amarillo, Tex., June 4, 1936; s. Arthur Greeley and Janet Karen (Miller) W.; m. Judith Diane Mumma, Dec. 30, 1961; children: Michael Allan, Sandra Kay, Melanie Diane, Patricia Karen. B.A., Tex. A. and M. U., 1958; LL.B., U. Tex., 1962. Bar: Tex. 1962. Practice law Pampa, Tex., 1962—; judge Municipal Ct., 1963-68; county atty. Gray County, Tex., 1969-76; discovery task force Tex. Supreme Ct., 1991-94. Dist. commr. Pampa Youth Coun., Inc., S.W. Indian Orgn., Inc., Master Home for Children, Inc., PHS Scholarship Fund, dir., 1988—; trustee Happy Haven Children's Home, 1970-71; coach Little League, 1974—; chmn. Gray County Dem. Party, 1987—; pres. Gray County chpt. Am. Cancer Soc., 1976-77; Sunday sch. tchr. 1st United Meth. Ch., 1962, chmn. adminstrv. bd., 1984, chmn. coun. ministries, 1986, lay leader, 1990-92. Recipient Adult Leader of Yr. award Pampa Jr. C. of C., 1969, Tru-Teens Leader of Yr. award, 1972, Pampa High Sch. Key Club Disting. Svc. award, 1966, 83, Spl. Achievement award panhandle Sports Hall of Fame, 1994. Mem. ABA, Tex. Bar Assn., Coll. State Bar Tex., Gray County Bar Assn., Assn. Trial Lawyers Am. (sustaining) Tex. Trial Lawyers Assn. (bd. dirs. 1988-92), Tex. Criminal Def. Lawyers Assn., Pampa C. of C., Pampa Jaycees (pres. 1968-69), Tex. Jaycees (legal counsel 1970-71), Kiwanis (pres. 1985-86), Optimists (pres. 1983-84, Optimist of Yr. award 1987). Home: 2111 Dogwood Ln Pampa TX 79065-3825 Office: Warner & Finney Box 645 Pampa TX 79066-0645 *The epitaph on my grandfather's grave reads: "He lived to serve." I have tried to live my life according to that philosophy.*

WARNER, JOHN WILLIAM, senator; b. Washington, DC, Feb. 18, 1927; s. John William and Martha Stuart (Budd) W.; children: Mary Conover, Virginia Stuart, John William IV. BS Engring., Washington and Lee U., 1949; LL.B., U. Va., 1953. Law clk. to U.S. judge, 1953-54, spl. asst. to U.S. atty., 1956-57; asst. U.S. atty. Dept. Justice, 1957-60; ptnr. Hogan & Hartson, 1960-68; owner, operator Cattle Farm, 1961—; undersec. of navy, 1969-72, sec. of navy, 1972-74; adminstr. Am. Revolution Bicentennial Adminstrn., 1974-76; U.S. senator from Va., 1979—. Served with USNR, 1944-46; to capt. USMCR, 1949-52. Mem. Bar Assn. D.C. Republican. Episcopalian. Club: Metropolitan. Office: Office of Senate 225 Russell Senate Bldg Washington DC 20510-4601

WARNER, KENNETH E., public health educator, consultant; b. Washington, Jan. 25, 1947; s. Edgar W. Jr. and Betty (Strasburger) W.; m. Patricia A. Hilty, Oct. 1, 1977; children—Peter, Andrew. A.B., Dartmouth Coll.,

1968; M.Phil., Yale U., 1970, Ph.D., 1974. Lectr. dept. health planning and adminstrn. Sch. Pub. Health, U. Mich., Ann Arbor, 1972-74; asst. prof. Sch. Pub. Health, U. Mich., 1974-77, assoc. prof., 1977-83, prof., 1983—, chmn., 1982-88, 92—, Office on Smoking and Health, USPHS, Rockville, Md., 1978—. Inst. Medicine, Nat. Acad. Scis., Washington, 1984—, numerous additional pub. and pvt. orgns.; mem. bd. sci. counselors div. cancer prevention and control Nat. Cancer Inst., Bethesda, Md., 1985-89. Author: (with Bryan Luce) Cost-Benefit & Cost Effectiveness Analysis in Health Care, 1982; contbr. articles to profl. jours. Trustee, Am. Lung Assn., Mich. Lansing, 1982; mem. subcom. on smoking Am. Heart Assn., Dallas, 1983-87; mem. com. on tobacco and cancer Am. Cancer Soc., N.Y.C., 1984—. Hon. Woodrow Wilson fellow, 1968; W.K. Kellog Found. fellow, 1980-83; vis. scholar Nat. Bur. Econ. Research, Stanford, Calif., 1975-76; recipient Surgeon Gen.'s medallion Dr. C. Everett Koop, 1989. Mem. Am. Pub. Health Assn., Am. Econ. Assn., Nat. Assn. Pub. Health Policy (sec. council on smoking prevention 1983-84), Phi Beta Kappa. Office: U Michigan Sch Pub Health Policy & Admin 109 Observatory St Ann Arbor MI 48109-2029

WARNER, KENNETH WILSON, JR., editor, association publications executive; b. Chgo., Dec. 22, 1928; s. Kenneth Wilson and Ann S. (Knapp) W.; m. Deborah Ann Bollo, Dec. 28, 1982 (div. Apr. 1995); 1 child, Joseph; children by previous marriages: Sara, Seth, Katharin. B.S. Ed., No. Ill. U., 1950. Staff editor Bldg. Supply News, Chgo., 1953-56; staff editor Elec. Merchandising, 1956-60; free-lance writer Sarasota, Fla., 1960-66; editor Gunsport Mag., Alexandria and Falls Church, Va., 1966-67; editor Gunfacts Mag., Arlington, Va., 1968-70, pub., 1968-70; exec. editor Am. Rifleman, Nat. Rifle Assn., Washington, 1971-78, asst. dir. publs. div., 1972-78; editor Am. Hunter, 1973-78, Am. Rifleman, 1976-78; dir. publs. NRA, Washington, 1977-78; editor in chief Gun Digest, Knives Annual-DBI Books Inc., Greenville, W.Va., 1979—; design cons. Blackjack Knives, Effingham, Ill. Author: The Practical Book of Knives, 1976; The Practical Book of Guns, 1978. Editor: The Bolt Action, 1976. Contbr. articles to profl. jours. Cpl. U.S. Army. 1951-53. Recipient Cutlery Hall of Fame. Mem. NRA (life), Knifemaker's Guild. Am. (assoc.). Office: Gun Digest Editorial Office PO Box 52 Greenville WV 24945-0052

WARNER, LAVERNE, education educator; b. Huntsville, Tex., Aug. 14, 1941; d. Clifton Partney and Velma Oneta (Steely) W. BS, Sam Houston State U., 1962, MEd, 1969; PhD, East Tex. State U., 1977. Cert. elem. sch. tchr., Tex. First grade tchr. Port Arthur (Tex.) Ind. Sch. Dist., 1962-64; kindergarten tchr. Burlington (Vt.) Community Schs., 1964-66; first grade tchr. Aldine Sch. Dist., Houston, 1967-68; music tchr. Crawfordsville (Ind.) Community Schs., 1968-71; prof. early childhood edn. Sam Houston State U., Huntsville, 1975—, chmn. faculty senate, 1988-89; chair faculty senate Sam Houston State U., 1990-91, chair-elect, 1989-90. Author: (with P. Berry) Tunes for Tots, 1982, (with K. Craycraft) Fun with Familiar Tunes, 1987, Language in Centers: Kids Communicating, 1991, Theme Escapapdes, 1992, What If...Themes, 1993; contrib. editor Good Apple, Inc., Carthage, Ill., 1986-88, 91-93; contbr. over 60 articles to profl. jours. Mem. Huntsville Leadership Inst., 1986-88, chmn. adv. bd. 1987-88, chmn. 1987-88; Community Child Care Assn., Huntsville, 1988-90. Recipient Sam Houston State U. Excellence in Teaching award, 1992, Tchr. Educator of Yr. award Tex. Assn. for Edn. Young Children, 1992. Mem. Tex. Assn. Coll. Tchrs. (life, past pres.), Nat. Assn. for Edn. Young Children (life), Tex. Elementary-Kindergarten Nursery Educators (state pres. 1982-84), Tex. Assn. for Edn. Young Children (v.p. 1988-89, newsletter editor, 1991-93, Teacher Educator of Yr. 1992, pres.-elect 1993—, pres. 1995), Huntsville Leadership Inst. Alumni Assn. (pres. 1988-89), Phi Delta Kappa (area 3H coord. 1986-92, Svc. Key 1987), Sam Houston Assn. for Edn. Young Children (charter, pres.-elect, 1991-92, pres. 1992-93), Sam Houston Univ. Women (pres. 1985-86), Huntsville High Sch. Ex-Students Assn. (charter, pres. 1989-91). Mem. Ch. of Christ. Avocations: music, reading, shopping. Office: Sam Houston State U Coll Edn and Applied Sci Huntsville TX 77341

WARNER, LEE HOWLAND, cultural programs director; b. Parkersburg, W.Va., Jan. 21, 1943; s. Edwin Brooks and Rebecca (Dailey) W.; m. Wenefred Gail Harter, Apr. 3, 1983; children by previous marriage: Jill, Gregory Lee. BA Juniata Coll., 1964; MA, U. Wis., 1965, PhD, 1971. Asst. prof. Fla. State U., Tallahassee, 1968-75; assoc. curator Hist. Tallahassee Pres. Bd., 1975-79; hist. preservation bd. coord. Fla. Dept. State, Tallahassee, 1979-81; asst. dir. Div. Archives History and Record Mgmt., Tallahassee, 1981-82; dir. Mus. Fla. History, Tallahassee, 1982-87; asst. dir. div. Hist. Resources, Tallahassee, 1987; exec. dir. Asolo Ctr. for Performing Arts, 1987—; trustee Tallahassee Jr. Mus., 1983-88; bd. dir., pres. Fla. History Assocs., Tallahassee, 1983-87. Editor: Photos of Alvin S. Harper, 1984; mng. editor: Jour. of Libr. History 1974-76; contbr. articles to profl. jours. NSF fellow, 1968; Council for Faculty Research grantee, 1974; Am. Philos. Soc. grantee, 1976. Mem. Am. Hist. Assn., Orgn. Am. Historians, Am. Assn. State and Local History (chmn. awards com. Region V), Fla. Hist. Records Com., Am. Assn. Mus. Home: 5240 Winding Way Sarasota FL 34242-1848 Office: Asolo Ctr 5555 N Tamiami Trl Sarasota FL 34243-2141

WARNER, MARK ROY, film editor. Editor: (films) (with Freeman Davies and Billy Weber) 48 Hours, 1982, (with Don Zimmerman) Rocky III, 1982, (with Zimmerman) Staying Alive, 1983, (with Caroline Biggerstaff) A Soldier's Story, 1984, (with Christopher Lebenzon and Scott Wallace) Weird Science, 1985, (with Steve Mirkovich and Edward A. Warschilka) Big Trouble in Little China, 1986, (with Warschilka and John Wright) The Running Man, 1987, Cocoon: The Return, 1988, Driving Miss Daisy, 1989 (Academy award nomination best film editing 1989?) Pacific Heights, 1990, Rush, 1992, (with John F. Burnett and Zimmerman) Leap of Faith, 1992, Rich in Love, 1992, Intersection, 1994, Dolores Claiborne, 1995. Office: care Motion Picture Editors 7715 Sunset Blvd #220 Los Angeles CA 90046*

WARNER, MICHAEL D., museum director; b. Salt Lake City, Nov. 1, 1949; s. Reed H. and Alma (Henline) W.; m. Ilene G. Reflow, Nov. 9, 1973; children: Ryan D., Joshua T. Student, Met. State Coll., 1969-71. Dist. mktg. mgr. Frontier Airlines, Inc., Denver, 1970-80; gen. mgr. Frontier Airlines, Inc., Colorado Springs, Colo., 1980-85; exec. dir. ProRodeo Hall of Fame, Colorado Springs, 1985—. Editor: (mag.) Roundup. Dir. Pikes Peak Sertoma, Colorado Springs, 1990, Tax Adv. Com., Colorado Springs, 1985-89; pres. Conv. and Vis. Bur., Colorado Springs, 1984. Republican. Avocations: golf, fishing, western art. Office: PRO Rodeo Hall of Fame & Mus Am Cowboy 101 Pro Rodeo Dr Colorado Springs CO 80919-2301

WARNER, MINER HILL, investment banker; b. N.Y.C., Aug. 13, 1942; s. Bradford Arnold and Nancy (Hill) W.; m. Ellen C. Murphy, Mar. 18, 1972; children—Alix Mallet-Prevost, Lily Wolcott. A.B., Harvard U., 1964; C.E.P., Institut d'Etudes Politiques, Paris, 1963; M.Sc. in Econs., London Sch. Econs., 1965; LL.B., U. Pa., 1968; postgrad., NYU. Grad. Sch. Bus. Adminstrn., 1971-73. Bar: N.Y. 1969. Assoc. Shearman & Sterling, N.Y.C., 1968-71; assoc. Salomon Bros. Inc., N.Y.C., 1971-73; v.p. Salomon Bros. Internat. Ltd., London, 1974-78; v.p., mgr. Salomon Bros. Inc., N.Y.C., 1979-87; dir. Merrill Lynch & Co., 1988-92; pres. Pub. Resources Internat., 1992—; former advisory dir. Council of the Americas, former dir. Woodwin Mgmt. Inc. Pres.'s Pvt. Sector Survey on Cost Control, Washington, 1982-83, 500 Club, N.Y.C. Republicans; sr. warden St. John's Ch., Fishers Island, N.Y., active Order of St. John's of Jerusalem; Pilgrims, N.Y.C.; trustee N.Y. Hist. Soc., Econ. Club, N.Y.; bd. dirs. Hay Harbor Club, Fishers Island. Recipient Order of St. John of Jerusalem. Mem. Mayflower Soc. Episcopalian. Clubs: Brook (sec.), Links, River, Downtown Assn. (N.Y.C.); Metropolitan (Washington); Fishers Island. Home: 148 E End Ave New York NY 10028-7503 Office: Pub Resources Internat 40 Rector St New York NY 10006

WARNER, PETER DAVID, publishing executive; b. Phila., Aug. 15, 1942; s. Robert and Myra (Spector) W.; m. Ruth Bluestein (div. 1982); m. Jill Sansone, 1983; children: Emily, Cynthia, Nicholas. BA, NYU, 1964. Asst. dir. membership and devel. Mus. Modern Art, N.Y.C., 1973-76; editor, promotion dir. Book-of-the-Month Club, N.Y.C., 1976-79; pres. Thames and Hudson, N.Y.C., 1979—. Author: Loose Ends, 1972, Lifestyle, 1986. Mem. The Writers Room (bd. dirs.). Office: Thames & Hudson Inc 500 Fifth Ave New York NY 10110-0001

WARNER, RAWLEIGH, JR., oil company executive; b. Chgo., Feb. 13, 1921; s. Rawleigh and Dorothy (Haskins) W.; m. Mary Ann deClairmont, Nov. 2, 1946; children: Alison W. Pyne, Suzanne W. Parsons. Grad. Lawrenceville (N.J.) Sch., 1940; A.B. cum laude, Princeton U., 1943. Sec. treas. Warner Bard Co., Chgo., 1946-48; with Continental Oil Co., 1948-53; asst. treas. Continental Oil Co., Houston, 1952-53; treas. Socony-Vacuum Overseas Supply Co., 1953-55; asst. treas. Mobil Overseas Oil Co., 1955-56; mgr. econs. dept., then mgr. Middle East dept. Socony Mobil Oil Co. Inc., 1956-59; regional v.p. Mobil Internat. Oil Co., 1959-60, exec. v.p., 1960-63, pres., 1963-64; exec. v.p., dir. Mobil Oil Corp. (formerly Socony Mobil Oil Co., Inc.), 1964, pres., 1965-69, chmn. bd., chief exec. officer, 1969-86; chmn. Mobil Corp., 1976-86. Trustee Solomon R. Guggenheim Found. Served to capt. F.A., AUS, 1943-45. Decorated Purple Heart, Bronze Star, Silver Star. Mem. Am. Petroleum Inst. Republican. Presbyn. Clubs: Augusta (Ga.) Nat. Golf; Links (N.Y.C.); New Canaan Country; Blind Brook (Rye Brook, N.Y.); Jupiter Island (Hobe Sound, Fla.); Chicago; Seminole (North Palm Beach, Fla.). Office: Mobil Corp PO Box 2072 New York NY 10163

WARNER, RICHARD DAVID, research foundation executive; b. Batavia, N.Y., July 22, 1943; s. Wesley Elmer and Adelia May (Elwell) W.; m. Susan Connelley, June 6, 1964; children: Mindy Sue, Craig Mathew; m. Eula Lorraine Anderson, Mar. 1, 1974; 1 child, Richard David Jr. BS, Houghton Coll., 1965; MS, Pa. State U., 1967. Rschr. Eastman Kodak Co., Rochester, N.Y., 1967-72; dir. computer programs Rayne Internat., N.Y.C., 1972-73; dir. R & D Consol. Internat., Chgo., 1973-74, Nashville Electrographics Co., 1975-76; rsch. dir. Graphic Arts Tech. Found., Pitts., 1977—; mem. Coun. Rsch. and Engring., Chadsford, Pa., 1989—; vice chmn. Internat. Assn. Rsch. Insts. for Graphic Arts Industries, Dramstadt, Fed. Republic Germany, 1990—. Contbr. articles to profl. publs. Achievements include invention of GATF's color communicator; patent for GATS's Dot Gain Scale-II; patent pending for GATF's acetuance guide. Office: Graphic Arts Tech Found 4615 Forbes Ave Pittsburgh PA 15213-3796

WARNER, ROBERT MARK, archivist, historian, university dean; b. Montrose, Colo., June 28, 1927; s. Mark Thomas and Bertha Margaret (Rich) W.; m. Eleanor Jane Bullock, Aug. 21, 1954; children: Mark Steven, Jennifer Jane. Student, U. Denver, 1945; B.A., Muskingum Coll., 1949, LL.D. (hon.), 1981; M.A., U. Mich., 1953, Ph.D., 1958; H.H.D. (hon.), Westminster (Pa.) Coll., 1981; L.H.D. (hon.), DePaul U., 1983. Tchr. high sch. Montrose, Colo. 1949-50; lectr. dept. history U. Mich., 1958-66, asso. prof., 1966-71, prof., 1971—, prof. Sch. Info. and Library Studies, 1974—, dean Sch. Info. and Library Studies, 1985-92, univ. historian, 1992—, interim dir. Univ. Libraries, 1988-90; asst. in rsch. Bentley Hist. Libr., 1953-57, asst. curator, 1957-61, asst. dir., 1961-66, dir., 1966-80; archivist of U.S., 1980-85; mem. exec. com. Bentley Hist. Libr., 1988—; bd. visitors Sch. Libr. Sci., Case Western Res. U., 1976-80, chmn., 1980-84, Maxwell Sch. Govt., Syracuse U., 1982-87; chmn. Gerald R. Ford Presdl. Libr. Bldg. Com., 1977-79; bd. dirs., sec. Gerald R. Ford Found., 1987—; trustee Woodrow Wilson Internat. Ctr. for Scholars, 1980-85, chmn. fellowship com., 1983-85; chmn. Nat. Hist. Publs. and Records Commn., 1980-85; mem. exec. com. Online Computer Libr. Ctr., 1990-93; bd. govs. Clements Libr., 1988-90, 93—, Clark Hist. Libr. Ctrl. Mich. U., 1987—; vis. prof. UCLA, 1993. Author: Chase S. Osborn, 1860-1949, 1960, Profile of a Profession, 1964, (with R. Bordin) The Modern Manuscript Library, 1966, (with C.W. Vanderhill) A Michigan Reader: 1865 to the Present, 1974, (with F. Blouin) Sources for the Study of Migration and Ethnicity, 1979, Diary of a Dream: A History of the National Archives Independence Movement, 1980-1995, 1995. Served with U.S. Army, 1950-52. Recipient Disting. Svc. award Muskingum Coll., 1990, Disting. Svc. award Nat. Hist. Pub. and Records Commn., 1992. Fellow Soc. Am. Archivists; mem. Am. Hist. Assn. (council 1981-85), Orgn. Am. Historians, ALA (council 1986-91), Assn. for Library and Info. Sci. Edn., Presbyn. Hist. Soc. (bd. dirs. 1987-91), Am. Assn. State and Local History, Hist. Soc. Mich. (trustee 1960-66, v.p. 1972-73, pres. 1973-74), Soc. Am. Archivists (mem. council 1967-71, sec., exec. dir. 1971-73, v.p. 1974-75, pres. 1976-77), Am. Antiquarian Soc., Phi Alpha Theta, Beta Phi Mu. Presbyterian. Club: U. Mich. Research. Lodge: Rotary. Home: 1821 Coronada Dr Ann Arbor MI 48103-5066 Office: U Mich Sch Info & Libr Studies 550 E University Ave Ann Arbor MI 48109-1092

WARNER, ROBERT S., company director, former accountant; b. Erie, Pa., Apr. 9, 1907; s. Spencer Roycraft and Anna Edith (MacDonald) W.; m. Doris Jean Squarey, June 29, 1931 (dec. Sept. 1987); children: Elizabeth S. (Mrs. Richard W. Bakenhus), Robert S. (dec.); m. Mary Catherine Moore, Oct. 13, 1990. Litt.B., Rutgers U., 1928. With Lybrand, Ross Bros. & Montgomery, C.P.A.s, N.Y.C., 1928-72; charge St. Louis office Lybrand, Ross Bros. & Montgomery, C.P.A.s, 1936-49; charge Los Angeles office Lybrand, Ross Bros. & Montgomery, C.P.A.s, Los Angeles, 1949-72; mem. firm Lybrand, Ross Bros. & Montgomery, C.P.A.s, 1944-72; mem. exec. com.; exec. com. Coopers & Lybrand; dir. Bixby Ranch Co. Trustee J.B. and Emily Van Nuys Charities, L.A., South Coast Med. Ctr. Found., South Laguna. Mem. Calif. N.Y. socs. C.P.A.s, Am. Inst. C.P.A.s. Clubs: Bohemian (San Francisco); Big Canyon Country (Newport Beach, Calif.). Home: 32 N La Senda Dr Laguna Beach CA 92677-3365

WARNER, SETH L., mathematician, educator; b. Muskegon, Mich., July 11, 1927; s. Seth LeMoyne and Agnes (Brustad) W.; m. Susan Emily Rose, June 16, 1962; children: Susan Emily, Sarah Southall, Seth Lawrence. B.S. Yale U., 1950; M.A., Harvard U., 1951, Ph.D., 1955. Rsch. instr. Duke U., 1955-57, asst. prof., 1957-61, asso. prof., 1961-65, prof. math., 1965—, dir. grad. studies math., 1960-68, chmn., 1968-70, 73-82; mem. Inst. Advanced Studies, 1959-60; vis. disting. prof. math. Reed Coll., 1970-71; visitor U. Paris, 1964-65, U. Oslo, 1982-83. Author: Modern Algebra, vols. I and II, 1965, re-issued, 1990, Classical Modern Algebra, 1971, Topological Fields, 1989, Topological Rings, 1993. Served with Med. Service Corps AUS, 1946-48. Mem. Phi Beta Kappa, Sigma Xi. Episcopalian. Home: 2433 Wrightwood Ave Durham NC 27705-5823 Office: Duke U Math Dept Durham NC 27708-0320

WARNER, THEODORE KUGLER, JR., lawyer; b. Phila., Sept. 13, 1909; s. Theodore Kugler and Anna (Allen) W.; m. Dorothy Wark Hoehler, Nov. 23, 1935; children—Betsy Ann (Mrs. Douglas R. Bulcher), Peter Joyce. A.B., U. Pa., 1931, LL.B. cum laude, 1934. Bar: Pa. 1934. With Pa. R.R., Phila., 1934-70; chief tax counsel Pa. R.R., 1952-58, dir. taxation, 1958-68, v.p. taxes, 1968, v.p. accounting and taxes, 1968-69, v.p. corp. adminstrn., 1969-70; pres. Can. So. Ry., 1968-70; v.p. Pitts. & Lake Erie R.R., 1968-70; officer, dir. other Penn Central cos., 1968-70; counsel Duane, Morris & Heckscher, Phila., 1970-71, Harper & Driver, 1975—; lectr. on consol. returns various tax forums. Bd. suprs. Easttown Twp., Pa., 1962-70, chmn., 1966-70; bd. dirs. Independence Found., 1991-92, sec., 1993, pres., 1993—. Mem. Nat. Tax Assn. (pres. 1965-66), Am. Law Inst. (life mem.), ABA, Pa. Bar Assn., Order of Coif, Aronimink Golf Club, Union League, Masons (33 deg., mem. com. on masonic homes 1970-84, chmn. 1975-77, 81-83, Franklin medal 1983, bd. dirs. treas. Masonic libr. and mus. 1991—), Tau Kappa Epsilon. Republican. Lutheran. Home: 39 Old Covered Bridge Rd Newtown Square PA 19073-1211 Office: 1000 N American Bldg Philadelphia PA 19107

WARNER, VINCENT W., bishop. Bishop Diocese of Olympia, Seattle, 1990—. Office: Diocese of Olympia PO Box 12126 1551 10th Ave E Seattle WA 98102-4298

WARNER, VINNIE, principal. Recipient Elem. Sch. Recognition award US Dept. Edn., 1989-90. Office: Barretts Sch 1780 Carman Rd Manchester MO 63021

WARNER, WAYNE HENRY, elementary and secondary educator; b. Phila., Oct. 11, 1941; s. Marion V. (Kreener) Warner; m. Mary JoAnn Halpert, Aug. 26, 1961; children: Stephen, Virginia, Matthew. BS in Elem. Edn., East Stroudsburg (Pa.) U., 1963; MEd, Temple U., 1969; postgrad., Trenton State Coll., Pa. State U. Cert. elem. tchr., phys. edn. tchr., ednl. media specialist. Elem. tchr., phys. edn. tchr. Bristol (Pa.) Twp. Schs., 1965-67; dir. media, tchr., head coach cross-country, gymnastics, track George Sch., Newtown, Pa., 1969-70; tchr. Centennial Schs., Warminster, Pa., 1963-65, 67-68, 1970-71; tchr. Oxford Hills Schs., South Paris, Maine, 1971-74;

regional mgr. Iams Co., Dania, Fla., 1974-86; asst. media dir., coach football and gymnastics, tchr. video prodn. Northfield (Mass.) Mount Hermon Sch., 1986-89; tchr., football coach Rogersville (Tenn.) City Sch., 1989-90; dir. phys. edn./athletics, head coach cross-country, baseball and track Brandon Hall Sch., Atlanta, 1990—; juror Nat. Film Festival, N.Y.C., 1988. Mem. NEA, Assn. Ednl. Rsch. and Tech., AAHPERD. Avocations: running, bicycling, camping, traveling, beekeeping. Office: Brandon Hall Sch 1701 Brandon Hall Dr Atlanta GA 30350-3799

WARNER, WILLIAM HAMER, applied mathematician; b. Pitts., Oct. 6, 1929; s. John Christian and Louise (Hamer) W.; m. Janet Louise West, June 29, 1957; 1 dau., Katherine Patricia. Student, Haverford Coll., 1946-48; B.S., Carnegie Inst. Tech., 1950, M.S., 1951, Ph.D., 1953. Research asso. grad. div. applied math. Brown U., Providence, 1953-55; asst. prof. dept. aerospace engring. and mechanics U. Minn., Mpls., 1955-58; asso. prof. U. Minn., 1958-68, prof., 1968—. Author: (with L.E. Goodman) Statics, 1963, Dynamics, 1964; contbr. articles to profl. jours. Mem. Am. Math. Soc., Soc. Indsl. and Applied Math., Math. Assn. Am., Soc. Natural Philosophy. Office: U Minn 107 Akerman Hall Minneapolis MN 55455

WARNICK, CHARLES TERRY, research biochemist; b. Brigham City, Utah, Jan. 29, 1943; s. Charles W. and Blanche (Richards) W.; m. Sandra Hathaway, Sept. 2, 1970; children: Derek, Darren, Bryan, Amber, Ashlee. BS, Brigham Young U., 1965; PhD, U. Utah, 1971. Postdoctoral fellow U. Ala., Edmonton, Alta., Can., 1970-72; rsch. assoc. U. Utah, Salt Lake City, 1972-74, clin. instr., 1974-79, asst. rsch. prof., 1979-81; asst. prof. biochemistry Latter Day Sts. Hosp. and U. Utah, Salt Lake City, 1981—; cons. clin. labs., 1985-90, also dir. rsch. lab., head R&D chemistry dept., 1990—. Contbr. articles to profl. jours. Fellow NASA, 1965, Nat. Cancer Inst. Can., 1970; grantee NIH, 1978, Utah Heart Assn., 1982. Mem. Am. Assoc. Clin. Chemists, Am. Chem. Soc., N.Y. Acad. Sci., Am. Inst. Chemists. Mormon. Avocations: marathon running, coin and stamp collecting. Office: Latter-day Saints Hosp Rsch Lab 325 8th Ave Salt Lake City UT 84143

WARNICK, WALTER LEE, mechanical engineer; b. Balt., May 31, 1947; s. Marvin Paul and Freda (Wilt) W.; m. Metta Ann Nichter, May 2, 1970; children: Ashlie Colleen, Leah Brooke. BS in Engring., Johns Hopkins U., 1969; PhD, U. Md., 1977. Registered profl. engr., Md. Engr. Westinghouse Electric Co., Linthicum, Md., 1969-71, U.S. Naval Rsch. Lab., Washington, 1971-77; engr. U.S. Dept. Energy, Washington, 1977-85, sr. exec., 1985—; Dept. Energy rep. Nat. Acid precipitation Assessment Program, Washington, 1981—; dep. dir. Program Analysis Office of Energy Rsch., 1995—. Author: Warnick Families of Western Maryland, 1988, 95, Wilt Families of Western Maryland, 1991. Pres. citizen's adv. com. to Howard County Bd. of Edn., Ellicott City, Md., 1980-82. Mem. ASME, Sigma Xi. Office: US Dept Energy Washington DC 20585

WARNKE, DETLEF ANDREAS, geologist, educator; b. Berlin, Fed. Republic of Germany, Jan. 29, 1928; came to U.S., 1955; s. Aloys and Martha (Konetzky) W.; m. Holly M. Menkel, Nov. 14, 1964 (div. 1993); children: Erik, D. Christian. Diploma in Geology, U. Freiburg, Fed. Republic of Germany, 1953; PhD in Geology, U. So. Calif., 1965. Jr. exploitation engr. Shell Oil, Houston and Los Angeles, 1956-58; research asst. U. So. Calif., Los Angeles, 1959-61; instr. various colls., Los Angeles and Long Beach, Calif., 1959-63; research assoc., asst. prof. Fla. State U., Tallahassee, 1963-71; from asst. prof. to prof. geology Calif. State U., Hayward, 1971—; exchange prof. Free U. Berlin, 1980-81. Contbr. articles to profl. jours. Fulbright scholar, 1987-88; NSF grantee. Mem. Geol. Soc. Am., Soc. Sedimentary Geology, Am. Geophys. Union, Am. Quaternary Assn., Geologische Vereinigung, Sigma Xi. Avocations: skiing, hiking. Office: Calif State U Dept Geol Scis Hayward CA 94542

WARNKE, PAUL CULLITON, lawyer; b. Webster, Mass., Jan. 31, 1920; s. Paul Martin and Lillian (Culliton) W.; m. Jean Farjeon Rowe, Sept. 9, 1948; children: Margaret Farjeon, Georgia Culliton, Thomas Martin, Stephen August, Benjamin Hyatt. A.B., Yale U., 1941; LL.B., Columbia U., 1948; LL.D. (hon.), Northland Coll., 1979, Franklin and Marshall Coll., 1983, George Washington U., 1984, Grinnell Coll., 1985, Amherst Coll., 1985, Haverford Coll., 1989. Bar: D.C. 1948. Assoc. Covington & Burling, Washington, 1948-57; ptnr. Covington & Burling, 1957-66; gen. counsel Dept. Def., 1966-67, asst. sec. def. for internat. security affairs, 1967-69; ptnr. Clifford, Warnke, Glass, McIlwain & Finney, 1969-77; dir. ACDA, Washington, 1977-78; chief U.S. arms control negotiator, 1977-78; ptnr. Clifford & Warnke, Washington, 1978-91, Howrey & Simon, Washington, 1991—; mem. Presdl. Adv. Bd. on Arms Proliferation Policy, 1995—; Scientific and Policy Adv. Com. of the Arms Control and Disarmament Agy., 1995—; spl. cons. to sec. state, 1978-81; mem. Md. and D.C. adv. coms. to U.S Commn. Civil Rights, 1962-66; trustee Lawyers Com. for Civil Rights Under Law; dir. Internat. Vol. Svcs., 1973-76; exec. com. Trilateral Commn., 1973-77; mem. China coun. Asia Soc., 1976-77; mem. disciplinary bd. D.C. Bar, 1973-75, bd. govs., 1976-77. Trustee Potomac Sch., 1958-66, chmn. bd., 1965-66; bd. dirs. Health and Welfare Coun. Nat. Capital Area, 1966-67; trustee Northland Coll., 1970-76, Columbia U., 1984-90; bd. dirs. Georgetown U., 1979-92, Wolftrap Found., 1978-83; bd. visitors Columbia U. Sch. Law; chmn. selection com. Albert Einstein Peace Prize Found., 1991-93; mem. governing bd. Common Cause, 1983-86. Lt. USCGR, 1942-46. Fellow Am. Bar Found.; mem. ABA, Fed. Bar Assn., D.C. Bar Assn., Coun. Am. Ambs., Am. Soc. Internat. Law, Coun. Fgn. Rels. Democrat. Clubs: Met. (Washington); Yale (N.Y.C.). Home: 5037 Garfield St NW Washington DC 20016-3465 Office: Howrey & Simon 3d Fl 1299 Pennsylvania Ave Washington DC 20004-2402

WARNKE, ROGER ALLEN, pathology educator; b. Peoria, Ill., Feb. 22, 1945; s. Delmar Carl and Ruth Armanelle (Peard) W.; m. Joan Marie Gebhart, Nov. 18, 1972; children: Kirsten Marie, Lisa Marie. BS, U. Ill., 1967; MD, Washington U., St. Louis, 1971. Diplomate Am. Bd. Pathology. Intern in pathology Stanford (Calif.) U. Med. Sch., 1971-72, resident in pathology, 1972-73, postdoctoral fellow in pathology, 1973-75, postdoctoral fellow in immunology, 1975-76, asst. prof. pathology, 1976-82, assoc. prof., 1983-90; prof., 1991—; cons. Becton Dickinson Monoclonal Ctr., Mountain View, Calif., 1982-88, IDEC, Mountain View, 1985-90; sci. advisor Ventana Med. Systems, Inc., Tucson, 1986—. Contbr. over 200 articles to med. jours., chpts. to books. Recipient Benjamin Castleman award Mass. Gen. Hosp., 1981; Agnes Axtel Moule faculty scholar Stanford U., 1979-82; Nat. Cancer Inst. and NIH rsch. grantee, 1978-95. Mem. So. Bay Pathology Soc., Calif. Soc. Pathologists, U.S. Can. Acad. Path., Am. Assn. Pathologists, Soc. for Hematopathology, European Assn. for Haematopathology. Home: 845 Tolman Dr Stanford CA 94305 Office: Stanford U Dept Pathology Stanford CA 94305

WARNKEN, DOUGLAS RICHARD, publishing consultant; b. N.Y.C., Apr. 17, 1930; s. Richard William and Juliette (Lindsay) W.; m. Virginia M. Thompson, Sept. 16, 1957; 1 child, William Monroe. A.B., Norwich U., 1952. Sales rep. Prentice-Hall, Inc., Nashville, 1954-56; regional sales mgr. Wadsworth Pub. Co., Inc., Chgo., 1957-59; nat. sales mgr. Wadsworth Pub. Co., Inc., Belmont, Calif., 1960-64; v.p. marketing mgr. Wadsworth Pub. Co., Inc., Belmont, 1964-68; exec. v.p. Wadsworth Pub. Co., Inc., 1968-70, pres., 1977-78, dir., 1971-78; pres. Wadsworth, Inc., 1978-85, chief exec. officer, 1980-84, vice chmn., 1985-86; chmn. bd. Wadsworth Pubs. of Can., Ltd., 1975-80; chmn. bd. Van Nostrand Reinhold Co. Inc., 1981-83, chmn. 1983-85; chmn. bd. Anaheim Pub. Co., Inc., 1982-85; dir. Van Nostrand Reinhold Co. Inc., Lange Med. Pubs., Inc., Internat. Thomson Orgn., Inc., 1982-85; chmn. HDL Communications, Inc., 1988—. Active Boy Scouts Am. Served to 1st lt. AUS, 1952-54. Named hon. Ky. coll., 1978. Mem. Vols. for Internat. Tech. Assistance, Belmont C. of C. (dir. 1970-80, pres. 1972-73), Western Book Pubs. Assn. (dir. 1971-78), Press Club of San Francisco. Republican. Presbyterian. Clubs: Carmel Valley Golf and Country, Monterey Country, Peninsula Golf and Country. Lodge: Knights of the Vine.

WARNKEN, PAULA NEUMAN, university library director, educator; b. La Crosse, Wis., Mar. 11, 1948; d. David M. and Gladys F. (Glickman) Neuman; m. Clifford H. Warnken, Sept. 12, 1970; children: Devin A., Jonathan D. BA, U. Wis., 1970; MLS, Kent (Ohio) State U., 1980; M of Edn. and Personnel Tng. and Devel., Xavier U., 1985. Pub. service librarian

Ohio U., Zanesville, 1976-80; head reader services Xavier U., Cin., 1980-84, dir. univ. libraries, 1984—, adj. instr. English, 1983—. Trustee OHIONET, 1987—. Mem. ALA, Acad. Library Assn. Ohio (pres. 1985-86). Office: Xavier U McDonald Meml Libr 3800 Victory Pky Cincinnati OH 45207-7332

WARNOCK, DAVID GENE, nephrologist; b. Parker, Ariz., Mar. 5, 1945. MD, U. Calif., San Francisco, 1970. Diplomate Am. Bd. Internal Medicine, Am. Bd. Nephrology. Intern U. Calif., San Francisco, 1970-71, resident, 1971-73; fellow nephrology NIH, Bethesda, Md., 1973-75; prof. medicine and pharmacology U. Calif., San Francisco, 1983; prof. U. Ala., Birmingham, 1988—; chief nephrology sect. VA Med. Ctr., Birmingham, 1983-88; prof., dir. divsn. nephrology U. Ala., Birmingham, 1988—, prof. medicine & physiology, 1988—. Mem. AAAS, Am. Physiol. Soc., Am. Soc. Clin. Investigation, Am. Soc. Nephrology. Office: U Ala Nephrology Rsch & Tng Ctr UAB Sta Birmingham AL 35294*

WARNS, RAYMOND H., judge; b. St. Paul, July 24, 1920; s. Henry John and Veronica (Jennings) W.; m. Ruth Elenor Fuhrman, Nov. 22, 1947; children—Stephen F., Mark J., Michael T., Raymond H. Student, U. Minn., 1941-42, 45-47; B.S.L., J.D., St. Paul Coll. Law, 1948-52. With law dept. Soo Line R.R., Mpls., 1952-57; with firm Battle, Neal, Harris, Minor & Williams, Charlottesville, Va., 1962-63; with Greyhound Corp., Chgo., 1957-61, 63-69, gen. counsel, 1965; v.p. claims Greyhound Lines, Inc. Greyhound Corp., 1969; gen. atty. Household Finance Corp., 1969-71; U.S. adminstrv. law judge Seattle, 1971-85; retired. Served as pilot USAAF, World War II. Mem. Ill. Bar, Am. Arbitration Assn. Home: 1890 Willow Ave NE Bainbridge Island WA 98110

WARONKER, LEONARD, record company executive; b. Los Angeles, Oct. 3, 1941; s. Simon and Jeanette (Gelber) W.; m. Donna Zuber, Mar. 24, 1968 (div. 1985); children: Joseph, Anna, Kate; m. Cathleen Hamro, Apr. 12, 1987. Grad., U. So. Calif., 1964. Pres. Warner Bros. Records, Burbank, Calif., 1983—. Office: Warner Bros Records 3300 W Warner Blvd Burbank CA 91505-4694*

WARREN, ALBERT, publishing executive; b. Warren, Ohio, May 18, 1920; s. David and Clara W.; m. Margaret Virginia Yeomans, Jan. 9, 1947; children: Ellen, Paul, Claire, Daniel, Thomas, Joan. BA in Journalism, Ohio State U., 1942. Assoc. editor TV Digest, Washington, 1945-50, sr. editor, 1950-58, chief Washington Bur., 1958-61; pres., editor, pub. Warren Pub., Inc., Washington, 1961—; lectr. Columbia Grad. Sch. Journalism, N.Y.C., 1962-75; mem. alumni adv. coun. Ohio State U., Columbus, 1982-88. Contbr. articles to profl. jours. Mem. adv. coun. to commitment Ohio State U., 1982—. With USNR, 1942-45, PTO. Mem. Ind. Newsletter Assn. (co-founder 1963, pres. 1965-66), Newsletter Pubs. Assn. (Pub. of Yr., 1985), Broadcast Pioneers, Cable TV Pioneers, Internat. Radio and TV Soc. Pubs., Mus. of Broadcasting, White House Corr. Assn., U.S. Congress Periodical Gallery, Soc. Profl. Journalists (Hall of Fame 1991). Home: 26 W Kirke St Chevy Chase MD 20815-4261 Office: Warren Pub Inc 2115 Ward Ct NW Washington DC 20037-1209

WARREN, ALEX MCLEAN, JR., automotive executive; b. Augusta, Ga., Aug. 4, 1940; s. Alex McLean and Bessie Clay (Farris) W.; m. Barbara Howell, Feb. 16, 1963 (div.); children: Elizabeth Clay, Brian Lee; m. Virginia A. Fitzgerald, Jan. 3, 1980. BA, U. Ky., 1962, LLB, 1965; MBA, U. Chgo., 1979. Bar: Ky. 1965, Pa. 1969. Labor atty. U.S. Steel Corp., Pitts., 1968-72; dir. indsl. rels. Rockwell Internat. Graphics Group, Chgo., 1972-75, dir. pers., 1975-77; corp. dir. human resources Allegheyn Internat. Chemetron Group, Chgo., 1977-80; v.p. human resources Leaseway Transp. Corp., Cleve., 1980-83, sr. v.p., 1983-86; sr. v.p. Toyota Motor Mfg. USA, Lexington, Ky., 1986—. Mem. task force Greater Cleve. Growth Assn., 1983-86, Ky. Econ. Devel. Corp., 1987—; bd. dirs. United Way Bluegrass, 1987—, Cleve. 500 Found., Fund for the Arts, 1988-90, Opera House Fund, 1988—, Ky. Ctr. for the Arts, 1993—; founder, co-chmn., bd. dirs. Bluegrass Tomorrow, 1988—. Capt. USAF, 1965-68. Mem. Georgetown C. of C., Champions of Golf Club. Republican. Presbyterian. Home: 890 Mcmeekin Pl Lexington KY 40502-2788 Office: Toyota Mfg USA Inc 1001 Cherry Blossom Way Georgetown KY 40324-9598

WARREN, ALFRED S., JR., automobile manufacturing company executive; b. 1926. BA, Muskingum Coll., 1948, LLD (hon.), 1988; MEd, U. Pitts., 1951. Conf. leader Gen. Motors Inst., Detroit, 1955-59; asst. personnel dir. Chevrolet div. Gen. Motors Corp., Buffalo, 1959-60, prodn. supr., 1960-64, gen. prodn. supr. axle plant, Buffalo, 1964-67, plant mgr. Chevrolet shell plant, St. Louis, then mgr. motor plant, Flint, Mich., 1967-68, mgr. axle plant, Warren, Mich., 1968-70, regional plant mgr. Chevrolet, Cleve., 1970-73, corp. dir. personnel devel., Detroit, 1973-77, gen. dir. personnel Fisher Body div., 1977-80, corp. v.p. indsl. relations, 1980—.

WARREN, ALVIN CLIFFORD, JR., lawyer, educator; b. Daytona Beach, Fla., May 14, 1944; s. Alvin Clifford and Barbara (Barnes) W.; m. Judith Blatt, Aug. 20, 1966; children—Allison, Matthew. BA, Yale U., 1966; J.D., U. Chgo., 1969. Bar: Conn. 1970, Pa. 1975. Prof. law U. Conn.-West Hartford, 1969-73, Duke U., Durham, N.C., 1973-74, U. Pa., Phila., 1974-79, Harvard U. Law Sch., Cambridge, Mass., 1979—. Mem. ABA (tax sect.). Contbr. articles to law jours. Office: Law Sch Harvard U Cambridge MA 02138

WARREN, CHARLES DAVID, library administrator; b. Martin, Tenn., June 12, 1944; s. Charles Alton and Evelyn (Bell) W.; m. Linda Ann Hild, July 10, 1971; children: Aaron David, Meredith Hild, Julia Myers. BS, U. Tenn., 1967; MS, U. Ill., Urbana, 1969. cert. pub. library adminstr. Dir. Shiloh Regional Library, Jackson, Tenn., 1969-72, Cumberland County Pub. Library, Fayetteville, N.C., 1973-79; exec. dir. Richland County Pub. Library, Columbia, S.C., 1979—; v.p. LHW Creations, Inc., 1979—; adv. bd. Simon & Schuster Co., 1989—. Bd. dirs. Civic Music Assn., Fayetteville, N.C., 1973-79, Fayetteville Symphony, 1973-78, Fayetteville Arts Commn., 1975, Friends of Librs. U.S.A., 1994—; mem. Columbia Coord. Coun., 1987-88; chmn. Richland County History Commn., 1987—; mem. John Cotton Dana Awards Commn., 1994—. Recipient Lucy Hampton Bostick award, 1993, S.C. Pub. Adminstr. Yr. award, 1993; named Young Man of Yr., Fayetteville Jaycees, 1977, S.C. Libr. of Yr., 1991. Mem. ALA (pres. Jr. Member Roundtable 1977, chmn. awards com. 1984), Southeastern Libr. Assn. (pres. pub. libr. sect. 1978), S.C. Libr. Assn. (bd. dirs. 1980), Caprician Club, Spring Valley Country Club, Rotary, Kiwanis. Democrat. Episcopalian. Home: 217 Cricket Hill Rd Columbia SC 29223-3003 Office: Richland County Pub Libr 1431 Assembly St Columbia SC 29201-3101

WARREN, CRAIG BISHOP, flavor and fragrance company executive, researcher; b. Phila., Oct. 21, 1939. AB, Franklin and Marshall Coll., 1961; MS, Villanova U., 1963; PhD, Cornell U., 1968. Rsch. chemist Monsanto Co., St. Louis, 1968-70, sr. rsch. chemist, 1970-72, rsch. specialist, 1973-75; group leader Internat. Flavors & Fragrances, Union Beach, N.J., 1975-77, sr. group leader, 1977-79, rsch. dir., 1979-83, v.p., 1983—. Editor: Odor Quality and Chemical Structure, 1981, Use of Computers in Flavor and Fragrance Research, 1983; contbr. 30 articles to profl. jours.; patentee in field. Mem. exec. coun. Boy Scouts Am., Monmouth County, N.J., 1981-85. Rsch. fellow NIH, 1964-68. Mem. Assn. Rsch. Dirs. (pres. 1989-90), Am. Chem. Soc. (chmn. Monmouth Country chpt. 1980-81), N.Y. Acad. Sci., Indsl. Rsch. Inst., ASTM. Avocations: bicycling, sailing, skiing, tropical fish, personal computers. Office: Internat Flavors & Frangrance 1515 Highway 36 Keyport NJ 07735

WARREN, DAVID BOARDMAN, museum director, art curator; b. Balt., Mar. 11, 1937; s. Robert Otey Yancey Warren and Florence Elizabeth Prickett Hershey; m. Gabrielle Lavielle Fraser, Apr. 24, 1971 (div. July 1978); 1 son, Robert Wilson Fraser; m. Janie Currie Lee, Jan. 2, 1980. AB cum laude, Princeton U., 1959; MA, U. Del., 1965. Curator Bayou Bend Collection, Mus. Fine Arts, Houston, 1965-86, assoc. dir. collection, 1974-86, 1986—, assoc. dir., sr. curator, 1986—; cons. Friends of Gov.'s Mansion, Austin; mem. bd. Winterthur Mus.; dir. Winterthur Corp.; mem. adv. com. Tex. area project Archives of Am. Art, Houston, 1979-83, Mt. Vernon Ladies Assn. of Union, 1989—. Author: Bayou Bend: American Furniture Paintings and Silver in the Bayou Bend Collection, 1975; (with others) Texas

Furniture: The Cabinetmakers and Their Work 1940-1880, 1975, Marks of Achievement: Four Centuries of American Presentation Silver, 1986, (with Katherine S. Howe) exhbn. catalogue The Gothic Revival style in America, 1830-1870, 1976; author, co-author other exhbn. catalogs. Served to lt. USNR, 1960-63. Mem. Philos. Soc. Tex. Republican. Episcopalian. Office: Museum of Fine Arts 1001 Bissonnet St Houston TX 77005-1896

WARREN, DAVID GRANT, lawyer, educator; b. Chgo.; m. Marsha White, 1959. A.B., Miami U., Oxford, Ohio, 1958; J.D., Duke U., 1964. Bar: N.C. 1964. Prof. Med. Ctr., Duke U., Durham, N.C., 1975—; exec. dir. N.C. Med. Malpractice Study Commn., 1986, Gov.'s Inst. on Alcohol and Substance Abuse, 1991—; faculty mem. U.N.C., U. London, Georgetown U., McGill U. News editor Jour. Health Politics, Policy and Law, 1977—. Office: Duke U Med Ctr PO Box 2914 Durham NC 27715-2914

WARREN, DAVID HARDY, psychology educator; b. Chelsea, Mass., July 28, 1943; s. Roland Leslie and Margaret (Hodges) W.; m. Katherine V. Warren; children: Michael Jonathan Warren, Gabriel Kristopher Coy. A.B. in Psychology, Yale U., 1965; Ph.D. in Child Devel, U. Minn., 1969. Prof. psychology U. Calif., Riverside, 1969—, dean Coll. Humanities and Social Scis., 1977-85, dir. Univ. honors program, 1989-92, chair dept. psychology, 1992-94, exec. vice chancellor, 1994—. Author: Blindness and Early Childhood Development, 1977, 84, Blindness and Children: An Individual Differences Approach, 1994; contbr. articles to profl. jours. Mem. Psychonomic Soc., AAAS. Office: U Calif Office of Exec Vice Chancellor Riverside CA 92521

WARREN, DAVID LILES, educational association executive; b. Goldsboro, N.C., Sept. 15, 1943; s. James Hubert and Katherine (Liles) W.; m. Ellen Elizabeth LeGendre, Mar. 1, 1969; children—Jamison, Mackenzie, Katrin. B.A. in English, Wash. State U., 1965; M. Urban Studies, Yale U., 1970, M.Div., 1970; Ph.D., U. Mich., 1976; LittD, LLD, Moravian Coll., 1994; LittD, Elmhurst Coll., 1994. Gen. sec. Dwight Hall, Yale U., New Haven, 1969-76, bd. dirs., 1976—; assoc dir. community relations Yale U., New Haven, 1976-78; sr. v.p., provost Antioch U., N.Y.C. and Yellow Springs, Ohio, 1978-82; chief adminstrv. officer City of New Haven, 1982-84; pres. Ohio Wesleyan U., Delaware, 1984-93, Nat. Assn. Indep. Colls. and Univs., Washington, 1993—; cons. to hosps., sch. systems, colls., univs.; bd. dirs. Delaware County Bank; chmn. NCAA Pres. Commn., Div. III, 1990-92. Contbr. chpts. to books, articles to Yale Alumni Mag. Mem. New Haven Bd. Alderman, 1973-75; vice chmn. New Haven Commn. on Poverty, 1981-82; pres. North Coast Athletic Conf., 1988-90; justice of peace New Haven Democratic Party, 1974-76; state chmn. People to People, 1987; chmn. Gov.'s Task Force on Dep. Registrar, 1987; chmn. Ohio Five Coll. Commn., 1985-95, Campus Compact Nat. Exec. Com., 1987-88; bd. dirs. U.S. Health Corp., Coun. Ethics and Econs.; exec. com. Great Lakes Colls. Assn., Cen. Ohio Symphony Orch.; chmn. Ohio Ethics Commn. Fulbright scholar Wash. State U., 1965-66; Rockefeller fellow Yale U., 1966; disting. Centennial Alumnus Wash. State U. Mem. Am. Assn. Higher Edn., Assn. Ind. Colls. Univs. (sec. 1987-88), Phi Beta Kappa. Democrat. Methodist. Clubs: University (Columbus, Ohio); Graduate (New Haven). Avocations: jogging; writing; tennis. Office: Nat Assn Ind Colls and Univs Ste 700 1025 Conecticut Ave NW Washington DC 20036-5405

WARREN, DONALD, university dean, education educator; b. Waco, Tex., Sept. 27, 1933; s. Loren H. and Oma (Chastain) W.; children: William Wood, Benjamin Loren, Jonathan Barnett (dec.). AB, U. Tex., 1957; MDiv, Harvard U., 1960; PhD, U. Chgo., 1968. Dir. program Cambridge (Mass.) Neighborhood House, 1958-60; dean students Coll. House Program U. Tex., Austin, 1960-62; dir. studies Ecumenical Inst., Chgo., 1962-64; rsch. assoc. U. Chgo., 1965-67; asst. prof. Chgo. State U., 1968-69; from asst. to assoc. prof. edn. U. Ill., Chgo., 1969-79, head dept. policy studies Coll. Edn., 1970-79, dir. joint PhD program in policy analysis, 1977-79, co-dir. project curriculum devel., 1974-76; prof., dept. chair edn. policy, planning, and adminstrn. Coll. Edn. U. Md., College Park, 1979-90; prof., U. Dean Sch. Edn. Ind. U., Bloomington, 1990—; vis. prof. edn. policy U. Hawaii Manoa, 1987; internat. and nat. presenter, cons. in field. Author: To Enforce Education: A History of the Founding Years of the United State Office of Education, 1974, (with others) Pride and Promise: Schools of Excellence for All the People, 1984; editor: American Teachers: Histories of a Profession at Work, 1989, History, Education, and Public Policy: Recovering the American Educational Past, 1978; contbr. chpts. to books, articles to profl. jours.; mem. editorial bd. Ednl. Founds., 1990-94, History Edn. Quar., 1980-84, 89-93, Ednl. Studies, 1982-85, 1976-79, Rev. Jour. Philosophy and Social Sci., 1982-85, Issues Edn., 1981-83; assoc. editor Ednl. Theory, 1976-79. Mem. policy adv. com. Ctr. Philanthropy, Indpls., 1990-93, adv. bd. Polaroid Corp. Edn. Project, 1985-88, nat. adv. bd. Sch. Edn. and Human Svcs. Gallaudet U., Washington, 1982-92, Md. Common. Secondary Edn., 1982-85, adv. bd. Paul and Jean Hanna Collection Edn. Hoover Instn., Stanford U., 1985—; bd. dirs. Ind. Pub. Sch.-Univ. Partnership, Indpls. 1990—. Mem. Am. Ednl. Rsch. Assn. (v.p. 1983-85 div. history and historiography), Coun. Learned Socs. Edn. (pres. 1979-83), Am. Ednl. Studies Assn. (pres. 1974-75), History Edn. Soc. (pres. 1990-91). Home: 2729 Brigs Bend Bloomington IN 47401-4402 Office: Ind U Sch Edn Wendell W Wright Edn Bldg 201 N Rose Ave Bloomington IN 47405-1006

WARREN, DONALD WILLIAM, physiology educator, dentistry educator; b. Bklyn., Mar. 22, 1935; s. Sol B. and Frances (Plotkin) W.; m. Priscilla Girardi, June 10, 1956; children: Donald W. Jr., Michael C. BS, U. N.C., 1956, DDS, 1959; MS, U. Pa., 1961, PhD, 1963; d Odontology honoris causa, U. Kuopio, Finland, 1991. Asst. prof. dentistry U. N.C., Chapel Hill, 1963-65, dir. Craniofacial Ctr., 1963—, assoc. prof., 1965-69, prof., 1969-80, chmn. dept. dental ecology, 1970-85, Kenan prof., 1980—, rsch. prof. otolaryngology, 1985—; cons. NIH, Bethesda, Md., 1967—; R. J. Reynolds-Nabisco, Winston-Salem, N.C., 1986—. Contbr. articles to profl. jours. Recipient Honor award Am. Cleft Palate Assn./Craniofacial Assn., 1992, O. Max Garner award U. N.C. Bd. Govs., 1993. Fellow AAAS, Internat. Coll. Dentists, Am. Speech and Hearing Lang. Assn., Internat. Assn. Dental Rsch., Acoustical Soc. Am., Am. Cleft Palate Assn. (pres. 1981-82, Disting. Svc. award 1984), Am. Cleft Palate Edn. Found. (pres. 1976-77). Avocations: horse related activities, running, farming. Home: PO Box 1356 Southern Pines NC 28388 Office: U NC Sch Dentistry CB # 7450 Chapel Hill NC 27599

WARREN, EDUS HOUSTON, JR., investment management executive; b. Danville, Va., Dec. 9, 1923; s. Edus Houston and Edith (Farley) W.; children: Ann Warren Ketchledge, Ralph Lounsbury, Sarah Randolph, Edus Houston III; m. Harriet C. Higgins, May 5, 1990. A.B., Harvard U., 1946. With Spencer Trask & Co., Inc., N.Y.C., 1951-77; gen. partner Spencer Trask & Co., Inc., 1959-68, pres., chief exec. officer, dir., 1974-77; vice chmn. Hornblower, Weeks, Noyes & Trask, Inc. (merger Spencer Trask & Co., Inc./Hornblower, Weeks, Hemphill, Noyes), 1977-78; exec. v.p., mem. fin. com., mem. exec. com. Loeb Rhoades, Hornblower & Co.; vice chmn. Capital Guardian Research Co., N.Y.C., from 1978; sr. v.p Capital Internat. Ltd., London, 1989—; sr. v.p., dir. Capital Guardian Trust Co.; sr. ptnr. Capital Group Cos.; treas., trustee Fin. Acctg. Found. Served to 1st lt. USAAF, 1943-45. Decorated D.F.C., Air medal. Mem. N.Y. Soc. Security Analysts, Fin. Analysts Fedn. (chmn.), Securities Industry Assn., Inst. Chartered Financial Analysts. Republican. Episcopalian. Home: Lynch Mountain Rd Sautee Nacoochee GA 30571 Office: Capital Guardian Trust Co 1230 Peachtree St NE Atlanta GA 30309

WARREN, EDWARD W., lawyer; b. Louisville, Ky., Apr. 2, 1944. BA, Yale U., 1966; JD, U. Chgo., 1969. Bar: Ill. 1969, D.C. 1970. Law clk. to Hon. Luther M. Swygert U.S. Ct. Appeals (7th cir.), 1969-70; ptnr. Kirkland & Ellis, Washington. Mem. ABA, D.C. Bar. Office: Kirkland & Ellis 655 15th St NW Ste 1200 Washington DC 20005-5701

WARREN, FRANK M., JR., construction company executive; b. 1932. Grad. Ga. Inst. Tech. 1958. With Raymond Internat. Builders, Charlotte, N.C., 1958-61, 64-83, Nat. Bulk Carriers, Inc., Charlotte, 1961-64; pres., dir. Jones Group, Inc., Charlotte, 1983-86; pvt. cons. Charlotte, 1986-88; pres., CEO Rogers Group, Inc., Nashville, 1988—. Office: Rogers Group Inc 421 Great Circle Rd Nashville TN 37228*

WARREN, GERALD LEE, newspaper editor; b. Hastings, Nebr., Aug. 17, 1930; s. Hie Elias and Linnie (Williamson) W.; m. Euphemia Florence Brownell, Nov. 20, 1965 (div.); children: Gerald Benjamin, Euphemia Brownell; m. Viviane M. Pratt, Apr. 27, 1986. A.B., U. Nebr., 1952. Reporter Lincoln Star, Nebr., 1951-52; reporter, asst. city editor San Diego Union, 1956-61; bus. rep. Copley News Service, 1961-63; city editor San Diego Union, 1963-68, asst. mng. editor, 1968-69, editor, 1975-92; editor San Diego Union-Tribune, 1992-95, asst. to pub., 1995—, 1995—; dep. press sec. to Pres. Richard Nixon, 1969-74, Pres. Gerald Ford, 1974-75. Mem. bd. Pacific coun. internat. policy Eureka Found. Lt. (j.g.) USNR, 1952-56. Mem. Am. Soc. Newspaper Editors, Coun. Fgn. Rels., Sigma Delta Chi, Sigma Nu. Republican. Episcopalian. Office: Copley Press Inc 350 Camino De La Reina San Diego CA 92108-3003

WARREN, HARRY VERNEY, geological sciences educator, consulting geological engineer; b. Anacortes, Wash., Aug. 27, 1904; s. Victor Mackenzie and Rosamond Ellice Burrell (Campion) W.; m. Margaret Bessie Tisdall, July 14, 1934; children: Charlotte Louisa Verney, Victor Henry Verney. BA, U. B.C., Vancouver, Can., 1926, BASc, 1927, DSc (hon.), 1978; postgrad., Rhodes Sch. for B.C., 1926-29; MSc, Oxford U., Eng., 1928, DPhil, 1929; DSc (hon.), Waterloo U., Ont., Can., 1975. Registered profl. engr., B.C. Lectr. U. B.C., 1932-35, asst. prof. geol. scis., 1935-39, assoc. prof., 1939-45, prof., 1945-73, hon. prof., 1973—; Commonwealth Fund fellow Calif. Inst. Tech., 1929-32. Contbr. articles to profl. jours. Mem. council Vancouver Bd. Trade, 1939-71 (life); pres. B.C. and Yukon Chamber of Mines, Vancouver, 1952-54, UN Assn. Can. (Vancouver br.), 1956-58. Decorated officer Order of Can., 1971, Order of B.C., 1991; named Disting. lectr. Can. Inst. Mining and Metallurgy, 1971; Hon. fellow Royal Coll. Gen. Practitioners, Eng., 1973; recipient "Spud" Huestis disting. prospectors award B.C./Yukon Chamber of Mines, 1986, Disting. Citizen award City of Vancouver Centennial, 1986, Disting. Svc. award Prospector and Developer's Assn. Can., 1990, Can. 125th Commemorative medal, 1992; inductee B.C. Sports Hall of Fame, 1990, U. B.C. Sports Hall of Fame, 1993. Fellow Inst. Mining and Metallurgy (life), Royal Soc. Can. (life), Geol. Soc. Am. (life); mem. Can. Council (Killam award), Assn. Profl. Engrs. B.C. (life), Sigma Xi. Mem. Ch. of England. Club: Faculty of U. B.C. Avocations: field hockey, rugby, cricket. Home: 1816 Western Pkwy, Vancouver, BC Canada V6T 1V4 Office: U BC Dept Geol Scis, 6339 Stores Rd, Vancouver, BC Canada V6T 2B4

WARREN, HENRY CLAY, JR., retired naturalist; b. Oakland, Calif., Mar. 25, 1937; s. Henry Clay and Nell Grace (Griffith) W.; m. Raedell Jean Walsh, Nov. 15, 1937; children: Deborah Colleen, Cynthia Doreen. BA, U. Calif., Berkeley, 1963. Probation officer, social worker Contra Costa County, Martinez, Calif., 1963-66; park ranger Austin Creek S.R.A., Guerneville, Calif., 1966-68; park ranger Lassen Volcanic Nat. Park, Mineral, Calif., 1968-69, asst. chief naturalist, 1970-73; chief naturalist Mount McKinley (Alaska) Nat. Park, 1973-75; asst. chief naturalist Pacific N.W. Regional Office Nat. Park Svc., Seattle, 1975-79; chief naturalist Olympic Nat. Park, Port Angeles, Wash., 1979-95; ret., 1995. Author: Olympic, Story Behind the Scenery, 1979. Pres. Four Seasons Maintenance Commn., Port Angeles, 1984, 85. Mem. Assn. Interpretive Naturalists (regional dir. 1981-83), Port Angeles Yacht Club (commodore 1989), Port Angeles Power Squadron (comdr. 1985). Avocations: hiking, skiing, boating, wildlife observation, travel.

WARREN, IRWIN HOWARD, lawyer; b. N.Y.C., May 16, 1950; s. Milton and Shirley (Glatman) W.; m. Elizabeth Vogel, Aug. 11, 1974. BA, Columbia U., 1971, JD, 1974. Bar: N.Y., U.S. Ct. Appeals (1st, 2d, 3d, 4th, 6th, 8th, 11th cirs.), U.S. Dist. Ct. (so. and ea. dists.). Assoc. Weil, Gotshal & Manges, N.Y.C., 1974-82, ptnr., 1982—. Contbr. articles to profl. jours. Mem. ABA (litigation sect., co-chair ethics and professionalism com., sect. litigation task force on ancillary bus. activities of lawyers). Office: Weil Gotshal & Manges 767 Fifth Ave New York NY 10153-0002

WARREN, J. BENEDICT, retired history educator; b. Waterflow, N.Mex., June 30, 1930; s. Benedict Alfred and Mary Ursula (Clark) W.; m. Patricia Susan Hyde, June 15, 1968. BA, Duns Scotus Coll., 1953; postgrad., Holy Family Sch. Theology, 1953-57, Cath. U. of Am., 1957-58; MA, U. N.Mex., 1960, PhD, 1963. Franciscan priest various chs., 1957-67; asst. prof. history U. Md., Coll. Park, 1968-70, assoc. prof. hist., 1970-77, prof. history, 1977-93; ret., 1993; cons. Library of Congress, Washington, 1967-77. Author: Vasco de Quiroga and His Pueblo-Hospitals of Santa Fe, 1963 (rev. Spanish edits. 1977, 90), Hans P. Kraus Collection of Hispanic American Manuscripts, a Guide, 1974, La conquista de Michoacán, 1521-1530, 1977 (rev. edit., 1989, rev. English version, 1985); editor: books including Diego Basalenque, Arte, 1994, Gonzalo Gómez primer poblador espanol de Guayangareo (Morelia), 1991, Diccionario grande de la lengua de Michoacan, 1991 (2 vol.), Maturino Gilberti, Arte, 1987, Vocabulario, 1989, Juan Baptista de Lagunas, 1983, Latin America: a Guide to the Historical Literature, 1971; editor: The Americas: A Quarterly Rev. of Inter-Am. Cultural History, 1963-66. John Carter Brown Library fellow, 1965, Fulbright fellow 1981-82. Mem. Conf. on Latin Am. History, Middle Atlantic Conf. on Latin Am. Studies. Democrat. Avocation: gardening. Office: Lic J Ma Mendoza Pardo 99, Col Nueva Chapultepec, 58280 Morelia Michoacan, Mexico

WARREN, JACK HAMILTON, former trade policy advisor; b. Apr. 10, 1921; m. Hilary J. Titterington; children: Hilary Warren Nicolson, Martin, Jennifer Warren Part, Ian. Student, Queens U., Kingston, Ont., Can., 1938-41. Joined Dept. External Affairs, 1945; assigned London, 1948-51; fin. counsellor Washington, 1954-57; asst. dep. minister trade and commerce, 1958-64, dep. minister industry, trade and commerce, 1964-71, high commr. to U.K., 1971-75; ambassador to U.S., 1975-77, Can. coordinator for multilateral trade negotiations, 1977-79; vice chmn. Bank of Montreal, Que., Can., 1979-86; prin. trade policy advisor Govt. Que., 1986-94. Served with Royal Canadian Navy, 1941-45; officer Order of Can., 1982. Home: PO Box 282 RR 1, Chelsea, PQ Canada J0X 1N0

WARREN, JAMES RONALD, retired museum director, author, columnist; b. Goldendale, Wash., May 25, 1925; stepson H.S. W.; m. Gwen Davis, June 25, 1949; children: Gail, Jeffrey. B.A., Wash. State U., 1949; M.A., U. Wash., 1953, Ph.D., 1963. Adminstrv. v.p. Seattle Community Coll., 1965-69; pres. Edmonds Community Coll., Lynnwood, Wash., 1969-79; dir. Mus. of History and Industry, Seattle, 1979-89; lectr. in field. Author history books; columnist Seattle Post Intelligencer, 1979-92, Seattle Times, 1992—. Served with U.S. Army, 1943-45, ETO, prisoner-of-war, Germany. Mem. VFW, Am. Ex-POW Assn., 42d (Rainbow) Div. Vets., others. Lodge: Rotary (Seattle). Home and Office: 3235 99th Ave NE Bellevue WA 98004-1803

WARREN, JAMES WALTER, JR., pharmaceutical company executive; b. Lincolnton, N.C., Aug. 17, 1944; s. James Walter and Edith (Abernethy) W.; m. Nancy Wallace Warlick, Jan. 19, 1964; children—James Walter, Beverly Joy. B.S. in Pharmacy, U. S.C., 1967; M.S. in Pharmaceutics, Butler U., Indpls., 1971; Ph.D. in Pharmaceutics, U. Ga., 1976. Pharmacy supr. Greenville Hosp., S.C., 1967-69; research pharmacist Eli Lilly & Co, Indpls., 1969-73; instr. U. Ga., Athens, 1973-76; prof., dir. Med. U. S.C., 1976-81; v.p. research and devel. R.P. Scherer Co., Clearwater, Fla., 1981-84; v.p. sci. div. Reid-Rowell, Inc., Atlanta, 1984—. Author numerous research papers. Mem. Am. Pharm. Assn., Acad. Pharm. Scis., Sigma Xi, Rho Chi. Episcopalian. Club: Gamecock. Avocations: golf, writing. Home: 4752 Township Chase Marietta GA 30066-1736 Office: Solvay Pharm Inc 901 Sawyer Rd Marietta GA 30062-2250

WARREN, KENNETH S., medical educator, physician; b. N.Y.C., June 11, 1929; m. Sylvia Marjorie Rothwell, Feb. 14, 1959; children: Christopher Harwood, Erica Marjorie. AB, Harvard U., 1951, MD, 1955; DSc (hon.), Mahidol U., Thailand, 1990. Intern, Harvard service Boston City Hosp., 1955-56; research assoc. Lab. Tropical Diseases, NIH, Bethesda, Md., 1956-62; asst. prof. medicine Case Western Res. U., 1963-68, assoc. prof., 1968-75, prof., 1975-77, profl. library sci., 1974-77; dir. health scis. Rockefeller Found., N.Y.C., 1977-87, assoc. v.p. 1988-89; adj. prof. Rockefeller U., 1977-89; prof. medicine NYU, 1977—; dir. sci. Maxwell Communication Corp., Maxwell Found., N.Y.C., 1989-92; Heath Clark lectr. London Sch. Hygiene and Tropical Medicine, 1988; adj. prof. medicine Tufts U., 1990—; cons. ed.

Charles Scribner's Sons, 1992-93; CEO Comprehensive Med. Sys., Inc., 1992-94; v.p. acad. affairs Picower Inst. Med. Rsch., 1993—; chmn. Global Libr. Sys., Inc., 1994—; mem. Inst. Medicine, Nat. Acad. Scis.; bd. dirs. Immunotherapy, Inc.; cons. WHO. Author: Schistosomiasis: The Evolution of a Medical Literature, Selected Abstracts and Citations, 1852-1972, 1973, Geographic Medicine for the Practitioner, 2d edit., 1985, Scientific Information Systems and the Principle of Selectivity, 1980, Coping with the Biomedical Literature, 1981, Tropical and Geographical Medicine, 2d edit., 1990, Immunology and Molecular Biology of Parasitic Diseases, 1993, Doing More Good Than Harm, 1993; founding editor: Jour. Molecular Medicine; contbr. numerous articles to profl. jours. Recipient Career Devel. award NIH, 1966-71, Mary Kingsley medal Liverpool Sch. Tropical Med., 1987, Frohlich award N.Y. Acad. Sci., 1988, Van Thiel medal Dutch Soc. Parasitology, 1989. Fellow ACP, Royal Coll. Physicians; mem. Am. Soc. Clin. Investigation, Assn. Am. Physicians, Am. Assn. Immunologists, Am. Assn. Study Liver Diseases, Am. Soc. Tropical Medicine and Hygiene (Bailey K. Ashford award 1974), Infectious Diseases Soc. Am. (Squibb award 1975), Royal Soc. Tropical Medicine and Hygiene, Soc. for Scholarly Pub., Internat. Fedn. Sci. Editors (exec. bd.), N.Y. Acad. Scis. (bd. govs. 1991-93), Royal Soc. Medicine Found. (bd. dirs. 1992—, treas. 1994—), Internat. Molecular Medicine Soc. (founding sec., treas.). Patentee diagnostic methods, drugs. Office: Picower Inst Med Rsch 350 Community Dr Manhasset NY 11030 *As an academic I achieved professorships in both medicine and library sciences. During my 33 year career in tropical medicine I have been fortunate to fulfill my three goals: to travel, to enjoy the challenge of medical research and to improve the health of our fellow human beings in the developing world. As an information scientist I did research on the quality of information, developed low-cost, efficient, integrated information systems for medical schools and ministries of health in the developing world and am engaged in putting these principles and models to work on the global level.*

WARREN, LESLEY ANN, actress; b. N.Y.C., Aug. 16, 1948. Studied ballet, N.Y.C.; studied acting, The Actors Studio, N.Y.C. TV appearances include Rodgers and Hammerstein's Cinderella, 1964, Fight for Jenny, 1986, 27 Wagons Full of Cotton, 1990, A Seduction in Travis County, 1991, In Sickness and in Health, 1991; Broadway debut in 110 in the Shade, 1963, Drat the Cat, 1964, Metamorphosis, Three Penny Opera; films include The Happiest Millionaire, 1967, Harry and Walter Go to New York, 1976, Victor/Victoria, 1982, Songwriter, Choose Me, Clue, Apology, 1986, Burglar, 1987, Cop, 1988, Baja Oklahoma, 1988, Worth Winning, 1989, Life Stinks, 1991, Pure Country, 1992, The Color of Night, 1994; TV mini-series include 79 Park Ave., 1977, Beulah Land, 1980, Pearl, Evergreen, 1985, Family of Spies, 1990; TV films include Seven in Darkness, 1969, Love Hate Love, 1971, Assignment Munich, 1972, The Daughters of Joshua Cabe, 1972, The Letters, 1973, The Legend of Valentino, 1975, Betrayal, 1978, Portrait of a Stripper, 1979, Beulah Land, 1980, Portrait of a Showgirl, 1982, A Flight for Jenny, 1986, Baja Oklahoma, 1988, Family of Spies, 1990, A Seduction in Travis County, 1991, In Sickness and Health, 1992, Willing to Kill: The Texas Cheerleader Story, 1992, Joseph, 1995. Office: care ICM 8942 Wilshire Blvd Beverly Hills CA 90211*

WARREN, MARK EDWARD, shipping company executive, lawyer; b. Rochester, Minn., Nov. 26, 1951; s. Edward Joseph and Eunice (Golberg) W.; m. Jasmine Margaret Syracuse, Feb. 18, 1984; children: Natalie, Stephanie. Cert., Instituto de Estudios Europeos, Madrid, 1972; BA, Gustavus Adolphus Coll., St. Peter, Minn., 1974; JD, U. Minn., 1977. Bar: Calif. 1977, U.S. Dist. Ct. (no. and cen. dists.) Calif. 1978, U.S. Ct. Appeals (9th cir.) 1985, U.S. Dist. Ct. (ea. dist.) Calif. 1986, U.S. Dist. Ct. (so. dist.) Calif. 1987, D.C. 1989, U.S. Supreme Ct. 1989, U.S. Ct. Appeals (D.C. cir.) 1989, U.S. Dist. Ct. (D.C. dist.) 1989, U.S. Dist. Ct. Md. 1991, Va. 1992. Assoc. Gibson, Dunn & Crutcher, L.A., 1977-78; spl. asst. to V.P. Walter Mondale Washington, 1979-80; assoc. Gibson, Dunn & Crutcher, L.A., 1980-84; ptnr. Gibson, Dunn & Crutcher, L.A. and Washington, 1985-93; sr. v.p., gen. counsel Princess Cruises, L.A., 1993—. Mem. U. Minn. Law Alumni Assn. (bd. dirs.). Office: Princess Cruises 10100 Santa Monica Blvd Los Angeles CA 90067

WARREN, PATRICIA J., museum director; b. Seattle, Dec. 12, 1950; d. Vernon Sidney and Ernestine Abernathy (Bilan) W. BA, U. Wash., 1972, BS, 1975, JD, 1978, MA, 1990. Atty. City Kirkland, Wash., 1978-80, City Bellevue, Wash., 1980-86; mus. dir. Jefferson County Hist. Soc., Port Townsend, Wash., 1990—. Precinct chair 46th Dist., Seattle, 1985-88; mem. Jefferson County AIDS Task Force, Port Townsend, 1991—. U. Wash. fellow, 1988-89. Mem. AAUW, Wash. State Bar Assn., Wash. Mus. Assn. (trustee 1991-93, v.p. 1993—), Rotary Club. Democrat. Office: Jefferson County Hist Soc City Hall 210 Madison St Port Townsend WA 98368

WARREN, RICHARD JORDAN, newspaper publisher; b. Bangor, Maine, May 28, 1945; s. Richard Kearney Warren and Joanne (Jordan) Van Namee; m. Barbara Burrowes Hall, Mar. 9, 1968 (div.); m. Elizabeth Carter, June 21, 1978; children—Courtney, George, Anne. B.A., Trinity Coll., Hartford, Conn., 1968; postgrad. smaller cos. mgmt. program Harvard Bus. Sch., 1977-80. Reporter, The Courant, Hartford, Conn., 1968-71; asst. pub. The Bangor Daily News 1971-84, v.p., 1974—, editor, 1980—, pub., 1984—; pres. Northeast Pub. Co., Presque Isle, Maine; dir. Bangor Pub. Co., Northeast Pub. Co., Merrill/Norstar Bank, Portland, Courier-Gazette, Inc.; past mem. UPI Newspaper Adv. Bd.; mem. Megantic Fish and Game Corp. Mem. Portland Com. on Fgn. Relations, U. Maine Devel. Council, Kent Moot Court, Columbia U. Law Sch., N.Y.C.; past mem. Bangor Bicentennial Com., Bangor Jaycees, adv. bd. Salvation Army, Bangor; bd. dirs. Counseling Center, Bangor Symphony Orch., C. of C. Ambassadors Club; trustee Unity Coll. Served to 1st lt., Air N.G., 1968-75. Mem. Am. Newspaper Pub. Assn. (chmn. bus. and workplace issues subcom., bd. dirs.), AP (audit com.), Maine Coast Heritage Trust (bd. dirs.), Quebec-Labrador Found. (bd. dirs.), Am. Soc. Newspaper Editors, New Eng. Newspaper Assn., Maine Daily Newspaper Assn. (past pres., v.p.), Alexander Grahm Bell Assn. for the Deaf Centennial Bd. (steering com.), Action Com. of Fifty (pres.), Bangor Mechanic Assn. Clubs: Nat. Press (Washington); Penobscot Salmon; Tarratine (Bangor), Univ. (N.Y.C.). Lodge: Rotary (Bangor). Office: Bangor Pub Co 491 Main St Bangor ME 04401-6296*

WARREN, RICHARD KEARNEY, newspaper publisher; b. N.Y.C., Apr. 13, 1920; s. George Earle and Anna (Kearney) W.; m. Joanne Jordan, Sept. 18, 1943 (div. Oct. 1969); children: Richard J., Carolyn; m. Susan Atwood Thibodeau, Oct. 1, 1970. B.S., Yale U., 1942; Litt.D., Ricker Coll., 1971. Shift supt. W.Va ordnance works Gen. Chem. Co., Point Pleasant, 1942-43; dir. Bangor Pub. Co., Maine, chmn. exec. com.; pres. Rockland Courier-Gazette, Inc., also dir.; bd. dirs. N.E. Pub. Co. Bd. dirs. William A. Farnsworth Libr. and Art Mus.; past trustee Ricker Coll.; past bd. dirs. Bangor YMCA. Lt. (j.g.) USNR, 1943-46. Mem. Maine Daily Newspaper Assn. (pres. 1953-54, 73-74), N.E. Daily Newspaper Assn. (pres. 1959-60), Am. Newspaper Pubs. Assn., New Eng. Soc. N.Y., N.E. Harbor Fleet Club (Maine), Penobscot Valley Country Club, Yale Club (N.Y.C.), N.E. Harbor Tennis Club, Rotary. Home: 28 W Broadway Bangor ME 04401-4541 Office: 96 Harlow St Ste F Bangor ME 04401-4920 also: 3 Huntington Pl Northeast Harbor ME 04662-0663

WARREN, RICHARD M., experimental psychologist, educator; b. N.Y.C., Apr. 8, 1925; s. Morris and Rae (Greenberg) W.; m. Roslyn Pauker, Mar. 31, 1950. BS in Chemistry, CCNY, 1946; PhD in Organic Chemistry, N.Y. U., 1951. Flavor chemist Gen. Foods Co., Hoboken, N.J., 1951-53; rsch. assoc. psychology Brown U., Providence, 1954-56; Carnegie sr. rsch. fellow Coll. Medicine NYU, 1956-57; Carnegie sr. rsch. fellow Cambridge (Eng.) U., 1957-58, rsch. psychologist applied psychology Rsch. Unit, 1958-59; rsch. psychologist NIMH, Bethesda, Md., 1959-61; chmn. psychology Shimer Coll., Mt. Carroll, Ill., 1961-64; assoc. prof. psychology U. Wis., Milw., 1964-66, prof., 1966-73, rsch. prof., 1973-75, disting. prof., 1975—; vis. scientist Inst. Exptl. Psychology, Oxford (Eng.) U., 1969-70, 77-78. Author: (with Roslyn Warren) Helmholtz on Perception: Its Physiology and Development, 1968, Auditory Perception: A New Synthesis, 1982; contbr. articles on sensation and perception to profl. jours. Fellow APA, Am. Psychol. Soc.; mem. AAAS, Acoustical Soc. Am., Am. Optom. Assn., Speech and Hearing Assn., Sigma Xi. Office: U Wis Dept Psychology Milwaukee WI 53201

WARREN, ROBERT CARLTON, manufacturing company executive; b. Portland, Oreg., Apr. 13, 1918; s. Floyd Carlton and Ethel (Wright) W.; m. Nani Marie Swigert, June 23, 1945; children: Catharine K., Robert Carlton, Wendy W., William S., Elizabeth B. Grad., Stanford U., 1940. With U.S. Steel Corp., Portland, 1940, Esco Corp., Portland, 1941, Oreg. Shipbldg. Corp., 1941-43; gen. mgr., dir. Cascade Corp., Portland, 1943-54; pres., CEO Cascade Corp., 1954-71, chmn., CEO, 1971-83, chmn. 1983-93, chmn. emeritus, 1993—; chmn., CEO Stair Assist Corp., 1983-93, chmn. emeritus, CEO, 1993—. Pres. Portland Art Assn., 1979-80; Mem. Pres.'s Export Council, 1981-84. Mem. NAM (dir. 1978-83), Chi Psi. Office: care Cascade Corp 2020 SW 4th Ave Portland OR 97201-4953

WARREN, ROBERT DAVIS, state senator; b. Sampson County, July 22, 1928; s. Opheus and Neta (Jackson) W.; m. Ann Sparks, Jan. 20, 1951; children—Robert Davis Jr., Gary Burrell. B.S., N.C. State U., 1950, M.Ed., 1968; postgrad. East Carolina U. Mem. N.C. Senate; vice chmn. agrl. com., edn. com.; mem. v-c appropriations com., appropriations com. edn., judiciary I com., redistricting Senate com., rules of operation of Senate, transp. com. 1981; mem. Gov.'s Adv. Com. Vocat. Edn., 1969-73, Benson Recreation Commn. Deacon, Benson Bapt. Ch., 1950-80, chmn., Sunday Sch. supt., Sunday sch. tchr., 1966-80. Recipient Young Man of Yr. award Benson Jaycees, 1960; Boss of Yr. award Johnston County; Benson Citizen of Yr. award, 1980; Hon. Chpt. Farmer Degree and Hon. State Farmer Degree, Future Farmers Am. Mem. N.C. Assn. Educators, NEA, N.C. Prins. and Asst. Prins. Assn., N.C. Farm Bur., Johnston County Arts Soc., N.C. Wildlife Fedn., Mental Health Assn. of Johnston County, Benson C. of C. Democrat. Club: Sampson County Dem. Men's. Lodges: Masons, Shriners. Office: NC Senate State Capitol Raleigh NC 27611 Other: RR 3 Box 25 Benson NC 27504-9803

WARREN, ROBERT WILLIS, federal judge; b. Raton, N.M., Aug. 30, 1925; s. George R. and Clara (Jolliffe) W.; m. Laverne D. Voagen, Aug. 23, 1947; children: Cheryl Lynn, Iver Eric, Gregg Alan, Treiva Mae, Lyle David, Tara Rae. BA magna cum laude, Macalester Coll., 1950; MA, U. Minn., 1951; JD, U. Wis., 1956; postgrad., Fgn. Service Inst., 1951-52. Bar: Wis. 1956. Fgn. affairs officer U.S. Dept. State, 1951-53; mem. firm Godfrey, Godfrey & Warren, Elkhorn, 1956-57; ptnr. firm Warren & Boltz, Attys., Green Bay, 1957-59, Smith, Will & Warren, 1965-69; asst. dist. atty. Brown County, Wis., 1959-61; dist. atty., 1961-65; mem. Wis. Senate, 1965-69; atty. gen. Wis., 1969-74; U.S. dist. judge Milw., 1974—; Mem. Gt. Lakes Commn., Wis. Council on Criminal Justice, Wis. Bd. Commrs. Pub. Lands, Four Lakes council Boy Scouts Am., Wis. Controlled Substances Bd., Wis. Council on Drug Abuse, Wis. State Urban Affairs. Served with AUS, 1943-46, ETO. Decorated Purple Heart. Mem. ABA, Wis. Bar Assn., Nat. Assn. Attys. Gen. (pres. 1973-74), Midwestern Conf. Attys. Gen., Wis. Dist. Attys. Assn., VFW, DAV. Republican. Methodist. Club: Optimist. Office: US Dist Ct 364 US Courthouse 517 E Wisconsin Ave Milwaukee WI 53202-4506

WARREN, ROSANNA, poet; b. Fairfield, Conn., July 27, 1953; d. Robert Penn Warren and Emily Clark; m. Stephen Scully, 1981; children: Benjamin, Katherine, Chiara. BA summa cum laude, Yale U., 1976; MA, Johns Hopkins U., 1980. Private art tchr., 1977-78; clerical worker St. Martin's Pr., N.Y.C., 1977-78; asst. prof. English Vanderbilt U., Nashville, 1981-82; vis. asst. prof. Boston U., 1982-88, asst. prof. English and modern fgn. langs., 1989—; poetry cons., contbg. editor Partisan Rev., 1985—; poet-in-residence Robert Frost Farm, 1990. Author: The Joey Story, 1963, Snow Day, 1981, Each Leaf Shines Separate, 1984, Stained Glass, 1993; editor, contbr.: The Art of Translation: Voices from the Field, 1989; editor: Eugenio Montale's Cuttlefish Bones, 1993; contbr. to periodicals including Agni Rev., Am. Poetry Rev., Antioch Rev., Atlantic Monthly, Chelsea, Chgo. Rev., Georgia Rev., Nation, New Yorker, N.Y. Times, Partisan Rev., Ploughshares, Southern Rev., Washington Post. Recipient McLaughlin English prize Yale U., 1973, Charles E. Clark award Yale U., 1976, Nat. Discovery award in poetry 92nd St. YMHA-YWCA, 1980, Newton Arts Coun. award, 1983, Lavan Younger Poets prize Acad. Am. Poets, 1992, Lamont Poetry prize Acad. Am. Poets, 1993, Lila Wallace Writers' Fund award, 1994, Witter Bynner prize in poetry Acad. Arts and Letters, 1994; named Scholar of House Yale U., 1975-76; Yaddo fellow, 1980; Ingram Merrill grantee, 1983, 93; Guggenheim fellow, 1985-86; Am. Coun. Learned Societies grantee, 1989-90. Mem. MLA. Home: 11 Robinwood Ave Needham MA 02192 Office: Univ Professors Program Boston Univ 745 Commonwealth Ave Boston MA 02215*

WARREN, RUSSELL GLEN, academic administrator; b. Balt., Apr. 29, 1942; s. Clarence N. and Kathryn (Butler) W. BBA, U. Richmond, 1964; PhD, Tulane U., 1968. Asst. prof., then assoc. prof. U. Richmond (Va.), 1971-74, dean of Richmond Coll., 1974-76, asst. to univ. v.p., then asst. to univ. pres., 1976-78; v.p. for acad. affairs U. Montevallo, Ala., Ala., 1978-84; v.p. for acad. affairs James Madison U., Harrisonburg, Va., 1984-90, acting pres., 1986-87; pres. N.E. Mo. State U., Kirksville, 1990-95; Disting. prof. mgmt. and econ. Hardin Simmons U., Abilene, Tex., 1995—; dir. Ctr. Rsch. on Teaching and Learning. Author: Antitrust in Theory and Practice, 1976, Carpe Diem, 1995. Bd. Dirs. Va. Rural Devel. Corp., Richmond, 1988-90. Capt. U.S. Army, 1969-71. Named One of Outstanding Young Men of Va., Va. Jaycees, 1976. Mem. Assn. Am. Coll. and Univs. (bd. dirs. 1994—). Methodist. Avocations: golf, collecting cars. Home: 71 Tamarisk Cir Abilene TX 79606 Office: Hardin-Simmons U Sch of Business Abilene TX 79606

WARREN, WILLIAM BRADFORD, lawyer; b. Boston, July 25, 1934; s. Minton Machado and Sarah Ripley (Robbins) W.; m. Mary Elizabeth Coolidge, Aug. 8, 1955 (div. July 1969); children: John Coolidge, Sarah Robbins; m. Elisabeth Bezold, July 4, 1975 (div. Dec. 1977); m. Arete B. Swartz, Sept. 20, 1985. A.B. magna cum laude, Harvard U., 1956, LL.B. cum laude, 1959. Bar: N.Y. 1960. Assoc. Dewey Ballantine, N.Y.C., 1959-68; ptnr. Dewey Ballantine, 1968—; lectr. Inst. Fed. Taxation, N.Y. U., So. Fed. Tax Inst., Practicing Law Inst. Pres. Cintas Found., N.Y.C.; bd. dirs. John Carter Brown Libr., Providence, R.I. Mem. Am. Law Inst., Am. Coll. Trust and Estate Counsel (former regent), Acad. Am. Poets (bd. dirs.), Internat. Acad. Estate and Trust Law (former exec. coun.), N.Y. Estate Bar Assn. (chmn. com. taxation of trust and estates sect. 1980-83), Assn. Bar City N.Y., Soc. Mayflower Descs., Harvard Club, Knickerbocker Club, Century Club, Grolier Club (pres.). Home: 520 E 86th St New York NY 10028-7534 Office: Dewey Ballantine 1301 Ave of the Americas New York NY 10019-6092

WARREN, WILLIAM CLEMENTS, lawyer, educator; b. Paris, Tex., Feb. 3, 1909; s. Archibald Levy and Elma (Clements) W.; m. Diana June Peel Willock, Jan. 13, 1945; children: Robert Peel, Larissa Eve, William Liversidge. AB, U. Tex., 1930, AM, 1931; LLB, Harvard U., 1935; LLD (hon.), L.I. U., 1955, Columbia U., 1981; D in Polit. Sci., U. Basle, 1965. Bar: Ohio 1937, N.Y. 1952, D.C. 1959. Assoc. Davis, Polk & Wardwell, N.Y.C., 1935-37, Holiday, Grossman & McAfee, Cleve., 1937-42, Milbank, Tweed, Hadley & McCloy, N.Y.C., 1942-47; prof. law Western Res. U., Cleve. 1937-42; mem. faculty Columbia Law Sch., N.Y.C., 1946-82, Kent prof. law, 1959-77, Kent prof. emeritus, 1977—, dean, 1952-70, dean emeritus, 1970—; ptnr., of counsel Roberts & Holland, N.Y.C., 1952; bd. dirs. Guardian Life Ins. Co. Am., Sterling Nat. Bank & Trust Co. N.Y.C., Barnwell Industries, Inc., Sterling Bancorp, CSS Industries, Aston-Martin LaGonda Group, Aladan Corp., Columbia Yeast, Inc., Internat. Yeast, Inc.; hon. chmn. bd. dirs. Sandoz U.S.; mem. N.Am. adv. bd. Swissair. Served as lt. col. U.S. Army, 1943-46. Decorated Bronze Star (2), Legion of Merit; comdr. Order of the Crown (Italy); recipient Medal for excellence Columbia Law Sch. Alumni Assn., 1969. Mem. ABA, Am. Judicature Soc., Am. Law Inst., Assn. Bar of City of N.Y., N.Y. County Lawyers Assn., N.Y. State Bar Assn., Inst. Internat. Edn. (trustee), Order Moral Scis. (fgn. corr.), Accademia delle Scienze dell' Instituto di Bologna (fgn. corr. mem.; Order Moral Scis. 1971). Presbyterian. Clubs: Broad Street, Century Assn., Cosmos, Links, Metropolitan, Univ. Co-author: U.S. Income Taxation of Foreign Corporations and Nonresident Aliens, 1966; Cases and Materials on Accounting and the Law, 1978; Cases and Materials on Federal Wealth Transfer Taxation, 1982; Cases and Materials on Federal Income Taxation, Vol. I, 1972, supplement, 1983, Vol. II, 1980; pres., dir. Columbia Law Rev. Office: Roberts & Holland 825 8th Ave New York NY 10019-7416

WARREN, WILLIAM GERALD, lawyer; b. Detroit, Apr. 22, 1930; s. William Grant and Margaret Kathryn (Matthews) W.; m. Martha Elsie Artz, Apr. 20, 1974; children: Mary Katharine, Elizabeth Bogo. A.B. with honors, U. Mich., 1952, LL.B. (Frederick L. Leckie scholar), 1955. Bar: Mich. 1956. Assoc. firm Dickinson, Wright, Moon, Van Dusen & Freeman, Detroit, 1955-63, ptnr., 1964—; bd. dirs. Mackinac Fin. Corp., Mackinac Corp., V.G. Nahrgang Co.; gen. counsel, sec. bd. Detroit Savs. Bank. Contbr. articles to profl. jours. Mem., chmn. Wayne County (Mich.) Grievance Com., 1966—; spl. counsel 4-H Found. Mich., 1966-68. Recipient Henry M. Campbell award, 1954, Roberts P. Hudson award State Bar Mich., 1978. Fellow Am. Coll. Trial Lawyers, Internat. Soc. Barristers, Am. Bar Found., Mich Bar Found.; mem. Phi Beta Kappa, Phi Kappa Phi, Pi Sigma Alpha, Phi Alpha Delta. Republican. Roman Catholic. Clubs: Detroit, University, Otsego Ski, Grosse Pointe, Witenagemote. Office: Dickinson Wright Moon Van Dusen & Freeman One Detroit Ctr Ste 4000 Detroit MI 48226

WARREN, WILLIAM HERBERT, business administration educator; b. Newport News, Va., July 21, 1924; s. William Herbert and Helen Virginia (Cofer) W.; m. Mary Virginia Shaw, Sept. 11, 1948; children: Katherine Warren Butt, Constance Warren Desaulniers, Suzanne Warren Huhn, David, John. BSBA, U. Richmond, 1948; MS, Purdue U., 1950, PhD, 1969. Dir. indsl. rels., plant mgr. Albemarle Paper Co. div. Ethyl Corp., 1954-66; dir. labor relations, cons. Newport News Shipbldg. div. Tenneco, 1970-73; asst. prof. U. Richmond, Va., 1950-53; assoc. prof. Purdue U., 1966-70; mem. faculty Coll. William and Mary, Williamsburg, Va., 1972—, D. Hillsdon Ryan prof. bus. adminstrn., 1979-92; prof. emeritus Williamsburg, Va., 1992—; cons. to industry and govt.; labor arbitrator. Served with USN, 1943-46. Mem. APA, Acad. Mgmt., Kiwanis, Omicron Delta Kappa. Republican. Baptist. Home: 110 Bowstring Dr Williamsburg VA 23185-4952 Office: Sch Business Coll William and Mary Williamsburg VA 23185

WARREN, WILLIAM KERMIT, newspaper managing editor; b. Harlem, Ga., May 27, 1941; s. William Kermit and Willie Garnell (Thaxton) W.; m. Nancy Carolyn Andrews, Sept. 5, 1964; children—Wendy Karen, William Kermit. B.A. in Journalism, U. Ga., 1964. Reporter Augusta Ga. Chronicle, Ga., 1964-65; reporter Chattanooga Times, Tenn., 1965-66, reporter, city editor, 1971-80; mng. editor Roanoke (Va.) Times & World News, 1980—. Served to capt. USAF, 1966-70. Recipient Best Feature Story award Ga, AP, 1964. Mem. AP Mng. Editors Assn., Sigma Delta Chi. Episcopalian. Avocation: reading. Home: 3355 Dawn Cir Roanoke VA 24018-3837 Office: Times World Corp PO Box 2491 201-209 W Campbell Ave Roanoke VA 24010

WARREN, WILLIAM MICHAEL, JR., utilities company executive; b. Bryan, Tex., June 8, 1947; s. William Michael and Rebecca Carolyn (Glass) W.; m. Anne Candler McLeod, June 5, 1968; children: William Powers, Laura Anne, Amy Lynn. BA, Auburn U., 1968; JD, Duke U., 1971. Bar: Ala. 1971. Assoc. Bradley, Arant, Rose & White, Birmingham, Ala., 1971-77, ptnr., 1977-83; v.p., gen. counsel Ala. Gas Corp., Birmingham, 1983-84, pres., chief operating officer, 1984—; pres, chief oper. officer Energen Corp., Birmingham, 1987-91, pres., chief ops. officer, 1991—; bd. dirs. AmSouth Bank Birmingham N.A., Energen Corp., Ala. Gas Corp., So. Gas Assn., Inst. Gas Tech. Contbr. articles to periodicals. Bd. dirs. Ala. Symphony Assn., 1988-90, pres., 1990—, chmn., 1991-92; chmn. Met. Devel. Bd., 1989-90; trustee Ala. Inst. for Deaf and Blind, 1988—, Children's Hosp. Birmingham, 1988—. 1st lt. USAF, 1971-72. Mem. ABA, Am. Gas Assn. (edn. 2000 com. 1991—), So. Gas Assn. (bd. dirs. 1989—), Inst. Gas Tech. (bd. trustees 1989—), Birmingham Area C. of C. (bd. dirs. 1986—, v.p. 1989), Summit Club (bd. dirs. 1989). Democrat. Methodist. Lodge: Rotary. Home: 3533 Mill Springs Rd Birmingham AL 35223-1637 Office: Ala Gas Corp 2101 6th Ave N Birmingham AL 35203-2748

WARREN, WILLIAM ROBINSON, real estate broker; b. St. Louis, Nov. 14, 1931; s. Edgar Lovett and Katharine (Cope) W.; m. Margaret Dorothea Ogilvy, June 13, 1953; children: Anne W. Bretting, Christina Margaret, Erica Katharine. B.S. in Math. and Physics, Bethany Coll., 1953; M.B.A., U. So. Calif., 1963; student, UCLA, 1951-56, Am. U., summer 1952. Vice pres. System Devel. Corp., Santa Monica, Calif., 1958-69; v.p. King Resources Co., Los Angeles, 1969-71; pres. Consol. Mgmt. Systems Los Angeles, 1971-72; sr. v.p. and region dir. Western Bancorp. and United Calif. Bank, Los Angeles, 1972-75; v.p. Fluor Corp., Irvine, Calif., 1975-84; pres. Consol. Realty, Newport Beach, Calif., 1984-93; Bishop Hawk, Newport Beach, 1993—; instr. U. Calif. Irvine Grad. Sch. Mgmt., 1985-87. Mem. Orange County Blue Ribbon Com., Santa Ana, 1980-81; trustee, exec. com. South Coast Repertory, Costa Mesa, Calif. Mem. Soc. Info. Mgmt., Am. Mgmt. Assn., Mgmt. Info. Continuing Seminar (chmn. 1980-81, exec. com. 1978-82), Realty Investment Assn. Calif. (dir. 1994—), Beta Theta Pi. Republican. Presbyterian. Clubs: Big Canyon Country (Newport Beach), Back Bay (Newport Beach). Home: 26 Pinehurst Ln Newport Beach CA 92660-5229 Office: 2424 SE Bristol St Ste 200 Newport Beach CA 92660

WARRICK, JAMES CRAIG, banker; b. Bangor, Pa., Oct. 9, 1938; s. Walter John and Florence Elizabeth (Lentz) W.; m. Diane Marie Higham, May 29, 1965; children—Scott, John. BS, Rider U., 1961; MBA, Seton Hall U., 1968. CPA, N.J. With KPMG Peat Marwick, N.J., 1965-71; audit mgr. KPMG Peat Marwick, 1971-74; v.p., regional controller Crestar Fin. Corp., Richmond, 1974-77; sr. v.p., corp. controller Crestar Fin. Corp., 1977-85, group exec. v.p., 1985—. Mem. long range planning com. United Way Svcs., Richmond, Va., 1984-85, fin. com., allocations com., 1975-84; councilman East Windsor Twp., N.J., 1969; bd. dirs. One Ocean Place Homeowners, Fin. Inst. Res. Risk Retention Group; fund raising chmn., class agt. Rider U. Lt. (j.g.) USN, 1961-64, capt. USNR. Fellow AICPA, Va. Soc. CPAs; mem. Fin. Execs. Inst. (pres. Va. chpt. 1985-86), Bryce Resort (dir. 1981-82, planning, fin. com. 1989—). Republican. Episcopalian. Avocations: skiing; swimming; golf; tennis. Home: 2120 Castlebridge Rd Midlothian VA 23113 Office: Crestar Fin Corp PO Box 26665 919 E Main St Richmond VA 23219-4625

WARRINGTON, CLAYTON LINWOOD, JR., advertising agency executive; b. Balt., Sept. 12, 1936; s. Clayton Linwood and Alice Theresa (Piccini) W.; m. Jacqueline Hoke Kiefer, Mar. 28, 1960 (div. 1974); children—Clayton Linwood, John Niles; m. Elizabeth Barbara Waizenegger, Sept. 28, 1974. B.S., U. Md., 1958; Postgrad. Am. U., 1962-63. Registered pharmacist. Mgr. market data systems Pfizer Labs., N.Y.C., 1966-68; v.p., account group supr. Dean L. Burdick Assocs. Inc., N.Y.C., 1968-72; sr. v.p., mgmt. supr. Sudler & Hennessey Inc., N.Y.C., 1972-74; pres., CEO Dugan/Farley Comm. Inc. div. Ally & Gargano, Inc., Upper Saddle River, N.J., 1974—. Served to lt. USN, 1959-64. Mem. U. Md. Alumni Internat. Methodist. Club: Ridgewood Country. Home: 16 Highwood Ter Glen Rock NJ 07452-1512 Office: Dugan/Farley Comm 600 E Crescent Ave Saddle River NJ 07458-1846

WARRINGTON, JOHN WESLEY, lawyer; b. Cin., June 6, 1914; s. George Howard and Eliza (Holmes) W.; m. Suzanne Mooney, May 5, 1951; children—Anne McGrath Warrington Wilson, George Howard, John Wesley, Mary Warrington Cassidy, Elizabeth Warrington Ott, Sarah Warrington Selnick, Rachel Warringotn Moss. A.B., Yale U., 1936; postgrad., Cambridge (Eng.) U., 1937; LL.B., Harvard U., 1940; D.F.A. (hon.), U. Cin., 1980. Bar: Ohio 1940. Since practiced in Cin.; sr. ptnr. Graydon, Head & Ritchey, 1951-89; dir. emeritus Fifth Third Bank. Chmn. emeritus planning commn., Indian Hill, Ohio, 1959-86; pres. emeritus Cin. Music Hall; chmn. Cin. Mus. Assn.; trustee emeritus Cin. Union Bethel, Am. Schs. Oriental Research, Seven Hills Schs., Cin. Natural History Mus., Cin. Inst. Fine Arts; sec. bd. trustees Episc. Diocese So. Ohio. Served to capt. Am. Field Service, 1942-45. Mentioned in dispatches Brit.). Mem. Am., Ohio, Cin. Bar Assns., Phi Beta Kappa. Republican. Episcopalian. Home: 8625 Camargo Club Dr Cincinnati OH 45243-3340 Office: PO Box 6464 Cincinnati OH 45201-6464

WARRINGTON, ROBERT O'NEIL, JR., mechanical engineering educator and administrator, researcher; b. Sparta, Wis., Mar. 13, 1945; s. Robert O'Neil and Virginia (Johnson) W.; m. Anne Cabell, Aug. 14, 1968; children: Robert O'Neil III, Daniel Scott, Kristy Cabell. BS in Aerospace Engring., Va. Poly. Inst., 1967; MS in Mech. Engring., U. Tex.-El Paso, 1971; PhD in Mech. Engring., Mont. State U., 1975. Instr. U. Tex.-El Paso, 1971; instr. Mont. State U., Bozeman, 1975-76, asst. prof., 1976-80, assoc. prof., 1980-83;

prof. mech. engring., dept. head La. Tech. U., Ruston, 1983—, track and field ofcl., 1983—; cons. Atlas Processing Co., Shreveport, La., 1984—. Author: Montana Energy Primer, 1978; contbr. articles to profl. jours. Coach Little League, Bozeman, 1978-83, Soccer League, Bozeman, 1981-83. Served with U.S. Army, 1968-70. Grantee NSF, Exxon Found., Hewlett-Packard Corp., C.E., Dept. Energy, 1975—, AT&T Found. Mem. ASME (K-8 com. 1983—), Am. Soc. for Engring Edn. (vice-chmn., program chmn. mech. engring. div.), Mont. Engring. Assocs. (sec.-treas. 1979—), Nat. Ski Patrol, Sigma Chi. Republican. Roman Catholic. Office: LA Tech Univ Mech Engring Dept PO Box 10348 Tech Sta Ruston LA 71272-0001

WARRINGTON, WILLARD GLADE, former university official; b. Macomb, Ill., Oct. 24, 1920; s. Henry K. and Farie V. (Prather) W.; m. A. Irene Windser, Aug. 9, 1945 (dec. 1969); m. Janette Moffatt Cooper, Apr. 26, 1972; children: David, Steven, Douglas, Jane Ann, Stephen Cooper. B.Ed., Western Ill. State Tchrs. Coll., 1941; M.S., U. Ill., 1949, U. Ill., 1950; Ed.D., U. Ill., 1952. Tchr. public high schs. Ill., 1941-42, 45-48; mem. faculty Mich. State U., 1952-58, dir. office evaluation services, 1958-74, asso. dean Univ. Coll., 1974-78, acting dean Univ. Coll., 1978-80, dir. undergrad. univ. div., 1980-85, dir. prof. emeritus, 1986—; cons. edn.; Ford Found. cons. U. Philippines. Contbr. articles on ednl. measurement to profl. publs.; editorial bd.: Ednl. and Psychol. Measurement, 1968-85. Active Boy Scouts Am., 1957-68. Served to lt. col. USAAF, 1942-45. Mem. Nat. Council on Measurement in Edn. (pres. 1973-74), Am. Ednl. Research Assn., Assn. for Gen. and Liberal Studies (sec.-treas. 1973-79). Methodist. Home: 510 W Silver Lake Rd Traverse City MI 49684

WARSAWER, HAROLD NEWTON, real estate appraiser and consultant; b. N.Y.C.; s. Sidney L. and Alice (Frachtman) W.; m. Sally Kingsbury; children: Alice Cooper, Nancy Arkuss, Carole Greenblatt. BA, U. Mo.; MBA, Harvard U. Property mgr. and real estate broker Sidney L. Warsawer & Son, N.Y.C.; appraiser Atlantic Appraisal Co., Inc., N.Y.C., 1960—; pres. Atlantic Appraisal Co., Inc., N.Y.C., 1960—, Consolidated Capital, N.Y.C., 1962-68; pres., bd. dirs. Contemporary Enterprises, N.Y.C., 1974-76. Mem. editorial bd. The Appraisal Jour., 1970-85. Candidate Teaneck N.J. Sch. Bd., Coun. Teaneck N.J.; chmn. bldg. com. Temple Emeth, Teaneck, 1954-64. Mem. Appraisal Inst. (pres. N.Y. chpt. 1977, bd. dirs. 1970-80, 90-92, gov. counsellor 1978), Nat. Assn. Rev. Appraisers, Real Estate Bd. N.Y., Nat. Realty Club (pres. 1992, bd. dirs.), Am. Arbitration Assn., Haworth Golf Club. Avocations: golf, clocks. Home: 430 Rutland Ave Teaneck NJ 07666-2823 Office: 60 E 42nd St Ste 2303 New York NY 10165-0001

WARSH, JEFFREY ALAN, state legislator, lawyer; b. New Milford, N.J., Sept. 21, 1960; s. Leonard and Estelle Warsh. BA, Franklin & Marshall Coll., 1982; JD, Emory U., 1985. Bar: N.J. 1985. Atty. N.J. Divsn. Alcoholic Beverage Control, Trenton, 1985-87; regulatory counsel N.J. Dept. Human Svcs., Trenton, 1988-90; pvt. practice New Brunswick, N.J., 1991; assoc. Ansell, Zaro, Bennett, & Grimm, Eatontown, N.J., 1992—; mem. N.J. Gen. Assembly, Trenton, 1992—, mem. transp. and comm. com.; chmn. Assembly Regulatory Oversight Com.; Biosolds Utilization Task Force; mem. Transportation and Comm. Com., Commerce and Regulatory Com. Vice chmn. Edison (N.J.) Rep. Orgn.; chief of staff State Senator Peter Garibaldi, Edison, 1985; mem. N.J.-Israel Commn., 1994—; bd. dirs. Metuchen-Edison Soccer Club; mem. Coalition for a Better Edison, 1990—; active Citizens Upset with Tax Situation; mem. N.J. State Commn. on Aging, 1992-94. Jewish. Avocations: outdoor activities, hiking, history, reading, soccer. Office: NJ Gen Assembly 100 Plainfield Ave Ste 1 Edison NJ 08817

WARSHAUER, IRENE CONRAD, lawyer; b. N.Y.C., May 4, 1942; d. Alfred and Sylvia (Bober) Conrad; m. Alan M. Warshauer, Nov. 27, 1966; 1 dau., Susan L. B.A. with distinction, U. Mich., 1963; LL.B. cum laude, Columbia U., 1966. Bar: N.Y. 1966, U.S. Dist. Ct. (so. and ea. dists.) N.Y. 1969, U.S. Ct. Appeals (2d cir.) 1969, U.S. Supreme Ct. 1972, U.S. Dist. Ct. (no. dist.) N.Y. 1980. With First Jud. Dept., N.Y. State Mental Health Info. Service, 1966-68; assoc. Chadbourne Parke Whiteside & Wolff, 1968-75; mem. Anderson Kill & Olick & Oshinsky, P.C., N.Y.C., 1975—; lectr. Def. Research Inst., Aspen Inst. Humanistic Studies, ABA, Rocky Mountain Mineral Law Found., CPR Inst. Dispute Resolution, panelist Am. Arbitration Assn., 1973—; mediator U.S. Dist. Ct. So. Dist., N.Y. Contbr. articles, chpts. to profl. lit. Mem. Democratic County Com., 1968—. Named to Hon. Order Ky. Cols. Mem. Assn. of Bar of City of N.Y. (judiciary com. 1982-84), N.Y. State Bar Assn. (chairperson subcom. mentally disabled and community 1978-82), ABA. Avocations: gardening, cooking, birding. Office: Anderson Kill Olick & Oshinsky 1251 Ave of the Americans New York NY 10020-1182

WARSHAUER, MYRON C., land use planner; b. 1939. BS in Fin., U. Ill., 1962; MBA, Northwestern U., 1963. With affiliate Standard Parking Corp., 1962—; now pres. Standard Parking Corp., Chgo. Office: Standard Parking Corp 55 E Monroe St Ste 3440 Chicago IL 60603*

WARSHAW, ALLEN CHARLES, lawyer; b. Harrisburg, Pa., Aug. 27, 1948; s. Julius and Miriam (Nepove) W.; m. Shirley Anne Nes, Aug. 23, 1970; children: Christopher James, Andrew Charles, William Robert. BA, U. Pa., 1970; JD, Villanova U., 1973. Bar: Pa. 1973, U.S. Dist. Ct. (ea. and mid. dists.) Pa. 1974, U.S. Ct. Appeals (3d cir.) 1975, U.S. Supreme Ct. 1977, Calif. 1978. Staff atty. Office Atty. Gen., State of Pa., Harrisburg, 1973-79, chief civil litigation, 1979-85, dir. civil law, 1985-86; ptnr. Duane, Morris & Heckscher, Harrisburg, 1986—. Coach, pres. Mechanicsburg Soccer Assn.; coach Upper Allen Baseball Assn. Mem. ABA, Pa. Bar Assn., Pa. Def. Inst. Home: 1035 Mccormick Rd Mechanicsburg PA 17055-5970 Office: Duane Morris & Heckscher 305 N Front St Harrisburg PA 17101-1236

WARSHAW, ANDREW LOUIS, surgeon, researcher; b. N.Y.C., Feb. 18, 1939; s. David and Florence (Rand) W.; m. Brenda Rose Flavin, Jan. 4, 1986; children: Jordan, Abigail, Daniel; stepchildren: Heather, Gretchen, Brenda. AB, Harvard U., 1959, MD, 1963. Diplomate Am. Bd. Surgery. Intern in surgery Mass. Gen. Hosp., Boston, 1963-64, resident in surgery, 1964-65, 67-70, rsch. fellow in medicine, 1970, chief resident in surgery, 1971; clin. assoc. in gastroenterology NIH, Bethesda, Md., 1965-67; from instr. surgery to prof. surgery Harvard Med. Sch., Boston, 1972-90, Harold & Ellen Danser prof. surgery, 1990—; assoc. chief surg. svcs. Mass. Gen. Hosp., Boston, 1990—, chief gen. surgery, 1992—. Editor: Pancreatitis, 1989, Current Practice of Surgery, 1993; contbr. over 200 articles, 131 book chpts., editorials to med. jours., revs., 8 med. ednl. films, videos. Lt. comdr. USPHS, 1965-67. Mem. Am. Bd. Surgery (chmn. 1992-93, dir. 1985-93), New Eng. Surgical Soc. (pres. 1993-94), Am. Coll. Surgeons (pres. Mass. chpt. 1991-92). Avocations: photography, fly fishing. Office: Mass Gen Hosp WACC-336 Boston MA 02114

WARSHAW, JERRY, insurance company executive; b. 1941. BA, U. Fla.; MBA, NYU. With Guardian Life Ins. Co., 1964-67, Trans World Life Ins. Co. Inc., 1967-68; with Presdl. Life Ins. Co., Nyack, N.Y., 1968—, pres. Office: Presidential Life Ins Co 69 Lydecker St Nyack NY 10960*

WARSHAW, JOSEPH BENNETT, pediatrician, educator; b. Miami Beach, Fla., July 17, 1936; s. Phillip Robert and Mona (Monashefsky) W.; m. Cynthia Ann Stober, June 6, 1961; children: Deborah, Kathryn, Lawrence. B.S., U. Fla., 1957; M.D., Duke U., 1961; M.S. (hon.), Yale U., 1976; M.D. (hon.), Catholic U.; Josiah Macy Jr. faculty scholar, U. Oxford, 1979-80. Diplomate Am. Bd. Pediatrics., subsplty bd. in neonatal-perinatal medicine. Intern, resident in pediatrics Strong Meml. Hosp., Rochester, N.Y., 1961-63; resident in pediatrics Duke Hosp., Durham, N.C., 1963-64; research assoc. NIH, 1964-66, Retina Found., Boston, 1966-68; assoc. in pediatrics Harvard U., 1968-71, asst. prof. pediatrics, 1971-72, assoc. prof., 1972-73; assoc. prof. pediatrics and ob-gyn Yale U., 1973-76, prof. pediatrics and ob-gyn, 1976-82; prof., chmn. dept. pediatrics U. Tex. Health Sci. Ctr., Dallas, 1982-87; chief staff Children's Med. Ctr., Dallas, 1982-87; chief pediatrics Parkland Meml. Hosp., Dallas, 1982-87 prof., chmn. dept. pediatrics Yale U. Sch. Medicine, New Haven, 1987—; physician-in-chief Children's Hosp. at Yale New Haven Hosp., 1987—; mem. human embryology and devel. study sect. NIH, 1974-78, nat. adv. council nat. inst. child health and human devel., 1987-91. Editor: Seminars in Perinatology, Principles and Practice of Pediatrics; contbr. articles on pediatrics, perinatology, devel. biology and biochemistry to profl. jours. Clin. research adv. com. Nat.

Found. March of Dimes, 1978-92; mem. rsch. com. United Cerebral Palsy, 1987—. Served with USPHS, 1964-66. Fellow Am. Acad. Pediatrics; mem. Inst. Medicine of NAS, Am. Pediatric Soc. (coun. mem. 1988-94), Am. Soc. Clin. Investigation, Am. Soc. Biol. Chemistry, Am. Soc. Cell Biology, Soc. Devel. Biology, Soc. Pediatric Rsch. (pres. 1981-82), Assn. Am. Physicians, Internat. Pediatric Rsch. Found. (chmn. bd. 1989-93), Conn. Acad. Arts and Scis. Home: 350 Vineyard Point Rd Guilford CT 06437-3255

WARSHAW, LEON J(OSEPH), physician; b. N.Y.C., July 20, 1917; s. Samuel and Bessie (Olken) W.; m. Mona Glassman, Aug. 31, 1941; children: Peter M., David C. A.B., Columbia U., 1938, M.D., 1942. Diplomate Am. Bd. Internal Medicine, Am. Bd. Preventive Medicine (occupational medicine). Intern, house physician 1st med. div. Bellevue Hosp., N.Y.C., 1942-44; from clin. asst. vis. physician to asso. vis. physician Bellevue Hosp., 1942-59; clin. asst., then adj. Beth Israel Hosp., N.Y.C., 1944-49; asso. attending physician Beth Israel Hosp., 1949-87, chief adult cardiac clinic, 1950-62; practice internal medicine N.Y.C., 1944-55, med. dir. and/or med. cons. various corps., 1944-69; with Equitable Life Assurance Soc., N.Y.C., 1967-80; v.p., chief med. dir. Equitable Life Assurance Soc., 1970-75, v.p., corp. med. dir., 1975-80; on leave as dep. dir. N.Y.C. Mayor's Office of Ops., 1978-80; clin. prof. environ. medicine NYU, 1980—; cons. health care delivery, 1980—; exec. dir. N.Y. Bus. Group on Health, 1980-93; mem. N.Y. Gov.'s Health Adv. Council, 1978-84, N.Y. State Adv. Coun. on Alcoholism Svcs., 1988—, chmn., 1990—; mem. faculty Columbia U. Coll. Physicians and Surgeons, 1944-60, NYU Med. Sch., 1945-47; chmn. bd. Equitable Environ. Health, Inc., Woodbury, N.Y., 1973-75; dir., 1975-78; trustee Ins. Med. Scientist Scholarship Fund, 1975-78; mem. adv. bd. Ctr. Productive Aging, N.Y. Ctr. for Policy on Aging; bd. dirs. Med. & Health Research Assn., 1984—; mem. N.Y. State Adv. Council on Alcoholism Svcs., 1987—, chmn., 1990—; mem. nat. adv. com. Pres.'s Com. Employment Handicapped, 1965-89; mem. Pres.'s Council Phys. Fitness and Sports, 1970-85; bd. sponsors Twin Cities Health Care Devel. Project, 1972-75; chmn. med. adv. com. Washington Bus. Group Health, 1977-79; mental health adv. bd. Cornell U., 1970-80; Sappington Meml. lectr. Indsl. Med. Assn.; dir. Health Systems Agy. N.Y.C., 1987-93; Thackrah lect. Soc. Occupational Medicine/Leeds U., 1988. Author: Malaria: Biography of a Killer, 1949, Managing Stress, 1979, The Heart in Industry, 1969; contbr. articles to profl. jours.; mem. editorial bd. jours. Fellow Am. Coll. Occupational & Environ. Medicine, Am. Coll. Cardiology, ACP, Am. Coll. Preventive Medicine, Am. Occupational Medicine Assn. (past dir.), N.Y. Acad. Scis.; mem. AMA, N.Y. State, N.Y. County med. socs., Am. Arbitration Assn. (adv. health council 1972-80), Am. Heart Assn. (chmn. heart industry com. 1966-68, dir. 1969-73), Conf. Board, Nat. Safety Council (dir. 1972-74, v.p. research 1972-74), Greater N.Y. Safety Council (1970), N.Y. C. of C., N.Y. Heart Assn. (dir. 1968-70, 76-82), Occupational Health Inst. (dir. 1970-87), N.Y. Acad. Medicine (chmn. sec. occupational medicine 1964-66), N.Y. State Soc. Occupational Medicine (pres. 1965-67, exec. com. 1967-77), Occupational Psychiatry Group, Soc. Occupational Medicine, Med. and Health Rsch. Assn. N.Y.C. (bd. dirs.), Alpha Omega Alpha, Beta Sigma Rho, Phi Delta Epsilon. Office: 180 W End Ave Apt 6C New York NY 10023-4926

WARSHAW, MARTIN RICHARD, marketing educator; b. N.Y.C., Sept. 17, 1924; s. Irving Gregg and Adelaide (Klein) W.; m. Alice M. Present, Mar. 28, 1948; children: Gregg, Mark, Lynn, Laurie. A.B., Columbia U., 1947; M.B.A., U. Mich., 1957, Ph.D., 1960. Salesman Daniels Jewelry Co., Battle Creek, Mich., 1947-50; store mgr. Daniels Jewelry Co., 1950-55; v.p., dir. Daniels Jewelry Co., Lansing, Mich., 1955-64; instr. mktg. U. Mich., 1957-60, asst. prof., 1960-64, assoc. prof., 1964-67, 1967-89, prof. emeritus, 1989—, chmn. mktg. faculty, 1973-79, 81-84. Author: (with Taylor and Scott) Introduction To Marketing Management, 5th edit, 1985, (with Engel and Kinnear) Promotional Strategy, 8th edit., 1994. Served with C.E. U.S. Army, 1943-46. Mem. Am. Mktg. Assn. (past pres. Detroit chpt.). Home: 5424 Parkgrove Rd Ann Arbor MI 48103-9202 Office: U Mich Sch Bus Adminstrn Ann Arbor MI 48109

WARSHAW, ROBERT S., police chief; b. Bklyn., Nov. 25, 1947; married, 2 children. BA in Sociology, Temple U., 1969; MS in Human Resources Adminstrn., Biscayne Coll., 1981. Police officer ops. divsn. Miami Police Dept., 1973-78, exec. asst. to chief, chief of staff, 1978-81, asst. chief of police, 1981-85; mgr. adminstrn. Dept. Pub. Safety, Dekalb County, Decatur, Ga., 1986-88; chief of police City of Statesville, N.C., 1988—; adj. faculty exec. devel. program Inst. of Govt., U.N.C., Chapel Hill. Mem. Internat. Assn. Chiefs of Police (exec. com.), Police Exec. Rsch. Forum, N.C. Assn. of Chiefs of Police. Office: Rochester Police Dept 150 South Plymouth Ave Rochester NY 14614

WARSHAW, STANLEY IRVING, government official; b. Boston, Nov. 5, 1931; s. Alec and Sarah (Laserson) W.; m. Wanda Faye Capino, Feb. 12, 1992; 1 child from previous marriage, Karen Beth. B.S. in Ceramic Engring. Ga. Tech. Inst., 1957; Sc.D. in Ceramics, M.I.T., 1961; grad., Advanced Mgmt. Program, Harvard Bus. Sch., 1978. Sr. scientist research div. Raytheon Co., Waltham, Mass., 1961-64; with Am. Standard, Inc., New Brunswick, N.J., 1964-75, gen. mgr. engring. and devel., 1972-75; dir. Ctr. for Consumer Product Tech., Nat. Inst. Stds. and Tech. (formerly Nat. Bur. Stds.), Washington, 1975-80, dir. Office Product Standards Policy, 1981-86, assoc. dir., 1987-89; dir. Office Standards Svcs. Nat. Inst. Stds. and Tech. (formerly Nat. Bur. Stds.), Gaithersburg, Md., 1989-93; sr. policy advisor Internat. Trade Adminstrn., U.S. Dept. Commerce, Washington, 1994—. Served to capt. U.S. Army, 1951-53. Fellow N.Y. Acad. Scis., Washington Acad. Scis. Home: 8051 Rising Ridge Rd Bethesda MD 20817-6951 Office: US Dept Commerce Rm 3527 Internat Trade Adminstrn Washington DC 20230

WARSOFF, STANLEY L., lawyer; b. N.Y.C., Aug. 30, 1946; s. Louis A. and Sylvia (Pearl) W.; m. Ruth Peterson, Dec. 6, 1987. BA, CUNY, 1968; JD, St. John's U., 1972. Bar: N.Y. 1973, U.S. Dist. Ct. (ea. and so. dist.) N.Y. 1975, Fla. 1976, U.S. Supreme Ct. 1980. Atty. Home Life Ins. Co., N.Y.C., 1972-75; counsel FDIC, N.Y.C., 1975-80; assoc. Squadran, Ellenoff, Pleasant & Lehrer, N.Y.C., 1981-82, Opton, Handler, Gottlieb & Feiler, N.Y.C., 1982-84; Phillips, Nizer, Benjamin, Krim & Ballon, N.Y.C., 1984—; lectr. NYU Real Estate Inst., 1986—. Mem. St. John's U. Law Rev. Consumer counsel N.Y.C. Civil Ct. and Small Claims Ct., 1976-77. With USAR, 1968-71. Named St. Thomas More scholar St. John's U., 1970-71. Mem. ABA, N.Y. County Lawyers, N.Y. State Bar Assn. (mem. com. cooperatives and condominiums real property law sect.), Shakespeare Lodge, Masons. Home: 415 E 52nd St New York NY 10022-6424 Office: Phillips Nizer Benjamin Krim & Ballon 40 W 57th St New York NY 10019-4001

WARSON, TOBY GENE, retired corporate executive; b. Ft. Madison, Iowa, Oct. 18, 1937; s. Harold Francis and Chelsea Irene (Holt) W.; m. Linda Muriel Beasley, Dec. 29, 1979; children: Leslie Lynn, Michael Douglas. BS in Engring., U.S. Naval Acad., 1959; MS in Physics, U.S. Naval Postgrad., 1968. Commd. ensign USN, 1959, advanced through grades to comdr., ret., 1979; dir. ops. Honeywell, Seattle, 1979-84; v.p., gen. mgr. Honeywell, West Covina, Calif., 1984-87; dir., chief exec. officer Honeywell, Ltd., Bracknell, Eng., 1987-90; v.p. internat. mktg. Honeywell, Mpls., 1990, pres. def. and marine divs., 1990; pres., CEO Alliant Techsystems, Edina, Minn., 1990-95; ret., 1995. Decorated D.S.M. Republican. Avocations: photography, scuba diving, golf.

WARTELL, ROGER MARTIN, biophysics educator; b. N.Y.C., Feb. 24, 1945; s. Hugh H. and Jennie (Silbermann) W.; m. Aila Irmeli Salo, Sept. 18, 1945; children: Zachary, Arlena. BSc, Stevens Inst. Tech., Hoboken, N.J., 1966; PhD, U. Rochester, N.Y., 1971. Postdoctoral fellow U. Wis., Madison, 1971-73; prof. physics and biology Ga. Inst. Tech., Atlanta, 1974—, dir. Sch. Biology, 1991—, dir. Biosciss. Ctr., 1991—; vis. fellow U. Wis., Madison, 1978-79; vis. scientist NIH, Bethesda, Md., 1986-87; cons. SCI-EXPO Inc., Tucson, 1984-86. Contbr. articles to profl. jours. Mem. Biophys. Soc., ACS. Office: Ga Inst Tech Sch of Biology Atlanta GA 30332

WARTELLA, ELLEN ANN, communications educator, consultant; b. Kingston, Pa., Oct. 16, 1949; d. Nicholas and Margaret (Lipko) W.; m. D. Charles Whitney, Aug. 1, 1976; children: David Charles, Stephen Wright. BA, U. Pitts., 1971; MA, U. Minn., 1974, PhD, 1977. Asst. prof. Ohio State U., Columbus, 1976-79; rsch. asst. prof. communications U. Ill., Champaign, 1979-83, rsch. assoc. prof. 1983-89, rsch. prof., 1989-93; dean

Coll. Comm., Walter Cronkite Regents Chair in Comm. U. Tex., Austin, 1993–; vis. prof. U. Calif., Santa Barbara, 1992-93; cons. Children's TV Workshop, N.Y.C., 1988-89, FTC, Washington, 1978, 1991-92, FCC, Washington, 1979. Co-author: How Children Learn to Buy, 1977; editor: Mass Communications Review Yearbook, 1982-83, Rethinking Communication, vols. I and II, 1989. Mem. bd. advisors Am. Children's TV Festival, Chgo., 1988—, The Learning Place, Champaign, 1992; bd. dirs. Headliners Found, Austin, 1993—, Sta. KLRU-TV (ex officio), Austin, 1993—. Recipient Krieghbaum award Assn. for Edn. in Journalism and Mass Communication, 1984; Univ. scholar U. Ill., 1989-93; Gannett Ctr. for Media Studies fellow, 1985-86. Fellow Internat. Comm. Assn. (pres. 1992-93), Broadcast Edn. Assn. (bd. dirs. 1990-94), Speech Comm. Assn., Soc. for Rsch. in Child Devel.

WARTH, ROBERT DOUGLAS, history educator; b. Houston, Dec. 16, 1921; s. Robert Douglas and Virginia (Adams) W.; m. Lillian Eleanor Terry, Sept. 18, 1945. B.S., U. Ky., 1943; M.A., U. Chgo., 1945, Ph.D., 1949. Instr. history U. Tenn., Knoxville, 1950-51; instr. Rutgers U., Newark, 1951-54; asst. prof. Rutgers U., 1954-58; vis. prof. Paine Coll., Augusta, Ga., 1960; asso. editor Grolier, Inc., N.Y.C., 1960-62, 63-64; lectr. Hunter Coll., N.Y.C., part time, 1962-63; asso. prof. S.I. Community Coll., 1964-68; prof. history U. Ky., Lexington, 1968-92; prof. emeritus history U. Ky., 1992—; Pres. So. Conf. Slavic Studies, 1982-83. Author: The Allies and the Russian Revolution, 1954, Soviet Russia in World Politics, 1963, Joseph Stalin, 1969, Lenin, 1973, Leon Trotsky, 1977. Served with AUS, 1943-44. Sr. scholar award So. Conf. Slavic Studies, 1992. Mem. Am. Hist. Assn., Am. Assn. Advancement Slavic Studies, AAUP. Home: 640 W Cooper Dr Lexington KY 40502-2277 Office: U Ky Dept History Lexington KY 40506

WARTHEN, HARRY JUSTICE, III, lawyer; b. Richmond, Va., July 8, 1939; s. Harry Justice Jr. and Martha Winston (Alsop) W.; m. Sally Berkeley Trapnell, Sept. 7, 1968; children: Martha Alsop, William Trapnell. BA, U. Va., 1961, LLB, 1967. Bar: Va. 1967, U.S. Ct. Appeals (4th cir.) 1967, U.S. Dist. Ct. (ea. dist.) Va. 1969. Law clk. to judge U.S. Ct. Appeals (4th cir.), Richmond, Va., 1967-68; assoc. Hunton & Williams, Richmond, 1968—; lectr. U. Va. Law Sch., Charlottesville, 1975-77, in field. Trustee exec. com. Hist. Richmond Found., 1986-95; dir. exec. com. Preservation Alliance of Va., 1991—, pres. 1994—; elder, trustee endowment fund Grace Covenant Presbyn. Ch.; moderator Hanover Presbytery, Presbyn. Ch. (USA), 1988. Lt. U.S. Army, 1962-64. Fellow Am. Coll. Trust and Estate Counsel, Va. Law Found.; mem. ABA, Richmond Bar Assn., Va. Bar Assn. (chmn. sect. on wills, trusts and estates 1981-89), Antiquarian Soc. Richmond (pres. 1977-78), Country Club Va., Deep Run Hunt Club. Republican. Home: 1319 Shallow Well Rd Manakin Sabot VA 23103-2305 Office: Hunton & Williams Riverfront Plaza East Tower 951 E Byrd St Richmond VA 23219-4040

WARTHIN, THOMAS ANGELL, physician, educator; b. Ann Arbor, Mich., Aug. 11, 1909; s. Aldred Scott and Katharine Louise (Angell) W.; m. Virginia Carver Whittier Warthin, Oct. 15, 1938; children: Jonathan Carver W., Richard Scott W., Thomas Whittier W. AB, U. Mich., 1930; MD cum laude, Harvard U., 1934. Diplomate Am. Bd. Internal Medicine. Intern medicine Boston City Hosp., 1934-36; resident intern medicine New Haven Hosp., Conn., 1936-37; fellow intern medicine Johns Hopkins Med. Sch., Balt., 1937-39; practice medicine Mass. Gen. Hosp., Boston, 1939-42; chief med. svc. VA Hosp., W. Roxbury, Mass., 1946-75; prof. of medicine Harvard Med. Sch., Boston, 1955-76, prof. of medicine emeritus, 1976—; cons. Surgeon Gen. U.S. Army, Washington, 1960-69, Internal Medicine VA Hosp., W. Roxbury, Mass., 1976-84. Contbr. articles to profl. jours. Brigadier Gen. U.S. Army, 1942-69. Recipient Legion of Merit, U.S. Army, 1969. Mem. ACP (master), Soc. Med. Cons. Armed Forces (pres. 1964), Internat. Soc. Internal Medicine (hon.), Mass. Med. Soc., Am. Clin. and Climatol. Assn. (coun., v.p. 1982), Aesculapian Club (pres. 1962), Alpha Omega Alpha. Avocation: gardening. Home: 180 Main St Apt 120 Walpole MA 02081-4033

WARTIK, THOMAS, chemistry educator, former college dean; b. Cin., Oct. 1, 1921; s. Abraham and Lena (Monnes) W.; m. Louise Dreifus, Apr. 8, 1952; children: Nancy, Steven Philip. A.B., U. Chgo., 1943; Ph.D., U. Chgo., 1949. Chemist, Manhattan project U. Chgo., 1944-46; faculty Pa. State U., University Park, 1950-88; prof. chemistry Pa. State U., 1960-88, chmn. dept., 1960-71; dean Pa. State U. (Coll. Sci.), 1971-88; Vis. scientist U. Calif. Radiation Labs., 1957, 59, 61; cons. in field. Mem. adv. bd. Petroleum Research Fund, Am. Chem. Soc., 1968-71; mem. Fulbright Scholar Selection Com. in Chemistry, 1966-72, chmn., 1969-72; mem. N.Y. State Doctoral Evaluation Com., 1974; chmn. chemistry vis. com. Tex. A. and M. U., 1979—; mem. Council Am. Colls. Selection Com. Nat. Sci. Bd., 1983. Contbr. profl. articles to jours.; Editor: Borax to Boranes, 1961. Fellow AAAS; mem. Am. Chem. Soc. (councillor 1967-69, vis. assoc. 1960—), Middle States Assn. (accreditation teams 1962—), Phi Beta Kappa, Sigma Xi. Club: Lake Glendale Sailing (dir.). Home: 333 S Allen St Apt 602 State College PA 16801-4839 Office: U Pa 120 Davey Lab University Park PA 16802-6300

WARWICK, DIONNE, singer; b. East Orange, N.J., Dec. 12, 1940; m. Bill Elliott (div. 1975); children: David, Damon. Ed., Hartt Coll. Music, Hartford, Conn. As teen-ager formed Gospelaires and Drinkard Singers, then sang background for rec. studio, 1966; debut, Philharmonic Hall, N.Y. Lincoln Center, 1966; appearances include London Palladium, Olympia, Paris, Lincoln Ctr. Performing Arts, N.Y.C.; records include Don't Make Me Over, 1962, Walk On By, Do You Know The Way to San José, What The World Needs Now, Message To Michael, I'll Never Fall In Love Again, I'll Never Love This Way Again, Deja Vu, Heartbreaker, That's What Friends Are For; albums include Valley of the Dolls and Others, 1968, Promises, Promises, 1975, Dionne, 1979, Then Came You, Friends, 1986, Reservations for Two, 1987, Greatest Hits, 1990, Dionne Warwick Sings Cole Porter, 1990, Hidden Gems; The Best of Dionne Warwick, Vol. 2, 1992, (with Whitney Houston) Friends Can Be Lovers, 1993; TV appearance in Sisters in the Name of Love, HBO, 1986; screen debut Slaves, 1969, No Night, So Long, also, Hot! Live and Otherwise; co-host: TV show Solid Gold; host: TV show A Gift of Music, 1981; star: TV show Dionne Warwick Spl. Founder Dionne Warwick Scholarship Fund, 1968, charity found BRAVO (Blood Revolves Around Victorious Optimism), Warwick Found. to Help Fight AIDS; spokeswoman Am. Sudden Infant Death Syndrome; participant U.S.A for Africa; Am. Amb. of Health, 1987. Recipient Grammy awards, 1969, 70, 80; NAACP Key of Life award, 1990. Address: Arista Records Inc 6 W 57th St New York NY 10019*

WARWICK, JOHN PETERSEN, advertising executive; b. New Rochelle, N.Y., Mar. 20, 1926; s. H. Paul and Hortense (Petersen) W.; m. Janet Mick, Sept. 29, 1962; children: Brian John, Jennifer Jean. Grad., Taft Sch., 1944; B.A., Dartmouth Coll., 1948. With sales dept. Hoffman Beverage Co., 1948-49; with Warwick Advt. Inc., 1949—; pres., chief exec. officer Warwick, Welsh & Miller, Inc., from 1964; formerly chmn., chief exec. officer Warwick Advt., Inc., N.Y.C., chmn. bd., 1986—; Trustee Met. Savs. Bank, N.Y.C. Served with USNR, 1944-46. Mem. Kappa Sigma. Republican. Presbyn. Clubs: Westhampton (N.Y.) Country; Winged Foot Golf (Mamaroneck, N.Y.); Nat. Links (Southampton, N.Y.). Office: Warwick Advt Inc 100 Avenue Of The Americas New York NY 10013-1605

WARWICK, WARREN J., pediatrics educator; b. Racine, Wis., Jan. 27, 1928; married; 2 children. BA, St. Olaf Coll., 1950; MD, U. Minn., 1954. Med. fellow pediatrics U. Minn., Mpls., 1955-57, med. fellow specialist, 1959-60, from instr. to assoc. prof. pediatrics, 1960-78, prof. pediatrics, 1978—; mem. ctr. program com. Nat. Cystic Fibrosis Rsch. Found., 1964-66, chmn. med. care com., 1966-71, coop. study com., 1971-72; mem. exec. bd. sci.-med. com. Internat. Cystic Fibrosis (Mucoviscidosis) Assn., 1970-80; mem. nat. data registry com. Cystic Fibrosis Found., 1972-86; Annalisa Marzotto cystic fibrosis chmn. Cardiovascular Rsch. fellow Alpha Omega Phi, 1955-57, Rsch. fellow Am. Heart Assn., 1959-60; recipient Rsch. Career Devel. award USPHS, 1961-66. Achievements include research in pulmonary diseases, experimental pathology, immunology, cystic fibrosis. Office: U Minn Hosp Cystic Fibrosis Ctr 420 Delaware St SE Minneapolis MN 55455

WASAN, DARSH TILAKCHAND, university official, chemical engineer educator; b. Sarai, Salah, West Pakistan, July 15, 1938; came to U.S., 1957,

naturalized, 1974; s. Tilakchand Gokalchand and Ishari Devi (Obhan) W.; m. Usha Kapur, Aug. 21, 1966; children: Ajay, Kern. BSChemE, U. Ill., 1960; PhD, U. Calif., Berkeley, 1965. Asst. prof. chem. engring. Ill. Inst. Tech., Chgo., 1964-67, assoc. prof., 1967-70, prof., 1970—, chmn. dept., 1971-77, 78-87, acting dean, 1977-78, 87-88, v.p. rsch. and tech., 1988-91, provost, 1991—, provost and sr. v.p., 1995—; cons. Inst. Gas Tech., 1965-70, Chgo. Bridge & Iron Co., 1967-71, Ill. EPA, 1971-72, NSF, 1971, 78-79, 87-89, Nelson Industries, 1976—, B.F. Goodrich Chem. Co., 1976-78, Exxon Rsch. & Engring. Co., 1977-89, Stauffer Chem. Co., 1980-88, ICI Ams., 1988—. Editor-in-chief Jour. Colloid and Interface Sci.; mem. publs. bd. Chem. Engring. Edn. Jour.; mem. adv. bd. Internat. Jour. Powder Tech., Jour. Separations Tech., Surfaces and Colloids Jour., Jour. of Dispersion Sci. and Tech.; contbr. articles to profl. jours. Recipient Donald Gage Stevens Disting. Lectureship award Syracuse U., 1991, Jakob J. Bikerman Lectureship award Case Western U., 1994, Robert Gilpin Lectr. award Clarkson U., 1995. Fellow Am. Inst. Chem. Engrs. (Ernest Thiele award 1989); mem. AAAS, Am. Chem. Soc., Soc. Rheology, Am. Soc. Engring. Edn. (Western Electric award 1972, 3M Lectureship award chem. engring. divsn. 1991), Am. Physics Inst., Fine Particles Soc. (pres. 1976-77, Hausner award 1982), Sigma Xi. Home: 8705 Royal Swan Ln Darien IL 60561-8433 Office: Ill Inst Tech 3300 S Federal St Chicago IL 60616-3732

WASFI, SADIQ HASSAN, chemistry educator; b. Basrah, Iraq, July 1, 1936; established residency in the U.S., 1978; s. Hassan Mohammed and Seniye (Omar) W.; m. Ellen Olivia Schwarz, Nov. 15, 1968; children: Yasmine, Dahlia, Ammar. BS in Chemistry Edn., Baghdad (Iraq) U., 1961; MS in Analytical Chemistry, Georgetown U., 1966, PhD in Inorganic Chemistry, 1971. Lectr. chemistry Basrah U., 1971-77; rsch. assoc. U. Hawaii, Honolulu, 1975-76, Georgetown U., Washington, 1977-78; assoc. prof. Montgomery Coll., Takoma Park, Md., 1978-79; prof. chemistry Del. State U., Dover, 1979—; vis. assoc. prof. Georgetown U., 1980, 81. Contbr. articles to profl. jours.; patent in antimony oxometalate complexes having anti-viral activity, 1991. Mem. Am.-Arab Anti-Discrimination Com. Mem. Am. Chem. Soc., Sigma Xi. Muslim. Home: 286 Pine Valley Rd Dover DE 19904 Office: Del State Univ Dept Chemistry 1200 N DuPont Hwy Dover DE 19901

WASHBURN, DAVID THACHER, lawyer; b. Claremont, N.H., May 2, 1930; s. Walter Henry and Josephine Emmeline (Dana) W.; m. Joycemarie Springer, June 10, 1957 (div. Dec. 1975); children: Margaret Dana, David Thacher Jr., Robert Springer, John Putnam. BA, U. Vt., 1952; JD, NYU, 1955. Bar: N.Y. 1956, D.C. 1970, U.S. Supreme Ct 1970. Assoc. Paul, Weiss, Rifkind, Wharton & Garrison, N.Y.C., 1955-65, ptnr., 1965—. Trustee Rye Neck Bd. Edn., Mamaroneck, N.Y., 1971-73, Cambridge (Mass.) Coll., 1980-88, The Yard, N.Y.C., 1986—, ARIA Found., Inc., Williston, Vt., 1991—; trustee, mem. exec. com. Rare Ctr. for Tropical Bird Conservation, Phila., 1979-80; dir. Sanctuary for Families, Inc., N.Y.C., 1994—, treas. 1995—. Mem. ABA, N.Y. State Bar Assn., Assn. of Bar of City of N.Y., The Coffee House (N.Y.C.), Doubles (N.Y.C.), Coveleigh Club (Rye, N.Y.), Westchester Country Club (Harrison, N.Y.). Home: 10 W 66th St New York NY 10023 Office: Paul Weiss Rifkind Wharton & Garrison 1285 Ave of Americas New York NY 10019-6064

WASHBURN, DONALD ARTHUR, business executive; b. Mankato, Minn., Sept. 24, 1944; s. Donald and Geraldine Helen (Pint) W.; m. Christine Carvell, Aug. 24, 1968; children: Timothy, Abigail. BBA with high honors, Loyola U., Chgo., 1971; MBA, Northwestern U., 1973, JD cum laude, 1978. Bar: Ill. 1978. With prodn. mgmt. dept. J.T. Ryerson/Inland Steel, Chgo., 1963-68; asst. to the pres. G.B. Frank, Inc., 1969-70; cons. Intec, Inc., 1970-72; mktg. mgmt., atty. Quaker Oats, Co., 1972-79; sr. cons. Booz, Allen & Hamilton, 1979-80; corp. v.p., then sr. v.p. Marriott Corp., Washington, 1980-90; sr. v.p. N.W. Airlines, Mpls., 1990-94, exec. v.p., 1994—. Contbr. articles to profl. jours. Mem. ABA, Ill. Bar Assn., Chgo. Bar Assn., Alpha Sigma Nu, Beta Gamma Sigma. Unitarian Universalist. Office: Northwest Airlines Inc 5101 Northwest Dr Saint Paul MN 55111-3027

WASHBURN, H. BRADFORD, JR., museum administrator, cartographer, photographer; b. Cambridge, Mass., June 7, 1910; s. Henry Bradford and Edith (Hall) W.; m. Barbara Teel Polk, Apr. 27, 1940; children: Dorothy Polk, Edward Hall, Elizabeth Bradford. Grad., Groton Sch., 1929; A.B., Harvard U., 1933, A.M., 1960, D.H.L. (hon.), 1975; postgrad., Inst. Geog. Exploration, 1934-35; postgrad. hon. degrees; Ph.D., U. Alaska, 1951; D.Sc., Tufts U., 1957, Colby Coll., 1957, Northeastern U., 1958, U. Mass., 1972, Curry Coll., 1982; D.F.A., Suffolk U., 1965; D.H.L., Boston Coll., 1974; LL.D., Babson Coll., 1980. Instr. Inst. Geog. Exploration, Harvard U., 1935-42; dir. Mus. Sci, Boston, 1939-80, chmn. of the corp., 1980-85, hon. dir., 1985—; dir. Mountaineer in Alps, 1926-31; explorer Alaska Coast Range, 1930-40; served as leader numerous mountain, subarctic area explorations; cons. various govtl. agys. on Alaska and cold climate equipment; leader in spl. expdns. investigating high altitude cosmic rays, Alaska, 1947; rep. Nat. Geog. Soc., 17th Internat. Geog. Congress, 1952; leader Nat. Geog. mapping expdns. to, Grand Canyon, 1971-75; chmn. Mass. Com. Rhodes Scholars, 1959-64; chmn. arts and scis. com. UNESCO conf., Boston, 1961; mem. adv. com. John F. Kennedy Library, 1977; mem. vis. com. Internat. Mus. Photography, 1978; mem. U.S. Nat. Commn. for UNESCO, 1978; lectr. work of Yukon Expdn., Royal Geog. Soc., London, 1936-37, on mapping Grand Canyon, 1976; lectr. Mus. Imaging Tech., Bangkok, 1989, Royal Geog. Soc., London, on mapping Mt. Everest, 1990; lectr. Antarctica, 1994. Contbr. articles, photographs on Alaska, Alps to glaciers, and mountains to mags., books.; editor, pub. lst large-scale map Mt. McKinley, Am. Acad. Arts and Scis.-Swiss Found. Alpine Rsch., Bern, 1960; mapped Mt. Kennedy for Nat. Geog. Soc., 1965, Grand Canyon, 1971-74, Muldrow Glacier (Mt. McKinley), 1977; editor new chart, Squam Lake, N.H., 1968, new Grand Canyon map for Nat. Geog. Soc., 1978, Bright Angel Trail map, 1981; photo-mapped Mt. Everest for Nat. Geog. Soc., 1984; dir., pub. large-scale map of Mt. Everest for Nat. Geog. Soc., 1984-88; project chief new 1:50,000 map of Mt. Everest for Nat. Geog. Soc. and Boston Sci. Mus., 1988; pub. Tourist Guide to Mt. McKinley, 1971, new map of Presdl. Range, N.H, 1989; completed new large-scale relief model Mt. Everest, 1990; one-man photographic shows Whyte Art Mus., Banff, Can., Internat. Mus. Photography, N.Y.C., Rochester, N.Y. Bd. overseers Harvard, 1955-61; trustee Smith Coll., 1962-68, Richard E. Byrd Found., 1979-84, Mt. Washington Obs., 1979—; mem. Task Force on Future Financing of Arts in Mass., 1978; hon. bd. dirs. Swiss Found. Alpine Research, 1984—. Recipient Royal Geog. Soc. Cuthbert Peek award for Alaska Exploration and Glacier Studies, 1938, Burr prize Nat. Geog. Soc., 1940, 65, Stratton prize Friends of Switzerland, 1970, Lantern award Rotary Club, Boston, 1978, New Englander of Yr. award New Eng. Coun., 1974, Gold Research medal Royal Scottish Geog. Soc. (with wife), 1979, Alexander Graham Bell award Nat. Geog. Soc., 1980, Disting. Grotonian award Groton Sch., 1979, Explorers medal Explorers Club, 1984, award for lifelong contbns. to cartography and surveying Explor. Soc. New Eng., 1985, King Albert medal of merit, 1994; named Bus. Statesman of Yr. Harvard Bus. Sch. Assn., Boston, 1970; named to Acad. Disting. Bostonians Boston C. of C., 1983; one of nine Photographic Masters, Boston U. Fellow Royal Geog. Soc. London, Harvard Travelers Club (Gold medal 1959), Nat. Geog. Soc. (with wife, Centennial award 1988), AAAS, Am. Acad. Arts and Scis., Am. Geog. Soc. (hon.), Calif. Acad. Sci, Assn. Sci. Tech. Centers (hon.), Arctic Inst. N.Am., U. Ariz. Ctr. for Creative Photography; mem. Explorers Club (hon. dir.), French Alpine (hon. mem. Groupe de Haute Montagne, Paris), Phi Beta Kappa (hon.), Chinese Assn. Sci. Expeditions (hon.). Clubs: Commercial, Harvard Varsity, St. Botolph (hon. life), Aero Club of New Eng. (hon.), Harvard Montaineering (Boston) (hon., past pres.), American Alpine (N.Y.C.) (hon.), Alpine (London) (hon.), Sierra of San Francisco (hon.), Mountaineers (Seattle) (hon.), Mountaineering of Alaska (hon.); hon. mem. several clubs. Leader 1st ascent Mt. Crillon, Alaska, 1934, Nat. Geog. Soc. Yukon Expdn., 1935; leader 1st aerial photog. exploration Mt. McKinley, 1936, ascended its summit, 1942; 47, 51; leader 1st aerial exploration St. Elias range, 1938; 1st ascents Mount Sanford and Mount Marcus Baker in Alaska, 1938, Mt. Lucania, Yukon, 1937, Mt. Bertha, Alaska, 1940, Mt. Hayes, Alaska, 1941; 1st ascent West side Mt. McKinley 1951; leader Nat. Geog. Soc. Mt. Everest mapping project, 1981-88; expdn. to S.E. Asia, guest Chinese Acad. Scis., met with King of Nepal, 1988; leader expdn. to Nepal, 1992; 1st laser-distance observation to summit of Mt. Everest, 1992; 50th trip to Alaska to open exhibit of own photos Anchorage Art Mus., 1993.

Home: 220 Somerset St Belmont MA 02178-2011 Office: Science Park Boston MA 02114

WASHBURN, LAWRENCE ROBERT, manufacturing executive; b. Jackson, Mich., Aug. 5, 1941; s. Lawrence Merton and Elvina Marie (Morgan) W.; m. Kay Frances Wieczerzak, Nov. 21, 1970; children: Lawrence Robert II, Alexa Kay. BA in History, Govt., So. Calif. Coll., 1974. Supr., engr. Tool Rsch. & Engring., Inc., Santa Ana, Calif., 1968-77; ops. mgr. Knudsen Systems, Inc., Anaheim, Calif., 1977-86; plant mgr. Flourcarbon, Anaheim, Calif., 1986-88; dir. engring. Ricoh Electronics, Inc., Tustin, Calif., 1988-92; chmn., CEO Teqcom Industries, Santa Ana, 1992—. Dist. commr. Boy Scouts Am., Orange County, Calif., 1982-90; exec. dir. Immanuel Luth. Ch. & Sch., 1987-92; bd. dirs. Luth. High Sch. Orange County, 1990—. With USN, 1966-68. Decorated Navy Achievement medal; recipient Scouter medal Boy Scouts Am., 1986, Award of Merit, 1988. Mem. Am. Soc. Mech. Engrs., Soc. Mfg. Engrs., Air Traffic Control Assn., Ridgeline Country Club. Republican. Avocations: golfing, body surfing, backpacking. Office: Teqcom Industries 1712 Newport Cir Ste O Santa Ana CA 92705-5118

WASHBURN, MELINDA WALL, nursing administrator; b. Dallas, Sept. 9, 1952; d. John E. and Irma B. (Cooper) Walll; m. Doug Washburn, Feb. 26, 1984. BSN, U. Tex., 1976. RN, Tex., Ky. Svc. supr. Baylor U. Med. Ctr., Dallas; v.p. nursing St. Joseph Hosp., Lexington, Ky. Mem. ANA, Am. Orgn. Nurse Execs., Assn. Operating Room Nurses, Ky. Heart Assn.

WASHBURN, ROBERT BROOKS, university dean, composer; b. Bouckville, N.Y., July 11, 1928; s. Robert Phelps and Florence (Brooks) W.; m. Beverly Jean Darnell, July 10, 1952; children—Brooks, Roberta. BS, SUNY, Potsdam, 1949, MS, 1956; PhD, Eastman Sch. Music, 1960. Dean, prof. music SUNY, Potsdam, 1954-95, dean emeritus, sr. fellow music, 1995—; cons. NEH, Ogdensburg, N.Y., 1984-87, N.Y. State Sch. Music Assn., 1976-80, U.S. Office Edn., Washington, 1978-80; del. Music Educators Nat. Conf. Composer over 150 mus. works, 1955—. Served as sgt. USAF, 1950-54. Nat. Endowment for the Arts grantee, 1979; fellow Danforth Found., 1958-59, Ford Found. grantee, 1959-60, Fulbright fellow, 1986. Mem. ASCAP, Soc. for Ethnomusicology. Avocation: traveling. Home: 87 State Hwy 72 Potsdam NY 13676-9466 Office: SUNY Crane Sch Music Potsdam NY 13676

WASHBURN, STAN, artist; b. N.Y.C., Jan. 2, 1943; s. Sherwood Larned and Henrietta (Pease) W.; m. Andrea Aall Stub, Mar. 5, 1966; children—Anne Elizabeth, John Larned. M.F.A., Calif. Coll. Arts and Crafts, 1968. Founding ptnr. The Griffin Co., Oakland, Calif., 1968-70. Author: George's Dragon, 1974, A Moral Alphabet of Vice and Folly, 1986, Intent to Harm, 1994; one-man shows at Achenbach Found., San Francisco, 1977, St. Botolph Club, Boston, 1977, Pucker/Safrai, Boston, 1975, 77, 80, 85, Ames, Berkeley, Calif., 1974, 78, 81, 84, Thackrey & Robertson, San Francisco, 1981, 86, Charles Campbell, San Francisco, 1983, 86, 88, 90, 91, Bannatyne, Santa Monica, 1990, North Point, San Francisco, 1993 ; represented in permanent collections at Bklyn. Mus., Achenbach Found., Chgo. Art Inst., Library of Congress, Houghton Library, Phila. Mus. Art, Boston Mus. Fine Arts. Mem. Berkeley Police Res., 1973-78; mem. Berkeley Police Rev. Commn., 1979-83; trustee The Coll. Prep. Sch., Oakland, 1986—. Address: 2010 Virginia St Berkeley CA 94709-2138

WASHBURN, WILCOMB EDWARD, historian, educator; b. Ottawa, Kans., Jan. 13, 1925; s. Harold Edward and Sidsell Marie (Nelson) W.; m. Lelia Elizabeth Kanavarioti, July 14, 1951 (div. June 1981); children—Harold Kitsos, Edward Alexandros; m. Kathryn Laffler Cousins, Jan 2, 1985. Grad., Phillips Exeter Acad., 1943; AB summa cum laude, Dartmouth Coll., 1948; MA, Harvard U., 1951, PhD, 1955; HHD (hon.), St. Mary's Coll. Md., 1970, Assumption Coll., 1983, St. Lawrence U., 1991. Teaching fellow history and lit. Harvard, 1954-55; fellow Inst. Early Am. History and Culture, Williamsburg, Va., 1955-58; instr. Coll. William and Mary, 1955-58; curator div. polit. history Smithsonian Instn., U.S. Nat. Mus., Washington, 1958-65; dir. Am. studies program Smithsonian Instn., 1965—; Professorial lectr. U., 1961-63, adj. prof., 1963-69; cons. in research Grad. Sch. Arts and Scis., professorial lectr. in Am. civilization George Washington U., 1966—; adj. prof. U. Md., 1975—; Civil info. and edn. officer Toyama Mil. Govt. Team, Toyama Prefecture, Japan, 1946-47. Author: The Governor and the Rebel: A History of Bacon's Rebellion in Virginia, 1957, Red Man's Land/White Man's Law: A Study of the Past and Present Status of The American Indian, 1971, The Assault on Indian Tribalism: General Allotment Law (Dawes Act) of 1887, 1975, The Indian in America, 1975, (with others) The Federal City: Plans and Realities, The Exhibition, 1976; Editor: (with others) The Indian and the White Man, 1964, Proc. of the Vinland Map Conf, 1971, The American Heritage History of the Indian Wars, 1977; Contbr. (with others) articles to profl. jours. Past pres. Hist. Soc. of Washington; active Am. Hist Assn., Va. Hist. Assn., Md. Hist. Assn., Mass. Hist. Soc. With USMCR, 1943-45, 51-52. Fellow Am. Anthropol. Assn.; mem. AAAS, Am. Soc. Ethnohistory (past pres.), Am. Studies Assn. (past pres.), Colonial Soc. Mass., Am. Antiquarian Soc., Orgn. Am. Historians, Japan-Am. Soc. Washington (past trustee), Instituto Histórico e Geográfico Brasileiro, Anthropol. Soc. Washington, Phi Beta Kappa, Cosmos Club. Club: Cosmos (Washington). Office: Smithsonian Instn Am Studies Program Nat Postal Museum Washington DC 20560

WASHINGTON, CRAIG A., congressman; b. Oct. 12, 1941. B.S., Prairie View A&M U.; J.D.; Tex. So. U. Mem. Tex. Ho. of Reps., 1973-83; mem. Tex. Senate, from 1984, mem. health and human resources, jurisprudence, and state affairs coms.; mem. 101st-103rd Congresses from 18th Tex. dist., Washington, D.C., 1989—; mem. Energy and Commerce com., subcom. Health and Environ., Energy and Power, govt. ops. com., judiciary com., subcoms. crime and criminal justice, civil and constnl. rights. Democrat. Office: US House of Reps 1711 Longworth House Office Bldg Washington DC 20515-4318

WASHINGTON, DELPHINE CYNTHIA, special education educator, artist; b. Logansport, La., June 24, 1945; d. Roy Thomas Washington and Cuevator Francez (Singleton) Washington-Taylor; m. Howard Littlejohn, Mar., 1969 (div. Sept., 1980); 1 child, Mona Lisa Francez Washington. BEd in Art Edn. and Mentally Retarded, Grambling State U., 1974, postgrad. in Edn., 1989; MEd in Elem. Edn., Prairie View A&M U., 1981. Spl. edn. tchr. Walnut Hill Jr. High Sch., Shreveport, La., 1979-80, Second Ward High Sch., Glaster, La., 1981-82; spl. edn. and art tchr. North DeSoto High Sch., Stonewall, La., 1982—; art tchr. summer program, Shreveveport Regional Arts Coun., 1992. Exhibited in group show at African Am. Art Exh., Ebony Expressions Art Gallery, Shreveport, La. (1st place water color painting "The Old Black Church"), 1993. Recipient Art Trophy, Spl. Edn. Supr., Mansfield La. Art Show, 1982, Key to City, Mayor Baton Rouge, La., 1992, Cert. of Appreciations, White House Art Exhibit, President Bush, 1992, Appreciation cert. Supr. Spl. Edn., 1992. Mem. NAUW, PTA (cert. appreciation 1990), Coun. Exceptional Children. Avocations: oil painting, drawing, water color, ceramics, music.

WASHINGTON, DENNIS, production designer. Prodn. designer: (films) Crossing the Line, 1992, (with Robert Fortune) White Men Can't Jump, 1992, Nowhere to Run, 1993, The Fugitive, 1993, Angels in the Outfield, 1994. Office: Smith/Gosnell/Nicholson & Assocs PO Box 1166 1515 Palisades Dr Pacific Palisades CA 90272*

WASHINGTON, DENZEL, actor; b. Mt. Vernon, N.Y., Dec. 28, 1954; m. Pauletta Pearson; children: John David, Katia, Malcolm and Olivia (twins). BA in Journalism, Fordham U.; student, Am. Conservatory Theatre, San Francisco. With N.Y. Shakespeare Festival, Manhattan Theatre Club. New Fed. Theatre. Actor: (stage prodns.) Coriolanus, 1979, Spell No. 7, The Mighty Gents, Richard III, One Tiger to a Hill, Ceremonies in Old Dark Men, When the Chicken Comes Home to Roost (Audelco award), A Soldier's Play (Obie award 1981), Checkmates, 1988, Split Second, (feature films) Carbon Copy, 1981, A Soldier's Story, 1981, Power, 1986, Cry Freedom, 1987, For Queen and Country, 1988, The Mighty Quinn, 1989, Glory, 1989 (Golden Globe award 1989, Acad. award 1990, NAACP Image award 1990), Heart Condition, 1990, Mo' Better Blues, 1990, Ricochet, 1991, Mississippi Masala, 1992, Malcolm X, 1992, Much Ado About Nothing, 1993, Philadelphia, 1993, The Pelican Brief, 1993, Crimson Tide, 1995, Virtuosity, 1995; (TV Movies) Wilma, 1977, License to Kill, 1984, The George

McKenna Story, 1986, (TV miniseries) Flesh and Blood, 1979; regular (TV series) St. Elsewhere, 1982-88. Am. Conservatory Theater scholar. Avocations: basketball, reading, cooking. Office: care ICM 8942 Wilshire Blvd Beverly Hills CA 90211*

WASHINGTON, GERALD, manufacturing executive; b. 1939. With Futorian Mfg. Co., New Albany, Miss., 1960-69, De Ville Furniture Co., Pontotoc, Miss., 1969-74, Astro Lounger Co., Okolona, Miss., 1974-76; with Washington Furniture Mfg. Co., Houlka, Miss., 1977—, now chmn. bd. Office: Washington Furniture Mfg Co 2 Mi N Of Hwy 32 N Houlka MS 38850

WASHINGTON, GROVER, JR., musician, producer, composer, arranger; b. Buffalo, Dec. 12, 1943; m. Christine; children: Grover III, Shana. Student, Wurlitzer Sch. Music, Temple U.; also pvt. instrn. Worked for record distbr., 1969-70; pres. pub. co. G.W. Jr. Music, Inc.; pres. prodn. co. G-Man Prodns., Inc. Played with musical group Four Clefs, to 1963, with Keith McAllister, 1963-65, 19th Army Band, 1965-67, played with various groups in Phila. and N.Y., with Billy Cobham, with Don Gardner's Sonotones, 1967-68, Charles Earland, 1971, rec. forKudu Records, Elektra Records, not under contract with Sony Records; plays soprano, tenor, alto. baritone saxophones; over 24 solo albums including Come Morning, Mr. Magic, Winelight, The Best is Yet to Come, Then and Now, Time Out of Mind, Next Exit, All My Tomorrows; numerous recs. as sideman or featured artist with Randy Weston, Bob James, Ralph MacDonald, Kathleen Battle, Don Sebesky, others, numerous TV and personal appearances throughout U.S., Can., Europe, Japan; performs Nat. Anthem regularly for Phila. Eagles and Phila. 76ers; producer 3 albums for group Pieces of a Dream, Jean Carne; first album of music from the Crosby Show. Performed at Inaugural events for Pres. Bill Clinton, 1993. Recipient numerous record industry awards including Grammy award, 6 gold albums, 1 platinum album, also many prestigious charitable and community awards. Office: care Lloyd Z Remick Zane Mgmt The Bellevue 6th Fl Broad & Walnut Sts Philadelphia PA 19102

WASHINGTON, JAMES WINSTON, JR., artist, sculptor; b. Gloster, Miss., Nov. 10, 1909; s. James and Lizie (Howard) W.; m. Janie R. Miller, Mar. 29, 1943. Student, Nat. Landscape Inst., 1944-47; D.F.A., Center Urban-Black Studies, 1975. tchr. summer class N.W. Theol. Union Seattle U., 1988. One man shows U.S.O. Gallery, Little Rock, 1943, Foster-White Gallery, Seattle, 1974, 78, 80, 83, 89 (also at Bellevue Art Mus., 89), Charles and Emma Frye Art Mus., Seattle, 1980, Mus. History and Industry, Seattle, 1981; exhibited in group shows Willard Gallery, N.Y.C., 1960-64, Feingarten Galleries, San Francisco, 1958-59, Grosvenor Gallery, London, Eng., 1964, Lee Nordness Gallery, N.Y.C., 1962, Woodside Gallery, Seattle, 1962-65, Foster-White Gallery, Seattle, 1974, 76, 89, Smithsonian Instn., 1974, San Diego, 1977, Foster/White Gallery, Seattle, 1992, others; retrospective exhbn. Bellevue Art Mus., Washington, 1989; represented in permanent collections Seattle, San Francisco, Oakland art museums, Seattle First Nat. Bank, Seattle Pub. Library YWCA, Seattle, Meany Jr. High Sch., Seattle World's Fair, Expo 70 Osaka, Japan., Whitney Mus. Am. Art, N.Y.C.; commd. sculpture: Bird With Covey, Wash. State Capitol Mus., Olympia, 1983, Obelisk with Phoenix and Esoteric Symbols of Nature in granite, Sheraton Hotel Seattle, 1982, Life Surrounding the Astral Alter, In Matrix, owner T.M. Rosenblume, Charles Z. Smith & Assocs., Seattle, 1986, The Oracle of Truth (6 1/2 ton sculpture at M. Zion Bapt. Ch., Seattle, 1987, commd. sculptures King County Arts Commn., 1989, Bailey Gatzent Elem. Sch., Seattle, 1991, Twin Eaglets of the Cosmic Cycle (Quincy Jones), 1993, Fountain of Triumph (Bangasser Assocs. Inc.), 1992-93, Seattle, 1994. Passover leader Mt. Zion Baptist Ch., Seattle, 1974-87. Recipient Spl. Commendation award for many contbns. to artistic heritage of state Gov., 1973, plaque City of Seattle, 1973, plaque Benefit Guild, Inc., 1973, arts service award King County Arts Commn., 1984, cert. of recognition Gov. of Wash., 1984, Editor's Choice award Outstanding Achievement in Poetry Nat. Libr. Poetry, 1993; named to Wash. State Centennial Hall of Honor, Wash. State Hist. Soc., 1984; home and studio designated historic landmark (city and state), 1991. Mem. Internat. Platform Assn., Internat. Soc. Poets (life, awards 1993), Profl. Artists Phila., Masons (33 degree Prince Hall Lodge #67). Home: 1816 26th Ave Seattle WA 98122-3110

WASHINGTON, JOHN AUGUSTINE, physician, pathologist; b. Istanbul, Turkey, May 29, 1936; (parents Am. citizens); s. Samuel Walter and Simone (Fleisher) Washington; m. Maaja Harms, July 11, 1959; children: Stephen L., Richard R., Mikaela A. BA with honors, U. Va., 1957; MD, Johns Hopkins U., 1961. Diplomate Am. Bd. Pathology, (Clin. Pathology, Med. Microbiology). Intern Duke U. Med. Ctr., Durham, N.C., 1961-62, resident in surgery, 1962-63; resident in clin. pathology NIH, Bethesda, Md., 1965-67, asst. chief microbiology svc., 1966-67; assoc. cons. microbiology Mayo Clinic, Rochester, Minn., 1967-68, dir. bacteriology lab., 1968-71, head sect. clin. microbiology, 1971-86; chmn. dept. microbiology Cleve. Clinic Found., 1986-92, vice chmn. divsn. pathology and lab. medicine, 1992—, chmn. dept. clin. pathology, 1992—, head microbiology sect., 1992—; trustee Am. Bd. Pathology, Tampa, Fla., 1989-94. Mem. editl. bd. Jour. Infectious Diseases, European Jour. Clin. Microbiology and Infectious Diseases; sect. editor Infectious Diseases in Clin. Practice; contbr. more than 300 articles to profl. jours.; author numerous chapters in books. Lt. comdr. USPHS, 1963-67. Fellow ACP, Coll. Am. Pathologists, Am. Soc. Clin. Pathologists, Am. Coll. Chest Physicians, Infectious Diseases Soc. Am., Am. Acad. Microbiology. Democrat. Avocations: gardening, swimming. Office: Cleve Clin Found 9500 Euclid Ave Cleveland OH 44195-0001

WASHINGTON, MALIVAI, professional tennis player; b. Swartz Creek, MI, June 20, 1969. Student, U. Mich. Ranked 6th in U.S. Tennis Assn., 1993. Named All-American NCAA, 1988-89; mem. U.S. Davis Cup Team, 1993; winner of Australian Open, 1994, U.S. Clay Courts Championship, 1992. *

WASHINGTON, REGINALD LOUIS, pediatric cardiologist; b. Colorado Springs, Colo., Dec. 31, 1949; s. Lucius Louis and Brenette Y. (Wheeler) W.; m. Billye Faye Ned, Aug. 18, 1973; children: Danielle Larae, Reginald Quinn. BS in Zoology, Colo. State U., 1971; MD, U. Colo., 1975. Diplomate Nat. Bd. Med. Examiners, Am. Bd. Pediatrics, Pediatric Cardiology. Intern in pediatrics U. Colo. Med. Ctr., Denver, 1975-76, resident in pediatrics, 1976-78, chief resident, instr., 1978-79, fellow in pediatric cardiology 1979-81, asst. prof. pediatrics, 1982-1988, assoc. prof. pediatrics, 1988-90, assoc. clin. prof. pediatrics, 1990—; staff cardiologist Children's Hosp., Denver, 1981-90; v.p. Rocky Mountain Pediatric Cardiology, Denver, 1990—; mem. admissions com. U. Colo. Sch. Medicine, Denver, 1985-89; chmn., bd. dirs. Coop. Health Care Agreements, 1994—. Cons. editor Your Patient and Fitness, 1989-92. Adv. bd. dirs. Equitable Bank of Littleton, Colo., 1984-86; bd. dirs. Rocky Mountain Heart Fund for Children, 1984-89, Cleo Parker Robinson Dance Co., 1992-94, Ctrl. City Opera, 1989—, Raindo Ironkids, 1989—, Nat. Coun. Patient Info. and Edn., 1992—, Childrens Heart Alliance, 1993-94, Regis U., Denver, 1994—, Colo. State U. Devel. Coun., 1994—; chmn. Coop Health Care Agreements Bd. State of Colo., 1994; trustee Denver Ctr. Performing Arts, 1994—; mem. Govs. Coun. Physical Fitness, 1990-91. Named Salute Vol. of Yr. Big Sisters of Colo., 1990; honoree NCCJ, 1994. Fellow Am. Acad. Pediatrics (cardiology subsect.), Am. Coll. Cardiology, Am. Heart Assn. (coun. on cardiovascular disease in the young, exec. com. 1988-91, nat. devel. program com. 1990-94, vol. of yr. 1989, pres. Colo. chpt. 1989-90, Torch of Hope 1987, Gold Heart award Colo. chpt. 1990, bd. dirs. Colo. chpt., exec. com. 1987—, grantee Colo. chpt. 1983-84, mem. editorial bd. Pediatric Exercise Sci. 1988—, Nat. Physician of the Yr., 1995), Soc. Critical Care Medicine; mem. Am. Acad. Pediatrics/Perinatology, N.Am. Soc. Pediatric Exercise Medicine (series 1986-87), Colo. Med. Soc. (chmn. sports medicine coun. 1993-94), Leadership Denver 1990, Denver Athletic Club, Met. Club, Glenmoor Golf Club. Democrat. Roman Catholic. Avocations: skiing, golf, fishing. Home: 7423 Berkeley Cir Castle Rock CO 80104-9278 Office: Rocky Mountain Pediatric Cardiology 1601 E 19th Ave Ste 5600 Denver CO 80218-1216

WASHINGTON, ROBERT ORLANDA, educator, former university administrator; b. Newport News, Va., Feb. 8, 1935; s. Robert Lee and Fannie (Bates) W.; m. Mary Louise Lewis, Apr. 7, 1955; children: Robert, Glynis, Cheryl, Nathan, Allyson, Terrence, Candace. B.S., Hampton Inst., 1956; M.S., Marquette U., 1966; M.A., U. Mo., 1968; Ph.D., Brandeis U.,

1973. Pub. Milw. Post, weekly newspaper, 1960-64; research assoc. Greenleigh Assocs., N.Y.C., 1965-72; instr. social work Simmons Coll., Boston, 1970-72; prof. Case Western Res. U., Cleve., 1972-74; dean Sch. Social Work, Ohio State U., Columbus, 1976-82, U. Ill., Champaign, 1982-86; cons. U.S. AID, Nigeria, 1970, 72, Cairo, 1975, 77; commr. accreditation Coun. on Social Work Edn., N.Y.C., 1978-81; cons. U.S. HHS, Washington, 1981; pres., CEO Social Policy Rsch. Group, Inc., Boston, 1986-88; vice-chancellor for rsch. and grad. studies U. New Orleans, 1988-93. Author: Programm Evaluation in the Human Services, 1980, (with others) Social Policy and Social Welfare, 1980, Marco Practice in Social Work, 1982, Social Work in the 1980's, 1982, Children in Need of Roots, 1985, Social Work in Schools, 1985, Toward a Theory of Social Planning, 1994. NDEA fellow, 1967. Mem. Council on Social Work Edn., Nat. Assn. Social Workers, Champaign Urban League, Ill. Guardianship and Advocacy Commn. Democrat. Home: 7135 Benson Ct New Orleans LA 70127-2001 Office: U New Orleans Lakefront New Orleans LA 70148

WASHINGTON, SHELLEY LYNNE, dancer; b. Washington, Nov. 3, 1954; d. Edward Freeman and Geraldine (Butler) W. Student, Interlochen Arts Acad., 1969-72, Juilliard Acad., N.Y.C., 1972-74. Dancer Martha Graham, N.Y.C., 1974-75, Twyla Tharp Dance Found., N.Y.C., 1975—, Am. Ballet Theatre, N.Y.C., 1988-91; ballet mistress and artistic assoc. dir. for Twyla Tharp, including repertory for Boston Ballet, Hubbard St. Dance Co., Martha Graham Dance Co. Dancer in film Hair, 1978; in Broadway show Singin in the Rain, 1985-86. Recipient Bessie Schonberg award for Outstanding Performing, 1987.

WASHINGTON, VALORA, foundation administrator; b. Columbus, Ohio, Dec. 16, 1953; d. Timothy Washington and Elizabeth (Jackson) Barbour; children: Omari, Kamilah. BA in Social Sci. with honors, Mich. State U., 1974; PhD, Ind. U., 1978; PhD (hon.), Bennett Coll., 1992. Assoc. instr. sch. edn. Ind. U., Bloomington, 1975-77; dir., cons. Urban League Ind., Indpls., 1977-78; substitute tchr. Indpl. Pub. Schs., 1978; dir. U. N.C., Chapel Hill, 1980-82; congrl. sci. fellow Soc. for Rsch. in Child Devel., Washington, 1981-82; prof. edn. U. N.C., Chapel Hill, 1978-83; asst. dean, assoc. prof. Howard U., Washington, 1983-86, Am. U., Washington, 1986-87; prof., v.p. Antioch Coll., Yellow Springs, Ohio, 1987-90; v.p. Kellogg Found., Battle Creek, Mich., 1990—; cons. Ford Found., N.Y.C., 1990; project evaluator Carnegie Corp., N.Y.C., 1989-90, Ohio Bd. Regents, Columbus, 1990—. Author: (with others) Creating New Linkages for the Adoption of Black Children, 1984, Project Head Start: Past, Present and Future Trends in the Context of Family Needs, 1987, Black Children and American Institutions: An Ecological Review and Resource Guide, 1988, Affirmative Rhetoric, Negative Action: The Status of Black and Hispanic Faculty in Higher Education, 1989; contbr. articles to profl. jours; contbr. chapters to numerous books. Recipient Capital U. award, 1990, award Springfield Alliance Black Educators, 1989; named one of Ten Outstanding Young Women Am., 1980, Outstanding Young Woman N.C., 1980, one of 100 Young Women of Promise Good Housekeeping Mag., 1985. Mem. Nat. Coun. Negro Women (chmn. 1982-83), Am. Assn. for Higher Edn. (sec. black caucus 1989), Soc. for Rsch. in Child Devel. (pres. black caucus 1987-89), Nat. Assn. for the Edn. of Young Children (sec. of bd. dir. 1990—), Phi Delta Kappa, Delta Kappa Gamma.

WASHINGTON, WALTER, retired college president; b. Hazlehurst, Miss., July 13, 1923; s. Kemp and Mable (Comous) W.; m. Carolyn Carter, July 31, 1949. BA, Tougaloo Coll., 1948, LLD (hon.), 1972; MS, Ind. U., 1952, LLD (hon.), 1983; Edn. Specialist, Peabody Coll., 1958; postgrad., Yale, 1953; EdD, U. So. Miss., 1969; postgrad., Harvard U., 1989; DSc (hon.), Purdue U., 1993. Tchr. Holtzclaw High Sch., Crystal Springs, Miss., 1948-49; asst. prin., tchr. Parrish High Sch., Hazlehurst, 1949-52; prin. Utica Jr. Coll. High Sch., Miss., 1951-54; dean Utica Jr. Coll., 1954-55, pres., 1957-69; prin. Sumner Hill High Sch., Clinton, Miss., 1955-57; pres. Alcorn (Miss.) State U., 1969-94, pres. emeritus, 1994—; past ptnr. Klinger Industries, Ltd. Pres. Nat. Pan-Hellenic Council, 1964-67, Nat. Alumni Council of United Negro Coll. Fund, 1959-60; past. mem. adv. council Miss. Vocational Edn. Program, Miss. Regional Med. Programs; mem. Miss. Econ. Council; mem. S.E. regional exec. com. Boy Scouts Am.; mem. exec. com. Andrew Jackson council; past mem. adv. council Miss. 4-H Clubs; bd. dirs. Miss. Mental Health Assn., Miss. Easter Seal Soc.; past bd. dirs. Miss. Heart Assn. Recipient Presdl. citation for Outstanding Leadership to Univ./Industry Cluster, 1980-81, Disting. Alumni award Vanderbilt-Peabody, 1991, George Washington Carver Lifetime Achievement award Tuskegee Inst.; named.to U. So. Miss. Alumni Hall of Fame, 1987; Walter Washington Bldgs. named in his honor U. So. Miss., Alcorn State U., 1994. Mem. NEA, ASCD, Am. Assn. Sch. Adminstrs. (So. Regional Edn. bd.), Nat. Assn. State Univs. and Land Grant Colls., So. Assn. Colls. Secondary Schs. (past bd. dirs., past chmn. secondary commn., past chmn. commn. on colls., past trustee), Miss. Educators Assn. (pres. 1964-65), Miss. Tchrs Assn., Nat. Soc. for Study of Higher Edn., Tougaloo Nat. Alumni Assn. (pres. 1960), George Peabody Coll. Alumni Assn. (past v.p. exec. com., Disting. Alumni of Yr. 1991), John Dewey Soc., Delta Kappa Pi, Phi Delta Kappa, Alpha Kappa Mu, Alpha Phi Alpha (gen. pres. 1974-76).

WASHINGTON, WARREN MORTON, meteorologist; b. Portland, Oreg., Aug. 28, 1936; s. Edwin and Dorothy Grace (Morton) W.; m. LaRae Herring, July 30, 1959 (div. Aug. 1975); children: Teri, Kim, Marc (dec.), Tracy; m. Jona Ann, July 3, 1978 (dec. Jan. 1987); m. Mary Elizabeth Washington, Apr., 1995. B.S. in Physics, Ore. State U., 1958, M.S. in Meteorology, 1960; Ph.D. in Meteorology, Pa. State U., 1964. Dir. of climate and global dynamics div. Nat. Center Atmospheric Research, Boulder, Colo.; affiliate prof. meteorology oceanography U. Mich. at Ann Arbor, 1968-71; mem. Nat. Adv. Com. for Oceans and Atmospheres, 1978-84; mem. sec. of energy adv. bd. U.S. Dept. Energy, 1990-93. Contbr. articles to meteorol. jours. Mem. Boulder Human Relations Commn., 1969-71; mem. Gov.'s Sci. Adv. Com., 1975-78. Fellow AAAS (bd. dirs.), Am. Meteorol. Soc. (pres. 1994); mem. Am. Geog. Union, Nat. Sci. Bd. Home: 725 Pinehurst Ct Louisville CO 80027 Office: PO Box 3000 Boulder CO 80307-3000

WASIELE, HARRY W., JR., diversified electrical manufacturing company executive; b. Chgo., June 29, 1926; s. Harry W. and Antoinette (Tuleja) W.; m. Loretta K. Anderson, Jan. 3, 1948; children: Kathleen Ann Wasiele Bach, Brian David, Larry Scott, Mark Thomas. Grad. high sch. Asst. sales mgr. Drake Mfg. Co., Chgo., 1950-55; sales engr. AMP, Inc., Chgo., 1955, Detroit, 1956-57; product mgr. AMP Inc., Harrisburg, Pa., 1958-61; industry mgr. AMP, Inc., 1961-67, dir. marketing, 1967-68; div. gen. mgr. Brand-Rex div. Am. Enka Corp., Willimantic, Conn., 1968-70; pres. Brand-Rex Co. subs. Akzona Inc., 1970-83; chmn. Brand-Rex Ltd., Glenrothes, Scotland, 1974-83; v.p. sales and corp. devel. Cablec Corp., New City, N.Y., 1985—; dir. Berkel Inc.; chmn., pres. Tarpon Springs (Fla.) Internat. Tannery, Inc., 1990—. Bd. dirs. Eastern Conn. State Coll. Found., 1972-83; trustee Windham Community Hosp., Willimantic, 1968-83, trustee emeritus, 1983—, pres. bd. trustees, 1981-83. With USNR, 1944-46. Mem. Nat. Elec. Mfrs. Assn. (chmn. wire and cable div., bd. govs. 1982-84), Conn. Bus. and Industry Assn. (emeritus dir.), New Seabury Country Club, Mariner Sands Country Club. Republican. Roman Catholic. Home (summer): 53 Shore Dr W PO Box 826 New Seabury MA 02649 Home (winter): Mariner Sands 6755 Barrington Dr Stuart FL 34997

WASIK, JOHN FRANCIS, editor, writer, publisher; b. Chgo., July 2, 1957; s. Arthur Stanley and Virginia Frances (Gray) W.; m. Kathleen Rose. BA in Psychology, U. Ill., Chgo., 1978, MA in Communication, 1988. Sr. editor Consumers Digest Inc., Chgo., 1986—; editor, pub. Conscious Consumer and Co. Newsletters. Author: Electronic Business Information Sourcebook, 1987, Green Company Resource Guide, 1992, The Green Supermarket Shopping Guide, 1993, The Investment Club Book, 1995. Mem. Soc. Profl. Journalists, Soc. Environ. Journalists. Office: Consumers Digest Inc 5705 N Lincoln Ave Chicago IL 60659-4707

WASILEWSKI, VINCENT THOMAS, retired lawyer; b. Athens, Ill., Dec. 17, 1922; s. Alex and Anna (Gillespie) W.; m. Patricia Callery, June 17, 1950 (dec. 1989); children: Jan, Susan, Catherine, Terese, Thomas, James; m. Marjorie Nohowel, June 19, 1992. A.B. in Polit. Sci., U. Ill., 1948, J.D., 1949. Bar: Ill. 1950, D.C. 1980. Mem. staff Nat. Assn. Broadcasters, Washington, 1949-82; v.p. govt. affairs Nat. Assn. Broadcasters, 1960-61, exec. v.p., 1961-65, pres., 1965-82; trustee Mus. Broadcasting. Served with

USAAF, 1942-45. Decorated D.F.C. with oak leaf cluster; Air medal with oak leaf cluster.; Recipient David Sarnoff award, Am. Women in Radio and TV Silver Satellite award, Commonwealth award. Mem. ABA, Nat. Assn. Broadcasters (Disting. Svc. award 1982), Fed. Comms. Bar Assn., Internat. Radio and TV Soc., Internat. Club (Washington), Burning Tree Club (Washington), George Town Club (Washington), Congl. Club (Potomac, Md.), John's Island Club (Vero Beach, Fla.), Knights of Malta, Order of Coif, Sigma Phi Epsilon, Phi Kappa Phi, Phi Alpha Delta. Roman Catholic. Clubs: Internat. (Washington), Burning Tree (Washington); Congressional Country (Potomac, Md.); Knights of Malta. Home: 6111 Davenport Ter Bethesda MD 20817 Office: Dow Lohnes & Albertson 1255 23d St Washington DC 20037

WASIOLEK, EDWARD, literary critic, language and literature educator; b. Camden, N.J., Apr. 27, 1924; s. Ignac and Mary (Szczesniewska) W.; m. Emma Jones Thomson, 1948; children: Mark Allan, Karen Lee, Eric Wade. B.A., Rutgers U., 1949; M.A., Harvard, 1950, Ph.D., 1955; postgrad., U. Bordeaux, France, 1950-51. Teaching fellow Harvard U., Cambridge, Mass., 1953-54, research fellow Russian Research Ctr., 1952-54; instr. English Ohio Wesleyan U., 1954-55; asst. prof. U. Chgo., 1955-60, assoc. prof. English and Russian, 1960-64, prof. Russian and comparative lit., 1964-69, Avalon prof. comparative lit. and Russian, 1969-76, Disting. Services prof. of English, comparative lit., and Slavic studies, 1976—, chmn. comparative lit. program, 1965-83, chmn. dept. Slavic langs. and lit., 1971-77; vis. prof. Slavic and comparative lit. Harvard, 1966-67. Author: (with R. Bauer) Nine Soviet Portraits, 1955, Crime and Punishment and the Critics, 1961, Dostoevsky: The Major Fiction, 1964, The Notebooks for Crime and Punishment, 1967, The Brothers Karamazov and the Critics, 1967, The Notebooks for the Idiot, 1968, The Notebooks for the Possessed, 1968, The Notebooks for A Raw Youth, 1969, The Notebooks for the Brothers Karamazov, 1970, The Gambler, with Paulina Suslova's Diary, 1972, Tolstoy's Major Fiction, 1978, Critical Essays on Tolstoy, 1986, Fathers and Sons: Russia at the Crossroads, 1993. Addressed UN on Tolstoy, 1988. With USNR, 1943-46. Recipient Quantrell teaching prize U. Chgo., 1961; Laing Press prize, 1972; Research fellow USSR, 1963; Guggenheim fellow, 1983-84. Mem. Modern Lang. Assn., Phi Beta Kappa, Lambda Chi Alpha. Home: 1832 Butterfield Ln Flossmoor IL 60422 Office: Univ Chicago Chicago IL 60637 *I believe in the life of the mind and I believe with Albert Camus that man's dignity lies in his lucidity: in seeing his fate clearly and in having the courage to accept it. Man is capable of sensitivity, courage, love, and compassion, and all of these are more human because he can think. He is also capable of cruelty, hatred, and destruction, and these are more tolerable because he can reason. Man is not man without reason.*

WASKOW, ARTHUR OCEAN, theologian, educator; b. Balt., Oct. 12, 1933; s. Henry B. and Hannah (Osnowitz) W.; m. Irene Elkin, 1956 (div. 1978); children: David, Shoshana; m. Phyllis Ocean Berman, 1986. B.A., Johns Hopkins, 1954; M.A., U. Wis., 1956, Ph.D., 1963. Legis. asst. Ho. of Reps., Washington, 1959-61; sr. staff mem. Peace Rsch. Inst., Washington, 1961-63; fellow Inst. Policy Studies, Washington, 1963-77; colleague Pub. Resource Ctr., Washington, 1977-82; faculty Reconstructionist Rabbinical Coll., Phila., 1982-89; dir. Shalom Ctr., 1983—; fellow ALEPH Alliance for Jewish Renewal, 1990—: mem. adv. bd. Temple of Understanding; vis. prof. religion Swarthmore Coll., 1982-83, Temple U., 1976-77, 87-88; sec.-treas. Conf. On Peace Rsch. in History, 1969-74. Author: The Limits of Defense, 1962, (with Stanley L. Newman) America in Hiding, 1962, Worried Man's Guide to World Peace, 1963, From Race Riot to Sit-In, 1966, The Freedom Seder, 1969, Running Riot, 1970, The Bush Is Burning, 1971, Godwrestling, 1978, Seasons of Our Joy, 1982, These Holy Sparks, 1983, (with Dabid and Shoshana Waskow) Before There Was A Before, 1984, (with Howard Waskow) Becoming Brothers, 1993, Down-to-Earth Judaism: Food, Money, Sex, and the Rest of Life, 1995; editor: Debate Over Thermonuclear Strategy, 1965, Menorah Jour, 1979—; screenwriter: In Every Generation, 1988; mem. editl. bd. Tikkun, Reconstructionist. Alt. del. Democratic nat. conv., 1968. Coolidge fellow Assn. Religion and Intellectual Life, 1983. Mem. Nat. Writers Union, Fabrangen, Nat. Havurah Com. (bd. dirs. 1979-80, 83-87), P'nai Or (bd. dirs. 1984-93, Aleph bd. dirs. 1993—), Internat. Coord. Com. on Religion and Earth (steering com. 1990-93), Phi Beta Kappa. Address: 6711 Lincoln Dr Philadelphia PA 19119 *For about 500 years the human race has made no "Sabbath" from ceaseless working, making, producing, doing and it therefore has raced to the brink of destroying itself and much of life on the planet. Just as individuals need rhythmic rest, so do societies—a spiritual truth that we should again learn from Torah. Time to be!.*

WASMUTH, CARL ERWIN, physician, lawyer; b. Pitts., Feb. 16, 1916; s. Edwin Hugo and Mary Blanche (Love) W.; m. Martha Conn., Aug. 25, 1939; children: Carl Erwin; m. Gertrude White Ruth, June 19, 1984; m. Wilhelmina Waterman Devine, May 12, 1990. BS, U. Pitts., 1935, MD, 1939; LLB, Cleve.- Marshall Law Sch., 1959. Bar: Ohio bar 1959; diplomate: Am. Bd. Anesthesiology. Intern Western Pa. Hosp., Pitts., 1939-40; fellow anesthesiology Cleve. Clinic Found., 1949-51, mem. emeritus staff, 1976—; pvt. practice medicine Dry Run, Pa., 1942-45, Scottdale, Pa., 1945-49; mem. dep. anesthesia Cleve. Clinic, 1951—, head dept., 1967-69; assoc. prof. law Cleve.-Marshall Law Sch., 1959-66; adj. prof. Cleve. Marshall Law Sch., 1966-73. Author: Anesthesia and the Law, 1961, Law for the Physician, 1966, Law and the Surgical Team, 1968; Editor: Legal Problems in the Practice of Anesthesiology, 1973; contbg. editor: Hale's Anesthesiology; editorial bd.: Med. World News; Contbr. articles to profl. jours. Trustee Cleve.- Marshall Law Sch., chmn., 1969-71; bd. dirs. Scottdale Hosp. Found.; chmn. bd. govs. Cleve. Clinic, 1969-77; trustee Cleve. Clinic Found., 1969-76, v.p., 1973-76; trustee Cleve. Clinic Ednl. Found., 1969-76, v.p., 1973-76; chmn. bd. trustees, pres. Cleve. Marshall Ednl. Found., 1972-81; bd. overseers Coll. Law, Cleve. State U., 1972-76; vis. com. Coll. Law, Case-Western Res. U., 1973-76; trustee United Torch Svcs., Tucson Symphony Soc., 1983-84, 88; trustee Santa Cruz Med. Found., 1977, pres., 1978; bd. govs. Ohio World Trade Center; trustee Cancer Center Cleve., Ohio Coll. Podiatric Medicine, 1976, Am. Coll. Legal Medicine Research Found., 1984—; mem. U. Ariz. Found., 1978, World Congress Med. Law, 1967—, Keynoter 3d World Congress, 1971; sec. Commn. Med. Malpractice, HEW, 1972-73; vestryman St. Francis-in-the-Valley Episcopal Ch., Green Valley. Named Distinguished Eagle Scout Nat. Council Boy Scouts Am., 1977; named Outstanding Citizen Eagle Cuyahoga council, 1976; Citizen of Year Cleve. Area Bd. Realtors, 1976. Fellow Am. Coll. Anesthesiologists, Am. Coll. Legal Medicine (pres. bd. govs. 1966-69), A.C.P., Am. Coll. Chest Physicians, Law Sci. Acad.; mem. Am. Soc. Anesthesiologists (dir., pres. 1968, speaker ho. of dels.), Ohio Soc. Anesthesiologists (dir. 1960-69), Cleve. Soc. Anesthesiologists (pres. 1963), Internat. Anesthesia Research Soc., World Fedn. Soc. Anesthesiologists (vice chmn. Am. delegation 1967), Acad. Anesthesiology (chmn. program com. 1967), Am. Ohio med. assns., N.Y. Acad. Scis., Nat. Acad. Sci., NRC, Com. Cadaver Utilization, Cleve. Acad. Medicine, AAAS, Transplantation Soc. (charter), Am., Ohio, Cuyahoga County, Cleve. bar assns., Phi Rho Sigma, Delta Theta Phi, Masons, Lions (past pres. local clubs), Old Pueblo Club, Tucson Club, Country of Green Valley Club, Pleasant Valley Country Club, Mt. Kenya Safari Club, Nanyuki, Kenya. Home: 727 W Quail Dr Green Valley AZ 85614-1740

WASS, HANNELORE LINA, educational psychology educator emeritus; b. Heidelberg, Germany, Sept. 12, 1926; came to U.S., 1957, naturalized, 1963; d. Hermann and Mina (Lasch) Kraft; m. Irvin R. Wass, Nov. 24, 1959 (dec.); 1 child, Brian C.; m. Harry H. Hisler, Apr. 13, 1978. B.A., Tchrs. Coll., Heidelberg, 1951; M.A., U. Mich., 1960, Ph.D., 1968. Tchr. W. Ger. Univ. Lab. Schs., 1958-60; mem. faculty U. Mich., Ann Arbor, 1958-60, U. Chgo. Lab. Sch., 1960-61, U. Mich., 1963-64, Eastern Mich., 1965-69; prof. ednl. psychology U. Fla., Gainesville, 1969-92; prof. emeritus, 1992—; faculty assoc. Ctr. for Gerontol. Studies U. Fla., Gainesville; cons., lectr. in thanatology. Author: The Professional Education of Teachers, 1974, Dying-Facing the Facts, 1979, 2d edit., 1988, 3d edit., 1994, Death Education: An Annotated Resource Guide, 1980, vol. 2, 1985, Helping Children Cope with Death, 1982, 2d edit., 1984, Childhood and Death, 1984; founding editor: (jour.) Death Studies, 1977—; cons. editor: Ednl. Gerontology, 1977—, (book series) Death Education, Aging, and Health Care; contbr. approximately 200 articles to profl. jours. and book chpts. Mem. Am. Psychol. Assn., Gerontol. Soc., Internat. Work Group Dying, Death and Bereavement (bd. dirs.), Assn. Death Edn. and Counseling. Home: 6014 NW 54th Way Gainesville FL 32606-3265 Office: U Fla 1418 Norman Hall Gainesville FL 32611

WASS, WALLACE MILTON, veterinarian, clinical science educator; b. Lake Park, Iowa, Nov. 19, 1929; s. Albert Carl and Esther (Moberg) W.; m. Doreen McCollum, May 31, 1953; children: Karen, Kimberly, Christopher, Kirby. Student, Minn. Jr. Coll., 1947-48; B.S., U. Minn., 1951, D.V.M., 1953, Ph.D., 1961. Diplomate: Am. Coll. Vet. Internal Medicine. Veterinarian Medford Vet. Clinic, Wis., 1953-58; instr. U. Minn. Coll. Vet. Medicine, St. Paul, 1958-63; prof. vet. medicine Iowa State U., Ames, 1964—, head dept. vet. clin. scis., 1964-83, prof., 1983—; cons. U.S. AID, Bogota, Columbia, 1963, U. Yola, Nigeria, 1983; staff veterinarian for med. rsch. sect. Brookhaven Nat. Lab., Upton, N.Y., 1963-64; cons. investigator fur seal harvest U.S. Dept. Commerce, Pribilof Islands, 1971, South Africa, 1974; use of antibiotics in animal feed U.S. FDA, 1972; cons. Farmland Ins. Co., 1971—; spl. cons. Kasetsart U., Bangkok, Thailand, 1974, Min. of Edn., Thailand, 1994. Contbr. articles, papers in field to profl. lit. Chmn. collegiate-ch. paster parish rels. com. United Methodist Ch., 1979, chmn. stewardship and fin. com., 1982. Served to 1st lt. USAF, 1953-55. Mem. AVMA (del. 1973-88), Iowa Vet. Med. Assn., Central Iowa Vet. Med. Assn. (pres. 1977), Am. Assn. Vet. Clinicians (pres. 1971-73), Phi Kappa Phi (sec. 1984-88, Iowa State U. chpt. pres. 1989-90), Phi Zeta, Alpha Zeta, Gamma Sigma Delta. Club: Wiltco Flying (sec. 1966-74). Home: 2166 Ashmore Dr Ames IA 50014-7840 Office: Iowa State U Dept Vet Clin Scis Ames IA 50011

WASSELL, IRENE MARTIN, food editor; b. Siloam Springs, Ark., Sept. 19, 1931; d. Leslie and Cora Etna (Jones) Martin; m. Bill J. Wassell, Mar. 29, 1953; children: Lisa Annette, Cynthia Lenore, Eric Lyndon. BA, U. Ark., 1978; MA, U. Ark., Little Rock, 1983. Woman's editor The Times of North Little Rock, 1978-80; staff features writer Ark. Gazette, Little Rock, 1980-90, food editor, 1990-91; food editor Ark. Dem.-Gazette, Little Rock, 1992—. Office: Ark Dem Gazette 121 E Capitol Ave Little Rock AR 72201-3819

WASSENICH, LINDA PILCHER, health policy analyst, fund raiser; b. Washington, Aug. 27, 1943; d. Mason Johnson and Vera Bell (Stephenson) Pilcher; m. Mark Wassenich, May 14, 1965; children: Paul Mason, David Mark. BA magna cum laude, Tex. Christian U., 1965; MSW, U. N.C., 1970. Licensed advanced practitioner, cert. social worker, Tex. Counselor family ct. Dallas County Juvenile Dept., Dallas, 1970-73, 75-76; dir. govt. rels. Vis. Nurse Assn., Dallas, 1980-84, exec. officer of hospice, 1984-85; exec. dir. Incest Recovery Assn., Dallas, 1985-86; assoc. exec. dir. Lone Star Coun. Camp Fire, Dallas, 1986-89; exec. v.p. Vis. Nurse Assn. Found., Dallas, 1989-91; dir. policy & resource devel. Vis. Nurse Assn., Dallas, 1992—. Contbr. articles to profl. pubs. Bd. dirs. Women's Coun. Dallas County, 1986-95, pres., 1992-93; chmn. Dallas County Welfare Adv. Bd., 1991-95; bd. dirs. United Way of Met. Dallas, 1992-94, Youth Impact Ctrs., Dallas, 1993-94; mem. adv. bd. Maternal Health and Family Planning Dallas, 1990-94; mem. Leadership Dallas, 1988-89. Recipient AAUW, Dallas, Laurel award, 1995. Mem. NASW (Tex. bd. dirs., nominating chmn. 1990-92, co-chmn. Dallas unit 1981-82, Social Worker of Yr. award 1988), LWV (bd. dirs. Dallas 1974-80, pres. 1995—), Acad. Cert. Social Workers, Nat. Soc. Fundraising Execs. (cert., bd. dirs. Dallas chpt. 1994—, v.p. governance 1995).

WASSER, HENRY, retired English educator; b. Pitts., Apr. 13, 1919; s. Nathan and Mollie (Mendelson) W.; m. Solidelle Felicité Fortier, Aug. 20, 1942; children: Michael Frederick (dec.), Eric Anthony (dec.), Frederick Anthony, Felicity Louise. B.A., M.A., Ohio State U., 1940; Ph.D., Columbia U., 1951. Teaching fellow George Washington U., 1940-42; analyst USAAF intelligence, 1941-43; chemist Goodyear Synthetic Rubber Co., 1943-45; from tutor to assoc. prof. City Coll., CUNY, 1946-66; prof. English, dean faculties Richmond Coll., CUNY, 1966-73; v.p. for acad. affairs Calif. State U., Sacramento, 1973-74; prof. English Coll. S.I., CUNY, 1974-89; dir. Center for European Studies, Grad. Sch. CUNY, 1979-93; Fulbright prof. U. Salonika, Greece, 1955-56; seminar assoc. Columbia U., 1961—, co-=chair, 1982-87, chair, 1987-89; mem. Colloquium on Higher Edn., Yale U., 1974-75; Fulbright prof. Am. Lit. U. Oslo, 1962-64, dir., prof. Am. Lit., 1963-64; vis. prof. U. Sussex, Eng., 1972; lectr. in field, Sweden, Norway, Eng., Germany, Poland, Yugoslavia, Italy, Turkey; Fulbright prof. Am. Lit. and Civilization U. Bergen, Norway, 1989-90, U. Aveiro, Portugal, 1993; rsch. scholar comparative higher edn. CUNY, 1989—. Author: The Scientific Thought of Henry Adams, 1956, (with others) Higher Education in Western Europe and North America: A Selected and Annotated Bibliography, 1979, American Literature and Language: A Selected and Annotated Bibliography, 1980; editor: (with Sigmund Skard) Americana Norvegica; Norwegian Contributions to American Studies, 1968, (with others) The Compleat University, 1983, Problems of the Urban University: A Comparative Perspective, 1984, Impact of Changing Labor Force on Higher Education, 1987; editor (with Ulrich Teichler) German and American Universities: Mutual Influences, 1992; mem. bd. editors History of European Ideas, 1986—, guest editor, summer, 1987; guest editor Higher Edn. Policy, spring, 1994; contbr. articles to newspapers and profl. jours. Faculty trustee CUNY, 1981-86, trustee emeritus, 1986—; bd. dirs. Scandinavian Seminar, 1978-86, sec., 1980-83, vice chmn., 1983-86. Recipient Am. Scandinavian Found. award, 1969, 71, German Acad. Exchange Service award, 1973, 80, Swedish Info. Service award, 1979, Norwegian Ministry of Culture award, 1983, NEH award, 1984, Foscolo medal U. Pavia, Italy, 1986, German Marshall Fund award, 1985, 87, Atheneum medal U. Pavia, Italy, 1988; Finnish Ministry Culture grantee, 1989. Mem. Am. Studies Assn. (pres. Met. N.Y. chpt. 1961-62, mem. nat. exec. council 1968-74), Melville Soc. Am. (historian 1969-74), MLA, Am. Scandinavian Found. (fellow 1971), Internat. Assn. Univ. Profs. English, Assn. Upper Level Colls. and Univs. (2d v.p. 1971-72), Assn. for World Edn. (internat. council), Phi Beta Kappa (sec. City Coll. chpt. 1957-62, 64-67, pres. CUNY Acad. for Humanities and Scis. 1991—), Internat. Conf. Higher Edn. (steering com. 1989—), Henry Adams Soc. (exec. coun. 1994—). Home: 333 E 34th St # 16C New York NY 10016-4927 also: 5517 Fieldstone Rd Bronx NY 10471 Office: CUNY Grad Sch New York NY 10036

WASSERBURG, GERALD JOSEPH, geology and geophysics educator; b. New Brunswick, N.J., Mar. 25, 1927; s. Charles and Sarah (Levine) W.; m. Naomi Z. Orlick, Dec. 21, 1951; children: Charles David, Daniel Morris. Student, Rutgers U.; BS in Physics, U. Chgo., 1951, MSc in Geology, 1952, PhD, 1954, DSc (hon.), 1992; Dr. Hon. Causa, Brussels U., 1985, U. Paris, 1986; DSc (hon.), Ariz. State U., 1987. Research assoc. Inst. Nuclear Studies, U. Chgo. 1954-55; asst. prof. Calif. Inst. Tech., Pasadena, 1955-59, assoc. prof., 1959-62, prof. geology and geophysics, 1962-82, John D. MacArthur prof. geology and geophysics, 1982—; served on Juneau Ice Field Research Project, 1950; cons. Argonne Nat. Lab., Lamont, Ill., 1952-55; former mem. U.S. Nat. Com. for Geochem., com. for Planetary Exploration Study, NRC, adv. council Petroleum Research Fund, Am. Chem. Soc.; mem. lunar sample analysis planning team (LSAPT) Manned Spacecraft Ctr., NASA, Houston, 1968-71, chmn., 1970; lunar sample rev. bd. 1970-72; mem. Facilities Working Group LSAPT, Johnson Space Ctr., 1972-82; mem. sci. working panel for Apollo missions, Johnson Space Ctr., 1971-73; advisor NASA, 1968-88, physical scis. com., 1971-75, mem. lunar base steering com., 1984; chmn. com. for planetary and lunar exploration, mem. space sci. bd. NAS, 1975-78; chmn. div. Geol. and Planetary Scis., Calif. Inst. Tech., 1987-89; vis. prof. U. Kiel, Fed. Republic of Germany, 1960, Harvard U., 1962, U. Bern, Switzerland, 1966, Swiss Fed. Tech. Inst., 1967, Max Planck Inst., Mainz and Heidelberg, Fed. Republic of Germany, 1985; invited lectr., Vinton Hayes Sr. Fellow, Harvard U., 1980, Jaeger-Hales lectr., Australian Nat. U., 1980, Harold Jeffreys lectr. Royal Astron. Soc., 1981, Ernst Cloos lectr., Johns Hopkins U., 1984, H.L. Welsh Disting. lectr. U. Toronto, Can. 1986., Danz lectr. U. Washington, 1989; Goldschmidt Centennial lectr. Norwegian Acad. Sci. and Letters, 1989; Green vis. prof. U.B.C. 1982; 60th Anniversary Symposium speaker, Hebrew U., Jerusalem, 1985. Served with U.S. Army, 1944-46. Decorated Combat Inf. badge. Recipient Group Achievement award, NASA, 1969, Exceptional Sci. Achievement award, NASA, 1970, Disting. Pub. Service medal, NASA, 1973, J.F. Kemp medal Columbia U., 1973, Profl. Achievement award U. Chgo. Alumni Assn., 1978, Disting. Pub. Service medal with cluster, NASA, 1978, Wollaston medal Geol. Soc. London, 1985, Sr. Scientist award, Alexander von Humboldt-Stiftung, 1985, Crafoord prize Royal Swedish Acad. Scis., 1986. Gold medal Royal Astron. Soc., 1991; named Hon. Fgn. Fellow European Union Geoscis., 1983, recipient Holmes medal 1987; Regents fellow Smithsonian Inst. Fellow AAAS, Am. Geophys. Union (planetology sect., Harry H. Hess medal 1985), Geol. Soc. Am. (life, Arthur L. Day medal 1970), Meteorol.

Soc. (pres. 1987-88, Leonard medal 1975); mem. Geochem. Soc. (Goldschmidt medal 1978), Nat. Acad. Scis. (Arthur L. Day prize and lectureship 1981, J. Lawrence Smith medal 1985), Norwegian Acad. Sci. and Letters, Am. Philos. Soc., Geol. Soc. London (hon. fellow 1995). Research interests include geochemistry and geophysics and the application of the methods of chemical physics to problems in the earth scis. Major researches have been the determination of the time scales of nucleosynthesis, connections between the interstellar medium and solar material, the time of the formation of the solar system, the chronology and evolution of the earth, moon and meteorites, the establishment of dating methods using long-lived natural radio-activities, the study of geologic and lunar processes using nuclear and isotopic effects as a tracer in nature, the origin of natural gases, and the application of thermodynamic methods to geologic systems. Office: Calif Inst of Tech Divsn Geol & Planetary Scis Pasadena CA 91125

WASSERMAN, ALBERT, writer, director; b. N.Y.C., Feb. 9, 1921; s. Martin S. and Beatrice (Schaffer) W.; m. Della Newmark, Aug. 5, 1943 (div. Mar. 1965); children—Paul, Vicki; m. Barbara Alson, June 19, 1968. B.S., Coll. City N.Y., 1941. Pres. Wasserman Prodns., Inc., N.Y.C., 1968-75. Writer documentary, ednl. and indsl. films, 1946-53; free lance writer, dir. TV documentary films, 1953-55; staff writer, dir., producer, CBS-TV, 1955-60; producer, dir., writer: NBC News, 1960-67; producer: 60 Minutes, 1976-86; writer, prod., dir.: Out of Darkness; writer film: First Steps; writer, dir. films for: CBS Pub. Affairs Series The Search; prod., writer dir.: NBC White Paper programs; prod., dir.: TV Spl. The Making of the President, 1972 (Sylvania TV award, Robert Flaherty film award, Acad. award 1947, Peabody award CBS Pub. Affairs series.). Recipient Lasker Med. Journalism awards (2); Edinburgh Film Festival silver medal, 1948, George Polk award, 1960, Journalism award Ohio State U., 1961. Mem. Writers Guild Am. East (treas. 1965-66), Dirs. Guild Am. (eastern regional council 1965-66, 69-70). Home: 259 W 11th St New York NY 10014-2414

WASSERMAN, ARNOLD SAUL, academic dean, industrial design executive; b. Washington, June 15, 1934; s. Joseph and Mildred (Jacobs) W. BA in Indsl. Design, Carnegie Mellon U., Pitts., 1956; MA in Design History, U. Chgo., 1965. Project dir. Peter Muller-Munk Assocs., Pitts., 1956-59; asst. dir. Compagnie de l'Esthetique Industrielle, Paris, 1961-63; project dir. Latham, Tyler, Jensen, Inc., Chgo., 1963-68; exec. dir. Product Planning Assocs., Santa Barbara, Calif., 1968-72; pres. Arnold Saul Wasserman Design, Santa Barbara, 1972-79; chmn. bd., dir. design TAG, Inc., Santa Barbara, 1976-79; dir. corp. indsl. design NCR Corp., Dayton, Ohio, 1979-80; mgr. indsl. design Xerox Corp., various locations, 1980-86; v.p. strategic planning RichardsonSmith, Inc., Columbus, Ohio, 1986-87; v.p. corp. indsl. design and human factors Unisys Corp., Blue Bell, Pa., 1987-91; dean Sch. Art & Design Pratt Inst., Bklyn., 1991—; mem. profl. adv. bd. Carnegie Mellon U., Pitts. 1987-89, Calif. State U., Long Beach, 1987-89, Stanford Design Forum, Palo Alto, 1988-89; design juror NEA, Washington, 1987-91. Author: Ergonomics, 1989. With U.S. Army, 1959-61. Carnegie Mellon U. fellow, 1952-55, U. Chgo. fellow, 1964-65, Ford Found. grantee, 1966, Nat. Endowment for Arts grantee, 1989. Mem. Indsl. Designers Soc. Am. (dir. 1979-80). Avocations: backpacking, art, music, sports. Home: 174 Emerson Pl Brooklyn NY 11205-3803 Office: Pratt Inst # Main-4 Brooklyn NY 11205

WASSERMAN, BARRY L(EE), architect; b. Cambridge, Mass., May 25, 1935; s. Theodore and Adelaide (Levin) W.; m. Wilma Louise Greenfield, June 21, 1957 (div. 1971); children: Tim Andrew, Andrew Glenn; m. Judith Ella Michaelowski, Apr. 22, 1979. B.A., Harvard U., 1957, M. Arch., 1960. Registered architect, Calif. Assoc. John S. Bolles Assocs., San Francisco, 1960-69; prin. Wasserman-Herman Assocs., San Francisco, 1969-72; prin., dir. Office Lawrence Halprin U Assocs., San Francisco, 1972-76; dep. state architect State of Calif., Sacramento, 1976-78, state architect, 1978-83; prof. dept. architecture, dir. Inst. Environ. Design, Sch. Environ. Design Calif. State Poly. U., Pomona, 1983-87, chair dept. architecture, Coll. Environ. Design, 1988—; cons. architecture, Sacramento, 1983—; program advisor Fla. A&M U., Tallahassee, 1981-83. Architect Wasserman House, San Rafael, Calif., 1963 (AIA-Sunset Mag. award of Merit) 1965-66), Anna Waden Library, San Francisco, 1969 (AIA award of Merit 1970)), Capitol Area Plan, Sacramento, 1977 (Central Valley chpt. AIA Honor award 1979). Recipient Awards citation Progressive Architecture 26th awards Program, 1979. Fellow AIA chmn. architecture in govt. com. (1979). Democrat. Jewish. Home: 6456 Fordham Way Sacramento CA 95831-2218

WASSERMAN, BERT W., communications and publishing company executive. With office of pres. Time-Warner Inc., N.Y.C.; exec. v.p., chief fin. officer Time-Warner Inc., until 1994. Office: Time-Warner Inc 1271 Ave of Americas New York NY 10020*

WASSERMAN, CHARLES, banker; b. Guayaquil, Ecuador, Aug. 31, 1929; came to U.S., 1948, naturalized, 1960; s. Mendel and Mary Wasserman; m. Jacqueline Royer, Oct. 4, 1960; children: Roger, Mark. BA, Farleigh Dickinson U., 1949; MBA, U. Havana, 1956. Trainee internat. dept. Chase Manhattan Bank, N.Y., 1958-60, Swiss Bank Corp. N.Y., 1960-64; area sr. credit analyst Am. Express Bank, N.Y., 1965-66; exec. v.p. Republic Nat. Bank, N.Y., 1967—, cons. to World Bank, 1989; chmn., pres. Republic Internat. Bank N.Y., L.A., 1988-89; hon. chmn. Meridian Capital Corp. Named Hon. Chmn., Meridian Capital Corp., 1994. Mem. Internat. Exec. Svc. Corps, Internat. Platform Assn. Home: 224 Nassau Ave Manhasset NY 11030-2440 Office: 127 E 59th St Rm 222 New York NY 10022-1225

WASSERMAN, DALE, playwright; b. Rhinelander, Wis., Nov. 2, 1917; s. Samuel and Hilda (Paykel) W. founder, artistic dir. Midwest Profl. Playwrights Lab.; Trustee, founding mem. Eugene O'Neill Theatre Center. Writer, producer, dir. for TV, motion pictures, theatre; author: (with Bruce Geller) musical Livin' the Life, 1957; stage plays The Pencil of God, 1961, 998, 1962, One Flew Over the Cuckoo's Nest, 1963, Man of La Mancha, 1965 (Tony award for best musical 1966, N.Y. Drama Critics' Circle award for best musical 1966, Outer Circle award 1966, Variety award 1966, Spanish Pavilion award 1966, others), Play with Fire, 1978, Great Big River, 1981, Shakespeare and The Indians, 1983; screenplays World of Strangers, 1955, The Vikings, 1958, Two Faces to Go, 1959, Aboard the Flying Swan, 1962, Jangadeiro, 1962, Cleopatra, 1963, Quick, Before It Melts, 1964; writer, co-prodr.: motion pictures Mister Buddwing, 1965, A Walk With Love and Death, 1969, Man of LaMancha, 1972; also numerous TV plays including Elisha and the Long Knives, 1954 (Publishers Guild award 1954), The Fog, 1957 (Writers Guild of Am. award 1957), Eichmann, 1958, Engineer of Death, 1959, The Citadel, 1959 (Writers Guild of Am. award 1959), I, Don Quixote, 1959, (Writers Guild of Am. award 1960), The Power and the Glory, 1960, The Lincoln Murder Case, 1961 (Writers Guild of Am. award 1961), Stranger, 1962, Burden of Proof, 1976, Scheherazade, 1977, The Seventh Dimension, 1984, My Name Is Esther, 1985, The Whole Truth, 1987, Green, 1987, A Fine American Family, 1988, Players in a Game, 1989, Murder Among the Saints, 1989, The Girl From Botany Bay, 1990, (mus.) Western Star, 1992, Beggar's Holiday, 1994; contbr. short stories, articles to Variety and other pubs. Recipient hon. degree U. Wis., 1980. Mem. Writers Guild Am. East (nat. council 1960-64), Writers Guild Am. West, Dramatists Guild, ALA, French Soc. Authors and Composers, The Jaques Brel Found. (gov.). Club: Players, Monte Cristo Soc. Office: c/o Harold Orenstein Atty 157 W 57th St New York NY 10019-2210

WASSERMAN, EDEL, scientist, executive; b. N.Y.C., July 29, 1932; s. Abraham and Ida (Ulano) W.; m. Zelda L. Rakowitz, Jan. 29, 1955; children: Stephen, Diane. B.A., Cornell U., 1953; M.A., Harvard, 1954, Ph.D. (NSF fellow 1953-56, Coffin fellow 1956-57), 1959. Mem. tech. staff Bell Telephone Labs., Murray Hill, N.J., 1957-76; prof. chemistry Rutgers U., New Brunswick, N.J., 1967-76; dir. Chem. Research Ctr., Allied Chem. Co., 1976-78, dir. Corp. Research Center, 1978-80, sr. staff scientist, 1980-81; mem. Chem. Scis. staff E.I. DuPont, 1981—, assoc. dir. rsch., 1983-93, sci. advisor ctrl. rsch. and devel., 1993—; Regents lectr. U. Calif., Irvine, 1973; mem. vis. com. Harvard U., Rutgers U., Argonne Nat. Lab., U. Tex.; mem. bd. on chem. scis. NRC, 1980-83; mem. adv. bd. on MPS, NSF, 1992-94, NREL Basic Rsch. Divsn., 1994—, BESAC, 1995—. Adv. editor: Chem. Physics Letters, 1967-79, Chem. Rev., 1982-89. Mem. Am. Chem. Soc. (numerous coms., adv. editor jour. 1971-75), Am. Inst. Physics. Research in complex organic and inorganic systems. Office: 328 E Dupont Exptl Sta Wilmington DE 19880

WASSERMAN, EDWARD ARNOLD, psychology educator; b. L.A., Apr. 2, 1946; s. Albert Leonard and May (Sabin) W. BA, UCLA, 1968; PhD, Ind. U., 1972. Postdoctoral fellow U. Sussex, Brighton, Eng. 1972; from asst. prof. to prof. psychology U. Iowa, Iowa City, 1972-83, prof., 1983—. Contbr. articles to profl. jours., chpts. to books; assoc. editor several jours. Bd. dirs. Big Bros., Big Sisters, Johnson County, Iowa, 1982-85. Ind. U. fellow, 1968, U. Iowa fellow, 1975, 82, NAS fellow, former USSR, 1976, James Van Allen Natural Scis. fellow, 1994-95. Fellow APA, Am. Psychol. Soc.; mem. Psychonomic Soc., Midwestern Psychol. Assn., Phi Beta Kappa. Office: U Iowa Dept Psychology Iowa City IA 52242

WASSERMAN, GERALD B., wholesale distribution executive. With Can-Star Sports, Inc., Can.; pres., CEO Weider Health & Fitness, Woodland Hills, Calif.; pres. Weider Health & Fitness 21100 Erwin St Woodland Hills CA 91367*

WASSERMAN, HARRY HERSHAL, chemistry educator; b. Boston, Mass., Dec. 1, 1920; s. Maurice Leonard and Rebecca (Franks) W.; m. Elga Ruth Steinherz, June 1, 1947; children: Daniel M., Diana R., Steven A. BS, MIT, 1941; MA, Harvard U., 1942, PhD, 1949; MA (hon.), Yale U., 1962. Rsch. asst. O.S.R.D. Penicillin Project, 1945; instr., asst. prof. dept. chemistry Yale U., New Haven, Conn., 1948-57, assoc. prof. dept. chemistry, 1957-62, prof. dept. chemistry, 1962-82, Eugene Higgins prof. chemistry, 1982-91; Eugene Higgins prof. chemistry emeritus, 1991—; cons. Union Carbide Corp., 1956-66, Sandoz Corp., 1966-74, SmithKline Beckman Corp., 1974-80, Ortho Pharmaceuticals, 1980-94. Author numerous articles on organic chemistry in sci. jours. Capt. USAF, 1942-45. Recipient William Devane Tchr.-Scholar award Phi Beta Kappa, 1977, Catalyst Teaching award Chem. Mfrs. Assn., 1985, Oustanding Tchr. award Yale U., 1985, Aldrich Synthetic Chemistry award, Am. Chem. Soc., 1987, Arthur Cope scholar award, 1990. Mem. NAS, Am. Acad. Scis., Conn. Acad. Scis. Avocation: watercolor painting. Home: 192 Bishop St New Haven CT 06511-3718 Office: Yale U Dept Chemistry 225 Prospect St New Haven CT 06512-1958

WASSERMAN, LEW R., film, recording and publishing company executive; b. Cleve., Mar. 15, 1913; m. Edith T. Beckerman, July 5, 1936; 1 dau., Lynne Kay. D (hon.), Brandeis U., NYU. Nat. dir. advt. and publicity Music Corp. Am., 1936-38, v.p., 1938-39, became v.p. charge motion picture div., 1940; now chmn., chief exec. officer, dir., mem. exec. com. MCA, Inc., also chmn. bd., chief exec. officer, dir. subsidiary corps.; chmn. emeritus Assn. Motion Picture and TV Producers. Trustee John F. Kennedy Libr., John F. Kennedy Ctr. Performing Arts, Jules Stein Eye Inst., Carter Presdl. Ctr., Lyndon Baines Johnson Found.; pres. Hollywood Canteen Found.; chmn. Rsch. to Prevent Blindness Found.; hon. chmn. bd. Ctr. Theatre Group L.A. Music Ctr.; bd. dirs. Amateur Athletic Found. of L.A. (chmn. fin. com.), L.A. Music Ctr. Found.; bd. gov.'s Ronald Reagan Presdl. Found. Recipient Jean Hersholt Humanitarian award Acad. Motion Picture Arts and Scis., 1973. Democrat. Office: Universal City Studios Inc 100 Universal City Plz Universal City CA 91608

WASSERMAN, LOUIS ROBERT, physician, educator; b. N.Y.C., July 11, 1910; s. Jacob and Ethel (Ballin) W.; m. Julia B. Wheeler, Feb. 20, 1957. A.B., Harvard U., 1931; M.D., U. Chgo., 1935. Diplomate: Am. Bd. Internal Medicine. Intern Michael Reese Hosp., Chgo., 1935-37; research fellow hematology Mt. Sinai Hosp., N.Y.C., 1937-39; research asst. Mt. Sinai Hosp., 1940-42, dir. dept. hematology, 1953-72, hematologist to hosp., 1950-72; research fellow med. physics U. Cal. at Berkeley, 1946-48, cons. radiation labs., 1948-51; asst. prof. Columbia Coll. Phys. and Surg., 1950-60, asso. clin. prof., 1960-66; prof. medicine Mt. Sinai Sch. Medicine, 1966-72, chmn. dept. clin. sci., 1967-72, Distinguished Service prof., 1972-79, emeritus, 1979—, Albert A. and Vera G. List prof. medicine (hematology), 1977-79, emeritus, 1979—; Research collaborator Brookhaven Nat. Labs., 1960-71; cons. practice specializing in hematology, N.Y.C., 1950—; Mem. nat. cancer planning com., chmn. polycythemia vera study group Nat. Cancer Inst., NIH, 1967—, mem. diagnostic research adv. com., 1972-75, co-chmn., 1975-77, chmn. bd. sci. counselors div. cancer treatment, 1974-76. Served to maj. AUS, 1942-46. Fellow ACP, AMA, N.Y. Acad. Medicine, N.Y. Acad. Sci., Internat. Soc. Hematology (v.p. 1972, counselor at-large 1973—); mem. Assn. Am. Physicians, Am. Soc. Hematology (exec. com. 1964-66, pres. 1968-69, adv. council 1969-74), Soc. Nuclear Medicine, Societe de Hopitaux de Paris, Soc. Exptl. Biology and Medicine, Harvey Soc., Soc. Study Blood, Am. Fedn. Clin. Research, Am. Soc. Clin. Nutrition, Am. Assn. Cancer Research, Am. Soc. Clin. Oncology, Reticulo-Endothelial Soc., Alpha Omega Alpha. Office: Mt Sinai Hosp 19 E 98th St New York NY 10029-6501

WASSERMAN, PAUL, library and information science educator; b. Newark, Jan. 8, 1924; s. Joseph and Sadie (Ringelescu) W.; m. Krystyna Ostrowska, 1973; children: Jacqueline R., Steven R. BBA, Coll. City N.Y., 1948; MS in L.S., Columbia, 1949, MS, 1950; PhD, U. Mich., 1960; postgrad., Western Res. U., 1963-64. Advt. mgr. Zuckerberg Co., N.Y.C., 1946-48; asst. to bus. libr. Bklyn. Pub. Library, 1949-51, chief sci. and industry div., 1951-53; librarian, asst. prof. Grad. Sch. Bus. and Pub. Adminstrn., Cornell U., 1953-56, libr., assoc. prof., 1956-62, librarian, prof., 1962-65; dean U. Md. Coll. Library and Info. Scis., 1965-70, prof., 1970—; vis. prof. U. Mich., summers 1960, 63, 64, Asian Inst. Tech., U. Hawaii, U. Hong Kong, summer 1988, Chulalalangkorn U., Bangkok, 1990, U. Washington, summer 1991, U. Wis., summer 1992, C.W. Post Coll. L.I.U., 1993; Isabel Nichol lectr. Denver U. Library Sch., 1968; market research cons. Laux Advt., Inc., 1955-59, Gale Research Co., Detroit, 1959-60, 63-64; research planning cons. Ind. U. Sch. Bus., 1961-62; cons. USPHS as mem. Nat. Library Medicine Manpower Tng. Rev. Com., 1966-69, Ohio Bd. Regents, 1969, Omngraphics, Inc., 1988-91, vols. tech. assistance, summer 1987; dir. Documentation Abstracts, Inc., 1970-73, v.p., 1971-73; Fulbright prof. Warsaw U., 1993-94. Author: Information for Administrators, 1956, (with Fred Silander) Decision Making, 1958, Measurement and Evaluation of Organization Performance, 1959, Sources of Commodity Prices, 1960, 2d edit., 1974, Sources for Hospital Administrators, 1961, Decision Making: An Annotated Bibliography, supplement, 1958-63, 1964, Librarian and the Machine, 1965; Book rev. editor: Adminstrv. Sci. Quar, 1956-61; editor: Service to Business, 1952-53, Directory of University Research Bureaus and Institutes, 1960, Health Organizations of the U.S. and Canada, 1961, and 2d to 4th edit., 1977, Statistics Sources, 1962 and 4th to 8th edits., 1984, (with Bundy) Reader in Library Adminstration, 1968, Reader in Research Methods in Librarianship, 1969; mng. editor: Mgmt. Information Guide Series, 1963-83, Consultants and Consulting Organizations, 1966, 4th edit., 1979, 5th edit., 1982, Who's Who in Consulting, 1968, 2d edit., 1974, Awards, Honors and Prizes: A Sourcebook and Directory, 1969, 2d edit., 1972, 4th edit. Vol. 1, 1978, International and Foreign Awards, 1975, New Consultants, 1973-74, 76-77, 78-79, Readers in Librarianship and Information Science, 1968-78, Ency. Bus. Information Sources, 1971, 3d edit., 1976, 4th edit., 1980, 5th edit., 1983, Library and Information Services Today, 1971-75, Consumer Sourcebook, 1974, 2d edit., 1978, 3d edit., 1980, 4th edit., 1983; series editor: Contributions in Librarianship and Information Science, 1969—; coordinating mgmt. editor: Information Guide Library, 1971-83, The New Librarianship-A Challenge for Change, 1972; mng. editor: Museum Media, 1973, Library Bibliographies and Indexes, 1975, Ethnic Groups in the United States, 1976, 2d edit., 1982, Training and Development Organizations, 1978, 2d edit., 1983, Speakers and Lecturers: How to Find Them, 1979, 2d edit., 1982, Learning Independently, 1979, 2d edit., 1983, Recreation and Outdoor Life Directory, 1979, Law and Legal Information Directory, 1980, 2d edit., 1982, Ency. Health Info. Sources, 1986, Ency. Sr. Citizen Info. Sources, 1987, Ency. Pub. Affairs Info. Sources, 1987, Ency. Legal Info. Sources, 1987; mem. editorial bd. Social Scis. Citation Index, Inst. Scientific Info., 1972—, Jour. Library Adminstrn., 1979-89, Social Sci. Info. Studies, 1979—, 1991 Education for Info.: The Internat. Rev. of Education and Tng. in Library and Info. Sci., 1983-88. Active U.S. Com. on Edn. and Tng. for Internat. Fedn. for Info. and Documentation, 1993-94. Served with U.S. Army, 1943-46. Decorated Purple Heart, Bronze Star; Fulbright scholar, Sri Lanka, 1986-87. Mem. AAUP, ALA, Am. Soc. Info. Sci., Spl. Librs. Assn. (editor, chmn. publ. project). Home: 4940 Sentinel Dr Apt 203 Bethesda MD 20816-3552 Office: U Md Coll Libr and Info Svcs College Park MD 20742

WASSERMAN, RICHARD LEO, lawyer; b. Balt., Aug. 6, 1948; s. Jack B. and Claire (Gutman) W.; m. Manuele Delbourgo, May 13, 1973; children: Alexander E., Lauren E. AB, Princeton U., 1970; JD, Columbia U., 1973. Bar: N.Y. 1975, Md. 1978, U.S. Dist. Ct. (so. and ea. dists.) N.Y. 1975, U.S. Dist. Ct. Md. 1978, U.S. Ct. Appeals (2d cir.) 1975, U.S. Ct. Appeals (4th cir.) 1979, U.S. Supreme Ct. 1982. Law clk. to hon. Roszel C. Thomsen U.S. Dist. Ct. Md., Balt., 1973-74; assoc. Proskauer Rose Goetz & Mendelsohn, N.Y.C., 1974-78; assoc. Venable, Baetjer & Howard, Balt., 1978-81, ptnr., 1982—. Mem. ABA (bus. bankruptcy com.), Md. Bar Assn. (sec. coun. bus. law sect. 1989-92), Bar Assn. Balt. City (chmn. banking bankruptcy and bus. law com. 1987-88), Bankruptcy Bar Assn. Dist. Md. (bd. dirs. 1988—, pres. 1990-91), Assn. of Bar Of City of N.Y., Am. Bankruptcy Inst., Princeton U. Alumni Assn. Md. (bd. dirs. 1980, pres. 1985-87), Suburban Club Balt. County (bd. govs. 1982-89, 94—, 2d v.p. 1986-87, sec. 1987-88, pres. elect 1994-95). Democrat. Jewish. Avocations: tennis, bridge. Office: Venable Baetjer & Howard 1800 Mercantile Bank Bldg Baltimore MD 21201

WASSERMAN, ROBERT HAROLD, biology educator; b. Schenectady, Feb. 11, 1926; s. Joseph and Sylvia (Rosenberg) W.; m. Marilyn Mintz, June 11, 1950; children: Diane Jean, Arlene Lee, Judith Rose. B.S., Cornell U., 1949, Ph.D., 1953; M.S., Mich. State U., 1951. Research assoc. AEC project U. Tenn., Oak Ridge, 1953-55; sr. scientist med. div. Oak Ridge Inst. Nuclear Studies, 1955-57; asso. prof. dept. phys. biology N.Y. State Vet. Coll., Cornell U., 1957-63, prof., 1963—, James Law prof. physiology, 1989—, acting head phys. biology dept., 1963-64, 71, 75-76, chmn. dept. / sect. physiology, 1983-87, mem. exec. com. div. biol. sci., 1983-87; vis. fellow Inst. Biol. Chemistry, Copenhagen, 1964-65; chmn. Conf. on Calcium Transport, 1962; co-chmn. Conf. on Cell Mechanisms for Calcium Transfer and Homeostasis, 1970; mem. adv. bd. Vitamin D Symposia, 1976—; mem. adv. bd. Symposia Calcium-Binding Proteins, 1977-88, chmn., 1977; mem. food and nutrition bd. NRC; cons. NIH, Oak Ridge Inst. Nuclear Studies; mem. pub. affairs com. Fedn. Am. Socs. Exptl. Biology, 1974-77 ; chmn. com. MPI, NRC. Bd. editors: Calcified Tissue Research, 1977-80, Procs. Soc. Exptl. Biol. Medicine, 1970-76, Cornell Veterinarian, Jour. Nutrition; contbr.: articles to profl. jours. Served with U.S. Army, 1944-45. Recipient Mead Johnson award, 1969, Andre Lichtwitz prize INSERM, 1982, W.F. Neuman award Am. Soc. Bone and Mineral Rsch., 1990, merit award NIH, 1993-96; Guggenheim fellow, 1964-65, 72, fellow NSF-OECD, 1964-65. Fellow Am. Inst. Nutrition, Am. Physiol. Soc., Soc. Exptl. Biology and Medicine, AAAS, Nat. Acad. Scis., Sigma Xi, Phi Kappa Phi, Phi Zeta. Home: 207 Texas Ln Ithaca NY 14850-1758

WASSERMAN, STEPHEN IRA, physician, educator; b. Los Angeles, Dec. 17, 1942; m. Linda Morgan; children: Matthew, Zachary. BA, Stanford U., 1964; MD, UCLA, 1968. Diplomate Am. Bd. Allergy & Immunology. Intern, resident Peter B. Brigham Hosp., Boston, 1968-70; fellow in allergy, immunology Robert B. Brigham Hosp., Boston, 1972-75; asst. prof. medicine Harvard U., Boston, 1975-79, assoc. prof., 1979; assoc. prof. U. Calif.-San Diego, La Jolla, 1979-85, prof., 1985—, chief allergy tng. program Sch. Medicine, 1979-85, chief allergy div. Sch. Medicine, 1985-93, acting chmn. dept. medicine, 1986-88, chmn. dept. medicine, 1988—, Helen M. Ranney prof., 1992—; co-dir. allergy sect. Robert B. and Peter B. Brigham Hosps., 1977-79; dir. Am. Bd. Allergy and Immunology, Am. Bd. Internal Medicine. Contbr. articles to profl. jours. Served to lt. comdr. USPHS, 1970-72, San Francisco. Fellow Am. Acad. Allergy and Immunology; mem. Am. Soc. Clin. Investigation, Assn. Am. Physicians, Am. Assn. Immunologists, Collegium INternationale Allergologicum, Phi Beta Kappa, Alpha Omega Alpha. Office: U Calif Med Ctr 402 Dickinson St Ste 380 San Diego CA 92103-6902*

WASSERMAN, STEVE, publisher; b. Vancouver, Wash., Aug. 3, 1952; s. Abraham and Ann (Dragoon) W.; m. Michelle Krisel, Mar. 7, 1982; children: Claire, Paul, Isaac. AB in Criminology, U. Calif., Berkeley, 1974. Asst. editor City Mag. of San Francisco, 1975-76; dep. editor opinion sect. Los Angeles Times, 1977-83; editor in chief New Republic Books The New Republic, N.Y.C., 1984-87; pub. Hill and Wang div. Farrar, Straus and Giroux Inc., N.Y.C., 1987-90, The Noonday Press div. Farrar, Straus and Giroux Inc., N.Y.C., 1987-90; editorial dir. Times Books divsn. Random House, N.Y.C., 1990—; cons. editor The Threepenny Rev., Berkeley, Calif., 1980-86, Tikkun, Oakland, Calif., 1986-90. Contbr. articles and revs. to mags. and newspapers. Mem. PEN. Office: Times Books/Random House 201 E 50th St New York NY 10022-7703

WASSERMAN, WALTER LEONARD, magnetics company executive; b. N.Y.C., Sept. 16, 1936; s. Soloman J. and Esther (Honigman) W.; m. Barbara Koenig, June 15, 1957 (div. 1973); children: Beth, Greg, Eli. BSEE, CUNY, 1957; MSEE, U. Pa., 1961, PhD in Bio Engring., 1964. Engring. supr. Hevey Mil. Electric GE, Syracuse, N.Y., 1958-60; engring. mgr. Philco Corp., Phila., 1960-65; v.p. bioengring. Hoffman-LaRoche, Nutley, N.J., 1965-67; pres. Health Tech. Corp., Moorestown, N.J., 1967-70; gen. mgr. Med. Data Systems, Dublin, Ireland, 1971-77; dir. mktg. El Scint (Israel), Inc., London, 1978-81; v.p. R&D Electro Biology, Inc., Parsippany, N.J., 1982-85; chief exec. officer Meditron Corp., Spring valley, N.Y., 1985-90, Modular Magnetics, New City, N.Y., 1990—; dir. dirs. Interpore Internat., Inc., Irvine, Calif., Theradyne, Inc., Salt Lake City, TriDyne, Inc., Salt Lake City. Contbr. articles to profl. jours.; patentee in field. Mem. Pres.'s Commn. for Handicapped, 1964. Capt. USAF, 1964-66, Vietnam. Recipient Gold medal Am. Assn. Rehab. Medicine, 1964. Democrat. Jewish. Avocations: stamp collecting, antiques. Office: Modular Magnetics Inc PO Box 119 New City NY 10956

WASSERMAN, WILLIAM PHILLIP, lawyer; b. Los Angeles, Sept. 13, 1945; s. Al and Ceil (Diamond) W.; married; children: Sam, George. BA, U. Calif., Berkeley, 1967; JD, U. Calif., 1970. Bar: Calif. 1971, U.S. Tax Ct. 1971. Ptnr. Loeb & Loeb, Los Angeles, 1970—; lectr. in field. field; participant in numerous programs, confs., and workshops in field in field. Mem. Editorial adv. bd.: Real Estate Taxation: A Practitioner's Guide, 1984—, Federal Tax Annual: Real Estate, 1982; contbr. numerous articles to profl. jours. Mem. ABA (nat. chmn Tax Sect. com. on real estate problems 1985-87), State Bar Calif., Los Angeles County Bar Assn., Calif. Bd. Legal Specialization (cert. taxation law specialist). Office: Loeb & Loeb 1000 Wilshire Blvd Ste 1800 Los Angeles CA 90017-2475

WASSERSPRING, FREDRIC R., securities trader; b. Bklyn., Jan. 12, 1947; s. Harold and Pearl W.; m. Barbara Grossman, Dec. 21, 1969; children: Karen, Amy. BS, U. R.I., 1969; MBA, NYU, 1970. CPA. Acct. Peat Marwick Mitchell, N.Y.C., 1970-74; v.p. Prudential-Bache Securities, N.Y.C., 1974-81; exec. v.p. Prudential-Bache Metal Co., Inc., N.Y.C., 1981-83, pres., 1983—; bus. Michael Anthony Jewelers. Trustee Village of Saddle Rock (N.Y.), 1986—. Office: Michael Anthony Jewelers Inc 115 S Macquesten Pky Mount Vernon NY 10550

WASSERSTEIN, BERNARD MANO JULIUS, historian; b. London, Jan. 22, 1948; came to U.S., 1980; s. Abraham and Margaret (Ecker) W.; m. Janet Barbara Sherrard, Nov. 29, 1981; 1 child, Charlotte Sophia. BA, Oxford U., 1969, MA, 1972, D.Phil., 1974. Rsch. fellow in politics Nuffield Coll. Oxford (Eng.) U., 1973-75, jr. lectr. politics Magdalen Coll., 1973, lectr. politics and internat. rels. Corpus Christi Coll., 1974-76; lectr. modern history U. Sheffield, Eng., 1976-80; assoc. prof. history Brandeis U., Waltham, Mass., 1980-82, prof. history, 1982—, dir. Tauber Inst., 1980-83, chmn. dept., 1986-90, dean grad. sch., 1992-99; vis. lectr. Hebrew U. of Jerusalem, 1979-80. Author: The British in Palestine, 1978, Britain and the Jews of Europe, 1939-45, 1979, The Secret Lives of Trebitsch Lincoln, 1988 (Golden Dagger award 1988), Herbert Samuel: A Political Life, 1992. Inst. for Advanced Studies fellow Hebrew U. of Jerusalem, 1984-85. Fellow Royal Hist. Soc.; mem. United Oxford Club, Cambridge Univs. Club, Athanaeum (London). Office: Brandeis U Dept of History Waltham MA 02254

WASSERSTEIN, BRUCE, investment banker; b. N.Y.C., Dec. 25, 1947; s. Morris and Lola Wasserstein; children: Pamela, Ben, Alex. BA with honors, U. Mich., 1967; MBA with high distinction, Harvard U., 1971, JD cum laude, 1971; diploma in law, Cambridge U., 1972. Assoc. Cravath, Swaine & Moore, N.Y.C., 1972-77; mng. dir. The First Boston Corp., N.Y.C., 1977-88; pres. Wasserstein, Perella and Co., NYC, 1988—. Author: Corporate Finance Law. Trustee Dalton Sch. Mem. Council on Fgn. Relations.

Democrat. Office: Wasserstein Perella & Co 31 W 52nd St 27th Fl New York NY 10019

WASSERSTEIN, WENDY, playwright; b. Bklyn., Oct. 18, 1950; d. Morris and Lola W. BA, Mt. Holyoke Coll., 1971; MA, CCNY, 1973; MFA, Yale Drama Sch., 1976. Author: (plays) Any Woman Can't, 1973, Happy Birthday, Montpelier Pizz-zazz, 1974, (with Christopher Durang) When Dinah Shore Ruled the Earth, 1975, Uncommon Women and Others, 1975, Isn't It Romantic, 1981, Tender Offer, 1983, The Man in a Case, 1986, Miami, 1986, The Heidi Chronicles, 1988 (Pulitzer prize for drama 1989, Outer Critics Circle award for best Broadway play 1989, Tony award for best play 1989, New York Drama Critics Circle award 1989, Susan Smith Blackburn prize 1989), The Sisters Rosensweig, 1993 (Outer Critics Circle award 1993); (essays) Bachelor Girls, 1990; (screenplays) Uncommon Women and Others, 1978, The Sorrows of Gin, 1979, (with Durang) House of Husbands, Isn't It Romantic, The Heidi Chronicles. Bd. dirs. Channel Thirteen MacDowell Colony, British Am. Arts. Assn. Am. Playwrights Project grantee, 1988, Brit.-Am. Arts Assn. grantee, Hale Matthews Found. award, Commissioning Program Phoenix Theater grantee, Guggenheim fellow, 1983. Mem. Coun. Dramatists Guild.

WASSHAUSEN, DIETER CARL, systematic botanist; b. Jena, Germany, Apr. 15, 1938; came to U.S., 1950, naturalized, 1957; s. Heinz P. and Elizabeth A. (Mueller) W.; m. Merrilee M. Locklin, Dec. 23, 1961; children—Lisa A., David B. B.S., George Washington U., 1962, M.S., 1965, Ph.D., 1972. Assoc. curator dept. botany Smithsonian Instn., Washington, 1969-76; chmn., curator dept. botany Nat. Mus. Natural History, Washington, 1976—. Recipient Smithsonian Research Found. awards, 1974, 75, Willdenow medal, 1979. Mem. Am. Soc. Plant Taxonomists, Internat. Assn. Plant Taxonomy, Neotropical Field Botanists Assn., Am. Inst. Biol. Scis., AAAS, Assn. Tropical Biology, Sigma Xi. Presbyterian. Research on systematics of neotropical Acanthaceae, floristic studies in Graminea of Brazil, floristic studies in Begoniaceae, revision of Nat. List Sci. Plant Names. Home: 9406 Chatteroy Pl Gaithersburg MD 20879-1424 Office: Nat Mus Natural History 10th St and Constitution Ave NW Washington DC 20560

WASSNER, STEVEN JOEL, pediatric nephrologist, educator; b. N.Y.C., Dec. 16, 1946; s. Abraham and Clara (Weitzner) W.; m. Enid K. Kling, June 11, 1972; children: Adam Jacob, Nancy Shane. B.S., CCNY, 1968; M.D., NYU, 1972. Diplomate Am. Bd. Pediatrics , Am. Bd. Pediatrics Nephrology. Intern, resident Children's Hosp. Los Angeles, 1972-74, fellow in pediatric nephrology, 1974-75; research fellow in pediatric nephrology U. Calif.-San Francisco, 1975-77; asst. prof. pediatrics Pa. State U. M.S. Hershey Med. Ctr., Hershey, 1978-83, assoc. prof. pediatrics, 1983-91, prof. pediatrics, 1991—, vice chmn. dept. pediatrics, 1990—, chief div. pediatrics nephrology, 1978—, chief div. pediatric diabetes, 1991—; vis. prof. human biochemistry Hebrew U., Hadassah Hosp., 1985-86; dir. Pediatric Diabetes Svc., 1988-91; bd. dirs. dialysis program for Pa. State U. students. Contbr. articles to med. jours. Mem. adv. bd. Kidney Found. S. Ctrl. Pa., Harrisburg, 1980—, sci. adv. coun. for pediatric nephrology/urology Nat. Kidney Found., 1986-92. Harrisburg com. for Hebrew U.; bd. dirs. Jewish Family Svc., Harrisburg, 1979-85, United Jewish Fedn., 1983-85, 94—, Yeshiva Acad., 1987-90. Recipient Rsch. Career Devel. award NIH, 1983; Musclar Dystrophy Assn. grantee, 1979-81; Sr. Internat. fellow Fogarty Internat. Ctr. NIH, 1985. Fellow Am. Acad. Pediatrics, Am. Bd. Pediatrics; mem. Soc. Pediatric Rsch., Am. Soc. Nephrology, Internat. Soc. Nephrology, Am. Soc. Pediatric Nephrology, Am. Physiol. Soc., Am. Diabetes Assn., Internat. Soc. Pediatric Nephrology, Internat. Pediatric Nephrology Assn. (counsellor 1989—). Office: MS Hershey Med Ctr PO Box 850 Hershey PA 17033-0850

WASSON, RICHARD HOWARD, English language educator; b. Chgo., Oct. 7, 1930; s. Robert Rock W. and Anna Hilbert Witt; m. Audrey Dohmeyer, 1956 (div. 1971); 1 child, Kristen Anna Wasson-Mirskin. BA, Cornell Coll., 1952; MA, U. Iowa, 1956; PhD, U. Wisc., 1962. Profl. Cert. English. Instr. U. W.Va., Morgantown, 1956-57; teaching asst. U. Wis., Madison, 1956-62; asst. prof. U. Ill., Champaign, Urbana, 1962-70; prof. Rutgers U., New Brunswick, N.J., 1970—; freshman com. dir. Rutgers U., 1977-81. Recipient Georgina Smith award for Creative and Disting. Leadership, 1992. Mem. AAUP (grievance chair 1987, 89, 92—, pres. New Brunswick chpt. 1990-93), MLA. Home: 61 Cleveland Ave Highland Park NJ 08904-1801 Office: English Dept Rutgers U New Brunswick NJ 08903

WATABE, NORIMITSU, biology and marine science educator; b. Kure, Hiroshima, Japan, Nov. 29, 1922; came to U.S., 1957; s. Isamu and Matsuko (Takamatsu) W.; m. Sakuko Kobayashi, Dec. 12, 1952; children: Shoichi, Sachiko. BS, 1st Nat. High Sch., Tokyo, 1945; MS, Tohoku U., Sendai, Japan, 1948, DSc, 1960. Rsch. investigator Fuji Pearl Co., Mie-ken, Japan, 1948-52; instr. Prefect U. Mie, Tsu, Mie-ken, Japan, 1952-55, asst. prof., 1955-59; rsch. assoc. Duke U., Durham, N.C., 1957-70; assoc. prof. U. S.C., Columbia, 1970-72, prof. biology, marine sci., 1972-93, disting. prof., 1993-94; disting. prof. emeritus, 1994—; dir. Electron Microscopy Ctr., 1970-95; cons. in field. Author: Studies on Pearls, 1959. Editor: Mechanisms of Mineralization, 1976; Mechanisms of Biomineralization, 1980, Hard Tissue Mineralization and Demineralization, 1991. Contbr. numerous sci. articles to profl. jours. Recipient Pearl Research award Elmer W. Ellsworth, 1952, Alexander Von Humboldt award Govt. of Germany, 1976, Russel award U. S.C., 1981; grantee NIH, 1971-76, NSF, 1973—. Fellow AAAS, Royal Micros. Soc. Gt. Britain; mem. Am. Micros. Soc. (rev. bd.), Am. Malacological Union (rev. bd.), Am. Soc. Zoologists, Electron Micros. Soc. Am. Avocations: music; piano playing. Home: 3510 Greenway Dr Columbia SC 29206-3416 Office: Electron Microscopy Ctr Univ S Carolina Columbia SC 29208

WATANABE, AUGUST MASARU, physician, scientist, medical educator, corporate executive; b. Portland, Oreg., Aug. 17, 1941; s. Frank H. and Mary Y. W.; m. Margaret Whildin Reese, Mar. 14, 1964; children: Nan Reiko, Todd Franklin, Scott Masaru. B.S., Wheaton (Ill.) Coll., 1963; M.D., Ind. U., 1967. Diplomate Am. Bd. Internal Medicine. Intern Ind. U. Med. Center, Indpls., 1967-68; resident Ind. U. Med. Center, 1968-69, 71-72; fellow in cardiology, 1972-74; clin. asso. NIH, 1969-71; clin. instr. medicine Georgetown U. Med. Sch., Washington, 1970-71; mem. faculty Ind. U. Sch. Medicine, Indpls., 1972—; prof. medicine and pharmacology, 1978—, chmn. dept. medicine, 1983-90; dir. Regenstrief Inst. for Health Care Ind. U. Sch. of Medicine, Indpls., 1984-90; v.p. Lilly Rsch. Labs. Eli Lilly & Co., Indpls., 1990-92, group v.p. Lilly Rsch. Labs., 1992-94, pres. labs, 1994—; v.p. Eli Lilly and Co., Indpls., 1994—, also bd. dirs., 1994—. Chmn. pharmacology study sect. NIH, 1979-81, chmn., 1981-83; mem. cardiovasc.-renal adv. com. FDA, 1982-85; mem. com. A, Nat. Heart, Lung and Blood Inst., 1984-88, chmn., 1986-88; cons. to fed. govt. and industry. Contbr. articles to profl. jours.; editorial bds. sci. jours. Served with USPHS, 1969-71. NIH grantee, 1972-92. Fellow ACP, Am. Coll. Cardiology, Am. Heart Assn. (councils on clin. cardiology and circulation, research rev. com. Ind. affiliate 1978-82, research and adv. com. North Central region 1978-82, adv. com. cardiovascular drugs 1976-79, chmn. com. 1979-81, chmn. program com. council on basic sci. 1982-84, chmn. com. on sci. sessions programs 1985-88, bd. dirs. 1985-88), Am. Coll. Cardiology (govt. relations com. 1979-81, trustee 1982-87); mem. Am. Fedn. Clin. Research (councilor Midwest sect. 1976-77, chmn.-elect Midwest sect. 1977-78, chmn. sect. 1978-79, chmn. sect. nominating com. 1979-80), Am. Soc. Clin. Investigation, Am. Soc. Clin. Pharmacology and Experimental Therapeutics, Am. Soc. Pharmacology and Exptl. Therapeutics (exec. com. div. clin. pharmacology 1978-81), Cardiac Muscle Soc., Central Soc. Clin. Research (councillor 1983-86, pres.-elect 1989, pres. 1990), Internat. Soc. Heart Research, Assn. Am. Physicians, Assn. Profs. of Medicine, Sigma Xi. Office: Eli Lilly & Co Drop Code 1209 Lilly Corp Ctr Indianapolis IN 46285

WATANABE, HIROSUKO, grain merchandising company executive. Pres., dir. Agrex Inc., Overland Park, Kans. Office: Agrex Inc 9300 110th St Ste 500 Shawnee Mission KS 66211-1524

WATANABE, KOUICHI, pharmacologist, educator; b. Manchuria, Japan, Aug. 26, 1942; s. Tetsuya and Mine W.; children: Toshikazu, Yoshihiro, Motohiro. BS, Tokyo Coll. Pharmacy, 1966; MS, Osaka U., 1968; PhD, 1971; LPIBA, 1986; DSc (hon.) Internat. U. Found., 1987, World U. Roundtable, 1988. Vis. fellow reprodn. rsch. br. Nat. Inst. Child Health and

WATANABE, KYOICHI A(LOYSIUS), chemist, researcher, pharmacology educator; b. Amagasaki, Hyogo, Japan, Feb. 28, 1935; s. Yujiro Paul and Yoshiko Francisca (Hashimoto) W.; m. Kikyoko Agatha Suzuki, Nov. 22, 1962; children: Kanna, Kay, Kenneth, Kim, Kelly, Katherine. BA, Hokkaido U., 1958, PhD, 1963. Lectr. Sophia U., Tokyo, 1963; rsch. assoc. Sloan-Kettering Inst., N.Y.C., 1963-66, assoc., 1968-72, assoc. mem., 1972-81, mem., prof., 1981—; rsch. fellow U. Alta., Edmonton, Can., 1966-68; assoc. prof. Cornell U. Med. Coll., N.Y.C., 1972-81, prof. pharmacology, 1981—; mem. study sect. NIH, Washington, 1981-84. Achievements include total synthesis of nucleoside antibiotics, novel heterocyle ring transformation, C-nucleose chemistry; antiviral and anticancer nucleosides; intercalating agents; modified oligonucleotides. Office: Sloan Kettering Inst 1275 York Ave New York NY 10021-6007

WATANABE, MAMORU, former university dean, physician, researcher; b. Vancouver, B.C., Can., Mar. 15, 1933; s. Takazo and Nao (Suginobu) W.; m. Marie Katie Bryndzak, June 1, 1974; 1 child, David. M.D., McGill U., 1957, Ph.D., 1963. Intern Royal Victoria Hosp., Montreal, 1957-58, resident in medicine, 1958-63; prof. medicine U. Alta., Edmonton, 1967-74; head internal medicine U. Calgary, Alta., 1974-76, assoc. dean edn., 1976-80, assoc. dean research, 1980-81, acting dean medicine, 1981-82, dean faculty medicine, 1982-92; med. staff Foothills Hosp., Calgary, 1974—. Fellow Royal Coll. Physicians and Surgeons (Can.); mem. Endocrine Soc., Can. soc. Clin. Investigation, Can. Soc. Endocrinology and Metabolism, Can. Hypertension Soc. Home: 162 Pumpridge Place SW, Calgary, AB Canada T2V 5B1 Office: U Calgary, 3330 Hospital Dr NW, Calgary, AB Canada T2N 1N4

WATANABE, RUTH TAIKO, music historian, library science educator; b. Los Angeles, May 12, 1916; d. Kohei and Iwa (Watanabe) W. B.Mus., U. So. Calif., 1937, A.B., 1939, A.M., 1941, M.Mus., 1942; postgrad., Eastman Sch. Music, Rochester, N.Y., 1942-46, Columbia U., 1947; Ph.D., U. Rochester, 1952. Dir. Sibley Music Library Eastman Sch. of Music, Rochester, N.Y., 1947-84; prof. music bibliography Eastman Sch. of Music, 1978-85, historian, archivist, 1984—; adj. prof. Sch. Library Sci. State U. Coll. at Geneseo, 1975-83; coordinator adult edn. program Rochester Civic Music Assn., 1963-75; mem. adv. com. Hochstein Music Sch.; lectr. on music, book reviewer, 1966—; program annotater Rochester Philharmonic Orch., 1959—. Author: Introduction to Music Research, 1967, Madrigali-II Verso, 1978; editor: Scribners New Music Library, Vols. 2, 5, 8, 1973, Treasury of Four Hand Piano Music, 1979; contbr. articles to profl. jours., contbr. symphony orchs. of U.S., 1986, internat. music jours.; modern music contbr. symphony orchs. of U.S., 1986, internat. music jours.; modern music librarianship, 1989; contbr. to Festschrift for Carleton Sprague Smith, 1989, De Mósica Hispana et aliis, 1990. Mem. overseers vis. com. Baxter Sch. Library Sci., Case Western Res. U., 1979-85, Alderman Book Com., 1986-89. Mem. ALA, AAUW (Pa.-Del. fellowship. 1949-50, 1st v.p. Rochester 1964-65, mem N.Y. state bd. 1965-66, mem. nat. com. on soc.'s reflection on arts 1967-69, nat. com. Am. fellowships awards 1969-74, br. pres. 1969-71, hon. co-chair Capital Fund Drive, 1986-88, Woman of Yr. award 1990), Internat. Assn. Music Libraries (2d v.p. commn. on conservatory libraries, commn. research libraries), Am. Musicol. Soc., Music Library Assn. (v.p. 1968-70, citation 1986, mem. editorial bd. 1967—, pres. 1979-81), Music Library Assn./Internat. Assn. Music Libraries (joint com., 1986-87), Civic Music Assn. Rochester, Riemenschneider Bach Inst. (hon.), Hanson Inst. Am. Music (bd. mem. 1981—), Univ. Club, Century Club, Phi Beta Kappa (pres. Iota chpt. of N.Y. 1969-71), Phi Kappa Phi, Mu Phi Epsilon (gen. chmn. nat. conv. 1956, nat. librarian 1958-60, recipient citation 1977, Ora Ashley Lambke award 1989), Pi Kappa Lambda (sec. 1978—, treas. 1980—), Delta Phi Alpha, Epsilon Phi, Delta Kappa Gamma (parliamentarian 1986-88). Home: 111 East Ave Apt 610 Rochester NY 14604-2539 Office: Eastman Sch Music Rochester NY 14604

WATANABE, TOSHIHARU, ecologist, educator; b. Kyoto, Japan, June 6, 1924; s. Seizo and Fusa Watanabe; m. Sumiko Isebo, Nov. 3, 1952; children: Ikuko, Naoki. DSc, Kyoto U., 1961. Prof. Nat. Kanazawa (Japan) U., 1972-75, Nat. (Japan) Women's U., 1975-88; prof. Fgn. Studies Kansai U., Hirakata/Osaka, Japan, 1988—; owner Diamond Resort Hawaii Owner's Club, 1989—; pres. Inst. Sci. Rsch. to Hydrospherical Ecology, 1990—. Author: Encyclopedia of Environmental Control Technology, 1990; editor: Japanese Jour. Diatomology, 1985, Japanese Jour. Water Treatment Biology, 1971. Profl. mem. Ministry of Constrn., Kinki dist., 1980—; vice-chmn. Com. on environ. pollution, Nara Prefecture and City, 1982—; com. mem. Wakayama, 1980—. Recipient Blue Ribbon Order of the Navy, 1961. Avocations: Indian ink drawing, music. Home: Higashigawa-cho 518, Shinkyogoku St Nakagyo-ku, Kyoto 604, Japan Office: Kansai U Fgn Studies, Kitakatahoko-cho 16-1, Hirakata Osaka 573, Japan

WATCHORN, WILLIAM ERNEST, diversified manufacturing executive; b. Toronto, Ont., Can., Aug. 8, 1943; s. Roy Elgin and Josephine (Swyrida) W.; m. Maureen Emmett, Dec. 28, 1967; 1 child, Meghan. Chartered Acct., Toronto, 1967. Mgr. fin. planning Found. Group of Cos., Toronto, 1968-70; cons. Pahang Tengarra Regional Master Planning Study, Malaysia, 1970-72; controller Selkirk Holdings, Ltd., Toronto, 1972-75; corp. contr. Torstar Corp., Toronto, 1975-78; v.p. fin. Canwest Capital Corp., Winnipeg, Man., 1978-82; exec. v.p. Kaiser Resources Ltd., Vancouver, B.C., 1982; sr. v.p., chief fin. officer Fed. Industries Ltd., Winnipeg, 1982-88; pres., chief exec. officer Fed. Industries Indsl. Group, Winnipeg, 1989-91, Ensis Corp., Inc., Winnipeg, 1991—; bd. dirs. Carte Internat. Inc., Ensis Corp., Inc., Heron Cable Industries Ltd., Infocorp Computer Solutions Ltd., Milltronics Ltd., Neo Industries S.A., Neo Europa S.A. Past chmn., bd. govs. Balmoral Hall Sch., Winnipeg; bd. dirs., vice chmn. western region com. C.D. Howe Inst., Toronto; bd. dirs., adv. bd. Vision Capital Fund; past exec. com. mem. Winnipeg 2000 Leaders Com.; dir. Can. Stds. Assn. Mem. Can. Inst. Chartered Accts., Man. Inst. Chartered Accts., B.C. Inst. Chartered Accts., Ont. Inst. Chartered Accts., Carleton Club, Winter Club. Avocations: squash, reading, travel, tennis. Home: 6453 Southboine Dr, Winnipeg, MB Canada R3R 0B7 Office: Ensis Corp Inc, Ste 1120/200 Graham Ave, Winnipeg, MB Canada R3C 4L5

WATERCUTTER, JACQUELINE A., health facility administrator; b. Dayton, Ohio, June 27, 1961; d. Francis E. and Leola J. (Meyer) Hoying; m. William E. Watercutter, Oct. 6, 1990; children: Alexandria Lee, Ashley Ann. BSN cum laude, Capital U., 1983; MS, Ohio State U., 1988. RN, Ohio. Order communication coord. Upper Valley Med. Ctr., Troy, Ohio. Mem. Sigma Theta Tau. Home: 101 Cliffton Dr Piqua OH 45356-4411

WATERFIELD, RANDOLPH HEARST, JR., accountant; b. Drexel Hill, Pa., Dec. 19, 1931; s. Randolph H. and Clara N. (Pontius) W.; m. Elizabeth Geistweit, Jan. 21, 1956; children: Adam D., Ellen. BS in Bus. Adminstrn., Drexel U., 1955. CPA, Pa. Staff acct. Ernst & Young, Phila., 1955-62; audit mgr. Arthur Young & Co., Phila., 1962-66, audit prin., 1966-68, ptnr., 1968-75; dir. east region acctg. and auditing Ernst & Young, N.Y.C. and Washington, 1975-85; office mng. ptnr. Ernst & Young, Washington, 1985-89; sr. ptnr. Arthur Young & Co., Washington, 1989—. Contbr. articles to profl. jours. Trustee Drexel U., Phila., 1983—; bd. dirs. Greater Washington Bd. Trade, 1988-89; corp. sponsors com. Washington Performing Arts Soc., Washington, 1987—. Mem. AICPA (chmn. ins. com. 1973-76, chmn. com. rels. with actuaries 1976-79), D.C. Inst. CPA's. Nat. Assn. Accts., Univ. Club, Washington Golf and Country Club, Pisces Club, Tower Club. Republican. Episcopal. Avocations: golf, fishing, art. Home: PO Box 921

Barnegat Light NJ 08006-0921 Office: Ernst & Young 1225 Connecticut Ave NW Washington DC 20036-2604

WATERFIELD, RICHARD DALLAS, bank executive, mortgage company executive; b. Ft. Wayne, Ind., Nov. 15, 1944; s. Richard Hobbs and Anne Kendrick (McGill) W.; m. Julie Ruth Rhinehart, July 6, 1968; children: Richard R., Richard R., Jill L. BA, Denison U., 1966; MBA, Northwestern U., 1968. V.p. Waterfield Mortgage, Ft. Wayne, 1972-76, exec. v.p., 1976-80, chmn., 1980—; chmn. Union Fed. Savs. Bank, Indpls., 1984—; bd. dirs. Ft. Wayne Nat. Bank, MSKTD Architects, Ft. Wayne. Bd. dirs. Ft. Wayne Downtown Coalition, 1980-83, Community Devel. Corp., 1978-84; mem. Mayors Task Force on Downtown Area, Ft. Wayne, 1985. Served as sgt. U.S. Army, 1968-74. Mem. Nat. Assn. Realtors, Young Pres. Orgn., Mortgage Bankers Assn., Ft. Wayne C. of C. (bd. dirs. 1985—). Presbyterian. Clubs: Ft. Wayne Country, Bus. Forum (dir. 1980, pres. 1981). Avocations: sports, travel. Office: Union Holding Co Inc 7500 W Jefferson Blvd Fort Wayne IN 46804-4131

WATERHOUSE, BLAKE E., health facility administrator; b. 1936. Physician Jackson Clinic, Madison, Wis., 1965-87, Physicians Plus Med. Group, Madison, 1987-90; with Straub Clinic Hosp. Inc., Honolulu, 1990—, pres., CEO. Office: Straub Clinic Hosp Inc 888 S King St Honolulu HI 96813*

WATERMAN, MICHAEL SPENCER, mathematics educator, biology educator; b. Coquille, Oreg., June 28, 1942; s. Ray S. and Bessie E. (Payne) W.; m. Vicki Lynn Buss, Aug. 14, 1962 (div. Mar. 1977); 1 child, Tracey Lynn. B.S., Oreg. State U., 1964, M.S., 1966; M.A., Mich. State U., 1968, Ph.D., 1969. Assoc. prof. Idaho State U., Pocatello, 1969-75; mem. staff Los Alamos Nat. Lab., 1975-82, cons., 1982—; USC Assocs. Endowed Chair U. So. Calif., L.A., prof. math. and biology, 1982—, U. So. Calif. Assocs. Endowed Chair, 1991—; vis. prof. math. U. Hawaii, Honolulu, 1979-80; vis. prof. structural biology U. Calif.-San Francisco, 1982; vis. prof. Mt. Sinai Med. Sch., N.Y.C., 1988. Editor: Mathematical Methods for DNA Sequences; assoc. editor Bull. Math. Biology; mem. editorial bd. Jour. Advances in Applied Math. jour., Molecular Phylongenetics adn Evolution, Genomics, Soc. for Indsl. and Applied Math. Jour. Applied MAth.; sr. editor: Jour. Computational Biology; contbr. numerous articles on amth., stats., biology to profl. jours., 1970—. Grantee NSF, 1971, 72, 75, Los Alamos Nat. Lab., 1976, 81, 88—; System Devel. Found., 1982-87, NIH, 1986—, Sloan Found., 1990-91. Fellow AAAS, Inst. Math. Stats; mem. Am. Statis. Assn., Soc. Math. Biology, Soc. Indsl. and Applied Math. Office: U So Calif Dept Math Los Angeles CA 90007

WATERS, BETTY LOU, newspaper reporter, writer; b. Texarkana, Tex., June 13, 1943; d. Chester Hinton and Una Erby (Walls) W.. AA, Texarkana Jr. Coll., 1963; BA, East Tex. State U., 1965. Gen. assignment reporter Galveston County Pub. Co., Galveston and Texas City, 1965-68; news and feature writer Ind. and Daily Mail, Anderson, S.C., 1968-69; reporter Citizen-Times newspaper, Asheville, N.C., 1969-74; edn. and med. reporter News Star World Pub. Co., Monroe, La., 1974-79; reporter, writer Delta Democrat Times, Greenville, Miss., 1980-89; staff writer Tyler (Tex.) Morning Telegraph, 1990—. Recipient 1st place award for articles La. Press Women's Contest, 1978, 1st place for interview, 1979; news media award N.C. Easter Seal Soc., 1973; 3d place award for feature writing Miss. Press Assn., 1984, for gen. news, 1983, for investigative reporting, 1988, 1st place for best series of articles, 1990; hon. mentions Tex. AP, 1966. Mem. Sigma Delta Chi.

WATERS, DANIEL W., electrical power industry executive. Exec. dir. So. Calif. Pub. Power Auth., Pasadena, Calif. Office: Southern Cal Pub Power Auth 200 S Los Robles Ave Pasadena CA 91101*

WATERS, DAVID ROGERS, retail executive; b. Akron, Ohio, Apr. 27, 1932; s. Herbert H. and Winifred Elsie (Kearns) W.; children: Ann S. Rohrbaugh, David Rogers, Thomas J., Peter M., Christopher C., Elizabeth E. Brewer, Jeffrey P. BS in Econs., U. Pa., 1954. Trainee, asst. to controller W.R. Grace & Co., N.Y.C., 1954-55; buyer M. O'Neil Co., Akron, 1957-62; div. mdse. mgr. May-Cohens, Jacksonville, Fla., 1962-66, Rich's, Atlanta, 1967; pres., gen. mdse. mgr. DePinna, N.Y.C., 1967-69; gen. mdse. mgr., then pres. Garfinckel's, Washington, 1969-73; pres., dir. Garfinckel, Brooks Bros., Miller & Rhoads, Inc., Washington, 1972-76, chmn., pres., CEO, 1976-81; chmn., dir. Frederick Atkins, Inc., 1980-81; pvt. practice cons., 1982-85, 90-92; exec. v.p., mem. mgmt. policy com., pres. Splty Retailing Group Gen Mills., Inc., 1985-88; chmn., dir., chief exec. officer Joseph A. Bank Clothiers, Inc., 1988-90; founder, pres., dir. Douglass & Waters, Inc., 1992-94; cons. DLJ Capital Corp., 1984-85; 1st vice-chmn. Nat. Retail Mchts. Assn., 1980-81; bd. dirs. Findings, Inc. Served with U.S. Army, 1955-57.

WATERS, DONALD JOSEPH, information services administrator; b. Balt., Sept. 16, 1952; s. Richard Hunter and Annette Catharine (Hannan) W.; m. Beverly Ann Brent, Apr. 5, 1974; children: Laura Elizabeth, Sarah Elizabeth. BA, U. Md., 1973; M Phil, Yale U., 1976, PhD, 1982. Resource specialist Yale Computer Ctr., New Haven, 1982-84; dir. computer services Yale Sch. Mgmt., New Haven, 1984-87; head, systems office Yale U. Library, New Haven, 1987-92, dir., libr. and adminstrv. systems, 1992-93, assoc. univ. librarian, 1993—. Author: Strange Ways and Sweet Dreams: Afro-American Folklore From the Hampton Institute, 1983. Mem. AAAS, ALA, Am. Soc. Info. Sci. Roman Catholic. Avocations: jazz, rowing, cabinet making. Home: 40 Overbrook Rd Madison CT 06443-1834 Office: Yale U Libr 120 High St New Haven CT 06520-8240

WATERS, GEORGE BAUSCH, newspaper publisher; b. Syracuse, N.Y., July 4, 1920; s. Louis Addison and Mildred Elaine (Bausch) W.; m. Shirley Kessinger Barnard, Sept. 23, 1943; children: Peter, Stephen, Nancy, Kristin, Dean. BA, Syracuse U., 1943. With Rome (N.Y.) Sentinel Co. Pub., 1947—, asst. gen. mgr., 1954-60, gen. mgr., 1960-66, pub., 1966-93, pres., 1993—; bd. dirs. N.Y. State Photonics Devel. Corp. Chmn. Rome Art and Community Ctr., 1967-85; trustee Stevens Kingsley Found., N.Y.C., 1966—, Kirkland Coll., Clinton, N.Y., 1973-79, Utica Coll. Syracuse U., Utica, 1963-78; past mem. Rome Bd. Edn., Rome Hosp.; bd. dirs. Cen. Assn. Blind. Capt. inf. U.S. Army, 1943-47, ETO. Mem. Am. Newspaper Pubs. Assn., N.Y. State Newspaper Pubs. Assn., N.Y. State Associated Dailies (pres. 1974), Am. Soc. Newspaper Editors, Jervis Libr. Assn. (pres. 1959-65), Soc. Profl. Journalists, Ft. Schuyler Club, Yale Club, Washington Press Club, Delta Kappa Epsilon. Republican. Presbyterian. Office: Rome Sentinel Co 333 W Dominick St Rome NY 13440-5701

WATERS, H. FRANKLIN, federal judge; b. Hackett, Ark., July 20, 1932; s. William A. and Wilma W.; m. Janie C. Waters, May 31, 1958; children—Carolyn Denise, Melanie Jane, Melissa Ann. B.S., U. Ark., 1955; LL.B., St. Louis U., 1964. Engr., atty. Ralston-Purina Co., St. Louis, 1958-66; ptnr. Crouch, Blair, Cypert & Waters, 1967-81; judge U.S. Dist. Ct. (we. dist.) Ark., from 1981, now chief judge. Former bd. govs. Washington Regional Med. Ctr. Mem. ABA, Ark. Bar Assn., Springdale C. of C. (past bd. dirs.). Office: US Dist Ct PO Box 1908 Fayetteville AR 72702-1908

WATERS, JAMES LOGAN, analytical instrument manufacturing executive; b. Lincoln, Nebr., Oct. 7, 1925; s. Leland L. and Marian L. (Yungblut) W.; m. Faith Cabot Pigors, Sept. 11, 1948; children: Richard Cabot, Barbara Faith. B.S., Columbia U., 1946; DSc (hon.), Northeastern U., 1993. Project mgr. Baird Assocs., Inc., Cambridge, Mass., 1947; founder, pres. James L. Waters, Inc., Framingham, Mass., 1947-58, Waters Assocs., Inc., Milford, Mass., 1957-82; chmn. bd. Waters Assocs., Inc., 1972-80; founder, pres. Waters Bus. Systems, Inc., Framingham, 1978—; bd. dirs. Markem Corp., Keene, N.H., Transtek Corp., Ellington, Conn. Mem. Framingham Town Meeting, 1952-61; mem. Framingham Sch. Com., 1961-70, chmn., 1962, 64; trustee Babson Coll., Wellesley, Mass., 1979-85; founder, trustee Waters Found., 1955—; trustee Northeastern U., 1984—. Served as ensign USNR, 1943-46. Mem. Tau Beta Pi. Patentee in field. Home: 1153 Grove St Framingham MA 01701-3701 Office: New York Ave Framingham MA 01701

WATERS, JENNIFER NASH, lawyer; b. Bridgeport, Conn., Dec. 21, 1951; d. Lewis William and Patricia (Cousins) W.; m. Todd David Peterson, Sept. 19, 1981; children: Elizabeth, Andrew. BA, Radcliffe, 1972; JD, Harvard, 1976. Bar: D.C. 1977, U.S. Supreme Ct. 1980. Clk. U.S. Ct. Appeals (D.C. cir.), Washington, 1976-77; assoc. Jones, Day, Reavis & Poque, Washington, 1977-79; assoc. Crowell & Moring, Washington, 1979-83, ptnr., 1983—. Mem. Fed. Energy Bar Assn. (bd. dirs. 1988-94, v.p. 1994-95, pres.-elect 1995—). Office: Crowell & Moring 1001 Pennsylvania Ave NW Washington DC 20004-2505

WATERS, JOHN, film director, writer, actor; b. Balt., Apr. 22, 1946; s. John Samuel and Patricia Ann (Whitaker) W. Student, NYU, 1966. Speaker various colls., comedy clubs, U.S., Europe, Australia, 1968—. Writer, dir. films Roman Candles, 1966, Eat Your Makeup, 1968, Mondo Trasho, 1969, Multiple Maniacs, 1970, Pink Flamingos, 1972, Female Trouble, 1974, Desperate Living, 1977, Polyester, 1981, Cry-Baby, 1990, Serial Mom, 1994; writer, dir., actor film Hairspray, 1987; actor Something Wild, 1988, Homer and Eddie, 1990, (TV show) 21 Jump Street, 1990; author: Shock Value, 1981, Crackpot, 1986, Trash Trio, 1988; contbr. articles to N.Y. Times, Am. Film, other mags. Fund raiser AIDS Action Balt.; spokesperson Anti-Violence Campaign, N.Y.C., 1991. John Waters Day named in his honor State of Md., 1985; John Waters Week named in his honor City of Balt., 1988. Mem. AFTRA, SAG, Dirs. Guild Am., Writers Guild Am., Acad. Motion Picture Arts and Scis. Avocation: study of extreme Catholic behavior before the Reformation. *

WATERS, JOHN B., lawyer; b. Sevierville, Tenn., July 15, 1929; s. J. B. and Myrtle (Paine) W.; m. Patsy Temple, Apr. 8, 1953; children: John B., Cynthia Beth. BS, U. Tenn., 1952, JD, 1961, D in Environ. Sci. (hon.), Milligan Coll., 1993. Bar: Tenn. 1961, U.S. Dist. Ct. (ea. dist.) Tenn. 1961, U.S. Dist. Ct. D.C. 1970, U.S. Supreme Ct. 1969. Mem. hearing com. Bd. Profl. Responsibility, Supreme Ct., 1974-80 Fed. co-chmn. Appalachian Regional Commn., 1969-71; chmn. Sevier County Indsl. Bd., Sevierville Library Found.; mem. Gov.'s Com. Econ. Devel.; Tenn. rep. to So. Growth Policies Bd., 1970-74; appointed dir. by Pres. Reagan Tenn. Valley Authority, Knoxville, 1984, appointed chmn. bd. dirs. by Pres. Bush 1992; trustee East Tenn. Baptist Hosp., Knoxville; mem. Tenn.-Tombigbee Waterway Authority, 1978-84; bd. dirs. Inst. of Nuclear Power Ops., 1985. Lt. USN, 1952-55. Fellow Am. Bar Found., Am. Coll. Probate Counsel; mem. Tenn. Bar Assn. (pres. 1983-84), Sevier County Bar Assn. (past pres.); mem. bd. Met. Knoxville Airport Authority. Republican. Baptist. Home: 405 Burridge Waters Edge Sevierville TN 37862 Office: Long Ragsdale & Waters PC PO Box 90384 Knoxville TN 37990-0384 also: 119 Commerce St Sevierville TN 37862-3524

WATERS, JOHN W, minister, educator; b. Atlanta, Feb. 5, 1936; s. Henry and Mary Annie (Randall) W. Cert., U. Geneva, Switzerland, 1962; BA, Fisk U., 1957; STB, Boston U., 1967, PhD, 1970. Ordained to ministry Bapt. Ch., 1967. Min. religious edn. Ebenezer Bapt. Ch., Boston, 1965-67, assoc. min., 1967-69; min. Myrtle Bapt. Ch., West Newton, Mass., 1969, Greater Solid Rock Bapt. Ch., Atlanta, 1981—; prof. Interdenominational Theol. Ctr. , Atlanta, 1976-86, trustee, 1980-83; bd. dirs. Habitat for Humanities, Atlanta, 1984-90; chmn. South Atlanta Joint Urban Ministries, 1983-93. Contbr. articles to profl. jours. Mem. Va. Highlands Neighborhood Assn., Atlanta, 1977-87, Butler St. YMCA, 1980-86, South Atlanta Civic League, 1983, others; treas. Prison Ministries with Women, Inc.; v.p. South Met. Ministries Fellowahip, Atlanta, 1990-94. Fund for Theol. Edn. fellow, 1965-67, Nat. Fellowship Fund fellow, 1968-70, Rockefeller doctoral fellow, 1969. Mem. AAUP (chpt. pres. 1971-72), Am. Acad. Religion, Soc. Bibl. Lit., Blacks in Bibl. Studies, New Era Missionary Bapt. Conv. Ga. Democrat. Home: 1516 Niskey Lake Trl SW Atlanta GA 30331-6318 Office: The Greater Solid Rock Bapt Ch 6280 Camp Rd Riverdale GA 30296-2803 *In life, each of us faces a variety of choices. The choices made determine our destiny, fate. When more of us assume responsibility and accountability for the choices made, the world in which we live will be decisively better.*

WATERS, LAUGHLIN EDWARD, federal judge; b. L.A., Aug. 16, 1914; s. Frank J. and Ida (Bauman) W.; m. Voula Davanis, Aug. 22, 1953; children: Laughlin Edward, Maura Kathleen, Deirdre Mary, Megan Ann, Eileen Brigid. A.B., UCLA, 1939; J.D., U. So. Calif., 1946. Bar: Calif. 1946. Dep. atty. gen. Calif., Los Angeles, 1946-47; individual practice law Los Angeles, 1947-53; sr. ptnr. Nossaman, Waters, Krueger & Marsh, 1961-76; U.S. atty. So. Dist. Calif., 1953-61; judge U.S. Dist. Ct. (cen. dist.) Calif., 1976—; cons. U.S. Dept. State in London, 1970; mem. U.S. Del. to Conf. Environ. Problems in Prague, 1971, White House Conf. on Aging, 1970-71; sr. dist. judge rep. Jud. Coun.; judge Atty Gen.'s Adv. Inst. Mem. Calif. Legislature, 1946-53; vice chmn. Rep. State Ctrl. Com., 1950-51, chmn., 1952-53; bd. dirs. Legal Aid Found., 1954-60; past pres. Cath. Big Brothers. Served as capt. U.S. Army, 1942-46. Decorated Bronze Star with oak leaf cluster, Purple Heart with oak leaf cluster, Combat Inf. badge. Fellow Am. Bar Found., Am. Coll. Trial Lawyers; mem. ABA (chmn. com. on housing and urban devel. 1977-79), Am. Judicature Soc., Assn. Bus. Trial Lawyers, U. So. Calif., UCLA Law Assn., Am. Legion, U. So. Calif. Legion Lex, Order Blue Shield, Town Hall, Polish Order Merit Cross with Swords, Hon. Citizen of Chambois, Trun, France, 10th Polish Dragons (hon.), Soc. Friendly Sons St. Patrick (past pres., Medallion of Merit award), Knights of Malta, Anchor Club, Calif. Club. Roman Catholic. Office: US Dist Ct 255 E Temple St Los Angeles CA 90012-3334

WATERS, M. JEAN, mortgage company executive; b. 1945. With Waters Mortgage Co., Ft. Lauderdale, Fla., 1976—, pres. Office: Waters Mortgage Corp 6190 NW 11th St Fort Lauderdale FL 33313*

WATERS, MAXINE, congresswoman; b. St. Louis, Aug. 15, 1938; d. Remus and Velma (Moore) Carr; m. Sidney Williams, July 23, 1977; children: Edward, Karen. Grad. in sociology Calif. State U., L.A.; hon. doctorates, Spelman Coll., N.C. Agrl. & Tech. State U., Morgan State U. Former tchr. Head Start; mem. Calif. Assembly from dist. 48, 1976-91, Dem. caucus chair, 1984; mem. 102nd-104th Congresses from Dist. 35, Calif. 1991—; mem. Banking, Fin., Urban Affairs com., Ho. subcom. on banking, capitol subcom. on banking, employment and tng. subcom. on vets., veterans affairs com. Mem. Dem. Nat. Com. Dem. Congrl. Campaign com.; del. Dem. Nat. Conv., 1972, 76, 80, 84, 88, 92, mem. rules com. 1984; mem. Nat. Adv. Com. for Women, 1978—; bd. dirs. TransAfrica Found., Nat. Women's Polit. Caucus, Ctr. Nat. Policy, Clara Elizabeth Jackson Carter Found. Spellman Coll., Nat. Minority AIDS Project, Women for a Meaningful Summit, Nat. Coun. Negro Women, Black Women's Agenda; founder Black Women's Forum. Office: US Ho of Reps 330 Cannon HOB Washington DC 20515

WATERS, MICHAEL COOPER, medical center and development corporation executive; b. Cisco, Tex., Oct. 29, 1942; m. Kathy Street, Apr. 17, 1976; children: Tiffany, Allison. Student, Baylor U., 1961-63; B.S., Lamar U., 1965; M.S., U. Pitts., 1967. Adminstrv. resident U. Tex. Med. Branch Hosp., Galveston, 1966-67; v.p. Meml. Hosp. System, Houston, 1969-78; exec. dir. Bapt. Meml. Hosp., Kansas City, Mo., 1978-80; pres. Hendrick Med. Ctr., Hendrick Med. Devel. Corp., Abilene, Tex., 1980—; dir. First Nat. Bank of Abilene. Bd. dirs. United Healthcare Systems, Kansas City; bd. dirs. Hospice of Abilene, 1981—, Hosp. Receivables, Carrollton, Tex., 1983—, United Way, Abilene, Pastoral Care and Counseling Ctr., 1981—. Served to lt. USPHS, 1967-69. Recipient W.F. Yates medallion William Jewell Coll., Liberty Mo., 1980. Mem. Am. Hosp. Assn., Am. Protestant Hosp. Assn. (bd. dirs. 1983—), Tex. Hosp. Assn. (chmn. Forts and Pecos div. 1983-84), Tex. Asn. Hosp. Auxs. (chmn. 1982-83), Abilene C. of C. (pres. 1986-87), Tex. Hosp. Assns. Bd. (treas. 1985-86, vice chmn. bd. dirs. 1986-87), Bapt. Hosp. Assn. (pres. 1985-87). Republican. Am. Baptist. Club: Abilene Kiwanis. Home: 2713 Southwest Dr Apt 208 Abilene TX 79605-6517 Office: Hendrick Med Ctr 1242 N 19th St Abilene TX 79601-2316

WATERS, RICHARD, retired publishing company executive; b. Sterling, Mass., May 13, 1926; s. Sherman Hoar and Viola (Arnold) W.; m. June Hollweg Dorer, Aug. 27, 1949; children: Karl (dec.), Kurt, Kris. B.A., Hobart Coll., 1950, LL.D. hon., 1970; M.B.A., Harvard U., 1951. Assoc. acct. Hunter & Weldon, N.Y.C., 1953-55; exec. v.p., chief fin. officer

Reader's Digest Assn., Pleasantville, N.Y., 1955-77; assoc. dean Harvard U. Bus. Sch., Boston, 1977-81; pres., chief exec. officer Sporting News, St. Louis, 1981-90, ret., 1990; bd. dirs. Republic Bank for Savs. (formerly Manhattan Savs. Bank), N.Y.C., Republic Nat. Bank, N.Y.C. Trustee Hobart Coll., 1971-91, William Smith Coll., 1971-91; regional v.p. Associated Industries N.Y. State, Albany, 1965-79; chmn. bd. Westchester Heart Assn., Port Chester, N.Y., 1975-76; bd. dirs. vice-chmn. Gateway chpt. Nat. Multiple Sclerosis Soc., 1991—. With USN, 1944-46, PTO; 1st lt. USAF, 1951-53. Mem. Nat. Assn. Pub. Accts.; mem Baseball Writers Assn. Am. Republican. Clubs: Old Warson Country; University (St. Louis); Sky (N.Y.C.). Home: 20 Somerset Downs Saint Louis MO 63124-1007

WATERS, RICHARD W., SR., mortgage company executive; b. 1943. With Dade County Sch. Bd., Miami, Fla., 1964-71, Waters Mortgage Investment Co., Ft. Lauderdale, Fla., 1971-76, Cmty. Mortgage Corp., Ft. Lauderdale, 1977-78; with Waters Mortgage Corp., Ft. Lauderdale, 1976—, chmn. bd. dirs. Office: Waters Mortgage Corp 6190 NW 11th St Fort Lauderdale FL 33313*

WATERS, ROGER, rock musician; b. Cambridge, England, Sept. 6, 1947. Bassist Sigma-6, T-Set, Megga Death, Screaming Abdabs, Pink FLoyd Sound, Pink Floyd, 1964-86; solo musician, 1987—. Albums include Music from the Body, 1970, The Pros & Cons of Hitchhiking, 1986, Radio KAOS, 1987, The Wall: Berlin 1990, 1990, Amused to Death, 1992; (with Pink Floyd) Piper at the Gates of Dawn, 1967, More, 1969, Atom Heart Mother, 1970, Relics, 1971, Darkside of the Moon, 1973, Wish You Were Here, 1976, The FInal Cut, 1983, A Collection of Great Dance Songs, 1994, The Division Bell, 1994.;. *

WATERS, RONALD W., church executive, pastor; b. Kokomo, Ind., July 23, 1951; s. Ronald Lee and Carolyn Elizabeth (Myers) W.; m. Norma Lee Grumbling Waters, June 16, 1973; 1 child, Melinda Ronee Waters. BA magna cum laude, Ashland (Ohio) Coll., 1973; MA in Comms. with high honors, Wheaton (Ill.) Coll., 1975; MDiv with high honors, Ashland (Ohio) Theol. Seminary, 1985; postgrad., Asbury Theol. Seminary, Wilmore, Ky., 1993—. Ordained elder Brethren Ch., 1986; lic. minister, 1985-86. Asst. to dir. Bd. of Christian Edn. The Brethren Ch., Ashland, Ohio, 1971-74; mng. editor of publs. Brethren Pub. Co., Ashland, Ohio, 1975-78, asst. to dir. and gen. mngr., 1978-80, exec. dir., 1980-82; dir. of Denom. Bus. The Brethren Ch. Nat. Office, Ashland, Ohio, 1982-84; cons. in mgmt. and computer applications, 1984-85; pastor Mt. Olive Brethren Ch., McGaheyville, Va., 1985-89; dir. Brethren Ch. Ministries The Brethren Ch. Nat. Office, Ashland, Ohio, 1989—; bd. dirs. corp. sec. Brethren Printing Co., Ashland, Ohio, 1989—; mission bd. Brethren Ch. Southeastern Dist., 1987-89; Gen. Conf. Brethren Ch., Statement of Faith Task Force, 1981-84, Polity Com., 1986-91; bd. reference, congl. adv. The Andrew Ctr., Elgin, Ill., 1994—; founder, tchr. Young Adult Sunday Sch. Class, Park St. Brethren Ch., Ashland, Ohio, 1990-93; Seminary Adv. Com., Ashland Theol. Seminary, 1990—; mem. Evangelism Mgmt. Team, Elgin, Ill., 1992—; spkr. in field. Author: Promise for the Future, 1993, Leader's Manual for Inviting and Welcoming New People, 1995; editor: The Brethren Evangelist mag., 1975-78; editl. asst.: New Beginnings mag., 1995—; contbr. numerous articles to religious jours. Adv. coun. World Relief Corp., Wheaton, Ill., 1990-92. Mem. Am. Soc. Ch. Growth, Nat. Assn. Brethren Ch. Elders, Nat. Assn. Evangs., Nat. Christian Edn. Assn., Evang. Press Assn., Denom. Prayer Leaders Network. Avocations: gardening. Office: The Brethren Ch Nat Office 524 College Ave Ashland OH 44805

WATERS, STEPHEN RUSSELL, state agency administrator; b. Quincy, Ill., Jan. 9, 1954; s. Russell O. and Dorothy Ann (Bartz) W.; m. Nancy K. Morris, Aug. 31, 1974; children: Leslie Ann, Ryan Patrick. BS in Law Enforcement, N.E. Mo. State, 1976. Police officer City of Kirksville, Mo., 1975; adminstrv. asst. to speaker pro-tem Mo. House of Reps., Jefferson City, 1976; investment counselor IDS Mktg., Dubuque, Iowa, 1977-78; dir. legal svcs. Mark Twain Legal Svcs., Canton, Mo., 1978-80; probation and parole officer State of Mo., Hannibal, 1980-84; juvenile officer 2d Jud. Cir., Edina, Mo., 1984-86; rep. Mo. Ho. of Reps., Canton, 1987-94; dir. Mo. Divsn. Transp. Dept. Econ. Devel., Jefferson City, 1994—. Chmn. parks City of Canton, 1980-82; alderman City of Canton, 1980-84. Mem. Am. Corrections Assn., Mo. Corrections Assn., N.E. Mo. Peace Officers, Moose, Kiwanis (bd. dirs. Canton chpt. 1979-80), Canton C. of C. (pres. 1979-82). Democrat. Mem. Christian Ch. Avocation: golf. Office: Mo Divsn Transp Dept Econ Devel PO Box 1216 Jefferson City MO 65101

WATERS, SYLVIA, dance company artistic director. Prin. dance Alvin Ailey Am. Dance Theater, N.Y.C.; artistic dir. Alvin Ailey Repertory Ensemble, N.Y.C., 1974—. Office: Alvin Ailey Repertory Ensemble 1515 Broadway New York NY 10036-5702*

WATERS, TIMOTHY J., lawyer; b. Santa Rosa, Calif., Apr. 18, 1943. BS, U. San Francisco, 1965; JD with honors, George Washington U., 1968. Bar: Va. 1968, D.C. 1973. Atty. FTC, Washington, 1968-73, asst. to dir. Bur. Competition, 1971, asst. to chmn., 1972; ptnr. McDermott, Will & Emory, Washington. Mem. D.C. Bar, Va. State Bar. Office: McDermott Will & Emory 1850 K St NW Washington DC 20006-2296

WATERS, WILL ESTEL, horticulturist, researcher, educator; b. Smithtown, Ky., Sept. 19, 1931; m. Elizabeth Sumler; children: Marie, Alan, Sheila. BS in Agronomy, U. Ky., 1954, MS in Soil Physics, 1958; PhD in Plant Nutrition, Vegetable Crops, U. Fla., 1960. Asst. prof. floricultural rsch. Gulf Coast Rsch. & Edn. Ctr., Bradenton, Fla., 1960-66; assoc. prof. ornamental horticulture Gulf Coast Experiment Sta., Bradenton, Fla., 1966-70; prof., horticulturist head Ridge Ornamental Hort. Lab., Apopka, Fla., 1968-70; prof., dir. Gulf Coast Rsch. & Edn. Ctr., Bradenton, 1970—; designer staff, equipment and programs, supr. devel. Agrl. Rsch. & Edn. Ctr. at Apopka, 1967-70; dir. Gulf Coast Rsch. & Edn. Ctr. at Dover, Fla., 1971—; dir. Agrl. Rsch. & Edn. Ctr. at Immokalee, Fla., 1971-86; author, supr. 4 fed. grants Gulf Coast Rsch. & Edn. Ctr., established MS and PhD coop. tng. programs and periodic formal undergrad. courses. Contbr. over 350 sci., tech. and popular articles to profl. jours. Named Ky. Col., Gov. Wendell Ford, 1972; recipient Appreciation award Fla. Flower Assn., 1978; named to Manatee County Agrl. Hall of Fame, 1988. Fellow Am. Soc. Hort. Sci. (Alex Laurie award 1968); mem. Soc. Am. Florists, So. Weed Conf., Soc. Region Am. Soc. Hort. Sci. (Leadership and Adminstrn. award 1990), Fla. Soil and Crop Sci. Soc., Fla. State Hort. Soc. (Outstanding Rsch. Paper award ornamental sect. 1967, Presdl. Gold Medal award 1968, sectional v.p. 1969), Fla. Ornamental Growers Assn. (Rsch. & Edn. award 1986), Fla. Nurserymen and Growers Assn. (Disting. Svc. award Manasota chpt. 1977, Outstanding Industry Person award 1981), Fla. Farm Bureau, Fla. Foliage Assn., Fla. Strawberry Growers Assn., Interamerican Soc. Tropical Horticulture. Achievements include development of horticultural production and handling recommendations in plant nutrition, growing media, soil and water chemistry, herbicides, post harvest keeping quality, and cultivar evaluations of primary flower, foliage and vegetable crops. Office: Gulf Coast Rsch & Ednl Ctr 5007-60th St E Bradenton FL 34203

WATERS, WILLIAM FRANCIS, financial services executive; b. Ithaca, N.Y., Apr. 1, 1932; s. William John and Helen (Lovelock) W.; m. Jane Collins, Sept. 28, 1957; children: Victoria, Anthony, Maria, Ned. AB in Econs., Cornel U., 1954, MBA in Fin., 1955; LLB, NYU, 1962. Bar: N.Y. 1962. With Merrill Lynch, N.Y.C., 1957—, CEO internat. pvt. banking group. Mem. Hatherly Country Club, Sheraton Steamboat Golf Club, Wee Burn Country Club, Killington (Vt.) Ski Club (pres. 1981-84). Office: Merrill Lynch World Financial Ctr 250 Vesey St New York NY 10281-1318

WATERS, WILLIE ANTHONY, opera and orchestra conductor; b. Goulds, Fla., Oct. 11, 1951. BMus, U Miami, 1973; postgrad., Memphis State U. Music dir. Greater Miami (Fla.) Opera, 1983-84, artistic dir. 1984-92, prin. condr., 1992-95; music dir. San Antonio Festival, 1983-85; guest condr. Detroit Symphony, Indpls. Orch., Norwegian Radio Orch., Philharm. Orch., Essen Philharm., Bavarian Radio Orch., Baden-Baden Radio Orch., Cologne Opera. Condr. San Diego Opera, Mich. Opera Theatre, Conn. Opera, San Francisco Opera, Australian Opera, Sydney, Ópera De Montréal; conducted Otello, Salome, Die Walkure, Bianca e Falliero (U.S. premiere), other operas; appeared in concert with Detroit Symphony,

Norwegian Radio Orch., Fla. Philharm., Dayton Philharm., Brucknerhaus Orch., Linz, Austria; rec. Philips Co. Recipient Prix de Martell, 1991.

WATERSTON, SAMUEL ATKINSON, actor; b. Cambridge, Mass., Nov. 15, 1940; s. George Chychele and Alice Tucker (Atkinson) W.; m. Lynn Louisa Woodruff, Jan. 26, 1976; children: Graham C., Elisabeth P., Katherine B.; child by previous marriage: James S. B.A., Yale U., 1962; student, Sorbonne, Paris, 1960-61. Theatrical appearances include: Indians, Oh Dad Poor Dad, Halfway Up the Tree, Lunch Hour, Hamlet, The Tempest, Measure for Measure, Much Ado About Nothing (recipient Obie, Drama Desk awards), Benefactors, 1986, A Walk in the Woods, 1988, Abe Lincoln in Illinois, 1993, Shakespeare & Szekspir, 1994; film appearances include: The Great Gatsby, 1975, Rancho Deluxe, 1976, Capricorn One, 1978, Interiors, 1978, Sweet William, 1978, Heaven's Gate, 1979, Eagle's Wing, 1983, The Killing Fields, 1984, Warning Sign, 1985, Savages, Hopscotch, 1980, Hannah and Her Sisters, 1986, Just Between Friends, 1986, The Devil's Paradise, September, 1987, Welcome Home, 1989, The Man in the moon, 1991, Mindwalk, 1991, Serial Mom, 1994; TV films include: Much Ado About Nothing, 1974, The Glass Menagerie, 1975, Diabolique, 1975, Friendly Fire, 1978, Oppenheimer, 1982, Q.E.D., 1982, Terrorist on Trial: The United States vs. Salim Ajami; TV miniseries appearance: Gore Vidal's Lincoln, 1988; regular TV series I'll Fly Away, NBC-TV, 1991-93 (Emmy award nomination, Lead actor, Drama, 1993), I'll Fly Away: Then and Now, PBS, 1993 (Emmy nomination, Lead Actor - Special, 1994), Law and Order. 1994—. Mem. Actors Equity Assn., Screen Actors Guild, AFTRA. Office: care Addis/Wechsler & Assocs 955 S Carrillo Dr 3rd Fl Los Angeles CA 90048*

WATERSTON, WILLIAM KING, minister, educator, academic administrator; b. Elizabeth, N.J., Feb. 12, 1937; s. John Robert and Sylvia (Eadie) W.; m. Judith Jane Schramm, Aug. 29, 1959; children: John Scott, Gregory Glenn, Robert Ormsby; m. Kathryn Larsen, Dec. 17, 1983; 1 child, Chad. AB, Bates Coll., 1959; BD, Eastern Bapt. Sem., 1962, M.Div., 1973. Ordained to ministry Am. Bapt. Chs. USA, 1962. Bus. mgr., editorial asst. Missions Mag., 1962-66, Crusader Mag., 1964-66; assoc. dir. radio and TV Am. Bapt. Chs. USA, 1966-69, dir. electronic media, 1969-72; host Dialogue TV Show, Phila., 1969-85; assoc. dir. communications div. Am. Bapt. Chs. USA, 1972-73; Parker Ford Bapt. Ch., 1973-81; dir. group homes ch. rels. devel. Bapt. Children's Svcs., Phila., 1981-92; sr. minister First Bapt. Warren, Warren, Pa., 1992—; pres. Warren County Ministerium, 1992—; instr. Eastern Bapt. Coll., 1973-85, Eastern Bapt. Sem., 1970-85. Editor Mediathink, 1973. Lodge: Rotary (pres. Cen. Perkiomen 1968). Home: 6 Jennie Ln Warren PA 16365 Office: First Bapt Warren 208 Market St Warren PA 16365-2306

WATFORD, JOHN HARDIN, bank executive; b. Hagerman, N.Mex., Oct. 8, 1931; s. Angus Elwood Watford and E. Joyce (West) Lankford; m. June J. Onorati, Aug. 31, 1952; children—Bill C., Lois A., Bob E., Jim A., Linda K. B.S. in Bus. Acctg., U. Colo., 1954. Vice-pres. data processing First Interstate Bank, Los Angeles, 1960-67; sr. v.p. ops. Seattle 1st Nat. Bank, 1967-75; exec. v.p. automation and ops. First Union Nat. Bank Fla., Jacksonville, 1975—; dir. Fla. Interchange Group, Orlando, Fla., 1983—; pres., dir. Computer Systems Inc., Seattle, 1973-75; faculty Bank Adminstrn. Inst. Grad. Sch. Banking, Madison, Wis., 1968-78; mem. Wash. State Data Processing Authority, Olympia, 1974-75; dir. Info. Tech. Edn. Consortium, Jacksonville. Named Outstanding Citizen, Gov. of Wash., 1975. Mem. Am. Bankers Assn. (automation com. 1970-73). Republican. Methodist. Club: Sawgrass (Ponte Vedra, Fla.). Office: First Union Nat Bank Fla 8324 Baymeadows Way Jacksonville FL 32256-8221

WATHEN, DANIEL EVERETT, state supreme court chief justice; b. Easton, Maine, Nov. 4, 1939; s. Joseph Jackson and Wilda Persis (Dow) W.; m. Judith Carol Foren, July 14, 1960; children: Julanne Carol, Daniel Arthur. AB, Ricker Coll., 1962; JD, U. Maine, 1965; LLM (hon.), U. Va. Law Sch., 1988. Bar: Maine 1965. Atty. Wathen & Wathen, Augusta, Maine, 1965-77; trial judge Superior Ct. Maine, Augusta, 1977-81; appellate judge Supreme Jud. Ct. Maine, Augusta, 1981-92; state chief justice Supreme Jud. Ct. Maine, 1992—. Office: ME Supreme Jud Ct 142 Federal St Portland ME 04101-4151

WATHNE, CARL NORMAN, hospital administrator; b. Johnstown, Mass., Oct. 16, 1930; s. Odd and Alice (Anderson) W.; m. Alice Adele Tucker, Jan. 25, 1958; children: John M., Carl K. BS, U. Pitts., 1952; MS, Columbia U., 1958. Asst. adminstr. Bayonne (N.J.) Hosp., 1958-60; assoc. adminstr. Binghamton (N.Y.) Gen. Hosp., 1960-63; chief exec. officer Putnam Community Hosp., Carmel, N.Y., 1963-65; v.p. A.J.J. Rourke, Inc., New Rochelle, N.Y., 1965-72; exec. dir. Lahey Clinic, Boston, 1972-79; pres., chief exec. officer Leonard Morse Health System, Natick, Mass., 1980-85, Leominster (Mass.) Health System, 1985-92; pres. Wathne Health Strategists, 1992—; adj. asst. prof. Boston U., 1981—; pres. Cen. New Eng. PHO, Leominster, 1991-92; hosp. cons. Contbr. articles to profl. jours. Mem. Mass. Hosp. Assn. (pres. 1987-88, chmn. 1987), New Eng. Hosp. Supts. Club (pres. 1986-88), North Cen. Mass. C. of C. (dir. 1988-91). Avocations: painting, sailing, photography. Home: 6 Colony Rd Lexington MA 02173-2004 Office: Wathne Health Strategists 6 Colony Rd Lexington MA 02173-2004

WATHNE, STEFAN, JR., consulting company executive. AB in Govt. & Soviet Studies with honors, Harvard Coll., 1991. Pres. Moscow Bus. Travel Svc., 1990—, The Moscow Inst. of Social and Polit. Studies, 1990—, Phoenicia Investments Ltd., 1990—. Author: Communism's Coup de Grace, 1991. ofcl. advisor Christian Dem. Movement of Russia, 1992—, Dem. Party of Russia, 19992—; founder Children of Russia, 1993—. Avocations: collecting antique and classic fly fishing equipment and tackle, fishing, tennis, skiing, sailing. Office: Phoenicia Investments Ltd 49th Fl 152 W 57th St New York NY 10019

WATKIN, DAVID, film director, cinematographer; b. Margate, Eng., Mar. 23, 1925. Filmmaker, 1948—; asst. cameraman Brit. Transport Films, 1950-55, cameraman, 1955-61; ind. filmmaker, 1961—. Motion pictures include The Knack, 1964, Help!, 1965, Marat/Sade, 1966, How I Won the War, 1967, Charge of the Light Brigade, 1968, Catch 22, 1970, The Devils, 1971, The Boyfriend, 1971, The Homecoming, A Delicate Balance, 1973, The Three Musketeers, 1974, The Four Musketeers, 1975, Jesus of Nazareth, Mahogany, 1975, To The Devil, a Daughter, 1976, Robin and Marian, 1976, Joseph Andrews, 1977, Cuba, 1979, Hanover Street, 1979, That Summer, 1979, Endless Love, 1981, Chariots of Fire, 1981, Yentl, 1983, The Hotel New Hampshire, 1984, White Nights, 1985, Out of Africa (Acad. award, 1985), Return to Oz, 1985, Sky Bandits, 1986, Moonstruck, 1987, The Good Mother, 1988, Masquerade, 1988, Memphis Belle, 1990, Hamlet, 1990, An Object of Beauty, 1991, The Cabinet of Dr. Ramirez, 1991, Used People, 1992, This Boy's Life, 1993, Bopha, 1993, Milk Money, 1993, Jane Eyre, 1994. Home: 6 Sussex Mews, Brighton BN2 1GZ, England

WATKIN, VIRGINIA GUILD, lawyer; b. Clinton, Mass., July 28, 1925; d. George Cheever and Dorothy Louise (Springer) Guild; m. Donald M. Watkin, June 22, 1946; children—Henry M., Mary Ellen, Edward G., Ann Kymry. B.A., Wellesley Coll., 1946; LL.B., Columbia U., 1949, LLD (hon.) Norwich U., 1986. Bar: N.Y. 1949, D.C. 1952, U.S. Ct. Appeals (D.C. cir.) 1952, U.S. Supreme Ct. 1954, Mass. 1963, U.S. Dist. Ct. Mass. 1968, U.S. Ct. Appeals (1st cir.) 1968, U.S. Ct. Appeals (9th cir.) 1976, U.S. Ct. Appeals (4th cir.) 1980, U.S. Ct. Fed. Claims 1983, U.S. Ct. Appeals (5th cir.) 1993. Assoc., Covington & Burling, Washington, 1952-58; assoc. counsel Mass. Crime Commn., 1963-64; assoc. Herrick, Smith, Donald, Farley & Ketchum, Boston, 1966-72, ptnr., 1973-74; ptnr. Covington & Burling, Washington, 1974—. Bd. vis. Columbia U. Sch. Law; trustee Northfield (Mass.) Mount Hermon Sch. Bd. 1978-83, Norwich U., Northfield, Vt., 1977-90, emertia 1990—, Wellesley Coll., 1989—; bd. overseers Wellesley Coll. Stone Ctr. for Developmt. Svcs. and Studies, 1989—, Wellesley Coll. Ctr. for Rsch. on Women, 1990—. Mem. Am. Law Inst., ABA, D.C. Bar (pres. 1993—), Soc. Woman Geographers, Columbia Law Sch. Alumni Assn. (regional v.p.), Wellesley Coll. Alumnae Assn. (bd. dirs. 1985-88). Club: Cosmos. Author: Taxes and Tax Harmonization in the Central American Common Market, 1967; contbr. articles to profl. jours. Home: 3001 Veazey Ter NW Washington DC 20008-5455 Office: Covington & Burling PO Box 7566 1201 Pennsylvania Ave NW Washington DC 20044-7566

WATKINS, BIRGE SWIFT, real estate investment executive; b. Grand Rapids, Mich., May 2, 1949; s. Robert Goodell and Betty Jane (Swift) W.; m. Elizabeth Beverly Price, Nov. 28, 1985; children: Elizabeth Porter, Benjamin Thorne Swift, Robert William MacIntosh. BA, Alma Coll., 1971; MBA, London Bus. Sch., 1981; MPA, Harvard U., 1989. Staff asst. to Pres. of U.S. Washington, 1974-77; congl. press sec. U.S. Ho. of Reps., Washington, 1977; v.p. Arbor Internat. Inc., McLean, Va., 1980-81; asst. office dir. AID, Washington, 1982-83; asst. dir. Pres.'s Task Force on Internal Pvt. Enterprise, Washington, 1983-85; dep. asst. sec. USDA, Washington, 1989-90; dir. investor outreach Resolution Trust Corp., Washington, 1991-94; ptnr. Benton Resources, Washington, 1994-95; cons. Com Mac, Washington, 1995—; bd. dirs. Corp. Healthcare Svcs. Inc., Springfield, Va.; cons. Washington Campus Inc., 1977, Va. Med. Assocs. Inc., Springfield, 1988. Mem. campaign staff Reagan-Bush campaign, Washington, 1980, Bush for President, 1988; mem. transition team office of Pres.-elect Bush, 1988. Mem. Urban Land Inst., Harvard Club (Washington). Avocations: skiing, running, contemporary art. Home: 832 Blackwell Rd Warrenton VA 22186-9442 Office: Com Mac 2620 P St NW Washington DC 20007

WATKINS, CALVIN W., government executive; b. Hendersonville, Tenn., Mar. 4, 1931; s. Calvin H. and Claris E. (Stinson) W.; m. Jessie L. Jolly, June 18, 1954; children: Glenn, Karen; m. Kathryn R. Snyder, Oct. 24, 1987; stepchildren: Melanie, Mary, Aaron. BS, Mid. Tenn. State U., 1958. Auditor Ralston Purina Co., Nashville, 1958-61, P&SA, U.S. Dept. Agr., Atlanta, 1961-65; regional supr. P&SA, U.S. Dept. Agr., L.A., 1965-76; br. chief P&SA, U.S. Dept. Agr., Washington, 1976-82, dep. adminstr., 1982-92, adminstr., 1992—. Mem. Sr. Exec. Assn. Avocations: fishing, golf, hiking. Home: Packers & Stockyards Admin 8626 Kerry Ln Springfield VA 22152 Office: P&SA USDA Rm 3039 So Bldg 14th and Independence Ave Washington DC 20250

WATKINS, CARLTON GUNTER, retired pediatrician; b. Wilmington, N.C., Aug. 25, 1919; s. Edison Lee and Maysie (Gunter) W.; m. Charlotte Jean Metcalf, Mar. 21, 1943; children—Lloyd Dixon Hollingsworth, Carlton Gunter, Mary Melissa, Charlotte Lou. A.B., U. N.C., 1939; M.D., Washington U., St. Louis, 1943. Rotating intern, asst. resident, resident pediatrics St. Louis City Hosp., 1943-45; resident pediatrics Duke Hosp., 1945-46; pvt. practice Charlotte, N.C., 1946-51, 53-73; chmn. dept. pediatrics Charlotte Meml. Hosp., 1958-61, 63-67; founder, sr. mem. Charlotte Pediatric Clinic, 1963-73; med. dir. Mecklenburg Center for Human Devel., Charlotte, 1973-89. Contbr. articles to med. jours. Pres. Charlotte-Mecklenburg Assn. for Children with Learning Disabilities, 1971-73, Mecklenburg Sr. Dems., 1993-94; mem. profl. adv. bd. Epilepsy Assn. N.C., 1976-86, v.p., 1986-88; mem. cons. bd. CPC Cedar Spring Hosp., 1992-94; mem. Charlotte-Mecklenburg Bd. Edn., 1966-74; mem. Mecklenburg Human Svcs. Coun., 1994—. Capt. M.C., U.S. Army, 1951-53. Fellow Am. Acad. Pediatrics (life); mem. AMA (life), N.C., Mecklenburg County med. socs., N.C. Pediatric Soc., Charlotte Pediatric Soc. (founder, 1st sec. 1950, pres. 1962), N.C. PTA (life), Alpha Kappa Kappa. Unitarian. Club: Old Catawba (Charlotte). Home: 8713 Gainsford Ct Charlotte NC 28210-5850

WATKINS, CHARLES BOOKER, JR., mechanical engineering educator; b. Petersburg, Va., Nov. 20, 1942; s. Charles Booker and Haseltine Lucy (Thurston) W.; m. Judith Griffin; children: Michael, Steven. B.S. in Mech. Engring. cum laude, Howard U., 1964; M.S., U. N.Mex., 1966, Ph.D., 1970. Registered profl. engr., D.C. Mem. tech. staff Sandia Nat. Labs., Albuquerque, 1964-71; asst. prof. dept. mech. engring. Howard U., Washington, 1971-73; prof., chmn. dept. mech. engring. Howard U., 1973-86; Herbert G. Keyser prof. mech. engring. dean Sch. Engring. CCNY, 1986—; cons. U.S. Army, U.S. Navy, NSF, pvt. industries, 1984-85; bd. dirs. Parsons Brinkerhoff, Inc., 1994—. Research grantee NSF, U.S. Navy, Nuclear Regulatory Commn.; research grantee Dept. Energy, NASA; recipient Ralph R. Teetor award Soc. Automotive Engrs., 1980; Sandia Labs. doctoral fellow; NDEA fellow. Fellow ASME, AIAA (assoc.); mem. AAAS, Soc. Automotive Engrs., Am. Soc. Engring. Edn., Sigma Xi, Omega Psi Phi, Tau Beta Pi. Home: 171 Sherman Ave Teaneck NJ 07666-4121 Office: CCNY Sch Engring Convent Ave New York NY 10031

WATKINS, CHERYL DENISE, special education educator; b. Chgo., Dec. 15, 1963; d. Henry Eugene and Jean (Ingram) W. BE in Spl. Edn., Chgo. State U., 1987; MEd, U. Ill., 1992. Tchr. children with autism Chgo. Bd. Edn., 1987—; cons. in field; adj. faculty Columbia Coll., Chgo., 1993, Nat. Louis U.; speaker ednl. topics Chgo., St. Louis, Ill., Iowa, Fla., Md. Author: You Can Do Anything: A Story for Ryan, 1993, Living with Autism, 1995. Scout master Scouting for People with Disabilities, 1989—; vol. workshops Cabrini Green Tutoring Program, Chgo. Recipient Golden Apple award Golden Apple Found., 1991, Disting. Alumni award Nat. Assn. for Equal Opportunity in Higher Edn./Chgo. State U., 1992, Kizzy award, 1992, Tchr. Achiever award Michael Jordan Found. Edn. Club; 1993; named Outstanding Young Woman in Am., 1986. Mem. Nat. Bd. Profl. Teaching Standards (spl. needs com.), Kappa Delta Pi, Phi Delta Kappa, Delta Sigma Theta. Avocations: roller skating, reading, cake decorating, writing, traveling. Office: Agassiz Elem Sch 2851 N Seminary Ave Chicago IL 60657-4343

WATKINS, DAVID, federal official; b. Hope, Ark., 1941; m. Ileene Renschler; 3 children. BS Bus. Adminstrn., U. Ark.; MBA, U. Ariz. Owner, operator advt. and mktg. firm, music co.; 2 telecom. cos., cellular phone co., nat. franchise co., farming venture, merchant banking firm; now asst. to President of U.S. for mgmt. and adminstrn. The White House, Washington. Mem. Sigma Chi, Blue Key, Cardinal XX. Office: Statutory Office Mgmt & Adminstrn 1600 Pennsylvania Ave NW Washington DC 20500

WATKINS, DEAN ALLEN, electronics executive, educator; b. Omaha, Oct. 23, 1922; s. Ernest E. and Pauline (Simpson) W.; m. Bessie Ena Hansen, June 28, 1944; children—Clark Lynn, Alan Scott, Eric Ross. B.S., Iowa State Coll., 1944; M.S., Calif. Inst. Tech., 1947; Ph.D., Stanford, 1951. Engr. Collins Radio Co., 1947-48; mem. staff Los Alamos Lab., 1948-49; tech. staff Hughes Research Labs., 1951-53; asso. prof. elec. engring. Stanford, 1953-56; prof., dir. Electron Devices Lab., 1956-64, lectr. elec. engring., 1964-70; co-founder, pres., chief exec. officer, dir. Watkins Johnson Co., Palo Alto, Calif., 1957-67; chmn., chief exec. officer, dir. Watkins Johnson Co., 1967-80, chmn., dir., 1980—; cons. Dept. Def., 1956-66; mem. White House Sci. Coun., 1988-89. Patentee in field; contbr. articles to profl. jours. Legis. chmn., dir. San Mateo County Sch. Bds. Assn., 1959-69; gov. San Francisco Bay Area Council, 1966-75; Republican precinct capt. Portola Valley, 1964; vice chmn. San Mateo County Finance Com., 1967-69; mem. Calif. Rep. Central Com. 1964-68; trustee Stanford, 1966-69; regent U. Calif., 1969—, chmn., 1972-74; mem. governing bd. Sequoia Union High Sch. Dist., 1964-68, chmn., 1967-68; mem. governing bd. Portola Valley Sch. Dist., 1958-66; mem. bd. overseers Hoover Instn. on War, Revolution and Peace, Stanford, 1969—, chmn., 1971-73, 85-86; adv. policy commn. Santa Clara County Jr. Achievement; trustee Nat. Security Indsl. Assn., 1965-78. Served from pvt. to 1st lt. C.E., O.R.C. AUS, 1943-46. Fellow IEEE (7th region Achievement award 1957, Frederik Philips award 1981), AAAS; mem. Am. Phys. Soc., Am. Mgmt. Assn., Western Electronic Mfrs. Assn. (chmn. San Francisco coun. 1967, v.p., dir.), Calif. C. of C. (dir. 1965-92, treas. 1978, pres. 1981), Nat. Acad. Engring., Mounted Patrol San Mateo County (spl. dep. sheriff 1960-70), San Mateo County Horseman's Assn., San Benito County Farm Bur., Calif. Cattlemen's Assn., Delta Upsilon. Clubs: Palo Alto (Palo Alto), University (Palo Alto); Shack Riders (San Mateo County); Commonwealth (San Francisco); Rancheros Visitadores. Office: Watkins-Johnson Co 3333 Hillview Ave Palo Alto CA 94304-1223

WATKINS, GEORGE DANIELS, physics educator; b. Evanston, Ill., Apr. 28, 1924; s. Paul F. and Lois V. (Daniels) W.; m. Carolyn Lenore Nevin, June 19, 1949; children: Lois Roberta, Paul Brent, Ann Romaine. B.S., Randolph-Macon Coll., 1943; D.Sc. (hon.), 1976; M.A., Harvard U., 1947, Ph.D., 1952. Research physicist Gen. Electric Research Lab., Schenectady, 1952-75; adj. prof. Rensselaer Poly. Inst., 1962-65, SUNY-Albany, 1969-72; Sherman Fairchild prof. physics Lehigh U., Bethlehem, Pa., 1975—; chmn. Gordon Research Conf. on Defects in Semiconductors, 1981; mem. solid state adv. com. Oak Ridge Nat. Lab., 1980-85. Mem. editorial bd. Phys. Rev. B, 1978-82; contbr. articles to profl. jours. Served to lt. (j.g.) USNR, 1943-46. NSF fellow, 1966-67; named Virginian of Yr. Va. Press Assn. 1980; recipient Alexander von Humboldt sr. U.S. Scientist award, 1983. Fellow Am. Phys. Soc. (Oliver E. Buckley award 1978), AAAS, Nat. Acad. Scis. Democrat. Unitarian. Office: Lehigh U Dept Physics Bethlehem PA 18015

WATKINS, HAROLD ROBERT, minister; b. Wauseon, Ohio, July 30, 1928; s. Orra Lynn and Florence Margaret (Bruner) W.; m. Evelyn Norma Earlywine, June 18, 1950; children: Mark Edwin, Nancy Jo Watkins Boyd. AB, Bethany Coll., 1950; BD, Lexington Theol. Sem., 1953; DD, Phillips U., 1985. Ordained minister Disciples of Christ, 1950. Min. Park Ave. Christian Ch., Tucson, 1953-56, First Christian Ch., Tuscaloosa, Ala., 1956-57; gen. ch. adminstr. Bd. Ch. Extension of Disciples of Christ, Indpls., 1958-95, pres., 1980-95; chmn. bd. dirs. Discipledata, Inc., Indpls. Trustee Bethany (W.Va.) Coll., 1976—, Nat. City Christian Ch. Corp., Washington, 1981—; bd. dirs. Ecumenical Ch. Loan Fund, Geneva; pres. World Conv. Chs. of Christ, Nashville, 1988-92. Recipient Outstanding Alumnus award Bethany Coll., 1975. Mem. Interfaith Forum on Religion, Art and Architecture (dir. officer 1979—, pres. 1981-82, Elbert M. Conover award 1989), Indpls. Athletic Club. Home: 7402 Somerset Bay # 118 Indianapolis IN 46240-3400 Office: Bd Ch Ext Disciples Christ 110 S Downey Ave Indianapolis IN 46219-6406

WATKINS, HAYS THOMAS, retired railroad executive; b. Fern Creek, Ky., Jan. 26, 1926; s. Hays Thomas Sr. and Minnie Catherine (Whiteley) W.; m. Betty Jean Wright, Apr. 15, 1950; 1 son, Hays Thomas III. BS in Acctg., Western Ky. U., 1947; MBA, Northwestern U., 1948; LLD (hon.), Baldwin Wallace Coll., 1975, Alderson Broaddus Coll., 1980, Coll. of William and Mary, 1982, Va. Union U., 1987. CPA, Ill., Ohio. With C. & O. Ry. Cleve., 1949-80, v.p. fin., 1964-67, v.p. adminstrv. group, 1967-71, pres., chief exec. officer, 1971-73, chmn. bd., chief exec. officer, 1973-80; with B. & O. R.R., 1964-80, v.p. finance, 1964-71, pres., chief exec. officer, 1971-73, vice chmn. bd., chief exec. officer, 1973-80; chmn., chief exec. officer Chessie System, Inc., 1973-80; pres. and co-chief exec. officer CSX Corp. (merger of Chessie System, Inc. and Seaboard Coast Line Industries, Inc.), Richmond, Va., 1980-82, chmn. bd., chief exec. officer, 1982-89, chmn. bd., 1989-91; chmn. emeritus, 1991—. Vice rector bd. visitors Coll. William and mary, 1984-87, rector, 1987-93. With AUS, 1945-47. Named Man of Yr., Modern R.R. mag., 1984; recipient Excellence in Mgmt. award Industry Week mag., 1982. Mem. Nat. Assn. Accts., Am. Inst. C.P.A.'s. Clubs: Commonwealth (Richmond, Va.); Country of Va. (Richmond). Home: 22 Lower Tuckahoe Rd W Richmond VA 23233-6108 Office: CSX Corp PO Box 85629 Richmond VA 23285-5629

WATKINS, HORTENSE CATHERINE, middle school educator; b. St. Louis, Nov. 29, 1924; d. Isaiah S. and Katie M. (Phelps) W. BA, Harris-Stowe State Coll., St. Louis, 1946; MEd, U. Ill., 1953; postgrad. U. Chgo., InterAm. U., Saltillo, Coahuila, Mex.; postgrad., U. Seville, Spain, Webster U., St. Louis. Cert. life tchr., reading specialist, Mo. Coord. urban rural programs Carver-Dunbar Schs., St. Louis, 1975-76; adminstrv. asst. Shaw Visual Performing Arts Sch., St. Louis, 1978-82; team IV leader Woerner IGE, St. Louis, 1982-87; tchr., head lang. arts dept. Nottingham Mid. Sch., St. Louis, 1987-92; tutor fgn.-speaking religious, presenter, lectr. numerous workshops; curriculum advisor St. Louis Pub. Schs. Active numerous cmty. orgns.; bd. dirs. St. Louis Cathedral Sch.; bd. dirs. Concert Series of St. Louis Cathedral. Mem. ASCD, Nat. Coun. Tchrs. English, Mo. State Tchrs. Assn., Greater St. Louis Coun. Social Studies, Delta Sigma Theta (Golden life), Delta Kappa Gamma. Home: 5070A Enright Ave Saint Louis MO 63108-1008

WATKINS, JAMES DAVID, food products executive; b. Rochester, Minn., Sept. 17, 1947; s. John Frederick and Lillian Kay (Johnson) W.; m. Elizabeth Smith Cieslowski; children: James David Jr., Joseph John. BA, U. Minn., 1969. Venture mgr. Pillsbury, Mpls., 1971-78; chief exec. officer Golden Valley Microwave Foods, Mpls., 1978—; bd. dirs. Country Lake Foods, Mpls. Bd. dirs. Big Brothers/Big Sisters, 1987. Home: 18591 Mushtown Rd Prior Lake MN 55372-3019 Office: Golden Valley Microwave Foods 7450 Metro Blvd Minneapolis MN 55439-3038

WATKINS, JERRY WEST, retired oil company executive, lawyer; b. Vernon, Tex., Dec. 10, 1931; s. Terrell Clark and Daisy (West) W.; m. Elizabeth Jill Cole, Sept. 3, 1955. Student, Hendrix Coll., 1949-50, La. Poly. Inst., 1950-51; JD, U. Ark., 1954. Bar: Ark. 1954. Law clk. Supreme Ct. Ark., Little Rock, 1954-55; with Murphy Oil Corp., El Dorado, Ark., 1955-89; sec., gen. atty., 1966-71, sec., gen. counsel, 1971-89, v.p., dir., 1975-88, exec. v.p., 1991-92, also dir., 1975-89; chief exec. officer, bd. dirs. Ocean Drilling and Exploration Co., New Orleans, 1989-91; mem. Ark. Bd. Law Examiners, 1969-74. Trustee Ark. State U., 1982-87; mem. Barton Libr. Bd., El Dorado 1966-89; bd. dirs. South Ark. Arts Ctr., El Dorado, 1979-82, 85-88, Warner Brown Hosp., El Dorado, 1984-87, South Ark. Med. Systems, 1987-89. Mem. ABA, Ark. Bar Assn., Union County Bar Assn. Home: 111 Watkins Dr El Dorado AR 71730-2752

WATKINS, JOAN MARIE, osteopath, occupational medicine physician; b. Anderson, Ind., Mar. 9, 1943; d. Curtis David and Dorothy Ruth (Beckett) W.; m. Stanley G. Nodvik, Dec. 25, 1969 (div. Apr. 1974). BS, West Liberty State Coll., 1965; Cert. of Grad. Phy. Therapy, Ohio State U., 1966; DO, Phila. Coll. Osteo., 1972; M of Health Professions Edn., U. Ill., Chgo., 1986; MPH, U. Ill., 1989. Diplomate Osteo. Nat. Bds., Am. Bd. Preventive Medicine. Emergency osteo. physician Cooper Med. Ctr., Camden, N.J., 1974-79, Shore Meml. Hosp., Somers Point, N.J., 1979-81, St. Francis Hosp., Blue Island, Ill., 1981-82; emergency osteo. physician Mercy Hosp. and Med. Ctr., Chgo., 1982-90, dir. emergency ctr., 1984-88; resident in occupational and preventive medicine U. Ill., 1988-90. Fellow Am. Coll. Preventive Medicine. Avocations: sailing, needlework, swimming. Home: 4306 Harbor House Dr Tampa FL 33615 Office: U Community Hosp Occupational Health Svcs 3100 E Fletcher Ave Tampa FL 33613

WATKINS, JOHN CHESTER ANDERSON, newspaper publisher; b. Corpus Christi, Tex., Oct. 2, 1912; s. Dudley Warren and Ruth (Woodruff) W.; m. Helen Danforth, Nov. 20, 1943 (div. 1959); children: Fanchon Metcalf Burnham, Robert Danforth, Stephen Danforth, Jane Pierce; m. Izetta Jewel Smith, Feb. 1960 (dec. 1989). Litt.D. Bryant Coll.; D.J. Roger Williams Coll., 1983. Reporter, makeup editor, aviation editor Dayton (Ohio) Jour. and Herald, 1934-35; reporter, aviation editor, mil. corr. Balt. Sun, 1935-41; asst. to pub., assoc. pub. Providence Jour.-Bull., 1945-54, pub., 1954-79; chmn. Providence Jour. Co., 1961-85, chmn. emeritus, 1985—; pres. Interam. Press Assn., 1971-72; also mem. adv. council. Served as fighter pilot USAAF, 1941-45; ops. officer 325th Fighter Group MTO. Decorated D.F.C., Air medal with 9 oak leaf clusters; knight comdr. Order of Merit (Italy), R.I. Heritage Hall of Fame. Fellow New Eng. Acad. Journalists (Yankee Quill award); mem. Air Force Assn., Am. Soc. Newspaper Editors, New Eng. Daily Newspaper Assn. (pres. 1966-68), Hope Club, Agawam Hunt Club, Cruising Am. Club, N.Y. Yacht Club, Spouting Rock Beach Assn. Home: PO Box 1085 Providence RI 02901-1085 Office: Providence Jour Co 75 Fountain St Providence RI 02902-0050

WATKINS, JOHN CUMMING, JR., law educator; b. Mobile, Ala., Apr. 2, 1935; s. John Cumming and Myrtle Lisette (van Devender) W.; m. Nancy Lee Parham, Sept. 24, 1964 (div. Oct. 1971); 1 child Scott Christopher; m. Sallie Ann Wilson, Aug. 12, 1972; children: Alicia Anne, Melissa Renee, John Cumming V. BS, U. Ala., Tuscaloosa, 1957; JD, U. Ala., 1962; MS, Fla. State U., 1964; LLM, Northwestern U., 1968. Bar: Ala. 1962, U.S. Dist Ct. (no. dist.) Ala. 1968, U.S. Ct. Appeals (5th cir.) 1970, U.S. Supreme Ct. 1973. Law clk. to assoc. justice Supreme Ct. Ala., Montgomery, 1962-63; law clk. to presiding justice U.S. Ct. Appeals (5th cir.), Tuscaloosa, Ala., 1965-66; asst. prof. bus. law Coll. Commerce U. Ala., Tuscaloosa, 1965-69, chmn. dept. criminal justice Coll. Arts and Scis., 1971-77, prof., 1975—; assoc. prof. criminology Sam Houston State U., Huntsville, Tex., 1969-71; cons. Am. Correctional Assn., 1969-71, W.K. Kellogg Found, 1976, Kresge Found., 1979-80, CHOICE, 1980—. Co-author: Introduction to Criminal Justice, 1982. Mem. adv. bd. Tuscaloosa County Juvenile Ct., 1984-88. 1st lt. U.S. Army, 1958-60. Mem. Ala. Bar Assn. (chmn. com. correctional instns. and procedures 1984-86). Democrat. Episcopalian. Avocations: mil. history, model trains. Home: 2324 Trenton Dr Tuscaloosa AL 35406-1623 Office: U Ala PO Box 870320 Tuscaloosa AL 35487-0320

WATKINS, JOHN FRANCIS, management consultant; b. Alhambra, Calif., May 21, 1925; s. Edward F. and Louise (Ward) W.; divorced; children—Stephen, Katherine, John Francis, William. B.S. in Civil Engring., U. Tex., Austin, 1947. With Earle M. Jorgensen Co., Lynwood, Calif., 1947-90, sr. v.p. adminstrn., 1978-90, ret.; owner John F. Watkins Assocs., Pasadena, Calif., 1990—. Bd. dirs. Boys Republic, Chino, Calif., 1970—, pres., 1977-80; bd. dirs. St. Luke Hosp., Pasadena, Calif., 1979-86, chmn. bd., 1982-86; pres. bd. Poly. Sch., Pasadena, 1978-80; bd. dirs. Econ. Literacy Coun. Calif., 1980-87, Pasadena Hist. Mus., 1990—, Holy Family Svcs., 1990—; mem. pres.' coun. Coll. Sci. and Engring., Loyla Marymount U., posse sheriff Huntington Westerners. Mem. U.S. Navy League (nat. bd. dirs. 1989—, pres. Pasadena coun. 1992-93), Calif. Club, Annandale Golf Club, Valley Club (San Marino, Calif.). Republican. Roman Catholic. Home & Office: 410 California Ter Pasadena CA 91105-2419

WATKINS, JOHN GOODRICH, psychologist, educator; b. Salmon, Idaho, Mar. 17, 1913; s. John Thomas and Ethel (Goodrich) W.; m. Evelyn Elizabeth Browne, Aug. 21, 1932; m. Doris Wade Tomlinson, June 8, 1946; m. Heien Verner Huth, Dec. 28, 1971; children: John Dean, Jonette Alison, Richard Douglas, Gregory Keith, Rodney Philip, Karen Stroobants, Marvin R. Huth. Student, Coll. Idaho, 1929-30, 31-32; BS, U. Idaho, 1933, MS, 1936; PhD, Columbia U., 1941. Instr. high sch. Idaho, 1933-39; faculty Ithaca Coll., 1940-41, Auburn U., 1941-43; assoc. prof. Wash. State Coll. 1944-49; chief clin. psychologist U.S. Army Welch Hosp., 1945-46; clin. psychologist VA Hosp., American Lake, Wash., 1949-50; chief clin. psychologist VA Mental Hygiene Clinic, Chgo., 1950-53, VA Hosp., Portland, Oreg., 1953-64; prof. psychology U. Mont., Missoula, 1964-84; prof. emeritus U. Mont., 1984—, dir. clin. tng., 1964-80; lectr. numerous univs.; clin. asso. U. Oreg. Med. Sch., 1957; pres. Am. Bd. Examiners in Psychol. Hypnosis, 1960-62. Author: Objective Measurement of Instrumental Performance, 1942, Hypnotherapy of War Neuroses, 1949, General Psychotherapy, 1960, The Therapeutic Self, 1978, (with others) We, The Divided Self, 1982, Hypnotherapeutic Techniques, 1987, Hypnoanalytic Techniques, 1992; contbr. articles to profl. jours. Mem. Internat. Soc. Clin. and Exptl. Hypnosis (co-founder, pres. 1965-67, recipient awards 1960-65), Soc. Clin. and Exptl. Hypnosis (pres. 1969-71, Morton Prince award), Am. Psychol. Assn. (pres. divsn. 30 1975-76, recipient award 1993), Sigma Xi, Phi Delta Kappa. Home and Office: 413 Evans Ave Missoula MT 59801-5827 *For a complete life one needs a job, a home, a love, a friend, and an enemy. My "enemies" are injustice, war, poverty, illness, and suffering, not people. Make your existence as meaningful as possible. Enjoy life fully, and when it comes time to leave, have no fear or regrets. Seek to leave this world a little better off because you lived. These are my values. Would that I were mature enough always to live up to them.*

WATKINS, JULIA M., university dean; b. Pocatello, Idaho, Sept. 24, 1941; d. Emory J. and Elaine (Steele) Herndon; m. Dennis A. Watkins, Sept. 20, 1963; children: Matthew, Christopher, Andrew. BS, U. Utah, 1963, MSW, 1965, PhD, 1970. Chmn. dept. sociology and social work U. Maine, Orono, 1984-87, acting dean Coll. Arts and Scis., 1988-89, dean Coll. Social and Behavioral Scis., 1989-92; interim v.p. for acad. affairs U. Maine, 1992—. Author: Social Policy and the Rural Setting; contbr. articles to profl. jours. Pres. Bangor Dist. Found.; bd. dirs. Bangor Dist. Nursing Assn. Grantee Adminstrn. on Aging, Am. Assn. Ret. Person Andrus Found., HHS, USPHS; recipient Disting. Alumni Career Svc. award Grad. Sch. of Social Work, U Utah, 1992. Mem. NASW, AAUW, Am. Assn. Higher Edn., Am. Coun. on Edn., Coun. on Social Work Edn., Nat. Assn. Women Deans, Adminstrs. and Counselors, Rotary, Phi Kappa Phi. Address: 122 Grant St Bangor ME 04401

WATKINS, LLOYD IRION, university president; b. Cape Girardeau, Mo., Aug. 29, 1928; s. Herman Lloyd and Lydia Mina (Irion) W.; m. Mary Ellen Caudle, Aug. 14, 1949; children: John Lloyd, Joseph William, Robert Lawrence. BEd, Southeast Mo. State U., 1949; MS, U. Wis., 1951, PhD, 1954; DH (hon.), U. Dubuque, 1974; EdD (hon.), Srinakharinwirot U., Thailand, 1986. Tchr. Jackson (Mo.) High Sch., 1948-50; asst. prof. Moorhead State Coll., 1954-56; assoc. prof. Ohio U., 1956-64, asst. to acad. v.p., assoc. prof., 1964-66; exec. v.p. Ida. State U., Pocatello, 1966-69; pres. Pvt. Colls. and Univs. Des Moines, 1969-73, West Tex. State U., 1973-77; pres. Ill. State U., Normal, 1977-88, prof., pres. emeritus, 1988-91, pres. emeritus, 1991—. Contbr. articles to profl. jours. Recipient Baker grant for Research Ohio U., 1963, Alumni Merit award S.E. Mo. State U., 1978. Mem. McLean County Humane Soc., McLean County Hist. Soc., Citizens' Com., The Alumni Club, Crestwicke Country Club, Kappa Delta Pi, Phi Alpha Theta, Rotary. Home: RR 13 Box 111 Bloomington IL 61704-8917

WATKINS, MICHAEL DEAN, town planner; b. Chillicothe, Ohio, June 14, 1961; s. James A. and Delores G. (Gloff) W. BArch, U. Cin., 1985. Registered architect, Md. Project architect Cho, Wilks & Benn, Balt., 1985-88; town architect Andres Duany & Elizabeth Plater-Zyberk, Architects, Washington, 1988—; speaker, panelist in field. Jr. high youth sponsor, mem. bldg. com., deacon Mountain Christian Ch., Joppa, Md. Recipient Young Arch.'s award Progressive Architecture mag., 1993. Office: DPZ Architects 320 Firehouse Ln Gaithersburg MD 20878-5643

WATKINS, PAUL B., academic research center administrator, medical educator; b. Schenectady, N.Y., Feb. 17, 1953; s. George Daniels and Carolyn Lenore (Nevin) W.; m. Joanne Carol Spalty, July 4, 1981; children: Andrew James, Melanie Ann. BA, Cornell U., 1975, MD, 1979. Intern N.Y. Hosp., 1979-80, resident, 1980-82; fellow Medical Coll. Va., 1982-84; physician admission ward Khao-I-Dang Cambodian Refuge Camp, Thailand, 1982; from instr. to asst. prof. Med. Coll. Va., 1984-86; asst. prof. U. Mich., Ann Arbor, 1986-91; assoc. prof. medicine, 1991—, assoc. dir. clin. rsch. ctr., 1991, dir. clin. rsch. ctr., 1991—; advisor toxic waste orgn. Inst. Medicine, Washington, 1993—; mem. toxicology study sect. NIH, Bethesda, Md., 1992—; sci. cons. Parke-Davis Pharm., Organon Internat., Wyeth-Ayerst, Proctor and Gamble, Abbott Labs., Bristol-Meyers Squibb. Contbr. articles to profl. jours. Asst. coach Burns Park Elem. Soccer Team, Ann Arbor, 1991—, softball team, 1993; mem. St. Andrews Ch., Ann Arbor, 1990—. Recipient VA Career Devel. Associate Investigator award, 1984-86, Rsch. Assoc. award, 1987-91. Fellow ACP; mem. AAAS, Am. Soc. Clin. Investigation (elected), Am. Assn. Study Liver Disease, Am. Gastroent. Assn., Am. Fedn. Clin. Rsch., Midwest Gut Club, Ctrl. Soc. Clin. Rsch., Internat. Assn. Study Liver, Internat. Soc. Study Xenobiotics. Avocations: jogging, skiing, wind surfing, tennis, scuba diving. Home: 2112 Wallingford Ann Arbor MI 48104 Office: U Mich Hosp Gen Clin Rsch Ctr 1500 E Med Ctr Dr A7119 Ann Arbor MI 48109-0108

WATKINS, SALLY MARIE, nursing administrator; b. Roswell, N.Mex., Aug. 17, 1954; d. William Chester and Pauline Ruth (Cmposten) Allbright; divorced; 1 child. BS in Nursing, U. Tex., Houston, 1976; MS, U. Utah, 1986. Staff nurse Univ. Hosp. Salt Lake City, 1976-77, 78-79, head nurse, 1980-84, dir. nursing, 1984-90; asst. head nurse St. Lukes Hosp., Boise, Idaho, 1977-78; assoc. adminstr. nursing Tacoma (Wash.) Gen. Hosp., 1990—; mem. clin. faculty Coll. Nursing U. Wash. Mem. Am. Orgn. Nursing Execs., Wash. Orgn. Nurse Execs. (mem. program com. 1994-95), Sigma Theta Tau. Avocations: hiking, quilting, reading, camping, piano. Office: Tacoma Gen Hosp. 315 S Martin Luther King Bl Tacoma WA 98405-4234

WATKINS, STANLEY, academic director; b. Bklyn., Feb. 23, 1929; s. Harry and Rose (Smith) W.; m. Dorothy Yaffe, Aug. 3, 1953; children: Leonard, Ellen. BSME, Cooper Union, 1962; MBA, St. Johns U., 1972. Adminstr. Loral Corp., N.Y.C., 1958-70; rsch. adminstr. City Coll. of CUNY, N.Y.C., 1970—. Served with U.S. Army, 1951-53, Korea. Mem. Soc. Rsch. Adminstrs., Nat. Coun. Univ. Rsch. Adminstrs. Avocations: skiing, biking. Home: 60 W 13th St New York NY 10011 Office: City Coll CUNY Convent Ave at 138th St New York NY 10031

WATKINS, STEPHEN EDWARD, accountant; b. Oklahoma City, Sept. 1, 1922; s. Ralph Bushnell and Jane (Howell) W.; m. Suzanne Fowler, Aug. 16, 1976; children—Elizabeth Ann Watkins Racicot, Stephen Edward. B.B.A., U. N.Mex., 1944. C.P.A., N.Mex. With Peat, Marwick, Mitchell & Co., 1944-67; pres. The New Mexican, Santa Fe, 1967-78, 90—; pvt. practice pub. acctg. Santa Fe, 1978—. Vestryman Ch. of Holy Faith; trustee St. Vincent Hosp., 1979-85, Orchestra Santa Fe, 1976-82, Hist. Santa Fe Found. (pres.

1990). Mem. AICPA, Sons of Am. Revolution, Rotary. Home: 1325 Don Gaspar Ave Santa Fe NM 87505-4627 Office: 223 E Palace Ave Santa Fe NM 87501-2044

WATKINS, WILLIAM, JR., electric power industry executive; b. Jersey City, N.J., Aug. 12, 1932; s. William James and Willie Ree (Blount) W.; m. Sylvia I. Mulzac, Oct. 16, 1955; children: Cheryl, Rene, Linda. BBA, Pace U., 1954; MBA, N.Y.U., 1962; postgrad. advanced mgmt. program, U. Mich., 1979; postgrad. exec. program, Edison Electric Inst., 1988. Staff asst. Consol. Edison Co. N.Y., N.Y.C., 1957-64; systems mgr. Volkswagen Am., Englewood Cliffs, N.J., 1964-71; v.p., dir. adminstrn. New Eng. Power Svc. Co., Westboro, Mass., 1972-82, v.p., dir. human resources, 1986-92; v.p., dist. mgr. Narragansett Electric Co., Providence, 1982-86, exec. v.p., 1992—; bd. dirs. Peerless Precision Corp., Lincoln, R.I., 1982-91. Chmn. R.I. Urban Project, Providence, 1984, R.I. Coun. for Econ. Edn., Providence, 1984; mem. Govs. Commn. on Health Care Reform, 1993-94; bd. trustees R.I. Hosp., 1995—; bd. dirs. R.I. Hosp. Trust Nat. Bank, Providence, 1987—, R.I. Hosp. Fin. Corp., Providence, 1987—, R.I. Hosp. Fin. Corp., Providence, 1987-91, Inroads, 1993—, Leadership R.I., 1993—, Nat. Conf. Christians and Jews, 1993—; mem. resource and devel. commn. Episcopal Diocese Mass., 1988-92; bd. trustees Roger Williams U., Bristol, R.I., 1991-94, R.I. Sch. Design, 1993—. Recipient Cmty. Svc. award Urban League R.I., 1986, Paris V. Sterett award John Hope Settlement House, 1987, Small Bus. Adminstrn. Adv. of the Yr. award, 1994. Mem. N.E. Indsl. Developers Assn. (bd. dirs. 1993—), R.I. Urban Bankers Assn., Kappa Alpha Psi. Avocations: swimming, biking, hiking, traveling. Home: 61 Stone Ridge Rd Franklin MA 02038-3121 Office: Narragansett Electric Co 280 Melrose St Providence RI 02907-2157

WATKINS, WILLIAM LAW, retired lawyer; b. Anderson, S.C., Dec. 26, 1910; s. Thomas Franklin and Agnes (Law) W.; m. Frances Sitton, Oct. 23, 1937; children: Sarah Watkins Marshall, Anna Watkins Hattaway, Elizabeth Watkins Kinghorn, Jane Watkins Mudd. A.B., Wofford Coll., 1932; LL.B., U. Va., 1933. Bar: S.C. 1933. Practice law Anderson, S.C., 1933; mem. Watkins & Prince, 1934-46, Watkins & Watkins, 1946-54, Watkins, Vandiver & Freeman, 1954-64, Watkins, Vandiver, Kriven & Long, 1964-67, Watkins, Vandiver, Kirven, Long & Gable, 1968-77; ptnr. Watkins, Vandiver, Kirven, Gable & Gray, 1977-85, of counsel, 1985-92; bd. dirs. Duke Power Co., 1975-84, Perpetual Bank, F.S.B., 1953-92. Mem. S.C. Ho. of Reps., 1935-36; mem. S.C. Probation, Parole and Pardon Bd., 1954-69; trustee Presbyterian Coll., Clinton, S.C., 1966-75, Anderson County Hosp. Assn., S.C., 1964-74. Served with AUS, 1942-46. Decorated Bronze Star with oak leaf cluster. Fellow Am. Coll. Trial Lawyers, Am. Bar Found.; mem. ABA, S.C. Bar, Anderson Bar Assn., Phi Beta Kappa, Sigma Alpha Epsilon. Presbyterian. Lodge: Rotary. Home: 317 North St Anderson SC 29621-5814

WATKINSON, PATRICIA GRIEVE, museum director; b. Merton, Surrey, Eng., Mar. 28, 1946; came to U.S., 1972; d. Thomas Wardle and Kathleen (Bredl) Grieve. BA in Art History and Langs. with honors, Bristol U., Eng., 1968. Sec. Mayfair Fine Arts and The Mayfair Gallery, London, 1969-71; adminstr. Bernard Jacobson, Print Pub., London, 1971-73; freelance exhbn. work, writer Kilkenny Design Ctr., Davis Gallery, Irish Arts Council in Dublin, Ireland, 1975-76; curator of art Mus. Art, Wash. State U., Pullman, 1978-83, dir., 1984—; asst. prof. art history Wash. State U., Pullman 1978. Co-author, co-editor: Gaylen Hansen: The Paintings of a Decade, 1985. Mem. Assn. Coll. & Univ. Museums and Galleries (western regional rep. 1987-89), Art. Mus. Assn. Am. (Wash. state rep. 1986-87), Internat. Council Museums (modern art com. 1986-89), Wash. Mus. Assn. (bd. dirs. 1984-87), Am. Fedn. Arts (western region rep. 1987-89). Office: Wash State U Mus Art Pullman WA 99164-7460

WATLINGTON, JOHN FRANCIS, JR., banker; b. Reidsville, N.C., Mar. 23, 1911; s. John Francis and Frances (Byers) W.; m. Margaret Jones, Feb. 22, 1947; children: John Francis III, Anne Wilson Watlington Curtis. A.B., Washington and Lee U., 1933. With Wachovia Bank & Trust Co., Winston-Salem, N.C., 1933-82; transit clk., asst. cashier, asst. v.p., v.p., sr. v.p. Wachovia Bank & Trust Co., 1933-56, pres., 1956-74, chmn., 1974-76, chmn. exec. com., 1977-82, also chmn. Charlotte office, 1946-56; chmn. Wachovia Corp., 1968-76; chmn. exec. com., 1977-82; ret. dir. Piedmont Natural Gas Co., Inc.; dir. emeritus USAir Group Inc. Trustee Union Theol. Sem.; chmn. Union Theol.-Sem., 1980-82; hon. life trustee Va. Found. for Ind. Colls.; hon. chmn. bd. visitors Bowman Gray Sch. Medicine; dir., past pres. Presbyn. Ch. U.S.A. Found. Mem. Winston-Salem C. of C. (pres. 1958-59), N.C. Citizens Assn. Presbyterian. Home: 17 Graylyn Place Ln Winston Salem NC 27106-5816 Office: 301 N Main St Winston Salem NC 27101-3802

WATRING, WATSON GLENN, gynecologic oncologist, educator; b. St. Albans, W.Va., June 2, 1936; m. Roberta Tawell. BS, Washington & Lee U., 1958; MD, W.Va. U., 1962. Diplomate Am. Bd. Ob-Gyn, Am. Bd. Gynecol. Oncology. Intern The Toledo Hosp., 1963; resident in ob-gyn Ind. U., Indpls., 1964-66, Tripler Gen. Hosp., Honolulu, 1968-70; resident in gen. and oncologic surgery City of Hope Nat. Med. Ctr., Duarte, Calif., 1970-71, assoc. dir. gynecol. oncology, sr. surgeon, 1973-77; fellow in gynecol. oncology City of Hope Nat. Med. Ctr. and UCLA Med. Ctr., 1972-74; asst. prof. ob-gyn UCLA Med. Ctr., 1972-77; assoc. prof., sr. gynecologist, sr. surgeon Tufts New Eng. Med. Ctr. Hosp., Boston, 1977-80, asst. prof. radiation therapy, 1978-80; practice medicine specializing in ob-gyn Boston, 1980-82; assoc. prof. ob-gyn U. Mass., Worcester, 1982; regional dir. gynecol. oncology So. Calif. Permanente Med. Group, Los Angeles, 1982—, asst. dir. residency tng., 1985—; dir. gynecol. oncology St. Margarets Hosp. for Women, Dorchester, Mass., 1977-80; clin. prof. ob-gyn U. Calif., Irvine, 1982—. Contbr. articles to profl. jours. Mem. ch. council Luth. Ch. of the Foothills, 1973-75. Served to lt. col. M.C., U.S. Army, 1965-71. Fellow Am. Coll. Ob-Gyn, Los Angeles Obstet. and Gynecol. Soc.; mem. AAAS, ACS (Calif. and Mass. chpts.), Boston Surg. Soc., AMA, Mass. Med. Soc., Mass. Suffolk Dist. Med. Soc., Internat. Soc. Gynecol. Pathologists, Western Soc. Gynecologists and Obstetricians, Am. Soc. Clin. Oncology, Soc. Gynecol. Oncologists, Western Assn. Gynecol. Oncologists (sec.-treas. 1976-81, program chmn. 1984, pres. 1985—), New Eng. Assn. Gynecol. Oncologists (chmn. charter com.), New Eng. Obstet. and Gynecol. Soc., Obstet. Soc. Boston, Am. Radium Soc., Soc. Study Breast Disease, New Eng. Cancer Soc., Internat. Gynecol. Cancer Soc., Daniel Morton Soc., Sigma Xi. Republican. Avocations: golf, skiing, horticulture. Office: So Calif Permanente Med Group 4950 W Sunset Blvd Los Angeles CA 90027-5821

WATROUS, WILLIAM RUSSELL, trombonist, composer, conductor; b. Middletown, Conn., June 8, 1939; s. Ralph Jarvas and Edna (Little) W.; m. Mary Ann Ackerman, Oct. 1978; children: Melody, Cheryl, Jason. Student pub. schs., New London, Conn. lectr. jazz edn., participant music seminars, brass confs.; bd. dirs. Internat. Trombone Workshop. Trombonist with bands of Woody Herman, Quincy Jones, Count Basie, leader own band, Manhattan Wildlife Refuge (now Calif. Wildlife Refuge), from 1970, composer: Dirty Dan and others (Voted Number One Trombonist, Downbeat Reader's Poll, 1975, 76, 77, 78, 79, 80, Internat. Critics Poll 1976, 77). Albums include The Tiger of San Pedro, Bone Straight Ahead, Watrous in Hollywood, I'll Play For You, Coronary Trombossa, La Zorra, Roarin' Back Into New York, New York, Someplace Else, 1986, Reflections, 1987, Bone-Ified, 1992, A Time for Love, 1993. Served with USNR, 1956-60. Mem. ASCAP, Am. Fedn. Musicians. Address: care Welk Records 1299 Ocean Ave Ste 800 Santa Monica CA 90401-1038*

WATSON, ALBERT MACKENZIE, photographer; b. Edinburgh, Scotland, Aug. 6, 1942; came to U.S., 1970; s. Albert and Gladys (Proctor) W.; m. Elizabeth Fergusson, Apr. 1, 1960; children: Albert Norman MacKenzie, Aaron Urquhart Munro. BA, Duncan of Jordanstone, Dundee, Scotland, 1966; MA (RCA), Royal Coll. Art, London, 1969. Pres. Albert Watson Photography Inc., N.Y.C., 1977—. Author: Cyclops, 1994 (subject of BBC documentary, 1994); photographer album cover Mason Profitt Come and Gone, Grammy winner, 1973. IBM traveling scholar, 1966; official photographer HRH Prince Andrew's wedding, 1986. Presbyterian. Avocations: golf, Egyptology, film. Office: 777 Washington St New York NY 10014-1748

WATSON, ALEXANDER FLETCHER, ambassador; b. Boston, Aug. 8, 1939; s. Fletcher G. and Alice Victoria (Hodson) W.; m. Judith Dawson Tuttle, June 23, 1962; children: David F., Caitlin H. BA, Harvard U., 1961;

MA, U. Wis., 1969. Consular officer Am. embassy, Santo Domingo, Dominican Republic, 1962-64, Madrid, 1964-66; internat. relations officer Dept. State, Washington, 1966-68, 73-75, spl. asst., 1975-77, dir. Office of Devel. Fin., 1978-79; polit. officer Am. embassy, Brasilia, Brazil, 1969-70; prin. officer Am. Consulate, Salvador, Brazil, 1970-73; dep. chief of mission Am. embassy, La Paz, Bolivia, 1979-81; dep. chief of mission Bogota, Colombia, 1981-84, Brasilia, Brazil, 1984-86; U.S. ambassador to Lima, Peru, 1986-89; dep. U.S. permanent rep. to UN, 1989-93; asst. sec. of state for inter-Am. affairs Dept. of State, Washington, 1993—. Decorated Order of San Carlos, Govt. of Colombia, 1984; Order of the Condor, Govt. of Bolivia, 1985; Labor Justice Order of Merit, Govt. of Brazil, 1987; Order of the Sun, Govt. of Peru, 1989. Mem. Am. Soc., Am. Fgn. Svc. Assn., Coun. on Fgn. Rels., Met. Mus. Art. Office: Dept State 3030 Arizona Ave NW Washington DC 20016

WATSON, ANDREW SAMUEL, psychiatry and law educator; b. Highland Park, Mich., May 2, 1920; s. Andrew Nicol and Eva Arvel (Barnes) W.; m. Catherine Mary Osborne, Sept. 1942; children: Andrew Nicol, John Lewis, David Winfield, Steven; m. Joyce Lynn Goldstein, July 21, 1967. BS in Zoology, U. Mich., 1942; MD, Temple U., 1950, M in Med. Sci., 1954. Intern, U. Pa. Grad. Hosp., 1950-51; resident in psychiatry Temple U., Phila., 1951-54; spl. lectr. Sch. Social Work, Bryn Mawr Coll., 1955-59; mem. med. faculty U. Pa., 1954-59, law faculty, 1955-59; prof. psychiatry U. Mich., Ann Arbor, 1959-80, mem. law faculty, 1959-90, prof. emeritus psychiatry and law, 1990; pvt. practice medicine, specializing in psychiatry, Ann Arbor, 1959—. Mem. Mich. Law Enforcement and Criminal Justice Commn., 1968-72. Served to capt. Med. Service Corps, AUS, 1942-46. Recipient Issac Ray award Am. Psychiat. Assn., 1978. Mem. Am. Psychiat. Assn., Am. Coll. Psychiatry, ABA (assoc.). Democrat. Unitarian. Author: Psychiatry for Lawyers, rev. edit., 1978; The Lawyer in the Interviewing and Counseling Process, 1976; others. Home: 21 Ridgeway St Ann Arbor MI 48104-1739 Office: 555 E William St Apt 21D Ann Arbor MI 48104-2427

WATSON, ANTHONY L., health facility executive; b. 1942. Supervising pub. health advisor dept.health edn. and welfare Ctr. for Disease Control, Pub. Health Svc., 1966-70; dep. dir. Comprehensive Health Planning Agy., N.Y.C., 1970-76; exec. v.p. Health Systems Agency of N.Y.C., 1976-85; pres. Health Ins. Plan Greater N.Y., N.Y.C. Mem. Community Council of Greater N.Y.; pres, CEO The N.Y. Urban Coalition. Mem. Am. Health Planning Assn., Am. Hosp. Assn. Office: Health Ins Plan Greater NY 7 W 34th St New York NY 10001

WATSON, ARTHUR DENNIS, government official; b. Brownsville, Pa., May 11, 1950; s. Arthur Francis Puglia and Margaret Teresa Mastile; stepson of John Leslie Watson; m. Kathleen Frances Zaccardo, July 16, 1983; 1 child, Fiona Kathleen. BSBA, U. Richmond, 1972; MS in Bus.-Govt. Rels. Am. U., 1977, MA in Lit., 1979; PhD in English Lang. and Lit. Cath. U., 1987. Statisical asst. U.S. Postal Svc. Hdqrs., Washington, 1972-73, economist assoc., 1973-74, staff economist, 1974-77, mktg. analyst, 1977; rate analyst U.S. Postal Rate Commn., Washington, 1977-79, dir. pub. affairs, 1979-82; spokesman, pub. affairs officer ICC, Washington, 1982-89, dep. dir. pub. affairs, 1989-93, assoc. dir. congl. and pub. affairs, 1993—; pres. Arthur D. Watson and Co., Clifton, Va., 1983—. Washington corr. Linn's Stamp News, Sidney, Ohio, 1983-84; pub. rels. columnist Arundel Communications, Reston, Va., 1991-92; contbr. articles to profl. jours.; reader Washington Ear, WETA-FM radio side channel, 1977. With USCG, 1972-78. Recipient Meritorious Svc. medal, Pub. Svc. award ICC, 1989. Mem. Nat. Assn. Govt. Communicators, E. Claiborne Robins Sch. Bus. Alumni Assn., Assn. Transp. Law, Logistics and Policy, USS Natoma Bay Assn., Pub. Rels. Soc. Am. Roman Catholic. Avocations: classical music, reading, writing, model building, travel. Home: 6521 Rockland Dr Clifton VA 22024-2415 Office: ICC Rm 3130 1201 Constitution Ave NW Washington DC 20423-0001

WATSON, BILLY, publishing executive, newspaper; b. Pitts, Ga., Sept. 7, 1938; m. Helen Turk; children: Kevin, Kim Holland. Degree in Journalism, U. Ga., 1960; postgrad., Ga. State U. With Cordele Dispatch, Wilcox County Chronicle, 1960-61; with Macon Telegraph, 1963, 67-78, bur. chief Atlanta, 1963-67; exec. editor Telegraph and News, 1978-83, gen. mgr., 1983-87; pres., pub. Columbus Ledger-Enquirer, 1987—; vis. instr. journalism Mercer U.; mem. journalism bd. U. Ga.; pres. Ga. AP, chmn. News Coun. AP. Founding chmn. Columbus Literate Community Program, Inc.; past chmn. Ga. Coun. Adult Literacy; bd. dirs. UPtown Columbus, Columbus Tech. Inst., Creek Indian Meml. Assn. With US Army. Mem. Ga. Press Assn. (former pres.), U. Ga. Journalism Alumni Assn. (former pres.), Columbus Rotary Club, Columbus Country Club, Chattahoochee River Club, Columbus C. of C. (bd. dirs.). Avocations: swimming, running, fishing, bluegrass music. Office: R W Page Corp 17 W 12th St Columbus GA 31901-2413

WATSON, C. L. (CHUCK WATSON), gas industry executive; b. 1950. Grad., Okla. State U., 1972. With Conoco, Inc., Houston, 1972-85; pres, CEO Natural Gas Clearinghouse, Houston, 1985—. Office: Natural Gas Clearinghouse 13430 Northwest Fwy Houston TX 77040

WATSON, CATHERINE ELAINE, journalist; b. Mpls., Feb. 9, 1944; d. Richard Edward and LaVonne (Slater) W.; m. Al Sicherman (div.); children: Joseph Sicherman, David Sicherman. B.A. in Journalism, U. Minn., 1967; M.A. in Teaching, Coll. of St. Thomas, 1971. Reporter Mpls. Star Tribune, 1966-72; editor Minneapolis, 1972-78, Travel sect., 1978—; editor in chief Galena (Ill.) Gazette, 1990-91. Author: Travel Basics, 1984. Contbr. articles to newspapers and travel mags. Recipient Newspaper Mag. Picture Editor's award Pictures of Yr. Competition, 1974, 75, awards for writing and photography Soc. Am. Travel Writers, 1983-94, Photographer of Yr. award, 1990, Alumna of Notable Achievement award U. Minn. Coll. Liberal Arts, 1994; named Lowell Thomas Travel Journalist of Yr., 1990. Mem. Am. Newspaper Guild, Soc. Am. Travel Writers, Phi Beta Kappa, Kappa Tau Alpha, Alpha Omicron Pi. Office: 425 Portland Ave Minneapolis MN 55488-0001

WATSON, DEAN, agricultural products. Pres. Koch Nitrogen Co., Inc., Wichita, Kas. Office: Koch Nitrogen Co Inc 4111 E 37th St N Wichita KS 67220*

WATSON, DENNIS WALLACE, microbiology educator, scientist; b. Morpeth, Ont., Can., Apr. 29, 1914; came to U.S., 1938, naturalized, 1946; s. William and Sarah (Verity) W.; m. Alicemay Whittier, June 15, 1941; children: Catherine W., William V. BSA, U. Toronto, 1934; MS, Dalhousie U., 1937; PhD, U. Wis., 1941, DSc (hon.), 1981. Rsch. assoc. U. Wis., 1942, asst. prof., 1946-49; vis. investigator Rockefeller Inst., 1942; investigator Connaught Lab. Med. Rsch. U. Toronto, 1942-44; assoc. prof. U. Minn., Mpls., 1949-52; prof. U. Minn., 1953-63, head dept. microbiology, 1964-84, Regents prof. microbiology, 1980-84, Regents prof. emeritus, 1984—; vis. prof. Med. Sch. U. Wash., 1950; mem. Commn. Immunization Armed Forces Epidemiology Bd., 1946-59; mem. bd. sci. counselors, div. biol. standards NIH, 1957-59, mem. Cont. Inst. Allergy and Infectious Diseases, 1964, mem. adv. coun., 1967-71; mem. microbiology panel Office Naval Rsch., 1963-66; vice chmn. Am. Soc. Microbiology Found., 1973; bd. dirs. Nat. Found. Infectious Diseases, 1976-81. Editorial bd. Infection and Immunity, 1971-72; editorial cons. Medcom Faculty Medicine, 1973—. With AUS, 1944-46. Recipient USPHS Research Career award, 1962-64; Spl. research fellow USPHS, 1960-61. Mem. AAAS, Am. Assn. Immunologists, Am. Chem. Soc., Am. Acad. Microbiology (vice chmn. bd. govs. 1967), Am. Soc. Microbiology (pres. 1969, v.p. Found. 1972-73), Soc. Exptl. Biology and Medicine (coun. 1977-79, pres. 1976-77), Lancefield Soc., Sigma Xi, Phi Zeta. Home: 2106 Hendon Ave Saint Paul MN 55108-1419 Office: U Minn Med Sch Dept Microbiology PO Box 196 Minneapolis MN 55455

WATSON, DOC (ARTHEL LANE WATSON), vocalist, guitarist, banjoist, recording artist; b. Deep Gap, N.C., Mar. 2, 1923; s. General Dixon and Annie (Greer) W.; m. Rosa Lee Carlton; children—Eddy Merle (dec.), Nancy Ellen. Ind. rec. artist, touring performer. Made first appearance at Boone (N.C.) Fiddler's Conf., rec. artist for Folkways in 1960's, signed with Vanguard Records, 1964, also recorded for United Artists, Columbia, Poppy, Sugar Hill, Verve and Flying Fish labels; performed at Newport Folk Festival, 1963, Smithsonian Inst., White House, 1980, Carnegie Hall, 1985; toured in Africa for Dept. State, 1970, also toured in Europe and Japan; albums include (many with Merle Watson) Southbound, Red Rocking Chair, The Guitar Album, Riding the Midnight Train (Grammy award for Best Traditional Folk album, 1986), Portrait, Songs for Little Pickers, On Praying Ground (Grammay award for best traditional folk album 1990); performed music for film Places in the Heart. Recipient Grammy award Nat. Acad. Rec. Arts and Scis., 1973, 74, 79, 86, 90, N.C. award State of N.C., 1985, Carolina prize N.Y. Times Corp., 1985, Grammy award for Best Traditional Folk Rec., 1990. Office: care Folklore Inc 1671 Appian Way Santa Monica CA 90401-3258

WATSON, DONALD RALPH, architect, universiity dean, author; b. Providence, Sept. 27, 1937; s. Ralph Giles W. and Ethel (Fletcher) Pastene; m. Marja Palmqvist, Sept. 8, 1966 (div. Jan. 1984); children: Petrik, Elise; m. Judith Criste, Jan. 3, 1986. A.B., Yale U., 1959, B.Arch., 1962, M.Ed., 1969. Lic. architect Nat. Council Archtl. Registration Bds. Architect Peace Corps, Tunisia, 1962-64; archtl. cons. Govt. of Tunisia, 1964-65; pvt. practice, Trumbull, Conn., 1969-90; dean Sch. Architecture, Rensselaer Poly. Inst., Troy, N.Y., 1990-95; chmn. environ. design program, Yale U., 1979-90; cons. UN, Bhutan, 1976, World Bank, North Yemen, 1979, Dept. of Energy, 1979, NAS, 1982, U.S. Advanced Bldg. Tech. Coun., 1991. Author: Designing and Building a Solar House, 1977, Energy Conservation Through Building Design, 1979, Climatic Design, 1983, Energy Design Handbook, 1993. Bd. dirs. Save the Children Fedn., 1979-82. Recipient Honor Design award Conn. Soc. Architects, 1974, Honor Design award region AIA, 1978, 84, 1st award Owens Corning Energy Conservation Bldg. Design Program, 1983, Excellence in housing award Energy Efficient Bldg. Assn., 1988, Lifetime Achievement award Passive and Low Energy Architecture, 1990; Assn. of Collegiate Schs. of Archtecture/Am. Metals Climax rsch. fellow, 1967-69; rsch. fellow Rockefeller Found., 1978. Fellow AIA; mem. Am. Solar Energy Soc. (editor). Home and Office: 54 Larkspur Dr Trumbull CT 06611

WATSON, EDWARD L., electric utility executive; b. Wichita Falls, Tex., Aug. 27, 1934; s. Samuel Edward and Dillie Ima (Thompson) W.; m. Martha Nann Lambert, May 31, 1953; children: Laura, Karan, Jeffrey. A. in EE, Arlington State U., 1955. Engring. asst. TU Elect., Wichita Falls, 1952-56, chief dispatcher, 1956-60; sales rep. TU Elect., Midland, Tex., 1960-64; mgr. TU Elect., Andrews, Tex., 1964-66, Odessa, Tex., 1966-72; div. mgr. TU Elect., Wichita Falls, 1972-76; v.p. TU Elect., Ft. Worth, Tex., 1976-85; sr. v.p. TU Elect., Dallas, 1985–; also bd. dirs. TU Elect., 1987–; chmn., dir. Industrial Found., 1963, 71. Mem. House Select com. on Statewide Energy Plan, Austin, 1988; bd. regents, Midwestern State U., 1986–. Named Outstanding Young Man Odessa Jaycees, 1972. Mem. Tex. Rsch. League (bd. dirs. 1987–), Assn. Elec. Cos. of Tex. (bd. dirs. 1988–), Tex. Assn. Taxpayers (bd. dirs. 1988–). Methodist. Avocations: swimming, travel. Office: Tex Utilities Electric Co 2001 Bryan St Dallas TX 75201-3002

WATSON, ELIZABETH MARION, protective services official; b. Phila., Aug. 25, 1949; d John Julian and Elizabeth Gertrude (Judge) Herrmann; m. Robert LLoyd Watson, June 18, 1976; children: Susan, Mark, David. BA in Psychology with honors, Tex. Tech. U., 1971. With Houston Police Dept., 1972-92, detective homicide, burglary and theft, 1976-81, lt. records div. northeast patrol div., 1981-84, capt. inspections div., auto theft div., 1984-87, dep. chief west patrol bur., 1987-90, police chief, 1990-92; with Austin, Tex. Police Dept., 1992–, police chief, 1992–; mem. editorial bd. S.W. Law Enforcement Inst., Richardson,Tex., 1990–. Mem. editorial bd. Am. Jour. Police, 1991–. mem. Internat. Assn. Chiefs of Police (mem. exec. com., mem. civil rights com.), Police Exec. Rsch. Form, Tex. Police Chiefs Assn. Roman Catholic. Office: Police Department PO Box 1088 Austin TX 78767-8801

WATSON, ELLEN L., academic administrator; b. Sioux City, Iowa, Jan. 14, 1948; d. Homer V. and Elsie (Bertelsen) W. AB, Wellesley Coll., 1970; MLS, U. Md., 1973. Cataloger Eisenhower Libr. Johns Hopkins U., Balt., 1970-74; appointments sec. to mayor City of Balt., 1974-75; libr. Community Coll. Balt., 1975-82, acting dir. librs., 1982-83; dir. learning resources ctr. Ark. Coll., Batesville, 1983-88; dir. Cullom-Davis Libr. Bradley U., Peoria, Ill., 1988–; interim assoc. provost info. technologies and resources Cullom-Davis Libr. Bradley U., Peoria, Ill., 1995–; adv. bd. Ill. Valley Libr. System, Pekin, 1989–. Contbr. articles to profl. jours. and chpts. to books. Mem. ALA, Assn. Coll. and Rsch. Librs., Libr. Adminstrn. and Mgmt. Assn., Libr. and Info. Tech. Assn., Ill. Libr. Assn., Ill. Assn. Coll. and Rsch. Librs., Phi Kappa Phi. Avocations: morgan horses, reading. Office: Bradley U Cullom-Davis Library 1511 W Bradley Ave Peoria IL 61625

WATSON, GEORGE HENRY, JR., broadcast executive, journalist; b. Birmingham, Ala., July 27, 1936; s. George Henry and Grace Elizabeth (Carr) W.; m. Ellen Havican Bradley, July 13, 1979; children—George H., III, Ellen Havican. B.A., Harvard U., 1959; M.S., Columbia U., 1960. Reporter Washington Post, 1960-61; corr. ABC News, 1962-75, Moscow bur. chief, 1966-69, London bur. chief, 1969-75, v.p., Washington bur. chief, 1976-80; v.p., mng. editor Cable News Network, 1980; v.p. news ABC News, N.Y.C., 1981-85; exec. in charge ABC News Viewpoint ABC News, 1981-85, v.p., Washington bur. chief, 1985-93, sr. contbg. editor, 1993–. Bd. advisors Grad. Sch. Journalism, Berkeley.Served with U.S. Army, 1958. Recipient Peabody award, 1982, DuPont Columbia award, 1983, nat. news Emmy award, 1984. Mem. Radio Television News Dirs. Assn., Soc. Profl. Journalists, Nat. Press Club, Overseas Press Club (award for best television documentary 1971, citation for excellence 1974), Washington Press Club, Com. to Protect Journalists. Club: Fed. City. Office: ABC News 1717 Desales St NW Washington DC 20036-4407

WATSON, GEORGE WILLIAM, lawyer, legal consultant; b. Eaton Rapids, Mich., Mar. 1, 1926; m. Ruth Carpenter Murphy, Oct. 1, 1949; children: G. William, Linda, Daniel, Thomas, Rose Mary. AB, U. Mich., 1947, JD, 1950. Bar: Mich. 1951, U.S. Dist. Ct. (ea. and we. dists.) Mich. 1951, U.S. Ct. Military Appeals, 1991. Pvt. practice law Charlotte, Mich., 1951-53; dir. Kalamazoo Legal Aid Bur., 1953-54; asst. pros. atty. Kalamazoo County, 1955-56; gen. atty. Office Civil and Def. Mobilization, Battle Creek, Mich., 1956-62, Def. Civil Preparedness Agy., Washington, 1962-80; assoc. gen. counsel Fed. Emergency Mgmt. Agy., Washington 1980–88, gen. counsel, 1988-91; cons. on adminstrn law and govtl. affairs pvt. practice, Alexandria, Va., 1991–. Pres. Mt. Vernon/Lee Enterprises, Alexandria, Va., 1988-94; commordor Nat. Yacht Club, Washington, 1981. With USN, 1944-46, PTO. Mem. State Bar of Mich. Episcopalian. Avocations: community svc., sailboat racing. Home and Office: 2108 Huntington Ave Alexandria VA 22303-1534

WATSON, GEORGIANNA, librarian; b. Lock Haven, Pa., Feb. 18, 1949; d. George and Anna (Eisenhower) Rhine; children: Sharga Nicolle, George Winfield-Martin. BS in Edn., Lock Haven State U., 1971; MLS, Brigham Young U., 1978; M in Pub. Adminstrn., John Jay Coll. Criminal Justice, N.Y.C., 1986. Tchr. Mifflin County Sch. Dist., Lewistown, Pa., 1971-72; librarian Shiprock Boarding Sch. Bur. Indian Affairs, Shiprock, N.Mex., 1972-79, Ft. Sill Indian Sch. Bur. Indian Affairs, Lawton, Okla., 1979-80; librarian U.S Mil. Acad., West Point, N.Y., 1980-83, head pub. services, library, 1983–. mem. Southeastern N.Y. Library Resource Council (mem. continuing edn. com., chairperson govt. documents interest group), Southeastern N.Y. Reference Library Interest Group, Am. Quarter Horse Assn., Internat. Arabian Horse Assn., Pi Alpha Alpha. Republican. Home: 176 Plains Rd Walden NY 12586-2443 Office: US Mil Acad Dept Army West Point NY 10996-1799

WATSON, H. MITCHELL, JR., business machines company executive. BA, U. Tenn, MS, U. Tenn. Systems engr. IBM Corp., 1962-66, br. mgr., Knoxville, Tenn., 1966-69, systems developer, 1969-71, dir. plans and controls system devel., 1971-73, v.p. plans and controls, 1973-74, v.p. tech com., mfg. systems com., 1974-77, asst. group exec. requirements Data Processing Mktg. Group, 1977-79, asst. group exec. plans and controls Data Processing Products Group, 1979-80, corp. v.p., pres. system products div., 1980-86, corp. v.p. mktg., 1986–. Office: Rolm Co PO Box 5017 Norwalk CT 06856-5017 Also: IBM Old Orchard Rd Armonk NY 10504

WATSON, HARLAN L(EROY), federal official, physicist, economist; b. Macomb, Ill., Dec. 17, 1944; s. Joseph Carroll and Helen Louise (Sanders)

W.; m. Sharon Ann Rinkus Diguette, Apr. 22, 1977. BA in Physics, Western Ill. U., 1967; PhD in Physics, Iowa State U., 1973; MA in Econs., Georgetown U., 1981. Postdoctoral fellow Argonne (Ill.) Nat. Lab., 1973-75; project scientist, then sr. scientist B-K Dynamics, Inc., Rockville, Md., 1975-78; tech. staff TRW Energy Systems Planning Group, Mc Lean, Va., 1978-80; profl. staff mem. subcom. on energy nuclear proliferation and govt. processes Com. on Govtl. Affairs, U.S. Senate, Washington, 1980-81; tech. and sci. cons. Com. on Sci. and Tech., U.S. Ho. of Reps., 1981-86; rep. energy and environ., coord. Com. on Sci., Space and Tech., U.S. Ho. of Reps., 1986-89; sci. adviser to sec. Dept. Interior, Washington, 1989-93, dep. asst. sec. for sci.-water and sci., 1989-90, prin. dep. asst. to sec. for water and sci., 1990-93; rep. spl. asst. subcom. energy, com. sci., space, tech. U.S. Ho. of Reps., Washington, 1993-95, staff dir. subcom. energy and environment, com. sci., 1995–. Contbr. articles to profl. jours. Mem. AAAS. Home: 6719 Tomlinson Ter Cabin John MD 20818 Office: B 374 Rayburn House Office Bldg Washington DC 20515

WATSON, HAROLD GEORGE, ordnance company executive, mechanical engineer; b. Phoenix, Oct. 19, 1931; s. Clarence Elmer and Eunice A. (Record) W.; m. Ruth May Thomas, Aug. 30, 1951 (dec.); children: Patricia Ruth, Linda Darlene, Harold George; m. Katherina Anna Kish, Sept. 22, 1990. B.S., U. Ariz., 1954. Engr. Shell Oil Co., L.A., 1954; project engr. Talco Engring. Co., Hamden Conn., 1956, area mgr., Mesa, Ariz., 1956-57, chief engr. Rocket Power, 1958-61, dir. engring., 1961-64; dir. engring. Space Ordnance Systems, El Segundo, Calif., 1964-68; dir. engring. Universal Propulsion Co., Riverside, Calif., 1968-70, gen. mgr., v.p. engring., Tempe, Ariz., 1970-76, v.p., mgr., 1976-77, pres., gen. mgr. Phoenix, 1977–. Patentee in field. 1st lt. USAR, 1954-56. Mem. Am. Mgmt. Assn., SAFE Assn. (past pres.), AIAA, Air Force Assn., Internat. Pyronetics Soc., Am. Def. Preparedness Assn. Office: Universal Propulsion Co Inc 25401 N Central Ave Phoenix AZ 85027

WATSON, JACK CROZIER, state supreme court justice; b. Jonesville, La., Sept. 17, 1928; s. Jesse Crozier and Gladys Lucille (Talbot) W.; m. Henrietta Sue Carter, Dec. 26, 1958; children: Carter Crozier (dec.), Wells Talbot. BA, U. Southwestern La., 1949; JD, La. State U., 1956; completed with honor, Appellate Judges Seminar, N.Y.U., 1974, Sr. Appellate Judges Seminar, 1980. Bar: La. 1956. Atty. King, Anderson & Swift, Lake Charles, La., 1956-58; prosecutor City of Lake Charles, 1960; asst. dist. atty. Calcasieu Parish, La., 1961-64; ptnr. Watson & Watson, Lake Charles, 1961-64; judge 14th Jud. Dist., La., 1964-72; judge ad hoc Ct. Appeals, 1st Circuit, Baton Rouge, 1972-73; judge Ct. Appeals, 3rd Circuit, Lake Charles, 1973-79; asso. justice La. Supreme Ct., New Orleans, 1979–; faculty advisor Nat. Coll. State Judiciary, Reno, 1970, 73; adj. prof. law summer sch. program in Greece, Tulane U., 1988-94; del. NEH Seminar, 1976 La. del. to Internat. Conf. Appellate Magistrates, The Philippines, 1977; mem. La. Jud. Coun., 1986-92. 1st lt. USAF, 1950-54. Mem. ABA, La. Bar Assn., S.W. La. Bar Assn. (pres. 1973), Law Inst. State of La., La. Coun. Juvenile Ct. Judges (pres. 1969-70), Am. Judicature Soc., S.W. La. Camellia Soc. (pres. 1973-74), Am. Legion (post comdr. 1963), Lake Charles Yacht Club (commodore 1974), Blue Key, Sigma Alpha Epsilon, Phi Delta Phi, Pi Kappa Delta. Democrat. Baptist. Office: La Supreme Ct 301 Loyola Ave New Orleans LA 70112-1800

WATSON, JACK H., JR., lawyer; b. El Paso, Tex., Oct. 24, 1938; children: Melissa Woodward, Lincoln Hearn. BA, Vanderbilt U., 1960; LLB, Harvard U., 1966. Bar: Ga. 1965, D.C. 1978. Assoc. King & Spalding, Atlanta, 1966-71; partner King & Spalding, 1972-77; asst. to Pres. for intergovtl. affairs and sec. to cabinet Washington, 1977-80; chief of staff White House, 1980-81; ptnr. Long, Aldridge & Norman, Atlanta, 1981–; mem. vis. com. Harvard Law Sch., 1987-93; permanent chmn. Ga. Joint Commn. on Alt. Dispute Resolution, 1990-93, chmn. Ga. Commn. on Dispute Resolution, 1993–. Counsel Met. Atlanta Commn. Crime and Juvenile Delinquency, 1966-67; trustee Milton S. Eisenhower Found., 1994–; pres. Met. Atlanta Mental Health Assn., 1971-72; chmn. Gov.'s Study Commn. Alcohol, 1971-72, Ga. Alcoholism Adv. Council, 1972; chmn. bd. Ga. Dept. Human Resources, 1972-77; candidate gov. of Ga., 1982; mem. nat. adv. com. Ctr. for Study of Presidency, 1983; mem. Franklin D. Roosevelt Library Bd., 1986–; chmn. 20th Century Fund Task Force on the U.S. Vice Presidency, 1987-88; active Franklin and Eleanor Roosevelt Instnl. Bd., 1990–. Served as officer USMC. Named One of Atlanta's Five Outstanding Young Men Jaycees, 1970. Mem. ABA (standing com. on dispute resolution 1991-93, coun. mem. sect. dispute resolution 1993–, chmn. ABA task force on N.Am. Free Trade Agreement 1993), State Bar Ga., Atlanta Bar Assn., Atlanta Lawyers Club, Phi Beta Kappa, Phi Eta Sigma, Omicron Delta Kappa. Office: Long Aldridge & Norman Ste 600 701 Pennsylvania Ave Washington DC 20004

WATSON, JAMES D., JR., principal; b. Phila., Apr. 8, 1943; s. James D. and Alice Geneva W.; m. Linda Watson, Aug. 1, 1987; children: D'Ana, Asher, Janine, Antonio. BS, Cheyney State Coll., 1966, MS; postgrad., Temple U.; student, Pa. State U. Cert. reading, elem. and secondary principalship, supt. Tchr., grade 6 Abington (Pa.) Sch. Dist.; tchr., grades 7-8 Chester (Pa.) Twp. Sch. Dist.; tchr., grades 5-8 Phila. (Pa.) Sch. Dist.; prin. Bensalem (Pa.) Sch. Dist.; developer High Expectations Program. Recipient commendations from Phila. City Coun., Mayor, Gov. and Bensalem Sch. Bd. Mem. Nat. Assn. for Elem. (Sch.) Prins., Am. Assn. for Elem. Sch. Prins., Nat. Assn. Black Sch. Educators.

WATSON, JAMES DEWEY, molecular biologist, educator; b. Chicago, Ill., Apr. 6, 1928; s. James Dewey and Jean (Mitchell) W.; m. Elizabeth Lewis, 1968; children: Rufus Robert, Duncan James. BS, U. Chgo., 1947, DSc (hon.), 1961; PhD in Zoology, Ind. U., 1950, DSc (hon.), 1963; LLD (hon.), U. Notre Dame, 1965; DSc (hon.), L.I. U., 1970, Adelphi U., 1972, Brandeis U., 1973, Albert Einstein Coll. Medicine, 1974, Hofstra U., 1976, Harvard U., 1978, Rockefeller U., 1980, Clarkson Coll., 1981, SUNY, 1983; MD (hon.), U. Buenos Aires, Argentina, 1986; DSc (hon.), Rutgers U., 1988, Bard Coll., 1991, U. Cambridge, 1993, Fairfield U., 1993, U. Stellenbosch, 1993. Rsch. fellow NRC, U. Copenhagen, 1950-51; Nat. Found. Infantile Paralysis fellow Cavendish Lab., Cambridge U., 1951-52, 55-56; sr. rsch. fellow biology Calif. Inst. Tech., 1953-55; asst. prof. biology Harvard U., 1955-58, assoc. prof., 1958-61, prof., 1961-76; dir. Cold Spring Harbor Lab., N.Y., 1968-94, pres., 1994–; assoc. dir. Nat. Ctr. for Human Genome Rsch. NIH, 1988-89, dir. Nat. Ctr. for Human Genome Rsch., 1989-92; Newton-Abraham vis. prof. Oxford U., 1994. Author: Molceular Biology of the Gene, 1965, 4th edit., 1986, The Double Helix, 1968, (with John Tooze) The DNA Story, 1981, (with others) The Molecular Biology of the Cell, 1983, 2d edit., 1989, (with John Tooze and David Kurtz) Recombinant DNA, A Short Course, 1983, 2d edit., 1992. Named Hopn. fellow Clare Coll., Cambridge U.; recipient (with F.H.C. Crick) John Collins Warren prize Mass. Gen. Hosp. 1959, Eli Lilly award in biochemistry Am. Chem. Soc., 1959, Albert Lasker prize Am. Pub. Health Assn., 1960, (with F.H.C. Crick) Rsch. Corp. prize, 1962, (with F.H.C. Crick and M.H.F. Wilkins) Nobel prize in medicine, 1962, Presdl. Medal of Freedom, 1977, Kaul Found. award for excellence, 1993, Nat. Biotech. Venture award, 1993, Copley Medal, 1993, Royal Society. Mem. NAS (Carty medal 1971), Am. Philos. Soc., Am. Assn. Cancer Rsch., Am. Acad. Arts and Scis., Am. Soc. Biol. Chemistry, Royal Soc. (London) (Copley medal 1993), Acad. Scis. Russia, Danish Acad. Arts and Scis. Home: Bungtown Rd Cold Spring Harbor NY 11724 Office: Cold Spring Harbor Lab PO Box 100 Cold Spring Harbor NY 11724-0100*

WATSON, J(AMES) HUGH, banker; b. Arcadia, La., Oct. 25, 1917; s. James Austin and Mary Virginia (Hays) W.; m. Harriet Jane Taylor, July 20, 1947; 1 child, Margaret W. Martin. Bus. cert., Chillicothe Coll. 1936. Nat. bank examiner Comptroller of Currency, 1946-48; with First Nat. Bank, Shreveport, La., 1948–, pres., 1964-81, chmn. bd., chief exec. officer, 1981-84, chmn. bd., 1984–; chmn. bd. First Nat. Bancorp, Inc., 1980-84; chmn. bd. First Mortgage Corp., 1982-84, La. Banshares, Inc., 1985-87, Premier Bancorp, Inc., 1987–; bd. dirs. Premier Investment Advisors, Inc., Premier Securities Corp. Trustee, chmn. exec. com. Centenary Coll. 1967–; bd. dirs. Council for A Better La., Baton Rouge, 1968-84, Pub. Solicitation Rev. Council, 1970–; mem. trust com. Norwela council Boy Scout Am., 1985–; pres. First Nat. Family Found., Shreveport, 1955–; bd. dirs. La. State Fair Assn., 1974–, Frost Found., Denver, 1975–; Neighborhood Housing Services, 1977-84. Served with U.S. Army, 1942-46. Recipient Clyde E. Fant Meml. award United Way, 1974, Humanitarian award Community Council,

1979; named Mr. Shreveport Optimist Club, 1977; Bus. Leader of Yr. C. of C., 1982; Heritage award Arcadia (La.) C. of C., 1986. Methodist. Clubs: East Ridge Country, Shreveport. Lodge: Rotary (Paul Harris Fellow award 1982). Office: Premier Bancorp Inc 451 Florida St Baton Rouge LA 70801-1705

WATSON, JAMES LOPEZ, federal judge; b. N.Y.C., May 21, 1922; s. James S. and Violet (Lopez) W.; m. D'Jaris Hinton Watson, July 14, 1956 (dec. Nov. 1989); children: Norman, Karen, Kris. B.A. in Govt, N.Y. U., 1947; LL.B., Bklyn. Law Sch., 1951. Bar: N.Y. bar 1951. Mem. N.Y. Senate from 21st Senatorial Dist., 1954-63; judge Civil Ct. N.Y., 1964-66; acting judge N.Y. State Supreme Ct., 1965; judge U.S. Customs Ct., 1966-80, U.S. Ct. Internat. Trade, 1980–. Bd. dirs. N.Y.C. Police Athletic League. Served with inf. AUS, World War II, ETO. Decorated Purple Heart, Combat Inf. badge. Mem. ABA, N.Y. State Bar Assn., Fed. Bar Council, World Peace Through Law. Home: 676 Riverside Dr New York NY 10031-5529 Office: US Ct Internat Trade 1 Federal Plz New York NY 10278-0001

WATSON, JENNIFER DARROW, foreign service and political officer, researcher; b. Raleigh, N.C., Apr. 18, 1960; d. William Randolph and Julie W. BA with highest honors, U. N.C., 1982; MA, U. Toronto, Canada, 1986, Johns Hopkins U., Bologna, Italy and Washington, 1987. Intern Greeley (Colo.) Police Dept., 1979; researcher/legal intern Dickstein, Shapiro & Morin, Washington, 1980; researcher/intern Govt. of Ontario, Toronto, 1981; resident asst. U. N.C. Housing Dept., Chapel Hill, N.C., 1980-81; math tchr., coach The Loomis Chaffee Sch., Windsor, Conn., 1982-84; v.p. Robert Ellsworth & Co., Inc., Washington, 1987-90; fgn. svc. and polit. officer Fgn. Svc. Inst. U.S. Dept. State, Rosslyn, Va., 1990–; tutor Saturday Learning Extension Program, Washington, 1988-89. Chair Morehead Found. Alumni (DC chpt.), 1988–; adv. Students Against Drunk Driving, 1982-84. Open fellow U. Toronto, 1984; John Motley Morehead Found. scholar, 1978. Mem. Japan-Am. Soc. Washington, Assn. Polit. Risk Analysts, Phi Beta Kappa. Democrat. Episcopalian. Avocations: volleyball, basketball, tennis, drawing, biking. Office: Dept of Labor Pub Affairs 200 Constitution Ave NW Washington DC 20210

WATSON, JERRY CARROLL, advertising executive; b. Greenville, Ala., Aug. 22, 1943; s. William J. and Georgia Katherine (Mixon) W.; m. Judith Zeigler Brooks, Sept. 16, 1988; 1 child, Theodore William. BS, U. Ala., Tuscaloosa, 1967. Staff writer Phillips, Eindhoven, The Netherlands, 1967-68; mgr. mktg. Fuller & Dees Mktg., Montgomery, Ala., 1968-70; v.p. Univ. Programs, Washington, 1970-73; pres. Coll. & Univ. Press, Washington, 1973-80; ptnr. Direct Response Consulting Svcs., McLean, Va., 1981–; bd. dirs. Foxhall Corp., The Art Co. Founding mem. Am. Inst. Cancer Rsch. Mem. Direct Mktg. Assn., Non-Profit Mailer Fedn., Promotional Mktg. Assn., Assn. Direct Response Fund Raising Coun., Am. Forestry Assn., Nature Conservancy, Sierra Club, Falls Church (Va.) C. of C. (bd. dirs.), Phi Kappa Psi. Avocation: gardening, astronomy. Home: 850 Dolley Madison Blvd Mc Lean VA 22101-1821 Office: Direct Response Cons Svcs 6849 Old Dominion Dr #300 Mc Lean VA 22101

WATSON, JOHN ALLEN, lawyer; b. Ft. Worth, Sept. 18, 1946; s. John and Mary (Barlow) W.; m. Patricia L. Clardy, Oct. 24, 1946; 1 child, Virginia E. B.A., Rice U., 1968; J.D., U. Tex., Austin, 1971. Bar: Tex. 1971. Assoc. Fulbright & Jaworski, Houston, 1971-78, ptnr., 1978–. Mem. ABA. Office: Fulbright & Jaworski LLP 1301 McKinney Ste 5100 Houston TX 77010-3095

WATSON, JOHN KING, JR., lawyer; b. Cambridge, Mass., Sept. 20, 1926; s. John King and Viola (Merz) W.; m. Audrey Margaret Williams, Aug. 25, 1951; children: John King III, Audrey Margaret, Jennifer Kathryn, Anne Mary, James King. BA, Harvard U., 1949; LLB, Columbia U., 1952. Bar: N.Y. 1953. Assoc. Lord, Day & Lord, Barrett Smith, N.Y.C., 1952-64; ptnr., 1965-87, counsel, 1987-92; of counsel Cadwalader, Wickersham & Taft, 1994–. Trustee Masters Sch., Dobbs Ferry, N.Y., 1978-84; mem. vis. com. Arms and Armor Dept. MEt. Mus. Art. Pvt. 1st class USMC, 1944-46. Mem. Downtown Assn., Harvard Club (N.Y.C.), Armor and Arms of N.Y. (pres. 1984-88), North Fork Country Club, Essex Yacht Club, Old Lyme Country Club. Republican. Avocation: antique arms. Home: 25 River Rd Essex CT 06426-1302 Office: Cadwalader Wickersham & Taft 100 Maiden Ln New York NY 10038

WATSON, JOHN LAWRENCE, III, trade association executive; b. Rome, Ga., Jan. 14, 1932; s. John Lawrence and Mary (Cowen) W.; m. Dorothy Palmer McLanahan, Aug. 9, 1958; children: Mary Palmer Watson Gard, Valerie Catherine Watson Bilbrough, John Lawrence IV. BS, Auburn U., 1954. Trader-over the counter J.C. Bradford & Co., Atlanta, 1957-58; with Robinson Humphrey & Co., Atlanta, 1958-64, dept. head-over the counter, 1964-74, dir. equity trading, 1974-83, dir. capital markets, 1983-85; pres. Security Traders Assn., N.Y.C., 1985–. mem. bd. visitors Babcock Sch. Mgmt. Wake forest U.; past chmn. Parent's Coun. Wofford Coll.; life trustee Pace Acad.; trustee Securities Industry Found. for Econ. Edn. Named Man of Yr., Equities mag. Mem. Nat. Assn. Securities Dealers (dist. chmn. 1982, bd. govs. 1983-85), Am. Mus. Fin. History (trustee), Capital City Club, Piedmont Driving Club (Atlanta), Ponte Vedra Club, Sawgrass Country Club (Ponte Vedra), Univ. Club (N.Y.C.). Home: 115 Central Park W New York NY 10023-4153 Office: Security Traders Assn 1 World Trade Ctr Ste 4511 New York NY 10048-0001

WATSON, JOHN R., landscape illuminating company executive; b. Temple, Tex., Feb. 22, 1922; s. J. Elmer and Florence Catherine (Granger) W.; m. Mary Adele Aspoas, Nov. 2, 1963; children: Suzanne Elizabeth, John Shannon. B.Landscape Architecture, Tex. A&M U., 1943, M.Landscape Architecture, 1946; postgrad., Sorbonne, Paris, Biarritz, France, 1945; studied under, Andrew Dasberg, Taos, 1954. Lighting designer Gen. Electric Co., Nela Park, Cleve., 1948-52; pres., owner John R Watson Landscape Illumination, Dallas, Houston, Austin, Tex., New Orleans, Atlanta, Conn., Charlotte,, Bahamas, P.R., San Francisco, Chgo., West Palm Beach, Hawaii, Tampa, 1953–; mem. com. on exterior lighting U.S. nat. com. Commn. Internat. de L'Eclairage. Contbr.: articles to London Mirror; numerous other publs. Served with AUS, 1942-45. Recipient Design award Nat. Soc. Interior Designers, 1965; various others. Mem. Illuminating Engring. Soc. Methodist. Clubs: Mason. (Dallas), Brookhollow Golf (Dallas); Argyle (San Antonio). Office: 1933 Regal Row Dallas TX 75235-2309

WATSON, JULIAN See BLAKE, BUD

WATSON, KATHARINE JOHNSON, art museum director, art historian; b. Providence, Nov. 11, 1942; d William Randolph and Katherine Johnson (Badger) W.; m. Paul Luther Nyhus, Dec. 17, 1983; stepchildren: Kristina Victoria, Karen Ida, Katharine Ellen. BA, Duke U., 1964; MA, U. Pa., 1967, PhD, 1973. Teaching asst. U. Pa., 1966-67; instr., curator exhbns. U. Pitts., 1969-70; curator of art before 1800 Allen Meml. Art Mus., Oberlin, Ohio, 1973-77; lectr. Oberlin Coll., 1973-77; dir. Peary-MacMillan Artic Mus. Bowdoin Coll., Brunswick, Maine, 1977-83, dir. Mus. of Art, 1977–; trustee Mus. Art of Ogunquit, 1977-89, Regional Art Conservation Lab., Williamstown, 1977-90, Surf Point Found., York, Maine; mem. Smithsonian Coun. Assoc.: Pietro Tacca, 1983; author text for exhbn. catalogues; co-editor: Allen Meml. Art Mus. Bull, 1974-77; contbr. articles to profl. jours. Mem. profl. adv. com. Victoria Soc. Maine, 1988-93; mem. adv. coun. Archives of Am. Art, 1982-90. Kress Found. fellow, 1967-68, Chester Dale Fellow, 1970-71, Am. Coun. Learned Socs. fellow, 1977-78, Villa I Tatti fellow, 1977-78. Mem. Am. Assn. Art Mus. Dirs., Am. Assn. Museums, Coll. Art Assn. Office: Bowdoin Coll Mus Art Walker Art Bldg Brunswick ME 04011

WATSON, KENNETH MARSHALL, physics educator; b. Des Moines, Sept. 7, 1921; s. Louis Erwin and Irene Nellie (Marshall) W.; m. Elaine Carol Miller, Mar. 30, 1946; children: Ronald M., Mark Louis. B.S., Iowa State U., 1943; Ph.D., U. Iowa, 1948; Sc.D. (hon.), U. Ind., 1976. Engr. resch. Naval Rsch. Lab., Washington, 1943-46; mem. staff Inst. Advanced Study Princeton (N.J.) U., 1948-49; rsch. fellow Lawrence Berkeley (Calif.) Lab., 1949-52, mem. staff, 1957-81; asst. prof. physics U. Ind., Bloomington, 1952-54; assoc. prof. physics U. Wis., Madison, 1954-57; prof. physics U. Calif.,

Berkeley, 1957-81; prof. oceanography, dir. marine physics lab. U. Calif., San Diego, 1981-93; cons. Mitre Corp., Sci. Application Corp.; mem. U.S. Pres.'s Sci. Adv. Com. Panels, 1962-71; adviser Nat. Security Coun., 1972-75; bd. dirs. Ctr. for Studies of Dynamics, 1979-88; mem. JASON Adv. Panel; mem. sci. adv. bd. George C. Marshall Inst., 1989—. Author: (with M.L. Goldberger) Collision Theory, 1964, (with J. Welch and J. Bond) Atomic Theory of Gas Dynamics, 1966, (with J. Nutall) Topics in Several Particle Dynamics, 1970, (with Flatté, Munk, Dashen) Sound Transmission Through a Fluctuating Ocean, 1979. Mem. Nat. Acad. Scis. Home: PO Box 9726 Rancho Santa Fe CA 92067-4726 Office: U Calif Marine Physics Lab La Jolla CA 92093

WATSON, LEE ANN, lawyer; b. Huntington, Ind., Oct. 28, 1952. BS, Ind. U., 1973; JD, Washington U., 1976. Bar: Ill. 1976. Ptnr. Katten Muchin & Zavis, Chgo. Mem. ABA, Ill. State Bar Assn., Chgo. Bar Assn. Office: Katten Muchin & Zavis 525 W Monroe St Ste 1600 Chicago IL 60661-3693

WATSON, LINDA ANNE, library director; b. New Milford, Conn., Nov. 26, 1951. Student, Georgetown U., 1969-71; BA summa cum laude, U. Conn., 1972; MLS, Simmons Coll., 1973. Libr., project mgr. Tracor-Jitco, Inc., Rockville, Md., 1974-75, libr. assoc., then AVLINE coord., 1975-79; asst. head selection and acquisitions sect. Nat. Libr. Medicine, NIH, Bethesda, Md., 1979-80, chief materials utilization br., 1980-82, head audiovisual resources sect., 1982-85; dir. info. svcs. Houston Acad. Medicine-Tex. Med. Ctr. Libr., 1985-86, assoc. dir. for pub. svcs., 1986-89, assoc. exec. dir. for libr. ops., 1989-90; dir. Claude Moore Health Scis. Libr., U. Va. Health Scis. Ctr., Charlottesville, 1990—, mem. gen. med. faculty, 1990—; sr. assoc. Cooper and Assocs., Charlottesville, 1985—; mem. adv. com. arthritis info. clearinghouse NIH, 1980-82, diabetes info. clearinghouse, 1984-85; mem. adv. com. combined health info. database HHS, 1983-85; adj. asst. prof. Baylor Coll. Medicine, Houston, 1986-90; adj. asst. prof. U. Tex. Med. Sch., Houston, 1986-90; mem. pub. rels. adv. coun. Tex. Med. Ctr., 1987-89; mem. planning panel on edn. and tng. health sci. librs. Nat. Libr. Medicine, 1993-94; presenter in field. Contbr. articles to profl. jours. Mem. Leadership Charlottesville, 1990—. Grantee Nat. Libr. Medicine, 1990-93, 94-95, Va. State Libr. and Archives, 1993-94, NSF, 1993-94. Mem. ALA, Assn. Coll. and Rsch. Librs., Libr. Adminstrn. and Mgmt. Assn., Am. Med. Informatics Assn., Va. Libr. Assn., Med. Libr. Assn. (chmn. ann. meeting nat. program com. 1992-95), Acad. Health Info. Profls. (disting.), Assn. Acad. Health Scis. Libr. Dirs. (vice chmn. joint legis. task force with Med. Libr. Assn. 1990-94), Va. Coun. Health Scis. Librs. (chmn. 1991-94). Avocations: horses, sports. Home: 200 George Rogers Rd Charlottesville VA 22901 Office: U Va Health Scis Ctr Claude Moore Health Scis Libr HSC Box 234 Charlottesville VA 22908

WATSON, MARY ALICE, academic administrator; b. Dublin, Ga., Apr. 10, 1943; d. Jonnie Cecil and Annie Hudson (Temples) Raffield; m. Ray James Watson, Sept. 1, 1963; children: Ray Jeffry, John Adam (dec.), Sally Ann Watson-Hall. BS in Bus. Edn., Ga. Coll., 1973, MEd in Bus. Edn., 1976; Ednl. Specialist in Vocat. Edn., U. Ga., 1982; EdD, Nova Southeastern U., 1995. Cert. postsecondary edn. adminstr., secondary tchr. and adminstr. Tchr. bus. edn. Treutlen County High Sch., Soperton, Ga., 1973-74, East Laurens High Sch., Dublin, 1974-77; coord. program edn. and career exploration East Laurens Elem. Sch., Dublin, 1977-80; dep. prin. East Laurens Comprehensive High Sch., Dublin, 1980-83; v.p. instrnl. svcs. Heart of Ga. Tech. Inst., Dublin, 1983—; chair v.ps. com. planning and evaluation Instrnl. Svcs. Coun. Ga. Dept. Tech. and Adult Edn., 1990, 91; mem. on-site evaluation team SACS-COEI, Paducah, Ky., 1990, Houston, Tex., 1989, Ochsner Allied Health Programs, Oschner Found. Hosp., New Orleans, 1993; George T. Baker Aviation Sch., Miami, 1993; Ft. Sam Houston Med. Programs, San Antonio, 1993; presenter practicum Nova U. Summer Inst., 1989; participant various seminars and workshops. Vol. Cancer Crusade, 1983—. Mem. Nat. Coun. Community Svcs. and Continuing Edn., Am. Tech. Edn. Assn., Internat. Tech. Edn. Assn., Nat. Coun. Instrnl. Adminstrs., Nat. Coun. Local Adminstrs. Vocat. Edn., Am. Vocat. Assn., Women Bus., Ga. Vocat. Assn., Ga. Assn. Local Adminstrs. Vocat. Edn., Dublin-Laurens County C. of C., Dodge County C. of C., Order Blarney Stones, Pi Omega Pi, Iota Lambda Sigma (v.p. 1994—). Baptist. Avocations: golf, walking, gardening, reading, sewing. Office: Heart of Ga Tech Inst 560 Pinehill Rd Dublin GA 31021-8896

WATSON, MAX P., JR., computer software company executive; b. 1946. Graduate, La. U. With IBM Corp., Houston, 1967-83, Wang Labs., Houston, 1985-90; with BMC Software, Inc., Houston, 1990—, now pres., CEO. Office: BMC Software Inc 2101 Citywest Blvd Houston TX 77042*

WATSON, PATRICIA L., library director; b. Jan. 15, 1939; m. Jack Samuel Watson, 1960; children: Bradley, Amanda. BA, Univ. Tenn., 1961, MS in Libr. and Info. Sci., 1975. Cataloging asst. tech. svcs. dept. Knoxville Pub. Libr., 1961-65; adminstrv. asst. Knoxville-Knox County Pub. Libr., 1975-78, head West Knoxville br. libr., 1978-85; dir. Knox County Pub. Libr. System, 1985—. Bd. dirs. Tanasi Girl Scout Coun., 1981-86; treas. Univ. Tenn. Grad. Sch. Libr. and Info. Sci. Alumni Orgn., 1983-84; elder Farragut Presbyn. Ch. Mem. ALA, Tenn. Libr. Assn. (v.p. 1991-92, pres. 1992-93), East Tenn. Libr. Assn. (pres. 1988-89). Office: Knox County Pub Libr System 500 W Church Ave Knoxville TN 37902-2505

WATSON, PAUL, photojournalist, correspondent. Photographer The Toronto Star, 1980—, Africa bur. chief, 1992-94, Asian bur. chief, 1994—. Recipient Robert Capa gold medal for photography, 1993, Nat. Newspaper award for spot news photography, 1994, Pulitzer Prize for spot news photography, 1994, Nat. Newspaper award for internat. reporting, 1994. Office: The Toronto Star, One Yonge St, Toronto, ON Canada M5E 1E6

WATSON, PAULA D., library administrator; b. N.Y.C., Mar. 6, 1945; d. Joseph Francis and Anna Julia (Miksza) De Simone; m. William Douglas Watson, Aug. 23, 1969; children—Lucia, Elizabeth. A.B., Barnard Coll., 1965; M.A., Columbia U., 1966; M.A.L.S., Syracuse U., 1972. Reference librarian U. Ill., Urbana, 1972-77, city planning and landscape architecture librarian, 1977-79, head documents library, 1979-81; asst. dir. gen. services U. Ill. Library, Urbana, 1981—, acting dir. gen. svcs., 1988-93, dir. ctrl. pub. svcs., 1989-93, asst. univ. libr., 1993—. Contbr. articles to profl. jours. N.Y. State Regents fellow Columbia U., N.Y.C., 1965-66; Council on Library Resources profl. edn. and tng. for librarianship grantee, 1983. Mem. ALA (sec. univ. librs. sect. ALA-Assn. Coll. and Rsch. Librs. 1989-91, mem. libr. adminstrn. mgmt. sect. com. on comparative libr. orgn. 1988-89, mem. conf. planning com. optical disk interest group 1988), Ill. Library Assn. Avocation: gardening. Home: 715 W Delaware Ave Urbana IL 61801-4806 Office: U Ill 246 A Library 1408 W Gregory Dr Urbana IL 61801-3692

WATSON, RICHARD ALLAN, philosophy educator, writer; b. New Market, Iowa, Feb. 23, 1931; s. Roscoe Richard and Daisy Belle (Penwell) W.; m. Patty Jo Andersen, July 30, 1955; 1 child, Anna Melissa. B.A., U. Iowa, 1953, M.A., 1957, Ph.D. in Philosophy, 1961; M.S. in Geology, U. Minn., 1959. Instr. philosophy U. Mich., Ann Arbor, 1961-64; asst. prof. Washington U., St. Louis, 1964-67; assoc. prof. Washington U., 1967-74, prof., 1974—; pres. Cave Research Found., Mammoth Cave, Ky., 1965-67; trustee Nat. Parks and Conservation Assn., Washington, 1969-81. Author: The Downfall of Cartesianism, 1966, Under Plowman's Floor, 1978, The Runner, 1981, The Philosopher's Diet, 1985, The Breakdown of Cartesian Metaphysics, 1987, The Philosopher's Joke, 1990, Writing Philosophy, 1992, Niagara, 1993; (with others) Man and Nature, 1969, The Longest Cave, 1976; editor: Classics in Speleology, 1968-73, Speleologia, 1974-79, Cave Books, 1980—, Jour. History of Philosophy, 1983, Jour. History of Philosophy Mongraph Series, 1985—. Served to 1st lt. USAF, 1953-55. NEH grantee, 1975; fellow Ctr. Advanced Study in Behavioral Scis., Stanford, Calif., 1967-68, 81-82, 91-92, Am. Coun. Learned Socs., 1967-68, Princeton Ctr. Internat. Studies, 1975-76. Mem. Nat. Speleological Soc. (hon. life), AAAS, Am. Philos. Assn., Cave Research Found. Office: Washington U Dept Philosophy Saint Louis MO 63130-4899

WATSON, RICHARD THOMAS, lawyer; b. Lakewood, Ohio, Aug. 21, 1933; s. Thomas Earl Watson and Sara Lucille (Whapham) Hadfield; m. Judith C. Briggs, Aug. 6, 1960; children: David, Andrew, Susan (dec.). AB, Harvard U., 1954, JD, 1960. Bar: Ohio 1960. Assoc. Spieth, Bell, McCurdy & Newell, Cleve., 1960, ptnr., 1965, mng. ptnr., 1987—; bd. dirs. numerous

corps. Chancellor Episcopal Diocese of Ohio, Cleve., 1986—; mem. vis. com. Harvard U. Div. Sch., Cambridge, Mass., 1988—, Harvard U. Univ. Resources, 1992—; v.p. bd. trustees Cleve. Mus. Art, 1991—; trustee Case Western Res. U., 1993—. Mem. Union Club Cleve. Office: Spieth Bell McCurdy & Newell 925 Euclid Ave Cleveland OH 44115

WATSON, ROBERT BARDEN, physicist; b. Champaign, Ill., Apr. 14, 1914; s. Floyd Rowe and Estelle Jane (Barden) W.; m. Genevieve L. Carter, Oct. 11, 1941; children: Ann Barden, Roberta Gail, Douglas Carter. AB, U. Ill., 1934; MA, UCLA, 1936; PhD, Harvard U., 1941. Teaching asst. UCLA, 1935-36; teaching asst., instr. Harvard U., Cambridge, Mass., 1936-41, rsch. assoc., 1940-41, rsch. assoc., Underwater Sound Lab., 1941-45; from asst. to assoc. prof. physics U. Tex., Austin, 1945-60, rsch. assoc., 1946-60; physical scis. adminstr. U.S. Dept. of the Army, Washington, 1960-76; cons. archtl. acoustics, Austin, 1946-60; rep. to various nat. and internat. sci. groups U.S. Army, Washington, 1960-76. Contbr. articles to Jour. Acoustical Soc. Am., Jour. Applied Physics. Fellow AAAS (Sci. Freedom and Responsibility award 1993), Acoustical Soc. Am.; mem. IEEE, Optical Soc. Am., Assn. Am. Physics Tchrs., Wash. Acad. Sci., Sigma Xi, Sigma Pi Sigma. Achievements include 3 patents concerning recorder, radar and sonar.

WATSON, ROBERT JOE, hospital administrator, retired career officer; b. Wellington, Kans., Nov. 12, 1934; s. Charles Bruce and Marguerite B. (Scholes) W.; m. Ursula Eschenroeder, Dec. 26, 1983; children: Stephanie, Stacy Watson Bruce, Susannah Watson Gold; stepchildren: Jurgen Wanke, Claudia Wanke. MS in Edn., Kans. State Tchrs. Coll., 1963; MBA, U. Hawaii, 1969; MHA, George Washington U., 1973, EdD, 1976; student, Command-Gen. Staff Coll., 1973, U.S. Army War Coll., 1986. Commd. 2nd lt. U.S. Army, 1963, advanced through grades to col., 1989; stationed at Tripler Army Med. Ctr., Honolulu, 1967-69, USARV Surgeons Office, Long Binh, Vietnam, 1969-70, Surgeon Gen.'s Office, Washington, 1970-74, Walter Reed Med. Ctr., Washington, 1974-76, Acad. Health Svcs., Ft. Sam Houston, Tex., 1976-80, 87-89, 68th Med. Group, Ziegenberg, Germany, 1980-82, U.S. Army Hosp., Ft. Riley, Kans., 1982-84, 34th Gen. Hosp., Augsburg, Germany, 1984-87; ret., 1989; assoc. dir. Student Health Ctr. U. Fla., Gainesville, 1989—. Fellow Am. Coll. Healthcare Execs. (adv. regent 1982-84). Episcopalian. Avocations: tennis, golf, gardening. Office: U Fla Student Health Ctr Gainesville FL 32611

WATSON, ROBERT R., lawyer; b. Buffalo, N.Y., Mar. 10, 1944. BA, Wheaton Coll., 1967; JD, U. Chgo., 1972. Bar: Ill. 1972. Law clerk to Hon. Richard W. McLaren U.S. Dist. Ct. (no. dist.), Ill., 1972-74; ptnr. Sidley & Austin, Chgo. Office: Sidley & Austin 1 First Nat Plz Chicago IL 60603

WATSON, ROBERT TANNER, physical scientist; b. Columbus, Ohio, Sept. 25, 1922; s. Rolla Don and Gladys Margaret (Tanner) W.; m. Jean Mehlig, Oct. 7, 1944; children—Melinda Jean, Parke Tanner, John Mehlig, Todd Pennell, Kate Ann. B.A., DePauw U., 1943; Ph.D., MIT, 1951. With photo products dept. E. I. duPont de Nemours & Co., Inc., Parlin, N.J., 1951-55; with electron tube div. RCA, Marion, Ind., 1955-59; with Internat. Tel. & Tel. Corp., 1959-71, v.p., gen. mgr. indsl. labs. div., 1962-63, pres., 1963-68; dept. tech. dir., other positions Aerospace and Def. Group, 1968-71; gen. phys. scientist OT and NTIA U.S. Dept. Commerce, 1971-90. Mem. Gov.'s Air Pollution Control Bd., 1966-70; Allen County chmn. Ind. Sesquicentennial, 1965; trustee Ind. Ednl. Services Found., 1968-71; bd. dirs. YMCA of Greater Ft. Wayne and Allen County, 1966-69. Served to lt. (j.g.) USNR 1943-46, combat, PTO; USNR, 1946-55. Mem. Am. Inst. Mgmt. (fellow pres.'s council 1970), Ft. Wayne C. of C. (dir. 1966-68), Allen County-Ft. Wayne Hist. Soc. (Old Fort com.), Optical Soc. Am., IEEE, Sigma Xi, Phi Eta Sigma, Beta Theta Pi. Research and engring. in x-ray diffraction, radioactive scattering, solid state energy levels, electron emission, magnetic and photog. media, electro-optical, Laser and telecommunication systems. Mgr. several engring. firsts. Patentee in field. Home: 1770 Lang Dr Crofton MD 21114-2145

WATSON, ROBERT WINTHROP, poet, English language educator; b. Passaic, N.J., Dec. 26, 1925; s. Winthrop and Laura Berdan (Trimble) W.; m. Elizabeth Ann Rean, Jan. 12, 1952; children: Winthrop, Caroline. B.A., Williams Coll., 1946; postgrad., U. Zurich, 1947; M.A., Johns Hopkins, 1950, Ph.D in English, 1955. Instr. English Williams Coll., 1946, 47-48, 52-53, Johns Hopkins, 1950-52; mem. faculty U. N.C., Greensboro, 1953—; prof. English U. N.C., 1963—; vis. poet, prof. English Calif. State U., Northridge, 1968-69. Author: (poems) A Paper Horse, 1962, Advantages of Dark, 1986, Christmas in Las Vegas, 1971, Selected Poems, 1974, Island of Bones, 1977, Night Blooming Cactus, 1980, The Pendulum: New and Selected Poems, 1995, (novels) Three Side of the Mirror, 1966, Lily Lang, 1977. Swiss-Am. exchange fellow, 1947; grantee Nat. Endowment Arts, 1973; recipient Am. Scholar Poetry prize, 1959, Lit. award Am. Acad. Inst. Arts Letters, 1977. Home: 9D Fountain Manor Dr Greensboro NC 27405-8001

WATSON, ROGER ELTON, human resources administrator; b. Goldsboro, N.C., Jan. 5, 1944; s. Robert Elton and Maggie (McCabe) W.; m. Barbara S. Baus, June 30, 1973; children: Michelle E., Stephanie Ann. BS, N.C. State U., 1968. Collection mgr. Planters Bank, Hopkinsville, Ky., 1976-80; pres., owner Watson Enterprises, Hopkinsville, 1980-85; cabinet for human resources Commonwealth of Ky., Hopkinsville, 1985—. Vice-pres. Hopkinsville Girsl Softball, 1979. Capt. AUS Spl. Forces, 1968-76, Vietnam. Decorated Disting. Svc. Cross, 2 Silver Stars, 2 Bronze Stars, Purple Heart. Mem. Lions Club (pres. 1978). Republican. Presbyterian. Home: 313 Mark Dr PO Box 1237 Hopkinsville KY 42241-7237

WATSON, SHARON GITIN, psychologist, executive; b. N.Y.C., Oct. 21, 1943; d. Louis Leonard and Miriam (Myers) Gitin; m. Eric Watson, Oct. 31, 1969; 1 child, Carrie Dunbar. B.A. cum laude, Cornell U., 1965; M.A., U. Ill., 1968, Ph.D., 1971. Psychologist City N.Y. Prison Mental Health, Riker's Island, 1973-74; psychologist Youth Services Ctr., Los Angeles County Dept. Pub. Social Services, Los Angeles, 1975-77, dir. clin. services, 1978, dir. Youth Services Ctr., 1978-80; exec. dir. Crittenton Ctr. for Young Women and Infants, Los Angeles, 1980-89, Assn. Children's Svcs. Agys. of So. Calif., L.A., 1989-92, L.A. County Children's Planning Coun., 1992—. Contbr. articles to profl. jours. Mem. Commn. for Children's Svcs. Family Preservation Policy Com., Mayor's Com. on Children, Youth and Families, L.A. Learning Ctrs. Design Team, Interagy. Coun. Child Abuse and Neglect Policy Com.; bd. dirs. L.A. Roundtable for Children, 1988-94, Adolescent Pregnancy Childwatch, 1985-89; trustee L.A. Ednl. Alliance for Restructuring Now; co-chmn. Los Angeles County Drug and Alcohol Abuse Task Force, 1990; mem. planning coun. Dept. Children's Svcs., 1986-88; mem. steering com. western region Child Welfare League Am., 1985-87. Mem. APA, Calif. Assn. Svcs. for Children (sec.-treas. 1983-84, pres. elect 1985-86, pres. 1986-87), Assn. Children's Svcs. Agys. So. Calif. (sec. 1981-83, pres. elect 1983-84, pres. 1984-85), Town Hall Calif., U.S. Figure Skating Assn. (bd. dirs., chair sanctions and eligibility com.), Inter-Club Assn. of Figure Skating Clubs (vice chair 1989-91, chair 1991-93), Pasadena Figure Skating Club (bd. dirs., pres. 1985-87, 89-90). Home: 4056 Campus Dr Los Angeles CA 90065-3928 Office: LA County Children's Planning Coun 500 W Temple St Rm B-26 Los Angeles CA 90012-2713

WATSON, SOLOMON BROWN, IV, lawyer, business executive; b. Salem, N.J., Apr. 14, 1944; s. Solomon Brown and Denise Amelia W.; m. Bernadette Aldrich, Mar. 18, 1967 (div.); children: Katitti Madrid, Kira Pallis (twins); m. Brenda J. Wilson, Apr. 28, 1984. B.A in English, Howard U., 1967; J.D., Harvard U., 1971. Bar: Mass. 1972, N.Y. 1977. Assoc. Bingham, Dana & Gould, Boston, 1971-74; corp. sec., asst. gen. counsel N.Y. Times Co., N.Y.C., 1979-89, gen. counsel 1989-90, v.p., gen. counsel 1990—. Active Vols. Legal Svc., Jobs for Youth Inc., until 1989; v.p. N.Y. Vietnam Vets. Leadership Program, Inc., until 1992, Agent Orange Assistance Fund, Vets. Adv. Bd.; bd. dirs. Legal Aid Soc. Lt. U.S. Army, 1966-68. Decorated Bronze Star with oak leaf cluster, Army Commendation medal with oak leaf cluster and V. Mem. ABA, Am. Arbitration Assn. (bd. dirs.), Assn. Bar City N.Y., Mass. Bar Assn., Newspaper Assn. Am. (mem. legal affairs com.), Legal Aid Soc. (bd. dirs.). Home: 341 W 87th St New York NY 10024-2635 Office: NY Times Co 229 W 43rd St New York NY 10036-3913

WATSON, STEVEN ELLIS, school district administrator; b. Columbus, Ind., Feb. 14, 1945; s. Emerson Ellis and Emma Lee (Freeman) W.; m. Janice Faye Grau, Aug. 1, 1970; children: Daniel, David. BS in Sociology, Polit. Sci., Ball State U., 1969, MA in Sociology, 1974, EdD in Ednl. Adminstrn., 1979. Tchr. social studies Frankton (Ind.) High Sch., 1969-70; dir. alternative edn. Muncie (Ind.) Community Schs., 1971-77; asst. prin. high sch. Hammond (Ind.) City Schs., 1978-82; dir. adult and extended svcs. At-Risk Program, Hammond (Ind.) City Schs., 1982—; mem., com. chair Gov.'s Adult Literacy Coalition, Indpls., 1983-87; bd. dirs. Calumet Area Literacy Coun., Hammond, 1988-92; cons. U.S. Dept. Edn., Ind. Div. Adult Edn., other ednl. orgns.; presenter workshops. Bd. dirs., v.p. Muncie Big Bros./Big Sisters, 1972-78, Northwest Ind. Big Bros./Big Sisters, 1981-85, Hammond YMCA, 1988—; bd. dirs. Northwest Ind. Boys and Girls Clubs, 1986-91; v.p. Hammond Lions Clubv, 1983—. Recipient award for outstanding adult and literacy program U.S. Dept. Edn., 1990; cited in Congl. Record, 1991; featured in spl. report NBC Nightly News, 1988, Parade mag., 1989; recipient program excellence award Erie (Pa.) C. of C., 1989. Mem. ASCD, Am. Assn. Adult and Continuing Edn., Ind. Assn. Adult and Continuing Edn. (bd. dirs., v.p. 1988-89, pres. 1990-91), Am. Contract Bridge League, Phi Delta Kappa. Avocations: duplicate bridge, coaching youth sports, baseball, basketball, movies. Home: 9408 Chestnut Ln Munster IN 46321-3802 Office: 5727 Sohl Ave Hammond IN 46320-2356

WATSON, STEWART CHARLES, construction company executive; b. Brock, Sask., Can., Sept. 17, 1922; s. Samuel Henry and Elva Jane (St. John) W.; student U. Buffalo; m. Irene Lillian Ahrens, Aug. 4, 1943; children: Judith Gail (Mrs. David Stafford), Wendy Carolyn (Mrs. Rocco Amuso), Ronald James, Candyce Louise. With Acme Steel & Malleable Iron Works, Buffalo, 1940-42; with Acme Hwy. Products, Buffalo, 1946-69, internat. mktg. mgr., 1955-69; pres. Watson-Bowman Assocs., Inc., Buffalo, 1970—, pres., Kinematics, 1984—. chmn. bd. Air Stewart Inc.; Internat. lectr. on kinetics of civil engring. structures; mem. U.S. Transp. Rsch. Bd.; bd. dirs. Internat. Bridge of Peace for Bering Strait Crossing. Served with AUS, 1943-45; ETO. Fellow Am. Concrete Inst. (dir. 1984—, Delmar Bloehm award 1984, Charles S. Whitney Medal 1987, hon. mem.); mem. Internat. Joints & Bearings Rsch. Coun. (chmn. 1988—), Internat. Activities Commn., ASTM, NAS, Masons (32 degree), Shriners. Home: 272 Lake Shore Rd, Fort Erie, ON Canada L2A 1B3

WATSON, SUSAN, newspaper columnist. Columnist Detroit Free Press. Office: Detroit Free Press 312 W Lafayette Detroit MI 48226-2706

WATSON, THOMAS CAMPBELL, economic development consulting company executive; b. Pensacola, Fla., Feb. 19, 1931; s. Thomas Campbell and Lucie Davis (Yonge) W.; m. Norma Lynn Lofberg, June 20, 1959; children: Thomas C., Valerie Lynn, Pamela Lucie. Student, The Citadel, 1949-50; B.S., U.S. Naval Acad., 1954; B.S.E.E., U.S. Naval Postgrad. Sch., 1962; postgrad., Armed Forces Staff Coll., 1978. Commd. ensign U.S. Navy, 1954, advanced through grades to rear adm., 1980; comdg. officer Attack Squadron 81, 1970-72, comdr. Carrier Air Wing 9, 1972-73, comdr. Light Attack Wing 1, 1973-75; exec. asst. DCNO Air Warfare, The Pentagon Washington, 1975-76; comdg. officer USS Truckee, 1976-78, comdg. officer USS Independence, 1978-80; dep. dir. for current ops. Joint Chiefs of Staff, The Pentagon Washington, 1980-82; ret. U.S. Navy, 1982; pres. Mars Electronics, U.S.A., West Chester, Pa., 1982-88, ret., Omega Ventures, 1988—; exec. dir. Mus. Sci. and History, Jacksonville, Fla., 1989; pres. CAVUAssoc., 1990—. Decorated Legion of Merit, D.F.C., Bronze Star, Air medal. Mem. Assn. Naval Aviation, Naval Acad. Alumni Assn. Roman Catholic. Club: Rotary. Home: 2371 Bridgette Way Green Cove Springs FL 32043-8763

WATSON, THOMAS STURGES, professional golfer; b. Kansas City, Mo., Sept. 4, 1949; s. Raymond Etheridge and Sarah Elizabeth (Ridge) W.; m. Linda Tova Rubin, July 8, 1973; children: Margaret Elizabeth, Michael Barrett. BS, Stanford U., 1971. Profl. golfer, 1971—. Winner Western Open, 1974, 1977, 1984; winner Byron Nelson Tournament, 1975, 78, 79, 80; winner Brit. Open, 1975, 77, 80, 82, 83; winner, U.S. Open, 1982; winner World Series, 1975, 80; winner Andy Williams San Diego Open, 1977, 80; winner El Prat, 1977; winner Masters, 1977, 81; winner Bing Crosby Nat. Pro-Am Golf Tournament, 1977, 78; winner Tucson Open, 1978, 84; winner Colgate Hall of Fame Classic, 1978, 79; winner Anheuser Busch Golf Classic, 1978; winner Meml. Tournament, 1979; winner Heritage Classic, 1979, 83; winner Tournament of Champions, 1979, 80, 84; Los Angeles Open, 1980, 82; Greater New Orleans Open, 1980, 81; Dunlop Phoenix, 1980, Atlantic Classic, 1981; Nabisco Championship, 1987, Hong Kong Open, 1992; Recipient Vardon Trophy, 1977, 78, 79, Byron Nelson award, 1977-78, 79-80; named to Ryder Cup Team, 1977, 81, 83, 89 (elected capt. 1992—); named Player of Year Profl. Golf Assn., 1977, 78, 79, 80, 82, 84; elected to PGA World Golf Hall of Fame, 1988, Kans. Golf Hall of Fame, 1991, William H. Richardson award 1990. Mem. U.S. Golf Assn., Profl. Golfers Assn., Golf Course Supts. Assn. of Am. (Old Tom Morris award 1992), Butler Nat. Golf Club, Shadow Glen Club, Preston Trails Golf Club, Oakwood Country Club, Par Club, Blue Hills Country Club. Leading money winner PGA, 1977-80, 84. Office: 1901 W 47th Pl Ste 200 Shawnee Mission KS 66205-1834*

WATSON, W. H., bishop. Bishop of N.W. Tex. Ch. of God in Christ, Lubbock. Office: Ch of God in Christ 1301 47th St Lubbock TX 80412

WATSON, W. ROBERT, president, chief executive officer; b. Corvallis, Oreg., Sept. 3, 1943; s. John Ernest and Sara (Rice) W.; m. Janice Gayle Blair, Mar. 18, 1978; children: Shelly, Rhonda, Melody, Brian. BS in Fin., Fla. State U., 1965, MBA, 1968. Mktg. mgr. Coca-Cola U.S.A., Atlanta, 1969-79, mgr. strategic planning, 1979-82, dir. fin. svcs., 1982-88; sr. v.p. Tex. Commerce Bank, Houston, 1988-89; pres. Watson & Assocs., Inc., Marietta, Ga., 1989-94; pres., CEO Harrison Direct, Inc., Atlanta, 1995—. Elder Presbyn. Ch., Marietta, 1985-86; active Johnson Ferry Bapt. Ch.; mem. Fla. State U. Boosters Club, President's Club. Capt. U.S. Army, 1965-67. Mem. WFW, Am. Legion, Emmaus, Kappa Alpha. Republican. Baptist. Avocations: golf, tennis, spectator sports.

WATSON, WARREN EDWARD, retired library administrator; b. Quincy, Mass., Apr. 5, 1925; s. Eimer Loring and Alice Loretta (Campbell) Watson; m. Elizabeth Mary Paul. AB, Boston Coll., 1948, MA, 1950; MLS, Simmons Coll., 1962. Broadcast news editor various radio stas., Mass., R.I., 1950-53; news editor Sta. WJAR-TV, Providence, 1953-55, spl. news assignments, 1958-59; spl. rgn. corr. on Operation Deepfreeze I CBS, Internat. News Svc., 1955-56; tech. writer Lincoln Lab., Lexington, Mass., 1956-58; libr. asst. Boston Pub. Libr., 1959-60, Boston Coll. Lib., 1960-61; asst. dir. Framingham (Mass.) Pub. Libr., 1961-64, dir., 1964-68; dir. librs. Thomas Crane Pub. Libr., Quincy, 1968-93; pres. Old Colony Libr. Network, Canton, Mass., 1984-86, Simmons Coll. Grad. Sch. of Libr. and Info. Sci. Alumni Bd., Boston, 1988-89. Mem. U.S. Power Squadrons, Raleigh, N.C., 1964—, Quincy (Mass.) Hist. Soc. Aviation Cadet US Army Air Corps, 1943-44. Mem. Mass. Libr. Assn. (pres. 1971), ALA, New England Libr. Assn. Democrat. Avocations: cons. libr. devel., reading. Home: 7 Dorchester St # 3 Quincy MA 02171-1152

WATSON, WILLIAM A. J., legal educator; b. 1933; MA, U. Glasgow, 1954, LLB, 1957; BA, Oxford U., 1957, MA, 1958, PhD, 1960. Lectr. Wadham Coll., Oxford U., 1957-59; fellow in jurisprudence Oriel Coll., Oxford U., 1959-65; pro-proctor Oxford U., 1962-63; Douglas prof. civil law U. Glasgow, 1965-68; prof. civil law U. Edinburgh, 1968-79; prof. law U. Pa., Phila., 1979-84, Gallichio prof., 1984—; vis. prof. Tulane U., 1967, U. Va., 1970, Cape Town (South Africa) U., 1974-75, U. Mich., 1977. Mem. Soc. Jean Bodin, Soc. Internationale des Droits de l'Antiquité, Soc. de l'Histoire du Droit, Am. Law Inst. Office: U Ga Law Sch Athens GA 30602

WATSON, WILLIAM D., lawyer; b. Buffalo, Sept. 1, 1943; s. William E. and Dorothy A. (Bowman) W.; m. Andrea L. Ehudin, Dec. 18, 1971; children: William A., Graham H. BA, Princeton U., 1965; LLB, Harvard U., 1968. Atty. Holme Roberts & Owen, Denver, 1970—; dir. Colo. Oil & Gas Assn. Author: The Gas Sellers Companion, 1992; editor Public Land and Resource Law Digest, 1966—. Capt. U.S. Army, 1968-70, Vietnam. Decorated 8 Bronze stars. Mem. ABA, Colo. Bar Assn., Fed. Energy Bar

Assn., Rocky Mountain Princeton Club (pres. 1991—). Office: Holme Roberts & Owen 1700 Lincoln St Ste 4100 Denver CO 80203

WATSON-BOONE, REBECCA A., educator; b. Springfield, Ohio, Mar. 7, 1946; d. Roger S. and Elizabeth Lupton (Walker) Boone; m. Dennis David Ash, 1967 (div. 1975); m. Frederick Kellogg, 1979 (div. 1988); m. Peter G. Watson-Boone, May 26, 1989. Student, Earlham Coll., 1964-67; BA, Case Western Res. U., 1968; MLS, U. N.C., 1971; postgrad. in libr. and info. scis., U. Wis., 1990—. Asst. reference libr. Princeton (N.J) U., 1970-76; head cen. reference dept. U. Ariz., Tucson, 1976-83, assoc. dean Coll. Arts and Scis., 1984-89; loaned exec. Ariz. Bd. Regents, 1988-89. Contbr. articles to profl. jours. Mem. ALA (div. pres. 1985-86, councilor 1988-92), Assn. for Libr. and Info. Sci. Edn., NAFE. Mem. Soc. of Friends. Home: 4333 W Grace Ave Mequon WI 53092-2136

WATT, DEAN DAY, retired biochemistry educator; b. McCammon, Idaho, Sept. 21, 1917; s. George William and Mary Amelia (Day) W.; m. Frances Elaine Murdock, Aug. 23, 1945; children: Sharon (Mrs. William E. Shull, Jr.), Nola Jean (Mrs. Thomas E. Barzee, Jr.), Barbara (Mrs. Robert Lauritzen), David, Stuart. Student, Idaho State U., 1936-37, 38-40; BS, U. Idaho, 1942; PhD, Iowa State U., 1949; postgrad., Case-Western Res. U., 1946-47. Research chemist Westvaco Chlorine Products, Newark, Calif., 1942-44; instr. Iowa State U., 1947-49; asst. prof. Purdue U., 1949-53; head dept. physiol. scis. Southeast La. Hosp., Mandeville, 1953-60; asso. prof. Tulane U., 1955-60, Ariz. State U., 1960-63; prin. biochemist Midwest Research Inst., Kansas City, Mo., 1963-69; prof. biochemistry Creighton U., 1969-88, prof. emeritus, 1988—. Fellow AAAS; mem. Internat. Soc. Toxinology (founding mem.), Sigma Xi. Mem. Ch. of Jesus Christ of Latter-day Saints. Research on animal venoms, biochemistry mental diseases. Home: 618 S 130th St Omaha NE 68154-2910

WATT, DOUGLAS (BENJAMIN WATT), writer, critic; b. N.Y.C., Jan. 20, 1914; s. Benjamin Douglas and Agnes Rita (Neimann) W.; m. Ray Mantel, Nov. 5, 1937 (div.); children—Richard David, James Douglas; m. Ethel Madsen, Aug. 13, 1951; children—Patricia, Katherine. A.B., Cornell U. 1934. Copy boy N.Y. News, 1936-37, radio columnist, 1937-40, drama reporter, 1940-71, sr. drama critic, 1971-87, critic-at-large, 1987—; staff writer New Yorker mag., 1946-95; profl. song writer; columnist Small World, 1955-70; critic-at-large, 1987-93. Pres. Hampton Animal Shelter, 1965-79. Served with USAAF, World War II. Mem. ASCAP, N.Y. Drama Critics Circle (pres. 1975-77). Club: Dutch Treat (N.Y.C.) (bd. govs.). Home: 27 W 86th St New York NY 10024-3615 *To say one has achieved success, except perhaps in isolated instances, is an exercise in vanity and contrary to man's experience. At best, some satisfaction can be gained in one's career, and then almost always because of intense effort.*

WATT, IAN PIERRE, retired English literature educator; b. Windermere, Westmorland, Eng., Mar. 9, 1917; s. Thomas and Renée (Guitton) W.; m. Ruth Mellinkoff, July 14, 1947; children—George, Josephine. B.A., St. John's Coll., Cambridge U. 1938, M.A., 1946; postgrad., Sorbonne, Paris, 1939, U. Calif. at Los Angeles, 1946-47, Harvard, 1947-48. Fellow St. John's Coll., 1948-52; asst. prof. English U. Calif. at Berkeley, 1952-55; assoc. prof. U. Calif.-Berkeley, 1955-58; prof. U. Calif. at Berkeley, 1958-62; dean Sch. English Studies U. East Anglia, Norwich, Eng., 1962-64; prof. English Stanford U., 1964-87, Eli Jackson Reynolds prof. humanities, 1971—; prof. emeritus, 1987—; dir. Stanford Humanities Center. Stanford U., 1980-85; vis. prof. U. Hawaii, 1967-68, Williams Coll., 1970, U. Nice, U. Paris, 1975-76; Alexander lectr. U. Toronto (Ont., Can.), 1974; lectr. Princeton U., 1980; broadcaster BBC. Author: The Rise of the Novel: Studies in Defoe, Richardson and Fielding, 1957, Conrad in the Nineteenth Century, 1980; editor: Wordsworth in Cambridge, 1950, Jane Austen: A Collection of Critical Essays, 1963, Lawrence Sterne, Tristram Shandy, 1963, The Augustan Age, 1968, The Victorian Novel: Modern Essays in Criticism, 1971, Joseph Conrad, The Secret Agent: A Casebook, 1973, The British Novel: Scott through Hardy, 1973, Joseph Conrad, Nostromo, 1988, Joseph Conrad, Almayer's Folly: A Story of an Eastern River, 1994; adv. editor: Nineteenth Century Fiction, 1960—, Eighteenth Century Studies, 1968—, Style, 1968—, Novel, 1968—; also scholarly editions Conrad, Smollett and Sterne. Served with Brit. Army, 1939-46; Japanese prisoner of War, 1942-45. Fellow Am. Acad. Arts and Scis. Home: 879 Mayfield Ave Palo Alto CA 94305-1052 Office: Dept of English Stanford Univ Stanford CA 94305

WATT, JAMES GAIUS, lawyer, former government official, legal consultant; b. Lusk, Wyo., Jan. 31, 1938; s. William G. and Lois M. (Williams) W.; m. Leilani Bomgardner, Nov. 2, 1957; children: Erin Gaia, Eric Gaius. B.S., U. Wyo., 1960, J.D., 1962. Bar: Wyo. 1962, U.S. Supreme Ct. 1966. Legis. asst., counsel to Senator Simpson of Wyo., 1962-66; sec. to natural resources com. and environ. pollution adv. panel C. of C. of U.S., 1966-69; dep. asst. sec. water and power devel. Interior Dept., 1969-72; dir. Bur. Outdoor Recreation, Washington, 1972-75; mem., vice chmn. Fed. Power Commn., 1975-77; pres., chief legal officer Mountain States Legal Found., Denver, 1977-80; sec. Dept. Interior, Washington, 1981-83; bus. cons. Washington, 1983-86, Jackson Hole, Wyo., 1986—; mem. bd. Environ. Diagnostics, 1984-87, Disease Detection Internat.. 1986-90; instr. Coll. Commerce and Industry, U. Wyo. Author: (with Doug Wead) The Courage of a Conservative, 1985. Mem. Phi Kappa Phi, Delta Theta Phi. Office: 755 Paintbrush Dr Jackson WY 83001-9354

WATT, JOHN H., financial executive; b. Jersey City, Aug. 31, 1927; s. John and Mary (Tollan) W.; m. Margaret Johnstone, Feb. 15, 1958; children: John, Jennifer, Andrew, R. Cameron. BS, Rutgers U., 1953; MBA cum laude, Fairleigh Dickinson U., 1965. Mgr. bus. planning NL Industries, Inc., N.Y.C., 1960-65, fin. mgr., 1965-69, asst. treas., 1969-82, treas., 1982-87; treas. Omnicom Group Inc., N.Y.C., 1988-92; CFO John H. Watt Assocs., Weston, Conn., 1993—. Served with USN, 1945-46, U.S. Army, 1953-55. Mem. Nat. Assn. Corp. Treas., Soc. Internat. Treas., University Club (N.Y.C.).

WATT, KENNETH EDMUND FERGUSON, zoology educator; b. Toronto, July 13, 1929; s. William Black Ferguson Watt and Irene Eleanor (Hubbard) Dodd; m. Genevieve Bernice Bendig, Oct. 28, 1955; children: Tanis Jocelyn, Tara Alexis. BA with honor, U. Toronto, 1951; PhD in Zoology, U. Chgo., 1954; LLD, Simon Fraser U., 1970. Biometrician Rsch. div. Dept. Lands and Forests, Ont., Canada, 1954-57; sr. biometrician Can. Dept. Agr., Ottawa, Ont., 1957-60; head, statis. rsch. and svcs. Canadian Dept. Forestry, Ottawa, 1960-63; from assoc. prof. to prof. dept. zoology Dept. Zoology, U. Calif., Davis, 1963—. Author: Ecology and Resource Management, 1968, Principles of Environmental Sciences, 1973, Understanding the Environment, 1982, Taming the Future, 1991. Recipient Gold medal Entomol. Soc., 1969. Achievements include development of new approach to forecasting future based on exhaustive statistics testing of nonlinear math. equations to long runs of historical data; discovery that change through time in real world systems violates Markov principles. Home: 1116 Dartmouth Pl Davis CA 95616-2312 Office: U Calif Dept of Zoology Davis CA 95616 *The actual causes of present events are much further back in time than most people suspect. Failure to understand this is why forecasting is such a disaster area.*

WATT, MELVIN L., congressman, lawyer; b. Mecklenburg County, N.C., Oct. 26, 1945; m. Eulada Paysour; children: Brian, Jason. BS in Bus. Adminstrn., U. N.C., 1967; JD, Yale U., 1970. Atty. Ferguson, Stein, Watt, Wallis, Adkins, & Grensham, 1971—; U.S. senator from N.C. 95th Congress, 1985-86; co-owner East Towne Manor, 1989—; mem. 103rd-104th Congress from 12th N.C. dist., Washington, D.C., 1993—; pres. Mecklenburg County Bar. Active CIC Found., Legal Aid of Southern Piedmont, N.C. NB Community Devel. Corp., Auditorium-Coliseum-Civic Ctr. Authority, United Way, Mint Mus., Family Housing Svcs., Pub. Edn. Forum, Dilworth Community Devel. Assn., Cities in Schs., Housing Authority Scholarship Bd., Morehead Scholarship Selection Com.; bd. visitors Johnson C. Smith Univ. Mem. N.C. Assn. Black Lawyers, N.C. Acad. Trial Lawyers, Charlotte C. of C. (sports action coun.), West Charlotte Bus. Incubator, Inroads Inc., Phi Beta Kappa. Democrat. Presbyterian. Office: US Ho of Reps 1232 Longworth Ho Office Bldg Washington DC 20515-3312

WATT, ROBERT DOUGLAS, Canadian government official; b. Picton, Ont., Can., Aug. 13, 1945; s. George Cuthill and Mary Amelia (Greer) W.; m. Alison Jean Logan, Sept. 29, 1973; children: Michael Andrew Logan, Catherine Nicola Logan. BA with honors, Carleton U., 1967, MA, 1968. Archivist Pub. Archives of Can., Ottawa, Ont., 1968-70; city archivist City of Vancouver, B.C., Can., 1971-72; curator of history Vancouver Centenial Mus., 1973-76, chief curator, 1976-77; head Vancouver Mus., 1977-79, dir., 1980-88; chief herald of Can., 1988—. Author: Shopping Guide of the West, 1977, (catalogue) Rainbows in Our Walls, 1978, Symbols of Splendour, 1983; editor: Museum on Stage, 1984; assoc. editor Material History Bull., 1976—; contbr. articles to profl. jours. Pres. Vancouver Hist. Soc., 1973-78. Fellow Heraldry Soc. Can., 1982 (bd. dirs., 1st v.p. 1977-87, pres. 1987-88); mem. Can. Mus. Assn., B.C. Mus. Assn. (councillor, pres., 1976-81), Académie internationale d'Héraldique, Can. Hist. Assn. Anglican. Office: Chief Herald of Can, 1 Sussex Dr Rideau Hall, Ottawa, ON Canada K1A 0A1

WATT, RONALD WILLIAM, public relations executive; b. Cleve., Oct. 10, 1943; s. Archie Gordon and Molly (Champa) W.; m. Elizabeth K. Strasshofer, May 15, 1965 (div. Dec. 1973); children: Cheryl Marie, Laurie Michelle; m. Simona Catherine Yesbak, Dec. 21, 1973; children: Ronald William Jr., Amanda Catherine. BJ, Bowling Green State U., 1965. Reporter Sta. WSPD-TV and Radio, Toledo, 1965-66; mgr. pub. relations Toledo-Lucas County Port Authority, Toledo, 1966-68; account exec. Flournoy & Gibbs, Toledo, 1968-73; v.p. Edward Howard and Co., Cleve., 1973-79; pres. Watt-Jayme Pub. Relations, Cleve., 1979-81; pres., chief operating officer Watt, Roop & Co., Cleve., 1981-86, chmn., chief exec. officer, 1987—. Grad. Leadership Cleve., 1988, alumni steering com., 1991—; chmn. Centennial ARC, Cleve., 1981; mem. vis. com. Coll. Urban Affairs Cleve. State U., chmn. In Tribute to Pub. Svc. program; co-founder Browns Buddies Program, Rainbow Babies, Childrens Hosp., Cleve., 1981; bd. dirs. Youth Opportunities, Inc., 1984-89, Downtown Cleve. Bus. Coun., 1987—, Cleve. chpt. NCCJ, 1988—, Citizens League of Cleve., 1988—, Marymount Hosp., 1988—, Cleve. chpt. Am. Cancer Soc., 1988—, N.E. Ohio Jazz Soc., Singing Angels, 1990—, Hiram House, 1991—, Clean-Land, Ohio, 1991—; co-chmn. Tri-C Jazzfest, 1990—, Tri-C Found., 1993—; leadership giving adv. com., image and presence Task Force Greater Cleve., United Way; voluntary communications dir., cabinet mem. 1990 campaign; steering com. Walter Hagen Invitational Golf Tournament; dir. Brian Brennan Boys Hope Golf Tournament, 1989—. Named one of Outstanding Young Men Am., 1971. Fellow Pub. Relations Soc. Am. (nat. chmn. profl. standards and bus. practices, bd. dirs. Counselors Acad. 1989—, chmn. 1993—, pres. Greater Cleve. chpt. 1981-82, 6 Silver Anvil awards 1969, 73, 87, 88, accredited); mem. Nat. Media Conf. (bd. dirs. 1985—), Cleve. Advt. Club (bd. dirs. 1985—, pres. 1991-92), Cleve. Press Club (bd. dirs. 1986-90), Greater Cleve. Press Club (co-chmn. centennial 1987), ARC Cleve. chpt. (vice chmn 1991-93, mktg. chair, 1989-92) Canterbury Golf Club (Shaker Heights, Ohio), Firestone Country Club (Akron, Ohio), Lakewood Country Club (Westlake, Ohio), Hermit Club (Cleve.), Clifton Club (Lakewood, Ohio), Union Club (Cleve.) Republican. Roman Catholic. Avocations: jazz music, piano, writing comedy. Office: Watt Roop & Co 1100 Superior Ave E Ste 1350 Cleveland OH 44114-2518

WATT, STUART GEORGE, engineering contracting company executive; b. Warsaw, N.Y., Apr. 26, 1934; s. George James and Elizabeth Fern (Fullington) W.; m. Dorothy Elayne McLeod, Aug. 13, 1957; children: Stuart George II, Eric Duncan. BS in Mineral Engring., Pa. State U., 1956, MS in Mineral Engring. (NSF fellow), 1958. Ops. research cons. Lukens Steel Co., Coatesville, Pa., 1959; sr. research engr. Internat. Minerals & Chems. Co., Mulberry, Fla., 1959-62; project mgr. Internat. Minerals & Chems. Co., Skokie, Ill., 1962-64; prodn. mgr. Internat. Minerals & Chems. Co., Carlsbad, N.Mex., 1964-66; exec. engr. Davy Powergas, Inc., Lakeland, Fla., 1966-69, v.p. bus. devel., 1970-71, sr. v.p., 1972-74; exec. v.p., chief exec. ops. Davy Powergas, Inc., Houston, 1974-78; exec. v.p. Davy Internat. Inc., 1978—; also dir.; exec. v.p. Davy McKee, 1979—; pres. Stuart G. Watt & Co., Pensacola, Fla.; bd. dirs. McKee-Kearney, Bricmont Enterprises, Aker Oil and Gas Tech., Inc., Aker Omega Inc. Mem. Am. Inst. Mining and Metal. Engrs., Pa. State Alumni Assn., Toastmasters Club, Jr. Achievement, Sigma Gamma Epsilon. Republican. Lutheran. Clubs: Houston University, Lone Palm Golf; Lakeside Country (Houston); University (Salt Lake City); Walden Golf. Home and Office: 14456 River Rd Pensacola FL 32507-9684

WATT, WILLIAM G., insurance company executive; b. 1934. Joined Royal Indemnity Co., Charlotte, N.C., 1957—, underwriter trainee, 1957-65, account contr., 1965-68, regional underwriting mgr., 1968-71, asst. sec., 1971-73, sec., 1973-75; regional mgr. Royal Indemnity Co., Southfield, Mich., 1975-77; asst. v.p. Royal Indemnity Co., Charlotte, 1977-78, v.p., 1978-82, sr. v.p. ops., 1982—. Office: Royal Ins Co of Am 9300 Arrow Point Blvd Charlotte NC 28273*

WATT, WILLIAM JOSEPH, academic administrator, chemistry educator; b. Carbondale, Ill., Dec. 15, 1925; s. Phillip Clinton and Ella (Dickey) W.; m. Helen Stevens Gravatt, Sept. 1, 1956; children: John Gravatt, Phyllis Cary, William Joseph. Student, U. Mich., 1943; BS in Chemistry, U. Ill., 1949; M.S., Cornell U., 1951, Ph.D., 1956. Asst. prof. chemistry Davidson (N.C.) Coll., 1951-53; asst. prof. to assoc. prof. Washington and Lee U., Lexington, Va., 1955-65, prof. chemistry, 1965-94; prof. and dean emeritus, 1994—; assoc. dean of coll. Washington and Lee U., Lexington, Va., 1968-71, dean, 1971-84, head dept. chemistry, 1986-91; vis. prof. High Sch. Tchrs., Ala. Coll., summers 1959-61, U. Va., summers 1964-66; Summer research participant Cornell U., 1956; Oak Ridge Nat. Lab., 1957, 58, U. Va., 1962. Contbr. articles to profl. jours. Pres. Rockbridge Co. Va. Mus. Fine Arts, 1963-65; bd. dirs. Rockbridge Concert Theater Series, 1960—, pres., 1971-77; trustee Episcopal High Sch., 1974-80; vestryman, sr. warden Episcopal Ch.; bd. dirs. Botetourt-Rockbridge Regional Library, 1971-80, chmn., 1975-77; sec.-treas. Conf. Acad. Deans of So. States, 1978-79, v.p., 1979-80, pres., 1980-81; chmn. Nat. Deans Conf., 1983, Commn. Ministry Higher Edn. Diocese of Southwestern Va., 1989—. Served with AUS, 1944-46. Mem. AAAS, Am. Chem. Soc., English-Speaking Union (nat. bd. dirs. 1993—), Soc. Chimique de France, Va. Acad. Sci., N.Y. Acad. Sci., Phi Eta Sigma, Alpha Chi Sigma, Omicron Delta Kappa (hon.). Democrat. Home: 7 Providence Pl Box 753 Lexington VA 24450 Office: Washington and Lee U Dept Chemistry Lexington VA 24450

WATT, WILLIAM VANCE, surgeon; b. Thomasville, Ga., Apr. 10, 1924; s. Charles Hansell and Elizabeth Gilkeson (Pancake) W.; m. Mary Mercer Pendleton, Apr. 7, 1951; children: Mercer Pendleton Watt Pember, Elizabeth Vance Watt Finch, Philip Cargill. Student, Davidson Coll., 1942-43, Duke U., 1943-44; MD, Johns Hopkins U., 1948. Diplomate Am. Bd. Surgery. Intern Union Meml. Hosp., Balt., 1948-49; resident surgery Jefferson Hosp., Roanoke, Va., 1949-51, 53-54; fellow surgery Lahey Clinic, Boston, 1954-55; mem. surg. staff Archbold Meml. Hosp., Thomasville, Ga., 1955-94. Lt. (j.g.) USNR, 1943-45, 50-52. Recipient Silver Beaver award Boy Scouts Am., 1974, Golden Eagle award, 1995. Mem. ACS, AMA, Am. Soc. Gastrointestinal Endoscopy, Southeastern Surg. Soc., Rotary. Republican. Episcopalian. Avocations: hunting, golfing, fishing. Home: 1104 Old Monticello Rd Thomasville GA 31792

WATTEL, HAROLD LOUIS, economics educator; b. Bklyn., Sept. 30, 1921; s. David Max and Carolyn (Abrams) W.; m. Sara Gordon, Sept. 1, 1946; children: Karen, Jill. B.A., Queens Coll., 1942; M.A., Columbia U., 1947; Ph.D. magna cum laude, New Sch. Social Research, 1954. Jr. economist WPB, 1942; economist Dept. Agr., 1946; econ. cons. Boni, Watkins & Mounteer, 1952; economist Bur. Bus. and Community Research, Hofstra U., 1954, 57, dir., 1957-58; prof. econs. Bur. Bus. and Community Rsch., Hofstra U., 1957-58; prof. emeritus, 1986—, chmn. dept. econs., 1957-61, chmn. div. bus., 1961—; dean Sch. Bus., 1965-73; econ. cons. to consumer counsel, staff Gov. N.Y., 1956-58; cons. N.Y. State Moreland Commn. on Alcoholic Beverage Control Law, 1963-64, Legislative Reference Bur., U. Hawaii, 1966, Schenley Industries, 1967—, Ralston Purina Co., 1967—; Am. Can Co., 1965—; econ. cons. Nat. Millinery Planning Bd., 1959-70; ednl. cons. U.S. Mcht. Marine Acad., Kings Point, 1972, Buluva Watch Co., 1975-82. Author and. publ.: The Millinery Industry; Editor: Planning in Higher Education, 1975, Chief Executive Officer Compensation, 1978, The Gross Personal Income Tax, 1981; Contbr. chpts. to books, encys., dictionaries, also reports.; Editor, contbr.: L.I. Bus, 1954-59. Mem. Comprehensive Health Planning Coun. 1970-75; bd. dirs., v. p., N.Y. State

unit Am. Lung Assn.; pres. Nassau-Suffolk unit; bd. dirs. Comprehensive Health Planning Coun., Nassau-Suffolk, N.Y., N.Y. State Citizen Coun., Consumer Farmer Found., Regional Med. Program Nassau-Suffolk, consumer rep., bd. dirs. Island Peer Rev. Orgn. , 1990. Lt. USNR, 1942-46. Edn. fellow, 1949; Hazen Found. fellow, 1952; Ford Found. regional fellow, 1960. Mem. Middle Atlantic Assn. Colls. Bus. Adminstrn. (pres. 1970-71), Am., Met. econs. assns., Am. Assn. U. Profs. (chpt. pres. 1953), N.Y. State Environ. Health Assn. (v.p.), Coop. Extension Assn. Nassau County (pres. 1984-85), Island Peer Rev. Orgn. (consumer/AARP rep. 1990—), Pi Gamma Mu, Omicron Chi Epsilon, Beta Gamma Sigma (hon. asso.). Home: 181 Shepherd Ln Roslyn Heights NY 11577-2525 Office: Hofstra U Hempstead NY 11550

WATTENBERG, ALBERT, physicist, educator; b. N.Y.C., Apr. 13, 1917; s. Louis and Bella (Wolff) W.; m. Alice von Neumann, May 23, 1992; children from a previous marriage: Beth, Jill, Nina Diane. B.S., Coll. City N.Y., 1938; M.A., Columbia, 1939; Ph.D., U. Chgo., 1947. Spectroscopist Schenley Distilleries, N.Y.C., 1939-42; physicist Manhattan Project, Metall. Lab., Chgo., 1942-46; group leader Argonne Nat. Lab., Chgo., 1946-50; asst. prof. U. Ill., Urbana, 1950-51; prof. physics U. Ill., 1958—; research physicist Mass. Inst. Tech., 1951-58. Recipient award for 1st nuclear reactor Am. Nuclear Soc., 1962; Nuclear Pioneer award Soc. Nuclear Medicine, 1977; NSF fellow U. Rome, 1962-63. Pioneered controlled nuclear reactor. Office: Univ Ill 1100 W Green St Urbana IL 61801-3003

WATTENMAKER, RICHARD JOEL, archive director, art scholar; b. Phila., Feb. 22, 1941; s. Nathan H. and Frances (Rynes) W.; m. Eva Augusta Oscarsson, June 25, 1968; children: Adrian Ezra, Barnaby Leo. B.A., U. Pa., 1963; M.A., NYU Inst Fine Arts, 1965; Ph.D., NYU Inst Arts, 1972. Dir. Rutgers U. Art Gallery, New Brunswick, N.J., 1966-69; chief curator Art Gallery Ont., Toronto, Can., 1972-78; dir. Chrysler Mus., Norfolk, Va., 1979-80, Flint (Mich.) Inst. Arts, 1980-88, Archives of Am. Art, Smithsonian Instn., Washington, 1990—; lectr. Barnes Found., 1991-92. Author: The Art of Charles Prendergast, 1968, The Art of Jean Hugo, 1973, Puvis de Chavannes and the Modern Tradition, 1975, Maurice Prendergast, 1994. Trustee Intermus. Conservation Lab., Oberlin, Ohio, 1982-88. Recipient Founders Day award NYU, 1972. Office: Smithsonian Instn Archives of Am Art 8th and G Sts NW Washington DC 20560

WATTERS, EDWARD McLAIN, III, lawyer; s. Edward McL. and Lucy F. (Disston) W.; m. Susan Secor, May 12, 1979; children—Jennifer Susan, Ann Elizabeth. B.A. cum laude, Yale U., 1965; J.D. cum laude, U. Pa., 1970. Bar: Pa. 1970. Ptnr., Pepper, Hamilton & Scheetz, Phila., 1977—; lectr. programs on estate planning and will drafting Pa. Bar Inst. Bd. dirs. Children's Cruise and Playground Soc. Pa., Sanitarium Playgrounds of N.J., others. Served to lt. USNR, 1965-75. Fellow Am. Coll. Trust and Estate Counsel (mem. com. state laws); mem. Phila. Bar Assn. , Pa. Bar Assn. (past chmn. legis. com. probate sect.), ABA (mem. com. on significant legislation probate sect.), Phila. Estate Planning Council (past pres.), Yale Club of Phila., Penn Club, Merion Golf Club. Office: Pepper Hamilton & Scheetz 1235 Westlakes Dr Ste 400 Berwyn PA 19312-2416

WATTERS, THOMAS ROBERT, geologist, museum administrator; b. West Chester, Pa., Feb. 1, 1955; s. Frank Edward Sr. and Beatrice Josephine (Speirs) W.; m. Nancy Rae Tracey, June 18, 1983; children: James T. Samantha E., Adam T. BS in Earth Scis., West Chester U., 1977; MA in Geology, Bryn Mawr Coll., 1979; PhD in Geology, George Washington U., 1985. Rsch. fellow Am. Mus. Natural History, 1978-80; rsch. asst. dept. terrestrial magnetism Carnegie Instn. Washington, 1980-81; rsch. geologist Ctr. for Earth and Planetary Studies Smithsonian Instn., Washington, 1981-89, supervisory geologist Ctr. for Earth and Planetary Studies, Nat. Air and Space Mus., 1989—, acting. chmn. Ctr. for Earth and Planetary Studies, 1989-92, chmn. Ctr. for Earth and Planetary Studies, 1992—; lectr. in field. Contbr. over 100 abstracts and papers; author Planets: A Smithsonian Guide, 1995. Active Plum Point Elem. PTA, 1991—, mem. exec. bd. 1991-92; coach Calvert T-Ball, 1992-93; coach Babe Ruth, 1994-95. William. P. Phillips Meml. scholar; grantee NASA, 1985-89, 86-88, 87-88, 87-90, 89-95 (two grants), 91-95, 95—; recipient cert. award Nat. Air Space Mus., 1983, 86, 89, 91, 92, 93. Mem. AAAS, Geol. Soc. Am. (mem. editorial bd. GEOLOGY 1993-95), Am. Geophysical Union (Editor's citation 1992), Kappa Delta Phi. Achievements include research in terrestrial and planetary tectonics and tectonophysics; morphological and structural comparisons of tectonic features on the terrestrial planets and analogous features on Earth; geologic mapping of Mars. Office: Smithsonian Instn Nat Air & Space Museum Rm 3789 Ctr Earth & Planetary Studies Washington DC 20560

WATTERSON, BILL, cartoonist; b. Washington, 1958; s. James and Kathryn W.; m. Melissa Watterson. Grad. polit. sci., Kenyon Coll., 1980. Editorial cartoonist Cincinnati Post, Cincinnati, OH, 1980; syndicated cartoon strip, Calvin and Hobbes Universal Press Syndicate, 1985—. Author, illustrator: Calvin and Hobbes, 1987, The Essential Calvin and Hobbes: A Calvin and Hobbes Treasury, 1988, Something Under the Bed is Drooling: A Calvin and Hobbes Collection, 1988, Yukon Ho!, 1989, The Calvin & Hobbes Lazy Sunday Book, 1989, The Authoritative Calvin and Hobbes, 1990, Weirdos from Another Planet!, 1990, The Revenge of the Baby-Sitter, 1991, Scientific Progress Goes "Boink", 1991, Attack of the Deranged Mutant Killer Monster Snow Goons, 1992, Indispensible Calvin and Hobbes: A Calvin and Hobbes Treasury, 1992, The Days are Just Packed, 1993, Homicidal Psycho Jungle Cat: A Calvin & Hobbes Collection, 1994; illustrator The Komplete Kolor Krazy Kat, vol. 1, 1990; wrote forward Fox Trot, 1989. Office: Universal Press Syndicate 4900 Main St Fl 9 Kansas City MO 64112-2644*

WATTERSON, JOYCE GRANDE, editor, publisher; b. Cleve., May 15, 1937; d. Anthony John Sr. and Helen Bernice (Kramer) Grande; m. Thomas Batchelor, Sept. 27, 1968; children: Sean Anthony, William Grande. BA, Notre Dame Ohio, 1960; Cert. Pratique, U. Paris, 1964; MA, Case Western Res., 1967. Cert. sales profl.; cert. tchr., Ohio. Tchr. Cleve. Bd. Edn., 1960-63, 64-65; asst. pers. dir. Cleve., Ohio Retail, 1965-66; tchr. Shaker Heights (Ohio) Bd. Edn., 1966-69, 71-72, 1983-85; lectr. Cleve. State U., 1987-88, Notre Dame Coll. Ohio, Cleve., 1990-91; adminstrv. dir. No. Ohio Acad. Pharmacy, Cleve., 1991-94. Author, editor, pub.; Cascade Valley Soups, 1989, Cascade Valley Beans, 1992; editor/pub. Concord Gazette, 1994—. Advisor Alateens, Cleve., 1970-73; pres. Parents of U. Sch., Hunting Valley, Ohio, 1986-87; mem. adv. com. Painesville Adult Basic and Literacy Edn. Project, 1995—. Mem. Le Cercle des Conférences Françaises of Cleve. (pres. 1986-88, life). Republican. Roman Catholic. Avocations: swimming, embroidery, crafts, book clubs. Home: 7067 Cascade Rd Concord OH 44077-9509 Office: GrandeLine Custom Comm 7067 Cascade Concord OH 44077

WATTERSON, SCOTT, wholesale fitness equipment distribution executive. Pres, CEO Proform Fitness Products, Inc.; also pres, CEO Weider Sporting Goods, Inc. Office: Proform Fitness Products Inc 1500 S 1000 W Logan UT 84321*

WATTLES, JOSHUA, motion picture studio executive. Sr., v.p. dep. gen. counsel Paramount Pictures Corp., subs. Gulf & Western Inc., N.Y.C. Office: Paramount Pictures Corp 1 Gulf Western Plz New York NY 10023

WATTLETON, (ALYCE) FAYE, association executive; b. St. Louis, July 8, 1943; d. George and Ozie (Garret) Wattleton; m. Franklin Gordon (div.); 1 child, Felicia. BS in Nursing, Ohio State U., 1964; MS in Maternal and Infant Health Care, Columbia U., 1967; LLD (hon.), Northeastern Univ. Law Sch., 1990; LHD (hon.), Long Island Univ., 1990, Univ. of Pa., 1990, Bard Coll., 1991; HHD (hon.), Oberlin Coll., 1991; LLD (hon.), Wesleyan Univ., 1991. Tchr. Miami Valley Hosp. Sch. Nursing, Dayton, Ohio, 1964-66; asst. dir. Montgomery County Combined Pub. Health Dist., Dayton, 1967-70; exec. dir. Planned Parenthood, Dayton, 1970-78; pres. Planned Parenthood Fedn. Am., Inc., N.Y.C, 1978-92; host syndicated TV show Tribune Entertainment, Chgo., 1992—. Author: How to Talk to Your Child About Sexuality, 1986. Bd. dirs. Kaiser Family Found., Calif. Wellness Found., WNET, Inst. for Internat. Edn., Quidel, Empire Blue Cross Blue Shield, Leslie Fay Cos. Recipient Claude Pepper Humanitarian award Internat. Platform Assn., 1990, Pioneer of Civil Rights and Human Rights award Nat. Conf. of Black Lawyers, 1990, Florina Lasker award N.Y. Civil Liberties Union Found., 1990, Whitney M. Young Jr. Service award Boy

Scouts of Am., 1990, Ministry of Women award Unitarian Universalist Women's Fed., 1990, Spirit of Achievement award Albert Einstein Coll. of Med. Yeshiva Univ., 1991, 20th Anniversary Advocacy award Nat. Family Planning and Reproductive Health Assn., 1991, Women of Achievement award Women's Projects and Production, 1991, Margaret Sanger award, 1992, Jefferson Public Service award, 1992, Dean's Distinguished Service award Columbia Sch. of Public Health, 1992. Office: care Fischer-Ross Agy 250 W 57th St New York NY 10107

WATTMAN, KENNETH E., chemical company executive; b. Orange, N.J., Feb. 9, 1928; s. George K. and Ruth P. (Anderson) W.; m. Margaret Nelson, May, 1954 (dec. Aug. 1984); children: George G., Mary Lou; m Anne Daley, June 14, 1986; stepchildren: Braford Trudeau, David Cramer, Katherine Trudeau. BChemE, Cornell U., 1950. Chemist Armour & Co., Chgo., 1950-55; sales mgr. Aquaness Corp., Houston, 1955-56; sr. v.p., dir. ICI Ams., Wilmington, Del., 1956-86; cons. Kao Corp., Toyko, 1987-88; pres., dir. Kao Corp. of Am., Wilmington, 1987—; chmn., dir. High Point (N.C.) Chem. Corp., 1987—; The Andrew Jergens Co., Cin., 1988—, Kao Infosystems Co., Plymouth, Pa., 1988—. Bd. dir. Salvation Army of Del., Wilmington, United Way of Del., Wilmington, 1974-88, chmn. fund raising, 1976; bd. dir. Jr. Achievement, Wilmington, 1985-86. Cpl. U.S. Army, 1950-52. Mem. Am. Chem. Soc., Greenville Country Club (pres. 1981, 83), Rodney Sq. Club, Coral Beach & Tennis Club, Bermuda. Avocations: fishing, reading, model building. Office: Kao Corp of Am 2711 Centerville Rd Wilmington DE 19808-1643

WATTMAN, MALCOLM PETER, lawyer; b. N.Y.C., June 27, 1941; s. William and Irma (Turtletaub) W.; m. Donna Weber, Sept. 1, 1963. BS in Indsl. Engring., U. Buffalo, 1963; postgrad., Syracuse U., 1963-64; JD, Fordham U., 1968. Bar: N.Y. 1969. Engr. US Air Material Command, Rome, N.Y., 1963-64, Uniroyal, Passaic, N.J., 1964-66, M&M Candies, Hackettown, N.J., 1966-68; cons. Touche Ross Co., N.Y.C., 1968-69; assoc. Cadwalader Wickersham & Taft, N.Y.C., 1969-78, ptnr., 1978—. Mem. ABA, N.Y. State Bar Assn., Assn. of Bar of City of N.Y. Home: 1185 Park Ave Apt 8K New York NY Office: Cadwalader Wickersham & Taft 100 Maiden Ln New York NY 10038-4818

WATTS, ANDRÉ, concert pianist; b. Nüremberg, Germany, June 20, 1946; s. Herman and Maria Alexandra (Gusmits) W. Student, Phila. Mus. Acad.; grad., Peabody Conservatory, Balt.; hon. doctorate, Yale U., 1973; HHD, Albright Coll., 1975; MusD (hon.), U. Pa., 1984. First pub. appearance at age 9, Phila. Orch. Children's Concerts, 1955, performed with Phila. Orch., 1956, with Leonard Bernstein and the N.Y. Philharmonic, 1963, European debut, London Symphony Orch., 1966, made world concert tour to 16 Asian and Western European cities for U.S. State Dept., 1967, including an appearance at The Berlin Festival, Soviet Union tour with San Francisco Symphony, 1973; appearances as soloist with all major U.S. and European orchs., solo tours, Europe, U.S., Japan, Israel; TV appearances include Live from Lincoln Center, Great Performers series, Lincoln Center, NET TV Spl. with Zubin Mehta and Los Angeles Philharm., Eugene Ormandy and the Phila. Orch.; rec. artist, CBS Records. Decorated Order of Zaire Congo; recipient Grammy award Nat. Acad. Rec. Arts and Scis., 1963; Lincoln Center medallion, 1974, Avery Fisher prize, 1988. Address: care IMG 22 E 71st St New York NY 10021-4911

WATTS, BARBARA GAYLE, law academic administrator; b. Covington, Ky., Oct. 18, 1946; d. William Samuel and LaVerne Barbara (Ziegler) W. BA, Purdue U., 1968; MEd, U. Cin., 1969, JD, 1978. Bar: Ohio 1978, U.S. Dist. Ct. (so. dist.) Ohio 1978. Residence dir. Ohio State U., Columbus, 1969-71, asst. dean students, 1971-75; assoc. Frost & Jacobs, Cin., 1978-81; asst. dean U. Cin. Coll. Law, 1981-84, assoc. dean, 1984—. Trustee Summerfair Inc., Cin., 1982-85. Schleman fellow Purdue U., 1968, Castleberry fellow AAUW, 1977. Mem. ABA, Ohio State Bar Assn., Cin. Bar Assn. (trustee 1992—, sec.1993-94), Nat. Assn. Women in Edn., Order of Coif, Chi Omega. Democrat. Office: U Cin Coll Law Clifton & Calhoun Sts Cincinnati OH 45221-0040

WATTS, CHARLES DEWITT, surgeon, corporate medical director; b. Atlanta, Sept. 21, 1917; s. Lewis G. and Ida H. (Hawes) W.; m. Constance Merrick, Jan. 5, 1945; children—Eileen Constance Watts Welch, Deborah Hill, Charles D., Winifred Anita Watts Hemphill. B.S., Morehouse Coll., 1938; M.D., Howard U., 1943; LHD (hon.), St. Pauls Coll., 1984; DSc (hon.), Duke U., 1991. Diplomate: Am. Bd. Surgery. Practice medicine specializing in surgery Durham, N.C., 1950—; med. dir. N.C. Mut. Life Ins. Co., Durham, 1960—; mem. faculty dept. surgery Howard U. Coll. Medicine, 1947-50; instr. surgery Howard U., Washington; asst. clin. prof. surgery Duke Med. Center; attending surgeon Durham County Gen. Hosp.; chmn. bd. Capital Health Systems Regional Agy., 1976; founder, dir. Lincoln Community Health Center, Durham, 1970. Trustee Howard U., Washington. Fellow Am. Coll. Surgery; mem. Inst. of Medicine of NSF. Home: 829 E Lawson St Durham NC 27701-4534 *As one looks back, he is impressed with the fact that whatever one accomplished was done with the help of others. It is an humbling experience to realize how interdependent we are as we go through life.*

WATTS, CHARLES HENRY, II, university administrator; b. N.Y.C., Oct. 17, 1926; s. Charles Henry and Mabel (Lamborn) W.; m. Patricia Dorothy McQuillen, June 9, 1951; children: Katharine L., Caroline W. Collins, Charles Henry III. AB, Brown U., 1947, PhD, 1953, LLD, 1975; MA, Columbia, 1948; LittD, Franklin Coll., 1965; LLD, Dickinson Sch. Law, 1968; HHD, Alderson-Broaddus Coll., 1969; LHD, Bucknell U., 1979. Mem. English dept. faculty Brown U., 1948-62, dean coll., 1958-62; exec. assoc. Am. Council on Edn., 1962-64; pres. Bucknell U., 1964-76; pres., chief exec. officer Wolf Trap Found. Performing Arts, 1976-77; cons., 1977-78; dir. campaign Brown U., 1978-80; dir. Beneficial Corp., Wilmington, Del., 1953—, gen. dir., 1980-87. Trustee emeritus Bucknell U., Lewisburg, Pa. Served to ensign USNR, WWII. Mem. Century Assn. (N.Y.C.), Cosmos Club (Washington), Knickerbocker Club (N.Y.C.), St. Botolph Club. Home: 191 Commonwealth Ave Apt 41 Boston MA 02116-2211

WATTS, CLAUDIUS ELMER, III, retired air force officer; b. Bennettsville, S.C., Sept. 22, 1936; s. Claudius Elmer and Blanche Robey (Wannamaker) W.; m. Patricia Jane Sims, July 23, 1960; children: Claudius Elmer IV, Patricia Watts Heck. A.B. in Polit. Sci., The Citadel, 1958; postgrad. (Fulbright scholar), London Sch. Econs. and Polit. Sci., 1958-59; M.B.A., Stanford U., 1967. Command. officer USAF, 1958, advanced through grades to lt. gen., 1986; comdr. 438th Mil. Airlift Group USAF, McGuire AFB, N.J., 1978-80; comdr. 63d Mil. Airlift Wing USAF, Norton AFB, Calif. 1980-82; asst. dep. chief staff plans Mil. Airlift Command USAF, Scott AFB, Ill., 1982-83, dep. chief staff plans Mil. Airlift Command, 1983-84; dir. budget Hdqrs. U.S. Air Force, Washington, 1984-85; sr. mil. asst. to dep. sec. def. U.S. Dept. Def., Washington, 1985-86; compt. USAF Washington, 1986-89; pres. The Citadel, Charleston, S.C., 1989—; adv. coun. grad. sch. bus. Stanford U.; mem. bd. visitors Air Univ., Def. Systems Mgmt. Coll.; mem. NCAA Coun., rep. on acad. requirements com. Bd. trustees Palmetto Partnership; chmn. Marion Sq. Commn. Decorated Def. Disting. Svc. medal, USAF Disting. Svc. medal, Legion of Merit with oak leaf cluster, D.F.C. with two oak leaf clusters, Air medal with ten oak leaf clusters, Gallantry Cross with Palm (Vietnam). Mem. Air Force Assn., Am. Soc. Mil. Comptrollers, Mil. Order World Wars, Air Force Sgts. Assn., Airlift Assn., Ranch Hand Assn., Vets. of War, Royal Order of St. Stanislas, Order of Daedalians, Rotary. Methodist. Avocations: golf; reading. Office: Mil Coll of SC The Citadel Charleston SC 29409

WATTS, DAVE HENRY, corporate executive; b. Montgomery, Ala., Jan. 18, 1932; s. Lawson Tate and Annie (Sherman) W.; m. Eleanor Lewis, Nov. 5, 1950; children—Anne Watts Durham, Martha Watts Keens, Susan Watts Balla. Student, U. Ala., 1950, U. Va. 1962; B.B.A., George Washington U., 1968, M.B.A., 1970, D.B.A., 1974. Comstr. clk. So. Ry., Birmingham, Ala., 1950-51, safety supr., various other positions, 1951-77; v.p. personnel So. Ry., Washington, 1977-82; v.p. personnel and corp. devel. Norfolk So. Corp., Va., 1982-85, exec. v.p. planning and devel., 1985-86, exec. v.p. mktg. 1986—; lectr. George Washington U., 1974—. Contbr. articles to publs. in field. Mem. Va. Opera Bd.; bd. trustees Va. Wesleyan Coll., The Italy-U.S. Bus. Conf. of Washington, Inc. Bd. Mem. Nat. Freight Transp. Assn. (exec. com.), Am. Soc. Transp. and Logistics, Nat. Indsl. Transp. League (chmn.

exec. adv. coun. rail execs.), Washington Golf and Country Club (Arlington, Va.), Princess Anne Country Club (Virginia Beach, Va.), Town Pt. Club (Norfolk, Va.) (bd. dirs.). Methodist. Avocations: tennis; golf. Office: Norfolk So Corp 3 Commercial Pl Norfolk VA 23510-2108

WATTS, DAVID EIDE, lawyer; b. Fairfield, Iowa, June 13, 1921. B.A., U. Iowa, 1941, J.D., 1942; postgrad., Columbia Law Sch., 1946-47. Bar: Iowa 1942, Mass. 1950, N.Y. 1954. Instr. U. Iowa, Iowa City, 1947-48; asst. prof. U. Pa., 1948-49, Harvard Law Sch., 1949-52; ptnr. Dewey Ballantine, N.Y.C., 1958-90; of counsel Dewey Ballantine, N.Y.C., 1990—; adj. assoc. prof. NYU, 1952-55; vis. lectr. Columbia U., 1954. Contbr. articles to legal jours. Mem. ABA, N.Y. State Bar Assn., Assn. Bar City N.Y., Am. Law Inst., Am. Coll. Tax Counsel. Home: 33 W 74th St New York NY 10023-2402 Office: Dewey Ballantine 1301 Ave of the Americas New York NY 10019-6092

WATTS, EMILY STIPES, English educator; b. Urbana, Ill., Mar. 16, 1936; d. Royal Arthur and Virginia Louise (Schenck) Stipes; m. Robert Allan Watts, Aug. 30, 1958; children: Benjamin, Edward, Thomas. Student, Smith Coll., 1954-56; A.B., U. Ill., 1958, M.A. (Woodrow Wilson Nat. fellow), 1959, Ph.D., 1963. Instr. English U. Ill., Urbana, 1963-67, asst. prof., 1967-73, assoc. prof., 1973-77, prof., dir. grad. studies dept. English, 1977—; bd. dirs. U. Ill. Athletic Assn., chmn., 1981-83; mem. faculty adv. com. Ill. Bd. Higher Edn., 1984—, vice chmn., 1986-87, chmn., 1987-88. Author: Ernest Hemingway and The Arts, 1971, The Poetry of American Women from 1632 to 1945, 1977, The Businessman in American Literature, 1982; contbg. editor: English Women Writers from the Middle Ages to the Present, 1990; contbr. articles on Jonathan Edwards, Anne Bradstreet to lit. jours. John Simon Guggenheim Meml. Found. fellow, 1973-74. Mem. MLA, AAUP, Midwest MLA, Authors Guild, Ill. Hist. Soc., Phi Beta Kappa, Phi Kappa Phi. Presbyterian. Home: 1009 W University Ave Champaign IL 61821-3317 Office: U Ill 208 English Urbana IL 61801

WATTS, ERNEST FRANCIS, manufacturing company executive; b. Chgo., Mar. 23, 1937; s. Ernest Francis and Frances A. (Roche) W.; student Spring Hill Coll., 1955-57; student No. Ill. U., 1958-59; m. Sept. 10, 1960; children: Ernest Francis, Peggy, Colin. Sales rep. Binks Mfg. Co., Dallas 1960-62, Memphis, 1962-65, asst. regional mgr., Dallas, 1971, v.p., gen. mgr., Mexico City, 1971-75, v.p. gen. mgr., Toronto, 1975-81, v.p. mktg., Franklin Park, Ill., 1981—; dir. Binks Can., Japan, Australia, Mex. Trustee, mem. exec. bd. Fenwick High Sch., 1983-89, lifetime trustee, 1989; trustee Rosary Coll. 1990. Served with USAR, 1960. Republican. Roman Catholic. Club: K.C. Office: Binks Mfg Co 9201 Belmont Ave Franklin Park IL 60131-2887

WATTS, GLENN ELLIS, union official; b. Stony Point, N.C., June 4, 1920; s. George Dewey and Nellie Viola (Ellis) W.; m. Bernice Elizabeth Willett, Nov. 8, 1941; children: Glenn Ellis II, Sharon Elizabeth Ann, Marianne Elizabeth Watts Erickson. With Chesapeake & Potomac Telephone Co., Washington, 1941-48; with Communications Workers Am., Washington, 1942-85, pres. div. 36, 1948-51, dir. dist. 2, 1951-56, asst. to pres., 1956-65, v.p., 1965-69, sec.-treas. union, 1969-74, pres., 1974-85, pres. emeritus, 1985—; v.p. exec. council AFL-CIO, 1974-85, v.p. emeritus, 1985—; v.p. indsl. union dept., 1968-85, mem. exec. bd. maritime trades dept., 1974-85; mem. Nat. Labor Com. for U.S. Savs. Bonds, 1975; nat. adv. bd. Labor Council for Latin Am. Advancement, 1975-85; mem. labor policy adv. com. for trade negotiations Dept. Labor, 1975-79; mem. industry-labor council White House Conf. on Handicapped Individuals, 1976; chmn. labor subcom. Pres.'s Com. on Employment of Handicapped, 1977; mem. sec.'s adv. council Dept. Commerce, 1976-77; mem. Pres.'s Commn. on Mental Health, 1977-78. Mem. Pres.'s Commn. on the Holocaust, 1978-79; mem. U.S. Holocaust Meml. Coun., 1979-93; past mem. D.C. Appeals and Rev. Bd., D.C. Wage and Hour Rev. Panel, Home Rule for D.C. Com.; mem. nat. advisory com. Nat. Congress Community Econ. Devel., 1974; past chmn. community chest relations com. Nat. Capital Area council Boy Scouts Am., past chmn. James E. West Dist., 1969-71; pres. Health and Welfare Council of Nat. Capital Area, 1967-69; mem. Inter-Am. adv. com. Postal Tel. and Telecom. Internat. 1968-74, mem. exec. com., 1977-85, v.p. 1978-81, pres., 1981-85; gen. chmn. United Giver's Fund, 1968, pres., 1971-75; sec. United Way of Am., 1971-76; bd. dirs., treas United Way Internat., 1974-78; mem.-at-large Dem. Nat. Com., 1974-85, mem. incomes policy study group of domestic affairs task group, 1974-76; trustee, sec.-treas. Am. Inst. Free Labor Devel., 1974-85; mem. U.S. Assn. for Club of Rome, 1978-80; trustee AFL-CIO Human Resources Devel. Inst., 1974-85, George Meany Ctr. for Labor Studies, 1976-85; trustee Ford Found., 1976-88; trustee Aspen Inst. for Humanistic Studies, 1974-89, trustee emeritus, 1989—; trustee Nat. Planning Assn., 1974-80; governing bd. Common Cause, United Way of Am., 1974-80; bd. dirs. Council on Fgn. Rels., 1987-90; Initiative Com. for Nat. Econ. Planning, 1975-76, Overseas Devel. Council, 1987-91; trustee, mem. exec. com. Joint Council Econ. Edn., 1976-79, Collective Bargaining Forum, 1983—, co-chmn. 1983-87, adv. bd. Collective Bargaining Inst. George Washington U., 1987-92; mem. Commn. on a Nat. Inst. Justice, 1976-79, Trilateral Commn., 1977—, Helsinki Watch, 1978-90, commn. Future U.S.-Mex. Relations, 1987-89, exec. com. Am. Agenda, 1988. Recipient Urban Trade Unionist award Nat. Urban Coalition, 1978, Silver Beaver award, 1965. Methodist.

WATTS, HAROLD ROSS, hospital administrator; b. Tillsonburg, Ont., Can., June 7, 1944; s. Leo Kirkland and Beatrice Josephine (Williams) W. MD, U. Western Ont., 1968. Licentiate Med. Council Can. Dist. med. officer Dept. of Health, Catalina, Nfld., Can., 1972-74; sr. med. officer Dept. of Health, Bell Island, Nfld., 1975-78; med. dir. Western Meml. Regional Hosp., Corner Brook, Nfld., 1978-79, chief exec. officer, med. dir., 1979-95; chief exec. officer, med. dir. Western Region Instl. Health Corp., 1995—; exec. mem. N.E. Can.-Am. Health Coun., Boston, 1988—; co-chmn. Royal Commn. Implementation Com., St. John's, Nfld., 1986-91. Pres. Soc. Prevention Cruelty to Animals, Corner Brook, 1983-86, 87-89, mem. exec. com.; mem. adv. com. on acad. and tech. Nfld., 1990-92; bd. dirs. Stephenville Festival of the Arts, 1986-91. Med. officer Royal Can. Navy, 1965-72. Mem. Nfld. Med. Assn. (bd. dirs. 1988-89, chmn. polit. action com. 1988—, pres. 1992-93, co-chmn. joint mgmt. com.), Can. Med. Assn. (gen. coun. 1991—, bd. dirs. 1994—) Corner Brook C. of C. (pres. 1990-91), Humber-St. Barbe-Bale Verte Progressive Conservative Assn. (past pres.), Alpha Omega Alpha. Anglican. Home: 13 Lomond St, Corner Brook, NF Canada A2H 3B1 Office: Western Meml Regional Hosp, PO Box 2005, Corner Brook, NF Canada A2H 6J7

WATTS, HAROLD WESLEY, economist, educator; b. Salem, Oreg., Sept. 30, 1932; s. Elton and Claire W.; m. Doris A. Roth, Sept. 28, 1951 (div. 1973); children—Michael Lee, Suzanne, Jane Marie, Kristin. B.A., U. Oreg., 1954; M.A., Yale U., 1956, Ph.D., 1957. From instr. to assoc. prof. Yale U., New Haven, 1957-63; from assoc. prof. to prof. econs. U. Wis., Madison, 1963-76, dir. Inst. Research on Poverty, 1966-71; prof. econs. and pub. policy Columbia U., N.Y.C., 1976—, dir. Pub. Policy Rsch. Ctr., 1988—; sr. fellow Mathematica Policy Research Princeton, N.J., 1979-92; sr. rsch. assoc. Urban Inst., 1994-95; sr. rsch. assoc. Urban Inst., 1994-95. Recipient Paul Lazarsfeld award, 1980; Guggenheim fellow, 1975. Fellow Assn. Pub. Policy Analysis and Mgmt., Econometric Soc.; mem. Am. Econ. Assn., Am. Statis. Assn. Democrat. Home: 448 Riverside Dr # 82 New York NY 10027-6818 Office: Columbia U Dept Economics New York NY 10027

WATTS, HEATHER, ballerina; b. Long Beach, Calif., Sept. 27, 1953; d. Keith Nevin and Sheelagh Maud (Woodhead) W. Student, Sch. Am. Ballet. N.Y.C. Mem. corps de ballet N.Y.C. Ballet Co., 1970-78, soloist, 1978-79, prin., 1979-95, retired, 1995; dir. N.Y. State Summer Sch. of Arts Sch. of Dance, Saratoga Springs, from 1982; organized dance troupe, Dancers, 1986. Created roles in George Balanchine's Robert Schumann's Davidsbündlertänze, Peter Martin's Rossini Pas de Deux, Lille Suite, Suite from Histoire du Soldat, Calcium Light Night, Sonate di Scarlatti, Concerto for Two Solo Pianos, Tango, A Schubertiad, Song of the Auvergne, Ecstatic Orange, Jerome Robbins' Piano Pieces, Chamber Works, I'm Old Fashioned, & The Four Seasons; performed in N.Y.C. Ballet's Balanchine Celebration, 1993; PBS-TV appearances include Bournonville Dances, The Magic Flute, A

Choreographer's Notebook (all Dance in America series), and Lincoln Center Special: Balanchine Celebrates Stravinsky. Recipient Dance Mag. award, 1985; L'Oreal Shining Star award, 1985, Lions of the Performing Arts award N.Y. Pub. Library, 1986. *

WATTS, HENRY MILLER, JR., stockbroker; b. Phila., Mar. 13, 1904; s. Henry Miller and Laura Esther (Barney) W.; m. Maxine Wieczorek, 1935; m. Anna Harris Pepper, 1952. Grad., St. Paul's Sch., 1921; A.B., Harvard U., 1925. With Robert Glendinning & Co., Phila., 1925-29; mem. N.Y. Stock Exchange, 1929—, gov., 1958-61, vice chmn. bd. govs., 1961-62, chmn. bd. govs., 1962-65; chmn. bd. Mitchel Schreiber, Watts & Co., Inc., N.Y.C. 1931-82; pres., chmn. bd. Independence Sq. Income Securities Inc., 1972—; dir. Teradyne Corp., Temporary Investment Fund, Inc., Municipal Fund for Temporary Investment; trustee Trust for Short-Term Fed. Securities; pres., mng. gen. partner Chestnut St. Exchange Fund. Bd. dirs. Muscular Dystrophy Assn. Am., 1965—, pres., 1968-75, mem. exec. com., 1975—. Lt. (j.g.) to comdr. USNR, 1941-45, capt. Res. ret. Rector's warden Christ Ch., Phila., 1964—. Decorated Bronze Star with combat V. Mem. Soc. Cincinnati of Pa. (pres. 1968-71), Mil. Order Fgn. Wars, 1st Troop Phila. City Cav. (hon.). Clubs: Racquet and Tennis (N.Y.C.), Union (N.Y.C.); Philadelphia. Home: 219 Spruce St Philadelphia PA 19106-3906 Office: 20 Broad St New York NY 10005-2601

WATTS, J. C., JR., congressman; b. Eufaula, Okla., Nov. 8, 1957; m. Frankie Watts; 5 children. BS in Journalism, U. Okla., 1981. Profl. football player Ottawa and Toronto Teams Can. Football League, 1981-86; youth min. Sunnyland So. Bapt. Ch., Del City, 1987-94; mem. Okla. Corp. Commn., 1990-94, chmn., 1993-94; mem. 104th Congress from 4th Okla. dist., 1995—; mem. Nat. Drinking Water Adv. Coun.; mem. electricity com. Nat. Assn. Regulatory Utility Commrs. Republican. Office: US House Reps 2344 Rayburn House Office Bldg Washington DC 20515-3604

WATTS, JOHN MCCLEAVE, financial services executive; b. Salt Lake City, July 20, 1933; s. Newell Edward and Mildred (McCleave) W.; m. Sharon Lee Sewell, Apr. 4, 2954 (div. Nov. 1969); children: John McCleave Jr., Christopher A., Kelly Lee Watts Cramer; m. Janis Marie Duncan, July 4, 1971; 1 stepson, Kenneth D. McCoy; BS, Mass. Inst. Tech., 1956; CLU; registered prin. Nat. Assn. Securities Dealers. In sales mgmt., Gen. Am. Life, Corpus Christi, Tex., 1957-65; mktg. dir., Am. Gen. Life, Houston, 1965-71; exec. v.p. Rsch. Mgmt. Assocs., Kansas City, Mo., 1971-79; pres., E.F. Hutton Agys., La Jolla, Calif., 1979-83; pres., Hartford (Conn.) Equity Corp., 1983-85; sr. v.p., Washington Nat. Corp., Evanston, Ill, 1985-90; chmn bd. Washington Equity Corp., 1985-90, Washington Nat. Fin. Services, Evanston, 1985-90; pres., CEO Xelan Inc., San Diego, 1991-93, bd. dirs., 1991-93; exec. v.p. Lamar Life Ins. Co., Jackson, Miss., 1993—; speaker mgmt., sales and data processing confs. Author: The Financial Services Shockwave, 1987; contbr. numerous articles to trade and profl. jours. City councilman, Leawood, Kans., 1973-78; chmn. Nueces County (Tex.) Republican Party, 1962-65; chmn. bd. dirs. Nat. Ctr. Fin. Edn., San Francisco, 1984—; bd. regents Coll. for Fin. Planning, Denver, 1986-91. Capt. AUS, 1956-57. Recipient Life Ins. Mktg. Inst. Achievement award Purdue U., 1960. Mem. Internat. Assn. Fin. Planners, Am. Soc. CLU's. Republican. Introduced nation's first universal life ins. product. Avocation: piloting. Home: 1537 Brobridge Dr Jackson MS 39211-2114 Office: Lamar Life Ins Co PO Box 880 Jackson MS 39205-0880

WATTS, MALCOLM S(TUART) M(CNEAL), physician, medical educator; b. N.Y.C., Apr. 30, 1915; s. Malcolm S.M. and Elizabeth (Forbes) W.; m. Genevieve Moffitt, July 12, 1947; children: Pauline, Elizabeth, Malcolm, James. A.B., Harvard U., 1937; M.D., 1941. Diplomate: Pan Am. Med. Assn. Group practice internal medicine San Francisco, 1948-76; clin. prof. medicine U. Calif. Sch. Medicine, 1972-89, assoc. dean, 1966-89, clin. prof. medicine emeritus, 1989—, dir. Extended Programs in Med. Edn., 1973-82; dir. Calif. Statewide Area Health Edn. System, 1979-89; chmn. bd. trustees San Francisco Consortium, 1968-74, trustee, 1974-80, exec. dir., 1981-94; dir. Soc. Med. Dirs. Continuing Med. Edn., 1975-82, pres., 1980-81; trustee Hospice of San Francisco, v.p., 1979-85; pres. Alliance Continuing Med. Edn., 1979-81. Editor Western Jour. Medicine. 1968-90, Jour. Continuing Edn. in the Health Professions, 1988-91. Served to capt. M.C. AUS, 1942-46. Recipient Outstanding Community Funds and Councils Am., 1964, U. Calif. San Francisco medal, 1983, Disting. Svc. award Alliance for Continuing Med. Edn., 1990, Disting. Svc. award soc. Med. Coll. Dirs. of Continuing Med. Edn., 1991. Master ACP; fellow Am. Coll. Hosp. Adminstrs. (hon.); mem. AMA, AAAS, Calif. Acad. Scis., Calif. Acad. Medicine, Am. Med. Writers Assn. (John T. McGovern award 1986), San Francisco Med. Soc. (pres. 1961), Am. Soc. Internal Medicine (pres. 1964-65), Calif. Med. Assn. (bd. dirs. 1962-90), Nat. Inst. Medicine, Soc. Med. Friends Wine, Coun. Biology Editors, Am. Acad. Polit. and Social Sci., Am. Acad. Polit. Sci., Acad. Mexicana Ciencias Mexicano de Cultura (corr.). Home: 270 Sea Cliff Ave San Francisco CA 94121-1028

WATTS, MARVIN LEE, minerals company executive, chemist, educator; b. Portales, N.Mex., Apr. 6, 1932; s. William Ellis and Jewel Reata (Holder) W.; m. Mary Myrtle Kiker, July 25, 1952; children: Marvin Lee, Mark Dwight, Wesley Lyle. BS in Chemistry and Math., Ea. N.Mex. U., 1959, MS in Chemistry, 1960; postgrad. U. Okla., 1966, U. Kans., 1967. Analytical chemist Dow Chem. Co., Midland, Mich., 1960-62; instr. chemistry N.Mex. Mil. Inst., Roswell, 1962-65, asst. prof., 1965-67; chief chemist AMAX Chem. Corp., Carlsbad, N.Mex., 1967-78, gen. surface supt., 1978-84; pres. N.Mex. Salt and Minerals Corp., 1984—; chem. cons. Western Soils Lab., Roswell, 1962-67; instr. chemistry N.Mex. State U., Carlsbad, 1967—; owner, operator cattle ranch, Carlsbad and Loving, N.Mex., 1969—; bd. dirs. Mountain States Mutual Casualty Co., 1991; gen. mgr. Eddy Potash, Inc., 1987—; dir. Soil Conservation Svc.; mem. Roswell dist. adv. bd. Bur. Land Mgmt.; bd. dirs. Southeastern N.Mex. Regional Sci. Fair, 1966; mem. adv. bd. Roswell dist. Bur. Land Mgmt.; mem. Eddy County Fair Bd., 1976—, chmn., 1978, 82; mem. pub. sch. reform com.; chmn. higher edn. reform com.; mem. sponsor of N.Mex. Pub. Sch. Reform Act; bd. dirs. Carlsbad Regional Med. Ctr., 1976-78; pres. bd. Carlsbad Found., 1979-82; adv. bd. N.Mex. State U. at Carlsbad, 1976-80; vice chmn. bd. Guadalupe Med. Ctr.; bd. dirs. N.Mex. State U. Found.; state senator N.Mex. Legis., 1984-89. Mem. Rep. State Exec. com., 1972—; Rep. chmn. Eddy County (N.Mex.), 1970-74, 78-82, dirs. Conquistador coun. Boy Scouts Am., Regional Environ. Ednl. Rsch. and Improvement Orgn. Served with Mil. Police Corps, AUS, 1953-55; Germany. Recipient Albert K. Mitchell award as outstanding Rep. in N.Mex., 1976; hon. state farmer N.Mex. Future Farmers Am.; hon. member. 4-H. Fellow N.Mex. Acad. Sci.; mem. Am. Chem. Soc. (chmn. subsect.), Western States Pub. Lands Coalition, Carlsbad C. of C. (dir. 1979-83), N.Mex. Mining Assn. (dir.), AIME (chmn. Carlsbad potash sect. 1975), Carlsbad Mental Health Assn., N.Mex. Inst. Mining and Tech. (adv. bd. mining dept.), Am. Angus Assn., Am. Quarter Horse Assn., N.Mex. Cattle Growers Assn. (bd. dirs. 1989—), Carlsbad Farm and Ranch Assn., Nat. Cattleman's Assn. Baptist. Kiwanis (Disting. lt. gov.), Elks. Home: PO Box 56 Carlsbad NM 88221-0056 Office: PO Box 31 Carlsbad NM 88221-5601

WATTS, OLIVER EDWARD, engineering consultancy company executive; b. Hayden, Colo., Sept. 22, 1939; s. Oliver Easton and Vera Irene (Hockett) W.; m. Charla Ann French, Aug. 12, 1962; children—Erik Sean, Oliver Eron, Sherilyn. BS, Colo. State U., 1962. Registered profl. engr., Colo., Calif.; profl. hand surveyor, Colo. Crew chief Colo. State U. Rsch. Found., Ft. Collins, 1962; with Calif. Dept. Water Resources, Gustine and Castaic, 1964-70; land and water engr. CF&I Steel Corp., Pueblo, Colo., 1971-76; engring. dir. United Western Engrs., Colorado Springs, Colo., 1971-76; ptnr. United Planning and Engring Co., Colorado Springs, 1976-79; owner Oliver E. Watts, Cons. Engr., Colorado Springs, 1979—. Dir. edn. local Ch. of Christ, 1969-71, deacon, 1977-87, elder, 1987—. 1st lt. C.E. AUS, 1962-64. Recipient Individual Achievement award Colo. State U. Coll. Engring., 1981. Fellow ASCE (v.p. Colorado Springs br. 1975, pres. 1978); mem. NSPE (pres. Pike's Peak chpt. 1976, Colo. sect. 1976 n.w. v.p. 1977, pres. 1978-79, Young Engr. award 1976, Pres.'s award 1979), Cons. Engrs. Coun. Colo. (bd. dirs. 1981-83), Am. Cons. Engrs. Coun., Profl. Land Surveyors Colo., Colo. Engrs. Coun. (del. 1980—), Colo. State U. Alumni Assn. (v.p., dir. Pike's Peak chpt. 1972-76), Lancers, Lambda Chi Alpha. Home: 7195 Dark Horse Pl Colorado Springs CO 80919-1442 Office: 614 Elkton Dr Colorado Springs CO 80907-3514

WATTS, QUINCY, track and field athlete. Olympic track and field participant Barcelona, Spain, 1992; Gold medalist and world record holder (with Valmon, Reynolds, Johnson) 4 x400 relay World Track and Field Championships, Stuttgart, Germany, 1993. Recipient 400m Track and Field, 4x4 Relay Gold medals Olympics, Barcelona, 1992. Office: c/o First Team Mktg 10100 Santa Monica Blvd Ste 46 Los Angeles CA 90067*

WATTS, RALPH S., social services administrator; b. Seoul, Korea, Apr. 15, 1934; s. Ralph Shore and Mildred (Hooper) W.; m. Patricia Ann Ortner, Aug. 17, 1952; children: Edie, Marcia, Ralph III, Laurie. BA in Religion, Union Coll., Lincoln, Nebr., 1956. Evangelist Seventh-Day Adventist, Nebr., 1956-57, pastor, 1957-60; ch. adminstr. Seventh-Day Adventist, N.D., 1961-63, Republic of Korea, 1963-66, Far East region, 1966-69; pres., chief exec. officer Seventh-Day Adventist, SE Asia, 1969-75, N.D. 1975-78, Minn., Iowa, Calif., 1978-85; pres., chief exec. officer Adventist Devel. and Relief Agy., Washington, 1985—. Author: Saigon-The Final Days, 1990. Bd. dirs. Loma Linda (Calif.) U., 1981—; Adventist Media Ctr., Thousand Oaks, Calif., 1981-90, Interaction, N.Y.C., 1986—. Office: ADRA Internat 12501 Old Columbia Pike Silver Spring MD 20904-6601

WATTS, ROBERT, wholesale distribution executive; b. 1948. Prin. Robert Watts, CPA, Atlanta, 1969-85; with EIS Mgmt. Corp., Atlanta, 1985—, sec.-treas., 1990—, v.p., sec.- treas. Office: EIS Mgmt Corp 1255 Collier Rd NW Atlanta GA 30318*

WATTS, ROBERT GLENN, retired pharmaceutical company executive; b. Norton, Va., Apr. 28, 1933; s. Clifford Amburgey and Stella Lee (Cornette) W.; m. Doris Juanita Slaughter, Aug. 29, 1953 (dec. 1980); children: Cynthia L. Watts Waller, Robert Glenn, Kelly L.; m. Sara Lowry Childrey, Aug. 20, 1982; stepchildren: J. Eric Alexander, Matthew R. Alexander. B.A., U. Richmond, 1959. Dir. ops. A.H. Robins Co., Inc., Richmond, Va., 1967-71, asst. v.p., 1971-73, v.p., 1973-75, sr. v.p., 1975-79, exec. v.p., 1979-92; ret., 1992; bd. dirs. Little Oil Co., Richmond, Fidelity Fed. Savs. Bank, Richmond. Bd. dirs. United Way, Richmond, 1982—; Pvt. Industry Council, Richmond, 1983—; sec. YMCA, Richmond, 1984— Served with USN, 1952-56. Mem. Met. Richmond C. of C. (chmn. 1985-86), Bull and Bear Club, Hermitage Country. Episcopalian. Home: 2409 Islandview Dr Richmond VA 23233-2525

WATTS, RONALD LESTER, retired military officer; b. Seneca, Mo., June 27, 1934; s. Lester N. and Naomi (Montgomery) W.; m. Anita Abelquist, Sept. 26, 1981; 1 child, Christina; children by previous marriage—Elizabeth Ann, Ronald Allen. B.S. in Edn., Pitts. State U., 1956; M.S. in Polit. Sci., Auburn U., 1976. Commd. officer U.S. Army, 1956, advanced through grades to lt. gen., 1987; asst. div. comdr. 1st Inf. Div., Ft. Riley, Kans., 1981-83; comdg. gen. U.S. Army Readiness, Fort Meade, Md., 1983; dep. comdg. gen. 1st U.S. Army, Fort Meade, Md., 1983-84; comdg. gen. 1st Inf. Div., Ft. Riley, Kans., 1984-86; chief staff Hdqrs. Forces Command, Ft. McPherson, Ga., 1986-87; commdg. gen. VII Corps, 1987-89, ret., 1989; pres. Watts Leadership Devel. Svcs., Greensboro, Ga., 1989—. Decorated D.S.M. with oak leaf cluster, Legion of Merit with 2 oak leaf clusters, Bronze Star, Air medal with 10 oak leaf clusters, Combat Inf. badge, Def. Superior Svc. medal with cluster.

WATTS, STEPHEN HURT, II, lawyer; b. Lynchburg, Va., Feb. 21, 1947; s. James Owen Jr. and Sarah Webb (Key) W.; m. Beverley Allan Brockenbrough, July 16, 1969 (div. 1986): children: Day Lowry, Stephen Hurt Jr.; m. Sally Yates Wood, May 24, 1986. BA, Washington & Lee U., 1968; JD, U. Va., 1972. Bar: Va. 1972, W.Va. 1973. Law clk. Taylor, Michie & Callahan, Charlottesville, Va., 1970-72; assoc. Spilman, Thomas, Battle & Klostermeyer, Charleston, W.Va., 1972-75; ptnr. Watts & Watts, Lynchburg, Va., 1975-77; v.p., counsel Commonwealth Gas Pipeline Corp., Richmond, 1977-81; gen. counsel Commonwealth Natural Resources, Inc., Richmond, 1980-81; assoc. McGuire, Woods & Battle, Richmond, 1981-83; ptnr. McGuire, Woods, Battle & Boothe, Richmond, 1983—. Bd. dirs. Lower Fan Civic Assn., Richmond, 1987-91, TheatreVirginia, Richmond, 1992-93, Va. Oil and Gas Assn., 1993; pres., bd. dirs Studio Theatre Richmond, 1991-93; chmn. outreach com. Grace and Holy Trinity Episcopal Ch., Richmond, 1993. Mem. ABA, Va. Bar Assn. (mem. adminstrv. law sect., dir.), Fed. Energy Bar Assn. Home: 3420 Grove Ave Richmond VA 23221 Office: McGuire Woods Battle & Boothe One James Center 901 E Cary St Richmond VA 23219

WAUCHOPE, KEITH L., diplomat; b. N.Y.C., Oct. 13, 1941; married; two children. A.B, Johns Hopkins U., 1963. Dep. prin. officer U.S. Consulate Gen. U.S. Dept. State, Asmara, Ethiopia, 1975-77; Sudan desk officer for East African Affairs U.S. Dept. State, 1977-79; dep. chief of mission U.S. Embassy U.S. Dept. State, Bamako, 1979-81; chief of assignments for Africa, Bur. of Pers. U.S. Dept. State, 1981-83, dep. dir. Office of West African Affairs, 1984-86; dep. chief of mission U.S. Dept. State, Monrovia, Liberia, 1986-89; amb. Gabonese Republic, Republic of Sao Tome, Principe, 1989—. Office: Am Embassy, Blvd de la Mer BP 4000, Libreville Gabon also: Libreville Dept State Washington DC 20521-2270

WAUD, ROGER NEIL, economics educator; b. Detroit, Mar. 26, 1938; s. Othneil Stockwell and Mary Josephine (Gough) W.; children: Heather, Neil. B.A., Harvard U., 1960; M.A., U. Calif., Berkeley, 1962; Ph.D. (Ford Found. fellow), U. Calif., Berkeley, 1965. Asst. prof. bus. econs. Grad. Sch. Bus. U. Chgo., 1964-69; assoc. prof. econs. U. N.C., Chapel Hill, 1969-72; prof. U. N.C., 1972—; sr. economist, bd. govs. Fed. Res. System, Washington, 1973-75; cons. Dept. Labor; mem. adv. bd. Taxpayers Ednl. Coalition, 1981; research assoc. Nat. Bur. Econ. Research, 1982-92; mem. N.C. Energy Policy Council, 1986-92. Author: Macroeconomics, 5th edit., 1992, Microeconomics, 5th edit., 1992; contbr. articles to profl. jours.; mem. editorial bd.: So. Econ. Jour, 1970-73. Mem. Am. Econ. Assn., Econometric Soc., So. Econ. Assn. (exec. com. 1977-79). Office: Univ NC Dept Econs Chapel Hill NC 27599-3305

WAUGAMAN, RICHARD MERLE, psychiatrist; b. Easton, Pa., Apr. 27, 1949; s. Charles Hoffmeier and Ruth Alviene (Melee) W.; m. Elisabeth Leone Pearson, June 20, 1970; children: Adele Marie, Garrett Dennis. AB, Princeton U., 1970; MD, Duke U., 1973. Cert. psychiatry, 1978, psychoanalysis, 1984. Resident Sheppard-Pratt Hosp., Towson, Md., 1973-76; Faculty Washington Sch. Psychiatry, Washington, 1983—; tng. and supervising analyst Washington Psychoanalytic Inst., 1989—; clin. assoc. prof. psychiatry Georgetown U. Sch. Medicine, Washington, 1985—; staff psychiatrist Chestnut Lodge, Rockville, Md., 1986—. Contbr. articles to profl. jours. Mem. Washington Psychoanalytic Soc., Am. Psychoanalytic Assn., Internat. Psychoanalytic Assn., Am. Psychiat. Assn. Methodist. Home: 8109 Horseshoe Ln Rockville MD 20854-3834 Office: Chestnut Lodge 500 W Montgomery Ave Rockville MD 20850-3892

WAUGH, DOUGLAS OLIVER WILLIAM, pathology educator; b. Hove, Sussex, Eng., Mar. 21, 1918; emigrated to Can., 1918; s. Oliver Sayles and Helen (Champion) W.; m. Sheila Louise Duff, Jan. 16, 1971. Student, U. Man., 1935-38; M.D.C.M., McGill U., 1942, M.S., 1948, Ph.D., 1950; LL.D. (hon.), Dalhousie U., 1992. Assoc. prof. pathology U. Alta., Edmonton, Can., 1950-51, McGill U., Montreal, Que., Can., 1951-57; assoc. prof. Queens U., Kingston, Ont., Can., 1958-60, prof., 1960-64, dean medicine, 1970-75, vice prin. health sci., 1971-72; prof., head pathology Dalhousie U., Halifax, N.S., Can., 1964-70; exec. dir. Assn. Can. Med. Colls., Ottawa, Ont., 1975-83; free-lance writer, essayist, biographer, 1983—; columnist Can. Med. Assn. Jour., 1983—; adj. prof. pathology U. Ottawa, 1978-83; chmn. adv. com. Can. Tumour Reference Ctr., NCI, Toronto, Ont., 1958-70; chmn. med. rsch. coun. Survey Path. Rsch, Ottawa, 1967; cons. Lab. Tech. Govt. B.C., 1977; sec. com. on accreditation Can. Med. Schs., 1978-83; mem. bd. accreditation Can. Assn. Univ. Schs. Nursing, 1984-93. Editor: ACMC Forum, 1975-83; contbr. articles to profl. jours. Served to capt. M.C., RCA, 1942-46. Named Prof. of Yr. Med. Undergrades, Dalhousie U., 1967; recipient Jubilee medal Queen Elizabeth II, 1977. Mem. Can. Med. Assn. (sr.), Can. Cytology Coun., Nat. Cancer Inst. Can. (pres. 1974-76), Social and Behavior Coun., Alcoholic Beverages Med. Rsch. Found., Royal Coll. Physicians and Surgeons Can. (coun. 1969-70), Can. Authors Assn. (nat. v.p. 1991-94). Home: 183 Marlborough Ave, Ottawa, ON Canada K1N 8G3

WAUGH, JOHN STEWART, chemist, educator; b. Willimantic, Conn., Apr. 25, 1929; s. Albert E. and Edith (Stewart) W.; married 1983; children: Alice Collier, Frederick Pierce. AB, Dartmouth Coll., 1949; PhD, Calif. Inst. Tech., 1953; ScD (hon.), Dartmouth Coll., 1989. Research fellow physics Calif. Inst. Tech., 1952-53; mem. faculty Mass. Inst. Tech., 1953—, prof. chemistry, 1962—, Albert Amos Noyes prof. chemistry, 1973-88, inst. prof., 1989—; vis. prof. U. Calif.-Berkeley, 1963-64; lectr. Robert Welch Found., 1968; Falk-Plaut lectr. Columbia U., 1973; DuPont lectr. U. S.C., 1974; Lucy Pickett lectr. Mt. Holyoke Coll., 1978; Reilly lectr. U. Notre Dame, 1978; Spedding lectr. Iowa State U., 1979; McElvain lectr. U. Wis., 1981; Vaughan lectr. Rocky Mountain Conf., 1981; G.N. Lewis meml. lectr. U. Calif., 1982; Dreyfus lectr. Dartmouth Coll., 1984; G.B. Kistiakowsky lectr. Harvard U., 1984; O.K. Rice lectr. U. N.C., Chapel Hill, 1986, Baker lectr. Cornell U., 1990; Smith lectr. Duke U., 1992; sr. fellow Alexander von Humboldt-Stiftung; also vis. prof. Max Planck Inst., Heidelberg, 1972; vis. scientist Harvard U., 1976; mem. chemistry adv. panel NSF, 1966-69, vice chmn., 1968-69; mem. rev. com. Argonne Nat. Lab., 1970-74; mem. sci. and edn. adv. com. Lawrence Berkeley Lab., 1980-86; exchange visitor USSR Acad. Scis., 1962, 75; mem. vis. com. Tufts U., 1966-69, Princeton, 1973-78; mem. fellowship com. Alfred P. Sloan Found., 1977-82; Joliot-Curie prof. École Supérieure de Physique et Chemie, Paris, 1985. Author: New NMR Methods in Solid State Physics, 1978; editor: Advances in Magnetic Resonance, 1965-87; assoc. editor: Jour. Chem. Physics, 1965-67, Spectrochimica Acta, 1964-78; mem. editorial bd. Chem. Revs., 1978-82, Jour. Magnetic Resonance, 1989—, Applied Magnetic Resonance, 1989—. Recipient Irving Langmuir award, 1976, Gold Pick Axe award, 1976, Pitts. award Spectroscopic Soc. Pitts., 1979, Wolf prize, 1984, Pauling medal, 1985, Calif. Inst. Tech. disting. alumnus award, 1987, Killian award, 1988, ISMAR prize, 1989, Richards medal, 1992, Evans award, 1994; Sloan fellow, 1958-62, Guggenheim fellow, 1963-64, 72; Sherman Fairchild scholar Calif. Inst. Tech., 1989. Fellow Am. Acad. Arts and Scis., Am. Phys. Soc. (chmn. div. chem., physics 1983-84), AAAS; mem. NAS, Slovenian Acad. Sci. and Arts (fgn. corr.), Phi Beta Kappa, Sigma Xi. Office: MIT 77 Massachusetts Ave Cambridge MA 02139-4307

WAUGH, ROBERT JAMES, aerospace company executive; b. Toronto, Ont., Can., May 8, 1934; s. James and Eleanor Curtis (Rogan) W.; m. Patricia Susan Fleming, Jan. 15, 1966 (div. Oct. 1973); m. Doris Janet Whitnable, Dec. 22, 1973. BS, U. Toronto, 1956; MBA, Harvard U., 1961. Registered profl. engr., Ont. Asst. supt. Hawaiian Dredging, Honolulu, 1961-62; field engr. Bechtel Corp., San Francisco, 1962-63; mgr. contracts Del E. Webb Co. Inc., Phoenix, Ariz., 1963-64; sr. dir. McKinsey & Co., Inc., N.Y.C., 1964-84; exec. v.p., sector pres. aerospace/aviation UNC Inc., Annapolis, Md., 1985—; bd. dirs. Clear Lake Land Co., Gouverneur, N.Y. Served with Royal Can. Air Force, 1956-59. Avocations: classical music, dog breeding, exercise, civil war history, reading. Office: UNC Inc 175 Admiral Cochrane Dr Annapolis MD 21401-7367

WAUGH, THEODORE ROGERS, orthopedic surgeon; b. Montreal, Sept. 21, 1926; s. Theodore Rogers and Anne Maude (Lawlor) W.; children: Susanne Rogers, Margaret Stewart, Theodore Rogers. BA, Yale U., 1949; MD, CM, McGill U., 1953; D Med.Sci., U. Goteborg, Sweden, 1968. Diplomate Am. Bd. Orthopaedic Surgery. Intern Royal Victoria Hosp., Montreal, 1953-54; asst. resident in pathology McGill U., 1954-55; asst. resident in surgery N.Y. U. Bellevue Med. Center, 1955-56; asst. resident, resident, fellow N.Y. Orthopedic Hosp., Columbia U., 1958-62, instr., clin. asst. prof. orthopedic surgery, 1962-68; asst. attending Presbyn. Hosp., N.Y.C., 1962-68; prof., chief div. orthopedic surgery U. Calif., Irvine, 1968-78; prof., chmn. dept. orthopedic surgery N.Y. U. Med. Center, 1978—. Contbr. numerous articles to profl. jours. Capt., M.C. USAF, 1956-58. Fellow ACS, Royal Coll. Surgeons (Can.), Am. Acad. Orthopaedic Surgeons, Scoliosis Research Soc., Assn. Bone and Joint Surgeons, Am. Orthopaedic Assn., Am. Orthopaedic Soc. for Sports Medicine; mem. Soc. Colonial Wars, Alpha Omega Alpha. Presbyterian. Club: 20th Century Orthopedic. Designer surg. devices used in orthopaedic surgery. Office: NYU Med Ctr 550 1st Ave New York NY 10016-6497

WAUGH, WILLIAM HOWARD, biomedical educator; b. N.Y.C., May 13, 1925; s. Richey Laughlin and Lyda Pearl (Leamer) W.; m. Eileen Loretta Garrigan, Oct. 4, 1952; children: Mark Howard, Kathleen Cary, William Peter. Student, Boston U., 1943, W.Va. U., 1944; MD, Tufts U., 1948, postgrad., 1949-50. Cardiovascular rsch. trainee Med. Coll. Ga., Augusta, 1954-55, asst. rsch. prof. physiology, 1955-60, assoc. medicine, 1957-60; assoc. prof. medicine U. Ky., Lexington, 1960-69; Ky. Heart Assn. Chair in cardiovascular rsch. medicine U. Ky., Lexington, 1963-71; prof. medicine U. Ky., Lexington, 1969-71; prof. medicine and physiology East Carolina U., Greenville, N.C., 1971—; head renal sect. U. Ky. Coll., Lexington, 1960-68; chmn. dept. clin. scis. E.Carolina U., Greenville, 1971-75; chmn. E. Carolina U. Policy and Rev. Com. on Human Rsch., Greenville, 1971-90. Contbr. articles to profl. jours. With AUS, 1943-46; capt. USAF, 1952-54. Fellow ACP; mem. AAAS, Am. Physiology Soc., Am. Heart Assn., Am. Soc. Nephrology, Microcirculatory Soc. Republican. Achievements include basic advances in excitation contraction coupling in vasc. smooth muscle; basic advances in autoregulation of renal blood flow and urine flow; adj. therapy in acute lung edema; noncovalent antisickling agents in sickle cell hemoglobinopathy. Home: 119 Oxford Rd Greenville NC 27858 Office: E Carolina U Sch Medicine Dept Physiology Greenville NC 27858

WAWRZYN, RONALD M., lawyer; b. Milw., July 25, 1945; s. Edmund T. and Virginia Marie (Mandt) W.; m. Mary Anne Koenig, June 20, 1970; children: Robert, Matthew, James. BS, U. Wis., 1968, JD, 1972. Bar: Wis. 1972, U.S. Dist. Ct. (ea. dist.) Wis. 1974, U.S. Dist. Ct. (we. dist.) Wis. 1978, U.S. Dist. Ct. (no. dist.) Ill. 1975, U.S. Ct. Appeals (7th and 10th circs.). Trial atty. U.S. Dept. Justice, Washington, 1972-74; ptnr. Foley & Lardner, Milw., 1974—. Contbr. articles to law jours. Mem. ABA, Milw. Bar Assn. Clubs: Milw. Athletic, Ozaukee Country (Mequon, Wis.). Office: Foley & Lardner Firstar Ctr 777 E Wisc Ave Milwaukee WI 53202

WAX, BERNARD, research and development consultant, lecturer; b. Phila., Apr. 4, 1930; s. Samuel and Anna (Kaminker) W.; m. Dolores Helen Nemchek, Mar. 21, 1953; children—Ann Susan Wax Loeb, Steven Albert, Stuart Michael, Rebecca Mara. B.A., U. Chgo., 1950, M.A., 1955; postgrad., U. Wis., 1955-59. Field rep., field services supr. Ill. State Hist. Library, 1959-66; dir. Am. Jewish Hist. Soc., Waltham, Mass., 1966-91, dir. spl. projects, 1991-93, dir. emeritus 1993—; mem. Ill. State Records Commn., 1961-66, Cook County State Records Commn., 1961-66. Editor: Assn. Jewish Libraries Bull, 1970-72, Bay State Hist. League Bull, 1971-73. Co-founder Joint Cultural Appeal, 1972; pres. Coun. on Archives and Rsch. Libns. in Jewish Studies, 1983-85. With Signal Corps, U.S. Army, 1953-55. Mem. Bay State Hist. League (editor, bd. dirs. 1971-76, pres. 1976-78). Home: 21 Blake Rd Brookline MA 02146-5803

WAX, DAVID M., orchestra executive. Gen. mgr. Minn. Symphony Orch.; exec. dir. Houston Symphony. Office: Houston Symphony 615 Louisiana St Houston TX 77002-2715

WAX, EDWARD L., advertising executive; b. 1937; 2 children: Elizabeth, Alex. BS, Northeastern U., 1959; MBA, U. Pa., 1961. Chmn., CEO Saatchi & Saatchi Advt. Worldwide, 1963-68; account exec. Compton Advt., N.Y.C., 1963-68; gen. mgr. Ace Compton Manila, Manila, Philippines, 1968-72; sr. v.p. Compton Advt., N.Y.C., 1972-77; pres. Saatchi & Saatchi Compton, Inc. (now Saatchi/Saatchi Advt.), N.Y.C., 1983-87; chief exec. officer Saatchi & Saatchi Compton Inc. (now Saatchi & Saatchi Advt.), N.Y.C., 1983-87, 1988-89; CEO Saatchi & Saatchi Compton, Inc. (now Saatchi/Saatchi Advt.), N.Y.C., 1987-89; chmn. Saatchi & Saatchi Compton Inc. (now Saatchi & Saatchi Advt.), N.Y.C., 1988-89; pres., chief exec. officer Saatchi & Saatchi Advt. Inc., N.Y.C., 1989—; also bd. dirs.; chmn., CEO Saatchi & Saatchi Compton, Inc. (now Saatchi & Saatchi Advt.), N.Y.C., 1989-92; past pres., CEO Saatchi & Saatchi N. Am., now chmn., CEO, dir.; pres., chief ops. officer Richard K. Manoff, Inc. (later Geers Gross Advt.), 1977-81. Capt. signal corps U.S. Army, 1965-67. Office: Saatchi & Saatchi Advt Worldwide 375 Hudson St Fl 12 New York NY 10014-3658

WAX, NADINE VIRGINIA, retired banker; b. Van Horne, Iowa, Dec. 7, 1927; d. Laurel Lloyd and Viola Henrietta (Schrader) Bobzien; divorced; 1 child, Sharlyn K. Wax Munns. Student, U. Iowa, 1970-71; grad. Nat. Sch. Real Estate and Fin., Ohio State U., 1980-81. Jr. acct. McGladrey, Hansen, Dunn (now McGladrey-Pullen Co., CPAs), Cedar Rapids, Iowa, 1944-47; office mgr. Iowa Securities Co. (now Norwest Mortgage Co.), Cedar Rapids, 1954-55; asst. cashier Mchts. Nat. Bank, Cedar Rapids, 1956-75, asst. v.p., 1976-78, v.p., 1979-91; ret., 1991. Bd. dirs. v.p. Kirkwood C.C. Facilities Found., Cedar Rapids, 1970-95; bd. dirs., treas. Kirkwood C.C., 1984-91; trustee Indian Creek Nature Ctr., Cedar Rapids, 1974—; vol. St. Luke's Hosp. Aux., Cedar Rapids, 1981-85; mem. Linn County Regional Planning Commn., 1982-92, Cedar Rapids-Marion Fine Arts Coun., 1994—; bd. suprs. Compensation Commn. for Condemnation, 1987-92; bd. dirs. Am. Heart Assn., Cedar Rapids, 1983-94; mem. Iowa Employment and Tng. Coun., Des Moines, 1982-83. Recipient Outstanding Woman award Cedar Rapids Tribute to Women and Industry, 1984. Mem. Fin. Women Internat. (state edn. chmn. 1982-83), Am. Inst. Banking (bd. dirs. 1968-70), Soc. Real Estate Appraisers (treas. 1978-80), Linn County Bankers Assn. (pres. 1979-80), Cedar Rapids Bd. Realtors, Cedar Rapids C. of C. (bus.-edn. com. 1986-91), Cedar Rapids Country Club. Republican. Lutheran. Avocations: travel, reading, walking. Home: 147 Ashcombe SE Cedar Rapids IA 52403-1700

WAX, WILLIAM EDWARD, photojournalist; b. Miami, Fla., Dec. 7, 1956; s. Ira and Rita (Gunshor) W. A.S., Berry Coll., Rome, Ga., 1976; B.S. in Engring., U. Fla., 1983. With Ind. Fla. Alligator, Gainesville, Fla., 1977-79; staff photographer Gainesville (Fla.) Sun, 1979-87; photo cons. N.Y. Times regional newspapers, 1984—; freelance photographer Miami, 1987—; pres. Wax Photographics, Inc., Miami Beach, Fla., 1989—; owner Studio Sobe, Miami Beach, 1992—, guest lectr. various univs.; faculty So. Short Course in News Photography, 1985—. Named So. Photographer of Yr., 1980, Regional Photographer of Yr., 1979, 82, 85; recipient Mark of Excellence, Sigma Delta Chi, 1978, Best of Show award Atlanta Seminar on Photojournalism, 1982, Best of Show and Silver medal Hearst Awards, 1978, design gold award Fla. Tech. Writers Assn., 1992, Design award, Gold award, Excellence award Soc. Tech. Comm. Internat. Tech. Art Competition, 1993, 94, Best of Show, 1994, Disting. Design award STC, 1993, Excellence Design award, 1993, Silver and Bronze Design awards Fla. Mag. Assn., 1994, nominated for Pulitzer Prize, 1979, 89. Mem. Nat. Press Photographers Assn. (Photographer of the Yr. 1980), Fla. Mag. Assn., Profl. Photographers Am., Nikon Profl. Svcs., Fla. Press Photographers Assn. Democrat. Jewish. Office: 350 Lincoln Rd Ste 516 Miami Beach FL 33139-3148

WAXENBERG, ALAN M., publisher; b. Davenport, Iowa, Mar. 1, 1935; s. George and Rose Waxenberg; m. Suzanne C. Ecker, Oct. 26, 1958; children: Robin Lynn, Scott Stephen. BA, U. Iowa, 1956. Cen. advt. dir. Good Housekeeping Mag., Detroit, 1958-71; mgr. Petersen Pub. Co., Detroit, 1971-72; v.p. nat. advt. dir. Petersen Pub. Co., N.Y.C., 1972-76; pub. Motor, N.Y.C., 1976-79; v.p., pub. Redbook, N.Y.C., 1982-88; sr. v.p., pub. Good Housekeeping, Hearst Pub. Co., N.Y.C. Active United Jewish Appeal Fedn., Anti-Defamation League, Jr. Achievement, United /fund; bd. dirs. adv. coun. Am. Health Found. Served with U.S. Army, 1956-58. Mem. Am. Advt. Fedn. (bd. dirs.), Mag. Pubs. Assn., Adcraft Club Detroit, U. Iowa Alumni Assn. Clubs: Franklin Hills Country (Franklin, Mich.), Metropolis Country (White Plains N.Y.); University (N.Y.). Office: Good Housekeeping Mag Hearst Mags 959 8th Ave New York NY 10019-3737

WAXLER, BEVERLY JEAN, anesthesiologist, physician; b. Chgo., Apr. 11, 1949; d. Isadore and Ada Belle (Gross) Marcus; m. Richard Norman Waxler, Dec. 24, 1972; 1 child, Adam R. BS in Biology, No. Ill. U., 1971; MD, U. Ill., Chgo., 1975. Diplomate Am. Bd. Anesthesiology, Am. Bd. Pathology. Intern dept. pathology Northwestern U., Chgo., 1975-76, resident, 1976-79; instr. Rush Presbyn. St. Luke's Med. Ctr., Chgo., 1979-81; asst. prof. pathology Loyola U., Maywood, Ill., 1981-84; resident dept. anesthesiology Cook County Hosp., Chgo., 1984-87, attending anesthesiologist, 1987—; clin. assoc. prof. U. Ill., Chgo., 1988—. Contbr. papers to Tissue and Cell, British Jour. Exptl. Pathology, Biochem. Medicine, Calcified Tissue Internat., Jour. Lab. Clin. Med. Recipient B.B. Sankey Anesthesia Advancement award Internat. Anesthesia Rsch. Soc., 1989; Nat. Rsch. Svc. award fellow Nat. Cancer Inst., 1980; grantee Varlen Corp., 1982. Mem. AAAS, Internat. Anesthesia Rsch. Soc., Am. Soc. Anesthesiologists, Sigma Xi. Achievements include research with future implications for the delivery of anesthesia for cancer patients and the effects of anesthetics on proteinase inhibitors and tumor behavior. Home: 7615 Church St Morton Grove IL 60053-1618 Office: Cook County Hosp Chicago IL 60612

WAXLER, ROBERT PHILLIP, university educator, consultant; b. Cambridge, Mass., Dec. 16, 1944; s. Felix Benjamin and Helen Ruth (Fonfara) W.; m. Linda Davida Lassoff, June 25, 1967; children: Jonathan Blake, Jeremy Regan. BA, Brown U., 1967; MA, Boston Coll., 1969; PhD, SUNY, Stony Brook, 1976. Instr. Whitman Coll., Walla Walla, Wash., 1974-75, asst. prof., 1975-80, assoc. prof., 1980-86, prof. lit., 1986—; asst. dean, 1987-88; assoc. dean Walla Walla, 1988-89; dean continuing edn. and summer programs U. Mass., Dartmouth, 1994—; co-dir. Ctr. for Jewish Culture, U. Mass., North Dartmouth, 1981—, chmn. Judaic studies, 1984—; ptnr. Comm. Mgmt. Co., Inc., South Dartmouth, 1981-85; comm. cons. Tricom, Inc., South Dartmouth, 1981-90; vis. fellow NEH Princeton U., summer 1983; participant 12th ann. acad. seminar Am. Jewish Com., Israel, 1981. Contbg. editor Compass Mag., 1981-85; contbr. lit. and communcation articles to profl. jours. and anthologies. Founding mem. Jewish Student Svc. Ctr., North Dartmouth, 1978-85; co-founder Changing Lives Through Lit. program, 1991—; mem. steering com. Labor Edn. Ctr., North Dartmouth, 1981—; mem. bd. of regents Mass. Task Force on Undergrad. Experience, Boston, 1988; bd. dirs. Tifereth Israel Synagogue, New Bedford, Mass., 1976-80, Jewish Fedn., New Bedford, 1981-83; chmn. Azorean Synagogue Restoration Com., 1989—. NEH summer grantee UCLA, 1978; grantee So. Mass. U. Found. 1984; recipient Eisner Citizenship award Boy Scouts Am., 1987, Richard M. Fontera award Labor Edn. Ctr., 1988, Hon. medal U. of the Azores, 1989. Mem. Mass. Speech Communication Assn. (exec. com. 1984-85). Avocation: tennis. Home: 25 Strathmore Rd North Dartmouth MA 02747-3113 Office: U Mass-Dartmouth Old Westport Rd North Dartmouth MA 02747

WAXMAN, DAVID, physician, university consultant; b. Albany, N.Y., Feb. 7, 1918; s. Meyer and Fannie (Strosberg) W.; m. Jane Zabel; children: Gail, Michael, Dan, Ann, Steve, Abby. B.S., Syracuse U., 1942, M.D., 1950. Intern Grace Hosp., Detroit, 1950-51; resident in medicine, fellow in cardiology Kans. U. Med. Ctr., Kansas City, 1958-61; instr. internal medicine Kans. U. Med. Ctr., 1961-64; asst. prof. internal medicine Kans. City Med. Ctr., 1964-69, assoc. prof., 1969-77, prof., 1977—, dir. dept. medicine outpatient service, 1970-74, asst. dean, 1970-71, assoc. dean for student affairs, 1971-72, dean of students, 1972-74, vice chancellor for students, 1974-76, vice chancellor, 1976-77, exec. vice chancellor, 1977-83, spl. cons. to chancellor for health affairs, 1983-94; ret.; nat. cons. to surgeon gen. USAF. Contbr. articles to med. jours. Mem. Kans. State Bd. Healing Arts, 1984-88. Maj. gen. USAFR ret. Decorated D.S.M., Legion of Merit with one oak leaf cluster. Fellow ACP, Alpha Omega Alpha; mem. Kans. Med. Soc., Soc. Med. Cons. to the Armed Forces. Office: Kans U Med Ctr Scis and Hosp 39th and Rainbow Blvd Kansas City KS 66103

WAXMAN, HENRY ARNOLD, congressman; b. Los Angeles, Sept. 12, 1939; s. Louis and Esther (Silverman) W.; m. Janet Kessler, Oct. 17, 1971; children: Carol Lynn, Michael David. B.A. in Polit. Sci, UCLA, 1961, J.D., 1964. Bar: Calif. 1965. Mem. Calif. State Assembly, 1969-74, chmn. com. on health, until 1974; mem. 94th-104th Congresses from 24th (now 29th) Calif. dist., 1975—; ranking minority mem. house subcom. on health and environment, 1979—; mem. govt. reform & oversight com. Pres. Calif. Fedn. Young Democrats, 1965-67. Mem. Calif. Bar Assn., Guardians Jewish Home for Aged, Am. Jewish Congress, Sierra Club, B'nai B'rith, Phi Sigma Alpha. Office: House of Representatives 2408 Rayburn House Ofc Washington DC 20515*

WAXMAN, MARGERY HOPE, lawyer; b. N.Y.C., Oct. 21, 1942; d. Lee and Florence Waxman; m. Willard H. Mitchell, Apr. 4, 1982. A.B., Smith Coll., 1964; J.D. with honors, George Washington U., 1967. Bar: D.C. 1968, U.S. Supreme Ct. 1971. Law clk. Honorable Spottswood W. Robinson III, U.S. Ct. Apls. for D.C. Cir., 1967-68; assoc. Covington & Burling, 1968-72; asst. gen. counsel Office Consumer Affairs, 1972-73; dep. gen. counsel Cost of Living Council, 1973-74; exec. asst. to chmn. FTC, 1975, asst. dir., dep. dir., acting dir. Bur. Consumer Protection, 1976-77, exec. dir., 1977-79; gen. counsel Office Personnel Mgmt., Washington, 1979-81; dep. gen. counsel Dept. Treasury, Washington, 1981-86; ptnr. Sidley & Austin, Washington, 1986-94, Greenberg, Traurig, Washington, 1994—. Recipient Meritorious Rank award, 1980, Presdl. Disting. Rank award, 1985. Mem. ABA, Am. Law Inst., Fed. Bar Assn., D.C. Bar Assn., Womens Bar Assn. Office: Greenberg Traurig 1501 M St NW Washington DC 20005

WAXMAN, RONALD, computer engineer; b. Newark, Nov. 28, 1933; s. Benjamin and Rose (Lifson) W.; m. Pearl Latterman, June 19, 1955; children: David, Roberta, Benjamin. BSEE, N.J. Inst. Tech., 1955; MEE, Syracuse U., 1963. Engr. IBM, Poughkeepsie, N.Y., 1955-56, 58-64, East Fishkill, N.Y., 1964-70, Poughkeepsie and Kingston, N.Y., 1970-80; sr. engr. IBM, Manassas, Va., 1980-87; prin. scientist U. Va., Charlottesville, 1987—; IEEE rep. and tech. advisor to Internat. Elec. Commn. U.S. tech. activities group for internat. design automation stds.; mem. steering com. very high speed integrated circuits hardware description lang. VHDL Users Group, 1987-91. Contbr. numerous articles to profl. jours. and tech. presentations. 1st lt. USAF, 1956-58. Fellow IEEE, IEEE Computer Soc. (bd. govs. 1989-94, founder, chmn. design automation standards subcom. 1983-88, steering com. 1989—, chmn. design automation tech. com. 1988-90, mem. steering com. 1991—, vice chmn. tech. activities bd. 1991-92, chmn. awards com. 1993, Disting. Vis. 1986-88, Meritorious Svc. cert. 1988, TAB Pioneer award 1989, v.p. membership activities bd. 1994), Internat. Fedn. Info. Processing (working group hardware description langs., rep. to tech. com.). Assn. Computing Machinery (mem. SIGDA). Achievements include patents in field. Office: U Va Ctr for Semicustom Integrated Systems Dept EE Thornton Hall Charlottesville VA 22903

WAXMAN, SETH PAUL, lawyer; b. Hartford, Conn., Nov. 28, 1951; s. Felix H. and Frieda (Goodman) W.; m. Debra F. Goldberg, Mar. 20, 1977; children: Noah, Sarah, Ethan. AB summa cum laude, Harvard U., 1973; JD, Yale U., 1977. Bar: D.C. 1978, U.S. Dist. Ct. D.C., U.S. Ct. Appeals (D.C., 3d, 4th, 5th, 9th and 11th cirs.) 1979, U.S. Supreme Ct. 1981. Law clk. to Judge Gerhard A. Gessell Washington, 1977-78; mng. ptnr. Miller Cassidy Larroca & Lewin, Washington, 1978-94; assoc. dep. atty. U.S. Dept. Justice, Washington, 1994—; instr. Nat. Inst. for Trial Advocacy. Contbr. numerous articles on litigation to legal jours. Michael C. Rockefeller fellow Harvard U., 1973-74; recipient Cardozo award for civil rights Anti-Defamation League, 1987. Mem. ABA (steering com. postconviction death penalty representation project, com. chmn. litigation sect., Pro Bono Publico award 1988), Jud. Conf. U.S. Office: US Dept Justice Rm 4208 Washington DC 20530

WAXMAN, STEPHEN GEORGE, neurologist, researcher; b. Newark, Aug. 17, 1945; s. Morris and Beatrice (Levitch) W.; m. Merle Applebaum, June 25, 1968; children: Matthew, David. AB, Harvard U., 1967; PhD, Albert Einstein Coll. Med., Yeshiva U., 1970, MD, 1972; MA (hon.), Yale U., 1986. Research fellow in neurosci. Albert Einstein Coll. Medicine, Bronx, N.Y., 1970-72; clin. fellow Boston City Hosp., 1972-75; asst. prof. neurology Med. Sch. Harvard U., Boston, 1975-77, assoc. prof., 1977-78; prof. Stanford (Calif.) U., 1978-86; chief neurology unit Palo Alto (Calif.) VA Hosp., 1978-86; prof., chmn. dept. neurology Yale U., New Haven, 1986—; chief neurology Yale-New Haven Hosp., 1986—; vis. asst. prof. biology MIT, Cambridge, 1975-77, vis. assoc. prof., 1977-78; vice chmn. Dept. Neurology Stanford U., 1981-86, chmn. Neuroscis. Program, 1982-86; adv. bd. Regeneration Programs VA, Washington, 1982-86; sci. adv. com. Nat. Spinal Cord Injury Assn., 1982—; sci. adv. bd. Paralyzed Vets. Am. 1981-91; dir. Ctr. Rsch. Neurol. Disease VA Med. Ctr., West Haven, Conn., 1986—; mem. corp. Marine Biol. Labs., Woods Hole, Mass., 1988; mem. sci. adv. coun. Am. Paralysis Assn., 1990, bd. sci. counselors Nat. Inst. Neurol. Diseases and Blindness, 1990—; mem. bd. Biobehavioral Scis., Inst. Medicine, 1990; fellow stroke coun. Am. Heart Assn., 1990; Adrian Meml. lectr., Kyoto, Japan, 1995. Author: Spinal Cord Compression, 1990, Correlative Neuroanatomy, 1993, The Atom, 1995; editor: Physiology and Pathobiology of Axons, 1978; editor-in-chief The Neuroscientist; assoc. editor Jour. Neurol. Scis.; editor The Axon, 1995; mem. editl. bd. Brain Rsch., Muscle and Nerve, Internat. Rev. Neurobiology, Annals of Neurology, Jour. Neurol. Rehab. Glia, Devel. Neurosci., Jour. Neurotrauma, Neurobiology of Disease, Cerebrovascular Disease. Recipient Trygve Tuve Meml. award NIH, 1973, Rsch. Career Devel. award NIH, 1975, Disting. Alumnus award Albert Einstein Coll. Medicine, 1990; rsch. fellow U. Coll., London, 1969; 6th ann. Denny-Brown lectr. Boston Soc. Neurology and Psychiatry, 1977, 3d ann. Dean's lectr. Brown U., 1989, Royal Coll. lectr. Can. Neurol. Assn., 1990; established investigator Nat. Multiple Sclerosis Soc., 1987, Adrian Lecture, 1995. Fellow Royal Soc. Medicine (Gr. Britain), Am. Heart Assn. (stroke coun.); mem. Am. Soc. Cell Biology, Am. Acad. Neurology, Internat. Brain Rsch. Orgn. (U.S. nat. com.), Soc. Neurosci., Am. Neurol. Assn. (counsillor 1980), World Fedn. Neurology, Assn. Rsch. in Nervous and Mental Diseases (trustee, pres. 1992), Assn. Univ. Profs. Neurology. Office: Yale U Sch Medicine 33 Cedar St New Haven CT 06519-2314

WAXSE, DAVID JOHN, lawyer; b. Oswego, Kans., June 29, 1945; s. I. Joseph and Mary (Poole) W.; m. Linda Schilling (div.); children: Rachel, Ryan, Rebecca; m. Judy Pfannenstiel, May 29, 1982; 1 child, Elayna. BA, U. Kans., 1967; teaching cert., Columbia U., 1968, JD, 1971. Bar: Kans. 1971, U.S. Ct. Appeals (10th cir.) 1971, U.S. Supreme Ct. 1975. Dean of students Intermediate Sch. 88, N.Y.C., 1968-70; spl. edn. tchr. Peter Cooper Sch., N.Y.C., 1971-72; assoc. Payne & Jones, Olathe, Kans., 1971-74, ptnr., 1974-84; of counsel Shook, Hardy & Bacon, Overland Park, Kans., 1984-86, ptnr., 1986—; shareholder Shook, Hardy & Bacon P.C., Overland Park, 1993—; mcpl. judge City of Shawnee, Kans., 1974-80; atty. City of DeSoto, Kans., 1972-79; adj. prof. U. Kans. Sch. Law, Lawrence, 1981-82; mem. juv. code adv. com. Kans. Jud. Coun., 1979-83, guardianship adv. com., 1982-83, atty. fees adv. com., 1986-87; mem. Civil Justice Reform Act Adv. Com., U.S. Dist. Ct. for Dist. Kans., 1991—; mem. Kans. Commn. on Jud. Qualifications, 1992-94, vice-chmn. 1994—; v.p. Kans. Legal Svcs., Inc., 1980-82, pres., 1985-87; bd. advisors Kans. Coll. Advocacy, 1979-80. Author: (with others) Kansas Employment Law, 1985, Litigating Employment Law Cases, 1987, Kansas Employment Law Handbook, 1991, supplement, 1992, Kansas Annual Survey, 1990—. Mem. Kan. Gov.'s Adv. Com. on Criminal Justice, 1974-77; gen. counsel Western Mo. Dist. ACLU, 1976-78, 86—, v.p., 1983-86, nat. bd. dirs., 1979-86, 91—, chmn. children's rights com., 1980-86; mem. AIDS Pol. Network, 1987—; med. treatment issues com., 1991—, constn. com., 1991—; mem. med./tech. com. AIDS Coun. Greater Kans. City, 1986—, ethics com consortium Midwest Bioethics Ctr., 1990—; bd. dirs. Parents Anonymous Kans., 1978-83, pres., 1979; bd. dirs., mem. fin. com. Kans. Com. for Prevention Child Abuse, 1980-83. Mem. ABA (chmn. children's rights com. and family law sects. 1985-86), Am. Employment Law Coun., Kans. Bar Assn. (chmn. legal aid com. 1978-83, bd. govs. 1988—, Pres.' Outstanding Svc. award 1982), Johnson County Bar Assn. (chmn. legal aid com. 1975-82, 92—), Amnesty Internat. (legal com. Kansas City chpt.), Common Cause, Sierra Club. Home: 9976 Hemlock Dr Shawnee Mission KS 66212-3447 Office: Shook Hardy & Bacon PC 40 Corporate Woods 6th flr 9401 Indian Creek Pky Overland Park KS 66210-2005

WAY, BARBARA HAIGHT, dermatologist; b. Franklin, N.J., Dec. 27, 1941; d. Charles Padley and Alice Barbara (Haight) Shoemaker; m. Anthony Biden Way; children: Matthew Shoemaker Way, Sarah Shoemaker Way. AB in Music cum laude, Bryn Mawr Coll., 1962, postgrad., 1963-64; MD, U. Pa., 1968. Diplomate Am. Bd. Dermatology. Systems engr. IBM, Balt., 1962-63; mem. dean's staff Bryn Mawr (Pa.) Coll., 1963-64; med. intern U. Wis. Hosps., Madison, 1968-69, resident in dermatology, 1969-72; physician emergency rm. St. Francis Hosp., La Crosse, Wis., 1969-72; asst. prof. dept. dermatology Tex. Tech U. Sch. Medicine, Lubbock, 1972-73, from asst. clin. to assoc. clin. prof., 1973-74, asst. prof., assoc. chair, 1974-76, assoc. prof., chair, 1976-81; assoc. clin. prof. Tex. Tech U. Health Scis. Ctr. (formerly Tex. Tech U. Sch. Medicine), Lubbock, 1981-92, founder, dir. dermatology residency tng. program, 1978-81; pvt. practice Lubbock, 1973-74, 81—; acting dir. Lubbock City Health Dept., 1982-83; mem. exec. com. Lubbock Gen. Hosp., 1978-81, mem. credentials com., 1978-81, chmn., 1979-81; mem. presdl. search com. Tex. Tech U., 1979, mem. univ. fringe benefits com., 1980-81; chmn. exec. com. ambulatory clinics Tex. Tech U. Health Scis. Ctr., 1980-81, mem. Med. Prachie Income Plan-bus. affairs subcom., 1980-81,

mem. space com., 1981, mem. anatomy search com., 1981; search com. for exec. dir. of Ambulatory Clinic, 1980-81; mem. active staff Meth. Hosp., Lubbock, mem. investigative rev. bd., 1989, subsection chief, 1992, 94; mem. active staff St. Mary of Plains Hosp., Lubbock, mem. credentials com., 1990, 92, 94, founding dir. phototherapy unit, 1990-91, 93, mem. exec. com., 1991, 93, chief dermatology sect., 1991, 93; cons., presenter, rschr. in field. Reviewer Archives Dermatology, Cutis, Pediatric Dermatology, Tex. Medicine; contbr. articles to profl. jours. Alumna admissions rep. Bryn Mawr Coll., 1972-75, 87—; pres. adult choir 1st Presbyn. Ch., 1974, mem. nominating com., 1975; mem. LEAP adv. bd. Lubbock Ind. Sch. Dist., 1979; mem. jud. hearing com. Lubbock Soccer Assn., 1980-82, chmn., 1981-82; mem. water safety com. Lubbock County chpt. ARC, 1982-83; chmn. fund raising com. soccer team Lubbock High Sch., 1986-87, mem. ad hoc parents' com. rev. closing of campus, 1988, sponsor cheerleading camp, 1989; active United Way Campaign, 1987-88; mem. adv. com. Lubbock Ind. Sch. Dist. for Re-Orgn. of Schs., 1990; mem. selection com. outstanding physician Lubbock chpt. Am. Cancer Soc., 1991-94, chmn., 1991; bd. dirs. Tex. Tech U. Med. Found., 1987-89, Double T Connection, 1988-90. Recipient Pathology Preceptorship award Pa. Hosp., 1966. Fellow Am. Acad. Dermatology (reviewer jour.); mem. AMA, Am. Soc. Dermatologic Surgery, Tex. Dermatol. Soc. (chmn. roster com. 1980), Tex. Med. Assn. (mem. sexually transmitted diseases com. 1986-90, mem. coun. pub. health 1990-92, vice councillor dist. III 1992—, chmn. reference com. fin. and orgnl. affairs ann. session 1992), Lubbock County-Garza County Med. Soc. (mem. various coms. 1980—, chmn. sch. and pub. health com. 1983, mem. bd. censors 1983-85, chair 1985, sec. 1986, v.p. 1987, liaison with Tex. Tech U. Health Scis. Ctr. com. 1988-91, co-chmn. pub. rels. com. 1988-89, alternate Tex. Med. Assn. del. 1988-89, del. 1990—, pres.-elect 1989, pres. 1990, chmn. ad hoc bylaws com. 1991-94, chmn. Hippocratic award 1991), Soc. Pediatric Dermatology, Women's Dermatologic Soc. (founding mem.). Office: 4102 24th St Ste 201 Lubbock TX 79410

WAY, CAROL JANE, non-profit organization administrator; b. Providence, Jan. 24, 1940; d. Wilfred Bartholomew and Lillian Elizabeth (Tainsh) Martineau; m. Paul Howard Way, June 28, 1958 (div. 1986); children: Laura L. Way Jordahl, P. Craig, Victoria L. Way Hermansen, J. Brent. EdB, R.I. Coll., 1960; postgrad., U. R.I., 1960; MPA, Mankato (Minn.) State U., 1978; postgrad., Universidad Internacional, Mexico City, 1985. Cert. in secondary edn.; lic. in real estate. Tchr. pub. secondary schs. Scotia, N.Y., 1962-64, 67-68, Schenectady, N.Y., 1968-69; reporter, freelance writer The Long Islander newspaper, Huntington, N.Y., 1969-71; tchr. pub. secondary schs. Avon, Conn., 1971-72; asst. to dir. Ret. Sr. Vol. program, Hartford, Conn., 1972-73; dir. pub. info. Mankato Schs., 1974-78; tchr. pub. secondary schs. Fairfield, Conn., 1979-80; assoc. dir. YWCA of Greater Bridgeport, Conn., 1980-81; dir. alumni relations Sacred Heart U., Fairfield, 1982-84; exec. dir. Westport (Conn.) C. of C., 1986-88, West Hartford (Conn.) C. of C., 1988-91, Greater Meriden (Conn.) C. of C., 1991—; bd. dirs. Child Guidance Ctr. of Greater Bridgeport, 1986—; participant English Inst. SUNY chpt. N.Y. State Tchrs. Assn., 1964. Contbr. articles to mags. and newspapers. Lt. gov. R.I. Girls' State, Providence, 1955; mem. Housewives for Rockefeller and Schenectady Reps., 1964; registered lobbyist various non-partisan groups, Minn. and Washington, 1975-78; chairwoman Blue Earth County (Minn.) Reps., 1975-78; town com. Fairfield Reps., 1980-83; bd. dirs. YMCA of West Hartford. Mem. Nat. Assn. Bus. Economists, Nat. Assn. Female Execs., AAUW (life, bd. dirs. 1963-81, nat. legis. com. 1976-78, 80-83), Women in the Arts (charter), Fairfield Network Exec. Women, Women in Mgmt., Farmington Woods Country Club. Episcopalian. Lodge: Rotary. Avocations: golf, skiing, swimming, needlepoint, the Arts. Home: 48 Gate Ridge Rd Fairfield CT 06432-1164 Office: Greater Meriden C of C 290 Pratt St Meriden CT 06450

WAY, E(DWARD) LEONG, pharmacologist, toxicologist, educator; b. Watsonville, Calif., July 10, 1916; s. Leong Man and Lai Har (Shew) W.; m. Madeline Li, Aug. 11, 1944; children: Eric, Linette. BS, U. Calif., Berkeley, 1938, MS, 1940; PhD, U. Calif., San Francisco, 1942. Pharm. chemist Merck & Co., Rahway, N.J., 1942; instr. pharmacology George Washington U., 1943-46, asst. prof., 1946-48; asst. prof. pharmacology U. Calif., San Francisco, 1949-52; assoc. prof. U. Calif., 1952-57, prof., 1957-87, prof. emeritus, 1987—, chmn. dept. pharmacology, 1973-78; USPHS spl. rsch. fellow U. Berne, Switzerland, 1955-56, China Med. Bd.; rsch. fellow, vis. prof. U. Hong Kong, 1962-63; Sterling Sullivan disting. vis. prof. martin Luther King U., 1982; hon. prof. pharmacology and neurosci. Guangzhou Med. Coll., 1987; mem. adv. com. Pharm. Rsch. Mfrs. Assn. Found.; 1968—; mem. coun. Am. Bur. for Med. Advancement in China, 1982; bd. dirs. Li Found., 1970—, pres., 1985—; bd. dirs Haight Ashbury Free Clinics, 1986-93; Tsumura prof. neuropsychopharmacology med. sch. Gunma U., Maebashi, Japan, 1989-90; sr. staff fellow Nat. Inst. on Drug Abuse, 1990-91; researcher on drug metabolism, analgetics, devel. pharmacology, drug tolerance, drug dependence and Chinese materia medica. Contbr. numerous articles and revs. to profl. publs.; editor: New Concepts in Pain, 1967, (with others) Fundamentals of Drug Metabolism and Drug Disposition, 1971, Endogenous and Exogenous Opiate Agonists and Antagonists, 1979; mem. editorial bd. Clin. Pharmacology, Therapeutics, 1975-87, Drug, Alcohol Dependence, 1976-87, Progress in Neuro-Psychopharmacology, 1977-91, Research Communications in Chem. Pathology and Pharmacology, 1978-91, Alcohol and Drug Dependence, 1986-91, Asian Pacific Jour. Pharm., 1985—. Recipient Faculty Rsch. Lectr. award U. Calif., San Francisco, 1974, San Francisco Chinese Hosp. award, 1976, Cultural citation and Gold medal Ministry of Edn., Republic of China, 1978, Nathan B. Eddy award Coll. on Problems in Drug Dependence, 1979, Chancellor's award for pub. svc. U. Calif., 1986, Disting. Alumnus award U. Calif., San Francisco, 1990, Asian Pacific Am. Systemwide Alliance award, 1993. Fellow AAAS, Am. Coll. Neuropsychopharmacology, Am. Coll. Clin. Pharmacology (hon.), Coll. on Problems of Drug Dependence (exec. com. 1978-92, chmn. bd. dirs. 1978-82); mem. Am. Soc. Pharmacology, Exptl. Therapeutics (bd. editors 1957-65, pres. 1976-77, Torald Sollman award 1992), Fedn. Am. Socs. Exptl. Biology (exec. bd. 1975-79, pres. 1977-78), Am. Pharm. Assn. (life, Rsch. Achievement award 1962), AMA (affiliate), Soc. Aid and Rehab. Drug Addicts (Hong Kong, life), Western Pharmacology Soc. (pres. 1963-64), Japanese Pharm. Soc. (hon.), Coun. Sci. Soc. Pres.' (exec. com. 1979-84, treas. 1980-84), Chinese Pharmacology Soc. (hon.), Academia Sinica. Office: U Calif Dept of Pharmacology San Francisco CA 94143-0450

WAY, JACOB EDSON, III, museum director; b. Chgo., May 18, 1947; s. Jacob Edson Jr. and Amelia (Evans) W.; m. Jean Ellwood Chappell, Sept. 6, 1969; children: Sarah Chappell, Rebecca Stoddard, Jacob Edson IV. BA, Beloit Coll., 1968; MA, U. Toronto, 1971, PhD, 1978. Instr. Beloit (Wis.) Coll., 1972-73, asst. prof. 1973-80, assoc. prof., 1980-85; dir. Logan Mus. Anthropology, Beloit, 1980-85, Wheelwright Mus. Am. Indian, Santa Fe, 1985-89; interim dir. N.Mex. Mus. Natural History, Albuquerque, 1990-91; exec. dir. Space Ctr. Internat. Space Hall of Fame, Alamogordo, N.Mex., 1991-94; dir. N.Mex. Farm and Ranch Heritage Mus., 1994—; evaluator Nat. Park Service, Denver, 1986. Contbr. articles to profl. jours. Mem. Nuke Watch, Beloit, 1983-84. Research grants Wis. Humanities Com., 1984, NSF, 1981; grantee Cullister Found., 1978-84; fellow U. Toronto, 1973. Mem. Am. Assn. Mus., Am. Assn. Phys. Anthropology, Can. Assn. for Phys. Anthropology, N.Mex. Assn. Mus. (pres. 1994-96), Soc. Am. Archaeology, Wis. Fedn. Mus. (adv. bd. 1982-85). Mem. Soc. Friends. Avocations: camping, skiing, fishing, reading, horseback riding. Office: N Mex Farm & Ranch Heritage Mus P O Drawer BB Las Cruces NM 88004

WAY, JAMES LEONG, pharmacology and toxicology educator; b. Watsonville, Calif., Mar. 21, 1926; s. Wong Bung Wee and Wow Wee (Wong) W.; children: Lani, Jon, Lori. BA, U. Calif., Berkeley, 1951; PhD, George Washington U., 1955. Asst. prof. U. Calif., Madison, 1959-62; assoc. prof. Marquette Med. Sch., Milw., 1962-67; prof. Washington State U., Pullman, 1967-82; endowed Shelton prof. pharmacology Tex. A&M U., College Station, 1982—; mem. toxicology study sect. NIH, Bethesda, Md., 1974-78; mem. toxicology data bank peer rev. com., NIH-NLM, 1978-85; mem. environ. health sci. study sect. NIEHS, 1985-90; vis. prof. pharmacology Nat. Def. Med. Ctr., Taipei, Taiwan, 1981-82; mem. toxicology data bank NLM, 1976-85; vis. scientist Med. Rsch. Coun./Nat. Inst. Med. Rsch., London, 1973-75. Contbr. over 200 articles to profl. jours. Recipient rsch. career devel. award NIH, 1959-72; Greenwald scholar U. Calif., Berkeley, 1960, Disting. scholar of U.S. NAS, 1986-88; N.Am. Baxter fellow, 1954-55, fellow NIH, 1979-80, Nat. Cancer Inst., 1955-58, also others. Mem. Am. Soc. Pharmacology and Exptl. Therapeutics (treas. 1989-90), Soc. Tox-

icology, Western Pharmacology Soc. (pres. 1978-79, mem. editorial bd. Toxicology and Applied Pharmacology 1978-90, Ann. Rev. Pharmacology and Toxicology 1986-91, assoc. editor 1991—), Internat. Soc. Resealed Erythrocyte (pres. 1993-95). Avocations: skiing, sky diving, windsurfing, scuba, handball. Office: Tex A&M U Health Sci Ctr Dept Med Pharmacology Med Sci Bldg College Station TX 77843-1114

WAY, KENNETH L., seat company executive; b. 1939. BS, Mich. State U., 1961, MBA, 1971. V.p. Lear Siegler, Inc., Southfield, Mich., 1966-88; chmn., chief exec. officer Lear Seating Co., Southfield, Mich., 1988—. With USAF, 1962-66. Office: LSS Holdings Corp Ten Hanover Sq New York NY 10005*

WAY, WALTER LEE, anesthetist, pharmacologist, educator; b. Rochester, N.Y., June 27, 1931; s. Kenneth F. and Mary F. (Faulkner) W.; m. Elizabeth J. Folwell, July 9, 1955; children: Barbara, Jonathan, Jeffrey. BS in Pharmacy, U. Buffalo, 1953; MD, SUNY, Syracuse, 1957; MS, U. Calif., San Francisco, 1962. Intern Highland Hosp., Rochester, N.Y., 1957-58; resident U. Calif., San Francisco, 1958-60, trainee, 1960-62, instr. anesthesia and oral medicine, 1960-64, asst. prof. anesthesia, 1962-64, asst. prof. anesthesia and pharmacology, 1964-68, assoc. prof. anesthesia and pharmacology, 1968-74, prof. anesthesia and pharmacology, 1974-94; prof. emeritus anesthesia and pharmacology, 1994—; vis. prof. various univs.; cons. in field. Mem. Am. Soc. Anesthesiologists, Calif. Soc. Anesthesiologists, Assn. Univ. Anesthesiologists, Am. Soc. Pharmacology and Exptl. Therapeutics. Office: Box 191 Ross CA 94957

WAYANS, DAMON, actor; b. N.Y.C., 1961. TV appearances include Saturday Night Live, 1985-86, Take No Prisoners: Robert Townsend and His Partners in Crime, 1988, The Mutiny Has Just Begun: Robert Townsend and His Partners in Crime, III, 1989, In Living Color, 1990-92 (Emmy Outstanding writing in variety program 1990, 91, Outstanding individual in variety program 1991); exec prodr.; actor: Damon Wayans: The Last Stand?, 1991 (film appearances) Beverly Hills Cop, 1984, Hollywood Shuffle, 1987, Roxanne, 1987, Colors, 1988, I'm Gonna Git You Sucka, 1988, Punchline, 1988, Earth Girls Are Easy, 1989, Look Who's Talking Too (voice), 1990, The Last Boy Scout, 1991; co-exec. prodr., screenwriter, actor Mo' Money, 1992, Blankman, 1994, Major Payne, 1995. Office: care CAA 9832 Wilshire Blvd Beverly Hills CA 90212*

WAYANS, KEENEN IVORY, actor, producer; b. N.Y.C., June 8, 1958; s. Howell and Elvira W. Film appearances include Star 80, 1983, Hollywood Shuffle (also co-screenwriter), 1987, Raw (also co-prodr., co-screenwriter), 1987, I'm Gonna Git You Sucka (also dir., screenwriter), 1988, Low Down Dirty Shame (also screenwriter), 1994; co-screenwriter The Five Heartbeats; TV series For Love and Honor, 1983-84, (also exec. prodr., creator) In Living Color (Emmy award outstanding variety, music or comedy program 1990), 1990-93; TV specials Robert Townsend and His Partners in Crime, HBO (also co-prodr., writer), 1987. Office: CAA 9832 Wilshire Blvd Beverly Hills CA 90212*

WAYBURN, LAURIE ANDREA, environmental and wildlife foundation administrator, conservationist; b. San Francisco, Sept. 27, 1954; d. Edgar A. and Cornelia (Elliott) W. BA, Harvard U., 1977. Program mgr. UN Environment Program, Nairobi, Kenya, 1978-81; program cons. UNESCO, Paris and Montevideo, Uruguay, 1983-86; cons. BBC, London, 1986-87; exec. dir. Point Reyes Bird Obs., Stinson Beach, Calif., 1987—; speaker numerous confs., 1987—; coord. Cen. Calif. Coast Biosphere Res., 1988—; com. mem. U.S. Nat. Program Man and Biosphere, Washington, 1989—; bd. dirs. UN Assn. Panel, San Francisco, People for A GGNRA, San Francisco, 1989—; del. Internat. Coun. Bird Preservation, Washington, 1989—. Contbr. articles to profl. jours. Advisor Switzer Found., San Francisco, 1990—. Avocations: hiking, birding, music writing.

WAYCASTER, BILL, chemicals executive; b. 1942. With Tex. Olefins Co., Houston, 1969—, CEO; with Tex. Petrochems., Houston, 1969—, CEO. Office: Tex Olefins Co 8707 Katy Fwy Ste 300 Houston TX 77024-1706 also: Tex Petrochems 8600 Park Place Blvd Houston TX 77017*

WAYGOOD, ERNEST ROY, plant physiology educator; b. Bramhall, Cheshire, Eng., Oct. 26, 1918; s. Edward Samuel and Alice (Harrison) W.; m. Adoree Magdalyn Woolf-LeBrooy, Dec. 30, 1950; 1 child, Pamela Mimi. B.S. in Agr., Ont. Agrl. Coll., 1941; M.S. in Agr., U. Toronto, 1947, Ph.D., 1949. Asst. prof. botany McGill U., Montreal, Que., Can., 1949-52, assoc. prof., 1952-54; prof., head dept. botany U. Man., Winnipeg, Can., 1954-74, prof. emeritus, 1979—. Flight lt. RCAF, 1941-45. Recipient Research award Lalor Found., 1956. Fellow Royal Soc. Can., Chem. Inst. Can.; mem. Can. Bot. Assn., Can. Soc. Plant Physiologists (pres. 1960), Am. Soc. Plant Physiologists, Am. Inst. Biol. Sci., Sigma Xi. Anglican. Home: 802-1245 Quayside Dr, New Westminster, BC Canada V3M 6J6

WAYLAN, CECIL JEROME, telecommunications executive; b. Herington, Kans., Sept. 13, 1941; s. Lewis Milo and Cecile Alice (Obermeyer) W.; m. Karen Sue Freeman, June 2, 1963; 1 child, Todd Cameron. BS, U. Kans., 1965; MSEE, Naval Postgrad., Monterey, Calif., 1972; PhD, Naval Postgrad., 1974. Cons. Sci. Applications, Vienna, Va., 1979-80, Waylan Assocs., Vienna, 1980-81; v.p. engring. Spacenet div. So. Pacific Communications Co., McLean, Va., 1981-82; v.p., gen. mgr. So. Pacific Satellite Co., McLean, 1982-83; pres. GTE Spacenet Corp., McLean, 1983—; mem. space applications bd. Nat. Rsch. Coun., 1986-88, GTE Ops. Com., 1989—; sr. advisor U.S. delegation World Adminstv. Radio Conf., 1988; bd. dirs. Nat. Ctr. for Telecommunications & Info. Policy Adv. Bd., Washington Airports Task Force, 1991—; mem. adv. com. on internat. comm. and info. policy, U.S. Dept. State, 1992—. Contbr. numerous articles to profl. jours. Mem. AIAA, Inst. Electrical and Electronic Engrs. (sr.), Sigma Xi, Eta Kappa Nu, Sigma Pi Sigma. Comdr. USN, 1959-79. Avocation: golf. Office: GTE Spacenet Corp 1700 Old Meadow Rd Mc Lean VA 22102-4304

WAYLAND, J(AMES) HAROLD, biomedical scientist, educator; b. Boise, Idaho, July 2, 1909; s. Charles William and Daisy (McConnell) W.; m. Virginia Jane Kartzke, June 24, 1933; children—Ann Marie Peters, Elizabeth Jane (Mrs. Paul T. Barber). B.S., U. Idaho, 1931, D.Sc. (hon.), 1977; M.S., Calif. Inst. Tech., 1935, Ph.D., 1937. Am. Scandinavian Found. fellow U. Copenhagen, 1937; asst. prof. physics U. Redlands, 1938-41; mil. research in mine warfare and torpedo devel., 1941-48; assoc. prof. applied mechanics Calif. Inst. Tech., Pasadena, 1949-57; prof. Calif. Inst. Tech., 1957-63, prof. engring. sci., 1963-79, prof. emeritus, 1979—; U.S. coordinator U.S.-Japan Coop. Seminars on Peripheral Circulation, 1967, 70; mem. cardiovascular and renal study sect. NIH, 1973-77; vis. prof. Shinshu U., Matsumoto, Japan, 1973, U. Limburg, Maastricht, The Netherlands, 1979, U. New South Wales, Australia, 1980, U. Heidelberg, 1982, U. of Tsukuba, Japan, 1987; Disting. vis. prof. U. Del., 1985. Contbr. articles to profl. publs., also books and articles on history of playing cards. Recipient Ordnance Devel. award U.S. Navy, 1945, Cert. of Recognition, NASA, 1975, Humboldt Sr. Scientist Rsch. award U. Heidelberg, 1982, 91, Malpighi prize, 1988; named to Alumni Hall of Fame, U. Idaho, 1990; Guggenheim fellow, 1953-54; rsch. grantee NIH, NSF, John A. Hartford Found., Kroc Found. Fellow AAAS (chmn. med. scis. sect. 1976); founding fellow Am. Inst. Med. and Biol. Engring.; mem. AAUP, Microcirculatory Soc. (pres. 1971-72, Landis award 1981), Am. Phys. Soc., Am. Physiol. Soc., European Microcirculatory Soc. (hon.), German Microcirculatory Soc. (hon.), Internat. Soc. Biorheology, Am. Heart Assn., Am. Inst. Archeology, Am. Soc. Enologists, Playing Card Soc., Sigma Xi, Phi Beta Kappa, Sigma Tau. Democrat. Unitarian. Club: Athenaeum. Achievements include patents for scanning confocal microscopy; development of quantitative methods for measuring blood flow in microvessels and macromolecular diffusion in living tissues, of servomicroscope for maintaining focus on moving tissue. Home: 900 E Harrison Ave Apt B-21 Pomona CA 91767-2024 Office: Calif Inst Tech Mail Code 104 # 44 Pasadena CA 91125

WAYLAND, L. C. NEWTON, public health pediatrician; b. Plainview, Tex., May 4, 1909; s. Levi Clarence and Connie Onita (Newton) W.; m. Helen Hart, June 18, 1938 (div. 1966); children: Newton, Elizabeth, Constance. Student Wayland Coll., Plainview, 1925-26, West Tex. State Tchrs. Coll., 1926-30; AB, Stanford U., 1932, MD, 1936; postgrad. U. Calif. Med. Sch.,

Children's, Gen. hosps., L.A. Intern, San Francisco City and County Hosp., Stanford Svc., 1936; house officer San Mateo County Hosp., 1937, Children's Hosp., L.A., 1938; dir. child health Santa Barbara (Calif.) County Health Dept., 1938-44; dir. health Santa Barbara City Schs., 1944-74; dir. health Santa Barbara City Coll., 1946-74; pvt. practice medicine specializing in pediatrics, 1955-70; ret. mem. pediatric staffs Santa Barbara Gen., St. Francis, Cottage, Goleta Valley hosps.; ret. med. cons. Calif. State Dept. Rehab., 1974-78; emeritus mem. med. staff Calif. State Prison at Soledad. Past non-nurse dir. exec. com., sch. nursing sect. Nat. Orgn. Pub. Health Nurses; past mem. adv. com. Calif. Dept. Edn. on Pub. Sch. Health; mem. Pub. Citizen Inc. Past 1st bd. dirs. Get Oil Out!; emeritus mem. vol. staff. Santa Barbara Zool. Gardens; mem. Internat. Peace Inst. Found., Children's Advocacy Coun., Calif., 1988—; Citizen Soldier. Recipient award Calif. Sch. Nurses Orgn., 1965, 71. Fellow Am. Pub. Health Assn., Am. Sch. Health Assn. (past pres. Calif. Div.); mem. NEA (ret.) NAACP, ACLU, NOW, ERA, LWV, OXFAM, WAND, YMCA, YWCA, Calif. Tchrs. Assn. Calif. Med. Assn. (ret.), Santa Barbara County Med. Soc. (ret.), Am. Acad. Pediatrics, L.A. pediatric socs. (ret.), World Coun. Chs., Nat. Coun. Chs. (founding mem. Laymen's Commn.), Christic Inst., No. Calif. Ecumenical Coun., UN Assn. (past pres. Santa Barbara chpt.), Ams. for Democratic Action, Calif. Congress Parents and Tchrs. (hon. life), Scholastic Socs. South, Nat. Audubon Soc., Save the Redwoods League, Wilderness Soc., Nat. Parks Assn., Calif. State Parks Assn., Sierra Club, So. Christian Leadership Conf., Internat. Peace Inst. Found., Vols. in Tech. Assistance, Planned Parenthood Fedn. Am., Environ. Protective Assn., U.S. Pub. Interest Rsch. Group (charter mem.), Fellowship Reconciliation, Inst. for Am. Democracy, Com. for Improvement Med. Care, Nat. Indian Youth Coun., Nat. Drug Policy Found. (charter mem.), Nat. and Internat. Wildlife Assn., Common Cause, Episcopal Peace Fellowship, Fund for Peace, Nat. and Internat. Nature Conservancy, Friends of the Earth, Greenpeace, Gray Panthers, Defenders of Wildlife, Internat. Physicians for Prevention of Nuclear War, Leadership Circle of Physicians for Social Responsibility, Nat. Urban League, Religious Coalition for Abortion Rights, Nat. Abortion Rights Action League, Freedom from Hunger Found., Alliance for Survival, Inst. Aerobic Rsch., Ctr. War/Peace Studies, Am. Farmland Trust, Rural Advancement Fund, So. Poverty Law Center, United World Federalists, Zero Population Growth, Negative Population Growth, Amnesty Internat., Coun. for Livable World, Clergymen and Laymen Concerned, Am. Fedn. Scientists, Planning and Conservation League Calif., Am. Indian Fund, Humane Soc. U.S., Assn. for Vol. Sterilization, Coun. on Econ. Priorities, N. Am. Congress on Latin Am., Ctr. Immigration Studies, Coalition for a New Fgn. Policy, Met. Opera Assn., Nat. Coun. on Aging, The Africa Fund., Ams. United for Separation of Ch. and State, Am. Friends Svc. Com., Nat. Assn. for R.R. Passengers, Calif. Tax Reform Assn., Nat. Com. for Peace in Cen. Am., Santa Barbara Citizens Planning Assn., Internat. Ctr. for Devel. Policy, Simon Wiesenthal Ctr., Am.-Israeli Civil Liberties Coalition, Internat. Platform Assn., Ctr. for Def. Info., Children's Aid Internat., Ctr. for Law in Pub. Interest, World Wildlife Fund, Solar Lobby, Rainforest Action Network, Educators for Social Responsibility, Bread for the World, PAX Ams., Nat. Cathedral Assn., People for the Am. Way, N.Y. Acad. of Scis., Nat. Assn. World Health, Santa Barbara Peace Resurce Ctr., Environ. Def. Ctr., mem. hon. steering com. Ron Dellum's Nat. Adv. Bd., charter mem. Nat. Civil Rights Hall of Fame (charter), numerous others. Contbr. articles to ednl. and other profl. jours. Home: 340 Old Mill Rd San Vicente 33 Santa Barbara CA 93110

WAYLAND, NEWTON HART, conductor; b. Santa Barbara, Calif., Nov. 5, 1940; s. L.C. Newton and Helen Bertha (Hart) W.; m. Judith Anne Curtis, July 3, 1969 (div. 1986). MusB, New Eng. Conservatory Music, 1964, MusM, 1966. Host, composer, performer Sta. WGBH-TV, Boston, 1963-82; pianist, harpsichordist Boston Symphony Orch., 1964-71; music dir. Charles Playhouse, 1965-67; pianist, guest condr., arranger Boston Pops Orch., 1971-74; resident Pops condr. Midwest Pops Orch., South Bend, Ind., 1979-91, Oakland Symphony Orch., Calif., 1980-85, Houston Symphony Orch., 1986-93; prin. Pops condr. Denver Symphony Orch., 1987-89, Vancouver (B.C.) Symphony Orch., 1993—; guest condr. numerous orchs. U.S. and Canada, 1977—. Recs. include: Music for Zoom (PBS Emmy-winning TV show), 1971-78, Music for Nova (award-winning PBS-TV show), 1972-78, America Swings, 1987, Gershwin Plays Gershwin, 1987, Pop Go the Beatles, 1987, Classical Jukebox, 1988, Stompin' at the Savoy, 1988, Sophisticated Ladies, 1988, A Touch of Fiedler, 1989, Prime Time, 1989; arranger, performer: Jazz Loves Bach, 1968, Fiedler in Rags, 1974; arranger, condr.: Berlin to Broadway with Kurt Weill, 1972; condr. Oedipus Tex (Grammy award 1991); arranger, composer, performer (songs A&M Records) Come On and Zoom, Zoom Tunes. Recipient highest honors New Eng. Conservatory Music, 1974, Chadwick Disting. Achievement medal New Eng. Conservatory Music, 1966. Avocations: hiking, swimming. Home and Office: 2970 Hidden Valley Ln Santa Barbara CA 93108-1619

WAYLAND, RUSSELL GIBSON, JR., geology consultant, retired government official; b. Treadwell, Alaska, Jan. 23, 1913; s. Russell Gibson and Fanchon (Borie) W.; m. Mary Mildred Brown, 1943 (div. 1964); children: Nancy, Paul R.; m. Virginia Bradford Phillis, Dec. 24, 1965. B.S., U. Wash., 1934; A.M., Harvard, 1937; M.S., U. Minn., 1935, Ph.D., 1939. Engr., geologist Homestake Mining Co., Lead, S.D., summers 1930-39; with U.S. Geol. Survey, 1939-42, 1952-80, chief conservation div., 1966-78; research phys. scientist Office of Dir., 1978-80; energy minerals cons., 1980—; Washington rep. Am. Inst. Profl. Geologists, 1982-88; commr. VA Oil and Gas Conservation Bd., 1982-90; with Army-Navy Munitions Bd., 1942-45, Office Mil. Govt. and Allied High Commn., Germany, 1945-52; instr. geology U. Minn., 1937-39. Author sci. bulls. in field. Served to lt. col. AUS, 1942-46. Decorated Army Commendation medal; recipient Distinguished Service award Dept. Interior. Mem. AIME, Mineral Soc. Am., Geol. Soc. Am., Am. Inst. Profl. Geologists, Soc. Econ. Geologists, Assn. Engring. Geologists, Cosmos Club, Sigma Xi, Tau Beta Pi, Phi Gamma Delta, Sigma Gamma Epsilon, Gamma Alpha, Phi Mu Alpha Sinfonia. Episcopalian. Home and Office: 4660 35th St N Arlington VA 22207-4462

WAYLAND, WILLIAM FRANCIS, diversified manufacturing company executive; b. Woonsocket, R.I., July 10, 1935; s. William F. and Cora (Dew) W.; m. Patricia Ann Whalen, Nov. 5, 1960; children: M. Scott, Pamela M., Catherine E. AB in Polit. Sci., Providence Coll., 1958; postgrad. in indsl. relations, U. Mich., 1964-65. Indsl. relations Chrysler Corp., 1961-75; dir. indsl. relations Schering Plough Corp., Kenilworth, N.J., 1975-77; v.p. adminstrn. A. Johnson & Co. Inc., N.Y.C., 1977-85; sr. v.p. human resources Textron Inc., Providence, 1985—. Bd. dirs. Providence Coll. Corp., 1985—, Roger William Gen. Hosp. Corp., Providence, 1986—. Served to 1st lt. U.S. Army, 1959-61. Recipient Personal Achievement award Providence Coll., 1984. Mem. Am. Soc. for Personnel Adminstrn. (human resources strategies and issues council 1985—), Human Resources Planning Soc., Providence Coll. Alumni Assn. (bd. dirs. 1985—). Roman Catholic. Club: Canoe Brook Country (Summit, N.J.). Office: Textron Inc 40 Westminster St Providence RI 02903-2525

WAYLAND-SMITH, ROBERT DEAN, banker; b. Oneida, N.Y., July 2, 1943; s. Robert and Prudence Cragin (Skinner) W-S.; m. Kathleen Anne Schultz, Aug. 24, 1968; children: Kristin, Debra. BA in Econs., U. Rochester, 1965. Mgr. equipment svc. Strong Meml. Hosp., Rochester, N.Y., 1965-67; mgmt. trainee Chase Lincoln First Bank, N.A., Rochester, 1967-68, mgr. mcpl. securities, 1968-81, mgr. portfolio mgmt. depart., 1981-84, mgr. fin. and investment svc. dept., 1984-87, mgr. trust and fin. svc. dept., 1987-88; pres. and CEO Rochester region Chase Manhattan Bank, N.A., 1988-93, upstate wealth segment exec., 1993—; mem. adv. bd. Roberts Wesleyan Coll., Rochester, 1989—; mem. adv. coun. J.W. Jones Sch. Bus. SUNY, Geneseo, 1990—. Trustee Ctr. for Govtl. Rsch., 1985—, Rochester Visitors Assn., 1990-93, Rochester Downtown Devel. Corp., 1991-93; dir. United Neighborhood Ctrs., Greater Rochester Found., 1992—; mem. fin. execs. adv. bd. Coll. Bus. Rochester Inst. Tech., 1994—; mem. adv. bd. Help Our World Found., 1990—. Fellow Assn. for Investment Mgmt. and Rsch.; mem. Internat. Assn. Fin. Planners, Rochester Soc. Security Analysts, Greater Rochester Met. C. of C. (dir. 1992—), Genesee Valley Club, Oak Hill Country Club. Avocations: golf, gardening, reading. Office: Chase Manhattan Bank NA One Chase Sq Rochester NY 14643

WAYLETT, THOMAS ROBERT, management consultant executive; b. Toronto, Ont., Can., Apr. 27, 1941; s. Robert George and Frances Jean (Thomson) W.; m. Nancy Jean Parkinson, May 12, 1961 (div.); children:

Cherie Lynne, Matthew; m. Karen P. Pritchard, Jan. 23, 1989. With Nat. Life, Imperial Life, Indsl. Life, Toronto; v.p. William M. Mercer Ltd., Toronto, 1966-75; dir. William M. Mercer Inc. N.Y.C., 1975-82; mng. dir. Marsh & McLennan Cos., N.Y.C., 1982-91; exec. v.p. William M. Mercer Cos., N.Y.C., 1991—; chmn. Mercer Mgmt. Consulting, Inc., N.Y.C., 1992—; bd. dirs. Nat. Econ. Rsch. Assocs., White Plains, N.Y., William M. Mercer Cos., Inc., N.Y.C. Office: Mercer Mgmt Consulting 1166 Avenue Of The Americas New York NY 10036-2708

WAYMAN, MORRIS, chemical engineering educator, consultant; b. Toronto, Can., Mar. 19, 1915; s. Harry and Martha (Alt) W.; m. Sara Gertrude Zadkin, Jan. 9, 1937; children: Michael Lash, Thomas Ethan. B.A., U. Toronto, 1936, M.A., 1937, Ph.D., 1941. Registered profl. engr., Ont. Researcher Can. Internat. Paper Co., Hawkesbury, Ont., 1942-52; tech. dir. Columbia Cellulose Co., Prince Rupert, B.C., 1958-63; prof. chem. engring. U. Toronto, 1963-93, prof. forestry 1973-93; pres. Morris Wayman, Ltd., Toronto, 1966—; adj. prof. chem. engring. U. Alberta, 1993—; cons., Can., U.S., Brazil, Sweden, UN. Author: Guide for Planning Pulp and Paper Enterprises, 1973, Wealth and Welfare, 1978, Biotechnology of Biomass Conversion: fuels and chemicals from renewable sources, 1990; contbr. numerous articles to sci. jours.; patentee in field. Mem. Ont. Waste Mgmt. Adv. Bd., 1975-80, Edmonton Philharm Orch. Hon. fellow Innis Coll., Toronto, 1977. Fellow AAAS, Royal Soc. Can., Chem. Inst. Can.; mem. Can. Wood Chemistry Symposium (chmn. 1979-82), Sigma Xi. Office: U Alberta, Dept Chem Engring, Edmonton, AB Canada T6G 2G6 *I believe that science and engineering have freed man from the centuries-old struggle for existence, and that our present - and, I believe, transient - discomfort and confusion arise from our hesitant acceptance of and adjustment to our new freedom. I expect to see a great burgeoning of the arts and humanities, as well as a vastly increased participation by men and women all over the world in the scientific way of life. We are truly bursting through to a better world.*

WAYMAN, ROBERT PAUL, electronics company executive; b. Chgo., July 5, 1945; s. Lowell Roger and Dorothy Emma (Francke) W.; m. Susan O. Humphrey; children: Jennifer, Allison, Grant, Kirsten, Clayton. BS in Sci. Engring., Northwestern U., 1967, MBA, 1969. Cost acct. Hewlett-Packard Co., Loveland, Calif., 1969-71, mgr. cost accounts, 1971-73, div. controller, 1973-76; instrument group controller Palo Alto, Calif., 1976-83, corp. controller, 1983-84, chief fin. officer, 1984—. Mem. Fin. Execs. Inst., Council Fin. Execs. Office: Hewlett-Packard Co 3000 Hanover St Palo Alto CA 94304-1112

WAYMOUTH, JOHN FRANCIS, physicist, consultant; b. Barahona, Dominican Republic, May 24, 1926; came to U.S., 1936; s. John Francis and Margaret Logan (Postell) W.; m. Frances O'Bannon Pope, Sept. 3, 1949; children: John F., George L., Anne K., Mark D. BS, U. of South, 1947; PhD in Physics, MIT, 1950. From sr. engr. to sect. head Sylvania Electric Products Co., Salem and Danvers, Mass., 1950-69; lab. dir. GTE Products Corp., Danvers, 1969-88; cons. physicist Marblehead, Mass., 1988—; chmn. exec. com. Phys. Electronic Conf., 1969-72; mem. evaluation panel heat div. Nat. Bur. Standards, Gaithersburg, Md., 1972-74; mem. tech. edc. products radiol. saftey standards com. Bur. of Radiol. Health, Rockville, Md., 1977-79; mem. adv. com. for physics NSF, Washington, 1981-83. Author: Electric Discharge Lamps; contbr. articles to profl. jours.; patentee in field. With U.S. Army, 1944-46, PTO. Recipient Elenbaas prize Dutch Phys. Soc., 1973. Fellow Am. Phys. Soc., Illuminating Engring. Soc. N.Am. (medal 1991).

WAYMOUTH, ROBERT, chemistry educator. Prof. dept. chemistry Stanford (Calif.) U. Recipient Arthur C. Cope Scholar award Am. Chem. Soc., 1995. Office: Stanford U Dept Chem S G Mudd Bldg Stanford CA 94305-5080*

WAYNE, LOWELL GRANT, air pollution scientist, consultant; b. Washington, Nov. 27, 1918; s. Glenn Lytten and Bonnie Jean (Leming) W.; m. Martha Lee Dolson, June 21, 1942; children: Garth Lee, Randall Rush. BS, U. Calif., Berkeley, 1937; student, U. Calif., Davis, 1939-41, Harvard U., 1942; PhD, Calif. Inst. Technology, 1948. Diplomate Am. Bd. Indsl. Hygiene. Fellow Mellon Inst. for Indsl. Rsch., Pitts., 1949-52; phys. chemist Stanford Rsch. Inst., Menlo Park, Calif., 1953-54; occupational health engr. U. Calif., L.A., 1954-56; rsch. photochemist Air Pollution Control Dist., L.A., 1956-62; rsch. analyst Hancock Found. U. So. Calif., L.A., 1962-72, section head Air Pollution Control Inst., 1966-72; v.p., sr. scientist Pacific Environ. Svcs., Inc., Santa Monica, Calif., 1972-85; cons. L.A., 1985—; sr. scientist Valley Rsch. Corp., Van Nuys, Calif., 1987—. Lt. comdr. USNR, 1942-46. Fellow AAAS; mem. So. Calif. Fedn. Scientists, Air and Waste Mgmt. Assn., Am. Chem. Soc., Sigma Xi. Unitarian. Avocation: chamber music. Home: 285 Bayside Rd Arcata CA 95521-6463

WAYNE, STEPHEN J., government educator, academic director, writer; b. N.Y.C., Mar. 22, 1939; s. Arthur G. and Muriel (Marks) W.; m. Cheryl Beil, May 22, 1982; children: Jared B., Jeremy B. BA with honors, U. Rochester, 1961; MA, Columbia U., 1963, PhD, 1968. Instr. polit. sci. U.S. Naval Postgrad. Sch., 1963-65; instr. politics and govt. Ohio Wesleyan U., 1966-68; asst. prof. polit. sci. and pub. affairs The George Washington U., 1968-73, assoc. prof., 1973-79, prof., 1979-89; prof. govt., head Am. govt. sect. Georgetown U., Washington, 1989—; adviser President-Elect Portillo and staff, Mexico City, 1976; dir. U.S. Studies program Ctr. Advanced Study of Ams., 1985-87; faculty assoc. pub. policy, grad. inst. pub. policy edn. and rsch. George Washington U., 1986-89; chair recruitment com. Am. govt. and pub. policy Georgetown U., 1989—; chair Merthan and Walsh lectureships; presenter and lectr. in field. Author: The Legislative Presidency, 1978, The Road to the White House, 1980, post election edit., 1981, 2d edit., 1984, 3d edit., 1988, 4th edit., 1992, (with George C. Edwards) Presidential Leadership: Politics and Policy Making, 1985, 2d edit., 1990; editor: Investigating the American Political System: Problems, Methods, and Projects, 1974, (with George C. Edwards) Studying the Presidency, 1983, (with Clyde Wilcox) The Quest for National Office, 1992; appeared on 3 one-hour programs on presidency Every Four Years, sta. WHYY-TV, PBS, 1980; election night analyst ARD-German TV, 1992; adv. editor polit. sci. McGraw Hill College Divsn., 1982—; series editor American Political Institutions and Public Policy, M. E. Sharpe, Inc., 1990—; contbr. numerous articles, chptrs. and book revs. to books and profl. jours. Office: Georgetown U Dept Govt 37th and O NW Washington DC 20057

WAYTE, (PAUL) ALAN, lawyer; b. Huntington Park, Calif., Dec. 30, 1936; s. Paul Henry and Helen Lucille (McCarthy) W.; m. Beverly A. Bruen, Feb. 19, 1959 (div. 1972); children: David Alan, Lawrence Andrew, Marcia Louise; m. Nancy Kelly Wayte, July 5, 1975. AB, Stanford U., 1958, JD, 1960. Bar: Calif. 1961, U.S. Dist. Ct. (so. dist.) Calif. 1961, U.S. Supreme Ct. 1984. Ptnr. Adams, Duque & Hazeltine, Los Angeles, 1966-85, Dewey Ballantine, Los Angeles, 1985—. Mem. L.A. County Bar Assn. (chmn. real property sect. 1981-82), Am. Coll. Real Estate Lawyers (bd. govs. 1989—, pres. 1994), Am. Coll. Mortgage Attys., Anglo-Am. Real Property Inst. (bd. govs. 1989-91), L.A. Philharm. Assn. (exec. com. bd. dirs. 1973—), Chancery Club, Calif. Club (L.A.), Valley Hunt Club (Pasadena). Home: 1745 Orlando Rd Pasadena CA 91106-4131 Office: Dewey Ballantine 333 S Hope St Los Angeles CA 90071-1406

WAZZAN, AHMED R(ASSEM) FRANK, engineering educator, dean; b. Lattakia, Syrian Arab Republic, Oct. 17, 1935; married, 1959; 3 children. BS, U. Calif., Berkeley, 1959, MS, 1961, PhD in Engring. Sci., 1963. From asst. prof. to assoc. prof. engring. UCLA, 1962-69, prof. engring. and applied sci., 1974—, assoc. dean Sch. Engring. and Applied Sci., 1981-86, dean Sch. Engring. and Applied Sci., 1986—; cons. McDonnell Douglas Corp., 1962-71, Lawrence Radiation Lab., 1965-67, Westinghouse Electric Corp., 1974-76, N.Am. Aviation, 1975-78, Aerojet Corp., 1975—; Honeywell Corp., 1976-78; vis. scholar Electricité de France, Paris, Office of Commr. Atomic Energy, Saclay, France, 1973-79. Reviewer Applied Mech. Rev., 1971-87. Guggenheim fellow, 1966. Fellow Am. Nuclear Soc. Research in modeling of fuel elements for fast breeder reactor, stability and transition of laminar flows, thermodynamics of solids and of dense gases, and thermal hydraulics of pressurized water reactors. Office: UCLA Sch of Engring Dean 405 Hilgard Ave Los Angeles CA 90024-1600

WEADOCK, DANIEL PETER, corporate executive; b. N.Y.C., June 21, 1939; m. Florence Towey, Oct. 5, 1961; children: Daniel, Bryan, Kevin, Ann,

Kathleen. B.S. in Fin, Fordham U., 1967; PhD (hon.), Georgian Ct. Coll., Lakewood, N.J., 1991. With central bookkeeping Chase Manhattan Bank, 1957-61; with ITT Corp., 1961—; spl. asst. to office of pres. ITT, 1969-75; dir. ops. ITT Africa and Middle East, Brussels, 1975-79; pres. ITT Africa and Middle East, 1979; v.p. ITT, 1979-83; pres. ITT Europe Inc., Brussels, 1983—; exec. v.p. ITT, 1983—, group exec.-Europe; pres. ITT-Europe, Inc.; chmn., pres., CEO ITT Comms. and Info. Svcs., Seacucus, N.J., 1988-93; pres., COO ITT Sheraton Corp., Boston, 1993—. Named Knight of the Order of the Crown by the King of Belgium, 1988. Office: ITT Sheraton Corp 60 State St Boston MA 02109

WEAKLAND, REMBERT G., archbishop; b. Patton, Pa., Apr. 2, 1927; s. Basil and Mary (Kane) W. AB, St. Vincent Coll., Latrobe, Pa., 1948, DD (hon.), 1963, LHD (hon.), 1987; MS in Piano, Juilliard Sch. Music, 1954; grad. studies sch. music, Columbia U., 1954-56; LHD (hon.), Duquesne U., 1964, Belmont Coll., 1964, Cath. U. Am., 1975, Xavier U., Cin., 1988, DePaul U., 1989, Loyola U., New Orleans, 1991, Dayton U., New Orleans, 1993, Marian Coll., Fond du Lac, 1995, Marian Coll., Fond du Lac, Wis., 1995; HHD (hon.), St. Ambrose U., Davenport, 1990, Aquinas Inst. Theology, St. Louis, 1991, St Mary's Coll., Notre Dame, Ind., 1994; LLD (hon.), Cardinal Stritch Coll., Milw., 1978, Marquette U., 1981, Loyola U., Chgo., 1986, U. Notre Dame, 1987, Mt. Mary Coll., Milw., 1989, Fairfield U., 1994; D of Sacred Music (hon.), St. Joseph's Coll., Rensselaer, Ind., 1979; DST (hon.), Jesuit Sch. Theology, 1989, St. John's U., Collegeville, Minn., 1991, Santa Clara U., 1991, Yale U., 1993; DD (hon.), Lakeland Coll., Sheboygan, 1991, Regis Coll., Toronto, 1993. Joined Benedictines, Roman Cath. Ch. 1945, ordained priest, 1951. Mem. faculty music dept. St. Vincent Coll., 1957-63, chmn., 1961-63, chancellor chmn. of bd. of Coll., 1963-67; elected co-adjutor archabbot, 1963; abbot primate Benedictine Confederation, 1967-77; archbishop of Milw., 1977—. Mem. Ch. Music Assn. Am. (pres. 1964-66), Am. Guild Organists. Office: PO Box 07912 Milwaukee WI 53207-0912

WEARE, ASHLEY, banker; b. Boston, Mar. 22, 1927; s. John and Helene W.; m. Marguerite Trocmé, Apr. 15, 1955; children—Isabelle, Cynthia, Christopher, Betsey Ann. AB, Harvard U., 1952, MBA, 1954. Contr. Bankers Trust Co., N.Y.C., 1966-72; contr. Bankers Trust N.Y. Corp., 1972, asst. to chmn., 1972-87, sr. v.p. corp. fin. and investor rels., 1978—. With USNR, 1945-46. Mem. Nat. Investor Rels. Inst., Investor Rels. Assn. (pres.), Bank Adminstrn. Inst., Fin. Execs. Inst. Home: 275 W 96th St Apt 21G New York NY 10025-6269 Office: Bankers Trust Co 280 Park Ave New York NY 10017-1216

WEARLY, WILLIAM LEVI, business executive; b. Warren, Ind., Dec. 5, 1915; s. Purvis Gardner and Ethel Ada (Jones) W.; m. Mary Jane Riddle, Mar. 8, 1941; children: Patricia Ann, Susan, William Levi, Elizabeth. B.S., Purdue U., 1937, Dr. Engring. (hon.), 1959. Student career engr. C.A. Dunham Co., Michigan City, Ind., 1936; mem. elec. design staff Joy Mfg. Co., Franklin, Pa., 1937-39; v.p., gen. sales mgr. Joy Mfg. Co., 1952-56, exec. v.p., 1956-57, pres., dir., 1957-62; v.p. dir. Ingersoll-Rand Co., 1964-66, exec. v.p., 1966-67, chmn., chief exec. officer, 1967-80, chmn. exec. com., 1981-85; dir. ASA Ltd., Med. Care Am.; trustee LMI; speaker engring. groups. Author tech. publs. relating to mining. Bd. dirs. Boys Clubs Am. Mem. NAE, IEEE, AIME, Nat. Acad. of Engring., C. of C. Sky Club N.Y.C., Blind Brook Golf Club, Desert Forest Golf Club, Ariz. Club, Masons, Shriners, Eta Kappa Nu, Tau Beta Pi, Beta Theta Pi. Republican. Methodist. Patentee in field. Home: One Milbank IIF Greenwich CT 06830 also: PO Box 1072 Carefree AZ 85377

WEARN, WILSON CANNON, retired media executive; b. Newberry, S.C., Oct. 7, 1919; s. George F. and Mary (Cannon) W.; m. Mildred Colson, Feb. 21, 1948; children: Jean Wearn Held, Joan Wearn Gilbert, Wilson Cannon Jr. B.E.E., Clemson U., 1941. Engr. Westinghouse Electric Corp., Pitts., 1941, FCC, Washington, 1946-48; assoc. cons. electronic engr. firm Weldon & Carr, Washington, 1948-50; ptnr. Vandivere, Cohen & Wearn (cons. engrs.), Washington, 1950-53; with Multimedia Broadcasting Co., Greenville, S.C., 1953—; organizer of corp. Multimedia Broadcasting Co., 1953, became corp. officer, 1960, pres., 1966-77; pres. Multimedia, Inc., Greenville, 1977-81; chief exec. officer Multimedia, Inc., 1978-84, chmn. bd., 1981-89; chmn. emeritus Multimedia, Inc., Greenville, 1989—; instr. electronic engring. Clemson U., 1946. Mem. S.C. Hosp. Adv. Council, 1969-71; bd. dirs. Family and Children Service of Greenville County, 1967-69, pres., 1969; bd. dirs. Newspaper Advt. Bur., 1981-85; trustee Greenville Symphony Assn., 1960-62, 71-77, pres., 1977; trustee Greenville Hosp. System, 1964-70, chmn., 1968-70; trustee Broadcast Rating Council, 1969-73, chmn., 1971-73; trustee Clemson U. Found., 1973-79, pres., 1979; trustee Presbyn. Coll., F.W. Symmes Found. Served to capt. Signal Corps, AUS, 1941-45, PTO. Decorated Bronze Star; recipient Outstanding Alumni award Clemson U., 1972. Mem. Nat. Assn. Broadcasters (chmn. bd. 1975-77), S.C. Broadcasters Assn. (pres. 1967), Greater Greenville C. of C. (pres. 1972), Nat. Assn. Securities Dealers (bd. govs. 1985-88). Presbyterian (elder). Clubs: Kiwanis (Greenville), Poinsett (Greenville), Green Valley Country (Greenville). Office: Multimedia Inc PO Box 1688 Greenville SC 29602-1688

WEART, SPENCER RICHARD, historian; b. Detroit, Mar. 8, 1942; s. Spencer Augustus and Janet (Streng) W.; m. Carole Ege, June 30, 1971; children: Lara Kimi, Spencer Gen. BA, Cornell U., 1963; PhD, U. Colo., 1968. Postdoctoral fellow Calif. Inst. Tech., 1968-71, U. Calif., Berkeley, 1971-74; dir. Ctr. for History Physics, Am. Inst. Physics, College Park, Md., 1974—. Author: Scientists in Power, 1979, Nuclear Fear, 1988; contbr. articles to profl. jours. Fellow AAAS. Home: 12 Buena Vista Dr Hastings Hdsn NY 10706-1104 Office: Am Inst Physics One Physics Ellipse College Park MD 20740-3843

WEARY, PEYTON EDWIN, medical educator; b. Evanston, Ill., Jan. 10, 1930; s. Leslie Albert and Conway Christian (Fleming) W.; m. Janet Edsall Gregory, Aug. 23, 1952; children—Terry, Conway Christian, Carolyn Fielder. B.A., Princeton U., 1970; M.D., U. Va., 1955. Diplomate: Am. Bd. Dermatology (dir. 1978-88, pres. 1987-88). Intern, case Western Res. U. Hosps., Cleve., 1955-56; rotating intern Univ. Hosp. Cleve., 1955-56; asst. resident dermatology U. Va., Charlottesville, 1958-60; resident dermatology U. Va., 1960-61, instr. dept. dermatology, 1961-62, asst. prof., 1962-65, assoc. prof., 1965-70, prof., chmn. dept. dermatology, 1970-93; mem. staff Univ. Hosp., mem. cancer com., 1979—, sec.-treas.; Univ. Hosp. house staff, 1960-61, clin. staff 1965-66, pres. clin. staff, 1966-67. Mem. editorial bd. Jour. Am. Acad. Dermatology, 1978-87; editorial adv. bd. Skin and Allergy News, 1978—; contbr. articles to profl. jours. Bd. dirs. Lupus Found. Am., 1980-84; trustee, mem. exec. com. Dermatology Found., 1975-79; pres. Albermarle County unit Am. Cancer Soc., 1967-69. Served from 1st lt. to capt., M.C. U.S. Army, 1956-58. Mem. ABA, Nat. Assn. Physicians Environ. (pres. 1995—), Va. Dermatol. Soc. (sec.-treas. 1965-71), Am. Acad. Dermatology (hon., bd. dirs. 1973-76, Gold medal 1990, pres. 1993-95), Soc. Investigative Dermatology (bd. dirs. 1976-81, v.p. 1985), Assn. Profs. Dermatology (sec.-treas. 1976-79), Am. Dermat. Assn. (bd. dirs. 1987—, pres. 1992-93), Dermatology Found., Albermarle County Med. Soc., Med. Soc. Va., So. Med. Assn., Reven Soc., Am. Bd. Med. Specialties (v.p. 1988, pres.-elect 1989, pres. 1990-92), Coun. Med. Splty. Socs. (bd. dirs. 1989-92, sec. 1992—), Alpha Omega Alpha, Sigma Xi. Republican. Presbyn. Club: Boar's Head Sports. Home: 110 Magnolia Dr Charlottesville VA 22901-2015 Office: Dept Dermatology Univ Va Hosp Charlottesville VA 22908

WEATHERBEE, ARTEMUS EDWIN, former federal government official; b. Bangor, Maine, Feb. 9, 1918; s. Ray Wellman Sherman (stepfather) and Lola (Yelland) W.; m. Pauline Jellison, June 18, 1940; children: Sue Weatherbee Adams, Richard Charles, Steven Sherman. A.B. with honors, U. Maine, 1939; intern, Nat. Inst. Pub. Affairs, 1939-40. Chief of classification, chief of placement F.C.A., 1941-42; sr. personnel officer Office Emergency Mgmt., 1942-43; dir. personnel Nat. War Labor Bd., 1943; W.S.B., 1946; chief exec. selection War Assets Adminstrn., 1946; chief fgn. service recruitment Dept. State, 1946-48, asst. chief allowances staff, 1948-49, chief, 1949-50, asst. chief deptl. personnel div., 1950-51, spl. asst. to dir. personnel, 1951-52, dep. dir. personnel, 1952-53; exec. dir., dep. asst. postmaster gen. Bur. Personnel, P.O. Dept., 1954-59; adminstrv. asst. sec., asst. sec. for adminstrn. Treasury Dept., 1959-70; U.S. dir. Asian Devel. Bank-Manila with personal rank of ambassador, 1970-73; exec. dir. Kennebunk-Kennebunkport C. of C., 1975-78; corporator Kennebunk Savs. Bank, 1978-81; cons. Maine Mgmt. and Cost Survey Commn., 1974. Mem.

nat. adv. com. Am. Security Coun., 1978-80; mem. Nat. Tax Limitation Com., 1979-80; chmn. U. Maine Devel. Coun., 1975-77; mem. Gov.'s adv. com. on U. Maine, 1975-78, Kennebunk Budget Bd., 1974-77; bd. dirs. Kennebunk Area Indsl. Corp., 1976-79, York County Community Concert Assn., 1978-80; mem. Nat. Rights to Work Com., 1975-80; trustee U. Maine, 1975-80; deacon United Community Ch., 1984-85, trustee, 1985-88; candidate for Maine Senate, 1978; bd. dirs. Security Patrol, 1982-83. Served to lt. (j.g.) USN, 1943-45; ret. comdr. Res. 1978. Recipient Meritorious Service award Dept. State, 1950, Arthur S. Flemming award U.S. Junior C. of C., 1956; Exceptional Service award Treasury Dept., 1965; Career Service award Nat. Civil Service League, 1965; Rockefeller Pub. Service award, 1968; Alexander Hamilton award Treasury Dept., 1970; Alumni Career Service award U. Maine, 1972. Mem. U. Maine Alumni Assn., Sun City Center C. of C. (exec. dir. 1981-83, pres. 1982), Naval Res. Assn., Nat. Assn. Retired Fed. Employees (bd. dirs. Sun City Ctr. chpt. 1985-88, pres. 1986-87), Cape Arundel Golf Club, Sun City Ctr. Golf and Country Club, Lions (dir. 1975-77), Rotary (Paul Harris fellow 1978—), Phi Beta Kappa, Beta Theta Pi, Phi Kappa Phi, Sigma Mu Sigma. Republican. Home: 1012 Del Webb Blvd E Sun City Center FL 33573-6203 also: 34 Wood Pond Ln Kennebunk ME 04043-1722

WEATHERBEE, DONALD EMERY, political scientist, educator; b. Portland, Maine, June 21, 1932; s. Perley Emery and Ruby Francis (Smith) W.; m. Mary Ellen Bailey, Sept. 4, 1954; children: Mercy Meria, Donald Bailey, Thais Elizabeth, Amy Francesca, Oliver Parks Emery. A.B. magna cum laude, Bates Coll., 1954; M.A., Johns Hopkins U. Sch. Advanced Internat. Studies, 1956, Ph.D. (Earhart dissertation fellow), 1968. Spl. lectr. Gajah Mada State U., Jogjakarta, Indonesia, 1957-61; Ford Found. fellow The Hague, Netherlands, 1962-64; asst. prof. to prof. U.S., 1964-74; Donald S. Russell prof. contemporary fgn. policy, 1981—; sr. Fulbright fellow Inst. Southeast Asian Studies, Singapore, 1981-82; asst. dean Coll. Social Scis., 1972; Henry L. Stimson prof. polit. sci. U.S. Army War Coll., 1974-77; vis. asst. prof. U. R.I., 1965; exchange prof. Free U. Berlin, 1969; vis. fellow Inst. Security and Internat. Studies, Chulalongkorn U., Bangkok, Thailand, 1988-89; panelist reviewer Nat. Endowment for Humanities; cons., lectr. for U.S. govt. agys. Author: Ideology in Indonesia, 1965, The United Front in Thailand, 1970, Ancient Indonesia, 1974, Indonesian Security Policy and Perceptions, 1978, Southeast Asia Divided: The Asean-Indochina Crisis, 1985; editorial bd.: Asian Survey; exec. editor: Asian Affairs; contbr. numerous articles, revs. to publs. on S.E. Asian politics and internat. relations. Recipient Disting. Civilian Service decoration Dept. of the Army, 1977. Fellow Inter-Univ. Seminar on Armed Forces and Soc.; mem. Assn. Asian Studies, Internat. Studies Assn., Koninklijke Instituut voor Taal, Land- en Volkenkunde (Leiden, Netherlands). Office: Dept Govt and Internat Studies U SC Columbia SC 29208

WEATHERFORD, GEORGE EDWARD, civil engineer; b. Oakdale, Tenn., Jan. 8, 1932; s. Walter Clyde and Kathleen (Hinds) W.; m. Martha Jeannette Beck, July 9, 1960; children: Kathleen Jeannette Weatherford-Hommelfoth, Elizabeth Lynn. BSCE, Ind. Inst. Tech., Fort Wayne, 1957; BS Engr. in Constrn., U. Mich., 1959; MSBA, St. Francis Coll., 1975. Registered profl. engr., Ind., Ga., Ohio, Minn., Iowa, S.C., Pa., Ky., Ill., Md., La., Tenn., Mich. Plant engr. Cen. Soya Co., Inc., Decatur, Ind., 1959; civil engr. Cen. Soya Co., Inc., Decatur, 1959-64; county hwy. engr. Allen County Ind. Govt., Ft. Wayne, 1964-66; sr. civil engr. Cen. Soya Co., Inc., Fort Wayne, 1966-69, engring. mgr., 1969-77, prin. engr., 1977—; ind. cons. 1964—. Author book chpts.; contbr. articles to profl. jours. Trustee Ft. Wayne YWCA, 1973-76, North Christian Ch. and Endowment Trust. Sgt. USMC, 1950-54. Mem. ASCE (state treas. 1957), NSPE, Am. Concrete Inst., Am. Inst. Steel Constrn., Nat. Grain and Feed Assn. (fire and explosion rsch. and edn. com.), Ill. Assn. Structural Engrs., Grain Elevator and Processing Soc. (edn. programming com.). Republican. Home: 3617 Delray Dr Fort Wayne IN 46815-6012

WEATHERFORD, WILLIS DUKE, JR., college president emeritus; b. Biltmore, N.C., June 24, 1916; m. Anne Smith, 1954; children: Edith, Julia, Willis III, Susan, Alice. B.A., Vanderbilt U., 1937; B.D., Yale U., 1940; postgrad., U. N.C., 1940-41; M.A., Harvard U., 1943, Ph.D in Econs., 1952; LL.D., Carleton Coll., 1969, Swarthmore Coll., 1981; L.H.D., Blackburn U., 1983, Transylvania U., 1983, Berea Coll., 1984; L.L.D. Tusculum Coll. 1987. Dir. youth work Methodist Commn. World Peace, 1943-44; relief worker Am. Friends Service Com., Europe, 1944-47; asst. prof. econs. Swarthmore Coll., 1948-54, asso. prof., 1954-64; acad. dean Carleton Coll., 1965-67; pres. Berea Coll., Ky., 1967-84; pres. emeritus, asst. to pres. Berea Coll., 1984-91. Author: Geographic Differentials in Agricultural Wages, 1957; co-author: Economies of the World Today, 1962, 65, 76; contbg. author: Labor in Developing Countries, 1962; Editor: The Goals of Higher Education, 1960. Rural devel. specialist Am. Friends Svc. Com., India, 1950-51, UN, Malaya, 1959-60, Rotary Club, India, 1993; bd. chmn. Pine Mountain Settlement Sch., 1967-84; pres. Black Mountain Pairing Project, 1988-89, 92-93; bd. dirs. Frontier Nursing Svc., Warren Wilson Coll., Blue Ridge YMCA Assembly N.C., The Morgan Sch., Black Mountain Rotary Club. Ford Found. fellow India, 1954-55. Mem. Am. Econ. Assn., Assn. Asian Studies, AAUP (pres. chpt. 1965), Phi Beta Kappa, Omicron Delta Kappa, Phi Kappa Phi. Address: 1 Briar Branch Rd Black Mountain NC 28711

WEATHERILL, JOHN FREDERICK WILLIAM, arbitrator; b. Oakville, Ont., Can., Aug. 3, 1932; s. John Francis and Elda Evelyn (Stinson) W.; m. Stephanie Goodman, 1957 (div. 1985); children: Timothy, Andrew, Katherine. B.A., U. Toronto, 1954, LLB, 1957; LLM, Harvard U., 1958. Bar: Ont. 1960. Asst. prof. Osgoode Hall Law Sch., 1960-63, U. Western Ont., 1963-64; part-time prof. U. Ottawa, 1975-78; vice chmn. Ont. Labour Rels. Bd., 1964-67; labour-mngt. arbitrator, 1968-89; arbitrator Can. Ry. Office Arbitration and Grievance Commr. , Inco Metals Ltd., United Steelworkers Am., 1968-83; chmn. Crown employees Grievance Settlement Bd., Ont., 1980-84; bd. dirs. adjudicator PSSRB, 1970-86; v.p. Nat. Acad. Arbitrators, 1971-76, bd. gpvs., 1974-77. chmn., 1991-93, co-chmn. 1986-89, dir. rsch. and edn. found., 1985—; chmn. Can. Labour Rels. Bd. Author: A Practical Guide to Labour Arbitration Procedure, 1987; contbr. articles to profl. jours. Fellow Chartered Inst. Arbitrators (U.K.), Ont. Labour Mngt. Arbitrators Assn. (past pres.), Internat., Can. Bar Assns., Cercle univ. d'Ottawa. Avocations: reading, music, tennis. Home: 24 Belvedere Cres, Ottawa, ON Canada K1M 2G4 Office: Can Labour Rels Bd, C D Howe Bldg 4th Fl W, Ottawa, ON Canada K1A 0X8

WEATHERLEY-WHITE, ROY CHRISTOPHER ANTHONY, surgeon, consultant; b. Peshawar, India, Dec. 1, 1931; S. Roy and Elfreda (Milward) Boehm, m. Dorian Jeanne Freeman Weatherley-White, Dec. 27, 1961; children: Carl Christopher, Matthew Richard, Larissa Chantal. MA, Cambridge U., 1953; MD, Harvard U., 1958. Surgeon Biomedical Cons., Denver, 1970—; pres., 1992—; chmn. Plastic Surgery Rsch. Coun., 1975-76; pres. Rocky Mountain Assn. Plastic Surgeons, 1973-74; v.p. Am. Cleft Palate Assn. Author: Plastic Surgeru of the Female Breast, 1982; contbr. over 45 articles to profl. jours. Cons. Colo. Biomedical Venture Ctr., Denver, 1993—. Recipient Rsch. award Am. Soc. Plastic Surgery, 1962, 64. Mem. Harvard Club of N.Y., Oxford-Cambridge Club, Denver Country Club, Denver Athletic Club. Episcopalian. Avocations: flying, skiing, scuba diving, archaeology. Home: 100 S Humboldt Denver CO Office: 4500 E 9th Ave Ste 470 Denver CO 80220-3923

WEATHERLY, ROBERT STONE, JR., banker; b. Birmingham, Ala., May 12, 1929; s. Robert Stone and Gladys (Manning) W.; m. Mary Anne Burr, May 1, 1955; children: Robert Stone, III, Henry, William. A.B., Princeton U., 1950; LL.B., Harvard U., 1953, grad. advanced mgmt. program, 1972. Bar: Ala. 1953. Assoc. firm Burr, McKamy Moore & Thomas, Birmingham, 1955-62; asst. gen. atty. Vulcan Materials Co., Birmingham, 1962-69; v.p. chems. div. Vulcan Materials Co., Wichita, Kans., 1969-71; treas. Vulcan Materials Co., 1971-74, v.p. and controller, 1974-77; pres. metals div. Vulcan Materials Co., Birmingham, Ala., 1977-87, pres. Middle East div., 1982-87; chmn., chief exec. officer Jefferson Fed. Savings, Birmingham, 1987-91; dir. All Seasons Travel, Birmingham, 1991—; disting. lectr.-practitioner U. Ga. Served with U.S. Army, 1953-55. Mem. Nat. Assn. Accts. (cert. mgmt. acct.). Presbyterian. Club: Country of Birmingham, Chattooga (Cashiers, N.C.). Home: 4608 Old Leeds Rd Birmingham AL 35213-1802 Office: All Seasons Travel 120 Office Park Dr Birmingham AL 35223-2402

WEATHERS, K. RUSSELL, organization executive; b. Harrison County, Mo., June 21, 1942; s. William Kenneth and Mildred Grace (Fitzpatrick) W.; B.S., U. Mo., 1964; m. Judith C. Cain, Aug. 12, 1961; children: Vince S., Kent A., Joy L. Tchr. vocat. agr. North Platte High Sch., Dearborn, Mo., 1964-66, Centralia (Mo.) Public High Sch., 1966-67; staff asst. and mem. services staff Farmland Industries, Inc., Kansas City, Mo., 1967-69, formerly dir. services div., exec. dir. mem. public relations staff, 1980-84; exec. dir. Liberty (Mo.) Hosp. Found., 1984-91; nat. exec. dir., CEO Camp Fire, Inc., Kansas City, 1991—; v.p. Nat. 4-H Coun., Washington, 1986-91, FCX, Inc., Raleigh, N.C. 1984-86. Asst. scoutmaster Boy Scouts Am., 1975; chmn. ch. bd. Liberty Christian Ch., 1974-75; co-chmn. Mo-Am. Royal Night, 1980—; chmn. Am. Royal 4-H Conf.; mem. council Kansas City Tomorrow, 1980-81; v.p. Ag Hall of Fame, 1980—, Earnest Shepherd Youth Center, 1976-78, chmn., 1978-80; bd. dirs., vice chmn. Mo. 4-H Found., 1979—; chmn. Liberty Econ. and Preservation Commn., 1980-81; active Liberty City Council, 1977-81, Leadership Liberty Coun., 1992, Ind. Sect. Com., 1993—, USDA Youth Devel. Task Force, USSR and Poland chair, 1990, Leadership Raleigh, 1986—, United Meth. Parish Com., 1993—; mayor City of Liberty, 1981-83; Liberty chmn. County Criminal Justice Center Bond Issue, 1980—; chmn. Kansas City FFA adv. com.; chmn. 4-H Found., 1983—; mem. sponsoring com. Nat. Future Farmers Am.; mem. Tri-County Mental Health Adv. Bd., Mo. Gov.'s Com. on Community Block Grant and Devel., Clay County Elected Ofcls. Commn., Nat. Ag Day Com., Northland Devel. Com., ARC Blood Doner's Gallon Club, 1980. Recipient Disting. Service award Nat. FFA; hon. awards State Young Farmers Assn. Okla., Iowa, Mo., Kans., Colo., Nebr. Mem. Guest Rels. Assn., Mo. Mcpl. League (revenue sharing commn. 1983—, Westgate div. coms.), U. Mo. Alumni Assn., C. of C. Liberty (office site com.), Northland C. of C. (govt. relations com. 1982-83), Rotary Club 13, KC Mo., Internat. Agribus. Club (v.p. 1979-80, pres. 1980-81). Mem. Christian Ch. Office: Camp Fire Boys And Girls 4601 Madison Ave Kansas City MO 64112

WEATHERS, MILLEDGE WRIGHT, retired economics educator; b. Augusta, Ga., May 11, 1926; s. Robert Edward Lee and Margaret Elizabeth (Johnson) W.; m. Anna-Maria Helene von Bertrab; children: Helen Boehmlein, Martin, Margarete, Banjamin. BA, George Washington U., 1949, MA, 1957; Dr. oec. publ., U. Munich, 1961. Rsch. analyst U.S. Dept. Air Force, Washington, 1951-57, Gen. Electric Co., Santa Barbara, Calif., 1959-62; prvt. practice cons. Munich, 1962-64; cons. Gesellschaft fuer Anlagewerte, Munich, 1964-66; sr. staff analyst Lockheed-Ga. Co., Marietta, 1966-68; prof. econs. Adrian (Mich.) Coll., 1968-91. Contbr. articles to profl. jours. With U.S. Army, 1944-46. Mem. Am. Econs. Assn., Assn. for Evolutionary Econs., Nat. Tax Assn., Economists Allied for Arms Reduction, Internat. Platform Assn., Kappa Sigma. Avocations: music, walking. Home: 930 Lincoln Ave Adrian MI 49221-3230

WEATHERSBY, GEORGE BYRON, investment management executive; b. Albany, Calif., Dec. 9, 1944; s. Byron and Fannie A. W.; m. Linda Rose Scheirer, June 29, 1979; children: Deborah Jane, Geoffrey Byron. BS, U. Calif., Berkeley, 1965, MS, 1966, MBA, 1967, MS, Harvard U., 1968, PhD, 1970; DHL (hon.), U. San Francisco, 1987; LLD (hon.), U. So. Ind., 1992. Mem. faculty, assoc. dir. analytical studies, dir. Ford Found. rsch. program U. Calif., Berkeley, 1969-72; spl. asst. to U.S. Sec. of State Washington, 1972-73; dir. rsch. Nat. Common. on Financing Higher Edn., Washington, 1973-74; assoc. prof. mgmt. Harvard U., Cambridge, Mass., 1974-78; commr. higher edn. State of Ind., 1977-83; pres. Curtis Pub. Co., 1983-86, New UPI Inc., Washington, 1985-86; corp. v.p. fin. Ontario Corp., Muncie, Ind., 1986-88, pres., 1988-91, also bd. dirs.; ptnr. Founders Court Inc., Princeton, N.J., 1991-93; independant cons., 1993—; pres. Oxford Mgmt. Corp., 1994—; chmn. bd. dirs. Otis Conner Cos., 1984-86, Curtis Media Corp., 1984-86, Curtis Internat. Ltd., 1985-86, Prince Gardner, Inc., 1991-93, Alma Industries, 1992-93, Hanes Holding Co., 1992-93; bd. dirs. Holnam Inc., Farm Fans Inc., Delta Consol. Industries, Cambridge Parallel Processing, Advanced Retail Mktg. Author: (books) Financing Postsecondary Education in the U.S, 1974, Colleges and Money, 1976; contbr. numerous articles to profl. jours., 1967—; cons. editor: Jour. Higher Edn., 1974—; exec. editor: Change mag., 1980-84. Bd. dirs. Nat. Ctr. for Higher Edn. Mgmt. Systems, 1980-83, U.S.A. Fund, 1989—; mem. steering com. Edn. Commn. of States, 1978-82; mem. Ind. Com. Humanities, 1981-87; trustee U. So. Ind., 1985-91, Pk. Tudor Sch. Indpls., 1986-91, Butler U., 1987-93. Calif. Regents scholar, 1963-65; NSF fellow, 1966-67; AEC fellow, 1966-67; Kent fellow, 1967-70; White House fellow, 1972-73; named 1 of 100 Outstanding Young Leaders in Higher Edn. Change Mag., 1978. Mem. Am. Coun. Edn., Ops. Rsch. Soc. Am., Inst. Mgmt. Scis., Econometrica, Young Pres. Orgn. Republican. Office: 540 Madison Ave 32d Fl New York NY 10022

WEATHERSTONE, DENNIS, trust company executive; b. London, Nov. 29, 1930; s. Henry Philip and Gladys (Hart) W.; m. Marion Blunsum, Apr. 4, 1959; children—Hazel, Cheryl, Gretel, Richard Paul. Student, Northwestern Poly., London, 1946-49. Sr. v.p. Morgan Guaranty Trust Co. N.Y., N.Y.C., 1972-77, exec. v.p., 1977-79, treas., 1977-79, vice chmn., 1979-80, chmn. exec. com., 1980-86; pres. J.P. Morgan & Co., Inc. (formerly Morgan Guaranty Trust Co. N.Y.), N.Y.C., 1987-90, chmn., chief exec. officer, 1990-95; bd. dirs. GM Corp., Merck & Co.; mem. internat. adv. council Inst. Internat. Studies. Mem. Assn. Res. City Bankers (bd. dirs.). Office: Morgan Guaranty Trust Co of NY 60 Wall St New York NY 10260-2807*

WEATHERUP, ROY GARFIELD, lawyer; b. Annapolis, Md., Apr. 20, 1947; s. Robert Alexander and Kathryn Crites (Hesser) W.; m. Wendy Gaines, Sept. 10, 1977; children: Jennifer, Christine. AB in Polit. Sci., Stanford U., 1968, JD, 1972. Bar: Calif. 1972, U.S. Dist. Ct. 1973, U.S. Ct. Appeals (9th cir.) 1975, U.S. Supreme Ct. 1980. Assoc. Haight, Brown & Bonesteel, L.A., Santa Monica and Santa Ana, Calif., 1972-78, ptnr., 1979—; judge Moot Ct. UCLA, Loyola U., Pepperdine U.; arbitrator Am. Arbitration Assn.; mem. com. Book Approved Jury Instructions L.A. Superior Ct. Mem. ABA, Calif. Acad. Appellate Lawyers, Town Hall Calif., L.A. County Bar Assn. Republican. Methodist. Home: 17260 Rayen St Northridge CA 91325-2919 Office: Haight Brown & Bonesteel 1620 26th St Santa Monica CA 90404-4013

WEAVER, ALBERT BRUCE, university administrator; b. Mont., May 27, 1917; s. John B. and Myrtle (Dragstedt) W.; m. Adeline Okerberg, Sept. 1945; children: Janet, Gail, John. Student, Mont. Sch. Mines, 1935-37; AB, U. Mont., 1940; MS, U. Ida., 1941; postgrad., U. Minn., 1941-42; PhD, U. Chgo., 1951. Physicist Naval Ordnance Lab., 1942-45; research asso. U. Chgo., 1952, U. Wash., 1952-54; mem. faculty U. Colo., 1954-58, asso. prof., 1957-58, chmn. dept. physics, 1956-58; prof., head dept. physics U. Ariz., 1958-70, asso. dean, 1961-70, provost acad. affairs, 1970-72, exec. v.p., 1972-83, exec. v.p. emeritus, 1983—. Fellow Am. Phys. Soc., AAAS; mem. Am. Assn. Physics Tchrs., Ariz. Acad. Sci., Sigma Xi. Home: 5726 E Holmes St Tucson AZ 85711-2426

WEAVER, BARBARA FRANCES, librarian; b. Boston, Aug. 29, 1927; d. Leo Francis and Nina Margaret (Durham) Weisse; m. George B. Weaver, June 6, 1951; 1 dau., Valerie S. Clark. B.A., Radcliffe Coll., 1949; M.L.S., U. R.I., 1968; Ed.M., Boston U., 1978. Head libr. Thompson (Conn.) Pub. Libr., 1961-69; dir. Conn. State Libr. Svc. Ctr., Willimantic, 1969-72; regional adminstr. Cen. Mass. Regional Libr. System, Worcester, 1972-78; asst. commr. of edn., state libr. State of N.J., Trenton, 1978-91; dir. R.I. Dept. State Libr. Svcs., Providence, 1991—; lectr. Simmons Coll., Boston, 1976-78. Mem. ALA, R.I. Libr. Assn., Chief Officers State Libr. Agys. Office: State Libr Svcs Dept 300 Richmond St Providence RI 02903-4222

WEAVER, CARLTON DAVIS, retired oil company executive; b. Grantsville, W.Va., May 27, 1921; s. Arley Ezra and Grace (Davis) W.; m. Nancy Mason McIntosh, Mar. 21, 1951; 1 child, Nancy Mason. B.S. Engr. Mines, W.va. U., 1948. Office engr. E.I. du Pont de Nemours & Co., 1941-42, tech. service rep., 1948-51; with Ashland (Ky.) Oil, Inc., 1951-81, exec. asst., 1960-67, v.p., 1967-72, sr. v.p., 1972-81, group operating officer, 1976-81, pres. Ashland Resources Co. div., 1970-74; chmn. bd. Ashland Coal, Inc., 1981-84, Ven-Black, Inc., 1983-86; chmn. vis. com. Coll. Mineral and Energy Resources, W.Va. U., 1967-80. Served to maj. USMCR, 1942-46, 52-53. Mem. Nat. Coal Assn. (dir.). Home: PO Box 2036 White Sulphur Springs WV 24986-6036 Office: 1409 Winchester Ave Ashland KY 41101-7555

WEAVER, CHARLES HENRY, business consulting executive; b. Phila., Aug. 10, 1914; s. Charles Henry and Isabel (Walker) W.; m. Louise Schildecker, Sept. 7, 1940 (dec. Nov. 1977); children—Patricia Ann Weaver Telkins, William Schildecker, Peter Charles; m. Lois S. Amper, May 20, 1979. B.S., U. Pa., 1936. With Westinghouse Electric Corp., 1936-79; beginning as trainee, successively sales dept. transp. and generator div., sales engr. marine sect., mgr. marine sect., mgr. marine dept. Westinghouse Electric Corp., Pitts., mgr. marine and aviation sales dept., mgr. ctrl. dist. sales office; mgr. atomic power div. Westinghouse Electric Corp., 1948-55, v.p. charge atomic power activities, 1955-62, group v.p. atomic, def. and space group, 1962-67, v.p. govt. affairs, 1967-71, pres. world regions, 1971-75, exec. v.p. corp. world relations, 1975-79; pres. Pitts. Cons. Group, Inc., 1979—; dir., vice chmn. IEM (S.A.), Mexico, 1973-78. Trustee Moore Sch. Elec. Engring. of U. Pa., also bd. overseers Sch. Engring. and Applied Sci.; chmn. Allegheny County Air Pollution Adv. Com., 1959-67; mem. Coun. on Fgn. Rels., Nat. Fgn. Trade Coun. (past dir.), World Affairs Coun. Pitts. (past pres.), trustee Pitts. Coun. Internat. Visitors; past trustee Bus. Coun. Internat. Understanding; adv. coun. Japan-U.S. Econ. Rels.; past vice chmn. U.S.-Korea; past chmn. U.S.-Yugoslav Econ. Coun., Polish-U.S. Econ. Coun. Recipient order of merit Westinghouse Elec. Corp., 1948; ann. Nat. Transp. award for outstanding contbns. transp. industry, 1955. Mem. IEEE, ASME, Atomic Indsl. Forum (past pres.), Soc. Naval Archs. and Marine Engrs., Am. Nuclear Soc., Nat. Security Indsl. Assn. (past chmn.), Coun. Def. and Space Industry Assn. (past chmn.), Internat. C. of C. (past dir. U.S. coun.), Duquesne Club, Concordia Club, River Forest Country Club. Home: 540 N Neville St Pittsburgh PA 15213-2815

WEAVER, CHARLES HORACE, educational administrator; b. Statesville, N.C., Nov. 11, 1927; s. Lucius Stacy and Elizabeth Roderick (Hallyburton) W.; m. Nancy Jane Veale, June 24, 1955; 1 child, Charles Horace. BA, Wofford Coll., Spartanburg, S.C., 1951; MA, Columbia U., 1956; PhD, U. N.C., 1961. Tchr. English Oak Ridge Mil. Inst., N.C., 1951-54, High Point (N.C.) Cen. High Sch., 1954-56; asst. prin. Ferndale Jr. High Sch., High Point, 1956-58; prin. N.E. Jr. High Sch., High Point, 1959-60, Ferndale Jr. High Sch., High Point, 1960-62; asst. supt. Asheboro (N.C.) City Schs., 1962-65; supt. Elizabeth City (N.C.) pub. schs., 1965-69, Burke County Pub. Schs., Morganton, N.C., 1969-79; with State Dept. Pub. Instrn., Raleigh, N.C., 1979—; asst. state supt. aux. svcs. State Dept. Pub. Instrn., 1989—; bd. dirs. We. Carolina Bank & Trust Co., Wilmington Food Sys., Inc., Greenville Food Sys., Inc. Contbr. articles to profl. ours. Bd. dirs. Burke County United Fund, Burke County Council on Alcoholism, We. Piedmont Mental Health Assn., We Piedmont Symphony. Mem. Am. Assn. Sch. Adminstrs., N.C. Assn. Sch. Adminstrs., Horace Mann League (pres. 1975-76), High Point Jr. C. of C. (bd. dirs.), Burke Country C. of C., Rotary, Asheboro Country Club, Raleigh Capital City Club. Democrat. Methodist. Avocations: reading, golf, antiques.

WEAVER, DAVID HUGH, journalism educator, communications researcher; b. Hammond, Ind., Dec. 23, 1946; s. David W. and Josephine L. (Taylor) W.; m. Gail Shriver, June 28, 1969; children: Quinn David, Lesley Jo. BA, Ind. U., Bloomington, 1968, MA, 1969; PhD, U. N.C., 1974. Copy editor The Post-Tribune, Gary, Ind., 1968; wire editor, reporter The Courier-Tribune, Bloomington, Ind., 1968; wire editor The Chapel Hill Newspaper, N.C., 1973; asst. prof. journalism Ind. U., Bloomington, 1974-78, assoc. prof., 1978-83, prof., 1983-88; Roy W. Howard prof. Ind. U., Bloomington, Ind., 1988—. Author: Videotex Journalism, 1983; co-author: Newsroom Guide to Polls and Surveys, 1980, 90, Media Agenda-Setting, 1981, The American Journalist, 1986 (award Soc. Profl. Journalists 1987), 2nd edit., 1991, The Formation of Campaign Agendas, 1991, Contemporary Public Opinion, 1991. Lt. U.S. Army, 1969-71. Fellow Midwest Assn. Pub. Opinion Rsch. (pres. 1986-87); mem. Assn. for Edn. in Journalism and Mass Comm. (pres. 1987-88, Krieghbaum award 1983), Soc. Profl. Journalists, Internat. Comm. Assn. Avocations: guitar, music. Office: Ind U Sch of Journalism Ernie Pyle Hall Bloomington IN 47405-6201

WEAVER, DELBERT ALLEN, lawyer; b. Shoshone, Idaho, May 28, 1931; s. Arlo Irving and Kate Rosamond (McCarter) W.; m. Jeanne Carol Alford, June 1959; children: Tobin Elizabeth, Michael Andrew, Matthew Stewart, Edward Malcolm. BA, U. Oreg., 1953, LLB, 1956. Bar: Oreg. 1956, U.S. Dist. Ct. Oreg. 1956, U.S. Ct. Appeals (9th cir.) 1968. Ptnr. Weaver & Oram, Eugene, Oreg., 1956-59; dep. atty. City of Portland, Oreg., 1959-68; assoc. Winfree, Latourette, Murphy, et al., Portland, 1968-71; stockbroker Dupont Glore Forgan, Portland, 1971-73; securities examiner corp. div. State of Oreg., Salem, 1973-75, dep. commr. corp. div., 1975-80; pvt. practice Portland, 1980-87; counsel Schwabe, Williamson & Wyatt, Portland, 1987-90, sr. ptnr., 1991—. Office: Schwabe Williamson & Wyatt 1211 SW 5th Ave Ste 1800 Portland OR 97204-3795

WEAVER, DENNIS, actor; b. Joplin, Mo., June 4, 1924; s. Walter and Lenna Weaver; m. Gerry Stowell, Oct. 20, 1945; children: Rick, Robby, Rusty. BFA, U. Okla., 1948. Appeared on N.Y. stage, 1948-52; appeared in Streetcar Named Desire, Hollywood, Calif., 1953; under contract to Universal Internat., Hollywood, 1952-53, freelance actor, Hollywood, 1953-55; appeared on: TV series Gunsmoke, 1955-64, Kentucky Jones, 1964-65, Gentle Ben, 1967-69, McCloud, 1970-77, Stone, 1980, Buck James, 1985-87, Lonesome Dove, 1994; also Movies of the Week: Duel, 1971, Forgotten Man, 1971, Rolling Man, 1973, Terror on the Beach, 1973, Female Artillery, 1973, Patty Hearst, 1979; spls. Intimate Strangers, 1977, Police Story-A Cry for Justice, 1977, Pearl, 1978, Ishi, 1978, Islander, 1978, Centennial-The Longhorns, 1978, Amber Waves, 1979, The Ordeal of Dr. Mud, 1979, The Day the Loving Stopped, 1981, Don't Go to Sleep, 1982, Cocaine: One Man's Seduction, 1983, Winners Never Quit, 1986, Bluffing It, 1987, Disaster at Silo 7, 1988, The Return of Sam McCloud, 1989, Mastergate, 1991, (pilot) Greyhounds, 1993, "Buffalo Bill" in Lonesome Dovs, the series, 1994-95. Mem. SAG (pres. 1973-75), AFTRA, Dirs. Guild. Office: care Alice Billings PO Box 257 Ridgway CO 81432

WEAVER, DIANA JANE, nursing administrator; b. St. Paul, Aug. 30, 1939; m. John H. Weaver, Sept. 3, 1960; children: J. Bradley, Stacey L. Weaver Goodrich. Diploma, Ball Meml. Hosp., 1960, DNS, 1981; BSN, Ind. U., 1968; MSN, N.W. State U., 1974. Staff nurse Meth. Hosp., Indpls., 1960-62, charge nurse labor and delivery, 1962-67; ob-gyn nursing supr. Doctor's Hosp., Shreveport, La., 1969-71, DON svc., 1971-75; assoc. prof. nursing Ea. Ky. U., Richmond, 1975-84; emergency rm. supr. Pattie Clay Hosp., Richmond, Va., 1978; instr. grad. nursing U. Evansville, Ind., 1980; staff nurse labor and delivery U. Ky. Med. Ctr., Lexington, 1982-83, from assoc. hosp. dir. to dir. nursing svc., 1984-91; asst. dean clin. affairs U. Ky. Coll. Nursing, Lexington, 1984-91; v.p. nursing Yale-New Haven Hosp., 1991—; mem. exec. com. Univ. Teaching Hosp., 1987-88; presenter, speaker and researcher in field. Contbr. articles to profl. jours. Bd. dirs. YWCA, Lexington, 1988-91, chair women of achievement awards, 1990; vol. Spl. Olympics, 1990. U. Pa. Johnson and Johnson Wharton fellow, 1984. Mem. ANA, Am. Ednl. Rsch. Assn., Am. Orgn. Nurse Execs. (bd. dirs. 1990-92, pres.-elect 1993), Ky. Nurses Assn. (bd. dirs. dist. II 1988-89), Ky. Orgn. Nurse Execs., Ky. Soc. Hosp. Nursing Svc. (pres. 1985-86), U. N.C. Nurse Execs. (chair 1990-92), Ball State U. Alumni Assn. (Outstanding Alumnus 1989), Sigma Theta Tau (Delta Psi chpt.). Office: Yale-New Haven Hosp 20 York St New Haven CT 06510-3220

WEAVER, DON L., lawyer; b. Inglewood, Calif., Dec. 1, 1951. BA with highest honors, U. Calif., Santa Barbara, 1973; JD, U. So. Calif., 1977. Bar: Calif. 1977. Ptnr. Mayer, Brown & Platt, L.A. Mem. ABA (mem. sect. corp., banking and bus. law, mem. sect. antitrust law), Beverley Hills Bar Assn. (mem. exec. com., chmn. corps. and comml. law sect. 1982), State Bar Calif. (mem. exec. com. bus. law sect. 1987-91, chmn. franchise legislation com. 1986-87), Am. Law Inst. Office: Mayer Brown & Platt 350 S Grand Ave Los Angeles CA 90071-3406

WEAVER, DONNA RAE, company executive; b. Chgo., Oct. 15, 1945; d. Albert Louis and Gloria Elaine (Graffis) Florence; m. Clifford L. Weaver, Aug. 20, 1966; 1 child, Megan Rae. BS in Ed. No. Ill. U., 1966, EdD, 1977; MEd, De Paul U., 1974. Tchr. H.L. Richards High Sch. Oak Lawn, Ill., 1966-71, Sawyer Coll. Bus., Evanston, Ill., 1971-72; asst. prof. Oakton Community Coll., Morton Grove, Ill., 1972-75; vis. prof. U. Ill., Chgo., 1977-78; dir. devel. Mallinckrodt Coll., Wilmette, Ill., 1978-80, dean, 1980-83; campus dir. Nat.-Louis U., Chgo., 1983-90, dean div. applied behavioral scis., 1985-89; dean Coll. Mgmt. and Bus., 1989-90; pres. The Oliver Group, Inc., Kenilworth, Ill., 1993—; cons. Nancy Lovely and Assocs., Wilmette, 1981-84, North Ctrl. Assn., Chgo., 1982-90. Contbr. articles to Am. Vocat. Jour., Ill. Bus. Edn. Assn. Monograph, Nat. Coll. Edn.'s ABS Rev., Nat. View. Mem. Ill. Quality of Work Life Coun., 1987-90, New Trier Twp. Health and Human Svcs. Adv. Bd., Winnetka, Ill., 1985-88; bd. dirs. Open Lands Project, 1985-87, Kenilworth (Ill.) Village House, 1986-87. Recipient Achievement award Women in Mgmt., 1981; Am. Bd. Master Educators charter disting. fellow, 1986. Mem. Nat. Bus. Edn. Assn., Delta Pi Epsilon (past pres.). Avocations: reading, traveling, decorating. Office: 505 N Lake Shore Dr Ste 4010 Chicago IL 60611-3408

WEAVER, EDWARD T., foundation executive, educator; b. Beggs, Okla., Dec. 13, 1931; s. Thurmon Wesley and Thelma Cleo (Wright) W.; m. Judith A. DeVliegher; children: Mark E., Kirk B. Student, S.W. Mo. State U., 1958-59; BA, Cen. Bible Coll., Springfield, Mo., 1959; M Social Work, Washington U., 1961; MPA, U. So. Calif., 1981, D Pub. Adminstrn., 1985. Adminstr. Lake Bluff (Ill.) Children's Home, 1961-64; regional dir. Ill. Dept. Children and Family Services, Champaign, 1964-66, Chgo., 1966-68; dir. Ill. Dept. Children and Family Services, Springfield, 1968-72, Ill Dept Pub. Aid, Springfield, 1971-73; sr. assoc. Booz, Allen & Hamilton, Washington, 1973-74; exec. dir. Am. Pub. Welfare Assn., Washington, 1974-85; v.p. Paramount Communications, Inc. (formerly Gulf & Western Inc.), N.Y.C., 1985-89; pres. Paramount Communications Found., N.Y.C., 1985-91; prof. Henry W. Bloch Sch. Bus. and Pub. Adminstrn. U. Mo.-Kansas City, 1989—; v.p., chief adminstrv. officer Ewing Marion Kauffman Found., 1992—; lectr. U. Ill., Champaign, 1966; vis. prof. Washington U., St. Louis, 1978-85, 90-92; bd. dirs. Independent Sector, Washington, 1987-92; trustee Lois and SamuelSilberman Fund, N.Y.C., 1988-91; Am. Humane Assn., 1990-94, Camp Fire Inc., 1992—, Mid-Am. Care Found., 1991—, Midwest Care Ctrs., Inc., 1995—. Mem. Internat. Council on Social Welfare (asst. treas. gen., treas. gen., v.p.). Presbyterian.

WEAVER, FRANKLIN THOMAS, newspaper executive; b. Johnstown, N.Y., Oct. 11, 1932; s. Edwin K. and Bertha J. (Wendt) W.; children: Thomas, James, Michael, David, Tammy, Kelly, Anna; m. Joyce W. Phelps, Oct. 23, 1991. B.A. with high honors in Journalism, Mich. State U., 1954. Advt. sales rep. Grand Rapids Press, Mich., 1955-64; controller Muskegon (Mich.) Chronicle, 1964-66; mgr. Bay City (Mich.) Times, 1966-73; mgr. Jackson (Mich.) Citizen Patriot, 1973-84, pub., 1984—. Trustee, pres. Ella Sharp Mus. Mem. Newspapers Assn. Am., Mich. Press Assn. (pres. 1991), Greater Jackson C. of C., Jackson Country Club. Office: Jackson Citizen Patriot 214 S Jackson St Jackson MI 49201-2213

WEAVER, FRITZ WILLIAM, actor; b. Pitts., Jan. 19, 1926; s. John Carson and Elsa (Stringaro) W.; m. Sylvia Short, Feb. 7, 1953; children: Lydia Charlotte, Anthony Ballou. Mem. Barter Theatre Va., 1951, 52, Group 20 Players, Wellesley, Mass., 1953, 54, Stratford Shakespeare Festival, 1956, 58, Vancouver Festival, 1961, Phoenix Theatre, N.Y.C., 1959-60, Edinl. TV Channel 13, N.Y.C., 1960, 65; Off-Broadway appearances include Doctor's Dilemma, 1953, The Way of the World, 1954, L'Histoire du Soldat, 1954, Family Reunion, 1958, Power and Glory, 1958, Peer Gynt, 1959, Henry IV, parts I and II; Broadway appearances include White Devil, 1955 (Carence Derwent award), Chalk Garden, 1956, Miss Lonelyhearts, 1957, A Shot in the Dark, 1962, Protective Custody, 1958, All American, 1962, Lorenzo, 1962-63, The White House, 1964, Baker Street, 1965, Child's Play, 1969-70, The Price, 1979, The Crucible; appearances with Am. Shakespeare Festival, 1955, 56, 57, 58, 73, Cambridge Drama Festival, 1960, N.Y. Philharm., 1962; starred in world premiere Sorrows of Frederick, Los Angeles, 1967, Absurd Person Singular, 1975, Lincoln, 1976, Cocktail Hour, 1990, Love Letters, 1989, 90, King Lear, 1991, The Professional, 1995; motion pictures include The Crimson Curtain, 1955, Fail-Safe, 1963, The Guns of August, 1965, The Maltese Bippy, 1969, A Walk in the Spring Rain, 1969, Company of Killers, 1970, The Day of the Dolphin, 1973, Marathon Man, 1976, Demon Seed, 1976, Black Sunday, 1976-77, The Big Fix, 1979, Creepshow, 1983, Power, 1986; numerous TV appearances, including The Borgia Stick, 1967, Berlin Affairs, 1970, Heat of Anger, 1972, The Snoop Sisters, 1972, Hunter, 1973, The Legend of Lizzy Borden, 1975, Captains Corageous, 1977, The Hearst and Davies Affair, 1985, A Death in California, 1985, My Name is Bill W, 1989, Ironclads, 1991, Citizen Cohn, 1992, Blind Spot, 1993. Recipient Antoinette Perry award; Drama Desk award Outer Critics Circle, also Variety. Office: The Gersh Agy 232 N Canon Dr Beverly Hills CA 90210*

WEAVER, HILDA, counselor, psychotherapist; b. Washington, Sept. 28, 1933; d. Frank Lowrie and Elisabeth (Wilson) Weaver; m. William Rudel Glover, July 12, 1958 (div. 1976); children: Gail Glover Madha, Gina Glover Russ. BA in English, Miami U., Oxford, Ohio, 1956; MS in Clin. Psychology, Va. Commonwealth U., 1973. Lic. chem. dependency counselor, marriage and family therapist, psychol. assoc. Tchr. English and music Quantico (Va.) Post High Sch., 1956-59; staff psychologist Tex. Rehab. Commn., Houston, 1971-77; dir. counseling Episcopal Ch. of the Epiphany, Houston, 1978-88; counselor Snowflake Counseling, Houston, 1988-92; program therapist IntraCare Hosp., Houston, 1991—, coord. adult psychiat. program svcs., 1991—; coord. adult counseling svcs., 1993—. Singer Bay Area Chorus, Houston, 1989—. Mem. APA, Tex. Psychol. Assn., Nat. Assn. Alcohol and Drug Abuse Counselors, Tex. Assn. Alcohol and Drug Abuse Counselors, Houston Assn. Alcohol and Drug Abuse Counselors. Democrat. Avocations: writing, sailing. Office: Intra Care Hosp 7601 Fannin Houston TX 77054

WEAVER, HOWARD CECIL, newspaper editor; b. Anchorage, Oct. 15, 1950; s. Howard Gilbert and Lurlene Eloise (Gamble) W.; m. Alice Laprele Gauchay, July 16, 1970 (div. 1974); m. Barbara Lynn Hodgin, Sept. 16, 1978. BA, Johns Hopkins U., 1972; MPhil, Cambridge U., 1993. Reporter, staff writer Anchorage Daily News, 1972-76, columnist, 1979-80, mng. editor, 1980-83, editor, 1983—; editor, owner Alaska Advocate, Anchorage, 1976-79; internat. co-chair Northern News Svc., 1989-94; disting. lectr. journalism U. Alaska, Fairbanks, 1991. Pulitzer Prize juror, 1988, 89, 94, 95. Recipient Pulitzer prize, 1976, 89, Pub. Svc. award AP Mng. Editor's Assn., 1976, 89, Headliner award Press Club of Atlantic City, 1976, 89, Gold medal Investigative Reporters and Editors, 1989. Mem. Am. Soc. Newspaper Editors, Investigative Reporters and Editors, Sigma Delta Chi (Nat. award 1989), Alaska Press Club (bd. dirs. 1972-84), Upper Yukon River Press Club (pres. 1972). Avocations: ice hockey, foreign travel, opera.

WEAVER, JERRY, entrepreneur, holding company executive; b. 1931. Chmn. bd. Mid South Industries, Inc., Gadsden, Ala., 1964—. Office: Mid South Industries Inc 418 Stone St Gadsden AL 35906*

WEAVER, JO NELL, elementary school educator; b. Dallas, Apr. 22, 1941; d. Robert Glen and Lottie (Harris) Bryant; m. L. Ben Weaver, Sr., June 20, 1963 (div. Mar. 1968); children: Carolyn Cantrell, L. Ben Weaver, Jr. BA, So. Meth. U., Dallas, 1968; MEd, U. North Tex., 1974. Cert. elem. tchr., elem. supr. Tchr. Richardson (Tex.) Ind. Sch. Dist., 1968—. Curriculum writer Delta Edn., Inc., 1984-85; critic reader Silver Burdett & Ginn, 1989. Mem. Sch. Dist. edn. coun., Richardson, Ind., 1994-95. Recipient Tex. Congress of Parents and Tchrs. scholarship/grant Tex. PTA, 1974, Ross Perot award for Excellence in Tchg., 1978; named one of Outstanding Elem. Tchrs. of Am., 1975. Mem. Richardson Edn. Assn., North Tex. Reading Assn., Assn. Tex. Profl. Educators, ASCD, TEx. State Tchrs.' Assn., Alpha Delta Kappa. Republican. Baptist. Avocations: travel, photography, reading. Home: 4505 Hanover Garland TX 75042 Office: Richardson Ind Sch Dist 2100 Copper Ridge Richardson TX 75080

WEAVER, JOHN B., electronics executive, metal products executive; b. 1932. With Mid South Industries Inc., Gadsden, Ala., 1964—, v.p.; v.p. Emco Inc., Gadsden, Mid-South Electronics, Gadsden, Dixie Tool & Die Co., Gadsden. Office: Mid South Industries Inc 418 Sutton Bridge Rd Gadsden AL 35906*

WEAVER, KENNETH, gynecologist, researcher; b. Whitetop, Va., Dec. 4, 1933; s. Grover Cleveland and Violet Elaine (Baldwin) W.; children: Teresa Marie, Janice Eileen, Beverly Lynn, Pamela Jean, Cynthia Ann; m. Shelby Jean Davis, June 15, 1966. BA, U. N.C., 1957, MD, 1960. Diplomate Am. Bd. Ob-Gyn. Intern U.S. Pub. Health Svc., Boston, 1960-61; med. officer

Cherokee (N.C.) Indian Hosp., 1961-64; gen. physician Haywood County Hosp., Waynesville, N.C., 1964-70; obstetrician, gynecologist Haywood County Hosp., Waynesville, 1974-77; resident U. Ark. Med. Ctr., Little Rock, 1970-74; asst. prof. U. Ark., Little Rock, 1977-78, acting chmn., dept. ob-gyn., 1978; pvt. practice Johnson City, Tenn., 1978—; mem. Gov. Com. on Cancer, Raleigh, N.C., 1970-71; dir. Maternity and Infant Care, Little Rock, 1977-78; assoc. prof. James H. Quillen Coll. Medicine, Johnson City, 1978-83. Contbr. articles to sci. jours. Fellow Am. Coll. Ob-Gyn., Am. Coll. Nutrition, Am. Asson. Gynecol. Laparoscopists, N.Y. Acad. Scis. Achievements include six patent devices having to do with laser surgery and other gynecol. and urol. uses; rsch. in magnesium and preeclampsia, in magnesium and migraine, in relationship between magnesium and blood platelet function. Home: 377 Tavern Hill Rd Jonesborough TN 37659-5026 Office: 1103 Jackson Blvd Jonesborough TN 37659

WEAVER, LINDA, textiles executive. Chmn. bd. dirs., sec., treas. Diamond Rug & Carpet Mills, Eton, Ga., 1969—. Office: Diamond Rug & Carpet Mills Hwy 411 Eton GA 30724*

WEAVER, LOIS JEAN, physician, educator; b. Wheeling, W.Va., May 23, 1944; d. Lewis Everett and Ann (Novak) W. BA, Oberlin Coll., 1966; MD, U. Chgo., 1970. Pulmonary fellow Northwestern U., Evanston, Ill., 1975-77; trauma fellow U. Wash. Harborview Hosp., Seattle, 1977-79, research assoc., instr. medicine, 1979-81, clin. asst. prof. medicine, 1983—; clin. research fellow Virginia Mason Med. Research Ctr., Seattle, 1981-82; mem. med. staff Swedish Hosp., Seattle, 1984-92; pulmonary cons. Fred Hutchinson Cancer Research Inst., Seattle, 1984-86, regional med. advisor and med. cons., disability quality br. Social Security, Seattle, 1985—. Contbr. sci. articles to profl. jours. La Verne Noyes scholar U. Chgo., 1966; Parker B. Francis fellow Northwestern U., 1975. Mem. AMA, Am. Thoracic Soc., Wash. Lung Assn., Sigma Xi. Avocations: gardening, music. Home: PO Box 2098 Kirkland WA 98083-2098 Office: 2201 6th Ave # 53 Seattle WA 98121-1832

WEAVER, LYNN EDWARD, academic administrator, consultant, editor; b. St. Louis, Jan. 12, 1930; s. Lienous E. and Estelle F. (Laspe) W.; m. JoAnn D., 1951 (div. 1980); children: Terry Sollenberger, Gwen, Bart, Stephen, Wes; m. Anita G. Gomez, Oct. 27, 1983. BSEE, U. Mo., 1951; MSEE, So. Meth. U., 1957; PhD, Purdue U., 1958. Devel. engr. McDonnell Aircraft, St. Louis, 1952-53; aerophysics engr. Convair Corp., Ft. Worth, 1953-55; instr. elec. engring. Purdue U., Lafayette, Ind., 1955-58; assoc. prof., then prof., dept. head U. Ariz., Tucson, 1959-69; assoc. dean coll. engring. U. Okla., Norman, 1969-70; exec. asst. to pres. Argonne Univs., Chgo., 1970-72; dir. sch. nuclear engring. and health physics Ga. Inst. Tech., 1972-82; dean engring., disting. prof. Auburn (Ala.) U., 1982-87; pres. Fla. Inst. Tech., Melbourne, 1987—; cons. Ga. Power; bd. dirs. Oak Ridge Associated Univs., 1984-87, DBA Systems, Inc., Melbourne, Fla.; chmn. pub. affairs coun. Am. Assn. Engring. Soc., Washington, 1984-87; bd. advisors Ctr. for Sci., Tech. & Media, Washington. Author: (textbook) Reactor Dynamics & Control, State Space Techniques, 1968; exec. editor Annals of Nuclear Energy; contbr. numerous articles to tech. jours. U.S. rep. World Fedn., Engring. Orgn. Energy Com., 1981-86. Served to lt. USAF, 1951-53. Fellow Am. Nuclear Soc.; mem. IEEE (sr.), Am. Soc. Engring. Edn., Sigma Xi. Republican. Roman Catholic. Club: Eau Gallie Yacht. Avocations: tennis, jogging. Office: Fla Inst Tech 150 W University Blvd Melbourne FL 32901-6967

WEAVER, MARTIN EDWARD, historic conservation educator, administrator; b. London, Eng., May 12, 1938; s. Edward William and Florence (Frost) Weaver; m. Kalliopi Kalathakis, Apr. 12, 1961 (div.); children: Alexandra, Helen, Sophia Marika; m. Leslie A. Perowne, Nov. 27, 1984; 1 child, Laura Krystyna. AA, Archtl. Assn. Sch. Architecture, London, 1961. With hist. bldgs. divsn. Greater London Coun.; rsch. assoc. dept. anthropology London U.; dir. tng. programs on conservation heritage structures and sites Dept. Indian and No. Affairs, Can.; dir. edn. and tech. svcs. Heritage Can. Found., 1979-86, dir. archtl. conservation svcs. program, 1986-88; pvt. practice cons., 1988—; dir. Ctr. for Preservation Rsch., prof. in charge hist. preservation program Columbia U., N.Y.C., 1991—; site surveyor, supr., architect, instr. various sites including Snail Down, Wiltshire, U.K., 1957, 58, Gwithian, Cornwall, U.K., 1957, 58, 59, 60, Knossos, Crete, Greece, 1959, 60, Pasargadae, Iran, 1961, 63, Swanscombe Pit, Galley Hill Pit, Kent, U.K., 1966, 67, Hornos de la Peña, North Spain, 1971, 72, 73, Dealy Island, High Arctic, N.W.T., Can., Louisbourg, Nova Scotia, Can., 1986; assoc. prof. Columbia U., N.Y.C., 1988, 89; vis. prof. U. Montreal, 1990; vis. Ford Found. lectr. Middle East Tech. U., Turkey; ALCAN lectr. Queen's U., Kingston, 1990; prin. lectr., co-dir. Masonry Conservation, Adelaide, South Australia, 1988; lectr. UNESCO/ICCROM/Norwegian Govt., 1988, 90, 92, U. Montreal, 1989, Alta. Govt./U. Calgary, 1989, Alta. Culture/U. Calgary, 1989; cons. Environment Can., 1986-87, Beaupré and Michaud, Montreal, Can., 1987, U.S. Dept. Interior/U.S. EPA, 1987, State of Wash., Olympia, 1988, Presbyn. Ch. St. Paul's, Hamilton, Ont., Can., 1987-89, Fiset and Miller, 1988, Nat. Rsch. Coun. Can., 1988, Getty Conservation Inst., 1988, City of Montreal, 1988, 89, 90, 91, City of Victoria, B.C., Can., 1988, Nat. Capital Commn., Ottawa, 1988, 90, Govt. USSR, 1988, Dorval et Fortin, 1988-89, Ont. Hist. Soc., 1989, ARCOP, Montreal, 1989, 1990, City of Hamilton, 1989, City of Winnipeg, 1989, Houston Mus. Fine Arts, 1989, St. Mary's Cathedral, Kingston, Ont., 1989-91, Victoria Jubilee Hosp., 1989, St. George's Sch., Vancouver, B.C., 1989, Hamilton Region Conservation Authority, 1989-91, U. Toronto, 1989-92, Can. Parks Svc., 1989, Cornell U., Ithaca, N.Y., 1989-92, LMC Corp., N.J., 1989, Bank of Montreal, 1989, 90-92, 93, JCM Archtl. Assocs., Syracuse, N.Y., 1990-92, Henry Ford Mus., Dearborn, Mich., 1990-92, Anglican Cathedral St. James, Toronto, 1990, Dominik, Thompson, Mallette, Kingston, 1990-92, New Zealand Nat. Trust for Hist. Places, 1990, Afemco Engrs., Pointe Claire, Quebec, 1990-92, Can. Pacific Ltd., 1990, Saltfleet War Memls., Ont., 1990, Ch. Ascension, Hamilton, 1990-92, Columbia U. 1990, Gersovitz Becker Moss, 1991, 92, Anrep and Assocs., Toronto, 1991, Soeurs de la Charité, 1991-92, Robert Halsall and Assocs., Toronto, 1991-92, 92, Hamilton Mus. Steam and Tech., 1992, St. Bartholomew's Ch., Ottawa, 1992, Beaver Hall, 1992-93, U. Victoria, 1992, Wells Centennial Hall, Sunset Theatre, Island Mountain Mine Office, 1992, Provincial Govt. B.C., 1992, Peterborough, Ont., 1992, Bridge St. United Ch., Belleville, Ont., 1992-93, Côté, Glouberman, 1992-93, Alan Seymour Architects, Toronto, 1992-93, Norr Partnership, Toronto, 1992-93, City of Ottawa, 1993, Raymond Plumer Architects, N.Y., 1993, U.S. Dept. Interior, 1993, Peter Stokes, Niagara-on-the-Lake, Ont., 1993, Humberto Saldaña and Assocs., 1993, Eric Jokinen, Toronto, 1993, Conservation Partnership, U.K., 1993; lectr. U.S. Nat. Park Svc., 1973, Columbia U., 1978. Author: Conserving Buildings: A Guide to Techniques and Materials, 1992; contbr. over 140 articles, reports and book reviews to profl. jours. and mags. Recipient Thomas B. McQuestin Archtl. Conservation award, 1994. Fellow Centro Camuno di Studi Preistorici (Italy); mem. Am. Inst. for Conservation (assoc.), Lighter-than-Air Soc., Internat. Coun. on Monuments and Sites (Am. and Can. sects., internat. wood com. past pres.), Assn. for Preservation Tech. (life, past pres.), Internat. Inst. for Conservation-Can. Group (past pres.), Internat. Inst. for Conservation (London), Brit. Inst. Persian Studies (London, Tehran), Cornwall Archeol. Soc. (U.K.), Ottawa Group Conservators (past chmn.), Can. Rock Art Rsch. Assn. (elected associate). Avocations: wood and stone sculpture, drawing, painting, aviation history, collecting antiques and books. Office: Columbia U Ctr Preservation Rsch 400 Avery Hall New York NY 10027

WEAVER, MICHAEL JAMES, lawyer; b. Bakersfield, Calif., Feb. 11, 1946; s. Kenneth James and Elsa Hope (Rogers) W.; m. Valerie Scott, Sept. 2, 1966; children: Christopher James, Brett Michael, Karen Ashley. AB, Calif. State U., Long Beach, 1968; JD magna cum laude, U. San Diego, 1973. Bar: Calif., 1973, U.S. Dist. Ct. (so. dist.) Calif. 1973, U.S. Ct. Appeals (9th cir.) 1975, U.S. Supreme Ct. 1977. Law clk. to chief judge U.S. Dist. Ct. (so. dist.) Calif., San Diego, 1973-75; assoc. Luce, Forward, Hamilton & Scripps, San Diego, 1975-80, ptnr., 1980-86; ptnr. Sheppard, Mullin, Richter & Hampton, San Diego, 1986—; judge pro tem San Diego Superior Ct.; master of the Bench of the Inn, Am. Inns of Ct., Louis M. Welch chpt.; lectr. Inn of Ct., San Diego, 1981—, Continuing Edn. of Bar, Calif., 1983—, workshop for Judges U.S. Ct. Appeals (9th cir.), 1990. Editor-in-chief: San Diego Law Rev., 1973; contbr. articles to profl. jours. Bd. dirs., pres. San Diego Kidney Found., 1985—; bd. dirs. San Diego Aerospace Mus., 1985—; trustee La Jolla (Calif.) Playhouse, 1990—. Served to lt., USNR, 1968-74. Fellow Am. Coll. Trial Lawyers; mem. San Diego

Assn. Bus. Trial Lawyers (founding mem., bd. govs.), San Diego Def. Lawyers Assn. (dir.), Am. Arbitration Assn., 9th Cir. Jud. Conf. (del. 1987-90), Safari Club Internat. (San Diego chpt.), San Diego Sportsmen's Club. Republican. Presbyterian. Avocations: reading, family activities, flying, skiing. Office: Sheppard Mullin Richter & Hampton 501 W Broadway Fl 19 San Diego CA 92101-3536

WEAVER, PAMELA ANN, hospitality research professional; b. Little Falls, N.Y., July 7, 1947; d. Floyd Aron Weaver and Norma May (Putnam) Hoyer; m. Ken Ward McCleary, Mar. 2, 1947; children: Brian Wilson, Blake McClary, Ryan McCleary. AA, Fulton Montgomery Community Co, Amsterdam, NY, 1968; BA, SUNY, 1970; MA, U. S. Fla., 1973; PhD, Mich. State U., East Lansing, 1978. Mem. Mathematics Dept., Riviera Jr. High Sch., Miami, Fla., 1970-72; grad. asst. Office of Med., Edn. Research and adminstrn., Mich. State U. East Lansing, 1973-74, Dept. of Mktg., Mich. State U., East Lansing, 1974-75; instr. mktg. Mich. State U., East Lansing; asst. prof. mktg., hospitality svcs. adminstrn., Cen. Mich. State U., Mt. Pleasant, 1978-79, Cen. Mich. U., 1982-86; chair acad. senate Cen. Mich. U., Mt. Pleasant, 1985-86, prof. mktg., hospitality svcs. adminstrn., 1986-89; prof. Dept. Hospitality and Tourism Mgmt. Va. Poly. Inst. and State U., Blacksburg, 1989—. Contbr. articles to profl. jours. Mem. Coun. on Hotel, Restaurant and Instln. Edn., Acad. Mktg. Sci., Am. Mktg. Assn., So. Mktg. Assn. Office: Va Poly Inst and State U Wallace Hall Blacksburg VA 24061-0429

WEAVER, PAUL DAVID, lawyer; b. Chgo., Feb. 15, 1943; s. Paul Stanley and Margaret Elizabeth (Wurster) W.; m. Carol Lynne Homan, July 1, 1978; children: Paul Tyson, Samuel Lincoln. AB, Yale U., 1965; JD, U. Mich., 1971. Bar: Mass. 1971, Ohio 1972. Mgr. west coast Big 3 Industries, Houston, 1965-68; assoc. Goodwin, Procter & Hoar, Boston, 1971-78; sec., gen. counsel Houghton Mifflin Co., Boston, 1979-88, sr. v.p., gen. counsel, 1989—. Mem. Beverly (Mass.) Hosp. Corp., 1978—; town counsel Town of Wenham, Mass., 1976—, moderator, 1987—. Mem. ABA, Mass. Bar Assn., Boston Bar Assn., Assn. Am. Publs. (chmn. lawyers com. 1985-86), Am. Soc. Corp. Secs., Mass. City Solicitors/Town Counsels Assn., Mass. Moderators Assn., Myopia Hunt Club (Hamilton, Mass.), Yale Club (N.Y.C.), Phi Delta Phi. Avocations: antiques, skiing. Home: 88 Walnut Rd Wenham MA 01984-1611 Office: Houghton Mifflin Co 222 Berkeley St 5th Fl Boston MA 02116-3764

WEAVER, RICHARD L, II, speech communication educator; b. Hanover, N.H., Dec. 5, 1941; s. Richard L. and Florence B. (Grow) W.; m. Andrea A. Willis; children: R. Scott, Jacquelynn Michelle, Anthony Keith, Joanna Corinne. A.B., U. Mich., 1964, M.A., 1965; Ph.D., Ind. U., 1969. Asst. prof. U. Mass., 1968-74; assoc. prof. speech communication Bowling Green State U., 1974-79, prof., 1979—, dir., basic speech communication course, 1974—; vis. prof. U. Hawaii-Manoa, 1981-82, Bond U., Queensland, Australia, 1990, St. Albans, Melbourne, Australia, 1990, Western Inst., Perth, Australia, 1990. Author: (with Saundra Hybels) Speech/Communication, 1974, 2d edit., 1979, Speech/Communication: A Reader, 1975, 2d edit., 1979, Speech/Communication: A Student Manual, 1976, 2d edit., 1979, Understanding Interpersonal Communication, 1978, 2d edit., 1981, 3d edit., 1984, 4th edit., 1987, 5th edit., 1990, 6th edit., 1993, (with Raymond K. Tucker, Cynthia Berryman-Fink) Research in Speech Communication, 1981, Foundations of Speech Communication: Perspectives of a Discipline, 1982, Speech Communication Skills, 1982, Understanding Public Communication, 1983, Understanding Business Communication, 1985, Understanding Speech Communication Skills, 1985, Readings in Speech Communication, 1985, (with Saundra Hybels) Communicating Effectively, 1986, 2d edit., 1989, 3d edit., 1992, Skills for Communicating Effectively, 1985, 2d edit., 1988, 3d edit., 1991, 4th edit., 1993, (with Howard W. Cotrell) Innovative Instructional Strategies, 1987, 2d edit. 1988, 3d edit. 1989, 4th edit., 1990, 5th edit., 1992, 6th edit., 1993, (with Curt Bechler) Listen to Win: A Guide to Effective Listening, 1994; contbr. over 100 articles, chpts. to profl. jours, books, speeches. Mem. Internat. Comm. Assn., Internat. Soc. Gen. Semantics, Speech Comm. Assn., World Comm. Assn., Ctrl. States Speech Assn., Ohio Speech Assn., Internat. Listening Assn., Midwest Basic Course Dirs. Conf., Golden Key, Phi Kappa Phi (Bowling Green Faculty Excellence award 1989). Home: 9583 Woodleigh Ct Perrysburg OH 43551-2669 Office: Bowling Green State U Dept Interpersonal Com Bowling Green OH 43403

WEAVER, ROBIN GEOFFREY, lawyer, educator; b. Columbus, Ohio, Aug. 19, 1948; s. Eugene Rudolph and Lois Ann (Banks) W.; m. Valerie Cheryl Waller, June 28, 1980; children: Allyson, Lauren, Meridith. BA, Ohio State U., 1970; JD, U. Mich., 1973. Bar: Ohio 1974, U.S. Dist. Ct. (no. dist.) Ohio 1974, U.S. Ct. Appeals (6th cir.) 1990. Assoc. Squire, Sanders & Dempsey, Cleve., 1973-83, ptnr., 1983—; mem. faculty Nat. Inst. for Trial Adv. Northwestern U., Chgo., 1983—; mem. Ohio Supreme Ct. Bd. of Commrs. on Grievances and Discipline. With U.S. Army, 1974. Fellow Am. Coll. Trial Lawyers, Internat. Soc. Barristers; mem. ABA, Ohio Bar Assn., Cleve. Assn. Trial Attys. (life), 8th Appellate Jud. Conf., Am. Inns of Ct. (master bencher Cleve. chpt.). Episcopalian. Office: Squire Sanders & Dempsey 4900 Society Ct Cleveland OH 44114

WEAVER, SIGOURNEY (SUSAN ALEXANDRA WEAVER), actress; b. N.Y.C., Oct. 8, 1949; d. Sylvester (Pat) Weaver and Elizabeth Inglish; m. James Simpson, 1984; 1 child, Charlotte. BA in English, Stanford U., 1971; MA in Drama, Yale U., 1974. First profl. theater appearance in The Constant Wife, 1974; other roles in Beyond Therapy, Hurlyburly, 1984, The Merchant of Venice, 1987; films include: Annie Hall, 1977, Alien, 1979, Eyewitness, 1981, The Year of Living Dangerously, 1982, Deal of the Century, 1983, Ghostbusters, 1984, Aliens, 1986 (Acad. award nomination for best actress), Half Moon Street, 1986, One Woman or Two, 1987, Working Girl, 1988, Gorillas in the Mist, 1988 (Golden Globe award 1989), Ghostbusters II, 1989, Alien 3, 1992, 1492: Conquest of Paradise, 1992, Dave, 1993, Death and the Maiden, 1994, Jeffrey, 1995. Office: ICM 8942 Wilshire Blvd Beverly Hills CA 90211*

WEAVER, SYLVESTER LAFLIN, JR., communications consultant; b. Los Angeles, Dec. 21, 1908; s. Sylvester Laflin and Isabel (Dixon) W.; m. Desiree Mary Hawkins, Jan. 23, 1942; children: Trajan Victor Charles, Susan Sigourney. B.A. magna cum laude, Dartmouth Coll., 1930. Writer, producer CBS, Los Angeles, 1932; program dir. CBS, San Francisco, 1933-35; supr. programs, mgr. Young & Rubicam, N.Y.C., 1935-38; v.p., mem. exec. com. Young & Rubicam, 1946-49; advt. mgr. Am. Tobacco Co., 1938-46; v.p. TV, vice chmn., pres., chmn. NBC, N.Y.C., 1949-56; chmn. McCann Erickson, N.Y.C., 1958-63; pres. Subscription TV, Los Angeles, 1963-66; cons. Wells, Rich, Greene, others, Santa Barbara, Calif., 1967—; TV cons. to Nelson A. Rockefeller, 1958, 60, 62, 66, 72, Com. on Critical Choices, 1973-75. Creator mag. concept of TV, Today Show, Tonight Show; author: The Best Seat in the House, 1994. Chmn. Am. Heart Assn., 1959-63; bd. dirs. Muscular Dystrophy Assn., 1967—, pres., 1975—. Served with USN, 1942-45. Recipient Peabody award, 1956, Emmy award, 1967, also Sylvania, Look and Variety awards; named to TV Hall of Fame, 1985. Mem. Phi Beta Kappa. Republican. Episcopalian. Clubs: University (N.Y.C.), Seawanhaka Corinthian Yacht (N.Y.C.); Thunderbird Country (Palm Springs); Casino; Valley (Montecito). Home: 818 Deerpath Rd Santa Barbara CA 93108-1826

WEAVER, THOMAS HAROLD, health facility administrator; b. Asheville, N.C., July 21, 1943; s. Thomas Harold and Evelyn (Morris) W.; m. Marsha Va Fossen, Dec. 17, 1982; 1 child, Sallie Jayne. BA, Va. Mil. Inst., 1964; MEd, U. Ga., 1970; MAHA, George Washington U., 1973. Vol. EMS, various locations, 1965-94; mgmt. analyst VA Med. Ctr., Martinez, Calif., 1972-74; health planner VA Ctrl. Hdqrs., Washington, 1974-76, sr. health sys. specialist, 1976-79; asst. dir. VA Med. Ctr., Lexington, Ky., 1979; COO, assoc. dir. VA Med. Ctr., Ft. Howard, Md., 1980-82; sr. exec. service specialist assoc. dir. VA Med. Ctr., Durham, N.C., 1982-85; COO, assoc. med. dir. VA Med. Ctr., Pitts., 1985-89; CEO, med. ctr. dir. VA Med. Ctr. Martinsburg, W.Va., 1989-94; CEO, dir. med. ctr. VA Med. Ctr., Bay Pines, Fla., 1994—; v.p., bd. dirs. Berkeley County Emergency Ambulance Authority, Martinsburg, 1989-94; pres., chmn. bd. Bedington Vol. Fire and Rescue Dept., 1989-93; disting. vis. lectr. W.Va. U., 1992-94; lectr., cons. in field. Contbr. articles to profl. jours. Emergency med. svcs. instr. various locations, 1967-94, W.Va., 1990-94. Recipient Nat. Temp. Svc. award Sec. Vets. Affairs, Washington, 1975, Cert. of Merit, Geico Pub. Svc., Washington, 1985, Spl. Act Commendation award DVA and County Commn. for outstanding actions during cmty. disaster, 1993. Fellow Am. Coll. Healthcare Execs. (Fed. Exec. of Yr. W.Va. chpt. 1994); mem. Nat. Registry EMTs, Rotary. Office: Dept VA Affairs Med Ctr 10000 Bay Pines Bay Pines FL 33504

WEAVER, VELATHER EDWARDS (VAL WEAVER), small business owner; b. Union Hall, Va., Feb. 20, 1944; d. Willie Henry and Ethel (Smith) Edwards; m. Ellersn Fitzpatrick Weaver; children: Frankie Lawrence Mattox Jr., Terence Leon Mattox, Christopher Lamar Williams, Sharon, Shelley, Stephanie. Student, Sonoma State Coll., 1972, U. Calif., Berkeley, 1972; BA, Calif. State U., Hayward, 1973; MBA, St. Mary's Coll., Moraga, Calif., 1989. Coach, counselor Opportunities Industrialization Ctr., Oakland, Calif., 1967-69; tchr. Berkeley Headstart, 1969-70; instr., cons. external degree program Antioch Coll.-West, San Francisco, 1971-74; market analyst World Airways, Inc., Oakland, 1972-75, affirmative action adminstr., 1975-78; cons. A.C. Transit, Oakland, 1982; owner, mgr. Val's Designs and Profl. Svcs., Lafayette, Calif., 1980—; mgr. adminstrn., tng. supr. North Oakland Pharmacy, Inc., 1970—, also bd. dirs.; adv. bd. The Tribune, Oakland, 1982-88. Author RAPRO Self Mgmt. Program, 1985. Program coord., publicity Lafayette Arts and Sci. Found., 1982-83; mem. admission bd. grad. bus. sch. St. Mary's Coll., 1990; bd. dirs. Acalanes High Sch., Lafayette, 1980-82, Lafayette Elem. Sch., 1975-80; mem. City of Lafayette Econ. Devel. Task Force, 1994—. Mem. Calif. State Pharmacists Assn. Aux. (pres. Contra Costa Aux. 1980, pres. state aux. 1986-88, recognition award 1987), Calif. Pharmacists Polit. Action Com. (appreciation award 1988), Diablo Valley Bus. and Profl. Women (pub. rels. com. 1986-87, best local orgn. award 1987, action yearbook 1987), No. Calif. Med., Dental and Pharm. Assn. Aux. (bd. dirs., com. chair 1975—, pres. elect 1991, pres. 1991-93), Internat. Platform Assn., Links, Inc. Avocations: reading, researching family businesses, travel, attending auctions. Office: North Oakland Pharmacy Inc 5705 Market St Emeryville CA 94608-2892

WEAVER, WARREN, JR., writer; b. Madison, Wis., Feb. 7, 1923; s. Warren and Mary (Hemenway) W.; m. Barbara J. Woodall, July 8, 1950 (div. Feb. 1975); children: Carolyn, Sally, Melissa, Anne; m. Marianne Means, Feb. 10, 1977. B.A., Amherst Coll., 1943; M.S., Columbia U., 1947; J.D., Albany (N.Y.) Law Sch., 1958. Bar: N.Y. bar 1959, D.C. bar 1980. Reporter, then asst. state editor Watertown (N.Y.) Daily Times, 1947-48; mem. staff N.Y. Times, 1948-89; bur. chief N.Y. Times, Albany, 1959-62; mem. staff Washington bur. N.Y. Times, 1962-89, nat. polit. corr., 1966-68, Congressional corr., 1969-72, 79-81, Supreme Ct. corr., 1973-75, 77-78, columnist, 1982-87. Author: Making Our Government Work, 1964, Both Your Houses, 1972; contg. author: The Kennedy Years, 1964, The New York Times Election Handbook, 1964, 2d edit., 1968, The Road to the White House, 1965, Washington D.C.: Guide to the Nations Capital, 1967. Mem. N.Y. State Legis. Corrs. Assn. (pres. 1957). Clubs: Washington Press (dir. 1980-81), Nat. Press, Gridiron. Home: 1521 31st St NW Washington DC 20007-3075

WEAVER, WILLIAM BRUCE, astronomer, research administrator; b. Catskill, N.Y., Sept. 1, 1946; s. William Ray and Bette (Martino) W.; m. Sandra Dale Wilford; children: Cristina Dawn, Robert Bruce Glen. BS, U. Ariz., 1968; MS, Case Western Res. U., 1971, PhD, 1972. Sr. prin. staff mem. BDM, Monterey, Calif., 1973—; astronomer Monterey Inst. for Rsch. in Astronomy, 1972—, pres., 1985-92, 94—, dir. rsch., 1992—, also bd. dirs., 1972-92, 94—. Contbr. articles to profl. jours. Recipient NSF traineeship, 1968-72. Fellow Royal Astron. Soc., Am. Astron. Soc.; mem. Calif. Acad. Sci., Astron. Soc. Pacific, Internat. Astron. Union. Office: Monterey Inst Rsch Astronomy 900 Major Sherman Ln Monterey CA 93940-4698

WEAVER, WILLIAM CHARLES, industrial executive; b. Pitts., Nov. 10, 1941; s. Curtis D. and Mary (Yahres) W.; BS in Edn., Indiana U. of Pa., 1963; postgrad. in acctg. Tex. Christian U., 1964-65; m. Karla Lee Kottas, June 13, 1964; children: Michael, Kelli. With Price Waterhouse & Co., Pitts., 1965-73, audit mgr., 1970-73; corp. contr. Kennametal Inc., Latrobe, Pa., 1973-78, v.p., contr. 1978-83, v.p. treas., 1983-86, v.p., chief fin. officer, 1987-89; sr. v.p., chief fin. officer Oak Industries, Inc., Waltham, Mass., 1990—. Trustee, Hampton United Presbyn. Ch., 1972-73; pres. Mountain View Parent Tchrs. Orgn., 1976-77; bd. dirs. East High Acres Civic Assn., 1976-77; treas. Greater Latrobe Hockey Club, 1982-87; chmn. bd. dirs., mem. adv. coun. Jr. Achievement, Latrobe, 1982-85; chmn. bd. trustees Latrob United Way, 1988-89. 1st lt. U.S. Army, 1963-65. Mem. AICPA, Pa. Inst. CPAs, Nat. Investors Rels. Inst., Fin. Execs. Inst., MAPI Fin. Coun. Office: Oak Ind Inc 100 Winter St Waltham MA 02154-0921

WEAVER, WILLIAM CLAIR, JR. (MIKE WEAVER), human resources development executive; b. Indiana, Pa., Apr. 11, 1936; s. William Clair and Zaida (Bley) W.; m. Janet Marcelle Boyd, Sept. 18, 1963 (div. 1978); 1 child, William Michael. m. Donna June Hubbuch, Feb. 10, 1984. B Aero Engring., Rensselaer Poly. Inst., 1958; MBA, Washington U., St. Louis, 1971; postgrad., Rutgers U.; grad., Armed Forces Indsl. Coll. Registered profl. engr. Engr. aerodynamics N.Am. Aviation, Los Angeles, 1959-60; engr. flight test ops. Boeing/Vertol, Phila., 1963-66; engr. flight test project Lockheed Electronics, Plainfield, N.J., 1966-69; project engr. advanced systems, sr. staff engr. Emerson Electric Co., St. Louis, 1969-72; pres. Achievement Assocs., Inc. St. Louis, 1972—; founder, charter mem. Catalyst, 1978—; speaker in field. Contbr. articles to profl. jours.; author: Winning Selling, 1983, Winning Manager, 1990. Mem. adv. com. Boy Scouts Am., Bridgeton, Mo., 1974. Served to capt. USAF, 1960-63, USAFR. Mem. Nat. Soc. Profl. Engrs.,Am. Soc. Bus. and Mgmt. Cons., Am. Ordnance Soc., Am. Inst. Aeronautics and Astrounautics, Assn. MBA Execs., Air Force Assn., Am. Helicopter Soc., Acacia Frat., St. Louis C. of C., Mensa, Beta Gamma Sigma. Republican. Lutheran. Avocations: photography, music, sports. Home and Office: 13018 Ray Trog Ct Saint Louis MO 63146-1802

WEAVER, WILLIAM H., newspaper editor; b. Burlington, Iowa, Oct. 10, 1950; s. William Otis and Margaret (Hall) W.; m. Erin Therese Malloy, June 29, 1974; children: Molly, Michael, Daniel. BA, U. Iowa, 1972. Editor, mgr. Des Moines County News, West Burlington, Iowa, 1972-73; mng. editor Nevada (Iowa) Evening Jour., 1973-75, Centerville (Iowa) Iowegian, 1975-81; editor The Union-Recorder, Milledgeville, Ga., 1981-86; metro editor The Macon (Ga.) Telegraph, 1986-93, asst. mng. editor, 1993—; mem. news coun. Ga. AP, Atlanta, 1987-88. Sec., coach Vine-Ingle Little League, Macon, 1993—; bd. dirs. Miller Mid. Sch., Macon, 1993-94; den leader Cub Scouts, Macon, 1990-91, cubmaster, 1991-93. Mem. Ga. Press Assn. (mem. contest com. 1990, mem. edn. com. 1993-94, chmn. edn. com. 1994-95). Avocations: golf, desktop publishing, woodworking, fishing, camping. Home: 811 Winchester Cir Macon GA 31210 Office: Macon Telegraph Pub Co 120 Broadway PO Box 4167 Macon GA 31201-3444

WEAVER, WILLIAM MERRITT, JR., investment banker; b. Phila., Jan. 7, 1912; s. William Merritt and Frances (Jones) W.; m. Rosemary R. Fine, May 9, 1972; children by previous marriage: Judith (Mrs. Ross Campbell), Patricia (Mrs. Clarence Wurts), Wendy, Alison M. Grad., Phillips Exeter Acad., 1930; BA, Princeton, 1934. Ptnr. Nathan Trotter & Co., Phila., 1934-40; pres., dir. Frank Samuel & Co., Inc., Phila., 1945- 59, Haile Mines, N.Y.C., 1957-58; pres. Howmet Corp., N.Y.C., 1958-65; chmn. bd. dirs. Howmet Corp., 1965-66; ptnr. Alexander Brown & Sons, Balt., 1966-86, ltd. ptnr. emeritus, 1986—; dir. Allen Group, Inc. Served to col. AUS, 1941-45. Decorated Legion of Merit, Bronze Star, Croix de Guerre (France and Belgium). Mem. Knickerbacker Club, River (N.Y.C.) Club, Lyford Cay (Nassau) Club, Country Club of Fairfield (Southport, Conn.), Phi Beta Kappa. Home: Lazy W Ranch Smith NV 89430

WEAVER, WILLIAM SCHILDECKER, electric power industry executive; b. Pitts., Jan. 15, 1944; s. Charles Henry and Louise (Schildecker) W.; m. Janet Kae Jones, Mar. 7, 1981. BA, Hamilton Coll., 1965; JD, U. Mich., 1968. Bar: Wash. 1968. Assoc. Perkins Coie, Seattle, 1968-74; ptnr. Perkins COIE, Seattle, 1975-91; exec. v.p., CFO Puget Sound Power & Light Co., Bellevue, Wash., 1991—; bd. dirs. Puget Sound Power & Light Co., Puget Electric Devel. Co., Bellevue. Bd. dirs. Wash. Rsch. Coun., Seattle, 1991—; trustee Seattle Repseatory Theatre, 1992—. Mem. ABA, Wash. State Bar Assn., Seattle Yacht Club, Rainier Club. Office: Puget Sound Power & Light Co PO Box 97034-obc- Bellevue WA 98009

WEAVER, WILLIAM TOWNSEND, laywer; b. Chgo., Sept. 10, 1943; s. William H. and Lorraine (Matthews) W.; m. Nancy Fleming (div.); children: Kristin, Karin; m. Amy L. Sherrard, July 10, 1982; children: Kelsey, Matthew. AB, Stanford U., 1965; JD, U. Calif., San Francisco, 1968. Bar: Ill. 1968, U.S. Dist. Ct. (no. dist.) Ill. 1970. Ptnr. Lord, Bissell & Brook, Chgo., 1970—. With U.S. Army, 1968-70, Vietnam. Mem. ABA, Ill. Bar Assn., Chgo. Bar Assn., Order of Coif., Union League Club (Chgo.). Avocations: skiing, tennis, squash. Office: Lord Bissell & Brook Harris Bank Bldg 115 S La Salle St Ste 2600-3600 Chicago IL 60603-0700

WEAVIL, DAVID CARLTON, clinical laboratory services executive; b. Winston-Salem, N.C., Feb. 13, 1951; s. Kenneth George and Dorothy Elvira (Kiser) W.; m. Teresa Ann Houser (div. 1988); children: Heather Leigh, Chelsea Anne, Lucas Alexander, Kendall McKenzie; m. Mila Dicecco, Mar. 2, 1991. BBA, U. N.C., 1974. CPA, N.C. Auditor Peat Marwick Main Co., Greensboro, N.C., 1974-77; treas. Biomed. Reference Labs., Inc., Burlington, N.C., 1977-79, v.p. fin., 1979-82; sr. v.p. fin. Roche Biomed. Labs., Inc. (acquired by Hoffmann-LaRoche Inc.), Burlington, 1982-87; sr. v.p. ops. Roche Biomed Labs., Inc., Burlington, 1988-89; chief oper. officer, sr. v.p. Roche Biomed. Labs., Inc. (acquired by Hoffman-LaRoche), Burlington, 1989—. Bd. dirs. YMCA, Burlington, 1984—; treas./sec. T.E. Powell Jr. Biology Found. Elon Coll., N.C., 1978-88; bd. dirs. First United Meth. Ch., Graham, N.C., 1983, 84. Fellow N.C. Assn. CPAs; mem. AICPA, U. N.C. Alumni Assn. (life), Rams Club U. N.C., Beta Gamma Sigma.. Office: Roche Biomed Labs Inc 430 S Spring St Burlington NC 27215-5865

WEBB, ALEXANDER, III, investment company executive; b. Raleigh, N.C., Aug. 19, 1945; s. Alexander Jr. and Mary (Hall) W.; m. Laura Lee Robinson; children: Alexander IV, William Robinson. BA, U. N.C., 1968; MBA, Columbia U., 1972. Investment analyst First Union Nat. Bank, Charlotte, N.C., 1968-69; investment officer New Eng. Life Ins. Co., Boston, 1972-73; exec. v.p., dir., chief investment officer State Street Research & Mgmt. Co., Boston, 1973-89; pres. Fidelity Mgmt. Trust Co. (Fidelity Investments), Boston, 1990—, also bd. dirs.; adv. com. Investment Counseling, Inc., 1995—. Investment com. Soc. Preservation New England Antiquities. Mem. Boston Security Analysts Soc., Fin. Analysts Fedn. Episcopalian. Avocations: running, hiking. Office: Fidelity Mgmt Trust Co 82 Devonshire St Boston MA 02109-3614

WEBB, ALI, federal agency administrator; b. South Pasadena, Calif.. BJ, Stanford U., 1979; MPA, Harvard U., 1989. Reporter The Eagle, Bryan-College-Station, Tex., 1979; Calif. press sec. Walter Mondale for Pres., L.A., 1984; state press sec. Bradley for Gov., L.A., 1986; press sec. to L.A. mayor Tom Bradley, 1980-87; nat. press sec. Dick Gephardt for Pres., 1987-88; teaching asst., rsch. fellow Barone Ctr. Press, Politics and Pub. Policy Kennedy Sch. of Govt., Harvard U., Cambridge, Mass., 1988-89; instr. polit. comm. Emerson Coll., Boston, 1989; assoc. dir. League of Conservation Voters, Washington, 1989-93; dir. pub. affairs USDA, Washington, 1993—. Home: 9006 Eton Rd Silver Spring MD 20902 Office: USDA Dept Comm 14th & Independence Ave SW Washington DC 20250*

WEBB, ANTHONY ALLAN, banker; b. Lincoln, Nebr., May 24, 1943; s. Robert McGraw and Ruth Irene (Good) W.; m. Micheline Touchette, July 10, 1971; children—Annie, Christian. B.A., U. Colo., 1965; B.Internat. Mgmt., Am. Grad. Sch. Internat. Mgmt., 1970. Various positions Royal Bank Can., Montreal and London, 1970-77; assoc. mgr. Royal Bank Can. Toronto, Ont., Can., 1977-80; v.p. Royal Bank Can., Toronto, 1980-83, sr. v.p. merchant banking, 1983-84; dir. gen. Royal Bank Can., Geneva, 1984-88; sr. v.p. personal fin. svcs. Royal Bank Can., Montreal, 1988-93; chmn. Royal Bank Can. Suisse, Royal Bank Can., Channel Islands; pres., CEO Royal Trust, Toronto, 1993—. Served to lt. comdr. USNR, 1965-69. Home: 48 Suncrest Dr, Don Mills, ON Canada M3C 2L3 Office: PO Box 7500 Sta A, Toronto, ON Canada M5W 1P9

WEBB, BRAINARD TROUTMAN, JR., distribution company executive, lawyer; b. Brooklyn, Conn., Feb. 13, 1943; s. Brainard Troutman and Loretta (Dwyer) W.; m. Leigh Wickersham, Apr. 6, 1968; children: Patrick Brewster, Elizabeth Ryan. B.S., Spring Hill Coll., 1965; J.D., Emory U., 1968. Bar: Ga. 1968. Assoc. Tarleton & Zion, Decatur, Ga., 1970-73; corp. counsel Barwick Industries, Inc., Chamblee, Ga., 1973-75; corp. counsel Genuine Parts Co., Atlanta, 1975—, sec. 1984—, v.p. 1988—. Served to capt. AUS, 1968-70; Vietnam. Decorated Bronze Star, Air medal. Mem. Ga. Bar Assn., Greater Atlanta Corp. Counsels Assn., Lawyers Club Atlanta, Am. Soc. Corp. Secs. Roman Catholic. Home: 7990 Innsbruck Dr Dunwoody GA 30350-4308 Office: Genuine Parts Co 2999 Circle 75 Pky NW Atlanta GA 30339-3073

WEBB, CHARLES HAIZLIP, JR., university dean; b. Dallas, Feb. 14, 1933; s. Charles Haizlip and Marion (Gilker) W.; m. Kenda McGibbon, June 21, 1958; children: Mark, Kent, Malcolm, Charles Haizlip III. AB, So. Meth. U., 1955, MMus, 1955; DMus, Ind. U., 1964; DMus (hon.), Anderson. Coll., 1979. Asst. to dean Sch. Music, So. Meth. U., 1957-58; mem. faculty Sch. Music, Ind. U., 1960—, dean, 1973—. dir. Indpls. Symphony Choir, 1967-81; guest condr. chorus and orch. festivals throughout U.S.; duopianist with Wallace Hornibrook in U.S. and Australian tour, 1973; organist First Meth. Ch., Bloomington, 1961—, mem. hymnal revision com. Meth. Ch.; mem. jury Chopin competition; mem. jury internat. piano competitions in Munich, Budapest, South Africa, Paris, Chile, Warsaw, Bolzano, London, Cologne, Japan. Chmn. adv. bd. Internat. Music Festivals, Inc.; mem. Ind. Arts Commn., 1975-83, U.S.-USSR Commn. on Music Performance Edn.; Am. Coun. Learned Socs./USSR Ministry of Culture; mem. adv. panel The Music Found.; mem. recommendation bd. Avery Fisher Prize Program; bd. dirs. Busoni Found.; mem. bd. advisors Van Cliburn Internat. Piano Competition; mem. nat. adv. bd. Am. Guild Organists; trustee Indpls. Symphony Orch. With U.S. Army, 1955-57. Decorated D.S.M.; recipient Disting. Alumni award So. Meth. U., 1980, Sagamore of Wabash Gov. award, 1987, 89, Thomas Hart Benton medal Ind. U., 1987, Disting. Alumni award Highland Park High Sch., Dallas, 1989, Ind. Gov. award for arts, 1989. Mem. Ind. Acad., Century Assn. of N.Y., Pi Kappa Lambda, Phi Mu Alpha, Phi Delta Theta. Home: 648 Woodscrest Dr Bloomington IN 47401 Office: Ind U Sch Music Bloomington IN 47405

WEBB, CHARLES RICHARD, retired university president; b. Berkeley, Calif., Oct. 4, 1919; s. Charles Richard and Adele (McDaniel) W.; m. Andrée Bonno; 1 child, Charles Richard III. AB, U. Calif., Berkeley, 1942, MA, 1944; MA, Harvard U., 1947, PhD, 1949. Faculty San Diego State Coll., 1949-64, prof., 1958-64, chmn. dept. history, 1956-58; dean acad. affairs Stanislaus State Coll., Turlock, Calif., 1964-66; prof. history San Diego State Coll., 1966-70; pres. Eastern Conn. State U., Willimantic, 1970-88; ret., 1988; former assoc. dean acad. planning Calif. State Colls., 1966-69, former dep. state coll. dean acad. planning. Author: Worldbook in Western Civilization, 2 vols, 1959, Western Civilization vol. 1 (with Schaefer), vol. 2 (with Palm), 1958, (with Crosby) The Past as Prologue, 2 vols, 1973; contbr. articles to profl. jours. Bd. dirs. Santa Rosa Symphony Assn., New Eng. Program, Windham Meml. Cmty. Hosp., Sea Rsch. Found.; mem. Commn. on Conn.'s Future. With USNR, 1941-45. Mem. AAUP, Am. Hist. Assn., Am. Fedn. Musicians, Nat. Pks. and Conservation, Sonoma Land Trust, Sierra Club, Nature Conservancy, New Eng. Hist. Assn., Assn. Calif. State Coll. Profls. (v.p. 1958-60), Save the Redwoods League, Conn. Employees Assn., Am. Assn. State Colls. and Unvis., Phi Alpha Theta, Kappa Delta Pi, Omicron Delta Pi. Clubs: University (San Diego), Commonwealth of Calif., Willimantic Country, Saddle Club, Santa Rosa, Montecito Heights Health & Raquet Club, Santa Rosa. Home: 6495 Timber Springs Dr Santa Rosa CA 95409-5900

WEBB, DAN K., lawyer; b. Macomb, Ill., Sept. 5, 1945; s. Keith L. and Phyllis I. (Clow) W.; student Western Ill. U., 1963-66; J.D., Loyola U., 1970; m. Laura A. Buscemi, Mar. 15, 1973; children—Jeffrey, Maggie, Michael, Melanie. Bar: Ill. 1970. Chief spl. prosecutions div. U.S. Atty.'s Office, Chgo., 1970-76; ptnr. firm Cummins, Decker & Webb, Chgo., 1976-79; dir. Ill. Dept. Law Enforcement, Chgo., 1979-80; ptnr. Pierce, Webb, Lydon & Griffin, Chgo., 1980-81; U.S. atty., Chgo., 1981-84; ptnr. Winston & Strawn, Chgo., 1984—; instr. John Marshall Law Sch., 1975—, Loyola U. Sch. Law, 1980—. Vice chmn. Met. Fair and Expn. Authority, 1978—; bd. advisers Mercy Hosp. and Med. Ctr.; mem. Chgo. Council on Arson. Recipient spl.

commendation award U.S. Justice Dept., 1975; named 1 of 10 Outstanding Young Chicagoans, Chgo. Jaycees, 1979. Mem. ABA, Ill. Bar Assn., Chgo. Bar Assn., Fed. Bar Assn., Legal Club Chgo., Execs. Club Chgo. Republican. Home: 10020 S Damen Ave Chicago IL 60643-2004 Office: Winston & Strawn 35 W Wacker Dr Chicago IL 60601-1614

WEBB, DAVID OWEN, petroleum engineer, association executive; b. Matador, Tex., July 21, 1938; s. Owen Raby Webb and Mary Ernest (Echols) West; m. Jean S. Skidmore, May 6, 1967; children: William David, Jon Patrick. BS in Petroleum Engring., Tex. Tech. U., 1962. With Sun Oil Co., Houston, 1962-63, Kentron Hawaii Ltd., Honolulu, 1963-73, LTU Aerospace Corp., Washington, 1973-75; asst. dir., congressional liason for fossil energy U.S. Energy Rsch. & Devel. Adminstrn., Washington, 1975-77, sr. dir. energy rsch. ctrs., 1977; v.p. policy and regulatory affairs Gas Rsch. Inst., Washington, 1977-83, sr. v.p. policy and regulatory affairs, 1983—; pres., CEO Gas Tech. Info., Inc., Washington; operating agt. Internat. Energy Agy. Internat. Ctr. for Gas Tech. Info., Paris, 1993—. Home: 8318 Chapel Lake Ct Annandale VA 22003-4401 Office: Gas Rsch Inst 1331 Pennsylvania Ave NW # 730N Washington DC 20004*

WEBB, DEAN LEROY, engineering executive, consultant, civil, forensic, structural and investigative engineer; b. Murray, Utah, Feb. 18, 1949; s. Dean B. and Lawana (Williams) W.; m. Marla LaRue Wood, Aug. 6, 1971; children: Chanin Therin, Lacey LaRue. BS, BEE, Utah State U., 1973. Registered profl. engr., Utah, Calif., Idaho, Wyo., Colo., Ariz., Mont., Nev. Structural engr. Coon, King & Knowlton, Salt Lake City, 1973-81, DMJM, Coon, King & Knowlton, Salt Lake City, 1981-84; pres. Dean L. Webb & Assocs., Salt Lake City, 1984—. Recipient 1983 Portland Concrete Assn. Award of Excellence. Mem. NSPE (pres. Utah chpt. 1986-87), Salt Lake Area C. of C., Constrn. Specifications Inst. (pres. Salt Lake chpt. 1982-83), Utah Soc. Profl. Engrs. (pres. Salt Lake City chpt. 1983-84), Utah Engrs. Council (chmn. 1987-88), Am. Cons. Engring. Council, Structural Engrs. Assn. Utah (founding mem.), Am. Concrete Inst. (award of excellence, 1983), Am. Inst. Steel Constrn., Nat. Forensic Ctr. Republican. Mormon. Avocation: golf. Office: 5330 S 900 E Salt Lake City UT 84117-7261

WEBB, DONALD ARTHUR, minister; b. Wales, May 4, 1926; came to U.S., 1958; s. Arthur and Emily W.; m. Renee Mowbray, May 18, 1946; children—Cheryl, Marian, Christopher, Alison, Ian. Student, Queen's Coll., Cambridge (Eng.) U., 1944-45; BA, Ohio Wesleyan U., 1960; MDiv, Methodist Theol. Sch. in Ohio, 1963; PhD, Drew U., 1966; postdoctoral, Lincoln Coll., Oxford (Eng.) U., 1969, 72; LLD, Centenary Coll. La., 1991. Ordained to ministry Methodist Ch., 1960. Insp. Brit. Social Services, 1953-58; pastor various chs. Ohio and N.J., 1958-68; dean admissions, asst. prof. theology and lit. Meth. Theol. Sch. in Ohio, 1968-75, v.p. adminstrn., 1975-77; pres. Centenary Coll. La., Shreveport, 1977-91; sr. pastor First United Meth. Ch., Shreveport, 1991—. Author: The Flame and Dusty Miller, 1970, We Hold These Truths, 1960; author: Dostoevsky and Christian Agnosticism, 1971; contbr. articles, revs. to profl. jours. Active Colloquium on Violence and Religion. Mem. Am. Acad. Religion, Phi Beta Kappa. Episcopalian. Home: 6911 57th Ave NE Seattle WA 98115-7834 Office: U Wash Thomson Hall Jackson Sch Internat Study Box 353650 Seattle WA 98195-3650

WEBB, ERMAN A., food products executive; b. 1926. With various grocery cos., 1948-63; owner, operator numerous grocery stores, Calif., 1963-78; ret., 1978-83; with Sav Max Foods Inc., Modesto, Calif., 1983—, now chmn. bd. dirs. Office: Sav Max Foods Inc 1101 Sylvan Ave Ste A25 Modesto CA 95350*

WEBB, EUGENE, English language educator; b. Santa Monica, Calif., Nov. 10, 1938; m. Marilyn Teruko Domoto, June 4, 1964. B.A., U. Calif., Los Angeles, 1960; M.A., Columbia U., 1962, Ph.D., 1965. Asst. prof. Simon Fraser U., 1965-66; asst. prof. U. Wash., Seattle, 1966-70, assoc. prof., 1970-75, prof. comparative lit. and comparative religion, 1975—. Author: Samuel Beckett: A Study of His Novels, 1970, The Plays of Samuel Beckett, 1972, The Dark Dove: The Sacred and Secular in Modern Literature, 1975, Eric Voegelin: Philosopher of History, 1981, Philosophers of Consciousness: Polanyi, Lonergan, Voegelin, Ricoeur, Girard, Kierkegaard, 1988, The Self Between: From Freud to the New Social Psychology of France, 1993. Active Colloquium on Violence and Religion. Mem. Am. Acad. Religion, Phi Beta Kappa. Episcopalian. Home: 6911 57th Ave NE Seattle WA 98115-7834 Office: U Wash Thomson Hall Jackson Sch Internat Study Box 353650 Seattle WA 98195-3650

WEBB, HOWARD WILLIAM, JR., humanities educator, university official; b. Dayton, Ohio, June 23, 1925; s. Howard William and Martha (Brown) W.; m. Joyce Moore Cooper, Nov. 20, 1947; children: Howard William (dec.), Amy Forrest, Sarah Winship. BA, Denison U., 1947; MA, State U. Iowa, 1950, PhD, 1953. Asst. prof. English Central Mo. State Coll., 1953-56, So. Ill. U., Carbondale, 1956-62; assoc. prof. So. Ill. U., 1962-67, prof., 1967-90, dir. grad. studies in English, 1961-67, acting chmn., 1968, chmn., 1968-72, acad. affairs officer on bd. trustees staff, 1974-79, system acad. officer on chancellor's staff, 1979-85, vice chancellor for acad. affairs, 1985-90; interim dir. SIU Press, 1993. Editor: Illinois Prose Writers: An Anthology, 1968; contbr. articles to profl. jours. With USNR, 1943-46. Mem. MLA, Melville Soc. Home: 904 S Oakland St Carbondale IL 62901-2557

WEBB, IGOR MICHAEL, university administrator; b. Malacky, Czechoslovakia, Nov. 8, 1941; came to U.S., 1952; s. Michael and Josephine (Nash) W.; m. Catherine Lamb (div. 1989); 1 child, Kelly Webb-Lamb; m. Marianne F. Walters, 1990; children: Rebecca Alice, Sarah Elizabeth, Benjamin Oliver. BA, Tufts U., 1963; MA, Stanford U., 1966, PhD, 1971. Asst. prof. English Loyola U. Montreal, Can., 1968-70; asst. prof. English U. Mass., Boston, 1971-77, assoc. prof., 1977-78; chair div. humanities Richmond Coll., London, 1979-86; spl. asst. to pres. Adelphi U., Garden City, N.Y., 1986-87, acting provost, 1987-89, provost, 1989—, sr. v.p., 1992—. Author: From Custom to Capital, 1981, Against Capitulation, 1984. Bd. dirs. East European Cultural Endowment, 1987—. Creative Writing fellow Nat. Endowment for Arts, 1978. Mem. Phi Beta Kappa. Office: Adelphi U Office of Provost Garden City NY 11530

WEBB, J. A., insurance company executive; b. 1935. With State Compensation Insurance, San Francisco, 1959-86, pres., 1986—. Office: State Compensation Insur 1275 Market St # 16 San Francisco CA 94103-1410

WEBB, JACK M., lawyer; b. Monroe, La., Feb. 23, 1936; s. Sam L. and Lillian Etta (McCowen) W.; m. Diane Adele Waterman, Aug. 22, 1964; children: Julia Lillian Pogue, Kathryn Joy, Samuel Logan. BS in Geology, Centenary Coll. La., 1957; JD, Tulane U., 1960. Bar: La. 1960, Tex. 1962. Atty. Standard Oil Co. Tex., Houston, 1961-66; staff atty. Trunkline Gas Co., Houston, 1966-71; sr. atty. M.W. Kellogg Co., Houston, 1971-73; sec., asst. gen. counsel Gulf Resources & Chem. Corp., Houston, 1973-78, v.p. govt. rels., adminstry. asst. to chmn. bd., 1978-82; pres. Jack M. Webb & Assocs., 1983—; spl. amb. Bolivia, 1985, Finland, 1986, Haiti, 1991, Angola, 1992, Ghana, 1993; bd. dirs. Houston Nat. Bank. Bd. dirs. Scotia Pacific Holding Co., Employers Indemnity Co., U.S. Peace Corps, 1986-86, Nat. Pk. Found., 1982-92. Capt. U.S. Army, 1960-61. Mem. Tex. Bar Assn., Houston Bar Assn. Methodist. Home: 3434 Locke Ln Houston TX 77027-4139 Office: 2028 Buffalo Ter Houston TX 77019-2408

WEBB, JAMES OKRUM, insurance company executive; b. Cleve., Nov. 25, 1931; s. James Okrum and Bessie Ruth (Eubanks) W.; m. Frankie L. Lowe, Feb. 19, 1954; children: Pamela Ruth, Lisa Suzanne. BA, Morehouse Coll., Atlanta, 1953; M.B.A. in Actuarial Sci, U. Mich., 1955-57. Actuarial asst. Mut. of N.Y., N.Y.C., 1957-62; asst. to pres., actuary Supreme Life Ins. Co. Am., Chgo., 1962-64; v.p., actuary Supreme Life Ins. Co. Am., 1964-66; asst. actuary Health Care Service Corp. (Blue Cross and Blue Shield), Chgo., 1966-68; asst. v.p. product devel. Health Care Service Corp. (Blue Cross and Blue Shield), 1968-69, v.p. product and project mgmt., 1970-73, v.p. finance, asst. treas., 1973-74, v.p. corp. planning and devel., 1975-79, sr. v.p. planning and devel., 1979-85; pres., chief exec. officer Effective Data Processing, Inc., Oakbrook Terrace, Ill., 1985-94; pres. Managed Dental Care of Can., Toronto, 1987-94; chmn., pres., CEO Dental Network Am., 1990-94; pres., CEO Advanced

Diagnostic Ctrs. (ADL Mgmt., Inc.), 1994—; pres. Village of Glencoe, Ill., 1993—; dir. South Shore Nat. Bank Chgo., 1975-87, Harris Bank Glencoe/Northbrook, 1994—, Harris Bankcorp, 1995—, Harris Bankmont, 1995—, Harris Trust and Savings Bank, 1995—; Mem. Ill. Ins. Adv. Com., 1965-67; mem. Ill. Commn. Urban Area Govt., 1970-72. Mem. Glencoe (Ill.) Sch. Bd., 1970-77, pres., 1976-77; pres. Glencoe Human Relations Com., 1970-71; Bd. dirs., mem. budget and finance com. Mid-Am. chpt. ARC, 1974-75; v.p. mem. exec. com., chmn. devel. com. Chgo. Black United Fund, 1974-76; pres., bd. dirs. Chgo. Caucus; founder, past pres. bd. dirs. Home Investments Fund, 1968—; mem. Gov.'s Commn. on Health Assistance Programs; bd. dirs., v.p. Leadership Coun. for Met. Open Cmtys. Served with C.E. AUS, 1953-55. Mem. Am. Acad. Actuaries (dir., treas. 1975-78), Conf. Actuaries in Pub. Practice (assoc.), Alpha Phi Alpha. Clubs: Economics, Executives (Chgo.). Home: 260 Wentworth Ave Glencoe IL 60022-1932

WEBB, JAMES WILLIAM, food products executive; b. Dayton, Ohio, Apr. 16, 1938; s. Jesse Allen Lucille (Bevan) W.; m. Susan Bay Hayes, Aug. 12, 1961; children: Scott Charles, Julie Elizabeth. BBA, U. Cin., 1960. Mgr. sales Procter & Gamble, Cin., 1961-69, Clorox Co., Oakland, Calif., 1969-80; mgr., v.p. sales Challenge Dairy Products, Dublin, Calif., 1980—. Served with U.S. Army, 1961-62. Mem. U. Cin. Alumni Assn. (pres. Bay Area chpt. 1975). Republican. Lutheran. Avocations: tennis, running, bonsai gardening. Home: 204 Via Mantilla Walnut Creek CA 94598-3526 Office: Challenge Dairy Products PO Box 2369 11875 Dublin Blvd B200 Dublin CA 94568-0706

WEBB, JERE MICHAEL, lawyer; b. Portland, Oreg., July 28, 1944; s. Jesse F. Webb and Olive Rea (Coble) Chin; m. Judith A. Hartmann, Sept. 11, 1966. AB with distinction, Stanford U., 1966; JD, U. Chgo., 1969. Law clk. to justice Oreg. Supreme Ct., Salem, 1969-70; with Stoel, Rives, Boley, Portland, 1970—; bd. dirs. Oreg. Law Inst., Pacific Computer Law Inst. Editor Advising Oreg. Businesses, 1994, Marketing and Trade Regulation Law News; contbr. articles to numerous profl. jours. Mem. Oreg. State Bar (bd. govs. 1986-89, chmn. continuing legal edn. com. 1984-85). Home: 5433 SW Vacuna St Portland OR 97219-7260 Office: Stoel Rives & Boley 900 SW 5th Ave Ste 2300 Portland OR 97204

WEBB, JOHN, state supreme court justice; b. Rocky Mount, N.C., Sept. 18, 1926; s. William Devin and Ella (Johnson) W.; m. Martha Carolyn Harris, Sept. 13, 1958; children: Caroline Webb Smart, William Devin. Student, U.N.C., 1946-49; LLB, Columbia U., 1952. Judge Superior Ct., Wilson, N.C., 1971-77, N.C. Ct. Appeals, Raleigh, 1977-86; justice Supreme Ct. N.C., Raleigh, 1986—. Served with USN, 1944-46. Mem. N.C. Bar Assn. Democrat. Baptist. Home: 808 Trinity Dr W Wilson NC 27893-2131 Office: NC Supreme Ct PO Box 1841 Raleigh NC 27602-1841

WEBB, LANCE, bishop; b. Boaz, N.Mex., Dec. 10, 1909; s. John Newton Shields and Delia (Lance) W.; m. Mary Elizabeth Hunt, June 30, 1933 (dec. Mar. 1990); children—Gloria Jeanne (Mrs. David B. Davis), Mary M. (Mrs. Lee Edlund), Ruth Elizabeth (Mrs. Allan Lindstrom); m. Marie S. White, June 22, 1991. B.A. with highest honors, McMurry Coll., 1931, D.D., 1948; B.D., So. Meth. U., 1934, M.A., 1934; summer student, Union Theol. Sem., 1939, 47, 54, 57, 59, 60, 63; D.D., Ohio Wesleyan, U., 1960, MacMurray Coll., 1967, McKendree Coll., 1970; Litt.D., Morningside Coll., 1977; H.H.D., Ill. Wesleyan U., 1966; LL.D., So. Meth. U., 1966; Litt.D., Simpson Coll., 1979; Litt.D. (hon.), Wiley Coll., 1986. Ordained to ministry Meth. Ch., 1935; pastor McCullough-Harrah Meth. Chs., Pampa, Tex., 1934-37; chaplain prof. religion McMurry Coll., Abilene, Tex., 1937-38; pastor Shamrock, Tex., 1938-40, Eastland, Tex., 1940-41; pastor University Park Meth. Ch., Dallas, 1941-52, North Broadway Meth. Ch., Columbus, Ohio, 1953-64; bishop Meth. Ch., 1964-80; resident bishop Meth. Ch. Ill. area, 1964-76, Iowa area, 1976-80; retired Meth. Ch.; Ann. Endowed Lance Webb lectr. on spiritual formation Cen. Ill. Conf., 1976—, cons. on spiritual formation for the upper rm., Nashville, 1980—; chmn. com. on worship Meth. Ch., 1964-72, mem. gen. and jurisdictional confs., 1956, 60, 64, co-chmn. world Meth. com. worship and liturgy, 1966-71; mem. World Meth. Council, 1961-81, sec., vice chmn. com. worship and liturgy, 1971-76, chmn. com., 1976-81; mem. gen. bd. higher edn. United Meth. Ch., 1972-80; pres. north central jurisdiction Coll. of Bishops, 1979-80; conducted goodwill tours Middle East and Round the World, 1961, 63; Nat. Council Chs. interchange preacher Britain, 1959; chancellor Disciplined Order of Christ, 1964-89, chancellor emeritus, 1989—. Author: Conquering the Seven Deadly Sins, 1955, Discovering Love, 1959, Point of Glad Return, 1960, Art of Personal Prayer, 1962, On the Edge of the Absurd, 1965, When God Comes Alive, 1968, Disciplines for Life in the Age of Aquarius, 1971, God's Surprises, 1976, Onesimus, 1980, Making Love Grow, 1983, How Bad Are Your Sins, 1983, How Good Are Your Virtues, 1983, Disciplines for Life, 1986, Onesimus-Rebel and Saint, 1988; Sin and the Human Predicament, Vol. I, When Virtues Become Sins: God's Love and Human Transformation, Vol. II, 1988; A Traveller in the Company of God's Friends, 1991, Escape from Ephesus: A Novel of the First Century, 1991, Rebel and Saint, 1992 (sequel to Escape from Ephesus). Mem. Mayor's Com. on Human Relations, Columbus, 1953-64; chaplain Ohio House Senate, 1963; internat. chaplain Civitain Internat., 1951; trustee Meth. Sch. Theology in Ohio, Garrett Evang. Theol. Sch., Evanston, Ill., McKendree Coll., Lebanon, Ill., Ill. Wesleyan U., MacMurray Coll., Iowa 1964-76; trustee Wiley Coll., 1972-87, emeritus, 1987—; chmn. bd. Wesley Found., U. Ill., 1964-76, Morningside Coll., Simpson Coll., Cornell Coll., Iowa Wesleyan Coll., Westmar Coll., 1976-80, Rust Coll., 1976-80. Clubs: Masons (Scottish Rite) (33 deg.), Torch (Columbus). Home: # 443 324 Stoney Rdg Garfield AR 72732-9601 My life has been one continuous series of surprises in which the worst that has happened to me has turned out for the best. Since the age of 18 I have consciously lived by the faith that the Spirit creating, sustaining, and ruling our universe is like the spirit that was seen in Jesus. Whenever I have given myself to love and to serve upon this living faith, I have found my darkest nights turn into brightest dawns.

WEBB, LEWIS M., retail executive; b. 1934. Owner Webb's Texaco Svc., Los Alamitos, Calif., 1960-72; pres. Bargain Rent-A-Car Inc., Cerritos, Calif., 1960—, L.M. Webb & Sons, Inc., Mission Viejo, Calif., 1988—; pres., CFO Webb Automotive Group, Inc., Cerritos, Calif., 1989—; pres. Buick Mart Inc., Cerritos, Cerritos Body Works, Inc., Irvine, Calif., Kit Fit Inc., Buena Park, Calif., Lew Webb's Irvine Toyota, Mr. Wheels Inc., Cerritos. Office: Webb Automotive Group Inc 18700 Studebaker Rd Cerritos CA 90701*

WEBB, MARTHA JEANNE, film producer; b. Grinnell, Iowa, Oct. 26, 1947; d. Frederick Winfield and Helen (Potter) W.; m. Bruce A. Clark; children: Marjorie, Paula, David. Student, St. Cloud State U., 1965-67, U. Minn., 1967-69, Coll. of St. Catherine, 1979-81. Personnel, pub. relations, drug abuse edn. NIH, 1967-77; account services Doremus & Co., Mpls., 1977-79; v.p. adminstrn. Webb Enterprises, Inc., 1979-81; v.p. Russell-Manning Prodns., Mpls. 1981-86; pres. Clark Webb, Inc., Mpls. 1986—; pres. Minn. Film Bd., 1986-87, BCW Corp., 1988—; com. mem. Minn. Media Tech. Adv. Com., 1986. Commr. Minn. Commn. Bicentennial US Constitution, St. Paul, 1986-87; bd. dirs. Woods Acad., Maple Plain, Minn., 1987-88; mem. Minn. Super Bowl Task Force, St. Paul, Minn. Task Force on Research and Tech. Recipient numerous film awards including Silver award Interant. Film and TV Festival of N.Y., 1983, 84, 85, 86, 87, Golden Eagle award CINE Festival, 1985, Gold award Best in the West Fest, 1986, Gold award Telly Awards, 1987. Avocations: traveling, gardening, reading, retail design. Office: BCW Corp 18 N 4th St Minneapolis MN 55401-1717

WEBB, MARTY FOX, principal; b. Des Moines, July 15, 1942; d. Joseph John and Jean (Way) Fox; m. Andrew H. Rudolph, Aug. 17, 1963 (div. Jan. 1988); children: Kristen Ann, Kevin Andrew; m. Eugene J. Webb, Nov. 23, 1991. BS, U. Mich., 1964; MEd, Houston Bapt. U., 1982; EdD, U. San Francisco, 1993. Cert. adminstr., Tex., elem. and spl. edn. educator, Mich., Tex. Tchr. spl. edn. Hawthorn Ctr., Northville, Mich., 1964-70; tchr. Bellaire (Tex.) Sch. for Children, 1977-80; dir., owner Ednl. Consulting, Houston, 1979-80; prin. Corpus Christi Sch., Houston, 1980—; cons. Hawthorn Ctr., Northville, 1970-72, Bellaire Sch. for Young Children, 1974-78; instr. Excellence in Edn. Seminars, Galveston, Houston, 1985—; speaker in field. Recipient Elem. Sch. Recognition award U.S. Dept. Edn., 1989-90,

Blue Ribbon Sch. award, 1990, Outstanding Doctoral Student award, 1994. Mem. ASCD, Nat. Cath. Edn. Assn., Child Abuse Prevention Network, U. Mich. Alumni. Avocations: reading, flyfishing, camping, exercise, hiking. Home: PO Box 36204 Houston TX 77236-6204 Office: Corpus Christi Sch 4005 Cheena Dr Houston TX 77025-4701

WEBB, MICHAEL A., food products executive; b. 1957; s. Erman A. W. With father's grocery store; supr. Tropicana Foods, San Jose, Calif., 1981-83; with Sav Max Foods, Inc., Modesto, Calif., 1983—; pres. Sav Max Foods, Inc., Calif. Office: Sav Max Foods Inc 1101 Sylvan Ave Ste A25 Modesto CA 95350*

WEBB, MYRTLE BAILEY, elementary school reading teacher; b. Balt., Jan. 3, 1943; d. Henry Sailie and Myrtle (Dalton) Bailey; m. Harold Webb, Oct. 6, 1990; 1 child, Michele Elaine Cockrell Rochon. BS with honors, Morgan State U., 1965; MEd, Johns Hopkins U., 1970; cert. advanced studies, 1976; EdD, Temple U., 1982. Elem. sch. tchr. Balt. City Pub. Schs., 1965-67; day care tchr. Balt. Dept. Social Svcs., 1967-69; elem. sch. tchr. Balt. City Pub. Schs., 1969-77, reading specialist, 1977—. Mem. NAACP, Women Power, Nat. Assn. Black Sch. Educators, State of Md. Internat. Reading Assn. (bd. dirs.), Balt. City Coun. Internat. Reading Assn. (pres. elect 1992). Democrat. Roman Catholic. Avocations: reading, writing, walking. Office: Balt City Pub Schs 101 S Ellwood Ave Baltimore MD 21224-2244

WEBB, O. GLENN, farm supplies company executive; b. 1936; married. B.S., U. Ill., 1957; Ph.D, U. Ill., 1973. With Growmark, Inc., Bloomington, Ill., 1965—, sec., 1968-72, v.p., 1972-80, pres., from 1980, chmn., 1980—, also dir.; trustee, chmn. Am. Inst. Coop.; dir. St. Louis Farm Credit Banks, Farmers Export Co., Nat. Coop. Refinery Assn., Ill. Agr. Leadership Found.; trustee Grad. Inst. Coop. Leadership. Office: Growmark Inc Box 2500 1701 N Towanda Ave Bloomington IL 61701-2040

WEBB, RALPH LEE, mechanical engineering educator; b. Parker, Kans., 1934; m. Sylvia Apple; children: Janet, Laura. BSME (with honors), Kans. State U., 1957; MME, Rensselaer Poly. Inst., 1962; PhD, U. Minn., 1969. Registered profl. engr., Wis. Instr. mech. engring. Kans. State U., 1957; engring. maintenance officer USAF, Nellis AFB, Nev., 1957-59; engr. Knolls Atomic Power Lab., Schenectady, N.Y., 1960-62; mgr. heat transfer tech. Trane Co., La Crosse, Wis., 1963-77; assoc. prof. mech. engring. Pa. State U., University Park, 1977-81, prof., 1981—; lectr., cons. in field; condr. various workshops. Author: Principles of Enhanced Heat Transfer, 1994; contbr. articles to profl. jours. Recipient Hall-Thermotank Gold medal Inst. Refrigeration, 1989; rsch. grantee NSF, 1978-80, 83-86, Dept. Energy, 1979-82, 90-92, Internat. Copper Rsch. Assn., 1984—, EPRI, 1988—, Improved Radiators Studies Assn., 1988—, Wolverine, 1988-89, York Internat., 1988-89. Fellow ASME (chmn. heat transfer divsn., honors and awards com. 1987—, nat. nominating com. 1983-86, heat transfer divsn. rep. to basic engring. group 1980-86, exec. com. heat transfer divsn. 1976-81, editor-in-chief Jour. Heat Transfer 1972-76, nat. heat transfer conf. coordinating com. 1972-77, Outstanding Svc. award 1973-76, 82, Heat Transfer Meml. award 1987); mem. AICE, ASHRAE (tech. editor Heat Transfer Engring. 1978—, Jour. Heat Recovery 1981—, Jour. Paper award 1985). Office: Pa State Univ Dept Mech Engring University Park PA 16802

WEBB, RICHARD ALAN, physicist; b. L.A., Sept. 10, 1946; married; 2 children. BA, U. Calif., Berkeley, 1968; MS, U. Calif., San Diego, 1970, PhD, 1973. Rsch. assoc. U. Calif., San Diego, 1973-75; from asst. to assoc. rsch. physicist Argonne Nat. Lab., 1975-78; mem., mgr. rsch. staff T.J. Watson Ctr. IBM, Yorktown Heights, 1978-93; Alford Ward chaired prof. semicondr. physics, dept. physics Ctr. Superconductivity Rsch., Univ. Md., College Park, 1993-. Recipient Simon Mem prize, 1989. Fellow Am. Physics Soc. (Oliver E. Buckley condensed Malter Physics prize 1992). Achievements include research in macroscopic quantum tunneling in Josephson junctions at low temperatures, investigations of the Aharonov-Bohm effect and universal conductance fluctuations in very small semiconducting and normal metal rings, measurement of temperature, magnetic field and Fermi Engery dependencies of the conduction process of very small Si MOSFET devices in both insulating and metallic regimes. Office: U Md Dept Physics College Park MD 20742

WEBB, RICHARD C., engineering company executive; b. Omaha, Sept. 2, 1915; m. Virginia; 1 son. B.S.E.E., U. Denver, 1937; M.S.E.E., Purdue U., 1944, Ph.D., 1951. Registered profl. engr., Colo. Traffic engr. Mountain States Telephone and Telegraph Co., Denver, 1937-39; research engr. RCA Labs. Div., Princeton, N.J., 1945-53; pres., founder, tech. dir. Colo. Research Corp. (subs. Carrier Corp.), Syracuse, N.Y., 1956-61; pres., founder. tech. dir. Colo. Instruments, Inc., Broomfield, Colo., 1961-71; pres., gen. mgr. Colo. Instruments div. Mohawk Data Scis. Corp., Utica, N.Y., 1971-73; pres. Webb Engring. Co. (name changed to Data Ray Corp.), Boulder, Colo., 1973-85; vis. lectr. U. Colo., 1962-82; prof. elec. engring. U. Denver, 1953-56, Iowa State U., 1950. Contbr. articles to profl. jours. Recipient Disting. Engring. Alumnus award Purdue U., 1970, Profl. Achievement award U. Denver Alumni Assn., 1983, Outstanding Elec. Engr. award Purdue U., 1992. Fellow IEEE; mem. Soc. Motion Picture and TV Engrs., Acoustical Soc. Am., Inst. Aerospace Scis., Am. Ordnance Assn., Western Electronics Mfrs. Assn. (past v.p., dir.), Sigma Xi, Tau Beta Pi, Eta Kappa Nu. Patentee in field. Home: PO Box 3078 Estes Park CO 80517-3078

WEBB, RICHARD GILBERT, financial executive; b. Tulsa, May 11, 1932; s. William Leslie and Cora (Kroshus) W.; m. Patricia S. Wagdin, Apr. 13, 1957 (div. Sept. 1974); children: Catherine, Andrea, Nicholas; m. Judith A. Burke, Jan. 12, 1980; stepchildren: Mara, Karen, Jennifer, Christopher. Student, U. Okla., 1950-52; BBA, So. Meth. U., 1954; MBA, Harvard U., 1956. CPA, Okla. Mgmt. cons. McKinsey & Co., N.Y.C., 1959-61; planning analyst Mobil Oil Co., N.Y.C., 1961-64; sub controller, treas. ITT, N.Y.C., 1964-66; v.p., mgr. corp. devel. Ill. Tool Works, Chgo., 1966-70; v.p. planning, treas., chief fin. officer Insterstate Bakers, Kansas City, Mo., 1970-78; v.p., treas., chief fin. officer Gen. Host Corp., Stamford, Conn., 1979-81; v.p., treas., chief fin. officer Grolier, Inc., Danbury, Conn., 1981-89, fin. cons., 1989—; cons. to State Ill., Springfield, 1969; adj. prof. fin. dept. We. Conn. State U., 1984; adv. bd. Conn. Bank and Trust Co., Danbury, 1986-88. Fundraiser, bd. dirs. United Way, Danbury, Conn., 1982-86; bd. dirs. Danbury YMCA, 1983-89, treas., 1985-87, chmn. bd. dirs., 1987-89, chmn. bd. trustees, 1981-91, trustee, 1991—; mem. bd. advisors dept. fin. U. Conn., 1984-88; trustee Conn. Pub. Expenditure Coun., 1986-88. 1st lt. U.S. Army, 1956-59. Mem. AICPA, Okla. Soc. CPAs, Greater Danbury C. of C. (bd. dirs. 1985-89, treas. 1986-88, chmn. bd.dirs 1988-89), Harvard Club (N.Y.C.). Fin. Execs. Inst., Beta Bamma Sigma. Republican. Avocations: swimming, reading, jogging, antiques, golf. Home and Office: 37 Saddle Ridge Rd Pound Ridge NY 10576

WEBB, RICHARD STEPHEN, manufacturing executive; b. Nottingham, Eng., Aug. 3, 1944; came to U.S., 1988; s. Sydney and Kathleen Florence (Day) W.; m. Pamela Anne Fowlds, Sept. 3, 1966 (dec. July 1976); children: Jane, Simon, Elizabeth; m. Anne Hessel, Aug. 19, 1978; children: Clare, Penelope. BSc, U. Sheffield, Eng., 1966, PhD, 1970. Rsch. scientist U. Sheffield, 1966-69; tech. asst. C.E. Ramsden & Co. Ltd., Stoke-on-Trent, Eng., 1969-74; mktg. exec. Magnesium Elektron Ltd., Manchester, Eng., 1974-80, mktg. mgr., 1980-84; bus. devel. mgr. Alcan Aluminium, Mont., Can., 1984-88; bus. mgr. Alanx Products Inc., Newark, Del., 1988-91; pres. Alanx Products Inc., Newark, 1992-95, Lanxide Coated Products (Div. Lanxide Corp.), Newark, Del., 1995—; chmn. Del. Mfg. Alliance. Contbr. articles to profl. jours. Fellow Inst. Materials U.K.; mem. Am. Ceramic Soc., Can. Ceramic Soc. Am. Chem. Soc. Avocations: marathon and road running. Office: Lanxide Coated Products PO Box 6077 1300 Marrows Rd Newark DE 19714-6077

WEBB, RICHMOND JEWEL, professional football player; b. Dallas, Jan. 11, 1967. BA in Indsl. Distbn., Texas A&M. Offensive tackle Miami Dolphins, 1990—. Named NFL Rookie of Yr., Sporting News, 1990, Sporting News All-Pro Team, 1992. Played in Pro Bowl, 1990-93. Office: Miami Dolphins 2269 NW 199th St Miami FL 33169*

WEBB, ROBERT ALLEN, lawyer; b. Ann Arbor, Mich., Oct. 2, 1944; s. Edgar August and Harriet Wilda (Feetham) W.; m. Judith Travostino, Aug. 25, 1973; children—William Anthony, Christine Elizabeth. B.A., Amherst Coll., 1966; J.D., Yale U., 1969. Bar: Tex., 1970. Atty., OEO, 1969-70; ptnr. Baker & Botts, Houston, 1970—; adj. prof. U. Houston, 1973—; trustee Gulf Coast Legal Found., 1975—, pres., 1981-82, 1985; chmn. pub. utility law sect. State Bar Tex., 1981-82, chmn. com. legal aid to indigent, 1980-83. Recipient Houston Young Lawyers award of Achievement, 1981. Mem. Houston Young Lawyers (pres. 1975). Republican. Episcopalian. Club: Houston Athletic. Home: 33 Carolane Trl Houston TX 77024-5120 Office: Baker & Botts 3000 One Shell Plaza Houston TX 77002

WEBB, ROBERT KIEFER, history educator; b. Toledo, Nov. 23, 1922; s. Charles Ellis and Melva Marie (Kiefer) W.; m. Patty Bradburn Shull, Dec. 28, 1957; children: Emily, Margaret. A.B. Oberlin Coll., 1947; A.M., Columbia U., 1948, Ph.D. 1951; postgrad., London Sch. Econs., 1949-51. Instr. history Wesleyan U., 1951-53; from asst. prof. to prof. history Columbia U., 1953-70; editor Am. Hist. Rev., Washington, 1968-75; prof. history U. Md. Baltimore County, 1975-89, Presdl. Rsch. prof., 1989-93, acting vice-chancellor for acad. affairs, 1978-79, prof. emeritus, 1993—; vis. professorial fellow Victorian Studies Centre of U. Leicester, Eng., 1967; mem. Inst. Advanced Study, Princeton, 1982-83; vis. fellow Australian Nat. U., 1986; fellow Ctr. for History of Freedom, Washington U., 1988; assoc. fellow Manchester Coll. Oxford, Eng., 1988—; Sorensen rsch. fellow St. Catherine's Coll. Oxford, 1992. Author: The British Working-Class Reader, 1790-1848: Literacy and Social Tension, 1955, Harriet Martineau, a Radical Victorian, 1960, Modern England, from the Eighteenth Century to the Present, 2d edit., 1980, (with Peter Gay) Modern Europe, 1973; editor: bull. AAUP, 1975-78, Academe, 1979-81. Served with AUS, 1943-46. Fulbright scholar, 1950-51; Guggenheim fellow, 1959-60, 73-74, Am. Coun. Learned Socs. fellow, 1966-67; NEH rsch. grantee, 1978-80, 85-88. Democrat. Club: Cosmos (Washington). Home: 3309 Highland Pl NW Washington DC 20008-3234

WEBB, ROBERT LEE, chemical company executive; b. Topeka, Nov. 19, 1926; s. Floyd William and Laura Leona (Arnold) W.; m. Mary Elizabeth White, Jan. 25, 1952; children: Robert, Brigitte. BS, Washburn U., 1949. Chemist IH Milling Co., Topeka, 1949-50; research chemist Glidden Co., Jacksonville, Fla., 1950-57, mgr. research and devel. labs., 1957-59, prodn. mgr., 1959-61, asst. tech. dir., 1961, dir. devel., 1961-62; v.p. cons. research chemistry Terpene Research Inst., Jacksonville, 1962-64; with Union Camp Corp., Jacksonville, 1964, gen. mgr. Terpene and Aromatic div., 1968-80, v.p., 1975-80, v.p. gen. mgr. Chem. Group, 1980-85, sr. v.p. chem. ops. worldwide, 1985-87; prin. R.L. Webb & Assocs., Inc. (cons.), Orange Park, Fla., 1987—. Contbr. articles to profl. jours. Patentee in field (50). Served with USNR, 1944-46. Mem. Am. Chem. Soc. (Jacksonville sect. award 1987), Pulp Chems. Assn. (pres. 1980-82, exec. com. 1978-86). Lutheran. Home: 2479 Holly Point Rd E Orange Park FL 32073-5630 Office: PO Box 2219 Orange Park FL 32067-2219

WEBB, RODNEY SCOTT, lawyer; b. Cavalier, N.D., June 21, 1935; s. Chester and Aylza (Martin) W.; m. Betty M. Lykken, Aug. 31, 1957; children: Sharon, Crystal, Todd, Wade, Susan. BS, U.N.D., 1957, JD, 1959. Bar: N.D. 1959, U.S. Dist. Ct. N.D. 1965, U.S. Ct. Appeals (8th cir.) 1981. Assoc. Ringsak, Webb, Rice & Metelman, Grafton, N.D., 1959-81; state's atty. Walsh County, Grafton, 1966-74; mcpl. judge City of Grafton, 1975-81; spl. asst. atty. gen. State of N.D., 1970-81; U.S. atty. Dist. of N.D., Fargo, 1981-87, judge U.S. Dist. Ct. N.D., 1987—. Col. JAG, N.D. Army N.G., ret. Mem. N.D. State Attys. Assn. (past pres.). Republican. Lutheran. Office: US Dist Ct PO Box 3164 Fargo ND 58108-3164

WEBB, ROGER PAUL, electrical engineer, educator; b. Cedar City, Utah, Dec. 28, 1936; married, 1957. BEE, U. Utah, 1957; MEE, U. So. Calif., 1959; PhD in Elec. Engring., Ga. Inst. Tech., 1963. Registered profl. engr., Ga. Engr. Douglas Aircraft Corp., 1957-59; project engr. Sperry Phoenix Co., 1959-60; project engr. Ga. Inst. Tech., 1963—, also bd. dirs.; cons. Lockheed-Ga. Co., 1966—; asst. prof. Ga. Tech. Sch. Elec. Engring., 1963—; chair prof. power systems engring. Ga. Power Co., 1972—, assoc. dir. 1978—, dir. 1990—. Recipient Engring. Educator award Edison Electric Inst. Power, 1983, Joseph P. Biedenbach award IEEE Southeast region, 1993; named Engr. Yr. in Edn. Metro Atlanta Engrs., 1993. Fellow IEEE. Office: Ga Inst Tech Sch Elec and Computer Engring Atlanta GA 30332-0001*

WEBB, RONALD WAYNE, hospital administrator; b. Tunica, Miss., Oct. 8, 1953; s. Norris Nall and Ruby Jean (Frazier) W.; m. Annette d'Allemand, Oct. 17, 1981. AS, Phillips County Community Coll., 1973; BS, Ark. State U., Jonesboro, 1975; MBA, MS, U. Mo., 1977. Adminstrv. asst. St. Elizabeth Community Health Ctr., Lincoln, Nebr., 1977-79, v.p., 1979-81; adminstr. Holdenville (Okla.) Gen. Hosp., 1981-85; v.p. St. Anthony Hosp., Oklahoma City, 1985-91; adminstr. Pike County Meml. Hosp., Louisiana, Mo., 1991-94; pres. St. Eugene Cmty. Hosp., Dillon, S.C., 1994—; treas. Task Force on Emergency Med. Svcs., Lincoln, 1979-81; chmn. exhibits com. Midwest Health Congress, 1987-88. Pres. bd. dirs. Lancaster County March of Dimes, Lincoln, 1980-81; bd. dirs. Holy Apostles Episc. Ch., Oklahoma City, 1987-91. Recipient Outstanding Com. Mem. award Boy Scouts Am., Shawnee, Okla., 1985. Fellow Am. Coll. Healthcare Execs.; mem. Coll. Okla. Young Adminstrs. Group, Retail Mchts. Assn. (pres. 1983-84), Holdenville C. of C. (pres. 1984-85), Kiwanis (bd. dirs. Holdenville chpt. 1983-85), Rotary. Avocations: camping, running, music. Home: 804 Edgewood Blvd Dillon SC 29536 Office: St Eugene Cmty Hosp 301 Jackson St Dillon SC 29536

WEBB, THEODORE STRATTON, JR., aerospace scientist, consultant; b. Oklahoma City, Mar. 4, 1930; s. Theodore S. and Helen (Klabzuba) W.; m. Cuba Evans, Sept. 2, 1952; children: Theodore S. III, Kelly Elizabeth. BS in Physics, Okla. U., 1951; PhD in Physics and Math., Calif. Inst. Tech., 1955. Engr. Ft. Worth div. Gen. Dynamics, 1955-62, program mgr., 1962-69, dir. aero. tech., 1969-75, v.p. rsch. and engring., 1975-80, v.p. F-16 programs, 1980-89; pvt. practice cons. Ft. Worth, 1989—; engring. adv. bd. U. Okla., Norman, 1983—; mem. aerospace coun. Soc. Automotive Engrs., 1975-81; bd. dirs. Lear Astronics Inc. Bd. mem. Engring. Found. U. Tex., Austin, 1975-81, Found. for Sci. and Engring. So. Meth. U., Dallas, 1974-81, Tarrant County Day Care Assn., Ft. Worth, 1975-80, 89—; All Saints Episcopal Hosp., 1989—, Goodwill Industries of Tarrant Country, 1989—. Mem. AAAS, Am. Phys. Soc., Rivercrest Country Club. Home: 4901 Westridge Ave Fort Worth TX 76116-8222 Office: 6100 Western Pl Ste 901 Fort Worth TX 76107-4679

WEBB, THOMAS EVAN, biochemistry educator; b. Edmonton, Alta., Can., Mar. 4, 1932; came to U.S., 1970, naturalized, 1978; s. Donald John and Sarah Jane (McMinis) W.; m. Ellen Adair Armstrong, Sept. 4, 1961; children: Linda Carol, Sharon Laura. B.S., U. Alta., 1955, M.S., 1957; Ph.D., U. Toronto, 1961. Rsch. assoc. Nat. Rsch. Coun., Ottawa, Can., W. Wis., Madison, 1963-65; 1961-63; asst. prof. biochemistry U. Man. (Can.), Winnipeg, 1965-66; asst. prof. McGill U., Montreal, Que., Can., 1966-70, acting dir. cancer unit, 1969-70; assoc. prof. med. biochemistry Ohio State U., Columbus, 1970-74, prof., 1974—. Contbr. numerous articles on biochemistry of cancer to profl. jours. Grantee NIH/Nat. Cancer Inst., 1970—; fellow Air Force Office Sci. Rsch., 1982. Mem. Am. Soc. Biol. Scientists, Am. Assn. Cancer Research, AAAS, Sigma Xi. Home: 2050 Nayland Rd Columbus OH 43220-4465 Office: Ohio State U 1645 Neil Ave Columbus OH 43210-1218

WEBB, THOMPSON, geological sciences educator, researcher; b. L.A., Jan. 13, 1944; s. Thompson and Diana (Stimson) W.; m. Joan Moscovitch Webb, Aug. 10, 1969; children: Rosanna, Sarah. BS with honors, Swarthmore Coll., 1966; Ph.D, U. Wis., 1971. Rsch. assoc. U. Mich., Ann Arbor, 1970-72; asst. prof. geol. sci. Brown U., Providence, 1972-75, assoc. prof., 1975-84, prof., 1984—; vis. assoc. prof. U. Wis., Madison, summer 1976; chair paleoclimate adv. panel NOAA, 1994. Author: (book chpt.) Late Quat. Environments of the US, vol. 2, 1983; editor: (book) Vegetation History, 1988 (publ.) Geographie Physique et Quat. v. 39, no. 2, 1985, Global Climates Since the Last Glacial Maximum, 1993. Interviewer Swarthmore Coll., Providence, R.I., 1972—; chmn. Internat. Meat and Poultry Alliance, 1994-95. NSF postdoctoral fellow, 1970; vis. fellow Clare Hall, U. Cambridge, England, 1977, CIRES, U. Colo., Boulder, 1988, Bullard fellow Harvard U, Cambridge, Mass., 1995. Fellow AAAS; mem. Am. Meteorological Soc. Office: Brown U Dept Geol Sci 324 Brook St Providence RI 02912-9019

WEBB, TODD (CHARLES CLAYTON WEBB), photographer; writer; b. Detroit, Sept. 15, 1905; s. Joseph Franklin and Bertha (Hollingshead) W.; m. Lucille Minqueau, Sept. 10, 1949. Student, U. Toronto, Ont., Can., 1924-25. Free-lance photographer Standard Oil, N.Y.C., 1947-48, Marshall Plan, Paris, 1948-52, UN, N.Y.C., Togoland, Ghana, Sudan, Italian Somaliland, Tanganyika, Kenya., Rhodesia, Zanzibar, 1956-60, Santa Fe, N.Mex., 1961-71, St. Restitut, Provence, France, 1971-74; free-lance photographer Avon, Eng., 1974-75, Bath, Maine, 1975—. Photographer Tex. Homes of 19th Century, 1968, Pub. Tex. Bldgs., 1974, Georgia O'Keeffe: The Artist and Her Landscape, 1986, photos of N.Y.C., 1986, Paris, 1987; author: (Western U.S. history) Gold Strikes and Ghost Towns, 1961, The Gold Rush Trail and the Road to Oregon, 1963; (memoirs) Looking Back, 1991. With USN, 1942-45, PTO. Guggenheim fellow, 1955, 56; NEA grantee for Photography, 1979. Democrat. Mem. Soc. of Friends. Avocation: traveling. Home and Studio: 120 North St Bath ME 04530-2224 also: Betsy Evans 148 Middle St Portland ME 04101-4150

WEBB, VERONICA, fashion model, journalist; b. Detroit, Feb. 25, 1965; d. Leonard Douglas and Marion (Stewart) W. Student, New Sch. Social Rsch., 1983; signed with, Ford Models, Inc., N.Y.C., 1992—. Contbg. editor, columnist Paper Mag., 1989—; contbg. editor features column Interview Mag., 1990—; spokesmodel Revlon, 1992—. First featured on cover of Vogue, 1988. First African-Am. to receive exclusive cosmetics contract. Mem. Lifebeat (bd. dirs. 1994—). Office: NS Bienstalk 1740 Broadway 24th flr New York NY 10019

WEBB, WATT WETMORE, physicist, educator; b. Kansas City, Mo., Aug. 27, 1927; s. Watt Jr. and Anna (Wetmore) W.; m. Page Chapman, Nov., 1950; children: Watt III, Spahr C., Bucknell C. BS, MIT, 1947, ScD, 1955. Rsch. engr., asst. dir. rsch. Union Carbide Metals Co., Niagara Falls, N.Y., 1947-52, 55-61; prof. applied physics Cornell U., Ithaca, N.Y., 1961—; dir. Sch. Applied and Engring. Physics, 1983-88; dir. NIH-NSF Resource Biophysical Imaging and Opto-electronics, 1988—; dir. Biophysics Program, 1991—; NIH scholar-in-residence Fogarty Internat. Ctr. for Advanced Study, 1988-92; mem. adv. panels Materials Adv. Bd., 1958-59, 63-64, NSF, 1974—; co-chair NAS panel on sci. interfaces and tech. applications, Physics Through the 90s, 1983-86. Mem. editorial adv. com. Physics Today, 1991—; assoc. editor Phys. Rev. Letters, 1975-91; mem. editorial bd. Biophysics Jour., 1975-78, mem. publ. com., 1976-83; contbr. 200 articles to profl. jours. Guggenheim fellow, 1974-75. Fellow AAAS, Am. Phys. Soc. (chmn. 1988-89, exec. com. div. biol. physics 1975-77, Biol. Physics prize 1991), Am. Inst. Med. and Biol. Engrs. (founding 1992); mem. NAS, Nat. Acad. Engrin., Biophys. Soc. (mem. coun. 1972-75, 82-85), Am. Soc. Cell Biology, Am. Soc. Gen. Physiology, Internat. Soc. Optical Engring., Cornell Rsch. Found. (bd. dirs., exec. com. 1983—), Ithaca Yacht Club, Rochester Yacht Club, N.Y. Yacht Club. Achievements include patents in optical instruments, two photon laser microscopy, fluorescent probes, microcrystals, welding technology. Office: Cornell U Clark Hall Ithaca NY 14853

WEBB, WATTS RANKIN, surgeon; b. Columbia, Ky., Sept. 8, 1922; s. Frank Elbert and Susie Josephine (Rankin) W.; m. Frances Luella Cooke, Aug. 19, 1944; children: Andrew Michael, Paul Alan, Harvey Elbert, Gordon Lewis. BA, U. Miss., 1942; MD, Johns Hopkins U., 1945. Diplomate Am. Bd. Surgery, Am. Bd. Thoracic Surgery, Am. Bd. Surg. Critical Care. Intern Barnes Hosp., St. Louis, 1945-48; resident in surgery VA Hosp., Biloxi, Miss., 1946-48; resident in gen. and thoracic surgery Barnes Hosp., 1948-52; chief surgeon Miss. State Sanatorium, 1952-63; instr. surgery U. Miss., 1955-56, asst. prof. surgery, 1956-58, prof., 1958-63; prof., chmn. div. thoracic and cardiovascular surgery U. Tex. Southwestern Med. Sch., Dallas, 1964-70; prof., chmn. dept. surgery SUNY Upstate Med. Center, Syracuse, 1970-77, Tulane U., New Orleans, 1989-93; prof. surgery La. State U., New Orleans, 1993—. Author: Pulmonary Problems in Surgery, 1974, Surgery in Acute Coronary Problems, 1974, Aneurysms, 1983, Cardiovascular Emergencies, 1986, Atlas of Pulmonary Resections, 1988, (with others) Surgical Management for Chest Injuries, Vol. VII, 1990; editorial bd.: Annals of Thoracic Surgery, 1968-79, Surg. Rounds, 1978-82, Surgery Clinics, 1980-82, Microcirculation, 1983-84, Brit. Jour. Surgery, 1981-89; contbr. over 450 articles to profl. jours. Recipient Hadassah award, 1965, Knockers Soc. Outstanding Tchr. award SUNY Upstate Med. Ctr., Syracuse, 1972, Owl Club Clin. Tchr. of Yr award Tulane Med. Sch., 1978, 86, 88-93, Gloria P. Walsh award for best tchr. in Med. Sch., 1992. Fellow ACS, Am. Coll. Chest Physicians; mem. AMA, Am. Assn. Thoracic Surgery, Am. Coll. Cardiology, Am. Fedn. Clin. Research, Am. Heart Assn. (Silver medal 1963), Am. Physiol. Soc., Am. Surg. Assn., Am. Thoracic Soc., Halsted Soc., La. Med. Soc., Orleans Parish Med. Soc., New Orleans Surg. Soc., Societe International de Chirurgie, Soc. Cryobiology, Soc. Thoracic Surgeons, Soc. Univ. Surgeons, Southeastern Surg. Congress, So. Med. Assn., So. Soc. Clin. Research, So. Surg. Assn., Surg. Assn. La., Surg. Biology Club II, Internat. Soc. Heart Transplantation, Gulf Coast Vascular Soc., Sigma Xi, Alpha Omega Alpha, Pi Kappa Pi, Beta Beta Beta, Alpha Epsilon Delta. Methodist. Home: 21 Park Island Dr New Orleans LA 70122-1228 Office: La State U Dept Surgery 1542 Tulane Ave New Orleans LA 70112-2825

WEBB, WAYNE EARL, JR., lawyer, engineer; b. East St. Louis, Ill., Apr. 3, 1951; s. Wayne E. and Esther T. (Koesterer) W.; m. Carla J. Lemons, June 24, 1975; children: Jennifer, Casey. BEE, Rice U., 1973; JD, U. Tex., 1976. Bar: Tex. 1976, U.S. Dist. Ct. (so. dist.) Tex. 1980, U.S. Ct. Appeals (Fed cir.) 1982, U.S. Ct. Appeals (5th cir.) 1983, U.S. Ct. Appeals (7th cir.) 1985, U.S. Dist. Ct. (no. and we. dists.) Tex. 1990. Assoc. Pravel, Gambrell, et al, Houston, 1980-84, ptnr., 1984-89; ptnr. Fulbright & Jaworski, Austin, Tex., 1989—. Contbr. articles to profl. jours. Lt. USN JAGC, 1976-80. Mem. Tex. Bar Assn. (intellectual property law sect. 1980-90, sec. 1984), Am. Intellectual Property Law Assn. (chmn. membership com. 1987-89), Houston Intellectual Property Law Assn. (chmn. trademark law com. 1985), Austin Intellectual Property Law Assn. Republican. Avocations: golf, guitar. Home: 603 Las Lomas Dr Austin TX 78746-5493 Office: Fulbright & Jaworski 600 Congress Ave Ste 2400 Austin TX 78701-3234

WEBB, WELLINGTON E., mayor; BA in Edn. State Coll., 1964, MA in Edn. Univ. No. Colo.; 1970; teacher, 1964-76; elected Colo. House of Reps., 1972, 74, 76; regional dir. HEW, 1977-81, governor's cabinet, 1981-87; elected auditor City of Denver, 1987-91, mayor, 1991—. Chmn. U.S. Conf. of Mayor's Task Forces on Violence, 1993—. Address: Office of Mayor City & County Bldg Rm 350 1437 Bannock St Denver CO 80202-5308

WEBB, WILLIAM DUNCAN, lawyer, investment executive; b. Dayton, Ohio, Feb. 14, 1930; s. Herbert Henry and Dorothy (Chamberlain) W.; m. Nancy Helen Regester, June 12, 1953; children: Joseph Chamberlain (dec.), Mary Helen, Nancy Katherine, Sarah Elizabeth, Lucy Ellen. AB, U. Mich., 1952, JD, 1956. Bar: Mo. 1956, Kans. 1958, U.S. Supreme Ct. 1969. Assoc. Stinson, Mag, Thomson, McEvers & Fizzell, Kansas City, Mo., 1956-58; sec. Kansas City (Mo.) Power & Light Co., 1960-78, asst. treas., 1969-78, asst. v.p. communications, 1978-79, asst. v.p. bd. affairs, 1979-84; legal counsel Fellowship of Christian Athletes. Mem. city coun. Roeland Park, Kans., 1960-62; chmn. Kansas City Myasthenia Gravis Found., 1965-67; bd. dirs. Boys Club of Kansas City, Mo., 1969-74, Greater Kansas City YMCA, Greater Kansas City chpt. ARC; chmn. bd. councilors Avila Coll., 1969-70; trustee, asst. sec., 1970-89; bd. dirs. Rural Water Dist. # 7, Johnson County, Kans., 1992-94. Mem. Internat. Maine-Anjou Assn. (dir., sec.-treas. 1969-76), Theta Delta Chi, Phi Alpha Delta. Presbyterian. Home: 37000 W 155th St Gardner KS 66030-9617 Office: 7500 College Blvd Ste 225 Overland Park KS 66210

WEBB, WILLIAM HESS, lawyer; b. Scottdale, Pa., Sept. 10, 1905; s. Austin Allison and Gertrude (Hess) W.; m. Marian Elizabeth Wellings, Nov. 26, 1931; children: John M. Patricia Ann (Mrs. Charles M. Small). BA, U. Pitts, 1926, LLB, 1929. Bar: Pa. 1929. Practiced in Pitts., 1929—; sr. ptnr. Webb, Ziesenheim, Bruening, Logsdon, Orkin & Hanson, Pitts., 1948—. Bd. dirs., v.p., treas. Pitts. Opera, Inc.; mem. Pitts. Symphony Soc. Served to 1st

lt. U.S. Army Res., 1926-34. Mem. ABA (ho. of dels. 1961-65), Am. Intellectual Property Law Assn. (bd. mgrs. 1953-62, pres. 1959-60), Pa. Bar Assn., Inter-Am. Law Inst., Delta Theta Phi, Theta Chi, Duquesne Club, Univ. Club (Pitts.), Edgeworth Club (Sewickley, Pa.), Allegheny Country Club. Home: 201 Grant St Apt 305 Sewickley PA 15143-1337 Office: Webb Ziesenheim Bruening Logsdon Orkin & Hanson 436 7th Ave Pittsburgh PA 15219

WEBB, WILLIAM JOHN, public relations counsel; b. Chgo., Jan. 9, 1922; s. Archibald Roy and Nina Spencer (Brown) W.; m. Madeline Betty Calkins, Oct. 24, 1989. BA, U. Calif., L.A., 1947; MA in Polit. Sci. and Pub. Adminstrn., Am. U., 1976. Spl. projects, plans and policy staff officer CIA, Washington, 1951-58; press sec., spl. asst. Senator William Knowland of Calif., Washington, 1958-59; spl. asst. pub. info. Army Chief R & D, 1959-63; spl. asst. Senator John Tower of Tex., Washington, 1963-64; spl. asst. to asst. dir. inspections and spl. projects OEO, 1965, spl. asst. regional rels., sr. pub. affairs officer, 1973-74; spl. asst. pub. affairs, chief public info. Navy Seabees Naval Facilities Engring. Command, Washington, 1966-69; dir. spl. projects Maritime Adminstrn., 1969-70; spl. asst. regional liaison-coordination Office of Sec. Dept. Transp., 1971-73; dir. congl. and pub. affairs Nat. Reading Ctr., 1972-73; spl. asst. communication liaison-coordination White House, Washington, 1974; regional and intergovtl. liaison officer Office of Adminstr. EPA, 1975; staff specialist in indsl. rels. communication Fed. Energy Adminstrn., Washington, 1976; sr. public affairs officer, dir. Health Care Financing Adminstrn. HHS, 1976-79; sr. staff officer intergovt. and regional affairs Office of Sec. Dept. Energy, 1980-81; dep. spl. asst. public affairs to Sec. of Labor, 1981. Mem. Pub. Rels. Soc. Am. (Nat. Capital chpt. bd. dirs. 1963, 65-67, 69-70, 72, 74, 76-77, 79, Silver Anvil award 1968), Nat. Assn. Govt. Communicators (dir. 1977-78, pres. Nat. Capital chpt. 1977-78, Blue Pencil awards), Mensa, Nat. Press Club, Am. Legion, Kappa Sigma. Home: 2124 Powhatan St Falls Church VA 22043-1910

WEBB, WILLIAM LOYD, JR., army officer; b. Mineral Wells, Tex., Sept. 30, 1925; s. William Loyd and Francis (Mayer) W.; m. Muriel Emma Hinson, Dec. 27, 1947; children: George Sidney, William Loyd III, Lucinda Adrienne, Alicia Muriel. Student, Tex. A & M Coll., 1942-44; B.S., U.S. Mil. Acad., 1947; M.A., U. Pa., 1958. Commd. 2d lt. U.S. Army, 1947, advanced through grades to maj. gen., 1974; co. comdr. Korea, 1950, Ft. Riley, Kans., 1951-52, Germany, 1953-54; assoc. prof. English U.S. Mil. Acad. West Point, N.Y., 1958-61; regimental comdr., dep. comdt. of cadets U.S. Mil. Acad., 1967-69; squadron comdr. 14th Armored Cavalry Germany, 1963-64; mem. faculty U.S Army War Coll., 1965-68; comdr. support command 1st Inf. Div. Vietnam, 1969; dep. comdg. gen. Ft. Ord, Calif., 1971-73; ops. officer 8th Army, U.S. Forces Korea, UN Command Korea, 1973-75; mem. UN Command Mil. Armistice Commn., 1975; comdr. 1st Armored Div., U.S. Army Europe W.Ger., 1975-78; dep. comdg. gen. V Corps, U.S. Army Europe W. Ger., 1978; asst. dep. chief of staff for personnel Dept. Army Washington, 1978-82. Decorated D.S.M., Legion of Merit with oak leaf cluster, D.F.C., Bronze Star medal with oak leaf cluster, Air medal with 5 oak leaf clusters, Army Commendation medal with 2 oak leaf clusters, Purple Heart. Mem. Assn. U.S. Army, Armor Assn. Episcopalian. Office: 10148 Hillington Ct Vienna VA 22182-2908

WEBBER, CATHERINE CARNEY, state legislator, lawyer, social worker, state official; b. New Bedford, Mass., Aug. 11, 1942; d. Henry D. Carney and Catherine (Breault) Richetson; m. William B. Webber, May 21, 1971 (div. 1981); 1 child, Carney. BA in Edn., U. Fla., 1964; MSW, U. Hawaii, 1971; M in Mgmt., Willamette U., 1985, JD, 1985. Bar: Oreg. Supr. social svcs. Dept. Pub. Welfare, Cambridge, Mass., 1966-73; program exec. Children's Svcs. Divsn., 1974-79; program mgr. Oreg. Advocacy Project, 1979-82; law clk.to Hon. Kurt Rossman Oreg. Ct. Appeals, 1985; adminstr./ counsel joint interim task force liability ins. Oreg. State Legislature, Salem, 1986; assoc. William, Troutwine & Bowersox, Portland, Oreg., 1987-88; mem. parole bd. Oreg. Bd. Parole and Post Prison Supervision, 1989-91; sr. policy advisor, adminstr. Gov.'s Office, Criminal Justice Svcs. Divsn., 1991-93; mem. Oreg. Senate, 1993—, chair senate edn. com., co-chair joint legis. com. data processing, mem. various coms.; sr. counsel, adminstr. ho. judiciary com. Oreg. Legislature, 1987, sr. counsel, adminstr. senate judiciary com., 1989; mem. exec. bd. Oreg. Coun. Crime and Delinquency. Mem. citizens' budget com. Salem-Keizer Sch. Bd.; mem. citizens budget adv. com., cable regulatory commn. Marion County/City of Salem; mem. Marion County Juvenile Svc. Commn., Oreg. Commn. Hispanic Affairs; bd. dirs. Cath. Community Svcs. Found. Recipient Women of Achievement award YWCA, 1993. Mem. Ladies Aux. VFW. Democrat. Roman Catholic. Office: Oregon Senate State Capital # 215 Salem OR 97310

WEBBER, HOWARD RODNEY, computer company executive; b. Berlin, N.H., Oct. 20, 1933; s. Robert Alfred and Amelia (Rousseau) W.; m. Helen Margaret McCubbin, May 6, 1959; children: Benjamin James, Adam Brooks, Holly Isabella. A.B., Dartmouth Coll., 1956; postgrad., Lehigh U., 1956-57. Editor in chief U. N.C. Press, Chapel Hill, 1960-63, Johns Hopkins Press, Balt., 1963-65; dir. Case Western Res. U. Press Cleve., 1965-70, MIT Press, Cambridge, 1970-74; v.p., gen. mgr., pub. Open Court Pub. Co., LaSalle, Ill., 1974-83; v.p., pub. Reference div. Houghton Mifflin Co., Boston, 1983-87; mgr. advanced devel. Groupware Systems Digital Equipment Corp., Nashua, N.H., 1987—. Served with AUS, 1957-59. Mem. Phi Beta Kappa. Democrat. Episcopalian. Home: 49 Wilson Rd Bedford MA 01730-1340 Office: Digital Equipment Corp ZK01-3/A10 110 Spit Brook Rd Nashua NH 03062-2711

WEBBER, JOHN BENTLEY, orthopedic surgeon; b. Morritown, N.J., Jan. 27, 1941; s. George Bentley and Gladys (Moody) W.; m. Mary Christina Thometz, Feb. 25, 1978; children: John Bentley, Edward Alan. B.A., Lehigh U., 1962; M.D., Temple U., 1966. Intern Rochester Gen. Hosp., N.Y., 1966-67; resident Temple U. Med. Ctr., Phila., 1967-70; Sterling Bunnell fellow in hand surgery Pacific Med. Ctr., San Francisco, 1971; practice medicine specializing in orthopedic surgery and surgery of hand Phila., 1973—; assoc. prof. orthopedic surgery and rehab. Hahnemann Med. Coll. and Hosp., Phila., 1973—, chief sect. on hand surgery, 1973—; cons. in hand surgery Mcpl. Med. Svcs., Phila., 1973-87, USPHS, Phila., 1973-76, burn ctr. St. Agnes Med. Ctr., Phila., 1973—, Phila. unit Shriners' Hosp. for Crippled Children, 1979-95. Served to maj. USAF, 1971-73. Fellow Am. Acad. Orthopedic Surgeons, ACS (Pa. com. on trauma); mem. Am. Soc. for Surgery of Hand, Bunnell Hand Club (pres. 1978-80), AMA, Assn. for Acad. Surgery; mem. Eastern Orthopedic Soc., Pa. Med. Soc., Phila. Orthopedic Soc., Phila. Hand Soc. (pres. 1987-89), Phila. County Med. Soc., Phila. Coll. Physicians, Meigs Med. Assn., Rotary Club, Union League, Riverside Yacht Club, Phila. Country Club, Delaware Valley Ducks Unltd. (chmn. 1983-88). Republican. Congregationalist. Home: 1139 Rock Creek Rd Gladwyne PA 19035-1439 Office: 221 N Broad St Philadelphia PA 19107-1511

WEBBER, RICHARD JOHN, lawyer; b. Mpls., July 27, 1948; s. Richard John and Mary Lee (Moore) W.; m. Susan Barbara Listerman, Jan. 8, 1972; children: Hillary, Joanna. BA, Princeton U., 1970; JD, U. Mich., 1973. Bar: D.C. Ct. Appeals 1974, U.S. Ct. Appeals (9th and D.C. cirs.) 1980, U.S. Dist. Ct. D.C. 1980, U.S. Claims Ct. 1974, U.S. Supreme Ct. 1980. Law clk. U.S. Ct. Claims, Washington, 1973-75; trial atty. U.S. Dept. Justice, Washington, 1975-80; assoc. Arent, Fox et al, Washington, 1980-85, ptnr., 1985—. Mem. ABA (chmn. fed. contract claims and remedies com. sect. pub. contract law 1986-91), Fed. Bar Assn. (chmn. ADP procurement com. govt. contracts sect. 1992-94, chmn. govt. contracts sect. 1994—). Office: Arent Fox Washington Sq 1050 Connecticut Ave NW Washington DC 20036-5303

WEBBER, WILLIAM ALEXANDER, university administrator, physician; b. Nfld., Can., Apr. 8, 1934; s. William Grant and Hester Mary (Constable) W.; m. Marilyn Joan Robson, May 17, 1958; children—Susan Joyce, Greg Michael, George David. M.D., U. B.C., Can., Vancouver, 1958. Intern Vancouver Gen. Hosp., 1958-59; postdoctoral fellow Cornell U. Med. Coll., N.Y.C., 1959-61; asst. prof. medicine U. B.C., 1961-66, assoc. prof., 1966-69, prof., 1969—, dean faculty medicine, 1977-90, assoc. v.p. acad., 1990—. Mem. B.C. Med. Assn., Can. Assn. Anatomists, Am. Assn. Anatomists, Can. Nephrological Soc. Research on renal structure and function. Home: 2478 Crown St, Vancouver, BC Canada V6R 3V8 Office: U BC Old

Administration Bldg, 6328 Memorial Rd Rm 132, Vancouver, BC Canada V6T 1Z2

WEBEL, RICHARD KARL, landscape architect; m. Janet Darling, July 25, 1947 (dec.); 1 son, Richard Crawford; m. Pauline Dodge Pratt, Sept. 27, 1969. BA, Harvard U., 1923, M.Landscape Architecture, 1926; hon. degrees, Wofford Coll., 1979, Furman U., 1983. Fellow Am. Acad. in Rome, 1926-29; asst. prof. Harvard U. Sch. Design, Cambridge, Mass., 1929-39; pvt. practice landscape architecture, 1931—; mem. N.Y.C. Fine Arts Commn.; mem. vis. com. Grad. Sch. Design, Harvard U., 1962-68. Prin. works include, colls., univs., racetracks, clubs and redesign of Washington Mall and Lincoln Meml. areas, Washington. Recipient numerous awards Am. Assn. Nurserymen, 1955-81, Nat. Landscape award Am. Assn. Nurserymen, 1991, Mrs. Oakleigh Thorne medal Garden Club Am., 1970. Fellow Am. Soc. Landscape Architects (pres. N.Y. chpt. 1954); mem. NAD, Archtl. League N.Y. Clubs: Harvard; Century Assn. (N.Y.C.); Jupiter Island (Hobe Sound, Fla.); Piping Rock (Locust Valley, N.Y.). Home: Cedar Swamp Rd Glen Head NY 11545 Office: Innocenti & Webel 85 Forest Ave Box 506 Locust Valley NY 11560

WEBER, ALEXIS KURPIEWSKI, nursing school executive; b. Pitts., Mar. 10, 1949; d. Joseph Paul and Nell (Wolowic) Kurpiewski; m. Clark E. Weber, May 19, 1984. BA, LaRoche Coll., 1977, BS in Nursing, 1980; MS in Nursing, Duquesne, U., 1981. RN, Pa. Assoc. dir., asst. dir. coord. psychiatric nursing St. Francis Med. Ctr., Pitts., dir. sch. nursing. Chair edn. com., mem. exec. com. ARC. Recipient Alumni Achievement award LaRoche Coll., 1990. Mem. NAFE, Nat. League for Nursing, Sigma Theta Tau. Home: 117 Sunset Dr Pittsburgh PA 15237-3740

WEBER, ALFONS, physicist; b. Dortmund, Germany, Oct. 8, 1927; s. Alexander and Ilona (Banda) W.; m. Jeannine K. Weber, Oct. 8, 1955; children: Karl, Louise, Paul. PhD, Ill. Inst. Tech., 1956. Instr. physics Ill. Inst. Tech., Chgo., 1953-56; from asst. prof. physics to prof. Fordham U., Bronx, N.Y., 1957-81, prof. physics and chemistry, 1976-81, chmn. dept. physics, 1964-70; rsch. physicist Nat. Inst. Standards and Tech., Gaithersburg, Md., 1977—, acting chief molecular spectroscopy div., 1980-81, chief molecular physics div., 1982—; with chem scis. divsn. U.S. Dept. Energy, 1991-92, chem. divsn. NSF, 1992—. Editor: Raman Spectroscopy of Gases and Liquids, 1979; Structure and Dynamics of Weakly Bound Molecular Complexes, 1987, Spectroscopy of the Earth's Atmosphere and Interstellar Medium, 1992; mem. editorial bd. Jour. of Raman Spectroscopy, Jour. Chem. and Phys. Reference Data. V.p. Union Free Dist. # 1 Sch. Bd., Eastchester, N.Y., 1970-73. Postdoctoral fellow NRC Can., U. Toronto, 1956-57; Ellis R. Lipponcott Awd., 1991, Optical Soc. Am. Fellow Am. Phys. Soc. (councillor 1987-91); mem. AAAS, Optical Soc. Am., Coblentz Soc. Office: Nat Inst Stds and Tech Molecular Physics Divsn Rm B 268 Bldg 221 Gaithersburg MD 20899

WEBER, ARNOLD R., university chancellor; b. N.Y.C., Sept. 20, 1929; s. Jack and Lena (Smith) W.; m. Edna M. Files, Feb. 7, 1954; children: David, Paul, Robert. B.A., U. Ill., 1951; M.A., MIT, 1958, Ph.D. in Econs., 1958. Instr., then asst. prof. econs. MIT, 1955-58; faculty U. Chgo. Grad. Sch. Bus., 1958-69, prof. indsl. relations, 1963-69; asst. sec. for manpower Dept. Labor, 1969-70; exec. dir. Cost of Living Council; also spl. asst. to Pres. Nixon, 1971; Gladys C. and Isidore Brown prof. urban and labor econs. U. Chgo., 1971-73; former provost Carnegie-Mellon U.; dean Carnegie-Mellon U. (Grad. Sch. Indsl. Adminstrn.), prof. labor econs. and pub. policy, 1973-80; pres. U. Colo., Boulder, 1980-85; pres. Northwestern U., Evanston, Ill., 1985-95, chancellor, 1995—; vis. prof. Stanford U., 1966; cons. manpower and govt. agys., 1960—; Dept. LAbor, 1965; mem. Pres.'s Adv. Com. Labor Mgmt. Policy, 1964, Orgn. Econ. Coop. and Devel., 1987; vice chmn. sec. labor task force improving employment services, 1965; chmn. research adv. com. U.S. Employment Service, 1966; adv. com. U.S. Employment Service, 1966; assoc. dir. Office Mgmt. and Budget, Exec. Office Pres. 1970-71; chmn. Presdl. Railroad Emergency Bd., 1982; trustee Com. for Econ. Devel., Joint Coun. on Econ. Edn.; bd. dirs. Aon Corp., Burlington Northern, Inc., Inland Steel Co., Pepsico Inc., Tribune Corp., Deere & Co. Author: Strategies for the Displaced Worker, 1966; Contbr. articles to profl. jours. Trustee com. con econ. devel. Bus. and Higher Edn. Forum; bd. dirs. Chgo. Coun. Fgn. Rels., Eurasia Found. Lt. (j.g.) USCGR, 1952-54. Ford Found. Faculty Research fellow, 1964-65. Mem. Am. Acad. Arts and Scis., Indsl. Relations Research Assn. (bus.-higher edn. forum), Nat. Acad. Pub. Adminstrn., Concorsium of Social Scis. Assns. (bd. dirs.), Comml. Club Chgo., Econ. Club Chgo. (pres. civic com.), Phi Beta Kappa. Jewish. Office: Northwestern U Office of Chancellor 555 Clark St Evanston IL 60208-0001 Office: Evanston IL 60208-1100

WEBER, ARTHUR, magazine executive; b. Chgo., Feb. 1, 1926; s. Philip and Mary (Arlinsky) W.; m. Sylvia Zollinger, Aug. 19, 1950; children—Randy, Lori. Student, Ill. Inst. Tech., 1943-44; B.S. in Elec. Engring. Northwestern U., 1946. Elec. design engr. Corn Products Refining Co., 1946-48, Naess & Murphy (architects & engrs.), Chgo., 1949-51, Ford Motor Co., 1952-53, Skidmore, Owings & Merill, Chgo., 1954-57, Shaw, Metz & Dolio, Chgo., 1958-59; pres. Consumers Digest mag., Chgo., 1959—; pub. Money Maker mag. (name changed to Your Money mag., 1991), 1979-91; pres., 1992—. Served with USNR, 1944-46. Office: Consumers Digest Inc 5705 N Lincoln Ave Chicago IL 60659-4707

WEBER, BARBARA A., research entomologist; b. Prairie du Chien, Wis., Nov. 15, 1947; married; 1 child. BA, Viterbo Coll., 1969; MS, U. Minn., St. Paul, 1971; PhD, So. Ill. U., 1982. Conservation forest pest specialist entom. Minn. Dept. Natural Resources, 1973-74; entomologist Dutch elm disease Minn. Dept. Agr., 1974-75; project leader USDA, 1983-86, legis. asst., 1987-88, staff asst., 1988-91, rsch. entomologist Forest Svc., 1975—, acting dir., 1991—. Editor Walnut Coun. Bull., 1981-85. Recipient Am. Black Walnut Rsch. award, 1983; Cong. fellow Am. Polit. Sci. Assn., 1986-87. Mem. Entom. Soc. Am., Soc. Am. Foresters, Sigma Xi. Achievements include research on insect pests of black walnut; disease transmission by insects; taxonomy of scolytid insects; silvicultural management of black walnut to control insect problems. Office: Pac SW Forest & Range Exp Sta 800 Buchanan St West Annex Albany CA 94706*

WEBER, BARBARA M., sales executive, consultant; b. Oneonta, N.Y., Apr. 27, 1945; d. Peter J. and Helen (Bettiol) Macaluso; m. Peter Biddle Weber, July 29, 1972 (div. July 1988). Student, SUNY, Cortland, 1963-67; AAS in Merchandising and Retail Mgmt., SUNY, Mohawk Valley. Service cons. N.Y. Telephone, Albany, N.Y., 1966-68; sr. service advisor N.Y. Telephone, Albany, 1970-73; data communications instr. AT & T, nationwide, 1968-70; equipment mgr. Rushmore & Weber, Albany, 1978-82; v.p. ops. Rushmore & Weber 1983-92, gen. mgr., v.p., 1987-88, pres., chief exec. officer, 1988-92, also bd. dirs.; ind. cons. Orange Handling, Inc., Latham, N.Y., 1992—. Republican. Roman Catholic. Club: Schuyler Meadows Country. Avocations: skiing, tennis, golf, sailing, knitting. Home: PO Box 236 Newtonville NY 12128-0236

WEBER, CHARLES EDWARD, management educator; b. Chgo., Feb. 21, 1930; s. Edward W. and Augusta (Lonk) W.; m. Suzanne Brodseller, Sept. 6, 1952; children: Paul Andrew, Mark Francis. Student, Marquette U., 1948-50; B.A., U. Ill., 1952, M.A. in Labor and Indsl. Relations, 1953; M.A. in Econs. (Hicks fellow), Princeton U., 1954, Ph.D. in Econs, 1958. Mem. research staff Princeton, 1954-56; from instr. to assoc. prof. bus. U. Pitts., 1956-66, research assoc. adminstrv. sci., 1961-63; acting dir. Adminstrv. Sci. Center, 1963-66; dean Sch. Bus. Adminstrn., U. Wis.-Milw., 1966-76, prof. policy and mgmt. studies, 1976—; cons. Arthur D. Little, 1964-66; pres. Wis. Cons. Assocs., 1979—; dir. The Milw. Co., 1984-86; field reader U.S. Office Edn., 1964-74; organizer, dir. Univ. Nat. Bank, Milw., 1970-76. Author: Stories of Virtue in Business, 1995; also articles. Commr. pub. debt City of Milw., 1976-85; co-chmn. com. to advise on reorgn. Milw. City Govt., 1968-72; pres. Task Force to Advise on Fire Investigation; mem. Gov.'s Coun. for Econ. Devel., 1972-74; bd. dirs. Citizen's Govt. Rsch. Bur., 1974-80, Cardinal Stritch Coll. 1986-92; deacon Roman Catholic Ch., 1981—; pres., CEO SHARE of SE Wis., 1994—. Ford Found. fellow, 1959-60, 62-63; Weber Exec. Alumni Assn. of U. Wis.-Milw. named in his honor. Mem. Soc. for Strategic Mgmt., Acad. Mgmt., Met. Milw. Assn. Commerce, Beta Gamma Sigma. Home: 3453 N Hackett Ave Milwaukee WI 53211-2946

WEBER, CHARLES WALTER, nutrition educator; b. Harold, S.D., Nov. 30, 1931; s. Walter Earl and Vera Jean (Scott) W.; m. Marylou Merkel Adam, Feb. 3, 1961; children: Matthew, Scott. BS, Colo. State U., 1956, MS, 1958; PhD, U. Ariz., 1966. Research asst. U. Ariz., Tucson, 1963-66, asst. prof., 1966-68, assoc. prof., 1969-72, prof. nutrition, 1973—; cons. Hermosillo, Mex., 1970-74, Inst. of Health, Cairo, 1981-82, U. Fortaleza, Rio de Janiero, 1986. Contbr. articles to sci. jours. Served as cpl. U.S. Army, 1952-54. Mem. Am. Assn. Cereal Chemists, Am. Inst. Nutrition, Inst. Food Technologists, N.Y. Acad. Scis., Am. Soc. Clin. Nutrition, Poultry Sci. Assn.-Ariz. Referees Assn., Sigma Xi. Club: Randolph Soccer (Tucson) (pres. 1976-79). Avocation: stamp collection. Home: 4031 E Calle De Jardin Tucson AZ 85721-0001 Office: U Ariz Dept Nutritional Sci 309 Shantz Bldg Tucson AZ 85721

WEBER, DANIEL E., marketing professional; b. Chgo., July 6, 1940. BS in Bus. Mgmt., DePaul U., 1962. Asst. to exec. dir. Am. Oil Chemists Soc., Chgo., 1962-67; administrv. mgr. Inst. Food Tech, Chgo., 1967-69, dir. conv. svcs., 1969-79, dir. mktg., 1979-91, assoc. exec., exec. dir., 1991—. Chmn. 25th Anniversary Com. City of Rolling Meadows, 2 term ind. mem. city coun., chmn. every major com., street dedicated "Weber Drive"; officer Crusade of Mercy; bd. dirs., treas., v.p. Northwest Mental Health Assn., Disting. Svc. award. Named Meeting Planner of Yr. Assn. Conv. Ops. Mgmt., 1990. Mem. Nat. Assn. Exposition Mgrs. (bd. dirs., officer, pres. 1988, v.p. 1987, cert. exposition mgr.), Trade Show Bur. (bd. dirs. 1987—), Coun. Engring. and Sci. Soc. Exec. (conv. liaison coun. del. 1980-81, program chmn. meetings, expositions), Profl. Conv. Mgmt. Assn. (bd. dirs. 1992, 93). Avocation: golf. Office: Inst of Food Techs 221 N La Salle St Fl 300 Chicago IL 60601-1207

WEBER, DAVID C(ARTER), librarian; b. Waterville, Maine, July 25, 1924; s. Carl J. and Clara (Carter) W.; m. Natalie McLeod, Dec. 26, 1952; children: L. Jefferson, Christopher Q., Natasha McLeod, Sarah N. A.B., Colby Coll., 1947; student, Bowdoin Coll., 1946; B.S., Columbia U., 1948; A.M., Harvard U., 1953; postgrad., Rutgers U., 1956. Cataloger, asst. to dir., asst. dir. libraries Harvard U., 1948-61; asst. dir., assoc. dir. Stanford (Calif.) U., 1961-69, dir. libraries, 1969-91, Ida M. Green chair, 1987-91, dir. librs. emeritus, 1991; cons. to acad. libraries, pub. and pvt. instns. and orgns., U.S. and Can. Author: (with others) College and University Accreditation Standards, 1958, (with R.D. Rogers) University Library Administration, 1971; (with P.D. Leighton) Planning Academic and Research Library Buildings, 1986; editor: Studies in Library Administrative Problems, 1960; contbr. articles to profl. jours. Served with AUS, 1943-46. Council on Library Resources fellow, 1970. Mem. ALA, Assn. Coll. and Rsch. Libraries (pres. 1981-82), Assn. Libr. Collections and Tech. Svcs. (pres. 1967-68). Clubs: Roxburghe (San Francisco); Book of Calif. Office: 863 Lathrop Dr Stanford CA 94305

WEBER, DELBERT DEAN, university administrator; b. Columbus, Nebr., July 23, 1932; s. Charles and Ella M. (Hueschen) W.; m. Lou Ann Ross, Dec. 29, 1954; children: William, Bethany, Kelly. BA, Midland Coll., Fremont, Nebr., 1954; MEd, U. Nebr., 1958, EdD, 1962; LittD (hon.), Shizuoka (Japan) U., 1982; LLD (hon.), U. City of Manila, 1984. Tchr. social studies and English, prin. Creston (Nebr.) High Sch., 1956-58; instr. ednl. founds. U. Nebr., Lincoln, 1958-60, instr. and coord. jr. high lab. sch., 1960-62; chancellor U. Nebr.-Omaha, 1977—; from asst. to assoc. prof. edn. Ariz. State U., Tempe, 1962-65, dean and prof. edn., 1969-77; asst. to pres. and sec. to trustees Cleve. State U., 1965-69; chmn. commn. on culture and sec. to trustees Cleve. State U., 1965-69; chmn. commn. on culture and edn. to Pakistan, U.S. Dept. of State, 1984; bd. dirs. Norwest Bank, Omaha. Author: (with N.L. Haggerson, L.H. Griffith) Secondary Education Today, 1968; contbr. articles to profl. jours. trustee Nebr. Meth. Hosp., Omaha Home for Boys, Nebr. Meth. Hosp., 1980—; bd. dirs. Midlands region NCCJ, Omaha Community Playhouse, numerous others; gen. campaign chmn. United Way of Midlands, 1983; chmn. midlands region Nat. Conf. Christians and Jews, 1989-92; mem. consultation com. Strategic Command, 1988—; adv. bd. Salvation Army, 1991—, Nebr. state exec. bd. U.S. West Comm., Inc., 1992—; merit selection panel for Magistrate Judge, 1992. With U.S. Army, 1954-56. Named Citizen of Yr., United Way of Midlands, 1984, Disting. Educator N. Cen. Region Boy Scouts Am., 1989, Outstanding Citizen, Woodmen of the World, 1990, King of Ak-Sar-Ben, 1990, Man of Yr. Omaha Club 1992, Merry Makers 1992; recipient Vision award Com. Prevention of Blindness, 1991, Svc. to Mankind award Sertoma Club, 1994. Mem. Am. Assn. Colls. for Tchr. Edn. (bd. dirs. 1976-79, chmn. ann. conv. 1975, appeals bd. 1984-85, task force 1984-85), Am. Assn. State Colls. and Univs. (task force on excellence in edn. 1982-84, bd. dirs., exec. com. 1983-86, com. communications tech. 1984-86, resource ctr. bd. liaison 1985, com. acad. affairs, com. on internat. programs 1987, com. on urban affairs 1987), Assn. Urban Univs. (bd. dirs. 1980-85), Nat. Assn. State Univs. and Land Grant Colls. (mem. exec. com 1982-83, chmn. urban affairs div. 1982-83), Nat. Assn. Colls. and Schs. of Edn. in State Univs. and Land Grant Colls. (bd. dirs. 1974-77, pres. 1977-78), Nat. Collegiate Athletic Assn. (pres. commn. 1984-89), Nat. Coun. for Accreditation of Tchr. Edn. (appeals bd. 1983), Omaha C. of C., Strategic Air Command (bd. dir. consultation com.). Lutheran. Avocation: golf. Home: 1816 N 132d Ave Cir Omaha NE 68154 Office: U Nebr Eppley 201 Omaha NE 68182

WEBER, DON, finance company executive. Pres. Norwest Funding, Inc., Mpls. Office: Norwest Funding Inc 3601 Minnesota Dr Ste 200 Minneapolis MN 55435*

WEBER, DONALD B., advertising and marketing executive; b. Jersey City, Nov. 6, 1932; s. John William and Rose Ann (Saroshi) W.; m. Ann McDermaid, 1955 (div. 1975); children: Martha Elizabeth, Margaret Ann; m. Jean Host, 1980. BA, Rollins Coll., 1954; MBA, Northwestern U., 1959. Account exec. Leo Burnett Co., Inc., Chgo., 1958-63; sr. v.p., mgmt. supr. Foote, Cone & Belding, Chgo., 1963-76; pres. Blau Bishop Assocs., 1976-79; v.p. Russell Reynolds Assocs., Chgo., 1979-82; sr. v.p., regional mgr. MSL Internat., Chgo., 1982-85; exec. v.p Rumrill-Hoyt, Inc., Rochester, N.Y., 1985-88; sr. v.p. D'Arcy Masius Benton & Bowles, Chgo., 1988—; lectr. Northwestern U. Lt. commdr. USNR, 1955-58. Mem. Chgo. Advtg. Fedn. (bd. dirs. 1988-93), Oak Hill Country Club, Exmoor Country Club, Tavern Club. Republican. Episcopalian. Office: D'Arcy Masius Benton & Bowles 200 E Randolph Dr 71st Fl Chicago IL 60601

WEBER, DONALD W., telephone company executive; b. Turtle Creek, Pa., Oct. 4, 1936; s. James J. and Hazel (Frederick) W.; m. Rose Mary Gaugler, Apr. 4, 1964; children: Jennifer A., Steven D., Christopher J. BSBA, Duquesne U., 1961. Sr. acct. Arthur Andersen & Co., Pitts., 1961-64; contr. Contel Corp. (formerly Continental Telephone Co. then Continental Telecom Inc.), Dryden, N.Y., 1964-65; contr. NE div. Contel Corp., Syracuse, N.Y., 1965-69; corp. contr. telephones Contel Corp., St. Louis, 1969-70; v.p. telephone acctg. Contel Corp., Bakersfield, Calif., 1970-72; v.p. Ea. region Contel Corp., Dublin, Va., 1972-75; v.p. revenue requirements Contel Corp., Bakersfield, 1975-76; v.p. telephone ops. Contel Corp., Atlanta, 1976-82, exec. v.p. telephone ops., 1982-87, pres., chief exec. officer, bd. dir., 1987—; bd. dirs. Contel Corp., Contel Cellular, Inc. Bd. dirs. Woodruff Arts Ctr. With U.S. Army, 1954-57. Mem. U.S. Telephone Assn. (bd. dirs. 1981-88), Atlanta C. of C. (bd. dirs.). Republican. Roman Catholic. Clubs: Dunwoody Country (Ga.); Ashford (Atlanta). Avocations: boating, tennis. Office: Contel Corp 245 Perimeter Center Pky NE Atlanta GA 30346-2304

WEBER, ERNST, engineering consultant; b. Vienna, Austria, Sept. 6, 1901; naturalized, 1936; married, 1936; 2 children. Diploma, Vienna Tech. U., 1924, DSc, 1927; PhD in Physics, U. Vienna, 1926; DSc (hon.), L.I. U., 1963; DEng (hon.), Newark Coll., 1959, U. Mich., 1964, Polytech. Inst. Bklyn., 1969. Research engr. Oesterreichische Siemens-Schuckert-Werke, Austria, 1924-29; research engr. Siemens-Schuckert-Werke, Fed. Republic Germany, 1929-30, vis. prof., 1930-31, research prof. elec. engring., 1931-41; investigator Office of Sci. Research and Devel. Contract, 1942-45; prof. elec. engring., head dept., dir. Microwave Research Inst., 1945-47, pres., 1957-69; emeritus pres. Polytech. Inst. N.Y., 1969—; sec. Polytech. Research and Devel. Co., Inc., 1944-52, pres., 1952-60; chmn. div. engring. Nat. Research Council, 1970-74, mem. commn. sociotech. systems, 1974-78, cons. 1978—. Recipient Howard Coonley medal Am. Standards Assn., 1966, L.E. Girdner award Engrs. Council Profl. Devel., 1978, Nat. Medal of Sci., 1987, Centennial medallion Am. Soc. Engring. Educators, 1993; named to Am. Soc. Engring. Educators Hall of Fame, 1993. Fellow Am. Physical Soc., IEEE

WEBER, EUGEN, historian, educator, author; b. Bucharest, Romania, Apr. 24, 1925; came to U.S., 1955; s. Emanuel and Sonia (Garrett) W.; m. Jacqueline Brument-Roth, June 12, 1950. Student, Institut d'etudes politiques, Paris, 1948-49, 51-52; M.A., Emmanuel Coll., Cambridge U., 1954, M.Litt., 1956. History supr. Emmanuel Coll., 1953-54; lectr. U. Alta., 1954-55; asst. prof. U. Iowa, 1955-56; asst. prof. history UCLA, 1956, assoc. prof., 1959-63, prof., 1963—, Joan Palevsky prof. modern European history, 1984—, chmn. dept., 1965-68; dir. study center UCLA, France, 1968-70; dean social scis. UCLA, 1976-77, dean Coll. Letters and Scis.,—, 1977-82; Ford faculty lectr. Stanford U., 1965; Patten lectr. Ind. U., 1981; vis. prof. Collège de France, Paris, 1983; directeur d'études Ecole des hautes études, Paris, 1984-85; Christian Gauss lectr., Princeton U., 1990. Author: Nationalist Revival in France, 1959, The Western Tradition, 1959, Paths to the Present, 1960, Action Française, 1962, Satan Franc-Maçon, 1964, Varieties of Fascism, 1964, (with H. Rogger) The European Right, 1965, A Modern History of Europe, 1970, Europe Since 1715, 1972, Peasants into Frenchmen, 1976 (Commonwealth prize Calif. 1977), La Fin des terroirs, 1983 (Prix de la Société des gens de lettres 1984), France Fin-de-siècle, 1986 (Commonwealth prize Calif. 1987), My France, 1990, Movements, Currents, Trends, 1991, The Hollow Years, 1994; adv. editor Jour. Contemporary History, 1966—, French History, 1985—, French Cultural Studies, 1990—, Am. Scholar, 1992—. Served as capt. inf. Brit. Army, 1943-47. Recipient Luckman Disting. Teaching award UCLA Alumnae Assn., 1992; decorated Ordre Nat. des Palmes Academiques, France; Fulbright fellow, 1952, 82-83; research fellow Am. Philos. Soc., 1959, Social Sci. Research Council, 1959-61, Am. Council Learned Socs., 1962; Guggenheim fellow, 1963-64; NEH sr. fellow, 1973-74, 82-83. Fellow Netherlands Inst. Advanced Studies, Assn. française de science politique, Am. Acad. Arts and Scis.; mem. Am. Hist. Assn., Soc. d'histoire moderne, Soc. French Hist. Studies, Phi Beta Kappa (hon., Ralph Waldo Emerson prize 1977, senator 1988—).

WEBER, FRED J., state supreme court justice; b. Deer Lodge, Mont., Oct. 6, 1919; s. Victor N. and Dorothy A. (Roberts) W.; m. Phyllis M. Schell, June 2, 1951; children: Anna Marie, Donald J., Mark W., Paul V. B.A., U. Mont., 1943, J.D., 1947. Bar: Mont. 1947. Atty. Kuhr & Weber, Havre, Mont., 1947-55, Weber, Bosch & Kuhr, and successors, 1956-80; justice Supreme Ct. Mont., Helena, 1981—. Served to capt. inf. U.S. Army, 1943-46. Fellow Am. Bar Found., Am. Coll. Probate Counsel; mem. ABA, Am. Judicature Soc. Office: Mont Supreme Ct Justice Bldg 215 N Sanders St Helena MT 59620

WEBER, FREDERIC, lawyer; b. Rochester, Minn., Mar. 23, 1939; s. Harry Matthew Weber and Kathleen (Osborn) Weber Thornton; m. Carole Barskis, June 14, 1968 (div. Dec. 1984); children: Peter Frederic, Anne Kathleen; m. Nancy Kay Bratrud, June 15, 1988. B.A. U. Notre Dame, 1962, JD, 1972. Bar: Ill. 1972, Minn. 1988. Assoc. Lord, Bissell & Brook, Chgo., 1972-80, ptnr., 1981—. Bd. govs. Luth. Social Svcs. Alcohol and Drug Dependency Program, Chgo., 1989—. Lt. Comdr. USN, 1962-68, Vietnam. Decorated 4 Air medals, Navy Commendation medal with V device, Air Force Commendation medal, Presdl. Unit citation Dept. Defense. Mem. ABA, Chgo. Bar Assn. Avocation: piloting. Office: Lord Bissell & Brook 115 S La Salle St Chicago IL 60603-3801

WEBER, FREDRIC ALAN, lawyer; b. Paterson, N.J., July 31, 1948; s. Frederick Edward and Alida (Hessels) W.; m. Mary Elizabeth Cook, June 18, 1983. BA in History, Rice U., 1970; JD, Yale U., 1976. Bar: Tex. 1976, U.S. Dist. Ct. (so. dist.) Tex. Assoc. Fulbright & Jaworski, Houston, 1976-80, participating assoc., 1980-83, ptnr., 1983—. Dir. Houston Symphony Soc., 1993—. Recipient Benjamin Scharps prize Yale Law Sch., 1976, Ambrose Gherihi prize Yale Law Sch., 1976. Mem. ABA, Nat. Assn. Bond Lawyers (bd. dirs. 1988-89, treas. 1989-90, pres.-elect 1991, pres. 1991-92), Houston Bar Assn. Office: Fulbright & Jaworski LLP 1301 Mckinney St Ste 5100 Houston TX 77010-3095

WEBER, GEORGE, oncology and pharmacology researcher, educator; b. Budapest, Hungary, Mar. 29, 1922; came to U.S., 1959; s. Salamon and Hajnalka (Arvai) W.; m. Catherine Elizabeth Forrest, June 30, 1958; children: Elizabeth Dolly Arvai, Julie Vibert Wallace, Jefferson James. BA, Queen's U., 1950, MD, 1952; MD (hon.), U. Chieti, Italy, 1979, Med. Faculty, Budapest, 1982, U. Leipzig, Fed. Republic of Germany, 1987, Tokushima (Japan) U., 1988; Kagawa (Japan) U., 1992. Rsch. assoc. Montreal Cancer Inst., 1953-59; prof. pharmacology Ind. U. Sch. Medicine, Indpls., 1959—; dir. Lab for Exptl. Oncology Sch. Medicine, Ind. U., Indpls., 1974—; Milan Panič prof. oncology Ind. U., Indpls., 1994—; prof. Lab. for Exptl. Oncology Sch. Medicine, Ind. U., Indpls., 1974-90, disting. prof. Lab. for Exptl. Oncology, 1990—; chmn. study sect. USPHS, Washington, 1976-78; sci. adv. com. Am. Cancer Soc., N.Y.C., 1972-76, 94—, Damon Runyon Fund, N.Y.C., 1971-76; mem. U.S. Nat. Com., Internat. Union Against Cancer, Washington, 1974-80, 90-94, NAS, Washington, 1974-80, 90-94. Editor: Advances in Enzyme Regulation, Vols. 1-35, 1962—; assoc. editor Jour. Cancer Rsch., 1969-80, 82-89. Recipient Alecce Prize for cancer rsch. Tiberine Acad., Rome, 1971, Best Prof. award Student AMA, Indpls., 1966, 68, G.F. Gallanti prize for enzymology Internat. Soc. Clin. Chemists, 1984, Outstanding Investigator award Nat. Cancer Inst., NIH, 1986-94. Mem. Am. Soc. for Pharmacology and Exptl. Therapeutics, Am. Assn. Cancer Rsch. (G.H.A. Clowes award 1982), Am. Physiol. Soc., Biochem. Soc., Russian Acad. Sci. (hon.), Hungarian Cancer Soc. (hon.), Hungarian Acad. Scis. (hon.), Acad. Scis. Bologna (Italy) (hon.). Home: 7307 Lakeside Dr Indianapolis IN 46278-1618 Office: Ind U Sch Medicine Lab Exptl Oncology 702 Barnhill Dr Indianapolis IN 46202-5200

WEBER, GEORGE RICHARD, financial consultant, writer; b. The Dalles, Oreg., Feb. 7, 1929; s. Richard Merle and Maud (Winchell) W.; m. Nadine Hanson, Oct. 12, 1957; children: Zachary Ann Weber Katooli, Karen Louise Weber Zaro, Linda Marie. BS, Oreg. State U., 1950; MBA, U. Oreg., 1962. CPA, Oreg. Sr. trainee U.S. Nat. Bank of Portland (Oreg.), 1950-51; jr. acct. Ben Musa, CPA, The Dalles, 1954; tax and audit asst. Price Waterhouse, Portland, 1955-59; sr. acct. Burton M. Smith, CPA, Portland, 1959-62; pvt. practice, Portland, 1962—; lectr. acctg. Portland State Coll.; expert witness fin. and tax matters. Sec.-treas. Mt. Hood Kiwanis Camp, Inc., 1965. Exec. counselor SBA; mem. fin. com., powerlifting team U.S. Powerlifting Fedn., 1984, amb. People to People, China, 1987. With AUS, 1951-53. Decorated Bronze Star. Mem. AICPA, Internat. Platform Assn., Oreg. Hist. Soc.,Oreg. City Traditional Jazz Soc., Order of the Holy Cross Jerusalem, Order St. Stephen the Martyr, Order St. Gregory the Illuminator, Knightly Assn. St. George the Martyr, World Literary Acad., Portland C.S. Lewis Soc., Beta Alpha Psi, Pi Kappa Alpha. Republican. Lutheran. Clubs: Kiwanis, Portland Track, City (Portland); Multnomah Athletic; Sunrise Toastmasters. Author: Small Business Long-term Finance, 1962, A History of the Coroner and Medical Examiner Offices, 1963, CPA Litigation Service References, 1991; contbr. to profl. pubs. and poetry jours. Home: 2603 NE 32nd Ave Portland OR 97212-3611 Office: 4380 SW Macadam Ave Ste 210 Portland OR 97201-6404

WEBER, GERALD JOSEPH, federal judge; b. Erie, Pa., Feb. 1, 1914; s. Joseph J. and Ruth M. (Sullivan) W.; m. Berta M. Drechsel, Aug. 21, 1947; children: Thomas, William, Mary. A.B., Harvard U., 1936; LL.B., U. Pa., 1939. Bar: Pa. 1940. Civilian with U.S. Forces, Austria, 1946-47; mem. firm Knox, Weber, Pearson & McLaughlin, Erie, 1957-64; city solicitor Erie, 1951-61; judge U.S. Dist. Ct. Western Dist. Pa., 1964—. Served with AUS, 1942-45. Decorated Bronze Star. Office: US Dist Ct US Post Office & Courthouse 7th St # 2 Pittsburgh PA 15215-2115 also: US Courthouse Erie PA 16501

WEBER, GLORIA RICHIE, minister, retired state representative; married; 4 children. BA, Washington U., St. Louis; MA, MDiv, Eden Theol. Sem., Webster Groves, Mo. Ordained to ministry Evang. Luth. Ch. Am., St. Louis, 1974-. Min. Am. Luth. Ch., St. Louis, 1974; family life educator Luth. Family & Children's Svcs. Mo.; state representative State of Mo., 1993-94; mem. Ho. of Reps., Mo./com. high edn.; vice-chmn. fed.-state rels. and vets. affairs com., pub. health and safety and social svcs com.; Medicaid and the elderly com., 1993—; Mo. state organizer, activist Interfaith Alliance. Exec. dir. Older Women's League. Recipient Woman of Achievement award St. Louis Globe-Dem., 1977, Unselfish Cmty. Svc. award St. Louis Sentinel Newspaper, 1985, Faith in Action award Luth. Svcs. St. Louis, 1994, Outstanding Woman award Coalition of St. Louis Labor Women, 1994; named Woman of Yr., Variety Club, 1978, Woman of Worth, Older Women's League, 1993. Democrat. Home and Office: 4910 Valley Crest Dr Saint Louis MO 63128

WEBER, HANNO, architect; b. Barranquilla, Colombia, Sept. 24, 1937; came to U.S., 1952; s. Hans and Ester (Oks) W. BA magna cum laude, Princeton U., 1959, MArch, 1961. Registered architect, Ill., Fla., Mo., Pa., N.J., Va. Urban designer, research assoc. Guayana project MIT and Harvard U., Caracas, Venezuela, 1961-63; project architect Paul Schweikher Assocs., Pitts., 1963-67; asst. architect Princeton U., 1967-73; assoc. prof. architecture Washington U., St. Louis, 1973-80; sr. design architect, studio head, assoc. Skidmore, Owings & Merrill, Chgo., 1980-83; prin. Hanno Weber & Assocs., Chgo., 1984—; vis. lectr. Escuela Nacional de Arquitectura Universidad Nacional de Mex., 1975; research assoc. Research Ctr. Urban and Environ. Planning, Princeton, N.J., 1967-70; project dir. The Community Design Workshop, Washington U. Sch. Architecture, St. Louis, 1973-78; assoc. prof. architecture U. Wis., Milw., 1983—. Contbr. articles to profl. jours. Mem. Pres.'s Commn. on Education of Women Princeton U., 1968-69. Fellow NEH, 1970, Graham Found.; 1973; 1st prize winner Flagler Dr. Waterfront Master Plan design competition, West Palm Beach, Fla., 1984, 1st prize winner Mcpl. Ctr. design competition, Leesburg, Va., 1987, Chgo. AIA Disting. Bldg. award Citation of Merit, Altamira, Terrace, Highland Park, Fla., 1987. Mem. AIA (Urban Design award Mcpl. Govt. Ctr., Leesburg, Va., 1992, Chgo. AIA Interior Architecture award citation of merit, Mcpl. Govt. Ctr., Leesburg, Va., 1992), The Arch. Assn., Phi Beta Kappa. Office: Hanno Weber & Assocs 417 S Dearborn St Chicago IL 60605-1120

WEBER, HANS JÜRGEN, physics educator; b. Berlin, May 3, 1939; came to U.S., 1966; naturalized, 1993; s. Hans Gustav Wilhelm and Hedwig Bertha Elisabeth (Angermann) W.; m. Edith E. Enzian, Aug. 19, 1966; 1 child, Chris H. MS in Math., U. Frankfurt, Fed. Republic Germany, 1961, PhD in Physics, 1965. Postdoctoral rsch. assoc. U. Frankfurt, 1965-66, Duke U., Durham, N.C., 1966-67; postdoctoral rsch. assoc. U. Va., Charlottesville, 1967, asst. prof. physics, 1968-71, assoc. prof., 1971-77, prof., 1977—; vis. scientist U. Mainz, Fed. Republic Germany, 1972, 77, 91, U. Paris-Sud, Orsay, France, 1979; vis. prof. U. Lyon, France, 1978. Contbr. to Physics Reports, Springer Tracts, Phys. Letters, Phys. Rev. Rsch. grantee NSF, 1971—. Mem. AAAS, Am. Phys. Soc., Am. Assn. Physics Tchrs., Sigma Xi. Lutheran. Achievements include development of a nuclear force (NN interaction) from quark models and a possible connection between quantum chromodynamics and meson dynamics; research on isobars in nuclei. Office: U Va Inst Nuclear and Particle Physics Mccormick Rd Charlottesville VA 22904

WEBER, HARM ALLEN, college chancellor, former college president; b. Pekin, Ill., Sept. 28, 1926; s. Harm Allen and Hilda (Meyer) W.; m. Arlene Olson, Dec. 18, 1948; children: Jan Christine, Harm Allen III, Matthew Karl. B.A., Bethel Coll. St. Paul, 1950; B.D., Bethel Sem., 1954; M.R.E. Christian Theol. Sem., Indpls., 1959; postgrad., Ball State U., Muncie, Ind., 1961-62; D.D., Judson Coll., Elgin, Ill., 1964. Ordained to ministry Baptist Ch., 1953; pastorates at Isle (Minn.) Bapt. Ch., 1950-53, Central Bapt. Ch., Indpls., 1954-60, First Bapt. Ch., Muncie, 1960-64, Covenant Bapt. Ch., Detroit, 1964-69; pres. Judson Coll., Elgin, 1969-91; vice chmn. bd. trustees Judson Coll., chancellor, 1992—; chmn. Indpls. Fedn. Chs., 1955-59; pres. Delaware County (Ind.) Coun. Chs., 1963-64; chmn. evangelism Detroit Coun. Chs., 1967-69; v.p. Am. Bapt. Home Mission Soc., 1969—; mem. exec. com. Gt. Lakes Coun. on Ministry, 1969—; mem. Ministers and Missionaries Benefit Bd., 1974-75; mem. gen. bd. Am. Bapt. Chs./USA; mem. nat. adv. com. Ednl. Assistance Ltd., 1987—. Mem. Ind. Gov.'s Multiple Sclerosis Bd., 1957-60; bd. dirs. Camp Isongal, Delaware County Crippled Children's Assn.; chmn. bd. dirs. Galloway Meml. Youth Camp, Wahkon, Minn.; mem. state exec. bd. Vols. of Am.-Minn., 1976—; trustee Am. Bapt. Sem. of the West, 1984-86. Mem. Am. Assn. Pres. Ind. Colls. and Univs., Elgin Area C. of C. (dir. 1975-78), Am. Bapt. Assn. Colls. and Univs. (pres. 1986-89). Club: Rotary. Office: Judson Coll 1151 N State St Elgin IL 60123-1498

WEBER, HERMAN C., JR., architect; b. Erie, Pa., Mar. 3, 1939; s. Herman C. and Patricia E. (Gallagher) W.; m. Lynn Carol Thomas, Sept. 1, 1962; children: Beth, Gretchen, Brian. BArch, Pa. State U., 1962; MS in Archtl. Design, Columbia U., 1963. Registered arch., Pa., N.Y., Ohio, Mich.; cert. Nat. Coun. Archtl. Registration Bds. Prin. Weber Murphy Fox, Erie, Pa.; instr. design U. Ky., 1964-65. Prin. works include Springhill Retirement Ctr., Erie, Erie County Libr. and Niagara Mus., Drumkerry Ctr., Comml. Ctr. Bracebridge, Ont., Can., Rice Ave. Mid. Sch., Girard, Pa., Perry's Landing Residential Marina Cmty., Erie, Harbor Creek Jr. High Sch., Harborcreek, Pa., others. Bd. dirs. Booker T. Washington Ctr., Erie Metro YMCA; bd. advisors Erie County Juvenile Detention Facility; mem. coun. fellows Pa. State U. Behrend Coll.; bd. corporators St. Vincent Health Ctr. Mem. AIA (past pres. local chpt.), Pa. Soc. Archs. Office: Weber Murphy Fox 300 State St Ste 200 Erie PA 16507-1429

WEBER, HERMAN JACOB, federal judge; b. Lima, Ohio, May 20, 1927; s. Herman Jacob and Ada Minola (Esterly) W.; m. Barbara L. Rice, May 22, 1948; children: Clayton, Deborah. BA, Otterbein Coll., 1949; JD summa cum laude, Ohio State U., 1951. Bar: Ohio 1952, U.S. Dist. Ct. (so. dist.) Ohio 1954. Ptnr. Weber & Hogue, Fairborn, Ohio, 1952-61; judge Fairborn Mayor's Ct., 1956-58; acting judge Fairborn Mcpl. Ct., 1958-60; judge Greene County Common Pleas Ct., Xenia, Ohio, 1961-82, Ohio Ct. Appeals (2d dist.), Dayton, 1982-85, U.S. Dist. Ct. (so. dist.) Ohio, Cin., 1985—; chmn. Ohio Jud. Conf., Columbus, 1980-82; pres. Ohio Common Pleas Judges Assn., Columbus, 1975. Vice mayor City of Fairborn, 1955-57, council mem., 1955-59. Served with USNR, 1945-46. Office: US Dist Ct 810 Potter Stewart Ct House 5th & Walnut Sts Cincinnati OH 45202

WEBER, JANET M., nurse; b. Lansdale, Pa., Mar. 12, 1936; d. Russell H. and Naomi (Moyer) W. Diploma in nursing, Washington County Hosp. Sch. Nursing, 1959; B.S. in Nursing, Grace Coll., 1960; M.Ed., Duquesne U., 1969. Staff nurse Murphy Med. Ctr., Warsaw, Ind., 1959-60; coll. nurse Grace Coll., Winona Lake, 1959-60; med. surg. nursing instr. Washington County Hosp. Sch. Nursing, Hagerstown, Md., 1961-64; pvt. duty nurse Washington County Hosp., Hagerstown, 1964; chmn. found. of nursing Presbyn. Univ. Hosp. Sch. Nursing, Pitts., 1964-72; curriculum coordinator Albert Einstein Med. Ctr. Sch. Nursing, Phila., 1972-73; assoc. dir. Albert Einstein Med. Ctr. Sch. Nursing, 1973-74, acting dir., 1974, dir., 1974-87; staff nurse ARC Penn-Jersey Blood Drive Donor Services, Phila., 1988-92, asst. nurse mgr., 1992—; nurse mgr. ARC Penn-Jersey Blood Drivce Donor Svcs., Phila., 1992—; cons. Med. Bd. Higher Edn., 1981-82. Author: The Faculty's Role in Policy Development, 1981, Assisting Students with Educational Deficiencies, 1975. Sec. coun. hosps. Schs. Nursing Washington County Hosp., 1979. Mem. Washington County Hosp. Nurses Alumni Assn. (pres. 1962-64), Grace Coll. Alumni Assn., Duquesne U. Alumni Assn. Republican. Home: 5640 Arbor St Philadelphia PA 19120-2502 Office: ARC Blood Donor Svcs 700 Spring Garden St Philadelphia PA 19123

WEBER, JEAN MACPHAIL, museum director; b. Boston, Apr. 2, 1933; d. Harold Percy and Dorothy Norma (Mutch) MacPhail; children: Julia Lee, Karin MacPhail, Laurie Stewart. Student, Brown U. and R.I. Sch. Design, 1950-52, Edinburgh U., Scotland, 1952-53; B.A. magna cum laude, Brown U., 1954; postgrad. Danforth scholar, State U. Iowa, 1954-55. Mgr. Lane Bryant Splty. Shop, Denver, 1956-57; campus advisor Saratoga Springs Council Chs.. Skidmore Coll., N.Y., 1960-64; art dir. Our Lady of Peace Hosp., Louisville, 1964-65; dir. Jr. Art Gallery, Louisville, 1965-69, Parrish Art Mus., Southampton, N.Y., 1969-79, Rochester Mus. N.Y., 1979-80, Rochester Mus. and Sci. Ctr., N.Y., 1979-80, Mus. N.Mex., Santa Fe, 1981-85; co-dir. Mus. Internat., 1990-94. Mus. Art, U. Hist. Soc. Wis. 1985-90; dir. Marine Maritime Mus., 1990-94, Mus. Art, U. Maine, 1991—; dir. Maine Maritime Mus., 1990-94; dir. U. Maine Mus. of Art, 1994; mem. mus. studies adv. com. Tufts U., Medford, Mass., 1993—; mem. Maine State Archives Commn.; mem. mus. panel Maine Arts Commn. Contbr. articles to profl. jours. Mem. cultural affairs adv. com. Suffolk

County, N.Y., 1974—; trustee Brown U., 1983—, Inter Pueblo Cultural Ctr., 1981-82; bd. dirs. Maine Community Cultural Alliance, 1991—. Met. Mus. grantee, 1971. Mem. Am. Assn. Mus. (accreditation commn. 1976-85, chmn. 1982-85, mem. coun. 1979-81, v.p. 1985—, bd. dirs. 1993—), N.E. Mus. Conf. (v.p. 1978-79, pres. 1979-80), Internat. Coun. Mus., N.Y. State Assn. Mus. (coun. 1977-80), Phi Beta Kappa. Mem. Soc. of Friends. Home: Rt 1 Box 2090 Surry ME 04684 Office: U Maine Mus of Art 5712 Carnegie Hall Orono ME 04469-5712

WEBER, JEROME CHARLES, education and human relations educator; former academic dean and provost; b. Bklyn., Sept. 1, 1938; s. Meyer and Ethel (Shier) W.; m. Elizabeth Lynn Wiley, July 18, 1975; children: Amy Elizabeth, Jeffrey Glenn. B.S., Bklyn. Coll., 1960; M.A., Mich. State U. 1961, Ph.D., 1966. Mem. faculty U. Okla., Norman, 1964—, prof. edn., phys. edn., human rels. and social work, 1973—, Regents' prof. edn. and human rels., 1991—, asst. and acting dean, 1969-72, dean Univ. Coll., 1973-91, vice provost instructional svcs., 1979-91; chmn. ednl. leadership and policy studies, 1993. Author: (with D.R. Lamb) Statistics and Research in Physical Education, 1970, (with G. Henderson) College Survival for Student-Athletes, 1985; contbr. articles to profl. jours. Bd. dirs. Univ. div. United Way, 1970; pres. Norman Kindergarten Assn., 1968; commr. Norman Bd. Parks, 1971-79. Fellow Am. Coun. Sports Medicine; mem. Am. Assn. Higher Edn., Coun. Sports Psychology, Am. Coun. on Edn. Democrat. Jewish. Home: 5 Pebblecreek Rd Norman OK 73072 Office: 630 Parrington Oval Norman OK 73069-8813

WEBER, JOHN BERTRAM, architect; b. Evanston, Ill., Oct. 15, 1930; s. Bertram Anton and Dorothea Hennecke (Brammer) W.; m. Sally Ann French; children: Suzanne French Weber Roulston, Jane Marie Weber McCarthy, Patricia Ann Weber Blodgett, Nancy Brammer. AB in Architecture, Princeton U., 1953; postgrad., Ill. Inst. Tech., 1959. Lic. architect. Field engr. United Constrn. Co., Riverdale, N.D., 1952; draftsman Bertram A. Weber Architect, Chgo., 1947-53; architect Betram A. Weber Architect, Chgo., 1958-1973; field engr. Atkinson United Constrn. Co., Greenup and Ashland, Ky., 1956-58; ptnr., proprietor Weber & Weber Architects, Chgo., Northbrook and Winnetka, Ill., 1973—; Mem. Ill. Architecture Act Revision task force, 1982-89. Prin. works include Prestwick Country Club, the 3175 Commercial Ave. Bldg., Northbrook, med. office bldg. and additions to Bi-county hospital, Warren, Mich., additions and alterations to Detroit Osteopathic Hosp., addition to Duraclean Internat. Bldg., Deerfield, additions to The Admiral (a retirement home in Chgo.), and numerous pvt. residences, churches, comml., ednl. and recreational bldgs. Active Winnetka (Ill.) Cmty. Caucus, 1965, 74, mayor's adv. com. on bldg. codes, Chgo., 1975-80; chmn. bldg. com. Winnetka Cmty. House, 1977-81, Winnetka Zoning Bd. Appeals, 1983-88, chmn., 1987-88, Winnetka ad hoc Zoning com., 1995; deacon, elder Winnetka Presbyn. Ch. With USN, 1953-56. Fellow Ill. Soc. Architects (bd. dirs. 1969-84, 91—, pres. 1976-78); mem. AIA Chicago Chpt. 1968— (health facility com. 1969-76), Ill. Architect-Engr. Coun. (chmn. 1981-82, del. 1976-87, 92—), Northbrook C. of C. Architects Club Chgo. (pres. 1981, bd. dirs. 1976-86, 94), Builders Clug Chgo. (bd. dirs. 1986—, pres. 1973-74), Am. Legion, Old Willow Club (pres. 1982-83, bd. dirs. 1980-82), Mchts. and Mfrs. Club, Dairymens Country Club. Home: 415 Berkeley Ave Winnetka IL 60093-2109 Office: Weber & Weber Architects 415 Berkeley Ave Winnetka IL 60093-2109 also: 464 Central Ave Northfield IL 60093

WEBER, JOSEPH H., communications company executive; b. N.Y.C., Dec. 10, 1930; s. Sol and Minna (Hoffman) W.; m. Sophie Ruderman, Apr. 10, 1954 (div. 1973); m. J. V. Hammar, Jan. 10, 1976; children—Leslie, Jonathan, David. B.E.E., Rensselaer Poly. Inst., 1952; M.S.E., George Washington U., 1956. Engr. Hazeltine Electronics Co., Little Neck, N.Y., 1952-53; mem. tech. staff Bell Telephone Labs., N.Y.C., 1956-61; head network analysis dept. Bell Telephone Labs., Holmdel, N.J., 1961-72; dir. data services AT&T Long Lines, N.Y.C., 1972-75; dir. network services planning Bell Telephone Labs., Holmdel, 1975-80; dir. tech. standards and regulatory planning AT&T, Basking Ridge, N.J., 1980-84; dir. strategic planning AT&T, N.Y.C., 1984-85; dir. venture tech. AT&T, Berkeley Heights, N.J., 1985-87; v.p. tech. Global Transactions Services Co., Parsippany, N.J., 1987-88; ptnr. T.E.L.A. Group, 1989-94, Weber Temin & Co., 1995—. Vice-pres. Holmdel Twp. Bd. Edn., 1970-72; mem. Morris Twp. Planning Bd., 1988—. Served with U.S. Navy, 1953-56. Mem. IEEE (sr.), IEEE Communications Soc. (chmn. switching com. 1972-73). Patentee in field. Home: Box 224 16 Canfield Rd Convent Station NJ 07961

WEBER, JULIAN L., lawyer, former publishing and entertainment company executive; b. Des Moines, July 19, 1929; s. Milton and Zelda (Robinson) W.; m. Idelle Feinberg, Apr. 17, 1957; children—Jonathan Todd, Suzanne. B.A., UCLA, 1951; J.D., Harvard U., 1955. Bar: N.Y. 1956. Partner Botein Hays & Sklar, 1964-79; pres. Nat. Lampoon Inc., N.Y.C., 1979-84; pvt. practice law N.Y.C., 1984—. Mem. ABA, Assn. of Bar of City of N.Y.

WEBER, KENNETH J., hotel executive; b. 1946. With Arthur Young & Co., N.Y.C., 1968-71, ITT-Grinnell Corp., Midland Park, N.J., 1971-73, Farmbest Foods Internat., Louisville, 1973-74; pres. Farrell's Ice Cream divsn. Marriott Corp., Washington, 1974-80; v.p., contr. Country Kitchens Internat. divsn. Carlson Cos., Inc., Mpls., 1980-81; sr. v.p. Poppin Fresh Restaurant divsn. Pillsbury Co., Mpls., 1981-83; with Marriott Hotels Corp., Washington, 1983-87; sr. v.p., corp. contr. Red Lion Hotels Corp., Vancouver, Wash., 1987-92; sr. v.p., CFO Omni Hotels Corp., Hampton, N.H., 1992—; also v.p., treas. Omni Ctr. Corp., Richmond, Va. Office: Omni Hotels Corp 500 Lafayette Rd Hampton NH 03842*

WEBER, LARRY, public relations executive. Founder, pres. Weber Group, Inc., Cambridge, Mass., 1987—. Office: The Weber Group Inc 101 Main St Cambridge MA 02142

WEBER, LAVERN JOHN, marine science administrator, educator; b. Isabel, S.D., June 7, 1933; s. Jacob and Irene Rose (Bock) W.; m. Shirley Jean Carlson, June 19, 1959 (div. 1992); children: Timothy L., Peter J., Pamela C., Elizabeth T.; m. Patricia Rae Lewis, Oct. 17, 1992. AAS, Everett Jr. Coll., 1956; BA, Pacific Luth. U., 1958; MS, U. Wash., 1962, PhD, 1964. Instr. U. Wash., Seattle, 1964-67, asst. prof., 1967-69, acting state toxicologist, 1968-69; assoc. prof. Oreg. State U., Corvallis, 1969-75, prof., 1976—, asst. dean grad. sch., 1974-77; dir. Hatfield Marine Sci. Ctr. Oregon State U., Newport, 1977—, supt. Coastal Oreg. Marine Exptl. Sta., 1989—. Pres., trustee Newport Pub. Libr., 1991-92, Yaquina Bay Econ. Found., Newport, 1991-92; pres. Oreg. Coast Aquarium, 1993—. Recipient Pres. award Newport Rotary, 1984-85. Mem. South Slough Mgmt. Commn., Am. Soc. Pharm. and Exptl. Therapy, West Pharm. Soc. Assn. Toxicology, Soc. Exptl. Biol. Med. (n.w. divsn., pres. 1978, 82, 87), Pacific N.W. Assn. Toxicologists (chair 1985-86, coun. 1991-93), Western Assn. Marine Lab. (pres. 1993). Avocations: woodworking, reading, walking, scuba, gardening. Office: Oregon State Univ Hatfield Marine Sci Ctr Aquarium 2030 SE Marine Science Dr Newport OR 97365

WEBER, MARY ELLEN HEALY, economist; b. San Francisco, May 28, 1943; d. Ignatius Bernard and Grace Marie (Hogan) Healy; B.A., Dominican Coll., 1965; postgrad. Nat. U. Mex., 1967, (vis. scholar) Stanford U., 1969-70, Cath. U. Chile, 1970-71, U. Chile, 1971-72; Ph.D., U. Utah, 1974; m. Stephen Francis Weber, Dec. 21, 1971. U. Utah teaching fellow, 1965-68; asst. prof. Smith Coll., 1972-75; country economist World Bank, IBRD, 1975-76; sr. economist Internat. Research & Tech. Corp., McLean, Va. 1976-78; dir. regulatory analysis, chief economist OSHA, U.S. Dept. Labor, Washington, 1979-84; pres. Weber Software Enterprises, 1984-86, Web-Wolf Data Systems, Inc., 1986-90; dir. econs. exposure and tech divsn. Office of Pollution Prevention & Toxics US EPA, Washington, 1990—. Social Sci. Research Council fgn. area fellow 1969-71. Mem. Sr. Execs. Assn., Exec. Women in Govt. Roman Catholic.

WEBER, MAX O., fibered glass fiber products manufacturing company executive; b. 1929. With Owens Corning Fiberglass Corp., Toledo, Ohio, 1955—, v.p., 1975-86, sr. v.p., pres. constrn. products group, 1986-88, v.p., 1975-81; sr. v.p. Owens Corning Fiberglass Corp., Toledo, 1986-88, group pres., COO, 1988-90, chmn., CEO, 1990-91, retired, 1992. Office: Owens-Corning Fiberglas Corp Fiberglas Towers Toledo OH 43604

WEBER, MERRILL EVAN, lawyer, business executive; b. Chgo., Sept. 1, 1956; s. Robert and Mildred (Kurchitzer) W.; m. Mindy Kallus, Mar. 29, 1987; children: Stephanie Margalit, Sarah Abigail. BA, Columbia Coll., 1978, MS in Journalism, 1978, JD, 1984. Bar: N.Y. 1985, U.S. Dist. Ct. (so. and ea. dists.) N.Y. 1985. Assoc. Fried, Frank, Harris, Shriver & Jacobson, N.Y.C., 1984-85, Mayer, Brown & Platt, N.Y.C., 1985-87, Paul, Weiss, Rifkind, Wharton & Garrison, N.Y.C., 1987-91, D'Ancona & Pflaum, Chgo., 1991-92; CEO, gen. counsel Merrill Weber & Co., Inc. (formerly Weber, Halpert & Co., Inc.), Chgo., 1992—. Harlan Fiske Stone scholar, Columbia Law Sch., 1982-83, 1983-84. Mem. ABA, N.Y. State Bar Assn., Assn. of Bar of City of N.Y. Jewish. Office: Merrill Weber & Co Inc 100 S Wacker Dr Ste 1850 Chicago IL 60606-4004

WEBER, MICHAEL, editor; b. N.Y.C., Sept. 25, 1945; s. David and Dorothy (Silverberg) W. BA in History magna cum laude, CUNY, 1966; postgrad., U. Wis., 1966-67; MA in Am. Civilization, NYU, 1968. Asst. editor in regional studies gen. ency. dept. Macmillan Pub. Co., N.Y.C., 1970-71; assoc. editor in regional studies New Columbia Ency. project Columbia U. Press, N.Y.C., 1971-74; editing supr. coll. divsn. McGraw-Hill Book Co., N.Y.C., 1974-76; assoc. editor in social studies sch. dept. Harcourt Brace Jovanovich, N.Y.C., 1976-79; project editor coll. divsn. St. Martin's Press, N.Y.C., 1979-81, acquisitions editor and devel. editor coll. divsn., 1981-89; exec. editor history and polit. sci. M. E. Sharpe, Inc., Armonk, N.Y., 1989—; copyeditor, proofreader, fact-checker for several pubs. house and Met. Mus. of Art. Author: Our National Parks, 1994, Our Congress, 1994; contbr. articles to The New Columbia Encyclopedia, 1975, also to other books in field. Mem. Phi Beta Kappa, Phi Alpha Theta. Democrat. Avocations: classical music, wines, hiking, photography. Home: 6 Peter Cooper Rd # 2D New York NY 10010 Office: ME Sharpe 80 Business Park Dr Armonk NY 10504

WEBER, MORTON M., microbial biochemist, educator; b. N.Y.C., May 26, 1922; s. Morris and Mollie (Scherer) W.; m. Phyllis Stern Levy, July 31, 1955; children—Stephen Abbott, Ethan Lenard. B.S., Coll. City N.Y., 1949; Sc.D., Johns Hopkins, 1953. Instr. microbiology Sch. Medicine, Johns Hopkins, 1951-55; Am. Cancer Soc. fellow in biochemistry McCollum-Pratt Inst., 1953-56; instr. bacteriology and immunology Med. Sch., Harvard, 1956-59; asst. prof. Sch. Medicine, St. Louis U., 1959-61, assoc. prof., 1961-63, prof., 1963—, chmn. dept. microbiology, 1964-87, chmn. emeritus, 1987—, prof. emeritus, 1992—; vis. scientist microbiology unit U. Oxford (Eng.) Dept. Biochemistry, 1970—; sr. mem. Linacre Coll. Oxford U., 1970—; mem. microbial chemistry study sect. NIH, USPHS, 1969-73. Served with USAAF, 1942-46. Fellow AAAS, Am. Acad. Microbiology, Infectious Disease Soc. Am., Johns Hopkins Soc. Scholars; mem. Am. Soc. Biol. Chemists, Am. Soc. Microbiology (sec. physiology div. 1964-65, vice chmn. 1965-66, chmn. 1966-67), Soc. Gen. Microbiology, N.Y. Acad. Scis., St. Louis Biochemistry Group (sec. 1968-69), Phi Beta Kappa (hon.), Sigma Xi. Research in biochemistry of microorganisms, with emphasis on pathways and mechanisms of electron transport, enzymatic regulatory mechanisms, and mode of action of antimicrobial drugs and antibiotics. Home: 7068 Waterman Ave Saint Louis MO 63130-4323 Office: St Louis U Sch Medicine Dept Microbiology Saint Louis MO 63104

WEBER, NANCY WALKER, charitable trust administrator; b. Adrian, W.Va., Aug. 26, 1936; d. James Everett and Wanna Virginia (Alderman) Walker; m. J. Raymond Jacob, Jr., June 12, 1955 (div. 1967); children: Paul M., Sharon L.; m. George Harry Weber, Apr. 27, 1983. Student, Peabody Prep. Mus., 1946-53, Peabody Conservatory Mus., 1954-56. Asst. buyer cosmetics Hutzler's Dept. Store, Balt., 1967-69; exec. sec. to exec. v.p. Martin Marietta Corp., Bethesda, Md., 1969-75; asst. exec. to exec. dir. hosp. U. Utah, Salt Lake City, 1976-80; dir. program adminstrn. Lucille P. Markey Charitable Trust, Miami, Fla., 1983—. Pianist, organist Middle River Bapt. Ch., Balt., 1953-61. Named Mrs. Del. in Mrs. Del./Am. Pagent, 1966. Avocations: piano, organ. Office: Lucille P Markey Charitable Trust 3250 Mary St Ste 405 Miami FL 33133-5232

WEBER, OWEN, broadcast executive; b. N.Y.C., Apr. 29, 1946; s. Francis and Margaret (Korn) W.; m. Barbara Burke, Oct. 28, 1978. BS in Broadcasting, U. Fla., 1968. Program dir. Sta. WLYH-TV, Lancaster, Pa., 1970-72; dir. affiliate rels. Mut. Radio Networks, Washington, 1972-77; account exec. Sta. WCBM, Balt., 1977-78; local sales mgr. Sta. WTOP, Washington, 1979-80; gen. sales mgr. Sta. WTOP-Radio Outlet Co., Washington, 1980-81; gen. sales mgr. Sta. WCBM-Radio Metromedia, Balt., 1981-83; gen. sales mgr. Sta. WPGC-AM-FM First Media Corp., Washington, 1983-85; v.p., gen. mgr. Stas. WCAO-Radio and WXYV-Radio Summit Broadcasting Corp., Balt., 1985-88; exec. v.p. Summit Broadcasting Corp., Atlanta, 1988-93; pres., CEO HMW Comm., Inc., Atlanta, 1993-95; v.p., gen. mgr. Sta. KIKK-AM-FM and Sta. KILT-AM-FM Westinghouse Broadcasting Co.-Group W, Houston, 1995—. Office: Group W Radio Houston Ste 1900 24 E Greenway Plz Houston TX 77046

WEBER, PHILIP JOSEPH, retired manufacturing company executive; b. Chgo., Mar. 15, 1909; s. Joseph and Theresa (Zollner); m. Esther P. White, Aug. 29, 1941; 1 child, Patricia G. B.B.A. Northwestern U., 1938. With Ernst & Ernst, Chgo., 1938-41; with Doall Co., Des Plaines, Ill., 1941—88; exec. v.p. Doall Co., 1960-69, pres., 1969-74, chmn. bd., 1974-88, ret. Clubs: Mason (Shriner), Elk, Park Ridge Country. Home: 709 N Merrill St Park Ridge IL 60068-2701 also: 4545 N Ocean Blvd Apt 9-d Boca Raton FL 33431-5342

WEBER, ROBERT CARL, lawyer; b. Chester, Pa., Dec. 18, 1950; s. Robert Francis and Lucille (Nobili) W.; m. Linda Brediger, June 30, 1972; children: Robert F., Mary Therese, David P., Joseph T. BA cum laude, Yale U., 1972; JD, Duke U. 1976. Bar: Ohio 1976, U.S. Dist. Ct. (no. dist.) Ohio 1976, U.S. Ct. Claims 1980, U.S. Ct. Appeals (6th cir.) 1981, U.S. Ct. Appeals (5th cir.) 1995. Assoc. Jones, Day, Reavis & Pogue, Cleve., 1976-83, ptnr., 1983—. Bd. dirs. United Way Svcs. of Cleve., 1992—. Fellow Am. Coll. Trial Lawyers; mem. ABA, Ohio Bar Assn., Am. Law Inst., Product Liability Adv. Coun., Cleve. Bar Assn. (chmn. jud. selection com. 1985-86, trustee 1990-93, pres.-elect 1994-95, pres. 1995-96), Jud. Conf. for 8th Jud. Dist. Ohio (life), Order of Coif. Roman Catholic. Office: Jones Day Reavis & Pogue 901 Lakeside Ave E Cleveland OH 44114-1116

WEBER, ROBERT GEORGE, lawyer; b. Chgo., Mar. 12, 1939; s. Edward S. and Loraine (Chapman) W.; m. Diane Tuomi, June 16, 1962; children: Charles, Christine, Peter. BBA, Loyola of south, New Orleans, 1962; JD, Northwestern U., 1965. Ptnr. Foley & Lardner, Milw., 1965—. Editor-in-chief Northwestern U. Law Rev., 1964-65. Mem. ABA, Wis. Bar Assn., Order of Coif. Office: Foley & Lardner Firstar Ctr 777 E Wisconsin Ave Milwaukee WI 53202-5302

WEBER, ROBERT MAXWELL, cartoonist; b. L.A., Apr. 22, 1924; p. Milton and Edith (Huston) W.; m. Marilyn Baum, Oct. 11, 1953 (div.); children—Peter, Lee; m. Debora Graves, Dec. 24, 1988. Student, Pratt Inst., 1945-48, Art Students League, 1948-50. Fashion illustrator, 1949-54; artist New Yorker mag., 1962—; work commd. by IBM, N.Y. Telephone, Am. Airlines, Mobil, Blue Cross/Blue Shield, U.S. Healthcare, Goodyear Co., J.C. Penney Co., Air Canada, Swissair, others; contbr. cartoons to nat. mags. Served with USCGR, 1942-45. Office: New Yorker 20 W 43rd St New York NY 10036-7400

WEBER, RONALD GILBERT, retired college president; b. Bergholz, Ohio, Feb. 18, 1916; s. George John and Elizabeth (Davis) W.; m. Mary Evelyn Cook, May 25, 1940 (dec. Dec. 1979); children: Constance (Mrs. Norman G. Coates), Judith L. (Mrs. Charles C. Watts). A.B., Mt. Union Coll., 1938; D.B.A. (hon.), Ohio No. U., 1963; LL.D. (hon.), Baldwin-Wallace Coll. 1976; L.H.D. (hon.), Mt. Union Coll., 1980. Loan rep., comml. rep., mgr. Household Finance Corp. & Beneficial Mgmt. Corp., Canton, O., Pitts., and McKeesport, Pa., 1938-43; alumni sec., dir. admissions and publicity Mt. Union Coll., Alliance, O., 1943-44; bus. mgr., sec. trustees Mt. Union Coll., 1945-50, v.p., sec., 1950-67, acting pres., 1967-68, pres., 1968-80, pres. emeritus, 1980—; comml. rep. First Nat. Bank McKeesport, 1944-45; cons. Ohio No. U., 1984—. Past bd. dirs. United Fund Alliance; past treas. Alliance Citizens Hosp. Assn.; past chmn. Ohio Meth. Common. High Edn., life trustee Ohio Found. Ind. Colls.; past trustee, past vice chmn., mem. exec. com. Assn. Ind. Colls. and Univs. Ohio; hon. trustee Mt. Union Coll.; past

pres. East Central Coll. Consortium. Recipient Alumni award Mt. Union Coll., 1943, Ohio No. U., 1991. Mem. Alliance Country Club, Blue Key, Psi Kappa Omega, Pi Gamma Mu, Alpha Tau Omega. Methodist. Home: 440 Vincent St Alliance OH 44601-3952

WEBER, ROY EDWIN, savings and loan association executive; b. Ann Arbor, Mich., Aug. 17, 1928; s. Edwin J. and Ruth E. (Nichols) W.; m. Carol Warren, Oct. 29, 1948; children—Michael R., Douglas J. Student, Mich. State U. 1946-48; D. Bus. Adminstrn. (hon.), Cleary Coll., 1987. With Great Lakes Bancorp, 1948-91, v.p., treas., 1959-68, exec. v.p., treas., 1968-69, pres., 1969-91, chmn. bd., 1973—; past dir. Fed. Home Loan Bank, Indpls.; 6th Dist. rep. to adv. council Fed. Home Loan Bank Bd., 1980-81; trustee Fin. Instns. Retirement Fund. Mem. city coun., Ann Arbor, 1969-71; mem. regional bd. Catherine McAuley Health Ctr.; trustee Ann Arbor Found.; bd. dirs. McKinley Found., 1986—, Glacier Hills Retirement and Nursing Ctr.; campaign chmn. Washtenaw United Way, 1989. Mem. Mich. Savs. and Loan League (dir. 1970, pres. 1976), U.S. Savs. and Loan League (legis. com. 1969—), Ann Arbor C. of C. (past dir.). Republican. Lutheran. Club: Barton Hills Country. Home: 3340 Riverbend Dr Ann Arbor MI 48105-9648 Office: Gt Lakes Bancorp-Fed Savs Bank 401 E Liberty St Ann Arbor MI 48104-2268

WEBER, SAMUEL, editor; b. N.Y.C., July 31, 1926; s. Bernard and Gertrude (Ellenberg) W.; m. Eileen Gloria Hornstein, Mar. 5, 1950; children—Bruce Jay, Robert Matthew. B.S. in Elec. Engring., Va. Poly. Inst., 1947. Engr. N.Y. Bd. Transp., 1948-50, U.S. Naval Shipyard, Bklyn., 1950-52, Barlow Engring. Co., N.Y.C., 1952-54; engring. supr. Curtiss Wright Corp., Woodridge, N.J., 1954-56; electronics engr. Loral Electronics Corp., N.Y.C., 1957-58; with Electronics mag., N.Y.C., 1958-67, assoc. mng. editor, 1968-70, exec. editor, 1970-79, editor in chief, 1979-84, exec. tech. editor, 1984-88, editor-at-large, 1988-92; editor in chief Electrotechnology mag., N.Y.C., 1990—; pres. Samuel Weber & Assocs., 1988-91, Samuel Weber & Assocs., Inc., 1991—; contbg. editor Asic & Eda Magazine, 1991—; spl. projects editor Electronic Engring. Times, 1992—. Author: Modern Digital Circuits, 1964, Optoelectronic Devices and Circuits, 1968, Large and Medium Scale Integration, 1974, Circuits for Electronics Engineers, 1977, Electronic Circuits Notebook, 1981. Served with AUS, 1944-46. Mem. IEEE (life). Home and Office: 4242 E Allison Rd Tucson AZ 85712

WEBER, SAMUEL LLOYD, tap dancer, choreographer; b. Washington, Oct. 16, 1950; s. Abe Charles and Mary Louise (Walker) W.; m. Rosine Anne Bena, July 28, 1973 (div. May 1986); 1 child, Ananda Bena. Grad., Calif. State U., L.A. Prin. dancer Peninsula Ballet Theatre, San Mateo, Calif., 1972-86; ballet master, prin. dancer Sacramento Ballet, 1986; prin. dancer Jazz Tap Ensemble, L.A., 1986—; instr. dance artist-in-residence L.A. County H.S. for Arts, 1989-91, Calif. State U., Fullerton, 1990, 94. Tap dancer Joyce Theatre season, 1992 (Bessie award 1993), soloist with Lyon Symphony Biennial, 1991. Home: 1163 Guerrero St San Francisco CA 94110-2934 Office: 1433 Yale St # B1 Santa Monica CA 90404-3133

WEBER, SHIRLEY BOWERS, retired management analyst, networking communicator; b. Columbus, Miss., Nov. 9, 1942; d. Durant Jr. and Myra Waldene (Davis) Bowers; m. Frank Thomas Weber, Sept. 28, 1963 (div. May 26, 1966). Student, Ga. State Coll. Bus. Adminstrn., 1960-61, Montgomery Coll., 1977-79. Budget & mgmt. analyst U.S. Dept. Commerce/NOAA, Rockville, Md., 1977-81; sr. mgmt. analyst U.S. Dept. Commerce/NOAA Silver Spring, Md., 1992-94; sr. budget & mgmt. analyst Nat. Weather Svc., Silver Spring, Md., 1981-88; chief, prodn. mgmt. branch U.S. Dept. Commerce/NEXRAD, Silver Spring, Md., 1988-92. Author, editor: Animal Organizations-VA & DC, 1985, Directory of Animal Org's-MD & DC, 1986, Project BREED Directory Vol. 1, 1989, Project BREED Directory-Red Book, 1993. Humanitarian of yr. Montgomery County (Md.) Humane Soc., 1990, President's award SPCA of Anne Arundel County (Md.), 1992, Top Dog award Washington Animal Rescue League. V.p., Project BREED (Breed Rescue Efforts & EDucation), Inc., (founding bd. dirs.) 1994—. Democrat. Established a nationwide vol. coalition currently comprising approximately 10,000 vols. who specialize in rescue of specific breeds or species of animals. Avocations: gardening, reading. Office: Project BREED, Inc. PO Box 15888 Chevy Chase MD 20825-5888

WEBER, STEPHEN LEWIS, academic administrator; b. Boston, Mar. 17, 1942; s. Lewis F. and Catherine (Warns) W.; m. Susan M. Keim, June 27, 1965; children: Richard, Matthew. BA, Bowling Green State U., 1964; postgrad., U. Colo., 1964-66; PhD, U. Notre Dame, 1969; EdD (hon.), Capital Normal U., China, 1993. Asst. prof. philosophy U. Maine, Orono, 1969-75, assoc. prof., 1975-79, asst. to pres., 1976-79; dean arts and scis. Fairfield (Conn.) U., 1979-84; v.p. acad. affairs St. Cloud (Minn.) State U., 1984-88; pres. SUNY Oswego, 1988—; participant Harvard Inst. Ednl. Mgmt., Cambridge, Mass., 1985; cons. Sloan Found., 1981. Contbr. numerous articles on philosophy and acad. adminstrn. to profl. jours. Mentor Am. Coun. Edn. Fellowship Program; co-chair Minn. State Bd. Edn. Curriculum Task Force on Educating the Black Learner, 1988; mem. Minn. Tech. Alliance, 1987; mem. program adv. com. Minn. Higher Edn. Coordinating Bd., 1986-88; mem. Gov.'s Commn. on Internat. Edn., 1988. Named Outstanding Humanities Tchr., U. Maine, 1975; Rsch. fellow U. Notre Dame, 1968-69. Mem. Am. Philos. Assn., Am. Assn. Higher Edn. Democrat. Avocations: art, woodworking, swimming, boating. Home: Shady Shore Oswego NY 13126 Office: SUNY 706 Culkin Hall Oswego NY 13126-3500

WEBER, SUSAN, research organization executive; b. Freiburg, Germany, Dec. 7, 1941; d. Willie and Anna Marie (Herold) W.; children: Illeny Maaza, Seble-Wengale Maaza. Asst. dir. pub. rels. Ams. for Dem. Action, Washington, 1966-71; legal asst. Strout, Adams, Payson & Pellicani, Rockland, Maine, 1971-72; adminstrv. assoc. Fund for Neighborhood Devel., Washington, 1972-74; sr. assoc. Ct. Internat. Policy, Washington, 1976-78; dir. office of support projects Pub. Citizen Inc., Washington, 1978-79; dir. adminstrn. New Directions, Washington, 1979-80; exec. dir. Zero Population Growth, Washington, 1984—; dep. dir. Zero Population Growth, 1983-84, devel. dir., 1981-83. Editor: USA by Numbers, 1988; dir. study Urban Stress Test, 1988. Mem. Wider Opportunities for Women (treas. bd. dir. 1976-82), Global Tomorrow Coalition (treas. bd. dir. 1987-93), Natural Resources Coun. Am. (bd. dirs. 1984-86, 88—), Nat. Immigration, Refugee, & Citizenship Forum (treas. 1984-86), InterAction (exec. com. 1992—). Office: Zero Population Growth Inc 1400 16th St NW # 320 Washington DC 20036-2290

WEBER, THOMAS ANDREW, federal agency executive; b. Tiffin, Ohio, June 8, 1944; s. Stanley Walter and Anna Louise (Decker) W.; m. Stephanie Helen Anthony, Aug. 17, 1968 (div.); children: Thomas, Lisa, Stefan, Alice, Andrea. BS in Chemistry, U. Notre Dame, 1966; PhD in Chemistry, Johns Hopkins U., 1970. Mem. tech. staff AT&T Bell Labs., Murray Hill, N.J., 1970-87; program officer chem. div. NSF, Washington, 1987-88, divsn. dir. advanced sci. computing, 1988-92, divsn. dir. info. systems, 1992-94; exec. officer MPS, Arlington, Va., 1994—. Contbr. numerous articles to profl. jours. Fellow Am. Phys. Soc.; mem. Phi Beta Kappa, Sigma Xi. Roman Catholic. Office: 4201 Wilson Blvd Arlington VA 22230

WEBER, THOMAS WILLIAM, chemical engineering educator; b. Orange, N.J., July 15, 1930; s. William A. and Dorothy (Negus) W.; m. Marianne S. Hartmann, June 4, 1966; children—Anne Louise, William Alois. B.Chem. Engring., Cornell U., 1953, Ph.D., 1963; M.S. in Chem. Engring., Newark Coll. Engring., 1958. Registered profl. engr., N.Y. Chem. engr. econs. and planning Esso Research & Engring., Linden, N.J., 1955-58; instr. Cornell U., 1961-62; assist. prof. SUNY-Buffalo, 1963-66, assoc. prof. chem. engring., 1966-82, prof., 1982—; assoc. chmn. dept., 1980-82, chmn. dept., 1982-89. Author: An Introduction to Process Dynamics and Control, 1973. Named Prof. of Yr., Tau Kappa Chi, 1965; recipient Chancellor's award for excellence in teaching, 1981, Tchr. of Yr. award Tau Beta Pi, 1982. Fellow Am. Inst. Chem. Engrs. (chmn. we. N.Y. sect. 1969-70, Profl. Achievement award we. N.Y. sect. 1978), Am. Soc. Engring. Edn. (chmn. instrumentation divsn. 1975-77, chmn. St. Lawrence sect. 1979-80, 92-94, chmn. divsn. experimentation and lab.-oriented studies 1985-86, Outstanding Zone Campus Rep. award 1988, AT&T Found. award 1987-88), Tech. Socs. Coun. Niagara Frontier (sec. 1973-75, pres. 1975-76, treas. 1978—), Sigma Xi, Phi Kappa

Phi, Tau Beta Pi, Theta Xi. Presbyterian. Club: Swedish of Buffalo (pres. 1974-76). Home: 52 Autumnview Rd Buffalo NY 14221-1602

WEBER, WALTER JACOB, JR., engineering educator; b. Pitts., June 16, 1934. Sc.B., Brown U., 1956; M.S.E., Rutgers U., 1959; A.M., Harvard, 1961, Ph.D., 1962. Registered profl. engr. Diplomate Am. Acad. Environ. Engrs. Engr. Caterpillar Tractor Co., Peoria, Ill., 1956-57; instr. Rutgers U., 1957-59; engr. Soil Conservation Service, New Brunswick, N.J., 1957-59; research, teaching asso. Harvard, 1959-63; faculty U. Mich., Ann Arbor, 1963—; prof., chmn. water resources program U. Mich., 1968-91, The Earnest Boyce Disting. Prof. of Engring., 1987-94; The Gordon Maskew Fair and Earnest Boyce Disting. U. Prof. U. Mich., Ann Arbor, 1994—; dir. Great Lakes & Mid-Atlantic Hazardous Substance Rsch. Ctr., Nat. Ctr. for Integrated Bioremediation R & D; Internat. cons. to industry, govt. Author: (with K.H. Mancy) Analysis of Industrial Wastewaters, 1971, Physicochemical Processes for Water Quality Control, 1972, (with F.A. DiGiano) Process Dynamics in Environmental Systems, 1995; editor-author: (with E. Matijevic) Adsorption from Aqueous Solution, 1968; contbr. numerous articles and chpts. to tech., profl. jours. and books. Recipient Disting. Faculty awards U. Mich., 1967, 78, Rsch. Excellence award U. Mich., 1980, Stephen S. Attwood award U. Mich., 1987, Disting. Faculty award Mich. chpt. Assn. Gov. Bds. of State Univs., 1989, Disting. Scientist award U.S. EPA, 1991; Faraday lectr. U. Mich., 1970; named Engr. of Distinction, Engrs. Joint Coun., 1973. Mem. NAE, Am. Acad. Environ. Engrs (Diplomate 1975, Gordon Maskew Fair award, 1995), .Am. Chem. Soc. (cert. of merit 1962, F. J. Zimmerman award 1982), Am. Inst. Chem. Engrs., ASCE (Rudolph Hering medal 1980, Thomas R. Camp award 1982, Simon W. Freese award 1984, G. Brooks Earnest award 1985), Am. Water Works Assn. (life, Acad. Achievement awards 1981, 89, A.P. Black Rsch. award 1991), Assn. Environ. Engring. Profs. (Disting. Faculty award 1968, NALCO research award 1979, Engring. Sci. rsch. award 1984, Outstanding Publ. award 1989, Disting. Lectr. award 1990), Internat. Assn. for Water Pollution Rsch. and Control (Founders Outstanding publication award 1987, 92), Water Pollution Control Fedn. (John R. Rumsey Meml. award 1975, Willard F. Shephard award 1980, Thomas R. Camp medal 1988, Gordon Maskew Fair medal 1990), Tau Beta Pi, Sigma Xi, Chi Epsilon, Delta Omega. Home: PO Box 7775 Ann Arbor MI 48107-7775 Office: U Mich Coll Engring Environ Engring Program Ste 181 EWRE Bldg Ann Arbor MI 48109-2125

WEBER, WENDELL WILLIAM, pharmacologist; b. Maplewood, Mo., Sept. 2, 1925; s. Theodore William and Flora Ann (Holt) W.; m. La Donna Tavis, Sept. 29, 1952; children—Jane Holt, Theodore Wendell. A.B., Central Coll., 1945; Ph.D. in Phys. Chemistry, Northwestern U., 1950; M.D., U. Chgo., 1959. Diplomate Am. Bd. Pediatrics; lic. Mich., N.Y., Calif. Asst. prof. chemistry U. Tenn., Knoxville, 1949-51; mem. ops. research staff U.S. Army Chem. Center, Edgewood, Md., 1951-55; successively instr., asst. prof., asso. prof., prof. pharmacology N.Y. U. Sch. Medicine, N.Y.C., 1963-74; prof. U. Mich., Ann Arbor, 1974—; Disting. Lectureship in Biomedical Rsch. U. Mich., 1993; mem. pharmacology-toxicology com. NIH, 1969-73, rev. coms., 1968—. NIH spl. fellow, 1962-65; research grantee, 1967—; recipient Career Scientist awards N.Y.C. Health Research Council, 1965-70, 70-74. Fellow N.Y. Acad. Scis.; mem. Am. Soc. Pharmacology and Therapeutics, Am. Chem. Soc., Am. Soc. Human Genetics, Soc. Toxicology (hon.), AAAS, Sigma Xi, Phi Lambda Upsilon. Research specialty in pharmacogenetics. Home: 14 Geddes Hts Ann Arbor MI 48104-1724 Office: Dept Pharmacology U Mich Ann Arbor MI 48109-0632

WEBER, WILFORD ALEXANDER, education educator; b. Allentown, Pa., Apr. 29, 1939; s. Alexander F. and Kathryn A. (Campbell) W.; children from previous marriage: Kendra L., Brad A.; m. Cheryl Angelo. Ba, Muhlenberg Coll., 1963; EdD, Temple U., 1967. Tchr., counselor New Life Boys Ranch, Harleysville, Pa., 1963-65; rsch. asst. Temple U., Phila., 1965-67; asst. prof. Syracuse (N.Y.) U., 1967-71; prof. U. Houston, 1971—; chair dept. curriculum & instrn. Author approximately 160 books, monographs, papers and articles. Grantee, Syracuse U., U. Houston. Mem. Am. Ednl. Rsch. Assn., Assn. Tchr. Educators. Avocation: sports. Home: 2015 Swift Blvd Houston TX 77030-1213

WEBER, WILLIAM P., electronics company executive; b. 1940; married. BS, Lamar U., 1962; MS, So. Meth. U., 1966. With Tex. Instruments, Inc., Dallas, 1962—; mgr. assembly and test equipment group, 1965-70, mfr. mgr. electro-optics div. equipment group, 1970-71, mgr. ops. digital systems, 1971-75, asst. v.p., mgr. missile div. equipment group, 1975-79, 1979-80, mgr. Lewisville site, 1979-80, v.p., mgr. electro optics div., 1980-81, mgr. Forest Ln. site, 1980-81, v.p., mgr. equipment group, 1981-82, v.p. and pres. defense systems and electronics group, 1982-84, exec. v.p., mgr. corp. devel., 1984-87, exec. v.p., pres. semiconductor group, 1987—, also bd. dirs. Office: Tex Instruments Inc PO Box 655474 13500 N Central Expy Dallas TX 75265

WEBER-ROOCHVARG, LYNN, consultant, adult education specialist, librarian; b. Long Beach, Calif., Jan. 5, 1945; d. Bernard R. and Ruth M. (Oehler) Weber; m. Edward A. Birge (div.); 1 child, Colin E.; m. Alan C. Roochvarg. BA, U. Wis., 1966, MA in Libr. Sci., 1967; PhD, Ariz. State U., 1980. Teaching asst. U. Wis., Madison, 1966-67; libr. Madison Pub. Libr., 1967-70, New Haven Free Pub. Libr., 1970-72; ESL instr. Tempe (Ariz.) Adult Basic Education Program, 1972-77, supr., 1977-80; pvt. practice Phoenix, 1980-82; libr. Phoenix Coll., 1982-84, Lansdale (Pa.) Sch. Bus., 1985-92; pres. LWR Assocs., Colmar, Pa., 1991—. Author: Serving Adult Learners, 1981; contbr. articles to profl. jours. Ford Found fellow, 1966; Ariz. Dept. Edn. grantee, 1978-80. Mem. ALA, Pa. TESOL, Phi Beta Kappa. Office: LWR Assocs PO Box 501 Colmar PA 18915-0501

WEBRE, SEPTIME, ballet company artistic director, choreographer; b. New Orleans, Dec. 7, 1961; s. Alfred L. and Juanita (Chisholm) W. BA, U. Tex., 1984. Dancer Merce Cunningham Dance Co., N.Y.C., 1981; dancer Am. Repertory Ballet/Princeton (N.J.) Ballet, 1987—, choreographer, 1988—, artistic dir., 1993—; freelance choreographer various ballet cos., 1988—; guest master tchr. various ballet cos., 1990—. Former mem. exec. bd. Young Dems. Am., Austin. Choreographic fellow N.J. Coun. on Arts, 1992. Roman Catholic. Office: Am Repertory Ballet 80 Albany St New Brunswick NJ 08901

WEBSTER, ALBERT KNICKERBOCKER, consultant in performing arts; b. Bklyn., Oct. 14, 1937; s. Albert Noyes and Janet (Knickerbocker) W.; m. Sara Beyer, Feb. 19, 1961; children: Albert Van Berghen, Katherine Lee. BA, Harvard Coll., 1959; student, L'Ecole de Musique de Fontainebleau, summers 1958-59. Asst. to mgr., asst. mgr. N.Y. Philharm., 1962-71, mng. dir., 1975-90, exec. v.p., 1978-90; gen. mgr. Cin. Symphony Orch., 1971-75; mem., co-chmn. planning sect., orch. sect., music panel Nat. Endowment for Arts, 1974-80, mem. inter-arts panel, 1981-82. Bd. dirs., treas. Am. Music Ctr.; bd. dirs Harvard Pieriou Found. Mem. Am. Symphony Orch. League (exec. com., bd. dirs.), Am. Arts Alliance (founding dir., bd. dirs., exec. com., sec.). Office: 5316 S Dorchester Ave Apt 408 Chicago IL 60615-5365

WEBSTER, DANIEL ROBERT, lawyer; b. Wayne, Mich., June 23, 1945. B.A. with high distinction, Ind. U., 1967; J.D., Harvard U., 1970. Bar: Ind. 1971, U.S. Dist. Ct. (so. dist.) Ind. 1971, U.S.C. Ct. Appeals (7th cir.) 1972, U.S. Supreme Ct. 1982; assoc. Hogan and Hartson, Washington, 1970-1; assoc. Ice, Miller, Donadio & Ryan, Indpls., 1971-77, 84—; dir. research Ind. Lawyers Commn., Indpls., 1977-81; sr. atty. Cummins Engine Co., Columbus, Ind., 1981-83; of counsel Ice Miller Donadio & Ryan, Indpls., 1983-85, ptnr., 1986—; mng. ptnr. Bamberger & Feibleman, Indpls. 1992—; chmn. corrections com. Indpls. Lawyers Commn., 1979-80, chmn. pub. defender com., 1977-80, mem. community services com., 1973-74, bd. dirs., 1974-80; mem. Greater Indpls. Progress Com. Task Force on Criminal Justice; mem. Legal Def. Panel; adv. com. The Carl Duisberg Soc., Ind. U. East Asian Studies Ctr.; mem. speakers bur. Indpls.; sec. bd. dirs Moore-Langen Printing Co. Inc. Co-editor: An Anatomy of Criminal Justice, 1980, Juvenile Intervention, 1982; contbr. articles to profl. jours.; producer TV Spl. Violence and the Public Response, 1978. Dem. nominee for Ind. Atty. Gen., 1980; Indpls., 1976-80; Am. del. Internat. YMCA Conf. on Disarmament and Detente, 1981; counsel Ind. Dem. Policy Com. 1980-81; mem. culture

com. Ind. Ptnrs. for the Americas, 1983—; bd. dirs. Am. Ctr. for Internat. Leadership, Indpls. Pan Am. Games Planning Com.; bd. dirs. Indpls. Internat. Ctr., CEO Indpls. World Trade Ctr., chmn. Ind. Asean Coun. Served with U.S. Army, 1971. Ind. U. merit scholar, 1966-67; Wheeler scholar, 1966-67; Ford P. Hall scholar, 1967. Mem. Ind. Assn. (internat. law sect.), Indpls. Bar Assn. NAACP, Ind. Hist. Soc., Ind. Lawyers Commn. (bd. dirs. 1982—), Ind. Council Fgn. Relations, Indpls. Lit. Club. Indpls. Econ. Club (bd. dirs.), Forum for Internat. Profl. Services, Inc. (bd. dirs., pres.), Internat. Sch. of Indpls. (bd. dirs.), Blue Key, Phi Beta Kappa, Phi Eta Sigma. Club: Phoenix. Office: Bamberger & Feibleman Ste 600 54 Monument Cir Indianapolis IN 46204

WEBSTER, DAVID A., lawyer; b. Jacksonville, Fla., Aug. 25, 1948. BBA summa cum laude, U. Ga., 1975, JD cum laude, 1977; LLM Taxation, NYU, 1979. Bar: Ga. 1977, U.S. Tax Ct. 1978, Fla. 1980. Ptnr. Baker & Hostetler, Orlando, Fla., 1980-94, Mahoney Adams & Criser PA, Jacksonville, 1994—; mem. Fla. Coun. Internat. Devel. 1981—, World Trade Coun. Ctrl. Fla. 1979—; chmn. Internat. Tax Discussion Group, 1989-90. Contbr. articles to profl. jours. Capt. U.S. Army, 1967-73. Mem. ABA (con. sect. taxation 1981-85), Internat. Bar Assn., Fla. Bar Assn. (exec. com. intenat. law, co-chmn. internat. tax com. 1986-87), State Bar Ga., Am. Assn. Atty. Cert. Pub. Accts., Orange County Bar Assn. (chmn. tax sect. 1986-87), adjunct prof. Unity of North Fla. Grad. Acctg. Program, Phi Kappa Phi. Office: Mahoney Adams & Criser PA 3300 Barnett Ctr 50 N Laura St Jacksonville FL 32202

WEBSTER, DAVID ARTHUR, life insurance company executive; b. Downs, Ill., July 20, 1937; s. Harold Sanford and Carmen Mildred (Moore) W.; m. Anna Elizabeth Prosch, June 10, 1956; children: Theodore David, Elizabeth Anna, Arthur Lee, William Harold. B.S., U. Ill., 1960. Actuarial asst. Mass. Mut. Life Ins. Co., Springfield, 1960-64; cons. actuary George Stennes & Assocs., Mpls., 1964-68; v.p., actuary Piedmont Life Ins. Co., Atlanta, 1968-72, Pacific Fidelity Life Ins. Co., Los Angeles, 1972-74; v.p., chief actuary U.S. Life Corp., N.Y.C., 1974-76; exec. v.p. U.S. Life Corp., 1976-78; dir., 1976-78; pres., dir. Beneficial Pension Svcs, BPS Agy., Inc.; v.p., treas., dir. Beneficial Assurance Co., 1978-82; asst. sec., dir. Beneficial Computer Svcs., Inc.; treas. Tel-Assurance Corp.; exec. v.p., dir. Beneficial Standard Life, 1978-82; pres., dir. U.S. Life Ins. Co. of Calif., 1982-84, Western World Fin. Group Inc., 1984-86; exec. v.p., COO R.W. Durham and Co., 1987—. Fellow Soc. Actuaries; mem. Am. Acad. Actuaries. Clubs: Actuaries of Pacific States, Woodland Hills Country. Home: 5131 Encino Ave Encino CA 91316-2523

WEBSTER, EDWARD WILLIAM, medical physicist; b. London, Apr. 12, 1922; came to U.S., 1949, naturalized, 1957; s. Edward and Bertha Louisa (Cornish) W.; m. Dorothea Anne Wood, June 24, 1961; children: John Stein, Peter Wood, D. Anne, Edward Russell, Mark Vincent, Susan Victoria. BSc in Elec. Engring., U. London, 1943, PhD, 1946; postgrad., MIT, 1949-51, 65-66, Columbia U., 1966; AM (hon.), Harvard U., 1989. Diplomate: Am. Bd. Radiology in radiol. physics (examiner 1958-84, chmn. physics com. 1966-76), Am. Bd. Health Physics. Research engr. English Electric Co., Stafford, Eng., 1943-49; travelling fellow lab. for nuclear sci. MIT, 1949-50, staff scientist, 1950-51; lectr. U. London, 1952-53; physicist Mass. Gen. Hosp., Boston, 1953—, chief radiol. scis. div., 1970—; prof. radiology Harvard U. Med. Sch., Boston, 1975—; prof. radiology div. health scis. and tech. Harvard-MIT, 1978-86; Langham lectr. U. Ky. Coll. Medicine, 1989; mem. adv. com. on environ. hazards VA, 1985, U.S. del. UN Sci. Com. on Effects of Atomic Radiation, 1987—; lectr. Harvard Sch. Pub. Health, 1971-86; cons. Radiation Effects Rsch. Found., Hiroshima, Japan, 1988; Taylor lectr. Nat. Coun. on Radiation Protection, 1992. Author: A Basic Radioisotopes Course, 1959, Atlas of Radiation Dose Distributions, 1965, Radiation Safety Manual of MGH, 1965, Physics in Diagnostic Radiology, 1970; co-author: Instrumentation and Monitoring Methods for Radiation Protection, 1978, Low-level Radiation Effects, 1982; co-editor: Advances in Medical Physics, 1971, Biological Risks of Medical Irradiations, 1980; inventor composite shields against low energy X-rays, 1970. Robert Blair travelling fellow London County Council, 1949; USPHS fellow, 1965; NIH grantee, 1958-80. Fellow Health Physics Soc. (Landauer award 1985, Failla award 1989), Am. Coll. Radiology (commn. mem. 1963—, Gold medal 1991); mem. Am. Assn. Physicists in Medicine (dir. 1958-65, pres. 1963-64, Coolidge medal 1983), Soc. Nuclear Medicine (trustee 1973-77), Radiol. Soc. N.Am. (v.p. 1977-78), New Eng. Roentgen Ray Soc. (hon., exec. com. 1976-77), Radiation Rsch. Soc., Sigma Xi (nat. lectr. 1988-89). Office: Mass Gen Hosp Fruit St Boston MA 02114-2620 *My efforts have focused on increasing and spreading knowledge which will improve man's control over his environment, including his health. Important principles include freedom to discuss and publish, respect for the rights of others and the acceptance of calls for difficult service.*

WEBSTER, ELROY, diversified supplies and machinery executive. Former 2d v.p., now chmn. Farmers Union Cen. Exch., Inc. Office: Farmers Union Cen Exch Inc 5500 Cenex Dr Inver Grove MN 55077-1733 also: Cenex PO Box 64089 Saint Paul MN 55164

WEBSTER, FREDERICK ELMER, JR., marketing educator, consultant; b. Auburn, N.Y., Oct. 22, 1937; s. Frederick Elmer and Evelyn May (Dudden) W.; m. Mary Alice Powers, Dec. 27, 1957; children: Lynn Marie, Mark Andrew (dec.), Lisa Ann. AB, Dartmouth Coll., 1959, MBA, 1960; PhD, Stanford U., 1964; Artium Magistrum (hon.), Dartmouth Coll., 1974. Asst. prof. mktg. Columbia U., N.Y.C., 1964-65; from asst. prof. to prof. bus. adminstrn. Dartmouth Coll., Hanover, N.H., 1965-79; assoc. dean Amos Tuck Sch. Dartmouth Coll., Hanover, 1976-83, E.B. Osborn prof. mktg., 1979-93, Charles Henry Jones Third Century prof. mgmt., 1993—; vis. prof. Internat. Mgmt. Inst., Geneva, 1970-88; vis. prof. bus. sch. Harvard U., Boston, 1987-89; exec. dir. Mktg. Sci. Inst., Cambridge, Mass., 1987-89; bd. dirs. Samuel Cabot, Inc., Mascoma Savs. Bank, Lebanon, N.H. Author: Marketing Communications, 1968, Social Aspects of Marketing, 1947, Marketing for Managers, 1974, Industrial Marketing Strategy, 1979, 2d edit., 1984, 3rd edit., 1991, Marketing Management Casebook, 1980, 4th edit., 1984, Field Sales Management, 1983, Market-Driven Management, 1994; editor: Ronald Series on Marketing Management, 1975-91; mem. editl. bd., sect. editor: Jour. Mktg., 1968—, Mktg. Letters, 1989—, Mktg. Mgmt., 1991—, Jour. Market-Formed Mgmt., 1995—; contbr. articles to profl. jours. Trustee Alice Peck Day Meml. Hosp., Lebanon, N.H., 1970-87, Mktg. Sci. Inst., 1989—; bd. overseers Hanover Inn, N.H., 1985-92; firefighter Town of Hanover, 1970—, lt. Etna Div., 1991—, mem. fin. com., 1973-78, com. chmn. 1977-78; bd. dirs. v.p. Vt. Pub. Radio, 1978-91, 92—; mem. fin. com. Dresden Sch. Dist., Hanover, 1973-76, chmn 1976-77; vestryman, treas. St. Thomas Episc. Ch., Hanover, 1967-70, 76-78, 91-92; mem. missions com. Episc. diocese N.H., Concord, 1988—. Gulf Oil fellow, 1959-60, U.S. Steel Found. fellow, 1961-63, Nat. Assn. Purchasing Agts. Doctoral fellow, 1963-64. Mem. Am. Mktg. Assn. (dir. 1972-74), Norford Lake Club. Republican. Episcopalian. Home: Deer Run Farm 80 Stevens Rd Hanover NH 03755-3114 Office: Dartmouth Coll Amos Tuck Sch Bus Adminstrn Hanover NH 03755

WEBSTER, GEORGE DRURY, lawyer; b. Jacksonville, Fla., Feb. 8, 1921; s. George D. and Mary Gaines (Walker) W.; m. Ann Kilpatrick; children: Aen Walker, George Drury, Hugh Kilpatrick. BA, Maryville Coll., 1941, LLD (hon.), 1984; LLB, Harvard U., 1948. Bar: Tenn. 1948, D.C. 1952, Md. 1976. Atty. tax div. Dept Justice, 1949-51; sr. partner Webster, Chamberlain & Bean, Washington; lectr. numerous tax. insts. Author: Business and Professional Political Action Committees, 1979, The Law of Associations, 1995. Trustee U.S. Naval Acad. Found., Annapolis, Md.; spl. U.S. ambassador, 1972. Served to lt. USNR, 1942-46. Mem. Am. Law Inst., Am. Bar Assn. Presbyn. Clubs: Chevy Chase (Md.); Metropolitan (Washington); Racquet and Tennis (N.Y.C.). Home: 5305 Cardinal Ct Bethesda MD 20816-2908 also: Webster Angus Farm Rogersville TN 37857 Office: Webster Chamberlain & Bean 1747 Pennsylvania Ave NW Washington DC 20006-4604

WEBSTER, HENRY DEFOREST, neuroscientist; b. N.Y.C., Apr. 22, 1927; s. Leslie Tillotson and Emily (deForest) W.; m. Marion Havas, June 12, 1951; children: Christopher, Henry, Sally, David, Steven. AB cum laude, Amherst Coll., 1948; MD, Harvard U., 1952. Intern Boston City Hosp., 1952-53, resident, 1953-54; resident in neurology Mass. Gen. Hosp., 1954-56,

research fellow in neuropathology, 1956-59; prin. investigator NIH research grants for electron microscopic studies of peripheral neuropathy, 1959-69; mem. staffs Mass. Gen., Newton-Wellesley hosps.; instr. neurology Harvard Med. Sch., 1959-63, assoc. in neurology, 1963-66, asst. prof. neuropathology, 1966; assoc. prof. neurology U. Miami Sch. Medicine, 1966-69, prof., 1969; head sect. cellular neuropathology Nat. Inst. Neurol. Diseases and Stroke, Bethesda, Md., 1969—; assoc. chief Lab. of Neuropathology and Neuroanat. Scis., 1975-84; chief Lab. Exptl. Neuropathology, 1984—; disting. scientist, lectr. dept. anatomy Tulane U. Sch. Medicine, 1973; Royal Coll. lectr. Can. Assn. Neuropathologists, 1982; Saul Korey lectr. Am. Assn. Neuropathologists, 1992; chmn. Winter Conf. on Brain Rsch., 1985, 86; head neuropathology delegation to visit China in 1990, Citizen Amb. Program, People to People Internat.; mem. exec. com. rsch. group on neuromuscular disease World Fedn. Neurology, 1986-93. Author: (with A. Peters and S.L. Palay) The Fine Structure of the Nervous System, 1970, 76, 91; contbr. articles to sci. jours. Recipient Superior Svc. award USPHS, 1977, A. von Humboldt award Fed. Republic Germany, 1985, Sci. award Peripheral Neuropathy Assn., 1994; named hon. prof. Norman Bethune U. of Med. Scis., Chanchun, China, 1991. Mem. Am. Assn. Neuropathologists (v.p. 1976-77, pres. 1978-79, Weil award 1960), Internat. Soc. Neuropathology (councillor 1976-80, v.p. 1980-84, exec. com. 1980-84, 86-94, pres. 1986-90), Internat. Congress Neuropathology (exec. gen. VIII 1978), Peripheral Nerve Study Group (exec. com. 1975-93, chmn. 1977 meeting), Japanese Soc. Neuropathology (hon.), Am. Neurol. Assn., Am. Acad. Neurology, Am. Soc. Cell Biologists, 1982; Am. Assn. Anatomists, Soc. Neurosci., Washington Ctr. Photography, Ausable Club. Office: NIH Bldg 36 Rm 4A 29 Bethesda MD 20892

WEBSTER, JAMES COLIN EDEN, oil company executive; b. Rangoon, Burma, Mar. 5, 1936; came to U.S., 1986; m. Susan Gorton Scarff, Sept. 13, 1965; children: Vanessa, Alexander, Benedict. BA, Trinity Coll., 1959, MA, 1967. With British Petroleum, London, 1959-85; pres. British Petroleum N.Am., N.Y.C., 1986; exec. v.p. British Petroleum Am., Cleve., 1987—, Standard Oil Co., Cleve., 1986-87. Office: BP Am Inc 200 Public Sq Cleveland OH 44114-2209

WEBSTER, JAMES RANDOLPH, JR., physician; b. Chgo., Aug. 25, 1931; s. James Randolph and Ruth Marian (Burtis) W.; m. Joan Burchfield, Dec. 28, 1954; children: Susan, Donovan, John. B.S., U. Chgo.-Northwestern U., 1953; M.D., M.S., Northwestern U., 1956. Diplomate: Am. Bd. Internal Medicine (sub bd. pulmonary disease and geriatrics). Intern Phila. Gen. Hosp., 1956-57; resident in medicine and fellow in pulmonary disease Northwestern U., 1957-60, 62-64; asst. chief medicine Northwestern Meml. Hosp., Chgo., 1968-73; chief medicine Northwestern Meml. Hosp., 1973-88; prof. medicine Northwestern U. Med. Sch., 1977—, chief gen. med. sect. Dept. Medicine, 1987-88; chief exec. officer Northwestern Med. Group Practice, 1978-88; dir. ctr. on aging/geriatrics Northwestern U. Med. Ctr., 1988—; chief staff Northwestern Meml. Hosp., 1988-90. Contbr. chpts. to books, articles to med. jours. Served with U.S. Army, 1960-62. Recipient Outstanding Clin. tchr. award Northwestern U. Med. Sch., 1974, 77, 84, 86, Alumni Merit award Northwestern U., 1979. Mem. Am. Fedn. Clin. Rsch. (ACP gov. for Ill. 1988-92, chair sub-com. on aging 1993—, Claypoole award 1994), Am. Thoracic Soc., Am. Geriatrics Soc., Ill. Geriatrics Soc. (pres. 1992-94), Soc. Rsch. and Edn. in Geriatrics. Home: 227 E Delaware Pl Chicago IL 60611-1743 Office: 750 N Lake Shore Dr Rm 601 Chicago IL 60611-4489 *Life should best be measured not by how long you live, but how.*

WEBSTER, JILL ROSEMARY, historian, educator; b. London, Sept. 29, 1931; arrived in Can., 1965; d. Harold James and Dora Elena (Andreini) W. BA in Hispanic Studies with honors, U. Liverpool, Eng., 1962, postgrad. cert. in edn., 1965; PhD in Spanish, U. Toronto, Can., 1969; MA in Spanish, U. Nottingham, Eng., 1964; BA in History with honors, U. London, Eng., 1978. Prof. U. Toronto, 1968-94, assoc. dean, 1978-81, dir. Ctr. for Medieval Studies, 1979-94, grad. chair dept. Spanish and Portuguese, 1993-94; prof. emeritus, 1995—. Author: Els Menorets: The Franciscans in the Realms of Aragon from St. Francis to the Black Death (1348), 1993. Fellow Royal Soc. Can.; mem. Am. Hist. Assn., Am. Cath. Hist. Assn., Can. Assn. Hispanists, Medieval Acad. Am., Am. Acad. Rsch. Historians of Medieval Spain (pres. 1990-94). Office: U Toronto St Michaels Coll, 81 St Mary St, Toronto, ON Canada M5S 1J4

WEBSTER, JOHN CHAS, human resources management consultant; b. L.A., May 5, 1944; s. Leo Paul and Agnes (Melavic) W.; m. Dawn Thompson, Nov. 13, 1993; children from a previous marriage: Miriam, Mark. BA in Sociology, German, Benedictine Coll., 1973; cert., Johns Hopkins U., 1974; MA in Social Psychology, U. No. Colo., 1975. Cert. alcohol, drug therapist. Staff psychologist, alcohol and drug programs U.S. Army, Ft. Carson, Colo., 1975-76; dir. alcohol and drug program Coconino County, Flagstaff, Ariz., 1976-78; dir. univ. rels. Intel Corp., Phoenix, Ariz., 1978-80; dir. employment G.T.E. Microcircuits, Phoenix, 1980-81; v.p. Monarch Computer Corp., Phoenix, 1981-83; dir. Found. for Human Resources, Santa Cruz, Calif., 1982—, v.p., 1983—; lectr. No. Ariz. U., Flagstaff, 1977-78, Regis Coll., Colorado Springs, Colo., 1985-88, U. Colo., Colorado Springs, 1985-88, Calif. State Employment Com., Sunnyvale, 1991-92; cons. Seagate Tech., Scotts Valley, Calif., 1991—. Designed Navajo Tribal Mental Health Program, Window Rock, Ariz., 1978. With U.S. Army, 1965-75. Recipient Outstanding Contbn. award Mental Health Dept., Colo., 1974, Ariz. Hwy. Patrol, 1978, Ariz. Adult Probation, 1978, Navajo tribe, Window Rock, Ariz., 1978. Mem. U. No. Colo. Alumni Assn. (Recognition award 1978), Benedictine Coll. Alumni Assn. (Svc. award 1991). Republican. Avocations: pilot, parachuting, Alpinist. Home: 16761 Corcel Ct Los Gatos CA 95032 Office: Found for Human Resources 140 Wissahickon Ave Los Gatos CA 95030

WEBSTER, JOHN GOODWIN, biomedical engineering educator, researcher; b. Plainfield, N.J., May 27, 1932; s. Franklin Folger and Emily Sykes (Boody) W.; m. Nancy Egan, Dec. 27, 1954; children: Paul, Robin, Mark, Lark. BEE, Cornell U., 1953; MSEE, U. Rochester, 1965, PhD, 1967. Registered profl. engr., Wis. Engr. North American Aviation, Downey, Calif., 1954-55; engr. Boeing Airplane Co. Seattle, 1955-59, Radiation Inc., Melbourne, Fla., 1959-61; staff engr. Mitre Corp., Bedford, Mass., 1961-62, IBM Corp., Kingston, N.Y., 1962-63; asst. prof. elec. engring. U. Wis.-Madison, 1967-70, assoc. prof. elec. engring., 1970-73, prof. elec. and computer engring., 1973—. Author: (with others) Medicine and Clinical Engineering, 1977, Sensors and Signal Conditioning, 1991; editor: Medical Instrumentation: Application and Design, 1978, 2d edit., 1992, Clinical Engineering: Principles and Practices, 1979, Design of Microcomputer-Based Medical Instrumentation, 1981, Therapeutic Medical Devices: Application and Design, 1982, Electronic Devices for Rehabilitation, 1985; Interfacing Sensors to the IBM-PC, 1988, Encyclopedia of Medical Devices and Instrumentation, 1988, Tactile Sensors for Robotics and Medicine, 1988, Electrical Impedance Tomography, 1990, Teaching Design in Electrical Engineering, 1990, Prevention of Pressure Sores, 1991, Design of Cardiac Pacemakers, 1995. Recipient Rsch. Career Devel. award NIH, 1971-76; NIH fellow, 1963-67. Fellow IEEE, Am. Inst. Med. and Biol. Engring., Instrument Soc. Am. (Donald P. Eckman Edn. award 1974); mem. Am. Soc. Engring. Edn. (Western Electric Fund award 1978, Theo C. Pilkington Outstanding Educator award 1994), Assn. Advancement Med. Instrumentation. Author: (with others) Medicine and Clinical Engineering, 1977, Sensors and Signal Conditioning, 1991; editor: Medical Instrumentation: Application and Design, 1978, 2d edit., 1992, Clinical Engineering: Principles and Practices, 1979, Design of Microcomputer-Based Medical Instrumentation, 1981, Therapeutic Medical Devices: Application and Design, 1982, Interfacing Sensors to the IBM-PC, 1988, Encyclopedia of Medical Devices and Instrumentation, 1988, Tactile Sensors for Robotics and Medicine, 1988, Electrical Impedance Tomography, 1990, Teaching Design in Electrical Engineering, 1990, Prevention of Pressure Sores, 1991, Design of Cardiac Pacemaker, 1995. Office: Univ Wis Dept Elec Computer Engring 1415 Engineering Dr Madison WI 53706-1691

WEBSTER, JOHN KIMBALL, investment executive; b. N.Y.C., June 7, 1934; s. Reginald Nathaniel and Lillian (McDonald) W.; m. Katherine Taylor Mulligan; children: John McDonald, Katherine Kimball. B.A., Yale U., 1956; postgrad., Wharton Sch., U. Pa., 1957-58. With Dominick & Dominick, N.Y.C., 1961-73; v.p. Dominick & Dominick, 1968-73; v.p., sec.

Dominick Fund, Inc., also Barclay Growth Fund, N.Y.C., 1971-73; v.p. Dominick Mgmt. Corp., N.Y.C., 1971-73, Monumental Capital Mgmt., Inc. Balt., 1974-75, Bernstein-Macaulay, Inc., N.Y.C., 1975-78; v.p., dir. Penmark Investments, Inc., Chgo., 1978-79; sr. v.p. Penmark Investments, Inc., 1979-80, exec. v.p., 1980-84; exec. v.p. Trust Banking Group, Sun Banks, Inc., 1984-85; v.p. MPT Assocs., 1986-90, Value Line Asset Mgmt., N.Y.C., 1990—; mem. no-load com. Investment Co. Inst., Washington, 1971-73; exec. com. No Load Mut. Fund Assn., N.Y.C., 1971-73; treas. No Load Mut. Fund Assn., 1972-73. Chmn. Nat. Telethon Com., Lawrenceville, Sch., 1986-88, chmn. Ann. Giving, 1988-89; vice chmn. Parents Fund Trinity Coll., Conn., 1987-90. Capt. USAF, 1958-61. Mem. Church Club (N.Y.C.), Yale Club (N.Y.C.), Rumson (N.J.) Country Club, Seabright (N.J.) Lawn Tennis Club, Baltusrol Golf Club, Summit Paddle Tennis Club. Episcopalian. Home: 46 Meadowview Ln Berkeley Heights NJ 07922-1308 Office: Value Line Asset Mgmt 220 E 42nd St 6th Fl New York NY 10017-5891

WEBSTER, LARRY RUSSELL, artist; b. Arlington, Mass., Mar. 18, 1930; s. James Burpee and Ethel (Hughes) W.; m. Rosemary Siekman, June 13, 1953; children: Wendy Lyn, Ricky Stewart, Holly Jean. B.F.A., Mass. Coll. Art, 1952; M.S., Boston U., 1953. Package designer Union Bag & Paper Co., N.Y.C., 1953-54; art dir., graphic designer, v.p., dir. Thomas Todd Co., Boston, 1956-78; asst. prof. design Mass. Coll. Art, 1964-66. Paintings in permanent collections including, DeCordova Mus., Lincoln, Mass., Grand Rapids (Mich.) Art Mus., Springfield (Mo.) Art Mus., Davenport (Iowa) Municipal Gallery, Colby Coll. Art Mus., Waterville, Maine, Peabody Mus. Salem, Mass. Served with U.S. Army, 1954-56. Recipient Silver medal Am. Watercolor Soc., 1968, 72; recipient C.F.S. award, 1963, Ed Whitney award, 1973, High winds medal, 1983, Rhinehold award, 1967, Ranger Fund Purchase prize, 1965, Adolph and Clara Obrig prize in watercolor NAD, 1970, gold medal Allied Artists Am., 1971, Washington Sch. Art award, 1977, Lena Newcastle award, 1978, Colo. Watermedia award, 1978, Golden award Rocky Mountain Nat. Watermedia Exhbn., 1979, Lorraine Fetzer Meml. award, 2d prize N.Am. Open Competition, 1990. Mem. NAD, Soc. Printers Boston (past mem. council), Am. Watercolor Soc. (Dolphin fellow 1981), Boston Watercolor Soc. (pres. 1974-75), Guild of Boston Artists. Home: 116 Perkins Row Topsfield MA 01983-1923

WEBSTER, LESLIE TILLOTSON, JR., pharmacologist, educator; b. N.Y.C., Mar. 31, 1926; s. Leslie Tillotson and Emily (de Forest) W.; m. Alice Katharine Holland, June 24, 1955; children—Katharine White, Susan Holland, Leslie Tillotson III, Romi Anne. B.A., Amherst Coll., 1947, Sc.D. (hon.), 1982; student, Union Coll., 1944; M.D., Harvard U., 1948. Diplomate: Am. Bd. Internal Medicine. Rotating intern Cleve. City Hosp., 1948-49, jr. asst. resident in medicine, 1949-50; asst. resident medicine Bellevue Hosp., N.Y.C., 1952-53; research fellow medicine Harvard and Boston City Hosp. Thorndike Meml. Lab., 1953-55; from demonstrator to instr. Sch. of Medicine Western Res. U., 1955-60; research assoc. to sr. instr. biochemistry Case Western Res. U. Sch. Medicine, 1959-60, asst. prof. medicine, 1960-70, asst. prof. biochemistry, 1960-65, asst. prof. pharmacology, 1965-67, asso. prof., 1967-70, prof. pharmacology, 1976-92, chmn. pharmacology dept., 1976-91, prof. pharmacology dept. emeritus, 1992, prof. medicine, 1980-86; prof., chmn. pharmacology dept. Northwestern U. Med. and Dental Sch. 1970-76. Served to lt. USNR, 1950-52. Russell M. Wilder fellow Nat. Vitamin Found., 1956-59; Sr. USPHS Research fellow, 1959-61; Research Career Devel. awardee, 1961-69; Macy faculty scholar, 1980-81. Mem. ACP (life), Central Soc. Clin. Rsch. (emeritus), Am. Soc. Clin. Investigation (emeritus), Am. Soc. Biochemistry and Molecular Biology (emeritus), Assn. Med. Sch. Pharmacology (emeritus), Am. Soc. Pharmacology and Exptl. Therapeutics (emeritus). Home: 2728 Leighton Rd Cleveland OH 44120-1325 Office: Univ Hosps of Cleve Rainbow Babies and Childrens Hosp 2074 Abington Rd Cleveland OH 44106-2602

WEBSTER, MELVILLE JAY, III, bank executive; b. South Bend, Ind., Feb. 21, 1944; s. Melville Jay Jr. and Mildred Grace (Spear) W. AB, Ind. U., 1966, MS, 1968. Cert. data processor, quality analyst. Scientific programmer Uniroyal, Inc., Mishawaka, Ind., 1968-71; sr. systems analyst G.D. Searle & Co., Skokie, Ill., 1971-74; systems mgr. Baxter Labs. Deerfield, Ill., 1974-77; data base administr. Union Spl. Machine Corp., Chgo., 1977-79; data base analyst Blue Cross of Calif., Oakland, 1979-81; sr. tech. specialist McKesson Corp., San Francisco, 1981-83; consulting systems engr. Bank of Am., San Francisco, 1983-89; cons. Computer Power Group, Oak Brook, Ill., 1989-91; systems mgr., v.p. First Bank Sys., Mpls., 1991—. Tchr. Jane Addams Resource Ctr., Chgo., 1990-91; mem. adv. coun. Mpls. Pub. Schs./Adult Basic Edn. Program, 1992-93. Mem. Twin Cities Quality Assurance Assn., Am. MENSA, Lions. Republican. Avocations: reading, gardening, contract bridge, urban renewal. Home: 4929 3rd Ave S Minneapolis MN 55409-2629 Office: First Bank System MPFP1901 601 2nd Ave S Minneapolis MN 55402-4301

WEBSTER, NORMAN ERIC, journalist, charitable foundation administrator; b. Summerside, P.E.I., Can., June 4, 1941; s. Eric and Elizabeth (Paterson) W.; m. Pat Roop, 1966; children: David, Andrew, Derek, Gillian, Hilary. BA, Bishop's U., Que., Can., 1962; MA, St. John's Coll., Oxford, Eng., 1964. Corr. Globe and Mail, Que., 1965; reporter Globe and Mail, Ottawa, Ont., Can., 1966; editor Globe Mag., Toronto, Ont., 1967-68; corr. Globe and Mail, Peking, China, 1969-71; asst. to pub. Winnipeg (Man., Can.) Free Press, 1971-72; bur. chief Globe and Mail, Toronto, 1972-74, columnist Ont. affairs, 1974-78; European corr. Globe and Mail, London, 1978-81; asst. editor Globe and Mail, Toronto, 1981-83, editor-in-chief, 1983-89; editor Montreal (Que.) Gazette, 1989-93; pres. RHW Found., Montreal, 1993—. Author: Discovering Today's China, 1972, The Pope in Poland, 1979. Recipient Nat. Newspaper award for Peking corr., 1971, for editorial writing, 1988; Rhodes scholar, 1962. Office: R Howard Webster Found Ste 2912, 1155 Rene Levesque Blvd W, Montreal, PQ Canada H3B 2L5

WEBSTER, ROBERT DAVID, lawyer; b. N.Y.C., Mar. 14, 1938; s. Louis W. and Thelma (Alcott) W.; m. Elizabeth Weld Brett, Apr. 4, 1964; children: Elizabeth A, Hope B., Christopher W. AB, Colgate U., 1959; LLB, Harvard U., 1962. Bar: N.Y. 1963, U.S. Dist. Ct. (so. dist.) N.Y. 1989. Assoc. Winthrop, Stimson, Putnam & Roberts, N.Y.C., 1962-68, ptnr., 1969—; bd. dirs. Dai-Ichi Kangyo Trust Co. N.Y., DKB Data Svcs. (USA), Inc. Trustee St. Bernard's Sch., 1977-82; vis. com. Grad. Faculties The New Sch. for Social Rsch., 1987-94; bd. dirs. 1090 Park Avenue Corp., 1990-95. Mem. Internat. Bar Assn. (vice chmn. banking law com. 1988-92, co-chmn. 1994—), Union Internationale des Avocats, Assn. of Bar of City of N.Y., Downtown Assn.

WEBSTER, ROBERT KENLY, lawyer; b. N.Y.C., May 16, 1933; s. Francis Kenly and Mary Louise (Rathbone) W.; m. Sally Irene Stratton, Apr. 16, 1960; children: Timothy Kenly, Kimberly Anne. AB, Princeton U., 1955; LLB, U. Va., 1960. Assoc. Cadwalader, Wickersham & Taft, N.Y.C., 1960-65; asst. U.S. atty. Dept. of Justice, Washington, 1965-68; prin. dep. gen. counsel Dept. of Army, Washington, 1968-73; ptnr. Kennedy & Webster, Washington, 1973-81, Shaw, Pittman, Potts & Trowbridge, Washington, 1981—; spl. investigator Iran FMS program Sec. of Def., Washington, 1977; advisor conflict of interest issues Watergate defendants Dept. Justice, Washington, 1977. Sec., gen. counsel, bd. dirs. Princeton (N.J.) Project 55, Inc., 1989—. Lt. (j.g.) USN, 1955-57. Mem. ABA, Fed. Bar Assn., Met. Club. Avocations: pottery, reading, traveling, squash, tennis. Office: Shaw Pittman Potts 2300 N St NW Washington DC 20037-1122

WEBSTER, ROBERT LOUDON, banker, lawyer; b. Dallas, May 11, 1954; s. Loudon Charles and Jane Ann (Bours) W.; m. Nadia Bernard, May 28, 1977; children: Kara Jane, Robert Alexander, Mackenzie Gene. BA, Duke U., 1976; JD, U. Tulsa, 1979. Bar: Wis. 1979; chartered fin. cons., CLU. Assoc. Axley & Brynelson, Madison, Wis., 1979-81; sr. v.p. 1st Wis. Nat. Bank Madison, 1981—. Bd. dirs. Am. Heart Assn. Madison, 1989—, Arthritis Found., Madison, 1989—, YMCA Madison, 1990—. Mem. Wis. Bar Assn., Dane County Bar Assn., Wis. Investment Mgmt. Sales Execs., Rotary. Republican. Presbyterian. Avocations: running, golf, tennis. Office: Firstar Bank Madison N.A. PO Box 7900 1 S Pinckney St Madison WI 53703

children: Noel, Michelle. BA, U. Wash., 1964; JD, Gonzaga U., 1969. Bar: Wash., U.S. Dist. Ct. (ea. and we. dists.) Wash., U.S. Ct. Appeals (9th cir.). Dep. pros. atty. Cowlitz County, Kelso, Wash., 1970-73; ptnr. Hickman, Webster, Ensley & Carpenter, Colfax, Wash., 1973-90, Hickman, Webster & Moulton, 1973-92, Hickman & Webster, 1992-95. Mem. Whitman County Bd. Mental Health, Pullman, Wash., 1973-83; chmn. civil svc. commn. Whitman County Sheriffs Office, Colfax, 1973—; pres. Colfax and Cmty. Fund, 1973-74; pres. Whitman Cmty. Concerts, 1990-93. Mem. Whitman County Bar Assn. (pres. 1981-82), Wash. State Bar Assn. (inter profl. com. 1986-89—, disciplinary com. 1986—). Club: Colfax Golf and Country. Lodge: Rotary (pres. Colfax club 1983-84). Home: 1801 N Oak St Colfax WA 99111-9801 Office: Hickman Webster & Moulton 302 N Mill St Colfax WA 99111-1826

WEBSTER, STEPHEN BURTIS, physician, educator; b. Chgo., Dec. 3, 1935; s. James Randolph Webster and Ruth Marion (Burtis) Holmes; m. Katherine Griffith Webster, Apr. 4, 1959; children: David Randolph, Margaret Elizabeth, James Lucian. BS, Northwestern U., 1957, MD, 1960. Diplomate Am. Bd. Dermatology. Intern Colo. Gen. Hosp., Denver, 1960-61; resident Walter Reed Gen. Hosp., Washington, 1962-65; staff physician Henry Ford Hosp., Detroit, 1969-71, Gundersen Clinic, La Crosse, 1971—; assoc. clin. prof. U. Wis., Madison, 1976—, U. Minn., Mpls., 1978—. Lt. col. U.S. Army, 1962-69. Fellow Am. Acad. Dermatology (sec.-treas. 1985-88, pres. 1991), Am. Bd. Dermatology (dir. 1992—); mem. AMA, Am. Dermatol. Assn., Wis. State Med. Soc., La Crosse County Med. Soc., Soc. Investigative Dermatology, Alpha Omega Alpha. Republican. Congregationalist. Avocations: bagpipes, model R.R. Home: 2062N Wedgewood Dr E La Crosse WI 54601 Office: Gundersen Clinic Ltd 1836 South Ave La Crosse WI 54601-5494

WEBSTER, THOMAS GLENN, psychiatrist; b. Topeka, Jan. 23, 1924; s. Guy Welland and Iva Amanda (Keefover) W.; m. Mary Tupper Dooly, June 27, 1948; children—Warnie Louise, Guy Weyman, David Michael. AB, Ft. Hays State Coll., 1946; MD, Wayne State U., 1949. Intern Los Angeles County Gen. Hosp., Calif., 1949-50; resident in psychiatry Mass. Mental Health Ctr., Boston, 1953-55, resident in child psychiatry, 1955-56; resident in child psychiatry James Jackson Putnam Children's Ctr., Boston, 1956-58; dir. presch. program for retarded children Greater Boston, 1958-62; coordinator 3d yr. med. student psychiatry clerkship Harvard U. Med. Sch.-Mass. Mental Health Ctr., Boston, 1960-63; practice medicine specializing in psychiatry Boston, 1953-62, Bethesda, Md., 1963-72, Washington, 1972—; tng. specialist psychiatry, then chief continuing edn. br. NIMH, Bethesda, Md., 1963-72; prof. psychiatry George Washington U., Washington, 1972-86, chmn. dept. psychiatry and behavioral scis., 1972-75, prof. emeritus, 1986—; vis. prof. Harvard U. Med. Sch., 1980-83, McLean Hosp., 1980-86; U.S.-Poland exchange health scientist, 1981. Pres. Woodhaven Citizens Assn. 1971-72. Served with AUS, 1943-46; as sr. asst. surgeon USPHS, 1951-53. Fellow Am. Psychiat. Assn., Am. Coll. Psychiatrists, Am. Coll. Psychoanalysts; mem. Assn. Acad. Psychiatry (pres. 1976-78), Group Advancement Psychiatry. Home: 8506 Woodhaven Blvd Bethesda MD 20817-3117 Office: 2112 F St NW Washington DC 20037-2715

WEBSTER, WILLIAM HEDGCOCK, lawyer; b. St. Louis, Mar. 6, 1924; s. Thomas M. and Katherine (Hedgcock) W.; m. Drusilla Lane, May 5, 1950 (dec. 1984); children: Drusilla Lane Busch, William Hedgcock, Katherine Hagee Roessle; m. Lynda Clugston, Oct. 20, 1990. AB, Amherst Coll., 1947, LLD, 1975; JD, Washington U., 1949, LLD, 1978; LLD (hon.), William Wood Coll., 1978, DePauw U., 1978, Drury Coll., Columbia Coll., U. Dayton, U. Notre Dame, Center Coll., Dickinson Coll., U. Miami, DePaul U., Am. U., John Jay Coll., Westminster Coll., Georgetown U., Rockhurst Coll., Pepperdine U. Bar: Mo. 1949, D.C. 1981. With Armstrong, Teasdale, Kramer and Vaughan (and predecessors), St. Louis, 1949-50, 52-59, 61-70; U.S. atty. U.S. Dist. Ct. (ea. dist.) Mo., 1960-61, judge, 1971-73; judge U.S. Ct. Appeals (8th cir.), 1973-78; dir. FBI, 1978-87, CIA, 1987-91; sr. ptnr. Millbank, Tweed, Hadley & McClay, Washington, 1991—; mem. Mo. Bd. Law Examiners, 1964-69, mem. adv. com. on criminal rules, 1971-78, mem. ct. adminstrs. com., 1975-78; bd. dirs. Anhauser-Busch Cos., Maritz Inc., Pinkertons Inc. Trustee Washington U., 1974—; bd. dirs. Atlantic Coun., Nat. Legal Ctr. for Pub. Interest, Police Found; hon. life pres. Big Bros. Orgn. St. Louis; bd. dirs. Big Bros. Am., 1966, hon. bd. dirs., 1978—. Lt. USN, 1943-46, 50-52. Recipient Disting. Alumnus award Washington U., 1977, Stein award Fordham U., Law award U. Va., Nat. Svc. medal Freedoms Found., Theodore Roosevelt award, Presdl. medal of Freedom, Nat. Security medal; named Father of Yr., 1986, Man of Yr., St. Louis Globe Dem., 1980. Fellow Am. Bar Found.; mem. ABA (chmn. sect. on corp. banking and bus. law 1977-78), Fed. Bar Assn., Mo. Bar Assn., St. Louis Bar Assn., Am. Law Inst. (mem. coun. 1978—), Washington U. Alumni Fedn. (pres. 1956-57), Washington U. Law Alumni (pres. 1961), Mo. Assn. Reps. (pres. 1958), Rotary, St. Louis Country Club, Noonday Club (St. Louis), Alfalfa Club, St. Alban's Tennis Club, Rotary, Order of Coif, Psi Upsilon, Delta Sigma Rho, Phi Delta Phi. Office: 1825 I St NW Ste 1100 Washington DC 20006-5403

WECHSLER, ALFRED ELLIOT, engineering executive, consultant, chemical engineer; b. Suffern, N.Y., Sept. 12, 1934; m. Nancy L. Lyons, Apr. 22, 1961; children: Charles, Elizabeth, Abigail. B.S. in Chem. Engring., M.I.T., 1955, M.S., 1958, Sc.D. in Chem. Engring. 1961. Registered profl. engr., Mass. Staff engr. Chevron Research Corp., 1957; asst. dir. M.I.T. Sch. Chem. Engring. Practice Buffalo Field Stas., Bangor, Maine, 1958; grad. research asst. chem. engring M.I.T., Cambridge, 1959-61; sr. research engr. engring. div. Arthur D. Little, Inc., Cambridge, 1961-66, leader research and experiments group, 1966-73, mgr. bio/enviro systems sect., v.p., 1973-80, corp. staff v.p., 1980—, sr. v.p., mgr. profl. ops. bus. unit, 1980-83, sr. v.p. gen. mgr. profl. ops., 1983-85, sr. v.p. chief profl. officer, 1985—. Contbr. articles to profl. jours. Trustee Environ. Careers Orgn. With U.S. Army, 1956-57. Fellow AAAS; mem. NSPE, Am. Chem. Soc., Am. Inst. Chem. Engrs. (bd. dirs. 1991-93). Office: Arthur D Little Inc 25 Acorn Park Cambridge MA 02140-2390

WECHSLER, HENRY, research psychologist; b. Warsaw, Poland, Aug. 16, 1932; came to U.S., 1941, naturalized, 1947; s. William and Lucy (Fryd) W.; m. Joan Goldstein, Oct. 16, 1955; children: Stephen Bruce, Pamela Jane, Peter Thomas. A.B. summa cum laude, Washington and Jefferson Coll., 1953; M.A. (Harvard Found. Advanced Study fellow, resident fellow), Harvard U., 1955, Ph.D. in Social Psychology, 1957. USPHS postdoctoral rsch. fellow, 1957; rsch. assoc. Joint Commn. Mental Illness and Health, 1957-58; rsch. assoc., asst. prof. Clark U., 1958-59; rsch. social psychologist Mass. Mental Health Ctr., 1959-65; rsch. assoc. in psychology Med. Sch., Harvard U., 1960-66; rsch. assoc. in psychology Harvard Sch. Pub. Health, 1963-66, lectr. social psychology, 1966—; dir. Youth Alcohol-Drug Program, dept. health & social behavior, 1988—; dir. rsch. and community health programs Med. Found., Inc., Boston, 1965-88; vis. lectr. Boston U., 1967-68; pres. SocioTech. Systems, 1969-74; lectr. in rsch. Simmons Coll. Sch. Social Work, 1969-80, adj. prof., 1981-84. Author, editor: The Threat of Impending Disaster; contbr. to books Psychology of Stress, 1964, Social Psychology and Mental Health, 1970, Emergency Medical Services: Behavioral and Planning Perspectives, 1973, Social Work Research in the Human Services, 1976, Handbook of Medical Specialties, 1976, The Horizons of Health, 1977, Explorations in Nursing Research, 1978, Handbook of Dental Specialties, 1979, Minimum Drinking Age Laws, 1980, The Social Context of Medical Research, 1981, Medical School Admissions, 1982; contbr. numerous articles to profl. jours. Fellow Am. Psychol. Assn., Mass. Psychol. Assn. (treas. 1967-68), Am. Sociol. Assn., Am. Pub. Health Assn.; mem. Mass. Pub. Health Assn., AAAS, Phi Beta Kappa. Club: Harvard (Boston). Home: 148 Puritan Dr Quincy MA 02169-1739 Office: Harvard Sch Pub Health Dept Health & Social Behavior 677 Huntington Ave Boston MA 02115-6023

WECHSLER, HERBERT, retired legal educator; b. N.Y.C., Dec. 4, 1909; s. Samuel and Anna (Weisberger) W.; m. Elzie S. Stix, May 29, 1933 (div. 1957); m. Doris L. Kläuber, Apr. 13, 1957. AB, CCNY, 1928; LLB, Columbia U., 1931, LLD (hon.), 1978; LLD (hon.), U. Chgo., 1962, Harvard U., 1967, Georgetown U., 1984, CUNY, 1988, Yale U., 1991. Bar: N.Y. 1933. Editor Columbia U. Law Rev., 1929-31; instr. law Columbia U., 1931-32, asst. prof., 1933-38, assoc. prof., 1938-45, prof., 1945— Harlan Fiske Stone prof. constl. law, 1957-78, emeritus, 1978—; law sec. to Mr. Justice

Harlan F. Stone, 1932-33; counsel to minority leader N.Y. State Constl. Conv., 1938; asst. atty. gen. of N.Y. (assigned Bklyn. investigation), 1938-40; exec. sec. U.S. Bd. Legal Examiners, 1941-42; mem. adv. com. on rules criminal procedure U.S. Supreme Ct., 1941-45; spl. asst. to atty. gen. of U.S., 1940-44; asst. atty. gen. of U.S., in charge war div. U.S. Dept. Justice, 1944-46; tech. adviser to U.S. mems. Internat. Mil. Tribunal, 1945-46; vis. prof. Harvard Law Sch., 1956-57, Oliver Wendell Holmes lectr., 1958-59; Am. Law Inst. reporter Model Penal Code, 1952-62; exec. dir. Am. Law Inst., 1963-84, mem. council, 1984—; dir. Social Sci. Research Council, 1953. Author: (with J. Michael) Criminal Law and Its Administration, 1940, The Federal Courts and the Federal System, (with H. Hart Jr.), 1953, 3d edit. (with others), 1988, Principles, Politics and Fundamental Law, 1961, The Nationalization of Civil Liberties and Civil Rights, 1969. Mem. Pres.'s Commn. on Law Enforcement and Adminstrn. of Justice, 1965-67, N.Y. Temporary Commn. Rev. Penal Law and Criminal Code, 1961-70; mem. permanent com. for Oliver Wendell Holmes Devise, 1966-74; mem. com. on rev. fed. ct. appellate system, 1973-75; chmn. N.Y. Jud. Nomination Commn., 1978-82. Recipient Henry J. Friendly medal Am. Law Inst., 1993. Fellow Am. Acad. Arts and Scis., Brit. Acad. (corr.); mem. ABA, Assn. of Bar of City of N.Y. (past v.p., medal), Am. Philos. Soc. (Townsend Harris medal, Learned Hand award), Order of Coif (hon.). Democrat. Club: Century Assn. Home: 179 E 70th St New York NY 10021-5154 Office: 435 W 116th St New York NY 10027-7201

WECHSLER, JUDITH GLATZER, art historian, filmmaker, educator; b. Chgo., Dec. 28, 1940; d. Nahum Norbert and Anne (Stiebel) Glatzer; m. Richard Wechsler, Sept. 15, 1963 (div. 1969); 1 child, Johanna; m. Benson Rowell Snyder, Apr. 30, 1976. BA, Brandeis U., 1962; MA, Columbia U., 1967; PhD, UCLA, 1972. From asst. prof. to assoc. prof. art history MIT, Cambridge, 1970-78; from assoc. prof. to prof. R.I. Sch. Design, Providence, 1980-89; producer, dir. Judith Wechsler, Inc., Brookline, Mass., 1985—; NEH art history, chmn. dept. Art and Art History Tufts U., Medford, Mass., 1989—; cons. in field; vis. prof. Harvard U., Cambridge, Mass., 1989, Hebrew U., Jerusalem, 1994, 96. Author: The Interpretation of Cézanne, 1982, A Human Comedy: Physiognomy and Caricature in 19th Century Paris, 1983; editor: Cézanne in Perspective, 1975, On Aesthetics in Science, 1978; dir. (films) (with Charles Eames) Daumier: Paris and the Spectator, Cézanne: The Late Work, 1978, Pissarro, 1981, Manet, 1983, (TV series) The Painter's World; producer, dir., screenwriter The Artist and the Nude, 1985, Training of Painters, 1987, The Arrested Moment, 1988, Portraits, 1988, Painting and the Public, 1988, Abstraction, 1989, Aaron Siskind: Making Pictures, 1991, (with Hans Namuth) Jasper Johns: Take an Object, 1990, Harry Callahan, 1993, Titian, Venus and Adonis, 1994; contbr. articles to profl. jours. and mus. catalogues. Juror Montreal Internat. Art Film Festival, 1989; bd. dirs. Swann Found. for Study of Caricature, 1985-93, Boston Film and Video Found., 1991-94. Recipient cine Golden Eagle award, 1983, 85, 88, 89, 92, 94, Red Ribbon, Am. Film Festival, 1989, 92, Gold Plaque, Chgo. Film Festival, 1991; grantee NEH, 1973, 85, 83-84, 84-85, 87-89, Nat. Endowment for Arts, 1980-81, 87-89. Mem. Coll. Art Assn. Democrat. Jewish. Office: Tufts U Dept of Art History Medford MA 02155

WECHSLER, RAYMOND HENRY, management company executive; b. Taunton, Mass., Apr. 2, 1945; s. Kurt and Ann (Schlessinger) W.; BA, Queens Coll., 1966; MBA, Columbia U., 1968; m. Louise Austin, July 29, 1979. CPA, N.Y. Mgmt. cons. Touche Ross & Co., N.Y.C., 1968-72; with RCA, N.Y.C., 1972-80, dir. internat. financing, 1976-77, dir. internat. treasury ops., 1977-80; CFO AT&T Internat., Basking Ridge, N.J., 1980-81, v.p., treas., CFO, 1981-83; pres. United Press Internat., Inc., 1985, Wechsler Mgmt. Corp. Inc., N.Y.C., 1983—; vice chmn. Protect Svcs. Industries, Inc., 1987—; chmn. bd., CEO ERC Industries, Inc., 1989-91, Mueller Industries, 1990-91, Accessory Place, Inc., 1993—; chmn., pres. Am. Equity Ptnrs., Inc., 1992—; bd. dirs. Crystal Oil Co., Jos. A. Bank Clothiers Inc. Office: 1301 Avenue of The Americas New York NY 10019

WECHTER, LARRY SCOT, retail food executive; b. South Bend, Ind., July 22, 1955; s. Monte and Betty May (Freeze) W.; m. Janis Marie Havens, Mar. 3, 1984; children: Jourdan Marie, Logan Scot. BS, Ball State U., 1976. CPA, Ill., Ind. Pub. acct. Fowler, Suttles & Co., CPA, Indpls., 1976-79; v.p. O'Malia Food Mkts., Noblesville, Ind., 1979—. Mem. Food Mktg. Inst. (electronic funds transfer com. 1985—), Nat. Assn. Accts., Am. Mgmt. Assn., Indpls. Soc. CPA's, Indpls. C of C (tax subcom., govtl. affairs com. 1985—, retail task force), Sigma Alpha Epsilon. Republican. Methodist. Avocations: tennis, working out, reading. Office: O'Malia Food Mkts 1555 Westfield Rd Noblesville IN 46060-8920 Also: Indpls Auto Auction Inc 4040 Office Plz Blvd Indianapolis IN 46254

WECHTER, VIVIENNE THAUL, artist, poet, educator; b. N.Y.C.; d. Samuel Joshua and Hilda (Thaul) Rosenthal; m. Nathan Wechter; 1 dau., Robyrta Joan Wechter Rapoport. B. Pedagogy, Jamaica Tchrs. Coll.; postgrad., Columbia U., N.Y. U., New Sch. for Social Research, Art Students League, Sculpture Center, Pratt Inst. Graphic Center; Ph.D. in Interarts and Psychology of Creativity, Union Inst. Artist in residence Fordham U., 1964—, asst. prof. art and esthetics, 1964, now prof. interdisciplinary creative arts, chmn. acquisitions and exhbns.; vis. poet-artist Kansas City Art Inst., 1975, Md. Inst. Coll. Art, 1975, New Sch., N.Y.C., 1976, Marist Coll., Poughkeepsie, N.Y., 1977; vis. prof. New Sch. for Social Rsch., spring 1986; past chmn. coll. liaison divsn. Bronx Coun. on Arts; vis. prof. creative devel. Miami (Fla.) Jewish Home and Hosp. for Aged, 1993; lect. Sch. Internat. Affairs U. Malta; sole U.S. rep. Internat. Brennale, Malta, 1995. Moderator: weekly radio broadcast Today's World, WFUV, 1951—, created 6 programs in South Pacific, 1986-87; illustrator: (Alfeo Marzi) book cover Park of Jonas, 1965; author: A View from the Ark, 1973; contbr. articles to profl. jours.; one-woman shows Castellane Gallery, East Hampton Gallery, N.Y.C., Cornell U., Ithaca, N.Y., Neville Pub. Mus., Green Bay, Wis., Nashville Fine Arts Ctr., Fairleigh Dickinson U., Rutgers U., Waterloo (Iowa) Mcpl. Galleries, Bodley Gallery, Gloria Cortella Gallery, N.Y.C., Manhattan Coll., N.Y.C., Kouros Gallery, N.Y.C., Everson Mus. Art, Syracuse, N.Y., CCNY, B.R. Kornblatt Gallery, Balt., New Sch. Social Research, N.Y.C., Arts Interaction, N.Y.C., 1993, Douglass Gardens, Miami, also Paris, Rejik, Yugoslavia, multimedia show, Everson Mus. Fine Art, Syracuse, 1979, Dyansen Gallery, N.Y.C., 1981, L.I. U., 1986, Schiller-Wapner, N.Y.C., Shapolsky Gallery, N.Y.C., 1989, New England Mus. Contemporary Arts, 1991, 92, Douglas Gardens, Miami, 1992, Nassau County Mus. Art, 1994; solo shows and poetry readings New Sch., N.Y.C., Arts Interaction, N.Y.C., L.I. U., 1988, Arts Interaction Gallery 12, N.Y.C., 1988, 93, Fordham U., N.Y.C., 1994; represented in permanent collections Corcoran Gallery, Washington, Houston Mus. Fine Arts, Jewish Mus. N.Y.C., Fordham U., N.Y.C., Univ. Art Museum Berkeley, Calif., Museum Art and Sci., Norfolk, Va., NYU, Mus. of Fine Arts, Moscow, Russia, Mus. of Fine Art, Newark, Ohio State U., Phoenix Mus. Fine Arts, Fairleigh Dickinson U., Madison, N.J., UN, Internat. Culture Ctr., Jerusalem, Mus. Modern Art Warsaw, Poland, Mus. Fine Arts Moscow, N.J. State Mus., Trenton, others; monumental outdoor sculpture The Emerging Sun commd. for Manhattan Psychiat. Ctr., Ward's Island, N.Y.C.; permanent sculpture installed George Meany Internat. Ctr. Labor Studies, Washington, 1981, Simple Justice on Columbus Ave. nr. Lincoln Ctr., N.Y.C., 1989; logo sculpture Miami Jewish Home & Hosp. for Aged; developer, curator, 1st Biennial of Outdoor Sculpture, Fordham U. Rose Hill Campus, 1983. Author: Art, Where Are We Today and Why?, 1985; solo exbn. and video presentation New Sch. for Social Research, Mar. and Apr., 1986, Wagner-Schiller Galleries, Sept., 1986; solo painting, sculpture, video presentation and poetry reading, Nov. Dec., 1986; sole exhbn. and poetry reading, The Silver Dream, Provincetown Art Assn. and Mus., July, 1987; chair, moderator Influences in Art (Italian Am. Roundtable Art & Lit., 1988, video on RAI TV, Rome, 1989; panelist St. Bartholomew's, N.Y.C., 1987; rep., exhbns. Leister Fine Arts, Ltd., London; prin. speaker annual cong. Arts Interaction, N.Y.C., 1993. Bd. dirs. Urban Arts Corps; founder, trustee, past pres. Bronx Mus. Art; v.p. U.S. Com. IAA-UNESCO; trustee Bronx Soc. Arts and Letters, 1988—, New England Ctr. Contemporary Arts, 1992—. Recipient awards Am. Acad. Arts and Letters, awards Am. Soc. Contemporary Art. Mem. Am. Abstract Artists, Univ. Council of Art Educators, Urban League Center Greater N.Y. (dir., mem. advisory bd. 1952—), United World Fedelists (1st chmn.), Fedn. Modern Painters and Sculptors (v.p.), Alpha Mu Gamma, Kappa Pi. To be an artist-poet who requires solitude in order to create yet has the urgent need to be actively involved in the human community is a frightening challenge. Yet I know that to live one without the other will be for me, neither.

WECK, THOMAS LINCOLN, consulting company executive; b. Norwalk, Conn., June 3, 1942; s. Frank A. and Wilnor Weck; m. Sandra L. Larson, Aug. 19, 1967; children: David Scot, Peter Michael, Kathryn Ann, Andrew Alan. AB, Stanford (Calif.) U., 1964; MBA, Harvard U., 1969. Assoc. Louis Berger & Assocs., Inc., East Orange, N.J., 1969-74; asst. v.p. Louis Berger Internat., Inc., East Orange, N.J., 1974-75, v.p., 1975-81, group v.p., 1981-93; pres. East Orange, N.J., 1993—; mem. transp. rsch. bd. Nat. Acad. Sci., 1981—; chmn. Com. on Environ. Analysis in Transp., 1992—. Author: Moving Up Quickly, 1979, Back-Back and The Lima Bear, 1983; contbr. articles to profl. jours. Mem. Environ. Commn., Madison, N.J., 1979-82, Rep. Nat. Com., Washington, 1986—. Hon. fellow Harvard U., 1967. Mem. Am. Econs. Assn., ASCE (affiliate). Office: Louis Berger Internat Inc 100 Halsted St East Orange NJ 07018-2699

WECKER, WILLIAM A., preventive medicine physician, neuropsychiatrist; b. N.Y.C., Mar. 14, 1923; s. Philip and Ruth (Frumkin) W.; m. Norma Cairney (dec. 1993); 1 child, Lyle Jeffery. BA, NYU, 1943, MD, 1946; MPH in Adminstrn., Harvard U., 1950; diploma Sch. Aviation Medicine, USAF, 1953. Lic. physician, surgeon, psychiatrist, N.Y.; cert. treating physician N.Y. State Workmen's Compensation Bd.; qualified psychiatrist N.Y. State Dept. Mental Health. Intern Bellevue Hosp., N.Y.C., 1946, Bayonne Gen. Hosp., 1946-47; health officer N.Y.C. Health Dept., 1948-50; dist. health officer N.Y. State Health Dept., Albany, 1950-52; pvt. practice medicine N.Y.C., 1954-59; grad. Sch. Aviation Medicine USAF, 1953; resident in psychiatry U.S. VA Hosp., N.Y.C., 1959-62, psychiatrist, 1962-64; psychiatrist Riverside Hosp., N.Y.C. Hosp. Dept., 1964-65, Postgrad. Ctr. for Mental Health, N.Y.C., 1964-65; pvt. practice preventive medicine, neuropsychiatry N.Y.C., 1948—; advisor Pan Am. Med. Assn., N.Y.C., 1952-55; cons. World Med. Assn., N.Y.C., 1954-61; staff physician Meml. Hosp., Queens, N.Y., 1955-64, Springfield (Mass.) Hosp., 1970-71; civil def. lectr. N.Y.C. Dept. of Health, 1955-58; advisor, charter mem. Acad. Religion and Mental Health, N.Y.C., 1959-62; psychiatrist, mgmt. cons., advisor in staff devel. program Youth House, N.Y.C., 1963-71; psychiatrist, cons. Mahoney Health Ctr., N.Y.C. Dept. Health, Bklyn., 1964-71; psychiatrist N.Y. State Narcotic Addiction Control Commn., 1970-71; med. examining physician N.Y.C. Workers Compensation Bd., 1971-76. Author: 3rd World Economics, 1981, Psychecology for Everybody, 1983, Comprehensive Psychenomics, 1983, American Confetti, 1990, Anatomy of an Asylum, 1968, The Story of "H", 1971, The Honduran Syndrome, 1973, Devil's Den, 1978, Growing Up in Honduras, 1980. Cons. Allen Haus, Zurich, 1990-91; advisor English Gentlemen's Club, Zurich, 1982-87, Centro Cultural, Honduras, 1978-82; corr. Harry Schulz Internat. Newsletter, Switzerland and Monaco, 1983-91. 2d lt. U.S. Army, 1943-45, capt. M.C. USAF, 1952-54; ATO. Decorated Nat. Def. Svc. medal. mem. Acad. Medicine Bklyn. (life), Nat. Inst. Mental Health, N.Y. State Med. Soc. (life), N.Y. Coun. Child Psychiatry, Kings County Med. Soc. (life), Royal Soc. Health (London). Avocations: composing classical music, poetry, painting. Home and Office: 52 Macdougal St # 1A New York NY 10012-2961

WECKESSER, ELDEN CHRISTIAN, surgery educator; b. Marshallville, Ohio, Mar. 31, 1910; s. Christian and Ella Elizabeth (Long) W.; m. Kathryn Alice Tuttle, Mar. 17, 1937; children: Jane, Elizabeth, Nancy, Mary. Student, Duke U., 1928-29; AB, Western Reserve U., 1933, MD, 1936. Diplomate Bd. of Surgery, Am. Coll. Surgeons. Intern Cin. Gen. Hosp., 1936-37; sr. intern surgery Univ. Hosps., Cleve., 1937-38, asst. resident gen. surgery, 1938-39, resident, 1939-40; from demonstrator in surgery to clin. prof. surgery Case Western Res. U., Cleve., 1940-74, prof. surgery, 1974-81, prof. emeritus surgery, 1981—; asst. surgeon Lakeside Hosp., Cleve., 1940-61, assoc. surgeon, 1961—; assoc. surgeon Highland View Hosp., St. Lukes Hosp., Cleve., 1961—; cons. surgeon VA Hosp., 1961—. Author: (books) Treatment of Hand Injuries, 1974, The Department of Surgery, Case Western Reserve University, 1843-1986, His Name Was Mudd, 1991; co-author: Flynn's Hand Surgery, 1966, rev. edits., 1975, 82, 91; co-author: (chpts.) Medicine in Cleveland and Cuyahoga County 1810-1976, 1977; contbr. numerous articles to profl. jours. Lt. col. Med. Corps U.S. Army, 1942-46, Australia, New Guinea. Named Disting. Alumnus, Case Western Res. U., 1981. Mem. AMA, ACS (mem. trauma com.), Am. Bd. Surgery, Acad. Medicine Cleve. (v.p. 1965-66, pres. 1966-67), Ohio State Med. Assn., Cleve. Surg. Soc. (pres. 1964-65), Am. Assn. Surgery Trauma, Am. Soc. Surgery of Hand, Cen. Surg. Assn., Internat. Soc. Surgery, Cleve. Med. Libr. Assn. (v.p. 1973-74, pres. 1974-75), Western Res. Med. Alumni Assn. (pres. 1965-66), Alpha Omega Alpha. Republican. Presbyterian. Avocations: author. Home and Office: 129 Manorbrook Dr Chagrin Falls OH 44022-4163

WECKESSER, ERNEST PROSPER, JR., publisher, educator; b. Akron, Ohio, Mar. 23, 1933; s. Ernest Prosper and Sadie (Liken) W.; m. Mary B. Hunter, Jan. 12, 1959; children—Jeffrey, Franz, Kathleen, Lynne. B.A., Bowling Green State U., 1955, M.A., 1960; Ph.D., Mich. State U., 1963. Asst. prof. speech SUNY-Oneonta, 1962-63, Kent State U., 1963-64; mem. faculty Purdue U., 1964-70, assoc. prof., 1968-70; prof. speech Montclair (N.J.) Coll., 1970-71; assoc. prof. speech Pa. State U., 1971-72; dir. Ernest Weckesser Assos.; chmn. bd. dirs. Green Tree Press, Inc., Dunkirk, N.Y.; pres. Bierhaus Internat., Inc., Erie, Pa. Author: The Radio Rhetoric of John L. Lewis, 1963, How To Succeed in College, 1971, The 12,000 Housewife, 1975, Dollars in Your Mailbox, 1975, Alternatives: A Network of Small Business Opportunities, 1992; co-author: The Bradley-Cooper Smoke Cessation Program, 1995. Bd. dirs. Florerence Crittenden Home, Erie.; Mem. Pres.'s Council Gannon U.; Mem. adv. bd. Villa Maria Coll. Served to capt. USAF, 1955-59. Named Disting. Pennsylvanian William Penn Soc., 1983.

WECKSTEIN, RICHARD SELIG, economics consultant; b. N.Y.C., Feb. 11, 1924; s. Isidore and Flo (Litwin) W.; m. Muriel Watenmaker, June 11, 1947; children: Beth Alison Harris, Leslie Ellen Hyman. Ph.B., U. Wis.-Madison, 1947; M.A., Yale U., 1948, Ph.D., 1953. Asst. prof. NYU, N.Y.C., 1951-53; asst. prof. U. Buffalo, 1953-57; vis. faculty Gadjah Mada U., Jogjakarta, Indonesia, 1957-58; vis. assoc. prof. U. Rochester, N.Y., 1958-59; asst. prof. Williams Coll., Williamstown, Mass., 1959-62; assoc. prof. Brandeis U., Waltham, Mass., 1962-66, prof., 1967-73, Carl Marks prof. econs., 1973-93, prof. emeritus, forensic economist, 1971—; mem. Consumers Council, Mass., 1964-72; cons. mission to Liberia Harvard Devel. Adv. Service, Cambridge, Mass., 1964, 66; cons. to Internal Bank of Reconstrn. Devel., Washington, 1971-72; vis. scholar Nuffield Coll., Oxford, 1972; lectr. Flaschner Jud. Inst. of Mass. Bar Found., 1981-83; lectr. Mass. Council Trial Attys., 1986-87. Editor: Expansion of World Trade and the Growth of National Economies, 1968; contbr. articles to profl. jours., ency. Bd. dirs. Beacon Hill Civic Assn., Boston, 1980-83; trustee Longy Sch. Music, Inc., Cambridge, Mass., 1990. Served to 1st lt. USAF, 1942-46. Social Sci. Research Council grantee, 1963-66; vis. fellow Harvard Law Sch. 1978. Mem. Am. Econ. Assn., Atlantic Econ. Soc., Nat. Assn. Forensic Econs., North Haven Yacht Club (Maine) (bd. dirs. 1983—, pres. 1988-92). Avocations: sailing, tennis, flying. Home: 22 Gray Gardens E Cambridge MA 02138 Office: Brandeis U Dept Econs Waltham MA 02254

WECLEW, ROBERT GEORGE, lawyer, educator; b. Chgo., Oct. 30, 1911; s. Victor T. and Mary (Tadrowski) W.; m. Jean Helen Vinson, Jan. 5, 1942; children: Harlene Villio, Robert Vinson Weclew. B.S. in Law, Northwestern U., 1932, J.D., 1935. Bar: Ill. 1934, U.S. Dist. Ct. (no. dist.) Ill. 1935, U.S. Supreme Ct. 1946. Assoc. Case and Lynn, Chgo., 1935-40; atty. Employers of Wausau, Chgo., 1940-42, VA, Chgo., 1945-57; prof. Law Sch., DePaul U., Chgo., 1957-78; acting dean Law Sch., DePaul U., 1968-71, prof. emeritus, 1978—; sole practice Chgo., 1978—; Mem. Am. Law Inst., 1968-71; counsel, co-founder Acad. of Gen. Dentistry, 1952-70. Contbr. articles on constl. law to profl. jours. Mem. Ill. Constl. Study Commn., Chgo., 1969-70. Fellow Acad. Continuing Edn. (counsel, co-founder 1974—); mem. Ill. Bar Assn. (council legal edn. 1969-71), Advocates Soc., Phi Kappa Theta, Delta Theta Phi.

WECLEW, VICTOR T., dentist; b. Chgo., Mar. 18, 1916; m. Gertrude David, 1945; 1 child, Victor T. III. B.S., U. Ill., 1939, D.D.S., 1943. Gen. practice dentistry Chgo., 1946—. Contbr. articles to profl. jours. Active Boy Scouts Am. Served to maj. A.C. U.S. Army, 1943-46. Fellow Acad. Gen. Dentistry (co-founder 1952, bd. dirs., asst. editor Jour. 21 yrs.), Acad. Continuing Edn. (co-founder 1974), Am. Coll. Dentists, Acad. of Dentistry Internat. (trustee); mem. ADA, Chgo. Dental Soc. (various coms., past dir., pres. N.W. br. 1969-70), U. Ill. Dental Alumni Assn. (bd. dirs. 10 yrs.,

Disting. Alumnus award 1985), Omicron Kappa Upsilon, Psi Omega. Roman Catholic. Home: 5781 N Forest Glen Ave Chicago IL 60646

WEDBUSH, EDWARD WILLIAM, investment banker; b. St. Louis, Sept. 14, 1932; s. William H. and Edith M. (Herman) W.; BSME, U. Cin., 1955; MBA, UCLA, 1957; m. Jean Lawrence, Dec. 18, 1960; children: Gary, Eric, Leigh Ann. Hughes fellow, 1955-58; pres. Wedbush & Co., L.A., 1957-69; pres., CEO Wedbush Morgan Securities, Inc., L.A., 1969—, Wedbush Corp., 1981—; bd. dirs. Securities Industry Assn., Great Am. First Savs. Bank; mem. adv. com. Am. Stock Exch., 1980—; dir. Pacific Stock Exch., 1974-78, chmn. bd., 1976-77; mem. Nat. Securities Clearing Corp., bd. dirs., 1981-84; chmn., mem. regional firms adv. com. N.Y. Stock Exch., 1984-88. Club: California. Home: Rancho Santa Fe CA 92067 Office: 1000 Wilshire Blvd Los Angeles CA 90017-2457

WEDDIG, LEE J(OHN), trade association executive; b. Fon du Lac, Wis., Sept. 22, 1935; s. Edward K. and Rose M. (Weddig); m. June M. Hennig, Jan. 28, 1956; children: Andrew J., Lisa M. B.S. in Journalism, Marquette U., 1956. Reporter UP, Milw., 1956, Fairchild Pubs., Chgo., 1957; nat. merchandising mgr. Motorola, Inc., Chgo., 1957-67; exec. dir. Nat. Fisheries Inst., Washington, 1967-73, exec. v.p., 1975—; pres. C.L. Watt, Inc., and Fin. Mgmt. Services, Inc., Dayton, Ohio, 1973-74; U.S. commr. Internat. Commn. for Conservation of Atlantic Tuna. Mem. Am. Soc. Assn. Execs. Republican. Roman Catholic. Club: Lakewood.

WEDDING, CHARLES RANDOLPH, architect; b. St. Petersburg, Fla., Nov. 16, 1934; s. Charles Reid and L. Marion (Whitaker) W.; m. Audrey Whitsel, Aug. 18, 1956 (div. Apr. 1979); children: Daryl L., Douglas R., Dorian B.; m. Vonnie Sue Hayes, June 22, 1984 (div. Dec. 1991); stepchildren: Stephanie M., Brian E.; m. June A. Free, Mar. 31, 1993; stepchildren: Gregory, Kristine. BArch, U. Fla., 1957. Registered architect, Fla., Ga., N.C., S.C., Del., Va., Tex., Ill., Ind., Kans., La., Mo., Okla., Tenn. Architect in tng. Harvard & Jolly AIA, St. Petersburg, 1957-60; architect, prin., pres. Wedding & Assocs., St. Petersburg, 1960—. Mayor City of St. Petersburg, 1973-75; past chmn. Pinellas County Com. of 100, Bldg. Dept. Survey Team, City of St. Petersburg; trustee All Children's Hosp., 1968-70; sect. leader St. Petersburg United Fund, 1965-70; mem. city council Action Team for Pier Redevel., 1967-68; mem. exec. com. Goals for City of St. Petersburg, 1970-72; den. leader Weblos, Boy Scouts Am., 1971-72; chmn., trustee Canterbury Sch. YMCA, 1968-72; mem. adv. com. Tomlinson Vocat. Sch., 1969-79; past trustee Mus. Fine Arts; past bd. dirs. Neighborly Ctr., Jr. Achievement Pinellas County. Served to 1st lt. U.S. Army, 1958-60. Fellow AIA (5 Silver Spike awards, Merit of Honor, Medal of Honor); mem. Am. Soc. Landscape Architects, St. Petersburg Assn. Architects (past. pres.), Fla. Assn. Architects (8 Merit Design awards). Republican. Episcopalian. Clubs: Suncoasters; St. Petersburg Yacht. Avocations: sailing, hunting, golfing, tennis. Home: 6900 10th Ave N Saint Petersburg FL 33710 Office: Wedding & Assocs Inc 300 1st Ave S Saint Petersburg FL 33701

WEDDINGTON, SARAH RAGLE, lawyer, educator; b. Abilene, Tex., Feb. 5, 1945; d. Herbert Doyle and Lena Catherine (Morrison) Ragle. BS magna cum laude, McMurry Coll., 1965, hon. doctorate, 1979; JD, U. Tex., 1967; hon. doctorate, Hamilton Coll., 1979, Southwestern U., 1989, Austin Coll., 1993. Bar: Tex. 1967, D.C. 1980, U.S. Dist. Ct. (we. no. and ea. dist.) Tex., U.S. Ct. Appeals (5th cir.), U.S. Supreme Ct. Pvt. practice law Austin, 1967-77; gen. counsel Dept. Agr., Washington, 1977-78; spl. asst. to Pres., Washington, 1978-79, asst. to Pres., 1979-80; chmn. Interdepartmental Task Force on Women, 1978-81; mem. Pres.'s Commn. on Exec. Exchange, 1981; Carl Hatch prof. law and pub. adminstrn. U. N.Mex., Albuquerque, 1982-83; pvt. practice law Austin, Tex., 1985—; dir. Tex. Office State-Fed. Relations, Austin, 1983-85; vis. prof. govt. Wheaton Coll., Norton, Mass., 1980-81; sr. lectr. Tex. Woman's U., Denton, 1981—, U. Tex., Austin, 1986—. Author: A Question of Choice, 1992; contbg. editor Glamour mag., 1981-83. Mem. Tex. Ho. of Reps., 1973-77. Recipient Woman of Yr. award Tex. Women's Polit. Caucus, 1973, Elizabeth Boyer award Equity Action League, 1978, Outstanding Woman award, 1979, Leadership awards Ladies Home Jour., 1979, spl. recognition Esquire mag., 1984, Woman Who Dares award Nat. Coun. Jewish Women, 1993, Woman of Distinction award Nat. Conf. for Coll. Women Student Leaders, 1993; named Lectr. of Yr. Nat. Assn. for Coll. Activities, 1990, 91. Mem. Tex. Bar Assn., Bus. and Profl. Women's Club, AAUW, Nat. Women's Polit. Caucus. Office: S Weddington Law Offices 709 W 14th St Austin TX 78701-1707

WEDDLE, STEPHEN SHIELDS, manufacturing company executive; b. Boston, Nov. 9, 1938; s. Harold Mansfield and Esther Letha (Bales) W.; m. Meredith Baldwin, June 10, 1961; children: Christopher, Timothy, Justin, Jamien. A.B., Harvard, 1960; LL.B., Columbia, 1963. Bar: N.Y. 1966, Conn. 1989. Lectr. in law (supported by Ford Found. Project for Staffing African Instns. for Legal Edn. and Research) Ahmadu Bello U., Zaria, Nigeria, 1963-65; assoc. firm Debevoise & Plimpton, N.Y.C., 1965-71; corporate counsel Technicon Corp., Tarrytown, N.Y., 1971-74; sec. Technicon Corp., 1972-78, sr. v.p., gen. counsel, 1974-78; v.p., gen. counsel, sec. Stanley Works, New Britain, Conn., 1978—. Mem. Assn. Bar City N.Y. (sec. com. on fgn. and comparative law 1968-70), Am., Conn., N.Y. bar assns., Am. Soc. Corp. Secs., Am. Corp. Counsel Assn. Office: Stanley Works 1000 Stanley Dr New Britain CT 06053

WEDEEN, MARVIN MEYER, hospital executive; b. Perth Amboy, N.J., Jan. 3, 1926; s. Nathan and Gertrude (Rappaport) W.; m. Hannah Haas; children: Rachel, Miriam. BS, Cornell U., 1949; MSc in Hosp. Adminstrn., Columbia U., 1971. Rsch. asst. Sealtest div. Kraft Foods, Schenectady, N.Y., 1949-55, dir. work simplification, 1955-59; pers. mgr. Dellwood Foods, Yonkers, N.Y., 1959-63; asst. v.p. Dellwood Foods, Yonkers, 1964-69; cons. pers. N.Y. Infirmary, N.Y.C. 1971; asst. adminstr. Sewickley Valley Hosp., Sewickley, Pa., 1971-80; v.p. Sewickley Valley Hosp., Sewickley, 1980-90; spl. advisor to pres. Sewickley (Pa.) Valley Hosp., 1991; ret., 1992; cons. Exec. Svc. Corp., 1992—; bd. dirs. Valley Care Assn., Sewickley, 1979—; mem. Human Resources Prog. Coun. Western Pa., 1987-89; cons. Sr. Med. Cons., N.Y.C., 1971. Chmn. oper. com. Health Systems Agy., Pitts.; class fund rep. Cornell U. Alumni Fund, 1967-72; bd. dirs. United Jewish Fedn. Bd., 1991—. Named Man of the Yr., Sewickley Hist. Soc. and Gateway Press, 1980. Fellow, Am. Coll. Health Care Execs.; mem. Am. Pub. Health Assn., Am. Hosp. Assn. Hosp. Assn. (planning and mktg. section, 1984—), Edgeworth Club. Avocations: racket sports, music, theater art. Home: RR 4 Sewickley PA 15143-9804

WEDEL, PAUL GEORGE, retired hospital administrator; b. Elizabeth, N.J., Jan. 1, 1927; s. Paul John and Helen (Cleary) W.; m. Jean Marie Martin, June 18, 1949; children: Dana Lyn Wedel, Laurie Ann Wedel Musser, Paul John II, Kurt Frederick. Grad., Peddie Sch., Hightstown, N.J., 1944; B.S. in Bus. Adminstrn., A.N. U., 1952; M.S. in Hosp. Adminstrn., Northwestern U., 1953. Adminstrv. resident Harrisburg (Pa.) Polyclinic Hosp., 1953-54; asst. adminstr. Williamsport (Pa.) Hosp., 1954-59, adminstr., 1959-64; pres. Lancaster (Pa.) Gen. Hosp., 1964-89; pres. Lancaster Gen. Hosp. Found., 1989-92, pres. emeritus, 1992-94; ret., 1994. Bd. dirs. Inter-County Hospitalization Plan, Inc., 1966-84, James Buchanan Found., Preservation Wheatland, 1968-80, Linden Hall Sch., 1984-91; sr. warden St. Thomas Episcopal Ch., 1979-81; trustee Millersville U., 1991—. Served with USNR, 1944-46, 50-51. Named Outstanding Young Man, Williamsport Jr. C. of C., 1957. Fellow Am. Coll. Health Care Execs. (regent Pa. 1984-89); mem. Am. Hosp. Assn., Hosp. Assn. Pa. (bd. dirs. 1970-73, 84-89), Lancaster Assn. Commerce and Industry (bd. dirs.), Hamilton Club, Pirates Club, Rotary (pres. 1978-79), Masons. Home: Rock Rimmon Ridges 203 Riveredge Dr Leola PA 17540-9745

WEDEMEYER, ERICH HANS, physicist; b. Osterode, Fed. Republic Germany, Aug. 16, 1927; s. Theodor and Ella (Osterwald) W.; m. Christel Seeringer, Aug. 18, 1956; 1 child, Sibylle. Diploma for physics, U. Göttingen, Fed. Republic Germany, 1956, D. Natural Scis., 1969. Rsch. physicist Aerodyn. Versuchsanstalt, Göttingen, 1956-61, Ballistic Rsch. Lab., Aberdeen, Md., 1962-66; head dept. Deutsche Forschungs-und Versuchsanstalt Luft und Raumfahrt, Göttingen, 1966-80, cons., 1990—, rsch. physicist, 1982-90; vis. prof. Von Karman Inst., Brussels, 1980-82. Contbr. articles to Ing. Arch., Jour. Fluid Mech., Jour. Aircraft; author: Liquid Filled Projectile Design, 1969. With German Air Force, 1943-45. Mem. AIAA. Evangelic Lutheran. Achievements include development of the theory of confined fluid

motion; research on Hydrodynamic Stability; on Wind Tunnel Techniques; 3 patents on adaptive wall test sections in wind tunnels. Home: Am Weinberg 37, 37176 Norten Hardenberg Germany Office: DLR Göttingen, Bunsenstrasse 10, 37073 Göttingen Germany

WEDEMEYER, W. ANNE LITTLE, pediatric cardiologist, educator, lawyer; b. Mercer County, Pa., May 29, 1937; d. Frederick and Lois (Waldorf) Little; m. Phillips Wedemeyer, May 18, 1963 (div. Dec. 1979); children: William J., Hope S., Christian K. BS, U. Pitts., 1959, MD, 1962; JD, Duquesne U., 1988. Diplomate Am. Bd. Pediatrics, Am. Bd. Pediatric Cardiology; bar: Pa. 1989. Intern U. Minn. Hosp., 1962-63, resident, 1966-67, fellow in pediat. cardiology, 1967-69; pediatrician U.S. Army, Hanau, Germany, 1965-66; asst. prof. pediat. U. Pitts., 1969-71; rschr. with Dr. Jessica H. Lewis, 1971-73; dir. pediat. cardiology Mercy Hosp. Pitts., 1972-88, active, adj. staff, 1988-93; clin. asst. prof. pediat. U. Pitts., 1971—; pvt. practice pediat. cardiology Pitts., 1972—; active staff physician Children's Hosp. Pitts., 1969—; cons. staff Allegheny Gen. Hosp., Pitts., 1978—. Co-chair NCCJ, Pitts., 1991-93, bd. dirs., 1989—, sec.; chair edn. and med. com. Pitts. Friends of Tibet, Trafford, Pa., 1993—, bd. dirs., 1994—, legal and tax com., 1993. Recipient Rsch. award Paul S. and Faith S. Cardiac Fund, 1968-69; rsch. grantee Minn. Heart Assn., 1968-69, Beaver County Heart Assn., 1970-71, HEALTH Rsch. and Svcs. Found., 1973-74; rsch. support grantee U. Pitts., 1971-72. Fellow Am. Acad. Pediat., Am. Coll. Cardiology; mem. AMA, Pa. Med. Soc., Pa. Bar Assn., Allegheny County Med. Soc. (med.-legal sect. 1991—), Allegheny County Bar Assn. (health law sect. 1991—), Fox Chapel Golf Club, Rivers Club (charter). Office: 1501 Locust St Ste 229 Pittsburgh PA 15219

WEDEPOHL, LEONHARD M., electrical engineering educator; b. Pretoria, Republic of South Africa, Jan. 26, 1933; s. Martin Willie and Liselotte B.M. (Franz) W.; m. Sylvia A.L. St. Jean; children: Martin, Graham. B.Sc. (Eng.), Rand U., 1953; Ph.D., U. Manchester, Eng., 1957. Registered profl. engr., Escom, Johannesburg, Republic of South Africa, 1957-61; mgr. L.M. Erricson, Pretoria, Republic of South Africa, 1961-62; sect. leader Reyrolle, Newcastle, Eng., 1962-64; prof., head dept. Manchester U., 1964-74; dean engring. U. Man., Winnipeg, Can., 1974-79; dean applied sci. U. B.C., Vancouver, Can., 1979-85, prof. elec. engring., 1985—; mem. Sci. Rsch. Coun., London, 1968-74; dir. Man. Hydro, Winnipeg, 1965-69, B.C. Hydro, Vancouver, 1980-84, B.C. Sci. Coun., 1981-84; cons. Horizon Robotics, Saskatoon, 1986; chmn. implementation team Sci. Place Can., 1985; cons. CEPEL, Rio de Janeiro; adv. Man. High Voltage D.C. Rsch. Ctr.; tech. advisor RTDS Techs., Inc., Winnipeg, 1994—. Contbr. articles to sci. jours.; patentee in field. Named Hon. Citizen City of Winnipeg, 1979. Fellow Instn. Elec. Engrs. (premium 1967); mem. Assn. Profl. Engrs. B.C. Avocations: music; cross-country skiing; hiking. Office: U BC Dept Elec Engring, 2356 Main Mall, Vancouver, BC Canada V6T 1Z4

WEDGE, THOMAS WILLIM, occult consultant, criminologist; b. Carey, Ohio, Oct. 16, 1943; s. Rosco Wedge and Margreat (Twining) Casper; m. Brenda Susan Krum, Oct. 6, 1966; 1 child, Gloria. BA, Cedarville Coll., 1981-84; diploma in Bible, Worthing Bible Inst., 1981; student, Central State Coll., 1984, Moody Bible Inst., 1984. Finish carpenter Columbus, Ohio, 1967-76; sales mgr. Key Renault, Columbus, Ohio, 1971-76, Miley's Sporting Goods, Delaware, Ohio, 1976-80; dir. Logan County Residential Treatment Ctr., Bellefontaine, Ohio, 1984-89; jail adminstr. Union County Sheriff's Dept., Marysville, Ohio, 1985-86; prin. Tom Wedge Co., Columbus, Ohio, 1989—; lectr. in field. Author: The Satan Hunter, 1989. With U.S. Army, 1963-66, Vietnam. Recipient Disting. Svc. award Sheriff's Office Punta Gorda, Fla., 1988, Sheriff's Office Jefferson Parish, 1990, Appreciation plaque La. State Police Acad., 1989; named for Disting. Svc., Atty. Gen. Ohio, 1992. Mem. Am. Soc. Law Enforcement Trainers, Nat. Sheriff's Assn., Internat. Assn. Asian Gangs, Ohio Crime Prevention Assn., Midwest Gang Investigation Assocs. (instr.). Republican. Baptist. Avocations: golf, fishing. Office: Tom Wedge Co PO Box 14425 Columbus OH 43214-0425

WEDGEWORTH, ANN, actress; b. Abilene, Tex., Jan. 21, 1935; m. Rip Torn (div.); 1 child, Danae; m. Ernest Martin; 1 child, Dianna. Attended U. Tex.; B.A. in Drama, So. Methodist U. Broadway debut in Make A Million, 1958; other Broadway appearances Chapter Two (Tony award), Thieves, Blues for Mr. Charlie, The Last Analysis; off-Broadway appearances Line, Chapparal, The Crucible, Days and Nights of Beebee Fenstermaker, Ludlow Fair, The Honest to God Shnozzola, A Lie of the Mind; toured with nat. cos. of The Sign in Sidney Brustein's Window and Kennedy's Children; appeared: in TV series Three's Company, The Edge of Night, Another World, Somerset, Filthy Rich, Evening Shade; other TV appearances All That Glitters, The Defenders, Bronk, Evening Shade, Twilight Zone, Trapper John, M.D.; TV film The War Between the Tates, Bogey, Right to Kill, A Stranger Waits; movies Handle With Care (Nat. Soc. Film Critics award), Thieves, Bang the Drum Slowly, Scarecrow, Catamount Killing, Law and Disorder, One Summer Love, Dragon-Fly, Birch Intervals, Soggy Bottom, USA, No Small Affair, Sweet Dreams, Mens Club, A Tiger's Tale, Made in Heaven, Far North, Miss Firecracker, Green Card. Office: care Paradigm Talent Agy 10100 Santa Monica Blvd 25th Fl Los Angeles CA 90067*

WEDGEWORTH, ROBERT, university librarian, dean, former association executive; b. Ennis, Tex., July 31, 1937; s. Robert and Jimmie (Johnson) W.; m. Chung Kyun, July 28, 1972; 1 child, Cicely Veronica. AB, Wabash Coll., 1959, DHL (hon.), 1980; MS, U. Ill., 1961; LittD, Park Coll., 1973; LLD, Atlanta U., 1982; DHL, Western Ill. U., 1983, Coll. William & Mary, 1988. Cataloger Kansas City Pub. Library, 1961-62; asst. librarian, then acting librarian Park Coll., Parkville, Mo., 1962-64; librarian Meramec Community Coll., Kirkwood, Mo., 1964-66; acquisitions librarian Brown U. Library, Providence, 1966-69; asst. prof. Rutgers U., New Brunswick, N.J., 1971-72; exec. dir. ALA, Chgo., 1972-85; dean Sch. Library Service Columbia U., N.Y.C., 1985-92; univ. libr., prof. libr. adminstrn. U. Ill., Urbana, 1992—; mem. Nat. Commn. on New Technol. Uses of Copyrighted Works, 1975-78, biomed. library rev. com. Nat. Library Medicine, 1975-78, chmn., 1978-79; mem. network adv. com. Library of Congress, 1975-78; dir. exec. bd., exec., coun., council Ctr. for the Book, Library of Congress, 1978-82; bd. dirs. Newberry Library, Chgo., 1979—, Pub. Service Satellite Consortium, 1975-85; bd. visitors U. Miami Libraries, Air U. Libr., 1987—; mem. exec. bd. Internat. Fedn. Library Assns. and Instns., The Hague, 1985-91, pres. 1991—; trustee Am. Library in Paris, 1986-92; trustee Wabash Coll., 1988—; alumni bd. Wabash Coll., pres. 1987-89; vis. prof. Sch. Library Sci. U. N.C., Chapel Hill, 1985; mem. adv. coun. Princeton U. Libraries, 1977-78, Stanford U. Libraries, 1989—; mem. nat. adv. com. Gannett Ctr. for Media Services; mem. Accrediting Council on Edn. in Journalism and Mass Communication. Editor: Library Resources and Tech. Services, 1971-73; editor-in-chief ALA Yearbook, 1976-85, World Encyclopedia of Library and Information Services, 3d edit., 1994. Chmn. U.S. Nat. Com. for UNESCO/PGI, 1976-81. Council on Library Resources fellow, 1969. Mem. ALA (life), NAACP (life), Am. Soc. Info. Sci., Grolier Club, Am. Antiquarian Soc. Home: 2008 Bentbrook Dr Champaign IL 61821 Office: Univ of Illinois 1408 W Gregory Rm 230 Urbana IL 61801

WEDIG, JOHN HARRISON, toxicologist, consultant; b. St. Louis, Dec. 25, 1941; s. John Harrison and Verla W.; m. M. Rita Thomas; children: Sara, Alison, Meredith. AB in Zoology, Washington U., St. Louis, 1964; M in Wildlife, U. Mich., 1967, PhD in Toxicology, 1971. Diplomate Am. Bd. of Toxicology. Toxicologist Olin Corp., New Haven, Conn., 1971-78, sr. toxicologist, 1978-1985; project dir. Great Ea. Devel., Grenwich, Conn., 1985-87; pvt. practice Grenwich, 1985-87; dir. toxicology T.P.S., Inc., Mt. Vernon, Ind., 1987-89, sci. dir., 1989—. Fellow Am. Acad. Vet. and Comparative Toxicology; mem. Am. Soc. Pharmacology and Exptl. Therapeutics, Soc. Toxicology. Achievements include 4 patents for drugs. Office: T P S Inc 1170 Hickory Hill Dr Watkinsville GA 30677-2121

WEDLOCK, ELDON DYMENT, JR., law educator; b. Providence, Oct. 29, 1942; s. Eldon Dyment and Madelyn Bernice (Daniels) W.; m. Janet Louise Nielsen, Aug. 1965; children: Stina Cole, Sara Nielsen. AB, Brown U., 1965; JD, Am. U., 1968; LLM, Yale U., 1969. Bar: D.C. 1969, U.S. Dist. Ct. D.C. 1968, U.S. Ct. Appeals (D.C. cir.) 1969. Assoc. prof. law U.S.C., Columbia, 1969-72, assoc. prof., 1972-77, prof., 1977-90, David H. Means chair, prof., 1990—. Author: (with others) The Emerging Rights of the Confined, 1972, The Tree of Liberty, 1986; editor The Jour. of Law and Edn., 1973—. Mem. D.C. Bar Assn., ACLU (pres. Columbia chpt. 1973-76). Democrat. Home:

200 S Edisto Ave Columbia SC 29205-3304 Office: U SC Sch Law Columbia SC 29208

WEDRAL, ELAINE REGINA, food chemist; b. Detroit, Feb. 29, 1944; d. Albert and Anna Amelia (Stalc) Maesso; m. William Wedral, May 23, 1970. B.S. with honorsin Biochemistry, Purdue U., 1966; M.S. in Microbiology, Cornell U., 1968, Ph.D. in Food Chemistry, 1970. Quality control foreman, supr. Holloway House subs. Green Giant Food, Lafayette, Ind., 1964-65; chemist Campbell Soup Co., Chgo., 1966; mgr. microbiology Western Farmers Assn., Seattle, 1970-71; project coordinator nutrition and prodn. safety Libby McNeill & Libby Inc., Chgo., 1972-74; assoc. dir. product devel. Libby McNeill & Libby Inc., 1974-76, dir. research and devel., 1976-79, v.p. research and devel., 1979-80; v.p. Westreco div. Nestle Inc., New Milford, Conn., 1981—; dir. Westreco div. Nestle Inc. Contbr. articles to various publs. Mem. Nat. Food Processors (sci. affairs council), Am. Meat Inst. (sci. research com. 1976-81), Grocery Mfrs. Am. (tech. rep. 1974-77). Office: Westreco Inc Boardman Rd New Milford CT 06776-5516

WEED, ITHAMAR DRYDEN, life insurance company executive; b. Pomeroy, Ohio, Sept. 3, 1914; s. Ithamar B. and Besse (Smith) W.; m. Sally Lemert, July 5, 1941; children—Judith Lynne (Mrs. Lloyd Lindner), Charles Boyd, Donald Lemert. A.B., Ohio U., 1938; J.D. summa cum laude, Ohio State U., 1939. Bar: Ohio 1939. Clk. U.S. Dist. Ct. So. Dist. Ohio, Columbus, 1939-41; assoc. firm Vorys, Sater, Seymour and Pease, Columbus, 1946-54; assoc. counsel Western and So. Life Ins. Co., Cin., 1954-63; v.p., chief counsel Western and So. Life Ins. Co., 1963-73, sr. v.p., chief counsel, 1973-81; sec., dir Eagle Savs. Assn., Cin., 1970-81, West Ad, Inc., Cin., 1970-81; lectr. Coll. Law, Ohio State U., 1949-53. Served to lt. col. AUS, 1941-46. Mem. Order of Coif, Beta Theta Pi, Phi Delta Pi. Home: 5538 E Galbraith Rd Apt 34 Cincinnati OH 45236

WEED, MAURICE JAMES, composer, retired music educator; b. Kalamazoo, Oct. 16, 1912; s. Frank Eugene and Ella May (Britton) W.; m. Berneice Laverne Pope, Aug. 23, 1937; children: Allison Gilbert (Mrs. Walter D. Herrick), Laurice Ellen (Mrs. Samuel L. Rich). BA, Western Mich. U., 1934; MusB, Eastman Sch. Music, 1940, MusM, 1952, PhD, 1954. Supr. instrumental music pub. schs. Ionia, Mich., 1934-36, Three Rivers, Mich., 1937-43; asst. prof. music, dir. instrumental music, tchr. music theory Ripon Coll., 1946-51; tchr. Eastman Sch. Music, summer 1954; prof., head dept. music No. Ill. U., 1954-61, prof. music, 1961-74; adj. prof. music Western Carolina U., 1974-75; ret., 1975. Composer in residence, MacDowell Colony, 1961; performances include: Serenity for chamber orch. Eastman-Rochester Symphony, 1953, Symphony Number 1, Nat. Symphony Orch., Washington, 1956, Symphony of the Air, Carnegie Hall, 1957, Wonder of the Starry Night, 1st ann. symposium Contemporary Am. Music, U. Kans., 1959, Serenity and Fanfare for Two Trumpets and Organ, 8th ann. symposium Univ. Composers Exchange, Valparaiso, Ind., 1959; Sept Cinquains for Soprano Voice and chamber instrumental group, No. Ill. U., 1964, 67, Symphonie Breve, 6th ann. symposium Contemporary Am. Music U. Kans., 1967, Symphonie Breve, Oklahoma City Symphony Orch.; MBS broadcast, 1965, U. Redlands, 1964, Asheville (N.C.) Symphony Orch., 1979; condr. symposium of 8 sacred choral and 2 organ works by 6 coll., univ., high sch. and ch. choirs, Atlanta, 1975; Serenity, Asheville Symphony Orch., 1977; composer: over 65 works including Ships, Witchery (songs for soprano and piano), 1937, Rain, for contralto and piano, 1940, Three Preludes for Organ, 1945, Introduction and Scherzo, symphonic band, 1948, Gratitude, for contralto with organ, 1950, An After Easter Prayer, 1950, Serenity, for chamber orch., 1953, Wonder of the Starry Night, a capella choir, 1958, Symphonie Breve, 1959, Trio for violin, cello and piano, 1961, Concertino for cello and orch, 1962, Psalm XIII (mixed choir and organ), 1964, Hopkins Park, concert march, 1966, Triptych for Voices, a cappella choir, 1966, Vestigia Nulla Retrorsum, processional march, 1968, Praise Ye the Lord (mixed choir), 1968, A Wedding Song (soprano and organ), 1969, In the Midnight Hour (soprano and organ), 1970, In Te, Domini, Speravi (mixed choir), 1970, 4 Anthems for Mixed Choir, 1973, Postlude for Organ, 1974, The Catamounts, concert march for band, 1974, Duo for Viola and C Trumpet, 1977, Choral Fanfare No. 2, 1977, An Appalachian Celebration for Choir and Band, 1978; Celebration (hymn-anthem), 1981; 3 anthems for mixed voices Let All the People Praise Thee, 1980, Sing Praises to God, 1981, Praise Ye the Lord, 1982, The 3Bs-Brass Sextet, 1982, Voices of Appalachia, 1986; numerous others. Recipient 25th Anniversary award Nat. Symphony Orch., 1956, Ostwald award, 1959, J. Fisher & Bro. Centennial award, 1964, Pedro Paz award, 1966; Eastman Sch. Music teaching fellow, 1951-54. Mem. Nat. Assn. Composers U.S.A., Am. Music Ctr., Music Edn. Nat. Conf., N.C. Music Educators, Am. Soc. Univ. Composers, ASCAP, Phi Mu Alpha. Methodist. Home: Givens Estates Sweeten Creek Rd Wesley Dr N Villa 21-F Asheville NC 28803

WEEDER, DANA NIXON, surgeon; b. Phila., July 30, 1934; s. Stephan Dean and Caroline Denny (Nixon) W.; m. Astrid Sundt, May 19, 1962; children: Dana Sundt, Kristian Nixon, Kari Sundt. AB, Princeton U., 1955; MD, U. Pa., 1959. Diplomate Am. Bd. Surgery. Staff surgeon Doylestown (Pa.) Hosp., 1965-66, 68-70, Exeter (N.H.) Hosp., 1970—. Lt. cmdr. USN, 1966-68. Fellow Am. Coll. Surgeons; mem. N.E. Surgical Soc. Avocations: boat building, tennis, golf. Office: Saltonstall Med Bldg Buzell Ave Exeter NH 03833

WEEDN, TRISH, state legislator; b. Oklahoma City, May 10, 1950; d. Carl R. and Teddeline (Morrell) Throckmorton; m. James A. Weedn; children: Marnie, Mindy. Assessor McClain County, Okla., 1979-88; mem. Okla. State Senate, 1989—. Former chmn. McClain County Dem. Com; sect./treas. Purcell Pentacostal Holiness Ch. Mem. Okla. Assn. Assessing Officers, S.W. Coll. Ministry. Democrat. Pentacostal. Office: Okla State Senate State Capitol Oklahoma City OK 73105

WEEDON, ALAN CHARLES, chemist, educator; b. Oxford, Eng., Mar. 29, 1951; arrived in Can., 1976; s. Charles Arthur Reginald and Marjorie Elsie (Cook) W. BSc, London U., 1973, PhD, 1976. Rsch. assoc. U. Western Ont., London, Can., 1976-80, asst. prof., 1980-86, assoc. prof., 1986-91, prof., 1991—. Contbr. articles to sci. jours. Recipient Merck-Frosst award Can. Soc. Chemistry, 1991. Fellow Chem. Inst. Can.; mem. Am. Chem. Soc. Office: U Western Ont, Dept of Chemistry, London, ON Canada N6A 5B7

WEEKES, TREVOR C., astrophysicist; b. Dublin, Ireland, May 21, 1940; came to U.S. 1966; s. Gerard and Florence (Murtagh) W.; m. Ann Katherine Owens, Sept. 30, 1964; children: Karina, Fiona, Lara. BSc, U. Coll. Dublin, 1962, PhD, 1966; DSc, Nat. U. Ireland, 1978. Lectr. Univ. Coll. Dublin, 1964-66; postdoctoral fellow NRC, Cambridge, Mass., 1966-67; astrophysicist Smithsonian Astrophys. Obs., 1967-92, sr. astrophysicist, 1992—; resident dir. Whipple Obs., Amado, Ariz., 1969-76; vis. prof. Royal Greenwich Obs., U.K., 1980-81. Mem. Am. Astron. Soc., Am. Phys. Soc., Royal Astron. Soc. Democrat. Roman Catholic. Office: Whipple Obs PO Box 97 Amado AZ 85645-0097

WEEKLEY, FREDERICK CLAY, JR., lawyer; b. San Antonio, Aug. 29, 1939; s. F. Clay and Topsy (Stevens) W.; m. Lynda Freeman; children: Amber Lee, Caroline Lee. BBA, Baylor U., 1962, JD, 1963; LLM, NYU, 1969. Bar: Tex. 1963. Ptnr. Bracewell & Patterson, Houston, 1974-90; trust counsel Bank One, Tex. N.A., 1990—; mem. coun. real property, probate and trust law sect., State Bar of Tex., 1987-90; mem. trust divsn. Tex. Bankers Assn., 1992—, chmn. legis. com., 1992-95. Editor: Texas Wills System, 1984. Fellow Am. Coll. Trust and Estate Counsel. Home: 1821 Mossy Oak St Arlington TX 76012-5619 Office: Bank One Texas NA Legal Dept 1717 Main Fl 9 Dallas TX 75201-3602

WEEKLY, JOHN WILLIAM, insurance company executive; b. Sioux City, Iowa, June 21, 1931; s. John E. Weekly and Alyce Beatrice (Preble) Nichols; m. Bette Lou Thomas, Dec. 31, 1949; children: John William Jr., Thomas Patrick, Michael Craig, James Matthew, Daniel Kevin. Grad. high sch., Omaha. V.p First Data Resources, Inc., Omaha, 1969-74; v.p Mut. United Omaha Ins. Co., Omaha, 1974-81, sr. exec. v.p., 1981-87; pres., chief oper. officer Mut. of Omaha Ins. Co., Omaha, 1987, also bd. dirs., 1987—; pres., COO, bd. dirs. United of Omaha Life Ins. Co., 1990—; bd. dirs. Harbor Holdings, Inc., Companion Life Ins. Co., Kirkpatrick, Pettis, Smith, Polian, Inc., Tele-Trip Omaha Property and Casualty Co., United World Life Ins.,

Mut. Asset Mgmt. Co., Norwest Bank Nebr., N.A., Omaha Fin. Life Ins. Co., Omaha Airport Authority, Mus. of Omaha Investor Svcs., Preferred HealthAlliance, Inc. Bd. dirs. Bellevue (Nebr.) Coll., 1986—. Mem. Health Ins. Assn. Am. (bd. dirs. 1992—), Greater Omaha C. of C. (bd. dirs. 1991—). Avocations: hunting, fishing, golf. Office: Mut Omaha Ins Co Mutual Omaha Plz Omaha NE 68175

WEEKS, ALBERT LOREN, author, educator, journalist; b. Highland Park, Mich., Mar. 28, 1923; s. Albert Loren and Vera Grace (Jarvis) W. Student, U. Mich., 1942-43; MA, U. Chgo., 1949; PhD, Columbia U., 1965; cert. Russian Inst., 1960. Reporter Chgo. City News Bur., 1946; polit. analyst U.S. Dept. State, 1950-53, Free Europe Com., Inc., 1953-56; editorial asst. Newsweek mag., 1957-58; Russian tech. glossary compiler McGraw-Hill Book Co., 1960-61; prof. continuing edn. NYU, 1959-89; lectr. U.S. diplomatic history and soviet govt. Columbia U., 1951-52; mem. adv. coun. Nat. Strategy Info. Ctr., 1979-89; instr. Ringling Sch. Art and Design, 1991—. Host: A Week's View of Red Press, Sta. WNBC, 1965-68; series Myths That Rule America, NBC-TV, 1979-82; author: Reading American History, 1963, The First Bolshevik: A Political Biography of Peter Tkachev, 1968, The Other Side of Coexistence: An Analysis of Russian Foreign Policy, 1970, Richard Hofstadter's The American Political Tradition and the Age of Reform, 1973, Andrei Sakharov and the Soviet Dissidents, 1975, The Troubled Detente, 1976, Solzhenitsyn's One Day in the Life of Ivan Denisovich, 1976, Myths That Rule America, 1980, War and Peace: Soviet Russia Speaks, 1983; editor/compiler Brassey's Soviet and Communist Quotations, 1987, The Soviet Nomenklatura, 1987-1991; internat. affairs editor Def. Sci. mag., 1982-85; columnist Def. Report, 1982-90; nat. sec., editor N.Y.C. Tribune, 1982-90; contbr. articles N.Y. Times, New Republic, New Leader, Annals, Russian, Slavic revs., Christian Sci. Monitor, Problems of Communism, Survey, Mil. Intelligence, Slavo, Strategic Rev., Air Univ. Rev., L.A. Times, Washington Times, Orbis, Global Affairs, Panorama, Sarasota Herald-Tribune, Bradenton Herald, Defense and Diplomacy, Rossiiskiye Vesti, Am. Intelligence Jour., USA Today, Rossiiskiye Vesti. Home: 4884 Kestral Park Cir Sarasota FL 34231-3369

WEEKS, ARTHUR ANDREW, lawyer, educator; b. Hanceville, Ala., Dec. 2, 1914; s. A.A. and Anna S. (Seibert) W.; m. Carol P. Weeks; children: John David, Carol Christine, Nancy Anna. A.B., Samford U., 1936; LL.B., U. Ala., 1939, J.D., 1939; LL.M., Duke U., 1950; LL.D. (hon.), Widener U., 1980. Bar: Ala. 1939, Tenn. 1948. Sole practice Birmingham, Ala., 1939-41, 1946-47, 1954-61; dean, prof. law Cumberland U. Sch. Law, 1947-54; dean, prof. Samford U., 1961-72, prof. law, 1972-74; prof. law Cumberland Sch. Law, Samford U., 1984—; prof. law Del. Sch. Law of Widener U., Wilmington, 1974-82, dean, 1974-80, interim dean, 1982-83, dean emeritus, prof., 1983—. Served to capt. AUS, 1941-46. Mem. ABA, Tenn. Bar Assn., Ala. Bar Assn., Birmingham Bar Assn., Del. Bar Assn. (assoc.), Phi Alpha Delta, Phi Kappa Phi, Delta Theta Phi. Home: 1105 Water Edge Ct Birmingham AL 35244-1437

WEEKS, BRIGITTE, publishing executive; b. Whitchurch, Hants, Eng., Aug. 28, 1943; came to U.S., 1965; d. Jack and Margery May (Millett) W.; m. Edward A. Herscher, Sept. 6, 1969; children—Hilary, Charlotte, Daniel. Student, Univ. Coll. of North Wales, Bangor, 1962-65. Asst. editor Boston Mag., 1966-70; editor Kodansha Internat., Tokyo, 1969-72, Resources for the Future, 1973-74; asst. editor The Washington Post Book World, 1974-78, editor, 1978-88; sr. v.p., editor-in-chief Book-of-the-Month Club, N.Y.C., 1988-94; editor-in-chief Guideposts Assocs., N.Y.C., 1994—; pres. Nat. Book Critics Circle, 1984-86; bd. dirs. Nat. Book Found. Office: Guideposts Assocs 16 E 34th St New York NY 10016

WEEKS, DAVID FRANK, foundation administrator; b. Salt Lake City, Sept. 9, 1926; s. Frank Harold and Myrtle June (Larsen) W.; m. Betty Alice Tellin, Aug. 14, 1949; children: David Rice, Clayton Frank. Student, So. Meth. U., 1945, U. Tex., 1946; B.S. (Union Pacific Carl Raymond Gray scholar), U. Idaho, 1949; HHD (hon.), U. Louisville, 1993. Pres. Assoc. Students U. Idaho, 1948-49; announcer Sta. KBIO, Burley, Idaho, 1949; Idaho rep. Nat. Found. for Infantile Paralysis, Boise, 1949-53; asst. to nat. dir. fund raising Nat. Found. for Infantile Paralysis, N.Y.C., 1953-57; asst. nat. dir. March of Dimes, N.Y.C., 1957-59; account exec. Kersting, Brown & Co., N.Y.C., 1959-61; exec. dir. Rsch. to Prevent Blindness, Inc., N.Y.C., 1961-70, exec. v.p. 1970-83, pres., 1983—; pres., trustee RPB Endowment Fund Inc., N.Y.C., 1988—; mem. borough coun. Borough of Ho-Ho-Kus, N.J., 1966-68; mayor Borough of Ho-Ho-Kus, 1968-75; consumer rep. subcom. ophthalmic prostheses HEW, 1976-79; cons. Bur. Med. Devices, FDA, 1977-80; mem. nat. adv. eye coun. NIH, HHS, 1985-90; trustee Okla. Eye Found., 1988-92. Mem. Ho-Ho-Kus Planning Bd., 1962-65, chmn., 1965; mem. Zoning Bd., 1975-85, Bergen County (N.J.) Ethics Bd., 1977-82; founder, pres. Ho-Ho-Kus Republican Club, 1983-86. Served with USN, 1944-46. Recipient Bronze Palm Eagle Scout award Boy Scouts Am., 1941, Disting. Pub. Svc. award Am. Acad. Ophthalmology and Otolaryngology, 1976, cert. of recognition Johns Hopkins U. Schs. Medicine, Hygiene and Pub. Health, 1984, Nat. Vision Rsch. Leadership award Assn. U. Profs. Ophthalmology, 1989, Disting. Svc. award Johns Hopkins Med. Instns.-Wilmer Ophthal. Inst., 1989; named Ky. col., 1969, U. of Idaho Alumni Hall of Fame award, 1992. Mem. Assn. Rsch. in Vision and Ophthalmology (hon.), Pan Am. Ophthalmol. Assn. (assoc.), Am. Soc. Assn. Execs., Internat. Assn. Eye Rsch., Bergen County Mayors Assn. (pres. 1975-77), Am. Tentative Soc. (treas. and trustee 1974-94, v.p. 1982-94), Met. Club. Home: 8 Brookview Ct Ho Ho Kus NJ 07423-1201 Office: Research To Prevent Blindness 598 Madison Ave New York NY 10022-1614

WEEKS, GERALD, psychology educator; b. Morehead City, N.C., Nov. 20, 1948; s. Marion G. and Ada (Willis) W.; m. Kathleen Glass, Sept. 2, 1972. BA in Philosophy and Psychology, East Carolina U., 1971, MA in Gen. Psychology, 1973; PhD in Clin. Psychology, Ga. State U., 1979. Diplomate Am. Bd. Profl. Psychology (pres. 1987-88, bd. dirs. 1982-87), Am. Bd. Family Psychology, Am. Bd. Sexology; cert. marital and family therapist; lic. practicing psychologist, N.C., Pa.; registered Health Care Providers in Psychology. Intern in family therapy Harlem Valley Psychiatric Ctr., Wingdale, N.Y., 1978-79; assoc. prof. psychology U. N.C., Wilmington, 1979-85; dir. tng. Marriage Coun. Phila., 1985—; clin. assoc. prof. psychology Sch. Medicine U. Pa., Phila., 1985-87, clin. assoc. prof., 1988—; pvt. practice Carolina Ob-gyn Ctr., Wilmington, 1980-85. Author: Promoting Change Through Paradoxical Therapy, 1985, Treating Couples: The Intersystem Model of the Marriage Council of Philadelphia, 1989, Promoting Change through Paradoxical Therapy, 1991, (with L. L'Abate) Paradoxical Psychotherapy: Theory and Practice with Individuals, Couples, and Families, 1982, (with R. Sauber, L. L'Abate) Family Therapy: Basic Concepts and Terms, 1985, (with L. Hof) Intergrating Sex and Marital Therapy: A Clinicans Guide, 1987, (with S. Treat) Couples in Treatment, 1992; editorial bd. Am. Jour. Family Therapy, Am. Jour. Family Psychology; contbr. articles to profl. jours. Fellow Am. Assn. Marital and Family Therapy (clin. mem., nat. adv. bd., approved supr.); mem. APA, Acad. Family Psychology, Interpersonal and Social Skills Assn. (founding mem.), Acad. Psychologists in Marital, Sex, and Family Therapy. Home: 210 Church St # D Philadelphia PA 19106-4519 Office: Penn Coun for Relationships 4025 Chestnut St Fl 2 Philadelphia PA 19104-3054

WEEKS, JEROME C., writer, drama critic; b. Detroit, Dec. 10, 1953; s. William Lawrence and Frances (Podgurski) W.; m. Sara Rankin; 1 child, Suzanna Beckett. Bachelor, U. Detroit, 1975; Master, U. Conn., 1977; postgrad., U. Tex., 1977-80. Rsch. asst. Detroit Free Press, 1973-75; columnist, editor Third Coast Mag., Austin, Tex., 1982-84; entertainment writer Houston Post, 1984-86; drama critic Dallas Morning News, 1986—. Recipient Katy award Dallas Press Club, 1993. Mem. Am. Theatre Critics Assn. Office: Dallas Morning News 508 Young St Dallas TX 75202

WEEKS, JOHN DAVID, chemistry and physical science educator; b. Birmingham, Ala., Oct. 11, 1943; s. Arthur Andrew Weeks and Grace Hicks (Ezell) Marquez; m. Kaja Parming, May 27, 1987; 1 child, Aili. AB, Harvard U., 1965; PhD, U. Chgo., 1969. Postdoctoral fellow U. Calif., San Diego, 1969-71, U. Cambridge, Eng., 1971-72; mem. tech. staff AT&T Bell Labs., Murray Hill, N.J., 1972-90; prof. Inst. Phys. Sci. and Tech., dept. chemistry U. Md., College Park, 1990-95, disting. univ. prof., 1995—. Contbr. articles to profl. jours. Fellow Am. Phys. Soc.; mem. AAAS, Am. Chem Soc. (chair, theoretical chem. subdiv. 1992-93, Hildebrand award

1990). Home: 15301 Watergate Rd Silver Spring MD 20905-5779 Office: U Md Inst Phys Sci and Tech College Park MD 20742

WEEKS, JOHN ROBERT, geographer, sociology educator; b. Sacramento, June 1, 1944; s. Robert Louis and Thelma Hope (Evans) W.; m. Deanna Jean Hosea, May 16, 1965; children: John Robert, Gregory, Jennifer. AB, U. Calif., Berkeley, 1966, MA, 1969, PhD, 1972. Asst. prof. sociology Mich. State U., East Lansing, 1971-74; asst. prof. sociology San Diego State U., 1974-78, assoc. prof., 1978-81, prof., 1981-92; prof. geography, 1992—; chmn. dept. San Diego State U., 1978-85; adminstrv. dir. Internat. Population Ctr., 1985—; vis. research demographer U. Calif.-Berkeley, 1972; cons. Allied Home Health Assn., 1978-80, Area Agy. on Aging, San Diego, 1979-81, Los Angeles Regional Family Planning Council, 1986—, East County Econ. Devel. Coun., 1986—. Author: Teenage Marriages, 1976, Population, updated 5th edit., 1994, Aging, 1984, Demography of Islamic Nations, 1988, High Fertility Among Indochinese Refugees, 1989, Demographic Dynamics of the U.S.-Mexico Border, 1992. Grantee USPHS, 1983-84, 87-88, 88-89, 90—, U.S. Administrn. on Aging, 1979-80, U.S. Bur. of Census, 1988-89; trainee USPHS, 1967-71. Mem. Population Assn. Am., Am. Sociol. Assn., Internat. Union for Sci. Study Population, Am. Assn. Geographers. Democrat. Office: San Diego State U Dept Geography San Diego CA 92182

WEEKS, JULIE RAE, marketing executive; b. Lansing, Mich., Nov. 2, 1957; d. George Compton and Mollie Ray (McKinley) W. BA, U. Mich., 1979, MA, 1981. Field rep. Baker for Pres., Lansing, 1979-80; research asst. Market Opinion Research, Detroit, 1980, research analyst, 1982-84, sr. research asst., 1984-87, dir. of research, 1988—. Republican. Episcopalian. Avocations: orienteering, reading, jigsaw puzzles. Office: Small Bus Admn Office Adv Office Econ Rsch 409 3rd St SW Washington DC 20416

WEEKS, MARTA JOAN, priest; b. Buenos Aires, May 24, 1930; came to U.S., 1932; d. Frederick Albert and Anne (Newman) Sutton; m. Lewis Austin Weeks, Aug. 17, 1951; children: Kermit Austin, Leslie Anne. BA in Polit. Sci., Stanford U., 1951; MDiv, Episcopal Theol. Sem. S.W., 1991. Ordained priest Episcopal Ch., 1992. Legal libr.; sec. Mene Grande Oil Co., Caracas, Venezuela, 1948; English tchr. Centro-Venezolano Americano, Caracas, 1948; sec. Household Fin. Corp., Salt Lake City, 1951; legal sec. McKelvey & McKelvey Attys., Durango, Colo., 1952; sec., dir. Weeks Air Mus., Miami, Fla., 1985—; chaplain Jackson Meml. Hosp., 1992-93; priest-at-large Episcopal Diocese of S.E. Fla., until 1995; interim asst. St. James Episcopal Ch., Salt Lake City, 1994—. Trustee Beloit (Wis.) Coll., 1980-82, U. Miami, 1983-88, 95—, Bishop Gray Inns, Lake Worth and Davenport, Fla., 1992—. Mem. Am. Soc. Order St. John of Jerusalem. Address: 7350 SW 162nd St Miami FL 33157-3820

WEEKS, PAUL MARTIN, plastic surgeon, educator; b. Clinton, N.C., June 11, 1932; m. Doris Hill, Apr. 28, 1956; children: Christopher, Heather, Paul, Thomas, Susan, Phillip. AB, Duke U., 1954; MD, U. N.C., 1958. Diplomate Am. Bd. Surgery, Am. Bd. Plastic Surgery. Intern N.C. Meml. Hosp., Chapel Hill, 1959-62, asst. resident in surgery, 1962-63, chief resident in gen. surgery, 1962-63, chief resident in plastic surgery, 1963-64; from instr. to asst. prof. surgery U. Ky., Louisville, 1964-68, assoc. prof. surgery, 1968-70; prof. surgery, plastic and reconstructive surgery, head of div. Washington U. Sch. Medicine, St. Louis, 1971—; plastic surgeon-in-chief Barnes Hosp., St. Louis, 1971—, St. Louis Children's Hosp., 1971—. Assoc. editor Jour. Hand Surgery, 1976—, Plastic and Reconstructive Surgery, 1978-84; contbr. articles to profl. jours. Mem. AMA, ACS (gov. 1991—), Soc. Univ. Surgeons, So. Med. Assn., Am. Surg. Assn., So. Surg. Assn., Assn. Academic Surgeons, Am. Soc. Plastic and Reconstructive Surgeons, Am. Soc. Surgery of the Hand, Plastic Surgery Research Council, Am. Burn Assn., Am. Assn. Plastic Surgeons (pres. elect 1990-91, pres. 1991-92), Am. Assn. Plastic and Reconstructive Surgeons, Mo. State Med. Assn., St. Louis Med. Soc., Canadian Soc. Plastic and Reconstructive Surgeons, Nathan Womack Soc. Republican. Avocations: golf, sailing, skiing. Home: 6470 Ellenwood Ave Saint Louis MO 63105-2229 Office: Barnes Hosp Barnes Hospital Plz Saint Louis MO 63110

WEEKS, RICHARD RALPH, marketing educator; b. Champaign, Ill., Sept. 18, 1932; s. Frank Cook and B. Caroline (Pool) W.; m. Sue Ann Grunwald, Aug. 29, 1953; children: Kimberly Sue, Bret William. B.S., U. Ill., 1955; M.B.A., Washington U., St. Louis, 1960, D.B.A., 1966. Exec. sec., editor bull. Am. Assembly Collegiate Schs. Bus., St. Louis, 1960-64; exec. sec. Beta Gamma Sigma; also editor Beta Gamma Sigma Exchange, 1961-64; 1st ann. A.A.C.B.S. doctoral fellow in bus. adminstrv., 1964-65; dir. MBA program asst. prof. mktg. Coll. Bus., Okla. State U., 1965-66, asst. dean, dir. MBA program, asso. prof. mktg., 1966-67; dean, prof. mktg. Walter E. Heller Coll. Bus. Adminstrn., Roosevelt U., 1967-70; dean Coll. Bus. Adminstrn. U.R.I., 1970-85, acting v.p. bus. and fin., 1976-77, provost for pub. policy, pub. service and mgmt., 1979-85, prof. mktg., 1970-92, prof. emeritus, dean emeritus, 1992—; dir. Potter Hazlehurst Inc., Providence Gas. Co., Providence Energy Co., Newport Am. Corp., Daly & Walcott, Inc. Editor: Faculty Personnel, 9th edit, 1965; contbg. editor Ency. Bus. Information Sources, 1964; editorial adv. bd. Bus. and Soc, 1968-70. Bd. dirs. Chgo. Econ. Devel. Corp., 1968-70, v.p., 1969-70; bd. dirs. Chgo. Fin. Devel. Corp., 1970, Progress Assn. for Econ. Devel., 1972-73; bd. dirs. Coun. on Postsecondary Accreditation, 1974-83, mem. exec. com., 1977-82, chmn., 1979-81; bd. dirs. Friends of Jamestown Philomenian Library, 1972-77, pres., 1974-76; mem. adv. bd. Intercollegiate Case Clearinghouse, 1976-79; pres. Friends of URI Library, 1986-88. Served to capt. USAF, 1955-63. Fulbright grantee, 1986. Mem. Am. Mktg. Assn. (dir. acad. placement 1966, 68), Ea. Fin. Assn. (dir. 1974-77), Council Profl. Edn. Bus. (sec.-treas. 1960-64, exec. com. 1961-64), Nat. Assn. State Univs. and Land-grant Colls., Commn. on Edn. for Bus. Professions (sec. 1973-76, chmn. 1976-78), New Eng. Assn. Schs. and Colls. (sec.-treas. 1983-85), Am. Assn. Collegiate Schs. Bus. (various com., bd. dirs. 1976-85, pres. 1983-84), Greater Providence C. of C. (dir. 1979-82), Delta Sigma Pi, Alpha Kappa Lambda, Beta Gamma Sigma (various coms., pres. 1978-80), Mu Kappa Tau, Pi Sigma Epsilon, Phi Kappa Phi. Home: 2048 Imperial Cir Naples FL 33942-1089

WEEKS, ROBET ANDREW, materials science researcher, educator; b. Birmingham, Ala., Aug. 23, 1924; s. William Andrew and Annie Bell (Hammond) W.; m. Jane Sutherland, Mar. 20, 1948; children—Kevin Dale, Robin Dee, Loren Hammond, Kerry Andrew. B.S., Birmingham-So. Coll., 1947; M.S. U. Tenn., 1951; Ph.D., Brown U., 1966. Sr. physicist Union Carbide Corp., Oak Ridge, Tenn., 1951-84; research prof. material sci. Vanderbilt U., 1984—; disting. vis. prof. Am. U. in Cairo, 1970-71; invited prof. Ecole Poly. Federale de Lausanne, Switzerland, 1981; vis. prof. Cath. U., Leuven, Belgium, 1983; cons. numerous pvt. corps. and fed. agys. Co-editor: Effects of Modes of Formation on Structure of Glass, 1985, 88, Editing the Refereed Scientific Journal, 1994; assoc. editor Jour. Geophys. Rsch., 1968-74; eidtor. Jour. Noncrystalline Solids, 1988—; contbr. numerous articles to profl. jours. Served with U.S. Army, 1943-46. Union Carbide fellow, 1964; Fulbright lectr., 1980; research fellow Reading U., 1971. Fellow Am. Ceramic Soc. (R.A. Weeks Symposium on Sci. and Tech. SiO2 2nd Related Materials named in his honor, Honolulu 1993, editl. com. jour. 1968-80); mem. AAAS, Am. Phys. Soc., Materials Rsch. Soc. Avocation: photography. Home: 331 Southshore Dr Greenback TN 37742 Office: Vanderbilt U PO Box 1678 Nashville TN 37240

WEEKS, ROLAND, JR., newspaper publisher; b. Knoxville, Tenn., July 8, 1936. B.S., Clemson (S.C.) U., 1958. Sales engr. Metal Products, Inc., Greenville, S.C., 1961-63; mgmt. trainee, then bus. mgr. Columbia Newspapers, Inc.; pubs. The State and Columbia (S.C.) Record newspapers, 1963-68; pres., pub. Gulf Pub. Co., Inc.; pubs. Biloxi-Gulfport (Miss.) Sun Herald, 1968—; dir. Hancock Bank, Gulfport. Pres. Pine Burr area council Boy Scouts Am., 1980; chmn. Miss. Bd. Corrections, 1982-88. Served to 1st lt. USAF, 1958-61. Mem. Am. Newspaper Assn., So. Newspaper Pubs. Assn. (pres. 1981), Young Pres. Orgn., Gulf Coast C. of C. (pres. 1989). Presbyterian. Office: Gulf Pub Co Inc 205 DeBuys Rd PO Box 4567 Biloxi MS 39533-4567

WEEKS, ROSS LEONARD, JR., museum foundation executive; b. Jamestown, N.Y., Sept. 11, 1936; s. Ross Leonard and Cecile Forbes (Carrie) W.; AB, Colgate U. 1958; MS, George Washington U., 1971, cert. Fed. Exec. Inst., 1988; m. Patricia Ann Earley, June 10, 1951; children: Susan Woodall, Ross Leonard, III, William Andrew, David James. Reporter, Jamestown

Post-Jour., 1958-60, Richmond (Va.) News Leader, 1960-65; dir. public info. Coll. William and Mary, Williamsburg, Va., 1965-71, asst. to exec. v.p. 1971-74, asst. to pres., dir. univ. communications, 1974-81; exec. dir. Jamestown (Va.)-Yorktown Found., 1981-91; exec. dir. Historic Crab Orchard Mus., Inc., Tazewell, Va., 1992—; grant reviewer U.S. Inst. Mus. Svcs. Editor William & Mary Alumni Gazette, 1966-81. Chmn. Williamsburg-James City Bicentennial, 1975-77; bd. dirs. Va. Fed. Savs. Bank, 1981-91, Williamsburg Pre-Sch. Spl. Children, 1970-75, Va. Travel Council, 1987-89; pres. Williamsburg Sch. PTA, 1974-77; bd. dirs. Williamsburg C. of C., 1982-87, Coalfield Regional Tourism Devel. Authority S.W. Va., 1993—; Va. Southwest Blue Ridge Highlands, Inc., 1993-95; sec./treas. Frontier Culture Found., 1982-86; exec. dir. Va. Independence Bicentennial Commn., 1981-83; trustee council, Thirteen Original States, 1982-87; chair Tazewell County Tourism Devel. Commn.; mem. exhibition mine com. Town of Pocahontas; lay reader Stras Meml. Episc. Ch., Tazewell. Recipient award excellence for programs Council Advancement and Support Edn., 1978, 79. Mem. Public Relations Soc. Am., Am. Assn. Mus. (mus. assessment coms. 1988—), Am. Assn. State and Local History, St. Andrews Soc., Masons, Rotary (Paul Harris fellow 1987), Clan Ross Assn. U.S. Sigma Delta Chi, Kappa Delta Rho (Ordo Honora 1986). Avocations: travel, landscaping, antiquities, historical research. Home: Hemlock Ridge PO Box 82 Tazewell VA 24651-0082 Office: Hist Crab Orchard Mus Rt 1 Box 194 Tazewell VA 24651

WEEKS, SINCLAIR, JR., silverware manufacturing company executive; b. Barnstable, Mass., July 28, 1923; s. Sinclair and Beatrice (Dowse) W.; m. Mary Birch Broeksmit, Feb. 25, 1950; children: Nathaniel S., Stuart B., Beatrice W., Bradford S. S.B., Harvard U., 1945, M.B.A., 1947. With United Carr Inc., 1947-61; with Reed & Barton Corp., Taunton, Mass., 1961—, pres., 1972-87, chief exec. officer, 1976-87, chmn., 1986—, also bd. dirs.; trustee Reed & Barton Found.; bd. dirs. Eureka Mfg. Co., Colonial Income Fund, Colonial Fund, Inc., Colonial Tax-Managed Trust, Colonial Growth Shares, Inc., Colonial High Yield Securities, Inc., Blue Cross Mass., Sheffield Silver Co., Inc., Kurt Gutmann Jewelry, Inc., Commonwealth Energy System, Colonial Option Growth Trust. Trustee Boston Mus. Sci., Boys and Girls Camps, Wentworth Inst. Tech.; pres., treas., trustee Lancaster Found.; chair Bus. and Industry Polit. Action Com.; bd. dirs. Mass. Taxpayers Found. Served as officer USAAF, 1943-45. Republican. Clubs: Somerset (Boston), Commercial (Boston); Harvard (N.Y.C.), Twenty-Four Karat (N.Y.C.); Taunton Rotary, Concord (Mass.) Country, University of Chgo. Office: Reed & Barton Corp 144 W Britannia St Taunton MA 02780-1643

WEEKS, STEVEN WILEY, lawyer; b. Topeka, Mar. 7, 1950; s. Glen Wiley and Grace Aileen (West) W.; m. Lee Nordgren, Aug. 1, 1974 (div. 1985); 1 child, Kirstin Nordgren. BS summa cum laude, Washburn U., 1972; JD cum laude, Harvard U., 1977. Bar: Ohio. Project leader Nat. Sanitation Found., Ann Arbor, Mich., 1972; engr. Kans. Dept. Health and Environ., Topeka, 1972-74; ptnr. Taft, Stettinius & Hollister, Cin., 1977—; dir. Cin. Schroder, Inc., The Myers Y. Cooper Co., Cin.; adj. faculty Chase Coll. Law, 1987-88. Mem. adv. com. prosecuting atty. Hamilton County, Cin., 1992. Mem. Ohio State Bar Assn., Cin. Bar Assn. Republican. Methodist. Avocations: computers, golf. Home: 3641 Michigan Ave Cincinnati OH 45208 Office: Taft Stettinius & Hollister 425 Walnut St Cincinnati OH 45202

WEEKS, THOMAS WESLEY, bishop; b. Boston, July 14, 1945; s. Thomas J. and Susan Weeks; m. Leona Brown, Sept. 3, 1966; children: Thomas Wesley Jr., Abdullah Azeez. B in Applied Sci., Boston U., 1969, M in Urban Affairs, 1974; MDiv, Luther Rice Sem., Jacksonville, Fla., 1990; DD (hon.), Aenon Bible Coll., 1984. Ordained to ministry Pentecostal Assemblies of the World, Inc. Asst. site mgr. rsch. ops. Rand Corp., South Bend, Ind., 1974-76, site mgr., 1974-80; pastor Greater Bethel Apostolic Temple, Wilmington, Del., 1980—; pastor, bishop Pentecostal Assemblies of the World, Inc., 1987—; pres. Aenon Bible Coll., Indpls., 1984—; pres. Mass. State Young People, 1960-67, Internat. Pentecostal Young People's Union, 1976-82, Interdenominational Mins. Coun. Del., 1986—; mem. com. Planning for Internat. Ministerial Conf., 1990—. Author: Pagan Holidays, 1983; editor Reachout jour. and newsletter. With USAR, 1963-71. Recipient Outstanding award Internat. Pentecostal Young People's Union, 1982, Betterment of Community award City of Indpls., 1982, commendations U.S. Senate, State of Del., Wilmington City Coun., 1984-87. Mem. NAACP (Disting. Svc. award Del. chpt. 1989). Home: PO Box 527 Wilmington DE 19899-0527 Office: Greater Bethel Apostolic Temple 2900 N Van Buren St Wilmington DE 19802-2998

WEEKS, WALTER LEROY, electrical engineering educator; b. Utica, N.Y., Mar. 30, 1923; s. Walter William and Emma (Conley) W.; children: Patricia, Walter William, Daniel, Sheryl, Joseph, Kathryn. BS, U. Mich., 1947; MS, Mich. State U., 1949; PhD, U. Ill., 1958. Instr. Mich. State Coll., 1947-51; asst. prof. N.Mex. State Coll., 1951-54, prof., 1959-60; asso. prof. U. Ill., 1954-59; asst. dir. research and devel. Collins Radio Co., Cedar Rapids, Iowa, Dallas, 1960-63; prof. elec. engring. Purdue U., 1963-89, prof. emeritus, 1989—; chmn. Purdue Electric Power Ctr., 1985-88; cons. Terronics Devel. Corp., Elwood, Ind., 1985—. Author: Electromagnetic Theory for Engineering Applications, 1964, Antenna Engineering, 1968, Transmission and Distribution of Electrical Energy, 1981. With USAAF, 1942-46. Inventor radiation leak detector, 1975, partial discharge locator, 1982, power cable fault locator, 1989. Home: 5517 Inverness Dr Sarasota FL 34243-4734 also: PO Box 2162 West Lafayette IN 47906-0162

WEEKS, WILFORD FRANK, geophysics educator, glaciologist; b. Champaign, Ill., Jan. 8, 1929; married; 2 children. BS, U. Ill., 1951, MS, 1953; PhD in Geology, U. Chgo., 1956. Geologist mineral deposits for U.S. Geol. Survey, 1952-55; glaciologist USAF Cambridge Research Ctr., 1955-57; asst. prof. Washington U., St. Louis, 1957-62; adj. prof. earth scis. Dartmouth Coll., Hanover, N.H., 1962-85; glaciologist Cold Regions Rsch. and Engring. Lab., Hanover, 1962-89; chief scientist Alaska Synthetic Aperture Radar Facility, Fairbanks, 1986-93; prof. geophysics Geophys. Inst. U. Alaska, Fairbanks, 1986—; vis. prof. Inst. Low Temperature Sci. Hokkaido U., Sapporo, Japan, 1973; chair Arctic marine sci. USN Postgrad. Sch., Monterey, Calif., 1978-79; mem. earth sys. sci. com. NASA, Washington, 1984-87; advisor U.S. Arctic Rsch. Commn., divsn. polar programs NSF, Washington, 1987-88; chmn. NAS Com. on Cooperation with Russia in Ice Mechanics, 1991-92; mem. environ. task force MEDEA Cons. Group, 1992—. Capt. USAF, 1955-57. Fellow Arctic Inst. N.Am., Am. Geophys. Union; mem. NAE, Internat. Glaciological Soc. (v.p. 1969-72, pres. 1973-75, Seligman Crystal award 1989). Avocations: skiing, diving, contrabassist. Office: U Alaska Fairbanks Geophys Inst PO Box 757320 Fairbanks AK 99775-7320

WEEMS, FRANCES ELIZABETH, lawyer, county official; b. Lutherville, Md., Mar. 3, 1945; d. Charles Louis and Mary-Elizabeth Kathleen (Bentley) W. BA, U. Ala., 1977; JD, Miles Law Sch., 1989. With Jefferson County Commn., Birmingham, Ala., 1976—, community devel. specialist; bd. dirs. Indsl. Devel. Bd., Birmingham, 1990—. Composer and lyricist: Message to His Deciples, 1978; photographer: Lest We Forget, 1980 (award 1980). Sponsor, trainer Spl. Olympics, Birmingham, 1979—; bd. dirs. Kiwanis Internat., Bessemer, Ala., 1990. Recipient Meritorious Svc. award United Negro Coll. Fund, Inc., 1990; named Minority Advocate of Yr. U.S. Dept. Commerce, 1991, Minority Enterprise Devel. award, 1992, 93. Mem. Nat. Assn. County Community and Econ. Devel., Assn. Pub. Adminstrs., Delta Theta Phi. Roman Catholic. Avocations: special olympics, music, photography. Office: Jefferson County Commn 805 22nd St N Birmingham AL 35203-2303

WEEMS, JOHN EDWARD, writer; b. Grand Prairie, Tex., Nov. 2, 1924; s. J. Eddie and Anna Lee (Scott) W.; m. Jane Ellen Homeyer, Sept. 11, 1946; children: Donald (dec.), Carol, Mary, Barbara, Janet. BJ, U. Tex., 1948, M.Journalism, 1949; MA in Libr. Sci., Fla. State U., 1954. Tel. editor Temple (Tex.) Daily Telegram, 1950; instr. Calif. State Poly. Coll., San Dimas, 1950-51; night news editor San Angelo (Tex.) Standard-Times, 1951; copy editor Dallas Morning News, 1952-53; asst. prof., head cataloger main library Baylor U., 1954-57; asst. prof. U. Ala., also asst. mgr. Ala. Press Assn., 1957-58; asst. to dir. U. Tex. Press, 1958-68; prof. English, Baylor U., 1968-71, lectr. creative writing, fall 1979; reference librarian McLennan Community Coll., Waco, Tex., 1969-70; freelance writer, 1971—. With USNR, 1943-46, 51-52; lt. Res. (ret.). Am. Philos. Soc. grantee, 1964. Fellow

Tex. State Hist. Assn., Tex. Inst. Letters; mem. PEN, Nat. Book Critics Circle, Authors Guild, Western Writers Am., Sigma Delta Chi, Beta Phi Mu. Author: A Weekend in September, 1957; The Fate of the Maine, 1958; Race for the Pole, 1960; Peary: The Explorer and the Man, 1967; Men Without Countries, 1969; Dream of Empire (Amon G. Carter award), 1971; To Conquer a Peace: The War Between the United States and Mexico (Richard Fleming award), 1974; Death Song, 1976; The Tornado, 1977; (with John Biggers and Carroll Simms) Black Art in Houston, 1978; "If You Don't Like the Weather," 1986; editor: A Texas Christmas: A Miscellany of Art, Poetry, Fiction, Vol. I, 1983, Vol. II, 1986; (San Antonio Conservation Soc. Spl. award), The Story of Texas, 1986, Austin (Texas): 1839-1989, 1989 (Tex. Inst. Letters Barbara McCombs Lon Tinkle award lifetime Writing achievement 1989). Address: 2012 Collins Dr Waco TX 76710-2626

WEEMS, ROBERT CICERO, economist, educator; b. Meridian, Miss., July 22, 1910; s. Robert Cicero and Susie (Vaughan) W.; m. Frances Dodds, Aug. 13, 1941; 1 dau., Susan. B.S. with honors, State U., 1931; M.B.A., Northwestern U., 1934; Ph.D. in Econs., Columbia U., 1951. Part-time staff Bank of Shubuta, Miss., 1924-33; teaching fellow econs. La. State U., 1933-34; instr. bus. adminstrn. Miss. State Coll., 1934-35, asst. prof. banking and finance, 1935-38, asso. prof., 1938-40, acting dean Sch. Bus. and Industry, 1940-42; dean Miss. State Coll. Sch. Bus. and Industry, 1942-56; dir. Bus. Research Sta. of Coll. Miss. State Coll., 1940-56, asst. dir. engring. sci. and mgmt. War Tng. Program, 1941-43; dean Coll. Bus. Adminstrn., dir. Bur. Research U. Nev., 1956-77; adviser-cons. U. Nev. Endowment Fund, 1975—; chmn. Regional (Nev.) Export Expansion Council, 1960-74; mem. Nat. Export Expansion Council, U.S. Dept. Commerce, 1960-74; chmn. adv. council Miss. Employment Security Commn., 1952-56; mem. Western Indsl. Nev., Nev. Public Employees Retirement Bd., 1963-78, vice chmn., 1975-78; mem. employment security council Nev. Employment Security Dept.; mem. nat. adv. council SBA, 1975-77. Trustee U.S. Travel Data Center, 1973-76, Calif.-Nev. Meth. Found., 1980—; trustee Am. Inst. Econ. Research, 1964—, chmn. bd., 1972-76. Served to lt. comdr. USN, 1943-46. Recipient cert. of appreciation U.S. Dept. Commerce, 1968, 1973. Mem. Am. Hotel and Motel Assn. (trustee ednl. inst.), Travel Research Assn. (treas.), Western Econ. Assn., Nev. World Trade and Internat. Tourism Assn. (trustee 1974—, pres. 1976-77), Blue Key, Omicron Delta Kappa (hon.), Chi Lambda Rho, Delta Sigma Pi, Beta Gamma Sigma (nat. exec. coun. 1970-74), Phi Kappa Phi, Pi Kappa Alpha, Kappa Kappa Psi. Methodist. Club: Rotary (Reno). Home: 1135 Williams Ave Reno NV 89503-2648

WEENING, RICHARD WILLIAM, JR., banker, finance and communications executive, venture capitalist; b. San Bernardino, Calif., Dec. 24, 1945; s. Richard William and Alice Louise (Young) W.; m. Elizabeth Louise Halmbacher, June, 1965 (div. Aug. 1973); children: Elicia Louise, Mia Lynn; M. Robin Lorraine Woodard, July, 1990. Student, St. Johns U., 1963-65, U Wis., 1966-68. Legis. asst. U.S. Congressman Henry S. Reuss, Washington, 1968-70; exec. sec., chief of staff Wis. Gov. Patrick J. Lucey, Madison, 1970-72; pres., pub., dir. Raintree Pubs., Inc., Milw., 1972-85; pres., chief exec. officer, dir. McDonald-Raintree, Inc., 1977-82, George Philip Raintree, Cartographers, Inc., 1977-82; chmn., dir. Raintree Pubs. Internat., Ltd., London, 1978-82, Raintree de Mexico Editores, SA, Mexico City, 1978-82; chief exec. officer AgriData Resources, Inc. (now known as ARI Network Svcs., Inc.), 1981-87, chmn., chief. exec. officer, 1987-89, chmn., 1989—; mng. prin. Quaestus Ltd. Ptnrs., 1990—; pres., chief exec. officer RPI Holdings, Inc., 1985—; owner Northcote Vineyards, 1979—; bd. dirs. CONNECT, Inc., MERX, Inc., Electronic Product Info. Corp., Dynatec Systems Corp.; chmn. Lakefront Devel. Task Force, Milw., 1974, Chenequa Cable Com., 1991—; pres. Bd Harbor Commrs., Port of Milw., 1976-78; commr. Lake Area Communications System, 1990—. Bd. dirs. FFA Found., 1983087; active Chenqua Police and Fire Commn., Lake Area Comm. System Commn. in Hartland, Wis., 1990—. Mem. Info. Industry Assn., Young Pres.'s Orgn., Milw. Athletic Club, Milw. Yacht Club. Office: 330 E Kilbourn Ave Milwaukee WI 53202-6636

WEERTMAN, JOHANNES, materials science educator; b. Fairfield, Ala., May 11, 1925; s. Roelof and Christina (van Vlaardingen) W.; m. Julia Ann Randall, Feb. 10, 1950; children: Julia Ann, Bruce Randall. Student, Pa. State Coll., 1943-44; BS, Carnegie Inst. Tech. (now Carnegie Mellon U.), 1948, DSc, 1951; postgrad., Ecole Normale Superieure, Paris, 1951-52. Solid State physicist U.S. Naval Rsch. Lab., Washington, 1952-58, cons., 1960-67; sci. liaison officer U.S. Office Naval Rsch., Am. Embassy, London, 1958-59; faculty Northwestern U., Evanston, Ill., 1959—, prof. materials sci. dept., 1961-68, chmn. dept., 1964-68, prof. geol. scis. dept., 1963—, Walter P. Murphy prof. materials sci., 1968—; vis. prof. geophysics Calif. Inst. Tech., 1964, Scott Polar Rsch. Inst., Cambridge (Eng.) U., 1970-71, Swiss Fed. Inst. Reactor Rsch., 1986; cons. Cold Regions Rsch. and Engring. Lab., U.S. Army, 1960-75, Oak Ridge (Tenn.) Nat. Lab., 1963-67, Los Alamos (N.Mex.) Sci. Lab., 1967—; co-editor materials sci. books MacMillan Co., 1962-76. Author: (with Julia Weertman) Elementary Dislocation Theory, 1964, 2d edit. 1992; mem. editorial bd. Metal. Trans, 1967-75, Jour. Glaciology, 1972—; assoc. editor Jour. Geophys. Research, 1973-75; contbr. articles to profl. jours. With USMC, 1943-46. Honored with naming of Weertman Island in Antarctica; Fulbright fellow, 1951-52; recipient Acta Metallurgica gold medal, 1980; Guggenheim fellow, 1970-71. Fellow Am. Soc. Metals, Am. Phys. Soc., Geol. Soc. Am., Am. Geophys. Union (Horton award 1972, AIME Mathewson Gold medal 1977; mem. AAAS, Nat. Acad. Engring., Am. Inst. Physics, Internat. Glaciol. Soc. (Seligman Crystal award 1983), Arctic Inst., Am. Quaternary Assn., Explorers Club, Fulbright Assn., Sigma Xi, Tau Beta Pi, Phi Kappa Phi, Alpha Sigma Mu, Pi Mu Epsilon. Home: 834 Lincoln St Evanston IL 60201-2405

WEERTMAN, JULIA RANDALL, materials science and engineering educator; b. Muskegon, Mich., Feb. 10, 1926. BS in Physics, Carnegie-Mellon U., 1946, MS in Physics, 1947, DSc in Physics, 1951. Physicist U.S. Naval Rsch. Lab., Washington, 1952-58; vis. asst. prof. materials sci. and engring. Northwestern U., Evanston, Ill., 1972-73, assoc. prof., 1978-82, prof., 1982—, Walter P. Murphy prof., 1989, chmn. dept., 1987-92, asst. to dean grad. studies and rsch. Tech. Inst., 1973-76; mem. various NRC coms. and panels. Co-author: Elementary Dislocation Theory, 1964, 1992, also pub. in French, Japanese and Polish; contbr. numerous articles to profl. jours. Mem. Evanston Environ. Control Bd., 1972-79. Recipient Creativity award NSF, 1981, 86; Guggenheim Found. fellow, 1986-87. Fellow Am. Soc. Metals Internat., Minerals, Metals and Materials Soc.; mem. ASTM, NAE, Am. Phys. Soc., Materials Rsch. Soc., Soc. Women Engrs. (disting. engring. educator award 1989, achievement award 1991). Home: 834 Lincoln St Evanston IL 60201-2405 Office: Northwestern U Dept Material Sci & Engring 2225 N Campus Dr Evanston IL 60208-3108

WEESE, BENJAMIN HORACE, architect; b. Evanston, Ill., June 4, 1929; s. Harry Ernest and Marjorie (Mohr) W.; m. Cynthia Rogers, July 5, 1963; children: Daniel Peter, Catharine Mohr. B.Arch., Harvard U., 1951, M.Arch., 1957; cert., Ecole des Beaux Arts, Fontainebleau, France, 1956. Assoc., Harry Weese & Assocs., Architects, Chgo., 1957-77; prin. Weese Langley Weese, Chgo., 1977—; co-founder, pres. Chgo. Arch. Found., Glessner House, Chgo., 1966—. Trustee Graham Found. for Advanced Studies in Fine Arts, 1988—. Fellow AIA; mem. Nat. Council Archtl. Registration Bds. Home: 2133 N Hudson Ave Chicago IL 60614-4522 Office: Weese Langley Weese Ltd 9 W Hubbard St Chicago IL 60610-4605

WEESE, SAMUEL H., academic administrator; b. Morgantown, W.Va., Mar. 28, 1935; m. Ellen C. Carros, Feb. 14, 1981; children: Marguerite, James. BS, W.Va. U., 1957, MBA, 1962; MA, U. Pa., 1967, PhD, 1969. Ins. commr. State of W.Va., Charleston, 1969-75; gen. mgr. Nat. Flood Insurers Assn., Arlington, Va., 1975-78; prof. ins. U. Hartford, Conn., 1978-81; prof., chair ins. Ea. Ky. U., Richmond, 1981-85; v.p., exec. asst. to pres., sec. bd. trustees Am. Coll., Bryn Mawr, Pa., 1985-86, v.p. acad. affairs, sec. bd. trustees, 1986-87, acting pres., v.p. acad. affairs, sec. bd. trustees, 1988, pres., CEO, 1988—; bd. dirs. Am. Soc., 1988—, Ins. Soc. Phila.', 1989—; instr. dept. bus. and econs. Davis and Elkins (W.Va.) Coll., 1962-67; asst. prof. dept. fin. and ins. Coll. Bus. Adminstrn., U. Fla., Gainesville, 1967-69; adj. lectr. Coll. Bus. Adminstrn., George Washington U., Washington, 1977-78. Author: Non-Admitted Insurance in the United States, 1971; contbr. articles, studies to profl. pubs. 1st lt. USAF, 1958-60. Mem. Am. Risk and Ins. Assn., Am. Soc. CLU, Risk and Ins. Mgmt. Soc., Ins. Rsch. Office: Am Coll 270 S Bryn Mawr Ave Bryn Mawr PA 19010-2110

WEFER, DONALD PETERS, lawyer; b. Bronxville, N.Y., Oct. 23, 1933; s. A. Ralph C. and Margaret E. (Peters) W.; m. Janet G. Schade, July 12, 1958; children: Douglas P., Ellen G., Amy L. BA, U. Rochester, 1954; LLB, Yale U., 1960. Bar: N.Y. 1960. Law clk. to presiding justice U.S. Dist. Ct. Conn., New Haven, 1960-61; assoc. Simpson, Thacher & Bartlett, N.Y.C., 1961-70, ptnr., 1970-80; v.p. legal dept. Assn. Metals and Minerals, White Plains, N.Y., 1980—; bd. dirs. Christiania Gen. Ins. Corp. N.Y., Tarrytown. Lt. (j.g.) USN, 1955-58. Mem. Port Washington (N.Y.) Yacht Club (commodore 1981-82). Home: 117 Country Club Dr Port Washington NY 11050-4538 Office: Associated Metals & Minerals Co 3 Corporate Park Dr White Plains NY 10604-3803

WEG, JOHN GERARD, physician; b. N.Y.C., Feb. 16, 1934; s. Leonard and Pauline M. (Kanzleiter) W.; m. Mary Loretta Flynn, June 2, 1956; children: Diane Marie, Kathryn Mary, Carol Ann, Loretta Louise, Veronica Susanne, Michelle Celeste. BA cum laude, Coll. Holy Cross, Worcester, Mass., 1955; MD, N.Y. Med. Coll., 1959. Diplomate: Am. Bd. Internal Medicine. Commd. 2nd lt. USAF, 1958, advanced through grades to capt.; 1967; intern Walter Reed Gen. Hosp., Washington, 1959-60; resident, then chief resident in internal medicine Wilford Hall USAF Hosp., Lackland AFB, Tex., 1960-64; chief pulmonary sect. Wilford Hall USAF Hosp., 1964-66, chief inhalation sect., 1964-66, chief pulmonary and infectious disease service, 1966-67; resigned, 1967; clin. dir. pulmonary disease div. Jefferson Davis Hosp., Houston, 1967-71; from asst. prof. to assoc. prof. medicine Baylor U. Coll. Medicine, Houston, 1967-71; assoc. prof. medicine U. Mich. Med. Sch. Univ. Hosp., Ann Arbor, 1971-74; prof. U. Mich. Med. Sch. Univ. Hosp., 1974—; physician-in-charge pulmonary div., 1971-81, physician-in-charge pulmonary and critical care med. div., 1981-85; cons. Ann Arbor VA, 1971—, Wayne County Gen. hosps., 1971-84; mem. adv. bd. Washtenaw County Health Dept., 1973—; mem. respiratory and nervous system panel, anesthesiology sect. Nat. Ctr. Devices and Radiol. Health, FDA, 1983—, chmn., 1985-88. Contbr. med. jours., reviewer, mem. editorial bds. Decorated Air Force Commendation medal; travelling fellow Nat. Tb and Respiratory Disease Assn., 1971; recipient Aesculapius award Tex. Med. Assn., 1971. Fellow Am. Coll. Chest Physicians (chmn. bd. govs. 1976-79, gov. Mich. 1975-79, chmn. membership com. 1976-79, prof.-in-residence 1972—, chmn. critical care coun. 1982-85), Am. Coll. Chest Physicians and Internat. Acad. Chest Physicians (exec. council 1976-82, pres. 1980-81), ACP (chmn. Mich. program com. 1974); mem. AAAS, Am. Fedn. Clin. Rsch., AMA, Am. Thoracic Soc. (sec-treas. 1974-76), Am. Assn. Inhalation Therapy, Air Force Soc. Internists and Allied Specialists, Soc. Med. Consultants to Armed Forces, Internat. Union Against Tb, Mich. Thoracic Soc. (pres. 1976-78), Mich. Lung Assn. (dir., Bruce Douglas award 1981), Am. Lung Assn., Rsch. Club U. Mich., Assn. Advancement Med. Instrumentation, Central Soc. Clin. Rsch., Am. Bd. Internal Medicine (subsplty. com. on pulmonary disease 1980-86, critical care medicine test com. 1985-87, critical care medicine policy com. 1986-87), N.Y. Med. Coll. Alumni Assn. (medal of honor 1990), Alpha Omega Alpha. Home: 3060 Exmoor Rd Ann Arbor MI 48104-4132 Office: B I H 245 Box 0026 1500 E Medical Center Dr Ann Arbor MI 48109-0999

WEGE, PETER M., office furniture manufacturing company executive. V.p., sec. Steelcase, Inc., Grand Rapids, Mich. Office: Steelcase Inc 901 44th St SE Grand Rapids MI 49508-7594*

WEGENER, MARK DOUGLAS, lawyer; b. Cedar Rapids, Iowa, Nov. 1, 1948; s. Virgil Albert and Jean Frances (Wilke) W.; m. Donna Chait, May 28, 1972; children: Tara, David, Marisa. BA cum laude, Cen. Coll., Pella, Iowa, 1970; JD, Rutgers U., 1973. Bar: D.C. 1974, U.S. Dist. Ct. D.C. 1974, U.S. Ct. Appeals (D.C. cir.) 1974. Assoc. Howrey & Simon, Washington, 1973-79, ptnr., 1979—. Mem. ABA (anti-trust sect., litigation sect.), D.C. Bar Assn., The Metropolitan Club, Stage Harbor Yacht Club. Home: 7523 Old Dominion Dr Mc Lean VA 22102 Office: Howrey & Simon 1299 Pennsylvania Ave NW Washington DC 20004-2402

WEGENER, PETER PAUL, educator, author; b. Berlin, Aug. 29, 1917; came to U.S., 1946; naturalized, 1953.; m. Annette Schleiermacher, Aug. 14, 1961; children: Paul, Christopher, Philip. Dr rer. nat., U. Berlin, 1943; MA (priv.), Yale U., 1960; Dr. Ing. (E.h.) (hon.), U. Karlsruhe, Germany, 1979. Researcher supersonic wind tunnels Kochel, Germany, 1943-45; researcher gasdynamics, hypersonic wind tunnels U.S. Naval Ordnance Lab., 1946-53, Jet Propulsion Lab. Calif. Inst. Tech., 1953-60; prof. applied sci. Yale U., New Haven, 1960-72, Harold Hodgkinson prof. engring. and applied sci., 1972—, chmn. dept. engring. applied sci., 1966-71, prof. emeritus, 1987—; sr. Am. scientist Humboldt Found., 1979;. Researcher and contbr. articles on hypersonics, condensation metastable state, chem. kinetics, flow systems real gases, bubbles to profl. jours. Inst. Advanced Study Berlin fellow, 1986. Fellow Am. Phys. Soc., Conn. Acad. Sci. & Engring. (charter). Home: 29 Montgomery Pky Branford CT 06405-5128 Office: Yale U PO Box 2159 New Haven CT 06520

WEGENKE, GARY L., school systems administrator; b. South Bend, Ind., Feb. 28, 1938; s. Edward and Blanche Wegenke; m. Sandra S. Gard, Aug. 17, 1963; children: Bart and Bret (twins), Blake. BA, DePauw U., 1961; MS, Ind. U., 1964; PhD, Ohio State U., 1971. Secondary tchr. South Bend (Ind.) Community Sch. Corp., 1961-69; grad. rsch. asst. Coll. Edn. Ohio State U., Columbus, 1969-71; prin. Hill High Sch., Lansing, Mich., 1972-76; dir. adminstrvs. svcs. Lansing Sch. Dist., 1976-78, asst. supt. Fiscal and Adminstrv. Svcs., 1979-81, dep. supt., 1981-83; supt. schs. Waterloo (Iowa) Community Sch. Dist., 1983-88, Des Moines (Iowa) Ind. Community Sch. Dist., 1988—; adj. asst. prof. Ohio State U., Columbus, 1971-72; adj. prof. Mich. State U., East Lansing, 1980-84, U. Northern Iowa, Cedar Falls, 1984—, Drake U., 1991; nat. adv. panel chairperson Ctr. for Rsch. on Ednl. Accountability and Tchr. Evaluation, Western Mich. U., Kalamazoo, 1990—; chairperson state outcomes and assessment Iowa State Dept. Edn., 1992-93; project dir. Statewide Libr. Planning and Evaluation, Ohio State U., 1971-72; lectr. various symposia. Contbr. articles to profl. jours. Bd. dirs. Cedar Valley United Way, 1985-88, Leadership Investment for Tomorrow, Waterloo/Cedar Falls, 1986-88, HMO Iowa, 1990-92, Boy Scouts Am., 1991—, Jr. Achievement, Des Moines, 1988—, Polk County United Way, 1989—, Community Focus, 1992—; chairperson Urban Edn. Network, 1987. Named Exec. Educator 100 Best Sch. Execs., 1993, Iowa Supt. of Yr., 1993-94; recipient Lansing Concerned Citizen award Jr. C. of C., 1972. Mem. Am. Assn. Sch. Adminstrs., Sch. Adminstrs. Iowa, Des Moines Sch. Adminstrs. Assn., Des Moines C. of C. (bd. dirs 1990), Waterloo C. of C. (bd. dirs. 1985-87, Public Servant of Yr. award 1985), Phi Delta Kappa (v.p. U. Nothern Iowa chpt., Des Moines area Outstanding Educator of Yr. award 1992). Office: Des Moines Pub School 1800 Grand Ave Des Moines IA 50309-3310

WEGGE, LEON LOUIS FRANÇOIS, economics educator; b. Breendonk, Antwerp, Belgium, June 9, 1933; came to U.S., 1959; s. Petrus Maria and Alberta (De Maeyer) W.; m. Beate Maria Teipel, Nov. 22, 1962; children: Simone, Robert, Elizabeth. B in Thomistical Philosophy, Cath. U. Louvain, Belgium, 1957, Licentiate in Econ. Sci., 1958; PhD in Indsl. Econs., MIT, 1963. Assoc. lectr. U. New S. Wales, Kensington, Australia, 1963-66; prof. econs. U. Calif., Davis, 1966—; vis. prof. U. Bonn, Fed. Republic Germany, 1980-81. Assoc. editor Jour. Internat. Econs., 1971-84; contbr. articles to profl. jours. Rsch. fellow Ctr. for Ops. Rsch. and Econometrics, 1972-73, fellow The Netherlands Inst. for Advanced Study, 1987-88. Mem. Econometric Soc., Am. Statistical Assn. Roman Catholic. Home: 26320 County Rd # 98 Davis CA 95616 Office: Univ of Calif Davis Dept Of Economics Davis CA 95616

WEGMAN, HAROLD HUGH, management consultant; b. Cin., June 29, 1916; s. Clarence H. and Lillian (de Tellem) W.; m. Ruth Ellen Volk, May 1, 1937; children—Susan Ruth (Mrs. Michael Manning), Sally Ann (Mrs. Larry Fine). B.B.A., U. Cin., 1941; M.B.A., Xavier U., 1954. Band leader, studio mgr. Rudolph Wurlitzer Co. 1946-50; Tng. supr., then asst. to v.p. Gruen Watch Co., 1950-55; personnel dir., asst. to v.p. indsl. relations, asst. to pres. Howard Paper Co., Dayton, Ohio, 1959-62; v.p., gen. mgr. Elano Corp., Xenia, Ohio, 1962-64; v.p., dir. indsl. relations Champion Papers Inc., Hamilton, Ohio, 1964-67; v.p. U.S. Plywood Champion Papers, Inc., 1967-71, Champion Internat. 1971-72; pres. PEP Group, 1972—; dir. Mgmt. Center, Sacred Heart U., 1974—. Contbr. articles to profl. publs. Trustee Foreman Found., 1965-71.

Served to lt. (j.g.) USNR, 1944-46. Mem. Am. Soc. Personnel Adminstrs. (bd. dirs. 1969—, treas. 1970), Am. Soc. for Tng. and Devel., NAM, Am. Paper Inst., Am. Mgmt. Assn., Conn. songwriters assn., Lambda Chi Alpha. Home: 3400 S Ocean Blvd Suite 7-D Highland Beach FL 33487

WEGMAN, MYRON EZRA, physician, educator; b. Bklyn., July 23, 1908; s. Max and Nettie (Finkelstein) W.; m. Isabel Howe, July 4, 1936; children: Judith (Mrs. John A. Hirst), David Howe, Jane (Mrs. David D. Dunatchik), Elizabeth Gooding (Mrs. Ralph A. Petersen). A.B., CCNY, 1928; M.D. cum laude, Yale U., 1932; M.P.H., Johns Hopkins U., 1938. Diplomate Am. Bd. Preventive Medicine, Am. Bd. Pediatrics (ofcl. examiner). Intern, asst. resident, resident in pediatrics New Haven Hosp., 1932-36; instr. pediatrics Yale U., 1933-36; cons. pediatrics Md. State Health Dept., 1936-41; asst. prof. child hygiene sch. Tropical Medicine, San Juan, P.R., 1941-42; dir. research and tng. in child health, dir. sch. health N.Y.C. Health Dept., 1942-46; instr. pediatrics and lectr. public health adminstrn. Johns Hopkins U., 1939-46; asst. prof. pediatrics and pub. health Cornell U., 1942-46; asst. prof. pub. health Columbia U., 1940-46; prof. pediatrics, head dept. La. State U., 1946-52; pediatrician-in-chief Charity Hosp., New Orleans, 1946-52; prof. public health Sch. Public Health, U. Mich., Ann Arbor, 1960-74; dean Sch. Public Health, U. Mich., 1960-74, dean emeritus, 1974—; prof. pediatrics U. Mich. Med. Sch., 1961-78, prof. emeritus, 1978—; chmn. div. health sci., 1970-74; John G. Searle prof. public health, 1974-78, emeritus, 1978—; vis. prof. U. Malaya, 1974, Centro Universitario de Salud Publica, U. Autónoma Madrid, 1990—, U Cin., 1993; external examiner Nat. U. Singapore, 1983; cons. Internat. Sci. and Tech. Inst., 1986—, Sch. Pub. Health U. Kinshasa, Zaire, 1987, Schs. Pub. Health Jakarta, Surabaya, Ujung Pandang, Medan, Semarang, Indonesia, 1988; coord. Mich.-Madrid Sch. Pub. Health collaboration, 1990—. Editor: Public Health in the People's Republic of China, 1973; author: also pediatrics and public health textbooks, articles in med. jours. Status of Pan American Centers; mem. editorial bd. Revista Mexicana de Salud Publica, 1990—. Chief div. edn. and tng. Pan-Am. San. Bur., Regional Office for Ams., WHO, 1952-56; sec. gen Pan Am. San. Bur., Who Regional Office, 1957-60; pres. Assn. Schs. Public Health, 1963-66; pres. Comprehensive Health Planning Council, SE Mich., 1970-74; trustee Pan Am. Health and Edn. Found., 1970-85, 86-92, 94—, pres. 1984-85, chmn. Devel. com., 1991—; trustee Nat. San. Found., 1969-84, emeritus trustee, 1984—; pres. Physicians for Social Responsibility, Ann Arbor, 1987-92; mem. com. on carcinogenesis of pesticides Nat. Acad. Sci., 1977-79, com. on advanced study in China, 1978-82; chmn. Task Force on Nat. Immunization Policy, HEW, 1975-76; adv. com. Kellogg Nat. Fellowship Program, 1982—; rsch. adv. com. Resources for Future, 1978-84; spl. cons. State U. System Fla., 1982-87; mem. com. on prevention ctrs. CDC, 1986-94. Recipient Man of Yr. award CCNY, 1955; Clifford G. Grulee award Am. Acad. Pediatrics, 1958; Townsend Harris medal CCNY, 1961; Bronfman prize Am. Public Health Assn., 1967; Disting. Service award Mich. Public Health Assn., 1974; Walter P. Reuther award for disting. service United Auto Workers, 1974; Sedgwick medal Am. Pub. Health Assn., 1974; Outstanding Alumnus award Johns Hopkins Sch. Hygiene, 1982; Disting. Service award Delta Omega Soc., 1982; Spes Hominum award Nat. Sanitation Found., 1986, Disting. Alumnus award Yale U. Med. Sch., 1987; Spl. award Korean Soc. Preventive Medicine, 1989. Fellow Royal Soc. Health (hon.), AAAS; mem. Johns Hopkins U. Soc. Scholars, Am. Pediatric Soc., Soc. Pediatric Research, Am. Acad. Pediatrics, Am. Assn. World Health (v.p. 1979-82, 85-88, pres. 1982-84), Am. Public Health Assn. (chmn. exec. bd. 1965-70, pres. 1971-72), Fedn. Assan. Schs. Health Professions (1st pres. 1968-70), Soc. Exptl. Biol. and Medicine, Peruvian, Ecuadorian, Argentinian pediatric socs. (hon.), P.R. Pub. Health Assn. (hon.), Sigma Xi, Alpha Omega Alpha, Delta Omega, Phi Kappa Phi, Phi Beta Kappa (hon.). Club: Cosmos (Washington). Home: 2760 Overridge Dr Ann Arbor MI 48104-4049 Office: Sch Public Health U Mich Ann Arbor MI 48109-2029

WEGMAN, ROBERT B., food service executive; b. 1918; married. BBA, Niagra U. With Wegman's Food Markets, Inc., Rochester, pres., 1950—, chmn., 1969—. With USMC, ret. Office: Wegmans Food Markets Inc 1500 Brooks Ave Rochester NY 14624*

WEGMAN, WILLIAM GEORGE, artist; b. Holyoke, Mass., Dec. 2, 1943; s. George W. and Eleanor (Vezina) W. B.F.A. in Painting, Mass. Coll. Art, 1965; M.F.A., U. Ill., 1967. One-man shows include Gallerie Sonnabend, Paris, 1971, Pomona Coll. Art Gallery, 1971, Sonnabend Gallery, N.Y.C., 1972, 77, Galerie Ernst, Hanover, Ger., 1972, Situation, London, 1972, Konrad Fischer Gallery, 1972, 75, 79, Courtney Sale Gallery, 1972, Tex. Gallery, Houston, 1973, 75, 79, L.A. County Mus. of Art, Calif., 1973, 112 Greene St., N.Y.C., 1974, Mayor Gallery, London, 1975, Galleria Alessandra Castelli, Milan, 1975, The Kitchen, N.Y., 1976, Bruna Soletti Gallery, Milan, 1977, 82, Rosamund Felsen Gallery, 1978, Holly Solomon Gallery, N.Y.C., 1979, 80, 82, 84, 86, 88, 90, 92, Arnolfini Gallery, Eng., 1979, U. Wis., Milw., 1979, U. Colo. Art Galleries, Boulder, 1980, Marianne Deson Gallery, Chgo., 1980, Vivianne Esders Gallery, Paris, 1981, Magnuson Lee Gallery, Boston, 1981, Robert Hull Fleming Mus., Burlington, Vt., 1981, Locus Solus, Genoa, Italy, 1982, Dart Gallery, Chgo., 1982, Fraenkel Gallery, San Francisco, 1982, 88, 90, 92, 93, James Corcoran Gallery, Los Angeles, 1982, 90, Nancy Drysdale Gallery, Washington, 1982, 87, 94, Walker Art Ctr, Mpls., 1982, Ft. Worth Art Mus., Tex., 1982, De Cordova & Dana Mus. & Park, Mass., 1982, Southeastern Ctr. for Contemporary Art, Winston-Salem, N.C., 1982, The Contemporary Arts Ctr., Ohio, 1982, Newport Harbor Mus., Calif., 1982, Inst. Contemporary Arts at Va. Mus., Richmond, 1983, Fine Arts Gallery, U. Mass., Amherst, 1983, Tex. Gallery, Houston, 1983, 86, Greenville County Mus. Art, 1984, Lowe Mus. Art, Miami, Fla, 1985, Cleve. Mus. Art, 1986, Honolulu Acad. Arts, 1987, Mass. Coll. Art, Boston, 1987, U. San Diego, La Jolla, Calif., 1988, Pace MacGill Gallery, N.Y., 1988, 90, 92, 93, San Francisco Mus. Modern Art, Calif., 1988, Galerie Durand-Dessert, Paris, 1989, Budoin Lebon, Paris, 1989, Maison de la Culture et de la Communication de Saint Etienne, France, 1989, Linda Cathcart Gallery, L.A., 1990, 92, 94, The Taft Mus. Cin., 1990, The Butler Inst., Ohio, 1990, Sperone Westwater Gallery, N.Y., 1992, Kunstmuseum, Lucerne, Switzerland, 1990, ICA, London, 1990, Stedelijk Mus., The Netherlands, 1990, Frankfurt Kunstverein, Germany, 1990, Pompidou Ctr., Paris, 1990, ICA, Boston, 1990, Ringling Mus., Fla., 1990, Whitney Mus., N.Y., Contemporary Arts Mus., Tex., 1990, Neuberger Mus., SUNY, 1991, Galerie Andreas Binder, Germany, 1992, Athenaeum Music & Arts Library, Calif., 1992, Lisa Sette Gallery, Phoenix, 1994, Greg Kucera Gallery, Seattle, 1994, others; exhibited in group shows at Walker Art Ctr., Mpls., 1968, N.J. State Mus., Trenton, 1968, Detroit Inst. Art, 1969, Mus. Contemporary Art, Chgo., 1969, 77, Allen Meml. Mus., 1970, L.A. County Mus., Calif., 1971, Pasadena Art Mus., 1972, Contemporary Arts Mus., Houston, 1972, Whitney Mus. Am. Art, N.Y.C, 1973, 81, 89, Sonnabend Gallery, N.Y.C., 1974, Milw. Art Ctr., 1975, Sarah Lawrence Coll. Gallery, 1975, Phila. Mus. Art, 1976, San Francisco Mus. Modern Art, 1976, U. Calif.-Berkeley Art Mus., 1976, U. Chgo., 1976, Ringling Mus. Art, Sarasota, Fla., 1977, Walker Art Gallery, Eng., 1978, Holly Solomon Gallery, N.Y.C., 1978, 82, 87, Mus. Fine Arts, Houston, 1978, Aspen Ctr. Visual Arts, 1979, Santa Barbara Mus. Art, 1979, Mus. Modern Art, N.Y.C., 1980, 82, 83, Sidney Janis Gallery, 1981, Art Inst. Chgo., 1981, 82, Young Hoffman Gallery, Chgo., 1983, Inst. Contemporary Art, Boston, 1983, Castelli Graphics, N.Y.C., 1983, Queens Mus., N.Y., 1986, James Madison U., Harrison, Va, 1987, Fay Gold Gallery, Atlanta, 1988, Hudson River Mus., 1989, Volcano Arts Ctr., 1989, Pace/MacGill, N.Y.C., 1990, The History of Travel, The Taft Museum, Cin., The Butler Inst. Youngstown, Ohio, 1990, William Wegman: Paintings, Drawings, Photographs, Videotapes, Kunstmuseum, Luzern, Stedelijk Museum, Amsterdam, Frankfurt Kunstverein Frankfurt, Centre Nat. d'Art et cle Culture Georges Pompidou, Paris, Inst. of Contemporary Art, London, Inst. of Contemporary Arts, Boston, Contemporary Arts Mus., Houston, J.M. Ringling Mus., Sarasota, Whitney Mus., of American Art, N.Y., 1990-92, Outdoor Photographs, Neuberger Mus., State U. of N.Y. at Purchase, 1991, William Wegman: L'oeuvre photographique, 1969-76, Fonds Regional d'Art Contemporary, Limousin, France, 1991, New Polaroids, Holly Solomon Gallery, N.Y.C., Early Black and White Photographs, Pace/MacGill Gallery, N.Y.C., New Paintings, Sperone Westwater Gallery, N.Y.C., 1992, many others; contbr. articles to profl. jours.; videography: Reel 1, 1970-72, Reel 2, 1972, Reel 3, 1972-73, Reel 4, 1973-74, Reel 5, 1975, Reel 6, 1975-76, Reel 7, 1976-77, Split Sandwich, 1970, Gray Hairs, 1974-75, Man Ray, Man Ray, 1978, The World of Photography, 1985, Sesame Street Videos, 1989, 92, 93; film: Dog Baseball, 1986; Publications: Man's Best Friend, 1982, Everyday Problems, 1984, William Wegman: Paintings, Drawings, Photographs, Vide-

otapes, 1990, Cinderella, 1993, Little Red Riding Hood, 1993, ABC, 1994. Recipient Creative Artists Pub. Svc. award, 1979; Guggenheim Found. fellow, 1975, 86, Nat. Endowment for the Arts grantee, 1976, 82. Office: 431 E 6th St New York NY 10009-6305

WEGMILLER, DONALD CHARLES, health care corporation executive; b. Cloquet, Minn., Sept. 25, 1938; m. Janet A. Listerud, Apr. 27, 1957; children: Katherine, Mark, Dean. BA, U. Minn., 1960, MHA, 1962. Asst. administr. Fairview Hosp., Mpls., 1962-65; asst. administr. Fairview-Southdale Hosp., Mpls., 1965-66, administr., 1966-76; sr. v.p. Health Central System, Mpls., 1976-78; pres. Health Central, Inc., Mpls., 1978-80, Health Central Corp., Mpls., 1980-87; pres., CEO Health One Corp., Mpls., 1987-92; pres. HealthSpan, Mpls., 1992-93; pres. & CEO Mgmt. Compensation Group/HealthCare, Mpls., 1993—; preceptor clin. faculty U. Minn., 1975—; lectr.; adj. faculty U. Mich., 1980—; clin. faculty, lectr. Duke U., 1981—; cons. div. med. services U.S. Dept. State, Washington, 1975; bd. dirs. Health Providers Ins. Co., Hosp. Rsch. and Ednl. Trust, Med. Graphics Corp., HBO & Co., G.D. Searle & Co., Minn. Power, Profile Group, LifeRate; U.S. del. Kings's Fund Internat., 1979-85, nat. coord., 1985; U.S. Internat. Hosp. Fedn., 1987; keynote speaker Australian Pvt. Hosps. Assn. 10th Nat. Congress, 1990; mem. leadership adv. com. Am. Coll. Healthcare Execs., 1994. Mem. adv. bd. Health Mgmt. Quar. mag.; editorial bd. of Frontiers an Am. Coll. of Healthcare Execs. publ.; contbr. articles to profl. jours. Chmn. Bd. Edn., Richfield, Minn., 1971-74; staff asst. to Presidents Nixon, Ford and Reagan, 1972-89; adv. com. Sen. Durenberger's Health Care, Mpls., 1979—; trustee Nat. Adv. Coun. on Social Security, 1989—, Nat. Com. for Quality Health Care. Recipient Outstanding Pres. of Yr. award Mpls. Jaycees, 1969, Young Man of Yr. award, 1971, Nat. Healthcare award B'nai B'rith, 1987, Merit award Duke U. Program in Healthcare Adminstrn. Alumni Assn., 1990. Fellow Am. Coll. Health Care Execs. (Robert S. Hudgen's award 1969), Am. Hosp. Assn. (chmn. bd. trustees 1987), Minn. Hosp. Assn. (Disting. Svc. award 1988). Republican. Methodist. Lodge: Rotary. Home: 7871 Chesshire Ln N Maple Grove MN 55311 Office: Mgt Compensation Group Health Care 608 2nd Ave S Ste 370 Minneapolis MN 55402

WEGNER, GARY ALAN, astronomer; b. Seattle, Dec. 26, 1944; s. Herbert Edward and Melba Jean (Gardner) W.; m. Cynthia Kay Goodfellow, June 25, 1966; children: Josef, Kurt, Christian, Peter-Jürgen, Emma. Student, Wash. State U., Pullman, 1963-65; BS, U. Ariz., 1967; PhD, U. Wash., Seattle, 1971. Fulbright fellow Mount Stromlo Obs., Camberra, A.C.T., 1971-72; departmental demonstrator in astrophysics Oxford U., Eng., 1972-75; sr. sci. rsch. officer South African Astron. Obs., Capetown, Republic of South Africa, 1975-78; Annie J. Cannon fellow U. Del., Newark, 1978-79; asst. prof. Pa. State U., State College, 1979-82; asst. prof. to assoc. prof. physics and astronomy Dartmouth Coll., Hanover, N.H., 1982-88, Margaret Anne and Edward Leede Disting. prof. physics and astronomy, 1988—; dir. Mich.-Dartmouth-MIT Obs., 1991—; vis. astronomer Cornell U., 1992. Editor: White Dwarfs, 1989; contbr. articles to jours. in field. Keeley fellow Wadham Coll., Oxford, 1992-93, vis. fellow in astrophysics Oxford U., 1992-93; vis. prof. Astron. Inst. Ruhr U. Bochum, Germany, 1993-94; recipient rsch. prize The Alexander von Humboldt Found., Germany, 1993-94, numerous grants NSF, NASA. Mem. Am. Astron. Soc., Internat. Astron. Union. Lutheran. Office: Dartmouth Coll Dept Physics & Astronomy Wilder Lab Hanover NH 03755

WEGNER, HELMUTH ADALBERT, lawyer, retired chemical company executive; b. Berlin, Germany, Feb. 5, 1917; came to U.S., 1936, naturalized, 1943; s. Leo Michael and Hertha Johanna (Erdmann) W.; m. Cordelia Elizabeth Claussen, Aug. 23, 1941; children: Harold C., Ruth Ellen Wegner Hennessey, Linda Ann. B.S., U. Ill., 1938; postgrad., U. Wis., 1939; J.D., Chgo.-Kent Coll. Law, 1950. Bar: Ill. 1950, Va. 1979, D.C. 1981. With G.D. Searle & Co., Skokie, Ill., 1939—; patent dir. G.D. Searle & Co., 1958-63, gen. counsel, 1963-78, sec., 1972-78, sr. counsel, 1978-79, 82-92; ptnr. Wegner, Cantor, Mueller and Player, Washington, 1992-94. Contbr. articles to profl. jours. Mem. ABA (past com. chmn.), Va. Bar Assn., Am. Internat. Property Law Assn. (past com. chmn.), Am. Chem. Soc. (past dir. Chgo. sect., exec. com.), Assn. Internat. Protection Propriété Industrielle, Licensing Execs. Soc., Chgo. Chemists Club, Phi Delta Phi. Mem. United Ch. of Christ. Home: 5000 Fairbanks Ave Box 275 Alexandria VA 22311

WEGNER, JUDITH WELCH, lawyer, educator, university dean; b. Hartford, Conn., Feb. 14, 1950; d. John Raymond and Ruth (Thulen) Welch; m. Warren W. Wegner, Oct. 13, 1972. BA with honors, U. Wis., 1972; JD, UCLA, 1976. Bar: Calif. 1976, D.C. 1977, U.S. Supreme Ct. 1980, NC 1988. Law clk. to Judge Warren Ferguson, U.S. Dist. Ct. for So. Dist. Calif., L.A., 1976-77; atty. U.S. Dept. Justice, Washington, 1977-79; spl. asst. to sec. U.S. Dept. Edn., Washington, 1979-80; vis. assoc. prof. U. Iowa Coll. Law, Iowa City, 1981; asst. prof. U. N.C. Sch. Law, Chapel Hill, 1981-84, assoc. prof., 1984-88, prof., 1988—, assoc. dean, 1986-88, dean, 1989—. Chief comment editor UCLA Law Rev., 1975-76; contbr. articles to legal publs. Mem. ABA, AAUP, N.C. Assn. Women Attys., N.C. Bar Assn., Assn. Am. Law Schs. (exec. com. 1992-96, accreditation com. 1986-91, chmn. 1989-91, pres. 1995), Soc. Am. Law Tchrs., Nat. League Cities (countmentor program 1989—), Order of the Coif (nat. exec. com. 1989-92), Phi Beta Kappa. Democrat. Office: U NC Sch Law Campus Box 3380 Chapel Hill NC 27599-3380

WEGNER, KARL HEINRICH, physician, educator; b. Pierre, S.D., Jan. 5, 1930; s. Lester Fred and Nellie (Norbeck) W.; m. Mary Josephine Waddell, June 15, 1957; children: Madeleine Jean, Peter Norbeck, Mary Nell. B.A., Yale U., 1952; M.D., Harvard U., 1959. Intern, resident Mass. Gen. Hosp./Harvard U., 1959-62; pathologist Sioux Valley Hosp., Sioux Falls, S.D., 1962-90; pathologist, dir. Lab. Clin. Medicine, Sioux Falls, 1962-90; prof., chmn. dept. pathology U.S.D., 1968-73, v.p. health affairs, dean Sch. Medicine, 1973-79, Regents Disting. prof. emeritus, 1992—; owner, operator Meadowlark Farms, Montrose, S.D.; mem. Bd. of Regents for Higher Edn., State of S.D. Bd. dirs. U.S.D. Found., Sioux Valley Hosp. Found., Sioux Falls Area Found. With USMC. Karl H. Wegner Endowed Professorship, Bd. of Regents for Higher Edn., 1979; recipient Disting. Svc. award S.D. State Med. Assn., 1984, Community Svc. award, 1975; inducted to S.D. Hall of Fame, 1987. Fellow Coll. Am. Pathologists, Internat. Acad. Pathologists, Am. Soc. Pathologists; mem. Am. Pathology Found. (pres. 1984-85, Am. pathologist of Yr award, 1989), Alpha Omega Alpha. Home: Sunnymede S Minn Rd Sioux Falls SD 57106 Office: 1212 S Euclid Ave Sioux Falls SD 57105-0413

WEGNER, PETER, computer science educator; b. Leningrad, Russia, Aug. 20, 1932; came to U.S., 1964, naturalized, 1971; s. Leo and Hermine W.; m. Judith Priscilla Romney, July 22, 1956; children—Simon, Mark, Jeremy, Michael. B.sc., London U., 1953, Ph.D., 1968. Research assoc. M.I.T., 1959-60, Harvard U., 1960-61; lectr. London U. Sch. Econs., 1961-64; asst. prof. Pa. State U., 1964-66; assoc. prof. Cornell U., 1966-69; assoc. prof. Brown U., 1969-75, prof. computer sci., 1975—. Author: Information Structures and Machine Organization, 1968, Research Directions in Software Technology, 1979, Programming with Ada, 1979. Mem. Assn. Computing Machinery, Math. Assn. Am., Sigma Xi. Office: Box 1910 Brown Univ Providence RI 02912

WEGNER, SAMUEL JOSEPH, historical society executive; b. Twin Falls, Idaho, Aug. 27, 1952; s. Albert Henry and Eleanor Esther (Wright) W.; m. Linda Louise Talley, May 27, 1972; children: Ethan, Elena. BA, U. Ariz., 1973; MA, U. Idaho, 1975. Curator Mansion Mus.-Oglebay Inst., Wheeling, W.Va., 1975-76; curator of edn. State Hist. Soc. Wis., Madison, 1976-78; asst. supt. Region I Mo. Dept. Nat. Resources, Brookfield, 1978-85; dir. ops. So. Oregon Hist. Soc., Jacksonville, Oreg., 1985-87; exec. dir. So. Oregon Hist. Soc. Medford, Oreg., 1987—. Adv. com. Medford (Oreg.) Vis. and Conv. Bur., 1988—. Mem. Am. Assn. Mus., Nat. Trust for Hist. Preservation, Oregon Mus. Assn. Home: 3196 Springbrook Rd Medford OR 97504-4972 Office: So Oreg Hist Soc 106 N Central Ave Medford OR 97501-5926

WEGNER, SANDRA SUE, library director; b. Hutchinson, Kans., July 30, 1938; d. John Wilbur and Evelyn Lucille (White) DeFore; m. Leroy Gene Wegner, Oct. 7, 1960; children: Ross Eugene, Barry John. BS in Journalism, Tex. Woman's U., 1960; MS in LS, North Tex. State U., 1985. Cert. county libr., Tex. Reporter oil sect. Midland (Tex.) Reporter-Telegram, 1960; libr. clk. Midland County Pub. Libr., Midland, 1974-82, spl. collections libr.,

1982-85, asst. dir., 1985-90, dir., 1990—. Literacy tutor Midland Need To Read, 1987-90, bd. dirs., 1988—. Mem. ALA, Tex. Libr. Assn., Midland Geneal. Soc. (bd. dirs.), DAR (registrar Col. Theunis Dey chpt. 1993-95), Beta Phi Mu. Republican. Methodist. Avocation: genealogy. Home: 1502 Seaboard Midland TX 79705 Office: Midland County Pub Libr 301 W Missouri Ave Midland TX 79701

WEHLAND, GRANVILLE WARREN PEARSON, lawyer, consultant; b. Sandy Spring, Md., Sept. 9, 1934; s. Henry Wadsworth and Ellen Alberta (Pearson) W.; m. Mary Constance Colbert, Aug. 21, 1963; children: Mary Jeanne McCabe, Matthew Henry Colbert. JD, U. Balt., 1959. Chief Bur. Highways Howard County Govt., Ellicott City, Md., 1960-93; cons Wehland Law Offices, Ellicott City, 1994—; cons. Greater Balt. Regional Planning Com., 1971-75, MD Motion Picture Commn., Howard County, Md., 1975-93; rep. Classic Realty, Ellicott City, 1993—, AFLAC Ins., Timonium, Md., 1994—; bd. dirs. County Engrs. Assn., Md., 1977-80, pres. 1980-81, hist., 1993—. Author: Howard County Road Code and Specifications, 1963. Bd. dirs. Howard County Hist. Soc., Ellicott City, pres. 1980-81; councillor Patpasco unit Boy Scouts Am., Ellicott City, 1993—. Mem. SAR (pres. 1986-87, nat. trustee, Patriots Award medal 1985, Silver Good Citizenship medal 1983), Order of Founders and Patriots of Am. (gov. gen. 1990, Disting. Svc. award 1994), Nat. Gavel Soc. (sec. 1993—, Diamond Gavel 1994), Sons and Daus. of Pilgrims (gov. 1988-90). Democrat. Episcopalian. Avocations: genealogy, history, travel. Home: 3892 College Ave Ellicott City MD 21043-4609 Office: Order Founders & Patriots 3982 College Ave Ellicott City MD 21043-4609

WEHLE, JOHN L., JR., brewing company executive; b. Rochester, N.Y., Mar. 11, 1946; s. John L. and Marjorie (Strong) W.; m. Patricia Hallock, June 12, 1968; children—Elizabeth Anne, Carolyn Strong. B.S., Rochester Inst. Tech., 1970. Asst. v.p. fin. Genessee Brewing Co., Rochester, N.Y., 1975-80, v.p. fin. planning, 1980-81, exec. v.p., 1981-82, pres., 1982—; dir. Rochester eigonal bd. Chase Lincoln 1st Bank, mem. trust com.; mem. gunsmithing adv. bd. Rochester Inst. Tech. vice pres., treas. Genessee Country Museum; trustee Louis A. Wehle Found., Genesee Region Home Care Assn., Ctr. for Govtl. Research; sec., trustee Allendale Columbia Sch., trustee, mem. Tourism Devel. Com. Rochester Monroe County Conv. & Visitors Bur.; bd. dirs. Otetiana Council Boy Scouts Am. Office: Genesee Brewing Co Inc 445 Saint Paul St Rochester NY 14605-1775

WEHLING, ROBERT LOUIS, household products company executive; b. Chgo., Nov. 27, 1938; s. Ralph Joseph and Rita Helen (Casey) W.; m. Carolyn Thierry Harmon, July 5, 1958; children: Susan, Mary, Jennifer, Linda, Karen, Sandra. BA magna cum laude, Denison U., 1960. Brand asst. Procter & Gamble Co., Cin., 1960, 63-64, asst. brand mgr., 1964-66, br. mgr., 1966-70, assoc. advt. mgr., 1970-74, advt. mgr. bar soap and household cleaning products div., 1974-77, div. mgr. gen. advt., 1977-84, assoc. gen. advt. mgr., 1984-87, gen. mktg. svcs. mgr., 1987-88, v.p. mktg. svcs., 1988-90; v.p. pub. affairs, 1990—; mem. adv. task force Bus. Roundtable, 1990—. Pres. March of Dimes, Cin., 1981-84; mem. allocations com. Fine Arts Fund, Cin., 1987—; bd. dirs. Just Say No Internat., 1991-93; co-founder with USA Today, Coalition on Edn. Initiatives, 1991—; mem. Mayor's Commn. on Children, 1992—; vice chmn. Downtown Cin., Inc.; exec. com. Cin. Youth Collaborative; trustee United Way Cin., Ohio Schs. Devel. Corp.; bd. dirs. Edn. Excellence Partnership; participant Gov.'s Edn. Mgmt. Coun.; mem. Hamilton county Family and Children First Coun. Named One of 200 Greater Cincinnatians, Cin. Bicentennial Commn., 1988. Mem. Assn. Nat. Advertisers, Advt. Coun. (campaign dir. 1988—), Greater Cin. C. of C. (trustee, exec. com.), Queen City Club, Commonwealth Club, Phi Beta Kappa. Republican. Methodist. Avocations: running, reading, education, children's issues. Office: Procter & Gamble Co 1 Proctor Gamble Plz Cincinnati OH 45202

WEHMEIER, HELGE H., chemical, health care and imaging technologies company executive; b. Goettingen, Germany, 1943; married; 2 children. Attended, Internat. Mgmt. Devel. Inst., Switzerland, Inst. Europeen d'Adminstrn. des Affaires, France. With Bayer AG, 1965; mktg. synthetic fibers U.S. and Can. Mobay, N.Y.C, 1969; mktg. mgr. Leverkusen, Ger., 1974-78; gen. mgr. U.K., 1978-80; mgr. organic chem. divsn., 1981-84; head indsl. photographic divsn. Agfa-Gevaert AG subs. Leverkusen, 1984-89; pres., CEO Afga Corp., Ridgefield Park, N.J., 1989-91; also bd. dirs., exec. com. Agfa Corp., Ridgefield Park, N.J.; pres., CEO Bayer Corp. (formerly Miles Inc.), 1991—; bd. dirs. PNC Bank Corp. Bd. dirs. Pitts. Symphony Soc.; mem. exec. com., officer Allegheny Conf. Cmty. Devel., Pitts.; mem. Conf. Bd., Trilateral Commn. Mem. Chem. Mfrs. Assn. (bd. dirs., exec. com., internat. com.). Office: Bayer Corp 500 Grant St Pittsburgh PA 15219-2507

WEHNER, ALFRED PETER, inhalation toxicologist, biomedical scientist; b. Wiesbaden, Germany, Oct. 23, 1926; came to U.S. 1953, naturalized, 1958; s. Paul Heinrich and Irma (Schulze) Wl; m. Ingeborg Hella Miller, Aug. 30, 1955; children: Patricia Ingeborg, Alfred Peter, Jr., Jackie Diane, Peter Hermann. Cand. med., Johannes Gutenberg U., 1949, Zahnarzt DDS, 1951, D.M.D. cum laude, 1953. Diplomate Acad. Toxicol. Scis., 1988. Individual practice dentistry Wiesbaden, 1951-53; fellow clin. pedodontia Guggenheim Dental Clinic, N.Y.C., 1953-54; dentist 7100th Hosp., USAF, 1954-56; rsch. asst. Mobil Oil Co., Dallas, 1957-62; sr. rsch. scientist Biometrics Instrument Corp., Plano, Tex., 1962-64; pres. Electro-Aerosol Inst., Plano, Tex.; dir. Electro-Aerosol Therapy Centers, 1964-67; prof., chmn. dept. sci. U. Plano, 1966-67; sr. rsch. scientist biology dept. Battelle Pacific Northwest Labs., Richland, Wash., 1967-78; mgr. environ. and indsl. toxicology Battelle Pacific Northwest Labs., 1978-80, project dir., task leader indsl. toxicology, 1980-89; founder, pres. Biomed. & Environ. Cons., Inc., 1989—; cons. VA Hosp., McKinney, Tex., 1963-65; chmn., guest speaker 16 internat. sci. congresses and symposia. Author: From Hitler Youth to U.S. Citizenship, 1972; more than 120 sci. publs., including chpts. to books.; editor-in-chief: Am. Inst. Biomed. Climatology Bull.; editor: MEDICEF Direct Information (Federal Republic of Germany); reviewer various sci. jours.; patentee in field. Fellow Internat. Soc. Med. Hydrology, Tex. Acad. Sci.; mem. Am. Inst. Biomed. Climatology (bd. dirs. 1972-90, sec 1972-83, pres. 1984-90), Accademia degli Abruzzi per le Scienze e le Arti, Italy (hon. academician, v.p.), Pacific N.W. Assn. Toxicologists, Internat. Soc. of Biometeorology (USA rep. 1972-79), Internat. Soc. Aerosols in Medicine (exec. bd. 1970-80), Dallas County Dental Soc. (hon.), Internat. Assn. Aerobiology, Sigma Xi. Home and Office: 312 Saint St Richland WA 99352-2033

WEHNER, HENRY OTTO, III, pharmacist, consultant; b. Birmingham, Ala., Mar. 3, 1942; s. Henry O. Jr. and Carolyn (Kirkland) W.; m. Sammye Ruth Murphy, June 8, 1974 (div. July 1989). AA, Daytona Beach Community Coll., 1967; BS in Biology, North Ga. Coll., Dahlonega, 1971; BS in Pharmacy, U. Ga., 1974. Registered pharmacist, Fla., Ga.; cert. sci. tchr. grades 7-12, Ga. Tchr. biology Irwin County High Sch., Ocilla, Ga., 1971-75; extern Eckerd Drugs, Athens, Ga., 1977; intern/extern St. Mary's Hosp., Athens, 1977; pharmacy intern Button Gwinnett Hosp., Lawrenceville, Ga., 1978; co-owner, mgr. Hiawassee (Ga.) Pharmacy, 1978-79; staff pharmacist Dyal's Pharmacy, Daytona Beach, Fla., 1979, Little Drug Co., New Smyrna Beach, Fla., 1979-80; staff pharmacist, mgr. Super X Drugs, New Smyrna Beach, 1980-81; staff pharmacist Fish Meml. Hosp., New Smyrna Beach, 1981-92, Halifax Med. Ctr., Daytona Beach, Fla., 1992—. With USAF, 1961-65. Mem. Am. Pharm. Assn., Fla. Soc. Hosp. Pharm., Volusia County Pharm. Assn., Eastern Shores Soc. Hosp. Pharmacists (charter mem., pres.-elect 1995), Phi Lambda Sigma, Phi Theta Kappa. Methodist. Avocations: painting, cycling, tennis. Office: Halifax Med Ctr PO Box 1350 303 N Clyde Morris Blvd Daytona Beach FL 32114-2709

WEHR, LYNN, food products executive. V.p T. Marzetti Co., Columbus, Ohio. Office: T Marzetti Co 1105 Schrock Rd Ste 600 Columbus OH 43229*

WEHR, THOMAS A., psychiatrist, researcher; b. Louisville, Ky., Oct. 15, 1941; s. Elmer A. and Lillian (Ashby) W.; m. Elizabeth Barker Jones, Mar. 30, 1963; 1 child, David Rowan. BA in English Lit., Yale U., 1965; MD, U. Louisville, 1969. Diplomate Am. Bd. Psychiatry. Intern Michael Reese Hosp. and Med. Ctr., Chgo., 1969-70; resident in psychiatry Yale U. Sch. Medicine, New Haven, 1970-73; clin. assoc. sect. psychiatry NIMH, Bethesda, Md., 1973-75, med. rsch. officer, 1975-76, staff psychiatrist, 1976, chief clin. rsch. unit, clin. psychobiology br., 1977-84, chief clin. psychobiology br., 1982—; pvt. practice psychiatry Bethesda, Md., 1977—; instr. Washington Sch. Psychiatry, 1976-78; vis. prof. U. Naples Med. Sch., Italy, 1984; adj. prof. dept. biol. scis. U. Md., 1986—; internat. adv. bd. Ctr. Design Industrial Schedules; adv. bd. Soc. Rsch. Biol. Rhythms. Author: (with D. Oren, N.E. Rosenthal and W. Reich) How To Beat Jet Lag: The Travelers' Guide, 1993; co-editor: Circadian Rhythms in Psychiatry, 1983; mem. editorial bd. Experimental and Clinical Psychiatry, 1987-93, Lithium, 1989-95, Jour. Biol. Rhythms, 1985-94; patentee portable light delivery system; contbr. articles to profl. jours. Med. dir. USPHS, 1973-75, 76—. Recipient Nat. Rsch. Svc. award, 1975-76, award for Rsch. in Depression Anna-Monika Found., 1981, 91; grantee NIMH 1966-68, 69. Mem. Am. Psychiatric Assn., Am. Coll. Neuropsychopharmacology, Soc. Biol. Psychiatry, Soc. Light Treatment and Biol. Rhythms (v.p. 1992-93, chmn. ann. meeting sci. program com. 1992-93), Internat. Soc. Psychoneuroendocrinology, Internat. Soc. Chronobiology, Sleep Rsch. Office: Nat Inst of Mental Health Rm 4S-239 Bldg 10 10 Center Dr MSC 1390 Bethesda MD 20892-1390

WEHRER, CHARLES SIECKE, business educator; b. Norfolk, Nebr., July 13, 1914; s. Charles C. and Ella (Augusta) W.; m. May Winther Hansen, Aug. 21, 1982 (dec. Oct. 27, 1991). BA, Nebr. State Tchrs. Coll., 1940; MA in Sch. Adminstrn., U. Nebr., 1950, postgrad., 1950; postgrad., Columbia U., 1950, U. So. Calif., 1954-55; PhD without dissertation, Ohio State U., 1961; LHD (hon.), Sioux Empire Coll., 1967. Asst. commandant, basketball coach Black-Foxe Mil. Inst., Hollywood, Calif., 1945-46; coach, supt. local schs. Wood Lake, Nebr., 1947-49; prin. Scottsbluff (Nebr.) Jr. High Sch., 1950-51; grad. asst. in edn. U. Nebr., 1949-50, U. So. Calif., 1954-55; grad. asst. prof. elem. edn. Ohio State U., 1960; tchr. pub. schs. Paramount, Calif., 1953-54; tchr. Excelsior Adult Sch., Norwalk, Calif., 1953-57; supt. local schs. Shandon, Calif., 1956-57; assoc. prof. edn., supr. student teaching Ohio No. U., Ada, 1958-60; assoc. prof., supr. elem. student teaching Capital U., Columbus, Ohio, 1961-62; prin. Norwalk Iowa Elem. Jr. High Sch., 1962-63; prof. edn., dir. student affairs, asst. to pres. Grand View Coll., Des Moines, 1962-64; with depts. youth, TV, ednl. programming City of Des Moines, 1965; cons. program Iowa Civil Def./Health Dept., 1966; prof. edn. and psychology S.W. Community Coll., Creston, Iowa, 1967; acad. dean Sioux Empire Coll., Hawarden, Iowa, 1967-68; chmn. depts. edn., psychology, dir. tchr. edn. J.F. Kennedy Coll., Wahoo, Nebr., 1970-71; producer, emcee youth TV program Let's Listen to Youth Sta. KOLN-TV, Lincoln, Nebr., 1971; prof. edn. Concordia Coll., Seward, Nebr., 1973; tng. coord., dir. spl. tng. programs for mgmt. State of Nebr., 1974-75; prof. bus. Metro Tech., Omaha, 1976-82; prof. mgmt. tng. Bus. Devel. Ctr. U. Nebr., Omaha, 1976-82; prof. bus. Nebr. State Coll., Wayne, 1982-88, ret.; pres. Bus. Mgmt. Cons. Co., Wisner, Nebr., 1982-90; lectr. in field. Author: Keep in Touch, My Students, 1966; contbr. articles to profl. jours. Phys. dir. YMCA, Norfolk, 1934-36, McCook, Nebr., 1937-38, L.A. Downtown Y, 1940-41; counselor, adv. Nebr. Boys' State, 1949-50; Nebr. del. White House Conf. on Children and Youth, 1950; chmn. Nebr. Com. on Juvenile Delinquency; mem. Gov.'s Com. on Youth, Calif., Nebr.; spl. youth cons. radio program Art Linkletter House Party, Calif., 1952; dir. dept. guest relis. NBC, Hollywood, Calif., 1952; dir. spl. project Iowa Dept. Health, 1965-66; contbr. to sub-com. on poverty-youth programs U.S. Congress, 1964-65; chmn. youth sect. Iowa Congress Parents & Tchrs., 1966-67; lay min. Protestant Chs., 1967—, past ch. official First Congl. United Ch. of Christ, Norfolk, Elkhorn Valley Hist. Soc. Capt. USAAF, 1941-45. Decorated Bronze Star, Soldiers medal, 3 Battle Stars, 15th AF Unit citation, Pres. Unit citation, others; recipient spl. awards/commendations for radio/TV programs State PTA and other civic and youth groups, 1960-75, numerous awards for tchg. and youth work; named Outstanding Sch. Adminstr. in Nebr. dept. sch. adminstrn. U. Nebr., 1949, Nebr. Dept. Edn., 1948-50; named to Hall of Honor, Nebr. Softball Assn., 1993; Spl. Proclamation for Edn. and Youth Svcs. State of Nebr., 1994. Mem. NEA (Spl. Commendation for tchr. edn. programs), AAUP, Am. Assn. Ret. Persons (Nebr. Sr. Citizen Spl. Commendation 1980-81), Assn. for Higher Edn., Nat. Assn. Sch. Adminstrs., Nat. Soc. for Study of Edn., Internat. Platform Assn. (spl. spkr. conv. 1970), Am. Legion, VFW, Lions (bd. dirs., past pres.), Kiwanis (past pres.), Rotary, Delta Sigma, Phi Delta Kappa (Spl. Recognition award 1992), Sigma Tau Delta (past pres.). Address: 1000 Village Green #1 Norfolk NE 68701 *We are living in a dangerous world of unrest, a difficult time for all of us to adjust to the emotional and mental problems of this changing environmental world. If we can be of help to those who are in need of a friendly act then let us do our best to be of help and service to young and old alike as we may not pass this way again.*

WEHRING, BERNARD WILLIAM, nuclear engineering educator; b. Monroe, Mich., Aug. 3, 1937; s. Bernard Albert and Alma Christina (Graf) W.; m. Margaret Mary Robinson, Sept. 5, 1959; children: Mary Ann, James, Susan, Barbara. B.S.E. in Physics, U. Mich., 1959, B.S.E. in Math, 1959; M.S. in Physics, U. Ill., 1961, Ph.D. in Nuclear Engring, 1966. Asst. prof. nuclear engring. U. Ill., Urbana, 1966-70, assoc. prof., 1970-77, prof., 1977-84, asst. dean engring., 1981-82; prof. nuclear engring. N.C. State U., Raleigh, 1984-89, dir. nuclear reactor program, 1984-89; prof. mech. engring. U. Tex., Austin, 1989—, dir. Nuclear Engring. Teaching Lab., 1989—; cons. Argonne and Los Alamos nat. labs.; mem. crosssect. evaluation working group Brookhaven Nat. Lab. Contbr. sects. to books, articles to profl. publs. AEC fellow, 1963-65; NSF grantee, 1968—. Fellow Am. Nuclear Soc.; mem. Am. Soc. Engring. Edn., Am. Nuclear Soc. (standards com.), Am. Phys. Soc., IEEE. Achievements include contributing in the generation of basic nuclear data and development of new instruments and experimental techniques. Home: 8907 Spring Lake Dr Austin TX 78750-2932 Office: U Tex Nuclear Engring Teaching Lab J J Pickle Rsch Campus Austin TX 78712

WEHRLE, HENRY BERNARD, JR., diversified manufacturing company executive; b. Charleston, W.Va., 1922. Grad., Princeton U., 1943. Chmn. McJunkin Corp., Charleston, also bd. dirs.; bd. dirs. Bank One W. Va., Petroleum Equipment Supplies Assn. Office: McJunkin Corp 835 Hillcrest Dr E Charleston WV 25311-1627

WEHRLE, LEROY SNYDER, economist, educator; b. St. Louis, Feb. 5, 1932; s. Fred Joseph and Eleanor (Snyder) W.; m. JoAnn Griffith, Aug. 29, 1959; children—Chandra Lee, Lon Joseph. B.S., Washington U., St. Louis, 1953; M.A. in Econs, Yale, 1956, Ph.D. with honors, 1959. Asst. instr. Yale, 1958-59; with econ. sect. AID mission to Laos, 1960-61; sr. staff economist President's Council Econ. Advisers, 1961-62; spl. econ. adviser to U.S. Ambassador Unger, Vientiane, 1962; dep. dir. AID mission to Laos, 1963-64; asst. dir. AID mission, also econ. counsellor to U.S. ambassador, Saigon, 1964-67; assoc. dir. AID Mission, Saigon, 1964-67; internat. adminstr. Vietnam, AID, Dept. State, 1967-68; univ. fellow Harvard, 1968-69; sr. fellow Brookings Instn., 1969-70; dir. Ill. Inst. for Social Policy, Springfield, 1970-72; aide to Lt. Gov. Paul Simon, 1972; prof. economics Sangamon State U., 1972-88; founding ptnr., chief exec. officer Health Econs. and Mkt. Analysis Inc., Springfield, 1987-94; pres. Healthcare Cost Analysis, Inc., 1994—; chmn. bd. Tie Collar, Ltd. Mem. spl. study group Alliance Progress, 1962; mem. Rockefeller Latin Am. Mission, 1969; chmn. study team world food and nutrition study Nat. Acad. Sci., 1976-77. Served with AUS, 1953-55. Recipient William A. Jump meml. award, 1966. Home and Office: 2001 S Bates Ave Springfield IL 62704-3304

WEHRLE, MARTHA GAINES, state legislator; b. Charleston, W.Va., Nov. 30, 1925; d. Ludwell Ebersole and Betty (Chilton) Gaines. AB, Vassar Coll., 1948; MA, Harvard U., 1954; m. Russell Schilling Wehrle, Oct. 16, 1954; children: Michael H., Ebersole Gaines, Katherine S., Philip N., Martha Chilton. Tchr. W.Va. schs., 1949-50, Belmont (Mass.) Day Sch., 1951-53; mem. W.Va. Ho. of Dels., 1974-84, vice chmn. edn. com., 1976, chmn. constl. revision com., 1977-84, mem. fin. com.; state senator W.Va. State Senate from Kanawha County dist., 1989-95; bd. dirs. United Bankshares, McJunkin Corp.; mem. adv. coun. W.Va. Woman's Commmn. Mem. LWV, Garden Club Am. (chmn. nat. affairs and legis. 1987-93), Kanawha Garden Club, Charleston Jr. League Club. Democrat. Episcopalian. Office: WVa Senate State Capitol Charleston WV 25305

WEI, BENJAMIN MIN, engineering educator; b. Hebei, Hebei, China, Aug. 11, 1930; s. Fu Shun and Yuan Qing (Zhang) W.; m. Diana Yun Dee; children: Victor Mark; Jane Jiang. BSME, Chung Cheng Inst. Tech., 1954;

MSME, Concordia U., 1970; PhD, Pa. State U., 1981. Mech. engr. Ordnance Corps Arsenal, Taipei, Taiwan, 1953-59; tchr. Wenshan High Sch., Taipei, 1960-61; teaching asst. New Brunswick (Can.) U., 1962-64; supr. Domtar Constrn. Materials Co., Can., 1964-66; computer programmer McGill U., Can., 1966-67, Montreal (Can.) U., 1967-68; tchr. Pierrefond Comprehensive High sch., Que., 1970-73; prof. Norfolk (Va.) State U., 1974—; hon. prof., cons. Taiyuan U. Polytech. Contbr. articles to profl. jours. Mem. U.S. Senatorial Club, Rep. Presdl. Task Force, 1984—. Mem. Statistical Quality Control of China. Home: 1152 Janaf Pl Norfolk VA 23502-2631 Office: Norfolk State U 2401 Corprew Ave Norfolk VA 23504-3907

WEI, I-YUAN, research and development consultant and director; b. Taipei, Taiwan, Republic of China, Nov. 1, 1940; came to U.S., 1967; s. Kun-Te and Kun (Lu) W.; m. Shirley Chen, Dec. 28, 1968; children: Jerray, Jiaying. BS, Nat. Taiwan Normal U., 1963; MS, Nat. Taiwan U., 1966; PhD, Tufts U., 1971. Rsch. assoc. U. N.C., Chapel Hill, 1972-75; scientist Sprague Electric Co., North Adams, Mass., 1976-77; mgr. R & D Republic Foil, Salisbury, N.C., 1977-81; sr. engr. AMP Inc., Harrisburg, Pa., 1981-86, mem. tech. staff, 1986-88, project mgr., 1988-90, mgr. plating rsch., 1990-93, dir. contacts materials, consulant tech., 1994—. Contbr. articles to Jour. Chinese Chem. Soc., Jour. Chem. Physics, Jour. Am. Chem. Soc., Inorganic Chemistry, Chem. Phys. Lett., Jour. Magna. Reson. Mem. Am. Electroplaters and Surface Finishers Soc. (chmn. electronics finishing com. 1991-94, chmn., meetings and symposia, 1993—, dir. tech. edn. 1993—, Bd. Recognition award 1994), Electrochem. Soc., Ctrl. Pa. Chinese Assn. (pres. 1984, chmn. bd. 1985-93). Achievements include rsch. in deuteron quadrupole coupling constants in nitrobenzenes, hydrogen-bonded systems of aluminum hydroxides and anodic oxide films by deutron magnetic resonance, palladium and palladium-nickel as contact materials, electronic materials, electroplating; patentee in field. Home: 1046 W Areba Ave Hershey PA 17033 Office: AMP Inc PO Box 3608 Harrisburg PA 17105

WEI, JAMES, chemical engineering educator, academic dean; b. Macao, China, Aug. 14, 1930; came to U.S., 1949, naturalized, 1960; s. Hsiang-chen and Nuen (Kwok) W.; m. Virginia Hong, Nov. 4, 1956; children: Alexander, Christina, Natasha, Randolph (dec.). B.S. in Chem. Engring, Ga. Inst. Tech., 1952; M.S., Mass. Inst. Tech., 1954, S.c.D., 1955; grad., Advanced Mgmt. Program Harvard, 1969. Research engr. to research assoc. Mobil Oil, Paulsboro, N.J., 1956-62; sr. scientist Princeton, N.J., 1963-68; mgr. corp. planning N.Y.C., 1969-70; Allan P. Colburn prof. U. Del., Newark, 1971-77; Sherman Fairchild distinguished scholar Calif. Inst. Tech., 1977; Warren K. Lewis prof. MIT, Cambridge, 1977-91, head dept. chem. engring., 1977-88; Pomeroy and Betty Smith prof. chem. engring., dean Sch. Engring. and Applied Sci. Princeton (N.J.) U., 1991—; vis. prof. Princeton, 1962-63, Calif. Inst. Tech., 1965; cons. Mobil Oil Corp.; cons. com. on motor vehicle emissions Nat. Acad. Sci., 1972-74, 79-80; mem. sci. adv. bd. EPA, 1976-79; mem. Presdl. Pvt. Sector Survey Task Force on Dept. Energy, 1982-83. Bd. editors Chem. Tech, 1971-80, Chem. Engring. Communications, 1972—; cons. editor chem. engring. series, McGraw-Hill, 1964—; editor-in-chief: Advances in Chemical Engineering, 1980; Contbr. papers, monographs to profl. lit., The Structure of Chemical Processing Industries, 1979. Recipient Am. Acad. Achievement Golden Plate award, 1966. Mem. AIChE. (dir. 1970-72, lectr. 1968, Profl. Progress award 1970, Walker award 1980, Lewis award 1985, v.p. 1987, pres. 1988, Founders award 1990), AAAS, Am. Chem. Soc. (award in petroleum chemistry 1966), Nat. Acad. Engring. (nominating com. 1981, peer com., 1980-82, membership com. 1983-85, Draper award com. 1995-96), Am. Acad. Arts. and Scis., Academica Sinica of Taiwan, Sigma Xi. Home: 571 Lake Dr Princeton NJ 08540-5263 Office: Princeton U Engring Quadrangle Princeton NJ 08544-5263

WEI, JEN YU, physiologist, researcher, educator; b. Fukien, China, Jan. 26, 1938; came to U.S., 1979; s. Soen Yu Wei and Soen Sang Hoeng; m. Lian Shen, Jan. 19, 1966; 1 child, Ching Wei. BS, Fu-Dan U., Shanghai, China, 1962; PhD in Neurophysiology, Shanghai Inst. Physiology, Chinese Acad. Scis., 1966; PhD in Sensory Physiology, U. Utah, 1987. Rsch. assoc. Inst. of Physiology, Shanghai, 1966-77, asst. rschr., 1977-78; rsch. assoc. dept. physiology U. Hong Kong, China, 1979; rsch. assoc. U. Utah, Salt Lake City, 1979-81, rsch. instr., 1981-87, rsch. asst. prof., 1987-89, asst. rsch. neurophysiologist, 1989-91; assoc. rsch. neurophysiologist dept. medicine Brain Rsch. Inst. and Ctr. Ulcer Rsch. and Edn./Gastroenteric Biol. Ctr., VA Wadsworth Med. Ctr. UCLA, 1991—. NIH Individual Investigator Rsch. grantee, 1990—. Mem. AAAS, The Chinese Physiology Soc., Soc. for Neurosci., Internat. Brain Rsch. Orgn., Sigma Xi. Avocations: hiking, fishing. Office: UCLA Dept Medicine & Brain Rsch Inst 10833 Le Conte Ave Los Angeles CA 90024-1761

WEIANT, WILLIAM MORROW, investment banking executive; b. Perth Amboy, N.J., Nov. 30, 1938; s. Monroe Alden and Lois May (Dayer) W.; m. Joan Claire Eberstadt, June 10, 1967; children: Clarissa Leigh, Pamela Anne. BA, Amherst Coll., 1960; MBA, NYU, 1964. Chartered fin. analyst. Ptnr. Blyth Eastman Dillon, N.Y.C., 1963-75; mng. dir. CS 1st Boston, N.Y.C., 1976-91, Dillon, Read & Co. Inc., N.Y.C., 1991-94, Morgan Stanley & Co., N.Y.C., 1994—. With USAF, 1960-61. Mem. Bank and Fin. Analysts (pres. 1976, 87). Avocations: tennis, golf, skiing, piano. Home: 46 Northover Pl Red Bank NJ 07701-6311

WEIBLE, ROBERT A., lawyer; b. Dover, Ohio, June 25, 1953. BA summa cum laude, Wittenberg U., 1975; JD summa cum laude, Ohio State U., 1978. Ptnr. Baker & Hostetler, Cleve. Editor Ohio State Law Jour., 1977-78. Mem. Order of Coif. Office: Baker & Hostetler 3200 Nat City Ctr 1900 E 9th St Cleveland OH 44114-3303

WEICH, RONALD H., lawyer; b. N.Y.C., Nov. 19, 1959. Student, London Sch. Econs., 1979; BA, Columbia U., 1980; JD, Yale U., 1983. Bar: N.Y. 1984, U.S. Ct. Appeals (D.C. dir.) 1988. Asst. dist. atty. N.Y. Dist. Atty's Office, N.Y.C., 1983-87; spl. counsel U.S. Sentencing Commn., Washington, 1987-89; minority counsel Senate Constitution Subcom., Washington, 1989; chief counsel drug policy Senate Labor & Human Resources Com., Washington, 1990—, gen. counsel, 1992—. Guest editor Federal Sentencing Reporter, 1991; contbr. articles to profl. jours. Mem. ABA (criminal justice sect., sentencing/prison coms.), Bar Assn. State N.Y. Office: Com on Labor & Human Rsrcs 428 Dirksen Senate Ofc Bldg Washington DC 20510

WEICHENTHAL, BURTON A., educational administrator, beef specialist; b. Stanton, Nebr., Nov. 7, 1937; s. Arthur W. and Bertha M. (Topp) W.; m. Phyllis A. Bonner, June 12, 1960; 1 child, Susan. BS, U. Nebr., 1959; MS, S.D. State U., 1962; PhD, Colo. State U., 1967. Beef specialist U. Ill., Urbana, 1967-81; assoc. dir. U. Nebr. Panhandle Ctr., Scottsbluff, 1982—; beef specialist, 1987—. Mem. Sugar Valley Singers (past pres., treas.), Lions (past pres.), Elks. Avocations: neighborhood chorus singing. Office: U Nebr Panhandle Ctr 4502 Avenue I Scottsbluff NE 69361-4939

WEICHERT, DIETER HORST, seismologist, researcher; b. Breslau, Silesia, Germany, May 2, 1937; came to Can., 1954; s. Kurt Herman and Margarete Adelheid (Buresch) W.; m. Edith Struning (div. 1983), children: Thomas, Andreas. BASc, U. B.C., Vancouver, Can., 1961, PhD, 1965; MS, McMaster U., Hamilton, Ont., Can., 1963. Rsch. scientist earth physics br. Dominion Obs., Ottawa, Ont., 1965-78; rsch. scientist Pacific Geosci. Ctr., Sidney, B.C., 1978-81, head earthquake studies, 1981-88, assoc. dir., acting dir., 1988-90; rsch. scientist Geol. Survey Can., Sidney, B.C., 1990-96, emeritus, 1996—; cons. U.K. Atomic Energy Authority, Blacknest, Eng., 1970; guest lectr. Fredericiana U. Karlsruhe, Germany, 1971; mem. Can. Earthquake Engring. Com., Ottawa, 1982—; supt. constrn. industry, Germany, 1951-57. Contbr. over 80 articles to profl. jours. Woodrow Wilson fellow, 1961; Inco fellow, 1962-64. Mem. Seismol. Soc. Am. Achievements include research on underground nuclear explosion detection and identification; seismic hazard and strong seismic ground motion. Office: Geol Survey Can 9860 W Saanich Box 6000, North Saanich, BC Canada V8L 4B2

WEICHSELBAUM, RALPH R., oncologist chairman. BS, U. Wis., 1967; MD, U. Ill., Chgo., 1971. Intern Alameda County Hosp., Oakland, Calif. 1971-72; resident in radiation therapy Harvard Med. Sch., Boston, 1972-75; assoc. prof. radiation therapy Harvard Med. Ctr., Boston, 1980-84; assoc. prof. dept. cancer biology Harvard Sch. Public Health, Boston, 1983-84; prof., chmn. dept. radiation and cellular omcology Pritzker Sch. Medicine U.

Chgo., 1984—, Harold H. Hines Jr. prof., chmn; 1990; head Michael Reese/U. Chgo. Ctr. Radiation Therapy, 1984—. Contbr. articles to profl. jours. Office: Ctr for Radiation Therapy Pritzker Sch of Medicine 5841 S Maryland Ave Chicago IL 60637-1404

WEICKSEL, CHARLENE MARIE, principal; b. York, Pa., June 16, 1945; d. Edward A. and Mary Elizabeth (Hoffman) Debes; m. Stephen A. Weicksel, Aug. 27, 1967; children: Andrew. B Music Edn., Westminster Choir Coll., 1967; MEd, Trenton State Coll., 1986. Cert. tchr., prin., supr., N.J. Tchr. Hillsborough Twp. Bd. Edn., Neshanic, N.J., 1967-87, curriculum supr. fine and performing arts, 1987-93; prin. Triangle Rd. Elem. Sch., Hillsborough, N.J., 1993—. Bd. dirs. Lenape Swim Club, Skillman, N.J., 1990-93, Raritan Valley Chorus, Belle Mead, N.J., 1991-92. Mem. NEA, N.J. Edn. Assn., Nat. Art Educators Assn., Art Educators N.J., Jazz Educators. Democrat. Presbyterian. Avocations: cross-stitch, crochet, knitting, writing, travel. Home: 302 Sunset Rd Skillman NJ 08558-1628 Office: Hillsborough Twp Bd Edn 555 Amwell Rd Neshanic Station NJ 08853-3409

WEIDA, LEWIS DIXON, marketing analyst, consultant; b. Moran, Ind., Apr. 23, 1924; s. Charles Ray and Luella Mildred (Dixon) W.; student Kenyon Coll., 1943, Purdue U., 1946; B.S., Ind. U., 1948; M.S., Columbia U., 1950. Mgr. statis. analysis unit Gen. Motors Acceptance Corp., N.Y.C., 1949-55; asst. to exec. v.p. Am. Express Co., 1955-82. Served with USAAF, 1943-46; PTO. Mem. Internat. Platform Assn. Democrat. Club: Masons. Home: 25 Tudor City Pl New York NY 10017-6819

WEIDE, JANICE LEE, librarian; b. Baker, Oreg., Aug. 12, 1948; d. Albert L. and Woodie Rue (Jeffords) Crowson; m. Roy Karl Weide, June 13, 1971; children: Megan, Alison. BA, Oreg. State U., 1971; MLA, U. Oreg., 1974. Online coord. Salem (Oreg.) Pub. Libr., 1974—. Contbr. articles to profl. publs. Recipient On the Frontline award OCLC, 1991. Avocations: reading, bicycling, swimming. Office: Salem Pub Libr 585 Liberty St SE Salem OR 97301

WEIDE, WILLIAM WOLFE, housing and recreational vehicles manufacturer; b. Toledo, Aug. 19, 1923; s. Samuel and Pearl Celia (Weide) W.; m. Beatrice Lieberman, June 4, 1950; children: Brian Samuel, Bruce Michael, Robert Benjamin. Student, U. Toledo, 1942, Marquette U., 1943-44; B.S., U. So. Calif., 1949. Asst. controller Eldon Mfg., 1950; mem. Calif. Franchise Tax Bd., 1951; controller Sutone Corp., 1951-53; contr., treas. Pacific Concessions Corp., 1953; treas. Descoware Corp., 1953-58; sr. v.p. dir. Fleetwood Enterprises, Inc., Riverside, Calif., 1958-73, pres., chief oper. officer, 1973-82, vice chmn., 1982—, dir.; treas. So. Eastern Manufactured Housing Inst., Atlanta., 1972-74; vice chmn. bd. dirs. Fleetwood Enterprises, Inc.. Mem. City of Riverside Housing Com.; mem. exec. com. of policy adv. bd. Joint Ctr. for Urban Studies, Harvard-MIT, Cambridge; trustee City of Hope Hosp., Duarte, Calif.; Orange County chmn. United Jewish Welfare Fund, 1982-83; mem. Pres.'s Circle of U. So. Calif.; pres. Orange County Jewish Community Found., 1986-88; chmn. Calif. Mfrs. Housing Inst. Polit Action Com., 1986-92; vice chmn., chmn. Calif. devel. Wellness Community of Orange County. With USNR, 1942-46. Recipient Jack E. Wells Meml. award for service to manufactured housing industry, 1976; named to Recreational Vehicle/Manufactured Housing Industry Hall of Fame Elkhart, Ind., 1981; named Man of Yr., City of Hope, 1986. Mem. Nat. Assn. Accts. (past v.p., dir. Los Angeles and Orange County chpt.), Manufactured Housing Inst. (chmn., founding com. Calif. chpt. 1986), Western Manufactured Housing Inst. (vice-chmn.), Trailer Coach Assn., NAM (public affairs com.), Riverside C. of C. Office: Fleetwood Enterprises Inc PO Box 7638 Riverside CA 92513 *Love your family. Love your job. Give all you can for what you wish to achieve. Be a Jonathan Livingston Seagull.*

WEIDEKING, W., automotive holding company. Pres. Porsche Enterprises, Inc., Reno, Nev. Office: Porsche Enterprises Inc 100 W Liberty St Reno NV 89501*

WEIDEMANN, CELIA JEAN, social scientist, international business and financial development consultant; b. Denver, Dec. 6, 1942; d. John Clement and Hazel (Van Tuyl) Kirlin; m. Wesley Clark Weidemann, July 1, 1972; 1 child, Stephanie Jean. BS, Iowa State U., 1964; MS, U. Wis.-Madison, 1970, PhD, 1973; postgrad. U. So. Calif., 1983. Advisor, UN Food & Agr. Orgn., Ibadan, Nigeria, 1973-77; ind. researcher, Asia and Near East, 1977-78; program coord., asst. prof., cons. U. Wis., Madison, 1979-81; chief institutional and human resources U.S. Agy. for Internat. Devel., Washington, 1982-85, team leader, cons., Sumatra, Indonesia, 1984; dir. fed. econs. program Midwest Rsch. Inst., Washington, 1985-86; pres., CEO Weidemann Assocs., Arlington, Va., 1986—; cons. U.S. Congress, Aspen Inst., Ford Found., World Bank, Egypt, Nigeria, Gambia, Pakistan, Indonesia, AID, Kenya, Jordan, Poland, India, Egypt, Russia, Finnish Internat. Devel. Agy., Namibia, pvt. client, Estonia, Lativa, Russia, Japan, Internat. Ctr. Rsch. on Women, Zaire, UN Food and Agriculture Orgn., Ghana, Internat. Statis. Inst., The Netherlands, Global Exchange, 1986-87. Author: Planning Home Economics Curriculum for Social and Economic Development, Agricultural Extension for Women Farmers in Africa, 1990, Financial Services for Women, 1992, Egyptian Women and Microenterprise: The Invisible Entrepreneurs, 1992, Small Enterprise Development in Poland: Does Gender Matter?, 1994; contbr. chpts. to books and articles to profl. jours. Am. Home Econs. Assns. fellow, 1969-73 (recipient research grant Ford Found. 1987-89). Mem. Internat. Devel., Am. Sociol. Assn., U.S. Dirs. of Internat. Agrl. Programs, Assn. for Women in Devel. (pres. 1989, founder, bd. dirs.), Internat. Devel. Conf. (bd. dirs., exec. com.), Am. Home Econs. Assn. (Wis. internat. chmn. 1980-81), Internat. Fedn. Home Econs., Internat. Platform Assn., Pi Lambda Theta, Omicron Nu. Roman Catholic. Avocations: mountain trekking, piano/pipe organ, canoeing, photography, poetry. Home and Office: 2607 24th St N Arlington VA 22207-4908

WEIDENAAR, DENNIS JAY, college dean; b. Grand Rapids, Mich., Oct. 4, 1936; s. John and Jennie (Beukema) W.; m. Kristin Andrews, July 14, 1943; children: Kaarin Jaye, John Andrews. AB, Calvin Coll., Grand Rapids, 1958; MA, U. Chgo., 1961; PhD, Purdue U., W. Lafayette, 1969. Asst. prof. of econs.. Purdue U., West Lafayette, 1966-72, assoc. prof. of econ., 1972-77, prof. of econs. 1977—; interim dean Krannert Sch. of Mgmt., West Lafayette, 1983-84, assoc. dean, 1984—; dean Krannert Grad. Sch. Mgmt., West Lafayette, Ind., 1990—; cons. TRW, B.F. Goodrich, Ea. Panhandle: Author: Economics. Contbr. articles to profl. jours. Bd. dirs. Ind. Coun. on Econ. Edn., Lafayette, 1974-83, St. Elizabeth Hosp., Lafayette, Greater Lafayette Comty. Found., Lafayette Ins. Co. Recipient The Leavey Awd for Excellence in Pvt. Enterprise Edn., Freedom's Found., Valley Forge, 1983, Distinguished Service Awd., Joint Council on Econ. Edn., N.Y., 1986, Golden Key Nat. Honor Soc. 1985. Mem. Rotary, Delta Sigma Pi, Beta Gamma Sigma, Phi Delta Kappa. Presbyterian. Home: 3703 Moss Hill Dr West Lafayette IN 47906-8885 Office: Purdue U Krannert Sch Mgmt West Lafayette IN 47907

WEIDENBAUM, MURRAY LEW, economics educator; b. Bronx, N.Y., Feb. 10, 1927; s. David and Rose (Warshaw) W.; m. Phyllis Green, June 13, 1954; children: Susan, James, Laurie. BBA, CCNY, 1948; MA, Columbia U., 1949; MPA, Princeton U., 1954, PhD, 1958; LLD, Baruch Coll., 1981, U. Evansville, 1983, McKendree Coll., 1993. chmn. rsch. adv. com. St. Louis Regional Indsl. Devel. Corp., 1965-69; exec. dir. Pres.'s Com. on Econ. Impact of Def. and Disarmament, 1964; mem. U.S. Fin. Investment Adv. Panel, 1970-72; cons. various firms and instns. Fiscal economist Bur. Budget, Washington, 1949-57; corp. economist Boeing Co., Seattle, 1958-62; sr. economist Stanford Rsch. Inst., Palo Alto, Calif., 1962-63; mem. faculty Washington U., St. Louis, 1964—, prof., chmn. dept. econs., 1966-69, Mallinckrodt prof., 1971—; dir. Ctr. for Study Am. Bus. Ctr. for Study Am. Bus., St. Louis, 1975-81, 82-95; chmn. Ctr. for Study Am. Bus. Washington U., St. Louis, 1995—; asst. sec. econ. policy Treasury Dept., 1969-71; chmn. Coun. of Econ. Advs., 1981-82. Author: Federal Budgeting, 1964, Modern Public Sector, 1969, Economics of Peacetime Defense, 1974, Economic Impact of the Vietnam War, 1967, Government-Mandated Price Increases, 1975, Business, Government, and the Public, 1990, The Future of Business Regulation, 1980, Rendezvous With Reality: The American Economy After Reagan, 1988, paperback edit., 1990, Small Wars, Big Defense, 1992, Business and Governmant in the Global Marketplace, 1995; mem. editorial bd. Publius, 1971—, Jour. Econ. Issues, 1972-75, Challenge, 1974-81, 83—. With AUS, 1945. Recipient Alexander Hamilton medal U.S. Dept.

Treasury, 1971, Disting. Writer award Georgetown U., award for disting. teaching Freedoms Found., 1980, award for best book in econs. Assn. Am. Pubs., 1992; named to Free Market Hall of Fame, 1983; Banbury fellow Princeton U., 1954. Fellow AIAA, Nat. Assn. Bus. Economists, City Coll. Alumni Assn. (Townsend Harris medal 1969), Assn. for Pvt. Enterprise Edn. (Adam Smith award 1986), Cosmos Club. Office: Washington Univ Ctr for Study Am Bus 1 Brookings Dr Saint Louis MO 63130-4899

WEIDENFELD, EDWARD LEE, lawyer; b. Akron, Ohio, July 15, 1943; s. Sam and Beatrice (Cooper) W.; m. Sheila Rabb, Aug. 11, 1968; children: Nicholas, Daniel. BS, U. Wis., 1965; JD, Columbia U., 1968. Bar: N.Y. 1968, U.S. Supreme Ct. 1972, D.C. 1973. Pvt. practice N.Y.C., 1969-71, 73-82, Washington, 1982—; counsel, dir. energy staff Com. on Interior and Insular Affairs, U.S. Ho. of Reps., 1971-73; mem. faculty Am. Law Inst.-Am. Bar Assn. Continuing Legal Edn. Programs; mem. internat. del. to observe Philippine Election, 1986, internat. del. to observe Republic Korea Election, 1987, Pakistan Election, 1988, Chilean Election, 1989; lectr. to profl. groups; spl. cons. N.Y.C. Dept. Bldgs., 1967. Editor in chief Atomic Energy Law Jour., 1975-76. Mem. Pres.'s Commn. on White House Fellowships, 1977; nat. chmn. Lawyers for Reagan/Bush, 1980; chief dep. counsel Reagan/Bush Campaign, 1980; chmn. Reagan/Bush '84 Legal Adv. Bd., 1984; mem. D.C. Rep. Com., 1984-92, vice chmn., 1984-88; mem. Coun. Adminstrv. Conf. of U.S., 1981-92, sr. fellow, 1992—; trustee Danny Kaye and Sylvia Fine Kaye Found. Mem. ABA, D.C. Bar Assn., Fed. Communications Bar Assn., Internat. Bar Assn., Am. Law Inst., Assn. Bar City N.Y., Internat. Human Rights Law Group (vice chmn. bd. dirs.). Club: Met. (Washington). Home: 3059 Q St NW Washington DC 20007-3081

WEIDENFELD, SHEILA RABB, television producer, author; b. Cambridge, Mass., Sept. 7, 1943; d. Maxwell M. and Ruth (Cryden) Rabb; BA, Brandeis U., 1965; m. Edward L. Weidenfeld, Aug. 11, 1968; children: Nicholas Rabb, Daniel Rabb. Assoc. producer Metromedia, Inc., WNEW-TV, N.Y.C., 1965-68; talent coord. That Show with Joan Rivers, NBC, N.Y.C., 1968-71; coord. NBC network game programs, N.Y.C., 1968-71; producer Metromedia, Inc., WTTG-TV, Washington, 1971-73; creator/producer Take It From Here, NBC (WRC-TV), Washington, 1973-74; press sec. to first lady Betty Ford and spl. asst. to Pres. Gerald R. Ford 1974-77; mem. Pres.'s Adv. Commn. on Historic Preservation, 1977-81; TV producer, moderator On the Record, NBC-TV, WRC-TV, Washington, 1978-79; pres. D.C. Prodns., Ltd., 1978; producer, host Your Personal Decorator, 1987; mem. Sec. State's Adv. Commn. on Fgn. Service Inst., 1972-74; founding mem. Project Censured Panel of Judges, 1976—. Author: First Lady's Lady, 1979. Mem. U.S. Holocaust Meml. Council, 1987—; corporator, Dana Hall Sch., Wellesley, Mass; bd. dirs. Wolf Trap Found., Women's Campaign Fund, 1978-79; bd. dirs. D.C. Contemporary Dance Theatre, 1986-88, D.C. Rep. Cen. Com., 1984—, D.C. Preservation League, 1987-90; chmn. C&O Canal Nat. Hist. Park Commn., 1988—; bd. dirs. Am. Univ. Home, 1988—. Recipient awards for outstanding achievement in the media AAUW, 1973, 74, Silver Screen award A Campaign to Remember for the U.S. Holocaust Meml. Coun., 1989, Bronze medal Internat. Film and Video Festival N.Y., 1990; named hon. consul gen. of Republic of San Marino to Washington; knighted by Order of St. Agatha, Republic of San Marino, 1986. Mem. NATAS (Emmy award 1972), Washington Press Club, Am. Newspaper Women's Club, Am. Women in Radio and TV, Cosmos Club, Consular Corps, Sigma Delta Chi. Home and Office: 3059 Q St NW Washington DC 20007-3081

WEIDENSAUL, THOMAS CRAIG, university administrator, researcher; b. Reedsville, Pa., Apr. 4, 1939; s. Thomson Becker and Grace Elizabeth (Kendig) W.; married, June 12, 1965; children: T. Luke, Susan E., Daniel J. BA in Biology, Gettysburg Coll., 1962; MF in Forest Mgmt. and Forest Pathology, Duke U., 1963; PhD in Plant Pathology, Pa. State U., 1969. Plant pathologist forests and forest products USDA U.S. Forest Svc., Harrisonburg, Va., 1963-66; grad. asst. dept. plant pathology Pa. State U., University Park, 1966-69; head lab. for environ. studies, asst. prof. plant pathology and forestry Ohio Agrl. Rsch. and Devel. Ctr., Lab. For Environ. Studies, Wooster, 1970; assoc. prof. Ohio State U., Ohio Agrl. Rsch. and Devel. Ctr., Lab. For Environ. Studies, 1973-79, prof., 1979—, asst. dir. experiment sta., 1986-87, asst. dir. sch. natural resources, 1990—; mem. NAS panel on sulphur oxides. Contbr. articles to profl. publs. Chmn. environ. quality task force Ohio Agrl. Rsch. and Devel. Ctr., mem. exec., 1973—; mem. stats. adv. com., 1976-87, mem. adminstrv. and program rev. panel for rsch. and extension analytical lab., 1988, mem. adminstrv. cabinet, 1986—; mem. steering com. centennial open house, 1982, chmn. task force on global change rsch., 1990; mem. steering com. Nat. Air Pollution Workshop, 1974-76. With USAR, 1963-69. Recipient Ohio League Sportsmen and Nat. Wildlife Fedn. Gov's. award, 1980; Pa. State Senatorial scholar, 1957-58, Duke U. scholar, 1962-63, Pa. State U. post doctoral, 1969-70. Fellow NASA; mem. Am. Phytopathological Soc. (air pollution damage to crops com. 1973-75, 77-81, 83-86, vice chmn. environ. quality com. 1974, environ. quality and plant health com. 1989-90, 91—), Am. Soc. Agronomy, Pa. Christmas Tree Growers Assn., Am. Phytopath. Soc., Am. Foresters, Soil Sci. Soc. Am., Ohio Acad. Sci., Phi Kappa Phi, Sigma Xi, Phi Sigma, Phi Epsilon Phi. Achievements include research in effects of gaseous and metallic pollutants on microorganisms and higher plants, sources and effects of atmospheric deposition, predisposing and/or protecting capabilities of gaseous, acidic and metallic materials re infectious plant diseases, epidemiology and etiology of forest and shade tree diseases, uses and effects of municipal sewage sludge on soils, plant growth and nutrient availability, control of plant diseases: silvicultural and/or horticultural, chemical and resistance, sustaining and enhancing income to sugar maple sap producers through identifying, modeling, and managing risks associated with maple stresses and subsequent tree decline, identification and assessment of air pollution injury and damage to plants, christmas tree production and forest pathology extension, determination of presence of stable pollutants in soils, water and plant and animal tissues. Home: 6550 Fredericksburg Rd Wooster OH 44691-9422 Office: Sch Natural Resources Ohio Agrl # R D Ctr Wooster OH 44691

WEIDENTHAL, MAURICE DAVID (BUD WEIDENTHAL), educational administrator, journalist; b. Cleve., Nov. 26, 1925; s. William and Evelyn (Kolinsky) W.; m. Grace Schwartz, Apr. 14, 1957; 1 child, Susan Elizabeth Weidenthal Saltzman. B.A., U. Mich., 1950. Mem. staff Cleve. Press, 1950-81, editorial writer, 1950-51, asst. city editor, 1956-58, edn. editor, 1958-81; v.p. public affairs Cuyahoga Community Coll. Dist., Cleve., 1981-88; dir. Urban Colls. Project Am. Assn. Community Colls., Washington, 1989—. Mem. pub. affairs com. Greater Cleve. Growth Assn., 1981-88; mem. bd. advisors Coun. for Advancement and Support of Edn., 1981-88, Nat. Coun. Mktg. and Pub. Rels., 1981—; alt. bd. dirs. St. Vincent Quadrangle, 1983-88; trustee Hebrew Free Loan Assn., 1975-86; mem. philanthropic adv. com. Jewish Community Fedn. Served with AUS, 1944-45. Decorated Air medal. Mem. Edn. Writers Assn., Soc. Profl. Journalists, Cleve. City Club (bd. dirs. 1969-76), Cleve. Press Club. Home: 25858 Fairmount Blvd Cleveland OH 44122-2214 Office: 4250 Richmond Rd Cleveland OH 44122

WEIDER, JOSEPH, wholesale distribution executive. Chmn. bd., treas. Weider Health and Fitness, Woodland Hills, Calif.; Mem. chmn. bd. Weider Health and Fitness, Great Am. Foods. Office: Men's Fitness 21100 Erwin St Woodland Hills CA 91367-3712*

WEIDERHOLZ, CONRAD, magazine publisher. Pub. First for Women mag., Englewood Cliffs, N.J. Office: First for Women Bauer Pub Co 270 Sylvan Ave Englewood Cliffs NJ 07632*

WEIDLINGER, PAUL, civil engineer; b. Budapest, Hungary, Dec. 22, 1914; came to U.S., 1944; s. Andrew and Juliete W.; m. Solveig Hojberg, Dec. 24, 1964; children—Thomas, Pauline, Jonathan. B.S., Tech. Inst., Brno, Czechoslovakia, 1934; M.S., Swiss Fed. Inst. Zurich, 1937. Registered profl. engr. 17 states. Chief engr. Atlas Aircraft Products, N.Y.C., 1944-46; chief rsch. cons. dir. Nat. Housing Agy.; Industrialization Program Div., Washington, 1946-47; dir. engring. div. United Indsl. Assocs., Washington, 1947-48; sr. ptnr. Weidlinger Assocs., cons. engrs., N.Y.C., 1948—; mem. seismic loads com. Am. Nat. Standards Inst., 1978-80; chmn. Nat. Acad. Sci. Evaluation Panel, Nat. Bur. Standards, 1978-80; mem. sci. adv. bd. to chief staff USAF, 1957-58; vis. lectr. Harvard U., 1955-64, MIT, 1952-64. Author: Aluminum in Modern Architecture, Vol. II, 1956; contbr.

papers to profl. jours. Recipient award Engring. News-Record, 1966. Fellow ASCE (Ernest E. Howard award, Moisseiff award 1975, J. James R. Cross medal 1963), Franklin Inst. (Frank P. Brown medal 1987); mem. AIAA, Am. Concrete Inst., Nat. Acad. Engring., Earthquake Engring. Rsch. Inst., Internat. Assn. Bridge and Structural Engrs., N.Y. Acad. Scis., Nat. Bldg. Mus. (bd. dirs. 1982-88). Office: Weidlinger Assocs 333 7th Ave New York NY 10001-5004

WEIDMAN, ANNA KATHRYN, publishing company financial executive; b. Redwood City, Calif., July 6, 1962; d. Ronald Frank and Jane (Cotton) W.; m. Charles Shaw Robinson, Nov. 1, 1993. BA, U. Calif., Berkeley, 1984, MBA, 1992. Asst. to dir. U. Calif. Press, Berkeley, 1985-91, exhibits/sales mgr., 1991-93, chief fin. officer, 1993—; bd. dirs. Mercury House Pubs.; ind. cons., Berkeley, 1993; treas., bd. dirs Assocs. of U. Calif. Press, Berkeley, 1992—. Mem. vestry, bd. dirs. St. Mark's Episcopal Ch., Berkeley, 1993—. Democrat. Avocations: theatre, reading, cross-country skiing. Office: U Calif Press 2120 Berkeley Way Berkeley CA 94720

WEIDMAN, GREGORY ROWLETT, curator, historic interiors consultant; b. Tampa, Fla., Nov. 9, 1950; d. Henry Sheip and Gregory (Rowlett) Weidman; m. John Michael Flanigan, June 8, 1985. B.A., Hollins Coll., 1972; postgrad. U. Del., 1972-74. Curator Hist. Annapolis, Inc., Md., 1974-77, Cloister's Children's Mus., Balt., 1977; curator of furniture Md. Hist. Soc., Balt., 1978—; cons. Govt. House, Md.'s Gov.'s Mansion, Annapolis, 1979—; cons. numerous local hist. socs., house museums in Md., 1974—; lectr. Johns Hopkins U., Winterthur Mus., Goucher Coll. Author: Furniture in Maryland, 1740-1940, 1984; contbr. articles to profl. jours. Vol. Jr. League of Balt., 1981—. Mem. Am. Assn. Museums, Soc. Winterthur Grads., Decorative Arts Soc. Democrat. Episcopalian. Office: Maryland Hist Soc 201 W Monument St Baltimore MD 21201-4674

WEIDMAN, HAZEL HITSON, anthropologist, educator; b. Taft, Calif., Aug. 3, 1923; d. Frederick Dhu and Estell M. (Griesemer) Hitson; m. William H. Weidman, Sept. 9, 1960; children: William, Charles. B.S. in Social Anthropology, Northwestern U., 1951; A.M. (Thomas Dana Scholar in Social Anthropology), Radcliffe Coll., 1957, Ph.D. (USPHS fellow), 1959. Staff anthropologist Mass. Dept. of Pub. Health, Boston, 1959-60; cons. social sci. USPHS, Washington, 1960, Calif. Dept. Pub. Health, 1964; asst. prof. sociology and anthropology Coll. of William and Mary, Williamsburg, Va., 1964-65; asst. prof. social anthropology dept. psychiatry U. Ala. Med. Center, Birmingham, 1965-67; asso. research fellow Social Sci. Research Inst., U. Hawaii, Honolulu, 1967-68; assoc. prof. social anthropology dept. psychiatry U. Miami Sch. Medicine, Miami, 1968-72; prof. U. Miami Sch. Medicine, 1972-89, prof. emerita, 1989—; staff anthropologist and sr. social scientist, 1979-81, dir. Office Transcultural Edn. and Research, 1981-89, ret. 1990; assoc. prof. dept. anthropology U. Miami, Coral Gables, 1968-72, prof., 1972-77; Cons. social sci. U. Ala. Hosps. and Clinics, Birmingham, 1965-67; cons. social anthropology Nat. Center for Health Services Research and Devel., 1970-71; social sci. cons. Am. Found. Blind, 1973-76; cons. to Miccosukee Indian tribe and sec. higher edn. exec. com. Miccosukee Corp., 1978-82; mental health research edn. rev. com. NIMH, 1980-84; mem. vis. com. So. Assn. Colls. and Schs., 1980; mem. med. adv. bd. Ednl. Film Prodn., Riverside, Calif., 1969-72; dir. programs in cross-cultural tng. health profls., 1981-89. Founding editor: Med. Anthropology Newsletter, 1968-71; Contbr. articles and book revs. on social anthropology to profl. jours.; contbr. book chpts. on social anthropology. Mem. nat. adv. com. for cross-cultural demonstration project, Epilepsy Found. Am., 1985-89; mem. nat. adv. council Transcultural Nursing Rsch. Inst. U. Miami, 1986-89. Am. Philos. Soc. research grantee, 1965; Commonwealth Fund research grantee, 1971-73; Continuation grantee, 1973-75; State of Fla. Community Hosp. Edn. Council research and tng. grantee, 1979-81. Fellow Soc. Applied Anthropology, Am. Anthrop. Assn. (chmn. steering com. group for med. anthropology 1967-69, mem. com. on membership 1968-70, chmn. organizing com. group for med. anthropology 1969-70); mem. So. Anthrop. Soc., Assn. for Behavioral Scis. and Med. Edn., Soc. for Med. Anthropology, Council on Anthropology and Edn., Soc. Anthropology of Visual Communication, Soc. Psychol. Anthropology (mem. bd. dirs. 1979-81), Assn. Anthropology and Gerontology, World Federn. Mental Health. Mental World Future Soc., Phi Beta Kappa. Home: 58 Park St Camden ME 04843-2012

WEIDMAN, JEROME, author; b. N.Y.C., Apr. 4, 1913; s. Joseph and Annie (Falkovitz) W.; m. Peggy Wright, 1943; children: Jeffrey, John Whitney. Ed., CCNY, 1930-33, Washington Sq. Coll., N.Y.C., 1933-34, N.Y.U. Law Sch., 1934-37. Author: (novel) I Can Get It for You Wholesale, 1937, (novel) What's in It for Me?, 1938; (short stories) The Horse that Could Whistle Dixie, 1939; (travel) Letter of Credit, 1940; (novel) I'll Never Go There Any More, 1941, (novel) The Lights Around the Shore, 1943, (novel) Too Early To Tell, 1946; (short stories) The Captain's Tiger, 1947; (novel) The Price is Right, 1949, (novel) The Hand of the Hunter, 1951, (novel) The Third Angel, 1953; (essays) Traveler's Cheque, 1954; (novel) Give Me Your Love, 1954, (novel) Your Daughter, Iris, 1955; (short stories) A Dime A Throw, 1957; (novel) The Enemy Camp, 1958; (play) Fiorello!, 1959; (novel) Before You Go, 1960; (play) Tenderloin, 1961; (short stories) My Father Sits In The Dark, 1961; (novel) The Sound of Bow Bells, 1962; (play) I Can Get It For You Wholesale, 1962; (essays) Back Talk, 1963; (short stories) Nine Stories, 1964; (novel) Word Of Mouth, 1964; (short stories) The Death of Dickie Draper, 1965; (novel) Other People's Money, 1968; (novel) The Center of The Action, 1969; (play) Ivory Tower, 1969, (play) Asterisk, 1969; (novel) Fourth Street East, 1971, (novel) Last Respects, 1972, (novel) Tiffany Street, 1974, (novel) The Temple, 1976, (novel) A Family Fortune, 1978; (novel) Counsellors-at-Law, 1980, (autobiography) Praying For Rain, 1986. Co-recipient Pulitzer prize in drama for play Fiorello!, 1960; recipient Antoinette Perry award, N.Y. Drama Critics Circle award. Mem. Authors League Am. (pres. 1969-74). Home: 1230 Park Ave New York NY 10128

WEIDNER, DONALD J., geophysicist educator; b. Dayton, Ohio, Apr. 26, 1945; s. Virgil Raymond and Aletha Winifred Weidner; m. Deborah Mary Ray, April 13, 1968; children: Raymond V., Jennifer L. AB in Physics cum laude, Harvard, 1967; PhD in Geophysics, Mass. Inst. Tech., 1972. Asst prof. SUNY, Stony Brook, N.Y., 1972-77, assoc. prof., 1977-82, prof. geophysics, 1982—; dir. Mineral Physics Inst., SUNY, 1988—, Ctr. for High Pressure Rsch. SUNY, 1991—. Am. Geophysical Union fellow, 1981; recipient James B. Macelwane award Am. Geophysical Union, 1981. Achievements include building (with others) the high pressure facility at Stony Brook SUNY; large volume high pressure studies with synchrotron radiation; determining the equation of state of earth materials; phase stability fields of minerals and has pioneered the use of this system to determine the yield strength of these materials; design team leader for the large volume experiments that the GeoCars program is preparing for the Advanced Photon Source. Office: SUNY Sci & Tech Ctr High Pressure Rsch Dept Earth & Space Scis Stony Brook NY 11794

WEIDNER, EDWARD WILLIAM, university chancellor, political scientist; b. Mpls., July 7, 1921; s. Peter Clifford and Lillian (Halbe) W.; m. Jean Elizabeth Blomquist, Mar. 23, 1944; children: Nancy Louise, Gary Richard, Karen, William. BA magna cum laude, U. Minn., 1942, MA, 1943, PhD, 1946; postgrad., U. Wis., 1943-45; LHD (hon.), No. Mich. U., 1969; PhD (hon.), Linköping U., Sweden, 1975. Staff mem. Nat. Mcpl. League, 1944, research assoc., 1944-45; cons. govts. div. U.S. Bur. Census, 1945; statistician U.S. Bur. Census, Washington, 1946; lectr. U. Wis., Madison, 1945; instr. U. Minn., Mpls., 1945-47, asst. prof., 1947-49, asst. dir. research in inter-govtl. relations, 1946-53; asst. prof. UCLA, 1949-50; faculty Mich. State U., East Lansing, 1950-62, from assoc. prof. dir. govtl. research bur., to prof. polit. sci., 1952-62, chmn. polit. sci. dept., 1952-57; coordinator, chief adviser Vietnam Project, 1955-57; dir. Inst. Research on Overseas Programs, 1957-61; vice chancellor E.W. Ctr., 1962-65; prof. polit. sci. dir. ctr. for devel. change U. Ky., Lexington, 1965-67; chancellor U. Wis., Green Bay, 1966-86, prof. polit. sci., 1966-89; chancellor prof. emeritus, prof. emeritus, 1989—; dir. Cofrin Arboretum, 1986-89; project dir. Edward W. Weidner Ctr. for Performing Arts U. Wis., Green Gay, 1987-92; bd. dirs. Univ. Bank, Green Bay; cons. Fgn. Ops. Adminstrn., Vietnam, 1954-55, Baltimore County (Md.) Reorgn. Commn., 1953-54, Ford Found., Pakistan, 1956, Nat. Assn. Fgn. Student Advisers, 1959-60, Pres.'s Task Force Fgn. Econ. Assistance, 1961, Dept. State, 1962-63, AID, 1964-65, Lees Coll., 1971-72, Internat. Inst. Mcpl. Clks., 1992—; mem. Gov. Mich. Commn. Inter-Govtl. Relations,

1954-55, UN Univ. Council, 1974-80. Author: (with William Anderson) American Government, 1951, State and Local Government, 1951, (with others) The International Programs of American Universities, 1958, Intergovernmental Relations as Seen by Public Officials, 1960, (with William Anderson, Clara Penniman) Government for the Fifty States, 1960, The World Role of Universities, 1962, Technical Assistance in Public Administration Overseas, 1964; editor: Development Administration in Asia, 1970. Mem. Wis. Gov.'s Commn. on UN, 1975-81; trustee Prairie Sch., 1969-91, mem. adv. bd., 1991—; bd. dirs. Inst. for Shipboard Edn., 1976-89, Lab. Ornithology, Cornell U., 1992—; chmn. adv. bd. Lakeland chpt. ARC, 1981-84; mem. N.Am. adv. group UN Environ. Programme, 1983-90; bd. advisers Nature Conservancy Wis., 1984-91; bd. dirs. Heritage Hill Found., 1987-92, 95—, pres., 1991-92; bd. dirs. Family Svc. Assn., 1988-93; chmn. Brown County Cultural Coun., 1991—; mem. nat. coun. ASPA, 1947-50; mem. internat. coun. UN U., 1974-80; bd. dirs. Am. Coun. on Edn., 1971-74, sec. bd., 1971-72; mem. nat. coun. Am. Polit. Sci. Assn., 1950-52. Recipient Outstanding Achievement award U. Minn., 1975. Mem. Assn. Am. Colls. (bd. dirs. 1978-80), Internat. Assn. Mcpl. Clks. Found., Nature Conservancy, Audubon Soc., Am. Birding Assn., Phi Beta Kappa, Pi Sigma Alpha. Home: 5953 N Shore Acres Rd New Franken WI 54229-9443

WEIDNER, RICHARD TILGHMAN, physicist, educator; b. Allentown, Pa., Mar. 31, 1921; s. Miles Percival and Mabel (Aichroth) W.; m. Jean Elizabeth Fritsch, June 28, 1947; children: Christopher, Allegra, Timothy. B.S. summa cum laude, Muhlenberg Coll., 1943; M.S., Yale U., 1943, Ph.D., 1948. Instr. physics Yale U., 1943-44; instr. Rutgers U., 1947-48, asst. prof., 1948-53, asso. prof., 1953-63, prof. physics 1963-88, prof. emeritus, 1988—; asst. dean Rutgers Coll., 1966-69, assoc. dean, 1969-77, acting dean, 1977-78; physicist U.S. Naval Research Lab., Washington, 1944-46. Author: (with R.L. Sells) Elementary Modern Physics, 3d edit, 1980, Elementary Classical Physics, 2d edit, 1973, Elementary Physics, Classical and Modern, 1975, (with H.Y. Carr) Physics from the Ground Up, 1971, Physics, 1985, rev. edit., 1988 (transls. in German, Spanish, Vietnamese); also articles in field; contbr. Physics sect. Ency. Brit., 15th edit, 1974; assoc. editor Jour. Internat. Trumpet Guild. Mem. Bd. Edn. Bridgewater Twp., N.J., 1957-63. Lt. (j.g.) USNR, 1944-45. Recipient Alumni Achievement award Muhlenberg Coll., 1994; Lindback award Rutgers U., 1984. Fellow Am. Phys. Soc.; mem. Internat. Trumpet Guild, Sigma Xi. Lutheran. Home: 1426 Calypso Ave Bethlehem PA 18018-4740 Office: 56 W Market St Bethlehem PA 18018-5734

WEIDNER, ROSWELL THEODORE, artist; b. Reading, Pa., Sept. 18, 1911; s. Harry and Amelia (Hughes) W.; m. Marilyn Kemp, Dec. 5, 1957; children: Roslyn, Janice. Student, Pa. Acad. Fine Arts, 1930-35, Barnes Found., 1933-35. sr. instr. Pa. Acad. Fine Arts, 1938—, Dawson metal, 1965, 72. One-man shows include Pa. Acad. Fine Arts, 1940, 60, 65, Reading Mus., 1961, William Penn Meml. Mus., Harrisburg, Pa., 1966, McCleaf Gallery, Phila., 1970, Newman Galleries, Phila., 1978, 87, Marion Locks Gallery, 1981, So. Alleghenies Mus. Art, Loretto, Pa., 1991, F.A.N. Gallery, Phila., 1995; represented in permanent collections Pa. Acad. Fine Arts, Phila. Mus. Art, Met. Mus. Art, Libr. Congress, U. Pa., Conn. State Libr., Hahnemann Hosp., Phila., Temple U., Phila. Maritime Mus., Free Libr. Phila., Smith Kline, Berwin Corp., Price Waterhouse, Nat. Assn. Broadcasters, Washington, Bell Atlantic Corp., Phila., Dauphin Deposit Bank and Trust Co., Harrisburg, Phila. Conv. Ctr.; work represented by F.A.N. Gallery; contbr. articles to profl. jours. Cresson Fgn. Travelling scholar, 1935-36; recipient Percy Owens award, 1975. Fellow Pa. Acad. Fine Arts (pres. 1955-70). Home: 612 Spruce St Philadelphia PA 19106-4114 Office: Pa Acad Fine Arts Broad and Cherry Sts Philadelphia PA 19102 Studio: 116 S 7th St Philadelphia PA 19106

WEIERSTALL, RICHARD PAUL, pharmaceutical chemist; b. Jersey City, N.J., Nov. 5, 1942; s. William August and Emily Lois (Haughey) W.; m. Gail Janet Thomsen, Aug. 17, 1968; children: Eric, Kurt, Karen. BS, Rutgers U., 1966, MS, 1969; PhD, U. Calif., San Francisco, 1973. Unit head drug metabolism Sandoz Pharm., East Hanover, N.J., 1973-74; dir. tech. svc. Banner Gelatin Products, Chatsworth, Calif., 1974-76; v.p. tech. svc. Banner Gelatin Prod., Chatsworth, Calif., 1976-81; dir. pharm. sci. Ayerst Labs Inc., Rouses Point, N.Y., 1981-87; asst. v.p. Wyeth Ayerst Rsch., Rouses Point, 1987—. Mem. Am. Assn. Pharm. Sci., Am. Pharm. Assn. Home: 7 Stewart St Rouses Point NY 12979-1511

WEIGAND, JAMES GARY, utility company executive, former military officer; b. Sheridan, Wyo., Aug. 11, 1935; s. Harold Frederick and Maribel (Ragan) W.; m. Mary Alice Moosey, Apr. 21, 1962; children: Janet, Gretchen, Caroline. BS, U.S. Naval Acad., 1958; MS, U. Wash., Seattle, 1962, PhD, 1964. Commd. ensign USN, 1958, advanced through grades to comdr., 1973, nuclear submarine officer, served in Vietnam; ret., 1978; asst. to chmn. Gulf States Utitlites Co., Beaumont, Tex., 1978-79, v.p., 1979-86; pres., chief exec. officer Vt. Yankee Nuclear Power Co., Brattleboro, 1986—, also bd. dirs.; bd. dirs. Seyton Inc., Tacoma. Trustee BMH Inc. Mem. Assoc. Industries Vt. (bd. dirs. 1987—), Am. Nuclear Soc. (regional v.p. 1982-83). Episcopalian. Avocation: tennis. Office: Vt Yankee Nuclear Power Corp Ferry Rd Brattleboro VT 05301

WEIGAND, WILLIAM KEITH, bishop; b. Bend, Oreg., May 23, 1937. Ed., Mt. Angel Sem., St. Benedict, Oreg., St. Edward's Sem. and St. Thomas Sem., Kenmore, Wash. Bishop Diocese Salt Lake City, 1980—; Ordained priest Roman Cath. Ch., 1963. Office: Pastoral Ctr 27 C St Salt Lake City UT 84103-2302*

WEIGEL, JOHN J., lawyer; b. New Orleans, Feb. 4, 1932; s. George Edward and Marian Rose (Martin) W.; m. Barbara Ann Laporte, July 9, 1955; children: Leslie Ann, John J Jr., Lynn Ann, Guy Edward. LLB, Tulane U., 1956. Bar: La. 1956, U.S. Dist. Ct. (ea., mid., we. dists.) La. 1959, U.S. Ct. Appeals (5th cir) 1959, U.S. Supreme Ct. Law clk. La. Supreme Ct., New Orleans, 1958-59; from assoc. to sr. ptnr. Jones, Walker, Waechter, Poitevent, Carrere & Denegre, New Orleans, 1959—. Pers. bd. Jefferson Parish, La., 1974-83; bd. dirs. La. Civil Svc. League, New Orleans, 1975—. Fellow Am. Coll. Trial Lawyers; mem. ABA, Am. Bd. Trial Advocates, La. Bar Assn., New Orleans Bar Assn. Office: Jones Walker Waechter Poitevent Carrere & Denegre 201 Saint Charles Ave New Orleans LA 70170-1000

WEIGEL, PAUL HENRY, biochemistry educator, researcher, consultant; b. N.Y.C., Aug. 11, 1946; s. Helmut and Jeanne (Wakeman) W.; m. Nancy Shulman, June 15, 1968 (div. Dec. 1987); 1 child, Dana J.; m. Janet Oka, May 17, 1992. BA in Chemistry, Cornell U., 1968; MS in Biochemistry, Johns Hopkins U., Balt., 1969, PhD in Biochemistry, 1975. NIH postdoctoral fellow Johns Hopkins U., Balt., 1975-78; asst. prof. U. Tex. Med. Br., Galveston, Tex., 1978-82, assoc. prof., 1982-87; prof. biochemistry and cell biology U. Tex. Med. Br., Galveston, 1987-94, vice chmn. dept. human biol. chemistry and genetics, 1990-93, acting chmn. dept. human biology, chemistry and genetics, 1992-93; prof., chmn. dept. biochemistry and molecular biology U. Okla. Health Scis Ctr., Oklahoma City, 1994—; mem. NIH Pathobiochemistry Study Sect., Washington, 1985-87; cons. Teltech, Mpls., 1995—. Contbr. articles to profl. jours.; patentee in field. Treas. Bayou Chateau Neighborhood Assn., Dickinson, Tex., 1981-83, v.p., 1983-84, pres., 1984-86. With U.S. Army, 1969-71. Grantee NIH, 1979—, Office Naval Rsch., 1983-87, Tex. Biotech., 1989-94; recipient Disting. Tchr. award U. Tex. Med. Br., 1989, Disting. Rsch. award, 1989. Mem. Am. Chem. Soc., Am. Soc. Cell Biology, Am. Soc. Biochemistry and Molecular Biology. Democrat. Lutheran. Avocations: racquetball, basketball card collecting, poetry, camping. Home: 817 Hollowdale Edmond OK 73003 Office: U Okla Health Scis Ctr Dept Biochem & Mol Biology BMSB Rm 860 Oklahoma City OK 73190

WEIGEL, RAINER R., lawyer; b. Thalheim, Germany, Nov. 22, 1933. BA, Lake Forest Coll., 1955; JD, U. Mich., 1958. Bar: Ill. 1958, Fla. 1977, D.C. 1989. Ptnr. McDermott Will & Emery, Miami, Fla. Contbr. articles. to profl. jours. Mem. ABA, Ill. State Bar, Chgo. Bar Assn., Fla. Bar Assn., D.C. Bar Assn., Am. Coll. Trust and Estate Counsel. Office: McDermott Will & Emery 700 Brickell Ave Miami FL 33131-2804 also: McDermott Will & Emery 227 W Monroe St Chicago IL 60606

WEIGEL, STANLEY ALEXANDER, judge; b. Helena, Mont., Dec. 9, 1905; s. Louis and Jennie (Hepner) W.; m. Anne Kauffman, Apr. 21, 1940; children: Jane Anne, Susan Mary. AB, Stanford U., 1926, JD, 1928. Bar: Calif. 1928. Pvt. practice law San Francisco, 1928-62; judge U.S. Dist. Ct. (no. dist.) Calif., 1962 now sr. judge; non-resident lectr. Stanford Law Sch., 1952—; mem. Jud. Panel on Multidist. Litigation, 1968-79; mem. temporary emergency Ct. Appeals of U.S., 1980—; pres. Internat. Hospitality Ctr. Bay Area, 1959-68, Nat. Council for Community Services to Internat. Visitors, 1972-73; adv. gov. Calif. on Automobile Accident Commn., 1959; chmn. bd. visitors Stanford Law Sch., 1958-63; trustee World Affairs Council No. Calif., 1960—, pres., 1973-74; chmn. Ford Found. vis. com. to study behavioral sci. depts. Stanford U., 1956-57; mem. jud. conf. com. on jud. ethics, 1982-87. Served to lt. USNR, 1943-45. Decorated chevalier Order Leopold II (Belgium). Mem. Delta Sigma Rho, Phi Alpha Delta, Sigma Delta Chi. Office: US Ct Appeals PO Box 36060 450 Golden Gate Ave San Francisco CA 94102-3400

WEIGEND, GUIDO GUSTAV, geographer, educator; b. Zeltweg, Austria, Jan. 2, 1920; came to U.S., 1939, naturalized, 1943; s. Gustav F. and Paula (Sorgo) W.; m. Areta Kelbie, June 26, 1947 (dec. 1993); children: Nina, Cynthia, Kenneth. B.S., U. Chgo., 1942, M.S., 1946, Ph.D., 1949. With OSS, 1943-45; with mil. intelligence U.S. War Dept., 1946; instr. geography U. Ill., Chgo., 1946-47; instr. then asst. prof. geography Beloit Coll., 1947-49; asst. prof. geography Rutgers U., 1949-51, assoc. prof., 1951-57, prof., 1957-76, acting dept. chmn., 1951-52, chmn. dept., 1953-67, assoc. dean, 1972-76; dean Coll. Liberal Arts, Prof. geography Ariz. State U., Tempe, 1976-84, prof. geography, 1976-89; ret., 1989; Fulbright lectr. U. Barcelona, 1960-61; vis. prof. geography Columbia U., 1963-67, NYU, 1967, U. Colo., summer 1968, U. Hawaii, summer 1969; liaison rep. Rutgers U. to UN, 1950-52; invited by Chinese Acad. Scis. to visit minority areas in Chinese Cent. Asia, 1988; mem. U.S. nat. com. Internat. Geog. Union, 1951-58, 61-65; chmn. Conf. on Polit. and Social Geography, 1968-69. Author articles, monographs, bulls. for profl. jours.; contbr.: (4th edit.) A Geography of Europe, 1977; geog. editor-in-chief: Odyssey World Atlas, 1966. Bd. adjustment Franklin Twp., N.J., 1959; mem. Highland Park (N.J.) Bd. Edn., 1973-75, v.p., 1975; mem. Ariz. Coun. on Humanities and Pub. Policy, 1976-80; vice chmn. Phoenix Com. on Fgn. Rels., 1976-79, chmn., 1979-81; mem. exec. com. Fedn. Pub. Programs in Humanities, 1977-82; bd. dirs. Coun. Colls. Arts and Scis., 1980-83, Phoenix Chamber Music Soc., 1995—; commr. N. Cen. Assn. Colls. and Schs., 1976-80, bd. dirs. commn. on instns. of higher edn., 1980-83. Research fellow Office Naval Research, 1952-55, Rutgers Research Council, 1970-71; grantee Social Sci. Research Council, 1956, Ford Found., 1966, Am. Philos. Soc., 1970-71, German Acad. Exchange Service, 1984; Fulbright travel grantee Netherlands, 1970-71. Mem. Assn. Am. Geographers (chmn. N.Y. Met. div. 1955-56, editorial bd. 1955-59, mem. coun. 1965-66, chmn. N.Y.-N.J. div. 1965-66), Am. Geog. Soc., Sigma Xi (pres. Ariz. State U. chpt. 1989-91). Home: 2094 E Golf Ave Tempe AZ 85282-4046 Office: Ariz State U Dept Geography Tempe AZ 85287

WEIGER, JOHN GEORGE, foreign language educator; b. Dresden, Germany, Feb. 6, 1933; came to U.S., 1938, naturalized, 1945; s. Willy and Elisabeth (Prinz) W.; m. Leslie Lawrence Carpenter, Dec. 28, 1955; children: Robert Boyden, Mark Owen, Heidi Elaine. B.A., Middlebury Coll., 1955; M.A., U. Colo., 1957; Ph.D. (NDEA fellow), Ind. U., 1966. Instr. U. Colo., Boulder, 1955-57, Lawrence Coll., Appleton, Wis., 1957-58; instr. Romance langs. U. Vt., Burlington, 1958-62, asst. prof., 1964-67, assoc. prof., 1973, prof., 1973—, vice chmn. Romance lang. dept., 1964-68; chmn., 1994-95; asst. dean U. Vt. (Coll. Arts and Scis.), Burlington, 1968-69, assoc. dean, 1969-71, dean, 1971-76; instnl. rep. for Rhodes scholarships, Danforth fellowships, Turrell Fund scholarships, 1971-76; program chmn. George Aiken lecture series, 1975; vis. lectr. U. Bologna, 1978, 87, U. Venice, Italy, 1987, U. Valencia, Spain, 1987; Cervantes lectr. Fordham U., 1990; cons. Eirik Borve, Inc., 1979—. Author: Introduction to the Youthful Deeds of the Cid, 1969, The Valencian Dramatists of Spain's Golden Age, 1976, Cristobal de Virues, 1978, Hacia la Comedia, 1978, The Individuated Self: Cervantes and the Emergence of the Individual, 1979, The Substance of Cervantes, 1985, In the Margins of Cervantes, 1988; editor: Las Hazañas del Cid, 1981, La Infelice Marcela, 1985; mem. editorial bd.: Bull. of Comediantes, 1978—; editorial bd.: Hispania, 1993—; contbr. articles to profl. jours., also chpts. to books. U. Vt. Faculty Research fellow, 1967, 83, 86; Am. Council Learned Socs. grantee, 1978; U. Vt. Univ. scholar for the humanities, 1985-86. Mem. MLA (chmn. comedia sect. 1970-71), Renaissance Soc. Am., Am. Assn. Tchrs. Spanish and Portuguese (chmn. com. hon. mems. and fellows 1984), The Comediantes, Internat. Assn. Hispanists, Cervantes Soc. Am., Phi Beta Kappa, Phi Sigma Iota, Phi Eta Sigma (hon.). Home: 8 Woodbine Rd Shelburne VT 05482-7268 Office: U Vermont 506A Waterman Bldg Burlington VT 05405

WEIGERT, ANDREW JOSEPH, sociology educator; b. N.Y.C., Apr. 8, 1934; s. Andrew Joseph and Marie Teresa (Kollmer) W.; m. Kathleen Rose Maas, Aug. 31, 1967; children: Karen Rose, Sheila Marie. BA, St. Louis U., 1958, PhL, 1959, MA, 1960; BTh, Woodstock (Md.) Coll., 1964; PhD, U. Minn., 1968. NIMH trainee U. Minn., Mpls., 1965-67; asst. prof. sociology U. Notre Dame, Ind., 1968-72, assoc. prof., 1972-76, prof., 1976—, chmn. dept., 1980-84, 88-89; vis. assoc. prof. Yale U., New Haven, 1973-74; participant nat. and regional profl. meetings. Co-author: Family Socialization, 1974, Interpretive Sociology, 1978, Society and Identity, 1986; author: Everyday Life, 1981, Social Psychology, 1983, Life and Society, 1983, Mixed Emotions, 1991; adv. editor various sociology jours.; contbr. over 50 articles to profl. jours., chpts. to books; translator various works. Grantee NSF, 1969. Mem. Am Sociol. Assn., Soc. for Study Symbolic Interaction, Soc. for Sci. Study Religion, Assn. for Sociology Religion. Avocation: woodlot management. Office: U Notre Dame Dept Sociology Notre Dame IN 46556

WEIGHT, GEORGE DALE, banker, educator; b. Salt Lake City, Mar. 25, 1934; s. Sheldon J. and Florence (Noe) W.; m. Carilee Kesler, June 16, 1959; children: Camille, Kristene, Denise, Marcie, Nancy. BS, U. Utah, 1961; MS, U. Oreg., 1965, PhD, 1968. Instr. U. Oreg., Eugene, 1963-68; economist Fed. Res. Bank, Cleve., 1968-69; asst. v.p. fiscal ops. Fed. Res. Bank, Pitts., 1969-71; v.p. bank ops. Fed. Home Loan Bank Bd., Pitts., 1971-73; exec. v.p. Syracuse Savs. Bank, N.Y., 1972-73, pres., chief exec. officer, 1973-83; chmn., chief exec. officer Ben Franklin Fed. Savs. and Loan Assn., Portland, Oreg., 1983-90; dean Atkinson Grad. Sch. Mgmt. Willamette U., Salem, Oreg., 1990—; adj. prof. Oreg. Grad. Inst. Sci. & Tech., 1994—, Syracuse U., 1974; chmn. bd. Savs. Banks Life Ins. Fund, N.Y.C., bd. dirs. Onondaga County Indsl. Devel. Agy., Fed. Res. Bank San Francisco, Portland Br., State Accident Ins. Fund, Fed. Home Loan Bank Seattle; chmn. Oreg. State Bd. Edn., 1991. Pres. Hiawatha coun. Boy Scouts Am., Syracuse, 1974-77; chmn. bd. Crouse-Irving Meml. Hosp., 1978-83; mem. Gov.'s Commn. Edn. Reforms, 1988, Oreg. State Bd. Edn., 1989-95, chmn., 1991-92; chmn. Associated Oreg. Industries Found., 1993—; pres. Canal Mus., bd. dirs. Oreg. Bus. Coun. Recipient Silver Beaver award Boy Scouts Am., 1978; recipient Vol. of Yr. award Am. Heart Assn., 1980, Community Service award Rotary, Syracuse, 1982. Mem. Am. Fin. Assn., Arlington Club, Beta Gamma Sigma. Republican. Home: 16057 NW Claremont Dr Portland OR 97229 Office: Willamette U Atkinson Grad Sch Mgmt 900 State St Salem OR 97301-3930

WEIGLE, ROBERT EDWARD, mechanical engineer, research director; b. Shiloh, Pa., Apr. 27, 1927; s. William Edgar and Hilda Geraldine (Fans) W.; m. Mona Jean Long, Aug. 13, 1949; 1 child, Geoffrey Robert. BCE in Structures, Rensselaer Poly. Inst., 1951, MS in Mechanics, 1957, PhD in Mechanics, 1959. Registered profl. engr., N.Y., Pa. Assoc. rsch. scientist Rensselaer Poly. Inst., Troy, N.Y., 1955-59; chief scientist Watervliet Arsenal, 1959-77; technical dir. U.S. Army and Armament R & D Command, 1977-82; dir. U.S. Army Rsch. Office, 1982-88; dir. phys. sci. lab. N.Mex. State U. Las Cruces, 1988—; tech. dir., then dir. Benet Weapons Lab., 1959-77; chmn. numerous DoD and Army coms. Contbr. articles to profl. jours. Recipient Meritorious Civilian Service award for cannon breech design U.S. Army, 1964, U.S. Army Materiel Command citation for engineering achievement in Vietnam, 1966, Presidential citation for development of cannon firing simulator, 1965, Exceptional Civilian Svc. medal U.S. Army; elected to Am. Acad. of Mechanics, 1972. Mem. NSPE, ASME, AAAS, SEM Am. Soc. Testing Materials, Am. Def. Preparedness Assn. (Crozier prize 1985), Nat. Conf. Advancement of Rsch. (program com. 1987, exec. conf. com. host rep. NCAR-46 ann. conf. 1992), Army Sci. Bd. (chmn. rsch.

and new initiatives group 1991), Soc. Exptl. Mechanics, Tau Beta Pi, Chi Epsilon, Sigma Xi. Office: N Mex State U Physical Sci Lab PO Box 30002 Las Cruces NM 88003

WEIGLE, WILLIAM OLIVER, immunologist, educator; b. Monaca, Pa., Apr. 28, 1927; s. Oliver James and Caroline Ellen (Alsing) W.; m. Kathryn May Lotz, Sept. 4, 1948 (div. 1980); children—William James, Cynthia Kay; m. Carole G. Romball, Sept. 24, 1983. B.S., U. Pitts., 1950, M.S., 1951, Ph.D., 1956. Research assoc. pathology U. Pitts., 1955-58, asst. prof. immunochemistry, 1959-61; assoc. div. exptl. pathology Scripps Rsch. Inst., La Jolla, Calif., 1961-62, assoc. mem. div., 1962-63; mem. dept. exptl. pathology Scripps Rsch. Inst., La Jolla, 1963-74, mem. dept. immunopathology, 1974-82, chmn. dept. immunopathology, 1980-82, mem., vice chmn. dept. immunology, 1982-85, mem. dept. immunology, 1982—, chmn. dept. immunology, 1985-87; adj. prof. biology U. Calif., San Diego; McLaughlin vis. prof. U. Tex., 1977; mem. adv. bd. Immunetech Pharms., San Diego, 1988—; cons. in field. Author: Natural and Acquired Immunologic Unresponsiveness, 1967; assoc. editor: Clin. and Exptl. Immunology, 1972-79; Jour. Exptl. Medicine, 1974-84; Immunochemistry 1964-71; Procs. Soc. Exptl. Biology and Medicine, 1967-72; Jour. Immunology, 1967-71; Infection and Immunity, 1969-86, assoc. editor; Immunology and Infectious Disease, 1987—; sect. editor: Jour. Immunology, 1971-75; editorial bd.: Contemporary Topics in Immunobiology, 1971-93; Cellular Immunology, 1984—; contbr. articles to profl. jours. Trustee Lovelace Med. Found., Albuquerque. With USNR, 1945-46. Pub. Health Research fellow, Nat. Inst. Neurol. Diseases and Blindness, 1956-59; NIH sr. research fellow, 1959-61, Research Career award, 1962. Mem. Am. Assn. Immunologists, Am. Soc. Exptl. Pathology (Parke Davis award 1967), Am. Soc. Microbiology, N.Y. Acad. Scis., Am. Assn. Pathologists, Soc. Exptl. Biology and Medicine. Home: 688 Via De La Vly Solana Beach CA 92075-2461 Office: Scripps Rsch Inst Dept Immunology IMM9 10666 N Torrey Pines Rd La Jolla CA 92037-1027

WEIGLEY, RUSSELL FRANK, history educator; b. Reading, Pa., July 2, 1930; s. Frank Francis and Meta Beulah (Rohrbach) W.; m. Emma Eleanor Seifrit, July 27, 1963; children: Jared Francis Guldin, Catherine Emma Rohrbach. BA, Albright Coll., 1952; MA, U. Pa., 1953, PhD, 1956; HLD (hon.), Albright Coll., 1978. Instr. history U. Pa., Phila., 1956-58; asst. prof. Drexel Inst. Tech., Phila., 1958-60, assoc. prof., 1960-62; assoc. prof. Temple U., Phila., 1962-64, prof. history, 1964-85, Disting. Univ. prof., 1985—; vis. prof. Dartmouth Coll., Hanover, N.H., 1967-68; U.S. Army vis. prof. mil. history rsch. U.S. Army War Coll., U.S. Army Mil. History Rsch. Collection, Carlisle Barrakcs, Pa., 1973-74; pres. Am. Mil. Inst., Washington, 1975-76. Author: Quartermaster General of the Union Army: A Biography of M.C. Meigs, 1959, Towards an American Army: Military Thought from Washington to Marshall, 1962, History of the United States Army, 1967, 84, The Partisan War: The South Carolina Campaign of 1780-82, 1970, The American Way of War, 1973, Eisenhower's Lieutenants, 1981 (Athenaeum of Phila. Spl. award for Nonfiction by a Phila. Author, 1983), The Age of Battles: The Quest for Decisive Warfare from Breitenfeld to Waterloo, 1991; editor: The American Military: Readings in the History of the Military in American Society, 1969, New Dimensions in Military History, 1976, Philadelphia: A 300-Year History, 1982. Mem. Dept. of the Army Hist. Adv. Commn., Washington, 1976-79, 88—, Pa. Hist. Records Adv. Com., Harrisburg, 1977-79; bd. dirs. Masonic Libr., Mus. of Pa., The Grand Lodge F & A.M. of Pa., Phila., 1990—. Penrose Fund grantee Am. Philos. Soc., 1958; fellow John Simon Guggenheim Meml. Found., 1969-70; recipient Samuel Eliot Morison prize Am. Mil. Inst., 1989. Mem. Hist. Soc. Pa. (vice chmn. 1989-93, councilor 1983-89, 92—), Pa. Hist. Assn. (pres. 1975-78, v.p. 1967-75, coun. 1967—, editor jour. 1962-67), Am. Hist. Assn., Orgn. Am. Historians, Soc. Mil. Hist. (Disting. Book award 1992), So. Hist. Assn., Soc. Am. Historians Inc., Interuniv. Seminar on Armed Forces and Soc. Mem. Am. Philos. Soc. Democrat. Unitarian. Home: 327 S Smedley St Philadelphia PA 19103-6717 Office: Temple U Dept History Philadelphia PA 19122

WEIGMANN, HANS-DIETRICH H., chemist; b. Rostock, Germany, Jan. 12, 1930; m. Christa Weigmann; 2 children, Stefanie, Jessica. Vordiplom. in Chemistry, U. Hamburg, Germany, 1954, Diplom. in Organic Chemistry, 1958; Dr. rer. nat. in Organic Chemistry, Technische Hochschule, Aachen, Germany, 1960. Scientist German Wool Rsch. Inst., 1960-61; postdoctoral fellow Textile Rsch. Inst., Princeton, N.J., 1961-63, sr. scientist, 1963-67, assoc. dir. chem. rsch., 1967-70, assoc. dir. rsch., 1970-93, v.p. rsch., 1993-94; rsch. assoc. Textile Rsch. Inst., 1995—; com. tech. programs 4th Internat. Wool Textile Conf., 1969-70; chmn. Gordon Rsch. Conf. Fiber Sci., 1975. Co-recipient Best Paper award Textile Chemist and Colorist, 1982, Lit. award Soc. Cosmetic Chemists, 1986. Mem. Am. Chem. Soc. (divsn. cellulose, wood and fiber chemistry, divsn. organic coatings and plastics chemistry, chmn. symposium 1970, Internat. Textile Sci. Can. 1982), Am. Assn. Textile Chemists and Colorists (com. RA91 applied dyeing theory, exec. com. rsch., com. RA33, colorfastness to atmospheric contaminants, Internat. Dyeing Symposium 1983, Millson award com. 1987, Olney Medal for achievement in textile chemistry 1990). Office: Textile Research Institute PO Box 625 Princeton NJ 08542*

WEIHAUPT, JOHN GEORGE, geosciences educator, scientist, university administrator; b. La Crosse, Wis., Mar. 5, 1930; s. John George and Gladys Mae (Ash) W.; m. Audrey Mae Reis, Jan. 28, 1961. Student, St. Norbert Coll., De Pere, Wis., 1948-49; B.S., U. Wis., 1952, M.S., 1953; M.S., U. Wis.-Milw., 1971; Ph.D., U. Wis., 1973. Exploration geologist Am. Smelting & Refining Co., Nfld., 1953, Anaconda Co., Chile, S.Am., 1956-57; seismologist United Geophys. Corp., 1958; geophysicist Arctic Inst. N.Am., Antarctica, 1958-60, Geophys. and Polar Research Center, U. Wis., Antarctica, 1960-63; dir. participating Coll. and Univ. program, chmn. dept. phys. and biol. sci. U.S. Armed Forces Inst., Dept. Def., 1963-73; assoc. dean for acad. affairs Sch. Sci., Ind. U.-Purdue U., Indpls., 1973-78; prof. geology Sch. Sci., Ind. U.-Purdue U., 1973-78; asst. dean (Grad. Sch., prof. geoscis. Purdue U.), 1975-78; prof. geology, assoc. acad. v.p., dean grad. studies and research, v.p. Univ. Research Found., San Jose (Calif.) State U., 1978-82; vice chancellor for acad. affairs U. Colo., Denver, 1982-86, prof. geoscis., 1987—; Sci. cons. mem. sci. adv. bd. Holt Reinhart and Winston, Inc., 1967—; sci. editor, cons. McGraw-Hill Co., 1966—; hon. lectr. U. Wis., 1963-73; geol. cons., 1968—; editorial cons. John Wiley & Sons, 1968; editorial adv. bd. Dushkin Pub. Group, 1971—. Author: Exploration of the Oceans: An Introduction to Oceanography; mem. editorial bd. Internat. Jour. Interdisciplinary Cycle Research, Leiden; co-discoverer USARP Mountain Range (Arctic Inst. Mountain Range), in Victoria Land, Antarctica, 1960; discoverer Wilkes Land Meteorite Crater, Antarctic. Mem. Capital Community Citizens Assn.; mem. Madison Transp. Study Com., Found. for Internat. Energy Research and Tng.; U.S. com. for UN Univ.; mem. sci. council Internat. Center for Interdisciplinary Cycle Research; mem. Internat. Awareness and Leadership Council; mem. governing bd. Moss Landing Marine Labs.; bd. dirs. San Jose State U. Found. Served as 1st lt. AUS, 1953-55, Korea. Mr. Weihaupt in Antarctica named for him, 1966; recipient Madisonian medal for outstanding community service, 1973; Outstanding Cote Meml. award, 1974; Antarctic medal, 1968. Fellow Geol. Soc. Am., Explorers Club; mem. Antarctican Soc., Nat. Sci. Tchrs. Assn., Am. Geophys. Union, Internat. Council Corr. Edu., Soc. Am. Mil. Engrs., Wis. Alumni Assn., Soc. Study Biol. Rhythms, Internat. Soc. for Chronobiology, Marine Tech. Soc. (AAAS, Univ. Indsl. Adv. Council, Am. Council on Edn., Expdn. Polaire France (hon.), Found. for Study Cycles, Assn. Am. Geographers, Nat. Council Univ. Research Adminstrs., Soc. Research Adminstrs., Man-Environ. Communication Center, Internat. Union Geol. Scis., Internat. Geog. Union, Internat. Soc. Study Time, Community Council Pub. TV, Internat. Platform Assn., Ind., Midwest assns. grad. schs., Western Assn. Grad. Schs., Council Grad. Schs. in U.S., Wis. Alumni Assn. of San Francisco, Kiwanis, Carmel Racquet Club (Rinconada), The Ridge at Hiwan (Evergreen, Colo., pres. 1991-93). Home: 23906 Currant Dr Golden CO 80401-9243 Office: U Colo Campus Box 172 PO Box 173364 Denver CO 80204-5310

WEIHER, CLAUDINE JACKSON, government archives official; b. Kansas City, Mo., Nov. 24, 1941; d. Claude James and Evalyn (Smith) Jackson; m. Rodney Fredrick Weiher, Nov. 26, 1966. B.S., U. Mo., 1963; M.A., Georgetown U., 1967. With Nat. Archives and Records Adminstrn., Washington, 1966—, asst. archivist for mgmt. and adminstrn., 1982-86, acting dep. archivist, 1986-87, dep. archivist, 1987—. Avocation: sailing. Home: 813 E Capitol St SE Washington DC 20003-1347 Office: Nat Archives and Records Adminstrn Rm 106 Archives Bldg Washington DC 20408

WEIHING, JOHN LAWSON, plant pathologist, state senator; b. Rocky Ford, Colo., Feb. 26, 1921; s. Henry John and Clara Adele (Krull) W.; m. Shirley Ruth Wilkerson, Aug. 18, 1948; children: Lawson James, Martin Roy, Adell Ann, Warren John. BS in Agronomy, Colo. State U., 1942; MSc in Agronomy, U. Nebr., 1949, PhD in Botany and Plant Pathology, 1954. Instr. plant pathology U. Nebr., Lincoln, 1950-54, asst. prof., 1954-56, assoc. prof., 1956-60, prof., 1960-61, 62-64, 66-71, prof., interim chmn. plant pathology dept., 1961-62; prof., dir. Panhandle Rsch. and Extension Ctr. U. Nebr., Scottsbluff, 1971-84; with Alumni Office, Panhandle Found. U. Nebr., Scottsbluf, 1984-86; prof., chmn. plant sci. dept. Ataturk U., Erzurum, Turkey, 1964-66; mem. dist. 48 Nebr. Legislature, Lincoln, 1987-91; cons. Am. Hydroponics Systems, Inc., Grapevine, Tex., 1966-72. Creator U. Nebr. TV series Backyard Farmer, The Equation of Nature, 1959-60. Campaign chmn. United Way, Scottsbluff and Gering, Nebr., 1978. Lt. U.S. Army, 1942-46. Recipient Honor award Soil Conservation Soc. Am., 1982, Merit award Gamma Sigma Delta, 1977, Disting. Svc. award Nebr. Turfgrass Found., 1982, Nebr. Coop. Extension, 1970; named to Nebr. Hall Agrl. Achievement, 1987. Mem. Am. Phytopathol. Soc. (chmn. nat. extension com. 1963, pres. north cen. dir. 1971-72), AAAS, Am. Inst. Biol. Scis., Scottsbluff/Gering United C. of C. (pres. 1980-81), Rotary (bd. dirs. 1977-80), Elks. Republican. Presbyterian. Avocation: archeology. Home: 1605 Holly Dr Gering NE 69341-1954

WEIHRICH, HEINZ, management educator; came to U.S., 1959; s. Paul and Anna Weihrich; m. Ursula Weihrich, Aug. 3, 1963. BS, UCLA, 1966, MBA, 1967, PhD, 1973. Assoc. Grad. Sch. Mgmt. UCLA, 1968-73; from asst. to assoc. prof. Ariz. State U., Tempe, 1973-80; prof. of internat mgmt. U. San Francisco 1980—; internat. mgmt. cons. in field. Author: (with Harold Koontz and Cyril O'Donnell) Management, 7th edit., 1980, Japanese, Chinese and Indonesian edits., 8th edit., 1984, Singapore edit., 1985, Indonesian edit., 1986, Philippines edit., Bengali edit., 1989, Taiwan edit., 1985 (with Harold Koontz) 9th edit., 1988, Singapore edit., 1988, Chinese edit., 1989, Spanish edit., 1990, best-seller Spanish speaking world, Korean edit., 1988, 90, Pengurusan (Malaysian) edit., 1991, Management: A Global Perspective, 10th edit. (with Harold Koontz), 1993, Administração Fundamentos da Teoriae da Cienca, Primeiro Volume 1986, Administração Organização Planejamento e Controle, Segundo Volume, 1987, Administração Recursos Humanos: Desenvolvimento de Administradores, Terceiro Volume, 1987, (with Harold Koontz and Cyril O'Donnell) Management: A Book of Readings, 5th edit., 1980, (with George Odiorne and Jack Mendleson) Executive Skills: A Management by Objectives Approach, 1980, (with Harold Koontz) Measuring Managers--A Double-Barreled Approach, 1981, (with Harold Koontz and Cyril O'Donnell) Essentials of Management, 3d edit. 1982, Taiwan, Philippines, Chinese and India edits., 4th edit., 1986, Singapore edit., 1986, 5th edit., 1990, (with Harold Koontz) Manajamen, Jilid 1, Indonesian edit., 1987, Manajamen, Jilid 2, 1986, Elementos de Administracion, 3d edit., 1983, 4th edit. 1988, Management Excellence--Productivity through MBO, 1985, Singapore edit. 1986, Japanese edit., 1990, Greek edit., Produttivita con L' Italian edit. 1987, Administracion, 1985, Management Basiswissen, 1986, Excelencia Administrativa (Mex.), 1987, (with Harold Koontz and Cyril O'Donnell) Adminstracion Moderna, Tomo 1, 1986, (with Harold Koontz) Management: A Global Perspective, internat. edit., 1993, Administración: Una Perspectiva Global, 1994; editor: (with Jack Mendleson) Management: An MBO Approach, 1978; contbr. numerous articles and papers to profl. jours. Grantee Am. Mgmt. Assn., 1970. Fellow Internat. Acad. Mgmt., mem. Acad. Mgmt., Assn. Mgmt. Excellence (trustee 1985-87), Assn. Bus. Simulation Exptl. Learning, Acad. Internat. Bus., Beta Gamma Sigma, Sigma Iota Epsilon. Roman Catholic. Office: U San Francisco 2130 Fulton St San Francisco CA 94117-1080

WEIKART, DAVID POWELL, educational research foundation administrator; b. Youngstown, Ohio, Aug. 26, 1931; s. Hubert James and Catherine (Powell) W.; m. Phyllis Saxton, Aug. 24, 1957; children: Cynthia, Catherine, Jennifer, Gretchen. AB, Oberlin Coll., 1953, DSc (hon.), 1992; PhD, U. Mich., 1966. Cert. sch. psychologist, Mich. Dir. sch. svcs. Ypsilanti (Mich.) Pub. Schs., 1957-70; pres. High Scope Edl. Rsch. Found., Ypsilanti, 1970—; dir. High Scope Inst., London, 1991—. Author: Young Children in Action, 1979, Changed Lives, 1984, Challenging the Potential, 1992, Significant Benefits, 1993, Educating Young Children, 1995; editor: How Nations Serve Young Children, 1991, Families Speak, 1994. Mem., Nat. Commn. on Children, 1990-93. 1st lt. USMC, 1953-55. Recipient Lela Rowland award Nat. Mental Health Assn., Washington, 1987. Mem. Nat. Assn. for Edn. of Young Children. Avocation: camping.

WEIKERT, JERARD LEE, real estate broker; b. Zanesfield, Ohio, Dec. 25, 1929; s. Paul Hoover and Thelma May (McKeever) W.; m. Beth Ann Houston, Aug. 24, 1983. Grad., Officer Candidate Sch., 1952; BA, Wittenberg U., 1961; MS, George Washington U., 1966. Enlisted U.S. Army, 1951, advanced through grades to col., 1967, ret., 1972; self-employed profl. horse trainer and judge Fairfax County, Va., 1972—; v.p. sales and plans Keyes Gateway, Inc., Dayton, Ohio, 1983—; pres. Darrowby Inc. Real Estate Brokerage Consultancy, 1994—; judge Am. Horse Show Assn., 1972—. Contbr. articles to U.S. Army and horse jours. Chmn. Human Rels. Bd., Springfield, Ohio, 1991-92; mem. Planning Commn., Clark County, Ohio, 1991-93; v.p., exec. bd. Community Leadership Acad., Springfield, 1991-93; fin. dir. Tackett for State Senate, Ohio, 1992. Decorated Legion of Merit (2), Combat Infantry Badge. Mem. U.S. Dressage Fedn. (exec. bd.), Dayton Dressage Assn. (chmn. bd. dirs. 1995—), Dayton Area Bd. Realtors (chmn. equal opportunity com. 1988-90, profl. stds. com. 1991-93, grievance com. 1993-94, chmn. grievance com. 1995—), Dayton Racquet Club, Troy Country Club. Democrat. Avocations: antique bronzes and icons, genealogy.

WEIL, ANDRE, mathematics educator and researcher. Doctorate, U. Paris, 1928. Prof. math. emeritus Inst. Advanced Study, Princeton, N.J., 1976—. Editor: works of Jacques Bernoulli, Pierre de Fermat. Recipient Kyoto prize, 1994. Achievements include rsch. of branches of number theory and algebraic geometry; created theorem of mathematical conjecturecalled the Riemann hypothesis; Weil conjectures; unification of arithmetic, algebra, geometry and topology, rsch. in the history of math. Office: Inst for Advanced Study Mathematics S Olden Ln Princeton NJ 08540*

WEIL, DAVID S., plastics manufacturing executive; b. Germany, Apr. 6, 1925; came to U.S., 1943; s. William and Martha Weil; m. Grace K. Pollack, Mar. 20, 1949; children: Aryeh L., Esther R. Weil Sturm. BA, CCNY, 1949. Pres., chief exec. officer Ampacet Corp., Tarrytown, N.Y., 1958—. Sgt. U.S. Army, 1943-46, CBI. Decorated Bronze Star. Mem. Soc. Plastics Engrs. (Internat. Excellence award 1986), Soc. Plastics Industry (bd. dirs. 1983-86). Avocations: tennis, swimming. Office: Ampacet Corp 660 White Plains Rd Tarrytown NY 10591-5107*

WEIL, D(ONALD) WALLACE, business administration educator; b. Cleve., July 20, 1923; s. Laurence J. and Carol S. (Wallace) W.; m. Jane A. Bittel, Dec. 29, 1947; children—John Wallace, Charles Andrew, Margaret Jane, Carol Wyn. B.A., Oberlin Coll., 1947; J.D., Willamette U., 1950. Pres. James Foundry Corp., Fort Atkinson, Wis., 1960-70; faculty bus. adminstrn. U. Wis., Eau Claire, 1971-74; chmn. dept. bus. adminstrn. U. Wis., 1974-77, prof., 1985—; pres. Diversified Industries, Inc., St. Louis, 1977-81, UHI Corp., Los Angeles, 1981-85; dir. U.H.I. Corp. Diversified Industries, Inc., St. Louis, Sales Investments, Mgmt. Inc., Elmwood, Wis., Jane B. Inc., Eau Claire. Served with AUS, 1942-45. Mem. Am. Security Council, Nat. Council Small Bus. Mgmt. Devel., Phi Kappa Phi, Beta Gamma Sigma. Republican. Congregationalist. Home: 1530 Canfield St Eau Claire WI 54701-4018 Office: U Wis-Eau Claire Dept Bus Adminstrn Eau Claire WI 54701

WEIL, EDWARD DAVID, research scientist, chemist, educator; b. Phila., June 13, 1928; s. Irving E. and Minna M. (Stainbrook) W.; m. Barbara Joy Hummel, Sept. 11, 1952; children: David L., Claudia E. BS in Chemistry, U. Pa., 1950; PhD in Organic Chemistry, U. Ill., 1953; MBA, Pace U., 1982. Chemist, supr. Hooker Chem. Co., Niagara Falls, N.Y., 1950-63; supr., sr. scientist Stauffer Chem. Co., Dobbs Ferry, N.Y., 1965-86; ind. cons., patent agt., propr. Intertech. Svcs., 1986—; dir. exploratory rsch. Adelphi Rsch. Ctr., Garden City, 1986-87; rsch. prof. Poly. U., Bklyn., 1987—; Contbr. articles to Kirk-Othmer Ency., Ency. Polymer Sci., Rsch. Mgmt. Jour., others. Recipient IR-100 award Indsl. Rsch. Mag. Achievements include over 210 patents for commercial pesticides, flame retardants, processes, agricultural chemicals, others. Mem. Am. Chem. Soc. (chmn. profl. rels. com. N.Y. sect. 1980-94), Assn. Cons. Chemists and Chem. Engrs., Sigma Xi. Home and Office: 6 Amherst Dr Hastings On Hudson NY 10706

WEIL, ERNST, oil industry executive. Chmn., chief exec. officer Phibro Energy Inc., Greenwich, Conn. Office: Phibro Energy Inc 500 Nyala Farms Rd Westport CT 06880-6262 also: Salomon Inc 1 New York Plz New York NY 10004-1902

WEIL, FRANK A., investment banker, lawyer; b. Bedford, N.Y., Feb. 14, 1931; s. Sylvan and Ruth Alice (Norman) W.; m. Denie Sandison, Feb. 10, 1951; children: Deborah Weil Harrington, Amanda, Sandison, William. A.B. cum laude, Harvard U., 1953, LL.B., 1956. Bar: N.Y. 1956. Practiced in N.Y.C., 1957-60; gen. partner Loeb, Rhoades & Co., N.Y.C., 1960-71; pres. Abacus Fund, Inc., 1968-72; chief fin. officer, dir. Paine, Webber, Jackson & Curtis, N.Y.C., 1972-77; asst. sec. industry and trade Dept. Commerce, Washington, 1977-79; partner firm Ginsburg, Feldman, Weil & Bress, Washington, 1979-83, Wald, Harkrader & Ross, Washington, 1983-85; chmn., chief exec. officer Abacus and Assocs., Inc., 1985—; dir. Dorr-Oliver, Inc., Stamford, Conn., 1968-77, Hamburg Savs. Bank, N.Y.C., 1975-77, J.B. Lippincott Co., Phila., 1975-77, Govt. Research Corp., 1975-77, 79-85; dir., pres. Norman Found., 1953-77, 79—. Trustee Tchrs. Coll., Columbia U., 1976-79, Montefiore Hosp., 1960-77; trustee, vice chmn. No. Westchester Hosp., 1971-77; past vice chmn. bd. govs. Atlantic Inst. Internat. Affairs; past pres. Ednl. Alliance, trustee, 1957-77; trustee, sec. Fedn. Jewish Philanthropies, N.Y.C., 1965-77; trustee, chmn. Harvey Sch., 1969-76; trustee Hurricane Island Outward Bound Sch., 1974—, Washington Opera, 1984-85, Asia Soc., 1993—; bd. dirs., pres. Hickrill Found., Inc., 1953-77, 79—; bd. dirs. Coun. Excellence in Govt., 1984—, chmn., 1988-93, Am. Assembly, 1992—, Smithsonian Inst., 1994—; mem. vis. com. Kennedy Sch. Govt., Harvard U.; chmn. tax com., mem. N.Y. State Econ. Devel. Bd., 1975-77; chmn., mem. N.Y. State Bd. Equalization and Assessment, 1976-77; adv. bd. Sch. Advanced Internat. Studies, Johns Hopkins U., 1979-88; mem. N.Y. State Council on Fiscal and Econ. Priorities, 1985-89, N.Y. Coun. Fgn. Rels.; mem. N.Y. State Adv. Commn. on Liability Ins., 1986. Mem. Century Assn., Harvard Club, The Links, River Club, Met. Club. Home: 1516 28th St NW Washington DC 20007-3058 Office: Abacus & Assocs Inc 147 E 48th St # 3fl New York NY 10017-1294

WEIL, GILBERT HARRY, lawyer; b. N.Y.C., Aug. 31, 1912; s. Alexis and Esther (Marks) W.; m. Louise Rhoda Cohen, Mar. 14, 1936; children: Allen Charles, Jeffrey Lee. B.S., NYU, 1933, J.D. 1937. Bar: N.Y. 1937, U.S. Dist. Ct. (so. dist.) N.Y. 1941, U.S. Ct. Appeals (2d cir.) 1949, U.S. Ct. Appeals (4th cir.) 1950, U.S. Dist. Ct. (ea. dist.) N.Y. 1952, U.S. Ct. Appeals (3d cir.) 1956, U.S. Dist. Ct. D.C. 1961, U.S. Supreme Ct. 1964, U.S. Ct. Appeals (9th cir.) 1964, U.S. Ct. Appeals (5th cir.) 1969, U.S. Ct. Appeals (7th cir.) 1976, U.S. Ct. Appeals (fed. cir.) 1982. Law clk. and assoc. to Isaac W. Digges, 1935-53; pvt. practice, 1953-65; partner Weil and Lee, N.Y.C., 1966-69, Weil, Lee & Bergin, N.Y.C., 1969-76, Weil, Guttman & Davis, N.Y.C., 1976-82, Weil, Guttman, Davis & Malkin, N.Y.C., 1982-86, Weil, Guttman & Malkin, N.Y.C., 1986—; lectr. in field, 1952—. Contbr. articles to profl. jours. Served to lt (j.g.) USNR, 1943-45. Office: Weil Guttman & Malkin 60 E 42d St New York NY 10165

WEIL, HERMAN, psychology educator; b. Regisheim, Alsace Lorraine, Dec. 15, 1905; came to U.S., 1938, naturalized, 1944; m. Bertha Weiler, July 26, 1931; 1 son, Gunther M. Ph.D. in Psychology, U. Marburg, Germany, 1929, state exam. in math., chemistry, physics, 1929, state exam. in edn., 1931; D.Pub. Service (hon.), U. Wis.-Milw., 1986. Instr. Realgymnasium for Girls, Hersfeld, Germany, 1931-33; instr., studienrat Philanthropin Realgymnasium, Frankfurt on Main, Germany, 1933-38; postdoctoral scholar U. Iowa, 1939; prof. sci. Nebr. Central Coll., 1939-40; prof. Milw. Sch. Engring., 1940-43; prof. edn. and psychology, head dept. Wis. State Coll., Milw., 1943-56; prof. psychology U. Wis., Milw., 1956-76; prof. emeritus U. Wis., 1976—, chmn. dept., 1956-61, chmn. honors program superior students Coll. Letters and Scis., 1960-74, asso. dean, 1966-71, faculty retirement counselor, 1973-75; vis. prof. Northwestern U., summers 1947, 48, 51; cons. Human Relations Workshop, U. Mich., summers 1952-56; lectr. Workshops on Human Relations, Wis. State Coll., summers 1952-56; lectr. Milw. Downer Coll., 1943-47; cons. Dept. State, also U.S. Office Edn., Jugenheim, Ger., 1954; Disting. Service fellow Temple Emanu-El B'ne Jeshurun, 1976-78, 79-84, emeritus, 1984—; dean adult Jewish studies, 1978-79; Disting. scholar-in-residence Milw. Jewish Community Ctr., 1977-80; invited speaker dedication ceremonies of permanent edn. exhbt. in former Jewish Gymnasium Philanthropin, as sole Holocaust survivor of tenured faculty, Frankfurt, Fed. Republic Germany, 1988; curator Rubenstein Ctr. for 20th Century Jewry, 1992-93. Author: In Quest of Excellence, 1975, University of Wisconsin-Milwaukee Faculty Retirement Guidebook, 1975, 2d edit., 1976; contbr. chpts. and sects. to books on psychol. subjects. Co-chmn. Wis. region NCCJ, 1952-72, mem. commn. on ednl. orgns., 1955-60, nat. bd. dirs., 1977-84, nat. co-chmn. schs. and colls. com. observance of Nat. Brotherhood Week, 1957; mem. Gov.'s Commn. on Human Rights, 1953-56; counselor Milw. B'nai B'rith Hillel Found., 1950-60; pres. New Home Club, Inc., 1940-57, hon. pres., 1977-87; chmn. Milw. chpt. Am. Jewish Com., 1973-75, mem. nat. exec. com., 1973-80. Recipient citation of merit for work in human rels. Milw. B'nai B'rith Couns., 1952, Brotherhood award Wis. region NCCJ, 1959, Citation award Internat. Inst. Milwaukee County, 1960, Disting. Merit citation NCCJ, 1973, Disting. Merit citation Wis. Soc. Jewish Learning, 1973, Disting. Svc. award U. Wis.-Milw. chpt. AAUP, 1975, Disting. Merit citation Coll. Letters and Sci., U. Wis.-Milw., 1976, Am. Jewish Com. Inst. Human Rels. award, 1978, Spl. Lifetime Svc. award Milw. Assn. for Jewish Edn., 1989; guest of honor Mayor and Senate, City of West Berlin, 1979; linden tree planted in his honor near courtyard of Gold Meir Libr., U. Wis., Milw., 1990; named as one of Milw. Ret. profs. who have made significant, enduring and institution wide contbns., U. Wis.-Milw., 1994. Mem. AAUP (pres. Wis. conf. 1973-74), Wis. Soc. Jewish Learning (past pres.), Wis. Psychol. Assn. (past pres.), Milwaukee County Psychol. Assn. (past pres.), Nat. Collegiate Honors Council (mem. exec. com. 1972-73), Ret. Faculty Assn. U. Wis.-Milw. (pres. 1977-79), Phi Kappa Phi (hon.). Jewish (past v.p., trustee temple). Home: Apt 1003 1400 N Prospect Ave Milwaukee WI 53202 *The alleviation of prejudice is one of the foremost challenges of our time. To assist in the process of reducing hate between man and man, group and group, nation and nation, requires a life of dedication and earnest commitment. It presents more than the utterances of words and good-will on special occasions of the year; it means the initiation and follow-through of appropriate action patterns in one's smaller and larger environment to bring closer to realization and fruition the ideal of the "Brotherhood of Man under the Fatherhood of God".*

WEIL, IRWIN, Slavic languages and literature educator; b. Cin., Apr. 16, 1928; s. Sidney and Florence (Levy) W.; m. Vivian Weil, Dec. 27, 1950; children: Martin, Alice, Daniel. A.B., U. Chgo., 1948, M.A., 1951; Ph.D., Harvard U., 1960. Sr. social sci. research analyst Library of Congress, 1951-54; teaching fellow Harvard U., 1956-58; mem. faculty Brandeis U., 1958-65; mem. faculty dept. Slavic langs. and lit. Northwestern U., Evanston, Ill., 1966—; prof. Northwestern U., 1976-82; vis. prof. U. Moscow, Soviet Acad. Scis.; set up series of internat. symposia between Am. scholars and USSR Acad. Scis.; founder 1st Soviet-Am. TV Student Competition in Lit., 1988-89. Author books and articles pub. in field, pub. in U.S.A. and Russia. Recipient Pushkin Internat. gold medal for outstanding teaching and research, 1984, Outstanding Teaching award Northwestern U. Alumni Assn., 1987, Tempo All-Professor Team, Humanities, Chicago Tribune, 1993; Ford Found. fellow, 1954-55. Mem. Am. Assn. Tchrs. Slavic and East European Langs. (exec. sec. 1962-68, Excellence in Teaching award 1993), Am. Coun. Tchrs. Russian (v.p. 1975-79, pres. 1980-84), Internat. Assn. Profs. Russian (founding U.S. mem.). Jewish. Established TV competition on American and Russian literature between American and Russian high schoolers. Office: Northwestern U Slavic Dept Evanston IL 60208 *As a scholar and teacher trying hard to develop mutual understanding and cultural exchange with the USSR, I have discovered how important and fruitful it is to apply the normal standards of friendly discourse with people from an entirely different country and historical background.*

WEIL, JACK BAUM, clothing manufacturing company executive; b. Denver, Nov. 13, 1928; s. Jack Arnold and Beatrice (Baum) W.; m. Elizabeth

Fried, 1956 (div. 1969); children: Steven Eugene, Judith B. Weil Oksner; m. Candace Helene Taylor, 1973 (div. 1983). BA, Tulane U., 1952. V.p. Rockmount Ranch Wear Mfg. Co., Denver, 1954—, designer, sales mgr., 1957—; designer western apparel. Head planning group Humboldt Island Hist. Dist., Denver; committeeman Denver Rep. Com., 1974—; del. Rep. county, dist. and state convs., 1974—; sec. Rep. Ctrl. Com., 1st Congl. Dist. Colo., 1993-94, chmn. 1995—; mem. exec. com. Colo. Rep. State Ctrl. Com., 1995—; bd. dirs. 1st Universalist Ch., Denver; mem. admissions com. Tulane U.; del. Rep. Nat. Conv., 1992. 1st lt. U.S. Army. Mem. West Coast Western Mktg. Assn., Midwest Western Wear and Equipment Assn. (bd. dirs.), N.W. Western Wear & Equipment Travelers Assn. (pres. Mpls.), S.E. Western, English and Equine Assn. (bd. dirs. Altanta), Denver Western Wear and Equipment Assn., Hat Inst. Am. (del. 1974—), Denver Athletic Club, Town Club, Lincoln Club, Rump Club, Kappa Delta Phi. Avocations: painting, politics, physical fitness, travel. Home: 1025 Humboldt St Denver CO 80218-3121 Office: Rockmount Ranch Wear Mfg Co 1626 Wazee St Denver CO 80202-1314

WEIL, JEFFREY GEORGE, lawyer; b. Allentown, Pa., Apr. 28, 1951; s. Russel G.E. and Irene Marie (Kozlowski) W.; divorced; children: Michael, Stephen; m. Rachel Eisner, 1994. AB, Princeton U., 1973; JD, Harvard U., 1976. Bar: Pa. 1976, U.S. Dist. Ct. (ea. dist.) Pa. 1976, U.S. Ct. Appeals (3d cir.) 1976, U.S. Supreme Ct., 1988. Assoc. Dechert, Price & Rhoads, Phila., 1976-84, ptnr., 1984—, chmn. firm hiring com., 1987-89, mem. firm exec. com., 1990-94. Chmn. com. United Way Southeastern Pa., Phila., 1982-85, trustee, 1983-89, mem. funding policy com., 1987-90; participant Community Leadership Seminar Program, Phila., 1986; bd. dirs. Hawk Mountain Sanctuary, 1993—. Mem. ABA (vice chmn. adminstrn. law com. on pub. advs. and pub. representation 1985-88, mem. antitrust sect. pvt. litigation subcom. 1991—), Pa. Bar Assn., Phila. Bar Assn. (fed. cts. com. 1985—), Princeton U. Alumni Schs. Com., Princeton Club Phila. Avocations: fly-fishing, reading, sports. Home: 2 Esprit Ter Wayne PA 19087-5557 Office: Dechert Price & Rhoads 1717 Arch St Philadelphia PA 19103-2713

WEIL, JERRY, animator. MS, Brown U. Sr. animator MetroLight Studios, L.A. Creator fringe animation opening sequence (TV program) ABC World of Discovery; producer several films. Office: MetroLight Studios 5724 W 3rd St Ste 400 Los Angeles CA 90036-3078

WEIL, JOHN DAVID, envelope company executive; b. Chgo., Sept. 28, 1947; s. Leslie Joseph and Carlyne (Strauss) W.; m. Marcie Bornfriend, July 4, 1981; children: Jessica Lauren, Michael Brandon, Samantha Leigh. BS in Econs., U. Ill., 1969; MBA in Fin., Northwestern U., 1971. Asst. to chmn. bd. Stanwood Industries, Lake Forest, Ill., 1971-74; pres. Kent Paper Co., Ridgewood, N.Y., 1974-81; pres., CEO Am. Envelope Co., Chgo., 1982-94; with CC Industries, Chgo., 1995—; bd. dirs. DEC Internat., Inc. Mem. Envelope Mfrs. Am. (bd. dirs. 1986-94), Northmoor Country Club, Stonebridge Country Club. Avocation: golf. Office: CC Industries 222 N LaSalle St Chicago IL 60601

WEIL, JOHN WILLIAM, technology management consultant; b. N.Y.C., Feb. 3, 1928; s. Frank Leopold and Henrietta Amelia (Simons) W.; m. Joan Leatrice Landis, June 15, 1950; children: Nancy Ellen, Linda Jill. B.S., MIT, 1948; Ph.D., Cornell U., 1953. Various positions in nuclear reactors and computers Gen. Electric Co. (various locations), 1953-70; v.p. advanced systems and tech. Honeywell Info. Systems, Inc., Waltham, Mass., 1970-74; v.p., chief tech. officer Bendix Corp., Southfield, Mich., 1974-77; sr. v.p., chief tech. officer Bendix Corp., Southfield, 1977-83; v.p. advanced tech. and engring. Allied Corp., Southfield, 1983; pres. Modular Bio Systems, Inc., 1983-85, Weil Assocs., Inc., Bloomfield Hills, Mich., 1985—; bd. dirs. Access Corp., Maxwell Labs.; founder Met. Detroit Sci. and Engring. Coalition, 1977, sec., 1977-80, pres., 1980-82; chmn. Mich. Biotech. Inst., 1981-85, trustee, 1985-92; mem. Army Sci. Bd., 1982-84. Contbr. articles to profl. jours. AEC fellow, 1950-51. Home and Office: 218 Guilford Rd Bloomfield Hills MI 48304-2737

WEIL, JON DAVID, psychologist, geneticist, administrator; b. Evansville, Ind., Mar. 24, 1937. BA, Swarthmore (Pa.) Coll., 1958; postgrad., U. Calif., Berkeley, 1958-60; PhD in Genetics, U. Calif., Davis, 1963; PhD in Clin. Psychology, Wright Inst., Berkeley, Calif., 1984. Lic. psychologist, Calif.; diplomate Am. Bd. Med. Genetics. Asst. prof. molecular biology Vanderbilt U., Nashville, 1967-72; assoc. prof. molecular biology, 1972-77; rsch. geneticist U. Calif., San Francisco, Calif., 1977-86; asst. adj. prof. pediats. U. Calif., San Francisco, 1986-93, assoc. adj. prof. pediats., 1993—; clin. dir. program in genetic counseling U. Calif., Berkeley, 1989—; pvt. practice clin. psychologist San Ramon, Calif., 1988—. Contbr. articles to profl. jours. Mem. AAAS, APA, Am. Soc. Human Genetics, Nat. Soc. Genetic Counselors. Office: 200 Porter Dr #300 San Ramon CA 94583

WEIL, LEON JEROME, diplomat; b. N.Y.C., June 15, 1927; m. Mabel Selig, Apr. 8, 1952; children: Leon Jerome Jr., Katherine A., Caroline E. A.B. cum laude, Princeton U. Ptnr. Herzfeld & Stern, N.Y.C., 1974-84, Steiner Rouse & Co., 1950-74; now with Gruntal & Co., N.Y.C.; U.S. ambassador to Nepal, 1984-87; cons. UN Devel. Programme, Financial Svcs. Vol. Corps., Internat. Found. for Electoral Systems; exch. ofcl. Am. Stock Exchange. Trustee Berkshire Sch., Sheffield, Mass., Outward Bound Inc., Greenwich, Conn., Robert Taft Inst. Govt., N.Y.C.; mem. Pres.'s Council on Phys. Fitness and Sports; bd. dirs. Media Rsch. Center of Alexandria, Va. Served with USN, 1945-46. Republican. Club: City Athletic (N.Y.C.). Home: 213 E 48th St New York NY 10017-1538

WEIL, LEONARD, banker; b. 1922; married. With U.S. Dept. State, Vienna, Austria, 1946; with Union Bank, Los Angeles, 1946-62; pres., CEO Mfrs. Bank, Los Angeles, 1962-86; pres. emeritus Mfrs. Bank, 1986—; bd. dirs. Bond Fund of Am., Inc., Capital World Bond Fund, Inc., Tax-Exempt Bond Fund of Am., Inc.; adj. asst. prof. fin. Anderson Grad. Sch. Mgmt., UCLA. Trustee UCLA Found.; bd. visitors UCLA Grad. Sch. Mgmt.; past pres. Town Hall; bd. dirs. Braille Inst. Served with U.S. Army, 1943-45. Mem. Calif. Bankers Assn. (bd. dirs., past pres.), Am. Mgmt. Assn., Am. Econs. Assn., Am. Bankers Assn. Office: 233 Wilshire Blvd Fl 6 Santa Monica CA 90401-1205

WEIL, LOUIS ARTHUR, III, newspaper publishing executive; b. Grand Rapids, Mich., Mar. 14, 1941; s. Louis Arthur, Jr. and Kathryn (Halligan) W.; m. Mary Elizabeth Buckingham, Sept. 7, 1963 (div. June 1977); children: Scott Arthur, Christopher Davison, Timothy Buckingham; m. Daryl Hopkins Goss, Jan. 26, 1980. B.A. in English, Ind. U., 1963; DHL (hon.), Mercy Coll., Grand Valley State U. Various positions Times Herald, Port Huron, Mich., 1966-68; personnel dir., pub. Journal and Courier, Lafayette, Ind., 1968-73; gen. mgr. Gannett Westchester Rockland Newspapers, White Plains, N.Y., 1973-74, pres., gen. mgr., 1974-77, pres., pub., 1977-79; v.p. devel. Gannett Co., Inc., N.Y.C., 1979-83, sr. v.p. planning and devel., 1982-86; chmn., pub. Gannett Westchester Rockland Newspapers, White Plains, 1984-86; pres. The Detroit News, 1986-89, pub., 1987-89; U.S. pub. Time Mag., 1989-91; pub., chief exec. officer, exec. v.p. Ariz. Republic, Phoenix Gazette, Ariz. Bus. Gazette, 1991—; bd. dirs. Ctrl. Newspapers, Inc., Prudential. Chmn. membership Trustee Found. for Am. Comm.; mem. Greater Phoenix Leadership; trustee Cronkite Endowment Sch. Journalism and Telecomm. Ariz. State U., Phoenix Art Mus.; bd. dirs. Found. Am. Comms.; mem. adv. bd. Ariz. Cancer Ctr. U. Ariz.; campaign chmn. Valley of the Sun United Way, 1992. With USN. Office: Phoenix Newspapers Inc 120 E Van Buren St Phoenix AZ 85004*

WEIL, MAX HARRY, physician, medical educator, medical scientist; b. Baden, Switzerland, Feb. 9, 1927; came to U.S., 1937, naturalized, 1944; s. Marcel and Gretl (Winter) W.; m. Marianne Judith Posner, Apr. 1955; children: Susan Margot, Carol Juliet. AB, U. Mich., 1948; MD, SUNY, N.Y.C., 1952; PhD, U. Minn., 1957. Diplomate Am. Bd. Internal Medicine and Critical Care Medicine, Nat. Bd. Med. Examiners. Interin in internal medicine Univ. of Cin. Med. Ctr., 1952-53; resident U. Minn. Hosps., Heart Hosp., VA Hosp., Mpls., 1953-55; rsch. fellow U. Minn., Mpls., 1955-56; sr. fellow Nat. Heart Inst., Mayo Clinic, Rochester, Minn., 1956-57; chief cardiology City of Hope Med. Ctr., Duarte, Calif., 1957-59; asst. clin. prof. U. So. Calif. Sch. Medicine, L.A., 1957-59, asst. prof., 1959-63, assoc. prof., 1963-71, prof., 1971-81; chmn. L.A. County com. on emerging svcs., 1968-73; disting. prof., chmn. dept. medicine, chief div. cardiol Chgo. Med. Sch.,

Finch U. Health Scis., North Chicago, Ill., 1982-91, disting. univ. prof., 1992-94, disting. univ. prof. emeritus, 1994—; prof. clin. med. bioengring. U. So. Calif., 1972-81, adj. prof. medicine, 1981—, dir. Shock Rsch. Unit, 1961-81, Inst. Critical Care Medicine Ann. Symposium, 1963—, Ctr. Critically Ill, U. So. Calif., L.A., 1968-80; pres. Inst. Critical Care Medicine, Palm Springs, Calif. and Northbrook, Ill., 1994—; attending cardiologist children's divsn. L.A. County/U. So. Calif. Med. Ctr., 1958-65, attending physician, 1958-71, sr. attending cardiologist, 1968-73, sr. attending physician, 1971-81; vis. prof. anesthesiology/critical care medicine U. Pitts., 1972—; clin. prof. anesthesiology UCLA, 1981—; adj. prof. Northwestern U. Med. Sch., Chgo., 1992—; numerous vis. professorships and lectureships; cons. in field; prin. rschr. numerous grants and rsch. projects; Weil Internat. lectr. in critical care medicine U. So. Calif., L.A., 1987. Sect. editor Archives Internal Medicine, 1983-86, JAMA, 1969-72; guest editor Am. Jour. Cardiology, 1982, Critical Care Medicine, 1985; mem. editl. bd. Am. Jour. Medicine, 1971-79, Chest, 1980-95, Jour. Circulatory Shock, 1979-92, Clin. Engring. Newsletter, 1980—, Methods of Info. in Medicine, 1977-91, Jour. Clin. Illness, 1986—, Clin. Intensive Care, 1989—; mem. editl. adv. bd. Emergency Medicine, 1978—, Issues in Health Care Tech., 1983-86; assoc. editor Critical Care Medicine, 1973-74, mem. editl. bd., 1973-91, 94—; editor-in-chief Acute Care, 1983-90; contbr. articles to profl. jours.; patentee in field. Pres. Temple Brotherhood, Wilshire Blvd. Temple, L.A., 1967-68; bd. dirs. Hollywood Presbyn. Med. Ctr., 1976-81, L.A. chpt. Met. Am. Heart Assn., 1962-67, Chgo. chpt. Met. Am. Heart Assn., 1982—. Served with U.S. Army, 1946-47. Recipient prize in internal medicine SUNY, 1952, Alumni medallion SUNY, 1970; Disting. Svc. award Soc. Critical Care Medicine, 1984; numerous rsch. grants, 1959—; named Disting. Alumni Lectr., 1967, Oscar Schwindetzky Meml. Lectr. Internat. Anesthesia Rsch. Soc., 1978; recipient Lawrence R. Medoff award Chgo. Med. Sch., 1987, Morris L. Parker Rsch. award, 1989; Lilly scholar, 1988-89. Master ACP; fellow Am. Coll. Cardiology (chmn. emergency cardiac care com. 1974-81), ACP, Am. Coll. Chest Physicians (coun. clin. cardiology, coun. critical care medicine), Am. Coll. Clin. Pharmacology, Am. Coll. Critical Care Medicine, Am. Heart Assn. (coun. circulation, coun. basic sci., coun. cardiopulmonary and critical care, coun. clin. cardiology), N.Y. Acad. Sci., Chgo. Soc. of Internal Medicine; mem. AMA (sect. editor jour. 1969-72), IEEE, Ill. Med. Assn., Lake County Med. Assn., Los Angeles County Med. Assn., Am. Physiol. Soc., Am. Soc. Pharmacology and Exptl. Therapeutics, Am. Soc. Echocardiography, Am. Soc. Nephrology, Am. Trauma Soc. (founding mem.), Assn. Computing Machinery, Assn. Am. Med. Colls., Cen. Soc. Clin. Rsch., Chgo. Cardiol. Group (sec.-treas. 1986—, chmn. 1988-90), Chgo. Soc. Internal Medicine, Lake County Heart As1983-86), Intensive Care Soc., U.K., L.A. Soc. Internal Medicine, Soc. Exptl. Biology and Medicine, Western Soc. Clin. Rsch., Fedn. Am. Socs. Exptl. Biology, Am. Soc. Parenteral and Enteral Nutrition, Nat. Acad. Practice (disting. practitioner), Skull and Dagger, Sigma Xi, Alpha Omega Alpha. Jewish. Avocations: swimming, tennis, photography, philosophy-economics. Office: Inst Critical Care Medicine Bldg # 3 1695 N Sunrise Way Palm Springs CA 92262-5309

WEIL, MYRON, retired banker; b. Lincoln, Nebr., Apr. 17, 1918; s. Julius and Fannie (Livingston) W.; m. Pauline Clayton, Sept. 26, 1945; children—Michele Susan, Judy Lynn, Layla. B.S., Yale, 1939. Exec. v.p., dir. Nat. Bank Commerce, Lincoln, 1939-67; bd. dir. First Nat. Bank, Clinton, Iowa, 1967-91, chmn. bd. dirs., 1974-91; exec. v.p. Hawkeye Bancorp., Des Moines, 1967-83, bd. dirs., 1967-91; vice chmn. bd Hawkeye Bancorp., 1983-86. Served to maj. Q.M.C. AUS, 1939-45. Decorated Bronze Star. Home: 1025 Crescent Dr Clinton IA 52732-4739

WEIL, PAUL P., lawyer; b. Evansville, Ind., Jan. 30, 1936; s. Henry A. and Clarice Emy (Peres) W.; m. Barbara Ann Podell; children: Cynthia Marie Weil Connolly, Leslie Renee Weil Masaki. Student, U. Pa., 1953-55; BSBA, Washington U., 1959, JD, 1959. Bar: Mo. 1960. Assoc. Thomas, Busse, Cullen & Godfrey, St. Louis, 1959-61, ptnr., 1968-73; ptnr. Bryan Cave (formerly Bryan, Cave, McPheeters & McRoberts), St. Louis, 1973—. Mem. handicapped budget panel United Way, 1976-77; bd. dirs. Kammergild Chamber Orch. St. Louis, 1986-88; trustee Rosalie Tilles Non-Sectarian Charity Fund, 1987—; pres. Congregation Temple Israel, St. Louis, 1980-83. Mem. ABA (IRS regional liaison), Mo. Bar Assn. (vice chmn. tax sect. 1970), St. Louis Bar Assn. (v.p. 1969-72, treas. 1972-73), Noonday Club, Mo. Athletic Club (chmn. art com. 1978-80, mem. bd. govs. 1988-91). Republican. Jewish. Office: Bryan Cave 1 Metropolitan Sq 211 N Broadway Saint Louis MO 63102-2750

WEIL, PETER HENRY, lawyer; b. N.Y.C., Nov. 20, 1933; s. Frank L. and Henrietta Amelia (Simons) W.; m. Helen Fay Kolodkin, Dec. 18, 1960; children: Karen W. Markus, Frank L. BA cum laude, Princeton U., 1954; LLB cum laude, Harvard U., 1957. Bar: N.Y. 1957, U.S. Dist. Cts. (so. and ea. dists.) N.Y. 1972. Assoc. Weil, Gotshal & Manges, N.Y.C., 1958-62; assoc. Kaye Scholer, N.Y.C., 1962-67, ptnr., 1967—; chmn. panel on asset based lending Practicing Law Inst. Program, 1980-93, chmn. panel on troubled leverage buyouts, 1989-90; lectr. SMU Inst. on Comml. Financing, 1985-94, Banking Law Inst., 1987-89. Author: Asset Based Lending: An Introductory Guide to Secured Financing, P.I., 1989, 2nd edit., 1992. Fellow Am. Coll. of Commercial Fin. Lawyers; former chmn. N.Y. bd. overseers, former bd. govs. Hebrew Union Coll., Jewish Inst. Religion, Cin., N.Y.; Los Angeles, Jerusalem. With U.S. Army 1957-58. Mem. Ringwood Golden Master Volleyball Team, U.S. Nat. Champions, 1983. Mem. ABA, Assn. of Bar of City of N.Y. (banking law com. 1975-78). Office: Kaye Scholer Fierman 425 Park Ave New York NY 10022-3506

WEIL, RAYMOND RICHARD, soil scientist; b. Detroit, May 27, 1948; s. Ulrich L. and Hilde C. (Levy) W.; m. Susan R. Boscov, Feb. 22, 1968 (div. Feb. 1982); children: Benjamin S., Joshua J.; m. Patricia Lynn Driggers, Feb. 5, 1983. BS, Mich. State U., 1970; MS, Purdue U., 1972; PhD, Va. Poly. Inst. and State U., 1977. Cert. profl. soil scientist. Vol Peace Corps, Ethiopia, 1970; Farm mgr. Nat. Sharecropper's Fund, Wadesboro, N.C., 1972-73; instr. Va. Poly. Inst. and State U., Blacksburg, 1975-77; lectr. U. Malawi, Lilongwe, 1977-79; asst. prof. U. Md., College Park, 1979-84, assoc. prof., 1984-91, prof., 1991—; cons. Forest Dept., Sri Lanka Govt., 1981; adv. bd. Com. on Agr. Sustainability for Developing Countries, Washington, 1988—; mem. task force Ecosystem Farm, Accokeek (Md.) Found., 1990—. Author: Lab Manual for Soil Science, 1993; co-author: Nature and Properties of Soil: A Study Guide, 1984; contbr. articles to profl. jours. Named Fulbright-Hayes Scholarship Exch. fellow, Zimbabwe, 1985, Fulbright-Hayes Africa Regional Rsch. scholar, Tanzania, 1994, Nat. Def. Edn. Act fellow, Ind. 1971-72; recipient rsch. grants U.S. Dept. Interior, Md., 1982, 86, 89, 90, USDA, Md., 1991, U.S. AID, Malawi, 1988-92. Mem. Am. Soc. Agronomy (internat. div. chair 1993-94), Soil Sci. Soc. Am., Internat. Soil Sci. Soc. Achievements include devel. of new methods of matching fertilizer use to soil requirements in peasant farming sectors by mapping soil and plant nutrient status, of improved cropping sys. for sustainable prodn. of cereals and legumes; devel. of new soil mgmt. sys. to reduce groundwater contamination by nitrates; contrns. to understanding how best to manage organic wastes such as animal manure and sewage sludge in farming systems; devel. of new method to indigenous nutrient sources to enhance soil fertility. Office: U Md Agronomy Dept College Park MD 20742

WEIL, ROLF ALFRED, economist, university president emeritus; b. Pforzheim, Germany, Oct. 29, 1921; came to U.S., 1936, naturalized, 1944; s. Henry and Lina (Landauer) W.; m. Leni Metzger, Nov. 3, 1945; children: Susan Linda, Ronald Alan. B.A., U. Chgo., 1942, Ph.D, 1950; D. Hebrew Letters, Coll. Jewish Studies, 1967; L.H.D., Loyola U., 1970; D.H.L., Bowling Green State U., Ohio, 1986. Rsch. asst. Cowles Commn. for Rsch. in Econs., 1942-44; rsch. analyst Ill. Dept. Revenue, 1944-46; mem. faculty Roosevelt U., Chgo., 1946—, prof. fin. and econs., also chmn. dept. fin., 1954-65, dean Coll. Bus. Adminstrn., 1957-64, acting pres., 1965-66, pres., 1966-88, pres. emeritus, 1988—; past pres. Selfhelp Home for the Aged, Chgo. Author: Through these Portals-from Immigrant to College President, 1991; contbr. articles on fin. Bd. dirs. Landmarks Preservation Coun. of Ill., 1988—; bd. dirs. trustees Roosevelt U., Selfhelp of Chgo., Inc. Mem. Am. Econ. Assn., Cliff Dwellers Club.

WEIL, ROMAN LEE, accounting educator; b. Montgomery, Ala., May 22, 1940; s. Roman L. and Charlotte (Alexander) W.; children: Alexis Cherie, Charles Alexander Roman, Lacey Lorraine. B.A., Yale U., 1962; M.S. in Indsl. Adminstrn, Carnegie-Mellon U., 1965, Ph.D. in Econs., 1966. C.P.A.;

Cert. Mgmt. Acct. From instr. to prof. U. Chgo., 1965-93, Sigmund E. Edelstone prof. acctg., 1993—; Mills B. Lane prof. indsl. mgmt. Ga. Inst. Tech., 1974-76; adv. com. replacement cost implementation SEC, 1976-77; prof. acctg. Stanford U., 1984, prof. econs., 1985, prof. law, 1990—; prof. acctg. and law NYU Sch. Law, 1985; mem. adv. coun. Fin. Acctg. Stds., 1989-94; mem. task force on consolidations Fin. Acctg. Stds. Bd., 1984-89, mem. task force on discounting, 1989—, mem. task force on fin. instruments, 1994—, mem. adv. coun., 1989-94. Author: Fundamentals of Accounting, 1975, Financial Accounting, 7th edit., 1994, Accounting: The Language of Business, 8th edit., 1990, Inflation Accounting, 1976, Replacement Cost Accounting, 1976, Managerial Accounting, 1979, 5th edit., 1994, Litigation Services Handbook, 1990-93; editor: Handbook of Modern Accounting, 1977, 3d edit., 1983, Handbook of Cost Accounting, 1980, 4th edit., 1985, Acctg. Rev., 1974-79, Fin. Analysts Jour., 1980-88. NSF grantee, 1967-81. Mem. AICPA, Ill. Soc. CPAs, Am. Econ. Assn., Inst. Mgmt. Scis., Nat. Assn. Accts. (cert. mgmt. acct.), Am. Acctg. Assn., Inst. Managerial Acctg., Assembly Am. Collegiate Schs. Bus. (acctg. accreditation com. 1987-88), Oenonomy Soc. (co-chmn.). Home: 175 E Delaware Pl Apt 8302 Chicago IL 60611-1732 Office: U Chgo Grad Sch Bus 1101 E 58th St Chicago IL 60637-1511

WEIL, STEPHEN EDWARD, museum official; b. N.Y.C., June 24, 1928; s. Sidney and Beatrice (Sachs) W.; m. Rose Reicherson, Oct. 15, 1950 (div.); children: Rachel J., David N., Michael J.; m. Elizabeth Carbone, Sept. 7, 1974 (div.); m. Wendy Luke, Apr. 8, 1990. A.B., Brown U., 1949; LL.B., Columbia U., 1956. Bar: N.Y. 1956. Assoc. firm Rosenman, Colin, Kaye, Petschek & Freund, N.Y.C., 1956-63; v.p., gen. mgr. Marlborough-Gerson Gallery, N.Y.C., 1963-67; administr., sec. trustee Whitney Mus. Am. Art, N.Y.C., 1967-74; dep. dir., sec. Hirshhorn Mus. and Sculpture Garden, Smithsonian Instn., Washington, 1974—; mem. cultural property adv. com. USIA, 1989—. Co-author: Art Works - Law, Policy, Practice, 1974, Art Law - Rights and Liabilities of Creators and Collectors, 1986; author: Beauty and the Beast, 1983, Rethinking the Museum, 1990, A Cabinet of Curiosities, 1995; co-editor: Art Galleries and Museums, 1973. Mem. mus. adv. panel N.Y. State Coun. on arts, 1974-78; mem. adv. panel Inst. for Mus. Scis.; trustee Brown U., 1989-95. Mem. Am. Assn. Mus. (treas., v.p., councilor), Am. Fedn. Arts (trustee). Jewish. Home: 2936 28th St NW Washington DC 20008-3413 Office: Hirshhorn Museum Washington DC 20560

WEIL, THOMAS ALEXANDER, electronics engineer; b. N.Y.C., Jan. 22, 1930; s. Frank Leopold and Henrietta Amelia (Simons) W.; m. Dianne Isaacs; children: Deborah, Elizabeth, Alexander. BSEE, MIT, 1951. Engr. modulator sect. Raytheon Co., Watertown, Mass., 1951-55, sect. mgr. transmitters, 1955-59, dept. mgr. transmitters, 1969-77, staff scientist equipment devel. labs., 1972—, lab. mgr. radar systems, 1977-79, lab. mgr. advanced devel., 1979-80, program mgr. oil shale program, 1980-84. Contbr. articles to profl. jours., chpts. to books; patentee in field. Recipient Excellence in Tech. award Raytheon Co., 1990; Raytheon Co. fellow, 1989. Fellow IEEE (tech. papers com. Modulator Symposia Microwave Tube Symposia, Germeshausen award 1994). Republican. Mem. Universalist-Unitarian Ch. Avocations: classical music, photography, mountain climbing. Home: 14 Lanark Rd Wellesley MA 02181-3029 Office: Raytheon Co 430 Boston Post Rd Wayland MA 01778-1824 *Evolution and survival of the fittest have left mankind aggressive and prone to make war. Peace depends on finding how to overcome this heritage. Shouldn't we be working on how to resteer mankind's instincts?.*

WEIL, THOMAS P., health services consultant; b. Mount Vernon, N.Y., Oct. 2, 1932; s. H.M. and Alice (Franc) W.; m. Janet Whalen, Feb. 13, 1965. BA, Union Coll., 1954; MPH, Yale U., 1958; PhD, U. Mich., 1964. S.S. Goldwater fellow Mount Sinai Med. Ctr., N.Y.C., 1957-58; assoc. cons. J.G. Steinle Assocs., Garden City, N.Y., 1958-61; asst. prof. UCLA, 1962-65; assoc. dir. Touro Infirmary, New Orleans, 1964-66; prof. dir. U. Mo., 1966-71; v.p. E.D. Rosenfeld Assocs., N.Y.C., 1971-75; pres. Bedford Health Assocs. Inc., N.Y., N.C., 1975—; chmn. Health Edn. & Applied Rsch. Found., Washington, 1981-83; bd. dirs. Albany (N.Y.) Med. Ctr., Inc., 1974-77; cons. to numerous hosps., med. schs., health related orgs., 1958—. Contbr. articles profl. jours. Named vis. prof. W.K. Kellogg Found., Sydney, Australia, 1969; recipient svc. award Am. Assn. Healthcare Cons., 1982; Weil Disting. Profl. in Health Svcs. Mgmt., U. Mo. established in 1991. Fellow emeritus Am. Assn. Healthcare Cons.; fellow Am. Coll. Healthcare Execs.; fellow Am. Pub. Health Assn. Jewish. Avocations: mantrailing bloodhounds, quarter horses. Home: 1400 Town Mountain Rd Asheville NC 28804-2936 Office: Bedford Health Assocs Inc Flat Iron Bldg Ste 900A Asheville NC 28801

WEILAND, CHARLES HANKES, lawyer; b. Billings, Mont., Feb. 19, 1921; s. George Michael and Elizabeth (Hankes) W. A.B. cum laude, Johns Hopkins U., 1942; J.D., Harvard U., 1948. Bar: Ill. 1949, U.S. Dist. Ct. (no. dist.) Ill. 1949, U.S. Ct. Appeals (7th cir.) 1949, U.S. Supreme Ct. 1968. Assoc. Lord, Bissell & Brook, Chgo., 1948-55, ptnr., 1956-83; chmn. Cook County Inquiry Bd., Supreme Ct. Ill. Atty. Regis. and Disciplinary Commn., 1974-75. Served with AUS, 1942-46. Mem. Ill. Bar Assn., Chgo. Bar Assn. Republican. Clubs: Law; Legal (Chgo.).

WEILAND, STEPHEN CASS, lawyer; b. San Antonio, Apr. 29, 1948; s. Frank H. and Elleen (Pitman) W.; m. Jessica Buhler; children: Bradley, Cartwright, Kathryn. AB, Coll. William and Mary, Williamsburg, Va., 1970; JD, U. Tex., 1973. Bar: Tex. 1973, D.C. 1974. Trial atty. U.S. Dept. Justice, Washington, 1973-80; asst. dir. Commodity Futures Trading Commn., Washington, 1980-81; chief counsel U.S. Senate Permanent Subcom. on Investigations, Washington, 1981-85; of counsel Matthews & Branscomb, Corpus Christi, Tex., 1985-86; litigation ptnr. Jackson & Walker, Dallas, 1986—. Mem. ABA (mem. white collar crime com., criminal justice sect.). Republican. Office: Jackson & Walker 901 Main St # 6000 Dallas TX 75202-3797

WEILBACHER, ROBERT JAMES, Micronesian goverment official; b. Lelu, Kosrae, Fed. State of Micronesia, Sept. 14, 1946; s. Bernard Fritz and Kenye (James) W.; m. Josephia Fausto Arriola; children: Debra, Robert Jr., Wayne, Bradley, Leigh, Trixie, Flora, Iona, Yvonne. BS in Marine Transport, Philipping Mcht. Marine Acad., 1970. Lic. master and harbor pilot. Master govt. vessels, Saipan, Mariana Islands, 1970-75; supr. air ops. TTPI Govt., Saipan, 1975-76, chief divsn. aviation Dept. Transp., 1976-80; chief transp. divsn. Fed. Republic of Micronesia, Pohnpei, 1980-87, sec. Dept. Transp. and Comm., 1987—; mem. Environ Protection Bd. Fed. State Micronesia, Pohnpei, 1983-87, mem. Banking Bd., 1983-87. Roman Catholic. Office: Dept Transp and Comm, Palikir Ponape FM 96941

WEILBACHER, WILLIAM MANNING, advertising and marketing consultant; b. Albany, N.Y., June 23, 1928; s. William Carl and Gladys (Manning) W.; m. Martha Ethel Meyer, May 19, 1962; children: Barbara Taylor, Elizabeth Manning. BS, Yale U., 1949; MS, Columbia, 1951. Super. product analysis Nat. Biscuit Co., 1951-53; v.p., dir. rsch. Dancer-Fitzgerald-Sample, Inc., 1953-62, sr. v.p., 1971-73, exec. v.p., 1973-74, vice chmn., 1974-79; bd. dir., sr. v.p. McCaffrey & McCall, 1962-66; exec. dir. Ctr. for Advanced Practice, 1966; ptnr. Jack Tinker and Ptnrs., Interpub. Inc., 1966-69; v.p., dir. rsch. J. Walter Thompson Co., 1969-70; pres. Master Jazz Recs., Inc., 1967—, D-F-S Realty Inc., 1975-79, D-F-S Holdings Inc., 1974-79, Bismark Corp., 1979—, Second Mktg. Opinion, Inc., 1981—; lectr. advt. Grad. Sch. Bus., Columbia U., 1956-64, adj. prof. mktg., 1976-77, 81-82, 83; lectr. mktg. CCNY, 1955-57; adj. prof. mktg. Grad. Sch. Bus., NYU, 1965-70, 80-81, 83; Spencer vis. prof. S.I. Newhouse Sch. Pub. Comms., Syracuse U., 1982-86; mem. Radio-TV Ratings Rev. Coun., 1958-65; bd. dirs. Audit Bur. Circulation, 1964-71, Broacast Rating Coun., 1963-67; mem. tech. adv. com. Robert Wood Johnson Found., 1994—. Author: (with L.O. Brown, R. S. Lessler) Advertising Media, 1957, (with H.C. Barksdale) Marketing Research; Selected Readings and Analytic Commentaries, 1966, (with R.A. Bauer, S.A. Greyser) Advertising in America: The Consumer View, 1968, Marketing Management Cases, 1970, 4th edit. 1986, Advertising, 1979, 2d edit. 1984, Cases in Advertising, 1981, Auditing Productivity, 1981, Choosing an Advertising Agency, 1983, Current Advertiser Practices in Compensating Their Advertising Agencies, 1983, 86, 89, 92, 95, Choosing and Working with Your Advertising Agency, 1991, Managing Agency Relations, 1991, Brand Marketing, 1993, contbg. editor: Marketing Handbook, 1965. Vice chmn. tech. com. Advt. Rsch. Found., 1960-63, chmn., 1963-65, bd. dirs.,

1965-67. Mem. Am. Assn. Advt. Agys. (past vice chmn. rsch. com.), Market Rsch. Coun. (pres. 1970-71), Yale Club of N.Y.C., Eastward Ho Country Club, Alpha Kappa Psi, Beta Gamma Sigma. Home: Box 2002 30 Bismark Way Dennis MA 02638-2207

WEILER, JEFFRY LOUIS, lawyer; b. N.Y.C., Dec. 31, 1942; s. Kurt and Elaine (Kabb) W.; m. Susan Karen Goodman, June 8, 1964; children: Philip K., June M. BS, Miami U., Oxford, Ohio, 1964; JD, Cleve. State U., 1970. Bar: Ohio 1970, Fla. 1981; CPA, Ohio 1968. Acct. Meaden & Moore, CPAs, Cleve., 1964-65; IRS agt. U.S. Dept. Treasury, Cleve., 1965-70; assoc. Ulmer & Berne, Cleve., 1970-71; ptnr. Benesch, Friedlander, Coplan & Aronoff, Cleve., 1971—; adj. assoc. prof. Cleve.-Marshall Coll. Law, Cleve. State U., 1980-87. Contbr. to profl. pubs. Former trustee, Jewish Community Fedn., Cleve., 1978-83. Fellow Am. Coll. Trust and Estate Counsel; mem. ABA (sect. taxation, estate and gift tax subcom.), Cleve. Estate Planning Inst. (chmn. 1980), Cleve. Tax Inst. (chmn. 1983), Cleve. Bar Assn. (chmn. 1993—, trustee 1989-91). Avocations: photography, sailboat racing, ice skating. Home: 24714 Maidstone Ln Cleveland OH 44122-1614 Office: Benesch Friedlander 2300 BP America Bldg 200 Public Sq Cleveland OH 44114-2378

WEILER, JOSEPH ASHBY, newspaper editor; b. St. Louis, Oct. 23, 1946; s. Thomas Joseph and Nancy Delaureal (Bakewell) W.; m. Lisa Gillenwater, Dec. 17, 1972 (div. 1979). BJ, U. Mo., 1968, postgrad., 1970-71. Reporter Topeka Daily Capital, 1968, The Comml. Appeal, Memphis, 1971-77; city editor The Oakland Press, Pontiac, Mich., 1977, metro editor, 1978; editor The News-Democrat, Belleville, Ill., 1978-81, gen. mgr., 1982; metro editor The News-Sentinel, Ft. Wayne, Ind., 1982-83, mng. editor, 1983-88, exec. editor, 1988—. Pres. Leadership Ft. Wayne Alumni Assn., 1988-89; bd. dirs. Opus 18, Ft. Wayne. With U.S. Army, 1968-70, Fed. Republic of Germany; bd. advisors YMCA Downtown.. Recipient Pub. Svce. awards Tenn. Press Assn., 1975, 76. Mem. Am. Soc. Newspaper Editors, Associated Press Mng. Editors, Phi Kappa Theta. Roman Catholic. Avocations: boating, racquetball. Home: 1137 Illsley Dr Fort Wayne IN 46807-2120 Office: The News Sentinel PO Box 100 Fort Wayne IN 46801-0100

WEILER, KURT WALTER, radio astronomer; b. Phoenix, Mar. 16, 1943; s. Henry Carl and Dorothy (Esser) w.; m. Geertje Stoelwinder, June 8, 1979; children: Corinn Nynke Yoon, Anil Erick Jivan, Sanna Femke Lee. BS, U. Ariz., 1964; PhD, Calif. Inst. Tech., 1970. Guest investigator Netherlands Found. for Radioastronomy, Groningen, 1970-74; sci. collaborator Inst. for Radioastronomy, Bologna, Italy, 1975-76; sr. scientist Max Planck Inst. for Radioastronomy, Bonn, W.Ger., 1976-79; program dir. NSF, Washington, 1979-85; radio astronomer Naval Rsch. Lab, Washington, 1985—; Halley steering com. NASA, Washington, 1981-85. Author: WSRT Users Guide, 1973, 75; editor Radio Astronomy from Space, 1987; contbr. over 100 articles to profl. jours. and mags. Mem. Am. Astron. Soc., Royal Astron. Soc., Internat. Astron. Union, Internat. Sci. Radio Union, Nederlandse Astronomen Club, Jaguar Club, Nat. Capital Club. Home: 6232 Cockspur Dr Alexandria VA 22310-1504 Office: Naval Rsch Lab Code 7214 4555 Overlook Ave SW Washington DC 20375-5300

WEILER, PAUL CRONIN, law educator; b. Port Arthur, Ont., Can., Jan. 28, 1939; s. G. Bernard and Marcella (Cronin) W.; m. Florrie Darwin, 1988; children: Virginia, John, Kathryn, Charles. B.A. with honors, U. Toronto, 1960, M.A. with honors, 1961; LL.B., Osgoode Hall Law Sch., 1964; LLM, Harvard Law Sch., 1965; LL.D., U. Victoria, 1981. Bar: Ont. Prof. law Osgoode Hall Law Sch., 1965-72; chmn. Labour Relations Bd. B.C., 1973-78; Mackenzie King prof. Can. studies Harvard Law Sch., 1978-80, prof. law, 1980—, Henry J. Friendly prof. law, 1993—; prof. law, 1993—; chief counsel U.S. Commn. Future of Worker-Mgmt. Rels.; prin. legal investigator Harvard U. Med. Practice Study Group; impartial umpire AFL-CIO; chief reporter Am. Law Inst. Tort Reform Project; cons. to U.S. Commn. on Comprehensive Health Care (Pepper Commn.); spl. counsel Govt. of Ont. Rev. of Workers' Compensation, 1980-88; mem. pub. rev. bd. United Auto Workers, chief counsel Pres.' commn. Future Worker-Mgmt. Rels., 1993—; panelist, US/Canada Free Trade Agreement Softwood Lumber Arbitration, 1992-93. Author: Labor Arbitration and Industrial Change, 1970; In the Last Resort: A Critical Study of the Supreme Court of Canada, 1974; (with others) Labor Relations Law in Canada, rev. edit. 1974; (with others) Studies in Sentencing in Canada, 1974; Reconcilable Differences: New Directions in Canadian Labour Law, 1980; Reforming Workers Compensation, 1980; MEGA Projects: The Collective Bargaining Dimensions, 1981; Protecting the Worker From Disability, 1983; Governing the Workplace: The Future of Labor and Employment Law, 1990; (with others) Patients, Doctors, and Lawyers: Medical Injury, Malpractice Litigation and Patient Compensation, 1990; Medical Malpractice on Trial, 1991; (with others) A Measure of Malpractice, 1992; Cases, Materials and Problems on Sports & the Law, 1993; contbr. articles to profl. jours. Mem. Nat. Acad. Arbitrators, Nat. Acad. Social Ins., Nat. Acad. Sci., Inst. Medicine. Roman Catholic. Club: Cambridge Tennis (Cambridge, Mass.). Office: Harvard U Law Sch 1525 Massachusetts Ave Cambridge MA 02138-2918

WEILER, TODD ALAN, army official; b. Texarkana, Tex., Oct. 7, 1964; s. Gerald and Mamie Ruth (Clements) Penny. BA, Tex. Christian U., 1987. Cert. comml. rated rotorcraft aviator. Mem. campaign staff Clinton for Pres., 1992; White House liaison Dept. Def., Washington, 1993; dep. asst. sec. U.S. Army, Washington, 1993—; Dept. of Army rep. Civil-Tiltrotor Commn., Washington, 1993—. With U.S. Army, 1987-91, Desert Storm. Decorated 2 Air medals. Mem. VFW, Am. Legion, Intel. Charities Am., 101st Airborne Assn., Clinton-Gore Adminstrn. Assn. Democrat. Avocations: boating, flying, skiing. Home: 326 Cloude's Mill Dr Alexandria VA 22304 Office: OASA M&RA The Pentagon Rm 2E 580 Washington DC 20310

WEIL-GARRIS BRANDT, KATHLEEN, art historian; d. Kurt Hermann and Charlotte (Garris) Weil; m. Werner Brandt (dec. 1983). BA with honors, Vassar Coll., 1956; postgrad., U. Bonn, 1956-57; MA, Radcliffe U., 1958; PhD, Harvard, 1966. Asst. prof. NYU, N.Y.C., 1963-67, assoc. prof., 1967-72, prof., 1973—; asst. prof. NYU Inst. Fine Arts, N.Y.C., 1966-67, assoc. prof., 1967-72, prof., 1973—; vis. prof. Harvard U., Cambridge, Mass., 1980; editor in chief The Art Bulletin, N.Y.C., 1977-81; cons. on Renaissance art Vatican Mus., 1987—; vis. fellow Bibliotheca Hartziana (Max-Planck Inst.) Rome. Author: Leonardo and Central Italian Art, 1974, Problems In Cinquecento Sculpture, 1977; author: (with J. d'Amico) The Renaissance Cardinal's Ideal Palace, 1981; contbr. numerous articles to profl. jours. Decorated officer Order of Merit (Italy); recipient rsch. award Humboldt Found., 1985, Disting. Tchg. award Lindback Found., 1967, Golden Dozen Tchr. award NYU, 1993; Guggenheim fellow, 1976; grantee Henkel Found., 1987. Mem. Coll. Art Assn. (bd. dirs. 1973-74, 77-81), Renaissance Soc. Am. (editl. bd. 1992—), Soc. Archtl. Historians, N.Y. Acad. Scis., Phi Beta Kappa (v.p. NYU chpt. 1979-81). Avocations: art films, conservation, music, dance. Office: NYU Inst Fine Arts 1 E 78th St New York NY 10021-0178

WEILL, GEORGES GUSTAVE, mathematics educator; b. Strasbourg, France, Apr. 9, 1926; came to U.S., 1956; s. Edmond and Germaine (Falck) W. Ed., Ecole Polytechnique, Paris, 1950; E.N.S., Telecom., Paris, 1952; Licence de Mathematiques, U. Paris, France, 1954, D.Sc. in Physics, 1955; Ph.D in Math, U. Calif. at Los Angeles, 1960. Research scientist Compagnie Generale de Telegraphie Sans Fil, France, 1952-56; research fellow dept. elec. engring. Calif. Inst. Tech., Pasadena, 1956-59; teaching asso. math. U. Calif. at Los Angeles, 1959-60; research fellow math. Harvard, 1960-62; lectr., research asso. Yale, 1962-64; vis. asst. prof. Belfer Grad. Sch. Sci., Yeshiva U., 1964-65; assoc. prof. math. Poly. U., Bklyn., 1964-65, prof., 1966—. Mem. Am. Math. Soc., Societe Mathematique de France, IEEE (sr. mem.), Sigma Xi, Pi Mu Epsilon. Office: Polytechnic Univ 333 Jay St Brooklyn NY 11201-2907

WEILL, GUS, JR., communications consultant; b. Lafayette, La., Sept. 14, 1962; s. Gus and Ann (Harris) W. Reporter WAFB-TV, Baton Rouge, 1984-85; press sec. City Coun. Pres. of N.Y.C., 1985-86; press advisor Sen. Daniel P. Moynihan, N.Y.C., 1987-88; v.p. Penn & Schoen Assocs., N.Y.C., 1988-90; exec. v.p., gen. mgr. Edelman Pub. Rels., N.Y.C., 1990—. Jewish. Office: Edelman 1500 Broadway New York NY 10036-4015

WEILL, HANS, physician, educator; b. Berlin, Aug. 31, 1933; came to U.S., 1939; s. Kurt and Gerda (Philipp) W.; m. Kathleen Burton, Apr. 3, 1958; children: Judith, Leslie, David. B.S., Tulane U., 1955, M.D., 1958. Diplomate: Am. Bd. Internal Medicine. Intern Mt. Sinai Hosp., N.Y.C., 1958-59; resident Tulane Med. Unit, Charity Hosp. La., New Orleans, 1959-60; chief resident Tulane Med. Unit, Charity Hosp. La., 1961-62, sr. vis. physician, 1972—; NIH research fellow dept. medicine and pulmonary lab. Sch. Medicine Tulane U., New Orleans, 1960-61; instr. medicine Sch. Medicine Tulane U., 1962-64, asst. prof. medicine, 1964-67, assoc. prof., 1967-71, prof. medicine, 1971—; Schlieder Found. prof. pulmonary medicine, 1985—; chief Environ. Medicine sect. Tulane Med. Center, 1980—; dir. univ. Ctr. for Bioenviron. Rsch., 1989-93; dir. interdisciplinary research group in occupational lung diseases Nat. Heart, Lung and Blood Inst., 1972-92, mem. nat. adv. council, 1986-90, chmn. pulmonary disease adv. com., 1982-84; active staff Tulane Med. Center Hosp., 1976—; program dir. Nat. Inst. for Environ. Health Sci., 1992—; cons. pulmonary diseases Touro Infirmary, New Orleans, 1962—; cons. NIH, Nat. Inst. Occupational Safety and Health, Occupational Safety and Health Adminstrn., USN, NAS, EPA; lectr., participant workshops and confs. profl. groups in U.S., France, Can., U.K.; dir. Nat. Inst. Environ. Health Scis Superfund. Basic Rsch. Program, 1992—. Mem. editorial bd. Am. Rev. of Respiratory Disease, 1980-85, CHEST, 1987-91; editor Respiratory Diseases Digest, 1981; guest editor Byssinosis conf. supplement, CHEST, 1981. Fellow Am. Acad. Allergy, Royal Soc. Medicine, ACP; mem. Am. Thoracic Soc. (pres. 1976), Am. Lung Assn. (bd. dirs. 1975-78), New Orleans Acad. Internal Medicine (sec., treas. 1973-75), Am. Coll. Chest Physicians (gov. for La. 1970-75), Am. Fedn. Clin. Research, So. Soc. Clin. Investigation, N.Y. Acad. Scis., Brit. Thoracic Assn., Internat. Epidemiol. Assn., Am. Heart Assn. (task force on environment and cardiovascular system 1978), Brit. Thoracic Soc., Phi Beta Kappa, Alpha Omega Alpha. Home: 333 Friedrichs Ave Metairie LA 70005-4518 Office: Tulane U Sch Medicine Sect Environ Medicine 1430 Tulane Ave New Orleans LA 70112-2699

WEILL, RICHARD L., lawyer; b. Lincoln, Nebr., Jan. 28, 1943; s. Walter and Irma (Heineman) W.; m. Judy A. Brumm, July 11, 1965; children: David, John. BS, U. Nebr., 1964; LLB, NYU, 1967. Bar: N.Y. 1967, Nebr. 1969. Assoc. Proskauer Rose Goetz & Mendelsohn, N.Y.C., 1967-69; ptnr. Kutak Rock, Omaha, 1969-89; gen. counsel MBIA Inc., Armonk, N.Y., 1989-91, exec. v.p., 1991—. Home: 24 Bretton Ridge Rd Mount Kisco NY 10549-9650 Office: MBIA Inc 113 King St Armonk NY 10504-1611

WEILL, SAMUEL, JR., automobile company executive; b. Rochester, N.Y., Dec. 22, 1916; s. Samuel and Bertha (Stein) W.; student U. Buffalo, 1934-35; m. Mercedes Weil, May 20, 1939 (div. Aug. 1943); children: Rita and Eric (twins); m. Cléanthe Kimball Carr, Aug. 12, 1960 (div. 1982); m. Jacqueline Natalie Bateman, Jan. 5, 1983. Co-owner, Brayton Air Coll., St. Louis, 1937-42; assoc. editor, advt. mgr., bus. mgr. Road and Track Mag., Los Angeles, 1951-53; pres. Volkswagen Pacific, Inc., Culver City, Calif., 1953-73, Porsche Audi Pacific, Culver City, 1953-73; chmn. bd. Minto Internat., Inc., London; v.p. fin. Chieftain Oil Co., Ojai, Calif. Recipient Tom May award Jewish Hosp. and Research Center, 1971. Served with USAAF, 1943-45. Home: 305 Pauma Rd Ojai CA 93023-2432 Office: Chieftain Oil Co 214 W Aliso St Ojai CA 93023-2599

WEILL, SANFORD I., banker; b. N.Y.C., Mar. 16, 1933; s. Max and Etta (Kalika) W.; m. Joan Mosher, June 20, 1955; children: Marc P., Jessica M. B.A., Cornell U., 1955, student Grad. Sch. Bus. and Pub. Adminstrn., 1954-55. Chmn. bd., chief exec. officer Carter, Berlind & Weill (name changed to CBWL-Hayden, Stone, Inc. 1970, to Hayden Stone Inc. 1972, to Shearson Hayden Stone 1974, to Shearson Loeb Rh, N.Y.C., 1960-84; dir., chmn. exec. com. Carter, Berlind & Weill (name changed to CBWL-Hayden, Stone, Inc. 1970, to Hayden Stone, Inc. 1972, to Shearson Hayden Stone 1974, to Shearson Loeb Rh, 1981-83, pres., 1983-85; chmn. Fireman's Fund, 1984-85; past pres., chmn. exec. com., mem. fin. com. Am. Express Co., until 1989; chmn., chief exec. officer Primerica Corp., N.Y.C., 1989—, pres., until 1992; chmn. Primerica Holdings Inc., N.Y.C.; chmn., pres., chief exec. officer Comml. Credit Co., Balt., 1986—; dir. IDS Mutual Funds Group; chmn. adv. council The Johnson Grad. Sch. of Mgmt.; founder Acad. of Fin. Mem. bd. overseers Cornell Med. Coll.; chmn. Carnegie Hall, N.Y.C.; mem. bus. com. Mus. of Modern Art, N.Y.C. Mem. N.Y. Soc. Security Analysts. Clubs: Cornell (N.Y.C.), Century Country (Purchase, N.Y.), Harmonie (N.Y.C.). Office: Travelers Inc 65 E 55th St New York NY 10022-3219*

WEIMAN, STEPHEN L., investment company executive; b. 1958. Grad., Ithaca Coll., 1982. With Hein & Assocs., CPA, Denver, 1982-87; sr. v.p., COO Asset Investors Corp, Denver, 1987—. Office: Asset Investors Corp 3600 S Yosemite St Denver CO 80237-1812*

WEIMER, JEAN ELAINE, nursing educator; b. Denver, June 8, 1932; d. John and Marquerite Christina (Friehauf) Jacoby; m. James David Weimer, Aug. 5, 1956; 1 dau., Lisa Marie. Diploma in nursing Children's Hosp. Sch. Nursing, Denver, 1953; BS in Nursing, U. Denver, 1954; MA, NYU, 1962. RN, Colo., S.D., N.Y., Ill. Staff nurse Children's Hosp., Denver, 1953-54, head nurse, 1954-56; dir. nursing edn. Yankton (S.D.) State Hosp., 1956-60; instr. Mt. Sinai Hosp. Sch. Nursing, N.Y.C., 1960-64, curriculum coord., 1964-67; asst. prof. nursing City Colls. Chgo., 1968-78, assoc. prof., 1978-85, prof., 1985—; co-chmn. nursing dept. Truman Coll., 1984-93, chmn. 1993—; chmn. program com. RN Tutoring project, 1988-92. Deacon United Ch. of Christ, 1988-90. NIMH grantee, 1960-62. Mem. Am. Nurses Assn., Coun. Advanced Practioners Psychiat. Coun. of Dirs. of Assoc. Degree Nursing Programs, Nursing Truman Coll. Faculty Coun., City Coll. Faculty Coun., Kappa Delta Pi, Pi Lambda Theta. Home: 50 E Bellevue Pl Apt 904 Chicago IL 60611-1167 Office: Truman Coll 1145 W Wilson Ave Box 184 Chicago IL 60640-5691

WEIMER, PAUL K(ESSLER), electrical engineer; b. Wabash, Ind., Nov. 5, 1914; s. Claude W. and Eva V. (Kessler) W.; m. Katherine E. Mounce, July 18, 1942; children: Katherine Weimer Lasslob, Barbara Weimer Blackwell, Patricia Weimer Hess. A.B., Manchester Coll., 1936, D.Sc. (hon.), 1968; M.A. in Physics, U. Kans., 1938; Ph.D. in Physics, Ohio State U., 1942. Prof. phys. sci. Tabor Coll., 1937-39; research engr. David Sarnoff Research Center, RCA Labs., Princeton, N.J., 1942-65; fellow tech. staff David Sarnoff Research Center, RCA Labs., 1965-81, cons., 1981—. Recipient TV Broadcasters award, 1946, Zworykin TV prize Inst. Radio Engrs., 1959, Sarnoff award in sci. RCA, 1963, Kulturpreis award German Photographic Soc., 1986, Albert Rose Electronic Imager of Yr. award, 1987, Pioneer award N.J. Inventors Hall of Fame, 1991. Fellow IEEE (Outstanding Paper award Solid State Circs. Conf. 1963, 65, Morris Liebmann prize 1966); mem. NAE. Holder 90 patents in field; active in initial devel. of TV camera tubes, solid state sensors and thin-film transistors. Home and Office: 112 Random Rd Princeton NJ 08540-4146

WEIMER, ROBERT JAY, geology educator, energy consultant, civic leader; b. Glendo, Wyo., Sept. 4, 1926; s. John L. and Helen (Mowrey) W.; m. Ruth Carol Adams, Sept. 12, 1948; children: Robert Thomas, Loren Edward (dec.), Paul Christner, Carl Scott. BA, U Wyo., 1948, MA, 1949; PhD, Stanford U., 1953. Registered profl. engr.. Geologist Union Oil Co. Calif., 1949-54; cons. geologist U.S. and fgn. petroleum exploration, 1954—; prof. geology Colo. Sch. Mines, 1957-83, prof. emeritus, 1983—, Getty prof. geology, 1978-83; vis. prof. U. Colo., 1961, U. Calgary, Can., 1970, Inst. Tech., Bandung, Indonesia, 1975; Fulbright lectr. U. Adelaide, South Australia, 1967; disting. lectr. and continuing edn. lectr. Am. Assn. Petroleum Geologists, Soc. Expl. Geophysicists; ednl. cons. to petroleum cos., 1964—; mem. energy rsch. adv. bd. Dept. Energy, 1985-90, Bd. on Mineral and Energy Resources, NAS, 1988. Editor: Guide to Geology of Colorado, 1960, Symposium on Cretaceous Rocks of Colorado and Adjacent Area, 1959, Denver Earthquakes, 1968, Fossil Fuel Exploration, 1974, Studies in Colorado Field Geology, 1976. Trustee Colo. Sch. Mines Research Found., 1967-70; pres. Rockland Found., 1982-83. With USNR, 1944-46. Recipient Disting. Alumnus award U. Wyo., 1982, Mines medal Colo. Sch. Mines, 1984, Brown medal, 1990, Parker medal Am. Inst. Profl. Geologists. Fellow Geol. Soc. Am. (chmn. Rocky Mountain sect. 1966-67), AAAS; mem. Am. Assn. Petroleum Geologists (pres. elect 1990, Sidney Powers medal), Soc. Econ. Paleontologists and Mineralogists (hon., sec.-treas. 1966-67, v.p. 1971, pres. 1972, Twenhofel medal 1995), Colo. Sci. Soc. (hon., pres. 1981), Rocky Mountain Assn. Geologists (pres. 1969, hon.

mem., Scientist of Yr. 1982), Wyo. Geol. .Assn. (hon.), Colo. Sch. Mines Alumni Assn. (hon., Coolbaugh award); Am. Geol. Inst. Found. (sec., treas. 1984-88), Nat. Acad. Engring., Mt. Vernon Country Club (Golden, bd. dirs. 1956-59, 81-84, pres. 1983-84). Home: RR 3 25853 Mt Vernon Rd Golden CO 80401-9699

WEIN, ALAN JEROME, urologist, educator, researcher; b. Newark, Dec. 15, 1941; s. Isadore R. and Jeanette Frances (Abrams) W. A.B. cum laude, Princeton U., 1962; M.D., U. Pa., 1966. Diplomate Am. Bd. Urology (trustee). Intern mixed surgery Hosp. U. Pa., Phila., 1966-67, resident surgery, 1967-68; resident urology U. Pa., Phila., 1969-72, fellow Harrison Dept. Surg. Rsch. Urology Medicine, 1968-69, asst. instr. surgery Sch. Medicine, 1967-68, asst. instr. urology, 1969-71, instr., 1971-72, asst. prof., 1974-76, assoc. prof., 1976-83, prof., 1983—, asst. chief urology, 1974-79, dir. Urodynamic Evaluation Ct., 1974—, chmn. div. urology, 1981—, chief urology, 1981—; dir. resident edn. com. div. urology Sch. Medicine U. Pa., 1976—, coord. program urologics oncology, 1976—; chief urology VA Hosp., Phila., 1974-82, attending urologist, 1982—; asst. surgeon Children's Hosp. Phila., 1974—; cons. CDC Coun. Incontinence, 1990—; assoc. surgeon Pa. Hosp., Phila., 1977—; attending urologist Grad. Hosp., Phila., 1980—. Author: (with D.M. Barrett) Controversies in Neuro-Urology, 1984, Voiding Functiona and Dysfunction: A Logical and Practical Approach, 1988, (with A.R. Mundy and T.P. Stephenson) Urodynamics: Principles, Practice and Application, 1984, 2d edit., 1994, (with P.M. Hanno) A Clinical Manual of Urology, 1987, 2d edit., 1994, (with Hanno, Staskin and Krane) Interstitial Cystitis, 1990; editl. bd. asst. Urol. Survey, 1978-81; editl. bd. World Jour. Urology, 1982—, Am. Urol. Assn. Update series, 1983—, Urol. Survey, 1987—, Internat. Jour. Impotence Rsch.: Basic and Clin. Studies, 1989—, Urology, 1991—; ad hoc reviewer Cancer, 1985—; cons. editor Sexuality and Disability, 1985—; asst. editor Jour. Urology, 1980-89, ad hoc reviewer clin. sect., 1989—, mem. editl. bd. investigative sect., 1989—; assoc. editor Neurology and Urodynamics, 1982—; contbr. over 560 articles and abstracts to profl. jours. Mem. coun. urology Nat. Kidney Found., Inc.; mem. lectrs. bur. Am. Cancer Soc., 1984—; mem. adv. panel Help for Incontinent People, 1987—; mem. adv. bd. Simon Found., 1987—; mem. med. adv. bd. Institial Cystitis Assn., 1987—; chmn. bladder health coun. Am. Found. Urologic Disease, 1990—; trustee Am. Bd. Urology, 1990—. Served to maj. MC, U.S. Army, 1972-74. Grantee VA, 1974-79, 79, 81, 81-84, 82-85, 85-88, 88-92, Eaton Labs., 1975-76, 78-80, McCabe Rsch. Fund, 1975-82, 87-88, Merrell Nat. Labs., 1979-82, 1980-82, Nat. Kidney Found., 1980-81, NIH, 1980-83, 83-88, 84-87, 87—, Roche Labs., 1981, Smith Kline and French Labs., 1982, 86-88, Eli Lilly Labs., 1986-88, 91, Found. Interstitial Cystitis, 1986-87, 87-88, Sterling Drug Co., 1991. Fellow ACS; mem. AAAS, AMA (cons. com. drug evaluation 1977—), Am. Acad. Clin. Neurophysiology, Am. Assn. Surgery of Trauma, Am. Assn. Clin. Urologists, Am. Assn. Genito-Urinary Surgeons , Am. Fertility Soc., Am. Inst. Ultrasound in Medicine, Am. Soc. Pharmacology and Exptl. Therapeutics, Am. Soc. Andrology, Am. Soc. Clin. Oncology, Am. Urol. Assn. (chmn. practical cases urology 1982—), rsch. com. 1985—, editorial com mid-Atlantic sect. 1988—), Assn. Acad. Surgery, Can. Urol. Assn., Clin. Soc. Genito-Urinary Surgeons , Ea. Cooperative Oncologic Group, Endourol. Soc., Internat. Continence Soc., Nat. Assn. VA Physicians, N.Y. Acad. Scis., Coll. Physicians Phila., Del. Valley Soc. Transplant Surgeons, John Morgan Soc., Pa. Med. Assn., Pa. Oncologic Soc., Phila. Acad. Surgery, Phila. County Med. Soc., Phila. Profl. Standards Rev. Orgn., Phila. Urologic Soc. (pres. 1990-91), Ravdin-Rhoads Surg. Soc., Urol. Assn. Pa., Radiation Therapy Oncology Group (genitourinary working com. 1980—), Royal Soc. Medicine, Soc. Internat. d'Urologie, Soc. Basic Urologic Rsch., Soc. Sex Therapy and Rsch., Soc. Govt. Sec. Urologists, Soc. Pelvic Surgeons, Soc. Univ. Surgeons, Soc. Univ. Urologists, Soc. Urologic Oncology, Univ. Uro-logic Forum, Urodynamics Soc. (exec. com. 1980—), Urologic Rsch. Soc., Urologist's Ca Omega Alpha. Home: 609 Robinson Ln Haverford PA 19041-1921 Office: Hosp U Pa 5 Silverstein Pavilion 3400 Spruce St Philadelphia PA 19104-4219

WEIN, BERNARD J., retail executive. BA, U. Pitts., 1962. With Gimbel's Dept. Stores, N.Y.C., 1963-72, Allied Stores Corp., Ohio and Pa., 1972-86; sr. v.p. Catherine's Inc., Memphis, 1986-87, pres., chief exec., 1987-92, chmn. bd. dirs., pres., CEO, 1992—; pres. Virginia Specialty Stores, Memphis. Office: Catherine's Stores Corp 3742 Lamar Ave Memphis TN 38118-3727*

WEINBACH, ARTHUR FREDERIC, computing services company executive; b. Waterbury, Conn., May 3, 1943; s. Max and Winifred (Eckstein) W.; m. Joanne Kaplan, Nov. 20, 1970; children: Michael Scott, Jonathan David. BS in Econs., U. Pa., 1965, MS in Acctg., 1966. CPA. Various positions with Touche Ross & Co., N.Y.C., 1966-75; ptnr. Touche Ross & Co., Stamford, Conn., 1976-79; v.p. Automatic Data Processing, Inc., Roseland, N.J., 1980-81; v.p. fin. Automatic Data Processing, Inc., Clifton, N.J., 1981-82, sr. v.p. adminstrn. and fin., 1982-91, exec. v.p., 1992-94, pres., 1994—; also bd. dirs. Automatic Data Processing, Inc., Roseland, 1989—. Editor mag. sect. Conn. CPA Mag., 1978-79. Chmn. task force Stamford Area Commerce and Industry Assn., 1979; bd. dirs. Boys Hope, 1991—, Overlook Hosp. Found., 1991—; Metro N.J. U. Pa. Club, 1993—. Mem. Fin. Execs. Inst. Jewish. Home: 372 Long Hill Dr Short Hills NJ 07078-1208 Office: ADP Inc 1 A D P Blvd Roseland NJ 07068-1728

WEINBACH, LAWRENCE ALLEN, accounting executive; b. N.Y.C., Jan. 8, 1940; s. Max N. and Winifred H. Weinbach; m. Patricia Leiter, Dec. 1961; children: Wendy, Peter, Daniel. BS in Econs., U. Pa., 1961. CPA, Conn., N.Y., other states. With Arthur Andersen & Co. (CPA's), N.Y.C., 1961—; mng. ptnr. Arthur Andersen & Co. (CPA's), Stamford, Conn., 1974-80; ptnr.-in-charge N.Y. acctg. and audit practice Arthur Andersen & Co., N.Y.C., 1980-83, mng. ptnr. N.Y. and N.Y. Met. area, 1983-87, mem. bd. ptnrs., 1984—, chmn. bd. ptnrs., 1986-87, mng. ptnr., COO, 1987-89, mng. ptnr., chief exec., 1989—; bd. dirs. U.S.-Japan Bus. Coun., 1989-94. Bd. dirs. Hartman Regional Theatre, Stamford, 1976-80, chmn. bd. dirs., 1977-78; mem. bd. incorporators Stamford Hosp., 1976-84; bd. dirs. United Way, Stamford, 1976-78, Phoenix House Inc., 1984-92, Coun. on Fgn. Rels., 1986—, Catalyst, 1991—; trustee Carnegie Hall, 1985—, Northwestern U., 1990—; mem. bd. overseers Wharton Sch., U. Pa., 1988—, Pub. Policy Inst., 1990—, Am. Bus. Conf., 1990—, Stern Sch., NYU, 1990—, Asia Soc., 1994—. Mem. AICPA, N.Y. Soc. CPAs, Conn. Soc. CPAs, Econs. Club N.Y. (mem. bd. overseere 1985—), Chgo. Club, Harmonie Club, Univ. Club, Beta Gamma Sigma, Beta Alpha Psi. Office: Arthur Andersen & Co 1345 Avenue Of The Americas New York NY 10105-0010

WEINBERG, ALVIN MARTIN, physicist; b. Chgo., Apr. 20, 1915; s. J.L. and Emma (Levinson) W.; m. Margaret Despres, June 14, 1940 (dec. 1969); children: David, Richard; m. Gene K. DePersio, Sept. 20, 1974. A.B., U. Chgo., 1935, A.M., 1936, Ph.D., 1939; LL.D., U. Chattanooga, Alfred U.; D.Sc., U. Pacific, Denison U., Kenyon Coll., Worcester Poly. Inst., U. Rochester, Stevens Inst. Tech., Butler U., U. Louisville, U. Bridgeport. Research assoc. math. biophysics U. Chgo., 1939-41, Metall. Lab., 1941-45; joined Oak Ridge Nat. Lab., 1945, dir. physics div., 1947-48, research dir. lab., 1948-55, dir. lab., 1955-74; dir. Office Energy R&D, Fed. Energy Adminstrn., 1974, Inst. Energy Analysis, Oak Ridge, 1975-85; disting. fellow Oak Ridge Associated Univs., 1985—; mem. Pres.'s Sci. Adv. Com., 1960-62, Pres.'s Medal of Sci. Com. Author: Reflections on Big Science, 1967, (with E.P. Wigner) Physical Theory of Neutron Chain Reactors, 1958, Continuing the Nuclear Dialogue, 1985, Nuclear Reactions: Science and Trans-Science, 1992, The First Nuclear Era: The Life and Times of a Technological Fixer, 1994; co-author: The Second Nuclear Era, 1985; co-editor: The Nuclear Connection, 1985, Stratetic Defenses and Arms Control, 1987; editor: Eugene Wigner's Collected Works on Nuclear Energy, 1992. Recipient Atoms for Peace award, 1960, E.O. Lawrence award, 1960, U. Chgo. Alumni medal, 1966, Heinrich Hertz award, 1975, N.Y. Acad. Scis. award, 1976, Enrico Fermi award, 1980, Harvey prize, 1982, Eugene Wigner award in reactor physics, 1992. Mem. Nat. Acad. Scis. (applied sci. sect.), Am. Nuclear Soc. (pres. 1959-60), Nat. Acad. Engring., Am. Acad. Arts and Scis., Am. Philos. Soc., Royal Netherlands Acad. Sci. (fgn. asso.). Home: 111 Moylan Ln Oak Ridge TN 37830-5351 Office: Oak Ridge Associated Univs PO Box 117 Oak Ridge TN 37831-0117

WEINBERG, D. MARK, health insurance company executive; b. Aug. 4, 1952; s. Melvin Weinberg; m. Allyson Weinberg; children: Amanda, Sarah, Tiffany, Sean. BS in Elec. Engring., U. Mo., 1975. Gen. mgr. CTX

Products div. Pet, Inc., St. Louis, 1975-81; prin. Touche-Ross and Co., Chgo., 1981-87; exec. v.p. Blue Cross of Calif., Thousand Oaks, 1987-92, Wellpoint Health Networks, Woodland Hills, 1992—. Contbr. articles to profl. jours. Mem. exec. bd. United Way; pres. Sr. Alliance, Inc.; vice-chmn. Calif. Ins. Mktg. Svc., Inc. Mem. Conejo Valley C. of C. (bd. dirs.). Office: Wellpoint Health Networks Inc 21555 Oxnard St Woodland Hills CA 91367*

WEINBERG, DAVID, chemicals executive. Co-chmn. bd., CEO Fel-Pro Inc., Skokie, Ill., 1965—. Office: Fel-Pro Inc 7450 Mccormick Blvd Skokie IL 60076-4046*

WEINBERG, DAVID B., lawyer; b. Chgo., Feb. 19, 1952; s. Judd A. and Marjorie (Gottlieb) W.; m. Lynne Ellen Mesirow, July 6, 1980; children: Julie, Jane, Jonathan. AB cum laude, Harvard U., 1974; JD, Georgetown U., 1977. Bar: Ill. 1977, U.S. Dist. Ct. (no. dist.) Ill. 1977, U.S. Ct. Appeals (7th cir.) 1978. Law clerk to Hon. William G. Clark Supreme Ct. Ill., 1977-79; assoc. Lord, Bissell & Brook, Chgo., 1979-84, ptnr., 1985-89; ptnr. Mayer, Brown & Platt, Chgo., 1989—; Ill. Supreme Ct. com. Profl. Responsibility, Chgo., 1984-94, chmn. subcom. lawyers certification. Founding mem. Friends of Prentice, Chgo., 1986-87; assocs. bd. Rush-Presbyn. St. Luke's Med. Ctr., 1989—; founder, 1st pres., sec., trustee Ravinia Festival Assn., Highland Park, Ill., 1989—; jr. gov. bd. Chgo. Symphony Orchestra, 1979-86, chmn. fundraising com. 1981-82, chmn. nominating com. 1984-85; trustee Northwestern U., 1994—. Mem. ABA (sect. bus. law, com. fed. regulation securities), Harvard Club Chgo. (v.p. 1985-89), Chgo. Club, Standard Club Chgo. (dir. 1988-90), Econ. Club Chgo., Lake Shore Country Club, Arts Club Chgo. Office: Mayer Brown & Platt 190 S La Salle St Chicago IL 60603-3410

WEINBERG, EDWARD, lawyer; b. Whitewater, Wis., Sept. 5, 1918; s. Bernhard and Molly (Schotzky) W.; m. Anne Goldsmith, June 13, 1943; children—Mark, Robert. B.A., U. Wis.-Madison, 1939, LL.B., 1941. Bar: Wis. 1941, D.C. 1964, U.S. Supreme Ct. 1965. Atty., then asst. chief counsel Bur. Reclamation, 1944-54; asst. solicitor Dept. Interior, 1955-61, assoc. solicitor, 1962-63, dep. solicitor, 1963-68, solicitor, 1968-69; practiced in Washington, 1969—; mem. firm Duncan, Weinberg, Miller & Pembroke, P.C., 1974—; prin. cons. Nat. Water Commn., 1969-73. Author: Intrastate, Interstate and International Problems of Large-scale Water Transfer, 1969, The Colorado River Salinity Dispute, 1973; co-author: Meandering Through the Interior Maze, 1985, Federal Reserved Water Rights, 1990. Mem. Am. Fed., D.C. bar assns., Order of Coif, Artus, Tau Epsilon Rho. Democrat. Jewish. Home: 540 N St SW Washington DC 20024-4557 Office: 1615 M St NW Washington DC 20036-3209

WEINBERG, EUGENE DAVID, microbiologist, educator; b. Chgo., Mar. 4, 1922; s. Philip and Lenore (Bergman) W.; m. Frances Murl Izen, Sept. 5, 1949; children—Barbara Ann, Marjorie Jean, Geoffrey Alan, Michael Benjamin. B.S., U. Chgo., 1942, M.A., 1948, Ph.D., 1950. Instr. dept. microbiology Ind. U., Bloomington, 1950-53; asst. prof. Ind. U., 1953-57, asso. prof., 1957-61, prof., 1961—, head microbiology sect., med. sci. program, 1978—. Served with AUS, 1942-45. Mem. AAAS, Am. Soc. Microbiology, Soc. Geochemistry and Environ. Health. Office: Ind U Biology Dept Jordan Hall Bloomington IN 47405

WEINBERG, GERHARD LUDWIG, history educator; b. Hannover, Germany, Jan. 1, 1928; came to U.S. 1940, naturalized, 1949; s. Max Bendix and Kate Sarah (Gruenebaum) W.; m. Janet Kabler White, Apr. 29, 1989. BA, N.Y. State Coll. Tchrs., Albany, 1948; MA, U. Chgo., 1949, PhD, 1951; LHD honoris causa, SUNY, Albany, 1989. Research analyst War Documentation project Columbia U., 1951-54; vis. lectr. history U. Chgo., 1954-55, U. Ky., Lexington, 1955-56; dir. project microfilming captured German documents Am. Hist. Assn., 1956-57; asst. prof. U. Ky., 1957-59; mem. faculty U. Mich., Ann Arbor, 1959-74; prof. history U. Mich., 1963-74, chmn. dept., 1972-73; William Rand Kenan, Jr. prof. history U. N.C., Chapel Hill, 1974—; acting chmn. dept., 1989-90; vis. prof. Bonn U., 1983, USAF Acad., 1990-91; bd. dirs. World War II Studies Assn., 1968—; cons. in field. Author: Guide to Captured German Documents, 1952, Germany and the Soviet Union, 1939-1941, 1954, The Foreign Policy of Hitler's Germany, 1933-1936, 1970, The Foreign Policy of Hitler's Germany, 1937-1939, 1980, World in the Balance: Behind the Scenes of World II, 1981, A World at Arms: A Global History of World War II, 1994, Germany, Hitler and World War II, 1995; co-author: Soviet Partisans in World War II, 1964; editor: Hitlers zweites Buch, 1961, Transformation of a Continent, 1975; bd. editors Jour. Modern History, 1970-72, Central European History, 1970-72, Kansas Humanities Series, 1987—, Internat. history Rev., 1990—. Chmn. Ann Arbor Democratic Com., 1961-63; mem. Mich. Dem. Central Com., 1963-67; mem. adv. com. on the air force history program Sec. of Air Force, 1987-90. Wwith AUS, 1946-47. Fellow Social Sci. Research Council, 1962-63; fellow Am. Council Learned Socs., 1965-66; fellow Guggenheim Found., 1971-72; fellow Nat. Endowment Humanities, 1978-79. Mem. Am. Hist. Assn. (George Louis Beer prize 1971, 95, v.p. rsch. 1982-84), So. Hist. Assn. (chmn. European sect. 1989), Conf. Group for Ctrl. European History (chmn. 1982), Coordinating Com. Women in Hist. Profession, German Studies Assn. (exec. com. 1989-92, Halverson prize 1981, v.p. 1994—), World War II Studies Assn., Phi Beta Kappa. Jewish. Home: 1416 Mount Willing Rd Efland NC 27243-9646 Office: Dept History Univ NC Chapel Hill NC 27599-3195

WEINBERG, H. BARBARA, art historian, educator, curator paintings and sculpture; b. N.Y.C., Jan. 23, 1942; d. Max and Evelyn Kallman; m. Michael B. Weinberg, Aug. 30, 1964. AB, Barnard Coll., 1962; MA, Columbia U., N.Y.C., 1964, PhD, 1972. From asst. prof. to prof. art history Queens Coll. and Grad. Sch. CUNY, 1972-94; curator dept. Am. paintings and sculpture Met. Mus. Art., 1990—. Author: The Decorative Work of John La Farge, 1977, The American Pupils of Jean-Léon Gérome, 1984, The Lure of Paris: Nineteenth-Century American Painters and Their French Teachers, 1991; co-author: American Impressionism and Realism: The Painting of Modern Life, 1885-1915, 1994; mem. editorial bd. Am. Art Jour., 1984—. Mem. Coll. Art Assn., Phi Beta Kappa. Office: Met Mus Art 1000 Fifth Ave New York NY 10028-0198

WEINBERG, HARRY BERNARD, cardiologist; b. Fremont, Nebr., Apr. 29, 1913; s. Ephraim and Goldie (Levynsky) W.; m. Evelyn Waxenberg, Mar. 26, 1939; 1 son, Steven M. B.S. in Medicine, U. Nebr., 1935, M.D., 1936. Intern, Univ. Hosp., Omaha, 1936-37; resident cardiovascular disease Michael Reese Hosp., Chgo., 1938-40; pvt. practice internal medicine and cardiology Davenport, Iowa, 1940-69; coordinator Iowa Regional Med. Program, clin. prof. internal medicine U. Iowa Coll. Medicine, 1969-72; dir. med. edn. Meml. Hosp., Hollywood, Fla., 1972-74; pvt. practice medicine specializing in cardiology Hollywood, 1974-82; physician utilization rev. com., 1982-91; Bd. dirs. Iowa Heart Assn., 1953-64, pres., 1955-56. Bd. dirs. Davenport C. of C., 1958-61, v.p., 1961. Served to lt. col. AUS, 1940-46. Fellow ACP, Am. Coll. Cardiology; mem. AMA, Am. Heart Assn. (bd. dirs. 1956-69, fellow council clin. cardiology 1965—), Alpha Omega Alpha. Home: 4040 N Hills Dr Apt 37 Hollywood FL 33021-2453

WEINBERG, HARVEY A., apparel company executive; b. 1937; married. BS, U. Wis., 1959. Pres., chief exec. officer James K. Wilson, 1969-81; with Splty. Stores Group, 1980—, chmn., chief exec. officer, 1981-84; with Hartmarx Corp., Chicago, Ill., 1984—, vice chmn., 1986-87, vice chmn., chief exec. officer, from 1984, chmn., chief exec. officer; also bd. dirs. Hartmarx Corp. Office: Raleigh Clothiers Inc (NC) 222 N La Salle St Chicago IL 60601

WEINBERG, HELEN ARNSTEIN, American art and literature educator; b. Orange, N.J., June 17, 1927; d. Morris Jerome and Jeannette (Tepperman) Arnstein; m. Kenneth Gene Weinberg, Sept. 12, 1949; children: Janet Sue Weinberg Strassner, Hugh Benjamin, John Arnstein. BA in English Lit., Wellesley Coll., 1949; MA in English Lit., Western Res. U., 1953, PhD in English Lit., 1966. Teaching fellow Ohio State U., Columbus, 1949-51; instr. to prof. English Cuyahoga Community Coll., Cleve., 1953-57; instr. to prof. Cleve. (Ohio) Inst. Art, 1958—; standing officer Coll. English Assn. Ohio, 1987-90; vis. fellow NYU, 1985, Sch. Visual Art's, 1981; lecture tours Israel, 1968, 70, 71. Author: The New Novel in America: The Kafkan Mode in Contemporary Fiction, 1970.

Recipient fellowship in art history NEH, Columbia U., N.Y.C., 1977-78; Recipient Am. Culture grantee NEH/Vassar Coll., 1993. Mem. AAUP, Modern Lang. Assn., Coll. Art Assn. Democrat. Jewish. Home: 3015 Huntington Rd Shaker Heights OH 44120-2407 Office: Cleve Inst Art 11141 East Blvd Cleveland OH 44106-1710

WEINBERG, HERSCHEL MAYER, lawyer; b. Bklyn., Oct. 13, 1927; s. Jacob and Gertrude (Wernick) W. B.A., Bklyn. Coll., 1948; LL.B., Harvard U., 1952. Bar: N.Y. 1952. Atty. firm Payne & Steingarten, N.Y.C., 1952-57, Jacobs, Persinger & Parker, N.Y.C., 1957-61; partner firm Rubin, Rubin, Weinberg & Di Paola, N.Y.C., 1961-78, Weinberg Tauber & Pressman, 1979-90; pvt. practice, N.Y.C., 1990—; dir. Milgray Electronics, Inc. Served with AUS, 1946-47. Mem. Assn. of Bar of City of N.Y., N.Y. State Bar Assn. Club: Harvard (N.Y.C.). Home: 50 Sutton Pl S New York NY 10022-4167 Office: 110 E 59th St New York NY 10022-1304

WEINBERG, JEFFREY J., lawyer; b. N.Y.C., Aug. 27, 1948; s. Arnold Mitchell and Lucile (Barton) W.; m. Bonnie J. Sandhaus, Aug. 23, 1970; children: Seth, Andrew. BA, SUNY, Stony Brook, 1969; JD, Georgetown U., 1973. Bar: N.Y., U.S. Dist. Ct. (so. and ea. dists.). Assoc. Weil, Gotshal & Manges, N.Y.C., 1973-81, ptnr., 1981—; acting judge Village of Roslyn Estates. Author: Sales of Troubled Business, 1991, 92, 93, 94. Former trustee Village of Roslyn Estate. Mem. Knickerbocker Y.C. (gov. 1990-91). Avocation: sailing. Office: Weil Gotshal & Manges 767 Fifth Ave New York NY 10153-0002

WEINBERG, JOHN LEE, federal judge; b. Chgo., Apr. 24, 1941; s. Louis Jr. and Jane Kitz (Goldstein) W.; m. Sarah Kibbee, July 6, 1963; children: Ruth, Leo. BA, Swarthmore Coll., 1962; JD, U. Chgo., 1965. Bar: Ill. 1966, Wash. 1967, U.S. Dist. Ct. (we. dist.) Wash. 1967, U.S. Ct. Appeals (9th cir.) 1967. Law clk. to Hon. Henry L. Burman Ill. Appellate Ct., Chgo., 1965-66; law clk. to Hom. Walter V. Schaefer Ill. Supreme Ct., Chgo., 1966; law clk. to Hon. William T. Beeks U.S. Dist. Ct. Wash., Seattle, 1967-68; atty. Perkins Coie Law Firm, Seattle, 1968-73; judge U.S Magistrate Ct., Seattle, 1973—. Author: Federal Bail and Detention Handbook, 1988. Mem. ABA, Am. Judicature Soc., Wash. State Bar Assn., Seattle-King County Bar Assn., Fed. Magistrate Judges Assn. (nat. pres. 1982-83). Avocations: sports and physical fitness activities, bridge. Office: US Magistrate Judge 304 US Courthouse 1010 5th Ave Seattle WA 98104-1130

WEINBERG, JOHN LIVINGSTON, investment banker; b. N.Y.C., Jan. 5, 1925; s. Sidney James and Helen (Livingston) W.; m. Sue Ann Gotshal, Dec. 6, 1952; children: Ann K. (dec.), John, Jean. A.B. cum laude, Princeton U., 1948; M.B.A., Harvard U., 1950. With Goldman, Sachs & Co., N.Y.C., 1950—, ptnr., 1956-76, sr. ptnr., 1976-90, co-chmn. mgmt. com., 1976-84, chmn. mgmt. com., 1984-90; sr. chmn. Goldman, Sachs & Co., 1990—; bd. dirs. B.F. Goodrich Co., Knight-Rider, Inc., Seagram Co. Ltd., Champion Internat. Corp.; mem. Conf. Bd. Bd. govs. N.Y. Hosp.-Cornell Med. Ctr.; mem. DeWitt Wallace fund for meml. Sloan-Kettering Cancer Ctr. Capt. USMCR, 1942-46, 51-52. Fellow AAAS; mem. Va. Neurol. Inst., Coun. on Fgn. Rels., Bus. Coun., DeWitt Wallace Fund for Meml. Sloan Kettering Cancer Ctr. Office: Goldman Sachs & Co 85 Broad St Fl 22 New York NY 10004-2434

WEINBERG, LEONARD BURTON, political scientist; b. N.Y.C., Nov. 10, 1939; s. Max R. and Rose (Levin) W.; m. Ellen Bach, Aug. 23, 1966 (div.); 1 son, David; m. Sinikka Palomaki, June 4, 1986. B.A., Syracuse U., 1961, Ph.D., 1967; M.A., U. Chgo., 1963. Instr. polit. sci. U. Wis., Milw., 1966-67; asst. prof. polit. sci. U. Nev., Reno, 1967-71; assoc. prof. U. Nev., 1971-78, prof., 1978—, chmn. dept., 1979-82; vis. prof. U. Florence, Italy, 1992. Author: Comparing Public Policies, 1977, After Mussolini, 1979, The Rise and Fall of Italian Terrorism, 1987, Introduction to Political Terrorism, 1989; editor: Political Parties and Terrorist Groups, 1992; co-editor: Encounters with the Radical Right, 1992, The Transformation of Italian Communism, 1994. Fulbright grantee, 1965-66; Fulbright research award, 1984; Italian Govt. Borsa di Studio, 1965-66. Mem. Am. Polit. Sci. Assn., Internat. Polit. Sci. Assn. (political sociology com.), Conf. Group on Italian Politics of Am. Polit. Sci. Assn., Phi Kappa Phi. Jewish. Office: Dept Political Science U Nevada Reno NV 89557

WEINBERG, LILA SHAFFER, writer, editor; d. Sam and Blanche (Hyman) Shaffer; m. Arthur Weinberg, Jan. 25, 1953; children: Hedy Merrill Cornfield, Anita Michelle Miller, Wendy Clare Rothman. Editor Ziff-Davis Pub. Co., 1944-53; assoc. chief manuscript editor jours. U. Chgo. Press, 1966-80, sr. manuscript editor books, 1980—; mem. faculty Sch. for New Learning DePaul U., Chgo., 1976—; vis. faculty continuing edn. programs U. Chgo., 1984—. Author: (with A. Weinberg) The Muckrakers, 1961 (selected for White House Library 1963), Verdicts Out of Court, 1963, Instead of Violence, 1963, Passport to Utopia, 1968, Some Dissenting Voices, 1970, Clarence Darrow: A Sentimental Rebel, 1980; contbr. articles and revs. to various pubs. Bd. dirs. Hillel Found. U. Chgo. Recipient Friends of Lit. award Chgo. Found. Lit., 1980, Social Justice award Darrow Community Ctr., 1980, Disting. Body of Work award Friends of Midwest Authors, 1987. Mem. Soc. Midland Authors (dir. 1977-83, pres. 1983-85, Best Biography award 1980), ACLU, Clarence Darrow Commemorative Com., 1980, YIVO, Authors' League. Home: 5421 S Cornell Ave Chicago IL 60615-5608

WEINBERG, LOUISE, lawyer, educator, author; b. N.Y.C.; m. Steven Weinberg; 1 child, Elizabeth. AB summa cum laude, Cornell U.; JD Harvard U., 1969, LL.M., 1972. Bar: Mass. Sr. law clk. Hon. Chas. E. Wyzanski, Jr., Boston, 1971-72; assoc. in law Bingham, Dana & Gould, Boston, 1969-72; teaching fellow Harvard Law Sch., Boston, 1972-74; lectr. law Brandeis U., Waltham, Mass., 1974; assoc. prof. law Suffolk U., Boston, 1974-76, prof., 1977-80; vis. assoc. prof. law Stanford U., Palo Alto, Calif., 1976-77; vis. prof. law U. Tex., Austin, 1979; prof. law Sch. Law, U. Tex., Austin, 1980-84, Thompson prof., 1984-90, Andrews and Kurth prof. law, 1990-92; Fulbright and Jaworski regents rsch. prof. U. Tex., Austin, 1991-92, Angus G. Wynne, Sr. prof. civil jurisprudence, 1992—, Eugene R. Smith Centennial rsch. prof. law, 1993; vis. scholar Hebrew U., Jerusalem, 1989; Forum fellow World Econ. Forum, Davos, 1995; lectr. in field. Author: Federal Courts: Judicial Federalism and Judicial Power, 1994, and ann. supplement; co-author: Conflict of Laws, 1990; contbr. chpts. to books and articles to profl. jours. Bd. dirs. Ballet Austin, 1986-88, Austin Coun. on Fgn. Affairs, 1985—. Mem. Am. Law Inst. (consultative com. complex litigation 1989-93, consultative com. enterprise liability 1990—), Assn. Am. Law Schs. (chmn. com. on conflict la ws 1991-93, exec. coun. 1989-90), faculty fellow World Econ. Forum, Davos, Switzerland, 1995, Maritime Law Assn., Scribes, Tuesday Club, Met. Club, Phi Beta Kappa, Phi Kappa Phi. Office: U Tex Sch Law 727 E 26th St Austin TX 78705-3224 *The right thing is usually also the humane and liberal thing.*

WEINBERG, MARTIN HERBERT, psychiatrist; b. Bklyn., Sept. 3, 1923; s. Abe and Ida (Levine) W.; m. Elizabeth Carwardine, Sept. 20, 1951; children: Mark David, Sheila Ann, Keith Warren. BS, CCNY, 1947; licentiate, Royal Coll. Surgeons, Edinburgh, Royal Coll. Physicians, Edinburgh, Royal Faculty Physicians and Surgeons, Glasgow. Diplomate: Am. Bd. Psychiatry and Neurology, certified mental hosp. adminstr. Intern Kings County Med. Center, Bklyn., 1952; resident psychiatry Essex County Overbrook Hosp., Cedar Grove, N.J., 1954-56; staff psychiatrist Ancora State Hosp., Hammonton, N.J., 1956; chief service Ancora State Hosp., 1957, clin. dir., 1958-60, asst. med. dir., 1960-62, med. dir., 1962-67; med. dir. Trenton Psychiat. Hosp., 1967-73; dir. div. mental health and hosps. N.J. Dept. Instns. and Agys., 1973-74; med. dir. Trenton Psychiat. Hosp., 1974-79; surveyor psychiat. programs Joint Commn. Accreditation of Hosps., 1979-80; asst. supt. clin. services Phila. State Hosp., 1980-81; individual practice medicine specializing in psychiatry, 1981-86; staff psychiatrist Woods Sch., Langhorne, Pa., to 1986; cons. N.J. Neuropsychiat. Inst., 1981-83, New Lisbon State Sch., to 1985. Fellow Am. Psychiat. Assn., AAAS; mem. N.J. Psychiat. Assn. (past pres.). Home: 26 Diane Dr Trenton NJ 08628-2621

WEINBERG, MEYER, humanities educator; b. N.Y.C., Dec. 16, 1920; s. Charles and Anna (Palatnik) W.; m. Erica C. Mueller, Sept. 5, 1943; children: Rachel (dec.), David, Daniel, Carl, Benjamin. B.A., U. Chgo., 1942, M.A., 1945; A.A. Herzl Jr. Coll., 1947. Faculty history Wright br. City Coll. Chgo., 1945-67, coordinator master planning, 1968-69, coordinator innovations center, 1970-71; prof. history City Coll. Chgo. (Loop br.), 1971-

78; dir. Ctr. for Equal Edn. Northwestern U., Evanston, Ill., 1972-78, prof. Sch. Edn., 1978-88; prof. Afro-Am. studies, dir. Horace Mann Bond Center for Equal Edn., U. Mass., Amherst, 1978-90, prof. emeritus, 1990-92, 94—; inaugural holder Veffie Milstead Jones chair in multicultural edn. Calif. State U., Long Beach, 1992-94; chmn. edn. com. Coordinating Council Community Orgns., 1963-67; cons. Howard U., 1964-65, Am. Inst. for Research, 1972, bds. of edn. various cities, univs., 1964-79; bds. of edn. various cities, univs. Fla. Desegregation Center, U. Miami, 1973, NAACP Legal Def. Fund, 1972, Ford Found., 1978, System Devel. Corp., 1975, Nat. Cath. Conf. on Interracial Justice, 1977-78, Stanford Research Inst., 1976, WTTW-TV, Chgo., 1975-78, Edn. Commn. of States, 1978, Cemrel, Inc., 1977, System Devel. Corp., 1979, ESAA Human Relations Study, 1977; mem. tech. adv. com. Ill. Bd. Edn., 1971-72. Author: (with O. E. Shabat) Society and Man, 1956, 65, TV in America - The Morality of Hard Cash, 1962, Race and Place - A Legal History of the Neighborhood School, 1968, Desegregation Research - An Appraisal, 1968, 70, Minority Students - A Research Appraisal, 1977, A Chance to Learn (A History of the Education of Black, Mexican American, American Indian and Puerto Rican Children), 1977, In Search of Quality Integrated Education, 1983, Because They Were Jews: A History of Antisemitism, 1986; editor: Issues in Social Science, 1959, Learning Together, 1964, Integrated Education - A Reader, 1968, Education of the Minority Child - A Comprehensive Bibliography of 10,000 Selected Entries, 1970, W.E.B. DuBois - A Reader, 1970, The Education of Poor and Minority Children: A World Bibliography, 2 vols, 1981, The Education of Poor and Minority Children: A World Bibliography Supplement, 1986, America's Economic Heritage: A Documentary History, 2 vols., 1983, Racism in the United States, 1990, World Racism and Related Inhumanities: A Country-by-Country Bibliography, 1992, The World of W.E.B. DuBois, 1992; editor Rsch. Rev. of Equal Edn., 1977-79, Integrateducation mag., 1963-86; contbr. chpts. to books, articles to profl. jours. Recipient Center for Human Relations award for creative leadership in edn. NEA, 1971, Human Relations award Mass. Tchrs. Assn., 1988. Mem. Am. Hist. Assn., Soc. for History of Tech., Am. Soc. for Legal History. Home: Apt 7-D 5140 S Hyde Park Blvd Chicago IL 60615-4261

WEINBERG, MICHAEL, JR., commodities broker; b. Chgo., Mar. 19, 1925; s. Michael H. and Leila (Eichberg) W.; m. Joan F. Rusnak, Feb. 25, 1951; children: Michael Alan, Wendy Lee, Jill Diane (Mrs. Avrum Miller). B.A., U. Chgo., 1943; student, Grad. Sch. Bus., 1946-49. Pres. Great Lakes Pub. Co., Chgo., 1950-53; editor Hyde Park Herald, also Oakland-Kenwood Outlook, Chgo., 1950-53; commodity broker, v.p. Weinberg Bros. & Co. (commodity brokers and wholesalers), Chgo., 1953-83; mem. Chgo. Mercantile Exch., 1954—; pres. Am. Futures Corp., 1983-88; exec. dir. Lincoln Park Zool. Soc., 1963-65; Chmn. bd. govs., chmn. exec. com. Chgo. Merc. Exchange, 1972-73; dir. Internat. Monetary Market; mem. adv. com. Commodity Futures Trading Commn., Washington, 1975-76. Served with AUS, World War II. Mem. U. Chgo. Alumni Assn., Zeta Beta Tau. Home and Office: 800 Deerfield Rd Highland Park IL 60035-3531

WEINBERG, MILTON, JR., cardiovascular-thoracic surgeon; b. Sumter, S.C., Aug. 8, 1924; s. Milton and Ethel (Harper) W.; m. Joan Ehrenstrom, Nov. 24, 1956; children: Caryl, Susan, Amy. Student, Duke U., 1941-43, MD, 1947. Diplomate Am. Bd. Surgery, Am. Bd. Thoracic Surgery. Attending surgeon Rush Presbyn.-St. Luke's Med. Ctr., Chgo., 1957-90, emeritus attending, 1990—; attending surgeon Cook County Hosp., Chgo., 1956—, Luth. Gen. Hosp., Park Ridge, Ill., 1986—; assoc. prof. Rush Med. Coll., Chgo., 1969-78, prof. surgery, 1978-90, emeritus prof., 1990—; clin. prof. U. Chgo., 1990—; chmn. dept. surgery Luth. Gen. Hosp., Park Ridge, 1988-94; chmn. emeritus, vice chmn. Dept. Surgery Luth. Gen. Hosp., 1994—; pres. med. staff Rush Med. Ctr., Chgo., 1977-79; presenter movies at meetings ACS. Mem. editorial bd. Annals of Thoracic Surgery, 1968-79; contbr. articles to profl. jours., chpts. to surg. textbooks. Trustee The Presbyn. Home, Evanston, Ill., 1984—; bd. dirs. Chgo. Symphony Orch., 1985-94. Maj. U.S. Army, 1951-53, Korea. Decorated Bronze Star. Fellow ACS, Am. Coll. Chest Physicians, Am. Coll. Cardiology; mem. Am. Assn. Thoracic Surgery, Soc. Thoracic Surgeons, Soc. Vascular Surgery, Internat. Cardiovascular Soc., Ctrl. Surg. Soc. Avocations: fly fishing, fly rod building. Home: 2550 Princeton Ave Evanston IL 60201-4941 Office: Luth Gen Hosp 1775 Dempster St Park Ridge IL 60068-1143

WEINBERG, NORMAN LOUIS, electrochemist; b. Toronto, Ont., Can., May 6, 1936; s. Samuel and Helen (Wise) W.; m. Hannah Rita Cohen, Aug. 30, 1959; children: Eric, Laurie. BSc, U. Toronto, 1959, MSc, 1960; PhD, U. Ottowa, Can., 1963; postdoctoral studies, Technion, Israel, 1963-64. Sr. rsch. chemist Bristol Labs. Can., Candiac, Que., 1964-66, Am. Cyanamid Co., Stamford, Conn., 1966-70; group leader Hooker Chems. & Plastics Corp., Grand Island, N.Y., 1970-74, supr./program leader, 1974-77; pres. Berg Color-Tone, Inc., Lancaster, N.Y., 1977—; The Electrosynthesis Co., inc., Lancaster, 1977—, Electrocinerator Techs., Inc., Lancaster; lectr. electrochem. courses Buffalo, 1986, 87, 89; lectr. in-house course DuPont, 1987, 88; lectr./editor Internat. Forum on Electrolysis in the Chem. Industry, 1987-94. Editor: Technique of Electroorganic Synthesis, vol. 1, 1974, vol. 2, 1975, (with Tilak) Technique of Electroorganic Synthesis: Scale-Up, vol. 3, 1982, (with Little) Electroorganic Synthesis: Festschrift in Honor of Manuel Baizer, 1991; contbr. numerous articles to profl. jours. including Jour. Am. Chem. Soc., Can. Jour. Chemistry, Jour. Organic Chemistry, Jour. Applied Electrochemistry. Recipient Inventor of Yr. award Niagara Frontier Patent Law Assn., 1990. Mem. ECS, ISE, Am. Chem. Soc. (lectr. 1972-78). Achievements include 27 patents including for Radiographic Image Enhancement, Methods for the Electrosynthesis of Polyols, Fluorinated Carbons and Method of Manufacture, (with others) Modified Carbons and Electrochemical Cells Containing Same, (with others) Reactions in an Electrochemical Cell Including an Electrode Comprising Magneli Phase Titanium Oxide, (with others) Methods for Paired Electrosynthesis with Simultaneous Ethylene Glycol Formation, (with other) Membrane Divided Aqueous-Nonaqueous System for Electrochemical Cells, others; 9 patent applications for flourinated carbons and uses thereof, (with others) porous electrodes for use in electrochemical gas sensors, (with others) methods for purification of air, (with others) manufacture of flourinated carbons, (with others) high surface area electrodes. Office: Electrosynthesis Co Inc 72 Ward Rd Lancaster NY 14086-9779

WEINBERG, RICHARD ALAN, psychologist, educator; b. Chgo. Jan. 28, 1943; s. Meyer and Mollie I. (Soell) W.; m. Gail E. Blumberg Aug. 25, 1964; children: Eric, Brett. BS, U. Wis., 1964; MAT, Northwestern U., 1965; PhD, U. Minn., 1968. Lic. cons. psychologist, Minn. Asst. prof. Tchrs. Coll., Columbia U., N.Y.C., 1968-70; prof. ednl. psychology, psychology and child psychology U. Minn., Mpls., 1970—, Birkmaier professorship, 1994—; dir. Inst. Child Devel., former dir. Ctr. for Early Edn. and Devel., chair adv. coun. Children, Youth & Family Consortium; cons. EPA; reviewer Office of Edn., NSF; guest speaker TV and radio shows. Mem. adv. com. Children's Mus. Minn.; pres. Am. Assn. State Psychol. Bds.; liaison Nat. Register for Health Care Providers in Psychology; chair Pub. Policy Coun. Grantee Bush Found.; NSF; NIH. Fellow Am. Psychol. Assn.; mem., Soc. for Research in Child Devel., Behavior Genetics Soc., Am. Edn. Rsch. Assn., Am. Psychol. Soc. (bd. dirs.), Phi Beta Kappa, Phi Kappa Phi. Author: (with A. Boehm) The Classroom Observer: Developing Observation Skills in Early Childhood Settings, 1987; (with Scarr and Levine) Understanding Development, 1986; former assoc. editor Contemporary Psychology; editor Applied Developmental Science. Office: U Minn 180 Child Devel 51 E River Rd Minneapolis MN 55455-0345

WEINBERG, ROBERT ALLAN, biochemist, educator; b. Pitts., Nov. 11, 1942; s. Fritz E. and Lore (Reichhardt) W.; m. Amy Shulman, Nov. 19, 1976; children—Aron, Leah Rosa. S.B., MIT, 1964, Ph.D, 1969; Ph.D (hon.), Northwestern U., 1984. Intern Stillman Coll., Tuscaloosa, Ala., 1965-66; research fellow Weizmann Inst., Rehovoth, Israel, 1969-70; Salk Inst., LaJolla, Calif., 1970-72; from asst. prof. to assoc. prof. dept. biology & ctr. cancer rsch. MIT, Cambridge, 1973-82, prof. biology, 1982—; mem. Whitehead Inst., Cambridge, 1984—. Contbr. articles to profl. jours. Recipient Bristol Myers award, 1984, Armand Hammer award, 1984, Brown-Hazen award N.Y. State Dept. Health, 1984, Sloan prize Gen. Motors Cancer Rsch. Found., 1987, Rsch. Recognition award Samuel Roberts Noble Found., 1990, Gairdner Found. Internat. award, 1992. Mem. Nat. Acad. Sci. (sci. award 1984). Avocations: genealogy, house building. Office: Whitehead Inst 9 Cambridge Ctr Cambridge MA 02142-1479*

WEINBERG, ROBERT LEONARD, retired lawyer; b. Balt., May 31, 1923; s. Leonard and Beatrice (Lansburgh) W. Student, Coll. William and Mary, 1940-43; BS, Johns Hopkins, 1952; JD, U. Md., 1949. Bar: Md. 1948. Assoc. Weinberg and Green (attys.), Balt., 1948-52; ptnr. Weinberg and Green (attys.), 1952-94; asst. atty. gen. Md., 1953; instr. labor law and contract law Ea. Coll. (name now U. Balt.), 1954-57, Md. State Bd. C.Cs., 1989-92; ret., 1994. Pres. Comprehensive Housing Assistance, Inc., 1969-71, United Way Cen. Md., 1976-77; v.p. Levindale Hebrew Hosp./Geriatric Ctr., 1971-75, Jewish Hist. Soc. Md., 1980-86; bd. dirs. Sinai Hosp., 1974-86, Associated Jewish Charities Balt., 1980-93, pres. 1991-94,; nat. bd. dirs. NCCJ, co-chmn. Md. region, 1968-70; mem. Policy Studies Inst. Johns Hopkins U., 1984-86, Md. Humanities Coun., 1986-91; bd. dirs. Am. Jewish Hist. Soc., 1982—, v.p. 1984-90, hon. v.p., 1990—; v.p. Md. Hist. Soc., 1973-76; others. Mem. ABA, Md. Bar Assn., Balt. Bar Assn., Balt. Bar Found., Am. Judicature Soc. (bd. dirs. 1976-78), Am. Coll. Real Estate Lawyers, Md. Bar Found., Md. C. of C. (v.p. 1981-82), Omicron Delta Kappa, Suburban Balt. Country Club (pres. 1971-74), Ctr. Club (bd. govs., sec., counsel 1962-72). Republican. Jewish.

WEINBERG, ROBERT LESTER, lawyer, educator; b. N.Y.C., May 23, 1931; s. Abraham Matthew and Beatrice (Kohn) W.; m. Patricia Wendy Yates, Aug. 19, 1956; children: Susan Clare, David Hal, Jeremy Michael. BA, Yale U., 1953, LLB, 1960; PhD in Econs., London Sch. Econs., U. London, 1960. Bar: D.C. 1961, Conn. 1960, U.S. Supreme Ct. 1963, U.S. Ct. Appeals (D.C. and 2d cirs.) 1961, U.S. Ct. Appeals (3d and 7th cirs.) 1965, U.S. Ct. Appeals (6th cir.) 1968, U.S. Ct. Appeals (9th cir.) 1976, U.S. Ct. Appeals (10th cir.) 1977, U.S. Ct. Appeals (5th cir.) 1978, U.S. Ct. Appeals (4th cir.) 1982. Assoc. Williams & Connolly and predecessors, Washington, 1960-66, ptnr., 1967—; vis. lectr. U. Va. Sch. Law, Charlottesville, 1965—; adj. prof. U. Tex. Sch. Law, summer 1986; chmn. standing com. on pro bono matters D.C. Cir. Jud. Conf., 1980—. Columnist No. Va. Sun, 1970s; contbr. articles to profl. jours. Pres. No. Va. Fair Housing, Inc., 1968-69; chmn. Arlington Pub. Utilities Commn. (Va.), 1968, Arlington County Dem. Com., 1969-71, 10th Congl. Dist. Dem. Com., No. Va., 1972-76; del. Dem. Nat. Conv., 1976; pres. Arlington County Civic Fedn., 1973-75; mem. governing coun. Am. Jewish Congress, 1984—. Served with U.S. Army, 1957-59. Recipient Outstanding Citizen of Yr. award Washington Evening Star and Arlington County Civic Fedn., 1975. Mem. ABA (ho. of dels. 1977-82, 93—), Bar Assn. D.C. (pres. 1994-95), Conn. Bar Assn., D.C. Bar (pres. 1977-79), D.C. Bar Found. (pres. 1988-89, 91-92), Internat. Assn. Jewish Lawyers & Jurors (bd. dirs.), Nat. Jewish Dem. Coun. (bd. dirs.). Home: 5171 N 37th Rd Arlington VA 22207-1825 Office: Williams & Connolly 725 12th St NW Washington DC 20005-3901

WEINBERG, STEVEN, physics educator; b. N.Y.C., NY, May 3, 1933; s. Fred and Eva (Israel) W.; m. Louise Goldwasser, July 6, 1954; 1 child, Elizabeth. BA, Cornell U., 1954; postgrad., Copenhagen Inst. Theoretical Physics, 1954-55; PhD, Princeton U., 1957; AM (hon.), Harvard U., 1973; ScD (hon.), Knox Coll., 1978, U. Chgo., 1978, U. Rochester, 1979, Yale U., 1979, CUNY, 1980, Clark U., 1982, Dartmouth Coll., 1984, Columbia U., 1990, U. Salamanca, 1992, U. Padua, 1992; PhD (hon.), Weizmann Inst., 1985; DLitt (hon.), Washington Coll., 1985. Rsch. assoc., instr. Columbia U., 1957-59; rsch. physicist Lawrence Radiation Lab., Berkeley, Calif., 1959-60; mem. faculty U. Calif., Berkeley, 1960-69, prof. physics, 1964-69; vis. prof. MIT, 1967-69, prof. physics, 1969-73; Higgins prof. physics Harvard U., 1973-83; sr. scientist Smithsonian Astrophys. Lab., 1973-83; Josey prof. sci. U. Tex., Austin, 1982—; sr. cons. Smithsonian Astrophys. Obs., 1983—; cons. Inst. Def. Analyses, Washington, 1960-73, ACDA, 1973; Sloan fellow, 1961-65; chair in physics Coll. de France, 1971; mem. Pres.'s Com. on Nat. Medal of Sci., 1979-82, Coun. of Scholars, Library of Congress, 1983-85; sr. adv. La Jolla Inst.; mem. Com. on Internat. Security and Arms Control, NRC, 1981, Bd. on Physics & Astronomy, 1989-90; dir. Jerusalem Winter Sch. Theoretical Physics, 1983-94; mem. adv. coun. Tex. Superconducting Supercollider High Energy Rsch. Facility, 1987; Loeb lectr. in physics Harvard U., 1966-67, Morris Loeb vis. prof. physics, 1983—; Richtmeyer lectr., 1974; Scott lectr. Cavendish Lab., 1975; Silliman lectr. Yale U., 1977; Lauritsen Meml. lectr. Calif. Inst. Tech., 1979; Bethe lectr. Cornell U., 1979; de Shalit lectr. Weizman Inst., 1979; Cherwell-Simon lectr. Oxford U., 1983; Bampton lectr. Columbia U., 1983; Einstein lectr. Israel Acad. Arts and Scis., 1984; Hilldale lectr. U. Wis., 1985; Clark lectr. U. Tex., Dallas, 1986; Dirac lectr. U. Cambridge, 1986; Klein lectr. U. Stockholm, 1989; Brittin lectr. U. Colo., 1994,; Sackler lectr. U. Copenhagen, 1994 Sloan fellow, 1961-65; mem. Supercollider Sci. Policy Com., 1989-93. Author: Gravitation and Cosmology: Principles and Application of the General Theory of Relativity, 1972, The First Three Minutes: A Modern View of the Origin of the Universe, 1977, The Discovery of Subatomic Particles, 1982; co-author (with R. Feynman) Elementary Particles and the Laws of Physics, 1987, Dreams of a Final Theory, 1992, The Quantum Theory of Fields - Vol. I: Foundations, 1995; rsch. and publs. on elementary particles, quantum field theory, cosmology; co-editor Cambridge U. Press, monographs on math. physics; mem. adv. bd. Issues in Sci. and Tech., 1984-87; mem. sci. book com. Sloan Found, 1985-91; mem. editorial bd. Jour. Math. Physics, 1986-88; mem. bd. editors Daedalus, 1990—; mem. bd. assoc. editors Nuclear Physics B. Bd. advisors Santa Barbara Inst. Theoretical Physics, 1983-86; bd. overseers SSC Accelerator, 1984-86; bd. dirs. Headliners Found., 1993—. Recipient J. Robert Oppenheimer meml. prize, 1973, Dannie Heineman prize in math. physics, 1977, Am. Inst. Physics-U.S. Steel Found. sci. writing award, 1977, Nobel prize in physics, 1979, Elliott Cresson medal Franklin Inst., 1979, Madison medal Princeton U., 1991, Nat. Medal of Sci. NSF, 1991. Mem. Am. Acad. Arts and Scis. (past councilor), Am. Phys. Soc. (past councilor at large, panel on faculty positions com. on status of women in physics), NAS (supercollider site evaluation com. 1987-88), Einstein Archives (adv. bd. 1988—), Internat. Astron. Union, Coun. Fgn. Rels., Am. Philos. Soc., Royal Soc. London (fgn. mem.), Am. Mediaeval Acad., History of Sci. Soc., Philos. Soc. Tex. (pres. 1994), Tex. Inst. of Letters, Phi Beta Kappa. Clubs: Saturday (Boston); Headliners, Tuesday (Austin); Cambridge Sci. Soc.

WEINBERG, SYDNEY STAHL, historian; b. N.Y.C., Oct. 2, 1938; d. David Leslie and Berenice (Jarvis) Stahl; B.A., Barnard Coll., 1960; M.A., Columbia U., 1964; Ph.D., 1969; divorced; children: Deborah Sara, Elisa Rachel. Instr. history N.J. Inst. Tech., 1967-69, asst. prof., 1969-72; assoc. prof. history Ramapo Coll. N.J., Mahwah, 1972-74, prof., 1974—dir. Master of Arts Program in Liberal Studies, 1994—; dir. Garden State Immigration History Consortium, 1987-89. Nat. Endowment for Humanities fellow, 1977-78; sec./treas. Berkshire Conf. Women Historians, 1994—. Mem. Inst. for Rsch. in History, Am. Hist. Assn., Orgn. Am. Historians, Am. Studies Assn., Jewish Studies Assn., Assn. of Graduate Liberal Studies Programs. Author: The World of Our Mothers: The Lives of Jewish Immigrant Women, 1988; contbr. articles to profl. jours. Home: 80 La Salle St 19F New York NY 10027-4711 Office: Ramapo Coll MA Liberal Studies Program Office Mahwah NJ 07430

WEINBERG, SYLVAN LEE, cardiologist, educator, author, editor; b. Nashville, June 14, 1923; s. Abraham J. and Beatrice (Kottler) W.; m. Joan Hutzler, Jan. 29, 1956; children: Andrew Lee, Leslie. BS, Northwestern U., 1945, BM, 1946, MD, 1947. From intern to resident, fellow Michael Reese Hosp., Chgo., 1947-51; attending physician Good Samaritan Hosp., Dayton, Ohio, 1953—, chief of cardiology, 1966—, founding dir. coronary care unit, 1967—; clin. prof. medicine Wright State U., Dayton, 1975—; panelist Med. Affairs, nat. TV; pres. Weinberg Marcus Cardiomed. Group, Inc. Author: An Epitaph for Merlin and Perhaps for Medicine, 1983; founding editor Dayton Medicine, 1980—, Heart & Lung, 1972-87; contbr. articles to profl jours. Capt. U.S. Army, 1951-53, Korea. Recipient Army Commendation medal; Outstanding Pub. Svc. award Ohio State Senate, 1980. Fellow Am. Coll. Cardiology (pres. 1993-94, editor in chief audio jour. ACCEL 1995—), Am. Coll. Chest Physicians (pres. 1984); mem. Montgomery County Med. Soc. (pres. 1980). Avocations: writing, travel, golf. Home: 4555 Southern Blvd Dayton OH 45429-1118 Office: Weinberg Marcus Cardiomed Group 9000 N Main St Ste 402 Dayton OH 45415

WEINBERG, WILLIAM HENRY, chemical engineer, chemical physicist, educator; b. Columbia, S.C., Dec. 5, 1944; s. Ulrich Vivian and Ruth Ann (Duncan) W. BS, U. S.C., 1966; PhD in Chem. Engring. U. Calif., Berkeley, 1970; NATO postdoctoral fellow in phys. chemistry, Cambridge U., Eng. 1971. Asst. prof. chem. engring. Calif. Inst. Tech., 1972-74, asso. prof., 1974-77, prof. chem. engring. and chem. physics, 1977-89, Chevron disting. prof. chem. engring. and chem. physics, 1981-86; prof. chem. engring. and

chemistry U. Calif., Santa Barbara, 1989—, assoc. dean Coll. Engring., 1992—; vis. prof. chemistry Harvard U., 1980, U. Pitts. 1987-88, Oxford U., 1991; Alexander von Humboldt Found. fellow U. Munich, 1982; cons. E.I. DuPont Co. Author: (with Van Hove and Chan) Low-Energy Electron Diffraction, 1986; editor 4 books in field; mem. editorial bd. Jour. Applications, Surface Sci. 1977-85, Handbook Surfaces and Interfaces, 1978-80, Surface Sci. Reports, 1980—, gen. editor, 1992—, Applied Surface Sci., 1985—, Langmuir, 1990—, Surface Sci., 1992—; contbr. articles to profl. jours., chpts. to books. Recipient Giuseppe Parravano award Mich. Catalysis Soc., 1989; fellow NSF, 1966-69, Alfred P. Sloan Found., 1976-78, Camille and Henry Dreyfus Found. fellow 1976-81. Fellow Am. Phys. Soc. (Nottingham prize 1973), Am. Vacuum Soc.; mem. AAAS, AIChE (Colburn award 1981), Am. Chem. Soc. (LaMer award 1973, Kendall award 1991, Arthur W. Adamson award, 1995), N.Am. Catalysis Soc., mem. Nat. Acad. of Engring. Phi Beta Kappa, Sigma Xi. Home: 877 Summit Rd Santa Barbara CA 93108-2321 Office: U Calif Dept Chem Nuclear Engr Santa Barbara CA 93106

WEINBERGER, ALAN DAVID, corporate executive; b. Washington, July 31, 1945; s. Theodore George and Shirley Sunshine (Gross) W.; m. Lauren Myra Kaminski, Dec. 2, 1979; children: Mark Henry, Benjamin Charles. BA, NYU, 1967, JD, 1970; LLM, Harvard U., 1973. Bar: N.Y. 1971, D.C. 1978, U.S. Supreme Ct. 1980. Assoc. White & Case, N.Y.C., 1970-72; founding law prof. Vt. Law Sch., South Royalton, 1973-75; atty. SEC and Fed. Home Loan Bank Bd., Washington, 1977-81; founder, chmn. bd., CEO The ASCII Group Inc., Washington, 1984—; mem. adv. bd. Ashton Tate Inc., Torrance, Calif., 1986-87; sponsor, agt. All Union Fgn. Trade Acad., Acad. Nat. Economy of USSR in U.S.A., 1988-90; chmn. govt. affairs com. Computer Tech. Industry Assn., 1993-95. Law rev. editor NYU Sch. Law, 1970. Named one of Top 25 Most Influential Execs. in Computer Industry, Computer Reseller News, 1988. Mem. Nat. Orgn. on Disability (CEO coun.), D.C. Bar Assn., Order of Coif, Kenwood Country Club. Avocation: tennis. Office: ASCII Group Inc 7475 Wisconsin Ave Bethesda MD 20814

WEINBERGER, ARNOLD, retired electrical engineer; b. Bardejov, Czechoslovakia, Oct. 23, 1924; came to U.S., 1939; s. Henry C. and Bina (Shapira) W.; widowed; children: Paul I., Ronda B., Keith A. BSEE, CCNY, 1950. Engr. Nat. Bur. Standards, Washington, 1950-60; rsch. staff mem. IBM, Yorktown Heights, N.Y., 1960-66; engr., Poughkeepsie, N.Y. IBM, 1966-91, ret., 1991. Contbr. articles on computer arithmetic, logic, large-scale integration, system organization, memories, design automation. Patentee in field. With U.S. Army, 1944-46, ETO. Fellow IEEE (Outstanding sect. award 1981). Avocation: table tennis.

WEINBERGER, CASPAR WILLARD, publishing executive, former secretary of defense; b. San Francisco, Aug. 18, 1917; s. Herman and Cerise Carpenter (Hampson) W.; m. Jane Dalton, Aug. 16, 1942; children: Arlin Cerise, Caspar Willard. AB magna cum laude, Harvard U., 1938, LLB, 1941; LLD (hon.), Eng., England, 1989; LittD (hon.), U. Buckingham, 1995. Bar: Calif., U.S. Ct. Appeals (D.C. cir.) 1990. Law clk. U.S. Judge William E. Orr, 1945-47; with firm Heller, Ehrman, White & McAuliffe, 1947-69, ptnr., 1959-69; mem. Calif. Legislature from 21st Dist., 1952-58; vice chmn. Calif. Rep. Cen. Com., 1960-62, chmn., 1962-64; chmn. Com. Calif. Govt. Orgn. and Econs., 1967-68; dir. fin. Calif., 1968-69; chmn. FTC, 1970; dep. dir. Office Mgmt. and Budget, 1970-72, dir., 1972-73; counsellor to the Pres., 1973; sec. HEW, 1973-75; gen. counsel, v.p., dir. Bechtel Power Corp., San Francisco, 1975-80, Bechtel, Inc., 1975-80, Bechtel Corp., 1975-80; sec. Dept. Def., Washington, 1981-87; counsel Law Firm of Rogers & Wells, Washington and N.Y.C., 1988-94; chmn. Forbes Magazine, New York, 1989—; formerly staff book reviewer San Francisco Chronicle; moderator weekly TV program Profile, Bay Area, sta. KQED, San Francisco, 1959-68; Frank Nelson Doubleday lectr., 1974. Writer column on Calif. govt., 1959-68; author: Fighting for Peace: Seven Critical Years in the Pentagon, 1990. Chmn. Pres.'s Com. on Mental Retardation, 1973-75; former mem. Trilaterial Commn.; former mem. adv. coun. Am. Ditchley Found.; former bd. dirs. Yosemite Inst.; former trustee St. Luke's Hosp., san Francisco, Mechanics Inst.; former chmn. nat. bd. trustees Nat. Symphony, Washington; former bd. govs. San Francisco Symphony; mem. bd. USA-ROC Econ. Coun., 1991-94; co-chmn. Winston Churchill Travelling Fellowships Found., 1989—. Served to capt., inf. AUS, 1941-45; PTO. Decorated Bronze Star, Grand Cordon of Order of the Rising Sun (Japan), Hon. Knight Grand Cross Civil Div. Order of Brit. Empire; recipient Presdl. medal Freedom with distinction, 1987, George Catlet Marshall medal, 1988, Civil award Hilal-i-Pakistan, 1989. Mem. ABA, State Bar Calif., D.C. Ct. Appeals, Century Club (N.Y.), Bohemian Club (San Francisco), Pacific Union Club (San Francisco), Harvard Club (Washington). Episcopalian (former treas. Diocese of Calif.). Office: Forbes Mag 60 Fifth Ave New York NY 10011-8865 also: Forbes Inc 1901 L St NW Washington DC 20036

WEINBERGER, DANIEL R., psychiatrist, neurologist; b. N.Y.C., May 24, 1947; married; 1 child. BA, Johns Hopkins U., 1969; MD, U. Pa., 1973. Diplomate Am. Bd. Psychiatry and Neurology. Intern L.A. County-Harbor Gen. Hosp., Torrance, Calif., 1973-74; grad. fellow in medicine UCLA Sch. Medicine, 1973-74; clin. fellow in psychiatry Harvard U., 1974-77; resident in psychiatry Mass. Mental Health Ctr., Boston, 1974-76, chief resident, 1976-77; assoc. in medicine, divsn. psychiatry Peter Bent Brigham Hosp., Boston, 1974-76; assoc. clin. prof. psychiatry George Washington U., Washington, 1978-81, assoc. clin. prof., 1982, assoc. clin. prof. neurology and psychiatry, 1984; resident in neurology George Washington U. Med. Ctr., Washington, 1980-83; dir. rsch. ward adult psychiatry br., intermural rsch. program NIHM, Washington, 1977-78, staff psychiatrist, 1977-81; head clin. neuropsychiatry and neurobehavior unit NIMH/St. Elizabeth's Hosp., Washington, 1981-82, chief sect., 1983-86, chief clin. brain disorders br., 1986—; dir. movement disorder, dementia clinic, experimental therapeutics br. Nat. Inst. Neurol. Diseases and Stroke, Washington, 1983-86; dir. behavioral neurology svc. St. Elizabeth's Hosp., Washington, 1983-88; part-time gen. practice Bridgewater Med. Ctr., East Bridgewater, Mass., 1974-76; emergency rm. physician Cardinal Cushing Gen. Hosp., Brockton, Mass., 1974-77; examiner Am. Bd. Psychiatry and Neurology; part-time gen. practice psychiatry and neurology, Washington, 1978—; scientists promotion review com. NIMH, 1984-87; elected to coun. Assembly of Scientists NIMH/Nat. Inst. Neurological Diseases and Stroke, 1985-88; Roerig vis. prof. U. N.Mex., 1990, U. Mich., 1992; adv. bd. Alzheimer Disease Found., 1990—, Adams Super Ctr. Brain Studies, Tel Aviv, 1993—; Neal Mysell lectr. Harvard Med. Sch., 1993; steering com. in vivo NMR Ctr., NIH, 1993—. Mem. editorial bd. Biol. Psychiatry, 1986—, Internat. Jour. Schizophrenia Rsch., 1987—, Jour. Neuropsychiatry and Clin. Neurosci., 1987—, Psychiatry, 1987—, Progress in Neuropsychiatry and Psychopharmacology, 1989—, Jour. Clin. Brain Imaging, 1989—, Psychiatry Research: Neuroimaging, 1990—, Jour. Psychiatry and Neurosci., 1990—, Neuropsychopharmacology, 1991—, Development and Psychopathology, 1991—, Harvard Review of Psychiatry, 1992—; contbr. articles to profl. jours.; patentee in field. Capt. USPHS, 1977-86. Recipient Morton Prince award Am. Psychopathol. Assn., 1984, Judith B. Silver award Nat. Alliance for Mentally Ill, 1985, Arthur S. Flemming award Washington Jaycees, 1986, Established Investigator award NARSAD, 1990, Lieber award, 1993, Dean award Am. Coll. Psychiatrists, 1994. Fellow Am. Coll. Neuropsychopharmacology (Joel Elkes internat. award 1989); mem. AMA, AAAS, Am. Psychiat. Assn. (Found. Fund prize for rsch. 1991), Am. Acad. Neurology (sci. program com. 1990—), Am. Neuropsychiatric Assn., Soc. Biol. Psychiatry (A.E. Benett Found. award clin. science 1981), Behavioral Neurology Soc., Neurosci. (pub. lectr. 20th ann. meeting 1990), Washington Neurology Soc., Washington Psychiat. Soc., Phi Beta Kappa, Alpha Omega Alpha. Office: St Elizabeth's Hosp Chief Clin Brain Disor Br Washington DC 20032

WEINBERGER, FRANK, information systems advisor; b. Chgo., Sept. 18, 1926; s. Rudolph and Elaine (Kellner) W.; m. Beatrice Natalie Fixler, June 27, 1953; children: Alan J., Bruce I. BSEE, Ill. Inst. of Tech., 1951; MBA, Northwestern U., Evanston, 1959. Registered profl. engr., Ill. Calif. Engr. Admiral Corp., Chgo., 1951-53; sr. engr. Cook Rsch., Chgo., 1953-59; mem. tech. staff Rockwell Internat., Downey, Calif., 1959-80, info. systems advisor, 1980-95; info. mgmt. cons. Rockwell Internat., Los Alamitos, Calif., 1995—. Pres. Temple Israel, Long Beach, Calif. 1985-87; bd. dirs. 1973-85. With USN, 1944-46. Mem. Assn. for Computer Machinery. Democrat. Jewish. Avocation: microcomputers. Home and Office: 3231 Yellowtail Dr Los Alamitos CA 90720-5253

WEINBERGER, GEORGE MARTIN, political scientist, government infosystems specialist; b. Darby, Pa., July 19, 1947; s. Sidney and Hilda Anna (Greenberg) W. BA, Temple U., 1969; MPA, U. Ga., 1971, DPA, 1973. Asst. to assoc. prof. S.W. Tex. State U., San Marcos, 1973-85, prof., 1985—. Editor: Soviet Cybernetic Technology, 1985, 2 vols.; contbr. articles to profl. jours. Home: PO Box 1412 San Marcos TX 78667-1412 Office: SW Tex State U Dept Polit Sci San Marcos TX 78666

WEINBERGER, HAROLD PAUL, lawyer; b. N.Y.C., Mar. 12, 1947; s. Fred and Elaine (Schonfeld) W.; m. Toby Ann Strassman, Dec. 15, 1968; children—James David, Karen Ellen. B.A., CCNY, 1967; J.D., Columbia U. 1970. Bar: N.Y. 1971, U.S. Dist. Cts. (so., ea. and no. dists.) N.Y. 1972, U.S. Ct. Appeals (2d cir.) N.Y.C., 1970-71; assoc. Kramer, Levin, Naftalis, Nessen & Frankel, N.Y.C., 1971-77, ptnr., 1978—. Recipient John Ordronaux prize Columbia U. Law Sch., 1970. Mem. Assn. Bar City N.Y. (com. fed. legislation 1975-78, com. on products liability 1983-86, mem. com. on trademarks and unfair competition 1995—). Democrat. Jewish. Home: 336 Central Park W New York NY 10025-7111 Office: Kramer Levin Naftalis Nessen Kamin & Frankel 919 3rd Ave New York NY 10022-3903

WEINBERGER, LEON JOSEPH, insurance company executive; b. Leroy, Wis., Nov. 15, 1931; s. James J. and Marie Ann (Bauer) W.; m. Janet M. Hietbrink, Mar. 28, 1977; children: Alan, Carol, Eric, Janet, Randal, Kelly, John. Student, St. Norbert Coll., 1949-50; BBA, U. Wis., 1957; postgrad., Harvard U., 1975. Staff acct. Peat, Marwick, Mitchell & Co., Milw., 1957-61; controller Lake to Lake Dairy Co., Sheboygan, Wis., 1961-67; exec. v.p. Sentry Ins. Co., Stevens Point, Wis., 1967-79; v.p. Nationwide Ins., Columbus, Ohio, 1980-85; pres., chief exec. officer Wausau (Wis.) Ins. Cos., 1985—, also bd. dirs. Served with U.S. Army, 1952-54. Mem. Am. Inst. CPA's. Office: Wausau Ins Cos PO Box 8017 Wausau WI 54402-8017

WEINBERGER, LEON WALTER, sanitary engineer; b. N.Y.C., Aug. 28, 1923; s. Nathan and Margaret (Feldman) W.; m. Greta Stovsky, Dec. 16, 1950; children: Jeffrey Howard, Paula Lynn, Gayle Ellen. BS in Civil Engring., Cooper Union Coll., 1943; MS, MIT, 1947, ScD, 1949. Diplomate, Am. Assn. Environ. Engrs. Rsch. assoc MIT, Cambridge, Mass., 1947-49; assoc. prof. Case Inst. Tech., Cleve., 1949-63; asst. com. R&D water pollution Depts. Interior & HEW, Washington, 1963-68; group v.p. Zurn Industries, Erie, Pa., 1968-70; v.p. EnviroControl, Washington, 1970; prin. Leon W. Weinberger & Assocs., Rockville, Md., 1970-76; chief engr. Peer Cons., Rockville, Md., 1978—. Contbr. articles to profl. jours., presentations to sci. meetings. Lt. US Navy 1943-46, PTO. Fellow ASCE; mem. Water Pollution Control Fed., Am. Water Works Assn., Sigma Xi. Jewish. Home: 7400 Masters Dr Potomac MD 20854-3852 Office: Peer Cons PC 12300 Twinbrook Pky Rockville MD 20852-1606

WEINBERGER, MILES M., physician, pediatric educator; b. McKeesport, Pa., June 28, 1938; divorced; 4 children; m. Leslie Kramer, Aug. 22, 1992. A.B., U. Pitts., 1960, M.D., 1965. Diplomate Am. Bd. Pediatrics, Am. Bd. Allergy and Immunology, Am. Bd. Pediatric Pulmonology. Intern U. Calif. Med. Ctr., San Francisco, 1965-66, pediatric resident, 1965-67; research assoc NIH, Bethesda, Md., 1967-69; allergy and pulmonary fellow U. Colo., Denver, 1969-71; staff Ross Valley Med. Clinic, Greenbrae, Calif., 1971-73; clin. pharmacology fellow U. Colo., Denver, 1973-75; div. chmn. U. Iowa, Iowa City, 1975—; cons. D.C.Hosp. for Sick Children, 1967-69, allergy and immunology Family Practice Program, Sonoma County Community Hosp., U. Calif. Sch. Medicine, 1972-73; clin. instr. pediatrics Georgetown U. Sch. Medicine, Washington, 1967-69; staff pediatrician parttime West Side Neighborhood Health Ctr., Denver, 1970-71; pediatric sr. staff mem. Nat.Jewish Hosp. and Research Ctr., 1973-75; clin. asst. U. Colo. Med.Ctr., 1974-75; assoc. prof. pediatrics, chmn. pediatric allergy and pulmonary div. U. Iowa Coll. Medicine, 1975-80, assoc. prof. pharmacology, 1975-79, dir. Cystic Fibrosis Ctr., 1977—, prof. pediatrics, 1980—, dir. pediatric allergy and pulmonary div., 1977—. Author: Managing Asthma, 1990; contbr. numerous articles to profl. jours., chpts. to books; also audiovisual materials, commentaries, pub. letters and presentations in field. Recipient Clemens von Pirquet award Am. Coll. Allergy, 1974; grantee NIH, 1980-85, Cystic Fibrosis Ctr., Pharm. Mfrs. Assn. Fellow Am. Acad. Pediatrics (allergy sect. 1972, sect. on clin. pharmacology and therapeutics 1978, diseases of chest 1978); mem. Am. Acad. Allergy, Am. Soc. Clin. Pharmacology and Therapeutics, Soc. for Pediatric Rsch., Am. Thoracic Soc. (pres. Iowa Thoracic Soc. 1992-93), Camp Superkids of Iowa (adv. bd. 1981—), Am. Lung Assn. (pediatric pulmonary ctr. task force com. 1984-86). Home: 7 Cottage Grove Dr NE Iowa City IA 52240-9171 Office: U Iowa Dept Pediatrics Iowa City IA 52242

WEINBERGER, MYRON HILMAR, medical educator; b. Cin., Sept. 21, 1937; s. Samuel and Helen Eleanor (Price) W.; m. Myrna M. Rosenberg, June 12, 1960; children: Howard David, Steven Neal, Debra Ellen. BS, Ind. U., Bloomington, 1959, MD, 1963. Intern Ind. U. Med. Ctr., Indpls., 1963-64, resident in internal medicine, 1964-66, asst. prof. medicine, 1969-73, assoc. prof., 1973-76, prof., 1976—, dir. Hypertension Research Ctr., 1981—; USPHS trainee in endocrinology and metabolism Stanford U. Med. Ctr., Calif., 1966-68, USPHS spl. fellow in hypertension, 1968-69. Contbr. articles to profl. jours. Fellow ACP, Am. Coll. Cardiology, Am. Coll. Nutrition, Am. Soc. for Clin. Pharmacology and Therapeutics; mem. AAAS, Am. Fedn. Clin. Research, AMA, Am. Heart Assn., Am. Soc. Nephrology, Internat. Soc. Nephrology, Central Soc. Clin. Research, Endocrine Soc., Internat. Soc. Hypertension, Soc. for Exptl. Biology and Medicine. Home: 135 Bow Ln Indianapolis IN 46220-1023 Office: Ind U Hypertension Research Ctr 541 Clinical Dr Indianapolis IN 46202-5111

WEINBERGER, SETH JAY, lawyer; b. Jersey City, Mar. 8, 1955; s. Martin I. and Shirley (Epstein) W.; m. Barbara L. Goodman, Aug. 21, 1983; 1 child, Ian Fredric. BA, U. Mich., 1977, JD, 1979. Bar: N.J. 1980, Ill. 1982. Assoc. Pitney, Hardin, Kipp & Szuch, Morristown, N.J., 1980-82; assoc., then ptnr. Mayer, Brown & Platt, Chgo., 1982—. Office: Mayer Brown & Platt 190 S La Salle St Chicago IL 60603-3410

WEINBERGER, SIEGBERT JACOB, food company executive; b. Berlin, Fed. Republic Germany, July 20, 1924; came to U.S., 1938; s. Adolf S. and Meta C. (Bettauer) W.; m. Violetta Brick (div. 1955). BA, Ind. U., 1945; MA, NYU, 1947. Editorial asst. Middle Eastern Affairs Jour., N.Y.C., 1950-53; asst. concert mgr. S.A. Gorlinsky, London, 1953-54; concert mgmt. cons. London, 1953-55; sales mgr. Eastern Transatlantic Corp., N.Y.C., 1956-58, v.p. sales mgr., 1958-67, pres., 1967—; cons. N.Y. Commodities Corp., N.Y.C., 1986-89; cons. for internat. devel. WMS Industries; agent/cons. for U.S.A. Lothar Krüger Co., Munich, 1991—. Contbr. articles and book revs. on the Middle East to mags. V.p., trustee Kaliski Found. for Gifted Children, Inc., N.Y.C., 1985—. Served to sgt. U.S. Army, 1943-46, ETO. Decorated Purple Heart; Order of Merit (Poland). Republican.

WEINBROT, HOWARD DAVID, English educator; b. Bklyn., May 14, 1936; s. William and Rose (Shapiro) W. BA, Antioch Coll., Yellow Springs, Ohio, 1958; MA with honors (Woodrow Wilson fellow 1959, grad. fellow 1959-63), U. Chgo., 1959, PhD, 1963. Teaching fellow U. Chgo., 1962-63; instr. English Yale U., 1963-66; asst. prof., then assoc. prof. U. Calif., Riverside, 1966-69; mem. faculty U. Wis., Madison, 1969—, prof. English, 1972-84, Ricardo Quintana prof., 1984-87, Vilas prof., 1987—; Andrew Mellon vis. prof. Inst. Advanced Studies, Princeton, N.J., 1993-94. Author: The Formal Strain, 1969, Augustus Caesar in Augustan England, 1978, Alexander Pope and the Traditions of Formal Verse Satire, 1982, Essays on 18th-Century Satire, 1988, Britannia's Issue, 1993; also numerous articles, revs.; editor: New Aspects of Lexicography, 1972, Northrop Frye and 18th Century Studies; co-editor: The 18th Century: A Current Bibliography for 1973, 1975, Poetry in English, An Anthology, 1987. Sr. fellow NEH, 1975-76; summer fellow Huntington Library, 1977; fellow Newberry Library-Brit. Acad., 1977-78; Guggenheim-NEH fellow, 1983; Huntington-Brit. Acad. fellow, 1984; Newberry-NEH fellow 1985-86; fellow Humanities Inst., U. Wis., 1987, 90—; Guggenheim fellow 1988-89. Fellow Inst. for Advanced Studies (Princeton); mem. MLA, Am. Soc. 18th Century Studies (mem. editorial bd. 1977-80), Johnson Soc. (sec.-treas. ctrl. region 1970-95), Midwest Soc. 18th Century Studies (pres. 1980). Home: 1505 Wood Ln Madison WI 53705-1456 Office: U Wis Dept English 600 N Park St Madison WI 53706-1403

WEINER, ANNETTE BARBARA, university dean, anthropology educator; b. Philadelphia, Pa., Feb. 14, 1933; d. Archibald W. and Phyllis M. (Stein-Goldman) Cohen; m. Martin Weiner, 1953 (div. 1973); children: Linda Matisse, Jonathan Weiner; m. Robert Palter, 1979 (div. 1982); m. William E. Mitchell, 1987. B.A., U. Pa., 1968; Ph.D., Bryn Mawr Coll., 1974. Vis. asst. prof. Franklin & Marshall Coll., Lancaster, Pa., 1973-74; assoc. prof. Clare Hall, Cambridge, Eng., 1976; asst. prof. anthropology U. Tex., Austin, 1974-80, assoc. prof., 1980-81; prof., chmn. dept. anthropology NYU, N.Y.C., 1981-91; David B. Kriser prof. NYU, 1985—; dean Grad. Sch. Arts and Scis. NYU, N.Y.C., 1991—, dean Social Scis., 1993—; mem. adv. com. NRC, 1993—; bd. dirs. Social Sci. Rsch. Coun. Author: Women of Value: Men of Renown: New Perspectives in Trobriand Exchange, 1976, The Trobrianders of Papua New Guinea, 1989; editor (with J. Schneider) Cloth and Human Experience, 1989, (film, with D. Wason) The Trobriand Islanders of Papua New Guinea, Bilan du Film Ethnographique, Paris, 1991 (Grand Prix award), Inalienable Possessions: The Paradox of Keeping-While-Giving, 1992. Guggenheim fellow, 1980; grantee Wenner-Gren Found. Anthrop. Rsch., 1982, 85, 86, NEH, 1976, 85, Am. Council Learned Socs., 1976, NIMH, 1972-73. Fellow Am. Anthrop. Assn. (pres. 1991-93), Royal Anthrop. Inst. Gt. Britain and Ireland, Assn. Social Anthropology in Oceania, Soc. Cultural Anthropology (bd. dirs. 1985-87, pres. 1988-89), N.Y. Inst. of the Humanities; mem. Cibola Anthrop. Assn. (pres. 1977-79), Commn. Visual Anthropology, Nat. Rsch. Coun. (adv. com. 1993—), Social Sci. Rsch. Coun. (bd. dirs. 1993-95). Office: NYU Dean Grad Sch 6 Washington Sq N New York NY 10003-6668

WEINER, CARL DORIAN, historian; b. N.Y.C., Mar. 26, 1934; s. Alexander and Ann (Goodson) W.; m. Ruth Ann Feinglass, Sept. 6, 1959; children—Nicholas, Kevin, Daniel. B.A., Queens Coll., 1955; postgrad., U. Wis., 1958-61; M.A., Columbia U., 1959. Instr. U. Pitts., 1961-62; mem. faculty Carleton Coll., Northfield, Minn., 1964—, chmn. dept. history, 1974-77, 95—; prof. Carleton Coll., 1982—. Served with U.S. Army, 1957. Recipient 2d Century award Carleton Coll., 1968; Bush grantee, 1983-84. Jewish. Home: 403 Laurel Ave Saint Paul MN 55102

WEINER, CHARLES, historian, educator; b. Bklyn., Aug. 11, 1931; s. Louis and Minnie (Florman) W.; m. Shirley Marks (div. 1976); 1 child, Susan. B.S., Case Inst. Tech., 1960, M.A., 1963, Ph.D., 1965. Asst. editor Tooling and Production mag., Cleve., 1958-60; assoc. editor, 1961; editor The Explorer, Cleve. Museum of Natural History, 1960-62; dir. Project on History of Recent Physics in the U.S., Am. Inst. Physics, N.Y.C., 1964-65, Center for History of Physics, 1965-74; prof. history of sci. and tech. Mass. Inst. Tech., 1974—, dir. oral history program, 1975—. Co-editor: The Legacy of George Ellery Hale, 1972, Robert Oppenheimer: Letters and Recollections, 1980; editor: Exploring the History of Nuclear Physics, 1972, History of 20th Century Physics, 1977; mem. editorial council: Bull. of Atomic Scientists, 1979-84. Mem. com. social orgn. sci. Social Sci. Research Council, 1968-71; adv. com. to Library of Congress on Nat. Union Catalog of Manuscript Collections, 1965-71; mem. editorial adv. bd. Joseph Henry Papers, Smithsonian Instn., 1968—; com. on history of recent biochemistry and molecular biology Am. Acad. Arts and Scis., 1968-80, project dir. com. history contemporary physics, 1966-74; mem. adv. bd. Center for the Study of Consumer Movement, Consumers Union; mem. humanities adv. bd. Sta. WGBH, Boston, 1978-79. Served with U.S. Army, 1951-53. Recipient Disting. Service citation Am. Physics Tchrs., 1974; Case fellow, 1961-64; Guggenheim fellow, 1970-71; NSF grantee, 1965, 68, 70, 73, 75, 77, 81, 86; Nat. Endowment Humanities grantee, 1976, 77, 81, 86. Fellow AAAS (council 1969-75, com. on meetings 1969-72), History of Sci. Soc. (council 1968-70, chmn. Met. N.Y. Sect. 1969-70), Am. Hist. Assn., Oral History Assn., Orgn. Am. Historians, Soc. for History of Tech. (adv. council 1977-79). Office: Mass Inst Tech Program in Sci Tech and Society Bldg E51-201 Cambridge MA 02139

WEINER, CHARLES R., federal judge; b. Phila., June 27, 1922; s. Max and Bessie (Chairney) W.; m. Edna Gerber, Aug. 24, 1947; children: William, Carole, Harvey. Grad., U. Pa., 1947, M.A., 1967, Ph.D., 1972; LL.B. Temple U., 1950. Bar: Pa. bar 1951. Asst. dist. atty. Philadelphia County, 1952-53; mem. Pa. Senate from Phila. County, 1952-67, minority floor leader, 1959-60, 63-64, majority floor leader, 1961-62; U.S. dist. judge Eastern Dist. Pa., 1967—; Mem. Phila. County Bd. Law Examiners, 1959—. Mem. Pres.'s Adv. Commn. Inter-Govtl. Rels., Phila., Pub. Policy Com., Phila. Crime Prevention Assn., Big Bros. Assn.; mem. Pa. Bd. Arts and Scis.; trustee, exec. com. Fedn. Jewish Philanthropies of Phila., Allied Jewish Appeal of Phila.; bd. dirs. Mental Health Assn. of Pa., Phila. Psychiat. Ctr., Phila. Tribune Charities, Phila. Wharton Ctr. Parkside YMCA, Jewish Publ. Soc. Am., The Athenaeum, and others. Recipient Phila. Fellowship award; Founder's Day award Temple U.; Alumni award U. Pa.; Founder's award Berean Inst.; others. Mem. ABA, Pa. Bar Assn., Phila. Bar Assn., Am. Law Inst. Office: US District Ct 6613 US Courthouse Ind Mall W 601 Market St Philadelphia PA 19106-1723

WEINER, EARL DAVID, lawyer; b. Balt., Aug. 21, 1939; s. Jacob Joseph and Sophia Gertrude (Rachanow) W.; m. Gina Helen Priestley Ingoglia, Mar. 30, 1962; children: Melissa Danis Balmain, John Barlow. A.B., Dickinson Coll., 1960; LL.B., Yale U., 1968. Bar: N.Y. 1969. Assoc. Sullivan & Cromwell, N.Y.C., 1968-76, ptnr., 1976—; adj. prof. Rutgers U. Sch. Law, 1987-88; bd. dirs. Solvay Techs. Inc., Hedwin Corp., The Acting Co., vice chair, 1992—, v.p., 1991-92. Gov. Bklyn. Heights Assn., 1980-87, pres., 1985-87, adv. com., 1987—; gov. The Heights Casino, 1979-84, pres., 1981-84; trustee Bklyn. Bot. Garden, 1985—, vice chmn., 1989—; trustee Green-Wood Cemetery, 1986—, vice chmn., 1991—; bd. advisors Dickinson Coll., Carlisle, Pa., 1986-90, chmn., 1988-90, trustee, 1988—; mem. adv. com. East Rock Inst., 1988—. Lt. USN, 1961-65. Mem. ABA, N.Y. State Bar Assn., Assn. of Bar of City of N.Y. Office: Sullivan & Cromwell 125 Broad St New York NY 10004

WEINER, GERRY, government official; b. Montreal, Que., Can., June 26, 1933; m. Judith Weiner; children: Roberta, Mark. BA in Sociology and Anthropology, McGill U., 1954; BSc in Pharmacy, U. Montreal, 1958. Pharmacist, 1950-60; with Ayerst Labs., 1960-62; sr. ptnr. Apothapharm Pharmacies, 1963—; mem. for Pierrefonds-Dollard riding Parliament, 1984; parliamentary sec. for external affairs, 1984, parliamentary sec. for employment and immigration, 1985, minister of state for immigration 1986-88, minister of state for multiculturalism and citizenship, 1988, also sec. of state of Can., 1989—; minister Multiculturalism and Citizenship, 1991. Bd. dirs. West Island Bus. Devel. Council, 1982-84; mem. planning com. Dollard-des-Ormeaux, 1978-82; co-chmn. Emergency Med. Service Council, 1978-82; city councillor Dollard-des-Ormeaux, 1978-82, mayor, 1982-84; initiator Neighbourhood Watch program Island of Montreal, 1978; pres. North Shore Youth Services, 1970-75; mem. Lakeshore Gen. Hosp. Found., 1975-78, Beechwood Home and Sch. Assn.; founding pres. Congregation Rodeph Shalom; mem. La Régie intermunicipale des bibliothèques Pierrefonds-Dollard-des-Ormeaux, 1978-84. Mem. L'Ordre des Pharmaciens (West Island coordinator Urgence Pharmacien). Lodge: B'nai B'rith Univ. (former exec. mem.). Office: Cab du Ministre du Multiculturalisme, et de la Citoyenneté, Ottawa, ON Canada K1A 0M5

WEINER, IRVING BERNARD, university administrator, psychologist, educator; b. Grand Rapids, Mich., Aug. 16, 1933; s. Jacob H. and Mollie Jean (Laevin) W.; m. Frances Shair, June 9, 1963; children: Jeremy Harris, Seth Howard. B.A., U. Mich., Ann Arbor, 1955, M.A., 1957, Ph.D., 1959. Diplomate Am. Bd. Profl. Psychology. From instr. to prof. psychiatry and pediatrics U. Rochester, N.Y., 1959-72; head div. psychology U. Rochester Med. Center, 1968-72; prof. psychology, chmn. dept. Case Western Res. U., 1972-77, dean grad. studies, 1976-79; vice chancellor for acad. affairs U. Denver, 1979-83, prof. psychology, 1979-85; v.p. for acad. affairs Fairleigh Dickinson U., Teaneck, N.J., 1985-89; prof. psychology Fairleigh Dickinson U., 1985-89; prof. psychiatry U. South Fla., Tampa, 1989—; adv. editor John Wiley & Sons, 1967-93, Lawrence Erlbaum Assocs., 1993—; psychology edn. rev. com. NIMH, 1977-81. Author: Psychodiagnosis in Schizophrenia, 1966, Psychological Disturbance in Adolescence, 1970, rev. edit., 1992, Rorschach Handbook, 1971, Child Development, 1972, Principles of Psychotherapy, 1975, Development of the Child, 1978, Child and Adolescent Psychopathology, 1982, Rorschach Assessment of Children and Adolescents, 1982, rev. edit., 1995, Adolescence, 1985, rev. edit., 1995, Handbook of Forensic Psychology, 1987; editor: Readings in Child Development, 1972,

Clinical Methods in Psychology, 1976, 83, Jour. Personality Assessment, 1985-93, Rorschachiana, 1989—; mem. editl. bd. Profl. Psychology, 1971-76, Jour. Adolescent Health Care, 1979-87, Children and Youth Svcs. Rev., 1979-91, Jour. Pediatric Psychology, 1981-87, Devel. and Behavioral Pediatrics, 1985—, Studi Rorschachiani, 1985—, European Jour. Psychol. Assessment, 1985—, Jour. Adolescent Rsch., 1986-91, Jour. Personality Disorders, 1986-92, Psychol. Assessment, 1994—. Recipient Disting. Profl. Achievement award Genesee Psychol. Assn., 1974. Fellow APA, Am. Psychol. Soc., Acad. Clin. Psychology; mem. Assn. Advancement Psychology, Soc. Personality Assessment (pres. 1976-78, Disting. Contbr. award 1983), Assn. Internship Ctrs. (exec. com. 1971-76), Soc. Rsch. in Adolescence, Soc. for Rsch. in Child and Adolescent Psychopathology, Soc. for Exploration Psychotherapy Integration, Soc. Pediatric Psychology, Am. Psychol. Law Soc., Phi Beta Kappa, Sigma Xi, Phi Kappa Phi. Home: 13716 Halliford Dr Tampa FL 33624-6903 Office: U South Florida Psychiatry Ctr 3515 E Fletcher Ave Tampa FL 33613-4788

WEINER, IRWIN M., medical educator, college dean, researcher; b. N.Y.C., Nov. 5, 1930; s. Samuel and Pearl (Levine) W.; m. Lois M. Fuxman, Apr. 18, 1961 (div. 1980); children: Stefanie F., Jeffrey N.; m. Lieselotte Roth, June 20, 1981. AB, Syracuse U., 1952; MD, SUNY-Syracuse, 1956. Postdoctoral fellow Johns Hopkins Sch. Medicine, Balt., 1956-58, instr., 1958-60, asst. prof., 1960-66; assoc. prof. SUNY, Upstate Med. Ctr., Syracuse, 1966-68, prof., chmn. dept., 1968-87, v.p. rsch., 1982-88, dean Coll. Medicine, 1987-91, v.p. for med. and biomed. edn., 1988-91; dean Coll. Medicine Health Sci. Ctr., SUNY, Bklyn., 1991—; vis. asst. prof. Albert Einstein Coll. Medicine, Bronx, N.Y., 1964-65; cons. Sterling-Winthrop Rsch. Inst., N.Y., 1968-82, mem. rsch. bd., 1973-76; mem. study sect. Pharmacology and Exptl. Therapeutics "A", NIH, 1965-72, ad hoc com. on comparative pharmacology, Nat. Inst. Gen. Med. Scis., 1966-68, ad hoc com. rsch. career devel. awards and fellowships pharmacology, 1975-76; mem. consensus devel. panel analgesic associated kidney disease NIH, 1984; mem. pharmacology com. Nat. Bd. Med. Examiners, 1977-82; mem. rsch. com. Am. Heart Assn., 1969-74, chmn., 1969-74; mem. pharmacology adv. com. Pharm. Mfrs. Assn. Found., 1981—, chmn. basic pharmacology adv. com., 1987—; mem. N.Y. State Health Rsch. Coun., 1987—, chmn., 1991—. Field editor for renal pharmacology Jour. Pharmacology & Exptl. Theapeutics, 1965-72, editorial adv. bd., 1981-86; editorial bd. Life Scis. jour., 1973-79, renal, fluid and electrolyte physiology Am. Jour. Physiology, 1982-86; editorial com Ann. Rev. Pharmacology and Toxicology, 1982-86; contbr. over 90 articles to profl. jours., chpts. to books. Trustee Loretto Geriatric Ctr., 1989-91; bd. regents L.I. Coll. Hosp., 1993—; bd. dirs. Rsch. Found. SUNY, 1994—. Predoctoral fellow in physiology SUNY Upstate Med. Ctr., 1953-54; recipient numerous fed. fellowships, grants, 1956—, Rsch. Career Devel. award NIH, 1964-65. Mem. AAAS, Am. Soc. Pharmacology and Exptl. Therapeutics (bd. publs. trustees 1973-79), N.Y. Acad. Scis., Am. Soc. Nephrology, Internat. Soc. Biochem. Pharmacology, Internat. Soc. Nephrology, Assn. Med. Sch. Pharmacologists, N.Y. Acad. Medicine. Democrat. Jewish. Home: 39 Plaza St W Apt 10A Brooklyn NY 11217-3932 Office: SUNY Health Sci Ctr 450 Clarkson Ave Brooklyn NY 11203-2098

WEINER, JEROME HARRIS, mechanical engineering educator; b. N.Y.C., Apr. 5, 1923; s. Barnet and Dora (Muchar) W.; m. Florence Mensch, June 24, 1950; children: Jonathan David, Eric Daniel. B. Mech. Engring., Cooper Union U., 1943; A.M., Columbia U., 1946, Ph.D., 1952. Mem. faculty Columbia U., N.Y.C., 1952-68; prof. mech. engring. Columbia U., 1960-68, acting chmn. dept., 1961-62; L. Herbert Ballou Univ. prof. Brown U., Providence, 1968-93; L. Herbert Ballou Univ. prof. emeritus, 1993—. Author: (with B.A. Boley) Theory of Thermal Stresses, 1960, Statistical Mechanics of Elasticity, 1983. Fulbright research scholar Rome, Italy, 1958-59, Haifa, Israel, 1965-66; Guggenheim fellow, 1965-66. Mem. Am. Phys. Soc., Am. Math. Soc., ASME. Home: 24 Taber Ave Providence RI 02906-4113 Office: Brown U 79 Waterman St Providence RI 02912-9079

WEINER, JOEL DAVID, retired food products executive; b. Chgo., Aug. 27, 1936; m. Judith L. Metzger; children: Beth, David. BBA, Northwestern U. Dir. new products and household div. Alberto-Culver Co., Melrose Park, Ill., 1963-66; group mktg. mgr. Bristol Myers Co., N.Y.C., 1966-74; v.p. new products Carter Wallace Co., N.Y.C., 1974-78; exec. v.p. Joseph E. Seagram Corp., N.Y.C., 1979-84; exec. v.p. corp. mktg. Kraft, Inc., Glenview, Ill., 1984-89. Home: 550 Park Dr Kenilworth IL 60043-1005

WEINER, JONATHAN, management consultant; b. N.Y.C., May 27, 1943; s. David and Paula Ganzer W.; divorced; 1 child, Joanna. BA, Harvard U., 1964. Asst. budget dir. City of N.Y., 1967-74; staff dir. N.Y. State Moreland Art Commn., N.Y.C., 1974-76; prin. McKinsey & Co. Inc., N.Y.C., 1976-91; dir. APM, Inc., N.Y.C., 1991—. Trustee Interfaith Med. Ctr., Bklyn., 1989-90, Citizens Budget Commn., N.Y.C., 1990—. Home: 393 W End Ave New York NY 10019 Office: Com Econ Advisers Old Executive Office Bldg Washington DC 20503

WEINER, JONATHAN DAVID, writer; b. N.Y.C., Nov. 26, 1953; s. Jerome Harris and Ponnie (Mensch) W.; m. Deborah Heiligman, April 24, 1982; 1 child, Aaron. BA cum laude, Harvard U., 1977. Asst. editor Moment, Boston, 1978; sr. editor The Sciences N.Y. Acad. of Scis., N.Y.C., 1978-84, contbg. editor, 1984—; columnist "Field Notes", 1984—; columnist "Quanta", The Sciences, "Tech Photo", Close-Up. Author: Planet Earth, 1986 (Am. Geol. Inst. award 1986), The Next One Hundred Years: Shaping the Fate of Our Living Earth, 1991, The Beak of the Finch: Evolution in Real Time, 1994 (Pulitzer Prize for non-fiction 1995). Mem. Nat. Assn Sci. Writers. Office: care Victoria Pryor Arcadia 20-A Old Neversink Rd Danbury CT 06811*

WEINER, LESLIE PHILIP, neurology educator, researcher; b. Bklyn., Mar. 17, 1936; s. Paul Larry and Sarah (Paris) W.; m. Judith Marilyn Hoffman, Dec. 26, 1959; children: Patrice Weiner Miller, Allison Hope, Matthew, Jonathan. BA, Wilkes Coll., 1957; MD, U. Cin., 1961. Diplomate Am. Bd. Psychiatry and Neurology. Intern in medicine SUNY, Syracuse, 1961-62; resident in neurology Johns Hopkins Hosp., Balt., 1962-65, fellow, 1967-69; resident Balt. City Hosp., 1962-63; fellow in virology Slow Virus Lab., Nat. Inst. Neurol. and Communicative Disorders-Stroke, NIH, Balt., 1969; asst. prof. neurology Johns Hopkins U., 1969-72, assoc. prof., 1972-75; prof. neurology and microbiology U. So. Calif. Sch. Medicine, L.A., 1975—, chmn. dept. neurology, 1979—, Richard Angus Grant Sr. chair in neurology, 1987—; chief neurologist U. So. Calif. Univ. Hosp., 1979—, mem. bd. govs.; chief neurologist Los Angeles County-U. So. Calif. Med. Ctr., 1979—; bd. dirs. John Douglas French Found., L.A., 1987—; mem. neurosci. tng. study sect. NIH, 1990, mem. sci. adv. bd. Hereditary Disease Found., 1992—. Contbr. over 100 articles on neurology, immunology and virology to med. jours., chpts. to books. Bd. dirs. Starbright Found., L.A., 1991. Capt. M.C., U.S. Army, 1965-67. Grantee NIH, 1990-95. Fellow Am. Acad. Neurology; mem. Am. Neurology Assn., Am. Health Assistance Found., Soc. Neurosci., Johns Hopkins U. Soc. Scholars. Democrat. Jewish. Avocations: collecting books, concerts, plays. Home: 625 S Rimpau Blvd Los Angeles CA 90005 Office: U So Calif Sch Medicine 1975 Zonal Ave Los Angeles CA 90033-1082

WEINER, LOUIS MAX, retired mathematics educator; b. Chgo., Nov. 11, 1926; s. Samuel and Lena (Adelman) W.; m. June Belmont, Aug. 18, 1957; children: Howard, Joel, Todd. BS, U. Chgo., 1947, MS, 1948, PhD, 1951. Examiner Civil Svc. Commn., Chgo., 1951-52; asst. prof. DePaul U., Chgo., 1952-58; rsch. engr. Gen. Am. Rsch. Divsn., Niles, Ill., 1958-64; prof. math. Northeastern Ill. U., Chgo., 1964-93, chmn. dept., 1968-74; instr. Oakton C.C. Des Plaines, Ill., 1974-92. Assoc. editor Math. mag., 1968-72; author: Introduction to Modern Algebra, 1970, Basic Mathematical Concepts, 1972. Mem. Am. Math. Soc., Math. Assn. Am., Sigma Xi, Phi Beta Kappa. Avocation: photography.

WEINER, MAX, educational psychology educator; b. Hartford, Conn., May 7, 1926; s. Harry Sam and Gertrude (Cohen) W.; m. Gloria Safi, Feb. 24, 1960; children: William Ronald, Jennifer Sharon. BA, U. Conn., 1950; MA, Trinity Coll., 1953; PhD, Yale U., 1957. Sci. tchr. Meriden (Conn.) Pub. Schs., 1952-55; guidance dir. White Plains (N.Y.) Pub. Schs., 1956-59; assoc. prof. Bklyn. Coll., CUNY, 1959-68; prof. Grad. Sch. CUNY, 1968-81, acting univ. dean, tchr. edn., 1973-74, exec. officer PhD program edn. psychology,

1970-76, dir. Ctr. for Advanced Study Edn., 1970-78, acting dean rsch. Grad. Sch., 1978-79; dean edn. Fordham U., N.Y.C., 1981-93, prof. ednl. psychology, 1981—; cons. psychologist SUNY Health Sci. Ctr., Bklyn., 1967-89; mem. nat. commn. on excellence in edn. adminstrn. Univ. Coun. for Edn. Adminstrn., 1985-87; mem. nat. adv. commn. Coll. Bd. Equity 2000, 1993—. Contbr. articles to profl. jours. Treas. N.Y. Alliance for Pub. Schs., N.Y.C., 1987-93; mem. Mayor's Commn. on Spl. Edn., N.Y.C., 1984-85; bd. dirs. Arthritis Found., Atlanta, 1974-76; trustee Beth El Synagogue, New Rochelle, N.Y., 1985—, La Scuola, N.Y., 1986—; mem. bd. visitors Sch. Edn., Scranton U., 1992—. Fellow Japan Soc. Promotion Scis., 1978. Fellow APA, Am. Psychol. Soc., N.Y. Acad. Scis.; mem. ACA (life), AAAS, Arthritis Health Professions Assn. (pres. 1974-75), Am. Ednl. Rsch. Assn., Assn. Colls. and Schs. Edn. in State Univs. and Land Grant Colls. and Affiliated Pvt. Univs. (mem. exec. com. 1986-89, 92-93), Assn. for Measurement and Evaluation in Guidance (senator 1966-72, sec. 1973-75), Nat. Coun. Measurement in Edn., Westchester Assn. Hebrew Schs. (pres. 1982-84), Sigma Xi, Phi Delta Kappa, Kappa Delta Pi. Office: Fordham U Grad Sch Edn 113 W 60th St New York NY 10023-7404

WEINER, MORTON DAVID, banker, insurance agent; b. Balt., Aug. 19, 1922; s. Max and Rose (Wolfe) W.; m. Joan M. Maggin; children: Bruce, Lori, Julie, Jeff. B.S., Towson State Coll., 1942; grad. exec. program, UCLA, 1959. Pres., dir. AVNET, Inc., N.Y.C., 1963-69; pres., owner Morton D. Weiner & Co., Inc., N.Y.C., 1969-70; dir. USLIFE Corp., 1970-77; chmn. bd. Nat. Investors Life Ins. Cos., 1970-78; exec. v.p. Norris Grain Co., 1971-78; pres., chief exec. officer Norin Corp., 1971-78; chmn. bd. Maple Leaf Mills, Ltd., Toronto, Ont., Can., 1974-78; chmn., dir. South Atlantic Fin. Corp., 1978-80, Atico Fin. Corp., 1980-81; chmn. Morton D. Weiner & Co., 1981—; bd. dirs. City Nat. Bank Fla., Fundamental Mgmt. Corp. Served to capt. Signal Corps, U.S. Army, 1942-46, CBI. Office: 200 SE 1st St Miami FL 33131-1903

WEINER, MYRON, political science educator; b. N.Y.C., Mar. 11, 1931; s. Hyman and Anna (Peretz) W.; m. Sheila Leiman, June 29, 1952; children: Beth, Saul Jeremy. B in Social Scis., CCNY, 1951; MA in Politics, Princeton U., 1953, PhD, 1955. Instr. Princeton (N.J.) U., 1951-52; asst. prof. U. Chgo., 1956-61; mem. faculty MIT, 1961—, prof. polit. sci., 1965—, Ford prof. polit. sci., 1977—, chmn. dept., 1974-77; sr. staff mem. Ctr. Internat. Studies, MIT, 1965—, dir., 1987-92; mem. com. on comparative politics Social Sci. Rsch. Coun., 1961-71; NAS chmn. project population policy in less-developed countries, 1972-75; mem. Ctr. for Population Studies, Sch. Pub. Health, Harvard U., 1973—; co-chmn. joint Harvard-MIT faculty seminar on polit. devel.; vis. prof. Inst. Econ. Growth, Delhi (India) U., 1970; vis. scholar U. Paris, 1966-67, Harry S Truman Inst., Hebrew U., 1979; chmn. joint com. on South Asia, Am. Coun. Learned Socs./Social Sci. Rsch. Coun., 1980-84; vis. prof. Harvard U., 1984; vis. scholar Balliol Coll., Oxford, 1992; mem. adv. com. UN High Commr. for Refugees, 1994; cons. to govt. and founds. Author: Party Politics in India, 1957, The Politics of Scarcity, 1962, Political Change in South Asia, 1963, Party Building in a New Nation: The Indian National Congress, 1967, Sons of the Soil, 1978, India at the Polls: The Parliamentary Elections of 1977, 1978, India at the Polls-1980, 1983, The Indian Paradox: Essays in Indian Politics, 1989, The Child and the State in India, 1993; co-author: Politics of the Developing Areas, 1960, Rapid Population Growth: Consequences and Policy Implications, 1972, Crises and Sequences in Political Development, 1972, Policy Sciences and Population, 1975, India's Preferential Policies: Migrants, the Middle Classes and Ethnic Equality, 1981; editor: Modernization: The Dynamics of Growth, 1966, Political Parties and Political Development, 1966, State Politics in India, 1968, International Migration and Security, 1993; co-editor: Indian Voting Behavior, 1963, Electoral Politics in Indian States, 4 vols., 1974-77,The State, Religion and Ethnic Politics: Afghanistan, Iran and Pakistan, 1986, Understanding Political Development, 1987, Competitive Elections in Developing Countries, 1987, The Political Culture of Foreign Area and International Studies, 1991; editorial bd.: Global Political Assessment, Asian Survey, Jour. Commonwealth and Comparative Studies, Jour. Interdisciplinary History, Third World Quarterly. Mem. adv. com. UN High Commr. for Refugees. Named Fulbright 40th Anniversary Disting. fellow, 1986-87; fellow Fulbright Found., 1953, Ford Found., 1953, 87, Soc. Sci. Rsch. Coun., 1957, 79, Rockefeller Found., 1961, Guggenheim Found., 1961, Carnegie Found., 1969, NSF, 1969, Rockefeller-Ford Found. program population policy, 1975, Nat. Inst. Child Health and Human Devel. NIH, 1976, Smithsonian Instn., 1985, MacArthur Found., 1992, Japan Found., 1994. Mem. Assn. Asian Studies (dir. 1961-69, chmn. adv. com. rsch. and devel. 1966-69, chmn. Indian state politics com. 1960-70), New Eng. Assn. Asian Studies (pres. 1980), Am. Polit. Sci. Assn. (sec. 1986, chmn. nominating com. 1987, editorial bd. rev. 1966-70), Am. Acad. Arts and Scis., Internat. Union for Sci. Study of Population, Coun. Fgn. Rels. Home: 1258 Beacon St Brookline MA 02146-3715 Office: MIT Dept Polit Sci E53-369 Cambridge MA 02142-1320

WEINER, RICHARD, public relations executive; b. Bklyn., May 10, 1927; s. George M. and Sally (Kosover) W.; m. Florence Chaiken, Dec. 9, 1956; children: Jessica Weiner Lampert, Stephanie Weiner Isobaker. B.S., U. Wis., 1949, M.S., 1950. Pres. Creative Radio Assocs., Madison, Wis., 1951-52, Weiner-Morton Assocs., Madison, 1952-53; sr. v.p. Ruder & Finn, Inc., N.Y.C., 1953-68; pres. Richard Weiner, Inc., N.Y.C., 1968-86; pres. N.Y. div. Porter/Novelli, N.Y.C., 1987-88, sr. counselor, 1988—. Author: Professional's Guide to Public Relations Services, 1968, News Bureaus in the U.S., 1970, Syndicated Columnists, 1972, Professional's Guide to Publicity, 1979, Military Publications, 1979, College Alumni Publications, 1980, Investment Newsletters, 1981, Webster's New World Dictionary of Media and Communications, 1990. Fellow Pub. Rels. Soc. Am. (accredited counselor, Silver Anvil award 1965, 84, 86, 87, John Hill award 1984, Gold Anvil award 1990), Am. Acad. Physician and Patient (bd. dirs.), Am. Arbitration Assn. Jewish. Office: Porter/Novelli 437 Madison Ave New York NY 10022-7001 *The essence of life is growth, adaptation, change. I hope to continue to succeed in living vigorously.*

WEINER, ROBERT MICHAEL, engineering design company executive, consulting engineer; b. N.Y.C., Jan. 20, 1936; s. Dudley John and Ruth Alice (McCormick) W.; m. Mary Carole Soetje, June 8, 1957; children: Michael, David, Therese, Paul, Kathryn, John, Thomas, James. BS in Chem. Engring. maxima cum laude, U. Notre Dame, 1957; grad., Bettis Reactor Engring. Sch., 1958; MS in Nuclear Engring., U. Md., 1965. Power systems engr. br. naval reactors AEC, Washington, 1957-62, sect. leader br. naval reactors, 1962-65; systems engr. MPR Assocs. Inc., Washington, 1965-68, sect. supr., 1968-87, prin. officer, 1987—. Contbr. articles to profl. jours. Parish rep., charter mem. Annandale (Va.) Christian Community for Action, 1967—; active Christian Family Movement, No. Va.); coach, leader youth activities Boys Sports Clubs, Boy Scouts Am., 1967-82. Served to lt. USN, 1957-61. Mem. K.C. Avocations: photography, camping, ch. related edn. and social action work. Home: 4820 Randolph Dr Annandale VA 22003-6222 Office: MPR Assocs Inc 320 King St Alexandria VA 22314

WEINER, ROBERT STEPHEN, federal agency administrator; b. Paterson, N.J., Apr. 3, 1947; s. Jess Joseph Weiner and Dorothea Violet (Slavin) Tabor. BA, Oberlin Coll., 1969; MA, U. Mass., 1974. Student coord. Hampshire County, dir. telephone bank Kennedy for U.S. Senate, Amherst, Mass., 1970; dir. nat. voter registration Young Dems. Am., Washington, 1971-72; dir. voter registration, media dir. get out the vote Dem. Nat. Com., Washington, 1972; legis. asst. Congressman Edward Koch, Washington, 1974-75; staff dir. subcom. health and long-term care U.S. Ho. of Reps., Washington, 1975-76, staff dir. com. aging, 1976-80, media dir., press sec. com. narcotics, 1987-90, press sec./communications dir. Com. on Govt. Ops., 1990—; nat. campaign aide Kennedy for Pres., Washington, 1990-95; sr. assoc. Mgmt. Recruiters Internat., Springfield, Mass., 1981-83; dir. Robert Weiner Assocs., Amherst, 1983-86; dir. comm. Ho. Judiciary Com. Minority and Cong. John Conyers Jr., 1995—; dir. gen. press room Dem. Nat. Convention, Atlanta, 1988, N.Y.C. 1992; cons. Carter-Mondale Transition, Washington, 1976-77, Congressman Claude Pepper, Washington, 1975-89. Represented in permanent exhbns. Nat. Mus. Am. History, Smithsonian Instn., Washington; contbr. numerous articles to profl. jours. Dem. nominee for U.S. Congress, Mass., 1986; chmn. Road Runners Am. Nat. 10 Mile Championship, Amherst, 1984; vice chmn. Dem. Town Com., Amherst, 1984-87; legis. chmn. Pioneer Valley Gray Panthers, Amherst, 1981-87. Named Communicator of Yr., Washington Crime News Svcs., 1988, 89, 90; 2d place U.S. Nat. 1500 Meter Age 45 Indoor Track Championship, 1994.

Mem. Assn. House Dem. Press Assts., Congl. Staff Club, Nat. Dem. Club, Sugarloaf Mountain Athletic Club (pres. 1984-86), Potomac Valley Track Club, Capitol Hill Runners (pres. 1991—). Avocations: running, attending performing arts. Home: 1104 Sanford Ln Accokeek MD 20607-2324 Office: US Ho of Reps Com on 2426 Rayburn House Ofc Bldg Washington DC 20515

WEINER, RONALD GARY, accounting firm executive; b. Newark, N.J., Nov. 24, 1945; s. Seymour and Beatrice (Goldberg) W.; m. Vicki Miles, Sept. 8, 1973; children: Jennie, Maureen. BSBA, Babson Coll. (Mass.), 1966; postgrad. NYU, 1968-69; Harvard U., 1982. CPA, N.Y., N.J., Pa. Mgmt. cons., acct., pres. Perelson Weiner, N.Y.C., 1971—. Bd. dirs. Jewish Cmty. Rels. Coun. N.Y.; officer; trustee Babson Coll., Citizens Budget Com., N.Y.C.; dir., v.p. Jewish Guild for the Blind, N.Y.C.; treas., dir. Roundtable Polit. Action Com., N.Y.C.; bd. govs. Am. Jewish Com.; mem. adv. com. Muehlenberg Coll., Nat. Polish Am.-Jewish Am. Com. Fellow Wexner Heritage Found, Adenauer Exch. Program; mem. AICPA, Accts. Club Am., Pa. State Soc. CPAs, N.J. State Soc. CPAs (dir.), N.Y. State Soc. CPAs., Young Pres.'s Orgn., Econ. Club, Harmonie Club, Harvard Club, Mt. Ridge Country Club, Pottsville Club. Office: Perelson Weiner One Dag Hammarskjold Plz New York NY 10017-2286

WEINER, STEPHEN ARTHUR, lawyer; b. Bklyn., Nov. 20, 1933; s. Joseph Lee W. and Ruth Lessall (Weiner) W.; m. Mina Rieur, Sept. 1, 1958; children: Karen, James. B.A. summa cum laude, Harvard U., 1954; J.D. cum laude, Yale U., 1957. Bar: N.Y. 1958, U.S. Supreme Ct. 1963. Assoc. Winthrop, Stimson, Putnam & Roberts, N.Y.C., 1958-65, ptnr., 1968—; vice chmn. mgmt. com., 1984—; acting prof. law U. Calif., Berkeley, 1965-68; lectr. Practising Law Inst., 1971—. Contbr. articles to legal publs. Comment editor Yale Law Jour., 1956-57. Fellow Am. Coll. Trial Lawyers, Am. Bar Found.; mem. Assn. Bar City N.Y. (chmn. recruitment of lawyers com., chmn. com. on Stimson medal), Fed. Bar Coun. (chmn. com. on 2d cir. cts., trustee), Order of Coif, Phi Beta Kappa. Home: 190 Harbor Rd Port Washington NY 11050-2508 Office: Winthrop Stimson One Battery Park Pla New York NY 10004-1490

WEINER, STEPHEN MARK, lawyer; b. Boston, Mar. 20, 1943; s. Meyer and Esther (Lowenstein) W.; m. Roslyn G. Weiner, Dec. 19, 1967 (div. 1992); children: Jeremiah, Ben, Miriam, Isaac. AB magna cum laude, Harvard U., 1964; LLB, Yale U., 1968. Bar: Mass. 1968. Teaching fellow Boston Coll. Law Sch., Chestnut Hill, Mass., 1968-69; assoc. Goodwin, Proctor & Hoar, Boston, 1969-71; spl. asst. to Gov. Francis W. Sargent Commonwealth of Mass., Boston, 1971-74; chmn. Mass. Rate Setting Commn., Boston, 1972-78; assoc. prof. Boston U. Sch. Law, 1978-81, dir. Ctr. for Law and Health Scis.; mem. Goulston & Storrs, Boston, 1981-90, Mintz, Levin, Cohn, Ferris, Glovsky and Popeo, P.C., Boston, 1990—; co-chair and sect. coord. health law sect. Mintz, Levin, Cohn, Ferris, Glovsky and Popeo, P.C.; adj. prof. law Boston U. Sch. Law, 1993-94; vis. lectr. Yale Law Sch., 1994-95. Mem. editorial bd. New Eng. Jour. Human Svcs., 1979-81; mem. adv. bd. Hosp. Risk Mgmt., 1979-83; contbr. articles to profl. jours. Mem. gov. task force to evaluate Mass. Determination of Need Program, 1979-80; mem. profl. adv. coun. Mass. Dept. Elder Affairs, 1979-81; dir., treas. AIDS Action Com. Mass.; bd. dirs. Boston Film/Video Found.; trustee Beth Israel Hosp., Boston, 1979-95, Spaulding Rehab. Hosp., Boston, 1979-95; mem. corp. Mass. Gen. Hosp., Boston. Mem. ABA, Nat. Health Lawyers Assn., Mass. Bar Assn., Boston Bar Assn. Home: 1302 La Grange St Chestnut Hill MA 02167 Office: Mintz Levin Cohn Ferris Glovsky and Popeo PC 1 Financial Ctr Boston MA 02111

WEINER, TIMOTHY EMLYN, newspaper journalist; b. June 20, 1956; s. Herbert and Dora B. Weiner. BA, Columbia U., 1978, MS in Journalism, 1979. Reporter, freelance writer N.Y.C., 1979-81; reporter Kansas City (Mo.) Times, 1981-82, Phila. Inquirer, 1982-93, N.Y. Times, Washington, 1993—. Author: Blank Check: The Pentagon's Black Budget, 1990. Recipient Pulitzer prize (with others) Kansas City Times, 1982, for nat. reporting, 1988. Office: NY Times 1627 I St NW Washington DC 20006-4007

WEINER, WALTER HERMAN, banker, lawyer; b. Bklyn., Aug. 29, 1930; s. Harry and Sylvia (Freifeld) W.; m. Nina Ester Avidar, Oct. 11, 1966; children: Thomas Field, Jon Michael. BA, U. Mich., 1952, JD, 1953. Bar: N.Y. 1953. Sr. ptnr. Kronish, Lieb, Weiner & Hellman, N.Y.C., 1965-79; chmn. exec. com., chief exec. officer Republic N.Y. Corp., 1980-81, pres., chief exec. officer, 1981-83, chmn. bd., chief exec. officer, 1983—; chmn. exec. com., chief exec. officer Republic Nat. Bank of N.Y., 1980-82, pres., chief exec. officer, 1981-86, chmn. bd., chief exec. officer, 1986—, also bd. dirs.; bd. dirs. Republic N.Y. Corp., Republic Nat. Bank of N.Y. Assoc. editor U. Mich. Law Rev. Bd. dirs., treas. Bryant Park Restoration Corp., Internat. Sephardic Edn. Found.; trustee Guild Hall, East Hampton, N.Y.; mem. N.Y. Holocaust Meml. Commn.; bd. visitors U. Mich. Law Sch. Recipient Humanitarian award NAACP, 1987, Human Rels. award Accts., Bankers, Factors and Fin. div. Am. Jewish Com., 1988, Man of Yr. award Bklyn. Sch. for Spl. Children, 1988. Mem. ABA, N.Y. State Bar Assn., Assn. of Bar of City of N.Y., Am. Bankers Assn. Home: 876 Park Ave New York NY 10021-1832 Office: Republic Nat Bank of NY 452 Fifth Ave New York NY 10018-2706

WEINER, DONALD G(REGORY), association executive, engineer; b. Aberdeen, S.D., Sept. 16, 1930; s. McDonald Donnegan and Susan Mae (Mathis) W. B.S., U.S. Mil. Acad., 1952; M.S.E., Purdue U., 1958; grad., Northwestern U. Inst. for Mgmt., 1974, Command Staff Gen. Coll., 1965, Armed Forces Staff Coll., 1967, Army War Coll., 1969. Registered profl. engr., Tex. Commd. 2d lt. U.S. Army C.E., 1952, advanced through grades to brig. gen., 1977; troop comdr. Korea, 1953-54, Ger., 1958-60, 67-68; dist. engr. Little Rock, Ark., 1972-75; staff officer Hdqrs. Dept. Army, Washington, 1970-72; dir. Engr. Studies Group, Washington, 1975-77; spl. asst. to Chief Engrs., C.E., Washington, 1978, ret., 1978; exec. dir., sec. NSPE, 1978; bd. dirs. Jr. Engring. Tech. Soc., Nat. Mathcounts. Decorated Legion of Merit (3), Bronze Star medal (2), Army Commendation medal (4). Mem. Soc. Am. Mil. Engrs., U.S. Army., Nat. Soc. Profl. Engrs. Republican. Home: 8121 Dunsinane Ct Mc Lean VA 22102-2719 Office: NSPE 1420 King St Alexandria VA 22314-2750

WEINERT, HENRY M., biomedical company executive; b. Nordhausen, Kassel, Fed. Republic Germany, May 31, 1940; s. Heinrich V. Nennenstiehl and Martha H. Weinert; m. Helen Koopmans, Feb. 14, 1966 (div. June 1982); children: Jason C., Brian T.; m. Kerri V. Keaton, Sept. 25, 1989. BA in Sci., Columbia Coll., 1962; MBA, Harvard Grad. Sch. Bus., 1970. Med. rsch. assoc. Columbia Univ., N.Y.C., 1964-65; exec. v.p., founder Clin. Diagnostic Lab., New Haven, Conn., 1966-68; dir. planning, bus. devel. Leefde Labs./Am. Cyan., Pearl River, N.Y., 1970-73, mktg. dir., 1973-74; bus. devel. mgr. Corning (N.Y.) Glass Works, 1974-77, pres., founder Boston Biomed. Cons., Waltham, Mass., 1977—; spl. ltd. ptnr. MedVenture Assocs., San Francisco, 1965—, Interwest Ptnrs., San Francisco, 1989; presenter, lectr. in field. Patentee laser fabrication of microsuture needles; contbr. articles to profl. jours. Pres. Svc. Soc., Columbia Coll., 1959; chmn. Student Union Com., Columbia Coll., 1961; treas. Class 1962, Columbia Coll., 1962-64; others. Recipient Alumni Achievement award Columbia Coll., 1962; grantee NIH, 1964-66. Mem. Biomed. Mktg. Assn. (bd. dirs. 1978-86, Recognition award 1986), Am. Assn. Clin. Chemistry, Van Slyke Soc. (bd. mem. 1991—). Lutheran. Avocations: reading sci. fiction and mystery novels, sailing, cars, landscaping. Home: 86 Myles Standish Rd Weston MA 02193-2124 Office: Boston Biomed Cons 100 Fifth Ave Waltham MA 02154

WEINGAND, DARLENE ERNA, librarian educator, consultant; b. Oak Park, Ill., Aug. 13, 1937; d. Edward Emil and Erna (Heidenway) W.; m. Wayne Anthony Weston, Sept. 7 (div. June 1976); children: Kathleen Mary, Lynda Anne, Judith Diane, Barbara Jeanne; m. Roger Paul Couture, Apr. 7, 1984. BA in History and English, Elmhurst Coll., 1972; MALS, Rosary Coll., 1973; PhD in Adult Edn./Libr. Sci., U. Minn., 1980. Asst. prof. U. Wis., Madison, 1981-86, assoc. prof., 1986-92, prof., 1992—, SLIS acting dir., summer 1986, 91, SLIS assoc. dir., 1990-94, adminstr. SLIS Continuing Edn. Svcs., 1981—; cons. in mktg., continuing edn., libr. futures, info. issues, and mgmt., 1980—; invited mentor Snowbird Leadership Inst., 1990, 92; vis. fellow Curtin U. Tech., Perth, Australia, 1990; Fulbright lectr. U. Iceland, 1988; lectr. Wis. State Supt. Conf., 1992, S.W. Wis. Librs., 1992, Wis. Assn.

for Acad. Librs., Eau Claire, 1993, Lakeshores Libr. Sys., 1993, 2nd World Conf. on Continuing Edn. for the Libr. and Info. Sci., Barcelona, 1993, Internat. Fedn. of Libr. Assns., Barcelona, 1993, Wis. Ednl. Media Assn. Fall Conf. Endnote Presentation, 1993. Author: Marketing/Planning Library and Information Services, 1987, Administration of the Small Public Library, 3d edit., 1992, Budgeting and the political Process in Libraries: Simulation Games, 1992 (with others), Connections: Literacy and Cultural Heritage: Lessons from Iceland, 1992, Managing Today's Public Library: Blueprint for Change, 1994, author (with others) Continuing Professional Education and Internat. Fed. of Libr. Assoc.: Past, Present, and a Vision for the Future, 1993, Keeping the Book$: Public Library Financial Management, 1992; contbr. articles to profl. jours. Recipient Excellence award Nat. U. Continuing Edn. Assn., 1989, Econ. and Comty. Devel. award, 1989, Outstanding Achievement in Audio Applications award Internat. Teleconferencing Assn., 1991. Mem. ALA, Internat. Fedn. Libr. Assn. (ALA rep.), Assn. for Libr. and Info. Sci. Edn. (dir. 1990-92, rsch. grant 1992, award 1994), Assn. of the Australian Libr. and Info. Assn., Nat. Univ. Continuing Edn. Assn., Wis. Libr. Assn., Wis. Assn. for Adult and Continuing Edn., World Future Soc., Phi Delta Kappa, Beta Phi Mu. Office: U Wis-Madison Helen White Hall 600 N Park St Madison WI 53706

WEINGART, CAROL JAYNE, university administrator, educator, psychotherapist; b. Schenectady, N.Y., Oct. 2, 1943; d. Clare James Murphy and Carolyn Marie (Jayne) Carroccio; m. Robert Edward Weingart, Apr. 2, 1966 (div. Feb. 1977); children: Julia M. Ashman, Anne E. Spencer, Kenneth L., Phillip M., Jayne E. Garro, Carolyn M. Garro; m. Prentiss E. Dwinell, May 29, 1992. Diploma in nursing, Parkview Meth. Sch. Nursing, 1965; BS, Defiance Coll., 1975; MA in Counseling, Norwich U., 1990; PhD, Summit U., 1995, Asst. Provost, 1995—. Psychiatric nursing instr. St. Joseph Hosp. Sch. Nursing, Ft. Wayne, Ind., 1975-76; nurse clinician Dr. Joseph Fiacable MD, Ft. Wayne, 1976-77, Wyo. State Hosp., Evanston, 1977, State Hosp. South, Blackfoot, Idaho, 1977-81; nurse supr. Bannock Meml. Hosp., Pocatello, Idaho, 1979-82; nurse Idaho Home Health, Blackfoot, 1982; nurse clinician Region I Mental Health, Coeur d'Alene, Idaho, 1983-88; nurse clinician, therapist Spokane (Wash.) Community Mental Health, 1988-89; crisis/intake therapist N.E. Kingdom Mental Health, Newport, Vt., 1989-94; asst. provost Summit U., 1995—; nurse Girl Scouts Day Camp, Kendallville, 1974-75; edn. chairperson Noble County Mental Health Assn., Kendallville, 1973; presenter N. Idaho Coll., Coeur d'Alene, 1988; lectr. Whitworth Coll. Spokane, 1989; ARC instr. expectant parents. Author: Childbirth with Hypnosis Expecting, 1970. Mem., pres. Assn. Retarded Citizens, Blackfoot, 1982-83; pres. Tiny Tots Games, Coeur d'Alene, 1983-89; mem. adv. bd. Orleans/Essex Home Health, Newport, 1989-93. Mem. P.E.O. (various offices). Quaker. Avocations: travel, reading, sewing, knitting. Home: RR 2 Box 217 North Troy VT 05859-9711

WEINGART, JEANNE, public relations executive. Ptnr., adminstv. dir. Fin. Rels. Bd., Chgo. Office: Fin Rels Bd John Hancock Ctr 875 N Michigan Ave Chicago IL 60611-1801*

WEINGARTEN, JOSEPH LEONARD, aerospace engineer; b. N.Y.C., June 5, 1944; s. Herman H. and Irene Jane (Binzer) W.; 1 child, Toby. B of Mech. Engring., NYU, 1966; postgrad., Air War Coll., 1976. Chief engr. Ait Transportability Test Loading Agy., Wright-Patterson AFB, Ohio, 1972-74; project engr. dept. engring. USAF, Wright-Patterson AFB, 1966-72, sr. project engr. dept. engring., 1974-76, planning and project engr. dept. engring., 1976-81, chief mgmt. ops. dept. engring., 1981-83, sr. tech. planner dept. engring., 1983-92; tech. asst. DCS Engring. and Tech. Mgmt. Air Force Material Command, Wright-Patterson AFB, 1992-93; founder, CEO Huffman Wright Inst., 1993—; CEO Weingarten Gallery, Dayton, Ohio, 1967—; sec., treas., v.p., bd. dirs. Ohio Designer Craftsmen, Columbus; sec. Ohio Designer Craftsmen Enterprise, Columbus, 1982—; chmn. continuing edn. design dept. Affiliate Socs. Coun., Dayton, 1971-84; chmn. edn. coord. com. Kettering Inst., Wright State U., 1974-76, chmn. scientist and engr. awards panel, 1990-91, mem., 1992—. Contbr. articles on systems engring. to Aeronautical Systems div. Mech. Engring. Jour. (1st place award nat. contest 1970), Procs. 4th Intersoc. Conf. on Transp., Air Force Systems Command, USAF, Spl. Purpose Report, Gems and Minerals, Ceramics Monthly, The Crafts Report, Friends Jour.-Air Force Mus. Macintosh Software. Scoutmaster Troop 81 Boy Scouts Am., Kettering, Ohio, 1985-91, com. mem., 1991-93, dist. chmn. Sequoia Dist. Miami Valley Coun., 1991-93, asst. coun. commr., 1993—; pres. Friends of Montessori Sch. South Dayton, 1978-94. Capt. USAF, 1967-71. Named Eagle Scout Boy Scouts Am., 1962; recipient Disting. Eagle award Boy Scouts Am., 1992. Mem. AIAA (sr. mem., air transport systems tech. com. 1976-78, 80-82, Lawrence Sperry award 1977), ASME (sr. mem.), Am. Nat. Standards Inst. (materials handling 5 com. 1968-70), Soc. Automotive Engrs. (aircraft ground support equiment com. 1969-75). Achievements include 11 patents for expendable air cargo pallet, mail container, collapsible air cargo container, process for reinforcing extruded articles, process for large scale extrusions, air flotation cargo handling system, integral aircraft barrier net, load distributive cargo platform, laminated plastic packaging material, computer printer paper support, and investment casting mold base; developments include 3g cargo restraint criteria used worldwide on aircraft/spacecraft/shuttles, rope extraction system for C-5A, system for large scale structural plastics extruxions, advanced planning documents for Air Force, report in new type of DOD procurement system; other achievements include the design and creation of jewelry sold in museums and retail stores.

WEINGARTEN, MURRAY, manufacturing executive; b. N.Y.C., Feb. 8, 1925; s. Ellis and Ethel (Gaies) B.; m. Shirley L. Bowersox, Apr. 30, 1955; children—Steven Ellis, Betsy Lori. E.E., Rensselaer Poly. Inst., 1947. With J.R. Rider, N.Y.C., 1947-48; engr. Bendix Radio, Towson, Md., 1948-50; with Bendix Field Engring. Corp., Columbia, Md.; became v.p. Bendix Field Engring. Corp., 1963; chmn. bd., pres., dir.; chmn. bd., pres., dir. Bendix Comml. Services Corp., Columbia, 1974; ret. Bendix Comml. Services Corp., 1989; chmn. bd., pres. Morrison & Knudsen Svcs. Inc., ret., 1992—; pres. United Geophys. Corp. (subs. Bendix Corp.); also dir.; pres. Skagit Corp. (subs. Bendix Corp.), Sedro-Woolley, Wash. Served with USNR, 1943-45. Mem. IEEE (sr.), Armed Forces Communication and Electronics Assn., Soc. Exploration Geophysicists (asso.), Engring. Soc. Balt. Home: 9442 Dunloggin Rd Ellicott City MD 21042-5148

WEINGARTEN, STEPHEN C., electronics executive; b. 1947. BA, City Coll. N.Y., 1968; JD, Columbia U., 1971. Assoc. gen. coun. MCI Comm. Corp., WUI (sub. Xerox Corp.); asst. sec., asst. gen. coun. Matsushita Comm., Peachtree City, Ga., 1987—. Office: Matsushita Comm 776 Hwy 74 S Peachtree City GA 30269*

WEINGARTEN, VICTOR I., engineering educator; b. N.Y.C., Jan. 18, 1931; s. Arnold and Sophia (Dickerman) W.; m. Myrna Marcia Rosenthal, July 31, 1954; children: Scott, Barbara. BME, CCNY, 1952; MSME, NYU, 1954; PhD in Engring., UCLA, 1964. Prof. computer structural mechanics U. So. Calif., Los Angeles, 1964—; br. head, cons. Northrop Aircraft, Hawthorne, Calif., 1964-66; cons. Hughes Aircraft, Canoga Park, Calif., 1964-86, Rockwell Internat., El Segundo, Calif., 1983-85; pres. Structural Research and Analysis Corp., Santa Monica, Calif., 1983—. Contbr. articles to profl. jours. Mem. ASME, ASCE. Office: Structural Rsch & Analysis Corp 2951 28th St Santa Monica CA 90405-2961

WEINGARTNER, H(ANS) MARTIN, finance educator; b. Heidelberg, Germany, Apr. 4, 1929; came to U.S., 1939, naturalized, 1944; s. Jacob and Grete (Kahn) W.; m. Joyce Trellis, June 12, 1959; children—Steven M., Susan C., Eric H., Kenneth L. A.B., S.B., U. Chgo., 1950, A.M., 1951; M.S., Carnegie Mellon U., 1956, Ph.D., 1962. Economist Dept. Commerce, 1951-53; instr. Grad. Sch. Indsl. Adminstrn., Carnegie Mellon U., 1956-57; instr., then asst. prof. Grad. Sch. Bus., U. Chgo., 1957-63; assoc. prof. fin. Alfred P. Sloan Sch. Mgmt., Mass. Inst. Tech., 1963-66; prof. Grad. Sch. Mgmt., U. Rochester, N.Y., 1966-77; Brownlee O. Currey prof. fin. Owen Grad. Sch. Mgmt., Vanderbilt U., Nashville, 1977—; dir. Computer Consoles, Inc., 1974-89; cons. to industry. Author: Mathematical Programming and the Analysis of Capital Budgeting Problems, 3d edit, 1974, (with George Benston and Dan Horsky) An Empirical Study of Mortgage Redlining, 1978; also articles.; Deptl. editor: Mgmt. Sci., 1967-73. Served with AUS, 1951-53. Mellon fellow, 1954-55; Ford Found. fellow, 1955-56, recipient first prize Dissertation Competition, 1963. Mem. Inst. Mgmt. Scis. (v.p. fin. 1978-84, pres. 1985-86), Coun.Sci. Soc. Pres.s, Am. Econ. Assn., Am. Fin. Assn., Beta Gamma Sigma. Home: 1616 Ash Valley Dr Nashville TN 37215-4202 Office: Vanderbilt U Owen Grad Sch Mgmt 401 21st Ave S Nashville TN 37203

WEINGARTNER, RUDOLPH HERBERT, philosophy educator; b. Heidelberg, Germany, Feb. 12, 1927; came to U.S., 1939, naturalized, 1944; s. Jacob and Grete (Kahn) W.; m. Fannia Goldberg-Rudkowski, Dec. 28, 1952; children: Mark H., Eleanor C. A.B., Columbia U., 1950, M.A., 1953, Ph.D., 1959. Fellow Inst. Philos. Research, San Francisco, 1953-55; instr. philosophy Columbia, 1955-59; from asst. prof. to prof., chmn. dept. philosophy San Francisco State Coll., 1959-68; prof. philosophy Vassar Coll., Poughkeepsie, 1968-74, chmn. dept., 1969-74, Taylor prof. philosophy, 1973-74, dean Coll. Arts and Scis.; prof. philosophy Northwestern U., Evanston, Ill., 1974-87; provost U. Pitts., 1987-89, prof. philosophy, 1987-94, fellow Ctr. for the Philosophy of Sci., 1990-94, chmn. dept. philosophy, 1991-93. Author: Experience and Culture: The Philosophy of Georg Simmel, 1962, The Unity of the Platonic Dialogue: The Cratylus, the Protagoras, The Parmenides, 1973, Undergraduate Education: Goals and Means, 1992 (Frederick W. Ness book award 1993); editor: (with Joseph Katz) Philosophy in the West, 1965; exhibited sculptures in Mendelson Gallery, 1992, 94, UP Gallery, 1992; contbr. articles to profl. jours. Bd. dirs. Chamber Music Chgo., 1982-87, pres., 1986-87; mem. bd. advisors Pitts. Symphony, 1991—; mem. adv. bd. dept. music Carnegie Mellon U., Pitts., 1992—. Social Sci. Rsch. Coun. fellow, 1958-59; Guggenheim fellow, 1965-66; Am. Coun. Learned Socs. fellow, 1971-72; residency Rockefeller Found. Study and Conf. Ctr. in Bellagio, 1994. Mem. Am. Philos. Assn., Am. Assn. Colls. (bd. dirs. 1985-89, task force on gen. edn. 1985-88, editorial bd. liberal edn. jours. 1986-94), Assoc. Artists Pitts. (artist mem.), Phi Beta Kappa. Home: 5448 Northumberland St Pittsburgh PA 15217-1129

WEINGAST, MARVIN, laboratory director; b. Bklyn., Jan. 1, 1943; s. Abe and Rose (Altein) W. BS, L.I. U., 1967, MS, 1971; postgrad., Poly. Inst., 1967-68. Analytic and pollution chemist Amerada Hess Corp., Pt. Reading, N.J., 1969-73; asst. lab. dir. Chem. Constrn., North Brunswick, N.J., 1973-74; dir. Indsl. Hygiene Lab. Nat. Starch and Chemical, Bridgewater, N.J., 1974—; grant com. mem. Ctr. for Hazardous and Toxic Substance Mgmt., Newark, 1988—; mem. Sourland Regional Citizens Planning Coun., Neshanic, N.J., 1989—. Contbr. articles to profl. jours. Recipient Chemistry Dept. award L.I. U., 1967, Teaching fellowship Poly. Inst., 1967, L.I. U., 1968. Mem. MENSA, Am. Chem. Soc., Am. Conf. Chem. Labeling, Soc. Toxicology. Achievements include development of improved system for identification of hazardous chemicals; organization of first global monitoring of indsl. workers to hazardous workplace chemicals. Office: Nat Starch & Chem Co 10 Finderne Ave Bridgewater NJ 08807-3355

WEINGEIST, THOMAS ALAN, ophthalmology educator; b. N.Y.C., Jan. 28, 1940; s. Samson and Fausta (Haim) W.; m. Carol Perera, Mar. 19, 1963 (div. Aug. 1977); children: Aaron P., Rachel; m. Catherine McGregor, Aug. 18, 1977; children: Robert M., David M. BA, Earlham Coll., 1963; PhD, Columbia U., 1969; MD, U. Iowa, 1972. Resident in ophthalmology U. Iowa, 1972-75, fellow in retina, 1976; asst. prof. ophthalmology U. Iowa, Iowa City, 1976-80, assoc. prof., 1980-83, prof., 1983—, prof., head dept. ophthalmology, 1986—. Mem. editl. bd. Documenta Ophthalmologica, The Netherlands, 1989-94, Ophthalmology World News, vice chair, 1994. Fellow Am. Acad. Ophthalmology (editl. bd. jour. 1982—, Honor award 1979, Sr. Hon. award 1989, assoc. sec. for self-assessment 1988-93, sec. continuing edn. 1993—, bd. trustees 1993—, sr. sec. clin. edn. 1994—); mem. Macula Soc., Retina Soc., Vitreous Soc., Am. Medico-Legal Found., Assn. Univ. Profs. Ophthalmology (bd. dirs., pres.-elect 1994, pres. 1995). Avocations: photography, tennis. Home: 3 Heather Ct Iowa City IA 52245-3226 Office: U Iowa Dept Ophthalmology Iowa City IA 52242

WEINGROW, HOWARD L., financial executive, investor; b. N.Y.C., Dec. 6, 1922; s. Nathan and Anna (Shaw) W.; m. Muriel Corrine Franzblau, Nov. 24, 1946; children: Terry Vaccaro, Caron Abby Haim. Owner Legion Fluorescent Corp., N.Y.C., 1946-56; ptnr. Hechler & Weingrow, Inc., N.Y.C., 1956-58, Hechler, Lifton & Weingrow, Inc., N.Y.C., 1958-78; exec. v.p. Tanscontinental Investing Corp., N.Y.C., 1960-67; pres. Tanscontinental Investing Corp., 1967-70; prin. Lifton & Weingrow, N.Y.C., 1970—; co-chmn. Marcade Group, Inc., N.Y.C., 1986-91, bd. dirs., 1986-93; pres. Cell Diagnostics, Inc. and Medis Ltd., 1992—, Stanoff Corp., 1980—, Wesak Internat., chmn. Wesak Chrysler, 1992—; bd. dirs. Preferred Health Care, N.Y.C., Four Winds Inc., N.Y.C.; founder Weingrow Family Pediatric Urology Lab., L.I.J. Hosp., 1990. Treas. Dem. Nat. Com., Washington, 1970-72; mem. bd. govs. Hifstra U. Law Sch., 1977-79; dep. fin. chmn. Pres. Carter, Washington, 1980; trustee Hofstra U., Hempstead, N.Y., 1973-76, James S. Brady Presdl. Found., 1982, Children's Med. Fund, L.A. Jewish Children's Hosp., Lake Success, N.Y., 1986—, Am. Jewish Congress, 1988—; treas. Nassau County Mus. Fine Arts, 1988—; advisor to Pres. Lyndon Johnson, OEO, Washington; fin. advisor to the Govt. of Grenada and Office of Prime Min. Garry, 1977-78; founder Howard and Muriel Weingrow Collection of Avant Garde Arts and Lit., Hofstra U. Libr., 1972; founder Weingrow Family Pediatric Urology Lab. L.B.J. Hosp., 1990. Decorated Air medal, Disting. Flying Cross, Presdl. Citation; recipient of Hofstra U. Presdl. medal. Office: Stanoff Corp 805 3rd Ave Fl 15 New York NY 10022-7513

WEINHARDT, JANICE, nursing educator; b. Washington, Pa., Dec. 26, 1951; d. Donald and Loretta (Ankenbrand) Braun; m. Robert Weinhardt, Mar. 31, 1976; children: Erin, Sara. BSN, Kent State U., 1973, MSN, 1982. RN, Ohio. Staff nurse med./surg. unit St. Thomas Hosp., Akron, Ohio; instr. nursing Kent (Ohio) State U.; curriculum coord. Sch. Nursing St. Thomas Med. Ctr., Akron, dir. nursing edn. Mem. Nat. League Nursing, Sigma Theta Tau.

WEINHAUER, WILLIAM GILLETTE, retired bishop; b. N.Y.C., Dec. 3, 1924; s. Nicholas Alfred and Florence Anastacia (Davis) W.; m. Jean Roberta Shanks, Mar. 20, 1948; children: Roberta Lynn, Cynthia Anne, Doris Jean. BS, Trinity Coll., Hartford, Conn., 1948; MDiv, Gen. Theol. Sem., 1951, STM, 1956, ThD, 1970. Ordained to ministry Episcopal Ch., 1951. Pastor Episcopal parishes Diocese N.Y., 1951-56; prof. N.T. St. Andrews Theol. Sem., Manila, Philippines, 1956-60; asst. prof. N.T. Gen. Theol. Sem., 1961-71; rector Christ Ch., Poughkeepsie, N.Y., 1971-73; bishop Episcopal Diocese of Western N.C., Black Mountain, 1973-90, ret., 1990; vis. prof. religion Western Carolina U., Cullowhee, N.C., 1991-94; adj. faculty Seabury-Western Theol. Sem., Evanston, Ill., 1991-94. Served with USN, 1943-46. Mem. Soc. Bibl. Lit. Office: PO Box 368 Black Mountain NC 28711-0368

WEINHOLD, VIRGINIA BEAMER, interior designer; b. Elizabeth, N.J., June 21, 1932; d. Clayton Mitchell and Rosemary (Behrend) Beamer; divorced; children: Thomas Craig, Robert Scott, Amy Linette. BA, Cornell U., 1955; BFA summa cum laude, Ohio State U., 1969; MA in Design Mgmt., Ohio State U., 1982. Freelance interior designer, 1969-72; interior designer, dir. interior design Karlsberger and Assocs. Inc., Columbus, Ohio, 1972-82; assoc. prof. dept. indsl. design Ohio State U., 1982—; lectr. indsl. design Ohio State U., 1972, 79-80. Trustee Found. for Interior Design Edn. and Research. Mem. Inst. Bus. Designers (chpt. treas. 1977-79, nat. trustee 1979-81, nat. chmn. contract documents com. 1979-84, chpt. pres. 1981-83), Constrn. Specifications Inst., Interior Design Educator's Coun. (nat. treas. 1989-93), Interior Design Educator's Coun. Found. (nat. treas. 1992-94), Illuminating Engring. Soc., assoc. mem. AIA. Prin. works include Grands Rapids (Mich.) Osteo. Hosp., Melrose (Mass.) Wakefield Hosp., Christopher Inn, Columbus, John W. Galbreath Hdqrs., Columbus, Guernsey Meml. Hosp., Cambridge, Ohio, Trinity Epis. Ch. and Parish House, Columbus, Hale Hosp., Haverhill, Mass., Ohio State U. Dept. Indsl. Design Lighting Lab., others. Author: IBO Forms and Documents Manual, Interior Finish Materials for Health Care Facilities, Subjective Impressions: Lighting Hotels and Resturants, 1989, Effects of Lighting on The Perception of Interior Spaces, 1993. Home: 112 Glen Dr Columbus OH 43085-4010 Office: Ohio State U/Grad Studies 128 N Oval Mall Columbus OH 43210-1363

WEINHOUSE, SIDNEY, biochemist, educator; b. Chgo., May 21, 1909; s. Harry and Dora (Cutler) W.; m. Sylvia Krawitz, Sept. 15, 1935 (dec. Aug.

1957); children: Doris Joan, James Lester, Barbara May; m. Adele Klein, Dec. 27, 1969. B.S., U. Chgo., 1933, Ph.D., 1936; D.M.S. (hon.), Med. Coll. Pa., 1973; D.Sc. (hon.), Temple U., 1976, U. Chieti, Italy, 1979, Jefferson Med. Coll., 1983. Eli Lilly fellow U. Chgo., 1936-38, Coman fellow, 1939-41; staff OSRD, 1941-44; with Houdry Process Corp., 1944-47; biochem. research dir. Temple U. Research Inst., 1947-50, prof. chemistry, 1952-77; emeritus prof. biochemistry Temple U. Med. Sch., 1977—; emeritus prof. Jefferson Med. Coll., 1991; sr. scientist Lankenau Med. Research Ctr., 1987—; head dept. metabolic chemistry Lankenau Hosp. Research Inst. and Inst. Cancer Research, 1950-57; chmn. div. biochemistry Inst. Cancer Research, 1957-61; assoc. dir. Fels Research Inst., Temple U. Med. Sch., Phila., 1961-64, dir., 1964-74; mem. bd. sci. advisers Inst. Environ. Health, NIH. Contbr. articles on original research to sci. jours.; editor: Jour. Cancer Research, 1969-79. Bd. dirs. Am. Cancer Soc. Mem. Am. Chem. Soc., Am. Soc. Biol. Chemists, Am. Assn. Cancer Research, Nat. Acad. Sci. Home: 1919 Chestnut St Philadelphia PA 19103-3401 Office: Lankenau Med Rsch Ctr 100 W Lancaster Ave Wynnewood PA 19096 also: Jefferson Cancer Inst Rm 1034 273 N 10th St Philadelphia PA 19107

WEINKAUF, MARY LOUISE STANLEY, clergywoman; b. Eau Claire, Wis., Sept. 22, 1938; d. Joseph Michael and Marie Barbara (Holzinger) Stanley; m. Alan D. Weinkauf, Oct. 12, 1962; children: Stephen, Xanti. BA, Wis. State U., 1961; MA, U. Tenn., 1962, PhD, 1966; MDiv Luth. Sch. Theology, Chgo., 1993. Grad. asst., instr. U. Tenn., 1961-66; asst. prof. English, Adrian Coll., 1966-69; prof., head dept. English, Dakota Wesleyan U., Mitchell, S.D., 1969-89; instr. Columbia Coll., 1989-91; pastor Siloa Lutheran Ch., Ontonagon Faith, White Pine, Mich., Gowrie, Iowa. Mem. Mitchell Arts Council; bd. trustees, The Ednl. Found., 1986—. Mem. Nat. Council Tchrs. English, S.D. Council Tchrs. English, Sci. Fiction Research Assn., Popular Culture Assn., Milton Soc., AAUW (div. pres. 1978-80), S.D. State Poetry Soc. (pres. 1982-83), Delta Kappa Gamma (pres. local chpt., mem. state bd. 1972-89, state v.p. 1979-83, state pres. 1983-85), Sigma Tau Delta, Pi Kappa Delta, Phi Kappa Phi. Republican. Lutheran.

WEINKAUF, WILLIAM CARL, instructional media company executive; b. Fond du Lac, Wis., Apr. 7, 1934; s. Carl Alfred and Erma Gertrude (Lueck) W.; m. Carole Jean Hill, May 3, 1958 (div.); children: Carl William, Mary Gretchen, Donald Hill; m. Jean Boyne Hawks, Sept. 10, 1988. BA, Ripon (Wis.) Coll., 1955; postgrad. U. Wis., 1954, 57-58. Dir. Wis. Cen. Lumber Co., 1959-63; with Carlton Films, Beloit, Wis., 1965-68; founder, pres. IMCO Inc., Green Lake, Wis., 1968—; founder, pres. initiator of distribution of ednl. instructional materials catalogs, IMCO Pub. Co., 1978—; bd. dirs. The Peterson System, Inc.; co-founder, chmn. Affluence Unltd., Inc., Dallas, 1986; Chmn. council Cub Scouts Am., 1968-69; mem. exec. com. county Reps., 1970-71. Served to maj. AUS, 1955-57. Mem. Nat. Audio Visual Assn. (chmn. legis. com. Wis. 1975—), Nat. Sch. Supply and Equipment Assn. (bd. dirs. 1986-87), U.S. Res. Officers Assn. (chpt. pres. 1966-70), Green Lake C. of C., Sigma Nu. Mem. United Ch. Christ bd. trustees Green Lake, Wis. 1965-66, mem. bd. deacons Dallas 1989-93, chmn. 1992-93). Lodges: Mason (32 degree), KT. Office: 2215 Commerce St Dallas TX 75201

WEINKOPF, FRIEDRICH J., lawyer; b. Bautsch, Germany, Feb. 17, 1930. Student, U. Marburg, Germany, 1954; LLM, U. Pa., 1958; JD, Chgo.-Kent Coll. Law, 1967. Bar: Ill. 1967. Ptnr. Baker & McKenzie, Chgo. Office: Baker & McKenzie 1 Prudential Plz 130 E Randolph Dr Chicago IL 60601-6206

WEINLANDER, MAX MARTIN, retired psychologist; b. Ann Arbor, Mich., Sept. 9, 1917; s. Paul and Emma Carol (Lindemann) W.; BA, Ea. Mich. Coll., 1940; MA, U. Mich., 1942, PhD, 1955; M.A., Wayne U., 1951; m. Albertina Adelheit Abrams, June 4, 1946; children: Bruce, Annette. Psychometrist, VA Hosp., Dearborn, Mich., 1947-51; sr. staff psychologist Ohio Div. Corrections, London, 1954-55; lectr. Dayton and Piqua Centers, Miami U., Oxford, Ohio, 1955-62; chief clin. psychologist Child Guidance Clinic, Springfield, Ohio, 1956-61, acting dir., 1961-65; clin. psychologist VA Center, Dayton, Ohio, 1964-79; cons. Ohio Divsn. Mental Hygiene; summer guest prof. Miami U., 1957, 58, Wittenberg U., 1958; adj. prof. Wright State U., Dayton, 1975-76; cons. State Ohio Bur. Vocat. Rehab.; Oesterlen Home Emotionally Disturbed Children. Pres. Clark County Mental Health Assn., 1960, Clark County Health and Welfare Club, 1961; mem. Community Welfare Coun. Clark County, 1964; chmn. Comprehensive Mental Health Planning Com. Clark County, 1964; trustee United Appeals Fund, 1960. Mem. citizens adv. coun. Columbus Psychiat. Inst., Ohio State U. Served as sgt. AUS, 1942-46. Fellow Ohio Psychol. Assn. (chmn. com. on utilization of pscyhologists; treas., exec. bd. 1968-71); mem. Am. Psychol. Assn., Ohio Psychol Assn., Mich. Psychol. Assn., DAV, U. Mich. Pres. Club, Pi Kappa Delta, Pi Gamma Mu, Phi Delta Kappa. Republican. Lutheran. Lodge: Kiwanis. Contbr. 18 articles to psychology jours. Home: 17185 Valley Dr Big Rapids MI 49307-9523

WEINMAN, HOWARD MARK, lawyer; b. N.Y.C., May 6, 1947; s. Joseph and Kate (Dorn) W.; m. Pamela Eve Brodie, Jan. 6, 1980; children: David Lewis, Nathaniel Saul. B.A. magna cum laude, Columbia U., 1969; M.P.P., Harvard U, 1973, J.D. cum laude, 1973; LL.M. with highest honors in Taxation, George Washington U., 1981. Assoc., Fried, Frank, Harris, Shriver & Kampelman, Washington and N.Y.C., 1973-78; legis. atty. Joint Com. on Taxation, U.S. Congress, Washington, 1978-80; assoc. Sachs, Greenebaum, & Tayler, Washington, 1980-82; assoc. Crowell & Moring, Washington, 1982-84, ptnr., 1984—; adj. prof. internat. tax Georgetown U. Law Ctr., 1988-89. Contbr. articles to profl. jours. Mem. ABA (sect. on taxation), Kenwood Club, Phi Beta Kappa. Jewish. Home: 5404 Center St Bethesda MD 20815 Office: Crowell & Moring 1001 Pennsylvania Ave NW Washington DC 20004-2595

WEINMAN, JAMES A., meteorologist. Sr. scientist NASA Goddard Space Flight Ctr., Greenbelt, Md. Recipient Losey Atmospheric Scis. award AIAA, 1995. Office: NASA Goddard Space Flight Ctr Greenbelt Rd Greenbelt MD 20771*

WEINMAN, ROBERT ALEXANDER, sculptor; b. N.Y.C., Mar. 19, 1915; s. Adolph Alexander and Margaret Lucille (Landman) W.; m. Jane Morrison, July 14, 1945; children: Paul Alexander, Christopher Robert. Student, NAD, 1931-39, Art Students League, N.Y.C., 1939-40. Exhbns. include, NAD, 1937, 38, 49, 53, 71, 83, Pa. Acad. Fine Arts, 1939, N.Y. State Nature Assn., 1939, Nat. Arts Club, 1941, Georg Jensen, Inc., 1941, Allied Artists Am., 1946, 3d Sculpture Internat., Phila., 1949, Nat. Sculpture Soc., 1952, 64, 68, 69, 71, 79, 81, Soc. Animal Artists, 1970, 72; works include bronze doors, Baylor U., Tex.; bronze overdoor motif, U. Tenn. Ctr.; bronze dolphin fountain group, S.I. Community Coll.; small bronze, Bessie the Belligerent; study of an Indian rhinoceros, and a watercolor, Great Blue Heron, Brook-green Gardens, Georgetown, S.C.; Stations of the Cross, chapel Manhattanville Coll. Sacred Heart, Purchase, N.Y., bronze airman, Tulsa Mcpl. Airport, granite eagle, Fed. Res. Bank, Buffalo, rood group and twelve apostles, Our Lady of Perpetual Help, Queens, N.Y., others; creator numerous medals for athletic, ednl., bus., mil., religious and cultural orgns. Served to sgt. U.S. Army 1942-45. Recipient Sanford Saltus medal award Am. Numis. Soc., 1964, Sculptor of Year award Am. Numis. Assn., 1975. Fellow Nat. Sculpture Soc. (pres. 1973-76, Bennett Prize 1952, Henry Hering medal 1985); mem. Nat. Acad. Design (academician). Address: 941 Old Post Rd Bedford NY 10506

WEINMAN, JOHN GIFFEN, lawyer, diplomat; b. New Orleans, Aug. 29, 1928; S. Rudolph John and Mary Victoria (Mills) W.; m. Virginia Lee Eason, June 11, 1955; children: Winston Eason, Robert St. George Tucker, John Giffen Jr. Mary Virginia Lewis, George Gustaf. BA. Tulane U., 1950, JD, 1952. Bar: La. 1952. Pvt. practice law Phelps Dunbar and predecessor firm, New Orleans; ptnr. Phelps Dunbar and predecessor firm, 1955-80, of counsel, 1981-83, 85-89; gen. counsel Times-Picayune Pub. Corp. 1968-80; pres., dir. Waverly Oil Corp., 1981-89; amb. to Finland Am. Embassy, Helsinki, 1989-91; amb., chief of protocol of White House Dept. of State, Washington, 1991—; lectr. bills and notes New Orleans chpt. Am. Inst. Banking, 1958-59; bd. dir. Eason Oil Co., 1961-81, chmn., 1977; bd. dir. 1st Nat. Bank of Oklahoma City, 1978-84, Am. Life Ins. Co. of N.Y., 1981-88, Allied Investment Corp., 1985-88; asst. sec. Am. Bar Endowment 1971-74, bd. dirs., sec., 1975-80. Mem. adv. bd. Tulane Law Rev., 1965-92. Bd. govs.

Tulane Med. Ctr., 1968-81; bd. adminstrs. Tulane Ednl. Fund, 1981-91, emeritus bd. mem., 1992—, chmn. devel. com., 1985-89, co-chmn. Tulane Parents Fund, 1980-81; nat. chmn. ann. giving Campaign for Tulane, 1983-85; bd. dirs. Coun. for Better La., 1987-89, Tulane Children's Ctr., 1981-84, WYES Ednl. TV Sta., 1981-82; trustee S.W. Legal Found., 1978-80, Metairie Park Country Day Sch., v.p., 1976-77, pres., 1978-80, U.S. commr. gen. for 1984 La. World Expn., 1983-85; U.S. del. Bur. Internat. Expositions, Paris, 1984-85, chmn. del., 1985; state fin. chmn. George Bush for Pres., and Victory La. '88, 1987-88; mem. Pres.'s Nat. Adv. Bd. Personnel, 1988-89. Named Outstanding Law Alumnus, Tulane U., 1985. Mem. ABA (chmn. jr. bar conf. 1963-64, mem. ho. dels. 1964-66, 70, 72-76, sec. com. ethics evaluation 1965, rep. to conv. Union des Jeunes Avocats de France 1964, chmn. sect. bar activities 1969-70), La. Bar Assn. (sec. treas. 1965-67, Outstanding Young Lawyer award), La. Soc. Colonial Wars (gov. 1976), Phi Beta Kappa, Order of Coif, Delta Kappa Epsilon, Omicron Delta Kappa. Episcopalian. Home: 611 Hector Ave Metairie LA 70005-4415 Office: Office of Chief of Protocol Rm 1232 Dept of State Washington DC 20520-2317

WEINMANN, ROBERT LEWIS, neurologist; b. Newark, Aug. 21, 1935; s. Isadore and Etta (Silverman) W.; m. Diana Weinmann, Dec. 13, 1980 (dec. Dec. 1989); children: Paul, Chris, Dana, Paige. BA, Yale U., 1957; MD, Stanford U., 1962. Diplomate Am. Bd. of EEG and Neurophysiology, v.p.; diplomate Am. Acad. Pain Mgmt. Intern Pacific Presbyn. Med. Ctr., San Francisco, 1962-63; resident in neurology Stanford U. Hosp., 1963-66, chief resident, 1965-66; pvt. practice San Jose, Calif., 1969—. Chmn. editorial bd. Clin. EEG Jour.; mem. editorial bd. Jour. Am. Acad. Pain Mgmt.; formerly mem. editorial bd. Clin. Evoked Potentials Jour.; contbr. articles to various publs. Capt. M.C., U.S. Army, 1966-68, Japan. Award recipient State of R.I., Santa Clara County Med. Soc., Epilepsy Soc., other orgns.; fellow Univ. Paris, 1957-58. Union of Am. Physicians and Dentists (pres. 1990—, bd. dirs. 1972—, pres. Calif. fedn. 1990—). Avocations: softball, tennis, music, theater, martial arts. Office: Union Am Physicians & Dentists 1330 Broadway Ste 730 Oakland CA 94612-2506

WEINMANN, ROBERTO, molecular biologist, educator; b. Buenos Aires, Dec. 30, 1941; came to U.S., 1967; s. Bernardo and Gerda (Tobias) W.; m. Nury Vicens, Dec. 25, 1967 (div.); children: Guillermo, Joslyne. Bachelor's degree, Nat. Coll. Buenos Aires, 1960; Lic. in Biology, Sch. of Scis., Buenos Aires, 1967; PhD, Iowa State U., 1972. Postdoctoral fellow Washington U. Sch. Medicine, St. Louis, 1972-76; asst. prof. to assoc. prof. Wistar Inst., Phila., 1976-93; from asst. to assoc. prof. molecular biology grad. group Med. Sch. U. Pa., 1976—; rsch. fellow Bristol-Myers Squibb PRI, Princeton, N.J., 1993—; vis. sr. rsch. scientist dept. molecular biology, Princeton U., 1993—; cons. Pew Latin Am. Fellows Program, San Francisco, 1991-95. Mem. editorial bd. Gene Expression, 1990—; contbr. rsch. articles to sci. jours. Humboldt fellow Inst. for Genetics, U. Cologne, West Germany, 1975, INSERM fellow Pasteur Inst., Paris, 1983. Mem. Internat. Cell Rsch. Orgn., Am. Soc. Virology, Am. Soc. Microbiology. Office: Bristol-Myers Squibb PO Box 4000 Princeton NJ 08543-4000

WEINREB, LLOYD LOBELL, law educator; b. N.Y.C., Oct. 9, 1936; s. Victor and Ernestine (Lobell) W.; m. Ruth Plaut, May 5, 1963; children—Jennifer, Elizabeth, Nicholas. B.A., Dartmouth, 1957; B.A., U. Oxford, 1959, M.A., 1963; LL.B., Harvard, 1962. Bar: N.Y. 1963, Mass. 1969. Faculty Harvard Law Sch., Cambridge, Mass., 1965—; prof. law Harvard Law Sch., 1968—. Home: 119 Russell Ave Watertown MA 02172-3453 Office: Law Sch Harvard U Cambridge MA 02138

WEINREICH, GABRIEL, physicist, minister, educator; b. Vilnius, Lithuania, Feb. 12, 1928; came to U.S., 1941, naturalized, 1949; s. Max and Regina (Szabad) W.; m. Alisa Lourié, Apr. 19, 1951 (dec. 1970); m. Gerane Siemering Benamou, Oct. 23, 1971; children—Catherine, Marc, Daniel, Rebecca, Natalie. A.B., Columbia U., 1948, M.A., 1949, Ph.D., 1954. Ordained priest Episcopal Ch., 1986. Mem. staff Bell Telephone Labs., Murray Hill, N.J., 1953-60; mem. faculty U. Mich., Ann Arbor, 1960—; prof. physics U. Mich., 1964-95; prof. emeritus, 1995—; Collegiate prof. U. Mich., 1974-76; adj. minister St. Clare's Episcopal Ch., Ann Arbor, 1986-90; rector St. Stephen's Episcopal Ch., Hamburg, Mich., 1993—. Author: Solids: Elementary Theory for Advanced Students, 1965, Fundamental Thermodynamics, 1968, Notes for General Physics, 1972. Recipient Disting. Teaching award U. Mich., 1968, Klopsteg award Am. Assn. Physics Tchrs., 1992, Internat. medal French Acoustical Soc., 1992. Fellow Acoustical Soc. Am. (assoc. editor Jour. 1987-89). Home: 754 Greenhills Dr Ann Arbor MI 48105-2718 Office: Randall Lab U Mich Ann Arbor MI 48109-1120

WEINRIB, SIDNEY, retired optometric and optical products and services executive; b. N.Y.C., Sept. 29, 1919; s. David and Rose (Lichtig) W.; m. Ruth Lois Simon, Aug. 25, 1946 (dec. 1988); children: Irene Henry, Donna Acker, Jeri Taylor. BS in Optometry, Columbia U., 1941. Practice optometry Sterling Optical, N.Y.C., 1947-66, from sec. to chmn. bd., 1966-87; v.p. Ipco Corp., White Plains, N.Y., 1971-87; tchr. Bernard Baruch Sch. Bus., N.Y.C., 1953-54. Served with U.S. Army Signal Corps, 1942-46. Recipient commendation U.S. War Dept., 1946. Mem. Nat. Assn. Optometrists and Opticians (pres. 1978-87), Am. Nat. Standards Inst. Pioneer in modern optical chain retailing. Home: 270 Grand Central Pky # 32D Floral Park NY 11005

WEINS, LEO MATTHEW, publishing company executive; b. Racine, Wis., Sept. 2, 1912; s. Leo Matthew and Lula (Vollman) W.; m. Margaret Killion, Oct. 19, 1955. Student, Loyola U., Chgo., 1935-36, Northwestern U., 1946-47, U. Chgo., 1937-38. Comptroller ALA, 1952-57; with H. W. Wilson Co., N.Y.C., 1957—; pres., treas. H. W. Wilson Co., 1967—; chmn. bd. Mansell Pub., Ltd., London, 1981-87; mem. editorial bd. Choice, 1963-70, 77-81; mem. govt. adv. com. book and library programs Dept. State, 1973-76; mem. Bronx adv. com. Chase Manhattan Bank, 1968-78; trustee Dollar Dry Dock Savs. Bank N.Y., 1969-83; trustee, treas. N.Y. Met. Reference and Research Library Agency, 1979-83. Mem. sci. info. coun. NSF, 1968-72; bd. dirs. Highbridge Conservation Program, Bronx, 1966-69; pres. H.W. Wilson Found., 1967—; trustee Maritime Coll. at Ft. Schuyler Found., Bronx, N.Y., 1978-90. Served with AUS, 1943-46. Mem. ALA, Am. Anitquarian Soc., Pgp. Policy Assn. (gov. 1981-94). Home: 20 Beekman Pl New York NY 10022-8032 Office: H W Wilson Co 950 University Ave Bronx NY 10452-4224

WEINSCHEL, ALAN JAY, lawyer; b. Bklyn., Feb. 9, 1946; m. Barbara Ellen Schure, Aug. 20, 1967; children: Lawrence, Adam, Naomi. BA, Bklyn. Coll., 1967; JD, NYU, 1969. Bar: N.Y. 1970, U.S. Dist. Ct. (so. and ea. dists.) N.Y. 1973, U.S. Ct. Appeals (2d cir.) 1979, U.S. Ct. Appeals (9th cir.) 1986, U.S. Ct. Appeals (3d cir.) 1993. Assoc. Breed, Abbott & Morgan, N.Y.C., 1969-74; assoc. Weil, Gotshal & Manges, N.Y.C., 1974-78, ptnr., 1978—; lectr. Practising Law Inst., Ohio Legal Ctr., Am. Mgmt. Assn., Law Jour. Seminars, Law and Bus. Seminars. Trustee N.Y. Inst. Tech., Old Westbury, N.Y., 1969-76, Temple Sinai, Roslyn, N.Y., 1981-87, 89—. Capt. U.S. Army res., 1969-76. Mem. ABA (editorial bd. dirs. Antitrust Devels. 1981-87), N.Y. State Bar Assn. (chmn. antitrust sect. 1994—), Assn. Bar of City of N.Y. Office: Weil Gotshal & Manges 767 Fifth Ave New York NY 10153-0002

WEINSCHEL, BRUNO OSCAR, engineering executive, physicist; b. Stuttgart, Federal Republic of Germany, May 26, 1919; came to U.S., 1939; m. Shirley Kittredge; 6 children. BA in Physics, Technische Hochschule, Stuttgart, 1938; Dr. Engring. Technische Hochschule, Munich, Fed. Republic of Germany, 1966; DSc (hon.), Capitol Inst. Tech., 1984. Registered profl. engr., Md., D.C. Sr. engr. Western Electric, 1943-44; chief engr. Indsl. Instruments Co., Jersey City, 1944-48; group leader, rsch. scientist Nat. Bur. of Standards, 1949-52; chief engr., pres. Weinschel Engring. Co., Inc. Gaithersburg, Md., 1952-86, cons., 1987-88; pres., chief engr. Weinschel Rsch. Found., Gaithersburg, Md., 1987—; chief engr. Weinschel Assocs., Gaithersburg, 1988—. Contbr. over 50 articles to profl. jours.; inventor and co-inventor with 20 patents. Mem. Pres. Reagan's Com. Medal of Sci., 1986-87. Recipient William A. Wildhack award Nat. Conf. of Standards Labs., 1985. Fellow IEEE (mem. Richard M. Emberson award 1992), Instn. Elec. Engrs.-U.K.; mem. Annapolis Yacht Club, Cosmos Club, Internat. Club. Republican. Avocations: sailing, snow and water skiing.

WEINSHEIMER, WILLIAM CYRUS, lawyer; b. Chgo., Jan. 12, 1941; s. Alfred John and Coress (Searing) W.; m. Roberta Limarzi, June 5, 1965; children: William C. Jr., Kurt R., Robert L. BBA in Mktg., U. Notre Dame, 1962; JD, Northwestern U., 1965. Bar: Ill. 1965, U.S. Dist. Ct. (no. dist.) Ill. 1967, U.S. Tax Ct. 1968. Assoc. Hopkins & Sutter, Chgo., 1967-73, ptnr., chmn. trust and estates sect., 1973—; lectr. continuing legal edn. programs; mem. estate planning adv. coun. Northwestern U. Author: (with others) The New Generation Skipping Tax; Analysis, Planning & Drafting, 1987; Drafting Wills and Trust Agreements, 1990; contbr. articles to profl. jours. Bd. dirs. The Ragdale Found., Lake Forest, Ill., 1987—, Lawyers for Creative Arts, 1973-90, Winnetka United Way, 1989-92; pres. Family Svc. Winnetka-Northfield, Inc., 1978-79. Capt. U.S. Army, 1965-67. Fellow Am. Coll. Trust and Estate Coun. (bus. planning com. 1993—, chair Ill. chpt. 1989-92, editor Actec Notes 1991-92, bd. regents 1992—, chair edit. bd. 1993—); mem. ABA (vice chmn. con. on generation-skipping tax 1988-92), Ill. Bar Assn., Chgo. Bar Assn. (chmn. probate practice com. 1989), Chgo. Bar Found. (bd. dirs. 1992—), Ill. Bar Found. (bd. dirs. 1985-91), Law Club, Econ. Club, Mid-Day Club, Skokie Country Club, Notre Dame Club Chgo. (bd. govs. 1984-90). Roman Catholic. Avocations: golf, visual arts, performing. Office: Hopkins & Sutter 3 First National Plz Chicago IL 60602

WEINSHIENK, ZITA LEESON, federal judge; b. St. Paul, Apr. 3, 1933; d. Louis and Ada (Dubov) Leeson; m. Hubert Troy Weinshienk, July 8, 1956 (dec. 1983); children: Edith Blair, Kay Anne, Darcy Jill; m. James N. Schaffner, Nov. 15, 1986. Student, U. Colo., 1952-53; BA magna cum laude, U. Ariz., 1955; JD cum laude, Harvard U., 1958; Fulbright grantee, U. Copenhagen, Denmark, 1959; LHD (hon.), Loretto Heights Coll., 1985; LLD (hon.), U. Denver, 1990. Bar: Colo. 1959. Probation counselor, legal adviser, referee Denver Juvenile Ct., 1959-64; judge Denver Mcpl. Ct., 1964-65, Denver County Ct., 1965-71, Denver Dist. Ct., 1972-79, U.S. Dist. Ct. Colo., Denver, 1979—. Precinct committeewoman Denver Democratic Com., 1963-64; bd. dirs. Crime Stoppers. Named one of 100 Women in Touch with Our Time Harper's Bazaar Mag., 1971, Woman of Yr., Denver Bus. and Profl. Women, 1969; recipient Women Helping Women award Soroptimist Internat. of Denver, 1983, Hanna G. Solomon award Nat. Coun. Jewish Women, Denver, 1986. Fellow Colo. Bar Found., Am. Bar Found.; mem. ABA, Denver Bar Assn., Colo. Bar Assn., Nat. Conf. Fed. Trial Judges (exec. com.), Dist. Judges' Assn. of 10th Cir. (past pres.), Colo. Women's Bar Assn., Fed. Judges Assn., Denver Crime Stoppers Inc. (bd.dirs.), Devner LWV, Women's Forum Colo., Harvard Law Sch. Assn., Phi Beta Kappa, Phi Kappa Phi, Order of Coif (hon. Colo. chpt.). Office: US Dist Ct 1929 Stout St Denver CO 80294-2900

WEINSIER, ROLAND LOUIS, nutrition educator and director. MD, PhD in Pub. Health, Harvard U., 1973. Prof. nutrition, dir. clin. divsn. med. ctr. U. Ala., Birmingham, 1975—. Office: U Ala at Birmingham Med Ctr Dept Nutrition Scis U Sta PO Box 188 Birmingham AL 35294-0001*

WEINSTEIN, ALAN, health care management executive; b. Orange, N.J., Oct. 31, 1942; s. Herbert Milton and Evelyn (Schneider) W.; m. Ronni Jane Klorman, July 1, 1967 (div.); children: Renée S., Kevin M.; m. Harriet Rose Grumet, May 2, 1987. BS, Allegheny Coll., 1994; postgrad., Cornell U., 1994—. Sr. asst. Colorado-Wyoming Regional Med. Program, Denver, 1968-69; exec. dir. Midtown Hosp. Assn., Denver, 1969-73, North Suburban Assn. for Health Resources, Glenview, Ill., 1973-78; sr. v.p. Ill. Hosp. Assn., Naperville, Ill., 1978-83; pres. Premier Health Alliance, Westchester, Ill., 1983—; bd. dirs. Am. Internat. Health Alliance, Washington. With USPHS, 1966-68. Avocations: tennis, fishing, gardening. Office: Premier Health Alliance 3 Westbrook Corp Ctr Fl 9 Westchester IL 60154

WEINSTEIN, ALAN EDWARD, lawyer; b. Bklyn., Apr. 20, 1945; s. John and Matilda W.; m. Patti Kantor, Dec. 18, 1965; children: Steven R., David A. AA, U. Fla., 1964; BBA, U. Miami (Fla.), 1965, JD cum laude, 1968. Bar: Fla. 1968, U.S. Dist. Ct. (so. dist.) Fla. 1968, U.S. Ct. Appeals (5th cir.) 1969, U.S. Supreme Ct. 1973, U.S. Ct. Appeals (4th & 11th cirs.) 1981. Assoc. Cohen & Hogan, Miami Beach, Fla., 1968-71; pvt. practice Miami Beach, 1972-81; sr. ptnr. Weinstein & Preira, Miami Beach, 1981-92; prin. Law Offices of Alan E. Weinstein, Miami, 1992—; lectr. continuing legal edn. programs. Mem. ABA (criminal and family law sect. 1968—), Nat. Assn. Criminal Def. Lawyers, Fla. Bar Assn. (criminal and family law sect. 1968—, ethics com. 1987-88, bench/bar com. 1988-89), Fla. Criminal Def. Attys. Assn. (1978-79), Fla. Assn. Criminal Def. Lawyers (treas. 1989-90), Miami Beach Bar Assn., Soc. Wig and Robe, Phi Kappa Phi. Avocations: marlin fishing, reading, travel. Office: 1801 West Ave Miami FL 33139-1431

WEINSTEIN, ALLAN M., medical device company executive; b. Bklyn., June 25, 1945; s. Henry I. Weinstein and Hannah L. (Broidy) Glasser; m. Phyllis Fishman, Aug. 28, 1965; children: Craig, Brett, Danielle. BS, Poly. Inst., Bklyn., 1965, MS, 1966, PhD, 1972. Registered profl. engr. Postdoctoral fellow U. Pa., Phila., 1971-72; asst. prof. Clemson U., 1972-75; prof., dir. biomaterials Tulane U., New Orleans, 1975-81; v.p. tech. affairs Intermedics Orthopaedics, Dublin, Calif., 1981-83, also bd. dirs.; pres., chief exec. officer Harrington Arthritis Rsch. Ctr., Phoenix, 1983-87; co-founder, chmn., pres., chief exec. officer OrthoLogic Corp., Phoenix, 1987—. Editor: spl. publs. 472, 601, Nat. Bur. Stds., 1977, 81; contbr. numerous articles to profl. jours.; patentee (3) in field. Rsch. grantee NIH, 1973-91. Mem. Soc. for Biomaterials (charter mem., pres. 1985-86, Clemson Award for contbns. to biomaterials lit. 1995), Orthopaedic Rsch. Soc., Am. Soc. Metals, N.Y. Acad. Scis., Sigma Xi. Republican. Jewish. Avocations: tennis, skiing, golf. Home: 11222 E del Timbre Scottsdale AZ 85259 Office: OrthoLogic Corp 2850 S 36th St Phoenix AZ 85034-7239

WEINSTEIN, ANDREW H., lawyer; b. Pitts. Oct. 5, 1943; s. Adolph J. and Meta I. (Schwartz) W.; m. Susan Balber, Aug. 11, 1968; children: Jodi L., Toby M., Jamie M. BSBA, Duquesne U., 1965; JD, U. Pitts., 1968; LLM in Tax Law, NYU, 1969. Bar: Pa. 1969, U.S. Tax Ct. 1969, Fla. 1970, U.S. Dist. Ct. (so. dist.) Fla., U.S. Claims Ct. Trial atty. IRS, L.A., 1969-70, Miami, Fla., 1970-73; ptnr. Glass, Schultz, Weinstein & Moss, Coral Gables, Fla., 1973-80, Holland & Knight, Miami, 1980—. Contbr. articles to profl. jours. Bd. dirs. New World Symphony, Miami, Miami City Ballet, Performing Arts Found., Zool. Soc. Fla. Fellow Am. Coll. Tax Counsel; mem. ABA (tax sect. com., chmn. subcom. 1981-87), The Fla. Bar Assn. Republican. Avocations: golf, swimming, travel. Office: Holland & Knight 701 Brickell Ave 30th Fl Miami FL 33101

WEINSTEIN, ARNOLD ABRAHAM, playwright, theater educator; b. June 10, 1927; s. Sidney and Ada Weinstein. BA, Hunter Coll., 1951; MA, Harvard U., 1953. Prof. drama Yale Univ., New Haven, 1965-69; prof. English Columbia Univ., N.Y.C., 1979—; vis. critic Eugene O'Neill Found.; lectr. in field. Author: (with F. Colombo) Verga, 1985, Lorca, 1988, Scribner's European Writers; playwright: Red Eye of Love, 1961 (Obie award 1962), adapted Ovid's Metamorphoses for Paul Sills' Story Theater, 1971 (L.A. Critics award), Brecht-Weill's Mahagony, 1970, (adapted) Lorca La Mama, 1973; opera: (music of William Bolcom) Dynamite Tonight, 1966, revived 1975, 79, 87, Casino Paradise, 1988, Cabaret Songs (recorded by RCA), McTeague, 1992; contbr. (with Paul Sills) Second City, N.Y.C., 1964; dir. Metamorphoses, Spoleto, Italy. Served with USN, 1944-46, PTO. Mem. Phi Beta Kappa.

WEINSTEIN, DAVID CARL, lawyer; b. Flushing, N.Y., Nov. 21, 1951; s. Philip and Molly (Rencoff) W.; m. Clare Villari, Aug. 14, 1988; 1 child, Matthew Charles. BA, Boston U., 1972; JD, Boston Coll., 1975. Bar: Mass. Assoc. gen. counsel Prucapital, Inc., Cambridge, Mass., 1976-84; v.p., corp. counsel Fidelity Investments, Boston, 1984—; bd. dirs. Empire Fidelity Investments Life Ins. Co., N.Y.C. Trustee Hebrew Coll., Brookline, Mass., 1993—; bd. dirs. Goodwill Industries, Boston, 1990—. Mem. Am. Corp. Counsel Assn., Mass. Bar Assn. Office: Fidelity Investments 82 Devonshire St Boston MA 02109-3614

WEINSTEIN, DIANE GILBERT, federal judge, lawyer; b. Rochester, N.Y., June 14, 1947; d. Myron Birne and Doris Isabelle (Robie) Gilbert; children: Andrew, David. BA, Smith Coll., Northampton, Mass., 1969; postgrad., Stanford U., 1977-78, Georgetown U., 1979; JD, Boston U., 1979. Bar: D.C. 1979, Mass. 1979. Law clk. to judge D.C. Ct. Appeals, Wash-

ington, 1979-80; assoc. Peabody, Lambert & Meyers, Washington, 1980-83; asst. gen. counsel Office of Mgmt. and Budget, Washington, 1983-86; dep. gen. counsel U.S. Dept. Edn., Washington, 1986-88, acting gen. counsel 1988-89; legal counselor to V.P. of U.S., White House; counsel Pres.'s Competitiveness Coun., Washington, 1989-90; judge U.S. Ct. Fed. Claims, Washington, 1990—. Recipient Young Lawyer's award Boston U. Law Sch., 1989. Mem. Fed. Am. Inn of Ct., Federalist Soc., Univ. Club. Republican. Home: 3927 Massachusetts Ave NW Washington DC 20016-5104

WEINSTEIN, EDWARD MICHAEL, architect, consultant; b. Bklyn., May 5, 1947; s. Hyman and Freda (Rochkes) W.; m. Melanie Jane Ross, June 22, 1969; children: Valerie, David. BS, CCNY, 1969. Registered architect; lic. N.Y., N.J. Jr. architect N.Y.C. Dept. Ports and Terminals, 1970-72, architect, 1972-75, sr. urban designer, 1975-80, dir. waterfront devel., 1980-84, asst. commr., 1984-87; pres. EMW Assocs., Hastings-On-Hudson, N.Y., 1984—; ptnr. The Hastings Design Group, Hastings-On-Hudson, 1987—; adv. bd. Metro Marine Express Ltd., N.Y.C., 1989-91. Mem. Planning Bd. Hastings-on-Hudson, 1990—; trustee Greenburgh Hebrew Ctr., Dobbs Ferry, N.Y., 1986-89, 92—; v.p. N.Y. Port Promotion Assn., N.Y.C., 1984-87; mem. adv. com. on waterfront devel. N.Y. State Assembly. Recipient Gold Key award House Plan Assn., 1969. Mem. AIA, Am. Assn. Port Authority, N.Y. Soc. Architects, CCNY Alumni Assn. Democrat. Jewish. Avocations: tennis, art. Office: The Hastings Design Group 14 Spring St Hastings On Hudson NY 10706

WEINSTEIN, GEORGE WILLIAM, ophthalmology educator; b. East Orange, N.J., Jan. 26, 1935; s. Henry J. and Irma C. (Klein) W.; m. Sheila Valerie Wohlreich, June 20, 1957; children: Bruce David, Elizabeth Joyce, Rachel Andrea. AB, U. Pa., 1955; MD, SUNY, Bklyn., 1959. Diplomate Am. Bd. Ophthalmology (bd. dirs. 1981—). Intern then resident in ophthalmology Kings County Hosp., Bklyn., 1959-63; asst. prof. ophthalmology Johns Hopkins U., Balt., 1967-70; head ophthalmology dept. U. Tex., San Antonio, 1970-80; prof., Jane McDermott Shott chmn. W.Va. U., Morgantown, 1980—. Author: Key Facts in Ophthalmology, 1984; editor: Open Angle Glaucoma, 1986; editor Ophthalmol Surgery jour., 1971-81, Current Opinion in Ophthalmology jour., 1988—; contbr. articles to profl. jours. Served to lt. comdr. USPHS, 1963-65. Sr. Internat. fellow Fogarty Internat. Ctr. NIH, 1987. Mem. ACS (bd. govs. 1983-85, bd. regents 1987-92), Assn. Univ. Profs. Ophthalmology (pres. 1986-87, exec. v.p. 1994), Am. Acad. Ophthalmology (bd. dirs. 1980-92, chmn. long range planning com. 1986-89, pub. and profl. sec. 1983-89, pres.-elect 1990, pres. 1991, Honor award, Sr. Honor award), Alpha Omega Alpha (faculty 1987), Am. Ophthalmology Soc. (coun. 1992—). Jewish. Avocations: music, photography, tennis, basketball. Home: 28 Lakeview Dr Morgantown WV 26505 Office: W Va U Coll Medicine Dept Ophthalmology Morgantown WV 26506

WEINSTEIN, HARRIS, lawyer; b. Providence, May 10, 1935; s. Joseph and Gertrude (Rusitzky) W.; m. Rosa Grunberg, June 3, 1956; children: Teme Feldman, Joshua, Jacob. BS in Math., MIT, 1956, MS in Math. 1958; LLB, Columbia U., 1961. Bar: D.C. 1962. Law clk. to judge U.S. Ct. Appeals (3d cir.), Phila., 1961-62; with Covington & Burling, Washington, 1962-67, 69-90, 1993—; chief counsel Office of Thrift Supervision U.S. Dept. of Treasury, Washington, 1990-92; asst. to solicitor gen. U.S. Dept. Justice, 1967-69; pub. mem. Administrv. Conf. of U.S., 1982-90. Treas. Jewish Social Svc. Agency, 1994-95. Mem. MIT Corp., Nat. Press Club. Home: 7717 Georgetown Pike McLean VA 22102 Office: Covington & Burling PO Box 7566 1201 Pennsylvania Ave NW Washington DC 20004-2401

WEINSTEIN, HARVEY, film company executive. Co-chmn. Miramax Films Corp., L.A. Office: Miramax Films Corp 375 Greenwich St New York NY 10013-2338*

WEINSTEIN, HERBERT, chemical engineer, educator; b. Bklyn., Mar. 10, 1933; s. Abraham and Pauline (Feldman) W.; m. Judith Cooper, Apr. 6, 1957; children: Michael Howard, Edward Marc, Ellen Rachel. B.Engring. in Chem. Engring., Coll. City N.Y., 1955; M.S. in Chem. Engring, Purdue U., 1957; Ph.D., Case Inst. Tech., 1963. Staff mem. Los Alamos Sci. Lab., 1956-58; research engr. NASA Lewis Research Center, Cleve., 1959-63; asst. prof. chem. engring. Ill. Inst. Tech., 1963-66, assoc. prof., 1966-72, prof., 1972-77; dir. Center for Biomed. Engring., 1973-77; prof. CUNY, 1977—; Herbert G. Kayser prof. of chem. engring., 1987—; vis. rsch. assoc., mem. Med. Rsch. Inst. Michael Reese Hosp. and Med. Ctr., Chgo., 1965-77; vis. prof. mech. engring. Technion-Israel Inst. Tech., 1972-73; vis. prof. biomed. engring. Rush Med. Coll., Chgo., 1973-76; summer prof. Exxon Rsch. and Engring. Co., annually, 1981-92; Lady Davis vis. prof. Technion-Israel Inst. Tech., 1985; cons. to industry, rsch. labs. Mem. Am. Inst. Chem. Engrs., Sigma Xi. Jewish. Research and publs. on fluidization, mass reactor engring., fluid mechanics, biomed. engring. Office: CUNY Dept Chem Engring New York NY 10031

WEINSTEIN, I. BERNARD, physician; b. Madison, Wis., Sept. 9, 1930; s. Max and Frieda (Blachman) W.; m. Joan Anker, Dec. 21, 1952; children: Tamara, Claudia, Matthew. BS, U. Wis., 1952, MD, 1955, DSc (hon.), 1992. Intern, then resident in medicine Montefiore Hosp., N.Y.C., 1955-57; clin. assoc. NIH, 1957-59; rsch. assoc. Med. Sch. Harvard Coll., 1959-60; rsch. assoc. MIT, 1960-61; rsch. assoc. Coll. Phys. and Surg. Columbia U., N.Y.C., 1961—; prof. medicine, pub. health and genetics, 1973—; dir. Columbia-Presbyn. Cancer Ctr., N.Y.C., 1985—; attending physician Presbyn. Hosp., N.Y.C.; cons. Nat. Cancer Inst., Nat. Inst. Environment Health Sci., Internat. Agy. Rsch. Cancer. Author rsch. papers on biochemistry, molecular biology, cancer biology, chem. carcinogenesis. With USPHS, 1957-59. Recipient Meltzer medal Soc. Exptl. Biology and Medicine, Alumni award Med. Sch. U. Wis., 1986, Conte award Environ. Health Inst., 1990; European Molecular Biology Orgn. fellow Imperial Cancer Rsch. Fund, London, 1970-71. Fellow AAAS, Royal Soc. Medicine mem. Inst. of Medicine of NAS, Am. Assn. Physicians, Am. Soc. Microbiology, Am. Soc. Clin. Investigation, Am. Soc. Biol. Chemists, Am. Soc. Cell Biology, Internat. Soc. Quantum Biology, Am. Assn. Cancer Rsch. (pres. 1990, Clowes award 1987), Phi Beta Kappa, Sigma Xi, Alpha Omega Alpha. Jewish. Home: 249 Chestnut St Englewood NJ 07631-3135 Office: Columbia-Presbyn Cancer Ctr Coll Physicians & Surgeons 630 W 168th St New York NY 10032-3702

WEINSTEIN, IRA PHILLIP, advertising executive; b. Chgo., June 10, 1919; s. Phillip Marshall and Lillian (Greenblatt) W.; m. Norma Randall; children: Terri, Laura Temkin. Student, Crane Tech. Inst., 1937, Northwestern U., 1945-46. Chmn. bd. Schram Advt. Co., Chgo., 1945—. 1st lt. USAAF, 1942-45, ETO. Decorated D.F.C., Air medal, Purple Heart, Ex-Prisoner of War medal; recipient Presdl. citation, 1988. Mem. Chgo. Direct Mail Assn., Air Force Assn., Ex-POW Assn., Bombardiers Assn., Caterpillar Assn., Air Force Heritage League, 2d Air Divsn. Assn., Mil. Order of Purple HEart, 8th Air Force Hist. Soc. Office: The Schram Advt Co 450 Skokie Blvd Ste 800 Northbrook IL 60062-7916

WEINSTEIN, IRWIN MARSHALL, internist, hematologist; b. Denver, Mar. 5, 1926; m. Judith Braun, 1951. Student, Dartmouth Coll., 1943-44, Williams Coll., 1944-45; MD, U. Colo., Denver, 1949. Diplomate Am. Bd. Internal Medicine (assoc. bd. govs. hematology subcom.). Intern Montefiore Hosp., N.Y.C., 1949-50; jr. asst. resident in medicine Montefiore Hosp., 1950-51; sr. asst. resident in medicine U. Chgo., 1951-52, resident in medicine, 1952-53, instr. in medicine, 1953-54, asst. prof. medicine, 1954-55; vis. assoc. med. U. Calif. Center for Health Scis., L.A., 1955-56, assoc. clin. prof., 1957-60, clin. prof., 1970—; sect. chief in medicine, hematology sect. Wadsworth Gen. Hosp., VA Center, L.A., 1956-59; pvt. practice medicine specializing in hematology and internal medicine Los Angeles, 1959—; mem. staff Cedars-Sinai Med. Center, L.A., 1959—; chief of med. staff Cedars-Sinai Med. Center, 1972-74; mem. staff U. Calif. Ctr. Health Scis., Wadsworth Gen. Hosp., VA Ctr.; vis. prof. Hadassah Med. Ctr., Jerusalem, 1967; adv. for health affairs to Hon. Alan Cranston, 1971-92; mem. com. on space biology and medicine Space Sci. Bd.; active UCLA Comprehensive Cancer Ctr. Contbr. articles to profl. publs.; editor: (with Ernest Beutler) Mechanisms of Anemia, 1962. Master ACP (gov. So. Calif. Region I 1989-93); fellow Israel Med. Assn. (hon.); mem. AAAS, Am. Fedn. Clin. Rsch., Am. Soc. Hematology (exec. com. 1974-78, chmn. com. on practice 1978-87, mem. council 1974-78), Am. Internal Medicine, Assn.

Am. Med. Colls., Internat. Soc. Hematology, Internat. Soc. Internal Medicine, L.A. Acad. Medicine, L.A. Soc. Nuclear Medicine, Inst. of Medicine NAS, N.Y. Acad. Sci., Reticulo-Endothelial Soc., Royal Soc. Medicine, Western Soc. Clin. Rsch., Alpha Omega Alpha. Office: 8635 W 3rd St Ste 665 Los Angeles CA 90048-6101

WEINSTEIN, JACK BERTRAND, federal judge; b. Wichita, Kans., Aug. 10, 1921; s. Harry Louis and Bessie Helen (Brodach) W.; m. Evelyn Horowitz, Oct. 10, 1946; children: Seth George, Michael David, Howard Lewis. BA, Bklyn. Coll., 1943; LLB, Columbia, 1948; LLD (hon.), Bklyn. Law Sch., Yeshiva U., Albany Law Sch., Hofstra Law Sch.; Yale U. Bar: N.Y. 1949. Assoc. Columbia Law Sch., 1948-49; law clk. N.Y. Ct. Appeals Judge Stanly H. Fuld, 1949-50; ptnr. William Rosenfeld, N.Y.C., 1950-52; mem. faculty Columbia Law Sch., 1952-67, prof. law, 1956-67, adj. prof., 1967—; U.S. judge (Eastern Dist. N.Y.), 1967-93, chief judge, 1980-88; sr. judge Ea. Dist. N.Y., 1993—; vis. prof. U. Tex., 1957, U. Colo., 1961, Harvard U., 1982, Georgetown U., 1991, Bklyn. Law Sch., 1988—, others; counsel N.Y. Joint Legis. Com. Motor Vehicle Problems, 1952-54, State Sen. Seymour Halpern, 1952-54; reporter adv. com. practice and procedure N.Y. State Temp. Commn. Cts., 1955-58; adv. com. practice N.Y. Judicial Conf., 1963-66; adv. com. rules of evidence U.S. Jud. Conf., 1965-75, mem. com. jurisdiction, 1969-75, mem., 1983-86; mem. 2d Cir. Jud. Coun., 1982-88, U.S. Jud. Conf., 1983-86, others in past. Author: (with Morgan and Maquire) Cases and Materials on Evidence, 4th edit., 1965, (with Maguire, Chadbourne and Mansfield, 5th edit.), 1971, 6th edit., 1975, (with Mansfield, Abrams and Bergen), 8th edit., 1988, (with Rosenberg) Cases and Materials on Civil Procedure, 1961, rev. edit, (with Smit), 1971, (with Smit, Rosenberg and Korn), 1976, (with Korn and Miller) New York Civil Procedure, 9 vols., rev. edit, 1966, Manual of New York Civil Procedure, 1967, Basic Problems of State and Federal Evidence, 1976, (with Berger) Weinstein's Evidence, 7 vols., 1967, rev. edit., 1993, Revising Rule Making Procedures, 1977, A New York Constitution Meeting Today's Needs and Tomorrow's Challenges, 1967, Disaster, A Legal Allegory, 1988, (with Greenawalt) Readings for Seminar on Equality and Law, 1979, (with Murphy) Readings for Seminar in Individual Rights in a Mass Society, 1990-91, (with Berger) Readings for Seminar in Science and Law, (with Feinberg) Mass Torts, 1992, 94, Individual Justice in Mass Litigation, 1995. Chmn. N.Y. Dem. adv. com. on Constl. Conv., 1955; bd. dirs. N.Y. Civil Liberties Union, 1956-62, Cardozo Sch. Law, Conf. on Jewish Social Studies, 1980-88; nat. adv. bd. Am. Jewish Congress, 1960-67, CARE, 1985-90, Fedn. Jewish Philanthropies, 1985-94; chmn. lay bd. Riverside Hosp. Adolescent Drug Users, 1954-55. Lt. USNR, 1943-46. Mem. ABA, N.Y. State Bar Assn., Assn. of Bar of City of N.Y., Nassau County Bar Assn., Am. Law Inst., Soc. Pub. Tchrs. Law (Eng.), Am. Acad. Arts and Scis. Jewish. Office: US Dist Ct US Courthouse 225 Cadman Plz E Brooklyn NY 11201-1876

WEINSTEIN, JAY A., social science educator, researcher; b. Chgo., Feb. 23, 1942; s. Lawrence E. and Jacqueline L. (Caplan) W.; m. Diana S. Staffin, Sept. 16, 1961; m. Marilyn L. Schwartz, Nov. 25, 1972; children—Liza, Bennett. A.B., U. Ill., 1963, Ph.D., 1973; M.A., Washington U. St. Louis, 1965. Teaching fellow U. Ill., Urbana, 1963-64; teaching asst. McGill U., Montreal, Que., Can., 1964-68; instr. Sir George Williams U., Montreal, Que., Can., 1967-68; lectr. Simon Fraser U., Vancouver, B.C., Can., 1968; asst. prof. North Central Coll., Naperville, Ill., 1970-71, U. Iowa, 1973-77; prof. social sci. Ga. Inst. Tech., Atlanta, 1977-86; head dept. sociology Eastern Mich. U., 1986-90, faculty rsch. fellow, 1990-91; U.S. Info. Agy. and Soros Found. grantee ednl. devel. projectsf, Bulgaria and Albania, 1992—; researcher; cons. pub. and pvt. agys. Author: Madras: An Analysis of Urban Ecological Structure in India, 1974, Demographic Transition and Social Change, 1976, Sociology-Technology: Foundations of Postacademic Social Science, 1982, The Grammar of Social Relations: The Major Essays of Louis Schneider, 1984; editor: Paradox and Society, 1986; (with Vinod Tewari and V.L.S. Prakash Rao) Indian Cities: Ecological Perspectives, 1987; Studies in Comparative International Development, 1978-88; mem. editorial bd. Social Development Issues, 1977-85; specialized contbr. Calcutta Mcpl. Gazette, 1979—; editor: Social and Cultural Change, 1974-75; editorial reviewer Jour. Asian Studies, Social Devel. Issues, Tech. and Culture, Am. Sociologist, Technol. Forecasting and Social Change; contbr. chpts. to books, articles to profl. jours. Fulbright prof. Ahmedabad, India, 1975-76, Hyderabad, India, 1981-82; grantee Ga. Tech. Found., 1981-82, World Order Studies Course, 1974-75; Steinberg fellow, 1967. Mem. Am. Sociol. Assn., Soc. for Applied Sociology, Soc. South Indian Studies, Mich. Sociol. Assn. (pres. 1988-89), Sigma Xi. Jewish. Office: Eastern Mich U Sociology Dept Ypsilanti MI 48197

WEINSTEIN, JEFFREY ALLEN, consumer products company executive, lawyer; b. N.Y.C., Jan. 20, 1951; s. Herbert and Pearl (Linksman) W.; children—Jamie Kate, Jonathan Alexander. B.A., Pa. State U., 1972; J.D. Villanova U., 1975. Bar: Pa. 1975, N.H. 1983, U.S. Dist. Ct. (ea. dist.) Pa. 1975, U.S. Dist. Ct. N.H. 1983. Litigator Arthur Alan Wolk Assocs., Phila. 1975-78; v.p. adminstrn., sec., gen. counsel Centronics Data Computer Corp., Hudson, N.H., 1978—; exec. v.p., sec., gen. counsel Ekco Group, Inc., also bd. dirs.; exec. v.p. sec. bd. dirs. Ekco Housewares, Inc., Woodstream Corp.; asst. clk., bd. dirs. Frem Corp. Bd. dirs. Boys Club, Nashua, N.H., 1982-83; mem. N.H. Library Adv. Bd., Concord. Mem. Pa. Bar Assn., N.H. Bar Assn. Office: Ekco Group Inc 98 Spit Brook Rd Nashua NH 03062-5737

WEINSTEIN, LEONARD HARLAN, institute program director; b. Springfield, Mass., Apr. 11, 1926; s. Barney Willard Weinstein and Ida Pauline (Feinberg) Weinstein Clark; m. Sylvia Jane Sherman, Oct. 15, 1950; children: Beth Rachel, David Harold (dec.). BS, Pa. State U., 1949; MS, U. Mass., 1950; PhD, Rutgers U., 1953. Postdoctorial fellow Rutgers U., New Brunswick, N.J., 1953-55; plant physiologist Boyce Thompson Inst., Yonkers, N.Y., 1955-63; program dir. Boyce Thompson Inst., Ithaca, N.Y., 1963-91, bd. dirs., 1976—; dir. ecosystem rsch. ctr. Cornell U., Ithaca, 1988-90; William Boyce Thompson scientist; bd. dirs. Boyce Thompson Southwestern Arboretum, Superior, Ariz.; adj. prof. dept. natural resources Cornell U., Ithaca, 1979—. Contbr. articles (150) to profl. jours. and chpts. to books. Mem. sci. adv. bd. EPA, Washington, 1988-91; mem. com. natural resources NASULGS, 1986-89. Grantee NIH, NSF, HEW, Am. Cancer Soc., NASA, EPA, DOE, USDA. Mem. AAAS, Am. Soc. Plant Physiologists, Soc. Environ. Toxicologists and Chemists, Sigma Xi, Pi Alpha Xi, Gamma Sigma Delta. Home: 608 Cayuga Heights Rd Ithaca NY 14850-1424 Office: Cornell U 125 Boyce Thompson Inst Tower Rd Ithaca NY 14853

WEINSTEIN, MARK MICHAEL, lawyer; b. N.Y.C., Apr. 20, 1942; s. Nathan and Caroline (Levine) W.; m. Adrienne Peni Kuba, Aug. 15, 1965; children: Samantha Beth, Caleb Jonathan. AB, Columbia Coll., 1964; LLB, U. Pa., 1968. Assoc. Paul Weiss, Rifkind, Wharton and Garrison, N.Y.C., 1968-76; asst. v.p., dep. gen. counsel Warner Communications Inc., N.Y.C. 1976-78, v.p., 1978-85; v.p., gen. counsel Viacom Internat. Inc., N.Y.C., 1985-87, sr. v.p., gen. counsel and sec., 1987-93, sr. v.p. govt. affairs, 1993—. Office: Viacom Inc 1515 Broadway New York NY 10036-5702 also: Viacom/DC 1501 M St Washington DC 20005

WEINSTEIN, MARK STEVEN, air force officer; b. Washington, Feb. 5, 1957; s. Alvin David and Selma (Schulman) W.; m. Julia Rachel Scheer, Oct. 15, 1983; children: Brian Daniel, Brooke Sara, Matthew Scott. BS in Polit. Sci., Towson (Md.) State U., 1979; MPA in Health Care, Am. U., 1981; grad., Air Command and Staff Coll., 1994. Commd. 2d lt. USAF, 1982, advanced through grades to maj.; in-charge med. plans and readiness and patient affairs Malcolm Grow USAF Med. Ctr., Andrews AFB, Md., 1982-85; asst. adminstr. outpatient facility USAF Clinic Geilenkirchen, Germany, 1985-88; chief med. recruitment Br. 3546th USAF Recruiting Squadron, Houston, 1988-91; sr. health policy fellow in managed health care Air Force Inst. Tech.-Humana Inc., Louisville, 1991-92; dir. managed care 6th Med. Group, MacDill AFB, Fla., 1992—. Fellow Am. Coll. Healthcare Execs. (comm. com.), SunCoast Health Care Execs. (bd. dirs.). Avocations: fitness, sports. Office: 56th Med Group MacDill AFB FL 33608

WEINSTEIN, MARTIN, aerospace manufacturing executive, materials scientist; b. Bklyn., Mar. 3, 1936; s. Benjamin and Dora (Lemo) W.; m. Sandra Rebecca Yaffie, June 5, 1961; children: Hilary Ann, Sarah Elizabeth, Joshua Aaron. BS in Metals Engring., Rensselaer Poly. Inst., 1957; MS, MIT, 1960, PhD, 1961. Mgr. materials sci. Tycolabs, Waltham, Mass., 1961-

68; tech. dir. turbine support div. Chromalloy Am. Corp., San Antonio, 1968-71, v.p., asst. gen. mgr., 1971-74, pres. 1975-79; pres. Chromalloy Compressor Techs., San Antonio, 1979-82; group pres. Chromalloy Gas Turbine, San Antonio, 1982-86, chmn., chief exec. officer, N.Y.C., 1986—; supervisory mng. dir. Turbine Support Europe, Tilburg, Netherlands, 1975—; bd. dirs. Turbine Support Thailand, Bankok, Chromalloy U.K., Nottingham, Eng., Internat. Coating Co. Tokyo, Japan, Heurchrome, Paris, Malichaud Orleans, France. Bd. dirs. Jewish Fedn., 1981-85, Chamber Players of San Antonio, 1979-83, NCCJ, 1982-85; mem. vis. com. dept. metallurgy and materials sci. MIT, 1992—. Recipient Turner Meml. award Electrochem. Soc., 1963; Achievement award NASA, 1965; Am. Iron and Steel Inst. fellow, 1960. Mem. Am. Soc. Metals, Am. Inst. Metall. Engrs., N.Y. Acad. Sci., Sigma Xi. Patentee diffusion coating of jet engine materials. Contbr. articles to profl. jours. Home: 111 Sheffield San Antonio TX 78213-2626 Office: Chromalloy Gas Turbine Corp 200 Park Ave New York NY 10166-0001

WEINSTEIN, MICHAEL ALAN, political science educator; b. Bklyn., Aug. 24, 1942; s. Aaron and Grace (Sosin) W.; m. Deena Schneiweiss, May 31, 1964. B.A. summa cum laude, NYU, 1964; M.A. in Polit. Sci., Case Western Res. U., 1965, Ph.D., 1967. Asst. prof. polit. sci. Case Western Res. U., summer 1967, Va. Poly. Inst., 1967-68; asst. prof. Purdue U., 1968-70, assoc. prof., 1970-72, prof., 1972—; Milward Simpson disting. prof. polit. sci. U. Wyo., 1979. Author: (with Deena Weinstein) Living Sociology, 1974, The Polarity of Mexican Thought, 1976, The Tragic Sense of Political Life, 1977, Meaning and Appreciation, 1978, The Structure of Human Life, 1979, The Wilderness and the City, 1982, Unity and Variety in the Philosophy of Samuel Alexander, 1984, Finite Perfection, 1985, Culture Critique: Fernand Dumont and New Quebec Sociology, 1985, (with Helmut Loiskandl and Deena Weinstein) Georg Simmel's Scopenhauer and Nietzsche, 1986; (with Deena Weinstein) Deconstruction as Cultural History/The Cultural History of Deconstruction, 1990, La Déconstruction un Jeu Symbolique, 1990, (with Deena Weinstein) Georg Simmel: Sociological Flâmeur/Bricoleur, 1991, Photographic Realism as a Moral Practice, 1992, (with Deena Weinstein) Postmodern(ized) Simmel, 1993, (with Arthur Kroker) Data Trash: The Theory of the Virtual Class, 1994; mem. editorial bd. Humanitas, Can. Jour. Polit. and Social Theory, Social Philosophy Rsch. Book Series. Recipient Best Paper prize Midwest Polit. Sci. Assn., 1969; Guggenheim fellow, 1974-75; Rockefeller Found. humanities fellow, 1976; fellow Center Humanistic Studies, Purdue U., 1981. Mem. Midwest Polit. Sci. Assn., Phi Beta Kappa. Home: 800 Princess Dr West Lafayette IN 47906-2038 Office: Dept Polit Sci Purdue U West Lafayette IN 47907 *And which is worse, to be arbitrary or to be contradictory? I have attempted to be the most consistent rationalist of all by refusing to harmonize what is irreconcilable in the name of reason.*

WEINSTEIN, MILTON CHARLES, health policy educator; b. Brookline, Mass., July 14, 1949; s. William and Ethel (Rosenbloom) W.; m. Rhonda Kruger, June 14, 1970; children—Jeffrey William, Daniel Jay. A.B., A.M., Harvard U., 1970, M.P.P. 1972, Ph.D., 1973. Asst. prof. John F. Kennedy Sch. Govt., Harvard U., Cambridge, Mass., 1973-76, assoc. prof., 1976-80; prof. policy and decision scis. Harvard Sch. Pub. Health, Boston, 1980-86, Henry J. Kaiser prof. health policy and mgmt., 1986—; adj. prof. community and family medicine Dartmouth Med. Sch., Hanover, N.H., 1981-87; cons. U.S. office Tech. Assessment, 1979—, HHS, 1979—, VA, 1984-86, EPA, 1983—, Smith Kline and French, 1984-87, Ciba-Geigy, 1987—, New Eng. Med. Ctr., 1986-87, Intermountain Health Care, 1987, Bristol Myers-Squibb, 1989-92, E.I. DuPont de Nemours Co., 1989-91, Schering-Plough Corp., 1991—, Marion Merrell Dow, Inc., 1992—, Upjohn Corp., 1993—; mem. adult treatment panel Nat. Cholesterol Edn. Program, NIH; co-chair Cost-Effectiveness Panel on Clin. Prevention Svcs, USPHS, 1993—. Author: Clinical Decision Analysis, 1980, Hypertension: A Policy Perspective, 1976; mem. editorial bd. Med. Decision Making, 1981—, Jour. Environ. Econs. and Mgmt., 1986-88; assoc. editor Med. Decision Making, 1994—. NSF fellow, 1972. Mem. INFORMS, Inst. Medicine of NAS (com. on priorities for new vaccine devel., com. to evaluate the NIH artificial heart program), Soc. Med. Decision Making (trustee 1980-82, pres. 1984-85), Soc. Risk Analysis, Internat. Soc. Tech. Assessment in Health Care, Am. Med. Joggers Assn., Phi Beta Kappa. Office: Harvard U Sch Pub Health Dept Health Policy & Mgmt Boston MA 02115

WEINSTEIN, PETER M., lawyer, state senator; b. N.Y.C., Feb. 3, 1947; s. Moses and Muriel W.; m. Janet E. Forman; children: Andrew, Michael. BS, NYU; JD, Bklyn. Law Sch. Bar: N.Y., Fla. Asst. dist. atty. Queens County, N.Y.; asst. state's atty. Broward County, Fla.; pvt. practice, Ft. Lauderdale, Fla.; mem. Fla. State Senate, Tallahassee, 1982—, chmn. Broward County legis. del., 1985-86. Mem. Broward County Charter Rev. Commn.; mem. Coral Springs Planning and Zoning Bd. Capt. U.S. Army. Recipient Allen Morris award Fla. Senate; named Most Effective Freshman, Fla. Senate. Mem. Jewish War Vets., Coral Springs Dem. (pres. 1980-82). Avocation: photography. Office: 7880 N University Dr Ste 301 Fort Lauderdale FL 33321-2124

WEINSTEIN, PHILIP MEYER, English educator, literary critic; b. Memphis, July 8, 1940; s. Jacob and Rose (Wahl) W.; m. Elizabeth Pendleton Ogden, June 7, 1963; children: Elizabeth, Katherine. BA, Princeton U., 1962; MA, Harvard U., 1966, PhD, 1968. Asst. prof. dept. English Harvard U., Cambridge, Mass., 1968-71; asst. prof. dept. English Swarthmore (Pa.) Coll., 1971-74, assoc. prof., 1974-81, prof. English, 1981—; assoc. prof. Ecole Normale Superieure, Paris, 1983; disting. vis. prof. Rhodes Coll., Memphis, 1987. Author: Henry James and Requirements of Imagination, 1971, The Semantics of Desire, 1984, A Cosmos No One Owns, 1992. Fellow NEH, 1974-75, 82-83, Mellon Found., 1978-79, ACLS, 1987-88. Mem. MLA, Faulkner Soc. Democrat. Avocations: golf, tennis, travel. Office: Swarthmore Coll Dept English Swarthmore PA 19081

WEINSTEIN, ROBERT, film company executive. Co-chmn. Miramax Films Corp., L.A. Office: Miramax Films Corp 375 Greenwich St New York NY 10013*

WEINSTEIN, ROY, physics educator, researcher; b. N.Y.C., Apr. 21, 1927; s. Harry and Lillian (Ehrenberg) W.; m. Janet E. Spiller, Mar. 26, 1954; children: Lee Davis, Sara Lynn. B.S., MIT, 1951, Ph.D., 1954; Sc.D. (hon.), Lycoming Coll., 1981. Research asst. Mass. Inst. Tech., 1951-54, asst. prof., 1956-59; asst. prof. Brandeis U., Waltham, Mass., 1954-56; assoc. prof. Northeastern U., Boston, 1960-63, prof. physics, 1963-82, exec. officer, chmn. grad. div. of physics dept., 1967-69, chmn. physics dept., 1974-81; spokesman MAC Detector Stanford U., 1981-82; dean Coll. Natural Scis. and Math. U. Houston, 1982-88; prof. physics, 1982—; dir. Inst. Beam Particle Dynamics U. Houston, 1985—; assoc. dir., spokesman Tex. Ctr. for Superconductivity, 1987-89; vis. scholar and physicist Stanford (Calif.) U., 1966-67, 81-82; bd. dirs. Perception Tech., Inc., Winchester, Mass., Omniwave Inc., Gloucester, Mass., Wincom Inc., Woburn, Mass.; cons. Visidyne Inc., Burlington, Mass., Houston Area, Rsch. Ctr. Stanford U., Hodotector Inc., Houston, Park Square Engring., Mariatta, Ga., Harvard U., Cambridge, Mass., Cambridge Electron Accelerator, mem. adv. com., 1967-69; mem. adv. com. portfolio evaluation com. Houston Venture Ptnrs., 1990—; chmn. bd. dirs. Xytron Corp., 1986-91; dir., mem. exec. com. Houston Area Rsch. Ctr., 1984-87; 3d ann. faculty lectr. Northeastern U., 1966; chmn. organizing com. 4th ann. Internat. Conf. on Meson Spectroscopy, 1974, chmn. program com. 5th ann., 1977, mem. organizing com. 6th ann., 1980, 83; chmn. Tex. High Energy Physicists, 1989-91; keynote speaker MIT Alumni series, 1988; permanent mem. exec. com. Large Vol. Detector (Underground Neutrino Telescope, Italy); organizer session High Temperature Superconducting Magnets 3d and 4th World Congress on Superconductivity, Munich, 1993, Orlando, 1994. Author: Atomic Physics, 1964, Nuclear Physics, 1964, Interactions of Radiation and Matter, 1964; editor: Nuclear Reactor Theory, 1964, Nuclear Materials, 1964; editor procs.: 5th Internat. Conf. on Mesons, 1977; contbr. numerous articles to profl. jours. Mem. Lexington (Mass.) Town Meeting, 1973-76, 77-84; vice chmn. Lexington Coun. on Aging, 1977-83. With USNR, 1945-46. Recipient Founders award World Congress Superconductivity, 1988; NSF fellow Bohr Inst., Copenhagen, 1959-60, Stanford U., 1969-70, Guggenheim fellow Harvard U., 1970-71; NSF grantee, 1961—; recipient Tex. Rsch. awards, 1986-87, 90—, U.S. Dept. Energy award, 1974, 77, 87—, NASA award, 1990—, Elec. Power Rsch. Inst. award 1990-95, Phi Beta Phi Founders

award world congress on hyperproductivity, 1988. Fellow Am. Phys. Soc. (organizer session SSC and High Energy Physics 1984); mem. Am. Assn. Physics Tchrs., Masons, Sigma Xi, Phi Kappa Phi (chpt. pres. 1977-79, Nat. Triennial Disting. Scholar prize 1980-83)), Pi Lambda Phi. Unitarian. Achievements include measurement of fine structure of positronium; first measurement of rho meson coupling to gamma rays, of phi meson decay to two muons; early observation of break down in SU3 symmetry; demonstration of electron-muon universality, discovery of non-applicability of Lorentz contraction to length measured by a single observer; disproof of splitting of A2 meson; independent discovery of upsilon meson (bottom quark); achievement of highest magnetic field for any permanent magnet, in YBa2Cu3O7, 8.3 Tesla. Home: 4368 Fiesta Ln Houston TX 77004-6603 Office: U Houston IBPD Rm 632 SR1 Houston TX 77204

WEINSTEIN, RUTH JOSEPH, lawyer; b. N.Y.C., Mar. 26, 1933; d. David Arthur and Toby (Landau) Joseph; m. Marvin Walter Weinstein, June 3, 1962; children: Rosalyn S., Steven M., Barbara E. AB magna cum laude, Radcliffe Coll., 1954; LLB, Harvard U., 1957. Bar: N.Y. 1957, D.C. 1966. Assoc. Hale Russell & Gray and predecessor firms, N.Y.C., 1957-66, ptnr., 1966-85; ptnr. Winthrop Stimson Putnam & Roberts, N.Y.C., 1985—; chairperson Practising Law Inst. Forum, N.Y.C., 1978. Mem. sch. bd. Union Free Sch. Dist. 5, Rye Town, N.Y., 1976-79, pres., 1978-79. Mem. ABA, Assn. of Bar of City of N.Y. (com. on Aeronautics Assn. 1987-90), Harvard-Radcliffe Club of Westchester, The Wings Club Inc. Avocations: boating, skiing. Home: 21 Meadowlark Rd Rye Brook NY 10573-1209 Office: Winthrop Stimson 1 Battery Park Plz New York NY 10004-1403

WEINSTEIN, SIDNEY, university program director; b. N.Y.C., July 1, 1920; s. Jacob and Yetta W.; m. Celia Kahn, Mar. 6, 1943 (dec.); children: Risa, Jeri; m. Florence Landau, June 21, 1988. B.A., Bklyn. Coll., 1951; M.A., Columbia U., 1955; DPA, Indsl. Coll. Armed Forces, 1964. Contract adminstr. U.S. Corps Engrs., 1941-43; mgmt. analyst Dept. Army, N.Y.C., 1946-55; dir. data processing procurement GSA, 1956-68; dep. asst. commr. automated data mgmt. services GSA, Washington, 1968-72; asst. commr. automated data and telecommunications GSA, 1972-75; exec. dir. Assn. Computing Machinery, N.Y.C., 1975-85; assoc. prof. affiliates program Ctr. Research Info. Systems, Leonard N. Stern. Sch. Bus. NYU, 1985—; cons. to chmn. U.S. CSC. Served with USAF, 1943-46. Recipient Exceptional service award U.S. Govt., 1975. Mem. ABA (arbitrator 1989—), Coun. Engring. and Sci. Soc. Execs. (dir.), N.Y. Soc. Assn. Execs., Assn. Indsl. Coll. Armed Forces, Assn. Fed. Execs. Inst., Assn. Computing Machinery, Soc. Info. Mgmt. Home: 360 E 72nd St New York NY 10021-4753 Office: 44 W 4th St New York NY 10012-1126

WEINSTEIN, STANLEY, Buddhist studies educator; b. Bklyn., Nov. 13, 1929; s. Louis Arthur and Ruth (Appleson) W.; m. Lucie Ruth Krebs, Sept. 23, 1951; 1 son, David Eli. BA, Komazawa U., Tokyo, 1954-58; MA, U. Tokyo, 1960; PhD, Harvard U., 1966; MAH (hon.), Yale U., 1974. Lectr. Sch. Oriental and African Studies, London, 1962-68; assoc. prof. Buddhist studies Yale U., New Haven, 1968-74, prof., 1974—, chmn. council East Asian studies, 1982-85. Author: Buddhism under T'ang, 1987. Served with U.S. Army, 1952-54. Ford Found. fgn. area fellow, 1958-62; NEH sr. fellow, 1974-75. Mem. Am. Oriental Soc., Assn. Asian Studies. Home: 270 Ridgewood Ave Hamden CT 06517-1426 Office: Yale U Hall Grad Studies New Haven CT 06520

WEINSTEIN, STEPHEN BRANT, communications executive, researcher, writer; b. N.Y.C., Nov. 25, 1938; s. Max S. and Evelyn A. (Brandt) W.; m. Judith Louise Benham, June 10, 1961; children: Brant M., Anna M. SB, MIT, 1960; MS, U. Mich., 1962; PhD, U. Calif. at Berkeley, 1966. Mem. tech. staff Philips Rsch. Labs., Eindhoven, The Netherlands, 1967-68, Bell Labs., Holmdel, N.J., 1968-79; v.p. tech. strategy Am. Express Co., N.Y.C., 1979-84; exec. dir. subscriber systems rsch. Bellcore (formerly, Bell Communications Rsch.), Morristown, N.J., 1984-93; fellow C&C Rsch. Lab. NEC USA, Inc., 1994—. Author: Getting the Picture: A Guide to CATV and the New Electronic Media, 1986; co-author: Data Communication Principles, 1992; contbr. articles to profl. jours.; patentee in field. Fellow IEEE (editor-in-chief Comms. mag. 1984-89, chmn. press. 1979-82, Centennial medal 1984), IEEE Comms. Soc. (v.p. tech. affairs 1994—, dir. publs. 1990-93). Avocations: skiing, woodworking, video editing. Home: 150 Woodland Ave Summit NJ 07901-2029 Office: NEC USA Inc C & C Res Lab 4 Independence Way Princeton NJ 08540

WEINSTEIN, STEVEN DAVID, lawyer; b. Phila., May 3, 1946; s. Leon and Elizabeth (Evantash) W.; m. Karin Elkis, Feb. 16, 1986. BA, Rutgers U., 1968, JD, 1975. Bar: N.J. 1975, Pa. 1975, U.S. Dist. Ct. N.J. 1975, U.S. Dist. Ct. (ea. dist.) Pa. 1975, U.S. Supreme Ct. 1979, U.S. Ct. Appeals (3d cir.) 1981, U.S. Ct. Claims 1986. Assoc. Lewis Katz P.C., Cherry Hill, N.J., 1975-78; pvt. practice law Collingswood, N.J., 1978-84; ptnr. Blank, Rome, Comisky & McCauley, Cherry Hill, 1984—; atty. Camden (N.J.) County Counsel, 1982-84; v.p. N.J. County Counsels Assn. 1983. Trustee Camden County Coll., Blackwood, N.J., 1983, West Jersey Hosps. Found., Camden, 1984—, chmn. 1989-91; trustee Rowan Coll., 1989-90; mem. N.J. Bus.-Higher Edn. forum. Mem. ABA, N.J. Bar Assn., Camden County Bar Assn. Democrat. Jewish. Office: Blank Rome Comisky & McCauley Woodland Falls Corporate Park 210 Lake Dr E Ste 200 Cherry Hill NJ 08002-1163

WEINSTOCK, HAROLD, lawyer; b. Stamford, Conn., Nov. 30, 1925; s. Elias and Sarah (Singer) W.; m. Barbara Lans, Aug. 27, 1950; children—Nathaniel, Michael, Philip. B.S. magna cum laude, N.Y. U., 1947; J.D., Harvard, 1950. Bar: Conn. bar 1950, Ill. bar 1950, Calif. bar 1958. Atty. SEC, Washington, 1950-52, IRS, 1952-56; tax atty. Hunt Foods & Industries, Inc., Los Angeles, 1956-58; pvt. practice Beverly Hills, Calif., 1958-71, Los Angeles, 1971—; mem. Weinstock, Manion, Reisman, Shore & Neumann (and predecessor firms), 1958—; Lectr. extension div., estate planning courses U. Calif. at Los Angeles, 1959—; estate planning and taxation courses Calif. Continuing Edn. of the Bar, 1960—. Author: Planning An Estate, 4th edit., 1995; contbr. articles to profl. publs. Nat. trustee Union Am. Hebrew Congregations, 1976-79; bd. trustees Jewish Cmty. Found., L.A.; adv. bd. Estate Planning Inst. UCLE Law Sch., 1979-92, NYU Inst. on Fed. Taxation, 1986-95. Mem. ABA, Calif. Bar Assn., Beverly Hills Bar Assn. (chmn. probate and trusts com. 1967-68), Los Angeles Bar Assn., Beverly Hills Estate Planning Council (pres. 1968-69), Estate Counselors Forum of Los Angeles (pres. 1963-64). Jewish (pres. temple 1974-76). Office: Weinstock Manion 1888 Century Park E Los Angeles CA 90067-1702

WEINSTOCK, HERBERT FRANK, public relations executive; b. Los Angeles, July 26, 1913; s. Frank and Sarah (Mantel) W.; m. Evelyn June Hanson, July 27, 1940; children—Allan Herbert, William Jay, Joan Louise. A.A., Los Angeles City Coll., 1933. Financial editor Los Angeles Daily News, 1939-54; pub. relations assoc. H. F. Weinstock & Assocs., 1955-61, 80-91; public relations dir. Burton, Booth & Weinstock, Inc., 1961-63; with Eisamen, Johns & Laws (advt.), Los Angeles, 1964; v.p. charge corporate and financial pub. relations Kennett Pub. Relations Assocs., 1966-71; pres. Conway/Weinstock/ Assos., Inc., 1971-80. Pres. Intercommunity Care Centers, Inc., long Beach, Calif. Served with AUS, 1943-45; with 3d Army 1944-45. Home: 533 21st St Manhattan Beach CA 90266-2201

WEINSTOCK, LEONARD, lawyer; b. Bklyn., Aug. 18, 1935; s. Samuel Morris and Evelyn (Reiser) W.; m. Rita Lee Itkowitz, May 25, 1963; children—Gregg Douglas, Valerie Lisa, Tara Diane. B.S., Bklyn. Coll., 1956; J.D., St. John's U., Bklyn., 1959. Bar: N.Y. 1961, U.S. Supreme Ct. 1964, U.S. Ct. Appeals (2d cir.) 1963, U.S. Dist. Ct. (ea. and so. dists.) N.Y. 1963, U.S. Tax Ct. 1963. Assoc. Bernard Helfenstein law practice, Bklyn., 1962-63; supr. All State Ins. Co., Bklyn., 1963-64; atty. Hertz Corp., N.Y.C., 1964-65; ptnr. Nicholas & Weinstock, Flushing, N.Y., 1965-68; v.p., ptnr. Garbarini & Scher, P.C., N.Y.C., 1968—; lectr. Practicing Law Inst. N.Y.C., 1975—; arbitrator Nassau County Dist. Ct., Mineola, N.Y., 1979—, U.S. Dist. Ct. (ea. dist.) N.Y. 1986—; mem. Med. Malpractice Mediation Panel, Mineola, 1978—; Legal counsel Massapequa Soccer Club (N.Y.), 1981—; county committeeman Democratic Party, Massapequa Park, N.Y., 1979—. Served with U.S. Army, 1959-62. Mem. ABA, N.Y. State Bar Assn., Nassau County Bar Assn. (mem. med. jurisprudence ins. com. 1978), N.Y. Trial Lawyers Assn., Queens County Bar Assn. (mem. legal referral com. 1969). Avoca-

tions: stamp collecting, softball, racquetball. Home: 38 Barstow Rd Great Neck NY 11021 Office: Garbarini and Scher PC 1114 Avenue Of The Americas # 35th Flr New York NY 10036-7701

WEINSTOCK, WALTER WOLFE, systems engineer; b. Phila., Aug. 18, 1925; s. Abraham and Jeanne (Feldman) W.; m. Doris Alpert, Sept. 21, 1946; children—Steven Eric, Bruce Alan. B.S.E.E., U.Pa., 1946, M.S.E.E., 1954, Ph.D., 1964. Design engr. Philco, 1946-49; with RCA Corp., 1949-87; prin. scientist RCA Corp. (Missile and Surface Radar div.), Moorestown, N.J., 1979-87; cons., 1987—; mem. planning and steering adv. group Surface Ship Security Panel, Dept. Navy, 1979-82. Contbg. author: Modern Radar, 1965, Practical Phased Array Antenna Systems, 1991; contbr. articles to profl. jours. Recipient David Sarnoff award for Outstanding Achievement in Enrging. RCA, 1972. Fellow IEEE; mem. Tau Beta Pi, Eta Kappa Nu, Sigma Tau, Pi Mu Epsilon. Patentee in field. Home: 6 Beryl Rd Cheltenham PA 19012-1206

WEINTRAUB, ALLEN, diversified financial services executive. With Putnam, Coftin & Burr, Hartford, Conn., 1955-77; chmn. bd., CEO. pres. Advest Group Inc., Hartford, Conn., 1977—. Office: Advest Inc 1 Comml Pla 280 Trumbull St Hartford CT 06103*

WEINTRAUB, DANIEL RALPH, social welfare administrator; b. N.Y.C., Apr. 23, 1939; s. Benjamin Zion and Ida (Barman) W.; BA in Biology, NYU, 1959; DDS, Columbia U., 1963; certificate pub. health U. Wash., 1963; m. Sally Ann Franco, Mar. 16, 1968; children—David Arlo, Jeremy Michael. Rural community devel. adviser AID, Dominican Republic, 1966-68, population and pub. health adviser, 1968-69; asso. planning dir. Alan Guttmacher Inst. (formerly Center for Family Planning Program Devel.), N.Y.C., 1969-74; dep. dir. Family Planning Internat. Assistance, N.Y.C., 1974-76, COO, 1977-95; v.p. internat. programs Planned Parenthood Fedn. Am., N.Y.C., 1978—; mem. speaker's bur., 1982—; vol. leader, coordinator U.S. Peace Corps, Bolivia, 1964-65; cons. HEW, 1971-74, Nat. Center Health Statistics, 1974. Recipient Certificate of Honor, Dominican Republic, 1969; commendation Dept. Interior, Cochabamba, Bolivia, 1965. Mem. ACLU, Nat. Geog. Soc., Nature Conservancy, Choice in Dying. Author books and manuals on community devel. theory and practice, plans for area-wide family planning programs in met. areas, family planning tech. assistance in developing nations, nat. studies including Need for Subsidized Family Planning Services: United States, Each State and County, 1971. Home: 8 Dock Ln Port Washington NY 11050-1732 Office: FPIA 810 7th Ave New York NY 10019-5818

WEINTRAUB, JERRY, motion picture producer, executive; b. Sept. 26, 1937; m. Jayne Morgan. Chmn., chief exec. officer, pres. United Artists Corp., New York, 1985-86; founder Weintraub Entertainment Group, 1987—. Producer: (films) including Nashville, 1975, Oh God!, 1977, Cruising, 1980, All Night Long, 1981, Diner, 1982, The Karate Kid, 1984, The Karate Kid, Part II, The Karate Kid, Part III, 1989, Pure Country, 1992, The Next Karate Kid, 1994; appeared in (film) The Firm, 1993. Office: Weintraub Prodns 4000 Warner Blvd # 1 Burbank CA 91522-0001

WEINTRAUB, JOSEPH BARTON, publishing executive; b. Phila., Dec. 2, 1945; s. George and Edith (Lubner) W.; m. Denise Waters, June 14, 1974. BA, U. Pitts., 1966; MA, U. Chgo., 1967, PhD, 1973. Assoc. faculty U. Ind., Gary, Ind., 1970-74; mktg. specialist journalism div. U. Chgo. Press, 1974-75, sr. copywriter journalism div., 1975-78; periodical specialist ABA Press, Chgo., 1978-80, mktg. mgr., 1980-92, dir. publ. planning, 1992—; mktg. cons. Teachers Coll. Record, N.Y.C., 1977-79, Repertoire Internat. de la Litterature de l'Art, N.Y.C., 1977-79, Am. Lung Assn., 1980-82. Contbr. essays, translations, poems, short fiction to lit. revs. and small press anthologies. Recipient award Ill. Art Coun. Mem. Phi Beta Kappa. Avocations: writing, language study. Office: Am Bar Assn 750 N Lake Shore Dr Chicago IL 60611-4403

WEINTRAUB, KARL JOACHIM, history educator; b. Darmstadt, Fed. Republic Germany, Dec. 31, 1924; came to U.S., 1948; s. Micha B. Weintraub and Elizabeth (Hammel) Anders; m. D. Kathryn Lamphiear, Mar. 16, 1957 (div. 1980); m. Katy O'Brien, Apr. 23, 1983. BA, U. Chgo., 1949, MA, 1952, PhD, 1957; LHD (hon.), Knox Coll. 1986. Bibliographer U. Chgo. Librs., 1953-60; instr. U. Chgo. Coll. 1954-57, asst. prof. 1957-63; assoc. prof. U. Chgo., 1963-70, prof., 1970—, Disting. Svc. prof. 1987—, dean humanities, 1973-83. Author: Visions of Culture, 1966, The Value of the Individual, 1978; contbr. articles to profl. jours. Trustee Knox Coll., Galesburg, Ill., 1978—, Art Inst., Chgo., 1984—; bd. govs. Sch. of the Art Inst., Chgo., 1981—. Recipient Quantrell Award for Excellence in Teachign, 1960, 86, E. Harris Harbison award Danforth Found., 1967; fellow Am. Acad. Arts & Scis., 1990. Mem. Am. Hist. Assn., Quadrangle Club (pres. 1960s). Mem. Soc. of Friends. Home: 5844 S Stony Island Ave Chicago IL 60637-2004 Office: U Chgo History Dept 1050 E 59th St Chicago IL 60637-1512

WEINTRAUB, MICHAEL IRA, neurologist; b. N.Y.C., Aug. 14, 1940; s. Abraham and Mildred Weintraub (Kuttner) W.; m. Anita Bellin, Aug. 2, 1964; children: Jeffrey Brian, Lisa Ellen. B.A., N.Y. U., 1962; M.D., State U. N.Y., Buffalo, 1966. Diplomate: Am. Bd. Psychiatry and Neurology, Am. Bd. EEG., Am. Acad. Pain Mgmt., Am. Bd. Prof. Disability Cons., Am. Soc. of Neurorehabilitation. Intern E. J. Meyer Hosp., Buffalo, 1966-67; fellow neurology State U. N.Y., Buffalo, 1967-68; fellow neurology Yale U.-New Haven Med. Center, 1968-70, chief resident, 1969-70; instr. neurology Boston U. Sch. Medicine, 1970-72; instr. Albert Einstein Sch. Medicine, Bronx, N.Y., 1972-73; asst. prof. neurology N.Y. Med. Coll., 1974-77, assoc. clin. prof., 1977-83, clin. prof. neurology, 1983—; chief pediatric neurology Westchester County Med. Center, Valhalla, N.Y., 1974-77; practice medicine specializing in neurology/pain mgmt. Briarcliff, N.Y., 1972—; attending neurologist Phelps Meml. Hosp., 1972—, chief of neurology, 1981—; sr. neurologist Putnam Community Hosp., 1981—. Contbr. articles to med. jours. Recipient Outstanding Young Men of Am. award U.S. Jr. C. of C., 1971. Fellow ACP, Am. Coll. Angiology, Am. Acad. Neurology, Am. Bd. Electroencephalography; mem. AMA, Westchester County Med. Soc. Home: Quaker Bridge Rd E Croton On Hudson NY 10520 Office: 325 S Highland Ave Briarcliff Manor NY 10510-2031

WEINTRAUB, RUSSELL JAY, lawyer, educator; b. N.Y.C., Dec. 20, 1929; s. Harry and Alice (Lieberman) W.; m. Zelda Kresshover, Sept. 6, 1953; children—Sharon Hope, Harry David, Steven Ross. BA, NYU, 1950; JD, Harvard U., 1953. Bar: N.Y. 1955, Iowa 1961, Tex. 1980. Teaching fellow Harvard U. Law Sch., 1955-57; asst. prof. law U. Iowa, 1957-61, prof., 1961-65; prof. U. Tex., 1965—, Marrs McLean prof. law, 1970-80, Bryant Smith chair, 1980-82, John B. Connally chair, 1982—; vis. prof. law U. Mich., 1965, UCLA, 1967, U. Calif., Berkeley, 1973-74, Inst. Internat. and Comparative Law, Paris, 1975, U. Houston, 1979-80, Inst. Internat. and Comparative Law, Oxford, Eng., 1982, 83, 86, 87, 92, Dublin, Ireland, 1991, La. State U., Aix-en-Provence, France, 1993; lectr. Hague Acad. Internat. Law, 1984; cons. in field. Author: International Litigation and Arbitration, 1994, (with Eugene Scoles) Cases and Materials on the Conflict of Laws, 1967, 2d rev. edit., 1972, supplement, 1978, Commentary on the Conflict of Laws, 1971, 3d rev. edit., 1986, supplement, 1991, (with Hamilton and Rau) Cases and Materials on Contracts, 1984, 2d rev. edit., 1992; contbr. articles to profl. jours. Trustee U. Iowa Sch. Religion, 1960-65. Served with U.S. Army, 1953-55. Recipient Disting. Prof. award U. Tex. Sch. Law, 1977, Teaching Excellence award, 1979, cert. of meritorious service Am. Bar Assn., 1977, cert. of meritorious service Tex. Bar Assn., 1978, Best Tchr. award U. Houston, 1980, Carl Fulda award scholarship in internat. law, 1993. Mem. Am. Law Inst., Am. Bar Found., Tex. Bar Found., Scribes. Jewish. Home: 7204 Sungate Dr Austin TX 78731-2141 Office: U Tex Sch Law 727 E 26th St Austin TX 78705-3224 *The only true happiness lies in useful work done to the best of your ability.*

WEINTRAUB, SIDNEY, economist, educator; b. N.Y.C., May 18, 1922; s. Reuben and Anna Weintraub; m. Gladys Katz, Aug. 11, 1946; children: Jeffrey, Marcia Weintraub Plunkett, Deborah Weintraub Chilewich. B.B.A., CCNY, 1943; B.J., M.A. in Journalism, U. Mo., 1948; M.A. in Econs., Yale U., 1958, Ph.D. in Econs, Am. U., 1966. Commd. fgn. service officer Dept. State, 1949; dep. asst. sec. of state for internat. fin. and devel. Dept. State, Washington, 1969-74; asst. adminstr. for interagy. devel. coordination AID,

1974-75, exec. dir. interagy devel. coordination com., 1974-75; ret., 1975; sr. fellow Brookings Instn., Washington, 1978-79; Dean Rusk prof. Lyndon B. Johnson Sch. Public Affairs, U. Tex., Austin, 1976—; also dir. Program for U.S.-Mex. Policy Studies Lyndon B. Johnson Sch. Public Affairs, U. Tex.; William E. Simon chair in polit. economy Ctr. Strategic and Internat. Studies, 1993—; Disting. vis. scholar Ctr. for Strategic and Internat. Studies, Washington, 1990. Author: Free Trade with Mexico, 1984, A Marriage of Convenience: Relations Between Mexico and The United States, 1990, NAFTA: What Comes Next, 1994; contbr. articles to profl. jours. Served with U.S. Army, 1943-46. Recipient Disting. Career Service award AID, 1975. Mem. Coun. on Fgn. Rels., Am. Econ. Assn., Am. Fgn. Service Assn. Club: Cosmos (Washington). Office: Lyndon B Johnson Sch Pub Affairs Drawer Y University Sta Austin TX 78712 *Once having been thrust into the Second World War, my main intellectual interest has been in foreign affairs. I had concluded, as President Kennedy did later, that domestic issues can hurt but misplaced foreign policy can kill. My drive has been to understand what motivates nations, what stimulates people within different nations, what is the U.S. national interest, and to become as expert as my talents would allow about such crucial issues as domestic security, international economic interaction, social mobility, and human development generally. This remains my ambition.*

WEINTRAUB, STANLEY, arts and humanities educator, author; b. Phila., Apr. 17, 1929; s. Ben and Ray (Segal) W.; m. Rodelle Horwitz, June 6, 1954; children: Mark, David, Erica. BS, West Chester (Pa.) State Coll., 1949; MA, Temple U., 1951; PhD, Pa. State U., 1956. Instr. Pa. State U., University Park, 1953-59; asst. prof. Pa. State U., 1959-62, asso. prof., 1962-65, prof. English, 1965-70, research prof., 1970-86, Evan Pugh prof. Arts and Humanities, 1986—; dir. Inst. for Arts and Humanistic Studies, 1970-90; Vis. prof. U. Calif. at Los Angeles, 1963, U. Hawaii, 1973, U. Malaya, 1977, Nat. U. Singapore, 1982. Author: Private Shaw and Public Shaw, 1963, The War in the Wards, 1964, Reggie, 1965, The Art of William Golding, 1965, Beardsley, 1967, The Last Great Cause, The Intellectuals and the Spanish Civil War, 1968, Evolution of a Revolt: Early Postwar Writings of T.E. Lawrence, 1968, The Literary Criticism of Oscar Wilde, 1968, Journey to Heartbreak, 1971, Whistler: A Biography, 1974, Lawrence of Arabia: the Literary Impulse, 1975, Four Rossettis, A Victorian Biography, 1977, Aubrey Beardsley: Imp of the Perverse, 1976, The London Yankees: Portraits of American Writers and Artists in England, 1894-1914, 1979, The Unexpected Shaw. Biographical Approaches to G.B. Shaw and His Work, 1982, A Stillness Heard Round the World: The End of the Great War, 1985, Victoria. An Intimate Biography, 1987, Long Day's Journey into War: December 7, 1941, 1991, Bernard Shaw: A Guide to Research, 1992, Disraeli: A Biography, 1993, The Last Great Victory-The End of World War II, July/August 1945, 1995; editor: An Unfinished Novel by Bernard Shaw, 1958, C.P. Snow: A Spectrum, 1963, The Yellow Book: Quintessence of the Nineties, 1964, The Savoy: Nineties Experiment, 1966, The Court Theatre, 1966, Biography and Truth, 1967, Evolution of a Revolt: Early Postwar Writings of T.E. Lawrence, 1968, The Literary Criticism of Oscar Wilde, 1968, Shaw: An Autobiography 1856-1898, 1969, Shaw: An Autobiography, The Playwright Years, 1898-1950, 1970, Bernard Shaw's Nondramatic Literary Criticism, 1972, Directions in Literary Criticism, 1973, Saint Joan Fifty Years After: 1923/24-1973/74, 1973, The Portable Bernard Shaw, 1977, (with Anne Wright) Heartbreak House. A Facsimile of the Revised Typescript, 1979, (with Richard Aldington) The Portable Oscar Wilde, 1981, Modern British Dramatists, 1900-1945, 1982, The Playwright and the Pirate. Bernard Shaw and Frank Harris: A Correspondence, 1982, British Dramatists Since World War II, 1983, Bernard Shaw, the Diaries, 1885-1897, 1986, Bernard Shaw on the London Art Scene, 1885-1950, 1989, also editor Comparative Literature Studies, 1987-92, Shaw, The Ann. of Bernard Shaw Studies, 1956-89. Pres. Jewish Community Council of Bellefonte (Pa.) State Coll., 1966-67. Served to 1st lt. AUS, 1951-53, Korea. Decorated Bronze Star medal.; Guggenheim fellow, 1968-69; recipient Disting. Humanist award Pa. Humanities Council, 1985. Mem. The Authors' Guild, PEN. Home: 840 Outer Dr State College PA 16801-8233 Office: Pa State U 202 Ihlseng Cottage University Park PA 16802-1704 *I subscribe to Bernard Shaw's declaration in the Preface to Man and Superman that "This is the true joy in life, the being used for a purpose recognized by yourself as mighty one; the being thoroughly worn out before you are thrown on the scrap heap; the being a force of Nature instead of a feverish selfish little clod of ailments and grievances complaining that the world will not devote itself to making you happy.".*

WEINTZ, CAROLINE GILES, non-profit association consultant, travel writer; b. Columbia, Tenn., Dec. 8, 1952; d. Raymond Clark Jr. and Caroline Higdon (Wagstaff) Giles; m. Walter Louis Weintz; children: Alexander Harwood, Elizabeth Pettus. AB, Princeton U., 1974; postgrad. diploma, U. London, 1976. Dir. advt. and promotion E.P. Dutton Pubs., N.Y.C., 1977-86; advt. cons. Assn. Jr. Leagues Internat., N.Y.C., 1986-91, advt. mgr., 1992-94, dir. of systems, 1994—. Author: The Discount Guide for Travelers over 55, 4th edit., 1988. Vol. researcher St. Paul's Nat. Hist. Site and Bill of Rights Mus., Westchester, N.Y., 1986—; treas. Soc. Nat. Shrine of The Bill of Rights; mem. Jr. League, Pelham, N.Y. Mem. Authors Guild, Nat. Soc. Colonial Dames, Huguenot Soc. Am., Daus. Cin., Mensa. Episcopalian. Home: 444 Wolfs Ln Pelham NY 10803-2127

WEINTZ, WALTER LOUIS, book publishing company executive; b. Westchester, N.Y., Apr. 19, 1952; s. Walter Henry and Helen (Bennett) W.; m. Caroline Harwood Giles, Aug. 31, 1974; children: Alexander Harwood, Elizabeth Pettus. AB, Princeton U., 1974; MPhil, U. London, 1976. Dir. sales and mktg. St. Martin's Press, N.Y.C., 1977-84; v.p., dir. mktg. Atlantic Monthly Press, N.Y.C., 1985-86; v.p. A.M.E. Pub., Ltd., N.Y.C., 1987-91; pres. Mondadori Pub. Co., N.Y.C., 1987-91; v.p., assoc. pub. Random House Inc., N.Y.C., 1991—. Co-author: Discount Guide for Travellers Over 55, 1983. Avocation: fencing. Office: Random House Inc 201 E 50th St New York NY 10022-7703

WEI-QIANG, ZHANG, dancer. Grad. with highest honors, Beijing Dance Acad., 1979; postgrad., Houston Ballet Acad. Prin. dancer Beijing Dance Acad. Ballet Co., 1981-84, Ctrl. Ballet of China, 1984-92, Royal Winnipeg (Man., Can.) Ballet, 1992—; guest artist Houston Ballet, Star Dancers Ballet, Japan, Asami Maki Ballet Co., Universal Ballet Co. of Korea, The Hong Kong Ballet, Goh Ballet, Can., Gala performance in memory of Anton Dolin, London, 1984, 2nd Internat. Ballet Competition Gala, Paris, 1986, 2d Aoyama Ballet Festival, Tokyo, 1988, Gala performance in memory of Prix de Lausanne, Tokyo, 1989, Japan Ballet Festival, Tokyo, 1989, 91, 92, and numerous other festivals and galas. Prin. roles include Giselle, Don Quixote, Swan Lake, Nutcracker, Raymonda, La Fille Mal Gardee, Coppelia, The Leaves Are Fading, The Afternoon of the Faun, Scotch Symphony, Allegro Brillante, Romeo & Juliet, Sleeping Beauty. Recipient Bronze medal 2nd Internat. Ballet Competition, Jackson, Miss., 1982, 2nd prize 4th World Ballet Competition, Osaka, Japan, 1984, Bronze medal 5th Moscow Internat. Ballet Competition, 1985, Highest Honor award 1st Nat. Ballet Competition, Beijing, 1985. Office: Royal Winnipeg Ballet, 380 Graham Ave, Winnipeg, MB Canada R3C 4K2*

WEIR, ALEXANDER, JR., utility consultant, inventor; b. Crossett, Ark., Dec. 19, 1922; s. Alexander and Mary Eloise (Field) W.; m. Florence Forschner, Dec. 28, 1946; children: Alexander III, Carol Jean, Bruce Richard. BSChemE, U. Ark., 1943; MChemE, Poly Inst. Bklyn., 1946; PhD, U. Mich., 1954; cert., U. So. Calif. Grad. Sch. Bus. Administrn., 1968. Chem. engr. Am. Cyanamid Co., Stamford Rsch. Labs., 1943-47; with U. Mich., 1948-58; rsch. assoc., project supr. Engring. Research Inst., U. Mich., 1948-57; lectr. chem. and metall. engring. dept. U. Mich., 1954-56, asst. prof., 1956-58; cons. Ramo-Wooldridge Corp., Los Angeles, 1956-57, mem. tech. staff, sect. head, asst. mgr., 1957-60, incharge Atlas Missile Captive test program, 1956-60; tech. advr. to pres. Northrop Corp., Beverly Hills, Calif., 1960-70; prin. scientist for air quality So. Calif. Edison Co., Los Angeles 1970-76, mgr. chem. systems research and devel., 1976-86, chief research scientist, 1986-88; utility cons. Playa Del Rey, Calif., 1988—; rep. Am. Rocket Soc. to Detroit Nuclear Council, 1954-57; chmn. session on chem. reactions Nuclear Sci. and Engring. Congress, Cleve., 1955; U.S. del. AGARD (NATO) Combustion Colloquium, Liege, Belgium, 1955; Western U.S. rep. task force on environ. research and devel. goals Electric Research Council, 1971; electric utility advisor Electric Power Research Inst., 1974-78, 84-87; industry advisor Dept. Chemistry and Biochemistry Calif. State U., Los Angeles, 1981-88. Author: Two and Three Dimensional Flow of Air

through Square-Edged Sonic Orifices, 1954; (with R.B. Morrison and T.C. Anderson) Notes on Combustion, 1955, also tech. papers; inventor acid rain prevention device used in 5 states. Sea Scout leader, Greenwich, Conn., 1944-48, Marina del Rey, Calif., 1965-70; bd. govs., past pres. Civic Union Playa del Rey, chmn. sch., police and fire, nominating, civil def., army liaison coms; mem. Senate, Westchester YMCA, chmn. Dads sponsoring com., active fundraising; chmn. nominating com. Paseco del Rey Sch. PTA, 1961; mem. Los Angeles Mayors Community Adv. Com.; asst. chmn. advancement com., merit badge dean Cantinella dist. Los Angeles Area council Boy Scouts Am. Recipient Nat. Rsch. Coun. Flue Gas Desulfurization Industrials Scale Reliability award NAS, 1975, Power Environ. Achievement award EPA, 1980, Excellence in Sulfur Dioxide Control award EPA, 1985. Mem. AICE, Am. Geophys. Union, Navy League U.S. (v.p. Palos Verdes Peninsula coun. 1961-62), N.Y. Acad. Scis., Sci. Rsch. Soc. Am., Am. Chem. Soc., U.S. Power Squadron, St. Andrews Soc. So. Calif., Clan Macmachtan Assn., Clan Buchanan Soc. in Am., Betty Washington Lewis Soc. of Children of Am. Revolution (past pres.), Ark. Soc. of Children of Am. Revolution (past pres.), Santa Monica Yacht Club, Sigma Xi, Phi Kappa Phi, Phi Lambda Upsilon, Alpha Chi Sigma, Lambda Chi Alpha. Office: 8229 Billowvista Dr Playa Del Rey CA 90293-7807

WEIR, BRYCE K. A., neurosurgeon, neurology educator; b. Edinburgh, Scotland, Apr. 29, 1936; came to U.S., 1992; s. Ernest John and Marion (Stewart) W.; m. Mary Lou Lauber, Feb. 25, 1976; children: Leanora, Glyncora, Brocke. BSc, McGill U., Montreal, Que., Can., 1958, MD, CM, 1960, MSc, 1963. Diplomate Am. Bd. Neurol. Surgery, Nat. Bd. Med. Examiners. Intern Montreal Gen. Hosp., 1960-61; resident in neurosurgery Neurological Inst., Montreal, 1962-64, 65-66, N.Y. Neurol. Inst., N.Y.C., 1964-65; neurosurgeon U. Alta., Edmonton, Can., 1967-72, dir. div. neurosurgery, Walter Anderson prof., chmn. dept. surgery, 1986-92; surgeon-in-chief U. Alta. Hosps.; Maurice Goldblatt prof. surgery and neurology U. Chgo., 1992—, dir. Brain Rsch. Inst., 1993—; past pres. V Internat. Symposium on Cerebral Vasospasm; mem. neurology A study sect. NIH, 1991-93; invited speaker at over 100 profl. meetings; vis. prof. over 50 univs., including Yale U., Cornell U., Columbia U., Duke U., U. Toronto, U. Calif., San Francisco; over 10 named lectureships, including White lectr. Harvard U., Gainey lectr., Mayo Clinic. Author: Aneurysms Affecting the Nervous System, 1987; mem. editl. bd. Jour. Neurosurgery, chmn. bd., 1993-94; mem. editl. bd. Neurosurgery Quar., Jour. Cerebrovascular Disease; contbr. over 200 articles to med. jours. Fellow ACS, Royal Coll. Surgeons Can., Royal Coll. Surgeons Edinburgh (hon.); mem. Am. Surg. Assn., James IV Assn. Surgeons, Am. Acad. Neurol. Surgeons, Soc. Neurol. Surgeons (Grass gold medal 1992). Achievements include contributions to the understanding of cerebral vasospasm and the surgical management of intracranial aneurysms. Office: U of Chgo Pritzker Sch of Medicine 5841 S Maryland Ave Chicago IL 60637

WEIR, D. ROBERT, company executive. Sr. v.p. Sherritt Inc., Ft. Saskatchewan, Alta., Can. Recipient H.T. Airey award, ASTzch award. Office: Sherritt Inc, Fort Saskatchewan, AB Canada T8L 3W4

WEIR, EDWARD KENNETH, cardiologist; b. Belfast, No. Ireland, Jan. 7, 1943; came to U.S. 1973; s. Thomas Kenneth and Violet Hilda (ffrench) W.; m. Elizabeth Vincent Pearman, May 29, 1971; children: Fergus G., Conor K. BA, U. Oxford, U.K., 1964; MA, BM, BCh, U. Oxford, 1967, DM, 1976. Diplomate Am. Bd. Internal Medicine. Sr. house physician Nuffield Dept. Medicine, Radcliffe Infirmary, Oxford, 1970-71; registrar in cardiology Groote Schuur Hosp., Cape Town, South Africa, 1971-73; postdoctoral rsch. fellow U. Colo., Denver, 1973-75; cons. pediatric cardiologist U. Cape Town Med. Sch., 1975-76; cons. cardiologist U. Natal Med. Sch., Durban, South Africa, 1976-77; assoc. prof. medicine U. Minn., Mpls., 1978-85, prof. medicine, 1985—; staff physician Va. Med. Ctr., Mpls., 1978—; dir. Grover Confs. on Pulmonary Circulation, 1984—. Co-editor: Pulmonary Hypertension, 1984, The Pulmonary Circulation in Health and Disease, 1987, Pulmonary Vascular Physiology and Pathophysiology, 1989, The Diagnosis and Treatment of Pulmonary Hypertension, 1992, Ion Flux in Pulmonary Vascular Control, 1993, The Pulmonary Circulation and Gas Exchange, 1994, Nitric Oxide and Oxygen Radicals in the Pulmonary Vasculature, 1995. Fulbright scholar, 1973-75; Sr. Internat. Fogarty fellow, 1993. Fellow Am. Coll. Cardiology, Royal Coll. Physicians London; mem. Am. Heart Assn. (Minn. affiliate bd. dirs. 1989-93, Nat. Cardiopulmonary Coun. (exec. com. 1992—), Pulmonary Circulation Found. (treas. 1985—). Office: VA Med Ctr 111C 1 Veteran's Dr Minneapolis MN 55391

WEIR, KENNETH WYNN, marine corps officer, experimental test pilot; b. Sherman, Tex., Oct. 20, 1930; s. Kenneth Herbert and Berye Lee (Wynn) W.; m. Nancy Corr Mosher, Oct. 10, 1953; children—Kenneth Mosher, David Wynn, William Scott. B.S., U.S. Naval Acad., 1952; M.S., U. So. Calif., 1968. Commd. 2d lt. USMC, 1952, advanced through grades to maj. gen., 1977, comdg. gen. 65th Marine Amphibian Brigade, 1978, dep. comdg. gen. Fleet Marine Force Pacific, 1981, comdg. gen. 4th Marine Air Wing, 1985; chief U-2/TR 1 Test Pilot Lockheed Skunk Works, Burbank, Calif., 1966-93; ret., 1993. Fellow Soc. Exptl. Test Pilots (pres. 1980-81). Achievements include more flight test experience above 60,000 feet altitude in high performance airplanes than anyone else in the world.

WEIR, MORTON WEBSTER, retired university chancellor and educator; b. Canton, Ill., July 18, 1934; s. James and Frances Mary (Johnson) W.; m. Cecelia Ann Rumler, June 23, 1956; children: Deborah, Kevin, Mark. AB, Knox Coll., 1955; MA, U. Tex., 1958, PhD, 1959. Rsch. assoc., asst. prof. child devel. U. Minn., Mpls., 1959; asst. prof. child devel. U. Ill., Urbana, 1960-64, assoc. prof., 1964-68, prof., 1968-93, prof. emeritus, 1993—; head dept. psychology, 1969-71, vice chancellor acad. affairs, 1971-79, v.p. acad. affairs, 1982-88, chancellor, 1988-93, chancellor emeritus, 1993—, sr. found. rep., 1993—; dir. Boys Town Center Study Youth Development, 1979-80. Contbr. numerous articles to profl. jours. Chmn. bd. trustees Knox Coll., 1995—. With AUS, 1960. NSF Predoctoral fellow, 1957-59. Fellow AAAS; mem. Soc. Rsch. in Child Devel. bd. publs. 1971, chmn. fin. com. 1993-95), Sigma Xi, Phi Beta Kappa, Phi Kappa Phi. Office: U Ill Found Harker Hall 1305 W Green St Urbana IL 61801-2919

WEIR, PETER FRANK, lawyer; b. Stuttgart, Ger., Mar. 26, 1933; s. Robert Henry and Ruth Sophie W.; m. Jean M., Sept. 27, 1958; children: Bradford F., Elizabeth A. BA, Williams Coll., 1955; LLB, Harvard U., 1958; MBA, N.Y.U., 1967. Bar: N.Y. 1959, Ga. 1957. Assoc. Winston & Strawn, N.Y.C., 1959-66, ptnr., 1966-92, ret. ptnr., 1992—. Bd. dirs. Episc. Ch. Found., 1981-93, sec.; 1989-93, also treas., chmn. fin. com., 1982-89, chmn. audit com., 1982-88, mem. exec. com., mem. steering com. N.Y. Regional Coun., 1975-81, chmn., 1979-81. Bd. dirs., counsel Point O'Woods Assn., N.Y., 1976-91, v.p., 1982-91; alt. bd. dirs. Fire Island Assn., 1976-86, 92—; sec. and dir. Elderworks Found., 1982-92; dir. Episc. Evangelism Found., 1995—. Served with Air N.G. 1958-63. Mem. ABA, Internat. Bar Assn., N.Y. State Bar Assn., Assn. of Bar of City of N.Y., Church Club (trustee 1988-91), Down Town Assn. Club, Williams Club, Club at Point O'Woods (v.p., gov. 1970-79), Hillsboro Club. Republican. Home: 530 E 86th St Apt 11C New York NY 10028-7535 Office: c/o Winston & Strawn 175 Water St New York NY 10038-4918

WEIR, PETER LINDSAY, film director; b. June 21, 1944, Sydney; s. Lindsay Weir and Peggy Barnsley; m. Wendy Stites, 1966; 2 children. Ed. Scots Coll., Sydney, Vaucluse Boys High Sch., Sydney. Worked in real estate until 1965; worked as stagehand in TV, Sydney, 1967; dir. film sequences in variety show, 1968; dir. amateur univ. revs., 1967-69; dir. for Film Australia, 1969-73; made own short films, 1969-73, ind. feature film producer, dir. and writer, 1973—. Films include: Cars that Ate Paris, 1973, Picnic at Hanging Rock, 1975, The Last Wave, 1977, The Plumber (TV), 1978, Gallipoli, 1980, The Year of Living Dangerously, 1982, Witness, 1985, The Mosquito Coast, 1986, Dead Poets Society, 1989, Green Card, 1990, Fearless, 1993. Mem. Australia A.M. Recipient various film awards. Office: CAA care John Ptak 9830 Wilshire Blvd Beverly Hills CA 90212

WEIR, ROBERT MCCOLLOCH, history educator; b. Phila., Aug. 26, 1933; s. Horace McColloch and Helen (Gillette) W.; m. Anne Highstree, Jan. 28, 1955; children: Carol Anne-Elisabeth, Suzanne Helen. BA, Pa. State U., 1958; MA, Western Res. U., 1961, PhD, 1966. Instr. history U. Houston, 1965-66, asst. prof., 1966-67; asst. prof. U. S.C., Columbia, 1967-

70, assoc. prof., 1970-78, prof., 1978—; vis. prof. U. Southampton (Eng.), 1988. Assoc. editor Am. Nat. Biography, Am. Coun. Learned Socs., 1990—; bd. editors Jour. So. History, 1982-85; author: Colonial South Carolina, A History, 1983, The Last of American Freemen, 1986; contbr. articles to profl. jours. With USNR, 1954-56. NEH fellow, 1967-68, summer fellow Huntington Libr., Sam Marino, Calif., 1982; NEH summer grantee, 1990; recipient South Eastern Am. Soc. for 18th Century Studies award. Mem. Am. Antiquarian Soc. (invited), So. Hist. Assn., Orgn. Am. Historians, Am. Hist. Assn., S.C. Hist. Assn. (pres. 1975-76), S.C. Hist. Soc. (editorial bd. 1983—). Democrat. Office: U SC History Dept Columbia SC 29208

WEIR, STEPHEN JAMES, financial executive; b. Calgary, Alta., Can., Mar. 22, 1940; s. Jack W. and Elizabeth T. (Speirs) W.; m. Janet R Suggitt, July 1961; children: James, Jennifer. C.A., U. Man., 1962; M.B.A., U. Western Ont., Can., 1967. Accountant Winnipeg, Man., 1957-63; mgr. credit and control 3M Co. of Can., London, Ont., 1963-65; asst. credit mgr. corporate credit Bank of Montreal, 1967-72; treas. Dominion Textile Inc., Montreal, 1972-77; compt., 1977-81; v.p. internat. divsn. Dominion Textile Inc., 1981-83, v.p. consumer div., 1983-84, v.p. ops. service, 1984-85, v.p. APP/IND div., 1985-87, v.p. fin. ops., 1987-88; v.p. fin. Telemedia Inc., Montreal, 1988-90, exec. v.p., chief fin. officer, 1990—. Mem. Can. Inst. Chartered Accountants, Financial Execs. Inst. Office: Telemedia Inc, 1411 Peel St, Montreal, PQ Canada H3A 1S5

WEIR, THOMAS CHARLES, banker; b. Sandwich, Ill., Oct. 18, 1933; s. Glendon V. and Eleanor (Hoge) W.; m. Angela Di Giovanni. Grad., Pacific Coast Banking Sch., U. Wash., 1966. Mgr. consumer loans Barnett Nat. Bank, Cocoa, Fla., 1955-58; with 1st Interstate Bank Ariz., 1958-79; head retail banking div. 1st Nat. Bank Ariz., various locations, 1974-79, exec. v.p., 1975-79; chmn., chief exec. officer Home Fed. Savs., Tucson, 1979-87; chmn. Ariz. Commerce Bank, 1987-88; pres. Tucson Resources, Inc., 1988-89; pres., chief exec. officer Tucson Electric Power Co., 1989-90; fin. cons. Tucson, 1990—; pres. WD Enterprises, Inc., 1994—, Dependable Personnel, Inc., 1994—; bd. dirs. Apollo Group, Inc.; pres. Dependable Nurses, Inc., 1994—. With AUS, 1953-55. Republican. Episcopalian. Clubs: Tucson Country, White Mountain Country.

WEIR, WILLIAM C., III, lighting manufacturing company executive; b. Orlando, Fla., Oct. 17, 1937. Grad. high sch., Orlando. Mail clk. Hughes Supply, Inc., Orlando, 1955-56; warehouse mgr., 1957-59, gen. oper. mgr., 1959-64, gen. mgr., 1964-72, v.p., gen. mgr., 1972-83, exec. v.p., 1983-90; ptnr. Accord Industries, Winter Park, Fla., 1990—; mem. nat. adv. coun. U.S. Small Bus. Adminstrn., 1986—; dir. Associated Gen. Contractors, 1970-72, Cen. Fla. Builders & Exchange, 1972-76, Associated Builders & Contractors, 1988—. Bd. dirs. Tri County Transp. Authority, 1985-90, Better Bus. Bur. Cen. Fla., 1985-90; chmn. Cen. Fla. Crime Line Program, 1986-89. Mem. Illuminating Engring. Soc. Republican. Methodist. Avocations: playing golf, fishing, photography. Office: Accord Industries 4001 Forsyth Rd Winter Park FL 32792-6814

WEIRICH, RICHARD DENIS, government official; b. Aurora, Ill. BS, U. Notre Dame, 1966; MBA, U. Chgo., 1968. Computer programmer/analyst Armour & Co., Chgo., 1966-68; software specialist NIMH, Washington, 1968-70; mgr. software support State of Ill., Springfield, 1970-73; dir. info. requirements U.S. Postal Svc., Washington, 1973-75; mgr. tech. support, 1975-80; dir. postal data ctr. U.S. Postal Svc., San Bruno, Calif., 1980-84; dir. comms. and tech. U.S. Postal Svc., Washington, 1984-88, asst. postmaster gen. tech. resources, 1988-89, asst. postmaster gen., v.p. info. systems, 1989—. Office: US Postal Svc Information Systems 475 L'Enfant Plz SW Washington DC 20260

WEIS, JOSEPH FRANCIS, JR., federal judge; b. Pitts., Mar. 12, 1923; s. Joseph Francis and Mary (Flaherty) W.; m. Margaret Horne, Dec. 27, 1958; children: Maureen, Joseph Francis, Christine. BA, Duquesne U., 1941-47; J.D., U. Pitts., 1950; LLD (hon.), Dickinson Coll., 1989. Bar: Pa. 1950. Individual practice law Pitts., 1950-68; judge Ct. Common Pleas, Allegheny County, Pa., 1968-70, U.S. Dist. Ct. (we. dist.) Pa., 1970-73, U.S. Ct. Appeals (3d cir.), Pitts., 1973—; lectr. trial procedures, 1965—; adj. prof. law U. Pitts., 1986—; chmn. Fed. Cts. Study Com., Jud. Conf. Com. on Experiment to Videotape Trial Proceedings within the 3rd Cir., Internat. Jud. Conf. the Joint Am.-Can. Appellate Judges Conf., Toronto, 1986, London, 1985, futurist subcom. bicentennial com. Ct. Common Pleas, Allegheny County, Pa., 1988; participant programs legal medicine, Rome, London; mem. Am.-Can. Legal Exchange, 1987. Contbr. articles to legal jours. Mem. Mental Health and Mental Retardation Bd., Allegheny County, 1970-73; mem. Leukemia Soc., 1970-73, Knights of Malta, Knights of Equity, Am. Legion, 4th Armored Div. Assn., Disabled Am. Vets., Cath. War Vets., Mil. Order of the World Wars; mem. bd. adminstrn. Cath. Diocese Pitts., 1971-83; trustee Forbes Hosp. System, Pitts., 1969-74. Capt. AUS, 1943-48. Decorated Bronze Star, Purple Heart with oak leaf cluster; recipient St. Thomas More award, 1971, Phillip Amram award, 1991, Edward J. Devitt Disting. Svc. to Justice award, 1993. Fellow Internat. Acad. Trial Lawyers (hon.), Am. Bar Found.; mem. ABA (chmn. appellate judges' conf. 1981-83), Pa. Bar Assn., Allegheny Bar Assn. (past v.p.), Acad. Trial Lawyers Allegheny County (past pres), Am. Judicature Soc., Jud. Conf. U.S. (chmn. civil rules com. 1986-87, com. on adminstrn. bankruptcy system 1983-87, subcom. on jud. improvements 1983-87, chmn. standing com. rules of practice and procedure 1988), Inst. Jud. Adminstrn., KC. Home: 225 Hillcrest Rd Pittsburgh PA 15238-2307 Office: US Ct Appeals 513 US PO & Courthouse 7th Grant St Pittsburgh PA 15219

WEIS, JUDITH SHULMAN, biology educator; b. N.Y.C., May 29, 1941; d. Saul B. and Pearl (Cooper) Shulman; m. Peddrick Weis; children: Jennifer, Eric. BA, Cornell U., 1962; MS, NYU, 1964, PhD, 1967. Faculty CUNY, 1964-67; asst. prof. Rutgers U., Newark, 1967-71, assoc. prof., 1971-76, prof., 1976—; Congl. sci. fellow U.S. Senate, Washington, 1983-84; mem. grant rev. panel NSF, Washington, 1976-82, program dir., 1988-90; mem. rev. panel EPA, 1984-92; vis. scientist EPA Lab., Gulf Breeze, Fla., 1992. Mem. marine bd. NAS, 1991—. Grantee NOAA, 1977—, N.J. EPA Rsch. 1978-79, 81-83, N.J. Marine Scis. Consortium Rsch., 1987—, NSF fellow, 1962-64. Mem. Am. Inst. for Biol. Scis. (bd. dirs. 1986-88, 89-91), Soc. Environ. Toxicology and Chemistry (bd. dirs. 1990-93), Estuarine Rsch. Fedn., Ecol. Soc. Am., NOW (pres. Essex County 1972), Sierra Club (bd. dirs. N.J. chpt. 1986-88). Avocations: choral singing, swimming, jogging. Office: Rutgers U Dept Biol Scis Newark NJ 07102

WEIS, KONRAD MAX, museum administrator, retired chemical company executive; b. Leipzig, Germany, Oct. 10, 1928; came to U.S., 1971, naturalized, 1985; s. Alfred and Margarete (Leipoldt) W.; m. Gisela Lueg, Aug. 3, 1956; children: Alfred, Bettina. PhD, U. Bonn, 1955. Joined Bayer AG, Leverkusen, Germany, 1956, mgmt./exec. positions, 1961-74; pres., CEO Mobay Corp. subs. Bayer AG, Pitts., 1974-81, pres., chmn., CEO, 1981-86; pres., CEO Bayer USA Inc., Pitts., 1986-91, ret., hon. chmn., 1991—; bd. dirs. Dravo Corp., Pitts., Michael Baker Corp., Pitts., Leipzip Trade Fair Corp., PNC Equity Mgmt. Corp. subs. PNC Bank, Pitts., Titan Pharms., Inc., San Francisco, Biol. Detection Sys., Pitts., Leipzig Gallerie for Contemporary Arts. Life trustee Carnegie-Mellon U., 1981—; life trustee, chmn. bd. dirs. The Carnegie, Pitts., 1984—; bd. dirs. Pitts. Symphony Soc., 1987-94; hon. consul of Germay in Pitts., 1978-88. Recipient Cultural award Pitts. Ctr. for Arts, 1987, Internat. Palladium medal Am. sect. Soc. de Chimie Indsl., 1981, Americanism award Anti-Defamation League, 1992; decorated Comdrs. Cross, Order of Merit of Germany, 1994. Mem. World Affairs Coun. Pitts. (dir. 1983—), Pitts. Golf Club, Rolling Rock Country Club Ligonier Pa., Fox Chapel Golf Club, Duquesne Club. Office: The Carnegie 4400 Forbes Ave Pittsburgh PA 15213-4080 also: Miles Inc 1 Mellon Ctr 500 Grant St Pittsburgh PA 15219-2502

WEIS, SIGFRIED, supermarket chain executive; b. 1916; married. BA, Yale U., 1938. With Weis Markets Inc., Sunbury, Pa., 1938—, v.p., treas., 1962, pres., 1962—, also dir. Office: Weis Markets Inc 1000 S 2nd St Sunbury PA 17801-3399

WEISBERG, D. KELLY, law educator; b. Pitts., Aug. 25, 1949; d. David and Ruth (Dysken) W.; m. George Blumenthal, Aug. 14, 1977; children: Aaron, Sarah. PhD, Brandeis U., 1976; JD, U. Calif., Berkeley, 1979. Bar: Calif. 1979. Asst. prof. Washington U., St. Louis, 1981-83; assoc. prof.

Hastings Coll. Law, St. Francisco, 1983-86, prof., 1986—; cons. ABA, Washington, Am. Justice Inst., Sacramento. Office: Hastings Coll of Law 200 Mcallister St San Francisco CA 94102

WEISBERG, HERBERT FRANK, political science educator; b. Mpls., Dec. 8, 1941; s. Nathan R. and Jean (Schlessinger) W.; m. Judith Ann Robinson, Dec. 16, 1979; 1 child, Bryan Bowen. BA, U. Minn., 1963; PhD, U. Mich., 1968. Asst. prof. polit. sci. U. Mich., Ann Arbor, 1967-73, assoc. prof. polit. sci., 1973-74; assoc. prof. polit. sci. Ohio State U., Columbus, 1974-77, prof. polit. sci., 1977—. Author: Central Tendency and Variation, 1992; co-author: Theory Building and Data Analysis, 1984, Controversies in Voting Behavior, 1984, 92, Classics in Voting Behavior, 1992; editor: Political Science: Science of Politics, 1985, Democracy's Feast: Elections in America, 1995; co-editor Am. Jour. Polit. Sci., 1979-82. Mem. Midwest Polit. Sci. Assn. (v.p. 1983-85), Am. Polit. Sci. Assn. (program chmn. 1983), Phi Beta Kappa, Pi Sigma Alpha, Phi Kappa Phi. Home: 742 Gatehouse Ln Columbus OH 43235-1732 Office: Ohio State U Dept Polit Sci Columbus OH 43210

WEISBERG, JONATHAN MARK, public relations executive; b. Troy, N.Y., Dec. 5, 1943; s. David G. and Elizabeth (Cohn) W.; m. Pamela Crowe, Apr. 30, 1972; children: Zoe, Amanda. BA, Syracuse U., 1965; MA, Newhouse Communications Ctr., Syracuse U., 1968. V.p. Harshe, Rotman & Druck, N.Y.C., 1972-74, Rowland Co., N.Y.C., 1974-76; exec. v.p. Richard Weiner Inc., N.Y.C., 1976-84; dir. consumer, med. device and nutritional communications Bristol-Myers Squibb Co., N.Y.C., dir. corp. comms., 1984—; dir. internat. pub. affairs Bristol-Myers Squibb Co., 1994—; cons. Interbank Card Assn., N.Y.C., 1972-74, Ky. Fried Chicken, Louisville, 1974-76, Cigar Assn. Am., Washington, 1984, Am. Soc. Journalists and Authors, N.Y.C., 1980-84, Belgian Endive Mktg. Bd., Brussels, 1982-84. Office: Bristol Myers Squibb Co 345 Park Ave New York NY 10154-0001

WEISBERG, LEONARD R., research and engineering executive, retired; b. N.Y.C., Oct. 17, 1929; s. Emanuel E. and Esther (Raynes) W.; m. Frances Simon, Mar. 23, 1980; children: Glenna Weisberg Andersen, Orren Weisberg Falk, Frances Weisberg Brookner. BA magna cum laude, Clark U., 1950; MA, Columbia U., 1952. Rsch. asst. Watson Labs. IBM, N.Y.C., 1953-55; with RCA Labs., Princeton, N.J., 1955-71; mem. tech. staff RCA Labs., 1955-66, head rsch. group, 1966-69, dir. semicondr. device rsch. lab., 1969-71; dir. materials tech. lab. Itek Corp., Lexington, Mass., 1972-74; v.p. dir. ctrl. rsch. lab. Itek Corp., 1974-75; dir. electronics tech U.S. Dept. Def., Washington, 1975-79; v.p. rsch. and engring. Honeywell Inc., Mpls., 1980-94, ret., 1994; mem. adv. group on electron devices U.S. Dept. Def.; bd. dirs. SubMicron Sys. Corp., XLI Corp. Contbr. articles to profl. jours. Fellow IEEE; mem. Am. Phys. Soc., Sigma Xi. Home: 1225 LaSalle Ave Apt 1407 Minneapolis MN 55403

WEISBERG, MORRIS L., retired lawyer; b. Phila., June 7, 1921; s. Alexander and Hilda (Lichtenstein) W.; m. Mildred Norma Lubich, July 7, 1948; children—Richard, James, John. B.A., U. Pa., 1943, LL.B. 1947; M.A., Yale U., 1944. Bar: Pa. 1950, U.S. Dist. Ct. (ea. dist.) Pa. 1950, U.S. Supreme Ct. 1962. Bigelow teaching fellow U. Chgo. Law Sch., 1947-48, Raymond grad. fellow, 1948-49; Gowen fellow U. Pa. Law Sch., Phila., 1948-49; ptnr. Harry Norman Ball, Phila., 1950-56; assoc. Blank, Rome, Comisky & McCauley, and predecessor, Phila., 1956-60, ptnr., 1960-93; permanent mem. Jud. Conf. 3d Cir. Fellow Am. Bar Found.; mem. Order of Coif, Phi Beta Kappa Assocs. Office: Blank Rome Comisky & McCauley 4 Penn Center Plz Philadelphia PA 19103-2521

WEISBERG, RUTH MAXINE, radio reporter, television talk show host; b. Phila., May 31, 1956; d. William and Libby (Magness W.; 1 child, Talia Genevieve. BS in Spl. Edn. with honors, Pa. State U., 1977. Reporter Shadow Traffic Network, Phila., 1978-82; news dir., morning anchor Sta. WIFI-FM, Phila., 1982-83; features editor Sta. WPEN, Phila., 1983-85; arts and entertainment editor Sta. WSNI-FM, Phila., 1985-88; TV, radio talk show host CBS, Phila., 1988—; ind. filmmaker, voice over narrator. Nat. corr., contb. editor Single Mother mag. Miss Am. Pageant scholar, 1980; recipient Radio Features awards Phila. Press Assn., 1983, AP, 1983, Women in Comm., 1984. Mem. Internat. TV Assn. (contbg. editor monthly newsletter Phila. 1982—, Video Craft award for voiceover narration 1992, Mem. of Yr. 1994), Nat. Orgn. Single Mothers, Inc. Avocations: bodybuilding, piano, juggling, ice skating. Home: 37 Sabine Ave Narberth PA 19072-1740 Office: PO Box 903 Narberth PA 19072

WEISBERG, STUART ELLIOT, federal official, lawyer; b. Bklyn., Feb. 2, 1949; s. Julius and Esther Weisberg; m. Elizabeth Jane Kraichardt, June 24, 1979; children: Andrew Jonathan, Eric Nathaniel. BA, Brandeis U., 1971; JD, U. Pa., 1974. Bar: N.Y. 1976, D.C. 1976, U.S. Ct. Appeals (9th cir.) 1976, U.S. Supreme Ct. 1979. Assoc. NLRB, Washington, 1975-84; staff dir., counsel employment and housing subcom. U.S. Ho. of Reps., Washington, 1984-93; now chmn. Occupational Safety and Health Review Commission, Washington. Democrat. Jewish. Avocations: basketball, tennis. Office: Occupational Safety and Health Review Commission 1120 20th St NW Washington DC 20036

WEISBERGER, BARBARA, choreographer, artistic director, educator; b. Bklyn., Feb. 28, 1926; d. Herman and Sally (Goldstein) Linshes; m. Sol Spiller, Sept. 3, 1945 (div. 1948); m. Ernest Weisberger, Nov. 15, 1949; children: Wendy, Steven. B.S. in Edn., Psychology, Pa. State U., 1945; L.H.D. (hon.), Swarthmore Coll., 1970; D.F.A. (hon.), Temple U., 1973, Kings Coll., 1978, Villanova U., 1978. Founder, dir., tchr. Wilkes-Barre (Pa.) Ballet Theater, 1953-63; founder, dir. Pa. Ballet, Phila., 1962-82, Carlisle (Pa.) Project, 1984—; vice chmn. dance panel Nat. Endowment for the Arts, Washington, 1975-79. Performed with Met. Opera Ballet, N.Y.C., 1937, 38, Mary Binney Montgomery Co., Phila., 1940-42, ballet mistress, choreographer, Ballet Co. of Phila. Lyric Opera, 1961-62; ; choreographic works include Italian Concerto, Bach, Symphonic Variations, Franck; also operas for, Phila. Lyric Opera Co. Named Disting. Dau. of Pa., 1972, Disting. Alumna, Pa. State U., 1972; recipient 46th ann. Gimbel Phila. award, 1978. Mem. Psi Chi. Office: 571 Charles Ave Kingston PA 18704-4711 also: Carlisle Project PO Box 724 Carlisle PA 17013-3212

WEISBERGER, JOSEPH ROBERT, chief state supreme court justice; b. Providence, Aug. 3, 1920; s. Samuel Joseph and Ann Elizabeth (Meighan) W.; m. Sylvia Blanche Pigeon, June 9, 1951; children: Joseph Robert, Paula Ann, Judith Marie. AB, Brown U., 1942; JD, Harvard U., 1949; LLD, R.I. Coll., Suffolk U., St. Joseph Coll.; DCL, Providence Coll.; DHL, Bryant Coll.; LLD, Roger Williams Coll., 1992, Brown U., 1992. Bar: Mass. 1949, R.I. 1950. With Quinn & Quinn, Providence, 1951-56; solicitor Glocester, R.I., 1953-56; judge R.I. Superior Ct., Providence, 1956-72, presiding justice, 1972-78, chief justice, 1993—; adj. prof. U. Nev., 1986—; mem. faculty Nat. Jud. Coll.; vis. lectr. Providence Coll., Suffolk Law Sch., Roger Williams Coll.; Chmn. New Eng. Regional Conf. Trial Judges, 1962, 63, 65; chmn. New Eng. Regional Commn. Disordered Offender, 1968-71, R.I. Com. Adoption on Rules Criminal Procedure, 1968-72, chmn. of R.I. Adv. Com. Corrections, 1973, Nat. Conf. State Trial Judges ABA, 1977-78; exec. com. Appelate Judges Conf. ABA, 1979—; vice chmn., 1983-85, chmn., 1985-86; bd. dirs. Nat. Ctr. for State Cts., 1975-81. Chmn. editorial bd. Judges Jour., 1973-75. Pres. R.I. Health Facilities Planning Coun., 1967-70; chmn. Gov. R.I. Coun. Mental Health, 1968-73; moderator Town of East Providence, 1954-56; mem. R.I. Senate, 1953-56, minority leader, 1955-56; vice chmn. bd. trustee R.I. Hosp., 1968-92, St. Joseph's Hosp., trustee, 1962—. Lt. comdr. USNR, 1941-46. Recipient Erwin Griswold award Nat. Jud. Coll., 1989; named to R.I. Hall of Fame; Paul Harris fellow Rotary Internat. Fellow Am. Bar Found.; mem. ABA (ho. of dels., task force on criminal justice stds. 1977-79), R.I. Bar Assn., Am. Judges Assn. (gov.), Inst. Jud. Adminstrn., Am. Judicature Soc. (Herbert Harley award 1990), Am. Law Inst., Phi Beta Kappa (past pres. Alpha chpt. Brown U.), K.C. Order of St. Gregory (knight comdr. with star 1989). Home: 60 Winthrop St Riverside RI 02915-2624 Office: RI Supreme Ct 250 Benefit St Providence RI 02903-2719 *My professional life for the last 40 years has been occupied with judicial duties. I have been blessed with the opportunity to meet ever changing challenges and to attempt to solve a myriad of problems. These opportunities have been rewarding and absorbing. I consider judicial work to be a great privilege.*

WEISBIN, CHARLES RICHARD, nuclear engineer; b. Bklyn., Jan. 4, 1944; s. Alma (Schwartz) Lovitt; m. Alison Norma Weisbin, June 20, 1964; children: Daniel Mark, Amy Gayle. MS in Nuclear Engring., Columbia U., 1965, DSc in Nuclear Engring., 1969. Group leader Oak Ridge (Tenn.) Nat. Lab., 1977-80, section head, 1980-89, dir. Ctr. for Engring. Systems Advanced Rsch., 1982-89, dir. robotics and intelligence systems, 1986-89; mgr. telerobotics tech. Jet Propulsion Lab., Pasadena, Calif., 1991-92, mgr. robotic systems and advanced computer tech. sect., 1989-93; mgr. rover and telerobotic tech., 1993-95, mgr. robotics and Mars exploration tech., 1995—; mem. joint tech. panel on robotics DOD Joint Dirs. Labs., 1986-89; assoc. prof. computer sci. U. Tenn., Knoxville, 1984-89; program chmn. 2nd Internat. Conf. on Artificial Intelligence, IEEE Computer Soc., 1985; co-chmn. U.S. NASA Telerobotics Working Group, robotics and telepresence Space Tech. Interagency Group, 1992—. Author: Sensitivity and Uncertainty Analysis of Reactor Performance Parameters, 1982; mem. editorial bd. Applied Intelligence, 1990-95; contbr. articles to profl. jours. Recipient NASA Exceptional Svc. medal, 1993. Mem. IEEE (Cert. Appreciation 1987), Am. Nuclear Soc. (program chmn. 1977-79), Robotics and Automation Soc., Sigma Chi, Tau Beta Pi. Republican. Jewish. Achievements include initiation of robotics and intelligent systems at Oak Ridge; rsch. on sensitivity analysis, non-destructive assay of spent nuclear fuel, supervised inspection, and emergency response robotics. Home: 775 Starlight Heights Dr La Canada Flintridge CA 91011-1854 Office: Jet Propulsion Lab 4800 Oak Grove Dr Pasadena CA 91109-8001

WEISBROD, CARL BARRY, lawyer, public official; b. N.Y.C., Oct. 5, 1944; s. Walter and Hilda (Pelzer) W.; m. Jody Adams, Jan. 21, 1979; 1 child, William. BS, Cornell U., 1965; JD, NYU, 1968. Bar: N.Y., 1968; U.S. Dist. Ct. (so. dist.) N.Y., 1969. asst comml. N.Y.C. Housing Dept., 1970-72; counsel, chief exec. officer Wildcat Svc. Corp., N.Y.C., 1972-77; gen. counsel Manpower Demonstration Rsch. Corp., N.Y.C., 1977-78; dir. Mayor's Office of Midtown Enforcement, N.Y.C., 1978-84; exec. dir. City Vol. Corps, N.Y.C., 1984-86, N.Y.C. Planning Commn., 1986-87; pres. 42d St. Devel. Project, N.Y.C., 1987-90; pres., chief exec. officer N.Y.C. Econ. Devel. Corp., 1990-94; pres. Alliance for Downtown N.Y., 1995—; chmn. N.Y.C. Loft Bd., 1982-84. Contbr. articles to profl. jours. Office: 120 Broadway New York NY 10271

WEISBUCH, ROBERT ALAN, English educator; b. Rochester, N.Y., Nov. 22, 1946; s. Irving Arthur and Ferne (Paull) W.; m. Susan Ann Remington, July 23, 1972 (div. 1979); 1 child, Max; m. Louise Wicks Freymann, Aug. 6, 1983 (div. 1994); children: Sarah, Michael. BA magna cum laude, Wesleyan U., Middletown, Conn., 1968; MPhil in English, Yale U., 1970, PhD in English, 1972. Asst. prof. English U. Mich., Ann Arbor, 1972-76, assoc. prof., 1976-85, prof., 1985—, assoc. chmn. dept. English, 1981-84, chmn., 1987-94, assoc. prof. rsch., assoc. dean faculty programs Racnhar Sch. Grad. Studies, 1994—; assoc. prof. Bread Loaf Sch. English, Middlebury, Vt., 1980, 84. Author: Emily Dickinson's Poetry, 1975, Atlantic Double-Cross, 1986; radio columnist Ann Arbor News, 1984-87. Am. Coun. Learned Socs. fellow, 1976-77, Rackham fellow, U. Mich., 1983; recipient Amoco teaching award U. Mich., 1986. Mem. MLA, Emily Dickinson Soc. (bd. dirs. 1987—), Phi Beta Kappa. Democrat. Avocations: radio, baseball, automobiles. Office: U Mich Dept English 7601 Haven Hall Ann Arbor MI 48109

WEISBURGER, ELIZABETH KREISER, retired chemist, editor; b. Greenlane, Pa., Apr. 9, 1924; d. Raymond Samuel and Amy Elizabeth (Snavely) Kreiser; m. John H. Weisburger, Apr. 7, 1947 (div. May 1974); children: William Raymond, Diane Susan, Andrew John. BS, Lebanon Valley Coll., Annville, Pa., 1944, DSc (hon.), 1989; PhD, U. Cin., 1947, DSc (hon.), 1981. Rsch. assoc. U. Cin., 1947-49; col. USPHS, 1951-89; postdoctoral fellow Nat. Cancer Inst., Bethesda, Md., 1949-51, chemist, 1951-73, chief carcinogen metabolism and toxicology br., 1972-75, chief Lab. Carcinogen Metabolism, 1975-81, asst. dir. chem. carcinogenesis, 1981-89, ret.; cons. in field; lectr. Found. for Advanced Edn. in Scis., Bethesda, 1980-95; adj. prof. Am. U., Washington, 1982—. Asst. editor-in-chief Jour. Nat. Cancer Inst., 1971-87; mem. editl. adv. bd. Environ. Health Perspectives, 1993—; mem. editl. bd. Chem. Health and Safety, 1994—; contbr. articles to profl. jours. Trustee Lebanon Valley Coll., 1970—, pres. bd. trustees, 1985-89. Recipient Meritorious Svc. medal USPHS, 1973, Disting. Svc. medal, 1985; Hillebrand prize Chem. Soc. Washington, 1981. Fellow AAAS (nominating com. 1978-81); mem. Am. Chem. Soc. (Garvan medal 1981), Am. Assn. Cancer Research, Soc. Toxicology, Am. Soc. Biochem. and Molecular Biology, Royal Soc. Chemistry, Am. Conf. Govtl. Indsl. Hygienists, Grad. Women in Sci. (hon.), Iota Sigma Pi (hon.). Lutheran.

WEISBURGER, JOHN HANS, medical researcher; b. Stuttgart, Germany, Sept. 15, 1921; came to U.S., 1943, naturalized, 1944; s. William and Selma (Barth) W.; children: William, Diane, Andrew. AB, U. Cin., 1947, MS, 1948, PhD, 1949; MD (hon.), U. Umeå, Sweden, 1980. Mem. staff Nat. Cancer Inst., NIH, Bethesda, Md., 1950-61, head carcinogen screening sect., 1961-72; dir. bioassay segment, Carcinogenesis Programs Nat. Cancer Inst., Bethesda, Md., 1971-72; v.p. rsch. Am. Health Found., Valhalla, N.Y., 1972-87; dir. Naylor Dana Inst. for Disease Prevention, Valhalla, 1972-87, dir. emeritus, sr. mem., 1987—; rsch. prof. pathology N.Y. Med. Coll., Valhalla, 1974—; pres. Weisburger Assocs., North White Plains, N.Y., 1987—; mem. biochemistry and nutrition study sect. NIH, 1957-58; mem. interdepartmental panel on carcinogens FDA, USDA, USPHS, 1962-71; chmn. subcom. Nat. Cancer Program Strategic Plan, 1971-74, chmn. carcinogenesis subcom. Nat. Large Bowel Cancer Project, 1972-75; chmn. subcom. positive controls NAS-NRC Conf. on Carcinogen Testing of New Drugs, 1973; mem. expert panel on nitrites and nitrosamines USDA, 1973-77; chmn. Workshop Colorectal Cancer, Unio Internat. Contra Cancrum, Geneva, 1975; mem. Nat. Cancer Inst. Clearinghouse on Environ. Carcinogens, 1976-78; program chmn. Toxicology Forum, 1977; co-chmn. organizing com. U.S.-Japan Coop. Workshop on GI Tract Cancer, 1979, Internat. Workshop on Nutrition and Cancer, 1982, Workshop on Dietary Fats and Fiber in Human Cancer, 1986; chmn. symposium on large bowel cancer 7th congress OMGE, 1982; chmn. symposium on natural carcinogens in human cancer devel. Unio Internat. Contra Cancrum, 1982; mem. program com. Internat. Congress of Toxicology III, 1982-83; mem. panel on irritants and vesicants Commn. on Life Scis., NRC, NAS, 1983; mem. cancer edn. com. N.Y. Med. Coll., 1983-88; bd. dirs., co-chmn. profl. edn. com. Westchester div. Am. Cancer Soc., 1983-89; mem. pancreas cancer working group, organ systems program Nat. Cancer Inst., 1985-86; mem. sci. adv. bd. Am. Water Works Assn., 1988; chmn. sci. rev. panel N.J. State Commn. Cancer Rsch., 1988-90; chmn. nutrition and cancer sect. 15th meeting Unio Internt. Contra Cancrum, Hamburg, Fed. Republic Germany, 1990; chmn. internat. discussion group Belgian Soc. Psychosocial Aspects of Cancer, Brussels, 1990; internat. lectr. on nutrition and cancer prevention, S.E. Asia, 1991; co-chmn. internat. symposium on health effects of tea, N.Y., 1991; chmn. nutrition and cancer sect. 3d anticarcinogenesis and antimutagenesis conf., Italy, 1991; chmn. study sect. NIH-Nat. Cancer Inst., Bethesda, Md., 1991; co-chmn. mechanisms nutrition cancer European Sch. Oncology, Venice, Italy, 1992; rsch. fellow Japanese Found. for Promotion of Cancer Rsch. Nat. Cancer Ctr. Rsch. Inst. Tokyo, 1992; advisor com. rev. RDA Food and Nutrition Bd. NAS, 1993; lectr. German Acad. Nutritional Medicine, Freiburg, 1994. Assoc. editor Jour. Nat. Cancer Inst., 1960-62, Xenobiotica, 1971—, Archives of Toxicology, 1977-87, Jour. Am. Coll. Toxicology, 1982—, preventive Medicine, 1988—; mem. internat. editl. adv. bd. Food and Chem. Toxicology, 1967—; assoc. editor Cancer Rsch., 1969-80, mem. cover editl. bd., 1987—; mem. editl. bd. Chemico-Biol. Interactions, 1969-88, Carcinogenesis, 1979-87, Inst. Sci. Info. Atlas of Sci., 1987-89, Cancer Epidemiology Biomarkers Prevention, 1991—, Cancer Detetion Prevention, 1994—; mem. guest editl. bd. Japanese Jour. Cancer Rsch., 1987—. With AUS, 1944-46; col. USPHS, 1950-72. Decorated D.S.M., 1964; recipient Meritorious Svc. medal USPHS HEW, 1970, Outstanding Service award Westchester div. Am. Cancer Soc., 1984, Meyer and Anna Prentis award Mich. Cancer Ctr., 1987; named one of 1000 most cited scientists, ISI List, 1981. Leadership plaque N.J. State Commn. Cancer Rsch., 1990. Fellow N.Y. Acad. Scis., Am. Coll. Nutrition; mem. Am. Assn. Cancer Rsch. (rep. to European Assn. Cancer Rsch. 1985-89), Am. Chem. Soc. (com. environ. improvement 1992—), astroent. Assn., Am. Conf. Govt. Indsl. Hygenists, Am. Soc. Biochem. Molecular Biologists, Am. Soc. Pharmacology and Exptl. Therapeutics, Am. Soc. Preventive Oncology (founding mem., bd. dirs. 1983-90, Disting. Svc. award 1990), Biochem. Soc. (London, emeritus), Environ. Mutagen Soc., European Assn. Cancer Rsch. (coun. 1985-90), Japan Cancer Assn. (hon.

life), Soc. Exptl. Biol. Medicine, Soc. Toxicology (chmn. bd. publs. 1968-71, councilor 1972-74, amb. toxicology Mid-Atlantic div. 1990, Award of Merit 1981), Sigma Xi, Alpha Chi Sigma (pres. Washington profl. chpt. 1967-68), Phi Lambda Upsilon. Home: 4 Whitewood Rd White Plains NY 10603-1137 Office: Am Health Found Naylor Dana Inst Valhalla NY 10595-1599 *In my lifetime a revolutionary change occurred in our knowledge of the causes and the mechanisms involved in the major premature killing diseases—heart disease, hypertension, stroke, many forms of cancer. These key advances stemmed from the partnership between the federal government, public-supported societies and academic institutions that encourage health research. The impact of these diseases can be reduced in virtually all countries of the world provided their political bodies can agree that peaceful endeavors and cooperation in fostering better health for their people can be made a high priority goal. Medical science now can implement successful prevention efforts. I am glad I have lived through this period and have played a role in this development.*

WEISE, CHARLES MARTIN, zoology educator; b. Bridgeville, Pa., July 8, 1926; s. Louis August and Alice (Martin) W.; m. Joan C. Spencer, July 18, 1951; children—Patricia, Carla, Christopher, Charles, Robert. B.S., Ohio U., 1950; M.S., U. Ill., 1951; Ph.D., 1956. Asst. prof. biology Fisk U., Nashville, 1953-56; asst. prof. zoology U. Wis., Milw., 1956-60, assoc. prof., 1960-66, prof., 1966—, chmn. dept. zoology, 1961-64, 78-84, chmn. dept. biol. scis., 1989-94. Served with USMCR, 1945-46. Mem. Am., Brit. ornithologists unions, Wis. Soc. Ornithology, Am. Soc. Zoologists, Phi Beta Kappa. Research physiology of bird migration, population ecology of vertebrates. Home: 2314 E Stratford Ct Milwaukee WI 53211-2630 Office: U Wis Dept Biol Sci Milwaukee WI 53201

WEISE, FRANK EARL, III, food products company executive; b. Williamsport, Pa., July 30, 1944; s. Frank E. and Marian (Hagerman) W.; m. Deborah Dunstan; children: Frank E. IV, Alison S. BA in Econs., Lehigh U., 1966, MS in Bus. Econs., 1967. Various fin. mgmt. Procter & Gamble Co., Cin., 1967-79, comptr., CFO health and personal care div., 1983-86, dir. pers. and fin., 1986-88, comptr., CFO food and beverages div., 1988-91; fin. dir., CFO Procter & Gamble Benelux, Brussels, 1979-83; sr. v.p. fin., CFO Campbell Soup Co., Camden, N.J., 1992—. Mem. Fin. Execs. Inst., Cin. Country Club, Merion Golf Club (Ardmore, Pa.). Republican. Avocations: golf, tennis. Office: Campbell Soup Co Campbell Pl Camden NJ 08101

WEISE, GEORGE J., commissioner; b. Scranton, Pa., Mar. 3, 1949; s. George Franklin and Rita Marie W.; m. Therese Lee Palmer, Oct. 20, 1984; children: Michelle Lyddane, Melissa Anne. BS, U. Md., 1971, JD with honors, 1975; MBA with honors, George Washington U., 1983. Bar: Md. 1975, Ct. Internat. Trade 1984. Import specialist U.S. Customs Svc., Dept. Treasury, Washington, 1972-75, commr., 1993—; atty. U.S. Internat. Trade Commn., Washington, 1975-83, IBM Corp., 1983-84; profl. staff mem. Subcom. on Trade, Ho. of Reps. Ways and Means Com., Washington, 1984-89, staff dir., 1989-93. Office: US Customs Svc Dept Treasury 1301 Constitution Ave NW Washington DC 20229

WEISE, RICHARD HENRY, lawyer, corporate executive; b. Davenport, Iowa, Apr. 5, 1935; s. F. Roe and Jane (Neiger) W.; m. Virginia Armstrong, Aug. 25, 1956; children: Kimberley, Steven, Richard. B.A., DePauw U., 1956; J.D., Northwestern and DePaul U., 1961. Bar: Ill. 1961. Cons. Standard Oil, 1958-61; atty. E.J. Brach & Sons, Chgo., 1961-65; div. counsel Kraft Co., Chgo., 1965-68; various positions law dept. Motorola, Schaumburg, Ill., 1968-77, v.p., gen. counsel, sec., 1977-85; sr. v.p., gen. counsel, sec. Motorola Inc., Schaumburg, Ill., 1985—; lectr. ITT Kent Coll., Chgo., 1982-83; adj. lectr. Loyola U. Law Sch., Chgo., Fla. Bar Edn.; pres. 1550 Corp. Mem. ABA, Ill. Bar Assn., Chgo Bar Assn. Republican. Episcopalian. Club: Meadow (Roselle, Ill.). Office: Motorola Inc 1303 E Algonquin Rd Schaumburg IL 60196

WEISE, THEODORE LEWIS, delivery service executive; b. Marion, Ohio, Apr. 14, 1944; s. Rudolph F.J. and Francis (Maxwell) W.; m. Sharon Linda Huffman, June 21, 1969; children: Chet Dale, Tessa Brooke. BSEE, U. Mo.-Rolla, 1967; MBA, U. West Fla., 1971. V.p. ops. Sun Airlines, Memphis, 1967-69; flight test engr. Gen. Dynamics Corp., Ft. Walton Beach, Fla., 1969-71; various mgmt. pos. Fed. Express Corp., Memphis, 1972-76, v.p. ops. planning, 1976-80, sr. v.p. ops. planning, 1980-82, sr. v.p. bus. service ctrs., 1982-85, sr. v.p. cen. support services, 1985-87, sr. v.p. domestic ground ops., 1987—. Mem. bldg. com. Farmington Presbyn. Ch., Germantown, Tenn., 1986—; pres., bd. dirs. Jr. Achievement, Memphis, 1979—. Mem. Kappa Alpha. Republican.

WEISENBURGER, RANDALL, company executive; b. 1958. With Coopers & Lybrand, 1980-85, First Boston Corp., 1987-88; mng. dir. Wasserstein Perella & Co., 1988—; CEO Wickes Mfg. Co., Inc., Southfield, Mich., 1990-93; vice chmn. Collins & Aikman, Maybelline, Inc.; chmn. Yardley of London. Office: Wasserstein Perella & Co 31 W 52nd St New York NY 10019

WEISER, MARK DAVID, computer scientist, researcher; b. Chgo., July 23, 1952; s. David Warren and Audra Laverne (Hunsaker) W.; m. Victoria Ann Reich, Dec. 16, 1976; children: Nicole Reich-Weiser, Corinne Reich-Weiser. Student, New Coll., Sarasota, Fla., 1969-71; MS, U. Mich., 1976, PhD, 1979. V.p. Cerberus Video, Ann Arbor, Mich., 1972-75; programmer Omnitext, Ann Arbor, Mich., 1971-76; project leader MIS, Romulus, Mich., 1975-76; from asst. to assoc. prof. computer sci. U. Md., College Park, 1979-87; prin. scientist Xerox Palo Alto (Calif.) Rsch. Ctr., 1987—, lab. mgr., 1988—; founder Cerberus Video, Ann Arbor, 1972-75. Contbr. over 70 articles to profl. jours. Mem. IEEE, AAAS, Assn. for Computing Machinery. Avocations: existential philosophy, Go, drummer for rock band Severe Tire Damage. Office: Xerox PARC Computer Sci Lab 3333 Coyote Hill Rd Palo Alto CA 94304-1314

WEISER, PAUL DAVID, manufacturing company executive; b. N.Y.C., May 30, 1936; s. Irving Julius and Rose (Peckerman) W.; m. Paula Lee Block, June 19, 1960; children: Amy Helen, Deborah Susan. B.S. in Metallurgy, M.I.T., 1959; LL.B. (editor law rev.), U. Calif., Berkeley, 1963. Bar: Calif. 1963. Assoc. firm Mitchell, Silberberg & Knupp, Los Angeles, 1963-68; with Dataproducts Corp., Woodland Hills, Calif., 1968—; sec., gen. counsel Dataproducts Corp., 1968—, sr. v.p., 1980—; chmn. adv. com. shareholder communications SEC, 1981. Contbr. articles legal publns. Served with USAR, 1959-60. Mem. Am. Bar Assn., Am. Soc. Corp. Secs. Jewish. Office: 6219 De Soto Ave Woodland Hills CA 91367-2602

WEISER, RALPH RAPHAEL, recovery company executive; b. N.Y.C., May 25, 1925; children: Jane, Jeffrey. BA, NYU, 1947; JSD, Harvard U., 1950. Bar: N.Y. 1950. Ptnr. Lotterman & Weiser, Esq., N.Y.C., 1955-64; pres. Dragor Shipping Inc., N.Y.C., 1964-65; chmn. Nat. Equipment Rental, N.Y.C., 1965-67; exec. v.p. Am. Export Industries, N.Y.C., 1967-69; pvt. practice investment, 1970-84; chmn. Internat. Recovery Corp. (N.Y. Stock Exch.), Miami, Fla., 1984—. Sgt. USAAF, 1943-45, PTO. Office: Internat Recovery Corp 700 S Royal Poinciana Blvd Miami FL 33166-6600

WEISER, SHERWOOD MANUEL, hotel and corporation executive, lawyer; b. Cleve., Mar. 9, 1931; s. Aaron A. and Helen (Scheiner) W.; m. Judith A. Zirkin, July 31, 1955; children: Douglas J., Warren P., Bradley A. BS, Ohio State U., 1952; LLB, Case Western Res. U., 1955. Bar: Ohio 1955. Ptnr. Weiser & Weiser, Attys., Cleve., 1955-65, Weiser & Lefton, Attys., Cleve., 1965-69; chmn., chief exec. officer TCC, Miami, Fla., 1970—; bd. dirs. United Nat. Bank, Miami, Carnival Cruise Lines, Miami. Trustee Fla. Internat. U. Found., Miami, 1984-94, U. Miami, 1988—, New World Symphony, Miami, 1987—; trustee, chmn. bd. Ransom-Everglades Sch., Miami, 1974-84; co-chmn. bd. advisors Coconut Grove Playhouse, 1986—. Mem. Am. Hotel and Motel Assn., Cleve. Bar Assn., Soc. of Benchers, Order of Coif. Jewish. Avocations: tennis, sailing, art. Office: TCC 3250 Mary St Miami FL 33133

WEISFELDT, MYRON LEE, physician, educator; b. Milw., Apr. 25, 1940; s. Simon Charles and Sophia (Price) W.; m. Linda Nan Zaremski, Dec. 29, 1963; children—Ellyn Joy, Lisa Janel, Sara Michelle. Student, Northwestern U., 1958-60; BA, Johns Hopkins U., 1962, MD, 1965. Intern and resident

Columbia-Presbyn. Med. Ctr., N.Y.C., 1965-67; fellow in cardiology Mass. Gen. Hosp., Boston, 1970-72; asst. prof. medicine Johns Hopkins U., Balt., 1972-78, prof. medicine, 1978-91, Robert L. Levy prof. cardiology, 1979-91; Samuel Bard prof. medicine, chair dept. Columbia-Presbyn. Med. Ctr., N.Y.C., 1991—; dir. cardiology Johns Hopkins Med. Inst., Balt., 1975-91, Peter Belfer Lab. for Johns Hopkins, Ischemic Heart Disease Spl. Ctr. Rsch., 1977-91; nat. pres. Am. Heart Assn., 1989-90; cardiology adv. com. Nat. Heart, Lung and Blood Inst., 1986-90, chmn., 1988-90. Editor: The Aging Heart, 1980; editorial bd. Jour. Clin. Investigation, 1984-88, Circulation, 1980-86, 88—; Jour. Am. Coll. Cardiology, 1987-93, Jour. Molecular and Cellular Cardiology, 1975-80, 86-89, Circulation Rsch., 1988-94. Served with USPHS, 1967-69. NIH grantee, 1977-91. Fellow AAAS; mem. Assn. Univ. Cardiologists, Am. Soc. Clin. Investigation, Assn. Am. Physicians, Assn. Prof. Medicine, Phi Beta Kappa, Alpha Omega Alpha, Interurban Clin. Club. Jewish. Home: 47 Havemeyer Rd Irvington NY 10533-2642 Office: Columbia Presbyn Med Ctr 630 W 168th St New York NY 10032-3702

WEISGALL, HUGO DAVID, composer, conductor; b. Ivancice, Czechoslovakia, Oct. 13, 1912; came to U.S., 1920, naturalized, 1926; s. Adolph Joseph and Aranka (Stricker) W.; m. Nathalie Shulman, Dec. 28, 1942; children: Deborah, Jonathan. Student, Johns Hopkins, 1929-31, Ph.D., 1940; musical edn., Peabody Conservatory, Baltimore, 1927-30, Curtis Inst., Phila., 1936-39; studied composition with, Roger Sessions. Instr. composition Cummington Sch. Arts, 1948-51; instr. Julliard Sch. Music Arts, 1957-69; Disting. prof. composition Queens Coll., 1960-83; disting. vis. prof. Penn State U., 1959-60; disting. prof. Peabody Inst., Balt., 1974-75; chmn. faculty Sem. Coll. of Jewish Music, Jewish Theol. Sem. of Am.; pres. Am. Music Ctr., 1964-73; assoc. Lincoln Ctr. Fund, 1965-68; dir. Hilltop Mus. Co., Balt., 1951-54. Condr. Har Sinai Temple Choir, 1931-42, Y-Alliance Orch., 1935-42, Balt. String Symphony, 1936-38, Md. N.Y.A. Orch., 1940-41; guest condr. London Symphony, London Philharmonic, BBC Symphony orchs., Orchestre de la Chapelle Musicale de la Reine Elizabeth, Belgium, Radio National Belge, dir. Balt. Inst. Mus. Arts, 1949, composer in residence Am. Acad. in Rome, 1966-67, 84; composer Songs, 1929, Quest; ballet, 1937, One Thing Is Certain, ballet, 1939, Hymn for chorus and orch, 1941; Overture in F, 1942, Soldier Songs, 1944-45, Outpost, 1947; opera The Tenor, 1949-50, The Stronger, 1952, Three Symphonic Songs for high voice and orch, 1952, Six Characters in Search of an Author, 1956, Purgatory, 1958, Athaliah, 1963, Nine Rivers from Jordan, 1968; song cycle Fancies and Inventions, 1970, Translations, 1971, End of Summer, 1974; cantata for soprano, tenor, chorus and orch. Song of Celebration, 1976; (opera) Jenny or the Hundred Nights, 1976, The Golden Peacock, 1976; song cycle Liebeslieder, 1979; opera The Gardens of Adonis, 1981, Piano Sonata, 1982, Prospect, 1983, 4 Birthday Cards, 1983, Lyrical Interval, song cycle for low voice and piano, 1984, Tekiatot: Rituals for Rosh Hashannah for orch., 1985, Tangents, 4 episodes for flute and marimba, 1985, Arioso and Burlesca for cello and piano, 1983, Loves Wounded 2 songs for baritone and orch., 1986, opera Will You Marry Me?, 1987, opera Esther, 1992; Ditson Opera commn., Columbia, 1952, Koussevitzky commn., 1961, Psalm of the Distant Dove canticle for mezzo soprano and piano, 1992. Enlisted as pvt. AUS, 1942; asst. mil. attache to govts. in exile, London, later to Czechoslovakia cultural attache Am. embassy 1946-47, Prague. Awarded Bearns prize Columbia, 1931; traveling Curtis Inst., 1938; Ditson fellow Columbia, 1944; grantee Nat. Inst. Arts and Letters, 1952; Guggenheim fellow, 1955-56, 61-62, 66-67. Mem. Nat. Inst. Arts and Letters, Am. Acad.-Inst. Arts and Letters (pres. 1990—), Phi Beta Kappa. Home: 81 Maple Dr Great Neck NY 11021-1909 Office: Jewish Theol Sem Broadway & 122d St New York NY 10027

WEISGERBER, DAVID WENDELIN, editor, chemist; b. Delphos, Ohio, May 20, 1938; s. Hubert Louis and Catherine Margaret (Laudick) W.; m. Carole Ann Friemoth, Oct. 23, 1965; children: Jason, Erik. B.S. Bowling Green State U., 1960; Ph.D., U. Ill., 1965. Research chemist E.I. duPont de Nemours & Co., Inc., Deepwater, N.J., 1964-69; indexer Chem. Abstracts Service, Columbus, Ohio, 1969-73, asst. to editor, 1973-77, mgr. chem. substance handling, 1977-79, dir. editorial ops., 1979-82, editor, 1982—. Mem. Am. Chem. Soc., N.Y. Acad. Sci., Am. Soc. Info. Sci. Roman Catholic. Home: 6178 Middlebury Dr E Worthington OH 43085-3375 Office: PO Box 3012 Columbus OH 43210-0012

WEISGERBER, JOHN SYLVESTER, provincial legislator; b. Barrhead, Alta., Can., June 12, 1940; s. Sylvester and Eva (Kilshaw) Harrison; m. Judith Muriel Janke, June 30, 1961; children: Joanne, Pamela. BBA, N. Alta. Inst. Tech., 1962. Owner Carland Ltd., 1975-81; econ. devel. commr. Peace River-Liard Regional Dist., Dawson Creek, 1982-84; sales mgr. Timberline Pontiac Buick GMC Ltd., Dawson Creek, 1984-86; mem. legis. assembly Govt. of B.C. (Can.), Victoria, 1986—, parliamentary sec. to min. of state, 1987-88, min. of state for Nechako and N.E., 1988-89, min. native affairs, 1989—; chmn. Cabinet Com. on Native Affairs, Victoria, 1988-90; mem. Cabinet Com. on Sustainable Devel., Victoria, 1988-90; mem. Select Standing Com. of Forests and Lands, Victoria, 1988-90; mem. Select Standing Com. on Agr. and Fisheries, Victoria, 1988-90; interim leader B.C. Social Credit Party, 1992-93; leader Reform Party of B.C., 1995. Bd. dirs., pres. Dawson Creek and Dist. Fall Fair, 1980-86. Mem. Rotary (past pres.), Mile O Riding Club (bd. dirs., pres. 1976-81). Avocations: hunting, fishing, downhill skiing. Office: Parliament Bldgs, Rm 101, Victoria, BC Canada V8V 1X4

WEISHEIT, JON CARLETON, physicist, educator; b. Mt. Vernon, Wash., Oct. 10, 1944; s. O. George and Shirley Ann (Spickerman) W.; m. Janet Carolyn Lucas, Nov. 24, 1965; children: Krista Marie, Lara Elizabeth. BS, U. Tex., 1966; MS, Rice U., 1969, PhD, 1970. Rsch. fellow astronomy Harvard U., Cambridge, Mass., 1970-72; rsch. physicist Lawrence Livermore Nat. Lab., Livermore, Calif., 1972-79, assoc. div. leader physics, 1981-88; rsch. physicist, lectr. Princeton (N.J.) U., 1979-81; prof. space physics and astronomy Rice U., Houston, 1988—; dept. chmn. space physics and astronomy, 1992—; cons. Los Alamos (N.Mex.) Nat. Lab., 1988—, Lawrence Livermore Nat. Lab., 1988—; mem. adv. com. NRC, Washington, 1984-87. Author: (with others) Applied Atomic Collision Physics Vol. 2, 1984, Advances Atomic: Molecular Physics, 1989; contbr. approx 60 articles to profl. jours. Dir. swim meets AAU, Calif., 1975-79; mem. fellowship com. Hertz Found., Livermore, 1977-92. Recipient fellowship Dept. Defense, 1966-69, post-doctoral fellowship NSF, 1970. Fellow Am. Physical Soc.; mem. Am. Astron. Soc., Internat. Astron. Union. Achievements include patent related to tokamak plasma heating; comprehensive research on atomic processes in dense plasmas; role of Auger transitions in astrophysics; interpretation of quasar spectra; intense magnetic field phenomena. Office: Rice U PO Box 1892 Houston TX 77251-1892

WEISKITTEL, RALPH JOSEPH, real estate executive; b. Covington, Ky., Jan. 1, 1924; s. Nelson I. and Hilda (Nieman) W.; m. Audrey Bushelman, June 19, 1948; children—Thomas, Carol Anne, Barbara Jane. Eve. student, Xavier U., Cin., 1946-47. Mem. staff Cin. Enquirer, 1942-43, 45—, home sect. editor, 1958-63, bus. editor, 1963-77; v.p. corp. markets Koetzle Corp. (Realtors), 1977-79; v.p. Devitt and Assocs (Realtors), 1979-90; v.p. sales and mktg. Toebben Cos., 1990-91; sr. v.p. The Chelsea-Moore Co., 1991-94; v.p. sales Cline Realtors, 1994—. Mem. city council, Ft. Wright, Ky., 1960-68; mem. St. Agnes Parish Council, 1974-77; mem. bishop's adv. council Diocese of Covington. Served with AUS, 1943-46. Mem. Nat. Assn. Real Estate Editors, Soc. Am. Bus. Writers. Club: Cincinnati. Home: 1571 St Anthony Dr Covington KY 41011-3752 Office: The Federated Bldg 7 W 7th St Ste 1900 Cincinnati OH 45202

WEISMAN, IRVING, social worker, educator; b. N.Y.C., May 6, 1918; s. Max and Sadie (Berkowitz) W.; m. Cyrille Gold, May 1, 1941; children: Seth, Adam. B.S., CCNY, 1939; M.S., U. Buffalo, 1942; Ed.D., Columbia U., 1962. Cert. social worker N.Y. State. Caseworker Nat. Refugee Service, N.Y.C., 1941; warden's asst. Fed. Detention Hdqrs., Bur. Prisons, Dept. Justice, N.Y.C., 1942-43; mil. svc. psychiat. social worker to chief social worker VA, Camden and Union Cos., N.J., 1946-49; case supr. Altro Health and Rehab. Service, N.Y., 1949-50; field instr., lectr. Columbia U. Sch. Social Work, 1950-57, assoc. prof., 1957-62, prof., 1962-84, prof. emeritus, 1984, adj. prof., 1984, acting dean, 1964-65; assoc. dean Hunter Coll. Sch. Social Work, 1967-69; exec. officer doctoral program social work Grad. Ctr. CUNY, 1975-78; clin. practice William Alanson White Inst., 1976-79; vis.

prof. Sch. Social Work, Barry U., 1984-85; adj. prof. Sch. Social Work, San Diego State U., 1988—; UN adv. on social welfare to Ceylon Sri Lanka, 1963-64; sr. Simon research fellow U. Manchester (Eng.), 1970-71; cons. U.S. Office Juvenile Delinquency and Youth Devel., U.S. Children's Bur., NIMH, NIDA, HEW, N.Y.C. Dept. Personnel, Westchester County (N.Y.) Dept. Mental Health, Community Service Soc., Council Social Work Edn., Moblzn. for Youth, N.Y.C., Universidad Católica Madre y Maestra, Santo Domingo, Dominican Republic, 1983-84, United Jewish Appeal-Fedn. Jewish Philanthropies of N.Y.C., 1986-87, U. Puertorriqueña de los Antillas Aguadilla, P.R., 1993; condr. continuing edn. workshops, various univs. Contbr. articles to profl. jours., also monographs. Served with USAAF, 1943-46. HEW and HHS grantee, 1961-62, 64-76, 77-81. Mem. Nat. Assn. Social Workers. Home: 4612 Monongahela St San Diego CA 92117

WEISMAN, JOEL, nuclear engineering educator, engineering consultant; b. N.Y.C., July 15, 1928; s. Abraham and Ethel (Marcus) W.; m. Bernice Newman, Feb. 6, 1955; 1 child, Jay (dec.). B.Ch.E., CCNY, 1948; M.S., Columbia U., 1949; Ph.D., U. Pitts. 1968. Registered profl. engr. N.Y., Ohio. Plant engr. Etched Products, N.Y.C., 1950-51; from jr. engr. to assoc. engr. Brookhaven Nat. Lab., Upton, N.Y., 1951-54; from engr. to fellow engr. Westinghouse Nuclear Energy Systems, Pitts., 1954-59, from fellow engr. to mgr. thermal and hydraulic analysis, 1960-68; sr. engr. Nuclear Devel. Assocs., White Plains, N.Y., 1959-60; assoc. prof. nuclear engring. U. Cin., 1968-72, prof. nuclear engring., 1972—, dir. nuclear engring. program, 1977-86, dir. lab. basic and applied nuclear research, 1984-94. Co-author: Thermal Analysis of Pressurized Water Reactors, 1970, 2d edit., 1979, Introduction to Optimization Theory, 1973, Modern Power Plant Engineering, 1985; editor: Elements of Nuclear Reactor Design, 1977, 2d edit., 1983; contbr. tech. articles to profl. jours.; patentee in field. Mem. Cin. Environ. Adv. Council, 1976-78; mem. Cin. Asian Art Soc., 1977—, v.p., 1980-82, pres., 1982-84; mem. exec. bd. Air Pollution League Greater Cin., 1980-90. Sr. NATO fellow, Winfrith Lab., U.K. Atomic Energy Authority, 1972; sr. fellow Argonne Nat. Lab., Ill., 1982; NSF research grantee, 1974-78, 82-85, 86-89; recipient Dean's award U. Cin. Coll. Engring., 1987. Fellow Am. Nuclear Soc. (v.p. Pitts. sect. 1957-58, mem. exec. com. thermal-hydraulics div. 1989-92); mem. Am. Inst. Chem. Engrs., Sigma Xi. Democrat. Jewish. Avocation: Japanese art. Home: 3419 Manor Hill Dr Cincinnati OH 45220-1522 Office: U Cin Dept Mech Ind & Nuclear Engring Cincinnati OH 45221

WEISMAN, JOHN, author; b. N.Y.C., Aug. 1, 1942; s. Abner I. Weisman and Syde (Lubowe) Kremer; m. Susan Lee Povenmire, Feb. 12, 1983. AB, Bard Coll., 1964. Mng. editor Coast mag., Los Angeles, 1969-70; staff writer Rolling Stone, San Francisco, 1971, Detroit Free Press, 1971-73; assoc. editor TV Guide, Radnor, Pa., 1973-77; bur. chief TV Guide, Washington, 1977-89; sr. fellow Annenberg Washington program Northwestern U., Washington, 1989-91; bd. dirs. Va. Writing mag. Author: (nonfiction) Guerrilla Theatre, 1973, Shadow Warrior, 1989, Rogue Warrior, 1992 (#1 bestseller N.Y. Times Book Rev.), (novels) Evidence, 1980, Watchdogs, 1983, Blood Cries, 1987, Rogue Warrior II: Red Cell, 1994 (bestseller N.Y. Times), Green Team, 1995 (bestseller N.Y. Times). Mem. Bard Coll. Alumni Assn. (bd. govs. 1975-81, pres. 1981-83). Club: Army and Navy (Washington). Home: 5522 Trent St Chevy Chase MD 20815-5512 also: Ground Zero Ledge Bluemont VA 22012

WEISMAN, LORENZO DAVID, investment banker; b. Guatemala, Apr. 22, 1945; came to U.S. 1957; s. Eduardo Tobias and Suzanne (Loeb) W.; m. Danielle Maysonnave, June 22, 1971; children—Melissa Anne, Alexia Maria, Thomas Alexander. B.A. in History and Lit. cum laude, Harvard U., 1966; postgrad., Conservatoire Nat. D'Art Dramatique, Paris, 1966-71; M.B.A. in Fin., Columbia U., 1973. V.p. Dillon, Read & Co., Inc., N.Y.C., 1977-80, sr. v.p., 1980-82; mng. dir. Dillon, Read & Co., Inc., London, 1982-84; pres., chief exec. officer Dillon Read Ltd., London, 1984-93; head Internat. Dillon Read & Co., N.Y.C., 1993—; bd. dirs. Sudimer Buy-Out Fund, Spain, Corporacion Borealis, Spain, France Capital Devel., France, Dillon, Read & Co., Inc., N.Y.C., Dillon, Read, Ltd., London; univ. resources Harvard U., 1991, mem. adv. com. David Rockefeller Ctr. for L.Am. Studies, 1995—; mem. internat. bd. overseers Columbia Bus. Sch., 1992; mem. bd. overseers Institut Français/Alliance Française, N.Y.C., 1995—. Trustee Institut Français/Alliance Française, N.Y.C., 1995. Mem. Travelers Club (Paris), RAC Club (London).

WEISMAN, DONALD LEROY, art educator, artist, filmmaker, writer; b. Milw., Oct. 12, 1914; s. Friedrich Othello and Stela Priscilla (Custer) W.; m. M. Virginia Stant; children: Anne Wilder, Christopher Thomas. B.S., U. Wis., Milw., 1935; Ph.M., U. Wis. Madison, 1940; Ph.D. Ohio State U., 1950. Asst. prof. art U. Ill. State U., Normal, 1940-42, 47-48, Wayne U., Detroit, 1949-51; prof., head dept. art U. Ky., Lexington, 1951-54; prof., chmn. dept. art U. Tex., Austin, 1954-58, Univ. prof. arts, 1959-81, prof. emeritus, 1981—; cons. Ford Found., N.Y.C., 1958, 66, U.S. Nat. Com. UNESCO, 1953, Rockefeller Found., 1956, Nat. Council Arts., 1966-72; spl. cons. USIS, Forence, Italy, 1961-62. Author: Language and Visual Form, 1968, Visual Arts as Human Experience, 1970, Duncan Phyfe & Drew, 1984, Follow the Bus with the Greek License Plates, 1981, Frank Reaugh, Painter to the Longhorns, 1985; contbr. articles, poems, stories and revs. to profl. jours.; painter, collagist one-man shows, Cushman Gallery, Houston, Nye Gallery, Dallas, Petite Gallery, N.Y.C., Art Mus. U. N. Mex., group shows, Bocur Gallery, N.Y.C., Chgo. Art Inst., Dallas Mus. Fine Arts, Rockefeller Ctr., N.Y.C., Vanucci Gallery, Pistoia, Italy, Villa Monte Carlo Chapala, Jalisco, Mexico; film-maker numerous productions. Served to lt. (j.g.) USN, 1942-45, PTO. Recipient Letter of Commendation Pres. U.S., 1972; recipient Teaching awards U. Tex., 1963, 65, 70, 77, honor for book Some Folks Went West 12th Annual Writers Conf., Austin, 1900; grantee U. Tex. Research Inst., Italy, Eng., 1961-62, 71, Pub. Broadcast Corp., 1970, 72; named fine arts scholar Harvard U., 1941. Mem. Nat. Humanities Faculty. Home: 1108 Yaupon Valley Rd Austin TX 78746-4329 Office: Am Studies U Tex Austin TX 78712

WEISMANTEL, GREGORY NELSON, management consultant and software executive; b. Houston, Sept. 8, 1940; s. Leo Joseph and Ellen Elizabeth (Zudis) W.; m. Marilyn Ann Fanger, June 18, 1966; children: Guy Gregory, Christopher Gregory, Andrea Rose. BA in English, U. Notre Dame, 1962; MBA in Internat. Bus., Loyola U., Chgo., 1979. With mgmt. staff Gen. Foods Corp., White Plains, N.Y., 1966-80; pres., chief exec. officer Manor House Foods, Inc., Addison, Ill., 1980-82, Weismantel & Assocs., Downers Grove, Ill., 1982-84; v.p. perishable div. Profl. Marketers, Inc., Lombard, Ill., 1984-86; group v.p. sales and mktg. services, dir. corp. strategy Profl. Marketers, Inc., Lombard, 1986-87; v.p. mng. prin. Louis A. Allen Assoc. Inc., Palo Alto, Calif., 1987-88; pres., chief exec. officer The Vista Group, St. Charles, Ill., 1989—; bd. dirs. Epicurean Foods, Ltd., Chgo.; pres., CEO The Vista Tech. Group, Ltd., The Vista Mgmt. Group. Chmn. fin. St. Edward's High Sch. Jubilee, Elgin, Ill., 1982-85; bd. dirs. Dist. 301 Sch. Bd., Burlington, Ill., 1980-84, St. Edward's Found., Elgin, 1982—. Capt. U.S. Army, 1962-66. Recipient ICP/Chgo. Software Assoc. Re-Engring. award, 1994; State of Ill. grantee, 1989, Build Ill. Investment Fund. Mem. Grocery Mfg. Sales Execs., Chgo. Software Assn., Chg. C. of C. (small bus. com.). Roman Catholic. Clubs: Merchandising Execs., Food Products, Am. Mktg. (Chgo.).

WEISMILLER, DAVID R., library administrator; b. Victoria, B.C., Can., Feb. 12, 1943. BA, U. B.C., 1967; B Library Sci., U. Toronto, 1968, MLS, 1972; MPA, Queen's U., Kingston, Ont., Can., 1986. Cataloguer, MAP libr., acquisitions libr. Trent U., Peterborough, Ont., 1968-74; asst. dist. libr. Scarborough (Ont.) Pub. Libr., 1974-77; cons. Waterloo-Brazil-CIDA Programme in Engring., Brazil, 1977-79; chief libr. Belleville (Ont.) Pub. Libr., 1979-85, Nepean (Ont.) Pub. Libr., 1985-88; city libr. Winnipeg (Man., Can.) Pub. Libr., 1988—. Mem. Inst. Pub. Administrn. Can., Can. Library Assn., Man. Library Assn., ALA. Office: Winnipeg Pub Libr, 251 Donald St, Winnipeg, MB Canada R3C 3P5

WEISNER, MAURICE FRANKLIN, former naval officer; b. Knoxville, Tenn., Nov. 20, 1917; s. Clinton Hall and Adra Inez (Ogg) W.; m. Norma Holland Smith, May 30, 1942; children: Maurice Hall, Franklin Lee, Stewart Holland. B.S., U.S. Naval Acad., 1941; aviation tng., 1943; grad., Nat. War Coll., 1959. Commd. ensign U.S. Navy, 1941, advanced through grades to adm., 1972; assigned U.S.S. Wasp, 1941-42; various aircraft squadrons in PTO, 1942-46, (U.S.S. Badoeng Strait), 1947-48; comdr. Patrol Squadron 46,

1949-51; assigned Office Chief Naval Operations, 1951-53; comdr. Fighter Squadron 193, 1954-55; assigned air striking forces study sect. Office Chief Naval Operations, 1955-58; comdr. Fighter Squadron 101, 1959-60, U.S.S. Guadalupe, 1960-61, U.S.S. Coral Sea, 1961-62; assigned Bur. Naval Personnel, 1962-64; dir. air weapons systems analysis staff Office Chief Naval Operations, 1964-65; comdr. Carrier Div. 1, 1965-67; dep. chief naval personnel, 1967-69; comdr. Attack Carrier Striking Force 7th Fleet, 1969-70, 7th Fleet, 1970-71; dep. chief naval operations (air warfare), 1971-72, vice chief of naval operations, 1972-73; comdr. in chief U.S. Pacific Fleet, 1973-76, Unified Pacific Comd., 1976-79. Decorated Def. D.S.M., Navy D.S.M. with 4 gold stars, Army D.S.M., Air Force D.S.M.; Legion of Merit with gold star; D.F.C. with gold star; Air medal with 5 gold stars; Navy Commendation medal. Home: 351 Woodbine Dr Pensacola FL 32503-3202

WEISS, ALAN, management consultant, author; b. Hoboken, N.J., Mar. 3, 1946; m. Maria Gallo, Aug. 3, 1968; children: Danielle, Jason. BA in Polit. Sci., Rutgers U., 1968; MA in Polit. Sci., Montclair Coll., 1972; MA in Psychology, Calif. Coast U., 1989, PhD in Psychology, 1991. Cert. mgmt. cons., profl. cons. Mgr. Prudential Ins., Newark, 1968-72; dir., v.p. Kepner-Tregoe, Inc., Princeton, N.J., 1972-81; pres. Kepner-Tregoe Continuing Edn., Princeton, 1981-83; pres., CEO Walter V. Clarke Assocs. Inc., Providence, 1984-85, Summit Cons. Group Inc., Providence, 1985—. Author: The Innovation Formula, 1988, Managing for Peak Performance, 1989, Making It Work, 1990, Million Dollar Consulting, 1992. Dir. EBC House for Battered Women, Warwick, R.I., 1992—; vol. Samaritans Suicide Hot Line, Providence, 1992—. Mem. Nat. Speakers Assn., New Eng. Speakers Assn. (pres.-elect 1992-93, pres. 1993-94), Univ. Club, Am. Soc. Journalists and Authors, Audobon Soc., Newport Preservation Soc., Save-The-Bay. Office: Summit Cons Group Inc Box 1009 East Greenwich RI 02818

WEISS, ALLAN JOSEPH, transport company executive, lawyer; b. Boston, N.J., 1932; s. Mark and Eve S. (Kane) W.; m. Sherrill Roecker, Feb. 18, 1973; children: Stephanie Eve, Mark Allan. B.S., U.S. Mcht. Marine Acad., 1955; J.D., Cornell U., 1961. Bar: N.Y. 1961, D.C. 1962, Calif. 1965, U.S. Supreme Ct. 1965. Trial atty. admiralty and shipping U.S. Dept. Justice, 1961-67; chief trial atty. admiralty office U.S. Dept. Justice, San Francisco, 1967-74; Pacific counsel Sea-Land Service, Inc., Oakland, Calif., 1974-76; dep. gen. counsel Sea-Land Service, Inc., 1977-78, gen. counsel, 1978-82, sec., 1979-82; assoc. gen. counsel Sea-Land Industries, 1979-82; pres. Freights Unltd., Inc., 1982—; gen. counsel Toledo, Peoria & Western Rwy., 1991—; adj. prof. law McGeorge Sch. Law, 1974-76. Served with U.S. Navy, 1955-57. Mem. Fed. Bar Assn., Calif. Bar Assn., D.C. Bar Assn., San Francisco Bar Assn., Maritime Law Assn. U.S., Cornell U. Law Assn., Kings Point Alumni Assn. Home: 126 Seney Dr Bernardsville NJ 07924-1818 Office: Freights Unlimited Inc PO Box 428 Peapack NJ 07977-0428

WEISS, ALVIN HARVEY, chemical engineering educator, catalysis researcher and consultant; b. Phila., Apr. 28, 1928; s. Louis and Helen F. (Wilinsky) W.; children: Linda S., Louis B.; m. Devorah Schwartz, June 10, 1979. BSChemE, U. Pa., 1949, PhD in Phys. Chemistry, 1965; MSChemE, Newark Coll. Engring., 1955. Registered profl. engr., Mass., Del. Chem. engr. Fiber Chem. Corp., Cliffwood, N.J., 1949-51, Colgate-Palmolive Co., Jersey City, 1953-55, Houdry Process and Chems. Co., Linwood, Pa., 1956-63; research assoc., lectr. U. Pa., Phila., 1963-66; prof. chem. engring. Worcester Poly. Inst., Mass., 1966-94, prof. emeritus, 1994—; NASA-ASEE summer faculty fellow Stanford U., Ames Research Ctr., 1967, 68; affiliate scientist Worcester Found. Exptl. Biology, 1972-74; Fulbright-Hays sr. faculty fellow to dept. chem. engring. Ben-Gurion U. of Negev, Beersheva, Israel, 1973-74, vis. prof. chem. engring., 1974; U.S. coord. U.S.-USSR Coop. Sci. Program in Chem. Catalysis, Topic IV, 1973-76, prin. investigator (with M.M. Sakharov), 1976-78; prin. investigator (with K.I. Ione) U.S.-USSR Coop. Sci. Program in Chem. Catalysis, Topic III, 1978-80; Fulbright-Hays vis. lectr. dept. chem. engring. Middle East Tech. U., Ankara, Turkey, 1974, vis. prof., 1991; vis. research scientist dept. organic chemistry Weizmann Inst., Rehovoth, Israel, 1974; vis. lectr. Inst. Isotopes and Central Inst. Chemistry, Hungarian Acad. Scis., Budapest, 1976; vis. prof. Inst. Cultural Relations and Inst. Isotopes, Hungarian Acad. Scis., 1978, 80; UNIDO chief tech. advisor to Petrochem. Complex of Bahia Blanca, Argentina, 1980; sr. research fellow chem. systems lab. Army Chem. Ctr., Md., 1981; UNIDO research fellow chem. process devel. Rsch. Inst. for Chem. Industry, Beijing, Peoples Republic of China, 1982; UNIDO expert in catalysis to YARPET Petrochemical Complex, Yarimca, Turkey, 1986-87; bd. dirs. U.S. com. for sci. coop. with Vietnam; vis. lectr. Nat. Ctr. for Sci. Rshc., Inst. of Indsl. Chemistry, 1986. translator: (with M. Delleo, G. Dembinski and J. Happel) Catalysis by Non-Metals (O.V. Krylov), 1970; contbr. articles to profl. jours.; patentee in field. With U.S. Army, 1951-53. Named Outstanding Researcher and Creative Scholar, Worcester Poly. Inst., 1984; recipient Sci. Achievement award Worcester Engring. Soc., 1984; research grantee NSF, PRF, NASA, DOD, DOE. Fellow Am. Inst. Chem. Engrs. (rsch. com. 1968-80, symposia chmn. 1973-84); mem.AAUP, ACS, Am. Inst. Chem. Engrs., Catalysis Soc. (bd. dirs., sec. 1968-88), Catalysis Soc. New England (founding pres. 1967-68, bd. dirs. 1968—), Am. Chem. Soc. (New England petroleum div. rep. 1970-88, session chmn. 1973—), Deutsche Gesellschaft für Chemische Apparatwesen. Office: Worcester Poly Inst 100 Institute Rd Worcester MA 01609-2276

WEISS, ARMAND BERL, economist, association management executive; b. Richmond, Va., Apr. 2, 1931; s. Maurice Herbert and Henrietta (Shapiro) W.; BS in Econs., Wharton Sch. Fin., U. Pa., 1953, MBA, 1954; D.B.A., George Washington U., 1971; m. Judith Bernstein, May 18, 1957; children: Jo Ann Michele, Rhett Louis. Cert. assn. exec. Officer, U.S. Navy, 1954-65; spl. asst. to auditor gen. Dept. Navy, 1964-65; sr. economist Center for Naval Analyses, Arlington, Va., 1965-68; project dir. Logistics Mgmt. Inst., Washington, 1968-74; dir. systems integration Fed. Energy Administrn., Washington, 1974-76; sr. economist Nat. Commn. Supplies and Shortages, 1976-77; tech. asst. to v.p. System Planning Corp., 1977-78; chmn. bd., pres., chief exec. officer Assns. Internat., Inc., 1978—; chmn. bd. dirs., chief fin. officer RAIL Digital Corp., 1988-91; v.p., treas. Tech. Frontiers, Inc., 1978-80; sr. v.p. Weiss Pub. Co., Inc., Richmond, Va., 1960—; v.p. Condo News Internat., Inc., 1981; v.p., bd. dirs. Leaders Digest Inc., 1987-88; sec., bd. dirs. Mgmt. Svcs. Internat., Inc., 1987-88; adj. prof. Am. U., 1979-80, 89-90; vis. lectr. George Washington U., 1971; assoc. prof. George Mason U., 1984; treas. Fairfax County (Va.) Dem. Com. 1992-94, assisted Pres. Clinton, v.p. Gore transition at White House, 1993, pres. Washington Mgmt. and Business Assn., 1993—; chmn. U.S. del., session chmn. NATO Symposium on Cost-Benefit Analysis, The Hague, Netherlands, 1969, NATO Conf. on Operational Rsch. in Indsl. Systems, St. Louis, France, 1970; pres. Nat. Council Assns. Policy Scis., 1971-77; chmn. adv. group Def. Econ. Adv. Council Dept. Def., 1970-74; resident assoc. Smithsonian Instn., 1973—; expert cons. Dept. State, GAO; undercover agt. FBI, 3 yrs. Del. Pres.'s Mid-Century White House Conf. on Children and Youth, 1950; scoutmaster Japan, U.S., leader World Jamborees, France, Can., U.S., 1945-61; Eagle scout, 1947; U.S. del. Internat. Conf. on Ops. Rsch., Dublin, Ireland, 1972; organizing com. Internat. Cost-Effectiveness Symposium, Washington, 1970; speaker Internat. Conf. Inst. Mgmt. Scis., Tel Aviv, 1973, del., Mexico City, 1967. Mem. bus. com. Nat. Symphony Orch., 1968-70, Washington Performing Arts Soc., 1974-88; bus. mgr. Nat. Lyric Opera Co., 1983—; mem. mktg. com. Fairfax Symphony Orch., 1984-91; bd. dirs. Mc Lean (Va.) Orch., 1992-94; exec. com. Mid Atlantic council Union Am. Hebrew Congregations, 1970-79, treas. 1974-79; mem. nat. MUM com., 1974-79; mem. dist. com. Boy Scouts Am., 1972-75; bd. dirs. Nat. Council Career Women, 1975-79 Va. Acad. Scis., 1991—. Recipient Silver medal 50-yard free style and half mile swimming meet No. Va. Sr. Olympics, 1990. Fellow AAAS, Washington Acad. Scis. (gov. 1981-92, v.p. 1987-88, pres.-elect 1989-90, pres. 1990-91, past pres. 1991-92); mem. Ops. Research Soc. Am. (chmn. meetings com. 1969-71, chmn. cost-effectiveness sect. 1969-70, Moving Spirit award 1994), Washington Ops. Research/Mgmt. Sci. Council (editor newsletter 1969-93, sec. 1971-72, pres. 1973-74, trustee 1975-77, bus. mgr. 1976-93), Internat. Inst. Strategic Studies (London), Am. Soc. Assn. Execs. (membership com. 1981-82, cert.), Inst. for Mgmt. Sci., Am. Econ. Assn., Wharton Grad. Sch. Alumni Assn. (exec. com. 1970-73), Am. Acad. Polit. and Social Sci., Nat. Eagle Scout Assn., Am. Legion, Navy League of the U.S., Greater Wash. Soc. Assn. Execs., Fairfax County C. of C., Vienna, Va. C. of C., Alumni Assn. George Washington U. (governing bd. 1974-82, chmn. univ. publs. com. 1976-78, Alumni Service award 1980), Alumni Assn. George Washington U. Sch. Govt. and Bus. Adminstrn. (exec. v.p. 1977-78, pres.

1978-79), George Washington U. Doctoral Assn. (sr. v.p. 1968-69), Nat. Assn. Acad. Sci. (del. 1991-93). Jewish. (pres. temple 1970-72). Club: Wharton Sch. Washington (sec. 1967-69, pres. 1969-70, exec. dir. 1987—; Joseph Wharton award 1991). Co-editor: Systems Analysis for Social Problems, 1970, The Relevance of Economic Analysis to Decision Making in the Departmenfense, 1972, Toward More Effective Public Programs: The Role of Analysis and Evaluation, 1975. Editor: Cost-Effectiveness Newsletter, 1966-70, Operations Research/Systems Analysis Today, 1971-73, Operation Research/Mgmt. Sci. Today, 1974-87; Feedback, 1969-93, Condo World, 1981; assoc. editor Ops. Research, 1973-75; publisher: IEEE Scanner, 1983-89, Spl. and Individual Needs Tech. (SAINT) Newsletter, 1987-88, Jour. Parametrics, 1984-88. Home: 6516 Truman Ln Falls Church VA 22043-1821

WEISS, BRIAN, lawyer; b. Bklyn., Aug. 16, 1945; s. Morris and Ruth (Schimelman) W.; m. Susan Rae Klarreich, July 3, 1983. BA cum laude, CUNY, 1965, MA, 1968, PhD, 1974; JD, Columbia U., 1978. Bar: N.Y. 1979. Instr. Eng. SUNY, Geneseo, 1968-72; adj. asst. prof. CUNY, Baruch, 1974-75; editorial cons. N.Y.C., 1974-75; staff researcher ABA, N.Y.C., 1979-80; pvt. practice Queens, N.Y., 1980-81; chief of appeals F. Lee Bailey & Aaron J. Broder Firm, N.Y.C., 1981-82; pvt. practice N.Y.C., 1982—; assigned counsel plan panels Supreme Ct. and Criminal Ct., N.Y.C. Editor The Broder N.Y. Tort Reporter, 1989-91. Adminstr. Harry Bermack Pro Bono Litigation Panel, B'nai B'rith, 1986—. NDEA fellow, 1965. Mem. N.Y. County Lawyers Assn. (legal assistance com.), Assn. of Bar of City of N.Y. (libr. com.), N.Y. Trial Lawyers Assn., N.Y. Criminal Bar Assn., Columbia Law Sch. Alumni Assn., Am. Mensa, MLA, N.Y. Lawyers Unit, B'nai Brith (v.p. 1983-92, pres. 1992—), Phi Beta Kappa (gamma chpt.). Democrat. Office: 11 Park Pl New York NY 10007-2800

WEISS, BRUCE JORDAN, academic administrator; b. N.Y.C., Mar. 17, 1945; s. Robert and Margolith (Goldsmith) W.; m. Dianne Mary McConville, Sept. 1, 1968; children: Jenna Lynn, Evan Michael. BA in Psychology, CUNY, 1965; MA in Psychology, U. Toledo, 1967; PhD in Psychology, U. Md., 1971. Lic. psychologist, Mass. Counseling psychologist Am. U., Washington, 1970-71, U. Calif., Berkeley, 1971-72; clin. dir. Pedregal House, San Mateo, Calif., 1973-74; dir. Berkeley Day Treatment Ctr., 1974-77; program dir. Mass. Sch. Profl. Psychology, Newton, 1977-79; dean Dedham, 1979-86; pres., 1986—. Contbr. chpt. to book. Fellow Mass. Psychol. Assn.; mem. Am. Psychol. Assn. Jewish. Office: Mass Sch Profl Psychology 322 Sprague St Dedham MA 02026-5250

WEISS, CARYL SHANDER, interior designer, educator; b. Phila., Aug. 4, 1949; d. Sidney Arron and Norma (Malish) S.; m. Milton B. Weiss, Sept. 21, 1974; 1 child, Dylan Shander. Student Pa. State U., 1968-69, Phila. Coll. Art, 1967-68; B.A. in Interior Design, Am. U., 1972; M.S., Drexel U., 1974; postgrad. Lawrence Inst. Tech., 1977. Prin. owner, interior designer Design Works, Phila., 1974-75; project designer Finger Office, Houston, 1975-77; lectr. interior design U. Houston, 1976-77; designer Hunter/Miller & Assocs., Alexandria, Va., 1978-79; asst. prof. Mt. Vernon Coll., Washington, 1979-81; program coordinator interior architecture and design dept. Mundelein Coll., Chgo., 1981-83; ind. cons. to design programs and designers Caryl Weiss, Westfield, N.J., 1983—. Bd. dirs. adv. bd. Mundelein Coll., 1981-83; bd. dirs. Inst. Bus. Designers, Chgo., 1982-83. Named Design Educator of Year, Am. Soc. Interior Designers, 1982; Mundelein Coll. Challenge grantee, 1982. Mem. Inst. Bus. Designers (dir. 1982-83), Am. Soc. Interior Designers, Interior Design Educator Council, Nat. Council Jewish Women. Home: 90 Kitchell Rd Lawrence Farms E Mount Kisco NY 10549

WEISS, CHARLES ANDREW, lawyer; b. Perryville, Mo., Jan. 24, 1942; s. Wallace Francis and Iola Frances Weiss; m. Marie Suzanne Desloge, June 10, 1972; children—Christopher, Robert, Julie, Anne. B.J. with highest honors, U. Mo., 1964, A.B. in History, 1965; J.D. cum laude, Notre Dame U., 1968. Bar: Mo. 1968, U.S. Dist. Ct. (ea. dist.) Mo. 1968, U.S. Ct. Appeals (8th cir.) 1968, U.S. Ct. Appeals (9th cir.) 1974. Law clk. to chief judge U.S. Ct. Appeals (8th cir.), 1968-69, U.S. Ct. Appeals (5th cir.) 1992; ptnr. Bryan Cave, St. Louis, 1969—; lectr., researcher St. Louis U. Law Sch., 1970-73. Supr., Red Cross Water Safety Program, Perry County, Mo., 1962-64; dir. Neighborhood Youth Corps., Perry County, 1965-66; pres. Perry County Young Democrats Club, 1965-67; committeeman Boy Scouts Am., 1982-86. Fellow Am. Coll. Trial Lawyers; mem. ABA (ho. of dels. 1986—), Met. Bar Assn. St. Louis (pres. 1984-85), Mo. Bar Assn. (bd. govs. 1985—), Roman Catholic. Clubs: Mo. Athletic (St. Louis), The Riverlands Assn., Inc. (pres. 1991-93), Jefferson Nat. Expansion Hist. Assn. (chmn. 1993—), Notre Dame of St. Louis (dir. 1983—). Office: Bryan Cave 211 N Broadway Saint Louis MO 63102-2733

WEISS, CHARLES MANUEL, environmental biologist; b. Scranton, Pa., Dec. 7, 1918; s. Morris and Fannie (Levy) W.; m. Shirley Friedlander, June 7, 1942. BS, Rutgers U., 1939, postgrad., 1939-40; postgrad., Harvard U., 1940; PhD, Johns Hopkins U., 1950. Fellow in marine microbiology, research assoc. in marine biology Woods Hole Oceanographic Instn., Mass., 1939-47; chemist, biologist Balt. Harbor Project, Johns Hopkins U. Dept. San Engring., 1947-50; basin biologist div. water pollution control USPHS, N.Y.C., 1950-52; biologist med. labs. Army Chem. Ctr., Edgewood, Md., 1952-56; prof. environ. scis. and engring. U. N.C., Chapel Hill, 1956-89, prof. emeritus, 1989—, creator/sponsor C. & S. Weiss Urban Livability program, 1992—; cons. limnology Duke Power Co.; mem. ad hoc panel waste treatment Space Sci. Bd., Nat. Acad. Sci., 1966-68, chmn. panel mgmt. of spacecraft solid and liquid wastes, 1968-69, subcom. atmosphere and water contaminants of manned spacecraft, 1971; mem. triennial water quality standards rev. com. N.C. Dept. Natural Resources and Community Devel., 1982-83; cons. Nat. Health Service, Santiago, Chile, 1971. Author: Water Quality Investigations, Guatemala: Lake Atitlan 1968-70, 1971, Water Quality Investigations, Guatemala: Lake Amatitlan 1969-70, 1971, The Trophic State of North Carolina Lakes, 1976, The Water Quality of the Upper Yadkin Drainage Basin, 1981, Water Quality Study, B. Everett Jordan Lake, N.C., 1981-85, 87; editor N.C. Conf. AAUP Newsletter, 1985-91. Mem. Chapel Hill Planning Bd., 1969-76, chmn., 1970-72, 75-76; trustee Chapel Hill Preservation Soc., 1972; bd. dirs. Triangle Theatre Opera, 1986, 89, 91—; mem. adv. coun. Santa Fe Chamber Music Festival, 1990-91, trustee, 1991—. Bigelow fellow Woods Hole Oceanographic Instn., 1970—. Fellow AAAS, Am. Pub. Health Assn., N.Y. Acad. Scis.; mem. Am. Chem. Soc., Am. Geophys. Union, Am. Fisheries Soc., Am. Soc. Limnology and Oceanography, Ecol. Soc. Am., Soc. Internat. Limnologie, Water Pollution Control Fedn. (chmn. research com. 1966-71), Am. Water Works Assn. (chmn. subcom. water quality sampling of com. quality control in reservoirs 1978-80), Am. Soc. Microbiology, AAUP (chpt. pres. 1980-81, pres. N.C. conf. 1982-83, William S. Tacey award Assembly of State Confs. 1992), Sigma Xi, Delta Omega. Home: 155 N Hamilton Rd Chapel Hill NC 27514-5628 Office: U NC Sch Pub Health CB7400 Rosenau Chapel Hill NC 27599-7400

WEISS, CHARLES STANARD, investment banker; b. San Antonio, Dec. 20, 1952; s. Charles Frederick and Bernice (Pearigan) W.; m. Wendy Avrett, Feb. 13, 1982; children: Victoria Elizabeth, Charles Avrett, Timothy McDow. BA, Vanderbilt U., 1974; MBA, U. Chgo., 1976. Asst. v.p. Citibank N.A., N.Y.C., 1976-81; exec. v.p. Smith Barney, Inc., N.Y.C., 1981—. Mem. Ind. Petroleum Assn. Am., Seawanhaka Corinthian Yacht Club (Oyster Bay, N.Y., treas. 1987-89, rear commodore 1989-91, vice commodore 1991-93, commodore 1993-95), 29 Club, Piping Rock Club (Matinecook, N.Y.), Les Cheneaux Club (Cedarville, Mich.). Republican. Presbyterian. Avocation: sailing, skiing. Home: 199 Cove Rd Oyster Bay NY 11771 Office: Smith Barney Harris Upham 1345 Ave of the Americas New York NY 10105

WEISS, DANIEL EDWIN, clergyman, educator; b. Kenosha, Wis., June 9, 1937; s. Edwin and Ruth J. (Stromquist) W.; m. Rachel A. Johnson, Aug. 9, 1958; children: Daniel E., Kristen R. BA, Wheaton Coll., 1959, MA, 1962; MDiv, Gordon Conwell Theol. Sem., South Hamilton, Mass., 1962; PhD, Mich. State U., 1964; DD (hon.), Judson Coll., 1976, Franklin Coll., 1990. Ordained to ministry Am. Bapt. Chs., 1962. Prof. ministry Gordon Div. Sch., Wenham, Mass., 1964-69; v.p. Gordon Coll., Wenham, 1969-73; pres. Eastern Coll., St. Davids, Pa., 1973-81, Eastern Bapt. Theol. Sem., Phila., 1973-81; v.p. Pace U., N.Y.C., 1981-83; exec. dir. Am. Bapt. Bd. Edn. and Publ., Valley Forge, Pa., 1983-88; gen. sec. Am. Bapt. Chs. U.S.A.,

Valley Forge, 1988—; mem. ctrl. com. World Coun. Chs., Geneva, 1989—; mem. gen. bd. Nat. Coun. Chs., N.Y.C., 1989—; mem. gen. coun. Bapt. World Alliance, Washington, 1985—. Office: Am Bapt Chs USA PO Box 851 Valley Forge PA 19482-0851

WEISS, DAVID, religion educator; b. Sighet, Rumania, Dec. 21, 1928; came to U.S., 1947, naturalized, 1953; s. Callel and Fanny (Weiss) Wiederman; m. Tzipora Hager, Dec. 9, 1953; children—Baruch, Ephraim, Isaiah. B.A., Bklyn. Coll., 1953; M.A., N.Y.U., 1956; M.H.L., Jewish Theol. Sem., 1957, D.H.L., 1958; PhD (hon.), Haifa U., Israel, 1993; DHL (hon.), Gratz Coll., 1994; DTh (hon.), U. Lund, Sweden, 1995. Instr. religion and Talmud Jewish Theol. Sem., 1957-62, asst. prof. Talmud, 1962-68, assoc. prof., 1968-86, prof. Rabbinics, 1970-86; lectr. religion Columbia U., N.Y.C., 1961-63, adj. asst. prof., 1963-65, adj. assoc. prof., 1965-68, adj. prof., 1968-86, prof., 1986—, Lucius N. Littauer prof. classical Jewish civilization, 1995—; vis. prof. Talmud Bar-Ilan U., Israel, 1974; Lady Davis vis. prof. Talmud Hebrew U., Israel, 1984. Author (under name Halivni): Sources and Traditions: A Source Ciritical Commentary on The Talmud, Vol. I on Seder Nashim, 1968; author Vol. II on Seder Moed, 1975, Vol. III on Tractate Shabbath, 1983, Vol. IV on Tractate Erubin and Pesahim, 1983, Vol. V on Tractate Baba Qama, 1993, Midrash, Mishnah and Gemara, 1986, Peshat and Derash, 1991, Revelation Restored, 1996. Recipient Bialik prize City of Tel-Aviv, Israel, 1984; grantee Council Research Humanities Columbia, 1964; Guggenheim fellow, 1970-71; recipient L. Ginzberg award Jewish Theol. Sem., 1971-72; Nat. Endowment for Humanities fellow, 1980; fellow Inst. for Advanced Studies Hebrew U., Jerusalem, Israel, 1981. Mem. Am. Acad. Jewish Rsch. (past pres.), Am. Acad. Arts and Scis. Home: 435 Riverside Dr New York NY 10025-7743

WEISS, DAVID, construction executive. CFO Beazer Homes USA, Inc., Atlanta. Office: Beazer Homes USA Inc 5775 Peachtree Rd Atlanta GA 30341*

WEISS, DAVID RAYMOND, lawyer; b. Port Washington, Wis., Mar. 18, 1948; s. Lawrence Martin and Laverne A. (Ansay) W.; m. Sandra Morton Williams, Aug. 11, 1972; children: Ian Tucker, Hickory Pearson. BA in Psychology, U. Wis., 1970, JD, 1973. Bar: Wis. 1973, U.S. Dist. Ct. (we. dist.) Wis. 1973, Wash. 1976, U.S. Dist. Ct. (we. dist.) Wash. 1976, Maine 1979, U.S. Dist. Ct. Maine 1979, U.S. Tax Ct. 1980. Trust counsel United Bank and Trust Co., Madison, Wis., 1973-75; assoc. Weinrich, Gilmore & Adolph, P.S., Seattle, 1975-78; mng. ptnr. Stinson, Lupton & Weiss, P.A., Bath, Maine, 1979—; mem. Commn. Alternative Dispute Resolution, Augusta, Maine, 1985-87; bd. dirs. New Eng. Bar Assn., Augusta. Contbr. articles to bar jour. Treas. YMCA, Bath, 1984-86; trustee YMCA Charitable Trust, Bath, 1988—, Maine Maritime Mus., 1992—; pres. Bath Area C. of C., 1987. Mem. ABA, Maine State Bar Assn. (pres. 1989), Maine Bar Found. (charter mem. Found. Fellows, bd. dirs. 1988-91, bd. govs. 1982-90), Wash. Bar Assn. Sagadahoc County Bar Assn., Wis. Bar Assn. Avocations: beekeeping, farming, bird watching, sailing. Office: Stinson Lupton & Weiss PA 280 Front St Bath ME 04530-2651

WEISS, DONALD L(OGAN), retired sports association executive; b. Aurora, Ill., Aug. 22, 1926; s. Harry H. and Esther (Cook) W.; m. Charlene Thomas, Aug. 23, 1947; children: Deborah Lynn Weiss Geline, Barbara Jane Weiss Junkett, Pamela Sue Weiss Ven der Lee. Student, Cornell Coll., Mt. Vernon, Iowa, 1943, 46; B.J., U. Mo., 1949. Newsman AP, Huntington, W.Va., 1949-51; sports writer-editor AP, N.Y.C., 1951-63; publs. editor, info. dir. U.S. Golf Assn., N.Y.C., 1963-65; dir. info. Nat. Football League, N.Y.C., 1965-68; dir. public relations Nat. Football League, 1968-77; exec. dir. Nat. Football League, N.Y.C., 1977-94. Contbr. articles on golf and football to profl. publs., 1963—. With submarine svc., USN, 1944-46. Recipient Journalistic Achievement awards Sigma Delta Chi, Kappa Tau Alpha, 1948-49, Trustees' award Ohio U., 1978, Nat. citation Nat. H.S. Athletic Coaches Assn., 1990. Methodist. Office: 410 Park Ave New York NY 10022-4407

WEISS, EARLE BURTON, physician; b. Waltham, Mass., Nov. 23, 1932; s. Murray E. and Ruth R. (Pill) W.; m. Ruth Lithwick, Dec. 1, 1963; children—Ilana, Joshua. BS with honors, Northeastern U., 1955; MS, M.I.T., 1957; MD, Albert Einstein Coll. Medicine, 1961. Intern King's County Hosp., Bklyn., 1961-62; resident Boston City Hosp., 1962-64, Nat. Heart Inst. fellow, 1964-66; assoc. dir. Tufts Med. Svc., 1969-70; dir. respiratory ICU, physician pulmonary svc. Boston City Hosp., 1964-71; dir. div. respiratory diseases St. Vincent Hosp., Worcester, Mass., 1971-89; also acting med. dir. St. Vincent Hosp., 1985-87; prof. medicine U. Mass. Med. Sch., 1977—; sr. pulmonary rsch. scientist, dept. anesthesia Rsch. Labs. Brigham and Womens Hosp., Boston, 1989—; lectr. Tufts Med. Sch.; assoc. affiliated prof. life scis. Worcester (Mass.) Poly. Inst.; vis. prof. anesthesia Harvard Med. Sch., 1990—; med. dir. Found. Rsch. in Bronchial Asthma and Related Diseases; Tb cons. Commonwealth of Mass., 1964-71. Author: Bronchial Asthma, 2d edit., 1976, 3d edit., 1993, Status Asthmaticus, 1978; contbr. to Ciba Collection: The Respiratory System, An Anthology of Medical Classics, 1995—. Served to capt. USAF, 1965-70. Recipient Dr. J. McKeever award for outstanding educator St. Vincent Hosp., 1970, Chadwick medal for meritorious contbn. thoracic diseases Mass. Thoracic Soc., 1990. Fellow ACP, Am. Coll. Chest Physicians, Royal Coll. Physicians (assoc.); mem. AAAS, AMA, Mass. Thoracic Soc. (pres. 1976-78, Chadwick medal for meritorious contbn. 1990), Mass. Med. Soc., Am. Thoracic Soc., Am. Assn. Clin. Scientists, Am. Soc. Internal Medicine, Soc. Free Radical Rsch., N.Y. Acad. Scis., Interasthma. Avocation: research in the role of calcium and oxygen toxic products in asthma and airways reactivit. Home: 57 South St Natick MA 01760-5526 Office: Brigham and Womens Hosp Dept Anesthesia Rsch L Boston MA 02115

WEISS, EDITH BROWN, law educator; b. Salem, Oreg., Feb. 19, 1942; d. Leon Michael and Edith E. Brown; m.B., Stanford U., 1963; J.D., Harvard U., 1966; Ph.D., U. Calif.-Berkeley, 1973; DDL (hon.) Chgo.-Kent Coll. Law, 1993; m. Charles Weiss, Jr., July 24, 1969; children—Jed, Tamara. Bar: D.C., 1967, U.S. Ct. Claims, 1967, U.S. Ct. Customs and Patent Appeals, 1967, U.S. Tax Ct., 1967, U.S. Ct. Mil. Appeals, 1967; atty. adv. ACDA, Washington, 1966-68; research assoc. Brookings Instn., Washington, 1972-74; asst. prof. civil engring. and politics Princeton U., 1974-78; prof. law Georgetown U., Washington, 1978—; cons. UN Environ. Program, 1974-78, NOAA, 1977-78, UN U., 1983—; chmn. Social Sci. Rsch. Coun. Com. on Rsch. on Global Environ. Change, 1989-94. Bd. editors Am. Jour. Internat. Law, Internat. Legal Materials, Global Governance. Recipient Dinkelspiel award Stanford U., 1963, Leland T. Chapin award, 1962, Mellinkoff award, 1963; Harold and Margaret Sprout award, 1979, Elizabeth Haub prize, 1994; Woodrow Wilson fellow, 1968. Mem. ABA (standing com. world order), Am. Soc. Internat. Law (chmn. ann. meeting 1979, nominating com. 1979-80, exec. coun. 1981-85, v.p. 1983-85, pres. 94—), Nat. Acad. Scis. (environ. studies bd. 1981-84, vice chmn. U.S. nat. com. for SCOPE 1984-85, water sci. and tech. bd. 1985-88, commn. on geoscis., environment and resources 1992-95), Coun. Fgn. Relations, Am. Law Inst., Internat. Coun. Environ Law, Cousteau Soc. (coun. advs.), Phi Beta Kappa, Sigma Xi. Club: Bannockburn Civic Assn. Author: (with Brown, Fabian, Cornell) Regimes for the Oceans, Outer Space and Weather, 1977, In Fairness to Future Generations: International Law, Common Patrimony and Intergenerational Equity, 1989;contbr. articles to profl. jours. Office: Georgetown U Law Ctr 1507 Isherwood St NE # 1 Washington DC 20002-5564

WEISS, EGON ARTHUR, retired library administrator; b. Vienna, Austria, June 7, 1919; Came to U.S., 1938; s. Arthur and Martha (Schrecker) W.; m. Renee Hansi Weiss, July 11, 1942; children—Helen Louise, Steven Arthur. Student Berea Coll., 1938-40; A.B., Harvard U., 1947; M.A., Boston U., 1949; M.S.L.S., Simmons Coll., Boston, 1951. Prof. asst. Brookline (Mass.) Pub. Library, 1949-51, br. dir. 1951-58; asst. dir. library U.S. Mil. Acad., West Point, N.Y., 1958-62, libr. dir. libr., 1962-87, libr. emeritus, 1987—; libr. cons., editor; trustee Southeast N.Y. Libr. Rsch. Coun., Poughkeepsie, 1966—; mem. John Cotton Dana Ctr., N.Y.C., 1975-79; cons. Pergamon Press, McLean, Va., 1983—. Co-author: Catalog Military Science Coll., 4 vols., 1969; contbr. to Funk & Wagnalls Ency., 1965—; appraiser rare books and spl. collections. Chmn. Black Rock Forest Preservation Council, Cornwall, N.Y., 1981—; trustee Mus. Hudson Highlands, Cornwall-on-Hudson, N.Y., 1968; vice chmn. Citizens Adv. Com.,

Cornwall, 1963-64; pres. Friends of Cornwall (N.Y.) Pub. Libr., 1989—, chmn. gifts and bequests, 1984—; counsellor Friends of West Point Libr., 1987—, trustee David Libr. of Am. Revolution, Pa., 1986—; alt. del. The White House Conf. on Libr. and Info. Svcs., 1991. Served to lt. col. U.S. Army, 1942-46, ETO. Mem. ALA (pres. armed forces sect. 1966), Spl. Libraries Assn. (chmn. mil. library div. 1970), Archons of Colophon, Res. Officers Assn. (pres. Orange County 1965—), Assn. U.S. Army (bd. govs. 1984—). Club: Harvard (v.p. schs. and scholarship) (Poughkeepsie, N.Y.) Lodges: Toastmasters (edn. v.p. Newburgh, N.Y. 1968), Masons. Avocations: reading; swimming; tennis; playing violin. Home: 33 Spruce St Cornwall On Hudson NY 12520-1124

WEISS, ELLYN RENEE, lawyer; b. Phila., Aug. 11, 1947; d. Samuel J. and Ruth G. (Miller) Paul; m. Robert Lowell Weiss Jr., June 26, 1969; 1 child, Nora Caroline. BA cum laude, Smith Coll., Northampton, Mass., 1969; JD cum laude, Boston U., 1972. Bar: Mass. 1972, D.C. 1978, U.S. Dist. Ct., Mass., U.S. Dist. Ct., D.C., U.S. Ct. Appeals (D.C., 1st and 3d cirs.), U.S. Supreme Ct. Lectr. environ. law Boston U., 1976-77; asst. atty. gen. Mass. Atty. Gen., Boston, 1973-77; ptnr. Harmon & Weiss, Washington, 1977-88, Foley, Hoag & Eliot, Washington, 1988—. Recipient Disting. Svc. Citation Mass. Atty. Gen., Boston, 1975. Mem. Union Concerned Scientists (dir. 1988—). Avocation: painting. Office: Foley Hoag & Eliot 1615 L St NW Washington DC 20036-5610

WEISS, ERIC ROBERT, lawyer; b. Phila., Feb. 5, 1958. BA, Rutgers U., 1980; JD, George Washington U., 1984. Counsel Mutual Broadcasting, Arlington, Va., 1984-85, dir. bus. affairs, 1985—; v.p. bus. and legal affairs Westwood One Inc., Los Angeles, 1986—. Mem. ABA, Beverly Hills Bar Assn. Office: Westwood One Inc 9540 Washington Blvd Culver City CA 90232-2689

WEISS, GAIL ELLEN, legislative staff director; b. N.Y.C., Apr. 11, 1946; d. Joseph and Elaine (Klein) W.; m. John A. Kelly. BA, U. Md., 1967. Staff asst. U.S. Office Econ. Opportunity/Job Corps, Washington, 1967-69; legis. asst. Hon. William L. Clay, Mem. Congress, Washington, 1969-72; rsch. asst. Rt. Hon. Roy Hattersley, Mem. Parliament, London, 1972-73; legis. asst. various coms. U.S. Ho. of Reps., Washington, 1973-90, staff dir. Com. on P.O. and Civil Svc., 1991-94, Dem. staff dir. Com. on Econ. and Ednl. Opportunities, 1995&; mem. working group Pres.'s Task Force on Nat. Health Reform, 1993. Democrat. Jewish. Office: Com on Econ and Ednl Opp 2101 Rayburn Ho Office Bldg 2100 Rayburn Ho Office Bldg Washington DC 20515

WEISS, GEORGE C., lawyer; b. Cornwall, N.Y., Dec. 18, 1946; s. George Joseph and Ella (Vacca) W.; m. Donna Irene Rysinger, June 17, 1967; children: Matthew, Christopher, Nora, Claire, Delia. BA, St. John's U., 1968, JD, 1971. Bar: N.Y. 1972, U.S. Dist. Ct. (so. dist.) N.Y. 1975, U.S. Ct. Appeals (2d cir.) 1975, Ct. Appeals (D.C. cir.) 1988. Ptnr. Dewey, Ballantine, Bushy, Palmer & Wood, N.Y.C., 1971—. Pres. parish coun. St. John the Evangelist Roman Cath. Ch., Goshen, N.Y., 1977-81, trustee, 1981-83. Mem. N.Y. State Bar Assn. (real property and banking law sects.). Republican. Office: Dewey Ballantine 1301 Ave of the Americas New York NY 10019-0002

WEISS, GEORGE HERBERT, mathematician, consultant; b. N.Y.C., Feb. 19, 1930; s. Morris and Violet (Mayer) W.; m. Delia Esther Orgel, Dec. 20, 1961; children: Miriam Judith, Alan Keith, Daniel Mordechai. BA, Columbia U., 1951; MA, U. Md., 1953, PhD, 1958. Physicist USN, White Oak, Md., 1951-61; asst. prof. U. Md., College Park, 1959-63; fellow Rockefeller U., N.Y.C., 1963-64, Weizmann Inst., Rehovot, Israel, 1958-59; mathematician NIH, Bethesda, Md., 1964—; cons. GM, IBM, GE. Author: Lattice Dynamics in the Harmonic Approximation, 1963, 2d edit., 1971, The Master Equation in Chemical Physics, 1977, Aspects of the Random Walk, 1993, Contemporary Problems in Statistical Physics, 1994, Aspects and Applications of the Random Walk, 1994, Introduction to Crystallographic Statistics, 1995. With U.S. Army, 1954-56. Recipient Disting. Svc. in Math. award Washington Acad. Sci., 1967, Disting. Svc. award NIH, 1970. Avocation: photography. Office: Nih Bethesda MD 20816

WEISS, GERHARD HANS, German language educator; b. Berlin, Aug. 6, 1926; came to U.S., 1946; s. Curt Erich and Gertrud (Grothus) W.; m. Janet Marilyn Smith, Dec. 27, 1953; children: John Martin, Susan Elizabeth Weiss Spencer, James David. BA, Washington U., St. Louis, 1950, MA, 1952; PhD, U. Wis., 1956. Prof. German U. Minn., Mpls., 1956—, assoc. dean, 1967-71, 79, chmn. dept. German, 1987—; mem. German-Am. Textbook Commn., Braunschweig, Fed. Republic Germany, 1985-88. Author: Begegnung mit Deutschland, 1970; editor: Unterrichtspraxis, 1975-80, Minn. Monographs in the Humanities, 1964-70; contbr. articles to profl. jours. Served to lt. col. USAR, 1946-75. Recipient Cross Merit, Fed. Republic Germany, 1982. Mem. MLA, Am. Assn. Tchrs German (pres. 1982-83, cert. of merit 1981, Disting. German Educator award 1991), German Studies Assn., Am. Council for the Teaching Fgn. Langs. (Nelson Brooks award 1987). Methodist. Home: 4101 Abbott Ave S Minneapolis MN 55410-1004

WEISS, GERSON, physician, educator; b. N.Y.C., Aug. 1, 1939; s. Samuel and Lillian (Wolpe) W.; m. Linda Gordon, Dec. 24, 1959; children: Jonathan, David, Michele, Andrew. B.A., NYU, 1960, M.D., 1964. Diplomate Am. Bd. Ob-Gyn. (mem. div. reproductive endocrinology 1985-90). Intern, fellow dept. medicine Johns Hopkins Sch. Medicine, 1964-65; resident ob-gyn NYU Med. Center, 1964-69; research fellow physiology U. Pitts. Sch. Medicine, 1971-73; asst. prof. ob-gyn NYU Med. Center, 1971-76, asso. prof., 1976-80, prof., 1980-85, dir. div. reproductive endocrinology, 1975-85; prof. ob-gyn U. Med. and Dentistry N.J.-N.J. Med. Sch., 1986—, chmn. dept., 1986—. Mem. editorial bd. Fertility and Sterility Jour., Gyn.-Ob. Investigation; contbr. rsch. articles reproductive endocrinology and gynecology to med. jours. Served to maj. MC U.S. Army, 1969-71. Rsch. grantee NIH, 1975—, United Cerebral Palsy Found., 1977-83, Mellon Found., 1982-85; John Polachek Found. Med. Rsch. fellow. Mem. Am. Coll. Obstetricians and Gynecologists, Am. Ob-Gyn. Soc., Am. Bd. Ob-Gyn. (bd. dirs. 1993—), Endocrine Soc. Gynecol. Investigation, N.Y. Obstet. Soc. (pres. 1990-91), N.Y. Gynecol. Soc. (pres. 1989-90), Soc. Study of Reprodn., Phi Beta Kappa, Sigma Xi, Alpha Omega Alpha. Home: 390 1st Ave Apt 11D New York NY 10010-4935 Office: UMDNJ NJ Med Sch Dept Ob-Gyn 185 S Orange Ave Newark NJ 07103-2714

WEISS, HERBERT KLEMM, aeronautical engineer; b. Lawrence, Mass., June 22, 1917; s. Herbert Julius and Louise (Klemm) W.; m. Ethel Celesta Giltner, May 14, 1945 (dec.); children: Janet Elaine, Jack Klemm (dec.). BS, MIT, 1937, M.S., 1938. Engr. U.S. Army Arty. Bds., Ft. Monroe, Va, 1938-42, Camp Davis, N.C., 1942-44, Ft. Bliss, Tex., 1944-46; chief WPN Systems Lab., Ballistic Research Labs., Aberdeen Proving Grounds, Md, 1946-53; chief WPN systems analysis dept. Northrop Aircraft Corp., 1953-58; mgr. advanced systems devel. mil. systems planning aerotronic div. Ford Motor Co., Newport Beach, Calif., 1958-61; group dir., plans devel. and analysis Aerospace Corp., El Segundo, Calif, 1961-65; sr. scientist Litton Industries, Van Nuys, Calif., 1965-82; cons. mil. systems analysis, 1982—. Mem. Sci. Adv. Bd. USAF, 1959-63, sci. adv. panel U.S. Army, 1965-74, sci. adv. commn. Army Ball Research Labs., 1973-77; advisor Pres.'s Commn. Law Enforcement and Adminstrn. Justice, 1966; cons. Office Dir. Def., Research and Engring., 1954-64. Contbr. articles to profl. jours. Patentee in field. Recipient Commendation for meritorious civilian service USAF, 1964, cert. appreciation U.S. Army, 1970. Fellow AAAS, AIAA (assoc.); mem. IEEE, Ops. Research Soc. Am. Republican. Presbyterian. Club: Cosmos. Home: PO Box 2668 Palos Verdes Peninsula CA 90274-8668

WEISS, HOWARD A., violinist, concertmaster, conductor, music educator; b. Chgo.; s. Morris X. and Rose (Weiner) W. B.Music, Chgo. Musical Coll. of Roosevelt U., 1960; M.Music with honors, Juilliard U., 1966. Founder, music dir., condr. Rochester Philharm. Youth Orch., N.Y., 1970-89; prof. violin Eastman Sch. Music, Rochester, 1981—, Nazareth Coll., Rochester, 1983-85; mem. adv. bd. Young Audiences of Rochester), 1975—, Rochester Chamber Orch., 1981—. Concertmaster Rochester Philharm. Orch., 1967-87, concertmaster emeritus, 1987—, concertmaster Rochester Oratorio Soc., 1987—, Chgo. Chamber Orch., 1962-70, Va. Symphony, 1964, San Francisco Ballet Orch., 1962, Eastern Music Festival, Greensboro, N.C., 1976-80,

Grand Teton Music Festival Seminar, Jackson Hole, Wyo., 1983-86, Bear Lake Mus. Festival, Utah, 1992-93; 1st violinist Cleve. Orch., 1965-67; violin soloist more than 40 concertos with Cleve. Orch., Rochester Philharm., New Orleans Philharm., Chgo. Grant Park Symphony, Cin. Chamber Orch., Chgo. Chamber Orch., Rochester Chamber Orch.; soloist in complete concerti, (5) of J.S. Bach for Violin and Orch. with Rochester Bach Festival; soloist in complete concerti, (3) of Haydn for Violin and orch. with Rochester Chamber Orch.; soloist rec. Amram Elegy for Violin and Orchestra, David Zinman, Rochester Philharm. Orch., on RCA Red Seal; performed chamber music with: Misha Dichter, Leonard Rose, Lynn Harrell, Yo-Yo Ma, Elly Ameling, Jaime Laredo, Walter Trampler, Lillian Fuchs, James Buswell, Gary Karr, Alan Civil, Lukas Foss; leader of Hartwell String Quartet, 1975-78; participant Casals Festival, Puerto Rico, 1975-80. As music dir. and condr. Rochester Philharm. Youth Orch. recorded 21 LPs including symphonies by Franck, Sibelius, Shostakovich, Dvorak, Borodin and Rachmaninoff, made 12 tours, including 4 abroad, Eng. and Scotland, 1984, Germany, Austria and Switzerland, 1986, Dominican Republic, 1987, Jamaica, 1989, and appears on Voice of Am. Named Outstanding Grad. of 1966, Roosevelt U., 1973; recipient Monroe County (N.Y.) Medallion, 1986. Home: 228 Castlebar Rd Rochester NY 14610-2914

WEISS, IRA FRANCIS, retired banker; b. Providence, Oct. 19, 1909; s. Abraham and Minnie (Chernoff) W.; m. Gladys Abbott (div. 1966); children: Abbott, Michael, John. Student, CCNY, 1926-28; LL.B., St. Lawrence U., 1931; postgrad., Columbia U., 1931-33, St. John's Coll., Annapolis, 1975-78; B.A., Seminar Coll., New Sch., 1980, M.A., 1982; postgrad., CUNY Grad. Ctr. Bar: N.Y. 1934. Pvt. practice N.Y.C., 1934-37; asst. sec. Credit Utility Co., Inc., N.Y.C., 1937-42; successively asst. sec., asst. v.p., v.p., adminstrv. v.p., sr. v.p. Trade Bank & Trust Co., 1926-33, 45-70; sr. v.p. Nat. Bank N. Am., N.Y.C., 1970-74; br. cons. Nat. Bank N.Am. (now NatWest Bank), 1975. Mem. Jewish Com. on Scouting, N.Y.C., 1950-53; asst. mgr. United Fund, Glen Ridge, N.J., 1959; mem. Civic Conf. Com., 1961-64, Mayor's Transp. Com., 1962-65, Speakers Bur. of United Cerebral Palsy Soc., N.Y.C., 1946-50; treas., exec. bd. N.Y. chpt.; mem. nat. exec. council Am. Jewish Com., 1962-75; mem. Nat. Com. on Am. Fgn. Policy. Sgt. U.S. Army, 1942-45. Mem. AIM, N.Y. Credit and Financial Mgmt. Assn., Am. Arbitration Assn. (nat. panel), Robert Morris Assocs., Fgn. Policy Assn., Carnegie Council on Ethics and Internat. Affairs, Ctr. for Study Presidency, Acad. Polit. Sci. Home: 8 Reservoir Rd Apt 101 Hanover NH 03755-1315

WEISS, JAMES LLOYD, cardiology educator; b. Chgo., Jan. 15, 1941; s. Edward Huhner and Ruth (Wingerhoff) W.; m. Susan Forscher Weiss. July 23, 1967; children: Ethan James, Lisa Fleur. BA, Harvard Coll., 1963; MD, Yale U., 1968. Intern, resident U. Mich. Hosp., Ann Arbor, 1968-70; staff fellow NIH, Bethesda, Md., 1970-72; resident medicine Johns Hopkins Hosp., Balt., 1972-73; fellow cardiology, 1973-75; dir. Heart Station, 1976—, asst. prof. Medicine, 1975-81, assoc. prof. Medicine, 1981-90, prof. Medicine, Cariology, 1990—; editorial bd. Johns Hopkins Med. Ctr., 1991—. Contbr. 100 articles to profl. jours. Recipient Harvard Book prize, 1959. Fellow Am. Coll. Cardiology, AHA Coun. on Circulation; mem. Harvard Club N.Y.C., Ctr. Club. Office: Cariology Div. Johns Hopkins Hosp. 600 N Wolfe St Baltimore MD 21287

WEISS, JAMES MICHAEL, financial analyst, portfolio manager; b. Chgo., July 20, 1946; s. Harold Cornelius and Elizabeth Josephine (Jesse) W.; m. Kathleen Jane Postorino, July 18, 1970; children: Elizabeth, Ann, Jane, William. BA, Marquette U., 1968; MBA, U. Pa., 1972. CFA; chartered investment counselor. Credit analyst Provident Nat. Bank, Phila., 1972; ptnr., sr. portfolio mgr. Stein Roe & Farnham Investment Counselors, Chgo., 1972-87, 1st v.p., sr. portfolio mgr., 1987-90, sr. v.p., prin., sr. portfolio mgr., 1991-92; exec. v.p., sr. portfolio mgr. IDS Adv. Group, Inc., Mpls., 1993—; bd. dirs. Colie & Harris, Inc., Tropp & Co., Chgo.; v.p. Stein Roe Cash Reserves Fund, Chgo., 1982-87. Author: (with others) Handbook of Cash Flow and Treasury Management, 1987; contbr. articles to profl. jours. Commr. Glenview (Ill.) Zoning Bd., 1978-80; trustee Glenview Village Bd. Trustees, 1980-86; chmn. Marquette U. Exec. Senate, Chgo., 1984-87; mem. Glenview Bus. Area Redevel. Com., 1990-93; mem. bus. adv. coun. Elmhurst (Ill.) Coll., 1986-93; founding bd. dirs. Glenview Edn. Found., 1990-93. With U.S. Army, 1968-70. Recipient Cert. Merit Village of Glenview, 1987. Mem. Investment Analysts Soc., Fin. Analysts Fedn., Investment Counsel Assn., Marquette U. Alumni Assn. (nat. bd. dirs. 1989-91, Nat. Svc. award 1995), North Shore Country Club (Glenview), Interlachen Country Club. Avocations: golf, travel, writing. Home: 4900 Bywood W Edina MN 55436-1309 Office: IDS Tower # 10 Minneapolis MN 55440

WEISS, JAMES MOSES AARON, psychiatrist, educator; b. St. Paul, Oct. 22, 1921; s. Louis Robert and Gertrude (Simon) W.; m. Bette Shapera, Apr. 7, 1946; children: Jenny Anne Weiss Ford, Jonathan James. AB summa cum laude, U. Minn., 1941, ScB, 1947, MB, 1949, MD, 1950; MPH with high honors, Yale U., 1951. Diplomate: Am. Bd. Psychiatry and Neurology (examiner 1963-83). Teaching asst. psychology St. Thomas Coll., St. Paul, 1941-42; intern USPHS Hosp., Seattle, 1949-50; resident, fellow psychiatry Yale Med. Sch., 1950-53; from instr. to asst. prof. psychiatry Washington U., St. Louis, 1954-60; mem. faculty U. Mo., 1959—, First Prof. Psychiatry, 1961—, founding chmn. dept., 1960-91, prof. community medicine, 1971—; univ. prof. emeritus, 1991—; vis. prof. Inst. Criminology, Cambridge (Eng.) U., 1968-69, All-India Inst. Med. Scis. and U. Malaya, 1984; internat. cons., 1958—; founding co-chmn. Asian-Am. Consortium on Psychiat. Disorders, 1986—; Kohler disting. lectr. St. Louis U., 1988. Author numerous articles in field; editor, co-author: Nurses, Patients, and Social Systems, 1968; corr. editor: Jour. Geriatric Psychiatry, 1967—; founding editor, chmn. bd. Jour. Operational Psychiatry, 1970-90; editorial advisor Community Mental Health Jour., 1979-87; trustee Mo. Rev., 1982-83. Served with M.C., AUS, 1942-46, PTO; to capt. M.C., AUS, 1953-54. Decorated Philippine Liberation medal, 1945; recipient Sir Henry Wellcome award, 1955, Israeli bronze medal, 1963, Basic Books award, 1974, Disting. Service commendation Nat. Council Community Mental Health Ctrs., 1982, 83, 86, Guhleman award for Clin. Excellence U. Mo., 1987, Hon. Achievement award U.Mo., 1991, Disting. Svc. award VA, 1991; named Chancellor's Emissary U. Mo., 1979; faculty fellow Inter-Univ. Council, 1958, sr. research fellow Am. Council Edn. and NSF, 1984. Found. fellow Royal Coll. Psychiatrists; fellow Royal Soc. Medicine, Am. Psychiat. Assn. (life), Am. Pub. Health Assn. (life), Am. Coll. Preventive Medicine (emeritus), Royal Soc. Health, AAAS, Am. Coll. Psychiatrists (life), Am. Assn. Psychoanalytic Physicians (hon.); mem. Assn. Mil. Surgeons U.S. (hon. life), Assn. Western Profs. Psychiatry (chmn. 1970-71), Mo. Acad. Psychiatry (1st pres. 1966-67), Mo. Psychiat. Assn. (life, pres. 1987-88), Assn. de Methodologie et Documentation en Psychiatrie, Mil. Order World Wars, Phi Beta Kappa, Sigma Xi, Psi Chi, Alpha Omega Alpha, Alpha Epsilon Sigma, Gamma Alpha. Clubs: Scholars (Cantab.); Wine Label (London); Yale (St. Louis); Univ. (Columbia). Research on suicide, homicide, antisocial behavior, aging, social psychiatry. Home: Crow Wing Farm RR 2 Box 2 Columbia MO 65201-9802 Office: U Mo Dept Psychiatry Columbia MO 65212 *Only this endures: creativity, the pursuit of excellence, and continuing concern for human civilization.*

WEISS, JAMES ROBERT, lawyer; b. Munich, Oct. 27, 1949; s. Norman Emanuel and Zelda Jane (Klein) W.; m. Lynn Marcia Levey, June 25, 1972; children: Allana, Tessa. BA, Northwestern U., 1971; JD, Cath. U. Am., 1974. Bar: Pa. 1974, D.C. 1985, Md. 1985. Trial atty. anti-trust div. U.S. Dept. Justice, Washington, 1974-80, asst. chief transp. sect. anti-trust div., 1980-86, chief transp., energy and agr. sect. anti-trust div., 1986-88; ptnr. Preston Gates Ellis & Rouvelas Meeds, Washington, 1988—. Contbr. articles to profl. jours. Mem. ABA (anti-trust sect. rep. to coordinating group on energy law 1988-91), D.C. Bar Assn., Fed. Energy Bar Assn., Md. Bar Assn. Avocations: tennis, bicycling, hiking. Office: Preston Gates Ellis & Rouvelas Meeds 1735 New York Ave NW Washington DC 20006-5209

WEISS, JAMES WILLIAM, healthcare executive; b. Wilkes-Barre, Pa., Dec. 16, 1940; s. William Anthony and Agnes Elizabeth (Wertzberger) W. BS, U.S. Mil. Acad., 1962; M in Health Adminstrn. with honors, Baylor U., 1977. Commd. 2d lt. U.S. Army, 1962, advanced through grades to lt. col., retired, 1982; adminstrv. resident West Point (N.Y.) Army Hosp., 1976-77; health care adminstr. Eisenhower Army Med. Ctr., Augusta, Ga., 1977-79; chief exec. officer 2nd Combat Support, Columbus, Ga., 1979-82; asst.

adminstr. Truckee Meadows Hosp., Reno, 1982-83; chief exec. officer HCA Parthenon Pavilion, Nashville, 1983-87; chief exec. officer and exec. dir. Inner Harbour Hosps. Ltd., Douglasville, Ga., 1987-91; chief exec. officer, adminstr. Lewis Gale Psychiatric Ctr., Salem, Va., 1991—; cons. quality assurance Hosp. Corp. Am., Nashville, 1984—. Mem. Emergency Med. Svcs. Coun., Augusta and Columbus, Ga., 1977-82, sec., 1977-79; steering com. Coalition for Equitable Health Ins., Nashville, 1985-86, Atlanta, 1988; dir. emergency med. technician course, Columbus, 1979-82; chair Douglas County United Way campaign, 1990; chmn. med. united United Way of Roanoke Valley, 1991, 92. Decorated Bronze Star; recipient Top Performance of Yr. award, HCA Psychiat. Co., 1984, 85. Fellow Am. Coll. Healthcare Execs. (cert. mental health adminstr.); mem. Assn. Mental Health Adminstrs., Fla. Assn. Pvt. Psychiat. Hosps. (pres. 1988-90), Nat. Assn. Psychiat. Health Systems (chmn. multi-facility for-profit section 1993), Fla. League Hosps., Ga. Hosp. Assn. (chmn. coun. psychiat. and chem. dependence hosps. 1990-91), Douglas C. of C. (bd. dirs.). Avocations: jogging, travel. Home: 3270 Standing Peachtree Trl Kennesaw GA 30144-5810 Office: Lewis Gale Psychiatric Ctr 1902 Braeburn Dr Salem VA 24153-7304

WEISS, JAY M(ICHAEL), psychologist, educator; b. Passaic, N.J., Mar. 20, 1941; s. Benjamin and Anne (Pearl) W.; m. Meryl Etta Levenson, June 9, 1963; children: Jennifer, Jason. BA, Lafayette Coll., 1962; PhD, Yale U., 1967. Asst. prof. Rockefeller U., N.Y.C., 1969-73, assoc. prof., 1973-84; prof. dept. psychiatry Med. Ctr., Duke U., Durham, N.C., 1984-92; prof. dept psychiatry behavioral scis. Emory U. Sch. Medicine, Atlanta, Ga., 1992—; adj. assoc. prof. NYU, 1973-84, CCNY, 1979-84. MacArthur Found. fellow, 1984-89. Fellow AAAS, Soc. for Behavioral Medicine. Office: Emory Univ Sch Medicine Ga Mental Health Inst 1256 Briarcliff Rd NE Atlanta GA 30306

WEISS, JEFFREY L., federal agency director; b. New Haven, July 13, 1945; s. Robert Weiss and Elsie (Altschular) Janis; m. Hemlata Nazli Pisharody, June 1, 1969; children: Vasanta, Jack. BA, Yale U., 1968; MPA, So. Meth. U., 1977. Vol. Peace Corps, India, 1968-72; country dir. Peace Corps, Seychelle Islands, 1977-80; agy. exec. ACTION, Tex., 1972-76, Small Bus. Agy., Washington, 1981-88; with Cmty. Rels. Svc., Dept. Justice, Washington, 1989-92, acting dir., 1993—. Vol. Orr Sch., Washington, 1991—, DuPont Cir. Citizens Assn., Washington, 1991—; active YMCA, 1988—. Mem. Am. Soc. Stoopers, Yale Club. Office: Dept Justice 10th and Constitution NW Washington DC 20530

WEISS, JEROME PAUL, lawyer; b. Binghamton, N.Y., May 16, 1934; s. Milton I. and Irene (Freeman) W.; m. Marion Levitt, June 30, 1963; children: Jonathan Peter, Andrew Stephen. AB magna cum laude, Princeton U., 1956; JD, Harvard U., 1961. Bar: N.Y. 1962, D.C. 1975. Assoc. Hitsch, Cowie, Bruce, Lee & Mawhinney, Syracuse, N.Y., 1961-64; asst. gen. counsel Agway, Inc., Syracuse, 1964-72; dep. gov. and gen. counsel Farm Credit Adminstrn., Washington, 1972-73; assoc. Hamel, Park, McCabe & Saunders, Washington, 1974-76, ptnr., 1976-78, sr. ptnr., 1978-83, mng. ptnr., 1983-86; mng. ptnr. Sonnenschein, Nath & Rosenthal, Washington, 1986—; adj. prof. Syracue U. Sch. Law, 1970-74, Antioch Sch. Law, 1974-76. Trustee Landon Sch., Bethesda, Md., 1982-88. Lt. USNR, 1956-58. Mem. ABA, N.Y. State Bar Assn., D.C. Bar Assn. Clubs: Riverbend Country (Great Falls, Va.); Naples (Fla.) Bath and Tennis. Contbr. articles to legal jours. Home: 488 River Rd Great Falls VA 22066 Office: Sonnenschein Nath & Rosenthal 1301 K St NW Washington DC 20005-3317

WEISS, JOSEPH JOEL, consulting company executive; b. Newark, July 27, 1931; s. Harry H. and Belle (Sass) W.; m. Leah Kneller, Apr. 10, 1954 (div. 1961); children: Sara, Daniel; m. Carol Lynn Seegott, Sept. 29, 1967; children: Laura, John. BSBA, Rutgers U., 1953, MBA, 1958. Dist. mgr. N.J. Bell Telephone Co., 1955-61; asst. comptroller ITT P.R. Telephone Co., San Juan, 1964-68; sr. cons. 1968-71; v.p. data services Rio De Janeiro, 1971-74; dir. ops. N.Y.C., 1975-80; v.p. Control Data Corp., Rio De Janeiro, 1974-75; exec. v.p., chief adminstrv. officer Burger King Corp., Miami, 1980-89; chief oper. officer Goode, Olcott, Knight & Assocs., Coral Gables, Fla., 1989-90; pres. Contraband Detection Internat., Miami, Fla., 1990-92, Cons. Group Internat., Solon, Ohio, 1992—; Seegot Environ., Solon, 1992—; bd. dirs. WPB TV. Pres. Civic Betterment Assn., Franklin Twp., N.J., 1961; trustee U. Miami Citizens Bd., 1987—; bd. dirs. Boy Scouts Am., 1982—. Maj. USAF, 1954-63. Recipient Strategic Planning Achievement award Boy Scouts Am., 1985. Mem. Hist. Soc. Fla. (bd. dirs. 1986—). Republican. Presbyterian. Club: Fisher Island. Avocations: oil painting, tennis. Home: 8216 Chagrin Rd Chagrin Falls OH 44022-4746 Office: Seegot Environ 10040 Aurora-Hudson Rd Streetsboro OH 44241

WEISS, JULIE, costume designer. Costume designer: (stage) The Elephant Man, 1979 (Tony award nomination best costume design 1979), (films) I'm Dancing as Fast as I Can, 1982, Independence Day, 1983, Second Thoughts, 1983, Spacehunter: Adventures in the Forbidden Zone, 1983, Testament, 1983, F/X, 1986, Masters of the Universe, 1987, The Whales of August, 1987, 1969, 1988, Tequila Sunrise, 1988, Steel Magnolias, 1989, Wicked Stepmother, 1989, The Freshman, 1990, Honeymoon in Vegas, 1992, House of Cards, 1993, Searching for Bobby Fischer, 1993, It Could Happen to You, 1994, (TV movies) The Gangster Chronicles, 1981, The Elephant Man, 1982 (Emmy award nomination best costume design 1982), Little Gloria...Happy at Last, 1982 (Emmy award nomination best costume design 1983), The Dollmaker, 1984 (Emmy award best costume design 1984), Do You Remember Love?, 1985, Evergreen, 1985 (Emmy award nomination best costume design 1985), Conspiracy of Love, 1987; costume cons.: (films) Cherry 2000, 1988. Office: care Costume Designer's Guild 13949 Ventura Blvd Ste 309 Sherman Oaks CA 91423*

WEISS, KENNETH ANDREW, lawyer, law educator; b. New Orleans, Jan. 16, 1951; s. Irving and Julia (Mayer) W.; m. Barbara Hollingsworth, June 30, 1979. BA, Tulane U., 1972, JD with honors, 1975; LLM in Taxation with highest honors, George Washington U., 1981. Bar: La. 1975, D.C. 1976. Edit. writer, Washington corr. The Times-Picayune, New Orleans and Washington, 1973-79; news editor Congl. Quarterly, Washington, 1979-81; mng. editor Reporters Com. for Freedom of the Press, Washington, 1981-82; assoc. atty. McGlinchey Stafford Lang, New Orleans, 1982-84, ptnr., 1984—; prof. Tulane U. Law Sch., New Orleans, 1987—; mem. trust code com. La. Law Inst., Baton Rouge, 1993—. Co-author: Bankers' Guide to Establishing, Managing and Operating Common Trust Funds, 1986, Business Uses of Life Insurance, 1986, Executive Compensation, 1990; assoc. editor Tulane Law Rev., 1974-75, mem. bd. adv. editors, 1992—; contbr. articles to profl. jours. Bd. dirs. Longue Vue House and Gardens Adv. Corp., 1993—; trustee Greater New Orleans Ednl. TV Found., Sta. WYES-TV, 1994—; mem. profl. adv. com. Jewish Endowment Found., 1982—; mem. planned gifts adv. com. Tulane U., 1989—; active Met. Area Com. Leadership Forum, New Orleans, 1983; fellow Inst. Politics, Loyola U., New Orleans, 1989-90. Recipient Addy award for polit. advt., 1989, awards for investigative reporting; Phi Delta Phi scholar, 1972-73. Fellow Am. Coll. Trust and Estate Counsel; mem. La. State Bar Assn. (taxation sect., bd. cert. tax atty.), New Orleans Bar Assn., New Orleans Estate Planning Coun., Order of the Coif. Republican. Jewish. Office: McGlinchey Stafford Lang 643 Magazine St New Orleans LA 70130

WEISS, LEONARD, mathematician, engineer, senate staff director; b. N.Y.C., Mar. 14, 1934; s. Max and Sadie (Albert) W.; m. Sandra Joyce Raynes, June 15, 1958; children: Madelyn, Eugene. B.E.E., CCNY, 1956, M.S., Columbia U., 1959; Ph.D., Johns Hopkins U., 1962. Lectr. CCNY, 1956-59; staff scientist Research Inst. for Advanced Studies, Balt., 1962-64; asst. prof. Brown U., Providence, 1964-66; assoc. prof. Brown U., 1966-68; prof. U. Md., College Park, 1968-78; lectr. asst. to Senator John Glenn of Ohio, 1976-77; cons. Naval Research Lab., Washington, 1970-77; staff dir. Senate Subcom. on Energy, Nuclear Proliferation and Govt. Processes, 1977-86, Senate Com. Govtl. Affairs, 1987—. Editor: Ordinary Differential Equations, 1972; contbr. articles to profl. jours.; author legislation on nuclear proliferation, energy, govt. orgn., and govt. mgmt. Alfred P. Sloan research fellow, 1966-68; IEEE Congl. fellow, 1975-76. Mem. AAAS, IEEE, Sigma Xi. Home: 11701 Auth Ln Silver Spring MD 20902-1644 Office: 340 Dirksen Washington DC 20510

WEISS, LEWIS STEPHEN, pharmaceutical executive; b. N.Y.C., June 5, 1934; s. Moe and Rose (Kiel) W.; m. Linda Sharon Freid, Jan 8, 1967; 1 child, Scott Jeffrey. BS in Pharmacy, L.I. U., 1956. Exec. v.p. Nysco Labs. div. Revlon Health Care, N.Y.C., 1962-77, Rexall Drug Co., N.Y.C., 1977-81; v.p. pharms. ICC Industries, N.Y.C., 1981-84; pres. L.S. Weiss & Co., Inc., N.Y.C., 1984-94; chmn. of bd. Pharmaceutical Recruiters, Inc., N.Y.C., 1994—; bd. dirs. Zenith Labs., Montvale, N.J., Medigum Corp. Contbr. articles to profl. jours. Mem. Nat. Assn. Pharm. Mfrs., Aircraft Owners and Pilots Assn., Drug, Chem. and Allied Trades Assn., Pvt. Label Mfrs. Assn. (founding, bd. dirs. 1979—), Delta Sigma Theta (pres. 1955-56). Jewish. Club: Concord Squash (N.Y.C.) (bd. dirs. 1987—). Avocations: flying, squash. Home: 315 E 68th St New York NY 10021-5692

WEISS, LIONEL EDWARD, geology educator; b. London, Eng., Dec. 11, 1927; came to U.S., 1956, naturalized, 1972; s. S. and E. (Carney) W.; m. Liv Mariane Nissen-Sollie, Dec. 27, 1964; children: Nicholas Erling, Elin Katrina. B.Sc. with 1st class honours, U. Birmingham, Eng., 1949, Ph.D., 1953; Sc.D., U. Edinburgh, Scotland, 1956. Commonwealth Fund fellow U. Calif. at Berkeley, 1951-53; sr. research fellow U. Edinburgh, 1953-56; mem. faculty U. Calif. at Berkeley, 1956—, prof. geology, 1964-89, emeritus prof. geology, 1989—; Miller research prof., 1965, 66; cons. in field. Author: (with F.J. Turner) Structural Analysis of Metamorphic Tectonites, 1963, (with others) The Earth, 1970, The Minor Structures of Deformed Rocks, 1972; also articles. Guggenheim fellow, 1962, 69; Fulbright scholar Norway, 1975. Home: 1954 Patricia Dr Pleasant Hill CA 94523-2930

WEISS, MAREDA RUTH, university administrator; b. Chgo., Sept. 23, 1941; d. William Arthur and Ruth Emily (Schauble) W. BBA, U. Wis., 1963. Acct., then super. rsch. adminstrn./fin. U. Wis. System, Madison, 1964-69; specialist, asst. dean, now assoc. dean, dir. rsch. svcs. U. Wis., Madison, 1969—; univ. chair State Employees Combined Campaign, Madison, 1986. Treas. Wis. Cen. Ctr. Aux., Madison, 1971-73, 75-77, 79-81, Frineds of WHA-TV pub. tv, Madison, 1989-91; chair nominating com. U. Wis. Credit Union, 1982-88. Mem. Nat. Coun. Univ. Rsch. Adminstrs. (presenter workshops, sec.-treas. 1980-83, chair, vice-chair mid-Am. region 1989-91, Disting. Svc. award 1989), Univ. Ins. Assn. (bd. dirs. 1982—). Avocations: skiing, golf, photography, travel. Office: U Wis Grad Sch 500 Lincoln Dr Madison WI 53706-1380

WEISS, MARINA, government official; b. Ann Arbor, Mich., Dec. 26, 1944; d. Lyndon E. and Marina Lee; m. Michael Edward Weiss, Jan. 9, 1971; children: Paige, Whitney. BA, Am. U., 1967; MA, U. Tex., 1971; PhD, Tex. A&M U., 1978. Mem. faculty Tex. A&M U., College Station, 1971-78; found. fin. and grants coord. City Hall, Waco, Tex., 1979-80; legis. asst. Senator Lloyd Bentsen, Washington, 1980-86; chief counsel health and income security U.S. Senate Fin. Com., Washington, 1986-93; dep. asst. sec. for health policy U.S. Treasury Dept., Washington, 1993—. Home: 2025 Turtle Pond Dr Reston VA 22091 Office: US Dept Treasury 1500 Pennsylvania Ave NW Washington DC 20220

WEISS, MARK, public relations executive; b. N.Y.C., Mar. 5, 1950. BA in Psychology, Queens Coll., 1972; MA om Social Psychology, New Sch. for Social Rsch., 1975. With Multimedia Advt./Pub. Rels., 1970-74; account rep. Edward Baker, Inc., 1974-78; account exec. Rowland Co., 1978-81, v.p., 1980-84, sr. v.p., 1984-86, exec. v.p., 1986-90, exec. v.p., COO, 1991-92, pres., CEO, 1992—. Office: Rowland Worldwide Inc 1675 Broadway New York NY 10019*

WEISS, MARK ANSCHEL, lawyer; b. N.Y.C., June 20, 1937; s. George and Ida (Galin) W.; m. Joan Roth, June 8, 1958; children—Rebecca, Sarabeth, Jonathan, Deborah. A.B., Columbia U., 1958; LL.B. magna cum laude, Harvard U., 1961; Bar: N.Y. 1961, D.C. 1962, U.S. Supreme Ct. 1965. Assoc. Covington & Burling, Washington, 1961-66, 69-70, ptnr., 1970—; spl. asst. to Under Sec. Treasury Dept., Washington, 1966-68, spl. asst. to sec., 1968-69. Mem. D.C. Bar, ABA, Fed. Bar Assn., City Club (Washington). Office: Covington & Burling PO Box 7566 1201 Pennsylvania Ave NW Washington DC 20044

WEISS, MARK LAWRENCE, anthropology educator; b. Bklyn., Nov. 1, 1945; s. Arthur A. and Ruth E. Heilbronn W.; m. Linda K. Spangler, July 31, 1993; children: Evan M., Emily C. BA, SUNY, Binghamton, 1966; MA, U. Calif., Berkeley, 1968, PhD, 1969. Asst. prof. anthropology Wayne State U., Detroit, 1969-73, assoc. prof., 1973-87, prof., 1987—; program dir. phys. anthropology NSF, Washington, 1990-92. Co-author: Human Biology and Behavior, 1975; contbr. articles to Nature, Am. Jour. Primatology, Yearbook, Phys. Anthropology, Jour. Molecular Biology; mem. editorial bd. Human Biology, 1988—, Yearbook of Phys. Anthropology, 1992—, Jour. Human Evolution, 1994—. Recipient award in excellence in teaching and rsch. Probus Club, 1973. Fellow Am. Anthrop. Assn., Am. Assn. Phys. Anthropologists (exec. com. 1993-96). Jewish. Office: Dept Anthropology Wayne State Univ. Detroit MI 48202

WEISS, MARTIN HARVEY, neurosurgeon, educator; b. Newark, Feb. 2, 1939; s. Max and Rae W.; m. R. Debora Rosenthal, Aug. 20, 1961; children: Brad, Jessica, Elisabeth. A.B. magna cum laude, Dartmouth Coll., 1960, B.M.S., 1961; M.D., Cornell U., 1963. Diplomate Am. Bd. Neurol. Surgery (bd. dirs. 1983-89, vice chmn. 1987-88, chmn. 1988-89). Intern Univ. Hosps., Cleve., 1963-64; resident in neurosurgery Univ. Hosps., 1966-70; sr. instr. to asst. prof. neurosurgery Case Western Res. U., 1970-73; asso. prof. neurosurgery U. So. Calif., 1973-76, prof., 1976-78, prof., chmn. dept., 1978—; chmn. neurology B study sect. NIH; mem. residency rev. com. for neurosurgery Accreditation Commn. for Grad. Med. Edn., 1989—, vice neurosurgery Accreditation Commn. for Grad. Med. Edn., 1989—, vice chmn., 1991-93, chmn., 1993—; Courville lectr. Sch. Medicine, Loma Linda U., 1989; W. James Gardner lectr. Cleve. Clinic, 1993; Edwin Boldrey vis. prof. U. Calif. San Francisco, 1994; hon. guest San Francisco Neurol. Soc., 1994; hon. guest San Francisco Neurol. Soc., 1994; Arthur Ward vis. prof. U. Wash., 1988; Afrox traveling prof. South African Cong. of Neurol. Surgeons, 1989; Loyal Davis lectr. Northwestern U., 1990. Author: Pituitary Diseases, 1980; mem. editl. bd. Neurosurgery, 1979-84, Neurol. Rsch., 1980—, Jour. Neurosurgery, 1987—, chmn., 1995—; editor-in-chief Clin. Neurosurgery, 1980-83; assoc. editor Bull. L.A. Neurol. Socs., 1976-81, Jour. Clin. Neurosci., 1981—. Served to capt. USAR, 1964-66. Spl. fellow in neurosurgery NIH, 1969-70. Mem. ACS (adv. coun. neurosurgery 1985-88), Soc. Neurol. Surgeons, Neurosurg. Soc. Am., Am. Acad. Neurol. Surgery (exec. com. 1988-89, v.p. 1992-93), Rsch. Soc. Neurol. Surgeons, Am. Assn. Neurol. Surgeons (bd. dirs. 1988-91, sec. 1994-97), Congress Neurol. Surgeons (v.p. 1982-83), Western Neurosurg. Soc., Neurosurg. Forum, So. Calif. Neurosurg. Soc. (pres. 1983-84), Phi Beta Kappa, Alpha Omega Alpha. Home: 357 Georgian Rd La Canada Flintridge CA 91011-3520 Office: 1200 N State St Los Angeles CA 90033-4525

WEISS, MAX TIBOR, aerospace company executive; b. Hajdunanas, Hungary, Dec. 29, 1922; came to U.S., 1929, naturalized, 1936; s. Samuel and Anna (Hornstein) W.; m. Melitta Newman, June 28, 1953; children: Samuel Harvey, Herschel William, David Nathaniel, Deborah Beth. BEE, CCNY, 1943; MS, MIT, 1947, PhD, 1950. Rsch. assoc. MIT, 1946-50; mem. tech. staff Bell Tel. Labs., Holmdel, N.J., 1950-59; assoc. head applied physics lab. Hughes Aircraft Co., Culver City, Calif., 1959-60; dir. electronics rsch. lab. The Aerospace Corp., L.A., 1961-63, gen. mgr. labs. div., 1963-67, gen. mgr. electronics and optics div., 1968-78, v.p., gen. mgr. lab. ops., 1978-81, v.p. engring. group, 1981-86; v.p. gen. mgr. labs. div. Northrop Corp., Hawthorne, Calif., 1991-94; corp. v.p., dep. gen. mgr. electronics/systems integration Northrop Grumman Corp., Bethpage, N.Y., 1994—; asst. mgr. engring. ops. TRW Systems, Redondo Beach, Calif., 1967-68; mem. sci. adv. bd. USAF. Contbr. articles to physics and electronics jours.; patentee in electronics and communications. With USNR, 1944-45. Fellow Am. Phys. Soc., IEEE, AIAA, AAAS; mem. NAE, Sigma Xi. Office: Northrop Corp 2301 W 120th St Hawthorne CA 90251-5032

WEISS, MELVYN I., lawyer; b. N.Y.C., Aug. 1, 1935; s. Joseph and Jean Weiss; m. Barbara Joan Kaplan, Dec. 27, 1958; children: Gary Michael, Stephen Andrew, Leslie Caryn. BBA, CCNY, 1957; JD, NYU, 1959. Bar: N.Y. 1960, U.S. Ct. Appeals (2d, 5th, 8th and 9th cirs.) 1975, U.S. Supreme Ct. 1976. Assoc. Strasser, Spiegelberg, Fried & Frank, N.Y.C., 1959-61, Galef & Jacobs, N.Y.C., 1962-65; founding ptnr. Milberg, Weiss, Bershad,

Specthrie & Lerach(now Milberg, Weiss, Bershad, Hynes & Lerach), N.Y.C., San Diego, 1966—; lectr., panelist universities, bar groups, continuing legal edn. orgns. Author: handbook; contbr. articles to profl. jours. Founder Melvyn and Barbara Weiss Pub. Interest Student Loan Repayment Found., NYU. Mem. ABA, Am. Coll. Trial Laywers, B'nai B'rith (Human Rels. award Anti Defamation League 1976), CCNY Alumni Assn. (Oustanding Alumni award 1982), Muttontown Golf and Country Club, Boca Rio Golf Club. Home: 34 The Hollows Muttontown NY 11732-1513 Office: Milberg Weiss Bershad Hynes & Lerach 1 Penn Plz New York NY 10119

WEISS, MICHAEL JAMES, chemistry educator; b. N.Y.C., May 29, 1941; s. Irving and Florence (James) W.; m. Myra Lee Landau, June 10, 1967; 1 child, Amy Merril Weiss Musikar. BS in Chemistry, Bklyn. Coll., 1964; MS in Chemistry, Adelphi U., 1966; PhD in Biochemistry, N.Y. Med. Coll., 1971. Supr. clin. chemistry Queens Gen. Hosp., N.Y.C. 1971-77; dir. biochemistry Kingsborough Med. Ctr., N.Y.C., 1977-78; lab. dir. Nassau (N.Y.) Diagnostic Lab., 1978-86; chemistry educator N.Y. Bd. Edn., 1986—; lab. cons., N.Y., 1986—. Author: (chpt.) The Antigenic Nature of Mamalian Cell Membranes, 1976; contbr. articles to profl. jours. Maj. U.S. Army, 1978—. Recipient Conspicous Svc. cross Howard Hughes Med. Inst., 1993, fellowship Howard Hughes Med. Inst., 1994. Mem. AAAS, N.Y. Acad. Sci., Armed Forces Soc. Med. Lab. Scientists. Achievements include research in oneofetal antigens.

WEISS, MORDECHAI, principal. Prin. Hebrew Acad. Atlantic County, Margate City, N.J. Recipient Elem. Sch. Recognition award U.S. Dept. Edn., 1989-90. Office: Hebrew Acad Atlantic County 601 N Jerome Ave Margate City NJ 08402-1599

WEISS, MORRY, greeting card company executive; b. Czechoslovakia, 1940; m. Judith Stone. Grad., Wayne State U. Salesman, field mgr. Am. Greetings Corp., Cleve., 1961-66, advt. mgr., 1966-68, v.p., 1969-73, group v.p. mktg. and sales, 1973-78, formerly chief operating officer, from 1978, pres., 1978-92, also bd. dirs., chief exec. officer, 1987—, chmn., 1992—. Office: Am Greetings Corp 10500 American Rd Cleveland OH 44144-2301*

WEISS, MYRNA GRACE, business consultant; b. N.Y.C., June 22, 1939; d. Herman and Blanche (Stiftel) Ziegler; m. Arthur H. Weiss; children: Debra Anne Huddleston, Louise Esther. BA, Barnard Coll., 1958; MA, Hunter Coll., 1968; MPA, NYU, 1978; cert. in Mktg., U. Pa. Tchr. N.Y.C. and Vallejo, Calif., 1959-68; dir. admissions Columbia Prep. Sch., N.Y.C., 1969-72; dir. PREP counselling NYU, N.Y.C., 1973-74; dept. head Hewitt Sch., N.Y.C., 1974-79; mgr. Met. Ins. Co., N.Y.C., 1979-84; mktg. exec. Rothschild, Inc., N.Y.C., 1984-85; pres. First Mktg. Capital Group Ltd., N.Y.C., 1985—; mng. dir. Wrap Co. Internat. N.V., 1992—; advisor Lared Group, N.Y.C., 1987—; advisor Gov.'s Hwy. Safety Com., N.Y.C., 1985-88; pres. Fin. Women's Assn. N.Y., 1984-85. Bd. dirs. 92nd Y, N.Y.C., 1972-90, ARC, N.Y.C., 1989—, asst. treas., 1993—. Mem. Internat. Women's Forum (bd. dirs. 1990-92), Econ. Club N.Y., Women's Econ. Roundtable (bd. dirs. 1988-90). Office: 1st Mktg Capital Group Ltd 1056 Fifth Ave New York NY 10028-0112

WEISS, PAUL, philosopher, educator; b. N.Y.C., May 19, 1901; s. Samuel and Emma (Rothschild) W.; m. Victoria Brodie, Oct. 27, 1928 (dec. Dec. 31, 1953); children: Judith, Jonathan. BSS, CCNY, 1927; MA, Harvard U., 1928, PhD (Sears Travelling fellow), 1929; hon. degrees, Grinnell Coll., 1960, Pace Coll., 1969, Bellarmine Coll., 1973, Haverford Coll., 1974, Boston U., 1989. Instr., tutor philosophy Harvard U., also instr. Radcliffe Coll., 1930-31; assoc. in philosophy Bryn Mawr (Pa.) Coll., 1931-33, assoc. prof., 1933-40, prof., 1940-46, chmn. dept., 1944-46; Guggenheim fellow, 1938; vis. prof. Yale U., 1945-46, prof. philosophy, 1946-62, Sterling prof. philosophy, 1962-69, Sterling prof. emeritus, 1969—; fellow Ezra Stiles Coll.; vis. prof. philosophy Hebrew U., Jerusalem, 1951; Luce-Rabinowitz grantee for study, Israel and India, 1954; lectr. Aspen Inst., 1952, Chancellor's Forum, U. Denver, 1952; Orde Wingate lectr., 1954; Powell lectr. U. Ind., 1958; Gates lectr. Grinnell Coll., 1960; Matchette lectr. Purdue U., 1961, Wesleyan Coll., 1963; Aquinas lectr. Marquette U., 1963; Townsend Harris medalist, 1963; Rhoades lectr. Haverford Coll., 1964; Phi Beta Kappa lectr., 1968-69; resident scholar State U. N.Y., 1969, 70; vis. prof. U. Denver spring 1969; Eliot lectr. Marquette U., 1970; William De Vane medalist Yale, 1971; Aquinas lectr. St. Mary's, 1971; medalist City Coll., 1973, Hofstra U., 1973; B. Means lectr. Trinity Coll.; Japan, 1981; Ann. McDermott Lectr. U. Dallas, 1983; vis. Heffer prof. Philosophy Cath. U. Am., 1969-91, 93-94. Author: Reality, 1938, Nature and Man, 1947, Man's Freedom, 1950 (Portugese transl., 1960), Modes of Being, 1958, Our Public Life, 1959, World of Art, 1961 (Hebrew transl., 1976), Nine Basic Arts, 1961, History: Written and Lived, 1962, Religion and Art, 1963, The God We Seek, 1964, Philosophy in Process, 12 vols., 1955-88, The Making of Men, 1967, Sport: A Philosophic Inquiry, 1969 (Japanese transl., 1985, Korean transl., 1993), Beyond All Appearances, 1974, Cinematics, 1975, First Considerations, 1977, You, I and the Others, 1980, Privacy, 1983, Toward a Perfected State, 1986, Creative Ventures, 1991, At Open Court, 1995, Being and Other Realities, 1995; co-author: Right and Wrong: A Philosophical Dialogue Between Father and Son, 1967, 71, Hebrew translation, 1971, Approaches to World Peace, 1944, Perspectives on a Troubled Decade, 1950, Moral Principles of Action, 1952, Personal Moments of Discovery, 1953, Perspectives on Peirce, 1965, Dimensions of Job, 1969, Mid-Century American Philosophy, 1974, Philosophy of Baruch Spinoza, 1980, Existence and Actuality, 1984, When the Worst That Can Happen Already Has, 1992; co-editor: Collected Papers of Charles S. Peirce, 6 vols.; founder, editor Rev. of Metaphysics, 1947-63; mem. editorial bd. Judaism, Jour. of Speculative Philosophy; contbr. to profl. periodicals. Mem. Assn. for Symbolic Logic (councillor 1936—), Am. Philos. Assn. (co-pres. 1966), Conf. on Sci. Philos. and Religion (founding mem.), C. S. Peirce Soc. (founding mem., pres.), Metaphys. Soc. Am. (founder, pres. 1951, 52, councillor 1953-58), Philos. Soc. for Study of Sport (founder, pres. 1973), Am. Friends of Hebrew U., Philos. Edn. Soc., Inc. (founder), Washington Philos. Club (C.S. Peirce award), Société Européenne de Culture, Academie Internationale de Philosophie de l'Art, Am. Assn. Middle East Studies, Aurelian Club, Elizabethan Club, Washington Philosophic Club, Phi Beta Kappa. Address: 2000 N St NW Washington DC 20036

WEISS, PAUL THOMAS, federal agency executive; b. Bismarck, N.D., Nov. 18, 1944; s. Earl Paul and Hazel Lucretia (Baker) W.; children: Mark David, Clare Elizabeth. BS, U. N.D., 1967. Pers. mgmt. specialist Dept. Justice, Washington, 1970-72; labor employee relations specialist Dept. Treasury, Washington, 1972-77; assoc. dir. human resources Comptr. of Currency, Washington, 1977-80; dep. dir. pers. Dept. Treasury, Washington, 1980-83, dir. pers., 1984-85; assoc. adminstr. for adminstrn. GSA, Washington, 1985-89; assoc. dir. mgmt. and budget U.S. Action Agy., Washington, 1989-90; dep. asst. sec. for adminstrn. Dept. Transp., Washington, 1990-95; mgmt. cons., 1995—; mem. Pres. Coun. Mgmt. Improvement, 1985-89; mem. panel on pub. svc. Nat. Acad. Pub. Adminstrn., 1986—; v.p., mem. exec. com. Am. Consortium for Internat. Pub. Adminstrn., 1986—; bd. dirs. Worldwide Assurance for Employees of Pub. Agys., Inc., 1986—. Author (booklet) You and Your Employees, 1974; author, reviewer numerous reports and govt. manuals. With Med. Svc. Corps, U.S. Army, 1969-70, Vietnam. Decorated Bronze Star medal with 3 oak leaf clusters; recipient Pres. Rank Meritorious Svc. award Pres. U.S., 1987, awards U.S. Treas., 1979, 85, Govt. Exec. Mag. Leadership award, 1992. Mem. Sr. Execs. Assn., Am. Soc. Pub. Adminstrs. (bd. dirs. Nat. Capital area chpt.). Roman Catholic. Avocations: bridge, jogging, reading. Office: US Dept Transp 400 7th St NW Washington DC 20590-0001

WEISS, RAINER, physics educator; b. Berlin, Sept. 29, 1932. BS, MIT, 1955, PhD, 1962. Instr. physics Tufts U., Medford, Mass., 1960-61, asst. prof. physics, 1961-62; rsch. assoc. in physics Princeton U., 1962-64; asst. prof. physics MIT, Cambridge, 1964-67, assoc. prof. 1967-73; prof. physics MIT, 1973—; mem. NASA phys. sci. com., 1970-74, SSSC com., 1982, infrared detector panel, 1978, others; mem. Panel on Joint Inst. of Lab. Astrophysics, Bd. on Assessment of NBS Programs, Nat. Acad. Scis., 1985—; coord. NSF Panel on Interferometric Obs. for Gravitational Waves, 1986; mem. Nat. Acad. Sci. space sci. bd., 1983-86, others. Recipient MIT Baker award for excellence in teaching, 1968; NASA Achievement Award (Monolithic Bolometers), 1984, Exceptional Sci. Achievement medal, 1991, Group Achievement medal, 1991; NASA/GSFC Group Achievement award, 1990. Mem. AAAS, Am. Phys. Soc., Am. Astron. Soc. Achievements include research in experimental atomic physics, atomic clocks, laser physics, experimental gravitation, millimeter and sub-millimeter astronomy, cosmic background measurements. Office: MIT Rm 20 F 001 77 Massachusetts Ave Boston MA 02139-4307

WEISS, RENÉE KAROL, editor, writer, musician; b. Allentown, Pa., Sept. 11, 1923; d. Abraham S. and Elizabeth (Levitt) Karol; m. Theodore Weiss. BA, Bard Coll., 1951; student, Conn. Sch. Dance; studied violin with, Sascha Jacobinoff, Boris Koutzen, Emile Hauser, Ivan Galamian. Mem. Miami U. Symphony Orch., 1941, N.C. State Sympnony, 1942-45, Oxford U. Symphony, Opera Orchs., Eng., 1953-54, Woodstock String Quartet, 1956-60, Bard Coll. Chamber Ensemble, 1950-66, Hudson Valley Philharmonic, 1960-66, Hudson Valley String Quartet, 1965, Princeton Chamber Orch., 1980-93; orchestral, chamber, solo work, 1966—; with Theodore Weiss poetry writing workshops, Princeton U., 1985, Hofstra Coll., 1985, Modern Poetry Cooper Union, 1988; tchr. modern dance to children Bard Coll., kindengarren Tivoli, N.Y. Pub. Sch., 1955-58. Author: (children's books) To Win A Race, 1966, A Paper Zoo, 1968 (best books for children N.Y. Times, Book World 1968, N.J. Author's award 1968, 70, 88), The Bird From the Sea, 1970, David Schubert: Works and Days, 1984; co-editor, mgr. Quar. Rev. Lit., 1945—; contbr. poems to various jours.; poetry readings (with Theodore Weiss) at various colls. in U.S. and abroad, including China. Office: Q R L Poetry Series 26 Haslet Ave Princeton NJ 08540-4914

WEISS, RICHARD R., rocket propulsion technology executive; b. Detroit, Nov. 4, 1934; s. Charles Max and Edna May (Guard) W.; m. Sally Anita Sparkman, Aug. 10, 1957; children: Mark, Kevin, Todd, Scott. BS in Aero. Engring., U. Mich., 1957; MSME, U. So. Calif., 1964; D of Mech. Engring., Purdue U., 1970. Devel. engr. Jupiter Missile rocket engine Rocketdyne, 1957-58; unit chief, test condr. THOR Missile test program Air Force Rocket Prop. Lab. 1958-61, various tech. positions, 1961-65, various engring. mgmt. positions, 1965-74, chief scientist, 1974-85, 1st dir. Strategic Def. Initiative Tech. Office, 1985-87; chief scientist Air Force Rocket Prop. Lab. (renamed Astronautics Lab.), 1987-89; dir. Astronautics Lab., 1989-90; chief scientist, dir. Astronautics Lab. (merger Phillips Lab.), 1990-91; dir. Propulsion Directorate Phillips Lab. Operating Location, Edwards AFB, Calif., 1991-92; dep. dir. space launch systems and tech. Office of Under Sec. of Def., Strategic and Space Systems, Missiles and Space Systems, 1993-94; ret., 1994; past tech. panel chmn. Space Launch Modernization Plan, 1994; mem. Nat. Rsch. Coun. Aeronautics & Space Engring. Bd., Advanced Space Tech. Panel, Washington, 1992-94; U.S. rep. Agard Propulsion & Energetics Panel, Paris, 1987—; mem. ad hoc panel on space launch USAF Sci., 1993—; chmn. Joint Army, Navy, AF (JANNAF) Interagy. Chem. Propulsion Exec. Com.; contbr. to rocket propulsion devels. for most of the nation's space and missile sys. including Apollo, Space Shuttle, Titan, Atlas, Peacekeeper, Minuteman, Strategic Def. Initiative;. 1st lt. USAF, 1958-61. Co-recipient Air Force Sys. Command Aerospace Primus award, 1986. Fellow AIAA (assoc., AIAA Wyld Propulsion award 1994). Home: 5912 Walnut Way Palmdale CA 93551*

WEISS, ROBERT BENJAMIN, lawyer; b. Perth Amboy, N.J., Aug. 27, 1948; s. Denes and Patricia (Chazin) W.; m. Susan Stern, June 11, 1972; children: Elana, Shira, Danielle. BA, Yeshiva U., 1971; JD, Case Western U., 1975. Bar: Mich. 1977, U.S. Dist. Ct. (ea. dist.) Mich. 1978. Assoc. Ulmer, Berne, Laronge, Glickman & Curtis, Cleve., 1975-76; staff atty. Gen. Motors Corp., Detroit, 1976-82; ptnr. Honigman Miller Schwartz & Cohn, Detroit, 1982—. Office: Honigman Miller Schwartz & Cohn 2290 1st National Bldg Detroit MI 48226

WEISS, ROBERT FRANCIS, former academic administrator, religious organization administrator, consultant; b. St. Louis, Aug. 27, 1924; s. Frank L. G. and Helen M. (Beck) W. B.A., St. Louis U., 1951, Ph.L., 1953, M.A., 1953, S.T.L., 1961; Ph.D., U. Minn., 1964. Joined Soc. of Jesus, 1946; ordained priest Roman Catholic Ch., 1959; tchr. Rockhurst High Sch., Kansas City, Mo., 1953-56; adminstrv. asst. to pres. St. Louis U., 1961-62; asst. dean Rockhurst Coll., Kansas City, Mo., 1964-66, dean, v.p., asst. prof. edn., 1966-72, pres., 1977-88; pres. St. Louis U. High Sch., 1973-77, interim pres., 1992; asst. for higher edn. and continuing formation Mo. Province S.J., St. Louis, 1989-92, treas., 1992—; mem. Commn. on Govtl. Rels., Am. Coun. Edn., 1985-87; bd. dirs. Kansas City Regional Coun. for Higher Edn., 1978-88, Boys Hope/Girls Hope, 1977—. Contbr. chpts. to books, articles to profl. jours. Trustee St. Louis U., 1973-87, 91—, Loyola U. New Orleans, 1973-82, 85-88, United Student Aid Funds, Inc., 1977-94, U. San Francisco, 1987—, Marymount Coll., Salina, Kans., 1986-88, St. Louis U. H.S., 1989—, Fontbonne Coll., St. Louis, 1973-77; bd. dirs. Creighton U., Omaha, 1981—; trustee Sacred Heart Program, Radio and TV Apostolate, St. Louis, 1990—, pres., 1992—; bd. dirs. Our Little Haven, 1992—. With U.S. Army, 1943-46. Decorated Bronze Star. Mem. Am. Assn. for Higher Edn., Rainbow Div. Vets. Assn. (nat. chaplain 1976-84, 88-90, pres.-elect 1990-91, pres. 1991-92), Alpha Sigma Nu, Alpha Phi Omega. Home and Office: 4511 W Pine Blvd Saint Louis MO 63108-2109 *The only way for me to look at life is in the light of faith, which I consider one of God's greatest gifts. Life for me is an opportunity to serve God and as many of my neighbors as I can. I am basically an optimist. There is so much beauty around us, so many good people, so many marvels to behold—that I thank the Lord for giving me the ability to know and experience this life and to look forward to eternal life with God, the Source of all life. Any success I have had I attribute to taking advantage of the opportunities that God has put in my path.*

WEISS, ROBERT JEROME, psychiatrist, educator; b. West New York, N.J., Dec. 9, 1917; s. Harry and Dora (Samuels) W.; m. Minnie Thompson Moore, Apr. 21, 1945; children:—Scott Tillman, James Woodrow, Elizabeth Thompson. Student, Johns Hopkins, 1937; A.B., George Washington U., 1947; M.D., Columbia, 1951; M.A. (hon.), Dartmouth, 1964. Intern Columbia div. Bellevue Hosp., 1951, asst. resident medicine, 1953; resident psychiatry N.Y. Psychiat. Inst., 1954-56; asst. attending Vanderbilt Clinic, 1957-58, Presbyn. Hosp., N.Y., 1958-59; chief psychiatry Mary Hitchcock Meml. Hosp., 1959-70; career tchr. trainee Nat. Inst. Mental Health, 1956-58; tchr., research Columbia Coll. Phys. and Surg., 1956-59; prof. psychiatry, chmn. dept. Dartmouth Med. Sch., 1959-70; psychiatrist Beth Israel Hosp., 1988-90; attending physician Presbyn. Hosp., 1975-85, cons., 1985—; vis. prof. community medicine Harvard Med. Sch., 1970-71, vis. prof. psychiatry, 1988-91; cons. Ednl. Devel. Ctr., 1989—; also assoc. dir. Ctr. for Community Health and Med. Care, 1970-75, assoc. dean health care planning, 1970-75; prof. psychiatry and social medicine Columbia Coll. Phys. & Surg., 1975-86, also dir. Centers for Community Health, 1975-86; De Lamar prof. public health practice, dean Columbia U. Sch. Public Health, 1980-86, dean and Delemar prof. of pub. health practice, prof. psychiatry, prof. social medicine, emeritus, 1986—; vis. prof. community medicine U. N.Mex. Med. Sch., 1986-89; cons. N.H. Div. Mental Health, 1959-70, Nat. Ctr. for Health Svcs. Rsch., 1975-86, NIMH, 1977-86; cons. psychiatry Mass. Gen. Hosp., 1970-75; chmn. adv. commn. N.H. Dept. Health and Welfare, 1961-65; exec. com. N.H. Mental Health Planning Project, 1964-66; mem. adv. commn. Mental Health Commn. for N.H., 1965-70; chmn. psychiatry tng. com. NIMH, 1967-68, mem. coord. panel, 1965-67; ad hoc com. interdisciplinary tng. program, 1966, mem. agenda com., 1966; Schumann lectr. Dartmouth Med. Sch., 1986; cons. AT&T, 1990-92; chmn. bd. Acamedica, 1992, Employee Managed Care Corp., 1994—. Co-editor: Columbia U. Coll. Physicians and Surgeons Complete Home Medical Guide, 1986, editor emeritus 2d edit., 1989; author articles, chpts. in books. Served to maj. AUS, 1941-46. Recipient Bi-Centennial medal Columbia Coll. Phys. and Surg., 1967. Fellow Am. Psychiat. Assn. (life); mem. N.Y. Soc. Clin. Psychiatry, N.Y. Psychiat. Inst. Alumni Assn. (pres. 1961), Acad. Psychoanalysis, Am. Assn. Med. Colls., AAAS, N.Y. Acad. Sci., N.Y. Acad. Medicine, Herman Biggs Soc., No. New Eng. Psychiat. Soc. (councillor 1969-75), Am. Assn. Chmn. Depts. Psychiatry (pres. 1969-70). Achievements include demonstrated social supports reduce disability due to mental illness; research in special health care delivery, health care preventive psychiatry. Home: 34 Allison Rd Princeton NJ 08540-3002

WEISS, ROBERT M., urologist, educator; b. N.Y.C., Jan. 13, 1936; s. David and Laura W.; m. Ilana Shemer, May 20, 1973; children—Erik Daniel, Dana Alexandra. B.S. magna cum laude, Franklin and Marshall Coll., Lancaster, Pa., 1957; M.D. SUNY, Bklyn., 1960; M.A. (hon.), Yale U., 1976. Diplomate: Am. Bd. Urology, Nat. Bd. Med. Examiners. Intern Cornell Med. Div., Bellevue Hosp., N.Y.C., 1960-61; resident in gen. surgery Beth Israel Hosp., N.Y.C., 1961-62; resident in urology Squier Urol. Clinic, Presbyn. Hosp., N.Y.C., 1963-64, 65-67; vs. fellow Columbia U. Coll. Physicians and Surgeons, N.Y.C., 1964-65, adj. assoc. prof. pharmacology, 1975-77, adj. prof. pharmacology, 1977—; mem. faculty Yale U. M.ed. Sch., New Haven, 1967—, prof. urology, 1976-88, prof., chief sect. of urology, 1988—; attending urology Yale-New Haven Hosp., New Haven, 1967-88, head sect. of urology, 1988—; cons. West Haven VA Hosp., Waterbury (Conn.) Hosp. Contbr. articles to med. publs. Served with USAR, 1962-63. Fellow ACS, Am. Acad. Pediatrics; mem. Am. Assn. Genito-Urinary Surgeons, Am. Physiol. Soc., Soc. Gen. Physiologists, Assn. Univ. Urologists, Soc. Pediatric Urology, Am. Urol. Assn., Am. Soc. Clin. Pharmacology and Therapeutics, Internat. Urodynamics Soc., AAAS, Internat. Soc. Dynamics of Upper Urinary Tract, Clin. Soc. Genito-Urinary Surgeons, Phi Beta Kappa, Sigma Xi. Office: Yale U Sch of Medicine 333 Cedar St New Haven CT 06510-3206

WEISS, ROBERT ORR, speech educator; b. Kalamazoo, Apr. 8, 1926; s. Nicholas John and Ruth (Orr) W.; m. Ann Lenore Lawson, Sept. 16, 1951; children: Elizabeth Ann, John Lawson, James Robert, Virginia Lenore. BA, Albion Coll., 1948; MA, Northwestern U., 1949, PhD, 1954. Instr. speech Wayne State U., Detroit, 1949-51; instr. pub. speaking Northwestern U., Evanston, Ill., 1954-55; mem. faculty DePauw U., Greencastle, Ind., 1955—, H.B. Gough prof. speech, 1965—, dir. forensics, head communication arts and scis., 1963-78, 85-86, 93. Author: Public Argument, 1995; editor: Speaker and Gavel, 1968-75; co-editor: Current Criticism, 1971; contbr. articles to profl. jours. Served with AUS, 1945-46. Mem. AAUP (pres. DePauw U. chpt. 1961-62), Speech Communication Assn. (legis. assembly 1966-68), Am. Forensic Assn. (sec.-treas. 1958-59), Cen. States Communication Assn., Internat. Communication Assn., Phi Beta Kappa, Delta Sigma Rho-Tau Kappa Alpha (nat. v.p. 1981-83, pres. 1983-85), Theta Alpha Phi, Omicron Delta Kappa, Sigma Nu. Home: 722 Highridge Ave Greencastle IN 46135-1402

WEISS, ROBERT STEPHEN, medical manufacturing and services company financial executive; b. Honesdale, Pa., Oct. 25, 1946; s. Stephen John and Anna Blanche (Lescinski) W.; BS in Acctg. cum laude, U. Scranton, 1968; m. Marilyn Annette Chesick, Oct. 29, 1970; children: Christopher Robert, Kim Marie, Douglas Paul. CPA, N.Y. Supr., Peat, Marwick, Mitchell & Co., N.Y.C., 1971-76; asst. corp. contr. Cooper Labs., Inc., Parsippany, N.J., 1977-78, v.p., corp. contr. Palo Alto, Calif., 1981-83; v.p., corp. contr. The Cooper Cos., Inc. (formerly CooperVision, Inc.), Palo Alto, Calif., 1984-89; v.p., treas., CFO The Cooper Cos., Inc., Pleasanton, Calif., 1989—, sr. v.p., 1992—; v.p. fin., contr. CooperVision Pharms., Mountain View, Calif., 1979, v.p. fin., contr. corp. contr., 1980; bd. dirs. The Cooper Cos., Inc., Ft. Lee, N.J., 1992-94. With U.S. Army, 1969-70. Decorated Bronze Star with oak leaf cluster, Army Commendation medal. Mem. AICPA, N.Y. State Soc. CPAs. Home: 446 Arlington Ct Pleasanton CA 94566-7708 Office: The Cooper Cos Inc 6140 Stoneridge Mall Rd Pleasanton CA 94588-3232

WEISS, RONALD WHITMAN, real estate executive, lawyer; b. N.Y.C., Aug. 13, 1939; s. Rudolph and Sandra (Walters) W.; m. Ellen Klein, Oct. 25, 1980; children: Hilary, Carolyn, Christopher. B.S. in Econs., U. Pa., 1961; J.D., L.L.B., Columbia U., 1964. Bar: N.Y. 1964; cert. prin. N.Y. Stock Exchange. Pvt. practice N.Y.C., 1964—; pres. Shearson Hamill Real Estate Corp., N.Y.C., 1971-73; pres., chmn. Shearson Hayden Stone Real Estate Corp., N.Y.C., 1973-75, Shearson Loeb Rhodes Real Estate Corp., N.Y.C., 1975-78, Shearson Am. Express Real Estate Corp., N.Y.C., 1979-84, Shearson Lehman Bros. Real Estate Corp., N.Y.C.; exec. v.p. Shearson Lehman Bros., Inc., N.Y.C., 1984-89; chmn., pres. CWS Fin. Group, N.Y.C., 1989—; exec.v.p., dir. Balcor/Am. Express, Inc.; pres., chmn. CWS Fin. Groupo, 1989—; mng. dir., asst. gen. counsel Primerica Corp. 1991—; sr. real estate analyst v.p. First Albany Corp., N.Y.C., 1994—. Mem. ABA, New York County Lawyers Assn., Real Estate Bd. N.Y., Security Industry Assn. Clubs: Quaker Ridge (Scarsdale, N.Y.); Harmonie (N.Y.C.). Home: 737 Park Ave New York NY 10021 Office: First Albany Corp 6 E 43rd St New York NY 10017

WEISS, SHIRLEY F., urban and regional planner, economist, educator; b. N.Y.C., Feb. 26, 1921; d. Max and Vera (Hendel) Friedlander; m. Charles M. Weiss, June 7, 1942. BA, Rutgers U., 1942; postgrad., Johns Hopkins U., 1949-50; M in Regional Planning, U. N.C., 1958; PhD, Duke U., 1973. Assoc. research dir. Ctr. for Urban and Regional Studies U. N.C., Chapel Hill, 1957-91, lectr. in planning, 1958-62, assoc. prof., 1962-73, prof., 1973-91, prof. emeritus, 1991—; joint creator-sponsor Charles and Shirley Weiss Urban Livability Program, U. N.C., Chapel Hill, 1992—; research assoc. Inst. for Research in Social Sci., U. N.C., 1957-73; research prof. U. N.C., Chapel Hill, 1973-91, acting dir. women's studies program Coll. Arts and Scis., 1985, faculty marshall, 1988-91; mem. tech. com. Water Resources Rsch. Inst., 1976-79; mem. adv. com. on housing for 1980 census Dept. Commerce, 1976-81; cons. Urban Inst., Washington, 1977-80; mem. rev. panel Exptl. Housing Allowance Program, HUD, 1977-80; mem. adv. bd. on built environ. Nat. Acad. Scis.-NRC, 1981-83, mem. program coordinating com. fed. constrn. coun. of adv. bd. on built environ., 1982-83; mem. Planning Accreditation Bd., Site Visitation Pool, Am. Inst. Cert. Planners and Assn. Collegiate Schs. Planning, 1985—; mem. discipline screening com. Fulbright Scholar awards in Architecture and City Planning, Coun. for Internat. Exchange of Scholars, 1985-88. Author: The Central Business District in Transition: Methodological Approaches to CBD Analysis and Forecasting Future Space Requirements, 1957, New Town Development in the United States: Experiment in Private Enterpreneurship, 1973; co-author: A Probabilistic Model for Residential Growth, 1964, Residential Developer Decisions: A Focused View of the Urban Growth Process, 1966, New Communities U.S.A., 1976; co-author, co-editor: Urban Growth Dynamics in a Regional Cluster of Cities, 1962; co-editor: New Community Development: Planning Process, Implementation and Emerging Social Concerns, vols. 1, 2, 1971, City Centers in Transition, 1976, New Communities Research Series, 1976-77; mem. editorial bd.: Jour. Am. Inst. Planners, 1963-68, Rev. of Regional Studies, 1969-74, 82—, Internat. Regional Sci. Rev, 1975-81. Trustee Friends of Libr., U. N.C., Chapel Hill, 1988-94, Santa Fe Chamber Music Festival, adv. coun., 1990-91, trustee, 1991—; bd. dirs. Triangle Opera Theatre, 1986-89, 91—. Adelaide M. Zagoren fellow Douglass Coll., Rutgers U., 1994; recipient Mary Turner Lane award Assn. Women Faculty, 1994. Fellow Urban Land Inst. (sr., exec. group, community devel. coun. 1978—); mem. Am. Inst. Planners (sec., treas. southeast chpt. 1957-59, v.p. 1960-61), Am. Inst. Cert. Planners, Am. Planning Assn., Am. Econ. Assn., So. Regional Sci. Assn. (pres. 1977-78), Regional Sci. Assn. (councillor 1971-74, v.p. 1976-77), Nat. Assn. Housing and Redevelopment Ofcls., Interamerican Planning Soc., Internat. Fedn. Housing and Planning, Town and Country Planning Assn., Internat. Urban Devel. Assn., Econ. History Assn., Am. Real Estate and Urban Econs. Assn. (regional membership chmn. 1976-82, 84-85, dir. 1977-80), AAUP (chpt. pres. 1976-77, pres. N.C. Conf. 1978-79, mem. nat. council 1983-86, William S. Tacey award Assembly of State Confs.), Douglass Soc., Order of Valkyries, Phi Beta Kappa. Home: 155 N Hamilton Rd Chapel Hill NC 27514-5628

WEISS, STANLEY ALAN, mining, chemicals and refractory company executive; b. Phila., Dec. 21, 1926; s. Walter Joseph and Anne Betty (Lubin) W.; m. Lisa Popper, May 23, 1958; children: Lori Christina Lurie, Anthony Walter. Student. Pa. Mil. Coll., 1947-48, Georgetown U., 1950-51; fellow Ctr. for Internat. Affairs, Harvard U., Cambridge, Mass., 1977-78; LHD (hon.), Point Park Coll., Pitts., 1994. Founder Minera La Mundial, SA, San Luis Potosi, Mexico, 1954-56, Manganeso Mexicano SA, Mexico City, 1957-61, Mercurio Internacional SA, Mexico City, 1957-61; founder Flux, SA, Mexico City, 1960-82, Sao Paulo, Brazil, 1964-74; founder, chmn. bd., chief exec. officer Am. Minerals, Inc., El Paso, Tex., 1960-91; co-founder, exec. v.p. Ralston Trading & Devel. Corp., 1968-91, chmn. bd. dirs., 1991; chmn. bd. dirs. Am. Premier, Inc., King of Prussia, Pa., 1991—. Author: Manganese: The Other Uses, 1976; contbr. articles on nat. security and internat. trade issues. Founder, chmn. bus. Execs. for Nat. Security, Washington, 1982—; bd. dirs. New Am. Schs. Devel. Corp., Washingto; mem. The Coun. for Excellence in Govt. With U.S. Army, 1944-46, ATO. Mem. Am. Bus. Conf., Am. Ditchley Found., Internat. Inst. Strategic Studies (Eng.), World Econ. Forum (Switzerland), Royal Inst. Gt. Britain (London), Garrick Club (London). Jewish. Avocations: tennis, skiing. Home: 2126 Connecticut Ave

NW # 5 Washington DC 20008-1729 Office: American Premier Inc 1615 L St NW Ste 330 Washington DC 20036-5610

WEISS, STANLEY C., electrical and electronics products wholesale distribution executive; b. Chgo., Apr. 20, 1929; s. Edward and Belle Rose (Heifler) W.; m. Fern Adrienne Dellheim, Feb. 26, 1956;children: Sharon Anne Weiss Maluth, Lisa Karen. BBA, So. Meth. U., 1951; postgrad., Northwestern U., Chgo., 1953. Asst. mgr. men's furnishings Gassman's, Chgo., 1951-53; restaurant and hotel supplies salesman Edward Don & Co., Chgo., 1953; sales trainee, mgr. EDP, Kuppenheimer Clothing, Chgo., 1954-56; with EESCO, Inc. (Englewood Electric), Chgo., 1956—; bd. dirs. Cameron Ashley Bldg. Material Supply; speaker at profl. meetings; adv. cons. various elec. mfrs., 1980-92. Contbr. articles to profl. mags. Banquet co-chmn. Better Boys Found., Chgo., 1983-93; bd. dirs. Jewish Cmty. Ctrs. of Chgo., 1994—. Recipient Banquet Co-chmn.'s award Better Boys Found. 1984-92. Mem. Nat. Assn. Elec. Distbrs. (bd. dirs., chmn. 1991-92), Nat. Assn. Wholesalers (product liability com. Chgo. 1984, bd. dirs. 1991-92), Nat. Assn. Credit Mgmt. (chmn. WES group Chgo. 1970-74), Lake Michigan Club (chmn., bd. dirs. 1975-85), Twin Orchard Country Club (Longwood, Ill., bd. dirs. 1988-92), DuPage Club (Oak Brook Terrace, Ill.), B'nai Brith (officer Chgo. 1954-64, bd. dirs. 1962-64). Avocations: reading, travel, golf. Office: EESCO Inc 3939 S Karlov Ave Chicago IL 60632-3881

WEISS, STANLEY IRWIN, engineering executive, aeronautical engineer; b. N.Y.C., Oct. 27, 1925; s. Maurice H. and Malvina (Toffler) W.; m. Catherine Jordan, Oct. 2, 1952; children: Ann, Audrey, Janet, Marion. B in Aero. Engring., Rensselaer Poly. Inst., 1945, MS, 1948; PhD, U. Ill., 1950; postgrad., Harvard Bus. Sch., 1969. Dynamicist, project engr. Goodyear Aerospace, Akron, Ohio, 1950-55; chief engr. Kawneer Corp., Niles, Mich., 1955-57; program mgr. mfg. and quality assurance mgmt., AGM-programs, v.p. engring., advanced programs and devel. space systems div. Lockheed Missiles and Space Co., Inc., Sunnyvale, Calif., 1957-78; dep. asst. sec. Dept. Energy, Washington, 1978-80; assoc. administr. chief engr. NASA, Washington, 1980-83; corp. v.p. engring., v.p. rsch. and devel. Lockheed Corp., Burbank and Palo Alto, Calif., 1983-90; Hunsaker prof. MIT, Cambridge, 1991-92, prof., 1992—; bd. dirs. AMTEC; lectr. Akron (Ohio) U., 1950-53; dir. Non-Ferrous Metals Rsch. Coun., Washington, 1973-78; exec.-in-residence U. Santa Clara (Calif.) Bus. Sch., 1976-78; chmn. engring. adv. bd. Rensselaer Poly. Inst., 1983—; mem. exec. com. adv. bd. Coll. Engring., U. Ill., Urbana, 1987—. Contbr. numerous articles to profl. jours. Lt. USNR, 1943-47. Recipient Meritorius Exec. award Dept. Energy, Washington, 1980, D.S.M. NASA, 1983. Fellow AIAA; mem. World Affairs Coun., Commonwealth Club, Sigma Xi. Avocations: flying, music, tennis, history. Home: 416 Commonwealth Ave Apt 502 Boston MA 02215-2810 Office: MIT Aero/Astron Dept 77 Massachusetts Ave Cambridge MA 02139-4307

WEISS, STEPHEN HENRY, investment firm executive; b. N.Y.C., Oct. 30, 1935; s. Milton and Nathalie (Segal) W.; m. Suzanne Rogers, May 7, 1983; children: Michael David, Jonathan Scott, Nathalie Christine; 1 stepchild, Heather Boose. A.B., Cornell U., 1957. With A.G. Becker, N.Y.C., 1959-70, v.p., 1964-70, dir., 1967-70; founder, mng. ptnr., chmn. exec. com. Weiss, Peck & Greer, N.Y.C., 1970—. Trustee Cornell U., 1984, chmn. bd. trustees, mem. investment com., mem. devel. com., bd. overseers, past chmn. Cornell Med. Coll.; mem. joint bd. N.Y. Hosp.-Cornell Med. Ctr.; mem. bd. visitors Sch. Medicine, U. Calif., Davis; bd. dirs. The Centurion Found.; trustee Spence Sch.; mem. Citizens Budge Commn. of N.Y.C., Citizens Com. Home: 10 Gracie Sq New York NY 10028-8031 Office: Weiss Peck & Greer 1 New York Plz New York NY 10004

WEISS, STEPHEN JOEL, lawyer; b. N.Y.C., Sept. 12, 1938; s. Morris and Frances (Dinkin) W.; m. Madeline Adler, Aug. 12, 1962; children: Lowell Andrew, Valerie Elizabeth, Bradley Lawrence. B.S., Queens Coll., 1959; LL.B., Cornell U., 1962; LL.M., Georgetown U., 1966. Bar: N.Y. 1963, D.C. 1966, U.S. Supreme Ct. 1975. Atty. SEC, Washington, 1962-65; assoc. firm Arent Fox Kintner Plotkin & Kahn, Washington, 1965-70, ptnr., 1971-94; ptnr. Holland & Knight, Washington, 1994—; lectr. securities and corp. law Am. Law Inst., ABA, Fed. Bar Assn., Practicing Law Inst., Bur. Nat. Affairs, Exec. Enterprises, Aspen Law & Bus. Orgn. Mgmt., Inc. Mem. adv. bd.; Securities Regulation and Law Report, Bus. Nat. Affairs, 1980—; contbr. articles on securities, corp. dirs. and officers liability and ins. law to legal and bus. jours.; author: Regulation D-A Practical Guide, 1994. Mem. ABA (fed. regulation securities com. 1970—, chmn. Rule 10b-5 subcom. 1976-78, chmn. civil liabilities subcom. 1978-81, chmn. ad hoc com. fgn. corrupt practices legislation 1976-77, Guiding Principles Task Force bus. ins. com. 1994—, devels. in bus. financing com. 1982—), Fed. Bar Assn. (chmn. securities law comm. 1968-70, mem. exec. com. of securities law com. 1971—, chmn. coun. on financing and taxation 1971-72, chmn. publs. bd. 1977-78, nat. coun. 1972-80, Leadership commendnation 1973). Club: Cornell Law (Washington) (pres. 1971-79). Office: Holland & Knight 2100 Pennsylvania Ave NW Washington DC 20037

WEISS, SUSAN, newspaper editor. Managing editor Life Section, USA Today, Arlington, Va. Office: USA Today 1000 Wilson Blvd Arlington VA 22209-3991

WEISS, THEODORE RUSSELL, poet, editor; b. Reading, Pa., Dec. 16, 1916; s. Nathan and Mollie T. (Weinberg) W.; m. Renée Karol, July 6, 1941. B.A., Muhlenberg Coll., 1938, Litt.D. (hon.), 1968; M.A., Columbia U., 1940, postgrad., 1940-41; Litt.D. (hon.) Bard Coll., 1973. Instr. English U. Md., 1941, U. N.C., 1942-44, Yale U., 1944-46; prof. English, Bard Coll., 1946-68; vis. prof. poetry MIT, 1961-62; resident fellow creative writing Princeton U., 1966-67, prof. English and creative writing, 1968-87, emeritus, William and Annie S. Paton prof. ancient and modern lit., 1977-87, emeritus; Fannie Hurst prof. lit. Washington U., St. Louis, 1978; prof. English poetry Cooper Union, 1988; poet-in-residence Monash U., Melbourne, Australia, 1982; lectr. New Sch. Social Research, 1955-56, N.Y.C. YMHA, 1965-67; lectr. for USIS in various countries; guest lectr. for Advanced Study, Princeton, N.J., 1986-87, 87-88, Villa Serbelloni, Bellagio, Italy, 1989; guest lectr. Peking U., Shanghai U., People's Republic China, 1991. Editor, pub. Quar. Rev. Lit., 1943—; editor poetry series Princeton U. Press, 1974-78; mem. poetry bd. poetry series Wesleyan U. Press, 1964-70; juror in poetry for poetry series, Bollingen Com., 1965, Nat. Book Awards, 1967, 77; author: Selections from the Note-Books of G.M. Hopkins, 1945; author: The Breath of Clowns and Kings: Shakespeare's Early Comedies and Histories, 1971, The Man from Porlock, Selected Essays, 1982; (poems) The Catch, 1951; Outlanders, 1960, Gunsight, 1962, The Medium, 1965, The Last Day and the First, 1968, The World Before Us: Poems, 1950-70, 1970, Fireweeds, 1976, Views and Spectacles, Selected Poems, 1978, Views and Spectacles, New and Selected Shorter Poems, 1979, Recoveries, 1982, A Slow Fuse, 1984, Collected Poems, 1987, paper back edit., 1988, A Sum of Destructions, 1994, Selected Poems, 1995; also articles and recs. Recipient Wallace Stevens award, 1956, Creative Arts award Brandeis U., 1977, Shelley Meml. award Poetry Soc. Am., 1989; Ford Found. fellow, 1953-54; hon. fellow Ezra Stiles Coll., Yale U.; grantee Nat. Found. Arts and Humanities, 1967-68; Ingram Merrill Found. fellow, 1974-75; Guggenheim Found. fellow, 1986-87. Home: 26 Haslet Ave Princeton NJ 08540-4914

WEISS, THOMAS EDWARD, physician; b. New Orleans, June 15, 1916; s. Carl Adam and Viola Maine W.; m. Catherine Torres Edwards, June 29, 1950; children: Thomas Edward, Hampton Carl. Student, La. State U. 1933-34; M.D., Tulane U., 1940. Diplomate: Am. Bd. Internal Medicine. Intern Touro Infirmary, New Orleans, 1940-41; resident in pathology Touro Infirmary, 1940; fellow in internal medicine Alton Ochsner Med. Found., New Orleans, 1946-47; staff physician specializing in internal medicine Ochsner Clinic, New Orleans, 1947-50; head rheumatology sect. Ochsner Clinic, 1960-77, now mem. staff emeritus rheumatology sect., bd. mgrs. clinic, 1966-74; mem. staff Ochsner Found. Hosp.; sr. vis. physician Charity Hosp. La.-New Orleans; mem. faculty Tulane U. Med. Sch., 1960-84, emeritus prof. clin. medicine, 1989—; chmn. vol. support com. Alton Ochsner Med. Found., 1984—, dir. alumni affairs, 1984—. Contbr. articles to profl. jours. Bd. dirs. Vis. Nurses Assn., Alton Ochsner Med. Found., also trustee; founder, bd. govs. La. Arthritis Found.; nat. bd. govs. Arthritis Found., 1968-74. Maj. AUS, 1941-45, ETO and PTO. Master Am. Coll. Rheumatology; Fellow ACP (Laureate award 1991); mem. AMA, Orleans Parish Med. Soc. (dir.), La. Med. Soc., So. Med. Assn., Nat. Soc. Clin. Rheu-

matologists, Am. Rheumatism Assn. (pres. 1973-74, exec. com.), Am. Coll. Rheumatology (hon.), Vis. Nurses Assn., New Orleans Country Club, Sigma Chi, Omega Kappa Kappa. Democrat. Roman Catholic. Home: 401 Metairie Rd Apt 625 Metairie LA 70005-4305 Office: 1514 Jefferson Hwy New Orleans LA 70121-2483

WEISS, THOMAS FISCHER, electrical engineering educator, biophysicist; b. Prague, Czechoslovakia, Oct. 17, 1934; came to U.S. 1941, naturalized citizen; s. Eugene and Erna (Frenkel) W.; m. Aurice B Vernon, June 10, 1962; children: Max Philip, Elisa Lane, Eric Radford. BSEE, CCNY, 1956; SM, MIT, 1959, PhD, 1963. Postdoctoral fellow Ford Found., 1963-65; engr. Douglas Aircraft Co., 1957; rsch. asst. dynamic analysis and control lab., rsch. lab. of electronics MIT, Cambridge, Mass., 1956-57, 57-63, cons., 1961-65, from asst. prof. to assoc. prof. electrical engring., 1963-1978, prof. electrical engring., 1978—; mem. many MIT comms.; rsch. assoc. dept. otolaryngology Mass. Eye & Ear Infirmary, 1964—; rsch. assoc. preventive medicine Harvard U. Med. Sch., 1964-69, instr. dept. preventive and social medicine, 1969-74; faculty Harvard-MIT divsn. health scis. and tech. Harvard U., 1980—; mem. bioelectric pheonmena com. Biomed. Engring. Group IEEE; cons. communicative disorders panel for nat. plan, NIH, 1978, mem. rev. com., 1978-83; participant multidisciplinary workshop on inner ear and hearing, NIH, 1974. Edit. bd. Hearing Rsch., 1986—; organ., chair workshops in field; contbr. numerous abstracts, articles to profl. jours.; invited lectr. in field. Recipient NIH Rsch. Career Devel. award, 1975-80, Javits Neurosci. Investigator award, 1984-91, Higher Edn. Software award best engring. software EDUCOM/NCRIPTAL, 1990; apptd. Thomas and Gerd Perkins prof. electrical and bioelectrical engring., 1992—. Home: 1607 Centre St Newton MA 02139 Office: MIT Rm 36-857 77 Massachusetts Ave Cambridge MA 02139

WEISS, VOLKER, university administrator, educator; b. Rottenmann, Austria, Sept. 2, 1930; came to U.S. 1953, naturalized, 1960; s. Othmar and Pauline (Morianz) W.; m. Peg Hake, Sept. 14, 1957; children: Erick V., Christopher J. Dipl.Ing. Physics, Tech. U. Vienna; Dipl.Ing. Physics (Fulbright scholar), 1955; Ph.D. in Solid State Sci. and Tech, Syracuse U., 1957. Rsch. metallurgist DEMKA Steel, Utrecht, The Netherlands, 1952; asst. prof. metallurgy Syracuse U., 1957-60, prof. materials sci., 1965—, prof. engring. and physics, 1986—, chmn. solid state sci. and tech. program, 1960-77, assoc. dean sponsored programs, 1972-78; dir. Inst. Energy Rsch., 1976-80, v.p. rsch. and grad. affairs, 1978-86, dir. engring physics program, 1988—, chmn. dept. mechanical, aerospace, mfg. engring., 1992-94; U.S.-Can Prof., 1993—; cons. indsl. firms Dept. Transp.; bd. dirs., past pres. Syracuse Friends of Chamber Music, Tech. Club Syracuse; v.p., bd. dirs. Discovery Ctr. of Sci. and Tech., 1979—; NATO sr. scientist fellow, Germany and Gt. Britain, 1967-68. Editor: Sagamore Conf. Procs, 1962-86; contbr. articles on mech. behavior of materials and phys. metallurgy to profl. jours. Fellow Am. Soc. Metals; mem. ASME, ASTM, Am. Physical Soc., Sigma Xi. Home: 238 Scottholm Ter Syracuse NY 13224-1738 Office: Syracuse U 449 Link Hall Syracuse NY 13244

WEISS, WALTER STANLEY, lawyer; b. Newark, Mar. 12, 1929; s. Jack and Mollie (Orkin) W.; m. Misty M. Moore; children from previous marriage: Jack Stephen, Andrew Scott. A.B., Rutgers U., 1949, J.D., 1952. Bar: D.C. 1952, N.J. 1956, Calif. 1961. Trial atty. IRS, Phila., Los Angeles, 1957-62; asst. U.S. atty., chief tax div. Los Angeles, 1962-63; ptnr. firm Goodson & Hannam, Los Angeles, 1963-67; mng. ptnr. firm Long & Levit, Los Angeles, 1967-79; ptnr. firm Greenberg & Glusker, Los Angeles, 1979-81, Rosenfeld, Meyer and Susman, Beverly Hills, Calif., 1981-93; prin. Law Office of Walter S. Weiss, L.A., 1993—. Contbr. articles to legal jours. Served to capt. JAGC USAF, 1953-56. Named Arbitrator Nat. Assn. Securities Dealers, 1974. Fellow Am. Coll. Trial Lawyers; mem. Am., Los Angeles County, Beverly Hills, Century City bar assns. Home: 1805 Westridge Rd Los Angeles CA 90049-2215 Office: Law Office Walter S Weiss Ninth Fl 12424 Wilshire Blvd Los Angeles CA 90025

WEISS, WILLIAM, retired pulmonary medicine-epidemiology educator; b. Phila., Jan. 30, 1919; s. William and Anna (Grossman) W.; m. Esther E. Sabul, June 22, 1941; children: Winifred A., Seth S., Deborah E. BA, U. Pa., 1940, MD, 1944. Clin. dir. pulmonary disease svc. Phila. Gen. Hosp., 1950-74; chest cons. Norristown (Pa.) State Hosp., 1951-60; dir. Pulmonary Neoplasm Rsch. Project, Phila., 1957-67; faculty U. Pa. Grad. Sch. Medicine, Phila., 1952-66, Med. Coll. Pa., Phila., 1952-86; from assoc. prof. to prof. medicine Hahnemann U. Med. Coll., Phila., 1966-84, prof. emeritus, 1984—; cons. to various indsl. cos., Pa., N.J., 1962—. Editor Phila. Medicine, 1976—; contbr. more than 220 articles and more than 100 edits. to profl. jours., 18 chpts. to books; mem. editl. bd. Arch. Environ. Health, 1968-86. Bd. dirs. Am. Cancer Soc., Phila. 1980-86; cons. on asbestos Bd. Edn., Phila., 1983—; mem. EPA Sci. Review Panel for Health Rsch., Washington, 1980-81, Toxics/Health Effects adv. com. Pa. Dept. Health, 1985-87. Capt. USAF, 1953-55. Recipient Ann. Sci. award Am. Cancer Soc., Phila. div., 1979, Cristol award Phila. County Med. Soc., 1989; picture on cover Cancer Rsch., Mar. 1, 1990 for lung cancer rsch. Fellow ACP, Coll. Physicians Phila., Am. Coll. Occupational and Environ. Medicine (merit in authorship award 1974, 85); mem. AMA, Laennec Soc. Phila. (pres. 1970), Phila. Occupational Med. Assn. (pres. 1980-81), Am. Thoracic Soc., Pa. Med. Soc., Phila. County Med. Soc. (Strittmatter award 1991). Avocation: classical music. Home: 3912 Netherfield Rd Philadelphia PA 19129-1014

WEISS, WILLIAM LEE, retired communications executive; b. Big Run, Pa., May 21, 1929; s. Harry W. and Dorothy Jane (McKee) W.; m. Josephine Elizabeth Berry, June 3, 1951; children: Susan Leigh Weiss Miller, David William, Steven Paul. BS in Indsl. Engring, Pa. State U., 1951; D of Mgmt. (hon.), Purdue U., 1988; LLD (hon.), DePaul U., 1990, Knox Coll., 1993. With Bell Telephone Co. of Pa., 1951, 1953-76; v.p. staff Bell Telephone Co. of Pa., Phila., 1973-74; v.p.; gen. mgr. Bell Telephone Co. of Pa. (western region), 1974-76; v.p. ops. Wis. Telephone Co., Milw., 1976-78; pres. Ind. Bell Telephone Co., Indpls., 1978-81; also dir. Ind. Bell Telephone Co.; pres. Ill. Bell Telephone Co., Chgo., 1981, chmn., 1982-83; chmn., CEO Ameritech, Chgo., 1983-94, chmn. emeritus, 1994—, ret., 1994; bd. dirs. Abbott Labs., Chgo., The Quaker Oats Co., Chgo., Merrill Lynch, N.Y.C., Tenneco, Houston. Bd. dirs. Chgo. Coun. Fgn. Rels., Lyric Opera Chgo. 1991-94; trustee Mus. Sci. and Industry, Chgo. bd. trustees, 1989-92, Chgo. Symphony Orch., 1982, Northwestern U., 1982, Pa. State U., 1994; with Bus. Coun. With USAF, 1951-53. Mem. Commercial Club (pres. 1989-90), Chgo. Club, Econ. Club, Mid-Am. Club (Chgo.), Glen View (Ill.) Club, Old Elm (Ill.) Country Club of N.C. (Pinehurst), Tau Beta Pi, Phi Delta Theta. Avocations: civic work, golf, travel, family activities.

WEISSBACH, HERBERT, biochemist; b. N.Y.C., Mar. 16, 1932; s. Louis and Vivian (Ruhalter) W.; m. Renee Kohl, Dec. 27, 1953; children—Lawrence, Nancy, Marjorie, Robert. B.S., CUNY, 1953; M.S., George Washington U., 1955, Ph.D., 1957. Chemist Nat. Heart Inst., Bethesda, Md., 1953-68; acting chief NIH, Bethesda, Md., 1968-69; assoc. dir. Roche Inst. Molecular Biology, Nutley, N.J., 1969-83, dir., 1983—; v.p. Hoffmann-La Roche, Nutley, N.J., 1983—; adj. prof. George Washington U., 1964-69, Columbia U. 1969-85, U. Medicine and Dentistry N.J., Newark, 1981-93, Princeton U., 1984-85. Editor: Molecular Mechanisms of Protein Biosynthesis, 1977, Archives of Biochemistry and Biophysics; contbr. articles to profl. jours. Recipient Superior Svc. award NEW, 1968, Enzyme award Am. Chem. Soc., 1970, Disting. Alumni award George Washington U., 1994. Mem. Am. Soc. Biol. Chemists, Am. Soc. Pharmacology and Exptl. Therapeutics, Nat. Acad. Scis., AAAS. Home: 5 Blackfoot Cir Wayne NJ 07470-4942 Office: Roche Inst Molecular Biology 340 Kingsland St Nutley NJ 07110-1150

WEISSBARD, DAVID RAYMOND, minister; b. Albany, N.Y., July 10, 1940; s. Alfred Henry and E. Ramona (Van Wie) W.; m. Mary Linda Roberts, Mar. 31, 1963 (dec. May 1987); children: Melissa Anne, Michele Lee Weissbard Burns, Andrew Van Wie (dec.), Meredith Lynn Weissbard Andrews; m. Karen Wells, Sept. 1, 1990; 1 child, Hilary Rebecca. BA, St. Lawrence U., 1962, MDiv., 1965; diploma in applied social studies, U. Southampton, Eng., 1973. Ordained to ministry Unitarian Universalist Assn., 1965; cert. social worker, Eng. Student min. 1st Universalist Ch., Dexter, N.Y., 1963-65, Henderson, N.Y., 1963-65; min. 1st Parish in Bedford (Mass.) Unitarian Universalist Ch., 1965-74; sr. min. Fairfax Unitarian Ch., Oakton, Va., 1974-79, The Unitarian Universalist Ch., Rockford, Ill.,

1979—; v.p. Cen. Midwest Dist. Unitarian Universalist Assn., 1989-92. Producer, host weekly TV program Fusion, WIFR-TV, 1980—. Mem. religious policy com. Rockford Sch. Dist., 1991. Recipient Skinner award Unitarian Universalist Assn., 1979; named One of Rockford's 15 Most Interesting People, 1990. Mem. ACLU (No. Ill. steering com.), Greater Rockford Clergy Assn., Unitarian Universalist Mins. Assn. (treas. 1976-78), Soc. for Profls. in Dispute Resolution. Democrat. Home: 1805 Clinton St Rockford IL 61103 Office: The Unitarian Ch 4848 Turner St Rockford IL 61107-5099

WEISSBARD, SAMUEL HELD, lawyer; b. N.Y.C., Mar. 3, 1947; children: Andrew Joshua, David S. BA, Case Western Res. U., 1967; JD with highest honors, George Washington U., 1970. Bar: D.C. 1970, U.S. Supreme Ct. 1974. Assoc. Fried, Frank, Harris, Shriver & Kampelman, 1970-73, Arent, Fox, Kintner, Plotkin & Kahn, 1973-78; prin. Weissbard & Fields, P.C., 1978-83; shareholder, v.p. Wilkes, Artis, Hedrick & Lane, Washington, 1983-86; ptnr. Foley & Lardner, Washington, 1986—; Co-chair Creditors' Rights Workout and Bankruptcy Group, 1992-95. Editor in chief George Washington U. Law Rev., 1969-70. Bd. dirs. Luther Rice Soc. George Washington U., 1985-87, Atlanta Coll. Art, 1993, Nat. Learning Ctr., 1993—, Georgetown Arts Commn., 1995—; chmn. steering com. of Lawyer's Alliance for Nat. Learning Ctr. and Capital Children's Mus., 1989-90; mem. steering com. DC/NLC Don't Drop Out Campaign, 1992, 93. Recipient John Bell Larner medal, 1970. Mem. ABA, D.C. Bar, Georgetown Bus. and Profl. Assn. (bd. dirs. 1993—), sec., gen. counsel 1994—), Order of Coif. Office: Foley & Lardner 3000 K St NW Ste 500 Washington DC 20007-5109

WEISSBERGER, RUTH MARION, health education company executive, psychologist; b. Syracuse, N.Y., Sept. 17, 1942; d. Alfred Ernest and Ruth Marion (Hughes) Delmonico; m. William Isenhart, Aug. 5, 1961 (div. 1974); children: Mark, Maria; m. Edward Weissberger, July 26, 1980. BA, St. John Fisher Coll., Rochester, N.Y., 1983; MS, U. Rochester, 1983, EdD, 1986. Cert. in counseling, hypnotherapy. Pvt. practice psychol. counseling Victor, N.Y., 1983-86, Rochester, 1986-92; CEO The Natural Response, Inc., Rochester, 1991—; cons. to Kodak Co., Rochester, 1989—, Fisons Corp., Rochester, 1991—), Bausch & Lomb, Rochester, 1992—, Gen. Rwy. Signal, Rochester, 1993—. Author tape recording: A Special Place, 1993; author manual: Stress Manual, 1992. Instr. ARC, Rochester, 1983-86; lectr. Schs. in the Community, Rochester, 1983—. Recipient Appreciation award Am. Mental Health Counseling, 1991, Multiple Sclerosis Assn., 1991. Mem. APA, Am. Counseling Assn., Am. Bd. Med. Psychotherapy, Am. Bd. Med. Psychotherapists (assoc.). Avocations: piano, orchids, travel. Home and Office: The Natural Response Inc 354 Woolston Rd Pittsford NY 14534-9776

WEISSBRODT, DAVID SAMUEL, law educator; b. Washington, Oct. 13, 1944; s. I. S. and Selma (Mushkin) W.; m. Patricia Schaffer, June 13, 1970; children: James, Bronwen. AB, Columbia U., 1966; JD, U. Calif., Berkeley, 1969. Bar: Calif. 1970, D.C. 1973, U.S. Supreme Ct. 1974, Minn. 1975. Law clk. Calif. Supreme Ct., San Francisco, 1969-71; intern Internat. Commn. of Jurists, Geneva, Switzerland, 1972-73; assoc. Covington & Burling, Washington, 1973-75; from assoc. prof. to prof. of law U. Minn., Mpls., 1975-89, Briggs & Morgan prof. law, 1989—; co-dir. Human Rights Ctr. U. Minn., Mpls.; legal counsel Minn. Advs. for Human Rights, Mpls., Ctr. for Victims of Torture, Mpls.; pub. mem. U.S. Del. to UN Commn. on Human Rights, 1993-95. Author (book) Immigration Law; co-author (book) International Human Rights, 1990. Office: U Minn 229 19th Ave S Minneapolis MN 55455-0400

WEISSENBUEHLER, WAYNE, bishop. Bishop of Rocky Mountain Evang. Luth. Ch. in Am., Denver. Office: Rocky Mountain Synod ABS Bldg #101 7000 Broadway Denver CO 80221-2907

WEISSFELD, JOACHIM ALEXANDER, lawyer; b. Wuppertal, Germany, Mar. 18, 1927; s. Samuel and Emma (Erb) W.; m. Mary Morton, June 27, 1953; children: Elizabeth Weissfeld Hopper, Katherine Weissfeld McGrady. AB, Brown U., 1950; JD, Harvard U., 1953. Bar: R.I. 1954, various Fed. Cts. 1955. Assoc., then ptnr. Graham, Reid, Ewing & Stapleton, Providence, 1957-70; ptnr. Tillinghast, Collins & Graham, Providence, 1970-81, Hinckley, Allen, Providence, 1981—. With USN, 1945-46. Fellow Am. Coll. Trust and Estate Counsel; mem. ABA, R.I. Bar Assn. Estate Planning Coun. R.I. (pres. 1989), Harvard Law Sch. Assn. (nat. coun. 1990—), Phi Beta Kappa. Congregationalist. Office: Hinckley Allen 1500 Fleet Ctr Providence RI 02903

WEISSKOPF, BERNARD, pediatrician, child behavior, development and genetics specialist, educator; b. Berlin, Dec. 11, 1929; came to U.S., 1939, naturalized, 1944; s. Benjamin and Bertha (Loew) W.; m. Penelope Allderdice, Dec. 26, 1965; children—Matthew David, Stephen Daniel. B.A., Syracuse U., 1951; M.D. U. Leiden, Netherlands, 1958. Diplomate Am. Bd. Med. Mgmt. Intern Meadowbrook Hosp., East Meadow, N.Y., 1958-59; resident Meadowbrook Hosp., 1959-60, Johns Hopkins Hosp., Balt., 1962-64; fellow child psychiatry Johns Hopkins U. Sch. Medicine, Balt., 1962-64; asst. prof. pediatrics U. Ill. Coll. Medicine, Chgo., 1964-66; faculty U. Louisville, 1966—, prof. pediatrics, 1970—; also assoc. in psychiatry, pathology and Ob-gyn, dir. Child Evaluation Ctr., Louisville, 1966—; chmn. Gov.'s Adv. Com. Early Childhood, Gov.'s Council on Early Childhood, Ky., 1986-88. Contbr. articles to profl. jours. Trustee Jewish Hosp., Louisville, 1974-77. Served to capt. USAF, 1960-62. Fellow Am. Acad. Pediatrics, Am. Assn. Mental Deficiency; mem. Am. Soc. Human Genetics, So. Soc. Pediatric Rsch., Am. Soc. Law and Medicine, Am. Coll. Physician Execs. Home: 6409 Deep Creek Dr Prospect KY 40059-9422 Office: Child Evaluation Ctr 224 E Broadway St Louisville KY 40202-1739

WEISSKOPF, VICTOR FREDERICK, physicist; b. Vienna, Austria, Sept. 19, 1908; came to U.S., 1937, naturalized, 1942; s. Emil and Martha (Gut) W.; m. Ellen Tvede, Sept. 5, 1934 (dec. Aug. 1989); children: Thomas Emil, Karen Louise; m. Duscha Schmid, May 1991. Ph.D., U. Goettingen, Germany, 1931. Rsch. assoc. U. Copenhagen, Denmark, 1932-34, Inst. of Tech., Zürich, Switzerland, 1934-37; asst. prof. physics U. Rochester, N.Y., 1937-43; with Manhattan Project, Los Alamos, N.M., 1943-46; prof. physics Mass. Inst. Tech., 1946-60; dir. gen. European Orgn. for Nuclear Research, Geneva, Switzerland, 1961-65; Inst. prof. Mass. Inst. Tech., 1965—; chmn. high energy physics adv. panel AEC, 1967-73. Author: (with J. Blatt) Theoretical Nuclear Physics, 1952, Knowledge and Wonder, 1962, Physics in the Twentieth Century, 1972; (with K. Gottfried) Concepts of Particle Physics, 1984; The Privilege of Being a Physicist, 1989; The Joy of Insight: Passions of a Physicist, 1991; also articles on nuclear physics, quantum theory, radiation theory, etc. in science jours. Recipient Max Planck medal Germany, 1956, Hi Majorana award, 1970, G. Gamov award, 1971, Boris Pregel award, 1971, Prix Mondial Cino del Duca France, 1972, L. Boltzmann prize Austria, 1977, Nat. Medal of Sci. U.S., 1980, Wolf prize, Jerusalem, 1982, Enrico Fermi award U. S. Dept. Energy, 1988, Pub. Welfare medal Nat. Acad. Scis., 1991, Compton medal for statesmanship in sci. Am. Inst. Physics, 1992. Fellow Am. Phys. Soc. (pres. 1960, Forum award 1991); mem. Nat. Acad. Scis., Am. Acad. Arts and Scis. (pres. 1975-79), French Academie des Scis. (corr.), Austrian Acad. Sci. (corr.), Danish Acad. Sci. (corr.), Bavarian Acad. Sci. (corr.), Scottish Acad. Sci. (corr.), Soviet Acad. Sci. (corr.), Pontifical Acad. Sci., Spanish Acad. Sci. (corr.), German Acad. Sci. Home: 20 Bartlett Ter Newton MA 02159-2314

WEISSMAN, DANIEL, journalist; b. N.Y.C., Nov. 19, 1938; s. Herman Reuben and Fanny (Goldstein) W.; m. Marcia Deborah Kaufman, June 2, 1962; children: Neil Edward, Charles Todd, Glen Scott. BS, NYU, 1962. Special asst. N.J. Dept. Commerce and Economic Devel., Trenton, N.J., 1965-67; newspaper reporter columnist Herald News, Passaic, N.J., 1967-71; newspaper columnist, political reporter The Star Ledger, Newark, N.J., 1971—. Bd. dirs. Easter Seal Soc., 1967—. With USAF, 1960-67. Recipient Opinion Writing award Sigma Delta Chi, 1993, Investigative Writing award Headline Club, 1993, Bus. Writing award C.I.T. Club, 1993. Home: 915 Pickering Dr Yardley PA 19067-4309 Office: The Star Ledger The State House Cn # 021 Trenton NJ 08625

WEISSMAN, EUGENE YEHUDA, chemical engineer; b. Bucharest, Romania, Sept. 23, 1931; came to U.S., 1958; s. Alfred A. and Paula D. (Braunstein) W.; children: Ian A., Michael L. BS, Israel Inst. Tech., 1953;

MS, U. Mich., 1959; PhD in chem. engr., Case Western Reserve U., 1963; MBA, U. Chgo., 1972. Registered profl. engr. Mgr. Israel Atomic Energy Comm., 1953-58; process engr. Hercules Powder Co., 1960-61; sr. engr. Gen. Electric Co., 1963-65, mgr. R&D, 1965-68; head rsch. dept. Johnson Controls, 1968-73; dir. rsch. B.A.S.F. Corp., 1973-91; dir. technology transfer Nat. Ctr. for Mfg. Scis., 1991-92; exec. dir. Ctr. for Process Analytical Chemistry U. Wash., 1992-94; pres. Weissman Assocs., Seattle, 1994—; adv. coun. Coll. Engring. U. Akron; mem. editorial and tech. adv. bd. PI Quality. Contbr. articles to profl. jours.; patentee in field. Fellow USPHS, 1959, 62. Mem. AAAS, AIChE (dir. heat transfer and energy conversion divsn.), NRC (co. rep.), Catalysis Soc. New Eng. (dir.), Electrochem. Soc., Nat. Membership Com., Am. Soc. for Quality Control, Indsl. Rsch. Inst. (bd. dirs., chmn. bd. editors, chmn. nominating com., univ. rels. com., advanced study groups com., fin. com.), Am. Chem. Soc. (corp. assocs. com.), Nat. Coun. Advancement of Rsch. (conf. com.), Coun. for Chem. Rsch. (Univ. Ind. interaction com.), Tech. Transfer Soc., Mich. Materials Processing Inst. (bd. dirs.), Internat. Forum Process Analytical Chemistry (sci. bd.). Home and Office: 4119 NE 142nd St Seattle WA 98125-3841

WEISSMAN, GAIL KUHN, nursing administrator; b. Sioux City, Iowa. BSN, Vanderbilt U., Nashville, 1960; MA in Nursing, Columbia U., 1963, EdD, 1988; postgrad., Tchr.'s Coll., Columbia U., 1979. Dir. nursing Montefiore Med. Ctr., N.Y.C.; asst. prof. dept. health care mgmt. The Mt. Sinai Hosp. Med. Sch., N.Y.C.; dean Sch. Continuing Edn. The Mt. Sinai Hosp., v.p. nursing; acting chairperson Ctr. for Nursing Rsch. and Edn. Mt. Sinai Sch. Medicine, N.Y.C. Contbr. articles to profl. jours. Named YWCA Woman Achiever, City of N.Y., 1989, Disting. Svc. Alumni award, Vanderbilt U., 1989, So. N.Y. League Nursing Dorothy McMullen-Pisani award, 1989, Jacobi Medallion for Disting. Achievement and Extraordinary Svc. to Hosp., Mt. Sinai Med. Ctr. 1989; recipient Jane Delano Disting. Svc. award N.Y. County RN Assn., 1991. Fellow Am. Acad. Nursing, Am. Pub. Health Assn., Am. Mgmt. Assn., Am. Hosp. Assn., Am. Orgn. Nurse Execs., Deans and Dirs. of Nursing in Greater N.Y., NLN, N.Y. State Nurses Assn., Sigma Theta Tau. Home: 1200 5th Ave New York NY 10029

WEISSMAN, JACK (GEORGE ANDERSON), editor; b. Chgo., June 6, 1921; s. Ben and Ida (Meyerson) W.; m. Bernice Platt, Nov. 13, 1949; children: Bruce, David, Ellen Montgomery. B.A. in Edn., Northwestern U., 1943, M.S. in Journalism, 1944. Asst. editor Bankers Monthly, Chgo., 1944-45; mng. editor Practical Knowledge, Chgo., 1945-50; with pub. relations dept. Roosevelt U., Chgo., 1947-50; editor Opportunity Mag., Chgo., 1950-89, ret. Author: Make Money at Home, 1963, How to Make Correct Decisions, 1964, Money Making Businesses You Can Start for $500 Or Less, 1965, Making It Big in Selling, 1987. Served to cpl. USAAF, 1945-46. Mem. Sigma Delta Chi, Phi Delta Kappa. Jewish.

WEISSMAN, JERROLD, metal products executive; b. Great Falls, Mont., June 25, 1936; m. Nadyne B. Weissman; children: Aaron, Leila. Student, Denver U., 1953, U. Mont., 1954-55; AB in History and Econs., U. Miami (Fla.), 1958, postgrad. in history, 1958-61. Chmn. bd. dirs., chief operating officer, chief exec.officer N.W. Steel, Inc., 1962-81; chief exec. officer N.W. Steel of Idaho, Inc., 1973-81; sales mgr., asst. v.p., exec. v.p., pres., chief exec. ofcr. Carl Weissman & Sons, Inc., Great Falls, 1987—; pres., bd. dirs. Mont. Compressed Steel, Inc., N.W. Fence Products Co., Nat. Gen. Supply, Inc.; pres., bd. dirs. N. Warehouse Distbrs. Bd. dirs. Great Falls Children's Receiving Home, 1971-75; active United Way, 1961—; mem. City Trade Commn., 1983-85; fundraiser ARC; chmn. univ. com. Forward Great Falls, 1984; asst. scout master Boy Scouts Am., 1985-86; pres. Great Falls Hebrew Assn., 1984-86, 94-95, v.p. 1987, bd. dirs., 1990—; mem. Mont. Assn. Jewish Communities, 1986—; founding mem. N.W. Assn. Against Malicious Harassment; mem. Mont. Hist. Soc., various mus.; campaign worker, del. Rep. Party. Mem. Inst. Scrap Iron and Steel (chpt. office, bd. dirs. 1963-86), Nat. Assn. Recycling Industries (mem. nat. legis. com. 1967-86), Inst. Scrap Recycling Industries, Nat. Assn. Steel Pipe Distbrs. (bd. dirs.1976-80, mem. standards com. 1976-80, convention dir. 1976-80), Masons (master 1969-70, mem. jr. exec. com. 1964-67, pres. jr. exec. com. 1966-67), Shriners, Meadowlark Country Club. Home: 2777 Greenbrier Dr Great Falls MT 59404-3639 Office: Carl Weissman & Sons Inc PO Box 1609 Great Falls MT 59403-1609

WEISSMAN, MICHAEL LEWIS, lawyer; b. Chgo., Sept. 11, 1934; s. Maurice and Sue (Goldberg) W.; m. Joanne Sherwin, Dec. 19, 1961; children: Mark Douglas, Greg Steven, Scott Adam, Brett Anthony. Student (White scholar), U. Chgo., 1951-52; BS in Econs, Northwestern U., 1954; MBA in Accounting, U. Pa., 1956; JD, Harvard U., 1958; postgrad. (Fulbright scholar), U. Sydney, Australia, 1958-59; postgrad., Hague Acad. Internat. Law, 1959. Bar: D.C. 1958, Ill. 1959. Asst. prof. bus. law Roosevelt U., Chgo., 1959-61; practice in Chgo., 1959—; mem. firm Aaron, Aaron, Schimberg & Hess, 1969-78; sr. ptnr. Boorstein & Weissman, 1978-82, Weissman, Smolev & Solow, 1982-88, Foley & Lardner, 1988-92, McBride Baker & Coles, 1992—; asst. prof. Roosevelt U., 1960-62; lectr. Lake Forest (Ill.) Coll., 1979-80; chmn. Banking Group, Union League Club Chgo.; mem. Com. on Bank Counsel Ill. Bankers Assn., 1987-88, vice chmn., 1988-90; panelist Robert Morris Assocs., Banking Law Inst., Midwest Fin. Conf., Greater O'Hare Assn., Miss. Law Inst., Bank Lending Inst.; Chgo. Assn. Commerce and Industry, State of Art Seminars, Infocast Inc., SBA, Fed. Res. Bank Chgo., Lenders Ednl. Inst., Bank Adminstrn. Inst. Found., Lender's Forum. Author: Lender Liability, 1988, Commercial Loan Documentation and Secured Lending, 1990; mem. bd. editors Commercial Damages, 1985—; contr. articles to profl. jours. and bus. orgns. Mem. adv. bd. Affective Disorders Clinic, U. Ill. Med. Sch., 1979-81. Mem. ABA, Ill. Bar Assn., Chgo. Bar Assn., Ill. Bankers Assn., Ill. Inst. Continuing Legal Edn. (bd. dirs. 1989-93), Assn. Comml. Fin. Attys. (bd. dirs.), Harvard Law Soc. Ill., Turnaround Mgmt. Assn. (steering com. Chgo. chpt.), Comml. Fin. Assn. Ednl. Found. (adv. bd.), Beta Alpha Psi. Home: 2067 Old Briar Rd Highland Park IL 60035-4245 Office: McBride Baker & Coles 500 W Madison St Ste 4000 Chicago IL 60661-2511

WEISSMAN, MORRIS, printing compnany company; b. 1942. Grad., NYU, 1962. With Midwest Rubber Reclaiming, 1963-86, U.S. Banknote Co., N.Y.C., 1086-90; chmn, Am. Bank Note Co., N.Y.C., 1990—; Mem. Chmn. Bd. Am. Bank Note Holographic, Elmsford, N.Y., Idamatics, N.Y.C., U.S. Bank Note Co. Office: American Bank Note Company 51 W 52nd St New York NY 10019-6119*

WEISSMAN, NORMAN, public relations executive; b. Newark, Apr. 12, 1925; s. Julius and Lenora (Schimmel) W.; m. Sheila Holtz, Dec. 12, 1950 (div. Dec. 1973); 1 son, Lee; m. Natalie Ruvell, Aug. 31, 1984. BA in English, Rutgers U., 1949; MA in Journalism, U. Wis., 1951. Asst. editor McGraw Hill Pub. Co., Inc., 1951-54; sec. to Dept. Air Pollution Control, N.Y.C., 1954-56; account exec. Ruder & Finn, N.Y.C., 1956-59, v.p., 1959-62, sr. v.p., 1962-68, pres., 1968-85, vice-chmn., 1983-85; vice-chmn. G.C.I. Group, Inc., N.Y.C. 1986-90; chmn. Edward Aycoth Worldwide, 1991-93, Citigate, Inc., N.Y.C., 1993—. Served with USN, 1943-46. Mem. Advt. Women N.Y. (hon.), Internat. Pub. Rels. Assn., Phi Beta Kappa, Sigma Delta Chi. Lodge: Rotary. Home: 162 E 93rd St New York NY 10128-3711 Office: Citigate Inc 63 Wall St New York NY 10005

WEISSMAN, PAUL MARSHALL, investment company executive; b. New Haven, Apr. 3, 1931; s. Abraham S. and Regina (Sanditz) W.; m. Harriet Levine, Sept. 30, 1961; children: Michael A., Peter A., Stephanie T. BA, Harvard U., 1952; MBA, U. Pa., 1954. Mng. dir. emeritus Bear, Stearns & Co., N.Y.C., 1958—. V.p., bd. dirs. Grand St. Settlement, N.Y.C.; bd. dirs. N.Y. Service for Handicapped, 1963-75, treas., 1969-71; exec. com., chmn. Harvard Coll. Fund; mem. nominating com. bd. overseers Harvard U., 1983-86; trustee, vice chmn. Conn. Coll., New London, Rye Country Day Sch., N.Y., 1982-91, Hopkins Grammar Sch., New Haven, 1981-86. 1st lt. U.S. Army, 1955-58. Recipient Richard T. Flood award Harvard U., 1977. Mem. Harvard Club of N.Y., Harvard Alumni Assn. (dir. 1978-81, sr. v.p. 1986-87, pres. 1987-88). Jewish. Home: 2 Oxford Rd White Plains NY 10605-3603 Office: 245 Park Ave New York NY 10167-0001

WEISSMAN, ROBERT EVAN, information services company executive; b. New Haven, May 22, 1940; s. Samuel and Lillian (Warren) W.; m. Janet Johl, Aug. 27, 1960; children: Gregory, Christopher, Michael. BSBA, Babson Coll., Wellesley, Mass., 1964. Exec. v.p. Rediffusion Inc., Saugus,

Mass, 1972-73; dir. corp. devel. Nat. CSS, Wilton, Conn., 1973-74, chmn., 1975-81; exec. v.p. Dun & Bradstreet Corp., N.Y.C. 1981-84, pres., 1985-93, CEO, 1995—, chmn., CEO, 1995—; bd. dirs. State St. Boston Corp.; mem. bus. roundtable com. econ. devel. U.S.-Japan Bus. Coun. Vice chmn. Babson Coll. Mem. IEEE, Info. Tech. Assn. Am., Inst. Mgmt. Accts., Soc. Mfg. Engrs. (sr.). Office: Dun & Bradstreet Corp 187 Danbury Rd Wilton CT 06897

WEISSMAN, WILLIAM R., lawyer; b. N.Y.C., Aug. 16, 1940; s. Emanuel and Gertrude (Halpern) W.; m. Barbra Phylis Gershman; 1 child, Adam; stepchildren: Eric, Jace, Julie Greenman. BA, Columbia U., 1962, JD cum laude, 1965. Bar: N.Y. 1965, D.C. 1969, U.S. Dist. Ct. (no. dist.) Tex. 1965, U.S. Dist. Ct. (so. and ea. dists.) N.Y. 1977, U.S. Ct. Appeals (5th cir.) 1966, U.S. Ct. Appeals (D.C. cir.) 1969, U.S. Ct. Appeals (9th cir.) 1973, U.S. Ct. Appeals (2d and 3d cirs.) 1974, U.S. Ct. Appeals (10th cir.) 1979, U.S. Ct. Appeals (11th cir.) 1981, U.S. Supreme Ct. 1968. News dir., program dir. WKCR-FM, N.Y.C., 1960-62; law clk. U.S. dist. judge, Dallas, 1965-66; trial atty. antitrust div. Dept. Justice, Washington, 1966-69; spl. asst. U.S. atty., Washington, 1967; assoc. Wald, Harkrader & Ross, Washington, 1969-72, ptnr., 1973-85; ptnr. Piper & Marbury, Washington, 1986—; instr. Georgetown U. Law Sch.-D.C. Bar Continuing Legal Edn. Program, 1980-89, environ. regulation course Exec. Enterprises, Inc., 1985—. Mem. Arlington (Va.) County Tenant-Landlord Commn., 1973-77, chmn., 1975-77; parliamentarian Arlington County Dem. Com., 1971-75; sec. Columbia Law Sch. Alumni Assn. of Washington, 1982-84, pres., 1984-86, bd. dirs. 1984-88. Mem. editorial adv. bd. Jour. Environ. Regulation, 1991—. Recipient James Gordon Bennett prize Columbia U., 1962, E.B. Convers prize Columbia U., 1965. Mem. ABA, Fed. Bar Assn., D.C. Bar Assn. Jewish. Club: Columbia U. of Washington (bd. dirs. 1987-93). Home: 3802 Lakeview Ter Falls Church VA 22041-1313 Office: Piper & Marbury LLP 1200 19th St NW Washington DC 20036

WEISSMANN, GERALD, medical educator, researcher, writer, editor; b. Vienna, Austria, Aug. 7, 1930; came to U.S., 1938; s. Adolf and Greta (Lustbader) W.; m. Ann Raphael, Apr. 1, 1953; children: Lisa, Andrew. BA with honors, Columbia U., N.Y.C., 1950; MD, NYU, 1954. Diplomate Am. Bd. Internal Medicine. Intern Mt. Sinai Hosp., N.Y.C., 1954-55, asst. resident medicine, 1957-58; chief resident medicine Bellevue Hosp., N.Y.C., 1959-60; fellow depts. biochemistry and medicine Arthritis and Rheumatism Fedn., NYU, 1958-59; rsch. asst. dept. medicine NYU Sch. Medicine, 1959-60, instr. medicine, 1959-62, asst. prof., 1962-65, assoc. prof., 1966-70, prof., 1970—, dir. div. cell biology, 1969-73, dir. div. rheumatology of dept. medicine, 1973—; USPHS spl. rsch. fellow dept. biophysics Strangeways Lab., Cambridge, Eng., 1960-61; sr. investigator Arthritis and Rheumatism Found., N.Y.C., 1961-65; career rsch. scientist Health Rsch. Coun. N.Y.C., 1966-71; instr. physiology Marine Biol. Lab., Woods Hole, Mass., 1973-77, investigator, 1970—, trustee 1993—; vis. investigator ARC Inst. Animal Physiology, Babraham, Eng., 1964-69, Centre de Physiologie et d'Immunologie Cellulaires, Hosp. St. Antoine, Paris, 1973-74, William Harvey Rsch. Inst., London, 1987; mem. postdoctoral fellowships rev. com. Pfizer, Internat., N.Y.C., 1983—; scholarship selection com. Pew Scholars in Biomed. Scis., New Haven, 1984—; lectr. Johns Hopkins U., 1976, 89, Med. Coll. Ga., Augusta, 1980, Med. Coll. Pa., 1988, William Harvey Rsch. Inst., London, 1987, others; nat. adv. bd. Pew Scholars Biomed. Sci., 1984—. Author: The Woods Hole Cantata, 1985, They All Laughed at Christopher Columbus, 1987, The Doctor With Two Heads, 1990, The Doctor Dilemma, 1992, Democracy and DNA, 1995; editor-in-chief Inflammation, 1975—, Advanced in Inflammation Rsch., 1979—, MD Mag., 1989-94; mem. editl. bd. Clin. Immunology and Immunopathology, 1972-88, Advances in Prostaglandin, Thromboxane and Leukotriene Rsch., 1975—, Am. Jour. Medicine, 1976-88, Tissue Reactions, 1979, Immunopharmacology, 1982; contbr. over 300 articles to profl. publs. and to the N.Y. Times, The New Republic, The Yale Rev., Sci. Am. Capt. M.C., U.S. Army, 1955-57. Recipient Allesandro Robecchi prize Internat. League Against Rheumatism, 1972, Marine Biol. Lab. award, 1974, 1979, U. Bologna medal, Italy, 1978, Lila Gruber Cancer Rsch. award Am. Acad. Dermatology, 1979, Solomon A. Berson Med. Alumni Achievement award NYU, 1980, Merit award NIH, 1987, Centennial award Marine Biol. Lab., 1988, C.M. Plotz award N.Y. Arthritis Found., 1993, others; Guggenheim Found. fellow, N.Y.C., 1973-74. Fellow AAAS; mem. Am. Coll. Rheumatology (pres. 1982-83, Disting. Investigator award 1992), Am. Fedn. Clin. Rsch., Soc. Exptl. Biology and Medicine, Am. Soc. Pharmacology and Exptl. Therapeutics, Am. Soc. Exptl. Pathology, Assn. Am. Immunologists, Am. Soc. Cell Biology, Am. Soc. Clin. Investigation, Am. Soc. Biol. Chemistry and Molecular Biology, Assn. Am. Physicians, Harvey Soc. of N.Y. (pres. 1981-82), Interurban Clin. Club, PEN Am. Ctr., Phi Beta Kappa, Alpha Omega Alpha. Avocation: tennis. Office: NYU Med Ctr Dept Medicine 550 1st Ave New York NY 10016-6497

WEISSMANN, HEIDI SEITELBLUM, radiologist, educator; b. N.Y.C., Feb. 4, 1951; d. Louis and June (Joseph) Seitel Bloom; m. Murray H. Weissmann, June 16, 1973; 1 dau., Lauren Erica. BS in Chemistry magna cum laude, Bklyn. Coll., CUNY, 1970; MD, Mt. Sinai Sch. Medicine, N.Y.C., 1974. Diplomate Nat. Bd. Med. Examiners. Intern Montefiore Med. Ctr. Bronx, N.Y., 1974-75, resident in diagnostic radiology, 1975-78; fellow in computerized transaxial tomography and ultrasonography N.Y. Hosp.-Cornell U. Med. Ctr., N.Y.C., N.Y., 1978-79; instr. in radiology and nuclear medicine Albert Einstein Coll. Medicine, Montefiore Med. Ctr., Bronx, N.Y., 1979-80; asst. prof. radiology and nuclear medicine Albert Einstein Coll. Medicine and Montefiore Med. Ctr., Bronx, N.Y., 1980-84, assoc. prof. nuclear medicine, 1984—, assoc. prof. radiology, 1986—; adj. attending physician Montefiore Med. Ctr., 1979-87; chmn. Nuclear Medicine Grand Rounds: Greater N.Y., 1980-87; physician coord. Nuclear Medicine Technologist In-Service Tng. Program, 1982-86; com. NIH, 1984-86, NIH Diagnostic Radiology, 1985-86. Assoc. editor Nuclear Medicine Ann., 5 vols., 1979-84, editor, 5 vols. 1985—; contbr. chpts. to books, articles to jours.; reviewer Jour. of Radiology, 1981—, mem. editorial adv. bd., 1985-86, assoc. editor, 1986—; reviewer Jour. of Nuclear Medicine, 1981—, Am. Jour. of Roentgenology, 1986—, Gastroenterology, 1986—, Western Jour. of Medicine, 1985—; contbr. audiovisual programs and films. Recipient Saul Horowitz, Jr., Meml. award (Disting. Alumnus award), Mt. Sinai Sch. Medicine, 1980, Pres.' award, Am. Roentgen Ray Soc., 1979, Berta Rubinstein, M.D., Resident award, 1978, others. Mem. Radiol. Soc. N.Am. (mem. subcom. for nuclear medicine of program com., 1981, 82, 83, chmn. 1984, 85, 86), Soc. Nuclear Medicine (trustee 1983-87, 88—, sec.-treas. Correlative Imaging Council 1979-82, exec. bd. 1982-84, pres. 1984-86, exec. bd. 1986—, mem. acad. council 1980—, task force on interrelationship between nuclear medicine and nuclear magnetic resonance 1983-85, gov. Greater N.Y. chpt. 1983-85, treas., 1985-86, 86-87, 2d ann. Tetalman award of Edn. and Research Found. 1982, mem., vice chmn. coms. and subcoms.), Soc. Gastrointestinal Radiologists, Am. Inst. Ultrasound in Medicine, N.Y. Acad. Scis., Assoc. Alumni Mt. Sinai Med. Ctr., Nuclear Radiology Club (chmn. 1983—). Phi Beta Kappa.

WEISS-SWEDE, FRANCES ROBERTA See ZAMIR, FRANCES ROBERTA

WEISSTEIN, ULRICH WERNER, English literature educator; b. Breslau, Germany, Nov. 14, 1925; came to U.S., 1950, naturalized, 1959; s. Rudolf and Berta (Wende) W.; m. Elisabeth Rieckh; children: Cristina, Cecily, Eric Wolfgang, Anton Edward. Student, Goethe-Universität, Frankfurt, 1947-50, 51-52, U. Iowa, 1950-51; MA, Ind. U., 1953, PhD, 1954; Doctorate (hon.), U. Lund, Sweden, 1993. Instr. Lehigh U., Bethlehem, Pa., 1954-58; asst. prof. Lehigh U., 1958; asst. prof. English and comparative lit. Ind. U., Bloomington, 1959-62; assoc. prof. Ind. U., 1962-66, prof. German and comparative lit., 1966-90, chmn. comparative lit. program, 1985-89; dir. Ind. U.-Purdue U. Studienprogramm U. Hamburg, 1981-82; vis. prof. U. Wis., summer. 1966, Middlebury Sch. German, summer 1970, U. Hamburg (Germany), spring 1971, U. Vienna, 1976, Stanford U., 1979, U. Hamburg, spring 1982, Graz U., Austria, 1985, U. Bologna, Italy, 1991, U. Antwerp, Belgium, 1992, U. Graz, Austria, 1995; external examiner comparative lit. U. Hong Kong, 1974-76. Author: Heinrich Mann, 1962, The Essence of Opera, 1964, Max Frisch, 1967, Einführung in die Vergleichende Literaturwissenschaft, 1968, English version: Comparative Literature and Literary Theory, 1973; Spanish version: Introducciòn a la Literatura Comparada, 1975, Chinese version, 1987, Japanese version, 1976, Korean version, 1979; Forschungsbericht zur Vergleichenden Literaturwissenschaft, 1968-1977, 1981, Links und links gesellt sich nicht: Gesammelte Aufsätze zum Werk Heinrich

Manns und Bertolt Brechts, 1985; editor: Literatur und Bildende Kunst: Ein Handbuch zur Theorie und Praxis eines komparatistischen Grenzgebiets, 1992; editor German sect. Twayne World Authors series, 1964-86, Yearbook of Comparative and General Literature, 1960-90, Expressionism as an International Literary Phenomenon, 1973; co-editor: Literature and the Other Arts, 1981, Texte und Kontexte: Festschrift für Norbert Fuerst, 1973, Intertextuality: German Literature and Visual Art from the Renaissance to the Twentieth Century, 1993; translator: The Grotesque in Art and Literature (W. Kayser), 1963. MLA grantee, 1958-59; Guggenheim fellow, 1974-75. Mem. MLA (exec. coun. 1983-86), Internat. Comparative Lit. Assn. (exec. coun. 1979-85, sec. 1985-89), Am. Comparative Lit. Assn., Coun. Internat. Exchange Scholars (area com. for W. Ger. and Austria 1983-85). Home: Baiernstrasse 54/IV, 8020 Gaz Austria

WEISTART, JOHN C., law educator; b. 1943. BA, Ill. Wesleyan U., 1965; JD, Duke U., 1968. Law clk. to presiding justice Ill. Supreme Ct., Springfield, 1968-69; asst. prof. Duke U., Durham, N.C., 1969-72, assoc. prof., 1972-73, prof., 1973—. Office: Sch Law Duke U Durham NC 27706

WEISWASSER, STEPHEN ANTHONY, lawyer, broadcast executive; b. Detroit, Nov. 21, 1940; s. Avery and Eleanor (Sherman) W.; m. July 3, 1962 (div. 1985); children: Jonathan, Gayle; m. Andrea Timko, Apr. 19, 1986; children: Anne, Emily. BA, Wayne State U., 1962; student, Johns Hopkins U., 1962-63; JD, Harvard U., 1966. Bar: D.C. 1967, U.S. Supreme Ct. 1970. Law clk. to chief judge U.S. Ct. Appeals, Washington, 1966-67; assoc. Wilmer, Cutler and Pickering, Washington, 1967-74, ptnr., 1974-86; sr. v.p., gen. counsel Capital Cities/ABC, Inc., N.Y.C., 1986-91, sr. v.p., exec. v.p. ABC-TV network group, 1991, sr. v.p., exec. v.p. ABC News, 1991-93, sr. v.p., 1993; sr. v.p., gen. counsel ABC News, N.Y.C., 1993-94; sr. v.p., pres. Multimedia Group, N.Y.C., 1993—; bd. dirs. Ctr. Comm.; pres. Internat. Radio and TV Soc. Found., Inc., 1995—. Trustee Woodrow Wilson Found., 1994—. Mem. ABA, Fed. Comm. Bar Assn. Jewish. Home: 2 Quincy St Chevy Chase MD 20815-4227 Office: Capital Cities/ABC Inc 77 W 66th St New York NY 10023-6290

WEISZ, PAUL B(URG), physicist, chemical engineer; b. Pilsen, Czechoslovakia, July 2, 1919; naturalized, 1946; s. Alexander and Amalia (Sulc) W.; m. Rhoda A.M. Burg, Sept. 4, 1943; children: Ingrid B., P. Randall. Student, Tech. U. Berlin, 1938-39; BS, Auburn U., 1940; ScD, Swiss Fed. Inst. Tech., Zurich, 1965, ScD (hon.), 1980. Research physicist Bartol Research Found., Swarthmore, Pa., 1940-46; Research physicist Mobil Oil Corp. (formerly Socony Mobil Oil Corp.), 1958-61, sr. scientist, 1961-69, mgr. process research sect., 1967-69; mgr. Central Research Lab. Mobil Research & Devel. Corp., Princeton, N.J., 1969-82, sr. scientist and sci. adv., 1982-84; Disting. prof. chem. and bio-engring. sci. U. Pa., 1984-90, prof. emeritus, 1990—; adj. prof. Pa. State U., 1992—; cons. rsch. and tech. strategy, 1984—; vis. prof. Princeton U., 1974-76, mem. adv. council dept. chem. engring., 1973-78; mem. adv. and resource council Princeton U. Sch. Engring., 1974-78; chmn. center policy bd. Center for Catalytic Sci. and Tech., U. Del., 1977-81; mem. energy research adv. bd. U.S. Dept. Energy, 1985-90. Editor: Advances in Catalysis, 1956-93; edtl. bd. Jour. Catalysis, 1962-83, Chem. Engring. Comms., 1972-78, Heterogeous Chem. Reviews, 1993—; monthly columnist Sci. of the Possible, Chemtech, 1980-83; contbr. numerous articles to sci. jours.; holder 80 patents. Recipient ann. award Catalysis Club Phila., 1973, Lavoisier medal, Socié té Chimique de France, 1983, Perkin medal Soc. Chem. Industries, 1985, Nat. Medal of Tech., 1992. Fellow Am. Phys. Soc., Am. Inst. Chemists (Chem. Pioneer award 1974); mem. AIChE (R.H. Wilhelm award 1978), Am. Chem. Soc. (sci. award South Jersey sect. 1963, E.V. Murphree award 1972, Leo Friend award 1977, Chemistry of Contemporary Tech. Problems award 1986, Carothers award 1987), N.Y. Acad. Sci., Nat. Acad. Engring., Nassau Club (Princeton). Quaker. Office: Univ of Pa Dept Bio-Engring Philadelphia PA 19104

WEISZ, WILLIAM JULIUS, electronics company executive; b. Chgo., Jan. 8, 1927; m. Barbara Becker, Dec. 25, 1947; children: George, Terri, David. B.S. in Elec. Engring., MIT, 1948; D.B.A. (hon.), St. Ambrose Coll., 1976. With Motorola, Inc., Chgo., 1948-90, exec. v.p., 1969-70, pres., 1970-80, chief oper. officer, 1972-86, vice chmn., 1980-93, chief exec. officer, 1986-87, officer of bd., 1988-89, ret., 1990, chmn. bd. dirs., 1993—; Pres. Motorola Communications Internat., 1966-90; Motorola Communications and Electronics, Inc., 1966-69; dir. (Motorola Israel), Harris Bankcorp Harris Trust and Savs. Bank; mem. exec. com. land mobile adv. com. to FCC. Com. chmn. Cub Scout Pack Evanston coun. Boy Scouts Am., 1960-62; trustee MIT, 1975-85, 91—; mem. Def. Policy Adv. Com. on Trade, 1988-92. Recipient award of merit Nat. Electronics Conf., 1970; Freedom Found. of Valley Forge award, 1974; MIT Corp. Leadership award, 1976. Fellow IEEE (past nat. chmn. vehicular communications group); mem. Electronic Industries Assn. (past chmn., bd. govs., past chmn. indsl. elec. div., medal of honor 1981), Bus. Roundtable, MIT Club (dirs. Chgo.), Sigma Xi, Tau Beta Pi, Eta Kappa Nu. Office: Motorola Inc 1303 E Algonquin Rd Schaumburg IL 60196

WEITHAS, WILLIAM VINCENT, advertising agency executive; b. Jamaica, N.Y., May 10, 1929; s. William and Margaret (Beese) W.; m. Mary Eileen Livingston, Sept. 1, 1956; children—Suzann Weithas Cahill, Bill, John, Jeremy, Claudia. B.S., Seton Hall U., 1951. Salesman Nabisco Co., 1951; v.p., account supr. Batten, Barton, Durstine & Osborn, Inc., N.Y.C., 1952-66; advt. mgr. P. Ballantine & Sons, N.Y.C., 1966-67, v.p., dir. mktg. services, 1967-68; v.p. SSC&B, Inc., N.Y.C., 1968-72, exec. v.p., 1972-79, pres., chief operating officer, 1979-81, chmn., chief exec. officer, 1981-83; vice chmn. SSC&B: Lintas Internat., London, 1981-82, chmn., chief exec., 1982-85; chmn., chief exec. officer Lintas Worldwide, N.Y.C. and London, 1985-91; vice chmn., dir. Interpub. Group of Cos., N.Y.C., 1991—; dir. The Advt. Coun., 1986—. Mem. N.Y. State Gov.'s Bus. Adv. Bd., 1986—. Mem. Am. Assn. Advt. Agys. (vice chmn. 1987—, chmn. 1988-89, dir.-at-large 1983-85, ops. com. 1984-85), Coun. for Comml. Freedom, Nat. Advt. Rev. Coun., Navesink Country Club, Madison Sq. Garden Club. Office: The Interpublic Group of Company 1271 Ave of the Americas New York NY 10020 also: 84 Eccleston Sq, London SW1V 1PX, England

WEITKAMP, WILLIAM GEORGE, nuclear physicist; b. Fremont, Nebr., June 22, 1934; s. Alvin Herman and Georgia Ann (Fuhrmeister) W.; m. Audrey Ann Jensen, June 2, 1956; children—Erick, Jay, Gretchen, Laurie. B.A., St. Olaf Coll., 1956; M.S., U. Wis., 1961, Ph.D., 1965. Research asst. prof. U. Wash., Seattle, 1965-67; asst. prof. U. Pitts., 1967-68; tech. dir., research prof. Nuclear Physics Lab., U. Wash., Seattle, 1968-95, retired, 1995. Served with USAF, 1956-59. Acad. guest Eidgenossische Technische Hochschule Zurich, Switzerland, 1974-75. Mem. Am. Phys. Soc. Home: 2019 E Louisa St Seattle WA 98112-2207 Office: Univ Wash Nuclear Physics Lab GL-10 Seattle WA 98195

WEITZ, BRUCE, retail executive; b. 1947. BBA, Pace U., 1969. With Walbaums, Cen. Islip, N.Y., 1973-77, Shop-Rite Supermarkets, Elizabeth, N.J., 1978-83; with merchandising and ops. Price Chopper, Schenectady, N.Y., 1978-83; various exec. pos. ea. divsn. First Nat. Supermarkets, Windsor Locks, Conn., 1983-88; pres. Grossman's, Inc., Braintree, Mass., 1989-92; CEO, COO Duane Reade, Long Island, N.Y., 1992—. Office: Duane Reade 49-29 30th Pl Long Island City NY 11101*

WEITZ, ERIC, chemistry educator; b. N.Y.C., Sept. 18, 1947; s. Harry and Charlotte Weitz; m. Elizabeth Burrell. BS, MIT, 1968; PhD, Columbia U., 1972. Postdocoral rsch. assoc. U. Calif., Berkeley, 1972-74; asst. prof. Northwestern U., Evanston, Ill., 1974-80, assoc. prof. 1980-84, prof., 1984—. Fellow Alfred P. Sloan Found., 1978-82, DuPont Young Faculty fellow E.I. DuPont, 1974, vis. fellow Joint Inst. Lab. Astrophysics 1983-84. Fellow Am. Physical Soc.; mem. Am. Chemical Soc.

WEITZ, JOHN, fashion designer, writer; b. Berlin, May 25, 1923; came to U.S., 1940, naturalized, 1943; s. Robert and Hedy (Jacob) W.; m. Susan Kohner, Aug. 30, 1964; children: Paul John, Christopher John; children by previous marriage: Karen Weitz Curtis, Robert. Student, Hall Sch., London, 1936, St. Paul's Sch., London, 1936-39; certificate, Oxford-Cambridge Sch. 1938. Founder John Weitz Designs, Inc., N.Y.C., 1954—. Designer various cos., until 1954; author: Value of Nothing, Man in Charge (Best Seller list 1974), Friends in High Places, 1982, Hitler's Diplomat, 1992. Bd. dirs. emeritus The Allen-Stevenson Sch., N.Y.C.; bd. dirs. Phoenix House, William J. Donovan Found., Vets. of OSS, Leo Baeck Inst., Am. Coun. on Germany; mem. pres.'s coun. Mus. City of N.Y. Capt. M.I. AUS, 1942-46, ETO. Decorated First Class Cross Order of Merit (Fed. Republic Germany), 1988, Comdr.'s Cross (Fed. Republic Germany), 1995; recipient Sports Illustrated award, 1959, NBC Today award, 1960, Phila. Mus. award, 1960, Caswell Massey awards 1963-66, Harpers Bazaar medallion, 1966, Moscow diploma, 1967, Coty award, 1974, Cartier Design award, 1981, Mayor's Liberty medal, N.Y.C., 1986, Cutty Sark Career Achievement award, 1986, Dallas Menswear Mart award, 1990, Pres.'s award of Fashion Inst. of Tech., 1990, Ellis Island medal of Honor, 1992; named to Internat. Best Dressed List Hall of Fame, 1971. Mem. The Pilgrims, Union Club, Century Assn., Spl. Forces Club, Old Pauline Club (v.p., London), Confrerie des Chevaliers du Tastevin, Beach Club (Palm Beach), Vintage Sports Car Club Am., Sports Car Club Am., Road Racing Drivers Club, USN Acad. Sailing Squadron, Sag Harbor Yacht Club. Office: 600 Madison Ave New York NY 10022-1615

WEITZEL, HARRY JOHN, JR., banker; b. Balt., July 27, 1938; s. Harry John Sr. and Edna (McCabe) W.; m. Susan Glass, Nov. 27, 1981; children: Harry John III, Alec D.; stepchildren: John P. Saladin, S. Austin Saladin, Jacque S. Saladin. AB, Johns Hopkins U., 1960; MBA, George Washington U., 1963; student, Stonier Grad. Sch. Banking, 1971. With Md. Nat. Bank, Balt., 1960—, credit analyst, 1962-64, asset cashier & officer, 1964-66, asst. v.p., regional loan officer, 1966-68, v.p., regional div. head, 1968-72, sr. v.p. entire county system, 1972-79, sr. v.p. strategic planning functions, 1979-81, exec. v.p., 1981-84, sr. exec. v.p., 1984-89; pres., chief oper. officer MNC Retail Svcs. Corp., 1989—. Officer, bd. dirs., mem. exec. com. Hist. Annapolis (Md.), Inc., 1970-85; trustee, mem. exec. bd. The Balt. Mus. Art, 1981—; bd. govs., trustee The Ctr. Club, Md., 1984—; pres. St. Mary's Coll. Found., 1988—; mem. bd. visitors U. Md., pres., 1989—. Served to capt. U.S. Army, 1961-62. Mem. Assn. Res. City Bankers (internat. banking com. 1988-89), Am. Bankers Assn. (mem. exec. com. 1981-84, co-chmn. corp. planning com. 1982-84), Johns Hopkins U. Balt. Com., U. Md.-Md. Indsl. Partnership Com. (mem. adv. bd.), Johns Hopkins Alumni Assn. Democrat. Episcopalian. Club: Robert Morris Assocs. Avocations: squash, tennis. Home: 203 Nottingham Hl Annapolis MD 21405 Office: MNC Retail Svcs Corp 10 Light St Fl 14 Baltimore MD 21202-1435

WEITZEL, JOHN PATTERSON, lawyer; b. Pitts., Aug. 24, 1923; s. Albert Philip and Elizabeth (Patterson) W.; m. Elisabeth Swan, Mar. 20, 1965; children: Mary Middleton, Paul Patterson. Student, Deerfield (Mass.) Acad., 1937-40; A.B., Yale U., 1946; LL.B., Harvard U., 1949. Bar: Mass. 1949, U.S. Supreme Ct. 1960. Assoc. Herrick, Smith, Donald, Farley & Ketchum (now Herrick & Smith), Boston, 1949-53, prtnr., 1961-86; prtnr. Palmer & Dodge, Boston, 1986-93; of counsel, 1993—, spl. asst. to sect. treasury, 1953-55, asst. to under sec. treas, 1955-56; asst. gen. counsel Treasury Dept., 1956-59, dep. to sec. treasury, 1959-60, asst. sec. treasury, 1960-61; U.S. exec. dir. IBRD, 1960-61; mem. planning bd. NSC, 1959-61; cons. to sec. def., 1973. Mem. Mass. Council Arts and Humanities, 1966-71; overseer, dir. sec. Boys and Girls Clubs, Boston; mem. corp. Mass. Gen. Hosp., Boston Mus. Sci.; trustee Roxbury Latin Sch. Served with USAAF, 1943-45. Mem. Am., Boston bar assns., Am. Law Inst. Clubs: Harvard (Boston), Union Boat (Boston). Home: 45 Devon Rd Chestnut Hill MA 02167-1851 Office: Palmer & Dodge 1 Beacon St Boston MA 02108-3190

WEITZEL, JOHN QUINN, bishop; b. Chgo., May 10, 1928; s. Carl Joseph and Patricia (Quinn) W. BA, Maryknoll (N.Y.) Sem., 1951, M of Religious Edn., 1953; PMD, Harvard U. Ordained priest Roman Cath. Ch., 1955. With ednl. devel. Cath. Fgn. Mission Soc. of Am., Maryknoll, 1955-63, nat. dir. vocations for Maryknoll, dir. devel. dept. and info. services, 1963-72, mem. gen. council, 1972-78; asst. parish priest Cath. Ch., Western Samoa, 1979-81, pastor, vicar gen., 1981-86; consecrated bishop, 1986; bishop Cath. Ch., Am. Samoa, 1986—. Office: Diocese Samoa-Pago Pago Fatuoaiga PO Box 596 Pago Pago AS 96799-0596

WEITZEL, PETER ANDRE, editor, newspaper; b. Akron, Ohio, July 5, 1936; s. Anthony Edmund Weitzel and Dorothy (Leininger) Simons; m. Sara Mitchell, June 28, 1958 (div. 1978); m. Linda Goodridge Steckley, Jan. 10, 1981; children: Tony, Philip, Mark, Matthew, Adam. AB Polit. Sci., U. Ill., 1958. Reporter Miami Herald, 1958-62, asst. city editor, 1965-69, govt. editor, 1969-71, state editor, 1971-78, asst. mng. editor, 1978-83, mng. editor, 1983-93, sr. mng. editor, 1993-95; ret., 1995; Pres. Fla. Soc. Newspaper Editors, 1979-80. Pres. Fla. First Amendment Found., Tallahassee, 1985—; chmn. Nat. Freedom Info. Coalition, Dallas, 1993—. Mem. Am. Soc. Newspaper Editors, Fla. Soc. Newspaper Editors (Freedom info. com. 1981—). Fla. First Amendment Found., Nat. Freedom Info. Coalition. Avocations: softball, swimming. Home: 721 Biltmore Way # 702 Coral Gables FL 33134 Office: The Miami Herald 1 Herald Plz Miami FL 33132

WEITZEL, WILLIAM CONRAD, JR., lawyer; b. Washington, Feb. 6, 1935; s. William Conrad and Pauline Lillian (Keeton) W.; m. Loretta LeVeck, Mar. 10, 1978; children: William Conrad III, Richard S., Sarah L., Andrew K. AB, Harvard U., 1956, LLB, 1959; postgrad., MIT, 1974. Bar: D.C. 1961. Law clk., chief judge U.S. Cts. Md., Balt., 1959-60; USA atty., Washington, 1961-66; atty. Texaco, Inc., White Plains, N.Y., 1966-73; assoc. gen. counsel Texaco, Inc., 1973-76, gen. counsel, 1977-82, v.p., gen. counsel, 1982-84, sr. v.p., gen. counsel, 1984-90; Pres. Texaco Philanthropic Found., Inc., 1980-90; ptnr., chmn. bus. clients dept. Cummings & Lockwood, Stamford, Conn., 1991—. Chmn. adv. bd. Southwestern Legal Found. With USN, 1960-61. Fellow Ctr. for Pub. Resources; mem. ABA, Am. Law Inst., Conn. Bar Assn., D.C. Bar Assn., Assn. Gen. Counsel (v.p., bd. dirs. 1988-90), Westchester-Fairfield Corp. Counsel Assn. (pres. 1981, chmn., chief legal officers com. 1982-90), Am. Petroleum Inst. (gen. com. on law, chmn. 1983-84), Darien (Conn.) Country Club, Harvard Club (dir. Harvard Alumni Assn. for Conn. 1990-93, pres. Fairfield County club 1987—). Republican. Episcopalian. Office: Cummings & Lockwood Ten Stamford Forum PO Box 120 Stamford CT 06904

WEITZER, BERNARD, telecommunications executive; b. Bronx, N.Y., Sept. 22, 1929; s. Morris R. and Eva (Kurtz) W.; m. Anne DeHaven Jones, Nov. 5, 1982. BS, CCNY, 1950; MS, NYU, 1951, postgrad., 1951-54. Mgr., asst. v.p. systems engring and analysis Western Union Telegraph Co., Upper Saddle River, N.J., 1966-71, v.p. engring. and computer systems, 1976-85, sr. v.p. ops., 1985-90; cons. pvt. practice, Fort Lee, N.J., 1990—; exec. v.p., gen. mgr. Western Union Teleprocessing Industries, Inc., Mahwah, N.J., 1971-76; dir. U.S. Telecomm. Tng. Inst.; mem. adv. com. TV comm. U.S. Info. Agy. Pres. Ft. Lee Bd. Edn.; pres., bd. trustees Ft. Lee Pub. Libr. Served to lt. U.S. Army, 1954-57. Mem. Chaines des Rotisseurs, Internat. Wine Food Soc. Home: 6 Horizon Rd Apt 2509 Fort Lee NJ 07024-6652

WEITZMAN, ARTHUR JOSHUA, English educator; b. Newark, Sept. 13, 1933; s. Louis I. and Cecele W.; m. Catherine Ezell, Aug. 8, 1982; children: Peter A., Anne E. BA, U. Chgo., 1956, M.A., 1957; Ph.D., NYU, 1964. Instr. English, Bklyn. Coll., 1960-63; asst. prof. Temple U., Phila., 1963-69; assoc. prof. Northeastern U., Boston, 1969-72; prof. Northeastern U., 1972—; field editor G.K. Hall (Macmillan Pub.). Editor: Letters Writ by a Turkish Spy (G.P. Marana), 1970; founder, co-editor: The Scriblerian, 1968—; co-editor: Milton and the Romantics, 1980-81; contbr.: revs. and articles to profl. jours. and newspapers including Los Angeles Times, Boston Globe, Miami Herald. NEH fellow, 1972-73; Mellon fellow, 1976; research grantee Temple U.; research grantee Northeastern U. Mem. MLA, Am. Soc. 18th Century Studies, Conf. Editors Learned Jours. Jewish. Home: 4 Bellis Ct Cambridge MA 02140-3240 Office: Northeastern U Dept English 406 Holmes Boston MA 02115

WEITZMAN, HOWARD L., lawyer; b. L.A., Sept. 21, 1939. BS, U. So. Calif., 1962, JD, 1965. Bar: Calif. 1966, U.S. Dist. Ct. (ctrl., ea. and so. dists.) Calif., U.S.Ct. Appeals (9th cir.), U.S. Supreme Ct. 1976, U.S. Ct. Appeals (6th cir.) 1983. Ptnr. Katten Muchin Zavis & Weitzman, L.A.; lectr. U. So. Calif., 1973-83. Mem. ABA, L.A. County Bar Assn., Beverly Hill Bar Assn. Office: Katten Muchin Zavis & Weitzman 1999 Ave of the Stars Ste 1400 Los Angeles CA 90067-6042

WEITZMAN, ROBERT HAROLD, investment company executive; b. Chgo., July 15, 1937; s. Nathan and Selma Weitzman; m. Marilynn Beth

Felzer, Sept. 5, 1965; children—Joshua C., Eliza S. B.A. in Bus., Econs., Grinnell Coll., 1959; J.D., DePaul U., 1963. Bar: Ill 1963. Vice pres. Weitzman Enterprises, Chgo., 1955-63; assoc. Lissner, Rothenberg, Reif & Barth, Chgo., 1963-68; real estate counsel Continental Ill. Nat. Bank and Trust Co., Chgo., 1968-74; v.p., group head Continental Ill. Investment Trust, Chgo., 1974-76; founding ptnr. Group One Investments, Chgo., 1977—; lectr. in field. Editor: Real Estate Finance Handbook, 1979. Contbr. articles to profl. jours. Trustee, advisor Weitzman Found., 1963-77, mng. trustee, 1978—; cons., advisor Ill. chpt. Big Bros. Am. Orgn., 1969-72; trustee The Wis. Real Estate Investment Trust, 1980, 81. Recipient Outstanding Young Man Am. award U.S. Jaycees, 1973. Mem. Ill. Bar Assn., Chgo. Bar Assn., Nat. Assn. Rev. Appraisers and Mortgage Underwriters (charter mem. cert. rev. appraiser designation), Real Estate Securities and Syndication Inst. (bd. dirs. Ill. chpt. 1982-90, pres. 1984, regional v. p. 1988, specialist in real estate securities designation 1988, chmn. nat. com. on continuing edn. 1989, 90). Real Estate Investment Assn. (founding mem., Nat. bd. dirs. 1990—, exec. com. nat assn. and Ill. chpt. 1990—, chmn. nat. com. for advanced edn., 1990—, specialist in real estate investment designation 1990), Am. Inst. Banking, Internat. Coll. Real Estate Cons. Profls., Internat. Real Estate Bd. Home: 535 Carriage Way Deerfield IL 60015-4534 Office: Group One Investments Suite 1005 77 W Washington St Ste 1005 Chicago IL 60602-2805

WEITZNER, HAROLD, mathematics educator; b. Boston, May 19, 1933; s. Morris and Alice Savitz W.; m. Lois S. Friedlander, June 12, 1962; children: Daniel J., Henry D. AB, U. Calif., Berkeley, 1954; AM, Harvard U., 1955, PhD, 1958. Assoc. rsch. scientist Courant Inst. NYU, N.Y.C., 1959-60, rsch. scientist, 1960-62, asst. prof., 1962-65, assoc. prof., 1965-69, prof., 1969—; assoc. dir. Magneto-Fluids div. Courant Inst. NYU, N.Y.C., 1988—, dir., 1973-79, 84-88; chmn. Math. Dept. Courant Inst. NYU, N.Y.C., 1989-91; cons. Oak Ridge Nat. Labs., Oak Ridge, Tenn., 1980—; mem. magnetic fusion adv. com. U.S. Dept. Energy, 1986-89, fusion energy adv. com., 1991-93; mem. adv. com. Gen. Atomics Corp., 1994—. Contbr. articles to sci. jours. Fellow Am. Phys. Soc.; mem. Soc. for Indsl. and Applied Math., Univ. Fusion Assn. (exec. com. 1993—). Home: 10 Cedar Ave Larchmont NY 10538-4121 Office: NYU Courant Inst 251 Mercer St New York NY 10012-1110

WEKSEL, WILLIAM, electronics executive. Chmn. bd. dirs., CEO E. F. Johnson Co., Burnsville, Minn. Office: E F Johnson Co 438 Gateway Blvd Burnsville MN 55337*

WEKSLER, MARC EDWARD, physician, educator; b. N.Y.C., Apr. 16, 1937; s. Jacob J. and Lillian W.; m. Babette Barbash; children: David J., Jennifer Lee. B.A., Swarthmore Coll., 1958; M.D., Columbia U., 1962. Intern Bronx (N.Y.) Mcpl. Hosp., 1962-63, resident in medicine, 1963-64; asst. prof. medicine Cornell U. Med. Coll., N.Y.C., 1970-75; assoc. prof. Cornell U. Med. Coll., 1975-78, Wright prof. medicine, 1978—, dir. div. geriatrics and gerontology, 1978—; attending physician N.Y. Hosp., Meml. Hosp., N.Y.C.; vis. prof. Pasteur Inst., Paris; cons. NIH, VA, N.Y.C., WHO, Pontifical Acad. Scis., Nat. Acad. Scis.; James Day lectr. Cornell U., 1980; pres. bd. trustees Am. Fedn. Aging Rsch., 1992-94. Editorial bd.: Jour. Clin. Immunology, Annals of Internal Medicine, Proc. Soc. Exptl. Biology and Medicine; asso. editor: Exptl. Aging Research. Founder, pres. Graphic Arts Coun. N.Y.; pres. Am. Fedn. Aging Rsch. Fellow Morgan Libr., Frick Collection; mem. ACP; mem. Am. Soc. Clin. Investigation, N.Y. Acad. Medicine (chmn. geriatric sect.), Gerontol. Soc. (humanities and arts com.), Assn. Am. Physicians, Interurban Clin. Club, Alpha Omega Alpha. Office: Cornell U Med Coll 1300 York Ave New York NY 10021-4805

WELANDER, BO, chemicals executive; b. 1942. Degree, U. Tech., Stockholm, 1966. With Nobel Industries Sweden, 1966-87; pres., mem. Eka Nobel, Inc., Marietta, Ga., 1987—. Office: Eka Nobel Inc 1519 Johnson Ferry Rd Marietta GA 30062*

WELBER, DAVID ALAN, accountant; b. York, Pa., Oct. 14, 1949; s. Harry and Julia Welber. BS in Acctg., York Coll., 1975. CPA, Pa.; cert. fin. planner, Coll. for Fin. Planners. Acct. Einhorn, Butler, Gingerich & Co., York, 1974-82; ptnr. Bergdoll & Martin, York, 1984-86; prin. David A. Welber, CPA, York, 1982-84, 86—; v.p. Bell Socialization Svcs., 1994-96. Bd. dirs. Jewish Family Svcs., Exch. Club Ctr. for Prevention of Child Abuse, Harrisburg, Pa., 1979-87, Rehab. and Indsl. Tng. Ctr., York, 1987-90, Bell Socialization Svcs., 1991—; mem. coun. Colony Park Homeowners Assn., York, 1982-84; co-chmn. Ohev Sholom Bd. Edn., York, 1987-90. Mem. Pa. Inst. CPAs (mem. personal fin. planning com. 1987—, Edn. award 1973), Exch. Club York (treas. 1984-90, pres. 1991-92), Greater York Rep. Club (treas. 1995—). Republican. Jewish. Avocations: reading, dancing, history, tropical birds, Compuserve network. Office: 212 E Market St York PA 17403-2013

WELBORN, CARYL BARTELMAN, lawyer; b. Phila., Jan. 29, 1951; d. Raymond C. and Helen Ann (Roach) Bartelman; m. Lucien Ruby, Apr. 11, 1987. AB, Stanford U., 1972; JD, UCLA, 1976. Bar: Ill. 1976, Calif. 1978. Assoc. Isham Lincoln & Beale, Chgo., 1976-78; from assoc. to ptnr. Morrison & Foerster, San Francisco and L.A., 1978—; lectr. real property law. Mem. ABA (chmn. com. on partnerships, real property sect. 1989-93), Am. Coll. Real Estate Lawyers (bd. govs. 1994). Office: Morrison & Foerster 345 California St San Francisco CA 94104

WELBORN, ELSIE ELENDER JENKINS, nurse executive, nurse; b. Crandall, Miss., May 13, 1937; d. Perry Lamar and Esther Lou (Napp) Jenkins; m. Eldon Coy Welborn, Apr. 4, 1957; children: Link Von, Coy. Diploma in nursing, South Miss. Charity Hosp., 1963; BSN, U. Miss., 1971; MS, U. South Fla., 1976. Cert. nurse adminstr. Relief house supr., float nurse Hinds Gen. Hosp., Jackson, Miss., 1970-71; asst. dir. nursing svcs. Kings Daughters Hosp., Greenville, Miss., 1971-72; supr., instr. VA Med. Ctr., Tampa, Fla., 1972-78; asst. chief nursing svc. VA Bay Pines, Fla., 1978-81, VA New Orleans, 1981-82; chief nursing svc. VA Med. Ctr., Boise, Idaho, 1982-84, Biloxi, Miss., 1984-91; chief nursing svc. VA Med. Ctr., Lake City, Fla., 1991—; preceptor grad. nursing program U. So. Miss., Long Beach; mem. adj. faculty dept. nursing grad. program La. State U. Sch. Nursing; mem. adj. faculty Boise State U.; mem. Nat. League Nursing com. Lake City C.C. Named VA Career Woman of Yr. 1990, Lighthouse Bus. and Profl. Women's Club, Biloxi, 1990. Mem. ANA, Miss. Nurses Assn., U. Miss. Sch. Nursing Alumnae Assn., Daus. of Nile, Sigma Theta Tau. Home: 14677 C R 137 Wellborn FL 32094 Office: Va Med Ctr 801 S Marion St Lake City FL 32055

WELBORN, JOHN ALVA, former state senator, small business owner; b. Kalamazoo, Mich., Dec. 20, 1932; s. H. Sterling and Elizabeth Catherine (Dougherty) W.; m. Dorothy Yeomans, Aug. 15, 1952; children: Kayla, John, Kami. Grad. high sch., Richland, Mich. Previously supr. Cooper Twp., Mich.; Mich. state rep. Lansing, 1972-74, Mich. sen., 1974-82, 83-94; dairy farmer Kalamazoo area, 1985-94; agt. Welborn Ins. Agy., Kalamazoo area; owner Welborn's Yesteryear Antiques. Candidate for gov. Mich., 1982; past chmn. Kalamazoo Rep. Exec. Com.; past mem. Gull Lake (Mich.) Sch. Bd.; past bd. suprs. Kalamazoo County, dir. Kalamazoo Soil Conservation Dist.; vol. fireman Cooper Twp. Fire Dept. Named Legislator of Yr. Police Officers Assn. Mich., 1988; recipient Golden Eagle Nat. Fedn. Police. Home: 6304 N Riverview Dr Kalamazoo MI 49004-9649

WELBORN, REICH LEE, lawyer; b. Winston-Salem, N.C., Nov. 1, 1945; s. Bishop M. and Hazel (Waterman) W.; m. Martha Huffstetler, Aug. 27, 1966; children: Judson Allen, Spencer Brooks. AB, U. N.C., 1968, JD with honors, 1971. Bar: N.C. 1971. Assoc. Moore & Van Allen, PLLC and predecessor Powe Porter & Alphin, P.A., Durham, N.C., 1971-76; ptnr. Moore & Van Allen and predecessor Powe Porter & Alphin, P.A., Durham, N.C., 1976—; v.p. Family Counseling Svc., Durham, 1978-79. Recipient Order of Long Leaf Pine award Gov. of N.C., 1991, Spl. Citation, 1983. Mem. ABA, N.C. Bar Assn.: Durham County Bar Assn. (v.p. 1987-89, pres. 1989-90), N.C. State Bar, Croasdaile Club (pres. 1989-90), Sertoma (pres. Durham chpt. 1987-88), Jaycees (pres. N.C. chpt. 1981-82), Durham C. of C. (bd. dirs. 1992-93). Home: 7 Lanecrest Pl Durham NC 27705-1854 Office: Moore & Van Allen PLLC 2200 W Main St Ste 800 Durham NC 27705-4677

WELBORN, VICTORIA LEE, science librarian, educator; b. Thomasville, N.C., Feb. 17, 1953; d. Ivan Edward and Mary Christine (Murphy) W.; m. Craig K. Weatherington, Apr. 20, 1993. BA, Wake Forest U., 1975; MLS, Kent State U., 1979. Ref. libr. Health Scis. Libr. Ohio State U., Columbus, 1980-83, head Biol. Scis. Libr. 1983-88; head sci. libr. U. Calif., Santa Cruz, 1988—; adj. instr. Libr. Sch., Kent (Ohio) State U., 1987-88. Mem. Internat. Assn. Marne Scis. Librs. and Info. Ctrs. Office: U Calif Sci Libr Santa Cruz CA 95063

WELCH, ARNOLD DEMERRITT, pharmacologist, biochemist; b. Nottingham, N.H., Nov. 7, 1908; s. Lewis H. and Stella M. (Batchelder) W.; m. Mary Grace Scott, June 15, 1933 (dec.); children: Michael Scott, Stephen Anthony, Gwyneth Jeanne Sinizer; m. Erika Petrová, Mar. 15, 1966. B.S., U. Fla., 1930, M.S., 1931, D.Sc. (hon.), 1973; Ph.D., U. Toronto, 1934; M.D., Washington U., 1939. Research asst. U. Fla., 1929-31; fellow pharmacology U. Toronto, 1931-35; asst. pharmacology Washington U., 1935-36, instr., 1936-40; dir. pharmacol. research Sharp and Dohme, Inc., Phila., 1940-44, dir. research, 1943-44; prof. pharmacology, dir. dept. Sch. Medicine, Western Res. U., 1944-53; Fulbright sr. research scholar Oxford U., 1952; prof. pharmacology, chmn. dept. Sch. Medicine, Yale U., 1953-67, Eugene Higgins prof. pharmacology, 1957-67; dir. Squibb Inst. Med. Research, 1967-72; pres. Squibb Inst. Med. Research, Princeton, N.J., 1972-74; chmn. dept. biochem. and clin. pharmacology St. Jude Children's Research Hosp., Memphis, 1974-81, rschr., mem. emeritus, 1981-83; cancer expert Nat. Cancer Inst., 1983-86, acting dep. dir. div. of cancer treatment, 1984; scientist emeritus NIH, 1988—; mem. com. on growth NRC, chmn. panel mech. action, 1946-48, chmn. sect. chemotherapy, 1948-52, chmn. com. on growth, 1952-54; mem. sci. adv. bds. Leonard Wood Meml., 1947-53, Nat. Vitamin Found., 1953-56, St. Jude Children's Research Hosp., Memphis, 1968-71; mem. div. biology and medicine NSF, 1953-55; mem. study sect. pharmacology and exptl. therapeutics USPHS, 1952-56, 1959-63, chmn., 1960-63, chmn. study sect. chemotherapy, 1963-65; mem. coordinating com. cancer chemotherapy Nat. Cancer Service Ctr., USPHS, 1955-57; mem. research adv. council Am. Cancer Soc., 1956-59; mem. adv. council biol. sci. Princeton, 1969-75; mem. working cadre Nat. Large Bowel Cancer program Nat. Cancer Inst., 1975-80; sci. adv. bd. La Jolla Cancer Research Found., 1978-81; mem. Memphis Med. Seminar, 1977-83, pres., 1981-82. Assoc. editor: Cancer Research, 1950-58, Pharmacological Revs., 1962-66, Ann. Rev. Pharmacol., 1965-69; editor: Biochem. Pharmacology, 1958-62, vice chmn. internat. bd. editors, 1962-83, chmn., 1983-93; mem. adv. bd. Advances in Pharmacology and Chemotherapy, 1962-85; mem. bd. editors Handbuch der experimentellen Pharmakologie, 1966-85; contbr. articles to profl. jours., chpts. to books. Recipient alumni award U. Fla., 1953, Washington U., 1957, Torald Sollmann award Am. Soc. Pharmacology and Exptl. Therapeutics, 1966, Chester Stock award Meml. Sloan-Kettering Cancer Ctr., 1987, J. Heyrovsky gold medal Czechoslovak Acad. Scis., 1989; Commonwealth fellow Inst. für Therapeutische Biochemie, U. Frankfurt, Germany and Acad. Scis., Prague, Czechoslovakia, 1964-65. Fellow AAAS; mem. Am. Soc. Pharmacol. and Exptl. Therapeutics, Assn. Am. Physicians, Am. Assn. Cancer Rsch., Am. Soc. Biol. Chemistry and Molecular Biology, Am. Soc. Clin. Pharmacology and Therapeutics, Am. Soc. Hematology, Am. Chem. Soc., Soc. Exptl. Biology and Medicine, Biochem. Soc. Gt. Britain, Cosmos Club (Washington), Phi Beta Kappa, Phi Kappa Phi, Sigma Xi, Alpha Omega Alpha, Delta Tau Delta. Home: Unit C-410 8101 Connecticut Ave Chevy Chase MD 20815

WELCH, ASHLEY JAMES, engineering educator; b. Ft. Worth, May 3, 1933; married, 1952; 3 children. BS, Tex. Tech U., 1955; MS, So. Meth. U., 1959; PhD in Elec. Engring., Rice U., 1964. Aerophys. engr. Gen. Dynamics, Ft. Worth, 1957-60; instr. elec. engring. Rice U., 1960-64, from asst. to assoc. prof., 1964-74, dir. engring. computing facility, 1970-71, dir. biomed. engring. program, 1971-75; prof. elec. and biomed. engring. U. Tex., Austin, 1975—, Marion E. Forsman Centennial prof. engring., 1985—. Fellow IEEE, Am. Soc. Lasers Surg. Medicine (bd. dirs. 1989-92). Research in laser-tissue interaction, application of lasers in medicine. Office: U Tex at Austin Dept Elec & Computer Engring Austin TX 78712

WELCH, BO (ROBERT W. WELCH, III), production designer; m. Catherine O'Hara. BArch., Univ. of Ariz., 1975. Production designer, films include Lost Boys, 1987, Beetle Juice, Accidental Tourist, Ghostbusters II, Joe VS the Volcano, Edward Scissor Hands (Brit. Acad. Award, 1992), Grand Canyon, Batman Returns; TV films Heart of Steel, Stark II; art dir., films Mommy Dearest, Star Chamber, Deal of the Century, Best Defense, Swing Shift, The Color Purple (Academy award nomination), Violets Are Blue. Mem. Acad. of Motion Pictures Arts & Scis., Soc. of Motion Picture and TV Art Dirs. Office: The Mirisch Agency Ste 500 10100 Santa Monica Blvd Los Angeles CA 90067

WELCH, BYRON EUGENE, communications educator; b. Kansas City, Mo., Mar. 3, 1928; s. Paul C. and Lucile Irene (Sherman) W.; m. Mabel Holmberg, May 18, 1947; 1 son, Byron Eugene, II. Ed., Swarthmore Coll., Tex. Christian U., U. Tex., Austin. Dir. devel. and planning Atlantic Christian Coll., Wilson, N.C., 1956-58; dir. devel. Chapman Coll., Orange, Calif., 1958-59; asst. to pres. Calif. Western U., San Diego, 1959-60, William Woods Coll., Fulton, Mo., 1960-62; pres. Welch Assocs., Inc.; fund raising and devel. cons. Welch Assocs., Inc., Houston, 1962-94; adj. prof. communication U. Tex., Austin, 1968—. Mem. exec. bd. Sam Houston Area coun. Boy Scouts Am., 1974-91; bd. dirs. population program Baylor U. Coll. Medicine, 1975—; sec., mem. exec. com. U. Amas., Pueblo, Mex., 1978—; chmn. bd. elders, chmn. ch. bd. Bethany Christian Ch., Houston, 1972-79, mem. pension fund bd., 1979-86; pres. Houston Community Found., 1980-91; chmn. bd. Excape Ctr., 1989-91. With USNR, 1945-46. Recipient Silver Beaver award Boy Scouts Am., 1981. Mem. Nat. Soc. Fund Raisers (pres. 1975-77, chmn. bd. 1977-78, mem. cert. bd. 1981-86), Southwest Soc. Fund Raisers (pres. 1968-70), U. Tex. Southwest Inst. Fund Raising (dean 1974-85, dean Rice U. fund raising 1986-91), Nat. Soc. Fund Raising Execs. Found. (pres. 1980-83). Home: 4515 W Alabama St Houston TX 77027-4803 *The supreme satisfaction is to give without counting the cost. I have tried to make it a rule of my life never to remember what I do for others, but never to forget what others do for me.*

WELCH, CAROL MAE, lawyer; b. Rockford, Ill., Oct. 23, 1947; d. Leonard John and LaVerna Helen (Ang) Nyberg; m. Donald Peter Welch, Nov. 23, 1968 (dec. Sept. 1976). B.A. in Spanish, Wheaton Coll., 1968; J.D., U. Denver, 1976. Bar: Colo. 1977, U.S. Dist. Ct. Colo. 1977, U.S. Ct. Appeals (10th cir.) 1977, U.S. Supreme Ct. 1981. Tchr. State Hosp., Dixon, Ill., 1969, Polo Community Schs., Ill., 1969-70; registrar Sch. Nursing Hosp. of U. Pa., Phila., 1970; assoc. Hall & Evans, Denver, 1977-81, ptnr., 1981-82; spec. counsel 1993-94; mem. Miller & Welch, L.L.C., Denver, 1995—. mem. Colo. Supreme Ct. Jury Inst., Denver, 1982—; vice chmn. com. on conduct U.S. Dist. Ct., Denver, 1982-83, chmn., 1983-84; lectr. in field; speaker Women and Bus. Conf., Denver, 1982. Pres. Family Tree, Inc. Named to Order St. Ives, U. Denver Coll. Law, 1977. Mem. ABA, Am. Trial Lawyers Assn. (state com.), Internat. Soc. Barristers, Internat. Assn. Def. Counsel, Am. Coll. Trial Lawyers, Am. Bd. Trial Advs. (treas. Colo. chpt. 1991-92, pres. 1992-93), Colo. Def. Lawyers Assn. (treas. 1982-83, v.p. 1983-84, pres. 1984-85), Denver Bar Assn., Colo. Bar Assn. (mem. litigation sect. coun. 1987-90), Colo. Bar Found. (trustee 1992—), Def. Rsch. Inst. (chmn. Colo. chpt. 1987-90, regional v.p. 1990-93, pres. 1992-94), William E. Doyle Inn. Office: Miller & Welch LLC 730 17th St #370 Denver CO 80202-3503

WELCH, CHARLES DAVID, diplomat; b. Munich, Germany, Dec. 25, 1953; s. Donald Mansel and Jackie (Brown) W.; m. Gretchen Anne Gerwe, May 14, 1983; children: Emma Frances, Margaret Elizabeth, Hannah Alice. Student, London Sch. Econs., 1973-74; BS in Fgn. Svc., Georgetown U., 1975; MA in Law and Diplomacy, MA, Tufts U., 1977. Staff asst. office of undersecretary U.S. State Dept. Security Assistance, Washington, 1977-79; polit. officer U.S. Embassy, Islamabad, Pakistan, 1979-81; country officer Syria desk U.S. State Dept. Bur. of Near Ea. and South Asian Affairs, Washington, 1981-82; country officer Lebanon desk; 1982-83; polit. sect. chief U.S. Embassy, Damascus, Syria, 1984-86; polit. counselor U.S. Embassy, Amman, Jordan, 1986-88; mem. sr. seminar fgn. policy U.S. State Dept. Fgn. Svc. Inst., Washington, 1988-89; dir. near Ea. and South Asian affairs Nat. Security Coun., White House, Washington, 1989-91; exec. asst. to undersec. for polit. affairs Dept. of State, Washington, 1991-92; dep. chief of mission U.S. Embassy, Riyadh, Saudi Arabia, 1992—. Mem. Coun. Fgn.

Rels., Am. Fgn. Svc. Assn., Phi Beta Kappa, Phi Alpha Phi. Presbyterian. Avocations: sports, books, music, history. Home and Office: Am Embassy Unit 61307 APO AE 09803-1307

WELCH, CLAUDE EMERSON, surgeon; b. Stanton, Nebr., Mar. 14, 1906; s. John Hayes and Lettie (Phelan) W.; m. Phyllis Heath Paton, Aug. 14, 1937; children: Claude Emerson Jr., John Paton. AB summa cum laude, Doane Coll., 1927, DSc (hon.), 1955; AM in Chemistry, U. Mo., 1928; MD magna cum laude, Harvard U., 1932; DSc, U. Nebr., 1970; DHC (hon.), U. Montevideo, Uruguay, 1982. Asst. instr. organic chemistry U. Mo., 1927-28; surg. resident Mass. Gen. Hosp., Boston, 1932-37, vis. surgeon, 1937—, chief tumor clinic, 1957-63; clin. prof. surgery Harvard Med. Sch., 1964-72, clin. prof. emeritus, 1972—; chmn. Bd. Registration in Medicine, Commonwealth of Mass., 1976-81; McLaughlin Gallie vis. prof., hon. fellow Royal Coll. Physicians and Surgeons of Can., 1978—; Claude E. Welch Professorship in Surgery, Harvard, 1992. Lt. col. M.C., AUS, 1942-45. Decorated Commendation medal; recipient Disting. Service award AMA, 1976, Leader in Am. Medicine award Countway Libr., 1985, Roswell Park medal Buffalo Surg. Soc., 1986. Fellow Internat. Soc. Univ. Colon and Rectal Surgeons (hon.), Boston Surg. Soc. (pres. 1965, Bigelow medal 1986, hon. fellow); mem. ACS (bd. govs. 1960-63, bd. regents 1963-72, pres. 1973-74), Mass. Med. Soc. (pres. 1965), Internat. Soc. Surgery (pres. U.S. chpt. 1978-80), Soc. Surgery Alimentary Tract (pres. 1965), Am. Surg. Assn. (pres. 1976-77), So. Surg. Assn., New Eng. Surg. Assn., Pan Pacific Surg. Assn. (v.p. 1971—), James IV Assn. Surgeons, N.Y. Soc. Colon and Rectal Surgeons, Harvard Med. Sch. Alumni Assn. (pres. 1972-73), Alpha Omega Alpha; hon. mem. Coll. Physicians and Surgeons, Costa Rica, L.A., Detroit, Kansas City, Portland, Cen., N.Y., B.C., Chile, St. Paul surg. socs., Que., Argentina socs. digestive surgery, Am. Soc. Colon and Rectal Surgeons. Home: 10 Longwood Dr Apt 163 Westwood MA 02090-1138 Office: Mass Gen Hosp Boston MA 02114

WELCH, CLAUDE (RAYMOND), theology educator; b. Genoa City, Wis., Mar. 10, 1922; s. Virgil Cleon and Deone West (Grenelle) W.; m. Eloise Janette Turner, May 31, 1942 (div. 1970); children—Eric, Thomas, Claudia; m. Theodosia Montigel Blewett, Oct. 5, 1970 (dec. 1978); m. Joy Neuman, Oct. 30, 1982. BA summa cum laude, Upper Iowa U., 1942; postgrad., Garrett Theol. Sem., 1942-43; BD cum laude, Yale U., 1945, PhD, 1950; DD (hon.), Ch. Div. Sch. of Pacific, 1972, Jesuit Sch. Theology, 1982; LHD (hon.), U. Judaism, 1976. Ordained to ministry Meth. Ch., 1947. Instr. religion Princeton (N.J.) U., 1947-50, asst. prof., 1950-51, vis. prof., 1962; asst. prof. theology Yale U. Div. Sch., New Haven, 1951-54, assoc. prof., 1954-60; Berg prof. religious thought, chmn. dept. U. Pa., Phila., 1960-71, assoc. dean Coll. Arts and Scis., 1964-68, acting chmn. dept. philosophy, 1965-66; prof. hist. theology Grad. Theol. Union, Berkeley, Calif., 1971—, dean, 1971-87, pres., 1972-82; vis. prof. Garrett Theol. Sem., 1951, Pacific Sch. Religion, 1958, Hartford Sem. Found., 1958-59, Princeton Theol. Sem., 1962-63, U. Va., 1987; Fulbright sr. lectr. U. Mainz, Germany, 1968; Sprunt lectr. Union Theol. Sem., Richmond, Va., 1958; Willson lectr. Southwestern U., Georgetown, Tex., 1994; dir. study of grad. edn. in religion Am. Coun. Learned Socs., 1969-71; del. World Conf. on Faith and Order, 1963. Author: In This Name: the Doctrine of the Trinity in Contemporary Theology, 1952, (with John Dillenberger) Protestant Christianity, interpreted through its Development, 1954, 2d rev. edit., 1988, The Reality of the Church, 1958, Graduate Education in Religion: A Critical Appraisal, 1971, Religion in the Undergraduate Curriculum, 1972, Protestant Thought in the 19th Century, vol. 1, 1799-1870, 1972, vol. 2, 1870-1914, 1985; Editor, translator: God and Incarnation in Mid-19th Century German Theology (Thomasius, Dorner and Biedermann), 1965; Contbr. to publs. in field. Recipient decennial prize Bross Found., 1970; Guggenheim fellow, 1976; NEH research fellow, 1984, Fulbright research fellow, 1956-57. Mem. Am. Acad. Religion (pres. 1969-70), Coun. of Socs. for Study of Religion (chmn. 1969-74, 85-90), Soc. for Values in Higher Edn. (pres. 1967-71), Am. Soc. Ch. History, Am. Theol. Soc., Phi Beta Kappa. Home: 123 Fairlawn Dr Berkeley CA 94708-2107

WELCH, DAVID C., advertising agency executive. Formerly pres., chief exec. officer Southfield office William Esty Co., Mich.; chief exec. officer Detroit office Campbell-Mithun-Esty, Southfield, 1988—. Office: Campbell Mithun Esty 222 S 9th St Minneapolis MN 55402-3389

WELCH, DOUGLAS LINDSAY, physics educator; b. Karamursel, Turkey, Oct. 8, 1958; s. Gene Armour and Katharin (Lindsay) W.; m. Carol Marie Gibbons, Aug. 28, 1982. BSc, U. Toronto, Ont., Can., 1981, MSc, 1983, PhD, 1985. Rsch. assoc. Nat. Rsch. Coun. Dom Astrophys. Obs., Victoria, B.C., Can., 1986-88; asst. prof., univ. rsch. fellow McMaster U., Hamilton, Ont., 1988—. Office: McMaster U Dept Physics & Astron, 1280 Main St W, Hamilton ON Canada L8S 4M1

WELCH, EDWARD P., lawyer; b. Columbus, Ohio, Mar. 12, 1950; s. Charles E. and Charma L. (Overbeck) W.; m. Noreen R. Welch, Sept. 8, 1973. BS in Bus. Administrn., Georgetown U., 1972; JD, Villanova U., 1976. Bar: Del. 1976, U.S. Dist. Ct. Del. 1977, U.S. Ct. Appeals (3d cir.) 1981, U.S. Supreme Ct. 1981, N.Y. 1982, U.S. Ct. Appeals (fed. cir.) 1985, (5th cir.) 1992. Law clk. Del Ct. Chancery, Wilmington, 1976-77; assoc. Prickett, Ward, Burt & Sanders, Wilmington, 1977-79; assoc. Skadden, Arps, Slate, Meagher & Flom, Wilmington, 1979-84, ptnr., 1984—; mem. com. charged with drafting evidence code Del., com. charged with drafting dir. liability legis., Wilmington 1977-78, Ct. Chancery Rules Com., Wilmington, 1990—. Author: Folk, Ward & Welch: Folk on the Delaware General Corporation Law, 1988, 2d edit., 1992; bimonthly Nat. Law Jour.; co-editor: Folk On The Delaware General Corporation Law Fundamentals, 1993. Bd. dirs. United Cerebral Palsy of Del., Wilmington, 1977-87, The Mary Campbell Ctr., 1987—; co-chmn. United Cerebral Palsy's Camp Manito, Wilmington, 1982-83; trustee The Tatnall Sch., Wilmington, 1992. Recipient Community Svc. award United Cerebral Palsy of Del., Wilmington, 1981. Mem. Del. Bar Assn. (mem. coun. corp. law, Young Lawyers award 1986), The Rodney Square Club, Corp. Law Coun. Office: Skadden Arps Slate Meagher & Flom PO Box 636 One Rodney Sq Wilmington DE 19801

WELCH, EDWIN HUGH, academic administrator; b. Balt., Apr. 11, 1944; s. Lester Kenneth and Catherine (Dodrer); m. Janet Gail Boggess, Nov. 22, 1977. BA, Western Md. Coll., 1965; STB, Boston U. Sch. Theology, 1968; postgrad., London Sch. Econs. and Polit. Sci., 1968-69; PhD, Boston U., 1971. Assoc. prof., chmn. W.Va. Wesleyan Coll., Buckhannon, 1971-75; assoc. prof., chmn. Lebanon Valley Coll., Annville, Pa., 1975-79, dir. weekend coll., 1979-80; dean Lakeland Coll., Sheboygan, Wis., 1980-81; provost Wartburg Coll., Waverly, Iowa, 1981-89; pres. U. Charleston, W.Va., 1989—; chmn. Iowa Deans Confs., Des Moines, 1988-89; title III evaluator Iowa Wesleyan Coll., Mt. Pleasant, 1983-85. Contbr. articles to edn. jours. Bd. dirs. Bus. and Indsl. Devel. Corp., One Valley Bank, Charleston Area Med. Ctr.; v.p. Nat. Inst. Chem. Studies; creator, dir. Community Leadership Devel. Program, Waverly, 1986-88; bd. dirs., pres. Lebanon (Pa.) Family Planning Assn., 1976-81. Named Tchr. of Yr., W.Va. Wesleyan Coll., 1974. Mem. Nat. Assn. Ind. Colls. and Univs., Balt. Conf. United Meth. Ch. (ordained), Appalachian Coll. Assn., Coun. Ind. Colls., Rotary Internat. (bd. dirs. Charleston). Democrat. Methodist. Office: U Charleston Office of Pres Charleston WV 25304-1099

WELCH, GARTH LARRY, chemistry educator; b. Brigham City, Utah, Feb. 14, 1937; s. Samuel and Minnie Jane (Hughes) W.; m. Melba Lael Coombs, Sept. 9, 1960; children: Larry Kent, Kathryn Louise, Richard Samuel, Garth Edward, Robert Irvine, David Jonathan. B.S., U. Utah, 1959, Ph.D., 1963. Teaching asst. U. Utah, 1959-62; postdoctoral research fellow UCLA, 1962-64; asst. prof. Weber State U., Ogden, Utah, 1964-68; assoc. prof. Weber State U., 1968-72; prof. Weber State U., Ogden, 1972—; dean Sch. Natural Sci., 1974-83, exec. dir. bus. affairs, 1983-89, assoc. v.p. phys. facilities, 1990—; mem. Utah State Council on Sci. and Tech., 1980-84. Mem. Mormon Tabernacle Choir, Salt Lake City, 1958-62, Jay Welch Chorale, 1983—; Pleasant View Planning Commn., 1988-91, chmn., 1990-91. Mem. Am. Chem. Soc., Sigma Xi, Phi Kappa Phi. Mem. LDS Ch. (bishop 1966-74). Home: 3910 N 800 W Ogden UT 84414-1066

WELCH, HARRY SCOVILLE, lawyer, retired gas pipeline company executive; b. Hugo, Okla., Nov. 14, 1923; s. John Calvin and Gaynell (Potts) W.; m. Peggy Joyce Weis, Dec. 18, 1954; children—Marshall Porter, Gay,

Harry Scoville, Mary Margaret, Anne. B.B.A., U. Tex. at Austin, 1947, LL.B., 1949. Bar: Tex. 1948. Atty. Am. Republics Corp., Houston, 1949-51; ptnr. Turner, White, Atwood, McLane & Francis, Dallas, 1951-59; exec. asst., then v.p. Tenneco Inc., Houston, 1959-73; v.p., gen. counsel Panhandle Ea. Corp., Houston, 1973-74, sr. v.p., gen. counsel, 1975-85; v.p., gen. counsel Tex. Ea. Corp., Houston, 1987-89; mem. bd. adjustment Hunter's Creek Village, Tex., 1970-77, chmn., 1973-77; mem. adv. bd. Internat. Oil and Gas Ednl. Ctr., Southwestern Legal Found., Dallas, 1975-85; bd. dirs. Plains Petroleum Co., Lakewood, Colo. Served with USNR, 1943-46. Fellow Tex. Bar Found.; mem. Am., Houston, Fed. Energy bar assns., State Bar Tex., Phi Kappa Sigma, Phi Alpha Delta. Presbyterian. Club: Ramada (Houston). Home: 10611 Twelve Oaks Dr Houston TX 77024-3135

WELCH, JENNIFER DIANE, lawyer; b. Boston, Apr. 11, 1965; d. George P. and Margery Welch. BA, Vanderbilt U., 1987; JD, Emery U., 1990. Assoc. Drew, Eckl & Farnhan, Atlanta, 1990-93; corp. counsel RaceTrac Petroleum, Inc., Atlanta, 1993-95; mgr. regulatory and legis. affairs Bell-South Corp., 1995—. Active Legal Clinic Homeless, 1990—, Jr. League, 1994—; com. chair Cancer Soc., Atlanta, 1990—. Mem. ABA, Ga. State Bar, Ky. State Bar, Atlanta Bar Assn., PEO. Methodist. Avocations: travel, photography, art, reading, painting. Home: 2222 Peachtree St NW A-S Atlanta GA 30309 Office: Racetrac Petroleum Inc 300 Technology Ct Smyrna GA 30082

WELCH, JOE BEN, academic administrator; b. Amite County, Miss., May 18, 1940; s. H.A. Joe and Mildred Pill (Bean) W.; m. Dorothy Louise Rostron, June 2, 1962; children: Wendi Jo Welch Sands, Robin Clare Welch Peveto, Sandra Tres Welch Dobbs, Roxana Merry. BS, La. Tech. U., 1963, MEd, Lamar U., 1967; EdD, McNeese State U., 1974. Instr. math., sci. Clinton (La.) High Sch., 1963-64; instr. math. Port Neches (Tex.) Groves High Sch., 1964-67; acting head math. and sci. dept. Trinity Christian Coll., Baton Rouge, 1967-68; head math. and sci. dept. Mid-City Bapt. Jr. Coll., New Orleans, 1968-69; instr. math. Orange (Tex.) Extension Ctr., Lamar U., 1969-70, dir., 1970-75; dean Lamar U. Ctr.-Orange, 1975-81, provost, 1981-83, pres., 1983-89; pres. Middle Ga. Coll., Cochran, 1989—. Mem. adv. bd. dirs. Bleckley Meml. Hosp., 1989—. Recipient Grateful Appreciation award West Orange-Cove Consol. Sch. Dist., 1976-82, Outstanding and Dedicated Svc. award ARC, Orange, 1985; named Citizen of Yr. C. of C., Orange, 1985. Mem. Am. Assn. Community and Jr. Colls., Cochran (Ga.) Bleckley C. of C., Macon City Club (bd. dirs. 1991—), Phi Delta Kappa. Baptist. Office: Mid Ga Coll 1100 2d St SE Cochran GA 31014

WELCH, JOHN DANA, urologist, performing arts association executive; b. Canton, Ill., Mar. 14, 1938; m. Myrna Lee Loring, Dec. 23, 1962; children: Timothy Lance, Christina Dawn. BS, U. Ill., 1960, MD, 1963. Diplomate Am. Bd. Urology, Nat. Bd. Med. Examiners, Fla. Bd. Med. Examiners. Rotating intern Tampa (Fla.) Gen. Hosp., 1963-64, resident in urology, 1964-68; pvt. practice, Sarasota, Fla., 1970—; bd. dirs. Bay Area Renal Stone Ctr.; chief surgery HCA Doctors Hosp., 1981, chief of staff, 1983, trustee, 1988-91. Bd. dirs. Asolo Ctr. for Performing Arts, 1980—, sec., 1989-90, v.p., 1990-93, pres., 1993-94. Major USAF, 1968-70. Mem. Fla. Med. Assn., Sarasota County Med. Soc., Am. Urological Assn. (SE sect.), Fla. Urological Soc. (pres. 1986), Am. Lithotripsy Soc. Home: 650 Mourning Dove Dr Sarasota FL 34236 Office: 1921 Waldemere St Sarasota FL 34239 also: Asolo Ctr Performing Arts 5555 N Tamiami Trail Sarasota FL 34243

WELCH, JOHN FRANCIS, JR. (JACK WELCH), electrical manufacturing company executive; b. Peabody, Mass., Nov. 19, 1935; s. John Francis and Grace (Andrews) W.; m. Carolyn B. Osburn, Nov. 1959 (div. 1987); children: Katherine, John, Anne, Mark; m. Jane Beasley, Apr. 1989. B.S. in Chem. Engring. U. Mass., 1957; M.S., U. Ill., 1958, Ph.D., 1960. With Gen. Electric Co., Fairfield, Conn., 1960—, v.p., 1972, v.p., group exec. components and materials group, 1973-77, sr. v.p., sector exec., consumer products and services sector, 1977-79, vice chmn., exec. officer, 1979-81, chmn., chief exec. officer, 1981—; also dir. Gen. Electric Capital Services. Patentee in field. Mem. NAE, The Bus. Coun. (former chmn.), Bus. Roundtable. Office: Gen Electric Co 3135 Easton Tpke Fairfield CT 06431-0002

WELCH, JOHN PATON, surgeon, educator; b. Boston, July 1, 1942; s. Claude Emerson and Phyllis (Paton) W.; m. Marylouise Dahl; children: Evan, Tyler. BA, Harvard Coll., 1964, MD, 1968. Diplomate Am. Bd. Surgery. Intern, then resident in surgery Mass. Gen. Hosp., Boston, 1968-71, 73-74; hon. rsch. registrar Royal Free Hosp., London, 1972; asst. prof. surgery U. Conn., Farmington, 1976-82, assoc. prof. surgery, 1982-92, clin. prof. surgery, 1992—; surgeon Pyrtek, Bloom & Welch, P.C., Hartford, Conn.; surgeon Pyrtek, Bloom & Welch, P.C., Hartford, Conn., 1976-94, Conn. Surg., P.C., Hartford, 1994—; adj. asst. prof. surgery Dartmouth U. Med. Sch., Hanover, N.H., 1977-94, adj. prof. surgery, 1994—. Author: Manual of Lower GI Tract Surgery, 1980, Intestinal Obstruction: Differential Diagnosis and Clinical Management, 1990; contbr. chpts. to several textbooks. With U.S. Army, 1974-76. Fellow ACS; mem. AMA (Physicians Recognition award 1974-77), Assn. Acad. Surgery, Soc. for Surgery of Alimentary Tract, Am. Gastroenterol. Assn., Soc. Surg. Oncology, New Eng. Surg. Soc., Am. Soc. Colon and Rectal Surgeons, Soc. Am. Gastrointestinal Endoscopic Surgeons, Internat. Surg. Soc., World Assn. Hepatobiliary Surgery, New Eng. Cancer Soc., Hartford Med. Soc., Surgeons Travel Club. Avocations: gardening, music, skiing. Office: Conn Surg Group PC 85 Seymour St Hartford CT 06106

WELCH, JOSEPH F., investment company executive; b. Binghamton, N.Y., Aug. 3, 1934; s. James Joseph and Winifred Frances (Doyle) W.; m. Marcia Pyle, Oct. 6, 1962; children: Winifred, Lorraine, Suzanne, Lucinda, Elizabeth. BS, Lehigh U., 1956; MBA, Cornell U., 1961. Mgmt. positions with Gen. Electric Co., Benton & Bowles, Internat. Salt, 1963-70; pres. Penske Corp., Reading, Pa., 1974-76; pres., owner J.F. Welch Interests, Inc., 1970—, The Bachman Co., Reading, 1980—; bd. dirs. Detroit Diesel Corp., Snack Food Assn., chmn.; mem. adv. bd. Meridian Bank, Del. to White House Conf. on Small Bus. Bd. dirs. YMCA, Phila. Zoo; mem. Pa. Ethics Commn., 1980-82; bd. dirs., treas. Pa. Energy Devel. Authority; mem. pres.'s council U. Vt. Bus. Sch.; trustee Miss Hall's Sch., St. Joseph Hosp., Lehigh U.; chmn. Bus. Adv. Coun., Coll. Bus. & Econs., Lehigh Univ. Mem. adv. coun. Johnson Grad. Sch. Mgmt. Served to maj. U.S. Army, 1956-58. Mem. Am. Mgmt. Assn. (pres. sect.), Berks County C. of C. (bd. dirs., v.p.), Lehigh U. Alumni Assn. (bd. dirs., pres.), Saucon Valley Country Club, Berkshire Country Club, Ocean Reef Club, Sankaty Head Club, Nantucket Yacht Club. Office: 1 Washington Tower Plz Reading PA 19601

WELCH, LINDA OGDEN, sales executive; b. Wabash, Ind., Apr. 3, 1958; d. Russell Devon and Nancy Rebecca (Bright) O.; m. Albert Darius Welch III. Jan. 31, 1990. BS, Oral Roberts U., 1980. Sales coord. Sta. KIRO, Seattle, 1980-81; account exec. Sta. KRAV/KGTO, Tulsa, 1981-84, Sta. KOTV-TV, Tulsa, 1984-86; Sta. KHOU-TV, Houston, 1986-87, Sta. KTXA-TV, Dallas, 1987-89, Sta. KATZ-TV, Dallas, 1989-90, Petry TV, Dallas, 1990-91; sales exec. IOPTEX Rsch., Inc., Irwindale, Calif., 1992-94; pres. Ogden-Welch Longhorn Co., 1992—; territory mgr. Allergan, Valley View, Tex., 1994—; cons. Synthes, Paoli, Pa., 1994—; pres. The Welch Group, Inc. Republican. Avocations: art, ranching, cooking, gardening. Office: Synthes USA 1690 Russell Rd PO Box 1766 Paoli PA 19301

WELCH, LLOYD RICHARD, electrical engineering educator, communications consultant; b. Detroit, Sept. 28, 1927; s. Richard C. and Helen (Felt) W.; m. Irene Althea Main, Sept. 12, 1953; children—Pamela Irene Welch Towery, Melinda Ann, Diana Lia Welch Worthington. B.S. in Math., U. Ill., 1951; Ph.D. in Math., Calif. Inst. Tech., 1958. Mathematician NASA-Jet Propulsion Lab., Pasadena, Calif., 1956-59; staff mathematician Inst. Def. Analyses, Princeton, N.J., 1959-65; prof. elec. engring. U. So. Calif., L.A., 1965—; cons. in field. Contbr. articles to profl. jours. Served with USN, 1945-49, 51-52. Fellow IEEE; mem. Nat. Acad. Engring., Am. Math. Soc. Math. Assn. Am., Soc. for Indsl. and Applied Math., Phi Beta Kappa, Sigma Xi, Phi Kappa Phi, Pi Mu Epsilon, Eta Kappa Nu. Office: U So Calif Elec Engring Bldg 500A Los Angeles CA 90089

WELCH, MARTIN E., III, manufacturing company executive; b. Detroit, June 25, 1948; s. Martin E. Jr. and Josephine E. (Gant) W.; m. Anne Mary

Westrick, Nov. 21, 1970; children: Michele, James, Mary, Brian. BS, U. Detroit, 1970, MBA, 1973. CPA, Mich. Audit mgr. Arthur Young & Co., Detroit, 1970-77; dir. mktg. acctg. Fruehauf Corp., Detroit, 1977-82; corp. acctg. mgr. Chrysler Corp., Highland Park, Mich., 1982-83, asst. controller, 1983-86; v.p., controller-treas. Chrysler-Can., Ltd., Windsor, Ont., Can., 1986-87; gen. auditor Chrysler Corp., Highland Park, Mich., 1987-88, asst. treas., 1988-91; sr. v.p., CFO Fed.-Mogul, Southfield, Mich., 1991—. Home: 2601 S Indian Mound Rd Bloomfield Hills MI 48301-2257 Office: Fed-Mogul Corp 26555 Northwestern Hwy Southfield MI 48034

WELCH, NEAL WILLIAM, retired electric company executive; b. North Adams, Mass., Sept. 16, 1908; s. Owen William and Mary Gertrude (McGovern) W.; m. Harriet Flood, June 27, 1935; children—Marian, Mary. Grad., Bently Coll., 1930. With Sprague Electric Co., North Adams, 1932-82; v.p. sales Sprague Electric Co., 1953-60, sr. v.p. mktg. and sales, 1960-67, exec. v.p., 1967-71, chmn. exec. com., 1968-71, chmn., chief exec. officer, 1971-81, chmn. bd., chmn. exec. com., 1981-82; dir. GK Techs.; chmn., cons., mem. exec. com. Spelco; ret., 1984. Home: Laurie Dr Williamstown MA 01267

WELCH, OLIVER WENDELL, retired pharmaceutical executive; b. Jacksonville, Tex., Jan. 9, 1930; s. Jackson Andrew and Annie Laura (Trapp) W.; m. Wanda Virginia Urrey, Nov. 14, 1948. BA, Tex. Tech U., 1952; MA, Columbia U., 1958. Pharm. rep., supr. mktg. research, manpower devel. Warner Lambert Co., Morris Plains, N.J., 1962-72; mgr. corp. devel. Boehringer Mannheim Corp., N.Y.C., 1972-75; v.p. Biomed. Data Co., N.Y.C., 1975-77; assoc. dir., dep. dir. regulatory affairs Sterling Winthrop Inc., N.Y.C., 1977-94; ret., 1994. Mem. Regulatory Affairs Profls. Soc., Drug Info. Assn., Order St. John of Jerusalem. Republican. Episcopalian. Avocations: music, travel, theatre.

WELCH, PATRICK DANIEL, state senator; b. Chgo., Dec. 12, 1948; s. William C. and Alice W. Student, So. Ill. U., 1970; JD, Chgo. Kent Coll. Law, 1974. Bar: Ill. 1974. Pvt. practice, Peru, Ill., 1974—; mem. Ill. Senate, 1983—; asst. minority leader, 1993—; former chmn. energy and environ. comm.; nat. Del., mem. credentials com. Dem. Nat. Conv., 1976, del., 1980, 84, 88, 92; precinct committeeman Peru Dem. Party, 1976-86; del. Dem. Nat. Mid-Term Conf., 1978, 82; committeeman Ill. Dem. Cen. Com., 1978—; mem. exec. com., 1983—; mem. Peru Citizens' Svc. Agency; vice-chmn. Ill. Dem. Party, 1990—. Recipient Disting. Svc. award Ill. Bicentennial Commn., 1976. Mem. Ill. Bar Assn., La Salle County Bar Assn. Office: State Senate State Capitol Springfield IL 62706

WELCH, PATRICK E., diversified financial services company executive; b. 1947. Student, Seattle U.; MS in Physics, U. Wash., 1970, MBA, 1973. Fin. analyst Ford Motor Com, Seattle, 1973-74; mgr. investment evals. dept. Weyerhaeuser Co., Inc., Federal Way, Wash., 1974-81; with Great Northern Insured Annuities, Seattle, 1981—, GNA Securities, Inc., Federal Way, Seattle; pres., CEO Gen. ELC Capital Assurance Co., Seattle, 1993—; now pres., CEO GNA Corp., Seattle. Office: First GNA Life Insur Co of NY 2 Manhattanville Rd Purchase NY 10577-2118*

WELCH, PHILIP BURLAND, electronics and office products company executive; b. Portland, Maine, Oct. 15, 1931; s. Philip Gerald Welch and Clara Jenny (Berry) Hawxwell; m. Sheila May Preston, May 19, 1960; children: Jahna Holly Welch Roth, Victoria Preston Welch Johnsen. Student, Berklee Coll., 1955-58. Nat. sales mgr. Akai Am. Ltd., Anaheim, Calif., 1970-73, BSR, USA, Blaupunkt, N.Y., 1973-76; nat. sales and mktg. mgr. Philips High Fidelity Labs, Ft. Wayne, Ind., 1976-79; dir. mktg. Pioneer Electronics, Moonachie, N.J., 1979-82; pres. Schneider N.Am. Ltd., Dayton, N.J., 1982-83; v.p. Lyons Assn., Insigh., 1986-88; pres. Nat. Electric Mktg. Co., Jacksonville, Fla., 1975—; Hemisphere Enterprises Corp., Jacksonville, 1988—; cons. ContraTech Corp., Portland, Oreg., 1986-87, Kukje Internat., N.Y.C., 1986, FCI Inc., N.J., 1985, others; cons. Multiform Products, Inc., Jacksonville, 1989-90, gen. mgr., 1990—; established Akai and Philips audio brand in U.S. Contbr. articles to profl. jours. With USAF, 1950-54. Named Man of Decade Audio/Video Cons. USA, 1982, Man of Yr. Soc. of Audio Cons., 1974. Republican. Avocations: flying, golf. Office: Ste 129 10991-55 San Jose Blvd Jacksonville FL 32223

WELCH, RAQUEL, actress; b. Chgo., Sept. 5, 1940; d. Arm and Josepha (Hall) Tejada; m. James Westley Welch, May 8, 1959 (div.); children: Damon, Tahnee; m. Patrick Curtis (div.); m. Andre Weinfeld, July 1980 (div.). Actress: (films) including Fantastic Voyage, 1966, One Million B.C., 1967, The Biggest Bundle of Them All, 1968, Fathom, 1967, The Queens, 1967, 100 Rifles, 1969, Magic Christian, 1970, Bedazzled, 1971, Fuzz, 1972, Bluebeard, 1972, Hannie Caulder, 1972, Kansas City Bomber, 1972, Myra Breckinridge, 1970, The Last of Sheila, 1973, The Three Musketeers, 1974 (Golden Globe award for best actress), The Wild Party, 1975, The Four Musketeers, 1975, Mother, Jugs and Speed, 1976, Crossed Swords, 1978, L'Animal, 1979, (TV movies) The Legend of Walks Far Woman, 1982, Right to Die, 1987, Scandal in a Small Town, 1988, Trouble in Paradise, 1989, Torch Song, 1993, Naked Gun 33 1/3, 1993, (Broadway debut) Woman of the Year, 1982; author: The Raquel Welch Total Beauty and Fitness Program, 1984. Address: RWP Inc # 514 9903 Santa Monica Blvd Beverly Hills CA 90212

WELCH, ROBERT BALLINGER, investment planner; b. Baton Rouge, Nov. 16, 1936; s. Jasper Arthur and Oramay (Ballinger) W.; m. Janice I. Perrine; children: Robert B. Jr., Mary Inger, Carlton Arthur; m. Judith Dorene Brace, Apr. 17, 1971. BA in Comm. and Mktg., U. Ill., 1961. Lic. investment broker and planner. Advt. account mgr., TV writer, dir. sales Nat. Advt. Agy. & TV Broadcasting, Baton Rouge, Dallas, Houston, until 1972; gen. ptnr. real estate devel. Nat. Firms, New Orleans, 1972-80, investment broker, 1980—; mem. adv. bd. Computer Mentors. Co-prod.: (TV documentary) No Bells at Carville, 1959 (Emmy award). Mem. student life adv. bd. Tulane U. Mem. Carl G. Jung Soc. (treas., bd. dirs.), Sigma Chi (regional officer). Home and Office: 106 Westchester Pl New Orleans LA 70131

WELCH, ROBERT BOND, ophthalmologist, educator; b. Balt., May 24, 1927; s. Robert S.G. and Sally (Bond) W.; m. Elizabeth Truslow, May 30, 1953. A.B., Princeton U., 1949; M.D., Johns Hopkins U., 1953. Diplomate: Am. Bd. Ophthalmology. Intern in internal medicine Duke U. Hosp., 1953-54; resident in ophthalmology Wilmer Inst., Johns Hopkins U., 1954-57, chief resident in ophthalmology, 1959, co-dir. retina service, 1959-84, dir. retina service, 1984-85; retinal cons. in ophthalmology Walter Reed Army Hosp., 1961—, Bethesda Naval Hosp, 1976—; assoc. prof. ophthalmology Johns Hopkins U.; chmn. dept. ophthalmology Greater Balt. Med. Ctr., 1985-91. Author: (with others) The Wilmer Institute 1925-1975, 1976; editor Transactions Am. Ophthal. Soc., 1984-91; mem. editorial staff Retina mag., 1980-86. Served with USNR, 1945-47. Mem. Am. Ophthal. Soc. (v.p. 1992-93, pres. 1993-94, editor 1984-90), Retina Soc. (pres. 1981-83), Pan. Pacific Surg. Assn. (v.p. 1972-80), Md. Soc. Eye Physicians and Surgeons (pres. 1963-64), Md. Club., Elkridge Club, South River Club. Democrat. Episcopalian. Home: 4409 Atwick Rd Baltimore MD 21210-2811 Office: 6565 N Charles St Baltimore MD 21204-6800 also: 86 State Cir Annapolis MD 21401-1906

WELCH, ROBERT MORROW, JR., lawyer; b. Wichita Falls, Tex., Dec. 17, 1927; s. Robert Morrow and Sue (Hays) W.; children: Catherine C., Robert Morrow III, Candice C.; m. Annette Y. Apodaca, Dec. 17, 1985. LL.B, Baylor U., 1951. Bar: Tex. 1951, Colo. 1989. Briefing clk. Supreme Ct. Tex., Austin, 1951-52; assoc., then ptnr. Fulbright & Jaworski, Houston, 1952-92, ret. sr. ptnr., 1992—. Sgt. USMC, 1946-48. Fellow Tex. Bar Found.; mem. ABA, Am. Acad. Matrimonial Lawyers, Houston Bar Assn. Home: 1436 W Gray Ste 189 Houston TX 77019 also: PO Box 1000 Ste 127 Silverthorne CO 80498-2980 Office: Fulbright & Jaworski 1301 Mckinney St Houston TX 77010-3095

WELCH, ROBERT W., production designer, art director. Prodn. designer: (TV movies) Heart of Steel, 1983, Slow Burn, 1986, Stark: Mirror Image, 1986, (films) The Lost Boys, 1987, The Accidental Tourist, 1988, Beetlejuice, 1988, Ghostbusters II, 1989, Joe Versus the Volcano, 1990, Edward Scissorhands, 1990, Grand Canyon, 1991, Batman Returns, 1992, Wolf, 1994; art dir.: (films) The Star Chamber, 1983, Deal of the Century, 1983, Swing Shift, 1984, Best Defense, 1984, The Color Purple, 1985 (Academy award nomination best art direction 1985). Office: care Lawrence Mirisch The Mirisch Agency 10100 Santa Monica Blvd Ste 700 Los Angeles CA 90067*

WELCH, RONALD J., actuary; b. Luling, Tex., June 26, 1945; s. Billie C. and Irene (Anton) W.; m. Leslie Ann Herman, Oct. 9, 1971; children: Kelley, Stephen. BBA, U. Tex., 1966; MS, Northeastern U., 1968. V.p., actuary Am. Nat. Ins. Co., Galveston, Tex., 1975-80, sr. v.p., actuary, 1980-86, sr. v.p., chief actuary, 1986—; bd. dirs. Standard Life & Accident Ins. Co., Oklahoma City, Am. Nat. Property & Casualty Ins., Springfield, Mo., Am. Nat. Life Ins. Co. of Tex., Galveston; chmn. bd. Garden State Life Ins. Co., Newark. Fellow Soc. of Actuaries; mem. Am. Acad. Actuaries. Office: Am Nat Ins Co 1 Moody Pla Galveston TX 77550

WELCH, ROSS MAYNARD, plant physiologist, researcher, educator; b. Lancaster, Calif., May 8, 1943; s. Lloyd C. and Theda W. (Slane) W.; m. Jill Susanne Varley, Aug. 22, 1965; children: Renell Cherie, Brent Ross. BS, Calif. Poly. U., 1966; MS, U. Calif., Davis, 1969, PhD, 1971. Plant physiologist USDA Agrl. Rsch. Svc., Ithaca, N.Y., 1971—; rsch. assoc. Cornell U., Ithaca, 1971-75, asst. prof. plant physiology, 1975-81, assoc. prof., 1981-87, prof., 1987—; disting. vis. scientist Murdoch U., Perth, Australia, 1980-81; vis. disting. scholar and lectr. U. Adelaide, Australia, 1991—; coord. food systems for health program coll. agriculture and life sci. Cornell U., 1994—. Editor: Crops as Sources of Nutrients for Humans, 1984; co-editor: Micronutrients in Agriculture, 2d edit., 1989; contbr. over 100 rsch. articles and 20 rev. articles to profl. jours. Fellow Am. Soc. Agronomy (Rsch. award N.E. br. 1992), Soil Sci. Soc. Am.; mem. Am. Soc. Plant Physiologists, AAAS, N.Y. Acad. Scis., Masons (master 1984-85), Sigma Xi. Republican. Mem. United Ch. of Christ. Achievements include discovery that nickel is an essential element for all higher plants; discovery that zinc plays a role in maintaining the integrity of root-cell plasma membranes. Home: 24 Hickory Cir Ithaca NY 14850-9673 Office: US Plant Soil & Nutrition Lab Tower Rd Ithaca NY 14853

WELCH, S(TEPHEN) ANTHONY, university dean, Islamic studies and arts educator; b. Phila., Apr. 29, 1942; s. Arnold DeMerritt and Mary Scott Welch; children: Nicholas, Bronwen, Emily. Student, U. Munich, Free U. of Berlin; BA in German Lit. with honors, Swarthmore Coll., 1965; MA, Harvard U., 1967, PhD (Fine Arts) History of Islamic Art and Architecture, 1972. Lectr. dept. history in art U. Victoria, B.C., 1971-72, asst. prof., 1972-75, assoc. prof., 1975-80, prof., 1980—, assoc. dean, 1982-85, Dean of Faculty of Fine Arts, 1985—; vis. prof. U. Minn., U. Wash., U. Chgo.; specialist in Iranian painting, Mughal painting in India, Islamic calligraphy and Sultanate architecture in medieval India. Author: Shah 'Abbas and the Arts of Isfahan, 1973, Artists for the Shah, 1976, Collection of Islamic Art, Prince Sadruddin Aga Khan, 4 Vols., 1972-78, Calligraphy in the Arts of the Muslim World, 1979, Arts of the Islamic Book, 1982, Treasures of Islam, 1985; contbr. articles to scholarly and profl. jours. Office: Dean Faculty Fine Arts, Univ Victoria, Victoria, BC Canada V8W 2Y2

WELCH, THOMAS ANDREW, lawyer; b. Lincoln, Nebr., Dec. 22, 1936; s. Lawrence William and Edna Alberta (Tangeman) W.; m. Ann Reinecke, Sept. 12, 1959; children: Jonathan Thomas, Michael Andrew, Susan Jennifer. Student, Stanford U., 1955-56; BA, UCLA, 1959; JD, Harvard U., 1965. Bar: Calif. 1966, U.S. Dist. Ct. (no. dist.) 1966, U.S. Ct. Appeals (9th cir.) 1966, U.S. Supreme Ct. 1976. Assoc. Brobeck, Phleger & Harrison, San Francisco, 1965-71, ptnr., 1972—; exec. com. Asia/Pacific Ctr. Resolution Internat. Disputes, San Francisco; bd. dirs. Ctr. Internat. Dispute Resolutions, Honolulu. Mem. bd. dirs. Youth Law Ctr., San Francisco, 1990—. Lt. USNR, 1959-66. Mem. ABA, Calif. Bar Assn., Am. Law Inst., Am. Arbitration Assn. (large complex case panel of neutrals). Republican. Presbyterian. Club: World Trade (San Francisco). Home: 38 Irving La Orinda CA 94563-1108 Office: Brobeck Phleger & Harrison 1 Market Pla 2800 Spear Tower San Francisco CA 94105

WELCH, THOMAS KENYON, lawyer; b. Ogden, Utah, Sept. 4, 1944; s. Harold L. and Florence (Perrin) W.; m. Alma Jean Fowler, Apr. 2, 1971; children: Melissa, Lindsay, Cameron, Christopher, Justin, David. BS, Weber State Coll., 1969; JD, George Washington U., 1971. Bar: Utah 1972, U.S. Dist. Ct. Utah 1972, U.S. Supreme Ct. 1975. Staff asst. Sen. Wallace F. Bennett, Washington, 1970-72; exec. v.p., pres., corp. counsel Smith's Mgmt. Corp., Salt Lake City, 1972—. Chmn. Gov. of Utah Task Force on Amateur Athletics, 1985—; bd. dirs. Salt Lake City Airport Authority, Salt Lake City/County Transp. Task Force. Named Outstanding Alumni Weber State Coll., Ogden, Utah, 1984; recipient Citation of Appreciation Salt Lake City. Mem. Utah Bar Assn., Salt Lake C. of C. (gov.). Republican. Mormon. Club: Timpanogas (Salt Lake City). Lodge: Rotary (Paul Harris fellow). Home: 3040 Sherwood Cir Salt Lake City UT 84108-2537 Office: Smith Mgmt Corp 1544 S Redwood Rd Salt Lake City UT 84104-5105

WELCH, WILLIAM HENRY, oil service company executive, consultant; b. Pharr, Tex., Nov. 24, 1929; married. AA, Edinburg (Tex.) Jr. Coll., 1949; BS, Trinity U., 1951. Sales engr. NL Baroid div. NL Industries, Inc., Liberty, Tex., 1955-58; dist. mgr. NL Industries, Inc., Liberty, Alvin (Tex.), New Orleans, Ardmore (Okla.), 1958-69; gen. mgr. Baroid de Venezuela NL Industries, Inc., Marcaibo, 1965-69; mgr. Latin Am. ops. Baroid Internat. NL Industries, Inc., Houston, 1969-71; mgr. ea. hemisphere ops. NL Baroid div., London NL Industries, Inc., 1971-74, dir. internat. drilling svcs. NL Baroid div., 1974-77, pres. NL Atlas Bradford, 1977-81; sr. v.p. NL Ind., 1981; pres. NL Oilfield Svcs. NL Industries, Inc., 1981-83, pres. NL Baroid, 1983-86, pres., chief operating officer NL Petroeum Svcs., 1986-87, cons., 1987; retired, 1987—; chmn. Valley Shamrock Inc., 1987—; chmn. bd. dirs. Cottonwood Ctrs., 1993. Bd. dirs. Jr. Achievement Southeast Tex., Houston, 1985-86; fund raiser United Way, Houston, 1985-86. 1st lt. U.S. Army, 1952-55. Mem. Petroleum Equipment Supplies Assn. (1st v.p. 1988-89), Nat. Oilfield Material and Del. Soc. (pres. 1984-85), Am. Petroleum Inst., Soc. Petroleum Engrs., Nat. Oil-Equipment Mfrs. and Dels. Soc., Petroleum Club, Sugar Creek Country Club. Avocations: golf, fishing, travel. Home: 26 Bendwood Dr Sugar Land TX 77478-3701

WELCH, WILLIAM JOHN, astronomer, educator; b. Chester, Pa., Jan. 17, 1934; s. William Taylor and Ruth (van Leuven) W.; m. Jill C. Tartar, July 4, 1980; children by previous marriage—Eric, Leslie, Jeanette. B.S., Stanford U., 1955; M.S., U. Calif., Berkeley, 1958, Ph.D. 1960; Hon. Dr., Universite de Bordeaux, 1979. Asst. prof. elec. engring. U. Calif., Berkeley, 1960-65; asso. prof. U. Calif., 1965-69, prof. astronomy and elec. engring., 1969—; dir. Radio Astronomy Lab., 1972. Contbr. numerous articles on radio astronomy and related fields to profl. jours. Bd. trustees Asso. Univs., Inc.; mem. Arecibo Adv. Bd. Grantee in radio astronomy NSF; Grantee in radio astronomy NASA. Mem. Internat. Astron. Union, Internat. Union Radio Sci., AAAS, Am. Astron. Soc. Home: 2727 Shasta Rd Berkeley CA 94708-1923 Office: U Calif-Berkeley Radio Astronomy Lab 601 Campbell Hall Berkeley CA 94720

WELD, JONATHAN MINOT, lawyer; b. Greenwich, Conn., Feb. 25, 1941; s. Alfred White and Sally (Duggan) W.; m. Jane Paige, June 19, 1965; children: Elizabeth, Eric. A.B. in History cum laude, Harvard U., 1963; J.D., Cornell U., 1967. Bar: N.Y. 1967, U.S. Ct. Appeals (2d cir.) 1969, U.S. Dist. Ct. (ea. and so. dist.) N.Y. 1970. Assoc. Shearman & Sterling, N.Y.C., 1967-75, ptnr., 1976—; ptnr. Shearman & Sterling, London, 1987-85; bd. dirs. Bank of N.S. Internat. Bd. dirs. Bkln. Hosp., St. Ann's Sch.; former bd. dirs. Bkln. Home for Children, Harvard Coll. Fund, Winent and Clayton Vols. Mem. ABA, N.Y. State Bar Assn. Office: Shearman & Sterling 599 Lexington Ave New York NY 10022-6030 also: 153 E 53rd St New York NY 10022-4611

WELD, TUESDAY KER (SUSAN KER WELD), actress; b. N.Y.C., Aug. 27, 1943; d. Lathrop Motley and Aileen (Ker) W.; m. Claude Harz, Oct., 1965 (div. 1971); 1 dau., Natasha; m. Dudley Moore, Sept. 20, 1975 (div.); 1 son, Patrick; m. Pinchas Zukerman, Oct. 18, 1985. Attended Hollywood (Calif.) Profl. Sch. Actress: (TV programs) including Cimarron Strip, Playhouse 90, Kraft Theatre, Alcoa Theatre, Climax, Ozzie and Harriet, The Many Loves of Dobie Gillis, 77 Sunset Strip, The Millionaire, Tab Hunter Show, Zane Grey Theatre, Follow the Sun, Bus Stop, Dick Powell Theatre,

Adventures in Paradise, Naked City, Eleventh Hour, DuPont Show of the Month, The Greatest Show on Earth, Mr. Broadway, Fugitive, The Crucible, (films) including debut in Rock, Rock, Rock, 1956, Rally Round the Flag Boys, The Five Pennies, 1959, The Private Lives of Adam and Eve, 1960, Return to Peyton Place, Wild in the Country, Bachelor Flat, 1961, Lord Love A Duck, 1966, Pretty Poison, 1968, I Walk the Line, 1970, A Safe Place, 1971, Play It As It Lays, 1972, Because They're Young, 1960, High Time, Sex Kittens Go to College, 1960, The Cincinnati Kid, 1965, Soldier in the Rain, I'll Take Sweden, 1965, Who'll Stop the Rain, 1978, Looking for Mr. Goodbar, 1977, Serial, 1980, Thief, 1981, Author! Author!, 1982, Once Upon a Time in America, 1984, Heartbreak Hotel, 1988, Falling Down, 1993 (TV movies) including Reflections of Murder, 1974, F. Scott Fitzgerald in Hollywood, 1976, A Question of Guilt, 1978, Mother and Daughter: The Loving War, 1980, Madame X, 1981, The Rainmaker, 1982, The Winter of Discontent, 1983, Scorned and Swindled, 1984, Circle of Violence, 1986. Began childhood career as fashion and catalogue model at age of three; by age of twelve appeared regularly on covers of mags. and performed child roles on TV programs, including Playhouse 90, Kraft Theatre, Alcoa Theatre, Climax. *

WELD, WILLIAM FLOYD, governor, lawyer; b. Smithtown, N.Y., July 31, 1945; s. David and Mary Blake (Nichols) W.; m. Susan Roosevelt, June 7, 1975; children: David Minot, Ethel Derby, Mary Blake, Quentin Roosevelt, Frances Wylie. A.B. summa cum laude, Harvard U., 1966, J.D. cum laude, 1970; diploma with distinction, Oxford (Eng.) U., 1967. Bar: Mass. 1970. Law clk. to Hon. R.A. Cutter, Supreme Jud. Ct. Mass., 1970-71; ptnr. firm Hill & Barlow, Boston, 1971-81; assoc. minority counsel U.S. Ho. of Reps. Judiciary Com. Impeachment Inquiry, 1973-74; U.S. atty. for the Dist. of Mass., 1981-86; asst. atty. gen., criminal div. U.S. Justice Dept., Washington, 1986-88; sr. ptnr. Hale & Dorr, Boston, Washington, 1988-90; gov. Commonwealth of Mass., 1990—. Republican nominee for atty. gen., Mass., 1978. Republican. Office: Office of Gov Executive Office State House Boston MA 02133

WELDEN, ARTHUR LUNA, biology educator; b. Birmingham, Ala., Jan. 27, 1927; s. Arthur Luna and Mary Woodson (Smith) W.; m. Frances Merkl Colvin, Aug. 19, 1950; children: Charles Woodson, Arthur Frederick. AB, Birmingham-So. Coll., 1950; MS, U. Tenn., 1951; PhD, U. Iowa, 1954. Asst. prof. Millikin U., Decatur, Ill., 1954-55; instr. in botany Tulane U., New Orleans, 1955-59, asst. prof., 1959-63, assoc. prof., 1963-68, prof. biology, 1968-79, Ida Richardson prof. botany, 1979—, chmn. dept. biology, 1979-93, prof. emeritus, 1994—; panel chmn. So. Assembly, Biloxi, Miss., 1970-71; program dir. Mesoam. Ecology Inst., New Orleans, 1982-87. Assoc. editor Tulane Studies in Zoology and Botany, 1966-78; contbr. articles to profl. jours. Served with U.S. Army, 1945-47. Grantee Am. Philos. Soc., 1957, NSF, 1960-75, NSF and Consejo Nacional de Mex., 1976-79, fellow AAAS, 1992; named to Socio Honorario, Sociedad Mexicana de Mex., 1982. Mem. Mycol. Soc. Am. (councilor 1967-69), Assn. for Tropical Biology, Swiss Mycol. Soc., Orgn. for Tropical Studies (life), Sigma Xi. Democrat. Home: 7826 Willow St New Orleans LA 70118-4056 Office: Tulane U Dept Biology 6823 Saint Charles Ave New Orleans LA 70118-5665

WELDON, DAVID BLACK, financial executive; b. London, Ont., Can., June 27, 1925; s. Douglas Black and Margaret (Black) W.; m. Ina G. Perry, July 7, 1951; children: Susan, Douglas, Anthony, Mardie, Kate. BA with honors, U. Western Ont., London, 1947, LLD (hon.). With Midland Doherty Fin. Corp. and predecessor cos., Toronto, Ont., 1950—, ret., 1989, dir.; chancellor U. Western Ont., 1984-88, chancellor emeritus, 1994—; dir. Dover Industries Ltd., Toronto, Emco Ltd., London, Goderich Elevators Ltd., Ont. Trustee Ont. Jockey Club; bd. dirs. Royal Agrl. Winter Fair, Toronto, 1970—, pres., 1980-82. Served with inf. Can. Army, 1944-45. Progressive Conservative. Anglican. Clubs: Toronto (bd. mgrs. 1983-85), York, Toronto Golf; London Hunt, London; Ristigouche Salmon (Quebec, Que., Can.); Griffith Island. Avocations: breeding and racing standardbred horses; fishing; hunting. Home: Prospect Farms, Arva, ON Canada N0M 1C0 also: 18A Hazelton Ave Apt 408, Toronto, ON Canada M5R 2E2 Office: Denison Mines Ltd, 40 Dundas St W Ste 320, Toronto, ON Canada M5G 2C2

WELDON, DAVID JOSEPH, JR., congressman, physician; b. Amityville, N.Y., Aug. 31, 1953; s. David Joseph and Anna (Mallardi) W.; m. Nancy Sourbeck, Nov. 26, 1956; 1 child, Kathryn. BS, SUNY, Stony Brook, 1978; MD, SUNY, Buffalo, 1981. Elder Zion Christian Fellowship, Palm Bay, Fla., 1991—; mem. 104th Congress from 15th Fla. dist., Washington, DC, 1995—; pvt. practice, Melbourne, Fla., 1987—; pres. Space Coast Family Forum, Melbourne, 1988-91. Maj. USAR, 1981—. Mem. AMA, Am. Coll. Physicians, Fla. Med. Assn. Home: 1602 Willard Rd NW Melbourne FL 32907-6320 Office: US Ho of Reps 432 Cannon Melbourne FL 20515-1015

WELDON, JEFFREY ALAN, state senator, historical research company executive; b. Billings, Mont., May 6, 1963; s. Richard Allen and Monica (Michaud) W.; m. Leslie Helen Boileau, July 7, 1990. BA, U. Mont., 1986, MPA, 1994. Rsch. analyst Heritage Rsch. Ctr., Missoula, Mont., 1989-91, v.p., 1991—; state senator Mont., 1993—. Democrat.

WELDON, NORMAN ROSS, manufacturing company executive; b. Greencastle, Ind., July 21, 1934; s. David M. and Lenora F. (Evens) W.; m. Carol J. Warne, Oct. 2, 1954; children: Thomas D., Cynthia M. B.S., Purdue U., 1956, M.S. in Indsl. Mgmt, 1962, Ph.D., 1964. With CTS Corp., Elkhart, Ind., 1964-79; exec. v.p. CTS Corp., 1970-76, pres., 1976-79, chief exec. officer, 1977-79, also dir.; pres. Cordis Corp., Miami, Fla., 1979-87; also chief exec. officer Cordis Corp.; pres., dir. Corvita Corp., Miami, 1987—; mem. adv. bd. Investment Co. Am., Inc.; trustee New Economy Fund; bd. dirs. SMALLCAP World Fund, Inc., Novoste Corp., Enable Med. Corp. Trustee Fla. Internat. U. Served to capt. USAF, 1956-60. Recipient Disting. Alumnus award Krannert Grad. Sch. Mgmt., Purdue U., 1979; NSF fellow, 1962-63; Ford Found. fellow, 1963-64. Mem. Tau Kappa Epsilon, Phi Eta Sigma, Alpha Zeta. Presbyterian. Club: Royal Palm Tennis, Weston Hills Country Club. Office: Corvita Corp 8210 NW 27th St Miami FL 33122-1900

WELDON, THEODORE TEFFT, JR., retail company executive; b. Evanston, Ill., July 19, 1932; s. Theodore Tefft and Dorothe Galbraith (Stover) W.; m. Barbara Ann Eskilson, Aug. 17, 1957; children: Lisa Courtney Weldon LeFevre, Theodore Tefft III, Margaret Helen. BA, Dartmouth Coll., 1954. Retail store salesman Sears Roebuck & Co., Gary, Ind., 1954-58; retail store mgr. Sears Roebuck & Co., Kankakee, Ill., 1958-62; sales mgr. Craftsman Sears Roebuck & Co., Chgo., 1962-69, advt. mgr. Craftsman, 1969-70, mktg. mgr. tires, 1970-81, sr. buyer sporting goods, 1981-82, nat. gen. catalog mgr., 1982-86; dir. home TV shopping Sears/QVC, Chgo., 1986-92; cons. Drake, Beam, Morin, Inc., Chog., 1992-94, Forcus Media, Inc., L.A., 1993—, Standard Mktg. Corp., Naperville, Ill., 1993—, King World, L.A., 1993—. Mem. Jr. Achievemnt, Chgo., 1966-68; rep. Winnetka (Ill.) Village Caucus, 1972-74; advisor Children's Theatre of Winnetka, 1972—; pres. Sunset Improvement Assn., Winnetka, 1975—. Avocations: internat. travel, theatre, swimming, biking, golf. Home: 426 Sunset Rd Winnetka IL 60093-4232

WELDON, W(AYNE) CURTIS, congressman; b. Marcus Hook, Pa., July 22, 1947; m. Mary Gallagher; children: Karen, Kristin, Kimberly, Curt, Andrew. BA in Humanities, West Chester State Coll., 1969; AAS in Fire Sci., Del. County Community Coll., Media, Pa., 1972; state instrn. cert., Cheyney State Coll.; postgrad., Cabrini Coll., Temple U., St. Joseph's U. Lic. tchr. Pa. From tchr. to head tchr. Walnut St. Sch., Darby-Colwyn-William Penn Sch. Dist., Pa., 1972-76; dir. tng. and manpower CIGNA (INA Corp.), Del. County, 1976-87; mayor City of Marcus Hook, 1977-81; councilman Del. County Council, 1981-87, vice chmn. then chmn., 1984-87; mem. 100th-103rd Congresses from 7th Pa. dist., Washington, D.C., 1987—; former chmn. Del. Valley Regional Planning Commn.; asst. dir. Elem. Secondary Edn. Act Title I Program, 1972-76; environ. specialist Project KARE, 1972-76; mem. Armed Svcs. Com., Merchant Marine and Fisheries Com.; co-chmn. Congl. Fire Svcs. Caucus. Named Man of Yr. Chester Bus. and Profl. Assn.; Most Effective Freshman Legislator Am. Security Coun.; Citizen of the Yr. Del. County C. of C., Clean Air Champion Sierra Club, Man of Yr. Internat. Soc. Fire Protection Engrs., 1988, taxpayers hero Citizen's Against Government Waste; recipient Outstanding Govt. Leader-

ship award Nat. Recycling Coalition, Fed. Legis. award Pa. Dirs. Assn. Community Action Agys., Spirit of Enterprise award U.S. C. of C., Golden Bulldog Watchdogs of Treasury award. Office: US Ho of Reps Office Ho Mems 2452 Rayburn Washington DC 20515

WELDON, WILLIAM FORREST, electrical and mechanical engineer, educator; b. San Marcos, Tex., Jan. 12, 1945; s. Forrest Jackson and Rubie Mae (Wilson) W.; m. Morey Sheppard McGonigle, July 30, 1968; children: William Embree, Seth Forrest. BS in Engring. Sci., Trinity U., San Antonio, 1967; MSME, U. Tex., 1970. Registered profl. engr., Tex. Engr. Cameron Iron Works, Houston, 1967-68; project engr. Glastron Boat Co., Austin, Tex., 1970-72; chief engr. Nalle Plastics Co., Austin, 1972-73; rsch. engr. U. Tex., Austin, 1973-77, tech. dir. Ctr. Electromechanics, 1977-85, dir. Ctr. Electromechanics, 1985-93, prof., 1985—; mem. permanent com. Symposium on Electromagnetic Launch Tech., 1978—, naval rsch. adv. com., 1992-96; cons. numerous cos. and govts., 1973—. Contbr. over 285 articles to profl. publs. Bd. dirs. Water Control & Improvement Dist. No. 10, Travis County, Tex., 1984—. Recipient Peter Mark medal Electromagnetic Launch Symposium, 1986, IR 100 award Indsl. Rsch. mag., 1983. Fellow ASME; mem. IEEE (sr.), NSPE. Achievements include 28 patents for rotating electrical machines, pulsed power, and electromagnetic propulsion. Office: U Tex Ctr Electromechanics Mail Code # 77000 Austin TX 78727

WELFELD, JOSEPH ALAN, healthcare consultant; b. Bklyn., May 8, 1948; s. Morris Welfeld and Shirley Schachner; m. Blossom Yablon, June 15, 1969; children: Robyn Elise, Michael Evan. BE, The Cooper Union, 1970; MBA, Baruch Coll., 1975. Asst. dir. Kings County Hosp., Bklyn., 1972-75; exec. dir. L.I. Cancer Coun., Inc., Melville, N.Y., 1975-78, Nassau Physicians Rev. Orgn., Inc., Westbury, N.Y., 1978-82; CEO Ocean State Physicians Health Plan, Providence, 1982-86; regional v.p. United Healthcare Corp., Providence, 1986-87; pres. Managed Care Resources, Inc., Miami, Fla., 1987-93; regional dir. healthcare cons. The Hay Group, N.Y.C., 1993—. Fellow Am. Coll. Healthcare Execs. (chmn. managed care execs. com. 1994-95), Metro N.Y. Healthcare Fin. Mgmt. Assn. (chmn. managed care com. 1992-95). Office: Hay Group 101 Hudson St Jersey City NJ 07302

WELFER, THOMAS, JR., utility company executive; b. Pitts., Sept. 21, 1936; s. Thomas and Gertrude (Myers) W.; m. Kathleen Ward, Aug. 25, 1962; children: Karen A. Welfer Rapp, Sharon A., Thomas III, Gary, Jeff, Kathy. BSBA cum laude, Duquesne U., 1961; postgrad., U. Pitts., 1962, C.C. Allegheny County, 1977. Lic. real estate salesman, Pa. Union relations statistician Duquesne Light Co., Pitts., 1965-68, union relations analyst, 1968-70, mgr. office of pres., 1970-80, corp. sec., 1980-84, coordinator human resources, 1984-85, benefits compliance coordinator, 1985—. Com. chmn. troop 670 Boy Scouts Am., 1975-87, mem.-at-large Seneca dist. Allegheny Trails coun., 1983-92; coach Westview-Ross Athletic Assn., Pitts., 1985-86; chmn. adminstrv. bd. McKnight United Meth. Ch., Pitts., 1976-77, mem. fin. com., 1978—, chmn., 1986—. With USAF, 1954-58. Mem. Pa. Electric Assn. (mem. econ. survey com. 1972-80, supr. ann. conv. registration 1975, 77, 79), Beta Alpha Phi. Republican. Avocations: travel; camping; fishing; photography; bowling. Office: Duquesne Light Co PO Box 1930 411 Seventh Ave Pittsburgh PA 15230-1930

WELGE, DONALD EDWARD, food manufacturing executive; b. St. Louis, July 11, 1935; s. William H. and Rudelle (Fritze) W.; m. Mary Alice Childers, Aug. 4, 1962; children: Robert, Tom. B.S., La. State U., 1957. With Gilster-Mary Lee Corp., Chester, Ill., 1957—, pres., gen. mgr., 1965—; dir. Buena Vista Bank of Chester. Former chmn. St. John's Luth. Bd. Edn. 1st lt. Transp. Corp, U.S. Army, 1958-63. Named So. Ill. Bus. Leader of Yr. So. Ill. U., 1988. Mem. Perryville C. of C. (pres. 1989), Chester, Ill. C. of C. (past pres.), Alpha Zeta, Phi Kappa Phi. Republican. Lutheran. Home: 5 Knollwood Dr Chester IL 62233-1416 Office: Gilster Mary Lee Co 1037 State St Chester IL 62233-1657

WELHAN, BEVERLY JEAN LUTZ, nursing educator, adminstrator; b. Phila., Dec. 7, 1950; d. Winfield E. and Mary Helen (James) Lutz; m. Robert John LeBar, Aug. 28, 1971 (div. July 1978); m. Joseph Welhan, Jan. 7, 1984; children: James Benjamin, Jillian Grace. Diploma, Montgomery Hosp. Sch. Nursing, 1971; B.S.N., Gwynedd Mercy Coll., 1974; M.Ed., Lehigh U., 1977; M.S.N., Villanova U., 1983; postgrad., Widener U. Staff nurse recovery room Montgomery Hosp., Norristown, Pa., 1971-72; charge nurse North Penn Convalescent Residence, Lansdale, Pa., 1972-74; instr. med./surg. nursing Episcopal Hosp., Phila., 1974-78; staff nurse Montgomery Hosp., Norristown, Pa., 1978-79; asst. dir. nursing edn. Episcopal Hosp., Phila., 1979-85, assoc. dir. nursing edn., 1985-89, dir. nursing edn., 1989—; part-time instr. Pa State U., 1983-84. Author: Testing Program for Scherer's Introductory Medical/Surgical Nursing, 1986. Mem. Nat. League Nursing (program evaluator 1990—, bd. rev. 1993—), Am. Nurses Assn., Pa. Nurses Assn. Southeastern Pa. League for Nursing (mem. nominating com. 1982-83, bd. dirs. 1983-85), Northwest Coalition of Hosp. & Diploma Schs. of Nursing (bd. dirs. 1993-94, chair nominating com., 1993-94, nominating com. 1991-92), Montgomery Hosp. Alumni Assn., Nurses' Alumni Assn. of Episcopal Hosp. (hon.), Sigma Theta Tau, Phi Kappa Phi. Republican. Home: 607 Overbrook Ln Oreland PA 19075-2403 Office: Episc Hosp Sch Nursing Front St and Lehigh Ave Philadelphia PA 19125

WELIKSON, JEFFREY ALAN, lawyer; b. Bklyn., Jan. 8, 1957; s. Bennet Joseph and Cynthia Ann Welikson; m. Laura Sanders, Aug. 19, 1979; children: Gregory Andrew, Joshua Stuart. BS, U. Pa., 1976, MBA, 1977; JD, Harvard U., 1980. CPA, N.Y.; bar: N.Y. 1981. Assoc. Shearman & Sterling, N.Y.C., 1980-83; staff counsel Reliance Group Holdings Inc., N.Y.C., 1983-84; dir. legal dept., 1984-85, asst. v.p., corp. counsel, 1985-88, v.p., asst. gen. counsel, asst. sec., 1988-94; exec. v.p. gen. counsel, sec. Reliance Nat. Ins. Co., N.Y.C., 1994—. Contbg. editor Harvard U. Internat. Law Jour., 1979-80. Mem. ABA, N.Y. State Bar Assn., Am. Inst. CPAs. Office: Reliance Nat Ins Co 77 Water St New York NY 10005

WELIN, WALTER, financial advisor; b. Lund, Sweden, Sept. 20, 1908; s. Lars and Adele (Hellegren) W.; m. Ulla Olsson, Nov. 25, 1950; 1 child, Lars. Grad. Econs. and Fin., U. Lund, MA in Polit. Sci. 1943, grad. law sch. 1945. Dir. dept. The Royal Swedish Patent Office, Stockholm, 1948-74; fin. advisor/cons. in pvt. practice, Lund. Club: St. Knut Guild. Mem. AAAS, N.Y. Acad. Scis., Nat. Geographic Soc., Planetary Soc. Address: Siriusgatan 25 S-224, 57 Lund Sweden

WELKE, ELTON GRINNELL, JR., publisher, writer; b. Berkeley, Calif., June 15, 1941; s. Elton Grinnell Sr. and Elsie Maud (Shattuck) W.; m. Anna Lange, July 28, 1963 (div. 1980); children: Allison Espy, Erik Grinnell; m. Bonnie Jean Lum, Jan. 24, 1981; 1 child, Erin Irene. BA in Zoology, U. Calif., Berkeley, 1962. Staff writer Sunset mag., Menlo Pk., Calif., 1962-65, assoc. editor, 1965-69, sr. editor, 1978-80; travel editor Better Homes & Gardens, Des Moines, 1969-71; mng. editor Apt. Life mag., Des Moines, 1971-72; exec. editor Sunset Spl. Interest mags., Menlo Pk., 1972-78; free-lance editorial cons. San Francisco and Seattle, 1981-84; v.p., dir. Livingston & Co., Seattle, 1984-89; publisher Microsoft Press, 1989—; cons. Holland Am. Line, Seattle, 1983-84, Livingston & Co. Advt., Seattle, 1983-84. Author: How to Survive Being Alive, 1977, Place's to go With Children Around Puget Sound, 1987. Bd. dirs. Olympic Nat. Pk. Assocs., Washington, 1965-69, March of Dimes, Western Washington, 1987—, chmn. campaign com., 1989—. Recipient 1st Pl. award Washington Press Assn., 1985, 86, 88, WPA award, 1987. Mem. Soc. Am. Travel Writers, Pub. Rels. Soc. of Am., Internat. Assn. Bus. Communicators (Golden Quill award 1985), Washington Athletic Club, Sierra Club. Avocations: gardening, plant collecting, fly fishing, cattle ranching, Asian art. Home: 11329 NE 103rd St Kirkland WA 98033-5178 Office: Microsoft Corp 1 Microsoft Way Redmond WA 98052

WELKER, WALLACE IRVING, neurophysiologist, educator; b. Batavia, N.Y., Dec. 17, 1926. Ph.D. in Psychology, U. Chgo., 1954. Mem. faculty U. Wis. Med. Sch., 1957—, prof. neurophysiology, 1965-90, emeritus prof., 1990—. Served with AUS, 1945-47. Sister Kenny Found. scholar, 1957-62; recipient NIH Career Devel. award, 1962-67. Mem. Am. Anat. Soc., Neurosci. Soc. Office: U Wis 275 Med Sci Bldg Madison WI 53706

WELKOWITZ, WALTER, biomedical engineer, educator; b. Bklyn., Aug. 3, 1926; s. Samuel and Shirley (Rosenblum) W.; m. Joan Horowitz, June 17, 1951; children: David, Lawrence, Julie. BS, The Cooper Union, N.Y.C., 1948; MS, U. Ill., 1949, PhD, 1954. Profl. engr., N.J. Rsch. assoc. U. Ill., Urbana, 1948-54, Columbia U., N.Y.C., 1954-55; asst. to pres., gen. mgr. Gulton Industries, Inc., Metuchen, N.J., 1955-64; prof., chmn. elec. engring. Rutgers U., Piscataway, N.J., 1964-86, prof. biomed. engring., 1986—, chmn. biomedical engring., 1986-90; cons. Gulton Industries, Metuchen, N.J., 1964-74. Author: Engineering Hemodynamics: Application to Cardiac Assist Devices, 1977, 2d edit., 1987; co-author: Biomedical Instruments: Theory and Design, 1976, 2d edit., 1992; author numerous chpts. in books; contbr. more than 100 articles to profl. jours. With U.S. Navy, 1944-46. Rutgers U. Rsch. Coun. fellow, 1974-75; recipient Centennial medal IEEE, 1984, Excellence in Rsch. award Rutgers Bd. Trustees, 1985, IEEE Career Achievement award Soc. Engring. Med. Biology, 1991; Llewellyn Thomas vis. prof. U. Toronto, Can., 1989. Fellow IEEE (engring. in medicine and biol. soc. career achievement award 1991), N.Y. Acad. Medicine, Am. Inst. of Medicine and Biol. Engring. Achievements include 26 patents for Electron Tube, Ultrasonic Flowmeter, Ultrasonic Transducer, Piezoelectric Heart Assist Apparatus, Method and Apparatus for Non-Invasive Monitoring Dynamic Cardiac Performance, and others. Home: 138 Highland Ave Metuchen NJ 08840-1942 Office: Rutgers U Biomed Engring PO Box 909 Piscataway NJ 08855-0909

WELL, IRWIN, language educator; b. Cin., Apr. 16, 1928; s. Sidney and Florence (Levy) W.; m. Vivian Max, Dec. 27, 1950; children: Martin, Alice, Daniel. BA, U. Chgo., 1948, MA, 1951; PhD, Harvard U., 1960. Teaching fellow Harvard U., Cambridge, Mass., 1955-58; asst. prof. Brandeis U., Waltham, Mass., 1958-65; assoc. prof. Northwestern U., Evanston, Ill., 1966-70, prof. Russian, Russian Lit., 1970—; pres., mem. bd. dirs. Am. Coun. Tchrs. of Russian, Washington, 1967—. Author numerous books in field; contbr. articles to scholarly jours. Recipient Pushkin medal Internat. Assn. of Russian Profs. Jewish. Avocations: music, singing. Office: Northwestern U Slavic Dept. Evanston IL 60208

WELLBORN, CHARLES IVEY, lawyer; b. Houston, Dec. 9, 1941; s. Fred W. and Emily R. (Gladu) W.; m. J.D. McCausland, Aug. 14, 1965; children: Westly O., Kerry S. BA in Econs., U. N.Mex., 1963, JD, 1966; LLM, NYU, 1972. Bar: N.Mex. 1966, U.S. Dist. Ct. N.Mex. 1966. Assoc. Neal & Matkins, Carlsbad, N.Mex., 1966-68; Robinson & Stevens, Albuquerque, 1969-71; ptnr. Schlenker, Parker, Payne & Wellborn, Albuquerque, 1971-76, Parker & Wellborn, Albuquerque, 1976-82; ptnr. Modrall, Sperling, Roehl, Harris & Sisk, Albuquerque, 1982-95; pres. U. N.Mex. Tech. Devel. Corp., Albuquerque, 1995—. Bd. dirs. N.Mex. Symphony Orch., 1988-91; bd. dirs. U. N.Mex. Anderson Schs. Mgmt. Found., 1989-94; vice chair U. N.Mex. Found., Inc., 1990-94; mem. Gov.'s Bus. Adv. Coun., 1989—; Small Bus. Adminstrn. Fin. Svcs. Adv., N.Mex., 1989; mem. venture capital mgmt. adv. com. N.Mex. State Investment Coun., 1991—; mem. Econ. Forum, vice-chair, 1993—; chmn. Roots & Wings Found., 1989—; v.p. N.Mex. Dem. Bus. Coun., 1992—; bd. dirs. Accion N.Mex., 1994—. Contbr. articles to law revs. Sgt. USAF, 1968-69, Korea. Fellow Am. Bar Found.; mem. ABA (ho. of dels. 1984-91), Albuquerque Bar Assn. (pres. 1977-78), N.Mex. Bar Found. (pres. 1980-82), State Bar N.Mex. (pres. 1982-83). Democrat. Roman Catholic. Office: U NMex Tech Devel Corp 851 University Blvd SE Ste 200 Albuquerque NM 87106

WELLBORN, OLIN GUY, III, law educator; b. Galveston, Tex., Oct. 21, 1947; s. Olin Guy Jr. and Betty Jean (Merriman) W.; m. Jodi Boston, July 1, 1983; children: Olivia Boston, Olin Guy IV. AB in English magna cum laude, Harvard U., 1970, JD magna cum laude, 1973. Law clk. Baker & Botts, Houston, 1972, U.S. Ct. Appeals, San Francisco, 1973-74; asst. prof. Sch. Law U. Tex., 1974-77, prof. Sch. Law, 1977—, William C. Liedtke sr. prof. Sch. Law, 1985—, assoc. dean acad. affairs Sch. Law, 1987-91; vis. prof. Harvard Law Sch., 1978, U. Mich. Law Sch., summer 1987; co-reporter liason com. rules evidence State Bar Tex., 1981-83, adv. com. subcom. on criminal matters Tex. Senate-House Select Com. on Judiciary, 1984, standing com. adminstrn. rules of evidence State Bar Tex., 1983-88, 94-95, fac. Criminal Justice Conf., Tex. Ctr. for Judiciary, 1985-86, Tex. COll. Advanced Judicial Studies, 1992—. Author: (with Charles T. McCormick and John F. Sutton Jr.) Cases and Materials on Evidence, 6th edit., 1989, 7th edit., 1992, (with Steven Goode and M. Michael Sharlot) Guide to the Texas Rules of Evidence: Civil and Criminal, 1988, 2d edit., 1993, Teacher's Manual to Accompany Cases and Materials on Evidence, 1992—, Courtroom Handbook on Texas Evidence, 1994, 95, (with Steven Goode) Courtroom Handbook on Federal Evidence, 1995, Courthouse Evidence Handbook, 1995. Mem. Phi Beta Kappa. Office: U Tex Sch Law 727 E 26th St Austin TX 78705-3299

WELLBURN, TIMOTHY, film editor. Editor: (films) The Irishman, 1978, Cathy's Child, 1979, Chain Reaction, 1980, Caddie, 1981, (with Michael Balson and David Stiven) The Road Warrior, 1982, The Killing of Angel Street, 1983, The Coolangatta Gold, 1984, Burke and Wills, 1985, The Fringe Dwellers, 1987, Dangerous Game, 1989, Judgment Night, 1993, Blown Away, 1994. Office: The Lyons/Sheldon Agency 8344 Melrose Ste 20 Los Angeles CA 90069*

WELLEK, RICHARD LEE, business executive; b. Chgo., Dec. 2, 1938; s. William I. and Mae (Silbert) W.; m. Susan Lee Pollack, Aug. 20, 1960; children: Jeffrey Alan, Marcia Rae, Deborah Lynn. BS, U. Ill., 1960. Material mgr. National Metalwares Inc., Aurora, Ill., 1963-65, sales mgr., 1968-73, exec. v.p. ops., 1977-80, pres., 1980-83; sales mgr. Decar Corp., Middleton, Wis., 1965-68; group exec. Varlen Corp., Naperville, Ill., 1983, pres., chief exec. officer, 1983—, also bd. dirs.; bd. dirs. AMCO Corp. Bd. dirs. Ill. Math. & Sci. Acad., Bus. Adv. Coun., Coll. Commerce & Bus. U. Ill., 1986—; bd. trustees Temple Bnai Israel, 1983—. Served to capt. USAF, 1960-63. Club: Economic (Chgo.). Avocations: motor sports, tennis. Office: Varlen Corp 55 Schuman Blvd PO Box 3089 Naperville IL 60566

WELLEN, ROBERT HOWARD, lawyer; b. Jersey City, Aug. 19, 1946; s. Abraham Louis and Helen Rose (Krieger) W.; m. Anita Fass, June 16, 1968; children: Elizabeth, Judith Maria. BA, Yale Coll., 1968; JD, Yale U., 1971; LLM in Taxation, Georgetown U., 1975. Bar: Conn. 1971, D.C. 1972, Colo. 1982. Assoc. Fulbright & Jaworski, Washington, 1975-76, participating assoc., 1976-79, ptnr.; ptnr. Ivins, Phillips & Barker, Washington, 1993—; adj. prof. law Georgetown U. Law Ctr., 1982-85. Mem. lawyers com. Democratic Nat. Com., Washington, 1988. Served to lt. JAGC, USNR, 1971-75. Mem. ABA (past chmn. com. on corp. tax, sect. taxation, supr. editor sect. taxation newsletter), Fed. Bar Assn. (council taxation), Phi Beta Kappa. Jewish. Contbr. articles to legal pubs. Office: Ivins Phillips & Barker 1700 Pennsylvania Ave NW Washington DC 20006-4700

WELLER, ANDREW MICHAEL, steel company executive. Gen. mgr., v.p., treas. Bethlehem (Pa.) Steel Corp. Office: Bethlehem Steel Corp 1170 8th Ave Bethlehem PA 18016

WELLER, EDGAR O., transportation executive; b. 1915. LLB, 1938. Sole practice Dallas, 1938-69; with Frozen Food Express Industries, Inc., Dallas, 1947—, now vice chmn. bd. dirs. Office: Frozen Food Express Industries Inc 1145 Empire Central Pl Dallas TX 75247-4300*

WELLER, GERALD C., congressman; b. Streator, Ill., July 7, 1994. Degree in Agriculture, U. Ill., 1979. Aide to U.S. Congressman Tom Corcoran, 1980-81, aide to U.S. Sec. of Agriculture John R. Block, 1981-85; active family farm, 1985-88; rep. State of Ill., 1988-94; mem. 104th Congress from 11th Ill. dist., 1994—; asst. majority whip; rep. House Republican steering com.; mem. Newt Gingrich's policy com., exec. com. NRCC, House Banking Com., House Veternas Affairs Com., House Transp. and Infrastructure Com. Mem. 1st Christian Ch. of Morris, Ill. Mem. Nat. Republican Legis. Assn. (legislator, Legislator of the Year). Office: US House Reps 1032 Longworth House Office Blsg Washington DC 20515-1311*

WELLER, GUNTER ERNST, geophysics educator; b. Haifa, June 14, 1934; came to U.S., 1968; s. Erich and Nella (Lange) W.; m. Sigrid Beilharz, Apr. 11, 1963; children: Yvette, Kara, Britta. BS, U. Melbourne, Australia, 1962, MS, 1964, PhD, 1968. Meteorologist Bur. Meteorology, Melbourne, 1959-61; glaciologist Australian Antarctic Exps., 1964-67; from asst. prof. to assoc. prof. geophysics Geophys. Inst., U. Alaska, Fairbanks, 1968-72, prof., 1973—, dep. dir., 1984-86, 90—; project dir. NASA-UAF Alaska SAR Facility, Fairbanks, 1983-93; program mgr. NSF, Washington, 1972-74; pres. Internat. Commn. Polar Meteorology, 1980-83; chmn. polar rsch. bd. NAS, 1985-90, Global Change Steering Com. Sci. com. on Antarctic Rsch., 1988-92; chmn. Global Change Working Group Internat. Arctic Sci. Com., 1990—; dir. Ctr. for Global Change and Arctic System Rsch., U. Alaska, 1990; dir. Coop. Inst. Arctic Rsch., 1994—. Contbr. numerous articles to profl. jours. Recipient Polar medal Govt. Australia, 1969; Mt. Weller named in his honor by Govt. Australia, Antarctica; Weller Bank named in his honor by U.S. Govt., Arctic. Fellow AAAS (exec. sec. arctic divsn. 1982—), Arctic Inst. N.Am.; mem. Internat. Glaciological Soc., Am. Meteorol. Soc. (chmn. polar meteorology com. 1980-83), Am. Geophys. Union. Home: PO Box 81024 Fairbanks AK 99708-1024 Office: U Alaska Geophys Institute Fairbanks AK 99775

WELLER, JANET LOUISE, lawyer; b. Boston, Sept. 17, 1953; d. Thomas Huckle and Kathleen (Fahey) W.; m. John Lee Holloway; children: Kelly Brianna, Janine Fahey. BA, Harvard U., 1975; JD, U. Mich., 1978. Bar: D.C. 1978, U.S. Dist. Ct. D.C. 1978, U.S. Ct. Appeals (D.C. cir.) 1979. Assoc. Cleary, Gottlieb, Steen & Hamilton, Washington, 1978-86, ptnr., 1986—. Office: Cleary Gottlieb Steen 1752 N St NW Washington DC 20036-2806

WELLER, JOSEPH C., brokerage house executive; b. 1939. BA, U. Miss. 1961. CPA. CPA Minor & Moore, Memphis, 1961-67; exec. v.p., sec., treas. Morgan, Keegan & Co. Inc., Memphis, 1969—. Office: Morgan Keegan & Co Inc Morgan Keegan Tower 50 Front St Memphis TN 38103*

WELLER, MICHAEL, playwright, screenwriter; b. Sept. 26, 1942; s. Paul and Rosa (Rush) W. BA, Brandeis U.; student, Manchester U. Author: plays Cello Days at Dixais Place, 1965, How Ho-Ho Rose and Fell in Seven Short Scenes, 1966, Happy Valley, 1969, The Bodybuilders, 1969, Now There's Just the Three of Us, 1969, Open Space, 1969, Poison Come Poison, 1970, Cancer, 1970, Moonchildren, 1972, Grant's Movie, 1971, Tira Tells Everything There is to Know About Herself, 1971, Twenty Three Years Later, 1973, Fishing, 1975, Alice, 1976, Split, 1978, Loose Ends, 1979, Dwarfman, 1980, The Ballad of Soapy Smith, 1983-84, Ghost On Fire, Broadway, 1985, Spoils of War, 1988, Lake No Bottom, 1990, Help!, 1992, Buying Time, 1993, The Heart of Art, 1994; lyricist (with Jim Steinman) More Than You Deserve, 1973; screenwriter Hair, 1979, Ragtime, 1980 (Academy award nomination for best adapted screenplay 1981), Lost Angels, 1989, Writing on the Wall, God Bless You Mr. Rosewater, 1991, Getting Rid of Alex, 1993, (TV) Spoils of War, 1994; adapter, composer: Fred, 1965, The Making of Theodore Thomas, Citizen, 1968. Recipient Drama Desk award for most promising playwright, 1971; Rockefeller fellowship, 1973; Creative Artists Pub. Svc. grantee, 1976. Office: CAA care Rob Scheidlinger 9830 Wilshire Blvd Beverly Hills CA 90212 also: McNaughton Lowe Representation, 200 Fulham Rd, London SW10 9PN, England

WELLER, PETER, actor; b. Stevens Point, Wis., June 24, 1947; s. Frederick and Dorothy Weller. BA, North Tex. State U., 1970; cert., Am. Acad. Dramatic Arts, N.Y.C., 1972; studies with Uta Hagen, H.B. Studios, N.Y.C., 1974-77. Appeared in various plays including Sticks and Bones, Streamers, The Woods, Daddy Wolf, Rebel Women, The Woolgatherer, Cat on a Hot Tin Roof; TV prodns. Kentucky Woman, 1983, Two Kinds of Love, 1983, Women and Men: Stories of Seduction, 1990, Rainbow Drive, 1990; films include Butch and Sundance: The Early Years, 1979, Just Tell Me What You Want, 1980, Shoot the Moon, 1982, Of Unknown Origin, 1983, Adventures of Buckaroo Bonzai, 1984, Firstborn, 1984, Robocop, 1987, Shakedown, 1988, A Killing Affair, 1988, Leviathan, 1989, Robocop II, 1990, Naked Lunch, 1992, Fifty-Fifty, 1993, The New Age, 1994; cable film My Sister's Keeper. Mem. Actor's Studio, 1979. Avocation: jazz. Office: care CAA 9830 Wilshire Blvd Beverly Hills CA 90212*

WELLER, ROBERT N(ORMAN), hotel executive; b. Harrisburg, Pa., Feb. 1, 1939; s. Charles Walter and Martha Ann (MacPherson) W.; m. Nancy M. Wood, June 21, 1975; children—Wendi Elizabeth, Terrie Lynn, Nikki Ann. B.S., Cornell U., 1969. Mgr. Hall's Motor Transit Co., Harrisburg, Pa., 1961-65; market research analyst Carrolls Devel. Corp., Syracuse, N.Y., 1970-72; asst. to pres. Econo-Travel Motor Hotel Corp., Norfolk, Va., 1972-74; dir. franchise sales Econo-Travel Motor Hotel Corp., 1975, pres., dir., 1976-84; pres., dir. Econo-Travel Devel. Corp., Norfolk, 1977-84; pres. Internat. Data Bank Ltd., 1985-86; pres., dir. Econo Lodges of Am., 1986-90; group pres., exec. v.p. Choice Hotels Internat., Silver Spring, Md., 1990-91; with Hospitality Ventures, Virginia Beach, 1991—; pres. Super 8 Motels, Inc. divsn. Hospitality Franchise Systems, Parsippany, N.J., 1993—. Served in USMC, 1957-60. Home: 3027 Lynndale Rd Virginia Beach VA 23452-6233 Office: Hospitality Ventures 2620 Southern Blvd Ste 104 Virginia Beach VA 23452

WELLER, SOL WILLIAM, chemical engineering educator; b. Detroit, July 27, 1918; s. Ira and Bessie (Wieselthier) W.; m. Miriam Damick, June 11, 1943; children—Judith, Susan, Robert, Ira. B.S., Wayne State U., 1938; Ph.D., U. Chgo., 1941. Asst. chief coal hydrogenation U.S. Bur. Mines, Pitts., 1945-50; head fundamental rsch. Houdry Process Corp., Linwood, Pa., 1950-58; mgr. propulsion rsch. Ford Aeronutronic Co., Newport Beach, Calif., 1958-61; dir. chem. lab. and materials rsch. lab. Philco-Ford Co., Newport Beach, 1961-65; prof. chem. engring. SUNY-Buffalo, 1965—; emeritus, 1989; C.C. Furnas prof. SUNY-Buffalo, 1983—; vis. fellow Oxford U., 1989. Author numerous sci. papers, book chpts., ency. entries. Fulbright lectr. Madrid, 1975, Istanbul, 1980. Mem. Am. Chem. Soc. (chmn. Orange County sect. 1964, H.H. Storch award 1981, E.V. Murphree award 1982, Schoellkopf medal 1984, Dean's award 1991), ASTM (founder com. D32 on catalysts). Achievements include patents in field. Office: SUNY Buffalo 305 Furnas Hall Buffalo NY 14260

WELLER, THOMAS HUCKLE, physician, emeritus educator; b. Ann Arbor, Mich., June 15, 1915; s. Carl V. and Elsie A. (Huckle) W.; m. Kathleen R. Fahey, Aug. 18, 1945; children: Peter Fahey, Nancy Kathleen, Robert Andrew, Janet Louise. A.B., U. Mich., 1936; M.S., 1937, LL.D. (hon.), 1956; M.D., Harvard, 1940; Sc.D., Gustavus Adolphus U., 1975, U. Mass., 1985; L.H.D., Lowell U., 1977. Diplomate Am. Bd. Pediatrics. Teaching fellow bacteriology Harvard Med. Sch., 1940-41; research fellow tropical medicine, pediatrics, 1947-48, instr. comparative pathology, tropical medicine, 1948-49, asst. prof. tropical pub. health Sch. Pub. Health, 1949-50, assoc. prof., 1950-54, Richard Pearson Strong prof. tropical pub. health, 1954-85, prof. emeritus, 1985—, head dept., 1954-81; intern bacteriology and pathology Children's Hosp., Boston, 1941; intern medicine Children's Hosp., 1942, asst. resident medicine, 1946, asst. dir. research div. infectious diseases, 1949-55; mem. commn. parasitic diseases Armed Forces Epidemiol. Bd., 1953-72, dir., 1953-59; charge parasitology, bacteriology, virology sections Antilles Dept. Med. Lab., P.R. Author sci. papers. Served to maj. M.C. AUS, 1942-46. Recipient E. Mead Johnson award for devel. tissue culture procedures in study virus diseases Am. Acad. Pediatrics, 1953, Kimble Methodology award, 1954, Nobel prize in physiology and medicine, 1954, George Ledlie prize, 1963, Weinstein Cerebral Palsy award, 1973, Stern Symposium honoree, 1972, Bristol award Infectious Diseases Soc. Am., 1980, Gold medal and diploma of honor U. Costa Rica, 1984, First Sci. Achievement award VZV Rsch. Found., 1993. Fellow Am. Acad. Arts and Scis.; mem. Harvey Soc., AMA, Am. Soc. Parasitologists, Am., Royal socs. tropical medicine and hygiene, Am. Pub. Health Assn., AAAS, Am. Epidemiological Soc., Nat. Acad. Scis., Am. Pediatric Soc., Assn. Am. Physicians, Soc. Exptl. Biology and Medicine, Am. Assn. Immunologists, Soc. Pediatric Research, Phi Beta Kappa, Sigma Xi, Alpha Omega Alpha. Home and Office: 56 Winding River Rd Needham MA 02192-1025

WELLES, JAMES BELL, JR., lawyer; b. Schenectady, N.Y., Aug. 27, 1918; s. James Bell and Grace E. (Frazer) W.; m. Ann Bouton Thom, Apr. 26, 1946; children—Ann, James Bell, III, William (dec.), Thomas, Amy. A.B., Columbia U., 1939, J.D., 1942. Bar: N.Y. 1943. Assoc. Mitchell, Capron, Marsh, Angulo & Cooney, N.Y.C., 1946-56; mem. firm. Angulo, Cooney, Marsh & Ouchterloney, N.Y.C., 1956-59, Debevoise & Plimpton, N.Y.C., 1960-93. Bd. visitors Columbia Law Sch., N.Y.C., 1974-94; bd. dirs. Burke Found., White Plains, N.Y., 1959—, pres.; trustee Emma Willard Sch., Troy, N.Y., 1974-82. Maj. USAAF, 1942-45. Fellow Am. Coll. Trust and Estate Counsel; mem. ABA, N.Y. State Bar Assn., Assn. of Bar of City of N.Y., Delta Phi, Phi Delta Phi. Republican. Episcopalian. Club: University (N.Y.C.). Home: 25 Ivy Hill Rd Chappaqua NY 10514-1805 Office: Debevoise & Plimpton 875 3rd Ave New York NY 10022-6225

WELLES, JOHN GALT, museum director; b. Orange, N.J., Aug. 24, 1925; s. Paul and Elizabeth Ash (Galt) W.; m. Barbara Lee Chrisman, Sept. 15, 1951; children: Virginia Chrisman, Deborah Galt, Barton Jeffery, Holly Page. BE, Yale U., 1946; MBA, U. Pa., 1949; LHD (hon.) U. Denver, 1994. Test engr. Gen. Electric Co., Lynn, Mass., 1947; labor relations staff New Departure div. Gen Motors Corp., Bristol, Conn., 1949-51; mem. staff Mountain States Employers Council, Denver, 1952-55; head indsl. econs. div. U. Denver Research Inst., Denver, 1956-74; v.p. planning and devel. Colo. Sch. Mines, Golden, 1974-83; regional adminstr. EPA, Denver, 1983-87; exec. dir. Denver Mus. Natural History, 1987-94, dir. emeritus, 1994—. Sr. cons. Secretariat, UN Conf. Human Environment, Geneva, 1971-72; cons. Bus. Internat., S.A., Geneva, 1972; trustee Tax Free Fund of Colo., N.Y., 1987—; exec. com. Denver Com. on Fgn. Rels., 1987—; chmn. Colo. Front Range Project, Denver, 1979-80. Contbr. articles to profl. jours., newspapers. Recipient Disting. Service award Denver Regional Council Govts., 1980, Barnes award EPA, 1987. Mem. AAAS, Am. Assn. Museums (ethics commn. 1991-94, v.p. 1992—), Sustainable Futures Soc. (nat. adv. bd. 1994—), Met. Denver Exec. Club (pres. 1967-68), World Future Soc., Univ. Club (Denver) Denver Athletic Club, Tau Beta Pi, Blue Key. Republican. Episcopalian.

WELLES, MELINDA FASSETT, artist, educator; b. Palo Alto, Calif., Jan. 4, 1943; d. George Edward and Barbara Helena (Todd) W. Student, San Francisco Inst. Art, 1959-60, U. Oreg., 1960-62; BA in Fine Arts, UCLA, 1964, MA in Spl. Edn., 1971, PhD in Ednl. Psychology, 1976; student fine arts and illustration Art Ctr. Coll. Design, 1977-80. Cert. ednl. psychologist, Calif. Asst. prof. Calif. State U., Northridge, 1978-82, Pepperdine U., L.A., 1979-82; assoc. prof. curriculum, teaching and spl. edn. U. So. Calif., L.A., 1980-89; mem. acad. faculty Pasadena City Coll., 1973-79, Art Ctr. Coll. Design, 1978—, Otis Coll. Art and Design, L.A., 1986—; UCLA Extension, 1980-84, Coll. Devel. Studies, L.A., 1978-87, El Camino C.C., Redondo Beach, Calif., 1982-86; cons. spl. edn.; pub. adminstrn. analyst UCLA Spl. Edn. Rsch. Project, 1973-76; exec. dir. Atwater Park Ctr. Disabled Children, L.A., 1976-78; coord. Pacific Oaks Coll. in svc. programs for L.A. Unified Schs., Pasadena, 1978-81; mem. Southwest Blue Book, Freedom's Found. at Valley Forge, Friends of French Art, Costume Coun. L.A. County Mus. of Art., Assistance League of So. Calif. Author: Calif. Dept. Edn. Tech. Reports, 1972-76; editor: Teaching Special Students in the Mainstream, 1981, Educating Special Learners, 1986, 88, Teaching Students with Learning Problems, 1988, Exceptional Children and Youth, 1989; group shows include: San Francisco Inst. Art, 1960, U. Hawaii, 1978, Barnsdall Gallery, L.A., 1979, 80; represented in various pvt. collections. HEW fellow, 1971-72; grantee Calif. Dept. Edn., 1975-76, Calif. Dept. Health, 1978. Mem. Am. Psych. Assn., Calif. Learning Disabilities Assn., Am. Council Learning Disabilities, Calif. Scholarship Fedn. (life), Alpha Chi Omega. Office: 700 Levering Ave Apt 1 Los Angeles CA 90024-2795

WELLFORD, HARRY WALKER, federal judge; b. Memphis, Aug. 6, 1924; s. Harry Alexander and Roberta Thompson (Prothro) W.; m. Katherine E. Potts, Dec. 8, 1951; children: Harry Walker, James B. Buckner P., Katherine T., Allison R. Student, U. N.C. 1943-44; BA, Washington and Lee U., 1947; postgrad. in law, U. Mich., 1947-48; LLD, Vanderbilt U., 1950. Bar: Tenn. 1950. Atty. McCloy, Myar & Wellford, Memphis, 1950-60, McCloy, Wellford & Clark, Memphis, 1960-70; judge U.S. Dist. Ct., Memphis, 1970-82; judge U.S. Ct. Appeals (6th cir.), Cin. and Memphis, 1982-92, sr. judge, 1992—; pres.' adv. com. Rhodes Coll., Christian Brothers U., LeMoyne-Owen Coll. Trustee Mary Baldwin Coll., Staunton, Va., 1991-93; chair Sen. Howard Baker campaigns, 1964-66; chair Tenn. Hist. Commn., Tenn. Constnl. Bicentennial Commn., 1987-88; mem. charter drafting com. City of Memphis, 1967, Tenn. Am. Revolution Bicentennial Commn., 1976, Com. on Adminstrn. Fed. Magistrates System, Jud. Conf. Subcom. Adminstrn. of Criminal Law Probation; clk. session, commr. Gen. Assembly; elder Presbyn. Ch.; moderator Memphis Presbytery, 1994. Recipient Sam A. Myar award for svc. to profession and community Memphis State Law U., 1963. Mem. Phi Beta Kappa, Omega Delta Kappa. Home: 91 N Perkins Rd Memphis TN 38117-2425 Office: US Ct Appeals 1176 Federal Bldg 167 N Main St Memphis TN 38103-1814

WELLFORD, HILL B., JR., lawyer; b. Tulsa, Okla., Apr. 30, 1942. AB, Davidson Coll., 1964; JD, U.N.C. 1967. Bar: Va. 1968. Ptnr. Hunton & Williams, Richmond, Va.; lectr. in field. Mem. ABA, Va. Bar Assn. (chmn. com. labor rels. and employment law 1977-87), Assn. Trial Lawyers Am., Phi Delta Phi. Office: Hunton & Williams Riverfront Plaza East Tower 951 E Byrd St Richmond VA 23219-4040

WELLIN, KEITH SEARS, investment banker; b. Grand Rapids, Mich., Aug. 13, 1926; s. Elmer G. and Ruth (Chamberlin) W.; m. Carol D. Woodhouse, Sept. 5, 1951 (dec. 1970); children: Cynthia Wellin Plum, Peter, Marjorie Wellin King; m. Nancy Brown Negley, Aug. 2, 1985. B.A., Hamilton Coll., 1950; M.B.A., Harvard U., 1952. With E.F. Hutton & Co., Inc., Chgo., 1952-71; regional v.p. dir. E.F. Hutton & Co., Inc., 1962-66; pres. E.F. Hutton & Co., Inc., N.Y.C., 1967-71; vice chmn. E.F. Hutton & Co., Inc., 1970-71; sr. v.p., treas., dir. Reynolds Securities Inc., 1971-74, pres., dir., 1974-78; exec. v.p., dir. Dean Witter Reynolds Orgn., from 1978; chmn. Dean Witter Reynolds Inter-Capital, from 1978; former vice chmn. Dean Witter Reynolds Inc.; chmn. bd. Moorco Internat., Houston; former gov., mem. exec. com. Assn. Stock Exchange Firms; mem. governing council Securities Industry Assn. Mem. investment com., trustee Hamilton Coll. Served to 2d lt., inf. AUS, 1945-47. Clubs: Knickerbocker (N.Y.C.); Clove Valley Rod and Gun (La Grangeville, N.Y.); Round Hill (Greenwich, Conn.); River Club. Home: El Tule Ranch Drawer C Falfurrias TX 78355 Office: care Moorco Internat Inc 2700 Post Oak Blvd Ste 2400 Houston TX 77056

WELLINGER, CHARLES H., health services company executive; b. 1945. BBA, Wichita State U., 1972; MPH, U. Mo., 1972. Various positions Kamen Supply Co., Wichita, Kans., 1963-72; adminstrv. resident St. Luke's Hosp., Kansas City, Mo., 1972-73, assoc. dir., 1977-80, assoc. exec. dir., 1980; adminstr., CEO Spelman Meml. Hosp., Smithville, Mo., 1980-82; sr. adminstr., COO Good Samaritan Med. Ctr., Phoenix, 1982-86, CEO, 1989-91; CEO Thunderbird Samaritan Hosp. and Health Ctr., Glendale, Arix., 1986-89; exec. v.p., COO Samaritan Health Svcs., Phoenix, 1991—; also chmn. Ariz. Physicians IPA Inc., Phoenix. Office: Ariz Physicians IPA Inc 4041 N Central Ave Bldg B Phoenix AZ 85012*

WELLINGTON, HARRY HILLEL, lawyer, educator; b. New Haven, Aug. 13, 1926; s. Alex M. and Jean (Ripps) W.; m. Sheila Wacks, June 22, 1952; children: John, Thomas. AB, U. Pa., 1947; LLB, Harvard U., 1952; MA (hon.), Yale U., 1960. Bar: D.C. 1952. Law clk. to U.S. Judge Magruder, 1953-54, Supreme Ct. Justice Frankfurter, 1955-56; asst. prof. law Stanford U., 1954-56; mem. faculty Yale U., 1956—, prof. law, 1956—, Edward J. Phelps prof. law, 1967-83, dean Law Sch., 1975-85, Sterling prof. law, 1983-92, Sterling prof. emeritus law, 1992—; pres., dean. prof. law N.Y. Law Sch., N.Y.C., 1992—; Ford fellow London Sch. Econs., 1965; Guggenheim fellow; sr. fellow Brookings Instn., 1968-71; Rockefeller Found. fellow Bellagio Study and Conf. Ctr., 1984; faculty mem. Salzburg Seminar in Am. Studies, 1985; John M. Harlan disting. vis. prof. N.Y. Law Sch., 1985-86; review person ITT-SEC; moderator Asbestos-Wellington Group; cons. domestic and fgn. govtl. agys.; trustee N.Y. Law Sch.; bd. govs. Yale U. Press; mem. jud. panel, exec. com. Ctr. Public Resources Legal Program; Harry H. Wellington lectr., 1995—. Author: (with Harold Shepherd) Contracts and Contract Remedies, 1957, Labor and the Legal Process, 1968, (with Clyde Summers) Labor Law, 1968, 2d edit., 1983, (with Ralph Winter) The Unions and the Cities, 1971, Interpreting the Constitution, 1990; contbr. articles to profl. jours. Mem. ABA, Bar Assn. Conn., Am. Law Inst., Am. Arbitration Assn., Am. Acad. Arts and Scis., Common Cause (nat governing bd.). Office: NY Law Sch 57 Worth St New York NY 10013-2926 also: Yale U Sch Law New Haven CT 06520

WELLINGTON, JEAN SUSORNEY, librarian; b. East Chicago, Ind., Oct. 23, 1945; d. Carl Matthew and Theresa Ann Susorney; m. Donald Clifford Wellington, June 12, 1976; 1 child, Evelin Patricia. BA, Purdue U., 1967; MA in LS, Rosary Coll., River Forest, Ill., 1969; MA, U. Cin., 1976. Head Burnam Classical Libr. U. Cin., 1970—. Compiler: Dictionary of Bibliographic Abbreviations Found in the Scholarship of Classical Studies and Related Disciplines, 1983. Mem. Art. Librs. Soc. N.Am. (chair Ohio br. 1984-85). Office: U Cin Classics Libr Box 210191 Cincinnati OH 45221-0191

WELLINGTON, JUDITH LYNN, cultural organization administrator; b. Yonkers, N.Y., Feb. 4, 1947; d. James William Wellington and Ardath (Sweet) Longden; m. Charles L. Lerman (div.); 1 child, Michael J. BA, Wheaton Coll., Norton, Mass., 1969; MA, Harvard U., 1971, PhD, 1975. Asst. prof. Juniata Coll., Huntingdon, Pa., 1974-76; asst. dir., assoc. mem. Monell Chem. Senses Ctr., Phila., 1976-86; v.p. Zool. Soc. Phila., 1986-92; pres., CEO N.J. Acad. for Aquatic Scis., Camden, N.J., 1992—. Bd. dirs. South Jersey Performing Arts Ctr., Camden, N.J., 1989—; bd. dirs., sec. Delaware River Ferry Co., Camden, 1988—. Office: Thomas H Kean NJ State Aquarium 1 Riverside Dr Camden NJ 08103-1060 Home: 18 Allendale Rd Philadelphia PA 19151

WELLINGTON, ROBERT HALL, manufacturing company executive; b. Atlanta, July 4, 1922; s. Robert H. and Ernestine V. (Vossbrinck) W.; m. Marjorie Jarchow, Nov. 15, 1947; children: Charles R., Robert H., Christian J., Jeanne L. B.S., McCormack Sch. of Engring. and Applied Scis. (formerly Northwestern Tech. Inst.), 1944; M.S. in Bus. Adminstrn, MBA, U. Chgo., 1958. With Griffin Wheel Co., 1946-61; v.p. parent co. Amsted Industries, Inc., Chgo., 1961-74, exec. v.p., 1974-80, pres., chief exec. officer 1981-88, chmn. bd., chief exec. officer, 1988-90; bd. dirs. Prudential Money Market Assets, Prudential Rsrch. Fund, Inc., Prudential Intermediate Income Fund, Inc. Served to lt. USN, 1943-46. Mem. Chgo. Athletic Club, Econ. Club, Mid-Am. Club, Comml. Club. Office: Amsted Industries Inc 205 N Michigan Ave Fl 44 Chicago IL 60601-5999

WELLINGTON, SHEILA WACKS, foundation administrator, psychiatry educator; b. N.Y.C., Dec. 24, 1932; d. Louis and Rose Feldman; m. Harry Hillel Wellington, June 22, 1952; children: John and Thomas. BA in Polit. Sci., Wellesley Coll., 1952; traineeship, USPHS, 1966-68; MUS, Yale U., 1968, MPH, 1968. Lectr. dept. psychiatry Sch. Medicine Yale U., New Haven, 1974-93; dir. Hill-West Haven div. Conn. Mental Health Ctr., 1977-80, Greater Bridgeport Community Mental Health Ctr., 1980-86; sec. Yale U., New Haven, Conn., 1987-93; pres. Catalyst, N.Y.C., 1993—; mem. plan and rev. panel Pres's. Com. Mental Health, exec. com Conn. Conf. Ind. Colls.; pres. New Haven Civil Svc. Com., Am. Coll. Mental Health Adminstrn., Human Invest Com., U.S. Vet. Adminstrn.; fellow Berkeley Coll. Contbr. articles to profl. jours. Gov. Mory's Assoc., New Haven Devel. Com.; bd. dirs. N.Y. Women's Agenda, Md. Found.'s Take Our Daughters to Work Day, Quinnipiac Coll., Shubert Performing Arts Ctr., Yale-New Haven Hosp., United Way, Lewis Walpole Libr., Yale U. Art Gallery, Yale U. Press; pres. Am. Coll. Mental Health Adminstrn., Human Investment Com., U.S. VA; mem. exec. com. Conn. Conf. Ind. Colls. Recipient New haven Mayoral Citation for Community Svc., 1981, Conn. Gov's Com. to Employ Handicapped Outstanding Svc. award, 1984, Ofcl. Citation Gen. Assembly State of Conn., 1985, Bridgeport YWCA Woman of yr. award, 1985, Spl. Citation for Pub. Svc. Gov. William O'Neill, 1986, New Haven YWCA Women in Leadership award, 1990, Marrakech Founders award, 1990, Elm Ivy award 1993. Mem. Phi Beta Kappa. Home: 55 Huntington St New Haven CT 06511 Office: Pres Catalyst 250 Park Ave S New York NY 10003

WELLINGTON, WILLIAM GEORGE, plant science and ecology educator; b. Vancouver, B.C., Can., Aug. 16, 1920; s. George and Lilly (Rae) W.; m. Margret Ellen Reiss, Sept. 22, 1959; children: Katherine Jean, Stephen Ross. B.A., U. B.C., 1941; M.A., U. Toronto, 1945, Ph.D., 1947. Meteorol. officer Can. Meteorol. Service, Toronto, 1942-45; research entomologist Can. Dept. Agr., Sault Ste. Marie, Ont., 1946-51; head bioclimatology sect. Can. Dept. Forestry, Sault Ste. Marie, Ont., Victoria, B.C., 1951-67; prin. scientist Can. Dept. Forestry, Victoria, 1964-68; prof. ecology U. Toronto, 1968-70; dir. Inst. Animal Resource Ecology, U. B.C., Vancouver, 1973-79; prof. plant sci. and resource ecology Inst. Animal Resource Ecology, U. B.C., 1970-86, hon. prof. dept. plant sci., 1986—, prof. emeritus, 1986—; Killam sr. research fellow U. B.C., 1980-81; inaugural lectr. C.E. Atwood Meml. Seminar Series, Dept. Zoology, U. Toronto, 1993. Contbr. articles to profl. jours. Named Prof. of Yr.; Faculty Agrl. Sci., U. B.C., 1986. Fellow Entomol. Soc. Can. (Gold medal 1968), Royal Soc. Can., Explorers Club; mem. Am. Meteorol. Soc. (award 1969), Entomol. Soc. Am. (C. J. Woodworth award 1979), Japanese Soc. Population Ecology, Entomol. Soc. Ont. Anglican. Club: Am. Philatelic Soc. Home: 2350 130A St, Surrey, BC Canada V4A 8Y5 Office: U BC, ARE and Dept Plant Sci, Vancouver, BC Canada V6T 1W5

WELLISCH, WILLIAM JEREMIAH, social psychology educator; b. Vienna, Austria, July 3, 1938; came to U.S., 1940; s. Max and Zelda (Schanser) W.; m. Geraldine Eve Miller (dec. Feb. 1970); children: Garth Kevin, Miriam Rhoda; m. Claudine Abbey Truman, Sept. 5, 1971; children: Rebecca Colleen, Marcus Joshua, Gabriel Jason. MA in Sociology, U. Mo., 1965, PhD in Sociology, 1968. Researcher urbanization Hemispheric Consultants, Columbia, Mo., 1968-69; cons. to local govt. ofcl. on L.Am. Bicultural Consultants, Inc., Denver, 1969-70; prof. Red Rocks Coll., Lakewood, Colo., 1970-76, 77—. Author: Bi-Cultural Development, 1971, Honduras: A Study in Sub-Development, 1978. Mem. citizen's adv. bd. Sta. KCFR Pub. Radio, Denver, 1989—. Republican. Mem. Unification Ch. Avocations: still-life photography, landscape gardening. Home: 2325 Clay St Denver CO 80211-5123 Office: Red Rocks CC 13300 W 6th Ave Lakewood CO 80401

WELLIVER, CHARLES HAROLD, hospital administrator; b. Wichita, Kans., Feb. 14, 1945; married. BA, Wichita State U., 1972, MHA, U. Mo., 1974. Asst. dir. St. Luke's Hosp., Kansas City, 1974-79, assoc. dir., 1979-80; adminstr. Spelman Meml. Hosp., Smithville, Mo., 1980-82; sr. adminstr., COO Good Samaritan Med. Ctr., Phoenix, 1982-86, v.p., CEO, 1989—; v.p., CEO Thunderbird Samaritan Hosp., Glendale, Ariz., 1986-89. Office: Good Samaritan Regional Med Ctr 1441 N 12th St Phoenix AZ 85006-2837

WELLIVER, WARREN DEE, lawyer, retired state supreme court justice; b. Butler, Mo., Feb. 24, 1920; s. Carl Winfield and Burdee Marie (Wolfe) W.; m. Ruth Rose Galey, Dec. 25, 1942; children: Gale Dee (Mrs. William B. Stone), Carla Camile (Mrs. Dayton Stone), Christy Marie. BA, U. Mo., 1945; JD, U. Mo., 1948. Bar: Mo. 1948. Asst. pros. atty. Boone County, Columbia, 1948-54; sr. ptnr. Welliver, Atkinson and Eng, Columbia, 1960-79; tchr. law Law Sch. U. Mo., 1948-49; mem. Mo. Senate, 1977-79; justice Supreme Ct. Mo., Jefferson City, 1979-89; mem. Gov. Mo. Adv. Coun. Alcoholism and Drug Abuse, chmn. drug coun., 1970-72; chmn. Task Force Revision Mo. Drug Laws, 1970-71; liaison mem. coun. Nat. Inst. Alcoholism and Alchohol Abuse, 1972-79; mem. Ctrl. Regional Adv. Coun. Comprehensive Psychiatric Svcs., 1990-92. Bd. dirs. Nat. Assn. Mental Health, 1970-76, regional v.p., 1973-76; mem. Mo. Assn. Mental Health 1968-69, Stephens Coll. Assocs., 1965-79; pres. Friends of Libr., U. Mo., 1976, bd. dirs., 1979-92; chmn. Dem. Com., 1954-64; hon. fellow Harry S. Truman Libr. Inst., 1979—; bd. dirs. Supreme Ct. Hist. Soc., 1982—; vice chair adv. bd. U. Mo. Multiple Sclerosis Inst., 1992—; bd. curators Stephen's Coll., 1980-92. With USNR, 1941-45. Recipient Disting. Alumni medal and award U. Mo., 1994. Fellow Am. Coll. Trial Lawyers, Am. Bar Found.; mem. ABA, Mo. Bar Assn. (pres. 1967-68), Boone County Bar Assn. (pres. 1970), Am. Judicature Soc., Am. Legion (past post comdr.), Multiple Sclerosis Soc. (Gateway chpt. bd. dirs. 1986-92), Order of Coif, Country Club of Mo., Columbia Country Club (past pres.). Home: 3430 Woodrail Ter Columbia MO 65203-0926

WELLMAN, CARL PIERCE, philosophy educator; b. Lynn, Mass., Sept. 3, 1926; s. Frank and Carolyn (Heath) W.; m. Farnell Parsons, June 20, 1953; children: Timothy, Philip, Lesley, Christopher. B.A., U. Ariz., 1949; M.A., Harvard U., 1951, Ph.D., 1954; postgrad., U. Cambridge, Eng., 1951-52. Instr. Lawrence U., Appleton, Wis., 1953-57; asst. prof. Lawrence U., 1957-62, assoc. prof., 1962-66 prof., chmn. dept. philosophy, 1966-68; prof. philosophy Washington U., St. Louis, 1968-88, Hortense and Tobias Lewin

Disting. prof. humanities, 1988—; Mem. rev. panel research grants NEH, 1968-71. Author: The Language of Ethics, 1961, Challenge and Response: Justification in Ethics, 1971, Morals and Ethics, 1975, Welfare Rights, 1982, A Theory of Rights, 1985, Real Rights, 1995. Recipient Uhrig Distinguished Teaching award Lawrence U., 1968; Am. Council Learned Socs. fellow, 1965-66; NEH sr. fellow, 1972-73; Nat. Humanities Center fellow, 1982-83. Mem. Am. Philos. Assn., Internat. Assn. for Philosophy Law and Social Philosophy. Home: 625 S Skinker Blvd # 902 Saint Louis MO 63105-2340

WELLMAN, HENRY NELSON, nuclear medicine specialist; b. Kans., Nov. 10, 1933; s. Henry F. and Nell M. (Burger) W.; m. Evelyn Marie Boone, Aug. 17, 1957; children: Bernadette, Karen, Anne, Maureen, Margaret, Suzanne. BS, Rockhurst Coll., 1956; MD, St. Louis U., 1960. Diplomate Am. Bd. Internal Medicine, Am. Bd. Nuclear Medicine. Intern St. Louis Univ. Hosp., 1960-61; resident pediatric medicine U. Cin., 1963-67; asst. attending div. internal medicine Cin. Gen. Hosp., 1967-70, staff physician, then attending physician, 1966-71; prof. medicine and radiology, dir. div. nuclear medicine Med. Ctr. Ind. U., 1971—; med. staff Ind. U. Hosps., Wishard Meml. Hosp., VA Hosp., Indpls.; cons. FDA, 1975-79, WHO, Belgium, Switzerland, Germany, Am. Standards Inst. subcom., Nuclear Medicine subcom.; U.S. tech. adviser Internat. Electrotech. Com., 1977-81. Contbr. numerous articles to profl. jours. Recipient Sci. Display award Ohio State Med. Assn., 1968, U.S. Sr. Scientist award Alexander Von Humboldt Found., 1979-80. Fellow ACP, Am. Coll. Radiology, Am. Coll. Nuclear Physicians, Soc. Nuclear Medicine, European Assn. Nuclear Medicine; mem. AMA (chair nuclear medicine residency rev. com. 1983-84), U.S. Pharmacopeia, Ind. State Med. Assn., Marion County Med. Soc., Ind. Roentgen Ray Soc., Alpha Omega Alpha. Home: 7651 W 88th St Indianapolis IN 46278-1109 Office: Ind Univ Med Ctr 926 W Michigan St Indianapolis IN 46202-5203

WELLMAN, RICHARD VANCE, legal educator; b. Worthington, Ohio, Sept. 10, 1922; s. Burton Singley and Blanche (Gardner) W.; m. Louise Dewey Laylin, Oct. 18, 1944 (dec. Dec. 1982); children: Martha, Anne, Jane, Sarah, Peter Burton, Charles Dewey; m. Natalie Lancaster Robertson, Dec. 12, 1983. A.B., U. Mich., 1947; J.D., 1949. Bar: Ohio 1949, Mich. 1960. Practice in Cleve., 1949-51, Mt. Vernon, Ohio, 1951-54; mem. faculty U. Mich. Law Sch., 1954-74; Alston prof. law U. Ga. Sch. Law, 1974-90, prof. emeritus, 1990—. Engaged in nat. effort to encourage state probate code revisions, 1965—; commr. Mich. Uniform State Laws, 1970-73, Ga. Uniform State Laws, 1974—; exec. dir. Joint Editorial Bd. Uniform Probate Code, 1990—. Served to 1st lt. AUS, 1943-46. Mem. Am. Bar Assn., Mich. Bar Assn., Am. Law Inst., Am. Coll. Trust and Estate Counsel. Home: 190 Tipperary Rd Athens GA 30606-3833

WELLNER, JON AUGUST, statistician, educator; b. Portland, Oreg., Aug. 17, 1945; s. Charles August and Ethel Dorothy (Wolf) W.; m. Cynthia Hickey, Mar. 21, 1992. BS in Math., U. Idaho, 1968; PhD in Stats., U. Wash., 1975. Asst. prof. stats. U. Rochester, N.Y., 1975-78, assoc. prof., 1978-83; prof. U. Wash., 1983—. Author: Empirical Processes with Applications to Statistics, 1986, Efficient and Adaptive Estimation for Semiparametric Models, 1993; contbr. articles to profl. jours. Served to lt. U.S. Army, 1969-71, Vietnam. Fellow John Simon Guggenheim Found., 1987-88. Fellow AAAS, Inst. Math. Stats. (assoc. editor Annals of Stats. 1983-89, 92-94). Avocations: mountain climbing, skiing, photography. Home: 1947 14th Ave E Seattle WA 98112-2801 Office: U Wash Dept Stats GN-22 Seattle WA 98195

WELLNER, MARCEL NAHUM, physics educator, researcher; b. Antwerp, Belgium, Feb. 8, 1930; came to U.S., 1949; s. Jules and Lucie (Rapoport) W.; m. Magdeleine Misselyn, Apr. 7, 1961; children: Pierre, Lucie. B.S., MIT, 1952; Ph.D., Princeton U., 1958. Instr. Brandeis U., Waltham, Mass., 1957-59; mem. Inst. Advanced Study, Princeton, N.J., 1959-60; research assoc. Ind. U., Bloomington, 1960-63; vis. scientist Atomic Energy Research Establishment, Harwell, Eng., 1963-64; from asst. prof. to prof. Syracuse U., 1964—. Author gen. physics textbook; contbr. numerous articles on quantum field theory to profl. jours. Mem. Am. Phys. Soc. Office: Syracuse U Dept Physics Syracuse NY 13244

WELLS, ARTHUR STANTON, manufacturing company executive; b. Kingsport, Tenn., Jan. 8, 1931; s. Arthur Stanton and Blanche Welch (Duncan) W.; m. Ellen N. Blackburn, June 15, 1957; children: Arthur S., Thomas B., Emily B., Richard R. B.S., Yale U., 1953; M.B.A., Harvard U., 1957. Fin. analyst Eastman Kodak Co., Kingsport, Tenn., 1957-65; mgr. profit analysis Xerox Corp., Rochester, N.Y., 1966-68; asst. treas. Xerox Corp., Stamford, Conn., 1969-76, treas., 1976-79; v.p. fin. Barnes Group Inc., Bristol, Conn., 1979-86, exec. v.p. fin., 1987-93, pres., CEO, dir., 1994—; bd. dirs. ValueCare Inc., Hartford. Trustee, treas. Wilton (Conn.) Libr. Assn., 1972-78; bd. dirs. New Eng. Opera Assn., 1972-78; assoc. bd. dirs. Conn. Bank and Trust Co., Hartford, 1984-90; chmn. bd. trustees, exec. com. Conn. Pub. Expenditure Coun., Inc., 1990-93. With AUS, 1953-55. Mem. Fin. Execs. Inst. Democrat. Home: 1 Wilton Crest Wilton CT 06897-4052 Office: Barnes Group Inc 123 Main St Bristol CT 06010-6307

WELLS, BEN HARRIS, retired beverage company executive; b. Saginaw, Mich., June 11, 1906; s. Ben W. and Florence (Harris) W.; m. Katherine Gladney, June 17, 1938; children: Katherine Graves, Ben Gladney. Student, Ind. U., 1922-25; A.B., U. Mich., 1929, M.A., 1931; L.H.D., Westminster Coll., 1979, U. Mo.-St. Louis, 1983. Tchr. John Burroughs Sch., St. Louis County, 1929-31, 33-38; critic tchr. U. Mich. Sch. Edn., 1931-33; with Seven-Up Co., St. Louis, 1938-78; pres. Seven-Up Co., 1965-74, chmn., 1974-78; Chmn. Consumer Research Inst., 1970-77. Pres. St. Louis Symphony Soc., 1970-78, chmn., 1978-84, v.p., 1985-89, life trustee, 1989—; pres. Laumeier Internat. Sculpture Park, St. Louis County, 1981-83; mem. community adv. bd. Sta. KWMU-Radio, U. Mo.; hon. life mem. Opera Theatre of St. Louis Bd.; bd. dirs. Community Found., 1977-87, St. Louis Conservatory and Schs. for Arts, 1979—, 1st St. Forum, 1979-89, Winston Churchill Meml. and Library, Fulton, Mo., Am. Symphony Orch. League, 1987—, Music Assocs. of Aspen (Colo.), 1979-87, others. Recipient Mo. Arts award, 1984, (with Katherine Gladney Wells) Lifetime Achievement in the Arts award St. Louis Arts and Edn. Coun., 1994. Mem. Nat. Assn. Mfrs. (bd. dirs. 1969-73), Grocery Mfrs. Am. (bd. dirs. 1969-77), St. Louis Symphony Orch. (hon. life), Am. Fedn. Musicians (hon. mem. musicians local), Phi Beta Kappa, Sigma Chi. Clubs: St. Louis, Bellerive Country, Bogey, Noonday, University, Racquet Club (St. Louis). Lodge: Rotary. Office: 560 Trinity At Delmar Saint Louis MO 63130 *Whatever I have accomplished has been done through people—good people, and expecting good people to do their best.*

WELLS, BENJAMIN GLADNEY, lawyer; b. St. Louis, Nov. 13, 1943; s. Benjamin Harris and Katherine Emma (Gladney) W.; m. Nancy Kathryn Harpster, June 7, 1967; children: Barbara Gladney, Benjamin Harpster. BA magna cum laude, Amherst (Mass.) Coll., 1965; JD cum laude, Harvard U., 1968. Bar: Ill. 1968, Tex. 1973, U.S. Tax Ct. 1973, U.S. Ct. Claims 1975, U.S. Ct. Appeals (5th cir.) 1981, U.S. Dist. Ct. (so. dist.) Tex. 1985, U.S. Dist. Ct. (we. dist.) Tex. 1993. Assoc. Kirkland & Ellis, Chgo., 1968-69; assoc. to ptnr. Baker & Botts, L.L.P., Houston, 1973—; mem. Harvard Legal Aid Bur., 1966-68. Contbr. articles to profl. jours. Mem. devel. com. St. John's Sch., Houston, 1987—; chmn. planned giving com., 1987—; active Harvard Legal Aid Bureau, 1966-68. Served U.S. Army, 1969-72. Mem. Houston Tax Roundtable (pres. 1994-95), The Forest Club, The Houston Club, Phi Beta Kappa. Presbyterian. Office: Baker & Botts LLP One Shell Plaza 910 Louisiana St Houston TX 77002-4995

WELLS, CAROLYN CRESSY, social work educator; b. Boston, July 26, 1943; d. Harris Shipman Wells and Marianne Elizabeth (Monroe) Glazier; m. Dale Reed Konle, Oct. 11, 1970 (div. Sept. 3, 1982); m. Dennis Alan Loeffler, Sept. 29, 1990. BA, U. Calif., Berkeley, 1965; MSW, U. Wis., 1968, PhD, 1993. Cert. ind. clin. social worker, marriage and family therapist. Vol. VISTA, Espanola, N.Mex., 1965-66; social worker Project Six Cen. Wis. Colony, Madison, 1968, Milw. Dept. Pub. Welfare, 1969, Shorewood (Wis.) Manor Nursing Home, 1972; sch. social worker Jefferson (Wis.) County Spl. Edn., 1977-78; lectr. sociology and social work Marquette U., Milw., 1972-73; dir. social work program, 1973-90, 93—; assoc. prof. social work, 1981-94, prof. social work, 1994—; social work therapist Lighthouse Counseling

Assocs., Racine, Wis., 1989-91, The Cambridge Group, 1991-92; Achievement Assocs., 1992—; vis. lectr. social work U. Canterbury, Christchurch, N.Z., 1983. Author: Social Work Day to Day, 1982, rev. edit., 1988, Social Work Ethics Day to Day, 1986; co-author: The Social Work Experience, 1991. Mem. NASW, Am. Assn. for Marriage and Family Therapy, Am. Assn. Profl. Hypnotherapists, Coun. on Social Work Edn. (publs. and media com. 1989-91, site vis. for accreditation 1987—), Acad. Cert. Social Workers, Assn. Baccalaureate Program Dirs., Wis. Coun. on Social Work Edn. (pres. 1980-82, sec. 1985-87, mem. exec. com. 1993). Democrat. Avocations: writing, silent sports. Home: 4173 Sleeping Dragon Rd West Bend WI 53095 Office: Marquette U Social Work Program 526 N 14th St Milwaukee WI 53233-2211

WELLS, CHARLES WILLIAM, utility executive; b. Springfield, Ill., June 25, 1934; s. William Ward and Maxine Deloris (Harris) W.; m. Lois Vasconcelles, Mar. 5, 1954; children: David, Susan, Amy. Student, Springfield Jr. Coll., 1952-54; B.S. in Elec. Engring., U. Ill., 1956; M.B.A., 1977. With Ill. Power Co., 1958—, v.p., 1972-76, exec. v.p., 1976—, also dir. Served with USN, 1956-58. Presbyterian. Clubs: Country of Decatur, Decatur Racquet. Home: 403 Southmoreland Pl Decatur IL 62521-3745 Office: Ill Power Co 500 S 27th St Decatur IL 62525

WELLS, CHRISTINE, foundation executive; b. Grayling, Mich., Aug. 6, 1948; d. Chester John and Mary W. BA, Mich. State U., 1970, MLIR, 1982; MLS, U. Mich., 1976. Head libr. Lansing State Jour., E. Lansing, Mich., 1973-82; mng. editor libr. svcs. USA TODAY, Washington, 1982-87; libr. dir. Gannett Co., Inc., Washington, 1985-87, chief staff, chmn. and CEO office, 1988-89; v.p. adminstrn. Gannett Found., Washington, 1989-90; v.p. internat. The Freedom Forum, Washington, 1991—; exec. dir. The Newseum, 1993-94; sr. v.p. The Freedom Forum, 1994—. Recipient Dising. Alumni award U. Mich., 1991. Mem. ALA, Spl. Librs. Assn. (Profl. award 1994). Office: The Freedom Forum 1101 Wilson Blvd Arlington VA 22209-2248

WELLS, CHRISTOPHER BRIAN, lawyer; b. Belleville, Ill., Jan. 23, 1948; s. Frederick Meyers and Ethel Pauline (Morris) W.; m. Gaynelle Vansandt, June 6, 1970. BA in Econs., U. Kans., BS in Bus., 1973, JD. Enforcement atty. SEC, Seattle, 1977-82; ptnr. Lane, Powell, Moss & Miller, Seattle, 1982—. Served to capt. U.S. Army, 1973-77. Mem. ABA, Wash. State Bar Assn., King County Trial Lawyers Assn., Wash. Soc. CPA's., Kans. Bar Assn. Democrat. Office: Lane Powell Spears Lubersky 1420 5th Ave Ste 4100 Seattle WA 98101-2338

WELLS, CLYDE KIRBY, Canadian provincial government official; b. Buchans Junction, Newfoundland, Nov. 9, 1937; s. Ralph and Maude (Kirby) W. B.A. in polit. sci., Meml. U., 1959; LL.B., Dalhousie U. Law Sch., 1962. Bar: N.S. 1963, Nfld. 1964. Pvt. practice, 1964-66; rep. dist. Humber East Nfld. Ho. of Assembly, 1966; mem. cabinet Premier Joseph R. Smallwood, 1966-68; pvt. practice, 1968-77; rep. from Nfld. Can. Bar Assn. com. constitutional changes, 1977-79; counsel to fed. govt. and Nfld. Supreme Ct., 1979-87; elected leader Liberal Party of Nfld. and Labrador, 1987; mem. Ho. of Assembly for dist. Windsor-Buchans, 1987; premier Nfld. and Labrador, 1989—; mem. Bay of Islands, 1989—. Liberal. Office: Office of Premier, Confederation Bldg 8th Fl, Saint John's, NF Canada A1B 4J6

WELLS, DAMON, JR., investment company executive; b. Houston, May 20, 1937; s. Damon and Margaret Corinne (Howze) W.; BA magna cum laude, Yale U., 1958; BA, Oxford U., 1964, MA, 1968; PhD, Rice U., 1968. Owner, CEO Damon Wells Interests, Houston, 1958—, pres., Damon Wells Found., 1993—. Bd. dirs. Child Guidance Ctr. of Houston, 1970-73; trustee Christ Ch. Cathedral Endowment Fund, 1970-73, 84-88, chmn., 1987-88, Kinkaid Sch., 1972-86, Kinkaid Sch. Endowment Fund, 1981-86; hon. friend of Somerville Coll., Oxford U., 1988—; mem. Sr. Common Room, Pembroke Coll., Oxford U. 1972—; trustee Camp Allen retreat of Episc. Diocese of Tex., 1976-78; founding bd. dirs. Brit. Inst. U.S., 1979-80; mem. pres.'s coun. Tex. A&M U., 1983-89. Named Hon. Comdr. Most Excellent Order of Brit. Empire by Her Majesty Queen Elizabeth II, 1991, Outstanding Alumnus Yr. by Kinkaid Sch., 1994. Fellow Jonathan Edwards Coll. (assoc.), Yale U., 1982—; hon. fellow Pembroke Coll., Oxford U., 1984—. Mem. English-Speaking Union (nat. dir. 1970-72, v.p. Houston br. 1966-73), Coun. Fgn. Rels., Phi Beta Kappa, Pi Sigma Alpha. Episcopalian. Clubs: Houston Country, Houston, Yale (N.Y.C.), United Oxford and Cambridge U. (London); Cosmos (Washington), Buck's (London), Coronado (Houston), Little Ship Club (London). Author: Stephen Douglas: The Last Years, 1857-1861, 1971 (Tex. Writer's Roundup prize 1971), paperback edit., 1990. Home: 5555 Del Monte Dr Houston TX 77056-4116 Office: 2001 Kirby Dr Ste 806 Houston TX 77019-6033

WELLS, DANIEL RUTH, physics educator; b. N.Y.C., May 2, 1921; s. Daniel R. and Charlotte T. (Danziger) W.; m. Mary E. O'Connell, 1944; children: Donna Mary, Christina Mary. BME, Cornell U., 1942; MS, NYU, 1953; PhD, Stevens Inst. Tech., 1963. Instrument rated comml. pilot. Aero. engr. Chance-Vought Aircraft, Stratford, Conn., 1942-43; aero. engr. Sunsdet Aircraft, N.Y.C., 1943; engr. Indsl. Tng. Co., N.Y.C, 1946-50; design engr. Republic Aircraft, L.I., N.Y., 1950-52; physicist Plasma Physics Lab. Princeton U., 1955-63; assoc. prof. physics U. Miami, Fla., 1963-66, prof. physics, 1966-92, prof. emeritus; nuclear physicist rsch. div. NYU, N.Y.C., 1952-53; assoc. prof. physics Seton Hall U., South Orange, N.J., 1962-63; cons. U.S. Army Piccatiny (N.J.) Arsenal, 1968-70, Sandia Labs. (N.Mex.), 1972-73, various Fla. cos., 1973—. Contbr. numerous articles to profl. jours.; patentee in field. 1st lt. U.S. Army Air Force, 1943-46. Recipient AFOSR (1964-73) and NSF (1973-78) grants for plasma rsch. Mem. Am. Phys. Soc., Sigma Xi, Theta Chi, Sigma Pi Sigma. Avocations: flying, boating, tennis, golf. Home: 6950 SW 62nd St Miami FL 33143-1842 Office: U Miami Physics Dept PO Box 248046 Miami FL 33124-8046

WELLS, DEWEY WALLACE, lawyer; b. Raleigh, N.C., Oct. 14, 1929; s. B.C. and Alma (Blanchard) W.; m. Ann D. Wells, Aug 25, 1951; children: Robert, Betty W., Daniel, Brady, Jeff. AA, Mars Hill Coll., 1950; BS, Wake Forest U., 1952, JD, 1954. Bar: N.C. 1954, U.S. Dist. Ct. (ea. dist.) N.C. 1960, U.S. Ct. Appeals (4th cir.) 1961, U.S. Dist. Ct. (mid. dist.) N.C. 1985. Exec. sec. N.C. Jud. Council, Raleigh, 1954-55; trust officer Planter's Nat. Bank & Trust Co., Rocky Mt., N.C., 1955-57; ptnr. LeRoy, Wells, Shaw, Hornthal & Riley, Elizabeth City, N.C. 1958-85, Womble, Carlyle, Sandridge & Rice, Winston Salem, N.C., 1985—; judge Superior Ct., 1st Jud. Dist. N.C., 1974. 1st lt. USAR, 1954-58. Fellow Am. Coll. Trial Lawyers, Am. Bar Found.; mem. ABA, N.C. Bar Assn. (pres. 1980-81), N.C. Natural Heritage Trust (trustee), Rotary. Republican. Baptist. Home: 1890 Pilot Ridge Rd Collettsville NC 28611 Office: Womble Carlyle Sandridge & Rice PO Drawer 84 1600 Southern Nat Fin Ctr Winston Salem NC 27102-0084

WELLS, DONALD EUGENE, hospital administrator; b. Phoenix, May 10, 1940; married. BHA, Ga. State U., 1970, MHA, 1972. Adminstrv. resident Emory Univ. Hosp., Atlanta, 1971-72, asst. adminstr., 1972-77, assoc. adminstr., 1977-78, dep. exec. dir., 1978-81, adminstrv. dir., 1981-91, exec. dir., 1991—. Mem. Ga. Hosp. Assn. (del., mem. coms.). Office: Emory U Hosp 1364 Clifton Rd NE Atlanta GA 30322-1102

WELLS, EDWARD PHILLIPS, radiologist; b. Hanover, N.H., Oct. 4, 1916; s. Harry Artemas and Madeleine Roberta (Lucky) W.; m. Barbara Mix, Jan. 25, 1941; children: James C., Phyllis L. Fahey, Lucinda W. Graves, Patricia Wells-Bogue, Kenneth R. BA, Dartmouth Coll., 1939; MD, NYU, 1942. Diplomate Am. Bd. Radiology. Intern rotating Mary Hitchcock Hosp., Hanover, N.H., 1942-43; maj. U.S. Army Med. Corps, 1943-46; resident in radiology Mary Hitchcock Hosp., Hanover, 1946-48; radiologist Rutland (Vt.) Hosp., 1949-51, North Shore Radiol. Assoc., Danvers, Mass., 1951-82; adj. radiologist Hitchcock Hosp., Hanover, 1982-82; intermittent radiologist V.A. Hosp., White River Junction, Vt., 1984-94. Named to U.S. Olympic Ski Team, 1940. Mem. AMA, New Eng. Med. Assn., Vt. Med. Assn., N.H. Med. Assn., Lake Mitchell Trout Club, Black Brook Salmon Club. Avocations: trout and salmon fishing. Home: Old Farm Rd HCR 63 Box 502 Grantham NH 03753

WELLS, EVERETT CLAYTON, JR., economic development executive; b. Hopkinsville, Ky., May 11, 1954; s. Everett Clayton and Lois Gertrude

(Aday) W.; m. Suzanne Walden. BS, Murray State U., 1977; postgrad., Memphis State U., 1978. Credit mgr. Dunlap Sales, Hopkinsville, 1979-85; asst. exec. dir. Hopkinsville C. of C., 1985-86; exec. dir. Hopkinsville Christian County C. of C., 1986-87; sr. econ. devel. coord. Mcpl. Electric Authority of Ga., Atlanta, 1987—; bd. dirs., vice-chmn. of promotions Ky. Western Waterways, Grand Rivers, 1986-87. Pres. Murray State U. Alumni Assn., 1985-86. Mem. Nat. Assn. Corp. Real Estate Execs. Profl., Am. Econ. Devel. Coun., Ga. C. of C. Execs. Assn., Ga. Indsl. Developers (chmn. Vol. of Yr. com. 1991), So. Indsl. Devel. Coun. (alt. state bd. dirs. 1993, bd. dirs. 1992-95, exec. com. 1995), Rotary (pub. rels. chmn. 1981-82, chmn. youth com. 1986-87, free enterprise chmn. 1986-87), Little River Rd. Runner's Club (co-founder, pres. 1981-83, state rep. 1983-88). Republican. Baptist. Avocations: running, basketball, reading, weight lifting. Home: 6507 Bermuda Ln Flowery Branch GA 30542-3108 Office: Mcpl Electric Authority Ga Ste 2105 285 Peachtree Ctr Ave Atlanta GA 30303

WELLS, FAY R., food products executive; b. 1925. Attended, U. Iowa, 1946-50. With Wells Dairy, Inc., Le Mars, Iowa, 1951—, ptnr., 1954-77, pres., 1977-80, chmn. bd. dirs., 1980—. With U.S. Army, 1943-46. Office: Wells Dairy Inc 1 Blue Bunny Dr Le Mars IA 51031*

WELLS, FRED D., food products executive; b. 1925. With Wells Dairy, Inc., Le Mars, Iowa, 1946—, ptnr., 1954-77, v.p., 1977-80, pres., 1980—. With U.S. Army, 1943-46. Office: Wells Dairy Inc 1 Blue Bunny Dr Le Mars IA 51031*

WELLS, GEORGE DOUGLAS, corporate executive; b. Clydebank, Scotland, Aug. 6, 1935; came to U.S., 1960; m. Roberta S. Rennie, 1959; children: Carole, George Leslie, Neil. BSc with honors, U. Glasgow, Scotland, 1957, MS, 1959. With Fairchild Camera & Instrument Corp., Mountain View, Calif., successively gen. mgr. diode div., gen. mgr. transistor div., gen. mgr. discrete group, gen. mgr. analog and discrete group, sr. v.p., from 1977, exec. v.p., until 1983; pres. Intersil Inc. div. GE, Cupertino, Calif., 1983-85; pres., chief oper. officer, mem. Office Chief Exec. L.S.I. Logic Corp., Milpitas, Calif., 1985-92; pres., CEO Exar Corp., 1992—. Home: 14580 Carnelian Cir Saratoga CA 95070-5966 Office: LSI Logic Corp 1551 Mccarthy Blvd Milpitas CA 95035-7424

WELLS, HERMAN B., university chancellor; b. Jamestown, Ind., June 7, 1902; s. Joseph Granville and Anna (Harting) W. Student, U. Ill., 1920-21; BS, Ind. U., 1924, AM, 1927, LLD, 1962; postgrad., U. Wis., 1927-28, LLD (hon.), 1946; LLD (hon.), Butler U., Rose Poly. Inst., DePauw U., 1939, Wabash Coll., 1942, Earlham, 1948, Valparaiso U., 1953, Miami U., Tri-State Coll., 1959, U. Louisville, 1961, Franklin Coll., Anderson Coll., 1962, Ball State Tchrs. Coll., Washington U., 1963, U. Notre Dame, St. Joseph's Coll., U. Calif., Ind. State Coll., 1964, Drury Coll., 1968, Columbia, 1969, Chgo. Circle Campus U. Ill., 1973, Howard U., 1976, U. S.C. 1980, L.H.D. 1963, Marian Coll., 1970; hon. doctorate in edn., Coll. Edn., Bangkok, 1968. Asst. cashier First Nat. Bank, Lebanon, Ind., 1924-26; asst. dept. econs. U. Wis., 1927-28; field sec. Ind. Bankers Assn. 1928-31; sec., research dir. Study Commn. for Ind. Fin. Instns., 1931-33; instr. econs. Ind. U., 1930-33, asst. prof., 1933-35, prof. adminstrn. sch. bus. adminstrn., 1935-72, dean sch. bus. adminstrn., 1935-37, acting pres. sch. bus. adminstrn., 1937-1938, pres. sch. bus. adminstrn., 1938-62, univ. chancellor, 1962—, interim pres., 1968; supr. div. of banks and trust cos., div. of research and statistics Ind. Dept. Fin. Instns., 1933-35; sec. Commn. for Ind. Fin. Instns. 1933-36; chmn. Ind. U. Found., 1937-62, 69-72, vice chmn., 1975—, pres., 1962-69, chmn. exec. com., 1969—; chmn. Fed. Home Loan Bank of Indpls., 1940-71; dir. Ind. Bell Telephone Co., 1951-72, Chemed Corp., 1970—, Lilly Endowment, Inc., 1973—; Spl. advisor on Liberated Areas, U.S. Dept. State, 1944; cons. U.S. delegation San Francisco Conf. for Am. Council on Edn., 1945; Mem. Allied Missions for Observation Greek elections, rank of Minister, 1946; adviser on cultural affairs to mil. gov. U.S. Zone, Germany, 1947-48; del. 12th Gen. Assembly of UN, 1957; adviser Ministry Edn. Pakistan, 1959; head U.S. delegation SEATO Prep. Commn. on Univ. Problems, Bangkok, 1960; mem. UN com. experts to rev. activities and orgn. UN Secretariat, 1960-61, Nat. Citizen's Commn. Internat. Cooperation, Com. Econ. Devel., 1958-61; chmn. legislature's com. higher edn. State N.Y., 1963-64; mem. Pres.'s Com. U.S. Soviet Trade Relations, 1965; mem. rev. com. on Haile Sellassie I U., Addis Ababa, 1966-75; mem. pres.'s Spl. Com. on Overseas Vol. Activities, 1967; mem. Nat. Commn. on U.S.-China Relations, 1969; tech. adv. bd. Milbank Meml. Fund, 1973-78; Ex-pres. Nat. Assn. State Univs., State U. Assn.; exec. com. Am. Council on Edn. (chmn. council), 1944-45; mem. 1st bd. regents Am. Savs. & Loan Inst. Grad. Sch. Savs. and Loan.; Trustee Edn. and World Affairs, 1963-71, chmn., 1963-70; trustee Howard U., 1956-75, Am. U. at Cairo, 1957-75, Ind. Inst. Tech. (emeritus), Earlham Coll. (hon.), Carnegie Found. for Advancement Teaching, 1941-62; former mem. adv. council Am. Sch. of Madrid; mem. nat. com. on govt. fin. Brookings Instn.; bd. visitors Tulane U.; chmn. Aerospace Research Applications Center, Ind. U., 1962-72; nat. bd. dirs. Goodwill Industries Am., 1962-69; bd. dirs. James Whitcomb Riley Meml. Assn. (hon. chmn.), Sigma Nu Ednl. Found., 1946—, Arthur M. Retz Foundation (v.p.), Learning Resources Inst., 1959-65, Council on Library Resources, Historic Landmarks Found. Ind., 1974—; chmn. adv. com. Acad. in Pub. Service, 1976-83; founder, active mem. Ind. Acad., 1971—. Author: (with others) Report of Study Commission for Indiana Financial Institutions, 1932, Being Lucky: Reminiscences and Reflections, 1980, articles in mags. Recipient Distinguished Service award Ind. Jr. C. of C., 1938; 1st ann. award N.Y. Alumni chpt. Beta Gamma Sigma, 1939; Gold medal award Internat. Benjamin Franklin Soc., 1959; Comdrs. Cross of Order of Merit Germany, 1960; Radio Sta. WHAS Ind. Man of Year, 1960; Man of Year awards Indpls. Times, 1961; Man of Yr. awards Ind. Optometric Assn., 1961; comdr. Most Exalted Order White Elephant, Thailand, 1962; knight comdr. 2d class Most Noble Order Crown, 1968, Most Exalted Order of White Elephant, Thailand, 1986; Nat. Interfrat. Conf. award, 1962; Hoosier of Yr. award Sons of Ind. in N.Y., 1963; Interfrat. Service award Lambda Chi Alpha, 1964; Robins of Am. award, 1964; Distinguished Service Sch. Adminstrn. award Am. Assn. Sch. Adminstrs., 1965; Ind. Arts award, 1977; Liberty Bell award, 1978, Lifetime Achievement award Ind. Coun. Fund-Raising Execs., 1985; Disting. award for Lifetime Achievement Am. Coun. on Edn., 1985; Diamond Jubilee award Kappa Alpha Psi, 1986; Hon. mem. United Steelworkers Am., 33d, 30. Nat. Exchange Clubs, DeMolay Legion of Honor, 1975; hon. v.p. AM. Sunday Sch. Union; recipient Ind. U. medal, 1989; Great Am. Traditions award B'nai B'rith Internat., 1991, Lifetime Achievement award Entrepreneur of Yr., 1992, Maynard K. Hine medal Ind. U.-Purdue U. Indpls., 1993. Fellow Internat. Coll. Dentists (hon.), Am. Coll. Dentists (hon.), AAUP, Am. Philos. Soc., Am. Assn. Sch. Adminstrs., Royal Soc. Art London (Benjamin Franklin fellow), Am. Econ. Assn., Internat. Assn. Univs. (v. 1955-60), Am. Research Inst. for Arts (chmn. bd. 1975-77), Nat. Commn. on Humanities (vice chmn. 1964-65), Ind. Acad. Social Scis. (past pres.), Ind. Soc. of Chgo., Ind. Soc. Pioneers, Ind. Hist. Soc. (dir. 1968—), Ind. Tchrs. Assn., Mortar Bd., Blue Key, Phi Beta Kappa, Phi Mu Alpha, Kappa Delta Pi, Beta Gamma Sigma, Alpha Kappa Psi, Kappa Kappa Psi, Sigma Nu (regent 1968-70). Methodist (trustee). Clubs: Mason (33 deg.), Kiwanian (hon.), Rotarian (hon.), Athenaeum; Columbia (Indpls.), Athletic (Indpls.); Century Assn. (N.Y.C.), University (N.Y.C.); University (Chgo.); Cosmos (Washington). Home: 1321 E 10th St Bloomington IN 47408-3964 Office: Ind U Owen Hall Office of Chancellor Bloomington IN 47405

WELLS, HERSCHEL JAMES, physician, former hospital administrator; b. Kirkland, Ala., Feb. 23, 1924; s. Alymer James and Martha Thelma (Cross) W.; m. Carmen Ruth Williams, Aug. 5, 1946; children: Judith Alliece Wells Jarecki, Pamela Elliece Wells McKinven, Joanne Olivia Wells Bennett. Student, Emory U., 1941-42, U. Ark., 1942-43; MD, U. Tenn. 1946. Rotating intern, then resident internal medicine Wayne County Gen. Hosp. (and Infirmary), Eloise, Mich., 1946-50; dir. infirmary div. Wayne County Gen. Hosp. (and Infirmary), 1955-65, gen. supt., 1965-74; dir. Wayne County Gen. Hosp. (Walter P. Reuther Meml. Long Term Care Facility), 1974-78; rev. physician DDS, SSA, Traverse City, Mich., 1978—. Served to maj. M.C. AUS, 1948-55. Mem. AMA, Mich. Med. Soc., Am. Fedn. Clin. Rsch., Masons (32 deg.), Alpha Kappa Kappa, Pi Kappa Alpha. Home and Office: 9651 N3 Rd Copemish MI 49625

WELLS, HOYT MELLOR, manufacturing executive; b. 1926; married. BME, U. Nebr., 1949, MME, 1951. V.p Goodyear Can. Inc., 1972; with Goodyear Tire & Rubber Co., 1951—, from v.p. to exec. v.p., from 1980, pres., COO, vice-chmn. the bd., pres., COO, 1994-95; ret., 1995. Office: Goodyear Tire & Rubber Co 1144 E Market St Akron OH 44316-0001

WELLS, J. LYLE, JR., bank executive. V. chmn. United Mo. Bank, Kansas City. Office: United Mo Bank 1010 Grand Blvd Kansas City MO 64106-2220*

WELLS, JAMES M., III, bank executive; b. 1946. Student, U. N.C., Rutgers U., U. Colo. Mgmt. trainee United Va. Bankshares, 1968-71, corporate adminstrv. officer, sec., 1971; br. officer, mgr. United Va. Bankshares/State-Planters, 1971-74; v.p. and treas. United Va. Mortgage Corp., 1974-79; pres., CEO United Va. Leasing Corp., 1974-79; exec. v.p. United Va. Bank, Norfolk, Va., 1979-83, pres. Ea. region, 1983-85, exec. v.p. corporate banking, 1985-86, exec. v.p. banking group, 1986-88; pres. Crestar Fin Corp, Richmond, Va., 1988—. Office: Crestar Fin Corp 919 E Main St PO Box 26665 Richmond VA 23261-6665

WELLS, JEFFREY M., state senator, lawyer, judge; b. Springfield, Mass., Sept. 26, 1948; s. William and Paulina Wells; m. Sherri; children: Pamela, Kimberly, Tom. BA, Duke U., 1970; MBA, Fla. State U., 1972, J.D., 1974. Ptnr. firm Wilder & Wells, P.C., Colorado Springs, 1974—; mem. Colo. State Senate, 1982—, majority leader, 1987—. Mem. El Paso Bar Assn., Colo. Bar Assn., Fla. Bar Assn., Colo. Trial Lawyers Assn., Moose Club. Republican. Presbyterian. Office: Wilder & Wells 524 S Cascade Ave Ste 1 Colorado Springs CO 80903-3992 Office: Office State Senate State Capitol Denver CO 80203

WELLS, JOEL FREEMAN, editor, author; b. Evansville, Ind., Mar. 17, 1930; s. William Jackson and Edith (Strasell) W.; m. Elizabeth Louise Hein, June 5, 1952; children: William, Eugenia, Susan, Steven, Daniel. A.B. in Journalism, U. Notre Dame, 1952; Litt.D. (hon.), Rosary Coll., 1980. Advt. and promotion dir. Thomas More Assn., Chgo., 1955-64; v.p. Thomas More Assn., 1967—, dir., 1968—; editor The Critic, Chgo., 1964-80; editor-in-chief Thomas More Press, Chgo., 1975-94; lectr. grad. dept. library sci. Rosary Coll., River Forest, Ill., 1964-67; mem. assoc. grad. faculty Loyola U., Chgo., 1984—. Author: Grim Fairy Tales for Adults: Parodies of the Literary Lions, 1967, A Funny Thing Happened To The Church, 1969, Under the Spreading Heresy, 1971, The Bad Children's Book, 1972, Second Collection, 1973, Here's to the Family, 1977, How To Survive with Your Teenager, 1982, Coping in the 80s: Eliminating Needless Stress and Guilt, 1986, No Rolling in the Aisles, 1987, Who Do You Think You Are?, 1989, The Manger Mouse, 1990; also articles. revs.; editor: Pilgrim's Regress, 1979; co-editor: anthologies Bodies and Souls, 1961, (with Dan Herr) Blithe Spirits, 1962, Bodies and Spirits, 1964, Through Other Eyes, 1965, Moments of Truth, 1966, Contrasts, 1972; contbr. to: Ann Landers Ency., A to Z, 1978. Served to lt. (j.g.) USNR, 1952-55. Home: 1500 Oak Ave # 5D Evanston IL 60201-4217 Office: Thomas More Assn 500 W Monroe St Chicago IL 60606-5013

WELLS, JOHN ANDREW, retail executive; b. Ft. Smith, Ark., Apr. 11, 1926; s. Aubrey J. and Bertie Lee (Stout) W.; m. Ila Marie Degen, Aug. 21, 1944; children: Alice Jane Wells Randall, John A. Jr. BSBA, U. Ark., 1949. Sect. mgr. J.C. Penney, Ft. Smith, 1949-54; sect. mgr. J.C. Penney, Oklahoma City, 1954-57, store mgr., 1963-65; sales, mdse. mgr. J.C. Penney, San Antonio, 1957-59, store mgr., 1959-63; dist. mgr. J.C. Penney, Dallas, 1965-68, sr. v.p. real estate and constrn svcs., 1988—; dist. mgr. J.C. Penney, Atlanta, 1968-69, regional v.p., 1978-86; dist. mgr. J.C. Penney, New Orleans, 1969-71, Tampa, Fla., 1972; coord. full line dept. J.C. Penney, N.Y.C., 1973-77, mgr. retail mktg., 1974-75, dir. treasury stores and supermarkets, 1976-77, sr. v.p. dir. mktg., 1986-87, sr. v.p. real estate and constrn. svcs., 1987; sr. v.p. real estate and constrn. svcs. J.C. Penney, Dallas, 1988—. Served with USN, 1944-46, PTO. Mem. Atlanta Athletic Club, Gleneagles Club. Republican. Methodist. Avocations: golf, gardening, woodworking. Office: J C Penney Co Inc 6501 Legacy Dr Plano TX 75024-3612

WELLS, JUDEE ANN, lawyer; b. Claremont, Okla., June 10, 1951. BS, S.W. Mo. State Coll., 1972; JD, U. Tex., 1977; LLM, NYU, 1985. Bar: Tex. 1977, Wash. 1978. Assoc. Strassburger & Price, Dallas, 1977-78; assoc. prof. Pacific Luth. U., Tacoma, Wash., 1978-79; tax atty. Exxon, Houston, 1979-81; assoc. Atlantic Richfield, Dallas, 1981-84; ptnr. Foster, Pepper & Shefelman, Seattle, 1985—; bd. dirs., officer Harrison Pub., Bellevue, Wash. Author: Real Estate Excise Tax, 1991. Mem. ABA, Wash. State Bar Assn., Tex. State Bar Assn. Office: Foster Pepper & Shefelman 1111 3rd Ave Ste 3400 Seattle WA 98101

WELLS, KITTY (MURIEL DEASON WRIGHT), country western singer; b. Nashville, Aug. 30, 1919; d. Charles Carey and Murtle Bell (Street) Deason; m. Johnnie Robert Wright, Oct. 30, 1937; children: Ruby Jean Wright Taylor, Bobby, Carol Sue Wright-Sturdivant. Grad. high sch. Country music singer; sang gospel in chs. as a child; performed on radio, early 1930s; with John and Jack and the Tenn. Mountain Boys, late 1930's-early 1940's, regular on Grand Ole Opry, from 1952, now with Johnny Wright, Bobby Wright and the Tennessee Mountain Boys; songs include: Release Me, It Wasn't God Who Made Honky Tonk Angels, Making Believe; author: Kitty Wells Cookbook. Bd. dirs. Nashville Meml. Hosp. Recipient award as number 1 female singer Cashbox Mag., 1953-62, Billboard 1954-65, award of yr. for top female country vocalist Record World mag. 1965, award for highest artistic achievement in rec. arts 1964, various awards Downbeat mag., 1964, Woman of Yr. award 1974, named Top Female Artist of Decade, Record World mag. 1974, named to Country Music Hall of Fame 1976. Mem. Country Music Assn., Nat. Assn. Rec. Arts and Scis. Mem. Ch. of Christ. First woman to hit No. 1 on the country charts with "It Wasn't God Who Made Honky Tonk Angels." Office: 240 Old Hickory Blvd Madison TN 37115

WELLS, LEONARD NATHANIEL DAVID, JR., lawyer; b. Akron, Ohio, Aug. 24, 1914; s. Leonard Nathaniel David and Lida Holmes (Carr) W.; m. Louise Cauker, July 31, 1937; children—Leonard Nathaniel David III, Sarah Ann (Bennett), Lida Louise (Angione), Joe Cauker. B.A., Tex. Christian U., 1934; LL.B., Columbia U., 1937. Bar: Tex. 1937. Regional atty. for NLRB, St. Louis, 1939-41; sr. atty. NLRB, Washington, 1941-44; assoc. dir. field div. NLRB, 1944-46; founding ptnr. Mullinax, Wells, Baab & Cloutman (and predecessors), Dallas, 1947-89; gen. counsel Tex. State Fedn. Labor, 1947-57; counsel So. Conf. Teamsters, 1956-92; monitor Internat. Brotherhood Teamsters, 1958-59; bd. dirs. lawyers coordinating com. AFL-CIO, 1984-93. Trustee Gulf Coast Trades Ctr., 1990—. Mem. Am. Bar Assn. Hon. mem. Ho. of Dels. 1959-60, chmn. labor law sect. 1954-55), Tex. State Bar (chmn. labor law sect. 1951-52). Democrat. Home: 7525 Fisher Rd Dallas TX 75214-2908 Office: 3301 Elm St Dallas TX 75226

WELLS, LINDA ANN, editor-in-chief; b. N.Y.C., Aug. 9, 1958; d. H. Wayne and Jean (Burchell) W.; m. Charles King Thompson, Nov., 1993. BA in English, Trinity Coll., 1980. Edit. asst. Vogue Mag., N.Y., 1980-83, assoc. editor beauty, 1983-85; style reporter New York Times, N.Y.C., 1985, beauty editor, food editor, 1985-90; founding editor, editor-in-chief Allure Mag., N.Y.C., 1990—; speaker Am. Womens' Econ. Devel. N.Y., 1988-89. Contbr. numerous articles to N.Y. Times Mag., Allure Mag., 1985—. Chmn. N.Y. Shakespeare Festival, 1993, 94. Recipient Fragrance Found. award, 1991, Nat. Mag. Design award, 1994, Legal Def. and Edn. Fund Equal Opportunity award NOW, 1994. Mem. Am. Soc. Mag. Editors (bd. dirs. 1993—). Office: Allure Mag Condé Nast Publs 360 Madison Ave New York NY 10017-3136

WELLS, LINTON, II, federal official; b. Luanda, Angola, Apr. 7, 1946; s. Linton and Helen Fay (Gillis) W.; m. Linda Marie Motta; children: Linton III, Frank. BS in Physics and Oceanography, U.S. Naval Acad., 1967; MSE in Math. Scis., PhD in Internat. Rels., Johns Hopkins U., 1975; student, Boueikeushusho (Japanese Nat. Def. Coll.), Tokyo. Commd. ensign USN, 1967; commdr. USS Joseph Strauss, 1984-86, Destroyer Squadron 21, 1989-91; advanced through grades to capt. USN, 1994, ret., 1994; asst. to under

sec. for policy Dept. Def., The Pentagon, Washington, 1991-93, dept. to under sec. for policy, 1993—. Decorated Def. Superior Svc. medal, Legion of Merit (2), others; recipient C.N.G. Hendrix award for excellence in oceanography, 1967, Arleigh Burke Leadership award, 1975, Silver medal Naval Inst. Prize Essay Contest, 1985. Mem. Nat. Space Soc., Army and Navy Club, Explorer's Club, Soc. Physics Students, Tau Beta Pi; Avocations: flying, scuba diving, reading, travel. Office: Dep to Under Sec Def for Policy The Pentagon Rm 2E812 Washington DC 20301-2200

WELLS, MELISSA FOELSCH, foreign service officer; b. Tallinn, Estonia, Nov. 18, 1932; emigrated to U.S., 1936, naturalized, 1941; d. Kuno Georg and Miliza (Korjus) Foelsch; m. Alfred Washburn Wells, 1960; children: Christopher, Gregory. BS in Fgn. Service, Georgetown U., 1956. Fgn. svc. officer Dept. State, Washington, 1958-61; consular officer Dept. State, Trinidad, 1961-64; econ. officer mission OECD, Paris, 1964-66; econ. officer London, 1966-71; internat. economist, 1971-73; dep. dir. maj. export projects Dept. Commerce, 1973-75; comml. counselor Brazil, 1975-76; amb. to Guinea-Bissau and Cape Verde Dept. of State, 1976-77; U.S. rep. ECOSOC, UN, N.Y.C., 1977-79; resident rep. UNDP, Kampala, Uganda, 1979-81; dir. IMPACT program UNDP, Geneva, 1982-86; amb. to Mozambique, 1987-90; amb. to Zaire (Kinshasa), Kinshasa, 1991-93; under-sec.-gen. for adminstrn. and mgmt. UN, N.Y., 1993—. Mem. Am. Fgn. Service Assn. Office: UN Hdqrs State Dept Rm S-2700 New York NY 10017

WELLS, MERLE WILLIAM, historian, state archivist; b. Lethbridge, Alta., Can., Dec. 1, 1918; s. Norman Danby and Minnie Muir (Huckett) W.; student Boise Jr. Coll., 1937-39; A.B., Coll. Idaho, 1941, L.H.D. (hon.), 1981; M.A., U. Calif., 1947, Ph.D., 1950; L.H.D., U. Idaho, 1990. Instr. history Coll. Idaho, Caldwell, 1942-46; assoc. prof. history Alliance Coll., Cambridge Springs, Pa., 1950-56, 58, dean students, 1955-56; cons. historian Idaho Hist. Soc., Boise, 1956-58, historian and archivist, 1959—; hist. preservation officer, archivist State of Idaho, Boise, 1968-86. Treas., So. Idaho Migrant Ministry, 1960-64, chmn., 1964-67; nat. migrant adv. com. Nat. Council Chs., 1964-67, gen. bd. Idaho council, 1967-75; bd. dirs. Idaho State Employees Credit Union, 1964-67, treas., 1966-67; mem. Idaho Commn. Arts and Humanities, 1966-67; mem. Idaho Lewis and Clark Trail Commn., 1968-70, 84-88; mem. Idaho Bicentennial Commn., 1971-76; bd. dirs. Sawtooth Interpretive Assn., 1972—; dept. history United Presbyn. Ch., 1978-84; v.p. Idaho Zool. Soc., 1982-84, bd. dirs., 1984-94, treas., 1988-90, historian, 1990—. State Hist. Preservation Officers (dir. 1976-81, chmn. Western states council on geog. names 1982-83), Am. Hist. Assn., Western History Assn. (council 1973-76), AAUP, Am. Assn. State and Local History (council 1973-77), Soc. Am. Archivists, Assn. Idaho Historians (pres., 1994), others. Author: Anti-Mormonism in Idaho, 1978, Boise: An Illustrated History, 1982, Gold Camps and Silver Cities, 1984, Idaho: Gem of the Mountains, 1985. Office: Idaho State Hist Soc 210 Main St Boise ID 83702

WELLS, NORMAN, JR., metal products executive. BS metallurgy, indsl. engring., U. Wash., 1971; MBA, Gonzaga U., 1980. With Castech Aluminum Group Inc., Akron, Ohio, 1989—. Office: Castech Aluminum Group Inc. 753 W Waterloo Rd Akron OH 44314*

WELLS, PETER RAYMOND, architect; b. Ridgewood, N.J., Aug. 18, 1956; s. Raymond Richard and Betty Louise (Martin) W.; m. Linda Rose DiMauro, Aug. 8, 1982; children: Jaclyn Marie, Philip Dimauro. Exchange student Thames Poly., London, 1978; B.F.A., R.I. Sch. Design, 1979, B.Arch., 1980. Registered arch., N.J., N.Y., Conn., Pa. Nat. Coun. Archtl. Registration; registered profl. planner, N.J.; Lic. bldg. inspector, sub code official, constrn. code offical. Dir. and zoning officer bldg. dept., Borough of Paramus, N.J. Campaign chmn. Pascack Valley Hosp. Found., 1992-94, bd. dir. 1993-95; bd. dirs. Bergen Cmty. Blood Ctr., 1989-94; adv. bd. dirs. Plaza Sch. Drafting; mem. Montvale Evangical Free Ch. Mem. AIA, BOCA, N.J. Soc. Archs., Archs. League No. N.J., Paramus C. of C. (pres. 1994-95), Jaycees (Paramus, N.J. v.p. 1982, pres. 1982-83), Paramus Rotary (sec. 1983, pres. 1985-86). Home: 251 Park Ave Park Ridge NJ 07656-2445

WELLS, RAYMOND O., JR., mathematics educator, researcher; b. Dallas, June 12, 1940; s. Raymond O. and Hazel (Rand) W.; m. Rena Schwarze, Aug. 1, 1963; children: Richard Andrew, René Michael. BA, Rice U., 1962; MS, NYU, 1964, PhD, 1965. Asst. prof. math. Rice U., Houston, 1965-69, assoc. prof., 1969-74, prof. math., 1974—; prof. edn., 1993—, chmn. dept. edn., 1994—, dir. sch. math. project, 1987—, dir. computational math. lab., 1990—, prof. edn., 1993—, chmn. dept. edn., 1994—; vis. asst. prof. Brandeis U., Waltham, Mass., 1967-68, U. Göttingen, Germany, 1974-75, U. Colo., Boulder, 1983-84; adj. prof. cmty. medicine Baylor Coll. Medicine, 1994—; active Inst. for Advanced Study, Princeton, N.J., 1970-71, 79-80; exch. visitor NAS, Sofia, Bulgaria, 1984. Author: Differential Analysis on Complex Manifolds, 1973, Mathematics in Civilization, 1973, Twister Geometry and Field Theory, 1990; editor: Mathematical Heritage of Herman Weyl, 1989; contbr. numerous articles to sci. jours. Pres. Stages Repertory Theater, Houston, 1989-90. Recipient Alexander von Humboldt Sr. U.S. Scientist award U. Göttingen, 1974-75; Fulbright fellow, 1968, Guggenheim fellow, 1974. Fellow AAAS (coun. 1989—), Aware, Inc.; mem. Am. Math. Soc. (coun., editor 1978-88), Cosmos Club Washington. Home: 5000 Montrose Blvd Apt 21B Houston TX 77006-6564 Office: Rice U Dept Math PO Box 1892 Houston TX 77251-1892

WELLS, RICHARD H., gaming research executive; b. Stillwater, Okla., June 24, 1940; s. James R. and Edna Ruth (McKnight) W.; m. Peggy P. Puyear, Aug. 9, 1988; children: Shanley Renne, Richard Carlyle, Amy Luru. BS in Gen. Bus., Okla. State U., 1964; student systems dynamics program, MIT, 1985-86. Sr. fin. analyst Conoco, Houston, 1964-69; v.p. planning Union Planters Nat. Bank, Memphis, 1969-75; v.p. fin. planning Inn devel. Holiday Inns, Memphis, 1975-78, v.p. corp. adminstrn., 1979-80; sr. v.p. planning-adminstrn. Harrah's, Reno, 1980-86; v.p. Bally's Casino Hotels, Reno, 1986-90; co-owner Pennington & Assocs., Reno, 1990—; founder, owner Casino Player Count Svc., Reno, 1990—; founder, pres. Wells Gaming Rsch., Reno, Nev., 1995—. Mem. Reno Downtown Redevel. Com., 1983-84, Reno Task Force for Econ. Diversification, 1984, Nev. Gov.'s Econ. Adv. Com., 1983-84, Reno-Sparks Conv. Authority Rsch. Coun., 1990; chmn. Washoe Med. Found. Project Mgmt. Group, 1990; mem. dir. Econ. Authority Western Nev., 1992—. Served with USAR, 1958-61. Mem. Reno C. of C. (dir. 1983-84), Fin. Execs. Inst. (pres. 1974-75). Home: PO Box 3781 Reno NV 89504-3781

WELLS, RICHARD LEWIS, insurance company executive. Pres. Farmers Ins. Columbus, Columbus, Ohio. Office: Farmers Ins Columbus 2400 Farmers Dr Columbus OH 43235*

WELLS, ROBERT STEVEN, law association executive; b. Pitts., July 7, 1951; s. Richard H. and Mary J. (Kimball) W. BS, Purdue U., 1972; JD, Ohio State U., 1976. Bar: Ohio 1977, U.S. Dist. Ct. (so. dist.) Ohio 1977, Ill. 1980, U.S. Dist. Ct. (no. dist.) Ill. 1981, U.S. Supreme Ct. 1983. Pvt. practice, Columbus, Ohio, 1977-78; rsch. counsel ABA Ctr. for Profl. Responsibility, Chgo., 1979-84, ethics counsel, 1985; exec. dir. S.C. Bar, 1985—. Editor: ABA/BNA Lawyers' Manual on Profl. Conduct, 1984, ABA Disciplinary Law and Procedure Rsch. System, 1979. Mem. S.C. Bar, Am. Judicature Soc., Nat. Assn. Bar Execs. (past chmn. long-range planning com., past chmn. bylaws com.). Office: SC Bar 950 Taylor St Columbia SC 29201-2745

WELLS, SAMUEL ALONZO, JR., surgeon, educator; b. Cuthbert, Ga., Mar. 16, 1936; s. Samuel Alonzo and Martha (Steele) W.; m. Barbara Anne Atwood, Feb. 13, 1964; children: Sarah, Susan. Student, Emory U., 1954-57, M.D., 1961. Diplomate: Am. Bd. Surgery (bd. dirs., exec. com. 1986-89, vice chmn. 1987-88, chmn. 1988-89). Intern Johns Hopkins Hosp., Balt., 1961-62, resident in internal medicine, 1962-63; asst. resident in surgery Barnes Hosp., St. Louis, 1963-64; resident in surgery Duke U., Durham, N.C., 1966-70; guest investigator dept. tumor biology Karolinska Inst., Stockholm, 1967-68; asst. prof. surgery Duke U., Durham, N.C. 1970-72, assoc. prof., 1972-76, prof., 1976-81; clin. assoc. surgery br. Nat. Cancer Inst., NIH, Bethesda, Md., 1964-66, sr. investigator surgery br., 1970-72, cons. surgery br., 1975—; prof., chmn. dept. surgery Washington U., St. Louis, 1981—; dir. Duke U. Clin. Rsch. Ctr., 1978-81. Mem. editorial bd. Annals of Surgery, 1975-93, Surgery, 1975-93, Jour. Surg. Rsch., 1981-93; editor in chief World Jour. Surgery, 1983-92, Jour. Am. Coll. Surgeons,

1994—. Served to lt. comdr. USPHS, 1964-66. Mem. ACS (bd. regents 1989—, residency rev. com. for surgery 1987-93, chmn. 1991-93, mem. editorial bd. Current Problems in Surgery, 1988—, editor-in-chief 1989—), Am. Surg. Assn. (recorder, mem. council 1986-91), Soc. Univ. Surgeons (exec. council 1976-78), Soc. Clin. Surgery (treas. 1980-86, v.p. 86-88, pres. 88-90), Am. Soc. Clin. Investigation, ACS, Inst. of Medicine of NAS, Am. Bd. of Surgery (vice chmn. 1987-88, chmn. 1988-89), Nat. Cancer Adv. Bd., Halsted Soc. (pres. 1987), Soc. of Surgical Oncology (pres. 1993-), Alpha Omega Alpha. Home: 46 Westmoreland Pl Saint Louis MO 63108-1244 Office: Washington U Sch Medicine 660 S Euclid Ave Saint Louis MO 63110-1010

WELLS, SAMUEL JOSEPH, insurance company executive; b. Cass City, Mich., Aug. 12, 1946; s. Harold J. and Evelyn E. (Schmidt) W.; Leslie Ann Buhs, Dec. 26, 1970; children: Samuel Joseph, Dace Elyse. BS in Mktg., Ferris State U., 1970; postgrad., Am. Coll., 1980, Am. Coll., 1983. CLU, chartered fin. cons. Agt. Farm Bur. Ins. Mich., 1970-72; agy. mgr. Farm Bur. Ins. Mich., Kalamazoo, 1972-75; dir. sales Farm Bur. Mktg. Mich., Adrian, 1975-76; dir. agys.; regional dir. agys. Vol. State Life, Adrian, 1982-84; v.p., gen. mgr. Farm Progress Ins. Co., Ill., 1984-88; pres. Allied Life Ins. Co., Des Moines, 1988—. Officer Adrian Maples Rd Runner, 1983. Mem. Town Life Underwriters, Iowa Soc. CLUs, Sigma Phi Epsilon. Republican. Methodist. Home: 105 S 32d St West Des Moines IA 50265 Office: Allied Life Ins Co 701 5th Ave Des Moines IA 50309-1304

WELLS, THEODORE V., JR., lawyer; b. 1950. BA, Holy Cross, 1972; MBA, Harvard U., 1976; JD, Harvard Law Sch., 1976. Bar: N.J. 1977. Law clerk to Hon. John J Gibbons U.S. Ct. Appeals (3rd cir.), 1976-77; ptnr. Lowenstein, Sandler, Kohl, Fisher & Boylan P.C., Roseland, N.J.; mem. adj. faculty trade regulation Sch. Law, Seton Hall U., 1980-81; mem. faculty trial advocacy Practicing Law Inst., 1982—; mem. lawyers adv. com. U.S. Ct. Appeals (3rd cir.), 1982-85, 88—. Bd. trustees Coll. Holy Cross, 1977—, Newark Mus., 1979-82; bd. dirs. Essex County Urban League, 1979-88. Mem. ABA (antitrust law sect., state antitrust law subcom. 1980—), Assn. Crimiunal Def. Lawyers (trustee 1984—), N.J. State Bar Assn. (antitrust law com. 1980—). Office: Lowenstein Sandler Kohl Fisher & Boylan 65 Livingston Ave Roseland NJ 07068

WELLS, THOMAS B., federal judge; b. 1945. BS, Miami U., 1967; JD, Emory U., 1973; LLM, NYU, 1978. Atty. Graham & Wells, Vidalia, Ga., Hurt, Richardson, Garner, Todd & Cadenhead, Vidalia, Ga., Shearer & Wells, Vidalia, Ga.; city atty. City of Vidalia; county atty. Toombs County, Ga.; judge U.S. Tax Ct., Washington, 1986—. With USNR, 1970. Mem. ABA. Office: US Tax Ct 400 2nd St NW Washington DC 20217-0002

WELLS, VICTOR HUGH, JR., advertising agency executive; b. Bloomington, Ill., Apr. 19, 1924; s. Victor Hugh and Wilma Julia (Codlin) W.; m. Jacqueline L. Wade, Nov. 25, 1949; children:—Victor Hugh, III, Polly Jo, Ken Douglas. BS., Bradley U., 1948. Copywriter Chgo. Tribune, 1949-54; copywriter Earle Ludgin & Co., Chgo., 1954-58, creative dir., 1959-64; group creative dir. Tatham-Laird, Chgo., 1958-59; founder, creative dir., pres. Rink Wells & Assos. (advt. agy.), Chgo., 1964-72; v.p., dir. creative services N.W. Ayer Inc., Chgo., 1972-84; exec. v.p., dir. creative services N.W. Ayer Inc., N.Y.C., 1984-86, also bd. dirs.; cons. N. W. Ayer Inc., N.Y.C., 1986—. Served to 2d lt. AC US Army, 1943-45. Recipient various advt. creative awards, including Clio, Andy awards. Office: One Worldwide Plaza 825 8th Ave New York NY 10019-7416

WELLS, WALTER E., prefabricated housing manufacturing executive; b. 1936. Exec. v.p. Schult Homes Corp., Middlebury, Ind., 1970-72, pres., 1972-84, CEO,dir., 1984—. Office: Schult Homes Corp 221 US Highway 20 Middlebury IN 46540*

WELLSTONE, PAUL, senator; b. Washington, July 21, 1944; s. Leon and Minnie W.; m. Sheila Wellstone, 1963; children: David, Marcia, Mark. BA, U. N.C., 1965, PhD Polit. Sci., 1969. Tchr. Carleton Coll., Minn.; U.S. senator from Minn., 1991—, mem. coms. on small bus., energy and natural resources, Indian affairs, labor and human resources, sen. dem. policy com., chmn. subcom. rural economy and family farming. Author: How the Rural Poor Got Power, Powerline. Dir. Minn. Community Energy Program. Office: US Senate 717 Hart Senate Office Bldg Washington DC 20510*

WELNA, CECILIA, mathematics educator; b. New Britain, Conn., July 15; d. Joseph and Sophie (Roman) W. B.S., St. Joseph Coll., 1949; M.A., U. Conn., 1952, Ph.D., 1960. Instr. Mt. St. Joseph Acad., 1949-52; asst. instr. U. Conn., 1950-55; instr. U. Mass., Amherst, 1955-56; prof., chmn. dept. math. and physics U. Hartford, 1982-91, prof. math., 1991—. Mem. Math. Assn. Am., Nat. Council Tchrs. Math., Assn. Tchrs. Math. Conn., Sigma Xi. Office: U Hartford Dana 295A Bloomfield Ave West Hartford CT 06117

WELNETZ, DAVID CHARLES, human resources executive; b. Antigo, Wis., Apr. 12, 1947; s. Francis P. and Marquette A. (Stengl) W.; m. Mary L. McCulley, Aug. 25, 1973; children: Andrew, Timothy. BS in Biology, U. Wis., Stevens Point, Wis., 1969; MS in Indsl. Rels., U. Wis. Madison, 1975. Mgr. coll. recruitment tng. Rexnord Inc., Milw., 1975-77; personnel mgr. Rexnord Inc., Sarasota, Fla., 1977-80; corp. dir. employee rels. Rexnord Inc., Milw., 1980-83; sr. cons. The Thompson Group, Brookfield, Wis., 1983-87; v.p. The Thompson Group, Brookfield, 1987-91; pres. Thompson Cons., Brookfield, 1991—; adv. bd. SUNY, Buffalo, 1982-88; bd. dirs. Matarah Industries. Mem. adv. bd. Wauwatosa Sch. Dist., Wis., 1983-84, Am. Cancer Soc., 1994—; bd. dirs. Matarah Ind., 1994—. 1st lt. U.S. Army, 1969-72. Recipient Bronze Star U.S. Army, 1972. Mem. Pers. Indsl. Rels. Assn. (program com. 1988-91, chmn. pers. rsch 1980-82), Human Resources Planning Soc., Human Resources Mgmt. Assn. Roman Catholic. Home: 1918 Forest St Wauwatosa WI 52313 Office: Thompson Cons Ltd 17700 W Capitol Dr Brookfield WI 53045-2006

WELPOTT, JACK WARREN, photographer, educator; b. Kansas City, Kans., Apr. 27, 1923; s. Ray Calvert and Dolores (Davenroy) W.; m. Doris Jean Franklin, June 12, 1949; children—Jan Marie, Matthew David; m. Judy Dater, May 22, 1969; m. Wendy Brooke Gray, May 11, 1986. B.S., Ind. U., 1949, M.S., 1954, M.F.A., 1959. Mem. acad. staff Ind. U., 1949-59; mem. faculty San Francisco State U., 1959-93, ret., 1993; artist in residence RISD, 1984; workshop leader Columbia Coll., 1985, Friends of Photo, 1985, Humboldt State U., 1985, Parsons Sch. Design, Paris, 1985, Volcano Hawaii, 1986, numerous others in France, England, Switzerland, Japan and Mexico. One man shows include, U. Calif., Davis, Art Inst. Chgo., 1972, Wall Street Gallery, Spokane, 1973, Gallery 113, Santa Cruz, Calif., 1974, San Francisco Mus. Art, 25 year retrospective, 1976, U. So. Calif., 25 year retrospective, 1977, Ind. U., 25 year retrospective, 1977, Silver Image Gallery, Seattle, 1977, Ohio State U., 1978, Center for Creative Photography, U. Ariz., 1979, Colo. Mountain Coll., 1980, Bard Coll., 1981, Jehu Gallery, San Francisco, 1981, Galerif Voor Fotografie, Antwerp, Belgium, 1983, R.I. Sch. Design, 1984, La Photographie Creative, Pavillon des Arts, Paris, 1984, New Sch. Social Research, N.Y.C., 1984, Foto Biennale Enschede, Netherlands, 1984, Vision Gallery, San Francisco, 1984, Min Gallery, Tokyo, 1987, Osaka (Japan) Cultrual Ctr., 1989, Retrospective Vision Gallery, San Francisco, 1992; two man shows include Musee Reattu, Arles, France, 1976, Photographers Gallery, Palo Alto, Calif., 1986, group exhbns. include Santa Barbara Mus., Mus. Modern Art, Mexico City, Photography in Am, Whitney Mus., N.Y.C., Photography in the 20th Century, George Eastman House, California Photography, Oakland Mus., San Francisco Mus. Art, U. Oreg. Commitment to Vision, 1986, U. Colo. Photographics, 1986, numerous others, Met. Mus. Art, N.Y.C., De Cordova Mus., Lincoln, Mass.; represented in permanent collections Graham Nash Collection, Mus. Modern Art, N.Y.C., Whitney Mus. Art, N.Y.C., Art Inst. Chgo., Bibliotheque Nat, Paris, Tokyo Coll. Photography, Open U., London, Internat. Mus. Photography, Rochester, N.Y., San Francisco Mus. Art, Musee Reattu, Arles, Frances, Oakland (Calif.) Mus., U. Colo., Center Creative Photography, Tucson, U. N.Mex., Pasadena Art Mus., Australian Nat. Gallery, Houston Mus. Fine Arts, Fogg Art Mus., Cambridge, Mass., Gallery Van Haarlem, Netherlands; author: The Halide Conversion, 1989; contbr. photos to books. Served with USAAF, 1943-46. NEA fellow, 1979; grantee Polaroid, 1983, Marin Arts Coun., 1991. Home: PO Box 496 Inverness CA 94937-0496

WELSCH, GLENN ALBERT, accounting educator; b. Woodward, Okla., Apr. 1, 1915; s. George Franklin and Minnie Melissa (Bowers) W.; m. Irma Richards, Apr. 5, 1942; children: Glenn Andrew, Linden Richards, Mary Ann Welsch Williamson. B.S., Northwestern State Coll., Alva, Okla., 1935; grad., Army Staff and Command Sch., 1943; M.S., Okla. State U., 1949; Ph.D., U. Tex., 1952. CPA, Okla., Tex. Comml. tchr. pub. high sch. Alva, Okla., 1937-40; mem. faculty Coll. Bus. Adminstrn., U. Tex., 1952-85, prof. acctg., 1956-85, chmn. dept., 1959-62, assoc. dean grad. studies, 1962-67, John Arch White prof. acctg., 1968-78, Peat, Marwick, Mitchell prof. acctg., 1978-83, Bayless chair in free enterprise, 1984-85, Bayless chair emeritus, 1985—; instr. Exec. Devel. Program, 1956-72; vis. prof. Carman G. Blough Disting. prof. U. Va., 1970-71; Prickett Disting. vis. prof. Ind. U., 1975; cons. various companies on fin. acctg. and profit planning and control; expert witness. Author: (with Ronald W. Hilton and Paul Gordon) Budgeting: Profit Planning and Control, 5th edit., 1988, (with B.H. Sord) Business Budgeting: A Survey of Management Planning and Control Practices, 1958, (with C.T. Zlatkovich) Intermediate Accounting, 8th edit., 1989, (with C.H. Griffin and T.H. Williams) Advanced Accounting, 1966, (with Daniel G. Short) Fundamentals of Financial Accounting, 6th edit., 1987, (with R.N. Anthony) Fundamentals of Management Accounting, 4th edit., 1984. Served to maj. AUS, 1940-46. Recipient numerous awards for teaching excellence and service to acctg. profession, including Outstanding Educators award Amn. Acctg. Assn., 1985; named to Hall of Fame, Coll. and Grad. Coll. of Bus. Adminstrn., U. Tex., 1988. Mem. Tex. Soc. CPA's (v.p. 1959-60), Am. Acctg. Assn. (pres. 1963), Am. Inst. CPA's (council 1968-73, acctg. prins. bd. 1970-73), Nat. Assn. Accts., Fin. Execs. Inst., Planning Execs. Inst., Beta Alpha Psi, Beta Gamma Sigma. Home: 3405 Taylors Dr Austin TX 78703-1047

WELSH, DENNIE M., business machines company executive. Gen. mgr. industry solutions IBM Corp., White Plains, N.Y. Office: IBM Corp 44 S Broadway White Plains NY 10601

WELSH, DONALD EMORY, publisher; b. Youngstown, Ohio, Oct. 6, 1943; s. Edward Francis and Clevelle Rose W.; m. Elizabeth Bourne Floyd, June 25, 1966; children: Leah Bourne, Emory Philip. A.B., Columbia U., 1965; J.D., Cleveland Marshall Sch. Law, 1969. Bar: Ohio 1969. Trust devel. officer Cleve. Trust Co., 1968-70; advt. sales rep. Fortune mag., Time, Inc., N.Y.C., 1970-75; advt. dir. Rolling Stone mag., N.Y.C., 1975-77; v.p., assoc. pub. Rolling Stone mag., 1977-78; pub. Outside mag., N.Y.C., 1978-82; pub. Muppet mag. and pres. Lorimar Pub. Group (formerly Telepictures Publs., Inc.), 1982-87; pres. Welsh Pub. Group, Inc., 1987-94; exec. v.p. Marvel Family Media, 1994—. Trustee Outward Bound, U.S.A.; bd. dirs. Big Apple Circus. Mem. ABA, Mag. Pubs. Assn. (former bd. dirs.), Ohio Bar Assn., Cleve. Bar Assn., Century Assn., Racquet and Tennis Club, Sharon Country Club (Conn.), Hyannis Port Club (Mass.). Clubs: Racquet and Tennis (N.Y.C.); Sharon (Conn.) Country, Hyannis Port (Mass.). Home: 501 E 79th St New York NY 10021 Office: Welsh Publishing Group Inc 300 Madison Ave New York NY 10017-6216

WELSH, PETER CORBETT, museum consultant, historian; b. Washington, Aug. 28, 1926; s. Arthur Brinkley and Susan Jane (Putney) W.; m. Catherine Beatrice Allen, Nov. 27, 1951 (div. 1969); children—Susan Jane, Peter Corbett; m. Caroline Levert Mastin, Sept. 8, 1970; 1 child, James Munson Corbett. B.A., Mt. Union Coll., Alliance, Ohio, 1950; postgrad., U. Va., 1950-51; M.A. (Hagley fellow), U. Del., 1956. Research asst., fellowship coordinator Eleutherian Mills-Hagley Found., Wilmington, Del., 1956-59; assoc. curator dept. civil history Mus. History and Tech., Smithsonian Instn., 1959-61; curator Growth U.S., 1962-64, curator dept. civil history, 1964-69, asst. dir. gen. mus. of instrn., 1969-70, dir. OfficeMus. Programs, 1970-71; dir. N.Y. State Hist. Assn., Cooperstown, 1971-74; vis. prof. Cooperstown Grad. Program, N.Y. State Hist. Assn.; dir. Cooperstown Grad. Programs, 1971-74; dir. spl. projects N.Y. State Mus., Albany, 1975-76; dir. Bur. Mus., Pa. Hist. and Mus. Commn., 1976-84; pres. The Welsh Group, 1984-86; curator The Adirondack Mus., Blue Mountain Lake, N.Y., 1986-88, sr. historian, 1988-89; mus. cons., lectr., 1989—; adj. prof. SUNY; cons. FDR Mus. and Little White House, Warm Springs, Ga., 1968-72; trustee Landon Sch., Bethesda, Md., 1964-70; bd. dirs., mem. exec. com. Ctr. for Conservation of Hist. Art and Artifacts, 1979-83; bd. dirs. Lake Placid Ctr. for the Arts, 1992—. Author: Tanning in the United States: A Brief HIstory, 1964, American Folk Art: The Art and Spirit of te People, 1967, Track and Road: The American Trotting Horse, 1820-1900, 1968, The Art of Enterprise: A Pennsylvania Tradition, 1983, Jacks, Jobbers and Kings: Logging the Adirondacks, 1994; also articles; editor: Smithsonian Jour. History, 1967-70. Served to 1st lt. AUS, 1951-54. Mem. Am. Hist. Assn., Am. Studies Assn., Am. Assn. Mus., N.Y. State Assn. Mus. (council 1971-75), Am. Assn. State and Local History (publ. com.), Soc. History of Tech., Sigma Nu. Democrat. Roman Catholic. Club: Country of Harrisburg. Office: 34 2nd St Tupper Lake NY 12986-2011

WELSH, ROBERT K., religous organization executive. Pres. Ch. Fin. Coun. Office: Ch Fin Coun PO Box 1986 Indianapolis IN 46206

WELSH, RONALD ARTHUR, physician, educator; b. Houston, Oct. 13, 1926; s. Leo Arthur and Octavia Virginia (Franssen) W.; m. Mary Jeanne Duncan, June 24, 1950; children: Mary Jeanne, William, James. A.B., U. Tex., 1947, M.D., 1950. Intern USPHS, Hosp., New Orleans, 1950-51; resident in pathology USPHS, Balt., 1951-55; chief pathology USPHS Hosp., Galveston, Tex., 1955-57; asst. prof. pathology L. Tex. Med. Br., Galveston, 1955-57, La. State U., New Orleans, 1957-59; asso. prof. La. State U., 1959-61, prof., 1961—; chief surg. pathology Charity Hosp., New Orleans, 1975-93; cons. forensic pathology Orleans Parish Coroner, 1961-79; cons. path. Va. Hosp., New Orleans, 1971—; Mem. La. Commn. on Narcotics and Rehab., 1970-72; Bd. dirs. La. div. Am. Cancer Soc., 1960-89, La. div Am. Cancer Soc. (nat. div.), 1966-68, nat. del. dir., 1980-86. Served with USNR, 1944-46; Served with USPHS, 1950-57. Recipient Distinguished Prof. award La. State U. Alumni Assn., 1973-74, Asclepian award Am. Cancer Soc., New Orleans unit, 1992. Mem. AMA, Internat. Acad. Pathology, Am. Soc. Clin. Pathologists, Coll. Am. Pathologists, Assn. Pathologists, La., Orleans Parish med. socs., Phi Beta Kappa, Alpha Omega Alpha, Nu Sigma Nu. Republican. Episcopalian. Home: 2429 Octavia St New Orleans LA 70115-6533 Office: 1901 Perdido St New Orleans LA 70112-1328

WELSH, THOMAS J., bishop; b. Weatherly, Pa., Dec. 20, 1921. Grad., St. Charles Borromeo Sem., Phila., Cath. U. Am. Ordained priest Roman Cath. Ch., 1946. Ordained titular bishop of Scattery Island and aux. bishop of Phila.-1970-74; 1st bishop of Arlington Va., 1974-83; bishop of Allentown Pa., 1983—. Office: Bishop of Allentown PO Box F 202 N 17th St Allentown PA 18105

WELSHANS, MERLE TALMADGE, management consultant; b. Murphysboro, Ill., June 17, 1918; s. Arthur Isaac and Martha Ellen (Blair) W.; B.Ed., So. Ill. U., 1940; M.A., Washington U., St. Louis, 1947, Ph.D., 1951; m. Mary Katherine Whitenbaugh, June 2, 1942; children: Elizabeth Margaret Van Steenbergh, Arthur Edmund, Janice Ann. Asst. v.p. Merc. Mortgage Co., Olney, Ill., 1940; exec. officer, dept. bus. adminstrn. George Washington U., 1950-54; prof. fin. grad. Sch. Bus. Adminstrn., Washington U., 1954-69; v.p. fin. Union Electric Co., St. Louis, 1969-83; mgmt. cons., 1983—; dir. Prudential Mutual Funds, Hotchkis & Wiley Funds. Trustee United Meth. Found. Served to capt. U.S. Army, 1942-45. Decorated Bronze Star medal. Mem. Fin. Mgmt. Assn. (dir.), Am. Econ. Assn., Am. Fin. Assn., Am. Soc. Fin. Analysis, Fin. Analysts Assn. St. Louis (trustee), Alpha Kappa Phi, Beta Gamma Sigma, Artus. Methodist. Author: (with R.W. Melcher) Finance, 8th edit., 1992; cons. economist, editor Fin. Newsletter, 1965-69. Address: 14360 Ladue Rd Chesterfield MO 63017-2524

WELSHIMER, GWEN R., state legislator, real estate broker, appraiser, tax consultant; b. Poughkeepsie, N.Y., Nov. 5, 1935; d. Freanor Ralph and Beulah M. (Reedy) Grant; m. Billy L. Blake (div. 1979); children: Donald E., Jerry A.; m. Robert E. Welshimer. Student, Kans. State U., 1953-54; cert., Jones Real Estate Coll., Colorado Springs, Colo., 1975. Cert. real estate appraiser, 1993. Exec. sec. Coll. Bd. Trustees, Bellevue, Wash., 1967-69; exec. sec. to chmn. bd. dirs. Garvey Industries, Wichita, Kans., 1969-73, adminstrv. asst. pers. and pub. affairs, 1969-73; copywriter Walter Drake & Sons, Colorado Springs, 1973-75; real estate agt. UTE Realty, Colorado Springs, 1975-76; newspaper pub., owner Black Forrest News, Colorado

Springs, 1976-79; real estate broker, appraiser Gwen Welshimer Real Estate, Wichita, 1979—; coord. Epic Real Estate Sch., Wichita, 1988—; legislator Kans. Ho. of Reps., Topeka, 1990—, minority leader local govt. com., 1994-95. Dem. precinct committeewomen, Wichita; bd. dirs. United Meth. Urban Ministries, Wichita, 1990—. Mem. NOW, AAUW, Colo. Press Assn., Colo. Bd. Realtors, Nat. Fedn. Women, Women's Home Extension (past pres.), Nat. Order Women Legislators (state dir. 1994-95). Democrat. Methodist. Home: 6103 Castle Wichita KS 67218 Office: Kans Ho of Reps State Capitol Topeka KS 66612

WELSOME, EILEEN, journalist; b. N.Y.C., Mar. 12, 1951; d. Richard H. and Jane M. (Garity) W.; m. James R. Martin, Aug. 3, 1983. BJ with honors, U. Tex., 1980. Reporter Beaumont (Tex.) Enterprise, 1980-82, San Antonio Light, 1982-83, San Antonio Express-News, 1983-86, Albuquerque Tribune, 1987-94. Recipient Clarion award, 1989, News Reporting award Nat. Headliners, 1989, John Hancock award, 1991, Mng. Editors Pub. Svc. award AP, 1991, 94, Roy Howard award 1994, James Aronson award, 1994, Gold Medal award Investigative Reporters and Editors, 1994, Sigma Delta Chi award, 1994, Investigative Reporting award Nat. Headliners, 1994, Selden Ring award, 1994, Heywood Broun award, 1994, George Polk award, 1994, Sidney Hillman Found. award, 1994, Pulitzer Prize for nat. reporting, 1994; John S. Knight fellow Stanford U., 1991-92.

WELTCHEK, PAUL RICHARD, lawyer; b. Elizabeth, N.J., Dec. 2, 1928; s. Lawrence L. and Fannie S. (Shor) W.; m. Edith Zanditon, July 11, 1954; children: Nancy Ellen, Ann Elizabeth, Peter Richard. B.A., U. Nebr., 1950; LL.B., Yale U., 1955. Bar: N.J. 1955, Calif. 1959, N.Y. 1962. Ptnr. Shearman & Sterling, N.Y.C., 1965—. Served to 1st lt. U.S. Army, 1951-52. Mem. Internat. Bar Assn., Internat. Fiscal Assn., ABA, N.Y. State Bar Assn., Assn. of Bar of City of N.Y., Phi Beta Kappa. Office: 153 E 53rd St New York NY 10022-4611

WELTER, WILLIAM MICHAEL, marketing and advertising executive; b. Evanston, Ill., Nov. 18, 1946; s. Roy Michael and Frances (DeShields) W.; m. Pamela Bassett, June 11, 1971; children: Barclay, Robert Michael. BS, Mo. Valley Coll., 1966. Account exec. Leo Burnett Co., Inc., Chgo., 1966-74; v.p., account supr. Needham Harper Worldwide, Chgo., 1974-80; v.p. mktg. Wendy's Internat., Inc., Dublin, Ohio, 1981; sr. v.p. mktg., 1981-84, exec. v.p., 1984-87; owner, chief exec. officer Haunty & Welter Advt. Agy., Worthington, Ohio, 1987-91; sr. exec. v.p. mktg. Rax Restaurants Inc., Dublin, 1992; exec. v.p. mktg. Metromedia Steakhouses, Inc., Dayton, 1992-93; sr. v.p. mktg. Metromedia Co., Dayton, 1993-95; exec. v.p., chief mktg. officer Heartland Foods Inc., Dublin, Ohio, 1995—. Founder Santa's Silent Helpers, Columbus, Ohio, 1985. Mem. Advt. Fedn. Columbus, Scioto Country Club, Lakes Golf and Country Club. Avocations: golf, fishing. Home: 4311 Woodhall Rd Columbus OH 43220-4379 Office: Heartland Food Systems Inc 4150 Tuller Rd Dublin OH 43017

WELTMAN, DAVID LEE, lawyer; b. Springfield, Mass., Jan. 12, 1933; s. Sol Walter and Esther (Ziskind) W.; m. Lois Handmaker, Sept. 2, 1956; children: John, Elizabeth, Herman, Sally. AB, Yale U., 1954; LLB, Harvard U., 1957. Bar: Mass. 1957. Assoc. Mintz, Levin & Cohn, Boston, 1957-60; v.p. Ansonia Mills, Inc., Taunton, Mass., 1960-63; assoc. Foley, Hoag & Eliot, Boston, 1963-67, ptnr., 1967—; sec., clk. Charles River Assocs., Boston, 1965—, Brigham Med. Group Found., 1972—, Siemens-Nixdorf Info. Systems, Burlington, Mass., 1979—, Am. Brush Co., Clairmont, N.H., 1982-92. Chmn. leadership devel. Coun. Jewish Fedns. and Welfare Funds, 1966-68; trustee New Eng. Med. Ctr., Boston, 1970-82, Combined Jewish Philanthropies, Boston, 1970—; chmn. Newbury Coll., Boston, 1972—, Lown Cardiovascular Rsch. Found., 1993—; incorporator Mus. Sci. Boston, 1972—, Boston U. Med. Ctr., 1965—; pres. Beaver Country Day Sch., Chestnut Hill, Mass., 1975-80, Jewish Cmty. Ctr., Brookline and Newton, 1968-71; bd. overseers South Shore Hosp. Found., Weymouth, Mass., 1990—. Chmn. leadership devel. Coun. Jewish Fedns. and Welfare Funds, 1966-68; trustee New Eng. Med. Ctr., Boston, 1970-82, Combined Jewish Philanthropies, Boston, 1970—; chmn. Newbury Coll., Boston, 1972—, Lown Cardiovascular Rsch. Found., 1993—; incorporator Mus. Sci., Boston, 1972—, Univ. Hosp., Boston, 1978—; pres. Beaver Country Day Sch., Chestnut Hill, Mass., 1975-80, Jewish Community Ctr., Brookline and Newton, 1968-71; bd. overseers South Shore Hosp. Found., Weymouth, Mass., 1990—. Recipient Young Leadership award Combined Jewish Philanthropies, 1968, Class of 1954 award Yale U., 1989, Founders Day award Beaver Country Day Sch., 1991. Mem. ABA, Boston Bar Assn., Nat. Health Lawyers Assn., Cohasset Yacht Club (Mass.), Downtown Club. Avocations: tennis, sailing. Home: 90 Gammons Rd Cohasset MA 02025-1406 Office: Foley Hoag & Eliot 1 Post Office Sq Boston MA 02109-2103

WELTNER, BETSEY, state art association administrator; b. Atlanta, Apr. 22, 1952; d. Charles Longstreet and Betty Jean (Center) W. AB, U. Ga., 1975. Pub. info. officer City of Atlanta Bur. Cultural Affairs, 1975-77; press sec. Sen. Wache Fowler, Washington, 1977-79; acct. exec. Hill and Knowlton, Washington, 1979-81; sr. v.p. Grey and Co., Washington, 1981-86; sr. v.p. Hill and Knowlton, Sydney, Australia, 1986-87, Washington, 1987-88; v.p. pub. affairs Cohn & Wolfe, Atlanta, 1988-90; exec. dir. Ga. Coun. for Arts, Atlanta, 1991—. Mem. affirmative action com. Dem. Party of Ga., Atlanta, 1991—, women in politics com., 1992, del. 1992 Dem. Nat. Conv.; adv. com. Ct. Appointed Spl. Advocates, Atlanta, 1992; trustee, chmn. communications com. The Ga. Conservancy, Atlanta, 1991—. Recipient Cert. of Excellence, Pub. Rels. Soc. Am., 1991, Role award The Arts Exch., 1992, DECA award Atlanta Bus. Chronicle, 1992. Mem. Nat. Assn. State Art Agys. (bd. dirs. 1991—), So. Assn. State Arts Agys., Ga. Citizens for Arts. Democrat. Episcopalian. Avocations: horseback riding, hiking, theatre, folk art. Office: Ga Council for the Arts 530 Means St NW Atlanta GA 30318-5793 Office: Ga Council for the Arts 930 Means St Ste 115 Atlanta GA 30318

WELTON, THEODORE ALLEN, theoretical physics educator, consultant; b. Saratoga Springs, N.Y., July 4, 1918; s. William Edwin and Mathilde (Hatton) W.; m. Jean Elizabeth Malloy, June 10, 1943 (dec. Dec. 1976); children: William Edwin, Caroline Elizabeth, Mary Louise, John Edward; m. Regina Bogden, Oct. 29, 1977; stepchildren: Melisande Regina, James Courtney. BS, MIT, 1939; PhD, U. Ill., 1943. Physics instr. U. Ill., Urbana, 1943-44; jr. scientist Los Alamos (N.Mex.) Sci. Lab., 1944-46; rsch. assoc. physics MIT, Cambridge, 1946-48; asst. prof. physics U. Pa., Phila., 1948-50; prin. physicist Oak Ridge (Tenn.) Nat. Lab., 1950-59, mem. sr. rsch. physics staff, 1959-82, cons., 1983—; adj. prof. physics U. Tenn., Knoxville, 1963-83; cons. Westinghouse Atomic Power Divsn., Pitts., 1949-50; vis. scientist Lawrence Radiation Lab., Berkeley, Calif., 1959-60. Author: (with others) Fast Neutron Physics, 1963, Bright Field Electron Microscopy, 1979. Reader, marking books in preparation for reading Recording for the Blind, Oak Ridge, 1982—; sec., bd. dirs. Oak Ridge Civic Music Assn., 1970-72, mem. guild, 1989—. Recipient Alexander von Humboldt Found. award, 1980. Fellow Am. Phys. Soc. Avocations: history, travel, computer programming, cosmological theory.

WELTY, EUDORA, author; b. Jackson, Miss.; d. Christian Webb and Chestina (Andrews) W. Student, Miss. State Coll. for Women; B.A., U. Wis., 1929; postgrad., Columbia Sch. Advt., 1930-31. Author: A Curtain of Green, 1941, The Robber Bridegroom, 1942, The Wide Net, 1943, Delta Wedding, 1946, Music From Spain, 1948, Short Stories, 1949, The Golden Apples, 1949, The Ponder Heart, 1954 (William Dean Howells medal Am. Acad. Arts and Letters 1955), The Bride of the Innisfallen, 1955, Place in Fiction, 1957, The Shoe Bird, 1964, Thirteen Stories, 1965, A Sweet Devouring, 1969, Losing Battles, 1970 (Nat. Book award nomination 1971), One Time, One Place, 1971 (Christopher Book award 1972), The Optimist's Daughter, 1972 (Pulitzer prize in fiction 1973), The Eye of the Story, 1978, The Collected Stories of Eudora Welty, 1980 (Notable Book award ALA 1980, Am. Book award 1981), One Writer's Beginnings, 1984 (Am. Book award 1984, Nat. Book Critics Circle award nomination 1984), Eudora Welty Photographs, 1989, A Writer's Eye: Collected Book Reviews, 1994, Monuments to Interruption: Collected Book Reviews, 1994; editor: (with Ronald A. Sharp) The Norton Book of Friendship, 1991; contbr.: New Yorker. Recipient O. Henry award, 1942, 43, 68, Creative Arts medal for fiction Brandeis U., 1966, Nat. Inst. Arts and Letters Gold Medal, 1972, Nat. Medal for Lit., 1980, Presdl. Medal of Freedom, 1980, Commonwealth medal MLA, 1984, Nat. Medal of Arts, 1987; Lit. grantee Nat. Inst. Arts and Letters, 1944; Guggenheim fellow, 1942; Chevalier de l'Ordre des Arts et Lettres (France), 1987. Mem. Am. Acad. Arts and Letters. Home: 1119 Pinehurst Pl Jackson MS 39202-1812

WELTY, JOHN DONALD, university president; b. Amboy, Ill., Aug. 24, 1944; s. John Donald and Doris (Donnelly) W.; children: Anne, Elisabeth. B.S., Western Ill. U., 1965; M.A., Mich. State U., 1967; Ed.D., Ind. U., 1974. Asst. v.p. for student affairs SW State U., Marshall, Minn., 1973-74; dir. residences SUNY-Albany, 1974-77, assoc. dean for student affairs, 1977-80; v.p. for student and univ. affairs Indiana U. of Pa., 1980-84, pres., 1984-91; pres. Calif. State U., Fresno, 1991—; lectr. in field. Contbr. articles to profl. jours. Chmn. Small Bus. Incubator of Indiana, 1985-91; bd. dirs. Open Door Crises and Counseling Ctr., Indiana, Big Bros./Big Sisters, Indiana, 1980-84. Recipient Chancellor's award SUNY, 1977. Mem. Pa. Assn. Student Personnel Adminstrs., Am. Coll. Personnel Assn., Am. Assn. State Colls. and Univs., Nat. Assn. Student Personnel Adminstrs., Indiana C. of C. (bd. dirs.), Assn. Gov. Bds. Roman Catholic. Lodge: Rotary. Office: Calif State U 5241 N Maple Ave Fresno CA 93740-8027

WELTY, JOHN RIDER, lawyer; b. Waynesboro, Pa., Nov. 5, 1948; s. Richard Samuel and Mary Catherine (Rider) W.; m. Susan Eileen Mescall, Aug. 7, 1970; children: John R. II, David Richard, Brian James. BA in Econs., Shippensburg State U., 1970; JD, Am. U., 1975. Bar: Pa. Economist bur. econ. analysis U.S. Dept. of Commerce, Washington, 1970-76; staff atty. to sr. atty. Carpenter Tech. Corp., Reading, Pa., 1976-82; assoc. gen. counsel Carpenter Tech. Corp., Reading, 1982-89, dir. law, 1989-90, dir. law, asst. sec., 1990-91, gen. counsel, asst. sec., 1991-92, gen. counsel, sec., 1993—, v.p. gen. counsel, sec.; sec. fed. polit. action com. Carpenter (Pa.) Tech. Corp., Reading, 1978—, sec. state polit. action com., 1978—. Founder Drexelwood Community Assn., Wyomssing, Pa., 1981-82; bd. dirs. Cornwall Terr. Community Assn., Sinking Spring, Pa., 1977-79; sch. dirs. Conrad Weiser Area Sch. Dist., 1992—; mem. dist. com., vice chmn. Hawk Mountain coun. Boy Scouts Am., 1991—. Mem. ABA, Pa. Bar Assn., Am. Corp. Counsel Assn., Pa. Self Insurers Assn. (bd. dirs. 1978-81), Phi Alpha Delta, Alpha Phi Omega. Republican. Avocations: tennis, reading. Office: Carpenter Tech Corp PO Box 14662 101 Bern St Reading PA 19601-1203

WELTY, WILLIAM JOHN, transportation executive, accountant; b. Dixon, Ill., Nov. 16, 1945; m. Judy L. Welty; children: Kelly, Bryce. BS in Acctg., No. Ill. U. CPA, Ill. Sr. auditor Coopers & Lybrand, Rockford, Ill., 1969-72; plant controller Walton Products Co., Atlantic, Iowa, 1972-73; mfg. group controller Caron Internat., Inc., Rochelle, Ill., 1973-77; asst. controller U.S. Reduction Co., E. Chgo., Ind., 1977-79; corp. controller Allied Van Lines, Inc., Broadview, Ill., 1979-82, v.p. fin., chief officer, 1982—; Mem. tax adv. panel Am. Movers Conf. Vol. YMCA-sponsored basketball. With USNG. Mem. AICPA, Ill. Soc. CPA's, Am. Trucking Assn. (household goods dir. Nat. Acctg. & Fin. Council). Avocations: golf, fishing, coaching Little League baseball and YMCA sponsored basketball. Office: Allied Van Lines Inc 2120 S 25th Ave Maywood IL 60153-2830

WELU, JAMES A., art museum director; b. Dubuque, Iowa, Dec. 15, 1943; s. Andrew L. and Anna E. (Riley) W. BA, Loras Coll., 1966; MA, U. Notre Dame, 1967, MFA, 1968; PhD, Boston U., 1977. Instr. St. Mary-of-the-Woods (Ind.) Coll., 1968-70; asst. curator Worcester (Mass.) Art Mus., 1974-76, assoc. curator, 1976-80, instr.; 1977-78, 80-81, chief curator, 1980-86, dir., 1986—; instr. Clark U., Worcester, 1980. Panelist Mass. Coun. on Arts and Humanities, Boston, 1981-82, 90, Utilization of Mus. Resources Nat. Endowment for the Arts, 1988; trustee Williamstown Regional Art Conservation Lab., Inc., Mass., 1981-86; mem. panel Utilization Mus. Resources, NEA, 1988. Boston U. grantee, 1973, NEA Mus.' Profl. grantee, 1976-81; Samuel H. Kress Found. fellow, 1973; recipient Netherland-Am. Found. award Netherland Found., 1973, Disting. Alumni award Boston U. Grad. Sch., 1986. Mem. Assn. Art Mus. Dirs., Coll. Art Assn. Am., Am. Assn. Museums, New Eng. Mus. Assn., Historians of Netherlandish Art. Home: 16 Rutland Ter Worcester MA 01609-1664 Office: Worcester Art Mus 55 Salisbury St Worcester MA 01609-3123

WEMPLE, WILLIAM, lawyer; b. N.Y., Nov. 3, 1912; s. William Lester and Dorothy (Gunnels) W.; m. Dorothea Dutcher, Nov. 1, 1941; children: Littlepaige, Katharine Holland, William Barent, Leslie, Wendy, Stephanie, Liana Ashley. AB, Harvard U., 1934; LLB, Columbia U., 1937. Bar: N.Y. 1938. Assoc. Cravath, deGersdorff, Swaine & Wood, N.Y.C., 1937-42; civilian with Office Gen. Counsel, Navy Dept., 1942-43, 45-46; assoc. Dewey, Ballantine, Bushby, Palmer & Wood, N.Y.C., 1946-52, ptnr., 1952—. Mem. planning commn. Village of Scarsdale, N.Y., 1957-64; bd. dirs. Scarsdale Community Fund and Council, 1955-60. Served to lt. comdr. USNR, 1943-45. Fellow Am. Bar Found.; mem. ABA (council corp., banking and bus. law sect. 1976-80), Am. Law Inst., N.Y. State Bar Assn. (chmn. banking, corp. and bus. law sect. 1969-70). Republican. Club: Town (Scarsdale) (gov. 1959-62, 75-76, chmn. edn. com. 1976-77). Home: 36 Old Farm Rd Charlottesville VA 22903-4723 Office: Dewey Ballantine 1301 Ave of the Americas New York NY 10019

WEMPNER, GERALD ARTHUR, engineering educator; b. Waupun, Wis.; s. Paul Christian and Thekla Nelda (Jung) W.; m. Lorraine Bischel, Sept. 6, 1952 (div. Apr. 1983); children: Susan K., Paul J. BS, U. Wis., 1952, MS, 1953; PhD, U. Ill., 1957. Instr. U. Ill., Urbana, 1953-57, asst. prof., 1957-59; assoc. prof. U. Ariz., Tucson, 1959-62; prof. U. Ala., Huntsville, 1964-73; prof. Ga. Inst. Tech., Atlanta, 1973-91, prof. emeritus, 1991—; vis. prof. U. Calif., Berkeley, 1962-63. Author: Mechanics of Solids, 1973; co-author: Mechanics of Deformable Bodies, 1961, Mechanics of Solids, 1995; contbr. articles to profl. jours. With U.S. Army, 1946-48. NSF fellow, Stanford (Calif.) U., 1963-64, Sr. fellow Alexander von Humboldt Found., Germany, 1973, Killam fellow U. Calgary, Can., 1983. Fellow ASME (asssoc. editor 1976-83), Am. Acad. Mechanics. Avocations: art, sculpture, photography, woodwork. Home and Office: Ga Inst Tech Sch Engring 3397 Hidden Acres Dr Doraville GA 30340

WEN, HELEN HWA JUNG, nurse; b. Tainan, Taiwan, Feb. 9, 1935; came to U.S., 1967; d. Yong-Shing and Jung-Yong (Lee) Wu; m. Michael M. Wen, Sept. 4, 1956; children: Tony, Ted. Diploma nursing, St. Anthony Hosp. Med. Ctr., Rockford, Ill., 1979; B Health Profession, S.W. Tex. State U., 1988; MA in Human Svcs., St. Edward's U., Austin, Tex., 1992. Cert. occupational health nurse, cert. for Angiometry, cert. for Pulmonary FUnction Test, 1990, cert. Emergency Care Asst., 1995. Tchr. Chung Chang Grade Sch., Tainan, 1953-67; med. asst. Beloit (Wis.) Clinic, 1973-76; nursing asst. Carlye Nursing Home, Beloit, 1977; staff nurse, team leader, surg. and med. Beloit Meml. Hosp., 1979-80, staff nurse, team leader, 1979-80; staff nurse, team leader, occasional charge nurse Seton Med. Ctr., Austin, 1980-94; occupational health nurse, sr. nurse, CPR instr. Motorola Inc., Austin, 1986—. Instr. CPR Seton Good Health, Austin, 1992—. Mem. Austin Assn. Occupational Health Nurses.

WEN, SHIH-LIANG, mathematics educator; came to U.S., 1959; s. S.W. and C.F. (Hsiao) W.; children: Dennis, Andy, Jue. BS, Nat. Taiwan U., Taipei, 1956; MS, U. Utah, 1961; PhD, Purdue U., 1968. Assoc. research engr. The Boeing Co., Seattle, 1961-63; with dept. math Ohio U., Athens, 1968—, successively asst. prof., assoc. prof. and prof., chmn. dept. math., 1985-93; rsch. analyst Applied Math Rsch. Lab. USAF, Wright-Patterson AFB, Ohio, summer, 1972; vis. rsch. scientist Courant Inst. Math. Scis. NYU, 1978-79; hon. prof. Jiangxi U., People's Republic of China, 1985; disting. vis. prof. Lanzhou U., People's Republic of China, 1989. Mem. Am. Math. Soc., Soc. for Indsl. and Applied Math., Math. Assn. Am. Avocations: fishing, bridge, music. Office: Ohio Univ Dept Of Math Athens OH 45701

WENDEBORN, RICHARD DONALD, retired manufacturing company executive; b. Winnipeg, Man., Can.; came to U.S., 1976; naturalized, 1948; s. Curtis and Rose (Lysecki) W.; m. Dorothy Ann Munn, Aug. 24, 1957; children: Margaret Gayle, Beverley Jane, Stephen Richard, Peter Donald, Ann Elizabeth. Diploma, Colo. Sch. Mines, 1952; grad. advanced mgmt. program, Harvard U., 1974. With Can. Ingersoll-Rand Co., Montreal, 1952—, gen. mgr., v.p., dir., 1968, pres., 1969-74, chmn. bd., 1976—; exec. v.p. Ingersoll-Rand Co., Woodcliff Lake, N.J., 1976-89; ret., 1989; mem. Can. Govt. Oil and Gas Tech. Exch. Program with USSR, 1972—, Minerals and Metals Mission to People's Republic of China, 1972—. Mem. Resource

Fund Colo. Sch. Mines; past pres., dir. Town and River Civic Assn. Mem. Machinery and Equipment Mfrs. Assn. Can. (bd. dirs. 1974—, past chmn.), Royal Palm Yacht Club (commodore 1994), Useppa Island Club, Tau Beta Pi. Home: 9990 Cypress Lake Dr Fort Myers FL 33919-6020

WENDEL, RICHARD FREDERICK, economist, educator, consultant; b. Chgo., Apr. 29, 1930; s. Elmer Carl and Victoria Matilda (Jeffrey) W.; m. Leslie Jane Travis, June 15, 1957; children: John Travis, Andrew Stewart. A.B., Augustana Coll., 1951; M.B.A., U. Pa., 1957, Ph.D. (fellow 1962-64), 1966. Asst. to pres. Flexonics Corp., Maywood, Ill., 1957-59; sales rep., product mgr. Kordite div. Nat. Distillers Corp., Macedon, N.Y., 1959-62; instr. Wharton Sch., U. Pa., 1964-65; asst. prof. mktg. Grad. Sch. Bus. Adminstrn., Washington U., St. Louis, 1965-69; assoc. prof. U. Conn., 1969-74, prof., 1974-90, prof. emeritus, 1990; mem. U.S. Census Field Adv. Commn., 1967-69; mem. acad. adv. commn. Bur. Labor Stats., U.S. Bur. Census Survey of Consumer Expenditures, 1971-76; mem. Conn. Export Devel. Council, Dept. Commerce, 1972-76; dir. Neon Software Inc. Author: (with M.L. Bell) Economic Importance of Highway Advertising, 1966; (with W. Gorman) Selling: Preparation. Persuasion. Strategy., 1983, 88; editor: Readings in Marketing, 1973-74, 75-76, 77-78, 78-79, 79-80, 80-81, (with C.L. Lapp) Add to Your Selling Know-How, 1968; editorial staff: jour. Mktg., 1965-74. Bd. dirs. Roper Center. Served with USAF, 1951-55. Center for Real Estate and Urban Econs. grantee, 1969-70. Mem. Am. Mktg. Assn., N.Y. Acad. Scis. Republican. Episcopalian. Home: Friendship Valley Brooklyn CT 06234

WENDEL, THOMAS MICHAEL, financial services company executive; b. Jamestown, N.D., July 15, 1936; s. Peter Thomas and Esther Marie (Jahnke) W.; m. Elise Ida Moennig, June 11, 1960; children—Gretchen, Heidi, Peter. B.S. in Math., Ursinus Coll., 1960; M.A. in Econs., San Jose State Coll., 1964; M.B.A., U. Santa Clara, 1969. Exec. Pan Am World Airways, N.Y.C., 1971-81, chief fin. officer, 1981-82; dir., chief fin. officer PaineWebber Inc., N.Y.C., 1982-85, exec. v.p., mng. dir., div. dir. fin. instns., 1985-86; pres., chief exec. officer Liberty Brokerage Inc., N.Y.C., 1986—. Author: Introduction to Data Processing: COBOL, 1969. Served with USMC, 1954-56. Nat. Def. fellow, 1960. Mem. Phi Kappa Phi. Office: Liberty Brokerage 77 Water St New York NY 10005-4401

WENDELIN, RUDOLPH ANDREW, artist; b. Herndon, Kans., Feb. 27, 1910; s. Paul Henry and Mary Wilhemina (Hauptman) W.; m. Carol Marie Bergmann, Mar. 11, 1944; children: Michael, David, Elizabeth. Student, U. Kans. Sch. Architects, 1929-32. Topographical draftsman U.S. Forest Svc./ USDA, Milw., 1933-34, exhibitor, illustrator, 1934-36; exhibitor, illustrator U.S. Forest Svc./USDA, Washington, 1934-73, ret., 1973; stamp designer U.S. Postal Svc., 1958, 60, 64, 69, 84; tchr. Holden Village, Lutheran Family Retreat Ctr., Chelan, Wash., 1981, 83; cons., artist Smokey Bear Program, 1973—. Designer Smokey Bear costume, 1952, Forest Conservation Stamp, 1958, Range Conservation Stamp, 1961, John Muir Commemorative Stamp, 1961, John Wesley Powell Stamp, 1969, Smokey Bear Commemorative Stamp, 1984, Centennial Stamp, 1991; co-designer Fifth World Forestry Congress Stamp, 1960; contbr. concepts Woodsy Owl, 1970, Spunky Squirrel, Am. Forestery Assn., 1981; illustrator: The City that Forgot Christmas, 1968; one-man show at Gifford Pinchot Inst. for Conservation Studies, Milford, Pa., 1984, Fed. Bldg. Plz., Milw., 1987, State Capitol, Topeka, Kans., 1987, Ludell (Kans.) Day, 1989, Rawlins County (Kans.) Hist. Mus., 1989; exhibited in group shows at Univ. Club, Washington, 1990, 91, Cosmos Club, Washington, 1990, George Mason Law Sch. Gallery, 1992; works represented in numerous pub. and pvt. collections. Mem. neighborhood conservation Arlington County, Va., 1955; active Arlington County Hist. Commn., 1960. With USN, 1942-45. Recipient Horace Hard award Graphic Arts Industry, 1969. Democrat. Home: 4516 7th St N Arlington VA 22203-2010

WENDELSTEDT, HARRY HUNTER, JR., umpire; b. Balt., July 27, 1938; m. Cheryl Maher, Nov. 2, 1970; children: Harry III, Amy. Student, Essex Community Coll.; BS in Edn., U. Md. Profl. baseball umpire, 1962—; with minor leagues, Ga.-Fla., 1962 (Northwest), 1963, Tex., 1964 (Internat.), 1965; with maj. leagues (Nat.). 1966—; umpire All-Star Game, 1968, 76, 83, 92, Nat. League championship series, 1970, 72, 77, 80, 82, 84, 88, 90, World Series, 1973, 80, 86, 91; owner, operator Harry Wendelstedt Umpire Sch. Named Top Umpire in Maj. League Baseball Md. Profl. Baseball Players Assns., 1975, Best Umpire in Nat. League Chgo. Tribune, 1982, Best Ball and Strike Umpire Sports Illustrated, 1982, Major League Umpire of Yr., 1992, Fla. Diamond Club, 1993. Mem. Major League Umpires Assn. (4 term past pres.). Office: Major League Umpires Assn 88 S St Andrews Dr Ormond Beach FL 32174-3857

WENDER, HERBERT, title company executive. Office: CMAC Investment Corp 1601 Market St Philadelphia PA 19103*

WENDER, IRA TENSARD, lawyer; b. Pitts., Jan. 5, 1927; s. Louis and Luba (Kibrick) W.; m. Phyllis M. Bellows, June 24, 1966; children: Justin B., Sarah T.; children by previous marriage: Theodore M., Matthew G., Abigail A., John B. Student Swarthmore Coll., 1942-45; JD, U. Chgo., 1948; LLM, NYU, 1951. Atty. Lord, Day and Lord, N.Y.C., 1950-52, 54-59; asst. dir. internat. program in taxation Harvard U. Law Sch., 1952-54; lectr. N.Y. U. Sch. Law, N.Y.C., 1954-59; ptnr. Baker and McKenzie, Chgo., 1959-61, founding ptnr. N.Y.C. office, 1961-71; sr. ptnr. Wender, Murase & White, 1971-82, of counsel, 1982-86; chmn. C. Brewer and Co., Ltd., Honolulu, 1969-75; pres., chief exec. officer A.G. Becker Paribas Inc., 1978-82; chmn., chief exec. officer Sussex Securities Inc., 1983-85; of counsel Patterson, Belknap, Webb & Tyler, N.Y.C., 1986-87, ptnr., 1988-93, of counsel, 1994, chmn. Perry Ellis Internat., Inc., N.Y.C., 1994; bd. dirs. REFAC Tech. Devel. Corp., N.Y.C., South and West Property Trust, Inc., Dallas, Dime Bancorp, Inc. Bd. mgrs. Swarthmore Coll., 1978-89; pres., bd. mgrs. PARC Vendome Condominium, 1990-94; trustee Brearley Sch., N.Y.C., 1980-85, Putney (Vt.) Sch., 1985—; active Council on Fgn. Relations. Mem. Am., N.Y. State bar assns., Assn. of Bar of City of N.Y. Author: (with E.R. Barlow) Foreign Investment and Taxation, 1955. Home: 340 W 57th St New York NY 10019 Office: Patterson Belknap Webb & Tyler 1133 Ave of the Americas New York NY 10036

WENDER, PAUL ANTHONY, chemistry educator. BS, Wilkes Coll., 1969; PhD, Yale U., 1973; PhD (hon.), Wilkes U., 1993. Asst. prof., assoc. prof. Harvard U., 1974-81; prof. Stanford U., 1981—, 1993—; cons. Eli Lilly & Co., 1980—, lectr. Am. Chem. Soc. Recipient Arthur C. Cope Sholan award Am. Chem. Soc., 1990, Guenther award Am. Chem Soc., ICI Am. Chem. award Stuart Pharmaceut, NIH Merit award. Mem. AAAS, Am. Chem. Soc. Office: Stanford U Dept Chemistry Stanford CA 94305*

WENDER, PHYLLIS BELLOWS, literary agent; b. N.Y.C., Jan. 6, 1934; d. Lee and Lillian (Frank) Bellows; m. Ira Tensard Wender, June 24, 1966; children: Justin Bellows, Sarah Tensard. B.A., Wells Coll., 1956. Asst. advt dir. Book Find Club, N.Y.C., 1957-58; publicity dir. Grove Press, N.Y.C., 1958-61, Dell Pub. Co., N.Y.C., 1961-63; theatrical agt. Artists Agy. Inc., N.Y.C., 1963-68; agt. Wender & Assocs., 1968-81; writers' agt. Rosenstone/Wender, N.Y.C., 1981—. Bd. dirs. Just Women Inc., Bklyn., 1982, mem. adv. com., 1983-87; bd. dirs. Fortune Soc., N.Y.C., 1977-80; trustee Wells Coll., Aurora, N.Y., 1981-90. Mem. Women's Media Group (dir. 1988-90). Club: Cosmopolitan (N.Y.C.). Office: Rosenstone/Wender 3 E 48th St New York NY 10017-1027

WENDEROTH, COLLIER, JR., food products executive; b. 1923. Chmn. bd. O. K. Instries Inc., Fort Smith, Ariz., 1985—. With U.S. Army, 1948-55. Office: O K Industries Inc 700 S B St Fort Smith AR 72901*

WENDERS, WIM, motion picture director; b. Dusseldorf, Germany, Aug. 14, 1945. Dir. films including Summer in the City, 1970, The Goalie's Anxiety at the Penalty Kick, 1972, The Scarlet Letter, 1974, Alice in the Cities, 1974, The Wrong Move, 1975, Kings of the Road, 1976, The American Friend, 1977, Lightning Over Water (Nick's Movie) (with Nicholas Ray), 1980, The State of Things, 1982, Hammett, 1982; Paris, Texas, 1984 (Palme d'Or, Cannes Internat. Film Festival), Tokyo-Ga, 1985, Wings of Desire, 1987 (Best Dir., Cannes Internat. Film Festival), Aufzeichnungen zu Kleiderund Stadten, 1989, Until the End of the World, 1991, Far Away, So

Close, 1993 (Cannes Internat. Film Festival Grand Prize). Office: Gray City Inc 853 Broadway New York NY 10007 Office: Paul Kohner Agy 9169 Sunset Blvd Los Angeles CA 90069*

WENDORF, DENVER FRED, JR., anthropology educator; b. Terrell, Tex., July 31, 1924; s. Denver Fred and Margaret (Hall) W.; children: Frederick Carl, Michael Andrew, Gail Susan, Cynthia Ann, Kelly Peta, Scott Frederick. B.A., U. Ariz., 1948; M.A., Harvard U., 1950, Ph.D., 1953. Research assoc. Mus. N.Mex., Santa Fe, 1950-56; assoc. dir. Mus. N.Mex., 1958-64; assoc. prof. Tex. Tech U., Lubbock, 1956-58; prof. anthropology So. Meth. U., Dallas, 1964—; chmn. dept. anthropology So. Meth. U., 1968-74, Henderson-Morrison prof. prehistory, 1974—; dir. Ft. Burgwin Research Ctr., Taos, N.Mex., 1957-76. Author: numerous books including The Prehistory of Nubia, 1968, The Midland Discovery, 1955, Paleoecology of the Llano Estacado, 1961, A Guide to Salvage Archaeology, Prehistory of the Eastern Sahara, 1980; also articles. Chmn. Tex. State Antiquities Com., 1969-82; mem. Nat. Park System Adv. Bd., 1983-87, chmn., 1985-87; mem. Cultural Properties Adv. Bd., 1984-90. Served with AUS, 1943-47. Decorated Purple Heart; decorated Bronze Star. Mem. Soc. for Am. Archaeology (treas. 1974-77, pres. 1979-81), Nat. Acad. Scis. Home: 401 S Centre Ave Lancaster TX 75146-3830

WENDORF, HULEN DEE, law educator, author, lecturer; b. West, Tex., Oct. 29, 1916; s. Reinhardt and Laura (Blume) W.; m. Mary Jane Pfeffer, June 13, 1939; children: Robert Joseph, Donald Joseph, Florence Ann. BS, U.S. Mil. Acad., 1939; JD, Yale U., 1951. Bar: Conn. 1951, Tex. 1961, U.S. Ct. Mil. Appeals 1952, U.S. Supreme Ct. 1958, U.S. Dist. Ct. 1960. Commd. 2d lt. U.S. Army, 1939, advanced through grades to col., ret. as chief of adminstrv. law div. Office Judge Adv. Gen., 1959; practice El Paso, Tex., 1959-61; prof. law Baylor U. Law Sch., 1961-86, prof. emeritus, 1986—; former chmn. and long-time mem. Citizens Adv. Com. to Juvenile Judge; former dir. Heart of Tex. Legal Aid Assn. Author: Texas Law of Evidence Manual, 1983, 3d rev. edit., 1991, also 3 law sch. casebooks; columnist United Retirement Bull.; contbr. various articles to law revs. Rsch. dir. Texans War on Drugs, 1980-81; chmn. Food For People, 1981—; elder, Presbyn. Ch. Decorated Legion of Merit, Bronze Star, Army Commendation medal. Mem. Waco-McLennan County Bar Assn. (former dir., former v.p.), Phi Delta Phi. Home: 2808 Cumberland Ave Waco TX 76707-1324

WENDORF, RICHARD HAROLD, library director, educator; b. Cedar Rapids, Iowa, Mar. 17, 1948; s. Harold Albert and Jeanne Ellen (Hamblin) W.; m. Barbara Hilderman, Sept. 12, 1970 (div. 1983); m. Diana Thanet French, Jan. 1, 1984; children: Reed Thanet Wendorf-French, Carolyn Thanet Wendorf-French. BA, Williams Coll., 1970; PhB, U. Oxford, Eng., 1972; MA, Princeton U., 1974, PhD, 1976. From asst. prof. English to assoc. prof. English Northwestern U., Evanston, Ill., 1976-86, assoc. dean, 1984-88, prof. English and art history, 1986-89; libr. dir. Houghton Libr., Harvard U., Cambridge, Mass., 1989—; sr. lectr. fine arts Harvard UY., 1990—; acting libr. Fine Arts Libr., Harvard U., 1991-92; lectr. Phi Beta Kappa Assocs., 1992—; dir. NEH summer seminars for coll. tchrs., Northwestern U., 1987, Harvard U., 1990, 92; Robert Sterling Clark vis. prof. art history Williams Coll., 1993. Author: William Collins and Eighteenth-Century English Poetry, 1981, The Elements of Life: Biography and Portrait-Painting in Stuart and Georgian England, 1990, paperback, 1991; editor: Articulate Images: The Sister Arts from Hogarth to Tennyson, 1983, Rare Book and Manuscript Libraries in the Twenty-First Century, 1993; editor (with Charles Ryskamp) The Works of William Collins, 1979; contbr. essays in field; mem. editl. bds. Studies in Eighteenth-Century Culture, 1985-89, Word and Image, 1992-95, Yale Edn. of the Writings of Samuel Johnson, 1992—. Rsch. grantee Folger Shakespeare Libr., Washington, 1976, Am. Philos. Soc., 1982, 87, Henry E. Huntington Libr., 1979, Yale Ctr. for Brit. Art, 1983; jr. rsch. fellow Am. Coun. Learned Socs., 1978-79; summer stipend NEH, 1979; sr. rsch. fellow Am. Coun. Learned Socs., 1981-82; NEH rsch. fellow Newberry Libr., Chgo., 1988-89; fellow John Simon Guggenheim Meml. Found., 1989-90. Mem. Signet Soc. (assoc.), Harvard Faculty Shop Club, Saturday Club, Cambridge Sci. Club, Club of Odd Volumes, Colonial Soc. Mass., Nat. Com. on Stds. in Arts, Keats-Shelley Assn. of Am. (dir. 1993—), Williams Club, The Johnsonians (chmn. 1994-95), Am. Soc. for 18th Century Studies (pres. Midwest regional soc. 1986), Grolier Club, Coll. Art Assn., Soc. Brit. Art Historians, Phi Beta Kappa (exec. bd. Chgo. 1984-87). Office: The Houghton Library Harvard U Cambridge MA 02138

WENDOWSKI, KATHLEEN CECELIA, hospital administrator; b. Phila., Aug. 12, 1933; d. William Harry and Eleanor Cecelia (Commo) Strain; m. Leonard Edwin Wendowski Sr., June 4, 1955; children: Leonard E. Jr., Joseph I., Steven Paul, Thomas Lester. Diploma in Nursing, Meth. Hosp., Phila., 1955; BS in Nursing Edn., Temple U., 1972; M Health Adminstrn., Jersey City State Coll., 1987. RN, N.J., Pa., Md. Nursing positions various hosps., 1958-84; dir. nursing Rancocas Valley Hosp., Willingboro, N.J., 1972-74; med. mgr. Afcon Ambulatory Care, Phila., 1974-75; dir. nursing Wallkill Valley Gen. Nee Alexander Linn Hosp., Sussex, N.J., 1976-81; asst. adminstr., adminstr. health ctr. ambulatory care Wallkill Valley Gen. Hoep., Sussex, 1982-84; pvt. cons. Leska Enterprises, Fairfield, N.J., 1984-86; dir. nursing Kennedy Meml. Hosp., Cherry Hill, N.J., 1984; asst. adminstr. Bayonne (N.J.) Hosp., 1986-91; adminstr. Oakridge Manor Nursing Home, Wayne, N.J., 1992—. Vol. Boy Scouts Am., 1980-84, 87—; bd. dirs. Am. Lung Assn. Central N.J., 1988-91, chmn. Bayonne adv. unit, 1989-91; chmn. program com. Am. Heart Assn., 1978-84; mem. edn. com. Am. Cancer Soc., 1988-91; participator March of Dimes, 1982-88; chmn. Teen Health Edn. and Svcs. Com. Bayonne, 1986-91; mem. adv. com. Bayonne Office on Aging, 1986-91; sec. Mayor's Task Force on AIDS, Bayonne, 1986-91. Mem. Am. Health Care Assn., N.J. Assn. Health Care Fac., N.J. Health Care Execs. (membership chmn. 1989-90), Am. Coll. Health Care Execs., N.J. Nat. League for Nursing, Am. Hosp. Assn., N.J. Soc. Respiratory Care, Inc., Midatlantic Health Congress, Wallkill Valley C. of C. (chmn. pub. rels.), N.W. Health and Breath Assn. (bd. dirs. 1977-91), N.J. Adult Day Care Assn., Soroptimists (pres. local chpt. 1980-84, 88-90), Bayonne Kiwanis, 1989—. Home: 158 Sand Rd Fairfield NJ 07004-1574 Office: Oakridge Manor Nursing Ctr 261 Terhune Dr Wayne NJ 07470

WENDT, CHARLES WILLIAM, soil physicist, educator; b. Plainview, Tex., July 12, 1931; s. Charles Gottlieb and Winnie Mae (Bean) W.; m. Clara Anne Diller, Oct. 15, 1955; children: Charles Diller, John William, Elaine Anne, Cynthia Lynne. B.S. in Agronomy, Tex. A&M U., 1951, Ph.D. in Soil Physics, 1966; M.S. in Agronomy, Tex. Tech U., 1957. Research asst. Tex. Tech Coll., 1953-55, instr. agronomy, 1957-61, asst. prof., 1961-63; research asst. soil physics Tex. A&M U., 1963-65, research assoc., 1965-66; asst. prof. Tex. A&M U. (Agrl. Research and Extension Center), Lubbock, 1966-69; assoc. prof. Tex. A&M U. (Agrl. Research and Extension Center), 1969-74, prof., 1974-91, prof. emeritus, 1991—; cons. cotton prodn. Ministry of Agr. Sudan, summer 1960; cons. Irrigation Assn., 1977-81, Office of Tech. and Assessment, 1982, S.E. Consortium for Internat. Devel., 1989, Rhone Poulenc Agri. Co., 1992-93; prin. backstop scientist U.S. AID West African Rsch. Program on Soil-Plant-Water Mgmt., 1982—; chmn. agrl. sect. Southwestern and Rocky Mountain div. AAAS, 1982-83. Contbr. articles to profl. jours., chpt. to book. Del. Lubbock County Rep. Conv., 1978; elder Westminster Presbyn. Ch.; Tex. rep. to Great Plains Coun. 1 com. on evapo-transpiration. 1st lt. U.S. Army, 1951-53. Named Outstanding Researcher High Plains Research Found., 1982; recipient Superior Achievement award for rsch., soil and crop scis. dept. Tex. A&M Univ., 1987; grantee industry and water dists. Dept. Interior, U.S. AID, EPA. Mem. Soil Sci. Soc. Am., Am. Soc. Agronomy, Brit. Plant Growth Regulator Soc., Optimist Club (1st v.p., bd. dirs.), Sigma Xi, Phi Kappa Phi. Home: 4518 22nd St Lubbock TX 79407-2515 Office: Texas Agrl Expt Station RR 3 Lubbock TX 79401-9803

WENDT, E. ALLAN, ambassador; b. Chgo., Nov. 8, 1935; s. John Arthur Frederick and Dorothy Hannah (Stephenson) W. BA magna cum laude, Yale U., 1957; certificat d'Etudes Politique, Institut d'Etudes Politiques, Paris, 1959; MPA, Harvard U., 1967. Econ. commnl. officer Am. Embassy Am. Embassy, Saigon, Vietnam, 1961-71; fin. officer U.S. Mission to European Cmtys., Brussels, 1971-74; State Dept. fellow Coun. on Fgn. Rels., N.Y.C., 1974-75; dir. Office Internat. Commodities, Dept. State, Washington, 1975-79; counselor for econ. and commnl. affairs Am. Embassy, Cairo, 1979-81; dep. asst. sec. of state for internat. energy and resources policy

Dept. State, 1981-86, sr. rep. for strategic tech. policy, 1987-92, with rank of amb., 1988-92; amb. to Republic of Slovenia Ljubljana, 1993—. Contbr. articles to profl. jours. Recipient award for heroism Dept. State, 1968, Presdl. Meritorious Svc. award, 1986, Superior Honor award Dept. State 1992. Mem. Coun. Fgn. Rels. Episcopalian. Avocation: tennis. Office: Dept State Ljubljana Washington DC 20521-7140

WENDT, GEORGE ROBERT, actor; b. Chgo., Oct. 17, 1948; m. Bernadette Birkette; children: Joshua, Andrew, Hilary. BA in Econs., Rockhurst Coll., 1971. Mem. Second City comedy troupe, Chgo., 1974-81. Actor: (feature films) My Bodyguard, 1980, Somewhere in Time, 1980, Airplane II: The Sequel, 1982, Jeckyl & Hyde: Together Again, 1982, The Women in Red, 1984, Thief of Hearts, 1984, No Small Affair, 1983, Fletch, 1985, House, 1986, Plain Clothes, 1988, Guilt by Suspicion, 1991, Forever Young, 1992, Man of the House, 1995; guest-star: (TV shows) Alice, Soap, Taxi, Hart to Hart, The American Dream; regular (TV show) Cheers, 1982-1993, The George Wendt Show, 1995; appeared in various commls.; appeared on stage with the Second City comedy troupe, also Wild Men, 1993. *

WENDT, HANS W., life scientist; b. Berlin, July 25, 1923; came to U.S., 1953; naturalized, 1967; s. Hans O. and Alice (Creutzburg) W.; m. Martha A. Linger, Dec. 23, 1956 (div. 1979); children: Alexander, Christopher, Sandra; m. Judith A. Hammer, June 25, 1988. MSc, U. Hamburg, Germany, 1949; PhD in Psychopharmacology, U. Marburg, Germany, 1953. Psychology diploma, Germany. Rsch. asst. U. Marburg, 1949-53; rsch. assoc. Wesleyan U. and Office Naval Rsch., Middletown, Conn., 1952-53; asst. prof., field dir. internat. project U. Mainz, Germany, 1955-59; engring. psychologist to prin. human factors scientist Link Aviation, Apollo Simulator Systems, Binghamton, N.Y., 1959-61; assoc. to prof. psychology Valparaiso (Ind.) U., 1961-68; prof. psychology Macalester Coll., St. Paul, 1968-93; rsch. fellow chronobiology U. Minn., Mpls., 1980—, cons. behavioral geomedicine, 1994—; vis. scholar Harvard U., 1953-54; cons. and reviewer, 1961—; hon. prof. sci. U. Marburg, Germany, 1971—; vis. prof. U. Victoria, B.C., Can., U. Marburg, U. Bochum, Germany, U. Bielefeld, Germany, U. Goettingen, Germay, 1966-89. Contbr. articles to profl. jours., chpts. to books. Recipient Disting. Sr. Scientist award, Alexander von Humboldt Found., 1976. Mem. Internat. Soc. Biometeorology, Internat. Soc. Chronobiology, Bioelectromagnetics Soc., Soc. Sci. Exploration, others. Home: 2180 Lower Saint Dennis Rd Saint Paul MN 55116-2831

WENDT, HENRY, III, pharmaceutical company executive; b. Neptune City, N.J., July 19, 1933; s. Henry II and Rachel L. (Wood) W.; m. Holly Peterson, June 23, 1956; children: Henry IV, Laura. AB, Princeton U., 1955. With Kline & French Labs, Phila., 1955-70, v.p. mktg., gen. mgr., 1970-71; pres., chief operating officer Smith Kline Corp., Phila., 1971-76, also bd. dirs.; chief exec. officer SmithKline Beckman Corp., Phila., 1982-87, pres., 1982, chmn., from 1987; now chmn. SmithKline Beecham, Phila.; bd. dirs. Atlantic Richfield Co., Allergan, Inc., Beckman Instruments, Inc., Wiggins, Teape & Appleton. Contbr. articles to profl. jours. Member adv. coun. dept. East Asian studies Princeton U. Mme. Japan Soc., U.S.-Japan Bus. Coun. (chmn.). Also: SmithKline Beecham PLC, New Horizons Ct, Great West Rd, Brentford Middlesex TW8 9EP, England

WENDT, LLOYD, writer; b. Spencer, S.D., May 16, 1908; s. Leo L. and Marie (Nylen) W.; m. Helen Sigler, June 16, 1932 (dec. June 1989); 1 child, Bette Joan; m. Martha Teale, 1981. Student, Sioux Falls Coll., 1928-29; S.B., Northwestern U., 1931, MS, 1934. Reporter, later columnist, drama reviewer Sioux Falls (S.D.) Press, 1927-28; publicity dir. S.D. Democratic Central Com., 1928; reporter Daily Argus-Leader, 1929, telegraph editor, 1932-33; also tchr. journalism Sioux Falls Coll.; joined staff Chgo. Tribune, 1934; as reporter, becoming spl. feature writer mag. sect., later editor Grafic mag., Sunday editor, until 1961, also Sunday editor, asso. editor, 1975-77; editor Chgo.'s Am. newspaper, 1961-69; pub., editor Chgo. Today, 1969-74, also pres.; lectr. fiction writing Northwestern U., 1946; chmn. fiction div. Medill Sch. Journalism, 1950-53. Free lance writer, 1977—; author: (with Herman Kogan) Lords of the Levee, 1943, Gunners Get Glory, 1944, Bright Tomorrow, 1945, Bet a Million, (with Herman Kogan) 1948, Give the Lady What She Wants, (with H. Kogan), 1952, Big Bill of Chicago, (with H. Kogan), 1953, Chicago: A Pictorial History, (with H. Kogan), 1958, Chicago Tribune, the Rise of a Great American Newspaper, 1979, The Wall Street Journal, the Story of Dow Jones and the Nation's Business Newspaper, 1982, Swift Walker, informal biography of Gurdon Saltonstall Hubbard, 1986 (non-fiction award Chgo. Found. for Lit., 1986). Pres. Soc. Midland Authors, 1947-50. Served to lt. comdr. USNR, 1942-46. Recipient Disting. Svc. award Nat. Soc. Journalists, 1980. Home: 4025 Murfield Dr E Bradenton FL 34203-4036

WENDZEL, ROBERT LEROY, political science educator; b. May 28, 1938; married; 3 children. BA in Polit. Sci. magna cum laude, Kalamazoo Coll., 1960; PhD in Polit. Sci., U. Fla., 1965. Assoc. prof. polit. sci. U. Maine, Orono, 1977-81, 82-83; prof. internat. affairs U.S. Air War Coll., Maxwell AFB, Ala., 1981-82; asst. dean arts & scis., prof. polit. sci., coord. internat. affairs program U. Maine, 1984-86; prof. internat. politics U.S. Air War Coll., Maxwell AFB, 1986-87, ednl. advisor to the Commandant, 1987—; mem. internat. affairs com., U. Maine, 1977-80, budget adv. com., 1983-86, coord. internat. affairs program, 1984-86. Author: International Relations: A Policymaker Focus, Thai edit., 1989, Relacoes Internacionais, 1985, International Politics: Policymakers and Policymaking, 1981, International Relations: A Policymaker Focus, 1977, 2d edit., 1980; co-author: America's Foreign Policy in a Changing World, 1994, Defending America's Security, 1983, 2d edit., 1990, To Preserve the Republic: The Foreign Policy of the United States, 1985; contbr. articles to profl. jours. Mem. Phi Beta Kappa. Home: 160 Old Field Dr Montgomery AL 36117 Office: Air War Coll Maxwell AFB AL

WENGER, LARRY BRUCE, law librarian, law educator; b. Everett, Wash., Dec. 21, 1941; s. Lester Edwin Wenger and Selma Marie (Norberg) W. Saterstrom; m. Marilyn Diane Watt, June 26, 1965; children: Bruce Daniel, Kathleen Marie. BA, U. Wash., 1964, JD, 1967; MLS, Simmons Coll., 1969. Reference libr. Sch. Law Harvard U., Cambridge, Mass., 1967-69; asst. law libr. SUNY, Buffalo, 1969-71, law libr., assoc. prof. law, 1971-76; law libr., prof. law U. Va., Charlottesville, 1976—; cons. to law librs.; bd. dirs. Nat. Ctr. for Preservation Law. Mem. Am. Assn. Law Librs., Internat. Assn. Law Libraries, Bibliog. Soc., Bibliog. Soc. Am. Home: 2630 Meriwether Dr Charlottesville VA 22901-9513 Office: U Va Law Libr N Grounds Charlottesville VA 22901

WENGER, LUKE HUBER, educational association executive, editor; b. Ephrata, Pa., Oct. 23, 1939; s. Luke Martin and Elva B. (Huber) W. BA., Eastern Mennonite Coll., Harrisonburg, Va., 1962; postgrad., U. Gottingen, W.Ger., 1962; U. Munich, W.Ger., 1967-78; Ph.D., Harvard U., 1973. Editor, asst. exec. dir. Medieval Acad. Am., Cambridge, Mass., 1973-81, exec. dir., 1981—. Editor: Speculum: A Jour. of Medieval Studies, 1981—. Fulbright fellow, 1962-63; Woodrow Wilson fellow, 1963-64; German Acad. Exchange fellow, 1967-68. Office: Speculum Jour Medieval Studies Medieval Acad of America 1430 Massachusetts Ave Cambridge MA 02138-3810

WENGER, VICKI, interior designer; b. Indpls., Aug. 30, 1928. Ed., U. Nebr., Internat. Inst. Interior Design, Parsons in Paris. Pres. Vicki Wenger Interiors, Bethesda, Md., 1963-71, Washington, 1982—; pres. Beautiful Spaces Inc., Washington, 1982—; chief designer Creative Design, Capitol Heights, Md., 1969-84; lectr. Nat. Assn. Home Builders, 1983-88; mem. programs com. D.C. Assn. Home Builders, 1983-88. Author-host: (patented TV interior design show) Beautiful Spaces 1984; producer, host (cable TV show) Design Edition, 1988—. Designer Gourmet Gala, March of Dimes, Washington, 1986-88; decorator showhouse Nat. Symphony Orch., Washington, 1983-94, chmn. women's com., 1991-92; decorator showhouse Am. Cancer Soc., Washington, 1983, Alexandria Comty. YWCA, 1990. Mem. Am. Soc. Interior Designers (profl., nat. bd. dirs. 1973-75, nat. examining com. 1977-78, pres. Md. chpt. 1976, bd. dirs. Washington Metro chpt. 1989-91, pres.-elect 1995, mem. pres.'s barrier free com. 1980), Nat. Trust Hist. Preservation, Smithsonian Instn. (sponsor), Nat. Presss Club. Democrat. Presbyterian. Office: Vicki Wenger Interiors 2801 New Mexico Ave NW Washington DC 20007-3921

WENGERT, NORMAN IRVING, political science educator; b. Milw., Nov. 7, 1916; s. Eugene F. and Lydia (Semmann) W.; m. Janet Mueller, Oct. 9, 1940; children: Eugene Mark, Christine Ann, Timothy John. B.A., U. Wis., 1938, J.D., 1942, Ph.D., 1947; M.A., Fletcher Sch., 1939. With TVA, 1941-48; faculty Case Coll. N.Y., 1948-51; mem. program staff Office Sec. Dept. Interior, 1951-52; prof., chmn. social sci. dept. N.D. State U., Fargo, 1952-56; research asso. Resources for Future, Inc., 1956; prof. pub. adminstrn. U. Md., 1956-59; dep. dir. Nat. Outdoor Recreation Resources Rev. Com., 1959-60; prof., chmn. dept. polit. sci. Wayne State U., Detroit, 1960-68; vis. prof. pub. adminstrn. Pa. State U., 1968-69; prof. polit. sci. Colo. State U., Ft. Collins, 1969-87, prof. emeritus; mem. policy analysis staff Office of Chief, U.S. Forest Service, 1978-79; vis. rsch. prof. U.S. Army Engr. Inst. Water resources, 1969-70; Royer lectr. U. Calif., Berkeley, 1975; lectr. U. Sarajevo, Yugoslavia, summer 1978, NATO Adv. Study Inst., Sicily, summer 1981; lectr. U. Linkoping, Sweden, summer, 1984; spl. adviser Govt. of India on food, agr., 1959; cons. U.S. Army Corps Engrs., 1968, Thorne Ecol. Inst., 1972-75, FAA, 1963, Atlantic Richfield Oil Corp., 1973-74, Nat. Water Quality Commn., 1974—, Office Water Resources and Tech., USDI, 1973-75, and states Colo., Md., Ga., Mich., also Western Interstate Nuclear Bd.; summer fellow Fonds für Umweltstudien, Bonn, Germany, 1973; cons. No. Colo. Water Conservancy Dist., 1988—; mem. comn. NAS/NRC. 1990. Author: Valley of Tomorrow: TVA and Agriculture, 1952, Natural Resources and the Political Struggle, 1955, Administration of Natural Resources, 1961, (with George M. Walker, Jr.) Urban Water Policies and Decision Making in Detroit Metro Region, 1970, Urban-Metropolitan Institutions for Water Planning, Development and Management, 1972, Impact on the Human Environment of Proposed Oil Shale Development in Garfield County, 1974, Property Rights in Land: A Comparative Exploration of German and American Concepts and Problems, 1974, Public Participation in Water Resources Development, 1974, The Political Allocation of Burdens and Benefits: Externalities and Due Process in Environmental Protection, 1976, Regional Factors in Siting and Managing Energy Facilities in the Eleven Western States, 1976, The Purposes of the National Forests, 1979; also chpts. in other books.; editor: (with others) Institutions for Urban-Metropolitan Water Management, 1972, Natural Resources Jour. issue, 1979; co-editor: (with others) The Energy Crisis: Reality or Myth, 1973; contbg. author: Planning the Use and Management of Land, 1979, Unified River Basin Management, 1981, Encyclopedia of Policy Studies, 1983, Operation of Complex Water Systems, 1983. Served as ensign USNR, 1944-45. Mem. Western Polit. Sci. Assn., Am. Soc. Pub. Adminstrn., State Bar Wis. (emeritus), Forest Hist. Soc. , Soil Conservation Soc. Am. (Nat. Honor award 1982), Order of Coif, Sigma Xi, Phi Kappa Phi. Home: 1225 Teakwood Dr Fort Collins CO 80525-1957

WENGLOWSKI, GARY MARTIN, economist; b. Rochester, N.Y., Sept. 2, 1942; s. Henry Bernard and Isabelle (Franc) W.; m. Joyce Richards, Oct. 3, 1964; children: Gary Martin, Catherine Jean. B.S. in Econs., U. Pa., 1964, M.A. (NDEA fellow), 1965, Ph.D. in Econs. (NDEA fellow), 1967. With Goldman Sachs & Co., N.Y.C., 1967—, v.p., economist, 1972-78, ptnr., dir. econ. research, 1978-86, ltd. ptnr., 1986—; adj. prof. NYU, Pace U.; tech. cons. The Bus. Coun., 1982-85; chmn. vis. com. econ. dept. U. Pa., 1985—. Author: Industry Profit Forecasting, 1972, Industry Profit Forecasting—Progress Report, 1975. Trustee CARE Found., 1991—, Haystack Mountain Sch., 1994—. Named Best Economist on Wall St., Ann. Instnl. Investor Mag. Polls, 1976-86. Fellow Nat. Assn. Bus. Economists; mem. Am. Econ. Assn., Deer Isle Yacht Club (vice commodire 1993-94, commodore 1994—). Office: Goldman Sachs & Co 85 Broad St Fl 2 New York NY 10004-2434

WENK, DANIEL N., landmark site administrator. Supt. Mt. Rushmore Nat. Meml., Keystone, S.D. Office: Mt Rushmore Nat Meml PO Box 268 Keystone SD 57751-0268*

WENK, EDWARD, JR., civil engineer, policy analyst, educator; b. Balt., Jan. 24, 1920; s. Edward and Lillie (Heller) W.; m. Carolyn Frances Lyford, Dec. 27, 1941; children: Lawrence Shelley, Robin Edward Alexander, Terry Allan. BE, Johns Hopkins U., 1940, DEng, 1950; MSc, Harvard U., 1947; DSc (hon.), U. R.I., 1968; LHD (hon.), Johns Hopkins U., 1989. Registered profl. engr. Head structures div. USN David Taylor Model Basin, Washington, 1942-56; chmn. dept. engring. mechanics S.W. Research Inst., San Antonio, 1956-59; sr. specialist sci. and tech. Legis. Reference Service, Library of Congress, Washington, 1959-61; chief sci. policy research div. Legis. Reference Service, Library of Congress, 1964-66; tech. asst. to U.S. President's sci. adviser and exec. sec. Fed. Council for Sci. and Tech., White House, Washington, 1961-64; exec. sec. Nat. Council on Marine Resources and Engring. Devel., Exec. Office of Pres., Washington, 1966-70; prof. engring. and pub. affairs U. Wash., Seattle, 1970-83, prof. emeritus, 1983—; dir. program in social mgmt. tech. U. Wash., 1973-79; tech. advisor to gov. State of Wash., 1993—; lectr. numerous univs.; cons. in pub. policy for environ. and tech. affairs, risk assessments, ocean engring., decision theory; Nat. Adv. Com. on Oceans and Atmosphere, 1972-73; vice chmn. U.S. Congress Tech. Assessment Adv. Council, 1973-79; adviser Congress, GAO, NSF, EPA, NOAA, White House, U.N. Secretariat, Wash. State, Alaska, U.K., Australia, Sweden, Philippines, Alaska Oil Spill Commn., 1989, Wash. State Marine Oversight Bd., 1992, pub. interest groups; vis. scholar Woodrow Wilson Internat. Center for Scholars, 1970-72, Harvard U., 1976, Woods Hole Oceanographic Instn., 1976, U. Sussex, 1977; tech. advisor to Wash. State gov. Author: The Politics of the Ocean, 1972, Margins for Survival, 1979, Tradeoffs-Imperatives of Choice in a High-Tech World, 1986, Making Waves–Engineering, Politics and the Social Management of Technology, 1995; editor: Engring. Mechs. Jour., 1958-60, Exptl. Mechs. Jour., 1954-56; mem. editl. bd. Tech. Forecasting, Tech. in Soc.; contbr. articles to profl. jours.; designer Aluminaut submarine, 1959; author of concept of tech. assessment, 1964. Bd. dirs. Human Interaction Research Inst., 1980-90, Smithsonian Sci. Info. Exchange., 1977-82, UPS Civilian, 1973-88. Ensign USNR, 1944-45. Recipient Navy Meritorious Civilian Svc. award, 1946; named Disting. Alumnus Johns Hopkins U., 1979, Tchr. of Yr., Wash. State Engrs., 1980, Tchr. of Yr., Students in Pub. Adminstrn., 1986, Disting. Alumnus, Balt. Poly. Inst., 1991; Ford Found. grantee, 1970; Rockefeller Found. Belagio fellow, 1976, 90; 1st Stuckenburg lectr. Wash. U., 1988; Regents lectr. U. Calif., Berkeley, 1989. Fellow ASME (exec.), AAAS; mem. ASCE, NSPE, Soc. Exptl. Mechs (past pres. and William M. Murray lectr.), Internat. Assn. Impact Assessment (pres. 1981-82), NAE (chmn. com. on pub. policy 1970-75), Nat. Acad. Pub. Adminstrn., Am. Soc. for Pub. Adminstrn. (chmn. com. on sci. and tech. in govt. 1974-78), Assembly Engring. and Marine Bd. NRC, Nat. Oceanography Assn. (v.p. pub. affairs 1979-72), Cousteau Soc. (chmn. adv. bd.), Explorers Club, Sigma Xi (nat. lectr.), Tau Beta Pi, Chi Epsilon. Club: Cosmos (Washington). Home: 111 Lake Ave W #302 Kirkland WA 98033-6155 *Each of us has the opportunity, indeed responsibility, to contribute to the human experience and to enrich the lives of future generations. In a world of change, cultural diversity and uncertainty, we must be ourselves and not merely slaves of conventional thought. We must act on the basis of what we believe to be right rather than only from the desire to be loved.*

WENNER, CHARLES RODERICK, lawyer; b. New Haven, Conn., Jan. 10, 1947; s. Charles Bellew and Joan Rhoda (Morrison) W. BS, Coll. Charleston, 1969; JD, U. Conn., 1973. Bar: Conn. D.C. 1977. Law clk. Conn. Superior Ct., Hartford, 1973-74; staff atty. SEC, Washington, 1974-76, spl. counsel to chmn., 1976-77; assoc. Fulbright & Jaworski, Washington, 1977-81, ptnr., 1981—; lectr. law Sch. Law U. Conn., 1973-74. Trustee Calvary United Meth. Ch., Arlington, Va., 1993-95; counselor Gospel Mission of Washington, 1991-95; bd. dirs. Operation Friendship Internat., Inc., Washington, 1993-95. Recipient Am. Hist. award DAR, Charleston, 1969. Mem. ABA, D.C. Bar Assn. Methodist. Avocations: running. Home: 1101 S Arlington Ridge Rd Arlington VA 22202-1951 Office: Fulbright & Jaworski 801 Pennsylvania Ave NW Washington DC 20004-2615

WENNER, GENE CHARLES, arts foundation executive; b. Catasauqua, Pa., Dec. 21, 1931; s. Clinton G. and Bertha (Taggert) W.; m. Carole Brunner, Aug. 15, 1953; children: Robert Larren, Laurel E. Wenner Carsell. BS in Music, West Chester (Pa.) State Coll., 1953; M.Ed. in Music, Pa. State U., 1954. Tchr. music Phila. pub. schs., 1945-55, 56-60; assoc. prof. Kutztown (Pa.) State Coll., 1960-66, dir. coll. choir, 1960-66; fine arts adv. Pa. Dept. Edn., 1966-69, U.S. Office Edn., 1969-71; asst. dir. arts in edn. program John D. Rockefeller 3d Fund, 1971-78; arts edn. coordinator

Office Commr., U.S. Office Edn., 1978-79; pres. Am. Music Conf., Wilmette, Ill., 1979-81; v.p. for programs Nat. Found. Advancement in Arts, Miami, Fla., 1983-87; pres. Arts and Edn. Cons., Inc., Reston, Va., 1987-91; sr. cons. Bus. & Industry for Arts Edn., 1990-91; exec. dir. Charlotte (N.C.) Community Sch. for the Arts, 1991—; fund raising cons. Nat. Pub. Radio, Funding Ctr., S.C. Gov. Sch.; sr. cons. Spl. Kids in Pub., 1991; master tchr. Inst. Arts; guest lectr. U. N.C., U. Tex., Loyola U.; mus. dir. Allentown (Pa.) Mcpl. Opera, 1962-63, Allentown Civic Little Theatre, 1964, Little Theatre Alexandria, Va., 1971; dir. Hershey (Pa.) Little Theatre, 1967-68, Hershey Community Chorus, 1967-69. Composer: I'll Never Forget You, 1968, Chorale of Dedication, 1974, Turn Thou to Me, 1975, Are You Nobody, Too?, 1976, Great Things God Hath Done, 1986, In My Father's House, 1986; original music and script Adventures in the Arts, Hershey, 1968; also original TV music, I Am the Way, 1985, When You Remember, 1985; author papers, reports in field. Served with AUS, 1955-56. Named Best Mus. Dir. Little Theatre Alexandria. Mem. Music Educators Nat. Conf., Nat. Guild of Community Schs. of the Arts. Club: Masons. Home: 4100B Bannockburn Pl Charlotte NC 28211-4532

WENNER, HERBERT ALLAN, pediatrician; b. Drums, Pa., Nov. 14, 1912; s. Herbert C. and Verna (Walp) W.; m. Ruth I. Berger, June 27, 1942; children—Peter W., James M., Susan T., Thomas H. B.S., Bucknell U., 1933; M.D., U. Rochester, 1939. Diplomate: Am. Bd. Microbiology, Am. Bd. Pediatrics. Intern in pathology Sch. Medicine, U. Colo., Denver, 1939-40; intern in pediatrics Yale Sch. Medicine, 1940-41, asst. resident and fellow in pediatrics, 1941-43, instr. preventive medicine, 1944-46; NRC fellow Yale U.-Johns Hopkins U., 1943-44; asst. prof. pediatrics and bacteriology Sch. Medicine, U. Kans., Kansas City, 1946-49; asso. prof. Sch. Medicine, U. Kans., 1949-51, research prof. pediatrics, 1951-69, adj. prof., 1975—; Joyce C. Hall Disting. prof. pediatrics U. Mo. Sch. Med., Kansas City, 1969-83; emeritus adj. prof. U. Mo. Sch. Med. (Sch. Dentistry), 1970—; formerly cons. epidemiology Kans. Bd. Health, Mo. Bd. Health. Asso. editor: Am. Jour. Epidemiology, 1967-79; mem. editorial bd.: Intervirology, 1972-79; past mem. editorial adv. bd.: Archives of Virology, 1975-79; contbr. articles to med. books and jours. NIH Research Career awardee, 1962. Fellow AAAS, Am. Public Health Assn., Am. Coll. Epidemiology, Am. Acad. Pediatrics; mem. Soc. Pediatric Research, Am. Pediatric Soc., Soc. Exptl. Biology and Medicine, Biometrics Soc., Mo. Med. Assn., AMA, Royal Soc. Health, AAUP, N.Y. Acad. Scis., Am. Epidemiology Soc., Infectious Disease Soc. Am. Episcopalian. Home: 9711 Johnson Dr Shawnee Mission KS 66203-3147 *Good parents, a devoted family, superb teachers and hard work have contributed to my career, and the rewards therein.*

WENNER, JANN SIMON, editor, publisher; b. N.Y.C., Jan. 7, 1946; s. Edward and Ruth N. (Simmons) W.; m. Jane Ellen Schindelheim, July 1, 1968; children: Alexander Jann, Theodore Simon, Edward Augustus. Student, U. Calif.-Berkeley, 1964-66. Editor, pub. Rolling Stone mag., N.Y.C., 1967—; Record, N.Y.C., 1981-86, Look mag., N.Y.C., 1979, Men's Jour., 1992—; editor in chief Outside Mag., San Francisco, 1977-78, US Mag., N.Y.C., 1985—, Men's Jour., 1992—; exec. v.p. Rock & Roll Hall of Fame. Author: Lennon Remembers, 1971, Garcia, 1972. Bd. dirs. Robinhood Found. Recipient Disting. Achievement award U. So. Calif. Sch. Journalism and Alumni Assn., 1976, Nat. Mag. award, 1970, 77, 86, 87, 88, 89. Mem. Am. Soc. Mag. Editors. Office: Rolling Stone Straight Arrow Publishing Co 1290 Ave of the Americas New York NY 10104*

WENNER, LETTIE MCSPADDEN, political science educator; b. Battle Creek, Mich., Apr. 9, 1937; d. John Dean and Isma Doolie (Sullivan) McSpadden; m. Manfred Wilhelm Wenner, Apr. 3, 1962; children: Eric Alexis, Adrian Edward. AB, U. Chgo., 1959; MA, U. Calif., Berkeley, 1962; PhD, U. Wis., 1972. Fgn. svc. officer Dept. State, Washington, 1961-63; rsch. assoc. Dept. HEW, Washington, 1965-67; asst. prof. polit. sci. U. Ill., Chgo., 1972-79, assoc. prof. polit. sci., 1979-88; prof. and chair dept. polit. sci. No. Ill. U., De Kalb, 1988—. Author: One Environment Under Law, 1976, The Environmental Decade in Court, 1982, United States Energy and Environmental Interest Groups, 1990. Mem. Am. Polit. Sci. Assn., Midwest Polit. Sci. Assn., Law and Society Assn., Pub. Policy Assn., Audubon Soc., Sierra Club. Democrat. Home: 3112 Fairway Oaks Dr De Kalb IL 60115-4925 Office: No Ill U Dept Polit Sci De Kalb IL 60115

WENRICH, JOHN WILLIAM, college president; b. York, Pa., June 8, 1937; s. Ralph Chester and Helen Louise (McCollam) W.; m. Linda Larsen, June 23, 1961 (dec. Sept. 1966); 1 child, Thomas Allen; m. Martha Gail Lofberg, Sept. 1, 1967; 1 child, Margaret Ann. A.B., Princeton U., 1959; M.A., U. Mich., 1961, Ph.D., 1968. Fgn. service officer Dept. State, Washington, 1962-65; rep. Internat. Devel. Found., N.Y.C., 1965-66; project dir. U. Mich. Ann Arbor, 1966-69; asst. to pres. Coll. San Mateo, Calif., 1969-71; v.p. Ferris State U., Big Rapids, Mich., 1971-75, pres., 1984-88; pres. Canada Coll., Redwood City, Calif., 1975-79, Santa Ana Coll., Calif., 1979-84; chancellor San Diego Community Coll. Dist., 1988-90, Dallas County Community Coll., 1990—. Co-author: Leadership in Administration of Technical and Vocational Education, 1974, Administration of Vocational Education. Recipient Meritorious Service medal Dept. State, 1966; Hinsdale scholar Sch. Edn. U. Mich., 1968. Avocations: bridge; tennis; travel. Home: 1520 Wyndmere Dr De Soto TX 75115-7808 Office: 701 Elm St Dallas TX 75202-3201

WENSINGER, ARTHUR STEVENS, German language and literature educator; b. Grosse Pointe, Mich., Mar. 9, 1926; s. Carl Franklin and Suzanne (Stevens) W. Grad., Phillips Acad. Andover, 1944; BA, Dartmouth Coll., 1948; MA, U. Mich., 1951; postgrad., U. Munich, 1948, 50-51, U. Innsbruck, 1953-54; PhD, U. Mich., 1958. Instr., asst. prof., assoc. prof. Wesleyan U., Middletown, Conn., 1955-68, prof. German and humanities, 1968-93, Marcus Taft prof. German and humanities, 1977-93, prof. emeritus, 1994—, chmn. dept. German lang. and lit., 1971-74, 78-93, also sr. tutor Coll. Letters; pres. passim Friends of Davison Art Ctr.; reader for NEH, 1980—; mem. selection com. German Acad. Exch. Svc., 1980—. Author: Hogarth on High Life, 1970, Plays by Arthur Schnitzler, 1982-83; translator, editor: The Theater of the Bauhaus, 1961, rev. edit., 1986, The Letters and Journals of Paula Modersohn-Becker, 1983, 2nd edit., 1990; translator, editor: Querelle: The Film Book, 1983; translator: Franz Kafka: Pictures of a Life, 1984, The Sons, 1989, Marlene Dietrich: Portraits, 1984, Shabbat (Peter Stefan Jungk), 1985, Hanna Schygulla and R.W. Fassbinder, 1986, Kaethe Kollwitz: The Work in Color, 1988, Niklas Frank, In the Shadow of the Reich, 1991; co-translator: Günter Grass, Two States-One Nation?, 1990; contbr. to R.W.Fassbinder, The Anarchy of the Imagination, 1992; editor: Stone Island (Peter S. Boynton), 1973; co-editor: Hesse's Siddhartha, 1962; continuing editor: Correspondence of Norman Douglas 1868-1952; contbr. articles to profl. jours.; Translator in field. Fellow Wesleyan Ctr. for Humanities, 1974, Reynolds fellow, 1950-51, Fulbright fellow, 1954-55, Danforth fellow, 1959, Ford Found. fellow, 1970-71; Inter Nations grantee, 1978, 82, NEH Rsch. Travel grantee, 1993. mem. MLA, Am. Assn. Tchrs. German, Heinrich von Kleist Gesellschaft, Internat. Brecht Soc., Kafka Soc. Am., Auden Soc., Soc. Preservation New Eng. Antiquities, Conn. Acad. Arts and Scis., Haddam, Conn. Land Trust, Phi Beta Kappa, Phi Kappa Phi, Delta Tau Delta. Home: Candlewood Farm 95 Jacoby Rd Higganum CT 06441-4225 Office: Wesleyan U PO Box 6090 Middletown CT 06459-6082

WENSITS, JAMES EMRICH, newspaper editor; b. South Bend, Ind., Oct. 8, 1944; s. John Andrew and Melva Mae (Betz) W.; m. Wendy Anne Reygaert, June 12, 1965; children: Cheryl Wensits Lightfoot, John, Kristin Wensits Hough, Amy; m. Catherine Marie Palmer Pope, Nov. 27, 1987; stepdaughter, Christina Pope. BA in Journalism, Purdue U., 1966. Reporter South Bend Tribune, 1966-92, assoc. editor, 1992—. Office: South Bend Tribune 225 W Colfax Ave South Bend IN 46626-1000

WENSTROM, FRANK AUGUSTUS, state senator, city and county official; b. Dover, N.D., July 27, 1903; s. James August and Anna Petra (Kringstad) W.; student public schs., Carrington, N.D.; LLD (hon.), U. N.D., 1990. m. Mary Esther Pickett, June 10, 1938. In oil bus., Carrington, 1932-38, Williston, N.D., 1938-45; mgr. Williston Co. of C., 1945-51; pub. rels. officer 1st Nat. Bank, Williston, 1951-53, mng. officer real estate mortgage dept., 1953-60; exec. officer Northwestern Fed. Savs. and Loan Assn. Williston, 1964-68; spl. cons. Am. State Bank Williston, 1968-73; mem. N.D. Senate, 1957-60, 67—, pres. pro tem, 1973-74; lt. gov. State of N.D., 1963-64; dir., sec. Williston Cmty. Hotel Co., 1950—; chmn. subscriber's com. N.W. dist. N.D.

Blue Cross-Blue Shield, 1972—. Mem. Williston Public Housing Authority, 1951—, Williams County Park Bd., 1951—, N.D. Yellowstone-Ft. Union Commn., 1957-64, Legis. Rsch. Coun., 1957-60, Legis. Coun., 1969-70; del. N.D. 2d Constl. Conv., 1970, pres., 1971-72; Williams County comn. U.S. Savs. Bonds Com., 1958-69; creator Frank A. Wenstrom Libr. for Student Rsch., Grank Forks, N.D., 1984; co-chair N.D. Constitution subcom. for developing and displaying hist. papers pertaining to U.S. constitution; mem. Constitutional Celebration com., 1985; pres. N.D. 2d Constitutional Conv., 1971-72; co-chair archives search com. N.D. Const. Conv., 1971-72; bd. dirs. N.D. Easter Seals Soc., 1960-75, state pres., 1970-71; bd. advisors Salvation Army, 1960-75; bd. dirs. Univ. Found., U. N.D. Williston Center, 1965—; mem. joint legis. com. Nat. Assn. Ret. Tchrs.-Am. Assn. Ret. Persons, 1975—, chmn., 1979-80. Recipient Liberty Bell award N.D. Bar Assn., 1977, Disting. Svc. award Bismarck Jr. Coll., 1981; award Nature Conservancy, 1982; Svc. award Greater N.D. Assn., 1983, C.P. Lura award Disting. Service to Edn. Minot State Coll., 1986, Award of Excellence Com. of Gov.'s Council on Human Resources, 1986. Mem. Upper Missouri Purebred Cattle Breeders Assn. (sec-treas. 1947-62), N.D. Wildlife Fedn. (state pres. 1947-48), Greater N.D. Assn. (dir. 1955-56, mem. Roosevelt Nat. Meml. Park com. 1957-63), U.S. Savs. and Loan League (dir. 1965-67). Republican. Congregationalist. Clubs: Rotary, Elks, Masons (hon. grand master), Shriners, Order Eastern Star. Office: PO Box 187 Williston ND 58802-0187

WENSTRUP, H. DANIEL, chemical executive; b. Cin., Sept. 27, 1934; s. Carl D. and Lucille (Cahill) W.; m. Eileen O'Brien, Nov. 24, 1956; children: Gary, Julie, Patrick, Kevin, Katy, Greg. BSBA, Xavier U., 1956. Sales rep. Chemcentral Corp., Cin., 1958-66; sales mgr. Chemcentral Corp., Detroit, 1966-72, gen. mgr., 1972-75, v.p. regional mgr., 1975-82; v.p. dir. mktg. Chemcentral Corp., Chgo., 1982-86, pres., 1986—, pres., chief exec. officer, 1988—, bd. dirs. Mem., supporter Mus. Sci. Industry, Chgo., 1991—, Ravinia Chgo. Symphony, 1991—, adv. com. Gov. Edgar. 1st lt. U.S. Army, 1956-58. Mem. Chem. Mfrs. Assn. (dir. 1989-92), Chem. Industry Coun. Ill. (dir. 1989—, pres.), Nat. Paint & Coatings Assn., Nat. Petroleum Refiners Assn., Ill. Mfrs. Assn., Ill. C. of C., Medinah Country Club, Oak Brook Tennis Club. Republican. Roman Catholic. Avocations: golf, tennis, jogging, reading, theatre. Office: Chemcentral Corp 7050 W 71st St Bedford Park IL 60638-5902

WENTE, PATRICIA ANN, radio executive; 1 child, Jessica. BA in Communications, Sangamon State U., 1978, MA in Communications, 1981. Vol. coord. Sta. WSSR-FM, Springfield, Ill., 1977-79; sta. mgr. Stas. WRRS, KMUW, Wichita, Kans., 1979-85; gen. mgr. Sta. KGOU, Norman, Okla., 1985-87; mgr. sta. grant programs Corp. for Pub. Broadcasting, Washington, 1987-89; gen. mgr. Sta. KWMU-FM, St. Louis, 1989—; participant NPR Pub. Radio Conf., 1979-90, Pub. Broadcasting Svc. Conf., 1987-89, Corp. for Pub. Broadcasting Conf., 1977-80, Rocky Mountain Pub. Radio Meetings, 1987-89, SECA Meetings, 1987-89; bd. dirs. Pub. Radio in Mid-Am. Conf., 1986-88; mem. gerontology faculty Wichita State u., 1983-84; promotion & pub. svc. announcer Sta. KPTS-TV, Wichita, 1979-80; judge coord. Ohio State Awards, 1986-87. Mem. adv. com. for handicapped svcs. Wichita State U., 1980-82. Mem. Pub. Telecommunication Fin. Mgmt. Assn. (bd. dirs. 1990—), Alpha Epsilon Rho (pres. 1979-84, advisor 1990). Office: Sta KWMU-FM Univ Mo-St Louis 8001 Natural Bridge Rd Saint Louis MO 63121-4401

WENTLEY, RICHARD TAYLOR, lawyer; b. Pitts., July 31, 1930; s. Howard Magee and Beatrice (Taylor) W.; m. Jane Francis Garvey, Aug. 18, 1956 (dec.); children: Richard Taylor, Anne Elizabeth, David William, Christopher James, Jane Margaret. B.A. in Polit. Sci., Bucknell U., 1953; J.D., U. Pitts., 1956. Bar: Pa. 1956, U.S. Ct. Appeals (3d cir.) 1956, U.S. Supreme Ct. 1967. Ptnr. Thorp, Reed & Armstrong, Pitts., 1956-68; judge Ct. Common Pleas of Allegheny County, Pitts., 1968-74; ptnr. Reed, Smith, Shaw & McClay, Pitts., 1974—; lectr. ednl. programs U. Pitts. Trustee Winchester Thurston Sch, Pitts.; vestry man Fox Chapel Episcopal Ch. Mem. ABA, Pa. Bar Assn., Allegheny County Bar Assn. (lectr. ednl. programs), Acad. Trial Lawyers Allegheny County. Republican. Clubs: Pittsburgh, Pitts. Athletic Assn., Rivers. Home: 221 Guyasuta Rd Pittsburgh PA 15215-1518 Office: Reed Smith Shaw & McClay 435 6th Ave Pittsburgh PA 15219-1886

WENTORF, ROBERT HENRY, physical chemist; b. West Bend, Wis., May 28, 1926; s. Robert H. and Sophia Wentorf; m. Vivian Marty, Aug. 20, 1949; children: Jill, Laine, Rolf; m. 2d Frances Gohn Gillespie, 1993. B.S. in Chem. Engring, U. Wis., 1948, Ph.D. in Chemistry, 1952. Teaching and research asst. U. Wis., Madison, 1948-52; vis. prof. U. Wis., 1966-67; mem. R & D staff GE Co., Schenectady, 1952-88; disting. research prof. Rensselaer Poly. Inst., Troy, N.Y., 1988—. Editor: Modern Very High Pressure Techniques, 1962, Advances in High Pressure Research, vol. IV, 1974; contbr. articles to sci. jours. Served with USN, 1944-45. Recipient New Materials prize Am. Phys. Soc., 1977. Mem. Am. Chem. Soc. (Ipatieff prize 1965), Nat. Acad. Engring., Mohawk Soaring Club (dir., instr. gliding), Sigma Xi, Alpha Chi Sigma, Tau Beta Pi. Patentee in field. Home: RR 3 Box 154A Greenwich NY 12834-9111 Office: Rensselaer Poly Tech Inst Chem Engring Dept Troy NY 12180

WENTSLER, GERTRUDE JOSEPHINE, secondary history educator; b. Campbell, Ohio, July 16, 1943; d. John Tofil and Irene S. (Glass) Wallace; m. Lawrence L. Murray, Dec. 29, 1967 (div. 1978); 1 child, Carolyn E. Murray; m. Wm. Scott Wentsler, Mar. 4, 1989. BA, Miami U., Oxford, Ohio, 1964; MEd, Xavier U., Cin., 1967. Cert. secondary tchr., Ohio. Tchr. history Cin. Pub. Schs., 1964-71, Northwest Sch. Dist., Cin., 1974—. Dist. dir. College Hill Forum, Cin., 1972, mem. edn. com., 1970-73. Jennings scholar, 1986-87; recipient Journalism awards, 1987-89, Outstanding Tchr. award U. Chgo., 1989, Tchr. award Friends of Wm. Howard Taft Birthplace, 1992. Mem. NOW, N.W. Tchrs. Assn. (bldg. rep. 1975-77), Nat. Coun. Social Studies, Cin. Fedn. Tchrs. (membership chair 1968, bldg. rep. 1966-69). Avocations: needlework, reading, travel. Home: 2075 Connecticut Ave Cincinnati OH 45224-2368

WENTWORTH, ANDREW STOWELL, lawyer; b. Boston, Mar. 3, 1938; s. Walter Adams and Helen (Goodrich) W.; m. Natalie Cobb, Mar. 3, 1968 (div.); children: Michelle, Nicole; m. Mary Ellen O'Brien, May 30, 1992. BA, Mich. State U., 1960; LLB, JD, Ohio State U., 1966. Bar: Ohio 1967, U.S. Dist. Ct. (so. dist.) Ohio 1968. Auditor U.S. Audit Agy., Paris, 1962-63; asst. pros. atty. Franklin County Prosecutor's Office, Columbus, Ohio, 1967-69; ptnr. Freda & Wentworth, Columbus, 1969-71, Schwenker, Reeves, Wentworth, Stridsberg & Perrin, Columbus, 1971-75, Connor & Wentworth, Columbus, 1975-79; pvt. practice Andrew S. Wentworth, LPA, Columbus, 1979—; law dir. Village of Thurston, Ohio, 1992—. Lectr. Maryhaven Hosp., Columbus, 1985—; fundraiser Mich. State U., East Lansing, 1989-91. 1st Lt. Q.M.C., U.S. Army, 1960-62, capt. USAR, 1962-66. Mem. Ohio Acad. Criminal Def. Lawyers, Ohio Acad. Trial Lawyers, Delta Tau Delta. Republican. Episcopalian. Avocations: Civil War, reading history and biography, travel, competitive amateur tennis. Home: 4207 Bluebonnet Ct Westerville OH 43081 Office: 501 S High St Columbus OH 43215

WENTWORTH, JACK ROBERTS, business educator, consultant; b. Elgin, Ill., June 11, 1928; s. William Franklin and Elizabeth (Roberts) W.; m. Rosemary Ann Pawlak, May 30, 1956; children—William, Barbara. Student, Carleton Coll., 1946-48; BS, Ind. U., 1950, MBA, 1954, DBA, 1959. Coord. displays Cadillac divsn., Gen. Motors Corp., Detroit, 1954-56; asst. prof. bus., assoc. dir. research Sch. of Bus. Ind. U., Bloomington, 1957-60, assoc. prof., dir. rsch., 1960-70, prof., 1970-93, chmn. MBA program, 1970-76, chmn. dept., faculty rep. NCAA, 1978-83, assoc. dean Sch. of Bus., 1984-93, Arthur M. Weimer prof., 1993—; mktg. cons., Bloomington, 1960—; bd. dirs. Kimball Internat., Jasper, Ind.; Bank One, Bloomington, Market Facts Inc., Chgo.; KPT Corp., Bloomfield, Lone Star Industries, Stamford, Conn. Editor: (monograph) Marketing Horizons, 1965; exec. editor Bus. Horizons, 1960-70. Served to 1st lt. USAF, 1950-53. Recipient Teaching award MBA Assn., 1973, 78, 81, 84, 85, Svc. award Assn. for Bus. and Econ. Rsch., 1983. Mem. Am. Mktg. Assn. (v.p. 1971-73), Grad. Mgmt. Admissions Coun. (chmn. bd. trustees 1977-78), Univ. Club, Masons, Beta Gamma Sigma (pres. Alpha of Ind. chpt. 1971-72, bd. govs 1986—, nat. pres. 1994—). Republican. Episcopalian. Avocations: athletic events;

travel; bicycling; model railroading; magic. Office: Indiana Univ Sch Bus Bloomington IN 47405

WENTWORTH, MICHAEL JUSTIN, curator; b. Detroit, June 15, 1938; s. Harold Arnold and Marian (Jones) W. MFA, U. Mich., 1962; PHD, Harvard U., 1976. Curator, acting dir. Smith Coll. Mus. Art, Northampton, Mass., 1968-69; dir. Rose Art Mus., Brandies U., Waltham, Mass., 1970-74; assoc. prof. Wellesley Coll., Mass., 1976; curator Boston Athenaeum, Mass., 1985—. Author: James Tissot, 1984. Office: Boston Athenaeum 10 1/2 Beacon St Boston MA 02108-3777

WENTWORTH, MURRAY JACKSON, artist, educator; b. Boston, Jan. 18, 1927; s. Harold Squires and Mary Louise (Murray) W.; m. Elaine Magnuson, June 16, 1953; 1 child, Janet Louise. Diploma, Art Inst. Boston, 1950. Advt. artist Agy. Art Svcs., Boston, 1950-58; instr. Art Inst. Boston, 1958-78; artist, instr. Norwell, Mass., 1968—. Group shows, Allied Artists Am., 1980, 82 (Silver medal 1980), Allied Art Am., 1982 (Obrig prize 1982), Am. Watercolor Soc., 1980 (Dolphin fellow 1980), Rocky Mount Nat. Exhibition, 1982 (Grumbacher award 1982). Cpl. U.S. Army, 1945-47. Recipient Hudson Valley Art Assn. award, 1991, Guild Boston Artists award, 1992. Mem. Allied Artists Am., Nat. Acad. Design (Pike Meml. award 1986), Am. Watercolor Soc., New England Watercolor Soc. (Grumbacher Gold medal award 1989). Home: 132 Central St Norwell MA 02061-1306

WENTWORTH, THEODORE SUMNER, lawyer; b. Bklyn., July 18, 1938; s. Theodore Sumner and Alice Ruth (Wortmann) W.; AA, Am. River Coll., 1958; JD, U. Calif., Hastings, 1962; m. Sharon Linelle Arkush, 1965 (dec. 1987); children: Christina Linn, Kathryn Allison; m. Diana Webb von Welanetz, 1989; 1 stepchild, Jan van Welanetz. Bar: Calif. 1963, U.S. Dist. Ct. (no., ctrl. dists.) Calif., U.S. Ct. Appeals (9th cir.), U.S. Supreme Ct.; cert. civil trial specialist; diplomate Nat. Bd. Trial Advocacy; assoc. Am. Bd. Trial Advocacy. Assoc. Adams, Hunt & Martin, Santa Ana, Calif., 1963-66; ptnr. Hunt, Liljestrom & Wentworth, Santa Ana, 1967-77; pres. Solabs Corp.; chmn. bd., exec. v.p. Plant Warehouse, Inc., Hawaii, 1974-82; prin. Law Offices of Theodore S. Wentworth, specializing in personal injury, product liability, profl. malpractice, bus. fraud, fire loss litigation, human rights issues, Irvine and Temecula, Calif.; judge pro tem Superior Ct. Attys. Panel, Harbor Mcpl. Ct.; owner Eagles Ridge Ranch, Temecula, 1977—. Pres., bd. dirs. Santa Ana-Tustin Community Chest, 1972; v.p., trustee South Orange County United Way, 1973-75; pres. Orange County Fedn. Funds, 1972-73; bd. dirs. Orange County Mental Health Assn. Mem. ABA, Am. Bd. Trial Advocates (assoc.), State Bar Calif., Orange County Bar Assn. (dir. 1972-76), Am. Trial Lawyers Assn., Calif. Trial Lawyers Assn. (bd. govs. 1968-70), Orange County Trial Lawyers Assn. (pres. 1967-68), Lawyer-Pilots Bar Assn., Aircraft Owners and Pilots Assn., Bahia Corinthian Yacht Club, Balboa Bay Club, Corsair Yacht Club, The Center Club, Pacific Club, Newport, Fourth of July Yacht Club (Catalina Island). Research in vedic prins., natural law, quantum physics and mechanics. Office: 4631 Teller Ave Ste 100 Newport Beach CA 92660 also: Wells Fargo Bank Bldg 41530 Enterprise Cir S Temecula CA 92590-4816

WENTZ, BILLY MELVIN, JR., finance executive; b. Charlotte, N.C., Aug. 11, 1953; s. Billy M. Wentz and Betty Jane (Harper) Bass; m. Cynthia Gardner, Aug. 2, 1975; children: Jessica, Kyle. BSBA, U. of N.C., 1975; MBA, U. of Tampa, 1979. CPA, N.C. Contr. Kerley and Edwards, Charlotte, N.C., 1975-76; plant acct. Rexham Corp., Charlotte, 1976-77; acctg. mgr. Rexham Corp., Sarasota, Fla., 1977-79, div. controller, 1979-80, group controller, 1980-82; corp. cost mgr. Rexham Corp., Charlotte, 1982-86, corp. dir. acctg., 1986-87, corp. estter, 1987-89, fin. dir., 1989—. Bd. dirs. YMCA, Charlotte. Mem. AICPA, N.C. Assn. CPA's, Country Haven Swim and Racquet Club (treas.).. Office: 4201 Congress St Ste 340 Charlotte NC 28209-4621

WENTZ, HOWARD BECK, JR., manufacturing company executive; b. Pitts., Jan. 10, 1930; s. Howard and Emmy Lou W.; m. Judith Ann Blough, June, 1958; children: Howard, Roger, Elizabeth. B.S.E., Princeton U., 1952; M.B.A., Harvard U., 1957. Mfg. exec. TRW Corp., 1957-60; assoc. Robert Heller and Assocs., Cleve., 1960-63; exec. v.p. Paterson-Leitch Co., Cleve., 1963-69; pres. Duff-Norton, Charlotte, N.C., 1969-72; corp. v.p. parent co. Amstar Corp., N.Y.C., 1972-79; exec. v.p. Amstar Corp., 1979-81, chief oper. officer, 1979-81, pres., 1981—, chief exec. officer, 1982-89, chmn., 1983—, also bd. dirs.; chmn. Eastar Inc., 1989—; bd. dirs. Colgate-Palmolive Co., Tam Brands, Inc., Crompton & Knowles Corp. Lt. USN, 1952-55. Office: Long Wharf Maritime Ctr 555 Long Wharf Dr Ste 12 New Haven CT 06511-5901*

WENTZ, JANET, principal. Prin. Los Ranchos Elem. Sch. Recipient Doe Elem. Sch. Recognition award, 1989-90. Office: Los Ranchos Elem Sch 5785 Los Ranchos Rd San Luis Obispo CA 93401-8247

WENTZ, SIDNEY FREDERICK, insurance company executive, foundation executive; b. Dallas, Mar. 27, 1932; s. Howard Beck and Emmy Lou (Cawthon) W.; m. Barbara Strait, Sept. 9, 1961; children: Eric, Jennifer, Robin. AB, Princeton U., 1954; LLB, Harvard U., 1961. Atty. White & Case, N.Y.C., 1960-65, Western Electric Co., 1965-66, AT&T Corp., 1966-67; with Crum & Forster Inc., Morristown, N.J., 1967—, v.p., gen. counsel, 1967-71, sr. v.p. gen. counsel, 1971-72, exec. v.p., 1972, pres., 1972-87, chmn. bd., 1987-88, chmn. exec. com., 1988-90, also bd. dirs.; chmn. bd. Robert Wood Johnson Found., Princeton, N.J., 1989—. Trustee Morristown Meml. Hosp., 1974—; Drew U., 1991—. Served to lt. (j.g.) USNR, 1954-57. Mem. Morris County Golf Club, Morristown Field Club, Sakonnet (R.I.) Golf Club, Baltusrol Golf Club, Jupiter Hills (Fla.) Golf Club, Loblolly Pines (Fla.) Golf Club. Office: Robert Wood Johnson Found PO Box 2316 College Rd E Princeton NJ 08540-6672

WENTZ, WALTER JOHN, health administration educator; b. Newburgh, Ohio, June 17, 1928; s. Walter John and Gladys Marjory W.; m. Lynne E. Putnam; children: Marcia, Sharon, Diane, Courtney, Richard, Jerry, Rick. B.A., U. Iowa, 1949, M.A., 1950, Ph.D., 1963. Pres. Meml. Hosp., Saulte Ste Marie, Mich., 1965-71; assoc. prof. Central Mich. U., Mt. Pleasant, 1977-78; prof. health adminstrn. Wichita State U., 1978-87, chmn. dept. health adminstrn. Coll. Health Professions, 1978-87; prof. div. health adminstrn. Gov's State U., Univ. Pk., Ill., 1987—. Contbr. articles to profl. jours., chpts. to books.; Mem. editorial bd.: Jour. Hosp. and Health Services Adminstrn. Fellow Am. Pub. Health Assn., AAAS, Royal Soc. Health, Am. Coll. Healthcare Execs.; mem. Phi Kappa Phi, Sigma Iota Epsilon, Omicron Delta Kappa, Beta Gamma Sigma, Alpha Eta. Republican. Methodist. Club: Rotary (dir.). Office: Governors State U Divsn Health Adminstrn University Park IL 60466

WENTZ, WILLIAM HENRY, JR., aerospace engineer, educator; b. Wichita, Kans., Dec. 18, 1933. BS in Mech. Engring. cum laude, Wichita State U., 1955, MS in Aeronautical Engring., 1961; PhD in Engring. Mechanics, U. Kans., 1969. Lic. profl. engr., Kans. Liaison engr. Beech Aircraft, 1952-53; propulsion engr. Boeing Co., Wichita, Kans., 1955; instr. mech. engring. Wichita State U., 1957-58; aerodynamicist Boeing Co., Wichita, 1958-63; from asst. prof. to assoc. prof. aeronautical engring. Wichita State U., 1963-75, prof. aeronautical engring., 1975-83, Gates-Learjet prof. aeronautical engring., 1983-86, disting. prof. aerospace engring., 1986—, dir. Ctr. Basic and Applied Rsch. Inst. Aviation Rsch., 1986-89, exec. dir. Nat. Inst. Aviation Rsch., 1988—; dir. rsch. projects Boeing Co., 1960, 61, NASA, 1964-66, 66-68, 70-71, 71-83, 85-87, 86-88, 82-87, Dept. of Def., 1986-88, Kans. Tech. Enterprise Corp., 1988—, FAA, 1986—. Contbr. articles to profl. jours. With USAF, 1955-57. Sci. Faculty fellow NSF, 1967-68. Fellow AIAA (assoc., past chmn. Wichita sect., Outstanding advisor student chpt. 1964, 65, 70, Gen. Aviation award 1981, Engr. of Yr. award Wichita sect. 1992, Engr. of Yr. award Region V 1991-92; mem. Soc. Automotive Engrs. (Ralph R. Teeter award 1973), Sigma Gamma Tau, Tau Beta Pi. Office: Wichita State U Nat Inst Aviation Rsch Campus Box 93 Wichita KS 67260-0093

WENTZEL, DAN R., title company executive; b. 1942. With Transamerica Title Ins., Seattle, 1962-82, Chicago Title Ins., L.A., 1981-83, N.Am. Title Co., Walnut Creek, Calif., 1983—; chmn., CEO N.Am. Asset Devel. Corp.,

Walnut Creek, 1991—. Office: No Am Asset Devel Corp 2185 N California Blvd Ste 575 Walnut Creek CA 94596*

WENZ, RICHARD L., school system and church administrator; b. Lincoln, Nebr., Sept. 24, 1934; s. Arthur Frederick and Mildred Iretha Wenz; m. Janet Helen, July 25, 1959; children: Jennifer, Jeffrey. BA, Concordia Tchrs. Coll., 1956; MA, Washington U., St. Louis, 1961. Tchr. Concordia Luth. Sch., Maplewood, Mo., 1956-61; prin. St. John's Luth. Sch., Hannibal, Mo., 1961-72, Ellisville, Mo., 1972-79; prin. ch. adminstr. Trinity Luth. Sch., Davenport, Iowa, 1979—; mem. Mo. Dist. Patterns Performance Com. 1960-71; pres. Mo. Dist. Tchrs. Conf., 1971, Mo. Dist. Prins. Conf., 1979, St. Louis Prins. Conf., 1979; chmn Mo. Dist. Sch. Com., 1974-76, Iowa Dist. East Sch. Com. 1981-84, evaluator, 1982-85; mem. evaluation team Concordia Tchrs. Coll., 1979; mem. Iowa Gov's Adv. Coun. for Non-Pub. Schs., 1984—; site visitor Blue Ribbon Sch. Award, 1986-88; mem. coors. coun. Iowa Dept. Edn., 1988-89; Iowa rep. to sch., Russia, 1989; evaluator Iowa Outcomes, 1992-93. Bd. dirs. Jr. C. of C., 1968-70; active doctinal review com. L.C.M.S., 1981-88, planning coun. for mission and ministry, 1990-92, reconciler, 1993—, tchr. rep. on 150th anniversary, 1993—. Named Alumnus of Yr., Concordia Tchrs. Coll., 1987, Iowa Exemplary Luth. Educator, 1988, Nat. Disting. Luth. Prin, 1993, Nat. Disting. Prin., U.S. Dept. Edn., 1993. Mem. Luth Edn. Assn. (treas. 1986-90), Dept. Luth. Elem. Sch. Prins. (conv. program com. 1986, conv. chmn. 1992), Iowa Assn. Non-Pub. Schs., Iowa Dist. East (bd. dirs. 1982—). Office: Trinity Luth Sch 1122 W Central Park Ave Davenport IA 52804-1805

WENZ, RODNEY E., public relations executive; b. North Platte, Nebr., Dec. 21, 1935. Student in Journalism, U. Nebr. Reporter, city editor Fremont Guide and Tribune, 1954-59; reporter, bur. chief Rockford Newspapers, 1959-66; coord. comm. Chrysler Corp., 1966-67; bus. editor Louisville Courier-Jour., 1967-70; pres. Wenz-Neely Co., Louisville, 1971-85, chmn. Recipient newswriting awards AP, UPI, Disting. Newswriting award Am. Polit. Sci. Assn., 1963; nominee Pulitzer prize, 1963. Mem. NIRI, Pub. Rels. Soc. Am. (counselors acad.). Office: The Wenz-Neely Co PO Box 1363 505 W Ormsby Ave Louisville KY 40203*

WENZEL, FRED WILLIAM, apparel manufacturing executive; b. St. Louis, Jan. 14, 1916; s. Frederick H. and Ella M. (Heuerman) W.; m. Mary Edna Cruzen; 1 child, Robert F. Grad., U. Wis., 1937. Chmn. H. Wenzel Tent & Duck Co. St. Louis, 1937-52; pres. Hawthorn Co., New Haven, Mo., 1952-64; v.p. Kellwood Co., Chgo., 1961-64; chmn. bd. Kellwood Co., St. Louis, 1964, pres., chmn., 1965-76, chmn., chief exec. officer, 1976-84, chmn. from 1984, now chmn. emeritus. Home: 13315 Fairfield Square Dr Chesterfield MO 63017-5925 Office: Kellwood Co PO Box 14374 Saint Louis MO 63178-4374*

WENZEL, JAMES GOTTLIEB, ocean engineering executive, consultant; b. Springfield, Minn., Oct. 16, 1926; s. Gottlieb Henry and Elvira Wilhemina (Runck) W.; m. Elaine Joyce Abrahamson, June 17, 1950; children: Lori Lynn, Jodi Ann, Sheri Lee, James G. II. BA in Aero Engring. with high distinction, U. Minn., 1948, MS, 1950; DHL (hon.), Calif. Luth. U., Thousand Oaks, 1985. Mgr. aerodynamics Convair, San Diego, 1950-56, asst. to v.p engring., 1956-58; asst. to sr. v.p. engring. Gen. Dynamics Corp., N.Y.C., 1958-60, mgr., govt. planning, 1960-62; v.p. ocean systems Lockheed Missiles & Space Co., Sunnyvale, Calif., 1962-84; pres., chmn. Ocean Minerals Co., Sunnyvale, 1977-84, Marine Devel. Assocs. Inc, Saratoga, Calif., 1984—; chmn. Oreg. Resource Exploration Co., Portland, 1985—; pres. Centry Systems Inc., Saratoga, 1994—; bd. dirs. Yr. of the Ocean Found., Washington, 1984-8; chmn., pres. Sea/Space Symposium, Phila. 1971—. Author (with others) Ocean Engineering, 1968; author 58 published papers on ocean engring., 1966-88; patentee in field. Regent Calif. Luth. U., Thousand Oaks, 1975-78, 85-87; pres., chmn. Jr. Achievement, Santa Clara County, Calif., 1976-81; chmn. Luth. Lay Renewal, No. Calif., 1975-81, 88—; pres. Immanuel Luth. Trusts, Saratoga, Calif., 1989-94. With USN, 1944-46. Recipient Mayor's award for Oceanology City of L.A., 1967, Japan Govt. Contbns. award Marine Facilities Panel, 1992. Fellow Marine Tech. Soc. (ocean sci. and engring. award 1988); mem. NAE (life), NRC Marine bd. 1978-84), Cosmos Club (Washington), Saratoga Mens Club, Tau Beta Pi, Tau Omega. Republican. Lutheran. Avocations: scuba diving, wood working, fishing. Office: Marine Devel Assocs Inc PO Box 3409 Saratoga CA 95070-1409

WENZEL, JOAN ELLEN, artist; b. N.Y.C., July 23, 1944; d. Irwin S. and Pearl (Silverman) Rever; m. Allen Jay Wenzel, June 12, 1966 (div. June 1987); 1 child, Kimberly Anne; m. Robert Harold Messing, July 23, 1987 (dec.). Student, Syracuse U., 1962-64; BS in Painting, NYU, 1966, MA in Painting, 1976; postgrad., Harvard U., 1967. One-woman shows include Helander Gallery, Palm Beach, Fla., 1985, 89, 95, Adamar Fine Art, Miami, 1993, Gallery Contemporena, Jacksonville, Fla., 1993, Alexander Brest Mus., Jacksonville, 1993, Albertson Peterson Gallery, Winter Park, Fla., 1992, Amerifest, Miami, 1991, Gallery Yves Arman, N.Y.C., 1982, Palm Beach County Court House, West Palm Beach, Fla., 1991, One Brickall Square, Miami, 1992; exhbns. include Aldrich Mus., Ridgefield, Conn., 1977, Queens Mus., N.Y.C., 1981. Democrat. Jewish. Home: 2275 Ibis Isle Rd W Palm Beach FL 33480-5307

WENZEL, LEONARD ANDREW, engineering educator; b. Palo Alto, Calif., Jan. 21, 1923; s. Robert N. and Frances A. (Browne) W.; m. Mary E. Leathers, Oct. 21, 1944; children: Frances B., Alma L., Jesse R., Sara V. BSChemE, Pa. State U., 1943; MSChemE, U. Mich., 1948, PhD in Chem. Engring., 1950. Registered profl. engr., Pa. Jr. rsch. engr. Phillips Petroleum Co., Bartlesville, Okla., 1943-44; jr. rsch. scientist Mellon Inst., Pitts., 1944; rsch. engr. Colgate-Palmolive, Jersey City, 1949-51; asst. prof. engring. Lehigh U., Bethlehem, Pa., 1951-56—, assoc. prof., 1956-60, prof., 1960-88, chmn. dep. chem. engring., 1962-83, prof. emeritus, 1988—; project dir. UNESCO, Bucaramanga, Colombia, 1969-70, cons. in chem. engring., Maracaibo, Venezuela, 1970-73; cons. Air Products and Chems., Allentown, Pa., 1951-80, Exxon, Baytown, Tex., 1983-86; chief scientist Arencidia Techs., Inc., Allentown, 1987—; pres. L.A. Wenzel Inc., Bethlehem, 1988—. Co-author: Principles of Unit Operations, 1960, Chemical Process Analysis: Mass and Energy Balances, 1987; author: Cryogenic Engineering, 1988. Bd. dirs. S.E. Neighborhood Assn., Bethlehem, 1986—, Bethlehem Housing Authority, 1988—. Lt. (j.g.) USN, 1944-46, PTO. Fellow Am. Inst. Chem. Engrs.; mem. Am. Chem. Soc., Am. Soc. for Engring. Edn. Avocations: stamps, gardening, travel. Home: 517 15th Ave Bethlehem PA 18018-6429 Office: Lehigh Univ Bldg #111 Bethlehem PA 18015

WENZLER, WILLIAM PAUL, architect; b. Milw., Feb. 9, 1929; s. Paul C. and Bertha R. (Froemming) W.; m. Dolores A. Rahn, June 17, 1950; children: Edward, Deborah, John, Joan. Student, U. Wis., 1947-48; BS in Archtl. Engring., U. Ill., 1952. Registered architect, Wis., Ill., Mich., Ga., others. Draftsman H.C. Haeuser (architect), Milw., 1952, A.H. Siewert (architect), Milw., 1952-54; designer Brust and Brust (architects), Milw., 1954-55; pvt. practice Milw., 1955—; pres. William Wenzler & Assoc. (Architects, Inc.), 1966—. Prin. works include Germantown (Wis.) Elementary Sch., 1956, St. Edmunds Episcopal Ch., Elm Grove, Wis., 1957, Zion Evangel. and Reformed Ch., Milw., 1958, 1st Congl. Ch., Mukwonago, Wis., 1959, Goldendale (Wis.) Elementary Sch., 1959, Bradford Terr., Milw., Protestant Home for Aged, 1962, Our Shepherd Luth. Ch., Greendale, Wis., 1963, Gerald H. Nickoll residence, Fox Point, Wis., 1963, Inland Steel Co. factory and office bldg., Milw., 1966, Brookfield (Wis.) Evangel. Luth. Ch., 1966, Luth. Social Services Wis. and Upper Mich. hdqrs., Milw., 1967, Lloyd A. Gerlach residence, Elm Grove, 1967, Eden Theol. Sem. Library, Webster Groves, Mo., 1968, Luth. Ch. Living Christ, Germantown, 1969, Grace Episcopal Ch., Galesburg, Ill., 1970, Calvary Bapt. Ch., Milw., 1970, Fine Arts Complex, U. Wis.-Stevens Point, 1971, Northridge Lakes Community Devel., Milw., 1971, phys. edn. bldg., U. Wis.-Parkside, 1972, Jewish Vocat. Services Milw., renovation, 1974, theater and anthropology bldg. Beloit Coll., 1975, Elmbrook Ch., Brookfield, Wis., 1975, Dubuque (Iowa) Theol. Library, 1976, Portage County Human Services Ctr., Stevens Point, 1979, Henry Reuss Interpretive Ctr., Dundee, Wis., 1981, Golda Meir House, Milw., 1981, Ctr. for Arts, U. Wis. Platteville, 1983, Cen. United Meth. Ch., Milw., 1983—, Greek Orthodox Manor, Wauwatosa, 1984, River House Condominiums, Milw., 1985, Usinger Factory addition, Milw., 1985, Oak Hill Terr., Waukesha, 1986, Laurel Oaks Retirement Community, Glendale, 1988, United Ch. Christ, Madison, Wis., 1993, Irving L. Young Audiorium,

Wis., 1993, univ. ctr. addition U. Wis.-Whitewater, 1988, ; also numerous exhbns. of works. Francis J. Plym fellow U. Ill., 1958; Ford Found. grantee U. Wis., 1961; named one of Wis. 5 Outstanding Young Men Wis. Jr. C. of C., 1961; recipient Gov. Wis. award for creativity in arts, 1967; various awards for archtl. works. Fellow AIA (housing com.); mem. Interfaith Forum on Religion, Art and Architecture, Gargoyle, Tau Beta Pi. Mem. Eastbrook Ch. Home: 2823 N Shepard Ave Milwaukee WI 53211-3433 Office: William Wenzler & Assocs 205 W Highland Ave Milwaukee WI 53203-1114

WERBA, GABRIEL, public relations consultant; b. Paris, Feb. 28, 1930; came to U.S., 1941; s. Aron and Dina (Lewin) W.; m. Barrie Celia Sakolsky, June 1, 1952; children: Dean Steffen, Annmarie Alexandra. BA in Journalism, U. Tex., 1948; postgrad., NYU Grad. Sch. Bus., 1948-49, NYU Sch. Law, 1961-62. Account exec. Harold C. Meyers & Co., N.Y.C., 1959-61; dir. pub. rels. and advt. Yardney Electric Corp., N.Y.C., 1961-63; sr. assoc. Shiefman & Assocs., Detroit, 1963-66; account exec. Merrill Lynch, Detroit, 1966-70; exec. v.p. Shiefman Werba & Assocs., Detroit, 1970-73; sr. v.p., exec. v.p., pres., chief oper. officer Anthony M. Franco, Inc., Detroit 1973-88; pres., chief exec. officer The Werba Group, Inc. and Gabriel Werba and Assocs., Inc., Detroit, 1988-94; prin. Durocher.Dixson.Werba, Inc., Detroit, 1994—; bd. dirs. Environ. Recovery Technologies, Inc., Troy, Mich.; Intrepid World Comm., Inc., Birmingham, Mich. Contbr. articles to profl. jours. Bd. dirs. Oakland Citizens League, Detroit, 1970—, Detroit Symphony Orch. Hall, 1983—, Detroit Chamber Winds, 1985-91, Common Ground, Royal Oak, Mich., 1988—, The Attic Theatre, Detroit, 1989-93, The Children's Ctr., Detroit, 1989-95, NATAS, Detroit, 1992—, The Jewish Cmty. Coun. Met. Detroit, 1989—, Margaret W. Montgomery Hsop., 1993—; mem. comm. com. Detroit Inst. Arts, 1986—, exhibits com., 1990—; chmn. comm. com.; mem. strategic planning com. The Children's Ctr., Detroit, 1989—; adv. bd., 1995—. Mem. Nat. Investor Rels. Inst. (past dir., pres. Detroit chpt., spkr., panelist), Pub. Rels. Soc. Am. (bd. dirs. Detroit chpt. 1988-94, pres. 1992-93, past treas. Detroit Counselors' sect., nat. membership com., nat exec. com. fin. sect., spkr., panelist), Fin. Analysts Soc. Detroit (past chmn. pub. info. com.), Am. Mensa (bd. dirs. 1975-91, nat. chmn. 1979-83), Internat. Mensa (bd. dirs. 1979-83, 85-93). Avocations: art collecting, concerts, theater. Home: 3320 Spinnaker Ln Apt 13C Detroit MI 48207-5006 Office: Durocher Dixson Werba Inc 400 Renaissance Ctr Ste 2250 Detroit MI 48243-1602

WERBITT, WARREN, gastroenterologist, educator; b. Phila., Jan. 29, 1939; s. Saull Boris and Pearl (Weiner) W.; m. Drue Natalie Engman Werbitt, Aug. 30, 1964; children: Julie Michele, Jeffrey Brian. BS in Pharmacy, Temple U., 1960; D in Osteopathy, Coll. Osteopathic Medicine, Des Moines, 1966; MD, Med. Coll. Pa., 1973. Diplomate Am. Osteo. Bd. Internal Medicine, also sub-splty. bd. Gastroenterology; diplomate Am. Bd. Internal Medicine, also sub-splty. bd. Gastroenterology. Internship Doctor's Hosp., Columbus, Ohio, 1966-67; residency in internal medicine Doctor's Hosp., Columbus, 1967-68, Cherry Hill (N.J.) Med. Ctr., 1968-69, Mercy Catholic Med. Ctr., Phila., 1969-70; residency in internal medicine Med. Coll. Pa. Hosp., Phila., 1971-72, fellow in gastroenterology, 1970-71, 72-74; instr. Med. Coll. Pa., Phila., 1971—; instr. Phila. Coll. Osteopathic Medicine, 1973-75, chmn. div. gastroenterology, 1975-77; clin. assoc. prof. medicine N.J. Coll. Medicine and Dentistry, 1977—; attending physician and cons. in gastroenterology Med. Coll. Pa., Phila., 1974—, Vet. Adminstrn. Hosp., Phila., 1972-75; chmn. Div. Gastroenterology, Dept. Medicine Phila. Coll. Osteopathic Medicine, 1975-77; chmn. Dept. Medicine Kennedy Meml. Hosp. U. Med. Ctr., Cherry Hill, 1979-81, chmn. subsect. Gastroenterology, 1979-87. Contbg. editor The N.J. Jour. for Ostepathic Physicians and Surgeons, 1980—; mem. scientific adv. com. Phila. chpt. Nat. Found. Ileitis & Colitis, Inc., 1982—; contbr. articles to profl. jours. Recipient Profl. Svc. award Med. Soc. N.J., 1991. Fellow Am. Coll. Physicians, Am. Coll. Gastroenterology, Acad. Med. N.J.; mem. AMA, Am. Soc. Gastrointestinal Endoscopy, Am. Gastroenterology Assn., Am. Soc. Parenteral and Enteric Nutrition, Am. Inst. Ultrasound in Medicine, Phila. Gastrointestinal Rsch. Forum, State Med. Soc. N.J., Camden County Med. Soc., N.J. Endoscopic Soc., Del. Valley Soc. for Gastrointestinal Endoscopy, South Jersey Gastroenterological Soc., Am. Osteopathic Assn., N.J. Soc. Osteopathic Physicians and Surgeons, Am. Coll. Osteopathic Internists, Camden County Osteopathic Assn., Am. Cancer Soc. (bd. dirs. N.J. chpt.), Pres.'s Circle Am. U., N.Y. Acad. Scis., John Sherman Myers Soc., Lambda Omicron Gamma. Avocations: golf, running, music, reading, American History. Office: Profl Gastroenterology Assn 1939 Route 70 E Ste 250 Cherry Hill NJ 08003-4507

WERBOS, PAUL JOHN, neural research director; b. Darby, Pa., Sept. 4, 1947; s. Walter Joseph and Margaret Mary (Donohue) W.; m. Lily Fountain, July 13, 1979; children: Elizabeth, Alexander, Maia. BA magna cum laude, Harvard U., 1967; MSc, London Sch. Econs., 1968; MA, Harvard U., 1969, PhD, 1974. Rsch. assoc. MIT, Cambridge, Mass., 1973-75; asst. prof. U. Md., College Park, 1975-78; math. statistician U.S. Census Bur., Suitland, Md., 1978-79; energy analyst U.S. Dept. Energy, Washington, 1979-88, 89; program dir. NSF, Washington, 1988, 89—. Author: The Roots of Back-propagation: From Ordered Derivatives to Neural Network & Political Forecasting, 1993; contbr. chpt. to Handbook of Intelligent Control, 1992. Regional dir., Washington rep. L-5 Soc. (merged with Nat. Space Soc.), Washington, 1980s. Mem. Internat. Neural Network Soc. (pres. 1991-92, sec. 1990). Quaker-Universalist. Achievements include patent pending for eleastic fuzzy logic and associated adaptation techniques; devised theory of intelligence; created alternative formulation of quantum theory. Home: 8411 48th Ave College Park MD 20740-2403 Office: NSF 1776 G St NW Rm 1151 Washington DC 20550

WERBOW, STANLEY NEWMAN, language educator; b. Phila., Apr. 19, 1922; s. Morris and Sadie (Newman) W.; m. Naomi Esther Ecker, June 1, 1952; children: Susan Linda, Emily Frances, Carol Martha. B.A., George Washington U., 1946; postgrad., Middlebury Coll., 1946, 47, U. Mich., 1948; Ph.D., Johns Hopkins, 1953. Tchr. Ea. High Sch., Washington, 1946-47; research analyst specialist U.S. Dept. Def., Washington, 1952-53; mem. faculty U. Tex., Austin, 1953—, prof., 1959-69, 78—, chmn. dept. Germanic langs., 1969-71, dean Coll. Humanities, 1971-78, acting dean Coll. Fine Arts, 1980-81; vis. prof. U. Marburg, 1963, U. N.Mex. German Summer Sch., 1984, 87, 89. Author: Martin von Amberg, 1957, (with Lehmann, Rehder, Shaw) Review and Progress in German, 1959; Editor: Formal Aspects of Medieval German Poetry, 1970. Served with Signal Corps AUS, 1943-45. Decorated Bronze Star medal; Bundesverdienstkreuz erster klasse W. Ger.; recipient Fulbright award to Netherlands, 1950-51; Guggenheim fellow, 1960; Fulbright research scholar Germany, 1960-61. Mem. Modern Lang. Assn. (pres. South Central assn. 1976—), Medieval Acad., Internat. Assn. Germanists, Phi Beta Kappa, Phi Kappa Phi, Delta Phi Alpha. Home: 4205 Prickly Pear Dr Austin TX 78731-2017 Office: Univ Texas Dept Germanic Langs Austin TX 78712

WERCKMEISTER, OTTO KARL, art historian and educator; b. Berlin, Apr. 26, 1934; came to U.S., 1965; s. Karl and Rose (Petzold) W.; m. Maria Eugenia Lacarra, July 3, 1965 (div. 1985); children: Christina, Robert, Veronica. PhD, Freie U. Berlin, 1958. Research assoc. German Archeol. Inst. Madrid, Spain, 1962-65; assoc. prof. to prof. UCLA, 1965-84; Mary Jane Crowe Disting. prof. Northwestern U., 1984—. Author: Ende der Asthetik, 1971, 1972, Ideologie und Kunst bei Marx und andere Essays, 1974, Versuche über Paul Klee, 1981, Zitadellenkultur, 1989, Eng. edit., 1991, The Making of Paul Klee's Career, 1914-20, 1989. Guggenheim fellow, 1981, Wissenschaftskolleg (Berlin) fellow, 1986. Office: Northwestern U Dept Art Hist Evanston IL 60208

WERGER, PAUL MYRON, bishop; b. Greenville, Pa., June 13, 1931; s. Jacob Paul and Laura Annetta (Greenwalt) W.; m. Diane Mae Ellison, July 26, 1957; children: Paul Myron, Jonathan David, Matthew James, Mary Dianne. BA, Thiel Coll., 1954; MDiv, Northwestern Theol. Sem., Mpls., 1957, DD (hon.), 1976; LHD (hon.), Grand View Coll., 1985. Ordained to ministry, Luth. Ch. Am., 1957. Pastor Apostles Luth. Ch., St. Paul, 1957-61, St. Luke's Luth. Ch., Bloomington, Minn. 1961-78; bishop Iowa Synod Luth. Ch. Am., Des Moines, 1978-88, S.E. Iowa Synod, Iowa City, 1987—; chmn. Conf. Bishops Evang. Luth. Ch. Am. 1987-91, mem. ch. coun. 1988-91, bishop adv. mem., 1988, stewardship and evangelism com. NW Synod, 1959-62; mem. bd. social ministry Minn. Synod, 1963-70, mem. exec. bd., dean south suburban dist.; pres., bd. dirs. Luth. Social Services in Minn.;

mem. mgmt. com. dir. mission N.Am. Luth. Ch. Am., 1983—; del. Luth. Ch. Am. convs.; pastor evangelist Evang. Outreach; corp. bd. dirs. Fairvi. Contbr. articles to profl. jours. Mem. Bloomington Human Rights Commn.; mem. citizens adv. com. Bloomington Sch. Dist. 271; bd. dirs. Luther Northwestern, 1976, Luth. Sch. Theology, Chgo., 1978-88, Luth. Ch. Am. Found., Grandview Coll., 1978, GrandView Coll., 1978-92, Iowa Luth. Hosp., 1978—, Luth. Soc. Svc. Iowa, 1978—, Fairview Corp., 1985—; bd. fellows Sch. Religion, U. Iowa; Luth. Ch. in Am. observer Wartburg Theol. Sem., 1986-88. Recipient Thiel Coll. Alumni award for profl. achievement, 1979. Mem. Assn. Bloomington Clergy, Conf. of Luth./Roman Cath. Bishops. Avocations: travel, photography, golf, fishing, sports. Office: SE Iowa Synod Hdqrs PO Box 3167 2635 Northgate Dr Iowa City IA 52244-3167

WERKHOVEN, KATHRYN REGINA, nursing administrator; b. Memphis Apr. 11, 1936; d. Stephen Grier and Mary (McKenize) Edmundson; m. William Edward Werkhoven, July 8, 1961; children—Thomas, Jerome, Michael, Mary Anne, John. Diploma nursing Nazareth Coll., 1957; B.Profl. Studies, Memphis State U., 1979. Cert. nursing adminstr. Scrub nurse Dr. McCarthy Demere, Memphis, 1960-62; instr. St. Joseph Hosp., Memphis, 1962-71, dir. surgery, 1971-74; dir. surgery St. Francis Hosp., Memphis, 1974-79, dir. nursing, 1979—. Wharton's fellow in nursing mgmt. Wharton's and Johnson & Johnson, 1984. Mem. Am. Soc. Nursing Adminstrs., Tenn. Hosp. Assn. (chmn. council on nursing 1984-85), Tenn. Soc. Nurse Adminstrs. (bd. dirs. 1982-84). Democrat. Roman Catholic. Avocations: swimming; reading. Office: St Francis Hosp 5959 Park Ave Memphis TN 38119-5198

WERKING, RICHARD HUME, librarian, historian, academic administrator; b. Charleston, S.C., Sept. 29, 1943; s. F. Woody and Mary S. (Prissinger) W. BA, U. Evansville, 1966; MA in Am. History, U. Wis., 1967, PhD in Am. History, 1973; MA in Librarianship, U. Chgo., 1975. Instr. history Northland Coll., Ashland, Wis., 1967-68; pers. staffing specialist U.S. Civil Svc. Commn., Indpls., 1968-69; reference libr. Lawrence U., Appleton, Wis., 1975-77; head reference dept., asst. prof. history U. Miss., Oxford, 1977-79, asst. libr. dir., asst. prof. history, 1979-80, acting libr. dir., asst. prof. history, 1980-81; assoc. libr. dir., asst. prof. history Trinity U., San Antonio, Tex., 1981-83, libr. dir., assoc. prof. history, 1983-91; libr. dir., assoc. dean, prof. history U.S. Naval Acad., Annapolis, Md., 1991—; With OCLC Adv. Com. on Coll. and Univ. Librs., Dublin, Ohio, 1986-92; sr. fellow Grad. Sch. Libr. & Info. Sci., UCLA, 1989. Author: The Master Architects: Building the U.S. Foreign Service, 1977; contbr. articles to profl. jours., chpts. to books, also papers, monographs and revs. With U.S. Army, 1962. Sparks fellow Phi Kappa Phi, 1966, postdoctoral fellow Coun. on Libr. Resources, 1974. Mem. ALA (comml. com. librs. sect. 1987-88), Orgn. Am. Historians. Office: US Naval Acad Nimitz Libr 589 Mcnair Rd Annapolis MD 21402-5028

WERKMAN, SIDNEY LEE, psychiatry educator; b. Washington, May 3, 1927. A.B., Williams Coll., 1948; M.D., Cornell U., 1952. Diplomate Am. Bd. Psychiatry and Neurology, Am. Bd. Child Psychiatry. Intern U. Va. Hosp., Charlottesville; resident in psychiatry Yale U., 1953-55, St. Elizabeth's Hosp., Washington, 1955-56; assoc. prof. psychiatry George Washington U., Washington, 1960-69; prof. U. Colo. Sch. Medicine, Denver, 1969-87; dir. div. adolescent psychiatry Children's Hosp. of Washington, 1965-69; clin. prof. Georgetown U. Sch. Medicine, Washington, 1989—; psychiatrist Capital Area Permanente Med. Group, Washington, 1990—; cons. grants NIMH, Washington, 1982—, guest researcher, 1984-85. Author: The Role of Psychiatry in Medical Education, 1966, Only a Little Time: A Chronicle of Dying, 1972, Bringing Up Children Overseas, 1977. Bd. dirs. Med. U. So. Africa, Performing Arts Soc., Washington Concert Operas. Master sgt. U.S. Army. Fellow Commonwealth Fund, Florence, Italy, 1963-64, NEH, 1979. Mem. Am. Psychiat. Assn., Am. Acad. Child Psychiatry, Group for Advancement Psychiatry, Am. Orthopsychiat. Assn. (bd. dirs. 1970-73), Colo. Psychiat. Soc. Office: 2918 33rd Pl NW Washington DC 20008-3527

WERLEIN, EWING, JR., federal judge, lawyer; b. Houston, Sept. 14, 1936; s. Ewing and Ruth (Storey) W.; m. Kay McGibbon Werlein, June 29, 1963; children: Ewing Kenneth, Emily Kay. BA, So. Meth. U., 1958; LLB, U. Tex., 1961. Bar: Tex. 1961, U.S. Dist. Ct. (so. dist.) Tex. 1965, U.S. Dist. Ct. (ea. dist.) Tex. 1990, U.S. Ct. Appeals (5th cir.) 1970, U.S. Ct. Appeals (10th cir.) 1980, U.S. Claims Ct. 1985, U.S. Tax Ct. 1985, U.S. Supreme Ct. 1983. Ptnr. Vinson & Elkins, Houston, 1964-92; dist. judge U.S. Dist. Ct. (so. dist.) Tex., 1992—. Trustee So. Meth. U., Dallas, 1976-92, Asbury Theol. Sem., Wilmore, Ky., 1989—; mem. gen. bd. pub. United Meth. Ch., Nashville, 1974-84, chmn., 1980-84, chancellor Tex. ann. conf., 1977—; mem. exec. com. World Meth. Counh., 1981—, treas., 1991-93. Capt. USAF, 1961-64. Fellow Am. Coll. Trial Lawyers, 1984, Internat. Soc. Barristers, 1987; recipient Disting. Alumni award SMU Alumni Assn., 1994. Fellow Am. Bar Found., Tex. Bar Found., Houston Bar Found.; mem. State Bar of Tex. (dir. 1990-93), Nat. Conf. of Bar Pres.'s, Houston Bar Assn. (pres. 1988-89), Houston C. of C. (life), SAR, Order of the Coif, Ramada Club (Houston), Phi Beta Kappa. Office: US Dist Ct Tex US Courthouse 515 Rusk St Ste 9136 Houston TX 77002-2605

WERLING, DONN PAUL, environmental educator; b. Ft. Wayne, Ind., Oct. 14, 1945; s. Paul Henry and Lydia Sophia (Rebber) W.; m. Diane Mueller, July 11, 1970; 1 child, Benjamin Paul. BS, Valparaiso U., 1967; MS, Mich. State U., 1968; MEd, Loyola U., 1970; Ph.D., U. Mich., 1979. Dir. nature project Raymond Sch., Chgo. Bd. Edn., 1969-72; dir. Evanston Environ. Assn., Ill., 1973-81; dir. Henry Ford Estate, U. Mich.-Dearborn, 1983—; adj. asst. prof. edn., 1984—; founder N.Am. Voyageur Conf., 1977. Author: Environmental Education and Your School Site, 1973; A School-Community Stewardship Model, 1979; Lake Michigan and Its Lighthouses, 1982, Lakes and Lighthouses, 1989, Lighthouse Digest of the Great Lakes, 1993, Lore and Legacy, 1994. Mem. state master plan com. on environ. edn. State of Ill., Springfield, 1970; mem. adv. com. Ill. Coastal Zone, Chgo., 1978; bd. dirs. Ill. Shore council Girl Scouts U.S., 1978-82, Chgo. Maritime Soc., 1982. Recipient Mayor's award City of Evanston, 1976, Russell E. Wilson award U. Mich. Sch. Edn., 1979, Service award Ill. Shore council Girl Scouts U.S., 1978, J. Lee Barrett award Met. Detroit Tourist & Conv. Bur., 1986, award for interpretative excellence Nat. Assn. for Interpretation, 1989; named to Outstanding Young Men Am., Jaycees, 1975. Mem. Nat. Assn. Interpretation, Am. Assn. Mus., Great Lakes Lighthouse Keepers Assn. (founder, pres. 1982-86), Tourist and Travel Assn. Southeast Mich. (chmn. 1984-86), Kiwanis. Avocations: historic restoration, gardening, writing, composing, singing Christian and bluewater music. Address: Henry Ford Estate-Fair Lane U of Michigan-Dearborn Evergreen Rd Dearborn MI 48128

WERMAN, DAVID SANFORD, psychiatrist, psychoanalyst, educator; b. N.Y.C., Jan. 1, 1922; s. Morris and Blanche (Heftel) W.; m. Marjolijn R. de Jager, Oct. 25, 1958 (div. 1975); children: Marco W., Claudia J. B.A., Queens Coll., 1942; postgrad., Columbia U., 1946-47; M.D., Cert. d'Etudes Medicales, U. Lausanne, Switzerland, 1952. Diplomate Am. Bd. Obstetrics and Gynecology, Am. Bd. Psychiatry and Neurology. Intern Beth Israel Hosp., N.Y.C., 1953-54; resident, 1954-57; resident Montefiore Hosp., Bronx, N.Y., 1964-67; pvt. practice specializing in ob-gyn. N.Y.C., 1957-64; faculty acad. psychiatry U.N.C., Chapel Hill, 1967-76, assoc. prof., instr. psychoanalytic tng. program, 1974—; prof. psychiatry Duke U. Med. Ctr., Durham, N.C., 1976—, supervising and tng. analyst psychoanalytic tng. program, 1981—, Honored prof. emeritus, 1992—; prof. emeritus, 1992—; cons. Durham VA Hosp. Author: The Practice of Supportive Psychotherapy, 1984. Contbr. chpts. to books, articles to profl. jours. With AUS, 1943-45. Named Outstanding Tchr. psychiatry U. N.C., 1975, honored tchr. psychiatry Duke U., 1978, hon. prof., 1990. Fellow ACS, Am. Psychiat. Assn., Am. Coll. Psychoanalysts, others. Home: 1503 Michaux Rd Chapel Hill NC 27514-7637 Office: Duke Univ Med Ctr Dept Psychiatry PO Box 3812 Durham NC 27702-3812

WERMAN, THOMAS EHRLICH, record producer; b. Newton, Mass., Mar. 2, 1945; s. Lester and Ruth (Ehrlich) W.; m. Susan Lynne Gould, Aug. 25, 1968; children—Julia Gould, Nina Eve, Daniel Lester. B.A., Columbia

U., 1967, M.B.A., 1969. Asst. account exec. Grey Advt., N.Y.C., 1969-70; asst. to dir. Epic Records Artistes and Repertoire, 1970-73; dir. talent acquisition Epic Records, 1973-76, staff producer, 1976-80; v.p., exec. producer CBS Records, Inc., L.A., 1980-81; sr. v.p. Elektra Records, 1981-82; pres. Julia's Music Inc., 1981—. Recipient N.Y.C. Civilian Commendation award for heroism, 1968, 14 platinum records awards Rec. Industry Assn. Am., 1977—, 8 Gold Record awards, 1977—. Mem. Nat. Assn. Recording Arts and Scis. Democrat. Jewish.

WERMERS, DONALD JOSEPH, registrar; b. Ethan, S.D., Nov. 19, 1934; s. Anthony J. and Margaret (Muntefering) W.; m. Verla Jean Blankenfeld, Oct. 14, 1961; children: Gregory, Leah. BS in Edn., No. State Coll., 1960; postgrad., U. S.D., summer 1964, 65; MEd, U. Fla., 1967; EdD, U. Ill., 1971. Tchr. bus. Wessington Springs (S.D.) High Sch., 1960-61; bus. mgr. Delaney Clinic, Mitchell, S.D., 1961-63; acting supt., prin., tchr. White Lake (S.D.) Schs., 1963-65; tchr. bus. Milford (Iowa) High Sch., 1965-66; residence hall counselor Ea. Ill. U., Charleston, 1967-68; asst. dir. Office Sch. and Coll. Rels. U. Ill., Champaign, 1970-80; dir. admissions, registrar U. N.D., Grand Forks, 1980-85; registrar U. Wis., Madison, 1985—. Editor chpt. in book; pubs. editor Transfer Credit Practices of Selected Insts., 1977-81. NDEA fellow U. Fla., 1966-67, U. Ill., 68-69. Mem. Am. Assn. Collegiate Registrars and Admissions Officer (v.p. 1995—), Coll. and Univ. Machine Records. Avocations: golf, classical and band music, athletic events. Office: U Wis 750 University Ave Rm 130 Madison WI 53706-1490

WERMUTH, PAUL CHARLES, retired English educator; b. Phila., Oct. 28, 1925; s. Paul C. and Susan (Manga) W.; m. Barbara Ethel Braun, Aug. 26, 1951; children—Geoffrey Paul, Paul Charles, Alan John, Stephen Mark. A.B., M.A., Boston U., 1951; Ph.D., Pa. State U., 1955. Instr. Clarkson Coll., Potsdam, N.Y., 1951-52; part-time instr., grad. asst. Pa. State U., 1952-55; asst. prof. Coll. William and Mary, 1955-57; mem. faculty Central Conn. State Coll., New Britain, 1957-68; assoc. prof. English Central Conn. State Coll., 1966-68; prof. English Northeastern U., 1968-90, prof. emeritus, 1990—, chmn. dept., 1968-75; vis. prof. Middlebury Coll., 1963-64. Author: Modern Essays on Writing and Style, 2d edit, 1969, Essays in English, 1967, Bayard Taylor, 1974, also articles. Served with USAAF, 1943-46. Danforth summer study grantee, 1961. Mem. Modern Lang. Assn., AAUP, Mensa. Home: 73 Mostyn St Swampscott MA 01907-1616 Office: Northeastern Univ Boston MA 02115

WERNER, CHARLES GEORGE, cartoonist; b. Marshfield, Wis., Mar. 23, 1909; s. George J. and Marie (Tippelt) W.; m. Eloise Robertson, Oct. 5, 1935 (dec. Jan. 1993); children: David, Jean, Stephen. Spl. courses at Northwestern U.; student, Art Ins. Chgo., 1943. Artist, photographer Springfield Leader, 1930-35; mem. art dept. Daily Oklahoma, 1935-37, editorial cartoonist, 1937-41; chief polit. cartoonist Chgo. Sun, 1941-46; cartoonist Indpls. Star, 1947-95; instr. cartooning pub. schs., Oklahoma City, 1939-41, lectr. history polit. cartoons. Recipient Pulitzer prize for cartoon, 1938; honorable mention for cartoon in auto safety contest, 1939; hon. mention Nat. Safety Council cartoons, 1943; Sigma Delta Chi award best cartoon, 1943; Nat. Headliners Club 1st place award, 1951; Freedoms Found. awards, 1951, 52, 53, 55, 56, 58, 62, 63; 1st place award Nat. Found. Hwy. Safety, 1965; winner one of 6 best caricatures Internat. Salon of Cartoons, Montreal, 1969. Hon. lifetime mem. Oklahoma City Jr. C. of C.; mem. Am. Assn. Editl. Cartoonists (pres. 1959-60), Nat. Cartoonists Soc., Masons (33 deg.), Shriners, Jesters, Indpls. Athletic Club (Indpls.), Sigma Delta Chi (hon.). Episcopalian. Clubs: Masons (33 deg.), Shriners, Jesters, Indianapolis Athletic (Indpls.), Columbia (Indpls.). Address: 4445 Brown Rd Indianapolis IN 46226-3147

WERNER, CLARENCE L., transportation executive; b. 1937. Asst. mgr. Larson Grain Co., Omaha, 1958-61; with Bus. Motor Express, Inc., Omaha, 1961-62; with Werner Enterprises, Inc., Omaha, 1956-82, pres., 1982-84, chmn. bd., CEO, 1984—. Office: Werner Enterprises Inc I-80 Highway 50 Omaha NE 68138

WERNER, ELIZABETH HELEN, librarian, Spanish language educator; b. Palo Alto, Calif., June 21, 1944; d. Fielding and Lucy Elizabeth (Hart) McDearmon; m. Michael Andrew Werner, Aug. 21, 1976. BA, Mills Coll., 1966; MA, Ind. U., 1968; MLS, U. Md., 1973. Instr. Spanish, Western Md. Coll., Westminster, 1968-72; libr., assoc. prof. Clearwater (Fla.) Christian Coll., 1975—; sec. Sunline Libr. users group Tampa Bay Libr. Consortium, Tampa, Fla., 1993-94. Contbr. book revs. to profl. jours. Com. mem. Upper Pinellas County Post Office Consumers Adv. Coun., Clearwater, 1992—. Mem. Fla. Libr. Assn., Assn. Christian Librs., Fla. Assn. Christian Librs. (pres. 1991-94), Friends of the Clearwater Libr., Am. Assn. Tchrs. Spanish and Portuguese. Avocations: reading, choir, travel, language study. Office: Clearwater Christian Coll 3400 Gulf To Bay Blvd Clearwater FL 34619-4514

WERNER, GERHARD, pharmacologist, psychoanalyst, educator; b. Vienna, Austria, Sept. 28, 1921; came to U.S., 1957, naturalized, 1965; s. Rudolf and Elizabeth (Lukas) W.; m. Marion E. Friedmann, July 25, 1958; children—Philip Ralph, Karen Nicole. M.D. U. Vienna, 1945. With dept. pharmacology U. Vienna, 1945-50; prof. pharmacology, head dept. U. Calcutta (India) Sch. Tropical Medicine, 1952-54, U. Sao Paulo (Brazil) Med. Sch. of Ribeirao Preto, 1955-57; assoc. prof. Cornell U. Med. Sch., 1957-61; assoc. prof. pharmacology and physiology Johns Hopkins U. Med. Sch., 1963-65; v.p. prof. affairs Univ. Health Ctr., Pitts., 1975-78; prof. pharmacology, head dept. U. Pitts. Med. Sch., 1965-75, dean, 1975-78, prof. psychiatry, 1978-89, F.S. Cheever Disting. prof., emeritus prof., 1990; pres. Med. Comp, Inc., 1990—; assoc, chief of staff Dept. Vets. Affairs Med. Ctr. Highland Drive, Pitts., 1991; cons. Ctr. for Emergent Technology, Motorola, Inc., 1995—; cons. technology program NSF, 1970-75, mem. adv. panel regulatory biology div. biology and med. sci., 1969-70, mem. primate ctr. rev. com., 1973-79; mem. chem. biol. info. panel NIH, 1967-70, mem. study sect. pharmacology and exptl. therapeutics, 1964-68; mem. study sect. Pitts. Psychoanalytic Inst., 1973-79; external examiner for Ph.D (med. sci.) U. Calcutta, 1953—; mem. adv. bd. Indian Coun. Med. Rsch., 1952-54. Mem. editorial bd. Jour. Neurophysiology, 1970-78, Internat. Jour. Neuropharmacology, Jour. Clin. Pharmacology; asso. editor Pharmacol. Revs, 1969-70; contbr. articles to profl. jours. Recipient Humboldt prize, 1984. Fellow N.Y. Acad. Sci.; mem. Soc. Neuroscis., AAAS, Harvey Soc., Am. Soc. Pharmacology and Exptl. Therapeutics, Am. Physiol. Soc., Soc. Gen. Systems Research, Internat. Union for Psychobiology, Soc. for Artificial Intelligence, Assn. for Computing Machinery, Internat. Brain Research Orgn., Am. Psychoanalytic Assn., Indian Soc. Biochemistry and Physiology, German Pharmacol. Soc., Sigma Xi. Home: 1307 Bennington Ave Pittsburgh PA 15217-1136

WERNER, GLORIA S., librarian; b. Seattle, Dec. 12, 1940; d. Irving L. and Eva H. Stolzoff; m. Newton Davis Werner, June 30, 1963; 1 son, Adam Davis. BA, Oberlin Coll., 1961; ML, U. Wash., 1962; postgrad. UCLA, 1962-63. Reference librarian UCLA Biomed Library, 1963-64, asst. head pub. services dept., 1964-66, head pub. services dept., head reference div., 1966-72, asst. biomed. librarian public services, 1972-77, asso. biomed. librarian, 1977-78, biomed. librarian, assoc. univ. librarian, dir. Pacific S.W. regional Med. Library Service, 1979-83; asst. dean library services UCLA Sch. Medicine, 1980-83; assoc. univ. librarian for tech. services, 1983-89, dir. libraries, acting univ. librarian, 1989-90, univ. librarian, 1990—; adj. lectr. UCLA Grad. Sch. Library and Info. Sci., 1977-83. Editor, Bull. Med. Library Assn., 1979-82, asso. editor, 1974-79; mem. editorial bd. Ann. Stats. Med. Sch. Libraries U.S. and Can., 1980-83; mem. accrediting commn. Western Assn. Schs. and Colls., N.W. Assn. Schs. and Colls. Mem. ALA, Assn. Rsch. Librs. (bd. dirs. 1993—). Office: UCLA Rsch Libr Libr Adminstrv Office 405 Hilgard Ave Los Angeles CA 90024-1575

WERNER, JOSEPH GRANBERRY, lawyer; b. Stamford, Tex., Sept. 10, 1940; s. Walter Crowell and Lily-(Granberry) W.; m. Bilye Buckner, Apr. 30, 1972; 1 dau., Susan Buckner. B.A., Rice U., 1962; LL.B., U. Tex., 1967. Bar: Tex. 1967, U.S. Dist. Ct. (no. dist.) Tex. 1969, U.S. Ct. Appeals (5th cir.) 1970, U.S. Supreme Ct. 1973. Asst. city atty. City of Dallas, 1969-72, 73-82, first asst. city atty., 1982-85; ptnr. Haynes and Boone, Dallas, 1985—; speaker Southwestern Legal Found., Nat. Inst. Mcpl. Law Officers, Nat. League of Cities, Tex. Mcpl. League, Tex. City Attys. Assn., Internat. Assn. Chiefs of Police, Ams. for Effective Law Enforcement. Mem. Dallas Bar Assn., State Bar Tex., ABA. Office: Haynes and Boone 3100 Nationsbank Plz 901 Main St Dallas TX 75201

WERNER, MARIO, pathology educator; b. Zurich, Switzerland, Aug. 21, 1931; came to U.S., 1961; s. Hans and Noemi (Martinello) W.; m. Elsbeth B. Nievergelt, May 26, 1961; 1 child, Conrad J. MD, U. Zurich, 1956, DMS, 1961. Diplomate Am. Bd. Pathology, Am. Bd. Clin. Chemistry. Resident in surgery Kantonsspital St. Gallen, Switzerland, 1957-58; resident in internal medicine U. Basel, Switzerland, 1958-61; fellow Swiss Acad. Med. Sci. Nat. Inst. Arthritis, Bethesda, Md., 1961-62, Rockefeller U., N.Y.C., 1962-64; chief cen. lab. U. Essen, Fed. Republic of Germany, 1964-66; asst. prof. pathology U. Calif., San Francisco, 1967-70; assoc. prof. Washington U., St. Louis, 1970-72; prof. George Washington U., Washington, 1973—. Editor-in-chief Clinica Chimica Acta, 1985—; editor Clin. Chemistry, 1978-85, Clin. Biochemistry, 1980-90, Med. Lab. Observer, 1980—, Am. Jour. Clin. Pathology, 1983-85, InVivo, 1987—; editor 19 books; contbr. more than 70 articles to profl. jours., 35 chpts. to books., more than 70 miscellaneous sci. comm. Chmn. health care delivery program, Bi-State Regional Med. Program, 1971-72. Fellow Am. Soc. Clin. Pathologists, Coll. Am. Pathologists, Nat. Acad. Clin. Biochemistry; mem. Internat. Soc. Clin. Enzymology (chmn. 4th congress 1983, pres. 1989-90), Acad. Clin. Lab. Physicians and Scientists, Nat. Coun. Health Lab. Svcs. (chmn. 1987-89), Am. Bd. Clin. Chemistry (bd. dirs. 1979-85, chmn. exam. com. 1981-83). Home: 2819 Mcgill Ter NW Washington DC 20008-2749 Office: George Washington U Med Ctr 901 23d St NW Washington DC 20037

WERNER, MARLIN SPIKE, speech pathologist and audiologist; b. Portland, Maine, Aug. 15, 1927; s. Leonard Matthews and Margaret (Steele) W.; m. Caroline Emma Paul, Dec. 23, 1985; children: Leo Hart, Joseph Hart. BA in Sociology and Social Work, U. Mo., 1950; ScM in Audiology and Speech Pathology, Johns Hopkins U., 1957; PhD in Speech and Hearing Sci., Ohio State U., 1966. Lic. in audiology, hearing aid dispensing, speech pathology, Hawaii; lic. in audiology and speech pathology, Calif. Audiologist/speech pathologist, dir. Speech and Hearing Ctr. Asheville (N.C.) Orthopedic Hosp., 1960-64; assoc. prof. speech pathology and audiology We. Carolina U., Cullowhee, N.C., 1965-69; assoc. prof. speech pathology, audiology and speech sci. Fed. City Coll. (now U. D.C.), Washington, 1969-73; pres. Friends of Nepal's Hearing Handicapped, Oakland, Calif., 1979-84; hearing aid dispenser, audiologist, speech pathologist pvt. practice, Oakland and Lafayette, Calif., 1973-85; pvt. practice Lafayette, 1985-87; pvt. practice speech pathology and audiology Hilo, Hawaii, 1987—; speech and hearing cons. VA Hosp., Oteen, N.C., 1960-64; clin. cons. Speech and Hearing Clinic, Asheville Orthopedic Hosp., 1966-67; lectr., presenter in field. Contbr. articles to profl. jours.; contbr. to Ency. Brit., Am. Heritage Book of Natural Wonders, others. Mem. hearing impaired svcs. task force State of Hawaii Dept. Health, 1987-88; mem. Hawaii County Mayor's Com. for Persons with Disabilities, 1988-94; adv. bd. Salvation Army, 1992; bd. dirs. Hawaii chpt. Am. Arthritis Found.; past pres. Big Island Safety Assn.; mem. Hawaii Gov's. bd. Hearing Aid Dealers And Fitters; mem. adv. com., pres. Older Adult Resource Ctr., Laney Coll., Oakland, Calif.; v.p. Hawaii Spelelogical Survey; chmn. Hawaii Grotto of N.S.S.; others. MCH fellow Johns Hopkins U., 1954, Pub. Health fellow Ohio State U., 1964. Fellow Nat. Speleological Soc.; mem. AAAS, Am. Speech and Hearing Assn., Acoustical Soc. Am., Calif. Speech and Hearing Assn., Calif. Writers Club (bd. dirs., past pres.), Hawaii Speech/Lang. Hearing Assn. Avocations: collecting and making musical instruments, graphic arts, photography, cave exploring, writing. Home: PO Box 11509 Hilo HI 96721-6509 Office: 400 Hualani St Ste 191-A Hilo HI 96720-4378

WERNER, R(ICHARD) BUDD, business executive; b. Lorain, Ohio, Aug. 27, 1931; s. Paul Henry and Bessie Marie (Budd) W.; m. Janet Sue Kelsey, Aug. 28, 1932; children: Richard Budd, David Kelsey, Mary Paula. BS in Commerce, Ohio U., 1953. CPA. Sr. auditor Arthur Andersen & Co., Cleve., 1955-59; various fin. positions Glidden Co., Cleve., 1959-65; v.p., asst. treas. Harshaw divsn. Kewanee Oil Co., Cleve., 1965-72; v.p. fin., treas. Weatherhead Co., Cleve., 1973-77; v.p. finance, treas. Hauserman, Inc., Cleve., 1977-81; v.p. fin., CFO SPX Corp., Muskegon, Mich., 1981-94, sr. v.p. planning and devel., 1994—; bd. dirs., chmn. fin. com. Mercy Health Svcs. Mem. Lakewood (Ohio) City Coun., 1972-73. Lt. Q.M.C., U.S. Army, 1953-55. Mem. Fin. Execs. Inst., Mich. Soc. CPAs, Spring Lake Country Club, Chgo. Athletic Assn., Grand Rapids Press Club. Office: SPX Corp PO Box 3301 700 Terrace St Muskegon MI 49443-3301

WERNER, ROBERT JOSEPH, college dean, music educator; b. Lackawanna, N.Y., Feb. 13, 1932; s. Edward Joseph and Marian L. (Gerringer) W.; m. Sharon Lynne Mohrfeld, June 22, 1957; children: Mark J., Kurt M., Erik J. BME, Northwestern U., 1953, MusM, 1954, PhD, 1967. Dir. instrumental music Evanston (Ill.) Twp. High Sch., 1956-66; assoc. prof. mus. Harpur Coll. SUNY, Binghamton, 1966-68, dir. Contemporary Music Project, 1968-73; dir. Sch. Mus. U. Ariz., Tucson, 1973-85, deanfine arts, 1981-82; dean Coll.-Conservatory of Music U. Cin., 1985—. Editor: Comprehensive Musicianship: An Anthology of Evolving Thought, 1971; contbr. articles to profl. jours. Mem. exec. bd. Tucson Symphony Orch., 1974-85; bd. dirs. Cultural Commn. Tucson, 1974-75, Cin. Symphony Orch., 1985—, Cin. Opera, 1985—, Cin. Ballet, 1985—. With U.S. Army, 1954-56. Mem. Nat. Assn. Schs. Music (pres. 1989-91), Coll. Music Soc. (pres. 1977-78), Internat. Soc. for Music Edn. (pres. 1984-86, treas. 1986—), Music Educators Nat.Conf., McDowell Soc., Coll. Music Soc., Pi Kappa Lambda, Mu Alpha Sinfonia. Office: U Cin Coll Conservatory of Music Cincinnati OH 45221-0003

WERNER, ROBERT L., lawyer; b. N.Y.C., Feb. 28, 1913; s. Abraham L. and Elsa (Ludwig) W.; m. Raye Davies, Oct. 13, 1945; children: William, John. A.B., Yale U., 1933; L.L.B., Harvard U., 1936. Bar: N.Y. 1936, U.S. Supreme Ct. 1936, also various fed. cts. and adminstrv. agys. 1936. Spl. asst. to U.S. atty. So. Dist. N.Y., 1936, asst. U.S. atty, 1937-40, confidential asst., 1940-42; 1st asst. civil div. U.S. Dept. Justice, Washington, 1946-47; spl. asst. to atty. gen. U.S., 1946-47; mem. law dept. RCA, N.Y.C., 1947; v.p., gen. atty. RCA, 1951-62, exec. v.p., gen. atty., 1962-66, exec. v.p., gen. counsel, 1966-78, dir., 1963-79, cons., 1978-83; mem. adv. bd. Internat. and Comparative Law Ctr. Southwestern Legal Found., Dallas, 1966—, treas., 1970-72, vice chmn., 1972-73, chmn. advisory bd., 1974-76, found. trustee 1976-88, hon. trustee 1988—; lectr. Conf. Bd., Practicing Law Inst., others; mem. nat. adv. council corp. law depts. Practising Law Inst., 1974-78; com. on restrictive bus. practices U.S. council Internat. C. of C., 1973-78; N.Y. Lawyers' Com. for Civil Rights under Law, 1972-78. Trustee Ithaca Coll., N.Y., 1968-88, hon. trustee, 1988—, chmn. bd., 1976-78; trustee Salisbury (Conn.) Sch., 1975-77, N.Y. Chiropractic Coll., 1986-89; bd. dirs. Midtown Arts Common at St. Peter's Ch., 1983-89. Capt. U.S. Army, 1942-44; to lt. col. USAAF, 1944-46, ETO. Recipient Disting. Service award Ithaca Coll., 1988. Fellow Am. Bar Found.; mem. Internat., Fed., Am., N.Y. State, City N.Y., FCC bar assns., IEEE (sr.), Am. Legion, Harvard Law Sch. Assn., Assn. Gen. Counsel (emeritus), U.S. Naval Inst., Internat. Law Assn. (Am. br.), Nat. Legal Aid and Defender Assn. (dir. 1974-79), Am. Judicature Soc., Newcomen Soc., N.Y. County Lawyers' Assn., Assn. Soc. Internat. Law, Yale Club, Harvard Club N.Y., The Rockefeller Ctr. Club, Nat. Lawyers Club, Army and Navy Club (Washington), Coral Beach Club (Bermuda). Home: 116 E 68th St New York NY I0021-5956

WERNER, SETH MITCHELL, advertising executive; b. N.Y.C., Sept. 23, 1954; s. Michael M. and Helen (Barasch) W.; 1 child, Zachary Michael. BS in Pub. Rels., Boston U., 1976. Writer Monett Media, Atlanta, Ga., 1976-

77; writer, copy chief Goldberg/Marchesano, Washington, 1977-79; writer The Marshalk Co., N.Y.C., 1979-86, Foote, Cone & Belding, San Francisco, 1986-87; then pres., exec. creative dir. Bloom FCA! (now Publicis/Bloom), Dallas, now vice chmn., exec. creative dir. Allstar Writer of Yr. Adweek mag., 1984, 87, Advt. Exec. of Yr., 1988. Office: Publicis/Bloom 3500 Maple Ave Dallas TX 75219-3901

WERNER, THOMAS LEE, hospital administrator; b. Hazen, N.D., Dec. 8, 1945; married. BA, Union Coll., 1967; MA, U. Nebr., 1969. Asst. dir. pers. Portland (Oreg.) Adventist Med. Ctr., 1971-72; v.p. Verticare Ambulatory Care Program, Portland, 1972-73; adminstr. Tillamook (Oreg.) CountyGen. Hosp., 1973-77, Walla Walla (Wash.)Gen. Hosp., 1977-81; exec. v.p. Fla. Hosp. Med. Ctr., Orlando, 1981-85, pres., 1985—. Office: Fla Hosp Med Ctr 601 E Rollins St Orlando FL 32803-1248

WERNER, TOM, television producer, professional baseball team executive; m. Jill Werner; 3 children, Teddy, Carolyn, Amanda. BA, Harvard Univ., 1971. With ABC Television, Inc., 1972-82; co-owner Carsey-Werner Co., Studio City, Calif., 1982—; chmn. San Diego Padres, 1991—; mem. bd. dirs. Old Globe Theatre; Sharp Hospital. Co-exec. producer TV series: Oh, Madeline, 1983; exec. producer: The Cosby Show, (Emmy awd. Outstanding Comedy Series-1985), 1984-92, A Different World, 1987-93, Roseanne, 1988—, Chicken Soup, 1989-90, Grand, 1990, Davis Rules, 1991, You Bet Your Life, 1993-93, Frannie's Turn, 1992. Office: San Diego Padres PO Box 2000 San Diego CA 92112-2000*

WERNER, WILLIAM ARNO, architect; b. San Francisco, Dec. 11, 1937; s. William Arno and Sophie (Menutis) W.; m. Wendy Rolston Wilson, Feb. 3, 1963 (div. Jan. 1983); 1 child, Christa Nichol. BA with honors, Yale U., 1959, BArch, 1962, MArch, 1963. Drafter Serge Chermayeff, Paul Rudolph and Charles Brewer, New Haven, 1961-63; project designer Johnson, Poole & Storm, San Francisco, 1963-64; project designer Leo S. Wou & Assocs., Honolulu, 1965-66, v.p. of design, 1971-72; project architect John Tatom Assocs., Honolulu, 1965-66; sr. designer Skidmore, Owings & Merrill, San Francisco, 1968-71, assoc./project architect, 1972-76; prin. W.A. Werner Assocs., San Francisco, 1976-80; ptnr. Werner & Sullivan, San Francisco, 1980—; chmn. Design Rev. Bd., City of Sausalito, Calif.; bd. govs. Yale U., New Haven; visitorship in architecture U. Auckland Found., New Zealand, 1994. Prin. works include Alameda Mcpl. Credit Union, Lane Pub. Co., Menlo Park, Calif., Pacific Data Images, Mountain View, Calif., Saga Corp., Menlo Park, Tiffany & Co., Union Square, San Francisco, Somerset Collection, Troy, Mich., Touche Ross & Co., Oakland, U.S. Post Office, San Francisco, (renovations) Fed. Express Co., San Francisco, KD's Grog N' Grocery, San Francisco, Jessie Street. Substation, San Francisco, Lakeside Tower Health Ctr./Mt. Zion Hosp., Qantas Bldg, San Francisco, Women's Care, San Francisco, Moon Residence, Dillon Beach, Calif., Shenkar Residence, San Francisco, Tacker Residence, Denver, Lasky Residence, San Francisco, Starring Residence, San Francisco, Whitehead Residence, Monte Rio, Calif., various laboratories, theatres and rsch. facilities, urban design. Recipient Progressive Architecture Design award Jessie St. Substation, 1980, DuPont Co. Design award Touche Ross & Co., 1983, award of Excellence Woodwork Inst. of Calif., 1989, USPS/NEA Nat. Honor award for Design Excellence, 1990, Tucker Design Excellence award Bldg. Stone Inst., Tiffany & Co., 1992. Mem. AIA (San Francisco chpt.), Found. for San Francisco's Architectural Heritage (hon.). Home: 213 Richardson St Sausalito CA 94965-2422

WERNER-JACOBSEN, EMMY ELISABETH, developmental psychologist; b. Eltville, Germany, May 26, 1929; came to U.S., 1952, naturalized, 1962; d. Peter Josef and Liesel (Kunz) W. B.S., Johannes Gutenberg U., Germany, 1950; M.A., U. Nebr., 1952, Ph.D., 1955; postgrad., U. Calif., Berkeley, 1953-54. Research asso. Inst. Child Welfare, U. Minn., 1956-59; vis. scientist NIH, 1959-62; asst. prof. to prof. human devel., rsch. child psychologist U. Calif., Davis, 1962-94, rsch. prof., 1995—. Sr. author: The Children of Kauai, 1971, Kauai's Children Come of Age, 1977, Cross-Cultural Child Development: A View from the Planet Earth, 1979, Vulnerable, but Invincible, 1982, 2d edit., 1989, Child Care: Kith, Kin and Hired Hands, 1984, Overcoming the Odds, 1992, Pioneer Children on the Journey West, 1995; contbr. articles to profl. jours. Mem. Internat. Assn. Cross-Cultural Psychologists, Soc. Rsch. in Child Devel., German Acad. Social Pediats. (hon.).

WERNICK, JACK HARRY, chemist; b. St. Paul, May 19, 1923; s. Joseph and Eva (Legan) W.; B.Met.E., U. Minn., 1947, M.S., 1948; Ph.D., Pa. State U., 1954; m. Sylvia Katz, Dec. 20, 1947 (dec.); children—Phyllis Roberta Wernick Lauer, Rosanne Pauline; m. 2d, Charlotte Adler, 1983. Staff, Manhattan Project, Los Alamos, 1944-46; mem. staff Bell Labs., Murray Hill, N.J., 1954-84, head solid state chemistry research dept., 1963-81, head device materials research dept., 1981-83; div. mgr. Bell Comm. Rsch., 1983-92; cons. U.S. Office Sci. and Tech., Nat. Bur. Standards, NSF; mem. steering com. div. nuclear fusion ERDA, 1977-79; mem. Gov.'s Roundtable on Superconductivity, N.J., 1989-90. Served in U.S. Army, 1944-46. Fellow N.Y. Acad. Scis., Am. Phys. Soc., AIME, Am. Soc. Metals (McFarland award 1969); mem. Nat. Acad. Engring., AAAS, IEEE, Electrochem. Soc., Sigma Xi, Phi Lambda Upsilon. Jewish. Author: (with E.A. Nesbitt) Rare Earth Permanent Magnets, 1973, (with J.L. Shay) Chalcopyrite Crystals, 1975; editor: Materials and Energy: Selected Topics, 1977; Materials Letters; contbr. articles to profl. jours. Home: 21 Haran Cir Millburn NJ 07041-1403 Office: AT&T Bell Labs Murray Hill NJ 07974

WERNICK, RICHARD FRANK, composer, conductor; b. Boston, Jan. 16, 1934; s. Louis and Irene (Prince) W.; m. Beatrice Messina, July 15, 1956; children: Lewis, Adam, Peter (dec.). B.A., Brandeis U., 1955; MA, Mills Coll., 1957. Instr. music U. Buffalo, 1964-65; asst. prof. music, dir. univ. symphony U. Chgo., 1965-68; Magnin prof. humanities Pa. Contemporary Players, U. Pa., 1968-93; co-founder Community Youth Orch. of Delaware County; cons. Contemporary Music, The Phil. Orch., 1983-89, spl. cons. to the music dir., 1989-93; bd. dirs. Theodore Presser Co. Music dir. Royal Winnipeg Ballet Can., 1957-58; composer: Haiku of Basho, 1967, A Prayer for Jerusalem, 1971 (Naumburg award 1975), Moonsongs from the Japanese, 1972, Kaddish Requiem, 1973, String Quartet 2, 1973, Songs of Remembrance, 1974, Visions of Terror and Wonder, 1976 (Pulitzer prize 1977), Contemplations of the Tenth Muse, Book I, 1976, Book II, 1978, Introits and Canons, 1977, A Poison Tree, 1979, Concerto for Cello and Ten Players, 1980, In Praise of Zephyrus, 1981, Piano Sonata: Reflections of a Dark Light, 1982, Sonata for cello and piano: Portraits of Antiquity, 1982, The Oracle of Shimon bar Yochai, 1983, Concerto for Violin and Orch., 1983-84 (Friedheim 1st prize 1986); Oracle II for soprano, oboe and piano, 1985, Concerto for Viola and Orch., 1985-86, Musica Ptolemeica brass quintet, 1987; Symphony #1, 1988, String Quartet #3, 1988, Concerto for Piano and Orch. (Friedheim award 1992), 1989-90, Fragments of Prophecy, 1990, String Quartet #4, 1991 (Friedheim 1st prize 1991), Concerto for Saxophone Quartet and Orch., 1991, Cello Concerto #2, 1992, Symphony #2, 1993, ...and a time for peace, 1994, String Quartet #5, 1995, Cassation music Tom Jefferson Knew, 1995. Recipient music award Nat. Inst. Arts and Letters, 1976, Nat. Endowment Arts grantee, 1975, 79, 82; Fellow Ford Found., 1962-64, Guggenheim Found., 1976. Mem. ASCAP. Democrat. Office: 201 S 34th St Philadelphia PA 19104-6313

WERNICK, SANDIE MARGOT, advertising and public relations executive; b. Tampa, Sept. 13, 1944; d. Nathan and Sylvia (Bessock) Rothstein. BA in English, U. Fla., 1966. Tchr. English Miami Beach (Fla.) Sr. High Sch., 1967; adminstrv. asst. pub. rels. Bozell & Jacobs, Inc., N.Y.C., 1968-69; asst. to dir. pub. rels. Waldorf-Astoria, N.Y.C., 1969-70; dir. advt. and pub. rels. Hyatt on Union Square, San Francisco, 1974-82; pres. Wernick Mktg. Group, San Francisco, 1982—. Bd. mem. Nat. Kidney Assn., San Francisco, 1985-87; advisor Swords to Plowshares, San Francisco, 1988-89. Recipient Award of Merit, San Francisco Advt. and Cable Car Awards, 1979, Award of Excellence, San Francisco Art Dirs, 1978, awards Am. Hotel and Motel Assn., 1981, 82, awards of excellence San Francisco Publicity Club, 1990. Mem. Women in Comms. (bd. dirs. 1987-89), Am. Women in Radio and TV (bd. dirs. 1989-90), Pub. Rels. Soc. Am., San Francisco Publicity Club (pres. 1989), Variety Club, Profl. Bus. Women's Assn., Calif. Pacific Med. Ctr. (aux. 1988—). Democrat. Jewish. Home: 1690 Broadway St Apt 705 San Francisco CA 94109-2419 Office: Wernick Marketing Group 444 Market St Ste 1125 San Francisco CA 94111

WERNICKE, BRIAN PHILIP, geologist, educator; b. L.A., June 26, 1958; married. BS in Geol. Scis., U. So. Calif., 1978; PhD in Earth and Planetary Scis., Mass. Inst. Tech., 1982. Asst. prof. geology Syracuse U., 1982-83; asst. prof. geology Harvard U., 1983-86, assoc. prof., 1986-87, prof. geology, 1987-92; prof. geology Calif. Inst. Tech., 1992—; vis. prof. Calif. Inst. Tech., 1990; cons. Mobil Oil Corp., 1980-82, Amoco, 1981-87, Sci. Applications, Inc., 1984-85, Marathon Oil Co., 1985-91, Exxon Prodn. Rsch. Co., 1987—, Ctr. Nuclear Waste Regulatory Analyses U.S. Nuclear Regulatory Commn., 1992—; mem. working group 3 Second Conf. on Scientific Oceanic Drilling, 1986-87; panelist U.S. Geol. Survey External Grants Program Nat. Hazards Reduction Program, 1987, continental dynamics program divsn. earth scis. NSF, 1993—; mem. continental margins com. ocean scis. bd. Nat. Rsch. Coun., 1987-89; mem. panel on coupled hydrolic/tetonic/hydrothermal processes at Yucca Mountain bd. radioactive waste mgmt. Nat. Rsch. Coun., 1990-92; mem. Antarctic adv. com. NSF, 1990-91; corresponding mem. working group 3 team D Interunion Commn. on the Lithosphere, 1986-90. Editor: Geol. Soc. of Am. Memoir 176, 1990;. Fellow Geol. Soc. Am. (Donath medal 1991), Am. Geophysical Union, Phi Beta Kappa. Office: Divsn Geol & Planetary Sci MS 170-25 Caltech Pasadena CA 91125

WERRIES, E. DEAN, food distribution company executive; b. Tescott, Kans., May 8, 1929; s. John William and Sophie E. Werries; m. Marjean Sparling, May 18, 1962. B.S., U. Kans., 1952. With Fleming Foods Co., Topeka, 1955-89, exec. v.p., 1973-76; exec. v.p. Eastern ops. Fleming Foods Co., Phila., 1976-78; pres. Fleming Foods Co., Oklahoma City, 1978-81; pres., chief operating officer Fleming Cos., Inc., Oklahoma City, 1981-88, also dir.; pres., chief exec. officer Fleming Cos., Inc., 1988-89, chmn., CEO, 1989-93; Sec. Commerce State Okla., 1995—; chmn. bd. Sonic Corp., 1995—. Sec. of commerce State of Okla., 1995—. With U.S. Army, 1952-54, Korea. Mem. Nat. Am. Wholesale Grocers Assn. (bd. dirs. 1979-93), Food Mktg. Inst. (bd. dirs. 1989-91), Ind. Grocers Alliance (bd. dirs. 1984-94). Republican. Presbyterian. Office: Fleming Cos Inc PO Box 26647 6301 Waterford Blvd Oklahoma City OK 73126-0647

WERSON, JAMES BYRD, lawyer; b. Butte, Mont., Dec. 29, 1916; s. Edward L. and Alma (Baker) W.; m. Elspeth Lamont Pollard, Feb. 26, 1943; children: Sallie Lamont, Janet Elspeth Werson Yantis, Alice Mary. AB, U. Calif., Berkeley, 1938, JD, 1942. Bar: Calif. 1945. Spl. agt. FBI, 1942-46; with Severson & Werson, San Francisco, 1946—; sr. ptnr. Severson, Werson, Berke & Melchior, San Francisco, 1965—; bd. dirs. Assocs. Nat. Bank, Nat. Corp. Housing Partnership, 1988. Recipient Disting. Service award Nat. Consumer Fin. Assn., 1968. Mem. ABA (vice chmn. consumer bankruptcy com. 1960—, mem. com. on fin. services 1976—), Am. Fin. Svcs. Assn. (chmn. law com. 1961—), Soc. Former Spl. Agts. FBI, Merchants Exchange Club, Villa Taverna Club, Capitol Hill Club, Richmond Country Club (dir. pres. 1979), Big C Soc. U. Calif. (bd. dirs. 1977-80, pres. 1989—). Mem. Am. swimming team touring Europe, 1938. Home: 8615 Thors Bay Rd El Cerrito CA 94530-2568 Office: Severson & Werson 1 Embarcadero Ctr San Francisco CA 94111-3600

WERSTLER, RICHARD EMERSON, museum director; b. Canton, Ohio, Feb. 6, 1927; s. Henry Howard and Dessie Bernice (Werstler) W.; m. Wilma Pauline Maurer, June 4, 1949; children: Beth Arlene, Jeffrey Loyal, Mark Emerson. BS, Wittenberg U., 1950; MS, U. N.Dak., 1952; EdD, Case Western Reserve U., 1964. Tchr. Clark County Schs., Springfield, Ohio, 1950-52, prin., 1952-54; tchr., sci. cons. Lakewood (Ohio) Pub. Schs., 1954-59; tchr., prin. Cleve. Hgts.-Univ. Hgts. Schs., 1959-64; prof. edn. Ctrl. Mich. U., Mt. Pleasant, 1964-65; dir. prof. studies edn. Adrian (Mich.) Coll., 1965-80, prof., dir. grad. studies, 1975-80, prof., dir. continuing edn., 1981-85; exec. dir., chief exec. officer The McKinley Nat. Mem., Mus. Hist., Sci. and Industry, Discover World, Canton, Ohio, 1985—; cons. pub. sch. dists., Ohio & Mich., 1964-85; founder, pres. Lenawee Edn. Credit Union, Adrian, 1969-83; mem. adv. counsels higher edn., elem./secondary edn., tchr. edn. State Bd. Edn., Lansing, 1966-83. Author: The Schools of Europe, 1967. Recipient Alumni Assn. citation Wittenberg U., Springfield, Ohio, 1984. Mem. Canton C. of C. (com.), Rotary Internat., Phi Delta Kappa (Educator of Yr. 1984, founder Lenawee chpt. 1980). Avocations: agriculture, conservation. Home: 8763 Kent Ave NE North Canton OH 44721-1314 Office: McKinley Nat Meml Discover World Mus of History Sci & Industry PO Box 20070 Canton OH 44701-0070

WERT, CHARLES ALLEN, metallurgical and mining engineering educator; b. Battle Creek, Iowa, Dec. 31, 1919; s. John Henry and Anna (Spotts) W.; m. Lucille Vivian Mathena, Sept. 5, 1943; children: John Arthur, Sara Ann. B.A., Morningside Coll., Sioux City, 1941; M.S., State U. Iowa, 1943, Ph.D., 1948. Mem. staff Radiation Lab., Mass. Inst. Tech., 1943-45; instr. physics U. Chgo., 1948-50; mem. faculty U. Ill. at Urbana, 1950—, prof., 1955, head dept. metall. and mining engring., 1967-86, prof. emeritus, 1989; cons. to industry. Author: Physics of Metals, 1970, Opportunities in Materials Science and Engineering, 1977; also articles.; Cons. editor, McGraw Hill Book Co. Recipient sr. scientist award von Humboldt-Stiftung. Fellow Am. Phys. Soc., Am. Soc. Metals, AAAS, AIME; mem. Sigma Xi. Home: 1708 W Green St Champaign IL 61821-3796 Office: U Ill Metallurgy & Mining Bldg Urbana IL 61801

WERT, JAMES JUNIOR, materials scientist, educator; b. Barron, Wis., Jan. 9, 1933; s. James Lewis and Bernice Janet (Walker) W.; m. Jane Alice Thornton, Aug. 16, 1958; children: Thaddeus Thornton, Melissa Jane. B.S., U. Wis., 1957, M.S., 1958, Ph.D., 1961; postgrad., Carnegie Tech. Inst., 1958-59. Assoc. engr. Westinghouse Electric Corp., Pitts., 1958-60; rsch. scientist A.O. Smith Corp., Milw., 1961-62; mem. faculty Vanderbilt U., Nashville, 1962—; prof. material sci. and engring. Vanderbilt U., 1967—, chmn. dept., 1969, chmn. materials, mechanics and structures div., 1969-72, chmn. materials sci. dept., 1975-82, chmn. dept. mech. and materials engring., 1976-82, George A. Sloan prof. metallurgy, 1976—; mayor City of Forest Hills, Tenn., 1990-95; dir. Ctr. for Coatings Sci. and Tech., Vanderbilt U., 1969-74; co.-dir. Ctr. for Materials Tribology, 1987—; vis. prof. Cambridge U., 1974; sr. Fulbright lectr. Mid. East; cons. Avco, 1964-71, Temco, 1964-71, Arnold Engring. Ctr., Tullahome, Tenn., 1966-71, Nat. Acad. Scis., 1969-70; pres. Technology Assocs., Inc., Nashville, 1975-85; pres. James Wert & Assocs., 1985—. Contbr. articles to profl. jours. Served with AUS, 1953-55. Ampco fellow, 1957-58; Westinghouse-Bettis fellow, 1958-59; Foundry Edn. fellow, 1952-57; recipient Adams award Am. Welding Soc., 1969, Teaching award Tau Beta Pi, 1970, 78. Fellow ASME, ASM Internat.; mem. ASTM, AIME, Am. Welding Soc., Am. Soc. Metals, Hillwood Country Club, Sigma Xi, Tau Beta Pi, Phi Eta Sigma, Alpha Sigma Mu, Pi Kappa Alpha, Pi Tau Sigma, Omicron Kappa Delta. Methodist. Patentee nuclear fuels and cladding materials. Home: 2510 Ridgewood Dr Nashville TN 37215-4518

WERT, JAMES WILLIAM, banker; b. Chgo., Sept. 22, 1946; s. Andrew J. and Clair Wert; m. Candace M. Cronwall, Apr. 2, 1976; children: James William, Catherine Claire. B.A. in Fin. with high honor, Mich. State U., 1971; postgrad., Northwestern U. Grad. Sch. Mgmt., 1971-75; postgrad. exec. program, Stanford U., 1982. With Continental Ill. Nat. Bank & Trust Co., Chgo., 1971-75; with Soc. Corp./Soc. Nat. Bank, Cleve., 1975—; sr. v.p. Soc. Nat. Bank, 1977, Soc. Corp., 1979-87; exec. v.p. Soc. Nat. Bank, 1981-85, sr. exec. v.p., 1986-87, exec. v.p, 1987-90, vice chmn. bd., 1987—; vice chmn., chief fin. officer Soc. Corp., 1990—; mem. faculty Grad. Sch. Banking, U. Wis., Madison, 1978-80. Trustee Dyke Coll., Cleve.; active St. Luke's Hosp. Assn., Cleve. chpt. ARC, Achievement Ctr. for Children, Cleve. Devel. Ptnrship, Clev. chpt. United Cerebal Palsey, WVIZ-TV Cleve. Pub. TV. Mem. Am. Bankers Assn. (econ. adv. com 1980-83, exec. com bank investment and funds mgmt. 1983-86), Assn. Res. City Bankers, Tavern Club, Country Club of Cleve., Pepper Pike Club, Trout Club, Hanger Club, Union Club (Cleve.), Beta Gamma Sigma, Phi Kappa Phi. Republican. Roman Catholic. Home: 32700 Meadowlark Way Pepper Pike OH 44124 Office: Soc Corp 800 Superior Ave E Cleveland OH 44114-2601

WERT, JONATHAN MAXWELL, II, management consultant; b. Port Royal, Pa., Nov. 8, 1939; s. Jonathan Maxwell I and Helen Leona (Leonard) W.; m. Monica Kay Manbeck; children: Jonathan Maxwell III, Kimberly Dee, Jon Adam, Justin Tyler, Amanda Elizabeth. B.S. in Biology, Austin Peay State U., 1966, M.S. in Biology, 1968; Ph.D. in Adminstrn., U. Ala., 1974. Park supt., chief interpretive services Bur. State Parks Pa. Dept. Environ. Resources, Harrisburg, 1968-69; chief naturalist Bays Mountain Park Environ. Edn. Ctr., Kingsport, Tenn., 1970-71; environ. and energy edn. specialist TVA, Knoxville, 1971-75; cons. energy, environment, conservation U. Tenn., Knoxville, 1975; sr. assoc.-energy Energy Extension Svc., Coop. Extension Svc., Pa. State U., 1977-80; pres. Energy-Environ. Consultants, Port Royal, Pa., 1981-85, Mgmt. Diagnostics. Cons. to Mgmt.; Port Royal, 1985—. Author: Writing Environmental Education Grant Proposals, 1974, Environmental Education Study Projects for High School Students, 1974, Environmental Education Study Projects for College Students, 1974, Developing Environmental Study Areas, 1974, Developing Environmental Education Curriculum Material, 1974, Finding Solutions to Environmental Problems . . . A Process Guide, 1975, Assessing an Issue in Relation to Environmental, Economic, and Social Impact . . . A Process Guide, 1976, Energy Conservation Measures for Mobile Home Dwellers, 1978, Selected Energy Conservation Options for the Home, 1978, Selected Energy Management Options for Small Business and Local Government, 1978, Life Lines: A Book of Poetry, Prose, and Axioms, 1983, Survivorship and Growth in Employment: A Question and Answer Guide, 1983; mem. adv. bd.: Environ. Edn. Report, 1974—; cons. editor: Jour. Environ. Edn, 1975; contbr. articles to profl. jours. Counselor Boy Scouts Am., 1975. Served with USMC, 1958-61. Recipient Conservation award Am. Motors Co., 1976. Mem. U.S. Energy Assn., Inst. Mgmt. Cons., Orgn. Devel. Inst., Phi Delta Kappa. Lutheran. Office: Mgmt Diagnostics PO Box 194 Port Royal PA 17082-0194

WERT, LUCILLE MATHENA, librarian, educator; b. Sioux City, Iowa, May 24, 1919; d. Arthur Edmund and Anna Sarah (Harrington) Mathena; m. Charles Allen Wert, Sept. 7, 1942; children: John Arthur, Sara Ann. B.A., Morningside Coll., 1942; B.S. in LS, Simmons Coll., 1945; M.A., U. Ill., 1963, Ph.D., 1969. Asst. librarian elec. engring. library M.I.T., Cambridge, 1944-45; math., physics and astronomy librarian U. Iowa, Iowa City, 1946-48, U. Chgo., 1948-51; research asst. Grad. Sch. Library Sci., U. Ill., Urbana, 1964-65; research assoc. Grad. Sch. Library Sci., U. Ill. 1966-67, vis. lectr., 1968-69, research asst. prof., 1969-71, research assoc. prof., dir. library research center, 1971-75, assoc. prof., 1975-77, prof. library adminstrn., chemistry librarian, 1977-86, asst. dir. pub. svcs. for phys. scis. & engring., 1981-86, emeritus prof., 1986—; library cons. Council for Advancement of Small Colls. Editor: Jour. Edn. for Librarianship, 1976-80. Mem. U. Ill. Pres.'s Coun., 1993—; sustaining fellow Art Inst. Chgo., 1987—. Recipient Disting. Alumni award Morningside Coll., 1992; U.S. Office of Edn. small rsch. project grantee, 1968-69. Mem. ALA (com. on accreditation site visitors pool 1972-92), Assn. Coll. and Rsch. Librs., Libr. Adminstrn. and Mgmt. Assn., Assn. Libr. and Info. Sci. (dir. 1974-77), Am. Chem. Soc. (liaison to Spl. Libr. Assn., mem. editorial bd. CHEMTECH 1987—, chair 1992, chem. info. div awards com. 1988-91), Am. Assn. Info. Scis. (chmn. spl. interest group biology and chemistry 1985-86, spl. interest group steering com. 1987-89), Spl. Librs. Assn. (chmn. chemistry div. 1986-87), Beta Phi Mu. Presbyterian. Office: 1708 W Green St Champaign IL 61821-3721

WERTH, ANDREW M., telecommunications executive; b. Saarbruck, Germany, Mar. 2, 1934; came to U.S., 1944; s. Steven S. and Margot Werth; m. Eileen B. Pighini, Jan. 30, 1954; children: Gregory, Jeffrey, Karen. BS, Columbia U., 1955, MS, 1961. Project engr. ITT Labs., Nutley, N.J., 1959-64; mem. tech. staff Comsat Corp., Washington, 1964-68; br. mgr. Comsat Labs., Clarksburg, Md., 1968-72; pres. Hughes Network Systems Internat., Germantown, Md., 1972—. Patentee in field. Capt. USAF, 1955-57. Fellow IEEE; mem. AIAA, Cosmos Club. Roman Catholic.

WERTH, SUSAN, lawyer; b. N.Y.C., Nov. 29, 1948. BA, Barnard Coll., 1970; JD, Columbia U., 1973. Bar: Fla. 1973, U.S. Dist. Ct. (so. dist.) Fla. 1974, U.S. Dist. Ct. (mid. dist.) Fla. 1975, U.S. Dist. Ct. (no. dist.) Fla. 1976, U.S. Ct. Appeals (5th cir.) 1974, U.S. Ct. Appeals (11th cir.) 1978, U.S. Supreme Ct. 1978, U.S. Ct. Appeals (11th cir.) 1981. Ptnr. Weil, Gotshal & Manges, Miami, Fla.; adj. prof. law Sch. Law U. Miami, 1976-77. Mem. Fla. Bar Found. (bd. dirs. 1986-88, sec.-treas. 1988-90, pres.-elect 1991-92, pres. 1992-93), Fla. Bar. Office: Weil Gotshal & Manges 701 Brickell Ave Ste 2100 Miami FL 33131

WERTHAMER, N. RICHARD, physicist; b. Milw., Feb. 9, 1935. BS, Harvard Coll., 1956; PhD in physics, U. Calif., 1961. Rsch. assoc. U. Calif., San Diego, 1961-62; mem. tech. staff Bell Labs, 1962-75; chmn. N.Y. State Energy Rsch. and Devel. Authority, 1976-78; dir. Becton Dickinson & Co., 1983-93; mgmt. cons. Chelsea Technols, N.Y.C., 1993—. Fellow AAAS, Am. Phys. Soc.; mem. Am. Assn., Clin. Chem. Office: Chelsea Technols 43 W 16th St Ste 7-D New York NY 10011*

WERTHEIM, GUNTHER KLAUS, physicist; b. Berlin, Feb. 26, 1927; came to U.S., 1939; s. Frederick Max and Elisabeth Anna (Seiffert) W.; m. Lee Hilles, Sept. 8, 1956; children: Elisabeth Lee Fraebel, Frederick Whiley, Charles Gunther. ME, Stevens Inst. Technology, 1951; AM, Harvard U., 1952, PhD, 1955. Rsch. assoc. Woods Hole (Mass.) Oceanographic Inst., 1950-55; tech. staff mem. AT&T Bell Labs., Murray Hill, N.J., 1955—; dept. head AT&T Bell Labs., Murray Hill, 1962-82, disting. mem. tech. staff, 1983—; mem. physics vis. com. Harvard U., Cambridge, Mass., 1973; mem. vis. com. Bartol Rsch. Found., Newark, Del., 1975-83. Author: Mössbauer Effect, Principles and Applications, 1964; contbr. over 250 articles to profl. jours., chpts. to books. With U.S. Army, 1945-46. Recipient Sr. Scientist award Alexander von Humboldt Found., 1986. Fellow Am. Phys. Soc., AAAS. Achievements include first electric measurement of gulf stream transport; discovery of Mössbauer effect isomer shift. Office: AT&T Bell Labs 600 Mountain Ave New Providence NJ 07974-0636

WERTHEIM, HARVEY J., human resource specialist. Grad., City Coll. N. Y., 1962. Acct. Price Waterhouse, N.Y., 1964-69, v.p., dir., 1969-81; v.p., dir. Rsch. and Sci. Dir., N.Y., 1969-81; pres. Harvest Ventures Inc., N.Y., 1981—; chmn. bd. Career Horizons, Inc., Woodbury, N.Y., 1990—. With U.S. Army, 1962-64. Office: Career Horizons Inc 177 Crossways Park Dr Woodbury NY 11797*

WERTHEIM, MITZI MALLINA, technology company executive; b. N.Y.C.; d. Rudolf and Myrtle B. (McGraw) Mallina; m. Ronald P. Wertheim, Feb. 25, 1965 (div. July 1988); children: Carter, Christiana. B.A., U. Mich., 1960. Asst. dir. div. research Peace Corps, Washington, 1961-66; sr. program officer Cafritz Found., Washington, 1970-76; dep. undersec. navy, 1977-81; with Fed. Sector Div. IBM, 1981-94; v.p. enterprise solutions Systems Rsch. and Applications Corp., 1994—; Woodrow Wilson vis. fellow, 1979, 80. Bd. dirs. Nat. Coalition for Sci. and Tech., 1983—, Youth Policy Inst., 1986-91, VITA, 1990—; mem. vis. com. MIT, 1983-89. Recipient Federally Employed Women award Def. Dept., 1980; Disting. Pub. Svc. medal Navy Dept., 1981. Mem. Coun. on Fgn. Rels. Episcopalian. Home: 3113 38th St NW Washington DC 20016-3726

WERTHEIM, ROBERT HALLEY, national security consultant; b. Carlsbad, N.Mex., Nov. 9, 1922; s. Joseph and Emma (Vorenberg) W.; m. Barbara Louise Selig, Dec. 26, 1946; children: Joseph Howard, David Andrew. Student, N.Mex. Mil. Inst., 1940-42; B.S., U.S. Naval Acad., 1945; M.S. in Physics, M.I.T., 1954; postgrad., Harvard U., 1969. Commd. ensign U.S. Navy, 1945, advanced through grades to rear adm., 1972; assigned Spl.

Projects Office, Washington, 1956-61, Naval Ordnance Test Sta., China Lake, 1961-62, Office Sec. Def., Washington, 1962-65; head Missile br. Strategic Systems Project Office, Washington, 1965-67; dep. tech. dir. Missile br. Strategic Systems Project Office, 1967-68, tech. dir., 1968-77, dir., 1977-80; sr. v.p. Lockheed Corp., 1981-88; cons. nat. def., 1988—; emeritus mem. Charles Stark Draper Lab., Inc.; mem. U. Calif. Pres. Adv. Coun.; mem. sci. adv. group Dept. Def., Dept. Energy, Inst. for Def. Analysis, Ctr. for Naval Analysis, U.S. Strategic Command; mem. nat. security adv. Los Alamos Nat. Lab., Lawrence Livermore Nat. Lab. Decorated Legion of Merit, D.S.M. with cluster, Navy Commendation medal, Joint Service Commendation medal; recipient Rear Adm. William S. Parsons award Navy League U.S., 1971. Fellow AIAA; mem. Am. Soc. Naval Engrs. (hon. mem., Gold medal 1972), Nat. Acad. Engring., U.S. Naval Inst., Nat. Acad. of Scis. (com. on internat. security and arms control), Army-Navy Country Club, Bernardo Heights Country Club, Masons, Sigma Xi, Tau Beta Pi. Home: 17705 Devereux Rd San Diego CA 92128-2084 Office: Sci Applications Internat Corp 1299 Prospect St La Jolla CA 92037

WERTHEIM, SALLY HARRIS, academic administrator, dean, education educator; b. Cleve., Nov. 1, 1931; d. Arthur I. and Anne (Manheim) Harris; m. Stanley E. Wertheim, Aug. 6, 1950; children: Kathryn, Susan B., Carole J. BS, Flora Stone Mather Coll., 1953; MA, Case Western Res. U., 1967, PhD, 1970. Cert. elem. and secondary edn. tchr., Ohio. Social worker U. Hosps., Cleve., 1953-54; tchr. Fairmount Temple Religious Sch., Cleve., 1957-72; mem. faculty John Carroll U., Cleve., 1969—, prof., 1980—, dean grad. sch., rsch. coord., 1986-93, acad. v.p., 1993-94; dean Grad. Sch., coord. faculty rsch. John Carrol U., Cleve., 1994—; cons. in field; cons. Jennings Found., Cleve.; chmn. sch. com. Cleve. Commn. on Higher Edn., 1987—. Contbr. articles to profl. jours. Sec. Cuyahoga County Mental Health Bd., Cleve., 1978-82; pres. Jewish Family Svc. Assn., Cleve. 1974-77, Montefiore Home for Aged, Clevel., 1987-90, bd. dirs. Mt. Sinai Med. Ctr., Cleve., 1984-93, Cleve. Edn. Fund, 1992-94; v.p. Jewish Cmty. Fedn., 1988-91, pres. 1994—, bd. trustees, 1992—; chairperson edn. com. Cleve. Found. Commn. on Poverty, 1988-93, pres. bd. trustees, 1994—, Cleve. Cmty. Bldg. Initiative, 1993—, United Way Svcs., 1994—. Named One of 100 Most Influential Women, Cleve. mag., 1983; recipient award Jewish Communty Fedn.; grantee Jennings Found., 1984-87, Cleve. and Gund Found., 1987-90, Lilly Found., 1988. Mem. Am. Assn. Colls. for Tchrs. Edn. (bd. dirs. 1982-85), Ohio Assn. Colls. for Tchrs. Edn. (pres. 1981-83), Coun. of Grad. Schs. Avocations: flower arranging, travel, antiques. Office: John Carroll U Grad Sch Cleveland OH 44118

WERTHEIMER, FRANC, retired corporate executive; b. Nuremberg, Germany, Sept. 26, 1927; came to U.S., 1938; s. Erich Z. and Sophie (Prager) W.; m. Sidelle Shaiken, Sept. 2, 1951; children: Laura S., David F. BA summa cum laude, Bklyn. Coll., 1950; MA, Columbia U., 1951. Head dept. systems analysis Vitro Labs., West Orange, N.J., 1952-68; pres., chief exec. officer ManTech Internat. Corp., Alexandria, Va., 1968-91; vice chmn. Forensic Techs. Internat. Corp., Annapolis, Md., 1968-92; adj. prof. math. Bklyn. Coll., CUNY, 1951-53, Fairleigh Dickinson U., Rutherford, N.J., 1954-58, Kean Coll., Union, N.J., 1968-72; instr. math. Emeritus Found. and Project Apply, AAAS, 1991—; mentor Dingman Ctr., U. Md. Sch. Bus. and Mgmt., 1991—, adj. prof. mgmt., 1995—. Contbr. over 500 reports, monographs, position papers, concept documents pub. and submitted to U.S. Govt. and pvt. sector clients, articles to profl. jours.; guest editor Technical Jour., 1969; session chmn. tech. seminar, 1980. Bd. dirs. Washington Urban League, 1979-84; bd. dirs., pres., v.p., sec. Sumner Village Condominium, Bethesda, Md., 1988—; mem. Com. on Coms., Montgomery County, Md., 1991-93; docent Nat. Archives and Record Adminstrn.; docent Phillips Collection, 1991—; mem. adv. coun., 1993—, mgr. vols., 1994—; asst. to dir. dir. men's group OASIS, 1993—. With U.S. Army. Grad. scholar Columbia U., 1950. Mem. Ops. Rsch. Soc. Am., Navy League U.S. (life), Bklyn. Coll. Alumni Assn. (pres. D.C. chpt. 1989), Cosmos Club, B'nai B'rith, Phi Beta Kappa, Pi Mu Epsilon. Home: 4956 Sentinel Dr Bethesda MD 20816-3512

WERTHEIMER, FREDRIC MICHAEL, association executive; b. Bklyn., Jan. 9, 1939; s. Irving Wertheimer and Mildred (Klein) Van Brink; m. Linda Cozby, June 15, 1969. B.A., U. Mich., 1959; LL.B., Harvard U., 1962. Bar: N.Y. bar 1963. Atty. SEC, 1963-66; legis. counsel Congressman Silvio Conte, 1967-68; counsel House Small Bus. Com., 1969-70; lobbyist, legis. dir., v.p. Common Cause, Washington, 1971-81; pres. Common Cause, 1981—. Author: Common Cause Manual on Money and Politics, 1972. Served with U.S. Army, 1962-63. Fellow Kennedy Inst. Politics, Harvard U., 1972. Jewish. Home: 1416 35th St NW Washington DC 20007-2805 Office: Common Cause 2030 M St NW Washington DC 20036-3306

WERTHEIMER, ROBERT E., paper company executive; b. 1928; married. BSME, U. Wash., 1950; MBA, Harvard U., 1952. With Longview (Wash.) Fibre Co., 1952—, package engr., 1955-59, asst. mgr. container ops., 1959-60, asst. mgr. container sales, 1960-63, v.p. container sales West, 1963-75, v.p. prodn., 1975, group v.p. containers, now exec. v.p., dir. Office: Longview Fibre Co 120 Montgomery St Ste 2200 San Francisco CA 94104-4325 Office: Longview Fiber Co Longview WA 98632

WERTHEIMER, SYDNEY BERNARD, lawyer; b. N.Y.C., Apr. 15, 1914; s. Sydney B. and Edna F. (Leimdorfer) W.; m. Jane B. Celler, Nov. 10, 1938; children: Sue Wertheimer Frank, Jill Wertheimer Rifkin. BS in Econs, U. Pa., 1935; LLB, Harvard U., 1938. Bar: N.Y. 1938, U.S. Customs Ct 1970, U.S. Supreme Ct 1976, D.C. Ct. Appeals 1973. Mem. firm Glass & Lynch, N.Y.C., 1938-39; asst. U.S. atty. So. Dist. N.Y., 1939-42; exec. of subs. Schenley Distillers, N.Y.C., 1946-48; from assoc. to ptnr. Weisman, Celler, Spett, Modlin & Wertheimer, N.Y.C., 1947-83; pres. Silas Worth, Inc., 1987—; former dir. Fedders Corp. Author: (with others) The Draft and You, 1940. Bd. dirs. Am. Red Magen David for Israel, 1951—, vice chmn., 1988—, Scarsdale Bd. Edn., N.Y., 1959-62. With USN, 1943-45. Mem. Assn. of Bar of City of N.Y. Club: Quaker Ridge Golf (Scarsdale, N.Y.). Home and Office: 5 Normandy Ln Scarsdale NY 10583-7620

WERTIMER, SIDNEY, economics educator; b. Buffalo, Oct. 28, 1920; s. Sidney and Florence Belle (Smith) W.; m. Eleanor M. Walsh, June 21, 1947. B.S., U. Pa., 1942; M.A., U. Buffalo, 1949; Ph.D., London Sch. Econs., 1952. Instr. U. Buffalo, 1947-50; asst. prof. econs. Hamilton Coll., 1952-56, assoc. prof., 1956-64, prof., 1964—, Leavenworth prof. econs., 1967-79, Marjorie and Robert W. McEwen prof. econs., 1987-91, prof. emeritus, 1991—, asso. dean, 1957-65, chmn. dept. econs., 1967-75, provost, 1975-80; dir. Otisca Industries, Ltd. Author: (with John S. Gambs) Economics and Man, 1958; contbr. articles to profl. publs. Served to lt., sr. grade USN, 1942-46. Mem. Am. Econs. Assn., Mask and Wig, Sadaquada, Delta Kappa Epsilon. Home: 305 College Hill Rd Clinton NY 13323-1209 Office: Hamilton Coll Clinton NY 13323

WERTKIN, GERARD CHARLES, museum director, lawyer; b. N.Y.C., Oct. 3, 1940; s. Murray and Cecelia (Bregman) W.; m. Barbara Susan Dansky, Sept. 25, 1965; children: Jennifer, Andrew Murray, Rebecca. AB, Syracuse U., 1962; LLB, NYU, 1965, LLM, 1970. Bar: N.Y. 1966. Assoc. Saxe, Bacon & O'Shea, N.Y.C., 1965-67; atty. Kayser-Roth Corp., N.Y.C., 1967-76; pvt. practice law N.Y.C., 1976-80; asst. dir. Mus. Am. Folk Art, N.Y.C., 1980-91, assoc. dir., then acting dir., 1991, dir., 1991—; instr. grad. program dept. folk art studies NYU, 1982-90, adj. assoc. prof., 1990—. Author: The Four Seasons of Shaker Life, 1986; co-author: The Jewish Heritage in American Folk Art, 1984; author forewords and introductions to many books and exhbn. catalogs. Bd. dirs. Friends of Shakers, Sabbathday Lake, Maine, 1975—, pres., 1979-82; trustee United Soc. of Shakers, Sabbathday Lake, 1979—; adv. com. grad. program mus. professions, Seton Hall U., South Orange, N.J., 1993—; bd. overseers Hancock Shaker Village, Pittsfield, Mass., 1993—; bd. adv. Hist. Soc. early Am. Decoration, 1993—; nat. adv. com. Folk Art Soc. Am., 1992—. Mem. Univ. Club N.Y.C. Office: Mus Am Folk Art 61 W 62nd St New York NY 10023-7015

WERTLIEB, DONALD LAWRENCE, psychologist, educator; b. Washington, Feb. 22, 1952; s. Norman N. and Helen (Rubin) W.; m. Lorre Beth Polinger, Aug. 12, 1973; children: Joshua Michael, Mollie Rebecca, Miriam Tamar. BS in Psychology summa cum laude, Tufts U., 1974, MA in Child Study, 1975; MA in Psychology, Boston U., PhD in Clin. and Community Psychology, 1979. Instr. psychology Harvard U. Med. Sch., Boston, 1978-81, also staff psychologist Judge Baker Guidance Ctr., Boston, 1978-81; asst.

prof. Eliot-Pearson dept. child study Tufts U., Medford, Mass., 1981-86, assoc. prof., 1986-89, chmn., 1989—, chmn. dept. edn. interim, 1990-91; sr. rsch. assoc. Harvard U. Community Health Plan, Boston, 1981-87; mem. faculty Inst. for Health Rsch., Harvard Sch. Pub. Health, 1983-87; lectr. dept. social medicine and health policy, Harvard Med. Sch., 1984-89; cons. mental health svcs. Mem. editorial bd. Profl. Psychology, 1979-82, Jour. Applied Devel. Psychology, 1981—, Jour. Clin. Child Psychology, 1981—, Jour. Pediatric Psychology, 1986—. Carmichael prize scholar, 1973; NIMH tng. fellow, 1974-76; NIMH rsch. grantee, 1977-81, 83-86; Office Spl. Edn. tng. grantee, 1981-83; NIH Biomed. Rsch. grantee, 1982; W.T. Grant Found. grantee, 1982-86; lic. psychologist, Mass. Fellow Am. Orthopsychiat. Assn., Am. Psychol. Soc. (charter); mem. Am. Psychol. Assn., Assn. Advancement Psychology, New Eng. Psychol. Assn., Mass. Psychol. Assn., Boston Inst. Devel. Infants and Parents, Soc. Psychol. Study of Social Issues, Soc. Rsch. in Child Devel., Phi Beta Kappa, Psi Chi.

WERTS, MERRILL HARMON, management consultant; b. Smith Center, Kans., Nov. 17, 1922; s. Mack Allen and Ruth Martha (Badger) W.; BS, Kans. State U., 1947; MS, Cornell U., 1948; m. Dorothy Wilson, Mar. 22, 1946; children: Stephen M., Riley J., Todd J., Kelly M. Beef sales mgr. John Morrell & Co., Topeka and Memphis, 1948-53; dir. mktg. Kans. Dept. Agr., Topeka, 1953-55; sec.-treas. Falley's Markets, Inc., Topeka, 1955-58; v.p. S.W. State Bank, Topeka, 1958-65; pres. First Nat. Bank, Junction City, Kans., 1965-78; pvt. practice mgmt. cons., Junction City, 1978—; mem. Kans. Senate, 1978-88; mem. Kans. Pub. Employee Rels. Bd., 1989-94, Kans. Comsn. on Future of Health Care, 1991-94; chmn. Kans. WWII Commemoration Com. 1995—, Kans. Commn. on Vets. Affairs, 1995—; dir. Stockgrowers State Bank, Maple Hill, Kans., J.C. Housing & Devel., Inc., Kans. State Hist. Soc., Transformer Disposal Specialists, Inc. Mem. Kans. Bank Mgmt. Commn., 1967-71; mem. adv. com. U.S. Comptroller of Currency, 1971-72. Mem. Topeka Bd. Edn., 1957-61; pres. Junction City-Geary County United Fund, 1967-68; pres. Junction City Indsl. Devel., Inc., 1966-72. Trustee Kans. State U. Endowment Assn., Kans. Synod Presbyn. Westminster Found., 1965-72. 1st lt., inf., AUS, 1943-46. Decorated Bronze Star medal, Purple Heart, Combat Inf. badge; named to Inf. Officer Candidate Hall Fame, 1981, Civilian Aide to Sec. of Army for Kans., 1991-95; named Outstanding State Legis. Am. Legis. Exchange Coun., 1988. Mem. Kans. State U. Alumni Assn. (pres. 1957), Am. Legion, VFW, Kans. Bankers Assn., Assn. U.S. Army, U.S., Kans. (bd. dirs., v.p. 1979-84), Junction City (pres. 1975-76) chambers commerce, Kans. Farm Bur., Kans. Livestock Assn., DAV, Junction City Country Club (past pres.), Masons, Shriners, Jesters, Rotary (dist. gov. 1973-74), Sigma Phi Epsilon. Republican. Presbyterian. Address: 1228 Miller Dr Junction City KS 66441-3312

WERTSMAN, VLADIMIR FILIP, librarian, information specialist, author; b. Secureni, Romania, Apr. 6, 1929; came to U.S., 1967; s. Filip and Anna Wertsman. LLM summa cum laude, U. A.I. Cuza, Romania, 1953; MLS, Columbia U., 1969. Judge lower and appellate cts. Romania, 1953-67; examiner stock certs. 1st Nat. City Bank, N.Y.C., 1967-68; reference libr. sci. div. Bklyn. Pub. Libr., N.Y.C., 1969-74, sr. libr. Canarsie br., 1974-77, sr. libr. Greenpoint br., 1977-80, sr. libr. Leonard br., 1980-82; sr. libr., Slavic and Romanian specialist Donnell Libr. Ctr. N.Y. Pub. Libr., 1982-86; sr. libr. Learner's Adv. and Job Info. Ctr., 1987-93. Author; editor: The Romanians in America, 1748-1974, 1975, The Ukrainians in America, 1608-1975, 1976, The Russians in America, 1727-1970, 1977, The Armenians in America, 1618-1976, 1978, The Romanians in America and Canada, 1980, Librarian's Companion: A Handbook of Thousands of Facts and Figures on Libraries/Librarians, 1987, Career Opportunities for Bilinguals and Multilinguals: A Directory of Resources in Education, Employment and Business, 1991, 2nd edit. 1994, What's Cooking in Multicultural America, 1995; co-author: Ukrainians in Canada and United States, 1981, Free Voices in Russian Literature, 1950s-1980s, 1986; editorial cons. Harvard Ency. Am. Ethnic Groups, 1980; contbr. Books, Libraries and Information in Slavic and East European Studies, 1986, Immigrant Labor Press in North America, 1840s-1970s, 1987. Through American Eyes, 1989, Ency. of N.Y.C., 1991; contbr. articles, book revs. to profl. jours. Recipient Disting. Lit. Achievement award Am. Soc. Writers, 1977. Mem. ALA, Am. Pub. Libr. Assn. (chair multilingual libr. materials and svcs. com. 1976-88, spl. merit award 1988, chair pub. & ethnic materials com. ethnic materials info. exch. roundtable 1989—), Am. Assn. Advancement of Slavic Studies, Am. Romanian Acad. Arts & Scis., Delta Tau Kappa. Avocations: chess playing, travel, stamp collecting, dancing. Home: 330 W 55th St New York NY 10019 America is by its very nature of historical formation and development a multiethnic, multicultural and multilingual society. And if variety is the spice of life then American ethno-linguistic and cultural mosaique is the spice of our society. America's pluralism is also a microcosm of the entire world its citizens representing virtually all continents.

WERTZ, JOHN ALAN, secondary school educator; b. Mpls., May 28, 1945; s. John Edward and Florence (Carlson) W.; m. Margaret M. Schlangen, 1993. BS, Hamline U., 1967; MS, St. Cloud State Coll., 1973; postgrad., George Washington U., 1985. Tchr. social sci. St. Cloud (Minn.) Community Schs., 1967—; trainer and field rep. New Games Found., San Francisco, 1980-83. Mem. com. social action Minn. Synod, Luth. Ch. Am., 1971-74; chair social action com. Salem Luth. Ch. Coun., St. Cloud, 1974-76; mem. affirmative action com. St. Cloud Cmty. Schs., 1975-78, co-chair student assistance com., 1982-83, mem. site coun. Apollo High Sch., 1994—; chair St. Cloud Human Rights Commn., 1979-83; adv. Ctrl. Minn. Sexual Assault Ctr., 1981-83; bd. dirs. St. Cloud Area Tenants' Assn., 1975-77, St. Cloud Area Spl. Olympics, 1982-83. Recipient Merit award St. Cloud Area Coun. for Handicapped, 1976; grad. St. Cloud Area Leadership Program, 1995. Mem. ASCD, NEA, Minn. Edn. Assn., St. Cloud Edn. Assn. (chair govtl. rels. coun. 1978-83, 88—), St. Cloud Area C of C. (edn. divsn. 1992—, vice-chmn. PreK-12 com. 1993-94, chair edn. recognition com. 1994—). Avocations: theatre arts, camping, computing. Home: 816 Rilla Rd Saint Cloud MN 56303 Office: St Cloud Pub Schs 1000 44th Ave N Saint Cloud MN 56303

WERTZ, KENNETH DEAN, real estate executive; b. Oklahoma City, July 14, 1946; s. Walter K. and Kathryn L. (Moore) W.; children: Adam Troy, Kirsten Paige. B.S. in Acctg., Okla. State U., 1968, M.S. in Acctg. and Econs., 1969; JD, U. San Francisco, 1978. CPA, Okla., Calif; lic. real estate broker, Okla. Sr. acct. Deloitte, Haskins & Sells, San Francisco, 1969-70, 71-75; v.p. acquisitions, mng. dir. Landsing Corp., Menlo Park, Calif., 1975-86; pres. Detrick Salsberry Mgmt. Inc., Tulsa, 1987-88; v.p. asset mgmt. Corporex Co., Cin., 1989-90; exec. v.p. real estate Brunner Cos., Dayton, Ohio, 1990-92; pres. Pillar Real Estate Advisors, Dayton, Ohio, 1992—. Lt. col. Med. Svc. corps U.S. Army, 1968—. Decorated Army Commendation medal with three oak leaf clusters. Mem. Am. Inst. CPA's, Okla. Soc. CPA's, Calif. CPA's, Nat. Assn. Securities Dealers (fin. prin., registered sales rep.). Republican. Methodist. Avocations: running, snow and water skiing, racquetball, camping, fishing. Home: 835 Hunterwknoll Ln Cincinnati OH 45230-4343 Office: Pillar Real Estate Advisors 5335 Far Hills Ave Ste 318 Dayton OH 45429-2317

WERTZ, SPENCER K., philosophy educator; b. Amarillo, Tex., Oct. 27, 1941; s. Ralph E. and Pauline (Tressler) W.; m. Linda Loflin, Aug. 12, 1967. BA, Tex. Christian U., 1965, MA, 1966; PhD, U. Okla., 1970. Instr. Austin Coll., Sherman, Tex., 1969; from instr. to full prof. philosophy Tex. Christian U., Ft. Worth, 1969—, chmn. dept. philosophy, 1983-92; instr. Tex. Christian U. Div. Extended Edn., Ft. Worth 1975—. Author: Talking a Good Game, 1991; co-editor: Sport Inside Out, 1985; contbr. over 60 articles to profl. jours. and mags. Mem. N.Mex.-West Tex. Philos. Soc. (pres. 1980-81), Southwestern Philos. Soc. (pres. 1985-86), Philos. Soc. Study Sport (pres. 1985-86), North Tex. Philos. Assn. (pres. 1987-88), Phi Sigma Tau, Phi Beta Kappa. Avocations: tennis, gardening, wilderness travel. Home: 303 Mini Ranch Rd Weatherford TX 76086-9078 Office: Tex Christian Univ Dept Of Philosophy Fort Worth TX 76129

WERZBERGER, ALAN, pediatrician; b. Toronto, Ont., Can.; Dec. 4, 1954; came to U.S., 1985; s. Bernard and Clara (Hilman) W.; m. Sabina Fischman, June 18, 1978; children: Samuel, Moshe, Yehuda, Jacob Joseph, Mayer, Joel, Susan, Henry, Rochelle Werzberger. MD, U. Toronto, 1981. Intern, resident Hosp. for Sick Children, Toronto, Ont., 1981-85; Pvt. practice Monroe, N.Y., 1985—; full attending Dept. Pediatrics Good Samaritan Hosp., Suffern, N.Y., 1985—; assoc. attending Dept. Pediatrics St. Agnes

Hosp., White Plains, N.Y., 1992—; clin. asst. prof. pediatrics N.Y. Med. Coll., Valhalla, 1991—; asst. prof. pediatrics NYU Med. Ctr., N.Y.C., 1994—; dir. Kiryas Joel Med. Rsch. Inst., N.Y.C., 1994—; dir. Kiryas Joel Med. Rsch. Inst., Monroe, 1991—. Fellow Am. Acad. Pediatrics; mem. Med. Group Mgmt. Assn. Achievements include publication of the first demonstration of efficacy of a vaccine against Hepatitis A. Office: RR 5 Box 157 Monroe NY 10950-2633

WESBERRY, JAMES PICKETT, JR., financial management consultant, auditor, international organization executive; b. Columbia, S.C., Sept. 22, 1934; s. James P. and Ruby L. (Perry) W.; m. Lea Esdras Casteneda, June 13, 1975; children: Jonathan Jesse, Perry Latimer, Ruby Lee Nilda; children by previous marriage: James Pickett III, Elisa Marie, Lillian Sue, Paul Armand. BBA, Ga. State U., 1955; LLD (hon.), Atlanta Law Sch., 1967; MPA, Am. U., 1983. CPA, Ga.; cert. internal auditor; cert. fraud examiner; cert. govt. fin. mgr. Page, U.S. Ho. of Reps., 1949-51; acct., mgmt. cons., Atlanta, 1956-67; v.p. fin. and adminstrn. Computer Tech. South, Atlanta, 1969-70; sr. cons. Inst. Pub. Adminstrn., N.Y.C., 1967-69, 70-76; cons. to comptroller gen. of Peru, 1970-74, of Ecuador, 1974-78; adv., prof. Latin Am. Inst. Auditing Scis., Peruvian and Ecuadorean Sch. Govtl. Auditing, 1971-78; pres. Internat. Profl. Devel. Inst., 1976-78; condr. seminars: dir. systems, standards and procedures Days of Inns Am., Inc., 1979-80; chief auditor OAS, Washington, 1980-82; cons. World Bank, 1982-83, prin. advisor acctg. and auditing pub. sector modernization divsn. Latin Am. and Caribbean region, 1994—; sr. adv. to comptroller gen. U.S., 1983-85; dir. internat. ops. Price Waterhouse, 1985-88; sr. fin. adviser AID, 1988-93, pres., CEO, Inst. Pub. Adminstrn., 1993-94, trustee, 1993-94; dir. N.Y. Bur. Mcpl. Rsch., 1993-94; mem. panel of experts in acctg. and auditing UN, 1972—; adj. prof. Am. U., Washington, 1981-85; founding dir. Internat. Consortium Govtl. Fin. Mgmt., 1977-88, 94—, pres., 1984-87; cons./tchr., all Spanish-speaking Western Henisphere nations, Brazil, Haiti, Jamaica, The Netherlands Antilles, Peoples Republic of China, The Philippines, Can., U.S. Co-author: UN Handbook on Government Auditing for Developing Countries, editor: Latin American Manual of Professional Auditing in the Public Sector; editor Spanish lang. newsletter Pistas de Auditoria, 1985-92; mem. editorial bd. Pub. Budgeting and Fin. Mgmt.; mem. editorial bd., 1982-92. The Govt. Accts. Jour.; contbr. articles to profl. jours. Mem. Ga. Senate, 1962-67; mem. Fulton County Democratic Exec. Com. (Ga.), 1962-66. Decorated Order of Merit (Peru), 1972; recipient Outstanding Career Achievement award USAID, 1993. Mem. AICPA (chmn. interam. com. 1988—), Interam. Acctg. Assn. (cert. assoc., bd. dirs. 1989—, chmn. pub. sector com. 1989-91, mem. exec. com. 1994—, Vet. Acct. Am. award 1987), Am. Acctg. Assn., Assn. Govt. Accts. (Authors award 1981-82, 89-90); chmn. internat. affairs com. 1981-82, 89-91), Inst. Internal Auditors (v.p. Latin Am. 1978-79, internat. relations com. 1977-82, 84-88, regional dir. Latin Am. 1986-88, chpt. bd. govs. 1981-87, v.p. 1982-84, pres. 1984-85, vice chmn. internat. membership com. 1989-90, chpt. Disting. Svc. award 1987, Bradford Cadmus Meml. award internat. orgn. 1989, Outstanding Contbr. Author's award 1990), Honduras CPA Soc. (hon. award 1990), Jr. Chamber Internat. (life senator), Quito (Ecuador) Inst. Internal Auditors (life bd. dirs.), Lima (Peru) Coll. Pub. Accts. (hon.), Lima Jr. C. of C. (hon.), No. Va. Inst. Internal Auditors (hon.). Baptist. Home: 4004 Franconia Rd Alexandria VA 22310-2136 Office: World Bank Pub Sector Modernization Divsn Rm I-8383 Washington DC 20433

WESBURY, STUART ARNOLD, JR., health administration and policy educator; b. Phila., Dec. 13, 1933; s. Stuart Arnold and Jennie (Glazewska) W.; m. June Carol Davis, Feb. 23, 1957; children—Brian, Brent, Bruce, Bradford. B.S., Temple U., 1955; M.Hosp. Adminstrn., U. Mich., 1960; Ph.D., U. Fla., 1972. Commd. pharmacist USPHS, 1955, served as adminstrv. officer, hosp. and clinic pharmacist, resigned, 1958; adminstrv. asst. Del. Hosp., 1960-61; asst. adminstrt. Bronson Meth. Hosp., 1961-66; asso. dir., asst. prof. U. Fla. Teaching Hosp., 1966-67, dir., asso. prof., 1967-69; v.p. Computer Mgmt. Corp., Gainesville, Fla., 1969-72; dir., prof. grad. studies in health services mgmt. U. Mo., Columbia, 1972-78; pres. Am. Coll. Healthcare Execs., Chgo., 1979-91; sr. v.p. TriBrook Group, Inc., Westmont, Ill., 1992-94; prof. Sch. of Health Adminstrn. and Policy Ariz. State U., Tempe, 1994—. Co-author: Why We Spend Too Much on Health Care; contbr. articles to profl. jours. Bd. dirs Health Tasc, Inc., Atlanta, Blood Sys., Inc., Scottsdale, Ariz., Boy Clubs, Gainesville, Heartland Inst.; chmn. bd. dirs. Mid-Am. chpt. ARC, 1988-91, DuPage County Dist., 1984-87; active Boy Scouts Am.; chmn. adminstrv. bd. Meth. Ch.; trustee Nat. Blood Found.; Rep. Congl. candidate Dist. 13, Ill. With USPHS, 1955-58. Fellow Am. Coll. Health Care Adminstrs. (hon.), Am. Coll. Healthcare Execs. (Silver Medal award, 1991); mem. Am. Hosp. Assn., Hosp. Mgmt. Systems Soc., Am. Public Health Assn., Assn. Univ. Programs in Health Adminstrn. (chmn. 1977-78), Am. Assn. Healthcare Con. (hon.). Lodge: Rotary (past pres.). Home: 6711 E Camelback Rd # 25 Scottsdale AZ 85251 Office: Ariz State Univ Sch Health Adminstrn Policy PO Box 874506 Tempe AZ 85287-4506

WESCHLER, ANITA, sculptor, painter; b. N.Y.C.; d. J. Charles and Hulda Eva (Mayer) W.; married. del. U.S. Com. Internat. Assn. Art, Fine Arts Fedn., N.Y. Exhibited Met. Mus. Art, Mus. Modern Art, Art Inst. Chgo., Phila. Mus. Internat., Am. Acad., Inst. Arts and Letters, Bklyn. Mus., Newark Mus., Hofstra Mus., U. Conn., Carnegie Inst. Internat., Whitney Mus. Annuals, Storm King Art Ctr., mus. and galleries throughout U.S. and Japan; represented in permanent collections U. Pa., Michael Wolfson Found., Miami, Fla., Met. Mus. Art, Syracuse U., Butler Art Inst., Whitney Mus., Norfolk Mus., Brandeis U., Middlebury Coll., Amherst Coll., Yale U., Wichita State Mus., SUNY-Binghamton, U. Iowa, U. Nebr., La Salle U., Pa. Acad. Fine Arts, Insts. for Achievement of Human Potential in Pa., Italy, and Brazil, Art Students League; one-man shows include Birmingham (Ala.) Mus. Art, Main Library, Winston-Salem, N.C., U. Wis., Milw., Miami Beach Art Ctr., Tel Fair Acad., Savannah, Ga., Columbia (S.C.) Mus., U. N.C.-Chapel Hill, Stover Mill Gallery, Erwinna, Pa., Suffolk Art Mus., N.Y., Stony Brook, N.Y., also 50 traveling and stationary shows in N.Y.C. and nationwide, 1993; exhibited in over 500 shows; creator plastic resins and fiberglass as sculpture medium (bonded bronze), synthetic glazes as painting medium; author: poetry book Nightshade, A Sculptor's Summary. Recipient prizes Corcoran Gallery, San Francisco Mus., Am. Fedn. Arts Traveling Show, Montclair Art Mus.; fellow MacDowell Colony, Yaddo. Mem. Archtl. League Sculptors Guild (past bd. dirs., treas.), Nat. Assn. Women Artists, Nat. Mus. Women in the Arts, Artist Craftsmen N.Y., Fedn. Modern Painters and Sculptors. Address: 136 Waverly Pl New York NY 10014 *Imposed overall are multiple work hours. The deliberate shift is in periods, to another form—a contrasting medium. A life can be won or lost for work. The focus of attention remains entirely on the creative project. It is replenished by travel and forays into the outer world, a cultural and human renascence.*

WESCHLER, LAWRENCE MICHAEL, writer, journalist; b. Van Nuys, Calif., Feb. 13, 1952; s. Irving R. and Franzi (Toch) W.; m. Joanna S. Wegrzynowicz, Feb. 22, 1984; 1 child, Sara Alice. BA in Philosophy and Cultural History, U. Calif., Santa Cruz, 1974. Interviewer, editor Oral History Program UCLA, 1974-78; freelance writer L.A., 1978-80; staff writer The New Yorker mag., N.Y.C., 1981—. Author: Seeing is Forgetting the Name of the Thing One Sees: A Life of Contemporary Artist Robert Irwin, 1982, The Passion of Poland, 1984 ; David Hockney's Cameraworks, 1986 (Kodakpreis 1986), Shapinsky's Karma, Boggs's Bills and Other True-Life Tales, 1988 (George Polk award 1988), A Miracle, A Universe: Settling Accounts with Torturers, 1990, Mr. Wilson's Cabinet of Wonder, 1995; contbr. to Village Voice, L.A. Times, Internat. Herald Tribune, L.A. Weekly, Rolling Stone, N.Y. Times, Artforum, ArtNews, The Nation, others. Co-dir. Ernst Toch Archive & Soc., L.A., 1972—. Recipient Hemingway prize Overseas Press Club, 1982, Sidney Hillman award, 1989, George Polk award for best mag. reporting, 1992; Pointer fellow Yale U., 1982, Guggenheim fellow, 1986-87, N.Y. Inst. for Humanities fellow, 1991—, Bard Ctr. fellow, 1992—. Mem. PEN, Nat. Writers Union. Jewish. Office: The New Yorker 20 W 43rd St New York NY 10036-7400

WESCOE, W(ILLIAM) CLARKE, physician; b. Allentown, Pa., May 3, 1920; s. Charles H. and Hattie G. (Gilham) W.; m. Barbara Benton, Apr. 29, 1944; children: Barbara, William, David. BS, Muhlenberg Coll., 1941; ScD, 1957; MD, Cornell U., 1944. Intern N.Y. Hosp., 1944-45, resident, 1945-46; asst. prof. pharmacology Med. Coll., Cornell U., 1949-51; prof. pharmacology and exptl. medicine U. Kans. Med. Center, from 1951, dir.,

1953-60; dean U. Kans. Med. Center (Sch. Medicine), 1952-60; chancellor U. Kan., 1960-69; v.p. med. affairs Sterling Drug Inc., N.Y.C., 1969-71; exec. v.p. Sterling Drug Inc., 1971-72, vice chmn., 1972-74, chmn., 1974-85; bd. dirs. N.Y. Stock Exch., 1986-92, Biofield Corp. Editor: Jour. Pharmacol. and Exptl. Therapeutics, 1953-57. Chmn. China Med. Bd. N.Y., N.Y.C., 1960-77; bd. dirs. Tinker Found., 1968-93, Minn. Opera; trustee emeritus Samuel Kress Found., Columbia U.; chmn. John Simon Guggenheim Meml. Found., 1983-91, Muhlenberg Coll. Markle scholar med. scis., 1949-54. Fellow ACP; mem. Am. Soc. Pharmacology and Exptl. Therapeutics, Phi Beta Kappa, Sigma Xi, Alpha omega Alpha, Alpha Tau Omega, Nu Sigma Nu. Home: 8935 N Shore Dr Spicer MN 56288

WESCOTT, ROGER WILLIAMS, anthropologist; b. Phila., Apr. 28, 1925; s. Ralph Wesley and Marion (Sturges-Jones) W.; m. Hilja J. Brigadier, Apr. 11, 1964; children: Walter, Wayne. Grad., Phillips Exeter Acad., 1942; B.A. summa cum laude, Princeton U., 1945, M.A., 1947, Ph.D., 1948; M.Litt., Oxford U., 1953. Asst. prof. history and human relations Boston U. and Mass. Inst. Tech., 1953-57; assoc. prof. English and social sci., also dir. African lang. program Mich. State U., 1957-62; prof. anthropology and history So. Conn. State Coll., 1962-66; prof., chmn. anthropology and linguistics Drew U., Madison, N.J., 1966—; Presdl. prof. Colo. Sch. Mines, 1980-81; first holder endowed Chair of Excellence in Humanities U. Tenn., 1988-89; shipboard lectr., 1980—; fgn. lang. cons. U.S. Office Edn., 1961; pres. Sch. Living, Brookville, Ohio, 1962-65; exec. dir. Inst. Exploratory Edn., N.Y.C., 1963-66; Korzybski lectr. Inst. Gen. Semantics, N.Y.C., 1976; forensic linguist N.J. State Cts., 1982-83; host Other Views, N.J. Cable TV, Trenton, 1985-87. Author: A Comparative Grammar of Albanian, 1955, Introductory Ibo, 1961, A Bini Grammar, 1963, An Outline of Anthropology, 1965, The Divine Animal, 1969, Language Origins, 1974, Visions, 1975, Sound and Sense, 1980, Language Families, 1986, Getting It Together, 1990; also poems and articles; host, program dir. Other Views, N.J. Cable TV, 1985-87. Rhodes scholar, 1948-50; Ford fellow, 1955-56; Am. Council Learned Socs. scholar, 1951-52. Fellow AAAS, Am. Anthrop. Assn., African Studies Assn.; mem. Acad. Ind. Scholars (life mem.), Assn. for Poetry Therapy, Internat. Soc. Comparative Study Civilizations (co-founder, pres. 1992—), Linguistic Assn. Can. and U.S. (pres. 1976-77), Internat. Linguistic Assn., Com. for Future, Soc. for Hist. Rsch. 9v.p.), Internat. Orgn. for Unification Terminological Neologisms (1st v.p.), World Hist. Assn., Phi Beta Kappa. Home: 16A Heritage Crest Southbury CT 06488-1370 *Since our lives are short, it seems appropriate that our reflections on them should be comparably brief. Success is transient and high regard, relative. Though my occupational classification is that of a teacher and administrator, I have rarely been able seriously to picture myself as an educational careerist. I have thought of myself, rather, as an intellectual explorer, perennially fascinated by the inadequately explained aspects of man and his world and powerfully impelled to share that sense of fascination with fellow explorers.*

WESELY, DONALD RAYMOND, state senator; b. David City, Nebr., Mar. 30, 1954; s. Raymond Ely and Irene (Sabata) W.; m. Geri Williams, 1982; children: Sarah, Amanda, Andrew. BA, U. Nebr., 1977; LLD (hon.), Kirksville Coll. Osteopathic Medicine, 1989. Mem. Nebr. Legislature, Lincoln, 1978—; exec. assoc. Selection Rsch., Inc., Lincoln, 1984-86; sr. rsch. assoc. Lincoln Telephone Co., 1985—. Del., Dem. Nat. Conv., 1984, 88, 92; chair Assembly on Legislature, Nat. Conf. State Legislatures., 1992-93; chair platform com. Dem. State Conv., 1986; del. Am. Coun. Young Polit. Leaders, 1993. Recipient Friend of Edn. award Nebr. State Edn. Assn., 1982, Disting. Svc. award Nebr. Pub. Health Assn., 1984, Disting. Alumni award Lincoln Northeast High Sch., 1991, Disting. Health Care award Nebr. Nurse Anesthetists Assn., 1992, Leadership award for Quality in Health Care, Nebr. League Nursing, 1992, Pres.'s award Nebr. Acad. Physicians Assts., 1993, U. Nebr.- Lincoln Outstanding Young Alumni award, 1994; named Mental Health Citizen of Yr., Nebr. Mental Health Assn., 1984, Outstanding Young Man, Nebr. Jaycees, 1985, Pub. Official of Yr., Nebr. Assn. Retarded Citizens, 1992, Advocate of Yr. Nebr. Family Day Care Assn., 1993. Roman Catholic. Office: State Capitol Lincoln NE 68509

WESELY, EDWIN JOSEPH, lawyer; b. N.Y.C., May 16, 1929; s. Joseph and Elizabeth (Peles) W.; children: Marissa Celeste, Adrienne Lee; m. Marcy Brownson, Sept. 23, 1992. Ed., Deep Springs Coll., 1945-47; A.B., Cornell U., 1949; J.D., Columbia U., 1954. Bar: N.Y. 1954, D.C. 1985, U.S. Supreme Ct. 1960, others. Law clk. to judge U.S. Dist. Ct. (so. dist.) N.Y., 1954-55; asst. U.S. atty. So. Dist. N.Y., 1955-57; assoc. Winthrop, Stimson, Putnam & Roberts, N.Y.C., 1957-63, ptnr., 1964—; chair spl. com. on effective discovery in civil cases U.S. Dist. Ct. (ea. dist.) N.Y., 1982-86, com. on civil caseflow, 1985-88, com. on civil litigation, 1988—, civil justice reform adv. group, 1990—; mem. com. on pretrial phase of civil cases of Jud. Coun. of 2d Cir., 1984-86, standing com. on improvement civil litigation, 1986-89; mem. ex-officio Civil Justice Reform Act adv. group U.S. Dist. Ct. (so. dist.) N.Y.; bd. dirs. CARE, 1964—, pres. 1986-89, chmn. 1978-86, 89-90, internat. bd. dirs. 1981-90, pres. 1986-89; bd. dirs. Internat. Rescue Ctr., 1964—; bd. dirs., mem. exec. com. Internat. Ctr. in N.Y., 1990—. Trustee Deep Springs Coll., 1991—. Decorated Order of Civil Merit (Republic of Korea); recipient World Humanitarian award Fgn. Press Assn., Commendation Bd. Judges U.S. Dist. Ct. (ea. dist.) N.Y. Fellow Am. Coll. Trial Lawyers (mem. com. on advancing rule of law abroad 1990—); mem. ABA (spl. adv. com. on internat. activities 1990-93, chmn. on discovery 1977-78, mem. spl. com. study of discovery abuse 1977-82, chair task force on liaison with internat. profl. assns. on matters of mutual concern, Civil Justice Reform Act task force 1991-93, task force on the state of the justice system 1993—), UN Assn. of U.S.A. (bd. govs. 1991), Assn. of Bar of City of N.Y. (mem. various coms., organized demonstration observation panel), Coun. on Fgn. Rels., India House. Office: Winthrop Stimson One Battery Park Pla New York NY 10004-1490

WESELY, MARISSA CELESTE, lawyer; b. N.Y.C., Apr. 25, 1955; d. Edwin Joseph and Yolanda Teresa (Pyles) W.; m. Paul Howard Allen, Sept. 17, 1983; 1 child, Emma Elizabeth Wesely Allen. BA magna cum laude, Williams Coll., 1976; JD cum laude, Harvard U., 1980. Bar: N.Y. 1981. Assoc. Simpson Thacher & Bartlett, N.Y.C., 1980-82, 84-88, ptnr., 1989—; assoc. Simpson Thacher & Bartlett, London, 1982-84; lectr., cons. Harvard Inst. Internat. Devel., Beijing, 1981, Jakarta, Indonesia, 1982; guest lectr. Yale Law Sch., New Haven, 1991. Bd. dirs. Lawyers Alliance for N.Y., N.Y.C., City Lore, N.Y.C. Mem. N.Y.C. Bar Assn., Womens Bar Assn., Phi Beta Kappa.

WESENBERG, JOHN HERMAN, association executive; b. Davenport, Iowa, Jan. 16, 1927; s. Herman B. and Nell (Watterson) W.; m. Alice Jane McMahill, Sept. 10, 1949; children: Anne, John, Sue, James. Student, Iowa State U., 1944-45, 47, Amherst Coll., 1946; B.A., U. Iowa, 1951, M.A., 1952; postgrad., Northwestern U., 1952-55, Mich. State U., 1956-67. Research asso. Bur. Bus. and Econ. Research, U. Iowa, 1949-52; asst. mgr. Danville (Ill.) C. of C., 1952-54; exec. v.p. Belleville (Ill.) C. of C., 1954-57; sec. Retail Mchts. and Central Dist. Bur., Des Moines, 1957-62; exec. v.p. Greater Des Moines C. of C., 1963-80; sec. Greater Des Moines Com., 1963-80; sr. exec. v.p. Greater Albuquerque C. of C., 1980-82, Met. Tulsa C. of C., 1982-91; dir. mgmt. adv. program Okla. State C. of C. and Industry, Tulsa, 1992—; sr. exec. counselor U.S.C. of C., 1993—; trustee Employee Stock Ownership Plan, Internat. Bank, Washington, 1977-80, 83-84; lectr. Inst. Orgn. Mgmt., Mich. State U., 1959-67, 69-70, U. Colo., 1970, 75, 78, 79, 81, 85, 87, 90, 91, Syracuse U., 1971, U. Santa Clara, Calif., 1972, 74-75; lectr. Tex. Christian U., 1971, 73, U. Del., 1973-76, 80, 82, U. Ga., 1973, 82, 86, U. Notre Dame, 1975, 81, So. Meth. U., 1975-76, 81, 84, 85, 87, 88, 89, 90, 91, Mills Coll., 1976, San Jose Coll., 1981, U. Okla., 1984, 86, 88, 90-91, Stanford U., 1990, Econ. Devel. Inst. U. Okla., 1994. Co-chmn. Des Moines Mail Users Council, 1963-68; sec.-treas. Des Moines Housing Corp., Baseball, Inc., 1963-80; sec. Des Moines Devel. Corp., Des Moines Industries, Inc., 1963-80, Community Improvement, Inc., 1968-80, Greater Des Moines Community Found., 1968-80; treas. Greater Des Moines Shippers Assn., 1971-80; trustee Fringe Benefits, Inc., Washington, 1969-82; mem. exec. com. Iowa Council on Econ. Edn. 1978-80; mem. planning com. Grand View Coll., 1976-80; mem. adv. council, region VIII SBA, 1973-80; Mem. bd. regents Inst. Orgn. Mgmt. Mich. State U., 1967-80; bd. regents U. Colo., 1977-80, So. Meth. U., 1980-81; vice chmn. nat. bd. regents Inst. for Orgn. Mgmt., 1978-79, chmn., 1979-80; trustee U. Albuquerque, 1980-82. Served with USAAF, 1944-46. Recipient Outstanding Community Leadership award Religious Heritage of Am., 1978. Mem. Am. Arbitration Assn.,

Am. Retail Execs. Assn. (dir. 1962-63), Am. C. of C. Execs. (dir. 1965-73, 84-91, hon. life dir./mem. 1992—, pres. 1971-72), U.S.C. of C. (dir. 1979-81, liaison officer 1989-91), Iowa C. of C. Execs. (dir. 1960-66, pres. 1964), Okla. C. of C. Execs. (dir. 1983-86, pres. 1986), Ill. Mfrs. Assn. (exec. com. So. div. 1955-57), St. Louis Indsl. Coun. (v.p. 1957), Okla. C. of C. and Industry (mem. exec. com. bd. dirs. 1986, fin. com. 1986-94), Industries for Tulsa (sec. 1986-91), Beta Theta Pi (gen. sec. 1974-81, adv. coun. former trustees 1981—), Mtn. States Assn. (v.p. 1980-81—), Des Moines Club, Petroleum Club. Home: 6718 E 65th Pl Tulsa OK 74133-4007 Office: Met Tulsa C of C 616 S Boston Ave Tulsa OK 74119-1215

WESLAGER, CLINTON ALFRED, historian, writer; b. Pitts., Apr. 30, 1909; s. Fred H. and Alice (Lowe) W.; m. Ruth G. Hurst, June 9, 1934; children: Ruth Ann (Mrs. George G. Tatnall), Clinton Alfred, Thomas Hurst. BA, U. Pitts., 1933; LHD, Widener U., 1986; LittD (hon.), Wesley Coll., 1993. Vis. prof. Am. history Wesley Coll., 1969, U. Del., 1971-73; vis. prof. Am. history Brandywine Coll., 1970-82, prof. emeritus, 1983—. Author: Delaware's Forgotten Folk, 1943, Delaware's Buried Past, 1944, Delaware's Forgotten River, 1947, The Nanticoke Indians, 1948, Brandywine Springs, 1949, Indian Place-Names in Delaware, 1950, Red Men on the Brandywine, 1953, Richardsons of Delaware, 1957, Dutch Explorers, Traders and Settlers, 1961, Garrett Snuff Fortune, 1965, English on the Delaware, 1967, Log Cabin in America, 1969, The Delaware Indians, A History, 1972, Magic Medicines of the Indians, 1973, The Stamp Act Congress, 1976, The Delaware Indian Westward Migration, 1978, The Delawares, A Critical Bibliography, 1978, The Nanticoke Indians, Past and Present, 1983, Swedes and Dutch at New Castle, 1987, New Sweden on the Delaware, 1988, A Man and His Ship: Peter Minuit and the Kalmar Nyckel, 1990; editor: Historic Red Clay Valley, Inc, 1961-69. Pres. trustees Richardson Park Sch., 1953-57. Recipient Merit award Am. Assn. State and Local History, 1965, 68, Christian Lindback award for teaching excellence, 1977, Trustee award Hist. Soc. Del., 1987, Medal of Distinction, U. Del., 1988, History medal DAR, 1990, del Tufo award Del. Humanities Forum, 1991. Fellow Archaeol. Soc. N.J., Holland Soc. N.Y.; mem. AAUP, Hist. Soc. Pa., Soc. Pa. Archaeology, Am. Name Soc., Archaeol. Soc. Del. (Archibald Crozier award 1987, pres. 1942-48), Ea. States Archaeol. Fedn. (pres. 1954-58), Dupont Country Club, Masons, Sigma Delta Chi. Home: 255 Possum Park Rd Newark DE 19711-3887

WESLER, KEN, theater company manager; b. Phila., Apr. 3, 1964; s. Irwin Harvey and Marcia Elaine (Trilling) W.; m. Deborah Lee Rader, Nov. 2, 1986; children: Alexander, Samantha. BA, Temple U., 1981-85. Prodn. mgr. The Wilma Theatre, Phila., 1983-89; gen. mgr. Gretna Prodns., Inc., Mt. Gretna, Pa., 1989, 90, Walnut St. Theatre, Phila., 1989—; guest lectr. Cabrini Coll., Phila., 1988, Temple U., Phila., 1988—. Mem. Stage Mgr.'s Assn., Actor's Equity. Office: Walnut St Theatre 825 Walnut St Philadelphia PA 19107-5107

WESLER, OSCAR, mathematician, educator; b. Bklyn., July 12, 1921; s. Israel Edward and Sarah (Hartman) W. B.S., Coll. City N.Y., 1942; M.S., N.Y. U., 1943; postgrad., Princeton U., 1943-46; Ph.D., Stanford U., 1955. Mem. faculty Stanford U., 1952-56, vis. prof. stats., 1978; mem. faculty U. Mich., 1956-64; prof. stats. and math. N.C. State U., Raleigh, 1964—; cons. Inst. Sci. and Tech., U. Mich., 1957-64, IBM, 1966; vis. prof. statistics Stanford, 1962-63, 73, 74, 78, U. Calif., Berkeley, 1972-73; vis. lectr. NSF Program vis. lectrs. in statistics, 1963—. Author: Solutions to Problems in Theory of Games and Statistical Decisions, 1954; also articles in profl. jours. Recipient Outstanding Tchr. award N.C. State U., 1966. Mem. Inst. Math. Statistics, Am. Math. Soc., Sigma Xi, Phi Kappa Phi. Research in statis. decision theory, probability, stochastic processes. Home: 1926 Smallwood Dr Raleigh NC 27605-1302

WESLEY, JOHN MERCER, artist; b. Los Angeles, Nov. 25, 1928; s. Ner Wesley and Elsa Marie (Patzwaldt) W.; m. Hannah Allen Green, Dec. 18, 1971; children: Christine Alice, Ner. Student, Los Angeles City Coll., UCLA, 1947-50. One-man shows include, Robert Elkon Gallery, N.Y.C., 1963-80, 84, Premio Internat., Instituto Torcuato di Tella, Buenos Aires, 1967, Documenta 5, Kassel, 1972, Carl Solway Gallery, Cin., 1972, 85, 89, Galerie Rudolf Zwirner, Cologne, 1973, Rush Rhees Gallery, U. Rochester, 1974, PS 1, N.Y.C., 1978, Reinhard Onnasch Ausstellungen, Berlin, 1982-83, 101 Spring St. Gallery, N.Y.C., 1987, fiction/non fiction, N.Y.C., 1990, 91, Chinati Found., Marfa, Tex., 1990, Daniel Weinberg Gallery, Santa Monica, Calif., 1992, Portikus, Frankfurt, 1993, Stedelijk Mus., Amsterdam, 1993, Kunstverein, Ludwigsburg, Germany, 1993, daad-Galerie, Berlin, 1993, Galerie Rolf Ricke, Cologne, 1994, José Freire Gallery, N.Y.C., 1994; group exhbns. include, Whitney Mus., 1968, 69, 76, Indpls. Mus., 1976, Royal Academy, London, 1991, Mus. Contemporary Art, L.A., 1992-93, Mus. Beaux Arts, Montreal, 1992-93; represented in permanent collections, Albright-Knox Mus., Buffalo, Mus. Modern Art, N.Y.C., U. Tex., Austin, Mpls. Soc. Fine Arts, Chinati Found., Marfa, Tex., Rose Art Gallery, Brandeis U., Waltham, Mass., U. Kentucky, Lexington, Kunstmuseum, Basel, Switzerland, Dayton (Ohio) Mus. Art, Portland (Oreg.) Art Mus., Whitney Mus., Stedelijk Mus., Speed Mus., Louisville, Ky. Guggenheim fellow, 1976; grantee Nat. Endowment Arts, 1989. Address: 52 Barrow St New York NY 10014

WESLEY, NORMAN H., metal products executive; b. 1949. BA, MBA, U. Utah, 1973. With Crown Zellerbach Corp., San Francisco, 1973-83; pres., CEO ACCO World Corp., Wheeling, Ill., 1983—. Office: ACCO World Corp 770 S Acco Plz Wheeling IL 60090*

WESLING, DONALD TRUMAN, English literature educator; b. Buffalo, May 6, 1939; s. Truman Albert and Helene Marie (Bullinger) W.; m. Judith Elaine Dulinawka, July 28, 1961; children: Benjamin, Molly, Natasha. BA, Harvard U., 1960, PhD, 1965; BA, Cambridge U., Eng., 1962. Asst. prof. U. Calif. at San Diego, La Jolla, 1965-67, assoc. prof., 1970-80, prof., 1981—; lectr. U. Essex, Colchester, Eng., 1967-70. Author: Wordsworth and Landscape, 1970, Chances of Rhyme, 1981, The New Poetries, 1985, The Scissors of meter, 1995, (with T. Slawek) Literary Voice, 1995. Mem. Amnesty Internat. Home: 4968 Foothill Blvd San Diego CA 92109-2234 Office: U Calif Lit # 0410 La Jolla CA 92093

WESSEL, HENRY, photographer; b. Teaneck, N.J., July 28, 1942; s. Henry and Jennie (Cincotta) W.; children by previous marriage: Nicholas, Rider. B.A., Pa. State U., 1966; M.F.A., SUNY, Buffalo, 1972. Propr., mgr. comml. photog. studio State Coll., Pa., 1966-68; cinematographer for documentary film Dept. HEW, 1967; instr. dept. art Pa. State U., Phila., 1967-69; prof. dept. photography San Francisco Art Inst., 1973-94, chmn. grad. program photography, 1977-78, chmn. dept. photography, 1987-93; asst. prof. San Francisco State U., 1974-75; vis. lectr. photography various colls. and art schs., 1967-81; propr., dir. Photographic Resources, Point Richmond, Calif., 1977—; vis. artist Mills Coll., 1987-88;. One-man show at Mus. Modern Art, N.Y.C., 1973; represented in permanent collections, Mus. Modern Art, N.Y.C., Phila. Mus. Art, Boston Mus. Fine Arts, Library of Congress, Am. Arts Documentation Center, Exeter, Eng., Nat. Gallery of Can., Ottawa; author: Henry Wessel, 1987, House Pictures, 1992. Guggenheim fellow, 1971, 78; Nat. Endowment Arts fellow, 1975, 77, 78. Home: PO Box 475 Richmond CA 94807-0475 Office: Photographic Resources PO Box 475 Richmond CA 94807-0475

WESSEL, JEFFREY HALL, bank executive; b. Duluth, Minn., Apr. 25, 1942; s. Leo R. and Mabel (Hall) W.; m. Susan E. Parker, July 22, 1967; children—Katherine M., Brandon J. B.A., U. Minn., 1964, J.D., 1967. With The Northern Trust Co., Chgo.; now exec. v.p., head subsidiary banks; chmn. No. Trust of Fla. Corp., No. Trust Bank of Tex.; bd. dirs. No. Trust Bank, Lake Forest, Ill., No. Trust Bank, O'Hare, No. Trust Bank, DuPage, No. Trust Bank Ariz. Club: Valley Lo (bd. dirs.). Home: 777 Sunset Ridge Rd Winnetka IL 60093-1030 Office: No Trust Co 700 Brickell Ave Miami FL 33131-2804

WESSEL, MORRIS ARTHUR, pediatrician; b. Providence, Nov. 1, 1917; s. Morris Jacob and Bessie (Bloom) W.; m. Irmgard Rosenzweig, June 1, 1952; children: David, Bruce, Paul, Lois. BA, Johns Hopkins U., 1939; MD, Yale U., 1943. Diplomate Am. Bd. Pediatrics. Intern Babies Hosp., N.Y.C., 1943-44; asst. dir. pediatric outpatient clinic Yale New Haven (Conn.) Hosp., 1951-52, dir. pediatric outpatient clinic, 1952-57; staff pediatrician, collaboration project Yale U. Sch. Medicine, 1957-62, instr. in pediatrics, 1950-53, clin. asst. prof., 1963-61, clin. assoc. prof. of pediatrics, 1961-75, clin. prof. pediatrics, 1975—; cons. pediatrician Clifford Beers Child Guidance Clinic, 1967—; bd. dirs. Clifford Beers Guidance Clinic, New Haven, 1950-55, Women's Health Svc., New Haven, 1992—, Child Welfare League, N.Y.C., 1979-91. Author: Parents Book on Raising a Healthy Child, 1987. Maj. AUS, 1944-47, ETO. Mem. Am. Acad. Pediat. (Practitioner Rsch. award 1994), Soc. Adolescent Medicine, Conn. Med. Soc., New Haven County Med. Soc. Office: 878 Howard Ave New Haven CT 06519-1106

WESSELINK, DAVID DUWAYNE, finance company executive; b. Webster City, Iowa, Sept. 5, 1942; s. William David and Lavina C. (Haahr) W.; m. Linda R. DeWitt, Dec. 27, 1971; children: Catherine, Bill. BA in Bus., Cen. Coll., 1964; MBA, Mich. State U., 1970. Tchr. Peace Corps, Turkey, 1964-66, Karabuk Koleji, Turkey, 1967-68, Robert Koleji, Turkey, 1969-70; research analyst Household Fin. Corp., Chgo., 1971-73, asst. dir. research, 1973-77; asst. treasurer Household Fin. Corp., Prospect Heights, Ill., 1977, v.p., dir. research, 1977-82, group v.p., chief fin. officer, 1982-86, sr. v.p., chief fin. officer, 1986—; v.p., treas. Household Internat., Prospect Heights, 1988-93; sr. v.p., CFO Advanta Corp., 1993—. Bd. dirs. Am. Cancer Soc., Northbrook, Ill., 1988—, Glenkirk Found., Northbrook, 1988—; mem. nat. leadership com. Cen. Challenge at Cen. Coll. Mem. Fin. Execs. Inst., Chgo. Coun. on Fgn. Rels., Econ. Club Chgo. Office: Advanta Corp 300 Welsh Rd Horsham PA 19044

WESSELMANN, GLENN ALLEN, hospital executive; b. Cleve., Mar. 21, 1932; s. Roy Arthur and Dorothy (Oakes) W.; m. Genevieve De Witt, Sept. 6, 1958; children: Debbie, Scott, Janet. A.B., Dartmouth, 1954; M.B.A. with distinction, Cornell U., 1959. Research aide Cornell U. Ithaca, N.Y., 1958-59; adminstrv. resident Meml. Hosp., N.Y.C., 1957-58; adminstrv. asst. Meml. Hosp., 1959-61, asst. adminstr., 1961-65, asst. v.p., 1965-68; v.p. for adminstrn. Meml. Hosp. for Cancer and Allied Diseases, N.Y.C., 1968-79; exec. v.p., chief operating officer St. John Hosp., Detroit, 1979-84; pres., CEO St. John Health System, 1984-95—; vice chmn., 1995—; chmn., pres., CEO St. John Hosp. & Med. Ctr., 1984-94; mem. bus. adv. bd. City of Detroit, 1991-95, chmn., 1993-94; mem. exec. com. Greater Detroit Area Health Coun.; bd. dirs. Caymich Ins. Co. Ltd., Mich. Health Care Alliance, SelectCare, Detroit Econ. Growth Corp. Trustee Sisters of St. Joseph Health System 1981-94, Sisters of St. Joseph Health Svc., 1983—, St. John Hosp. and Med. Ctr., 1979-95, St. John Health System, 1984—, The Oxford Inst., 1984-95, Eastwood Clinics, 1992-95; mem. bus. adv. bd., City of Detroit, 1991—, chmn. 1993-94. Served with MC AUS, 1955-57. Fellow ACHE; mem. Am. Hosp. Assn., Internat. Hosp. Fedn., Mich. Hosp. Assn. (trustee, chmn. 1994—, mem. exec. com.), Assn. Am. Med. Colls. (Coth rep.), Am. Cancer Soc. (regional adv. bd. 1994—), Med. Group Mgmt. Assn., Soc. Health Service Adminstrs., Sigma Phi Epsilon. Home: 63 Big Woods Dr Hilton Head Island SC 29926 Office: St John Health Sys Office of the Pres 22101 Moross Rd Detroit MI 48236-2148

WESSELS, BRUCE W., materials scientist, educator; b. N.Y.C., Oct. 18, 1946; m. Beverly T. Wessels; children: David, Kirsten. BS in Metallurgy and Materials Sci., U. Pa., 1968; PhD in Materials Sci., MIT, 1973. Mem. tech. staff GE R&D Ctr., 1972-77, acting branch mgr., 1976; from asst. prof. to assoc. prof. Northwestern U., Evanston, Ill., 1977-83, prof. materials sci. and engring., 1984—; vis. sci. Argonne Nat. Lab., 1978; mem. program com. 3d Internat. Conf. Superlattices, Microdevices and Microstructures, 1987; vice chair TMS electronic, magnetic and photonic materials divsn. exec. coun., 1991-92, chair, 1993—. Editor: (with G.Y. Chin) Advances in Electronic Materials, 1986; mem. edit. bd. Jour. Electronic Materials, 1982-88; contbr. over 140 articles to profl. jours. Mem. Minerals, Metals and Materials Soc.-AIME (chmn. electronic materials com. 1987-89, conf. program chmn. 1986-87, key reader Trans. of AIME, 1985—, bd. dirs. 1993—), Electrochem. Soc., Materials Rsch. Soc. (symposium organizer 1993, 95), Sigma Xi, Tau Beta Pi. Office: Materials Science & Engring Northwestern U 2225 N Campus Dr Evanston IL 60208

WESSINGER, W. DAVID, management consultant; b. Leesville, S.C., Aug. 8, 1924; s. Noah F. and Willye W. (Quattlebaum) W.; m. Virginia Lou Hinsch, June 30, 1945; children: David, Clifford, Carol, Virginia Anne. BS in Bus., George Washington U., 1962; MS in Mgmt., U.S. Navy Postgrad. Sch., 1963. Cert. mgmt. cons. Ensign USN, 1943, advanced through grades to capt., 1964; cons. Orgn. Resources Counselors, Inc., N.Y.C., 1968-78, v.p., 1978-85, sr. v.p., 1985-93. Mem. Arbitration Assn., Am. Compensation Assn., Inst. Mgmt. Cons. Presbyterian. Avocations: woodworking, fishing, tennis, golf. Office: Organization Resources Counselors Inc 1211 6th Ave New York NY 10036-8701

WESSLER, RICHARD LEE, psychology educator, psychotherapist; b. St. Louis, Sept. 11, 1936; s. Harry Edward and Lorraine Grace (Hoffman) W.; m. Sheenah Hankin, Mar. 28, 1984; 1 child, Lisa. Student, U. Mo., 1954-55; A.B., Washington U., 1958, Ph.D., 1966. Research assoc. St. Louis U., 1962-66, asst. prof. sociology, 1966-69; assoc. prof. psychology Parsons Coll., Farifield, Iowa, 1969-73; prof. psychology Pace U., Pleasantville, N.Y., 1974—; postdoctoral fellow, dir. tng. Inst. for Rational-Emotive Therapy, N.Y.C., 1973-75, 76-82; pvt. practice psychotherapy N.Y.C., 1976—; vis. prof. Rijksuniversiteit te Leiden, Netherlands, 1981-82, U. Aston, Eng., 1982; cons. govt. agys., hosps., bus. Author: (with R.A. Wessler) The Principles and Practice of Rational Emotive Therapy, 1980, (with S.R. Wolen and R.D. Giuseppe) A Practioner's Guide to Rational-Emotive Therapy, 1980; editor: Rational Living, 1974-83; assoc. editor: Brit. Jour. Cognitive Psychotherapy. Mem. Am. Psychol. Assn., Assn. for Advancement Behavior Therapy.

WESSLER, SHEENAH HANKIN, psychotherapist, consultant; b. Tamworth, England, Nov. 4, 1939; came to U.S., 1982; d. Alexander Rolfe Mackenzie and Irene May Richards; m. Philip Raymond Hankin, Apr. 16, 1962 (div. Mar. 1984); children: Stuart, James, Robin, Nicholas; m. Richard L. Wessler, Mar. 28, 1984. BA with honors, Birmingham Univ., 1961, diploma in sr. edn., 1963; diploma in counseling psychology, Aston Univ., 1979. Dir. Irish Pregnancy Counseling Clinic, Dublin, Ireland, 1979-81; counselor trainer Well Woman Clinic, Dublin, Ireland, 1979-81; pvt. practice Dublin, Ireland, 1979-81; co-dir. Cognitive Psychotherapy Assocs., N.Y.C., 1983—; cons. Coolemine Therapeutic Community, Dublin, 1983—. Contbr. articles to profl. jours. Mem. Am. Counseling Assn. Office: Cognitive Psychotherapy Svcs 18 E 93 St New York NY 10128

WESSLER, STANFORD, physician, educator; b. N.Y.C., Apr. 20, 1917; S. Hugo and Minerva (Miller) W.; m. Margaret Barnet Muhlfelder, Dec. 17, 1942; children—John Stanford, Stephen Lawrence, James Hugh. Grad.; Fieldston Sch., N.Y.C., 1934; B.A., Harvard, 1938; M.D., N.Y.U., 1942. From fellow to asst. prof. medicine Harvard U. Med. Sch., 1946-64; from resident to assoc. chief med. svc. Beth Israel Hosp., Boston, 1946-64; prof. medicine Washington U. Sch. Medicine, St. Louis, 1964-74; John L. and Adalaine Simon prof. Washington U. Sch. Medicine, 1966-74; prof. medicine, assoc. dean postgrad. programs NYU Sch. Medicine, 1974-90; physician in chief Jewish Hosp., St. Louis, 1964-74; assoc. physician Barnes Hosp., St. Louis, 1964-74; attending physician NYU Med. Center, Univ. Hosp., N.Y.C., 1974-90; Bellevue Hosp. Center, N.Y.C., 1974-90; Manhattan VA Hosp. Med. Ctr., 1974-90; Mem. coms. NRC, Inst. of Medicine, Nat. Heart, Lung and Blood Inst.; bd. dirs. N.Y. Heart Assn., 1980-86; pres. Council Continuing Med. Edn., N.Y., 1979-85. Contbr. articles on vascular disease.; mem. editorial bds. jours. in field. Served with M.C. AUS, 1943-46. Recipient James A. Mitchell award, 1972. Mem. Am. Physiol. Soc., Am. Soc. Clin. Investigation, Am. Physicians, Am. Heart Assn. (investigator 1955-59, bd. dirs. 1971-76, chmn. publs. com. 1972-76, chmn. coun. on thrombosis 1974-76, v.p. 1974-76, mem. sci. adv. com. 1986-90, Merit award 1978, Disting. Achievement award 1989), Alpha Omega Alpha. Home: 60 Rye Rd Rye NY 10580-2228

WESSLING, FRANCIS CHRISTOPHER, mechanical engineer, educator; b. St. Louis, June 7, 1939; s. Francis Christopher and Olivia Marie (Buss) W.; m. Susan Jane Hoyt, June 15, 1963; children: Laura, Francis III, Paul, Angela, Stephen. BSME, Washington U., St. Louis, 1961; MSME, U. N.Mex., 1963; PhD in Mech. Engring., U. Minn., 1968. Registered profl. engr., N.Mex. Prof. mech. engr. U. N.Mex., Albuquerque, 1967-79; mgr. Tenn. Valley Authority, Chattanooga, 1979-82; pres. Wessling Cons., Chat-

tanooga, 1982-83; sr. program analyst Sverdrup Tech. Inc., Tullahoma, Tenn., 1983-84; sr. rsch. scientist U. Ala., Huntsville, 1984-87, prof., mech. engr., 1988—; assoc. dir. Consortium for Materials Devel. in Space U. Ala. Huntsville, 1985—, project mgr. Consort & Joust Sounding Rocket Programs, 1988—; cons. U.S. Dept. Energy, Albuquerque, 1978-79, Solar Energy Industries Assn., Sacramento, 1980-81. Contbr. articles to profl. jours. Bd. dirs. Diocesan Bd. Edn., Birmingham, 1987-90; sec. North Ala. Soccer Ofcls. Assn., Huntsville, 1987-90. Mem. AIAA, ASME. Home: 3275 Maysville Rd NE Huntsville AL 35811-9540 Office: U Ala Huntsville RI M65 Huntsville AL 35899

WESSLING, ROBERT BRUCE, lawyer; b. Chgo., Oct. 8, 1937; s. Robert Euans and Marguerite (Rickert) W.; m. Judith Ann Hanson, Aug. 26, 1961; children: Katherine, Jennifer, Carolyn. BA, DePauw U., 1959; JD, U. Mich., 1962. Bar: Calif. 1963, U.S. Dist. Ct. (cen. dist.) Calif. 1963, U.S. Ct. Appeals (9th cir.) 1965. Assoc. Latham & Watkins, L.A., 1962-70, ptnr., 1970-94, of counsel, 1995—; bd. govs. Fin. Lawyers Conf., Los Angeles, 1974—. Mem. World Affairs Coun., L.A., Town Hall, L.A.; trustee DePauw U. Mem. ABA, Calif. Bar Assn., Los Angeles Bar Assn., Phi Beta Kappa, Phi Delta Phi, Phi Eta Sigma, Order of Coif. Democrat. Methodist. Avocations: tennis, travel. Office: Latham & Watkins 633 W 5th St Ste 4000 Los Angeles CA 90071-2059

WESSMAN, JOAN FEENEY, nurse administrator; b. Phila., Mar. 28, 1950; d. Walter James and Elizabeth Mary (Nangle) Bennis; children: Megan, Kate, Matthew; m. Robert E. Wessman, April 17. 1993. Diploma in nursing, Fairview Gen. Hosp. Sch. Nsg., Cleve., 1971; BS in Nursing, Miami U., Oxford, Ohio, 1981; MS, Ohio State U., 1982. RN, Ohio. Staff nurse Southwest Gen. Hosp., Berea, Ohio, 1971; staff/charge nurse Children's Med. Ctr., Dayton, Ohio, 1971-72, Mercy Hosp., Hamilton, Ohio, 1973-74; supr. McCullough Hyde Meml. Hosp., Oxford, Ohio, 1974-78; staff nurse St. Elizabeth Med. Ctr., Dayton, 1978-79, instr., coord., 1979-80, supr., 1980-83; dir. nursing Miami Valley Hosp., Dayton, 1983-87; sr. v.p. nursing Akron (Ohio) Gen. Med. Ctr., Akron, Ohio, 1987-90; sr. v.p. patient svcs. Akron (Ohio) Gen. Med. Ctr., 1990—; adj. faculty mem. U. Akron, 1987—, Kent (Ohio) State U., 1987—; mem. VHA Cen. Nurse Exec. Task Force, Nat. Nursing Adv. Coun., Health Care Forum; mem. Midwest Alliance in Nursing, 1992—. Adv. bd. mem. Recruitment and Retention Report, 1989—; contbr. articles to profl. jours. Mem. adv. com. ARC, Dayton, 1987; mem. program com. Midwest Alliance in Nursing, 1992—; chair Pvt. Industry Coun., 1991-92, chair, 1992—; mem. adv. bd. Recruitment and Retention Report, 1989—. Recipient Rsch. Incentive award Wright State U., 1986, Excellence in Nursing Leadership award Delta Omega, 1990; Johnson and Johnson Wharton fellow 1991. Mem. AACN, Am. Orgn. Nurse Execs., Am. Hosp. Assn., Ohio Orgn. Nursing Execs. (pres. 1992—), Ohio Hosp. Assn., Ohio Nurses Assn. (del.), Pentagon Coun. (chmn. 1989), Women's Network, Health Care Forum, Nat. League for Nursing, Phi Kappa Phi, Sigma Theta Tau. Roman Catholic. Office: Akron Gen Med Ctr 400 Wabash Ave Akron OH 44307-2433

WESSON, WILLIAM SIMPSON, retired paper company executive; b. Seattle, June 5, 1929; s. Edward Phineas and Margaret (Simpson) W.; m. Janet Hudson Knowles, Jan. 31, 1981; children by previous marriage: Edward, Anne, Lee. A.B., Cornell U., 1951, M.B.A., 1954. With Scott Paper Co., Phila., 1954-87; v.p. Edn. div. Scott Paper Co., Holyoke, Mass., 1969-74; pres. Scott Graphics, 1974-76; mng. dir. Bowater-Scott Corp. Ltd., U.K., 1976-81; pres. Scott Paper Internat., Phila., 1981-87; chmn. bd. Bowater-Scott Corp., Ltd., 1978-87, ret., 1987. Pres. Nat. Grocers Benevolent Fund, U.K., 1977-78; mem. Cornell U. Council, N.Y., 1982-86. Served to 1st lt. U.S. Army, 1951-53. Republican.

WEST, ALFRED PAUL, JR., financial services executive; b. Brooksville, Fla., Dec. 7, 1942; s. Alfred Paul Sr. and Jane (Coogler) W.; m. Loralee Smith, June 16, 1964; children: Angela Paige, Alfred Paul III, Andrew Palmer. B in Aerospace Engring., Ga. Inst. Tech., 1964; MBA, U. Pa., 1967, postgrad., 1967-68. Chmn., chief exec. officer SEI Corp., Wayne, Pa., 1968—, pres., 1973—. Bd. dirs. All-Star Forum, Phila., 1983—, Paoli Meml. Hosp., 1990—; grad. exec. bd. Wharton Sch. of Bus., 1983—; chmn. bd. dirs. Wharton's SEI Ctr. for Advanced Studies in Mgmt., 1989—; bd. dirs. World Affairs Council, Phila., 1985-89, mem. exec. com., 1989, chmn. adv. com., 1989—. Republican. Presbyterian. Avocations: skiing, golf, photography. Office: SEI Corp 680 E Swedesford Rd Wayne PA 19087-1610

WEST, A(RNOLD) SUMNER, chemical engineer; b. Phila., Jan. 12, 1922; s. Arnold and Mary (Sumner) W.; m. Beverly Helen Lehman, Oct. 5, 1946; children: Barbara Ann, Richard Sumner. BSChemE, U. Pa., 1943; MS, Pa. State U., 1946. With Rohm and Haas Co., Phila., 1946-87, rsch. engr., 1946-62, rsch. supr., 1962-72, mgr. research dept., 1972-77, sr. tech. specialist govt. and regulatory affairs, 1978-87; owner, prin. A.S. West Assocs., Huntingdon Valley, Pa., 1987—; cons. dept. chem. engring. U. Pa., 1952-72; mem. indsl. and profl. adv. com. Coll. Engring., Pa. State U., 1978-84, chmn. chem. engring. div., 1980-81, chmn. com., 1982-83. Mem. Lower Moreland Twp. (Montgomery County) Authority, 1970, sec., 1971—; vice-chmn. bd. dirs. Chemical Heritage Found., 1984-92; pres. United Engring. Trustees, 1986-87. Fellow Am. Inst. Chem. Engrs. (dir. 1964-66, treas. 1973-75, v.p. 1976, pres. 1977); mem. Engrs. Joint Council (dir. 1976-79), Am. Assn. Engring. Socs. (vice chmn. public affairs council 1981, chmn. council 1982-83), Am. Chem. Soc., Nat. Soc. Profl. Engrs., Soc. Automotive Engrs., Water Environ. Fedn. Club: The Valley (Huntington Valley). Home and Office: 3896 Sidney Rd Huntingdon Valley PA 19006-2347

WEST, ARTHUR JAMES, II, biologist; b. Boston, Dec. 14, 1927; s. Arthur James and Lillian (Laming) W.; BS, Suffolk U., 1951, MA in Edn., 1956; MS, U. N.H., 1962, PhD in Zoology, 1964; m. Carolyn Barbara Ross, June 4, 1948 (div. May 1972); children: Arthur James, Gregory Thomas, Donald Robert; m. Linda Jean Cummings, July 21, 1985 (div. Sept. 1993); children: Melissa Ida, Benjamin Cummings. Faculty, Suffolk U., Boston, 1952-68, assoc. prof. biology, 1964-65, prof., 1965-68, co-chmn. biology, 1964-68; dean, prof. div. natural sci. New Eng. Coll., Henniker, N.H., 1968-70; prof. chmn. dept. biology Suffolk U., 1970-72, 78-88; assoc. program dir. Pre-coll. Edn. in Scis., NSF, 1972-73; prof. dept. biology Suffolk U., 1973-89, prof. emeritus, 1989—; acad. v.p. for curriculum devel. U. San Juan Capistrano, 1992-93; owner, operator Subway of Farmington and Skowhegan, Maine, chmn.adv. coun. 1993-94; dir. R.S. Friedman Cobscook Bay Lab., 1975-88; exec. com. M.I.T./Sea Grant Consortium Program, 1979-85; asst. prof., chmn. biology Mass. Coll. Optometry, 1957-60; instr., chmn. sci. Emerson Coll., 1956-59; staff Norwich U., 1960; cons. Ginn & Co. Sci. Publs., 1967-70; hon. cons., parasitologist Akvapatologisk Lab., 1987; civil svc. examiner Mass. Dept. Natural Resources, 1965-72. Founding pres. Keltown Civic Assn., 1954; chmn. Woburn United Fund, 1958; mem. Woburn Sch. Com., 1955-60, chmn. 1957; chmn. Woburn YMCA, 1958, Woburn Rep. City Com., 1959, New Vineyard Town Com., 1990; vice chmn. Franklin County Rep. Com.; mem. common. on ocean mgmt. Mass. Served with USN, 1946-47, with Res., 1947-52. NSF grantee, 1968-71, 70-71, 75-82. Mem. Mass. Bay Marine Studies Consortium (pres. 1982-85), Mass. Marine Educators, Inc. (com. 1978-86), AAAS, Am. Inst. Biol. Scis., Nat. Marine Edn. Assn. (dir. 1976-78, pres. 1985-86), Ea. Star, Rotary, Masons, Sigma Xi (Suffolk U. club pres. 1972), Sigma Zeta, Phi Beta Chi (pres. 1951), Beta Beta Beta, Phi Sigma. Research and publs. on Acanthocephala and undergrad. marine edn. Home: PO Box 104 New Vineyard ME 04956-0104

WEST, BERNARD, investor; b. N.Y.C., Nov. 16, 1931; s. Milton and Lillian (Perlbinder) W.; m. Joyce M. Loewenthal, June 30, 1956; children: Stacy E. West-Clark, Jane A. AB, Cornell U., 1953, JD, 1955. Bar: N.Y. 1987. Assoc. Paul R. Shaw, Esq., N.Y.C., 1957-62; ptnr. West & Wolk, Esqs., N.Y.C., 1962-68; exec. v.p., owner Charles H. Greenthal Group, Inc., N.Y.C., 1968-91. Past bd. dirs. Realty Adv. Bd., N.Y.; bd. dirs. Ctr. for Am. Culture Studies Columbia U. Jewish Guild for the Blind. Mem. ABA, Am. Booksellers Assn., Internat. Map Trade Assn., Harmonie Club (N.Y.C.), City Athletic Club (N.Y.C.), Quaker Ridge Golf Club (Scarsdale, N.Y.), Beaver Creek (Colo.) Club. Avocations: reading, skiing, gardening, golf. Offic: Westhaven Ltd 220 E 42nd St New York NY 10017-5806

WEST, BOB, pharmaceutical company executive; b. Ellenville, N.Y., Mar. 7, 1931; s. Harry and Elsie May Wisentowsky; m. Betty Parker, May 9, 1957 (div.); children: Debra Ellen, Elizabeth Ann, Sharon Lynn; m. Jacqueline

Cutler, Jan. 3, 1982. BS, Union U., 1952; MS, Purdue U., 1954, PhD, 1956; postgrad. mgmt. seminar, U. Chgo., 1972. Pres., dir. research Food, Drug, Chem. Svcs., Stamford, Conn., 1975—; pres., dir. research Bob West Assocs., Inc., Stamford, 1975—; pres. Drug Info. Assn., Phila., 1974-75; sci. adv. bd. Fountain Pharms., Inc., Largo, Fla., 1993—. Editorial bd. Drug Info. Assn. Jour., Phila., 1977-85; contbr. articles to profl. jours. Mem. ASPET, Am. Soc. Toxicology, Acad. Pharm. Scis., Assn. Rsch. Dirs., Drug Info. Assn., Assn. Univ. Tech. Mgrs. Home and office: Food Drug Chem Svcs 3771 Center Way Fairfax VA 22033-2602

WEST, BURTON CAREY, physician; b. Pitts., Feb. 21, 1941; s. Pemberton Burton and Maree (Van Scoyoc) W.; m. Katherine Ann Young, Dec. 27, 1963; children: Amy Fay Chandler, Holly Katherine Brewer, John Pemberton, Abigail Coleman, Emily Van Scoyoc. AB, AMherst Coll., 1963; MD, Cornell U., 1967. Diplomate Am. Bd. Internal Medicine and Infectious Diseases. Resident U. Hosps., Seattle, 1967-69; clin. assoc., sr. staff fellow NIAID, NIH, Bethesda, Md., 1969-72; resident Vanderbilt Hosp., Nashville, 1972-74; from asst. prof. to prof. medicine La. State U. Sch. Medicine, Shreveport, 1974-89, chief sect. infectious diseases, 1974-89; chmn. dept. medicine Meridia Huron Hosp., Cleve., 1989—. Contbr. articles to profl. jours. Lt. comdr. USPHS, 1969-71. Fellow Infectious Diseases Soc. Am. (pres. elect 1994-95), Am. Coll. Physicians (Ohio chpt. chmn. program dirs. 1995—). Independent. Office: Meridia Huron Hosp 13951 Terr Rd Cleveland OH 44112

WEST, BYRON KENNETH, banker; b. Denver, Sept. 18, 1933; s. Willis Byron and Cecil Bernice (Leathers) W.; m. Barbara Huth, June 25, 1955. AB, U. Ill., 1955; MBA, U. Chgo., 1960. With Harris Bank, Chgo., 1957—, investment analyst, 1957-62, v.p., 1966-76; group exec. Harris Bank Internat. Banking Group, Chgo., 1974-76, head banking dept., exec. v.p., 1976-80, pres., 1980; chmn. bd., chief exec. officer Harris Bankcorp, Inc., Chgo., 1984—, also bd. dirs.; chmn., chief exec. officer Harris Trust and Savs. Bank, Chgo., 1985—; bd. dirs. Motorola, Inc., Assn. Res. City Bankers. Trustee U. Chgo., Rush-Presbyn.-St. Luke's Med Center; mem. governing bd. Chgo. Orchestral Assn.; bd. dirs. U. Ill. Found. Served with USN, 1955-57. Mem. Res. City Bankers Assn., Christian Laymen of Chgo., Phi Beta Kappa. Republican. Clubs: Skokie Country (Glencoe, Ill.); Pine Valley (N.J.); Univ., Chgo., Commonwealth, Comml., Econ. (Chgo.). Home: 134 Green Bay Rd Apt 205 Winnetka IL 60093-4046 Office: Harris Bankcorp Inc PO Box 755 111 W Monroe St Chicago IL 60603-4095

WEST, CHARLES CONVERSE, theologian, educator; b. Plainfield, N.J., Feb. 3, 1921; s. George Parsons and Florence (Farish) W.; m. Ruth Floy Carson, Sept. 6, 1944; children: Russell Arthur, Walter Lawrence, Glenn Andrew. B.A., Columbia U., 1942; B.D., Union Theol. Sem., N.Y.C., 1945; Ph.D., Yale U., 1955. Ordained to ministry Presbyterian Ch. U.S.A., 1946; missionary, fraternal worker Bd. Fgn. Missions Presbyn. Ch. U.S.A., 1946-56; instr., chaplain Cheeloo U., Hangchow, China, 1948-49; instr. Nanking Theol. Sem., 1949-50; indsl. mission work Gossner Mission, Mainz-Kastel, Germany, 1950-51; lectr. Kirchliche Hochschule, Berlin, 1951-53; Lectr. Hartford Sem. Found., 1955-56; asso. dir. Ecumenical Inst., Bossey, Switzerland under World Council Chs., 1956-61; chargé de cours U. Geneva, 1956-61; instr. Peking Nat. U., 1948; assoc. prof. Christian ethics Princeton Theol. Sem., 1961-63, Stephen Colwell prof. Christian ethics, 1963-91, prof. emeritus, 1991—, acad. dean, 1979-84; mem. Commn. to Form Statement Faith U.P. Ch. U.S.A., 1961-67, chmn. internat. affairs adv. com., 1963-66; Chmn. U.S. Com. for Christian Peace Conf., 1965-72; chmn. working com. Dept. Studies in Mission, Evangelism World Council Chs., 1967-68; member Commn. on Internat. Affairs, Nat. Council Chs., 1968-73. Author: Communism and the Theologians, 1958, Outside the Camp, 1959, Ethics, Biolence and Revolution, 1969, The Power to be Human, 1971, Perspective on South Africa, 1985; editor: The Sufficiency of God, Essays in Honor of Dr. W.A. Visser't Hooft, 1963; assoc. editor: Religion in Eastern Europe, 1985—; translator: J. Hamel-A Christian in East Germany, 1960. Mem. Am. Soc. Christian Ethics (v.p. 1972-73, pres. 1973-74), Am. Theol. Soc. (v.p. 1982-83, pres. 1983-84), Presbytery N.Y.C., Ams. for Dem. Action., Christians Associated for Rels. with Eastern Europe (pres. 1988-92). Home: 157 Mountain Rd Ringoes NJ 08551-1402 Office: Princeton Theological Seminary CN821 Princeton NJ 08542

WEST, CHARLES PATRICK, agronomist, educator; b. Mpls., June 13, 1952; s. Howard George and Margaret Mary (Colburn) W.; m. Jane Marie Scott, May 24, 1980; children: Scott Patrick, Grant Howard. BS, U. Minn., 1974, MS, 1978; PhD, Iowa State U., 1981. Vol. agronomist Peace Corps, Morocco, 1974-76; agronomy researcher Ministry of Agr. and Fisheries, Hamilton, New Zealand, 1982-84; asst. prof. agronomy U. Ark., Fayetteville, 1984-90, assoc. prof., 1990—. Contbr. 40 articles to profl. jours. N.Z. Nat. Rsch. Adv. Coun. postdoctoral rsch. fellow 1982-84. Mem. Am. Soc. Agronomy, Crop Sci. Soc. Am., Am. Forage and Grassland Coun. (Merit award), Sigma Xi, Gamma Sigma Delta. Office: 276 Altheimer Dr Fayetteville AR 72703-6804

WEST, CLARK DARWIN, pediatric nephrologist, educator; b. Jamestown, N.Y., July 4, 1918; s. Clark Darwin and Frances Isabel (Blanchard) W.; m. Ruthann Asbury, Apr. 12, 1944 (div.); children: Charles Michael, John Clark, Lucy Frances; m. Dolores Lachenman, Mar. 1, 1986. A.B., Coll. of Wooster, 1940; M.D., U. Mich., 1943. Intern Univ. Hosp., Ann Arbor, Mich., 1943-44; resident in pediatrics Univ. Hosp., 1944-46; fellow in pediatrics Children's Hosp. Research Found., Cin., 1948-49; research assoc. Children's Hosp. Research Found., 1951—, asso. dir., 1963—; dir. div. immunology and nephrology, 1958—; with cardiopulmonary lab. chest service Bellevue Hosp., N.Y.C., 1949-51; attending pediatrician Children's Hosp., 1951—; asst. prof. pediatrics U. Cin., 1951-55, asso. prof., 1955-62, prof., 1962—; mem. comm. NIH, 1965-69, 1972-73. Mem. editorial bd.: Jour. Pediatrics, 1960-79, Kidney Internat., 1977-89, Clin. Nephrology, 1989—; contbr. articles to profl. jours. Served to capt. M.C., AUS, 1946-47. Decorated Army Commendation medal; recipient Recognition award Cin. Pediatric Soc., 1980, Mitchell I. Rubin award, 1986, Henry L. Barnett award, 1995. Mem. Soc. Pediatric Research (sec.-treas. 1958-62, pres. 1963-64), Am. Pediatric Soc., Am. Soc. Pediatric Nephrologists (pres. 1973-74), Am. Physiol. Soc., Am. Assn. Immunologists, Am. Soc. Nephrology, Internat. Pediatric Nephrology Assn., Sigma Xi, Alpha Omega Alpha. Research on immunopathogenesis and treatment of glomerulonephritides and in the complement system. Home: 11688 Aristocrat Dr Harrison OH 45030 Office: Children's Hosp Med Ctr Cincinnati OH 45229

WEST, CORNEL, philosopher, writer; b. Tulsa, June 2, 1953; s. Clifton L. W.; 1 child from previous marriage, Clifton; m. Elleni Gebre Amlak. BA, Harvard U., 1973; PhD, Princeton U., 1977. Prof. religion Union Theol. Sem., N.Y., 1977-84, 87-88, Yale U. Divinity Sch., New Haven, 1984-87; prof. religion, dir. dept. Afro-Am. Studies Princeton (N.J.) U., 1988-94; prof. Afro-Am. Studies, philosophy of religion, Du Bois fellow Harvard U., Cambridge, Mass., 1994—; Am. corr. Le Monde Diplomatique; vis. prof. U. Paris. Author: Prophesy Deliverance! An Afro-American Revolutionary Christianity, 1982, Prophetic Fragments, 1988, The American Evasion of Philosophy: A Genealogy of Pragmatism, 1990, Breaking Bread: Insurgent Black Intellectual Life, 1991, The Ethical Dimensions of Marxist Thought, 1991, Race Matters, 1993, Beyond Eurocentrism and Multiculturalism, Vol. I: Prophetic Thought in Postmodern Times, 1993, Vol. II: Notes on Race, Class and Power, 1993, Keeping Faith: Philosophy and Race in America, 1993, (with Paula Giddings) Regarding Malcolm X, 1994, (with Michael Lerner) Jews and Blacks: Let the Healing Begin, 1995. Recipient Literary Lion award N.Y. Pub. Libr., 1993. Office: Harvard U Dept Afro-Am Studies Cambridge MA 02138-6502

WEST, DANIEL JONES, hospital administrator, rehabilitator counselor; b. Coaldale, Pa., Sept. 19, 1949; s. Daniel J. and Mildred Elizabeth (Kreiger) W.; m. Linda Jean Werdt, Sep. 18, 1971; children: Jeffrey Bryan, Christopher Jones. BS cum laude, Pa. State U., 1971, EdM summa cum laude, 1972; postgrad., Montgomery County Community Coll., 1973, Rutgers U., 1974. Cert. rehab. counselor. Psychol. svcs. assoc. Commonwealth of Pa./Harrisburg State Hosp., 1972; adminstrv. dir., counselor Good Samaritan Hosp., Pottsville, Pa., 1972-74, adminstrv. 1975—; cons. in drug abuse and alcoholism, 1974—; instr., dept. counselor edn. Pa. State U. Schuylkill campus, 1973—; adviser to undergrad. rehab. edn. orgn., 1975; cons. Temple U. Sch. Social Adminstrn., 1974; moderator First Ann. Conf.

on Drug and Alcohol Abuse, Bedford, Pa., 1977. Author manuals on mgmt. and counseling, various tng. programs for rehab. counseling. Chmn. planning and implementation coun. Schuylkill County Gov.'s Coun. on Drug and Alcohol Abuse, State of Pa., 1973-74; mem. Drug Adv. Task Force, 1973-74, Task Force Child and Family Resource Devel. Program, Schuylkill County, 1973—, Criminal Justice System Task Force, Schuylkill County, 1975—; mem. adv. bd. Holy FAmily Home Health Care Agy, Schuylkill County, 1977—, chmn. bd. edn. com., 1977—; bd. dirs. St. David's Soc. Schuylkill and Carbon Counties, 1976—, Health Systems Agy., Northeast Pa., 1977—. Mem. AAAS, Nat. Vocat. Guidance Assn., Am. Ednl. Assn., Am. Pers. and Guidance Assn., Am. Ednl. Rsch. Assn., Am. Pub. Health Assn., Assn. for Advancement of Psychology, Assn. Mental Health Adminstrs., Am. Psychol. Assn., Assn. for Advancement of Behavior Theraphy, Pa. State Alumni Assn., Elks, Masons, Iota Alpha Delta. Home: PO Box 2208 Moscow PA 18444 Office: Scranton U O'Hara Hall 3rd fl Scranton PA 18510

WEST, DONALD VALENTINE, editor, journalist; b. Memphis, Tex., Jan. 5, 1930; s. Raynes V. and Kathleen Inez (Thornton) W.; m. Carroll Virginia Warren, July 24, 1951 (div.); children: Kathleen, Susan, James, Teresa, Michael, Mark, Thomas. BA, N.Mex. A&M U., 1950. Mng. editor Roswell (N.Mex.) Dispatch, 1947-48; desk editor El Paso (Tex.) Times, 1950-51; writer Broadcasting Mag., Washington and N.Y.C., 1953-60; mng. editor Television Mag., N.Y.C., 1961-66; asst. to pres. CBS Inc., N.Y.C., 1966-70; mng. editor, editor Broadcasting Mag., Broadcasting & Cable Mag., Washington, 1971—; TV prodr. SQN Prodns., 1970-71. Sgt. U.S. Army, 1951-53. Recipient Presdl. award Reed Pub. U.S.A., 1994. Office: Broadcasting & Cable Mag 1705 Desales St NW Washington DC 20036-4405

WEST, EMERY JOSEPH, financial analyst, investment portfolio manager; b. Kingston, Pa., Nov. 24, 1940; s. David Dimon and Elizabeth Irene (Emery) W.; m. Darla Jean Payne, Oct. 13, 1962 (div. Aug. 1972); 1 child, Emery Joseph II; m. Karen Marie Rowlands, Jan. 1, 1981. Grad., Mercersburg Acad., 1959, U.S. Air Force Acad., 1962; cert., Northwestern U., Evanston, Ill., 1964, U. Windsor, Ont., 1972, 73, 79, Rockford Coll., Ill., 1982; cert. investment mgmt., Princeton U., 1984; MBA, Coll. William & Mary, 1990. Chartered fin. analyst. Jr. investment analyst Tech. Stock Rev., Inc., N.Y.C., 1962-63; analyst, broker Grant, Jones & Co., Inc., Washington, 1963-64; sr. account exec. W.E. Hutton & Co., Washington, 1964-74; investment exec. E.F. Hutton & Co., Washington, 1974-78; 1st v.p. investments and portfolio mgr. Drexel Burnham Lambert, Inc., Washington, 1978-89; 1st v.p., portfolio mgr. Smith Barney Inc., Washington, 1989—; bd. dirs. Fairfax Cable Channel 10, 1985-88; trustee and chmn. investment com. Fairfax County Retirement System, 1985-89. Active mem. Fairfax County (Va.) Rep. Com., 11th Congl. dist. fin. com.; mem. Fairfax County Econ. Adv. Commn., 1992—; mem. Fairfax County Com. of 100, 1984—; mem. No. Va. Tech. Coun. Recipient Award Appreciation County of Fairfax Retirement System, 1989. Fellow Fin. Analysts Fedn., Inst. Chartered Fin. Analysts, Internat. Soc. Fin. Analysts; mem. Assn. for Investment Mgmt. and Rsch., Washington Soc. Investment Analysts, Nat. Assn. Bus. Economists, Nat. Economists Club, Washington Assn. Money Mgrs., Mercersburg Acad. Alumni Coun., Fairfax County C. of C, Belle Haven Country Club, Tower Club. Republican. Lutheran. Avocations: golf, crossword puzzles, backgammon, bridge. Office: Smith Barney Inc 1776 I St NW Washington DC 20006-3709

WEST, FELTON, newspaper writer; b. Houston, May 9, 1926; s. Felton Eber and Clara Viola (Ross) W.; m. Jean Frances Osborn, Oct. 27, 1945; children—Felton Dale, Bruce Eugene, Wade Osborn, Barbara Jean. Student, U. N.Mex., 1944-46; B.S., U. Houston, 1952, M.Litt., 1957. Mem. staff Houston Post, 1943-95, Washington corr., 1961-65, chief Austin (Tex.) capitol bur., 1966-85, columnist, 1985-93, editorial writer, 1993-95, ret., 1995. Served with USNR, World War II. Mem. Soc. Profl. Journalists, Phi Kappa Phi. Home and Office: 2251 CR 284 Liberty Hill TX 78642-9761

WEST, GAIL BERRY, lawyer; b. Cin.; d. Theodore Moody and Johnnie Mae (Newton) W.; m. Togo D. West, Jr., June 18, 1966; children: Tiffany Berry, Hilary Carter. B.A. magna cum laude, Fisk U., 1964; M.A., U. Cin., 1965; J.D., Howard U., 1968. Bar: D.C. 1969, U.S. Supreme Ct. 1978. Staff atty. IBM, 1969-76; spl. asst. to sec. HUD, 1977-78; staff asst. to spl. asst. to Pres., Washington, 1978-80; dep. asst. sec. for manpower res. affairs installations Dept. Air Force, 1980-81; atty. AT&T, Washington, 1983-84; exec. dir. govt. affairs Bell Comms. Rsch. Inc., Washington, 1984-95; dir. govt. rels. Armstrong World Industries, Inc., Washington, 1995—. Mem. exec. com. ARC, Washington, 1974-85; bd. dirs. Family and Child Svcs., Washington, 1974-87; trustee Corcoran Gallery Art, Arena Stage, Decatur House; bd. dirs. Meridian House. Ford Found. fellow, 1965-68. Mem. ABA, D.C. Bar Assn., Unified Bar D.C. Democrat. Episcopalian. Home: 4934 Rockwood Pky NW Washington DC 20016-3211 Office: 1025 Connecticut Ave NW Washington DC 20036

WEST, GLENN EDWARD, business organization executive; b. Kansas City, Mo., Nov. 19, 1944; s. Ernest and Helen Cecil (Johnson) W.; m. Vicki Lynn Knox, May 22, 1970; children: Keele Kay, Kollen Chandler, Ashley Knox. BS in Acctg. and Mktg. cum laude, Northwest Mo. State U., 1966; student U. Colo. Inst. Orgn. Mgmt., 1974; student Notre Dame U. Acad. Orgn. Mgmt., 1977. Auditor Arthur Young & Co., Kansas City, Mo., 1966-68; sales mgr. Procter & Gamble, Kansas City, Mo., 1968-69; mgr. pub. relations St. Joseph Area C. of C., 1969-71, mgr. econ. devel., 1971-74; exec. v.p. Lawrence C. of C, Kans., 1974-81, Greater Macon C. of C., Ga., from 1981; now pres. Austin C. of C. Contbr. articles to profl. jours. Chmn. chpt. ARC, Macon, 1984; pres. Quality of Life Found. Austin, Greater Austin Sports Found. Recipient Leadership award Kiwanis Club, St. Joseph, Mo., 1974. Served with USNG, 1967-73. Mem. Kans Assn. Commerce and Industry (bd. dirs. 1977-79, leadership award 1981), Kans. C. of C. Execs (bd. dirs. 1977-80, pres. 1979), Ga. C. of C. Execs. (bd. dirs. 1982—), Am. C. of C. Execs. (bd. dirs. 1979-81, 83-84, vice chmn. 1989—, chmn.-elect 1990, chmn. 1991, cert. chamber exec. 1980), C. of C. of U.S. (adv. com. 1981-89, bd. dir. 1995), Rotary, Barton Creek Country Club. Republican. Methodist. Office: Greater Austin C of C PO Box 1967 111 Congress Ave Plz Austin TX 78767-1967

WEST, J. ROBINSON, petroleum finance company executive, former government official; b. Bryn Mawr, Pa., Sept. 16, 1946; m. Eileen Shields, May 1992; children: Lily Eileen, Kate Cristy, Laura Shields, John Weyth. B.A., U. N.C., 1968; J.D., Temple U., 1973. Mem. staff White House, Washington, 1974-76; asst. to sec. of def. Dept. Def., Washington, 1976, dep. asst. sec. for internat. econ. affairs, 1976-77; v.p., 1st v.p. Blyth, Eastman, Dillon and Co., 1977-80; mem. Reagan Transition Team, 1980-81; asst. sec. Dept. Interior, Washington, 1981-83, pvt. cons., 1983-84; pres., chief exec. officer Petroleum Fin Co., 1984—; mng. dir. Petroleum Intelligence Group, Ltd., 1988—; chmn. Generation Ventures Assocs., 1991—. Trustee German Marshall Fund of U.S.; dir. Fr.-Am. Found.; pres. Weyth Endowment for Am. Art. Mem. Coun. Fgn. Rels., Internat. Inst. Strategic Studies. Home: 1524 28th St NW Washington DC 20007-3058 Office: Petroleum Fin Co Ltd 1140 Connecticut Ave NW Ste 700 Washington DC 20036-4001

WEST, JAMES HAROLD, accounting company executive; b. San Diego, Oct. 11, 1926; s. Robert Reed and Clara Leona (Moses) W.; m. Norma Jean, 1953 (div.); 1 son, Timothy James; m. Jerel Lynn Smith, Nov. 16, 1976; 1 child, James Nelson. BS, U. So. Calif., Los Angeles, 1949. CPA, Calif. Ptnr., McCracken & Co., San Diego, 1950-61; mgr. Ernst & Ernst, San Diego, 1961-64; ptnr. West Turnquist & Schmitt, San Diego, 1964—. Bd. govs. ARC, Washington, 1981-87; pres., bd. dirs. Combined Arts and Edn. Coun., San Diego, 1980-83; pres. Francis Parker Sch., 1988-90; bd. dirs. San Diego Hosp. Assn., 1981—, San Diegans Inc., 1989-92, Mus. Photographic Arts, 1990-92; trustee Calif. Western Sch. Law, 1985—; mem. bd. advisors U. So. Calif. Sch. Acctg., 1985—; treas. San Diego Nat. Sports Tng. Found., 1988-92; mem. acctg. exec. bd. U. San Diego, 1992—. With AUS, 1945-46; PTO. Mem. AICPA, Calif. Soc. CPAs (bd. dirs. 1963-64), University Club (San Diego), Capital Hill Club (Washington), Masons. Republican. Home: 3311 Lucinda St San Diego CA 92106-2931 Office: West Turnquist & Schmitt 2550 5th Ave Fl 10 San Diego CA 92103-6612

WEST, JAMES JOSEPH, lawyer; b. Tarentum, Pa. Nov. 26, 1945; s. Samuel Elwood and Rose (McIntyre) W.; m. Kathleen Geslak, Aug. 19,

1967; children: Joseph Allen, Yvonne Michelle, KaiLynn Ann. BS in Econs., St. Vincent Coll., 1967; JD, Duquesne U., 1970. Bar: Pa. 1971, U.S. Dist. Ct. (we. dist.) Pa. 1971, U.S. Ct. Appeals (3d cir.) 1971, U.S. Dist. Ct. (mid. dist.) Pa., 1980. Law clk. to presiding justice U.S. Dist. Ct., Pa., 1970-74; asst. U.S. atty. chief appellate sect. U.S. Atty.'s Office, Pitts., 1974-79; dep. dir. criminal law Pa. Atty. Gen.'s Office, Harrisburg, 1979-82; 1st asst. U.S. atty. U.S. Dist. Ct. (mid. dist.) Pa., Harrisburg, 1982-84, U.S. atty., 1984-93; assoc. Sprague & Sprague, Phila., 1993—. Mem. Nat. Environ. Enforcement Council. Recipient Outstanding Performance award U.S. Dept. Justice, 1974-78, Commendation Gov. of Pa., 1981. Mem. Pa. Bar Assn., Allegheny County Bar Assn., Dauphin County Bar Assn. Republican. Roman Catholic. Home: 129 Oxford Ln North Wales PA 19454-4402 Office: Sprague & Sprague 135 S 19th St Ste 400 Philadelphia PA 19103

WEST, JERRY ALAN, professional basketball team executive; b. Chelyan, W.Va., Aug. 28, 1938; s. Howard Stewart and Cecil Sue (Creasey) W.; m. Martha Jane Kane, May, 1960 (div. 1977); children: David, Michael, Mark; m. Karen Christine Bua, May 28, 1978; 1 son, Ryan. BS, W.Va. Coll.; LHD (hon.), W.Va. Wesleyan Coll. Mem. Los Angeles Lakers, Nat. Basketball Assn., 1960-74, coach, 1976-79, spl. cons., 1979-82, gen. mgr., 1982-94; exec. v.p. basketball operations L. A. Lakers, 1994—; mem. first team Nat. Basketball Assn. All-Star Team, 1962-67, 70-73, mem. second team, 1968, 69. Author: (with William Libby) Mr. Clutch: The Jerry West Story, 1969. Capt. U.S. Olympic Basketball Team, 1960; named Most Valuable Player NBA Playoff, 1969, All-Star Game Most Valuable Player, 1972; named to Naismith Meml. Basketball Hall of Fame, 1979, NBA Hall of Fame, 1980; mem. NBA 35th Anniversity All-Time Team, 1980. Office: LA Lakers 3900 W Manchester Blvd PO Box 10 Inglewood CA 90306*

WEST, JOE EARL, veterinarian, clinical pathologist; b. Woodward, Tex., Mar. 8, 1932; s. Joe Conner and Jozie Marie (Oakes) W.; m. Carolyn Kay Francis, Dec. 16, 1967; children: Katherine, Gary, April, Jeremy. DVM, Tex. A&M U., 1956; MS, U. Rochester, 1961; PhD, U. Calif., 1971. Veterinarian Riser Animal Hosp., Skokie, Ill., 1956-57; commd. 1st lt. USAF, 1957, advanced through grades to col., 1974; base veterinarian USAF, Nellis AFB, Nev., 1957-59; research scientist Hanford labs. USAF, Richland, Wash., 1959-60; chief nuclear med. sect. Med. Service Sch. USAF, Gunter AFB, Ala., 1961-65; chmn. dept. radiation biology Armed Forces Radiobiol. Research Inst., Nat. Naval Med. Ctr., Bethesda, Md., 1972-75; command veterinarian US Air Forces Europe, Ramstein AB, Germany, 1975-78; med. insp. USAF, Norton AFB, Calif., 1978-79; ret. USAF, 1979; clin. pathologist, assoc. prof. Miss. State U., Starkville, 1980-82; clin. pathologist Tex. Vet. Med. Diagnostic Lab., College Station, 1982—; cons. radiation biology and biophysics Office Surgeon Gen., Hdqrs. USAF, Washington, 1974-79; clin. pathology cons. to vet. perceptors Miss. State U., Starkville, 1981-82. Contbr. biomed. research and clin. lab. diagnosis to profl. jours. Bd. dirs. A&M United Meth. Ch., College Station, 1986-89. Mem. AVMA, Am. Soc. Vet. Clin. Pathologists, Am. Assn. Vet. Lab. Diagnosticians, Am. Assn. Equine Practitioners, Brazos Valley Vet. Med. Assn. (v.p. progs. 1982-87, pres. 1987-88), Tex. Acad. Vet. Practice (v.p. 1987-88, pres. 1989-90, Pres. award 1990), Tex. Vet. Med. Assn. (chmn. equine practice com. 1986-87, co-chmn. conv. com. 1989-90, Veterinarian of the Yr. Distng. Achievement award 1988, elected to soc. phi zeta, alternate del., 1991, del. ho. of del. 1992—, chair animal welfare task force, 1991-93, Pres. award 1992), Delta Soc., Brazos County A&M Club (pres. 1986-87), Nat. Cap A&M Club (Washington) (pres. 1973-74, area 26 rep. assn. former student coun., 1993—), mem. aggic hostel com., 1990-94, Yell Leader Agt. 1994—), Masons, Lions (songleader, bd. dirs., chmn. Tex. Lions Camp com., sec. treas. sight first campaign, Melvin James award 1994). Republican. Methodist. Avocations: gardening, racquetball, jogging, tennis, reading. Office: Tex Vet Med Diagnostic Lab PO Box 3040 College Station TX 77841-3040

WEST, JOHN BURNARD, physiologist, educator; b. Adelaide, Australia, Dec. 27, 1928; came to U.S., 1969; s. Esmond Frank and Meta Pauline (Spehr) W.; m. Penelope Hall Banks, Oct. 28, 1967; children: Robert Burnard, Joanna Ruth. M.B.B.S., Adelaide U., 1951, M.D., 1958, D.Sc., 1980; Ph.D., London U., 1960; Dr. honoris causa, U. Barcelona, Spain, 1987. Resident Royal Adelaide Hosp., 1952, Hammersmith Hosp., London 1953-55; physiologist Sir Edmund Hillary's Himalayan Expdn., 1960-61; dir. respiratory research group Postgrad. Med. Sch., London, 1962-67; reader medicine Postgrad. Med. Sch., 1968; prof. medicine and physiology U. Calif. at San Diego, 1969—; Wiltshire lectr., London, 1977, Schwidetzky lectr., 1975, Fleischner lectr., 1977, Robertson lectr. Adelaide U., 1978; leader Am. Med. Rsch. Expdn. to Mt. Everest, 1981; U.S. organizer China-U.S. Conf. on respiratory failure, Nanjing, 1986; mem. life scis. adv. com. NASA, 1988-89, task force sci. uses of space sta., 1984-87, aerospace med. adv. com., 1988-89, chmn. sci. verification com. Spacelab SLS-1, 1983-92; prin. investigator, Spacelabs SLS 1, 2, LMS, Neurolab, 1983—; co-investigator European Spacelabs 5, D2, Euromir 1987—; mem. commn. on respiratory physiol., 1985—; mem. commn. on clin. physiol., 1991—, mem. commn. gravitation physiol., 1986—; mem. U.S. nat. com. Internat. Union Physiol. Scis., 1984-87; mem. study sect. NIH, chmn., 1973-75; external examiner Nat. U. Singapore, 1995. Author: Ventilation/Blood Flow and Gas Exchange, 1965, Respiratory Physiology-The Essentials, 1974, Translations in Respiratory Physiology, 1976, Pulmonary Pathophysiology-The Essentials, 1977, Translations in Respiratory Physiology, 1977, Bioengineering Aspects of the Lung, 1977, Regional Differences in the Lung, 1977, Pulmonary Gas Exchange (2 vols.), 1980, High Altitude Physiology, 1981, High Altitude and Man, 1984, Everest-The Testing Place, 1985, Best and Taylor's Physiological Basis of Medical Practice, 1985, 91, Study Guide for Best and Taylor, 1985, High Altitude Medicine and Physiology, 1989, The Lung: Scientific Foundations, 1991, Lung Injury, 1992. Recipient Ernest Jung prize for medicine, Hamburg, 1977, Presdl. citation Am. Coll. Chest Physicians, 1977, Reynolds Prize for history Am. Physiol. Soc., 1987; I.J. Flance lectr. Washington U., 1978; G.C. Griffith lectr. Am. Heart Assn., 1978; scholar Macy Found., 1974; Kaiser teaching award 1980; W.A. Smith lectr. Med. Coll. S.C., 1982; S. Kronheim lect. Undersea Med. Soc., 1984; D.W. Richards lectr. Am. Heart Assn., 1980, E.M. Papper lectr. Columbia U., 1981, I.S. Ravdin lectr. ACS, 1982, Burns Amberson lectr. Am. Thoracic Soc., 1984, Harry G. Armstrong lectr. Aerospace Med. Assn., 1984, Annual Space Life Scis. lectr. Federation Associated Socs. of Experimental Biology, 1991, Hermann Rahn lectr. SUNY Buffalo, 1992, Menkes lectr. Johns Hopkins, 1992, Jeffries Med. Rsch. award Am. Inst. Aeronautics and Astronautics, 1992; Mcleod lectr. Macallum lectr. U. Toronto, Can., 1989, Southampton U., U.K., 1990, Blatto lectr. U. Philippines, Manila, 1990, Mohaideen lectr. Long Is. Coll., Brooklyn, 1993, Bullard lectr. Uniformed Svcs. U., Bethesda, Md., 1993. Fellow Royal Coll. Physicians (London), Royal Australasian Coll. Physicians, Royal Geog. Soc. (London), AAAS (med. sci. nominating com. 1987-93, coun. del. sect. med. scis.), Am. Inst. for Med. and Biol. Engring. (founder fellow 1992), Internat. Soc. for Mountain Medicine (pres. 1991-94); mem. NAS (com. space biology and medicine 1986-90, subcom. on space biology 1984-85, com. advanced space tech. 1992-94, panel on small spacecraft technology 1994), Nat. Bd. Med. Examiners (physiology test com. 1973-76), Am. Physiol. Soc. (pres. 1984-85, coun. 1981-86, chmn. sect. on history of physiology 1984-92, hist. pubs. adv. com.), Am. Soc. Clin. Investigation, Physiol. Soc. Great Britain, Am. Thoracic Soc., Assn. Am. Physicians, Western Assn. Physicians, Russian Acad Sci. (elected fgn. mem.), Explorers Club, Fleisr Soc. (pres. 1985), Harveian Soc. (London), Royal Instn. Gt. Britain, Hurlingham Club (London), La Jolla Beach & Tennis Club. Home: 9626 Blackgold Rd La Jolla CA 92037-1110 Office: U Calif San Diego Sch Medicine 0623 Dept Medicine La Jolla CA 92093

Funds, All Asia Funds; bd. dir., chmn. Seibels Bruce Group, Inc.; adv. bd. Donaldson, Lufkin & Jenrette, Inc. Trustee Presbyn. Coll., So. Center Internat. Studies. Maj. AUS, 1942-46. Decorated Army Commendation medal; comdr. Order of Merit (W. Ger.), Freedom award S.C. C. of C. Mem. Phi Beta Kappa. Democrat. Presbyterian. Address: PO Drawer 13 Hilton Head Island SC 29938

WEST, JOHN MERLE, retired physicist, nuclear consultant; b. Stilwell, Okla., Jan. 18, 1920; s. James M. and Maude B. (Bacon) W.; m. Navlion F. Farmer, Oct. 5, 1945; children: J. Cornel L. Clark. BS in Phys. Sci. and Math. with highest honors, Northeastern State U., 1939; MS in Physics, U. Iowa, 1941. Physicist, supr. Du Pont Co., Carney's Point, N.J., 1941-42, Pryor, Okla., 1942-43; physicist, supr. U. Chgo. Manhattan Project, 1943-44, Hanford Works Manhattan Project, 1944-46, GE, Hanford Works, Richland, Wash., 1946-49; asst. dir. reactor engring., project mgr. Argonne Nat. Lab., Lemont, Ill., 1949-57; exec. v.p. Gen. Nuclear Engring. Corp., Dunedin, Fla., 1957-65; v.p. nuclear activities Combustion Engring. Inc., Windsor, Conn., 1965-84; sr. v.p. Nuclear Combustion Engring. Inc., Windsor, Conn., 1984-85; nuclear cons., Cape Coral, Fla., 1985—. Contbr. numerous articles to profl. jours.; papers at profl. meetings; holder numerous patents. Recipient Charles Coffin award GE, 1949. Fellow Am. Nuclear Soc. (charter mem., Walter Zinn award 1983); mem. NAE, Engrs. Club. Republican. Presbyterian. Home and Office: 1608 SE 40th Ter Cape Coral FL 33904-7467

WEST, JOHN THOMAS, surgeon; b. Live Oak, Fla., June 23, 1924; s. James Whitaker and Lelah Eulalia (Moore) W.; m. Ruth Marit Blakely, June 18, 1948; children: Phyllis Ann, Rebecca Ruth, James Carl, Jeffrey Moore, Paul Blakely. BS, U. Mich., 1946; MD, Vanderbilt U., 1951. Diplomate Am. Bd. Surgery. Commd. officer USPHS, 1951, advanced through grades to capt., 1963; rotating intern USPHS Hosp., Seattle, 1951-52; chief surgery USPHS Alaska Native Hosp., Anchorage, 1957-60, resident gen. surgery, 1954-57; chief surgery USPHS Hosp., Seattle, 1963-69, USPHS Indian Hosp., Phoenix, 1969-71; sr. investigator surg. br. Nat. Cancer Inst., USPHS, Bethesda, Md., 1960-63; ret., 1971; clin. assoc. prof. Tex. Tech U., Lubbock, 1974-77; pvt. practice La Grange, Ga., 1971-74, 77-94; ret., 1994; mem. active staff West Ga. Med. Ctr., La Grange, 1971-74, 77-94. Bd. dirs. Ga. divsn. Am. Cancer Soc., 1972-77, 77-92. Recipient Meritorious Svc. medal USPHS, 1968. Fellow ACS, Soc. Surg. Oncology. Presbyterian. Achievements include report of facilitation of major hepatic resection by an innovation in the surgical exposure of the liver. Home: 134 Hickory Ln La Grange GA 30240-8622

WEST, LEE ROY, federal judge; b. Clayton, Okla., Nov. 26, 1929; s. Calvin and Nicie (Hill) W.; m. MaryAnn Ellis, Aug. 29, 1952; children: Kimberly Ellis, Jennifer Lee. B.A., U. Okla., 1952, J.D., 1956; LL.M. (Ford Found. fellow), Harvard U., 1963. Bar: Okla. 1956. Individual practice law Ada, Okla., 1956-61, 63-65; faculty U. Okla. Coll. Law, 1961-62; Ford Found. fellow in law teaching Harvard U., Cambridge, Mass., 1962-63; judge 22d Jud. Dist. Okla., Ada, 1965-73; mem. CAB, Washington, 1973-78; acting chmn. CAB, 1977; practice law Tulsa, 1978-79; spl. justice Okla. Supreme Ct., 1965; judge U.S. Dist Ct. (we. dist.) Okla., 1979—. Editor: Okla. Law Rev. Served to capt. USMC, 1952-54. Mem. U. Okla. Alumni Assn. (dir.), Phi Delta Phi (pres. 1956), Phi Eta Sigma, Order of Coif. Home: 6500 E Danforth Rd Edmond OK 73034-7601 Office: US Dist Ct 3001 US Courthouse 200 NW 4th St Oklahoma City OK 73102-3003

WEST, LINDA LEA, administrator; b. Sparta, Wis., Oct. 5, 1943; d. Larry C. and Florance M. (Haskell) Lomax; m. Thomas C. West, Aug. 29, 1964; children: Timothy C., Daniel H., Deborah R. AB magna cum laude, Occidential Coll., 1965; MLS, UCLA, 1966. Cert. preliminary adminstrv. svcs.; cert. tchr. Calif. Libr. young adult L.A. Pub. Libr., 1966-67; libr. edn., psychology Humbolt State Coll. Libr., Arcata, Calif., 1967-68; reference libr. Monterey (Calif.) Bay Area Coop. Libr., 1969-70; instr. Hacienda La Puente & El Monte (Calif.) Adult Edn., 1976-78; instr., curriculum writer Indochinese RAP, Hacienda La Puente (Calif.) Sch. Dist., 1978-81, coord. refugee project, 1981-88; instr. adult edn. UCLA Extension, 1988—; resource tchr. Baldwin Park (Calif.) Adult Sch., 1988-90; archives mgr. Outreach & Tech. Assistance Network Hacienda La Puente Sch. Dist., 1990—; cons. in field. Comtbr. articles to profl. jours. Jr. troop leader Girl Scouts Am., West Covina, Calif., 1985-88. Mem. ALA, AAUW, Am. Assn. Adult Continuing Edn., Am. Vocat. Assn., Calif. Tchrs. English to Speakers Other Langs. (asst. adult level chmn. 1985-86, adult level chmn. 1986-87), Calif. Coun. Adult Edn., Calif. Libr. Assn., Calif. Tchrs. English to Speakers Other Langs., Phi Beta Kappa, Beta Phi Mu, Phi Alpha Theta. Democrat. Episcopalian. Avocations: tennis, tropical fish, choral singing. Home: 912 S Coral Tree Dr West Covina CA 91791 Office: Hacienda La Puente Sch Dist 15377 E Proctor Ave Hacienda Heights CA 91745

WEST, MARJORIE EDITH, elementary education educator; b. Lawrence, Kans., Aug. 18, 1940; d. Merwin Hales and Helen Aletha (Fellows) Wilson Polzin; m. Hammond Dean Watkins, Feb. 17, 1968 (div. 1971); 1 child, Michele Dawn; m. Merlin Avery West, Apr. 2, 1975 (div. 1984). BA in Elem. Edn., U. No. Colo., 1962, MA in Reading, 1970; postgrad., La. State U., 1981-82, U. New Orleans, 1981-82. Cert. tchr., Colo. Tchr. Sch. Dist. 11, Colorado Springs, Colo., 1962-64, Nat. Def. Overseas Teaching Program, Wiesbaden, Fed. Republic Germany, 1964-65, Alaska On-Base Schs., Fairbanks, 1965-66, Great Bend (Kans.) Sch. Dist., 1966-67, Killeen (Tex.) Sch. Dist., 1967-68, Jefferson County Schs., Lakewood, Colo., 1969—. Recipient Alumni Trail Blazer award U. No. Colo., 1988; named Colo. Tchr. of Yr., 1994, finalist Nat. Tchr. of Yr., 1994. Mem. NAFE, AAUW, NEA, PTA (by-laws com. 1989-90, hon. life mem.), Colo. Edn. Assn. (del. to assembly 1985-90), Jefferson County Edn. Assn. (spl. svcs. com. 1989-90), Internat. Reading Assn., Phi Delta Kappa, Pi Lambda Theta, Epsilon Sigma Alpha (etn. chair 1989-90, chair ways and means com. 1990-91, publicity chair 1991-93). Democrat. Avocations: football, travel, golf, reading. Home: 10810 W Exposition Ave Lakewood CO 80226-3818

WEST, MARVIN LEON, managing editor; b. Knoxville, May 1, 1934; s. Alvin Leon and Alma Oneta (Bishop) W.; m. Sarah Jane Blackburn, July 24, 1954; children: Michael, Gary, Jayne, Donna. BA in Journalism, U. Tenn., 1955. Sports writer Knoxville News-Sentinel, Tenn., 1955-80, sports editor, 1980-83, mng. editor, 1983-85; nat. sports editor Scripps Howard News Svc., Washington, 1985-95, mng. editor, 1995—. Named Sportswriter of Yr., Tenn. Nat. Broadcasters and Sports Writers Assn., Salisbury, N.C., 1967, 1974. Mem. U.S. Basketball Writers Assn. (pres. 1983-84). Presbyterian. Avocation: fishing. Home: PO Box 327 Mount Vernon VA 22121-0327 Office: Scripps Howard News Svc 1090 Vermont Ave NW Washington DC 20005-4905

WEST, MICHAEL ALAN, hospital administrator; b. Waseca, Minn., Aug. 4, 1938; s. Ralph Lel and Elizabeth Mary (Brann) W.; m. Mary Thissen, Jan. 21, 1961; children—Anne, Nancy, Douglas. B.A., U. Minn., 1961, M.H.A., 1963. Sales corr. Physicians and Hosps. Supply Co., Mpls., 1959-60; adminstrv. resident R.I. Hosp., Providence, 1962-63; adminstrv. asst. R.I. Hosp., 1963-65, asst. dir., 1965-68; exec. asst. dir. Med. Center U. Mo., Columbia, 1968-70; assoc. dir. Med. Center U. Mo., 1970-74, asst. prof. community health and med. practice, 1968-74; v.p. for adminstrn. Luth. Gen. Hosp., Park Ridge, Ill., 1974-80; exec. v.p. Luth. Gen. Hosp., 1980-84; pres., CEO Akron Gen. Med. Ctr., Ohio, 1984—; bd. dirs. Vol. Hosps. Am. Inc., Emerald Health Network; bd. dirs., chair VHA-Central, Inc. Mem. Am. Coll. Healthcare Execs., Akron Regional Hosp. Assn. (chmn.), Portage Country Club, Akron City Club, Rotary. Home: 495 Woodbury Dr Akron OH 44333-2780 Office: Akron Gen Med Ctr 400 Wabash Ave Akron OH 44307-2433

WEST, MORRIS LANGLO, novelist; b. Melbourne, Australia, Apr. 26, 1916; s. Charles Langlo and Florence Guilfoyle (Hanlon) W.; m. Joyce Lawford, Aug. 14, 1952. BA, U. Melbourne, Australia, 1937; DLitt. (hon.), Santa Clara U., 1968, Mercy Coll., Dobbs Ferry, N.Y., 1982, U. Western Sydney, 1993; DLitt (hon.), Australian Nat. U., Canberra, 1995. Tchr. modern langs. and math New South Wales, Australia and Tasmania, 1933-39; sec. to William Morris Hughes, Prime Minister Australia, 1943; mng. dir. Australian Radio Prodns., 1943-53; publicity mgr. Mudroch Newspaper Chain, Melbourne, Australia, 1945-46; film, drama writer Shell Co. and Australian Broadcasting Network, from 1954. Author: Moon in My Pocket,

1945, Gallows on the Sand, 1955, Kundu, 1956, Children of the Shadows (English title: Children of the Sun), 1957, The Crooked Road (English title: The Big Story), 1957, McCreary Moves In, 1958, Backlash (English title: The Second Victory), 1958, The Devil's Advocate, 1959 (Nat. Brotherhood award Nat. Council Christians and Jews 1960, James Tait Black Meml. award 1960, William Heinemann award Royal Soc. 1959), The Naked Country, 1960, Daughter of Silence, 1961, The Shoes of the Fisherman, 1963 (Bestsellers Paperback of Yr. award 1965), The Ambassador, 1965, Tower of Babel, 1967, (with R. Francis) Scandal in the Assembly, 1970, The Heretic, A Play in Three Acts, 1970, Summer of the Red Wolf, 1971, The Salamander, 1973, Harlequin, 1974, The Navigator, 1976, Proteus, 1979, The Clowns of God, 1981 (Universe Lit. Prize 1981), The World is Made of Glass, 1983, Cassidy, 1986, Masterclass, 1988, Lazarus, 1990, The Ringmaster, 1991, The Lovers, 1993. Served to lt. Australian Imperial Forces, 1939-43, PTO. Recipient Internat. Dag Hammarskjold prize Diplomatic Acad. of Peace (grand collar of merit), 1978. Fellow Royal Soc. Lit., World Acad. Arts and Sci., Order of Australia. Clubs: Royal Prince Alfred Yacht (Sydney, Australia), Australian (Sydney). Office: PO Box 102, Avalon NSW 2107, Australia

WEST, PAUL NODEN, author; b. Eckington, Derbyshire, Eng., Feb. 23, 1930; came to U.S., 1961, naturalized, 1971; s. Alfred Massick and Mildred (Noden) W. Student, Oxford U., 1950-53; MA, Columbia U., 1953. Asst. prof. English Meml. U. Nfld., Can., 1957-58; assoc. prof. Meml. U. Nfld. 1958-60; faculty Pa. State U., 1962-95, prof. English and comparative lit. 1968-95; prof. emeritus, 1995—; Crawshaw prof. Colgate U., 1972; Melvin Hill disting. vis. prof. Hobart and William Smith Colls., 1973; vis. English prof. Cornell U., 1986; disting. writer in residence Wichita State U., 1982; vis. prof. English Brown U., 1992; fiction judge Creative Artists Pub. Svc. Program, N.Y.C., 1974, 81; writer-in-residence U. Ariz., 1984; judge Katherine Ann Porter Prize for Fiction 1984, Artists Found. Author: Byron and the Spoiler's Art, 1960, rev., 1990, I, Said the Sparrow, 1963, The Snow Leopard, 1965, Tenement of Clay, 1965, The Wine of Absurdity, 1966, Alley Jaggers, 1967, I'm Expecting to Live Quite Soon, 1970, Words for a Deaf Daughter, 1970, Caliban's Filibuster, 1971, Beta Lugosi's White Christmas, 1972, Colonel Mint, 1973, Gala, 1976, The Very Rich Hours of Count von Stauffenberg, 1980, Out of My Depths: A Swimmer in the Universe, 1983, Rat Man of Paris, 1986, Sheer Fiction, 1987, The Universe and Other Fictions, 1988 The Place in Flowers Where Pollen Rests, 198, Lord Byron's Doctor, 1989, Portable People, The Women of Whitechapel and Jack the Ripper, 1991 Sheer Fiction: II. 1991, James Ensor, 1991, Love's Mansion, 1992, Tenement of Clay, 2d edit., 1993, Sheer Fiction, III, 1994, A Stroke of Genius, 1995, The Tent of Orange Mist, 1995; contbr. Washington Post and N.Y. Times, 1962—, Harper's Mag., CQ Mag., Paris Rev., Yale Rev.; fiction judge N.Y. Found. for the Arts, Nat. Book Award, 1990. Served with RAF, 1954-57. Recipient Aga Khan Fiction prize, 1973, Hazlett Meml. award for Excellence in Arts (lit.), 1981, Lit. award Am. Acad. and Inst. Arts and Letters, 1985, Pushcart Prize, 1987, 91, The Best Am. Essays award, 1990, Outstanding Achievement medal Pa. State U., 1991, Grand Prix Halpérine Kaminsky award, 1992, Lannan Fiction award, 1993, Tchg. award Northeastern Assn. Grad. Schs., 1994; named Lit. Lion N.Y. Pub. Libr., 1987; Guggenheim fellow, 1963-63; Nat. Endowment for Arts Creative Writing fellow, 1979, 84; nominated for Médicis, Femina and Meilleur Livre Etranger prizes, France, 1991, Lannan Lit. Videos #35. Mem. Authors Guild. Office: Elaine Markson Agy 44 Greenwich Ave New York NY 10011-9999 *The unexamined life may not be worth having, but the examined life is endurable only to an open mind, through which life holistically flows, keeping that mind as incomplete as our knowledge of the universe itself.*

WEST, PHILIP WILLIAM, chemistry educator; b. Crookston, Minn., Apr. 12, 1913; s. William Leonard and Anne (Thompson) W.; m. Tenney Constance Johnson, July 5, 1935 (dec. Feb. 1964); children: Dorothy West/ Farwell, Linda West Gueho (dec.), Patty West Elstrott; m. Foymae S. Kelso, July 1, 1964. B.S., U. N.D., 1935, M.S., 1936, D.Sc. (hon.), 1958; Ph.D., State U. Iowa, 1939; postgrad., Rio de Janeiro, 1946. Chemist N.D. Geol. Survey, 1935-36; research asst. san. chemistry U. Iowa, 1936-37; asst. chemist Iowa Dept. Health, 1937-40; research microchemist Econ. Lab., Inc., St. Paul, 1940; faculty La. State U., 1940-80, prof. chemistry, 1951-80, Boyd prof., 1953-80, emeritus, 1980—; chmn. an. symposium modern methods of analytical chemistry, 1948-65, dir. Inst. for Environmental Scis.,; 1967-80; co-founder, chmn. bd. West-Paine Labs. Inc., Baton Rouge, 1980-93; O. M. Smith lectr. Okla. State U., 1955; vis. prof. U. Colo., 1963, Rand Afrikaans U., 1980; adj. prof. EPA, 1969-80; founder Kem-Tech. Labs., Inc., Baton Rouge, 1954, chmn. bd., 1965-74; co-founder West-Paine Labs., Inc., Baton Rouge, 1978, pres., 1978-93, chmn. bd., lab dir., 1990; mem. 1st working party sci. com. on problems of environment, 1971-74; pres. analytical sect. Internat. Union Pure and Applied Chemistry, 1965-69, mem. sect. indsl. hygiene and toxicology, 1971-73, mem. air quality sect., 1973-75; mem. tech. adv. com. La. Air Pollution Control Com., 1979—; mem. Gov.'s Task Force Environ. Health, 1983-85; mem. sci. adv. bd. EPA, 1983-84; cons. WHO; tech. expert Nat. Bur. Standards Nat. Vol. Lab. Accreditation Program, 1988—; chmn. bd., CEO West & Assoc., Inc., 1992—. Author: Chemical Calculations, 1948, (with Vick) Qualitative Analysis and Analytical Chemical Separations, 2d edit., 1959, (with Bustin) Experience Approach to Experimental Chemistry, 1975; editor: (with Hamilton) Science of the Total Environment, 1973-78, (with Macdonald) Analytica Chimica Acta, 1959-78, Reagents and Reaction for Qualitative Inorganic Analysis; co-editor: Analytical Chemistry, 1963; asst. editor: Mikrochemica Acta, 1952-78, Microchem. Jour, 1957-75; adv. bd.: Analytical Chemistry, 1959-60; publ. bd.: Jour. Chem. Edn, 1954-57; contbr. articles to profl. jours. Recipient Honor Scroll award La. sect. Am. Inst. Chemistry, 1972. Fellow AAAS; mem. Am. Chem. Soc. (Southwest award 1954, Charles E. Coates award 1967, Analytical Chemistry award 1974, award for Creative Advances in Environ. Sci. and Tech.), La. Acad. Sci., Air Pollution Control Assn., Am. Indsl. Hygiene Assn., Austrian Microchem. Soc. (hon.), Soc. of Analysts Eng. (hon.), Internat. Union Pure and Applied Chemistry (pres. commn. 1, pres. analytical div.), Japan Soc. for Analytical Chemistry (hon.), La. Cancer and Health Found., Sigma Xi, Phi Lambda Upsilon, Phi Kappa Phi, Alpha Epsilon Delta, Alpha Chi Sigma, Tau Kappa Epsilon. Office: West-Paine Labs Inc 7979 G S R I Ave Baton Rouge LA 70820-7499

WEST, RALPH LELAND, veterinarian; b. Grand Rapids, Minn., Apr. 23, 1915; s. Ralph Leland and Elsie (Wardall) W.; m. Mary Elizabeth Brann, June 14, 1937; children: Michael Alan, Janet Lee West Friedrich, Thomas James. DVM, Iowa State U., 1936; MS, Purdue U., 1972. Pvt. practice Waseca, Minn., 1936-42, 46-70; grad. asst. Sch. Vet. Medicine Purdue U., West Lafayette, Ind., 1970-72; asst. dir. sci. activities Am. Vet. Med. Assn., Schaumburg, Ill., 1972-77, dir. sci. activities, 1977-87. Contbr. articles to jours. in field. Mem. Pk. Bd., Waseca, 1948-50, Youth Commn., 1948-52; mem., chmn. Waseca Hosp. Bd., 1954-64; trustee Sunny Acres Villas Inc., Denver, 1988—. Maj. U.S. Army, 1942-46, ETO. Recipient Stange award Iowa State U., 1983. Mem. AMVA (award 1990), Am. Assn. Ret. Vets. (dir. 1987-90), Am. Vet. History Soc., Colo. Vet. Med. Assn., Minn. Vet. Med. Assn., Iowa State U. Vet. Alumni Assn., Phi Zeta. Republican. Avocations: reading, bridge, stock market. Home: 1719 E Bijou St Apt 611 Colorado Springs CO 80909-5732

WEST, REXFORD LEON, banker; b. Syracuse, N.Y., Feb. 18, 1938; s. Rexford A. and Nina (Crysler) W.; children: Lisa, Julie, Gregory, Kristen. A.A.S., Auburn Community Coll., N.Y., 1957; B.S. magna cum laude, Syracuse U., N.Y., 1972; Advanced Mgmt. Program, Harvard Bus. Sch., Boston, 1984. Accountant Marine Midland Bank, Syracuse, N.Y., 1959-67, v.p., asst. treas., 1967-72; v.p., controller Marine Midland Services Corp., Buffalo, N.Y., 1972-76; sr. v.p., ops. div. Marine Midland Bank, N.A., Buffalo, N.Y., 1976-77, sr. v.p., sr. ops. officer, 1977-79, exec. v.p., sr. ops. officer, 1979-85, divsn. exec. ops., 1985-87, sector exec. ops. and fin. mgmt., 1987-90, sr. exec. v.p. corp. engrng., 1990-92; exec. v.p. adminstrv. svc. Fleet Bank, Melville, N.Y., 1992-94; exec. v.p. loan servicing Fleet Mortgage Group, Columbia, S.C., 1994—. Served with U.S. Army, 1957-61. Office: Fleet Mortgage Group 1333 Main St Columbia SC 29201

WEST, RICHARD CHARLES, construction company executive; b. Tampa, Fla., June 13, 1945; s. Walter Graham and Helen (Springer) W.; m. Pamela Edds, June 18, 1966; 1 child, Chandra Lorene. B in Bldg. Constrn., U. Fla., 1968. Project mgr. Porfiri Constrn., Miami, Fla., 1970-71, Preston H. Haskell Co., Jacksonville, Fla. 1971-74; sr. project mgr. Ira H. Hardin Co., Atlanta, 1974-81; with McDevitt & Street Co., 1981-85, 86-88; sr. project mgr. Atlanta, 1981-83; v.p. ops. Dallas, 1983, Charlotte, N.C., 1983; sr. v.p.,

div. mgr. Richmond, Va., 1984-85, Atlanta, 1986-88; exec. v.p. A.R. Weeks & Assocs., Atlanta, 1985-86; sr. mgr. Forest City Comml. Co., Inc., Cleve., 1988-89; exec. v.p., ptnr. The C.M. Group, Inc., Atlanta, 1989—. Vol. worker Woodruff Arts Ctr.-Arts Alliance, Atlanta, 1982-86, team capt., 1987. Served to 1st lt. U.S. Army, 1968-70. Mem. Pi Kappa Alpha. Republican. Clubs: Atlanta Athletic. Avocations: golf, tennis, drawing, painting. Home: 568 N Palisades Cir Marietta GA 30067-5114 Office: The C M Group Inc 1303 Hightower Trl Atlanta GA 30350-2919

WEST, RICHARD LUTHER, military association executive, defense consultant, retired army officer; b. Ithaca, N.Y., Jan. 8, 1925; s. Luther W. and Beatrice E. (Ryan) W.; m. June D. Kirby, June 5, 1945; children—John R., Lesley A., Peter L. Student, No. Mich. Coll., 1941-42; B.S., U.S. Mil. Acad., 1945; M.S., Princeton U., 1954; M.S. in Bus. Adminstrn, George Washington U., 1965. Commd. 2d lt. U.S. Army, 1945, advanced through grades to lt. gen., 1977; comptr. of the Army Washington, 1977-81, ret., 1981, cons. def., 1982—; dir. Inst. Land Warfare Assn. U.S. Army, 1988—. Decorated D.S.M., Legion of Merit with 3 oak leaf clusters, Bronze Star, Air medal with 2 oak leaf clusters, Army Commendation medal with oak leaf cluster. Mem. Assn. U.S. Army (v.p. 1992—), Am. Mil. Engrs., Am. Soc. Mil. Comptrs., Am. Def. Preparedness Assn., Sigma Xi. Home: 1509 Laurel Hill Rd Vienna VA 22182-1713

WEST, RICHARD VINCENT, art museum official; b. Prague, Czechoslovakia, Nov. 26, 1934; came to U.S., 1938, naturalized, 1947; s. Jan Josef and Katherine Frieda (Mayer) Vyslouzil; 1 child, Jessica Katherine. Student, UCLA, 1952-55, Music Acad. of the West, 1958-60; BA with highest honors, U. Calif., Santa Barbara, 1961; postgrad., Akademie der Bildenden Kuenste, Vienna, 1961-62, Hochschule fur Musik und darstellende Kuenste, Vienna, 1961-62; MA, U. Calif., Berkeley, 1965. Curatorial intern Cleve. Art Mus., 1965-66, Albright-Knox Art Gallery, Buffalo, 1966-67; curator Mus. Art Bowdoin Coll., Brunswick, Maine, 1967-69, dir., 1969-72; dir. Crocker Art Mus., Sacramento, Calif., 1973-82, Santa Barbara Mus. Art, Calif., 1983-91; pres. Artmuse Assocs., Benicia, Calif., 1991-92; dir. Newport (R.I.) Art Mus., 1992-94, Frye Art Mus., Seattle, 1995—; mem. Joint Yugoslav-Am. Excavations at Sirmium, 1971; bd. dirs. Sacramento Regional Art Coun., 1973-77; bd. overseers Strawbery Banke, 1993—. Author: Painters of the Section d'Or, 1967, Language of the Print, 1968; The Walker Art Building Murals, 1972, Munich and American Realism in the 19th Cen., 1978, An Enkindled Eye: The Paintings of Rockwell Kent, 1985, Standing in the Tempest: Painters of the Hungarian Avant-Garde, 1991, America in Art, 1991, A Significant Story: American Painting and Decorative Arts from the Karolik Collection, 1993; exhbn. catalogues, also various revs. and articles. Active Newport Reading Room; founding mem. New England Community Mus. Consortium. Served with USN, 1956-57. Ford Found. fellow, 1964-65; Smithsonian fellow, 1971. Mem. Am. Assn. Mus., Coll. Art Assn., Internat. Coun. Mus., Western Assn. Art Mus. (pres. 1975-78), Calif. Assn. Mus. (bd. dirs. 1980-82, v.p. 1986-91), Newport Reading Rm., Rotary. Office: Frye Art Mus PO Box 3005 Seattle WA 98114

WEST, ROBERT C., engineering company executive; b. Keytesville, Mo., 1920; BCE, Ga. Inst. Tech., 1949; married. With Sverdrup Corp., St. Louis, 1953—, chief engr., 1967-68, v.p., 1968-69, exec. v.p., 1969-73, chief operating officer, 1973-75, pres., chief exec. officer, 1975-77, chmn. bd., pres., 1977-82, chmn. bd., 1982-88, chmn. emeritus, 1988; bd. dirs. Centerre Bank, St. Louis, Angelica Corp; mem. adv. com. Export-Import Bank U.S. Bd. dirs. St. Louis Region Commerce and Growth Assn., Laclede St. Law, Ranken Tech. Inst.; chmn. bd. Webster U., 1982-87; emeritus bd. dirs. Mo. Goodwill Industries; bd. dirs. St. Louis Area council Boy Scouts Am., now pres. North Cen. Region Nat. Exec. Bd.; mem. nat. adv. bd. Ga. Inst. Tech. Recipient Engr. of Yr. award, 1976, Herbert Hoover medal, 1985; Achievement award medal Engrs. Club St. Louis, 1977; Mo. Honor award for disting. service in engring., 1981; Silver Beaver award Boy Scouts Am., 1985. Registered profl. engr. Fellow Am. Cons. Engrs. Council, ASCE (Profl. Recognition award 1981); mem. Mo. Corp. for Sci. and Tech. (chmn. bd. dirs.). Office: Sverdrup Corp 801 N 11th St Saint Louis MO 63101-1000

WEST, ROBERT COOPER, geography educator; b. Enid, Okla., June 30, 1913; s. George Washington and Elva A. (Cooper) W.; m. Phyllis Devereaux, May 11, 1968. A.B., U. Calif. at Los Angeles, 1935, M.A., 1938; Ph.D., U. Calif. at Berkeley, 1946. Cartographer OSS, Washington, 1941-45; geographer Smithsonian Instn. (Mexico City office), 1946-48; asst. prof. to prof. La. State U. at Baton Rouge, 1948—, Boyd prof., 1970-80, prof. emeritus, 1980—; vis. prof. U. Wis. at Madison, 1966, U. Calif. at Los Angeles, 1968, U. Ariz. at Tucson, 1972, 76. Author: (with others) Middle America, its lands and peoples, 3d edit., 1989, others; vol. editor: (with others) Handbook Middle American Indians, vol. 1, Natural Environment and Early Cultures, 1964, Sonora, Its Geographical Personality, 1993. Recipient Alumni Faculty award La. State U., 1965; Guggenheim fellow, 1955. Mem. A.A.A.S., Assn. Am. Geographers (citation for meritorious contbn. 1964, Outstanding Achievement award 1973), Latin Am. Studies Assn., Conf. Latin Amercanist Geographers, Sigma Xi. Home: 4815 Tulane Dr Baton Rouge LA 70808-4762 Office: Dept Geography and Anthropology La State U Baton Rouge LA 70803

WEST, ROBERT CULBERTSON, chemistry educator; b. Glen Ridge, N.J., Mar. 18, 1928; s. Robert C. and Constance (MacKinnon) W.; children: David Russell, Arthur Scott, Derek. B.A., Cornell U., 1950; A.M., Harvard U., 1952, Ph.D., 1954. Asst. prof. Lehigh U., 1954-56; mem. faculty U. Wis.-Madison, 1956—, prof. chemistry, 1963—, Eugene G. Rochow prof., 1980; adj. prof. So. Oreg. State Coll., 1984—; indsl. and govt. cons., 1961—; Fulbright lectr. Kyoto and Osaka U., 1964-65; vis. prof. U. Würzburg, 1968-69, Haile Selassie I U., 1972, U. Calif.-Santa Cruz 1977, U. Utah, 1981, Inst. Chem. Physics Chinese Acad. Sci., 1984, Justus Liebig U., Giessen, Fed. Republic Germany, U. Estadual de Campinas, Brazil, 1989; Abbott lectr. U. N.D., 1964, Seydel-Wooley lectr. Ga. Inst. Tech., 1970, Sun Oil lectr. Ohio U., 1971, Edgar C. Britton lectr. Dow, Midland, Mich., 1971, Jean Day Meml. lectr. Rutgers U., 1973; Japan Soc. for Promotion Sci. vis. prof. Tohoku U., 1976, Gunma U., 1987; Lady Davis vis. prof. Hebrew U., 1979; Cecil and Ida Green honors prof. Tex. Christian U., 1983; Karcher lectr. U. Okla., 1986; Broberg lectr. N.D. State U., 1986; Xerox lectr. U. B.C., 1986, McGregory lectr. Colgate U., 1988; Lady Davis vis. prof. Technion Israel Inst. Tech., 1990; Humboldt prof. Tech. U. Munich, Fed. Republic Germany, 1990; George W. Watt lectr. U. Tex., Austin, 1992; vis. prof. U. Estadual de Campinas, Brazil, 1993; Dozor vis. fellow Ben Gurion U. of the Negev, Israel, 1993. Co-editor: Advances in Organometallic Chemistry, Vols. I-XXXVI, 1964—, Organometallic Chemistry--A Monograph Series, 1968—; contbr. articles to profl. jours. Pres. Madison Community Sch., 1970-81; founder, bd. dirs. Women's Med. Fund, 1971—; nat. bd. dirs. Zero Population Growth, 1980-86; bd. dirs., v.p. Protect Abortion Rights Inc., 1980; lay minister Prairie Unitarian Universalist Soc., 1982. Recipient F.S. Kipping award, 1970; Outstanding Sci. Innovator award Sci. Digest, 1985; Chem. Pioneering award Am. Inst. Chemists, 1988; Wacker Silicon prize, 1989; Humboldt U.S. Scientist award, 1990. Mem. Am. Chem. Soc., Chem. Soc. (London), Japan Chem. Soc., AAAS, Wis. Acad. Sci. Home: 305 Nautilus Dr Madison WI 53705-4333

WEST, ROBERT MACLELLAN, science education consultant; b. Appleton, Wis., Sept. 1, 1942; s. Clarence John and Elizabeth Ophelia (Moore) W.; m. Jean Sydow, June 19, 1965; 1 child, Christopher. BA, Lawrence Coll., 1963; SM, U. Chgo., 1964, PhD, 1968. Rsch. assoc. Princeton (N.J.) U., 1968-69; asst. prof. Adelphi U., Garden City, N.Y., 1969-74; curator of geology Milw. Pub. Mus., 1974-83; dir. Carnegie Mus. Natural History, Pitts., 1983-87, Cranbrook Inst. Sci., Bloomfield Hills, Mich., 1987-91; prin. RMW Sci. Action, Washington, 1992—; CEO Informal Sci., Inc., Washington, 1993—; adj. prof. U. Wis., Milw., 1974-83; comm. mem. Indo-U.S. Subcom., 1990—. Contbr. articles to profl. jours. Bd. dirs. Friends of the New Zoo, Pitts., 1984-87; treas. East Mich. Environ. Action Coun., Birmingham, Mich., 1987-92. Recipient Arnold Guyot prize Nat. Geographic Soc., 1982; named Man of Yr. in Sci. by Vectors Pitts., 1988; NSF fellow, 1968; NSF rsch. grantee, 1970-80, Nat. Geographic Soc. rsch. grantee, 1973, 76, 77, 79, 80, 82. Mem. Nat. Coun. Sci. Edn. (bd. dirs. 1984-88, 92—), Nepal Natural History Soc. (advisor 1992—), Soc. Vertebrate Paleontology, Geol. Soc. Am., Paleontology Soc., Am. Soc. Mammalogists, Am. Assn. Mus., Rotary. Avocations: history, sports. Office: Informal Sci Inc PO Box 42328 Washington DC 20015-0928

WEST, ROBERT VAN OSDELL, JR., retired petroleum executive; b. Kansas City, Mo., Apr. 29, 1921; s. Robert Van Osdell and Josephine (Quistgaard) W.; divorced; children: Robert Van Osdell III, Kathryn Anne, Suzanne Small, Patricia Lynn; m. Helen L. Boecking, 1978. BS, U. Tex., 1942, MS, 1943, PhD, 1949. Registered profl engr. Tex. Petroleum engr. Slick Urschel Oil Co., 1949-56; pres. Slick Secondary Recovery Corp., 1956-59; v.p. Texstar Corp., 1959; pres. Texstar Petroleum Co. subs. Texstar Corp., 1959-64; founder Tesoro Petroleum Corp., San Antonio, 1964, chmn. bd. dirs., chief exec. officer, 1971-88, chmn. bd., 1989-92; chief executive officer Tesoro Petroleum Corp., 1964-92; bd. dirs. Frost Nat. Bank. Mem. engring. found. adv. coun. U. Tex., mem. at large and life Centennial Commm.; former bd. visitors McDonald Obs. and Astronomy; mem. devel. bd. U. Tex. San Antonio Health Sci. Ctr.; assoc. mem. bd. visitors U. Tex. M.D. Anderson Cancer Ctr., Houston; Trinity U. Assoc., San Antonio; mem. adv. coun., trustee St. Mary's U. Sch. Bus.; past trustee San Antonio City Public Service Bd.; trustee S.W. Research Inst.; past chmn. San Antonio Econ. Devel. Found.; bd. dirs. World Affairs Council, San Antonio; chmn. St. Luke's Luth. Hosp. Found., San Antonio; emeritus chmn. bd. trustees San Antonio Symphony; founder, former chmn. bd. dirs Tiwanaku Archaeol. Found., Bolivia.; founder, former chmn. exec. com. Caribbean/L.Am. Action, Washington; trustee Ams. Soc. N.Y.; chmn. gen. campaign United Way of San Antonio and Bexar County, 1986, vice chmn. bd. trustees, 1988—; chmn. pub. sector campaign subcom. United Way of Am., 1988—. Named Disting. Grad., U. Tex. Coll. Engring., 1973; recipient People of Vision award Nat. Soc. Prevention of Blindness, 1982, Internat. Citizens award World Affairs Coun., 1986, Good Scout award Boy Scouts Am., 1987, Alexis de Tocqueville award United Way of San Antonio and Bexar County, 1990. Mem. Ind. Petroleum Assn. Am., Soc. Petroleum Engrs. (past chmn. San Antonio-Austin chpt.), 25 Yr. Club Petroleum Industry, Pvt. Enterprise Edn. (Herman W. Lay Meml. award 1986), Am.'s Soc., All-Am. Wildcatters Club, Sigma Chi (Significant Sig award 1979). Episcopalian. Office: 1250 NE Loop 410 Ste 805 San Antonio TX 78209

WEST, ROBERTA BERTHA, writer; b. Saline County, Mo., Sept. 7, 1904; d. Robert and Amanda Melvina (Driver) Baur; m. Harold Clinton West, Aug. 27, 1932; children: Arle Faith W. Lohof, Lydia Ann (Lyda) F.H. Hyde, Danna Rose F.H. Burns. AB, William Jewell Coll., 1928; AM, U. Mo., 1930. Cert. tchr., Mo., Mont. Elem. and secondary sch. tchr. Mo. and Mont. Schs., 1922-47; supt. schs. Hogeland (Mont.) Schs., 1947-48, 55; prof. fgn. langs. Will Mayfield Coll., Marble Hill, Mo., 1930; columnist Quad County Star, Viburnum, Mo., 1982—; writer and researcher ch. history, 1964-91; cons. Yellowstone Conf. Meth. Ch.; compiler Mont. list of Meth. Mins. 1784-1984. Author: Northern Montana Methodist History, 3 vols., 1974, Faith, Hope and Love in the West, 1971; editor: Brother Van by Those Who Knew Him, 1975, reprinted, 1989;; also contbr. articles. Recipient 1st John M. Templeton prize, 1959. Democrat. Avocation: crocheting. Home: PO Box 583 Viburnum MO 65566 Office: Quad County Star Viburnum MO 65566

WEST, RUTH TINSLEY, lawyer; b. Scranton, Pa., Mar. 4, 1945; d. Joseph Woodford and Martha McLendon (Ross) W.; children: Bowman Staples Garrett, III, McLendon West Garrett. BA in Polit. Sci., Duke U., 1966; JD, Mercer U., 1974. Bar: Ga. Claims adjuster Aetna Casualty & Surety, 1966-67, Liberty Mut. Ins. Co., 1967-68; methods analyst Am. Cyanamid Co., 1968-69; ptnr. King & Spalding, Atlanta, 1980—. Editor-in-chief Mercer Law Rev. Bd. visitors Walter F. George Sch. Law Mercer U., 1979-80, sec. bd. visitors, 1980-81, chmn. bd. visitors, 1981-82, bd. visitors, 1987. Mem. Atlanta YMCA, 1988-90, Nexus Contemporary Art Ctr., 1983-93, New Visions Gallery, 1987-89, Ga. Justice Project, 1989—, Pro-Choice, 1990—, Mercer Univ. Press, 1991—, Atlanta Women's Fund, 1993—; participant Leadership Ga., 1981, Leadership Atlanta, 1986-87, exec. com., 1991-92; mem. Commerce Club, 1987—; trustee Ga. Ctr. for Children, 1994—. Mem. ABA (tax-exempt fin. sect. taxation com. 1978—), State Bar Ga. (pub. com. 1976-78, long range planning com. 1978-86, Legal Aid com. 1979-80, editor newsletter younger lawyers sect. 1976-78, dir. 1978-79), Atlanta Bar Assn. (dir. 1985-86, chmn. minority clerkship program 1985-87, adv. bd. 1989—), Bond Attys. Workshop (chmn. 1978-79, steering com. 1977-78, 85-86, instr. 1979-89), Nat. Assn. Bond Lawyers (dir. 1977-80, treas. 1978-80, instr. fundamentals mcpl. bonds 1980, chmn. legis. seminar 1987), Lawyers Club Atlanta (treas. 1983-85, sec. 1986-87, exec. com. 1983-89), Ga. Bar Found., Inc. (trustee 1993), Mercer U. Alumni Assn. (sec. 1982-83, v.p. 1983-84, pres.-elect 1984-85, pres. 1985-86), Phi Alpha Delta. Democrat. Episcopalian. Avocations: outsider folk art, travel. Home: 245 Peachtree Cir NE Atlanta GA 30309-3206 Office: King & Spalding 191 Peachtree St Atlanta GA 30303

WEST, STEPHEN ALLAN, lawyer; b. Salt Lake City, Mar. 23, 1935; s. Allan Morrell and Ferne (Page) W.; m. Martha Sears, Mar. 21, 1960; children: Stephen Allan, Jr., Page, Adam. JD, U. Utah, 1961, BS in Philosophy, 1962. Law clk. to judge U.S. Dist. Ct., Utah, 1961-62; assoc. Marr, Wilkins & Cannon, Salt Lake City, 1962-65; ptnr. Marr, Wilkins & Cannon, 1965-67; atty. Jennings, Strouss, Salmon & Trask, Washington, 1967-68; atty. Marriott Corp., Washington, 1968-71, asst. gen. counsel, 1971-74, v.p. and assoc. gen. counsel, 1974-87, v.p. and dep. gen. counsel, 1987-93; sr. v.p., gen. counsel Marriott Internat., Inc., Washington, 1993-94. Bishop LDS Ch., 1977-81; mem. exec. bd. Interfaith Conf. Met. Washington, 1989-93, vice chmn., 1992-93; mem. exec. bd. Christa McAuliffe Inst. Task Force of Nat. Found. for Improvement Edn. Mem. ABA (exec. coun. young lawyers sect. 1964-65), Utah Bar Assn. (exec. com. young lawyers sect. 1962-67), D.C. Bar Assn., Utah Profl. Rels. Com., U. Utah Aluni Assn. (Disting. Alumni award 1971), Skull and Bones, Owl and Key, Phi Delta Phi, Sigma Chi. Lodges: Skull & Bones, Owl & Key.

WEST, STEPHEN KINGSBURY, lawyer; b. Pittsfield, Mass., Sept. 28, 1928; s. William Bradford and Ruth (Ostyee) W.; m. Ann Wick, Apr. 30, 1955; children: Timothy Wick, Lucy West Engebretson, Todd Kingsbury, Daniel Wick. B.A., Yale U., 1950; LL.B., Harvard U., 1953. Assoc. Sullivan & Cromwell, N.Y.C., 1957-64, ptnr., 1964—; dir. ING Am. Life Ins. Co., Netherlands Ins. Co., Pioneer Mut. Fund, Boston, Aim, Inc., Houston, Winthrop Focus Funds, N.Y.C. Served to 1st lt. inf. U.S. Army, 1953-56. Mem. ABA, N.Y. State Bar Assn., Assn. Bar City N.Y. Office: Sullivan & Cromwell 125 Broad St New York NY 10004-2400

WEST, THOMAS MEADE, insurance company executive; b. Owensboro, Ky., Aug. 15, 1940; s. Frank Thomas and Vivian (Brown) W.; 1 child, Thomas Meade. B.A. cum laude, Vanderbilt U., 1962; M.A. magna cum laude, U. Mich., 1964. Various mgmt. positions Lincoln Nat. Life Ins. Co., Fort Wayne, Ind., 1964-75, v.p., 1975-78, sr. v.p., 1978-81, exec. v.p., 1981-94; pres., CEO Lincoln Nat Reins. Cos.; prin. West Cons. Corp.; bd. dirs. Union Fed. Savs. Bank of Indpls. Area pres. Boy Scouts Am., Ind.; dir. Jr. Achievement, Ft. Wayne. With U.S. Army, 1964-66. Fellow Soc. of Actuaries; mem. Am. Acad. Actuaries, Fort Wayne C. of C. (bd. dirs.). Presbyterian. Home: 6914 Woodcroft Ln Fort Wayne IN 46804

WEST, TOGO DENNIS, JR., secretary of Army, former aerospace executive; b. Winston-Salem, N.C., June 21, 1942; s. Togo Dennis and Evelyn (Carter) W.; m. Gail Estelle Berry, June 18, 1966; children: Tiffany Berry, Hilary Carter. BSEE, Howard U., 1965, JD cum laude, 1968. Bar: D.C. 1968, N.Y. 1969, U.S Ct. Mil. Appeals 1969, U.S. Supreme Ct. 1978, U.S. Ct. Claims 1981. Elec. engr. Duquesne Light and Power Co., 1965; patent researcher Sughrue, Rothwell, Mion, Zinn and McPeak, 1966-67; legal intern U.S. EEOC, 1967; law clk. firm Covington & Burling, Washington, 1967-68; summer assoc. Covington & Burling, 1968, assoc. 1973-75, 76-77; law clk. to judge U.S. Dist. Ct. for So. Dist. N.Y., 1968-69; assoc. dep. atty. gen. U.S. Dept. Justice, Washington, 1975-76; gen. counsel Dept. Navy, Washington, 1977-79; spl. asst. to sec. and dep. sec. Dept. Def., Washington, 1979-80, gen. counsel, 1980-81; ptnr. Patterson, Belknap, Webb & Tyler, Washington, 1981-90; sr. v.p. govt. rels. Northrop Corp, Washington, 1990-93; sec. of Army, Washington, 1993—; adj. prof. Duke U. Sch. Law, 1980-81; bd. cons. Riggs Nat. Bank, Washington, 1990-93. Mng. editor: Howard Law Jour, 1968. Commr. D.C. Law Rev. Comm., 1982-89, chmn., 1985-89; mem. Nat. Council of Friends of John F. Kennedy Ctr. for Performing Arts, 1984-91, treas., 1987-91; bd. govs. Antioch U. Sch. Law, 1983-87, vice chmn., 1986-87; chmn. Greater Washington Bd. Trade, legis. bur., 1987-89, bd. dirs., 1987-93, mem. exec. com. 1987-92; mem. fed. legis. com., 1990-93; chmn. Kennedy Ctr. Community and Friends Bd., 1991—; mem. Washington

Lawyers' Com. Civil Rights Under Law, 1987-93, D.C. Com. on Pub. Edn., 1988-93, chmn.; 1990-91; trustee The Aerospace Corp., 1983-90, Ctr. for Strategic and Internat. Studies, 1987-90, Nat. Lawyers Com. for Civil Rights Under Law, 1987-93, Inst. for Def. Analyses, 1989-91, Protestant Episcopal Cathedral Found., 1989—, Shakespeare Theatre at The Folger, 1990-93, N.C. Sch. Arts, 1990—, Aerospace Edn. Found. of Air Force Assn., 1991-93; bd. dirs. D.C. Law Students in Ct. Program, 1986-92, World Affairs Coun., 1991-93, Atlantic Coun., 1991-93; mem. fin. com. Episcopal Diocese of Washington, 1989—, mem. standing com., 1990-92; sr. warden St. John's Ch., Lafayette Sq.; chmn. trustee coun. YMCA Metro. Wash., 1990-92; mem. nat. adv. com. UN Assn. USA, 1991-93; D.C. Ct. Appeals Admissions Com., 1990-93.. Served to capt. Judge Adv. Gen. Corps U.S. Army, 1969-73. Decorated Legion of Merit; recipient Disting. Pub. Service medal Dept. Def., 1981, Eagle Scout award with Bronze Palm Boy Scouts Am., 1957, Service to Howard U. award, 1965. Mem. ABA, Nat. Bar Assn., Washington Coun. Lawyers (dir. 1973-75), Sigma Pi Phi, Phi Alpha Delta, Omega Psi Phi, Alpha Phi Omega, Met. Club, Univ. Club (Washington), F St. Club. Democrat. Episcopalian. Clubs: Metropolitan, University (Washington). Democrat. Episcopalian. Office: Office of Sec Army 101 Army Pentagon Washington DC 20310-0101

WEST, W. RICHARD, JR., museum director; b. San Bernardino, Calif., Jan. 6, 1943; s. W. Richard Sr. and Maribelle (McCrea) W.; m. Mary Beth Braden, June 29, 1968; children: Amy Elizabeth, Benjamin Braden. BA magna cum laude in Am. History, U. Redlands, 1965; AM in Am. History, Harvard U., 1968; JD, Stanford U., 1971; LHD (hon.), Bacone Coll., 1992, Ottawa U., 1994, U. Okla., 1995. Bar: Calif., D.C., U.S. Ct. Appeals (8th cir.), U.S. Supreme Ct. Clk. to Hon. Benjamin C. Duniway U.S. Ct. Appeals (9th cir.), 1971-72; assoc. Fried, Frank, Harris, Shriver & Jacobson, Washington, 1973-79, ptnr., 1979-88; dir. direct support component Am. Indian Lawyer Tng. Program, Inc., 1976-77; ptnr. Gover, Stetson Williams & West P.C., Albuquerque, 1988-90; founding dir. Smithsonian Instn's Nat. Mus. Am. Indian, Washington, 1990—; treas. Am. Indian Lawyer Tng. Program, Inc., 1973—; adj. prof. Indian law Stanford U., 1977. Mem. edit. bd. Am. Indian Historian, 1969-71; note editor Stanford Law Review, 1970-71; contbr. articles to profl. jours. coord., treas. Native Am. Coun. Regents Inst. Am. Indian Arts, 1975-80; bd. visitors Stanford Law Sch., 1978-81; trustee Phelps Stokes Fund, 1981-87, Bush Found., 1991—, Bacone Coll., 1986-89, chmn., 1989-89, Morning Star Found., 1987-93, U. Redlands, 1991—, alumni bd., 1987-89, Ednl. Found. Am., 1993—; bd. dirs. Amerindian Circle, Inc., 1981-88, Nat. Indian Justice Ctr., 1982-89; cultural edn. com. Smithsonian Inst., 1987-90; nat. support com. Native Am. Rights Fund, 1990—; adv. com. Winslow Found., 1991—; hon. coun. Wings Am., 1993—. Recipient Career Achievement award U. Redlands, 1987, Disting. Svc. award, 1992, award Appreciation and Recognition, Cheyenne and Arapaho Tribes Okla., 1990, Spirit of the People award Okla. Inst. Indian Heritage, 1990; named (with another) Amb. of Yr. Red Earth Indian Ctr. Okla., 1993. Mem. Am. Indian Bar Assn. (charter pres. 1976-77). Mem. Cheyenne and Arapaho Tribes Okla. Home: 3311 Rowland Pl NW Washington DC 20008 Office: Nat Mus of Am Indian 470 L'Enfant Plz Ste 7102 Washington DC 20560

WEST, WILLIAM BEVERLEY, III, lawyer; b. Ft. Worth, Feb. 5, 1922; s. William Beverley Jr. and Ella Louise (Moore) W. B.A., U. Tex., 1942, LL.B., 1948; Indsl. Adminstr., Harvard Grad. Sch. Bus. Adminstrn., 1943; LL.M., Columbia, 1949; grad., Command and Gen. Staff Sch. Bar: Tex. 1949. Practice in Ft. Worth; asst. U.S. atty. No. Dist. Tex., 1953, 1st asst. U.S. atty., 1957-58, U.S. atty., 1958-61; exec. asst. to asst. atty. gen., lands div. Dept. Justice, 1961-63; ptnr. Clark, West, Keller, Butler & Ellis, Dallas, 1963-89, of counsel, 1989—; mem. adv. bd. Southwestern Law Enforcement Inst., Dallas, 1959-82; mem. adv. com. on criminal rules U.S. Jud. Conf., 1973-77; mem. lawyers adv. com. U.S. Ct. Appeals, 5th cir., 1985-87. Bd. dirs. prison ministry Kairos, Inc. of Tex., 1990-93, chmn., 1992; mem. nat. bd. Kairos, Inc., 1991—, sec., 1992—; lay eucharistic min. Episcopalian Ch. Capt. AUS, 1942-46. Decorated Bronze Star. Fellow Tex. Bar Found., Southwestern Legal Found.; mem. ABA (chmn. sect. jud. adinstrn. 1970-71, ho. dels. 1971-74, sect. litigation, co-editor Antitrust Litigator 1988-92), Inst. Jud. Adminstrn. N.Y.C., Nat. Assn. Former U.S. Attys. (bd. dirs. 1990-93), Nat. Inst. for Trial Advocacy (dir. 1970-83), Fed. Bar Assn., Am. Judicature Soc., Ft. Worth Club, City Club (Dallas), Delta Tau Delta, Phi Alpha Delta, Pi Sigma Alpha. Home: 3701 Turtle Creek Blvd Apt 8H Dallas TX 75219-5530 Office: Clark West Keller Butler & Ellis 4800 Renaissance Tower Dallas TX 75270-2146

WESTALL, SANDRA THORNTON, special education educator; b. Rochester, N.Y., Jan. 31, 1940; d. William Heldrith and Janice (King) Thornton; m. Thomas Keith Westall, Jan. 10, 1965 (div. 1980); children: William Thornton, Robert Theodore. AS in Bus., So. Va. Coll. Women, 1962; BA in Early Childhood Edn., Mars Hill Coll., 1982; MA in Spl. Edn., Appalachian State U., 1989; MA in Behavioral Emotional Edn., Western Carolina U., 1990. Cert. tchr. spl. edn., learning disabilities, emotional handicapped, N.C., Fla. Tchr.'s asst. spl. edn. Mitchell County Sch., Spruce Pine, N.C., 1964-70; tchr. Pine Ridge Sch. for Learning Disabilities, Williston, Vt., summer 1985, 88, Summit Acad. for Learning Disabled Students, Waynesville, N.C., 1986-88; resource tchr. Ire B. Jones Elem. Sch. and Asheville Jr. High Sch., N.C., 1988-89; tchr. Irene Worthem Sch. for Severe/Profound Mentally Retarded, Asheville, 1989-90; resource tchr. G. Holmes Braddock High Sch., Miami, Fla., 1990-91, Kelsey L. Pharr Elem. Sch., Miami, 1991-94; tchr. Tyrone Mid. Sch., St. Petersburg, Fla., 1994—; night tchr. Nova U., Ft. Lauderdale, Fla., 1992—, Fla. Meml. Coll., Miami, 1992—; tutor, counselor Black Mountain (N.C.) Correctional Ctr. for Women, 1989-90; trainer behavior disorders No. Colo. U., Breckenridge, 1989, Willie M. Workshop, Asheville, 1989; condr. workshops on left and right brain teaching, 1980-87; speaker on learning disabled adults Harvard U., 1989; tchr. day camps for handicapped students, 1983, 84; advocate for learning disabled students and adults; del. Citizen Amb. Program field of learning disabilities, Diagnostic Ctr., various schs., Vilnius, Siauliai Pedagogical Inst., Dept. Spl. Pedagogics, Lithuania, inst. Defectology, Russian Acad. Pedagogical, Moscow, City Coun., Inst. Econ. Problem Studies, St. Petersburg, Russia, 1993. Vol. Dade County Helpline and Dade County Schs. (in aid of Hurricane Andrew victims), swimming courses for ARC, 1980—; bd. dirs. N.C. Advocacy Ctr. for Children's Edn. and Parent Tng., 1986-90. Grantee Creative Learning for Behavior Handicapped Students, 1989; honoree ARC, 1980. Mem. Am. Coun. on Rural Spl. Edn., Assn. for Children and Adults with Learning Disabilities, The Orton Dyslexia Soc., Coun. for Exceptional Children, Coun. for Behavior Emotionally Handicapped Children. Episcopalian. Avocations: teaching, swimming, drawing, attending flea markets. Home: 540 Carillon Pky Apt 1071 Saint Petersburg FL 33716 Office: Tyrone Mid Sch 6421 22nd Ave N Saint Petersburg FL 33710

WESTBERG, ROBERT MYERS, lawyer; b. Seattle, July 12, 1932; s. Alfred John and Jean Jackson (Myers) W.; m. Nancy Lyon, June 18, 1955; children: R. Britt, Jennifer J., Catherine C. Student, Princeton U., 1950-53; LL.B., U Wash., 1956. Bar: Calif. 1957, Wash. 1957, D.C. 1981, N.Y. 1983. Ptnr. Pillsbury, Madison & Sutro, San Francisco, 1957—. Bd. dirs. Legal Aid Soc. San Francisco, 1972—. Mem. State Bar Calif., Wash. State Bar Assn., D.C. Bar Assn. Democrat. Episcopalian. Club: Princeton of N.Y. Office: Pillsbury Madison & Sutro 225 Bush St San Francisco CA 94104-4207

WESTBERRY, BILLY MURRY, lawyer; b. Georgetown, La., Nov. 5, 1926; s. Iley Donley and Julia Frances (Thornton) W.; m. Nancy Elizabeth Kent, Aug. 7, 1953; children—Robert Kent, William Bishop. Student, Murray (Ky.) State U., 1946-48; LL.B., U. Louisville, 1950. Bar: Ky. 1950. Since practiced in Marion; county atty. Crittenden County, 1954-62, 1967-73; city atty. Marion, 1965-67; partner firm Westberry & Roberts, 1968—; chmn. Jud. Ethics Com. Ky., 1979—; mem. Ky. Commn. Law Enforcement and Crime Prevention, 1968—. Served with USAAF, 1944-45; Served with USAF, 1951-53. Mem. Am. Bar Assn., Ky. Bar Assn. (pres. 1978-79), Crittenden County Bar Assn., Am. Legion. Republican. Episcopalian. Clubs: Rotary, Shriners. Home: 125 Brookfield Paducah KY 42001 Office: 113 S 4th St Paducah KY 42001

WESTBROOK, DON ARLEN, minister; b. Clinton, N.C., June 2, 1941; s. Ennis and Geneva (Gainey) W.; m. Carrol Ann Holder, Sept. 15, 1963;

children: Felisha Ann, Neal Vance. Student, Logos Bible Coll./Grad. Sch., 1989, Duke Univ. Ordained to ministry Full Gospel Fellowship Chs. and Mins. Internat., 1965. Pastor Bethel Christian Ctr., Durham, N.C., 1969—; v.p. Full Gospel Fellowship Chs. and Mins. Internat., Dallas, 1982—; missionary to India, Nicaragua and Haiti, 1990. Chmn. Concerned Citizens for Moral Govt., Durham, 1989. Home: 4401 B American Dr Durham NC 27705 Office: Bethel Christian Ctr 3518 Rose Of Sharon Rd Durham NC 27712

WESTBROOK, JAMES EDWIN, lawyer, educator; b. Camden, Ark., Sept. 7, 1934; s. Loy Edwin and Helen Lucille (Bethea) W.; m. Elizabeth Kay Farris, Dec. 23, 1956; children: William Michael, Robert Bruce, Matthew David. BA with high honors, Hendrix Coll., 1956; JD with distinction, Duke U., 1959; LLM, Georgetown U., 1965. Bar: Ark. 1959, Okla. 1977, Mo. 1982. Assoc. Mehaffy, Smith & Williams, Little Rock, 1959-62; asst. counsel, subcom. of U.S. Senate Jud. Com., Washington, 1963; legis. asst. U.S. Senate, Washington, 1963-65; asst. prof. law U. Mo. at Columbia, 1965-68, asst. dean, 1966-68, asso. prof., 1968-70, prof., 1970-76, 80—; James S. Rollins prof. law, 1974-76, 80—; Earl F. Nelson prof. law, 1982—, interim dean, 1981-82; dean U. Okla. Coll. Law, Norman, 1976-80; George Allen vis. prof. law, U. Richmond, 1987; vis. prof. law Duke U., 1988; arbitrator on roster of Fed. Mediation and Conciliation Service, 1974—; reporter Mid-Am. Assembly on Role of State in Urban Crisis, 1970; dir. Summer Internship Program in Local Govt., 1968; cons. various Mo. cities on drafting homerule charters; mem. Gov.'s Adv. Council on Local Govt. Law, 1967-68, Fed. Practice Com. U.S. Dist. Ct. (we. dist.) Mo., 1986-90; chmn. Columbia Charter Revision Commn., 1973-74; mem. spl. com. labor relations Mo. Dept. Labor and Indsl. Relations, 1975; mem. Task Force on Gender and Justice, Mo. Jud. Conf., 1990-93; mem. com. to rev. govtl. structure of Boone County, Mo., 1991. Author: (with L. Riskin) Dispute Resolution and Lawyers, 1987, supplement, 1993; contbr. articles to profl. jours. Chair search com. for chancellor U. Mo., Columbia, 1992. Mem. ABA, Mo. Bar Assn. (vice chmn. labor law com. 1986-87, chmn. 1987-88), Nat. Acad. Arbitrators, Assn. Am. Law Schs. (chmn. local govt. law round table coun. 1972), Central States Law Sch. Assn. (pres. 1982-83), Order of Coif, Blue Key, Alpha Chi. Roman Catholic. Home: 3609 Woods Edge Rd Columbia MO 65203 Office: U Mo Sch Law Columbia MO 65211

WESTBROOK, JAY LAWRENCE, law educator; b. Morristown, N.J., Dec. 11, 1943; s. Joel W. and Elaine Frances (Summers) W.; m. Pauline June Travis, Feb. 15, 1969; 1 child, Joel Mastin. BA in Polit. Sci./Philosophy, U. Tex., 1965, JD, 1968. Bar: Tex. 1968, D.C. 1969, U.S. Ct. Appeals (D.C. cir.) 1969, U.S. Supreme Ct. 1976, U.S. Ct. Appeals (4th cir.) 1978, U.S. Ct. Appeals (2d cir.) 1979. Assoc. Surrey & Morse (name now Jones, Day, Reavis, Pogue), Washington, 1969-74; ptnr. Surrey & Morse (name now Jones, Day, Reavis, Pogue, Surrey & Morse), Washington, 1974-80; mem. law faculty U. Tex., Austin, 1980—, Benno C. Schmidt Chair Bus. Law, 1991—; vis. prof. U. London, 1990, Harvard Law Sch., 1991-92; advisor Tex. Internat. Law Jour., 1985-91; reporter Am. Law Inst. Transnat. Insolvency Project, 1994—. Co-author: As We Forgive Our Debtors: Bankruptcy and Consumer Credit in America 1989 (Silver Gravel award ABA 1989), The Law of Debtors and Creditors: Text, Cases and Problems, 2d edit. 1991, Teacher's Manual, The Law of Debtors and Creditors, 2d edit. 1991; contbr. articles to profl. jours. Grantee U. Tex. Law Sch. Found., 1982, U. Rsch. Inst., 1982-83, NSF, 1983-86, Policy Rsch. Inst., Lyndon Johnson Sch. Pub. Affairs, 1984, Tex. Bar Found., 1985, Nat. Inst. Child Health and Human Devel., 1986, Nat. Conf. Bankruptcy Judges, 1991, 93. Mem. ABA (bus. bankruptcy com., internat. bankruptcy subcom., internat. sect., Meyer Rsch. grant 1986), Am. Law Inst., Am. Coll. Bankruptcy, Nat. Bankruptcy Conf., State Bar Tex. (governing coun. internat. sect. 1987-89), Internat. Bar Assn., Internat. Bankruptcy Com. (com. J), Order of the Coif. Office: U Tex Sch Law 727 E 26th St Austin TX 78705-3224

WESTBROOK, JOEL WHITSITT, III, lawyer; b. San Angelo, Tex., June 19, 1916; s. Lawrence Whittington and Minnie Frances (Millspaugh) W.; m. Elaine Frances Summers, Feb. 13, 1943; 1 son, Jay Lawrence. Student, U. Va., 1934-35; B.A., U. Tex., 1937, J.D., 1940. Bar: Tex. 1940. 1st asst. U.S. Atty., San Antonio, 1946-51; 1st asst. dist. atty. Bexar County, San Antonio, 1951-52; dist. atty. pro tem, 1956; pvt.practice San Antonio, 1952-54; partner Trueheart, McMillan, Russell & Westbrook, San Antonio, 1954-61; ptnr. Jones, Boyd, Westbrook & Lovelace, Waco, Tex., 1962-68, Sheehy, Cureton, Westbrook, Lovelace & Nielsen, Waco, 1968-74, Trueheart, McMillan, Westbrook & Hoffman, San Antonio, 1974-80, Westbrook & Goldston, 1980-81, Westbrook Schroeder & Piker, San Antonio, 1981-84; pvt. practice San Antonio, 1984—; adj. prof. criminal law, legal ethics and evidence St. Mary's Sch. Law, San Antonio, 1971-61, 74-76; adj. prof. med. malpractice U. Tex. Law Sch., Austin, 1985, 86. Author: (with others) Texas Torts and Remedies, 1987; contbr. articles to legal and mil. jours. Chmn. San Antonio Crime Prevention Com., 1954-56; pres. Action Planning Coun., Waco, 1966-68; chmn. Waco-McLennan County Mental Health-Mental Retardation Bd. Trustees, 1967-70; pres. adv. bd. Providence Hosp., Waco, 1969-70, Model City com., Waco, 1969-72, chmn., 1971-72. Served to maj., inf. AUS, 1940-46, ETO, MTO. Decorated Combat Inf. badge, Silver Star, Bronze Star, Purple Heart. Fellow Tex. Bar Found. (life sustaining, charter); mem. Waco-McLennan County Bar Assn. (bd. dirs. 1963-66), San Antonio Bar Assn. (pres. 1957-58), State Bar of Tex. (bd. dirs. 1965-68, chmn. com. for local bar svcs 1968-79, chmn. com. for legal svcs to elderly 1976-79, mem. com. for ct. costs and delay 1980-81, mem. coll. bd. 1981-83, vice chmn. membership rels. 1981-83, mem. history and traditions of bar 1983—, chmn. spl. projects), Tex. Assn. Def. Counsel (v.p 1970-71), U. Tex. Law Sch. Alumni Assn. (dir. 1969-72), Mil. Order World Wars (comdr. San Antonio chpt. 1952-53), Delta Theta Phi, Sigma Alpha Epsilon. Episcopalian. Clubs: Giraud (San Antonio); Army-Navy (Washington). Episcopalian. Home: 7709 Broadway St Apt 208 San Antonio TX 78209-3203 *I have expected responsibility in others, and I have wanted others to expect responsibility in me.*

WESTBROOK, NICHOLAS KILMER, museum administrator, historian; b. Boston, July 10, 1948; s. Jack Hall and Elizabeth (Kirkland) W.; m. Virginia Lee Macleod, June 12, 1971; children: Benjamin Macoun, Samuel Farley. AB cum laude, Amherst Coll., 1971; MA, U. Conn., 1973; postgrad., U. Pa., 1973-76. Seasonal ranger-historian Nat. Park Svc., Stillwater, N.Y., 1969-71; asst. to v.p. for interpretation Old Sturbridge Village, Sturbridge, Mass., 1972-75; ednl. materials developer Uni-Coll Corp., Phila., 1975-76; exhibits coord. Minn. Hist. Soc., St. Paul, 1976-78, curator of exhibits, 1978-88; exec. dir. Ft. Ticonderoga, Ticonderoga, N.Y., 1989—; panelist NEH, Washington, 1985—, Inst. Mus. Svcs., Washington, 1991—; bd. dirs. N.Y. State Mil. Heritage Mus. Editor: Industrial Archeology of the Twin Cities, 1983, Bull. Ft. Ticonderoga Mus., 1991—; book rev. editor Indsl. Archeology, 1983-89; curator several exhibits. Trustee Fedn. for Hist. Svcs., 1990—, treas., 1992—; bd. dirs. Mohican Coun. Boy Scouts Am. Winston Churchill travelling fellow Gt. Britain, 1981, Andrew W. Mellon fellowship, 1995. Mem. Soc. for Indsl. Archeology (bd. dirs. 1983-85, sec. 1986-91), Am. Assn. for State and Local History, Am. Assn. Mus., Soc. for Indsl. Archeology, Soc. for History of Tech., Am. Printing History Assn., Ticonderoga C. of C. (v.p. 1989—), Kiwanis, Antiquarian Soc. Presbyterian. Avocation: letterpress printing. Home: Creek Rd Box 8 Crown Point NY 12928 Office: Ft Ticonderoga Fort Rd Ticonderoga NY 12883

WESTBROOK, T. L., bishop. Bishop of Wash. Ch. of God in Christ, Spanaway. Office: Ch of God in Christ 1256 176th St Spanaway WA 98387-7901

WESTBROOKS, ALPHONSO, public relations executive; b. Memphis, May 30, 1934; s. Al Sr. and Erma (Bowen) W.; m. Alice Malcolm Moore, Aug. 3, 1956; children: Alicia J., Aricka M., Alpha D. Student, Tallacega Coll., 1953; BJ, Lincoln U., 1956; MA in Communications, U. Chgo. 1958. Ordained to ministry Ch. of God in Christ: Market rsch. dir. Johnson Pub. Co., Chgo. 1958-59; divsn. supt. Commonwealth Edison, Chgo., 1961-90; dir. pub. rels. Ch. of God in Christ, Chgo., 1990—. Officer DuSable Mus. of African Am. History, Chgo., 1983—, Chgo. Boys and Girls Club, 1985—; mem. Operation PUSH; trustee St. Paul Ch. of God in Christ, Chgo. Lt. U.S. Army, 1959-61. Named Robert S. Abbot scholar Lincoln U., 1953. Mem. Chgo. Urban League, Omega Psi Phi. Democrat. Avocations: golf, tennis, stamp collecting. Home: 9357 S Pleasant Chicago IL 60620

WESTBY, ARMIN, clergy member, church administrator. Exec. dir. Home Missions of the Church of the Lutheran Brethren of America, Fergus Falls, Minn. Office: Church Lutheran Brethren of Am World Missions 1007 Westside Dr Box 655 Fergus Falls MN 56538

WESTCOTT, JOHN MCMAHON, JR., lawyer; b. N.Y.C., Aug. 1, 1944; s. John M. Sr. and Mary Sabin (Pitkin) W.; m. Suzanne Halland Laporte, June 27, 1970; children: Valerie, John M. III, Jeffrey. BA cum laude, Yale U., 1966; JD, Harvard U., 1969. Bar: Mass. 1969. Assoc. Hale and Dorr, Boston, 1969-75, jr. ptnr., 1975-79, sr. ptnr., 1979—, asst. mng. ptnr., 1980—; gen. ptnr. Haldor Investment Adv., Boston, 1988—. Mem. corp. Winsor Sch., Boston, 1986—, clk., trustee, 1989—. Served with USAR, 1969-75. Mem. Brookline Country Club, Union Boat Club, Somerset Club. Republican. Episcopal. Office: Hale and Dorr 60 State St Boston MA 02109-1803

WESTEN, PETER, legal educator; b. 1943. B.A., Harvard Coll., 1964; J.D., U. Calif.-Berkeley, 1968. Bar: Calif. 1970, D.C. 1971, Mich. 1973. Law clk. to Justice William O. Douglas, U.S. Supreme Ct., 1968-69; fellow Internat. Legal Ctr., 1969-71; assoc. Paul, Weiss, Rifkind, et al, 1971-73; asst. prof. U. Mich., 1973-76, assoc. prof., 1976-78, prof., 1978—. Guggenheim fellow, 1981-82. Mem. Order of Coif. Office: U Mich Law Sch 625 S State St Ann Arbor MI 48109-1215

WESTER, KEITH ALBERT, film and television recording engineer, television executive; b. Seattle, Feb. 21, 1940; s. Albert John and Evelyn Grayce (Nettell) W., m. Judith Elizabeth Jones, 1968 (div. Mar. 1974); 1 child, Wendy Elizabeth. AA, Am. River Coll., Sacramento, 1959; BA, Calif. State U., L.A., 1962; MA, UCLA, 1965. Lic. multi-engine rated pilot. Prodn. asst. KCRA-TV, Sacramento, 1956; announcer KSFM, Sacramento, 1960; film editor, sound rec. technician Urie & Assocs., Hollywood, Calif., 1963-66; co-owner Steckler-Wester Film Prodns., Hollywood, 1966-70; owner Profl. Sound Recorders, Studio City, Calif., 1970—, Aerocharter, Studio City, 1974—; owner Wester Devel., Sun Valley, Coeur d'Alene, Idaho, 1989—, also Studio City, 1989—; ptnr. Sta. KDQ-TV, Coeur d'Alene/Spokane, Idaho, 1993—. Mem. NATAS (Emmy award An Early Frost 1986, Emmy nominations in 1982, 84, 85, 87), Acad. Motion Picture Arts and Scis. (Acad. award nomination for best sound Black Rain 1990), Cinema Audio Soc. (sec. 1985-91, Sound award 1987), Soc. Motion Picture and TV Engrs., Internat. Sound Technicians, Local 695, Assn. Film Craftsmen (sec. 1967-73, treas. 1973-76), Screen Actors Guild, Aircraft Owners and Pilots Assn. (Confederate Air Force col.), Am. Radio Relay League. Home: 4146 Bellingham Ave Studio City CA 91604-1601 Office: Profl Sound Recorders 22440 Clarendon St Woodland Hills CA 91367-4467

WESTERBECK, KENNETH EDWARD, retired insurance company executive; b. Des Moines, Sept. 5, 1919; s. Joseph David and Florence Alice (King) W.; m. Miriam M. Martens, Jan. 24, 1942; children: Kent E., Marcia M. Westerbeck Waltersheide. D.B.A., Upper Iowa U., 1979. With Equitable Life Ins. Co. of Iowa, 1938-84; v.p., chief fin. officer Equitable of Iowa Cos., 1977-84, v.p., treas., 1980-84; v.p., sec. Equitable Life Ins. Co. of Iowa, 1973-84; ret., 1984; pres. Equitable Investment Svcs. Inc., Des Moines, 1982-84. Bd. Trustees Upper Iowa U.; bd. dirs. A.R.C.; mem. West Des Moines City Council, 1976-93. Mem. Des Moines Soc. Fin. Analysts. Republican. Presbyterian. Home: 715 10th St West Des Moines IA 50265-3506

WESTERBERG, ARTHUR WILLIAM, chemical engineering educator; b. St. Paul, Oct. 9, 1938; s. Kenneth Waldorf and Marjorie Claire (Darling) W.; m. Barbara Ann Dyson, July 14, 1963; children: Kenneth, Karl. B.S., U. Minn., 1960; M.S., Princeton U., 1961; Ph.D., Imperial Coll., London, 1964. Pres. Farm Engring. Sales Inc., Savage, Minn., 1964-65; sr. analyst Control Data Corp., San Diego, Calif., 1965-67; asst. prof., assoc. prof., prof. U. Fla., Gainesville, 1967-76; prof. chem. engring. Carnegie-Mellon U., Pitts., 1976—, chmn. dept., 1980-83, Swearingen prof., 1982—; dir. Design Research Ctr., 1978-80, Univ. prof., 1992—; dir. Engring. Design Research Ctr., 1986-89. Co-author: Process Flowsheeting, 1979. Fellow AIChE (lectr. 1989, Computers and Systems Tech. div. award 1983, Walker award 1987, McAfee award 1990); mem. NAE, Am. Soc. Engring. Edn. (chem. engring. div. lectr. 1981). Home: 5564 Beacon St Pittsburgh PA 15217-1972 Office: Carnegie-Mellon U Pittsburgh PA 15213

WESTERBERG, VERNE EDWARD, magazine publisher; b. Evanston, Ill., May 7, 1931; s. Verne and Martha (Hillestad) W.; m. Lee Hanley, July 10, 1954; children—Scott, Steve. BA, U. Colo., 1950-54. Sales devel. mgr. House and Garden, N.Y.C., 1967-70, advt. mgr., 1970-73, advt. dir., 1973-77; pub. Bride's Mag., N.Y.C., 1977-80, Self Mag., N.Y.C., 1980-83, Gourmet Mag., N.Y.C., 1983-86, Vogue Mag., 1987-90; v.p. Conde Nast Publs. Inc., 1987-90; mng. dir. Conde Nast Publs. Pty Ltd, Australia, 1991—. Served to 1st lt. USAF, 1954-57. Clubs: Royal Sydney Yacht Squadron, N.Y. Yacht, Riverside Yacht, Am. Club (Sydney). Office: Conde Nast Publs Pty Ltd, 170 Pacific Hwy, Greenwich N.S.W. 2065, Australia

WESTERDAHL, JOHN BRIAN, nutritionist, health educator; b. Tucson, Dec. 3, 1954; s. Jay E. and Margaret (Meyer) W.; m. Doris Mui Lian Tan, Nov. 18, 1989. AA, Orange Coast Coll., 1977; BS, Pacific Union Coll., 1979; MPH, Loma Linda U., 1981. Registered dietitian; chartered herbalist; cert. nutrition specialist. Nutritionist, health educator Castle Med. Ctr., Kailua, Hawaii, 1981-84; health promotion coord., 1984-87, asst. dir. health promotion, 1987-88, dir. health promotion, 1988-89; dir. nutrition and health rsch. Health Sci., Santa Barbara, Calif., 1989-90; sr. nutritionist, project mgr. Shaklee Corp., San Francisco, 1990—; talk show host Nutrition and You, Sta. KGU Radio, Honolulu, 1983-89; cons. med. mem. Hawaii div. Am. Heart Assn., Honolulu, 1984-87; mem. nutrition study group Govs. Conf. Health Promotion and Disease Prevention for Hawaii, 1985. Mem. AAAS, Am. Coll. Sports Medicine, Am. Dietetic Assn., Am. Nutritionists Assn., Am. Coll. Nutrition, Soc. for Nutrition Edn., Nat. Wellness Assn., Nutrition Today Soc., Am. Soc. Pharmacognosy, Inst. Food Technologists, Hawaii Nutrition Coun. (v.p. 1983-86,m pres.-elect 1988-89, pres. 1989), Hawaii Dietetic Assn., Calif. Dietetic Assn., N.Y. Acad. Scis., Seventh-day Adventist Dietetic Assn., several other profl. assns. Republican. Seventh-Day Adventist. Avocations: swimming, scuba diving. Office: Shaklee Corp 444 Market St San Francisco CA 94111-5325 *Personal philosophy: "Beloved, I wish above all things that thou mayest prosper and be in health, even as thy soul prospereth." 3 John 2.*

WESTERFIELD, HOLT BRADFORD, political scientist, educator; b. Rome, Italy, Mar. 7, 1928; s. Ray Bert and Mary Beatrice (Putney) W.; m. Carolyn Elizabeth Hess, Dec. 17, 1960; children—Pamela Bradford, Leland Avery. Grad., Choate Sch., 1944; B.A., Yale U., 1947; M.A., Harvard U., 1951, Ph.D., 1952. Instr. govt. Harvard U., 1952-56; asst. prof. polit. sci. U. Chgo., 1956-57; mem. faculty Yale U., 1957—, prof. polit. sci., 1965—, chmn. dept., 1970-72, Damon Wells prof. internat. studies, 1985—; research asso. Washington Center Fgn. Policy Research, Johns Hopkins Sch. Advanced Internat. Studies, 1965-66; vis. prof. Wesleyan U., Middletown, Conn., 1967, 71. Author: Foreign Policy and Party Politics: Pearl Harbor to Korea, 1955, The Instruments of America's Foreign Policy, 1963; editor: Inside CIA's Private World: Declassified Articles from the Agency's Internal Journal, 1955-1995, 1995. Sheldon traveling fellow Harvard, 1951-52; Henry L. Stimson fellow Yale, 1962, 73; sr. Fulbright-Hays scholar, 1973; hon. vis. fellow Australian Nat. U., 1973. Mem. Am. Polit. Sci. Assn. (Congl. fellow 1953-54), Internat. Polit. Sci. Assn. Home: 115 Rogers Rd Hamden CT 06517-3533 Office: Yale Univ Dept Polit Sci PO Box 208301 New Haven CT 06520-8301

WESTERFIELD, PUTNEY, management consulting executive; b. New Haven, Feb. 9, 1930; s. Ray Bert and Mary Beatrice (Putney) W.; m. Anne Montgomery, Apr. 17, 1954; children: Bradford, Geoffrey, Clare. Grad., Choate Sch., 1942-47; B.A., Yale U., 1952. Co-founder, v.p. Careers, Inc., N.Y.C., 1950-52; mgr. S.E. Asia Swen Publs., Inc., Manila, Philippines, 1952; mem. joint adv. commn. Korea, 1953-54; polit. officer Am. embassy, Saigon, Vietnam, 1955-57; asst. to pub. Time mag., N.Y.C. 1957-59, asst. circulation dir. 1959-61; circulation dir. Time mag., 1965-66, asst. pub., 1966-68; asst. pub. Life mag., N.Y.C., 1968; pub. Fortune mag., N.Y.C., 1969-73; pres. Chase World Info. Corp., N.Y.C., 1973-75; v.p. Boyden Assocs. Internat., San Francisco, 1976-80, sr. v.p., western mgr., 1980-84; pres., chief exec. officer Boyden Assocs. Internat., N.Y.C. and San Francisco, 1984-90, mng. dir., 1990—; bd. dirs. Upside Publ. Co. Bd. dirs. Urban League, N.Y.C., 1969-71, Children's Village, 1968-71, Mediterranean Sch. Found., 1969-71, Nat. Boys Club, 1970-73, U.S. -S. Africa Leaders Exch. Program, 1971—, Bus. Coun. for Internat. Understanding, 1974-76, Yale-China Assn., 1975-78, East Meets West Found., 1991—; trustee Choate Sch., Wallingford, Conn., 1967-76, Westover Sch., Middlebury, Conn., 1975-79, Watch Hill Chapel Soc., 1963-77, Assn. Yale Alumni, 1972-75, 80-83. Mem. Burlingame Country Club, Pacific Union Club, Bohemian Club. Home: 10 Greenview Ln Hillsborough CA 94010-6424 Office: Boyden Internat 275 Battery St Ste 420 San Francisco CA 94111-3331

WESTERGAARD, PETER TALBOT, composer, music educator; b. Champaign, Ill., May 28, 1931; s. Harald Malcolm and Rachel (Talbot) W.; m. Barbara Jay, Sept. 11, 1955; children: Elizabeth, Margaret. BA, Harvard, 1953; MFA, Princeton, 1956. Fulbright guest lectr. Staatliche Hochschule, Freiburg, Germany, 1957-58; instr. Columbia, 1958-63, asst. prof., 1963-66; vis. lectr. Princeton U., 1966-67; assoc. prof. Amherst Coll., Mass., 1967-68; from assoc. prof. music to prof. Princeton U., 1968—, chmn. dept. music, 1974-78, 83-86, William Shubael Conant prof. music, 1995—; vis. prof. U. B.C., 1987; lectr. internat. music seminar Univ. Bahia, Brazil, 1992; endowed prof. U. Ala., 1995. Condr. Princeton U. Orch., 1968-73; dir. Princeton U. Opera Theater, 1970—, June Opera Festival of N.J., 1983-86; Composer: Cantata I (The Plot against the Giant), 1956, Five Movements for Small Orchestra, 1958, Cantata II (A Refusal to Mourn the Death, by Fire, of a Child in London), 1958, Quartet for Violin, Vibraphone, Clarinet and Violoncello, 1960, Spring and Fall, To a Young Child, 1960, 64, Cantata III (Leda and the Swan), 1961, Trio for Flute, Violoncello and Piano, 1962, Variations for Six Players, 1963, Mr. and Mrs. Discobbolos, 1965, Divertimento on Discobbolic Fragments, 1967, Noises, Sounds and Sweet Airs, 1968, Tuckets and Sennets, 1969, Moto Perpetuo for Six Wind Instruments, 1976, Alonso's Grief, 1977, There Was a Little Man, 1979, Ariel Music, 1987, Two Fanfares, 1988, Ariel Songs, 1988, Ode, 1989, The Tempest, 1990; Author: Introduction to Tonal Theory, 1975; translator operas: The Magic Flute, 1977, Don Giovanni, 1979, Der Freischutz, 1980, Fidelio (original version of 1805), 1982, Cosi fan tutte, 1983, The Marriage of Figaro, 1984, Cinderella, 1986. Guggenheim fellow, 1964-65, N.J. State Council on the Arts fellow, 1986-87, 89-90; grantee Nat. Endowment for Arts, 1990-91. Office: Princeton U Dept Music Princeton NJ 08544

WESTERHOFF, GARRET PETER, environmental engineer, executive; b. Fairlawn, N.J., Oct. 12, 1935; s. Garret Peter and Elizabeth (Ullmer) W.; m. Helga Ann Kasch, May 31, 1958; children: Garret Peter, Eric John, Paul Keith. BS in Civil Engring., N.J. Inst. Tech., 1957, MS in Sanitary Engring., 1967. Registered profl. engr. N.J., N.Y., Ohio, Va., Ariz., Calif., Md., Fla., Ala., La., Maine, Mass., Nebr., N.Mex., Nev., N.C., Pa.; profl. planner/diplomate Am. Acad. Environ. Engrs. Loss prevention engr. Factory Mutual Engring. Co., 1960-64; project engr. Jersey Engring. Assocs., 1964-65; from v.p. to exec. v.p. Malcolm Pirnie, Inc., White Plains, N.Y., 1967—; mem. tech. adv. coun. Nat. Water Rsch. Inst.; internat. rapporteur on water quality and treatment in U.S. Internat. Water Supply Assn., World Congress, Budapest, 1993, Durbon, S. Africa, 1995; tech. cons. Office Drinking Water U.S. EPA; presenter in field. Contbr. articles to profl. jours. 1st lt. USAF, 1957-60. Mem. Am. Water Works Assn. (former stds. coun., chmn. Internat. Water Supply Assn. N.Am. com., former chmn. water supply planning and coord. com., former trustee engring. and constrn. divsn.), former chmn. water reuse comm., former chmn. water treatment plant wastes disposal com., former chmn. alum recovery rsch. adv. com., rsch. adv. coun. Rsch. Found.), Am. Soc. Civil Engrs., NSPE, Water Environment Fedn. Avocations: fishing, photography, writing. Office: Malcolm Pirnie Inc 102 Corporate Park Dr White Plains NY 10604-3802

WESTERHOFF, JOHN HENRY, III, clergyman, theologian, educator; b. Paterson, N.J., June 28, 1933; s. John Henry and Nona Celia (Walsh) W.; m. Alberta Louise Barnhart, Dec. 27, 1955 (div. 1991); childen: Jill Louise, John Jeffrey, Beth Anne; m. Caroline Askew Hughes, Oct. 27, 1991. BS, Ursinus Coll., 1955; STB, Harvard U., 1958; EdD, Columbia U., 1974; DD, Ursinus Coll., 1990. Ordained to ministry United Ch. of Christ, 1958, Episcopal Ch., 1978; pastor Congl. Ch., Presque Isle, Maine, 1958-60; assoc. pastor Congl. Ch., Needham, Mass., 1960-64; pastor 1st Congl. Ch., Williamstown, Mass., 1964-66; edn. sec., editor Colloquy (United Ch. Bd. for Homeland Ministries), N.Y.C., 1966-73; Lentz lectr. Harvard U. Div. Sch., 1973-74; prof. Duke U. Div. Sch., Durham, N.C., 1974-94; dir. Inst. Pastoral Studies, Atlanta, 1992—; interim rector St. Bartholomew Episcopal Ch., Atlanta, 1993-94; assoc. rector St. Lukes Episcopal Ch., Atlanta, 1994—. Author: Values for Tomorrows Children, 1970, A Colloquy on Christian Education, 1972, Generation to Generation, 1974, Tomorrow's Church, 1976, Will Our Children Have Faith?, 1976, McGuffey and His Readers, 1978, Who Are We?, 1978, Learning Through Liturgy, 1978, Inner Growth-Outer Change, 1979, The Church's Ministry in Higher Education, 1979, Liturgy and Learning Through the Life Cycle, 1980, Christian Believing, 1980, Bringing Up Children in The Christian Church, 1980, A Faithful Church, 1981, The Spiritual Life: Learning East and West, 1981, Building God's People, 1983, A Pilgrim People, 1984, Living the Faith Community, 1985, On the Threshold of God's Future, 1986, Living Into Our Baptism, 1990, Schooling Christians, 1992, The Spiritual Life: Foundation for Preaching and Teaching, 1994; editor: Religious Edn, 1979-89. Mem. Assn. Profs. and Researchers in Religious Edn., Religious Edn. Assn. Democrat. Episcopalian. Office: Saint Luke's Episcopal Ch 435 Peachtree St NE Atlanta GA 30365

WESTERHOUT, GART, retired astronomer; b. The Hague, The Netherlands, June 15, 1927; came to U.S., 1962, naturalized, 1969; s. Gerrit and Magdalena (Foppe) W.; m. Judith Mary Monaghan, Nov. 14, 1956; children: Magda C., Gart T., Brigit M., Julian C., Anthony K. Drs., Leiden U., Netherlands, 1954, Ph.D., 1958. Asst. Leiden U. Observatory, 1952-56, sci. officer, 1956-59, chief sci. officer, 1959-62; prof., dir. astronomy U. Md., 1962-73, chmn. div. math. and phys. scis. and engring., 1972-73, prof. astronomy, 1973-77; sci. dir. U.S. Naval Observatory, Washington, 1977-93; vis. astronomer Max Planck Inst. Radio Astronomy, Bonn, Germany, 1973-74, mem. adv. bd., 1976-79; vice chmn. divsn. phys. sci. NRC, 1969-73; mem. com. on radio frequencies, 1971-92; trustee Assoc. Univs. Inc., 1971-74; mem. Intern Union Commn. on Allocation of Frequencies, 1974-82; mem. sci. coun. Stellar Data Ctr., Strasbourg, France, 1978-84, chmn., 1981; chmn. working group on astrometry, astronomy survey com. NAS, 1979-81; mem. adv. bd. Haystac-N.E. Radio Obs. Consortium, 1974-77; mem. Arecibo adv. bd. Nat. Astronomy and Ionosphere Ctr., 1977-80, chmn., 1979-80. Contbr. on radio astronomy, spiral structure of our galaxy and astrometry to profl. jours. Recipient citation for teaching excellence Washington Acad. Scis., 1972; U.S. Sr. Scientist award Alexander von Humboldt Stiftung, Ger., 1973; NATO fellow, 1959. Mem. Internat. Astron. Union (chmn. working group on astron. data 1985-91), Internat. Sci. Radio Union (pres. commn. on radio astronomy 1975-78), Am. Astron. Soc. (councilor 1975-78, v.p. 1985-87), Royal Astron. Soc. Roman Catholic. Home: 811 W 38th St Baltimore MD 21211-2203

WESTERMAN, GAYL SHAW, law educator; b. Hobbs, N.Mex., July 17, 1939; d. Travis Bowen and Xena Zonelle (Brooks) Shaw; m. George G. Westerman (div. 1971); children: Kara K., Christopher C.; m. Lawrence C. Olin. BA, Stanford U., 1961; MS, U. Pa., 1965; JD, Pace U., 1981; LLM, Yale U., 1982, D of Jud. Sci., 1984. Bar: Conn. 1986. Teaching positions in regular and spl. edn., 1962-68; learning specialist The Child Ctr., Kentfield, Calif., 1968-69, sr. learning specialist, program dir., adj. prof. edn., 1969-78; prof. law Pace U. Sch. Law, White Plains, N.Y., 1982—; vis. lectr. Yale Law Sch., New Haven, 1988, 91; dir. London law program Pace U., 1983-92, 93—; cons. Conn. Civil Liberties Union, 1991-92. Author: Reading Skills Development Program, 1970, Spelling and Writing, 1971, Operational Assessment Tool, 1972, Operational Assessment Tool Reading Program, 1976, The Juridical Bay, 1987, Straight Baselines in International Maritime Boundary Delimitation, 1992; contbr. articles to profl. jours. Mem. ABA, ACLU, Am. Arbitration Assn., Am. Soc. Internat. Law, Nat. Trust Hist. Preservation, New Haven Preservation Trust, Greenpeace. Democrat. Avocations: opera, theater, music. Office: Pace U Law Sch 78 N Broadway White Plains NY 10603-3710

WESTERMAN, HOWARD G., oil and gas company executive; b. Cin., Oct. 11, 1928; s. Carl George and Loretta Rose (Meis) W.; m. Laura Jane David,

Jan. 22, 1952; children: Howard G., Mark, Paul, Celeste Westerman Lewis, Robert, Lene Westerman Pecorari, Jason. BS in Petroleum Engring., U. Okla., 1950; LLD (hon.), Benedictine Coll., Atchison, Kans., 1987. Registered profl. engr., Okla. Engr. Bethlehem Supply Co., Tulsa, 1954-59, Dallas, 1959-60; founder, exec., engr., CEO, chmn. bd. J-W Operating Co., Dallas, 1960—; pres., chmn. bd. Cohort Energy Co., Excell Drilling Co., J-W Gathering Co., United Oil and Gas Co., Cohort Engring. Co., Q-West Energy Co.; mgmt. advisor Westerman Holding Co., Ltd., J-W Holding N.V., J-W Reins. Ltd.; mng. ptnr. United Exploration Co. Ltd., Program One, Two, Four and Five, United '81 Co., Westerman Farm Co. Patentee in field. Dir. emeritus Benedictine Coll., Atchison, Kans.; mem. Rep. Nat. Com.; sustaining mem. Boy Scouts Am. 1st lt. U.S. Army, 1950-54. Mem. Soc. Petroleum Engrs., Aircraft Owners and Pilots Assn., Mid-Continent Oil and Gas Assn., Dallas Petroleum Club. Republican. Roman Catholic. Office: J-W Operating Co 15508 Wright Brothers Dr Dallas TX 75244-2137

WESTERMAN, SYLVIA HEWITT, journalist, university official; b. Columbus, Ohio; d. Harry James and Grace (Doyle) W. BA, Ohio State U. With Sta. WLW-C, WTVN and WBNS, Columbus, 1954-63; with CBS News, 1963-79, radio TV producer, 1964-67, producer Face the Nation, 1967-74, dep. dir. news, 1974-78, v.p. spl. events and polit. coverage, 1978-79; v.p., exec. asst. to pres. NBC News, N.Y.C., 1979-82; v.p. spl. projects UPI, N.Y.C., 1983-84; pres. Sylvia Westerman Enterprises, N.Y.C.; dir. planning and new programs Fordham Grad. Sch. Bus. Adminstrn., N.Y.C. 1989—. Recipient Emmy award Nat. Acad. TV Arts and Scis. 1974. Bd. dirs. Ohio State U. Devel. Fund; adv. bd. Critical Difference for Women; coun. advisors Ohio State U. libr.; mem. steering com. Acad. Quality Consortium. Mem. Jr. League Columbus, Cosmopolitan Club, Sigma Delta Chi, Theta Sigma Phi, Kappa Alpha Theta. Home: 220 E 63rd St Apt 5-a New York NY 10021-7648 Office: 113 W 60th St New York NY 10023-7404

WESTERMANN, DAVID, lawyer, educator, electronics industry executive; b. N.Y.C., Mar. 2, 1920; s. John Jacob and Margaret (Maher) W.; m. Edith E. West, Mar. 11, 1972; children by previous marriage: Nancy, John Jacob, David. AB, Columbia U., 1941, LLB, 1943; LLD (hon.), Adelphi U., 1979. Bar: N.Y. 1943. Assoc. Donald A. Gray, N.Y.C., 1947-48, William P. McCool, N.Y.C., 1948-50; atty. Hazeltine Corp., Greenlawn, N.Y., 1950—, v.p., gen. counsel, 1961-66, pres., 1966-77, chief exec. officer, 1966-80, chmn., 1977-80, dir., 1965-80; prof. James Forrestal chair Def. Systems Mgmt. Coll., Ft. Belvoir, Va., 1981-89, adj. prof., 1989-91; prof. emeritus Def. Systems Mgmt. Coll., 1991—; of counsel Westermann & Tryon, Garden City, N.Y., 1987—; trustee Optic-Electronic Corp., 1987-90; Bannerman lectr. Naval Postgrad. Sch., 1975; bd. dirs. Procurement Roundtable; admissions com. rep. Columbia Coll. Mem. bd. edn. South Huntington schs., Union Free Sch. Dist. 13, 1956-59, pres., 1959-60; adv. trustee Poly. U.; past trustee Urban League L.I.; past. bd. dirs. Action Com. for L.I.; past chmn. bd. dirs. Performing Arts Found. L.I. Served to 1st lt. AUS, 1942-46. Recipient Distinguished Pub. Svc. medal Dept. Def., 1989. Fellow Nat. Contract Mgmt. Assn. (bd. advisors 1983-89); mem. ABA, Columbia Coll., Columbia Law Sch. Alumni Assn., John Jay Assocs. (life), Nat. Security Indsl. Assn. (trustee 1969-81, chmn. 1975-76, trustee emeritus 1989—), L.I. Forum for Tech. (founding chmn. 1977—), Am. Legion, Air Force Assn., Assn. U.S. Army, Westhampton Country Club, Varsity "C", Wings, Delta Psi, Phi Delta Phi. Home: 220 Cathedral Ave Hempstead NY 11550-1100 Office: 100 Quentin Roosevelt Blvd Garden City NY 11530

WESTERMANN, HORACE CLIFFORD, sculptor; b. Los Angeles, Dec. 11, 1922; s. Horace Clifford and Florita Lynd (Bloom) W.; m. Joanna May Beall, Mar. 31, 1959. Student, Art Inst. Chgo., 1947-50, 52-54. Exhibited in one-man shows Frumkin Gallery, Chgo., 1958, 74, Corcoran Gallery, Los Angeles, 1974, Moore Coll., Phila., 1972, others; group shows Smithsonian Instn., 1974, Guggenheim Mus., N.Y.C., 1970, Carnegie Mus., 1971, Mus. Modern Art, N.Y.C., 1960, Whitney Mus. Am. Art, 1976, Venice Biennale, 1976, others; retrospective exhbns. Los Angeles County Mus., Calif., 1968, Mus. Contemporary Art, Chgo., 1968, Galerie Thomas Borgmann, Cologne, Fed. Republic Germany, 1970, Galerie Neuendorf, Hamburg, Fed. Republic Germany, 1973, Whitney Mus. Am. Art, New Orleans Mus. Art, Des Moines Mus. Art, Seattle Mus. Art, San Francisco Mus. Modern Art, 1978, Serpentine Gallery, London, 1980, Xavier Fourcade, N.Y.C., 1981, John Berggruen Gallery, San Francisco, 1985, Lennon, Weinberg Inc., N.Y.C., 1988, 90; author: Letters from H.C. Westermann, 1988; represented in pvt. collections. Served with USMC, 1942-46, 50-52. Recipient Nat. Arts Council award, 1967, Sao Paulo Biennial award, 1972. Studio: PO Box 5028 Brookfield CT 06804-5028

WESTERVELT, JAMES JOSEPH, insurance company executive; b. Bklyn., July 8, 1946; s. Cornealius V. and Regina Elizabeth (May) W.; m. Sue Jane Brubaker, Aug. 5, 1972; children: Kevin K., Natalie M. BBA, Manhattan Coll., 1967. Mgr. auditing Peat, Marwick & Mitchell, N.Y.C., 1967-78; dir. auditing City Investing, N.Y.C., 1978-81; asst. v.p., asst. contr. ITT Hartford, Conn., 1981-89, v.p., group contr., 1989—. With U.S. Army, 1968-69. Mem. AICPA, Hawaii Soc. CPAs, Conn. Soc. CPAs, Am. Ins. Assn. Roman Catholic. Avocations: skiing, wine tasting, tennis, chess, electronics. Office: Hartford Fire Insurance Co Hartford Plz Hartford CT 06115

WESTERVELT, PETER JOCELYN, physics educator; b. Albany, N.Y., Dec. 16, 1919; s. William Irving and Dorothy (Jocelyn) W.; m. Alice Francis Brown, June 2, 1956; children: Dirck Edgell, Abby Brown. B.S., MIT, 1947, M.S., 1949, Ph.D., 1951. Mem. staff radiation lab. MIT, 1940-41, underwater sound lab., 1941-45, asst. in physics, 1946-47, rsch. assoc., 1948-50; asst. prof. physics Brown U., 1951-58, assoc. prof., 1958-63, prof., 1963-90, prof. emeritus, 1990—; mem. subcom. aircraft noise NASA, 1954-59; mem. com. hearing and bio-acoustics NRC, 1957-83, exec. council, 1960-61, 78-83, chmn., 1967-68, 80-83; mem. sonic boom com. Nat. Acad. Sci., 1968-71; mem. R.I. Atomic Energy Commn., 1968-73; cons. applied research lab. U. Tex., Austin, 1973-83. Recipient Rayleigh medal Inst. Acoustics U.K., 1985. Fellow Am. Physics Soc., Acoustical Soc. Am. Home: 16 John St Providence RI 02906-1008 Office: Brown U Dept Physics Providence RI 02912

WESTERVELT, ROBERT MOORE, physics educator; b. Phila., Oct. 9, 1949; s. Robert Moore and Marie Louise (Jefferson) W. BS in Physics with honors, Calif. Inst. Tech., 1971; PhD in Physics, U. Calif., Berkeley, 1977; AM (hon.), Harvard U., 1986. Prof. physics and applied physics Harvard U., Cambridge, Mass., 1979-84, assoc. prof. physics and applied physics, 1984-86, prof. physics, Gordon McKay prof. applied physics, 1986—; cochmn. Gordon Conf. on Condensed Matter Physics, 1988; bd. editors Physica D-Nonlinear Phenomena, 1986-90. Recipient Ross N. Tucker Meml. award Intel Corp., 1977; Chancellor's fellow U. Calif. Berkeley, 1971. Mem. Am. Phys. Soc. Office: Harvard U Div Applied Scis Cambridge MA 02138

WESTFALL, BERNARD G., university hospital executive; b. Lockney, W.Va., July 12, 1941; s. Edward C. and Wilma (Dotson) W.; m. Marion Williams, July 26, 1969; 1 child, Gregory. BS, W. Va. U., 1963, MBA, 1972. Tchr. sci. Monongalia County Schs., Morgantown, W.Va., 1963-65; assoc. dir. purchasing W. Va. U., Morgantown, 1965-73; hosp. computer mgr. W. Va. U. Hosp., Morgantown, 1973-74, assoc. adminstr. fin. and systems, 1974-82; interim adminstr. W.Va. U. Hosp., Morgantown, 1982-83, sr. assoc. adminstr., 1983-84, contr. v.p., adminstr., 1984-87, pres., 1987—; bd. dirs. One Valley Bank; guest lectr. W. Va. U., 1984—. Author: Central Breakout at West Virginia University, 1970. Trustee W.Va. Hosp. Assn. Mem. Am. Coll. Hosp. Adminstrs., Hosp. Fin. Mgmt. Assn. Lodge: Rotary. Home: RR 9 Box 69A Morgantown WV 26505-9809

WESTFALL, CARROLL WILLIAM, architectural historian; b. Fresno, Calif., Dec. 23, 1937; s. Carroll W. and Alice Margaret (DeVore) W.; m. Cheryl Ludwig, June 6, 1964 (div. 1971); m. Relling Rossi, June 26, 1982; 1 child, Nicholas William. BA, U. Calif., Berkeley, 1961; MArch, U. Manchester, Eng., 1963; PhD, Columbia U., 1967. Asst. prof. Amherst (Mass.) Coll., 1966-72; asst. prof. U. Ill., Chgo., 1972-75, assoc. prof., 1975-82; assoc. prof. U. Va., Charlottesville, 1982-88, profl. archtl. history, 1988—, chmn. dept., 1983-89; cons. in field. Author: In This Most Perfect Paradise, 1974, Italian edit., 1984, (with Robert Jan van Pelt) Architectural Principles in the Age of Historicism, 1991; contbr. articles to profl. jours. Bd. dirs.

Landmarks Preservation Coun., Chgo., 1973-82, pres., 1974-76. Mem. Soc. Archtl. Historians, Coll. Art Assn., Nat. Trust Historic Preservation, Cliffdwellers (Chgo.). Republican. Avocation: travel. Home: 1 Cottage Ln Charlottesville VA 22903 Office: Univ Va Sch Architecture Charlottesville VA 22903

WESTFALL, DAVID, lawyer, educator; b. Columbia, Mo., Apr. 16, 1927; s. Wilhelmus David A. and Ruth (Rollins) W.; m. Elizabeth Putnam Beatty; children: Elizabeth Stewart, William Beatty, Thomas Curwen, Katharine Putnam. AB, U. Mo., 1947; LLB magna cum laude, Harvard U., 1950. Bar: Ill. 1950, Mass. 1956. Assoc. Bell, Boyd, Marshall & Lloyd, Chgo., 1950-55; asst. prof. law Harvard Law Sch., 1955-58, prof., 1958—, John L. Gray prof., 1983—. Author: Estate Planning Cases and Text, 1985, Everly Woman's Guide to Financial Planning, 1984, Family Law, 1993; co-author: Estate Planning Law and Taxation, 3rd edit., 1994; co-editor: Readings in Federal Taxation, 1983. Served as 1st lt. JAGC, AUS, 1951-53. Fellow Am. Coll. Trust and Estate Counsel (acad.); mem. ABA, Mass. Bar Assn., Am. Law Inst., Phi Beta Kappa, Phi Delta Theta. Home: 5103 Stearns Hill Rd Waltham MA 02154 Office: Law Sch Harvard U Cambridge MA 02138

WESTFALL, RICHARD SAMUEL, historian; b. Fort Collins, Colo., Apr. 22, 1924; s. Alfred Rensselaer and Dorothy (Towne) W.; m. Gloria Marilyn Dunn, Aug. 23, 1952; children: Alfred, Jennifer, Kristin. B.A., Yale U., 1948; M.A., 1949, Ph.D., 1955; postgrad., London U., 1951-52. Instr. history Calif. Inst. Tech., Pasadena, 1952-53; instr., asst. prof. history State U. Iowa, Iowa City, 1953-57; asst. prof. history Grinnell Coll., 1957-60, assoc. prof., 1960-63; prof. history Ind. U., Bloomington, 1963-89; prof. history Ind. U., 1965-89, disting. prof. of history and philosophy of sci., 1976-89, chmn. dept., 1967-73; prof. emeritus Ind. U., Bloomington, 1989—. Author: Science and Religion in Seventeenth Century England, 1958, Force in Newton's Physics, 1971, Construction of Modern Science, 1971, Never at Rest: A Biography of Isaac Newton, 1980, Essays on the Trial of Galileo, 1990, Life of Isaac Newton, 1993; editor: (with V.E. Thoren) Steps in the Scientific Tradition, 1969. Mem. United Ministry Bd., Bloomington, 1964-73; elder First Presbyterian Ch., Bloomington. Served with USNR, 1944-46. Fellow Am. Acad. Arts and Scis., Royal Soc. Lit.; mem. AAUP, Am. Hist. Assn. (Leo Gershoy award 1981), History of Sci. Soc. (2d v.p. 1973-74, v.p. 1975-76, pres. 1977-78, Pfizer award 1972, 83, Sarton medal 1985), Societe internationale d'histoire des sciences. Home: 2222 N Browncliff Ln Bloomington IN 47408-1302 Office: Ind Univ Dept Hist & Phil Sci Bloomington IN 47405

WESTFIELD, FRED M., economics educator; b. Essen, Germany, Nov. 7, 1926; came to U.S., 1940; s. Dietrich and Grete (Stern) W.; m. Joyce A. Horwitz Nochlin, Nov. 15, 1968; stepchildren: Steven Nochlin, Keith Nochlin. BA magna cum laude, Vanderbilt U., 1950; PhD in Indsl. Econs., MIT, 1957. Teaching asst., instr. MIT, Cambridge, 1952-53; lectr. Northwestern U., Evanston, Ill., 1953-57, asst. prof., 1957-60, assoc. prof., 1960-65; prof. econs. Vanderbilt U., Nashville, 1965—, mem. faculty coun. Coll. Arts and Sci., 1974-76, mem. faculty senate, 1979-82, 94-95, dir. undergrad. studies dept. econs. and bus. adminstrn., 1984-87, mem. grad. faculty coun., 1991; vis. prof. U. Colo., summers 1973-74; condr. seminars, lectr., participant univs. and rsch. orgns.; Fulbright sr. lectr. U. Nac. del Sur, Argentina, 1986; cons. Coun. Econ. Advisers, Exec. Office Pres., 1968, World Bank and Water and Power Devel. Authority, Pakistan, 1970-72, World Bank and East African Power and Light Co., Kenya, 1975, NSF, 1975, FTC, 1976-78, World Bank, UN Devel. Program and Econ. Planning Bd. South Korea, 1975-76; expert witness Tenn. Pub. Svc. Commn., 1980-89, Consumer Advocate Tenn. Atty. Gen., 1994; also others. Mem. editorial bd. Utilities Policy, 1990—; mem. bd. editors So. Econ. Jour., 1973-75; editorial referee Am. Econ. Rev., Jour. Polit. Economy, Econometrica, So. Econ. Jour., Econ. Inquiry; contbr. articles and book revs. to profl. jours. With U.S. Army, 1945-46. Fellow Gen. Edn. Bd., MIT, Ford Found., 1958-59. Mem. Am. Econ. Assn., Econometric Soc. (program com. 1967, chmn. conf. sessions), So. Econ. Assn. (v.p. 1976-77, chmn. conf. sessions), Phi Beta Kappa (chmn. audit com. Tenn. Alpha chpt.). Home: 1097 Lynnwood Blvd Nashville TN 37215-4540 Office: Vanderbilt U PO Box 1681 Sta B Nashville TN 37235

WESTHAVER, LAWRENCE ALBERT, electronics engineer, consultant; b. Washington, Oct. 24, 1936; s. James Waldo and Hattie Virginia (Bush) W.; m. Jo Ann Turner, Jan. 5, 1957; children: Lawrence Albert Jr., Wendy Jo Westhaver Roski, Bonnie Jo. Cert. engring., U. Va., 1966. Electronic design, cons. Westhaver Assocs., Inc., Laurel, Md., 1971—; engring. draftsman Office Rsch. and Devel. Nat. Security Agy., Arlington Hall, Va., 1955-57; engring. technician Office Rsch. and Engring. Nat. Security Agy. Ft. G.G. Meade, Md., 1958-66, electronic engr. Office Rsch. and Engring., 1967-82, sr. engr. Office of Rsch. and Engring., 1982-84; sr. engr. Communications Systems Support Group, Laurel, Md., 1984-93. Patentee method for photographic aperture control, photographic light integrator, switching current regulator, photographic test equipment, electronic tuner for stringed musical instruments, microcomputer-based Ni-Cd battery charger, and color-correcting filter for underwater photography. Avocations: scuba diving, snorkeling, biking, hiking, bird watching. Home: 8609 Portsmouth Dr Laurel MD 20708-1819

WESTHEIMER, DAVID KAPLAN, novelist; b. Houston, Apr. 11, 1917; s. Adolf and Esther (Kaplan) W.; m. Doris Gertrude Rothstein, Oct. 9, 1945; children: Fred, Eric. B.A., Rice Inst., Houston, 1937. Successively asst. amusement editor, radio editor, mag. editor, TV editor Houston Post, 1939-41, 45-46, 50, 53-60, columnist, 1984-88. Author: Summer on the Water, 1948, The Magic Fallacy, 1950, Watching Out for Dulie, 1960, Von Ryan's Express, 1964, My Sweet Charlie, 1965, Song of the Young Sentry, 1968, Lighter Than a Feather, 1971, Over the Edge, 1972, Going Public, 1973, The Avila Gold, 1974, The Olmec Head, 1974, Rider on the Wind, 1979, Von Ryan's Return, 1980, (with John Sherlock) The Amindra Gamble, 1982, Sitting It Out, 1992, Death Is Lighter Than a Feather, 1995 (play) My Sweet Charlie, 1966, (TV films) Trouble Comes to Town, 1972, A Killer Among Us, 1990. Served to capt. USAAF, 1941-45, ETO; served to capt. USAF, 1950-53; lt. col. USAF; ret. Decorated Air medal, D.F.C. Mem. ACLU, NAACP, PEN, Writer's Guild Am. West. Author's Guild, Ret. Officer Assn., Calif. Writers Club. Democrat. Avocations: travel, reading, walking. Home and Office: 11722 Darlington Ave Apt 2 Los Angeles CA 90049-5525

WESTHEIMER, FRANK HENRY, chemist, educator; b. Balt., Jan. 15, 1912; s. Henry Ferdinand and Carrie (Burgunder) W.; m. Jeanne Friedmann, Aug. 31, 1937; children: Ruth Susan, Ellen. AB, Dartmouth Coll., 1932, ScD (hon.), 1961; MA, Harvard U., 1933, PhD, 1935; ScD (hon.), U. Chgo., 1973, U. Cin., 1976, Tufts U., 1978, U. N.C., 1983, Bard Coll., 1983, Weizmann Inst., 1987, U. Ill. at Chgo., 1988. Rsch. assoc. U. Chgo., 1936-37, instr., 1937-41, asst. prof., 1941-44, assoc. prof., 1946-48, prof. chemistry, 1948-53; vis. prof. Harvard U., 1953-54, prof. chemistry, 1954-82, sr. prof., 1982-83, prof. emeritus, 1983—, chmn. dept., 1959-62; Overseas fellow Churchill Coll., U. Cambridge, Eng., 1962-63; mem. Pres.'s Sci. Adv. Com., 1967-70; research supr. Explosives Research Lab., Nat. Def. Research Com., 1944-45; chmn. com. survey chemistry Nat. Acad. Scis., 1964-65. Assoc. editor Jour. Chem. Physics, 1942-44, 52-54; editorial bd. Jour. Am. Chem. Soc, 1960-69, Procs. Nat. Acad. Scis., 1983-89; contbr. articles to profl. jours. Recipient Naval Ordnance Development award, 1946, Army-Navy cert. of appreciation, 1946, James Flack Norris award in phys.-organic chemistry, 1970, Willard Gibbs medal, 1970, Theodore W. Richards medal, 1976; award in chem. scis. Nat. Acad. Sci., 1980, Richard Kokes award, 1980, Charles Frederick Chandler medal, 1980, Rosenstiel award, 1981, Nichols medal, 1982, Robert A. Welch award, 1982, Ingold medal, 1983, Cope award, 1982, Nat. Medal of Sci., 1986, Paracelsus medal, 1988, Priestley medal, 1988, Repligen award, 1992; fellow Columbia U. NRC, 1935-36, Guggenheim Found., 1962-63, Fulbright-Hays Found., 1974. Mem. Nat. Acad. Sci. (council 1971-75, 76-79), Am. Philos. Soc. (council 1981-84), Am. Acad. Arts and Scis. (sec. 1985-90), Royal Soc. (fgn. mem.). Home: 3 Berkeley St Cambridge MA 02138-3409

WESTHEIMER, GERALD, optometrist, educator; b. Berlin, Germany, May 13, 1924; naturalized, 1944, came to U.S., 1951; s. Isaak and Ilse (Cohn) W. Optometry diploma, Sydney (Australia) Tech. Coll., 1943, fellowship diploma, 1950; BSc, U. Sydney, 1947; PhD, Ohio State U., 1953; DSc (hon.), U. NSW, Australia, 1988; ScD (hon.), SUNY, 1990. Practice optometry Sydney, 1945-51; research fellow Ohio State U., 1951-53; prof.

physiol. optics U. Houston, 1953-54; asst. prof., then assoc. prof. physiol. optics Ohio State U., 1954-60; postdoctoral fellow neurophysiology Marine Biol. Lab., Woods Hole, Mass., 1957; vis. researcher Physiol. Lab., U. Cambridge, Eng., 1958-59; mem. faculty U. Calif. at Berkeley, 1960—, prof. physiol. optics, 1963-68, chmn. group physiol. optics, 1964-67, prof. physiology, 1968-89, prof. neurobiology, 1989—, head div. neurobiology, 1987-92; adj. prof. Rockefeller U., N.Y., 1992—; Sackler lectr. Tel Aviv U. Med. Sch., 1988, D.O. Hebb lectr. McGill U., 1991, Grass Found. lectr. U. Ill., 1991; mem. com. vision NRC, 1957-72; mem. visual scis. study sect. NIH, 1966-70, chmn. visual scis. B study sect., 1977-79; mem. vision, research and tng. com. Nat. Eye Inst., NIH, 1970-74, chmn. bd. sci. counselors, 1981-83; mem. exec. council com. vision NAS-NRC, 1969-72; mem. communicative scis. cluster Pres.'s Biomed. Rsch. Panel, 1975. Author rsch. papers; editor: Vision Rsch., 1972-79; editl. bd. Investigative Ophthalmology, 1973-77, Exptl. Brain Rsch., 1973-89, Optics Letters, 1977-78, Spatial Vision, 1985—, Ophthalmic and Physiological Optics, 1985—, Vision Rsch., 1985-92, Jour. of Physiology, 1987-94; editor: procs. of Royal Soc. London, 1990—. Recipient Von Sallman prize Columbia U., 1986; Prentice medal Am. Acad. Optometry, 1986, Bicentennial medal Australian Optometric Assn., 1988. Fellow AAAS, Royal Soc. London (Ferrier lectr. 1992), Am. Acad. Arts and Scis., Optical Soc. Am. (Tillyer medal 1978, assoc. editor jour. 1980-83), Am. Acad. Optometry; mem. Royal Soc. New So. Wales, Soc. Neurosci., Assn. Rsch. in Vision and Ophthalmology (Proctor medal 1979), Internat. Brain Rsch. Orgn., Physiol. Soc. Gt. Britain, Sigma Xi. Home: 582 Santa Barbara Rd Berkeley CA 94707

WESTHEIMER, RUTH SIEGEL (KAROLA RUTH SIEGEL WESTHEIMER), psychologist, television personality; b. Frankfurt, Fed. Republic Germany; came to U.S., 1956; m. Manfred Westheimer; children: Miriam, Joel. Grad. psychology U. Paris Sorbonne; Master's degree, New Sch. for Social Research, N.Y.C., 1959; EdD, Columbia U., 1970. Research asst. Columbia U. Sch. Pub. Health, N.Y.C., 1967-70; assoc. prof. Lehman Coll., Bronx, N.Y., 1970-77; with Bklyn. Coll., West Point Milit. Acad.; counsellor, radio talk show hostess Sexually Speaking Sta. WYNY-FM, N.Y.C., 1980—; hostess TV series Good Sex, Dr. Ruth Show, Ask Dr. Ruth, 1987—; pvt. practice N.Y.C.; adj. assoc. prof. NYU. Author: Dr. Ruth's Guide to Good Sex, 1983, First Love: A Young People's Guide to Sexual Information, 1985, Dr. Ruth's Guide for Married Lovers, 1986, (autobiography) All In a Lifetime, 1987, Sex and Morality: Who is Teaching Out Sex Standards?, 1988, Dr. Ruth's Guide to Erotic and Sensuous Pleasures, 1991, Dr. Ruth's Guide to Safer Sex, 1992, Dr. Ruth Talks to Kids, 1993, The Art of Arousal, 1993, Dr. Ruth's Encyclopedia of Sex, 1994; contbr. articles to mags.; appeared in film A Woman or Two, 1986; appeared on TV show Quantum Leap, 1993. Fellow N.Y. Acad. Medicine. Office: King Features Syndicate Inc 235 E 45th St New York NY 10017-3305 also: Lifetime TV 36-12 35th Ave Astoria NY 11106

WESTHEIMER, RUTH WELLING, retired management consultant; b. Detroit, May 17, 1922; d. Benjamin Dennis and Elsa (Friedenberg) Welling; m. Robert Irvin. BA, U. Wis., 1944. V.p., bd. dirs. Sterling Stones Ctr., Cin., 1976-85; chmn., developer Vol. Action Ctr., Cin., 1979-82; trustee United Way Community Chest, Cin., 1980-88; organizer Cooporate Voluntarism Council, Cin., 1982-85; v.p., exec. com. United Way Community Chest, Cin., 1983-85; chmn. Evaluation Com. United Way, Cin., 1985-88; advisor YWCA Career Women Achievement, Cin., 1981—; bd. dirs. Cancer Family Care, Cin., 1986—; chmn. United Way Agy. Partnership Devel., Cin., 1988—; treas. Workum Scholarship Found., Cin., 1969-86; chmn. Fine Arts Fund;. Trustee Cin. Psychoanalytic Found., 1974-78, Ohio Citizens Coun., Columbus, 1967-70; bd. dirs. Planned Parenthood Assn., Cin., 1991—. Mem. Woman's City Club, League of Women Voters (treas. 1959-68),. Avocations: tennis, golf, horticulture, travel. Home: 2525 Rookwood Pl Cincinnati OH 45208-3340

WESTIN, ALAN FURMAN, political science educator; b. N.Y.C., Nov. 11, 1929; s. Irving and Etta (Furman) W.; m. Beatrice Patricia Shapoff, June 20, 1954; children: David, Debra, Jeremy. B.A., U. Fla., 1948; LL.B., Harvard U., 1951; Ph.D. teaching fellow, 1965. Bar: D.C. 1951. Sr. fellow Yale U. Law Sch., New Haven, 1956-57, vis. prof. sch., 1960-61; asst. prof. govt. Cornell U., Ithaca, N.Y., 1957-59; assoc. prof. pub. law and govt. Columbia U., N.Y.C., 1959-66; prof. Columbia U., 1966—; dir. Ctr. Research and Edn. in Am. Liberties, 1965-71; founder, pres. Ednl. Fund Individual Rights, N.Y.C., 1978-86; pres. Changing Workplaces, Englewood, N.J., 1982-87; program assoc. Harvard U., 1968-72; cons. IBM, 1973-75, U.S. Office Tech. Assessment, 1973—; pres. Ctr. Social and Legal Rsch., 1987—, Ref. Point Found., 1987—; ptnr. Privacy and Legis. Assocs., Washington, 1993—; cons. on privacy to Equifax, Citicorp, IBM, Am. Express, U.S. Social Security Adminstrn., U.S. Gen. Svcs. Adminstrn., Chrysler, Health Data Exch., Bell Atlantic; acad. advisor nat. pub. surveys on privacy Louis Harris and Assocs., 1979, 90, 91, 92, 93, 94, 95; dir. privacy and human genome project U.S. Dept. Energy, 1992-95; chmn. Res. Coun. Healthy Cos., 1991—. Author: The Anatomy of a Constitutional Law Case, 1958, Privacy and Freedom, 1967 (George Polk award, Sidney Hillman award, Melcher award, Van Am. Soc. award 1967), (with Barry Mahoney) The Trial of Martin Luther King, 1975, (with Michael A. Baker) Databanks in a Free Society, 1972; editor: Whistle Blowing! Loyalty and Dissent in the Corporation, 1980, Information Technology in a Democracy, 1971, (with Alfred Feliu) Resolving Employment Disputes Without Litigation, 1988, (with John D. Aram) Managerial Dilemmas: Cases in Social, Legal, and Technological Change, 1988; editor-in-chief: The Civil Liberties Rev., 1973-79; polit. sci. editor: Casebook Series, 1960-66; contbr. numerous chpts. to books, articles to legal and popular publs.; mem. editorial bd. Employee Rights and Responsibilities Jour, Information Age, Jour. Computing and Society, Transnational Data Report; writer-narrator: CBS-TV Series, The Road to the White House, 1964; cons. spl. programs: ABC-TV.; pub. editor-in-chief Privacy and American Business, 1993—. Mem. Nat. Wiretapping Commn., 1973-76; vice-chmn. N.J. Commn. Individual Liberty, 1977-81; sr. cons. U.S. Privacy Protection Study Commn., 1975-77. Recipient Mark Van Doren award Columbia U., 1972; recipient Disting. Alumnus award Delta Sigma Rho-Tau-Kappa Alpha, 1965; grantee Rockefeller Found., 1983, Russell Saga Found., 1969-71, 81-82. Mem. Nat. Acad. Scis. (computer sci. and engring. bd. 1969-72), Am. Polit. Sci. Assn., Assn. Computing Machinery (chmn. task force privacy 1972-73). Home: 1100 Trafalgar St Teaneck NJ 07666-1928 Office: 118th St And Amsterdam Ave New York NY 10027 also: Ref Pt and Ctr Social/Legal Rsch/Ste 414 2 University Plz Hackensack NJ 07601-6202

WESTIN, DAVID LAWRENCE, lawyer; b. Flint, Mich., July 29, 1952; s. Lawrence Rae and Mary Louise (Holman) W.; m. Victoria Peters; children: Victoria, Elizabeth. BA, U. Mich., 1974, JD, 1977. Bar: D.C. 1979. Law clk. U.S. Ct. Appeals (2d cir.), N.Y.C., 1977-78, U.S. Supreme Ct., Washington, 1979; assoc. Wilmer, Cutler & Pickering, Washington, 1979-84, ptnr., 1985-91; sr. v.p., gen. counsel Capital Cities/ABC, Inc., N.Y.C., 1991-93; pres. of prodn. ABC TV Network, N.Y.C., 1993-94; pres. ABC TV Network News Group, N.Y.C., 1993-94; lectr. Harvard U. Law Sch., Cambridge, Mass., 1986; adj. prof. Georgetown U. Law Ctr., Washington, 1989-91. Bd. dirs. Lincoln Ctr. Film. Soc., 1994—, Am. Arbitration Assn., 1991—. Democrat. Presbyterian. Club: Chevy Chase (Md.). Home: 4103 Bradley Ln Chevy Chase MD 20815 Office: Capital Cities/ABC Inc 77 W 66th St New York NY 10023-6201

WESTLAKE, DONALD EDWIN, author; b. N.Y.C., July 12, 1933; s. Albert Joseph and Lillian Marguerite (Bounds) W.; m. Nedra Henderson, Aug. 10, 1957 (div. 1966); m. Sandra Foley, Apr. 9, 1967 (div. 1975); m. Abigail Adams, May 18, 1979; children: Sean, Steven, Tod, Paul; stepchildren: Adrienne Adams, Patrick Adams, Katharine Adams. Student, SUNY, Plattsburgh and Binghamton. Author. 50 novels including The Mercenaries, 1960, Killing Time, 1961, 361, 1962, Killy, 1963, Pity Him Afterwards, 1964, The Fugitive Pigeon, 1965, The Busy Body, 1966, The Spy in the Ointment, 1966, God Save the Mark, 1967 (Edgar Allen Poe award Mystery Writers Am. 1967), Philip, 1967, The Curious Facts Preceding My Execution, and Other Fictions, 1968, Who Stole Sassi Manoon, 1968?, Somebody Owes Me Money, 1969, Up' Your Banners, 1969, The Hot Rock, 1970, Adios, Scheherezade, 1970, I Gave at The Office, 1971, Under An English Heaven, 1971, Bank Shot, 1972, Cops and Robbers, 1972, (with Brian Garfield) Gangway, 1972, Help I Am Being Held Prisoner, 1974, Jimmy The Kid, 1974, Two Much, 1975, A Travesty, 1975, Brothers Keepers, 1975, Dancing Aztecs, 1976, Enough!, 1977, Nobody's Perfect, 1977, Castle in the Air,

1980, Kahawa, 1982, Why Me?, 1983, Levine, 1984, A Likely Story, 1984, High Adventure, 1985, Good Behavior, 1986, (with Abby Westlake) High Jinx, 1987, (with A. Westlake) Transylvania Station, 1987, Trust Me On This, 1988, Sacred Monster, 1989, Tomorrow's Crimes, 1989, Drowned Hopes, 1990, Humans, 1992, Don't Ask, 1993, Baby, Would I Lie?, 1994, Smoke, 1995; (as John B. Allan) Elizabeth Taylor: A Fascinating Story of America's Most Talented Actress and the World's Most Beautiful Woman, 1961; (as Tucker Coe) Kinds of Love, Kinds of Death, 1966, Murder among Children, 1968, Wax Apple, 1970, A Jade in Aries, 1971, Don't Lie to Me, 1972; (as Richard Stark) The Hunter, 1963 (pub. as Point Blank, 1973), The Man with the Getaway Face, 1963 (pub. as The Steel Hit, 1971), The Outfit, 1963, The Mourner, 1963, The Score, 1964, The Jugger, 1965, The Seventh, 1966, The Handle, 1966 (pub. as Run Lethal, 1966), The Damsel, 1967, The Dame, 1967, The Rare Coin Score, 1967, The Green Eagle Score, 1967, The Black Ice Score, 1968, The Sour Lemon Score, 1969, The Blackbird, 1969, Deadly Edge, 1971, Slayground, 1971, Lemons Never Lie, 1971, Plunder Squad, 1972, Butcher's Moon, 1974, Stark Mysteries, 1981; screenwriter: Cops and Robbers, 1973, (with Michael Kane) Hot Stuff, 1979, The Stepfather, 1986, Why Me?, 1990, The Grifters, 1990 (Academy award nomination best adapted screenplay 1990), (TV movies) Supertrain, 1979, Jimmy the Kid, 1985, Fatal Confession: A Father Dowling Mystery, 1987. Served with USAF, 1954-56. Recipient Edgar Allen Poe Grand Master award Mystery Writers Am., 1992. Office: c/o Knox Burger Assocs 39 1/2 Washington Sq S New York NY 10012-1004•

WESTLAKE, ROBERT ELMER, SR., physician; b. Jersey City, Oct. 2, 1918; s. Henry Ebenezer and Bertha (Fowle) W.; m. Agnes Vivian Kumpf, Oct. 1, 1944; children—Robert Elmer, Barbara Elizabeth, Richard Louis. Grad., Lawrenceville Sch., 1936; A.B., Princeton, 1940; M.D., Columbia, 1943. Diplomate: Am. Bd. Internal Medicine. Intern Englewood (N.J.) Hosp., 1944, 46-47; resident Univ. Hosp., Syracuse, N.Y., 1947-49; instr. medicine State U. N.Y. Med. Center, Syracuse, 1949-50; asst. prof. State U. N.Y. Med. Center, 1950-52, clin. asso. prof., 1956-67, clin. prof., 1967-81, clin. prof. emeritus, 1981—; pvt. practice internal medicine Syracuse, 1952-81; mem. staff State Univ., Crouse-Irving-Meml. VA hosps.; dir. profl. services Community Gen. Hosp., 1967-81; cons. USPHS, 1966-72, Social Security Adminstrn., 1968-71; mem. Com. Rev. Regional Med. Programs, NIH, 1966-67; med. adv. council Dept. Def., 1969-74; pres. Profl. Standards Rev. Orgn. Central N.Y., 1974-77. Contbr. articles to profl. jours. Pres. Onondaga Found. Med. Care, 1961-68; v.p. Blue Shield Central N.Y., 1965-73, chmn. bd., 1973-81. Served to lt. (j.g.) M.C. USNR, 1944-46. Fellow A.C.P.; mem. Am. Soc. Internal Medicine (pres. 1965-66), Onondaga County Heart Assn. (pres. 1963-64). Home: 5056 SE Bent Wood Dr Stuart FL 34997-1603

WESTLEY, JOHN RICHARD, foreign service officer; b. Fairmont, Minn., Feb. 25, 1939; s. Richard and Margaret (Kindschi) W.; m. Sidney Kathryn Bohanna, Mar. 26, 1966(div. Sept. 1977); children: Elizabeth Laura, Karen Margaret, Marian Bohanna; m. Joan Nancy Ehrlich, Apr. 12, 1980; 1 child, Katherine Matthea. BA in Philosophy, Yale U., 1961; MA in Econs., Columbia U., 1966; PhD in Econs., Am. Univ., 1983. Internat. economist U.S. Dept. Treasury, Washington, 1966-69; loan officer U.S. AID, Addis Ababa, Ethiopia, 1970-72; economist U.S. AID, Nairobi, Kenya, 1973-75, Washington, 1976-78; program officer U.S. AID, New Delhi, India, 1979-84; dir. mission to Bangladesh U.S. AID, Dhaka, 1985-87; assoc. asst. adminstr. bur. Africa U.S. AID, Washington, 1987-90; dir. mission to Kenya U.S. AID, Nairobi, 1990-94; dir. Mission to Egypt US AID, Cairo, 1994—. Author: Agriculture and Equitable Growth, 1986. With U.S. Army, 1961-64. Mem. Am. Econ. Assn., Soc. for Internat. Devel., Phi Beta Kappa. Presbyterian. Home and Office: USAID Unit 64902 APO AE 09839

WESTLING, JON, university administrator; b. Yakima, Wash., June 7, 1942; s. Norman L. and Jean R. (Bergamini) W.; m. Elizabeth A. Wüthrich, Oct. 14, 1977; children: Emma E., Matthew R., Andrew N. BA, Reed Coll., 1964; postgrad., St. John's Coll. Oxford (Eng.) U., 1964-67, UCLA, 1971-74. Instr. history Centre Coll., Danville, Ky., 1967-68; asst. prof. history and humanities Reed Coll., Portland, Oreg., 1968-71; assoc. dir. Boston Univ. Prodns., 1974-76; asst. to pres. Boston U., 1976-79, assoc. provost, 1979-83, provost ad interim, 1983-84, provost, 1984-88, exec. v.p., 1988-90, interim pres., 1990, exec. v.p., provost, 1991-95, provost, pres.-elect, 1995—; bd. dirs. Century Bank. Bd. dirs. Mass. Corp. for Ednl. Telecomms., 1990—; trustee Boston Mus. Sci., 1990—. Gen. Motors Nat. scholar, 1960-64, Rhodes scholar, 1964-67. Home: 7 Churchill Ln Lexington MA 02173-5801 Office: Boston U Office Provost 145 Bay State Rd Boston MA 02215-1790

WESTMAN, CARL EDWARD, lawyer; b. Youngstown, Ohio, Dec. 12, 1943; s. Carl H. and Mary Lillis (Powell) W.; m. Carolyn J., July 17, 1965; children: C. Forrest, Stephanie A. BBA, Sam Houston State U., 1966; JD, U. Miami, 1969, LLM in Taxation, 1972. Bar: Fla. 1969. Ptnr. Frost & Jacobs, 1983-93, Roetzel & Andress, Naples, Fla., 1993—. S.W. Fla. coun. Boy Scouts Am. Eagle Bd. of Review, 1987—; trustee David Lawrence Found. for Mental Health, Inc., 1976-86, chmn. 1985-86; trustee Pikeville Coll., 1993—, Naples Cmty. Hosp., 1992—; past pres. bd. trustees, elder Moorings Presbyn. Ch. Mem. ABA, Fla. Bar, Collier County Bar Assn., Estate Planning Coun, Coral Reef Yacht Club, Useppa Island Club. Home: 1952 Crayton Rd Naples FL 33940-5070 Office: Roetzel & Andress 3003 Tamiami Trl N Naples FL 33940-4102

WESTMAN, JACK CONRAD, child psychiatrist, educator; b. Cadillac, Mich., Oct. 28, 1927; s. Conrad A. and Alice (Pedersen) W.; m. Nancy K. Baehre, July 17, 1953; children—Daniel P., John C., Eric C. M.D., U. Mich., 1952. Diplomate: Am. Bd. Psychiatry and Neurology. Intern Duke Hosp., Durham, N.C., 1952-53; resident U. Mich. Med. Center, 1955-59; dir. Outpatient Services, Children's Psychiatric Hosp., Ann Arbor, Mich., 1961-65; assoc. prof. U. Mich. Med. Sch., 1964-65; coordinator Diagnostic and Treatment Unit, Washington Center, U. Wis., Madison, 1966-74; prof. psychiatry, 1965—; cons. Joint Commn. on Mental Health of Children, 1967-69, Madison (Wis.) Pub. Schs., 1965-74, Children's Treatment Center, Mendota Mental Health Inst., 1965-69. Author: Individual Differences in Children, 1973, Child Advocacy, 1979, Handbook of Learning Disabilities, 1990, Who Speaks for the Children?, 1991, Licensing Parents, 1994; editor: Child Psychiatry and Human Development; contbr. articles to profl. jours. Vice-pres. Big Bros. of Dane County, 1970-73; v.p. Wis. Assn. Mental Health, 1968-72; co-chmn. Project Understanding, 1968-75. Served with USNR, 1953-55. Fellow Am. Psychiat. Assn., Am. Coll. Psychiatrists, Am. Acad. Child and Adolescent Psychiatry, Am. Orthopsychiat. Assn. (bd. dirs. 1973-76); mem. Am. Assn. Psychiat. Svcs. for Children (pres. 1978-80), Multidisciplinary Acad. Clin. Edn. (pres. 1992—). Home: 1234 Dartmouth Rd Madison WI 53705-2214 Office: 600 Highland Ave Madison WI 53792-0001

WESTMORE, MICHAEL GEORGE, make-up artist; b. Hollywood, Calif., Mar. 22, 1938; s. Montague George and Edith Adeline W.; m. Marion Christine Bergeson, Dec. 4, 1966; children: Michael George, Michele, McKenzie. BA, U. Calif. Santa Barbara, 1961. Apprentice make-up artist Universal City Studios, Universal City, Calif., 1961-63, staff make-up artist, 1964, asst. head dept. make-up lab., 1965-71; freelance make-up artist various studios, Hollywood, Calif., 1971-87; make-up supr. and designer Paramount Studios, Studio City, 1987—; Instr. theatre arts dept. Los Angeles Valley Coll., 1966—; pres. Cosmetic Control Centers, Inc., 1971-76; pres. Hollywood Magic Cosmetics, 1985-87; research cons., lectr. therapeutic cosmetics for med. assns. Author: The Art of Theatrical Make-Up for Stage and Screen, 1971, also chpts. in books; co-author: Star Trek Makeup FX Journal; make-up artist for TV spls. Eleanor and Franklin (Emmy award Nat. Acad. TV Arts and Scis. 1984), Why Me? (Emmy award 1984), Three Wishes of Billy Grier (Emmy award 1985), Star Trek (Emmy award 1988, 1992, 1993), Amazing Stories (Emmy award 1987), (films) 2010 (Acad. award nomination Acad. Motion Picture Arts and Scis. 1985), Mask (Acad. award 1986), Clan of the Cave Bear (Acad. award nomination 1987). Served with AUS, 1956. Mem. Internat. Alliance Theatrical Stage Employees, Soc. Make-up Artists, Vikings of Scandia, Lambda Chi Alpha (life). Address: 3830 Sunswept Dr Studio City CA 91604

WESTMORELAND, BARRY KEITH, state legislator; b. Kingsport, Tenn., Aug. 26, 1946; s. Horace Arnold and Ruth (Taylor) W.; m. Alice Charles, Feb. 1, 1977; children: Joel Keith, Stoney Lee. BS in Criminal Justice cum laude, East Tenn. State U., 1973; postgrad., U. Tenn., Walter State C.C.

Policeman Kingsport Police Dept., 1968-69; dep. sheriff Sullivan County Sheriff's Dept., Blountville, Tenn., 1973-75, chief dep., adminstr., 1976-86; law enforcement planner 1st Tenn. Regional Law Enforcement Planning Agy., Johnson City, 1975-76; CEO Sullivan County, Blountville, 1986-90; mem. Tenn. Ho. of Reps., Nashville, 1992—; cons. Alternative Correction Systems, Johnson City, 1993—; mem. criminal justice adv. bd. Walters State C.C., East Tenn. State U. Former chmn. exec. com. Tri-Cities Airport Commn.; former chmn. Sullivan County Indsl. Commn.; former mem. bd. dirs. 1st Tenn. Devel. Dist., Upper East Tenn. Human Devel. Agy.; bd. dirs. Holston Valley Hosp. and Med. Ctr., Upper East Tenn. Jevenile Detention Ctr., 1st Tenn. Human Resource Agy.; mem. adv. bd. Salvation Army; mem. adv. bd. N.E. Tenn. Community Coll.; mem. Kingsport Visitors Coun., Legis. Com. for Econ. Devel., East Tenn. Tourism Coun.; also others. Sgt. USAF, 1964-68; bd. dirs. Sullivan County Children's Advocacy Ctr.. Job Tng. Partnership Act. Named Legislator of Yr. Tenn. Devel. Dists., 1994, Outstanding Legislator Tenn. Forestry Assn., 1994; recipient award of merit Tenn. Human Resources Agy. Assn., 1994. Mem. NRA, Tenn. County Execs. Assn. (v.p.), Tenn. County Svcs. Assn., United Comml. Travelers, Outdoorsman, Kingsport Interfraternal Coun., Eagles, Moose. Republican. Methodist. Avocations: hunting, fishing, golf. Address: 3216 Kenridge St Kingsport TN 37664 Office: Tenn Ho of Reps 214 War Memorial Bldg Nashville TN 37243

WESTMORELAND, KENT EWING, lawyer; b. Tulsa, May 17, 1949; s. Earl E. and Adeline (Burckhalter) W.; m. Mary Kathleen Price, June 14, 1981. B.B.A., So. Meth. U., 1971; J.D., U. Tex., 1975. Bar: Tex. 1975, U.S. Dist. Ct. (so. dist.) Tex. 1976, U.S. Dist. Ct. (ea. dist.) Tex. 1977, U.S. Ct. Appeals (5th cir.) 1977, U.S. Ct. Appeals (11th cir.) 1982, U.S. Dist. Ct. (no. dist.) Tex. 1984, U.S. Supreme Ct. 1985; cert. Tex. Bd. Legal Specialization, Civil Trial Law, Personal Injury Trial Law. Atty., Kronzer, Abraham & Watkins, Houston, 1975-76, Eastham, Watson, Dale & Forney, Houston, 1976-79, Ross, Griggs & Harrison, Houston, 1979-90, Phelps Dunbar, 1990—. Served with USNR, 1972-78. Mem. Maritime Law Assn. U.S. (proctor 1977), Tex. Assn. Def. Lawyers, Metro. Racquet Club, Sweetwater Country Club. Republican. Methodist. Home: 5303 Pine St Bellaire TX 77401-4810 Office: Phelps Dunbar 1331 Lamar St Ste 501 Houston TX 77010-3026

WESTMORELAND, REGINALD CONWAY, journalism educator; b. Navarro, Tex., Oct. 31, 1926; s. Mark Arthur Westmoreland and Grace Beryl (Knight) Westmoreland Denton; m. Mary Nell Burns, Feb. 6, 1949; children: Linda Carol, Lisa Kay, David Conway. BA, U. North Tex., 1947, MA, 1956; PhD, U. Mo., 1961. Reporter, editor Dallas Times Herald, 1947-55; tchr. journalism Abilene (Tex.) Christian U., 1955-64; chair U. North Tex., Denton, 1974-88; prof., assoc. dean Pepperdine U., Malibu, Calif., 1983-85. Author: How to Write for Newspapers, 1966, A Guide to Church Publicity, 1971; (Times Herald history) 100 Years, 1979; editor: Columbia Missourian, summers, 1959, 60. Capt. USAR, 1950-59. Southern Fund fellow, 1959-61. Mem. Am. Assn. Schs. and Depts. Journalism (pres. 1980-81), Am. Soc. Journalism Sch. Adminstrs. (pres. 1978-79), Assn. Edn. Journalism and Mass Comms. (exec. com. 1978-81), Tex. Journalism Edn. Coun. (pres. 1976-77). Avocations: writing, computers, reading, travel. Home: 2021 N Lake Trl Denton TX 76201-0603 Office: U North Tex PO Box 5278 Denton TX 76203-5278

WESTOFF, CHARLES FRANCIS, demographer, educator; b. N.Y.C., July 23, 1927; s. Frank Barnett and Evelyn (Bales) W.; m. Joan P. Uszynski, Sept. 11, 1948 (div. Jan. 1969); children: David, Carol; m. Leslie Aldridge, Aug. 1969 (div. Feb. 1993). A.B., Syracuse U., 1949, M.A., 1950; Ph.D., U. Pa., 1953. Instr. sociology U. Pa., 1950-52; research assoc. Milbank Meml. Fund, N.Y.C., 1952-55; research assoc. Office Population Research Princeton U., 1955-62, prof. sociology, 1962—; Maurice P. During '22 prof. demographic studies and sociology, 1972—, chmn. dept. sociology, 1965-70, assoc. dir. Office Population Research, 1962-75, dir., 1975-92; assoc. prof. sociology N.Y.U., also chmn. dept. sociology Washington Sq. Coll., 1959-62; vis. sr. fellow East-West Population Inst., Honolulu, 1979, 81; Disting. vis. prof. Am. U., Cairo, 1979; mem. vis. com. Harvard-M.I.T. Joint Center for Urban Studies, 1980-83; exec. dir. Commn. Population growth and Am. Future, 1970-72; mem. adv. com. on population stats. U.S. Bur. Census, 1973-79; chmn. Nat. Com. for Rsch. on 1980 Census, 1981-88; bd. dirs. Alan Guttmacher Inst., 1977-88, 89—; sr. tech. advisor Demographic Health Surveys, 1984—; bd. dirs. Population Resource Ctr., 1985—, Population Ref. Bur., 1988-94, Population Comms. Internat., 1992—; com. on population NAS, 1983-88. Co-author: Family Growth in Metropolitan America, 1961, The Third Child, 1963, College Women and Fertility Values, 1967, The Later Years of Childbearing, 1970, From Now to Zero, 1971, Reproduction in the United States, 1965, 71, Toward the End of Growth: Population in America, 1973, The Contraceptive Revolution, 1976, Demographic Dynamics in America, 1977, Age at Marriage, Age at First Birth, and Fertility in Africa, 1992; contbr. articles on demography and sociology to profl. jours. Fellow Am. Sociol. Assn., Am. Acad. Arts and Scis.; mem. Inst. Medicine Nat. Acad. Sci., Planned Parenthood Fedn. Am. (dir. 1978-81), Population Assn. Am. (bd. dirs. 1960-62, 68-70, 1st v.p. 1972-73, pres. 1974-75), Internat. Union Sci. Study Population. Home: 537 Drakes Corner Rd Princeton NJ 08540-7515

WESTON, ARTHUR WALTER, chemist, scientific and business executive; b. Smith Falls, Ont. Can., Feb. 13, 1914; came to U.S., 1935, naturalized, 1952; s. Herbert W. and Alice M. (Houghton) W.; m. V. Dawn Thompson, Sept. 10, 1940; children: Roger L., Randall K., Cynthia B. BA, Queen's U., Kingston, Ont., 1934, MA, 1935; PhD, Northwestern U., 1938. Postdoctoral fellow Northwestern U, Evanston, Ill., 1938-40; with Abbott Labs., North Chgo., Ill., 1940-79, dir. rsch. and devel., 1959-61, v.p. rsch. and devel. 1961-68, dir. company, 1959-68, v.p. sci. affairs, 1968-77, v.p. corp. licensing, 1977-79; v.p., dir. San-Abbott, Japan, 1976-79; cons. Abbott Labs., North Chgo., Ill., 1979-85; pres. Arthur W. Weston & Assocs., Lake Forest, Ill., 1979—. Contbr. profl. jours. and books. Patentee in field. Mem. Office Sci. Rsch. and Devel., War Manpower Commn., 1942-45; mem. exec. com. indsl. chemistry, div. chemistry and chem. tech. NRC, 1961-65; mem. indsl. panel on sci. and tech. NSF, 1974-80; mem. ad hoc com. chem. agts. Dept. Def., 1961-65. Mem. Rsch. Dirs. Assn. Chgo. (pres. 1965-66), Am. Chem. Soc. (trustee Chgo. 1965—, dir. Chgo. sect. 1952-59, nat. com. corp. assocs. 1967-72), Dirs. Indsl. Rsch., Indsl. Rsch. Inst. (bd. dirs. 1970-73), Phi Beta Kappa, Sigma Xi, Phi Lambda Upsilon. Home and Office: 349 Hilldale Pl Lake Forest IL 60045-3031

WESTON, BURNS HUMPHREY, law educator; b. Cleve., Nov. 5, 1933; s. Stephen Burns and Simonne Humphrey Weston; m. Marta Cullberg; children: Timothy Bergmann, Rebecca Burns. Student, Oberlin Conservatory of Music, 1952-53, Western Res. U., 1954, U. Edinburgh, Scotland, 1954-55; BA, Oberlin Coll., 1956; LLB, Yale U., 1961, D of Jud. Sci., 1970. Bar: N.Y. 1963, Iowa 1968. Assoc. Paul, Weiss, Rifkind, Wharton & Garrison, N.Y.C., 1961-64; assoc. prof. law U. Iowa, Iowa City, 1966-67, assoc. prof. law, 1967-69, prof. law, 1969-83, Bessie Dutton Murray disting. prof. law, 1983—, founding dir. ctr. for world order studies, 1972-76, chair internat. and comparative law program, 1990-92; assoc. dean for internat. and comparative legal studies, 1992—, chair grad. program in internat. and comparative law, 1992—; vis. prof. Grinnell Coll., 1974, UCLA, 1981; sr. fellow, dir. Transnational Acad. Program Inst. for World Order, 1976-78; vis. prof. summer program A. Schweitzer U., Aix-en-Provence, 1991; cons. internat. law Naval War Coll., 1968-69, Club of Rome Project on Global Learning, 1977-79. Author: International Claims: Postwar French Practice, 1971, (with Richard B. Lillich) International Claims: Their Settlement by Lump Sum Agreements, 2 vols., 1975; editor, author: (with W. Michael Reisman) Toward World Order and Human Dignity: Essays in Honor of Myres S. McDougal, 1976, Peace and World Order Studies: A Curriculum Guide, 1978; (with Richard A. Falk and Anthony A. D'Amato) International Law and World Order, 1980, (with Lillich) International Claims: Contemporary European Practice, 1982, Toward Nuclear Disarmament and Global Security: A Search for Alternatives, 1984, (with Richard P. Claude) Human Rights in the World Community: Issues and Action, 1989, Alternative Security: Living Without Nuclear Deterrence, 1990, (with Richard A. Falk and Anthony D'Amato) International Law and World Order: A Problem-Oriented Coursebook, 2d ed., 1990, Basic Documents in International Law and World Order, 2d ed., 1990; contbr. numerous writings to many publs. in field; mem. bd. editors Am. Jour. Internat. Law, editorial com. Bull. Peace Proposals; mem. editorial adv. bd. Innovation in Internat. Law Series,

Transnational Pubs.; mem. editorial rev. bd. Human Rights Quarterly; mem. editorial bd. Jour. World Peace. Mem. Internat. Studies Assn. Consortium of Peace Rsch. Edn. and Devel., Coun. on Fgn. Rels., Global Edn. Assocs., Iowa City Fgn. Rels. Coun., World Future Studies Fedn., Lawyers Com. on Nuclear Policy, Internat. Assn. of Lawyers Against Nuclear Arms; mem. peace law and edn. project Meiklejohn Civil Liberties Inst.; bd. dirs. Iowa divsn. UN Assn.-USA. Rockefeller Found. and Sterling fellow Yale U. Law Sch., 1964-66, rsch. fellow Procedural Aspects Internat. Law Inst., 1967-74; sr. fellow World Policy Inst., 1974-91, World Order Teaching fellow, 1980-83, World Acad. Art and Sci. fellow, 1982—; recipient Scroll of Honor award UN Assn. Iowa div., 1991. Mem. ABA (past standing com. on World order under law, internat. law and practice sect., individual rights and responsibility sect.), Am. Assn. for Internat. Commn. on Jurists, Am. Soc. Internat. Law (spl. commendation 1978, award 1982), Internat. Human Rights Law Group, Lawyers Alliance for World Security, Internat. Peace Rsch. Assn., Procedural Aspects Internat. Law Inst., Am. Soc. Internat. Law (v.p. 1992—), U.S. Assn. for Club of Rome. Avocations: music, mountain climbing, gardening. Office: Univ Iowa Coll Law Boyd Law Bldg Iowa City IA 52242

WESTON, I. DONALD, architect; b. Bklyn., Feb. 16, 1928; s. Martyn N. and Betty (Lash) W.; m. Sylvia Stone, Oct. 23, 1952; children: Suzanne, Pamela. BArch, MIT, 1950; MArch, Pratt Inst., 1959, M in City and Regional Planning, 1981. Cert. Nat. Coun. Archtl. Regis. Bd.; lic. architect N.Y., Mass. Ptnr., prin. Martyn & Don Weston Architects, Bklyn., 1956—. Co-authored 2 studies for determining methods of reducing the cost of pub. housing, 1960. Mem. Mayor's Blue Ribbon Panel to Investigate the Bldg. Process in N.Y.C., 1987-88; pro bono pub. mem., sec. Cadman Plz. Co-op., Bklyn., 1972-78. Fellow AIA (mem. Bklyn. chpt. 1954—, pres. 1964-65); mem. Nat. Sculpture Soc. (v.p. 1990—), Fine Arts Fedn. N.Y. (v.p. 1981—, pres. 1984-87, 90-91), Art Cccommn. Assocs. (pres. 1991-92). Avocations: tennis, golf, community activism. Office: Martyn & Don Weston Arch 100 Remsem St Brooklyn NY 11201

WESTON, JOHN FREDERICK, business educator, consultant; b. Ft. Wayne, Ind., Feb. 6, 1916; s. David Thomas and Bertha (Schwartz) W.; children: Kenneth F., Byron L., Ellen J. B.A., U. Chgo., 1937, M.B.A., 1943, Ph.D., 1948. Instr. U. Chgo. Sch. Bus., 1940-42, asst. prof., 1947-48; prof. Anderson Grad. Sch. Mgmt. UCLA, 1949—, Cordner prof. Anderson Grad. Sch. Mgmt., 1981-94; prof. emeritus Anderson Grad. Sch. Mgmt. UCLA, 1986—; econ. cons. to pres. Am. Bankers Assn., 1945-46; disting. lecture series U. Okla., 1967, U. Utah, 1972, Miss. State U., 1972, Miami State U., 1975; dir. UCLA Anderson Grad. Sch. Mgmt. Rsch. Program in Competition and Bus. Policy, 1969—, Ctr. for Managerial Econs. and Pub. Policy, 1983-86. Author: Scope and Methodology of Finance, 1966, International Managerial Finance, 1972, Impact of Large Firms on U.S. Economy, 1973, Financial Theory and Corporate Policy, 1979, 2d edit., 1983, 3d edit., 1988, Managerial Finance, 9th edit, 1992; assoc. editor: Jour. of Finance, 1948-55; mem. editorial bd., 1957-59; editorial bd. Bus. Econs., Jour. Fin. Rsch.; Managerial and Decision Econs.; manuscript referee Am. Econ. Rev., Rev. of Econs. and Statistics, Engring. Economist. Bd. dirs. Bunker Hill Fund. Served with Ordnance Dept. AUS, 1943-45. Recipient Abramson Scroll award Bus. Econs., 1989-93; McKinsey Found. grantee, 1965-68; GE grantee, 1967; Ford Found. Faculty Rsch. fellow, 1961-62. Mem. Am. Finance Assn. (pres. 1966, adv. bd. 1967-71), Am. Econ. Assn., Western Econ. Assn. (pres. 1962), Econometric Soc., Am. Statis. Assn., Royal Econ. Soc., Fin. Analysts Soc., Fin. Mgmt. Assn. (pres. 1979-80). Home: 258 Tavistock Ave Los Angeles CA 90049-3229 Office: UCLA Anderson Grad Sch Mgmt Los Angeles CA 90095-1481

WESTON, JOSH S., data processing company executive; b. Bklyn., Dec. 22, 1928; married. B.S., CCNY, 1950; M.A., U. New Zealand, 1951. Exec. v.p. Popular Services, Inc., 1955-70; v.p. planning adminstrn. Automatic Data Processing, Inc., Roseland, N.J., 1970-75, exec. v.p., 1975-77, pres. from 1977, chief exec. officer, 1982—; former chief operating officer, now also chmn.; dir. Shared Med. Systems, Pub. Service Electric & Gas Co. Office: ADP Inc 1 A D P Blvd Roseland NJ 07068-1728*

WESTON, M. MORAN, II, educator, real estate developer, banker, clergyman; b. Tarboro, N.C., Sept. 10, 1910; s. Milton Moran and Catharine C. (Perry) W.; m. June 27, 1946; children: Karann Christine, Gregory. BA, Columbia U., 1930, PhD, 1954, STD (hon.), 1968; DD (hon.), Va. Theol. Sch., 1964; DHL (hon.), Fordham U., 1988. Bus. mgr. St. Philips Episcopal Ch., N.Y.C., 1948-51; exec. sec. Christian Citizenship Nat. Council, Episcopal Ch., N.Y.C., 1951-57; rector, chief executive officer St. Philips Ch. and Community Svc. Council, N.Y.C., 1957-82; sr. prof. SUNY, Albany, 1959-77, prof. emeritus, 1977—; pvt. housing developer, 1982—; vis. prof. U. Ife, Ile-Ife, Nigeria, 1977; chmn. bd. Carver Fed. Savs. Bank, N.Y.C., 1980—; bd. mem., founder, Carver Fed. Bank, N.Y.C., 1948—; trustee Columbia U., 1969-81, trustee emeritus, 1981—; trustee St. Augustine Coll., Raleigh, N.C., 1970—, Mt. Sinai Hosp. Med. Sch. and Ctr., N.Y.C., 1971—; trustee emeritus, Columbia U., 1981—; pres. 6 housing corps. Co-developer (two 24-story condominium bldgs.) Towers-on-the-Park, 1986; author: Social Policy, 1964. Founder, pres. Weston United for Cmty. Devel., N.Y.C., 1981, Tri-Continental Assn.; trustee NAACP Legal Def. Fund, N.Y.C., 1965—, Fgn. Policy Assn., N.Y., 1980-89, Phelps Stokes Fund, N.Y.C., 1970-80; cons. 3d Internat. UN Conf. Against Apartheid, 1977. Recipient St. Augustine's Cross, Archbishop of Canterbury, London, 1981, Excellence award Columbia Grad. Sch., N.Y.C., 1982, Humanitarian awards N.Y. Urban League, N.Y.C., 1982, N.Y. YMCA, 1982, Mickey Leland award Hope for the Homeless, 1989, Lifetime of Excellence in Pub. Svc. award Nat. Housing Assn., 1991, Phoenix award Abyssinian Devel. Corp. Mem. Housing for People (founder, pres. 1980—), Nat. Assn. for Affordable Housing, (founder, pres. 1987—), Sigma Pi Phi (pres. Zeta chpt. 1983-86). Club: Lotos (N.Y.C.). Lodge: Elks (Hon. Supreme Exalted Ruler 1946-50). Home: 253 Boulevard E New Rochelle NY 10801-2002 Office: Carver Fed Savs Bank 75 W 125th St New York NY 10027-4512

WESTON, MICHAEL C., lawyer; b. Asheville, N.C., Aug. 13, 1938; m. May Ann Damme; two children. AB in English, Brown U., 1960; JD, U. Mich., 1963. Bar: Mich. 1964, Ill. 1973. Assoc. Hill, Lewis, Adams, Goodrich & Tait, Detroit, 1963-68; from sec. to pres. corp. and indsl. consortium Econ. Devel. Corp. of Greater Detroit, 1969-73; chief staff atty. Northwestern U., Evanston, Ill., 1973-81, v.p. legal affairs, 1981-89; v.p. and gen. counsel, 1990—; lectr. minority bus. devel. Inst. Continuing Legal Edn., conflicts of interest Nat. Coun. Univ. Rsch. Adminstrs. Contbr. articles to profl. jours. Chmn. Univ. Gallery Com., 1982-85; bd. dirs. Northwestern U. Press. Mem. ABA (sect. of taxation, com. on exempt orgns., lectr. Inst. on Minority Bus. Devel.), Chgo. Bar Assn., Chgo. Coun. of Lawyers, Nat. Assn. Coll. and Univ. Attys. (lectr. fed. tax matters, outside activities faculty mems. univ.-community rels., med. risk mgmt., bd. dirs. 1985-88, 1992—, pres. 1995—). Office: Northwestern U 633 Clark St Evanston IL 60208-0002

WESTON, PAUL, composer, arranger, conductor; b. Springfield, Mass.; m. Jo Stafford, 1952; children: Tim, Amy. B in Econs. cum laude, Dartmouth U., 1933; postgrad., Columbia U. Currently pres. Hanover Music Corp., Corinthian Records. free lance arranger for Rudy Vallee, Phil Harris and his Orch., Joe Haymes, Fleischman Radio Hour, 1934-35; worked for Tommy and Jimmy Dorsey, 1935-40, arranged Song of India, Stardust, Night and Day, Who, other songs; 1st motion picture arranging with Bing Crosby Band for Holiday Inn, 1941; other work at Parmount Pictures for Crosby, Bob Hope, Bett Hutton, etc.; as musical dir. at Capitol Records made his own albums in style to be known as Mood Music and accompanied Johnny Mercer, Gordon MacRae, Jo Stafford, Betty Hutton, Dean Martin, others; 1st Capitol album Music for Dreaming; from 1943-50 on radio and making albums; in 1950 with Columbia Records, making instrumental albums, working as West Coast dir. of Artists and Repertoire, and with his own orch. accompanying singers Doris Day, Rosemary Clooney, Jo Stafford, Frankie Laine, others; CBS radio series The Paul Weston Show aired 1951-52; musical dir. NBC-TV, 1957-62; musical dir. Danny Kaye TV show, 1963-67, then with Jonathan Winters and Jim Nabors on CBS; after retiring from TV served as musical dir. for Disney on Parade for 3 yrs. Composer: (pop songs) Day By Day, I Should Care, Shrimp Boats, Autumn in Rome, When April Comes Again; (symphonic suites) Crescent City Suite, The Mercy Partridge Suite; (choral work) The Bells of Santa Ynez; also various religious works

including two masses; 4 comedy albums with Jo Stafford including Grammy award winner Jonathan and Darlene in Paris. Former pres. Crippled Children's Soc. Los Angeles; bd. dirs. Westlake Sch.; active internat. hymnal project with Maryknoll Mission Soc. Founder, 1st nat. pres. Nat. Acad. Recording Arts and Scis., awarded the Acad.'s Trustees award, 1971. Office: Corinthian Records PO Box 6296 Beverly Hills CA 90212-1296*

WESTON, RANDY (RANDOLPH EDWARD WESTON), pianist, composer; b. Bklyn., Apr. 6, 1926; s. Frank Edward and Vivian (Moore) W.; children: Cherryl, Pamela, Niles, Kim. Student, Parkway Music Inst., Bklyn., 1950-52. lectr. on African music UN. Pianist Am. Soc. African Culture tour, Lagos, Nigeria, 1961, 63; toured with Randy Weston's sextet for State Dept., North and West Africa, 1967; appearances include Newport Festival, 1958, Monterey Festival, 1966, Carnegie Hall, 1973, Philharm. Hall, N.Y.C., 1973; appearances maj. jazz clubs in N.Y.C.; also numerous UN concerts, Billie Holiday Theatre, N.Y.U.; European tours include Kingsberg Jazz Festival, Oslo, 1974, Montreux (Switzerland) Jazz Festival, 1974, Festival de Costa del Sol, Marbella, Spain, 1974, Ahus Jazz Festival, Kristianstad, Sweden, 1974, Festival at Antibes, 1974; Tour of Brazil, 1981, Festival de Vienne, France, 1985, Pompeii Jazz Festival, Italy, 1985, Internat. Festival Marrahesh, Marocco, 1986, 1st Festival Gnaoua Culture, Morocco, 1987, Lygano Festival Jazz, Switzerland, 1988, Jazzaldia, San Sebastian, Spain, 1988; Caribbean Cultural Ctrs. Expressions Festival, N.Y.C., 1988, Roots Festival, Lagos, Nigeria, 1988; featured quest artist One Hundred Yrs. of Jazz, Amsterdam, The Netherlands, 1989; lecture-concerts in Europe including Bern, Basel, Zurich, Lyons, 1975; recs. include Blue Moses, 1972 (number 1 in Record World's jazz chart), Volcano Blues, 1993, Monterey '66, 1994; compositions include Pam's Waltz, 1950, Little Niles, 1950, Hi Fly, 1958, Portrait of Vivian, 1959, Berkshire Blues, 1960, Uhruru Africa suite, 4 movements, 1960, African Cook Book, 1965, The Last Day, 1966, The Ganawa, 1971, Portrait of F.E. Weston, 1974, Carnival, Blues to Africa, Nuits Americani, Blue, Trilogy: Portraits of Ellington; Portraits of Monk; Self-Portrait of Weston, Verve, The Spirits of Our Ancestors, 1992; concert artist for radio-TV and maj. U.S. museums including Smithsonian Instn.; performed benefit concerts for anti-apartheid com. at UN through African-Am. Musicians Soc., 1961; appeared in film Jamboree, 1986; commd. The Africans, Spoleto Festival, U.S.A., 1981, The African Queens, Boston Pops, 1981, Portrait of Billie Holiday, Orch. Symphonique de Lyons and Ensemble Instrumental et Big Band de Grenoble, France, 1985, African Sunrise, City of Chicago, 1985; Spanish TV films: Jazz Entre Amigos, 1987, Randy in Tangier; Randy Weston, African Rhythms, Boston TV, 1989. Recipient New Star Pianist award Down Beat Internat. Critics Poll 1955, Pianist Most Deserving of Wider Recognition award, 1972, Broadway award Hollywood Advt. Club 1965, Premier prix de l'Academie du Jazz, France 1975; named World's Best Jazz Pianist Internat. Roots Festival, Lagos, Nigeria, 1988; Randy Weston Week declared in his honor Bklyn. Borough Pres.'s Office/ Bklyn. Acad. Music, 1986; French Office Nationale de Diffusion Artistique grantee, 1976; Nat. Endowment for Arts grantee, 1974. Mem. ASCAP (Composers awards), Am. Fedn. Musicians. Sufi. Address: PO Box 749 Maplewood NJ 07040-0749 also: care Louise Billotte 595 Connecticut St San Francisco CA 94107-2832*

WESTON, ROGER LANCE, banker; b. Waukegan, Ill., Mar. 2, 1943; s. Arthur Walter and Vivian Dawn (Thompson) W.; m. Kathleen Plotzke, Sept. 15, 1979; children: Cynthia Page, Kent Andrew, Arthur Eladio, Rebecca Dawn, Alice Sinclair, Elliott Churchill, Evan Walter, Spencer Lance. BS, MacMurray Coll., 1965; MBA, Washington U., St. Louis, 1967. Investment adviser Harris Trust & Savs. Bank, Chgo., 1967-69; sr. investment counselor Security Suprs., Chgo., 1969-70; exec. v.p., treas., chief fin. officer Telemed Corp., Hoffman Estates, Ill., 1971-79; vice chmn. Bank Lincolnwood, Ill., 1979-85; pres., chief exec. officer GSC Enterprises, Lincolnwood, 1979-85, EVCO, Inc., Itasca, Ill., 1985-87; vice chmn., chief exec. officer Evanston (Ill.) Bank, 1985-88; chmn. bd. dirs., pres., chief exec. officer GreatBanc, Inc., Aurora, Ill., 1986—. Mem. Barrington Hills (Ill.) Zoning Bd. Appeals, 1987, com. Asian art Art Inst. Chgo., 1987. Mem. Washington U. Eliot Soc. (chmn. membership com. 1986-91), Univ. Club. Republican. Presbyterian. Office: GreatBanc Inc 2300 N Barrington Rd Hoffman Estates IL 60195

WESTON, ROY FRANCIS, environmental consultant; b. Reedsburg, Wis., June 25, 1911; s. Charles Frederick and Hattie (Jensen) W.; m. Madeleen Elizabeth Kellner, Dec. 31, 1934; children: Susan Weston Thompson, Katherine Weston Swoyer Fittipaldi. B.C.E., U. Wis., 1933; M.C.E., NYU, 1939; D.Engring. (hon.), Drexel U., 1981. Registered profl. engr.: U. States; diplomate Am. Acad. Environ. Engrs. (pres. 1973-74). Jr. hwy. engr. Wis. Hwy. Dept., 1934-36; dist. engr. Wis. Dept. Health, 1936-37; san. engring. research fellow NYU, N.Y.C., 1937-39; san. engr. Atlantic Refining Co., Phila., 1939-55; chmn. bd. Roy F. Weston, Inc., West Chester, Pa., 1955-91, chmn. emeritus, 1991—; environ. cons. Contbr. numerous articles on environ. control and sustainable devel. to profl. publs. vis. com. dept. civil and urban engring. U. Pa., Phila., also Ctr. for Marine and Environ. Studies, Lehigh U.; bd. overseers Sch. Engring., Pa. State U., former mem. indsl. and profl. adv. com. Pa. State U.; past bd. overseers Duke U. Sch. Engring.; past trustee Phila. Coll. Pharmacy and Sci.; former mem. Pa. Gov.'s Energy Coun. Recipient Disting. Svc. citation U. Wis., 1975, George Washington medal Phila. Engrs., 1973, Samual S. Baxter Meml. award Water Resources Assn. of Delaware River Basin, 1994, Nat. Engring. award Am. Assn. Engring. Socs., 1994, Gordon Maskew Fair award Am. Acad. Environ. Engrs., 1977. Mem. ASCE, APHA, NSPE (Engr. of Yr. award 1973), NAE, AIChE (environ. divsn. Lawrence K. Cecil award 1993), ASCE (hon. mem. award 1994), Am. Assn. Engring. Socs. (nat. engring. award 1994), Pa. Soc. Profl. Engrs. (Engr. of Yr. 1970, 73), Water Pollution Control Fedn. (Arthur Sidney Bedell award 1959, Indsl. Wastes meda 1950, hon.), Am. Chem. Soc., Air Pollution Control Assn., Cons. Engrs. Coun., Water Resources Assn. Delaware River Assn. (pres. 1976-77), Overbrook Golf Club, Phila. Engrs. Club. Office: Roy F Weston Inc 1 Weston Way West Chester PA 19380-1499

WESTON, THEODORE BRETT, photographer; b. Los Angeles, Dec. 16, 1911; s. Edward and Flora (Chandler) W.; divorced; 1 dau. Freelance photographer Calif. One-man shows include: U. Ariz. Ctr. for Creative Photography, Tucson, 1983, San Francisco Mus. Modern Art, 1983; represented in permanent collections: Mus. Modern Art, N.Y.C., Library of Congress, Washington, Art Inst. Chgo.; photography books: Brett Weston Photographs, Brett Weston Voyage of the Eye; Photographs from Five Decades. Recipient Guggenheim award, 1946. Office: PO Box 5427 Carmel CA 93921-5427

WESTON, WILLARD GALEN, diversified holdings executive; b. Eng., Oct. 29, 1940; s. W. Garfield Weston and Reta L. Howard; m. Hilary Frayne, 1966; 2 children. BA, U. Western Ont., LLD (hon.). Chmn. bd. Wittington Investments, Ltd., George Weston Ltd., Toronto, Ont., Can., Holt, Renfrew & Co. Ltd., Loblaw Cos. Ltd., Weston Foods Ltd., Weston Resources Ltd.; vice chmn. bd. dirs. Fortnun and Mason PLC (U.K.); bd. dirs. Assoc. Brit. Foods PLC (U.K.), Can. Imperial Bank Commerce, Brown Thomas Group Ltd. (Ireland). Pres. The W. Garfield Weston Found.; chmn. bd. dirs. Lester B. Pearson Coll. Pacific, United World Colls.; life mem. Royal Ont. Mus., Art Gallery Ont. Officer Order of Can. Mem. Badminton and Racquet Club, York Club, Toronto Club, Guards Polo Club, Lyford Cay Club, Windsor Club (Fla.). Avocations: polo, tennis. Office: George Weston Ltd, 22 St Clair Ave E Ste 1900, Toronto, ON Canada M4T 2S3 also: Wittington Investments Ltd, 22 St Clair Ave E Ste 2000, Toronto, ON Canada M4T 2S3

WESTON, WILLIAM LEE, dermatologist; b. Grand Rapids, Minn., Aug. 13, 1938; s. Eugene and Edith Kathryn (Lee) W.; m. Janet J. Atkinson, June 9, 1964; children: Elizabeth Carol, William Kemp. AB, Whitman Coll., 1960; B in Med. Sci., U.S.D. 1963; MD, U. Colo., 1965. Resident in pediatrics U. Calif., San Francisco, 1967-68; intern, then resident in pediatrics U. Colo., Denver, 1965-67, resident in dermatology, 1970-72, asst. prof. dermatology and pediatrics, 1972-76, prof., 1976—, chmn. dept. dermatology, 1976—. Author: Practical Pediatric Dermatology, 1979, rev. edit., 1985, Color Textbook of Pediatric Dermatology, 1991; editor-in-chief Current Problems in Dermatology, 1988-93. With AUS, 1968-70. Mem. Soc. Pediatric Dermatology (founder, sec.-treas. 1975-80, pres. 1984-85), Colo. Dermatol. Soc. (pres.), Soc. Investigative Dermatology (bd. dirs.), Am.

Acad. Dermatology (bd. dirs.). Methodist. Home: 8550 E Ponderosa Dr Parker CO 80134-8233 Office: 4200 E 9th Ave Denver CO 80220-3706

WESTOVER, SAMUEL LEE, insurance company executive; b. Soap Lake, Wash., May 30, 1955; s. Gordon Kent Westover and Janice Lelia (Matlock) Jensen; m. Susan Kern, July 13, 1977; children: Michael, S. Fielding, Austin, Clinton, Cassandra. BS in Acctg., Brigham Young U., 1978. Acct. Price Waterhouse, L.A., 1978-80; chief fin. officer, sr. v.p. Maxicare Health Plans, Inc., L.A., 1981-88; chief exec. officer and chief operating officer Western Health Plans, Inc. San Diego, 1988-90; chief fin. officer, sr. v.p. Blue Cross of Calif., Woodland Hills, 1990-93; CFO, sr. v.p. WellPoint Health Networks, Inc., Woodland Hills, 1993; pres., CEO SysteMed, Inc., Torrance, Calif., 1993—. Office: SysteMed Inc Ste 400 970 W 190th St Torrance CA 90502

WESTPHAL, JAMES ADOLPH, planetary science educator; b. Dubuque, Iowa, June 13, 1930; s. Henry Ludwig and Nancy Kathryn (Wise) W.; m. Lois Jean, Apr. 1956 (div. 1966); 1 child, Andrew Johnathan; m. Barbara Jean Webster, Nov. 2, 1967. BS, U. Tulsa, 1954. Team leader Sinclair Rsch. Labs., Tulsa, 1955-61; sr. engr. Calif. Inst. Tech., Pasadena, 1961-66, sr. rsch. fellow, 1966-71, assoc. prof., 1971-76, prof., 1976—, dir. Palomar Obs., 1994—; prin. investigator Hubble space telescope NASA, Calif. Inst. Tech., Pasadena, 1977—; dir. Palomar Obs. Fellow MacArthur Found., 1991; recipient Space Science award Am. Inst. Aeronautics and Astronautics, 1995. Mem. Am. Astron. Soc. Office: Calif Inst Tech MS 170-25 Pasadena CA 91125

WESTPHAL, KLAUS WILHELM, university museum director; b. Berlin, Mar. 20, 1939; came to U.S., 1969; s. Wilhelm Heinrich and Irmgard (Henze) W.; m. Margaret Elisabeth Dorothea Wagner, May 16, 1969; children: Barbara, Marianne, Christine. BS in Geology, Eberhard-Karls Universität, Germany, 1960, MS, 1964, PhD in Paleontology, 1969. Dir. geology mus. U. Wis. Madison, 1969—; bd. dirs. natural history coun. U. Wis. Madison, 1973—, Friends of Geology Mus., Inc., 1977—; nat. speaker on paleontology Outreach, 1977—; instr. paleontology U. Wis., 1977—; leader expeditions fossil vertebrates including dinosaurs, 1977—. Participant various tchr.-ing. projects Wis. Pub. Schs. Lutheran. Home: 3709 High Rd Middleton WI 53562-1003 Office: U Wis Geology Mus 1215 W Dayton St Madison WI 53706-1692

WESTPHAL, LEONARD WYRICK, health care executive, consultant; b. Kansas City, Mo., Sept. 28, 1946; s. Leonard Henry and Elizabeth (Wyrick) W.; m. Sandra Sanders, Aug. 13, 1972; children: Michael Weston, Margaret Elizabeth. BFA, So. Meth. U., 1969; MA, S.W. Mo. State U., 1972; postgrad., U. Mich., Cen. Mo. State U., Lincoln U. of Mo., Century U. Lic. nursing home adminstr., Mo., Ark. Exec. dir. Dist. III Area Agy. on Aging, Warrensburg, 1972-83; state dir. Mo. Div. of Aging, Jefferson City, Mo., 83-85; spl. asst. to dir. Mo. Dept. Mental Health, Jefferson City, 1985-86; exec. dir. Missouri River Health Care, Jefferson City, 1986-88; health care adminstr., cons., 1988—; continuing edn. instr., mem. adv. coun. continuing edn. SW Mo. State U., 1993—; adj. instr., internship supr. Cen. Mo. State U., Warrensburg, 1974-83; mem. rev. panel State of Mo., 1974-76, HEW, 1984-85; cons. Adminstrn. on Aging, Fed. Emergency Mgmt. Agy., 1977-83; bd. dirs. Mid-Am. Congress on Aging, 1975; chmn. Mo. Gov.'s Task Force, Hearings and Conf. on Alternative Care for Elderly, 1982-83; mem. Mo. Bd. Nursing Home Adminstrs., 1983-85; founder, coord. Older Missourians Craft Festival, 1978-83; pres., v.p. Mo. Alliance Area Agys. on aging, 1974-76; host radio programs Sta. Kmos-TV, Sta. KCMW-FM, Sta. KWTO, 1993—; mem. adv. com. health care adm. program S.W. Mo. State U.; presenter in field. Author articles in disaster assistance. Mem. Mo. Rep. Com., 1970—, rev. panel United Way, Warrensburg, 1978; mem. coun. ministries 1st United Meth. Ch., Warrensburg, 1979-83, mem. adminstrv. coun., 1981-83, pres. Meth. Men, 1982-83; mem. commn. on missions, Wesley United Meth. Ch., Jefferson City, 1984-86, liturgist, 1985-89; mem. ch. and soc. commn. Wesley United Methodist Ch., Springfield, 1989—; pres. PTA, Warrensburg, 1982; coach Little League Football and Basketball, Warrensburg, 1981-82; bd. dirs. Warrensburg Community Betterment, 1976-78; mem. adminstrv. coun., mem. chancel choir Grace United Meth. Ch., Springfield, 1993—. Recipient Boss of Yr. award Warrensburg Jaycees, 1976, svc. recognition Mo. Office Aging, 1977, Mo. Alliance Area Agys. on Aging, 1977, Older Adult Transp. Svc., Columbia, Mo., 1983, Mo. State Fair, 1983, Mo. Dept. Mental Health, 1986; Exceptional Svc. in Disaster Assistance award City of Sedalia, 1977, 80; Outstanding Contbns. award Ret. Sr. Vol. Programs, 1977, 79, Excellence in Adminstrn. award Mo. Office Aging, 1977, Outstanding Svcs. award Hickory County, Mo., 1984, also others. Fellow Am. Coll. Healthcare Adminstrs. (cert.); mem. Am. Coll. Healthcare Execs., Gerontol. Soc., Am., Am. Soc. Pub. Adminstrn., Mo. Alliance for Homecare, Mo. League Nursing Home Adminstrs., Am. Coll. Healthcare Profls., Jefferson City C. of C., Springfield C. of C. (mem. retirement and devel. coms.), Optimists (v.p. Warrensburg 1979-81), Rotary, Elks, Delta Sigma Rho-Tau Kappa Alpha, Delta Chi (alumni advisor, alumni bd. trustees, achievement award). Avocations: political activities, hiking, travel, literature, canoeing. Home: 1420 S Lovers Ln Springfield MO 65804-2123

WESTPHAL, PAUL, professional basketball coach; b. Torrance, Calif., Nov. 30, 1950; m. Cindy Westphal; children: Victoria, Michael Paul. Degree in phys. edn., U.S.C., 1972. Player Boston Celtics, 1972-75, Phoenix Suns, 1975-80, 83-84, Seattle Supersonics, 1980-81, N.Y. Knicks, 1981-83; coach S.W. Coll., Phoenix, 1985-86, Grand Canyon Coll., 1986-88; asst. coach. Phoenix Suns, 1988-92, head coach, 1992—. Named All-Star 5 times, Comeback Player of Yr.; uniform number retired by Suns, 1989. Office: Phoenix Suns 201 E Jefferson Phoenix AZ 85004*

WESTPHAL, RAINER JOHN, software company executive; b. Huntington Station, N.Y., July 7, 1935; s. Frank and Gertrude M. (Zebedies) W.; m. Antoinette M. Passo, May 7, 1960; children: Jeffrey, Stefanie, Amanda. BS in Bus. Adminstrn., Drexel U., 1959. Programmer RCA, Camden, N.J., 1960-62; sys. analyst, mgr. Ednl. Testing Svc., Princeton, N.J., 1962-67; cons. Peat, Marwick, Mitchell, Phila., 1968-72; v.p. Sorbus, Inc., King of Prussia, Pa., 1973-78; pres. Vertex, Inc., Berwyn, Pa., 1978—; ptnr. Westford Devel., Berwyn, Pa., 1990—; mem. Drexel U. Adv. Bd., Phila., 1992—. Author: (directory) National Sales Tax Rate, 1973; contbr. articles to profl. jours. Mem. N.J. Jaycees, Somerville, 1965; vol. mem. Phila. (Pa.) City Task Force, 1992. Mem. Inst. Product Dirs., Union League Phila., Chester Valley Golf Club (treas. 1985-86), Bear's Paw Golf Club. Republican. Roman Catholic. Avocations: golf, travel, bridge, chess, hiking. Office: Vertex Inc 1041 Old Cassatt Rd Berwyn PA 19312

WESTREICH, BENZION JOSEPH, lawyer; b. N.Y.C., June 2, 1952; s. Osias and Gerda (Gerwitz) W.; m. Joyce M. Mayer, Sept. 13, 1978; children: Jonathan Michael, Daniel Stephan, Zachary Mark. BS summa cum laude, CUNY, 1974, postgrad., 1974-75; JD, Columbia U., 1978. Bar: N.Y. 1979, U.S. Dist. Ct. (ea. and so. dists.) N.Y., Calif. 1988. Assoc. Shearman & Sterling, N.Y.C., 1978-86, ptnr., 1987-88; ptnr. Shearman & Sterling, L.A., 1988—. Stone scholar Columbia U., 1977, 78. Mem. Phi Beta Kappa. Office: 500 S Grand Ave # 18 Los Angeles CA 90071-2609

WESTWATER, JAMES WILLIAM, chemical engineering educator; b. Danville, Ill., Nov. 24, 1919; s. John and Lois (Maxwell) W.; m. Elizabeth Jean Keener, June 9, 1942; children: Barbara, Judith, David, Beverly. B.S., U. Ill., 1941; Ph.D., U. Del., 1948. Mem. faculty U. Ill., Urbana, 1948—; prof. chem. engring. U. Ill., 1962—, head dept., 1962-80; papers chmn. 5th Nat. Heat Transfer Conf., Buffalo, 1960; chmn. 3d Internat. Heat Transfer Conf., Chgo., 1966; Reilly lectr. Notre Dame U., 1958; Donald L. Katz lectr. U. Mich., 1978. Contbr. articles profl. jours. Recipient Conf. award 8th Nat. Heat Transfer Conf., 1965. Fellow AIChE (dir. past divsn. chmn., inst. lectr. 1964, named eminent chem. engr., William H. Walker award 1966, Max Jakob award ASME 1972, Founders award 1984, heat transfer and energy conversion award 1989, Ernest Thiele award 1992). mem. ASME, NAE, Am. Chem. Soc., Am. Soc. Engring. Edn. (Vincent Bendix award 1974). Home: 116 W Iowa St Urbana IL 61801-5035

WESTWICK, CARMEN ROSE, nursing educator, consultant; b. Holstein, Iowa, Feb. 2, 1936; d. J. Alfred and Hazel C. (Lage) Armiger; m. Richard A. Westwick, Dec. 28, 1957; children: Timothy, Ann. BS in Nursing, U. Iowa, 1958; MS, U. Colo. 1960; PhD, Denver U., 1972. RN, Tenn. Instr. Sch.

Nursing West Suburban Hosp., Oak Park, Ill., 1958-59, 60-62; nurse Navajo Presch., Carson's Trading Post, N.Mex., 1967; lectr. then prof. U. Colo., Denver, 1968-69, 72-77; program dir. Western Coun. on Higher Edn. in Nursing, Boulder, Colo., 1976-77; prof. nursing, dean U. N.Mex, Albuquerque, 1977-81, Boston U., 1982-85, S.D. State U., Brookings, 1988-91; NHC chair of excellence in nursing NHC, Murfreesboro, 1993—; exec. dir. N.H. Bd. Nursing, Concord, 1986-87; case reviewer Joint Underwriters Assn., Boston, 1983-92; mem. publs. and rsch. com. Aberdeen (S.D.) Area Indian Health Svc., 1989-91; manuscript reviewer Midwest Alliance in Nursing, Indpls., 1989-92, Holistic Nursing Jour.; mem. adv. coun. S.D. Office Rural Health, Pierre, 1989-91. Contbr. articles to profl. jours. Nurse trainee fellow Nursing div. Dept. Health and Human Svcs., 1959-60, Predoctoral fellow, 1969-72; Nat. Merit scholar, 1954-56. Fellow Am. Acad. Nursing; mem. Sigma Theta Tau (nat. 1st v.p. 1968), Phi Kappa Phi, Kappa Delta Phi. Lutheran. Avocations: antiques, quilting. Office: Mid Tenn State U Dept Nursing Box 81 Murfreesboro TN 37132

WESTWOOD, ALBERT RONALD CLIFTON, engineer; b. Birmingham, Eng., June 9, 1932; came to U.S., 1958, naturalized, 1974; s. Albert Sydney and Ena Emily (Clifton) W.; m. Jean Mavis Bullock, 1956; children: Abigail, Andrea. B.S. with honors, U. Birmingham, 1953, Ph.D. in Phys. Metallurgy, 1956, D.Sc. in Materials Sci., 1968. Chartered engr. and physicist, U.K. Tech. officer research dept., metals div. Imperial Chem. Industries, Birmingham, 1956-58, successively scientist, sr. scientist, assoc. dir., head materials sci. dept., dir., 1958-74; dir. Martin Marietta Labs., Balt., 1974-84, corp. dir. R & D, 1984-87; v.p. R & D Martin Marietta Corp., Bethesda, Md., 1987-90, v.p. sci., 1990, v.p. rsch. and tech., 1990-93; v.p. rsch. and exploratory tech. Sandia Nat. Labs. divsn. Lockheed Martin Corp., Albuquerque, 1993—; mem. various govt. and univ. adv. coms. including Office Sci. and Tech. Policy, NASA, NRC, NAE, NSF, Nat. Inst. Standards and Tech., U. Md., U. Fla., MIT, Ga. Inst. Tech., Coun. on Competitivemess; dir. Martin Marietta Energy Systems. Contbr. more than 120 articles to sci. jours. Chmn. Md. Humanities Coun.; trustee New Mex. Symphony Orch., Santa Fe Opera. Recipient Disting. Young Scientist award Md. Acad. Scis., 1966, Centennial award U. Md., 1994; Beilby Gold medal Royal Inst. Chemsitry, 1970, Tewksbury lectr. U. Melbourne, 1974, Wenk lectr. Johns Hopkins U., 1995. Fellow AAAS (chmn. ind. sci. sect.), Am. Soc. Metals Internat. (Burgess lectr. 1984, Campbell Meml. lectr. 1987, Disting. lectr. 1995), The Minerals, Metals and Materials Soc. (dir., fin. officer, pres. 1990, Krumb lectr. 1988, Leadership award 1992); mem. NRC (commr. 1985-88, chmn. 1992—, com. engring. and tech. systems), NAFE (chmn. pub. info. adv. com. 1992—), ASME (Disting. lectr. 1989), Royal Swedish Acad. Engring. Scis., Md. Acad. Scis. (mem. coun.), Md. Inst. Metals (pres.), Indsl Rsch. Inst. (bd. dirs., pres. 1989-90). Home: 1413 Pinnacle View Dr NE Albuquerque NM 87112-6558 Office: Sandia Nat Labs Org # 1000 Albuquerque NM 87185-1431

WESTWOOD, JAMES NICHOLSON, lawyer; b. Portland, Oreg., Dec. 3, 1944; s. Frederick Alton and Catherine (Nicholson) W.; m. Janet Sue Butler, Feb. 23, 1980; children: Laura, David. BA, Portland State U., 1967; JD, Columbia U., 1974. Bar: Oreg. 1974, U.S. Dist. Ct. Oreg. 1974, U.S. Ct. Appeals (9th cir.) 1978, U.S. Supreme Ct. 1981, U.S. Ct. Appeals (fed. cir.) 1984. Assoc. Miller, Anderson, Nash, Yerke & Wiener, Portland, 1974-76, 78-81; asst. to pres. Portland State U., 1976-78; ptnr. Miller, Nash, Wiener, Hager & Carlsen, Portland, 1981—. Recipient Disting. Svc. award Portland State U. Found., 1984, Outstanding Alumni award Portland State U., 1992. Mem. ABA (chmn. forest resources com. 1987-89), Oreg. Bar Assn., Am. Acad. Appellate Lawyers, Univ. Club (bd. govs. 1994), City Club (pres. 1991-92). Republican. Unitarian. Home: 3121 NE Thompson St Portland OR 97212-4908 Office: Miller Nash Wiener Hager & Carlsen 111 SW 5th Ave Portland OR 97204

WESTWOOD, MELVIN NEIL, horticulturist, pomologist; b. Hiawatha, Utah, Mar. 25, 1923; s. Neil and Ida (Blake) W.; m. Wanda Mae Shields, Oct. 12, 1946; children: Rose Dawn, Nancy Gwen, Robert Melvin, Kathryn Mae. Student, U. Utah, 1948-50; BS in Pomology, Utah State U., 1952; PhD in Pomology, Wash. State U., 1956. Field botanist Utah State U., Logan, 1951-52, supt. Howell Field Sta., 1952-53; rsch. asst. State Coll. Wash., 1953-55; rsch. horticulturist Agrl. Rsch. Svc. USDA, Wenatchee, Wash., 1955-60; assoc. prof. Oreg. State U., Corvallis, 1960-67, prof., 1967-80, prof. emeritus, 1986—; rsch. dir. Nat. Clonal Germplasm Repository, Corvallis, 1980-82, nat. tech. advisor, 1984-86. Author: Deciduous Fruit and Nut Production, 1976, Temperate-Zone Pomology: Physiology and Culture, 1978, 3d edit., 1993, Contract Military Air Transport From the Ground Up, 1995; co-author: Cherry Nutrition, 1966, Pear Rootstocks, 1987, Management and Utilization of Plant Germplasm, 1988, Maintenance and Storage: Clonal Germplasm, 1989, Genetic Resources of Malus, 1991; contbr. more than 200 articles to profl. jours. With USAAF, 1946-47. Grantee NSF, 1966; recipient Hartman Cup award Oreg. Hort. Soc., 1989. Fellow Am. Soc. Hort. Sci. (bd. dirs. 1974-75, chmn. com. environ. quality 1971, adv. coun. 1974-79, mem. pomology sect. 1967-74, publs. com. 1971-74, pres. western region 1974, Joseph Harvey Gourley award for Pomology 1958, 77, Stark award for Pomology 1969, 77, Outstanding Researcher award 1986); mem. AAAS, Am. Soc. Plant Physiologists, Am. Pomological Soc. (adv. bd. 1970-75, exec. bd. 1980-84, Paul Howe Shepard award 1968, 82, Wilder medal 1980), UN Assn. USA, Ams. United for Separation of Ch. and State, Amnesty Internat., Phi Kappa Phi, Gamma Sigma Delta. Baptist. Achievements include patent for Autumn Blaze ornamental pear; research on Pyrus (pear), Malus (apple) and Prunus (plum, cherry, peach) and on the physiology of rootstock genera. Office: Oreg State U Dept Horticulture Corvallis OR 97331

WESTWOOD, VIVIENNE, fashion designer; 2 children. Dr. h.c., Royal Coll. Art, 1992. created Pirate Collection, 1980, Pagan 5 Collection, 1989; launched Mini Crini, 1985; developed New Glamour movement; introduced corset after 200 years, Harris tweed collection, 1987, cut & slash, 1990, new silouette with bustle and shoulders; shows include Paris, 1991, Salon, 1991, Always on Camera, 1992, Grand Hotel, 1992, Anglomania, 1993, Cafe Society, 1993, On Liberty, 1994, Erotic Zones, 1994, others. Named Designer of Yr., 1990, 91.

WETHERILL, EIKINS, lawyer, stock exchange executive; b. Phila., Oct. 3, 1919; s. A. Hecksher and Edwina (Brunner) W. LL.B., U. Pa., 1948. Practiced in Phila., 1948-55, Norristown, 1955—; assoc. firm Evans, Bayard & Frick, 1948-50; ptnr. Reilly, Hepburn, Earle & Wetherill, 1950-55; firm Henderson, Wetherill, O'Hey & Horsey, 1955—; pres. Phila. Stock Exchange, Inc., 1965-81; bd. dirs. Germantown Savs. Bank; fin. commentator CBS-TV News, 1966-68; chmn. bd. Sta. WHYY-TV, 1970-76, dir., 1976-90; dir. 1st Pa. Corp., 1st Pa. Bank, solicitor to lt. gov. Pa., 1951-55, asst. U.S. atty. gen., 1953-55, treas. Montgomery County, 1956-59; pres. Montgomery County Bd. Commrs., 1960-63; chmn. Pa. Securities Commn., 1963-65; commr. Delaware Valley Regional Planning Commn., 1965—, chmn., 1968-69, 70-71, 78-79. Former bd. dirs. Greater Phila. Partnership; chmn. Phila. Drama Guild, 1975-80, dir., 1980-87; trustee Davis and Elkins Coll., 1973-91. Served to capt., cav. Signal Corps, OSS, AUS, 1941-45. Mem. Am., Phila. bar assns., Delta Psi. Episcopalian. Clubs: Phila. (Phila.), Racquet (Phila.). Office: 1 Montgomery Plz Ste 902 Norristown PA 19404

WETHERILL, GEORGE WEST, geophysicist, planetary scientist; b. Phila., Aug. 12, 1925; s. George West and Leah Victoria (Hardwick) W.; m. Phyllis May Steiss, June 17, 1950 (dec. Jan. 1995); children: Rachel, George, Sarah. Ph.B., U. Chgo., 1948, S.B. in Physics, 1949, S.M., 1951, Ph.D. in Physics, 1953. Mem. staff dept. terrestrial magnetism Carnegie Inst., Washington, 1953-60; prof. geophysics and geology UCLA, 1960-75, chmn. dept. planetary and space sci., 1968-72; dir. dept. terrestrial magnetism Carnegie Inst., Washington, 1975-91, mem. sci. staff, 1991—; cons. NASA, NSF, Nat. Acad. Sci. Editor Ann. Rev. of Earth and Planetary Sci.; assoc. editor. Meteoritics, Icarus; contbr. articles to profl. jours. With USN, 1943-46. Recipient G.K. Gilbert award Geol. Soc. Am., 1984, Profl. Achievement Citation U. Chgo. Alumni Assn., 1985. Fellow Am. Acad. Arts and Scis., Am. Geophys. Union (pres. planetology sect. 1970-72, recipient H.H. Hess medal, 1991), Meteoritical Soc. (v.p. 1971-74, 81-83, pres. 1983-85, Leonard medal 1981); mem. NAS, Geochem. Soc. (v.p. 1973-74, pres. 1974-75), Internat. Assn. Geochem. and Cosmochemistry (pres. 1977-80), Internat. Astron. Union, Am. Astron. Soc. Div. Planetary Scis. and Div. Dynamic Astronomy (G.P. Kuiper prize 1986), Religious Soc. Free Quakers, Internat.

Soc. for Study of Origin of Life. Episcopalian. Office: Carnegie Inst 5241 Broad Branch Rd NW Washington DC 20015-1305 *Seek him that maketh the Pleiades and Orion, and turneth the shadow of death into morning. Amos 5:8.*

WETHERINGTON, ROGER VINCENT, journalism educator, newspaper copy editor; b. Jacksonville, Fla., Mar. 12, 1942; s. Roger Vincent and Ruby Estelle (Jones) W.; m. Andra Marie Miller, Aug. 31, 1972; 1 child, Brady Miller. BA in English Lit., Columbia U., 1965; MA in Journalism, U. So. Calif., 1979, PhD in Comm., 1986. Copyboy, reporter, asst. city editor Daily News, N.Y.C., 1963-76; lectr. journalism Calif. State U., Long Beach, 1976-78, 87-90; asst. prof. Calif. State U., Northridge, 1979-84; asst. prof. comm. St. John's U., Jamaica, N.Y., 1990-93, assoc. prof., 1993—; copy editor N.Y. Times, N.Y.C., 1992—. Recipient media award for incisive reporting Cancer Care, Inc., 1974, faculty devel. award Calif. State U.-Northridge, 1983; teaching fellow Gannett Found., 1977. Mem. AAUP, Assn. for Edn. in Journalism and Mass Comm., Soc. Profl. Journalists, Investigative Reporters and Editors, Newspaper Guild, Deadline Club. Avocation: opera. Office: St John's U 8000 Utopia Pky Jamaica NY 11439

WETHINGTON, CHARLES T., JR., academic administrator. AB, Ea. Ky. U., 1956; postgrad., Syracuse U., 1958-59; MA, U. Ky., 1962, PhD, 1965. Instr. ednl. psychology U. Ky., Lexington, 1965-66; dir. Maysville (Ky.) C.C., 1967-71; asst. v.p. c.c. system U. Ky., Lexington, 1971-81, v.p. c.c. system, 1981-82, chancellor c.c. system, 1982-88, chancellor c.c. system and univ. rels., 1988-89, interim pres., 1989-90, pres., 1990—; chmn. legis. com. State Dirs. Community and Jr. Colls., 1983-85, chmn. nat. coun., 1985-86; mem. commn. on colls. So. Assn. Schs. and Colls., 1978-84, vice chmn. exec. coun., 1984, trustee, 1986-89; mem. So. Regional Edn. Bd., 1988—, mem. exec. com., 1989-93, vice chmn., 1991-93. Bd. dirs. Bluegrass State Skills Corp., 1984-91, vice chmn. bd. dirs., 1986-87; bd. visitors Community Coll. of Air Force, 1986-90; mem. Ky. Ednl. TV Adv. Com., 1984—; mem. jud. nominating commn. 22nd Jud. Dist., Fayette County, Ky., 1988-91; mem. Ky. Coal Authority, 1991—, So. Growth Policies Bd., 1990—; served with sec. svc. USAF, 1957-61. Home: Maxwell Pl 47 Rose St Lexington KY 40508 Office: U Ky 104 Administration Bldg Lexington KY 40506

WETHINGTON, JOHN ABNER, JR., retired nuclear engineering educator; b. Tallahassee, Apr. 18, 1921; s. John Abner and Mary McQueen (Hale) W.; m. Kathryn Kemp Greene, Aug. 19, 1943; 1 son, John Abner III. A.B., Emory U., 1942, M.A., 1943; Ph.D., Northwestern U., 1950. Vis. research asst. Princeton, 1943-44; chemist Ferclove Corp., Oak Ridge, 1944-46; chemist to sr. chemist Oak Ridge Nat. Lab., 1949-53; asst. prof. to prof. nuclear engring. U. Fla., 1953-85, prof. emeritus, 1985—; on leave as fellow Lawrence Livermore Lab., Calif., 1971-72; vis. scientist P.R. Nuclear Center, 1962-63, Oak Ridge Nat. Lab., 1979-80; U.S. del. to Radiation Congress, Haregate, Eng., 1963, 2d Internat. Conf. Peaceful Uses of Atomic Energy, Switzerland, 1958; faculty participant Oak Ridge Sch. Reactor Tech., 1957-58. Contbr. articles to profl. jours. Fellow AAAS; mem. Am. Chem. Soc., Am. Nuclear Soc., Phi Beta Kappa, Sigma Xi, Alpha Chi Sigma. Democrat. Methodist. Home: 109 NW 22nd Dr Gainesville FL 32603-1426

WETLAUFER, DONALD BURTON, biochemist, educator; b. New Berlin, N.Y., Apr. 4, 1925; s George C. and Olga (Kirckhoff) W.; m. Lucille D. Croce, May 5, 1950; children—Lise, Eric. B.S. in Chemistry, U. Wis., Madison, 1946, M.S. in Biochemistry, 1952, Ph.D., 1954. Chemist Argonne (Ill.) Nat. Lab., 1944, 46-47, Bjorksten Lab., Madison, 1948-50; Carlsberg Lab., Copenhagen, 1955-56; research asso. Harvard U., 1956-61, tutor biochem. sci., 1958-61; asst. prof. biochemistry Ind. U. Med. Sch., 1961-62; asso. prof., then prof. biochemistry U. Minn. Med. Sch., 1962-75; DuPont prof. chemistry U. Del., Newark, 1975—, chmn. dept., 1975-85; vis. investigator Max Planck Inst. Ernahrungsphy., 1974-78; mem. fellowship rev. com. NATO, 1970; cons. Nat. Inst. Gen. Med. Sci., 1964—, NSF, 1980—. Author research papers in field of protein biochemistry, protein folding and high performance protein purification; indsl. cons. NSF predoctoral fellow, 1952-54; Nat. Found. Infantile Paralysis postdoctoral fellow, 1955-56; Am. Heart Assn. postdoctoral fellow, 1956-58; grantee USPHS, 1961—; grantee NATO, 1974-77; grantee NSF, 1977—; grantee AEC, 1962; recipient Career Devel. award USPHS, 1961-62. Mem. AAAS, Am. Chem. Soc. (councilor, alt. councilor divsn. biol. chemistry 1975-87), Am. Soc. Biochemistry and Molecular Biology, The Protein Soc., Chromatography Forum, Phi Beta Kappa. Office: U Del Dept Chemistry & Biochemistry Newark DE 19716

WETMORE, BYRON F., construction company executive; b. 1932. Grad., Mansfield State Coll., 1954, Pa. State U., 1957. Joined Lane Constrn. Corp., Meriden, Conn., 1957, from various mgmt. positions to pres., 1957—. Office: Lane Constrn Corp 965 E Main St Meriden CT 06450-6004

WETMORE, THOMAS TRASK, III, retired foundation administrator, retired coast guard officer; b. New London, Conn., Oct. 15, 1925; s. Thomas Trask and Vivian (Brown) W.; m. Joan M. Hancock, Feb. 5, 1949; children: Thomas Trask IV, James R., Jennifer Wetmore Sellers, Daniel H., Judith J. Wetmore Logan. Student, Yale U., 1943-44; B.S. in Marine Engring, U.S. Coast Guard Acad., 1948; postgrad., U.S. Naval Postgrad. Sch., 1951; M.A., N.Y. U., 1973. Commd. ensign U.S. Coast Guard, 1948, advanced through grades to rear adm., 1977; instr. profl. studies dept. C. G. Acad., New London, Conn., 1957-61; comdg. officer tender USCGC Papaw, Charleston, S.C., 1961-63; chief communications br. 5th C. G. Dist., Portsmouth, Va., 1963-67; comdg. officer USCGC Chincoteague, Norfolk, Va., 1967-69; communications officer C. G. Atlantic Area, Governors Island, N.Y., 1969-72; chief aids to nav. br. 3d C. G. Dist., Governors Island, N.Y., 1969-72; chief ops. 3d C. G. Dist., 1974-75; dep. comdr. Atlantic Area, 1975-76; asst. supt. C. G. Acad., New London, 1976-77; chief Office of Reserve, U.S. C. G. Hdqrs., Washington, 1977-79; dist. comdr. 5th C. G. Dist., 1979-81; ret., 1981; exec. dir. Pequot Community Found., 1983-93; ret., 1993. Effective cycling instr. League Am. Bicyclists. Decorated Legion of Merit, Meritorious Service medal with gold star, C. G. Commendation medal with gold star, C. G. Achievement medal with ops. disting. device. Mem. U.S. C. G. Acad. Alumni Assn., Ret. Officers Assn., Pequot Cycling Club. Club: Rotary. Home: 62 Glenwood Pl New London CT 06320-2907

WETSTEIN, GARY M., accountant, company executive. CPA, Mich. N.Y. Chmn., chief exec. officer BDO Seidman, Detroit, 1990—. Office: BDO Seidman Ste 1900 755 W Big Beaver Rd Troy MI 48084-4903 Office: BDO Seidman 330 Madison Ave New York NY 10017

WETTACK, F. SHELDON, academic administrator. AB, San Jose State U., 1960, MA, 1962; PhD, U. Tex., Austin, 1967. From asst. prof. to prof. Hope Coll., Holland, Mich., 1967-82, dean nat. and social scis., 1974-82; dean faculty arts and scis. U. Richmond, 1982-89; pres. Wabash Coll., Crawfordsville, Ind., 1989-93; v.p., dean of faculty Harvey Mudd Coll., Claremont, Calif., 1993—. Office: Harvey Mudd Coll 301 E 12th Claremont CA 91711

WETTER, EDWARD, broadcasting executive; b. Hoboken, N.J., Feb. 2, 1919; s. Edward and Ottilie (Steup) W.; m. Alice Kornat, Nov. 6, 1940 (div. 1946); 1 son, Robert Edward; m. Ruth Lowenstein, Oct. 26, 1954 (div. 1971); 1 dau., Karen Deborah; m. Virginia F. Pate, Apr. 7, 1972. B.A., U. Mich., 1939, M.S., 1941. Dir. spl. ops. Office Sec. Def., 1946-57; bus. broker Allen Kander & Co., N.Y.C., 1957-59; pres. Edward Wetter & Co., Inc., Havre de Grace, Md., 1959—; Harford Enterprises, Havre de Grace, 1978—; v.p. Edwin Tornberg and Co., Inc., N.Y.C., 1959-73; sec-treas. Radio One Five Hundred, Inc., Indpls., 1964—, Radio 900, Inc. Louisville, 1966-90, Radio 780, Inc., Arlington, Va., 1977—. Contbr. to: Biol. Scis. Vol. 2, 1955. Chmn. Zoning Appeals Bd., Havre de Grace, 1982. Served to capt. AUS, 1941-46. Lodge: Rotary. Home and Office: 1000 Chesapeake Dr Havre De Grace MD 21078-3902

WETTERAU, THEODORE C., diversified food wholesaler; b. St. Louis, Nov. 13, 1927; s. Theodore C. and Edna (Ehrlich) W.; m. Helen Elizabeth Killion, Dec. 20, 1954; children: T. Conrad, Mark Stephen, Elizabeth Killion. BA, Westminster Coll., Fulton, Mo., 1952, LLD (hon.), 1977, LHD (hon.), Westminster Coll. With Wetterau, Inc., Hazelwood, Mo., 1952—, v.p. mktg., 1960-63, exec. v.p., 1963-70, pres., chief exec. officer, 1970-74, chmn., chief exec. officer, 1974-89, chmn., pres., chief exec. officer, 1989—;

also bd. dirs.; bd. dirs. Maritz Inc., Food Mktg. Inst. Bd. dirs. Boatmen's Nat. Bank, Barnes Hosp., Gen. Am. Life Ins. Co., V.P. Fair Found., United Way of St. Louis, Mark Twain Inst., Boy Scouts Am., St. Louis Symphony Soc., (all St. Louis); dir. Automobile Club Mo., Ranken Tech. Inst.; trustee Westminster Coll.; past chmn., adv. bd. St. Louis Salvation Army; mem. Pres.'s Council of Community Assn. Schs. for the Arts, St. Louis; ex officio trustee Food Industry Crusade Against Hunger, hon. chmn., 1988. Served with U.S. Army, 1946-47, Korea. Named Man of Month, Progressive Grocer mag., 1966, Sales Exec. of Yr., Sales and Mktg. Execs. St. Louis, 1977; recipient Aggus Disting. Pub. Service award, 1980, Nat. Disting. Service award Am. Jewish Com., 1980, Bus. and Profl. award Religious Heritage of Am., 1980. Mem. Nat. Am. Wholesale Grocers Assn. (gov., past chmn. bd.), Ind. Grocers Alliance (past chmn., bd. dirs.), U.S.C. of C. (bd. dirs., mem. food agr. com.), Knights of Round Table (bd. dirs.), Knights of the Cauliflower Ear. Clubs: Old Warson Country, St. Louis. Office: Wetterau Inc 8920 Pershall Rd Hazelwood MO 63042

WETTEREAU, RICHARD BRADWAY, editor, writer; b. N.Y.C., Jan. 21, 1932; s. James Oswald and Elizabeth Saeger Bradway W.; BA, Columbia U., 1954; m. Cynthia Fairhurst Parks, Oct. 1, 1972; 1 stepdaughter, Catherine Elston Parks. Reporter, asst. mng. editor L.I. Press, 1959-77; L.I. editor, editor Sunday edit., editor, writer Week-in-Rev., editor-at-large N.Y. Post, 1977—. Active, Central Manhasset Civic Assn. Served as 2d lt. U.S. Army. Decorated Purple Heart. Mem. Nat. Ry. Hist. Soc., N. Hempstead Hist. Soc., L.I. Press Club, N.Y. Press Club, Sigma Delta Chi, The Salurians. Quaker. Editor: Homes of the Signers of the Declaration, 1976, The Pennsy Era on Long Island, 1987; co-author: Victorian Railroad Stations on Long Island, 1988. Home: 195 Thompson Shore Rd PO Box 189 Manhasset NY 11030

WETTERHAHN, KAREN ELIZABETH, chemistry educator; b. Plattsburgh, N.Y., Oct. 16, 1948; d. Gustave George and Mary Elizabeth (Thibault) W.; m. Leon H. Webb, June 19, 1982; children—Leon Ashley, Charlotte Elizabeth. B.S., St. Lawrence U., 1970; Ph.D., Columbia U., 1975. Chemist, Mearl Corp., Ossining, N.Y., 1970-71; research fellow Columbia U., N.Y.C., 1971-75, postdoctoral fellow, 1975-76; asst. prof. chemistry Dartmouth Coll., Hanover, N.H., 1976-82, assoc. prof., 1982-86, prof., 1986—; assoc. dean faculty scis., 1990-94, acting dean faculty, 1995—. Contbr. articles to profl. jours. A.P. Sloan fellow, 1981. Mem. Am. Chem. Soc., Am. Assn. Cancer Research, AAAS, N.Y. Acad. Scis. Office: Dartmouth Coll Dept Chemistry 6128 Burke Lab Hanover NH 03755-3564

WETTIG, PATRICIA, actress; b. Cin., Dec. 4, 1951; m. Ken Olin, 1982; children: Clifford, Roxanne. Student, Ohio Wesleyan U., U. Aberdeen, Scotland; grad. in drama, Temple U.; studies with Bill Esper, Neighborhood Playhouse, N.Y.C. Personal dresser to Shirley MacLaine; mem. Circle Repertory Co. Appeared in theater prodns. including The Wooglatherer, 1980, The Diviners, 1981, Talking With, 1984, TV series St. Elsewhere, 1986-88, thirtysomething, 1987-91 (Emmy award for best supporting actress in drama 1988, for best lead actress in drama 1990, 1991), Courthouse, 1995—; guest appearances on L.A. Law, Hill Street Blues; appeared TV movies Silent Motive, 1992, Taking Back my Life: The Nancy Ziegenmeyer Story, 1992, Parallel Lives, 1994, The Langoliers, 1995; appeared in motion pictures, Guilty by Suspicion, 1991, City Slickers, 1991, City Slickers II: The Legend of Curley's Gold, 1994.

WETZEL, CARROLL ROBBINS, lawyer; b. Trenton, N.J., Apr. 5, 1906; s. William and V. Caroline (Wieand) W.; m. Phoebe Meade Francine, June 21, 1935; children: Anne F., Phoebe Wetzel Griswold, Carroll Robbins. A.B., Wesleyan U., Middletown, Conn., 1927; LL.B., U. Pa., 1930, Gowen fellow, 1931. Bar: Pa. 1931, N.J. 1931, U.S. Suprene Ct. 1962. Since practiced Phila.; partner firm Dechert, Price & Rhoads, 1934-73, of counsel, 1973—; mem. adv. com. to Comptroller of Currency, 1962. Bd. dirs. Libr. Co. Phila., 1952-83, pres., 1975-83; trustee Phila. Gen. Hosp., 1958-67; bd. dirs. Bok Tower Gardens, 1962-88, bd. dirs. emeritus, 1989—; bd. dirs. Phila. Maritime Mus., 1976-86, U. Pa. Law Sch., 1978-83. With USAAF, 1942-45, ETO. Mem. ABA (chmn. sect. bus. law 1966-67, editor Bus. Lawyer 1964-65), Pa. Hort. Soc. (bd. dirs. 1954-70, pres. 1967-70), Phila. Club. Democrat. Episcopalian. Home: 353 Lewis Ln Ambler PA 19002-5166 Office: Dechert Price & Rhoads 4000 Bell Atlantic Tower 1717 Arch St Philadelphia PA 19103-2713

WETZEL, CHERIE LALAINE RIVERS, biologist; b. Lewiston, Idaho, June 20, 1930; d. Edwin Bagnal and Mary Elizabeth (Rose) Rivers; m. Herbert Don Wetzel, July 3, 1948; children: Margaret Elizabeth, Don Louis. AA, Chabot Coll., 1966; BA in Biology, Stanford U., 1968, MA, 1970; PhD in Botany, U. Calif., Berkeley, 1979. Asst. curator Dudley Herbarium Stanford (Calif.) U., 1968-70; instr. Calif. flora U. Calif., Berkeley, summer 1971, vis. assoc. prof. botany, biology, 1977-85; instr. gen. biology, ecology, microbiology Chabot Coll., Hayward, Calif., 1970-71, 74-77; instr. botany, field ecology, biology San Francisco City Coll., 1977—; chmn. dept. biol. scis., 1980-84; participant various profl. meetings; invited speaker XIV Internat. Bot. Conf., Berlin, 1987. Contbr. bot. and electron microscopy articles to profl. jours. Trustee Strybing Arboretum Soc. of Golden Gate Park, also mem. plant collections com., bot. publs., libr. com.; bd. dirs. Pacific Horticulture Found. Recipient Outstanding Scholarship Faculty award Chabot Coll., 1966, Gordon Ferris $1,000 award Stanford U., 1969, Reed L. Buffington Outstanding Alumnus award Chabot Coll., 1987; NIH grantee, 1976. Fellow Calif. Acad. Scis. (hon.); mem. AAAS, Am. Soc. Cell Biology, Bot. Soc. Am., Calif. Bot. Soc., Calif. Native Plant Soc., Electron Microscope Soc. Am., Am. Friends of U. Calif. Bot. Garden, No. Calif. Electron Microscope Soc., Friends of Jepson Herbarium, Sigma Xi. Home: PO Box 3969 Hayward CA 94540-3969 Office: San Francisco City Coll Dept Biol Scis 50 Phelan Ave San Francisco CA 94112-1821

WETZEL, SISTER DAMIAN, health care administrator; b. Biloxi, Miss., Nov. 18, 1931; d. Milton James and Hyacinth Vivan (Tew) W. B.S. in Nursing, Marillac Coll., St. Louis, 1959; M.A. in Administra., George Washington U., 1972. Joined Daus. of Charity of St. Vincent de Paul, 1953; staff nurse, head nurse, supr. med.-surg. St. Mary's Hosp., Milw., 1955-57; supr. operating room, emergency and intensive care St. Mary's Hosp., Evansville, Ind., 1960-64; nursing instr. St. Margaret's Sch. Nursing, Montgomery, Ala., 1964-67; dir. hosp. nursing service St. Margaret's Sch. Nursing, Montgomery, Ala., 1967-69; adminstrv. resident St. Vincent's Hosp. and Med. Ctr., N.Y.C., 1971-72; adminstr. De Paul Hosp., New Orleans, 1972-74, Setan Med. Ctr., Austin, Tex., 1974-76, Hotel Dieu Hosp., New Orleans, 1976-80; adminstr. St. Paul Hosp., Dallas, 1980—, also dir.; mem. health services adv. council U. Tex., Dallas, 1980—; dir. children's Oncology, Inc., Dallas, 1980—; preceptor Dept. Health Services Adminstrn. Tulane U., New Orleans, 1983. Chmn. bd. trustees St. Joseph Hosp., Chgo., 1981—; bd. dirs. Tex. Cath. Conf. of Health Facilities, Austin, 1982—; mem. adv. council Tex. Women's U., Dallas, 1982—. Recipient Nat. Brotherhood and Humanitarian award NCCJ, Dallas, 1983. Fellow Am. Coll. Hosp. Adminstrs.; mem. Am. Hosp. Assn., Cath. Health Assn., Dallas Ft. Worth Hosp. Council (Dallas), Tex. Hosp. Assn., Market Ctr. Bus. & Profl. Assn. Office: Daughters Charity W Central Province Saint Louis MO 63121-4694

WETZEL, DONALD TRUMAN, engineering company executive; b. Thayer, Mo., June 22, 1937; s. Ralph Noel and Jane Stiles (Hoyt) W.; m. Betty Ann Benbenek, June 20, 1959; children: James Douglas, Kathleen, Margaret. BS in Engring., U. Mo., 1959; postgrad., London Sch. Bus. Studies, 1981. Registered profl. engr., Mo., Ohio, Pa. Project engr. Ralston Purina Co., St. Louis, 1965-73; mgr. engring. Europe Ralston Purina Co., Brussels, 1973-75; project mgr. A.G. McKee Co., Chgo., 1976-80, v.p. ops., 1980-82; v.p., gen. mgr. Davy-McKee Corp., Chgo., 1982-88; v.p., dep. div. mgr. Sverdrup Corp., St. Louis, 1989-90, v.p., ops. mgr., 1990-93, v.p., prin., 1993—. Capt. USAF, 1959-65, Europe. Decorated Air Force Commendation medal, Pres.'s Unit citation. Mem. NSPE, Nat. Inst. Food Technologists. Avocations: upland bird and water fowl hunting, fishing.

WETZEL, EDWARD THOMAS, investment company executive; b. Indpls., Apr. 16, 1937; s. Edward George and Sarah Catherine Wetzel; divorced; children: Raymond, Cynthia. BA, Bethany (W.Va.) Coll., 1959; MBA, U. Mass., Amherst, 1963. Market research analyst Gen. Electric Co. Pittsfield, Mass., 1960-63; editor, spl. projects dir., asst. v.p. DMS, Inc., Greenwich, Conn., 1964-70; pres. Industry News Service, Inc., Wilton, Conn., 1970-92;

v.p. Wright Investor's Svc., Bridgeport, Conn., 1992—. Pres. Wilton Vol. Ambulance Corps, 1976-81, 83-87. Served to 2d lt. USAFR, 1959-65. Recipient Disting. Citizen award Town of Wilton, 1986. Mem. Planning Forum, Info. Industry Assn., Newsletter Pub. Assn., Kiwanis (pres. bd. dirs. Wilton chpt. 1991-92). Office: Wright Investor's Svc 1000 Lafayette Blvd Bridgeport CT 06604

WETZEL, GILBERT A., telephone company executive; b. 1932; married. BS, Pa. State U., 1954. With Standard Oil Ind., 1954-55, AT&T, 1967-68; with Bell Telephone Co. of Pa., Phila., 1958-67, 68—, comptroller, 1968-82, v.p. pub. affairs, 1982-85, pres., 1985—, also bd. dirs.; v.p. pub. affairs Diamond State Telephone Co., Wilmington, Del., 1982-85, pres., chief exec. officer, 1985—, also bd. dirs. Served to 1st lt. USAF, 1955-58. Office: Bell Tel Co Pa 1 Parkway-13B Philadelphia PA 19102

WETZEL, HEINZ, foreign language educator; b. Ziesar, Germany, May 11, 1935; immigrated to Can., 1965; s. Ernst and Katharina (Jentzsch) W.; m. Marianne Dummin, Mar. 19, 1957; children: Andreas, Suzanne, Claudia. Staatsexamen, Free Univ., Berlin, 1960; Dr. phil., U. Göttingen, Fed. Republic Germany, 1967. Asst. prof. German dept. Queen's U., Kingston, Can., 1965-69; assoc. prof., grad. sec. German dept. U. Toronto, Can., 1969-72, prof. German dept., 1972—; chmn. German dept. U. Toronto, 1984-89; vis. prof. U. Calif., San Diego, 1973, Technische Universität Braunschweig, Fed. Republic Germany, 1973. Author: (book) Konkordanz zu den Dichtungen Georg Trakis, 1971, Klang und Bild in den Dichtungen Georg Trakis, 1972, The Seer in the Spring: On Eliot's The Waste Land, 1974; editor: Seminar: A Jou. of Germanic Studies, 1980-85; contbr.50 articles to German and comparative lit. to profl. jours. Fellowships and grants from Social Scis. and Humanities Rsch. Coun. of Can., 1967-87, 73, 79, 86, 90-91, 93. Mem. MLA of Am., Can. Assn. Univ. Tchrs. German. Office: U Toronto Dept German, Univ College, Toronto, ON Canada M5S 1A1

WETZEL, KARL JOSEPH, physics educator, university official and dean; b. Waynesboro, Va., May 29, 1937; s. Mark Ernest and Margaret K. (Jungbluth) W.; m. Barbara Carol Damutz, Aug. 3, 1968; children: Sebastian P., Christopher M. BS in Physics, Georgetown U., 1959; MS in Physics, Yale U., 1960, PhD in Physics, 1965. Physicist Nat. Bur. Standards, Washington, 1959; postdoctoral fellow Inst. Nuclear Physics, Darmstadt, Germany, 1965-67, Argonne (Ill.) Nat. Lab., 1967-69; asst. prof. physics U. Portland, Oreg., 1969-72, assoc. prof., 1972-80, prof., 1980—, chmn. sci. dept., 1980-86, dean Grad. Sch., 1987—, asst. acad. v.p.; cons. in field; adj. prof. State of Oreg. Dept. Continuing Edn., Portland, 1976—. Contbr. articles to profl. publs. Bd. dirs. Friendly House Ctr., Portland, 1979-82, Choral Arts Ensemble, Portland, 1988—. NSF fellow, 1965, 76-77; recipient Pres.' award Oreg. Mus. Sci. and Industry, 1972, Outstanding Advisor award Am. Coll. Test/ Nat. Academic Advising Assn., 1984. Mem. Am. Phys. Soc., AAUP. Achievements include first to describe experiments using germanium detectors with neutron-capture gamma-ray spectroscopy; first measurement of Delbrück effect in photon scattering. Office: U Portland 5000 N Willamette Blvd Portland OR 97203-5743

WETZEL, ROBERT GEORGE, botany educator; b. Ann Arbor, Mich., Aug. 16, 1936; s. Wilhelm and Eugenia (Wagner) W.; m. Carol Ann Andree, Aug. 9, 1959; children: Paul Robert, Pamela Jeanette, Timothy Mark, Kristina Marie. BS, U. Mich., 1958, MS, 1959; PhD, U. Calif. at Davis, 1962; PhD (hon.), U. Uppsala, Sweden, 1984. Research assoc. Ind. U., Bloomington, 1962-65; asst. prof. botany Mich. State U., Hickory Corners, 1965-68; assoc. prof. Mich. State U., 1968-71, prof., 1971-86; prof. U. Mich., Ann Arbor, 1986-90; Bishop prof. biology U. Ala., Tuscaloosa, 1990—; cons. Internat. Biol. Program, London, 1967-75; chmn. Internat. Seagrass Commn., 1974-75; founding mem. Internat. Lake Environment Com., 1986—. Author: Limnology, 1975, 2d rev. edit., 1983, Limnological Analyses, 1979, 2d rev. edit., 1990, To Quench Our Thirst: Present and Future Freshwater Resources of the United States, 1983; editor: Periphyton of Freshwater Ecosystems, 1983; contbr. numerous articles on ecology and freshwater biol. systems to profl. jours.; mem. editorial bd. Aquatic Botany, 1975—; N.Am. editor Archiv f. Hydrobiologie, 1989—. Served with USNR, 1954-62. Recipient First T. Erlander Nat. professorship Swedish Nat. Research Council and U Uppsala, 1982-83, award of Distinction U. Calif. at Davis, 1989; AEC grantee, 1965-75; NSF grantee, 1962—; ERDA grantee, 1975-77; Dept. Energy grantee, 1978—. Fellow AAAS, mem. Royal Danish Acad. Scis. (elected fgn. mem. 1986), Am. Acad. Arts. Scis. (elected mem. 1993), Am. Inst. Biol. Scis., Am. Soc. Limnology and Oceanography (editorial bd. 1971-74, v.p. 1979-80, pres. 1980-81, G.E. Hutchinson medal 1992), Aquatic Plant Mgmt. Soc., Ecol. Soc. Am., Internat. Assn. Ecology, Freshwater Biol. Assn. U.K., Internat. Assn. Theoretical and Applied Limnology (gen. sec., treas. 1968—, Baldi Meml. award 1989, Naumann-Thienemann medal 1992), Internat. Phycological Soc., Mich. Acad. Scis., N.Am. Benthological Soc., Phycological Soc. Am., Internat. Assn. Great Lakes Research, Internat. Consortium Salt Lake Rsch. (editorial bd. 1991—), Japanese Soc. Limnology, Mich. Bot. Soc., Internat. Assn. Aquatic Vascular Plant Biologists (founder, pres. 1979—), Water Assn. Finland (editorial bd. 1990—), Asociacion Argentina de Limnologia (hon.), Brazilian Soc. Limnology, Finnish Limnological Soc. (mem. editorial bd. 1989—), Internat. Lake Environ. Comm. Found. (mem. exec. bd. 1986—), Netherlands Soc. Aquatic Ecology, N.Am. Lake Mgmt. Soc., Russian Soc. Aquatic Ecology, Soc. Wetland Scientists, Sigma Xi, Phi Sigma. Home: 16 Dunbrook Tuscaloosa AL 35406-1949 Office: U Ala Dept Biology Tuscaloosa AL 35487-0344

WETZLER, JAMES WARREN, economist; b. N.Y.C., Dec. 27, 1947; s. Benjamin and Deborah (Rabinowitz) W. B.S., U. Pa., 1969; PhD, Harvard U., 1973. Economist Joint Com. on Taxation, U.S. Congress, Washington, 1973-76; chief economist Joint Com. on Taxation, U.S. Congress, 1976-83, dep. chief staff, 1983-84; investment banker Bear Stearns and Co., Inc., N.Y.C., 1985-88; commr. N.Y. State Dept. Taxation and Finance, Albany, 1988-94; dir. econ. consulting and multistate tax policy Deloitte & Touche LLP, N.Y.C., 1995—. Office: Deloitte & Touche LLP 2 World Fin Ctr New York NY 10281

WETZLER, MONTE EDWIN, lawyer; b. N.Y.C., May 7, 1936; s. Alvin and Sally (Epstein) W.; m. Sally Jane Elsas, Dec. 19, 1963; 1 child, Andrew Elsas. AB, Brown U., 1957; LLB, U. Va., 1960; LLM in Taxation, NYU, 1966. Bar: N.Y. 1960, Calif. 1979. Assoc. Regan Goldfarb Heller Wetzler & Quinn, N.Y.C., 1960-66, ptnr., 1966-73, mng. ptnr., 1973-81; sr. v.p., gen. counsel Damson Oil Corp., N.Y.C., 1981-86, exec. v.p., chief fin. officer, 1986-88; pres. B&D Equities Inc., 1986-88; ptnr. Breed, Abbott & Morgan, N.Y.C., 1988-93, mng. ptnr.; ptnr. Whitman Breed Abbott & Morgan, N.Y.C., 1993—. Editor: Selected Problems in Securities Law, 1972, Joint Ventures and Privatization in Eastern Europe, 1991-92. Counsel, N.Y. State Senate Com. on Housing, N.Y.C. Recipient Svc. award Practicing Law Inst., N.Y.C., 1973. Mem. ABA, N.Y. State Bar Assn. (exec. com. bus. law sect. 1993-94, securities law com.), Bar Assn. City N.Y., Corp. Law com.; Harmonie Club (gov. 1983-84, 86-88), Cedar Point Yacht Club, Essex Yacht Club, Phi Delta Phi, Order of Coif. Republican. Jewish. Home: 8 River Road Dr Essex CT 06426 Office: Whitman Breed Abbott & Morgan 200 Park Ave New York NY 10166

WETZSTEIN, SANDRA LYNNE, elementary school educator; b. San Angelo, Tex., Mar. 28, 1944; d. Robert Hans and Arline Edwina (Milleville) Jensen; m. Merrell W. Wetzstein, July 17, 1966; children: Raechel, Joel, Rebecca. BA, Concordia Coll., River Forest, Ill., 1966; MEd, U. Okla., Norman, 1985. Cert. coop. learning trainer. Elem. tchr. St. Paul's Luth. Sch., West Point, Nebr., 1966-67; tchr. English Centro Cultural Brasil-Estados Unidos, Belem, Brazil, 1972-76; elem. tchr. St. Mary's Sch., Balboa, Republic Panama, 1981-82, Dept. Def. Dependent Sch., Howard AFB, Republic Panama, 1982-95, Curundu Middle Sch. Republic Panama, 1995—. Mem. ASCD, Nat. Coun. Math. Tchrs., Phi Delta Kappa. Home: PSC 07 Box 573 APO AA 34007

WEVERS, JOHN WILLIAM, retired Semitic languages educator; b. Baldwin, Wis., June 4, 1919; emigrated to Can., 1951; s. Bernard and Wilemina (Te Grootenhuis) W.; m. Grace Della Brondsema, May 22, 1942; children: Robert Dick, John William, Harold George, James Merritt. A.B. Calvin Coll., Grand Rapids, Mich., 1940; Th.B., Calvin Sem., 1943; Th.D., Princeton Theol. Sem., 1945; D.D. (hon.), Knox Coll., Toronto, 1973;

D.H.C. (hon.), Leiden U., 1985. Lectr., then asst. prof. O.T. and Semitic langs. Princeton Theol. Sem., 1946-51; mem. faculty U. Toronto, Ont., Can., 1951—, prof. Near Eastern studies, 1963—, prof. emeritus, 1984—; grad. chmn., 1972-75, chmn. dept., 1975-80; chmn. adminstrv. council Presbyn. Ch. Can., 1960-65. Author: Commentary on the Book of Ezekiel, 1969, Septuaginta Vetus Testamentum Graecum: Genesis, 1974, Deuteronomium, 1977, Numeri, 1981, Leviticus, 1986, Exodus, 1991; also text histories, 1974, 78, 83, 86, 92, Notes on the Greek Text of Exodus, 1990, Genesis, 1993; editor-in-chief Can. Jour. Linguistics, 1960-67. Bd. govs. Central Hosp. Toronto, 1963—, chmn., 1967-80; chmn. Hosp. Council Met. Toronto, 1974-75; bd. govs. Ont. Hosp. Assn., 1974-84, pres., 1978-79. Recipient Queen's Jubilee medal, 1978. Fellow Royal Soc. Can.; mem. Oriental Club Toronto, Internat. Orgn. Septuagint and Cognate Studies (pres. 1972-80, hon. pres. 1989—), Can. Bibl. Studies (hon. life), Akademie Wissenschaften Goettingen (corr.), Arts and Letters Club (Toronto). Home: 116 Briar Hill Ave, Toronto, ON Canada M4R 1H9 Office: U Toronto, Dept Near Eastern Studies, Toronto, ON Canada M5S 1A1

WEXLER, ANNE, government relations and public affairs consultant; b. N.Y.C., Feb. 10, 1930; d. Leon R. and Edith R. (Rau) Levy; m. Joseph Duffey, Sept. 17, 1974; children by previous marriage: David Wexler, Daniel Wexler. B.A., Skidmore Coll., 1951, LL.D. (hon.), 1978; D.Sc. in Bus. (hon.), Bryant Coll., 1978. Assoc. pub. Rolling Stone mag., 1974-76; personnel adviser Carter-Mondale transition planning group, 1976-77; dep. undersec. regional affairs Dept. Commerce, 1977-78; asst. to Pres. of U.S., Washington, 1978-81; pres. Wexler and Assocs., Washington, 1981-82; govt. relations and pub. affairs cons., chmn. Wexler, Reynolds, Harrison & Schule, Inc., Washington, 1981-90; vice chmn. Hill and Knowlton PA Worldwide, Washington, 1990-92; chmn. The Wexler Group, div. Hill & Knowlton, Washington, 1992—; bd. dirs. Alumax, Inc., NOVA, Nat. Park Found., Am. Cyanamid Co., New Eng. Electric System, Continental Corp., Comcast Corp., Dreyfus Index funds; mem. vis. com. J.F. Kennedy Sch. of Govt., Harvard U., pub. responsibility com. bd. advisors Carter Ctr., Emory U.; bd. visitors U. Md. Sch. Pub. Affairs. Named Outstanding Alumna Skidmore Coll., 1972, recipient most disting. alumni award, 1984, Bryce Harlow award, 1989. Mem. Council on Fgn. Relations., Com. of 200, Nat. Womens Forum. Jewish. Office: 1317 F St NW Ste 600 Washington DC 20004-1105

WEXLER, GINIA DAVIS, singer, association executive; b. Phila., Mar. 10, 1923; d. Meyer and Hilda (Emery) D.; m. Morris M. Wexler, Oct. 1968. Student drama, Carnegie Inst. Tech., 1939-41; vocal pupil, Frances Lewando, Doris Monteux, 1939-50; coached with, Povla Frijsh, Pierre Monteux, Queena Mario, Pablo Casals, Madeleine Grey. Voice tchr. Mich. State U., East Lansing, 1962; dir. Hancock County Chamber Music Soc. (now Hancock County Friends of Arts), East Sullivan, Maine, 1962—; dir. free programs for children Farmstead Barn, Sullivan, Maine, 1970—. Performed as Polly Peachum in The Beggar's Opera, 1941, Bar Harbor (Maine) Stock Co., Chautauqua, N.Y. Bucks County Playhouse; leading roles New Moon, Toledo Light Opera Co., 1945; appeared on Broadway in Susan and God, 1942, Call Me Mister, 1946; made operatic debut as Gretel in Hansel and Gretel with Pitts. Opera Soc., 1943; ann. recital N.Y.C., 1948-65; toured U.S.A., 1947-67, Europe, 1949, 50; appeared at Holland Festival, 1950; in 1st U.S. performances of Flaminio of Pergolesi, 1953; with 1st U.S. performances of Royal Opera of Brussels, 1953, broadcasts, U.S., Europe; appeared with symphony orch., U.S., Europe, Middle-East, 1955-67; made six months world tour, Africa, Asia, 1966, guitar concerts, 1965; dir. performing arts for children series, Hancock Grand County Auditorium, 1976-89, high sch. touring program, 1980-89, recs. songs Music Library Records, Inc.; folk music div., Library of Congress; mem. Surry, Maine Opera Co., 1984-90; dir. Sullivan Bicentennial Chorus, 1989; lead role in play All Thru the Night, 1989; appearances Am. Folksong Festival; adviser folk music, Nat Arts Found.; authority on folksongs; collecter, transcriber, interpreter: (with Jean Thomas) folklore Ky. mountains (the Traipsin' Woman), 1950-55, also other locations; entertainer Armed Forces, U.S., Europe. (Recipient grand prize Internat. contest interpretation French song 1958). Chmn. Sullivan (Me.) Conservation Commn., 1973-83. Developer unique recital program Portraits in Song, 1947. Home: RR 1 Box 8 Gouldsboro ME 04607-9703 also: 3850 Galt Ocean Dr Fort Lauderdale FL 33308

WEXLER, HASKELL, film producer, cameraman; b. Chgo., 1922; s. Simon Wexler; m. Nancy Ashenhurst (div.); two children; m. Marian Witt (div.); 1 son, Mark; m. Rita Taggart. Grad., U. Chgo. Ednl. documentaries, Chgo., for eleven years; cinematographer films: The Hoodlum Priest, The Best Man, America America, The Loved One, In the Heat of the Night, Who's Afraid of Virginia Woolf? (Acad. award), The Thomas Crown Affair, American Graffiti, One Flew Over the Cuckoo's Nest, Introduction to the Enemy, Bound for Glory (Acad. award), Coming Home, Colors, Three Fugitives, 1988, Blaze, 1989, Lookin' to Get Out, Matewan, Other People's Money, The Babe, (with others) Days of Heaven, (with others) Rolling Stones-IMAX, The Secret of Roan Inish, Canadian Bacon; producer, writer, dir., photographer: (with others) films Medium Cool, 1969; wrote and directed Latino, 1985. Mem. Acad. Motion Picture Arts and Scis. (bd. govs. cinematographers br.). Address: 1341 Ocean Ave Ste #111 Santa Monica CA 90401 Agent: Internat Creative Mgmt c/o Paul Hook 8942 Wilshire Blvd Beverly Hills CA 90211

WEXLER, HERBERT IRA, retail company executive; b. Newark, Sept. 6, 1916; s. Irving and Jeanette (Lesser) W.; m. Elaine L. Ellis, Oct. 10, 1948; children: Susan, Peter, Toni. Student, Rutgers U., 1939-41; student advanced mgmt. program, Harvard U., 1956. Stock boy, salesman, asst. buyer L. Bamberger & Co., 1935-41, asst. buyer, 1946-47; buyer appliances R.H. Macy & Co., N.Y.C., 1947-48, TV radio buyer, 1949-54, mdse. adminstr., v.p., 1955-67, sr. v.p., mem. exec. com., dir., 1968-73; pres., chmn. bd., chief exec. officer Marcade Group Inc., N.Y.C., 1973-86, bd. dirs., cons., 1987—. Vice chmn. Greater N.Y. council Boy Scouts Am.; organizer, fundraiser Yale Grace New Haven Hosp.; mem. Gov. Harriman's Com. to Investigate Fraud and Misrepresentation in Consumer Products; mem. adv. council to bd. trustees Greens Farms Acad., Westport, Conn.; gen. chmn. State of Israel Bond Drive, 1980, testimonial, 1978; gen. chmn. N.Y. Community Service Soc.; chmn. N.Y. sect. for fundraising Denver Jewish Hosp; dir. Children's Blood Found. N.Y. Hosp. Served to capt. AUS, 1941-46. Named Key Man of Yr. Am. Jewish Com. and B'nai B'rith, 1957; named B'nai B'rith Man of Yr., 1976; recipient Disting. Service award Am. Jewish Com. and Anti-Defamation League, 1960, Award of Honor Fedn. Jewish Philanthropies of N.Y., 1961, Scroll of Honor United Jewish Appeal of Greater N.Y., 1964, Man of Yr. award Conn. Digestive Disease Soc., 1973. Clubs: Harvard, Harmonie, Birchwood Country. Home: 26 Burr Farms Rd Westport CT 06880-3817

WEXLER, JACQUELINE GRENNAN (MRS. PAUL J. WEXLER), former association executive and college president; b. Sterling, Ill., Aug. 2, 1926; d. Edward W. and Florence (Dawson) Grennan; m. Paul J. Wexler, June 1, 1969; stepchildren: Wendy, Wayne. A.B., Webster Coll., 1948; M.A., U. Notre Dame, 1957; LL.D., Franklin and Marshall Coll., 1968, Phila. Coll. Textiles and Sci., 1987; D.H.L., Brandeis U., 1968; LL.D., Skidmore Coll., 1967, Smith Coll., 1975; HHD, U. Mich., 1967, U. Ohio, 1976; D.H.L., Carnegie Inst., 1966, Colo. Coll., 1967, U. Pa., 1979, U. South Fla., 1991; HHD (hon.), U. Hartford, 1987; DH, St. Ambrose Coll., 1981; DD, Lafayette Coll., 1990. Tchr. English and math. Loretto Acad., El Paso, Tex., 1951-54; tchr. English and math. Nerinx Hall, St. Louis, 1954-59; tchr. English Webster Coll., 1959-60, asst. to pres., 1959, v.p. devel., 1960, exec. v.p., 1962-65, pres., 1965-69; v.p., dir. internat. univ. studies Acad. for Ednl. Devel., N.Y.C., 1969; pres. Hunter Coll., City U. N.Y., 1969-79, Acad. Cons. Assoc., N.Y.C., 1982-90; ret., 1990; pres. NCCJ, 1982-90; writer, commentator, cons.; mem. Am. Council on Edn., Commn. on Internat. Edn., 1967; mem. adv. com. to dir. NIH, 1978-80; mem. exec. panel chief naval ops. U.S. Navy, 1978-81; dc examiners Fgn. Service, Dept. State, 1981-83; dir. Interpublic Group of Cos., Inc., United Techs. Corp.; mem. Pres.'s Adv. Panel on Research and Devel. in Edn., 1961-65; mem. Pres.'s Task Force on Urban Ednl. Opportunities, 1967. Author: Where I Am Going, 1968; contbr. articles to profl. jours. Trustee U. Pa. Recipient NYU Sch. Edn. Ann. award for creative leadership in edn., 1968, Elizabeth Cutter Morrow award YWCA, 1978, Abraham L. Sachar Silver medallion Brandeis U.'s Nat. Women's Com., 1988, The Albert Einstein award Am. Soc. Technion, 1989; named One of Six Outstanding Women of St. Louis Area St. Louis chpt. Theta Sigma Phi, 1963, Woman of Achievement in Edn. St. Louis

Globe-Democrat, 1964, Woman of Accomplishment Harpers Bazaar, 1967, one of Am.'s Most Important 100 Women Ladies Home Jour., 1988; Kenyon lectr. Vassar Coll., 1967. Mem. Mo. Acad. Squires, Kappa Gamma Pi.

WEXLER, KENNETH NORMAN, psychology educator; b. Jersey City, N.J., Dec. 27, 1942; s. Benjamin and Rose (Seiden) W.; m. Sherry Mitnik, Aug. 16, 1968; children: Paul, Stephanie. BA in Math., U. Pa., 1964; PhD in Psychology, Stanford U., 1970. Asst. prof. psychology U. Calif., Irvine, 1969-72, assoc. prof., 1973-78 prof. psychology, 1978-88; prof. psychology and linguistics, dept brain and cognitive sci. MIT, Cambridge, 1989—; dir. grad. studies sch. social sci. U. Calif., Irvine, 1976-78; dir. research program in perception and high mental processes, 1979-82, co-dir. research program computers and learning, 1985—; Sloan vis. scientist U. Mass. Dept. Linguistics, 1979; invited lectr. Assn. Computer Machinery, 1970, U. London, 1975, UCLA, 1977 numerous others. Co-author: Formal Principles of Language Acquisition, 1983; contbr. articles to profl. jours. Grantee NSF, 1975-79, 79-84, 85; fellow NSF, 1963-64, NIMH, 1966-68, John Simon Guggenheim Meml. Found., 1985. Fellow AAAS; mem. Linguistic Soc. Am., Assn. Computational Linguistics, Soc. Math. Psychology, Cognitive Sci. Soc. Office: MIT 77 Massachusetts Ave Cambridge MA 02139-3594

WEXLER, LEONARD D., federal judge; b. Bklyn., Nov. 11, 1924; s. Jacob and Bessie (Herman) W.; m. Barbara Blum, Mar. 1953; children: Allison Wexler Smeitanka, Robert, William. BS, Ind. U., 1947; JD, NYU, 1950. Bar: N.Y. 1983, U.S. Dist. Ct. (ea. dist.) N.Y. 1983. Assoc. Siben & Siben Esqs., Bay Shore, N.Y., 1950-56; ptnr. Meyer & Wexler Esqs., Smithtown, N.Y., 1956-83; judge U.S. Dist. Ct. (eastern dist.) N.Y. 1983—; atty. Suffolk County Police Conf., 1956-83; 1st atty. Suffolk County Patrolmen's Benevolent Assn., 1960-75; 1st atty. Suffolk County Detectives Assn., 1964-70; temporary state chmn., legal counsel Com. for Rev. Juvenile Justice System, N.Y. State Bar Assn.; speaker, lectr.; 1st adminstr. Assigned Counsel Plan N.Y. State, 1966-83. Served with U.S. Army, 1943-45. Mem. Suffolk County Criminal Bar Assn. (founder 1965, dir. 1956-60). Republican. Jewish. Avocations: travelling; sailing. Home: 94 W Bayberry Rd Islip NY 11751-4905 Office: US Dist Ct 300 Rabro Dr Hauppauge NY 11788-4256

WEXLER, NANCY SABIN, clinical neuropsychology educator; b. Washington, July 19, 1945; d. Milton and Leonore Wexler. AB cum laude, Radcliffe Coll., 1967; PhD in Clin. Psychology, U. Mich., 1974; DHL (hon.), N.Y. Med. Coll., 1991; DSc (hon.), U. Mich. 1991. Lic. psychologist, N.Y. Psychol. intern, teaching fellow U. Mich., 1968-74; asst. prof. psychology grad. faculty New Sch. Social Rsch., N.Y.C., 1974-76; pvt. practice psychology N.Y.C., 1974-76; health sci. adminstr. Nat. Inst. Neurol., Comm. Disorders and Stroke, NIH, 1978-83; pres. Hereditary Disease Found., Santa Monica, Calif., 1983—; prof. neuropsychology Coll. Phys. and Surgeons, Columbia U., N.Y.C., 1985-92, prof. clin. neuropsychology, 1992—; mem. Ctr. for Brain and Behavior Coll. Phys. and Surgeons of Columbia U., 1985; mem. adv. com. Human Genome Ctr., Lawrence Berkeley Labs. and U. Calif., 1988—; mem. external adv. com. Ctr. for Human Genome Studies, Los Alamos Nat. Labs., 1990—; co-chairperson ethical, legal and social issues com. Human Genome Orgn., 1991—, mem. dir. search Nat. Ctr. for Human Genome Rsch., NIH, 1992; chairperson Joint NIH/Dept. of Energy Ethical, Legal, Social Issues Working Group on Human Genome, 1989—. Contbr. articles to profl. jours. Trustee Nat. Huntington's Disease Assn., 1983-85, Marine Biol. Lab., 1984-86, Eleanor Roosevelt Inst. Cancer Rsch., 1985-91, Found. for Care and Cure of Huntington's Disease, 1988—. Fulbright scholar U. West Indies, Jamaica, 1967-68; fellow The Hastings Ctr., 1990—; recipient award Robert J. and Claire Pasarow Found., 1987, Living Legacy award Women's Internat. Soc., 1988, Alumnae Athena award Alumnae Coun. U. Mich., 1989, award Gov.'s Office, Zulia, Venezuela, 1989, Venezuelan Presdl. award, 1990, Legis. Commendation N.Y. State, 1990, Disting. Svc. award Nat. Assn. Biology Tchrs., 1993, Nat. Med. Rsch. award Nat. Health Coun., 1993, Albert Lasker Pub. Svc. award, 1993. Mem. AAAS (bd. dirs. 1993—), APA, Am. Soc. Law and Medicine, Soc. Neurosci. (chairperson social issues com. 1988-90, organizing com. Neurobiology of Human Disesase Workshop 1980—), Am. Psychol. Soc., Am. Soc. Human Genetics, World Fedn. Nuerology, Rsch. Group on Huntington's Disease, Am. Neurol. Assn. Office: Columbia U Coll Physicians & Surgeons Dept Neuropsychology 630 W 168th St New York NY 10032 Office: Hereditary Disease Found 1427 7th St # 2 Santa Monica CA 90401 also: Columbia U Coll Phys & Surg NY State Psychiat Inst 722 W 168th St Box 58 New York NY 10032

WEXLER, PETER JOHN, producer, director, set designer; b. N.Y.C., Oct. 31, 1936; s. S. David and Berda (Sarnoff) W.; m. Constance Ann Ross, Nov. 30, 1962. BS in Design, U. Mich., 1958; student, Yale Sch. Drama, 1958. Designs include White House stage, 1961, War and Peace, 1964, The White Devil, 1965, A Joyful Noise, 1966, The Happy Time, 1967, In the Matter of J. Robert Oppenheimer, 1968, Merv Griffin TV show, 1965, Terra Nova, 1979 (L.A. Dramalogue Critics award); prin. designer, Center Theatre Group, L.A., 1967-70, designer, N.Y. Philharmonic Promenades, 1965-78; play and film The Trial of the Catonsville 9, 1971-72; Leonard Bernstein's Mass, L.A., 1973, N.Y. Philharmonic Rug Concerts, 1973-77, Les Troyens, Met. Opera Co., 1973, Le Prophète, Met. Opera Co., 1977, Un Ballo in Maschera, Met. Opera Co., 1980, Theatre Space Prodns., Pitts. Pub. Theatre, 1975-77; mem. design team for Frank O. Gehry & Assocs., redesign Hollywood Bowl; designer: Albert Herring, Savonlinna Opera Festival, Finland, 1981; centennial prodn. Les Troyens, Met. Opera, 1983; directed: Cold Storage, Ariz. Theatre Co., 1978, Terra Nova, Pitts. Public Theatre, 1981; producer, Dallas Symphony Orch.'s Star Fest 80; producer Rocky Mountain Music Festival, Denver Symphony Orch., 1983-84, Star Spangled Banner, Permanent Exhibition U.S. Nat. Emblem, Smithsonian Instn., Washington, 1982; producer, design exhbn. Am. Anthem, LTV Ctr., Dallas/Smithsonian Instn., 1985; designer, broker exhbn. Liberties with Liberty, Trammell Crow Co./Mus. Am. Folk Art, 1985; designer Horizons '86, N.Y. Philharmonic, 1986; co-producer, designer video, exhbn. and space Albany Urban Cultural Park, Albany, N.Y., 1986; producer, dir. Pletka, multimedia theatre piece for orch., Dallas Symphony Orch., 1987; programmer, designer Trans-Hudson Ferry for the Port Authority of N.Y. and N.J., 1987-88; producer The Search for Life, Smithsonian Inst., 1987; producer Mstislav Rostropovich 60th Anniv. Gala Concert, Nat. Symphony Orch., Kennedy Ctr., Washington, 1987, Navy 87, Navy 89, USN multi-media orchestral prodn., Washington, 1987; producer, artistic dir. Spring Creek Music Festival, Garland, Tex. Dallas Ft. Worth Metroplex, 1992-94; dir. Lost in the Stars, A.C.O., Carnegie Hall, 1989; visual cons. Lifetime Med. (cable TV), 1989-90; design cons. Reebok River Stage - Radio City Music Hall Prodns, 1989; program designer Mega-Mall, Oxford Devel. Co., Pitts., Infinished Stories, 1994, A Salute to Slava, Kennedy Ctr., Washington, 1994. Project leader Outdoor Performance Facility, Met. Opera Co., N.Y. Philharmonic Symphony, Dept. Cultural Affairs City of N.Y. Recipient Internat. Theatre Inst. competition award ANTA, 1965, most imaginative use of scene design award Saturday Rev., 1965, Drama Desk-Joseph Maharam award for The Happy Time as best designer of mus., 1968, L.A. Drama Critics Circle award, 1971. Address: 277 W End Ave New York NY 10023

WEXLER, RAYMOND P., lawyer; b. St. Louis, May 17, 1942; s. Morris J. and Augusta W.; m. Mary Anne Lacks, Mar. 5, 1967; Children: Jennifer, Randy, Colin. BA, Washington U. St. Louis, 1964, JD, 1967; LLM, N.Y.U., 1972. Bar: Mo. 1967, Ill. 1972. Ptnr. Kirkland & Ellis, Chgo., 1972—; dir. Internat. Tax Forum, Chgo., 1974, 1967-71. Office: Kirkland & Ellis 200 W Randolph St Chicago IL 60606-1812

WEXLER, RICHARD LEWIS, lawyer; b. Chgo. June 19, 1941; s. Stanley and Lottie (Pinkert) W.; m. Roberta Seigel, June 13, 1962; children: Deborah (Mrs. Jonathan Sokobin), Joshua, Jonathan. Student, U. Mich., 1959-1962; JD cum laude, John Marshall Law Sch., 1965. Bar: Ill. 1965, US. Dist. Ct. (no. dist.) Ill. 1967. Gen. counsel Metro. Planning Council, Chgo., 1965-67; ptnr. Wexler, Kane, Rosenzweig & Shaw, Chgo., 1967-71, Taussig, Wexler & Shaw, Chgo., 1971-78, Wexler, Siegel & Shaw, Chgo., 1978-83; ptnr. Sachnoff & Weaver, Ltd., Chgo., 1983-91, chair real estate dept., 1985-91, mng. ptnr., 1985-90; ptnr., co-chairperson real estate dept. Lord Bissell & Brook, Chgo., 1991—; legal cons. Zoning Laws Study Commn., Ill. Gen. Assembly, Springfield, 1969-71, Urban Counties Study Commn., Springfield, 1971-72; legal counsel Ill. Coastal Zone Mgmt. Program, Springfield, 1979-81, Northeastern Ill. Planning Commn., Chgo., 1969—. Contbr. numerous articles to profl. jours. Pres. Jewish Fedn. Met. Chgo., 1986-88, mem. numerous coms., also bd. dirs. 1978-90; pres. Jewish United Fund, 1986-88; bd. dirs. Coun. Jewish Fedns., 1980, mem. exec. com., 1985—, v.p., 1988—, chmn. planning steering com., 1990—, chmn. fed./agy. rels. com., 1989-90; co-chmn. Task Force on Poverty and Low Income, 1985-87; nat. vice-chmn. United Jewish Appeal, 1988—, regional allocations chmn., 1987-88, chmn. region II, 1988-90, budget com., 1989-92, allocations com., 1990-91; campaign exec., 1991—; chmn. Operation Exodus II, 1993-94; bd. dirs. Jewish Edn. Soc. N.Am., 1982-85, Hebrew Immigrant Aid Soc., 1988—, Nat. Conf. on Soviet Jewry, 1989—, vice chair, 1989-92, nat. chair, 1992—; bd. dirs. Nat. Jewish Community Rels. Adv. Coun., 1988—, vice chair, 1988-92; chmn. Jewish Com. Rels. Coun. Chgo., 1988-89. Fellow Eta Lambda; mem. ABA, Ill. State Bar Assn. (Lincoln award, Legal Writing, 1966). Avocations: tennis, reading, travel. Office: Lord Bissell & Brook 115 S La Salle St Ste 3400 Chicago IL 60603-3903

WEXLER, ROBERT, university administrator. Pres. U. of Judaism, L.A. Office: U Judaism 15600 Mulholland Dr Los Angeles CA 90077-1519

WEXNER, LESLIE HERBERT, retail executive; b. Dayton, Ohio, 1937. BSBA, Ohio State U., 1959, HHD (hon.), 1986; LLD (hon.), Hofstra U., 1987; LHD (hon.), Brandeis U., 1990; PhD (hon.), Jewish Theol. Sem. Founder, pres., chmn. bd. The Limited, Inc., fashion chain, Columbus, 1963—; dir. mem. exec. com. Banc One Corp., Sotheby's Holdings Inc., vis. com. Grad. Sch. Design Harvard U.; mem. bus. adminstrn. adv. coun. Ohio State U.; chmn. Retail Industry Trade Action Coalition. Bd. dirs. Columbus Urban League, 1982-84, Hebrew Immigrant Aid Soc., N.Y.C., 1982—; co-chmn. Internat. United Jewish Appeal Com.; nat. vice chmn. United Jewish Appeal; bd. dirs., mem. exec. com. Am. Jewish Joint Distbn. Com., Inc.; trustee Columbus Jewish Fedn., 1972, Columbus Jewish Found., Aspen Inst., Ohio State U., Columbus Capital Corp. for Civic Improvement; former trustee Columbus Mus. Art, Columbus Symphony Orch., Whitney Mus. Am. Art, Capitol South Community Urban Redevel. Corp.; former mem. Governing Com. Columbus Found.; founding mem., first chair The Ohio State U. Found.; exec. com. Am. Israel Pub. Affairs Com. Decorated cavaliere Republic of Italy. Named Man of Yr. Am. Mktg. Assn., 1974. Mem. Young Presidents Orgn., Sigma Alpha Mu. Club: B'nai B'rith. Office: Ltd Inc PO Box 16000 3 Limited Pkwy Columbus OH 43216-6000

WEY, JONG-SHINN, research laboratory manager; b. Kaohsiung, Taiwan, Oct. 26, 1944; came to U.S. 1968; s. Tan-Ding and Chao (Lee) W.; m. Hseh-Yi Su, 1965; children: John, Nancy. BS in Chem. Engring., Nat. Taiwan U., 1967; PhD, Clarkson U., 1973. Sr. rsch. chemist Eastman Kodak Co., Rochester, N.Y., 1973-80, rsch. assoc., 1980-84, lab. head, 1984-91, sr. lab. head, 1991—. Co-author: Preparation and Properties of Solid State Materials, 1981, Handbook of Industrial Crystallization, 1992. Recipient Jour. award Photographic Sci. and Engring. Fellow Soc. Photographic Scientists and Engrs.; mem. AIChE. Achievements include patents in field; published papers on crystallization, precipitation, nucleation, growth, size distribution control and photographic emulsion. Home: 259 Hillary Ln Penfield NY 14526 Office: Eastman Kodak Co Rsch Labs Bldg 59 Rochester NY 14650-1736

WEYAND, FREDERICK CARLTON, retired military officer; b. Arbuckle, Calif., Sept. 15, 1916; s. Frederick C. W. and Velma Semans (Weyand); m. Lora Arline Langhart, Sept. 20, 1940; children: Carolyn Ann, Robert Carlton, Nancy Diane. A.B., U. Calif.-Berkeley, 1939; LL.D. (hon.), U. Akron, 1975. Officer U.S. Army, advanced to gen. chief of staff, 1940-76; sr. v.p. First Hawaiian Bank, Honolulu, 1976-82; trustee Estate of S.M. Damon, Honolulu, 1982—; bd. dirs. First Hawaiian, Inc., Ltd., First Hawaiian Bank, First Hawaiian Credit Corp. Chmn. ARC, Honolulu, 1982, Hawaiian Open golf Tourney, 1981-82. Decorated D.S.C. U.S. Army, 1967, D.S.M. Army (3), Dept. Def. (1), 1966-76, other U.S. and fgn. mil. decorations. Mem. Am. Def. Preparedness Assn., Assn. U.S. Army, U.S. Strategic Inst. (v.p. 1976—), USAF Assn. Lutheran. Clubs: Waialae Country. Lodge: Masons. Home: 2121 Ala Wai Blvd Ph 1 Honolulu HI 96815-2211 Office: SM Damon Estate 1132 Bishop St Ste 1520 Honolulu HI 96813-2809

WEYENBERG, DONALD RICHARD, chemist; b. Glenvil, Nebr., July 11, 1930; s. Clyde H. and Elva I. (Hlavaty) W.; m. Barbara Ann Oppenheim, Dec. 26, 1955; children: Ann Louise, Thomas Richard. B.S. in Chemistry, U. Nebr., 1951; Ph.D., Pa. State U., 1958; P.M.D. Program, Harvard U., 1968. Research chemist Dow Corning Corp., Midland, Mich., 1951-65, research mgr., 1965-68, dir. corp. devel., 1968-69, dir. silicone research, 1969-71, bus. mgr., 1971-76, dir. research, 1976-79, v.p. research and devel., 1979-86, chief sci. and sr. v.p. research and devel., 1987-93, sci. emeritus, 1993—; bd. dirs. Dow Corning, Dendritech; Hurd lectr. Northwestern U., 1992—. Bd. editors Organometallics Jour., 1980-86; contbr. articles to sci. jours., chpts. to books; patentee silicone materials. Bd. visitors Memphis State U., 1981-87; mem. indsl. bd. advisors U. Nebr., 1988. Named Alumni fellow Pa. State U., 1988. Mem. Am. Chem. Soc. (chmn. Midland sect. 1967 Outstanding Achievement in Promotion Chem. Scis. award Midland sect.), Indsl. Research Inst., N.Y. Acad. Scis., Sigma Xi. Lodge: Rotary. Home: 4601 Arbor Dr Midland MI 48640-2644 Office: Dow Corning Corp PO Box 994 2200 Salzburg St Midland MI 48640-8594

WEYERHAEUSER, GEORGE HUNT, forest products company executive; b. Seattle, July 8, 1926; s. John Philip and Helen (Walker) W.; m. Wendy Wagner, July 10, 1948; children: Virginia Lee, George Hunt, Susan W., Phyllis A., David M., Merrill W. BS with honors in Indsl. Engring., Yale U., 1949. With Weyerhaeuser Co., Tacoma, 1949—, successively mill foreman, br. mgr., 1949-56, v.p., 1957-66, exec. v.p., 1966-88, pres., chief exec. officer, 1988, chmn. bd., chief exec. officer, 1988-91, chmn. bd., past CEO, also bd. dirs.; bd. dirs. Boeing Co., SAFECO Corp., Chevron Corp.; mem. Bus. Coun., Bus. Roundtable, Wash. State Bus. Roundtable. Office: Weyerhaeuser Fin Svcs 33663 Weyerhauser Way S Auburn WA 98001*

WEYFORTH, MIMI See DAWSON, MIMI

WEYGAND, ROBERT A., lieutenant governor, landscape architect; b. Attleboro, Mass., May 10, 1948. BA in Fine Arts, U. R.I., 1971, BS in Civil and Environ. Engring., 1976. Project mgr. R.I. Dept. Nat. Resources, 1973-82; owner Weygand, Orciuch & Christie, Inc., 1982-92; mem. R.I. Ho. of Reps. from 84th dist., 1984-92; lt. gov. State of R.I., 1993—; chmn. house com. on corps., 1990; chmn. E. Providence Planning Bd., 1978-84, R.I. Small Bus. Advocacy Coun., 1992—, R.I. Long Term Care Coord. Coun., 1992—, R.I. Delegation/White House Conf. on Aging, 1995; bd. dirs. R.I. Scenic Hwy, 1988-92. Bd. dirs. Save the Bay, 1984-87, United Way, 1993—, Meeting St. Ctr., 1993—; pres. bd. dirs. R.I. Parks Assn., 1983-92; chmn. R.I. Land Use Commn., 1987-92. Recipient Legislator of Yr. award R.I. League Cities and Towns, 1988, Exceptional Pub. Svc. award FBI, 1992, Disting. Svc. Star State of R.I., 1992. Mem. Am. Soc. Landscape Architects; Am. Planning Assn. (Outstanding Pub. Svc. award New Eng. chpt. 1992). Office: State House Rm 313 Providence RI 02903

WEYHER, HARRY FREDERICK, lawyer; b. Wilson, N.C., Aug. 19, 1921; s. Harry Frederick and Laura Gray (Carter) W.; m. Barbara Dore McCusker, Sept. 9, 1950 (div. May 1971); children: Barbara Brandon, Harry Frederick III, Laura Carter; m. Laura Hyman Harvey, Oct. 17, 1971 (div. Sept. 1986); m. Michelle Eimers, Dec. 29, 1989. B.S., U. N.C., 1946; student, U. Glasgow, Scotland, 1946; LL.B. magna cum laude, Harvard U. 1949. Bar: N.Y., 1950. Assoc. Cravath, Swaine & Moore, N.Y.C., 1949-54; sr. assoc. counsel N.Y. State Crime Commn., 1950-52; ptnr., counsel Olwine, Connelly, Chase, O'Donnell & Weyher, N.Y.C., 1954-91; adj. assoc. prof. N.Y.U. Sch. Law, 1952-62; bd. dirs. AFA Protective Systems, Inc., The Pioneer Fund, Inc. Author: (with Hiram Knott) ESOP-Employee Stock Ownership Plan, 2d ed., 1985, Hanging Out a Shingle, 1987; contbr. articles to profl. jours. Mem. ABA, N.Y. State Bar Assn., Assn. of Bar of City of N.Y., Phi Beta Kappa, Beta Gamma Sigma, Zeta Psi. Clubs: Harvard, Racquet and Tennis (N.Y.C.), Lyford Cay (Nassau), Boone & Crockett. Home: 211 E 70th St Apt 17B New York NY 10021-5207 Office: 551 Fifth Ave 27th FL New York NY 10176

WEYHER, HARRY FREDERICK, III, metals company executive; b. N.Y.C., Mar. 9, 1956; s. Harry F. and Barbara (McCusker) W.; m. Anda

Gailitis, July 7, 1984; children: Harry F. IV, Jesse D. BA, Middlebury Coll., 1977. Treas. Bunge Corp., N.Y.C., 1977-90; v.p. fin. Gerald Metals Inc., Stamford, Conn., 1990—. Mem. Racquet & Tennis Club. Home: 215 Ridgefield Rd Wilton CT 06897-2432 Office: Gerald Metals Inc High Ridge Park Stamford CT 06904

WEYLER, WALTER EUGEN, manufacturing company executive; b. Berwyn, Ill., Sept. 21, 1939; s. Eugen J. and Else E. (Deeg) W.; m. Nancy Prudence Haines; children—Walter Eugen, Peter C., Amy H. B.E.E., Mich. State U., 1961; M.B.A., Harvard U., 1963. Mktg. mgr. integrated circuit product line Tex. Instruments Corp., Dallas, 1963-68; mfg. mgr. semicondr. div. ITT, West Palm Beach, Fla., 1968-74; various positions Gen. Electric Co., Waterford, N.Y., 1974-82; v.p., gen. mgr. mobile communications Gen. Electric Co., Lynchburg, Va., 1982-85; pres., chief operating officer Graco, Inc., Mpls., 1985—. Trustee Minn. Orch., Mpls., 1985. Mem. Mpls. C. of C. (trustee 1987). Clubs: Interlachen (Mpls.), Minneapolis. Home: 7715 Stonewood Ct Minneapolis MN 55439-2642

WEYRAUCH, PAUL TURNEY, retired army officer; b. Alpine, Tex., July 22, 1941; s. Paul Russell and Margaret Fischer (Fletcher) W.; m. Nancy Virginia Haight, Dec. 18, 1965; children: Julie Lynn, Paul C. BS, U.S. Mil. Acad., West Point, N.Y., 1963; MBA, Tulane U., 1976. Commd. 2d lt. U.S. Army, 1963, advanced through grades to brig. gen.; bn. comdr. 1st Bn., 5th F.A., Ft. Riley, Kans., 1978-80; asst. chief of staff 1st Inf. Div., Ft. Riley, 1980-81; comdr. 1st Cav. Div. Arty., Ft. Hood, 1982-85; chief of staff U.S. Army F.A. Ctr., Ft. Sill, Okla., 1985-86; asst. chief of staff for plans and policy Allied Forces So. Europe, Naples, Italy, 1986-89; chief of staff III Corps and Ft. Hood, 1989-91; ret., 1991. Tchr. Sunday sch. local Protestant chs., pres. chapel couns., leader, coord. Bible studies. Decorated D.S.M., Def. Superior Svc. Medal, Legion of Merit, Bronze Star medal with V. device, Bronze Star medal with 1 oak leaf cluster, Meritorious Svc. medal with 3 oak leaf clusters. Mem. 1st Cav. Div. Assn. Avocations: running, collecting military insignia. Home: 320 S Ridge Cir Georgetown TX 78628-8213

WEYRAUCH, WALTER OTTO, legal educator; b. Lindau, Germany, Aug. 27, 1919; came to U.S., 1952; s. Hans Ernst Winand and Meta Margarete (Lönholdt) W.; m. Jill Carolyn White, Mar. 17, 1973; children from previous marriages—Kurt Roman, Corinne Harriet Irene, Bettina Elaine (dec.). Student, U. Freiburg, 1937, U. Frankfurt Main, Germany, 1940-43; Dr. iur, U. Frankfurt Main, Germany, 1951; LL.B., Georgetown U., 1955; LL.M., Harvard, 1956; J.S.D., Yale, 1962. Referendar Frankfurt, Germany, 1943-48; atty. German cts. U.S. Ct. Appeals, Allied High Commn., Frankfurt, 1949-52; expert on trade regulations, visit in U.S. under auspices Dept. State, 1950; Harvard U. Dumbarton Oaks Library and Collection, Washington, 1953-55; asst. in instrn. Law Sch., Yale, 1956-57; assoc. prof. law U. Fla., Gainesville, 1957-60, prof., 1960-89, Clarence J. TeSelle prof. law, 1989-94, Stephen C. O'Connell chair, 1994—; hon. prof. law Johann Wolfgang Goethe U., Frankfurt Main, 1980—; vis. cons. U. Calif. at Berkeley, Space Scis. Lab., 1965-66; vis. prof. law Rutgers U., 1968; vis. prof. polit. sci. U. Calif. at Berkeley, 1968-69; vis. prof. law U. Frankfurt, 1975; cons. Commn. of Experts on Problems of Succession of the Hague Conf. on Pvt. Internat. Law, U.S. Dept. State, 1968-71; Rockefeller Found. fellow, Europe, 1958-59. Author: The Personality of Lawyers, 1964, Zum Gesellschaftsbild des Juristen, 1970, Hierarchie der Ausbildungsstätten, Rechtsstudium und Recht in den Vereinigten Staaten, 1976, Gestapo V-Leute: Tatsachen und Theorie des Geheimdienstes, 1989, 2d edit., 1992; co-author: (with Sanford N. Katz) American Family Law in Transition, 1983, (with Katz and Frances E. Olsen) Cases and Materials on Family Law: Legal Concepts and Changing Human Relationships, 1994; contbr. to: Clinical Law Training-Interviewing and Counseling, 1972, Law, Justice, and the Individual in Society-Psychological and Legal Issues, 1977, Marriage and Cohabitation in Contemporary Societies: Areas of Legal, Social and Ethical Change-An International and Interdisciplinary Study, 1980, Dutch trans., 1981, Group Dynamic Law: Exposition and Practice, 1988. Mem. Am. Acad. Fgn. Law, Law and Soc. Assn., Internat. Soc. on Family Law, Assn. Am. Law Schs. (chmn. coms. studies beyond 1st degree in law 1965-67), Order of Coif. Home: 2713 SW 5th Pl Gainesville FL 32607-3113 Office: U Fla Coll Law Gainesville FL 32611

WEYRICH, PAUL MICHAEL, political organizations executive; b. Racine, Wis., Oct. 7, 1942; s. Ignatius A. and Virginia M. (Wickstrom) W.; m. Joyce Anne Smigun, July 6, 1963; children: Dawn, Peter, Diana, Stephen, Andrew. AA, U. Wis., 1962. Ordained deacon Melkite Greek Eparchy, 1990. News dir. Service Broadcasting, Kenosha, Wis., 1962-63; reporter Milw. Sentinel, 1963-64; polit. reporter, newscaster CBS, Milw., 1964-65; news dir. Sta. KQXI, Denver, 1966; asst. U.S. Sen. Gordon Allott of Colo., 1966-73; asst. to Sen. Carl T. Curtis, Nebr., 1973-77; founder, pres. Heritage Found., 1973-74; nat. chmn. Free Congress PAC, Coalitions for Am., BOD, AMTRAK, 1987-93; pres. Free Congress Found., Krieble Inst. of Free Congress Found., NET-Polit. Newstalk Network; Washington editor The Wanderer, 1969-71; nat. editor Transport Central, 1968-73; treas. Coun. Nat. Policy, 1981-92; bd. dirs. All News Radio WEEI, Boston, 1984-90; vice chmn. Com. for Effective State Govt. Recipient Youth of Yr. award Racine Optimist Club, 1960, Excellence in Reporting citation Milw. Common Council, 1964, Documentary of Yr. award for Wis. TV, 1965. Mem. Central Electric Railroaders Assn., Internat. Policy Forum (chmn. 1983-94); former mem. HUD Adv. Commn. on Regulatory Barriers to Affordable Housing. Greek Catholic. Author: The Role of Rails series, 1964; pub. Polit. Report, 1975-89, The New Electric Rwy. Jour., 1988—; Spotlight on Congress, 1989-93; host (daily talk show) Direct Line, 1993—; co-host The New Electric Railway Jour., 1994—, Ways & Means, 1994—. Home: 12615 Lake Normandy Ln Fairfax VA 22030-7262 Office: Free Congress Found 717 2d St NE Washington DC 20002

WHALE, ARTHUR RICHARD, lawyer; b. Detroit, Oct. 28, 1923; s. Arthur B. and Orpha Louella (Doak) W.; m. Roberta Lou Donaldson, Oct. 29, 1949; children: Richard Donaldson, Linda Jean. BSChemE, Northwestern U., 1945; LLB, George Washington U., 1956. Bar: D.C. 1957, Mich. 1957, Ind. 1977, Office of U.S. Patent and Trademark 1957. Chem. engr. Ansul Chem. Co., Marinette, Wis., 1946-47, Parke, Davis & Co., Detroit, 1947-50; writer med. lit. Parke, Davis & Co., 1950-52; chem. engr. Bur. Ships, U.S. Dept. Navy, Washington, 1952-55; dep. sect. head, indsl. gas sect. Bur. Ships, U.S. Dept. Navy, 1954-55; patent engr. Swift & Co., Washington, 1955-56; patent atty. Upjohn Co., Kalamazoo, 1956-65; asst. mgr. organic chems. sect. patent dept. Dow Chem. Co., Midland, Mich., 1965-66; mgr. Dow Chem. Co., 1967-73, mng. counsel, 1973-75; asst. sec., gen. patent counsel Eli Lilly & Co., Indpls., 1975-86; of counsel Miller, Morriss & Pappas, Lansing, Mich., 1986-89, Baker & Daniels, Indpls., 1987—; bd. dirs. Wyckoff Chem. Co., South Haven, Mich.; lectr. Practicing Law Inst., John Marshall Law Sch. Contbr. articles to profl. jours. Pres. Nat. Inventors Hall of Fame Found., 1978-79; bd. dirs. Holcomb Rsch. Inst., INdpls, 1982-86. Served to lt. (j.g.) USNR, 1943-46. Mem. State Bar Mich. (chmn. patent trademark copyright sect. 1967-69), D.C. Bar Assn. (mem. patent trademark copyright div.), Midland County Bar Assn. (pres. 1974-75), Am. Bar Assn. (mem. patent trademark copyright sect.), Assn. Corp. Patent Counsel, Nat. Coun. Patent Law Assns. (chmn. 1979-80), Am. Intellectual Property Law Assn. (pres. 1974-75), Ashlar Lodge, Masons, Shriners. Republican. Presbyterian. Avocation: golf. Home: 3513 Admiralty Ln Indianapolis IN 46240-3568 also: 2363 Gulf Shore Blvd N Naples FL 33940-4356 Office: Baker & Daniels 300 N Meridian St Ste 2700 Indianapolis IN 46204-1782

WHALEN, CHARLES WILLIAM, JR., author, business executive, educator; b. Dayton, Ohio, July 31, 1920; s. Charles William and Colette (Kelleher) W.; m. Mary Barbara Gleason, Dec. 27, 1958; children—Charles E., Daniel D., Edward J., Joseph M., Anne E., Mary B. B.S., U. Dayton, 1942, H.H.D. (hon.), 1980; M.B.A., Harvard U., 1946; postgrad., Ohio State U. 1959-60; LL.D., Central State U. Ohio, 1966. Vice pres. Dayton Dress Co., 1946-52; faculty U. Dayton, 1952-66; mem. 90th-95th Congresses 3d Dist. Ohio; pres. New Directions, Washington, 1978-79; fellow Woodrow Wilson Internat. Center for Scholars, 1980; adj. prof. N.C. Internat. Service, Am. U. 1981. Mem. Ohio Ho. of Reps., 1954-60, Ohio Senate, 1960-66; mem. Internat. Vol. Svcs., Inc.; v.p. Washington Inst. Fgn. Affairs; mem. U. Dayton adv. bd. Ctr. for Internat. Studies; bd. dirs. Harvard Bus. Sch., Washington. 1st lt. AUS, 1943-46. Recipient Disting. Alumnus award U.

Dayton Alumni Assn., 1975;. Roman Catholic. Clubs: Capitol Hill, Kenwood Country, Dayton Bicycle.

WHALEN, JAMES JOSEPH, college president; b. Pottsville, Pa., Mar. 6, 1927; s. Frank Leo and Mary M. (McCusker) W.; m. Gillian Stuart Hamer, Sept. 29, 1956. AB, Franklin and Marshall Coll., 1950; MS (VA fellow), Pa. State U., 1952, PhD in Clin. Psychology (VA fellow), 1955; LLD (hon.), Newton (Mass.) Coll., 1975. Lic. psychologist, Mass. VA tng. intern clin. psychology Roanoke (Va.) VA Hosp., 1951-52, Wilkes-Barre (Pa.) VA Hosp., 1954-55; clin. psychologist VA Hosp., Pitts., 1955-58; asst. dean, psychologist European div. U. Md., Munich, Germany, 1958-60; prof. psychology, lectr. European div. U. Md., Heidelberg, Germany, 1960-63; asst. dir., asst. prof. psychology U. Md., European Div., 1963-64; assoc. prof., prof. psychology Ohio U., 1964-69, dir. ctr. for psychol. services, 1964-65, dean students, 1965-66, adminstry. v.p., 1966-67, exec. v.p., 1967-69; pres., prof. Newton Coll., 1969-75; pres. Ithaca (N.Y.) Coll., 1975—, prof., 1975—; past chmn. Am. Coun. Edn., chmn. nominating com., 1994, Ad Hoc study com., Commn. on Ednl. Credit and Credentials, 1992—, chmn. membership com., 1988-90, bd. dirs., 1984-91, chmn. constn. and by-laws rev. com., 1991-92; past mem. pres.'s commn. NCAA, past chmn. div. III subcom., mem. com. on rev. and planning, 1990—; co-chair NCAA Gender Equity Task Force, 1992-93; mem. Edn. Commn. States Task Force on State Policy and Ind. Higher Edn.; past chmn. bd. visitors Air U. USAF; cons., chmn. Joint Chiefs of Staff Profl. Mil. Edn. Rev. Panel, mem. exec. com. Joint Chiefs of Staff Process for Accreditation of Joint Edn., 1991—; mem. Knight Found. Commn. on Intercoll. Athletics, 1989-93; mem. bd. visitors U. N.C., Asheville, 1986-89; past chmn. Nat. Assn. Ind. Colls. and Univs., bd. dirs., 1982-85, mem. pub. rels. adv. com., 1989-90, mem. govt. rels. com., 1985-89, chmn. govt. rels. com. on state rels., 1988-89; mem. Commn. on Ind. Colls. and Univs. in N.Y. State, past chmn. bd., past chmn. fed. rels. Com., trustee, 1978-84, 89-92, chmn. fin. com., 1990-92, treas. CICU/NYSCICU bd. 1991-92; mem. regents adv. coun. for Planning in Higher Edn., State of N.Y.; mem. nat. adv. com. Ctr. for Study of Sports in Soc.; mem. commr. edns. adv. coms. state N.Y., mem. commrs. edns. task force to reorganize state edn. dept.; chmn. adv. bd. Fleet Bank, Ithaca; bd. dirs. Fleet Investment Svcs., Rochester, N.Y. Contbr. articles on exec. leadership and ednl. adminstrn. to profl. jours. Served with USNR, 1945-46. Recipient Keiper award Franklin and Marshall Coll., 1948, medal USAF, 1990; Pa. State U. scholar, 1950-52. Mem. Am. Psychol. Assn., Mass. Psycho. Assn., Internat. Assn. Univ. Pres., N.Y. Acad. Scis., N.Y. State C. of C. (edn. com.), Ind. Coll. Fund N.Y. State (past mem. exec. com.), Assn. Colls. and Univs. N.Y. State (past mem. exec. com., bd. trustees), Oracle Soc., Univ. Club, Royal Auto Club, Ithaca Garden Club, Rotary, Phi Kappa Phi (editorial adv. bd. Nat. Forum 1989-94), Phi Delta Kappa, Psi Chi, Phi Kappa Tau, Phi Mu Alpha, Delta Phi Alpha. Home: 2 Fountain Pl Ithaca NY 14850-4428 Office: Ithaca Coll 953 Danby Rd Ithaca NY 14850-7001

WHALEN, JEROME DEMARIS, lawyer; b. Portland, Oreg., Feb. 9, 1943; s. William F. and Rose (Demaris) W. BA, U. Wash., 1965; JD, Harvard U., 1969. Bar: Wash. 1969. Assoc. Foster Pepper & Shefelman, Seattle, 1969-74, ptnr., 1974-91, mng. ptnr., 1982-85; ptnr. Whalen & Firestone, Seattle, 1991—; adj. prof. corps. Law Sch., U. Puget Sound, Tacoma, 1976-77; instr. securities regulation Law Sch., U. Wash., Seattle, 1979; bd. dirs. Wright Runstad & Co., Seattle. Author: Commercial Ground Leases, 1988. Mem. Port of Seattle Ctrl. Waterfront Devel. Panel, 1988-90; trustee Corp. Coun. for Arts, Seattle, 1989—; trustee Pratt Fine Arts Ctr., Seattle, 1989-94, pres., 1991-93, Seattle Internat. Music Festival, 1992—. Mem. Wash. State Bar Assn. (chmn. corp. bus. and banking law sect. 1980-81), Phi Beta Kappa. Office: Whalen & Firestone 1221 2nd Ave Ste 410 Seattle WA 98101-2942

WHALEN, JOHN PHILIP, retired educational administrator, clergyman, lawyer; b. Troy, N.Y., Jan. 4, 1928; s. Philip Joseph and Mary Catherine (Doyle) W.; B.A. summa cum laude, St. Mary's Sem. and Univ., Balt.; 1949; S.T.L., Cath. U., 1953, M.A., 1954, S.T.D. summa cum laude, 1965; J.D., George Washington U., 1976; postgrad. Johns Hopkins U., 1959-60, U. Md., College Park, 1958-59, Fordham U., 1953-54; LHD (hon.), Marymount U., 1987. Ordained priest Roman Cath. Ch., 1953. Instr. Mater Christi Sem., Albany, N.Y., 1953-58; asst. prof. Mt. St. Mary's Coll., Emmitsburg, Md., 1959-61; assoc. prof. Cath. U. Am., Washington, 1961-67, acting pres., 1968-69; pastor St. Mary's Ch., Oneonta, N.Y., 1970-72; pres. Consortium of Univs. of Washington area, 1972-88; mng. editor New Cath. Ency., 1963-67; pres., editor-in-chief Corpus Publs., 1967-94; ret. 1994. cons. 12 colls. and univs.; chmn. Univ. Support Services Inc., 1986-94, pres., chief exec. officer; cons. student loans, capital access trust, capital loans to colls.; bd. dirs. U.S. Fund for Improvement Postsecondary Edn., 1988-91. Bd. dirs. Sta. WETA-TV, 1968-69, Washington Ctr. for Met. Studies, 1968-69, Met. Bd. Trade, D.C., 1975-90, sec. bd. dirs., 1983-85; bd. dirs. Cath. U. Am., 1968-69, Nat. Shrine of Immaculate Conception, 1968-69, Dumbarton Coll., 1970-72, Trinity Coll., 1969-72, St. Mary's Coll. (South Bend, Ind.), 1970-74, St. Anselm's, 1979-85, Mt. Vernon Coll., 1982-84; pres. Univ. Extension Ednl. Corp., 1974-94; mem. Fed. City Council, 1982—; mem. Council for Ct. Excellence, 1984-90; chmn. Ctr. Advanced Studies of the Ams., 1984-90. Named Man of the Yr. 1984; recipient Disting. Alumnus award George Washington U., 1988. Mem. Nat. Cath. Edn. Assn., Cath. Theol. Soc. Am. (dir. 1966-68), Higher Edn. Group Washington (pres. 1974-75). Clubs: Tired Hands (pres. 1982-84), Cosmos (Washington), City Club; Rotary. Editorial bd. Law and Edn.; weekly columnist Evangelist, Albany; contbr. to Nat. Geog. mag.; contbr. articles to ednl. and theol. jours. Office: 1614 Parham Rd Silver Spring MD 20903-2256

WHALEN, JOHN SYDNEY, management consultant; b. Moncton, N.B., Can., Sept. 26, 1934; s. Harry Edward and Sarah Maude (Bourgeois) W.; m. Margaret Joan Carruthers, May 3, 1958; children: Bradley Graham, Elizabeth Ann. Grad., Can. Inst. Chartered Accts., 1959. Chartered acct. Coopers & Lybrand (formerly McDonald, Currie & Co.), St. John, N.B., 1954-63; with Kaiser Services, Oakland, Calif., 1963-75; telecommunications mgr. Kaiser Services, 1966-69, asst. controller, 1969-70, controller, 1970-74; mgr. corp. acctg. Kaiser Industries Corp., Oakland, 1975; controller Kaiser Engrs., Inc., Oakland, 1975-76; v.p. fin. and adminstrn. Kaiser Engrs., Inc., 1976-82; mgmt. cons., owner Whalen & Assocs., Inc., Alamo, Calif., 1983—; prin. Corp. Restructuring Group, Inc., Alamo, Calif., 1989—; pres. Round Hill Securities, Inc., 1993—. Mem. Fin. Execs. Inst., Turnaround Mgmt. Assn. Club: Round Hill Golf and Country; Commonwealth. Home: 2216 Nelda Way Alamo CA 94507-2004 Office: 3158 Danville Blvd Alamo CA 94507-1540

WHALEN, LAURENCE J., federal judge; b. 1944. BA, Georgetown Coll.; 1967; JD, Georgetown U., 1970, LLM in Taxation, 1971. Judge U.S. Tax Ct., Washington, 1987—; atty. Crowe & Dunlevy, Oklahoma City, Hamel & Park, Washington; spl. asst. to Asst. Atty. Gen.; trial atty., tax div. U.S. Dept. Justice. With USAR, 1971. Mem. ABA (taxation, litigation and bus. law sects.), Fed. Bar Assn. Office: US Tax Ct 400 2nd St NW Washington DC 20217-0002

WHALEN, LUCILLE, academic administrator; b. Los Angeles, July 26, 1925; d. Edward Cleveland and Mary Lucille (Perrault) W. B.A. in English, Immaculate Heart Coll., Los Angeles, 1949; M.S.L.S., Catholic U. Am., 1955; D.L.S., Columbia U., 1965. Tchr. elem. and secondary parochial schs. Los Angeles, Long Beach, Calif., 1945-52; high sch. librarian Conaty Meml. High Sch., Los Angeles, 1950-52; reference/serials librarian, instr. in library sci. Immaculate Heart Coll., 1955-58; dean Immaculate Heart Coll. (Sch. Library Sci.), 1958-60, 65-70; assoc. dean, prof. SUNY, Albany, 1971-78, 84-87; prof. Sch. Info. Sci. and Policy SUNY, 1979-83; dean grad. programs, libr. Immaculate Heart Coll. Ctr., Los Angeles, 1987-90; ref. libr. (part-time) Glendale Community Coll., 1990—; dir. U.S. Office Edn. Instn. Author, editor: (with others) Reference Services in Archives, 1986. author: Human Rights: A Reference Handbook, 1989. Mem. ACLU, Common Cause, Amnesty Internat. Democrat. Roman Catholic. Home: 320 S Gramercy Pl Apt 101 Los Angeles CA 90020-4542 Office: Glendale Community Coll 1500 N Verdugo Rd Glendale CA 91208-2894

WHALEN, MARTIN J., corporate executive, lawyer; b. Chgo., May 6, 1940; s. Frank Gervais and Beatrice (Granger) W.; m. Mary-Jo McMahon, Aug. 17, 1963; children: Maureen, Michael, Cathryn, Matthew. JD, DePaul U., 1965. Bar: Ill., U.S. Tax Ct., U.S. Supreme Ct. Dir. labor relation-flight Ea. Airlines Inc., Miami, Fla., 1973-76; dir. labor rels. Hughes Airwest div.

Hughes Air Corp., San Francisco and Phoenix, 1976-77, gen. atty., 1977-79, sr. dir. pers., 1979-80; assoc. gen. counsel Hughes Helicopters, Inc., Culver City, Calif. and Mesa, Ariz., 1980-84; v.p. adminstrn. McDonnel Douglas Helicopter Co., Mesa, 1984-86; sr. v.p. adminstrn., gen. counsel Am. West Airlines, Inc., Phoenix, 1986—; exec. com. Airline Indsl. Rels. Conf., Washington, 1986—. Chmn. Mesa Econ. Growth Assn., 1989, treas., 1985-87, vice chmn., 1988; bd. dirs. Prehab of Ariz., Mesa, 1988—, East Valley Partnership, 1989. Roman Catholic. Avocations: light aircraft, golf, bricklaying. Office: Am W Airlines Inc 4000 E Sky Harbor Blvd Phoenix AZ 85034-3802

WHALEN, MICHAEL P., architect; b. Seattle, May 13, 1949; s. Jack R. and Dorothy (Welsh) W.; m. Leslie Porter, Aug. 26, 1978; children: Stephanie Hope, Edward David. BArch, U. Wash., 1972; MArch, U. Calif., Berkeley, 1976. Cert. NCARB. Architect Eden & Eden, San Francisco, 1972-74, Media Five, Ltd., Honolulu, 1974-75, Kaplan McLaughlin Diaz, San Francisco, 1976-77; prin. Callison Partnership, Seattle, 1978—. Prin. works include (mixed use devel.) Carillon Point, 1988-89, (resort hotel) Semiahmoo, 1987, (dept. store) Nordstrom, Tyson's Corner, Va., 1988, pvt. club, Tokyo, 1990. Branner Traveling fellow U. Calif., Berkeley, 1977-78. Mem. AIA (cert., award Seattel chpt. 1988, 89), Urban Land Inst., Internat. Coun. Shopping Ctrs., Japan Am. Soc., City Club, Wash. Athletic Club. Office: Callison 1420 5th Ave Seattle WA 98101-2333

WHALEN, PHILIP GLENN, poet, novelist; b. Portland, Oreg., Oct. 20, 1923; s. Glenn Henry and Phyllis Bush W. B.A., Reed Coll., 1951. Ordained Zen Buddhist priest, 1973. Head monk Dharma Sangha, Santa Fe, 1984-87; abbot Hartford St. Zen Ctr., San Francisco, 1991; lectr., tchr., 1955—. Author: poetry Three Satires, 1951, Self-Portrait, From Another Direction, 1959, Like I Say, 1960, Memoirs of an Inter-Glacial Age, 1960, Every Day, 1965, Highgrade, 1966, On Bear's Head, 1969, Severance Pay, 1971, Scenes of Life at the Capitol, 1971, The Kindness of Strangers, 1975, Enough Said, 1980, Heavy Breathing, 1983; novels You Didn't Even Try, 1967, Imaginary Speeches for a Brazen Head, 1972; interviews Off the Wall, 1978; prose text The Diamond Noodle, 1980; juvenile The Invention of the Letter, 1967; Recipient Poet's Found. award 1962, V.K. Ratcliff award 1964; By & Large, tape cassette reading his own poems, 1987. Served with USAAF, 1943-46. Am. Acad. Arts and Letters grantee-in-aid, 1965, 91, Morton Dauwen Zabel award for Poetry, 1986, Fund for Poetry award, 1987, 91; Com. on Poetry grantee, 1968, 70, 71. Office: 57 Hartford St San Francisco CA 94114-2013

WHALEN, RICHARD JAMES, author, consultant; b. N.Y.C., Sept. 23, 1935; s. George C. and Veronica (Southwick) W.; m. Joan Marie Giuffré, Oct. 19, 1957; children: Richard Christopher, Laura, Michael. B.A., Queen's Coll., 1957. Asso. editor Richmond (Va.) News Leader, 1957-59; contbg. editor Time mag., 1959-60; editorial writer Wall St. Jour., 1960-62; asso. editor Fortune mag., 1962-66, sr. editor, 1966; writer-in-residence Center Strategic Studies Georgetown U., Washington, 1966-70; cons. State Dept., 1970-72; sr. policy adviser to Ronald Reagan, 1978-80; chmn. The Whalen Co., Inc. Author: The Founding Father: The Story of Joseph P. Kennedy, 1964, rev. edit. 1993, A City Destroying Itself, 1965, Catch the Falling Flag, 1972, Taking Sides, 1974, The Wealth Weapon, 1980, Trade Warriors, 1986, 2d edit., 1990; editor: The Report of The President's Commission on an All-Volunteer Armed Force, 1970, Report of the President's Commission on Financial Structure and Regulation, 1971. Mem. Council on Fgn. Relations. Club: Cosmos (Washington). Home: 3220 Volta Pl NW Washington DC 20007-2731

WHALEN, THOMAS EARL, psychology educator; b. Toledo, June 26, 1938; s. T. Mylo and Alice E. (Tallman) W.; m. Carolyn Margaret Lapham, Dec. 24, 1960; children: Jennifer Susan, Holly Elizabeth. BA, UCLA, 1960; MA, San Diego State U., 1967; PhD, U. Conn., 1970. Cert. secondary tchr., Calif. Secondary tchr. San Diego City Schs., 1964-68; rsch. assoc. Southwest Regional Lab., Inglewood, Calif., 1969; prof. Calif. State U., Hayward, Calif., 1970—; indsl. psychology dept. chair 1977-79, assoc. dean sch. edn. 1987-89, Calif. State U. Hayward; rsch. cons. Evaluation Assocs. San Francisco Bay Area Schs., 1971-88, Lawrence Livermore Nat. Lab., Livermore, Calif., 1982-83. Author: (text book) Ten Steps to Behavioral Research, 1989; contbr. articles to profl. jours. Lt. USN, 1960-63. Recipient U.S. Office of Edn. fellowship, U. Conn., 1968-70, post doctoral scholarship Am. Edn. Rsch. Assn., U. Iowa, 1972. Mem. Am. Edn. Rsch. Assn., APA, Calif. Ednl. Rsch. Assn. (bd. dirs. 1982-84), Bay Area Coun. on Measurement and Evaluation in Edn. (pres. 1976-77), United Profs. of Calif. (exec. bd. Calif. State U. Hayward 1975-76). Avocations: golf, travel, gardening. Home: 325 Conway Dr Danville CA 94526-5511 Office: Calif State U 25800 Carlos Bee Blvd Hayward CA 94542-3000

WHALEN, WAYNE W., lawyer; b. Savanna, Ill., Aug. 22, 1939; s. Leo R. and Esther M. (Yackley) W.; m. Paula Wolff, Apr. 22, 1970; children: Amanda, Clementine, Antonia, Nathaniel. BS, U.S. Air Force Acad., 1961; JD, Northwestern U., 1967. Bar: Ill. 1967, U.S. Ct. Appeals (7th cir.) 1968, U.S. Supreme Ct. 1972. Commd. 1st lt. USAF, 1961, ret., 1964; assoc. Mayer, Brown & Platt, Chgo., 1967-74, ptnr., 1974-84; ptnr. Skadden, Arps, Slate, Meagher & Flom, Chgo., 1984—; bd. dirs. Van Kampel Am. Capital Family Mut. Funds, Oak Brook, Ill. Author: Annotated Illinois Constitution, 1972. Del. 6th Ill. Constitutional Conv., 1969-70, chmn. style drafting and submission com. Named Outstanding Young Lawyer, Chgo. Bar Found., 1970. Mem. Chgo. Club. Home: 4920 S Greenwood Ave Chicago IL 60615-2816 Office: Skadden Arps Slate 333 W Wacker Dr Chicago IL 60606-1218

WHALEY, LYNNE ANN, senior vice president nursing; b. Chgo., June 26, 1951; c. Clarence Richard and Evelyn Kathleen (Dinkel) W. BSN, U. No. Colo., Greeley, 1973; MS in Nursing Adminstrn., Calif. State U., L.A., 1987; postgrad., U. Calif., Berkeley, 1990; degree in exec. mgmt., U. So. Calif., 1995. Clin. nurse St Lukes Hosp., Denver, 1973-74; clin. nurse Long Beach (Calif.) Meml. Med. Ctr., 1974-78, nursing supr., 1978-86, DON, 1986-90, nursing adminstr. med.-surg., 1990-91; sr. v.p. nursing, 1991—; clin. asst. prof. nursing dept. nursing U. So. Calif., 1987—. Bd. dirs. Allied Hosp. Fed. Credit Union. Mem. Am. Orgn. Nurse Execs., Calif. Orgn. Nurse Execs., others.

WHALEY, STORM HAMMOND, retired government official, consultant; b. Sulphur Springs, Ark., Mar. 15, 1916; s. Storm Onus and Mabel Etta (Prater) W.; m. Jane Florence Bucy, Oct. 6, 1935; children: Carroll Jean Whaley Anderson, Ann Marie Whaley Adams, Rebecca Glenn Whaley Dyess. B.A., John Brown U., 1935; LL.D. (hon.), 1959; postgrad., U. Ark. Law Sch., 1954; D.Sc. hon., U. Ark. for Med. Scis., 1983. Mgr. Sta. KUOA, Siloam Springs, Ark., 1935-53, Sta. KGER, Long Beach, 1948-53, KOME, Tulsa, 1951; asst. to Congressman J.W. Trimble, 1953-54; asst. to pres. U. Ark., 1954-59, acting pres., 1959-60, v.p. health scis., 1960-70; assoc. dir. communications NIH, Bethesda, Md., 1970-92; retired, 1992; mem. U.S. del. World Health Assembly, 1962, 63, 64; mem. nat. adv. health council USPHS, 1963-66; chmn. ad hoc com. Report to Pres. and Congress Regional Med. Programs, 1967; mem. U.S. Sr. Exec. Service, 1979. Author: They Call It, 1951. Del. Democratic Nat. Conv., 1940, 44, 48, 52. Recipient Superior Service award HEW, 1974, SES Performance award, 1982, Superior Service award USPHS, 1987. Fellow AAAS; mem. Broadcast Pioneers, Ark. Broadcasters Assn., Am. Med. Writers Assn., Internat. Sci. Writers Assn., NIH Alumni Assn. (bd. dirs. 1992—), Omicron Delta Kappa, Lambda Chi Alpha, Masons (33 deg.), KT Club, Nat. Press Club (Washington). Home and Office: 4400 E West Hwy Bethesda MD 20814-4524

WHALEY, VERNON, church administrator. Chmn. Music Commission of the Nat. Assn. of Free Will Baptists, Nashville, Tenn. Office: PO Box 50117 Nashville TN 37205

WHALLEY-KILMER, JOANNE, actress; b. Manchester, England, Aug. 25, 1964; m. Val Kilmer. Actress (theater) Bows and Arrows, 1982, Rita, Sue, and Bob Too, 1982, The Genius, 1983, Kate, 1983, The Crimes of Vautrin, 1983, The Pope's Wedding, 1984, Saved, 1984, As I Lay Dying, 1985, Women Beware Women, 1986, Three Sisters, 1987, What the Butler Saw, 1989 (Theatre World award 1989); (films) Pink Floyd-The Wall, 1982, Dance With a Stranger, 1985, The Good Father, 1986, No Surrender, 1986, Willow, 1988, Popielusko, (To Kill a Priest), 1989, Scandal, 1989, Kill Me

Again, 1989, Navy SEALS, 1990, Crossing the Rapture, 1994, Trial By Jury, 1994, A Good Man in Africa, 1995 (TV) A Christmas Carol, 1984, A Kind of Loving, A Quiet Life, The Gentle Touch, Reilly, Save Your Kisses, Will You Love Me Tomorrow?, (TV mini-series) Edge of Darkness, 1986, The Singing Detective, 1988, Channel Crossings, 1988, Scarlett, 1994. Office: Creative Artists Agency 9830 Wilshire Blvd Beverly Hills CA 90212*

WHALLON, EVAN ARTHUR, JR., orchestra conductor; b. Akron, Ind., July 24, 1923; s. Evan Arthur and Katharine (Kistler) W.; m. Jean Borgman, Aug. 28, 1948 (dec. 1977); children: Paul Evan, Eric Andrew; m. Rachael Shumate, Dec. 29, 1983 (div. 1992. MusB, Eastman Sch. Music, 1948, MusM, 1949; MusD (hon.), Denison U., 1963, Otterbein U., 1969, Ohio Dominican U., 1970. Debut with Phila. Orch., 1948; condr.: opera The Consul, 1949-50, Springfield (Ohio) Symphony, 1951-56, Columbus (Ohio) Symphony, 1956-82, guest condr., Spoleto (Italy) Festival, Phila. Orch., Cleve. Orch., San Francisco Symphony, Buffalo Philharmonic, Boston Arts Festival, N.Y.C. Opera, San Francisco Spring Opera, Balt. Symphony, Prague Symphony Orch., Budapest Mav Symphony, condr., mus. dir. Chatauqua (N.Y.) Opera Assn., 1966-81; mus. dir. Merola program and Western Opera Theater, San Francisco Opera, 1982-87, Ohio Light Opera, 1988-93. Lt. (j.g.) USNR, WWII. Recipient citation Columbus City Council, 1963, Ohio citation Ohioana Assn., 1983. Mem. Condrs. Guild (bd. dirs., pres. 1988-90). Home: 95 Orchard Dr Gaithersburg MD 20878-2223

WHALLON, WILLIAM, literature educator; b. Richmond, Ind., Sept. 24, 1928; s. Arthur J. and Adelaide (Wheeler) W.; m. Joanne Holland, Aug. 22, 1957; children: Andrew, Nicholas. B.A., McGill U., 1950; Ph.D., Yale U., 1957. Prof. Mich. State U., East Lansing, 1963—. Author: Formula, Character, and Context, 1969, Problem and Spectacle, 1980, Inconsistencies, 1983, (poetry) A Book of Time, 1990. Fellow Center for Hellenic Studies, 1962-63; Fulbright prof. comparative lit., U. Bayreuth, 1984-85. Home: 1655 Walnut Heights East Lansing MI 48823-2943

WHAM, DOROTHY STONECIPHER, state legislator; b. Centralia, Ill., Jan. 5, 1925; d. Ernest Joseph and Vera Thelma (Shafer) Stonecipher; m. Robert S. Wham, Jan. 26, 1947; children: Nancy S. Wham Mitchell, Jeanne Wham Ryan, Robert S. II. BA, MacMurray Coll., 1946; MA, U. Ill., 1949; D of Pub. Adminstrn. (hon.), MacMurray Coll., 1992. Counsellor Student Counselling Bur. U. Ill., Urbana, 1946-49; state dir. ACTION program, Colo./Wyo. U.S. Govt., Denver, 1972-82; mem. Colo. Ho. of Reps., 1986-87; mem. Colo. Senate, 1987—, chair jud. com., 1988—; with capital devel. com., health, environ, welfare, instns., fin. appropriations, legal svcs. Mem. LWV, Civil Rights Commn. Denver, 1972-80; bd. dirs. Denver Com. on Mental Health, 1985-88, Denver Symphony, 1985-88. Mem. Am. Psychol. Assn., Colo. Mental Health Assn. (bd. dirs. 1986-88), Colo. Hemophilia Soc. Republican. Methodist. Lodge: Civitan. Avocations: travel, furniture refinishing. Home: 2790 S High St Denver CO 80210-6352 Office: State Capitol Rm 342 Denver CO 80203

WHAM, GEORGE SIMS, publishing executive; b. Laurens, S.C., Jan. 27, 1920; s. George Sims and Nellie (Melette) W.; m. Beth Keeler, Sept. 13, 1947; children—Norman Brent, Bonnie Beth, Barry Keeler. B.S., Clemson U., 1941; M.S., U. Tenn., 1947; Ph.D., Pa. State U., 1951. Textile technologist USDA, 1947-49; research assoc. Sch. Chemistry and Physics, Pa. State U., 1949-51; prof., asst. dean Tex. Women's U., 1951-54; sr. editor Good Housekeeping mag., N.Y.C., 1954-60; v.p. tech. dir. Good Housekeeping mag., 1961-87; tech. cons.; Disting. vis. fellow U. N.C., 1987-88; dir. R & D, Phillips Van Heusen, Inc., 1960-61; guest lectr. Purdue U., U. Md., Ariz. State U., U. Conn., U. Del., Clemson U., U. R.I., Mich. State U.; leader U.S. del. Internat. Standards Confs., 1968, 71, 86, 87. Contbr. articles to profl. jours. Pres. Governing Council, Washington, N.J., 1960-62; mem. Bd. Edn., Hightstown, 1959-61. Served to maj. AUS, 1941-46. Decorated Silver Star, Purple Heart. Mem. Am. Assn. Textile Chemists and Colorists (past pres., Harold C. Chapin award), Am. Nat. Standards Inst. (chmn. bd. dirs. 1986-88, chmn. textile standards bd. 1966-68, Howard Coonley medal 1985, George S. Wham Leadership medal 1990), Consumer Coun. (chmn. 1985), Sigma Xi, Phi Psi, Omicron Nu. Home: 201 E Ward St Hightstown NJ 08520-3313 Office: 959 8th Ave New York NY 10019-3737

WHAM, WILLIAM NEIL, publisher; b. N.Y.C., Dec. 28, 1934; s. William and Jessie (Neill) W.; m. Lynn McCorvie, Mar. 6, 1966; children: McCorvie, Avery. B.S., Syracuse U., 1956. Salesman Mut. N.Y., N.Y.C., 1959-61; regional sales mgr. Doubleday Pub. Co., N.Y.C., 1961-64, Reinhold Pub. Co., N.Y.C., 1964-68; sales mgr. United Bus. Publs., N.Y.C., 1968; pres., pub. jours. Internat. Scientific Communications, Inc., Shelton, Conn., 1968—. Founder: sci. jours. Am. Lab., Internat. Lab., Am. Biotech. Lab., Am. Clin. Lab., Internat. Biotech. Lab., Lab. Products Tech., Am. Lab. News, European Clin. Lab., Internat. Lab. News, Internat. Biotech. News, European Clin. Lab. News, Am. Environ. Lab. Served with AUS, 1956-58. Home: 157 Pinewood Trl Trumbull CT 06611-3312 Office: Internat Sci Communications Inc 30 Control Dr Shelton CT 06484-6111

WHANG, YUN CHOW, space science educator; b. Foochow, China, Dec. 13, 1931; came to U.S., 1955; s. Ta Chun and Wenlun (Lin) W.; m. Yeong-Ping Chu, Aug. 29, 1959; children: Ruth, Joyce, Kenneth. Ph.D., U. Minn., 1961. Asst. prof. U. Fla., 1961-62; assist. prof. The Cath. U. Am., 1962-63, assoc. prof., 1963-67, prof., 1968—, chmn. dept., 1971-83; sr. research assoc. Nat. Acad. Scis., 1967-68; vis. prof. Royal Inst. Tech., Stockholm, Sweden, 1972-73. Mem. Am. Geophys. Union, ASME. Research on slow shocks, solar wind theory, termination shock and heliopause, interaction solar wind with moon and planets. Home: 8003 Grand Teton Dr Potomac MD 20854-4073

WHANGER, PHILIP DANIEL, biochemistry educator and researcher, nutrition educator; b. Lewisburg, W.Va., Aug. 30, 1936; married, 1964; 2 children. BS, Berry Coll., 1959; MS, W.Va. U., 1961; PhD in Nutrition, N.C. State U., 1965. From asst. to assoc. prof. Oreg. State U., Corvallis, 1966-78, prof. nutrition & biochemistry, 1978—; rsch. assoc. biochemistry Mich. State U., 1965-66; mem. assoc. staff Harvard Med. Sch., 1972-73; vis. scientist Gen. Acad. Exch. Svc., U. Tubingen, 1986, Commonwealth Sci. & Industry Rsch. Orgn., Wembley, Western Australia, Acad. Preventive Medicine, Beijing, 1988. Rsch. fellow NIH, 1966-67, Spl. fellow, 1972; Internat. fellow NSF, 1980-81; Rsch. grantee Oreg. State U., 1968—. Mem. Am. Inst. Nutrition, Am. Soc. Animal Sci., Internat. Bioinorg Scientists, Soc. Environ. Geochemistry and Health. Achievements include research in altered metabolic pathways under selenium deficiency, relationships of vitamin E and selenium in myopathies, biochemical properties of selenium and cadmium metallo-proteins, metabolic pathways for incorporation of selenium into proteins, selenium and gluthathione peroxidise in human blood fractions, selenium deficiencies in primates, selenium intake on human blood and urine fractions. Office: Oreg State U Dept Agrl Chemistry Corvallis OR 97331*

WHARE, WANDA SNYDER, lawyer; b. Columbia, Pa., Nov. 5, 1959; d. William Sylvester and Dorothy Jacqueline (Luttman) W.; m. James Robert Snyder, Nov. 14, 1987; 1 child, Eric James. BA, Franklin & Marshall Coll., 1981; JD, Dickinson Sch. Law, 1984. Bar: Pa. 1984. Asst. counsel Pa. Dept. Labor and Industry, Harrisburg, 1984-87; assoc. Gibbel, Kraybill & Hess, Lancaster, Pa., 1987-89; corp. counsel Irex Corp., Lancaster, 1990—. Mem. parish-staff rels. com. 1st Meth. Ch., Lancaster, 1987-92, mem. com. on status and role of women, 1989—, chair 1992—. Democrat. Office: Irex Corp 120 N Lime St Lancaster PA 17602-2951

WHARTON, BEVERLY ANN, utility company executive; b. St. Louis, Nov. 17, 1953; d. Lawrence A. and Helen M. Bextermueller; m. James R. Wharton, March 30, 1974; 1 child, Laura. BS, So. Ill. U., 1975; MBA, U of S.D., 1980. Tax acct. supr. Iowa Pub. Service Co., Sioux City, Iowa, 1978-84; asst. sec. Iowa Pub. Service Co., Sioux City, 1981-84; sec., 1984-88, v.p staff services, 1985-88, sr. v.p. support group, 1988-91; corp. sec. Midwest Energy Co., Sioux City, 1988-91, 1986-88, sr. v.p., 1988-90; gen. mgr. Midwest Gas, Sioux City, 1991—, group v.p., gen. mgr., 1992—; bd. dirs. Midwest Power Systems, Inc., Sioux City, Am. Gas Assn., Inst. Gas Technology. Bd. dirs. Security Nat. Bank, Marian Health Ctr., Briar Cliff Coll. Mem. Midwest Gas Assn. (bd. dirs. 1992—), Rotary (Sioux City club). Roman Catholic. Office: Midwest Gas 401 Douglas St Sioux City IA 51101-1443

WHARTON, CLIFTON REGINALD, JR., former university president, former government official, former insurance executive; b. Boston, Sept. 13, 1926; m. Dolores Duncan, 1950; children: Clifton, Bruce. BA, Harvard U., 1947; MA, Johns Hopkins U., 1948, U. Chgo., 1956; PhD in Econs., U. Chgo., 1958; LLD (hon.), Johns Hopkins U., 1970, U. Mich., 1970, Wayne State U., 1970, Hahneman Med. Sch., 1975, Georgetown U., 1976, Va. State U., 1977, CCNY, 1978, Wright State U., 1979, Lincoln U., 1979, Albany Law Sch., 1980, Duke U., 1981, Amherst Coll., 1983, U. Ill., 1984, U. Vt., 1987, Colgate U., 1987, Tuskegee U., 1987, Tufts U., 1988, Mich. State U., 1988, Claremont U. Ctr. and Grad. Sch., 1989, U. Notre Dame, 1989, Clark Atlanta U., 1990, Howard U., 1991, Shippensburg U., 1991, Miami U. Ohio, 1991, Washington U., 1991, Harvard U., 1992, Kenyon Coll., 1992, Ind. U. of Pa., 1992, Lehigh U., 1993; DPS (hon.), Ctrl. Mich. U., 1970, U. Pitts., 1989; LittD (hon.), N.C. Agrl. and Tech. State U., 1986, MacMurray Coll., 1993; LHD (hon.), Oakland U., 1971, No. Mich. U., 1975, Columbia U., 1978, Brandeis U., 1981, NYU, 1981, U. Conn., 1983, U. Mass., Boston, 1985, So. Ill. U., 1987, George Mason U., 1988, L.I. U., 1989, U. Ala., Birmingham, 1989, Va. Commonwealth U., 1990, SUNY, 1990, St. Paul's Coll., 1992, Johnson C. Smith U., 1994, Western Conn. State U., 1994, Northeastern U., 1994, DSc (hon.), Mercy Coll., 1989, Bryant Coll., 1990; PhD Internat. Rels. (hon.), Am. U., 1993; D. Mgmt. (hon.), GMI Inst. Engring. and Mgmt., 1992. Exec. trainee Am. Internat. Assn. Econ. and Social Devel., 1948-49, program analyst, 1949-51, head reports and analysis, 1951-53; rsch. asst. econs. U. Chgo., 1953-56, rsch. assoc., 1956-57; exec. agri. Devel. Coun., 1957-58, assoc., 1958-64, dir. Am. univs. rsch., 1964-67, v.p., 1967-69; pres. Mich. State U., 1970-78; chancellor SUNY System, 1978-87; chmn., CEO Tchrs. Ins. & Annuity Assn. Coll. Retirement Equities Fund, N.Y.C., 1987-93; dep. Sec. State U.S. Dept. State, Washington, 1993; bd. dirs. Ford Motor Co., Detroit, Tenneco, Harcourt Gen., N.Y. Stock Exch. Co-author: Patterns for Lifelong Learning, 1973; editor: Subsistence Agriculture and Economic Development, 1969; contbr. articles to profl. jours. Trustee Rockefeller Found., 1970-87, chmn., 1982-87; trustee Asia Soc., 1967-77, Overseas Devel. Coun., 1969-79, 94—, Carnegie Found., 1970-79, Agrl. Devel. Coun., 1973-80, Aspen Inst., 1980-93, Com. Econ. Devel., 1980-93, 94—, Coun. Fin. Aid to Edn., 1983-86, Coun. Fgn. Rels., 1983-93, Fgn. Policy Assn., 1983-87, MIT Corp., 1984-86, Acad. Ednl. Devel., 1985-86, Clark Found., 1991-93, Winrock Internat., 1994—; mem. Commn. on Intercollegiate Athletics, Knight Found., 1990-93, N.Y.C. Mayor's Coun. Econ. Advisors, 1990-93, Adv. Commn. on Trade Policy and Negotiations, 1990-92; bd. overseers Rockefeller Inst. of Govt., SUNY, 1994—. Mem. Am. Agrl. Econs. Assn., Assn. Asian Studies, Nat. Acad. Edn., Univ. Club (N.Y.C.), Country Club (Cooperstown, N.Y.). Office: TIAA-CREF 730 3rd Ave New York NY 10017-3206

WHARTON, DANNY CARROLL, zoo biologist; b. Ontario, Oreg., Mar. 13, 1947; s. Carroll Curtis and Norma (Grigg) W.; m. Marilyn Christine Hoyt, Sept. 22, 1973; children: Amanda, Catherine, Margaret, Arcadio. BA in Psychology, Coll. Idaho, 1969; MA in Internat. Adminstrn., Sch. for Internat. Tng., 1975; PhD in Biology, Fordham U., 1990. Rsch. assoc. Foresta Inst., Carson City, Nev., 1973-74; curatorial asst. Woodland Park Zool. Garden, Seattle, 1974-79; asst. curator N.Y. Zool. Soc./The Wildlife Conservation Soc., Bronx, 1979-85; assoc. curator N.Y. Zool. Soc., Bronx, 1985-89, curator, 1989—; dir. Ctrl. Pk. Wildlife Ctr., N.Y.C., 1994—; advisor Internat. Snow Leopard Trust, Seattle, 1986; mem. US-USSR Environ. Agreement of U.S. Fish and Wildlife Svc., 1983. Contbr. articles to profl. jours. Vol. U.S. Peace Corps, Ecuador, 1969-71. Fulbright scholar, U. Münster, Fed. Republic Germany, 1976-77. Fellow Am. Assn. Zool. Parks and Aquariums (chmn. gorilla species survival plan 1992—, chmn. snow leopard species survival plan 1986—, co-chmn. marsupial and monotreme taxon adv. group 1990-94); mem. Soc. for Conservation Biology, Internat. Union for Conservation of Nature/Species Survival Commn. (mem. captive breeding specialist group). Office: Wildlife Conservation Soc Ctrl Park Wildlife Ctr 830 Fifth Ave New York NY 10021-7095

WHARTON, KAY KAROLE, special education educator; b. Butler, Pa., Nov. 19, 1943; d. Clarence Henry Jr. and Alberta Elizabeth (Yost) Gilkey; m. David Burton Wharton, Nov. 28, 1975 (dec. May 1987). BS in Edn., Geneva Coll., 1965. Cert. spl. edn. tchr., Md. Tchr. 2d grade Butler Area Sch., 1965-71; resource tchr. Queen Anne County Bd. of Edn., Centreville, Md., 1971—; facilitator sch. improvement team Centreville Mid. Sch., 1992-95. Music dir. Diocese of Easton (Md.) Mid. Convocation Episcopal Cursillo, Old St. Paul's, Kent, 1989-91, St. Paul's, Hillsboro, 1993—; Sunday sch. supt. primary dept. St. Mark's Luth. Ch., 1966-71, St. Paul's Episcopal Ch., 1985-87; program dir. Queen Anne's County chpt. Am. Cancer Soc., Centreville, 1981-85; mem. PTA. Mem. NEA, Queen Anne County Edn. Assn., Md. State Tchrs. Assn., Coun. for Exceptional Children, Internat. Reading Assn., Upper Shore Reading Assn. (sec. 1985-91, 93—), Learning Disabled Am., Guardians Learning Disabled (sec. 1991-92), Internat. Wildlife Fedn., Smithsonian Assocs., Order Ea. Star (worthy matron Centreville 1977, sec. 1982-93), Nat. Geographic Soc., Town and Country Women's Club (pres. 1977, 79), Delta Kappa Gamma (Nu chpt. pres. 1992—, rsch. com. chairperson Alpha Beta State 1993-95, mem. chair 1995—). Republican. Avocations: piano, embroidery, handicrafts. Home: PO Box 237 Centreville MD 21617-0237 Office: Centreville Mid Sch 231 Ruthsburg Rd Centreville MD 21617-9702

WHARTON, LENNARD, engineering company executive; b. Boston, Dec. 10, 1933; s. Nathaniel Philip and Deeda (Levine) W.; m. Judith R. Gordon, Dec. 26, 1957; children: Ruth, Rebecca, Nathaniel. B.S. in Chem. Engring. MIT, 1955; B.A., Cambridge U., 1957, M.A., 1957; A.M., Harvard U.; A.M. (NSF fellow 1957-60), 1960, Ph.D. (Sr. fellow Soc. of Fellows 1960-63), 1963. Registered profl. engr., N.J., Ill. Prof. dept. chemistry U. Chgo., 1963-80; v.p. engring. ITE Imperial Corp., 1972-73; v.p. tech. Studebaker-Worthington, Barrington, Ill., 1978-79, McGraw Edison Co., Rolling Meadows, Ill., 1979-80; v.p. engring. and tech. Worthington group McGraw Edison Co., Mountainside, N.J., 1980-85; corp. v.p. tech. Material Research Corp., Pearl River, N.Y., 1985-87; v.p. Packer Engring. Inc., Naperville, Ill., 1987-95, chmn. bd., 1994-95; pres. Evidentia Engring. Inc., Short Hills, N.J., 1995—. Sloan fellow, 1964-66; named Outstanding Young Man of Chgo. Chgo. Jr. Assn. Commerce and Industry, 1968. Mem. IEEE (sr.), Nat. Fire Protection Assn., Am. Inst. Chem. Engrs. Office: 10 Park Pl Short Hills NJ 07078-2826

WHARTON, SHIRLEY GRANGER, hospital administrator, nurse; b. Portsmouth, Va., Nov. 3, 1947; d. William Woodard and Norma Mae (White) Granger; m. Earin D. Wharton, May 3, 1969; 1 child, Ryan Granger. Diploma in Nursing, Norfolk Gen. Hosp. Schs., 1968. RN, Va. Staff nurse Sentara Norfolk (Va.) Gen. Hosp., 1968-73; head nurse, 1973-76, asst. dir. nursing, 1976-79, asst. adminstr. nursing, 1979-86, sr. v.p., 1986—. Active Keel Club-United Way Hampton Roads, Va., 1987-89, Green Run High Sch. PTA, 1987—, Salem High Sch. PTA, 1990, Lake James Homeowners Assn., Virginia Beach, Va., 1986—, Sentara Hosps. Aux., 1980—. Mem. Am. Orgn. Nurse Execs., Exec. Women Internat. (pres. Hampton Roads chpt. 1989—), Va. Orgn. Nurse Execs. (bd. dirs. 1987-89), Pilot Club of Virginia Beach, Inc. (pres. 1990). Baptist. Avocations: reading, walking, cooking. Office: Sentara Norfolk Gen Hosp 600 Gresham Dr Norfolk VA 23507-1904

WHARTON, THOMAS HEARD, JR., lawyer; b. Houston, Dec. 18, 1930; s. Thomas Heard and Laura (Wellhausen) W. B.A., Rice U., 1952; LL.B., U. Tex., 1955. Bar: Tex. 1955, U.S. Dist. Ct. (so. dist.) Tex. 1966, U.S. Ct. Appeals (5th cir.) 1972. Assoc. firm Vinson & Elkins, Houston, 1959-70, ptnr., 1970—. Co-author: How to Live and Die with Texas Probate, 1969; Texas Estate Administration, 1975. Served with USN, 1956-59. Fellow Am. Coll. Probate Counsel, Tex. Bar Found. (life); mem. ABA, Houston Bar Assn. Republican. Methodist. Clubs: Houston, Houston City, Governors, Met. Racquet (Houston). Home: 2210 Welch St Houston TX 77019-5618 Office: Vinson & Elkins 3400 1st City Tower 1001 Fannin Houston TX 77002

WHATCOTT, MARSHA RASMUSSEN, elementary educator; b. Fillmore, Utah, Mar. 29, 1941; d. William Hans and Evangelyn (Robison) Rasmussen; m. Robert LaGrand Whatcott, Sept. 14, 1961; children: Sherry, Cindy, Jay Robert, Justin William. Assoc. Sci. So. Utah State U., 1962; BS, Brigham Young U., 1968. Cert. tchr. early childhood, Utah. Tchr. Provost Elem. Sch., Provo, Utah, 1968-84, 91—, kindergarten tchr., 1984-91, music specialist, 93-94, art specialist, 1984-85, math. specialist, 1988-89, sci. specialist, 1994—. Mem. polit. action com. Provo Sch. Dist., 1982, 90, mem. profl. devel. com., 1972-79; mem. profl. devel. com. Benniville Uniserve (Provo, Alpine and Nebo Sch. Dist.), 1994-95. Recipient Millard County Utah PTA scholarship, 1959-62, Golden Apple award Provo City PTA, 1984, Recognition Disting. Svc. in Edn. award Utah State Legis., 1992; named Outstanding Educator in Utah Legis. Dist. # 64, 1992. Mem. Utah Edn. Assn. (del. 1989-90), Provo Edn. Assn. (bldg. rep. 1983—), Bonneville Uniserve (profl. devel. com). Mem. LDS Ch. Avocations: music, gardening, art, drama, crafts. Office: Provost Elem Sch 629 S 1000 E Provo UT 84606-5204

WHEALEY, LOIS DEIMEL, humanities scholar; b. N.Y.C., June 20, 1932; d. Edgar Bertram Deimel and Lois Elizabeth (Hatch) Washburn; m. Robert Howard Whealey, July 2, 1954; children: Richard William, David John, Alice Ann Whealey Dediu. BA in History, Stanford U., 1951; MA in Edn., U. Mich., 1955; MA in Polit. Sci., Ohio U., 1975. Tchr. 5th grade Swayne Sch., Owyhee, Nev., 1952-53; tchr. 7th grade Ft. Knox (Ky.) Dependent's Sch., 1955-56; tchr. adult basic edn. USAF, Oxford, 1956-57; tchr. 6th grade Amerman Sch., Northville, Mich., 1957-58; tchr. 8th grade English, social studies Slauson Jr. High Sch., Ann Arbor, Mich., 1958-59; adminstrv. asst. humanities conf. Ohio U., Athens, 1974-76, 83; part-time instr. Ohio U., Athens, 1966-68, 75. Contbr. articles to profl. jours. Mem. Athens County Regional Planning Commn., 1974-78, treas., 1976-78; bd. dirs. Ohio-Meadville Dist. Unitarian-Universalist Assn., 1975-81; mem. Ohio coord. com. Internat. Women's Yr., 1977; v.p. Black Diamond Girl Scout Coun., 1980-86; chair New Day for Equal Rights Amendment, 1982; mem. Athens City Bd. Edn., 1984-90, v.p., 1984, pres., 1985 ; mem. Tri County Vocat. Sch. Bd., Nelsonville, Ohio, 1984-90, v.p., 1988-89; mem. adv. com. Ohio River Valley Water Sanitation Commn., 1986—; bd. dirs. Ohio Environ. Coun., 1984-90, sec., 1986-90; bd. dirs. Ohio Alliance for Environ., 1993—. Recipient Unsung UU award Ohio-Meadville Dist. Unitarian Universalist Assn., 1984, Thanks badge Black Diamond Girl Scout Coun., 1986, How to award Ednl. Press Assn. Am., 1990, Donna Chen Women's Equity award Ohio U., 1994; named Woman of Achievement, Black Diamond Girl Scout Coun., 1987. Mem. AAUW (pres. articles dir. 1969-70, 89-90, 93—, nat. pub. policy chair 1995—), LWV (pres. 1975-77), Phi Lambda Theta (life). Democrat. Avocations: classical music, square dancing, choral singing. Home: 14 Oak St Athens OH 45701-2605

WHEAT, FRANCIS MILLSPAUGH, retired lawyer; b. L.A., Feb. 4, 1921; s. Carl Irving and Helen (Millspaugh) W.; m. Nancy Loring Warner, Oct. 14, 1944; children—Douglas Loring, Carl Irving, Gordon Warner. A.B., Pomona Coll., 1942; LL.B. cum laude, Harvard U., 1948. Bar: Calif. 1949. With firm Gibson, Dunn & Crutcher, Los Angeles, 1948-64; partner Gibson, Dunn & Crutcher, 1955-64, 69-89; commr. SEC, 1964-69. Contbr. articles to profl. jours. Trustee S.W. Mus., L.A., 1964, Pomona Coll., 1967—, vice chmn., 1972—, Ralph Parson Found., 1995—; bd. dirs. UN Assn. L.A., 1963-64, Assn. Governing Bds. Univs. and Colls., 1968-70, Ctr. for Law in Pub. Interest, 1974—, Alliance for Children's Rights (pres. 1992-94), Calif. Commn. on Campaign Fin. (co-chmn. 1985—), Sierra Club Legal Def. Fund, 1978—. Lt. USNR, 1942-45. Mem. Am. Law Inst., Los Angeles County Bar Assn. (mem. corps. 1963-64, com. juvenile cts. 1957, trustee 1971-76, pres. 1975-76), Alumni Assn. Pomona Coll. (pres. 1964-65), Nat. Assn. Securities Dealers (bd. govs. 1973-76), Phi Beta Kappa. Democrat. Congregationalist (pres. 1961). Home: 2130 Lombardy Rd San Marino CA 91108-1302 Office: 333 S Grand Ave Fl 46 Los Angeles CA 90071-1504

WHEAT, JOE BEN, anthropologist; b. Van Horn, Tex., Apr. 21, 1916; s. Luther Peers and Elizabeth (Wellborn) W.; m. Frances Irene Moore, Apr. 6, 1947 (dec. Nov. 1987); m. Barbara K. Zernickow, Mar. 18, 1992. B.A., U. Calif.-Berkeley, 1937; M.A., U. Ariz., 1947, Ph.D. (Fund for Advancement Edn. fellow), 1953. Field dir. W.P.A. Archaeol. Project, Tech. Tech. Coll., Lubbock, 1939-41; archaeologist Smithsonian Instrn. River Basin Survey, Houston, 1947; fellow U. Ariz., Tucson, 1947-48; instr. anthropology U. Ariz., 1949-51; ranger, archaeologist Grand Canyon Nat. Park, U.S. Nat. Park Service, 1952-53; co-dir. Nubian Expdn., U. Colo., 1962-67; curator anthropology, prof. natural history Univ. Mus., 1953-87, prof. emeritus, 1987—; cons. to numerous profl. pubs.; mem. anthropology rev. bd. NSF, 1978-79. Contbr. numerous articles to profl. jours. Served with USAAF, 1941-45. Recipient Colo. State Archeologists award, 1981, Robert L. Stearns award, 1982, Clarence T. Hurst award, 1990, Byron S. Cummings award, 1991; NSF grantee, 1968, 70-71; Graham Found. grantee, 1976-79; Smithsonian Instrn. grantee, 1962-66, 70. Fellow Am. Anthrop. Assn., AAAS; mem. Soc. Am. Archaeology (pres. 1966-67, 50th Anniversary award), Council Mus. Anthropology (pres. 1977-78), Internat. Congress Americanists, Am. Ethnol. Soc. Club: Town and Gown. Home: 1515 Baseline Rd Boulder CO 80302-7650 Office: U Colo Museum Boulder CO 80309

WHEAT, MYRON WILLIAM, JR., cardiothoracic surgeon; b. Sapulpa, Okla., Mar. 24, 1924; s. Myron William and Mary Lee (Hudiburg) W.; m. Erlene Adele Plank, June 12, 1949 (div. June 1970); children: Penelope Louise, Myron William III, Pamela Lynn, Douglas Plank; m. Carol Ann Karmgard, June 18, 1971; 1 child, Christopher West. AB, Washington U., St. Louis, 1949; MD cum laude, Washington U., 1951. Diplomate Am. Bd. Surgery, Am. Bd. Thoracic Surgery. Instr., clin. fellow Washington U., St. Louis, 1956-58; asst. prof. surgery U. Fla., Gainesville, 1958-65, prof. surgery, 1965-72; dir. profl. svcs., chief clin. physician U. Fla. Shands Teaching Hosp., Gainesville, 1968-72; prof. surgery, dir. thoracic and cardiothoracic surgery U. Louisville Sch. Medicine, 1972-75; cardiothoracic surgeon Cardiac Surg. Assocs., P.A., St. Petersburg, Fla., 1975-91, Clearwater, Fla., 1978—. Author (with others) 14 books; contbr. over 100 articles to profl. jours.; developed drug therapy for acute dissecting aneurysms of the aorta. 1st lt. USAF, 1943-46, ETO. Named First Howard W. Lilienthal Meml. lectr. Mt. Sinai Hosp., 1963. Fellow Am. Coll. Cardiology (chmn. bd. govs. 1968-69), Am. Coll. Surgeons (gov.); mem. Am. Surg. Assn., Am. Assn. for Thoracic Surgery, So. Surg. Assn., So. Thoracic Surg. Assn., Soc. Thoracic Surgeons, Soc. Thoracic Surgeons Great Britain and Ireland, Alpha Omega Alpha. Republican. Avocation: field trials-bird dogs. Home: 1772 Long Bow Ln Clearwater FL 34624-6402 Office: Myron W Wheat Jr MD 1260 S Greenwood Ave Ste E Clearwater FL 24616-4195

WHEAT, WILLIS JAMES, university dean, management educator; b. Oklahoma City, Feb. 28, 1926; s. Willis R. and Aubyn (Roach) W.; m. Julia Francis Maguire, July 4, 1946; children—Willis J., Chatham James. B.S., Okla. State U.-Stillwater, 1949, M.S., 1950; DPA in Pub. Adminstrn., U. Pacific, 1968; LL.D., Tex. Wesleyan Coll., 1962; Dr. Comml. Sci., Oklahoma City U., 1980. Prof. mgmt., dean Sch. Bus., Oklahoma City U., 1954-64; exec. v.p., dir. mktg. Liberty Nat. Bank & Trust Co., Oklahoma City, 1964-87; dean Meinders Sch. Bus. Okla. City U., 1987—, T.K. Hendricks prof. mktg. and mgmt., 1987—; mem. faculty Stonier Grad. Sch. Banking, Rutgers U., 1975—, Essentials of Banking Sch., Norman, Okla., 1980-82, Grad. Sch. Banking of South, Baton Rouge, 1981-83. Contbr. articles to profl. jours. Chmn. Oklahoma City Plan Adv. Com., 1974-81, Okla. Employment Security Commn., Oklahoma City, 1981—; trustee, mem. exec. com. Oklahoma City U., 1975—; bd. dirs., chmn. United Bank Okla.; bd. dirs. Pace Co., Baldor Electric Co. Served with U.S. Army, World War II. Recipient Disting. Service citation U.S. SBA, 1978; Disting. Service award Oklahoma City U., 1980, Okla. Council on Econ. Edn., 1982. Mem. Am. Bankers Assn., Soc. Advancement of Mgmt. (past pres.), Nat. Council for Small Bus. Mgmt. Devel., Okla. Polit. Sci. Assn., Okla. Council on Econ. Edn., Delta Sigma Pi, Beta Gamma Sigma. Methodist. Lodges: Masons, Shriners, Jesters. Office: Okla City U Meinders Sch Bus PO Box 60804 Oklahoma City OK 73146-0804

WHEATER, ASHLEY, dancer; b. Cutler, Scotland. Student, Royal Ballet Sch. Mem. Royal Ballet, London Festival Ballet, Australian Ballet, Joffrey Ballet; soloist San Francisco Ballet, 1989-90, prin. dancer, 1990—. Performances with the San Francisco Ballet include The Sleeping Beauty, Swan Lake, Romeo and Juliet, Menuetto, Valses Poeticos (Love Letters), Handel-a Celebration, Forevermore, Bugaku, Who Cares?, The Four Temperaments, Duo Concertant, Symphony in C, Company B, In G Major, In the Night, In the middle, somewhat elevated, New Sleep, Maelstrom, Tagore, The End, La Fille mal gardée, La Sylphide, Nutcracker, Forgotten Land, Pulcinella, Connotations, Job, The Son of Horus, The Wanderer

Fantasy; with other cos. include La Fille mal gardée, Monotones II, The Dream, Wedding Bouquet, Romeo and Juliet, La Sylphide, Love Songs, Remembrances, Return to the Strange Land, Etudes, Echoing of Trumpets, Sphinx, Greening; performed at Reykjavik Arts Festivals, Iceland, 1990, Jacob's Pillow, 1990. Office: San Francisco Ballet 455 Franklin St San Francisco CA 94102-4471*

WHEATLAND, RICHARD, II, fiduciary services executive, museum executive; b. Boston, Nov. 25, 1923; s. Stephen and Dorothy (Parker) W.; m. Cynthia McAdoo, Feb. 13, 1954; 1 child, Sarah Wheatland Fisher. AB, Harvard U., 1944, postgrad., 1946-47; JD, Columbia U., 1949. Various positions with Marshall Plan adminstrn. Office Spl. Rep. in Europe, Dept. State, Paris, 1950-53; v.p. N.Y. Airways, N.Y.C., 1953-68; pres. Acadia Mgmt. Co., Inc., Boston, 1968-93, chmn., 1993—; bd. dirs., v.p. Pingree Assocs., Bangor, Maine. Mem. Mayor's Com. Insl. Leaders for Youth, N.Y.C., 1963-66; mem. corp. New Eng. Forestry Found.; mem., former chmn. Fund for Preservation of Wild Life and Natural Areas, Boston, 1980-92, bd. dirs. 1980-91; trustee Penobscot Marine Mus., Searsport, Maine, 1968-90, hon. trustee, 1990—; bd. dirs. Friends of Pub. Garden, Boston, 1972-89, 90—, Beacon Hill Civic Assn., Boston, 1985-89, Boston Natural Areas Fund, 1987—, asst. treas., 1993-94, treas. 1994—; treas. Frank Hatch for Gov. com., Boston, 1977-78; chmn., bd. trustees & overseers Peabody Essex Mus., Salem, Mass., 1992—, trustee, 1972-92, pres., 1983-92. Lt. (j.g.) USN, 1943-46, PTO. Mem. Am. Assn. Mus. (bd. dirs. trustee com. 1976-86, govt. affairs com. 1985—), Mus. Trustee Assn. (founder, bd. dirs. 1986—, sec. 1986-92), City Club Corp. (former bd. mgrs., former treas.). Avocations: jogging, sailing, travel. Office: Acadia Mgmt Co Inc 31 Milk St Boston MA 02109-5104

WHEATLEY, GEORGE MILHOLLAND, medical administrator; b. Balt., Mar. 21, 1909; s. William Francis and Teresa Genevieve (Milholland) W.; m. Eleanor Dodge, June 28, 1933 (dec. June 1969); children: George Milholland, Jr., Mary Ellen Rausch, Sarah Grinnell Nichols, William Bradford; m. Virginia Connelly Garling, Feb. 21, 1970. BS, Cath. U., 1929; MD, Harvard U., 1933; MPH, Columbia U., 1942. Diplomate Am. Bd. Pediatrics, Am. Bd. Preventive Medicine. Intern Hartford Hosp., Conn., 1933-35; house officer pediatrics Johns Hopkins Hosp., Balt., 1935-36; rsch. fellow N.Y. Post. Grad. Hosp., N.Y.C., 1936-37; prin. pediatrician Health Dept., N.Y.C., 1937-40; asst. med. dir. Met. Life Ins. Co., N.Y.C., 1940-45, asst. v.p., 1945-69, v.p., chief med. dir., 1969-74; med. dir. Dept. Social Svcs., Hauppauge, N.Y., 1974—; founder, 1st chmn. com. for joint action with Am. Coll. Surgeons and Assn. Surgery of Trauma Nat. Safety Coun. Author: Health Observation of School Children, 3d edit., 1965; contbr. articles to profl. jours. Bd. dirs. Med. Alert Found. Internat., Calif., 1974-84. Recipient Disting. Svc. award Am. Heart Assn., 1968. Fellow Am. Acad. Pediatrics (pres. 1960-61, trustee Partnership for Child Health 1987—, Clifford Grulee award 1964, Injury and Poison Prevention award 1993); mem. Union League and Piping Rock Club. Avocations: civil war history, water-color painting. Office: Dept Social Svcs PO Box 2000 Smithtown NY 11787-0758

WHEATLEY, MELVIN ERNEST, JR., retired bishop; b. Lewisville, Pa., May 7, 1915; s. Melvin Ernest and Gertrude Elizabeth (Mitchell) W.; m. Lucile Elizabeth Maris, June 15, 1939; children: Paul Melvin, James Maris, John Sherwood. AB magna cum laude, Am. U., 1936, DD, 1958; BD summa cum laude, Drew U., 1939; DD, U. of Pacific, 1948. Ordained to ministry Meth. Ch., 1939. Pastor area Meth. ch., Lincoln, Del., 1939-41; assoc. pastor First Meth. Ch., Fresno, Calif., 1941-43; pastor Centenary Meth. Ch., Modesto, Calif., 1943-46, Cen. Meth. Ch., Stockton, Calif., 1946-54, Westwood Meth. Ch., L.A., 1954-72; bishop Denver Area, 1972-84, ret., 1984; instr. philosophy Modesto Jr. Coll., 1944; summer session instr. Hebrew-Christian heritage U. of Pacific; instr. Homiletics U. So. Calif., So. Calif. Sch. Theology, Claremont; lectr. St. Luke's Lectures, Houston, 1966; mem. Bd. of Ch. and Soc., Commn. on Status and Role of Women, United Meth. Ch., 1976-84; condr. European Christian Heritage tour, 1961, Alaska and Hawaii Missions, 1952, 54. Author: Going His Way, 1957, Our Man and the Church, 1968, The Power of Worship, 1970, Family Ministries Manual, 1970, Christmas Is for Celebrating, 1977; contbr. articles to profl. jours. Chmn. Community Rels. Conf. So. Calif., 1966-69; pres. So. Calif. Ariz. Conf. Bd. Edn., 1960-68; hon. trustee Iliff Sch. Theology; hon. dir., active mem. Parents and Friends of Lesbians and Gays, 1980—. Recipient Disting. Alumnus award Am. U., 1979, Ball award Meth. Fedn. Social Action, 1984, Prophetic Leadership award The Consultation on Homosexuality, Tolerance and Roman Cath. Theology, 1985, Human Rights award Universal Fellowship of Met. Community Congregations, 1985. Home: 859A Ronda Mendoza Laguna Hills CA 92653-5940

WHEATLEY, WILLIAM ARTHUR, architect, musician; b. Knoxville, Tenn., Sept. 23, 1944; s. Arthur Cornwallis and Inda Mary (Benway) W.; m. Celeste Ann George, Mar. 25, 1970 (div.); children: Charles Arthur, James Harris Giddings. Student, Rice U., 1962-66; BA, U. St. Thomas, 1972. Registered architect, Pa., Md., N.J. Design draftsman W.W. Alexander, Houston, 1966-70; chief of prodn. W.W. Scarborough, Houston, 1970-74; project architect Ronald H. Waldie & Assocs., Houston, 1972-74; pres. Wheatley & Assocs., Houston, 1974-81; project architect Brooks Assocs., Houston, 1977-79; mgr. design Stone Bldg. Systems, Inc., Houston, 1979-81; project architect Bechtel, Houston, 1981-84; prin. Wheatley & Assocs., Houston, 1984-87; project mgr. STV/Sanders & Thomas, Pottstown, Pa. 1987-88, Day & Zimmerman, Inc., Radnor, Pa., 1988—. Composer: piano solos, chorales, oratorio and cantata, 1961-92; co-contbr. articles to profl. jours. Del. Tex. Rep. Convs., 1980, 82, 84. Mem. AIA (Phila. chpt.), Am. Arbitration Assn., Pa. Soc. Architects, Building Officials & Code Administrs. Internat., Forest Products Soc., The Mastersingers (bd. dirs. 1989—, treas. 1990-91), Choral Soc. Montgomery County (bd. dirs. 1990—, pres., 1992—). Episcopalian. Avocations: writing poetry and fiction, drawing, painting, sculpture. Office: Day & Zimmerman 230 King Of Prussia Rd Radnor PA 19087-5220

WHEATON, DAVID, professional tennis player; b. Mpls., Minn., June 2, 1969; s. Bruce and Mary Jane W. Student, Stanford U. 9th in U.S. Tennis Assn. rankings, 1992. Office: US Tennis Assn 70 W Red Oak Ln White Plains NY 10604-3602*

WHEATON, DAVID JOE, aerospace manufacturing company executive; b. Las Vegas, N.Mex., June 5, 1940; s. Joseph Charles and Estella Marie (Grubbs) W.; BS, U. Colo., 1962; m. Gail Ellen Moody, July 17, 1942; children—Deanna Lynn, Kimberly Gail, Joseph Charles II. Predesign engr., mktg. mgr. Convair div. Gen. Dynamics, San Diego, 1967-75, F-16 mktg. mgr. Fort Worth div., 1975-77, engring. program mgr., 1977-79, dir. F-16 domestic mktg., 1979-80, v.p mktg., 1980-88, corp. v.p. program devel. and planning, 1989-91, v.p. Ax program, 1991-93, New Bus. Devel., 1993—. Served with USN, 1962-67. Decorated Air medal (6). Mem. Air Force Assn., Am. Def. Preparedness Assn., Navy Tailhook Assn., Red River Fighter Pilots Assn., Nat. Mgmt. Assn., Sigma Tau, Scabbard and Blade, Tau Beta Phi. Republican. Office: General Dynamics Corp Fort Worth Div PO Box 748 Fort Worth TX 76101-0748

WHEATON, HARRY JAMES, corporate executive; b. Alliance, Ohio, May 11, 1941; s. Harry E. and Eila F. (Cowles) W.; m. Margo Ann Stubblefield, Oct. 2, 1965. BSBA, Franklin U., 1975. Salesman Texaco, Chgo., 1971-75; v.p. sales Cushion Foam Corp., Haverhill, Mass., 1975-81; gen mgr. Voltek, Inc., Lawrence, Mass., 1983-87; pres., CEO, bd. dirs. Cantrick Corp Corp., Lexington, Mich., 1983-87; v.p., gen. mgr. Besco, Inc., Seattle, 1993—; bd. dirs. U.S. Tool, Chgo., Tarva Industries, Detroit. With USN, 1967-71, Vietnam. Buddhist. Avocations: body building, golf. Home: 8006 45th Ave W Mukilteo WA 98275 Office: Besco 6141 4th Ave S Seattle WA 98108

WHEATON, PERRY LEE, management consultant; b. Corning, N.Y., Jan. 31, 1942; s. Raymond Elmer and Beatrice Estella (Rose) W.; A.B., Hamilton Coll., 1963; M.B.A., Rutgers U., 1964; m. Diane Lynn Mathewson, Sept. 18, 1971; children: James Gardner, William Bard, Lynley Mathewson. Mgr. mgmt. cons. services Coopers & Lybrand, Boston, 1966-76; prin., regional mgr. Theodore Barry & Assocs., 1976-81; sr. v.p., Putnam Fin. Services, Inc., 1981-85; dir. Theodore Barry & Assocs., 1985-90; mng. dir. Barrington Wellesley Group, Inc., 1990—. Served with N.G., 1965-71. C.P.A.; cert. mgmt. cons. Mem. AICPA, N.Y. Soc. C.P.A.s, Inst. Mgmt. Cons. Republican.

Unitarian. Home: 23 Poor Rd New London NH 03257-2390 Office: Barrington Wellesley Group Inc PO Box 2390 New London NH 03257-2390

WHEATON, T. FREDERIC, III, psychiatrist, retired naval officer; b. Sheboygan, Wis., Feb. 26, 1950; s. Thomas Rockerfeller II and Helen Woodword (Lodge) W.; m. Kim Harding Tiller, Apr. 3, 1961; 1 child, T. Frederic IV. BA in Polit. Sci., Harvard U., 1960; MHA, U. Mich., 1962; MD, Dartmouth Coll., 1967; MA in Sociology, Yale U., 1971. Diplomate Am. Bd. Psychiatry and Neurology. Commd. 2d lt. U.S. Navy, 1963, advanced through grades to adm.; comdr. U.S. Naval Hosps., various loations, 1976-82; chief psychiatry svc. U.S. Navy, Bethesda, Md., 1982-84, comdr. Naval intelligence 1984-86; spl. asst. to chief naval ops. U.S. Navy, Washington, 1986-89; ret. U.S. Navy, 1993; dep. assoc. sec. U.S. Dept. Vets. Affairs, Lake City, Fla., 1989—; bd. dirs., mem. adv. bd. IBM Corp., N.Y.C., 1991-94. Author: Case Book of Psychiatry, 1984, also numerous articles. Chmn. Mantee County Rep. Party, Bradenton, Fla., 1994; dep. chmn. Columbia County Rep. Party, Lake City, 1994—. Recipient Presdl. citation, 1992, Superior Performance award Sec. of Navy, 1989, others. Fellow Am. Psychiat. Assn. (citation 1986); mem. Naval Officers Assn., Nat. Assn. Health Profls., Am. Coll. Psychiatry (bd. dirs.), Res. Officers Assn. Baptist. Achievements include writing of official U.S. Navy policy on psychiatric intervention for all members of U.S. Navy. Office: Nat Med Ctr 801 S Marion St Lake City FL 32055

WHEATON, WARDE FRANKLIN, manufacturing company executive; b. Mpls., Feb. 20, 1929; s. Carlos Frederick and Berenice (Russell) W.; B.S., U.S. Mil. Acad., 1950; m. Joanne Molan, Mar. 8, 1952; children—Cheryl, David, John, Jim, Susan, Elizabeth, Paul, Anne. With McDonald Lumber Co., New Brighton, Minn., 1955-56; with Honeywell Inc., Mpls., 1957—, now exec. v.p. Honeywell Aerospace and Def.; dir. ADC, magnetic controls, Mpls. Bd. dirs. Mpls. Jr. Achievement, Meth. Hosp., Mpls. Served with U.S. Army, 1950-54. Mem. Aerospace Industries Assn. (gov.). Republican. Roman Catholic. Clubs: Minneapolis; Lafayette (Excelsior, Minn.).

WHEDON, GEORGE DONALD, medical administrator, researcher; b. Geneva, N.Y., July 4, 1915; s. George Dunton and Elizabeth (Crockett) W.; m. Margaret Brunssen, May 12, 1942 (div. Sept. 1982); children: Karen Anne, David Marshall. AB, Hobart Coll., 1936, ScD (hon.), 1967; MD, U. Rochester, 1941, ScD (hon.), 1978. Diplomate Am. Bd. Internal Medicine, Am. Bd. Nutrition. Intern in medicine Mary Imogene Bassett Hosp., Cooperstown, N.Y., 1941-42; asst. in medicine U. Rochester Sch. Medicine; also asst. resident physician medicine Strong Meml. Hosp., Rochester, 1942-44; instr. medicine Cornell U. Med. Coll., 1944-50, asst. prof. medicine, 1950-52; chief metabolic diseases br. Nat. Inst. Arthritis, Diabetes, Digestive and Kidney Diseases, NIH, Bethesda, Md., 1952-65, asst. dir., 1956-62, dir., 1962-81, sr. sci. adv., 1981-82; sr. assoc., dir. conf. program Kroc Found., Santa Ynez, Calif., 1982-84; adj. prof. medicine (endocrinology) UCLA Sch. Medicine, 1982-84; dir. med. rsch. programs Shriners Hosps. for Crippled Children, Tampa, 1984-91; mem. subcom. on calcium, com. dietary allowances Food and Nutrition Bd., NRC, 1959-64; cons. to office manned space flight NASA, 1963-78, chmn. Am. Inst. Biol. Scis. med. program adv. panel to, 1971-75, chmn. NASA life scis. com., 1974-78, mem. space program adv. coun., NASA, 1974-78; cons. on endocrinology and metabolism adv. com. Bur. Drugs, FDA, 1977-82; mem. subcommn. on gravitational biology Com. on Space Rsch., Internat. Union Physiol. Scis., 1979-85; mem. rsch. adv. bd. Shriners Hosps., 1981-84; mem. subcom. spacecraft maximum allowable concentrations, com. toxicology, bd. on environ. studies and toxicology Commn. on Life Scis. NRC, 1989—; cons. in medicine Wadsworth Den. Hosp. VA Ctr., L.A., 1982-84; mem. U.S. Del. of U.S.-Japan Coop. Med. Sci. Program, 1984-93; mem. internat. Soc. Gravitational Physiol., 1991—. Mem. editorial bd. Jour. Clin. Endocrinology and Metabolism, 1960-67; adv. editor Calcified Tissue Rsch., 1967-76; contbr. articles to profl. publs. Mem. med. alumni coun. Sch. Medicine, mem. trustees' coun. U. Rochester, 1971-76, vice chmn. trustees' coun., 1973-74, chmn., 1974-75; trustee Dermatology Found., 1978-82; bd. dirs. Osteogenesis Imperfecta Found., 1991—, med. adv. coun., 1993—. Recipient Superior Svc. award USPHS, 1967, Alumni citation U. Rochester, 1971, Alumni citation Hobart Coll., 1986, Exceptional Sci. Achievement medal NASA, 1974. Fellow Royal Soc. Medicine; mem. AAAS, Am. Fedn. Clin. Rsch. Assn. Am. Physicians, Aerospace Med. Assn. (Arnold D. Tuttle Meml. award 1978), Md. Acad. Scis. (sci. coun. 1964-70, 81-82), Endocrine Soc. (Robert H. Williams Disting. Leadership award in endocrinology 1982, Ayerst award 1974), Am. Physiol. Soc., Am. Inst. Nutrition, Am. Acad. Orthopaedic Surgeons (hon.), Am. Soc. Bone & Mineral Rsch., Orthopaedic Rsch. Soc., Am. Soc. Gravitational/Space Biology (Founders award 1994), Theta Delta Chi. Episcopalian. Home: 880 Mandalay Ave Apt 1002S Clearwater FL 34630-1230

WHEDON, MARGARET BRUNSSEN, television and radio producer; b. N.Y.C.; d. Henry and Anna Margaret (Nickel) Brunssen; m. G. Donald Whedon, 1942 (div. Sept. 1982); children: Karen Whedon Green, David Marshall. BA, U. Rochester, 1948; postgrad., CUNY-Hunter Coll., 1950. With ABC-TV and Radio News; asst. prodr. Coll. News Conf., 1952-60; prodr. This Week with David Brinkley, 1981-84. Prodr.: Issues and Answers, 1960-81, From the Capitol, ABC Radio, 1962-69; nres prodr. Pub. Affairs Satellite Sys., Inc., 1983—, Pubs at Pub. Affairs Satellite, Washington, 1986—; mem. Capitol Speakers, lectr., pub. speaker; commentator Flair Reports, 1962-64; music critic The Hill Rag; author: Always on Sunday, 1980, Dining in the Great Embassies, 1987. Recipient NCCJ award, 1968; nominee NATAS award, 1968. Mem. White House Corrs. Assn., Nat. Press Club, Am. Newspaper Women's Club (pres. 1983), Am. Women in Radio and TV, Radio-TV Corrs. Assn. Home: 4201 Cathedral Ave NW Apt 702E Washington DC 20016-4901 *Getting to know the leaders of the world, interviewing them in their capitols, and presenting their views to national and international TV and radio audiences were the fulfillment of my dreams since childhood. Next to my family, it has been the most important achievement of my life.*

WHEDON, RALPH GIBBS, manufacturing executive; b. Elizabeth, N.J., Aug. 10, 1949; s. Ralph Gibbs and Jane (MacMaster) W.; m. Lorna Jean Neebe, June 3, 1972; children: Deborah, David. Student, Clarkson Coll., 1968-70; BS, St. Lawrence U., 1972; student, Rensselaer Polytech. Inst., 1978; MBA, De Paul U., 1985. CPA, Ohio. Credit rep. Internat. Harvester Credit Corp., Albany, N.Y., 1972-75, ops. supr., 1975-79; mgr. export ops. Internat. Harvester Co., Chgo., 1979-86; treas. Pettibone Corp., Des Plaines, Ill., 1986-91; mgr. cash resources Bailey Controls Co., Wickliffe, Ohio, 1991—, acting dir. treas., 1992—, mgr. adminstrn., 1993—; dir. planning HMI Industries, 1994—. Bd. dirs. Naperville (Ill.) Cmty. Chorus, 1985-87; troop leader Boy Scouts Am., Naperville, 1985—; adv. coun. United Way, 1993—; adv. coun. Cleve. Treas. Club, 1992—; bd. dirs., 1994—. Episcopalian. Avocations: sailing, flying. Home: 7066 Brightwood Dr Concord OH 44077-2167 also: Branchview Dr East Holden ME 04429-9516

WHEEL, LESLEY, design firm executive; b. N.Y.C.; d. Lester and Helené (Nelson) W. BA, Brwyn Mawr Coll. Free-lance theater design N.Y.C. 1957-61; prin. Wheel Gersztoff Friedman Assocs. Inc. (formerly Wheel-Garon Inc.), N.Y.C., 1961-72, pres., 1972—. Mem. Internat. Assn. Lighting Designers (founding, past pres.), Lighting Research Inst. (past bd. dirs.). Office: Wheel Gersztoff Friedman Assocs 12100 Wilshire Blvd Suite 480 Los Angeles CA 90025

WHEELAN, R(ICHELIEU) E(DWARD), lawyer; b. N.Y.C., July 10, 1945; s. Richard Fairfax and Margaret (Murray) W. BS, Springfield (Mass.) Coll., 1967; MS, Iona Coll., 1977; JD, Pace U., 1981. Bar: N.Y. 1982, Minn. 1983, Colo. 1989, Tex. 1990, U.S. Dist. Ct. (no dist.) 1982, (so. dist.) Tex. 1991, U.S. Internat. Trade 1982, U.S. Ct. Appeals (2d cir.) 1982, (9th cir.) 1983, (5th cir.) 1993, U.S. Supreme Ct. 1994; bd. cert. criminal law, Tex. Lt. of detectives White Plains (N.Y.) Police Dept., 1969-81; area counsel IBM, Armonk, N.Y., 1981-89; gen. counsel Kroll Assocs. (Asia), Hong Kong, 1989-91; pvt. practice, Houston, 1991—. Mem. ABA (sentencing guidelines com.), Nat. Assn. Criminal Def. Lawyers (death penalty com.), Houston Bar Assn., Coll. of State Bar Tex., Pro Bono Coll. State Bar Tex., Nat. Criminal Def. Lawyers Assn., Tex. Assn. Criminal Def. Lawyers, Harris County Criminal Def. Lawyers Assn. (treas. 1993). Office: 602 Sawyer Ste 480 Houston TX 77007

WHEELAND, D. A., church administrator. V.p. gen. svcs. The Christian and Missionary Alliance, Colorado Springs. Office: The Christian & Missionary Alliance PO Box 35000 Colorado Springs CO 80935

WHEELER, ALBIN GRAY, U.S. Army career officer, educator, retail executive, law firm executive; b. Huntington, W.Va., Mar. 16, 1935; s. Harvey Gray and Hattie Benson (Weddle) W.; m. Beatrice Thomas, May 17, 1958; children: Dianne, Michelle, Patrice. BA, Marshall U., 1958; MBA, Pepperdine U., 1975; postgrad., Army War Coll., Carlisle Barracks, Pa., 1976, Harvard U., 1990. Enlisted U.S. Army, 1952, commd. 2nd lt., 1959, advanced through grades to maj. gen., 1985; comdr. divsn. spt. command, chief of staff 1st Inf. Divsn., Ft. Riley, Kans., 1978-80; dep. comdr. U.S. Army Logistics Ctr., Ft. Lee, Va., 1980-81; chief exec. officer Army AF Exch. Svc.-Europe, Munich, 1981-83; comdr. 2d Spt. Command, VII U.S. Corps, Germany, 1983-85; pres. Indsl. Coll. Armed Forces, Washington, 1985-89; dir. human resources Army Materiel Command, Washington, 1989-91; CEO Army and Air Force Exch. Svc., Dallas, 1991-93; ret. U.S. Army, 1993; exec. dir. Arent Fox Kitner Plotkin & Kahn, Washington, 1993—. Mem. Yeager Scholars Bd., Marshall U., 1986—. Decorated Def. and Army D.S.M., Bronze Star with two oak leaf clusters. Mem. Marshall U. Alumni Assn. Office: Arent Fox Kitner Plotkin & Kahn 1050 Connecticut Ave NW Washington DC 20036-5303

WHEELER, BURTON M., literature educator, higher education consultant, college dean; b. Mullins, S.C., Mar. 12, 1927; s. Paul and Elizabeth (Cleveland) W.; m. Jacquelyn Mulkey, Aug. 20, 1950; children—Paul, Geoffrey, Kristin. A.B., U. S.C., 1948, M.A., 1951; Ph.D., Harvard U., 1961. Teaching fellow Harvard U., Cambridge, Mass., 1953-56; mem. faculty Washington U., St. Louis, 1956—, prof., 1974—, dean Coll. Arts and Scis., 1966-78, interim dean univ. librs., 1988-89; cons., panelist Danforth Found., St. Louis, 1958-82; mem. GPEP panel Assn. Am. Med. Colls., Washington, 1981-84; cons.-evaluator North Cen. Assn., Chgo. Contbr. articles to profl. jours. Eli Lilly Found. fellow, 1965-66. Mem. Soc. Values in Higher Edn., Kent Fellow, Phi Beta Kappa (senator, chmn. qualifications com.). Office: Washington U English Dept Saint Louis MO 63130

WHEELER, C. HERBERT, architect, consultant, educator; b. Merchantville, N.J., June 6, 1915; s. Clarence Herbert and Louise Emma (Pennell) W.; m. Cicely Pointer, Aug. 29, 1940; children—Pamela, Janet, Betsy. B.Arch., U. Pa., 1937; M.Arch., MIT, 1940, postgrad. in acoustics and creative engring., 1953, 56; postgrad. bus. program, Alexander Hamilton Inst., 1947. Registered architect N.Y., N.J., Pa., Mich.; cert. Nat. Council Archtl. Registration Bds. Archtl. designer Austin Co., N.Y.C., 1938-41; architect, then chief architect J.G. White Engring. Co., N.Y.C., 1941-55; mgr. engring. Stran Steel Corp., Detroit, 1955-58; mgr. environ. systems Curtiss-Wright Corp., Quehanna, Pa., 1958-64; prof. archtl. engring. Pa. State U., University Park, 1964-80, prof. emeritus, 1980—. author: Public Organizations and Public Architecture, 1987; co-author: Emerging Techniques of Architectural Practice, 1966, Emerging Techniques of Architectural Programming, 1969. Served to maj. C.E., U.S. Army, 1942-46. Decorated Commendation Ribbon U.S. Army CE, 1945. Fellow AIA (emeritus, internat. relations com. 1981-84, v.p. Central Pa. chpt. 1984), Union Internat. des Architects Paris (permanent sec. profl. devel. work group 1980-85, coll. dels. 1981-85), mem. Am. Soc. Engring. Edn. (emeritus, chmn. archtl. engring. div. 1970), constrn. Specifications Inst., Ret. Officers Assn., Theta Xi (v.p. St. Louis 1953-54). Republican. Episcopalian/Methodist. Avocations: travel; precanceled stamp collecting; geography; literature. Home: 638 Franklin St State College PA 16803-3459 Office: Pa State U 104 Engring A Unit University Park PA 16802

WHEELER, CHARLES BERTAN, pathologist; b. Kansas City, Mo., Aug. 10, 1926; s. Charles Bertan and Florence (Martin) W.; m. Marjorie Martin, Aug. 21, 1949; children—Gordon, Mark, Marion, Graham, Nina. A.B., U. Louisville, 1946; M.D., U. Kans., 1950; J.D., U. Mo., Kansas City, 1959. Diplomate: Am. Bd. Pathology. Pathologist, dir. labs. Kansas City (Mo.) Gen. Hosp. and Med. Center, 1957-63; asso. pathologist Research Hosp. and Med. Center, Kansas City, Mo., 1963-65, N. Kansas City (Mo.) Meml. Hosp., 1966-68; dir. Wheeler Med. Labs., Kansas City, Mo., 1965—; clin. asst. prof. pathology U. Kans. Med. Sch., Kansas City; coroner Jackson County, Mo., 1965-67; Western judge Jackson County Ct., 1967-71; mayor of Kansas City Mo., 1971-79; adj. prof., cons. Sch. Medicine & Henry W. Bloch Sch. bus. & Pub. Adminstrn. U. Mo. Author: Doctor in Politics, 1974; contbr. articles to Am. Jour. Ob.-Gyn., New Eng. Jour. Medicine. Served with USNR, 1944-46; to capt. M.C. USAF, 1950-53. Named Alumnus of Yr. U. Mo., 1975; co-recipient Benjamin Rush award AMA, 1981. Fellow Am. Coll. Legal Medicine; mem. Mo. Soc. Pathologists (past pres.), Mo. Med. Assn., Jackson County Med. Soc., Coll. Am. Pathologists, Am. Soc. Clin. Pathologists, U. Kans. Med. Alumni Assn. (pres. 1969), Sigma Nu, Nu Sigma Nu. Democrat. Episcopalian. Club: Rotary. Office: 4320 Wornall Rd Ste 144 Kansas City MO 64111-3110

WHEELER, CLAYTON EUGENE, JR., dermatologist, educator; b. Viroqua, Wis., June 30, 1917; s. Clayton Eugene and Vista Beulah (Heal) W.; m. Susie Brooks Overton, Oct. 11, 1952; children: Susan Brooks, Margaret Ann, Elizabeth Clayton. B.A., U. Wis., 1938, M.D., 1941. Diplomate Am. Bd. Internal Medicine, Am. Bd. Dermatology (vice pres. 1977-78, pres. 1978-79). Intern Cin. Gen. Hosp., 1941-42; resident in internal medicine U. Mich. Hosps., 1942-44, research fellow endocrinology and metabolism, 1947-48, resident in dermatology, 1948-51; from asst. prof. to prof. dermatology U. Va. Med. Sch., 1951-62; prof. dermatology U. N.C. Med. Sch., Chapel Hill, 1962—, chmn. div., 1962-72, chmn. dept., 1972-87, chmn., exec. com. Med. Faculty Practice Plan, 1986-90; Clayton E. Wheeler Jr. prof. dermatology Sch. Medicine, U. N.C., 1991. Author: Practical Dermatology, 3d edit, 1967, also articles. Served to maj. M.C. AUS, 1944-47. Mem. Soc. Investigative Dermatology (pres. 1974-75, Rothman award 1979, hon. mem. 1993), Assn. Profs. Dermatology (pres. 1975-76), Am. Dermatol. Assn. (pres. 1982-83), Am. Acad. Dermatology (past dir., pres.-elect 1983-84, pres. 1984-85, past pres. 1985-86, hon. mem. 1988, masters in dermatology 1993, Gold medal 1993), Phi Beta Kappa, Alpha Omega Alpha. Methodist. Home: 2120 N Lakeshore Dr Chapel Hill NC 27514-2027 Office: NC Meml Hosp Manning Dr Chapel Hill NC 27514

WHEELER, DANIEL SCOTT, publishing executive, editor; b. Richmond, Va., Apr. 23, 1947; s. Arthur Bruce Jr. and Lavinia (Akers) W.; m. Kathy E. Wheeler; children: Matthew, Beth Marie, Jennifer Lynne, Brandy, Jennifer Ann. Student, Va. Commonwealth U., 1966-69, Butler U., 1981, Ind. U., 1984-85. Spl. agt. Northwestern Mut. Life, Richmond, 1969-71; enlisted USN, 1971, resigned, 1979; editor Am. Legion Mag., Indpls., 1979-85, pub., editor-in-chief, 1985—; bd. dirs. HP Direct. pres. Citizens Flag Alliance, Inc. Mem. Am. Legion, Mensa. Republican. Avocation: oil painting. Home: 4518 Fairhope Dr Indianapolis IN 46237-2951 Office: The American Legion Mag PO Box 1055 Indianapolis IN 46206-1055

WHEELER, DAVID LAURIE, university dean; b. Saginaw, Mich., July 30, 1934; s. Clayton Final and Blanche Beatrice (Hunt) W.; m. Jane Louise Manchester, Sept. 6, 1958; children: Elizabeth, Anne. AB, U. Mich., 1956, AM, 1958, Ph.D., 1962. Asst. dean student service Ill. State U., Normal, 1967-68, assoc. dean, 1968-69, assoc. dean grad. sch., 1969-72; dean grad. sch. West Tex. State U., Canyon, 1972-79, Ball State U., Muncie, Ind., 1979—; cons. McGraw-Hill Pub. Co., N.Y.C., Van Nostrand Reinhold Pub. Co., N.Y.C. Editor: The Human Habitat: Contemporary Readings, 1971. Woodrow Wilson fellow, 1961. Mem. Assn. Am. Geographers, Nat. Coun. Univ. Rsch. Adminstrs., Western History Assn., Tex. State Hist. Assn., Sigma Xi, Phi Kappa Phi. Republican. Presbyterian. Home: 4205 W Riverside Ave Muncie IN 47304-3653 Office: Grad Sch Ball State U Muncie IN 47306

WHEELER, DENNIS EARL, mining company executive, lawyer; b. Wallace, Idaho, Dec. 17, 1942; s. Earl L. and Virginia (Rice) W.; m. Jacquline Rae, May 16, 1971; children: Michelle, Maura, Wendy, Brad. BS in Bus., U. Idaho, 1965, JD, 1967. Bar: Idaho 1967. Ptnr. Hull, Hull & Wheeler, Wallace, 1967-78; sr. v.p., gen. counsel Coeur d'Alene (Idaho) Mines Corp., 1978-80, pres., 1980-86, CEO, 1986—, chmn., 1992—; bd. dirs. Sierra Pacific Resources, Pres. Idaho Bd. Edn., 1984-87; founder Jobs Plus, Coeur d'Alene, 1987—; bd. dirs. Ctr. for Democracy, Washington, 1992—, Children's Village, Coeur d'Alene, 1994—, Wildlife Habitat Enhancement Coun.,

WHEELER, DIANA JEAN MILLER, secondary education educator; b. Long Beach, Calif., May 12, 1945; d. Edward Joseph and Myrtle (Burchett) Miller. AA, Long Beach City Coll., 1965; BA, U. Calif., Long Beach, 1968; MA, Pepperdine U., 1983, credential in adminstr., 1983. Tchr. Long Beach Unified Sch. Dist., 1968—, acting co-adminstr., 1987—; dept. head Stephens Mid. Sch., Long Beach, 1975-85, faculty pres., 1984-89, faculty v.p., sch. site coun., new tchr. assoc. mentor, 1992—; speaker Regional Mid. Sch. Conf., Palm Springs, Calif., 1992, Nat. Mid. Sch. Conf., Long Beach, Calif., 1990, Louisville, 1991. Mem. ASCD, NEA, Nat. Coun. for Self-Esteem, Nat. Mid. Sch. Assn., Calif. Tchrs. Assn., Tchrs. Assn. Long Beach (Golden Apple award 1987). Avocations: keeping in shape, fishing, bike riding. Office: 1830 W Columbia St Long Beach CA 90810-2913

WHEELER, DOUGLAS PAUL, conservationist, government official, lawyer; b. Bklyn., Jan. 10, 1942; s. Robert S. and Lottie (Neubauer) W.; m. Heather A. Campbell, Aug. 28, 1965; children—Clay Campbell, Christopher Campbell. AB in Govt. with honors, Hamilton Coll., Clinton, N.Y., 1963; LLB, Duke U., 1966. Bar: N.C. 1966. Assoc. Levine, Goodman & Murchison, Charlotte, N.C., 1966-69; legis. atty. to asst. legis. counsel U.S. Dept. Interior, Washington, 1969-72, dep. asst. sec. Fish and Wildlife and Pks., 1972-77; exec. v.p. Nat. Trust for Hist. Preservation, Washington, 1977-80; pres. Am. Farmland Trust, Washington, 1980-85, now life mem.; exec. dir. Sierra Club, San Francisco, 1985-86; v.p. Land Heritage and Wildlife Conservation Found., Washington, 1986-88, exec. v.p., 1989-91; sec. for resources State of Calif., 1991—; advisor Pres.'s Commn. on Am. Outdoors. Bd. dirs. Calif. Nature Conservancy, Calif. Environ. Forum; mem. nat. coun. World Wildlife Fund, Am. Farmland Trust; candidate N.C. Ho. of Reps., 1968; mem. D.C. Rep. Ctrl. Com., 1984-85. Lt. JAGC, USNR, 1969-75. Recipient commendation U.S. Dept. Interior, 1976, Achievement award, 1980; Conservation award Gulf Oil Corp., 1985. Mem. N.C. Bar Assn., Sierra Club (life). Episcopalian. Home: PO Box 3164 El Macero CA 95618-0764

WHEELER, ED RAY, mathematics educator; b. Bowling Green, Ky., June 13, 1947; m. Claire Mosteller; children: Aaron, Jodi. BA, Samford U., 1969; PhD, U. Va., 1973. Instr. Lynchburg (Va.) Coll., 1969-70; teaching asst. U. Va., Charlottesville, 1970-73; asst. prof. No. Ky. U., Highland Heights, 1973-77, assoc. prof., 1977-80; dept. head Meredith Coll., Raleigh, N.C., 1980-87, Armstrong State Coll., Savannah, Ga., 1987—. Author: (with others) Mathematics: An Every Day Language, 1979, Modern Mathematics, 1995, Activity Manual for Elementary School Teachers, 1995; contbr. articles to profl. jours. Woodrow Wilson Found. fellow, 1969. Mem. Maths. Assn. Am., Am. Math. Soc., Am. Sci. Affiliation. Baptist. Avocations: tennis, jogging, reading. Office: Armstrong State Coll 11935 Abercorn St Savannah GA 31419-9901

WHEELER, EDWARD KENDALL, lawyer; b. Butte, Mont., Oct. 23, 1913; s. Burton K. and Lulu M. (White) W.; m. Charlotte D. Sharp, Apr. 15, 1939; children: Frederica Wheeler Smith, Kendall W. van Orman. AB, George Washington U., 1935; LLB, Harvard U., 1938; LLD (hon.), Mont. State U., 1994. Bar: D.C. 1939. Since practiced in Washington; ptnr. Wheeler & Wheeler, 1947—; chmn. bd. dirs. Rexcom, Inc.; bd. dirs. Wilmer Inst.; Greater Mont. Found., Wheeler Ctr., Charlotte & Edward Wheeler Found.; pres., CEO Advantage Paging. Served as lt. USNR, 1943-46. Mem. ABA, Fed. Bar Assn. Clubs: Chevy Chase; Met. (Washington), Burning Tree (Washington). Home: 6005 Highland Dr Chevy Chase MD 20815-6611 Office: Ste 400 808 17th St NW Washington DC 20006-3910

WHEELER, EVELYN A., communications specialist; b. Cedartown, Ga., May 1, 1955; d. W.F. and Alta E. (Pierce) W. BS in Psychology, Biology and Journalism, Berry Coll., Rome, Ga., 1977. Editor, dir. publs. Precept Ministries, Chattanooga, 1977-83; editor Youth with a Mission, Tujunga, Calif., 1983-84; tchr. Cobb Christian Sch., Marietta, Ga., 1984-85; chief comm. officer Precept Ministries, 1985—. Home: 4120 Albermarle Ave Chattanooga TN 37411-5203

WHEELER, GENEVIEVE STUTES, library administrator, educator; b. Duson, La., Dec. 13, 1937; d. Noah and Natalie (Falcon) Stutes; m. Richard Anthony Musemeche, Feb. 3, 1956 (div. 1975); children—Sabrina Marie Musemeche Beckham, Susan Ann; m. 2d, Berle Steele Wheeler, July 1, 1978. B.A., U. Southwest La., Lafayette, 1959; MS in Library Sci., La. State U., Baton Rouge, 1970. Cert. tchr. Tchr. Iberia Schs., New Iberia, La., 1959-60; sch. librarian Lafayette Parish Sch., 1960-69; tchr., librarian La. State Sch. Deaf, Baton Rouge, 1970-71; librarian East Baton Rouge System, 1971-78; library adminstr. St. Bernard Community Coll., Chalmette, La., 1978—; cons., 1978-92; dir. libr. sci. Nunez Community Coll., Chalmette, 1992—; cons. library La. State Dept. Edn., Baton Rouge, 1975-76. Author: tchr. guides, 1975, 77. Co-organizer, co-sponsor Project LesEnfants, 1975. Mem. Am. Library Assn., Am. Assn. Jr. and Community Colls., La. Assn. Sch. Librarians (pres. 1982-83), ALA, La. Assn. Sch. Execs., La. Library Assn. Gov.'s Conf. Libraries, Delta Kappa Gamma (v.p. Baton Rouge 1975-76), Phi Kappa Phi. Club: Republican Women's (New Orleans). Home: 12987 N Lake Carmel Dr New Orleans LA 70128-2523 Office: Nunex CC 3700 LaFontaine St Chalmette LA 70043

WHEELER, GEORGE CHARLES, quality assurance professional; b. Balt., Oct. 9, 1923; s. George Charles and Julia Elizabeth (Watrous) W.; m. Dorothy W. Whittemore, Sept. 13, 1947; children: Scott, Craig, Mark, Matthew, Tracy, Bruce; m. Clare Frances Weiner, Jan. 21, 1978. BS in Metall. Engring., Lehigh U., 1944. Various engring. and supervisory positions GE, Mass. and N.Y., 1944-62; mgr. materials, welding and nondestructive test engring. Knolls Atomic Power Lab., G.E., Schenectady, N.Y., 1962-68; mgr. nondestructive testing G.E. Power Sys., Schenectady, N.Y., 1968-85; pres., chief exec. officer Wheeler Nondestructive Testing, Inc., Schenectady, 1985—; mgr. tech. svcs. Am. Soc. for Nondestructive Testing, Columbus, Ohio, 1993—; cons. UN, N.Y.C., 1985—, Internat. Atomic Energy Agy., Vienna, Austria, 1985—, numerous others; guest lectr. Rensselaer Poly. Inst., Troy, N.Y., Union Coll., Schenectady, 1978-87; mem. math. sci. and tech. com. Schenectady County Community Coll., 1978-85, adj. prof., 1987—; U.S. del. Internat. Stds. Orgn., com. TC 135/SC7 NDT Pers. Qualification, 1987—; convenor working group #2, ISO-9712. Author: Guide to Developing Certification Exams, 1992; tech. editor: Nondestructive Testing Handbook, 3d edit.; contbg. editor Jour. of ASNT. Fellow Am. Soc. Nondestructive Testing (hon. life, bd. dirs. 1976-85, pres. 1983-84, chmn. cert. com. 1976-80, 86-89, mem. 1995—); mem. ASTM (com. internat. stds., com. nondestructive testing), NRA (life), Am. Soc. Metals, Nature Conservancy (life). Avocations: mountaineering, flying, gunning, photography.

WHEELER, GEORGE WILLIAM, university provost, physicist, educator; b. Dedham, Mass., Dec. 23, 1924; s. John Brooks, Jr. and Alice (Chamberli) W.; m. Margaret C. Pirie, Oct. 27, 1957; children: William Cameron, Alice Chamberlin. BS in Physics, Union Coll., Schenectady, 1949; PhD, Yale U., 1953. Research assoc. Woods Hole (Mass.) Oceanographic Inst., 1953-54; asst. prof. physics, sr. research asso. Yale U., 1954-64; physicist, div. head accelerator dept. Brookhaven Nat. Labs. Upton, N.Y., 1964-72; br. chief high energy physics program, div. phys. research AEC, Washington, 1972-74; dean natural and social sci., prof. physics Herbert H. Lehman Coll., CUNY, Bronx, 1974-79; prof. physics Temple U., Phila., 1979-83; dean Coll. Arts and Scis. Temple U., 1979-83; provost, prof. physics U. Tenn., Knoxville, 1984-90, ret. 1990; Trustee Southeastern Univs. Research Assn. 1984-92, chmn. 1985-89; dir. Oak Ridge Associated Univs., 1985-91; cons. in field; mem. bd. overseers Super Conducting Super Collider, 1988-91. Author papers on physics, particle accelerators. Mem. Branford (Conn.) Bd. Edn., 1961-64; trustee Village of Belle Terre, N.Y., 1967-69, bd. dirs. Southeastern Libraries Network, 1992-95; trustee Webb Sch. of Knoxville, 1985-94. Decorated Bronze Star. Mem. IEEE (sr.), AAAS, Am. Phys. Soc., Phi Beta Kappa, Sigma Xi. Home: 4909 Scenic Pt Channel Louisville TN 37777-3221

WHEELER, HAROLD ALDEN, retired radio engineer; b. St. Paul, May 10, 1903; s. William Archie Wheeler and Harriet Maria Alden; m. Ruth Gregory, Aug. 25, 1926 (dec. Feb. 1986); children: Dorothy, Caroline, Alden Gregory. BS in Physics, George Washington U., 1925, DSc (hon.), 1972; DEngring. (hon.), Stevens Inst. Tech., 1978, Polytechnic U., 1992. Engr. Hazeltine Service Corp., N.Y.C. and Bayside, N.Y., 1929-39; v.p., chief cons. engr. Hazeltine Service Corp., Little Neck, N.Y., 1940-45; cons. radio physicist Great Neck, N.Y., 1946-59; pres. Wheeler Labs Inc., Great Neck, 1947-68; dir. Hazeltine Corp., Little Neck, 1959-70, v.p., 1959-65, chmn., 1965-70; dir. Hazeltine Corp., Greenlawn, N.Y., 1971-83, chmn., 1971-77, chmn. emeritus, 1977-87, chief scientist, 1971-87; cons. Office of Sec. of Def., Washington, 1950-53; mem. Def. Sci. Bd., Washington, 1961-64. About 180 patents in field, including diode automatic volume control, 1932; author: Wheeler Monographs, Vol. 1, 1953, Hazeltine the Professor, 1978, Early Days of Wheeler and Hazeltine Corporation, 1982, Hazeltine Corporation in World War II, 1993; numerous papers in, procs. and transactions of IRE and IEEE. Recipient Modern Pioneer award Nat. Assn. Mfrs., 1940. Fellow IEEE (medal of honor 1964), IRE (Morris Liebmann prize 1940), Radio Club Am. (Armstrong medal 1964); mem. Nat. Acad. Engring., Inst. Elec. Engrs. (U.K.), Sigma Xi, Tau Beta Pi, Gamma Alpha. Republican. Unitarian. Home: 4900 Telegraph Rd Apt 523 Ventura CA 93003-4125

WHEELER, HENRY CLARK, manufacturing company executive; b. Bridgeport, Conn., Apr. 27, 1916; s. Dwight Clark and Louise (Carstesen) W.; m. Phyllis Francis Seeley, Sept. 6, 1940; children: Dwight Clark II, Louise Seeley, Philip Gregory. B.S., Yale U., 1939. With Acme Shear Co. (name changed to Acme United Corp., 1971), Bridgeport, 1939—, pres., 1941-90, CEO, 1952-94, chmn., 1990—. Served with USNR, 1941. Republican. Congregationalist. Office: Acme United Corp 75 Kings Hwy Cutoff Fairfield CT 06430-5340

WHEELER, HEWITT BROWNELL, surgeon, educator; b. Louisville, July 21, 1929; s. Arville and Lois (Vance) W.; m. Elizabeth Jane Maxwell, July 21, 1956; children: Stephen, Elizabeth, Jane, Mary. Student, Vanderbilt U., 1945-48; M.D. Harvard U., 1952. Diplomate Am. Bd. Surgery (bd. dirs. 1984-90). Cushing fellow Harvard Med. Sch., Boston, 1953, Peters fellow, 1956, research fellow, 1959-60, instr. surgery, 1961-64, clin. assoc. surgery, 1964-67, asst. clin. prof. surgery, 1967-70, assoc. prof. surgery, 1970-71; asst. in surgery Peter Bent Brigham Hosp., Boston, 1959-60, jr. assoc. surgery, 1961-64, assoc. surgery, 1964-69, sr. assoc. surgery, 1969-71; asst. chief surgery Roxbury VA Hosp., Boston, 1961-62, chief surgery, 1962-71, chief of staff, 1968-71; cons. surgery U. Mass. Med. Sch. at Worcester, 1966-71, prof., chmn. dept. surgery, 1971—, Harry M. Haidak disting. prof. surgery, 1985—; chief staff U. Mass. Hosp., 1974-76, surgeon-in-chief, 1976—; affiliate prof. biomed. engring. Worcester Poly. Inst., 1974—; lectr. surgery Harvard Med. Sch., 1974—; chief surgery St. Vincent Hosp., Worcester, 1971-75; cons. Meml. Hosp., Worcester City Hosp., 1970—, Worcester Hahnemann Hosp., 1974—, Peter Bent Brigham Hosp., 1973—; chmn. surg. research program com. VA, Washington, 1965-67, nat. participant surg. cons., 1965-69, chmn. ad hoc adv. com. surgery, 1969—. Trustee Cen. Mass. Health Care Found., 1975-77. Served to 1st lt., M.C. AUS, 1953-55. Mem. ACS (bd. govs. 1984-90, coun. Mass. chpt. 1973-76, pres. 1980), AAAS, AMA, Am. Surg. Assn., Soc. Univ. Surgeons, Internat. Cardiovascular Soc., Soc. Surg. Chairmen, New Eng. Surg. Soc. (treas. 1977-84, v.p. 1986-87, pres. 1989-91), Boston Worcester Surg. Soc. (pres. 1973-75, pres.-elect 1994), Transplantation Soc., Mass. Med. Soc. (100th Shattuck lectr. 1990), Worcester Dist. Med. Soc., New Eng. Vascular Soc. (v.p. 1985-86, pres. 1988-89), Internat. Chirurg. Soc. Research exptl. transplantation, blood vessel surgery, method to detect blood clots. Home: 10 Old English Rd Worcester MA 01609-1306

WHEELER, JACK COX, army officer; b. Canton, Ga., Feb. 2, 1939; s. Clinton Alfred and Juanita I. (Cox) W.; m. Marjorie Gunn, May 5, 1962; children: Leigh Ann, Clinton Alan. BA in History, North Ga. Coll., 1961; MA in Pub. Adminstrn., Shippensburg State U., 1979; postgrad., Harvard U., 1988. Commd. 2d lt. U.S. Army, 1961, advanced through grades to maj. gen., 1989; chief, officer mgmt. br. Mil. Assistance Command Vietnam, Tan Son Nat, 1969-70; pers. staff officer Dep. Chief of Staff for Pers., Washington, 1971-75; asst. to dir. army staff Office U.S. Army Chief of Staff, Washington, 1975-76; adj. gen. 1st Armored Div., Ansbach, Fed. Republic Germany, 1976-78; student Army War Coll., Carlisle Barracks, Pa., 1979; chief structure br. Dep. Chief of Staff for Pers., Washington, 1979-80, chief enlisted div., 1980-82, chief profl. devel., 1982-84; comdr. 8th Pers. Command-Korea, Youngsan Seoul, 1984-86; dir. Enlisted Pers. Mgmt., Alexandria, Va., 1986-88; dep. comdg. gen. U.S. Army Recruiting Command, Ft. Sheridan, Ill., 1988-89, comdg. gen., 1989—. Decorated D.S.M., Legion of Merit, Bronze Star. Mem. Assn. U.S. Army. Methodist.

WHEELER, JOHN ARCHIBALD, physicist, educator; b. Jacksonville, Fla., July 9, 1911; s. Joseph Lewis and Mabel (Archibald) W.; m. Janette Hegner, June 10, 1935; children: Isabel Letitia Wheeler Ufford, James English, Alison Christie Wheeler Lahnston. PhD, Johns Hopkins U., 1933; ScD (hon.), Western Res. U., 1958, U. N.C., 1959, U. Pa., 1968, Middlebury Coll., 1969, Rutgers U., 1969, Yeshiva U., 1973, Yale U., 1974, U. Uppsala, 1975, U. Md., 1977, Gustavus Adolphus U., 1981, Cath. U. Am., 1982, U. Newcastle-upon-Tyne, 1983, Princeton U., 1986, U. Conn., 1989, U. Maine, 1992; ScD, Tufts U., 1992; LLD (hon.), Johns Hopkins U., 1977; LittD (hon.), Drexel U., 1987. NRC fellow N.Y., Copenhagen, 1933-35; asst. prof. physics U. N.C., 1935-38; assoc. prof. physics Princeton U., 1938-42, assoc. prof., 1945-47, prof., 1947-76, Joseph Henry prof. physics, 1966-76, Joseph Henry prof. physics emeritus, 1976—; prof. physics and dir. Ctr. for Theoretical Physics, U. Tex., Austin, 1976-86; Ashbel Smith prof. U. Tex., Austin, 1979-86, Blumberg prof., 1981-86, Smith and Blumberg prof. emeritus, 1986—; cons. and physicist on atomic energy projects Princeton U., 1939-42, U. Chgo., 1942, E.I. duPont de Nemours & Co., Wilmington, Del., and Richland, Wash., 1943-45, Los Alamos, 1950-53; dir. project Matterhorn (H-bomb) Princeton U., 1951-53; Guggenheim fellow, Paris and Copenhagen, 1949-50; summer lectr. U. Mich., U. Chgo., Columbia U.; Lorentz prof. U. Leiden, 1956; Fulbright prof. Kyoto U., 1962; 1st vis. fellow Clare Coll. Cambridge U., 1964; Ritchie lectr. Edinburgh, 1958; vis. prof. U. Calif.-Berkeley, 1960; Battelle prof. U. Wash., 1975; sci. adviser U.S. Senate del. to 3d ann. conf. NATO Parliamentarians, Paris, 1957; mem. adv. com. Oak Ridge Nat. Lab., 1957-65, U. Calif., Los Alamos and Livermore, 1972-77; v.p. Internat. Union Physics, 1951-54; chmn. joint com. Am. Phys. Soc. and Am. Philos. Soc. on history theoretical physics in 20th Century, 1960-72; sci. adv. bd. USAF, 1961, 62; chmn. Dept. Def. Advanced Research Projects Agy. Project 137, (now Project Jason) 1958; mem. U.S. Gen. Adv. Com. Arms Control and Disarmament, 1969-72, 74-77. Author: Geometrodynamics, 1962, Gravitation Theory and Gravitational Collapse, 1965, Spacetime Physics, 1966, 2d edition with E. Taylor, 1992, Einsteins Vision, 1968, (with C.W. Misner and K.S. Thorne) Gravitation, 1973, Black Holes, (M. Rees and R. Ruffini) Gravitational Waves and Cosmology, 1974, Frontiers of Time, 1979, (with W. Zurek) Quantum Theory and Measurement, 1983, A Journey into Gravity and Spacetime, 1990, transl. German, Japanese, Italian, At Home in the Universe, 1993, Gravitation and Inertia, 1995; also translations, 1991-92; contbr. 375 articles to profl. jours. Trustee Battelle Meml. Inst., 1959-89, S.W. Rsch. Inst., San Antonio, 1977-92. Recipient A. Cressy Morrison prize N.Y. Acad. Sci. for work on nuclear physics, 1947, Albert Einstein prize Strauss Found., 1965, Enrico Fermi award AEC, 1968, Franklin medal Franklin Inst., 1969, Nat. medal of Sci., 1971, Herzfeld award, 1975, Outstanding Grad. Teaching award U. Tex., 1981, Niels Bohr Internat. Gold medal, 1982, Oersted medal Am. Assn. Physics Tchrs., 1983, J. Robert Oppenheimer meml. prize, 1984, Matteucci medal Nat. Acad. Sci. Rome, Soc. of the Forty, 1994. Fellow AAAS (dir. 1963-66, 76-79, v.p. 1971-73, Franklin medal 1989), Royal Acad. Sci. (Uppsala, Sweden), Tex. Philos. Soc., l'Academie Internationale de Philosophie des Sciences (v.p. 1987-90), Internat. Union Physics (v.p. 1951-54), Accademia Nazionale Dei Lincei, Royal Soc. (London), Century Assn. (N.Y.C.), Royal Danish Acad. Scis., Princeton Club (N.Y.C.), Phi Beta Kappa, Sigma Xi. Unitarian (trustee 1965). Office: Princeton U Dept Physics Princeton NJ 08544 *We will first understand how simple the universe is when we recognize how strange it is.*

WHEELER, JOHN CRAIG, astrophysicist, writer; b. Glendale, Calif., Apr. 5, 1943; s. G.L. and Peggy Wheeler; m. Hsueh Lie, Oct. 29, 1967; children:

Diek Winters, J. Robinson. BS in Physics, MIT, 1965; PhD in Physics, U. Colo., 1969. Asst. prof. astronomy Harvard U., Cambridge, Mass., 1971-74; assoc. prof. U. Tex., Austin, 1974-80, prof., 1980—, Samuel T. and Fern Yanagisawa Regents prof. astronomy, 1985—, chmn. astronomy dept., 1986-90; vis. fellow Joint Inst. Lab. Astrophysics, Boulder, Colo., 1978-79, Japan Soc. for Promotion of Sci., 1983; vis. prof. Assn. Univs. for Rsch. in Astronomy, 1990; mem. exec. com. astrophysics workshop Aspen (Colo.) Ctr. for Physics, Tex. Symposium on Relativistic Astrophysics. Author: The Krone Experiment, 1986. Recipient undergrad. teaching award Coll. Natural Scis., U. Tex., 1984, teaching award Bd. Visitors, Dept. Astronomy, U. Tex., 1986; Fulbright fellow, Italy, 1991. Mem. Internat. Astron. Union, Am. Astron. Soc., Sigma Xi. Avocations: running, writing, reading. Office: U Tex Dept Astronomy Austin TX 78712

WHEELER, JOHN ERNEST, JR., oil company executive; b. Leonardtown, Md., Nov. 28, 1952; s. John Ernest and Margaret Louise (Johnson) W.; m. Catherine Maria McConville, Oct. 21, 1978; children: Justin, Christian. BA in Acctg., Loyola Coll., Balt., 1974, MBA in Fin., 1985. CPA, Md. Staff acct. Ernst & Young, Balt., 1974-76; auditor Crown Cen. Petroleum, Balt., 1976-77, sr. auditor, 1977-78, acctg. mgr., 1978-79, div. contr., 1979-81, contr., 1981—, v.p., 1984—, treas., 1991—. Treas. Crown Cen. Polit. Action Com., 1985—; bd. dirs. Easter Seals of Md., 1989—. Mem. AICPA, Md. Assn. CPA's, Fin. Execs. Inst., KC. Roman Catholic. Office: Crown Cen Petroleum Corp One N Charles St 1 N Charles St Baltimore MD 21201-3709

WHEELER, JOHN HARVEY, political scientist; b. Waco, Tex., Oct. 17, 1918; m. Norene Burleigh; children: David Carroll, John Harvey III, Mark Jefferson. B.A., U. Md., 1946, M.A., 1947; Ph.D., Harvard U., 1950. Instr. dept. govt., asst. dir. Summer Sch., Harvard U., 1950; asst. prof. Johns Hopkins U., 1950-54; assoc. prof. Washington and Lee U., 1954-56, prof. polit. sci., 1956-60; fellow in residence Ctr. for Study Dem. Insitns., 1960-69, program dir., 1970-75; chmn., pres. Inst. Higher Studies, Carpinteria, Calif., 1975—; Martha Boaz rsch. prof. in acad. info. systems U. So. Calif. Libr. Systems, 1986—, Martha Boaz disting. rsch. prof., 1987—; cons. Fund for Republic, 1958-61; adj. prof. New Sch., 1986—, ISIM, 1989—; founder, bd. dirs. The Virtual Acad., 1987; mem. faculty Western Behavioral Scis. Inst., 1990—; mem. BESTnet, Nat. Rsch. and Edn. Network; pres. C-Mode Inst., 1992—; bd. dirs. Silicon Beach Comm. Author: The Conservative Crisis, 1958, (with Eugene Burdick) Fail-Safe, 1962, Democracy in a Revolutionary Era, 1968, The Politics of Revolution, 1971, The Virtual Library, 1987, The Virtual Society, 1988, 2d edit., 1992; editor, contbg. author: Beyond Punitive Society, 1973, Structure of Ancient Wisdom, 1983, Bioalgebra of Judgment, 1986, Fundamental Structures Human Reflexion, 1990; editor: (with George Boas) Lattimore, The Scholar, 1953; co-founder, joint chief editor: (with James Danielli) Jour. Social and Biol. Structures, 1973—; joint editor Goethe's Science, 1986; developed computer-mediated "Freshman Academy", 1993; contbr. articles to profl. jours. Served with AUS, 1941-46. Home: 7200 Casitas Pass Rd Carpinteria CA 93013-3120 Office: Inst Higher Studies PO Box 704 Carpinteria CA 93014-0704

WHEELER, JOHN OLIVER, geologist; b. Mussoorie, India, Dec. 19, 1924; s. Edward Oliver and Dorothea Sophie (Danielsen) W.; m. Nora Jean Hughes, May 17, 1952; children: Kathleen Anna Wheeler Hunter, Jennifer Margaret Wheeler Crompton. B.A.Sc. in Geol. Engring., U. B.C., 1947; Ph.D. in Geology, Columbia U., 1956. Geologist Geol. Survey Can., Ottawa, Ont., 1951-61, Vancouver, B.C., 1961-65; rsch. scientist Geol. Survey Can., 1965-70; rsch. mgr. Geol. Survey Can., Ottawa, 1970—; chief regional and econ. geology div. Geol. Survey Can., 1970-73, dep. dir. gen., 1973-79; rsch. scientist Geol. Survey Can. (Cordilleran div.), 1979-90, rsch. scientist emeritus, 1990—. Compiler of regional geol. maps of we. Can., Can. and no. N.Am. and Greenland; contbr. articles to profl. jours. Fellow Royal Soc. Can., Geol. Assn. Can. (pres. 1970-71, Logan medal 1983), Geol. Soc. Am. (councillor 1971-74); Can. Geosci. Council (pres. 1981); mem. Can. Inst. Mining and Metallurgy, Can. Geol. Found. (pres. 1974-79). Anglican. Clubs: Can. Alpine, Am. Alpine. Office: Geol Survey Can, 100 W Pender St, Vancouver, BC Canada V6B 1R8

WHEELER, JOHN WATSON, lawyer; b. Murfreesboro, Tenn., Sept. 11, 1938; s. James William and Grace (Fann) W.; m. Dorothy Anita Pressgrove, Aug. 5, 1959; children: Jeffrey William, John Harold. BS in Journalism, U. Tenn., 1960, JD, 1968. Bar: Tenn. 1968, U.S. Dist. Ct. (ea. dist.) Tenn. 1968, U.S. Supreme Ct. 1974, U.S. Ct. Appeals (6th cir.) 1975. Editor The Covington (Tenn.) Leader, 1963-65; adminstrv. asst. to lab. dir. UT-AEC Rsch. Lab., Oak Ridge, Tenn., 1965-68; assoc. Hodges, Doughty & Carson, Knoxville, Tenn., 1968-72; ptnr. Hodges, Doughty & Carson, Knoxville, 1972—; mem. commn. to study Appellate Cts. in Tenn.; chair U.S. Magistrate Merit Selection Panel, Ea. Dist., Tenn., 1991; mem. Bankruptcy Judge Merit Selection Panel, Ea. Dist. Tenn., 1992-93. Chmn. Hist. Soc. U.S. Dist. Ct. Ea. Dist. Tenn. U.S. Army, 1961-63, capt. Res. Fellow Am. Bar Found. (life), Tenn. Bar Found.; mem. ABA (ho. of dels. 1986—), Tenn. Bar Assn. (pres. 1989-90, bd. govs. 1981-91), Nat. Conf. Bar Pres., Am. Inns. of Ct. (master of bench), Internat. Assn. Def. Counsel, So. Conf. Bar Pres., Fox Den Country Club. Republican. Lutheran. Avocations: golf, travel. Home: 12009 N Fox Den Dr Knoxville TN 37922-2540 Office: Hodges Doughty & Carson PO Box 869 Knoxville TN 37901-0869

WHEELER, KATHERINE FRAZIER (KATE WHEELER), writer; b. Tulsa, July 27, 1955; d. Charles Bowen and Jan Nette (Moses) W. BA in English Fine Arts, Rice U., 1977; MA in Creative Writing, Stanford U., 1981. News reporter The Miami (Fla.) Herald, 1977-79; tchr. English composition Middlesex C.C., Lawrence, Mass., 1991; tchr. meditation Insight Meditation Soc., Barre, Mass., 1991—. Author: (short stories) Not Where I Started From, 1993; editor: (essays) In This Very Life, 1990; translator: (poems) Borrowed Time/Lo Esperady Lo Vivido, 1987; contg. editor: Tricycle Mag. Buddhist nun Mahasi Sasana Yeiktha, Rangoon, Burma, 1988; vol. Pet Share, Somerville (Mass.) Hosp., 1994. Recipient Pushcart Press prize, 1983-84, Best Am. Short Stories award Houghton Miflin, 1992, O. Henry award Doubleday, Inc., 1982, 93; nominee PEN/Faulkner award, 1994, Whiting Found. award, 1994; grantee NEA, 1994. Avocations: travel, dog training, sky gazing. Home: 72 Rev Nazareno Properzi Wy Somerville MA 02143

WHEELER, KATHERINE WELLS, state legislator; b. St. Louis, Feb. 8, 1940; d. Benjamin Harris and Katherine (Gladney) Wells; m. Douglas Lanphier Wheeler, June 13, 1964; children: Katherine Gladney, Lucille Lanphier. BA, Smith Coll., 1961; MA, Washington U., St. Louis, 1966. Founder auction N.H. Pub. TV, Durham, 1973-76; pub. mem. N.H. Pub. Broadcasting Council, Durham, 1975-80; founding mem. bd. govs. N.H. Pub. TV, 1980-88; elected N.H. Ho. of Reps., Concord, 1988—; coord. internat. visitors program N.H. Coun. World Affairs, 1981—; bd. dirs. Planned Parenthood No. New Eng., Gt. Bay Sch. and Tng. Ctr., Newington, N.H. Vice chair Strafford County Legis. Delegation, 1993-94; active Commn. on Health, Human Svcs. and Elderly Affairs N.H. Ho. of Reps., Concord, 1988; bd. dirs. Devel. Svcs. Strafford County, Inc., 1991—. Named Woman of Yr. Union Leader Newspaper, 1984, Citizen of Yr. Homemakers of Strafford County, 1990, Legislator of Yr. N.H. Assn. of Social Workers, 1993, Legislator of Yr. N.H. NASW, 1993; recipient Elizabeth Campbell Outstanding Pub. TV Vol. award N.H. Friends Pub. Broadcasting, 1984, Meritorious Svc. award N.H. Women's Lobby, 1992, Dist. Contbn. award N.H. Psychol. Orgn., Inc., 1994, Cert. of Achievement for Outstanding Legis. Leadership N.H. Citizen Action, 1994. Mem. AAWU, AARP, LWV, Order of Women Legis., N.H. Smith Coll. Club (v.p. 1974-76, pres. 1976-78), N.H. Assn. Social Workers (legislator of yr. 1993), N.H. Psychol. Orgn. Inc. (disting. contbn. award 1994). Democrat. United Ch. Christ. Home and office: 27 Mill Rd Durham NH 03824-3098

WHEELER, KENNETH WILLIAM, historian, educator; b. Amarillo, Tex., Mar. 7, 1929; s. Homer N. and Bertha (Campbell) W.; children: Amanda, Philip, David. B.A., U. Tex., 1951; diplome D'etudes Degré Superiur, Sorbonne, Paris, 1956; Ph.D., U. Rochester, 1963. Lectr. history and city planning, asst. dean Grad. Sch. Ohio State U. 1960-66; asso. dean Met. Coll.; acting dean, dir. MetroCenter; assoc. prof. history Boston U., 1967-69; prof. history, dean Univ. Coll., Rutgers U., 1969-72, provost 1972-87; sr. v.p. acad. affairs Rutgers U., 1987-91, Univ. prof. history, 1974—; mem. vis. com. Harvard U., 1972-80, adv. com. Lahey Clinic, 1989—, Planned

---

Parenthood, 1988—. Author: To Wear a City's Crown, 1968, Women, The Arts, and The 1920's in New York and Paris, 1982; editor: For the Union, 1968. Trustee New Brunswick Tomorrow, George Street Theatre, Rutgers Prep. Sch. Served with AUS, 1951-53. Recipient award Am. Philos. Assn., 1966; fellow Am. Council Edn., 1966-67. Mem. Am. Hist. Assn., Orgn. Am. Historians, Soc. des amis des Univs. de Paris, Urban League, Phi Kappa Psi, Delta Sigma Pi. Clubs: Century Assn. (N.Y.C.), Palo Duro (Tex.). Office: Rutgers U 172 College Ave New Brunswick NJ 08901-1157

WHEELER, LADD, psychology educator; b. Rosenberg, Tex., June 22, 1937; s. John DeWitt and Fredda (Stewart) W.; m. Clara McKee, June 20, 1961; 1 son, Scott; m. 2d Barbara Fox, Sept. 26, 1980; children: Karen, Robin; m. Helen Lee, Mar. 27, 1986; children: Natalie, Andrew. B.A., Stanford U., 1959; Ph.D., U. Minn., 1962. Research scientist Human Resources Research Office, Monterey, Calif., 1962-63, Nava. Med. Research Inst., Bethesda, Md., 1963-67; assoc. prof. Duke U., Durham, N.C., 1967-68, NYU, N.Y.C., 1968-71; prof. U. Rochester, (N.Y.), 1972—. Author: Interpersonal Influence, 1970, Interpersonal Influence, 2d edit., 1978, General Psychology, 1975; editor: Review of Personality and Social Psychology, Vols. 1-4, 1980-83. Fellow Am. Psychol. Assn., Am. Psychol. Soc., Soc. Personality and Social Psychology (pres. 1986). Home: 24 Locust Hill Dr Rochester NY 14618-5415 Office: U Rochester Rochester NY 14627

WHEELER, M. CATHERINE, organization executive; b. Plainfield, N.J., May 31, 1942; d. William R. and Josephine S. (Ford) W. BA in Politics, Hollins Coll., 1964; MA in Theatre, U. Kans., 1966. Asst. mgr. South Shore Music Circus, Cohasset, Mass., 1967; pub. rels. asst. Trinity Square Repertory Co., Providence, 1967-68; co. mgr. Acad. Playhouse, Wilmette, Ill., 1968; adminstrv. asst. Am. U. Theatre, Washington, 1968-71; pub. rels. asst. Winterthur Mus. and Gardens, Wilmington, Del., 1972-76, dir. pub. rels., 1976-84; dir. Del. Tourism Office, Dover, 1984-93; pub. rels. coord. New Castle County Bd. of Realtors, Wilmington, 1994-95, dir. polit. affairs and comm., 1995—; pub. rels. cons. Historic Deerfield, Mass., 1983, Tourism Coun. Frederick County, Md., Bristol Riverside Theatre, Pa., 1994; bd. dirs. U.S. Travel Data Ctr., 1989-93. Editor Winterthur Newsletter, 1972-84. Mem. Del. Heritage Commn., 1984-93, Del. Coastal Heritage Greenways Coun., 1991-93. Mem. Nat. Coun. State Travel Dirs. (chmn. nominating com. 1987-89, chmn. edn. com. 1989-91, chmn. rsch. task force 1991-92), Travel Industry Assn. (bd. dirs. 1990-94, chmn. Mid-Atlantic U.S.A (1989-92). Avocations: theatre, music, museums, travel, writing. Office: New Castle Cty Bd Realtors 3615 Miller Rd Wilmington DE 19802-2523

WHEELER, MALCOLM EDWARD, lawyer, law educator; b. Berkeley, Calif., Nov. 29, 1944; s. Malcolm Ross and Frances Dolores (Kane) W.; m. Donna Marie Stambaugh, July 21, 1981; children: Jessica Ross, M. Connor. SB, MIT, 1966; JD, Stanford U., 1969. Bar: Calif. 1970, Colo. 1992, U.S. Dist. Ct (cen. dist.) Calif. 1970, U.S. Ct. Appeals (9th cir.) 1970, U.S. Ct. Appeals (10th cir.) 1973, U.S. Dist. Ct. (no., so., ea. and cen. dists.) Calif. 1975, U.S. Ct. Appeals (11th cir.) 1987, U.S. Ct. Appeals (D.C. cir.) 1987, U.S. Supreme Ct. 1976, U.S. Ct. Appeals (3d cir.) 1989, (4th cir.) 1992. Assoc. Howard, Prim, Smith, Rice & Downs, San Francisco, 1969-71; assoc. prof. law U. Kans., Lawrence, 1971-74; assoc. Hughes Hubbard & Reed, Los Angeles, 1974-77, ptnr., 1977-81, 83-85, cons. 1981-83; ptnr. Skadden, Arps, Slate, Meagher & Flom, Los Angeles, 1985-91; dir. Parcel, Mauro, Hultin & Spaanstra P.C., Denver, 1991—; vis. prof. U. Iowa, 1978, prof., 1979; prof. U. Kans., Lawrence, 1981-83; chief counsel U.S. Senate Select Com. to Study Law Enforcement Undercover Activities, Washington, 1982-83. Mem. editorial bd. Jour. Products Liability, 1984—; bd. editors Fed. Litigation Guide Reporter, 1986—; contbr. articles to profl. jours. Mem. ABA, Calif. Bar Assn., Colo. Bar Assn., Am. Law Inst. Office: Parcel Mauro Hultin & Spaanstra PC 1801 California St Denver CO 80202-2658

WHEELER, MARSHALL RALPH, zoologist, educator; b. Carlinville, Ill., Apr. 7, 1917; s. Ralph Adelbert and Hester May (Ward) W.; m. Edna Vivian Cronquist, July 3, 1944; 1 dau., Sandra Wheeler King; m. Linda Carol Lackner, May 10, 1966; children: Karen, Carson. Student, Blackburn Coll., 1935-37; B.A., Baylor U., 1939; postgrad., Tex. A&M U., 1939-41; Ph.D. (NRC fellow), U. Tex., 1947. Mem. faculty U. Tex., Austin, 1947—; assoc. prof. zoology, 1955-61, prof., 1961-78, emeritus prof., 1978—; Gosney fellow Calif. Inst. Tech.; former dir. Nat. Drosophila Species Resources Ctr.; mem. Nat. Wildflower Rsch. Ctr. Editor: Studies in Genetics, 1960-72. Served with USN, 1941-45. NSF grantee; NIH grantee. Mem. Entomol. Soc. Am. (editor Annals 1970-75), S.W. Assn. Naturalists (pres. 1961), Southwestern Entomol. Soc. (pres. 1978), Am. Hemerocallis Soc., Wilderness Soc., Nature Conservancy, Sierra Club. Home: 1313 Ardenwood Rd Austin TX 78722-1105 Office: U Tex Dept Zoology Austin TX 78712

WHEELER, ORVILLE EUGENE, university dean, civil and mechanical engineering educator; b. Memphis, Dec. 31, 1932; s. Eugene Lloyd and Sarah Josephine (Craig) W.; m. Mary Bea Rychlik, June 6, 1956; 1 dau., Lynnette Layne. B.Engring. cum laude, Vanderbilt U., 1954; M.S. in Civil Engring. U. Mo., 1956; Ph.D., Tex. A&M U., 1966. Registered profl. engr., Ala., Tenn., Wis. With Chance Vought Co., Dallas, 1959-60, Hayes Aircraft Co., Birmingham, Ala., 1960-61, Brown Engring. Co., Huntsville, Ala., 1961-62, NASA, Huntsville, 1962-66; design specialist Gen. Dynamics Co., Ft. Worth, 1966-72; chief structures engr. Bucyrus Erie Co., Milw., 1972-78; prof. civil and mech. engring., dean Herff Coll. Engring. Memphis State U., 1978-87, Herff prof. structural mechanics, 1987—. Served with USN, 1956-59. Mem. ASCE, ASTM, Assn. for Computing Machinery, Am. Inst. Steel Constrn., Memphis Engrs. Club. Methodist. Home: 3307 E Monticello Cir Memphis TN 38115-0640 Office: U Memphis Memphis TN 38152

WHEELER, OTIS BULLARD, academic administrator, educator emeritus; b. Mansfield, Ark., Feb. 1, 1921; s. Clarence Charles and Georgia Elizabeth (Bullard) W.; m. Doris Louise Alexander, Jan. 17, 1943; children: Ann Carolyn, Ross Charles; m. Anne Carol Loveland, Mar. 23, 1991. B.A., U. Okla., 1942; M.A., U. Tex., 1947; Ph.D., U. Minn., 1951. Faculty La. State U., Baton Rouge, 1952—; prof. English La. State U., 1965-81, prof. emeritus, 1981—, chmn. dept., 1974, asst. dean grad. sch., 1962-67, vice chancellor for acad. affairs, 1974-80, acting chancellor, 1981; Fulbright-Hayes lectr. U. Innsbruck, Austria, 1968-69. Author: The Literary Career of Maurice Thompson, 1965. Served with U.S. Army, 1942-46, 51-52. Decorated Bronze Star medal. Mem. Phi Kappa Phi, Omicron Delta Kappa. Democrat. Methodist. Home: 162 Clara Dr Baton Rouge LA 70808-4709

WHEELER, OTIS V., JR., public school principal; b. Silex, Mo., Oct. 1, 1925; s. Otis V. and Pearla F. (Howell) W.; m. Virginia Rogers, June 7, 1947; children: Jan Leigh, Mark Patrick. BBA, U. Mo., 1948, MEd, 1965, EdD, 1971. USN, 1948-52, Bus. mgr., 1952-61; sci. tchr. Columbia (Mo.) Pub. Schs., 1961-63, principal, 1963-91; supt. Boone County Sch. Dist., Mo., 1971; instr. U. Mo., Columbia, 1970-72, asst. prof. 1972-75, 78-79; cons. Midwest Ctr for Equal Ednl. Opportunities, 1972-75. Served to lt. USNR, 1943-85, World War II, Korea. Mem. Nat. Assn. Elem. Sch. Prins. (U.S. Dept. Edn., Nat. Disting. Prin. award 1985, Excellence in Edn. award 1986), Mo. Assn. Elem. Sch. Prins. (Disting. Service award 1984, editor jours. 1967-88), Mo. State Tchrs. Assn., Retired Officers Assn., U. Mo. Columbia Coll. Edn. Alumni (Citation of Merit award 1987), Phi Delta Kappa, Phi Delta Theta, Kappa Delta Pi. Methodist. Club: Lake Ozark Yachting Assn. (Mo.). Avocations: boating, dancing, travel, scuba diving. Home: 916 W Ash St Columbia MO 65203-2636 Office: Ridgeway IGE Sch 107 E Sexton Rd Columbia MO 65203-4082

WHEELER, PAUL JAMES, real estate executive; b. Mpls., Jan. 8, 1953; s. Philip James and Phyllis Lavonne (Holmquist) W.; m. Marianne Marie Stanton, June 3, 1978; children: Allison, Nathan, Kathryn. BA in Econs., DePauw U., 1975; MBA in Mgmt., Northwestern U., 1977. CPA, Ill. Acct. Deloitte, Haskins & Sells, Chgo., 1976-79; v.p. fin. Quinlan & Tyson, Inc., Evanston, Ill., 1979-82; sr. v.p. The Inland Group, Inc., Oakbrook, Ill. 1982—; bd. dirs. Am. Nat. Downers Grove, Inland Am. Ins. Co., Inland Securities Corp., Oak Brook, Ill. Mem. Ill. Soc. CPA's, Nat. Assn. Real Estate Investment Trusts, Nat. Multi Housing Coun., Investment Program Assn., Libertyville Sunrise Rotary. Republican. Evangelical Free. Home: 255 Ridgeway Ln Libertyville IL 60048-2457 Office: The Inland Group Inc 2901 Butterfield Rd Hinsdale IL 60521-1190

WHEELER, RAYMOND DAWSON, accountant; b. Sackville, N.B., Can., Oct. 26, 1946; s. James Allison and Hazel Hanna (MacElroy) W.; m. Jennifer Grace McKee, July 31, 1971. B Commerce, Mt. Alison U., Sackville, 1968; MBA, U. Toronto, Ont., Can., 1992. Chartered acct., N.S., B.C., Ont. Regional mng. ptnr. Doane Raymond, Toronto. Fellow B.C. Inst. Chartered Accts., Ont. Inst. Chartered Accts., Oakville Curling Club, Islington Golf Club, Ont. Progressive Conservative-Cornerstone Club. Office: Doane Raymond, 200 Bay St, Toronto, ON Canada M5J 2P9

WHEELER, RAYMOND LOUIS, lawyer; b. Ft. Sill, Okla., Feb. 10, 1945; s. Raymond Louis and Dorothy Marie (Hutcherson) W.; m. Priscilla Wheeler, July 1, 1966 (div. 1982); children: Jennifer, Hilary; m. Cynthia Lee Jackson, July 14, 1984; children: Matthew Raymond, Madeline Elizabeth. BA, U. Tex., 1967; JD, Harvard U., 1970. Bar: Calif. 1972, U.S. Dist. Ct. no. dist. Calif. 1972, U.S. Ct. Appeals 5th cir. Calif. 1970-71; assoc. Morrison & Foerster, San Francisco, 1971-76, ptnr., 1976-90; ptnr. Morrison & Foerster, Palo Alto, Calif., 1990—; chmn. labor and employment law dept. Morrison & Foerster, San Francisco, 1984-88, 92—; lectr. labor and EEO law. Exec. editor Harvard Law Rev., 1969-70; editor in chief The Developing Labor Law; mem. nat. adv. bd. Indsl. Rels. Law Jour., 1980—; contbr. articles to law jours. Mem. ABA (chmn. com. on law devel. under labor rels. act 1990-93). Republican. Office: Morrison & Foerster 755 Page Mill Rd Palo Alto CA 94304-1018

WHEELER, R(ICHARD) KENNETH, lawyer; b. Washington, July 25, 1934; s. Nathaniel Dudley and Ruth Lee (Matthews) W.; m. Christine Kandris, Jan. 11, 1990; children by previous marriage: Jennifer L., Ruth E. BA, Emory and Henry Coll., U. Richmond, 1957; LLB, U. Richmond, 1964. Bar: Va. 1963, D.C. 1977. Assoc., then ptnr. Hunton, Williams, Gay, Powell & Gibson and successor firms, Richmond, 1963-88; sr. ptnr. Kane, Wheeler, Fenderson & Jeffries, Richmond, 1988-90; counsel Durrette, Irvin, Lemons & Fenderson, P.C., Richmond, 1990-94; ptnr. Wallace, Harris & Wheeler, Richmond, 1994—; adj. prof. law T.C. Williams Sch. Law, U. Richmond, 1966, 83, bd. dirs., 1977-79; adj. prof. law Va. Commonwealth U., 1970; lectr. trial practice U. Va., 1981-82, 85, 87; arbitrator Am. Arbitration Assn. Served to capt. USMCR, 1957-61. Williams scholar U. Richmond, 1961-63. Mem. ABA, Fed. Bar Assn., Nat. Assn. R.R. Trial Counsel, Am. Judicature Soc., Am. Law Inst., Va. State Bar (chmn. com. liaison with law schs. 1977-78, chmn. com. legal edn. and admission to bar 1978-80, spcl. com. on professionalism 1987-88), Va. Bar Assn., Bar Assn. D.C., Richmond Trial Lawyers Assn., Va. Trial Lawyers Assn., Richmond Bar Assn., Chesterfield-Colonial Heights Bar Assn., Henrico Bar Assn., Web Soc., McNeill Law Soc., Supreme Ct. Hist. Soc., Marine Corps League (life), Rector's Club (U. Richmond), Pi Sigma Alpha, Phi Delta Phi, Omicron Delta Kappa (hon.). Office: Wallace Harris & Wheeler 1100 Boulders Pky Ste 100 Richmond VA 23225-4035

WHEELER, RICHARD WARREN, banker; b. Boston, Feb. 8, 1929; s. Wilfrid and Sybil Constance (Leckenby) W.; m. Betty Ann Owens, Sept. 9, 1950; children: Emily, Susan Knight, Thomas Adams, Alice Owens, Sarah Bennett. BA, Williams Coll., 1952; PMD, Harvard Bus. Sch., 1962. With Citibank, N.A., 1952-82; assigned to Citibank, N.A., Hongkong, Manila and Tokyo, 1953-69, v.p., 1967-69, head Asia Pacific div., 1969-75, dep. overseas div., 1975-77; sr. v.p. Citibank, N.A., N.Y.C., 1969-82; head internat. relations unit Citibank, N.A., 1977-82; exec. v.p. Asia Soc., 1982-84; pres. Asia Internat. Bank, 1984-85; sr. v.p., gen. mgr. Bank of the Philippine Islands, N.Y.C., 1985-90; internat. fin. cons., 1991—. Bd. dirs. v.p. Am. Australian Assn., 1972-88; organizing dir. Nat. Coun. U.S.-China Trade; bd. dirs., chmn. exec. com. Presiding Bishop's Fund for World Relief, 1976-82; mem. Episcopal Church Standing Committee on Stewardship, 1978-84; mem. spl. refugee adv. panel Dept. State, 1982; chmn. adv. coun. Havard Ctr. for Study World Religions, 1974-89; mem. adv. bd. Georgetown Ctr. for Contemporary Arab Studies, 1977-79, Harvard U. Ctr. for East Asian Studies, 1971-76, Ctr. for Strategic and Internat. Studies, 1970-80; v.p. exec. coun. Harvard U. Bus. Sch., 1971-75; chmn. bus. and industry adv. coun. to OECD com. on capital markets and capital movements 1980-82; mem. exec. com. ASEAN-U.S. Bus. Coun., 1976-82, Sudan-U.S. Bus. Coun., India-U.S. Bus. coun., 1976-82, U.S.-Korea Econ. Coun., 1978-82, also pres., bd. dirs.; mem. exec. com. Philippine-Am. Found., 1987-92; chmn. adv. coun. Episc. Migration Ministries; trustee Cambridge Sch. Weston, Mass. With AUS, 1946-47. Mem. Japan Soc. (chmn. exec. com., bd. dirs. 1970-82), Nat. Planning Assn. (trustee, treas. 1976-82), Nat. Fgn. Trade Coun. (bd. dirs., exec. com. 1976-82), Internat. C. of C. (vice chmn., trustee U.S. coun. 1976-82), Philippine Am. C. of C. (v.p., bd. dirs. 1987-92), U.S. Assn. for Internat. Migration (pres., bd. dirs., exec. com. 1987-92, bd. assessors), Coun. on Fgn. Rels., Univ. Club, Bronxville Field Club, Hodegaya Golf Club, Tokyo Lawn Tennis Club. Episcopalian. Home: 99 Sudbury Rd Concord MA 01742-2421 Office: Wheeler Realty Trust 150 Wheeler Rd Marstons Mills MA 02648-1110

WHEELER, STANTON, law and social science educator; b. 1930. BA, Pomona Coll., 1952; MA, U. Wash., 1956, PhD, 1958. Instr. sociology U. Wash., 1956-58, assoc. prof. sociology, 1963-64; instr. social relations Harvard U., Cambridge, Mass., 1958-60, asst. prof. social relations, 1961-63; Fulbright research fellow U. Oslo, Norway, 1960-61; sociologist Russell Sage Found., 1964-68, cons., 1968—; adj. prof. Yale U., New Haven, 1965-68, prof., 1968—, Ford Found. prof. law and social scis., 1985—; fellow Ctr. Advanced Study in Behavioral Scis., Stanford (Calif.) U., 1970-71; pres. Amateur Athletic Found. L.A., 1985-87 (on leave). Mem. Am. Sociol. Assn., Soc. Study of Social Problems, Law and Soc. Assn. Office: Yale Law Sch Yale Ave # 401A New Haven CT 06515

WHEELER, THOMAS BEARDSLEY, insurance company executive; b. Buffalo, Aug. 2, 1936; s. William Henry and Ruth (Matthews) W.; m. Anne Tuck Robertson, Nov. 25, 1961; children: Elizabeth Wheeler Soule, Wendy Bennett. B.A., Yale U., 1958. C.L.U. Sales rep. IBM, White Plains, N.Y., 1961-62; sales rep., asst. gen. agt. Mass. Mut. Life Ins. Co., Boston, 1962, gen. agt., 1972-83; exec. v.p. Mass. Mut. Life Ins. Co., Springfield, 1983-86, pres., 1987-88, pres., chief exec. officer, 1988—; chmn. bd. dirs. Oppenheimer Acquisition Corp., Concert Capital Mgmt., Inc.; bd. dirs. Bank of Boston Corp., Textron, Inc.; pres. Jobs for Mass. Co-author: Managing Sales Professionals, 1984. Trustee Springfield Coll., 1985—; Am. Coll., Bryn Mawr, Pa., 1987-90, Baystate Health Systems, Inc., Springfield, 1983-92, Springfield Orch. Assn., Basketball Hall of Fame, Springfield; Mass. state chmn. U.S. Olympic Com. Lt. USNR, 1958-60. Mem. Yale Univ. Devel. Bd., Springfield Life Underwriter's Assn., Am. Soc. C.L.U.'s (Pioneer Valley chpt., pres. Boston chpt. 1980-81), Boston Underwriter's Assn. (pres. 1972-73), Mass. Assn. Life Underwriters (pres. 1976-77), Health Ins. Assn. Am. (bd. dirs. 1990-93), Million Dollar Round Table, Yale Club of N.Y., Colony (Springfield), Longmeadow Country Club, Boca Grande, Chapoquoit Yacht Club (sec. 1973-75), The Links (N.Y.C.). Republican. Avocations: skiing, boating, art, antiques, music. Office: Mass Mut Life Ins Co 1295 State St Springfield MA 01111-0001

WHEELER, THOMAS EDGAR, communications technology executive; b. Redlands, Calif., Apr. 5, 1946; s. Charles Taylor and Martha (Edgar) W.; married; children: Nicole Pierce, David Maxwell. B.S., Ohio State U., 1968. Asst. dir. Ohio State U. Alumni Assn., Columbus, 1968-69; v.p. Grocery Mfrs. Am., Inc., Washington, 1969-76; exec. v.p. Nat. Cable TV Assn., Washington, 1976-79, pres., chief exec. officer, 1979-85; pres., chief exec. officer NABU: The Home Computer Network, 1985-86; chmn., chief exec. officer NuCable Resources Corp., Washington, 1986—; pres., dir. Media Enterprises Corp., 1982—; pres., chief exec. officer Cellular Telecommunications Industry Assn., 1992—; bd. dirs. NuMedia Corp. Bd. trustees John F. Kennedy Ctr. for Performing Arts; bd. dirs. Vincent T. Lombardi Found.; Cibernet Corp., Cellular Found., Inc., Youth Serve Am. Democrat. Office: Cellular Telecom Ind Assn 1133 21st St NW Washington DC 20036-3390

WHEELER, TIMOTHY ARNEAL, assistant superintendent; b. Carrollton, Ga., Aug. 26, 1943; s. Ronnie Arneal and Lizzie Lillian (Huckeba) W.; m. Frances Ethelyn Massey, Dec. 20, 1970; children: Martha Marie, Ethelyn Anne, Wesley Arneal. AB, W. Ga. Coll., 1966; MS, Ga. So. Coll., 1970; EdS, U. Ga., 1979. Cert. tchr., adminstr., Ga. Band dir., fine arts coord. Douglas County Sch. System, Douglasville, Ga., 1966-76; music dir. Jefferson City (Ga.) Schs., 1976-77; elem. prin. Jackson County Schs., Jefferson,

Ga., 1977-79; high sch. prin. Jackson County Schs., Jefferson, 1979-80, supt., 1980-88; supt. Carroll County Sch. System, Carrollton, Ga., 1988-90, bond dir. Stephens County Sch. System, Toccoa, Ga., 1990-91; asst. supt. Elbert County Sch. System, Elberton, Ga., 1991—; music dir. Midway United Meth. Ch., Douglasville, Ga., 1966-76, '90, Jefferson 1st United Meth. Ch., 1976-88, '92—; cons. So. Assn. Colls. and Schs., 1990—; adj. prof. W. Ga. Coll., 1989—; judge at many parades and band festivals. Presenter Pub. Broadcasting System, Curriculum Issues in Ga., 1986. Vice chmn. Carroll County Bd. Health, Carrollton, 1990; mem. Jackson County Bd. Health, Jackson County Child Abuse Task Force, adv. coun. Sch. Edn. W. Ga. Coll., Carrollton, 1988-90, Emmanuel Coll., Franklin Springs, Ga., 1992—. Named Man of Yr. Douglas County C. of C., 1969, Hon. Chpt. Mem., FHA Jackson County Comprehensive High Sch., 1980, FFA, 1981, Outstanding Educator, Ga. Art Edn. Assn., 1983; recipient Leadership award, Phi Delta Kappa, 1990, Carroll County Ednl. Found., 1990; bands he directed were honored many times including invitation to play at Presidential inauguration, 1972. Mem. ASCD, Ga. Assn. Supervision and Curriculum Devel., Ga. Sch. Bds. Assn., Ga. Assn. Sch. Supts. (bd. dirs. 1985-87, pres. 9th dist. assn. 1985-86), Ga. Assn. Ednl. Leaders, Elbert County C. of C., Phi Delta Kappa. Methodist. Home: 2274 Old Kings Bridge Rd Nicholson GA 30565-2912 Office: Elbert County Bd Edn 50 Laurel Dr Elberton GA 30635-1842

WHEELER, WARREN G(AGE), JR., retired publishing executive; b. Boston, Dec. 6, 1921; s. Warren Gage and Helen (Hoagl) W.; m. Jean Frances Moseley, Feb. 22, 1945; children: Richard, Michael, Ann, Duncan. B.S., Bowdoin Coll., 1943; B.J., U. Mo., 1947, M.A., 1948. With South Bend (Ind.) Tribune (name changed to Schurz Communications, Inc. 1976), 1948-82, gen. mgr., 1964-71, exec. v.p., 1971-75, pres., 1975-82. Campaign chmn. United Community Services, South Bend, 1960, pres., 1946 treas. South Bend Urban League, 1962-63; trustee St. Joseph's Hosp., South Bend, 1969-77; gen. chmn. St. Joseph County (Ind.) Hosp. Devel., 1969-71; deacon, elder, pres. session 1st Presbyn. Ch., South Bend; chmn. trustees United Ch. of Marco Island, 1992-93. Served with USN, 1943-46. Protestant recipient Brotherhood award South Bend-Mishawaka chpt. NCCJ, 1970. Mem. Am. Newspaper Pubs. Assn., Am. Mgmt. Assn., Newspaper Personnel Relations Assn. (pres. 1955-56), Hoosier State Press Assn. (dir. 1967-70), Inland Daily Press Assn. (pres. 1972, pres. found. 1974-78), Sailing Assn. Marco Island, South Bend Press Club, Signal Point Club, Hideaway Beach Golf and Tennis Club, Sigma Delta Chi, Kappa Tau Alpha, Kappa Mu. Home: 6000 Royal Marco Way Apt 657 Marco Island FL 33937-1886

WHEELER, WESLEY DREER, marine engineer, naval architect, consultant; b. N.Y.C., Aug. 3, 1933; s. Wesley Lunn and Rosalie (Smith) W.; m. Dolores Janes-Wheeler, May 27, 1989; children: Wesley P., Jonathan H., Deborah B. BS in Mech. Engring., Worcester Poly. Inst., 1954; MSE in Naval Architecture and Marine Engring., U. Mich., 1958. Naval architect Am. Bulk Carriers, N.Y.C., 1966-68; port engr. Am. Trade and Prodn. Co., N.Y.C., 1968-69; pres. Techmarine, Inc., N.Y.C., 1969-71; asesor tecnico Astilleros Espanoles SA, Cadiz, Spain, 1971-72; tech. dir. Am. Bulk Carriers, N.Y.C., 1972-74; pres. Wesley D. Wheeler Assoc., Ltd., N.Y.C., 1974-83; v.p. J.J. Henry Co. Inc., N.Y.C., 1983; pres. Wheeler Assocs., N.Y.C., 1983—; Am. rep. Blohm & Voss, Astilleros Españoles, Dakar Marine, Shanghai Shipyard, Tandanor. Elder and trustee Fifth Ave. Presbyn. Ch., N.Y.C., sec.; dir. Sutton Area Community, N.Y.C., Soc. Naval Architects and Marine Engrs., N.Y.C., 1990-92, treas.; chmn. Soc. Marine Cons., N.Y.C., 1987-94. Mem. Maritime Assn. Port of N.Y./N.J., Soc. Marine Port Engrs. N.Y., Soc. Maritime Arbitrators Inc., Royal Inst. Naval Architects, Inst. Marine Engrs., Asociacion Ingenieros Navales Madrid. Presbyterian. Avocations: boating, skiing, tennis, golf, travel. Home: 60 Sutton Pl S New York NY 10022-4168

WHEELER, WILLIAM CRAWFORD, agricultural engineer, educator; b. Maysville, Ga., Feb. 19, 1914; s. James D. and Pearl (Chandler) W.; B.S. in Agrl. Engring., U. Ga., 1940; student U. Tenn., 1941-42; M.S. in Agrl. Engring., Va. Polytech. Inst., 1951; postgrad. Mich State U., 1954-55; m. Annie Adams, May 23, 1942; children—Betty Catherine, James David. Supr. farm Ga. Vocational and Trade Sch., Monroe, 1932-36, instr. farm mechanics, 1940-41; jr. engr. U.S. Dept. Agr. Soil Conservation Service, Monroe; instr. dept. agrl. engrng. U. Tenn., 1941-42, asso. prof. agrl. engr-ing., 1946-53, specializing in rural electrification; prof. agrl. engring. U. Conn., 1953-72, head dept., 1953-69, prof. emeritus, 1972—; sabbatical leave for waste disposal study in Europe and Can., 1969; conducted summer course in farm mechanics U. Ark., Fayetteville, 1948; partner Lynwood Devels., Storrs, Conn. Mem. N.E. Regional Research Techn. Com. on Poultry Housing, 1953-65, Com. on Mechanization of Forage Crops, 1954-58; com. on Mechanization of Fruit and Vegetable Harvest, 1959-71, Com. on Improvement Efficiency in Harvesting Apples, 1966-71; chmn. projects com. Conn. Electrification Council, 1953-66; mem. farm electric service com. N.E. Council, 1953-72; mem. water resources Inst. U. Conn., 1964-69. Served as maj. 329th inf. 83d Div., U.S. Army, 1942-46. Decorated Bronze Star, Purple Heart. Registered engr., Tenn. Fellow Am. Soc. Agrl. Engrs. (chmn. North Atlantic sect. 1962); mem. Am. Soc. Engring. Edn., Nat. Soc. Profl. Engrs., Alpha Zeta, Scabbard and Blade, Gridiron, Aghon, Gamma Sigma Delta. Conglist. (chmn. council 1964). Author articles in field. Home: 1116 Linkside Dr Atlantic Beach FL 32233-4387

WHEELER, WILMOT FITCH, JR., diversified manufacturing company executive; b. Southport, Conn., June 5, 1923; s. Wilmot Fitch and Hulda Day (Chapman) W.; m. Barbara Rutherford, Sept. 30, 1944 (dec. Sept. 1971); children: Wilmot Fitch III, James Alexander, John R. (dec.), Susan; m. Nonnye Landers, Dec. 20, 1973; children: Tracy Lynne, Alexa Margaret. BA, Yale U., 1945; postgrad., NYU, 1947-48. Staff engr. Stevenson, Jordan & Harrison, Inc. (mgmt. cons.), 1946-51; with Am. Chain & Cable Co., Inc., N.Y.C., 1951-76; pres., chmn., chief exec. officer Am. Chain & Cable Co., Inc., 1967-76; chmn., dir. Jelliff Corp., Southport, Conn., 1976—; prin. Case & Co. Inc. (mgmt. cons.), 1977-82; trustee Dollar Savs. Bank, 1974-83, chmn., chief exec. officer, 1982-83; chmn., trustee, chief exec. officer Dollar Dry Dock Savs. Bank, 1983-84; chmn. bd. dirs., CEO Manhattan Nat. Corp., 1986-87, vice-chmn. 1987-90; bd. dirs. People's Bank, Conn.; trustee People's Mut. Holdings, Bridgeport Hosp. Bd. dirs. Wilmot T. Morris Found., Wilmot Wheeler Found., Sormir Petroleum Inc. With AUS, 1943-46. Decorated Bronze Star. Episcopalian. Clubs: Yale (N.Y.C.), Sky (N.Y.C.); Country of Fairfield. Home: PO Box 429 Southport CT 06490-0429 Office: Jelliff Corp PO Box 758 354 Pequot Ave Southport CT 06490-1345

WHEELOCK, ARTHUR KINGSLAND, JR., art historian; b. Worcester, Mass., May 13, 1943; s. Arthur Kingsland and Anne (Kneass) W.; m. Susan Hoffman, June 13, 1964 (div. June 1988); children: Arthur Tobey, Laura, Matthew; m. Perry Carpenter Swain, Aug. 24, 1991. BA, Williams Coll., 1965; PhD, Harvard U., 1973. Instr. Bement Sch., Deerfield, Mass., 1965-66; asst. prof. art history U. Md., College Park, 1974-84, assoc. prof., 1984-88, prof., 1988—; David E. Finley fellow Nat. Gallery Art, Washington, 1971-74; research curator Nat. Gallery Art, 1974-75, curator Dutch and Flemish painting, 1976-84, curator No. Baroque painting, 1984—; cons. Centraal Laboratorium voor Onderzoek van Voorwerpen van Kunst en Wetenschap, Amsterdam, 1969-70. Author: Perspective; Optics and Delft Artists around 1650, 1977, Jan Vermeer, 1981, 2nd rev. edit., 1988, Dutch Painting in the Age of Rembrandt, 1984; co-author: exhbn. catalogue Gods, Saints and Heroes: Dutch Painting in the Age of Rembrandt, 1980, British Painting in the National Gallery of Art, 1987, Masterworks from Munich: Sixteenth-to Eighteenth-Century Paintings from the Alte Pinakothek, 1988, Still Lifes of the Golden Age: Northern European Paintings from the Heinz Family Collection, 1989, Anthony Van Dyck, 1990; contbr. exhbn. catalogue Leonardo's Last Supper: Precedents and Reflections, 1984, Images of Reality, Images of Arcadia: Seventeenth-century Netherlandish Paintings from Swiss Collections, Art for the Nation: Gifts in Honor of the 50th Anniversary of the National Gallery of Art, 1989; contbr. articles and revs. to profl. jours. and encys. Decorated Knight officer Order Orange-Nassau (Netherlands); NDEA fellow, 1967-70; Nat. Endowment Arts grantee, 1979-80; Nat. Gallery Art curatorial fellow Ctr. Advanced Study Visual Arts, 1983-84, 87-88, Robert H. Smith curatorial rsch. fellow, 1990. Mem. Coll. Art Assn. Democrat. Episcopalian. Office: National Gallery Art Washington DC 20565

WHEELOCK, LARRY ARTHUR, engineer, consultant; b. Chgo., Nov. 20, 1938; s. Preston J. and Rozella (Schonert) W.; m. Ruth E. Pruess (div. Sept. 1975); children: John P., J. Robert, William D., Thomas K.; m. Norma Jane Fair, Oct. 22, 1984. BSEE, U. Evansville, 1962. Registered profl. engr., Ind.; cert. instrument rated comml. pilot, airframe and powerplant mechanic, FAA. Co-op student engr. Naval Avionics Facility, Indpls., 1958-59; co-op student engr. Naval Weapons Support Ctr., Crane, Ind., 1959-62, elec. engr., 1963-78; elec. engr. Delco Electronics, Kokomo, Ind., 1962-63; sr. mfg. eng. Ford Aerospace & Comm., Bedford, Ind., 1979-80; plant engr. Ethyl Corp., Terre Haute, Ind., 1980-81; plant mgr. Tredegar Industries/Ethyl Corp., Terre Haute, 1981-91. Patentee in field. Pres. Hulman Regional Airport Authority, 1992, Greene County Airport Bd. Commrs., Bloomfield, Ind., 1972-81. Mem. IEEE, NSPE, Aircraft Owners & Pilots Assn., Exptl. Aircraft Assn., Antique Aircraft Assn., Mensa, Internat. Fellowship of Flying Rotarians, Rotary Internat. Avocations: aviation, agriculture, mechanics, amateur radio, computers. Home: 7480 State Road 42 Terre Haute IN 47803-9778

WHEELOCK, MAJOR WILLIAM, JR., college administrator; b. Fall River, Mass., Dec. 12, 1936; s. Major William and Mildred Mary (Rogers) W.; m. Rita Pauline Gauthier, Feb. 22, 1962; children: Major William III, Nancy Beth. B.S., Providence Coll., 1958. Budget examiner, spl. asst. to asst. sec. of Navy Washington, 1963-66; legis. analyst, budget examiner Bur. of Budget, Exec. Office of Pres., Washington, 1966-71; exec. asst. to the gov. State of N.H., 1971-73; supt. N.H. Hosp., Concord, 1973-77; preceptor George Washington U. Sch. Hosp. Adminstrn.; exec. dir. N.H. Charitable Fund, Concord, 1977-78; pres. Rumford Nat. Graphics, Inc., Concord, 1978-82; sr. v.p. N.H. Savs. Bank, 1982-85; exec. v.p. Franklin Pierce Coll., Rindge, N.H., 1985—; trustee N.H. Savs. Bank, 1981-83; bd. dirs. Yankee Pub. Co. Inc., Peterborough, Fall River, Mass., 1957-58; bd. dirs. N.H. Indsl. Devel. Authority, 1972-75; bd. dirs. Community Health Care Assn., 1974-75, v.p., 1976; bd. dirs. N.H. Mental Health Assn., 1979-82, pres., 1980-82; bd. dirs. Crotched Mountain Found., 1980—; bd. dirs. N.H. Coun. for Humanities, 1980-86, chmn., 1984-86; bd. dirs. N.H. Social Welfare Coun., 1983-90—, pres., 1986-90; bd. dirs. New Eng. Found. Humanities, 1990—, Monadnock Family Svcs., 1990—, Monadnock Comm. Day Care Ctr., 1992—. Served with U.S. Army, 1959-61. Named N.H. Citizen of Yr., 1977; recipient Bancroft award N.H. Psychiat. Soc., 1977, Granite State award Plymouth State Coll., 1987. Mem. N.H. Hosp. Assn., Am. Coll. Hosp. Adminstrs. Roman Catholic. Clubs: Concord Country (pres. 1976-77), Keene Country (1986—); Lodge: Rotary (v.p. 1982-83, pres. 1983-84). Office: Crockett Mountain Foundation 1 Verny Dr Greenfield NH 03047 Office: College Rd Rindge NH 03461

WHEELON, ALBERT DEWELL, physicist; b. Moline, Ill., Jan. 18, 1929; s. Orville Albert and Alice Geltz (Dewell) W.; m. Nancy Helen Hermanson, Feb. 28, 1953 (dec. May 1980); children—Elizabeth Anne, Cynthia Helen; m. Cicely J. Evans, Feb. 4, 1984. B.Sc., Stanford U., 1949; Ph.D., Mass. Inst. Tech., 1952. Teaching fellow, then rsch. assoc. physics MIT, Boston, 1949-52; with Douglas Aircraft Co., 1952-53, Ramo-Wooldridge Corp., 1953-62; dep. dir. sci. and tech. CIA, Washington, 1962-66; with Hughes Aircraft Co., L.A., 1966-88, chmn., chief exec. officer, 1987-88; vis. prof. MIT, 1989; mem. Def. Sci. Bd., 1968-76; mem. Pres.'s Fgn. Intelligence, 1983-88; mem. Presdl. Commn. on Space Shuttle Challenger Accident, 1986; trustee Aerospace Corp., 1990-93, Calif. Inst. Tech., Rand Corp. Author 30 papers on radio-wave propagation and guidance systems. Recipient R.V. Jones Intelligence award, 1994. Fellow IEEE, AIAA (Von Karman medal 1986); mem. NAE, Am. Phys. Soc., Sigma Chi. Republican. Episcopalian. Address: 181 Sheffield Dr Montecito CA 93108

WHEELWRIGHT, STEVEN C., religious organization administrator, business educator; b. Salt Lake City, Sept. 13, 1943; s. Max and Deborah Ann (Coulam) W.; m. Margaret Steele, Dec. 21, 1965; children: Marianne, Melinda, Kristen, Matthew, Spencer. BS, U. Utah, 1966; MBA, Stanford U., 1969, PhD, 1970. Asst. prof. European Inst. Bus. Adminstrn., France, 1970-71; assoc. prof. Harvard U., Cambridge, Mass., 1971-73, 74-79; v.p. mktg. Wheelwright Lithographing, Utah, 1973-74; prof. Stanford (Calif.) U., 1979-88, Harvard U., Cambridge, MA, 1988—; bd. dirs. TJ Internat., Allegheny Ludlum Corp., Quantum Corp. Co-author: (with Spyros G. Makridakis) Computer-Aided Modeling for Managers, 1972, Forecasting Methods for Management, 1973, (with Spyros G. Makridakis and V. McGee) Forecasting Methods and Applications, 1988, (with Robert H. Hayes) Restoring Our Competitive Edge: Competing Through Manufacturing, 1984; (with Hayes and Kim B. Clark) Dynamic Manufacturing: Creating the Learning Organization, 1988, (with Kim B. Clark) Revolutionizing Product Development, 1992, Managing New Product and Process Development, 1993, Leading Product Development, 1995, (with Robert A. Burgelman and Modesto Maidique), Stategic Management of Technology and Innovation, 1995; co-editor: (with Spyros G. Makridakis) Handbook of Forecasting, 1987; assoc. editor various jours. Fellow Decision Scis. Inst. Office: Harvard U Bus Sch Boston MA 02163

WHELAN, ELIZABETH ANN MURPHY, epidemiologist; b. N.Y.C., Dec. 4, 1943; d. Joseph and Marion (Barrett) Murphy; m. Stephen T. Whelan, Apr. 3, 1971; 1 child, Christine B. BA, Conn. Coll., 1965; MPH, Yale U., 1967; MS, Harvard U., 1968, ScD, 1971. Coordinator County study Planned Parenthood, 1971-72; research assoc. Harvard Sch. Pub. Health, Boston, 1975-80; exec. dir. Am. Council Sci. and Health, N.Y.C., 1980-92, pres., 1992—; mem. com. on pesticides and toxics EPA; mem. U.S. Com. of Vital Stats., HHS; mem. Nat. Adv. Com. on Meat and Poultry Inspection, USDA; guest lectr. Queen Elizabeth II (Cunard Line). Author: Sex and Sensibility, 1973, Making Sense Out of Sex, 1974, Panic in the Pantry, 1975, 92, A Baby?...Maybe, 1975, Boy or Girl?, 1976, The Pregnancy Experience, 1977, Preventing Cancer, 1978, The Nutrition Hoax, 1983, A Smoking Gun, 1984, Toxic Terror, 1984, 86, 93, Balanced Nutrition, 1988; contbr. articles to profl. jours. and consumer publs. Bd. dirs. Food and Drug Law Inst., Nat. Agrl. Legal Fund, Media Inst., N.Y. divsn. Am. Cancer Soc. Recipient Disting. Achievement medal Conn. Coll., 1979, award Harvard U., 1994/95. Mem. APHA (Early Career award 1982, Homer Calver award 1992), Am. Inst. Nutrition, Am. Med. Writers Assn. (Walter Alvarez award 1986), U.S. Com. Vital Stats. Office: Am Council Sci and Health 1995 Broadway 2nd FL New York NY 10023-5882

WHELAN, FRANCIS C., federal judge; b. O'Neill, Nebr., Dec. 11, 1907; s. Edward H. and Susan (Quilty) W.; m. Patricia Brophy Lawo, Feb. 25, 1978. Student, San Diego State Coll., 1925-28; LL.B., U. Calif., 1932. Bar: Calif. 1932. Pvt. practice San Diego, 1932-35, Los Angeles, 1948-61; asst. U.S. atty., 1935-39; spl. asst. Dept. Justice; also spl. asst. to U.S. atty. gen., 1939-48; U.S. atty. So. Dist. Calif., 1961-64; U.S. dist. judge Central Dist. Calif., 1964—; now sr. judge. Mem. ABA, Los Angeles County Bar Assn., Am. Judicature Soc. Roman Catholic. Club: K.C. Office: US Dist Ct 47176 El Agadir Palm Desert CA 92260-5806

WHELAN, JAMES ROBERT, communications executive, international trade and investment consultant, author, educator; b. Buffalo, July 27, 1933; s. Robert and Margaret (Southard) W.; children from previous marriage: Robert J., Heather Elizabeth; m. Guadalupe Aguirre, 1990. Student, U. Buffalo, 1951-53, U. R.I., 1955-57; BA, Fla. Internat. U., 1974. Staff corr., fgn. corr., country mgr., divsn. mgr. UPI, Buffalo, 1952-53; staff corr., fgn. corr., country mgr., div. mgr. UPI, Providence, 1955-57, Boston, 1957-58, Buenos Aires, Argentina, 1958-61, Caracas, Venezuela, 1961-66, San Juan, P.R., 1966, 68; regional dir. corp. rels., then v.p. ops. ITT World Directories, ITT, San Juan, 1968-70; Latin Am. corr. Scripps-Howard Newspaper Alliance, Washington, 1970-71; mng. editor Miami (Fla.) News, 1971-73; freelance writer, 1973-74; freelance writer Hialeah (Fla.) Pub. Co., 1975-77; v.p., editl. dir. Panax Corp., Washington, 1977-80; v.p., editor Sacramento Union, 1980-82; editor, pub. Washington Times, 1982-84; mng. dir. CBN News, 1985-86; pres Capital Comm. Internat., 1986—; editor-in-chief Conservative Digest, 1988-89; vice chmn. Inter-Am. Found., Arlington, Va., 1991-94; cons. external affairs advisor Inter-Am. Investment Corp., 1992-93; dir. strategic planning Cocotel Holding, Santiago, Chile, 1993-94; pres. Minera Silver Standard S.A., 1994—; vis. prof. Polit. Sci. Inst., U. Chile, 1993—; assoc. prof. Finis Terrae U., 1993—; adj. prof. U. Md., 1993; guest lectr. ednl. instns. including Boston U., U. Miami, Ctrl. U. Venezuela, Cath. U., Andres Bello U., Chile, U. Chile, U. Tex., Austin, U. Concepcion, U. Santi-

ago; guest prof. U. Fla., 1973. Author: Through the American Looking Glass; Central America's Crisis, 1980, Allende: Death of a Marxis: Dream, 1981, Catastrophe in the Caribbean: The Failure of America's Human Rights Policy in Central America, 1984, The Soviet Assault on America's Southern Flank, 1988, Out of the Ashes: Life, Death and Transfiguration of Democracy in Chile, 1833-1988, 1989, Hunters in the Sky, 1991, Desde las Cenizas: Vida, Muerte y Transfiguracion de la Democracia en Chile, 1833-1988, 1993. Bd. dirs. Christian Community Service Agy., Miami, 1973, Hialeah-Miami Springs (Fla.) C. of C., 1976-77, Wolf Trap Found., 1984-87; bd. dirs. Nat. Council for Better Edn.; chmn. print media div. United Way campaign, Sacramento, 1981; bd. govs. Council on Nat. Policy, Washington, 1981-87; del. Commn. of Californias, 1981; chmn. Council for Inter-Am. Security Ednl. Inst., 1986-90; mem. spl. task force on pub. safety Greater Washington Bd. Trade; mem. Nat. Commn. on Free and Responsible Media, 1983-84; bd. dirs. Nat. Bus. Consortium for Gifted and Talented Children, 1985-87; bd. govs. Internat. Policy Forum, 1985—; mem. Presdl. Bd. Fgn. Scholarships (Fulbright Commn.). 1986-92, exec. planning com., 1987-92. With Signal Corps U.S. Army, 1953-55. Nieman fellow Harvard U., 1966-67; recipient citation of excellence Overseas Press Club, 1971, Unity award Lincoln U., 1976, Golden Press award Am. Legion Aux., 1977, Freedom award Valley Forge Found., 1981, Bernardo O'Higgins award Chilean Govt., 1990, presented at Chilean Embassy by Amb. Octavio Errazuriz. Mem. Nat. Press Club, Overseas Press Club, Univ. Club (Washington), Georgetown Club, Cosmos Club, Harvard Club (N.Y.C.), Club de la Union, Club de Ofcls. de La Fuerza Aerea (Santiago), Club Militar Lo Curro (Santiago). Home: Apt 902, Hernando de Aguirre 731, Providencia Santiago Chile

WHELAN, JOHN MARTIN, insurance executive; b. Phila., Aug. 22, 1944; s. John Martin and Catherine (Clarke) W.; m. Kathleen Rosamond, Apr. 11, 1970; children: Erika, Beth, Maura, John. BS, Drexel U., 1966; MBA, Columbia U., 1972. With corp. n. bus. devel. Continental Group, N.Y.C., 1970-71; mgr. mgmt. consulting Peat Marwick Mitchell & Co., Chgo., 1972-79; dir. Golden Rule Fin. Corp., Lawrenceville, Ill., 1983—, pres., chief operating officer, 1979-90, pres., chief exec. officer, 1990—, v.p., chief operating officer, chief operating officer, 1979-83, bd. dirs., pres., chief operating officer, 1983-90; pres., chief exec. officer, bd. dirs. Golden Rule Ins. Co., Lawrenceville, IL, 1990—; bd. dirs. Ad-Ventures, Indpls., 1985—; chmn. bd. dirs. All Savers Ins. Co. & Value Ins., Indpls, 1986—; pres., bd. dirs. Cen. States Securities Inc., Indpls., 1983—; bd. dirs., sec.-treas. Exec. Systems Inc., Indpls, 1983—; bd. dirs., v.p. M.A. Rooney, Indpls., 1984—. Bd. dirs. Vols. in Prevention, Probation & Prisons, Inc., Royal Oak, Mich., Greater Indpls. Progress Com., U.S. Bus. & Indsl. Coun., Washington; chmn. bd. Health & Hosp. Corp., Indpls. Capt. USAF, 1968-70. Named Sagamore of the Wabash, Gov. of Ind., 1990. Mem. Legatus. Roman Catholic. Avocations: golf, swimming. Office: Golden Rule Ins Co 7440 Woodland Dr Indianapolis IN 46278-1720

WHELAN, JOHN WILLIAM, lawyer, educator, consultant; b. Cleve., Apr. 23, 1922; s. Walter Edmund and Stacia Miriam W.; m. Maryrose Shields, May 29, 1947; children: Moira Ann Whelan Dykstra, Thomas M. AB, John Carroll U., 1943; JD, Georgetown U., 1948. Assoc. prof. law Columbus U., Washington, 1948-50; asst. prof. law U. Va., Charlottesville, 1955-56; asso. prof. law U. Wis., Madison, 1956-59; prof. law Georgetown U., Washington, 1959-67, U. Calif., Davis, 1967-75, Hastings Coll. Law U. Calif., San Francisco, 1975-91; prof. emeritus Hastings Coll. Law U. Calif., San Francisco, 1991—; vis. prof. Ninon U. Coll. Law, Tokyo, summer 1989; cons. to atty. gen. Trust Ty. Pacific Islands, 1976-78; mem. atomic energy com. Bd. Contract Appeals, 1965-73; hearing examiner Medi-Cal Fiscal Intermediary Contract, 1979-82; adminstrn. law judge constrn. contracts Trust Ter. Pacific Island, 1984-86; cons. on govt. contracts to Polish govt., 1992. Author: (with R.S. Pasley) Federal Government Contracts, 1975; (with K.H. York) Insurance, 1983, 2d edit., 1988, Federal Government Contracts, 1985, Supplement, 1989, Understanding Government Contracts, 1994; (with K.H. York, Leo Martinez) Insurance, 3rd edit., 1994; editor: Yearbook of Procurement Articles, 1965-90; mem. editl. bd. Pub. Procurement Law Rev. (U.K. pub.), 1991—; contbr. articles to profl. jours. Served with infl. AUS, 1943-45; served with J.A.G., 1950-55., Decorated Bronze Star; Ford Found. grantee, 1958-59, 63-64, summer 1970. Mem. ABA, Fed. Bar Assn., D.C. Bar Assn., Nat. Contract Mgmt. Assn. Home: 306 Bristol Pl Mill Valley CA 94941-4005 Office: U Calif Hastings Coll Law 200 Mcallister St San Francisco CA 94102

WHELAN, JOSEPH L(EO), neurologist; b. Chisholm, Minn., Aug. 13, 1917; s. James Gorman and Johanna (Quilty) W.; m. Gloria Ann Rewoldt, June 12, 1948; children: Joe, Jennifer. Student, Hibbing Jr. Coll., 1935-38; BS, U. Minn., 1940, MB, 1942, MD, 1943. Diplomate Am. Bd. Psychiatry and Neurology. Intern Detroit Receiving Hosp., 1942-43; fellow neurology U. Pa. Hosp., Phila., 1946-47; resident neurology U. Minn. Hosps., Mpls., 1947-49; chief neurology svc. VA Hosp., Mpls., 1949; spl. fellow electroencephalography Mayo Clinic, Rochester, Minn., 1951; practice medicine specializing in neurology Detroit, 1949-73, Petoskey and Gaylord, Mich., 1973-87; asst. prof. Wayne State U., 1957-63; chief neurology svcs. Grace Hosp., St. John's Hosp., Bon Secour Hosp. Detroit; cons. neurologist No. Mich. Hosps., Charlevoix Area Hosp.; instr. Med. Sch. U. Minn., 1949; cons. USPHS, Detroit Bd. Edn. Contbr. articles to profl. jours. Founder, mem. ad hoc Com. to Force Lawyers Out of Govt. Fellow Am. Acad. Neurology (treas. 1955-57), Am. Electroencephalography Soc.; mem. AMA, AAAS, Assn. Rsch. Nervous and Mental Diseases, Soc. Clin. Neurologists, Mich. Neurol. Assn. (sec.-treas. 1967-76, Disting. Physician award 1988), Mich. Med. Soc., No. Mich. Med. Soc., Grosse Pointe (Mich.) Club. Address: Oxbow 9797 Twin Lake Rd NE Mancelona MI 49659-9202

WHELAN, KAREN MAE LEPPO, manufacturing executive; b. Lancaster, Pa., Mar. 20, 1947; children: Katherine, John. BA, U. Pitts., 1967; MS in Bus., Va. Commonwealth U., 1977. Sr. acct. Arthur Young, Richmond, Va., 1977-80; various positions, advanced to v.p. fin. reporting James River Corp., Richmond, 1980-92; v.p., treas. Universal Corp, Richmond, 1993—. Mem. AICPA (Elijah Watts Sells award 1976), Nat. Investor Rels. Inst., Fin. Execs. Inst., Va. Soc. CPAs (cert. CPA, gold medal award 1976). Office: Universal Corp 1501 N Hamilton St Richmond VA 23219

WHELAN, MICHAEL RAYMOND, artist, illustrator; b. Culver City, Calif., June 29, 1950; s. William Raymond and Nancy (Sloet) W.; m. Diana Marie Thomas, July 27, 1972 (div. Apr. 1977); m. Audrey Elise Price, Dec. 24, 1978; children: Alexa Mari Price-Whelan, Adrian Michael Price-Whelan. BA, San Jose State U., 1973; postgrad., Art Ctr. Coll. Design, 1974. Freelance illustrator, Conn., 1974—. Author: Wonderworks, 1979, Michael Whelan's Works of Wonder, 1987. Recipient 10 Hugo awards World SF Conv., 1979-88, 3 Howard awards World Fantasy Conv., 1981, 82, 83, many others. Mem. Nat. Assn. Fantastic Art (v.p. 1984—), Soc. Illustrators, Graphic Artists Guild, Assn. Sci. Fiction and Fantasy Artists, Sci. Fiction Writers Am., Chinese-Okinawan Karate Assn. Avocations: oriental martial arts, traveling, computers, astronautics, electronic music. Office: PO Box 88 Brookfield CT 06804-0088

WHELAN, RICHARD J., director special education and pediatrics programs, academic administrator; b. Emmett, Kans, June 23, 1931; s. Richard Joseph and Margaret Alma (Cox) W.; m. Carol Ann King, Nov. 21, 1959; children—Mark Richard, Cheryl Lynne. B.A., Washburn U., 1955; Ed.D., U. Kans., 1966. Dir. edn. Menninger Clinic, Topeka, Kans., 1959-62; dir. edn. children's rehab. unit U. Kans. Med. Ctr., Kansas City, Kans., 1966—; prof. spl. edn. and pediatrics, chmn. dept. spl. edn. U. Kans., Lawrence, 1966-72, 78-80, 83-88, assoc. dean grad. studies and outreach, 1988-94, Ralph L. Smith disting. prof. child devel., 1968—, dean sch. edn., 1992-94; dir. div. U.S. Office Edn., Washington, 1972-74; cons. colls. and univs., state and fed. agys.; chmn. policy bd. Evaluation Tng., Kalamazoo, 1975-81. Author, editor: Promising Practices..., 1983; cons. editor Ednl. Research Ency., 1982; contbr. articles to profl. jours., chpts. to books. Chmn. adv. bd. Kans. Bd. Edn., Topeka, 1982-92; mem. adv. bd. Shawnee Mission Sch. Dist., Kans., 1984-92; mem. Gov.'s Task Force on Early Childhood, 1984-92; hearing officer various sch. dists. Served with U.S. Army, 1952-54. Mem. Soc. for Learning Disabilities (pres. 1980-81), Council for Exceptional Children, Assn. for Persons with Severe Handicaps (bd. dirs. 1975-79), Kans. Council for Exceptional Children (pres. 1963-64, Service award 1978), Phi Kappa Phi. Avocations: reading, music, golf, running, flying. Home: 7204 High Dr Shawnee Mission KS 66208-3355 Office: U Kans Med Ctr 39th and Rainbow Sts Kansas City KS 66160-7335

WHELAN, ROGER MICHAEL, lawyer, educator; b. Montclair, N.J., Nov. 12, 1936; s. John Leslie and Helen Louise (Callahan) W.; m. Rosemary Bogdan, Aug. 26, 1961; children: Helen, Theresa, John, James, Kathleen (dec.), Julie, Jennifer. AB cum laude, Georgetown U., 1959, JD, 1962. Bar: D.C. 1962, U.S. Dist. Ct. D.C. 1962, U.S. Ct. Appeals (D.C. cir.) 1962, U.S. Supreme Ct. 1968, U.S. Dist. Ct. Md. 1985. Assoc. Fried, Rogers & Ritz, Washington, 1961-66; ptnr. Doctor & Whelan, Washington, 1967-72; judge U.S. Bankruptcy Ct., Washington, 1972-83; sr. mem. Verner, Liipfert, Bernhard, McPherson & Hand, Chartered, Washington, 1984-89; sr. counsel Shaw, Pittman, Potts & Trowbridge, Washington, 1989—; dir. Lincoln Ctr. for Legal Studies, Arlington, Va., 1974-84; disting. lectr. Columbus Sch. Law, Cath. U. Am., Washington, 1975—. Sec. local campaign com., Alexandria, Va., 1964; trustee YMCAA, Silver Spring, Md., 1972-74. Recipient award D.C. Cir. Jud. Conf., 1984. Fellow Am. Coll. Bankruptcy (bd. regents 1989—); mem. Fed. Bar Assn. (chmn. bankruptcy subcom. 1988, exec. com. 1993—), Am. Bankruptcy Inst. (bd. dirs. 1991—, exec. com. 1993—, chmn. legis. com. 1991—), Walter Chandler Inn of Ct. (master emeritus 1990—). Republican. Roman Catholic. Avocations: fishing, hunting, boating. Home: 17908 Ednor View Ter Ashton MD 20861-9757 Office: Shaw Pittman Potts & Trowbridge 2300 N St NW Washington DC 20037-1122

WHELAN, STEPHEN THOMAS, lawyer; b. Phila., July 28, 1947; s. Stephen Thomas and Virginia King (Ball) W.; m. Elizabeth Ann Murphy, Apr. 3, 1971; children: Christine Barrett. BA magna cum laude, Princeton U., 1968; JD, Harvard U., 1971. Bar: N.Y. 1972, U.S. Dist. Ct. (so. dist.) N.Y. 1975. Assoc. Mudge Rose Guthrie & Alexander, N.Y.C., 1971-75; assoc. Thacher Proffitt & Wood, N.Y.C., 1975-77, ptnr., 1978—; chmn. corp. dept. Thacher Proffitt & Wood, 1992—. Co-author: New York's Uniform Commercial Code Article 2-A, 1994; contbr. articles to profl. jours. Bd. dirs. Sons Revolution, N.Y., 1979—; active N.Y. County Rep. Com., 1985—; active Princeton U. Alumni Coun., 1993—. Fellow Am. Coll. Investment Counsel; mem. ABA (chmn. subcom. on leasing 1994—), N.Y. State Bar Assn., Equipment Leasing Assn. Am. (mem. fed. govt. rels. com. 1992—). Roman Catholic. Avocations: road racing, secondary sch. students mentor, golf. Office: Thacher Proffitt & Wood 2 World Trade Ctr New York NY 10048-0002

WHELAN, WAYNE LOUIS, higher education administrator; b. Colonial Heights, Va., Jan. 10, 1939; s. Clarence Roscoe and Ruby Elizabeth (Farris) W.; m. Charlotte Harville Whelan, Aug. 25, 1961; children: Karen Lynne Smith, Whitney Hoffman Whelan. BA in History, U. Va., 1960, M in Edn. Adminstrn., 1967; EdD, Pacific States U., L.A., 1977. Tchr., administr. Hopewell (Va.) H.S., 1961-64; dir. guidance Colonial Heights (Va.) H.S., 1964-68; dir. evening and summer sessions Richard Bland Coll. Coll. William and Mary, 1968-72; assoc. dean evening and summer sessions Va. State U., 1972-78; dir. confs. and non-credit programs U. Tenn., 1978-86; assoc. v.p. continuing edn. and econ. devel. Trident Tech Coll., Charleston, 1986—. Oustanding Young Man Colonial Heights, Va. Jaycees, 1977. Mem. Assn. Continuing Higher Edn. (exec. v.p., meritorious svc. award, 1989), N. Charleston Breakfast Rotary, Trident Metro C. of C. Avocations: sailing, naval history. Home: 553 Planter's Loop Mount Pleasant SC 29464 Office: Trident Tech Coll PO 118067 Charleston SC 29423

WHELAN, WENDY, ballet dancer; b. Louisville; d. Rich and Kay Whelan. Student, Louisville Ballet Acad., Sch. Am. Ballet. Apprentice N.Y.C. Ballet, 1984-86, mem. corps de ballet, 1986-89, soloist, 1989-91, prin., 1991—. Appeared in feature roles in George Balanchine's ballets such as Apollo, Raymonda Variations, Swan Lake, Who Cares?, Symphony in Three Movements, Danses Concertantes, Episodes, Cortege Hongrois, The Four Temperaments, Brahms-Schoenberg Quartet, Divertimento # 15, A Midsummer Night's Dream, Bournonville Divertissements, The Nutcracker, Walpurgisnacht Ballet, Brahms-Schoenberg Quartet Pieces, Union Jack, The Cage; in Jerome Robbins' Antique Epigraphs and Glass Pieces; in Peter Martins' Ash, Jazz, Les Petits Riens, Sleeping Beauty; in William Forsythe's Behind the China Dogs and Herman Scherman; in Christopher D'Amboise's The Bounding Line in Richard Tanner's A Schubert Sonata; and performed in N.Y.C. Ballet's Balanchine Celebration, 1993. Office: NYC Ballet NY State Theater 20 Lincoln Ctr New York NY 10023*

WHELEHAN, PATRICIA ELIZABETH, anthropology educator; b. Rochester, N.Y., Mar. 4, 1947; d. Charles Thomas and Betty F. (Freisner) W.; 1 child, Rachel Alexandra Scout Galgoul. BA, SUNY, Potsdam, 1969; MA, SUNY, Albany, 1973, PhD, 1979. Cert. sex therapist, AIDS instr./counselor; diplomate Am. Bd. Sexologists. Group home houseparent LaSalle Sch. for Boys, Albany, 1973-75; grad. assist. SUNY, Albany, 1976-78; adj. assoc. prof. Counseling Ctr. Potsdam (N.Y.) Coll., 1985-87, assoc. prof. anthropology, 1978-94, prof., 1994—; sex and relationship therapist referral North Country MDs, 1982—; campus AIDS coordinator, assoc. prof. Inst. for Advanced Study Human Sexuality, San Francisco, 1988—; cons. Polaris Inst., San Francisco, 1988—. Co-author: Human Sexuality Text, 1989; editor: Women and Health, 1988; cons. editor Jour. Sex Edn. and Therapy, 1987-89; contbr. articles to profl. jours. Bd. dirs. Citizens Against Violent Acts, Potsdam, N.Y., 1986-87, AIDS Task Force Ctrl. N.Y., Syracuse, N.Y., 1988-91, St. Lawrence County Coun. on AIDS, Potsdam, 1988— SUNY travel grantee, 1987-88, 95; Potsdam Coll. mini grantee, 1979, 88, Rsch. and Creative Endeavors grantee, 1994-95. Mem. Am. Anthropol. Assn., Am. Coll. Sexology, Soc. Sci. Study Sex, AAUW, NORAL, NARAL, Phi Delta Kappa. Avocations: gourmet cooking, travel, long distance walking, reading. Office: SUNY Anthropology Dept 122 Macvicar Hall Potsdam NY 13676

WHELPLEY, DENNIS PORTER, lawyer; b. Mpls., Feb. 16, 1951; s. John Olsen and Harriet Marie (Porter) W.; m. Patricia Jan Adamy, Nov. 27, 1976; children: Heather Nicolle, Christopher Eric. BA, U. Minn., 1973, JD magna cum laude, 1976. Bar: Minn. 1976. Assoc. Oppenheimer Wolff & Donnelly, St. Paul, 1976-83, ptnr., 1983—. Mem. Order of Coif (Minn. chpt.), Phi Beta Kappa (Alpha of Minn. chpt.), Psi Upsilon (Mu chpt.), Dellwood Hills Golf & Country Club. Avocations: golf, tennis, squash, boating. Home: 49 Locust St Mahtomedi MN 55115-1542 Office: Oppenheimer Wolff & Donnelly 1700 First Bank Bldg Saint Paul MN 55101

WHELTON, PAUL K., medical educator, researcher; b. Cork, Ireland, Nov. 25, 1946; came to U.S., 1970; s. Andrew and Helen (Keane) W.; m. Shelagh Rosemary; children: Seamus, Megan. MD, Nat. U. Ireland, U. Coll. Cork, 1970; MSc in Epidemiology, U. London, 1980. Tng. in internal medicine sch. medicine Johns Hopkins U., Balt., 1970-73, tng. in nephrology sch. medicine, 1973-75, instr., asst. prof., assoc. prof., 1975-91, prof. sch. medicine, 1991—, from assoc. prof. to prof. sch. hygiene and pub. health, 1987—, dir. Welch Ctr. for Prevention, Epidemiology, and Clin. Rsch., 1989—; dir. Outpatient Gen. Clinic Rsch. Ctr., Balt., 1981—. Editor book on potassium and end stage renal disease; contbr. over 100 sci. articles to peer reviewed jours. Fellow. Am. Coll. Clin. Pharmacology, Am. Heart Assn. (coun. on cardiovascular epidemiology), Royal. Coll. Physicians (Ireland). Office: Johns Hopkins U Hosp Carnegie 292 600 N Wolfe St Baltimore MD 21287-0002

WHETTEN, JOHN D., food products executive. V.p. mktg. The Clorox Corp., Oakland, Calif., Danish Creamery Assn., Inc., Fresno, Calif.; with Challenge Dairy Products, Inc., Dublin, Calif., 1982—, pres., gen. mgr. Office: Challenge Dairy Products Inc 11875 Dublin Blvd B200 Dublin CA 94568*

WHETTEN, JOHN THEODORE, geologist; b. Willimantic, Conn., Mar. 16, 1935; s. Nathan Laselle and Theora Lucille (Johnson) W.; m. Carol Annette Jacobsen, July 14, 1960; children—Andrea, Krista, Michelle. A.B. with high honors, Princeton U., 1957; Ph.D., 1962; M.S., U. Calif.-Berkeley, 1959. Mem. faculty U. Wash., Seattle, 1963-81; research instr. oceanography U. Wash., 1963-64, asst. prof., 1964-68, assoc. prof., 1968-72, prof. geol. scis. and oceanography, 1972-81, chmn. dept. geol. scis., 1969-74; assoc. dean Grad. Sch., 1968-69; geologist U.S. Geol. Survey, Seattle, 1975-80; asst. div. leader geoscis. div. Los Alamos Nat. Lab., 1980-81, dep. div. leader earth and space scis. div., 1981-84, div. leader earth and space scis. div., 1984-86, assoc. dir. energy and tech., 1986-92, assoc. dir. quality, policy

and performance, 1992-93; lab. affiliate, 1994—; cons. in environ., safety and health and mfg. techs. Motorola Corp., 1994—. Contbr. articles to profl. jours. Fulbright fellow, 1962-63. Home: 154 Piedra Loop Los Alamos NM 87544-3837 Office: Los Alamos Nat Lab MS J-591 Los Alamos NM 87545

WHETTEN, LAWRENCE LESTER, international relations educator; b. Provo, Utah, June 12, 1932; s. Lester B. and Kate (Allred) W.; m. Gabriele Indra, Oct. 28, 1974 (dec. May 1985). B.A., Brigham U., 1954, M.A., 1955; Ph.D. with honors, NYU, 1963. Sr. polit. analyst Hdqrs. USAFE, Wiesbaden, Fed. Republic Germany, 1963-70; resident dir. grad. program in internat. relations U. So. Calif., Munich, Fed. Republic Germany, 1971-78, dir. studies USC/SIR grad. program in Germany, 1978-86; Erich Voegelin Gast prof. Munich U., 1987-88; lectr. Boston U., 1988—; lectr. Profl. Assoc. Ctr. Def. and Strategic Studies S.W. Mo. State U., Springfield, 1991—; cons. Fgn. Policy Inst., Phila., 1969-71, 76-79, R & D Assocs., Munich, 1977; lectr. Hoshschule für Politik, Munich; adj. prof., profl. assoc. Ctr. for Def. ans Strategic Studies, S.W. Mo. State U., 1991—. Author: Germany's Ostpolitik, 1971, Contemporary American Foreign Policy, 1974, The Canal War: Four Power Conflict, 1974, Germany East and West, 1981. Author, editor: Present State Communist Internationalism, 1983, The Interaction of Political Reforms Within the East Block, 1989. Served to capt. USAF, 1960-63. Penfield fellow NYU, 1957-59; grantee Ford Found., 1970, Royal Inst. Internat. Affairs, London, 1970, Thyssen Found., Cologne, Germany, 1974-82, 89, Volkswagen Found., 1982-85. Mem. Am. Acad. Polit. and Social Scis., Internat. Inst. Stratetic Studies, Am. Assn. Advancement of Soviet Studies, Gesellschaft für Auslandskunde, English Speaking Union, German Am. Assn. Home: Widenmayerstrasse 41, 80538 Munich Germany

WHETZEL, JOSHUA CLYDE, JR., museum executive, conservationist; b. Pitts., Mar. 8, 1921; s. Joshua Clyde and Gladys May (Porter) W.; m. Ann Farley Walton, Sept. 27, 1947; children: Joshua C., William M., Rachel W., Thomas P. B.S. in Chemistry, Va. Mil. Inst., 1943; postgrad., U. Pitts., 1963-66. Research assoc. Mellon Inst., Pitts., 1945-48; ptnr. Allegheny Refining Co., Verona, Pa., 1948-63; sec., treas. Conservation Found., Washington, 1967-69; pres. Western Pa. Conservancy, Pitts., 1969-80, chmn., 1980-95; pres. Buhl Sci. Ctr., Pitts., 1982-87; bd. dirs. Student Conservation Assn., Charlestown, N.H., 1978-85, 88, chmn., 1985-87; trustee Carnegie Inst., Pitts., 1983-87; chmn. sci. ctr. com. Carnegie Inst. Bd. Trustees, 1987-94; dir. Met. Pitts. Pub. Broadcasting, Inc., 1984-90. Mem. citizens adv. council Pa. Environ. Resources, Harrisburg, 1976-83; chmn. Park Commn. Fox Chapel Borough, Pa., 1970-79; elder Shadyside Presbyterian Ch., Pitts., 1973-79; treas. Three Rivers Arts Festival, 1961-67, Ellis Sch., 1963-67; co-chmn. Gov's Garden Commn., Harrisburg, Pa., 1979-81. Served to 1st lt. AUS, 1943-45, ETO. Named Man of Yr. in Conservation Pitts. Jaycees, 1974, Pa. Conservationist of Yr., Pa. Wildlife Fedn., 1986; recipient W.E. Clyde Todd award Audubon Soc. of W. Pa., 1980, Western Pa. Conservation award, 1985. Mem. Duquesne Club, Pitts. Golf Club, Rolling Rock Club (Ligonier, Pa.). Home and Office: 5036 Castleman St Pittsburgh PA 15232-2107

WHICHARD, WILLIS PADGETT, state supreme court justice; b. Durham, N.C., May 24, 1940; s. Willis Guilford and Beulah (Padgett) W.; m. Leona Irene Paschal, June 14, 1961; children: Jennifer Diane, Ida Gilbert. AB, U. N.C., 1962, JD, 1965; LLM, U. Va., 1984, SJD, 1994. Bar: N.C. 1965. Law clk. N.C. Supreme Ct., Raleigh, 1965-66; ptnr. Powe, Porter, Alphin & Whichard, Durham, 1966-80; assoc. judge N.C. Ct. Appeals, Raleigh, 1980-86; assoc. justice N.C. Supreme Ct., Raleigh, 1986—; instr. grad. sch. bus. adminstrn. Duke U., 1978; vis. lectr. U. N.C. Sch. Law, 1986—. Contbr. articles to profl. jours. Rep. N.C. Ho. of Reps., Raleigh, 1970-74; senator N.C. Senate, 1974-80, chair numerous coms. and commns.; N.C. legis. rsch. commn., 1971-73, 75-77, land policy coun., 1975-79; bd. dirs. Sr. Citizens Coordinating Coun., 1972-74; chair local crusade Am. Cancer Soc., 1977, state crusade chair, 1980, chair pub. issues com., 1980-84; pres., bd. chmn. Downtown Durham Devel. Corp., 1980-84; bd. dirs. Durham County chpt. ARC, 1971-79; Durham county campaign dir. March of Dimes, 1968, 69, chmn., 1969-74, bd. dirs. Triangle chpt., 1974-79; bd. advisors Duke Hosp., 1982-85, U. N.C. Sch. Pub. Health, 1985—, U. N.C. Sch. Social Work, 1989—; bd. visitors N.C. Ctrl. U. Sch. Law, 1987—; mem. law sch. dean search com. U. N.C., 1978-79, 88-89, self-study com., 1985-86; pres. N.C. Inst. Justice, 1984-94; bd. dirs. N.C. Ctr. Crime and Punishment, 1984-94. Staff asst. N.C. Army NG, 1966-72. Recipient Disting. Service award Durham Jaycees, 1971, Outstanding Legis. award N.C. Acad. Trial Lawyers, 1975, Outstanding Youth Service award N.C. Juvenile Correctional Assn., 1975, Citizen of Yr., Eno Valley Civitan Club, Durham, 1982, Faith Active in Pub. Life award N.C. Council of Churches, 1983, Outstanding Appellate Judge award N.C. Acad. Trial Lawyers, 1983, inducted Durham High Sch. Hall of Fame, 1987. Mem. ABA, N.C. Bar Assn. (v.p. 1983-84), Durham County Bar Assn., U. N.C. Law Alumni Assn. (pres. 1978-79, bd. dirs. 1979-82), Nat. Guard Assn. (judge advocate 1972-73, legis. com. 1974-76), Order of Golden Fleece, Order of Grail, Order of Old Well, Amphoterothen Soc., Order of Coif, Phi Alpha Theta, Phi Kappa Alpha. Democrat. Baptist. Clubs: Durham-Chapel Hill Torch (pres. 1984-85), Watauga (Raleigh, pres. 1994—). Home: 5608 Woodberry Rd Durham NC 27707-5335 Office: NC Supreme Ct 2 E Morgan St Raleigh NC 27602

WHIDDEN, STANLEY JOHN, physiologist, physician; b. N.Y.C., Oct. 10, 1947; s. Stanley Graham and Maybell (Van Houten) W.; m. Jan Venable Whidden, 1987. AS, Delgado Coll., 1969; BS, Southeastern La. U., 1971, MS, 1973; PhD, Auburn U., 1979; MD, U. Auto. De Ciudad Juarez, Mex., 1984; postgrad. Hyperbaric Physicians Ctr., NOAA, Nat. Def. U., 1986, Naval War Coll., 1995. Asst. head ops. Nuclear Sci. Ctr., Auburn U., Ala., 1976-78; lectr. physiology U. Wis.-Madison, 1978-79; asst. prof. U. New Orleans, 1979-80; postdoctoral fellow shock physiology La. State U. Med. Ctr., New Orleans, 1980-82; rsch., med. staff JESM Baromed. Inst., New Orleans, 1984-86; asst. prof. rsch. physiology dept., La. State U. Med. Ctr. New Orleans, 1988-89; mgr. program Dept. of Justice, Nat. Inst. Justice; fellow Naval War Coll. Contbr. chpt. to books: Handbook of Shock and Trauma, 1983, Physiological Basis of Decompression Sickness, 1987, Active Duty Army Combat Operation "Just Cause" Panama, 1990. Lt. col. USAR, 1966—, Desert Storm/Shield, Saudia Action, 1991, Op. Provide Hope, Somalia, 1993. Decorated Bronze Star; recipient Meritorious Svc. medal, Acom medal, UN medal, 1994; named to Hon. Col., La. Gov. Staff, 1985; named one of Outstanding Young Men of Am., 1986; USAF fellow, Sch. Aero. Medicine, Brooks AFB, Tex., 1986, 87, NASA fellow, Johnson Space Ctr., 1987; named Outstanding Young Men in Am., 1986; recipient Md. Gov.'s Citation, 1991. Mem. AAUP, AAAS, Am. Physiology Soc., Soc. Neurosci. Am. Chem. Soc., Aerospace Med. Assn., Aerospace Physiol. Soc., Am. Vet. Physiology and Pharmacology Soc., Am. Burn Assn., N.Y. Acad. Sci., Shock Soc., Undersea Med. Soc. Republican. Club: Spl. Forces assn. (New Orleans) (pres. 1983-84). Current work: Underlining cardiovascular and metabolic responses during shock with resuscitation and hyperbaric medical treatment. Subspecialties: Physiology (medicine); Space medicine. Office: PO Box 1252 Temple Hills MD 20757-1252

WHIDDON, CAROL PRICE, writer, editor, consultant; b. Gadsden, Ala., Nov. 18, 1947; d. Curtis Ray and Vivian (Dooly) Price; m. John Earl Caulking, Jan. 18, 1969 (div. July 1987); m. Ronald Alton Whiddon, Apr. 13, 1988. Student, McNeese State U., 1966-68; BA in English, George Mason U., 1984. Flute instr. Lake Charles, La., 1966-68; flutist Lake Charles Civic Symphony, 1966-69, Beaumont (Tex.) Symphony, 1967-68; freelance editor The Washington Lit. Rev., 1983-84, ARC Hdqrs., Washington, 1984; writer, editor Jaycor, Vienna, Va., 1985-87; writer, editor Jaycor, Albuquerque, 1987-90, publs. mgr., 1990-91; writer, editor Proteus Corp., Albuquerque, 1991-92; owner Whiddon Editorial Svcs., Albuquerque, 1989—; mem. S.W. Writer's Workshop, 1991—. Co-author: The Spirit That Wants Me: A New Mexico Anthology, 1991; contbr. various articles to Albuquerque Woman and mil. dependent pubs. in Fed. Republic Germany. Bd. dirs. Channel 27-Pub. Access TV, 1991-93, exec. bd. sec., 1992, v.p., 1993; dep. mgr. Fed. Women's Program, Ansbach, Fed. Republic Germany, 1980-81; pres. Ansbach German-Am. Club, 1980-82; sec. Am. Women's Activities, Fed. Republic Germany, 1980-81, chairwoman, 1981-82. Recipient cert. of appreciation from Am. amb. to Germany Arthur T. Burns, 1982, medal of appreciation from comdr. 1st Armored Div., Ansbach, Germany, 1982. Mem. NAFE, Women in Comm. (newsletter editor 1989-90, 91-92, 94-95, v.p. 1990-91, pres.-elect 1992-93, pres. 1993-94, chair programs com. Nat. Profl. Conf. 1994), Soc. Tech. Comm. (membership 1993-94), Nat. Assn. Desktop Pubs., Am. Mktg. Assn.; Greater Albu-

querque C. of C., N.Mex. Caucus Soc. (historian 1989-94, sec. 1991, newsletter editor 1992—, various show ribbons 1989-91). Republican. Avocations: reading, writing, gardening, camping, music. Home: 1129 Turner Dr NE Albuquerque NM 87123-1917

WHIDDON, FREDERICK PALMER, university president; b. Newville, Ala., Mar. 2, 1930; s. Samuel Wilson and Mary (Palmer) W.; m. June Marie Ledyard, June 14, 1952; children: Charles Wilson, John Tracy, Karen Marie and Keith Frederick (twins). AB, Birmingham So. Coll., 1952; BD cum laude, Emory U., 1955, PhD in Philosophy, 1963, LittD (hon.), 1991. Asst. prof. philosophy, dean of students Athens (Ala.) Coll., 1957-59; dir. Mobile Ctr. U. Ala., 1960-63; pres. U. South Ala., Mobile, 1963—; mem. presdl. adv. com. Fed. Home Loan Bank, Atlanta. Contbr. articles to profl. jours. Chmn. Marine Environ Scis. Consortium. Named Outstanding Adminstr. in Ala., Am. Assn. Univ. Adminstrs., 1981. Mem. Am. Assn. Univ. Adminstrs., Phi Kappa Phi. Lodge: Kiwanis (Mobile). Office: Univ South AL University Of South Alabama AL 36688

WHIDDON, JERRY B., artistic director, actor, educator; b. Washington, Nov. 30, 1947; s. Robert Lee and Vera (Raney) W.; m. Jean Patricia Brown, Oct. 29, 1983; children: Amelia, Hannah. BA, Towson State U., 1970. Tchr. English, drama, spl. edn. Sherwood High Sch., Sandy Springs, Md., 1970-71; founder, artistic dir. Street 70 Theatre Co., Rockville, Md., 1970-78; founding mem., actor Round House Theatre, Wheaton, Md., 1977-78, producing artistic dir., 1985—; tng. program coord. Double Image Theatre, N.Y.C., 1983-85; mem. adv. panel Md. State Arts Coun., 1990-93. Mem. League Washington Theatres (v.p.). Office: Round House Theatre 12210 Bushey Dr Wheaton MD 20902-1015

WHIFFEN, JAMES DOUGLASS, surgeon, educator; b. N.Y.C., Jan. 16, 1931; s. John Phillips and Lorna Elizabeth (Douglass) W.; child from a previous marriage, Gregory James; m. Sally Vilas Runge, Aug. 21, 1993. B.S., U. Wis., 1952, M.D., 1955. Diplomate: Am. Bd. Surgery. Intern Ohio State U. Hosp., 1955-56; resident U. Wis. Hosp., 1956-57, 59-61; instr. dept. surgery U. Wis. Med. Sch., 1962-64, asst. prof., 1964-67, assoc. prof., 1967-71, prof., 1971—, vice chmn. dept., 1970-72, acting chmn., 1972-74; asst. dean Med. Sch., 1975—; mem. exam. council State of Wis. Emergency Med. Services, 1974-77. Bd. dirs. Wis. Heart Assn. Served to lt. comdr. USNR, 1957-59. John and Mary R. Markle scholar in acad. medicine, also; Research Career Devel. award NIH, 1965-75. Fellow A.C.S., Am. Soc. Artificial Internal Organs. Club: Maple Bluff Country. Research, publs. on biomaterials, thrombo-resistant surfaces and the physiology of heart-lung bypass procedures. Home: 17 Cambridge Ct Madison WI 53704-5906 Office: 600 Highland Ave Madison WI 53792-0001

WHILLOCK, CARL SIMPSON, electric cooperative executive, former academic administrator; b. Scotland, Ark., May 7, 1926; s. Joe and Johnnie (Simpson) W.; m. Margaret Moore Carter; children and stepchildren: Timothy, Tom, Sally Whillock Conduff, Susan Whillock Lipe, Sallie Starr, Jenny Dakil, Melissa Campbell, Larry, Brennam, Benjamin. BS in Social Welfare, U. Ark., 1948, MA in History and Polit. Sci., 1951; JD, George Washington U., 1960. High sch. tchr., 1946-47, in family bus. livestock feeds, wholesale petroleum co., 1949-55; exec. asst. to Congressman J.W. Trimble, Berryville, Ark., 1955-63; pvt. practice law Clinton, Ark., 1963-66; pros. atty. 14th Jud. Dist., Ark., 1965-66; asst. to pres., dir. univ. rels., part-time instr. polit. sci. U. Ark., Fayetteville, 1966-71, v.p. govtl. rels. and pub. affairs, 1975-78; pres. Ark. State U., Jonesboro, 1978-80, Ark. Electric Coops. Inc., 1980—, Ark. Electric Coop. Corp., 1980—; bd. dirs. 1st Comml. Bank, Little Rock; campaign mgr. David Pryor for Gov. of Ark. Campaign, 1974-75; exec. sec. Gov. of Ark., 1975, mem., bd. of trustees Univ. of Ark. Mem. Ark. Ho. of Reps., two terms, 1953-56; chmn. Ark. Tax Reform Commn., 1987-88, mem. Pres.'s Ark. Adv. Coun. for Winrock, mem. bd. dirs. Winrock Internat. Inst. for Agrl. Devel.. Democrat. Home: PO Box 194208 Little Rock AR 72219-4208 *It is my belief that the success of any organization or effort depends on the caliber of the people involved in it. It is important that people be intelligent, imaginative, compassionate, willing to listen to others, courageous, conscientious, honest, and dependable. People who have these qualities have been the greatest inspiration to me.*

WHINNERY, JAMES ELLIOTT, aerospace medical scientist, flight surgeon; b. Amarillo, Tex., May 1, 1946; s. John Clark and Virginia Faye (Elliott) W.; m. Angela Marie Geraci, 1 child, Chance Typ Geraci. BS in Chemistry, West Tex. State U., 1968; MAT, Tex. Christian U., 1972, PhD in Phys. Chemistry, 1972; MD, U. Tex. Med. Br., Galveston, 1975; diploma, Air War Coll., 1976. Commd. 2d lt. USAF, 1972; flight surgeon Sch. Aerospace Medicine USAF, Brooks AFB, Tex., 1975-76, biomedical scientist Sch. Aerospace Medicine, 1978-81, head acceleration rsch. Sch. Aerospace Medicine, 1983-86; resident in internal medicine Wilford Hall USAF, Lackland AFB, Tex., 1976-78; dir. cardiovascular and renal clin. rsch. Merck, Sharp & Dohme Rsch. Labs., West Point, Pa., 1981-83; spec. rsch. fellow Air War Coll./Airpower Rsch. Inst., 1985-86; chief aerospace med. scientist Naval Air Warfare Ctr., Warminster, Pa., 1987—; advanced through grades to col. USAF, 1986, Air Nat. Guard asst. to europe command surgeon, 1986-90, 91-93; asst. command surg. USAF, Europe & Air Force Surg., Ops. Dessert Shield-Desert Strom, Sembach AB, Germany, 1990-91; air surgeon N.G. Bur., 1991—; adj. prof. Drexel U., Phila., 1986—; team physician U.S. Nat. Swimming Team, 1979-83; cons. USAF, 1991. Author: Neurophysiologic and Cardiovascular Research in Aviation Medicine, 1975; mem. editorial bd. Aviation Space & Environ. Medicine, 1980—; contbr. over 200 articles to profl. jours. Recipient Malcolm C. Grow Award Air N.G., 1986; named Chief Flight Surgeon, 1991. Fellow Am. Inst. Chemists, Am. Coll. Cardiology, Aerospace Med. Assn. (recipient Arnold D. Tuttle award, 1979, 86); mem. Am. Chem. Soc., Sigma Xi. Home: 1122 Columbus Cir # 2 Washington DC 20335-5490 Office: Office Chief of AeroMed Sci Naval Air Devel Ctr Warminster PA 18974*

WHINNERY, JOHN ROY, electrical engineering educator; b. Read, Colo., July 26, 1916; s. Ralph V. and Edith Mable (Bent) W.; m. Patricia Barry, Sept. 17, 1944; children—Carol Joanne, Catherine, Barbara. B.S. in Elec. Engring, U. Calif. at Berkeley, 1937, Ph.D., 1948. With GE, 1937-46; part-time lectr. Union Coll., Schenectady, 1945-46; asso. prof. elec. engring. U. Calif., Berkeley, 1946-52, prof., vice chmn. div. elec. engring., 1952-56, chmn., 1956-59, dean Coll. Engring., 1959-63, prof. elec. engring., 1963-80, Univ. prof. Coll. Engring., 1980—; vis. mem. tech. staff Bell Telephone Labs., 1963-64; research sci. electron tubes Hughes Aircraft Co., Culver City, 1951-52; disting. lectr. IEEE Microwave Theory and Technique Soc., 1989-92. Author: (with Simon Ramo) Fields and Waves in Modern Radio, 1944, 3d edit. (with Ramo and Van Duzar), 1994, (with D.O. Pederson and J.J. Studer) Introduction to Electronic Systems, Circuits and Devices; also tech. articles. Chmn. Commn. Engring. Edn., 1966-68; mem. sci. and tech. com. Manned Space Flight, NASA, 1963-69; mem. Pres.'s Com. on Nat. Sci. Medal, 1970-73, 79-80; standing com. controlled thermonuclear research AEC, 1970-73. Recipient Lamme medal Am. Soc. Engring. Edn., 1975, Centennial medal, 1993, Engring. Alumni award U. Calif.-Berkeley, 1980, Nat. Medal of Sci. NSF, 1992; named to Hall of Fame Modesto High Sch. (Calif.), 1983, ASEE Hall of Fame, 1993.; Guggenheim fellow, 1959. Fellow IRE (bd. dirs. 1956-59), IEEE (life, bd. dirs. 1969-71, sec. 1971, Edn. medal 1967, Centennial medal 1984, Medal of Honor 1985), Optical Soc. Am., Am. Acad. Arts and Scis.; mem. NAS, NAE (Founders award 1986), IEEE Microwave Theory and Techniques Soc. (Microwave Career award 1977), Phi Beta Kappa, Sigma Xi, Tau Beta Pi, Eta Kappa Nu. Congregationalist. Home: One Daphne Ct Orinda CA 94563 Office: U Calif Dept Electrical Engineering Berkeley CA 94720*

WHINSTON, ARTHUR LEWIS, lawyer; b. N.Y.C., Feb. 5, 1925; s. Charles Nathaniel and Charlotte (Nalen) W.; m. Melicent Ames Kingsbury, Mar. 19, 1949; children: Ann Kingsbury, James Pierce, Melicent Ames, Louise Ellen, Patricia Kingsbury. B.C.E., Cornell U., 1945; M.S.E., Princeton U., 1947; J.D., N.Y. U., 1957. Bar: N.Y. 1957, Oreg. 1964, U.S. Supreme Ct 1966, U.S. Patent Office 1958, U.S.C. Appeals (fed. cir.) 1959; registered profl. engr., N.Y., Oreg. Engr. Chas. N. & Selig Whinston, N.Y.C., 1947-50; lectr. Coll. City N.Y., 1950-51; structures engr. Republic Aviation Corp., Farmingdale, N.Y., 1951-57; practice in N.Y.C., 1957-64, Portland, Oreg., 1964—; patent lawyer Arthur, Dry & Kalish, 1957-64; partner Klarquist, Sparkman, Campbell, Leigh & Whinston, 1964—; chmn. Oreg. Bar com. on patent, trademark and copyright law, 1968-69, 77-78, mem. com. unauthorized practice law, 1970-73, chmn., 1972-73, com. on profl. responsibility, 1973-75. Served as ensign, C.E. USNR, 1945-46. Recipient Fuertes medal Cornell U. Sch. Civil Engring., 1945. Mem. ABA, Oreg. Bar Assn., N.Y. Bar Assn., Multnomah County Bar Assn., Am. Intellectual Property Law Assn., N.Y. Intellectual Property Law Assn., Oreg. Patent Law Assn. (pres. 1977-78), Profl. Engrs. Oreg. (past state legis. chmn.), Sigma Xi, Chi Epsilon, Phi Kappa Phi. Republican. Unitarian. Club: Multnomah Athletic. Home: 3824 SW 50th Ave Portland OR 97221-2112 Office: One World Trade Ctr Ste 1600 Portland OR 97204

WHIPPLE, DAVID DOTY, association executive; b. Akron, Ohio, Dec. 26, 1923; s. Hugh Scott and Helene Eleanore (Doty) W.; m. Carolyn Terhune Decker, Feb. 28, 1953; children: Susan Casselman, Marc Evan, Tim Decker, Scott Adams Montgomery. BA, Dartmouth Coll., 1949; postgrad., Johns Hopkins U., 1949-50, The Nat. War Coll., Washington, 1966-67. From ops. officer to counterterrorism nat. intelligence ofc. CIA, Washington, 1950-85; cons. internat. terrorism, 1985-89; exec. dir. Assn. Former Intelligence Officers, McLean, Va., 1989—; exec. v.p. Pagan Internat., Washington, 1987-89. Sgt. U.S. Army, 1945-46, Italy, Philippines. Mem. Assn. Former Intelligence Officers (exec. dir. 1989—), Nat. War Coll. Alumni Assn., CIA Retirees Assn. Office: Assn Former Intel Officers 6723 Whittier Ave Ste 303A McLean VA 22101

WHIPPLE, DEAN, federal judge; b. 1938. BS, Drury Coll., 1961; postgrad., U. Tulsa, 1961-62; JD, U. Mo., 1965, postgrad., 1965. Pvt. practice Lebanon, Mo., 1965-75; cir. judge div. II 26th Jud. Cir. Mo., 1975-87; dist. judge U.S. Dist. Ct., Kansas City, Mo., 1987—; prosecuting atty. Laclede County, Mo., 1967-71. Mem. Cen. United Meth. Ch., Kansas City. With Mo. N.G., 1956-61; USAR, 1961-66. Mem. Mo. Bar Assn. (mem. pub. info. com. 1971-72, mem. judiciary com. 1971-72, mem. bd. govs. 1975-87, mem. exec. com. 1983-84, 86-87, mem. planning com. for ann. meeting 1985, 87, chmn. 1986, mem. selection com. for Lon Hocker award 1986), Mo. Trial Judges Assn., 26th Jud. Bar Assn., Laclede County Bar Assn. (pres. 1968-69, 72-73), Kansas City Met. Bar Assn., Kansas City Inn of Ct. (instr. 1988-93), Mo. Hist. Soc., Phi Delta Phi. Office: US Dist Ct US Courthouse 811 Grand Ave Rm 613 Kansas City MO 64106-1909

WHIPPLE, FRED LAWRENCE, astronomer; b. Red Oak, Iowa, Nov. 5, 1906; s. Harry Lawrence and Celestia (MacFarl) W.; m. Dorothy Woods, 1928 (div. 1935); 1 son, Earle Raymond; m. Babette F. Samelson, Aug. 20, 1946; children: Dorothy Sandra, Laura. Student, Occidental Coll., 1923-24; AB, UCLA, 1927; PhD, U. Calif., 1931; AM (hon.), Harvard, 1945; ScD, Am. Internat. Coll., 1958; DLitt (hon.), Northeastern U., 1961; DSc (hon.), Temple U., 1961, U. Ariz., 1979; LLD (hon.), C.W. Post Coll., L.I. U., 1962. Teaching fellow U. Calif. at Berkeley, 1927-29, Lick Obs. fellow, 1930-31; instr. Stanford U., summer 1929, U. Calif., summer 1931; staff mem. Harvard Obs., 1931-77; instr. Harvard U., 1932-38, lectr., 1938-45; research asso. Radio Research Lab., 1942-45, asso. prof. astronomy, 1945-50, prof. astronomy, 1950-77, chmn. dept., 1949-56, Phillips prof. astronomy, 1968-77; dir. Smithsonian Astrophys. Obs., 1955-73, sr. scientist, 1973—; mem. Rocket Rsch. Panel U.S., 1946-57; U.S. subcom. NASA, 1946-52, U.S. Rsch. and Devel. Bd. Panel, 1947-52; chmn. Tech. Panel on Rocketry; mem. Tech. Panel on Earth Satellite Program, 1955-59; others coms. Internat. Geophys. Year, 1955-59; mem., past officer Internat. Astron. Union; coms. missions to U.K. and MTO, 1944; del. Inter-Am. Astrophys. Congress, Mexico, 1942; active leader project on Upper-Atmospheric Rsch. via Meteor Photog. sponsored by Bur. Ordnance, U.S. Navy, 1946-51; by Bur. Ordnance, U.S. Navy (Office Naval Rsch.), 1951-57, USAF, 1948-52; mem. com. meteorology, space sci. bd., com. on atmospheric scis. Nat. Acad. Scis.-NRC, 1958-65; project dir. Harvard Radio Meteor Project, 1957-65; adviser Sci. Adv. Bd., USAF, 1963-67; spl. cons. com. Sci. and Astronautics U.S. Ho. Reps., 1960-73; chmn. Gordon Rsch. Confs., 1963; dir. Optical Satellite Tracking Project, NASA, 1958-73; project dir. Orbiting Astron. Obs., 1958-72; dir. Meteorite Photography and Recovery Program, 1962-73, cons. working group on Orbiting planetary atmospheres, 1962-69; mem. space scis. working group on Orbiting Astron. Observatories, 1959-70; chmn. sci. council geodetic uses artificial satellites Com. Space Rsch., 1965-70. Author: Earth, Moon and Planets, rev. edit, 1968, Orbiting The Sun: Planets and Satellites of The Solar System, The Mystery of Comets, 1985; co-author: Survey of the Universe; Contbr.: sci. papers on astron. and upper atmosphere to Ency. Brit; mags., other publs.; Asso. editor: Astronomical Jour, 1954-56, 64-71; editor: Smithsonian Contributions to Astrophysics, 1956-73, Planetary and Space Science, 1958-83, hon. editor, 1983—; Science Revs, 1961-70; editorial bd.: Earth and Planetary Sci. Letters, 1966-73; inventor tanometer, meteor bumper; a developer window as radar countermeasure, 1944. Decorated comdr. Order of Merit for rsch. and invention, Esnault-Pelterie award France; recipient Donohue medals for ind. discovery of 6 new comets; Presdl. Cert. of Merit for sci. work during World War II; J. Lawrence Smith medal Nat. Acad. Scis. for rsch. on meteors, 1949; medal for astron. rsch. U. Liege, 1960; Space Flight award Am. Astronautical Soc., 1961; Disting. Fed. Civilian Svc. award, 1963; Space Pioneers medallion for contbns. to fed. space program, 1968; Public Svc. award for contbns. to OAO2 devel. NASA, 1969; Leonard medal Meteoritical Soc., 1970; Kepler medal AAAS, 1971; Career Svc. award Nat. Civil Svc. League, 1972; Henry medal Smithsonian Instn., 1973; Alumnus of Yr. Achievement award UCLA, 1976; Golden Plate award Am. Acad. Achievement, 1981; Gold medal Royal Astron. Soc., 1983; Bruce Medal, Astron. Soc. Pacific, 1986; Benjamin Franklin fellow Royal Soc. Arts, London, 1968—; depicted on postal stamp of Mauritania, 1986, of St. Vincent, 1994. Fellow Am. Astron. Soc. (v.p. 1962-64, 1987 Russell lecturer), Am. Rocket Soc., Am. Geophys. Union (Fred L. Whipple yearly lectr. estab. in honor planetary div. 1990), Royal Astron. Soc. (assoc.); mem. AAAS, Nat. Acad. Scis., AIAA Astronautics (aerospace tech. panel space physics 1960-63), Astronautical . Pacific, Solar Assos., Internat. Sci. Radio Union (U.S.A. nat. com. 1949-61), Am. Meteoritical Soc., Am. Standards Assn., Am. Acad. Arts and Scis., Am. Philos. Soc. (councillor sect. astronomy and earth scis. 1966-70), Royal Soc. Scis. Belgium (corr.), Internat. Acad. Astronautics (sci. advisory com. 1962-65), Internat. Astronautical Fedn., Am. Meteorol. Soc., Royal Astron. Soc. (assoc.), Phi Beta Kappa, Sigma Xi, Pi Mu Epsilon. Clubs: Examiner (Boston); Cosmos (Washington). Office: 60 Garden St Cambridge MA 02138-1596

WHIPPLE, HARRY, newspaper publishing executive. Now pres., pub. Cin. Enquirer. Office: Cin Enquirer 312 Elm St Cincinnati OH 45202-2739*

WHIPPLE, JUDITH ROY, book editor; b. N.Y.C., May 14, 1935; d. Edwin Paul and Elizabeth (Levis) Roy; m. William Whipple, Oct. 26, 1963. AB, Mount Holyoke Coll., 1957. Head libr. Am. Sch. Lima (Peru), S.A., 1957-59; asst. editor children's books G.P. Putnam's Sons, N.Y.C., 1959-62; assoc. editor W.W. Norton & Co., Inc., N.Y.C., 1962-68; editor Four Winds Press, 1968-75; editor-in-chief Scholastic Gen. Book Divsn., 1975-77; pub. Four Winds Press subs. Scholastic Inc., N.Y.C., 1977-82; pub., v.p. Macmillan Pub. Co., N.Y.C., 1982-89, exec. editor, 1989-94; editl. dir. Benchmark Books, Marshall Cavendish Corp., Tarrytown, N.Y., 1994—. Mem. PEN, Children's Book Coun. (pres. 1977, bd. dirs. 1970-79), Women's Nat. Book Assn., Soc. Children's Book Writers and Illustrators. Avocations: gardening, swimming, piano, travel. Office: Marshall Cavendish Corp 99 White Plains Rd Tarrytown NY 10591

WHIPPLE, KENNETH, automotive company executive; b. 1934. BS, MIT, 1958. With Ford Motor Co., Dearborn, Mich., 1958—, systems mgr. Ford Credit, 1966-69, mgr. mgmt. svcs. dept. fin. staff, 1969-71, systems analysis mgr. fin. staff, 1971-74, asst. contr. internat. fin. staff, 1974-75, v.p fin. Ford Credit, 1975-77, exec. v.p Ford Credit, 1977-80, pres. Ford Credit, 1980-84, v.p. corp. strategy, 1984-86; v.p chmn. Ford of Europe, 1986-88; exec. v.p., pres. Ford Fin. Svcs. Group, Dearborn, 1988—. Office: Ford Motor Co The American Rd Dearborn MI 48121-1899

WHIPPLE, THOMAS A., food marketing professional. With Lucky Stores, Inc., Tampa, Fla., 1962-88; exec. v.p. Kash-N-Karry Food Stores, Inc., Tampa, Fla., 1988—. Office: Kash-N-Karry Food Stores Inc 6422 Harney Rd Tampa FL 33610-9592

WHIPPS, EDWARD FRANKLIN, lawyer; b. Columbus, Ohio, Dec. 17, 1936; s. Rusk Henry and Agnes Lucille (Green) W.; children: Edward Scott, Rusk Huot, Sylvia Louise, Rudyard Christian. B.A., Ohio Wesleyan U., 1958; J.D., Ohio State U., 1961. Bar: Ohio 1961, U.S. Dist. Ct. (so. dist.)

Ohio 1962, U.S. Dist. Ct. (no. dist.) Ohio 1964, U.S. Ct. Claims 1963, U.S. Supreme Ct. 1963, Miss. 1965, U.S. Ct. Appeals (6th cir.) 1980. Assoc. George, Greek, King & McMahon, Columbus, 1961-66; ptnr. George, Greek, King, McMahon & McConnaughey, Columbus, 1966-79, McConnaughey, Stradley, Mone & Moul, Columbus, 1979-81, Thompson, Hine & Flory, Columbus, 1981-93; prin. Edward F. Whipps & Assocs., Columbus, 1993-94; ptnr. Whipps & Wistner, Columbus, 1995—; founder, trustee Creative Living, Inc., 1969—; trustee, v.p. Unverferth House, Inc., 1989. Host: TV programs Upper Arlington Plain Talk, 1979-82; TV program Briding Disability, 1981-82, Lawyers on Call, 1982—, U.A. Today, 1982-86, The Ohio Wesleyan Experience, 1984—. Mem. Ohio Bd. Psychology, 1992—; mem. Upper Arlington (Ohio) Bd. Edn., 1971-80, pres., 1978-79; mem. bd. alumni dirs. Ohio Wesleyan U., 1975-79; trustee Walden Ravines Assn., 1992—, pres. 1993—. Mem. ABA, Columbus Bar Assn., Ohio State Bar Assn., Assn. Trial Lawyers Am., Ohio Acad. Trial Lawyers, Franklin County Trial Lawyers Assn., Am. Judicature Soc., Columbus Bar Found., Ohio Bd. Pscyhology, Columbus C. of C., Upper Arlington Area C. of C. (trustee 1978—), Lawyers Club, Barrister Club, Columbus Athletic Club, Columbus Touchdown Club, Downtown Quarterback Club, Ohio State U. Faculty (Columbus) Club, Ohio State U. Golf Club, Highlands Country Club, Delta Tau Delta (nat. v.p. 1976-78). Republican. Home: 3111 Walden Ravines Columbus OH 43221 Office: Edward F Whipps & Assocs 500 S Front St Columbus OH 43215 *Personal philosophy: Commitment to personal growth, the development of interpersonal communication skills, the rule of law and a firm belief in the unique value of every individual are the primary factors seen in my approach to life.*

WHISENAND, JAMES DUDLEY, lawyer; b. Iowa City, Aug. 14, 1947; s. J.D. and Barbara Pauline (Huxford) W. BA in Mktg. cum laude, U. No. Iowa, 1970; MBA, Fla. State U., 1973, JD cum laude, 1973. Bar: Fla. 1973, U.S. Dist. Ct. (no., mid. and so. dists.) Fla. 1974, U.S. Tax Ct. 1974, U.S. Ct. Appeals (11th cir.) 1975, U.S. Supreme Ct. 1976. Law clk. U.S. Dept. Justice, Fla., 1972, Office of Fla. Atty. Gen., 1971-73; asst. atty. gen. Tax Div., 1973-74; head administr. law div., 1974-75; cabinet counsel Atty. Gen. Office, Fla., 1975; dep. atty. gen. Fla., 1975-78; ptnr. Sage, Gray, Todd & Sims, N.Y.C., Miami, 1979-81; of counsel Paul & Thomson, Miami, 1981-82; founding ptnr. Hornsby & Whisenand, Miami, 1982-90, Whisenand & Assocs., P.A., Miami, 1990-91; ptnr. Patton Boggs & Blow, Washington and Miami, 1991-93; founding ptnr. Whisenand & Turner, P.A., Miami, Fla., 1993—; pres. Americas Conf. Corp., 1994—. Publ.: The Cuba Report, 1992—; contbr. articles to profl. jours. Bd. advisors New World Sch. Arts, Miami, 1988; bd. dirs. Fla. State U. Sch. Law Alumni Assn., 1988-89; bd. trustees U. No. Iowa Found., 1993—; mem. bd. advisors Ctrl. European (Euromoney). Mem. Fla. Bar Assn., D.C. Bar Assn., Inter-Am. Bar Assn., Internat. Bar Assn., Greater Miami C. of C., European Forum. Avocations: polo, equestrian events, skiing, bicycling. Office: Whisenand & Turner PA 501 Brickell Key Dr Ste 200 Miami FL 33131-2608

WHISENHUNT, DONALD WAYNE, history educator; b. Meadow, Tex., May 16, 1938; s. William Alexander Whisenhunt and Beulah (Johnson) King; m. Betsy Ann Baker, Aug. 27, 1960; children: Donald Wayne Jr., William Benton. BA, McMurry Coll., 1960; MA, Tex. Tech U., 1962, PhD, 1966. Tchr. Elida (N.Mex.) High Sch., 1961-63; from asst. to assoc. prof. history Murray (Ky.) State U., 1966-69; assoc. prof., chmn. dept. Thiel Coll., Greenville, Pa., 1973-77; Dean Sch. Liberal Arts and Scis., Ea. N.Mex. U., Portales, 1977-77; v.p. acad. affairs U. Tex., Tyler, 1977-83; v.p. provost Wayne (Nebr.) State Coll., 1983-91, interim pres., 1985; prof. history, chmn. dept. Western Wash. U., Bellingham, 1991—. Author: Environment and American Experience, 1974, Depression in the Southwest, 1979, Chronological History of Texas, Vol. 1, 1982, Vol.2, 1987, Texas: Sesquicentennial Celebration, 1984; editor: Encyclopedia USA, 1988—. Democrat. Methodist. Office: Western Wash U Dept History Bellingham WA 98225

WHISLER, JAMES STEVEN, lawyer, mining and manufacturing executive; b. Centerville, Iowa, Nov. 23, 1954; s. James Thomas and Betty Lou (Clark) W.; m. Ardyce Dawn Christensen, Jan. 20, 1979; children: James Kyle, Kristen Elyse. BS, U. Colo., Boulder, 1975; JD, U. Denver, 1978; MS, Colo. Sch. Mines, Golden, 1984. Bar: Colo. 1978; CPA, Ariz. Assoc. gen. counsel, sec. Western Nuclear, Inc., Denver, 1979-81; exploration counsel Phelps Dodge Corp., N.Y.C., 1981-85; legal and adminstrv. mgr. Phelps Dodge Corp., Phoenix, 1985-87, v.p. gen. counsel, 1987-88, sr. v.p., gen. counsel, 1988-91; pres. Phelps Dodge Mining Co., Phoenix, 1991—; bd. dirs. Unocal Corp., 1st Interstate Bank Ariz., N.A.; chmn. Western Regional Coun.'s Working Group on Environ. Texas, 1990-93; mem. Ariz. Fed. Dist. Ct. Adv. group, 1991-92. Trustee Heard Mus., Phoenix, 1989-94, Rocky Mountain Mineral Law Found., 1989-92; mem. Dean's Coun. of 100, Ariz. State U., 1992—; mem. nat. bd. advisors Coll. Bus. and Pub. Adminstrn., U. Ariz., 1992—; bd. dirs. Met. Phoenix YMCA, 1989-92, Copper Bowl Found., Tucson, 1990-91, Ariz. Town Hall, 1991—, We. Regional Coun., 1991—; mem. Maricopa County Sports Authority, Phoenix, 1990—; mem. Phoenix Com. on Fgn. Rels., 1991-94. Mem. AICPA, AIME, Am. Corp. Counsel Assn., Soc. Mining Engrs., Colo. Bar Assn., Phoenix Thunderbirds, Phoenix Country Club. Home: 11438 N 54th Pl Scottsdale AZ 85254-5712 Office: Phelps Dodge Corp 2600 N Central Ave Phoenix AZ 85004-3050

WHISMAN, LINDA ANNE, law librarian; b. Santa Monica, Calif., May 28, 1954; d. Richard W. and Helen T. (Voss) Schulte; m. Timothy C. Whisman, Feb. 12, 1983; 2 children. BA, U. Calif., Irvine, 1976; MLS, UCLA, 1978; JD, Southwestern U., 1983. Bar: Calif. 1983, U.S. Dist. Ct. (cen. dist.) Calif. 1987. Reference librarian Southwestern U., L.A., 1978-82, law librarian, assoc. prof. law, 1982-89, prof., 1989—. Contbr. articles to legal jours. Mem. ABA, Am. Assn. Law Libraries, So. Calif. Assn. Law Libraries. Office: Southwestern U 675 S Westmoreland Ave Los Angeles CA 90005-3992

WHISNAND, ROY VAN ARSDEL, investment management executive; b. Providence, Jan. 26, 1944; s. Roy V. and Jane Ann (Morris) W.; m. Campbell Baker, June 11, 1966; children: Tyler, Carter. AB, Brown U., 1966; MBA, U. Va., 1968. V.p. Stone and Webster Inc., N.Y.C., 1972-86, exec. v.p., 1986-87; pres. Stone and Webster Mgmt. Cons. Inc., N.Y.C., 1984-86; ptnr. Combined Capital Mgmt., N.Y.C., 1987—; bd. dirs. NUI Corp., Bridgewater, N.J. Mem. N.Y. Soc. Security Analysts. Office: Combined Capital Mgmt 1 Penn Plz New York NY 10119-0001

WHISNANT, JACK PAGE, neurologist; b. Little Rock, Oct. 26, 1924; s. John Clifton and Zula I. (Page) W.; m. Patricia Anne Rimmey, May 12, 1944; children: Elizabeth Anne, John David, James Michael. B.S., U. Ark., 1948, M.D., 1951; M.S., U. Minn., 1955. Intern Balt. City Hosp., 1951-52; resident in medicine and neurology Mayo Grad. Sch. Medicine, Rochester, Minn., 1952-55; instr. neurology Mayo Grad. Sch. Medicine, 1956-60, asst. prof., 1960-64, asso. prof., 1964-69, prof., 1969—; Meyer prof. neurosci. Mayo Med. Sch.; chmn. dept. neurology Mayo Clinic, Mayo Med. Sch., Mayo Grad. Sch. Medicine, 1971-81; chmn. dept. health scis. research Mayo Clinic and Mayo Med. Sch., 1987-93; cons. neurology Mayo Clinic, 1955—, head sect. neurology, 1963-71; dir. Mayo Cerebrovascular Clin. Research Center, 1975—. Contbr. articles on neurology and cerebrovascular disease to med. jours. Trustee YMCA, Rochester. With USAAF, 1942-45. Decorated Air medal. NIH grantee, 1955—. Fellow Am. Heart Assn., Am. Acad. Neurology (pres. 1993—); mem. Am. Neurol. Assn. (pres. 1981-82), Am. Bd. Psychiatry and Neurology (bd. dirs. 1983-90, pres. 1989), Zumbro Valley Med. Soc., Minn. Med. Assn., Minn. Soc. Neurol. Scis., Ctrl. Soc. Neurol. Rsch., Nat. Adv. Neurol. Disease and Stroke Coun., Alumni Assn. Mayo Found. Presbyterian. Home: 1005 7th Ave NE Rochester MN 55906-7074 Office: Mayo Found Dept Health Scis Rsch 201 1st St SW Rochester MN 55905-0010

WHISTLER, ROY LESTER, chemist, educator, industrialist; b. Morgantown, W.Va., Mar. 31, 1912; s. Park H. and Cloe (Martin) W.; m. Leila Anna Barbara Kaufman, Sept. 6, 1935; 1 child, William Harris. B.S., Heidelberg Coll., 1934, D.Sc. (hon.), 1957; M.S., Ohio State U., 1935; Ph.D., Iowa State U., 1938; D.Litt. (hon.), St. Thomas Inst., 1982; D.Agr., Purdue U., 1985. Instr. chemistry Iowa State U., 1935-38; research fellow Bur. Standards, 1938-40; sect. leader dept. agr. No. Regional Rsch. Lab., 1940-46; prof. biochemistry Purdue U., 1946-76, Hillenbrand distinguished prof., asst. dept. head, 1974-82; Hillenbrand disting. prof. emeritus Purdue U., Lafayette, Ind., 1982—; chmn. Inst. Agrl. Utilization Research, 1961-75;

pres. Lafayette Applied Chemistry Inc., 1980—; vis. lectr. U. Witwatersrand, 1961, 65, 77, 85, Czechoslovakia and Hungary, 1968, 85, Japan, 1969, Taiwan, 1970, Argentina, 1971, New Zealand, Australia, 1967, 74; vis. lectr. Acad. Sci., France, 1975, Vladivostock Acad. Sci., 1976, Brazil, 1977, Egypt, 1979; lectr. Bradley Polytech. Inst., 1941-42, People's Republic China, 1985; adv. Whistler Ctr. for Carbohydrate Chemistry; indsl. cons. dir. Pfanstiehl Lab., Inc., Greenwich Pharm. Inc., FruteTec; mem. NRC sub-com. nomenclature biochemistry; pres. Lafayette (Ind.) Applied Chemistry. Author: Polysaccharide Chemistry, 1953, Industrial Gums, 1959, 2d rev. edit., 1976, 3d rev. edit. 1992; rev. edit.: Methods of Carbohydrate Chemistry, series, 1962—; co-author: Guar, 1979; editor: Starch-Chemistry and Technology, 2 vols., 1965, 67, rev. edit., 1984; editorial bd. Jour. Carbohydrate Research, 1960-91, Starchs Chemistry and Technology, 1985; bd. advisors Advances in Carbohydrate Chemistry, 1950—, Organic Preparations and Procedures Internat., 1970—, Jour. Carbo-Nucleosides-Nucleotides, 1973-77, Starke, Starch, 1979—; contbr. 500 articles to profl. jours. Recipient Sigma Xi rsch. award Purdue U., 1953, Medal of Merit, Japanese Starch Tech. Soc., 1967, German Saare medal, 1974, Thomas Burr Osborne award Am. Assn. Cereal Chemists, 1974, Sterling Henricks award USDA, 1991, 93, Nicholas Appert award Inst. Food Technologists, 1994; Roy L. Whistler internat. award in carbohydrates named in his hon.; Fred W. Tanner lectr., Chgo., 1994. Fellow AAAS, Am. Chem. Soc. (chmn. Purdue sect. 1949-50, carbohydrate divsn. 1951, cellular divsn. 1962, nat. councilor 1953-87, bd. dirs. 5th dist. 1955-58, chmn. com. edn. and students, chmn. sub-com. polysaccharide nomenclature, symposium dedicated in his honor 1979, hon. fellow award cellulose divsn. 1983, Hudson award 1960, Anselme Payen award 1967, Carl Lucas Alsburg award 1970, Spencer award 1970, 75, Disting. Svc. award 1983, named one of 10 outstanding chemists Chgo. sect. 1948), Am. Inst. Chemists (pres. 1982-83, Gold Medal 1992), Am. Assn. Cereal Chemists (pres. 1978, Thomas Burr Osborne award 1974), Internat. Carbohydrate Union (pres. 1972-74); mem. Lafayette Applied Chemistry (pres. 1970—), Argentine Chem. Soc. (life), Rotary (pres. 1966), Sigma Xi (pres. Purdue sect. 1957-59, nat. exec. com. 1958-62, hon. life mem. 1983—), Phi Lambda Upsilon. Lodge: Rotary (pres. 1966).

WHISTON, RICHARD MICHAEL, lawyer; b. N.Y.C., Mar. 1, 1944; s. Michael W. and Dorothy M. (Kussman) W. BS in Econs. cum laude, U. Pa., 1964; JD, Harvard U., 1968. Bar: N.Y. 1968, Conn. 1978, Fla. 1979, D.C. 1992, U.S. Dist. Ct. (so. and ea. dists.) N.Y. 1977, U.S. Dist. Ct. Conn. 1978, U.S. Ct. Claims 1979, U.S. Tax Ct. 1977, U.S. Ct. Appeals (5th cir.) 1979, U.S. Supreme Ct. 1977. Assoc. Kelley, Drye, Warren, N.Y.C., 1970-77; dep. div. counsel Hamilton Standard, Windsor Locks, Conn., 1977-78; asst. gen. counsel United Techs. Corp., Hartford, Conn., 1980-82; div. counsel Latin Am. ops. Otis Elevator Co., West Palm Beach, Fla., 1978-80; div. counsel European ops. Otis Elevator Co., Paris, 1982-83; v.p. counsel No. Am. ops. Otis Elevator Co., Farmington, Conn., 1983-85, v.p., gen. counsel, sec., 1985-90; v.p., gen. counsel, sec. Carrier World Hdqtrs., Farmington, 1990-92; sr. v.p., gen. counsel united techs. Pratt & Whitney, East Hartford, Conn., 1993—. Served to capt. U.S. Army, 1968-70. Mem. Alpha Beta Psi, Beta Gamma Sigma. Episcopalian. Avocations: comml. pilot. Office: Pratt & Whitney M/S 101-10 400 Main St East Hartford CT 06118-1888

WHITACRE, EDWARD E., JR., telecommunications executive; b. Ennis, Tex., Nov. 4, 1941. BS in Indsl. Engring., Tex. Tech U., 1964. With Southwestern Bell Telephone Co., 1963-85; various positions in ops. depts. Tex., Ark., Kans.; pres. Kans. div. Topeka, 1984-85; group pres. Southwestern Bell Corp., 1985-86; v.p. revenues and pub. affairs, vice-chmn., chief fin. officer Southwestern Bell Corp., St. Louis, 1986-88, pres., chief oper. officer, 1988-89, chmn., chief exec. officer, 1990—, also bd. dirs.; bd. dirs. Anheuser-Busch Cos., Inc., May Dept. Stores Co., Emerson Electric Co., Burlington No., Inc. Bd. regents Tex. Tech. U. and Health Scis., Lubbock; mem. exec. bd. nat. coun. and so. region Boy Scouts Am. Presbyterian. Office: SBC Communications Inc PO Box 2933 175 E Houston St 6th Fl San Antonio TX 78299-2933

WHITACRE, JOHN, apparel executive; b. 1953. Student, U. Wash. With Nordstrom Inc., 1976—; co-pres. Nordstrom Inc., Seattle, 1991—. Office: Nordstrom Inc 1501 5th Ave Seattle WA 98101-1603

WHITAKER, A(LBERT) DUNCAN, lawyer; b. Ft. Wayne, Ind., Jan. 3, 1932; s. Robert Lynn and Rhoda Irene (Duncan) W.; m. Adelaide B. Saccone, Aug. 13, 1955; children: Brent Robert, Alene G., Karen E. B.A., Yale U., 1954; J.D., U. Mich., 1957. Bar: Mich. 1957, U.S. Ct. Appeals D.C. 1959, U.S. Supreme Ct. 1961. Atty. antitrust div. U.S. Dept. Justice, 1957-59; assoc. Howrey & Simon, Washington, 1959-65, ptnr., 1965—; lectr. George Washington U., George Mason U. Law Sch. Contbr. articles to profl. jours. Mem. ABA, Fed. Bar Assn., D.C. Bar Assn., Order of Coif, Phi Beta Kappa. Clubs: Metropolitan. Office: Howrey & Simon 1299 Pennsylvania Ave NW Washington DC 20004

WHITAKER, BRUCE EZELL, college president; b. Cleveland County, N.C., June 27, 1921; m. Esther Adams, Aug. 22, 1947; children: Barry Eugene, Garry Bruce. BA, Wake Forest U., 1944; BD, So. Bapt. Theol. Sem., 1947, ThM, 1948, PhD, 1950; postgrad., George Peabody Coll., 1952; DL, Wake Forest U., 1987. Ordained to ministry Bapt. Ch., 1945; pastor Smithfield, Ky., 1945-49; instr. sociology and philosophy Ind. U., 1947-50; prof. religion Cumberland U., Lebanon, Tenn., 1950-51, Belmont Coll., Nashville, 1951-52; prof. sociology, asst. to pres. Shorter Coll., Rome, Ga., 1952-53; assn. pastor, minister edn. Atlanta, 1953-54; state sec., student dept. Bapt. State Conv., N.C., 1954-57; pres. Chowan Coll., Murfreesboro, N.C., 1957-89, pres. emeritus, 1989—; mem. adv. com. to Bd. Higher Edn., 1962-66; to N.C. Commn. Higher Edn. Facilities, 1964—; pres. N.C. Conf. Social Service, 1965-67, Assn. Governing Bds., 1973-82, Assn. So. Baptist Colls. and Schs., 1967-68, Assn. Eastern N.C. Colls., 1968-69; bd. dirs. Regional Edn. Lab. for Carolinas and Va. Pres. bd. trustees N.C. Found. Church-Related Colls., 1970-74; bd. dirs., v.p. Nat. Council Ind. Jr. Colls., 1974-75, pres., 1975-76; mem. advisory council presidents Assn. Governing Bds., from 1973; mem. N.C. Bd. Mental Health, from 1966; bd. dirs. Am. Assn. Community and Jr. Colls., 1976-82; pres. N.C. Assn. Colls. and Univs., 1977-78; chmn. N.C. Commn. Mental Health/Mental Retardation Sers., 1978-81. V.p. Bapt. State Conv. N.C., 1989-91. Named Tarheel of Week Raleigh News and Observer, 1962, Boss of Year N.C. Jaycees, 1972; tribute paid in Congl. Record, 1962, 89; Whitaker Libr. at Chowan Coll. named for him; Whitaker Sch. at Butner, N.C. named for him; selected one of nation's 18 most effective coll. presidents in 1985, funded study Exxon Found.; featured in We the People of North Carolina, 1989. Mem. N.C. Lit. and Hist. Assn. (pres. 1970-71), Am. Acad. Polit. and Social Scis., NEA, Am. Assn. Community and Jr. Colls. (dir. 1976-82, Leadership Recognition award 1989), Nat. Assn. Ind. Colls. and Univs. (dir. 1977-78, 81-85), Am. Assn. Higher Edn., Am. Coun. Edn. (bd. dirs. 1985-89), Internat. Platform Assn., Omicron Delta Kappa. Clubs: Capital City (Raleigh, N.C.), Capitol Club (Raleigh); Rotary (chmn. dist. student exchange com. 1969-72, Paul Harris fellow); Optimist; Beechwood Country (Ahoskie, N.C.); Harbor (Norfolk, Va.). Office: PO Box 40 Murfreesboro NC 27855-0040

WHITAKER, CHARLES LARIMORE, lawyer; b. Guntersville, Ala., Apr. 20, 1943; s. James G. and Pearl (Hastings) W.; m. Ann Clark, Sept. 2, 1962; children: Paula C., Clark L. BA, Vanderbilt U., 1965; LLB, U. Va., 1968. Assoc. Bradley, Arant, Rose & White, Birmingham, Ala., 1968-74, ptnr., 1974—. Contbr. articles to law revs. Mem. ABA, Birmingham Bar Assn. Avocations: reading, golf. Office: Bradley Arant Rose White 1400 Park Pl Towers Birmingham AL 35203

WHITAKER, CLEM, JR., advertising and public relations executive; b. Sacramento, Aug. 30, 1922; s. Clem and Harriett (Reynolds) W.; 1 child, Isabella Alexandra. Student, Sacramento Jr. Coll., 1942, U. Calif.-Berkeley, 1943. Reporter, Sacramento Union, 1938-40; staff mem. Campaigns, Inc.-Whitaker & Baxter, San Francisco, 1946-50; partner Campaigns, Inc.-Whitaker & Baxter, 1950-58, pres., 1958—; partner Whitaker & Baxter Advt. Agy., San Francisco, 1950-58; pres. Whitaker & Baxter Advt. Agy., 1958—. co-pub. Calif. Feature Svc., San Francisco, 1950—; chmn. Wye Energy Group. Bd. dirs. San Francisco Opera Assn. With USAAF, 1942-46, ETO. Mem. Cercle de L'Union. Home: 2040 Broadway St San Francisco CA 94115-1500 Office: Box 334 2443 Fillmore St San Francisco CA 94115-1825

WHITAKER, EILEEN MONAGHAN, artist; b. Holyoke, Mass., Nov. 22, 1911; d. Thomas F. and Mary (Doona) Monaghan; m. Frederic Whitaker. Ed., Mass. Coll. Art, Boston. Annual exhibits in nat. and regional watercolor shows; represented in permanent collections, Charles and Emma Frye Mus., Seattle, NAD, Hispanic Soc., N.Y.C., High Mus. Art, Atlanta, U. Mass., Norfolk (Va.) Mus., Springfield (Mass.) Mus. Art, Reading (Pa.) Art Mus., Nat. Acad. Design, U. Mass., Okla. Mus. Art, St. Lawrence U., Wichita State U., Retrospective show, Founders Gallery U. San Diego, 1988, invitational one-person show Charles and Emma Frye Art Mus., 1990; included in pvt. collections; featured in cover article of American Artist mag., Mar. 1987, in article Art of Calif. mag., July 1991; invitational Am. Realism Exhbn. Cir. Gallery, San Diego, 1992; author: Eileen Monaghan Whitaker Paints San Diego 1986. Recipient numerous major awards, including Allied Artists Am., Am. Watercolor Soc., 1st prize Providence Water Color Club, Wong award Calif. Watercolor Soc., De Young award Soc. Western Artists, 1st award Springville (Utah) Mus., Ranger Fund purchase prize, Orbrig prize NAD, Walter Biggs Meml. award, 1987; silver medal Am. Watercolor Soc., Watercolor West; fellow Huntington Hartford Found., 1964. Academician NAD; mem. Am. Watercolor Soc. (Dolphin fellow), Watercolor West (hon.), San Diego Watercolor Soc. (hon.). Home and Studio: 1579 Alta La Jolla Dr La Jolla CA 92037-7101

WHITAKER, FOREST, actor; b. Longview, Tex., July 15, 1961. Student voice, U. So. Calif. Stage appearances (London) Swan, Romeo and Juliet, Hamlet, Ring Around the Moon, Craig's Wife, Whose Life Is It Anyway?, The Greeks; other stage appearances include Patchwork Shakespeare, Beggar's Opera, Jesus Christ Superstar; TV appearances include Amazing Stories, Hill Street Blues, Cagney and Lacey, Trapper John, M.D., The Fall Guy, Different Strokes; TV movies Hands of a Stranger, 1987, Criminal Justice, 1990, Last Light, 1993; mini-series North & South, Parts I and II; films: Fast Times at Ridgemont High, 1982, Vision Quest, 1985, The Color of Money, 1986, Platoon, 1986, Stakeout, 1987, Good Morning, Vietnam, 1987, Bloodsport, 1988, Bird, 1988 (best actor Cannes Festival 1988), Johnny Handsome, 1989, Downtown, 1990, (also co-prodr.) Rage in Harlem, 1991, Article 99, 1992, Diary of a Hit Man, 1992, Consenting Adults, 1992, Body Snatchers, 1993, The Crying Game, 1993, Blown Away, 1994, Jason's Lyric, 1994, Prêt-à-Porter, 1994, Species, 1995, Smoke, 1995. office: care ICM 8942 Wilshire Blvd Beverly Hills CA 90211*

WHITAKER, GILBERT RILEY, JR., academic administrator, business economist; b. Oklahoma City, Oct. 8, 1931; s. Gilbert Riley and Melodese (Kilpatrick) W.; m. Ruth Pauline Tonn, Dec. 18, 1953; children: Kathleen, David Edward, Thomas Gilbert. B.A. Rice U., 1953; postgrad., So. Methodist U., 1956-57; M.S. in Econs., U. Wis., Madison, 1958, Ph.D. in Econs. (Ford Found. dissertation fellow), 1961. Instr., Sch. of Bus. Northwestern U., 1960-61, asst. prof. bus. econs., Sch. of Bus., 1961-64, asso. prof., Sch. of Bus., 1964-66, research assoc. Transp. Center, Sch. of Bus., 1962-66; asso. prof. Washington U., St. Louis, 1966-67; prof. Washington U., 1967-76, adj. prof. econs., 1968-76, asso. dean Sch. Bus. Adminstrn., 1969-76; dean, prof. bus. econs. M.J. Neeley Sch. Bus. Tex. Christian U., 1976-79; dean, prof., Sch. Bus. Adminstrn. U. Mich., 1979-90; provost, v.p. acad. affairs U. Mich., Ann Arbor, 1990-93, provost, exec. v.p. acad. affairs, 1993—; dir. Am. Assembly of Collegiate Schs. of Bus., 1984-91, v.p. and pres.-elect, 1988-89, pres. 1989-90, dir. Washington campus, 1980-89, chmn. 1985-88; bd. dirs. Lincoln Nat. Corp., Johnson Controls, Inc., Structural Dynamics Rsch. Corp., Handleman Co.; sr. economist banking and currency com. U.S. Ho. of Reps., 1964; Grad. Mgmt. Admissions Coun., 1972-75, chmn., 1974-75; bd. dirs. Washtenaw County United Way, 1990—. Author: (with Marshall Colberg and Dascomb Forbush) books including Business Economics, 6th edit., 1981, (with Roger Chisholm) Forecasting Methods, 1971. Served with USN, 1953-56. Mem. Am. Econ. Assn., Am. Fin. Assn., Ft. Worth Boat Club. Home: 2360 Londonderry Rd Ann Arbor MI 48104-4014 Office: U Mich Fleming Adminstrn Buil Ann Arbor MI 48109

WHITAKER, JOHN KING, economics educator; b. Burnley, Lancashire, Eng., Jan. 30, 1933; came to U.S., 1967; s. Ben and Mary (King) W.; m. Sally Bell Cross, Aug. 24, 1957; children: Ann Elizabeth, Jane Claire, David John. B.A. in Econs. U. Manchester, 1956; A.M., Johns Hopkins U., 1957; Ph.D., Cambridge U., 1962. Lectr. U. Bristol, Eng., 1960-66; prof., 1966-69; vis. prof. U. Va., Charlottesville, 1967-68; prof. econs. U. Va., 1969-86, chmn. dept. econs., 1979-82, Paul Goodloe McIntire prof. of econs., 1986-92; Georgia Bankard prof. of econs. U. Va., Charlottesville, 1992—. Author: The Early Economic Writings of Alfred Marshall, 1867-1890, 2 vols, 1975. Mem. Am. Econ. Assn., Royal Econ. Soc., Econometric Soc., History of Econs. Soc. Home: 1615 Yorktown Dr Charlottesville VA 22901-3046 Office: U Va Dept Econs Rouss Hall Charlottesville VA 22901

WHITAKER, KATHLEEN K., gifted education facilitator; b. Kansas City, Mo., Mar. 26, 1940; d. Richard Ingram and Rosemary (Frost) Kidd; m. William P. Whitaker, Feb. 24, 1962 (div. 1971); children: Lorie Beth, Minda Corinne. BA, U. Mo., 1962; MS, Kans. U., 1982. Cert. learning disabilities, gifted edn. and social studies tchr.; cert. psychol. examiner. Tchr. learning disabilities Wyandotte County Spl. Edn. Coop., Kansas City, Kans., 1980-84; learning specialist diagnostic team Children's Rehab. Unit Kans. U. Med. Ctr., 1984-85; tchr. learning disabilities Turner Sch. Dist., Kansas City, Kans., 1985-89, tchr. gifted edn., 1988-89, 94—; facilitator underachieving gifted edn. Shawnee Mission (Kans.) Schs., 1989—; tchr. of gifted, 1994—; presenter, staff mem. Rimm Underachievement Inst., 1992; presenter, developer larning materials in field; tchr., designer materials for parenting classes. Chmn. worship com. Shawnee Mission Unitarian Soc., 1991, trustee, 1992-93; adv. bd. Samaras Teddy Bear Comfort. Mem. Assn. for Edn. Gifted Underachieving Students, Kans. Assn. for Gifted, Talented and Creative, Phi Delta Kappa. Avocations: bicycling, bridge. Home: 4406 W 70th Ter Shawnee Mission KS 66208-2562 Office: Old Mission Multi-Use Ctr 4901 Reinhardt Dr Shawnee Mission KS 66205

WHITAKER, LINTON ANDIN, plastic surgeon; b. Navasota, Tex., Nov. 16, 1936; s. Ira Andin and Lena Rivers (Stedman) W.; m. Renata Grasmanis, Dec. 20, 1963; children: Derek Andin (dec.), Ingrid Marlena, Brandon Andrew. BA, Tex., 1958; MD, Tulane U., 1962. Diplomate Am. Bd. Surgery, Am. Bd. Plastic Surgery. Intern Montreal Gen. Hosp., 1962-63; resident in gen. surgery Dartmouth Affiliated Hosps., Hanover, N.H., 1965-69; resident in plastic surgery U. Pa. Hosp., Phila., 1969-71, chief plastic surgery, 1971-77, 87—, attending surgeon, 1971—; chief plastic surgery Children's Hosp. Phila., 1981—, attending surgeon, 1971—; attending physician VA Hosp., 1971—, Phila. Gen. Hosp., 1971-77; assoc. in plastic surgery Sch. Medicine, U. Pa., Phila., 1971-73, asst. prof. in plastic surgery, 1973-76, assoc. prof., 1976-81, prof., 1981—; founder, dir. Ctr. Human Appearance U. Pa. Med. Ctr., Phila., 1988—; vis. prof. Walter Reed Army Med. Ctr., Washington, 1976, Ohio State U. Med. Ctr., Columbus, 1977, Cleve. Clinic, 1980, Wilmington Med. Ctr., 1980, South Australia Craniofacial Unit, Adelaide, Australia and New Zealand, 1981, U. Hawaii, 1983, Brown U., Providence, 1983, Mass. Gen. Hosp., Boston, 1984, U. Utah, Salt Lake City, 1984, U. B.C., Vancouver, 1986, U. Pitts., 1988, U. Calif., San Diego, 1992, Ohio Valley Soc. for Plastic and Reconstructive Surgery, 1992; Curtis vis. prof. Dartmouth U. Med. Ctr., Hanover, N.H., 1990, Kazanjian vis. prof. Mass. Gen. Hosp., Boston, 1990; First Seiichi Ohmori Meml. lectr. All Asiatic Congress on Aesthetic Surgery, Tokyo, 1988; vis. speaker Inst. Cosmotology and Inst. Stomatology, Moskow, Russia, 1985; lectr., speaker at univs., assns. in field. Co-author: Atlas of Cranio-maxillofacial Surgery, 1982, Aesthetic Surgery of the Facial Skelton, 1992; editor: (with P. Randall) Symposium on the Reconstruction of Jaw Deformity, Clinics in Plastic Surgery, 1987, 91; co-editor: Yearbook of Plastic and Reconstructive Surgery, 1980—; mem. editorial bd. Jour. Cutaneous Aging and Cosmetic Dermatology, 1988—; contbr. articles to profl. jours. Capt. U.S. Army Med. Corps, 1963-65. Foederer fellow Foederer Fund for Excellence, 1985; NIH grantee, 1976-79, 81-87, 82-85, 89, Plastic Surgery Edn. Found. Rsch. grantee; recipient James IV Surg. Traveller award, 1979. Fellow Am. Coll. Surgeons, Am. Soc. Ophthalmic Plastic and Reconstructive Surgery (hon.); mem. AMA (mem. coun. sci. affairs, diagnostic and therapeutic tech. assessment reference panel 1982), Am. Assn. Plastic Surgeons (mem. program com. 1988, chmn. 1989, Rsch. grantee 1984-85), Am. Surg. Soc., Am. Alpine Workshop in Plastic Surgery (founding mem.), Am. Cleft Palate Assn. (chmn. com. classification craniofacial anomalies 1976-80, mem. program com. for 1978 mtg. 1977, mem. long-range planning com 1980, mem. coun. 1981-84, chmn. internat. rels. com. 1981-83), Am. Cleft Palate Ednl. Found. (bd. dirs. 1975-84, chmn. rsch. com. 1975-78, chmn. instrl. courses 1980-81),

Am. Soc. Aesthetic Plastic Surgery, Am. Soc. Craniofacial Surgery (mem. coun. 1992), Am. Soc. Maxillofacial Surgeons, Am. Soc. Plastic and Reconstructive Surgeons (mem. pub. rels com. 1974-76, mem. plastic surgery speakers bur. 1977—), Am. Soc. Plastic and Reconstructive Surgeons Ednl. Found. (chmn. ednl. assessment com., maxillofacial truama and craniofacial anomalies 1975-78, mem. clin. symposia com. 1978-82, chmn. clin. symposia com. 1981-82), Internat. Cleft Palate & Related Craniofacial Anomalies Soc. (mem. program com. 1981, 89), Internat. Soc. Aesthetic Surgery, Internat. Soc. Craniomaxillofacial Reconstruction (founding mem., organizer, mem. exec. com. 1987—), Phila. Med. Soc., Phila. Acad. Surgery, Coll. Physicians Phila., Assn. Acad. Surgery, Northeastern Soc. Plastic Surgeons N.Y. (chmn. program com. 1987, mem. programcom. 1988), Plastic Surgery Rsch. Coun., John Morgan Soc., Robert H. Ivy Soc., The Columbian Soc. Plastic, Maxillofacial and Hand Surgery (hon.), Academia Medica Lombarda (Italy, hon.), mie Planas de Cirugia Plastica (Spain, hon.), Mt. Kenya Safari Club (hon.), Soc. Former Residents and Assocs. Plastic Surgery (hon.), Phila. Club, Merion Cricket Club. Avocations: mountain climbing, skiing, wines. Office: U Pa Med Ctr 10 Penn Tower 3400 Spruce St Philadelphia PA 19104

WHITAKER, MEADE, federal judge; b. Washington, Mar. 22, 1919; s. Spier and Haidee (Meade) W.; m. Frances Dunn Baldwin, Feb. 10, 1945; children: Meade, Martin Baldwin (dec.), Frances Dunn Whitaker Schoonover; m. Carol Dekleva, Dec. 26, 1972. B.A., Yale U., 1940; LL.B., U. Va., 1948. Bar: Ala. 1948. Ptnr. Cabaniss & Johnston and successor firms, Birmingham, 1948-69, 70-73; tax legis. counsel Treasury Dept., Washington, 1969-70; chief counsel (IRS), Washington, 1973-76; ptnr. Arter & Hadden, Cleve., 1977-78; asst. gen. counsel Ford Motor Co., Dearborn, Mich., 1978-81; judge U.S. Tax Ct., Washington, 1982—. Served as officer USMCR, 1941-46. Mem. ABA, Am. Law Inst., D.C. Bar Assn. Episcopalian. Office: US Tax Ct 400 2nd St NW Washington DC 20217-0002

WHITAKER, PERNELL (SWEET PEA), professional boxer. Olympic Gold Medalist, boxing, lightweight divsn. L.A., 1984; lightweight champion Internat. Boxing Fedn., 1989; jr. lightweight champion World Boxing Coun.; lightweight champion World Boxing Assn., 1990; welterweight champion World Boxing Coun., 1993—; middleweight champion World Boxing Assn., 1995. Recipient Gold medal boxing lightweight divsn. Olympics, 1984; named pound for pound best boxer in the world Ring Mag., 1995, winner record 6 world championship titles in 4 weight classes, 1995. Office: World Boxing Coun, Genova 33 Colonia Juarez, Cuauhtemoc Mexico City Mexico*

WHITAKER, SUSANNE KANIS, veterinary medical librarian; b. Clinton, Mass., Sept. 10, 1947; d. Harry and Elizabeth P. (Cantwell) Kanis; m. Daniel Brown Whitaker, Jan. 1, 1977. A.B. in Biology, Clark U., 1969; M.S. in Library Sci., Case Western Res. U., 1970. Regional reference librarian Yale Med. Library, New Haven, 1970-72; med. librarian Hartford Hosp., Conn., 1972-77; asst. librarian Cornell U., Ithaca, N.Y., 1977-78; vet. med. librarian Coll. Vet. Medicine, Cornell U., 1978—; sec. SUNY Council Head Librarians, 1981-83. Mem. Med. Libr. Assn. (sec.-treas. vet. med. librs. sect. 1983-84, chmn. 1984-85), Med. Libr. Assn. (upstate N.Y. and Ont. chpt.), Acad. Health Info. Profls. Home: 231 Highgate Rd Ithaca NY 14850-1435 Office: Cornell U Coll Vet Medicine Flower-Sprecher Libr Ithaca NY 14853-6401

WHITAKER, THOMAS RUSSELL, English literature educator; b. Marquette, Mich., Aug. 7, 1925; s. Joe Russell and Sarah Genevieve (Houk) W.; m. Dorothy Vera Barnes, June 17, 1950; children: Thomas O'Hara, Sarah Mae, Mary Beth, Gwendolyn Anne. BA summa cum laude, Oberlin Coll., 1949; MA, Yale U., 1950, PhD, 1953. Instr. English Oberlin (Ohio) Coll., 1952-55, asst. prof., 1955-59, assoc. prof., 1959-63, prof., 1963-64; tchr. lit. Goddard Coll., Plainfield, Vt., 1964-66; prof. English U. Iowa, Iowa City, 1966-75; prof. English Yale U. New Haven, Conn., 1975-95, prof. theater studies, 1986-95, chmn. dept. English, 1979-85, Frederick W. Hilles prof. English emeritus, 1989-95. Author: Swan and Shadow: Yeats's Dialogue with History, 1964, 2d edit. with new preface, 1989, William Carlos Williams, 1968, rev. edit., 1989, Fields of Play in Modern Drama, 1977, Tom Stoppard, 1983, augmented edit., 1984; editor: Twentieth Century Interpretations of the Playboy of the Western World, 1969, Iowa Rev, 1974-77, Teaching in New Haven: The Common Challenge, 1991; chmn. editl. bd. On Common Ground, 1993-95. Served with C.E. U.S. Army, 1944-46. Recipient Harbison award for gifted teaching Danforth Found., 1972; Am. Council Learned Socs. fellow, 1969-70; NEH-Huntington fellow, 1981. Mem. MLA. Home: 882 Moose Hill Rd Guilford CT 06437-2303

WHITBREAD, THOMAS BACON, English educator, author; b. Bronxville, N.Y., Aug. 22, 1931; s. Thomas Francis and Caroline Nancy (Bacon) W. B.A., Amherst Coll., 1952; A.M., Harvard U., 1953, Ph.D. 1959. Instr. English, U. Tex. at Austin, 1959-62, asst. prof., 1962-65, asso. prof., 1965-71, prof., 1971—; Vis. assoc. prof. Rice U., 1969-70; mem. lit. adv. panel Tex. Commn. on Arts and Humanities, 1972-76. Author (poetry): Four Infinitives, 1964, Whomp and Moonshiver, 1982; contbg. author: Prize Stories, 1962, The O. Henry Awards, 1962; editor: Seven Contemporary Authors, 1966. Recipient third Aga Khan prize for fiction Paris Rev., 1960, Lit. Anthology Program award Nat. Endowment for Arts, 1968, Outstanding Freshman Tchr. award Phi Eta Sigma, 1972-73. Mem. MLA, AAUP, Tex. Inst. Letters (Poetry award 1965, 83), Nat., Am. amateur press assns., Phi Beta Kappa. Democrat. Home: 1014 E 38th St Austin TX 78705-1835 Office: U Tex Dept English Austin TX 78712

WHITBURN, GERALD, state agency administrator; b. Wakefield, Mich., July 12, 1944; s. Donald and Ruby E. (Nichols) W.; m. Charmaine M. Heise, May 3, 1969; children: Bree, Luke. BS, U. Wis., Oshkosh, 1966; MA, U. Wis., Madison, 1968; postgrad., Harvard U., 1988. Aide Gov. Warren P. Knowles, Wis., 1966-69; personal asst. USN sec. John H. Chafee, Washington, 1969-72; automobile dealer, real estate developer Merrill, Wis., 1973-80; exec. asst. to senator Robert W. Kasten U.S. Senate, Washington, 1981-87; dep. sec. Wis. Dept. Adminstrn., Madison, 1989-91, Wis. Dept. Health and Social Svcs., Madison, 1991-95; sec. exec. office of health and human svcs. Commonwealth of Mass., 1995—; Mem. U.S. Labor Sec.'s Commn. on Achieving Necessary Skills, Washington, 1990-92. Contbr. articles to newspapers. Del. Rep. Nat. Conv., 1988, 92. Recipient Disting. Alumni award U. Wis., Oshkosh, 1991. Home: 390 Main St Lynnfield MA 01940 Office: Wis Dept Health & Social Svcs 1 Ashburton Pl Rm 1109 Boston MA 02108

WHITBURN, MERRILL DUANE, English literature educator; b. Mpls., Apr. 29, 1938; s. George and Marie Ellen (Carlstedt) W.; m. Diane Robertson, June 15, 1960; children: Stephen, Mark, Elizabeth. AB, U. Mich., 1960, AM, 1968; PhD, U. Iowa, 1973. With Western Electric Co., N.Y.C. and Indpls., 1965-67; asst. prof. Tex. A&M U., College Station, 1973-77, assoc. prof., 1977-79; assoc. prof. Rensselaer Poly. Inst., Troy, N.Y., 1979-83, prof., 1983-89, Louis Ellsworth Laflin prof., 1989—, chmn. dept., 1979-85, 88—; co-owner Pride and Prejudice Books, Ballston Lake, N.Y., 1985—. Co-author (booklet) Guide for Departments of English, 1985; contbr. articles to profl. publs. Recipient Disting Svc. award Tex. A&M U., 1976, Disting. Teaching award, 1979, Jay R. Gould award for excellence in tchg. tech. com. Soc. Tech. Comm., 1995; grantee Fund for the Improvement of Postsecondary Edn., 1983. Mem. MLA, Soc. for Tech. Communication, Nat. Coun. Tchrs. English (best article in tech. writing award 1981), Coun. for Programs in Tech. and Sci. Communication, Assn. Depts. English. Office: Rensselaer Poly Inst Troy NY 12180

WHITCOMB, BENJAMIN BRADFORD, JR., neurosurgeon; b. Ellsworth, Maine, Dec. 13, 1908; s. Benjamin Bradford and Katherine Evelyn (Laffin) W.; m. Margaret Pike, Aug. 1, 1936; children: Stuart Pike, Katherine (Mrs. Paul Joseph Dudzinski), Judith (Mrs. Horace Hunt), Benjamin Bradford III. A.B., Bowdoin Coll., 1930; M.D., C.M., McGill U., Montreal, Que., Can., 1935. Diplomate: Am. Bd. Neurol. Surgery (vice chmn. 1969-70). Intern Hartford (Conn.) Hosp., 1935-37, John A. Wentworth fellow, 1937-38, resident neurosurgery, 1941-42, neurosurgeon, 1942—, dir. dept. neurosurgery, 1968-75; asst. resident in surgery and neurosurgery New Haven Hosp., 1938-41; asst. clin. prof. neurosurgery Yale Med. Sch., 1949-65, asso. clin. prof., 1965-73, clin. prof., 1973-76; clin. prof. neurosurgery dept. surgery U. Conn. Med. Sch., 1973—. Contbg. author: Medical History of World War II; Author articles treatment for spinal disc pathology and various disorders of the brain. Served with AUS, 1943-46. Mem. Am. Acad.

Neurol. Surgery (v.p. 1966-67, pres. 1973-74), A.C.S., A.M.A., Am. Assn. Neurol. Surgeons (v.p. 1971—), New Eng. Neurosurg. Soc. (pres. 1959-60), New Eng. Surg. Soc., Soc. Brit. Neurol. Surgeons (hon.), Scandanavian Neurosurg. Soc., New England Neurol. Surgeons (v.p. 1967-68). Home: RR 1 Box 124 Surry ME 04684-9712 *To have a goal and pursue it with tenacity and patience controls ambition. To admire and commend the good work of others controls pride. To discipline oneself to work more insures growth. To hold each person in genuine affection insures cooperation. To hold honesty paramount controls men.*

WHITCOMB, JAMES HALL, geophysicist, foundation administrator; b. Sterling, Colo., Dec. 10, 1940; s. Clay Thane and Julia Melvina W.; m. Sandra Lynn McMurdo, July 13, 1965 (div. 1978); m. Teresa R. Idoni, Feb. 3, 1989. Geophysics engring. degree, Colo. Sch. of Mines, 1962; MS in Oceanography, Geophysics, Oreg. State U., 1964; PhD in Geophysics, Calif. Inst. Tech., 1973. Grad. rsch. asst. dept. oceanography Oreg. State U., Corvallis, 1962-64; geophysicist ctr. astrogeology U.S. Geol. Survey, Flagstaff, Ariz., 1964-66; Fullbright-Hayes program rsch. fellow seismol. inst. U. Uppsala, Sweden, 1966-67; grad. rsch. asst. seismol. lab. Calif. Inst. Tech., Pasadena, 1967-73, sr. rsch. fellow seismol. lab., 1973-79; assoc. prof. attendant rank dept. geol. scis. U. Colo., Boulder, 1979-82, fellow Coop. Inst. Rsch. in Environ. Scis., 1979-84; v.p. technical applications and mktg. ISTAC, Inc., Pasadena, 1984-88; program dir. seismology NSF, Washington, 1989—; expert witness U.S. Ho. Reps. Com. on Sci. and Tech., 1977; mem. geodynamics rev. bd. Jet Propulsion Lab., 1980-82, com. on geodesy Nat. Acad. Scis., 1982-85; pres. Boulder Systems, Inc., Pasadena, 1987-88. Scholar State of Colo., 1958-62, Mobil Oil Co., 1960; recipient Outstanding Achievement award U.S. Geol. Survey, 1966; fellow Sweden-Am. Found., 1966. Mem. AAAS, Am. Geophysical Union, Seismol. Soc. Am., Soc. Exploration Geophysicists (scholar 1963), Tau Beta Pi, Phi Kappa Phi, Sigma Xi. Office: Nat Sci Found Geosciences 4201 Wilson Blvd Arlington VA 22230

WHITCOMB, ROBERT BASSETT, journalist, editor; s. Robert B. and Alberta (Gillette) W.; m. Nancy Davison Spears, July 26, 1975; children: Lydia D., Elizabeth T. BA, Dartmouth Coll., 1970; MS, Columbia U., 1972. Cert. Am. Press Inst. Writer Boston Herald Traveler, 1970-71; editor, writer Wall Street Jour., N.Y.C., 1972-75; fin. editor Internat. Herald Tribune, Paris, 1983-87; news and bus. editor Providence Jour., 1976-82, news editor, 1987-89, editorial writer, 1989-92, editorial page editor, 1992—; mng. editor Brown World Bus. Adv., Providence, 1987-91; consulting editor, chmn. editorial adv. bd. Manisses Comm., Providence, 1987—; mem. exec. bd. Com. Fgn. Rels., Providence, 1989-93; bd. trustees Am. Libr. Paris, 1984-87; co-moderator Truman Taylor Show, Providence, 1994—. Clapp-Poliak fellow Columbia U., 1972. Episcopalian. Office: Providence Jour Co 75 Fountain St Providence RI 02902-0050

WHITCRAFT, EDWARD C. R., investment banker; b. Lutherville, Md., 1914; s. Franklin Pierce and Louise Virginia (Regester) W. B.A., Yale, 1936. With Bank of New York, 1936-58, v.p. investment research, trust investment com., 1952-58; with Clark, Dodge & Co., N.Y.C., 1958-74; sr. v.p. Kidder, Peabody & Co., Inc., 1974-87; assoc. Shields & Co., 1987—. With USNR, 1944-46. Mem. N.Y. Soc. Security Analysts. Home: PO Box 486 Locust Valley NY 11560-0486 Office: 71 Broadway New York NY 10006-2601 also: 230 Birch Hill Rd Locust Valley NY 11560-1832

WHITE, ADRIAN MICHAEL STEPHEN, financial executive; b. Erith, Eng., Aug. 15, 1940; s. Malcolm Royston and Joan May (Richards) W.; m. Elaine M. Dorion, 1966; children: Malcolm, Catherine. Grad., McGill U., Montreal, 1964. Chartered accountant, Que., Ont. With Coopers & Lybrand, chartered accountants, 1962-66; acting treas. Rothesay Paper Corp., 1965; asst. treas. Genstar Ltd., 1967-71; treas. Brinco Ltd.; also Churchill Falls (Labrador) Corp., 1971-75; treas. Algoma Steel Corp., Ltd., Sault Ste. Marie, Ont., 1975-80; v.p., chief fin. officer Little Long Lac Gold Mines Ltd., Toronto, Ont., 1980-81; v.p. Bank of Montreal, Toronto, 1981-88; exec. v.p., CFO, bd. dirs. Curragh Inc., Toronto, 1988-93; also bd. dirs. Curragh Resources Group, Toronto; fin. columnist Indsl. Mgmt. mag.; Curragh Inc.; chmn. White-Maven Corp., 1993—; mng. ptnr. Scallwags Group, 1993—; bd. dirs. Anvil Range Mining Corp., exec. v.p., CFO, 1994—; bd. dirs. Doctor's Hosp. Bd. dirs. Doctor's Hosp Found., 1986. Mem. Fin. Execs. Inst (past pres. Toronto chpt.), Can. Tax Found. Address: 72 Sir Williams Ln, Islington, ON Canada M9A 1V3 Office: Anvil Range Mining, 145 Wellington St W, Toronto, ON Canada M5J 1H8

WHITE, ALBERT J., health products executive; b. 1933. BA, Tufts U., 1955; JD, Harvard U., 1958. Asst. sec. asst. gen. counsel Avis, Inc., 1959-63; v.p. sec. dir. Beecham, Inc., 1963—; v.p. sec., gen. counsel SmithKline Beecham Corp., Phila., 1989—. Office: SmithKline Beecham Corp PO Box 7929 1 Franklin Plz Philadelphia PA 19101

WHITE, ALICE ELIZABETH, physicist, researcher; b. Glen Ridge, N.J., Apr. 5, 1954; d. Alan David and Elizabeth Joyce (Jones) W.; m. Donald Paul Monroe, Oct. 13, 1990; 1 child, Ellen Elizabeth Monroe. BA in Physics, Middlebury (Vt.) Coll., 1976; MA in Physics, Harvard U., 1978, PhD in Physics, 1982. Postdoctoral mem. tech. staff AT&T Bell Labs., Murray Hill, N.J., 1982-84, mem. tech. staff, 1984-88, dept. head, 1988—. Contbr. over 100 articles to profl. jours. Mem. Am. Phys. Soc. (Maria Goeppert-Mayer award 1991), Optical Soc. of Am., Materials Rsch. Soc., Phi Beta Kappa. Achievements include patents in field. Office: AT&T Bell Labs PO Box 636 Murray Hill NJ 07974-0636

WHITE, ALVIN MURRAY, mathematics educator, consultant; b. N.Y.C., N.Y., June 21, 1925; s. Max and Beatrice White; m. Myra Goldstein, Dec. 4, 1946; children: Louis, Michael. BA, Columbia U., 1949; MA, UCLA, 1951; PhD, Stanford U., 1961. Acting instr. Stanford (Calif.) U., 1950-54; asst. prof. U. Santa Clara, Calif., 1954-61; prof. Harvey Mudd Coll., Claremont, Calif., 1962—; mem. math. rsch. ctr. U. Wis., Madison, 1961-62; vis. scholar MIT, 1975; initiator-facilitator humanistic math. network of over 1300 mathematicians worldwide; cons. coop. learning tutorial program Claremont Unified Sch. Dist. Editor: Interdisciplinary Teaching, 1981; editor, pub: Essays in Humanistic Mathematics, 1993; contbg. editor Humanistic Math. Network Jour.; contbr. articles to profl. jours. Served with USN, 1943-46, PTO. Grantee Fund for Improvement of Post-secondary Edn., Exxon Found. Mem. Am. Math. Soc., Math. Assn. Am., Nat. Coun. Tchrs. Math., Profl. Organizational Developers Network, Fedn. Am. Scientists, AAUP, Sigma Xi. Office: Harvey Mudd Coll 1250 N Dartmouth Ave Claremont CA 91711

WHITE, ALVIN SWAUGER, aerospace scientist, consultant; b. Berkeley, Calif., Dec. 9, 1918; s. Harold Hubbard and Ruth Amelia (Winkleman) W.; m. Betty Tomsett, Apr. 6, 1991; children: Stephen Alan, Cathie Lee, Leslie Ann. Student, U. Calif. at Davis, 1936-37, U. Calif. at Berkeley, 1937, 39-41; BME, U. Calif. at Berkeley, 1947. Engr., test pilot N.Am. Aviation, Inc., Los Angeles, 1954-61; chief test pilot N.Am. Aviation, Inc. (Los Angeles div.), 1961-66; mgr. flight ops., research and devel. Trans World Airlines, N.Y.C., 1967-69; aerospace cons. Tuscon, 1969—. Served with USAAF, 1941-46; with USAF, 1948-54. Decorated D.F.C., Air medal with 9 oak leaf clusters; recipient Warsaw Uprising Cross, Republic of Poland, 1944, Iven C. Kincheloe award Soc. Exptl. Test Pilots, 1965, Golden Plate award Am. Acad. Achievement, 1966, Harmon Internat. trophy, 1967, Richard Hansford Burroughs Jr. award Flight Safety Found., 1969, Aerospace Walk of Honor, 1994. Fellow Soc. Exptl. Test Pilots (pres. 1960-61); assoc. fellow AIAA (Octave Chanute award 1965); mem. Delta Upsilon. Republican. Episcopalian. Home and Office: 201 Pecan Ln Georgetown TX 78628 *As I grow older I look more and more for honesty in my associates. Without it you don't have much. An honest person probably knows better than anyone else how much courage it takes to be honest in some situations; so when you find honesty you find courage and character as well. And since I look for that in other people, I try very hard to be honest myself; I said, I try very hard!*

WHITE, ARTHUR CLINTON, physician; b. Williamsburg, Ky., Aug. 1, 1925; s. Herman Roy and Ethel Margaret (Goins) W.; m. Mary Katherine Pope, Dec. 27, 1949; children: Anne Litton White Davis, Arthur Clinton Jr., Herman Roy II. BS, U. Ky., 1948; MD, Harvard U., 1952. Intern, then resident in medicine Vanderbilt U. Hosp., Nashville, 1952-57; asst. prof.

medicine U. Louisville Med. Sch., 1958-63; assoc. prof. Med. Coll. Ga., 1963-67; prof. medicine, dir. infectious disease div. Ind. U. Med. Sch., 1967—; mem. drug efficacy study com. Nat. Acad. Scis., 1967. Contbr. articles med. publns. Served with USAAF, 1944-45. John and Mary R. Markle scholar, 1958-63. Mem. Infectious Disease Soc. Am., Cen. Soc. Clin. Rsch., Am. Clin. and Climatol. Assn., Med. Benevolence Found. (trustee 1986—), Meridian Hills Country Club, Skyline Club. Republican. Presbyterian. Home: 6363 Glen Coe Dr Indianapolis IN 46260-4736 Office: 1100 W Michigan St Indianapolis IN 46202-5208

WHITE, AUGUSTUS AARON, III, orthopaedic surgeon; b. Memphis, June 4, 1936; s. Augustus Aaron and Vivian (Dandridge) W. AB in Psychology cum laude, Brown U., 1957; MD, Stanford U., 1961; D of Med Sci, Karolinska Inst., Sweden, 1969; Advanced Mgmt. Program, Harvard U., 1984; DHL (hon.), U. New Haven, 1987. Diplomate Nat. Bd. Examiners, Am. Bd. Orthopaedic Surgery. Intern U. Mich. Hosp., Ann Arbor, 1961-62; asst. resident in gen. surgery Presbyn. Med. Center, San Francisco, 1962-63; asst. resident in orthopaedic surgery Yale Med. Center, New Haven, 1963-65, sr. instr., resident orthopaedic surgery, 1965-66; asst. prof. orthopaedic surgery Yale Med. Sch., 1969-72, assoc. prof., 1972-76, prof., 1977-78, dir. biomech. research dept. orthopedics, 1978-89; prof. orthopedic surgery Harvard Med. Sch., 1978—; orthopedic surgeon-in-chief Beth Israel Hosp., Boston, 1978-91, chief spine surgery div., 1991-92; sr. assoc. orthopedic surgery Children's Hosp. Med. Ctr., Boston, 1979-89; assoc. in orthopedic surgery Brigham & Women's Hosp., Boston, 1980-89; cons. div. surgery Sidney Farber Cancer Inst., Boston, 1980—; researcher biomechanics lab. Beth Israel Hosp.; chair sci. adv. bd., dir. OrthoLogic, Inc., Phoenix; bd. dirs. Am. Shared Hosp. Svcs., San Francisco; cons. orthopaedic surgery West Haven (Conn.) VA Hosp., 1970—; Hill Health Ctr., New Haven, 1970—; chief orthopedic surgery Conn. Health Care Plan, 1976-78; mem. adv. coun. Nat. Inst. Arthritis, Metabolism and Digestive Disease, NIH, 1979-82; mem. admissions com. Yale Med. Sch., 1970-72; presenter, moderator Symposium on Cervical Myelopathy, San Francisco, 1987; chmn. grant rev. com. NIH, 1985; chmn. scientific adv. bd., dir. Orthologic Corp., Phoenix; dir. Am. Shared Hosp. Svcs., San Francisco. Author: (monograph) Analysis of the Mechanics of the Thoracic Spine in Man, Leprosy, The Foot and The Orthopaedic Surgeon at Am. Acad. Orthopaedic Surgeons, 1970; book Clinical Biomechanics of the Spine, 1978, 2d edit., 1990; Symposium on Idiopathic Low Back Pain, 1982, Your Aching Back-A Doctor's Guide to Relief, 1983, rev. and updated edit., 1990, translated in German, 1992; contbr. articles to profl. jours., chpts. to sci. books. Trustee Brown U., Providence, 1971-76, bd. fellows, 1981-92; trustee Northfield Mt. Hermon Sch., Northfield, Mass., 1976-81; chmn. corp. com. on minority affairs Brown U., Providence, 1981-86, chmn. corp. com. med. edn. med. sch.; mem. The Partnership, Boston, 1984—. Served to capt. AUS, 1966-68. Decorated Bronze Star medal; named 1 of 10 Outstanding Young Men U.S. Jr. C. of C., 1969, Selected for Exceptional Black Scientist poster series CIBA-GEIGY Corp., 1982; recipient Martin Luther King, Jr. Achievement award, 1972, Kappa Delta award, nat. prize for outstanding research in orthopaedics field, 1975; nat. award for spinal research Eastern Orthopaedic Assn., 1980; Disting. Service award Northfield Mt. Hermon Sch. Alumni Assn., 1983; William Rogers award Associated Alumni Brown U., 1984; Outstanding Achievement award Delta Upsilon, 1986; Am.-Brit.-Canadian Travelling fellow Am. Orthopedic Assn., 1975. Fellow Am. Acad. Orthopaedic Surgeons, Scoliosis Research Soc.; mem. Orthopaedic Research Soc., Cervical Spine Research Soc., Internat. Soc. for Study Lumbar Spine, Internat. Soc. Orthopaedic Surgery and Traumatology, Nat. Med. Assn., Cervical Spine Research Soc. (pres. 1988), Scoliosis Research Soc., N.Am. Spine Soc., Acad. Orthopaedic Soc., Sigma Xi, Sigma Pi Phi.

WHITE, B. JOSEPH, university dean. Dean bus. administrn. U. Mich., Ann Arbor. Office: Dean School of Business Admin University of Michigan Ann Arbor Ann Arbor MI 48109*

WHITE, BARRY A., lawyer; b. Chgo., May 26, 1948. BA, U. Wis., 1970; JD cum laude, Northwestern U., 1973. Bar: Ill. 1973. Ptnr. Mayer, Brown & Platt, Chgo. Mem. Phi Eta Sigma, Phi Kappa Phi. Office: Mayer Brown & Platt 190 S La Salle St Chicago IL 60603-3410

WHITE, BARRY BENNETT, lawyer; b. Boston, Feb. 13, 1943; s. Harold and Rosalyn (Schneider) W.; m. Eleanor Greenberg; Joshua S., Adam J., Benjamin D. AB magna cum laude, Harvard U., 1964; JD magna cum laude, Harvard U., 1967. Bar: Mass. 1967, U.S. Dist. Ct. Mass. 1967, U.S. Ct. Appeals, (1st cir.) 1967. Assoc. Foley Hoag & Eliot, Boston, 1969-74, ptnr., 1975—, mem. exec. com., 1981-92, 93—, chmn. exec. com., 1991-97, mng. ptnr., 1991-92, 93—; mem. exec. com. 1991—; sec. 1992-93; chmn. Lex Mundi, 1994. Bd. dirs. Mass. affiliate Am. Diabetes Assn., 1975-82; bd. dirs., exec. com. Mass. Assn. Mental Health, 1985—, pres., 1993—; bd. dirs. Boston Mcpl. Rsch. Bureau, Home Owners Options for Mass. Edlers, Inc., 1986—, Vol. Lawyers Project, 1987—, Support Ctr. of Mass., 1988—; mem. Jewish Family and Children's Services, Boston, 1979-87; bd. visitors Boston U. Grad. Sch. Dentistry, 1981—; bd. dirs. Bur. Jewish Edn., 1987-88; bd. trustees Jewish Community Relations Council, 1988-92; chmn. com. for Clinton/Gore New Eng. Lawyers, 1992; chmn. Tsongas for Pres. Com., 1991—. With USPHS, 1967-69. Mem. ABA, Mass. Bar Assn., Boston Bar Assn., Am. Acad. Hosp. Attys., Am. Hosp. Assn. (adj. task force on health planning, 1982-84, contbg. editor hosp. law manual, 1981-84). Democrat. Clubs: Harvard of Boston, Badminton & Tennis. Editor: Harvard Law Rev., 1965-67. Office: Foley Hoag & Eliot 1 Post Office Sq Boston MA 02109-2103

WHITE, BENJAMIN TAYLOR, lawyer; b. Atlanta, Nov. 10, 1946; s. Edward Street and Jane Shannon (Taylor) W.; m. Ramona Taylor, Aug. 14, 1971; 1 child, Alexander Taylor. AB with honors, U. N.C., 1969; JD cum laude, Harvard U., 1973. Bar: Ga. 1973. Assoc. Alston & Bird, Atlanta, 1973-79, ptnr., 1979—. Trustee The Taft Sch., Watertown, Conn., 1978-81, Woodruff Arts Ctr., Atlanta, 1983—; pres., founder Ga. Vol. Lawyers for the Arts, 1979-82; chmn. Lee Harper and Dancers, Atlanta, 1979-83; pres. Alliance Theatre Co., Atlanta, 1985—. Fellow Am. Coll. Probate Counselors; mem. ABA, State Bar of Ga. (chmn. fiduciary law sect. 1986—), Atlanta Bar Assn., Internat. Bar Assn., Atlanta Tax Forum, Atlanta Estate Planning Council, Harvard Law Sch. Assn. Ga. (pres. 1981-82). Home: 3315 Valley Rd NW Atlanta GA 30305-1150 Office: Alston & Bird 1 Atlantic Ctr 1201 W Peachtree St NW Atlanta GA 30309-3400

WHITE, BENJAMIN VROOM, III, lawyer; b. Hartford, Conn., Nov. 25, 1941; s. Benjamin Vroom and Charlotte (Conover) W.; m. Elizabeth Dodge, Sept. 6, 1969; children: Constance Atwood, Charles Conover. AB, Harvard U., 1964; MA, Harvard Grad. Sch. of Edn., 1970; JD, Boston U., 1974. Law clk. to presiding justice R.I. Supreme Ct., Providence, 1974-75; assoc. ptnr. Hinckley, Allen, Salisbury & Parsons, Providence, 1975-81; ptnr. Vetter & White, Providence, 1981—; mem. faculty MCLE and Nat. inst. Trial Advocacy, Boston, 1983—. Contbr. articles to law review. Bd. govs. Gordon Sch., East Providence, 1981-82, 1st v.p., 1984—, bd. dirs. Lipptt Hill Tutorial, Providence, 1978-82. Served to lt. USNR, 1964-68, Vietnam. Mem. ABA (litigation sect.), R.I. Bar Assn. (fed. ct. bench and bar com. 1982—) Boston Bar Assn., R.I. Fed. Ct. Bd. of Bar Examiners. Republican. Episcopalian. Clubs: Harvard (R.I and N.Y.); Hope (Providence); Acoaset (Westport, Mass.). Office: Vetter & White Inc 20 Washington Pl Providence RI 02903-1328

WHITE, BETTY, actress, comedienne; b. Oak Park, Ill., Jan. 17, 1922; m. Allen Ludden, 1963 (dec.). Student pub. schs., Beverly Hills, Calif. Appearances on radio shows This Is Your FBI, Blondie, The Great Gildersleeve; actress: (TV series) including Hollywood on Television, The Betty White Show, 1954-58, Life With Elizabeth 1953-55, A Date With The Angels, 1957-58, The Pet Set, 1971, Mary Tyler Moore Show, 1974-77, The Betty White Show, 1977, The Golden Girls, 1985-92 (Emmy award for best actress 1986), The Golden Palace, 1992-93, Maybe This Time, 1995—; (TV miniseries) The Best Place to be, 1979, The Gossip Columnist, 1980, (film) Advise and Consent, 1962; guest appearances on other programs; summer stock appearances Guys and Dolls, Take Me Along, The King and I, Who Was That Lady?, Critic's Choice, Bells are Ringing. Recipient Emmy award NATAS, 1975, 76, 86; L.A. Area Emmy award, 1952. Mem. AFTRA, Am. Humane Assn., Greater L.A. Zoo Assn. (dir.). Office: care William Morris Agy 151 S El Camino Dr Beverly Hills CA 90212-2704*

WHITE, BEVERLY J., cytogeneticist; b. Seattle, Oct. 9, 1938. Grad., U. Wash., 1959, MD, 1963. Diplomate Nat. Bd. Med. Examiners, Am. Bd. Pediatrics, Am. Bd. Med. Genetics; lic physician and surgeon, Wash., Va. Rsch. trainee dept. anatomy Sch. Medicine U. Wash., Seattle, 1960-62, pediatric resident dept. pediatrics, 1967-69; rotating intern Phila. Gen. Hosp., 1963-64; rsch. fellow med. ob-gyn. unit Cardiovascular Rsch. Inst. U. Calif. Med. Ctr., San Francisco, 1964-65; staff fellow lab. biomed. scis. Nat. Inst. Child Health and Human Devel. NIH, Bethesda, Md., 1965-67, sr. staff fellow, attending physician lab. exptl. pathology Nat. Inst. Arthritis, Metabolism and Digestive Diseases, 1969-74, acting chief sect. cytogenetics, 1975-76, rsch. med. officer, attending physician sect. cytogenetics lab. cellular biology and genetics, 1974-86, dir. cytogenetics unit, interinstitute med. genetics program clin. ctr., 1987—. vis. scientist dept. pediatrics divsn. genetics Sch. Medicine, U. Wash., 1983-84; intramural cons. NIH, 1975—; cons. to assoc. editor Jour. Nat. Cancer Inst., 1976; med. staff cons. dept. ob-gyn. Naval Hosp. Bethesda, 1988-89; lectr. and presenter in field. Recipient Mosby Book award, 1963, Women of Excellence award U. Wash. and Seattle Profl. chpt. Women in Comm., 1963, Reuben award Am. Soc. for Study Sterility, 1963. Fellow Am. Coll. Med. Genetics (founding), Am. Acad. Pediatrics; mem. AMA, Am. Soc. Human Genetics, Fed. Physicians Assn., Assn. Cytogenetic Technologists (program com. 1989). Home: 20630 Highland Hall Dr Gaithersburg MD 20879 Office: NIH Cytogenetics Unit Bldg 8 Rm 108 Bethesda MD 20892

WHITE, BURTON LEONARD, educational psychologist, author; b. Boston, June 27, 1929; s. Jack J. and Evelyn S. W.; m. Janet Hodgson-White; children—Laura, Emily, David, Daniel. B.S.M.E., Tufts Coll., 1949; B.A., Boston U., 1956, M.A., 1957; Ph.D., Brandeis U., 1960. Research assoc. Brandeis U., 1960-62, M.I.T., 1962-65; sr. research assoc. Harvard Grad. Sch. Edn., 1965-78; head Center Parent Edn., Newton, Mass., 1978—. Author: books including Human Infants, 1971, Experience and Environment, Vol. I, 1973, Vol. II, 1978, The First Three Years of Life, 1975, 2d edit., 1985, The Origins of Competence, 1979, Educating the Infant and Toddler, 1988, Raising a Happy, Unspoiled Child, 1994; contbr. articles to profl. jours. Served with AUS, 1951-53. Home: 115 Pine Ridge Rd Newton MA 02168-1616 Office: 81 Wyman St Newton MA 02168-1519

WHITE, BYRON R., former U.S. supreme court justice; b. Ft. Collins, Colo., June 8, 1917; m. Marion Stearns; children: Charles, Nancy. Grad., U. Colo., 1938; Rhodes scholar, Oxford (Eng.) U.; grad., Yale Law Sch. Clk. to chief justice U.S., 1946-47; atty. firm Lewis, Grant & Davis, Denver, 1947-60; dep. atty. gen. U.S., 1961-62; assoc. justice Supreme Ct., U.S., 1962-93; ret., 1993. Served with USNR, World War II, Pacific. Mem. Phi Beta Kappa, Phi Gamma Delta, Order of Coif. Address: US Supreme Ct Supreme Ct Bldg 1 First St NE Washington DC 20543

WHITE, C. THOMAS, state supreme court justice; b. Humphrey, Nebr., Oct. 5, 1928; s. John Ambrose and Margaret Elizabeth (Costello) W.; m. Joan White, Oct. 9, 1971; children: Michaela, Thomas, Patrick. JD, Creighton U., 1952. Bar: Nebr. County atty. Platte County (Nebr.), Columbus, 1955-65; judge 21st Dist. Ct. Nebr., Columbus, 1965-77; justice Nebr. Supreme Ct., Lincoln, 1977—. Served with U.S. Army, 1946-47. Roman Catholic. Clubs: Elks, KC. Office: Nebr Supreme Ct 2219 St Capitol Bldg Lincoln NE 68509

WHITE, CALVIN JOHN, zoo executive, financial manager, zoological association executive; b. Twillingate, Nfld., Can., Feb. 28, 1948; s. Harold and Meta Blanche (Abbott) W.; m. Lorna Joan Maclachlan; children: Chelsea Elizabeth, Evan Alexander. B in Commerce, U. Toronto, Ont., Can., 1971. Fin. analyst Can. GE Co. Ltd., Toronto, 1971-72, Ford Motor Co. Can., Oakville, Ont., 1972-74; sr. fin. analyst Municipality of Met. Toronto, 1974-77, asst. dir. budget and ops. analysis, 1977-81, dir. budget analysis and internal control, 1981-86; gen. mgr. Met. Toronto Zoo, 1986—; pres. Zool. Soc. Met. Toronto, 1994—; bd. dirs. Met. Toronto Conv. and Visitors Assn., Can. Assn. Zool. Parks and Aquariums. Fellow Am. Zoo and Aquarium Assn.; mem. Am. Assn. Zoo Keepers, Inst. Pub. Adminstrn. Can. (bd. dirs. 1989-91), Zool. Soc. Met. Toronto (bd. dirs 1991—, pres. 1994—), World Conservation Union, Internat. Union Dirs. Zool. Gardens, Toronto Sportmen's Assn., Mensa. Office: Met Toronto Zoo, PO Box 280, Toronto, ON Canada M1E 4R5

WHITE, CHARLES ALBERT, JR., medical educator, obstetrician-gynecologist; b. San Diego, Aug. 1, 1922; s. Charles Albert and Helen (Hardy) W.; m. Suzan A. Alikadi, Dec. 6, 1960; children: Craig, Scott, Jennifer. D.V.M., Colo. State U., 1945; M.D., U. Utah, 1955. Diplomate: Am. Bd. Ob-Gyn. Intern Salt Lake County Hosp., 1955; resident in ob-gyn U. Iowa, 1959-61, mem. faculty ob-gyn, 1961-74; chmn. dept. ob-gyn W. Va. U., Morgantown, 1974-80; prof., chmn. dept. ob-gyn La. State U. Med. Ctr., New Orleans, 1980-92. Served to lt. comdr. USNR, 1957-59. Fellow ACS, Am. Gyn-Ob Soc.; mem. Am. Coll. Ob-Gyn, Central Assn. Ob-Gyn. Home: 33 Chateau Du Jardin Kenner LA 70065 Office: LSU Med Ctr 1542 Tulane Ave New Orleans LA 70112-2825

WHITE, CHARLES H., food science and technology educator; b. Birmingham, Ala., Mar. 15, 1943. BS, Miss. State U., 1965, MS, 1969; PhD, U. Mo., 1971. Sr. foods scientist Archer Daniels Midland Co., 1971-72; asst. prof. U. Ga., 1972-76; dir. quality assurance Dean Foods Co., 1976-80; prof. La. State U., 1980-85; E.W. Custer prof. dairy foods Miss. State U., 1985—, head dept. food sci. and tech., 1991—; mem. sci. adv. com. Dairy Rsch. Found.; mem. sci. adv. com. Nat. Dairy Promotion and Rsch. Bd., 1987-90; mem. task force on dairy tech., bd. on agr. NAS, 1988—; cons. with dairy food plants throughout U.S. and Can. Mem. editorial bd. Cultured Dairy Products Jour., Jour. Dairy Sci.; contbr. chpts. to books, articles to profl. jours. Served to col. U.S. Army Res., 1982-87. Recipient numerous grants. Mem. Am. Cultured Dairy Products Inst. (sec. 1988-89, tech. coun. 1979—), Am. Dairy Sci. Assn. (bd. dirs. 1984-87, v.p. So. div. 1988-89, pres. 1989-90), Internat. Assn. Milk, Food, and Environ. Sanitarians (pubs. com. 1979-82), Am. Men and Women of Sci., Inst. Food Technologists (microbiology sect., quality assurance sect.), Environ. Mgmt. Assn. Office: Miss State U Drawer NH Dept Food Sci and Tech Mississippi State MS 39762

WHITE, CHRISTIAN S., lawyer; b. Washington, Dec. 18, 1945; s. Milton Christian Jr. and Jean Caroline (Kirkwood) W.; m. Judith Dillard Walsh, Sept. 6, 1975. BA, Williams Coll. 1967; JD, U. Pa., 1970. Bar: D.C. 1970. Atty. advisor FTC, Washington, dep. asst. dir. mktg. practices, asst. dir. spl. statutes, exec. asst. to chmn., exec. dir., asst. gen. counsel, acting dir. bur. consumer protection. Mem. D.C. Bar. Avocation: sailing. Home: 4105 Woodbine St Chevy Chase MD 20015 Office: FTC Consumer Protection Bur 6th & Pennsylvania Ave NW Washington DC 20580

WHITE, CHRISTINE LYONS, oncology nurse, nursing researcher; b. Pa., Mar. 8, 1943; d. Eldred M. and Madeline (Whetzel) Lyons; m. James White, Nov. 1988; children: William Mackey Jr., David Mackey, Kirsten Mackey, January, Andrew. BSN, U. Pitts., 1965; MS in Nursing, George Mason U. 1983. RN, N.Y., Pa., Va., D.C.; cert. oncology nurse. Dir. nursing edn. and rsch. Mount Vernon Hosp., Alexandria, Va., 1982-89; oncology rsch. nurse specialist Washington Cancer Inst. Washington Hosp. Ctr., 1993—; adj. faculty U. Va. No. Va. Ctr., 1989. Contbr. articles to profl. jours.; presenter in field. Mem. Oncology Nursing Soc.

WHITE, CLEVELAND STUART, JR., architect; b. Norwalk, Conn., Jan. 10, 1937; s. Cleveland Stuart and Helen Thurston (Stephenson) W.; m. Matilda Bowen Romaine, Sept. 14, 1963; children: Cleveland Stuart III, Laura Brewster. AB, Princeton U., 1959; BArch, Columbia U., 1963. Registered architect, Vt., N.H., N.Y., Mass. Conn. Draftsman, designer Hill & Assocs., Cambridge, Mass., 1964-68, Roy W. Banwell, Jr., Hanover, N.H. 1968-71; prin. Banwell White & Arnold, Hanover, N.H., 1968-84, Banwell White Arnold Hemberger & Ptnrs., Hanover, N.H., 1984—; cons. Brookhaven (N.Y.) Nat. Lab., 1979-83; adj. prof. environ. studies Dartmouth Coll., Hanover, 1981; lectr. MIT Summer Inst., Cambridge, 1979, 80, 81. Author, editor: Case Study: 424 W 33rd Street Apartment Conversion, 1981; prin. works include Dartmouth Coll. Boathouse, Madbury (N.H.) Elem. Sch.; Pinckney Boathouse, Wolfeboro, N.H., Addition to Barton Hall-U. N.H., Durham, Soc. for Protection of N.H. Forests Conservation Ctr., Concord, Whitetail Ski and Summer Resort, Franklin County, Pa., Center

Moriches (N.Y.) Free Pub. Libr. Recipient Merit award Am. Wood Coun., 1981, 2 Energy Innovation award U.S. Dept. Energy, 1984, 87, 1st Honor award New Eng. Reg. Coun. Architects, 1978, Internat. Solar Energy Soc./Progressive Architecture Mag., 1982. Mem. AIA (chmn. environ. task force N.H. chpt. 1993-95, honor awards 1990, 92). Democrat. Avocations: sailing, skiing, music, gardening, art. Home: PO Box 40 Norwich VT 05055-0040 Office: Banwell White Arnold Hemberger & Ptnrs 2 W Wheelock St Hanover NH 03755-1709

WHITE, CONSTANCE BURNHAM, state official; b. Odgen, Utah, July 2, 1954; d. Owen W. and Colleen (Redd) Burnham; m. Wesley Robert White, Mar. 18, 1977. BA in English magna cum laude, U. Utah, 1976, postgrad., 1977; postgrad., Boston Coll., 1979; JD, Loyola U., 1981. Law clerk Kruse, Landa, Zimmerman & Maycock, Salt Lake City, 1979; law clerk legal dept. Bell & Howell, Lincolnwood, Ill., 1980; clerk, assoc. Parsons, Behle & Latimer, Salt Lake City, 1981-82; assoc. Reynolds, Vance, Deason & Smith, Salt Lake City, 1982-83; chief enforcement sect. Utah Securities Divsn., Salt Lake City, 1984-87, chief licensing sect., 1988, asst. dir., 1989-90; legal counsel Utah Dept. Commerce, Salt Lake City, 1990-92, exec. dir., 1993—; mem. Gov.'s Securities Fraud Task Force, 1984; spl. asst. atty. gen., 1986-88; spl. asst. U.S. atty., 1986—. Mem. North Am. Securities Adminstrs. Assn. (vice chair market manipulation com. 1988-89, penny stock/telecom. fraud com. 1989-90, chair uniform examinations com. 1990-92, chair forms revision com. 1992), Utah State Bar (securities adv. com. 1991—, task force on community-based mediation 1991—, chair securities sect. 1992-93). Office: Utah Dept Commerce 160 E 300th S Salt Lake City UT 84103

WHITE, CRAIG MITCHELL, lawyer; b. Phoenixville, Pa., Aug. 12, 1952. BA, Dartmouth Coll., 1974; JD, Ind. U., 1977. Bar: Ill. 1977, U.S. Dist. Ct. (no. dist.) Ill. 1977, U.S. Dist. Ct. (cen. dist.) Ill. 1980, U.S. Dist. Ct. (no. dist.) Ind. 1983. Ptnr. Wildman, Harrold, Allen & Dixon, Chgo., 1977—. Mem. Order of the Coif, Phi Beta Kappa. Office: Wildman Harrold Allen & Dixon 30th Fl 225 W Wacker Dr Fl 30 Chicago IL 60606-1224

WHITE, DALE ANDREW, journalist; b. Jacksonville, Fla., Feb. 17, 1958; s. John Andrew and Jeannelle Corinne White. B in Journalism, U. Fla., 1983. Reporter UPI, Miami, Fla., 1980, Orlando (Fla.) Sentinel Star, 1981; corr. Fla. Times-Union, Gainesville, 1982; reporter, columnist, editorial writer Sarasota Herald-Tribune, Bradenton, Fla., 1983—. Contbr. short stories to profl. publs. Recipient Chmn.'s award N.Y. Times, 1987, 3d Pl. Editorial Writing award Fla. Soc. Newspaper Editors, 1993. Office: PO Box 1695 Bradenton FL 34206

WHITE, DAVID CALVIN, electrical engineer, energy educator, consultant; b. Sunnyside, Wash., Feb. 18, 1922; s. David Calvin Sr. and Leafie Eloise (Scott) W.; m. Glorianna Guilii, July 30, 1949 (dec. Dec. 1965); 1 child, Julie Anne White Coman (dec.); m. Margot Ann Fuller, June 4, 1966; 1 child, Constance Anne. B.S., Stanford U., 1946, M.S., 1947, Ph.D., 1949. Registered profl. engr. Elec. engr. Kaiser Industries, Vancouver, Wash., 1941-42, 43-45; assoc. prof. elec. engring. U. Fla., Gainesville, 1949-52; asst. prof. elec. engring. MIT, Cambridge, 1952-54, assoc. prof., 1954-58, prof., 1958-62, Ford prof. engring., 1962-92, dir. energy lab., 1972-89, Ford prof. engring. emeritus, 1992—; pres., dir. Energy Conversion, Inc., 1961-64; cons. Gulf Oil, 1976-84, Johnson Controls, 1980—; sr. advisor and vis. prof. Birla Inst., India, 1968-70; mem. corp. Woods Hole Oceanographic Inst., Mass., 1977-84; mem. research coordinating panel Gas Research Inst., Chgo., 1977-85; chmn. adv. council Electric Power Research Inst., Palo Alto, Calif., 1984-86, mem., 1980-87. Author: (with others) Electromechanical Energy Conversion, 1959. Commr. Electric Light Plant, Concord, Mass., 1959-64, Kalmia Woods Water Dist., Concord, 1960-63. Named hon. prof. Instituto Politecnico Nacional, Mex., 1961. Fellow IEEE; mem. Nat. Acad. Engring., Am. Acad. Arts and Scis., Am. Soc. Engring. Edn. (George Westinghouse award 1961), Phi Beta Kappa, Sigma Xi, Tau Beta Pi, Eta Kappa Nu. Republican. Clubs: New Seabury Country, Woodfield Country. Avocations: golf; boating. Home: 8 Chart Way Popponesset Island New Seabury MA 02649 also: 799 E Jeffery St Apt 314 Boca Raton FL 33487 Office: MIT 77 Massachusetts Ave Rm E40-473 Cambridge MA 02139

WHITE, DAVID CLEAVELAND, microbial ecologist, environmental toxicologist; b. Moline, Ill., May 18, 1929; s. Frederick Berryhill and Dorothy (Cleaveland) W.; m. Sandra Jean Shoults, July 7, 1957; children: Winifred Shoults, Christopher Cleaveland, Andrew Berryhill. AB magna cum laude, Dartmouth Coll., 1951; MD, Tufts U., 1955; PhD, Rockefeller U., 1962. Rotating intern Hosp. of U. Pa., 1955-56; asst. prof., assoc. prof., then prof. biochemistry U. Ky., Lexington, 1962-72; prof. biol. sci. Fla. State U., Tallahassee, 1972-86; disting. scientist U. Tenn./Oak Ridge Nat. Lab., Knoxville, 1986—; prof. microbiology, ecology U. Tenn., Knoxville, 1986—; prin. investigator Oak Ridge (Tenn.) Nat. Lab., 1988—; mem. adv. com. Ctr. Theol. Inquiry, Princeton (N.J.) U., 1986-91, dir. Ctr. for Environ. Biotech., 1991—, Inst. Applied Microbiology, Knoxville, 1986-91; mem. sci. adv. panel Mich. State Ctr. Microbial Ecology, Lansing, 1989—, Mont. State Ctr. for Biofilm Engring., Bozeman, Mont., 1991—; mem. sci. adv. bd. Nat. Water Rsch. Inst., 1993—; dir. Microbial Insights, Inc., Knoxville; Welcome vis. prof. U. Okla., Norman, 1984-85; speaker at profl. confs. Author: Sex, Drugs and Pollution, 1983, 2d edit., 1985; founding editor-in-chief Jour. Microbiol. Methods 1985—; author 340 refereed sci. publs. Lt. M.C. USN, 1956-58. Recipient P.R. Edwards award S.E. br. Am. Soc. Microbiology, 1981, Proctor & Gamble Applied and Environ. Microbiology award Am. Soc. Microbiology, 1993, Applied and Environ. Microbiol. award ASM, 1993, Antarctic Svc. medal USN/NSF, 1984, Sci. and Tech. Achievement award U.S. EPA, 1987. Presbyterian. Achievements include discovery of signature biomarker technique for microbial biomass, community structure and nutritional status from environmental samples, microbial ecology of deep subsurface, tropical and antarctic sediments, microbial biofilms in microbial influenced corrosion, biosensors environmental characteristics. Office: Ctr for Environ Biotech 10515 Research Dr Ste 300 Knoxville TN 37932-2572

WHITE, DAVID HYWEL, physics educator; b. Cardiff, Wales, June 4, 1931; came to U.S. 1959, naturalized, 1966; s. William Richard and Bessie (Morgan) W.; m. Frances Mary Shearman, July 23, 1954; children: Richard Gerwyn, Christopher David. B.S., U. Wales, 1953; Ph.D., Birmingham U., 1956. Asst. lectr. Birmingham U., 1958-59; asst. prof. U. Pa., 1961-64; assoc. prof. Cornell U., Ithaca, N.Y., 1964-69; prof. Cornell U., 1969-78; sr. physicist, head exptl. facilities div. Isabelle Project, Brookhaven Nat. Lab. Upton, L.I., N.Y., 1978-82; group leader nuclear and particle physics rsch. P divsn. Los Alamos (N.Mex.) Nat. Lab., 1986-94; cons., 1967-69, 76-78. Author: Elementary Electronics, 1967; Editor: Scintillation Counters, 1966. NSF sr. postdoctoral fellow, 1970; JSPS fellow, 1981. Fellow Am. Phys. Soc., AAAS. Home: 913 Calle Vistoso Santa Fe NM 87501-1031

WHITE, DAVID LEE, journalist; b. Cleve., Nov. 17, 1946; s. Royden Lee and Loretta Elizabeth (Wolf) W.; m. Sandra Jean Sweet, Aug. 25, 1983. Student, Cuyahoga C.C., 1965-67. Sports corr. The Cleve. Plain Dealer, 1966-67; sports reporter The Willoughby (Ohio) News Herald, 1968, asst. sports editor, 1968-69; editor sports makeup Cleve. Press, 1969-70, sports reporter, 1970-73, editor night news, 1973-78, asst. community weekly editor, 1978-80, asst. editor world news, 1980-81, editor page makeup, PM edits., 1981-82, weekend chief copy desk, 1982-82, editor weekend news, 1981-82, asst. Sunday editor, 1981-82; editor prodn. The Charlotte (N.C.) Observer/Charlotte News, 1982-84, asst. editor features/lifestyles, 1984-86, editor TV week, 1986—; asst. coverage Ky. Derby United Press Internat. 1970, 71, 72, 74, 75, U.S. Open Golf Tournament, 1971. Coeditor: (book) Cleveland-Yesterday, Today and Tomorrow, 1976. Office: Charlotte Observer/Knight Pub Co PO Box 32188 600 S Tryon St Charlotte NC 28232

WHITE, DAVID OLIVER, museum executive; b. Phila., Mar. 3, 1938; s. Thomas Morton and Bernice Lorraine (Twist) W.; B.A., Glassboro State Coll., 1969; M.A., U. Conn., 1970; m. Lorraine Carolyn Wilt, June 19, 1965; children—Kristin Leigh, Andrew David. Acctg. clk. Penn Mut. Life Ins. Co., Phila., 1955-65; mus. dir. Conn. Hist. Commn., Hartford, 1970-74, 1992—; dir. Mus. Conn. History, State Library, Hartford, 1974-92; liaison to Conn. Hist. Commn., 1977-86, Conn. Film Festival com., 1977-80. Vice pres. Tolland Hist. Soc., 1972, 73, 79, pres., 1974, 75, 80; bd. dirs., 1977-79, 84—. Served with U.S. Army, 1961-63. Mem. Conn. Humanities Coun., N.E. Mus. Assn., Assn. for Study of Conn. History, Conn. Hist. Soc. Methodist.

Author: Connecticut's Black Soldiers 1775-83, 1973. Office: Conn Hist Comm 59 S Prospect St Hartford CT 06106

WHITE, DEVON MARKES, professional baseball player; b. Kingston, Jamaica, Dec. 29, 1962. With Calif. Angels, 1981-90, Toronto Blue Jays, 1990—; player Am. League All Star Team, 1989, 93. Recipient Gold Glove award, 1988-89, 91-94; named Am. League leader put outs by outfielder, 1987, 91-92. Office: Toronto Blue Jays, One Blue Jay Way Ste 3200, Toronto, ON Canada M5V 3B3*

WHITE, DONALD HARVEY, physicist, educator; b. Berkeley, Calif., Apr. 30, 1931; s. Harvey Elliott and Adeline White; m. Beverly Evalina Jones, Aug. 8, 1953; children: Jeri, Brett, Holly, Scott, Erin. AB, U. Calif. Berkeley, 1953; PhD, Cornell U., 1960. Rsch. physicist Lawrence Livermore (Calif.) Nat. Lab., 1960-71, cons.; prof. physics Western Oreg. State Coll., Monmouth, 1971—; vis. rsch. scientist Inst. Laue-Langevin, Grenoble, France, 1977-78, 84-85, 91-92. Author: (with others) Physics, an Experimental Science, 1968, Physics and Music, 1980. Pres. Monmouth-Independence Community Arts, 1983; pres. E. Smith Fine Arts Series, Monmouth, 1987. DuPont scholar, 1958; Minna-Heineman Found. fellow, Hannover, Fed. Republic Germany, 1977. Mem. Am. Phys. Soc., Am. Assn. Physics Tchrs. (pres. Oreg. sect. 1974-75), Oreg. Acad. Sci. (pres. 1979-80), Phi Kappa Phi (pres. West Oreg. chpt. 1989-90). Democrat. Presbyterian. Home: 411 S Walnut Dr Monmouth OR 97361-1948 Office: Western Oreg State Coll Dept Phys Earth Scis Monmouth OR 97361

WHITE, DORIS ANNE, artist; b. Eau Claire, Wis., July 27, 1924; d. William I. and Mary (Dietz) W. Grad., Art Inst. Chgo., 1950. One woman shows, IFA Galleries, Washington, Bergstrum Art Center and Museum, Neenah, Wis., Bradley Gallery, Milw.; exhibited in group shows, Ill. Mus., Springfield, 1963, Art Alliance, Phila., 1963, Museum Modern Art, N.Y.C., 1967, Pa. Acad. Fine Arts, Phila., 1963, 64, 66, Art Inst. Chgo., 1963, Met. Museum, 1966, N.A.D., N.Y.C., 1962, 63, 64, 65, 67, Butler Inst. Am. Art, Youngstown, Ohio, 1960, 61, 63, 64, 65, Smithsonian Instn., Washington, 1960, Walker Art Center, Mpls., 1963, 64, Madison (Wis.) Salon Art, 1958-63, 64, Spanish Internat. Pavilion, St. Louis, 1969, Utah State U., Logan, 1969, 70, Cleve. Inst. Art, Miami (Fla.) U., Chautauqua (N.Y.) Art Assn., Soc. Four Arts, Palm Beach, Fla., Instituto de arte de Mexico, others; represented in permanent collection, Butler Inst. Am. Art, Walker Art Center, Milw. Art Center. Recipient grand award Am. WWatercolor Soc., 1963, Grumbacker award, 1965, Paul Remmy award, 1964; medal of honor Knickerbocker Artists, 1963, Four Arts award Soc. Four ARts, 1963. Mem. NAD (Ranger fund purchase award 1965, Obrig award 1967). I allow myself complete freedom in expressing myself visually. I am constantly experimenting with new thoughts, new medias, and new directions. It is a constant challenge to take a fragment of visual thought and explore all possibilities. Changes and risks are involved. My external and internal world combine to provide the source of my creativity, therefore my goals are consequently shifting as I respond to these influences.

WHITE, DORIS GNAUCK, science educator, biochemical and biophysics researcher; b. Milw., Dec. 24, 1926; d. Paul Benjamin and Johanna (Syring) Gnauck; m. Donald Lawrence White Sr., Oct. 9, 1954 (div. Jan. 1986); children: Stanley, Dean, Victor, Donald Lawrence Jr. BS with honors, U. Wis., 1947, MS, 1949, PhD, 1956. Cert. tchr., Wis. Tchr. agr. U.S. Army Disciplinary Barracks, Milw.; 4-H leader extension div. USDA, Wis., N.J., 1950—; tchr. prof. U. Wis. Lab. High Sch., Madison, 1951-56; grad. teaching asst. health, rural, adult edn. U. Wis., Madison, 1951-56; prof. sci. edn., curriculum and instrn. William Paterson Coll., Wayne, N.J., 1957—; sci. teaching specialist Frankford (N.J.) Twp. Schs., 1962; steering com. N.J. Sci. Conv., 1977—; coll. liaison N.J. Sci. Suprs., 1979—; sr. faculty and grand marshall William Paterson Coll., 1992—; Eisenhower grant participant Belleville (N.J.) Pub. Schs., 1992-94; participant N.J. Sci. and Math. Coalition NSF grant, 1993; judge Seiko Youth Challenge, 1994; R&D judge 100 top internat. inventions, 1994. Mem. nat. sci. tchrs. manuscript rev. panel Jour. Coll. Sci. Teaching, 1991-94. Active 4-H Club Leadership, 1951— (N.J. Alumni award 1991), Geraldine Rockefeller Dodge Found. Animal Shelter, Madison, N.J., 1968—; St. Hubert's Giralda; transporter of clothes and food for poor and homeless of Paterson, N.J., 1971—; lic. blood tester for salmonella/fowl typhoid U.S. Dept. Agr.; 1987—; mem. panel on curriculum improvement N.J. Commr. Edn., 1990-91, program com. N.J. Sci. Conv., 1978—, sex equality com. N.J. Dept. Edn., 1987, sci. core proficiencies panel, N.J. Sci. Coalition, 1989-90; judge sci. fairs Carteret, N.J., 1991, N.J. Sci. Dept. Edn., Trenton, 1985-88; judge sci. fairs Carteret, N.J., 1991, N.J. Sci. Olympiad, 1993—; seer Morristown, 1986-92, Haledon, N.J., 1957-60; trustee N.J. Sci. Suprs. Assn., 1980—. Recipient Educator award Am. Cancer Soc., 1967, Meth. Layleader award, 1995; Dyes Rsch. grantee William Paterson Coll. Alumni Found., 1989-90; grantee NSF. Fellow N.J. Sci. Tchrs. Assn. (exec. bd. 1978—, indsl. liaison com. 1990-92); mem. Am. Poultry Assn. (life, lic. judge 1948—), Am. Chem. Soc., Am. Minor Breeds Assn., Nat. Sci. Tchrs. Assn., Nat. Sci. Suprs. Assn., N.J. Acad. Sci. (chair sci. edn. divsn. 1990—, liaison to sci. tchrs. 1992—), N.J. Sci. Suprs. Assn. (exec. bd. 1979—, pres. 1981, Outstanding Sci. Supr. award 1986, President's award 1992), N.J. Physics Tchrs. Assn., N.J. Sci. and Tech. Assn., Liberty Sci. Mus. (charter). Republican. Methodist. Achievements include development of chromosome mapping of fowl genes, two new breeds of squash which are now commercial varieties, penguin-like ducks; research in poultry genetics, genetics of Cucurbitaceae, ultrasound treatment of plant seeds as related to seed germination and plant growth, laser holographic interferometry to measure plant growth occuring in seconds, measurement in angstroms of light, growth regulators in plants, cat eye genetics, catatonic effects in fowl, herpes virus research with fowl; rodent remains and hanta virus; experiments with leaf berms for highway sound barriers, stuffing leaf berms with waste tires for highway median barriers, stuffing leaf berms with waste paper for highway sound barriers; experiments with tom turkey head ornaments colors of red, white and blue as indicators of contentment or stress, color changes during turkey copulation; new uses for incinerator ash, sewage sludge, and firework pollution; design of ocean wave and tidal pumps to transport glacial melt; design of portable methane gas generator; cereal grains genetics research. Home: 7 Beaver Brook Rd Annandale NJ 08801-2018 Office: William Paterson Coll 408 Raubinger Hall 300 Pompton Rd Wayne NJ 07470-2153

WHITE, DOUGLAS JAMES, JR., lawyer; b. N.Y.C., Mar. 20, 1934; s. Douglas James and Margaret (Stillman) W.; m. Denise Beale, May 28, 1960; children: Brian Douglas, James Roderick. BA, U. Oreg., 1955; LLB, Willamette U., 1958. Bar: Oreg. 1958. Law clk. to assoc. justice Oreg. Supreme Ct., Salem, 1958-59; assoc. Schwabe, Williamson & Wyatt (formerly known as Maxutt, Souther, Spaulding, Kinsey & Williamson), Portland, Oreg., 1959-69; shareholder, gen. ptnr. Schwabe, Williamson & Wyatt, P.C. (formerly known as Schwabe, Williamson, Wyatt, Moore & Roberts), Portland, Oreg., 1969-79, sr. ptnr., 1979-93; shareholder, 1994—; bd. dirs. Portland Iron Works and Affiliates; gen. outside counsel Oreg. Grad. Inst. Sci. Tech., Beaverton. Trustee Jesuit H.S., Beaverton, 1991-94; bd. dirs. St. Vincent de Paul Child Devel. Ctr., Portland, 1979-90, Portland Coun., Soc. St. Vincent de Paul, 1989-92; bd. dirs., officer Maryville Nursing Home, Beaverton, 1993—, St. Vincent de Paul Conf. of St. Thomas More, Portland, 1966—; active Saturday Acad., Beaverton, 1982—. Mem. ABA, Oreg. State Bar Assn. (real estate and land use sect. exec. com 1984-85), Multnomah County Bar Assn., Multnomah Athletic Club (Portland), Arlington Club (Portland), Flyfisher Club of Oreg. Republican. Roman Catholic. Avocations: flyfishing, cross-country skiing, bridge, hiking, jogging. Home: 6725 SW Preslynn Dr Portland OR 97225-2668 Office: Schwabe Williamson & Wyatt 1211 SW 5th Ave Portland OR 97204-3713

WHITE, DOUGLAS R., anthropology educator; b. Mpls., Mar. 13, 1942; s. Asher Abbott and Margaret McQuestin (Richie) W.; m. Jayne Chamberlain (div. Feb. 1971); m. Lilyan Amdur Brudner, Mar. 21, 1971; 1 child, Scott Douglas. BA, U. Minn., 1964, MA, 1967, PhD, 1969. Asst. prof. U. Pitts., 1967-72, assoc. prof., 1972-76; assoc. prof. U. Calif., Irvine, 1976-79, prof., 1979—; dep. dir. Lang. Artifutils Rsch. Project, Dublin, Ireland, 1971-73; vis. prof. U. Tex., Austin, 1974-75; chmn. Linkages: World Devel. Res. Coun., Md., 1986—, pres. 1986-90. Co-editor: Research Methods in Social Networks, 1989, Anthropology of Urban Environments, 1972; founder, gen. editor World Cultures Jour., 1985-90; author sci. software packages; contbr.

articles to profl. jours. Fellow Ctr. for Advanced Studies, Western Behavioral Sci. Inst., La Jolla, Calif., 1981-84; recipient Sr. Scientist award Alexander von Humboldt Stiftung, Bonn, Germany, 1989-91, Bourse de Haute Niveau award Ministry of Rsch. and Tech., Paris, 1992. Mem. Social Sci. Computing Assn. (pres. elect 1991, pres. 1992.). Democrat. Home: 8888 La Jolla Scenic Dr N La Jolla CA 92037 Office: U Calif Irvine School of Social Sci Irvine CA 92717

WHITE, DUANE E., mortgage company executive. Pres., CEO FBS Mortgage Corp., Saint Paul, Minn. Office: FBS Mortgage Corp 2550 University Ave W Saint Paul MN 55114*

WHITE, EDMUND VALENTINE, author; b. Cin., Jan. 13, 1940; s. Edmund Valentine and Delilah (Teddlie) W. B.A., U. Mich., 1962. Writer Time-Life Books, N.Y.C., 1962-70; sr. editor Saturday Rev., N.Y.C., 1972-73; exec. dir. N.Y. Inst. for Humanities, N.Y.C., 1982-83; asst. prof. writing seminars John Hopkins U., Balt., 1977-79; adj. prof. Columbia U. Sch. Arts, N.Y.C., 1981-83; prof. Brown U., Providence, 1990-92. Novelist: Forgetting Elena, 1973, Nocturnes for the King of Naples, 1978, A Boy's Own Story, 1982, Caracole, 1985, The Darker Proof, 1987, The Beautiful Room is Empty, 1988, Skinned Alive, 1995, Our Paris, 1995; author: States of Desire, 1980, The Faber Book of Gay Short Fiction, 1991, Genet: A Biography, 1993, The Burning Library, 1994. Named Ingram Merrill fellow, 1978, Guggenheim fellow, 1983; recipient Chevalier de l'ordre des arts et lettres, 1993, Nat. Book Critics Circle award, 1994. Office: care Maxine Groffsky 2 Fifth Ave New York NY 10011

WHITE, EDWARD ALLEN, electronics company executive; b. Cambridge, Jan. 1, 1928; s. Joseph and Bessie (Allen) W.; m. Joan Dixon, Dec. 22, 1949 (div. Aug. 1978); children: Dixon Richard, Leslie Ann White Lollar; m. Nancy Rhoads, Oct. 6, 1979. B.S., Tufts U., 1947. Chmn. Bowmar Instrument Corp., Phoenix, Mass., 1951—, White Technology Inc., Phoenix, 1980-86; pres. Ariz. Digital Corp., Phoenix, 1975-91; chmn., chief exec. officer AHI, Inc., Ft. Wayne, Ind., 1970-88; mem. World Pres's. Orgn., Washington D.C., 1978—. Patentee in field. Bd. dirs. Gov.'s Council Children, Youth and Families, Phoenix, 1982-84, Planned Parenthood Fedn. Am., 1984-88; pres., bd. dirs. Planned Parenthood Central and No. Ariz., 1984-88; trustee Internat House, N.Y.C., 1973-75, Tufts U., 1973-83. Mem. Tau Beta Pi. Club: Paradise Valley Country. Home: 5786 N Echo Canyon Cir Phoenix AZ 85018-1242 Office: Bowmar Instrument Corp 5080 N 40th St Ste 475 Phoenix AZ 85018-2150

WHITE, EMIL HENRY, chemistry educator; b. Akron, Ohio, Aug. 17, 1926. B.S., U. Akron, 1947; M.S., Purdue U., 1948, Ph.D. in Chemistry, 1950. Fellow U. Chgo., 1950-51; fellow Harvard U., 1951-52; instr. organic chemistry Yale U., New Haven, 1952-56; from asst. prof. to assoc. prof. Johns Hopkins U., Balt., 1957-64, prof. organic chemistry, 1964-80, D. Mead Johnson prof. chemistry, 1980—. Recipient Md. Chemist of Yr. award, 1980; Guggenheim fellow, 1958-59, NIH sr. fellow, 1965-66, 72-73. Home: 4400 Green Valley Rd Union Bridge MD 21791-9030 Office: Johns Hopkins U Dept Chemistry Baltimore MD 21218

WHITE, ERSKINE NORMAN, JR., management company executive; b. N.Y.C., July 21, 1924; s. Erskine Norman and Catharine (Putman) W.; m. Eileen E. Lutz, Nov. 5, 1949; children: Erskine Norman III, Carol Putnam White Wolfe, Catharine Lutz. BE, Yale U., 1947; MS, MIT, 1949. Staff mem. rsch. devel. bd. Dept. Def., 1949; plant mgr. Gorham Mfg. Co. (became Gorham Corp. 1961, Gorham div. Textron Inc. 1968), Asheville, N.C., 1956-57, 1956-57, exec. v.p., 1964-68, pres., 1968-69, dir., 1960-69; group v.p. Textron Inc., Providence, 1969-71; exec. v.p. ops. Textron Inc., 1971-75, exec. v.p., 1975-79, exec. v.p. corp. affairs, 1979-81; pres. E.N. White Mgmt. Corp., Providence, 1981—; v.p., treas. Cadwagan Assoc.; bd. dirs. Keyport Life Ins. Co., R.I. Hosp., Trust Nat. Bank, Carlisle Cos. Inc. Trustee Women and Infants Hosp., R.I., 1974-93, R.I. Sch. Design, 1966-72, 82—, chmn. fin. com., 1988—, treas., 1990—; bd. dirs., exec. com. New Eng. Coun., 1979-81; chmn. NCCJ, 1987-89. With USN, 1944-46, PTO. Mem. NAM (bd. dir. 1974-80, regional v.p. 1975, div. vice chmn. 1978-80, exec. com.), Urban League (bd. dir. R.I. chpt. 1989—), Greater Providence C. of C. (bd. dir., pres. 1978), R.I. C. of C. Fedn. (pres. 1979), Sigma Xi, Tau Beta Pi. Office: E N White Mgmt Corp 56 Pine St Ste 3A Providence RI 02903-2819

WHITE, ETHYLE HERMAN (MRS. S. ROY WHITE), artist; b. San Antonio, Apr. 10, 1904; d. Ferdinand and Minnie (Simmang) Herman; ed. pvt. schs., instrs.; m. S. Roy White, Mar. 3, 1924 (dec.); children: Mrs. William Marion Mohrle, Patsyruth Wheeler. Exhibited numerous one-man, group shows, Tex.; represented pub. collections in U.S., pvt. collections in Switzerland, Germany, Sweden. Del. Internat. Com. Centro Studi E. Scambi Internationali. Mem. Anahuac Fine Arts Group, San Antonio, Beaumont, Galveston, Houston art leagues, Daus. Republic Tex., UDC, Pastel Soc. Tex., Watercolor Soc., Nat. League Am. Pen Women, Dallas Tex. Sumie Soc. of Am., Baytown (Tex.) Porcelain Guild. Episcopalian. Mem. Order Eastern Star. Clubs: Fine Arts (Anahuac); Artist and Craftsmen (Dallas). Author, illustrator: Arabella. Author: Poet's Hour. Home: PO Box 176 Anahuac TX 77514-0176

WHITE, EUGENE JAMES, retired technology company executive; b. Hartford, Conn., Feb. 28, 1928; s. Mark James and Bernice Katherine (Humphry) W.; m. Vivian Pickral, June 16, 1951; children—Timothy, John, Eugene James. B.S. in Finance and Econs, U. Hartford, 1951. Corp. controller Kaman Corp., Bloomfield, Conn., 1951-60; sr. v.p. fin. EG&G Wellesley, Mass., 1960-83; trustee Boston Five Cents Savs. Bank; dir. E.T. Ryan Iron Works, Inc., Thompson Steel Co., BKW Inc. Mem. alumni mgmt. group U. Hartford; past mem. Natick Redevel. Commn.; mem. trustee council Leonard Morse Hosp., Natick, Mass.; bd. regents U. Hartford; chmn. bd. Nat. Alliance for Hydroelectric Energy. Served with USCGR, 1945-46. Recipient Distinguished Alumnus award U. Hartford Alumni Assn., 1976. Mem. Am. Mgmt. Assn., Fin. Execs. Inst. (pres. N.E. area, nat. dir.), Treas's Club Boston (past pres.), New Eng. Council (dir.). Roman Catholic. Club: Brae Burn Country (Newton, Mass.); Oyster Harbors (Osterville, Mass.), Monarch Country (Stuart, Fla.). Home: 2360 SW Longwood Dr Palm City FL 34990-4733

WHITE, EUGENE R., computer manufacturing company executive. With Gen. Electric Co., Fairfield, Conn., 1958-70, Fairchild Camera & Instrument Corp., 1970-74; chmn., chief exec. officer Amdahl Corp., Sunnyvale, Calif., from 1974, now vice chmn., also bd. dirs. Office: Amdahl Corp PO Box 3470 1250 E Arques Ave Sunnyvale CA 94088

WHITE, EUGENE VADEN, pharmacist; b. Cape Charles, Va., Aug. 13, 1924; s. Paul Randolph and Louise (Townsend) W.; m. Laura Juanita LaFontaine, Aug. 28, 1948; children: Lynda Sue, Patricia Louise. BS in Pharmacy, Med. Coll. Va., 1950; PharM (hon.), Phila. Coll. Pharmacy and Sci., 1966. Pharmacist McKim & Huffman Drug Store, Luray, Va., 1950, Miller's Drug Store, Winchester, Va., 1950-53; pharmacist, ptnr. Shiner's Drug Store, Front Royal, Va., 1953-56; pharmacist, owner Eugene V. White, Pharmacist, P.C., Berryville, Va., 1956—; Sturmer lectr. Phila. Coll. Pharmacy and Sci., 1979; Lubin vis. prof. U. Tenn. Sch. Pharmacy, Memphis, 1974; mem. bd. visitors Sch. Pharmacy, U. Pitts., 1969. Author: The Office-Based Family Pharmacist, 1978; created first office practice in community pharmacy, 1960, developed patient medication profile record, 1960. 2d lt. USAAC, 1943-45. Recipient Nat. Leadership award Phi Lambda Sigma, 1979, Outstanding Pharmacy Alumnus award Med. Coll. Va. Sch. Pharmacy Alumni Assn., 1989. Fellow Am. Coll. Apothecaries (J. Leon Lascoff award 1973); mem. Am. Pharm Assn. (Daniel B. Smith award 1965, Remington Honor medal 1978), Va. Pharm. Assn. (Pharmacist of Yr. award 1966, Outstanding Pharmacist award 1992). Methodist. Avocations: reading, woodworking, computer. Office: 1 W Main St Berryville VA 22611-1340

WHITE, FRED ROLLIN, JR., mining and shipping company executive; b. Cleve., Mar. 23, 1913; s. Fred Rollin and Miriam (Norton) W.; m. Emma Garretson Raymond, Dec. 21, 1940; children: Emma Stone White Seymour, Carolyn White Barr, Margaret Raymond White Ziering. B.A., Yale U., 1935. With Oglebay Norton Co., Cleve., 1935—, successively accountant, in

vessel ops., 1935-57, v.p. 1949-57, sr. v.p. transp. and docks, 1957-59, sr. v.p., 1959-78, treas., 1960-63, vice chmn. bd. emeritus, 1969-92; chm. exec. com. Oglebay Norton Co., 1978-92, dir., 1949—; v.p. Columbia Transp. Co. 1950-57, dir., 1950—; trustee Oglebay Norton Found.; treas. Fortune Lake Mining Co., 1950-60, v.p. 1952-60, dir., 1958-60; treas., dir. David Z. Norton Co., 1936—, v.p., 1959-60, 94—, pres., 1960-94; pres., dir. Internat. Great Lakes Shipping Co., 1959-61, Toledo Overseas Terminals Co., 1959-72; mem. Lake View Cemetery Assn., 1940-81 (emeritus), trustee, 1949-75, pres., 1954-71; v.p. Cleve. Vessel Agy., Inc., 1964-71, dir., 1958-71; v.p., dir. Chillicothe-Center Co., 1960-78; pres., dir. Silloc Ltd., 1966-73; v.p. Can. Ferro Hot Metal Spltys., Ltd., 1971-78; dir. Oglebay Norton Taconite Co., ONCO Eveleth Co., Central Silica Co., T&B Foundry Co., ON Coast Petroleum Co., Superior Land Co., 1973-86, Licking River Terminal Co., Tex. Mining Co., Saginaw Mining Co.; dir. Union Commerce Corp., Union Commerce Bank, 1959-82. Trustee Lake Carriers Assn.; treas. Great Lakes Protective Assn., 1965-76; treas., trustee Amasa Stone House, Inc., Cleve., 1946-85; asst. sec., asst. treas., trustee Horace Kelley Art Found. Served from 1st lt. to lt. col. AUS, 1941-45. Decorated Bronze Star. Mem. Am. Bur. Shipping (bd. mgrs. 1976-82), Am. Iron and Steel Inst., Internat. Shipmasters Assn. (hon. life), Soc. Naval Architects and Marine Engrs., First Cleve. Cavalry Assn. (pres. 1967-68, 83-85), Musical Arts Assn., SAR, Western Res. Hist. Soc. (v.p. 1964-68, trustee 1960-89, hon.), Greater Cleve. Growth Assn., Early Settlers Assn. Western Res., Lake County Hist. Soc. (hon. life, trustee 1961-79). Republican. Episcopalian. Clubs: Eastern Point Yacht (Gloucester, Mass.); Winous Point Shooting (Port Clinton, Ohio) (dir. 1957-89, v.p. 1965-69, pres. 1969-77); Kirtland Country (Cleve.) (dir. 1950-59), Union (Cleve.) (trustee 1959-70, 1st v.p. 1965-67, pres. 1967-69). Home: 18900 Shelburne Rd Cleveland OH 44118-4945 Office: 1100 Superior Ave E Cleveland OH 44114-2501

WHITE, FREDERICK ANDREW, physics educator, physicist; b. Detroit, Mar. 11, 1918; s. Andrew Bracken and Mildred (Witzel) W.; m. Dorothy Janet Sibley, Nov. 7, 1942 (dec.); children: Wendell William, Lawrence Sibley, Eric Sibley, Roger Randolph (dec.). B.S., Wayne State U., 1940; M.S., U. Mich., 1941; postgrad., U. Rochester, 1943-46; Ph.D., U. Wis., 1959. Insp. U.S. Army Ordnance, Rochester N.Y., 1941-43; research asst. Manhattan project U. Rochester, 1943-45, grad. instr. in research, 1946; research asst., research asso., cons. physicist Gen. Electric Co. Knolls Atomic Power Lab., Schenectady, 1947-62; adj. prof. nuclear sci. Rensselaer Poly. Inst., Troy, N.Y., 1961-62; prof. nuclear engring. and environmental engring., indsl. liaison scientist Rensselaer Poly. Inst., 1962-81, prof. emeritus, 1981—; mem. staff Bell Telephone Labs., 1969; research and liaison scientist Rochester Gas & Electric Co., N.Y., 1978—; adj. prof. physics SUNY, Albany, 1981-88; cons. NASA, 1965—; organist and acoustic cons. 1952—. Author: American Industrial Research Laboratories, 1961, Mass Spectrometry in Science and Technology, 1968, Our Acoustic Environment, 1975; Mass Spectrometry: Applications in Science and Engineering, 1986. Mem. AIAA, AAAS, IEEE, Am. Nuclear Soc., Am. Phys. Soc., Optical Soc. Am., Acoustical Soc. Am., Am. Chem. Soc., Am. Guild Organists, Soc. Applied Spectroscopy, Sigma Xi. Developer mass spectrometric instrumentation and its uses in measurements relating to nuclear and atomic physics; co-discoverer last naturally-occurring stable isotope. Home: 2456 Hilltop Rd Niskayuna NY 12309-2405 Office: Rensselaer Poly Inst Linac Lab Troy NY 12181

WHITE, GARY L., trucking executive; b. 1932. Dir. minority devel. Ford Motor Co., Dearborn, Mich., 1955-86; pres., chmn. bd. Jones Transfer Co., Monroe, Mich., 1986—. Office: Jones Transfer Co 300 Jones Ave Monroe MI 48161-1397

WHITE, GAYLE COLQUITT, religion writer, journalist; b. Lamar County, Ga., Nov. 4, 1950; d. Albert Candler and Ethel Eugenia (Moore) Colquitt; m. Robert Eugene White, Jr., Apr. 9, 1972; children: Margaret Candler, Robert Eugene III. AB in Journalism, U. Ga., 1972. Reporter Atlanta Jour. & Constn., 1972—. Named Templeton Reporter of Yr., Religion Newswriters Assn., 1992. Presbyterian. Office: Atlanta Journal & Constitution 72 Marietta St NW Atlanta GA 30303-2804

WHITE, GEORGE, government official, physical scientist; b. Bklyn., Dec. 19, 1937; s. Samuel Louis and Mollie (Telson) W.; m. Susan Jane Doppelhammer, Apr. 13, 1969; 1 child, Jeffrey Steven. B.S., CUNY, 1960; M.S., NYU, 1964; postgrad. NYU, 1966-68. Research asst. Rockefeller Inst., N.Y.C., 1960, NYU, N.Y.C., 1961-64; research scientist Atlantic Research Corp., Alexandria, Va., 1965-72; sr. staff officer Nat. Acad. Scis., Washington, 1973-80; div. chief, asst. to dir. U.S. Bur. Mines, Dept. Interior, Washington, 1981—; lectr. chemistry, No. Va. Community Coll., Alexandria, Va., 1972-78, Bronx Community Coll., 1961-64. Staff editor: Chemistry of Coal Utilization, 1980, Minerals and Materials, 1983—, Minerals Position of the U.S., 1985—. Named Presdl. Sci. Intern, Nat. Sci. Found., Dept. Transp., 1972; Legis. fellow U.S. Congress, 1992. Mem. Am. Chem. Soc., AAAS, Am. Inst. Mining Engrs., Washington Chem. Soc. Democrat. Jewish. Home: 3903 Forest Grove Dr Annandale VA 22003-1961 Office: Dept Interior US Bur Mines 810 7th St NW Washington DC 20241-9999

WHITE, GEORGE COOKE, theater director, foundation executive; b. New London, Conn., Aug. 16, 1935; s. Nelson Cooke and Aida (Rovetti) W.; m. Elizabeth Conant Darling, July 5, 1958; children: George Conant, Caleb Ensign, Juliette Darling. Student, U. Paris, 1956; BA, Yale U., 1957, MFA, 1961; student, Shakespeare Inst. 1959; ArtsD (hon.), Conn. Coll., 1994. Stage mgr. Imperial Japanese Azumakabuki Co., 1955; asst. mgr. Internat. Ballet Festival, Nervi, Italy, 1955; prodn. coordinator Talent Assos., 1961-63; adminstrv. v.p. score prodns. Paramount Pictures, 1963-65; founder, pres. Eugene O'Neill Meml. Theatre Found., 1965—; adviser, dir. Theatre One, Conn. Coll. Women, 1967-70; regional theater cons. Nat. Ednl. TV Network; guest lectr. Wagner Coll. 1970; acting dir. Hunter Coll. Hunter Arts, 1972-73; adj. prof. U. N.C.; prof. theater adminstrn. program Yale U., 1978-91; co-chmn. Yale Drama Sch.; mem. exec. com. Theatre Library Assn., 1967; bd. govs. Am. Playwrights Theatre; mem. bd. ANTA, 1967-68; mem. Mayor N.Y.C.'s Theatre Adv. Com.; advisory bd. Internat. Theatre Inst.; panel mem. Exptl. Theatre; U.S. State Dept. cultural exchange grantee to Australia; guest adminstr. Australian Nat. Playwrights Conf., 1973; U.S. del. Internat. Theatre Inst. Congress, Moscow, 1973; mem. Conn. Commn. on Arts, 1978-93, mem. exec. com., 1979-83, vice chair, 1992-93; co-founder Caribbean-U.S. Theatre Exchange; dir. Actors Theatre St. Paul, 1979, 80, 82, 83, 86, Hartman Repertory Theatre, 1980; guest dir. Chinese Theater Assn., Beijing, 1984, 87, Hedgerow Theatre, 1986; mem. nominating com. Antoinette Perry Awards, 1984-86, 88, 94; dir. Anna Christie Beijing Cen. Dramatic Theater, 1984, 87. Appeared in TV series Citizen Soldier, 1959-61; appeared in off-Broadway prodn. John Brown's Body. Trustee Goodspeed Opera House, 1966-68, Nat. Theatre Conf., 1973—, Eastern Conn. Symphony, Dance Arts Coun., Conn. Opera Assn., Conn. Pub. TV, 1973-83; Trustee Conn. Edn. Telecommunications Corp., 1973-83, chmn., 1982; mem. planning bd. Op. Rescue; bd. dirs. Rehearsal Club, Centre for Inter-Am. Rels., Theater of Latin Am., Manhattan Theatre Club, 1970-80, Met. Opera Guild; Performance mag.; exec. com. Yale Drama Alumni, 1963-73; mem. Yale Alumni Bd.; bd. overseers drama dept. Brandeis U.; adv. bd. Am. Musical Theatre Program, Hartford Conservatory, Bd. Arts & Bus. Coun., Brandeis Creative Arts Award Jury, Theater and New Music Theatre Works Panel, NEA; mem. Waterford (Conn.) Rep. Town Meeting, 1975-77; presdl. appointment to Nat. Coun. NEA, 1992; mem. Coast Guard Auxillary, Crew mem. U.S. Coast Guard Barque Eagle. Served with AUS, 1957-59. Recipient spl. citation New Eng. Theatre Conf., 1968, Margo Jones award, 1968, Pub. Svc. award New London County Bar Assn., 1975, Disting. Citizen's award Town of Waterford, 1976, Disting. Service award Conn. mag., Contbns. to State award, 1981, Lifetime Contbn. to Theatre award Am. Theater Assn., Contbn. to Conn. Arts award Quinnipiac Coll., 1989; Internat. Communications Agy. cultural exch. grantee to People's Republic of China, 1980; Officer first class Royal Swedish Order of Polar Star; Chevalier des artes et des lettres (France). Fellow Royal Soc. Arts; mem. Chinese Theatre Assn. (hon.). Clubs: Century; Cosmos (Washington); Thames (New London); White's Point Yacht. Office: O'Neill Theater Ctr 305 Great Neck Rd Waterford CT 06385

WHITE, GEORGE EDWARD, legal educator, lawyer; b. Northampton, Mass., Mar. 19, 1941; s. George LeRoy and Frances Dorothy (McCafferty) W.; m. Susan Valre Davis, Dec. 31, 1966; children: Alexandra V., Elisabeth

McC. BA, Amherst Coll., 1963; MA, Yale U., 1964, PhD, 1967; J.D., Harvard U., 1970. Bar: D.C. 1970, Va. 1975, U.S. Supreme Ct. 1973. Vis. scholar Am. Bar Found., 1970-71; law clk. to Chief Justice Warren, U.S. Supreme Ct., 1971-72; asst. prof. law U. Va., 1972-74, assoc. prof., 1974-77, prof., 1977-86, John B. Minor prof. law and history, 1987-92, Disting. Univ. prof., John B. Minor prof. law and history, 1992—; vis. prof. Marshall-Wythe Law Sch. spring 1988, N.Y. Law Sch., fall 1988. Mem. Am. Acad. Arts and Scis., Am. Law Inst., Am. Soc. Legal History (bd. dirs. 1978-81), Soc. Am. Historians. Author books, including The American Judicial Tradition, 1976, 2d edit., 1988, Tort Law in America: An Intellectual History (Gavel award ABA 1981), 1980, Earl Warren: A Public Life (Gavel award ABA 1983), 1982, The Marshall Court and Cultural Change, 1988, 2d edit. 1991 (James Willard Hurst prize 1990), Justice Oliver Wendell Holmes: Law and the Inner Self, 1993 (Gavel award ABA 1994, Scribes award 1994, Littleton-Griswold prize 1994), Intervention and Detachment: Essays in Legal History and Jurisprudence, 1994; editor Studies in Legal History, 1980-86. Office: U Va Law Sch Charlottesville VA 22903

WHITE, GEORGE MALCOLM, architect; b. Cleve., Nov. 1, 1920; m. Susanne Neiley Daniels, Apr. 21, 1973; children: Stephanie, Jocelyn, Geoffrey, Pamela. B.S., MIT, 1942, M.S., 1942; M.B.A., Harvard, 1948; LL.B., Case Western Res. U., 1959. Design engr. Gen. Electric Co., Schenectady, 1942-47; practice architecture and law Cleve., 1948-71; Architect of Capitol, Washington, 1971—; Mem. D.C. Zoning Commn.; acting dir. U.S. Bot. Garden; mem. U.S. Capitol Police Bd., U.S. Capitol Guide Bd., U.S. Ho. of Reps. Page Bd., Adv. Council on Hist. Preservation, Internat. Centre Com., Nat. Conservation Adv. Council, Nat. Capital Meml. Commn.; bd. dirs., chmn. design com. Pennsylvania Ave. Devel. Corp.; bd. dirs. Nat. Building Mus.; trustee Federal City Council; mem. art adv. com. Washington Met. Area Transit Authority; bd. regents Am. Archtl. Found.; former chmn. archtl. adv. com. Restoration of Statue of Liberty; chmn. com. for Statue of Liberty Mus.; mem. nat. panel arbitrators Am. Arbitration Assn.; former mem. vis. com. dept. architecture and planning MIT; mem. bd. cons. Nubian monuments at Philae, Egypt.; mem. internat. com. cons. for Egyptian Mus., Cairo; chmn. rev. com. Nat. Capital Devel. Commn. for Canberra, Australia. Works include First Unitarian Ch., Cleve., 1959, Preformed Line Products Co. Office Bldg., Cleve., 1960, Mentor Harbor Yacht Club, 1968, restoration, Old Senate and Supreme Ct. Chambers, U.S. Capitol, 1975, Libr. of Congress James Madison Meml. Bldg., 1979, U.S. Capitol Power Plant Extension, 1979, master plan for U.S. Capitol, 1981, Hart Senate Office Bldg., 1982, restoration of the west cen. front U.S. Capitol Bldg., 1987, Thurgood Marshall Fed. Judiciary Bldg., 1992, U.S. Capitol west terr. restoration and courtyard addt., 1993. Recipient Gold medal Archtl. Soc. Ohio, 1971, Burton award for Disting. Pub. Svc. Cleve. Club, 1991. Fellow AIA (Thomas Jefferson award 1992), Nat. Soc. Profl. Engrs., ASCE (hon. fellow); mem. Sigma Xi, Eta Kappa Nu, Lambda Alpha, Tau Beta Pi. Office: Architect of Capitol US Capitol Bldg Washington DC 20515-9994

WHITE, GEORGE W., federal judge; b. 1931. Student, Baldwin-Wallace Coll., 1948-51; J.D., Cleveland-Marshall Coll. Law, 1955. Sole practice law Cleve., 1956-68; judge Ct. Common Pleas, Ohio, 1968-80; judge U.S. Dist. Ct. (no. dist.) Ohio, 1980-95, chief judge, 1995—; referee Ct. Common Pleas, Cuyahoga County, 1957-62. Councilman, Cleve., 1963-68. Mem. ABA, Fed. Bar Assn., 6th Circuit Jud. Coun. (exec. com. 1995—). Office: US Dist Ct 135 US Courthouse 201 Superior Ave E Cleveland OH 44114-1203

WHITE, GERALD ANDREW, chemical company executive; b. L.I., N.Y., Aug. 2, 1934; s. Charles Eugene and Grace Mary (Trojan) W.; m. Mary Alice Turvey, June 8, 1957; children—Kevin, Patricia, Timothy, Megan. B in Chem. Engring., Villanova U., 1957; cert. advanced mgmt. program, Harvard Bus. Sch., 1975. Staff engr. Air Products and Chems., Inc., Allentown, Pa., 1962-65, mgr. systems devel., 1965-66, group controller, 1969-72, corp. controller, 1974-76, v.p. planning, 1977-82, v.p. fin., chief fin. officer, 1982-87, sr. v.p. fin., chief fin. officer, 1987—. Pres. United Way in Lehigh County, 1981; bd. dirs. Pa. Coun. on Econ. Edn., 1981, Lord Corp., 1994; trustee, treas. Allentown Art Mus., 1984; trustee, chmn. bd. trustees Allentown Coll. St. Francis de Sales, Center Valley, 1983. Lt. USN, 1957-62. Recipient J. Stanley Morehouse Meml. award Villanova U. Coll. Engring., 1983. Mem. AICE, Fin. Execs. Inst. (pres. northeastern Pa. chpt. 1974-75), Fin. Execs. Rsch. Found. (trustee 1992), Tau Beta Pi. Avocation: squash.

WHITE, GILBERT F(OWLER), geographer, educator; b. Chgo., Nov. 26, 1911; s. Arthur E. and Mary (Guthrie) W.; m. Anne Elizabeth Underwood, Apr. 28, 1944; children: William D., Mary, Frances. BS, U. Chgo., 1932, SM, 1934, PhD, 1942; LLD (hon.), Hamilton Coll., 1951, Swarthmore Coll.; LL.D. (hon.), Earlham Coll., Richmond, Ind., Mich. State U., Augustana Coll.; ScD (hon.), Haverford Coll.; hon. degree, Northland Coll. Geographer Miss. Valley Com. of P.W.A., 1934, Nat. Resources Bd., 1934-35; sec. land and water com. Nat. Resources Com. and Nat. Resources Planning Bd., 1935-40; with Exec. Office Pres., Bur. Budget, 1941-42; asst. exec. sec. Am. Friends Service Com., 1945-46; relief administr. in France, 1942-43; interned Baden-Baden, 1943-44; sec. Am. Relief for India, 1945-46; pres. Haverford Coll., 1946-55; prof. geography U. Chgo., 1956-69; prof. geography, dir. Inst. Behavioral Sci., U. Colo., Boulder, 1970-78; Gustavson disting. prof. emeritus Inst. Behavioral Sci., U. Colo., 1979—; dir. Natural Hazards Info. Ctr., 1978-84, 92-94; exec. editor Environment mag., 1983-93; vis. prof. Oxford U., 1962-63; cons. Investigations Lower Mekong Basin, 1961-62, 70; U.S. mem. UNESCO adv. com. on arid zone research, 1954-55; mem. mission Am. Vol. Agys. Relief Germany, 1946; vice chmn. Pres.'s Water Resources Policy Commn., 1950; mem. com. natural resources Hoover Commn., 1948; chmn. UN Panel Integrated River Basin Devel., 1956-57; chmn. Task Force Fed. Flood Control Policy, 1965-66; sci. adv. to administr. UN Devel. Program, 1966-71; chmn. adv. bd. Energy Policy Project, 1972-74; chmn. Am. Friends Service Com., 1963-69; chmn. com. on man and environment IGU, 1969-76; chmn. steering com. High Sch. Geography com., 1964-70; mem. Tech. Assessment Adv. Council, 1974-76; chmn. environ. studies bd. NRC, 1975-77; pres. Sci. Com. on Problems of Environment, 1976-82; chmn. bd. Resources for Future, 1973-79; co-chmn. U.S.-Egypt Joint Consultative Com. on Sci. and Tech., 1981-86; mem. adv. group on greenhouse gases World Meteorol. Orgn., Internat. Council of Scientific Unions, UN Environ. Program., 1986-90; chmn. tech. rev. com. Nev. Nuclear Waste Project, 1987-93; mem. adv. group on water UN Environ. Program, 1989-93, working group for Action Plan for Aral Sea Basin, USSR, 1990-93; chmn. nat. rev. com. Status U.S. Floodplain Mgmt., 1989. Author: Human Adjustment to Floods, 1942, Science and Future of Arid Lands, 1960, Social and Economic Aspects of Natural Resources, 1962, Choice of Adjustment to Floods, 1964, Strategies of American Water Management, 1969; co-author: Drawers of Water, 1972, Assessment of Research on Natural Hazards, 1975, Flood Hazard in the United States, 1975, The Environment as Hazard, 1978, also various govt. reports, 1937-45; editor: Natural Hazards: Local, National and Global, 1974, Environmental Aspects of Complex River Development, 1977; co-editor: Environmental Issues, 1977, The World Environment, 1972-1982, 1982, Environmental Effects of Nuclear War, 1983. Recipient Daly medal Am. Geog. Soc., 1971, Eben award Am. Water Resources Assn., 1972, Caulfield medal, 1989, Alumni medal U. Chgo., 1979, Outstanding Achievement award Nat. Coun. for Geog. Edn., 1981, Sasakawa UN Environ. prize, 1985, Tyler prize, 1987, Laureat d'Honneur award Internat. Geog. Union, 1988, Vautrin Lud Internat. Geog. prize, 1992, Hubbard medal Nat. Geog. Soc., 1994. Mem. NAS (mem. commn. on natural resources 1973-80, chmn. 1977-80, chmn. com. on water 1964-68, Environ. award 1980), Assn. Am. Geographers (pres., Outstanding Achievement award 1955, 74, Anderson medal 1986), Internat. Coun. Sci. Unions (mem. steering com. on study of environ. consequences of nuclear

war 1983-87, mem. adv. com. on environ. 1990—), Russian Geog. Soc. (hon.), Royal Geog. Soc. (hon.), Russian Acad. Scis. (fgn.), Am. Philos. Soc., Cosmos Club (Washington, award 1993), Sigma Xi,. Mem. Soc. Friends. Home: 624 Pearl St Apt 302 Boulder CO 80302-5072

WHITE, GORDON ELIOT, historian; b. Glen Ridge, N.J., Oct. 25, 1933; s. Maurice Brewster and Sarah Fullove (Gordon) W.; m. Nancy Johnson, 1955 (div. 1957); m. Mary Joan Briggs, Aug. 6, 1960 (dec. Nov. 1987); children: Sarah Elizabeth and Gordon O'Neal Brewster (twins), David McIntyre; m. Francis C. Barrineau, 1989. B.A., Cornell U., 1955; M.S. in Journalism, Columbia U., 1957. Lic. master mariner USCG; lic. pilot FAA. Stringer Nassau Daily Rev.-Star, Rockville Centre, L.I., N.Y., 1948-50; stringer Freeport (N.Y.) Leader, 1949-50; sports writer Morris County (N.J.) Citizen, 1950-51; stringer Ithaca (N.Y.) Evening News, 1951-55; photo editor, editorial writer Cornell Daily Sun, 1951-55; copy editor Am. Banker, N.Y.C., 1958; Washington corr. Chgo. Am., 1958-61; chief Washington bur. Deseret News, Salt Lake City, 1961-88; also corr. in Europe, U.S. and Antarctic for WJR, Detroit; KSL-KSL-TV, Salt Lake City, also KGMB, Honolulu; free lance writer with U.S. Navy, Army and Air Force, 1959; cons. Nat. Air and Space Mus.; auto racing, mil. aviation electronics historian. Advisor auto racing Nat. Mus. Am. History, Smithsonian Instn., 1989—. Recipient 1st prize for newsphoto Sigma Delta Chi, 1954; Raymond Clapper Meml. award White House Corrs. Assn., 1978; award for excellence in reporting Exec. Dept. and White House; award for excellence in reporting Nat. Press Club, 1979; award for investigative reporting Utah-Idaho-Spokane Regional AP; Nat. Sigma Delta Chi award for disting. work as Washington Corr., 1979; Roy W. Howard award for outstanding public service by a newspaper corr., 1979; award for disting. investigative reporting Investigative Reporters and Editors, 1980; Disting. Public Service Reporting Service Scripps Howard Found., 1980; Mark E. Peterson award, 1980; Reser-Tuthill award for writing on history of automobile racing, Indpls., 1985. Mem. Sigma Delta Chi, Pi Kappa Phi, Pi Delta Epsilon. Episcopalian. Club: Nat. Press (Washington). Home and Office: 2402 King St Alexandria VA 22301-2730

WHITE, SIR (VINCENT) GORDON LINDSAY, textile company executive; b. May 11, 1923; s. Charles and Lily May (Wilson) W.; m. Virginia Anne White, 1974; 3 children. Grad., De Aston Sch., Lincolnshire, Eng. Chmn. Welbecson Ltd., 1947-65; dept. chmn. Hanson Trust Ltd., 1965-73; chmn. Hanson Industries N.Am., Iselin, N.J., 1983-; mem. spl. commn. Hanson's Trust's opportunities overseas, 1979-83. Mem. Council for Police Rehab. Appeal, 1985—; bd. dirs. Shakespeare Theatre, Golger Library, Washington, 1985—; bd. dirs., chmn. internat. com. Congl. Award, 1984—; gov. BFI, 1982-84. Served with British mil., 1940-46. Named Knight Comd. Order of the Brit. Empire; St. Peter's Coll. hon. fellow, 1984; recipient Nat. Vol. Leadership award, Congl. award, 1984, Aims of Industry Free Enterprise award, 1985. Clubs: Spl. Forces; Brook, Explorer's (N.Y.C.); Mid-Ocean (Bermuda). Avocations: flying helicopters, horseback riding, skiing, tennis. Office: Hanson Industries Inc 99 Wood Ave S Iselin NJ 08830*

WHITE, H. BLAIR, lawyer; b. Burlington, Iowa, Aug. 2, 1927; s. Harold B. and Harriet E. (St. Clair) W.; m. Joan Van Alstine, Oct. 2, 1954; children—Blair W., Brian J. B.A., U. Iowa, 1950, J.D., 1951. Bar: Ill. 1951. Assoc. Sidley & Austin and predecessor firms, 1951-61, ptnr., 1962—; dir. DeKalb Energy Corp., 1967—, Kimberly-Clark Corp., 1971—, R.R. Donnelley & Sons Co., 1979—, Bankmont Fin. Corp., 1986-92, DeKalb Genetics Co., 1988—. Pres., bd. dirs. Cook County (Ill.) Sch. Nursing, 1966-71; bd. dirs. Rush-Presbyn.-St. Lukes Med. Ctr., 1986-93, life trustee; bd. dirs. Children's Meml. Hosp., Chgo., 1980—, chmn. bd. dirs., 1993—. Mem. ABA, Ill. Bar Assn., Chgo. Bar Assn., Am. Coll. Trial Lawyers, 7th Fed. Cir. Bar Assn., Commercial Club, Legal Club, Law Club, Chgo. Club, Econ. Club (Chgo.), Skokie Country Club, Old Elm Country Club, Lost Tree Club. Office: Sidley & Austin 1 First Nat Plz Chicago IL 60603

WHITE, HAROLD F., bankruptcy judge, retired federal judge; b. Hartford, Conn., Apr. 29, 1920; s. Harry and Maude C. (Strange) W.; m. Edna Jeanette Murie, 1943; children: Francis James, Susan, Harold. BSc, Ohio U., 1946; JD, U. Akron, 1952. Bar: Ohio 1952. Chief police prosecutor City of Akron, Ohio, 1953; asst. prosecutor Summit County, Akron, 1957-58; bankruptcy referee, bankruptcy judge U.S. Cts., Akron, 1958-94; on recall as sr. bankruptcy judge U.S. Cts., 1994—. Trustee Summit County Kidney Found; elder Westminster Presbyn. Ch., Akron. Named Disting. Alumni Ohio U., 1979, Outstanding Alumni U. Akron Sch. Law, 1983; recipient John Quine adj. lectr. of law award U. Akron Sch. Law, 1991. Mem. Akron Bar Assn., Ohio State Bar Assn., Nat. Conf. Bankruptcy Judges (twice gov. 6th cir.), Commercial Law League, Am. Bankruptcy Inst. Office: US Bankruptcy Ct Fed Bldg 2 S Main St Akron OH 44308-1810

WHITE, HAROLD TREDWAY, III, management consultant; b. Stamford, Conn., Nov. 3, 1947; m. Elizabeth Phillips. BA in History, Northwestern U., 1970; MBA, Darmouth U., 1974. Asst. to dir. urban affairs Am. Bankers Assn., Washington, 1972-73; sr. assoc. Cresap, McCormick & Paget Cons., 1974-75; dir. planning and devel. Tilton (N.H.) Sch., 1975-78; dir. alumni affairs Amos Tuck Sch. Dartmouth U., Hanover, N.H., 1978-82; chief devel. officer Manhattanville Coll., Purchase, N.Y., 1982-84; cons., 1985; pres. Resource Dynamics Group, White Plains, N.Y., 1987—; adj. asst. prof. Iona Coll., New Rochelle, N.Y., 1989-93; assoc. mem. cons. bd. Nat. Ctr. Nonprofit Bds., Washington, 1991—. Contbr. articles to profl. jours. Trustee, v.p., chmn. planning, devel. and mktg. coms. Tilton Sch., 1978—, pres. bd., 1992—; bd. dirs. Legal Awareness of Westchester, 1990—; Westchester Ctr. for Tng. and Devel., 1992—; pres. bd. Sci. Ctr. N.H., 1979-82, Nat. Coun. on Alcoholism and Other Drug Addictions/Westchester, 1985-89, Middle Patent Assn., 1988—; trustee Millbrook (N.Y.) Sch., 1981-87. Avocations: cross-country running, skiing, hiking, sailing. Office: Resource Dynamics Group 215 Katonah Ave Katonah NY 10536-2138

WHITE, HARRISON COLYAR, sociology educator; b. Washington, Mar. 21, 1930. BSc in Physics, Mass. Inst. Tech., 1950, PhD in Theoretical Physics, 1955; PhD in Sociology, Princeton U., 1960. Ops. analyst, ops. rsch. office Johns Hopkins U., 1955-56; asst. prof. indsl. adminstrn. and sociology Grad. Sch. Indsl. Adminstrn., Carnegie-Mellon U., 1957-59; asst. prof. sociology U. Chgo., 1959-63; assoc. prof., social relations dept. Harvard U., 1963-68, acting chair, social relations dept., 1970; vis. prof., dept. sociology U. Edinburgh, U.K., 1973-74; chair, dept spciology Harvard U., 1975-78, prof. sociology, 1968-86; head and chmn., dept. sociology U. Ariz., 1986-88; Eller prof. of mgmt. and policy, Coll. Bus. & Pub. Adminstrn., U. Ariz., 1986-88; dir. Center for the Social Studies, Columbia U., 1988—; prof., dept sociology Columbia U., 1988—, chair, dept. sociology, 1990—, Giddings prof. of sociology, 1992—. Author: An Anatomy of Kinship: Mathematical Models for Structures of Cumulated Roles, 1963, Chains of Opportunity: System Models of Mobility in Organizations, 1970, Research and Development as a Pattern in Industrial Management: A Case Study of Institutionalization and Uncertainty, 1981, Identity and Control: A Structural Theory of Social Action, 1992, Careers and Creativity: Social Forces in the Arts, 1993, (with Cynthia White) Canvases and Careers: Institutional Change in the French Painting World, 1965, rev. edit. 1993; mem. editorial bd. Social Networks, 1989—, Poetics, 1991—, Sociological Forum, 1990—. Netherlands Inst. for Advanced Study fellow in Residence, 1990, Ctr. for Advanced Study in Behavioral Scis., fellow 1956-57, Guggenheim fellow, 1973; recipient co-winner Sorokin award Am. Sociol. Assn., 1971, co-winner Samuel A. Stouffer Methodology award Am. Sociol. Assn., 1975. Mem. Nat. Acad. Scis., Am. Acad. Arts and Scis., Am. Assn. Advancement Of Sci., Sociol. Rsch. Assn. (bd. mem. 1992—), Am. Sociol. Assn. Office: Columbia U Ctr Social Scis 420 W 118th St New York NY 10027 also: Columbia U Dept Sociology Fayerweather Hall New York NY 10027 also: Center for Social Sciences Columbia U 814 International Affairs New York NY 10027

WHITE, HARRY EDWARD, JR., lawyer; b. Menominee, Mich., Apr. 26, 1939; s. Harry Edward and Verena Charlotte (Leisen) W.; m. Mary P.A. Sheaffer, June 7, 1980. BS in Fgn. Svc., Georgetown U., Washington, 1961; LLB, Columbia U., 1964. Bar: N.Y. 1965, U.S. Supreme Ct. 1970, U.S. Dist. Ct. (so. dist.) N.Y. 1979, U.S. Tax Ct. 1980. Assoc. Milbank, Tweed, Hadley & McCloy, N.Y.C., 1964-65, 67-73, ptnr., 1974—. Contbr. chpts. to books, articles to legal jours. Served with M.I., U.S. Army, 1965-66, Vietnam. Decorated Bronze Star. Mem. ABA, Internat. Bar Assn., N.Y. State Bar Assn. (chmn. taxation com. internat. law practice sect. 1987-90, co-chmn. exempt orgns. com. tax sect. 1987-88), Internat. Law Assn., Am. Soc. Internat. Law, Assn. Bar of City of N.Y., Internat. Fiscal Assn. Republican. Roman Catholic. Home: 333 E 55th St New York NY 10022-8316 Office: Milbank Tweed Hadley & McCloy 1 Chase Manhattan Plz New York NY 10005-1401

WHITE, HELEN FRANCES PEARSON, language educator, real estate broker; b. Bucoda, Mo., Sept. 26, 1925; d. William Sidney and Ella Myrtle Isaacs) Pearson; m. Jewel Porter White, June 21, 1942; children: Sydney LaVergne, Betty Ann, John Patrick. BA, Ark. State U., 1955; postgrad., U. Toulouse, 1965, U. Okla., 1962-64, U. Mex., 1966, Tex. A&M U., 1969; credited study tour on Creole Lang., Tex. A&M, 1969. Life time teaching lic. Mo., Tex., lic. real estate broker, lic. 1st class radio repr., FCC. High sch. English tchr. Manila, Ark., 1955-57; high sch. English, French tchr. New Madrid, Mo., 1958-63; Spanish, French tchr. Hardin Jefferson High Sch., Sour Lake, Tex., 1964-71; cons., instr. Radio Stas. KKAS & KWDX, Silsbee, Tex., 1969—; broker Accent Corner Real Estate, Silsbee, 1981—; tour dir. Robbins Ednl. Tours, Marquand, Mo., 1957-64, Whites' Tours, Silsbee, 1968—; host family, S.E. Tex. area rep. Youth for Understanding, 1968-75; workshop participant, job tng. instr., Programs for Human Svcs., 1981-84; pvt. lang. tutor, Portageville, Mo., Silsbee. Preservationist Hist. Landmark, 1991 (Tex. Hist. Commn. award for Old Silsbee Ice House); mem. Concept of Care, Kountze, Tex., 1985-88, Hardin County Tourist Bur.; charter commr. S.E. Tex. Women's Commn., 1985-88; coun. mem. County Assn. for Retarded Persons, Silsbee, 1986-89; pres. Silsbee Libr. Adv. Bd., 1986; founder, pres. Hardin County Arts and Ednl. Found., 1987—; mem. First Meth. Ch. Grantee Tex. A&M U., 1969. Mem. AAUW (life, pres. Hardin County br. 1983-86), Hardin County Geneal. Soc., Alpha Delta Kappa. Avocations: philatelist, numismatist, writing, art appreciation. Home: 1300 White Meadows RR 6 Box 75 Silsbee TX 77656-9232 Office: Accent Corner Real Estate Highway 327 W Silsbee TX 77656

WHITE, HERBERT SPENCER, research library educator, university dean; b. Vienna, Austria, Sept. 5, 1927; came to U.S., 1938, naturalized, 1944; s. Leon and Ernestine (Lichteneger) Hochweis; m. Mary Virginia Dyer, Feb. 19, 1953; 1 son, Jerome. BS in Chemistry, CCNY, 1949; MSLS, Syracuse U., 1950. Intern Libr. of Congress, Washington, 1950, mem. tech. info. divsn., 1950-53; tech. libr. AEC, Oak Ridge, Tenn., 1953-54; organizer, mgr. corp. libr. Chance Vought Aircraft, Dallas, 1954-59; mgr. engring. libr. IBM Corp., Kingston, N.Y., 1959-62; mgr. tech. info. ctr. IBM Corp., Poughkeepsie, N.Y., 1962-64; exec. dir. NASA Sci. and Tech. Info. Facility, College Park, Md., 1964-68; v.p. info. mgmt. Leasco Systems & Rsch. Corp., Bethesda, Md., 1968-70; sr. v.p. Inst. Sci. Info., Phila., 1970-74, corp. dir., 1971-74; pres. Stechert-Macmillan, Inc., Pennsaucken, N.J., 1974-75; prof. dir. Rsch. Ctr. Grad. Libr. Sch. Ind. U., Bloomington, 1975-80, dean Sch. Libr. and Info. Scis., 1980-90, disting. prof., 1991-95; prof. emeritus, 1995—; adj. prof. U. Ariz. Sch. Libr. Studies, 1995—, lectr. Author books; contbr. articles to profl. publs.; columnist Libr. Jour. Mem. Pres.'s Adv. Com. for Adminstrn. Title II-B Higher Edn. Act, 1965-68, Libr. Rsch. Planning Com. for 1980s, U.S. Dept. Edn. With USAAF, 1946-47. Spl. honoree, U. of Essen (Germany) Conf., 1992. Fellow Spl. Libraries Assn. (pres. 1969-70, J.C. Dana award 1985, Hall of Fame 1994); mem. ALA (councillor 1988—, planning com. 1989-91, Dewey medal 1987), Am. Soc. Info. Sci. (pres. 1973-74, W. Davis award 1977, award of merit 1981, named Pioneer, 1987), Assn. Libr. and Info. Sci. Edn. (chmn. govtl. rels. com. 1980-88), Am. Fedn. Info. Processing Socs. (dir. 1972-78), Federation Internationale de Documentation (Netherlands, bd. dir. 1976-78, treas. 1978-82), Soc. for Scholarly Pub. (bd. dirs. 1981-82), Assn. Rsch. Libraries (com. on libr. edn. 1983-85), Coun. Libr. Resources (rsch. priorities task force 1984-88, Ind. Libr. Lifetime Achievement award 1990), Beta Phi Mu (Svc. award 1995). Address: 330 E El Viento Green Valley AZ 85614

WHITE, HUGH VERNON, JR., lawyer; b. Suffolk, Va., July 24, 1933; s. Hugh Vernon and Mary Lois (Claud) W.; m. Mary Margaret Flowers, Nov. 25, 1961; children: Hunter, William, John. BS in Civil Engring., Va. Mil. Inst., 1954; LLB, Washington & Lee U., 1961. Bar: Va. 1961. Engr. E.I. DuPont de Nemours & Co., Parlin, N.J., 1954-55; exec. dir. Va. Legis. Study Commn., Richmond, Va., 1961-63; assoc. Hunton & Williams, Richmond, 1963-69, ptnr., 1969—; bd. dirs. Pulaski Furniture Corp., Pulaski, Va. Mem. Richmond First, 1966—, pres., 1971. Served to capt. USAF, 1955-58. Mem. ABA, Va. Bar Assn., Richmond Bar Assn., Phi Beta Kappa, Omicron Delta Kappa. Presbyterian. Clubs: Commonwealth, Country (Richmond). Home: 512 Gaskins Rd S Richmond VA 23233-5710 Office: Hunton & Williams Riverfront Plaza East Tower 951 E Byrd St Richmond VA 23219-4040

WHITE, JAMES ARTHUR, college president; b. Louisa, Ky., Mar. 29, 1933; s. Arthur and Cynthia Anne (Layne) W.; m. Margaret Biancy Shelton (div. 1988); children: Virginia White Silver, Margaret Leigh, James Christian. BS in Marine Engring. with honors, U.S. Naval Acad., 1956; MS, U. Kans., 1968; DBA, George Washington U., 1975. Commd. ensign USN, 1956, advanced through grades to comdr., 1969; mgr. strategic planning and analysis, nuclear fuels Potomac Electric Power Co., Washington, 1975-79; sr. policy analyst Office Mgmt. & Budget, Washington, 1979-80; dir. program planning and devel. Standard Oil Co. Ind., Chgo., 1980-84; dir. industry rels., govt. rels. U.S. Synthetic Fuels Corp., Washington, 1984-86; dir. tech. and engring. systems, assoc. dean U. Md. Grad. Sch., College Park, 1986-88; dean, prof. of mgmt. Mercer U. Sch. of Bus. and Econs., Atlanta, 1988-91; pres. Abu Dhabi (United Arab Emirates) Men's Coll., 1991-93; pvt. cons., 1993—; project mgr. Egyptian Manpower Devel. Project, 1994; vice-chmn. Internat. Assn. Knowledge Engrs., Washington, 1988—; chmn. resource base com. Am. Petroleum Inst., Washington, 1982-84; propr. Le Crocodile Restaurant, Atlanta. Mem. Joint Industry-Govt.-Citizens Task Force on Oil Shale Regulation, Denver, 1983; Rep. precinct chmn., Cook County, Ill., 1980-81. Mem. So. Bus. Adminstrn. Assn., Advanced Tech. Devel. Inst. (adv. coun.), Ga. Seed Capital Adv. Com., Atlanta Venture Forum, Exec. Forum Steering Com., Annapolis C. of C. (legis. com. 1987-88), Atlanta C. of C., Am. Bus. Coun. (Abu Dhabi, UAE). Republican. Presbyterian. Avocations: golf, reading, gardening, sailing.

WHITE, JAMES BARR, lawyer, real estate investor, consultant; b. Haverhill, Mass., June 13, 1941; s. Ned and Shirlee (Easter) W.; m. Carol Klein, June 23, 1963; children: Michael Andrew, Laurie Alison, Elizabeth Ellen. BS, Tufts U., 1962; LLB, Columbia U., 1965; MPA, Harvard U., 1988. Bar: Mass. 1965. Assoc. Goulston & Storrs, Boston, 1965-71, ptnr., 1971-74; ptnr. Palmer & Dodge, Boston, 1974-89; pvt. practice cons. Boston, 1989—; with ELAW Corp., Concord, Mass.; mem. adv. com. MIT Ctr. for Real Estate Devel., Cambridge, 1987-89; dir. Nat. Realty Com., Washington, 1987-89. Chmn. Town of Wayland (Mass.) Planning Bd., 1974-78; mem. Route 128 Area Com., Lincoln, Mass., 1985-87; mem. Town of Lincoln Planning Bd., 1991—; Town of Lincoln Hist. Dist. Commn., 1992—; bd. overseers New Eng. Conservatory, 1995—. Mem. Mass. Bar Assn., Boston Bar Assn., Handel and Haydn Soc. (gov. 1985-90, overseer 1990-94), Bostonian Soc. (bd. dirs. 1990—). Home: 38 Bedford Rd Lincoln MA 01773-2037 Office: ELAW Corp Office of Pres 175 Sudbury Rd Concord MA 01742-3419

WHITE, JAMES BOYD, law educator; b. Boston, July 28, 1938; s. Benjamin Vroom and Charlotte Green (Conover) W.; m. Mary Louise Fitch, Jan. 1, 1978; children: Emma Lillian, Henry Alfred; children by previous marriage: Catherine Conover, John Southworth. A.B., Amherst Coll., 1960; A.M., Harvard U., 1961, LL.B., 1964. Assoc. Foley, Hoag & Eliot, Boston, 1964-67; asst. prof. law U. Colo., 1967-69, assoc. prof., 1969-73, prof., 1973-75; prof. law U. Chgo., 1975-83; Hart Wright prof. law and English U. Mich., Ann Arbor, 1983—; vis. assoc. prof. Stanford U., 1972. Author: The Legal Imagination, 1973, (with Scarboro) Constitutional Criminal Procedure, 1976, When Words Lose Their Meaning, 1981, Heracles' Bow, 1985, Justice as Translation, 1990, "This Book of Starres", 1994, Acts of Hope, 1994. Sinclair Kennedy Traveling fellow, 1964-65; Nat. Endowment for Humanities fellow, 1979-80, 92; Guggenheim fellow, 1993. Mem. AAAS, Am. Law Inst. Office: U Mich Law Sch 625 S State St Ann Arbor MI 48109-1215

WHITE, JAMES EDWARD, geophysicist; b. Cherokee, Tex., May 10, 1918; s. William Cleburne and Willie (Carter) W.; m. Courtenay Brumby, Feb. 1, 1941; children: Rebecca White Vanderslice, Peter McDuffie, Margaret Marie White Jamleson, Courtenay White Forte. B.A., U. Tex., 1941, M.A., 1946; Ph.D., MIT, 1949. Dir. Underwater Sound Lab., MIT, Cambridge, 1941-45; scientist Def. Research Lab. Austin, Tex., 1945-46; research assoc. MIT, 1946-49; group leader, field research lab. Mobil Oil Co., Dallas, 1949-55; mgr. physics dept. Denver Research Center, Marathon Oil Co., 1955-69; v.p. Globe Universal Scis., Midland, Tex., 1969-71; adj. prof. dept. geophysics Colo. Sch. Mines, Golden, 1972-73, C.H. Green prof., 1976-87, prof. emeritus, 1986—; L.A. Nelson prof. U. Tex., El Paso, 1973-76; Esso vis. prof. U. Sydney, Australia, 1975; vis. prof. MIT, 1982, U. Tex.-Austin, 1985, Macquarie U., Sydney, 1988; del. U.S.-USSR geophysics exchange Dept. State, 1965; mem. bd. Am. Geol. Inst., 1972; mem. space applications bd. Nat. Acad. Engring., 1972-77; exchange scientist Nat. Acad. Sci., 1973-74; del. conf. on oil exploration China Geophys. Soc.-Soc. Exploration Geophysicists, 1981; cons. world bank Chinese U. Devel. Project II, 1987. Author: Seismic Waves: Radiation, Transmission, Attenuation, 1965, Underground Sound: Application of Seismic Waves, 1983, (with R.L. Sengbush) Production Seismology, 1987; editor: Vertical Seismic Profiling (E.I. Galperin), 1974; contbr. articles to profl. jours.; patentee in field. Recipient Halliburton award, 1987. Fellow Acoustical Soc. Am.; mem. NAE, Soc. Exploration Geophysicists (hon., Maurice Ewing medal 1986), Cosmos Club, Sigma Xi. Unitarian. Office: Colo Sch Mines Dept Geophysics Golden CO 80401

WHITE, JAMES FLOYD, theology educator; b. Boston, Jan. 23, 1932; s. Edwin Turner and Madeline (Rinker) W.; m. Marilyn Atkinson, Aug. 23, 1959 (div. 1982); children: Louise, Robert, Ellen, Laura, Martin; m. Susan Jan Waller, Oct. 28, 1982 (div. 1993). Grad., Phillips Acad., Andover, Mass., 1949; AB, Harvard U., 1953; BD, Union Theol. Sem., 1956; PhD, Duke U., 1960. Ordained to ministry United Meth. Ch., 1955. Instr. Ohio Wesleyan U., Delaware, 1959-61, Meth. Theol. Sch. in Ohio, Delaware, 1960-61; prof. Perkins Sch. Theology, So. Meth. U., Dallas, 1961-83, U. Notre Dame, 1983—. Author: Cambridge Movement, 1962, New Forms of Worship, 1971, Introduction to Christian Worship, 1980, Protestant Worship, 1989, others; mem. editorial bd. Religious Book Club, 1980—. Named one of 100 most Influential People in Am. Religion, Christian Century mag., 1982. Mem. N.Am. Acad. Liturgy (pres. 1979, Berakah award 1983), Am. Soc. Ch. History, Liturgical Conf., Societas Liturgica, United Meth. Soc. for Worship. Avocations: hiking, travel, book and antiques collecting. Office: U Notre Dame Dept Theology Notre Dame IN 46556

WHITE, JAMES GEORGE, pediatrician, hematologist, pathologist, educator; b. Aug. 28, 1929; s. Robert James and Catherine Annunciata (Sinnott) W.; m. Mary Simonet, June 18, 1955; children: Catherine, Gregory, Thomas, James, Michael. BS, St. Thomas Coll., 1951, U. Minn., 1952; MD, U. Minn., 1955. Diplomate Am. Bd. Pediatrics. Rotating intern Detroit Receiving Hosp., 1955-56; intern and resident U. Minn., Mpls., 1958-60, chief resident in pediatrics, 1960-61, asst. prof. pediatrics, 1963-66, assoc. prof., 1966-70, prof., 1970—, prof. lab. medicine and pathology, 1974—, Regents prof. pediatrics, lab medicine and pathology, 1984—, assoc. dean Sch. Medicine, 1985. Contbr. over 500 articles to profl. jours. Capt. U.S. Army, 1956-58. Recipient Jane Nugents Cochems award U. Colo., 1964, H.P. Smith award Am. Soc. Clin. Pathology, 1978, Edward Kowalski award Internat. Soc. Thrombosis and Hemostasis, 1981. Mem. Am. Heart Assn. (past chmn., mem. exec. com. coun. on thrombosis 1970—, v.p. rsch. 1975-76), Am. Soc. Clin. Investigation, Am. Soc. Pediatric Rsch., Assn. Am. Physicians, Am. Pediatrics Soc. (Mead Johnson award 1973). Democrat. Roman Catholic. Avocations: reading, walking, golf. Home: 1919 Humboldt Ave S Minneapolis MN 55403-2816 Office: U Minn Sch Medicine Mayo Bldg Box 490 Minneapolis MN 55455

WHITE, JAMES JUSTESEN, legal educator; b. Omaha, Feb. 19, 1934; s. Leland Cobb and Vernie Marie (Bisgard) W.; m. Nancy Ann Coleman, Dec. 23, 1956; children: James, Patricia, Christopher. B.A., Amherst Coll., 1956; J.D., U. Mich., 1962. Bar: Mich. 1967. Assoc. Latham & Watkins, Los Angeles, 1962-64; prof. law U. Mich., Ann Arbor, 1964-78, 81-82, assoc. dean, 1978-81, Robert A. Sullivan prof. law, 1982—; exec. dir. Nat. Inst. Consumer Justice, 1972-74; chmn. Gov.'s Adv. Commn. on Regulation of Fin. Instn., 1976; bd. dirs. Southeast Mich. Legal Services, 1978—; pres. U. Mich. Credit Union, 1983. Author: (with Speidel and Summers) Commercial and Consumer Law, 4th edit., 1987, (with Summers) Handbook of the Law Under the Uniform Commercial Code, 3d edit., 1988, (with Symons) Banking Law Teaching Materials, 2d edit., 1984, (with Edwards) Negotiations Materials and Problems, 1976. Trustee Ann Arbor Bd. Edn., 1981-84. Served to 1st lt. USAF, 1956-59, 62. Mem. Am. Law Inst., Mich. Bar Assn., Order of Coif, Phi Beta Kappa. Republican. Congregationalist. Home: 1603 Granger Ave Ann Arbor MI 48104-4428 Office: U Mich Law Sch 625 S State St Ann Arbor MI 48109-1215

WHITE, JAMES PATRICK, law educator; b. Iowa City, Sept. 29, 1931; s. Raymond Patrick and Besse (Kanak) W.; m. Anna R. Seim, July 2, 1964. BA, U. Iowa, 1953, JD, 1956; LLM, George Washington U., 1959; LLD (hon.), U. Pacific, 1964, John Marshall Law Sch., 1989, Weidner U., 1989, Campbell U., 1993; Jur D (hon.), Whittier Coll., 1992; LLD (hon.), Campbell U., 1993; Southwestern U., 1995. Bar: Iowa 1956, D.C. 1959, U.S. Supreme Ct. 1959. Teaching fellow George Washington U. Law Sch., 1958-59; asst. prof. U. N.D. Law Sch., Grand Forks, 1959-62; assoc. prof., acting dean U. N.D. Law Sch., 1962-63, prof., asst. dean, 1963-67; dir. agrl. law rsch. program, prof. law Ind. U. Law Sch., Indpls., 1967—, also dir. urban legal studies program, 1971-74; dean acad. devel. and planning, spl. asst. to chancellor Ind. Univ., Indpls., 1974-83; mem. for N.D. Commn. on Uniform State Laws, 1961-66; cons. legal edn. ABA, Indpls., 1974—. Contbr. papers to tech. lit. 1st lt. JAGC, USAF, 1956-58. Carnegie postdoctoral fellow U. Mich. Ctr. for Study Higher Edn., 1964-65. Fellow Am. Bar Found.; mem. ABA, Am. Law Inst., Order of Coif. Roman Catholic. Home: 7707 N Meridian St Indianapolis IN 46260-3651 Office: Ind U 550 W North St Indianapolis IN 46202-3162

WHITE, JAMES RICHARD, lawyer; b. McKinney, Tex., Jan. 22, 1948; s. James Ray and Maxine (Brown) W.; m. Marian Olivia Gates, Feb. 3, 1979; children: Nicole Olivia, Mandi Leigh, James Derek. BBA, So. Meth. U., 1969, MBA, 1970, JD, 1973, LLM, 1977. Bar: Tex. 1973, U.S. Tax Ct. 1975, U.S. Supreme Ct. 1989, U.S. Ct. Appeals (5th cir.) 1989; cert. Comml. Real Estate Law Tex. Bd. Legal Specialization. Assoc. Elliot, Meer, Vetter, Denton & Bates, Dallas, 1973-74, Atwell, Cain & Davenport, Dallas, 1974-75; atty. Saphire Corp., Dallas, 1975-77; assoc. Brice & Barron, Dallas, 1977-79; ptnr. Millard & Olson, Dallas, 1979-82, Johnson & Swanson, Dallas, 1982-83, Winstead, Sechrest & Minick P.C., Dallas, 1983—; mem. staff Southwestern Law Jour., Dallas, 1971-73; mem. So. Meth. U. Moot Ct. Bd., Order Barristers, Dallas, 1972-73; prof. North Lake Coll., Dallas, 1985; bd. dirs. Tex. Assn. Young Lawyers, Austin, 1980-82; sec. bd. dirs. Dallas Assn. Young Lawyers, 1976-80. Contbr. articles to profl. jours. Chmn. bd. dirs. Tex. Lawyers Credit Union, Austin, 1980-82; pres. North Tex. Premier Soccer Assocs., Dallas, 1979-81; mem. regional mobility task force Real Estate Coun., City of Dallas, 1991-92, mem. downtown revitalization com., 1995—; mem. Dallas Indsl. Devel. Bd., 1992-93, Dallas Higher Edn. Authority Bd., 1994—; speakers' bur. and accreditation divsn. World Cup USA '94. Mem. ABA (mem. survey, accreditation and opinion coms.), Tex. Bar Assn. (cert. 1973, mem. mortgage loan opinion com.), Tex. Coll. Real Estate Attys., Coll. State Bar Tex. Methodist. Avocations: soccer, golf, skiing, racquetball. Home: 8003 Hundley Ct Dallas TX 75231-4728 Office: Winstead Sechrest & Minick 5400 Renaissance Tower 1201 Elm St Dallas TX 75270-2016

WHITE, JAMES SPRATT, IV, textiles executive, lawyer; b. Rock Hill, S.C., June 23, 1941; s. James Spratt III and Grace (Huggin) W.; m. Sandra Hagler, July 27, 1963; children: James Spratt V, Walter McElhaney, Samuel Crawford. AB in History, Wofford Coll., 1963; JD, U. S.C., 1968. Bar: S.C. 1968. Atty. Whaley, McCutchen & Blanton, Columbia, S.C., 1968-71; atty.

Springs Industries, Inc., Fort Mill, S.C., 1971-81, gen. atty., 1981-83, sr. v.p. human resources, sec., 1983-88, sr. v.p., sec., gen. counsel, 1988-90; sr. v.p., pres. Diversified Products Group, 1990—. Chmn. Fort Mill Sch. Bd., 1985-92. Avocations: jogging, hiking, camping, tennis, music. Office: Springs Industries Inc Box 70 205 N White St Fort Mill SC 29715-1654

WHITE, JEFFREY GEORGE, healthcare consultant, educator; b. Lawrence, Mass., Apr. 16, 1944; s. Alfred James and Ruth Virginia (Maylum) W.; children: Jennifer L, Tracy E. AB in Econs., Bowdoin Coll., 1966; MBA, U. N.H., 1985. Asst. pers. dir., then asst. adminstr. Maine Med. Ctr., Portland, 1967-71; asst. adminstr. Regional Meml. Hosp., Brunswick, Maine, 1971, adminstr., 1971-74; assoc. dir. Elizabeth Ann Seton Hosp. (now Mid-Maine Med. Ctr.), Waterville, 1974-75; assoc. adminstr. Mid-Maine Med. Ctr., 1975-79, v.p. ops., 1979-83; asst. dir. Wentworth-Douglass Hosp., Dover, N.H., 1983-85; exec. v.p. Frisbie Meml. Hosp., Rochester, N.H., 1985-89, pres., 1989-92; sr. cons., prin. Helms & Co., Inc., Concord, N.H., 1992—; preceptor dept. health mgmt. and policy U. N.H., Durham, 1985-92; adj. asst. prof., 1991-93, asst. prof., 1993—; mem. instrnl. conf. coun. New Eng. Healthcare Assembly, 1992—. Vol. pub. TV sta.; bd. dirs. Greater Seacoast United Way, 1991—, chmn. cmty. campaign, 1993; pres. Greater Rochester C. of C., 1990. Fellow Am. Coll. Healthcare Execs. (past regent for N.H.); mem. N.H. Hosp. Assn. (trustee emeritus). Republican. Avocations: running, skiing, reading, travel. Home: 37 Mill Pond Rd Durham NH 03824 Office: Helms & Co Inc 14 South St Concord NH 03301

WHITE, JEFFREY LEE, middle school educator; b. Atlanta, June 30, 1957; s. Herbert Buel and Mildred Patricia (Carroll) W.; m. Leslie Ann Mayer, Aug. 7, 1982; children: Jeremy Andrew, Allison LeeAnn. BSEd in Sci., U. Ga., 1980; MEd in Sci., Ga. State U., 1985. Cert. secondary tchr. sci., Ga. Tchr. biology Berkmar High Sch., Lilburn, Ga., 1980-81, tchr. phys. sci., 1980-89, tchr. chemistry, 1983—, tchr. physics, 1985—; spl. assignment tchr. Gwinnett County Pub. Schs., Lawrenceville, Ga., 1991; instr. Trickum Mid. Sch., Lilburn; instr. Berkmar Community Sch., Lilburn, 1985, Gwinnett Area Tech. Inst., Lawrenceville, 1990-91, Open Campus High Sch., Lilburn, 1988-89; mem. faculty Teach for Am. Summer Inst., L.A., 1990; curriculum writer Ga. Power Edn. and Environ. Ctr., Atlanta, 1991; cons. Scitrek Sci. Mus., Atlanta, 1991. Subject nat. broadcast TBS Super Teacher Award, 1990. Deacon 1st Bapt. Ch. Decatur, Ga., 1991; mem. Rivercliff Manor Homeowners Assn., Lilburn, 1990—; sponsor Students Against Drunk Driving, 1983-90, Sci. Club, 1984-90, Scholars' Bowl Acad. Team, 1989-90. Woodrow Wilson fellow, Princeton U., 1988; recipient Honor Tchr. award Atlanta Jour. Constitution, 1991; named STAR Tchr. Gwinnett County C. of C., 1986, Ga. Tchr. of Yr., 1991. Mem. Am. Assn. Physic Tchrs., Nat. Sci. Tchrs. Assn., Ga. Sci. Tchrs. Assn., Metro-Atlanta Physics Tchrs. Assn., Profl. Assn. of Ga. Educators. Avocations: fatherhood, water sports, golf, physics toys. Home: 4607 Robie Rd SW Lilburn GA 30247-4777 Office: Trickum Middle School 948 Cole Rd SW Lilburn GA 30247-5498

WHITE, JERRY ALLEN, career officer; b. Raven Rock, W.Va., May 24, 1937; s. Don and Pearl (Northcraft) W.; m. Linda Pickens, Sept. 6, 1958; children: Jerry A. II, Jane Ann. BS in Geology, Marshall U., 1960; MS in Pub. Adminstrn., Shippensburg State U., 1977. Commd. 2d lt. U.S. Army, 1960, advanced through grades to maj. gen., 1989; comdr. 1st brigade 25th Inf. Div., Schofield Barracks, Hawaii, chief staff; team chief Nat. Mil. Command Ctr., Washington, 1980-81; chief of staff 25th Inf. Div., Schofield Barracks, Hawaii, 1981-83; comdr. 1st Brigade, 25th Inf. Div., Schofield Barracks, 1983-85; comdg. gen. 2d ROTC Region, Ft. Knox, Ky., 1985-87; asst. div. comdr. 7th Inf. Div., Ft. Ord, Calif., 1987-88; dir. ops. Forces Command, Ft. McPherson, Ga., 1988-90; comdg. gen. 7th Inf. Div., Ft. Ord, 1990-91, U.S. Army Inf. Ctr., Ft. Benning, Ga., 1991—. Decorated D.S.M., Silver Star, Legion of Merit. Mem. Rotary. Avocation: golf. Office: Commanding Gen US Army Infantry Ctr Fort Benning GA 31905-5000

WHITE, JESSE MARC, actor; b. Buffalo, Jan. 3; s. Elias and Freda Weidenfeld; m. Celia Kahn, Jan. 18, 1942; children—Carole, Janet. Appeared in: 17 Broadway plays including Harvey, 1944; appeared in 64 movies; TV series Ann Sothern Show, 1956-62, Danny Thomas' Make Room for Daddy, 1952-58, Marlo Thomas Show, 1969-71; numerous dramatic and comedy TV shows, 1945—; TV spokesman, Maytag Co., 1967-89, Acura automobiles, 1990—. Mem. AFTRA, SAG, Actors Equity Assn. Club: Friars of Calif. Office: care Craig Wykoff Epstein & Samonna 280 S Beverly Dr Beverly Hills CA 90212 *At age seven I knew what I wanted in life-to bring a little laughter and joy to the world. I've been blessed twice-to be able to do the thing I know and do best and to make a decent and respectable living at it. I have had a good life in show business and feel sorry for people who are not in it.*

WHITE, JILL CAROLYN, lawyer; b. Santa Barbara, Calif., Mar. 20, 1934; d. Douglas Cameron and Gladys Louise (Ashley) W.; m. Walter Otto Weyrauch, Mar. 17, 1973. BA, Occidental Coll., L.A., 1955; JD, U. Calif., Berkeley, 1972. Bar: Fla. 1974, Calif. 1975, D.C. 1981, U.S. Dist. Ct. (no. and mid. dists.) Fla., U.S. Ct. Appeals. (5th and 11th cirs.), U.S. Supreme Ct. Staff mem. U.S. Dept. State, U.S. Embassy, Rio de Janeiro, Brazil, 1956-58; with psychol. rsch. units Inst. Human Devel., Inst. Personality Assessment and Rsch., U. Calif., Berkeley, 1961-68; adj. prof. U. Fla. Criminal Justice Program, Gainesville, Fla., 1976-78; pvt. practice immigration and nationality law Gainesville, 1976—; appointed mem. Fla. Bar Inaugural Immigration and Nationality Certification Com., 1994—. Contbr. articles to profl. jours. Mem. ABA, Am. Immigration Lawyers Assn. (bd. dirs. Ctrl. Fla. chpt. 1985-94, chair Ctrl. Fla. chpt. 1988-89), co-chmn. So. Regional Liaison com. 1990-92, nat. bd. dirs 1988-89), Fla. Assn. Women Lawyers (8th jud. cir. chpt.), Bar Assn. 8th Jud. Cir. Fla., Gainesville Area C. of C., Gainesville Area Innovation Network, Altrusa Club Gainesville. Democrat. Office: 1330 NW 6th St Ste C Gainesville FL 32601-2213

WHITE, JOE LLOYD, soil scientist, educator; b. Pierce, Okla., Nov. 8, 1921; s. Claud Amos and Alta Maurice (Denney) W.; m. Wanita Irene Robertson, May 29, 1945; children—Lerrill, Darla, Ronna, Bren, Janeil. Student, Connors State Agrl. Coll., 1940-42; B.S., Okla. State U., 1944, M.S., 1945; Ph.D., U. Wis., 1947. Asst. prof. agronomy Purdue U., West Lafayette, Ind., 1947-51, assoc. prof., 1951-57, prof., 1957-88; cons. Bancroft Co., William H. Rorer Co., Chattem Chem. Co., Merck Sharp & Dohme Rsch. Lab. Patentee in field. Fellow NSF, 1965-66, Guggenheim Found., 1972-73; Fulbright scholar, 1973; recipient U.S. Scientist award Alexander von Humboldt Found., 1980-81. Fellow AAAS, Am. Soc. Agronomy, Am. Inst. Chemists, Soil Sci. Soc. Am., Mineral Soc. Am., Royal Soc. Chemistry; mem. Am. Chem. Soc., Clay Minerals Soc. (disting.), Am. Pharm. Assn., Coblentz Soc., Geochem. Soc., Internat. Soil Sci. Soc., Internat. Assn. Colloid and Interface Scientists, N.Y. Acad. Sci., Royal Soc. Chemists (chartered chemist), Soc. Petroleum Engrs. of AIME, Internat. Zeolite Assn., Soc. Applied Spectroscopy, Sigma Xi, Phi Kappa Phi, Phi Lambda Upsilon. Mem. Ch. of Christ. Achievements include patents for use of zeolites in ruminant nutrition, for stable dried aluminum hydroxide gel, for method and composition for treatment of hyperphosphatemia; establishment of the role of carbonate in inhibiting crystallization of aluminum hydroxide; definitive characterization of aluminum-containing adjuvants used in vaccines. Home: 2505 Roselawn Ave Lafayette IN 47904-2319 Office: Purdue U Dept Agronomy West Lafayette IN 47907

WHITE, JOHN, food marketing executive; b. 1953. BA, Washington U., 1975, MBA, 1976. With First Nat. Bank of St. Louis, Mo., 1976-80, Schneider Nat. Inc., Green Bay, Wis., 1980-86, Copeland Lumber Yards, Inc., Portland, Oreg., 1986-87; v.p., CFO United Grocers, Inc., Portland, Oreg., 1987—. Office: United Grocers Inc PO Box 22187 Milwaukie OR 97222

WHITE, JOHN, JR., insurance company executive, farm organization executive; b. 1930; married. With Ill Farm Bur., 1948—; pres. Ill. Farm Bur. Country Cos. Ins. Group, Bloomington, 1983—, IAA Trust Co., Bloomington, AgriVisor Svcs. Mem. Am. Farm Bur. Fedn. (bd. dirs.). Office: Country Cos 1701 N Towanda Ave Bloomington IL 61701-2040

WHITE, JOHN ABIATHAR, pilot, consultant; b. Chgo., May 29, 1948; s. Abiathar Jr. and Gretchen Elizabeth (Zuber) W.; m. Therese Ann Denz, June 21, 1980; children: Kathryn Ann, Laura Ellen. Student, Art Ctr. Coll.

of Design, 1969-70, Calif. Inst. Tech.; 1966-67; BArch, U. Ill., 1972. Archtl. apprentice Farner Und Gründer Industriearchitekten, Zürich, Switzerland, 1972; archtl. draftsman Walter Carlson Assocs., Elk Grove, Ill., 1973; architectural job capt. Unteed Assocs., Palatine, Ill., 1974-75; flight instr. Planemasters, Inc., West Chicago, Ill., 1976; pilot Aero Am. Aviation, West Chicago, 1977, Beckett Aviation, Cleve., 1978; pilot Am. Airlines, Chgo. and L.A., 1979—, capt., 1988—; archtl. cons. Nat. Accelerator Lab., Batavia, Ill., 1980, Constrn. Collaborative, Park Ridge, Ill., 1982, L.K. White Assocs., San Diego, 1988-92. Nat. Coun. Tchrs. of English scholar, 1966. Mem. Nat. Assn. Flight Instrs. Unitarian. Avocations: skiing, photography, travel. Home: 25400 N Bridge Rd Hawthorn Woods IL 60047 Office: Am Airlines O'Hare Internat Airport Chicago IL 60666

WHITE, JOHN ARNOLD, physics educator, research scientist; b. Chgo., Jan. 30, 1933; s. Maxwell Richard and Dorothy Edith (Arnold) W.; m. Rebecca Anne Cotten, June 20, 1964; children: Lauren, Thomas, Julia. B.A., Oberlin Coll., 1954; M.S., Yale U., 1955, Ph.D., 1959. Instr. physics Yale U., 1958-59, Harvard U., 1959-62; research assoc. Yale U., 1962-63; research physicist Nat. Bur. Standards, Washington, 1963-64; research assoc. U. Md., College Park, 1965-66; assoc. prof. Am. U., Washington, 1966-68; prof. Am. U., 1968—; cons. Nat. Bur. Standards, 1965-72; mem. tech. staff Bell Telephone Labs., summers 1954, 60-62; vis. scientist MIT, fall 1972, Nat. Bur. Standards, Washington, summer 1981; vis. prof. Inst. for Phys. Sci. and Tech., U. Md., College Park, fall 1993. Author sci. papers on atomic structure and fluorescence, magnetism, lasers, speed of light, thermodynamic fluctuations, critical point phenomena, extended renormalization group theory of fluids. Recipient (with Zoltan Bay) Boyden Premium Franklin Inst., Phila., 1980; honor scholar, 1950-54; Noyes Clark fellow, 1954-57; NSF fellow, 1957-58; grantee NSF, 1966, 67, 69, 71; grantee Office Naval Research, 1973, 74; mem. Soc. Engring. Edn. faculty fellow Naval Research Lab., Washington, summer 1985; Dept. Energy Office Basic Energy Scis. grantee, 1986, 88, 90. Fellow Am. Phys. Soc.; mem. AAUP, Washington Philos. Soc., Phi Beta Kappa, Sigma Xi. Home: 7107 Fairfax Rd Bethesda MD 20814-1234 Office: Am U Dept Physics Washington DC 20016-8058

WHITE, JOHN AUSTIN, JR., engineering educator, dean, consultant; b. Portland, Ark., Dec. 5, 1939; s. John Austin and Ella Mae (McDermott) W.; m. Mary Elizabeth Quarles, Apr. 13, 1963; children: Kimberly Elizabeth White Brakmann, John Austin III. BS in Indsl. Engring., U. Ark., 1962; MS in Indsl. Engring., Va. Poly. Inst., 1966; PhD, Ohio State U., 1969; PhD (hon.), Cath. U. of Leuven, Belgium, 1985, George Washington U., 1991. Registered profl. engr., Va. Indsl. engr. Tenn. Eastman Co., Kingsport, 1961-63, Ethyl Corp., Baton Rouge, 1965; instr. Va. Poly. Inst. and State U., Blacksburg, 1963-66, asst. prof., 1967-70, assoc. prof., 1970-72; teaching assoc. Ohio State U., Columbus, 1966-70; assoc. prof. Ga. Inst. Tech., Atlanta, 1975-77, prof., 1977-84, Regents' prof., 1984—, Gwaltney prof., 1988—, dean engring., 1991—; asst. dir. engring. NSF, 1988-91; founder, chmn. SysteCon Inc., Duluth, Ga., 1977-84; exec. cons. Coopers & Lybrand, N.Y.C., 1984-93; mem. mfg. studies bd. NRC, Washington, 1986-88; bd. dirs. CAPS Logistics, Russell Corp., Eastman Chem. Co., Motorola Corp.; pres. Nat. Consortium for Grad. Degrees for Minorities in Engring. and Sci., Inc., 1993-95; bd. dirs. Southeastern Consortium for Minorities in Engring.; appointed by U.S. Sec. of Commerce as U.S. del. to internat. steering com. of Intelligent Mfg. Sys. multinat. initiative, 1995-97; mem. Nat. Sci. Bd., 1994-2000. Co-author: Facility Layout and Location: An Analytical Approach, 1974 (Inst. Indsl. Engrs. Book of Yr. award 1974), 2d edit., 1991, Analysis of Queueing Systems, 1975, Principles of Engineering Economic Analysis, 3d edit., 1989, Capital Investment Decision Analysis for Management and Engineering, 1980, Facilities Planning, 1984 (Inst. Indsl. Engrs. Book of Yr. award 1984); editor: Production Handbook, 1987; co-editor: Progress in Materials Handling and Logistics, Vol. 1, 1989; also numerous articles to profl. jours., chpts. to books and handbooks in field, conf. procs. Recipient Outstanding Tchr. award Ga. Inst. Tech., 1982, Disting. Alumnus award Ohio State U. Coll. Engring., 1984, Disting. Indsl. Engring. alumnus award Va. Polytech. Inst. and State U., 1993, Reed-Apple award Material Handling Edn. Found., 1985, Disting. Svc. award NSF, 1991, Rodney D. Chipp Meml. award Soc. Women Engrs., 1994. Fellow Am. Inst. Indsl. Engrs. (pres. 1983-84, facilities planning and design award 1980, Outstanding Indsl. Engr. award-region III 1974, region IV 1984, Albert G. Holzman Disting. Educator award 1988, Outstanding Pub. award, 1988, David F. Baker Disting. Rsch. award 1990, Frank and Lillian Gilbreth award 1994), Am. Assn. Engring. Socs. (bd. govs., chmn. 1986, Kenneth Andrew Roe award 1989); mem. Nat. Acad. Engring., Ark. Acad. Indsl. Engring., Am. Soc. Engring. Edn. (Donald E. Marlowe Award 1994), Coun. Logistics Mgmt., Internat. Material Mgmt. Soc. (Material Mgr. of Yr. 1989), Soc. Mfg. Engrs. (Mfg. Educator award 1990), Nat. Soc. Profl. Engrs., Ops. Rsch. Soc. Am. (hon.), Golden Key Honor Soc., Sigma Xi, Alpha Pi Mu, Omicron Delta Kappa, Phi Kappa Phi, Tau Beta Pi, Omega Rho. Baptist. Avocations: reading, golf, writing. Office: Ga Inst Tech Coll Engring Office of Dean Atlanta GA 30332

WHITE, JOHN CHARLES, historian; b. Washington, Apr. 14, 1939; s. Bennett Sexton, Jr. and Mary Elizabeth (Wildman) W.; m. Carolyn R. West, July 6, 1963. A.B. magna cum laude with excptl. distinction in History (Robert E. Lee scholar), Washington and Lee U., 1960; M.A. (So. fellow), Duke U., 1962, Ph.D. (So. fellow), 1964. Asst. prof. U. Ala., Huntsville, 1967-70, assoc. prof., 1970-76 prof., 1976-91, chmn. dept. history, 1970-91, dir., acting chmn. dept. langs. and lits., 1988-91, ret., 1991; dir., sec.-treas. Consortium on Revolutionary Europe, 1972-86; European travel cons., 1991—. Editor: Procs. Consortium on Revolutionary Europe, 1977, 81; contbr. articles on French adminstrv. history to profl. jours. Bd. dirs Ala. Preservation Alliance, 1989-95, Ala. com. humanitites NEH, 1979-82, mem. exec. com., 1980-81; vice chmn. bd. Ala. Constn. Hall, 1979-81, chmn. bd. dirs., 1982-84; bd. dirs. Ala. Humanities Found., 1985-89, vice chmn. bd. 1988-89; assoc. Ala. Humanities, 1982-85; pres. Alliance Francaise, 1970; active Huntsville Lit. Assn., Huntsville Mus. Assn. Served to capt. Recipient Chalons and Dunkirk City medals, 1964-65, Ala. Hist. Commn. award of merit, 1978, Multi-Cultural Svcs. Recognition award U. Ala., Huntsville, 1991, appreciation award U. Ala. Alumni Assn., 1991, cert. of appreciation Gov. of Ala., 1991, Ala. Senate, 1991, award of merit Ala. Preservation Alliance, 1994, others; Woodrow Wilson summer grantee, 1961-62, U. Ala. rsch. grantee, 1969, 70, 74. Mem. Ala. Assn. Historians (pres. 1978-80), Ala. Hist. Soc., Consortium on Revolutionary Europe, Phi Alpha Theta (Nat. Scholarship medal 1991), Phi Kappa Phi, Omicron Delta Kappa (Founder's Day Leadership award 1991), Phi Sigma Iota (Nat. Svc. award 1991). Club: Rotary. Home: 220 Longwood Dr Huntsville AL 35801

WHITE, JOHN DAVID, composer, theorist, cellist; b. Rochester, Minn., Nov. 28, 1931; s. Leslie David and Millie (Solum) W.; m. Marjorie Manuel, Dec. 27, 1952; children: Jeffrey Alan, Michele Kay, David Eliot. BA magna cum laude, U. Minn., 1953; MA, U. Rochester, 1954, PhD, 1960. Mem. faculty Kent (Ohio) State U., 1956-58, 60-63, 65-73, prof. music, assoc. dean Grad. Sch., 1967-73; asst. prof. U. Mich., 1963-65; dean Sch. Music, Ithaca (N.Y.) Coll., 1973-74; vis. prof. U. Wis., 1975-78; chmn. music dept. Whitman Coll., 1978-80; prof. U. Fla., 1980—. Prin. cellist Eastman Philharmonia, 1959, Akron Symphony Orch., 1969-73; cellist Fla. Baroque Ensemble, 1980—, Fla. Arts Trio, 1986-93; dir. Fla. Musica Nova, 1991—; author: (with A. Cohen) Anthology of Music for Analysis, 1965, Understanding and Enjoying Music, 1968 (pub. in Japanese 1978), Music in Western Culture, 1972, The Analysis of Music, 1976, 2d edit., 1984, Guidelines for College Teaching of Music Theory, 1981, Comprehensive Musical Analysis, 1994, Theories of Musical Texture in Western History, 1995; editor: Music and Man; editl. Jour. for Musicological Research, Jour. Music Theory Pedagogy; contbr. articles to profl. jours.; Composer: Symphony No. 2, 1960, Blake Songs, 1961, Divertimento for Flute, Violin and Viola, 1961; opera The Legend of Sleepy Hollow, 1962; Three Choruses From Goethe's Faust, 1965, Three Joyce Songs, 1966, Ode to Darkness, 1967, Cantos of the Year, 1969, Variations for Clarinet and Piano, 1971, Whitman Music, 1972, Three Madrigals for Chorus and Orchestra, 1971, Russian Songs for Voices and Winds, 1972, Prayer (Solzhenytsin), 1973, String Quartet 1, 1975, Variations for Piano, 1976, Ode on the Morning of Christ's Nativity (Donne), 1977, Music for Oriana for violin, cello and piano, 1978, Pied Beauty, 1980, Sonata for Cello and Piano, 1981, Zodiac, 1981, Music for Violin and Piano, 1982, The Soft Voice, 1983, Concerto for Flute and Wind Ensemble, 1983, Dialogues for Trombone and Piano, 1984, Symphony for Wind Band, 1985, Concerto da Camera for Cello and Orch., 1985, Symphony for a Saint, 1986,

The Heavens are Telling, 1988, Music for Cello and Percussion, 1988, Songs of the Shulamite, 1989, Mirrors for Piano and Orchestra, 1990, But God's Own Descent, 1991, Music of the Open Road, 1993, Daylight and Moonlight, 1993, O Sing to the Lord a New Song, 1993, Illusions for Three, 1994, Music for Trumpet and Cello, 1994; recs. on Advent, Mark, Capstone and Opus One Labels. Served with AUS, 1954-56. Recipient Benjamin award, 1960, award Nat. Fedn. Music Clubs, 1962, internat. composition award U. Wis.-Oriana Trio, 1979, composition award Am. Choral Dirs. Assn., 1984; grantee NEA. Mem. ASCAP (awards 1965—), Soc. Composers (nat. coun. 1987-89, 93-96), Soc. Music Theory, Pi Kappa Lambda, Delta Omicron, Phi Mu Alpha, Phi Beta Delta. Home: 3102 NW 57th Ter Gainesville FL 32606-6939

WHITE, JOHN DAVID, lawyer; b. Kenedy, Tex., Aug. 26, 1948; s. Alton Eugene and Neva Mary (Schorp) W.; m. Daisy Mary Sloan, Aug. 29, 1970; children: Neva Nicole, Jacqueline Alice. BS in Polit. Sci., Tex. A&M U., 1970; JD, U. Tex., 1972. Bar: Tex. 1978. Staff atty. Texaco, Inc., Houston, 1978-81; assoc. Woods, Aston, Mayes, Harman & Watt, Houston, 1981-82; ptnr. Watt, White & Craig, Houston, 1982-90. Bd. dirs. Tex. Lyceum Assn. 1986-89. With JAGC, USAF, 1973-78. Fellow Tex. Bar Found.; Houston Bar Found.; mem. Tex. Bar Assn. (grievance com. 1983-85), Tex. Young Lawyers Assn. (bd. dirs. 1980-82, chmn. bd. dirs. 1981-82), Leadership Houston Assn. Episcopalian. Avocations: hunting, ranching. Office: Winstead Sechrest & Minick 910 Travis St Ste 1700 Houston TX 77002-5807

WHITE, JOHN FRANCIS, retired corporate executive; b. Madison, Wis., Dec. 2, 1929; s. Francis Bernard and Helen Margaret (Brown) W.; 1 dau., Susan Jeanne. B.S., U. Wis., 1951; grad., Harvard U. Advanced Mgmt. Program, 1974. With Kraft Inc., Glenview, Ill., v.p., dir. R&D, 1974-85, gen. mgr. spl. projects, retail venture group, 1985-87. Served with AUS, 1951-53. Mem. Inst. Food Technologists, Am. Chem. Soc., AAAS. Republican. Roman Catholic. Club: North Shore Country (Glenview). Home: 1439 Pebble Creek Dr Glenview IL 60025-2029

WHITE, JOHN GRAHAM, scientist; b. Prestatyn, Wales, Aug. 9, 1943; came to U.S., 1993; s. Bernard and Norah (Bannister) W.; m. Donna Albertson, July 26, 1980 (div. Apr. 1994); children: Phoebe, Ben, Amelia, Ruth; m. Claudia Cummins, Nov. 8, 1994. BTech, Brunel U., London, 1969; PhD, Cambridge (Eng.) U., 1974. Technician Med. Rsch. Coun., London, 1964-69, scientist, 1969-93; prof., dir. integrated microscopy resource U. Wis., Madison, 1993—; cons. Bio-Rad, Herculese, Calif., 1988—. Recipient Queen's award for Tech., 1991, Mullard award Royal Soc., 1994. Achievements include two patents for confocal microscopy. Office: U Wis Lab Molecular Biology 1525 Linden Dr Madison WI 53706*

WHITE, JOHN LINDSEY, lawyer; b. Camden, N.J., Apr. 1, 1930; s. John R. and Jean L. (Lord) W.; m. Jane V. Evans, Dec. 27, 1952; children: Linda White McFadden, John Lindsey Jr., Douglas A., Karen R. Ulmer. AB, Franklin and Marshall Coll., 1952; LLB, Temple U., 1955. Bar: N.J. 1955, U.S. Dist. Ct. N.J. 1955, U.S. Supreme Ct. 1960, U.S. Ct. Appeals (3d cir.) 1984. Sr. ptnr. LaBrum & Doak, Woodbury, N.J. Mem. N.J. Assembly, Trenton, 1964-68, N.J. State Senate, Trenton, 1968-72; trustee Underwood-Meml. Hosp., Woodbury, chmn. bd., 1994—. Recipient Disting. Svc. award Woodbury Jaycees, 1966. Fellow Am. Bar Found., Am. Coll. Trial Lawyers; mem. ABA, N.J. Bar Assn. (pres. 1985-86), Internat. Assn. Def. Counsel, N.J. Def. Assn. (pres. 1992-93), Trial Attys. N.J. (Trial Bar award 1991), Masons, Shriners. Republican. Presbyterian. Avocations: hunting, fishing, boating. Home: 193 Briar Hill Ln Woodbury NJ 08096-5916 Office: LaBrum & Doak 66 Euclid St Woodbury NJ 08096-7913

WHITE, JOHN MICHAEL, chemistry educator; b. Danville, Ill., Nov. 26, 1938; married, 1960; 3 children. BS, Harding Coll., 1960; MS, U. Ill., 1962, PhD in Chemistry, 1966. From asst. to assoc. prof. U. Tex., Austin, 1966-77, prof. chemistry, 1977—, now Hackerman prof. chemistry, dir. Sci. and Tech. Ctr. Mem. Am. Chem. Soc., Am. Phys. Soc. Research in surface and materials chemistry. Office: U Tex Dept Chemistry Welch Hall # 310 Austin TX 78712

WHITE, JOHN SIMON, opera director; b. Vienna, Austria, Mar. 4, 1910; came to U.S., 1938, naturalized, 1943; s. Emil and Martha (Pollack) Schwarzkopf. PhD, U. Vienna, 1933; student, Sorbonne, U. Besançon, France, U. Perugia, Italy. Mem. faculty Schotten Realschule, Vienna, 1934, New Sch. Social Rsch., N.Y.C., Lycée Français, N.Y.C., 1942-43; cons. Ford Found., 1974—; Columbia Artists Mgmt., 1979; asst. stage dir., N.Y.C. Opera Assn., 1946-51, assoc. dir., 1952-68, mng. dir., 1968-81, artistic cons., 1981—; exec. dir., Vienna Burgtheater guest appearance in N.Y.C., 1968; dir. U.S. tour Spanish Riding Sch., 1980, 82, 84. Author: The Renaissance Cavalier, 1959, also rsch. papers. Co-founder Am. Dressage Inst. for Classical Horsemanship, Saratoga, N.Y., 1967; Bd. dirs. Gert von Gontard Found., 1968—. Served with AUS, 1942-45. Recipient 1st prize, scholarship Italian Cultural Inst., Vienna, 1933; elected to Friends of Lipizzans Vienna Hofburg, 1976. Office: NYC Opera Lincoln Ctr Pla New York NY 10023

WHITE, JOHN WESLEY, JR., university president; b. Nashville, Oct. 20, 1933; s. John W. and Ernestine (Engle) W.; m. Martha Ellen Bragg, June 24, 1956; children: Marcus Wesley, Michelle Suzanne. Student, Martin Jr. Coll., 1952-54; BA, Vanderbilt U., 1956, BD, 1959; MA, George Peabody Coll., 1966, PhD, 1966; LHD, U. Nebr., 1983; LLD, Kwansai Gakuin U., Japan, 1991. Dean admissions, dir. student affairs Martin Coll., 1960-65; asst. to acad. v.p. George Peabody Coll., 1965-67; assoc. dean for humanities Oklahoma City U., 1968-70, dean Coll. Arts and Scis., 1970-77, assoc. prof. English, 1968-73, prof., 1973-77; pres. Nebr. Wesleyan U., 1977—; cons., speaker in field; bd. dirs. Norwest Bank, Woodmen Accident and Life Co. Immediate past pres. U. Senate, United Meth. Ch. Eli Lilly Sr. scholar Vanderbilt U., 1959. Mem. Nat. Assn. Ind. Colls. and Univs. (bd. dirs. 1989-93), Newcomen Soc. N.Am., Lincoln C. of C. (bd. dirs. 1990-93), Rotary (pres. West Oklahoma City sect. 1976), Kappa Delta Pi, Phi Kappa Phi, Alpha Mu Gamma, Blue Key. Office: Nebr Wesleyan U 5000 St Paul Ave Lincoln NE 68504-2760 *Two principles have been paramount in my life: One, related to the attitude toward myself, is that we can help to shape life, not simply endure it. We are "creative" creatures, not just "surviving" creatures. The second principle, related to the attitude toward others, is that communication is essential to coexistence; and only as we make a real effort to hear what is meant, rather than simply what is said or written, are we able to communicate effectively.*

WHITE, JOSEPH B., reporter; b. N.Y.C., 1959. Attended, Harvard U. Reporter The Wall Street Journal. Author: (with Paul Ingrassia) Comeback: The Fall and Rise of the American Automobile Industry, 1994. Recipient Pulitzer Prize for beat reporting, 1993. Office: The Wall Street Journal Detroit Bureau 500 Woodward Ave Ste 1950 Detroit MI 48226*

WHITE, JOSEPH CHARLES, manufacturing and retailing company executive; b. Toronto, Ont., Can., Aug. 14, 1922; s. Joseph Cleveland and Edith Parker (Johnson) W.; m. G. Evelyn Vipond, July 15, 1944; children—Ronald, Richard, JoAnne. Chartered acct., Queen's U., Kingston, Ont.; B.Commerce, U. Toronto. Vice-pres., dir. Agnew-Surpass, Inc., Brantford, Ont., Can., 1964-78; v.p., dir. Genesco Can., Inc., Cambridge, Ont., Can., 1978-82, exec. v.p., dir. 1982-87; pres. gen. mgr. retail op. Genesco Can., Inc., Cambridge, Ont., 1986-87; dir., v.p. Genesco Group Inc.; dir. Genesco Fin. Ltd. Chmn. Ross MacDonald Found., Brantford, Ont., 1983-86; pres. YMCA, Brantford, 1968-69; chmn. Brant County Post-Secondary Edn. Corp., Brantford, 1973-76. Served with Royal Can. Air Force, 1943-45. Mem. Ont. Inst. Chartered Accts., Can. Council Distbn. (pres. 1972-73), Brant County C. of C. (treas. 1966-68). Mem. United Ch. of Can. Avocations: downhill skiing; tennis. Home: 47 Golfdale Rd, Brantford, ON Canada N3T 5H6 Office: Genesco Can Inc, 401 Fountain St, Cambridge, ON Canada N3H 4V5

WHITE, KATE, editor-in-chief. Former editor-in-chief Child mag.; editor-in-chief Working Woman mag., N.Y.C., 1989-91, McCall's mag, N.Y.C., 1991-94, Redbook, N.Y.C., 1994—. Office: Redbook Hearst Magazines 224 W 57th St New York NY 10019-3299*

WHITE, KATHLEEN MERRITT, geologist; b. Long Beach, Calif., Nov. 19, 1921; d. Edward Clendenning and Gladys Alice (Merritt) White; m. Alexander Kennedy Baird IV, Oct. 1, 1965 (dec. 1985); children: Pamela Roberts, Peter Madlem, Stephen Madlem, Mari Afify. Attended Sch. Boston Mus. Fine Arts, Art Students League, 1940-42; BS in Geology, Pomona Coll., 1962; MS in Geochemistry, Claremont Grad. Sch., 1964. Rsch. asst. geology Pomona Coll., Claremont, Calif., 1940-62, rsch. assoc. geology, 1966-75; cons. geology Claremont, Calif., 1975-77; sr. scientist Jet Propulsion Lab./NASA, Pasadena, 1977-79, mem. tech. staff, 1979-86; ind. rschr. Claremont, 1986—; owner Kittie Tales, Videos and CDs for Children, Claremont, 1992—. Contbr. Geosat Report, 1986; contbr. articles to profl. jours. Grantee NASA, 1984, 85; Pomona Coll. scholar, 1963. Mem. Geol. Soc. Am. (invited paper 1994), Am. Geophys. Union, Pomona Coll. Alumni Assn. Republican. Avocations: painting, piano playing, weaving, hiking, swimming. Home: 265 W 11th St Claremont CA 91711-3804

WHITE, KENNETH RAY, health administration educator, consultant; b. Okmulgee, Okla., June 28, 1956; s. Miles Delano and Ollie Jane (Roberts) W. BS, Oral Roberts U., 1979; MPH, U. Okla., Oklahoma City, 1980; postgrad., Va. Commonwealth U., 1993—. Dir. planning Mercy Health Ctr., Oklahoma City, 1980-81, adminstrv. asst., 1981-86, v.p. mktg., 1987-89; v.p. ops. Harris Hosp.-HEB, Bedford, Tex., 1986-87; sr. cons. Mercy Internat., Farmington Hills, Mich., 1989-93; instr. health adminstrn. Va. Commonwealth U., Richmond, 1993—. Contbr. articles to profl. jours. Bd. dirs., officer March of Dimes, Oklahoma City, 1980-89, Am. Heart Assn., Oklahoma City, 1984-89. Named Outstanding Alumni, U. Okla., 1983. Fellow Am. Coll. Healthcare Execs. Avocations: travel, home renovation, foreign films. Office: 6319 Kensington Ave Richmond VA 23226

WHITE, KERR LACHLAN, physician, foundation director; b. Winnipeg, Man., Can., Jan. 23, 1917; s. John Alexander and Ruth Cecelia (Preston) W.; m. Isabel Anne Pennefather, Nov. 26, 1943; children: Susan Isabel, Margot Edith. BA with honors (Oliver Gold medal), McGill U., 1940, M.D., C.M., 1949; M.D. (hon.), U. Leuven, 1978; postgrad., London Sch. Hygiene and Tropical Medicine, 1960; DSc (hon.), McMaster U., 1983. Intern, resident in medicine Mary Hitchcock Meml. Hosp., Hanover, N.H., 1949-52; Hosmer fellow McGill U. and Royal Victoria Hosp., Montreal, Que., Can., 1952-53; asst. prof. medicine U. N.C. Sch. Medicine, Chapel Hill, 1953-57, assoc. prof. medicine and preventive medicine, 1957-62; Commonwealth advanced fellow Med. Rsch. Coun., Social Medicine Rsch. unit London Hosp., 1959-60; chmn., prof. epidemiology and community medicine U. Vt., Burlington, 1962-64; prof. Sch. Hygiene and Pub. Health Johns Hopkins U., Balt., 1965-76, chmn. dept. health care orgn., 1965-72; dir. Inst. Health Care Studies United Hosp. Fund N.Y., 1977-78; dep. dir. health scis. Rockefeller Found., N.Y.C., 1978—; chmn. U.S. Nat. Com. Vital and Health Stats., 1975-79; mem. health adv. panel Office of Tech. Assessment, U.S. Congress, 1975-82; cons. Nat. Ctr. Health Stats., 1967-83, WHO, 1967—. Editor: Manual for Examination of Patients, 1960, Medical Care Research, 1965, Health Care: An International Study, 1976, Epidemiology as a Fundamental Science, 1976, Task of Medicine, 1988, Healing the Schism, 1991; contbr. articles to profl. jours., chpts. to books in field; mem. editl. bd. Med. Care, 1962-73, Inquiry, 1967-79, Internat. Jour. Epidemiology, 1971-81, Internat. Jour. Health Svcs., 1971—. Bd. dirs. Found. for Child Devel., 1969-80; trustee Case-Western Res. U., 1974-79. With Can. Army, 1942-45. Fellow ACP, AAAS, NAS (Inst. Medicine, coun. 1974-76, chmn. membership com. 1975-77), APHA (gov. coun. 1964-68, 71-73, coun. med. care sect. 1962-65), Am. Acad. Preventive Medicine, Am. Heart Assn, Royal Soc. Medicine (hon.); mem. AMA, Internat. Epidemiol. Assn. (hon. life, pres. 1974-77, treas., exec. com. 1964-71, 74-77, coun. 1971-81), Assn. Tchrs. Preventive Medicine (coun. 1963-68), Am. Hosp. Assn. (adv. coun. ednl. and rsch. trust 1965-68), Ken L. White Inst. Health Svcs. Rsch. (hon. dir. 1995—), Cosmos Club (Washington), Century Club (N.Y.C.), Sigma Xi, Alpha Omega Alpha. Office: Rockefeller Found Div Health Scis 1133 Ave Of The Americas New York NY 10036-6710

WHITE, LAWRENCE J., economics educator; b. N.Y.C., June 1, 1943; s. Martin H. and Florence M. (Meiman) W. AB, Harvard U., 1964, PhD, 1969; MS in Econs., London Sch. Econs., 1965. Econ. adviser Harvard Devel. Adv. Svc., Pakistan and Indonesia, 1969-70; asst. prof. econs. Princeton U., N.J., 1970-76; mem. faculty Stern Sch. Bus., NYU, 1976—; prof. econs. Stern Sch. Bus., NYU, 1979—, chmn. dept., 1992-83; sr. staff economist U.S. Council Econ. Advisers, 1978-79; dir. econ. policy office, antitrust div. Dept. Justice, Washington, 1982-83; mem. Fed. Home Loan Bank Bd., 1986-89; cons. in field. Author: The Automobile Industry Since 1945, 1971, Industrial Concentration and Economic Power in Pakistan, 1974, Reforming Regulation: Processes and Problems, 1981, The Regulation of Air Pollutant Emission from Motor Vehicles, 1982, The Public Library in the 1980s: The Problems of Choice, 1983, International Trade in Ocean Shipping Services: The U.S. and the World, 1988, The S&L Debacle: Public Policy Lessons for Bank and Thrift Regulation, 1991; N.Am. editor Jour. Indsl. Econs., 1984-87, 90—. NSF fellow, 1965-69. Mem. Am. Econ. Assn., Phi Beta Kappa. Office: NYU Stern Sch Bus 44 W 4th St New York NY 10012-1126

WHITE, LEE CALVIN, lawyer; b. Omaha, Sept. 1, 1923; s. Herman Henry and Ann Ruth (Ackerman) W.; m. Cecile R. Zorinsky, Nov. 19, 1989; children: Bruce D., Rosalyn A., Murray L., Sheldon R., Laura H., Lori J. BS in Elec. Engring., U. Nebr., 1948, LL.B., 1950. Bar: Nebr. 1950, D.C. 1958. Atty. legal div. TVA, 1950-54; legis. asst. to Senator John F. Kennedy, 1954-57; asst. to Joseph P. Kennedy; mem. Hoover Commn., 1954-55; counsel U.S. Senate Small Bus. Com., 1957-58; adminstrv. asst. to Senator John S. Cooper, 1958-61; asst. spl. counsel to Pres. Kennedy, 1961-63; assoc. counsel to Pres. Johnson, 1963-65, spl. counsel, 1965-66; chmn. Fed. Power Commn., 1966-69; campaign mgr. R. Sargent Shriver (Democratic candidate v.p. U.S.), 1972; dir. Central Hudson Gas and Electric Corp., 1984-88. Bd. govs. N.Y. Merc. Exchange, 1980-84, 87-91. Served with AUS, 1943-46. Mem. D.C. Bar (gov. 1977-80). Home: 435 N St SW Washington DC 20024-3701 Office: Ste 300 1225 Eye St NW Washington DC 20005

WHITE, LELAND I., hospital administrator; b. Bklyn., Aug. 30, 1946; s. Milton Leonard and Jean W.; m. Lene Petersen, Aug. 16, 1969; children: Kevin, Jason, Erik. A.B., Rutgers U., 1968; M.P.H., U. Calif., 1970. Adminstrv. asst. Jersey City Med. Ctr., 1971-73, asst. adminstr., 1973-76; assoc. adminstr. Med. Coll. Pa., Phila., 1976-79, hosp. adminstr., 1979-84; exec. dir. Med. Coll. Pa., 1984-87, asst. prof. dept. community medicine, 1984-87; pres., chmn. bd. dirs. Health Ptnrs. of Phila., 1985-86; pres. Paoli (Pa.) Meml. Hosp., 1987—; v.p. Main Line Health, Inc., 1987—; chmn., bd. dirs. Health Ptnrs. of Phila., 1985-86; trustee Health Systems Agy. of Southeastern Pa. Served to capt. Med. Service Corps. U.S. Army, 1968-76. Fellow Am. Coll. Healthcare Execs. (mem. policy rev. group 1987—); mem. Am. Coll. Hosp. Adminstrs., Am. Hosp. Assn., Hosp. Assn. Pa. (trustee, chmn. com. on health care delivery systems 1983-86, mem. audit com.) Delaware Valley Hosp. Council (treas. 1981-83, trustee, chmn. com. on quality assurance 1983-86, fin. com. 1987—), Hosp. Purchasing Services Assn. (mktg. com., trustee 1984-87), Old York Rd. Country Club (Spirng House, Pa.) (trustee 1990), Maple Manor Swim Club, Riverside Racquet Club (Bala Cynwd, Pa.). Office: Paoli Meml Hosp 255 W Lancaster Ave Paoli PA 19301-1792

WHITE, LEONARD, motion picture company executive. Pres., chief exec. officer Orion Pictures Corp. Office: Orion Pictures Corp 1888 Century Park E Ste 6 Los Angeles CA 90067

WHITE, LINDA DIANE, lawyer; b. N.Y.C., Apr. 1, 1952; d. Bernard and Elaine (Simons) Schwartz; m. Thomas M. White, Aug. 16, 1975; 1 child, Alexandra Nicole. AB, U. Pa., 1973; JD, Northwestern U., 1976. Bar: Ill. 1976. Assoc. Walsh, Case, Coale & Brown, Chgo., 1976-77, Greenberger & Kaufmann (merged into Katten, Muchin), Chgo., 1977-82; ptnr. Greenberger & Kaufmann (merged into Katten, Muchin), 1982-85, Sonnenschein Nath & Rosenthal, Chgo., 1985—. Mem. ABA (real property fin. com., comml. leasing com., real property, probate and trust law sect. 1987—), Ill. Bar Assn., Chgo. Bar Assn., Internat. Assn. Corp. Real Estate Execs. Office: Sonnenschein Nath & Rosenthal 8000 Sears Tower 233 S Wacker Dr Chicago IL 60606

WHITE, LINDA ELAINE, nursing administrator; b. June 17, 1949. Student, Ind. U., 1966; BS in Maths., Purdue U., 1967-68, Ind. State U., Terre Haute, 1970; RN, Deaconess Hosp. Sch. Nursing, 1974; BSN, U. Evansville, Ind., 1976, MBA, 1983. Cert. nurse adminstr. Computer programmer Systems Tech. Corp., Terre Haute, 1970-71; nurse mgmt. analyst Deaconess Hosp., Inc., Evansville, 1974-76, staff specialist clin. study and nursing staff devel., 1976-81, adminstrv. asst. budget and project devel., 1981-84, dir. nursing med. surg. unit, 1985-87, v.p. nursing, 1987—; asst. v.p. nursing Cen. DuPage Hosp., Winfield, Ill., 1984-85; mem. adj. faculty U. Evansville, 1987-88. Active Operation City Beautiful. Wharton fellow, 1991. Mem. Am. Orgn. Nurse Execs., Ind. Orgn. Nurse Execs., Southwestern Dist. Ind. Orgn. Nurse Execs., Nursing Coalition of Evansville, Tri-State Nurse Assn., Leadership of Evansville, Jr. League of Evansville, Sigma Theta Tau. Home: 162 Hartin Dr Evansville IN 47711-3160

WHITE, LORAY BETTY, writer, actress, producer; b. Houston, Nov. 27, 1934; d. Harold White and Joyce Mae (Jenkins) Mills; m. Sammy Davis Jr., 1957 (div. 1959); 1 child, Deborah R. DeHart. Student, UCLA, 1948-50, 90-91, Nichiren Shoshu Acad., 1988-92; AA in Bus., Sayer Bus. Sch., 1970; study div. mem. dept. L.A., Soka U., Japan, 1970-86. Editor entertainment writer L.A. Community New, 1970-81; exec. sec. guest rels. KNBC Prodns., Burbank, Calif., 1969-75; security specialist Xerox X10 Think Tank, L.A., 1975-80; exec. asst. Ralph Powell & Assocs., L.A., 1980-82; pres., owner, producer LBW & Assocs. Pub. Rels., L.A., 1980—; owner, producer, writer, host TV prodn. co. Pub. Rels. Rels., L.A., 1987—; dir., producer L.B.W. Prodn. "Yesterday, Today, Tomorrow, L.A., 1981—. Actress (film) Ten Commandments, 1956, (Broadway) Joy Ride; appeared in the following endorsements including Budweiser Beer, Old Gold Cigarettes, Salem Cigarettes, TV commls. including Cheer, Puffs Tissue, Coca Cola, Buffern, others; entertainment editor L.A. Community News, 1970-73; writer (column) Balance News, 1980-82. Mem. Soka Gakkai Internat. Youth divsn. ARC, Urban League, Nat. Audubon Found., Nat. Parks Assn., Smithsonian Instn., Lupus Found. of Am. (so. Calif. chpt.), World Peace Cultural Festival '72, Bicentennial Celebration '76, United High Blood Pressure Telethon, Com. for Sr. Citizens, Beverly Hills-Westwood Sr. Citizen Cmty. Ctr. Recipient award ARC, 1955, Cert. of Honor, Internat. Orgn. Soka Gakkai Internat. of Japan, Cmty. Vols. of Am. award, 1994; named Performer of Yr. Cardella Demillo, 1976-77. Mem. ULCA Alumni Assn., Lupus Found. Am. (so. Calif. chpt.). Buddhist. Avocations: singing, acting, TV, writing, producing.

WHITE, LOWELL E., JR., medical educator; b. Tacoma, Wash., Jan. 16, 1928; s. Lowell E. and Hazel (Conley) W.; m. Margie Mae Lamb, June 21, 1947; children: Henry, Leanna White Maynes, Inger-Britt. B.S., U. Wash., 1951, M.D., 1953. Diplomate Am. Bd. Neurol. Surgery. Intern. N.C. Meml. Hosp., Chapel Hill, 1953-54; resident neurosurgery, asst. to instr. U. Wash., 1954-60, asst. prof., 1960-64, asso. prof., 1964-70; asso. dean U. Wash. (Sch. Medicine), 1965-68; prof., chief div. neurol. surgery U. Fla. 1970-72; prof. U. South Ala., 1972-94, chmn. div. neurosci., 1972-77, ret., 1994; adj. prof. Ala. Sch. of Math. and Sci., 1993-94; chmn. nat. adv. com. Animal Resources, 1964-70; cons. rsch. facilities and resources NIH; cons. divsn. hosp. and med. facilities USPHS; cons. grants adminstrn. policy Dept. HEW. Contbr. articles profl. jours. Bd. dirs. Mobile County Emergency Med. Svcs. Coun., 1973-82, Mobile chpt. Myasthenia Gravis Found., 1973-85, Gulf Coast chpt. Epilepsy Found. Am., 1974—, Mobile Mental Health Assn., 1979-89, Spl. Edn. Action Com., 1985—. With USN, 1946-47, USNR, 1948-66. Guggenheim fellow, 1958-59. Mem. Am. Assn. Neurol. Surgeons, Cajal Club, Am. Assn. Neuropathologists, Am. Acad. Neurol. Surgeons, Soc. for Neurosci., Assn. Am. Med. Colls., Am. Assn. Anatomists, Research Soc. Neurol. Surgeons, Neurosurg. Soc. Ala. (pres. 1975), AMA, Skyline Country Club (Mobile), Masons, Kiwanis, Sigma Xi. Home: 5750 Huffman Dr N Mobile AL 36693-3013

WHITE, LUTHER WESLEY, lawyer; b. Norfolk, Va., Aug. 29, 1923; s. Luther Wesley White Jr. and Edith Prettyman; m. Patricia Bowers; children: Luther, John P., Nell White King, Mary Dix. BA, Randolph-Macon Coll., 1947, LLD (hon.), 1989; LLB, Washington & Lee U., 1949, LLD, 1969; LHD (hon.), Bridgewater Coll., 1979; HHD (hon.), Ky. Wesleyan Coll., 1988. Bar: Va. 1949. Pvt. practice law Norfolk, 1949-67; pres. Randolph-Macon Coll., Ashland, Va., 1967-1979, Ky. Wesleyan Coll., Owensboro, 1979-88; atty. Eggleston & Thelen, Lovingston, Va., 1989—; HD (hon.); pres. Nat. Assn. Colls. and Univs. of United Meth. Ch., 1977-78. Pres. Norfolk Symphony Orch., 1966, Owensboro Symphony Orch., 1987. Lt. (j.g.) USN, 1943-46, PTO. Recipient Liberty Bell award Daviess County (Ky.) Bar Assn., Owensboro, 1983. Mem. Rotary (pres. Owensboro club 1982-83). Republican. Methodist. Avocations: music, tennis, gardening. Home: 31 Ashlawn Blvd Palmyra VA 22963-3329

WHITE, LYNN TOWNSEND, III, political science educator; b. Stanford, Calif., Sept. 16, 1941; s. Lynn Townsend Jr. and Maude (McArthur) W.; m. Barbara Sue White, May 30, 1965; children: Jeremy Townsend, Kevin McArthur. BA in Polit. Economy, Williams Coll., 1963; MA in Polit. Sci., U. Calif., Berkeley, 1965, PhD in Polit. Sci., 1972. With resjs. rsch. div. Dem. Study Group, Washington, 1962; instr. New Asia Coll., Hong Kong, 1963; rsch. assoc. Ctr. for SE Asian Studies Kyoto U., Japan, 1970-71; instr. polit. sci. dept. U. Calif., Berkeley, 1972-73, 88—; prof. Woodrow Wilson Sch. Politics and East Asian Studies Princeton (N.J.) U., 1973—; vis. scholar U. Hong Kong Ctr. for Asian Studies, 1988-89. Author: Careers in Shanghai, 1978, Policies of Chaos: Causes of Violence in the Cultural Revolution, 1989, (with others) The Modernization of China, 1981. Master Forbes Coll., 1987-88; trustee Princeton-in-Asia, 1982—. U. Calif. fellow, 1963-67, Harry Frank Guggenheim Found. fellow, 1988-89. Mem. Assn. for Asian Studies, Am. Polit. Sci. Assn. Democrat. Presbyterian. Avocations: singing, classical music, reading. Office: Princeton U Woodrow Wilson School Princeton NJ 08544

WHITE, MARGITA EKLUND, television association executive; b. Linköping, Sweden, June 27, 1937; came to U.S., 1948; d. Eyvind O. and Ella Maria (Eriksson) Eklund; m. Stuart Crawford White, June 24, 1961 (div. 1987); children: Suzanne Margareta Morgan, Stuart Crawford Jr. B.A. magna cum laude in Govt, U. Redlands, 1959, LL.D. (hon.), 1977, M.A. in Polit. Sci. (Woodrow Wilson fellow), Rutgers U., 1960. Asst. to press sec. Richard M. Nixon Presdl. Campaign, Washington, 1960; adminstrv. asst. Whitaker & Baxter Advt. Agy., Honolulu, 1961-62; minority news sec. Hawaii Ho. of Reps., 1963; research asst. to Senator Barry Goldwater and Republican Nat. Com., 1963-64; research asst., writer Free Society Assn., 1965-66; research asst. to syndicated columnist Raymond Moley, 1967; asst. to Herbert G. Klein, White House dir. communications, 1969-73; asst. dir. USIA, 1973-75; asst. press sec. to Pres. Gerald R. Ford, 1975; asst. press sec. to Pres., dir. White House Office of Communications, Washington, 1975-76; commr. FCC, 1976-79; dir. Radio Free Europe-Radio Liberty Inc., 1979-82, vice chmn., 1982; dir. Taft Broadcasting Co., 1980-87, Armtek Corp., 1987-88, Rayonier Forest Resources Co., 1985-93; pres. Assn. Maximum Svc. Television; bd. dirs. ITT Sheraton Corp., ITT Edn. Svcs., Caesars World, Inc., Washington Mut. Investors Fund, Growth Fund Washington, Leitch Tech. Corp.; U.S. del. Internat. Telecomm. Union Plenipotentiary Conf., Nairobi, 1982; coord. TV Operators Caucus, Inc., 1985-88. Mem. George Foster Peabody Adv. Bd., 1979-86. Recipient Disting. Service award U. Redlands Alumni Assn., 1974; Superior Honor award USIA, 1975. Mem. Exec. Women in Govt. (founding mem., sec. 1975), Women's Forum of Washington. Home: 1533 28th St NW Washington DC 20007 Office: 1776 Massachusetts Ave NW Washington DC 20036-1904

WHITE, MARILYN DOMAS, information science educator; b. Franklin, La., Aug. 16, 1940; d. George Julian and Norma Edwina (Melancon) Domas; m. Roger Stuart White, Aug. 31, 1968; 1 child, Joshua Stuart. BA, Our Lady of the Lake Coll., San Antonio, 1962; MS, U. Wis. 1963; PhD, U. Ill., 1971. Dir. Commerce Libr. U. Wis., Madison, 1963-65; head Social Sci./Bus. Libr. So. Ill. U., Edwardsville, 1965-67; cons. So. Ill. U./U.S. AID Adv. Team, South Vietnam, 1967; asst. prof. SUNY, Buffalo, 1972-74; lectr., vis. asst. prof. U. Md., College Park, 1976-77, asst. prof. info sci., 1977-82, assoc. prof. info. sci., 1982—; cons. USIA, Washington and abroad, 1977-83, Inst. for Def. Analyses, Bowie, Md.,Supercomputing Rsch. Ctr., 1990-91, Am. Health Care Assn., Washington, 1990-92, Am. Coun. on Edn., 1995. Contbr. articles to Libr. Quar., Drexel Libr. Quar., Reference Libr., others. James Lyman Whitney grantee ALA, 1983, Spl. Libr. Assn. rsch. grantee,

1993-94. Mem. Am. Soc. for Info. Sci., Spl. Libr. Assn. Roman Catholic. Office: U Md Coll Libr and Info Svcs Hornbake 4117F South Wing College Park MD 20742

WHITE, MARK N., lawyer; b. San Diego, Sept. 17, 1953; s. Don R. and Janice (Hodges) W.; m. Susan K. McGinnis. BA, Stanford U., 1975; JD, U. Pa., 1979. Bar: Calif. 1979, U.S. Ct. of Appeals (9th cir.) 1981, U.S. Supreme Ct. 1985. Assoc. Pillsbury, Madison & Sutro, San Francisco, 1979-87, ptnr., 1988—. Office: Pillsbury Madison & Sutro PO Box 7880 San Francisco CA 94120-7880

WHITE, MARTIN CHRISTOPHER, academic administrator; b. Anderson, S.C., Oct. 16, 1943; s. Jesse Martin and Christine Freida (Powell) W.; m. Linda Ann Fleming, July 31, 1965; children: Martin Lynn, Andrew Christopher. AB, Mercer U., 1965; MDiv, So. Bapt. Theol. Sem., 1968; PhD, Emory U., 1972. Prof. Elon Coll. (N.C.), 1972-76, dean acad. affairs, 1976-82, v.p. for acad. and student affairs, 1982-86; pres. Gardner-Webb U., Boiling Springs, N.C., 1986—; cons. So. Assn. Colls. and Schs., Atlanta, 1982—. Contbr. articles in field. Bd. dirs. United Way, Shelby, N.C., 1987. Woodrow Wilson fellow, 1971. Mem. Soc. Bibl. Lit., Nat. Assn. Bapt. Profs. of Religion, N.C. Ind. Coll. Assn., Alpha Chi, Omicron Delta Kappa. Democrat. Baptist. Lodge: Rotary (bd. dirs. Burlington, N.C. chpt. 1986). Avocations: golfing, tennis, music, traveling. Home: 303 W Marion St Shelby NC 28150-5335 Office: Gardner-Webb U Campus Mail Boiling Springs NC 28017

WHITE, MARY LOU, fundraiser, writer, educator; b. Davenport, Iowa, Feb. 17, 1939; d. Edward Joseph and Madeleine (Levart) Briglia; m. Morton Bartho White. Dec. 6, 1965 (dec. Jan. 1973). Cert. d'etudes francaises, U. Grenoble, France, 1959; BA, Gettysburg Coll., 1960; postgrad. Sorbonne, Paris, 1961; MA, Middlebury Coll., 1962; MS, U. Bridgeport, 1972. Writer CIA, N.Y.C., 1962-64; tchr. French Miss Porter's Sch., Farmington, Conn., 1964-66; fundraiser N.Y. Philharm., N.Y.C., 1966-72; tchr. French Fairfield (Conn.) Country Day Sch., 1973-77, Greens Farms (Conn.) Acad., 1977-79; spl. events coord. N.Y. Philharm., N.Y.C., 1979-80; econ. devel. Broward C.C., Ft. Lauderdale, Fla., 1989-91; programming grants writer Broward Ctr. for the Performing Arts, Ft. Lauderdale, 1992—. Vol. Polit. Party, Ft. Lauderdale, 1990-93. Mem. Hereditary Register of U.S. Avocations: chess, piano, breeding dachshunds. Home: 888 Intracoastal Dr Fort Lauderdale FL 33304

WHITE, MARY RUTH WATHEN, social services administrator; b. Athens, Tex., Dec. 27, 1927; d. Benedict Hudson and Sara Elizabeth (Evans) W.; m. Robert M. White, Nov. 10, 1946; children: Martha Elizabeth, Robert Miles, Jr., William Benedict, Mary Ruth, Jesse Wathen, Margaret Fay, Maureen Adele, Thomas Evan. BA, Stephen F. Austin State U., Nacogdoches, Tex., 1948. Chmn. Regional Drug Abuse Com. San Antonio, 1975-81, Met. Youth Council, San Antonio, 1976-78; state chmn. Citizens United for Rehab. Errants, San Antonio, 1978-91; sec. Bexar County Detention Ministries, San Antonio, 1979-88; chmn. Bexar County (Tex.) Jail Commn., 1980-82; chmn. com. on role of family in reducing recidivism Tex. Dept. Criminal Justice, Austin, 1985—; chmn. Met. Community Corrections Com., San Antonio, 1986-90; bd. dirs. Tex. Coalition for Juvenile Justice, 1975-93, Target 90 Youth Coordinating Coun., San Antonio, 1986-89; local chmn. vol. adv. bd. Tex. Youth Commn., 1986-87. Pres. San Antonio City Coun. PTA, 1976-78, Rep. Bus. Women Bexar County, San Antonio, 1984-86; bd. dirs. CURE, 1978-92; legis. chmn. Archdiocese of San Antonio Coun. Cath. Women, San Antonio Alliance Mental Illness; pres. North Urban Deanery; mem. allocation com. United Way, San Antonio, 1986-91. Named Today's Woman, San Antonio Light newspaper, 1985, Outstanding Rep. Woman, Rep. Bus. Women Bexar County, 1987; honoree Rep. Women Stars over Tex., 1992. Mem. Am. Corrections Assn. Criminal Justice Planners, LWV (pres. San Antonio chpt. 1984-86), Conservation Soc., Fedn. Women (bd. dirs. 1984-90), DAR (regent), Colonial Dames (pres.), Cath. Daus. Am. (registered parliamentarian, past regent Ct. of St. Anthony), Tex. Cath. Daus. Am. (state legis. chair). Home: 701 E Sunshine Dr San Antonio TX 78228-2516 Office: 7461 Callaghan Rd Ste 307 San Antonio TX 78229-2988

WHITE, MICHAEL DENNIS, food manufacturing company executive; b. Norwood, Mass., Jan. 11, 1952; s. Thomas Michael and Sally (Davenport) W.; m. Susan Lee Burns, June 30, 1972; children: Larissa, Paul, Jennifer. BA, Boston Coll., Newton, Mass., 1974; cert. of proficiency, Leningrad (USSR) State U., 1974; MA in Internat. Rels., Johns Hopkins U., 1976. CPA, Mass. Cons. Arthur Andersen & Co., Mgmt. Info. Cons. Div., Washington, Boston, 1976-80; mgr. Arthur Andersen & Co., Mgmt. Info. Cons. Div., 1980-81; cons. Bain & Co., Boston, 1981-84; mgr. Bain & Co., 1984-86; v.p. planning, devel. Avon Products, N.Y.C., 1986-87; v.p. retail devel. Avon Products, 1987-88; sr. v.p., gen. mgr. internat. Parfums Stern Inc. (subs. Avon Products), N.Y.C., 1988-90; v.p. planning Frito-Lay Inc., Plano, Tex., 1990, sr. v.p. fin., chief fin. officer, 1991—. Active Tri-State United Way, 1993; v.p. Westport (Conn.)-Weston United Way, 1988-90. Home: 1704 Anglebluff Ln Plano TX 75093-2803 Office: Frito-Lay Inc 7701 Legacy Dr Plano TX 75024-4099

WHITE, MICHAEL REED, mayor; b. Cleve., Aug. 13, 1951; s. Robert and Audrey (Silver) W.; m. Tamera K. White. BA, Ohio State U., 1973, MPA, 1974. Spl. asst. Columbus (Ohio) Mayor's Office, 1974-76; administrv. asst. Cleve. City Coun., 1976-77; sales mgr. Burks Electric Co., Cleve., 1978-84; state senator Ohio Senate, Columbus, 1984-89; mayor Cleve., 1990—; minority whip Ohio Senate Dems., 1987-89. City councilman City of Cleve., 1978-84; bd. dirs. Glenville Devel. Corp., Cleve., 1978—, Glenville Festival Found., Cleve., 1978—, United Black Fund, Cleve., 1986, Greater Cleve. Dome Corp., 1986. Named one of Outstanding Young Men Am., 1985, Outstanding Young Leader of Cleve.; recipient Outstanding Svc. award Cleve. chpt. Nat. Assn. Black Vets., 1985, Community Svcs. award East Side Jaycees. Democrat. Home: 1057 East Blvd Cleveland OH 44108-2984 Office: Office of Mayor 601 Lakeside Ave NE Cleveland OH 44114-1012*

WHITE, MICHELLE JO, economics educator; b. Washington, Dec. 3, 1945; d. Harry L. and Irene (Silverman) Rich; m. Roger Hall Gordon, July 25, 1982. AB, Harvard U., 1967; MSc in Econs., London Sch. Econs., 1968; PhD, Princeton U., 1973. Asst. prof. U. Pa., Phila., 1973-78; from assoc. prof. to prof. NYU, N.Y.C., 1978-83; prof. econs. U. Mich., Ann Arbor, 1984—; dir. PhD program in econs. U. Mich., 1992-94; vis. asst. prof. Yale U., New Haven, 1978; vis. prof. People's U., Beijing, 1986, U. Warsaw, 1990, U. Wis., Madison, 1991, U. Munich, 1992, Catholic U. Brabant, The Netherlands, 1993, 95, U. Chgo., 1993; cons. Pension Benefit Guaranty Corp., Washington, 1987; chmn. adv. com. dept. econs. Princeton U., 1988-90. Editor: The Non-profit Sector in a Three Sector Economy, 1981; contbr. numerous articles to profl. jours. Bd. dirs. Com. on Status of Women in Econs. Profession, 1984-86. Resources for Future fellow, 1972-73; grantee NSF, 1979, 82, 88, 91, 93, Sloan Found., 1984, Fund for Rsch. in Dispute Resolution, 1989; Fulbright scholar, Poland, 1990. Mem. Am. Econ. Assn., Am. Law and Econ. Assn. (bd. dirs. 1991-92), Am. Real Estate and Urban Econs. Assn. (bd. dirs. 1992-95), Social Scis. Rsch. Coun. (bd. dirs. 1994—). Office: Univ Mich Dept Economics 611 Tappan Ave Ann Arbor MI 48109-1220

WHITE, MORTON GABRIEL, philosopher, author; b. N.Y.C., Apr. 29, 1917; s. Robert and Esther (Levine) Weisberger; m. Lucia Perry, Aug. 29, 1940; children: Nicholas Perry, Stephen Daniel. B.S., CCNY, 1936; L.H.D., CUNY, 1975; A.M., Columbia U., 1938, Ph.D., 1942. Instr. philosophy Columbia U., 1942-46; instr. physics CCNY, 1942-43; asst. prof. philosophy U. Pa., 1946-48; asst. prof. philosophy Harvard U., 1948-50, asso. prof., 1950-53, prof., 1953-70, chmn. dept., 1954-57, acting chmn. dept., 1967-69; prof. Inst. Advanced Study, 1970-87; prof. emeritus, 1987—; Guggenheim research fellow, 1950-51; vis. prof. Tokyo U., 1952, 60, 66, U. Oslo, 1977-78; Neesima lectr. Doshisha U., Kyoto, 1985, CUNY, 1968-69, Rutgers U., 1987-88, 88-89; mem. Inst. Advanced Study, 1953-54, 62-63, 67-68, 68-69. Author: The Origin of Dewey's Instrumentalism, 1943, Social Thought in America, 1949, The Age of Analysis, 1955, Toward Reunion in Philosophy, 1956, Religion, Politics, and the Higher Learning, 1959, (with Lucia White) The Intellectual Versus the City, 1962; Editor: (with Arthur M. Schlesinger, Jr.) Paths of American Thought, 1963, Foundations of Historical Knowledge, 1965, Science and Sentiment in America, 1972, Documents in

the History of American Philosophy, 1972, Pragmatism and the American Mind, 1973, The Philosophy of the American Revolution, 1978, What Is and What Ought to Be Done, 1981, (with Lucia White) Journeys to the Japanese, 1952-79, 1986, Philosophy, The Federalist and the Constitution, 1987, The Question of Free Will, 1993. Fellow Center Advanced Study Behavioral Scis., 1959-60; fellow Am. Council Learned Socs., 1962-63. Mem. Am. Acad. Arts and Scis., Am. Antiquarian Soc., Am. Philos. Soc. Office: Inst for Advanced Study Princeton NJ 08540

WHITE, NATHAN EMMETT, JR., lawyer; b. Dallas, Nov. 28, 1941; s. Nathan Emmett and Martha Eleanor (Scogin) W.; m. Wanda Joyce Cason, Feb. 28, 1964; children: Steven Kelly, Russell Bradley. BBA, So. Meth. U., 1964, JD, 1972; postgrad. George Washington U., 1969-71. Bar: Tex. 1972, U.S. Dist. Ct. (no. dist.) Tex. 1976. Sole practice, Plano, Tex., 1972-89; county judge, Collin County, McKinney, Tex., 1975-82, county treas., 1983-85. Chmn. Collin County Rep. Party, 1972-74; mem. exec. com. State Rep. Party, 1982-84. Served to lt. USNR, 1966-71. Named Citizen of Yr., Plano C. of C., 1982. Mem. State Bar Tex. (chmn. sch. law sect. 1981-82). Mormon. Lodges: Rotary (pres. 1975-76, dist. gov. 1979-80), Masons. Home: 2406 Forest Ct Mc Kinney TX 75070 Office: PO Box 808 Mc Kinney TX 75070

WHITE, NICHOLAS J., retail company executive; b. Sacramento, 1945. Grad., Mo. So. State Coll. Exec. v.p. Wal-Mart Supercenter div. Wal-Mart Stores Inc. Home: 81 Champions Blvd Rogers AR 72758 Office: Wal-Mart Stores Inc 702 SW 8th St Bentonville AR 72716-9102

WHITE, NORVAL CRAWFORD, architect; b. N.Y.C., June 12, 1926; s. William Crawford and Caroline Ruth (Taylor) W.; m. Joyce Leslie Lee, May 24, 1958 (div.); children: William Crawford, Thomas Taylor, Gordon Crawford, Alistair David; m. Camilla Cecilia Crowe, June 7, 1992. B.S., Mass. Inst. Tech., 1949; student, Sch. Fine Arts, Fontainbleau, 1954; M.F.A., Princeton, 1955. Designer, assoc. Lathrop Douglass (Architect), 1955-59; prin. Norval C. White (Architect), N.Y.C., 1959-62, 66-67; partner Rowan & White (Architects), N.Y.C., 1962-66, Gruzen & Partners, N.Y.C., 1967-70; prin. Norval C. White & Assos., N.Y.C., 1970-74; ptnr. Levien, Deliso & White, 1974-80, Levien Deliso White Songer, 1980-86; asst. prof. architecture Cooper Union, 1961-67; prof. architecture City Coll., CUNY, 1970—, chmn. dept., 1970-77. Author: (with E. Willensky) AIA Guide to New York City, 1968, 2d edit., 1978, 3d edit., 1988, The Architecture Book, 1976, New York: A Physical History, 1987, The Guide to the Architecture of Paris, 1991; prin. works include Seiden House, Tenafly, N.J., 1960, Essex Terrace (housing), Bklyn., 1970, N.Y.C. Police Hdqrs., 1973, Brookhaven Parks (L.I.) San Landfill, 1971, Forsgate Indsl. Park, South Brunswick, N.J., 1978-86, Del Vista Condominiums, Miami, 1981, 61 Christopher Street, Greenwich Village, 1987. Trustee Bklyn. Inst. Arts and Scis., 1973-82, Bklyn. Pub. Libr., 1993—; gov. Bklyn. Mus., 1973-82, mem. adv. com., 1982—; mem. N.Y.C. Art Commn., 1975-86, sec., 1975-77, v.p., 1978-80. Served with USNR, 1944-46. Fellow AIA; mem. Soc. Archtl. Historians, N.Y. State Assn. Architects. Democrat. Home: 104 Pierrepont St Brooklyn NY 11201-2761 Office: CCNY Sch Architecture 138th St and Convent Ave New York NY 10031

WHITE, OWEN KENDALL, JR., sociologist, educator; b. Salt Lake City, Oct. 23, 1938; s. Owen Kendall and Thelma Clark White; m. Arlene Burraston; 1 child, C.A. Wood. BS in Sociology, U. Utah, 1964, MS in Sociology, 1967; PhD in Sociology, Vanderbilt U., 1975. Instr. part-time Vanderbilt U., Nashville, 1968; instr. sociology Washington and Lee U., Lexington, Va., 1969-75, asst. prof. sociology, 1975-80, assoc. prof. sociology, 1980-86, prof. sociology, 1986—, chair dept. sociology and anthropology, 1987—; vis. asst. prof. Inst. Urban Studies, U. Tex., summer 1978; referee Dialogue: A Jour. of Mormon Thought, 1989, Jour. of Urban Affairs, 1990—, Jour for Sci. Study of Religion, 1993—; lectr. in field. Author: Mormon Neo-Orthodoxy: A Crisis Theology, 1987, 2d printing, 1988; contbr. articles and book revs. to profl. pubs. Recipient Glenn grant Washington and Lee U., 1970, 75, 81-93, Silver award The Silver Found., 1971, Mednick fellowship Va. Found. for Ind. Colls., 1985, 93. Mem. Am. Anthrop. Assn., Am. Sociol. Assn., Assn. for the Sociology of Religion, Soc. for Sociol. Study of Mormon Life (pres. 1991-93), So. Anthrop. Soc., So. Sociol. Soc., Religious Rsch. Assn., Va. Sociol. Sci. Assn. Office: Washington and Lee U Dept Sociology/Anthropology Lexington VA 24450

WHITE, PAMELA JANICE, lawyer; b. Elizabeth, N.J., July 13, 1952; d. Emmet Talmadge and June (Howlett) W. BA, Mary Washington Coll., 1974; JD, Washington and Lee U., 1977. Bar: Md. 1977, U.S. Dist. Ct. Md. 1978, D.C. 1979, U.S. Dist. Ct. D.C. 1979, U.S. Ct. Appeals (4th cir.) 1979, U.S. Ct. Appeals (D.C. cir.) 1981, U.S. Ct. Claims 1981, U.S. Ct. Appeals (2d cir.) 1983, N.Y. 1983, U.S. Dist. Ct. (so. dist.) N.Y. 1983, U.S. Ct. Appeals (9th cir.) 1988, U.S. Supreme Ct. 1981. Assoc. Ober, Kaler, Grimes & Shriver, Balt., 1977-84, ptnr., 1985—; mem. Md. Bd. Law Examiners, 1986-94; select com. on Gender Equality, 1989—; fed. dist. ct. adv. group, Civil Justice Reform Act, 1990. Note and comment editor Washington and Lee Law Rev. 1976-77, Washington and Lee Law Council 1983-87, emeritus mem., 1988—, pres. 1991-92. Mem. Fed. Ct. Bicentennial Com., 1988-90; vol. Profl. Gov.'s Drug-Free Workplace Initiative, 1990-93; bd. trustees Washington and Lee U., 1995—. Named Disting. Alumna, Washington and Lee U., 1994, Hon. mem. Order of the Coif. Mem. Am. Bar Found., mem. ABA, Nat. Conf. Lawyers Corp. Fiduciaries, N.Y. State Bar Assn., Md. State Bar Assn. (mem. legal edn. sect. coun. 1987—, mem. labor sect. coun. 1992—, chair legal edn. sect. 1992-93, mem. professionalism com. 1992—, chair 1994—, bd. govs. 1993-95, mem. exec. com. 1994-95), D.C. Bar Assn., Balt. City Bar Assn., Fed. Bar Assn., Women's Bar Assn. Md. (treas. 1986-87, v.p 1987-88, pres.-elect 1988-89, pres. 1989-90, bd. dirs. 1984-86), Nat. Conf. of Women's Bar Assns. (bd. dirs. 1990-91), Md. Assn. Def. Counsel. Presbyterian. Avocations: hiking, softball, baseball. Office: Ober Kaler Grimes & Shriver 120 E Baltimore St Baltimore MD 21202-1674

WHITE, PAUL DUNBAR, lawyer; b. LaGrange, Ky., Oct. 20, 1917; s. Isham Forrest and Florence (Harris) W.; m. Marion Loutenas Stallworth, Sept. 2, 1949; children: Paulette, Ronald. A.B., Ky. State Coll., 1940; LL.B., Western Res. U., 1950. Bar: Ohio 1950, U.S. Supreme Ct. 1972. Supr. Ind. State Boys Sch., 1940-41; group worker spl. projects Karamu, Cleve., 1941-43; visitor Cuyahoga County Agy., 1946-47; individual practice law Cleve., 1950-51; police prosecutor City of Cleve., 1951-59, 1st asst. prosecutor, 1960-63, dir. law, 1967-68; judge Cleve. Mcpl. Ct., 1964-67; assoc. Baker & Hostetler, Cleve., 1968-70; ptnr. Baker & Hostetler, 1970—; mem. State of Ohio Bd. Examiners, 1972-78. Trustee NCCJ, Cleve., 1972-87; trustee Ohio Law Opportunity Fund, 1975-87, Cleve. Urban League, 1975-78, Dyke Coll., Cleve., 1976-86; bd. commrs. Cleve. Met. Park, 1975-78. Served with U.S. Army, 1943-46. Mem. ABA, Ohio Bar Assn., Greater Cleve. Bar Assn. (trustee 1976-79, del. 8th Jud. Dist. Ohio conf. 1985—), Nat. Bar Assn., Soc. Benchers (Case Western Res. U.), Norman S. Minor Bar Assn. Home: 16210 Telfair Ave Cleveland OH 44128-3736 Office: Baker & Hostetler 3200 National City Ctr 1900 E 9th St Cleveland OH 44114

WHITE, PERRY MERRILL, JR., orthopedic surgeon; b. Texarkana, Ark., Oct. 11, 1925; s. Perry Merrill and Mary Gladys (Shelton) W.; m. Lucy Katherine Freeman, Dec. 23, 1947; children: Perry Merrill III, Georgia Lynette, Katherine Landis White Long, John David. B.S., Baylor U., 1948, M.D., 1953; postgrad., Vanderbilt U., 1948-49. Diplomate Am. Bd. Orthopedic Surgery. Intern VA Hosp., Houston, 1953-54; gen. practice medicine Spearman, Tex., 1955-57; resident orthopedic surgery Eugene Talmadge Meml. Hosp., Augusta, Ga., 1957-61; chief Ga. Adult Amputee Clinic, 1965-79; active staff Scottish Rite Hosp. for Crippled Children, Decatur, Ga., 1965-73; instr. orthopedic surgery residency program Ga. Bapt. Hosp., 1965-83; orthopedic panelist Ga. Dept. Vocat. Rehab.; cons. Ga. Crippled Children's Service, 1965-76. Former mem. bd. dirs. Haggai Inst., Atlanta, London, Singapore. Served with USNR, 1944-46. Fellow ACS, Am. Acad. Orthopedic Surgeons; mem. So., Ga. Atlanta med. assns., Eastern Orthopedic Assn., Ga. Atlanta orthopedic socs., Alpha Kappa Kappa. Republican. Baptist (deacon). Home: 1547 Cave Rd NW Atlanta GA 30327-3119

WHITE, PHILIP BUTLER, artist; b. Chgo., Jan. 23, 1935; s. Ralph Gerald and Mary (Butler) W.; m. Anita Malisani; children—David, Daniel. B.F.A.,

U. So. Calif., 1957. juror 24th ann. exhbn. Tenn. Watercolor Soc., 1995. One-man show, Oehlschlaeger Art Gallery, Chgo., 1976, 78, 80; exhibited in group shows 2d, 3d, ann. nat. art round-ups, Las Vegas, 1957, 58, Union League Club, Chgo., 1959, 63, 65, 67, 69, 72, 74, 76, Ill. State Fair, 1959, 60, 61, 62, 63, 64, 65, 66, 67, 68, Brotherhood Week Art Exhbn., Chgo., 1960, N. Miss. Valley Artists exhibit, Ill. State Mus., Springfield, 1961, 63, 65, 67, 69, 70, Magnificent Mile, Chgo., 1961, ann. midyear shows, Butler Inst. Am. Art, Youngstown, Ohio, 1962, 63, 64, ann. Chgo. Sun Times exhbns., 1962, 63, 21st ann. exhbn. Audubon Artists, N.Y.C., 1963, ann. exhbns., Nat. Acad. Design, N.Y.C., 1963, 64, 65, 67, 68, 69, 70, 74, 75, 76, Okla. Mus. Art, 1969, 70, Ball State U., 1970, Am. Watercolor Soc. ann., 1970-71, one-man show, Oak Park (Ill.) High Sch., 1968; rep., Art Inst. Chgo., various art fairs including, Oakbrook, Ill., 1963, Old Capitol at Springfield, 1963, 68, Oak Park, 1963, 78 subject of cover story, Am. Artist mag., 1978. Served with AUS, 1958-59. Recipient John Deluca medal Las Vegas, 1957; Henry Ward Ranger Fund Purchase prize Nat. Acad. Design, 1963; Julius Hallgarten award, 1964, 67, 69; Thomas B. Clark award, 1965, 68, 70; Helen H. Chambers Purchase prize Union League Club, 1959; 1st prize in oils Union League Club, 1963, 67; 1st prize in oils Ill. State Fair, 1960, 65, Emily Goldsmith award, 1971; Juror of awards 71st annual exhibition Nat. Watercolor Soc., 1991. Address: 710 Clinton Pl River Forest IL 60305

WHITE, PHILLIP E., technology company executive; b. Paylorville, Ill., Dec. 24, 1943; s. Phillip Conrad and Lois Marion (Elliott) W.; m. Sheryl Faye Meyer (div. Feb. 1992); children: thler, Todd, Trevor. BA, Ill. Wesleyan, 1966; MBA, Ill. U., 1968. Dir. of planning IBM, White Plains, N.Y., 1968-84; exec. v.p. sales and mktg. Altos Computer System, San Jose, Calif., 1984-86; pres. Wyse Tech., San Jose, Calif., 1986-88; pres., chief exec. officer Informix Corp., Menlo Park, Calif., 1989—; bd. dirs. Intellicorp, Mountain View, Calif., 1989— Informix Corp., Menlo Park, Calif., 1989— Sam and Libby of Calif., San Carlos, 1992—. Bd. dirs. Santa Clara U., Calif., 1989—. Mem. Am. Electronics Assn. Republican. Methodist. Office: Informix Software 4100 Bohannon Dr Menlo Park CA 94025-1013

WHITE, R. QUINCY, lawyer; b. Chgo., Jan. 16, 1933; s. Roger Q. and Carolyn Jane (Everett) W.; m. Joyce Caldwell, Aug. 4, 1962; children: Cleaver Dorothea, Annelia Everett. BA, Yale U., 1954; JD, Harvard U., 1960. Bar: Ill. 1960, U.S. Dist. Ct. (no. dist.) Ill. 1960, U.S. Ct. Appeals (9th cir.) 1989. Assoc. Leibman, Williams, Bennett, Baird & Minow, Chgo., 1960-67, ptnr. 1973-77; ptnr. Sidley & Austin, Chgo., 1973-93, of counsel, 1994—; sec., dir. W.F. McLaughlin Co., Chgo., 1964-68; hon. consul gen. Islamic Republic Pakistan, Chgo., 1978-92; designated mem. U.S. Trademark Assn., 1985-94. Bd. dirs., counsel Off the Street Club, Chgo., 1974-84; sec. nat. governing bd. Ripon Soc., 1971-72; mem. exec. com. 43d-44th ward Regular Rep. orgn., Chgo., 1970-73, mem. Coun. Fgn. and Domestic Affairs, 1970-76; v.p., bd. dirs. Juvenile Protective Assn., 1965-87. Recipient Sitara-i-Quaid-i-Azam Pakistan, 1982. Mem. ABA, Chgo. Coun. Lawyers, Chgo. Bar Assn., Harvard Law Soc. of Ill. (dir. 1988-93). Home: 316 W Willow St Chicago IL 60614-5717 Office: Sidley & Austin 1 First Nat Plz Chicago IL 60603

WHITE, RALPH DALLAS, retired health insurance executive; b. Oklahoma City, Feb. 11, 1919; s. Ralph Allen and Ora Della (Lamberson) W.; m. Ramona Corrine Caffee, Aug. 29, 1943; children: Richard Dallas, Linda Diane. Grad., Okla. Sch. Bus., 1938; B.C.S., Okla. Sch. Accountancy, Law and Fin., 1941; postgrad., U. Tulsa, 1947, Mgmt. Inst., U. Mich., 1965-66. Discount clk. Gen. Motors Acceptance Corp., 1939-42; payroll supr. Douglas Aircraft Corp., 1942-45; with Blue Cross-Blue Shield of Okla., Tulsa, 1945-87, from acctg. supr., mgr. personnel and systems, office mgr., dir. adminstrn., sec.-treas., v.p. and sec.-treas., v.p., treas., to exec. v.p., treas., 1945-80, sr. v.p., 1980-81, cons. to pres., 1981-87, ret., 1987; v.p., treas. Mems. Service Life Ins. Co., 1977-79, dir., 1977-87. Mem. Internat. Com. Tulsa, Ark. Basin Devel. Assn. Named Boss of Yr. Am. Bus. Women's Assn., 1961; recipient Hall of Fame award Okla. Coll. of Bus., 1984. Mem. Nat. Office Mgmt. Assn. Adminstrv. Mgmt. Soc. (pres. 1957-58, Merit award key 1958, Diamond Merit award key 1968), Tulsa C. of C., Tulsa Farm Club, Downtown Kiwanis Club, Tulsa Computer Soc. Methodist. Home: 4709 E 22nd Pl Tulsa OK 74114-2127

WHITE, RALPH DAVID, retired editor and writer; b. Cleve., Mar. 10, 1931; s. Ralph Davis and Mildred Eva (Stein) W.; m. Lucy Margaret Sturm, Aug. 20, 1960; children: Randall, Eric, Karen, Kathleen. BA, Hamilton Coll., 1953; postgrad., SUNY, Buffalo. With Buffalo Evening News, 1956-89, reporter, 1956-61, successively copy editor, asst. city editor, feature editor, to, 1974, picture editor and dir. editorial art dept., 1974-83, gen. features editor, 1983-89, antiques columnist, 1983-89; guest lectr. SUNY, Buffalo. Served with U.S. Army, 1953-55, Far East. Recipient local awards Buffalo Newspaper Guild. Home: 1389 Whitehaven Rd Grand Island NY 14072-1915

WHITE, RALPH PAUL, automotive executive, consultant; b. Watertown, Mass., Aug. 1, 1926; s. Irving William and Margaret Sarah (McGowan) W.; m. Shirley Irene Christie, Nov. 22, 1947; children: Karin Ann, Eric John. BS in Indsl. Engring., Columbia U., 1951; postgrad., Yale U., 1958-59. Instr. engring. mechanics U. Conn., Torrington, 1956-57; mgr. data processing. B.F. Goodrich Co., Shelton, Conn., 1958-61; ptnr., mgmt. cons. Bavier, Bulger & Goodyear, New Haven, 1961-66; v.p. Davidson Rubber Co., Dover, N.H., 1966-69; pres. Davidson Rubber Co., Dover, 1969-80; group v.p. parent co. Ex-Cell-O, Troy, Mich., 1980-83; pres. Troy (N.H.) Mills Inc., 1983-86, chief exec. officer, 1983-89, chmn., 1987-89, also bd. dirs.; cons., 1989—; bd. dirs. J.A. Wright Co., Keene, N.H., J.D. Cahill Co., Hampton, N.H., Exeter Trust Co. Mem. N.H. Indsl. Devel. Authority, 1972-80, 85-88, Pease Devel. Authority, State of N.H., N.H. Bus. and Fin. Authority, 1992—; exec. bd. Whittemore Sch. Bus., U. N.H., Durham, 1984—. Mem. Am. Inst. Indsl. Engrs., Soc. Automotive Engrs., N.H. Bus. and Industry Assn. (bd. dirs. 1970-80, pres. 1972-73, vice chmn. 1984-86), Abenaqui Country Club, Rye Beach Club, Coral Beach Club. Democrat. Roman Catholic. Avocations: skiing, golf. Home: 70 Woodland Rd # 667 North Hampton NH 03862-2234

WHITE, RANDALL WAYNE, educational development executive; b. Keystone, Okla., Jan. 11, 1942; s. Wiley and Helen (Ottinger) W.; m. Carol L. Thompson, Feb. 1, 1964; children: Craig M., Todd R. BS, Okla. State U., 1963. Acctg. mgr. Mapco, Tulsa, 1963-69; controller CCI Corp., Tulsa, 1969-71, PepsiCo., Tulsa, 1971-74; pres. Arctic Express, Tulsa, 1975-80; chief fin. officer NICOR Drilling, Tulsa, 1980-83; pres. Ednl. Devel. Corp. Tulsa, 1983—; bd. dirs. Okla. Osteopathic Hosp. Tulsa, 1987—, Original Chili Bowl, Inc., 1986—. Mem. Shadow Mountain Racquet Club, Kiwanis (bd. dirs. Tulsa club 1988). Republican. Methodist. Home: 10385 S 76th East Ave Tulsa OK 74133-6828 Office: Ednl Devel Corp 10302 E 55th Pl Tulsa OK 74146-6507

WHITE, RANDY, retired professional football player; b. Wilmington, Del., Jan. 15, 1953; s. Guy and Laverne W.; m. Vicci Hanes, 1978; 1 child, Jordan. Student, U. Md. Defensive tackle Dallas Cowboys, 1975-88; played in Super Bowl X, 1975, XII, 1977, XIII, 1978. Winner Outland Trophy for best coll. lineman, 1974, (with Harvey Martin) Most Valuable Player award Super Bowl XII, 1977; named to Pro Bowl team, 1977-85, Pro Football Hall of Fame, 1994. *

WHITE, RAYMOND PETRIE, JR., dentist, educator; b. N.Y.C., Feb. 13, 1937; s. Raymond Petrie and Mabel Sarah (Shutze) W.; m. Betty Pritchett, Dec. 27, 1961; children—Karen Elizabeth, Michael Wood. Student, Washington and Lee U., 1955-58; D.D.S., Med. Coll. Va., 1962, Ph.D., 1967. Diplomate: Am. Bd. Oral and Maxillofacial Surgery. Postdoctoral fellow anatomy Med. Coll. Va., Richmond, 1962-67; resident in oral surgery Med. Coll. Va., 1964-67; asst. prof. U. Ky., Lexington, 1967-70; asso. prof. U. Ky., 1970-71, chmn. dept. oral surgery, 1969-71; prof., asst. dean adminstrn. Va. Commonwealth U., Richmond, 1971-74; prof. Sch. Dentistry U. N.C., Chapel Hill, 1974—, Dalton L. McMichael disting. prof., 1993—; dean Sch. Dentistry, U. N.C., Chapel Hill, 1974-81, assoc. dean Sch. Medicine, 1981-92; cons. Portsmouth Naval Hosp., Fayetteville VA Hosp.; mem. staff U. N.C. Hosps., mem. exec. com., 1974—, sec. 1977-78, assoc. chief staff, 1981-92; mem. adver. panel on dentistry U.S. Pharmacopeial Com., 1985—; sr. program cons. The Robert Wood Johnson Found., 1982-90. Author: (with E.R. Costich) Fundamentals of Oral Surgery, 1971, (with Bell and Proffit)

Surgical Correction of Dentofacial Deformities, 1980, (with W.R. Proffit) Surgical Orthodontic Treatment, 1990, (with M.R. Tucker, B.C. Terry, J.E. Van Sickels) Rigid Fixations for Maxillofacial Surgery, 1991; co-editor Internat. Jour. Adult Orthodontics and Orthodontic Surgery, 1985—; asst. editor Jour. Oral and Maxillofacial Surgery, 1993—; contbr. sci. articles to profl. jours. Bd. dirs. Am. Fund for Dental Health, 1978-86, v.p.; 1982-85. Recipient Outstanding Tchr. award U. Ky., 1971, Disting. Service award Am. Fund Dental Health, 1987. Mem. ADA, AAAS, N.C. Dental Soc., Internat. Assn. for Dental Rsch. (pres. Ky. sect. 1970), Inst. of Medicine of NAS, Chalmers J. Lyons Acad. Oral Surgery, Am. Assn. Oral and Maxillofacial Surgeons (gen. chmn. sci. sessions com. 1974-76, Outstanding Service award as committeeman 1976, chmn. strategic planning com. 1990—), N.C. Soc. Oral and Maxillofacial Surgeons, Sigma Xi, Psi Omega, Delta Tau Delta, Alpha Sigma Chi, Sigma Zeta, Psi Omega (Scholarship award 1962), Omicron Kappa Upsilon. Roman Catholic. Home: 1506 Velma Rd Chapel Hill NC 27514-7601 Office: U NC Sch Dentistry Dept Oral/Maxillofacial Surgery Chapel Hill NC 27514-7450

WHITE, REGGIE (REGINALD HOWARD WHITE), professional football player; b. Chattanooga, Dec. 19, 1961; m. Sara Copeland; children: Jeremy, Jecolia. Student, U. Tenn. With Memphis Showboats, 1984-85, Phila. Eagles, 1985-93, Green Bay Packers, 1993—. Named to Sporting News Coll. All-Am. team, 1983, Sporting News United States Football League All-Star team, 1985, Pro Bowl team, 1986-93, Sporting News All-Pro team, 1987, 88, 91, 93. Holds NFL career record for sacks, 137—. Office: Green Bay Packers PO Box 10628 Green Bay WI 54307-0628*

WHITE, RENE, public relations executive; b. L.A., Dec. 18, 1951. BA in Journalism, Calif. State U., 1974. Reporter Orange County Newspapers, 1973; with dept. pub. rels. San Francisco, Am., 1973-74; account mgr. Basso/Boatman, Inc., 1974-76; with Regis McKenna, 1977-80, v.p., 1980-82, exec. v.p., 1982; gen. mgr., dir. high tech. B-M, 1982-84; sr. v.p., dir. tech. mktg. Burson-Marsteller, 1984-86; sr. v.p. bd. dirs Fleishman-Hillard/L.A., 1986-87; pres. White Cromer Bellack, 1987-91; prin. WHite & Cromer, 1992—. Office: White & Co 50 Osgood Ste 120 San Francisco CA 94133

WHITE, RICHARD A., congressman; b. Bloomington, Ind., Nov. 6, 1953; m. Vikki; 4 children. BA in Govt., Dartmouth Coll., 1975; JD, Georgetown U., 1980. Law clk. to Hon. Charles Clark U.S Ct. Appeals (5th dist.), 1980-81; assoc. Covington & Burling, 1981-83; assoc. Perkins Coie, 1983-88, ptnr., 1988—; mem. 104th Congress from 1st Wash. dist., 1994—. Del. to dist. county, State GOP Convs., 1984—; founder Farm Team; founder, trustee Books for Kids. Office: US House Reps 1520 Longworth House Office Bldg Washington DC 20515-4701*

WHITE, RICHARD BOOTH, management consultant; b. N.Y.C., Aug. 26, 1930; s. Frank K. and Doris (Booth) W.; m. Mary Kane Russell, Dec. 9, 1961; children: Katherine Learned, Richard Booth (dec.), Anne Tristram, Leslie Russell. B.A., Yale U., 1952. Asst. account exec. Batten, Barton, Durstine & Osborn, N.Y.C., 1955; account exec. Batten, Barton, Durstine & Osborn, 1956-58, account supr., 1958-63, v.p., 1959-70, mgmt. supr., 1963-76, sr. v.p., 1970-76, exec. v.p., 1976-83, also dir., chmn. exec. com.; dir. BBDO Internat. Inc.; sr. dir., ptnr. Spencer Stuart & Assocs., N.Y.C., 1984—. Pres. bd. Wavency Care Ctr., New Canaan, Conn. 1st lt. USMCR, 1952-54. Mem. Beta Theta Pi. Presbyterian. Clubs: Yale, Racquet and Tennis (N.Y.C.); Country of New Canaan. Home: 774 Oenoke Rdg New Canaan CT 06840-9999 Office: Spencer Stuart & Assocs 695 E Main St Stamford CT 06901

WHITE, RICHARD CLARENCE, lawyer; b. Sioux City, Iowa, Oct. 31, 1933; m. Beverly Frances Fitzpatrick, Feb. 22, 1955; children—Anne, Richard, William, Christopher. B.A.; LL.B., Stanford U., 1962. Bar: Calif. 1963, U.S. Supreme Ct. 1970, N.Y. 1983. Assoc. O'Melveny & Myers, L.A., 1962-70, ptnr., 1970—. Lectr. in field. Bd. dirs. Equal Employment Adv. Coun., Washington, 1976-80, 83, Performing Arts Ctr. of Orange County 1983-86. Capt. USMC 1954-59; Mem. ABA (co-chmn. on practice and procedure labor and employment law sect. 1977-80, mem. equal opportunity law com. 1980-85, co-chmn. com. on insts. and meetings 1985-87, coun. 1987—), Orange County Bar Assn., Lincoln Club (Orange County). Republican. Contbr. articles to profl. publs.

WHITE, RICHARD DAVID, managing director; b. Flushing, N.Y., Dec. 8, 1953; s. Jerome and Marjorie White; m. Karen J. Newman, Nov. 18, 1979; children: Elizabeth Newman White, Alexandra Newman White. BA, Tufts U., 1976; MBA, Wharton Sch., 1978. CPA. Supr. cons. Coopers & Lybrand, N.Y.C., 1978-81; managing dir. Ardshiel Inc., N.Y.C., 1981-85, Oppenheimer & Co. Inc., N.Y.C., 1985—. Office: Oppenheimer & Co Inc Oppenheimer Tower World FInancial Ctr New York NY 10281

WHITE, RICHARD HUGH, dean student affairs; b. Brigham City, Utah, Dec. 3, 1933; s. Leroy Davis and Maude (Clark) White; m. Donna Mae Wood, Nov. 9, 1952 (dec. Dec. 1972); children: Richard, Marcus; m. Mary Jane Griffin, Mar. 8, 1985; children: Rhonda, Konrad. AS in Edn., Weber State Coll., 1952; BS in Edn., Utah State U., 1956, MS in Edn., 1962; D in Ednl. Adminstrn., U. Utah, 1968. Adminstrv. asst. dept. ednl. adminstrn. U. Utah, Salt Lake City, 1964-65; prin. Granite Sch. Dist., Salt Lake City 1965-68; asst. supt. schs. Okemos (Mich.) Pub. Schs., 1968-70, Salt Lake City (Utah) Schs., 1970-72; dir. secondary edn. Am. Sch. Found., Mexico City, 1974-76; supt. schs. Pinehill (N.Mex.) Schs., 1976-80; state asst. supt. Wyo. State Dept. Edn., Cheyenne, 1985-88; state deputy supt. Nev. Stae Dept. Edn., Carson City, 1988-89; dir. tchr. edn. Sierra Nev. Coll. Lake Tahoe, Incline Village, Nev., 1989-91; dean student affairs Sierra Nev. Coll. Lake Tahoe, Incline Village, 1991—; pres., cons. Educators Resource, Salt Lake City, 1972-74; pres., ptnr. Ednl. Mgmt. Systems, Tucson, 1980-83; fiscal analyst edn. Okla. State Senate, Oklahoma City, 1983-85. Active Rotarian, Murry, Utah, 1968, Lions Club, Price, Utah, 1987; instn. coord. United Fund, Salt Lake City, 1972, Carson City, 1990. Mem. AACD, Am. Assn. Sch. Adminstrs., Calif. Credential Analysts. LDS. Avocations: computers, golf, writing, genealogy. Office: Sierra Nev Coll PO Box 4269 800 College Dr Incline Vlg NV 89451-9114

WHITE, RICHARD L., chemicals company executive; b. 1939. With Mobay Corp., 1967—, v.p., then gourp v.p., 1981-86, exec. v.p. mktg., 1986—, also bd. dirs. Office: Mobay Corp Mobay Rd Pittsburgh PA 15205-9741

WHITE, RICHARD MANNING, electrical engineering educator; b. Denver, Apr. 25, 1930; s. Rolland Manning and Freeda Blanche (Behny) W.; m. Chissie Lee Chamberlain, Feb. 1, 1964 (div. 1975); children: Rolland Kenneth, William Brendan. AB, Harvard U., 1951, AM, 1952, PhD in Applied Physics, 1956. Rsch. assoc. Harvard U., Cambridge, Mass., 1956; mem. tech. staff GE Microwave Lab., Palo Alto, Calif., 1956-63; prof. elect. engring. U. Calif., Berkeley, 1963—; chmn. Grad. Group on Sci. and Math. Edn., U. Calif. at Berkeley, 1981-85; co-dir. Berkeley Sensor and Actuator Ctr., 1986—. Co-author: Solar Cells: From Basics to Advanced Systems, Microsensors, 1991; editor ElectroTechnology Rev.; patentee in field. Guggenheim fellow, 1968. Fellow AAAS, IEEE (Cledo Brunetto award 1986, Achievement award 1988, Disting. lectr. 1989); mem. Nat. Acad. Engring., Acoustical Soc. Am., Am. Phys. Soc., Phi Beta Kappa, Sigma Xi. Avocations: photography, hiking, skiing, running, music. Office: U Calif Sensor & Actuator Ctr Eecs Dept Berkeley CA 94720

WHITE, RICHARD NORMAN, civil and environmental engineering educator; b. Chetek, Wis., Dec. 21, 1933; s. Norman Lester and Lorna Elwilda (Robinson) W.; m. Margaret Claire Howell, Dec. 28, 1957; children—Barbara Ann, David Charles. BSCE, U. Wis.-Madison, 1956, MS, 1957, PhD, 1961. Registered profl. engr. N.Y. Staff assoc. Gulf Gen. Atomic, San Diego, 1967-68; assoc. prof. civil and environ. engring. Cornell U., 1965-72, prof. structural engring., 1972—, dir. Sch. Civil and Environ. Engring., 1978-84, assoc. dean for undergrad. programs, 1987-89, James A. Friend Family prof. engring., 1988—; vis. prof. U. Calif.-Berkeley, 1974-75, U. P.R., Mayaguez, 1982; cons. Def. Nuclear Agy., Washington, 1983-84, Sandia Nat. Lab., Albuquerque, 1981—, Stone & Webster Engring., 1983-87, SRI Internat., Palo Alto, Calif., 1979-83, Bakhtar Assoc., 1988—, Kamtech, 1994—, numerous others. Author: Structural Engineering, vols. I and II,

1976, Vol. III, 1974; Structural Modeling and Experimental Techniques, 1982, Building Structural Design Handbook, 1987; contbr. numerous articles to tech. jours. Served with AUS, 1957. Fellow ASCE (Collingwood prize, 1967), Am. Concrete Inst. (Kelly award 1992, Wason medal 1993, Structural Rsch. award 1994, v.p. 1995-97); mem. NAE, NSPE, Am. Soc. Engring. Edn., Precast/Prestressed Contrete Inst., Earthquake Engring. Rsch. Inst., Reinforced Concrete Rsch. Coun., Sigma Xi, Tau Beta Pi, Chi Epsilon. Republican. Presbyterian. Office: Hollister Hall Cornell U Ithaca NY 14853

WHITE, ROBB, author; b. Baguio, Luzon, The Philippines, June 20, 1909; s. Robb and Laura Placidia (Bridgers) W.; m. Rosalie Mason, Jan. 24, 1937 (div. 1964); children: Robb IV, Barbara Mason, June; m. Ann C. Saunders, 1985. BS, U.S. Naval Acad., 1931. Author: The Nub, 1935, The Smuggler's Sloop, 1937, Run Masked, 1938, Midshipman Lee, 1938, In Privateer's Bay, 1939, Three Against the Sea, 1940, Sailor in the Sun, 1941, The Lion's Paw, 1946, Secret Sea, 1947, Sail Away, 1948, Candy, 1949, The Haunted Hound, 1950, Deep Danger, 1952, Our Virgin Island, 1953, Midshipman Lee of the Naval Academy, 1954, Up Periscope, 1956, Flight Deck, 1961, Torpedo Run, 1962, The Survivor, 1964, Surrender, 1966, Silent Ship, Silent Sea, 1967 (Commonwealth Club medal for best juvenile book), No Man's Land, 1969, Deathwatch, 1972, The Frogmen, 1973, The Long Way Down, 1977, Fire Storm, 1979, Two on the Isle, 1985; screenwriter: Macabre, House on Haunted Hill, 13 Ghosts, The Tingler, Homicidal, (TV scripts) Perry Mason, Silent Service, Men of Annapolis. Active duty as capt. USNR. *I have lived the good life of a decent scoundrel.*

WHITE, ROBERT, church administrator. Asst. gen. overseer Ch. of God. Office: Church of God PO Box 2430 Cleveland TN 37320-2430

WHITE, ROBERT BRUCE, keyboard instruments company acoustical consultant; b. Casper, Wyo., Aug. 16, 1937; s. Steel Bruce and Julia Doris (Mace) W.; m. Nancy Inez Christian, Sept. 3, 1961; children: Jane Marie, Richard Bruce. BS, Okla. State U., 1959. Field engr. GE, Charlotte, N.C., 1961-63; physics, electronics specialist Derring-Milliken Rsch., Spartanburg, S.C., 1963-66; engring. mgr. Consultants, Inc., Woodruff, S.C., 1966-67; div. mgr. Case Bros., Spartanburg, 1967—; acoustical cons. for religious bldgs.; tchr. Spartanburg Tech. Coll.,1965-66. Contbg. author cookbooks. With USAF, 1959-61. Mem. Inst. Radio Engring., Am. Soc. Engring. Technicians, Am. Guild Organ Technicians, Elks, Masons. Republican. Methodist. Avocations: woodworking, cooking. Home: 225 Singing Woods Ln Spartanburg SC 29301-2622 Office: Case Bros 906 S Pine St Spartanburg SC 29302-3311

WHITE, ROBERT EDWARD, chemical engineering educator, consultant; b. Jersey City, Aug. 31, 1917; s. Frank Armour and Frances (deGeorge) W.; m. Gloria Elizabeth Ingersoll, June 12, 1943; children: Jeffrey R., Donna L., Barbara J., Linda L., Thomas F. BChE, Poly. Inst. Bklyn., 1938, MChE, 1940, DChE, 1942. Jr. engr. Vulcan Engring., Cin., 1939, 40; rsch. engr. York (Pa.) Corp., Pa., 1942-47; asst. prof. chem. engring. Bucknell U., 1947-49; assoc. prof. Villanova (Pa.) U., 1949-51, prof., 1951-86, prof. emeritus, 1986—, chmn. dept., 1949-83; cons. chem. engr. petroleum, paper industries, wastewater treatment. Contbr. articles to profl. jours. Chmn. bd. Newtown (Pa.) Mcpl. Authority, 1969-89; founder, chmn. Citizens for Better Govt., 1966-68. Recipient Centennial Achievement award Poly. Inst. Bklyn., 1956, Disting. award in chemistry Am. Inst. Chemists, 1979, Lindback award for outstanding teaching, 1980; Foster Wheeler grad. fellow Poly. Inst. Bklyn., 1942. Fellow AIChE (bd. dirs. 1970-72), TAPPI, Am. Soc. Engring. Edn. (chmn. Mid-Atlantic sect. 1963-64), Sigma Xi, Tau Beta Pi, Phi Lambda Upsilon, Alpha Chi Sigma. Patentee in field. Office: Villanova U Dept Chem Engring Villanova PA 19085

WHITE, ROBERT FREDERICK, landscape architect; b. Pitts., June 18, 1912; s. Edward John and Sarah Ann (Romaine) W.; m. Florence Hilda Kusian, Aug. 21, 1937; children: Hans Willi, Ross (by adoption). BS in Landscape Architecture, Pa. State U., College Park, 1934; MA in Landscape Architecture, U. Mich., 1951. Park staff City of Pitts., 1934-35, 2 parks mgr., 1934-37, mem. planning dept., 1937-43, 45; assoc. Office of Ruth Z. London, Houston, 1946-47; asst. prof. Coll. of Architecture Tex. A&M U., College Station, 1947-58, prof., head landscape architecture dept., 1962-75, prof. emeritus Coll. of Architecture, 1975—; prin. Robert F. White Assoc., Houston, 1958-62; cons. LB Johnson Home Site Restoration, Stone Wall, Tex., 1965. Judge hwy. dept. contest award LB Johnson, Ranch, Tex., 1970, nat. contest ASLA Mag., Washington, 1978; mem. Action Group, Houston, 1960-61, Planning Com., College Station, 1967-68. With USAF, 1943-45. Recipient Citation award Ho. of Reps./State of Tex., 1975. Fellow Am. Soc. Landscape Architecture (S.W. chpt. emeritus); mem. Alpha Gamma Rho, Tau Sigma Delta. Avocations: gardening, traveling, birding, drawing, jewelry making.

WHITE, ROBERT GORDON, educator, researcher, research director; b. Lithgow, NSW, Australia, Jan. 17, 1938; s. Richard Robert and Francis Elsie (Schubert) W.; m. Sandra Elizabeth Ferrier, Dec. 9, 1961; children: Robert Ian, Andrew Douglas. B. in Agrl. Sci., Melbourne U., Australia, 1962; M in Rural Sci./Physiology, U. New Eng., Australia, 1968, PhD, 1974. Rsch. asst. Melbourne U., 1962-63; demonstrator U. New Eng., Armidale, Australia, 1963-66, teaching fellow, 1966-69; asst. prof. zoophysiology and nutrition Inst. Arctic Biology, U. Alaska, Fairbanks, 1970-75; assoc. prof. U. Alaska, Fairbanks, 1975-81, prof., 1981—; acting dir. Inst. Arctic Biology, U. Alaska, Fairbanks, 1985, 92, dir., 1993—; dir. Large Animal Rsch. Sta., 1979—. Co-editor: (with Hudson) Bioenergetics of Wild Herbivores, 1985; editor: (proceedings, with Klein, Keller) First International Muskox Symposium, 1984 (proceedings, with Luick, Lent, Klein) First International Reindeer and Caribou Symposium, 1975; editorial bd.: Rangifer/Biol. Papers U. Alaska; contbr. over 100 papers to profl. jours. Pipe major Fairbanks Red Hackle Pipe Band, 1975-90; pres. Fairbanks Nordic Ski Club, 1973-75. NATO Rsch. fellow, Trondheim, Norway, 1975-76. Fellow AAAS (Alaska chmn. 1985-95), Artic Inst. N.Am.; mem. Am. Physiol. Soc. Wildlife Soc., Am. Soc. Mammologists, The Wildlife Mgmt. Soc., Australasian Soc. Wildlife Mgmt., Australian Soc. Animal Prodn., Australian Soc. Biochemistry and Molecular Biology, Sigma Xi. Avocations: cross country skiing, river boating, hunting, playing bagpipes. Office: U Alaska Inst Arctic Biology Fairbanks AK 99775

WHITE, ROBERT J., neurosurgeon, neuroscientist, educator; b. Duluth, Minn., Jan. 21, 1926; married, 1950; children: Robert, Christopher, Patricia, Michael, Daniel, Pamela, James, Richard, Marguerite, Ruth. B.S., Coll. St. Thomas, U. Minn., 1951, Ph.D. in Neurosurg. Physiology, 1962; M.D., Harvard, 1953; D.Sc. (hon.), John Carroll U., 1979, Cleve. State U., 1981. Intern surgery Peter Bent Brigham Hosp., Boston, 1953-54; resident Boston Children's Hosp. and Peter Bent Brigham Hosp., 1954-55; fellow neurosurgery Mayo Clinic, 1955-58; asst. to staff, 1958-59, research asso. neuro physiol., 1959-61; mem. faculty Case Western Res. U. Sch. Medicine, 1961—, prof. neurosurgery, 1966—, co-dir. neurosurgery, 1972, co-chmn. neurosurgery, 1973—; dir. neurosurg. and brain research lab. Cleve. Met. Gen. Hosp., 1961—; neurosurgeon Univ. Hosps.; also sr. attending neurosurgeon VA Hosp., 1961—; lectr. USSR, 1966, 68, 70, 72, 78, 79, 93, China, 1977, 81; adviser to Vatican authorities on bio-ethics; appointed mem. Pontifical Acad. Sci., 1994. Gen. editor: Internat. Soc. Angiol. Jour, 1966; editor: Western Hemisphere Jour. Resuscitation, 1971—, Surg. Neurology Resuscitation, Jour. of Trauma; co-editor: Surg. Neurology, 1973—; Contbr. numerous articles to profl. jours. Served with AUS, 1944-46. Recipient Mayo Clinic Research award, 1958; Med. Mut. Honor award, 1975; L.W. Freeman award PF, 1977. Mem. ACS (com. on trauma task force), AMA, Harvey Cushing Soc., Soc. Univ. Surgeons, Am. Physiol. Soc. Soc. Univ. Neurosurgeons (pres. 1978-79), Ohio Neurosurg. Soc. (pres. 1975), N.E. Ohio Neurosurg. Soc. (pres. 1971), Soc. Expt. Biology, Internat. Soc. Cybernetic Medicine (internat. bd. 1971—), Internat. Soc. Surgery, Soc. Neurol. Surgeons, Neurosurg. Soc. Am., Acad. Medicine Cleve. (bd. dirs., pres. 1978-79), Pontifical Acad. Scis. (adv. com. for biotech. applied to man 1994). Developed 1st isolated brain models; pioneered brain and cephalon transplant in animals, deep hypothermia techniques in brain and spinal surgery. Office: 2500 Metro Health Dr Cleveland OH 44109-1998 Home: 2895 Lee Rd Shaker Heights OH 44120-1833 *My professional work deals with the human brain, and I must treat its maladies through surgical and pharmacological intervention. These intimate experiences have convinced me of both the Divinity and the naturalness of man. For me, the very essence of*

what makes us what we are is centered in the tissues of the human brain. Operating and experimenting on this, the most complex organ of the body, has only intensified my respect for man and the acknowledgment that all of his (her) accomplishments have resulted through the processes of the single biological entity, the human brain.

WHITE, ROBERT JAMES, newspaper editor, columnist; b. Mpls., Nov. 6, 1927; s. Robert Howard and Claire Lillian (Horner) W.; m. Adrienne Hoffman, Sept. 24, 1955; children—Claire, Pamela, Sarah. B.S., U.S. Naval Acad., 1950. Vice pres. White Investment Co., Mpls., 1957-67; editorial writer Mpls. Tribune, 1967-73, assoc. editor, 1973-82; editor editorial pages Mpls. Star Tribune, 1982-93, columnist, 1993—. Recipient cert. of excellence Overseas Press Club, 1981. Mem. Council Fgn. Relations, Refugee Policy Group (bd. trustees). Presbyterian. Club: Minneapolis. Home: 4721 Girard Ave S Minneapolis MN 55409-2212 Office: Mpls Star Tribune 425 Portland Ave Minneapolis MN 55488-0001

WHITE, ROBERT JOEL, lawyer; b. Chgo., Nov. 1, 1946; s. Melvin and Margaret (Hoffman) W.; m. Gail Janet Edenson, June 29, 1969 (div. Dec. 1982); m. Penelope K. Bloch, Dec. 22, 1985. BS in Accountancy, U. Ill., 1968; JD, U. Mich., 1972. Bar: Calif. 1972, N.Y. 1975, U.S. Dist. Ct. (cen., ea., so. dists.) Calif. 1972, U.S. Ct. Appeals (9th cir.) 1978, U.S. Ct. Appeals (5th cir.) 1983, U.S. Ct. Appeals (6th cir.) 1984, U.S. Supreme Ct. 1977. Staff auditor Haskin & Sells, Chgo., 1968-69; assoc. O'Melveny & Myers, L.A., 1972-79, ptnr., 1980—; vis. lectr. Law Sch. U. Mich., Ann Arbor, 1986; lectr. Profl. Edn. Systems, Inc., Dallas and L.A., 1987, L.A., 1989, Phoenix, 1990, Practicing Law Inst., San Francisco and N.Y., 1989-93, Southwestern Legal Found., Dallas, 1991, UCLA Bankruptcy Inst., 1993, U. Calif., Los Angeles, 1993; commr. L.A. Productivity Commn., 1993—. Contbr. articles to profl. jours. Active Constl. Rights Found., 1980—, Am. Cancer Soc., 1989—. With U.S. Army, 1968-74. Fellow Am. Coll. Brankruptcy; mem. ABA (litigation sect., mem. comml. law and bankruptcy com. 1972—), L.A. County Bar Assn. (comml. law and bankruptcy sect., chmn. fed. cts. com. 1981-82, exec. com. 1982—), Assn. Bus. Trial Lawyers (bd. govs. 1983-85), Fin. Lawyers Conf. (bd. govs. 1986—, pres. 1990-91), Am. Bankruptcy Inst. Avocations: skiing, running, U.S. history. Office: O'Melveny & Myers 400 S Hope St Los Angeles CA 90071

WHITE, ROBERT JOHN, journalist; b. Cin., Mar. 12, 1953; s. Robert John and Jean W.; m. Mary C. Cupito, Apr. 26, 1986. BA in English & Journalism, Miami U., 1975. Intern Cin. Enquirer, 1975-76; reporter, photographer Franklin (Ind.) Daily Jour., 1976-79; reporter Charleston (S.C.) News and Courier, 1979-80, Evansville (Ind.) Courier, 1981; reporter Cin. Post, 1981-83, asst. met. editor, 1983-86, statehouse bur. chief, 1986-92, editorial page editor, 1993—. Recipient Investigative Reporters and Editors, Inc. award, 1988, ABA cert. merit, 1988. Mem. Nat. Conf. Editorial Writers, Cin. Assn., Leadership Cin., Cin. Hist. Soc. Office: Cin Post 125 E Ct St Cincinnati OH 45202

WHITE, ROBERT LEE, electrical engineer, educator; b. Plainfield, N.J., Feb. 14, 1927; s. Claude and Ruby Hemsworth Emerson (Levick) W.; m. Phyllis Lillian Arlt, June 14, 1952; children: Lauren A., Kimberly A., Christopher L., Matthew P. BA in Physics, Columbia U., 1949, MA, 1951, PhD, 1954. Assoc. head atomic physics dept. Hughes Rsch. Labs., Malibu, Calif., 1954-61; head magnetics dept. Gen. Tel. and Electronics Rsch. Lab., Palo Alto, Calif., 1961-63; prof. elec. engring., materials sci. and engring. Stanford U., Palo Alto, 1963, chmn. elec. engring. dept., 1981-86; William E. Ayer prof. elec. engring. Stanford U., 1985-88; exec. dir. The Exploratorium, San Francisco, 1987-89; dir. Inst. for Electronics in Medicine, 1973-87, Stanford Ctr. for Rsch. on Info. Storage Materials, 1991—; initial Ind. ptnr. Mayfield Fund, Mayfield II and Alpha II Fund, Rainbow Co-Investment Ptnrs., Halo Ptnrs.; vis. prof. Tokyo U., 1975; cons. in field. Author: (with K.A. Wickersheim) Magnetism and Magnetic Materials, 1965, Basic Quantum Mechanics, 1967; Contbr. numerous articles to profl. jours. With USN, 1945-46. Fellow Guggenheim Oxford U., 1969-70, Canton Hosp., Swiss Fed. Inst. Tech., Zurich, 1977-78, Christensen fellow Oxford U., 1986; Sony sabbatical chair, 1994. Fellow Am. Phys. Soc., IEEE; mem. Sigma Xi, Phi Beta Kappa. Home: 450 El Escarpado Stanford CA 94305-8431 Office: Stanford U Dept Material Sci Engr Stanford CA 94305

WHITE, ROBERT M., federal engineering agency administrator, engineer; b. Boston, Mass., Feb. 13, 1923; m. Mavis Seagle, Apr. 18, 1948; 2 children. BA, Harvard U., 1944; MS, MIT, 1949, ScD, 1950. Rsch. scientist Meteorology Devel. Lab. Air Force Cambridge Rsch. Ctr., 1950-52, dir. Meteorology Rsch. Ctr., 1952-59; rsch. assoc. MIT, 1959; assoc. dir. rsch. Travelers Ins. Co., 1959-60; pres. Travelers Rsch. Ctr., Inc., 1960-63; chief U.S. Weather Bur., 1963-65; administr. Environ. Sci. Svcs. Administrn. Dept. Commerce, 1965-70, administr.Nat. Oceanic and Atmospheric Administrn., 1970-77; pres. Joint Oceanographic Inst., Inc., 1977-79; exec. officer NAS, Washington, 1979-80; administr. Nat. Nat. Rsch. Coun. NAS, 1979-83; vice. chmn. Nat. Rsch. Coun. NAS, Washington, 1983—; pres. U. Corp. for Atmospheric Rsch. 1980-83, Nat. Acad. Engring., Washington, 1983—; bd. dirs. Charles Stark Draper Lab., Inc.; mem. Dept. of State adv. com. on oceans and internat. environ. and scientific affairs. Bd. dirs. Nat. Sci. Ctr. for Comms. and Electronics Found. With U.S. Army, 1942-45. Recipient Godfrey L. Cabot award Aero Club of New Eng., 1966, Rosenberger medal U. Chgo., 1971, Rockefeller Pub. Svc. award Princeton U., 1974, David B. Stone award New Eng. Aquarium, 1975, Matthew Fontaine maury award mithsonian Instn., 1976, Internat. Conservation award Nat. Wildlife Fedn., 1977, Neptune award Am. Oceanic Orgn., 1977, spl. award for Contributions to Marine AffairsMarine Tech. Soc., 1978, prize Internat. Meteorological Orgn., 1980; decorated Chevalier de la Legion d'Honneur, 1980. Mem. AAAS. Am. Geophys. Union, Am. Meteorological Soc. (councillor 1963-67, 76—, Cleveland Abbe award 1969, Anniversary medal 1970). Resources for the Future, Cosmos Club. Office: National Academy of Engineering 2101 Constitution Ave NW Washington DC 20418*

WHITE, ROBERT M., II, newspaper executive, editor, columnist; b. Mexico, Mo., Apr. 6, 1915; s. L. Mitchell and Maude (See) W.; m. Barbara Whitney Spurgeon, Aug. 19, 1948 (dec. Feb., 1983); children: Barbara Whitney, Jane See, Laura L., Robert M. III; m. Linda Hess Grimsley, July 11, 1992. Grad., Mo. Mil. Acad., 1933; A.B., Washington and Lee U., 1938, LL.B. (hon.), 1972. Writer of newspaper articles Australia, Africa, S.Am., Europe, USSR, 1966, 86, People's Republic China, 1972, 77; reporter Mexico (Mo.) Eve. Ledger, 1938-39, editor, pub., 1945; vice. prof. Sch. Journalism, Mo. U., 1968-69; reporter UP Bur., Kansas City, 1939-40; pres. Ledger Newspapers, Inc., Mexico, Mo., 1945-86; spl. cons. to pub. Chgo. Sun-Times, 1956-58; pres. See TV Co., Mexico, 1966-81; editor, pres., bd. dirs. N.Y. Herald Tribune, 1959-61; juror Pulitzer prize journalism, 1964-65; bd. dirs World Press Freedom Com. Co-author: A Study of the Printing and Publishing Business in the Soviet Union. President Gen. Douglas MacArthur Found., 1981—. Lt. col. AUS, 1940-45. Decorated Bronze Star; recipient nat. disting. service award for editorials Sigma Delta Chi, 1952, 68; editorial award N.Y. Silurians, 1959; Disting. Service to Journalism award U. Mo., 1967; Pres. award of merit Nat. Newspapers Assn., 1967; Ralph D. Casey Minn. award disting. service in journalism, 1983; finalist Journalist in Space 1986—. Mem. Am. Soc. Newspaper Editors (dir. 1968-69, chmn. freedom of info. com. 1970-72), Am. Newspaper Pubs. Assn. (nat. treas. 1963, dir. 1955-63, chmn. internat. group 1982-86), Washington Inst. Fgn. Affairs, Inland Daily Press Assn. (chmn. bd. 1958-59, pres., past sec., v.p.), Mo. Press Assn. (dir., v.p. 1981-83, pres. 1983-84), Mo. Press-Bar Commn. (chmn. 1972-74), Internat. Press Inst. (chmn. Am. com. 1982-85), Nat. Press Club, Bohemian Club, Dutch Treat Club, Burning Tree Club, Cosmos Club, Internat. Club, Masons, Rotary, Sigma Delta Chi (nat. pres. 1967, pres. found. 1968), Beta Theta Pi. Office: Ste 1537 4000 Massachusetts Ave NW Washington DC 20016

WHITE, ROBERT MARSHALL, physicist, government official, educator; b. Reading, Pa., Oct. 2, 1938; s. Carl M. and Miriam E. White; m. Sara Tolles; children: Victoria, Jonathan. B.S. in Physics, MIT, 1960; Ph.D., Stanford U., 1964. Vis. scientist Osaka U., Japan, 1963; NSF postdoctoral fellow U. Calif., Berkeley, 1965-66; asst. prof. physics Stanford U., 1966-70; NSF postdoctoral fellow, Cambridge, Eng., 1970-71; mgr. solid state research area Xerox PARC, 1971-78, mgr. storage technology, 1978-83, prin. scientist, 1983-84; v.p. research and tech. Control Data Corp. Data Storage Products Group, Mpls., 1984-86, chief tech. officer, v.p. research and engring, 1986-89; v.p., dir. advanced computer techs. Microelectronics & Computer Tech. Corp., Austin, Tex., 1989-90; under-sec. of commerce for tech., Dept. Commerce, Washington, 1990-93; prof., head dept. electrical and computer engring. Carnegie Mellon U., Pitts., 1993—; lectr. dept. applied physics Stanford U., 1971-81; vis. scientist Ecole Polytechnique, Paris, 1976-78, U. Pernambuco, Brazil, 1978; cons. prof. applied physics, prin. investigator Magnetic Thin Film Program, Stanford U., 1982-93; adj. prof. dept. physics U. Minn., 1987-89; guest Chinese Acad. Scis., 1982. Author: Quantum Theory of Magnetism, 1970 (Russian transl., 1972, Polish transl., 1979); Long Range Order in Solids, 1979 (Russian transl., 1982); Quantum Theory of Magnetism, 1983; Introduction to Magnetic Recording, 1985. Contbr. articles to profl. jours. Bd. advisors Inst. Tech. U. Minn., 1987; mem. State Minn. Com. on Sci. and Tech. Research and Devel., 1987-90; mem. adv. bd. U. Ill. Coll. Engring. Recipient Alexander von Humboldt Prize, Fed. Republic of Germany, 1981, Tyler Prize for Environmental Achievement, U. Southern California, 1992, Fellow AAAS, IEEE (disting. lectr. Magnetics Soc., mem. editorial bd. SPECTRUM, IEEE Disting. Pub. Svc. award 1993); Am. Phys. Soc.; mem. NAE, NRC (mem. nat. materials adv. bd., chmn. com. magnetic materials 1984, material sci. and engring., nat. steering com. advanced steady state neutron source, vice chmn. IUPAP commn. on magnetism), Conf. Magnetism and Magnetic Materials (adv. com. 1976-78, 80-95, program com. 1973-75, chmn. 1981, chmn. Intermag Conf. 1991), Internat. Conf. Magnetism (program chmn. 1985), Found. Nat. Medals Sci. and Tech. (bd. dirs. 1993—), Ontrack Computer Systems (bd. dirs. 1994—); mem. Panel on Advanced Computing of the Japanese Tech. Evaluation Ctr.; mem. Nat. Adv. Com. on Semiconductors, 1990-92, Mfg. Forum, 1991, Nat.Critical Techs. Panel, 1990-91. Office: Carnegie Mellon U Elec & Computer Engring Dept Pittsburgh PA 15213-3890

WHITE, ROBERT MAYER, meteorologist; b. Boston, Feb. 13, 1923; s. David and Mary (Winkeller) W.; m. Mavis Seagle, Apr. 18, 1948; children—Richard Mary, Edwina Janet. B.A., Harvard, 1944; M.S., Mass. Inst. Tech., 1949, Sc.D., 1950; D.Sc. (hon.), L.I. U., 1976, Rensselaer Poly. Inst., 1977, U. Wis., Milw., 1978; ScD (hon.), U. Bridgeport, 1984, U. R.I. 1986, Clarkson U.; PhD (hon.), Johns Hopkins U., 1982, Drexel U., 1985. Project scientist Air Force Cambridge Research Center, 1950-58, chief meteorol. devel. lab., 1958-59; asso. dir. research dept. Travelers Ins. Co., 1959-60; pres. Travelers Research Center, Inc., 1960-63; chief U.S. Weather Bur., 1963-65; administr. Environ. Sci. Services Adminstrn., 1965-70, NOAA, 1970-77; pres. Joint Oceanographic Inst., Inc., 1977-79; chmn. Climate Research Bd., exec. officer Nat. Acad. Scis., 1977-79; administr. Nat. Research Council, 1979-80; pres. Univ. Corp. Atmospheric Research, 1980-83; chmn. commn. natural resources Nat. Acad. Scis., 1980-83; pres. Nat. Acad. Engring., Washington, 1983—; permanent U.S. rep., mem. exec. com. World Meteorol. Orgn., 1963-77; fed. coord. Meteorol. Svcs. and Supporting Rsch., 1964-70; mem. Presdl. Commn. on Marine Sci. Engring. Rsch., 1967-68, U.S. del. UN Conf. on Human Environment, Stockholm, 1972, U.S. del.; governing coun., UN Environment Program, 1973-74; chief U.S. del. Intergovtl. Oceanographic Commn., UNESCO, Paris, 1972-73; U.S. commr. Internat. Whaling Commn., 1973-77; chmn. Marine Fisheries Adv. Com., 1970-77, U.S. chmn. U.S./France Coop. Program in Oceanography, 1973-77, U.S./USSR Joint Commn. for Exploration World Oceans, 1974-77; chm. Com. on Climate Change, White House Domestic Coun., 1975; World Climate Conf., 1979; mem. Nat. Adv. Com. Oceans and Atmosphere, 1979—, Nat. Sci. Ctr. Communications and Electronics Found., 1985—; mem. nat. adv. com. Govt. and Pub. Affairs U. Ill., 1987—; bd. dirs. The Charles Stark Draper Lab. Inc., Cambridge, Mass., 1982—; chmn. U.S. Com. for Internat. Inst. for Applied Systems Analysis, Laxenburg, Austria, 1990—. Author articles in field; mem. editorial bd. Am. Soc. Engring. Edn. jour. Bd. overseers Harvard U., 1977—; vis. com. meteorology and planetary sci. Mass. Inst. Tech.; Mem. vis. com. Kennedy Sch. Govt., Harvard U.; bd. dirs. Resources for Future, 1980—. Served to capt. USAAF, World War II. Decorated Legion of Honor France; recipient Jesse L. Rosenberger medal U. Chgo., 1971; Cleveland Abbe award Am. Meteorol. Soc., 1969; Godfrey L. Cabot award Aero Club Boston, 1966; Rockefeller Pub. Service award, 1974; David B. Stone award New Eng. Aquarium, 1975; Neptune award Am. Oceanic Orgn., 1977; Matthew Fontaine Maury award Smithsonian Instn., 1976; Internat. Cooperation award Nat. Wildlife Fedn., 1976; Internat. Meteorol. Orgn. prize, 1980, Tyler prize for Environ. Achievement U. Calif., 1992. Fellow Am. Meterol. Soc. (council 1965-67, 77—, Charles Franklin Brooks award 1978, pres. 1980), Am. Geophys. Union, World Acad. Art and Scis., Australian Acad. Tech. Scis. and Engring., Am. Acad. Arts and Scis., AAAS; mem. NAE (coun. 1977), Marine Tech. Soc., Coun. Fgn. Rels., Nat. Action Coun. Minorities in Engring. Inc., Finnish Acad. Tech. (fgn. mem. 1991—), Am. Philos. Soc., Nat. Commn. on the Environment World Wildlife Fund, Engring. Acad. Japan (fgn. assoc. 1988—), Internat. Acad. Astronautics (Paris), Cosmos Club (Washington). Club: Cosmos. Home: Somerset House II 5610 Wisconsin Ave Apt 1506 Bethesda MD 20815 Office: 2101 Constitution Ave NW Washington DC 20418-0007

WHITE, ROBERT ROY, chemical engineer; b. Bklyn., Mar. 1, 1916; s. Laurance S. and Grace A. (Diffin) W.; m. Elizabeth R. Clark, July 2, 1940; children: Robert Roy, William Wesley, Elizabeth Ann, Margaret. B.S., Cooper Union Inst. Tech., 1936; student, Bklyn. Poly. Inst., 1936-37; M.S. (Horace H. Rackham predoctoral fellow 1938), U. Mich., 1938; Ph.D., 1941; student, DePaul U. Law Sch., 1940-41. Jr. chem. engr. Calco Chem. Co. Bound Brook, N.J., 1936-37; research chem. engr. Dow Chem. Co., 1937-38; chem. engr. Standard Oil Co. Calif., 1940, Universal Oil Products Co., 1940-42; mem. faculty U. Mich., 1942-60, prof. chem. engring., 1945-60, assoc. dean Horace H. Rackham Sch. Grad. Studies, 1958-60; assoc. dean Coll. Engring. U. Mich. (Coll. Engring.), 1958-60; dir. Inst. Sci. and Tech. U. Mich., 1959-60; v.p., gen. mgr. research and devel. Atlantic Refining Co., Phila., 1960-62; sr. staff mgmt. service div. Arthur D. Little, Inc., 1962; v.p. devel. Champion Papers, Inc., Hamilton, Ohio, 1962-66; pres. research div. W.R. Grace & Co., 1966-67; dean Sch. Mgmt., Case Western Res. U., Cleve., 1967-71; spl. asst. to pres., dir. forum Nat. Acad. Sci., Washington, 1971-1981; adj. prof. chem. engring. U. Md., 1982—85, Cath. U. Am., Am. U.; v.p. JC Tech., 1986—; bd. dirs. Enterprise Chem. Co.; chem. engring. cons. Author: (with others) Unit Operations, 1950; Contbr. articles to profl. jours. Recipient Henry Russell award U. Mich., 1945; teaching award Phi Lambda Upsilon chpt. U. Mich., 1949; sesquicentennial award U. Mich., 1967; prof. award Cooper Union Inst., 1975; McCormack-Freud hon. lectr. Ill. Inst. Tech. Mem. AAAS, SAR, Am. Inst. Chem. Engrs. (jr. award 1945, Presentation award 1951, Profl. Progress award 1956), Am. Chem. Soc., Am. Soc. Engring. Edn. (George Westinghouse award 1955), Soc. Profl. Engrs., Am. Mgmt. Assn., Cosmos Club, St. Andrews Club, Sigma Xi, Alpha Chi Sigma, Phi Lambda Upsilon, Phi Kappa Phi, Tau Beta Pi, Iota Alpha. Office: 2440 Virginia Ave NW Washington DC 20037-2601

WHITE, ROBERT STEPHEN, physics educator; b. Ellsworth, Kans., Dec. 28, 1920; s. Byron F. and Sebina (Leighty) W.; m. Freda Marie Bridgewater, Aug. 30, 1942; children: Nancy Lynn, Margaret Diane, John Stephen, David Bruce. AB, Southwestern Coll., 1942, DSc hon., 1971; MS, U. Ill., 1943; PhD, U. Calif., Berkeley, 1951. Physicist Lawrence Radiation Lab., Berkeley, Livermore, Calif., 1946-61; head dept. particles and fields Space Physics Lab. Aerospace Corp., El Segundo, Calif., 1962-67; physics prof. U. Calif., Riverside, 1967-92, dir. Inst. Geophysics and Planetary Physics, 1967-92, chmn. dept. physics, 1970-73, prof. emeritus physics dept., 1992—; rsch. physicist Inst. Geophys. and Planetary Physics, 1992—; lectr. U. Calif., Berkeley, 1953-54, 57-59. Author: Space Physics 1970; contbr. articles to profl. jours. Served USNR, 1944-46. Sr. Postdoctoral fellow NSF, 1961-62; grantee NASA, NSF, USAF, numerous others. Fellow Am. Phys. Soc. (exec. com. 1972-74); mem. AAAS, AAUP, Am. Geophys. Union, Am. Astron. Soc. Home: 5225 Austin Rd Santa Barbara CA 93111 Office: U Calif Inst Geophysics & Planetary Physics Riverside CA 92521

WHITE, ROBERT WINSLOW, oilfield service company executive; b. Somerville, Mass., Mar. 28, 1934; s. T. Leo and Margaret G. (Canniff) W.; m. Deborah J. Fritsche, Sept. 3, 1981; children: Kathleen K., Robert W. SB, MIT, 1955; PhD, U. Ill., 1958. Sr. scientist Rohm & Haas Co., Phila., 1958-69; lab. mgr. CRL, NL Industries, Hightstown, N.J., 1969-72; tech. dir. Baker Castor Oil Co., Bayonne, N.J., 1972-73; mgr. coatings bus. NL Chems., Hightstown, 1974-79, dir. bus. strategy, 1979-82; div. pres. NL Treating Chems. div. NL Industries, Houston, 1982-89; pres., chief exec. officer Simon Environ. Svcs. N.Am. subs. Simon Engring., Houston, 1990-91, Simon Chem. Svcs. N.Am. subs. Simon Engring., Houston, 1991-93; pres. Western Unichem divsn. Western Co., Houston, Tex., 1994—; mem.

vis. com., chemistry dept. U. Tex., Austin, 1985—. Contbr. several papers to sci. jours.; 20 patents in field. Served to 1st lt. USAR, 1955-59. Mem. AAAS, Am. Chem. Soc., Soc. Petroleum Engrs. Avocations: travel, cross-country skiing, cooking, jogging. Home: One N Autumnwood Way The Woodlands TX 77380 Office: Unichem B-8 515 Post Oak Blvd Houston TX 77027

WHITE, RONALD LEON, financial management consultant; b. West York, Pa., July 14, 1930; s. Clarence William and Grace Elizabeth (Gingerich) W.; m. Estheranne Wieder, June 16, 1951; children: Bradford William, Clifford Allen, Erick David. BS in Econs, U. Pa., 1952, MBA, 1957. Cost analysis supr. Air Products & Chem. Corp., Allentown, Pa., 1957-60; cost control mgr. Mack Trucks, Inc., Allentown, 1960-64; mgmt. cons. Peat, Marwick, Mitchell & Co., Phila., 1964-66; mgr. profit planning Monroe, The Calculator Co. (div. Litton Industries), Orange, N.J., 1966-67, controller, 1967-68; v.p. fin. Bus. Systems Group of Litton Industries, Beverly Hills, Calif., 1968-70; pres. Royal Typewriter Co. div., Hartford, Conn., 1970-73; exec. v.p., chief operating officer, treas. Tenna Corp., Cleve., 1973-75, pres., dir., 1975-77; v.p. fin Arby's, Inc., Youngstown, Ohio, 1978-79; exec. v.p., dir. Roxbury Am., Inc., 1979-81; v.p. fin., treas. Royal Crown Cos., Inc., Atlanta and Miami Beach, Fla., 1981-86, TDS Healthcare Systems Corp., Atlanta, 1987-88; v.p. Corp. Fin. Assocs., Atlanta, 1988-90; prin. The Janelle Co., Atlanta, 1991—; instr. acctg. Wharton Sch. U. Pa., 1952-53, instr. industry, 1953-54. Served to lt. USNR, 1954-57. Mem. Am. Mgmt. Assn., Nat. Assn. Accountants, Nat. Assn. Corp. Dirs., Fin. Execs. Inst., Acacia. Mem. United Ch. Christ (deacon). Lodges: Masons, Rotary. Home: 2362 Kingsgate Ct Atlanta GA 30338-5931 Office: The Janelle Co 2362 Kingsgate Ct Atlanta GA 30338-5931

WHITE, ROY BERNARD, theater executive; b. Cin.; s. Maurice and Anna (Rudin) W.; m. Sally Lee Ostrom, June 17, 1951; children: Maurice Ostrom, Barbara Dee, Daniel Robert. B.A., U. Cin., 1949. Formerly mem. sales staff Twentieth Century Fox Films, Cin.; now pres. Mid-States Theatres; dir. Nat. Assn. Theatre Owners, nat. pres., exec. com., chmn. bd.; Mem. film adv. panel Ohio Arts Coun.; bd. dirs. Will Rogers Meml. Fund, Found. Motion Picture Pioneers, Inc.; mem. media arts panel Nat. Endowment for Arts. Served with USAAF, 1944-45. Named Exhibitor of Year Internat. Film Importers and Distbrs. Am. Mem. Nat. Assn. Theater Owners (pres.), Am. Film Inst. (trustee 1972-75, exec. com. 1972-75), Fedn. Motion Picture Pioneers (v.p.), Masons, Queen City Racquet, Crest Hills Country, Amberley Village (Ohio) Tennis Club (pres. 1972-73), Bankers Club, Quail Creek Country Club (Naples, Fla.), Alpha Epsilon Pi, Phi Eta Sigma. Home: 8171 Bay Colony Dr # 1904 Naples FL 33963

WHITE, RUTH LILLIAN, French language educator, researcher; b. Vancouver, B.C., Can., June 6, 1924; d. George Brooks and Olive (Wells) W. B.A., U. B.C.; A.R.C.T. in Piano, U. Toronto; Docteur, U. Paris, Sorbonne. Cert. profl. advanced phonetics Institut de Phonetique, Paris. Tchr. Vancouver Sch. Bd., 1946-66; head dept. lang. King Edward Continuing Edn. Ctr., B.C., 1962-65, Vancouver City Coll., 1965-66; prof. U. B.C., Vancouver, 1966-89, prof. edn. and arts, 1971-77, prof. arts, 1977-89; mem., chmn. numerous coms. B.C. Tchrs. Fedn., 1950-75; exec., chmn. Standing Com. on Lang., Acad. Council, B.C., 1968-82; mem., chmn. exam and revision coms. Govt. of B.C., 1952-76; mem. adv. bd. Can. Modern Lang. Rev., Toronto, 1979-90; scholar-in-residence Rockefeller Found., Bellagio Study and Conf. Ctr., Italy, 1979. Author: L'Avenir de La Mennais, 1974, Louis-Joseph Papineau et Lamennais, 1983, (with C.-L. Rogers) Relations Hugo-Lamennais, 1821-54, 1988, Verlaine et les musiciens, 1992; mem. editorial bd. Can. Modern Lang. Rev., 1971-79. Decorated chevalier Ordre des Palmes academiques (France), 1984; Can. Council fellow, 1978-79. Mem. Can. Assn. Univ. Tchrs., Association Internat. des Docteurs des Univs. de France, Soc. des Amis de Lamennais (Can. rep. 1971-89), Assn. des Ecrivains de Langue Française, Coll. and Univ. Tchrs. Assn., Coll. and Univ. Lang. Tchrs. Assn. Home: 206-1315 W 7th Ave, Vancouver, BC Canada V6H 1B8

WHITE, RUTH O'BRIEN (MRS. WALLACE B. WHITE), civic worker; b. N.Y.C., Dec. 20, 1907; d. Francis Athos and Caroline Rebecca (Young) O'Brien; m. Wallace Beasley White, June 5, 1931; 1 child, John Wallace. Student, Packer Collegiate Inst., 1921-27, Parsons Sch. for Design, New Sch. Social Rsch., 1927-30. Dir.-at-large Nat. Tb Assn., 1949-73, sec. bd., 1957-60; chmn. med. social service com. United Hosp. Fund Bklyn., 1949-53, mem. med. social service com. city wide orgn., 1962-66, mem. legis. com., 1970-72, vice chair legis. com., 1970—; mem. exec. com. United Hosp. Fund, 1972-74; del., mem. exec. com. Northeastern Tb Conf., 1960—, pres., 1962-63; dir. Brooklyn Tb and Health Assn., 1946—, v.p., 1957-60, pres., 1960-62, sec. bd., 1966-72, v.p. legis. com., 1978-80; advisory com. N.Y. State Bd. Edn., div. vocational rehab., 1954-57. Bd. mgrs., exec. com. Bklyn. Thoracic Hosp., 1940-48, bd. trustees, 1948-57, pres. women's aux., 1956-57; women's exec. bd. Bklyn. Hosp., 1957—, v.p. bd. dirs., 1967-72, chmn. med. social service com., 1963-91, chmn. com. legislation, 1972-91; chmn. ann. meeting program com. Am. Lung Assn., 1973, 74; v.p. mem. women's exec. bd. Bklyn. Phil., 1967-70; del. Nat. Social Welfare Assembly, 1957-68; mem. social service com. Cancer Care, Inc., 1966—, pub. relations com., 1969, bd. dirs., 1974-83, pub. affairs com., 1976—; mem. program and budget com. Nat. Tb and Respiratory Disease Assns., 1967-69; mem. Council Tb and Respiratory Disease Assns. N.Y. State, 1968—; vice chmn. Council Lung Assns. N.Y. State, 1973-75, chmn., 1975-77, treas., 1980-89, vice chmn. 1989—; mem. Action for Clean Air Com., 1965—; mem. housing and community task force Met. Assn., 1978-80; chmn. legis. com. Bklyn. Lung Assn., 1980-84; mem. com. on community health concerns United Hosp. Fund, 1979-82, legis. com., 1982—; mem. Hist. dist. Commn., Francestown, N.H., 1992. Recipient Will Ross medal Am. Lung Assn., 1987. Congregationalist. Signer Nat. Christmas Seal Appeal letter, 1974—; Ruth White day named in her honor, Bklyn. Borough, Sept. 30, 1986; Ruth White ann. award established to honor an outstanding vol. hon. life mem. Am. Lung Assn., 1988. Home: Biddle Hill Rd Francestown NH 03043 *To love and be loved. To be needed. To be engaged in pursuits whose outcome may make life better for some.*

WHITE, STANLEY ARCHIBALD, research electrical engineer; b. Providence, Sept. 25, 1931; s. Clarence Archibald White and Lou Ella (Givens) Arford; m. Edda Maria Castaño-Benítez, June 6, 1956; children: Dianne, Stanley Jr., Paul, John. BSEE, Purdue U., 1957, MSEE, 1959, PhD, 1965. Registered profl. engr., Ind., Calif. Engr. Rockwell Internat., Anaheim, Calif., 1959-68, mgr., 1968-84, sr. scientist, 1984-90; pres. Signal Processing and Controls Engring. Corp., 1990—; adj. prof. elec. engring. U. Calif., 1984—; cons. and lectr. in field; bd. dirs. Asilomar Signals, Systems and Computers Conf. Corp. Publisher, composer music; contbr. chpts. to books; articles to profl. jours.; patentee in field. Fellow N.Am. Aviation Sci. Engring., 1963-65; recipient Disting. Lectr. award Nat. Electronics Conf., Chgo., 1973, Engr. of Yr. award Orange County (Calif.) Engring. Coun., 1984, Engr. of Yr. award Rockwell Internat., 1985, Leonardo Da Vinci Medallion, 1986, Sci. Achievement award, 1987, Disting. Engring. Alumnus award Purdue U., 1988, Meritorious Inventor's award Rockwell Internat. Corp., 1989, Outstanding Elec. Engr. award Purdue U., 1992. Fellow AAAS, IEEE (founding chmn. Orange County chpt.), Acoustics, Speech and Signal Processing Soc. (vice chmn. 1983, gen. chmn. Internat. Symposium Circs. and Sys., 1992, Internat. Conf. Acoustics, Speech and Signal Processing 1984, Centennial medal 1984), IEEE Signal Processing Soc. (disting. lectr. 1991-92), Inst. Advancement Engring., N.Y. Acad. Scis.; mem. AIAA, Air Force Assn., Sci. Rsch. Soc., Sigma Xi (founding pres. Orange County chpt.), Tau Beta Pi, Eta Kappa Nu (internat. dir. emeritus). Avocation: choral music. Home: 433 E Avenida Cordoba San Clemente CA 92672-2350

WHITE, STEPHEN HALLEY, biophysicist, educator; b. Wewoka, Okla., May 14, 1940; s. James Halley and Gertrude June (Wyatt) W.; m. Buff Ertl, Aug. 20, 1961 (div. 1982); children: Saill, Shell, Storn, Sharr, Skye, Sunde; m. Jackie Marie Dooley, Apr. 14, 1984. BS in Physics, U. Colo., 1963; MS in Physics, U. Wash., 1965, PhD in Physiology and Biophysics, 1969. USPHS postdoctoral fellow biochemistry U.A. Charlottesville, 1971-72; asst. prof. physiology and biophysics U. Calif., Irvine, 1972-75, assoc. prof. physiology and biophysics, 1975-78, prof. physiology and biophysics, 1978—, vice chmn. physiology and biophysics, 1974-75, chmn. physiology and biophysics, 1977-89; guest biophysicist Brookhaven Nat. Lab., Upton, L.I., N.Y., 1977—; bd. dirs. Brian Pharms., San Juan Capistrano. Contbr. numerous articles to

profl. jours. Served to capt. USAR, 1969-71. Recipient Research Career Devel. award USPHS, 1975-80, Kaiser-Permanente award, 1975, 92; grantee NIH, 1971—, NSF, 1971—. Mem. Biophys. Soc. (chmn. membrane biophysics subgroup 1977-78, acting sec., treas. 1979-80, council 1981-84, exec. bd. 1981-83, program chmn. 1985 ann. meeting, sec. 1987-95, pres.-elect 1995-96, pres. 1996-97), Am. Physiol. Soc. (editl. bd. 1981-93, membership com. 1985-86, publ. com. 1987-91), Assn. Chem. Depts. Physiology (rep. to council acad. socs. 1981-82, councilor 1982-83, pres. 1986-87), Soc. Gen. Physiologists (treas. 1985-88, The Protein Soc. (electronic pub. coord. 1993—), NSF (adv. panel for molecular biology 1982-85, mem. nat. steering com. advanced neutron source 1992—). Avocations: skiing, cooking, travel. Office: Univ of Calif Dept of Physiology & Biophysics Irvine CA 92717

WHITE, SUE JEAN, lawyer; b. Liberal, Kans., May 16, 1955; d. Albert Leon and Arlene W. (Bunker) W. BBA, Washburn U., Topeka, 1977, JD, 1980. Bar: Kans. 1980, U.S. Dist. Ct. Kans. 1980, Tex. 1983. Law clk to presiding justice U.S. Dist. Ct. Kans., Kansas City, Kans., 1980-82; atty. Shell Oil Co., Houston, 1982—. Bd. dirs. Houston Area Women's Rape Crisis Ctr., 1985; mem. Houston Proud, 1986—. Mem. ABA, Tex. Bar Assn. Methodist. Avocations: antiques, quilting, bicycling. Office: Shell Oil Co PO Box 2463 Houston TX 77252-2463

WHITE, TERRENCE HAROLD, academic administrator, sociologist; b. Ottawa, Ont., Canada, Mar. 31, 1943; s. William Harold and Shirley Margaret (Ballantine) W.; m. Susan Elizabeth Hornaday; children: Christine Susan, Julie Pamela. Ph.D., U. Toronto, 1972. Head dept. sociology and anthropology U. Windsor, Ont., Can., 1973-75; prof., chmn. dept. sociology U. Alta., Edmonton, 1975-80, dean faculty of arts, 1980-88; pres. Brock U., St. Catharines, Ont., 1988—, T.H. White Orgn. Research Services Ltd., Edmonton, 1975—; dir. Labatt's Brewing Alta., Edmonton, 1981-88. Author: Power or Pawns: Boards of Directors, 1978, Human Resource Management, 1979; editor: Introduction to Work Science, 1981, QWL in Canada: Case Studies, 1983. Bd. dirs. Progressive Conservative Assn., Edmonton South, 1976-81, 1st v.p., 1981-85, pres., 1985-87; bd. dirs. Tri-Bach Festival Found., Edmonton, 1981-88, Alta. Ballet Co., 1985-88, Edmonton Conv. and Tourism Authority, Arch Enterprises, 1984-88, Niagara Symphony Soc., YMCA, St. Catharines, 1988-92; chair United Way Campaign St. Catharines, 1992, Fox Found., 1990—; bd. dirs. Edmonton Symphony Soc., v.p., 1986-88; bd. govs. U. Alta., 1984-88, Brock U., 1988—, Ridley Coll., 1990—. Recipient Can. 125 Commemorative medal, Govt. of Can. Mem. St. Catharines Club, Garden Ct. Racquet Club, Rotary (pres. Edmonton South 1981-82), Delta Tau Kappa, Alpha Kappa Delta. Home: 15 Deer Park Cres, Fonthill, ON Canada L0S 1E1 Office: Brock U, Saint Catharines, ON Canada L2S 3A1

WHITE, TERRY R., hospital administrator; b. Athens, Ohio, Nov. 6, 1940; married. BA, Ohio U., 1962; MHA, Xavier U., 1966. Adminstrv. resident Charleston (W.Va.) Gen. Hosp., 1965-66, adminstrv. asst., 1966-67; asst. adminstr. Youngstown (Ohio) Gen. Hosp., 1967-68, adminstr., 1968-74; pres. Lutheran Med. Ctr., Cleve., 1974-88; exec. v.p. Univ. Hosps. Cleve., 1988-89, sr. exec. v.p., 1989-91; dir., CEO U. Cin. Hosp. and Clinics, Cleve., 1991—. Mem. ACHE, Ohio Hosp. Assn. (bd. dirs., mem. coms.). Office: U Cin Hosp 234 Goodman St Cincinnati OH 45219-2374

WHITE, TERRY WAYNE, hospital administration executive; b. Rocky Mountain House, Alta., Can., Mar. 27, 1952; s. Arnold N. and Mildred J. W.; m. Darlene Y. Rockwell, July 31, 1977; children: Danae, Derek. BSc, Pacific Union Coll., 1973; MPH, Loma Linda U., 1977. Sr. v.p. Shawnee Mission (Kans.) Med. Ctr., 1977-84; pres. Castle Med. Ctr., Kailua, Hawaii, 1984—; mem. nat. adv. bd. The Healthcare Forum, San Francisco, 1986—; chmn. pacific region Inst. Svc. Excellence, 1993, Quality Mgmt. Exchange Forum, 1993. Trustee Le Jardin Academy, Kailua, 1989—. Maffly scholar The Healthcare Forum, 1993. Fellow Am. Coll. Healthcare Execs.; mem. Am. Hosp. Assn. (del. for state 1993—), Am. Soc. Quality and Control, Healthcare Assn. Hawaii (bd. dirs. 1991-93, chmn. 1990, Disting. Svc. award 1992), Rotary. Office: Castle Med Ctr 640 Ulukahiki St Kailua HI 96734-4498

WHITE, THOMAS EDWARD, government park official; b. Bozeman, Mont., Dec. 29, 1936; s. James Henry and Louesa (Coon) W.; m. Sylvia Moon Young, July 17, 1965 (dec. Aug. 1974); children—James Allen, Edward Paul; m. Patricia Lee Swanson, Mar. 1, 1975; 1 child, Andrew Todd. B.S., Mont. State U., 1959, M.S., 1963. Cert. tchr., Mont. Tchr. pub. schs. Mont., 1959-62; park historian Manassas Nat. Battlefield Park, Nat. Park Service, Va., 1964-66, Central Nat. Capital Parks, Nat. Park Service, Washington, 1966-68; supervisory park historian Fort Laramie Nat. Hist. Site, Nat. Park Service, Wyo., 1968-73; interpretive specialist So. Ariz. Group, Nat. Park Service, Phoenix, 1973-83; chief park interpreter Hawaii Volcanoes Nat. Park, 1983-87; interpretive planner Harpers Ferry (W.Va.) Ctr., Nat. Park Svc., 1987—; interpretive planner, internat. exchange assignment Can. Nat. Hist. Sites Service, Ottawa, Ont., 1969. Author: Garrison Life Trail: An Illustrated Guide to Fort Laramie, 1972 (Fed. Editors Assn. Blue Pencil award 1973). Adult adviser Order DeMolay, Mont., Va., Wyo., Ariz., 1960-83; Cub Scout and Boy Scout leader Theodore Roosevelt (Ariz.), Aloha (Hawaii), Shenandoah Area (W.Va.) coun. Boy Scouts Am., 1978—; adminstrv. bd. chmn. Hilo United Meth. Ch. 1985-87; scouting coord. New St. United Meth. Ch., 1988—. Recipient Chevalier Degree Order DeMolay, 1954, Legion of Honor award Order DeMolay, 1968; named Father of Yr., 1st Bapt. Ch., Scottsdale, Ariz., 1978, Statuette award Shenandoah Area coun. Boy Scouts Am., 1994, Cross and Flame Religious award for adult scout leaders Boy Scouts Am., 1995. Mem. Nat. Assn. Interpreters, Nat. Assn. United Meth. Scouters, NPS Employees and Alumni Assn., Sigma Nu. Lodge: Masons. Avocations: collecting stamps, hiking, model railroading, singing in church choir, genealogy. Office: Harpers Ferry Ctr NPS Div Interpretive Planning PO Box 50 Harpers Ferry WV 25410-0050

WHITE, THOMAS EDWARD, lawyer; b. N.Y.C., July 11, 1933; s. Thomas Aubrey and Gladys Mary (Piper) W.; m. Joan Carolyn Olsen, Dec. 2, 1967 (dec.); children: Charles Garret, Nancy Carolyn, Linda Marie, Penelope Lindsay, Elizabeth Ann. A.B., Princeton U., 1955; LL.B, Columbia U., 1960. Bar: N.Y. 1961. Atty. Seward & Kissel, N.Y.C., 1960-69; gen. counsel Howmet Corp., N.Y.C., 1969-70; v.p., gen. counsel, sec. Howmedica, Inc., N.Y.C., 1970-74; sr. v.p. dir. Howmedica, Inc., 1974-83; pvt. practice N.Y.C., 1983—; ptnr. Westmed Venture Ptnrs. (formerly Integrated Med. Venture Ptnrs.), N.Y.C., 1987—; chmn. Shoreside Cons. Ltd., Miami, Fla., 1987—. Mem. Mamaroneck Town Council, 1971-75; vestry Episcopalian Ch., 1987-90. Served to U.S. Army, 1955-57. Republican. Clubs: Larchmont (N.Y.) Yacht; Princeton (N.Y.C.). Home: 260 Barnard Rd Larchmont NY 10538-1941 Office: 485 Madison Ave New York NY 10022-5803

WHITE, THOMAS JEFFREY, healthcare management educator; b. Boston, Oct. 25, 1945; m. Tomoe Niijima White, Nov. 6, 1970; children: Tammy P., Treacy C. BA in Bus., U. Md., 1972; MS in Edn., Troy State U., 1974; MS in Sys. Mgmt., U. So. Calif., L.A., 1977; MBA in Healthcare Mgmt., Western New Eng. Coll., 1985. Dir. cert. hosp. adminstr. Commd. 2d lt. USAF, 1963, advanced through grades to lt. col., devel. officer edn. program USAF Air U., 1972-74, asst. adminstr. pers. adminstrn., 1974-75, asst. adminstr. resources mgmt., 1975-76, asst. adminstr. patient affairs mgmt., 1976-80; adminstr., CEO USAF Hosp., Yokota Air Base, Japan, 1980-81, USAF Comty. Med. Group Facility, L.A. AFB, El Segundo, Calif., 1981-83; adminstr., COO USAF Comty. Med. Group Facility, Hanscom AFB, Boston, 1983-86; mgmt. fellow spl. assignment Arthur D. Little, Inc., 1986-87; healthcare mgmt. cons./auditor Air Force Med. Inspection Ctr., 1987-90; chief plans and programs Air Force Inspection & Safety Ctr., 1990-91; sr. devel. officer Brim Enterprises, 1991-92; mem. adj. faculty grad. program health svcs. adminstrn. Chapman U., 1990—. Recipient So. Calif. Fed. Exec. Bd. Profl. Devel. award, 1983. Fellow Am. Coll. Healthcare Execs., Am. Hosp. Assn. Roman Catholic. Home: 29127 Lake Ridge Ln Highland CA 92346 Office: Chapman U Graeber St Riverside CA 92518

WHITE, THOMAS PATRICK, county official, small business owner; b. Red Bank, N.J., Mar. 17, 1945; s. Edwin Hardy and Alice G. (Olah) W.; m. Jeanette Haydee Gonzalez, Oct. 22, 1966; children: Kimberley Ann, Tiffany Lynne. AS in Criminal Justice, Indian River C.C., Ft. Pierce, Fla., 1977;

student, Northeastern U., 1964-65, Rutgers U., 1969, U. Fla., 1984. Cert. law enforcement officer, N.J., Fla.; cert. evaluator, Fla. State ranger N.J. Bur. Forests and Parks, Trenton, 1966-70; pres., owner Whiteford Enterprises Inc. T/A Colonial Automotive Svc. Ctr., Eatontown, N.J., 1970-75; dep. sheriff, criminal investigator, instr. firearms Indian River County Sheriff's Dept., Vero Beach, Fla., 1975-90; dir. investigations Indian River County Property Appraiser's Office, Vero Beach, 1990—; owner TeeJays' Awards, Vero Beach, 1978—. Dir. Rep. Club Indian River County, Vero Beach, 1994-95; treas. Men's Rep. Club, Vero Beach, 1995; former v.p. and pres. Fla. Police Combat League; former mem. Econ. Crime Coun. With USCG, 1962-66. Named Man of Yr., March of Dimes, 1987, Entrepreneur of Yr., Vero Beach Jaycees, 1992. Mem. Internat. Assn. Assessing Officers, Fraternal Order Police (state trustee 1978-85, state asst. dir. 1987-88, state dist. dir. 1989-90, pres. 1985-87, lodge v.p. 1993-94, Mem. of Yr. award 1982, 84, 88), Ducks Unltd. (1990—), 100 Club Indian River County, Elks, Kiwanis (v.p. Vero Beach 1991-92, pres. 1992-93, lt. gov. 1994-95, Kiwanian of Yr. award 1992). Roman Catholic. Avocations: golf, gun collecting, motorcycle riding, camping, freshwater fishing. Home: 1556 30th Ave Vero Beach FL 32960 Office: Indian River County Property Appraiser's Office 1840 25th St Vero Beach FL 32960

WHITE, THOMAS RAEBURN, III, law educator, consultant; b. Phila., Aug. 18, 1938; s. Thomas Raeburn Jr. and Charlotte (Gerhard) W.; m. Margaret Bardwell, Dec. 12, 1960 (div. June 1975); children: Elizabeth Krusenstjerma, Kathleen Harris, Thomas Ray IV; m. Maria Llanes, Oct. 19, 1975. BA, Williams Coll., 1960; LLB, U. Pa., 1963. Bar: Pa. 1964, Va. 1971. Assoc. White and Williams, Phila., 1963-65; atty.-advisor TLC U.S. Treasury Dept., Washington, 1965-67; assoc. prof. U. Va., Charlottesville, 1967-70, prof. law, 1970—; legis. atty. Joint Com. on Tax U.S. Congress, Washington, 1973-75; cons. adminstrn. conf. IRS Project, Washington, 1975-76; vis. prof. NYU Law Sch., N.Y.C., 1978-79. Mem. ABA (com. chair tax sect. 1985-87), Am. Coll. of Tax Coun., Va. Bar Assn., Va. State Bar Assn., Phila. Bar Assn., Charlottesville-Albermarle Bar Assn. Home: 12 Deer Path Charlottesville VA 22903-4707 Office: U Va Sch Law 580 Massie Rd Charlottesville VA 22903-1789

WHITE, TIMOTHY DOUGLAS, biology educator; b. Los Angeles, Aug. 24, 1950; s. Robert Julian and Georgia Johnston (McDougall) W. B.S. in Biology, U. Calif., Riverside, 1972, B.S. in Anthropology, 1972; M.A., U. Mich., 1974, Ph.D., 1977. Paleontologist East Rudolf Research Project, N. Kenya, 1974-77, Laetolil Expdn., N. Tanzania, 1978, 88, Middle Awash Valley, Ethiopia, 1981—, Olduvai Gorge, 1985-86, Paleoanthropological Inventory of Ethiopia, 1988—; prof. U. Calif., Berkeley, 1977-95, prof. integrative biology, 1995—. Grantee NSF, Nat. Geog. Soc. Fellow Calif. Acad. Sci.; mem. Soc. Vertebrate Paleontology, AAAS. An excavator earliest human ancestor footprints, Tanzania, 1978; co-discoverer earliest human ancestors A. afarensis 1978-79; A. ramidus 1994. Office: U of Calif Dept of Integrative Biology Berkeley CA 94720

WHITE, TIMOTHY OLIVER, newspaper editor; b. Albany, N.Y., June 29, 1948; s. Oliver C. and Yvonne (Letourneau) W.; 1 child, Eric B. BA in English, Siena Coll., 1971. Reporter Cape Cod Times, Hyannis, Mass., 1971-72, asst. Sunday editor, 1972-75, news editor, 1975-79, asst. editor, 1979-83, mng. editor, 1983—. Mem. AP Mng. Editors, New Eng. AP News Exec. Assn. (v.p. 1992, 93, pres. 1994), New Eng. Soc. Newspaper Editors. Avocations: community TV producer, photography, wilderness travel, bicycling, cooking, sailing. Home: PO Box 1187 56 Jolly's Crossing Rd Brewster MA 02631 Office: Cape Cod Times 319 Main St Hyannis MA 02601

WHITE, TIMOTHY THOMAS ANTHONY, writer, editor, broadcaster; b. Paterson, N.J., Jan. 25, 1952; s. John Alexander and Gloria Marie (Thomas) W.; m. Judith Anne Garlan, June 28, 1987; children: (twins) Alexander and Christopher. BA, Fordham U., 1972. Copyboy, sports and entertainment writer AP, N.Y.C., 1972-76; mng. editor Crawdaddy mag., N.Y.C., 1976-77, sr. editor, 1977-78; assoc. editor Rolling Stone mag., N.Y.C., 1978-79, sr. editor, 1979-82; host, co-producer Timothy White's Rock Stars/The Timothy White Sessions nationally syndicated radio series ABC Radio Network, 1986; LBS Radio Network, 1987, Westwood One Radio Network, 1988—; editor in chief Billboard mag., N.Y.C., 1991—. Author: Catch a Fire: The Life of Bob Marley, 1983, rev. enlarged edit., 1989, meml. edit., 1991, rev. edit., 1994, Rock Stars, 1984, Rock Lives: Profiles and Interviews, 1990, rev. edit., 1994; co-author: Rolling Stone Visits Saturday Night Live, 1979; (with others) Roadside Food, 1986; contbr.: The Best of the Music Makers, 1979, The 80s: A Look Back at the Tumultuous Decade, 1979, The Rolling Stone Interviews, 1981, Reggae International, 1982, Suddenly Four! A Guide for Downwardly Mobile, 1983, Twenty Years of Rolling Stone, 1987, A & M Records: The First 25 Years, 1987, The Nearest Faraway Place: Brian Wilson, the Beach Boys and the Southern California Experience, 1994; contbg. editor Musician, 1982—, Spin, 1985—; contbr. articles to various mags. Recipient ASCAP-Deems Taylor award, 1991, 93. Democrat. Avocations: drums, dancing, Caribbean history, folklore, music. Office: Billboard Mag 1515 Broadway New York NY 10036-5702

WHITE, TONY L, health and medical products executive. BA, We. Carolina U., 1969. Sales rep. Baxter Internat. Inc., 1970-74, dist. mgr., 1974-76, export mgr. Latin Am., 1976-82, v.p. AMPAC, pres. Travenol-Can., 1982-85, pres. Fenwal divsn., 1985-86, pres. scientific products, biomedical divsn., 1986; v.p. diagnostics Baxter Internat. Inc., Deerfield, Ill., 1989-95; exec. vp Baxter Internat. Inc. With USAR, 1968-74. Office: Baxter Internat Inc 1 Baxter Pky Deerfield IL 60015-4634

WHITE, VICTOR DEA, airport management executive; b. Ft. Worth, Tex., Mar. 16, 1951; s. Victor George and Louise Emily (Roach) W.; m. Denise Sue Bonzo, Sept. 3, 1977; children: Kathy, Tiffany, Daniel. BS in Bus. and Transportation with honors, St. Louis U., 1974. Airport mgmt. intern St. Louis Internat. Airport, 1974-75; airport mgmt. cons. Landrum & Brown, Cinn., 1975-77; airport duty mgr. Dallas/Ft. Worth Internat. Airport, 1977-81; exec. dir Waukegan (Ill.) Port Authority, 1981-83; dir. airports City of Midland (Tex.)/Odessa, 1983-90; dep. dir. airports Salt Lake City Airport Authority, 1990—; pres. U.S. Airport Svcs. Corp., Salt Lake City, 1983—; Bedford Industries Corp., Ft. Worth, 1977—. Author: Small Hub Airport Management, 1985. Chmn. Midland/Odessa Interant. Task Force, 1986-90, Mayor's Transp. Task Force 1991-95, Mayor's Americans with Disabilities Task Force 1991-94, Internat. Airport Rescue/Firefighting Acad. 1986-89, Internat. Airport Facilities Conf. 1993; mem. The Midland Com. 1986-90. Alpha Sigma Nu scholar, 1974, Alpha Chi scholar, 1974. Mem. Am. Assn. Airport Execs (pres. Northwest chpt. 1993-95, Southcentral chpt. 1988-90), Midland C. of C. (chmn. aviation task force 1986—). Republican. Roman Catholic. Avocations: flying, skiing, racquetball, photography, organ. Office: Salt Lake City Internat Airport AMF Box 22084 776 N Terminal Dr Salt Lake City UT 84122

WHITE, WARREN WURTELE, retailing executive; b. McKeesport, Pa., Feb. 29, 1932; s. Jay Leonard and Elizabeth Katherine (Fehr) W.; m. Marjorie Ada Shuman, Mar. 20, 1954; 1 dau., Laura Lynn. B.S., Duquesne U., 1954; M.Retailing, U. Pitts., 1957. With Strawbridge & Clothier, Phila., 1957—; buyer Strawbridge & Clothier, 1960-67, budget store divisional mdse. mgr., 1968-70, Clover Div. gen. mdse. mgr., 1970-76, v.p. for mdse. and sales promotion, 1978—, exec. v.p., 1978—, also dir., 1981—; gen. mgr. Strawbridge & Clothier (Clover Div.), 1978—. Bd. dirs. Ea. Star Charity Found. N.J., 1978-83. Served to 1st lt. arty. U.S. Army, 1954-56. Mem. Internat. Mass Retail Assn. (officer 1987-93, bd. dirs. 1981—, chmn. bd. 1991-93), South Jersey C. of C. (bd. dirs. 1991—), Am. Lung Assn. (bd. dirs. Phila. chpt. 1991-94). Republican. Methodist. Club: Tavistock. Lodge: Masons. Home: 1 Heritage Rd Haddonfield NJ 08033-3405 Office: Strawbridge & Clothier Clover Divsn 801 Market St Philadelphia PA 19107-3199

WHITE, WILL WALTER, III, public relations consultant, writer; b. Glen Ridge, N.J., July 3, 1930; s. Will Walter and Miriam Chandler (Milburn) W.; m. Phyllis Marcia DuFlocq, Dec. 28, 1951 (div. 1971); children: Will Walter IV, Scott, Alan; m. Anne Elizabeth Levenson, Nov. 21, 1971 (div. 1992); children: Duncan, Christopher; stepchildren: Michael, Susan; m. Catherine Laur, Aug. 26, 1992. B.A., Cornell U., 1952. Supr. Union Carbide Corp., N.Y.C., 1954-59; account exec. Ketchum, MacLeod & Grove, N.Y.C., 1959-62; sr. v.p. Wilson, Haight & Welch, Hartford, Conn., 1962-72; chmn., chief

exec. officer Lowengard & Brotherhood, Hartford, 1972-83; pres., chief exec. officer Harland & Tine & White, Hartford, 1983-87; chmn. Donahue Inc., Hartford, 1987-89; ptnr. Laur, White & White, Sarasota, Fla., 1992—; exec. com. Conn. Dist. Export Council, 1979-88. Author: The Sunfish Book, 1983; contbg. editor Mid-Gulf Sailing Mag., 1994—. Exec. com. Hartford Stage Co., 1982-86; pres. Vis. Nurse Assn., Hartford, 1979; fin. chmn. Vis. Nurse & Home Care, Inc., Hartford-Waterbury, 1982-91; pub. relations com. Fairfield County Republican Com., 1961. Served to 1st lt. U.S. Army, 1952-54. Nat. champion Sunfish Racing Class, 1966, 68. Mem. Pub. Rels. Soc. Am. (chmn. investor rels. sect. 1983, accredited, charter mem. Hall of Fame 1990), Bus. Profl. Advt. Assn. (cert. bus. communicator), Nat. Investor Rels. Inst., U.S. Sunfish Class Assn. (pres. 1985-88, charter mem. Hall of Fame 1991), Boaters Action & Info. League (v.p. edn. 1993—), Hist. Soc. Sarasota County (bd. dirs. 1995—), Sarasota Sailing Squadron. Address: 7362 Palomino Ln Sarasota FL 34241-9779

WHITE, W(ILLIAM) ARTHUR, geologist; b. Sumner, Ill., Dec. 9, 1916; s. Millard Otto and Joy Olive (Atkins) W.; m. Alma Evelyn Simonton McCullough, June 21, 1941. B.S., U. Ill., 1940, M.S., 1947, Ph.D., 1955. With Ill. Geol. Survey, Urbana, 1947-58, geologist, 1955-58, head clay resources and clay mineral tech. sect., 1958-72, geologist, 1972-79, geologist emeritus, 1979—; pvt. cons. geologist Urbana, 1979-88; prof. geology Fed. U. Rio Grande do Sul, Brazil, 1970. Contbr. articles to profl. jours. Fellow Geol. Soc. Am., Mineral. Soc. Am., AAAS; mem. Internat. Clay Mineral Soc., Am. Clay Mineral Soc., Ill. Acad. Sci., Mus. Natural History (assoc.), Nat. Geog. Soc., Am. Chem. Soc., Colloid Chem. Soc., Soc. Econ. Paleontologists and Mineralogists, Inter-Am. Soc., Charter mem. Order United Comml. Travelers Am., U. Ill. Alumni Assn., Sigma Xi. Home: 603 E Colorado Ave Urbana IL 61801-5923

WHITE, WILLIAM BLAINE, geochemist, educator; b. Huntingdon, Pa., Jan. 5, 1934; s. William Bruce and Eleanor Mae (Barr) W.; m. Elizabeth Loczi, Mar. 27, 1959; children: Nikki Elizabeth White McCurry, William Brion (dec.). BS, Juniata Coll., 1954; PhD, Pa. State U., 1962. Rsch. assoc. Mellon Inst., Pitts., 1954-58; asst. prof. Pa. State U., University Park, 1963-67; assoc. prof. Pa. State U., 1967-72, prof. geochemistry, 1972—, chmn. grad. program in materials, 1990-93. Assoc. editor: Am. Mineralogist, 1972-75, Materials Rsch. Bull., 1979-93, Jour. Am. Ceramic Soc., 1985-93, Water Resources Bull., 1992-93; editor earth scis. Nat. Speleol. Soc. Bull., 1964-94; author: Geomorphology and Hydrology of Karst Terrains, 1988, (with Elizabeth L. White) Karst Hydrology: Concepts from the Mammoth Cave Area, 1989, (with Susan Barger) Daguerreotype: Nineteenth-Century Technology and Modern Science, 1991; contbr. articles to profl. jours. Home: 542 Glenn Rd State College PA 16803-3472 Office: Pa State U Materials Rsch Lab University Park PA 16802

WHITE, WILLIAM DEKOVA (BILL WHITE), baseball league executive; b. Lakewood, Fla., Jan. 28, 1934; div.; 5 children. Student, Hiram Coll., 1952-53. With various minor league teams, 1953-55; with N.Y. Giants (later San Francisco Giants), 1956, 58, St. Louis Cardinals, 1959-65, 69, Phila. Phillies, 1966-68; broadcaster Sta. WPIX-TV, N.Y.C., 1970-88; pres. Nat. League, N.Y.C., 1989—. Recipient 7 Gold Glove awards; named to All-Star team 6 times. Office: Nat League Profl Baseball Clubs 350 Park Ave New York NY 10022

WHITE, WILLIAM FREDRICK, lawyer; b. Elmhurst, Ill., Sept. 30, 1948; s. William Daniel and Carol Ruth (Laier) W.; m. Kathie Jean Nichols, May 27, 1979; children: Nicholas Roland, Andrew William. BA, U. Ill., 1970; JD, Antioch Sch. of Law, 1976. Bar: U.S. Ct. Appeals (D.C. cir.) 1976, Wis. 1982, U.S. Dist. Ct. (we. dist.) Wis. 1982, U.S. Dist. Ct. D.C. 1976, U.S. Ct. Claims 1978, U.S. Ct. Appeals (7th and 10th cirs.) 1982. With U.S. Dept. Labor, Washington, 1976; interim exec. dir. Common Cause, Washington, 1977; asst. counsel Nat. Treasury Employees Union, Washington, 1977-79, assoc. gen. counsel, 1979-81, dir. litigation, 1981-82; assoc. Michael, Best & Friedrich, Madison, Wis., 1982-88, ptnr., chmn. assoc. devel. com., 1988—; pres., bd. dirs. Med. Physics Publ. Co., 1991—. Mem. strategic planning com. Hospice-Care, Madison, 1986—; treas. The Lufler com., Madison, 1984—; chmn. Pub. Health Commn., Madison, 1983-89; bd. dirs. exec. com. Dane County Mediation Program, Madison, 1983—, Perinatal Found., Madison, 1984—, Arthritis Found., Madison, 1986—, chmn. 1991-92, Commonhealth, Madison, 1986-88; bd. dirs. Dane County Natural Heritage Found., 1988-91; mem. Dane County Regional Airport commn., 1991—; pres., chancellor, Wisc. Conf. United Methodist Ch., 1992—, gen coun. Fin. and Adminstrn., 1991—, chmn. Legal Svcs. Found. 1991—, Robert A. Rohr Assn., Med. Physics Found. (bd. dirs. 1987—), Dane County Bar Assn., State Bar Assn. (sec. Health Law sect.). Democrat. Methodist. Avocations: cycling, skiing, volleyball, softball. Office: Michael Best & Friedrich 1 S Pinckney St Madison WI 53703-2808

WHITE, WILLIAM J., lawyer; b. Chgo., Oct. 1, 1948; s. William Joseph and Jeanette Ruth (Madden) W.; m. Mary Jane Yardley, Nov. 20, 1988; children: Christopher W., Timothy M., Kathleen M. BS in Chemistry, U. Ill., 1970; JD, John Marshall Law Sch., 1974. Bar: Ill. 1974, U.S. Dist. Ct. (no. dist.) Ill. 1974. Chemist Kraft Corp., Glenview, Ill., 1970-72; assoc. Lord, Bissell & Brook, Chgo., 1974-81, ptnr., 1982—; instr. John Marshall Law Sch., 1974-79. Mem. Chgo. Bar Assn. (exec. com. jud. evaluation com. 1985—), Assn. Advancement Automotive Medicine, Soc. Automotive Engrs., Union League. Roman Catholic. Home: 2117 N Magnolia Ave Chicago IL 60614-4011 Office: Lord Bissell & Brook 115 S La Salle St Ste 3300 Chicago IL 60603-3903

WHITE, WILLIAM JAMES, information and services company executive; b. Kenosha, Wis., May 30, 1938; s. William H. and Dorothy Caroline White; m. Jane Schulte, Aug. 13, 1960; children: James N., Thomas G., Maria, Gretchen S. BS, Northwestern U., 1961; MBA, Harvard U., 1963. Mech. planning engr. Procter & Gamble Corp., 1961-62; bd. dirs. TJ Internat., Boise, Idaho; corp. v.p. Hartmarx Corp., Chgo., 1963-74; group v.p. Mead Corp., Dayton, Ohio, 1974-81; pres., chief oper. officer, dir. Masonite Corp., Chgo., 1981-85; exec. v.p. and dir. USG Corp., 1985-88, pres., chief exec. officer Whitestar Enterprises, Inc., 1989-90; chmn., pres., chief exec. officer Bell & Howell Co., 1990-95; chmn. CEO Bell & Howell Holdings Co., 1995—. Author: (with Henderson et al) Creative Collective Bargaining, 1965. Alumni trustee Northwestern U., mem. adv. coun. The McCormick Sch. of Engring. and Applied Scis.; mem. bus. adv. coun. U. Ill., Chgo., 1981—; bd. dirs. TJ Internat, IMSA Fund for the Advancement of Edn., Aurora; past chmn. bd. Ill. div. Am. Cancer Soc. Mem. Econ. Club, The Chgo. Com., Chgo. Club, Glen View Country Club. Office: Bell & Howell Co 5215 Old Orchard Rd Skokie IL 60077-1035

WHITE, WILLIAM NORTH, chemistry educator; b. Walton, N.Y., Sept. 16, 1925; s. George Fitch and Frances (Peck) W.; m. Hilda R. Sauter, Sept. 8, 1951; children: Carla Ann, Eric Jeffrey. A.B., Cornell U., 1950; M.A., Harvard U., 1951, Ph.D., 1953. NRC postdoctoral fellow Calif. Inst. Tech., Pasadena, 1953-54; asst. prof. Ohio State U., Columbus, 1954-59; assoc. prof. Ohio State U., 1959-63; prof. chemistry U. Vt., Burlington, 1963-76, 77—; chmn. dept. U. Vt., 1963-70, acting chmn. dept., 1975-76; prof. chemistry U. Tex. at Arlington, 1976-77, chmn. dept., 1976-77; NSF sr. postdoctoral fellow Brookhaven Nat. Lab., Upton, N.Y., 1963-64, Harvard U., 1965; vis. scholar Brandeis U., 1974-75; chmn. arrangements com. Nat. Organic Chemistry Symposium, 1965-67. Contbr. articles on organic chemistry profl. jours. Selectman Town of Shelburne, Vt., 1968-74, water commr., 1973-74, justice of the peace, 1981—, sewer commr., 1991-93; mem. Chittenden County Regional Planning Commn., 1983-91. Served with AUS, 1943-46. Mem. Am. Chem. Soc. (chmn. Western Vt. sect. 1966-67), Royal Soc. Chemistry, New Eng. Assn. Chemistry Tchrs., AAAS, N.Y. Acad. Scis., Phi Beta Kappa, Sigma Xi, Phi Kappa Phi, Phi Lambda Upsilon. Home: Pierson Dr Shelburn VT 05482-7224 Office: U Vt Dept Chemistry Burlington VT 05405-0125

WHITE, WILLIAM SAMUEL, foundation executive; b. Cin., May 8, 1937; s. Nathaniel Ridgway and Mary (Loundes) W.; m. Claire Mott, July 1, 1961; children: Tiffany Loundes, Ridgway Harding. BA, Dartmouth Coll., 1959, MBA, 1960; LL.D. (hon.), Eastern Mich. U., 1975. With Barrett & Williams, N.Y.C., 1961-62; sr. assoc. Bruce Payne & Assocs., N.Y.C., 1962-71; v.p. C. S. Mott Found., Flint, Mich., 1971-75; pres. C. S. Mott Found., 1976—, trustee, 1971—, also chmn. bd. dirs.; bd. dirs. Continental Water

Corp; chmn. bd. dirs. U.S. Sugar Corp. Mem. exec. com. Daycroft Sch., Greenwich, Conn., 1966-70; bd. dirs. Flint Area Conf., 1971-84, Coun. on Founds., 1985-90, Independent Sector, 1994—, European Found. Centre, 1994—, Civicus, 1995—; mem. citizens adv. task force U. Mich., Flint, 1974-79; chmn. Coun. of Mich. Founds., 1979-81, Flint Area Focus Coun., 1988—; mem. Pres.'s Task Force on Pvt. Sector Initiatives, 1982; trustee GMI Engring. and Mgmt. Inst., 1982-86. Served with U.S. Army, 1960-62. Office: C S Mott Foundation 1200 Mott Foundation Bldg Flint MI 48502-1807

WHITE, WILLIS SHERIDAN, JR., retired utilities company executive; b. nr. Portsmouth, Va., Dec. 17, 1926; s. Willis Sheridan and Carrie (Culpepper) W.; m. LaVerne Behrends, Oct. 8, 1949; children: Willis Sheridan III, Marguerite Louise White Spangler, Cynthia D.W. Haight. B.S., Va. Poly. Inst., 1948; M.S., Mass. Inst. Tech., 1958. With Am. Electric Power Co. Inc., 1948-91; chmn., chief exec. officer Am. Electric Power Co., Inc. and its subs., N.Y.C., 1976-90, chmn., 1991, mem. bd. dirs., 1972-92; pres., bd. dirs. Ohio Valley Electric Corp., Ind.-KTV Electric Corp., 1977-91; bd. dirs. Bank of N.Y. Trustee Battelee Meml. Inst., Riverside Meth. Hosp., Columbus. With USNR, 1945-46. Sloan fellow, 1957-58. Mem. IEEE, NAE, Eta Kappa Nu, Omicron Delta Kappa. Methodist.

WHITE, WILLMON LEE, magazine editor; b. Lamesa, Tex., Mar. 10, 1932; s. Aubrey F. and Jewel (Henderson) W.; m. Carol A. Nelson, Nov. 2, 1957 (div.); children—Tracy, Wrenn, Gehrig, Bob; m. Barbara K. Kelly, Sept. 16, 1977; 1 dau., Theresa. B.A., McMurry Coll., Abilene, Tex., 1953; M.A., U. Tex., 1956. Reporter Abilene Reporter-News, 1953-54; public relations writer Tex. Ins. Adv. Assn., Austin, 1955-56; asst. editor Humble Way mag. Humble Oil & Refining Co. (Exxon), Houston, 1956-65; assoc. editor, news editor Together mag. Methodist Ch., Park Ridge, Ill., 1965-69; sr. editor World Book Ency., Chgo., 1969-70; asst. editor, then assoc. editor Rotarian mag. (publ. Rotary Internat.), Evanston, Ill., 1970-74, editor, 1974—, mgr. communications and pub. rels. div., 1979-95; asst. gen. sec. Rotarian mag. (publ. Rotary Internat.), Evanston, 1995—; intern Newsweek mag., 1954. Mem. Am. Soc. Mag. Editors, Am. Soc. Assn. Execs., Sigma Delta Chi. Club: Evanston Rotary. Office: Rotarian 1560 Sherman Ave Evanston IL 60201-3698

WHITEFIELD, ANNE C., secondary school principal. Prin. Hum-Fogg High Sch., Nashville. Recipient Elem. Sch. Recognition award U.S. Dept. Edn., 1989-90. Office: Hum-Fogg High Sch 700 Broadway Nashville TN 37203-3900

WHITEFORD, ANDREW HUNTER, anthropologist; b. Winnipeg, Man., Can., 1913; came to U.S., 1923, naturalized, 1928; s. John and Janet Cardiff (Hunter) W.; m. Marion Bonneville Salmon, Sept. 2, 1939; children: John Hunter, Michael Bonneville, Linda McMillan Whiteford Uzzell, Laurie Andrea Whiteford Richards. B.A., Beloit (Wis.) Coll., 1937, LL.D. (hon.), 1981; M.A., U. Chgo., 1943, Ph.D. 1950. Archaeologist N.Mex., 1938; supr. U. Tenn.-WPA, 1938-42; mem. faculty Beloit Coll., 1942-74, prof. anthropology, 1955-74, George L. Collie prof., 1955-74, chmn. dept., 1944-73, emeritus, 1974—; vis. prof. Mich. State U., 1975, 76, 79; vis. prof. art history U. N.Mex., 1980; Faye Laverne Bumpass lectr. Tex. Tech. U., 1981; rsch. fellow com. human rels. U. Chgo., 1945-46; dir. Logan Mus. Anthropology, Beloit Coll., 1946-74; urban rschr., Mex., Colombia, Spain; rsch. curator Indian Art Research Ctr., Sch. Am. Research, Santa Fe, 1980-84, 90—, interim adminstr. dir., 1981-84; research assoc. Wheelwright Mus. Am. Indian, Santa Fe, 1980—, trustee, 1979-85; adv. bd. Florence H. Ellis Mus., Ghost Ranch Conf. Ctr., Abiquiu, N.Mex., 1979—; guest curator, rsch. assoc. N.Mex. Mus. of Indian Arts and Culture, 1987—. Author: Two Cities of Latin America, 1964, North American Indian Arts, 1970, An Andean City at Mid-Century, 1977, Southwestern Indian Baskets: Their History and Makers, 1988, (chpts.) The Thaw Collection of Indian Art, 1995; mem. editl. adv. bd. Am. Indian Art mag.; contbr. articles to profl. jours., encys. and festschrifts. NSF faculty fellow, 1960-61; Social Sci. Research Council-Am. Council Learned Socs. fellow, 1961-62; grantee Wenner Gren Found.; grantee Social Sci. Research Council; grantee NSF; grantee USPHS; grantee Am. Philos. Soc. Fellow Am. Anthrop. Assn.; mem. Coun. for Mus. Anthropology, Soc. for Latin Am. Anthropology, Phi Beta Kappa, Sigma Xi, Beta Theta Pi, Omicron Delta Kappa. Address: 447 Camino Monte Vis Santa Fe NM 87501-4585

WHITEHEAD, E. DOUGLAS, urology educator; b. Galashiels, Scotland, Aug. 24, 1939; m. Patricia Robbins, June 26, 1966; 1 child, Robin Stacey. BA, Vanderbilt U., 1961; MD, Ind. U., 1965; postgrad., U. London, 1972. Diplomate Am. Bd. Urology; med. lic. Ind., Ill., N.Y., Calif., N.J. Intern. surgery Mount Sinai Hosp., N.Y.C., 1965-66; resident in surgery Presbyn.-St.-Luke's Hosp., Chgo., 1966-67; resident in urology N.Y.U. Med. Ctr., 1969-73; clin. assoc. urology Mount Sinai Sch. Medicine, N.Y.C., 1973-77, sr. clin. instr. urology 1977-80, asst. clin. prof. urology, 1980-92; pvt. practice, N.Y.C., 1973—; assoc. clin. prof. urology, 1992—; assoc. attending Beth Israel Med. Ctr., N.Y.C.; asst. attending Hosp. for Joint Diseases, Orthopaedic Inst., N.Y.C.; courtesy staff Gracie Square Hosp., N.Y.C.; attending physician N.Y.C. Eye and Ear Informary; med. advisor Impotence Anonymous & Jr., Diabetes Self-Mgmt., 1983-85, Jour. Urol. Nursing; editorial adv. bd. The Female Patient, Med. Aspects of Human Sexuality; mem. med. adv. bd. Colostomy Soc. N.Y., Inc.; com. and speaker in field. Editor: Current Operative Urology, 1975, 2d rev. edit., 1984, ann. edits., 1989-92, Mgmt. Impotence and Infertility, 1994, Sex Over Forty, 1990—, Atlas of Surgical Techniques in Urology; contbr. articles to profl. jours.; patentee in field. Grantee U.S.P.H., Clin. Research Ctr. Fellow Am. Coll. Surgeons, Clin. Soc. Am. Diabetes Assn., N.Y. Diabetes Affiliate; mem. AMA, Am. Urol. Assn., Internat. Soc. Urology (U.S. sect.), Am. Assn. Clin. Urologists, N.Y. State Urol. Assn., Internat. Soc. for Artificial Organs, Am. Soc. Nephrology, Med. Soc. State N.Y., Med. Soc. County N.Y., Am. Assn. Sex Edrs, Counselors and Therapists, Soc. for the Scientific Study of Sex, Sex Info. and Edn. Council of the U.S. Coalition on Sexuality and Disability, Am. Cancer Soc., Nat. Kidney Found., AAAS, Am. Geriatric Soc., N.Y. Acad. Sci., N.Y. Acad. Medicine, N.Y. Urodynamic Soc., Internat. Continence Soc. Home and Office: 785 Park Ave New York NY 10021-3552

WHITEHEAD, GEORGE WILLIAM, retired mathematician; b. Bloomington, Ill., Aug. 2, 1918; s. George William and (Christine) Mary (Gutschlag) W.; m. Kathleen Ethelwyn Butcher, June 7, 1947. SB, U. Chgo., 1937, SM, 1938, PhD, 1941. Instr. math. Purdue U., West Lafayette, Ind., 1941-45, Princeton (N.J.) U., 1945-47; asst. prof. Brown U., Providence, 1947-48, assoc. prof., 1948-49; asst. prof. MIT, Cambridge, 1949-51, assoc. prof., 1951-57, prof., 1957-85, prof. emeritus, 1985—. Author: Homotopy Theory, 1966, Elements of Homotopy Theory, 1978, Recent Advances in Homotopy Theory, 1970. Fellow Guggenheim Found., 1955-56, sr. post-doctoral fellow NSF, 1965-66; Fulbright Rsch. scholar, 1955-56. Fellow Am. Acad. Arts & Scis.; mem. NAS, mem. Math. Soc. (v.p.), Math. Soc. Am. Avocations: archeology, bridge, genealogy. Home: 25 Bellevue Rd Arlington MA 02174-7919

WHITEHEAD, IAN, insurance company executive. CEO, pres. London PCF Lf & Annuity Co., Raleigh, N.C. Office: London PCF Lf & Annuity Co 3109 Poplarwood Ct Raleigh NC 27604*

WHITEHEAD, J. RENNIE, science consultant; s. William and Beatrice Cora (Fenning) W.; m. Nesta Doone James, Jan. 11, 1944; children—Valerie Lesley (dec.), Michael James Rennie. B.Sc. in Physics, Manchester U., Lancashire, Eng., 1939; Ph.D. in Phys. Chemistry, Cambridge U., Eng., 1949. Cert. profl. engr., Ont.; chartered engr. U.K. Sci. officer TRE (UK Radar), Eng., 1939-51; assoc. prof. McGill U., Montreal, P.Q., Can., 1951-55; dir. research RCA Victor Co Ltd., Montreal, 1955-65; prin. sci. adviser Govt. of Can., Ottawa, Ont., 1965-75; sr. v.p. Philip A. Lapp Ltd., Ottawa, 1975-82; pvt. practice sci. cons. Ottawa, 1982—; bd. dirs. Hancock-Lapp Assocs., Ottawa, 1986-89; bd. dirs. Found. for Internat. Tng., Toronto, 1976-86. Author: Superregenerative Receivers, 1949. Fellow Royal Soc. Can., Inst. Physics, Instn. Elec. Engrs. Can. Aeronautics and Space Inst., Can. Assn. for Club of Rome (chmn. 1976-81). Anglican. Avocations: automobiles; philately; carpentry; computers. Home and Office: 1368 Chattaway Ave, Ottawa, ON Canada K1H 7S3

WHITEHEAD, JAMES S., lawyer; b. Rockford, Ill., Dec. 22, 1948; s. John B. and Beverley (Williams) W.; m. Pamela A. Miller, June 26, 1970; children: Jennifer, John. BA, Yale U., 1970; JD, U. Chgo., 1974. Bar: Ill. 1974, U.S. Ct. Appeals (D.C., 2d, 3d, 6th, 7th, 8th, 11th cirs.), U.S. Supreme Ct., U.S. Dist. Ct. (no. and so. dists.) Ill., U.S. Dist. Ct. (ea. dist.) Mich. Assoc. Sidley & Austin, Chgo., 1975-80, ptnr., 1981—. Office: Sidley & Austin 1 First Nat Plz Chicago IL 60603

WHITEHEAD, JOHN C., state judge; b. Loup City, Nebr., Mar. 4, 1939; s. Cyrus C. and Regina (Costello) W.; m. Linda L. Lykins, Sept. 11, 1965; children: Sarah, Amy. AB in History, Benedictine Coll., 1961; LLB, Washburn U., 1964. Bar: Nebr. 1964, Kans. 1964. Mem. firm Snell & Whitehead, Columbus, Nebr., 1965-66, Walker Luckey & Whitehead, Columbus, 1966-71, Walker, Luckey, Whitehead & Sipple, Columbus, 1971-77; judge Nebr. State Dist. Ct., Columbus, 1977—; dep. county atty. Platte County, Nebr., 1965-67; atty. City of Columbus, 1967-72. Bd. dirs. Lower Loup Natural Resource Dist., 1971-74, vice chmn., 1975-76; bd. dirs. Columbus Family YMCA, 1974-80, pres., 1978-80; bd. dirs. Platte County Playhouse, 1972-74. Mem. ABA (regional rep. Nat. Assn. State Trial Judges 1994—), Nebr. Bar Assn., Platte County Bar Assn. (pres. 1976-77), Nebr. Dist. Judges Assn. (sec.-treas. 1988-90, v.p. 1990, pres. 1991-92), Columbus C. of C. (bd. dirs. 1977-81, pres. 1979), Elks, Optimists (pres. 1971-72, lt. gov. Nebr. dist. 1972-73), Toastmasters (mem. 1968—), Am. Vets. (comdr. 1994—). Roman Catholic. Home: 3365 Pershing Rd Columbus NE 68601-8117 Office: State Dist Ct PO Box 445 Columbus NE 68602-0445 *What bothers me about America today is that we have become a nation of spectators, not just in sports, but in life itself. Life, like sports, provides the most rewards and enjoyment to the participant. The spectators only gain from the association, and when it's over find they have only the memories and no tangible benefits.*

WHITEHEAD, JOHN CUNNINGHAM, investment executive; b. Evanston, Ill., Apr. 2, 1922; s. Eugene C. and Winifred W.; m. Helene E. Shannon, Sept. 28, 1946 (div. Dec. 1971); children: Anne Elizabeth, John Gregory; m. Jaan W. Chartener, Oct. 22, 1972 (div. 1986); 1 child, Sarah; m. Nancy Dickerson, 1989. BA, Haverford Coll., 1943; MBA, Harvard U., 1947; LLD (hon.), Pace. U., Rutgers U., Haverford Coll., Amherst Coll. With Goldman, Sachs & Co., N.Y.C., 1947-84, ptnr., 1976-84, sr. ptnr., cochmn., 1976-84; dep. sec. Dept. State, Washington, 1985-89; now chmn. AEA Investors Inc., N.Y.C., 1989—. Trustee Haverford Coll., also former chmn.; trustee Paul Getty Trust, Rockefeller U., Lincoln Ctr. Theater, Outward Bound, Schumann Found.; past pres. bd. overseers Harvard U.; mem., past chmn. trustees coun. Nat. Gallery Art; co-chmn. Greater N.Y. coun. Boy Scouts Am.; chmn. Internat. Rescue Com., Andrew W. Mellon Found., Asia Soc., UN Assn. of U.S.A., Youth for Understanding, Internat. House; chmn. emeritus Brookings Inst. With USNR, 1943-46. Mem. Coun. on Fgn. Rels., Links Club, Univ. Club, Met. Club, F Street Club. Office: AEA Investors Inc 65 E 55th St New York NY 10022-3219

WHITEHEAD, JOHN JED, computer systems company executive; b. N.Y.C., June 1, 1945; s. Edwin Carl and Constance Rosemary (Raywid) W.; m. Christian Juillet, Sept. 24, 1985 (div. 1994). B.A., Williams Coll., 1967; postgrad., Case Western Res. U., 1967-68. Dir. chem. mktg., chem. div. Technicon Corp., Tarrytown, N.Y., 1969-70; sr. v.p., gen. mgr. indsl. div. Technicon Corp., 1970-71, sr. v.p. clin. div., 1971-74, sr. v.p. corp. planning, 1974-75, sr. v.p. research and devel., 1975-81, sr. v.p. bus. devel. and market planning, 1981-83, pres. diagnostic systems div., 1983-85; pres., dir., CEO TDS Corp., 1985-92, chmn., CEO, dir., 1992-93; bd. dirs. Whitehead Assocs., 1980—; bd. dirs. Digene Diagnostics, Inc., Rsch. Am., I-Stat Corp.; mem. adv. coun. Nat. Inst. Environ. Health Scis., NIH, 1971-73. Mem. Rockefeller adv. group to Pres.'s 1976 Bicentennial Planning Commn., 1971-72; bd. dirs. Westchester Urban League, 1973-74, Whitehead Biomed. Rsch. Inst., 1974—; Primary Care Network, 1985-87, Friends Nat. Libr. Medicine, 1992—, Sci. and Tech. Mus. of Atlanta (SciTrek), 1992—, Ams. Med. Progress 1993—; trustee Nat. Mus. Health and Medicine Found., 1991—. Home: Park Place on Peachtree 2660 Peachtree Rd Atlanta GA 30305 Office: Whitehead Ptnrs 200 Ashford Center N Atlanta GA 30338

WHITEHEAD, JOHN WAYNE, law educator, organization administrator, author; b. Pulaski, Tenn., July 14, 1946; s. John M. and Alatha (Weaver) W.; m. Virginia Carolyn Nichols, Aug. 26, 1967; children: Jayson Reau, Jonathan Mathew, Elisabeth Anne, Joel Christofer, Joshua Benjamen. BA, U. Ark., 1969, JD, 1974. Bar: Ark. 1974, U.S. Dist. Ct. (ea. and we. dists.) Ark. 1974, U.S. Supreme Ct. 1977, U.S. Ct. Appeals (9th cir.) 1980, Va. 1981, U.S. Ct. Appeals (7th cir.) 1981, U.S. Ct. Appeals (4th and 5th cirs.). Spl. counsel Christian Legal Soc., Oak Park, Ill., 1977-78; assoc. Gibbs & Craze, Cleve., 1978-79; sole practice law Manassas, Va., 1979-82; pres. The Rutherford Inst., Charlottesville, Va., 1982—, also bd. dirs.; frequent lectr. colls., law schs.; past adj. prof. O.W. Coburn Sch. Law. Author: The Separation Illusion, 1977, Schools on Fire, 1980, The New Tyranny, 1982, The Second American Revolution, 1982, The Stealing of America, 1983, The Freedom of Religious Expression in Public High Schools, 1983, The End of Man, 1986, An American Dream, 1987, The Rights of Religious Persons in Public Education, 1991, Home Education: Rights and Reasons, 1993, Religious Apartheid, 1994, several others; contbr. numerous articles to profl. jours.; contbr. numerous chpts. to books. Served to 1st lt. U.S. Army, 1969-71. Named Christian Leader of Yr. Christian World Affairs Conf., Washington, 1986; recipient Man of profl. and Profl. award Religious Heritage Am., 1990, Hungarian Freedom medal, Budapest, 1991. Mem. ABA, Ark. Bar Assn., Va. Bar Assn. Office: The Rutherford Inst PO Box 7482 Charlottesville VA 22906-7482

WHITEHEAD, KENNETH DEAN, author, translator, retired federal government official; b. Rupert, Idaho, Dec. 14, 1930; s. Clarence Christian and May Bell (Allen) W.; m. Margaret Mary O'Donohue, Aug. 2, 1958; children: Paul Daniel, Steven Francis, Matthew Patrick, David Joseph. BA in French, U. Utah, 1955; postgrad., U. Paris, 1956-57; cert. in Arabic and Middle East studies, Fgn. Service Inst., Beirut, 1962. Instr. English U. Utah, Salt Lake City, 1955-56; fgn. service officer Dept. State, Rome, Beirut and Tripoli, Libya, 1957-65; chief Arabic service Voice of Am., Washington, 1965-67; dep. dir. fgn. currency program Smithsonian Instn., Washington, 1967-72; assoc. v.p. Caths. United for Faith Inc., New Rochelle, N.Y., 1972-81; dir. Ctr. for Internat. Edn. U.S. Dept. Edn., Washington, 1982-86, dep. asst. sec. for higher edn. programs, 1986-88, asst. sec. for postsecondary edn., 1988-89. Author: Respectable Killing: The New Abortion Imperative, 1972, Agenda for the Sexual Revolution, 1981, Catholic Colleges and Federal Funding, 1988, DOA: The Ambush of the Universal Catechism, 1993; coauthor: The Pope, The Council and the Mass, 1981; sr. editor World Almanac Book of Dates, 1982, Macmillan Concise Dictionary of World History, 1983; translator 19 books from French, German, Italian, 1980-94. Bd. dirs. Notre Dame Inst. for Advanced Study, Arlington, Va., 1986-94. Fulbright scholar U.S. Dept. State, 1956-57. Mem. Fellowship Cath. Scholars (bd. dirs. 1990—), Brent Soc. Cath. Profls. (bd. dirs. 1992—), Cath. League for Religious and Civil Rights (bd. dirs. 1992—), KC. Republican. Home: 809 Ridge Pl Falls Church VA 22046-3631

WHITEHEAD, LEWIS E, JR., automotive consultant, management consultant; b. Gainesville, Ga., Aug. 3, 1927; s. Lewis Eugene and Lottie Bell (Wolford) W.; m. Mary Bryant Hinnant, Dec. 5, 1953; children: Lewis III, William H., Michael B., Charles A. BSEE, Clemson A&M, 1948; degree in Bus. Mgmt., U. Ga., 1950. Dist. mgr. Firestone Tire & Rubber Co., Charlotte, N.C., 1952-65; TBA merchandiser J.C. Penny Co., N.Y.C., 1965-67; nat. mktg. mgr. Computerized Auto Reporting Svcs., Inc., Birmingham, Ala., 1968-70; chmn., CEO Automotive Svc. Cons., Inc., Birmingham. Author tng. programs Nissan, Toyota, Ford, GM. Mem. Inst. Mgmt. Cons. (cert.), Assn. Mgmt. Cons. (cert., bd. dirs. 1979-82), Rotary Internat. Republican. Presbyterian. Avocations: golf, boating, walking. Home: 3508 S Woodridge Rd Birmingham AL 35223-1416 Office: Automotive Service Cons Inc 2131 Data Office Dr Birmingham AL 35244-1233

WHITEHEAD, MARVIN DELBERT, plant pathologist; b. Paoli, Okla., Dec. 18, 1917; s. Chester Arthur and Lola Elizabeth (Donnell) W.; 1 child, James Mark. BS, Okla. State U., 1939, MS, 1946; PhD (fellow), U. Wis. 1949. Seed analyst Soil Conservation Svc. USDA, Stillwater, Okla., 1936-38; asst. in agronomy Okla. State U., 1939-40; sr. seed analyst Fed. State Seed Lab., Montgomery, Ala., 1940-42; asst. plant pathologist U. Wis., Madison,

1946-48; asst. prof. plant pathology Tex. A&M U., College Station, 1949-55; assoc. prof. U. Mo., Columbia, 1955-60; prof. botany Edinboro State Coll., Pa., 1960-63; prof. plant pathology Ga. So. Coll., Statesboro, Ga., 1963-68; prof. botany and plant pathology Ga. State U., Atlanta, 1968-75; owner, dir. Marvern Plant Health, Inc., Atlanta, 1978—; cons. control of plant diseases. Editor Ga. Jour.-Sci., 1969-75; contbr. 59 articles to rsch. jours. and publs.; developer fungicide Phyton 27 for control of Dutch Elm Disease. With USAAF, 1941-46, PTO. Mem. AAAS, VFW, Am. Phytopathol. Soc., Mycol. Soc. Am., Bot. Soc. Am., Am. Inst. Biol. Scis., Crop Sci. Soc. Am., Am. Soc. Agronomy, Ofcl. Seed Analysts N.Am., Ga. Acad. Sci., Wis. Acad. Sci., Druid Hills Golf Club (Atlanta). Democrat. Home and Office: Apt 5E 2211 Massachusetts Ave Lemon Grove CA 91945-3616

WHITEHEAD, MICHAEL ANTHONY, chemistry educator; b. London, June 30, 1935; emigrated to Can., 1962; s. Francis Henry and Edith Downes (Rotherham) W.; 1 son, Christopher Mark. B.Sc. in Chemistry with honors, Queen Mary Coll., U. London, 1956, Ph.D., 1960, D.Sc., 1974. Asst. lectr. Queen Mary Coll., U. London, 1958-60; postdoctoral fellow U. Cin., 1960, asst. prof., 1961; asst. prof. theoretical chemistry McGill U., Montreal, Que, Can., 1962-66; asso. prof. McGill U., 1966-74, prof., 1974—; vis. prof. U. Cambridge, Eng., 1971-72, U. Oxford, Eng., 1972-74; vis. professorial fellow Univ. Coll. Wales, Aberystwyth, 1980, U. Oxford, 1990-91; invited prof. U. Geneva, 1983-84; life guest prof. Nat. U. Def. Tech., Changsha, People's Republic of China; mem. Internat. Com. on Nuclear Quadrupole Resonance.; co-chmn. 7th Internat. Symposium on Nuclear Quadrupole Resonance, Kingston, Ont., Can., 1983. Research, over 200 publs. in field of quantum chemistry and radio spectroscopy. Fellow Royal Chem. Soc., Chem. Inst. Can., Royal Soc. Arts; mem. Am. Chem. Soc., Am. Phys. Soc., James McGill Soc. (pres. 1993-95), Sigma Xi (pres. McGill chpt. 1971-72, 81-82, 92-95), Phi Lambda Upsilon. Anglican. Office: McGill U Dept Chemistry, 801 Sherbrooke St W, Montreal, PQ Canada H3A 2K6 *My faith in God and belief in Christ.*

WHITEHEAD, RICHARD LEE, insurance company executive; b. Pitts., Feb. 26, 1927; m. Shirley Ann Fritz, Aug. 19, 1950; children: David Lee, Deborah Ann Head. A.B. in Polit. Sci., Otterbein Coll., 1950; student, U. Pa. Law Sch., 1950-52. Claims adjuster Lumberman's Mut. Casualty Ins. Co., Phila., 1951-52; dir. admissions Otterbein Coll., 1952-54; indsl. relations asst. Westinghouse Electric Corp., Pitts., 1954-56; personnel mgr. Home Life Ins. Co., N.Y.C., 1956-63; dir. employee relations, then v.p. personnel and co. relations Berkshire Life Ins. Co., Pittsfield, Mass., 1963-73; sr. v.p., sec. Berkshire Life Ins. Co., 1973-84, exec. v.p., sec., 1984-90, chmn. bd., chief adminstrv. officer, 1990-92, chmn. bd., 1992—; guest speaker mgmt. edn. seminars. Vice pres., dir. Action for Opportunity, 1964-66; pres., dir. Berkshire County Action Coun., 1966-68, Berkshire County chpt. United Cerebral Palsy, 1966-67; v.p., bd. dirs. Pittsfield YMCA; bd. dirs., past pres. Pittsfield Urban Coalition; bd. dirs. North Adams Coll. Found.; chmn. Pittsfield Devel. Com., 1976-80, Berkshire Bus. Com. for Arts; trustee Berkshire C.C., 1992—; chmn. bd. trustees Berkshire Med. Ctr., 1992—. Served with USAAF, 1945-47. Mem. Eastern Coll. Personnel Officers (hon.), Life Office Mgmt. Assn. (past dir.), Life Ins. Assn. Mass. (past chmn. exec. com.), Central Berkshire C. of C. (chmn. 1986), Silver Bay Assn. (past v.p. fin. devel.), Soc. Preservation and Encouragement Barbershop Quartet Singing Am. Methodist.

WHITEHEAD, ROBERT, theatrical producer; b. Montreal, Can., Mar. 3, 1916; s. William Thomas and Lena Mary (Labatt) S.; m. Zoe Caldwell, 1968. Student, Trinity Coll. Sch., Port Hope, Can. Comml. photographer, 1936-38, actor, 1938-42, producer, 1946—; Dir ANTA Am. Shakespeare Festival. Producer: plays include Medea (Robinson Jeffers), starring Judith Anderson, 1947, Crime and Punishment, starring John Gielgud, 1947, Member of the Wedding (Carson McCullers), 1950 (N.Y. Times Drama Critics Circle award), Waltz of the Toreadors, 1957 (N.Y. Times Drama Critics Circle award), Separate Tables (Terrence Rattigan), 1956-57, A Touch of the Poet (Eugene O'Neill), 1958, The Visit (Friedrich Durrenmatt), 1958 (N.Y. Times Drama Critics Circle award 1958), Much Ado About Nothing (Shakespeare), 1959, A Man for All Seasons (Robert Bolt), 1961-62 (Tony award 1962, N.Y. Times Drama Critics Circle award 1961), The Physicists (Durrenmatt), 1964, The Price (Arthur Miller), 1968, The Prime of Miss Jean Brodie (Jay Presson Allen), 1968, Sheep On The Runway, 1970, Bequest to the Nation, 1970, The Creation of the World and Other Business (Miller), 1972, Finishing Touches, 1973-74, A Matter of Gravity, 1976, A Texas Trilogy, 1976, No Man's Land (Harold Pinter), 1976, The Prince of Grand Street, 1979, Betrayal (Harold Pinter), 1979, Lunch Hour, 1980-81, The West Side Waltz, 1980-81, Death of a Salesman (Miller), 1983-84, The Petition, 1986, The Speed of Darkness, 1991, Park Your Car in Harvard Yard (Israel Horowitz), 1991-92, Broken Glass (Miller), 1994, Master Class (Terrence McNally), 1995; co-producer: Artist Descending a Staircase (Tom Stoppard), 1989; dir. plays: Medea, N.Y.C., 1982, Melbourne, Australia, 1984, Lillian, 1986. Served Am. Field Service AUS, 1942-45. Recipient Sam S. Shubert Found. award, 1973, Edwin Booth award, 1990, United Jewish Appeal/Fedn. Lifetime Achievement award, 1991. Clubs: Century (N.Y.C.), Players (N.Y.C.). Office: 1501 Broadway New York NY 10036-5502

WHITEHILL, CLIFFORD LANE, lawyer; b. Houston, Apr. 14, 1931; s. Clifford R. and Catalina (Yarza) W.; m. Daisy Mae Woodruff, Apr. 18, 1959; children: Clifford Scott, Alicia Anne, Stephen Lane. BA, Rice U., 1954; LLB, U. Tex., 1957; LLM, Harvard U., 1958. Bar: Tex. 1957, Minn. 1962. Assoc. Childress, Port and Crady, Houston, 1957-59; auditor Haskins and Sells, 1959; asst. gen. counsel Tex. Butadiene and Chem. Co., N.Y.C., 1959-62; with Gen. Mills, Inc., Mpls., 1962—; gen. counsel, 1975-94, sr. v.p., gen. counsel, 1981—, sec., 1981-94. Mem. Minn. Minority Corp. Counsel; mem. corp. adv. bd., mem. adv. com. Nat. Chamber Litigation Ctr.; trustee William Mitchell Coll. Law; assoc. bd. dirs. Minn. Opera; bd. dirs. Minn. Uruguay Ptnrs. Am., Nat. Hispanic Scholarship Fund, Fund Legal Aid Soc., Minn. Spl. Olympics, Greater Minn. Coun. Chs. Minn.; chmn. Better Bus. Bur.; chmn. coun. Better Bus. Burs.; mem. exec. com. Ctr. Pub. Resources. Mem. ABA, Minn. Bar Assn., Tex. Bar Assn., Am. Arbitration Assn. (bd. dirs.), Nat. Assn. Mfrs. (bd. dirs., state dir.), UN Assn. U.S., Assn. of Gen. Counsel, Harvard Club, Lafayette Club. Republican. Roman Catholic. Avocations: boating, flying, skiing, tennis. Office: Gen Mills Inc PO Box 1113 1 General Mills Blvd Minneapolis MN 55426-1347

WHITEHOUSE, ALTON WINSLOW, JR., retired oil company executive; b. Albany, N.Y., Aug. 1, 1927; s. Alton Winslow and Catherine (Lyda) W.; m. Helen MacDonald, Nov. 28, 1953; children: Alton, Sarah, Peter. B.S., U. Va., 1949, LL.B., 1952. Bar: Ohio 1953. Assoc. partner firm McAfree, Hanning, Newcomer, Hazlett & Wheeler, Cleve., 1952-68; v.p., gen. counsel Standard Oil Co., Ohio, 1968- 69; sr. v.p. Standard Oil Co., 1969-70, pres., chief operating officer, 1970-77, vice chmn. bd., 1977-78, chmn. bd., chief exec. officer, 1978-86; bd. dirs. Timken Co., Canton, Ohio, McGean-Rohco, Cleve., Cleve-Cliffs Inc., Orvis, Inc. Trustee Cleve. Clinic Found., Holden Arboretum; mem. Cleve. Mus. Art. Mem. Am. Petroleum Inst. Republican. Episcopalian.

WHITEHOUSE, DAVID BRYN, museum director; b. Worksop, Nottinghamshire, Eng., Oct. 15, 1941; came to U.S., 1984; s. Brindley Charles and Alice Margaret (Dobson) W.; m. Ruth Delamain Ainger, 1963; children—Sarah, Susan, Peter; m. Elizabeth-Anne Ollemans, 1975; children—Julia, Simon, Nicola. B.A., Cambridge U., 1963, M.A., 1965, Ph.D., 1967. Wainwright fellow Oxford U., Eng., 1966-73; dir. Brit. Inst. Afghan Studies, Kabul, Afghanistan, 1973-74, Brit. Sch., Rome, 1974-84; chief curator Corning Mus. of Glass, N.Y., 1984-87, dep. dir., 1988-92, dir., 1992—; dir. Siraf expdn. Brit. Inst. Persian Studies, Tehran, Iran, 1966-73. Author: (with Ruth Whitehouse) Archaeological Atlas of the World, 1975; (with David Andrews and John Osborne) Aspects of Medieval Lazio, 1982, (with Donald B. Harden and others) Glass of the Caesars, 1987, Glass of the Roman Empire, 1988; (with Richard Hodges) Mohammed, Charlemagne and the Origins of Europe, 1983, Glass: A Pocket Dictionary, 1993, English Cameo Glass, 1994. Contbr. numerous articles and revs. to profl. jours. Fellow Soc. Antiquaries (London), Royal Geog. Soc., Pontificia Accademia Romana di Archeologia; mem. Accademia Fiorentina delle Arti del Disegno, Accademia di Archeologia, Lettere e Belle Arti, Deutsches Archaologisches Inst., Internat. Assn. for the History of Glass (pres. 1991—). Club: Athenaeum (London). Office: Corning Mus of Glass One Museum Way Corning NY 14830-2253

WHITEHOUSE, DAVID REMPFER, physicist; b. Evanston, Ill., Nov. 13, 1929; s. Horace and Emma (Rempfer) W.; m. Ruth Agnes Walker, June 23, 1956; children—Walker Philip, Laura Lees, Sanford Davis. B.S., Northwestern U., 1952; M.S., M.I.T., 1954, Sc.D., 1958. Assoc. prof. elec. engring. M.I.T., 1958-65; prin. research scientist Raytheon Co., Waltham, Mass., 1965-67; mgr. laser center Raytheon Co., Burlington, Mass., 1967-85; pres. Whitehouse Assocs., Weston, Mass., 1985—; co-founder, dir. Magnion Inc., Burlington, 1960-63; co-founder, chm. bd. DYMED Corp., Marlboro, Mass., 1989-91. Bd. dirs. New Eng. Bapt. Hosp., Boston, 1976—. Fellow Laser Inst. Am. (pres. 1981, bd. dirs. 1977—); mem. IEEE, Am. Inst. Physics. Episcopalian. Patentee in plasma physics, laser engring. Home and Office: 99 South Ave Weston MA 02193-2324

WHITEHOUSE, FRED WAITE, endocrinologist, researcher; b. Chgo., May 6, 1926; s. Fred Trafton Waite and Grace Caroline (Peters) W.; m. Iris Jean Dawson, June 6, 1953; children: Martha, Amy, Sarah. BS, Northwestern U., 1947; MD, U. Ill., Chgo., 1949. Diplomate Am. Bd. Internal Medicine; cert. endocrinology and metabolism. Intern, then resident Henry Ford Hosp., Detroit, 1949-53, staff physician, 1955—, chief div. metabolism, 1962-88; chief div. endocrinology and metabolism Henry Ford Hosp., 1988-95; fellow Joslin Clinic, Boston, 1954-55; cons. FDA, Washington, 1980—; mem. Coalition on Diabetes Edn. and Minority Health, 1989-91. Contbr. articles to profl. jours. Bd. dirs. Wheat Ridge Found., 1984-93. Lt. USNR, 1951-53. Fellow ACP; mem. NIH (nat. diabetes adv. bd. 1984-88), Am. Diabetes Assn. (pres. 1978-79, Banting medal 1979, Outstanding Clinician award 1989, Outstanding Physician Educators award 1994), Detroit Med. Club (pres. 1976), Detroit Acad. Medicine (pres. 1991-92). Lutheran. Avocations: bicycling, gardening. Home: 1265 Blairmoor Ct Grosse Pointe MI 48236-1230 Office: Henry Ford Hosp 2799 W Grand Blvd Detroit MI 48202-2689

WHITEHURST, BROOKS MORRIS, chemical engineer; b. Reading, Pa., Apr. 9, 1930; s. David Brooks and Bessie Ann (Lowry) W.; B.S., Va. Poly. Inst. and State U., 1951; m. Carolyn Sue Boyer, July 4, 1951; children: Garnett, Anita, Robert. Sr. process asst. Am. Enka Corp., Lowland, Tenn., 1951-56; sr. process devel. engr. Va.-Carolina Chem. Corp., Richmond, Va., 1956-63; project engr. Texaco Inc., Richmond, 1963-66; mgr. engring. services Texasgulf, Inc., Aurora, N.C., 1967-80, mgr. spl. projects and long range planning, 1980-81; pres. Whitehurst Assocs., Inc., New Bern, N.C., 1981—; instr., lectr., cons. alternative sources of energy community colls. and univs.; presenter paper Solar World Forum, Brighton, Eng., 1981. Cochmn. N.C. state supt. task force on secondary edn., 1974—; mem. N.C. Personnel Commn. for Public Sch. Employees; mem. N.C. state adv. com. on trade and indsl. edn., 1971-77; chmn. Gov.'s Task Force Vols. in the Workplace, 1981; chmn. State Adv. Council Career Edn., 1977—; gov.'s liaison for edn. and bus., 1978-79. Registered profl. engr., N.C. Recipient commendation Pres. U.S., 1981. Mem. Am. Inst. Chem. Engrs., Am. Inst. Chemists (dir. 1980-84, cert.), N.C. Inst. Chemists (pres. 1975-77), Nat. Soc. Profl. Engrs., N.C. Soc. Profl. Engrs., Royal Soc. Chemistry. Achievements include patents, and current work on biodegradable chelate systems, muncipal yard waste disposal, micronutrients for agriculture, waste rubber recycling. Home: 1983 Hoods Creek Rd New Bern NC 28564-9103 Office: PO Box 3335 New Bern NC 28564-3335

WHITEHURST, HARRY BERNARD, chemistry educator; b. Dallas, Sept. 13, 1922; s. Clement Monroe and Grace Annette (Walton) W.; m. Audry Lucile Hale, June 12, 1948; children: Jonathan Monroe, Katherine Annette Whitehurst Hilburn. BA, Rice U., 1944, MA, 1948, PhD, 1950. Rsch. chemist Manhattan Project, Oak Ridge, Tenn., 1944-46, U.S. Naval Radiol. Def. Lab., San Francisco, 1959; postdoctoral fellow U. Minn., Mpls., 1950-51; rsch. chemist Owens-Corning Fiberglas Corp., Newark, Ohio, 1951-55, rsch. dept. head, 1955-59; assoc. prof. chemistry Ariz. State U., Tempe, 1959-70, prof., 1970-92. Contbr. articles on oxides to profl. jours.; patentee glass fibers field. With C.E., AUS, 1944-46. Fellow Am. Inst. Chemists, AAAS, Ariz. Acad. Sci. (pres. 1960-61); mem. Am. Chem. Soc., Phi Lambda Upsilon. Democrat. Baptist. Avocation: photography. Home: 630 E Concorda Dr Tempe AZ 85282-2319

WHITEHURST, WILLIAM WILFRED, JR., management consultant; b. Balt., Mar. 4, 1937; s. William Wilfred and Elizabeth (Hogg) W.; B.A., Princeton, 1958; M.S., Carnegie Inst. Tech., 1963; m. Linda Joan Potter, July 1, 1961; children—Catherine Elizabeth, William Wilfred, III. Mathematician Nat. Security Agy., Fort George G. Meade, Md., 1961-63; mgmt. cons. McKinsey & Co., Inc., Washington, 1963-66; partner L.E. Peabody & Assos., Washington, 1966-69, exec. v.p., dir. L.E. Peabody & Assos., Inc., Lanham, Md., 1969-82, pres., dir., 1983-86, pres. W.W. Whitehurst & Assoc., Inc., Cockeysville, Md., 1986—. Contbr. to Code of Fed. Regulations 49 C.F.R. Sect. 1157. Served to lt. comdr. USNR, 1958-61. Recipient Diploma De Honor 14th Pan Am. Rwy. Congress. Mem. Am. Railway Engring. Assn., Transportation Rsch. Forum, Assn. for Investment Mgmt. and Rsch., Ops. Rsch. Soc. Am., Inst. Mgmt. Scis., Washington Soc. Investment Analysts. Episcopalian. Clubs: University, Princeton (Washington), Princeton (N.J.) Quadrangle. Home and Office: 12421 Happy Hollow Rd Cockeysville Hunt Valley MD 21030-1711

WHITEKER, ROY ARCHIE, retired chemistry educator; b. Long Beach, Calif., Aug. 22, 1927; s. Ewing Harris and Mabel Mary (Williams) W.; m. Jean Fiske MacLean, June 3, 1960; 1 son, Scott MacLean. BS, UCLA, 1950, MS, 1952; PhD, Calif. Inst. Tech., 1956. Instr. chemistry M.I.T., 1955-57; asst. prof. Harvey Mudd Coll., Claremont, Calif., 1957-61; asso. prof. Harvey Mudd Coll., 1961-67, prof. chemistry, 1967-73; assoc. dir. fellowships Nat. Acad. Scis., Washington, 1967-68; dep. exec. sec. Council Internat. Exchange Scholar, Washington, 1971-72; exec. sec. Council Internat. Exchange Scholar, 1972-75; dir. Coun. Internat. Exchange Scholar, 1975-76; prof. chemistry U. Pacific, Stockton, Calif., 1976-92, dean Coll. Pacific, 1976-89. Bd. dirs. Stockton Symphony Assn., 1978-80; dir. cmty. adv. bd. Sta. KUOP, 1981-89; bd. dirs. Stockton Chorale, 1989—; pres. U. of the Pacific Emeriti Soc., 1992-94. With USNR, 1945-46. Recipient Dow Chem. Co. fellowship, 1953-54; DuPont Teaching fellowship, 1954-55; NSF Sci. Faculty fellowship Royal Inst. Tech., Stockholm, Sweden, 1963-64. Mem. Am. Chem. Soc., Alpha Chi Sigma, Phi Beta Kappa, Phi Kappa Phi, Sigma Xi. Home: 3734 Portsmouth Cir N Stockton CA 95219-3843

WHITELEY, BENJAMIN ROBERT, insurance company executive; b. Des Moines, July 13, 1929; s. Hiram Everett and Martha Jane (Walker) W.; m. Elaine Marie Yunker, June 14, 1953; children—Stephen Robert, Benjamin Walker. B.S., Oreg. State U., 1951; M.S., U. Oreg.; postgrad. advanced mgmt. program, Harvard U. Clk. group dept. Standard Ins. Co., Portland, Oreg., 1956-69, asst. actuary group dept. then asst. actuary actuarial dept., 1959-63, asst. v.p., asst. actuary, 1963-64, asst. v.p., assoc. actuary, 1964-70, v.p. group ins. adminstrn., 1970-72, v.p. group ins. div., 1972-80, exec. v.p. group ins., 1980-81, exec. v.p. 1981-83, pres., CEO, 1983-92, chmn. bd. dirs., CEO 1993-94, chmn. bd. dirs., 1994—; bd. dirs. Gunderson, Inc., Portland, U.S. Bancorp., N.W. Natural Gas Co., Willamette Industries, Inc., Oreg. Natural Gas Devel. Corp., Canor Energy Ltd., The Greenbrier Cos. Past pres. Columbia Pacific coun. Boy Scouts Am.; past chmn. bd. trustee Pacific U., Forest Grove, Oreg.; bd. dirs. St. Vincent Med. Found., Portland, U.S. Bank of Oreg. 1st lt. USAF, 1952-55. Recipient Silver Beaver award Boy Scouts Am., 1983, Harvey and Emiline Clark medal Pacific U., 1991, Alumni fellow award Oreg. State U., 1991, Aubrey R. Watzek award Lewis and Clark Coll., 1994. Fellow Soc. Actuaries; mem. Am. Acad. Actuaries (bd. dirs. 1984-86), Am. Council of Life Ins. (bd. dirs. 1986-89), Internat. Congress Actuaries, Portland C. of C. (bd. dirs. 1983-89). Republican. Methodist. Clubs: Arlington, Waverley Country, Multnomah Athletic (Portland, Oreg.). Office: Standard Ins Co PO Box 711 Portland OR 97207-0711

WHITELEY, SANDRA MARIE, librarian, editor; b. May 24, 1943; d. Samuel Smythe and Kathryn Marie (Voigt) Whiteley; m. R. Russell Maylone, Jan. 8, 1977; 1 child, Cybele Elizabeth. BA, Pa. State U., 1963; MLS, Columbia U., 1970; MA, U. Pa., 1975; postgrad., Northwestern U., 1985—. Tchr. Amerikan Kiz Koleji, Izmir, Turkey, 1967-69; reference libr. Yale U., New Haven, Conn., 1970-74; head reference dept. Northwestern U., Evanston, Ill., 1975-80; asst. editor Who's Who in Libr. and Info. ALA, Chgo., 1980-81, editor Reference Books Bull., 1985—; lectr. Grad. Libr. Sch. U. Chgo., 1982-83; assoc. exec. dir. Assn. Coll. and Rsch. Librs., Chgo.,

1981-85. Author: Purchasing an Encyclopaedia, 4th edit., 1992, The American Library Association Guide to Information Access, 1994. Mem. ALA (various coms. 1977-81), Beta Phi Mu. Democrat. Congregationalist. Avocations: reading, hiking, travel. Home: 1205 Noyes St Evanston IL 60201-2635 Office: ALA 50 E Huron St Chicago IL 60611-2795

WHITEMAN, DOUGLAS E., publisher; b. Emporia, Kans., Mar. 4, 1961; s. Floyd E. and Phyllis E. (Troyer) W.; m. Susan R. Anderson, Sept. 14, 1985; 1 child, Aaron Anderson Douglas. BS in Bus. Adminstrn., U. Kans., 1983. With Putnam Pub. Group, Denver and N.Y.C., 1983—; dir. trade sales and mktg., internat. sales mgr. Putnam Pub. Group, N.Y.C., 1987-89, v.p. sales and mktg., 1989-94; sr. v.p., pub. Putnam and Grosset Book Group, 1994—. Methodist. Avocations: literature, tennis, golf, fantasy baseball. Office: Putnam Pub Group 200 Madison Ave New York NY 10016-3903

WHITEMAN, H(ORACE) CLIFTON, banker; b. Visalia, Calif., July 23, 1925; s. Horace Clifton and Henrietta Emma (Stewart) W.; m. Shirley Deyo, Nov. 28, 1953 (div. Apr. 1977); children: Susan Elizabeth, Pamela Stewart Ritz, Elizabeth Lyle Braun; m. Joan Coffin Leib, June 6, 1977. BA, Dartmouth Coll., 1950, MBA, 1951. V.p. Morgan Guaranty Trust Co., N.Y.C., 1951-68; v.p. to officer Investors Diversified Services, Inc., Mpls., 1968-76; pres. trustee The Bowery Savs. Bank, N.Y.C., 1976-78; sr. v.p. The Irving Trust Co., N.Y.C., 1978-82; exec. v.p. The Bank of Tokyo Trust Co., N.Y.C., 1982-89; sr. dep. gen. mgr. The Bank of Tokyo, Ltd., N.Y.C., 1984-89; cons. The Bank of Tokyo Group, N.Y.C., 1989-92; bd. dirs. York Rsch. Corp., Keene Corp. Mem. Down Town Club (N.Y.C.), Piping Rock Club (Locust Valley, N.Y.). Republican. Presbyterian. Home: 136 E 64th St New York NY 10021-7360 Office: 280 Park Ave New York NY 10017

WHITEMAN, JOHN O., rental company executive; s. Jack W. W. BA, Ariz. State U., 1962. With Empire Southwest Co., Mesa, Ariz., 1960—, officer, 1970—, exec. v.p., 1982—, also chmn. bd., pres. Empire Machinery Divsn., 1984—. Office: Empire Southwest Co 1725 S Country Club Dr Mesa AZ 85210*

WHITEMAN, JOSEPH DAVID, lawyer, manufacturing company executive; b. Sioux Falls, S.D., Sept. 12, 1933; s. Samuel D. and Margaret (Wallace) W.; m. Mary Kelly, Dec. 29, 1962; children: Anne Margaret, Mary Ellen, Joseph David, Sarah Kelly, Jane. B.A., U. Mich., 1955, J.D., 1960. Bar: D.C. 1960, Ohio 1976. Assoc. Cox, Langford, Stoddard & Cutler, Washington, 1959-64; sec., gen. counsel Studebaker group Studebaker Worthington, Inc., N.Y.C., 1964-71; asst. gen. counsel. United Telecommunications, Inc., Kansas City, Mo., 1971-74; v.p., gen. counsel, sec. Weatherhead Co., Cleve., 1974-77, Parker Hannifin Corp., Cleve., 1977—. Chmn. bd. dirs. St. Lukes Med. Ctr.; bd. dirs Judson Retirement Community. Served as lt. USNR, 1955-57. Mem. ABA, Beta Theta Pi, Phi Delta Phi. Republican. Roman Catholic. Home: 23349 Shaker Blvd Cleveland OH 44122-2670 Office: Parker Hannifin Corp 17325 Euclid Ave Cleveland OH 44112-1290

WHITEMAN, RICHARD FRANK, architect; b. Mankato, Minn., Mar. 24, 1925; s. Lester Raymond and Mary Grace (Dawald) W.; m. Jean Frances Waite, June 20, 1948 (dec. May 1980); children: David, Sarah, Lynn, Ann, Carol, Frank, Marie, Steven; m. Mavis Patricia Knutsen, May 30, 1982. BArch, U. Minn., 1945; MArch, Harvard U., 1948. Registered architect, Minn. Designer Ellerbe Co., St. Paul, Minn., 1946; architect Thorshov and Cerny, Mpls., 1948-53; prin. Jyring and Whiteman, Hibbing, Minn., 1953-62; pres. AJWM Inc., Hibbing and Duluth, Minn., 1963-72, Architects Four, Duluth, 1972-83; owner Richard Whiteman, Duluth, 1983—; sr. architect U. Minn., Duluth, 1972-80; chmn. Architect Sect. Registration Bd., Minn., 1972-80. Prin. works include Washington Sch., Hibbing, 1957 (Minn. Soc. Architects Design award 1957), Whiteman Summer Home, Pengilly, Minn. (Minn. Soc. Architects Design award 1959), Bemidji State Coll. Phys. Edn. Bldg. (Minn. Soc. Architects Design award 1960), Whiteman Residence, Griggs Hall UMD, 1990. Pres. U. for Srs., 1993-94; bd. govs. St. Louis County Hist. Soc.; mem. adv. com. Glensheen, U. Minn. Duluth. With USN, 1943-46, PTO. Mem. Minn. Soc. Architects (pres. 1972), Northeast Minn. Architects (pres. 1962), Service Corps Retired Execs. (chmn. Northeast Minn. chpt. 1986), Minn. Designer Selection Bd. (chmn. 1990). Mem. Democratic Farm Labor Party. Roman Catholic. Club: Kitchi Gammi (Duluth). Lodge: Kiwanis. Avocations: photography, fishing, cross-country skiing, travel. Home: 3500 E 3rd St Duluth MN 55804-1812

WHITEMAN, STEVEN, science adminstrator. V.p., gen. coun. EG&G Energy Measurements, Inc., North La Vegas. Office: EG&G Energy Measurements Inc 2621 Losee Rd North Las Vegas NV 89030*

WHITENER, WILLIAM GARNETT, dancer, choreographer; b. Seattle, Aug. 17, 1951; s. Warren G. and Virginia Louise (Garnett) W. Student, Cornish Sch. Allied Arts, Seattle, 1958-69. Dancer N.Y.C. Opera, 1969, Joffrey Ballet, N.Y.C., 1969-77, Twyla Tharp Dance, N.Y.C., 1978-87; asst. to choreographer Jerome Robbins for Robbins' Broadway, N.Y.C., 1988; artistic dir. Les Ballets Jazz de Montréal, 1991-93, Royal Winnipeg Ballet, 1993—; coord. dance dept. Concord Acad., Mass., 1988; vis. artist U. Wash., 1989-91; tchr. Harvard U. Summer Dance, 1989-90, NYU, 1985. Appeared in original Broadway cast Dancin', 1978; choreographer for Princeton Ballet, Joffrey II, John Curry Ice Theatre, Ballet Hispanico of N.Y., Boston Ballet Internat. Choreography Competition, Tommy Tune, Martine Van Hamel/ Kevin McKenzie, Ann Reinking, Seattle Repertory Theatre, Am. Ballroom Theater, N.Y.C., Hartford (Conn.) Ballet, On the Boards, (with Bill Irwin) Alive From Off Center (PBS-TV), (opera ensemble of N.Y.) A Little Night Music, Pacific Northwest Ballet, (Seattle Opera) Rusalka, Aida; dancer (films) Amadeus, Zelig, (TV shows) The Catherine Wheel, Dance in America; performer Garden of Earthly Delights, 1988. Mem. Actor's Equity, Am. Guild Mus. Artists. Home: 484 W 43rd St Apt 44D New York NY 10036-6327 Office: Royal Winnipeg Ballet, 380 Graham Ave, Winnipeg, MB Canada R3C 4K2*

WHITESELL, DALE EDWARD, retired association executive, natural resources consultant; b. Miamisburg, Ohio, Oct. 12, 1925; s. Harry Parker and Carmen Lucille (Holtzman) W.; m. Alma Irene Wells, Mar. 24, 1945; children: Catherine Elizabeth, Kimberly Lynn. B.S., Ohio State U., 1950, M.S. in Wildlife Mgmt., 1951. Game mgmt. supr. Ohio Div. Wildlife, Xenia, 1951-63, author farmer attitude survey, 1951-58; chief Ohio Div. Wildlife, Columbus, 1963-65; sr. exec. v.p. Ducks Unltd., Inc., Long Grove, Ill., 1965-87; ret. Ducks Unltd., Inc., 1987; bd. dirs. Safari Club Internat. Conservation Found., Tucson, 1982-83. Served as 2d lt. USAAF, 1943-46. Fellow Ohio State U., 1950; recipient Conservation award Gulf Oil Co., 1985. Mem. Ohio Wildlife Mgmt. Assn. (pres.), Internat. Assn. Fish, Game and Conservation Commrs. Office: Ducks Unltd Inc 1 Waterfowl Way Memphis TN 38120-2350 *Natural resource conservation means wise use—anything more or less will be manifested in additional zoos, museums, junk yards and the bone yards of fertilizer plants.*

WHITESELL, JOHN EDWIN, motion picture company executive; b. DuBois, Pa., Feb. 23, 1938; s. Guy Roosevelt and Grace Ethlyn (Brisbin) W.; m. Amy H. Jacobs, June 12, 1960; 1 child, Scott Howard; m. Martha Kathlyn Hall, Sept. 3, 1975; m. Phyllis Doyle, May 8, 1993. B.A., Pa. State U., 1962. Asst. mgr. non-theatrical div. Columbia Pictures Corp., N.Y.C., 1963-66; with Warner Bros., Inc., 1966—; nat. sales mgr. non-theatrical div. Warner Bros., Inc., Burbank, Calif., 1968-75; v.p. Warner Bros., Inc., 1975-76; v.p. internat. sales and adminstrn. Warner Bros. Internat. TV Distbn. 1976—; bd. dirs. Mastermedia Internat. Inc.; past bd. dirs. Found. Entertainment Programming in Higher Edu.; mem. self-study com. Nat. Entertainment Conf., 1974-75. Served with USNR, 1956-58. Mem. Nat. Audio-Visual Assn. (motion picture coun. 1973-76, exec. com. film coun. 1969-76, ednl. materials producers coun. 1976-82), Acad. TV Arts and Scis., Nat. Assn. Media Educators (adv. com. 1973-76). Home: 4414 Moorpark Way # 9 Toluca Lake CA 91602

WHITESIDE, CAROL GORDON, state official, former mayor; b. Chgo., Dec. 15, 1942; d. Paul George and Helen Louise (Barre) G.; m. John

Gregory Whiteside, Aug. 15, 1964; children: Brian Paul, Derek James. BA, U. Calif., Davis, 1964. Pers. mgr. Emporium Capwell Co., Santa Rosa, 1964-67; pers. asst. Levi Strauss & Co., San Francisco, 1967-69; project leader Interdatum, San Francisco, 1983-88; with City Coun. Modesto, 1983-87; mayor City of Modesto, 1987-91; asst. sec. for intergovtl. rels. The Resources Agy., State of Calif., Sacramento, 1991-93; dir. intergovtl. affairs Gov.'s Office, Sacramento, 1993—. Trustee Modesto City Schs., 1979-83; nat. pres. Rep. Mayors and Local Ofcls., 1990. Named Outstanding Woman of Yr. Women's Commn., Stanislaus County, Calif., 1988, Woman of Yr. 27th Assembly Dist., 1991. Republican. Lutheran. Office: Governor's Office 1400 10th St Sacramento CA 95814-5569

WHITESIDE, WILLIAM ANTHONY, JR., lawyer; b. Phila. Feb. 23, 1929; s. William Anthony and Ellen T. (Hensler) W.; m. Eileen Ann Ferrick, Feb. 27, 1954; children: William Anthony III, Michael P., Eileen A., Richard F., Christopher J., Mary P. BS Notre Dame U., 1951; LLB U. Pa., 1954. Bar: Pa. 1955. Assoc. Speiser, Satinsky, Gilliland & Packel, Phila., 1956-58, ptnr., 1958-61; ptnr. Fox, Rothschild, O'Brien & Frankel, Phila., 1961—. Served to 1st lt. USAF, 1954-56; chmn. bd. of trustees & chmn. exec. comm., Rochester Inst. Tech.; mem. pres. adv. coun. U. Notre Dame; bd. dirs. PAL, mem. exec. com.; emeritus trustee Germantown Acad (past pres.). Named Man of Yr., Notre Dame Club Phila., 1967. Mem. ABA, Pa. Bar Assn., Phila. Bar Assn., mem. Genesee Valley Club, Rochester, N.Y., Union League Club, Pyramid Club, Wissahickon Skating Club, Pa. Soc. (Phila.), Atlantic City (N.J.) Country Club. Republican. Roman Catholic. Home: 7808 Cobden Rd Laverock PA 19038 also: 901 Gardens Plz Ocean City NJ 08226-4719 Office: Fox Rothschild O'Brien 2000 Market St Fl 10 Philadelphia PA 19103-3231

WHITESIDES, GEORGE MCCLELLAND, chemistry educator; b. Louisville, Kty., Aug. 3, 1939; m. Barbara Breasted; children: George Thomas, Benjamin Haile. AB, Harvard U., 1960; PhD, Calif. Inst. Tech., 1964. Asst. prof. dept. chemistry MIT, Cambridge, 1963-69, assoc. prof., 1969-71, prof., 1971-75, Arthur C. Cope prof., 1975-80, Haslam and Dewey prof., 1980-82; prof. dept. chemistry Harvard U., Cambridge, 1982-86, Mallinckrodt prof., 1986—. Recipient Pure Chemistry award Am. Chem. Soc., 1975, Harrison Howe award Rochester sect., 1979, Remsen award, 1983, Arthur C. Cope Scholar award , 1989, James Flack Norris award, 1994, Disting. Alumni award Calif. Inst. Tech., 1980; Alfred P. Sloan fellow, 1968. Fellow AAAS; mem. NAS, Am. Acad. Arts and Scis. Office: Harvard U Dept of Chemistry 12 Oxford St Cambridge MA 02138-2902

WHITESIDES, THOMAS EDWARD, JR., orthopaedic surgeon; b. Gastonia, N.C., Nov. 4, 1929; s. Thomas Edward and Ferne (Bell) W.; m. Peggy Sue Patrick, Jan. 28, 1967; children: William Taylor, Lisa Elizabeth, Edward Patrick, John Thomas. BS, Emory U., 1952, MD, 1955. Diplomate Am. Bd. Orthopaedic Surgeons (dir. 1980-90, trustee 1991—). Resident in orthopaedics Barnes Hosp.-Washington U., St. Louis, 1957-60; asst. prof. surgery Emory U., 1962-66, assoc. prof. surgery, 1966-70, prof. orthopaedic surgery, 1970—, chmn. dept. orthopaedics, 1974-81; instr. orthopaedics Washington U., St. Louis, 1957-60; Alan DeForrest Smith lectr., Columbia U., N.Y.C., 1974, McCannoll lectr., Washington U., St. Louis,1978, Stein Meml. lectr., 1982, Phesant Meml. lectr., U. So. Calif.; vis. prof., Washington U., St. Louis, Harvard U., Iowa U., U. Pa., others. Author, editor: Evarts Surgery of Musculoskeletal System, 1984, Spine Section, 1984; contbr. numerous articles to profl. jours. Capt.,orthopedist MC, USAF, 1960-62. Recipient Kappa Delta rsch. award, Am. Acad. Orthopaedic Surgeons/ Orthopaedic Rsch. Soc., 1980. Mem. Am. Acad. Orthopaedic Surgeons; mem. Am. Orthopaedic Assn., Alpha Omega Alpha. Republican. Presbyterian. Avocations: cooking, photography. Home: 958 Calvert Ln NE Atlanta GA 30319-1202 Office: Emory Clinic Spine Ctr 1265 N Decatur Rd Decatur GA 30033

WHITE-THOMSON, IAN LEONARD, mining company executive; b. Halstead, Eng., May 3, 1936; came to U.S., 1969; s. Walter Norman and Leonore (Turney) W-T.; m. Barbara Montgomery, Nov. 24, 1971. B.A. with 1st class honors, New Coll., Oxford U., 1960, M.A., 1969. Mgmt. trainee Borax Consol. Ltd., London, 1960-61; asst. to sales mgr. Borax Consol. Ltd., 1961-64, asst. to sales dir., 1964; comml. dir. Hardman & Holden Ltd., Manchester, Eng., 1965-67; joint mng. dir. Hardman & Holden Ltd., 1967-69; v.p. mktg. dept. U.S. Borax Inc., Los Angeles, 1969-73; exec. v.p. mktg. U.S. Borax Inc., 1973-88, pres., 1988—, also dir.; group exec. Pa. Glass Sand Corp., Ottawa Silica Co., U.S. Silica Co., 1985-87; bd. dirs. Canpotex Ltd., chmn. bd., 1974-76; bd. dirs. KCET. Served with Brit. Army, 1954-56. Mem. Can. POtash Prodrs. Assn. (v.p. 1976-77, dir. 1972-77), Chem. Industry Coun. of Calif. (bd. dirs. 1982-85, chmn. 1984), Am. Mining Congress (bd. dirs. 1989), RTZ Borax and Minerals (bd. dirs. 1992, chief exec. 1995—), Oryx Energy Co. (bd. dirs. 1993), Calif. Club. Home: 851 Lyndon St South Pasadena CA 91030-3712

WHITFIELD, EDWARD, congressman; b. Hopkinsville, Ky., May 25, 1943; m. Constance Harriman. BS in Bus., U. Ky., 1965, JD, 1969. Mem. Ky. Ho. of Reps., 1973-74; owner, operator Rhodes Oil Co., 1973-82; counsel to pres. Seaboard Sys. Railroad (subs. CSX Corp.), 1979-82; v.p. state rels. CSX Corp., 1983-88, v.p. fed. railroad affairs, 1988-91; legal counsel to chmn. Interstate Commerce Commn., 1991-93; mem. 104th Congress from 1st Ky. dist., 1995—. 1st lt. USAR. Republican. Office: US Ho of Reps 1541 Longworth HOB Washington DC 20515

WHITFIELD, PRINCESS D., principal. Prin. Lemon G. Hine Jr. High Sch., Washington. Recipient Blue Ribbon award U.S. Dept. Edn., 1990-91. Office: Lemon G Hine Jr High Sch 8th And Pennsylvania Ave SE Washington DC 20003

WHITFIELD, RICHARD, publishing executive. Gen. mgr. Bonni Buy'rr Inc., Geneva, Ill. Office: Bonni Buy'rr Inc 2700 Keslinger Rd Geneva IL 60134*

WHITFORD, JOSEPH P., lawyer; b. N.Y.C., Apr. 30, 1950. BA, Union Coll., 1972; JD, Syracuse U., 1975; LLM in Taxation, George Washington U., 1978. Bar: N.Y. 1976, D.C. 1977, Wash. 1979. Staff atty. divsn. corp. fin. SEC, Washington, 1975-78; assoc. Foster, Pepper & Shefelman, Seattle, 1978-83, ptnr., 1983—; chmn. bd. dirs. MIT Forum on the Northwest, 1992-93. Office: Foster Pepper & Shefelman 1111 3rd Ave 34th Fl Seattle WA 98101

WHITHAM, GERALD BERESFORD, mathematics educator; b. Halifax, Eng., Dec. 13, 1927; came to U.S., 1956; s. Harry and Elizabeth (Howarth) W.; m. Nancy Lord, Sept. 1, 1951; children: Ruth H., Michael G., Susan C. BS, Manchester U., Eng., 1948, MS, 1949, PhD, 1953. Lectr. Manchester U., 1953-56; assoc. prof. NYU, 1956-59; prof. math. MIT, Cambridge, 1959-62; prof. aeros. and math. Calif. Inst. Tech., Pasadena, 1962-67, prof. applied math., 1967-83, Charles Lee Powell prof. applied math., 1983—. Author: Linear and Nonlinear Waves, 1974; also research papers on applied math. and fluid dynamics. Recipient Wiener prize in applied math., 1980. Fellow Royal Soc., Am. Acad. Arts and Scis. Home: 1689 E Altadena Dr Altadena CA 91001-1855 Office: Calif Inst Tech Applied Math 217-50 Pasadena CA 91125

WHITHAM, KENNETH, science and technology consultant; b. Chesterfield, Derbyshire, Eng., Nov. 6, 1927; emigrated to Can., 1948; s. Joseph and Evelyn (Murphy) W.; m. Joan Dorothy Glasspool, Nov., 1953; children—Melanie Judith, Katherine Hilary, Stephanie Frances. B.A. with honors, Cambridge U., Eng., 1948, M.A., 1952; M.A., Toronto U., 1949, Ph.D., 1951. Research scientist Dominion Observatory, Ottawa, Ont., 1951-59, 60-64; mem. UN Tech. Assistance Adminstrn., Nairobi, Kenya, 1959-60; dir. div. seismology and geothermal studies Earth Physics Br., Dept. Energy, Mines and Resources, Ottawa, 1964-73, dir. gen., 1973-80, asst. dep. minister conservation and non-petroleum energy, 1980-81, asst. dep. minister research and tech., 1981-87, chief sci. advisor, 1987; cons. in sci. and tech. Ottawa, 1987—. Contbr. articles to profl. jours. Recipient Outstanding Achievement award Public Service of Can., 1970. Fellow Royal Soc., Am. Acad. Arts and Scis. Home and Office: 1367 Morley Blvd, Ottawa, ON Canada K2C 1R4

WHITING, ALBERT NATHANIEL, former university chancellor; b. Jersey City, July 3, 1917; s. Hezekiah Oliver and Hildegarde Freida (Lyons) W.; m. Charlotte Luck, June 10, 1950; 1 dau., Brooke Elizabeth. A.B., Amherst Coll., 1938; student, Columbia, summer 1938, U. Pitts., 1938-39; M.A. in Sociology, Fisk U., 1941, L.H.D. (hon.), 1980; P.D. in Sociology, Am. U., 1952; LL.D., Amherst Coll., 1968, Western Mich. U., 1974, Duke, 1974, Kyung Hee U., Seoul, Korea; L.H.D., N.C. Central U., 1983. Research and teaching asst. Fisk U., 1939-41; instr. sociology, dir. rural community study Bennett Coll., Greensboro, N.C., 1941-43, 46-47; asst. prof. sociology Atlanta U., 1948-53; dean coll., prof. sociology Morris Brown Coll., Atlanta, 1953-57; asst. dean coll. Morgan State Coll., Balt., 1957-59; dean of college Morgan State Coll., 1960-67; pres. N.C. Central U., Durham, 1967-72; chancellor N.C. Central U., 1972-83; mem. bd. regents U. Md. System, 1988—; bd. dirs. Gen. Telephone of Southeast, Roses Stores, Inc. Contbr. articles profl. jours. Bd. dirs. Am. Council Edn., Ednl. Testing Service; bd. dirs., past pres. Assn. State Colls. and Univs.; v.p. Internat. Assn. Univ. Pres.; bd. dirs. Research Triangle Inst. N.C. Served to 1st lt. AUS, 1943-46. Episcopalian. Home: 11253B Slalom Ln Columbia MD 21044-2810

WHITING, ALLEN SUESS, political science educator, writer, consultant; b. Perth Amboy, N.J., Oct. 27, 1926; s. Leo Robert and Viola Allen (Suess) W.; m. Alice Marie Conroy, May 29, 1950; children: Deborah Jean, David Neal, Jeffrey Michael, Jennifer Hollister. B.A., Cornell U., 1948; M.A., Columbia U., 1950, cert. Russian Inst., 1950, Ph.D., 1952. Instr. polit. sci. Northwestern U., 1951-53; asst. prof. Mich. State U., East Lansing, 1955-57; social scientist The Rand Corp., Santa Monica, Calif., 1957-61; dir. Office Research and Analysis Far East U.S. Dept. State, Washington, 1961-66; dep. consul gen. Am. Consulate Gen., Hong Kong, 1966-68; prof. polit. sci. U. Mich., Ann Arbor, 1968-82; prof. U. Ariz., Tucson, 1982-93, Regents prof., 1993—, dir. Ctr. for East Asian Studies, 1982-93; cons. U.S. Dept. State, 1968-88; dir. Nat. Com. on U.S.-China Relations, N.Y.C., 1977-94; assoc. The China Council, 1978-88; pres. So. Ariz. China Coun., Tucson, 1983-95. Author: Soviet Policies in China: 1917-1924, 1954, China Crosses the Yalu, 1968, Chinese Calculus of Deterrence, 1975, Siberian Development and East Asia, 1981, China Eyes Japan, 1989, others; contbr. articles to profl. jours.; spl. commentator McNeill-Lehrer Program; CBS and NBC Spls. on China. Served with U.S. Army, 1945. Social Sci. Rsch. Coun. fellow, 1950, 74-75; Ford Found. fellow, 1953-55; Rockefeller Found. fellow, 1978; Woodrow Wilson Ctr. fellow, 1995—. Mem. Assn. Asian Studies. Home: 125 E Canyon View Dr Tucson AZ 85704-5901 Office: U Ariz Dept Polit Sci Tucson AZ 85721

WHITING, HENRY H., state supreme court justice. LLB, Univ. Va., 1949. Former judge 26th Jud. Cir. of Va.; justice Va. Supreme Ct., Richmond, 1987—. Office: Va Supreme Ct Judicial Ctr 5 N Kent St Winchester VA 22601-5037

WHITING, HUGH RICHARD, lawyer; b. East Chicago, Ind., Dec. 8, 1945; s. Harold C. and Nina (Hofstetter) W.; m. Sherry Ballast, July 2, 1965; 1 child, Kristin Anne. BA, U. Mich., 1967; JD, Ohio State U., 1974. Bar: Ohio 1974, Tex. 1981. Salesman, adminstr. Procter & Gamble, Cin., 1967-71; law clk. to Judge George Edwards U.S.C. Appeals (6th cir.) Ohio, Cin., 1974-75; assoc. Jones, Day, Reavis & Pogue, Cleve., 1975-81, ptnr., 1982—; chmn. Firmwide Profl. Svcs. Com.; mem. civil justice reform act adv. com. No. Dist. Ohio Adv. Com., Cleve., 1990—; mem. Ohio State U. Coll. Law Nat. Coun., Columbus, 1984—; speaker, presenter on legal practice and practice mgmt. various confs. and seminars. Co-chmn. Gen. Bus. Campaign Cleve. Orch., 1992. Mem. ABA (litigation sect., sect. bus. law), Tex. Bar Assn., Cleve. Bar Assn., Mayfield Country Club, Order of Coif. Avocations: golf, travel, reading. Office: Jones Day Reavis & Pogue 901 Lakeside Ave E Cleveland OH 44114-1190

WHITING, JOHN RANDOLPH, publisher, writer, editor; b. N.Y.C., Apr. 22, 1914; s. John Clapp and Elizabeth Margaret (Zittel) W.; m. Helen Louise Gamertsfelder, June 3, 1937; children: Wendy Helen Whiting Livingston, Merry Natalie Whiting Coleman, Robin Elizabeth Whiting Uhr. AB in Journalism, Ohio U., 1936. Reporter newspapers Ohio and N.Y. State, 1935-36; asso. editor Lit. Digest, 1936-37, True mag., 1937-38; free-lance writer for mags., 1938-40; mng. editor Click mag., 1940-41, Popular Photography mag., 1942-46; editor Sci. Illustrated mag., 1947-49; pub., editor Flower Grower mag., 1949-60; exec. v.p. Popular Sci. Pub. Co., 1961-66; pres. Communigraphics Coms., 1966-67; pub. Motor Boating and Sailing Mag., Hearst Mag. div., 1967-75, editor and pub. motor boating and sailing books, 1975-79; pub., editor Hearst Marine Books, 1979-81, cons. editor, 1981—; dir. Hastings Fed. Savs. & Loan Assn.; lectr. Colonial Williamsburg, univs., corps. and assns. on photo-journalism, illustrative photography. Author: Photography is a Language, 1946, You Can Sail, 1981, On Deck, 1985; editor and co-author books on photography, boating, picture books various subjects; contbr. to mags. on photography, scis. Trustee Community Hosp. Dobbs Ferry, N.Y. Recipient Editors' award Am. Seed Trade Assn., 1960. Mem. AAAS, Boating Writers Internat. (pres. 1973-79), Nat. Assn. Sci. Writers, Garden Writers Assn. (past pres.), Photog. Soc. Am., Phi Delta Theta, Sigma Delta Chi, Kappa Alpha Mu. Presbyterian. Clubs: N.Y. Yacht (N.Y.C.), Overseas Press (N.Y.C.); Cliffdwellers (Chgo.). Home: 44 Shady Ln Dobbs Ferry NY 10522-2019 *The computer, especially the word processor, is making "creativity" out of a technical tool—just as the camera did a century ago. The writer is freed from most of the dull copying work, just as the photographer was able to concentrate on seeing.*

WHITING, PAUL L., holding company executive; b. 1943. BA in Econs., Ill. Benedictine Coll.; grad. courses, U. Ill. With Am. Nat. Bank & Trust Co. of Chgo., 1967-72, Lawrence Sys., Inc. Tampa, Fla., 1972-74; v.p. planning and control Questor Corp., 1978-81, v.p. fin., 1981-82; v.p. treas. E & S Holdings Corp. (Spauding Co. & Evenflo Co. Divsns.), Tampa, Fla., 1982—. Office: E & S Holdings Corp PO Box 30101 Tampa FL 33630*

WHITING, RICHARD ALBERT, lawyer; b. Cambridge, Mass., Dec. 2, 1922; s. Albert S. and Jessie (Coleman) W.; m. Marvelene Nash, Feb. 22, 1948 (div. 1984); children—Richard A. Jr., Stephen C., Jeffrey D., Gary S., Kimberly G.; m. Joanne Sherry, Oct. 14, 1984. A.B., Dartmouth Coll., 1944; J.D., Yale U., 1949. Bar: D.C. 1949. Assoc. Steptoe & Johnson, Washington, 1949-55, ptnr., 1956-86, of counsel, 1987—; adj. prof. Vt. Law Sch., South Royalton, 1985-90; mem. exec. com. Yale Law Sch. Assn., New Haven, 1985-88; mem. adv. bd. The Antitrust Bull., N.Y.C., 1975—. Contbr. articles to profl. jours. Trustee Colby-Sawyer Coll., 1987—. Served to 1st lt. U.S. Army, 1945-46. Mem. ABA (council mem. Antitrust Law sect. 1977-85, del. to Ho. Dels. 1982-83, chmn. 1984-85). Presbyterian. Home: PO Box 749 Grantham NH 03753-0749 Office: 1330 Connecticut Ave NW Washington DC 20036-1704

WHITING, RICHARD BROOKE, retired investment banker; b. Cleve., June 28, 1947; s. Howard Langford and Mary Elizabeth (Livers) W.; m. Rosemarie Rykken, Dec. 20, 1965; children: Lisa, Paul, David, Matthew. BS, U. Minn., 1970. Asst. v.p. Security Pacific Bank, L.A., 1970-72; exec. v.p. Blyth Capital Markets Inc., Blyth Eastman Dillion & Co., N.Y.C., 1972-79; v.p., head trader City Bank N.Am., N.Y.C., 1979-82; v.p. Refco Arbitrage, N.Y.C., 1982-84; exec. v.p. Drexel Burnham, N.Y.C., 1984-86; 1st v.p., mgr. mortgage-backed securities E.F. Hutton, N.Y.C., 1986-88; v.p. mortgage-backed securities Donaldson Lufkin & Jenrette, N.Y.C., 1988-94; ret., 1994; pres. DLJ Mortgage Capital, DLJ Mortgage Capital Corp. Mem. Essex Hunt Club (Peapack, N.J.), Roxiticus Golf Club (Mendham, N.J.). Roman Catholic. Office: Donaldson Lufkin & Jenrette Securities Corp 140 Broadway New York NY 10005-1101

WHITINGTON, PETER FRANK, pediatrics educator, pediatric hepatologist; b. Memphis, May 8, 1947; s. Frank Everett and Mary Lena (Hollingsworth) W.; m. Susan Maurine Hoagland, June 6, 1967; children: Helen Frances, Mary Louise Whitington Mays, Katherine Daphne. BA in Econs., Tulane U., 1968; MD, U. Tenn., Memphis, 1971. Diplomate Am. Bd. Pediatrics, Am. Bd. Pediatric Gastroenterology. Resident in pediatrics, then chief resident U. Tenn. Ctr. for Health Scis., 1972-74, instr., 1975, asst. prof., 1978-81, assoc. prof., 1981-84, chief div. pediatric gastroenterology, 1984; rsch. fellow in gastroenterology Johns Hopkins Hosp., Balt., 1975-77; rsch. fellow in gastroenterology dept. pediatrics U. Wis., Madison, 1977-78; assoc. prof. dept. pediat. U. Chgo. Pritzker Sch. Medicine, 1984-87, assoc. prof. depts. pediat. and medicine, 1987-92, prof., 1992—; chief gastroenterology

LeBonheur Children's Med. Ctr., Memphis, 1978-84; numerous invited lectures and guest speaker at profl. meetings, workshops, symposia, hosps., confs.; vis. prof. Yale U., New Haven, 1993, U. Torino, Italy, 1994; mem. United Network for Organ Sharing pediatric transplantation com. Nat. Organ Procurement and Transplantation Network, 1992-94; reviewer numerous med. jours. including New Eng. Jour. Medicine, Gastroenterology, Hepatology, Jour. Pediat., Digestive Diseases and Scis., Pediatrics, Transplant. Mem. editl. bd. Jour. Pediatric Gastroenterology and Nutrition, 1991—, Liver Surgery and Transplantation, 1994—; sect. editor Birth Defects Compendium, 1987—; contbr. numerous articles and abstracts to med. jours. Mem. sci. adv. bd. Mid-South chpt. Nat. Found. for Ileitis and Colitis, Memphis, 1983-84; bd. dirs. Liver/Organ Transplant Fund, Memphis, 1983-84, Parents for Ctrl. H.S., Memphis, 1983-84; mem. med. adv. com. Chgo. Met. chpt. Am. Liver Found., 1985—, mem., med. adv. on bd. dirs., 1993—; med. dir. The Johnny Genna Found., Chgo., 1987—. Recipient Cmty. Svc. award NCCJ, Memphis, 1983; postdoctoral rsch. fellow NIH, 1977. Mem. Am. Assn. for Study Liver Diseases, Gastroenterology Rsch. Group, Am. Gastroent. Assn., Soc. for Pediatric Rsch., N.Am. Soc. for Pediatric Gastroenterology and Nutrition, Internat. Gastro-Surg. Club, Chgo. Pediatric Soc. Avocations: making fine furniture, fly fishing. Home: Apt 8 North 5490 South Shore Dr Chicago IL 60615 Office: U Chgo Wyler Children's Hosp 5841 S Maryland Ave MC 4065 Chicago IL 60637-1470

WHITIS, GRACE RUTH, nursing educator; b. San Antonio, Sept. 14, 1942; d. Allan and Jewel (Conlee) Richardson; m. Robert E. Whitis, Mar. 6, 1965; children: Jay, Jennifer. PhD, U. Tex., 1981; BS, U. Mary Hardin - Baylor, 1968; MS, Baylor U., 1970; MS in Nursing, U. Tex., 1972. Staff nurse Providence Hosp., Waco, Tex., 1965-67; prof., asst., dean U. Mary Hardin-Baylor, Belton, Tex., 1970-83; vis. prof. La. Tech. U., Ruston, La., 1982-84; prof. nursing Ark. State U., Jonesboro, Ark., 1985—. Contbr. articles to profl. jours. Mem. ANA, Nat. League for Nursing, Ark. State Nurses Assn., Sigma Theta Tau, Alpha Chi. Home: 2403 Paula Dr Jonesboro AR 72401-8015 Office: Ark State U PO Box 69 State University AR 72467-0069

WHITKO, JEAN PHILLIPS, academic administrator; b. Dover, Del., Oct. 31, 1940; d. Albert Leroy and Helen (Busch) Phillips; m. Donald A. Whitko, July 1, 1972; children: Lenore Ann, Wayne P., Donna J., Sheri L. BS, U. Del., 1962; MEd, Pa. State U., 1968, postgrad., 1968-72. Cert. tchr., Del., Pa. Tchr. Newcastle (Del.) Sch. Dist., 1962-68; rsch. asst. Pa. State U., University Park, 1969, instr. edn., grad. asst., 1969-72; substitute tchr. Jerusalem Lutheran Nursery Sch. and Day Care, Schwenksville, Pa., 1983-85; supr. student teaching Pa. State U., 1988—; evaluator fed. title I and III projects Pa. Dept. Edn., Harrisburg, 1970-72. Officer Women's Civ. Club Schwenksville, 1972—; vol. tchr. Perkiomen Valley Schs., Schwenksville, 1976-86; bd. dirs. Jerusalem Lutheran Nursery Sch. and Day Care, 1983-85. Named Friend of Edn., Perkiomen Valley Edn. Assn., 1983; recipient Commendation from Gov. Richard Thornburg, 1985. Mem. ASCD, Pa. Assn. Colls. and Tchr. Educators. Avocations: reading, photography. Home: 623 Main St Schwenksville PA 19473 Office: Pa State Univ 172 Chambers Bldg University Park PA 16802

WHITLEY, ARTHUR FRANCIS, retired international consulting company executive, engineer, lawyer; b. Bklyn., Apr. 14, 1927; s. John Boyd and Ellen (Walls) W.; m. Isabella Mary Passidomo, Apr. 9, 1950; children: Brent John, Scott Michael, Todd Joseph. B.E.E., Poly. Inst. N.Y., 1951; J.D., Seton Hall U., 1955; LL.M., Bklyn. Law Sch., 1958. Bar: N.J. 1960, U.S. Customs Ct. 1967, U.S. Patent Office 1972. Sales engr., atty. Pub. Service E&G, Newark, 1951-60; mgmt. cons. Nelson Walker Assocs., N.Y.C., 1961; atty. assoc. gen. counsel Engelhard Industries, Newark, 1962-75; v.p., group v.p. Engelhard Industries, Iselin, N.J., 1976-80, sr. v.p., 1981, exec. v.p., 1982-83; pres. Bro-Whit Assocs. Inc., 1983-89. Pres. World Trade Assn. N.J., 1965. Served with USN, 1945-46. Republican. Roman Catholic. Home: 24 Puddingstone Way Florham Park NJ 07932-2625

WHITLEY, DOUGLAS L., telecommunications industry executive. With Ill. Bell Telephone Co., 1993—, pres., chief exec. officer, 1993—; dir. Ill. Dept. Revenue. Office: Ill Bell Tel Co 225 W Randolph St Chicago IL 60606*

WHITLEY, JOE DALLY, lawyer; b. Atlanta, Nov. 12, 1950; s. Thomas Youngie and Mary Jo (Dally) W.; m. Kathleen Pinion, Sept. 27, 1975; children: Lauren Jacqueline, Thomas McMillan. BA, U. Ga., 1972, JD, 1975. Bar: Ga. 1975, U.S. Supreme Ct. 1989. Assoc. Kelly, Denney, Pease & Allison, Columbus, Ga., 1975-78; asst. dist. atty. Chattahoochee Jud. Cir., Columbus, 1978-79; assoc. Hirsch, Beil & Partin, P.C., Columbus, 1979-81; U.S. atty. Dept. Justice, Macon, Ga., 1981-87; dep. asst. atty. gen., Criminal Div. Dept. Justice, Washington, 1987-88, dep. assoc. atty. gen., 1988-89, acting assoc. atty. gen., 1989; ptnr. Smith, Gambrell & Russell, Atlanta, 1989-90; U.S. atty. Dept. of Justice, Atlanta, 1990-93; ptnr. Kilpatrick & Cody, Atlanta, 1993—; mem. atty. gen.'s adv. com. Dept. Justice, Washington, 1982-85; chmn. organized crime and violent crime subcom. Atty. Gen.'s Adv. Com., 1990-93, mem. investigative subcom., 1990-93, chmn. white collar crime subcom., 1993. Treas. Muscogee County Young Reps., Columbus, 1979-80. Mem. Ga. Bar Assn., Macon Bar Assn., Young Lawyers Club (pres. Columbus chpt. 1980-81), Lawyers Club of Atlanta. Republican. Presbyterian. Office: Kilpatrick & Cody Ste 2800 1100 Peachtree St Atlanta GA 30309-4530

WHITLEY, MICHAEL R., utilities executive; b. 1943. BA, Campbellsville Coll., 1963. Various positions Ky. Utilities Co., Lexington, Ky., 1964-78, corp. sec.; 1978-87, sr. v.p., 1987—. Office: Ky Utilities Co 1 Quality St Lexington KY 40507-1428

WHITLEY, NANCY O'NEIL, retired radiology educator; b. Winston-Salem, N.C., Feb. 21, 1932; d. Norris Lawrence and Thelma Mae (Hardy) O'Neil; m. J.E. Whitley, Dec. 20, 1958; children—John O'Neil, Catherine Anne. Student, Duke U., 1950-53; M.D., Bowman Gray Sch. Medicine, 1957. Fellow in cardiology Bowman Gray Sch. Medicine, Winston-Salem, 1958-60; intern Jefferson Davis Hosp., Houston, 1957-58; resident in radiology Bowman Gray Sch. Medicine, 1966-69, instr., 1969-70, asst. prof., 1970-74, assoc. prof., 1974-78; prof. radiology U. Md. Sch. Medicine, Balt., 1978-92; prof. oncology U. Md. Cancer Ctr., Balt., 1988-92; prof. radiology Med. U. S.C., Charleston, 1992-94; ret., 1994. Author: (with J.E. Whitley) Angiography, Techniques and Procedures, 1971.

WHITLEY, RALPH C., diversified financial services company executive; b. 1943. Grad., U. Calif., L.A., 1968. With Photo Reproductions, Inc., L.A., 1969-72; with CCH Computax, Inc., Torrance, Calif., 1972—, pres. Office: CCH Computax Inc 21250 Hawthorne Blvd Torrance CA 90503-6604*

WHITLOCK, BENNETT CLARKE, JR., retired association executive; b. Charleston, S.C., June 10, 1927; s. Bennett C. and Isabel Price (Beckman) W.; m. Elizabeth Darley Marshall, July 18, 1959; children: Mary Elizabeth, Bennett C. III. A.B., Presbyn. Coll., 1946; LL.B., U. S.C., 1949. With Am. Trucking Assns., Inc., Washington, 1949-89, asst. to mng. dir., 1961-70, asst. to pres., 1970-73, v.p., 1973-75, exec. v.p., chief oper. officer, 1975-76, pres., 1976-84, spl. adviser, pres., 1984-89; ret., 1989. Bd. dirs Braddock Road Boys Club; bd. visitors Mary Washington Coll., 1985-93, vice rector, 1986-88, rector 1990-92. Mem. Hwy. Users Fedn. for Safety and Mobility (dir.) Country Club of Fairfax, Kiawah Island Club, Blue Key, Pi Kappa Alpha. Episcopalian.

WHITLOCK, CHARLES PRESTON, former university dean; b. Highland Park, N.J., June 19, 1919; s. Frank Boudinot and Rosena Craig (Foster) W.; m. Patricia Hamilton Hoey, Mar. 10, 1960; children: Carol Foster, Adam Hoey, Susan Boudinot, Matthew Fitzsimmons, Beth Brewer. BA, Rutgers U., 1941; MA, Harvard U., 1947. Asso. dir. Bur. Study Counsel Harvard U., 1944-52, Allston Burr sr. tutor, 1952-58, lectr. social psychology, 1955-72, asst. to pres., 1958-70, assoc. dean of coll., 1970-72, dean of coll., 1972-76, assoc. dean faculty, 1976-82, master Dudley House, 1976-82; Dir. Cambridgeport Savs. Bank.; Mem. Mass. Higher Edn. Facilities Commn. Co-author: Harvard University Reading Films. Trustee Charity of Edward Hopkins, Lesley Coll.; bd. corporators New Eng. Deaconess Hosp. Col. USAF. Decorated Silver Star, D.F.C., Air medal. Home: 9 Barberry

Heights Rd Gloucester MA 01930-1201 Office: Harvard U Cambridge MA 02138

WHITLOCK, DAVID C., retired military officer; b. Little Rock, Ark., Jan. 24, 1935; m. Rosemarie Binik (dec.); children: D. Patrick, David D. B Bus., U. Nebr., 1962; grad., Squadron Officer Sch., 1965; MA Speech and Drama, U. Colo., 1966, PhD Communication, 1970; grad., Air Command and Staff Coll., 1978, Air War Coll., 1983. With USAF, 1952-62, tech. sgt., 1962; audiovisual tng. officer, 2d Lt., 1st lt. Hdqs. N. Am. Air Defense Command USAF, Colo., 1962-67; from English, speech intr., asst., dir. forensics, capt. to prof., major USAF Acad., 1967-74, prof. English, Speech, dir. Forensics, lt. col., 1979, pres. Tenure Coun., 1981-82; dir. Disting. Visitors Bureau Hdqs. USAF, Ramstein AFB, Germany, 1982-84; assoc. dean Civilian Inst. programs, col. AF Inst. Tech., Ohio, 1984-86; base comdr. 26th Combat Support Group Zweibrucken AFB, Germany, 1986-88; dean Civilian Inst. Programs Wright Patterson AFB, Ohio, 1989, commandant emeritus AF Inst. Tech. Air U., 1992-93. Recipient Legion of Merit, Meritorious Svc. medal with four oak leaf clusters, Air Force Commendation medal with two oak leaf clusters. Achievements include qualified parachutist. Home: 441 Green Vista Dr Enon OH 45323 Office: Air Force Institute of Tech Dayton OH 45433

WHITLOCK, JOHN JOSEPH, museum director; b. South Bend, Ind., Jan. 7, 1935; s. Joseph Mark and Helen Marcella (Cramer) W.; m. Sue Ann Kirkman, June 10, 1956; children—Kelly Ann, Michele Lynn, Mark. BS in Art, Ball State U., 1957, MA in Art, 1963; EdD, Ind. U., 1971. Tchr. art Union City (Ind.) Pub. Schs., 1957-59; tchr. art, art dir. Madison (Ind.) City Schs., 1959-64; prof. art, dir. gallery Hanover (Ind.) Coll., 1964-69; dir. Burpee Art Mus., Rockford, Ill., 1970-72; prof. arts and humanities Elgin (Ill.) Community Coll., 1970-72; dir. Brooks Meml. Art Gallery, Memphis, 1972-78; prof. mus. studies Southwestern Coll., Memphis, 1973-78; adj. asst. prof. art and museology Memphis State U., 1976-78; dir. Univ. Mus., mem. grad. faculty So. Ill. U., Carbondale, 1978—, also dir. mus. studies, adj. assoc. prof. anthropology, 1978—, adj. assoc. prof. polit. sci., 1988—, adj. assoc. prof. history, 1994—. dir. mus. studies, 1989—, mem. ROTC acad. avc. coun., 1988—, mem. president's coun., 1988-93, adj. assoc. prof. art Univ. Mus., 1978-88; chmn. bd. Nat. Coal Mus.; mem. Newsfront adv. bd. NC Broadcast News, Washington; sr. cons. Marine Mil. Acad. Mus., 1988—, mem. bd. advisors, 1991—. Mem. Rockford Human Rels. Commn., 1971-72; mem. president's coun. Southwestern Coll., 1973-78. Mem. Am. Assn. Mus., Internat. Coun. Mus., Midwest Assn. Mus., Assn. Art Mus. Dirs., Marine Corps League (commandant Shawnee detachment 1994—, comdr. USCG Aux, 1994—). Office: So Ill U Univ Mus Carbondale IL 62901

WHITLOCK, JOHN L., lawyer; b. New Orleans, Oct. 24, 1946; s. John Bert and Virginia Katherine (Marzolf) W.; m. Dorothy Florence Oeste, Sept. 13, 1969; children: Sarah Katherine, Thomas John. AB, Harvard U., 1968, JD, 1973. Bar: Mass. 1973, U.S. Dist. Ct. Mass. 1974, U.S. Ct. Appeals (1st cir.) 1975. Assoc. Herrick & Smith, Boston, 1973-80, ptnr., 1981-86; ptnr. Palmer & Dodge, Boston, 1986—. Bd. dirs., sec. Harvard-Radcliffe Collegiate Mus. Found., Inc., 1978—; treas. The Cecilia Soc., 1974-85, bd. dirs., 1974-86, 94—, pres., 1994—. With U.S. Army, 1968-70. Lutheran. Avocation: singing. Office: Palmer & Dodge 1 Beacon St Boston MA 02108

WHITLOCK, LUDER GRADICK, JR., seminary president; b. Jacksonville, Fla., June 20, 1940; s. Luder G. and Juanita O. (Nessmith) W.; m. Mary Louise Patton, Aug. 29, 1959; children: Frank Christopher, Alissa Ann, Beth LaVerne. BA, U. Fla., 1962; MDiv, Westminster Theol. Sem., 1966; D of Ministry, Vanderbilt U., 1973. Ordained to ministry Presbyn. Ch. in Am., 1966. Pastor Sharon Presbyn. Ch., Hialeah, Fla., 1966-69, West Hills Presbyn. Ch., Harriman, Tenn., 1969-75; prof. Reformed Theol. Sem., Jackson, Miss., 1975—, acting pres., 1978-79, pres., 1979—; bd. dirs Ligonier Ministries, Orlando, Fla. Editorial adv. bd. Leadership, Wheaton, 1992—. Trustee Westminster Theol. Sem., Phila., 1973-76, Covenant Coll., Chattanooga, 1973-80; bd. dirs. Internat. Grad. Sch. Theology, Seoul, Republic of Korea, 1987—; dir. Greater Orlando Leadership Found., 1989-92, Found. for Reformation, Orlando, Fla., 1994—, Key Life, 1995—. World Evangelical Fellowship N.Am. Region, Wheaton, Ill., 1992—, Internat. Christian Leadership Univ., Campus Crusade for Christ, exec. com., 1992—, Internat. Reformed Fellowship, co-pres., 1993—. Mem. Evang. Theol. Soc., Nat. Assn. Evangs. (bd. adminstrn. 1992—, dir. 1995, chmn. theology com. 1994—, nat. commn. higher edn. 1995—), Assn. Theol. Schs. (nominating com., exec. com. 1994—), Fellowship of Evang. Sem. Pres. (chmn. 1990-93, 94—), Citrus Club. Republican. Office: Reformed Theol Sem 1015 Maitland Center Common Bl Maitland FL 32751-7130

WHITLOCK, WILLIAM ABEL, lawyer; b. Faribault, Minn., Feb. 6, 1929; s. William Abel and Alice Eleanor (Bartel) W.; m. Shirley Rae Ohlausen; children: Anne, William, Justin, Jane, Thomas. BSL, U. Minn., 1951, LLB, 1953. Law clk. to justice Minn. Supreme Ct., St. Paul, 1952-53; law clk. to presiding justice U.S. Dist. Ct. Minn., 1953-54; assoc. Dorsey & Whitney, Mpls., 1957-62, ptnr., 1962-95, of counsel, 1995—. Served to capt. USAR, 1954-57. Mem. Order of the Coif. Office: Dorsey & Whitney 2200 Pillsbury Center S Minneapolis MN 55402

WHITMAN, BRADFORD F., lawyer; b. N.Y.C., 1945. AB, Harvard U., 1966; JD, U. Pa., 1969. Bar: N.Y. 1969, D.C. 1974, Pa. 1979. Atty., asst. chief pollution control sect. U.S. Dept. Justice, 1971-79; ptnr. Reed Smith Shaw & McClay, Phila. Mem. Phila. Bar Assn. (former chair environ. law com.). Office: Reed Smith Shaw & McClay 2500 One Liberty Pl Philadelphia PA 19103

WHITMAN, BRUCE NAIRN, flight safety executive; b. N.Y.C., Aug. 4, 1933; s. Stewart Lane and Josephine (McQueen) W.; m. Sarah Beach; children—Bruce Jr., Stewart, John. BA, Trinity Coll., 1955; postgrad., George Washington U., 1958-60. Sr. exec. asst. Nat. Bus. Aircraft Assn., Washington, 1958-60; exec. v.p. FlightSafety Internat., Flushing, N.Y., 1961—, also bd. dirs.; bd. dirs. PowerSafety Internat., MarineSafety, FlightSafety Svcs. Corp.; pres., chmn. Belle Haven Land Assn. Bd. gov. Flight Safety Found. Capt. USAF, 1955-58. Mem. Nat. Bus. Aircraft Assn. (assoc. coun., bd. dirs.), The Belle Haven Club (bd. dirs., sec. 1981-83, treas. 1984, vice commodore 1985, commodore 1986), Sailfish Point Yacht Club (bd. dirs.). Home: 54 Harbor Dr Greenwich CT 06830-7018 Office: Flight Safety Internat Marine Air Terminal La Guardia Airport New York NY 11371

WHITMAN, CHRISTINA BROOKS, law educator; b. 1947. BA, U. Mich., 1968, MA, 1970, JD, 1974. Law clk. to judge Harold Leventhal U.S. Ct. Appeals, Washington, 1974-75; law clk. to justice Powell U.S. Supreme Ct., Washington, 1975-76; asst. prof. U. Mich., Ann Arbor, 1976-79, assoc. prof., 1979-82, prof., 1982—. Office: U Mich Law Sch 625 S State St Ann Arbor MI 48109-1215

WHITMAN, CHRISTINE TODD, governor. Former freeholder Somerset County, N.J.; former pres. State Bd. Pub. Utilities; host radio talk show Sta. WKXW, Trenton, N.J.; gov. State of N.J., 1994—; chmn. Com. for an Affordable N.J. Columnist newspapers. Rep. candidate for senator State of N.J., 1990. Office: State House Office of Governor Trenton NJ 08625*

WHITMAN, DALE ALAN, lawyer, university professor; b. Charleston, W.Va., Feb. 18, 1939; m. Marjorie Miller; 8 children. Student, Ohio State U., 1956-59; BES, Brigham Young U., 1963; LLB, Duke U., 1966. Bar: Calif. 1967, Utah 1974. Assoc. O'Melveny & Myers, Los Angeles, 1966-67; asst. prof., then assoc. prof. Sch. Law, U. N.C., Chapel Hill, 1967-70; vis. prof. law N.C. Cen. U., Durham, 1968, 69; vis. assoc. prof. law UCLA, 1970-71; dep. dir. Office Housing and Urban Development, Fed. Home Loan Bank Bd., Washington, 1971-72; sr. program analyst FHA, HUD, Washington, 1972-73; prof. law Brigham Young U., 1973-78, 92—; vis. prof. law U. Tulsa, 1976, U. Mo., Columbia, 1976; prof. law, assoc. dean U. Wash., Seattle, 1978-82; prof., dean U. Mo. Sch. Law, Columbia, 1982-88, prof., 1988-91; cons., lectr. in field. Co-author: Cases and Materials on Real Estate Finance and Development, 1976, Real Estate Finance Law, 1979, 3d edit., 1994, Cases and Materials on Real Estate Transfer, Finance and Development, 1981, 3d edit., 1992, Land Transactions and Finance, 1983, The Law of Property, 1984, 2d edit., 1993, Basic Property Law, 1989; contbr. articles to

profl. jours. Fellow Am. Bar Found.; mem. Am. Law Inst., Am. Coll. Real Estate Lawyers. Home: 480 E 450 S Orem UT 84058 Office: BYU Law Sch Provo UT 84602

WHITMAN, GERALD JOHN, diplomat; b. N.Y.C., Nov. 26, 1943; s. John and Anne Joan (Serkes) W.; m. Stella Lin Whitman; children: Michael John, David Gerald. BS in Engring., Calif. State U., 1967. Consular officer U.S. Embassy, Bogota, 1973-75; consular officer U.S. Embassy, Buenos Aires, 1975-77, sci. counselor, 1983-85; sci. counselor U.S. Embassy, Rome, 1985-89; dep. chief mission U.S. Embassy, Montevideo, Uruguay, 1991—; fgn. affairs analyst Current Intelligence Staff, Washington, 1977-79; desk officer Office So. Cone Aff., Washington, 1979-81; prin. officer U.S. Consulate, Barranquilla, Columbia, 1981-83; dir. Office Advanced Tech., Washington, 1989-91. Lt. USN, 1967-70. Mem. Am. Fgn. Svc. Assn. Avocations: bicycling, computers, chess. Office: US Embassy Montevideo APO AA 34035 Office: US Embassy, Lauro Muller 1776, Montevideo Uruguay

WHITMAN, HOMER WILLIAM, JR., investment counseling company executive; b. Sarasota, Fla., Jan. 8, 1932; s. Homer William and Phoebe (Corr) W.; m. Anne Virginia Sarran, May 8, 1954; children: Burke William, Michael Wayne. BA in Econs. optime merens, U. South, 1953; grad., U.S. Naval Officer Candidate Sch., 1953; postgrad., Emory U., 1969. Served to group v.p. 1st Nat. Bank Atlanta, 1956-72; pres., dir. Palmer 1st Nat. Bank & Trust Co., Sarasota, 1973-74, Hamilton Bank & Trust Co., Atlanta, 1974-76; v.p. Lionel D. Edie & Co., Atlanta, 1976-78, Mfrs. Hanover Trust Co., Atlanta, 1978-85; sr. v.p. Montag & Caldwell, Inc., Atlanta, 1985—. Dir. Asolo State Theatre. Trustee Selby Found., 1973-74, West Paces Ferry Hosp., Ringling Sch. Art, St. Stephens's Sch.; bd. vis. Emory U.; mem. Leadership Atlanta. Lt. j.g. USNR, 1953-56. Named Hon. French Consul, Atlanta, Atlanta's Outstanding Young Man of Yr., 1963. Mem. Govt. Fin. Officers Assn., Fla. Govt. Fin. Officers Assn., Ga. Govt. Fin. Officers Assn., Assn. Investment Mgmt. Sales Execs., Atlanta Soc. Fin. Analysts, Health-care Fin. Mgmt. Assn., Fla. Pub. Pension Trustees Assn., Assn. Pvt. Pension and Welfare Plans (regl. chmn.), Am. Cancer Soc. (dir. Atlanta city unit), Newcomer Soc., 300 Club, Atlanta C. of C. (life mem.), Piedmont Driving Club, Peachtree Golf Club, Commerce Club, Buckhead Club (bd. govs.), Breakfast Club, Sarasota U. Club (bd. dirs.), Rotary. Episcopalian. Home: 77 E Andrews Dr NW Apt 353 Atlanta GA 30305-1344 Office: Montag & Caldwell Inc 1100 Atlanta Fin Ctr 3343 Peachtree Rd NE Atlanta GA 30326-1450

WHITMAN, KENNETH JAY, advertising executive; b. N.Y.C., May 4, 1947; s. Howard Jay and Suzanne Marcia (Desberg) W.; m. Susan M. Hall, Feb. 8, 1995. Student, Berklee Sch. Mus., 1965-66, Hubbard Acad., 1968-70. Nat. dep. dir. Pub. Relations Bur., Los Angeles, 1970-75; pres. Creative Cons., Los Angeles, 1975-82; pres., creative dir. Whitman & Green Advt., Toluca Lake, Calif., 1982-86, Whitman-Olson, Toluca Lake, 1986-92; v.p. mktg. Maxa Corp., 1992-93; creative dir. Whitman-Hall, L.A., 1993—. Co-author: Strategic Advertising, 1986; editor Freedom news jour., 1971-79; contbr. newspaper column Shape of Things, 1971-79. Pres. Los Angeles Citizens Comm. Human Rights, 1971-75. Recipient Cert. of Design Excellence Print Regional Design Ann., 1985, 87, Award of Excellence Consolidated Papers, 1985, Award of Excellence Print Mag., 1985, 87, 1st place award Sunny Creative Radio, 2 Telly awards, 1988, Belding award Advt. Club Los Angeles, Excellence award Bus. and Profl. Advt. Assn., 1987, Internat. Gold Medallion award Broadcast Promotion and Mktg. Execs. Mem. Art Dirs. Club of Los Angeles, VSC (pres. 1964-65), CEOs Circle. Avocations: underwater photography, music composition and recording, painting, interior design. Office: Whitman-Hall 2200 Brier Ave Dr Los Angeles CA 90039

WHITMAN, MARINA VON NEUMANN, economist; b. N.Y.C., Mar. 6, 1935; d. John and Mariette (Kovesi) von Neumann; m. Robert Freeman Whitman, June 23, 1956; children: Malcolm Russell, Laura Mariette. BA summa cum laude, Radcliffe Coll., 1956; MA, Columbia U., 1959, PhD, 1962; LHD (hon.), Russell Sage Coll., 1972, U. Mass., 1975, N.Y. Poly Inst., 1975, Baruch Coll., 1980; LLD (hon.), Cedar Crest Coll., 1973, Hobart and William Smith Coll., 1973, Coe Coll., 1975, Marietta Coll., 1976, Rollins Coll., 1976, Wilson Coll., 1977, Allegheny Coll., 1977, Amherst Coll., 1978, Ripon Coll., 1980, Mt. Holyoke Coll., 1980; LittD (hon.), Williams Coll., 1980, Lehigh U., 1981, Denison U., 1983, Claremont U., 1984, Notre Dame U., 1984, Eastern Mich. U., 1992. Mem. faculty U. Pitts., 1962-79, prof. econs., 1971-73, disting. pub. svc. prof. econs., 1973-79; mem. chief economist Gen. Motors Corp., N.Y.C., 1979-85, group exec. v.p. pub. affairs, 1985-92; disting. vis. prof. bus. adminstrn. & pub. policy U. Mich., Ann Arbor, 1992-94, prof. bus. adminstrn. and pub. policy, 1994—; mem. U.S. Price Commn., 1971-72, Coun. Econ. Advisers, Exec. Office of Pres., 1972-73; bd. dirs. Chemical Banking Corp., ALCOA, Procter & Gamble Co., Browning-Ferris Industries, UNOCAL, Inst. Internat. Econs.; mem. Trilateral Commn.; mem. Pres. Adv. Com. on Trade Policy and Negotiations, 1987-93; mem. tech. assessment adv. coun. U.S. Congress Office of Tech. Assessment, 1990—, Dept. Treasury, from 1977; mem. Consultative Group on Internat. Econs. and Monetary Affairs, from 1979; trustee Nat. Bur. Econ. Rsch., 1993—. Bd. dirs. Inst. for Internat. Econs, 1986, Eurasia Found, 1992—; bd. overseers Harvard U., 1972-78, mem. vis. com. Kennedy Sch., 1992—; trustee Princeton U., 1980-90. Fellow Earhart Found., 1959-60, AAUW, 1960-61, NSF, 1968-70, also Social Security Rsch. Coun.; recipient Columbia medal for excellence, 1973; George Washington award Am. Hungarian Found., 1975. Mem. Am. Econ. Assn. (exec. com. 1977-80), Am. Acad. Arts & Scis., Coun. Fgn. Rels. (dir. 1977-87), Phi Beta Kappa. Author: Government Risk-Sharing in Foreign Investment, 1965; International and Interregional Payments Adjustment, 1967; Economic Goals and Policy Instruments, 1970; Reflections of Interdependence: Issues for Economic Theory and U.S. Policy, 1979; also articles; bd. editors Am. Econ. Rev., 1974-77; mem. editorial bd. Fgn. Policy. Office: U Mich Sch Pub Policy 411 Lorch Hall Ann Arbor MI 48109-1220

WHITMAN, NANCY IRENE, nursing educator; b. Hornell, N.Y., Nov. 27, 1947; d. Jack Almy and Miriam Sue (Brook) W.; m. Robert Earl Campbell, Dec. 24, 1988. BSN, Alfred U., 1969; MSN, U. Va., Charlottesville, 1978; PhD, U. Tex., 1988. Staff nurse adult medicine Tufts New Eng. Med. Ctr., Boston, 1969-70; staff nurse pediatrics N. Shore Children's Hosp., Salem, Mass., 1970-71, Tufts New Eng. Med. Ctr., Boston, 1971-72; staff nurse rsch. unit Children's Med. Ctr., Boston, 1972-73; asst. instr. Mass. Gen. Hosp. Sch. Nursing, Boston, 1973-74; instr. nursing U. Va., Charlottesville, 1978-81; asst. prof. nursing U. Va., 1981-91; assoc. prof., chmn. dept. Lynchburg (Va.) Coll., 1991—. Co-author: Teaching in Nursing Practice, 1988, 2d edit., 1992, Computers in Small Bytes, 1992; contbr. articles to profl. jours. Recipient New Investigator award Soc. for Rsch. in Nursing Edn., Nat. League for Nursing, 1989; HBO and Co. Nurse scholar, 1990. Mem. ANA, Va. Nurses Assn. (1st v.p. 1988-90), Nat. League Nursing, Assn. for Care Children's Health, Sigma Theta Tau (counselor 1988-90, Nancy Ballard award 1987), Phi Kappa Phi. Home: RR 1 Box 355H Covesville VA 22931-9732 Office: Lynchburg Coll Lynchburg VA 24501

WHITMAN, REGINALD NORMAN, railroad official; b. Jasmin, Sask. Can., Oct. 15, 1909; s. Norman L. and Irene (Haverlock) W.; m. Opal Vales, Jan. 31, 1932; children: James, Richard, Donna (Mrs. Larry Ekland). Grad., St. Joseph Coll., Yorkton, Sask., 1928, Advanced Mgmt. Program, Harvard, 1958. With Great No. Ry., 1929-69; gen. mgr. Alaska R.R. Dept. Interior, 1955-56; fed. r.r. adminstr. Dept. Transp., 1969-70; chmn. bd., chief exec. officer M.-K.-T. R.R., 1970-88; Mem. Alaska North Commn., 1967-69. With AUS, 1943-44. Mem. Nat. Def. Transp. Assn., Am. Legion. Republican. Roman Catholic. Home: 7408 Glen Albens Cir Dallas TX 75225-1810

WHITMAN, ROBERT, lawyer, educator; b. N.Y.C., May 18, 1936; m. Edith Cybul, June 25, 1961; children—Mara, Miles. B.B.A., CCNY, 1956; J.D., Columbia U., 1959; LL.M., NYU, 1970. Bar: N.Y. 1959, Conn. 1966. Assoc. in law Columbia U., N.Y.C., 1959-60; asst. prof. law U. Md., 1960-62; assoc. firm Cravath, Swaine and Moore, N.Y.C., 1962-64, Tenzer, Greenblatt, Fallon & Kaplan, N.Y.C., 1964-66; assoc. prof. U. Conn., West Hartford, 1966-69, prof., 1969—, dir. Grad. Group and continuing edn. estate planning courses; also cons. Cadwalader, Wickersham & Taft; vis. prof. Yale U., U. So. Calif., Brunel U., Uxbridge, Eng., other instns.; spl. adv. joint editorial bd. Uniform Probate Code. Author: Simplified Guide to Estate Planning and Administration, 1981; co-author: Accounting and the

Law, 1978, CCH Financial and Estate Planning Reporter, 4 vols, 1980; (with others) ALI-ABA Basic Accounting for Lawyers, 1987; reporter: Nat. Fiduciary Acctg. study; contbr. articles legal jours. Editor: Warren, Gorham & Lamont's Estate Planning and Administration Service. Mem. Am. Bar Assn., Conn. Bar Assn., Am. Law Inst., Am. Coll. Trusts and Estates Counsel. Home: 86 Norwood Rd West Hartford CT 06117-2236 Office: U Conn Sch Law Greater Hartford Campus West Hartford CT 06117

WHITMAN, ROBERT VAN DUYNE, civil engineer, educator; b. Pitts., Feb. 2, 1928; s. Edwin A. and Elsie (Van Duyne) W.; m. Elizabeth Cushman, June 19, 1954; children: Jill Martyne Whitman Marsee, Martha Allerton (dec.), Gweneth Giles Whitman Kaebnick. BS, Swarthmore Coll., 1948, DSc (hon.), 1990; SM, MIT, 1949, ScD, 1951. Mem. faculty MIT, 1953—; prof. civil engring., 1963-93, head structural engring., 1970-74, head soil mechanics div., 1970-72; prof. emeritus, 1993—; vis. scholar U. Cambridge, Eng., 1976-77; cons. to govt. and industry, 1953—; mem. adv. com. for nat. earthquake hazard reduction program Fed. Emergency Mgmt. Agy., 1991-94, mem. commn. engring. and tech. systems NRC, 1992—. Author: (with T. W. Lambe) Soil Mechanics. Mem. Town Meeting Lexington, Mass., 1962-76, 85—, mem. permanent bldg. com., 1968-75, mem. bd. appeals, 1979-81, 84—. Lt. (j.g.) USNR, 1954-56. Recipient U.S. Scientist award Humboldt Found., 1984-90; Norwegian Geotech. Inst. rsch. fellow, 1984. Mem. NAE, ASCE (Rsch. award 1962, Terzaghi Lecture 1981, Terzaghi award 1987, C. Martin Duke Lifeline Earthquake Engring. award 1992, James Croes medal 1994), Boston Soc. Civil Engrs. (Structural Sect. prize 1963, Desmond Fitzgerald medal 1973, Ralph W. Horne Fund award 1977), Internat. Soc. Soil Mechanics and Found. Engrs., Earthquake Engring. Rsch. Inst. (dir. 1978-81, 84-88, v.p. 1979-81, pres. 1985-87, Disting. lectr. 1994). Research in soil mechanics, soil dynamics and earthquake engring. Home: 5 Hancock Ave Lexington MA 02173-3412 Office: MIT Dept Civil & Environ Engring Cambridge MA 02139

WHITMAN, RUSSELL WILSON, lawyer; b. Phila., Feb. 20, 1940; s. Russell W. Whitman and Amelia M. (Schauer) Richard; m. Mary Carol Tyson, Sept. 16, 1961; children: Russell Whitman III, Douglas W. BS, Drexel Inst. Tech., 1964; LLB, U. Pa., 1967. Bar: N.Y. 1968, Pa. 1969, N.J. 1990. Ptnr. Dechert Price & Rhoads, Phila., 1969-93. Office: Ste 200 Box 5072 1322 Hooper Ave Toms River NJ 08754

WHITMAN, RUTH, poet, educator, translator; b. N.Y.C., May 28, 1922; d. Meyer David and Martha Harriet (Sherman) Bashein; m. Cedric Whitman, Oct. 13, 1941; children: Rachel Claudia, Leda Miriam; m. Firman Houghton, July 22, 1959; 1 child, David Will; m. Morton Sacks, Oct. 6, 1966. B.A., Radcliffe Coll., 1944; M.A., Harvard, 1947. Editor Harvard U. Press, 1947-60; dir. poetry workshop Cambridge Ctr. Adult Edn., 1964-68; fellow poetry and translation Bunting Inst., Radcliffe Coll., 1968-70; instr. Radcliffe Seminars, 1969—; faculty Harvard U., 1979-84; vis. poet Tufts U., 1972, 73; vis. poet in Israel, 1974, 77, 79, 81; poet-in-residence Hamden Sydney Coll., 1974, Trinity Coll., 1975, U. Denver, 1976, Holy Cross Coll., 1978, MIT, 1979, 1989, U. Mass., 1980, Centre Coll., Ky., 1980, 87, Ky. Arts Commn., 1981; founder, pres. Poets Who Teach, Inc., 1974—; dir. poetry writing program Mass. Council Arts, 1970-73; vis. prof. poetry MIT, 1989-92. Author: Selected Poems of Alain Bosquet, 1963, Anthology of Modern Yiddish Poetry, 1966, Blood and Milk Poems, 1963, Marriage Wig and other poems, 1968, Selected Poems of Jacob Glatstein, 1972, The Passion of Lizzie Borden: New and Selected Poems, 1973; editor: Poemmaking: Poets in Classrooms, 1975, Tamsen Donner: A Woman's Journey, 1977, Permanant Address: New Poems, 1973-80, 1980, Becoming a Poet: Source, Process and Practice, 1982, The Testing of Hanna Senesh, 1986, The Fiddle Rose, 1990, Laughing Gas: Poems New and Selected, 1963-90, 91, Hatshepsut, Speak to Me, 1992, An Anthology of Modern Yiddish Poetry, 3d edit., 1995. Recipient Alice Fay di Castagnola award, 1968, Kovner award, 1968, Chanin award, 1972, Guiness Internat. award, 1973; John Masefield award, 1976; grantee Nat. Found. Jewish Culture, 1968; Nat. Endowment Arts, 1974-75; Tananbaum Found. grantee, 1979, 80; R.I. Council grantee in lit., 1980; sr. Fulbright writer-in-residence fellow Hebrew U., Jerusalem, 1984-85. Mem. Authors League, P.E.N., Poetry Soc. Am., New Eng. Poetry Club, Phi Beta Kappa. Address: 40 Tuckerman Ave Middletown RI 02842-6044

WHITMER, FREDERICK LEE, lawyer; b. Terre Haute, Ind., Nov. 5, 1947; s. Lee Arthur and Ella (Diekhoff) W.; m. Valeri Cade; children: Caitlin Margaret, Meghan Connors, Christian Frederick. BA, Wabash Coll., 1969; JD, Columbia U., 1973. Bar: N.Y. 1975, U.S. Dist. Ct. (so. dist.) N.Y. 1975, N.J. 1976, U.S. Dist. Ct. N.J. 1976, U.S. Dist. Ct. Appeals (3d cir.) 1977, U.S. Ct. Appeals (fed. cir.) 1983, U.S. Ct. Appeals (2d cir.) 1987, U.S. Supreme Ct. 1988, U.S. Ct. Appeals (7th cir.) 1994. Assoc. Kaye, Scholer, Fierman, Hays & Handler, N.Y.C., 1973-76, Pitney, Hardin & Kipp, Mor-ristown, 1976-78; ptnr. Pitney, Hardin, Kipp & Szuch, Morristown, 1979—. Mem. ABA, N.J. Bar Assn., Phi Beta Kappa. Republican. Lutheran. Home: 190 Hurlbutt St Wilton CT 06897-2706 Office: Pitney Hardin Kipp & Szuch Park Ave at Morris County PO Box 1945 Morristown NJ 07962-1945

WHITMER, JOSEPH MORTON, benefits consulting firm executive; re-tired; b. Sacramento, Apr. 29, 1942; s. Carlos Raymond and Elizabeth Ellen (McDonald) W.; m. Judith Leigh Johnson, Aug. 11, 1963 (dec. Jan. 1985); children: Karen L., Brian D., Julia A.; m. Paula Ann Thurman, Mar. 19, 1986. BS in Acctg., U. Ky., 1964, JD, 1967. Ptnr. Veal & Whitmer, Nicholasville, Ky., 1967-68; v.p., sec., gen. counsel and dir. Consol. Mgmt. Svcs., Eagles Nat. Life Ins. Co., First Mut. Ins. Co., First. Mut. Life Ins. Co., Lexington, Ky., 1970-75; pvt. practice Lexington, 1975-89; exec. v.p., dir. Profl. Adminstrs. Ltd., Lexington, 1968-86, pres. chief exec. officer, 1987-90, dir., 1990-93. Mem. bd. overseers Duke U. Comprehensive Cancer Ctr., Durham, N.C., 1987—; co-chair Melanoma Consortium, 1987-90. Named one of Outstanding Young Men Am., 1975. Mem. ABA, Ky. Bar Assn. Democrat. Methodist. Avocation: computers.

WHITMER, KEVIN, newspaper sports editor. Sports editor The Daily News, N.Y.C. Office: NY News Inc 220 E 42 St New York NY 10017*

WHITMIRE, JOHN LEE, daycare provider; b. Brevard, N.C., June 17, 1924; s. John Leander and Betty Burr (Owen) W.; m. Eva Lee Wilson, Aug. 13, 1950; 1 child, Bonita Dawn. Student, Brevard Coll., 1948-49; BS in Acctg., U. Balt., 1960. Asst. tchr. agr. pub. schs., Brevard, 1946-48; office mgr. Peninsula Poultry Co., Balt., 1955-59; auditor, with accounts receivable dept. Ea. Products Corp., Balt., 1959-62; chief acct. Texize Corp., Mauldin, S.C., 1962-63; contr. Atlas Vending Co., Greenville, S.C., 1966-69; owner, dir. Twinkle Kiddie Kollege & Day Care, Greenville, 1969—; lobbyist state day care regulation for better child care, Columbia, S.C. 1977-81; mem. Adv. Com. on Regulation Child Day Care Facilities, Columbia, 1982-83; field counselor Day Care Child Trend, N.C., S.C., Ga., Ala., Miss., Tenn., Ark. Recipient 100% Dist. Leader Dog award Leader Dogs for the Blind, 1992, 100% Dist. Gov.'s award 1992. Mem. long range planning com. Grove Sch., East Gantt Sch., Greenville; precinct committeeman Greenville Dem. Com., 1970—. Sgt. AUS, 1944-46, ETO; with U.S. Army, 1950-52, Korea. Decorated Purple Heart. Recipient Model Sector Coord. award Campaign Sight First, 1993, Key Leader award, 1993. Mem. ASCD, Lions (1st v.p. Pleasantburg, L.C. 1985-86, pres. 1987-88, zone chmn. dist. 32-A 1988-89, region chmn. 1989-90, lt. gov. 1990-91, dist. gov. 1991-92, bd. dirs. S.C. Lions Sight Conservation Assn., contbr. Internat. Lions Mag., 1992, Palmetto Lion, 1993-94, Lion of Yr. award 1985, cert. of appreciation from internat. pres. 1989, 91, S.C. Eye Bank Vol. of Yr. award 1992). Baptist. Avocations: collecting old clocks and watches, fishing. Home: 13 Pecan Dr Greenville SC 29605-3729

WHITMIRE, MELBURN G., pharmaceutical distribution company execu-tive; b. 1939. Student, Valley St. Coll. With Synergex Corp., Fresno, Calif., from 1958; pres. Drug Svcs., Inc., Fresno, Calif., 1980-85; with Amfac Distbn., Folsom, Calif., 1985-88; pres., c.e.o. MWC, Inc., Amfac Health Care (now known as Whitmire Distbn. Co.), Folsom, 1988—. With USAR, 1961-67. Office: Whitmire Distbn Co 81 Blue Ravine Rd Folsom CA 95630-4720

WHITMORE, CHARLES HORACE, utility executive, lawyer, manage-ment consultant; b. Atlantic, Iowa, June 29, 1914; s. Tom Cornell and Adda Maria (Baldwin) W.; m. Millicent Stahly, May 3, 1935; children: Jacqueline, Tom Cornell. B.A., Grinnell Coll., 1935; J.D., State U. Iowa, 1940; LL.D.,

St. Ambrose Coll., 1960. Bar: Iowa bar 1937, Ill. bar 1939. Asst. counsel United Light & Power Co., 1937-41, exec. operating asst., 1942-43; asst. to pres. Iowa-Ill. Gas & Electric Co., Davenport, Iowa, 1946-47; gen. counsel Iowa-Ill. Gas & Electric Co., 1948-54, v.p., 1950-54, dir., 1950-80, pres., 1954-75, chmn. bd., 1956-79, chmn. exec. com., 1979-80; v.p., dir. Overseas Adv. Assos., Inc., Riyadh, Saudi Arabia, 1979-80; pres. Quad-City Devel. Group, 1971-73; chmn. Mid-Am. Interpool Network; also founding mem. Nat. Elec. Reliability Council, 1968-69. Served as lt., aviation supply officer USNR, 1944-45. Mem. Outing Club (Davenport), Rock Island Arsenal Golf Club (Ill.). Presbyterian. Home: Steepmeadow Rock Island IL 61201-4412 Office: 1800 Third Ave Rm 507 Rock Island IL 61201-8019

WHITMORE, DONALD CLARK, retired engineer; b. Seattle, Sept. 15, 1932; s. Floyd Robinson and Lois Mildred (Clark) W.; m. Alice Elinor Winter, Jan. 8, 1955; children: Catherine Ruth, William Owen, Matthew Clark, Nancy Lynn, Peggy Ann, Stuart John. BS, U. Wash., 1955. Prin. engr. The Boeing Co., Seattle, 1955-87, ret., 1987; developer, owner mobile home pk., Auburn, Wash., 1979—. Author: Towards Security, 1983, (monograph) SDI Software Feasibility, 1990, Characterization of the Nuclear Proliferation Threat, 1993, Rationale for Nuclear Disarmament, 1995. Ac-tivist for arms control, Auburn, Wash., 1962—; chmn. Seattle Coun. ORgns. for Internat. Affairs, 1973, Auburn Citizens for Schs., 1975; v.p. Boeing Employees Goof Neighbor Fund, Seattle, 1977, Spl. Svc. award, 1977; bd. dirs. 8th Congl. Dist. Sane/Freeze, 1992—; pres. founder Third Millennium Found., 1994. Avocations: hiking, travel, collecting. Home and Office: 16202 SE Lake Moneysmith Rd Auburn WA 98092

WHITMORE, FRANK CLIFFORD, JR., geologist; b. Cambridge, Mass., Nov. 17, 1915; s. Frank Clifford and Marion Gertrude (Mason) W.; m. Martha Burling Kremers, June 24, 1939; children–Geoffrey, John, Katherine, Susan. B.A., Amherst Coll., 1938; M.S., Pa. State U., 1939; M.A., Harvard U., 1941, Ph.D., 1942. Teaching fellow Harvard U., Cambridge, Mass., 1940-42; instr. geology R.I. State Coll., Kingston, 1942-44; geologist U.S. Geol. Survey, Washington, 1944-84, scientist emeritus, 1984—; mem. com. on research and exploration Nat. Geog. Soc., 1970—, vice chmn., 1990—; research assoc. dept. Paleobiology Smithsonian Instn., Washington, 1967—; mem. adv. bd. Ctr. for Study of Early Man, U. Maine, Orono, 1985-90. Editor: Resources for 21st Century, 1982. Contbr. articles on geology and vertebrate paleontology to profl. jours. Bd. dirs. Prince Georges County Boys Clubs, Md., 1954-56; mem. program com. Nat. Capital council Girl Scouts U.S.A., Washington, 1967-69; pres. Thornton Soc., Washington, 1977-84. Recipient Medal of Freedom, U.S. Army, 1946; spl. achievement award, U.S. Geol. Survey, 1980; Meritorious Service award, U.S. Dept. Interior, 1981, Arnold Guyot Meml. award Nat. Geographic Soc., 1993. Fellow Geol. Soc. Am., AAAS; mem. Soc. Vertebrate Paleontology (hon. life, exec. com. 1960-62). Democrat. Clubs: Midriver, Harvard. Avocations: architectural history. Home: 20 Woodmoor Dr Silver Spring MD 20901-2447 Office: US Geol Survey Nat Nus Natural History MRC NHB 137 Wash-ington DC 20560

WHITMORE, GEORGE MERLE, JR., management consulting executive; b. Tarrytown, N.Y., Jan. 1, 1928; s. George Merle and Elizabeth Helen (Knodel) W.; m. Priscilla Elizabeth Norman, Mar. 30, 1963; children: Elizabeth Lawrence Lippincott, George Norman, Stephen Bradford. BE, Yale U., 1949; MBA, Harvard U., 1951. Test engr. Gen. Electric Co., Bridgeport, Conn., Erie, Pa., 1949; rsch. assoc. Harvard Bus. Sch., Boston, 1951-52; assoc. Cresap, McCormick Paget Inc., N.Y.C., 1954-59, prin., 1959-61, ptnr., 1961-69, v.p., dir., 1969-79, mng. dir., chief exec. officer, 1979-81; mng. dir. Ayers, Whitmore & Co., Inc., N.Y.C., 1981-88, Ayers, Whitmore div. A.T. Kearney, Inc., N.Y.C., 1988-90; mng. dir. Whitmore & Co., Gree-nwich, Conn., 1990—; chmn. bd. The Advantage Ptnrs., Inc., Chatham, N.J., Rathbone, King & Seeley, Inc., Stamford, Conn., Philo Smith & Co., Inc., Stamford; bd. dirs. Carroll Enterprises, Inc., Worcester, Mass., RTI Inc., Rockaway, N.J. Hon. trustee, former bd. pres. Hackley Sch., Tar-rytown, N.Y.; former trustee, bd. chmn. Greenwich (Conn.) Acad.; former trustee, treas. Salisbury (Conn.) Sch. With USAF, 1952-53. Mem. Inst. Mgmt. Cons. (founding mem.), Newcomen Soc., Tau Beta Pi. Presbyterian. Clubs: Stanwich (former dir.) (Greenwich); Yale (N.Y.C.). Home and Office: 4 Cedarwood Dr Greenwich CT 06830-3905

WHITMORE, JAMES ALLEN, actor; b. White Plains, N.Y., Oct. 1, 1921; s. James Allen and Florence Belle (Crane) W.; m. Nancy Mygatt, Mar. 24, 1978 (div.); m. Audra Lindley; children: James, Steven, Daniel. B.A., Yale U., 1942; postgrad. Am. Wing Theatre Sch. Performances include: (Broadway plays) debut in Command Decision, 1947, Elba, Manhattan Theatre Club, Winesburg, Ohio, 1956, Inquest, 1970, Will Rogers U.S.A., Give 'Em Hell Harry, 1974, The Magnificent Yankee, Washington, 1976, Bully, 1977, Handy Dandy, 1985, (films) Battleground, 1949, Next Voice You Hear, 1950, Asphalt Jungle, 1950, Mrs. O'Malley and Mr. Malone, 1950, Outsiders, 1950, Please Believe Me, 1950, Across de Vide Missouri, 1951, It's a Big Country, 1951, Because You're Mine, 1952, Above and Beyond, 1952, Girl Who Had Everything, 1953, All the Brothers Were Valiant, 1953, Kiss Me Kate, 1953, The Command, 1954, Them!, 1954, Oklahoma, 1955, Battle Cry, 1955, McConnell Story, 1955, Eddy Duchin Story, 1956, Face of Fire, 1959, Who Was That Lady?, 1960, Black Like Me, 1964, Chuka, 1967, Waterhole 3, 1967, Nobody's Perfect, 1968, Planet of the Apes, 1968, Madigan, 1968, The Split, 1968, Guns of the Magnificent Seven, 1969, Chato's Land, 1972, Where the Red Fern Grows, 1974, Give 'Em Hell Harry, 1974 (Acad. award nomination 1975), Bully, 1978, The Serpent's Egg, 1978, First Deadly Sin, 1980, Nuts, 1987, The Shawshank Redemption, 1994, numerous others, (TV appearances) including The Law and Mr. Jones, 1960-61, My Friend Tony, 1969, Temperature Rising, 1972-73, Will Rogers U.S.A., 1973, (TV miniseries) Celebrity, 1986, Favorite Son, 1988. Served with USMCR, 1942-46. Nominated Acad. award, 1949; recipient Antoinette Perry award, 1947, Comedy award Am. Acad. Humor, Ace award, 1989; named Most Promising Newcomer, 1947. Office: J Michael Bloom LTD 9200 Sunset Blvd Ste 710 Los Angeles CA 90069*

WHITMORE, JOHN ROGERS, banker; b. Columbia, Mo., Nov. 19, 1933; s. Rogers and Catherine (Gray) W.; m. Suzanne Smith, Dec. 21, 1965; children–Elizabeth Anne, Margaret Penn. A.B. in Polit. Sci., U. Mo., 1954, J.D., 1958. Bar: Ill. 1958, Mo. 1958, D.C. 1967. Asst. sec. trust div. Continental Ill. Nat. Bank & Trust Co., Chgo., 1958-66; sr. v.p., trust officer Am. Security and Trust Co., Washington, 1967-75; pres., chief exec. officer Bessemer Trust Co. (N.A.), N.Y.C., from 1975, Bessemer Trust Co., Newark, from 1975, Bessemer Trust Co. Fla., Palm Beach, from 1975, Bes-semer Group Inc., N.Y.C., 1981—; dir. Bessemer Securities Corp., N.Y.C., B. F. Saul Real Estate Investment Trust, Chevy Chase. Trustee Leonard Wood Meml. Nat. Found. Eradication Leprosy, Washington; trustee Found. Center, N.Y.C.; chmn. bd. trustees Greenwich (Conn.) Acad., 1984-87. Served to lt. comdr. USNR, 1955-57. Mem. Am. Ill., Mo., D.C., Chgo. bar assns., Phi Delta Phi. Mem. Community Ch. Clubs: University, Brook (N.Y.C.); Field, Belle Haven (Greenwich); Metropolitan, Chevy Chase (Washington); Travellers (Paris); Everglades (Palm Beach, Fla.). Office: Bessemer Group Inc 630 5th Ave New York NY 10111-0001

WHITMORE, JON SCOTT, theater educator; b. Seattle, Mar. 22, 1945; s. Walter James and Eurma (Thody) W.; m. Jennifer Gean Gross, Aug. 17, 1985; children: Ian Scott, Amy Lee. BA in Speech and Theatre, Wash. State U., 1967, MA in Speech and Theatre, 1968; PhD in Dramatic Arts, U. Calif., Santa Barbara, 1974. Instr. theatre Highline Coll., Seattle, 1968-71; grad. asst. U. Calif., Santa Barbara, 1971-74; asst. prof. theatre W.Va. U., Mor-gantown, 1974-78, assoc. prof., 1978-82, prof., 1979-85, chmn. dept., 1979-84, interim dean, 1984-85; prof., dean Faculty Arts and Letters SUNY, Buffalo, 1985-90; dean Coll. of Fine Arts, U. Tex., Austin, 1990—. Dir. plays including Suddenly Last Summer, The Miracle Worker, Equus, Romeo and Juliet, Long Days Journey Into Night, The Sea Gull, The Comedy of Errors, The Glass Menagerie, Blithe Spirit, The Tavern, Black Comedy, You're a Good Man Charlie Brown, Vanities, The Effect of Gamma Rays on Man-In-The-Moon Marigolds, Epiphany, Endgame, The Miser, J.B., The Mousetrap, Knapp's Last Tape, Miss Julie, Servant of Two Masters, Before We Were; actor various classical, modern and contemporary plays and performance pieces; author: Directing Postmodern Theater, 1994, William Saroyan, 1994. Mem. Erie County (N.Y.) Cultural Resources Adv. Bd., 1986-89, long range planning com. Studio Arena Theatre, Buffalo, 1986-90, trustee, 1987-90; mem. coun. fellows Am. Coun. Edn., 1984—; pres. W.Va.

Theater Conf., 1978-80, pres.-elect, 1977-78, founding mem., bd. dirs., 1975-81. Recipient ACE Fellow award Am. Council Edn., 1983-84; fellow U. Calif., Santa Barbara, 1973-74, Lilly Found., 1976-77; Maynard Lee Daggy scholar Wash. State U., 1967. Mem. Internat. Council Fine Arts Deans, Am. Council Arts, Assn. Theatre in Higher Edn. (v.p. adminstrn. 1991—, chmn. nat. conf. planning com. chief adminstrs. program, 1987), Assn. Communication Adminstrn. (elected to exec. com. 1982-85, chmn. task force theatre adminstrn., 1982-84), Speech Communication Assn., Council Colls. Arts and Scis., Assn. Coll., Univ. and Community Arts Adminstrs., Nat. Assn. State Univs. and Land-Grant Colls. (chair elect commn. arts, 1990-92, chair 1992—). Home: 4503 Tortuga Cv Austin TX 78731-4541 Office: U Texas Coll Fine Arts Office of Dean Austin TX 78712

WHITMORE, KAY REX, retired photographic company executive; b. Salt Lake City, July 24, 1932; s. Rex Grange and Ferrol Terry (Smith) W.; m. Yvonne Schofield, June 6, 1956; children: Richard, Kimberly, Michele, Cynthia, Suzanne, Scott. Student, U. Utah, 1950-53, BS, 1957; MS, MIT, 1975. With Eastman Kodak Co., Rochester, N.Y., 1957-93, engr. film mfg., 1957-67; with factory start-up Eastman Kodak Co., Guadalajara, Mex., 1967-71; various mgmt. positions film mfg. Eastman Kodak Co., Rochester, 1971-74, asst. v.p., gen. mgr. Latin Am. Region, 1975-79, v.p., asst. gen. mgr. U.S. and Can. Photog. Div., 1979-80, exec. v.p. and gen. mgr., 1981-83, pres., 1983-90, chmn. bd., pres., chief exec. officer, 1990-93; bd. dirs. The Chase Manhattan Corp. Trustee U. Rochester. With U.S. Army, 1953-55. Mem. Am. Soc. for Quality Control, World Wildlife Fund. Mem. LDS Ch. Office: Eastman Kodak Co 343 State St Rochester NY 14650-0001

WHITMORE, SHARP, lawyer; b. Price, Utah, Apr. 26, 1918; s. Leland and Anne (Sharp) W.; m. Frances Dorr, Aug. 15, 1940; children: Richard, Wil-liam, Ann. A.B., Stanford U., 1939; J.D., U. Calif.-Berkeley, 1942; LL.D., U. Pacific, 1982. Bar: Calif. 1944. Asso. Gibson, Dunn & Crutcher, Los Angeles, 1946-50; partner Gibson, Dunn & Crutcher, 1951—; chmn. Calif. Com. Bar Examiners, 1956-58. Bd. dirs. Nat. Jud. Coll., 1989-92. Fellow Am. Bar Found. (chmn. 1982-83); mem. L.A. County Bar Assn. (pres. 1970-71), Nat. Conf. Bar Examiners (chmn. 1957-58), State Bar Calif. (bd. govs. 1962-65, v.p. treas. 1964-65), ABA (ho. of dels. 1957-58, 68-93, bd. govs. 1985-88, editl. bd. jour. 1994—), Order of Coif (hon.). Republican. Clubs: Bohemian, Sunset, Chancery (pres. 1962-63). Home: 2005 Gird Rd Fallb-rook CA 92028-9685 Office: 750 B St Ste 3300 San Diego CA 92101-8115

WHITNEY, A(DELBERT) GRANT, mercantile and insurance company executive; b. Lowell, Mass., July 25, 1917; s. Adelbert Howard and Julia (Sheehan) W.; m. Lillian Ritch DeArmon, Nov. 17, 1950; children: Julia Woodley, A. Grant, Frank DeArmon. B.S. in Bus. Adminstrn, Boston U., 1940. Asst. to v.p. Belk Stores, Charlotte, N.C., 1946-52; asst. to pres. Belk Stores, 1952-55; v.p. sec.-treas. Belk Stores, Inc. Reciprocal, Belk Under-writers, Inc., Charlotte, 1950-58; exec. v.p., sec.-treas. Belk Stores, Inc. Reciprocal, Belk Underwriters, Inc., 1958—; sec.-treas. Archdale Mut. Ins. Co., 1962-65, exec. v.p., sec.-treas., 1965—; gen. mgr. ins. dept. Belk Stores Services, Inc., 1951—, sec., mem. exec. com., 1959-68, v.p., 1964-68, em-ployee ins. operating com., 1971, 72; v.p. sec.-treas. Providence Realty Corp., Charlotte, 1950-63, pres., 1959-60, pres., sec.-treas., 1964-75; v.p. Queen City Investors, Inc., Charlotte, 1959-62; sec. Thrifty Investors, Inc., Charlotte, 1961-62, investment chmn., 1964-65, v.p., 1967-68. Trustee Elmira (N.Y.) Coll., 1978—; mem. adv. com. on state workmen's compensation laws to Council State Govts.; Mem. exec. com. Arthritis and Rheumatism Found., Charlotte, 1959-60, dir., 1959-60; mem. ins. adv. council U. Tex., 1968-69; gen. chmn. host com. Billy Graham Appreciation Day, 1968, Billy Graham 60th Birthday Party, 1978; chmn. Billy Graham Reception, 1983; bd. dirs. Jr. Achievement, Inc.; mem. exec. bd. Mecklenburg council Boy Scouts Am., 1949—, v.p., 1962-66, chmn. exploring, 1970-72, exec. bd., S.E. region, 1973—, mem.-at-large nat. council, 1974—; mem. Charlotte 3d U.S. Army Adv. Com., 1953-68, civilian adv., 1968—; chmn. N.C. USO, 1959-73; spl. gifts chmn. N.C. div. Am. Cancer Soc., 1967, crusade chmn., 1969, 70, bd. dirs., 1968—, pres., 1972-73; vice chmn. Shrine Bowl of Carolinas, 1963-66, gen. chmn., 1967-69; bd. govs. Shrine Bowl, 1980; mem. Mayor's Com. Better Charlotte, 1974—; program chmn. Charlotte Bi-Centennial Celebra-tion Com., 1968—; chmn. Charlotte/Mecklenburg Bicentennial Com., 1975, 76; gen. chmn. Pres. Eisenhower's visit to Charlotte, Mecklenburg Declara-tion of Independence-Freedom Celebration Day, 1975, 76; industry chmn. laymen's nat. com. Nat. Bible Week, 1967-70, asso. chmn., 1971—; chmn. adv. com. Charlotte Youth for Christ; chmn. advance gifts and profl. div. United Appeal, 1955-56; bd. dirs. Mecklenburg Citizens Better Libraries, 1967-71, Charlotte Council on Alcholism, Contact of Charlotte, Rescue Mission, Goodwill Industries, Charlotte, Inc., United Arts Council, N.C. Multiple Sclerosis Soc., Charlotte Symphony Soc., 1949-55; creator, dir. Fes-tival in the Park, 1964—; v.p. Christian Rehab. Center, 1979—; chmn. Sun Belt Conf. Festival, 1978; bd. visitors Brevard Music Center; trustee United Community Services; chmn. promotional activities planning com. Downtown Charlotte Assn., 1965-68; bd. govs. Insts. Religion and Health; parents' council Davidson Coll., 1972-73; mem. U.S. Olympic Com., 1982; mem. steering com. Bicentennial Celebration U.S. Constitution, 1987. Served as officer AUS, World War II; col. Res. ret. Recipient Distinguished Service award Jr. C. of C., 1952; named Charlotte Young Man of Year, 1952; recipient Silver Beaver award Boy Scouts Am., 1956, Freedom Found. Bronze medal, 1954, Freedom Found. Bronze medal Printing Industry of the Carolinas, Franklin Medallion award, 1973, Soldiers medal for Heroism U.S. Army; Exemplary Service award N.C. Soc. for Prevention Blindness, 1972; elected to Exec. and Profl. Hall Fame, 1966; mem. selection com., 1967—; recipient Distinguished Service award Charlotte Rotary Club, 1966, Dist-inguished Service award Charlotte Exchange Club, 1967, Distinguished Ser-vice award Jungle Aviation and Radio Service, Inc., 1971; Distinguished Service certificate USO, 1973; A. Grant Whitney Day, City of Charlotte named for him, 1975; Community Bicentennial certificate of commendation U.S. Conf. Mayors, 1976; service to Mankind award Sertoma Clubs of Charlotte, 1977; Distinguished Ser. award Hornets Nest Council Girl Scouts Am., 1976, 77; named Man of Year Charlotte News, 1975; City proclama-tion, 1977; Bus. and Profl. award Religious Heritage of Am., 1986; named to Hon. Order Ky. Cols.; presented Bronze Bust Festival in the Park, 1987. Mem. Risk and Ins. Mgmt. Soc. (formerly Am. Soc. Ins. Mgmt.) (pres. Va.-Carolinas chpt. 1957-58, Carolinas chpt. 1963-64, nat. v.p. conf. activities 1965-66, 1st v.p. 1966-67, pres. 1967-68, nat. dir. 1968-70, nat. legis. com., joint industry/risk mgmt. com., Man of Yr. award, Pres.'s award 1971), Internat. Ins. Seminars Inc., Am. Mgmt. Assn. (participant confs. seminars 1972), Ins. Hall Fame (internat. bd. electors 1968-70, chamber electors 1972—), Nat. Assn. Ind. Insurers (v.p. 1953-67, dir. 1968—, vice chmn. 1977-78, chmn. 1978-79, chmn. fin. com. 1980, mem. property casualty ins. council 1979), Captive Ins. Cos. Assn. (v.p. 1973-74, sec. 1974—, pres. 1985-87), U.S. C. of C. (ins. com. 1967-69), Charlotte C. of C., Mil. Order World Wars, Am. Legion, Carolina Carrousel (dir. 1952-57, 70-71, hon. grand marshall parade 1976), Newcomen Soc. N.Am., Royal Soc. Knights Car-rousel (pres. 1955-64, chmn. governing council 1964-68, chmn. exec. com. 1968-69), Soc. 1st Div. Inf. Assn. U.S. Army, Res. Officers Assn., Am. Found. Religion and Psychiatry (pres. 1959-72), French Fgn. Legion (hon.). Presbyterian (elder). Clubs: Masons (33 deg.), Shriners, Lions, Carolina Clowns (hon.), Lions; Boston U. Alumni of the Carolinas (Charlotte) (pres. 1949-51, nat. alumni council 1962—), Execs. (Charlotte) (pres. 1963-64), Myers Park Country (Charlotte), Charlotte City (Charlotte), Goodfellows (Charlotte). Home: 684 Colville Rd Charlotte NC 28207-2308 Office: 308 E 5th St Charlotte NC 28202-2410 *Each of us, endowed with certain talents, has much to do to utilize them to their fullest extent, within the realm of our ability, in order to meet the challenge of life and not let indecision or inaction deter us from accomplishing the meaningful life work of which we are capable.*

WHITNEY, BARRY LYN, religious studies educator; b. Cornwall, Ont., Can., Dec. 10, 1947; s. Earl Stanley Whitney and Gwendolyn Grace (Mel-drum) Whitney. BA with honors, Carleton U., 1971; PhD in Religious Studies, McMaster U., Hamilton, Ont., 1977. Prof. religious studies U. Windsor, Ont., 1976—, rsch prof., 1992-93; prof. pastoral edn. Southwestern Regional Ctr., Cedar Springs, Ont., 1977-79; mem. Anglican commn. Canterbury Coll., London and Windsor, 1977-79, tutor of admissions, Windsor, 1979-82, fellow, 1979-82; regional coord. Ctr. for Process Studies, 1979—. Author: Evil and the Process God, 1985, What are They Saying About God and Evil?, 1989, Theodicy, 1993; contbr. articles to profl. jours. Scholar Carleton U., 1967-71, McMaster U., 1971-76, Can. Coun. scholar McMaster, U., 1972-75; rsch. grantee Social Scis. and Humanities Rsch.

Coun., 1988-90. Mem. Soc. for Study Process Philosophies, Coll. Theology Soc., Am. Acad. Religion, Coun. for Study Religion. Home: RR 1, Amherstburg, ON Canada N9V 2Y7 Office: U Windsor Dept Religious Studies, 401 Sunset Ave, Windsor, ON Canada N9B 3P4 *Committed to the process vision of reality (Whitehead, Hartshorne) as a viable vision of God and a major advance in dealing with the terrible agony of suffering and injustice.*

WHITNEY, CHARLES ALLEN, astronomer, writer; b. Milw., Jan. 31, 1929; s. Charles Smith and Gertrude (Schuyler) W.; m. Jane Ann Hall, Jan. 27, 1951 (dec. Nov. 1993); children: Elizabeth Ann, David Hall, Thomas Charles, Peter Schuyler, James Andrew; m. Elizabeth Manson Pyle, Apr. 23, 1995. B.S., Mass. Inst. Tech., 1951; A.M., Harvard U., 1953, Ph.D. (Agassiz fellow, NSF fellow), 1955. Physicist Smithsonian Astrophys. Obs., 1956-94; research asso. Harvard Coll. Obs., 1956-62; mem. faculty Harvard, 1958—, asso. prof. astronomy, 1963-68, prof., 1968-89, prof. emeritus, 1989—. Author: The Discovery of Our Galaxy, 1971, Whitney's Star Finder, 1974, rev. edit., 1989, Random Processes in Physical Systems, 1990; co-author: Wanderers in Space, 1990, Learn to Navigate, 1992, Astrophysics Simulations, 1995; editor Jour. of the Am. Assn. of Variable Star Observers, 1979—; contbr. articles to mags. and profl. jours. Mem. Am. Astron. Soc., Am. Acad. Arts and Scis., Internat. Astron. Union. Home: 60 Bradford Rd Weston MA 02193-2141 Office: Harvard Obs Cambridge MA 02138

WHITNEY, DAVID CLAY, business educator, consultant, writer; b. Astoria, Oreg., May 30, 1937; s. Rolla Vernon and Barbara (Clay) W.; m. Kathleen Donnelley, 1956 (div. 1963); children: David Jr., Gordon, Sara; m. Zelda Gifford, 1967 (div. 1973); m. Emily Jane Williams, 1992. BS in Chemistry, San Diego State U., 1959; PhD in Chemistry, U. Calif., Berkeley, 1963. Cert. data processor, cert. data educator. Acting asst. prof. U. Calif., Davis, 1962-63; chemist, mathematician Shell Devel. Corp., Emeryville, Calif., 1963-72; dir. computer services Systems Applications, Inc., San Rafael, Calif., 1973-77; prof. Sch. Bus. Coll. Bus. San Francisco State U., 1977—; info. systems cons. numerous cos., 1977—; textbook reviewer numerous pubs., 1979—. Author: Instructors' Guides to Understanding Fortran, 1977, 83, 87, Understanding Fortran, 1984, 88, Basic, 1988, 89, 95. Mem. Assn. Computing Machinery, Data Processing Mgmt. Assn., Soc. Data Educators, Mensa. Home: 1501 S Norfolk St San Mateo CA 94401-3605 Office: San Francisco State U Coll of Bus San Francisco CA 94132

WHITNEY, EDWARD BONNER, investment banker; b. Glen Cove, N.Y., June 6, 1945; s. Edward Farley and Millicent Bonner (Bowring) W.; m. Martha Congleton Howell, Aug. 17, 1974; children: William Howell, John Howell. B.A., Harvard U., 1966, M.B.A., 1969. Systems engr. IBM, Cambridge, Mass., 1966-67; assoc. Dillon, Read & Co. Inc., N.Y.C., 1969-74, v.p., 1975-79, sr. v.p., 1980-83, mng. dir., 1984—, also bd. dirs. Mem. Heights Casino Club (Bklyn.). Office: Dillon Read & Co Inc 535 Madison Ave New York NY 10022-4212

WHITNEY, JOHN FREEMAN, JR., political science educator; b. Balt., Feb. 14, 1944; s. John Freeman and Agnese Jay (Taliaferro) W.; m. Carolyn Nordyke, Aug. 5, 1966; children: Cristina Elizabeth Whitney Waits, John Freeman III, William David. BA, Baylor U., 1967; MS, Tex. A&M U., 1968; PhD, Fla. State U., 1970. Instr. polit. sci. Fla. State U., Tallahassee, 1968-70, Tex. A&I U., Kingsville, 1967-68, Lamar U., Beaumont, Tex., 1970-71; adminstrv. asst. mgr. Ill. State Fair Agy., Springfield, Ill., 1973-77; mayor Chatham, Ill., 1977-85; exec. dir. Ill. Soc. Opticianry, Springfield, 1982-86; prof. polit. sci. Lincoln Land Community Coll., Springfield, 1971—; commr., chmn. Comptroller Merit Commn., State of Ill., Springfield, 1981—; cons. in field. Author (instrs. manual) Irony of Democracy, 1984, Uniform Welfare Systems and the State of Florida, 1970. Precinct committeeman Sangamon County Dem. Orgn., Springfield, 1974-80; del. Dem. Nat. Conv., N.Y.C., 1976, Dem. Nat. Midterm Conf., Phila., 1982; Ill. state steering com., campaign dir. Carter for Pres., 1976-80, Dukakis for Pres., 1986-88. Recipient Disting. Achievement award VFW, 1978, Polit. Sci. Hon. award Pi Sigma Alpha, 1970, NISOD Teaching Excellence award, 1995; named Ford Found. Legis. staff intern Fla. State U., 1970. Fellow Am. Polit. Sci. Assn.; mem. Nat. Assn. Civil Svc. Commrs. (cen. region pres. 1988-91), Internat. Pers. Mgmt. Assn., Soc. for Human Resource Mgmt., Am. Polit. Sci. Assn. Democrat. Methodist. Home: 18 Pheasant Run Dr Chatham IL 62629-1029 Office: Lincoln Land C C Shepherd Rd Shepherd Rd Springfield IL 62708

WHITNEY, JONATHAN ROBERT, gas company executive; b. 1944; married. BS, Colo. State U., 1965. Sr. acct. Alvin J. Krutchen CAA, 1966-68; acct. Colo. Interstate Gas Co., Colorado Springs, 1968-69, supr. acct., then rate analyst, 1969-71, sr. rate analyst, 1971-73, mgr. rates, 1973-75, contr., 1975—, v.p., 1980-84, sr. v.p., exec. v.p., pres., CEO Colo. Interstate Gas Co., Colorado Springs, Colo. Office: Colo Interstate Gas Co PO Box 1087 Colorado Springs CO 80944

WHITNEY, RALPH ROYAL, JR., financial executive; b. Phila., Dec. 10, 1934; s. Ralph Royal and Florence Elizabeth (Whitney) W.; m. Fay Wadsworth, Apr. 4, 1959; children: Lynn Marie, Paula Sue, Brian Ralph. BA, U. Rochester, 1957, MBA, 1972. Spl. agt. Prudential Ins. Co., Rochester, N.Y., 1958-59, divsn. mgr., 1959-63; gen. agt. Nat. Life Vt., Syracuse, 1963-64; contr. Wadsworth Mfg. Assocs. Inc., Syracuse, 1964-65, v.p., 1965-68, pres., 1968-71; pres. Warren (Pa.) Components Corp., 1968-72; pres., mng. prin. ptnr. Hammond Kennedy Whitney & Co., N.Y.C., 1972—; chmn. IFR Sys., Inc., Seneca Printing Inc.; chmn. CEO Holbrook Patterson Inc., Globe Ticket & Label Co., Grobot File Co., Am. Maine Rubber Co., Miltco Inc., Control Devices Inc.; bd. dirs. Excel Industries, Inc., Baldwin Tech. Corp., Selas Corp. Am., M. Mossberg & Son, Inc., Keene Corp., Adage Inc., MedTek Inc. Mem. N.Y. Yacht Club, Lotus Club (N.Y.C.), Century Club (Syracuse), Merion Cricket Club, Princeton Club. Episcopalian. Home: 3441 Highway 34 Wheatland WY 82201-8714

WHITNEY, RICHARD BUCKNER, lawyer; b. Corpus Christi, Tex., Mar. 1, 1948; s. Franklyn Loren and Elizabeth Wolcott (Fish) W.; m. Chantal Marie Gindt, Aug. 18, 1972; children: Jennifer L., James R., Katherine E. BA in Polit. Sci., Union Coll., 1970; JD, Case Western Res. U., 1973. Bar: Ohio 1973, U.S. Dist. Ct. (no. dist.) Ohio 1974, U.S. Ct. Appeals (6th cir.) 1974, U.S. Ct. Appeals (3d cir.) 1987. From assoc. to ptnr. Jones, Day, Reavis & Pogue, Cleve., 1973—. Mem. ABA, Ohio Bar Assn., Cuyahoga County Bar Assn., Cleve. Bar Assn. (grievance com., unauthorized practice of law com.), Order of the Coif. Home: 2750 Southington Rd Cleveland OH 44120-1603 Office: Jones Day Reavis & Pogue 901 Lakeside Ave E Cleveland OH 44114-1190

WHITNEY, ROBERT A., JR., veterinarian, government public health executive; b. Oklahoma City, July 27, 1935; m. Elizabeth Teeple, June 29, 1986; children: Stacy, Tara, Mark, Laura. BS, Okla. State U., Stillwater, 1958, DVM, 1959; MS in Pharmacology, Ohio State U., Columbus, 1965. Lic. veterinarian. Chief vet. resources br. NIH, Bethesda, Md., 1972-85, acting dir. Div. Rsch. Svcs., 1984-85, dir. Div. Rsch. Svcs., 1985-90, acting dir. Rsch. Res., 1988-90; dir. Nat. Ctr. Rsch. Res., Bethesda, Md., 1990-92, dir. office of animal care and use, 1986-92; chief vet. officer USPHS, 1986-90, dep. surgeon gen., 1992—; cons. Pan. Am. Health Orgn., 1975—. Co-author: Laboratory Primate Handbook, 1973. Assoc. editor Jour. of Med. Primatology, 1971—; bd. Lab. Animal Sci., 1986-82; cons. editor Am. Jour. Primatology, 1980—. Lt. col. U.S. Army. 1959-71. Decorated DSM, 1987; recipient USPHS Commendation medal, 1976, Meritorious Svc. medal, 1984, Surgeon Gen.'s Exemplary Svc. medal, 1988; NIH Director's award 1984, Disting. Alumnus award Ohio State U., 1986, Disting. Grad. Recognition award Okla. State U., 1989, The Charles River Found. prize, 1989, Karl F. Meyer award Am. Vet. Epidemiol. Soc., 1989. Mem. AVMA, Am. Assn. Lab. Animal Sci. (pres. 1977-78), Am. Assn. Lab. Animal Practitioners, Am. Coll. Lab. Animal Medicine (bd. dirs. 1968-69, pres. 1992), Am. Soc. Primatologists. Home: 5213 Bangor Dr Kensington MD 20895-1104 Office: Office of Surgeon Gen Parklawn Bldg Rm 18-67 5600 Fishers Ln Rockville MD 20857

WHITNEY, ROBERT MICHAEL, lawyer; b. Green Bay, Wis., Jan. 29, 1949; s. John Clarence and Helen (Mayer) W. Student, U. Wis., 1967-70, JD, 1974. Bar: Wis. 1974, U.S. Dist. Ct. (we. dist.) Wis. 1979, U.S. Ct. Appeals (7th cir.) 1980, U.S. Dist. Ct. (ea. dist.) Wis. 1984, U.S. Supreme Ct. 1990. Legal counsel Wis. State Election Bd., Madison, 1976-78; ptnr. Walsh,

Walsh, Sweeney & Whitney, S.C., Madison, 1979-86, Foley & Lardner, Madison, 1986—; counsel Advocacy Assn. for Retarded Citizens, Madison, 1977-79. bd. dirs. Community TV, Inc., Madison, 1984-87. Mem. Assn. Trial Lawyers Am., Wis. Acad. Trial Lawyers, Wis. Bar Assn., Dane County Bar Assn., Rugby Club of Madison. Home: 3100 Lake Mendota Dr #803 Madison WI 53705 Office: Foley & Lardner First Wis Pla 1 S Pickney St PO Box 1497 Madison WI 53701

WHITNEY, RUTH REINKE, magazine editor; b. Oshkosh, Wis., July 23, 1928; d. Leonard G. and Helen (Diestler) Reinke; m. Daniel A. Whitney, Nov. 19, 1949; 1 son, Philip. BA, Northwestern U., 1949. Copywriter edn. dept. circulation div. Time, Inc., 1949-53; editor-in-chief Better Living mag., 1953-56; assoc. editor Seventeen magazine, 1956-62, exec. editor, 1962-67; editor-in-chief Glamour mag., N.Y.C., 1967—. Recipient Nat. Mag. award gen. excellence, 1981, 91, Pub. Interest, 1992, Cosmetic Executive Women Achiever award, 1993, honor award Women's City Club N.Y.; honoree Gala 11 Birmingham, So. Coll., 1993. Mem. Fashion Group, Am. Soc. Mag. Editors (pres. 1975-77, exec. com. 1989-92), Women in Communication (Matrix award 1980), Women in Media, U.S. Info. Agy. (mag. and print com. 1989-93), Alpha Chi Omega. Office: Glamour Condé Nast Bldg 350 Madison Ave New York NY 10017-3704

WHITNEY, WILLIAM CHOWNING, retired banker, financial consultant; b. Fullerton, Nebr., June 28, 1920; s. Barlow N. and Lena C. (Price) W.; m. Joan F. Whitney; children—William H., David M., Terri Lynn, Sherri Lee, Jonathan P., Laura Louise. B.S. cum laude, Loyola U., Chgo., 1949. Asst. bank examiner Fed. Res. Bank, Chgo., 1938-41; asst. auditor South Side Bank and Trust Co., Chgo., 1946-49; comptroller Peoples Nat. Bank, Bay City, Mich., 1949-52; asst. v.p., comptroller Tex. Bank and Trust Co., Dallas, 1952-54; with Old Kent Bank and Trust Co., Grand Rapids, Mich. 1954-86; sr. v.p., cashier, sec. bd., dir. Old Kent Fin. Corp., 1965-86; cons. Amway Corp., 1986—. Chmn. Met. Hosp., 1986-93, Met. Health Corp., 1987-95. Capt. AUS, 1941-46. Mem. Fin. Execs. Inst., Mich. Banks Assn., Bank Adminstrn. Inst., Grand Rapids C. of C., Rotary (Grand Rapids), Peninsular Club (Grand Rapids), Cascade Country Club (Grand Rapids), University Club (Grand Rapids), Kent Country Club (Grand Rapids), Grand Lodge Masons (fin. com.), Econ. Club. Home: 742 Apple Tree Dr Suttons Bay MI 49682-9778

WHITNEY, WILLIAM ELLIOT, JR., advertising agency executive; b. Albany, N.Y., Feb. 22, 1933; s. William Elliot and Louise E. (Goldsmith) W.; m. Nancy B. Bivings, Mar. 1, 1958; children—Susan, James, Douglas. B.A. cum laude, Amherst Coll., 1954; M.B.A., Harvard U., 1956. Account exec. McCann-Erickson, N.Y.C., 1956-58, Marschalk Co., N.Y.C., 1958-60; v.p., then sr. v.p. Ogilvy & Mather, N.Y.C., 1960-80; sr. v.p., mng. dir. Ogilvy & Mather, Chgo., 1980-85, exec. v.p., 1985-87, pres., 1987-89, chmn., 1990-91; cons. ptnr. Redirections, Inc., 1991—; lectr. U. Chgo. Grad. Sch. Bus., 1991—. Bd. dirs., v.p. Chgo. coun. Boy Scouts Am., 1978-81, 88—, Off-the-St. Club, Chgo., 1979—, pres. 1988-89; bd. dirs. Hinsdale (Ill.) Cmty. House, 1981, King-Bruwaert House, 1988—; v.p. civic adv. bd. Hinsdale Hosp., 1989-93; cons. Exec. Svc. Corps of Chgo., 1991—; trustee Village of Hinsdale, 1993—. Mem. Oldwick Advt. Club (pres.), Econs. Club, Hinsdale Golf Club. Home: 736 S Park Ave Hinsdale IL 60521-4646

WHITSEL, RICHARD HARRY, biologist, entomologist; b. Denver, Feb. 23, 1931; s. Richard Elstun and Edith Muriel (Harry) W.; children by previous marriages: Russell David, Robert Alan, Michael Dale, Steven Deane. BA, U. Calif., Berkeley, 1954; MA, San Jose State Coll., 1962. Sr. rsch. biologist San Mateo County Mosquito Abatement Dist., Burlingame, Calif., 1959-72; environ. program mgr., chief of watershed mgmt., chief of planning Calif. Regional Water Quality Control Bd., Oakland, 1972—; mem. grad. faculty water resource mgmt. U. San Francisco, 1987-89. Served with Med. Service Corps, U.S. Army, 1954-56. Mem. Entomol. Soc. Am., Entomol. Soc. Wash., Am. Mosquito Control Assn., Calif. Alumni Assn., The Benjamin Ide Wheeler Soc., Nat. Parks and Conservation Assn. (life), Sierra Club. Democrat. Episcopalian. Contbr. articles to profl. jours. Home: 4331 Blenheim Way Concord CA 94521-4258 Office: Calif Regional Water Quality Control Bd 2101 Webster St Oakland CA 94612-3027

WHITSEL, ROBERT MALCOLM, insurance company executive; b. Lafayette, Ind., Dec. 30, 1929; s. Earl Newton and Elizabeth (Bader) W.; m. Marilyn Katherine House, Oct. 15, 1955; children—Rebecca Sue, Cynthia Ann. B.S., Ind. U., 1951, M.B.A., 1954. With Lafayette Life Ins. Co., 1954—, dir., 1966—, mem. exec. com., 1968—, v.p., 1973, pres., 1973—; bd. dirs. INB Nat. Bank, N.W.; chmn. N. Cen. Health Svcs., Inc. Elder, trustee, deacon Presbyterian Ch., 1965-74; dir., past pres. Jr. Achievement Greater Lafayette, Inc., 1976-77, Central Presbyn. Found., Edgelea PTA; past pres., bd. dirs., past campaign chmn. United Way of Greater Lafayette; past v.p., bd. dirs. Wabash Sch. for Mentally Retarded; mem. adv. bd. Purdue Ctr. for Econ. Edn.; bd. dirs. Purdue Research Found.; past pres., bd. dirs. Capital Funds Found. Greater Lafayette; bd. dirs. Lafayette Home Hosp., 1972—, mem. finance com., 1976—, past pres.; trustee YWCA Found.; chmn. Greater Lafayette Progress Inc., Westminster Village Retirement Ctr.; pres. Greater Lafayette Community Found.; chmn. North Cen. Health Svcs., Inc. Served to 1st lt. USAF, 1951-53. Recipient Nat. Bus. Leadership award, 1977. Mem. Soc. Residential Appraisers, Ind. Mortgage Bankers Assn. (past pres.), Am. Coun. Life Ins. Co. (past pres.), Ind. C. of C. (dir.), Greater Lafayette C. of C. past pres.), Ind. Soc. of Chgo., Lafayette Country Club (past pres., dir.), Town and Gown Club, Masons, Beta Gamma Sigma. Republican. Home: 541 Old Farm Rd Lafayette IN 47905-3515 Office: Lafayette Life Ins Co 1905 Teal Rd # 7007 Lafayette IN 47905-2225

WHITSELL, DORIS BENNER, retired educator; b. Poplar Grove, Ill., Mar. 17, 1923; d. Ralph Erwin and Sarah McKay (Mulligan) Wheeler; m. Robert M. Benner, Dec. 1945 (div. 1955); 1 child Geoffrey Mark Benner (dec.); m. Eugene B. Whitsell, Feb. 1969 (dec. 1972). BS, No. Ill. U., 1944, MS in Edn., 1967; postgrad. Rockford Coll., 1964. Tchr. English and home econs. Lee (Ill.) High Sch., 1944-45; tchr. English Ashton (Ill.) Community High Sch., 1945-46; tchr. Morris Kennedy Sch., Rockford, Ill., 1952-55, William Nashold Sch., Rockford, 1955-56; tchr. English, drama Jefferson Jr. High Sch., Rockford, 1956-69; tchr. English Richwoods High Sch., Peoria, Ill., 1969-71; tchr. Calvin Coolidge Sch., Peoria, 1972-81; mem. textbook selection com. Dist. 150, Peoria, 1973-75, curriculum planning com., 1974-75, tutor for homebound, 1982-83, cons. competency test seminar; cons. textbook div. Harcourt, Brace, Jovanovich, 1981-83; evaluator North Cen. Accreditation Team, Jefferson High Sch., Rockford, 1980. Counselor Operation Sr. Security, Peoria, 1986-89; treas. Rockford Women's Club Fortnightly Dept., 1961-62; past deaconess 1st Federated Ch., Peoria; pres. Willow Heights Homeowners Assn., Peoria, 1979-81; vol. Rockford Midway Village and Mus. Ctr., 1993—; bd. dirs. Forest Vale Estates Condominiums, Meadows Assn., Rockford, treas., 1995. Named for Significant Svc. to the Community, Ret. Sr. Vol. Program, Peoria, 1986. Mem. Ill. Ret. Tchrs. Assn. (life, sec. 1982-90, bd. dirs. Found. Inc. 1965-93, moderator conv. panel 1990, Outstanding Svc. award 1989), Peoria Area Ret. Tchrs. Assn. (2d v.p. 1987-88, pres. 1989-90, chmn. state bldg. fund com. 1987-88), AAUW (program v.p. 1988-89), Nat. Ret. Tchrs. Assn. (life), No. Ill. U. Alumni Assn., Delta Kappa Gamma (chmn. ins. com. Beta Gamma chpt. 1956-60, v.p. 1962-64, pres. 1964-66, profl. affairs com. 1992-95, chmn. personal growth and svc. com. Nu chpt. 1988-90, program com. Lambda chpt. 1978-80). Avocations: reading, traveling, interior decorating, theatre. Home: 1283 Aarons St Rockford IL 61108-1536

WHITSELL, HELEN JO, lumber executive; b. Portland, Oreg., July 20, 1938; d. Joseph William and Helen (Cornwell) Copeland; m. William A. Whitsell, Sept. 2, 1960; 2 children. BA, U. So. Calif., 1960. With Copeland Lumber Yard Inc., Portland, 1960—, pres., chief exec. officer, 1973-84, chmn., chief exec. officer, 1984—; bd. dirs. First Interstate Bank of Orgn. Office: Copeland Lumber Yards Inc 901 NE Glisan St Portland OR 97232-2784

WHITSETT, KINGSLEY P., school administrator; b. St. Louis, Jan. 31, 1943; s. Thomas P. and Chrystalene (Huse) W.; m. Nancy M. Whitsett, Aug. 8, 1965; children: Edward W., Theodore (Teddy) D. BA, So. Coll. of Seventh-day Adv., Collegedale, Tenn., 1965; BD, Andrew's U., Berrien Springs, Mich., 1967. Dir. youth ministry Mo. Conf. 7th-day Adventists,

Raytown, 1975-80; pastor, sch. adminstr. Roanoke (Va.) 7th-day Adventist Ch. and Sch., 1980-82, Frederick (Md.) 7th-day Adventist Ch. and Sch., 1982-86; dir. youth ministry Mountain View Conf. 7th-day Adventists, Parkersburg, W.Va., 1986—, supt. edn., exec. sec., ministerial dir., 1989—; pastor sch. adminstr. Springfield (Mo.) Seventh-day Adventist Ch. and Sch., 1975-76; secondary tchr. Greater Miami Acad., Fla., 1973-75, Highland View Acad., Hagerstown, Md., 1971-73. Bd. dirs. Highland View Acad., Shenandoah Valley Acad., Mountain State Acad. Avocations: hiking, nature study, nature photography, reading, writing. Home: 3 Oak Cir Parkersburg WV 26101-9089 Office: Mountain View Conference 1400 Liberty St Parkersburg WV 26101-4124

WHITSON, JAMES NORFLEET, JR., diversified company executive; b. Clinton, Okla., Mar. 14, 1935; s. James Norfleet and Georgia (Webb) W.; m. Lyda Lee Gibson, Apr. 19, 1956; 1 child, James Mark. BBA, Tex. Tech U., 1957. Acctg. supr. LTV, Inc., Dallas, 1960-70; v.p. fin. Omega-Alpha, Inc., 1970-73; pres. Sammons Communications, Inc., Dallas, 1973-89; exec. v.p., chief operating officer Sammons Enterprises, Inc., Dallas, 1989—; bd. dirs. Sammons Enterprises, Inc., C-Span, Tri-Continental Corp. Mem. Alpha Tau Omega. Home: 6606 Forestshire Dr Dallas TX 75230-2856 Office: Sammons Enterprises Inc 300 Crescent Ct Dallas TX 75201-1836

WHITT, DAVID VIRGEL, insurance company executive; b. N.Y.C., Jan. 17, 1935; s. Virgel E. and Youland (ReDavid) W.; m. Charlotte Forsyth, Dec. 23, 1961; children—William D., Thomas F. B.S. in Ins./Econs, Butler U., 1957. Group rep. Am. United Life Ins. Co., Chgo., 1957-69; coordinator Am. United Life Ins. Co. (Student Life Plan), Indpls., 1960; regional group mgr. Am. United Life Ins. Co., Chgo., 1961-63, Phila., 1963-64; mgr. group sales and adminstrn. Am. United Life Ins. Co., Indpls., 1965-69; v.p., dir. group ins. Capitol Life Ins. Co., Denver, 1969-71; sr. v.p. Nat. Investors Life Ins. Co., Little Rock, 1971; exec. v.p., dir. Nat. Investors Life Ins. Co., 1972-81; v.p., dir. Nat. Investors Fire & Casualty Co., 1971-81; sr. v.p., dir. Gt. Atlantic Life Ins. Co., 1971-73; exec. v.p., dir. Mid-West Nat. Life Ins. Co., 1973-81; v.p., dir. Nat. Investors Pension Co., 1979-81; pres. G.I.C. Ins. Co., San Antonio, 1981; exec. v.p. Keystone Provident Life Ins Co, 1982-88; sr. v.p. Mass. Keystone Group, Boston, 1982-88; pres., chief exec. officer, dir. Beneficial Standard Life Ins. Co., L.A., 1988—. Chmn. bd. Westside YMCA, 1973-76. Served with USNR, 1952-60. Mem. Life Office Mgmt. Assn. Presbyterian. Office: Monarch Life Ins Co 1 Monarch Pl Springfield MA 01144

WHITT, GREGORY SIDNEY, molecular phylogenetics, evolution educator; b. Detroit, June 13, 1938; s. Sidney Abram and Millicent (Ward) W.; m. Dixie Lee Dailey, Aug. 25, 1963. B.S. Colo. State U., 1962, M.S., 1965; Ph.D., Yale U., 1970. Asst. prof. zoology U. Ill., Urbana, 1969-72; asso. prof. genetics and devel. U. Ill., 1972-77, prof., 1977-87, prof. ecology, ethology and evolution, 1987—; affiliate Ill. Natural History Survey, 1981—; mem. NIH study sect., 1975-76. Co-editor: Isozymes: Current Topics in Biological and Medical Research, 1977-87; editor: Isozyme Bull., 1978-81; mem. editorial bd. Biochem. Genetics, 1975—, Devel. Genetics, 1978-83, Jour. Molecular Evolution, 1979—, Molecular Biology and Evolution, 1983-93, Molecular Phylogenetics and Evolution, 1992—; contbr. articles to profl. jours. Fellow AAAS; mem. Am. Genetics Assn., Am. Soc. Icthyologists and Herpetologists, Soc. for the Protection of Old Fishes, Internat. Soc. Molecular Evolution, Soc. Systematic Biologists. Home: 1510 Trails Dr Urbana IL 61801-7052 Office: U Ill Dept Ecol Ethol/Evol 515 Morrill Hall 505 S Goodwin Urbana IL 61801

WHITT, RICHARD ERNEST, reporter; b. Greenup County, Ky., Dec. 15, 1944; s. Walter Charles and Irene (Hayes) W.; children: Hayes Chadwick, Emily. Student, Ashland (Ky.) Community Coll., 1966-68; B.A. in Journalism, U. Ky., 1970. Reporter Middlesboro (Ky.) Daily News, 1970-71; asst. state editor Waterloo (Iowa) Courier, 1971-72; city editor Kingsport (Tenn.) Times, 1972-76; No. Ky. bur. chief Courier-Jour., Louisville, 1977; Frankfort bur. chief Courier-Jour., 1977-80, spl. projects reporter, 1980-89; investigative reporter Atlanta Jour. & Constn., 1989—. Served with USN, 1962-66. Decorated Air medal; recipient Pulitzer prize for coverage of Beverly Hills Supper Club fire, 1978; named Outstanding Ky. Journalist, 1978; recipient John Hancock award for excellence, 1983. Democrat. Office: Atlanta Jour & Constn 72 Marietta St NW Atlanta GA 30303-2804

WHITT, ROBERT AMPUDIA, III, advertising executive, marketing professional; b. San Antonio, Oct. 15, 1930; s. Robert and Alice (Whitt) Ampudia; m. Mary Jane Kothmann, June 2, 1951; children: April Whitt Horner, Robert IV, Roxanne Seaman. BA in Internat. Trade, U. of the Ams., Mexico City, 1955; postgrad., Am. Grad. Sch. Internat. Mgmt., Phoenix, 1991, 92. Sales mgr. Sinclair & Valentine Co., Cali, Colombia, 1956-59; CEO for L.Am. Vision, Inc., Mexico City, 1960-74; pres., CEO Tex. Parade, Inc., Austin, 1974-77; CEO world ops. Novedades Editores, Mexico City, 1977-82; chmn., CEO Mktg. Mercadeo Internat., Dallas, 1982—; bd. dirs. Robea, S.A., Mexico City, Poliform, S.A., Mexico City, Tex. Bus. Hall of Fame Foundation, Dallas; mem. Alliance for Progress Task Force, 1963-67. Co-author: How to Market and Distribute in Mexico; editor: (Spanish lang.) Dallas Cowboys Mag., 1979, 80, 91 (Best Content award), Bienestar Mag., 1978 (Best Content award); contbr. articles to profl. jours. Sgt. U.S. Airborne, 1950-53. Recipient Nat. Winner award Silver Microphone, 1991, Nat. Finalist award, 1991, Addy award Am. Advt. Fedn., 1992, Nat. Winner award Telly awards (4), 1993, 95; named Speaker of the Year Toastmasters Internat., 1980. Mem. Fgn. Corr. Club, 11th Airborne Div. Assn. (life), Brookhaven Country Club (Dallas), Univ. Club (Dallas), Univ. Club (Mexico City), Metropolitan Soc. of Clubs. Office: Mktg Mercadeo Internat 2929 Mossrock Ste 205 San Antonio TX 78230-5141

WHITT, WILBY WAYNE, newspaper editor; b. Athens, Ala., July 18, 1924; s. A.A. and Eva (Matlock) W.; m. Mildred Brame, Sept. 7, 1947; children—Cynthia Whitt Castleberry, Wilby Wayne. B.A., U. Ala., 1945. Reporter UPI, Columbus, Cleve. and Charleston, W.Va., 1945-46; reporter Tennessean, Nashville, 1946-76, mng. editor, 1976—. Nieman fellow Harvard U., 1953-54. Mem. AP. Mng. Editors, UPI Tenn. Assn. Newspapers, Sigma Delta Chi. Office: The Tennessean 1100 Broadway Nashville TN 37203-3116

WHITTAKER, BILL DOUGLAS, minister; b. Bowling Green, Ky., June 14, 1943; s. Ewing A. and Lois (Jenkins) W.; m. Rebecca Kaye Howard, June 18, 1966; children: John, Karen, Mary. BA, Western Ky. U., 1965; MDiv, So. Bapt. Theol. Sem., Louisville, 1969, D of Ministry, 1974. Ordained to ministry So. Bapt. Conv., 1964. Pastor 1st Bapt. Ch., Sturgis, Ky., 1969-76, Murray, Ky., 1976-82; missionary Fgn. Mission Bd., So. Bapt. Conv., The Philippines, 1983-86; pastor Downtown Bapt. Ch., Orlando, Fla., 1986-88; pres. Clear Creek Bapt. Bible Coll., Pineville, Ky., 1988—. Author: Preparing to Preach, 1986; columnist Western Recorder newspaper, 1988—, Pineville Sun, 1993—. Bd. dirs. Coalition for the Homeless, Cen. Fla. YMCA, Orlando, 1986-88. Mem. Am. Assn. Bible Colls. (del. 1988), Assn. So. Bapt. Colls. and Schs. (del. 1988—), Ky. Bapt. Hist. Soc., Kiwanis (pres. Pineville chpt. 1994-95), Ky. Bapt. Conv. (pres. 1980). Home and Office: 300 Clear Creek Rd Pineville KY 40409-0212

WHITTAKER, JEANNE EVANS, former newspaper columnist; b. Detroit, Jan. 1, 1934; d. Alfred Heacock and Margaret (Evans) W.; m. Charles Martin Hines Jr., Sept. 29, 1962 (div. Feb. 1970); children: Charles M. Hines III, Margaret Helen Whittaker. Student, Northwestern U., 1952-53; BS in History, U. Mich., 1956. Columbia worker UN forces ARC, Korea, 1956-58; staff programmer ARC, Chaumont, Evreux, France, 1958-61; dir. Bexar County chpt. youth ARC, San Antonio, 1961-62; staff writer/columnist Detroit Free Press, 1970-75; editor Mich. Social Register, 1975-77; Lifestyle editor Observer and Eccentric newspapers, Birmingham, Mich., 1977-87; staff writer, columnist Detroit News, 1987-91. Contbr. articles to mags. Bd. dirs. Southeastern Mich. chpt. ARC (bd. dirs. 1987-93). Episcopalian. Avocations: writing, reading, travel. Home: 552 Cadieux Rd Grosse Pointe MI 48230-1508

WHITTEMORE, ANNE MARIE, lawyer; b. Southampton, Eng., Mar. 19, 1946; (parents Am. citizens); d. Rober R. and Vera (McMullen) Grimes; m. F. Case Whittemore, June 22, 1968; 1 child, Robert Pendleton. AB, Vassar Coll., 1967; LLB, Yale U., 1970. Bar: Va. 1970. Law clk. to presiding judge U.S. Ct. Appeals (4th cir.), Alexandria, Va., 1970-71; assoc. McGuire, Woods, Battle & Boothe, Richmond, Va., 1971-77, ptnr., 1977—; bd. dirs. Fed. Res. Bank of Richmond. Bd. of govs. Greater Richmond Community Found., 1978—; bd. advisors Va. Commonwealth U., Richmond, 1981—; trustee Confederate Meml. Library Soc., Richmond, 1988—. Mem. Richmond Bar Assn. (exec. com. 1986—), Va. Law Found. (bd. of govs. 1986—), Downtown Club (bd. dirs.). Republican. Roman Catholic. Home: 1 Huntley Rd Richmond VA 23226-3305 Office: McGuire Woods Battle & Boothe 1 James Ctr 6th Fl Richmond VA 23219

WHITTEMORE, EDWARD REED, II, poet, retired educator; b. New Haven, Sept. 11, 1919; s. Edward Reed and Margaret Eleanor (Carr) W.; m. Helen Lundeen, Oct. 3, 1952; children: Catherine Carr, Edward Reed III, John Lundeen, Margaret Goodhue. A.B., Yale U., 1941; postgrad., Princeton U., 1945-46; Litt.D., Carleton Coll., 1971. Mem. faculty Carleton Coll., 1947-67, prof. English, 1962-67, chmn. dept., 1964-67; program assoc. Nat. Inst. Pub. Affairs, 1966-68; editor Carleton Miscellany, 1960-64; cons. in poetry Libr. of Congress, 1964-65, 84-85; Bain-Swiggett lectr. Princeton, 1967; prof. U. Md., 1968-84, prof. emeritus, 1984—; poet laureate State of Md., 1985-88; lit. editor New Republic, 1969-74. Author: Heroes and Heroines, 1947, An American Takes a Walk, 1956, The Self-Made Man, 1959, The Boy From Iowa, 1962, The Fascination of the Abomination, 1963, Poems, New and Selected, 1967, From Zero to the Absolute, 1967, 50 Poems 50, 1970, The Mother's Breast and the Father's House, 1974, William Carlos Williams: Poet from Jersey, 1975, The Poet as Journalist, 1976, The Feel of Rock, 1982, Pure Lives, 1988, Whole Lives, 1989, The Past, the Future, the Present, 1990, Six Literary Lives, 1993; editor: Furioso, 1939-53, Browning, 1960, Delos mag., 1988-91. Capt. USAAF, 1941-45. Recipient award merit AAAL, 1971. Home: 4526 Albion Rd College Park MD 20740-3610

WHITTEMORE, LAURENCE FREDERICK, private banker; b. Bangor, Maine, Mar. 7, 1929; s. John Cambridge and Elizabeth Payson (Prentiss) W.; m. Sarah Lee Arnold, Aug. 9, 1958; children—Arianna, Gioia, Lia, Nike. B.A., Yale U., 1951; M.B.A., Harvard U., 1953; student, Balliol Coll., Oxford U., Eng., 1950. Account mgr. Brown Bros. Harriman, N.Y.C., 1956-72; gen. mgr. Brown Bros. Harriman, 1972-74; ptnr. Brown Bros. Harriman & Co., 1974—; dir. Manhattan Life Ins. Co., N.Y.C., Otto Wolff US Holding Co., 1982-86, Hurricane Industries, Houston, 1982-85, Albany Ins. Co., N.Y.C., Atlas Assurance Co. of Am., N.Y.C., 1984-86; mem. investment adv. com. Union Investment GmbH, Frankfurt, West Germany, 1973—; mem. Chgo. Stock Exch., 1975—. Trustee Sarah Lawrence Coll., 1988—, Am. Inst. Contemporary German Studies, 1994—; mem. Nat. Com. on U.S. China Rels., N.Y.C., 1982—, Chgo. Coun. on Fgn. Rels. 1980—; del. Assn. Yale Alumni, New Haven, 1982-86; chmn. Yale 35th Reunion Gift Drive, 1983-86. Served to comdr. USNR, 1953-56. Mem. Econ. Club of Chgo., N.Y. Soc. Security Analysts, Investment Analysts Soc. Chgo., Assn. for Investment Mgmt. and Rsch. Republican. Episcopalian. Clubs: Links, Yale, India House (N.Y.C.); Chicago; Minneapolis (Mpls.). Office: Brown Bros Harriman & Co 59 Wall St New York NY 10005-2818

WHITTEN, CHARLES ALEXANDER, JR., physics educator; b. Harrisburg, Pa., Jan. 20, 1940; s. Charles Alexander and Helen (Shoop) W.; m. Joan Emann, Nov. 20, 1965; 1 son, Charles Alexander III. B.S. summa cum laude, Yale U., 1961; Ph.D. in Physics, Princeton U., 1966. Research asso. A.W. Wright Nuclear Structure Lab., Yale U., 1966-68; asst. prof. physics UCLA, 1968-74, asso. prof., 1974-80, prof., 1980—, vice chmn. physics dept., 1982-86; vis. scientist Centre d'Etudes Nucléaires de Saclay-Moyenne Energie, 1980-81, 86-87. Contbr. articles to profl. jours. Mem. Am. Phys. Soc., Sigma Pi Sigma, Phi Beta Kappa. Home: 9844 Vicar St Los Angeles CA 90034-2719

WHITTEN, DAVID GEORGE, chemistry educator, researcher; b. Washington, Jan. 15, 1938; s. David Guy and Miriam Deland (Price) W.; m. Jo Wright, July 9, 1960; children: Jenifer Marie, Guy David. A.B., Johns Hopkins U., 1959; M.A., John Hopkins U., 1961, Ph.D., 1963. Asst. prof. chemistry U. N.C., Chapel Hill, 1966-70, asso. prof., 1970-73, prof., 1973-80, M.A. Smith prof., 1980-83; C.E. Kenneth Mees prof. U. Rochester, N.Y., 1983—, chair dept. chemistry, 1988-91; dir. Ctr. for Photoinduced charge transfer, 1989—; mem. adv. com. for chemistry NSF; cons. Eastman Kodak Co.; Rochester, N.Y. Alfred P. Sloan fellow, 1970; John van Geuns fellow, 1973; recipient special U.S. scientist award Alexander von Humboldt Found., 1975; Japan Soc. for Promotion of Sci. fellow, 1982. Mem. AAAS, Am. Chem. Soc. (award in colloid and surface chemistry 1992), Internat. Union of Pure and Applied Chemistry (commn. on photochemistry), Interam. Photochem. Soc. (pres.). Democrat. Episcopalian. Home: 72 Canterbury Rd Rochester NY 14607-3405 Office: U Rochester Dept Chemistry 404 Hutchinson Hall Rochester NY 14627

WHITTEN, DOLPHUS, JR., former university administrator, educational consortium executive; b. Hope, Ark., June 20, 1916; s. Dolphus and Annie Tyree (Logan) W.; m. Marie Braden, May 1, 1939; 1 dau., Suzanne (Mrs. H. Robert Guy). B.A., Ouachita Coll., 1936; M.A., U. Tex., 1940, Ph.D., 1961; postgrad., Western Res. U.; LL.D., McMurry Coll., Abilene, Tex., 1964. High Sch. tchr. and prin., Ark. pub. schs., 1936-42; prin. Hope Jr.-Sr. High Sch., 1945-47; dir. extension and placement services, asso. prof. history Henderson State Tchrs. Coll., Arkadelphia, Ark., 1947-58; adminstrv. dean Oklahoma City U., 1958-61, adminstrv. v.p., 1961-70, acting pres., 1962-63, 69-70, pres. 1970-79, pres. emeritus, 1979—; adj. prof. history Elon Coll., 1979-80; exec. dir. Joint Edni. Consortium, Arkadelphia, Ark., 1980-90. Bd. dirs. Ark. Humanities Coun., 1992—. Served with USAAF, 1942-45; lt. col. ret. Inducted into Okla. Hall of Fame, 1975. Mem. Am. Hist. Assn., Ark. Hist. Assn., Okla. Heritage Assn., Rotary (gov. local dist. 1991-92), Alpha Chi (past pres. region II), Pi Gamma Mu, Phi Alpha Theta, Sigma Alpha Iota. Methodist.

WHITTEN, JERRY LYNN, chemistry educator; b. Bartow, Fla., Aug. 13, 1937; s. John Graves and Dorothy Iola (Jordan) W.; m. Mary Hill (div. Sept. 1977); 1 child, Jerrard John; m. Adela Chrzeszczyk, June 21, 1980; 1 child, Christina. BS in Chemistry, Ga. Inst. Tech., 1960, PhD, 1964. Cert. chemist. Rsch. assoc. to instr. Princeton (N.J.) U., 1963-65; asst. prof. chemistry Mich. State U. East Lansing, 1965-67; asst. prof. chemistry SUNY, Stony Brook, 1967-68, assoc. prof., 1968-73, prof., 1973-89, chmn. chemistry dept., 1985-89; prof. chemistry, dean Coll. Phys. and Math. Scis. N.C. State U., Raleigh, 1989—, vis. prof. Centre Européen de Calcul Atomique et Moléculaire, Orsay, France, 1974-75, Univ. Bonn and Wuppertal, Fed. Republic Germany, 1979-80, Eidgenossische Technische Hochschule, Zurich, Switzerland, 1984. Contbr. over 100 articles to profl. jours. Recipient Alexander von Humboldt U.S. Sr. Scientist award, 1979; grantee Petroleum Rsch. Fund, 1966-67, 74-76, 77-81, NSF, 1967-72, U.S. Dept. Energy, 1977—; SDIO/ONR grantee, 1991—; Alfred P. Sloan fellow, 1969-71. Mem. AAAS, Am. Phys. Soc., Am. Chem. Soc., N.Y. Acad. Scis., Burroughs Wellcome Fund (bd. dirs.), Sigma Xi. Democrat. Episcopalian. Avocations: boating, tennis, skiing. Office: NC State U Coll Dept Phy and Math Scis Box 8201 Raleigh NC 27695-8201

WHITTEN, LESLIE HUNTER, JR., author, newspaper reporter; b. Jacksonville, Fla., Feb. 21, 1928; s. Leslie Hunter and Linnora (Harvey) W.; m. Phyllis Webber, Nov. 11, 1951; children: Leslie Hunter III, Andrew, Daniel, Deborah Wilson Gordon. B.A. in Journalism and English magna cum laude, Lehigh U., 1950, LHD, 1989. Newsman Radio Free Europe, 1952-57, I.N.S., 1957-58, U.P.I., 1958, Washington Post, 1958-63; with Hearst Newspapers, 1963-66; asst. bur. chief Hearst Newspapers, Washington, 1966-69; sr. investigator Jack Anderson's Washington Merry-Go-Round, 1969-92; pres. Athanor Inc., 1977-93; vis. assoc. prof. Lehigh U., 1967-69; adj. prof. So. Ill. U., 1984. Author: Progeny of the Adder, 1965, Moon of the Wolf, 1967, Pinion the Golden Eagle, 1968, The Abyss, 1970, F. Lee Baily, 1971, The Alchemist, 1973, Conflict of Interest, 1976, Washington Cycle, 1979, Sometimes a Hero, 1979, A Killing Pace, 1983, A Day Without Sunshine, 1985, The Lost Disciple, 1989, The Fangs of Morning, 1994. Served with AUS, 1946-48. Recipient hon. mention pub. service Washington Newspaper Guild, 1963, Edgerton award ACLU, 1974. Home and Office: 114 Eastmoor Dr Silver Spring MD 20901-1507

WHITTERS, JAMES PAYTON, III, lawyer, university administrator; b. Boston, Oct. 23, 1939; s. James P. Jr. and Norene (Jones) W.; m. Elizabeth Robertson, July 19, 1969; children: James P. IV, Catharine A. BA in History, Trinity Coll., Hartford, Conn., 1962; JD, Boston Coll., 1969; postgrad, U. Mass., Boston. Bar: Mass. 1969, U.S. Dist. Ct. Mass. 1970, U.S. Ct. Appeals (1st cir.) 1972. Assoc. Ely, Bartlett, Brown & Proctor, Boston, 1969-74; assoc. Gaston Snow & Ely Bartlett, Boston, 1974-79, ptnr., 1979-88; ptnr. Gaston & Snow, Boston, 1988-91; of counsel Peabody & Brown, Boston, 1991-95; dir. Office Career Svcs. Suffolk Univ. Law Sch., 1995—; bd. dirs., sec. Robertson Factories Inc., Taunton, Mass., 1979—; bd. dirs., v.p. Alkalol Co., Taunton, 1976—; vis. tchr. Groton (Mass.) Sch., 1993-94. Bd. dirs. New Eng. com. NAACP Legal Def. Fund, 1982—, Beacon Hill Nursery Sch., 1976-78; chmn. Mass. Outdoor Advt. Bd., Boston, 1975-81; vice chmn. Mass. Jud. Nominating Coun., Boston, 1983-87; trustee Trinity Coll., 1983—; trustee, sec. Hurrican Island Outward Bound Sch., 1977-87; vice chmn., bd. dirs. Mass. affiliate Am. Heart Assn., 1979—, chmn., 1989-91; bd. dirs. Greater Boston Legal Svcs., 1982-84, 93—, Mass. Assn. Mediation Programs, 1993—. Lt. (j.g.) USN, 1962-65. Recipient Alumni Excellence award Trinity Coll., 1987. Mem. Boston Bar Assn., Mass. Bar Assn., ABA, The Country Club (Brookline, Mass.). Democrat. Unitarian. Avocations: reading history, mountain climbing & jogging. Home: 44 Mt Vernon St Boston MA 02108

WHITTINGHAM, CHARLES ARTHUR, library administrator, publisher; b. Chgo., Feb. 11, 1930; s. Charles Arthur and Virginia (Hartke) W.; m. Jean Bragger Whittingham, June 4, 1955; children: Mary Elizabeth, Charles Arthur III, Philip Alexander, Leigh Ann. B.S. in English Lit. cum laude, Loyola U., Chgo., 1951. With McCall Corp., Chgo., 1956-59, Time, Inc., Chgo., 1959-62; pub.'s rep. Fortune mag., Time, Inc., N.Y.C., 1962-65; mgr. Fortune mag., Time, Inc. (San Francisco Office), 1965-69; asst. to pub. Fortune, N.Y.C., 1969-70, asst. pub., 1970-78; pub. Life mag., N.Y.C., 1978-88; sr. v.p. N.Y. Pub. Libr., 1989-92. Served to lt. (j.g.) USNR, 1951-55. Named to Athletic Hall of Fame Loyola U. Mem. Century Assn., Brook Club. Home and Office: 11 Woodmill Rd Chappaqua NY 10514-1128 also: 5884 Bartram St Boca Raton FL 33433-7265

WHITTINGHAM, CHARLES EDWARD, thoroughbred race horse owner and trainer; b. San Diego, Apr. 13, 1913; s. Edward and Ellen (Taylor) W.; m. Peggy Boone, Oct. 12, 1944; children: Michael Charles, Charlene. Trainer thoroughbred horses, Calif., 1930-42; asst. trainer Luro Pub. Stable, N.Y., 1945-49; owner, trainer Whittingham Pub. Stable, Sierra Madre, Calif., 1949—; winner Ky. Derby with Ferdinand, 1986, with Sunday Silence, 1989. Mem. Rep. Senatorial Inner-Circle, Washington, 1983—, nat. advisor bd. Am. Security Council, Washington, 1976—; campaigner mem. Rep. Nat. Com., Washington, 1976—. Served to master sgt. USMC, 1942-45, PTO. Recipient Eclipse awards Thoroughbred Race Track Assn./Daily Racing Form/Nat. Turf Writers Assn., 1971, 82, 89; named to Nat. Racing Hall of Fame, 1974, Brietbard Hall of Fame/Hall of Champions, San Diego, 1993. Mem. Horsemens Benevolent & Protective Assn. (v.p 1976—). Republican. Roman Catholic. Avocation: anything related to thoroughbred race horses. Home: 88 Lowell Ave Sierra Madre CA 91024-2510 Office: Charles Whittingham Inc 145 S Baldwin Sierra Madre CA 91024-2526

WHITTINGHAM, HARRY EDWARD, JR., retired banker; b. Albany, N.Y., Dec. 25, 1918; s. Harry E. and Mary (Baer) W.; m. Gladys D. Willstaedt, Sept. 2, 1942; children: Jeffrey A., Neal E. Grad., Stonier Grad. Sch. Banking, 1961. With Schenectady Trust Co., 1947-84, pres., chief exec. officer, 1974-82, chmn., chief exec. officer, 1982-84. Author: (with Purdy, Schneider, Aldom) Automation in Banking, 1962. Served with AUS, 1941-46. Episcopalian (vestryman). Clubs: Mohawk Golf (Schenectady). Home: 2314 Brookshire Dr Niskayuna NY 12309-4838

WHITTINGTON, BERNARD WILEY, electrical engineer, consultant; b. Charleston, W.Va., July 19, 1920; s. Owen Wiley and Ethel Parker (Thaxton) W.; m. Jean Wilhelm, Feb. 2, 1950; children: David Brian, Ann Leslie, Brenda Wiley. B.S. in Elec. Engring., W.Va. U., 1951. Registered profl. engr., W.Va. Elec. engr. Appalachian Power Co., Charleston, W.Va., 1951-56; mgr. sales Virginian Electric Co., Charleston, W.Va., 1956-59; engring. cons. Union Carbide Corp., Charleston, W.Va., 1959-82; pres. Whittington Engring., Inc., Charleston, W.Va., 1983—; chmn. bd. dirs. Bank of Sissonville, Pocatalico, W.Va.; pres. W.Va. Assn. Pub. Svc. Dists., 1983-86. Chmn. Water and Sewage Bd., Pocatalico, W.Va., 1958-89. Served to cpl. U.S. Army, 1942-45. Fellow IEEE (Standards Medallion award 1976, Outstanding Achievement award 1978, Centennial medal 1984, Richard Harold Kaufman award 1989); mem. Industry Applications Soc. (pres. 1982), Acad. Elec. Engring. Republican. Methodist. Lodge: Lions. Home and Office: 100 Whittingshire Ln Charleston WV 25312

WHITTINGTON, FLOYD LEON, economist, business consultant, retired oil company executive, foreign service officer; b. Fairfield, Iowa, May 27, 1909; s. Thomas Clyde and Ora E. (Trail) W.; m. Winifred Carol McDonald, July 31, 1933; children: Susan Whittington West, Thomas Lee. A.B., Parsons Coll., 1931; M.A., U. Iowa, 1936; student, U. Minn., 1940, Northwestern U., 1941-42. Econs., speech instr. Fairfield High Sch., 1931-36, Superior (Wis.) High Sch., 1936-40; supr. tchr. tng. Superior State Tchrs. Coll., 1936-40; econs., finance instr. Carroll Coll., Waukesha, Wis., 1940-42; price exec. OPA, Wis. and Iowa, 1942-46; indsl. relations mgr. Armstrong Tire & Rubber Co., Des Moines, 1946-48; dir. price and distbn. div. SCAP, Tokyo, Japan, 1948-51; Far East economist ODM, Washington, 1951-52; asst. adviser to sec. on Japanese financial and econ. problems Dept. State, Washington, 1952-53; chief Far Eastern sect. Internat. Finance div.; bd. govs. FRS, Washington, 1953-56; officer charge econ. affairs Office S.E. Asian Affairs, Dept. State, 1956-57, dep. dir., 1957-58; became counselor of embassy Am. embassy, Bangkok, 1958; counselor, polit. officer Am. embassy, Djakarta, Indonesia, 1962-65; counselor of embassy for econ. affairs Seoul, Korea, 1965-66; v.p. Pacific Gulf Oil, Ltd., Seoul, 1966—; exec. v.p. S.E. Asia Gulf Co., Bangkok, 1967-72, Gulf Oil Co. Siam, Ltd., Bangkok, 1967-72; v.p. Gulf Oil Co.-South Asia, Singapore, 1970-72; now Asian bus. cons. Recipient Meritorious Civilian Service citation Dept. Army, 1950. Mem. Am. Econ. Assn., Am. Acad. Polit. Sci., World Affairs Council Seattle (pres.), Seattle Com. Fgn. Relations, Pi Kappa Delta, Theta Alpha Phi. Presbyterian. Clubs: Royal Bangkok (Thailand); Sports; Lakes (Sun City, Ariz.). Lodges: Masons; Shriners; Rotary. Home: 1 Towers Park Ln Apt 515 San Antonio TX 78209-6421

WHITTINGTON, FREDERICK BROWN, JR., business administration educator; b. Sept. 22, 1934; m. Marjorie Ann Babington; children: Frederick Brown III, Marjorie Ellen, Lisa Anne. SB, MIT, 1958; MBA, Tulane U., 1965; PhD, La. State U., 1969. Staff economist Miss. Rsch. Commn., Jackson, 1961-64; sr. assoc. econ. rsch. Gulf South Rsch. Inst., Baton Rouge, 1966-69; asst. prof. bus. adminstrn. Emory U., Atlanta, 1969-73, assoc. prof., 1973-79, prof. bus. adminstr., 1979—, dir. customer bus. devel. track, 1991—; bd. dirs. Gwinnett Industries, Inc; mem. forecasting panel Fed. Res. Bank Atlanta; vis. prof. Johannes Kepler U., Linz, Austria, 1983, 84, 89; guest lectr. Austrian Univs., Linz, Vienna, Innsbruck and Klagenfurt; presenter workshops; cons. in field. Contbr. articles and reports to profl. jours. Mktg. plan, mgmt. audit State of Miss., Park Commn.; past chmn., bd. deacons Decatur Presbyn. Ch.; mem. adv. bd. DeKalb/Rockdale Svc. Ctr., ARC. Sears, Roebuck Found. fellow, 1965-66. Mem. Am. Mktg. Assn., Nat. Assn. Purchasing Mgmt., So. Mktg. Assn., Coun. for Logistics Mgmt., Warehousing Edn. and Rsch. Coun., Omicron Delta Kappa, Beta Gamma Sigma, Delta Tau Delta. Office: Goizueta Bus Sch Emory Univ Atlanta GA 30322

WHITTINGTON, ROBERT BRUCE, retired publishing company executive; b. Oakland, Calif., Mar. 5, 1927; s. Edward and Loretta (Edalgo) W.; m. Marie D. Sanguinetti, June 18, 1950; children: Mark, Lynn. Student, Stockton Jr. Coll., 1946-48; B.A. in Journalism and Polit. Sci. (Friend W. Richardson fellow), U. Calif., Berkeley, 1950. Reporter Stockton (Calif.) Record, 1950-60, exec. news editor, 1965-68, asso. pub., 1968-69, pub., 1969-72; v.p., dir. Speidel Newspapers, Reno, 1972-77; regional pres., dir. Gannett Co., Inc., Reno, 1977-82; publ. Reno (Nev.) newspapers, 1980-82; v.p., trustee Gannett Found., 1982-85; dir. Sierra Pacific Resources; pres. Speidel Newspapers Charitable Found. Served with USNR, 1944-46, PTO. Roman Catholic. Home: 2432 Pheasant Run Cir Stockton CA 95207-5212

WHITTINGTON, STUART GORDON, chemistry educator; b. Chesterfield, England, Apr. 16, 1942; came to Can., 1967; s. Frank and Eva May (Gretton) W.; m. Ann Fretwell, Aug. 3, 1964; children: Graeme, Megan. BA, U. Cambridge, Eng., 1963, PhD, 1967. Scientist Unilever Research, Welwyn, U.K., 1963-66, 68-70; postdoctoral fellow U. Calif., La Jolla, 1966-67; postdoctoral fellow U. Toronto, Can., 1967-68, asst. prof., 1970-75, assoc. prof., 1975-80, prof. chemistry, 1980—, chmn. dept. chemistry, 1985-88. Contbr. 150 articles to profl. jours. Mem. Am. Math. Soc. Internat. Soc. Math. Chemistry, Can. Assn. Theoretical Chemists. Mem. New Democratic Party. Avocations: music, natural history. Home: 173 Airdrie Rd Toronto, ON Canada M4G 1M7 Office: U of Toronto, Dept Chemistry, Toronto, ON Canada M5S 1A1

WHITTINGTON-GOLD, IRIS, community college educator. Dir. ctr. for Applied Gerontology Cuyahoga Comm. Coll., Cleveland, Ohio. Recipient Regional Person of the Yr. awd., Nat. Coun. on Community Services and Continuing Education, 1993. Office: Cuyahoga Community Coll Eastern Campus 4250 Richmond Rd Cleveland OH 44122

WHITTLE, CHARLES EDWARD, JR., consultant, lecturer; b. Brownsville, Ky., Mar. 8, 1931; s. Charles Edward and Lillian (Skaggs) W.; m. Suzanne Lee Miller, June 22, 1952; children: Charles, Jane, Jessica, Gayl, Tamara, Thomas, David, Jeffrey, Mary, Michael. AB, Centre Coll., Ky., 1949; PhD, Washington U., St. Louis, 1953; postgrad., U. Leiden, Netherlands, 1953-54, U. Tenn., 1975. Registered land surveyor, Ky. Engr. Union Carbide Corp., N.Y.C., 1954-56; physicist Western Ky. U., Bowling Green, 1956-62; prof., dean Centre Coll., Danville, Ky., 1962-74; researcher Inst. Energy Analysis-Oak Ridge Associated Univs., 1974-85, dir., 1985-88; v.p. C & S Assocs., Oak Ridge, Tenn., 1988-93; dean Pikeville (Ky.) Coll., 1988-93; v.p. M.W. Garay Assocs., Oak Ridge, 1993—; bd. dirs. Ky. World Trade Ctr.; cons. and lectr. in field. Author: Nuclear Moratorium, 1977; contbr. articles to profl. jours. Life mem. Ky. Hist. Soc. Fulbright scholar, 1953-54; Danforth Found. grantee, 1970. Mem. Am. Phys. Soc. (S.E. sect.), East Tenn. Hist. Soc., Oak Ridge C. of C. (indsl. recruitment com. 1984-89), Phi Beta Kappa, Sigma Xi, Rotary (Oak Ridge). bd. dirs. 1980-86, 89-90, pres. 1984-85, group study exch. team leader to Mex. 1986, chmn. dist. group study exch. com. 1987-89). Republican. Episcopalian. Avocation: genealogy. Home: 109 Trevose Ln Oak Ridge TN 37830-5454 Office: MW Garay Assocs PO Box 111 Oak Ridge TN 37831-0111

WHITTLE, JOHN JOSEPH, insurance company executive; b. Harrisburg, Pa., Mar. 3, 1936; s. Ernest James and Stephanie W.; m. Sarah A. Rausch, 1960; children: Jennifer, Jack, Lisabette. B.S., Pa. State U., 1958; grad. exec. devel. seminar, Cornell U., 1973; Masters, Am. Coll., 1986. C.L.U. Sales asst. Mut. Life Ins. Co. of N.Y., N.Y.C., 1958-65; mgr. Tacoma agy. Mut. Life Ins. Co. of N.Y., 1965-67, field sales dir. Eastern region, 1967-69, regional v.p. Central region, 1969-72, 2d v.p. for sales adminstrn., 1972-74, v.p. for sales service, 1974-76, v.p. for human resources/corp. services, 1976-79, v.p. for sales, 1979-80, sr. v.p. sales, 1980-83, sr. v.p. operating services, 1983-84, sr. v.p. Syracuse ops. MONY Fin. Services, 1984-89; pres., chief exec. officer Farmers & Traders Life Ins. Co., Cazenovia, N.Y., 1989-91, chmn., pres., chief exec. officer, 1991—; also bd. dirs. Farmers & Traders Life Ins. Co., Syracuse, N.Y.; bd. dirs. Syracuse div. Chase Manhattan Bank Adv. Bd. Bd. dirs. Community-Gen. Hosp. and Found., Met. Devel. Assn. Syracuse and Ctrl. N.Y., Inc., Syracuse Stage, Wellness Coun., LeMoyne Coll. Bd. Regents, United Way, Everson Mus. Art; mem. underwriting adv. com. WCNY-TV. With USAFR, 1961-62. Mem. Gen. Agts. and Mgrs. Assn., C.L.U. Soc., Life Underwriters Assn., Am. Coun. Life Ins. (pub. rels. policy com., bd. govs.), Syracuse C. of C. (bd. dirs.), Life Ins. Coun. N.Y., Onondaga Golf and Country Club. Republican. Methodist. Office: Farmers & Traders Life Ins Co 960 James St Syracuse NY 13203-2554

WHITTY, RAYMOND JOHN, hotel company executive; b. N.Y.C., Mar. 22, 1945; s. Raymond John and Agnes (Delaney) W.; m. Jacqueline Rae Howard, June 1, 1968; 1 son, Joseph. B.B.A., U. Portland, 1967. C.P.A., Wash. Acct., Peat Marwick Mitchell, Seattle, 1967-75; controller Arctic Marine Freighters div. Crowley Maritime Corp., Seattle, 1975-76; v.p., controller Westin Hotel Co., Seattle, 1976-84, sr. v.p., treas., 1984—. Trustee Seattle Children's Home, 1981-84. Mem. Am. Inst. C.P.A.s, Wash. Soc. C.P.A.s. Club: Sandpoint Country (Seattle). Office: Westin Hotel Co The Westin Bldg 2001 6th Ave Seattle WA 98121-2522

WHITWAM, DAVID RAY, appliance manufacturing company executive; b. Stanley, Wis., Jan. 30, 1942; s. Donald R. and Lorraine (Stoye) W.; m. Barbara Lynne Peterson, Apr. 13, 1963; children: Mark, Laura, Thomas. B.S., U. Wis., 1967. Gen. mgr. sales So. Calif. div. Whirlpool Corp., Los Angeles, 1975-77; mdse. mgr. ranges Whirlpool Corp., Benton Harbor, Mich., 1977-79, dir. builder mktg., 1979-80, v.p. builder mktg., 1980-83, v.p. whirlpool sales, 1983-85, vice chmn., chief mktg. officer, 1985-87, chmn., pres., chief exec. officer, 1987—; also bd. dirs.; bd. dirs. Combustion Engring. Inc., Stamford, Conn. Pres. bd. dirs. The Soup Kitchen, Benton Harbor, 1980—; mem. Nat. Council Housing Industry, Washington. Served to capt. U.S. Army. Fellow Aspen Inst. Republican. Lutheran. Club: Point O'Woods (Benton Harbor). Office: Whirlpool Corp 2000 M63 North Benton Harbor MI 49022*

WHITWORTH, HALL BAKER, forest products company executive; b. St. Paul, N.C., Feb. 15, 1919; s. A. Frederick and Maude Ethel (Baker) W.; m. Mary Margaret Mease, May 18, 1946; children: Hall Baker, Laura Ellen, David Allen. Student, Miss. So. Coll., 1942, U. N.C., 1957. With Champion Internat., Canton, N.C., 1936-62; mgr. materials Champion Internat., Canton, 1956-62; dir. materials packages div. Champion Internat., Chgo., 1962-65; dir. purchase U.S. Plywood-Champion Papers, Inc. (now champion Internat. Corp.) Champion Internat., Hamilton, Ohio, 1965-68, dep. dir. corporate materials services, 1966, v.p., dir. purchase, 1968-75; v.p. materials Champion Internat., Stamford, Conn., 1975—, dir., 1975—, now ret.; v.p., dir. So. Agri. Co., 1985—; pres., dir. H. Whitworth Enterprises, Inc., 1985—; dir. Pathfork-Harlan Coal Co. Served with U.S. Army, 1942-46. Recipient Thomas award Carolina-Va. Purchasing Agts. Assn., 1963. Mem. Am. Paper Inst. (chmn. energy subcom.), Am. Mgmt. Assn. (v.p. purchasing, transp. and phys. distbn. div. council). Methodist. Club: Canton Toastmakers (founder, 1st pres.). Lodges: Elks; Lions. Home and Office: 858 Lullwater Dr Oviedo FL 32765-8512

WHITWORTH, JOHN HARVEY, JR., lawyer; b. Pontotoc, Miss., Aug. 13, 1933; s. John Harvey Sr. and Clara Gladys (Tudor) W. BBA, U. Miss. 1955, JD, 1961; student, U. Delhi, India, 1958-59. Bar: Miss. 1961, N.Y. 1962, U.S. Supreme Ct.1965. Assoc. Dewey Ballantine, N.Y.C., 1961-69, ptnr., 1969-93. Editor in chief U. Miss. Law Jour., 1961. Mem. adv. bd. Nat. Arboretum, Washington, 1986-88; mem. vestry St. Peter's Ch. at Lithgow, Millbrook, N.Y., 1987—. Served with U.S. Army, 1955-57. Mem. Southwestern Legal Found. (trustee 1986—, chmn. Internat. and Comp. Law Ctr. 1984-85). Republican. Episcopalian. Clubs: Knickerbocker (N.Y.C.), Sandanona Hare Hounds (Millbrook, N.Y.). Avocations: landscape gardening, dogs. Home: PO Box 398 Millbrook NY 12545-0398 Office: Dewey Ballantine 1301 Avenue Of The Americas New York NY 10019-6092

WHITWORTH, KATHRYNNE ANN, professional golfer; b. Monahans, Tex., Sept. 27, 1939; d. Morris Clark and Dama Ann (Robinson) W. Student, Odessa (Tex.) Jr. Coll., 1958. Joined tour Ladies Profl. Golf Assn., 1959—; mem. adv. staff Walter Hagen Golf Co., Wilson Sporting Goods Co. Named to Hall of Fame Ladies Profl. Golf Assn., Tex. Sports Hall of Fame, Tex. Golf Hall of Fame, World Golf Hall of Fame; Capt. of Solheim Cup, 1990-92. Mem. Ladies Profl. Golf Assn. (sec. 1962-63, v.p. 1965, 73, 88, pres. 1967, 68, 71, 89, 1st mem. to win over $1,000,000). Office: care Ladies Profl Golf Assn 2570 Volusia Ave Daytona Beach FL 32114-1119

WHITWORTH, WILLIAM A., magazine editor; b. Hot Springs, Ark., Feb. 13, 1937; s. William C. and Lois Virginia (McNabb) W.; m. Carolyn Hubbard, Dec. 27, 1969; children—Matthew, Katherine. B.A., U. Okla., 1960. Reporter Ark. Gazette, Little Rock, 1960-63; reporter N.Y. Herald Tribune, 1963-65; staff writer The New Yorker, 1966-72, assoc. editor, 1973-80; editor-in-chief The Atlantic Monthly, Boston, 1981—. Office: Atlantic Monthly 745 Boylston St Boston MA 02116-2636

WHORISKEY, ROBERT DONALD, lawyer; b. Cambridge, Mass., May 9, 1929; s. John Joseph and Katherine Euphemia (MacDonald) W.; m. Martha Beebe Poutas, Apr. 16, 1966; children: Alexandra, Jonathan, Eliza. A.B., Harvard U., 1952; J.D., Boston Coll., 1958; LL.M., NYU, 1960. Bar: Mass. 1958, N.Y. 1963, U.S. Tax Ct. 1961, U.S. Claims Ct. 1969, U.S. Dist. Ct. (so. dist.) N.Y. 1969, U.S. Ct. Customs 1971, U.S. Ct. Appeals (2d cir.) 1972, U.S. Ct. Appeals (3d cir.) 1983, U.S. Ct. Appeals (D.C. cir.) 1991, U.S. Supreme Ct. 1974. Sr. trial atty. Office Chief Counsel, IRS, N.Y.C., 1960-67; assoc. Curtis, Mallet-Prevost, Colt & Mosle, N.Y.C., 1967-70, ptnr., 1970—, mem. exec. com., 1978-82, chmn. tax dept., 1982-87; bd. dirs. Internat. Tax Inst., v.p., lectr., 1980-84, chmn. bd., pres., lectr., 1985-87; lectr. Practicing Law Inst., World Trade Inst., Tax Execs. Inst., Am. Mgmt. Assn., Coun. for Internat. Tax Edn.; bd. dirs. Life Ins. Co. of Boston and N.Y., Inc. Author: Foreign Trusts, 1977, Annual Institute on International Taxation, 1966, 80, 81 (with Sidney Pine, Ralph Seligman) Tax and Business Benefits of the Bahamas, 1986; contbg. author: International Boycotts, Bender's Federal Tax Service, 1988, Third Party Information, John Wiley and Sons, Inc.'s Transfer Pricing, 1993. Trustee, treas. Montessori Sch. Westchester, 1974-77; mem. bd. ethics Village of Larchmont, N.Y., 1988—. Served with U.S. Army, 1952-54. Mem. ABA (com. on value added tax tax sect. 1994—), N.Y. State Bar Assn. (com. on practice and procedure tax sect. 1990—), Assn. of the Bar of the City of N.Y., Harvard Club, Larchmont Yacht Club. Democrat. Roman Catholic. Office: Curtis Mallet-Prevost Colt & Mosle 101 Park Ave New York NY 10178-0061

WHORTON, M. DONALD, occupational and environmental health physician, epidemiologist; b. Las Vegas, N.Mex., Jan. 25, 1943; s. R.H. and Rachel (Siegal) W.; m. Diana L. Obrinsky, Apr. 9, 1972; children: R. Matthew Richard, Laura Elizabeth, Julie Hannah. Student, U.S. Naval Acad., 1961-62; B.Biology, N. Mex. Highlands U., 1964; M.D., U. N.Mex., 1968; M.P.H., Johns Hopkins U., 1973. Intern Boston City Hosp., 1968-69; resident in pathology U. N.Mex., Albuquerque, 1969-71; instr., resident in medicine Balt. City Hosp., 1972-74; instr. Johns Hopkins U., Balt.; assoc. dir. div. emergency medicine Balt. City Hosps., 1974-75; clin. asst. prof. div. ambulatory and community medicine Sch. Medicine, U. Calif.-San Francisco, 1975-77; lectr. sch. pub. health program Inst. Indsl. Relations, Ctr. for Labor Research and Edn., 1975-79, med. dir. labor occupational program, 1975-79, assoc. clin. prof. occupational medicine, 1979-88; prin. Environ. Health Assocs., Inc., Oakland, 1978-88; v.p. ENSR Health Scis., 1988-94; pvt. practice Alameda, Calif., 1994—; chmn. adv. com. for hazard evaluation service and info. system Indsl. Relations Dept. State of Calif., 1979-84; cons. in field. Contbr. articles to profl. jours. Recipient Upjohn Achievement award, 1968; Robert Wood Johnson Found. clin. scholar, 1972-74. Fellow Am. Coll. Epidemiology, Am. Coll. Occupational and Environ. Medicine; mem. Am. Pub. Health Assn., Soc. for Occupational and Environ. Health, Am. Coll. Emergency Physicians, Calif. Med. Assn., AAAS, Inst. Medicine, Nat. Acad. Sci., Alpha Omega Alpha. Office: 1135 Atlantic Ave Alameda CA 94501

WHYBARK, DAVID CLAY, educator, researcher; b. Tacoma, Wash., Sept. 18, 1935; s. Clay Alfred and Irene (Stanton) W.; m. Neva Jo Richardson, July 6, 1957; children: Michael David, Suzanne Marie (dec.). BS, U. Washington, 1957; MBA, Cornell U., 1960; PhD, Stanford U., 1967. Rsch. assoc. Stanford (Calif.) U., 1962-67; asst. prof. Ariz. State U., Tempe, 1965-66; assoc. prof. Purdue U., West Lafayette, Ind., 1967-76; prof. Ind. U., Bloomington, 1976-90; Macon G. Patton disting. prof. U. N.C., Chapel Hill, 1990—; vis. prof. Shanghai Inst. Mech. Engring., 1986-87; adj. prof. Inst. for Mgmt. Devel., Lausanne, Switzerland, 1981-82, 85-90; dir., founder Global Mfg. Rsch. Group, 1990—; cons. in field. Author: Master Production Scheduling: Theory and Practice, 1979, Manufacturing Planning Control Systems, 1984, 2d edit., 1988, 3d edit., 1992, International Operations Management, 1989, Integrated Production and Inventory Management, 1993; editor: Global Manufacturing Practices, 1993; editor Internat. Jour. Prodn. Econs., 1991—. Recipient Lilly Alumni MBA Teaching Excellence award, 1990. Fellow Decision Scis. Inst. (past pres., disting. svc. award 1984), Pan Pacific Bus. Assn. (mem. coun.); mem. Ops. Mgmt. Assn. (pres. 1992-93), Am. Prodn. Inventory Control Soc., Internat. Soc. Inventory Rsch. (mem. coun., chair mgmt. sect.), Assn. Mfg. Excellence. Avocations: travel, winemaking. Office: U NC Kenan-Flagler Sch Global Mfg Rsch Ctr Chapel Hill NC 27599-3490

WHYBROW, PETER CHARLES, psychiatrist, educator; b. Hertforshire, Eng., June 13, 1939; came to U.S., 1964, naturalized, 1975; s. Charles Ernest and Doris Beatrice (Abbott) W.; m. Margaret Ruth Steele, Dec. 11, 1962 (div. 1988); children: Katherine, Helen. Student, Univ. Coll., London, 1956-59; M.B., B.S., Univ. Coll. Hosp. Med. Sch., 1962; diploma psychol. medicine, Conjoint Bd., London, 1968; M.A. (hon.), Dartmouth Coll., 1974, U. Pa., 1984. House officer endocrinology Univ. Coll. Hosp., 1962, sr. house physician psychiatry, 1963-64; house surgeon St. Helier Hosp., Surrey, Eng., 1963; house officer pediatrics Prince of Wales Hosp., London, 1964; resident psychiatry U. N.C. Hosp., 1965-67, instr., research fellow, 1967-68; asst. prof. psychiatry, 1968-69; dir. residency tng. psychiatry Dartmouth Med. Sch., Hanover, N.H., 1969-71; prof. psychiatry Dartmouth Med. Sch., 1970-84, chmn. dept., 1970-78, exec. dean, 1980-83; prof., chmn. dept. psychiatry U. Pa., Phila., 1984—, Ruth Meltzer prof. psychiatry, 1992; psychiatrist-in-chief Hosp. U. Pa., 1984—; dir. psychiatry Dartmouth Hitchcock Affiliated Hosp., 1970-78; vis. scientist NIMH, 1978-79; cons. VA, 1970—, NIMH, 1972—; chmn. test com. Nat. Bd. Med. Examiners, 1977-84; researcher psychoendocrinology. Author: Mood Disorders: Toward a New Psychobiology, 1984, The Hibernation Response, 1988; editor: Psychosomatic Medicine, 1977; mem. editl. bd. Cmty. Psychiatry, Psychiat. Times, Directions in Psychiatry, Neuropsychopharmacology; contbr. articles to profl. jours. Recipient Anclote Manor award psychiat. rsch. U. N.C., 1967, Sr. Investigator award Nat. Alliance for Rsch. into Schizophrenia and Depression, 1989; Josiah Macy Jr. Found. scholar, 1978-79; fellow Cen. for Advanced Studies in Behavioral Sci., Stanford, 1993-94. Fellow Am. Psychiat. Assn., Royal Coll. Psychiatrists (founding mem.), Am. Coll. Psychiatrists (Knight of Merit, Sovereign Order of St. John of Jerusalem 1993), Ctr. Advanced Study of Behavioral Scis., AAAS; mem. Assn. Am. Med. Colls., Soc. Psychosomatic Rsch., Am. Assn. Chmn. Depts. Psychiatry (pres. 1977-78), Royal Soc. Medicine, Am. Psychopath Assn., Soc. Biol. Psychiatry, N.Y. Acad. Scis., Soc. Neurosci., Sigma Xi, Alpha Omega Alpha, Cosmos Club (Washington). Club: Cosmos (Washington). Office: U Pa Dept Psychiatry 305 Blockley Hall Philadelphia PA 19104 also: 135 S 19th St Philadelphia PA 19103-4912

WHYTE, ANNE VERONICA, social science researcher, educator; b. Thorne, U.K., Apr. 14, 1942; arrived in Can., 1975; d. Philip and Grace Grant Mathieson (Tennant) Whyte; m. Robert Dewfall Auger; children from previous marriages: David Philip Kirkby, Clare Anne Kirkby, Joanna Catherine Whyte Burton. BA with honors, Cambridge U., Eng., 1963, MA, 1967; PhD, Johns Hopkins U., 1971. Geographer div. anthropology Smithsonian Inst., Washington, 1965-66; rsch. fellow Centre Latin-Am. Studies, U. Cambridge, 1967-68; rsch. assoc. depts. geography and psychology U. Bristol, Eng., 1968-74; univ. lectr. dept. geography U. Coll., U. London, 1974-75; assoc. prof. geography U. Toronto, Ont., Can., 1976-78, dir. undergrad. environ. studies Innis Coll., 1976-88; programme specialist MAB Programme Div. Ecol. Scis. UNESCO, Paris, 1984-86; dir. social scis. div. Internat. Devel. Rsch. Centre, Ottawa, Ont., Can., 1986-92, dir. gen., environment and natural resources div., 1992—; chairperson African Econ. Rsch. Consortium Inc., N.Y.C., 1987-90, Can. Nat. Com. UNESCO/MAB, Ottawa, 1989-93; Can. Global Change Program, Ottawa, 1990-92; mem. exec. bd. Can. Commn. for UNESCO, Ottawa, 1988-92; mem. internat. adv. com. Internat. Coun. Sci. Unions; active Ont. Roundtable for Environment and Economy, 1993—. Author: Land and Water Resources in Oaxaca, Mexico, 1973, Field Studies in Environmental Perception, 1977, Environmental Risk Assessment, 1980. Open Exhbn. and State scholar Girton Coll., Eng., 1961-63, Fulbright scholar Cambridge U., 1963-65. Fellow Royal Soc. Can., World Acad. Arts and Sci.; mem. Am. Assn. Geography, Can. Assn. Geographers (v.p.), Can. Assn. Geographers (v.p. 1993-94, pres. 1994—), Internat. Coun. Sci. Unions (mem. internat. adv. com.), Cambridge Club, McGill U. Club, Sigma Xi. Avocations: farming, ferns. Home: White House Farm, RR 2, Russell, ON Canada K4R 1E5 Office: Internat Devel Rsch Centre, 250 Albert St PO Box 8500, Ottawa, ON Canada K1G 3H9

WHYTE, GEORGE KENNETH, JR., lawyer; b. Waukegan, Ill., Oct. 10, 1936; s. George K. and Ella Margaret (Osgood) W.; m. Ann B. Challoner, June 20, 1964; children: Mary, Douglas. AB in Polit. Sci., Duke U., 1958;

LLB, U. Wis., 1965. Bar: Wis. 1965. Law clk. to chief justice Wis. Supreme Ct., Madison, 1965-66; assoc. Quarles & Brady, Milw., 1966-73, ptnr., 1973—. Lt. USN, 1958-62. Mem. ABA (employment law sect.), Wis. Bar Assn. (former chmn. labor and employment law sect.), Rotary. Congregationalist. Clubs: The Town, Milw. Athletic, Milw. Country. Home: 906 E Circle Dr Milwaukee WI 53217 Office: Quarles & Brady 411 E Wisconsin Ave Milwaukee WI 53202-4409

WHYTE, JAMES PRIMROSE, JR., former law educator; b. Columbus, Miss., Aug. 25, 1921; s. James P. and Mary (Savage) W.; m. Martha Ann Jones, Sept. 11, 1948; children—James Jones, Stuart Ward, Wilson Scott. A.B., Bucknell U., 1943; M.A., Syracuse U., 1948; J.D., U. Colo., 1951. Bar: Okla. 1951, Mo. 1957, Va. 1961. With firm Gordon & Whyte, McAlester, Okla., 1951-55; county atty. Pittsburg County, Okla., 1955-56; atty. Great Lakes Pipe Line Co., Kansas City, Mo., 1957; prof. law Coll. William and Mary, 1958-82, asst. dean, 1958-68, asso. dean, 1969-70, dean, 1970-75; ad hoc arbitrator Fed. Mediation and Conciliation Svc., Va. Dept. Labor, also industry and govt. panels. Contbr. profl. jours.; Mem. editorial adv. bd.: John Marshall Papers, 1966-77. Mem. Bd. Zoning Appeals, Williamsburg, 1971-77, chmn., 1977; trustee, pres. Williamsburg Regional Libr., 1965; trustee Williamsburg Area Meml. Community Ctr., 1963-68, pres., 1966-67. Served with USNR, 1943-46. Mem. Nat. Acad. Arbitrators, Va. State Bar, Phi Beta Kappa, Tau Kappa Alpha, Sigma Tau Delta. Home and Office: 1109 Jamestown Rd Williamsburg VA 23185-3315

WHYTE, MARTIN KING, sociology and Chinese studies educator; b. Oklahoma City, Nov. 4, 1942; s. William Foote and Kathleen (King) W.; m. Veronica Mueller, Nov. 5, 1966 (div. 1990); children: Adam, Tracy; m. Alice Hogan, Sept. 14, 1991; 1 child, Julia. A.B., Cornell U., 1964; M.A., Harvard U., 1966, Ph.D., 1971. From asst. prof. to prof. dept. sociology U. Mich., Ann Arbor, 1969-95; assoc. chmn. dept. sociology U. Mich., 1972-73, 79-81; dir. Univs. Service Ctr., Hong Kong, 1973-74; program dir.Sociology Program NSF, Washington, 1993-94; prof. dept. sociology George Washington U., Washington, 1995—; vis. prof. George Washington U., 1994-95; mem. joint com. on Chinese studies Am. Coun. of Learned Socs., 1978-81, 84-87; dir. Ctr. for Rsch. on Social Orgn., 1984-87, 90-92. Author: Small Groups and Political Rituals in China, 1974, The Status of Women in Preindustrial Societies, 1978; (with others) Village and Family in Contemporary China, 1978, Urban Life in Contemporary China, 1984, Dating, Mating and Marriage, 1990. Mem. Am. Sociol. Assn., Assn. Asian Studies, Phi Beta Kappa. Democrat. Avocation: tennis. Home: 10403 Muir Pl Kensington MD 20895-2929 Office: Dept Sociology The George Washington U 2129 G St NW Washington DC 20052

WHYTE, MICHAEL PETER, medicine and pediatrics educator, research director; b. N.Y.C., Dec. 19, 1946; s. Michael Paul and Sophie (Dziuk) W.; m. Gloria Frances Golenda, Oct. 26, 1974; 1 child, Catherine Alexandra. BA in Chemistry, NYU, 1968; MD, SUNY, N.Y.C., 1972. Diplomate Am. Bd. Internal Medicine, Nat. Bd. Med. Examiners. Intern, 1st yr. resident dept. medicine NYU Sch. Medicine Bellevue Hosp., N.Y.C., 1972-74; clin. assoc. devel. and metabolic neurology br. Nat. Inst. Neurol. and Communicative Disorders and Stroke NIH, Bethesda, Md., 1974-76; fellow divsn. bone and mineral metabolism dept. medicine Wash. U. Sch. Medicine, 1976-79, instr. dept. medicine, 1979-80, asst. sci. dir. Clin. Rsch. Ctr., 1979—; asst. physician Barnes Hosp., 1979—; dir. Metabolism Clinic Shriners Hosp. Crippled Children, St. Louis, 1979—; staff physician St. Louis Children's Hosp., 1979—; NIH clin. assoc. physician Clin. Rsch. Ctr. Wash. U. Sch. Medicine, 1980-82, asst. prof. medicine dept. medicine, 1980-86, assoc. prof. medicine dept. medicine, 1986-91, asst. prof. pediatrics Edward Mallinckrodt dept. pediatrics, 1982-89, assoc. prof. pediatrics Edward Mallinckrodt dept. pediatrics, 1989-92, prof. medicine dept. medicine, 1991—, prof. pediatrics Edward Mallinckrodt dept. pediatrics, 1992—; med. dir. Metabolic Rsch. Unit Shriners Hosp. Crippled Children, St. Louis, 1982—, mem. staff, 1983—; assoc. attending physician Jewish Hosp. St. Louis, 1983—; staff cons. Shriners Hosp. Crippled Children, St. Louis, 1979-83, Mexico City, 1991—; mem. consulting med. staff St. Louis Zoo, 1992—; mem. editorial bd. Calcified Tissue Internat., 1985-88, Jour. Bone and Mineral Rsch., 1994; mem. med. adv. bd. Osteogenesis Imperfecta Found., 1986—, med. adv. panel Paget's Disease Found., 1986—; chmn. med. adv. coun., bd. dirs. Osteogenesis Found., 1995—. Editor: Primer on Metabolic Bone Diseases and Disorders of Mineral Metabolism, 1990; assoc. editor Calcified Tissue Internat., 1989—; contbr. chpts. to books; contbr. over 100 articles to profl. jours. Lt. comdr. USPHS, 1974-76. Mem. Am. Soc. Cell Biology, Am. Soc. Clin. Investigation, Am. Coll. Physicians (assoc.), Am. Fedn. Clin. Rsch., Am. Soc. Advancement Sci., Am. Soc. Bone and Mineral Rsch. (ednl. com. 1987—, Fuller Albright award 1987, Young Investigator award 1983), Am. Soc. Human Genetics, Endocrine Soc., Soc. Experimental Biology and Medicine, Japanese Soc. Inherited Metabolic Disease. Office: Jewish Hosp St Louis 216 S Kings Hwy Saint Louis MO 63110

WHYTE, RONALD M., federal judge; b. 1942. BA in Math, Wesleyan U., 1964; JD, U. So. Calif., 1967. Bar: Calif. 1967, U.S. Dist. Ct. (no. dist.) Calif. 1967, U.S. Dist. Ct. (cen. dist.) Calif. 1968, U.S. Ct. Appeals (9th cir.) 1986. Assoc. Hoge, Fenton Jones & Appel, Inc., San Jose, Calif., 1971-77, mem., 1977-89; judge Superior Ct. State of Calif., 1989-92, U.S. Dist. Ct. (no. dist.) Calif., San Jose, 1992—; judge pro-tempore Superior Ct. Calif., 1977-89; lectr. Calif. Continuing Edn. of Bar, Rutter Group, Santa Clara Bar Assn., State Bar Calif.; legal counsel Santa CLara County Bar Assn., 1986-89; mem. county select com. Criminal Conflicts Program, 1988. Bd. trustees Santa Clara County Bar Assn., 1978-79, 84-85. U. Judge Advocate Gen.'s Corps, USNR, 1968-71. Recipient Judge of Yr. award Santa Clara County Trial Lawyers Assn., 1992, Am. Jurisprudence award. Mem. Calif. Judges Assn., Assn. Bus. Trial Lawyers (bd. govs. 1991-93). Office: US Courthouse 280 S 1st St San Jose CA 95113-3002

WHYTE, WILLIAM FOOTE, industrial relations educator, author; b. Springfield, Mass., June 27, 1914; s. John and Isabel (VanSickle) W.; m. Kathleen King, May 28, 1938; children: Joyce, Martin, Lucy, John. A.B., Swarthmore Coll., 1936, L.H.D. (hon.), 1984; mem., Soc. of Fellows, Harvard U., 1936-40; Ph.D., U. Chgo., 1943. Asst. prof. sociology, acting chmn. dept. anthropology U. Okla., 1942-43; asst., then assoc. prof. sociology U. Chgo., 1944-48, exec. sec. Com. Human Relations in Industry, 1946-48; prof. indsl. relations N.Y. State Sch. Indsl. and Labor Relations, Cornell U., 1948-79; dir. Social Sci. Research Center, 1956-61; rsch. dir. Programs for Employment and Workplace Systems Sch. Indsl. and Labor Rels., 1984—; dir. O & O Investment Fund, 1983. Author: Street Corner Society, 1943, Human Relations in the Restaurant Industry, 1948, Pattern for Industrial Peace, 1951, Money and Motivation, 1955, Man and Organization, 1959, Men at Work, 1961, Organizational Behavior, 1969, Organizing for Agricultural Development, 1975, Learning from the Field, 1984, Participatory Action Research, 1990, Participant Observer: An Autobiography, 1994; co-author: Action Research for Management, 1965, Toward an Integrated Theory of Development, 1968, Dominación y Cambios en el Peru Rural, 1969, Power, Politics, and Progress, 1976, Worker Participation and Ownership, 1983, Higher Yielding Human Systems for Agriculture, 1983, Making Mondragón, 1988, 91, Social Theory for Action, 1991; editor: Industry and Society, 1946, Human Organization, 1956-61, 62-63, Street Corner Society (4th expanded edit. 50th anniversary), 1993. Trustee Found. Research Human Behavior, 1960-67; bd. dirs. Nat. Ctr. for Employee Ownership, 1981-88. Fulbright fellow Peru, 1961-62; recipient Career Research award NIMH. Mem. Am. Sociol. Assn. (pres. 1981), Am. Acad. Arts and Scis., Soc. Applied Anthropology (pres. 1964), Indsl. Rels. Rsch. Assn. (pres. 1963). Home: 1 Sundowns Rd Ithaca NY 14850 *In social research, I have been as much concerned with practical applications as with scientific knowledge, and I have always sought to express findings in simple and clear prose.*

WIANT, SARAH KIRSTEN, law library administrator, educator; b. Waverly, Iowa, Nov. 20, 1946; s. James Allen and Eva (Jorgensen) W.; m. Robert E. Akins. BA, Western State Coll., 1968; MLS, U. North Tex., 1970; JD, Washington & Lee U., 1978. Asst. law librarian Tex. Tech. U., 1970-72; asst. law librarian Washington & Lee U., 1972—, 1978—, asst. prof. law, 1978-83, assoc. prof. law, 1984-92, prof. law, 1993—. Co-author: Copyright Handbook, 1984, Librarians and Copyright Law in the 1990s, 1994 Legal Research In the District of Columbia, Maryland and Virginia; contbr. chpts. to books; mem. adv. bd. Westlaw, 1990-93. Mem. ABA (com.

on libraries 1987-93), Am. Assn. Law Libraries (program chmn. for ann. meeting 1987, copyright office rep.), Am. Law Sch. (chmn. sec. on librs. 1990-92, accreditation com. 1991-94), Spl. Libraries Assn. (chair copyright com. 1990—), Maritime Law Assn., U.S. Trademark Assn. Office: Washington & Lee U Law Libr Lewis Hall Lexington VA 24450

WIATT, JAMES ANTHONY, theatrical agency executive; b. L.A., Oct. 18, 1946; s. Norman and Catherine (Sonners) W.; m. Randie Laine. BA, U. So. Calif., 1969. Campaign coord. Tunney for Senate, L.A., 1969-71; admnstrv. asst. Senator John V. Tunney, L.A., 1972-75; agt. FCA, L.A., 1976-78; lit. agt. Internat. Creative Mgmt., L.A., 1978-81, motion picture agt., 1981-83, head of motion picture dept., 1983-85, pres., COO, 1985—. Office: Internat Creative Mgmt 8899 Beverly Blvd Los Angeles CA 90048*

WIBERG, KENNETH BERLE, chemist, educator; b. Bklyn., Sept. 22, 1927; s. Dan and Solveig Berle W.; m. Marguerite Koch, Mar. 18, 1951; children—Patricia, Robert, William. B.S., Mass. Inst. Tech., 1948; Ph.D., Columbia, 1950. Mem. faculty U. Wash., 1950-62, prof. chemistry, 1958-62; prof. chemistry Yale U., 1962—, Whitehead prof., 1968-90, Eugene Higgins prof., 1990—, chmn. chem. dept., 1987-71; Boomer lectr. U. Alta., Can., 1959; Mem. chemistry advisory panel Air Force Office Sci. Research, 1960-66, NSF, 1965-68, chmn., 1967-68. Author: Laboratory Technique in Organic Chemistry, 1960, Interpretation of NMR Spectra, 1962, Physical Organic Chemistry, 1964, Computer Programming for Chemists, 1966, also articles.; Editor: Oxidation in Organic Chemistry, 1966, Sigma M.O. Theory, 1970; mem. editorial bd.: Organic Syntheses, 1963-71, Jour. Organic Chemistry, 1968-72, J. Computer Chem., 1982—, Tetrahedron, 1981—, Chemical Revs., 1986—; bd. editors: Jour. Am. Chem. Soc, 1969-72. Recipient James Flack Norris award, 1973, Arthur C. Cope award 1988; Sloan Found. fellow, 1958-62; Guggenheim fellow, 1961-62; Cope scholar, 1986. Mem. Nat. Acad. Scis., Am. Acad. Arts and Scis., Am. Chem. Soc. (exec. com. organic div. 1961-63, Calif. sect. award 1963, Linus Pauling award 1992). Home: 160 Carmalt Rd Hamden CT 06517-1904 Office: Yale U Chemistry Dept New Haven CT 06520

WIBERG, LARS-ERIK, human resources consultant; b. Wakefield, Mass., June 1, 1928; s. Sverker Clauson and Ingrid (Heurlin) W.; m. Elizabeth Margaret Allenbrook, Oct. 18, 1957; children: Kirsten, Margaret, Brenda. BS in Geology, MIT, 1950; MA in Teaching, Harvard U., 1952. From engr. to dir. corp. communications EG&G Inc., Boston and Bedford, Mass., 1956-69; from asst. v.p. to v.p. compensation and orgnl. planning First Nat. Bank of Boston, 1969-81; cons. Rockport, Mass., 1981—; lectr. human resources mgmt. Boston U., 1988-92; lectr. job search and career planning U. Karlstad, Sweden, 1992. Author: It's Your Move, 1991; inventor in field. Mem. Planning Bd., Rockport, 1965-72, chmn., 1969-72; pres. ch. coun. Swedenborg Chapel, Cambridge, Mass., 1984—; dir. Mass. New Ch. Union, 1990—; mem. Zoning Bd. Appeals, Rockport, 1986—. 1st lt. USAF, 1953-55. Mem. Affiliated New Eng. Cons. (founder Lexington, Mass. 1985—), Heritage Found., Swedenborg Sci. Assn. Republican. Avocations: church work, home repairs, music, gardening, reading. Home and Office: 156 South St Rockport MA 01966

WIBERLEY, STEPHEN EDWARD, chemistry educator, consultant; b. Troy, N.Y., May 31, 1919; s. Irving Charles and Ruth (Stanley) W.; m. Mary Elizabeth Bartle, Feb. 21, 1942; children: Stephen Edward, Sharon Elizabeth. B.A., Williams Coll., 1941; M.S., Rensselaer Poly. Inst., 1948, Ph.D., 1950. Sr. chemist Congoleum Nairn, Inc., Kearny, N.J., 1941-44; prof. chemistry Rensselaer Poly. Inst., Troy, N.Y., 1946—, chmn. dept. chemistry, 1984-88; dean Rensselaer Poly. Inst. (Grad. Sch.), 1964-79, vice provost, 1969-79; vis. sr. physicist Brookhaven Nat. Lab., Upton, N.Y., 1950; cons. Imperial Paper & Color Corp., Glens Falls, N.Y., 1957—, Socony Mobil Oil Co., Bklyn., 1957—, Huyck Felt Co., Rensselaer, N.Y., 1958—, Schenectady Chems. Inc., 1961—, U.S. Gypsum Co., Buffalo, 1962—. Author: Instrumental Analysis, 1954, Laboratory Manual for General Chemistry, 1963, Introduction to Infrared and Raman Spectroscopy, 1964. Served with AUS, 1944-46. Mem. Am. Chem. Soc., AAUP, Sigma Xi, Phi Lambda Upsilon. Home: 1676 Tibbits Ave Troy NY 12180-3726

WIBORG, JAMES HOOKER, chemicals distribution company executive; b. Seattle, Aug. 26, 1924; s. John R. and Hazel (Hooker) W.; m. Ann Rogers, July 1948; children: Katherine Ann, Mary Ellen, Caroline Joan, John Stewart. B.A., U. Wash., 1946. Owner, Wiborg Mfg. Co., Tacoma, 1946-50; securities analyst Pacific N.W. Co., Seattle, 1950-53; founder Western Plastics Corp., Tacoma, 1953; pres. Western Plastics Corp., 1953-55, chmn. bd., dir.; exec. v.p. Wash. Steel Products Co., Tacoma, 1955-58; mgmt. cons. Tacoma, 1958-60; v.p. United Pacific Corp., Seattle, 1960; pres. Pacific Small Bus. Investment Corp., Seattle, 1963-65; sr. v.p. indsl. div. United Pacific Corp., Seattle, 1963-65; pres., chief exec. officer, dir. United Pacific Corp., 1965; past pres., chief exec. officer, dir. Univar Corp. (formerly VWR United Corp.), Seattle, from 1966; chmn., chief exec. officer Univar Corp. (formerly VWR United Corp.), 1983-86; chief strategist, 1986-91, chmn., 1991—; dir., chmn., chief strategist VWR Corp., 1986—; dir. PACCAR Inc., Gensco Inc., Tacoma, Penwest Ltd., PrimeSource Corp. Clubs: Tacoma Country and Golf, Tacoma, Tacoma Yacht; Rainier (Seattle), Columbia Tower (Seattle). Office: Univar Corp PO Box 34325 Seattle WA 98124-1325

WICE, PAUL CLINTON, news director, educator; b. West Branch, Mich., Sept. 30, 1944; s. Clinton Harold and Viola Ruth (Potratz) W.; m. Dolores Ann Janovec, Sept. 30, 1967. BA, Kearney State Coll., 1966; MA, U. Nebr., Kearney, 1989. News anchor Sta. KHGI-TV, Kearney, Nebr., 1965-66; news editor Sta. KWBE Radio, Beatrice, Nebr., 1966-67; city editor Kearney Hub, 1968-69; news dir. Sta. KGFW-AM, Kearney, 1967-68, 69—; adj. faculty speech communication U. Nebr., Kearney, 1981—. Bd. dirs. Buffalo County Crimestoppers, Kearny Area Habitat for Humanity, Luth. Family Svcs. of Nebr.; bd. dirs., patron chair Community Concert Assn. Mem. Soc. Profl. Jours. (bd. dirs. Nebr. chpt.). Home: Box 1754 3602 11th Ave Kearney NE 68848-1754 Office: Sta KGFW-AM PO Box 666 Kearney NE 68848-0666

WICHA, MAX S., oncologist, educator; b. N.Y.C., Mar. 24, 1949; m. Sheila Crowley; children: Jason, Allyson. BS in Biology summa cum laude with honors, SUNY, Stony Brook, 1970; MD, Stanford U., 1974. Diplomate Am. Bd. Internal Medicine; lic. physician, Mich., Ill. Intern in internal medicine U. Chgo. Hosps. and Clinics, 1974-75, jr., sr. resident in internal medicine, 1975-77; rsch. assoc. lab. pathophysiology Nat. Cancer Inst./NIH, Bethesda, Md., 1977-79, fellow in clin. oncology, 1978-80, investigator lab. pathophysiology, 1979-80; asst. prof. internal medicine divsn. hematology and oncology U. Mich., Ann Arbor, 1980-83, assoc. prof., 1983-88, prof., 1988—, mem. tumor metastasis, extracellular matrrix, reproductive endocrinology programs, 1982—, dir. divsn. hematology and oncology, dir. Simpson Meml. Rsch. Inst., 1984-93, mem. program in cellular and molecular biology, 1984—, dir. Comprehensive Cancer Ctr., 1987—; mem. cancer rsch. com. U. Mich., 1981—, sci. adv. bd. dental rsch. inst., 1983—, dean's adv., 1988—, reproductive endocrinology selection com., breast care ctr. exec. com., 1988—, exec. dir.'s adv. coun., 1992—, chair instl. rev. com. gene therapy program project., 1992—, dean's adv. com. Howard Hughes Med. Inst., 1992—, strategic planning policy and organizational com. health scis. info. tech. and networking 1992—; vis. prof. Mich. State U., 1985, Harvard U., Boston, 1986, Wash. State U., 1986, Boston U., 1986, Wayne State U./Harper Grace Hosps., 1987, U. Ill., 1987, Med. Coll. Wis., 1987., U. Chgo., 1987, Eppley Inst. for Rsch. in Cancer and Allied Diseases, Omaha, 1988, U. Nebr., Omaha, 1988, U. Minn./Minn. VA Hosp., 1988, MD Anderson Cancer Ctr., Houston., Mt. Sinai Med. Ctr., N.Y.C., Am. Cancer Soc., Kalamazoo, 1989, Gainesville, Fla., 1990, Orlando, Fla., 1990, Pezcoller Symposium, Rovereto, Italy, 1990, Prince Henry's Hosp., Melbourne, Australia, 1990, Northwestern U. Med. Ctr., Chgo., 1990, Meml. Sloan-Kettering Cancer Ctr., N.Y.C., 1990, Tex. S.W. U., Dallas, 1990, Mich. State U., 1991; lectr. U. Mich., 1990; mem. NIH Site Visit team U. Calif. Cancer Rsch. Lab., Berkeley, 1985; ad hoc mem. cell biology and physiology study sect. NIH, 1985, 86, study sect., Bethesda, 1991; mem. NCI Site Visit team Norris Cotton Dartmouth Cancer Ctr., 1989, Howard U., Wash., 1989, Howard U. Parent Com. 1989, MD Anderson Cancer Ctr., Houston, 1992; sci. advisor U. Colo. Cancer Ctr., Denver, 1990, Samuel Waxman Cancer Rsch. Found., Mt. Sinai Med. Ctr., N.Y.C., 1988-93; mem. NCI Adv. Panel, Bethesda, 1991; mem. sci. adv. com. U. Tex. San Antonio Cancer Ctr., U.

Miami Sylvester Cancer Ctr., Mich. State U., East Lansing, Norris-Cotton Cancer Ctr., Dartmouth-Hitchcock Med. Ctr., Hanover, N.H., Mich. Cancer Found., Detroit, V. T. Lombardi Cancer Rsch. Ctr., Georgetown U., Washington, 1992—, MD Anderson Cancer Ctr., Houston, 1992—; mem. extramural sci. adv. bd. UCI Clin. Cancer Ctr., U. Calif. Irvine, Orange, 1992—; mem. NCI SPORE in Prostate Cancer Study Sect., 1992; chair NCI Cancer Ctr. Support Rev. Com., 1993; NCI Site Visit chair Jefferson Cancer Ctr., Phila., 1992, Worcester (Mass.) Cancer Found., 1993, Duke U. Cancer Ctr., Durham, N.C., 1993, Lineberger Comprehensive Ctr., Chapel Hill, N.C., 1993; mem. NCI Comprehensive Cancer Ctrs. Review, 1993, chmn. parent com. Cancer Ctr. Support Rev. Com., 1992—; cons. Warner Lambert Co., 1980—. Assoc. editor: Molecular and Cellular Differentation, 1993; co-editor: The Hematopoietic Microenvironment, 1993; mem. editorial bd. Blood, Molecular and Cellular Differentiation, Jour. Lab. and Clin. Medicine, Cancer Rsch., 1993—, Oncology, Cancer Prevention Internat.; reviewer Nature, Science, Proceedings of NAS, Jour. Clin. Investigation, Jour. Cell Biology, Exptl. Cell Rsch., Exptl. Hematology, Cancer., Clin. and Exptl. Metastasis, Jour. Nat. Cancer Inst., Tissue & Cell, Am. Inst. Biol. Scis., Am. Jour. Pathology, Jour Immunology, Jour. Med. Scis., NSF, Oncology Rsch., Lab. Investigatiosch. and Treatment; contbr. over 110 articles and to profl. jours., chpts. to books.; invited lectr. in field. With USPHS, 1977-80. Recipient NSF RSch. award SUNY, 1969, Eli Luke and David Jacob Rsch. award Stanford U. Sch. Medicine, 1974, Upjohn Achievement Excellence in Medicine award, Outstanding Med. Resident award U. Chgo. Hosps., 1977, Jerome Conn Excellence in Rsch. award, 1983; grantee NIH, 1991—, 93—, Am. Cancer Soc., 1992—, Suntory Rsch. Inst., 1992-93. Mem. AAASN, Am. Assn. for Cancer Rsch. (state legis. com. 1992—, finance com. 1992—), Am. Fedn. for Clin. Rsch. (selections com. midwest sect. 1986—, comm. com., 1986—, awards com., 1986—), Am. Soc. for Cell Biology, Am. Soc. Hematology (com. on publs. 1991-93), Assn. Am. Cancer Insts. (bd. dirs. 1993—), Am. Soc. for Clin. Investigation, Am. Soc. Clin. Oncology (award selection com. 1992—), Ctrl. Soc. for Clin. Rsch., Mich. Soc. Hematology and Oncology, Southwest Oncology Group, Assn. Community Cancer Ctrs. Achievements include patents for antibodies to human mammary cell growth inhibitor and methods of production and use, human mammary cell growth inhibitor and methods of production and use; research in regulation of cell growth and differentiation, molecular mechanisms of tumor metastasis. Office: U Mich Simpson Meml Inst Med Rsch 102 Observatory St Ann Arbor MI 48109-0724

WICHERN, DEAN WILLIAM, business educator; b. Medford, Wis., Apr. 29, 1942; s. Arthur William and Rebecca Ann (Ambler) W.; m. Dorothy Jean Rutkowski, Dec. 7, 1968; children: Michael, Andrew. B.S. in Math., U. Wis., 1964, M.S. in Stats., 1965, Ph.D. in Stats., 1969. Instr. Sch. Bus. U. Wis.-Madison, 1967-69, asst. prof., 1969-72, assoc. prof., 1972-76, prof., 1976-84, chmn. quantitative analysis dept., 1975-78; prof. Coll. Bus. Adminstrn. Tex. A&M U., 1984—, head bus. analysis and research dept., 1984-88, assoc. dean, 1988—, John E. Pearson prof. bus. adminstrn., 1985—; vis. prof. Math. Research Ctr., 1978-79. Co-author: Intermediate Business Statistics, 1977, Applied Multivariate Statistical Analysis, 3d edit., 1992; assoc. editor Jour. Bus. and Econ. Stats., 1983-91. Mem. Royal Statis. Soc., Am. Statis. Assn., Inst. Mgmt. Sci., Beta Gamma Sigma, Phi Kappa Phi. Home: 9217 Riverstone Ct College Station TX 77845-8333 Office: Tex A&M U Coll Bus Adminstrn Dept Bus Analysis College Station TX 77843

WICK, G. PHIL, retail executive; b. 1944. Sales & svc. Tire Ctr. Store, 1965-67, asst. mgr., 1967-69; mgr. Tire Ctrs., 1969-80; exec. v.p. retail ops., 1980-83; pres. Les Scwab Warehouse Ctr., Inc., Prineville, Oreg., 1984—. Office: Les Schwab Warehouse Ctr Inc 1015 Madras Hwy Prineville OR 97754-0667*

WICK, HILTON ADDISON, lawyer; b. Mt. Pleasant, Pa., Feb. 11, 1920; m. Barbara G. Shaw; children: James H., William S., B. Jane, Ann W. Julia A. BA, Maryville Coll., 1942; LLB, Harvard U., 1948. Bar: Vt. 1948. Practiced in Burlington; ptnr. Wick, Dinse & Allen, 1949-72; of counsel Dinse, Allen & Erdmann, Burlington, 1972-80; Wick & Maddocks, Burlington, 1980—; state senator Vt., 1989-91; COO Gifford Med. Ctr., Inc., Randolph, 1993-95; bd. dirs. Nat. Life Ins. Co., Vt. Pub. Radio, chmn., 1990—; bd. dirs. Blue Cross/Blue Shield Vt., Beach Properties, Inc. Trustee Middlebury Coll., 1969-85, Champlain Coll., 1974-94, Maryville Coll., 1981-86, Shelburne Mus., 1985-94, Ethan Allen Homestead, 1989—, Vt. Assn. for Blind and Visually Impaired, 1992—; bd. dirs. Vt. divsn., Am. Cancer Soc., 1979-93; pres. bd. trustees V. Law Sch., 1975-90; chmn. bd. trustees Vt. Community Found., 1985-91; chancellor Vt. State Colls., 1984-85. Mem. ABA, Vt. Bar Assn. (pres. 1967-68), Chittenden County Bar Assn. (pres. 1963-64), Internat. Soc. Barristers, Am. Bankers Assn. (bd. dirs. 1975-76), Vt. Bankers Assn. (pres. 1973-74), Ethan Allen Club, Harvard Club (Boston and N.Y.C.), Phi Kappa Delta. Home: Two Appletree Point Ln Burlington VT 05401 Office: 308 College St Burlington VT 05401-8319

WICK, JOHN WILLIAM, education educator, author; b. Mankato, Minn., Jan. 4, 1935; s. William Thure and Esther (Gustafson) W.; m. Janet Olson, Dec. 27, 1956 (div. Nov. 1974); children: Patricia Susan, Nancy Lynn, Peter John; m. Martha Cogen, Nov. 30, 1974; children: Adam Cogen, Jacob Thure. BA, Mankato (Minn.) State Tchrs. Coll., 1960; MS, U. Iowa, 1965, PhD, 1967. Tchr. Lone Tree (Iowa) High Sch., 1962-63, Mt. Vernon (Iowa) High Sch., 1963-64; prof. edn. Northwestern U., Evanston, 1967—; dir. rsch. and evaluation Chgo. Pub. Schs., 1974-79; lead author Am. Testronics, Iowa City, 1978—; dir. R & D, North Ctrl. Assn. Author: School-based Evaluation, 1987, Annotated Bibliographic Measures, 1992, Student Performance Improvement, 1993; author, moderator: (TV series) Improving Student Performance, 1994. With U.S. Army, 1953-56. Mem. Am. Ednl. Rsch. Assn., Phi Delta Kappa. Avocations: reading, travel. Home: 953 Oak Dr Glencoe IL 60022-1457 Office: Northwestern U 2003 Sheridan Rd Evanston IL 60201-2925

WICK, SISTER MARGARET, college administrator; b. Sibley, Iowa, June 30, 1942. BA in Sociology, Briar Cliff Coll., 1965; MA in Sociology, Loyola U., Chgo., 1971; PhD in Higher Edn., U. Denver, 1976. Instr. sociology Briar Cliff Coll., Sioux City, Iowa, 1966-71, dir. academic advising, 1971-72, v.p., acad. dean, 1972-74, 76-84, pres., 1987—; pres. Colls. of Mid-Am., 1985-87; bd. dirs. Boatmen's Bank, Sioux City. Bd. dirs. Mary J. Treglia Cmty. House, 1976-84, Marian Health Ctr., 1987—, Iowa Pub. TV—. Mem. North Ctrl. Edn. Assn. (cons.-evaluator for accrediting teams 1980-84, 89—), Siouxland Initiative (adv. bd.), Assn. Cath. Colls. and Univs. (bd. dirs.), Quota Internat., Rotary. Home: 75 W Clifton # 113 Sioux City IA 51104-1122 Office: Briar Cliff Coll Office of the President 3303 Rebecca St Sioux City IA 51104-2340

WICK, ROBERT THOMAS, retired supermarket executive; b. St. Louis, Nov. 26, 1927; s. Robert Berninger and Katherine (Burke) W.; m. Virginia Rose Allen, Sept. 6, 1952; children: Susan, Patrick, Nancy, Robert J. BS, St. Louis U., 1955; cert. in food distbn., Mich. State U., 1956. Sales mgr. Nat. Tea Co., St. Louis, 1966-68, asst. div. mgr., 1968-69; div. mgr. Nat. Tea Co. Sioux City, Iowa, 1969-71, Milw., 1971-73, Chgo., 1973-74; ops. gen. mgr. A&P Food Stores, Indpls., 1975-77; div. v.p. Colonial Food Stores- Grand Union, Norfolk, Va., 1977-79; pres., chief exec. officer Bonnie Be-Lo Markets, Inc., Norfolk, 1979-90, ret., 1990. Bd. dirs. Virginia Beach (Va.) Community Svcs. Bd., 1985-89; mem. adv. bd. Straight, Inc., Chesapeake, Va., 1987-91; dir. Community Alternatives, Inc., Virginia Beach, 1991-92. Tech. sgt. U.S. Army, 1946-48. Recipient Citizen of Yr. award St. Louis Argus Newspaper, 1968. Mem. Food Mktg. Inst. (bd. dirs. 1982-89), Va. Food Dealers Assn. (bd. dirs. 1981-87), Tidewater Retail Mchts. Assn. (pres., bd. dirs. 1981-91). Republican. Roman Catholic. Avocations: travel, stamp collecting, golf, cycling. Home: 801 Winthrope Dr Virginia Beach VA 23452-3940

WICK, WILLIAM DAVID, lawyer; b. Dayton, Ohio, Aug. 18, 1949; s. Wilhelm Palmer and Esther (Brehm) W.; m. Barbara Helene Maco; children: Chelsea Maco, Jenna Maco. BA, Northwestern U., 1971; JD, Georgetown U., 1974. Bar: Calif. 1974. Legis. asst. U.S. Rep. Charles Whalen, Washington, 1971-75; assoc. McCutchen, Doyle, Brown & Enersen, San Francisco 1975-78; atty. Office Regional Counsel U.S. EPA, San Francisco, 1978-85, chief hazardous waste br. Office Regional Counsel, 1985-91; ptnr. Crosby, Heafey, Roach & May, Oakland, Calif., 1991—; adj. prof. law Golden Gate U., San Francisco, 1981—. Editor Shepard's Calif. Environ. Law and Regu-

lation Reporter, 1992-95. Mem. ABA, San Francisco Bar Assn. Office: Crosby Heafey Roach & May 1999 Harrison St Oakland CA 94612

WICK, WILLIAM SHINN, clergyman, chaplain; b. West Chester, Pa.; s. William R. and Barbara (Shinn) W.; m. Debra R. Smith, Apr. 1, 1989; 1 child, Christopher R. BA, Trinity Coll. Deerfield, Ill., 1975; MDiv, Trinity Evang. Div. Sch., Deerfield, 1978. Ordained to ministry Evang. Free Ch. Am., 1978. Pastor Bradford (Vt.) Evang. Free Ch.1978-85, Evang. Free Ch. Newport, Vt., 1985-89, Grace Evang. Free Ch., Northfield, Vt., 1989—; chaplain Norwich U., Northfield, 1989—; bd. dirs. Evang. Free Ch. Am., Mpls., 1991—. Avocations: alpine skiing, racquetball, tennis, scuba diving, sailing. Home: The Evang Free Ch Am 92 S Main Northfield VT 05663-1438 Office: Grace Evang Free Ch PO Box 245 Northfield VT 05663-0245

WICKBERG, JENS ERIK, industrial executive; b. Uppsala, Sweden, July 11, 1943; s. Nils Erik and Gerd Margareta (Andersson) W.; m. Karin Gunnarsson, Nov. 20, 1968; children: Eva, Anna. MBA, Stockholm Sch. Econs., 1967. Market analyst Exxon, Stockholm, 1967-70; fin. mgr. Fagersta AB, Sao Paulo, Brazil, 1970-73; mng. dir. Fagersta AB, Sao Paulo, 1973-76, AGA A/S, Copenhagen, 1976-78, AGA Gas AB, Sundbyberg, Sweden, 1978-81; corp. v.p. AGA AB, Lidingö, Sweden, 1981-89, sr. v.p., 1989-94; pres. AGA AB, Stockholm, 1994—. Home: Sturegatan 64, S-114 36 Stockholm Sweden Office: AGA AB, S-181 81 Lidingö Sweden

WICKENS, DONALD LEE, engineer executive, consultant, rancher; b. Oklahoma City, Aug. 11, 1934; s. Claude Preston and Idora Bell (Wainscott) W.; m. Sylvia Ann Knopp, Aug. 25, 1957; children: Julia Ann, Donna Sue. BS, Okla. State U., 1957, MS, 1962. Engr. HTB Inc., Oklahoma City, 1961-65; chief structural engr. The Benham Group, Oklahoma City, 1965-70, prin. structural engr., 1970-75, sr. v.p. indsl., 1975-80; pres. Houston div. The Benham Group, 1980-82, pres. St. Louis div., 1982-88; pres. The Benham Group, Oklahoma City, 1988—, chmn., chief exec. officer, pres., 1991—; chmn., chief exec. officer, pres. The Benham Cos., Oklahoma City, Benham Real Estate & Devel., Oklahoma City, Benham Internat., Oklahoma City; chmn. bd. dirs. Roberts-Schornick & Assocs., Norman, Okla.; bd. dirs. Dynalogic, Detroit; chmn. Benham Internat. Eurasia Moscow, Stainless Equipment and Sys. Co., Atlanta, Beham Constructors. Lt. USAF, 1958-60. Mem. NSPE, ASCE, Am. Soc. Mil. Engrs., Southern U.S. Japan Assn. (gov.'s internat. exec. com. 1993), Phi Delta Theta, Sigma Tau, Chi Epsilon. Republican. Lutheran. Home: 2604 Charleston Rd Edmond OK 73034-7831 Office: The Benham Group 9400 N Broadway Ext Oklahoma City OK 73114-7401

WICKER, DENNIS A., lieutenant governor; b. Sanford, N.C., 1952; s. J. Shelton and Clarice (Burns) W.; m. Alisa O'Quinn; children: Quinn Edward, Jackson Dennis, Harrison Lee. BA in Econs. with honors, U. N.C., 1974; JD, Wake Forest U., 1978. Atty. Love & Wicker, 1978-92; mem. N.C. Ho. of Reps., 1981-92; lt. gov. State of N.C., 1993—; chmn. law enorcement com., 1983, house com. cts. and adminstrn. justice, 1985, house jud. com., 1987; chmn. N.C. Small Bus. Coun., 1993—, N.C. State C.C. Bd., 1993—, N.C. State Health Purchasing Alliance Bd., 1993—, Gov.'s Task Force on Driving While Impaired, 1994—, N.C. Local Govt. Partnership Coun.; mem. N.C. Capitol Planning Com., 1993—, N.C. Coun. of State, 1993, N.C. Commn. on Bus. Laws and The Economy. Home: 2601 N.C. Local Govt. Partnership Coun.; chmn. Gov.'s Task Force on Driving While Impaired; bd. visitors U. N.C. Named Legis. of Yr., Children's Learning Disability Assn. N.C.; recipient Jane Alexander Pub. Svc. award MADD, 1993, Pres.'s award N.C. Assn. Educators; listed among 10 most effective legis. N.C. Ctr. Pub. Policy Rsch. Mem. Phi Beta Kappa. Democrat. Methodist. Office: State Capitol Raleigh NC 27603-8006

WICKER, ROGER F., congressman; b. Pontotoc, Miss., July 5, 1951; m. Gayle Wicker; children: Margaret, Caroline, McDaniel. BA in Polit. Sci. and Journalism, U. Miss., 1973; JD, Ole Miss Law Sch., 1975. Judge advocate USAF, 1975-79; mem. staff rules com. Staff of U.S. Rep. Trent Lott, 1980-82; pvt. practice, 1982—; mem. 104th Congress from 1st Miss. dist., 1995—. Republican. Office: US House Reps Office House Mem Washington DC 20515

WICKER, THOMAS GREY, retired journalist; b. Hamlet, N.C., June 18, 1926; s. Delancey David and Esta (Cameron) W.; m. Neva Jewett McLean, Aug. 20, 1949 (div. 1973); children: Cameron McLean, Thomas Grey; m. Pamela Abel Hill, Mar. 9, 1974. AB in Journalism, U. N.C., 1948. Exec dir. Southern Pines (N.C.) C. of C., 1948-49; editor Sandhill Citizen, Aberdeen, N.C., 1949; mng. editor The Robesonian, Lumberton, N.C., 1949-50; pub. info. dir. N.C. Bd. Pub. Welfare, 1950-51; copy editor Winston-Salem (N.C.) Jour., 1951-52, sports editor, 1954-55, Sunday feature editor, 1955-56, Washington corr., 1957, editorial writer, city hall corr., 1958-59; assoc editor Nashville Tennessean, 1959-60; mem. staff Washington bur. N.Y. Times, 1960-71, chief bur., 1964-68; assoc. editor N.Y. Times, 1968-85, columnist, 1966-91. Author: (novels) The Kingpin, 1953, The Devil Must, 1957, The Judgment, 1961, Facing the Lions, 1973, Unto This Hour, 1984, Donovan's Wife, 1992, (non-fiction) Kennedy without Tears, 1964, JFK and LBJ: The Influence of Personality upon Politics, 1968, A Time To Die, 1975, One Press, 1978, One of Us: Richard Nixon and the American Dream, 1991. Served to lt. (j.g.) USNR, 1952-54. Nieman fellow Harvard, 1957-58, fellow Joan Shorenstein Barone Ctr. on the Press, Politics and Pub. Policy Harvard, 1993. Mem. Soc. Nieman Fellows, Century Assn., Soc. Am. Historians.

WICKER, WILLIAM WALTER, librarian; b. Canaan, Miss., Sept. 11, 1930; s. Richard Fenton and Willie Thomas (Dunn) W.; m. Nella Ruth Harris, Sept. 5, 1954; children: Carolyn, William W. Jr., Deborah Lynne. BA, U. Miss., 1951; MLS, La. State U., 1955; AM, Fla. State U., 1970, PhD, 1977. Libr. dir. Capital Area Regional Libr., Raymond, Miss., 1955-57, Sch. of Ozarks, Point Lookout, Mo., 1957-61; head serials dept. Memphis State U., 1961-62, assoc. dir., 1966-73; libr. dir. Frederick Coll., Portsmouth, Va., 1962-65; head circulation dept. Miss. State U., Starkville, 1965-66; dir. learning resources U. Houston-Clear Lake, 1973-86, interim dean Sch. Edn., 1984-85; libr. dir. La. Tech. U., Ruston, 1986—. Capt. USAF, 1951-53. Mem. La. Libr. Assn. (pres. 1994-95), Space City Rotary Club (bd. dirs. 1980-83, Paul Harris fellow 1981), Ruston Rotary Club (bd. dirs. 1988-89). Republican. Methodist. Home: 287 Stow Creek Rd Ruston LA 71270-9767 Office: Prescott Meml Libr La Tech Univ Ruston LA 71272

WICKES, GEORGE, English educator, writer; b. Antwerp, Belgium, Jan. 6, 1923; came to U.S., 1923; s. Francis Cogswell and Germaine (Attout) W.; m. Louise Westling, Nov. 8, 1975; children by previous marriage: Gregory, Geoffrey, Madeleine (dec.), Thomas, Jonathan. BA, U. Toronto, Ont., Can., 1944; MA, Columbia, U. 1949; PhD, U. Calif., Berkeley, 1954. Asst. sec. Belgian Am. Ednl. Found., N.Y.C., 1947-49; exec. dir. U.S. Ednl. Found. in Belgium, 1952-54; instr. Duke U., Durham, N.C., 1954-57; from asst. prof. to prof. Harvey Mudd Coll. and Claremont Grad. Sch., Calif., 1957-70; prof. English and comparative lit. U. Oreg., Eugene, 1970—; dir. comparative lit. U. Oreg., 1974-77, head English dept., 1976-83; lectr. U.S. Info. Service, Europe, 1969, Africa, 1978, 79; vis. prof. U. Rouen, France, 1970, U. Tubingen, W. Ger., 1981. Editor: Lawrence Durrell and Henry Miller Correspondence, 1963, Henry Miller, Letters to Emil, 1989, Henry Miller and James Laughlin: Selected Letters, 1995; author: Henry Miller, 1966, Americans in Paris, 1969, The Amazon of Letters, 1976; adv. editor: N.W. Rev., 1972—; translator: The Memoirs of Frederic Mistral, 1986. Served with U.S. Army, 1943-46. Fulbright lectr. France, 1962-63, 66, 78; sr. fellow Ctr. for Twentieth Century Studies, U. Wis.-Milw. Milwaukee, 1971, Creative Writing fellow Nat. Endowment Arts, 1973, Camargo fellow, 1991. Mem. PEN. Office: U Oreg English Dept Eugene OR 97403

WICKES, MARY, actress; b. St. Louis, June 13, 1916; d. Frank A. and Mary Isabella (Shannon) Wickenhauser. A.B., D.Arts (hon.), Washington U., St. Louis; postgrad., UCLA, 1972—. Lectr. seminars on acting in comedy Coll. William and Mary, Williamsburg, Va.—. Washington U. at St. Louis, Am. Conservatory Theatre, San Francisco. Debut at Berkshire Playhouse, Stockbridge, Mass.; appeared in: Broadway plays Stage Door, 1936, Father Malachy's Miracle, 1937, The Man Who Came to Dinner, 1939, Jackpot (musical), 1944, Hollywood Pinafore (musical), 1945, Town House, 1948, Park Avenue (musical), 1946, Oklahoma (revival), 1979, others; numerous appearances in dramatic and musical stock, including St. Louis Mcpl. Opera, Cape Playhouse, Dennis, Mass., Bucks County Playhouse, Pa., Alliance

Theater, Atlanta, The Coconut Grove Playhouse, Miami, Fla., Burt Reynolds Theatre, Jupiter, Fla., Fox Theatre, St. Louis, Mark Taper Forum, Ahmanson Theater and Chandler Pavilion, Los Angeles, Am. Shakespeare Festival, Stratford, Conn., Am. Conservatory Theater, San Francisco, Berkshire Playhouse, Mass. 1937-78; film debut in The Man Who Came to Dinner, 1942; other film appearances include Now Voyager, 1942, Higher and Higher, 1943, June Bride, 1948, Anna Lucasta, 1949, On Moonlight Bay, 1951, By the Light of the Silvery Moon, 1952, The Actress, 1953, White Christmas, 1959, The Music Man, 1962, The Trouble with Angels, 1966, Where Angels Go, Trouble Follows, 1968, Touched by Love, 1979, Postcards from the Edge, 1990, Sister Act, 1992, Sister Act II, 1993, Little Women, 1994; TV debut as Mary Poppins: other TV appearances include Studio One, 1946; regular: TV series Doc, Halls of Ivy, Lucy shows, Dennis the Menace, The Canterville Ghost, Murder, She Wrote, Wonderworks (PBS), Twigs, Highway to Heaven, others; co-star ABC series Father Dowling Mysteries, 1989-91. Mem. aux. Hosp. Good Samaritan, L.A.; chmn. Nat. Crippled Children's Soc., Mo., 1969; bd. dirs. Med. Aux. Ctr. for Health Scis., UCLA, 1977—, St. Barnabas Sr. Ctr., L.A., 1994—. Recipient numerous awards including Outstanding Actress award Variety Clubs, 1967; awards for vol. work UCLA; Humanitarian award Masons; elected to St. Louis Mcpl. Opera Hall of Fame, 1987; 1st annual Starbiird lectr. Washington U., St. Louis, 1988; nominated best comedy supporting-actress for Sister Act Am. Comedy awards, 1993. Mem. AFTRA, NATAS (Emmy award nomination), SAG, Actors Equity Assn., Acad. Motion Picture Arts and Scis., Phi Mu. Republican. Episcopalian. Office: care Artists Agy 10000 Santa Monica Blvd Los Angeles CA 90067

WICKES, R(ICHARD) PAUL, lawyer; b. Camden, N.J., June 11, 1948; s. Richard Gordon and Nancy Elizabeth (Roy) W.; m. Jane Avis Hunter, June 8, 1970, (div. Feb. 1978); m. Gail Thain Parker, Apr. 9, 1978. BA, Williams Coll., 1970; JD, Harvard U., 1973. Bar: Vt. 1973, U.S. Supreme Ct. 1976, Okla. 1982, N.Y. 1991. Ptnr. Williams & Wickes, Bennington, Vt., 1973-77; commr. Vt. Dept. Taxes, Montpelier, 1977-78; assoc. Gravel, Shea & Wright, Burlington, Vt., 1978-80; counsel to Gov. State of Vt., Montpelier, 1980-82; ptnr. Watson & McKenzie, Oklahoma City, 1982-84, Thompson & Knight, Dallas, 1984-90, Sherman & Sterling, N.Y.C., 1990—. Office: Shearman & Sterling 153 E 53rd St New York NY 10022

WICKESBERG, ALBERT KLUMB, retired management educator; b. Neenah, Wis., Apr. 2, 1921; s. Albert Henry and Lydia (Klumb) W.; m. Dorothy Louise Ahrensfeld, Oct. 28, 1944; children—Robert, William, James. B.A., Lawrence Coll., 1943; M.B.A., Stanford U., 1948; Ph.D., Ohio State U., 1955. Staff accountant S.C. Johnson & Son, Inc., Racine, Wis., 1948-50; asst. prof. Sacramento State Coll., 1950-51; prof. U. Minn., Mpls., 1953-86; prof. emeritus U. Minn., 1987—, chmn. dept. bus. adminstrn., 1959-62, dir. grad. studies, 1963-66, chmn. dept. mgmt. and transp., 1971-77. Author: Management Organization, 1966. Served with AUS, 1943-46, 51-52. Soc. Advancement Mgmt. fellow, 1972. Mem. Acad. Mgmt., Soc. Advancement Mgmt. (pres. Twin Cities chpt. 1961-62), Am. Assn. for Study Mental Imagery. Congregationalist. Home: 4501 Roanoke Rd Minneapolis MN 55422-5268 Office: U Minn Sch Mgmt Minneapolis MN 55455

WICKHAM, JOHN ADAMS, JR., retired army officer; b. Dobbs Ferry, N.Y., June 25, 1928; s. John Adams and Jean Gordon (Koch) W.; m. Ann Lindsley Prior, June 18, 1955; children: Lindsley, John Adams, Matthew. B.S., U.S. Mil. Acad., 1950; M.A., Harvard U., 1955, M.P.A., 1956; grad., Nat. War Coll., 1967. Commd. 2d lt. U.S. Army, 1950, advanced through grades to gen., 1979; asst. prof. social scis. U.S. Mil. Acad., 1956-60; bn. comdr. 1st Cavalry Div., Republic of Vietnam, 1967; brigade comdr., chief of staff 3d Inf. Div., Fed. Republic of Germany, 1969-70; army mem. chmn.'s staff group Office of Chmn. Joint Chiefs of Staff, Washington, 1970-71; dep. chief of staff for econ. affairs Mil. Assistance Command, Republic of Vietnam, 1971-73; dep. chief, negotiator U.S. del. Four Party Joint Mil. Commnn., Republic of Vietnam, 1973; sr. mil. asst. to Sec. Def. Washington, 1973-76; comdr. 101st Airborne Div. (Air Assault), Ft. Campbell, Ky., 1976-78; dir. Joint Staff Orgn. Washington, 1978-79; comdr. in chief UN Command, Republic of Korea-U.S. Combined Forces Command, Korea, 1979-82; vice chief of staff U.S Army, Washington, 1982-83, chief of staff, 1983-87, ret., 1987; pres., chief exec officer Armed Forces Communications and Electronics Assn., Fairfax, Va., 1987-92; bd. dirs. Cooper Inst. for Aerobic Rsch., Xsirius, Inc., Honeywell Fed. Sys., Advanced Photonics, Nortel Inc. Decorated D.S.M. (8), Silver Star (2), Legion of Merit (4), Bronze Star with V device, Air medal (11), Purple Heart, Legion of Honor (France), Order of Mil. Merit (Rep. of Korea), Royal Order of Polar Star (Sweden). Mem. assn. U.S. Army, 101st Airborne Assn. Home: 13590 N Fawnbrooke Dr Tucson AZ 85737

WICKHAM, KENNETH GREGORY, retired army officer, institute official; b. Hayti, Mo., Apr. 8, 1913; s. Charles Lawrence and Nell (Lively) W.; m. Helen Wickham, July 12, 1938 (dec.); 1 dau.; Mary Harvey Wickham Anderson; m. Norma A. Newcomb, Aug. 21, 1982. B.S., U.S. Mil. Acad., 1938; M.A., George Washington U., 1963; grad., Armed Forces Staff Coll., 1948, Army War Coll., 1956. Commd. 2d lt. U.S. Army, 1938, advanced through grades to maj. gen., 1964; assigned arty. U.S. and Hawaii, 1938-42; with inf. in PTO, ETO, 1942-45; various staff and command assignments, 1945-54; assigned Korea, 1954-55; comdt. (Adj. Gen.'s Sch.), 1959-61; comdg. gen. (Combat Service Support Group, Combat Devel. Command), 1964-66; adj. gen. U.S. Army, 1966-71; with Bus. Mgmt. Inst., Western Assn. Coll. and Univ. Bus. Officers, Stanford, Calif., 1975-80; Area dir. in Korea ARC campaign, 1955; bd. dirs. Army Emergency Relief Assn., U.S. Olympic Com., Army Mut. Aid Assn., Internat. Mil. Sports Council; pres. 1969-70; mem. exec. com. Council Internat. Mil. Sports, 1967-71; pres. Calif. Assn. Mil. Personnel, 1972-78, U.S. Mil. Sports Assn., 1982-84. Decorated D.S.M., Legion of Merit with 2 oak leaf clusters, Bronze Star with oak leaf cluster, Purple Heart, Commendation medal; Legion of Honor (France); 2 Croix de Guerre (France); Cross of Haakon VII (Norway); Ulchi Disting. Svc. medal (Korea). Home: 15 Sunkist Ln Los Altos CA 94022-2334

WICKHAM, MICHAEL W., transportation executive; b. 1946. With Roadway Express, Inc., Akron, Ohio, 1968—, terminal mgr., 1971-77, dist. mgr., 1977-81, v.p. N.E. divsn., 1981-85, v.p. western divsn., 1985-88, v.p. adminstrn. and fin., 1988-89, exec. v.p. adminstrn. and fin., 1989-90, pres., CEO, 1990—. Office: Roadway Express Inc PO Box 471 Akron OH 44309-0471

WICKISER, RALPH LEWANDA, painter, educator, author; b. Greenup, Ill., Mar. 20, 1910; s. Herk and Lydia (Denny) W.; m. Jane Bisson, June 1, 1936; children: Eric Lee, Lydia, Walter. Student, Chgo. Art Inst., 1928-31, Vanderbilt U., 1934-37; B.Ed., Eastern Ill. Coll., 1934, Ph.D. (hon.), 1956; A.M., Peabody Coll., 1935, Ph.D., 1938. Art writer also Peabody Reflector, 1934-35; instr. art La. State U., 1937-40, asst. prof., 1940, head fine arts dept., 1941, assoc. prof., 1944-49, prof., 1949-56; dir. art edn. SUNY Tchrs. Coll., New Paltz, 1956-59; chmn. art edn. dept. Pratt Inst., 1959-62, dir. grad. programs art and design, 1962-65, acting dean Sch. Art and Design, 1970-71, dir. grad. programs in art and design, 1971-75, emeritus prof., 1975—; lectr. art Vassar Coll., 1949; Mem. council National Com. Art Edn. One-man shows include Gallery 630B, New Orleans, 1990, Z Gallery, N.Y.C., 1990-91, Gallery at Park West, Kingston, N.Y., 1992, Walter Wickiser Gallery, 1993; exhibited in group shows at Grand Central Galleries, N.Y.C., Tiffany Found. Group, 1934-35, A New So. Group, Gresham Gallery, New Orleans, travelling show, 1937-41, Pa. Acad., 1946, Dallas Mus., 1947, The Arts Club, Washington, Library of Congress Annual Print Exhbn., U. Chattanooga, Assoc. Am. Artists Gallery, N.Y.C., Bklyn. Mus., Corcoran Gallery, Washington, Pa. Acad., Phila., Print Club, Phila., San Francisco Mus., Dayton (Ohio) Mus., Dallas Mus., Delgado Mus., Met. Mus., Whitney Mus., New Realism show Suffolk Mus., 1971, Lerner-Miraschi Gallery, N.Y.C., 1972, Pacem in Terris Gallery, UN, N.Y.C., 1975, Lotus Gallery, N.Y.C., 1976-77, Esta Robinson Gallery, N.Y.C., 1982, Ulster County Council for Arts, 1983, Princeton Gallery of Fine Art, N.J., 1987, The Thompson Gallery, N.Y.C., 1987, Z Squared Fine Art Gallery, N.Y.C. 1990-91, Woodstock Artists Assn., 1990, Pratt Schafler Gallery, 1990, Pratt Inst., 1991, Pratt Manhattan Gallery, 1991, Woodstock Art Assn., 1993, Haenah-Kent Gallery, N.Y.C. 1993; retrospective exhbn., Eastern Ill. U., 1968, color lithographs for Standard Oil Co., N.J., June 1947, water colors for, Ford Motor Co., 1948, creative painting, Woodstock, N.Y., 1948; cons., adv. bd., Unicorn Press for New Standard Ency. of Funk and

Wagnalls; author: (with Capt. P. E. McDowell) Military Leadership, 1944, Introduction to Art Activities, 1947, An Introduction to Art Education, 1957; Editor: (with Caroline Durieux) Mardi Gras Day, 1948; contbg. editor: Ency. of the Arts, 1946; contbr.: Cath. Ency.; author: book rev. Sat. Rev, 1952, 53, 54. Served with USNR, 1945-46. Ford Found. grant advancement edn., 1952-53. Mem. Artists Equity, Am. Soc. Aesthetics, Coll. Art Assn., Phi Delta Kappa, Kappa Delta Pi. Home: PO Box 263 Bearsville NY 12409-0263 *It has been a mystery to me why it takes a lifetime to become fully aware of one's self, one's life. Even for the person who constantly studies there is not enough time to learn all one needs to know, to see all the marvelous things to be seen in nature and fully respond to a falling leaf. It is ironic that we begin to value life when it ebbs. I say all of this because my life has been a search for understanding, to discover the principles behind life and nature and the ideas that defined the principles. Art and education have both offered me a life of activity and quiet contemplation. They have, by diligent pursuit, given me a greater appreciation of things thought and seen, felt and intuited.*

WICKIZER, MARY ALICE See BURGESS, MARY ALICE

WICKLEIN, JOHN FREDERICK, journalist, educator; b. Reading, Pa., July 20, 1924; s. Raymond Roland and Parmilla Catherine (Miller) W.; m. Myra Jane Winchester, July 31, 1948; children: Elizabeth, Peter, Joanna. Litt.B., Rutgers U., 1947; M.S. in Journalism, Columbia, 1948. Reporter Newark (N.J.) Evening News, 1947-51; news mng. editor Elec. World (McGraw-Hill weekly), N.Y.C., 1951-54; reporter, editor N.Y. Times, 1954-62; news dir. Sta. WNET-TV, N.Y.C., 1962-64; exec. producer news Sta. WABC-TV, N.Y.C., 1964-67; exec. producer Washington Bur. chief Pub. Broadcast Lab. (Nat. Ednl. TV), 1967-70; mng. news and pub. affairs broadcasts Sta. WCBS-TV, N.Y.C., 1970-71; gen. mgr. Sta. WRVR, N.Y.C., 1971-74; prof. journalism and broadcasting Boston U., 1974-80; dean Sch. Public Communication Boston U., 1974-78; vis. prof. communication Meth. U., São Paulo, Brazil, 1979; program officer for news and pub. affairs programs Corp. for Pub. Broadcasting, 1980-84; Willard M. Kiplinger chair in pub. affairs reporting, dir. Kiplinger mid-career program for journalists Ohio State U., 1984-89; Fulbright rsch. scholar Sturt U., Bathurst, NSW, Australia, 1990; lectr., cons. to Rutgers U. Media Resources Ctr., Warsaw, Poland, 1992; Ayers vis. prof. of Journalism, Jacksonville (Ala.) State U., 1992-93; producer news documentaries for public and comml. TV; lectr., cons. in field; coord. Working Group for Pub. Broadcasting, 1987—; spl. com. on regulation of media Am. Civil Liberties Union, 1988-92; adj. faculty, Poynter Inst. for Media Studies, 1988; adj. prof. journalism for rsch. Ohio State U., 1991-93; at-large mem., media ethics com. Nat. Coun. Chs., 1975—; fellow Inst. Democratic Communication Boston U., 1975-78; lectr. journalism Columbia Grad. Sch. Journalism, 1966-67; Danforth lectr. Barnard Coll., 1960-61; cons. Dept. Journalism, Jagiellonian U, Krakow, Poland, 1994. Author: (with Monroe Price) Cable Television: A Guide for Citizen Action, 1972, Electronic Nightmare: The New Communications and Freedom, 1981; editor: Investigative Reporting: The Lessons of Watergate, 1975; contbg. editor The Washington Monthly, 1969-72; contbr. to The Progressive, TV Quar., Atlantic Monthly, Columbia Journalism Rev, Archeology, Australian Journalism Rev., others. Recipient Polk award, 1963, documentary award Venice Film Festival, 1968, Dupont award, 1973, Brechner Freedom Info. prize, 1987. Mem. ACLU, Investigative Reporters and Editors, Amnesty Internat. U.S.A., Soc. Prof. Jours., Phi Beta Kappa. Democrat. Home and Office: 23200 Wilderness Walk Ct Gaithersburg MD 20882-2732

WICKLIFFE, JERRY L., lawyer; b. Dallas, Jan. 12, 1941; s. John A. and Ola (Kirk) W.; m. Lynda Hart, Aug. 26, 1961; children: Lisa Schmalhausen, Jeffrey, Mark. BBA, U. Tex., 1963, JD, 1965. Bar: Tex. 1965. Assoc. Fulbright & Jaworski, Houston, 1965-73, ptnr., 1973—. Office: Fulbright & Jaworski 1301 Mckinney St Fl 51 Houston TX 77010-3049

WICKLINE, SAMUEL ALAN, cardiologist, educator; b. Huntington, W.Va., Oct. 23, 1952. BA in Philosophy cum laude, Pomona Coll., 1974; MD, U. Hawaii, 1980. Diplomate Am. Bd. Internal Medicine, Am. Bd. Cardiology. Intern, resident in internal medicine Barnes Hosp. Barnes/Washington U. Sch. Medicine, St. Louis, 1980-83, clin. fellow in cardiology, 1983-85, rsch. fellow in cardiology, 1985-87; asst. prof. medicine Sch. Medicine Washington U. Sch. Medicine, St. Louis, 1987-93, assoc. prof., 1993—, adj. asst. prof. physics, 1990, adj. assoc. prof. physics, 1994, attending cardiologist, dir. echocardiology Jewish Hosp., 1992—, dir. divsn. cardiology, 1993—. Reviewer Jour. Clin. Investigation, Circulation, Arteriosclerosis and Thrombosis, Hypertension, Ultrasound in Medicine and Biology; contbr. over 60 articles to med. and sci. jours., chpts. to books on topics related to basic rsch. in cardiovascular biophysics and acoustics/ ultrasonics. Grantee NIH, 1990—, 92 — (two grants), 95—. Fellow Am. Coll. Cardiology (reviewer jour.); mem. IEEE Soc. Ultrasonics, Ferroelectrics and Frequency Control (tech. program com. ultrasonics symposium), Am. Heart Assn. (coun. on radiology and clin. cardiology, Clinician-Scientist award 1988-93, Established Investigator award 1993—), Am. Soc. Clin. Investigation, Am. Inst. Ultrasound in Medicine, Acoustical Soc. Am., Alpha Omega Alpha. Home: 11211 Pointe Ct Saint Louis MO 63127-1741 Office: Jewish Hosp Cardiology 216 S Kingshighway Blvd Saint Louis MO 63110

WICKMAN, HERBERT HOLLIS, physical chemist, condensed matter physicist; b. Omaha, Sept. 30, 1936. AB, Mcpl. U. Omaha, 1959; PhD, U. Calif., Berkeley, 1965. Mem. tech. staff Bell Telephone Labs., Murray Hill, N.J., 1964-71; prof. phys. chemistry Oreg. State U., Corvallis, 1971-87; program dir. condensed matter physics NSF, Washington, 1987—. Contbr. over 60 articles to profl. jours. Fellow Am. Phys. Soc.

WICKMAN, JOHN EDWARD, librarian, historian; b. Villa Park, Ill., May 24, 1929; s. John Edward and Elsie (Voss) W.; m. Shirley Jean Swanson, Mar. 17, 1951; children—Lisa Annette, Eric John. A.B., Elmhurst Coll., 1953; A.M., Ind. U., 1958, Ph.D., 1964; LL.D., Lincoln Coll., 1973. Instr. history Hanover (Ind.) Coll., 1959-62, Southeast Campus, Ind. U., Jeffersonville, 1962; asst. prof. history Northwest Mo. State Coll., Maryville, 1962-64; asst. to Gov. William H. Avery of Kans., Topeka, 1964-65; asst. prof. history Regional Campus, Purdue U., Fort Wayne, Ind., 1965-66; dir. Dwight D. Eisenhower Libr., Abilene, Kans., 1966-89; ret., 1989. Contbr. articles on Am. West, archival mgmt., adminstrv. history, oral history to profl. publs. Served with U.S. Army, 1953-55. Nat. Ctr. for Edn. in Politics faculty fellow, 1964-65; Am. Polit. Sci. Assn. Congl. fellow, 1975-76. Mem. Oral History Assn. (v.p. 1971-72, pres. 1972-73), Western History Assn. (coun. 1972-75), Kans. Hist. Soc. (2d v.p. 1974-75, pres. 1976-77, dir.). Home: PO Box 325 Enterprise KS 67441-0325

WICKMAN, PAUL EVERETT, public relations executive; b. Bisbee, Ariz., Aug. 21, 1912; s. Julius and Hilda Wilhelmina (Soderholm) W.; m. Evelyn Gorman, Nov. 22, 1969; children by previous marriage: Robert Bruce, Bette Jane, Marilyn Faye. Student, LaSierra U., Arlington, Calif., 1928-30, Pacific Union Coll., Angwin, Cal., 1931-32; spl. student, Am. U., 1946. Min., 1931-53, Internat. traveler, lectr., writer, 1937-44; assoc. sec Internat. Religious Liberty Assn., 1944-46; travel lectr. Nat. Lecture Bur., 1944-55; exec. sec., dir. internat. radio and TV prodns. Voice of Prophecy Corp., Faith for Today Corp., 1953-63; v.p. Western Advt. Agy., Los Angeles, 1953-55; dir. devel. Nat. Soc. Crippled Children and Adults, Inc., Chgo., 1955-56; exec. dir. Pub. Relations Soc. Am., Inc., N.Y.C., 1956-57; dir. corp. pub. relations Schering Corps., Bloomfield, N.J. 1957-58; pres. Wickman Pharm. Co., Inc., Calif., 1959-83, Paul Wickman Co., 1984—. Mem. Newport Beach CSC, mem. Orange County Children's Hosp. Fund; trustee Walla Walla (Wash.) Coll., 1989-91. Mem. Newcomen Soc., Pub. Rels. Soc. Am. (accredited), Internat. Platform Assn., Swedish Club (L.A., past pres.), Vikings, 552 Hoag Hosp. Club, Elks, Masons, Shriners, Royal Order Jesters, Kiwanis (past pres. Newport Beach club, lt. gov. div. 41 Cal-Neva Hi 1990-91). Home and Office: 28 Point Loma Dr Corona Del Mar CA 92625-1026

WICKMANN, DAVID L., clergyman. V.p. and sec. ea. dist. Moravian Ch. Am. Office: Moravian Church in Am 1021 Center St PO Box 1245 Bethlehem PA 18016-1245

WICKS, EUGENE CLAUDE, college president, art educator; b. Coleharbor, N.D., Oct. 7, 1931; s. Claude Edward and Grace Ann (Wilkin-

son) W.; m. Lavonne Maureen Yineman, June 21, 1953; children: Christopher Edwin, Louis Eugene, James Edward. B.F.A., U. Colo., 1957, M.F.A., 1959. Mem. faculty U. Ill., Urbana, 1959-94; assoc. head U. Ill., 1961-76, head Sch. Art and Design, 1977-80, dir., 1981-89; also prof. art U. Ill. (Sch. Art and Design); pres. Burren Coll. Art, Newtown Castle, Ireland, 1994—; cons. in field. Represented in permanent collections at, Phila. Print Club, Art Inst. Chgo., Am. Fed. Arts, others. Served with USN, 1951-54. U. Ill. research grantee, 1960, 61, 67, 68, 69, 74, 75; Fulbright grantee, 1988-89. Mem. Coll. Art Assn., Nat. Assn. Schs. Art and Design (dir. commn. on accreditation 1978-81, v.p. 1981-84, pres. 1984-87). Home: Tigín, Ballyvaughan Ireland Office: Burren Coll Art, Newtown Castle, Ballyvaughan, County Clare Ireland

WICKS, JOHN R., lawyer; b. Ottumwa, Iowa, Dec. 8, 1937; m. Nedra Morgan, Mar. 27, 1940; children: Catherine, John. BSC, U. Iowa, 1959, JD, 1964. Bar: Iowa 1964, Minn. 1966. Assoc. Dorsey & Whitney, Mpls., 1966-71; ptnr. Dorsey & Whitney, Rochester, Minn., 1972-92. Fellow Am. Coll. Trusts and Estates Counsel; mem. Minn. State Bar Assn. (probate and trusts law coun. 1989-92), Olmsted County Minn. Bar Assn. Office: Dorsey & Whitney 201 1st Ave SW Ste 340 Rochester MN 55902-3155

WICKS, WILLIAM WITHINGTON, retired public relations executive; b. Chgo., Dec. 20, 1923; s. William and Alice (Withington) W.; m. Frances M. Horner, Nov. 29, 1947; children: Barbara Anne, Christine Frances. BNS, U. Notre Dame, 1944, AB in Journalism magna cum laude, 1947. Staff corr. United Press Assn., Milw., 1947; pub. rels. mgr. Internat. Harvester Co., Louisville, 1948-58; mgr. field svcs. pub. rels. Standard Oil Co. (Ind.), Chgo., 1959-60; v.p. pub. rels. Griswold-Eshleman Co., Chgo., 1961-68; dir. pub. rels. G. D. Searle & Co., Chgo., 1968-74; dir. pub. rels./investor rels. Kimberly-Clark Corp., Neenah, Wis., 1974, staff v.p., 1974-80; v.p Kimberly-Clark Corp., Neenah (hdqrs. relocated to Dallas in 1985), 1980-89; v.p. and asst. to chmn. bd. Kimberly-Clark Corp., Irving, Tex., 1989-92; chmn. pub. relations sect. Pharm. Mfrs. Assn., Washington, 1974. Pres. Jr. Achievement Neenah-Menasha, 1978-81. Served to lt. (j.g.) USNR, 1944-46, PTO. Recipient Silver Anvil award Pub. Rels. Soc. Am., 1963, 79. Mem. PRSA (founder, pres. Bluegrass chpt. 1957-58), Optimist (pres. South End Club in Louisville 1957), Publicity Club of Chgo. (pres. 1967-68). Republican. Roman Catholic. Home: 1312 S Travis Cir Irving TX 75038-6243

WICKSER, JOHN PHILIP, lawyer; b. Buffalo, Oct. 14, 1922; s. Philip John and Margaretta Melissa (Fryer) W.; m. Frances M. Halsey, July 2, 1949; children: Margaretta Melissa, Philip John, Gaius Halsey. B.A., Yale U., 1945; J.D., Columbia U., 1949. Bar: N.Y. 1949. Since practiced in Buffalo; mem. firm Palmer, Houck & Wickser, 1949-50; ptnr. Palmer, Heffernan Wickser & Beyer, 1950-94; of counsel Magavern, Magavern & Grimm, 1994; pres. Main-Pearl Corp., 1963-82; dir. Union-Am. Re-Ins. Co., 1975-77; pres. Kleinhans Music Hall Mgmt., Inc. Life mem. adv. bd. Salvation Army, Internat. Inst., 1951-54; council State Tchrs. Coll., Buffalo, 1954-55; bd. dirs. Greater Buffalo Devel. Found., Grosvenor Soc.; chmn. bd. trustees Buffalo and Erie County Pub. Library; bd. dirs. Buffalo Fine Arts Acad., 1954-77. Served to lt. (j.g.) USN, World War II. Mem. Johnson Soc. London, Sons of Revolution, Buffalo Hist. Soc. (trustee), N.Y. State, Erie County bar assns., Am. Judicature Soc. Republican. Episcopalian. Clubs: Buffalo Country (Buffalo), Pack (Buffalo), Saturn (Buffalo); Yale (N.Y.C.); Elizabethan (New Haven); Pacific, Nantucket Yacht. Home: 22 Oakland Pl Buffalo NY 14222-2009 Office: Rand Bldg Buffalo NY 14203

WICKSTROM, KARL YOUNGERT, publishing company executive; b. Moline, Ill., Sept. 20, 1935; s. George Washington and Harriet L. (Youngert) W.; m. Patricia Pinkerton, 1959 (div.); children: Eric, Blair, Drew, Holly; m. Sheila Zehner, June 9, 1979. B.S.J., U. Fla., 1957. Writer, editor Orlando (Fla.) Sentinel-Star, 1958-60; writer Miami (Fla.) Herald, 1960-67; adminstrv. asst. Fla. Senate, Tallahassee, 1968; founder, pres., publisher Wickstrom Pubs. Inc., mags., books, Miami, 1968—. Original pub.: Aloft Mag., for Nat. Airlines passengers, 1968-80; pub.: Fla. Sportsman, 1969—, Ryder World for Ryder System, Inc, 1980—. Bd. dirs. Nat. Coalition for Marine Conservation; v.p Fla. Conservation Assn. Served with USAF, 1967-68. Recipient 1st pl. award for pub. service Fla. AP, 1967. Mem. Sigma Delta Chi (nat. 1st pl. award for investigative reporting Miami area crime, corruption 1967). Home: 745 S Alhambra Cir Miami FL 33146-3801 Office: Florida Sportsman 5901 SW 74th St Miami FL 33143-5150

WIDDEL, JOHN EARL, JR., lawyer; b. Minot, N.D., Nov. 17, 1936; s. John Earl Sr. and Angela Victoria (Gefroh) W.; m. Yvonne J. Haugen, Dec. 21, 1973; children: John P., James M., Susan N., Andrea K. B in Philosophy, BS in Bus. Adminstrn., U. N.D., 1966, BSBA, 1971. Bar: N.D. 1971, U.S. Dist. Ct. N.D., 1971, U.S. Ct. Appeals (8th cir.) 1989. Ptnr. Thorsen & Widdel, Grand Forks, N.D., 1971—; mcpl. judge City of Grand Forks, 1972—; st. magistrate Grand Forks County, 1975. Mem. N.D. Foster Parent Program, 1974-87; bd. dirs. YMCA, Grand Forks, 1982; dist. chmn. Boy Scouts Am., 1987-88; corp. mem. United Hosp. Served with U.S. Army, 1960-62. Mem. State Bar Assn. N.D. (bd. govs. 1983-88, pres. 1986-87), Greater Grand Forks County Bar Assn. (pres. 1982), N.E. Cen. Jud. Dist. (pres. 1983), Grand Forks Cemetery Assn. (bd. dirs. 1984—, pres. 1989-1994), Grand Forks Hist. Soc. (pres. 1983), Jaycees (Grand Forks), Antique Automobile Club of Am. (nat. dir. 1984—, v.p. 1985—, sec.-treas. 1989, N.D. region pres. 1977, 78, 83, 84), Elks (exalted ruler 1985-86), Masonic Bodies-Kem Temple Potentate, Sertoma (bd. dirs. 1984). Roman Catholic. Home: 2820 Belmont Rd Box 5624 Grand Forks ND 58206-1524 Office: Thorsen & Widdel 215A S 4th St Grand Forks ND 58206-5624

WIDDER, WILLARD GRAVES, retired banker; b. Kansas City, Kans., June 21, 1924; s. George A. and Dorothy B. (Graves) W. B.S. in Mech. Engring., U. Kans., 1946, LL.B., 1949. Bar: Kans. 1949. Pvt. practice Kansas City, Kans., 1949-53; with First Nat. Bank Kansas City, Mo., 1953-84; trust officer First Nat. Bank Kansas City, 1961-66, v.p., 1966-71, sr. v.p., 1971-84. Sec., dir. 1st Nat. Found., Kansas City Estate Planning Coun.; sec. Edward F. Swinney Found. With USNR, 1943-46. Mem. Masons (master 1958—), Phi Alpha Delta. Republican. Methodist. Home: 5303 W 122nd Ter Shawnee Mission KS 66209-3517

WIDDICOMBE, RICHARD PALMER, librarian; b. Paterson, N.J., Apr. 12, 1941; s. Robert Lord and Elvira Barbara (Guttila) W.; m. Martha Elizabeth Bruyn, Feb. 26, 1972. B.A., Alfred U., 1963; M.S. L.S., Syracuse U., 1964. Asst. librarian Yonkers Pub. Library, N.Y., 1964-65; asst. librarian Cooper Union, N.Y.C., 1965-66; asst. librarian Stevens Inst., Hoboken, N.J., 1966-72, dir. library, 1973—. Episcopalian. Home: Castle Point Sta PO Box S-1342 Hoboken NJ 07030 Office: SC Williams Libr Stevens Inst Hoboken NJ 07030

WIDDRINGTON, PETER NIGEL TINLING, professional baseball team executive; b. Toronto, Ont., Can., June 2, 1930; s. Gerard and Margery (MacDonald) W.; m. Betty Ann Lawrence, Oct. 12, 1956; children: Lucinda Ann, Andrea Stacy. B.A. with honors, Queen's U., Kingston, Ont., 1953; M.B.A., Harvard, 1955. Salesman Labatt's Inc. Canada, Ont., 1955-57; regional mgr. Ont. Labatt's Co., 1957-58, gen. mgr. Man., 1958-61, gen. mgr. B.C., 1962-65; gen. mgr. Kiewel & Pelissiers, Winnipeg, 1961-62; pres. Lucky Breweries Inc., San Francisco, 1968-71; v.p. corp. devel. John Labatt Ltd., 1971-73, sr. v.p., 1973-87, pres., chief exec. officer, 1973-89, chmn., 1987-91; chmn. Laidlaw Inc., 1990—, Toronto Blue Jays Baseball Club, 1989—; bd. dirs. Chief Execs. Orgn., Inc., Dialysis Ctrs. Am., Talisman Energy Inc., Can. Imperial Bank of Commerce, Ellis-Don Inc., Hayes-Dana Inc., SNC-Lavalin Group, ADT Ltd., Toronto Blue Jays Baseball Club, Major League Baseball Properties, Inc., chmn.; hon. dir. John Labatt Ltd. Address: 248 Pall Mall St Ste 400, London, ON Canada

WIDEMAN, JOHN EDGAR, English literature educator, novelist; b. Washington, DC, June 14, 1941; married, 3 children. BA, U. Pa., 1963; BPhil, Oxford U. Eng., 1966; postgrad., U. Iowa Writers Workshop, 1967; DLitt (hon.), U. Pa., 1985, Rutgers U. Mem. faculty U. Wyo., Laramie; prof. English U. Wyo., 1974-85, U. Mass., Amherst 1986—; USIS lectr. in Eastern Europe. Author: A Glance Away, 1967, Hurry Home, 1969, The Lynchers, 1973, Hiding Place, 1981, Damballah, 1981, Sent for You Yesterday, 1983 (PEN/Faulkner award for fiction 1984), Brothers and Keepers, 1984, Reuben, 1987, Fever, 1989, Philadelphia Fire, 1990 (PEN/Faulkner award for fiction 1991), The Homewood Books, 1992, The Stories of John

Edgar Wideman, 1992, All Stories Are True, 1993, Fatheralong, 1994; contbr. numerous articles and revs. to profl. jours., mags. Ben Franklin scholar; Lannan award, 1991; Kent fellow; Rhodes scholar; Nat. Endowment for Humanities grantee; MacArthur fellow 1993. Mem. Am. Assn. Rhodes Scholars (dir.), Am. Studies Assn. (council 1980-81), MLA, Am. Acad. Arts Scis. (elected), (Phi Beta Kappa). Office: Univ Mass Dept English Amherst MA 01003

WIDENER, HIRAM EMORY, JR., federal judge; b. Abingdon, Va., Apr. 30, 1923; s. Hiram Emory and Nita Douglas (Peck) W.; children: Molly Berendt, Hiram Emory III. Student, W. Va. Poly. Inst., 1940-41; B.S., U.S. Naval Acad., 1944; LL.B., Washington and Lee U., 1953, LL.D., 1977. Bar: Va. 1951. Pvt. practice law Abingdon, 1953-69; judge U.S. Dist. Ct. Western Dist. Va., Abingdon, 1969-71; chief judge U.S. Dist. Ct. Western Dist. Va., 1971-72; judge U.S. Ct. Appeals 4th Circuit, Abingdon, 1972—; U.S. commr. Western Dist. Va., 1963-66; mem. Va. Election Laws Study Commn., 1968-69. Chmn. Rep. party 9th Dist. Va., 1966-69; mem. Va. Rep. State Ctrl. Com., 1966-69, state exec. com., 1966-69. Served to lt. (j.g.) USN, 1944-49; to lt. USNR, 1951-52. Decorated Bronze Star with combat V. Mem. Am. Law Inst., Va. Bar Assn., Va. State Bar, Phi Alpha Delta. Republican. Presbyterian. Home and Office: PO Box 868 Abingdon VA 24212

WIDENER, PERI ANN, business development executive; b. Wichita, Kans., May 1, 1956; d. Wayne Robert and LuAnne (Harris) W. BS, Wichita State U., 1978; MBA, Fla. Tech., 1992. Advt. intern Associated Advt., Wichita, 1978; pub. rels. asst. Fourth Nat. Bank, Wichita, 1978-79; mktg. communications rep. Boeing Co., Wichita, 1979-83, pub. rels. rep., Huntsville, Ala., 1983-85, pub. rels. mgr., 1985-92; sr. pub. rels. mgr. Boeing Mil. Airplanes, Seattle, 1992-95; bus. devel. mgr. Boeing Defense & Space Group, Washington, D.C., 1995—. mem. exec. devel. program Boeing Def. & Space Group, 1993—. Preston Huston scholar, Wichita State U., 1978; recipient Best Electronic Ad award Def. Electronics mag., 1982, Best Total Pub. Rels. Program award Huntsville Press Club, 1985, Huntsville Media awards, 1986, 87, 88, 89, 90, 91, Huntsville Advt. Fedn. Addys, 1988. Mem. Pub. Rels. Soc. Am. (Seattle chpt.), Women in Communications, Pub. Rels. Coun. Ala. (bd. dirs. 1985-92, state pres. 1992, officer Huntsville chpt. 1984-91, pres No. Ala. chpt. 1989, Excellence award 1986-91, Achievement award 1986-91, Pres.'s award Huntsville chpt. 1985, State Practitioner of Yr. 1989, PRCA Medallion award excellence, numerous others), Internat. Assn. Bus. Communicators (D2 Silver Quills award 1985, 91, D6 Silver Quills 1993, 94), Pub. Rels. Soc. Am. (accredited 1989—), So. Pub. Rels. Fedn. (practitioner of yr. 1991, Excellence award 1986-91, Lantern award 1991), Huntsville-Madison County C. of C. (pub. rels. adv. com. 1987-92), Huntsville Press Club (bd. dirs. 1989-92), Sigma Delta Chi (pres.'s award 1991). Methodist. Office: Boeing Mil Airplanes MS 4C-98 PO Box 3707 # 14 Seattle WA 98124-2207

WIDERA, G. E. OTTO, mechanical engineering educator, consultant; b. Dortmund, Germany, Feb. 16, 1938; came to U.S., 1950; s. Otto and Gertrude (Yzermann) W.; m. Kristel Kornas, June 21, 1974; children: Erika, Nicholas. BS, U. Wis., 1960, MS, 1962, PhD, 1965. Asst. prof., then prof. materials engring. dept. U. Ill.-Chgo., 1965-91, prof. mech. engring., 1982-91, 1983-91, acting head indsl. systems engring. dept., 1985-86, dir. off-campus engring. programs, 1987-88; prof., chmn. mech. and indsl. engring. dept. Marquette U., Milw., 1991—; Gastdozent U. Stuttgart, Fed. Republic of Germany, 1968; vis. prof. U. Wis.-Milw., 1973-74, Marquette U., Milw., 1978-79; cons. Ladish Co., Cudahy, Wis., 1967-76, Howmedica, Inc., Chgo., 1977-75, Sargent & Lundy, 1970-88, Nat. Bur. Standards, 1980; vis. sci. Argonne Nat. Lab., Ill., 1968; bd. dirs. Wis. Ctr. for Mfg. Productivity. Editor: Procs. Innovations in Structural Engring., 1974, Pressure Vessel Design, 1982; assoc. editor: Pressure Vessel Tech., 1977-81, Applied Mechanics Revs., 1987-94, Manufacturing Review, 1991—; editorial adv. bd. Acta Mechanica Sinica, 1990—; mem. editorial bd. Pressure Vessels and Piping Design Technology, 1982; tech. editor Pressure Vessel Technology, 1982-93; co-editor: SME Handbook of Metalforming, 1985, 94, Design and Analysis of Plates and Shells, 1986. Standard Oil Co. Calif. fellow, 1961-63; NASA fellow, 1966; NAS travel grantee, Russia, 1972; von Humboldt fellow, Fed. Republic Germany, 1968-69. Fellow ASME (v.p. materials and structures 1993—, chmn. pressure vessel rsch. com. 1982-87, chmn. design and analysis com. pressure vessel and piping div. 1980-83, chmn. jr. awards com. applied mechanics div. 1973-76, chmn. machine design div. of Chgo. sect., 1967-68, editor newsletter Chgo. sect. 1971-73, exec. com. Chgo. sect. 1970-73, honors and awards chmn. Milw. sect. 1990—, mem. exec. com. and program chmn. pressure vessel and piping div. 1985-89, vice-chmn., sec. pressure vessel and piping div., 1989-90, chmn. pressure vessel and piping div., 1990-91, historian, senate pressure vessel and piping div., 1991-92, pres. senate pressure vessel and piping div., 1992-93, bd. editors, 1983-93, mem. materials and structures group, 1990-91, mem. coun. on engring. 1993—, mem. bd. on pressure tech. codes and standards, 1989-94, soc. rep. to Fedn. Materials Socs. 1994—, mem. tech. execs. com. 1993—, Pressure Valve and Piping award 1995), ASCE (sec.-treas. structural div. of Ill. sect. 1972-73, chmn. div. 1976-77, chmn. peer review com., tech. coun. on rsch. 1984, coun. on structural plastics), NSPE, Soc. Mfg. Engrs. (sr. mem.), Am. Soc. for Engring. Edn., French Pressure Vessel Assn., So. Plastics Engrs., Gesellschaft für Angewandte Mathematik und Mechanik, Am. Acad. Mechanics, WRC (pressure vessel rsch. coun., chmn. subcom. on design procedures for shell intersections, 1983-87, chmn. com. on reinforced openings and external loads, 1987-91, vice chmn. com. on polymer pressure components 1991—, chmn. com. shells and ligaments 1994—), Internat. Coun. on Pressure Vessel Tech. (chmn. Am. regional com 1988—, internat. chmn. 1992—), 2nd China Nat. Standards Com. for Pressure Vessels (hon. cons.), Wis. Club. Research on mechanics of composite materials, plates and shells, asymptotic methods in elasticity, pressure vessels and piping, mechanics of deformation processing. Home: 19440 Killarney Way Brookfield WI 53045 Office: Marquette U Dept Mech & Indsl Engring 1515 W Wisconsin Ave Milwaukee WI 53233-2286

WIDGOFF, MILDRED, physicist, educator; b. Buffalo, Aug. 24, 1924; d. Leo Widgoff and Rebecca Shulimson; children—Eve Widgoff Shapiro, Jonathan Bernard Widgoff Shapiro. B.A., U. Buffalo, 1944; Ph.D., Cornell U., 1952. Rsch. assoc. Brookhaven Nat. Lab., Yaphank, N.Y., 1952-54; rsch. fellow Harvard U., Cambridge, Mass., 1955-58; asst. prof. rsch. Brown U., Providence, 1959-66, assoc. prof. rsch., 1966-74, prof. physics, 1974—. Fellow Am. Phys. Soc.; mem. Sigma Xi, Phi Beta Kappa, Phi Kappa Phi. Office: Brown U Dept Physics PO Box 1843 Providence RI 02912-1843

WIDISS, ALAN I., lawyer, educator; b. L.A., Sept. 28, 1938; s. Al and Rose H. (Sobole) W.; m. Ellen Louise Magaziner, June 28, 1964; children: Benjamin I., Deborah Anne, Rebecca Elizabeth. BS, U. So. Calif., 1960, LLB, 1963; LLM, Harvard U., 1964. Bar: Calif. 1963. Teaching fellow Harvard U., 1964-65; asst. prof. law U. Iowa, Iowa City, 1965-68; assо. prof. U. Iowa, 1968-69, prof., 1969-78, Josephine R. Witte prof., 1978—; vis. prof. U. So. Calif., U. San Diego; dir. CLRS Mass. No-Fault Automobile Ins. Study, 1971-76. Author: A Guide to Uninsured Motorist Coverage, 1969; (with others) No-Fault Automobile Insurance in Action: The Experiences in Massachusetts, Florida, Delaware and New York, 1977, Uninsured and Underinsured Motorist Insurance (3d edit.), Vol. I, 1991, Vol. 2, 1992, Vol. 3, 1995; author, editor: (with others) Arbitration: Commercial Disputes, Insurance and Tort Claims, 1979 (with Judge Robert E. Keeton) Insurance Law, 1988 and Course Supplement, 1988; Insurance: Materials on the General Principles, Legal Doctrines and Regulatory Acts, 1989; contbr. articles to law jours. Bd. fellows U. Iowa Sch. Religion, 1976, vice chmn., 1991-93, chmn., 1993-95; chmn. Johnson County Citizens Adv. Com. for Regional Transp. Study, 1971-75; pres. Agudas Achim Synagogue, 1983-85, Iowa City Youth Orch., 1991-92. Mem. ABA, Am. Law Inst., Calif. Bar Assn., Assn. Am. Law Schs., Order of Coif, Phi Kappa Phi, Delta Sigma Rho. Avocations: tennis, theater. Home: 316 Kimball Rd Iowa City IA 52245-5825 Office: U Iowa Coll Law Iowa City IA 52242

WIDLUND, OLOF BERTIL, computer science educator; b. Stockholm, Feb. 11, 1938; s. Sten O. and Dagmar W.; m. Nadine H. Taub, June 13, 1972. M.S. in Engring., Royal Inst. Tech., Stockholm, 1960, Ph.D., 1964; ScD, Uppsala U., Sweden, 1966. Asst. prof. NYU, N.Y.C., 1968-72, assoc. prof., 1972-75, prof. computer sci., 1975—, chmn. dept. computer sci., 1980-

86. Contbr. articles to various publs. Office: NYU Courant Inst 251 Mercer St New York NY 10012-1110

WIDLUS, HANNAH BEVERLY, lawyer; b. Montreal, Quebec, Can., Jan. 23, 1955; d. William Jayson and Martha (Klein) Widlus; m. Moses W. Gaynor, Dec. 20, 1986. BSBA cum laude, Miami U., Oxford, Ohio, 1976; JD with honors, George Washington U., 1979. Bar: Tex. 1979, N.Y. 1984, Ill. 1988, D.C. 1990. Assoc. Johnson & Gibbs (formerly Johnson, Swanson & Barbee), Dallas, 1979-82, Proskauer Rose Goetz & Mendelsohn, N.Y.C., 1982-83, Patterson, Belknap, Webb & Tyler, N.Y.C., 1983-86; assoc. Kirkland & Ellis, Chgo., 1987-88, ptnr., 1988-91; counsel benefits Waste Management, Inc., Oak Brook, Ill., 1991-94; assoc. D'Ancona & Pflaum, Chgo., 1994—; lectr. on pension and profit sharing plans, 1988-92; seminar on employment regulations in Ill., 1987-91, seminar on basic employee benefits, 1988-90, NYU 45th Ann. Inst. on Fed. Taxation, 1986, inst. for paralegal studies NYU Sch. Continuing Edn., 1984-86, tax seminar Dallas Gen. Agts. and Mgrs. Assn., 1980, 81, Corpus Christi chpt. Tex. Soc. CPAs, 1981, sect. taxation Dallas Bar Assn., 1980. Contbr. articles to profl. jours. Mem. ABA (sect. taxation), State Bar Tex., State Bar N.Y., Ill. Bar, D.C. Bar. Jewish.

WIDMAN, GARY LEE, lawyer, former government official; b. Fremont, Nebr., June 1, 1936; s. Benjamin H. and Alice C. (Negley) W.; m. Mary Margaret Donnelly, Mar. 5, 1972(div. 1988); children: Andrew Scott, Natalie Claire. BS, U. Nebr., 1957; JD, Hastings Coll. Law U. Calif., 1962; LLM, U. Mich., 1966. Bar: Calif. 1962, D.C. 1982. Assoc. Thelen, Marrin, Johnson & Bridges, San Francisco, 1962-65; assoc. prof. law U. Denver, 1966-69; prof., dir. resource and environ. law program Hastings Coll. Law, U. Calif., San Francisco 1969-80; gen. counsel Coun. Environ. Quality, Exec. Office Pres., Washington, 1974-76; lectr. U. Calif. at Davis, 1978, Boalt Hall, 1977-79; assoc. solicitor Dept. Interior, Washington, 1980-81; of counsel Fulbright & Jaworski, 1981-85; dir. staff attys. U.S. Ct. of Appeals (9th cir.), San Francisco, 1985-87; atty. Bronson, Bronson & McKinnon, San Francisco, 1988—; trustee Rocky Mountain Mineral Law Found., 1969-74, 77-80; apptd. by gov. P. Wilson to Bay-Delta Oversight coun., 1993. Author and project dir.: Legal Study of Oil Shale on Public Lands, 1969. Served with U.S. Army, 1957-59. Mem. ABA (council sect. natural resources 1975-77, spl. com. energy law 1977-82, council lawyers and scientists 1984-90), Fed. Bar Assn. (chmn. com. natural resources 1977), Calif. Bar Assn., D.C. Bar Assn., Trout Unlimited Calif. (pres. 1986-90). Home: 28 Marinero Cir Apt 31 Belvedere Tiburon CA 94920-1614 Office: Bronson Bronson & McKinnon 505 Montgomery St San Francisco CA 94111-2514

WIDMAN, RICHARD GUSTAVE, engineering and construction company executive; b. Detroit, Jan. 28, 1922; s. Edward J. and Lena E. (Hurrle) W.; m. Barbara Jean Roehm, Sept 7, 1946; children: Richard Thomas, Linda Widman Wyer, Jeanne Widman Overby. B.C.E., U. Mich., 1947. Various positions Arthur G. McKee & Co. and McKee Corp., 1948-65, gen. mgr. petroleum and chems. div., 1966-68, v.p., 1968-69, exec. v.p., dir., 1969, pres., 1970-71, pres., chief exec. officer, chmn. bd., 1971-79, also dir.; chmn. bd., dir. Am. Automobile Assn.; bd. dirs. Ohio Motorists Assn. Served with C.E. AUS, 1943-46. Mem. Tau Beta Pi. Clubs: Royal Poinciana Golf. (Naples, Fla.). Lodges: Rotary, Shriners, Jesters. Home: 2901 Gulf Shore Blvd N Naples FL 33940-3901

WIDMANN, GLENN ROGER, electrical engineer; b. Newark, Jan. 8, 1957; s. Elmer and Ellen (Eccles) W. BSEE, Rutgers U., 1979; MSEE, Purdue U., 1981, PhDEE, 1988. Engr. N.J. Bell Telephone Co., Hopelawn, 1979; instr. Purdue U., West Lafayette, Ind., 1979-81, 83-88; prof. elec. engring. Colo. State U., Ft. Collins, 1989-91; engr. Hughes Aircraft Co., Canoga Park, Calif., 1980-83, scientist, project mgr., 1991-94; sr. sci. Hughes Rsch. Labs. Hughes Aircraft Co., Malibu, Calif., 1994—; cons. Bur. Reclamation, Denver, 1989, Benjamin Cummings Pub. Co., Ft. Collins, 1989; mem. program com. Internat. Symposium Robotics and Mfg., Santa Fe, N.Mex., 1991—. Contbr. articles to tech. jours.; patentee in robotics field. Recipient presentation award Am. Controls Conf., 1990. Mem. IEEE, Soc. Automotive Engrs., Tau Beta Pi, Eta Kappa Nu. Avocation: coin collecting. Home: 3434 Delilah St Simi Valley CA 93063-2720 Office: Hughes Aircraft Co Hughes Rsch Labs MS RL 71 3011 Malibu Canyon Rd Malibu CA 90265

WIDMANN, NANCY C., broadcast executive. Pres. radio div. CBS, N.Y.C., 1988—. Office: CBS Radio Networks 524 W 57th St New York NY 10019-2902

WIDMARK, RICHARD, actor; b. Sunrise, Minn., Dec. 26, 1914; s. Carl H. and Ethel Mae (Barr) W.; m. Ora Jean Hazlewood, Apr. 5, 1942; 1 dau., Anne Heath. B.A., Lake Forest (Ill.) Coll., 1936, D.F.A. (hon.), 1973. Instr. drama dept. Lake Forest Coll., 1936-38; Pres. Heath Prodns., 1955—; v.p. Widmark Cattle Enterprises, 1957—. Actor various radio networks, N.Y.C., 1938-47; Broadway appearances include Kiss and Tell, 1943, Get Away Old Man, 1943, Trio, 1944, Kiss Them for Me, 1944, Dunnigan's Daughter, 1945, Dream Girl, 1946-47; summer stock appearances include The Bo Tree, 1939, Joan of Lorraine, 1947; motion picture appearances include Kiss of Death, 1947, Street with No Name, 1948, Yellow Sky, 1948, Roadhouse, 1948, Down to the Sea in Ships, 1949, Night and the City, 1949, No Way Out, 1949, Panic in the Streets, 1950, Slattery's Hurricane, 1949, Halls of Montezuma, 1950, The Frogmen, 1950, Price of Gold, 1954, Co Blue, 1954, Broken Lance, 1954, Backlash, 1955, St. Joan, 1956, Time Limit, 1957, Warlock, 1958, The Alamo, 1959, Judgement at Nuremberg, 1961, Flight from Ashiya, 1962, How the West Was Won, 1962, The Long Ships, 1963, Cheyenne Autumn, 1963, Bedford Incident, 1964, Alvarez Kelly, 1965, The Way West, 1966, Madigan, 1967, Patch, 1968, Talent for Loving, 1968, The Moonshine War, 1969, When the Legends Die, 1971, Murder on the Orient Express, 1974, The Sellout, 1975, To the Devil, A Daughter, 1975, The Twilight's Last Gleaming, 1976, The Domino Principle, 1976, Roller Coaster, 1976, Coma, 1978, The Swarm, 1977, Hanky Panky, 1982, The Final Option, 1983, Against All Odds, 1984, True Colors, 1990; NBC TV appearance in Vanished, 1971, TV series Madigan, 1972; TV appearance in Benjamin Franklin, 1974, Mr. Horn, 1979, Bear Island, 1979, All God's Children, 1980, A Whale for the Killing, 1981, Blackout, 1985, A Gathering of Old Men, 1986, Once Upon a Texas Train, 1987, Cold Sassy Tree, 1989. True Colors, 1990. Bd. dirs. Hope for Hearing. Named Comdr. of Arts and Letters (France), 1987. Mem. Valley Club (Montecito, Calif.), Century Club (N.Y.C.), Phi Epsilon.

WIDMER, KEMBLE, geologist; b. New Rochelle, N.Y., Feb. 26, 1913; s. George Ellis and Beth (Kemble) W.; m. Virginia Maiers, Mar. 10, 1939; children—Kemble II, Katharine. A.B., Lehigh U., 1937; postgrad., Stanford, 1937-39; M.A., Princeton, 1947, Ph.D. 1950. Geologist Newfoundland Geol. Survey, summers 1937-41, 46, 47; asst. prof. geology Rutgers U., 1949-51; assoc. prof. geology Chaplain Coll., State U. N.Y., 1951-53; prin. geologist N.J. Bur. Geology, 1953-58; state geologist N.J., 1958-81; seminar assoc. Columbia U., 1967-83; N.J. nuclear indsl. officer, 1964-74; mem. fed. adv. com. on water data for public use U.S. Geol. Survey, 1978-81; ret., 1981; cons. U.S. Mil. Acad., 1964-83. Served to lt. col. AUS, 1941-46; col. Res. (ret.). Recipient Outstanding Civilian Svc. medal Dept. Army, 1983. Fellow Geol. Soc. Am., N.J. Acad. Sci., AAAS, Company Mil. Historians; mem. Sigma Xi. Club: Explorers (N.Y.C.). Home: 228 King George Rd Pennington NJ 08534-2324

WIDNALL, SHEILA EVANS, federal official, air force officer, former aeronautical educator, former university official; b. Tacoma, July 13, 1938; d. Rolland John and Genievieve Alice (Krause) Evans; m. William Soule Widnall, June 11, 1960; children: William, Ann. BS in Aero. and Astronautics, MIT, 1960, MS in Aero. and Astronautics, 1961, DSc, 1964; PhD (hon.), New Eng. Coll., 1975, Lawrence U., 1987, Cedar Crest Coll., 1988, Smith Coll., 1990, Mt. Holyoke Coll., 1991, Ill. Inst. Tech., 1991, Columbia U., 1994, Simmons Coll., 1994, Suffolk U., 1994, Princeton U., 1994. Asst. prof. aeros. and astronautics MIT, Cambridge, 1964-70, assoc. prof., 1970-74, prof., 1974-93, head divsn. fluid mechanics, 1975-79; dir. Fluid Dynamics Rsch. Lab., MIT, Cambridge, 1979-90; chmn. faculty MIT, Cambridge, 1979-80, chairperson com. on acad. responsibility, 1991-92, assoc. provost, 1992-93; sec. USAF, 1993—. Author: numerous articles to profl. jours. Bd. dirs. Carnegie Corp., N.Y., Chemfab Inc., Bennington, Vt., Aerospace Corp., L.A., Draper Labs., Cambridge; past trustee Carnegie Corp., 1984-92, Charles Stark Draper Lab. Inc.; mem. Carnegie Commn. Sci., Tech. and Govt. Contbr. articles to profl. jours.; patentee in field; assoc. editor

AIAA Jour. Aircraft, 1972-75, Physics of Fluids, 1981-88, Jour. Applied Mechanics, 1983-87; mem. editorial bd. Sci., 1984-86. Bd. visitors USAF Acad., Colorado Springs, Colo., 1978-84, bd. chairperson, 1980-82; trustee Boston Mus. Sci., 1989—. Recipient Washburn award Boston Mus. Sci., 1987. Fellow AAAS (bd. dirs. 1982-89, pres. 1987-88, chmn. 1988-89), AIAA (bd. dirs. 1975-77, Lawrence Sperry award 1972), Am. Phys. Soc. (exec. com. 1979-82); mem. ASME, NAE (coun. 1992—), NAS (panel on sci. responsibility), Am. Acad. Arts and Scis., Soc. Women Engrs. (Outstanding Achievement award 1975), Internat. Acad. Astronautics, Seattle Mountaineers. Office: USAF Office of Sec 1670 AF Pentagon Washington DC 20330-1670

WIDNER, RALPH RANDOLPH, civic executive; b. Phila., Oct. 21, 1930; s. Ralph Litteer and Viola (Cunningham) W.; m. Joan Sundelius Ziegler, July 9, 1955; children: Jennifer Anne, Wendy Rowe. B.A., Duke U., 1952; student, Georgetown U., 1958; D.H.L. (hon.), Union Coll., Ky., 1970, Capital U., Columbus, Ohio, 1971. Journalist Paterson (N.J.) Evening News, 1955-56, N.Y. Times, 1956-58; Congressional fellow Am. Polit. Sci. Assn., 1958; dir. pub. affairs Pa. Dept. Forests and Waters, 1959-60; asst. dir. Pa. Planning Bd., 1960-62; legis. asst. to U.S. Senator Clark, 1962-65; exec. dir. Appalachian Regional Commn., 1965-71; pres. Acad. for State and Local Govt., 1971-82; adj. prof. pub. adminstrn. and city planning Ohio State U., 1971-82; pres. Nat. Tng. and Devel. Service for State and Local Govt., 1979-81; staff v.p. Urban Land Inst., 1982-83; exec. dir. Greater Phila. First Corp., 1983-87; chmn., chief exec. officer Fairfax House Internat., Alexandria, Va., 1987—; dir. devel. Psaras Fund and Am. Community Svc. Network; mng. dir. Civic TN Network. Lt. (j.g.) USN, 1952-55. Fellow Nat. Acad. Pub. Administrn. Democrat. Methodist. Home: 2210 Belle Haven Rd Alexandria VA 22307-1100 Office: 21 Dupont Cir NW Washington DC 20036-1110

WIDNEY, MARILYN EDITH (MARILYN PERRY), international finance and real estate executive, television producer; b. N.Y.C., Feb. 11, 1939; d. Henry William Patrick and Edna May (Bown) Perry; m. Charles Leonidas Widney (dec. Sept. 1981). BA, Mexico City Coll., 1957. Pres. Marilyn Perry TV Prodns., Inc., N.Y.C., 1970—, C.L. Widney Internat., Inc., N.Y.C., 1977—; mng. dir. Donerail Corp., N.Y.C., 1980-88, Lancer, N.Y.C., 1980-88, Assawata, N.Y.C., 1980-88. Producer, host TV program Internat. Byline, series of more than 90 documentaries on the UN; host radio series Internat. Byline-mem. nations UN for PBS in S.C., N.C., Ga., Tenn., 1995—. Bd. dirs. UN After Sch. Program; ambassadorial candidate Pres. Bush., 1989. Recipient U.S. Indsl. Film Festival award, CINE Golden Eagle award, Bronze medal Internat. Film & TV Festival of N.Y., Bronzenen Urkinde, Berlin, award for superior quality Intercom-Chgo. Internat. Film Festival, Knights of Malta Trophy award for superior programming from Min. of Tourism, Internationales Tourismus award Filmfestival, Vienna, Manhattan Cable Ten Year award for continuous programming, citations from former pres. Ford and Carter. Mem. Asia Soc., UN Corrs. Assn., Rep. Presdl. Task Force (charter mem.), Rep. Nat. Com., Harbour Club (S.C.). Avocations: music, art and antiques collecting, travel. Home: 211 E 70th St New York NY 10021 Office: C L Widney Internat Inc 677 Fifth Ave New York NY 10022

WIDOM, BENJAMIN, chemistry educator; b. Newark, Oct. 13, 1927; s. Morris and Rebecca (Hertz) W.; m. Joanne McCurdy, Dec. 21, 1953; children: Jonathan, Michael, Elisabeth. AB, Columbia U., 1949; PhD, Cornell U., 1953; DSc (hon.), U. Chgo., 1991. Rsch. assoc. U. N.C., Chapel Hill, 1952-54; instr. chemistry Cornell U., Ithaca, N.Y., 1954-55, asst. prof., 1955-59, assoc. prof., 1959-63, prof., 1963-83, Goldwin Smith prof., 1983—; van der Waals prof. U. Amsterdam, The Netherlands, 1972; vis. prof. Harvard U., Cambridge, Mass., 1975; IBM vis. prof. Oxford (Eng.) U., 1978; Lorentz prof. U. Leiden, The Netherlands, 1985; vis. prof. Cath. U. Louvain, Belgium, 1988. Author: (with J.S. Rowlinson) Molecular Theory of Capillarity, 1982. With U.S. Army, 1946-47. Recipient Clark disting. tchg. award Cornell U., 1973, Dickson prize for sci. Carnegie-Mellon U., 1986, Hirschfelder Prize in Theoretical Chemistry U. Wis., 1991, Bakhuis Roozeboom medal Royal Netherlands Acad. Arts & Scis., 1994, Onsager medal U. Trondheim, Norway, 1994. Fellow Am. Phys. Soc., Am. Acad. Arts and Scis., N.Y. Acad. Scis. (Boris Pregel award for chem. physics rsch. 1976); mem. NAS, Am. Philos. Soc., Am. Chem. Soc. (Langmuir award in chem. physics 1982, Hildebrand award in theoretical and exptl. chemistry of liquids 1992). Home: 204 The Parkway Ithaca NY 14850-2247 Office: Cornell U Chemistry Dept Ithaca NY 14853

WIDROW, BERNARD, electrical engineering educator; b. Norwich, Conn., Dec. 24, 1929. BS, MIT, 1951, MS, 1953, DSc, 1956. Prof. Stanford (Calif.) U. Dept. Elec. Engring.; holder Francqui Chair, U. Louvain, Belgium, 1967. Fellow AAAS, IEEE (Centennial medal 1984, Alexander Graham Bell medal 1986); mem. Tau Beta Pi. Office: Stanford U Dept Elec Engring Durand Bldg Rm 139 Stanford CA 94305-4055*

WIEBE, BERNIE, conflict resolution studies educator; b. Altona, Man., Can., Jan. 30, 1935; s. Peter D. and Susanna (Hiebert) W.; m. Marge Dora Letkeman, July 8, 1956; Glen (dec.), Gayle, Gregory, Grant. BA, Goshen Coll., 1961; BD, Mennonite Biblical Sem., 1965; MA, U. N.D., 1972, PhD, 1974. Tchr. Mennonites in Man., Winnipeg, 1953-56, conf. min., 1965-71; pres. Freeman Jr. Coll., S.D., 1973-76; med. messenger Mennonites in Man.; mng. editor Mennonite Med. Assn., 1980-89; editor The Mennonite Gen. Conf. Mennonite Ch., 1976-86; prof. in CRS Menno Simons Coll., 1986—. Author: (book) Biblical Mutual Aid for the 1980's, 1987; contbr. chpts. to books, articles to profl. jours. lay min. Ft. Garry Mennonite Fellowship, 1977-80, exec. mem. Liberal Party, 1978-80, mem. edn. com. 1984-86, active spl. GC-MC inter-mennonite listening com. for homosexual concerns, 1990-92, mem. worship com. 1991-93; conf. moderator Mennonites in Man., 1979-82, 85-88, chair Can. program com. 1985-88, elected mem. divsn. sves. bd., 1989-92, mem. spl. com. to work with conflict in churches and to provide guidelines to CMM, 1992—, mem. GC Higher Edn. Coun., 1992—, appointee GC program com., 1992—, asst. moderator GC Conf., 1992—; mem. NDP task force on environ. Province Manitoba, 1988-89. Mem. Gideons. Home: 46 Belair Rd, Winnipeg, MB Canada R3T 0S2 Office: Menno Simons Coll, 380 Spence St 3d fl, Winnipeg, MB Canada R3B 2E9

WIEBE, J. E. N., province official. Lt. gov. Govt. Saskatchewan, Regina, Can. Office: Government House, 4607 Dewdney Ave, Regina, SK Canada S4P 3V7*

WIEBE, LEONARD IRVING, radiopharmacist, educator; b. Swift Current, Sask., Can., Oct. 14, 1941; s. Cornelius C. and Margaret (Teichroeb) W.; m. Grace E. McIntyre, Sept. 5, 1964; children: Glenis, Kirsten, Megan. BSP, U. Sask., 1963, MS, 1966; PhD, U. Sydney, Australia, 1970. Pharmacist Swift Current Union Hosp., 1963-64; sessional lectr. U. Sask., Can., 1965-66; asst. prof. U. Alta., Can., 1970-73, assoc. prof., 1973-78, prof., 1978—; dir. Slowpoke Reactor Facility, 1975-89, asst. dean rsch., 1984-87; assoc. dean U. Alta., 1990—; sessional lectr. U. Sydney, Australia, 1973; pres. Internat. Bionucleonics Cons. Lts., 1991—; dir. BMH, Australian Nuclear Sci. Tech. Orgn., 1990, Noujaim Inst. Pharm. Oncology, 1994—; rsch. assoc. Cross Cancer Inst., Edmonton, 1978—, Med. Rsch. Coun. Can.; vis. prof. Royal P.A. Hosp., Sydney, 1983-84, Searle vis. profl., 1986; MRC vis. profl. Toronto, 1987; PMAC vis. prof., 1988; McCalla prof. U. Alta, 1993-94; radiopharmacy cons. Australian Atomic Energy Commn., Sydney, 1983-84; mem. MRC standing com. on sci. and rsch., 1995—. Editor: Liquid Scintillation: Science and Technology, 1976, Advances in Scintillation Counting, 1983; guest editor Jour. of Radioanalytical Chemistry, 1981; editor Internat. Jour. Applied Radiation Instrumentation Part A, 1988-90; regional editor Internat. Jour. Nuclear Biology and Medicine, 1992-95. Commonwealth Univs. Exchange grantee, 1966; Alexander von Humboldt fellow, 1976-79, 82. Mem. Pharm. Bd. of New South Wales, Sask. Pharm. Assn., Soc. Nuclear Medicine, Assn. Faculties of Pharmacy of Can. (McNeil Rsch. award 1988), Can. Radiation Protection Assn., Can. Assn. Radiopharm. Scientists, Am. Pharm. Assn., Am. Assn. Pharm. Sci., Australian Nuclear Sci. Tech. Orgn. (dir., biomedicine and health 1990), Internat. Assn. Radiopharmacy (exec. sec. 1991-95), Univ. Club (Edmonton) (pres. 1985). Mem. Mennonite Ch.

WIEBE, RICHARD HERBERT, reproductive endocrinologist, educator; b. Herbert, Sask., Can., Dec. 28, 1937; came to U.S., 1971; s. Herbert and Olga

Maragratha (Jahnke) W.; m. Jacquelyn Dee Yancy, Aug. 30, 1975; 1 child, Richard Herbert, Jr. MD, U. Sask., 1962. Resident Queen's Univ., Kingston, Ont., Can., 1970; asst. to assoc. prof. Duke U., Durham, N.C., 1972-81; assoc. prof. to prof. U. So. Ala., Mobile, 1981-88; chmn. and prof. Dept. Ob-Gyn. U. S.D., Sioux Falls, 1988—; editorial cons. Fertility/Sterility, Birmingham, Ala., 1978—; sec., Univ. Physicians, Sioux Falls, 1991—. Contbr. numerous articles to profl. jours. Recipient, Rsch. Grant, NIH, Ala., 1981-89, Edn./Svc. Grant, USPHS, S.D., 1989—. Mem. ACOG, Assn. Profs. of Ob-Gyn., Am. Soc. Primatologists, Soc. for Gynecol. Investigation, Soc. for Study of Reproduction, Am. Fertility Soc., Endocrine Soc. Home: 1400 22nd St Sioux Falls SD 57105 Office: U SD Sch of Medicine Dept of Ob-Gyn 1400 22d St Sioux Falls SD 57105

WIEBE, RUDY HENRY, writer; b. Fairholme, Sask., Can., Oct. 4, 1934; s. Abram J. and Tena (Knelson) W.; m. Tena F. Isaak, 1958; children: Adrienne, Michael, Christopher. BA, U. Alta., 1956, MA, 1960; BTh, Mennonite Brethren Bible Coll., 1961; DLitt (hon.), U. Winnipeg, 1986, Wilfred Laurier U., 1991; LLD (hon.), Brock U., 1991. Fgn. svc. officer Govt. of Canada, Ottawa, Ont., 1960; editor Mennonite Brethren Herald, Winnipeg, Man., 1962-63; asst. prof. English Goshen Coll., Ind., 1963-67; asst. prof. U. Alta., Edmonton, 1967-70, assoc. prof., 1970-76, prof. English, 1976-92, prof. emeritus, 1992—; rsch. writer Glenbow Found., Calgary, 1956; chmn. Can. studies U. Kiel, Germany, 1984. Author: Peace Shall Destroy Many, 1962, First and Vital Candle, 1966, The Blue Mountains of China, 1970, The Temptations of Big Bear, 1973 (Governor General's award for fiction 1973), Riel and Gabriel, 1973, Where Is the Voice Coming From?, 1974, The Scorched-Wood People, 1977, Alberta: A Celebration, 1979, The Mad Trapper, 1980, The Angel of the Tar Sands and Other Stories, 1982, My Lovely Enemy, 1983, Playing Dead, 1989, Chinook Christmas, 1992, A Discovery of Strangers, 1994 (Governor General's award for fiction 1994); playwright: As Far as the Eye Can See, 1977; editor: The Story Makers: A Selection of Modern Short Stories, 1970, Stories from Western Canada, 1972, Stories from Pacific and Arctic Canada, 1974, Double Vision, 1976, Getting Here, 1977, More Stories from Western Canada, 1980, West of Fiction, 1983; compiler: War in the West: Voices of the 1885 Rebellion, 1985; contbr. to periodicals including Fiddlehead, Tamarack Rev., Camrose Rev., Canadian Lit., Maclean's, Saturday Night, The Bote. Rotary Internat. fellow, 1957-58; recipient Lorne Pierce medal Royal Soc. Can., 1987. Mem. Writers Union Can. (pres. 1985-86), Writers Guild Alta. (pres. 1980-81). Office: 105 10610-83 Ave, Edmonton, AB Canada T6E 2E2*

WIEBENSON, DORA LOUISE, architectural historian, educator, author; b. Cleve., July 29, 1926; d. Edward Ralph and Jeannette (Rodier) W. BA, Vassar Coll., 1946; MArch, Harvard U., 1951; MA, NYU, 1958, PhD, 1964. Architect N.Y., 1951-66; lectr. Columbia U., 1966-68; assoc. prof. U. Md., 1968-72, prof., 1972-77; vis. prof. Cornell U., 1974; prof. U. Va., Charlottesville, 1977-92, prof. emerita, 1992—, chmn. div. archtl. history, 1977-79, assoc. fellow U. Va. Ctr. Advanced Studies, 1982-83; pres. Archtl. Publs., N.Y.C., 1982—. Editor: Marsyas XI: 1962-64, 1965, Essays in Honor of Walter Friedlaender, 1965; Architectural Theory and Practice from Alberti to Ledoux, 1982, rev., 1983, Spanish transl., 1988; Guide to Graduate Degree Programs in Architectural History, 1982, rev., 1984, 86, 88, 90; author: Sources of Greek Revival Architecture, 1969, Tony Garnier: The Cité Industrielle, 1969, Japanese transl., 1983, The Picturesque Garden in France, 1978, Mark J. Millard Architectural Collection, Vol. I: French Books: Sixteenth through Nineteenth Centuries, 1993; contbr. articles to profl. jours. Student fellow Inst. Fine Arts, 1961-62, 62-63; grantee Am. Philos. Soc., 1964-65, 70, Samuel H. Kress Found., 1966, Gen. Rsch. Fund, U. Md., 1969, 74, 76, NEH, 1972-73, Samuel H. Kress Found., 1972-73, Am. Coun. Learned Socs., 1976, 81, 85, Ctr. Advanced Studies, U. Va., 1982, 1989, 1991, Graham Found. Advanced Studies Fine Arts, 1982, 93; fellow Yale Ctr. Brit. Art, 1983; sr. rsch. fellow NEH, 1986-87. Mem. Soc. Archtl. Historians (bd. dirs. 1974-77, 80-83, chair edn. com. 1976-90), Coll. Art Assn., Am. Soc. Eighteenth Century (mem. exec. bd. 1991-94).

WIECEK, WILLIAM MICHAEL, law educator; b. Cleve., Jan. 31, 1938; s. Michael Frank and Mary (Kotecki) W.; m. Maryann Pickarski, June 17, 1961 (div. 1979); children: Michael, Sophie, Kristen. BA, Cath. U., 1959; LLB, Harvard U., 1962; PhD, U. Wis., 1968. Bar: N.H. 1962. Atty. Snierson & Chandler, Laconia, N.H., 1962-64; prof. history U. Mo., Columbia, 1964-84; prof. law. Syracuse (N.Y.) U., 1985—. Author: The Guarantee Clause of the U.S. Constitution, 1972, The Sources of Antislavery Constitutionalism in America, 1760-1848, 1977, Constitutional Development in a Modernizing Society: The United States, 1803-1917, 1985, (with Harold M. Hyman) Equal Justice Under Law: Constitutional Development, 1835-1875, 1982, (with Gerard H. Clarfield) Nuclear America: Military and Civilian Nuclear Power in the United States, 1940-1980, 1984, Liberty Under Law: The Supreme Court in American Life, 1988, (with Kermit Hall and Paul Finkelman) American Legal History: Cases and Materials, 1991 (with Kermit Hall, James Ely and Joel Grossman) The Oxford Companion to the Supreme Court of the United States, 1992; contbr. numerous articles, chpts. and papers on law to profl. books, jours. and confs. Vol. emergency med. technician, firefighter Fayetteville (N.Y.) Fire Dept. Mem. ABA, Am. Law Inst., Am. Soc. for Legal History (bd. dirs. 1987-90), Orgn. Am. Historians, Selden Soc., Am. Hist. Assn., Supreme Ct. Hist. Soc. (mem. editorial bd. 1984-86), Phi Beta Kappa. Democrat. Roman Catholic. Home: 137 Stanwood Ln Manlius NY 13104-1411 Office: Syracuse U Coll Of Law Syracuse NY 13244

WIECHA, JOSEPH AUGUSTINE, linguist, educator; b. Chorzów II, Poland, Sept. 20, 1926; came to U.S., 1955, naturalized, 1958; s. Karol and Gertruda (Rudzki) W.; m. Mary Ruth Moore, 1953; children: Joseph Damian, Charles Francis, John Moore. B.A. with 1st class honors, Nat. U. Ireland, 1950; Ph.D. with highest distinction, N.Y. U., 1963. Instr. fgn. langs. U.S. Third Air Force, London, 1951-55; instr. German and Spanish U. Md., London, 1951-55; tchr. Spanish and math. Bklyn. Friends Sch., 1955-56; instr. German N.Y. U., N.Y.C., summer, 1958; lectr. German and humanities Harvard U., Boston, 1959-63; lectr. German Ill. Colby Coll., summer 1963; prof. German SUNY, Oswego, 1963-69; chmn. dept. fgn. langs. and lit. SUNY, 1963-69, chmn. dept. Germanic and Slavic langs. and lit., 1969-72, Disting. Teaching prof., 1973-92, prof. emeritus, 1992—; chmn. SUNY (Fgn. Studies Center), 1972-73; lectr. and cons. methodology of tchg. fgn. langs., 1959—; condr. seminars tchg. methodology fgn. langs. Nat. U. of Pedro Enriquez Ureña, Santo Domingo, 1972, U. Pisa, Italy, 1974, Moscow State Pedagogical Inst.; Fgn. Langs., USSR, 1976; vis. prof. U. Wroctaw, Poland, 1977. Developed Wiecha Progressive-Reflex method of teaching fgn. langs. Served as officer 2d Polish Corps Brit. Army, 1944-47. Decorated Bronze medal Polish Army, also; Brit. Def. medal; French Star; Star of Italy; recipient diploma of spl. recognition Universidad Nacional de Pedro Enriquez Ureña, 1973; Galileo medal U. Pisa, 1974; Ogden Butler fellow, 1958-59; Fels fellow, 1956-59; Kosciuszko Found. fellow, 1959. Mem. MLA, N.Y. State Assn. Fgn. Lang. Tchrs. (dir. 1975-78, Disting. Tchr. award 1975, Disting. Bd. Dirs. award 1978, Spl. Contbn. to Teaching Fgn. Langs. award 1979), Am. Assn. Tchrs. of German, Polish Inst. Arts and Scis. in Am., Nat. Spanish Honors Soc. (hon.), Am. Coun. on Edn. (nat. honor roll), Delta Phi Alpha (hon.), Dobro Slovo (hon.). Home: 710 Copa De Oro Marathon FL 33050-5406 also: PO Box 1409 RD #1 Beefast ME 04915

WIECHMANN, ERIC WATT, lawyer; b. Schenectady, N.Y., June 12, 1948; s. Richard Jerdone and Ann (Watt) W.; m. Merrill Metzger, May 22, 1971. B.A., Hamilton Coll. 1970; J.D., Cornell U., 1974. Bar: Conn. 1975, U.S. Dist. Ct. (so. and ea. dists.) N.Y. 1975, U.S. Dist. Ct. Conn. 1975, U.S. Ct. Appeals (2d cir.) 1975, U.S. Supreme Ct. 1978, U.S. Ct. Appeals (9th cir.) 1980, D.C. 1981, U.S. Dist. Ct. D.C. 1981, U.S. Ct. Appeals D.C. 1982, U.S. Ct. Appeals (5th cir.) 1986, U.S. Ct. Appeals (10th cir.) 1989. Assoc., Cummings & Lockwood, Stamford, 1974-82, ptnr.; spl. pretrial master U.S. Dist. Ct. Conn. 1984—; state atty. trial referee, 1986—, mem. law revision commn., evidence code drafting com.; mem. civil task force Ct. Superior Ct. Contbr. articles to profl. jours. Mem. Zoning Bd. Appeals, New Canaan, Conn., 1984-85. Mem. ABA, Def. Research Inst., Internat. Assn. Def. Counsel, Conn. Bar Assn. (exec. com. antitrust sect. 1982—, ct. rules adv. com., chmn. 1991—), Fed. Bar Coun., Hartford Club, Golf Club Avon. Republican. Episcopalian. Home: 21 Foxcroft Run Avon CT 06001-2509

WIECK, PAUL HANS, fraternal organization executive; b. Tama County, Iowa, Sept. 19, 1932; s. Hans B. and Ella W. (Wieben) W.; m. Catharine J. Weaver, June 3, 1951; children: Paul H. II, Charlotte Haselhuhn, Linda Lyons. Student, Iowa State U., 1949. Bookkeeper Wieck's Feed and Livestock, Inc., Dysart, Iowa, 1950-64; owner, operator Dysart Oil Co., 1964-79; dep. grand sec. Grand Lodge of Iowa Ancient Free and Accepted Masons, Cedar Rapids, 1980-91, grand sec., 1991-94. Mem. Masons (Ascalon Lodg No. 393, master 1971-72), various Masonic orgns. Mem. United Methodist Ch. Home: PO Box 250 Dysart IA 52224-0250

WIECKOWSKI, ZDISLAW WLADYSLAW, lawyer; b. Toronto, Mar. 28, 1954; s. Wladyslaw Antoni and Mary (Mosiewicz) W.; children: Anastazja, Stefan, Alina. AB summa cum laude, Boston U., 1975; JD, Harvard U., 1978. Bar: Mass. 1978. Assoc. Choate, Hall & Stewart, Boston, 1978-80; asst. v.p. The First Nat. Bank of Boston, 1980-85; ptnr. Nutter, McClennen & Fish, Boston, 1985—. Mem. fin. com., Rep. town com. Town of Hingham, Mass. Mem. South Shore C. of C., Sportsmen's Tennis Club (bd. dirs.), Phi Beta Kappa. Avocations: politics, skiing, mountain biking, tennis, model railroading. Office: Nutter McClennen & Fish One International Pl Boston MA 02110

WIECZYNSKI, FRANK ROBERT, insurance brokerage executive; b. Balt., Jan. 14, 1939; s. Joseph John and Margaret Anna (Baranowski) W.; children: Dina, Steven. BS., Loyola Coll., Balt., 1961; postgrad. in law, U. Balt., 1964-68. Sr. revenue agt. IRS, Balt., 1961-69; sr. v.p. Alexander & Alexander Services, Inc., Balt., 1969—. Served to 1st lt. U.S. Army, 1962-64. Mem. Am. Soc. Corp. Secs. Republican. Office: Alexander & Alexander Inc 10451 Mill Run Cir Owings Mills MD 21117-5577

WIED, GEORGE LUDWIG, physician; b. Carlsbad, Czechoslovakia, Feb. 7, 1921; came to U.S., 1953, naturalized, 1960; s. Ernst George and Anna (Travnicek) W.; m. Daga M. Graaz, Mar. 19, 1949 (dec. Aug. 1977); m. Kayoko Y. Yamauchi, Nov. 1, 1990. M.D., Charles U., Prague, 1945, MD (hon.), 1995. Intern County Hosp., Carlsbad, Czechoslovakia, 1945; intern U. Chgo. Hosps., 1955; resident in ob-gyn U. Munich, Fed. Republic Germany, 1946-48; practice medicine specializing in ob-gyn West Berlin, 1948-53; asst. ob-gyn Free U., West Berlin, 1948-52; assoc. chmn. dept. ob-gyn Moabit Hosp., Free U., West Berlin, 1953; asst. prof., dir. cytology U. Chgo., 1954-59, assoc. prof., 1959-65, prof., 1965-91, mem. bd. adult edn., 1964-68, prof. pathology, 1967-91, Blum-Riese prof. ob-gyn, 1968-91, acting chmn. dept. ob-gyn, 1974-75. Editor-in-chief Jour. Reproductive Medicine, Acta Cytologica, Analytical and Quantitative Cytology, Clinical Cytology; editor: Introduction to Quantitative Cytochemistry, Automated Cell Identification and Cell Sorting, Compendium on Clinical Cytology, Compendium on the Computerized Cytology and Histology Laboratory, Compendium on Quality Assurance in Clinical Cytology. Hon. dir. Chgo. Cancer Prevention Ctr., 1959-83; chmn. jury Maurice Goldblatt Cytology award, 1963-92. Recipient Cert. of Merit, U.S. Surgeon Gen., 1952, Maurice Goldblatt Cytology award, 1961, George N. Papanicolaou Cytology award, 1970. Mem. Am. Soc. Cytology (pres. 1965-66), Mex. Soc. Cytology (hon.), Spanish Soc. Cytology (hon.), Brazilian Soc. Cytology (fgn. corr.), Indian Acad. Cytology (hon.) Latin-Am. Soc. Cytology (hon.), Japanese Soc. Cytology (hon.), German Soc. Cytology (pres. 1977-80), Central Soc. Clin. Rsch., Chgo. Path. Soc., Chgo. Gynecol. Soc. (hon.), Am. Soc. Cell Biology, German Soc. Ob-Gyn. Bavarian Soc., Ob-Gyn. German Soc. Endocrinology, Russian Assn. Cytologists (hon.), Swedish Soc. Medicine (hon.), Austrian Soc. Clim. Cytology (hon.), Russian Assn. Cytologists (hon.), Sigma Xi. Home and Office: 1640 E 50th St Chicago IL 60615-3161

WIEDEMAN, GEOFFREY PAUL, physician, air force officer; b. London, Eng., Mar. 9, 1917; came to U.S., 1934, naturalized, 1942; s. Julius William Paul and Fanny (Poile) W.; m. Carolyn Sterling, Feb. 2, 1947; 1 son, Geoffrey Paul. B.S., U. Vt., 1938, M.D., 1941. Diplomate: Am. Bd. Preventive Medicine. Commd 1st lt. USAAF, 1942; advanced through grades to brig. gen. USAF, 1970; surgeon Eastern Transport Air Force, McGuire AFB, N.J., 1958-61; comdr. USAF Hosp., Tachikawa, Japan; surgeon 315th Air Div., Japan; also surgeon Kanto Base Command, Japan, 1962-65; comdr. USAF Sch. Health Care Scis., 1965-69; command surgeon Air Tng. Command, Randolph AFB, Tex., 1969-74; retired USAF, 1974; physician Brooks AFB Clinic, Tex., retired, 1989. Decorated D.S.M., Legion of Merit, Bronze Star, Air medal, Air Force Commendation medal with oak leaf cluster, 1972. Fellow Am. Coll. Preventive Medicine; mem. Aerospace Medicine Assn., Assn. Mil. Surgeons, Am. Pub. Health Assn., Air Force Assn. Home: 6134 Windrock Dr San Antonio TX 78239-2707

WIEDEMAN, JOHN HERMAN, civil engineer; b. Atlanta, Oct. 31, 1935; s. Herman F. and Annie (Crum) W.; m. Joan B. Denson, May 10, 1959; children: Harold, Jonna, Justin. BCE, Ga. Inst. Tech., 1957, M in Pub. Health Engring., 1957. Registered profl. engr., 12 states. With Wiedeman & Singleton, Atlanta, 1959—; ptnr., civil engr. Wiedeman & Singleton, 1962—. Lt. (j.g.) USN, 1957-59. Mem. ASCE (pres. 1982-83), NSPE, Am. Water Works Assn., Water Pollution Control Fedn., Atlanta Athletic Club (bd. dirs. 1979-81). Methodist. Office: Wiedeman & Singleton 1789 Peachtree Rd NE Atlanta GA 30309-2329

WIEDEMANN, JOSEPH ROBERT, insurance company executive; b. Chgo., June 18, 1928; s. Joseph Matthew and Ann Elizabeth (Zittman) W.; m. Ree McClure, Dec. 26, 1950; children: Sue Wiedemann Evans, Patti Wiedemann Podziomek, Jane Wiedemann Candela, Mary Wiedemann Darling, Julie Wiedemann Gotsch, Joseph, Thomas. BBA, Loyola U., Chgo., 1950. Sr. v.p. CNA Ins. Co., Chgo., 1952-77; v.p. Frank B. Hall Co., N.Y.C., 1977-79; pres., dir. Union Indemnity Ins. Co., N.Y.C., 1977-79, BCS Fin. Corp., Chgo., 1979-83; pres. C.V. Starr & Co., San Francisco, 1983-84, Lexington Ins. Co., Boston, 1985-87, Landmark Ins. Co., Los Angeles, 1986-87; pres. Am. Home Assurance Co., N.Y.C. 1987-92, chmn., 1992-93; 1992-93; v.p. Am. Internat. Group, N.Y.C., 1986-93; sr. v.p. Starr Excess Liability Ins. Co. Ltd., 1993—. City parking commr. Reading, Pa., 1970-73. Served to sgt. U.S. Army, 1950-52, Korea. Mem. Riddell's Bay Golf and Country Club (Bermuda), Royal Bermuda Yacht Club. Republican. Roman Catholic. Home: 12 Smithfield Manor, 9 Riddell's Bay Rd, Warwick WK 04, Bermuda Office: Starr Excess Liability Ins Co Ltd, 29 Richmond Rd, Pembroke HM 08, Bermuda

WIEDEMANN, KENT M., federal official. BA in History, San Jose State U.; MA in Internat. Rels., U. Oreg. Vol. Peace Corps, Micronesia, Truk; dir. mgmt. tng. European hdqrs. Hewlett-Packard Co.; joined Fgn. Svc.; officer Dept. State, Poznan, Poland; officer Office L.Am. Affairs Dept. State, 1985-88, dir. Office Chinese and Mongolian Affairs; various positions to counselor for econ. affairs Am. Embassy, Beijing; dep. chief mission Am. Embassy, Singapore, Tel Aviv; spl. asst. to President U.S., sr. dir. Asian Affairs Nat. Security Coun., Washington, 1993—; diplomat-in-residence, sr. fellow East-West Ctr., Honolulu. Office: Nat Security Coun Rm 493 Old Executive Office Bldg Washington DC 20506

WIEDEN, DAN G., advertising executive. Pres. Wieden & Kennedy, Inc., Portland, Oreg. Office: Wieden & Kennedy Inc 320 SW Washington St Portland OR 97204-2640*

WIEDENMAN, JERE WAYNE, lawyer; b. Madison, Wis., Oct. 22, 1950; s. William George and Janet Mae W.; m. Kathleen Louise Wescott, Jan. 30, 1971; 1 child, Karl Hans. BS, U. Wis., 1972; JD, Marquette U., 1976. Bar: Wis., U.S. Dist. Ct. (ea. and we. dists.) Wis., U.S. Dist. Ct. (we. dist.) Ky., U.S. Dist. Ct. (ea. dist.) Pa., U.S. Ct. Appeals (6th and 7th cirs.). Assoc. Foley and Lardner, Milw., 1976-83; ptnr., 1983—. Editor: Employment Law for Wisconsin Employees, 1987. Active Zoning Bd. Appeals, Nashotah, Wis., 1986-88; trustee Village of Nashotah, 1988—. Mem. ABA (labor law sect., litigation sect.), Wis. Bar Assn. (dir. labor law sect. 1987—). Office: Foley & Lardner 777 E Wisconsin Ave Milwaukee WI 53202-5302

WIEDENMAYER, CHRISTOPHER M., writing instrument manufacturer, distributor; b. Orange, N.J., May 16, 1941; s. Gustave E. and Margaret W.; m. Anne Iselin Morgan, June 18, 1966; children: Amanda, Elizabeth, Christopher. BA, Dartmouth Coll., 1963; MBA, Columbia U., 1968. Gen. mgr. Faber-Castell Corp., Parsippany, N.J., 1970-72, pres., chief exec. officer, 1972-84, chmn., chief exec. officer, 1984—; bd. dirs. DSG Internat. Ltd.,

Chem. Bank New Jersey N.A. Treas. Newark Mus., 1983—; bd. govs. Fairmount Cemetery Assn., Newark, 1978—; bd. dirs. Morristown YMCA, 1975-77. Mem. Writing Instrument Mfg. Assn. (bd. dirs. 1973—, v.p. 1989-93, pres. 1993—). Office: Faber-Castell Corp 4 Century Dr Parsippany NJ 07054-4606

WIEDLE, GARY EUGENE, real estate management company executive; b. San Antonio, July 28, 1944; s. Eugene Wiley and Melba Frances (Keeney) W.; m. Regena Zokosky, July 7, 1977 (div. June 1983); children: Ana Lauren, Aric Brandt. AA, Coll. of the Desert, Palm Desert, Calif., 1975; BA, Calif. State U., Long Beach, 1967; MA, U. So. Calif., 1973. Lic. real estate broker, Calif.; cert. profl. community assn. mgr. Adminstrv. asst. City of Inglewood, Calif., 1967-68, asst. city mgr., 1970-74; exec. dir. Coachella Valley Assn. of Govts., Palm Desert, 1974-84; mgr. The Springs Country Club, Rancho Mirage, Calif., 1984-87; profl. polit. sci. Coll of the Desert, Palm Desert, 1987-90; owner Fortune West Mgmt., Palm Desert, 1990—; cons. polit. orgns., bus. and community groups, Riverside County, Calif., 1984—. State comdr. DAV, Dept. Calif., 1982. 1st lt. U.S. Army, 1968-70, Vietnam. Decorated Bronze Star for valor, Purple Heart, Commendation of valor. Mem. Am. Inst. Cert. Planners (cert. planner), Cmty. Assns. Inst. (pres. 1986-89), Calif. Assn. Cmty. Mgrs., Real Estate Educators Cert. Inst., Bd. Realtors Palm Desert, Am. Planning Assn., Western Govtl. Rsch. Assn., Gideons Internat. Republican. Lutheran. Avocation: reading history. Home: 82-362 Gable Dr Indio CA 92201-7439 Office: Fortune West Mgmt GE Wiedle Co 73-900 El Paseo Ste 3 (rear) Palm Desert CA 92260

WIEDMAN, WAYNE RENTCHLER, retired association executive; b. Oklahoma City, Aug. 29, 1928; s. Lester Amon and Frieda Clara (Rentchler) W.; m. Nancy Jane Whitenight, Dec. 26, 1955; children: Kathryn Anne, Mary Francis. BA, U. Okla., 1950. Ind. credit mgr. Nat. Supply Co., Pitts., 1954-61; dist. sales rep. ARMCO Steel Corp., Chgo., 1961-71; automotive market mgr. Middletown, Ohio, 1972-74; dist. account mgr. ARMCO, Inc., Louisville, 1975-82; cons. mktg. Louisville, 1982-85; exec. dir. Nat. Soc. of SAR, Louisville, 1986-89, ret., 1990. Mayor City of Manor Creek, Ky., 1981-85; dist. commr. Jefferson County Preservation Commn., Louisville, 1985-86; bd. dirs. Friends of Ky. Pub. Archives, Frankfort, 1985-86. Named Eagle Scout, Boy Scouts Am., 1944. Episcopalian. Club: Blairwood. Avocations: travel, history. Home: 211 Marksfield Cir Louisville KY 40222-5234

WIEDMANN, TIEN-WEN TAO, medical scientist, educator; b. Shanghai, China, Jan. 12, 1938; came to U.S., 1955; d. Pai-chuan and Su-chuin (Chang) T.; m. Walter Wiedmann, June 20, 1966; children: Christian, Ulrich. Student, Nat. Taiwan U., Republic of China, 1953-55; BS, U. Okla., 1957; PhD, Harvard U., 1963. Rsch. assoc. Harvard U., Boston, 1965-69; scientist Basel (Switzerland) Inst. for Immunology, 1970-74, Bioctr., Basel, 1975-80; sr. rsch. assoc. Stanford (Calif.) U., 1980-84, assoc. prof. nuclear medicine, 1984-91; founder, organizer Health Corps, 1990—; v.p., rsch. dir., bd. dirs. Pharmagenesis, Calif., 1991—. Contbr. articles to profl. jours. Office: Pharmagenesis 3183 Porter Dr Palo Alto CA 94304

WIEDYK, GERALD M., union welfare fund administrator; b. Grosse Point Farms, Mich., May 18, 1949; s. William M. Wiedyk and Helena M. (Hodnicak) Wroblewski; m. Kathleen Yvonne Garsky, Oct. 30, 1969; 1 child, Rachel M. Student, Macomb County Community Coll., Warren, Mich., 1970-74. Asst. br. mgr. Household Finance Corp., Detroit, 1968-69; br. mgr. Pacific Finance Corp., Detroit, 1969-70, Mut. Finance Corp., Detroit, 1970-72; collection mgr. William Beaumont Hosp., Royal Oak, Mich., 1972-74; credit/billing asst. mgr. Detroit Macomb Hosp. Assn., 1974-78; controller Nat. Health Labs., Oak Park, Mich., 1978-80; exec. dir. Mich. Conf. of Teamsters Welfare Fund, Detroit, 1980—. Mem. Friends of Archbishop of Detroit, 1986—. Mem. Hosp. Patient Acctg. Assn., Health Care Fin. Mgmt. Assn. Roman Catholic. Avocations: golf, bowling. Office: Mich Conf Teamsters Welfare Fund 2700 Trumbull St Detroit MI 48216-1269

WIEGAND, BRUCE, lawyer; b. Dallas, Nov. 27, 1947; s. Frank Louis and Undine (Phillips) W.; m. Barbara Louise McKenna, July 18, 1970; children: Christy C., Laura C., Bruce Phillips. AB cum laude, Harvard U., 1969; JD, U. Pitts., 1973. Bar: Pa. 1973, U.S. Dist. Ct. (we. dist.) Pa. 1973, U.S. Ct. Appeals (3d cir.) 1973. Assoc. Kirkpatrick & Lockhart, Pitts., 1973-80, ptnr., 1980—; bd. dirs., pres. TWP, Inc. parent co. of T.W. Phillips, Butler, Pa.; bd. dirs., gen. counsel, sec. Phillips Resources, Inc., Butler, 1984—. Mem. ABA, Pa. Bar Assn., Allegheny County Bar Assn., Pa. Oil., Gas and Minerals, Duquesne Club, Rolling Rock Club, St. Clair Country Club, Rivers Club, Harvard U. Club, Yale U. Club, Princeton U. Club. Republican. Home: 94 Hoodridge Pittsburgh PA 15228-1805 Office: Kirkpatrick & Lockhart 1500 Oliver Bldg Pittsburgh PA 15222

WIEGAND, SYLVIA MARGARET, mathematician, educator; b. Cape Town, South Africa, Mar. 8, 1945; came to U.S., 1949; d. Laurence Chisholm and Joan Elizabeth (Dunnett) Young; m. Roger Allan Wiegand, Aug. 27, 1966; children: David Chisholm, Andrea Elizabeth. AB, Bryn Mawr Coll., 1966; MA, U. Wash., 1967; PhD, U. Wis., Madison, 1972. Mem. faculty U. Nebr., Lincoln, 1967—, now prof. math.; vis. assoc. prof. U. Conn., Storrs, 1978-79, U. Wis., Madison, 1985-86; vis. prof. Purdue U., 1992-93. Editor Communications in Algebra jour., 1990, Rocky Mountain Jour. Math., 1991—; contbr. rsch. articles to profl. jours. Troop leader Lincoln area Girl Scouts U.S., 1988-92. Grantee NSF, 1985-88, 90-93, Vis. Professorship for Women, 1992. Mem. AAUP, Am. Math. Soc. (mem.-at-large, coun.), Assn. Women in Math., London Math. soc., Math. Assn. Am. Avocations: running, family activities. Office: U Nebr Dept Math Lincoln NE 68588-0323

WIEGEL, ROBERT LOUIS, consulting engineering executive; b. San Francisco, Oct. 17, 1922; s. Louis Henry and Antionette L. (Decker) W.; m. Anne Pearce, Dec. 10, 1948; children: John M., Carol E., Diana L. BS, U. Calif. at Berkeley, 1943, MS, 1949. Mem. faculty U. Calif. at Berkeley, 1946—, prof. civil engring., 1963-87, prof. emeritus 1987—, asst. dean Coll. Engring., 1963-72, acting dean, 1972-73; dir. state tech. svcs. program for Calif. U. Calif., 1965-68, sec. acad. senate, 1988-89; vis. prof. Nat. U. Mex., summer 1965, Punjab Acad. Sci., 1976, 88, U. Cairo, 1978; sr. Queen's fellow in marine sci. Australia, 1977; cons. to govt. and industry, 1946—; chmn. U.S. com. for internat. com. oceanic resources, mem. marine bd. Nat. Acad. Engring., 1975-81; pres. Internat. Engring. com. on Oceanic Resources, 1972-75; hon. mem., 1988; mem. coastal engring. research bd. Dept. Army, 1974-85; mem. IDOE adv. panel NSF, 1974-77, Gov. Calif. Adv. Commn. Ocean Resources, 1967-73, Tsunami Tech. Adv. Council, Hawaii, 1964-66; U.S. del. U.S.-Japan coop. sci. programs, 1964, 65. Author publs. in field; editor Shore and Beach jour.; patentee in field. V.p., bd. dirs. Am. Shore and Beach Preservation Assn.; mem. Nat. Rsch. Coun. com. on Beach Nourishment and Protection, 1992-95. Recipient Outstanding Civilian Svc. medal Dept. Army, 1985, Berkeley citation U. Calif., 1987, Joe W. Johnson Outstanding Beach Preservation award Calif. Shore and Beach Preservation Assn., 1993, Coastal Zone Found. award, 1993. Fellow AAAS; mem. NAE, ASCE (hon., chmn. exec. com. waterways, harbors, coastal engring. div. 1974-75, vice chmn. coastal engring. rsch. coun. 1964-78, chmn. 1978-92, chmn. task com. wave forces on structures 1960-67, chmn. com. on coastal engring 1970-71, Rsch. prize 1962, Moffatt-Nichol Coastal Engring. award 1978, Internat. Coastal Engring. award 1985), Sigma Xi. Home: 1030 Keeler Ave Berkeley CA 94708-1404

WIEGENSTEIN, JOHN GERALD, physician; b. Fredericktown, Mo., June 22, 1930; s. John Joseph and Dorothy Faye (Mulkey) W.; m. Dorothy Iris Scifers, Dec. 27, 1952; children: Mark, Barbara, Paula, Cynthia. BS, U. Mich., 1956, MD, 1960. Dir. dept. emergency medicine Mich. Capital Med. Ctr., Lansing, 1975—; prof., chief sect. emergency medicine Mich. State U., 1982—; founder Internat. Rsch. Inst. for Emergency Medicine, pres., 1983-85; founder, pres. Am. Bd. Emergency Medicine, 1982-83; pres. Physician Assocs., P.C., 1976—, Occupational Med. Assocs., P.C., 1989—. With USAF, 1951-53; M.C., U.S. Army, 1960-63. Mem. AMA, Am. Coll. Emergency Physicians (founder, pres., chmn. bd. 1968-71, bd. dirs. 1968-76), Mich. State Med. Soc. (award 1971, 82), Ingham County Med. Soc., Galens Hon. Med. Soc., Soc. Acad. Emergency Medicine. Office: Mich Capital Med Ctr Dept Emergency Medicine 401 W Greenlawn Ave Lansing MI 48910-2819

WIEGERS, GEORGE ANTHONY, investment banker; b. N.Y.C., Aug. 23, 1936; s. Anthony F. and Florence Wiegers; m. Elizabeth Colwill, Oct. 30, 1965; 1 child, Alexander. B.A., Niagara U., 1958; M.B.A., Columbia U., 1961. Ptnr. Dean Witter & Co., N.Y.C., 1961-70; ptnr. Lehman Bros., N.Y.C., 1971-83; mng. dir. Dillon Read & Co., N.Y.C., 1983—; dir. Pulte Corp., Detroit, Technimetrics Inc., N.Y.C., Am. City Bus. Jours. Inc., Charlotte, N.C. 1st lt. U.S. Army, 1958-59. Clubs: Links, Anglers (N.Y.C.). Avocations: ranching. Office: Dillon Read & Co 535 Madison Ave New York NY 10022-4212

WIEGERSMA, NAN, economics educator; b. Grafton, Mass., July 16, 1942; d. Oscar John and Esther Marie (Polson) Wiegersma; 1 child, Chandra Hancock. BS, U. Md., 1966, MA, 1969, PhD, 1976. Economist US Dept. Agr., Washington, 1969-72; vis. asst. prof. econs. Antioch Coll., Yellow Springs, Ohio, 1972-73, San Diego State U., 1973-74; assoc. prof. econs. No. Va. Community Coll., Annandale, Va., 1974-79; prof. econs. Fitchburg (Mass.) State Coll., 1979—; cons. UN, 1987, FAO, 1994. Author: Vietnam: Peasant Land, Peasant Revolution, 1988; co-author: Agriculture in Vietnam's Economy, 1973; editl. bd. Vietnam Generation, 1988-93; contbr. articles to profl. jours., chpts. to books. Recipient Disting. Svc. award USDA, 1973; Joiner Ctr. grantee, 1987; Grad. Assoc. Faculty rsch. fellow Fitchburg State Coll., 1989-90; Fulbright fellow, 1991. Mem. NEA, Am. Econs. Assn., New Eng. Women and Devel. Group, N.E. Feminist Scholars, Women's Work Project (coord. 1974-79), Mass. Tchrs. Assn. (chpt. treas. 1986-90, pres. 1992-94), Women for Economic Justice (econ. literacy campaign), Montague (Mass.) Lottery Arts Coun. Democrat. Avocations: photography, hiking. Office: Fitchburg State Coll Pearl St Fitchburg MA 01420

WIEGLEY, ROGER DOUGLAS, lawyer; b. Buffalo, Dec. 8, 1948; s. Richard John and Georgianna (Eggleston) W.; m. Susan Carol Straus, Nov. 22, 1969; children: John William, Douglas James, Jennifer Jeanne. BA, SUNY, Buffalo, 1970; JD magna cum laude, U. Wis., 1977. Bar: Wis. 1977, Hawaii 1978, N.Y. 1982, D.C. 1982, Calif. 1986. Spl. asst. U.S. atty. U.S. Justice Dept., Honolulu, 1978-81; spl. asst. to gen. counsel Dept. of the Navy, Washington, 1981-82; assoc. Sullivan & Cromwell, Washington, 1982-85, 86-88; ptnr. Sidley & Austin, Washington, 1989-94, Winthrop, Stimson, Putnam & Roberts, Washington, 1994—; gen. counsel Benson, Inc. and Sentry, San Jose, Calif., 1985-86; arbitrator nat. panel Am. Arbitration Assn., 1988—. Contbg. editor The SEC Today, 1989—; contbr. numerous articles to profl. jours. Mem. pvt. sector study on cost control, Washington, 1982-83. Served with USN, 1973-82. Mem. ABA, Order of Coif. Office: Winthrop Stimson Putnam Rob 1133 Connecticut Ave NW Washington DC 20036

WIEGMAN, EUGENE WILLIAM, minister, former college administrator; b. Fort Wayne, Ind., Oct. 27, 1929; s. A. Henry and E. Catherine (McDonald) W.; m. Kathleen Wyatt, Apr. 26, 1952; children: Kathryn, Rose Marie, Mark, Jeanine, Gretchen, Matthew. BS, Concordia Coll., 1953; MS, U. Kans., 1956, EdD, 1962; grad., Pacific Luth. Theol. Sem., 1985. Tchr., coach Trinity Luth. Sch., Atchison, Kans., 1954-58; prin. tchr. St. John's Coll., Winfield, Kans., 1958-61; prof. Concordia Coll., Seward, Nebr., 1961-65; adminstrv. asst. to Rep. Clair Callan, Lincoln, Nebr., 1965-66; asst. to adminstr. fed. extension service Dept. Agr., Washington, 1966-67; dean community edn. Fed. City Coll., Washington, 1967-69; pres. Pacific Luth. U., Tacoma, 1969-75, Independent Colls. Wash., 1975-76; dir. Wash. Office Community Devel., 1977-78; commr. Dept. of Employment Security, 1978-81; exec. dir., pres., chief exec. officer Family Counseling Service of Tacoma and Pierce County, Wash., 1987—; assoc. pastor Luther Meml. Ch., Tacoma, 1987-90; pastor Gethsemane Luth. Ch., Tacoma, 1990—; dean clin. pastoral edn. Grad. Sch. of Korea, 1992—; mem. Wash. State Employment and Tng. Council; mem. cabinet Gov. of Wash., 1977-81; lectr., nat. public speaker, 1981—; pres. The Wiegman Inst., Tacoma, 1981—. Candidate for U.S. Congress from 6th dist. Wash., 1976; mem. Council on Washington's Future; exec. bd. dirs. Pacific Harbors Coun. Boy Scouts Am.; bd. dirs. Tacoma Area Urban Coalition; past chmn. Wash. Friends Higher Edn.; bd. dirs. Tacoma Urban League, Nat. Alliance Businessmen, Bellarmine Prep. Sch., Tacoma, Camp Brotherhood; trustee Tacoma Gen. Hosp., Pacific Sci. Center; mem. Commn. on Children for Tacoma and Pierce County, Coalition on Child Sexual Abuse, 1989—; mem. com. Faith Homes for Young Women; pres. Second City chamber of Tacoma. Recipient Disting. Teaching award City Winfield, Kans., 1960, Freedom Found. Teaching award, 1961, Disting. Eagle Scout award, 1982, Pres. award St. Martins Coll., 1980. Fellow Philosophy of Edn. Soc.; mem. Tacoma C. of C., N.W. Assn. Pvt. Colls., Assn. Higher Edn., Kiwanis, Phi Delta Kappa. Home: 405 N Stadium Way Tacoma WA 98403-3228

WIEGNER, ALLEN WALTER, biomedical engineering educator, researcher; b. Bethlehem, Pa., July 22, 1947; s. Howard Jay and Anna (Strouse) W.; m. Sandra A. Waddock, Aug. 26, 1978; 1 child, Benjamin Waddock. SB, SM, MIT, 1970, PhD, 1978. Rsch. assoc. Harvard U. Med. Sch., Boston, 1978-87, asst. prof. neurology (biomed. engring.), 1987—; asst. biomed. engr. Mass. Gen. Hosp., Boston, 1980—; cons. rsch. svc. VA Med. Ctr., 1984—, biomed. engr., 1987—. Contbr. articles, book chpts. to profl. publs. Lt. USPHS, 1970-72. Mem. IEEE (sr.), Biomed. Engring. Soc. (sr.), Soc. for Neurosci. Office: VA Med Ctr Spinal Cord Injury Svc 1400 Vfw Pky West Roxbury MA 02132-4927

WIEGNER, EDWARD ALEX, multi-industry executive; b. Waukesha, Wis., Dec. 13, 1939; s. Roy Edward and Margaret (Kuehnlein) W.; m. Cathryn J. Mullens, Oct. 16, 1970; children: Carlin, Ryan. BBA, U. Wis., 1961, MS in Econs., 1965, PhD in Econs., 1969. Asst. prof. bus. adminstrn. Marquette U., Milw., 1965-71; assoc. prof U. Wis., Madison, 1972-73; sec. Wis. Dept. Revenue, Madison, 1971-74; sr. v.p. fin., bd. dirs. Wis. Power and Light Co., Madison, 1974-76, sr. v.p. consumer, pub. and fin. affairs dir., 1976-80, exec. v.p., bd. dirs. 1980-82; sr. v.p., chief fin. officer, bd. dirs. Am. Natural Resources Co., 1982-85, exec. v.p., chief adminstrv. officer, bd. dirs., 1985-86; sr. v.p. Coastal Corp., 1985-86; sr. v.p., chief fin. officer Household Internat., Inc. 1986-88; exec. v.p., chief fin. officer The Progressive Corp., Mayfield Heights, Ohio, 1988-91, pres. fin. svcs. div., 1989-93; gen. ptnr. Aurora Ptnrs., 1994—; vice chmn. 1st Am. Ins. Co., Kansas City, Mo., 1994—. Contbr. articles to Northwestern Law Rev., others. Mem. Grand Harbor Country Club. Home: 1330 N St David's Ln Vero Beach FL 32967

WIEHL, JOHN JACK, foundry executive; b. Bklyn., May 4, 1920; s. Ferdinand and Theresa (Kogut) W.; m. Ruth Dorothy Anderson, May 11, 1946; children: John R., Edward, Robert, Fred. Grad. high sch., Elmhurst, N.Y. Cert. molder. Pres. Wiehl Bros. Brass Foundry, Bklyn., 1946-53, Hoboken (N.J.) Bronze Foundry, 1968-72, Franklin (N.H.) Non-Ferrous Foundry, 1981—; owner Wiehl Daily Farm, Milford, N.Y., 1954-67; foundry mgr. Perkins Marine, Miami, Fla., 1973-74, Watts Regulator, Lawrence, Mass., 1974-76, Samuel Eastman, Concord, N.H., 1976-78, Hayes Fluid Control, Gastonia, N.C., 1978-79, Jenkins Bros., Bridgeport, Conn., 1979-81. With USN, 1944-46, ETO, PTO. Mem. Am. Legion, Elks (brother). Avocation: music. Office: Franklin Non-Ferrous Foundry PO Box 35 Calef Hill Rd Franklin NH 03235

WIELAND, FERDINAND, hotel executive, entrepreneur; b. Unternberg Salzburg, Austria, Mar. 20, 1943; came to U.S., 1966; naturalized, 1969; s. Rupert and Elisabeth (Bernthaler) W.; m. Edda Hafner, Apr. 19, 1966. Dipl., Hotel and Restaurant Sch., Salzburg, 1961; BS, Widener U., 1985. Cert. hotel administrator (CHA), 1979. Hotel trainee Hotel Elite and Beau Rivage Palace, Biel and Lausanne, Switzerland, 1961; chef de rang Holland Am. Lines, Rotterdam, 1962-66; maitre d' Salum Sanctorum, N.Y.C., 1966, Hotel du Pont, 1967-68; food and beverage dir. Hotel du Pont, Wilmington, Del., 1971-77, gen. mgr., 1978-91; pres., chmn. Preferred Hotel & Resorts Worldwide, Oakbrook, Ill., 1985-90, also bd. dirs.; pres. Global Mktg. Assocs., Wilmington, 1988—. Co-Author: Managing Service in Hotel Food and Beverage Operations, 1985. Pres. Wilmington Conv. and Visitors Bur., 1983-84; commd. mem. gov.'s tourism adv. bd., Dover, Del., 1981-91; chmn. adv. bd. Hotel Sch., U. Del. 1981-91; bd. dirs. ARC, Wilmington, 1984-86; mem. Del. Rep. State Com., 1988—, Rep. Nat. Com., 1987—. With USN, army, 1968-71; USAR, 1971-74. Named to Honorable Order of Ky. Cols., 1987; decorated Army Commendation medal, 1971. Mem. Am. Hotel Assn. (corp.), Internat. Hotel Assn., Internat. Protocol Officers Assn., Am. Hotel and Motel Assn. (bd. dirs., mem. exec. com. 1978-91, trustee Ednl. Inst. 1983-88), Govs. Fgn. Trade Coun., Assn. Internat Skal Clubs,

Tavern Club, Rotary, (bd. dirs. Wilmington club 1989—). Republican. Roman Catholic. Avocations: chess, cycling, skiing, reading, travelling. Home: 3905 Ardleigh Dr Wilmington DE 19807-2109

WIELGUS, CHARLES JOSEPH, information services company executive; b. Hadley, Mass., Jan. 2, 1923; s. Joseph John and Anna Mary (Armata) W.; m. Irene Helen Graham, Jan. 1, 1947; children: Charles, Paul, Martha Jane. B.S. summa cum laude in Bus. Adminstrn, Bryant Coll., 1947, D.S. in Bus. Adminstrn. (hon.), 1977. With Bigelow-Sanford Carpet Co., Enfield, Conn. and N.Y.C., 1947-56; with Reuben H. Donnelley Corp. (subs. Dun & Bradstreet Corp.), Chicago and N.Y.C., 1956-71; v.p. personnel Dun & Bradstreet, Inc. (subs.), 1971-73; v.p. personnel Dun & Bradstreet Corp., 1973-76, sr. v.p. human resources, 1976-82, exec. v.p. human resources and communications, 1983-88, ret., 1988; nature photographer, 1989—; adj. faculty New Sch. Social Research, 1977-88, mem. adv. com. Masters program in human resources, 1977-88, ret., 1988; mem. adv. council on mgmt. edn. N.Y.C. C. of C., 1975-80; mem. bus. edn. adv. com. N.Y.C. Bd. Edn., 1977-88; dir. Nat. Ctr. Career Life Planning, 1986—; mem. adv. council on human resources mgmt. Nat. Conf. Bd., 1987-88. Bd. dirs. United Cerebral Palsy Assn. Westchester, 1966-75; trustee Operation Hope, Inc., 1966-75, active local and state Republican orgns., 1965-75. Served in USAF, 1943-46. Mem. Am. Arbitration Assn. (arbitrator 1988—), Nat. Alliance Bus. (dir., steering com.). Clubs: Univ, Larchmont Shore. Home: 151 Rockingstone Ave Larchmont NY 10538-1512 also: 7 Hummingbird Ln Hilton Head Island SC 29926

WIEMAN, CARL E., physics educator; b. Corvallis, Oreg., Mar. 26, 1951; m. Sarah Gilbert. BS, MIT, 1973; PhD, Stanford U., 1977. Asst. rsch. physicist dept. physics U. Mich., Ann Arbor, 1977-79, asst. prof. physics, 1979-84; assoc. prof. physics U. Colo., Boulder, 1984-87, prof. physics, 1987—; fellow Joint Inst. for Lab. Astrophysics, Boulder, 1985—; Loeb lectr. Harvard U., 1990-91; Rosenthal Meml. lectr. Yale U., Columbia U. 1988. Fellow Guggenheim Found., 1990-91; recipient Ernest Orlando Lawrence Mem. Award, U.S. Dept. of Energy, 1993. Fellow Am. Phys. Soc. (Davisson-Germer prize 1994); mem. Optical Soc. Am. Office: U Colo Box 390 Boulder CO 80309

WIEMANN, JOHN MORITZ, communications educator, consultant; b. New Orleans, July 11, 1947; s. John M. and Mockie (Oosthuizen) W.; m. Mary Eileen O'Loghlin, June 7, 1969; children: Molly E., John M. BA, Loyola U., New Orleans, 1969; postgrad., NYU, 1970-71; MS, Purdue U., 1973, PhD, 1975. With employee comm. dept. IBM, East Fishkill, N.Y., 1969-71; asst. prof. comm. Rutgers U., New Brunswick, N.J., 1975-77; from asst. prof. to prof. U. Calif., Santa Barbara, 1977—, prof., 1988—, prof. comm. and Asian Am. studies, 1994—, acting vice chancellor instnl. advancement, 1994—. Editor: Nonverbal Interaction, 1983, Advancing Communication Science, 1988, Communication, Health and the Elderly, 1990, Miscommunication and the Problematic Talk, 1991, Strategic Interpersonal Communication, 1994, Interpersonal Communication in Older Adulthood, 1994; author: Competent Communication, 1995; series editor Sage Ann. Rev. Communication Rsch., 1988-94. Bd. dirs. Goleta Youth Basketball Assn., 1987-92; mem. sch. site coun. Foothill Elem. Sch., 1987-88; mem. budget adv. com. Goleta Union Sch. Dist., 1982-84. David Ross fellow Purdue U., 1975, W.K. Kellogg Found. fellow, 1980-83; Fulbright-Hayes sr. rsch. scholar U. Bristol, Eng., 1985. Mem. APA, Internat. Comm. Assn. (bd. dirs. 1988-90), Speech Comm. Assn. (bd. dirs. 1984-86), Western States Comm. Assn., Internat. Network on Personal Rels., Internat. Pragmatics Assn., Sigma Xi, Phi Kappa Phi. Democrat. Roman Catholic. Avocations: cooking, squash, swimming. Office: U Calif Dept Comm Santa Barbara CA 93106-4020

WIEMER, ROBERT ERNEST, film and television producer, writer, director; b. Highland Park, Mich., Jan. 30, 1938; s. Carl Ernest and Marion (Israelian) W.; m. Rhea Dale McGeath, June 14, 1958; children: Robert Marshall, Rhea Whitney. BA, Ohio Wesleyan U., 1959. Ind. producer, 1956-60; dir. documentary ops. WCBS-TV, N.Y.C., 1964-67; ind. producer of television, theatrical and bus. films N.Y.C., 1967-72; exec. producer motion pictures and TV, ITT, N.Y.C., 1973-84; pres. subs. Blue Marble Co., Inc., Telemontage, Inc., Alphaventure Music, Inc., Betaventure Music, Inc. ITT, 1973-84; founder, chmn., chief exec. officer Tigerfilm, Inc., 1984—; chmn., bd. dirs. Golden Tiger Pictures, Hollywood, Calif., 1988—; pres, CEO Tuxedo Pictures Corp., Hollywood, Calif., 1993—. Writer, prodr., dir.: (feature films) My Seventeenth Summer, Witch's Sister, Do Me a Favor, Anna to the Infinite Power, Somewhere, Tomorrow, Night Train to Kathmandu; exec. prodr.: (children's TV series) Big Blue Marble (Emmy and Peabody awards); dir. (TV episodes) seaQuest DSV, Star Trek: The Next Generation, Deep Space Nine, The Adventures of Superboy; composer (country-western ballad) Tell Me What To Do. Recipient CINE award, 1974, 76, 77, 79, 81, Emmy award, 1978. Mem. NATAS, ASCAP, Ind. Film Producers Assn. (Outstanding Producer award), Nat. Assn. TV Programming Execs., Am. Women in Radio and TV, N.J. Broadcasters Assn., Dirs. Guild Am. Office: Golden Tiger Pictures 3896 Ruskin St Las Vegas NV 89117

WIEN, STUART LEWIS, retired supermarket chain executive; b. Milw., Sept. 11, 1923; s. Julius and Mildred (Rosenberg) W.; m. Charlotte Jean Milgram, June 4, 1949; children: Steven, John, William, Thomas.; m. Sheila B. Davis, July 25, 1982; stepchildren: Andrew, Stephen, Laurence, Geoffrey. B.S., UCLA, 1947. Chmn. bd. Milgram Food Stores, Inc., Kansas City, Mo., 1979-84; bd. dirs. UMB Funds. Trustee Menorah Med. Ctr.; bd. regents Rockhurst Coll. Mem. Oakwood Country Club, Jewish-Chautauqua Soc.

WIENER, DANIEL NORMAN, psychologist; b. Duluth, Minn., Feb. 6, 1921; s. Joseph Baxter and Fannie (Winer) W.; m. Phyllis Eileen Zager, Dec. 9, 1971; children: Jonathan Marc, Paul Aaron, Sara Ruth Wiener Pearson. BA, U. Minn., 1941, MA, 1942, PhD, 1950. Diplomate in Clin. Psychology Am. Bd. Profl. Psychology; lic. psychologist, Minn. Psychologist State of Conn., Hartford, 1943-44; chief psychologist VA Rehab. and Mental Hygiene Clinic, St. Paul and Mpls., 1944-76; Comty. Clinic, Two Harbors, Minn., 1968-89; pvt. practice psychology Mpls., 1952—; clin. prof. psychiatry and psychology U. Minn., Mpls., 1952—; cons. Hennepin County Dist. Ct., Mpls., 1982—. Author: Discipline, Achievement and Mental Health, 1960, Dimensions of Psychotherapy, 1965, Short-Term Psychotherapy and Structured Behavior Change, 1966, Training Children, 1968, Practical Guide to Psychotherapy, 1968, Classroom Management, 1972, Consumers Guide to Psychotherapy, 1975, Albert Ellis: Passionate Skeptic, 1988, B.F. Skinner: Benign Anarchist, 1995; book reviewer: Star-Tribune, Mpls. With USAF, 1942-43. Mem. Fellow APA, Am. Psychol. Soc.; mem. PEN, Minn. Psychol. Assn. (life, exec. coun.), Nat. Book Critics Cir. Avocations: tennis, squash. Home and Office: Apt 801 1225 Lasalle Ave Minneapolis MN 55403-2329

WIENER, HESH (HAROLD FREDERIC WIENER), publisher, editor, consultant; b. Bklyn., July 20, 1946; s. Jesse Leonard and Regina (Rappaport) W. B.S. in Polit. Sci., MIT, 1969. Mem. staff systems devel. Data Gen. Corp., Southboro, Mass., 1969-70; dir. computer edn. project U. Calif., Berkeley, 1970-72; editor Computer Decisions Mag., Rochelle Park, N.J., 1973-78; editor, pub. Tech. News Am., N.Y.C., 1976-88; pres. Tech. News of Am. Co., Inc., N.Y.C., 1982—; mng. dir. Tech. News Ltd., London, 1992—; pub. Computer and Communications Buyer Newsletter, 1979-95, Mainstream Newsletter, 1980-82, Infoperspectives Newsletter, 1982—, Storage Tech. Monitor, 1984-87, Infoperspectives Internat. (U.K.), 1989—, (Mid. East), 1991—, The Four Hundred Newsletter (U.K.), 1990—, The Four Hundred Newsletter (U.S.), 1990—; editor Infoperspectives Internat. (Italy), 1991—, The Four Hundred Newsletter (Italy), 1995—; pub. U.S. edit. Computergram Internat. Newsletter, 1985-90; corr. Processeurs mag., 1989—; cons. Hewlett-Packard Co. (Paris), 1971-72, Xerox Corp., 1972-73; advisor NSF, 1975. Author: Big Blue and You, The IBM Atlas, The Mainframe; corr. Computer Weekly, U.K., 1975-81, Computable, Amsterdam, 1976-87, Computing Can., 1977-78, Ordinateurs, Paris, 1977-89, Data News, Brussels, 1979-86, Informatics, U.K., 1981-85, Datanytt, Copenhagen, 1982-89, Mgmt. Tech. mag., 1983-85; editor BusinessWeek Newsletter for Info. Execs., 1987-90, Datamation Mag., 1983-90, Infoperspectives Internat. (Milan) 1991—; contbg. editor Bus. and Soc. Rev., 1978-85; contbr. N.Y. Times Syndicate, Los Angeles Times Syndicate, N.Am.

Newspaper Alliance Wireservice, Newsday, Manhattan, Inc., Rom Mag., Informatique (Paris), The Economist (London), Dun's Bus. Month, Software News, Intermedia, Digital News, Data Communications, Bus. Week Newsletter for Info. Execs., Bus. Strategy Internat., Nikkei Watcher on IBM (Tokyo), 1989—. Club: Overseas Press. Home: 246 6th Ave Brooklyn NY 11215-2103 Office: Tech News Am 110 Greene St New York NY 10012-3813

WIENER, JACQUES LOEB, JR., federal judge; b. Shreveport, La., Oct. 2, 1934; s. Jacques L. and Betty (Eichenbaum) W.; children: Patricia Wiener Shifke, Jacques L. III, Betty Ellen Wiener Spomer, Donald B. BA, Tulane U., 1956, JD, 1961. Bar: La. 1961, U.S. Dist. Ct. (we. dist.) La. 1961. Ptnr. Wiener, Weiss, Madison & Howell, A.P.C., Shreveport, 1961-90; judge U.S. Ct. Appeals (5th cir.), Shreveport, 1990—; mem. coun. La. State Law Inst., 1965—; master of the bench Am. Inn of Ct., 1990—. Pres. United Way N.W. La., 1975, Shreveport Jewish Fedn., 1969-70. Fellow Am. Coll. Trust & Estates Counsel, Am. Bar Found., La. Bar Found.; mem. ABA, La. State Bar Assn., Shreveport Bar Assn. (pres. 1982), Am. Law Inst., Internat. Acad. Trust & Estate Law (academician). Avocations: fly fishing, upland game bird hunting, photography, travel. Office: US Ct Appeals 5th Cir US Ct House 300 Fannin St # 5101 Shreveport LA 71101-3070

WIENER, JON, history educator; b. St. Paul, May 16, 1944; s. Daniel N. and Gladys (Aronsohn) Spratt. BA, Princeton U., 1966; PhD, Harvard U., 1971. Vis. prof. U. Calif.-Santa Cruz, 1973; acting asst. prof. UCLA, 1973-74; asst. prof. history U. Calif.-Irvine, 1974-83, prof., 1984—; plaintiff Freedom of Info. Lawsuit against FBI for John Lennon Files, 1983—. Author: Social Origins of the New South, 1979; Come Together: John Lennon in His Time, 1984, Professors, Politics, and Pop, 1991; contbg. editor The Nation mag.; contbr. articles to profl. jours. including The New Republic and New York Times Book Review. Bd. dirs. Liberty Hill Found. Rockefeller Found. fellow, 1979, Am. Council Learned Socs.-Ford Found. fellow, 1985. Mem. Am. Hist. Assn., Nat. Book Critics Circle, Orgn. Am. Historians, Nat. Writers' Union, The Authors' Guild, Liberty Hill Found. (bd. dir.) Office: U Calif Dept History Irvine CA 92717

WIENER, JOSEPH, pathologist; b. Toronto, Can., Sept. 21, 1927; came to U.S., 1949, naturalized, 1960; s. Louis and Minnie (Salem) W.; m. Judith Hesta Ross, June 20, 1954; children: Carolyn L., Adam L. M.D., U. Toronto, 1953. Intern Detroit Receiving Hosp., 1953-54; resident to chief resident pathology Mallory Inst. Pathology, 1954-55, Boston City Hosp., 1957-60; assoc. prof. pathology Columbia U., N.Y.C., 1960-68; prof. pathology N.Y. Med. Coll., N.Y.C., 1968-78; prof. pathology Wayne State U., Detroit, 1978—, chmn. dept., 1978-90; cons. NIH, 1970—. Served to capt. M.C. U.S. Army, 1955-57. Heart, Lung and Blood Inst. grantee, 1971; Coun. for High Blood Pressure Rsch. fellow, 1982—. Mem. AAAS, Am. Soc. Investigative Pathology, Am. Soc. Cell Biology, Mich. Path. Soc., Internat. Acad. Pathology, Am. Heart Assn., U.S./Can. Acad. Pathology, Mich. Heart Assn., Alpha Omega Alpha. Research on exptl. cardiovascular pathology and hypertension. Office: 540 E Canfield St Detroit MI 48201-1998

WIENER, MALCOLM HEWITT, investment management company executive; b. Tsingtao, China, July 3, 1935; (parents Am. citizens); s. Myron and Ethel (Zimmerman) W.; m. Carolyn Talbot Seely, June 8, 1990; 1 child, Catherine Diktynna Talbot. BA, Harvard U., 1957, JD, 1963. Bar: N.Y. 1964. Atty. N.Y.C., 1963-71, pvt. practice investing, 1971—; chmn. Millburn Corp., N.Y.C., 1977—, Millburn Ridgefield Corp., Ridgefield, Conn., 1982—, ShareInVest, Ridgefield, 1982—; lectr. in field; fellow faculty of govt., John F. Kennedy Sch. Govt., Harvard U., 1985; advisor U.S. Dept. State on Internat. Conv. on Illicit Traffic in Antiquities, 1970-75. Columnist Newsday; contbr. articles to profl. publs. Co-dir. Aegean Bronze Age Colloquium, NYU Inst. Fine Arts, 1975—; founder, exec. dir. Inst. Aegean Prehistory, 1982-89, pres., 1990—; trustee Am. Sch. Classical Studies in Athens; bd. dirs. Internat. Found. for Art Rsch., 1982-91; co-chmn. vis. com. Dept. Egyptian Art, mem. vis. com. Dept. Painting Conservation; vice chmn. bus. com., Met. Mus. Art; com. to visit Harvard Art Mus.; adv. bd. Malcolm Wiener Ctr. for Social Policy; mem. vis. com. Kennedy Sch. Govt., Harvard U.; mem. vis. com., paintings, Boston Mus. Fine Arts, 1985-91; chmn. coun. Greek and Roman Art Drawings and Prints Frick Collection; founder Wiener Lab. Am. Sch. Classical Studies, Athens; sponsor Malcolm and Carolyn Wiener Lab. for Aegean and Nr. Ea. Dendochronology Cornell U. With USN, 1957-60. Fellow Archaeol. Inst. Am. (hon. life), Met. Mus. Art (life), Frick Collection; mem. ABA, Coun. on Fgn. Rels. Office: 1270 Ave Of The Americas New York NY 10020-1700

WIENER, MARK SETH, health facility administrator; b. S.I., N.Y., July 7, 1956; s. Joseph and Audrey (Stone) W.; m. Marcie G. Gordon, Oct. 12, 1980; children: Aaron Lee, Jeffrey Daniel. BS, Wagner Coll., 1977; MA in Health Care Adminstrn., Wash. U., 1979. Exec. asst. Iowa Meth. Med. Ctr., Des Moines, 1979-82; asst. hosp. dir. U. Nebr. Med. Ctr., 1982-86; v.p. clin. svcs. Rsch. Med. Ctr., Kansas City, Mo., 1986-91; sr. v.p., COO Trinity Luth. Hosp., Kansas City, 1991—; bd. dirs. Shalom Geriatric Ctr., Hosp. Linen Svcs. Inc. Mem. healthcare adv. com. Presbyn. Metro Ministries Omaha, 1985; chmn. task force Cen. Iowa Assn. for Ind. Health Promotion, 1981-82; pres. Kansas City Assn. of Healthcare Execs., 1994. Mem. Am. Coll. Healthcare Execs., Am. Hosp. Assn., Mo. Hosp. Assn., Lions. Democrat. Jewish. Avocations: running, bicycling, tennis. Home: 9056 W 113th St Shawnee Mission KS 66210-1787 Office: Trinity Luth Hosp 3030 Baltimore Ave Kansas City MO 64108-3488

WIENER, MARTIN JOEL, historian; b. Bklyn., June 1, 1941; s. Harold H. and Eva (Richter) W.; m. Carol Ann Zisowitz, Sept. 22, 1964 (div. 1977); children: Wendy, Julie; m. Meredith Anne Skura, May 17, 1981; children: Rebecca, Vivian. BA, Brandeis U., 1962; MA, Harvard U., 1963, PhD in History, 1967. Asst. prof. Rice U., 1967-72, assoc. prof., 1972-80, prof. history, 1980-82, May Gibbs Jones prof., 1982—; chair dept. history, 1990-94. Author: Between Two Worlds: The Political Thought of Graham Wallas, 1971, English Culture and the Decline of the Industrial Spirit, 1850-1980, 1981 (Schuyler prize Am. Hist. Assn. 1981), Reconstructing the Criminal, 1990. Research fellow NEH, 1973, 86, Am. Council Learned Socs., 1982. Fellow Royal Hist. Soc.; mem. Am. Hist. Assn., Am. Soc. Legal History, Coun. for European Studies (steering com. 1985-90), Conf. on Brit. Studies (nominating com. 1982-84, coun. 1992-96), Social History Soc. (U.K.), Am. Hist. Assn. (coun. 1987-90). Jewish. Home: 5510 Yarwell Dr Houston TX 77096-4012 Office: Rice U Dept of History 6100 S Main Houston TX 77005

WIENER, MARVIN S., rabbi, editor, executive; b. N.Y.C., Mar. 16, 1925; s. Max and Rebecca (Dodell) W.; m. Sylvia Bodek, Mar. 2, 1952; children: David Hillel, Judith Rachel. B.S., CCNY, 1944, M.S., 1945; B.H.L., Jewish Theol. Sem.-Am. 1947, M.H.L., Rabbi, 1951, D.D. (hon.), 1977. Registrar, sec. faculty Rabbinical Sch., Jewish Theol. Sem. Am., 1951-57; cons. Frontiers of Faith TV Series, NBC, 1951-57; dir., instr. liturgy Cantors Inst.-Sem. Coll. Jewish Music, Jewish Theol. Sem. Am., 1954-58; faculty coordinator Sem. Sch. and Women's Inst., 1958-64; dir. Nat. Acad. for Adult Jewish Studies, United Synagogue Am., N.Y.C., 1958-78; editor Burning Bush Press, 1958-78, United Synagogue Rev. 1978-86; dir. com. congrl. standards United Synagogue Am., 1976-86, cons. community relations and social action, 1981-87, editor, exec. joint newsletter bd. 1986—; mem. Joint Commn. on Rabbinic Placement, 1951-57, Joint Prayer Book Commn., 1957-62; mem. exec. coun. Rabbinical Assembly, 1958-86; editorial coms. N.Y. Bd. Rabbis, 1987-89; trustee joint retirement bd. Jewish Theol. Sem. Am., Rabbinical Assembly and United Synagogue Am., 1959-86, sec., 1968-76, 84-85, vice chmn., 1976-82, 85-86, chmn., 1982, treas., 1983-84; co-chmn. Jewish Bible Assn., 1960-64; mem. bd. rev. Nat. Coun. Jewish Audio-Visual Materials, 1968-69; mem. exec. com. Nat. Coun. Adult Jewish Edn., 1966—; mem. exec. bd., editorial adv. bd., v.p. Jewish Book Coun.; chmn. Internat. Conf. Adult Jewish Edn., Jerusalem, 1972. Editor: Nat. Acad. Adult Jewish Studies Bull., 1958-78, Past and Present: Selected Essays (Israel Friedlaender), 1961, Jewish Tract Series, Issue 74-78 (15 titles), Adult Jewish Edn., 1958-78, Talmudic Law and the Modern State (Moshe Silberg), 1973. Mem. Am. Acad. Jewish Research, Assn. Jewish Studies, N.Y. Bd. Rabbis, Rabbinical Assembly. Home: 67-66 108th St Apt D-46 Forest Hills NY 11375 Office: Joint Retirement Bd 7 Penn Plz Ste 720 New York NY 10001-2005

WIENER, NORMAN JOSEPH, lawyer; b. Portland, Oreg., Sept. 10, 1919; s. Peter and Anna Wiener; m. Elizabeth Bentley, Jan. 26, 1945; children: Jane, Jon, Lisa. BA, U. Oreg., 1941, JD, 1947. Bar: Oreg. 1947. Assoc. King, Wood, Miller & Anderson, Portland, 1947-51; ptnr. Miller, Nash, Wiener, Hager & Carlsen, Portland, 1952—. Pres. United Way, Portland, 1977, Rehab. Inst. Oreg., Portland; trustee U. Oreg. Found. 1st lt. U.S. Army, 1942-46, World War II, 1951-52, Korea. Mem. ABA, Oreg. Bar Assn., Am. Bar Found. (life), Arlington Club (pres.), Portland Golf Club (pres.). Republican. Avocations: golf, swimming. Office: Miller Nash Wiener Hager & Carlsen 111 SW 5th Ave Ste 3500 Portland OR 97204

WIENER, ROBERT ALVIN, accountant; b. N.Y.C., Jan. 9, 1918; s. George and Rose Vivian (Fink) W.; m. Annabelle Kalbfeld, Jan. 1, 1941; children—Marilyn Wiener Grunewald, Marjorie Wiener Petit, Mark. B.C.S., NYU, 1938. CPA, N.Y., Ill.; cert. insolvency and reorgn. acct. Sr. ptnr. Robert A. Wiener & Co. (CPAs), N.Y.C., 1946-71; ptnr. Grant Thornton & Co. (CPAs), N.Y.C., 1971-73; v.p., gen. auditor Seaboard Industries, Inc. N.Y.C., 1973-77; pvt. practice acctg., 1978—; asst. prof. Pace Coll., 1956-77; lectr. Baruch Coll., 1947-77; acctg. cons. Unistar Programme UN Devel. Programme, 1991. Author: Insolvency Accounting, 1977. Served with AUS, 1943-46. Decorated Bronze Star. Mem. AICPA, N.Y. State Soc. C.P.A.s, Accts. Club Am., Fin. Execs. Inst., Inst. Internal Auditors, Assn. Insolvency Accts., Am. Arbitration Assn. (arbitration panel), Pi Lambda Phi. Home: 30 Waterside Plz New York NY 10010-2622

WIENER, RONALD MARTIN, lawyer; b. Phila., June 1, 1939; s. William V. and Sylvia (Bookbinder) W.; m. Susan Cooper, June 16, 1963; children: Carol Jan, Alan Mark; m. 2d, Linda A. Fisher, Feb. 21, 1981. A.B., U. Pa., 1961; J.D. magna cum laude, Harvard U., 1964. Bar: D.C. 1965, Pa. 1966. Law clk., U.S. Tax Ct., 1964-66; assoc. Wolf, Block, Schorr and Solis-Cohen, Phila., 1966-72, ptnr., 1972—; mem. commr.'s adv. group IRS, 1992-93. Mem. ABA, Pa. Bar Assn., Phila. Bar Assn. (chair tax sect. 1989-90). Office: Wolf Block Schorr and Solis-Cohen 12th Floor Packard Bldg SE Corner 15 & Chestnut Sts Philadelphia PA 19102

WIENER, SOLOMON, author, consultant, former city official; b. N.Y.C., Mar. 5, 1915; s. Morris David and Anna (Pinchuk) W.; m. Gertrude Klings, Feb. 24, 1946; children: Marjorie Diane Wein, Willa Kay Ehrlich. BS, Cornell, 1936; MPA, NYU, 1946. Exam. asst. N.Y.C. Dept. Personnel, 1937-42, civil service examiner, 1946-55, asst. div. chief, 1955-59, div. chief, 1959-67, asst. dir. exams., 1967-70, dir. exams., 1970-72, asst. personnel dir. exams., 1972-75; author, cons., 1975—; tchr. Washington Irving Evening Adult Sch., N.Y.C., 1949-60, tchr.-in-charge, 1960-67. Served with AUS, 1942-46, PTO. Decorated Bronze Star. Mem. Am. Soc. Pub. Adminstrn., Internat. Personnel Mgmt. Assn., Authors Guild, Res. Officers Assn., Ret. Officers Assn., Assn. of U.S. Army, Am. Def. Preparedness Assn. Author: A Handy Book of Commonly Used American Idioms, rev. edit., 1981, Manual de Modismos Americanos Más Comunes, rev. edit., 1981, A Handy Guide to Irregular Verbs and the Use and Formation of Tenses, 1959, Guía Completa de Los Verbos Irregulares en Inglés y el Uso y Formación de los Tiempos, 1959, Questions and Answers on American Citizenship, rev. edit., 1982, Clear and Simple Guide to Business Letter Writing, rev. edit., 1978, The College Graduate Guide for Scoring High on Employment Tests, 1981, The High School Graduate Guide for Scoring High on Civil Service Tests, 1981, How to Take and Pass Simple Tests for Civil Service Jobs, 1981, Officer Candidate Tests, 3d edit., 1993, Military Flight Aptitude Tests, 2d edit., 1994; co-author Practice for the Armed Forces Test, ASVAB, 14th edit., 1994, Practica para el Examen de las Fuerzas Armadas, ASVAB En Español, 1989; contbr. to ARCO ROTC Coll. Guide, 1988. Home: 523 E 14th St New York NY 10009-2927

WIENER, THOMAS ELI, lawyer; b. Dallas, Nov. 29, 1940; s. Samson and Fan (Gardner) W.; m. Felice Gloria Goodwin, Jan. 24, 1970; children: Gary Allen, Debra Roslyn, Allison Beth, Todd David. B.A., U. Tex., 1962, J.D. with honors, 1968. Bar: Tex. 1968, D.C. 1969, Pa. 1972, U.S. Supreme Ct. 1972. Atty.-advisor office chief counsel IRS, Washington, 1968-72; assoc. Pepper Hamilton & Scheetz, Phila., 1972-74, Abrahams & Loewenstein, Phila., 1974-76, Goodis, Greenfield, Henry & Edelstein, Phila., 1976-77, Mesirov, Gelman, Jaffe, Cramer & Jamieson, Phila., 1977-78; prin. Franklin, Margulies & Huntington, 1978-91, Riley & DeFalice, P.C., Phila., 1991-92, Wiener & Caplan, P.C., 1992—; Dir. Lufkin (Tex.) Inds., Inc., Wiener Lumber Co., Dallas. Author: (with others) Tax Problems of Fiduciaries, 1977. Trustee Golden Slipper Club; pres. Main Line Reform Temple, 1992-94, pres. brotherhood 1981-83; pres. Rotary Gundaker Found., 1986-87; v.p. Nat. Fedn. Temple Brotherhoods, 1994—, N. Am. Bd. World Union Progressive Judaism; v.p. Phila. Fedn. Reform Synagogues, 1993—; chair Synagogue Fedn. Coun. of Phila., 1994—. Mem. ABA, D.C. Bar Assn., Pa. Bar Assn., Tex. Bar Assn., Phila. Bar Assn., Am. Law Inst., Order of Coif. Lodges: Masons (32 degree K.C.C.H., past master), Rotary (pres. elect 1985-86). Home: 1233 Remington Rd Wynnewood PA 19096-2329 Office: 1608 Walnut St Ste 801 Philadelphia PA 19103-5450

WIENER, VALERIE, communications company owner; b. Las Vegas, Nev., Oct. 30, 1948; d. Louis Isaac Weiner and Tui Ava Knight. BJ, U. Mo., 1971, MA, 1972; MA, Sangamon State U., 1974; postgrad., McGeorge Sch. Law, 1976-79. Producer TV show "Checkpoint" Sta. KOMU-TV, Columbia, Mo., 1972-73; v.p., owner Broadcast Assocs., Inc., Las Vegas, 1972-86; pub. affairs dir. First Ill. Cable TV, Springfield, 1973-74; editor Ill. State Register, Springfield, 1973-74; producer and talent "Nevada Realities" Sta. KLVX-TV, Las Vegas, 1974-75; account exec. Sta. KBMI (now KFMS), Las Vegas, 1975-79; nat. traffic dir. six radio stas., Las Vegas, Albuquerque and El Paso, Tex., 1979-80; exec. v.p., gen. mgr. Stas. KXKS and KKJY, Albuquerque, 1980-81; exec. adminstr. Stas. KSET AM/FM, KVEG, KFMS and KKJY, 1981-83; press sec. U.S. Congressman Harry Reid, Washington, 1983-87; adminstrv. asst Friends for Harry Reid, Nev., 1986; press sec. U.S. Senator Harry Reid, Washington, 1987-88; owner Wiener Communications Inc., Las Vegas, 1988—. Author: Power Communications: Positioning Yourself for High Visibility (Fortune Book Club main selection 1994); contbg. writer The Pacesetter. Sponsor Futures for Children, Las Vegas, Albuquerque and El Paso, 1979-83; mem. Exec. Women's Coun., El Paso, 1981-83; mem. VIP bd. Easter Seals, El Paso 1982; appointee, media chair Gov.'s Coun. Small Bus., 1989-93, Clark Coun. Sch. Dist. and Bus. Cmty. PAYBAC Spkrs. and Partnership Programs, 1989-93; media dir. 1990 Conf. on Women Gov. of Nev.; media chair Congl. Awards Coun., 1989-93; media chair, nat. rep. Nat. Assn. Women Bus. Owners, So. Nev., 1990-91, appointee, vice chair Gov.'s Commn. on Postsecondary Edn.; bd. dirs. Better Bus. Bureau So. Nev. Named Outstanding Vol. United Way, El Paso, 1983, SBA Nev. Small Bus. Media Advocate of Yr., 1992; recipient Woman of Achievement in Media award, 1992, numerous 1st place Nev. Press Women Media awards, 1990—, Outstanding Achievement award Nat. Fedn. Press Women, 1991, Disting. Leader award Nat. Assn. for Community Leadership, 1993, Cir. of Excellence Award Las Vegas C. of C., 1993, numerous other awards. Mem. NAFE, Nev. Press Women, Nat. Speakers Assn., Internat. Speakers Network, Nat. Assn. Women Bus. Owners (Nev. Advocate of Yr. 1992), Dem. Press Secs. Assn., El Paso Assn. Radio Stas., Am. Soc. Assn. Execs., U.S. Senate Staff Club, Las Vegas C. of C. (Circle of Excellence 1993), Soc. Profl. Journalists. Democrat. Avocations: reading, writing, fitness training, pub. speaking, community involvement. Office: 1500 Foremaster Ln Ste 2 Las Vegas NV 89101-1103

WIENS, ARTHUR NICHOLAI, psychology educator; b. McPherson, Kans., Sept. 7, 1926; s. Jacob T. and Helen E. (Kroeker) W.; m. Ruth Helen Avery, June 11, 1949; children: Barbara, Bradley, Donald. B.A., U. Kans., 1948, M.A., 1952; Ph.D., U. Portland, 1956. Diplomate: Am. Bd. Examiners Profl. Psychology. Clin. psychologist Topeka State Hosp. 1949-53; sr. psychologist outpatient dept. Oreg. State Hosp., Salem, 1954-58; chief psychologist Oreg. State Hosp., 1958-61, dir. clin. psychology internship program, 1958-61; clin. instr. U. Oreg. Med. Sch., Portland, 1958-61; asst. prof. U. Oreg. Med. Sch., 1961-65, asso. prof., 1965-66, prof. med. psychology, 1966—; clin. asso. prof. psychology U. Portland, 1959-61; field assessment officer Peace Corps, 1965; cons. psychologist Portland Center for Hearing and Speech, 1964-67, Dammasch State Hosp., 1967-69, Raleigh Hills Hosp., 1968-84, Oreg. Vocat. Rehab. Div., 1973—, mem. state adv. com., 1976-93; cons. William Temple Rehab. House, Episcopal Laymen's Mission Soc., 1968-88; chmn. State Oreg. Bd. Social Protection, 1971-84, State Oreg. Bd. Psychologist Examiners, 1974-77; v.p. bd. dirs. Raleigh Hills

Research Found., 1974-80. Contbr. articles to profl. jours. Fellow AAAS, APA (chmn. com. on vis. psychologist program 1972-76, chmn. accreditation com. 1978, mem. task force edn. and credentialing 1979-84); mem. Am. Assn. State Psychology Bds. (pres. 1978-79), Nat. Register Health Svc. Providers in Psychology (bd. dirs. 1985-92), Profl. Exam. Svc. (bd. dirs. 1982-88, 90—, chmn. 1986-88), Sigma Xi. Home: 74 Condolea Way Lake Oswego OR 97035-1010 Office: Oreg Health Scis U Portland OR 97201

WIER, PATRICIA ANN, publishing executive, consultant; b. Coal Hill, Ark., Nov. 10, 1937; d. Horace L. and Bridget B. (McMahon) Norton; m. Richard A. Wier, Feb. 24, 1962; 1 child, Rebecca Ann. B.A., U. Mo., Kansas City, 1964; M.B.A., U. Chgo., 1978. Computer programmer AT&T, 1960-62; lead programmer City of Kansas City, Mo., 1963-65; with Playboy Enterprises, Chgo., 1965-71; mgr. systems and programming Playboy Enterprises, 1971; with Ency. Britannica, Inc., Chgo. 1971—; v.p. mgmt. svcs. Ency. Britannica USA, 1975-83, exec. v.p. adminstrn., 1983-84; v.p. planning and devel. Ency. Britannica, Inc., 1985, pres. Compton's Learning Co. div., 1985; pres. Ency. Britannica (USA), 1986-91, Ency. Britannica N.A., 1991-92; exec. v.p. Ency. Britannica, Inc., 1986-91; pres. Ency. Britannica N.Am., 1991-94; mgmt. cons. pvt. practice, Chgo., 1994—; cons. pvt. practice, Chgo., 1994—; bd. dirs. NICOR, Inc., Golden Rule Ins., Enrich. Internat., Alcas Corp.; mem. coun. Northwestern U. Assocs. Mem. fin. Coun. Archdiocese of Chgo., Coun. of Grad. Sch. of Bus. U. of Chgo. Mem. Direct Selling Assn. (bd. dirs. 1984-93, chmn. 1987-88, named to Hall of Fame 1991), Women's Coun. U. Mo. Kansas City (hon. life) Com. 200, The Chgo. Network. Roman Catholic. Office: Patricia A Wier Inc 175 E Delaware Ste 8305 Chicago IL 60611

WIER, RICHARD ROYAL, JR., lawyer, inventor; b. Wilmington, Del., May 19, 1941; s. Richard Royal and Anne (Kurtz) W.; m. Anne E. Edwards, Nov. 25, 1978; children—Melissa Royal, Emma Kurtz; children from previous marriage: Richard Royal, III, Mimi Poole. BA in English, Hamilton Coll., 1963; LLB, U. Pa., 1966; postgrad. in labor law, Temple U. 1983. Bar: D.C. 1967, Del. 1967, Pa. 1980, U.S. Dist. Ct. Del., U.S. Ct. Appeals (3d cir.), U.S. Supreme Ct. Assoc. Connolly, Bove & Lodge. Wilmington, 1966-68; dep. atty. gen. State of Del., Wilmington, 1968-70; state prosecutor Del. Dept. Justice, Wilmington, 1970-74; atty. gen. State of Del., Wilmington, 1975-79; ptnr. Prickett, Jones, Elliott, Kristol & Schnee, Wilmington, 1979-92, Weiner and Wier, P.A., Wilmington, 1992-93; sole practice lawyer Wilmington, 1993—; lectr. criminal and labor law various instns. Active United Way campaign, 1976, 77; mem. supervisory bd. Gov.'s Commn. on Criminal Justice; bd. dirs. Del. Coun. Crime and Justice, 1982-89; mem. adv. coun. Diabetes Control, 1990-92; dir. Project Assist, 1992—. Recipient Law Enforcement award Newark Police Dept., 1974; Law Enforcement Commendation medal Nat. Soc. SAR, 1976; Ideal Citizen award Am. Found. for Sci. Creative Intelligence, 1976; Commendation Del. Gen. Assembly Senate, 1976, 77, 80; Outstanding Achievement award, 1976. Mem. ABA, Nat. Dist. Attys. Assn. (state dir.), Del. Bar Assn. (chmn. criminal law sect. 1987-91, com. on drug crisis 1993—, vice chmn. labor law sect. 1987-88, chmn. 1989-90), Pa. Bar Assn., D.C. Bar Assn., Nat. Assn. Attys. Gen. (hon. life, exec. com.), Am. Judicature Soc., Am. Del. Trial Lawyers Assn., Nat. Assn. Extradition Ofcls. (hon. life, regional v.p., exec. dir., Outstanding Achievement award), Italian Radio/TV Assn. (hon.), Internat. Platform Assn., Pi Delta Epsilon. Office: Richard R Wier Jr PA 1220 N Market St Ste 600 Wilmington DE 19801-1131

WIERMAN, JOHN CHARLES, mathematician, educator; b. Prosser, Wash., June 30, 1949; s. John Nathaniel and Edith Elizabeth (Ashley) W.; m. Susan Shelley Graupmann, Aug. 13, 1971; 1 child, Adam Christopher. BS in Math., U. Wash., 1971, PhD in Math., 1976. Asst. prof. math. U. Minn., Mpls., 1976-81; asst. prof. Johns Hopkins U., Balt., 1981-82, assoc. prof., 1982-87, prof., 1987—, chmn. math. scis. dept., 1988—; sr. rsch. fellow Inst. Applied Math. and its Applications, Mpls., 1987-88. Co-author: First-Passage Percolation on the Square Lattice, 1978; editor numerous jours.; contbr. articles to profl. jours. Grad. fellow NSF, 1971-74; NSF rsch. grantee, 1976-93. Fellow Inst. Math. Stats. (organizer spl. session on percolation theory 1982, organizer spl. session on probability and math. stats. 1986); mem. Am. Soc. Quality Control, Bernoulli Soc., Am. Math. Soc., Am. Statis. Assn., Math. Assn. Am., Sigma Xi, Phi Beta Kappa. Office: Johns Hopkins U Dept Math Scis 34th & Charles Sts Baltimore MD 21218

WIERNIK, PETER HARRIS, oncologist, educator; b. Crocket, Tex., June 16, 1939; s. Harris and Molly (Emmerman) W.; m. Roberta Joan Fuller, Sept. 6, 1961; children: Julie Anne, Lisa Britt, Peter Harrison. B.A. with distinction, U. Va., 1961, M.D., 1965; Dr. h.c., U. of Republic, Montevideo, Uruguay, 1982. Diplomate Am. Bd. Internal Medicine, Am. Bd. Med. Oncology (mem. writing com. 1981-87). Intern Cleve. Met. Gen. Hosp., 1965-66, resident, 1969-70; resident Osler Svc. Johns Hopkins Hosp., Balt., 1970-71; sr. asst. surgeon USPHS, 1966, advanced through grades to med. dir., 1976; sr. staff assoc. Balt. Cancer Rsch. Ctr., 1966-71, chief sect. med. oncology, 1971-76, chief clin. oncology br., 1976-82, dir., 1976-82; assoc. dir. div. cancer treatment Nat. Cancer Inst., 1976-82; asst. prof. medicine U. Md. Sch. Medicine, Balt., 1971-74, assoc. prof., 1974-76, prof., 1976-82; Gutman prof., chmn. dept. oncology Montefiore Med. Ctr., 1982-94; head div. med. oncology Albert Einstein Coll., 1982-94; assoc. dir. for clin. rsch. Albert Einstein Cancer Ctr., 1982-94; prof. medicine Albert Einstein Coll. Medicine, 1982—; cons. hematology and med. oncology Union Meml. Hosp., Greater Balt. Med. Center, Franklin Sq. Hosp.; bd. dirs. Balt. City unit Am. Cancer Soc., 1971-78, chmn. patient care com., 1972-75, mem. profl. edn. and grants com. N.Y.C. div., 1983-90, mem. nat. clin. fellowship com., 1984—; mem. med. adv. com. Nat. Leukemia Assn., 1976-88, chmn. med. adv. com., 1989—; chmn. adult leukemia com. Cancer and Leukemia Group B, 1976-82; prin. investigator Eastern Coop. Oncology Group, 1982-94; mem. gynecol. oncology com., 1986-88, chmn. leukemia com., 1988-94; sci. cons. Vt. Regional Cancer Ctr., 1987—. Editor: Controversies in Oncology, 1982, Supportive Care of the Cancer Patient, 1983, Neoplastic Diseases of the Blood, 1985, 2d edit., 1991; assoc. editor Medical Oncology and Tumor Pharmacotherapy, 1987-91, sr. editor, 1991—; assoc. editor oncology Am. Jour. Therapeutics, 1994—; co-editor: Year Book of Hematology, 1986—, Handbook of Hematologic and Oncologic Emergencies, 1988, Am. Jour. Med. Scis., 1976-81; N.Am. editor Jour. Cancer Research and Clin. Oncology, 1994-89; mem. editorial bd. Cancer Treatment Reports, 1972-76, Leukemia Research, 1976-86, 91—, Leukemia, 1986—, Cancer Clin. Trials, 1977—, Jour. Therapeutic Rsch., 1994—, Hosp. Practice, 1979—, Jour. Clin. Oncology, 1989-91, PDQ Nat. Cancer Inst., 1984-94; sect. editor antineoplastic drugs Jour. Clin. Pharmacology, 1985—; editor-in-chief Medical Oncology, 1993—; also articles, chpts. in books. Recipient Z Soc. award U. Va., 1961, Byrd S. Leavell Hematology award U. Va. Sch. Medicine, 1965. Fellow AAAS, ACP, Am. Coll. Clin. Pharmacology, Internat. Soc. Hematology, Royal Soc. Medicine (London); mem. Am. Soc. Clin. Investigation, Am. Soc. Clin. Oncology (chmn. edn. and tng. com. 1976-79, 84, subcom. on clin. investigation 1980-82, program com. 1990, pub. issues com., 1990—), Am. Assn. Cancer Rsch., Am. Soc. Hematology, Am. Fedn. Clin. Rsch., Am. Acad. Clin. Toxicology, Internat. Soc. Exptl. Hematology, N.Y. Acad. Sci., Am. Soc. Hosp. Pharmacy, Am. Soc. Clin. Pharmacology and Therapeutics, Am. Radium Soc. (program com. 1987—, exec. com. 1988—, publ. com. 1988-92, sec. 1990-91, pres.-elect, 1992-93; pres. 1993-94), Polish Oncology Soc. (hon.), Harvey Soc., Uruguan Hematology Soc. (hon.), European Assn. Cancer Rsch., Phi Beta Kappa (assoc. 1991—), Sigma Xi, Alpha Omega Alpha, Phi Sigma (award 1961). Home: 43 Longview Ln Chappaqua NY 10514-1304 Office: Montefiore Med Ctr 111 E 210th St Bronx NY 10467-2401 *Always remember why you entered a profession in the first place. Leave the politics to those who have forgotten.*

WIERSBE, WARREN WENDELL, clergyman, author, lecturer; b. East Chicago, Ind., May 16, 1929; s. Fred and Gladys Anna (Forsberg) W.; m. Betty Lorraine Warren, June 20, 1953; children: David, Carolyn, Robert, Judy. B.Th., No. Baptist Sem., 1953; D.D. (hon.), Temple Sem., Chattanooga, 1965, Trinity Evr-Div. Sch., 1986; LittD (hon.). Cedarville Coll. 1987. Ordained to ministry Bapt. Ch., 1951; pastor Central Bapt. Ch., East Chicago, 1951-57; editorial dir. Youth for Christ Internat., Wheaton, Ill., 1957-61; pastor Calvary Bapt. Ch., Covington, Ky., 1961-71; sr. minister Moody Ch., Chgo., 1971-78; bd. dirs. Slavic Gospel Assn., Wheaton, 1973-87; columnist Moody Monthly, Chgo., 1971-77; author, conf. minister, 1978-80; vis. instr. pastoral theology Trinity Div. Sch., Deerfield, Ill.; gen. dir. Back to the Bible Radio Ministries, Lincoln, Nebr., 1984-89; writer-in-residence Cornerstone Coll., Grand Rapids, Mich.; disting. prof. preaching

Grand Rapids Bapt. Sem.; sr. contbg. editor Baker Book House, Grand Rapids. Author: over 100 books including William Culbertson, A Man of God, 1974, Live Like a King, 1976, Walking with the Giants, 1976, Be Right, 1977, (with David Wiersbe) Making Sense of the Ministry, 1983, Why Us? Why Bad Things Happen to God's People, 1984, Real Worship: It Can Transform Your Life, 1986, Be Compassionate, 1988, The Integrity Crisis, 1988, Be What You Are, 1988, The New Pilgrim's Progress, 1989, Be Courageous, 1989. Home and Office: 441 Lakewood Dr Lincoln NE 68510-2419

WIERSMA, G. BRUCE, dean, forest resources educator; b. Paterson, N.J., Oct. 26, 1942; s. George and Marjorie (Zeedyk) W.; m. Ann Becker, Aug. 15, 1964; children: Heather, Robin, Jennifer, Joshua. BS, U. Maine, 1964; MF in Forestry, Yale U., 1965; PhD Coll. Environ. Sci. & Forestry, SUNY, 1968. Teaching asst., 1965-66; rsch. biologist Coll. Environ. Sci. and Forestry SUNY, 1968; combat devels. staff officer U.S. Army Inst. Land Combat, Alexandria, Va., 1968-70; head monitoring sect. U.S. EPA, Washington, 1970-72, chief colic. monitoring branch, 1972-74; chief pollutant pathways br. U.S. EPA, Las Vegas, Nev., 1974-79, sr. ecologist, 1979-80; mgr. environ. earth scis. group, Idaho Nat. Engring. Lab. EG&G Idaho, Inc., 1980-87; instr. Idaho Falls Campus of Higher Edn. U. Idaho, 1981-90, affiliate grad. faculty Coll. Forestry Wildlife and Range Scis., 1988-90; mgr., dir. Ctr. Environ. Monitoring and Assesment Environ. Sci. and Tech. Group, 1989-90; dir. Ctr. Environ. Monitoring and Assesment Idaho Nat. Engring. Lab., EG&G Idaho, Inc., Idaho Falls, 1988-90; dean Coll. Forest Resources, assoc. dir. Maine Agrl. Experiment Sta., prof. Forest Resources U. Maine, Orono, 1991-93, dean Coll. Natural Resources, Forestry & Agrl., dir. Maine Agrl. and Forest Experiment Sta., prof. Forest Resources, 1993—; dir. Ctr. Environ. Monitoring and Assessment, Idaho Falls, Idaho, 1980-90; mem. adhoc task force to plan global environ. monitoring sys., 1993—; trustee Nature Conservancy, 1993—; mem. U.N. Ad hoc Task Force to plan Global Terrestrial Observing Sys., 1993—; mem. bd. dirs. Maine Forest Products Coun., 1993—; mem. U.S. Nat. Com. on Data for Sci. and Tech., 1990-92, others. Contbr. chpts. to books, articles to profl. jours; editor, founder Jour. Environ. Monitoring and Assesment. Capt. U.S. Army, 1968-70. Recipient numerous rsch. grants from various orgns. Mem. EPA (mem. sci. adv. bd. 1986-90), Nat. Rsch. Coun. (chair com. on databases, 1990-94, mem. com. on marine monitoring, 1986-90, Nat. Assn. Profl. Forestry Schs. (mem. exec. com. 1993—). Avocations: jogging, swimming, cross country skiing, backpacking, mountain climbing. Home: 30 Wildwood Dr East Holden ME 04429-9708 Office: Univ of Maine Coll Natural Res Forestry and Agrl 5782 Winslow Hall Orono ME 04469-5782

WIERZBICKI, RONALD GERARD, auditor; b. Amsterdam, N.Y., June 14, 1937; s. Michael Gerard and Irene Bernadette (Zarecki) W.; m. Alice C. Tammany, Jan. 15, 1958 (div. Mar. 1971); children: Gretchen, Gerard, Gail, Karin, Michael, Eric; m. Jean E. Slusas, Sept. 14, 1979. BSBA, U. Southwestern La., 1973. Loan mgr. Beneficial Fin. Co., Lafayette, La., 1960-69; supervising auditor N.Y. State Dept. Transp., Albany, 1973—; organizer S.W. La. Credit Rsch., Lafayette, 1965. Chpt. pres. Jaycees, Lafayette, 1968. With U.S. Army, 1956. Mem. Elks (exalted ruler Amsterdam 1988-89, v.p. N.Y. state 1992-93), Am. Legion (exec. bd. 1991-93). Avocations: travel, camping. Office: NY State Dept Transp State Campus Albany NY 12232

WIESE, JOHN PAUL, federal judge; b. Bklyn., Apr. 19, 1934; s. Gustav and Margaret W.; m. Alice Mary Donoghue, June 1961; 1 child,John Patrick. BA cum laude, Hobart College, Geneva, NY, 1962; LLB, U. of Va., Charlottesville, 1965. With Cox, Langford & Brown, Washington, DC, 1967-1969, Hodson & Creyke, 1969-74; trial commr. U.S. Claims Court, Washington, DC, 1974-1986, judge, 1986—. Mem. Phi Beta Kappa. Office: US Claims Ct 717 Madison Pl NW Washington DC 20005-1011

WIESE, LARRY CLEVENGER, lawyer; b. Huntsville, Tex., May 30, 1949; s. Arthur Edward and Lola Irene (Clevenger) W.; m. Patricia Petty Barr, Aug. 12, 1972; 1 son, Hugh Clevenger. B.S., Sam Houston State U., 1971; J.D., Tex. Tech. U., 1974; M.B.A., George Washington U., 1978. Bar: Tex. 1974, U.S. Ct. Mil. Appeals 1975, U.S. Supreme Ct. 1976, U.S. Dist. Ct. (so. dist.) Tex. 1979, U.S. Dist. Ct. (ea. dist.) Tex. 1980, U.S. Ct. Appeals (5th cir.) 1982. Staff atty. Shell Oil Co., Houston, 1978-80; atty. Houston div. Marathon Oil Co., 1980-84, Marathon Internat. Oil Co., London, 1984-87; sr. counsel internat. E & P Marathon Oil Co., Houston, 1987—. Contbr. article to profl. jour. Lectr. Ea. Mineral Law Found.; precinct chmn. Mayor Kathy Whitmire campaign, Houston, 1982; mem. Western Harris County Republican Men's Club, 1980-84, Gulf Coast Council Fgn. Affairs, Galveston, 1980-84. Served to lt. comdr. USCG, 1974-78. Named one of Outstanding Young Men in Am., 1981. Mem. Tex. Bar Assn., Houston Bar Assn. (chmn. corp. counsel sect. 1983-84), Houston Young Lawyers Assn. (program chmn. 1982-83), Maritime Law Assn., Res. Officers Assn., Navy League. Lutheran. Club: Luth. Men. Office: Marathon Oil Co PO Box 3128 Houston TX 77253-3128

WIESE, WOLFGANG LOTHAR, physicist; b. Tilsit, Fed. Republic Germany, Apr. 21, 1931; came to U.S., 1957; naturalized, 1965; s. Werner Max and Charlotte (Donath) W.; m. Gesa Ladehoff, Oct. 12, 1957; children: Margrit, Cosima. BS, U. Kiel, Fed. Republic Germany, 1954, PhD, 1957, PhD (hon.), 1993. Rsch. assoc. U. Md., College Park, 1958-59; rsch. physicist Nat. Bur. Standards, Gaithersburg, Md., 1960-62; chief plasma spectrosc. sect. Nat. Bur. Standards, Gaithersburg, 1962-77, chief atomic and plasma radiation div., 1978-91, chief atomic physics div., 1991—; lectr. U. Calif., 1963, 64. Author: Atomic Transition Probabilities, Vol. I, 1966, Vol. II, 1969, Vol. III, 1988, Vol. IV, 1988. Recipient Silver Medal award Dept. Commerce, 1962, Gold Medal award, 1971, Humboldt award, 1986, A.S. Fleming award U.S.C. of C., 1971, Disting. Career in Sci. award Wash. Acad. Sci., 1992; Guggenheim fellow, 1966. Fellow Am. Phys. Soc., Optical Soc. Am., Wash. Acad. Sci.; mem. Internat. Astron. Union, Sigma Xi. Lutheran. Home: 8229 Stone Trail Dr Bethesda MD 20817-4555 Office: Nat Inst Standards and Tech Gaithersburg MD 20899

WIESEL, ELIE, writer, educator; b. Sighet, Romania, Sept. 30, 1928; arrived in Paris, 1945; came to U.S., 1956, naturalized, 1963; s. Shlomo and Sarah (Feig) W.; m. Marion Erster, 1969; 1 child, Shlomo Elisha. Student, The Sorbonne, Paris, 1948-51; LittD (hon.), Jewish Theol. Sem., N.Y.C., 1967, Marquette U., 1975, Simmons Coll., 1976, Anna Maria Coll., 1980, Yale U., 1981, Wake Forest U., 1985, Haverford Coll., 1985, Capital U., 1986, L.I. U., 1986, U. Paris, 1987, U. Conn., 1988, U. Cen. Fla., 1988, Wittenberg U., 1989, Wheeling Jesuit Coll., 1989, Fairleigh Dickenson U., 1993; LHD (hon.), Hebrew Union Coll., 1968, Manhattanville Coll., 1972, Yeshiva U., 1973, Boston U., 1974, Coll. of St. Scholastica, 1978, Wesleyan U., 1979, Brandeis U., 1980, Kenyon Coll., 1982, Hobart/William Smith Coll., 1982, Emory U., 1983, Fla. Internat. U., 1983, Siena Heights Coll., 1983, Fairfield U., 1983, Dropsie Coll., 1983, Moravian Coll., 1983, Colgate U., 1984, SUNY, Binghamton, 1985, Lehigh U., 1985, Coll. of New Rochelle, 1986, Tufts U., 1986, Georgetown U., 1986, Hamilton Coll., 1986, Rockford Coll., 1986, Villanova U., 1987, Coll. of St. Thomas, 1987, U. Denver, 1987, Walsh Coll., 1987, Loyola Coll., 1987, Ohio U., 1988, Concordia Coll., 1990, N.Y.U., 1990, Fordham U., 1990, Conn. Coll., 1990, Upsala Coll., 1991, Duquesne U., 1991, Roosevelt U., 1991; PhD (hon.), Bar-Ilan U., 1973, U. Haifa, 1986, Ben Gurion U., 1988; LLD (hon.), Hofstra U., 1975, Talmudic U, Fla., 1979; U. Notre Dame, 1980, La Salle U., 1988, Bates Coll., 1995; HHD (hon.), U. Hartford, 1985, Lycoming Coll., 1987, U. Miami, 1988, Brigham Young U., 1989; D of Hebrew Letters, Spertus Coll. Judaica, 1973; DSc (hon.), U. Health Scis./Chgo. Med. Sch., 1989; ThD, U. Åbo Akadem, 1990; LHD (hon.), Hunter Coll., 1992, Susquehanna U., 1992, Am. U., 1992, Millersville U., 1993; hon. degree, U. Dayton, 1993, U. Mich., 1993; LHD (hon.), U. Bordeaux, 1993, Gustavus Adolphus Coll., 1994, McGill U., 1994, Mt. Sinai Med. Sch., 1994, Spelman Coll., 1995. Disting. prof. Judaic studies CCNY, 1972-76; prof. religious studies and univ. prof. Boston U., 1976—; prof. philosophy, 1988—; Disting. vis. prof. Henry Luce, 1982-83, Eckerd 'Coll., 1994; chmn. U.S. Pres.'s Commn. on the Holocaust, 1979-80, U.S. Holocaust Meml. Coun., 1980-86; founder Elie Wiesel Found. for Humanity, 1987; founding pres. Paris-based Universal Acad. Cultures; hon. chmn. Nat. Jewish Resource Ctr.; U.S. Holocaust Meml. Commn., Am. Friends of Ghetto Fighter's House; hon. pres. Am. Gathering of Jewish Holocaust Survivors; bd. dirs. Nat. Com. on Am. Fgn. Policy, 1983—; Elaine Kaufman Cultural ctr., advisory bd. The Raoul Wallenberg Comm. of U.S., 1981—; Humanitas, Am. Assocs. Ben-

Gurion U. of the Negev, Mut. of Am., France Libertés; v.p. Internat. Rescue Com., 1985—; bd. trustees Annenberg Rsch. Inst., 1983-89, Am. Jour. World Svc., 1985—; Haifa U., Tel-Aviv U.; bd. trustees Yeshiva U., 1977—; colleague Cathedral St. John the Divine, 1975—; mem. adv. bd. Boston U. Inst. for Philosophy & Religion, Nat. Inst. Against Prejudice & Violence, Internat. Ctr. in N.Y., Friends of Akim USA, Friends of LeChambon; mem. jury Neustadt Internat. Prize Lit., 1984; lectr. Andrew W. Mellon Ann. Lecture Series Boston U., 92d St. YMHA, YWHA Ann. Lectr. Series, ann. radio broadcast series Eternal Light for Jewish Theol. Sem. Am., advisory bd. Rena Costa Ctr. for Yiddish Studies at Bar-Ilan U., 1994, advisory Coun. Carnegie Commn. on Preventing Deadly Conflict, 1994. Author: Night, 1960, Dawn, 1961, The Accident, 1962, The Town Beyond the Wall, 1964, The Gates of the Forest, 1966, The Jews of Silence, 1966, Legends of Our Time, 1968, A Beggar in Jerusalem, 1970, One Generation After, 1970, Souls on Fire, 1972, The Oath, 1973, Ani Maamin, 1973, Zalmen, or the Madness of God, 1974, Messengers of God, 1976, A Jew Today, 1978, Four Hasidic Masters, 1978, The Trial of God, 1979, The Testament, 1980, Le Testament D'Un Poète Juif Assassiné (France's Prix Livre-Inter 1980, Bourse Goncourt, 1980, Prix des Bibliothécaires, 1981), 1985, Images from the Bible, 1980, Five Biblical Portraits, 1981, Somewhere A Master, 1982, Paroles d'Étranger, 1982, The Golem, 1983, The Fifth Son (Grand Prix de la Littérature, City of Paris), 1985, Signes d'Exode, 1985, Against Silence (3 vols., ed. Irving Abrahamson), 1985, Job ou Dieu dans la Tempête, 1986, A Song for Hope, 1987, The Nobel Address, 1987, Twilight, 1988; (essays) Silences et Mémoire d'hommes, 1989, L'Oublié, 1989, From the Kingdom of Memory, 1990, Célébration Talmudique, 1991, Sages and Dreamers, 1991, The Forgotten, 1992, (with John Cardinal O'Connor) A Journey of Faith, 1990, (with Albert Friedlander) The Six Days of Destruction, 1988, (dialogues with Philippe-Michaël Saint-Cheron) Evil and Exile, 1990; commentaries to A Passover Haggadah, 1993, Tous les fleuves vont à la mer (a memoir), 1994; editorial and adv. bds. Midstream, Religion and Lit. (U. Notre Dame), Sh'ma: Jour. of Responsibility, Hadassah Mag., Acad. of the Air for Jewish Studies, Holocaust and Genocide Studies: An Internat. Jour.; subject of 29 books; journalist Israeli, French and Am. newspapers. Chmn. adv. bd. World Union Jewish Students, 1985—; comité d'Honneur Ligue International Contre le Racisme et l'Antisemitisme, 1985—; founder Nat. Jewish Ctr. Learning and Leadership, 1974; mem. soc. fellows Ctr. Judaic Studies, U. Denver, 1980, bd. overseer Bar-Ilan U., 1970—. Recipient Prix Rivarol, 1963, Prix de l'Universite de la langue Francaise, 1963, Ingram Merrill award, 1964, Jewish Heritage award, Haifa U., 1975, Remembrance award, 1965, Prix du Souvenir, 1965, Nat. Jewish Book Council award, 1965, 73, Prix Médicis, 1968, Prix Bordin French Acad., 1972, Eleanor Roosevelt Meml. award, N.Y. United Jewish Appeal, 1972, Am. Liberties medallion Am. Jewish Com., 1972, Martin Luther King Jr. medallion, CCNY, 1973, Annual award for Disting. Service to Am. Jewry, Nat. Fedn. of Jewish Men's Clubs, 1973, Faculty Disting. Scholar award Hofstra U., 1974, Rambam award Am. Mizrachi Women, 1974, Meml. award N.Y. Soc. Clin. Psychologists, 1975, First Spertus Internat. award, 1976, Myrtle Wreath award Hadassah, 1977, King Solomon award, 1977, Liberty award HIAS, 1977, Jewish Heritage award, B'nai B'rith, 1966, Avodah award, Jewish Tchrs. Assn., 1972, Humanitarian award, B'rith Sholom, 1978, Joseph Prize for Human Rights, Anti-Defamation League, 1978, Zalman Shazar award State of Israel, 1979, Presdl. Citation, NYU, 1979, Inaugural award for Lit., Israel Bonds Prime Minister's Com., 1979, Jabotinsky medal, State of Israel, 1980, Rabbanit Sarah Herzog award Emunah Women of Am., 1981, Le Grand Prix Littéraire du Festival Internat. Deauville, 1983, Internat. Lit. prize for Peace, Royal Acad. Belgium, 1983, Lit. Lions award N.Y. Pub. Library, 1983, Jordan Davidson Humanitarian award Fla. Internat. U., 1983, Anatoly Scharansky Humanitarian award, 1983, Grand Officer, Legion of Honor, France, Congressional gold medal, 1985, Voice of Conscience award Am. Jewish Congress, 1985, Remembrance award, Israel Bonds, 1985, Anne Frank award, 1985, 4 Freedoms award FDR 4 Freedoms Found., 1985, Medal of Liberty award Statue of Liberty Presentation, 1986, Nobel Peace Prize, 1986, First Herzl Lit. award, First David Ben-Gurion award, Nat. UJA, Gov.'s award, Shaarei Tzedek, Internat. Kaplun Found. award Hebrew U. Jerusalem, Scopus award, 1974, Am.-Israeli Friendship award, Disting. Writers award Lincolnwood Library, 1984, First Chancellor Joseph H. Lookstein award Bar-Ilan U., 1984, Sam Levenson Meml. award Jewish Community Relations Council, 1985, Comenius award Moravian Coll., 1985, Henrietta Szold award Hadassah, 1985, Disting. Community Service award Mut. Am., 1985, Covenant Peace award Synagogue Council Am., 1985, Jacob Pat award World Congress Jewish Culture, 1985, Humanitarian award Internat. League Human Rights, 1985, Disting. Foreign-Born Am. award Internat. Ctr. N.Y., Inc., 1986, Freedom Cup award Women's League Israel, 1986, First Jacob Javits Humanitarian award UJA Young Leadership, 1986, Boston City Coun. Commendation, 1986, medal of Jerusalem, 1986, Freedom award Internat. Rescue Com., 1987, Achievement award Artist and Writers for Peace in the Middle East, 1987, La Grande Médaille de Vermeil de la Ville de Paris, 1987, La Médaille de la Chancellerie de l'Université de Paris, 1987, La Médaille de l'Université de Paris, 1987, First Eitinger Prize, U. Oslo, 1987, Lifetime Achievment award Present Tense mag., 1987, Spl. Christopher award The Christophers, 1987, Achievement award State Israel, 1987, Sem. medal Jewish Theol. Sem. Am., 1987, Metcalf Cup and Prize for Excellence in Teaching, Boston U., 1987, Spl. award Nat. Com. on Am. Fgn. Policy, 1987, Grã-Cruz da Ordem Nacional do Cruzeiro do Sul, Brazil's highest distinction, 1987, Profiles of Courage award B'nai B'rith, 1987, Centennial medal U. Scranton, 1987, Citation from Religious Edn. Assn., 1987, Golda Meir Sr. Humanitarian award, 1987, Presdl. medal Hofstra U., 1988, Human Rights Law award Internat. Human Rights Law Group, 1988, Bicentennial medal Georgetown U., 1988, Janus Korczak Humanitarian award NAHE, Kent State U., 1989, Count Sforza award in Philanthropy Interphil, 1989, Lily Edelman award for Excellence in Continuing Jewish Edn. B'nai B'rith Internat., 1989, George Washington award Am. Hungarian Found., 1989, Bicentennial medal N.Y.U., 1989, Humanitarian award Human Rights Campaign Fund, 1989, Internat. Brotherhood award C.O.R.E., 1990, Frank Weil award for Disting. Contbn. to Adv. of N.Am. Jewish Culture Jewish Community Ctrs. Assn. N.Am., 1990, 1st Raoul Wallenberg medal U. Mich., 1990, Award of Highest Honor Soka U., 1991, Facing History and Ourselves Humanity award, 1991, La Medaille de la Ville de Toulouse, 1991, 5th Centennial Christopher Columbus medal City of Genoa, 1992, 1st Primo Levi award, 1992, Lit. Arts award Nat. Found. for Jewish Culture, 1992, Ellis Island Medal of Honor, 1992, Guardian of the Children award AKIM USA, 1992, Bishop Francis J. Mugavero award for religious and racial harmony Cath. Newman Ctr. Queens Coll., 1994, Golden Slipper Humanitarian award, 1994, Interfaith Coun. on the Holocaust Humanitarian award, 1994, Crystal award Davos World Economic Forum, 1995, First Niebuhr award, Elmhurst Coll., 1995; named Humanitarian of the Century Coun. Jewish Orgns., Presdl. medal Freedom, 1992; Beth Hatefutsoth hon. fellow, 1988; honors established in his name: Elie Wiesel award for Holocaust Rsch., U. Haifa, Elie Wiesel Chair in Holocaust Studies, Bar-Ilan U., Elie Wiesel Endowment Fund for Jewish Culture, U. Denver, 1987, Elie Wiesel Disting. Svc. award, U. Fla., 1988, Elie Wiesel awards for Jewish Arts and Culture B'nai B'rith Hillel Founds., 1988, Elie Wiesel Chair in Judaic Studies Conn. Coll., 1990. Fellow Jewish Acad. Arts and Scis., Am. Acad. Arts & Scis., Timothy Dwight Coll., Yale U.; mem. Fgn. Press Assn. (hon. life), Amnesty Internat., PEN, Writers & Artists for Peace in Middle East, Writers Guild of Am. East, The Author's Guild,Royal Norwegian Soc. Scis. and Letters, Soc. des auteurs Paris, European Acad. of Arts, Sci. and Humanities, 1992; Phi Beta Kappa. Office: Boston U Univ Profs Program 745 Commonwealth Ave Boston MA 02215-1401

WIESEL, TORSTEN NILS, neurobiologist, educator; b. Upsala, Sweden, June 3, 1924; came to U.S., 1955; s. Fritz Samuel and Anna-Lisa Elisabet (Bentzer) W.; 1 dau., Sara Elisabet. MD, Karolinska Inst., Stockholm, 1954; D Medicine (hon.), Karolinska Inst, Stockholm 1989; AM (hon.), Harvard U., 1967; ScD (hon.), NYU, 1987, U. Pavia, 1987. Instr. physiology Karolinska Inst., 1954-55; asst. dept. child psychiatry Karolinska Hosp., 1954-55; fellow in ophthalmology Johns Hopkins U., 1955-58, asst. prof. ophthalmic physiology, 1958-59; assoc. in neurophysiology and neuropharmacology Harvard U. Med. Sch., Boston, 1959-60; asst. prof. neurophysiology and neuropharmacology Harvard U. Med. Sch., 1960-64, asst. prof. neurophysiology, dept. psychiatry, 1964-67, prof. physiology, 1967-68, prof. neurobiology, 1968-74, Robert Winthrop prof. neurobiology, 1974-83, chmn. dept. neurobiology, 1973-82; Vincent and Brooke Astor prof. neurobiology, head lab. Rockefeller U. N.Y.C., 1983—, pres., 1992—; Ferrier lectr. Royal Soc. London, 1972; NIH lectr., 1975; Grass lectr. Soc. Neurosci., 1976; lectr. Coll. of France, 1977; Hitchcock prof. U. Calif.-Berkeley, 1980; Sharpey-Schafer lectr. Phys. Soc. London; George Cotzias lectr. Am. Acad. Neurology, 1983. Contbr. numerous articles to profl. jours. Recipient Jules Stein award Trustees for Prevention of Blindness, 1971, Lewis S. Rosenstiel prize Brandeis U., 1972, Friedenwald award Assn. Rsch. in Vision and Ophthalmology, 1975, Karl Spencer Lashley prize Am. Philos. Soc., 1977, Louisa Gross Horwitz prize Columbia U., 1978, Dickson prize U. Pitts., 1979, Nobel prize in physiology and medicine, 1981, W.H. Helmerich III award 1989. Mem. Am. Physiol. Soc., Am. Philos. Soc., AAAS, Am. Acad. Arts and Scis., Nat. Acad. Arts and Scis., Swedish Physiol. Soc., Soc. Neurosci. (pres. 1978-79), Royal Soc. (gen. mem.), Physiol. Soc. (Eng.) (hon. mem.). Office: Rockefeller U Office Pres 1230 York Ave New York NY 10021

WIESEN, DONALD GUY, retired diversified manufacturing company executive; b. N.Y.C., July 4, 1928; s. Benjamin and Grace (Heath) W.; m. Patricia Ann Elfers, Apr. 29, 1950; children: Mara, Caitlin, Elizabeth, Anne, Megan. B.S., Columbia U., 1948, M.S., 1954. C.P.A., N.Y. Sr. tax specialist Price Waterhouse & Co., N.Y.C., 1950-58; with Chesebrough-Pond's, Greenwich, Conn., 1958-87; gen. mgr. ops. Europe Chesebrough-Pond's Inc., 1965-70, treas., 1970-72, group v.p., chief fin. officer, 1972-77, group v.p., internat., 1977-82, sr. group v.p., 1982-84, vice chmn., chief fin. officer, 1984-87, also dir., ret., 1987; bd. dirs. Skandia Am. Corp., 1985-91. Trustee Greenwich Libr., 1974-80; bd. govs. St. Bernard Coll., Cullman, Ala., 1973-75; rep. Columbia U. Alumni, Geneva, 1968; bd. dirs. Inner-City Found. for Charity and Edn., Bridgeport, Conn., 1992-93. Capt. USMC, 1951-54. Mem. AICPA, Indian Harbor Yacht Club, Univ. Club (N.Y.). Roman Catholic.

WIESEN, RICHARD A., academic administrator, educator; b. Sharon, Pa., Sept. 23, 1937. BS in Edn. Clarion State U., 1959; MS, Syracuse U., 1964; EdD, SUNY, Buffalo, 1970. Asst. prof. Buffalo State Coll., 1964-67, assoc. prof., 1967-71, assoc. dean, 1976, prof., 1971-92, assoc.v.p., 1979-83, v.p., 1983-90, provost, v.p. for acad. affairs, 1990-92; sr. v.p. D'Youville Coll., Buffalo, 1992—. Recipient Disting. Alumni award SUNY-Buffalo, 1990, Outstanding Alumni award 1990. Mem. Am. Assn. U. Adminstrs., Am. Assn. for Higher Edn. Office: D'Youville Coll 320 Porter Ave Buffalo NY 14201

WIESENECK, ROBERT L., credit manager; b. 1938. Graduate, Roosevelt U., 1958; MBA, U. Chgo., 1963. With Sears Roebuck and Co., Chgo., 1963—; nowpres. SPS Syss., Inc., Deerfield, Ill. Office: SPS Payment Systems Inc 2500 Lake Cook Rd Deerfield IL 60015*

WIESENFELD, BESS GAZEVITZ, business executive, real estate developer; b. Elizabeth, N.J., May 6, 1915; d. Morris and Rebecca (Sokolov) Gazevitz; m. Benjamin Wiesenfeld, Oct. 23, 1938 (dec.); children: Myra Judith Wiesenfeld Lewis, Elaine Phyllis Wiesenfeld Livingston, Ira Bertram (dec.), Sarah Ann Wiesenfeld Wasserman. BFA, N.Y. Sch. Design, N.Y.C., 1982. Pres. Anasarca Corp., 1958—; real estate devel. Colonia, N.J., 1961—; interior designer, 1961—; chair Bess & Co., Phila., 1982—; pres. Carolier Lns., Inc., 1986—. Patron Met. Opera Guild, Friends Music at Princeton; mem. pres.' coun. Norton Gallery and Sch. Art, Inc.; sustaining mem. N.J. Symphony Orch. Mem. AAUW, Nat. Trust for Hist. Preservation (assoc.), Am. Soc. Interior Designers (allied mem.), Met. Mus. Art, Mus. Modern Art, Smithsonian Inst., Victorian Soc. of Met. Opera Guild, Preservation, N.J., Inc., N.J. Symphony Orgn., Friends of Art Mus., Princeton, N.J., Friends of Music at Princeton. Republican. Jewish. Avocations: tennis, art history lectures, home tours, mus. tours, travel. Home: 374 New Dover Rd Colonia NJ 07067-2799 also: 2600 South Ocean Blvd Palm Beach FL 33480

WIESENFELD, JOHN RICHARD, chemistry educator; b. N.Y.C., July 26, 1944; s. Walter and Trude (Rosenberg) W. Stokes fellow, Pembroke Coll., Cambridge, Eng., 1971-72; BS with honors, CCNY, 1965; PhD, Case Inst. Tech., Cleve., 1969; MA, U. Cambridge, Eng., 1970. Asst. prof. Cornell U., Ithaca, N.Y., 1972-77, assoc. prof., 1978-84, prof., 1984-95, chair dept. chemistry, 1985-88, dep. v.p. for rsch., 1988-90, v.p. for plan, 1990-94; v.p. academic programs and planning, 1994-95; dean of sci. Fla. Atlantic U., Boca Raton, 1995—; vis. scholar Stanford U. Calif., 1978-79, U. Wash., 1988; cons. E.I. DuPont, Wilmington, Del., 1975, Phys. Dynamics, La Jolla, Calif., 1980-82, U.S. Dept. Energy, Pitts., 1982, NIH, 1994; bd. dirs. Associated Univs., 1989-92. Contbr. more than 100 sci. articles to profl. jours. Sloan Found. research fellow, 1975; recipient Tchr.-Scholar award, Dreyfus Found., 1975. Fellow AAAS; mem. Am. Chem. Soc., Coun. Chem. Rsch. (governing bd. 1987-90). Home: 3011 Jasmine Ct Delray Beach FL 33483 Office: Fla Atlantic U PO Box 3091 Boca Raton FL 33431

WIESER, SIEGFRIED, planetarium executive director; b. Linz, Austria, Oct. 30, 1933; came to Can., 1955; s. Florian Wieser and Michaela Josepha (Kaufmann) Wieser-Burgstaller; m. Joan Xaven Quick, Sept. 8, 1962; children: Leonard Franz, Bernard Sidney. BS in Physics, U. Calgary, Alta., Can., 1966. Lead chorus singer, dancer Landes Theatre, Linz, 1949-53; project engr. EBG, Linz, 1952-54; with Griffith Farms Ltd., Eng., 1954-55; seismic computer operator Shell Can., Calgary, 1956-61; GTA systems analyst U. Calgary, 1961-66; planetarium dir. Centennial Planetarium, Calgary, 1966-84, exec. dir., 1984-91; exec. dir. emeritus Alberta Sci. Ctr., 1991—; cons. Electro Controls, Salt Lake City, 1978-79. Contbr. articles to profl. publs. Recipient Violet Taylor award U. Calgary, 1964; Queen Elizabeth scholar Province Alta., 1961; Paul Harris fellow Rotary Internat. Mem. AAAS, Royal Astron. Soc. Can., Internat. Planetarium Soc., Can. Planetarium Soc., Can. Mus. Assn., Alberta Coll. of Art Alumni Assn. (pres. 1991-92). Anglican. Club: Magic Circle (Calgary). Avocations: swimming, hiking, astronomy, lecturing.

WIESLER, JAMES BALLARD, retired banker; b. San Diego, July 25, 1927; s. Harry J. and Della B. (Ballard) W.; m. Mary Jane Hall, Oct. 3, 1953; children: Tom, Ann, Larry. B.S., U. Colo., 1949; postgrad., Stonier Sch. Banking, Rutgers U., 1962, Advanced Mgmt. Program, Harvard U., 1973. With Bank of Am., NT & SA, 1949-87; v.p., mgr. main office San Jose, Calif., 1964-69, regional v.p. Cen. Coast adminstrn., 1969-74; sr. v.p., head No. European Area office Frankfurt, Fed. Republic of Germany, 1974-78; exec. v.p., head Asia div. Tokyo, 1978-81; exec. v.p., head N.Am. div. Los Angeles, 1981-82; vice chmn., head retail banking San Francisco, 1982-87; ret., 1987; bd. dirs. Visa USA, Visa Internat., Sci. Applications Internat. Corp., Wahlco Environ. Systems Inc.; bd. dirs., chmn. Bank Adminstrn. Inst., 1986-87. Pres. Santa Clara County Unit Fund, 1969, 70, San Jose C. of C., 1968; fin. chmn. Santa Clara County Reps., 1967-74; bd. dirs. San Diego Armed Svcs., YMCA, San Diego Regional Cancer Ctr.; trustee Sharp Hosp.; hon. consul-gen. for Japan. With USN, 1945-46. Mem. San Diego Zool. Soc., Bohemian Club, DeAnza Country Club, San Diego Country Club, San Diego Yacht Club. Presbyterian. Home: 605 San Fernando St San Diego CA 92106-3312 Office: Bank Am Nat Trust & Savs 450 B St San Diego CA 92101-8001

WIESNER, DAVID, illustrator, children's writer. Author, illustrator: Free Fall, 1988, Hurricane, 1990, Tuesday, 1991 (Caldecott medal 1992), June 29, 1999, 1992; illustrator: Kite Flier, 1986, The Sorcerer's Apprentice, 1989, The Rainbow People, 1989, Tongues of Jade, 1991, Man From the Sky, 1992, Night of the Gargoyles, 1994. Office: care Houghton Mifflin 222 Berkeley St Boston MA 02116*

WIESNER, JOHN JOSEPH, retail chain store executive; b. Kansas City, Mo., Mar. 31, 1918; s. Vincent A. and Jane Ann (Hagerty) W.; m. Georgiana Schild, Oct. 15, 1960; children: Susan, John V., Gretchen. BS in Bus. Adminstrn., Rockhurst Coll., 1960. Vice pres., contr. Fisher Foods, Cleve., 1970-77; asst. corp. contr. Richardson Vicks, N.Y.C., 1960-70; sr. exec. v.p. Pamida, Inc., Omaha, 1977-85, vice chmn., chief exec. officer, 1985-87; CEO C.R. Anthony Co., Oklahoma City, 1987—. Bd. dirs. Omaha Girls' Club, 1983—, Omaha Area Council on Alcohol and Drug Abuse, 1983—; bd. dirs. Fontenelle Forest, Omaha, chmn., 1983, 84, A Chance to Change Fedn.; mem. bd. regents Rockhurst Coll., Okla. City Golf & Country Club, Beacon Club, Oklahoma City, Kansas City, Mo. Named Bus. Assoc. of Yr., Am. Bus. Women's Assn., 1983. Mem. Nat. Assn. Accts. Republican. Roman Catholic.

WIESSLER, DAVID ALBERT, correspondent; b. Cambridge, Mass., July 20, 1942; s. Albert Francis and Vivian Mary (Thomas) W.; m. Mary Judith Burton, Dec. 28, 1968. AB, Princeton U., 1964; MA, U. Tex., 1968. Editor UPI, Dallas, N.Y.C., Washington, 1966-82; assoc. editor U.S. News & World Report, Washington, 1982-84; Washington Bur. chief UPI, Washington, 1984-90, sr. editor, 1990-93; news editor Bloomberg News Svc., 1994-95; editor nat. news Reuters, Washington, 1995—. Recipient Best Feature Writer award Dallas Press Club, 1970. Mem. Washington Gridiron Club. Avocations: reading, travel, cooking.

WIEST, DIANNE, actress; b. Kansas City, Mo., Mar. 28, 1948. Student, U. Md. Appeared in numerous plays including Ashes (off-Broadway), 1976, Leave It to Beaver is Dead, The Art of Dining (Obie award, 1979, Theatre World award 1983), Bonjour La Bonjour, Three Sisters, Serenading Louie (Obie award, 1983), Othello, After the Fall, Heartbreak House, Our Town, and Hunting Cockroaches, 1987, In the Summer House, 1993, Blue Light, 1994; appeared in films including It's My Turn, 1980, I'm Dancing as Fast as I Can, 1982, Independence Day, 1982, Footloose, 1984, Falling in Love, 1984, The Purple Rose of Cairo, 1985, Hannah and Her Sisters, 1986 (Acad. award for Best Supporting Actress 1987), Radio Days, 1987, Lost Boys, 1987, September, 1987, Bright Lights, Big City, 1988, Parenthood, 1989 (Acad. award nominee), Cookie, 1989, Edward Scissorhands, 1990, Little Man Tate, 1991, Cops and Robbersons, 1994, The Scout, 1994, Bullets Over Broadway, 1994 (Golden Globe award Best Supporting Actress-Drama 1995, Acad. award for Best Supporting Actress 1995); TV appearances include The Wall, 1982, The Face of Rage, 1983. Office: care Paul Wolfowitz Internat Creative Mgmt 59 E 54th St Ste 22 New York NY 10022-4001*

WIEST, WILLIAM MARVIN, education educator, psychologist; b. Loveland, Colo., May 8, 1933; s. William Walter and Katherine Elizabeth (Buxman) W.; m. Thelma Lee Bartel, Aug. 18, 1955; children: William Albert, Suzanne Kay, Cynthia May. BA in Psychology summa cum laude, Tabor Coll., 1955; MA, U. Kans., 1957; PhD, U. Calif., 1962. Rsch. asst. psychol. ecology U. Kans., 1955-57; rsch. asst. measurement cooperative behavior in dyads U. Calif., Berkeley, 1958-59; from asst. to assoc. prof. Reed Coll., Portland, Oreg., 1961-74, prof., 1974—; adj. investigator Ctr. Health Rsch., Portland, 1985—; project coord. WHO, Geneva, 1976-84; fgn. travel leader Assiniboine Travel, Winnipeg, Manitoba, Can., 1990-91, Willamette Internat. Travel, Portland, 1993-95; lectr. Fgn. Travel Club, Portland, 1990, 94; vis. scientist Oceanic Inst., Waimanalo, Hawaii, 1967-68; chmn. dept. psychology Reed Coll., Portland, 1973-75, 86; social sci. adv. com. Population Resource Ctr., N.Y.C., 1978—; vis. investigator Health Svcs. Rsch. Ctr., Portland, 1975-76, cons. 1976-80; com. protection human subjects Kaiser Permanente Med. Care Program, Portland, 1978-81; cons. WHO, 1980-81, U.S. Dept. Energy, 1980-83; mem. panel population study sect. HHS. Consulting editor Population and Environment, 1981—; jour. referee Health Psychology, Jour. Social Biology, Jour. Personality and Social Psychology, Memory and Cognition; contbr. articles to profl. jours. Sloan Found. Faculty Rsch. fellow, 1972-73, NSF fellow, 1975-76, USPSH fellow U. Calif., 1957-58, Woodrow Wilson Found. fellow U. Calif., 1960-61. Mem. AAAS, APHA, Am. Hist. Soc. Germans from Russia (conv. speaker 1991), Germans from Russia Heritage Soc., Am. Psychol. Assn., Population Assn. Am., Phi Beta Kappa, Sigma Xi. Home: 5009 SE 46th Ave Portland OR 97206-5048 Office: Reed Coll Psych Dept SE Woodstock Blvd Portland OR 97202

WIGDALE, JAMES B., bank executive. Chmn., chief exec. officer Marshall & Ilsley Bank, Milw., vice chmn. holding co., also bd. dirs. Office: Marshall & Ilsley Corp 770 N Water St Milwaukee WI 53202-3509*

WIGDOR, LAWRENCE ALLEN, chemical company executive; b. N.Y.C., Sept. 7, 1941; s. Irving and Gertrude (Kuhlman) W.; divorced; children: Paul, Evan. BChemE, NYU, 1962; MBA, CUNY, 1964, PhD, 1969. Group v.p. chems. Tenneco, Saddle Brook, N.J., 1976-78, exec. v.p. chems. & plastics, 1978-82; exec. v.p., COO Nuodex, Piscataway, N.J., 1982-85, pres., CEO, 1985-87; pres., CEO Huls Am., Piscataway, 1987-90; CEO Kronos Inc., East Houston, Tex., 1990—; exec. v.p. NL Industries, 1992—; chmn. bd. dirs. MEMC, St. Louis; bd. dirs. Nuodex Mexicana, Guadalajara, Mex., Huls Can., Toronto; chmn. bd. dirs., CEO Rheox, Inc., 1990—. Contbr. articels to profl. jours. 2d lt. U.S. Army. Mem. Chem. Mfrs. Assn. (bd. dirs. 1989-91). Republican. Avocation: pvt. investments.

WIGGIN, KENDALL FRENCH, state librarian; b. Manchester, N.H., Aug. 21, 1951; s. Ralph M. Jr. and Frances (Miltimore) W.; m. Elaine M. Elliott, June 2, 1973 (div. Jan. 1989); children: Sara, Douglas; m. Laura A. Larson, May 26, 1990; children: Lindsey, Tess. BA, U. N.H., 1974; MS in LS, Simmons Coll., 1975. Libr. Litchfield (N.H.) Pub. Libr., 1975; dir. Merrimack (N.H.) Pub. Libr., 1975-83; coord. tech. svcs. Manchester City Libr., 1983-90; state libr. N.H. State Libr., Concord, 1990—. Mem. ALA, New Eng. Libr. Assn., N.H. Libr. Assn., Chief Officers State Libr. Agys., Chief Officers State Libr. Agys. in N.E. N.H. Writers and Publishers Project. Republican. Presbyterian. Avocations: philately, gardening. Office: Cultural Affairs Dept 20 Park St Concord NH 03301-6314

WIGGINS, CHARLES, secondary education educator; b. Boston, July 8, 1938; s. John and Jeanne Lee (Sargeant) W.; children: Sam, Christy. AB, Colby Coll., 1962; AM, Columbia U., 1967. Cert. tchr., Conn. Tchr. social studies Wilton (Conn.) High Sch., 1967-70, Brien McMahon High Sch., Norwalk, Conn., 1970—. Contbr. articles to profl. jours. Co-chair, cofounder Edn. 2000; mem. Sec. of State's Citizenship Task Force, 1992-93. Cpl. U.S. Army, 1963-65. NDEA grantee, U. Bridgeport, 1968, Fulbright scholar U. Ghana, 1969; named Outstanding Educator, Cornell U., 1992. Mem. Am. Fedn. Tchrs. (steward 1986-93), Conn. Coun. Social Studies (bd. dirs. 1986-89, editor Yankee Forum 1985-91). Democrat. Avocations: carpentry, travel. Office: Brien McMahon High Sch Highland St Norwalk CT 06854

WIGGINS, CHARLES EDWARD, federal judge; b. El Monte, Calif., Dec. 3, 1927; s. Louis J. and Margaret E. (Fanning) W.; m. Yvonne L. Boots, Dec. 30, 1946 (dec. Sept. 1971); children: Steven L., Scott D.; m. Betty J. Koontz, July 12, 1972. B.S., U. So. Calif., 1953, LL.B., 1956; LL.B. (hon.) Ohio Wesleyan, 1975, Han Yang U., Seoul, Korea, 1976. Bar: Calif. 1957, D.C. 1978. Lawyer, Wood & Wiggins, El Monte, Calif., 1956-66, Musick, Peeler & Garrett, Los Angeles, 1979-81, Pierson, Ball & Dowd, Washington, 1982-84, Pillsbury, Madison & Sutro, San Francisco, 1984; mem. 90-95th congresses from 25th and 39th Calif. Dist.; judge U.S. Ct. Appeals 9th Circuit, 1984—. Mayor City of El Monte, Calif., 1964-66; mem. Planning Commn. City of El Monte, 1956-60; mem. Commn. on Bicentennial of U.S. Constitution, 1985—, mem. standing com. on rules of practice and procedure, 1987—. Served to 1st lt. U.S. Army, 1945-48, 50-52, Korea. Mem. ABA, State Bar Calif., D.C. Bar Assn. Republican. Lodge: Lions. Office: US Ct Appeals 9th Cir 50 W Liberty St Ste 950 Reno NV 89501-1949

WIGGINS, CHARLES HENRY, JR., lawyer; b. Balt., July 15, 1939; s. Charles Henry and Kathryn Wilson (Walker) W.; m. Wendy Jane Horn, June 20, 1964; children: Charles Hunter, Rebecca Rae, Melinda Marie. BSEE, U. Ill., Urbana, 1962; JD with honors, U. Ill., 1965. Bar: Ill. 1965, U.S. Dist. (no. dist.) Ill. 1970, U.S. Tax Ct. 1974, U.S. Ct. Appeals (7th cir.) 1983. Assoc. Vedder, Price, Kaufman & Kammholz, Chgo., 1969-73, ptnr., 1974—. Mem. zoning bd. appeals Village of Indian Head Pk., Ill., 1984-91. Capt. U.S. Army, 1965-68. Mem. Chgo. Bar Assn., University Club (Chgo.), Edgewood Valley Country Club (LaGrange, Ill., bd. dirs. 1991—), SAR. Avocations: golf, tennis, bridge. Office: Vedder Price Kaufman & Kammholz 222 N La Salle St Fl 26 Chicago IL 60601-1003

WIGGINS, HARRY, state senator, lawyer; b. Kansas City, Mo., Aug. 1, 1934; s. John M. and Helen F. (Murphy) W. BA, Rockhurst Coll.; JD, St. Louis U. Bar: Mo. 1957, U.S. Dist. Ct. (we. dist.) Mo. 1959, U.S. Ct. Appeals (8th cir.) 1962, U.S. Supreme Ct. 1963. Asst. U.S. atty. U.S. Dist. Ct. (we. dist.) Mo., Kansas City, 1961-67; supr. liquor control State Mo. Jefferson City, 1967-70, gen. counsel dept. pub. svcs., 1973-74; western judge Jackson County Ct., Kansas City, 1971-73; state senator Mo. 10th Dist., Kansas City, 1974—. Mem. Alpha Delta Gamma (past nat. pres.), Alpha Sigma Nu. Democrat. Roman Catholic. Home: 7817 Terrace St Kansas City MO 64114-1672 Office: Mo Senate The Capitol Rm 423 Jefferson City MO 65101

WIGGINS, JAMES BRYAN, religion educator; b. Mexia, Tex., Aug. 24, 1935; m. Kay Wiggins, Aug. 15, 1956; children: Bryan, Karis. BA, Tex. Wesleyan U., 1957; BD, So. Meth. U., 1959; PhD, Drew U., 1963; postgrad., Tübingen U., Fed. Republic Germany, 1968-69. Ordained to ministry Meth. Ch., 1959. Instr. humanities Union Jr. Coll., Cranford, N.J., 1960-63; asst. prof. religion Syracuse (N.Y.) U., 1963-69, assoc. prof., 1969-75, prof., 1975—, dir. grad. studies, 1975-80, chair dept., 1980—; exec. dir. Am. Acad. Religion, 1983-91, dir., 1973-75, 83-91; cons. in field; People to People del. leader to former Soviet Union, 1992. Author: The Embattled Saint, 1966, Foundations of Christianity, 1970; editor: Religion as Story, 1975, Christianity: A Cultural Perspective, 1987; contbr. articles to profl. jours. Trustee Scholars Press, Atlanta, 1983-91, chmn., 1986-91. Rockefeller Found. fellow, 1962-63; Lilly Endowment rsch. grantee, 1992-93. Fellow Soc. for Arts (bd. dirs. 1976—), Religion and Culture; mem. AAUP, Am. Acad. Religion, Am. Soc. Ch. History. Democrat. Avocations: golf, tennis, music, reading, travel. Office: Syracuse U Dept Religion 501 Hall of Langs Syracuse NY 13244

WIGGINS, JAMES RUSSELL, newspaper editor; b. Luverne, Minn., Dec. 4, 1903; s. James and Edith (Binford) W.; m. Mabel E. Preston, Feb. 8, 1923 (widowed Oct. 1990); children: William James (dec.), Geraldine Wiggins Thomssen (dec.), Patricia Wiggins Schroth, John Russell. Grad. high sch., Luverne; LLD (hon.), Colby Coll., 1954, U. Maine, Bates Coll., 1968; DLitt (hon.), Anna Maria Coll., 1976, Clark U., 1977; LHD (hon.), Husson Coll., Bangor, Maine, 1979, U. New Eng., 1983; DSci (hon.), Maine Maritime Acad., 1987; LittD (hon.), Bowdoin Coll., 1988. Reporter Rock County Star, Luverne, 1922-25; editor, pub. Luverne Star, 1925-30; editorial writer Dispatch-Pioneer Press, St. Paul, 1930-33, Washington corr., 1933-38, mng. editor, 1938-45, editor, 1945-46; asst. to pub. N.Y. Times, 1946-47; mng. editor Washington Post, 1947-53, v.p. mng. editor, 1953-55; v.p., exec. editor Washington Post and Times Herald, 1955-60, editor, exec. v.p., 1960-68; U.S. amb. to UN, 1968-69; editor, pub. Ellsworth (Maine) Am., 1969-91, editor, 1969—. Author: Freedom or Secrecy, 1956. Served to maj. USAAF, 1943-45; air combat intelligence officer 1943-44, MTO. Mem. Am. Soc. Newspaper Editors (past pres.), Am. Antiquarian Soc. (pres. 1969-77), Sigma Delta Chi. Clubs: Nat. Press, Cosmos, Gridiron (past pres.) (Washington). Lodge: Masons. Home: Carlton Cove HCR 64 Box 506 Brooklin ME 04616-9709 Office: Ellsworth Am 63 Main St Ellsworth ME 04605-1902

WIGGINS, JEROME MEYER, apparel textile industry financial executive; b. Portsmouth, Ohio, July 28, 1940; s. Jerome M. and Mary Vallee (Harold) W.; m. Mary Lou Wetta, Aug. 3, 1963; children: Laura, Kelly, Kristin, Patrick. BA, U. Notre Dame, 1962; postgrad., Ohio State U., 1964-66. CPA, Ohio. Acct. Ernst & Young, Columbus, Ohio, 1965-72; v.p. fin. Greater Ohio Corp., Columbus, 1972-75; gen. auditor VF Corp., Reading, Pa., 1975-80, contr., 1980-81, v.p. fin., 1981-89; chief fin. officer Dyersburg (Tenn.) Corp., 1989—. Mem. Am. Inst. CPA's. Republican. Roman Catholic. Avocations: golf, sailing, bridge. Office: Dyersburg Corp Phillips St Dyersburg TN 38024

WIGGINS, KIP ACKER, lawyer; b. Springfield, Mo., Mar. 17, 1950; s. Edward R. and Frances E. (Acker) W.; m. Mary E. Peacock, Oct. 29, 1977; children: Molly E., Matthew E.. BSBA, U. Mo., Columbia, 1972; JD, U. Mo., Kansas City, 1975. Bar: Mo. 1975. Ptnr. Hoskins, King, McGannon & Hahn, Kansas City, 1975-84, Shook, Hardy & Bacon, Kansas City, 1985-92, Morrison & Hecker, Kansas City, 1992—. Mem. ABA, Lawyers Assn. Kansas City, Kansas City Met. Bar Assn. Republican. Home: 12333 High Dr Shawnee Mission KS 66209-1301 Office: Morrison & Hecker 2600 Grand Blvd Kansas City MO 64108-4600

WIGGINS, NORMAN ADRIAN, university administrator, legal educator; b. Burlington, N.C., Feb. 6, 1924; s. Walter James and Margaret Ann (Chason) W.; m. Mildred Alice Harmon. AA, Campbell Coll., 1948; BA, Wake Forest Coll., 1950, LLB, 1952; LLM, Columbia U., 1956, JSD, 1964; Exec. Program, U. N.C., 1968-69; LLD, Gardner-Webb Coll., 1972. Deacon Wake Forest Baptist Ch., Winston-Salem, N.C., 1963-66, Buies Creek (N.C.) Bapt. Ch., 1973—; deacon, tchr. Sunday sch., 1952—, lay preacher, 1953—; pres. N.C. Found. of Ch.-Related Coll., 1969-70, Campbell U., Buies Creek, 1967—; prof. law Campbell U., 1976—. Author: Wills and Administration of Estates in North Carolina, mem., (with Gilbert T. Stephenson) Estates and Trusts, 1973; Editor: N.C. Will Manual, 1958—, Trust Functions and Services, 1978; Contbr. articles to legal jours. Chmn. Gov.'s Task Force Com. on Adjudication of the Com. on Law and Order, 1969-71; mem. Com. on Drafting Interstate Succession Act for N.C. 1957-59; mem. Com. for Revision of the Laws Relating to the Adminstrn. of Descs.' Estates, 1959-67, chmn., 1964-67; trustee Sunday Sch. Bd., So. Bapt. Conv., 1975—, chmn. bd. trustees, 1978—, nominations com., 1988—; pres. Bapt. State Conv. N.C., 1983-85; bd. dirs. N.C. Citizens for Bus. and Industry, 1982—. Recipient Outstanding Civilian Svc. award Dept. Army, 1985; Campbell Law Sch. renamed in his honor the Norman Adrian Wiggins Sch. of Law, 1989; recognized for outstanding svc. to high edn. and legal edn. Newcomen Soc. U.S., 1993. Mem. ABA, Nat. Assn. Coll. and Univ. Attys. (pres. 1972-73, Disting. Svc. award 1991), Am. Assn. Presidents Ind. Colls. and Univs. (pres. 1981-83), N.C. Assn. Colls. and Univs. (pres. 1970-72, exec. com. 1980-81), N.C. Bar Assn., Harnett County Bar Assn., Nat. Fellowship Baptist Men (pres. 1987-90), Jay Waugh Evang. Assn. (dir./pres. 1970-72), Dunn Area C. of C., Wake Forest Alumni Assn., Rotary (hon. mem. Dunn club), Phi Alpha Delta, Phi Kappa Phi, Omicron Delta Kappa. Office: Campbell U PO Box 127 Buies Creek NC 27506-0127

WIGGINS, ROSALIND ZELDINA, lawyer; b. Newark, Aug. 23, 1959. BA, Yale U., 1981; JD, Stanford U., 1984. Bar: Conn. 1984, U.S. Dist. Ct. 1985, U.S. Claim Ct. 1988. Assoc. Day, Berry & Howard, Hartford, Conn., 1984-89; counsel Pitney Bowes, Stamford, Conn., 1989-90; sr. counsel Pitney Bowes, Stamford 1991—. Contbr. articles to Conn. Bar Jour. Commr. Conn. Commn. on Human Rights and Opprtunities, Hartford, 1990. Mem. Nat. Black MBA Assn. Office: Pitney Bowes Inc World Hdqrs Location 5001 1 Elmcraft Rd Stamford CT 06926-0700

WIGGINS, SAMUEL PAUL, educator; b. Salisbury, N.C., Sept. 20, 1919; s. James Andrew and Mollie (Wilhelm) W.; m. Linda Jean Bessent, June 29, 1947; children: Stanley, David, Timothy, Mark. B.S., Ga. Tchrs. Coll., 1940; M.Ed., Duke U., 1942; Ph.D., Peabody Coll., 1952. Teaching prin. Alma, Ga., 1939-40; dir. lab. sch. Ga. Southwestern Coll., 1940-42; dir. student teaching Emory U., 1947-53; prof., adminstr. Peabody Coll., 1953-67; dean Coll. Edn., Cleve. State U., 1967-75, prof., 1975-85; prof. Norfolk State U., 1985—; chief advisor ICA (AID), Korea Tchr. Edn. Project, 1961-62; Fulbright lectr., Colombia, S.Am., 1966, Lisbon, Portugal, 1978; pres. Am. Assn. Colls. Tchr. Edn., 1974-75; mem. forum of leaders Nat. Edn. Orgns. USOE, 1975-77. Author: Successful High School Teaching, 1958, Student Teacher in Action, 1957, Southern High Schools and Jobless Youth, 1961, The Desegregation Era in Higher Education, 1966, Higher Education in the South, 1966, Battlefields in Teacher Education, 1964, Educating Personnel for Urban Schools, 1972, Improving Education for the Youth of Portugal, 1980, Revolution in Teacher Education: A Review of Reform Reports 1985; co-author: Equity and Excellence for Minorities in T.Ed. (A.T.E.), 1988. Served with USNR, 1942-47, comdr. Res. ret. Home: 609 Abbey Dr Virginia Beach VA 23455-6504

WIGGINS, TIMOTHY J., metal products executive; b. 1956. BA in Acctg., Mich. State U., 1979. CPA, 1981. Sr. mgr. Deloitte Haskins & Sells, Detroit, 1979-88; chief exec. officer Autodie Corp., Grand Rapids, Mich., 1988-93; cons. Glass & Assocs., Canton, Ohio, 1993; with Fruehauf Trailer Corp., Southfield, Mich., 1993—, exec. v.p. fin./adminstrn., chief fin. officer. Office: Fruehauf Trailer Corp 26999 Central Park Blvd Southfield MI 48076*

WIGGINTON, EUGENE H., publishing executive; b. Louisville, Mar. 4, 1935; m. Shirley Walter; children: Denise Wigginton Hamilton, Tressa Wigginton Treadway. BA, Cin. Christian Coll.; LLD (hon.), Milligan Coll. Sr. min. South Jefferson Christian Ch., Louisville, 1957-60; dir. pub. rels. Cin. Christian Coll., 1960-63; sr. min. Westside Christian Ch., Atlanta, 1963-71; exec. v.p. Milligan Coll. (Tenn.), 1971-82; v.p., pub. Standard Pub., Cin., 1982—; bd. dirs. Evang. Christian Pubs. Assn. Trustee Milligan Coll., 1983—. Recipient Citizenship award DAR and Am. Legion, I Dare You award Danforth Found., Fide et Amore award Milligan Coll. Home: 9383 Flemington Rd Cincinnati OH 45231-4051 Office: Standard Pub Co 8121 Hamilton Ave Cincinnati OH 45231-2323

WIGGS, DAVID HAROLD, JR., utilities company executive; b. El Paso, Tex., May 1, 1947; s. David Harold and Mary Louise W.; m. Suzanne Dobbs; children: David, Tracy, Logan. BBA, Tex. Tech U., 1969; JD, U. Tex., 1971. Assoc. Kemp, Smith Duncan and Hammond, El Paso, 1972-74, ptnr., 1974-87; ptnr., chief ops. officer El Paso Electric Co., 1988-89, chmn., pres., chief exec. officer, 1989—. Bd. dirs., pres. Sun Bowl, El Paso, 1987-88; bd. dirs. YMCA, El Paso, 1989—, U. Tex. at El Paso/El Dorado, 1989—. Named El Paso Outstanding Young Man El Paso Jaycees, 1982, One of Five Outstand ing Young Texans, 1982. Mem. Tex. State Bar, Tex. Utilities Lawyers, Tex. Rsch. League. Republican. Presbyterian. Avocations: golfing, skiing. Office: El Paso Electric Co 303 N Oregon St El Paso TX 79901-1329

WIGGS, EUGENE OVERBEY, ophthalmologist, educator; b. Louisville, Apr. 27, 1928; s. Eugene Overbey and Marie Helen (Martin) W.; children: Susan, Christopher, Karen, Mark. AB, Johns Hopkins U., 1950; MD, Duke U., 1955. Intern Denver Gen. Hosp., 1955-56; resident in ophthalmology Wilmer Inst. Johns Hopkins Hosp., 1956-59; ophthalmic plastic fellow Byron Smith, MD, N.Y.C., 1969; pvt. practice specializing in oculoplastic surgery Denver, 1961—; clin. prof. U. Colo. Med. Ctr.; lectr. ophthalmic plastic surgery various med. ctrs. Contbr. articles to med. jours. With USNR, 1959-61. Mem. AMA, Denver Med. Soc., Colo. Med. Soc., Am. Soc. Ophthalmic Plastic and Reconstructive Surgery, Am. Acad. Ophthalmology (svc. award 1982), Colo. Ophthalmology Soc. Republican. Roman Catholic. Office: 2005 Franklin St Denver CO 80205-5401

WIGHERS, ARTHUR, real estate developer; b. 1945. BA, U. Wis., 1967, MBA, 1969. CPA Wis. With Towne Reality, Inc., Milw., 1969—, pres. Office: Towne Reality Inc 710 N Plankinton Ave Milwaukee WI 53203*

WIGHT, JAMES K., civil engineer, research scientist, educator; b. Lansing, Mich., Feb. 27, 1947; s. Claude O. and Zella T. (Mills) W.; m. Linda K. Magley, June 10, 1969; children: Danielle, Evan, Blair. BSCE, Mich. State U., 1969, MSCE, 1970. Asst. prof. U. Mich., Ann Arbor, 1973-78, assoc. prof., 1978-86, prof., 1986—, dir. Structural Engring. Lab., 1987—. Editor: Earthquake Effects on Reinforced Concrete Structures, 1985—. Chair West Side United Meth. Ch., 1992-93. Am. Concrete Inst. fellow, 1984; recipient Delmar Bloem award Am. Concrete Inst., 1991. Mem. Kiwanis. Avocations: soccer coach, golf. Home: 616 Wembley Ct Ann Arbor MI 48103 Office: U Mich Dept Civil and Environ Engring 2340 G G Brown Bldg Ann Arbor MI 48109-2125

WIGHT, NANCY ELIZABETH, neonatologist; b. N.Y.C., Aug. 27, 1947; d. John Joseph and Gisela (Landers) Probst; m. Robert C.S. Wight, Oct. 1, 1988; 1 child, Robert C.S. II. Student, Cornell U., 1965-67; AB in Psychology, U. Calif., Berkeley, 1968; postgrad., George Washington U., 1971-72; MD, U. N.C., 1976. Diplomate Am. Bd. Pediatrics. Resident in pediatrics U. N.C., Chapel Hill, 1976-79; fellow in neonatal/perinatal medicine U. Calif., San Diego, 1979-81; clin. instr. Dept. of Pediatrics La. State U. Sch. of Medicine, Baton Rouge, 1982-86; neonatologist The Baton Rouge Neonatology Group, 1981-86; co-dir. neonatology, med. dir. respiratory therapy Woman's Hosp., Baton Rouge, 1981-85; med. dir. newborn svcs., neonatal respiratory therapy HCA West Side Hosp. Centennial Med. Ctr., Nashville, 1986-88; staff pediatrician, neonatologist Balboa Naval Hosp., San Diego, 1988-89; attending neonatologist Sharp Meml. Hosp., San Diego, 1990—, Children's Hosp.-San Diego, 1990—; asst. clin. prof. U. Calif. San Diego, 1991—; physician assoc. La Leche League. Contbr. articles to profl. jours. mem. exec. bd. Capital Area Plantation chpt. March of Dimes, Baton Rouge, 1981-86, chmn. health adv. com., 1982-86; mem. health com. Capital Area United Way, Baton Rouge, 1982-86; bd. mem. Baton Rouge Coun. for Child Protection, 1983-86, NICU Parents, Baton Rouge, 1981-86; mem. health adv. com. Nashville Area March of Dime, 1987-88. Recipient Am. Med. Women's Assn. award. Mem. AMA, Am. Acad. Pediatrics, Calif. Med. Assn., So. Med. Assn., San Diego County Med. Assn., Calif. Perinatal Assn., So. Perinatal Assn., Nat. Perinatal Assn., La. Perinatal Assn. (past 1st v.p. and pres.), Internat. Lactation Cons. Assn. (cert.), Hastings Soc. Home: 3226 Newell St San Diego CA 92106 Office: Children's Assoc Med Group 8001 Frost St San Diego CA 92123

WIGHTMAN, ALEC, lawyer; b. Cleve., Jan. 23, 1951; s. John and Betty Jane (Follis) W.; m. Kathleen A. Little, June 19, 1976; children: Nora, Emily. BA, Duke U., 1972; JD, Ohio State U., 1975. Bar: Ohio 1975, U.S. Tax Ct. 1982, U.S. Ct. Appeals (6th cir.) 1983. Assoc. Krupman, Fromson & Henson, Columbus, Ohio, 1975-77; ptnr. Krupman, Fromson, Bownas & Wightman, Columbus, 1978-82; assoc. Baker & Hostetler, Columbus, 1982-83, ptnr., 1984—. Mem. ABA, Ohio Bar Assn., Columbus Bar Assn. (com. bankruptcy law), Ohio Oil and Gas Assn. Avocation: tennis. Office: Baker & Hostetler 65 E State St Ste 2100 Columbus OH 43215

WIGHTMAN, ARTHUR STRONG, physicist, educator; b. Rochester, N.Y., Mar. 30, 1922; s. Eugene Pinckney and Edith Victoria (Stephenson) W.; m. Anna-Greta Larsson, Apr. 28, 1945 (dec. Feb. 11, 1976); 1 dau., Robin Letitia; m. Ludmilla Popova, Jan. 14, 1977. B.A., Yale, 1942; Ph.D., Princeton, 1949; D.Sc., Swiss Fed. Inst. Tech., Zurich, 1968, Göttingen U., 1987. Instr. physics Yale, 1943-44; from instr. to asso. prof. physics Princeton, 1949-60, prof. math. physics, 1960-92; prof. emeritus, 1992—; Thomas D. Jones prof. math. physics Princeton, 1971—; vis. prof. Sorbonne, 1957, École Polytechnique, 1977-78. Served to lt. (j.g.) USNR, 1944-46. NRC postdoctoral fellow Inst. Teoretisk Fysik, Copenhagen, Denmark, 1951-52; NSF sr. postdoctoral fellow, 1956-57; recipient Dannie Heineman prize math. physics, 1969. Fellow Am. Acad. Arts and Scis., Royal Acad. Arts; mem. Nat. Acad. Scis., Am. Math. Soc., Am. Phys. Soc., AAAS. Office: Princeton U 350 Jadwin Hall Princeton NJ 08544

WIGHTMAN, THOMAS VALENTINE, rancher, researcher; b. Sacramento, Oct. 7, 1921; s. Thomas Valentine and Pearl Mae (Cutbirth) W.; m. Lan Do Wightman. Student, U. Calif., Berkeley, 1945-46; B of Animal Husbandry, U. Calif., Davis, 1949; student, Cal. Poly. Inst., 1949-50. Jr. aircraft mechanic SAD (War Dept.), Sacramento, Calif.; rancher Wightman Ranch, Elk Grove, Calif., 1950-59; machinest Craig Ship-Bldg. Co., Long Beach, Calif., 1959-70; rancher Wightman Ranch, Austin, Nev., 1970-88; dir. Wightman Found., Sacramento, 1988—. Dir. med. rsch. Staff sgt. U.S. Army, 1942-45. Recipient scholarship U.S. Fed. Govt., 1945-50. Fellow NRA, VFW, U. Calif. Alumni Assn., U. Calif. Davis Alumni Assn., Bowles Hall Assn.; mem. Confederate Air Force. Republican. Avocations: antique automobiles and aircraft. Home and Office: Wightman Found PO Box 278016 Sacramento CA 95827-8016

WIGINGTON, RONALD LEE, retired chemical information services executive; b. Topeka, May 11, 1932; s. Oscar and Virginia C. (Ritchie) W.; m. Margaret E. Willey, Aug. 17, 1951; children: Linda, Carol, David, Brian. BS in Engring. Physics, U. Kans., 1953; MEE, U. Md., 1959; PhD in Elec. Engring., U. Kans., 1964; postgrad. in advanced mgmt. program, Harvard Bus. Sch., 1976-77. Tech. staff mem. Bell Telephone Labs., Murray Hill, N.J., 1953-54; div. chief Dept. Def., Washington, 1956-68; dir. rsch. and devel. Chem. Abstracts Svc., Am. Chem. Soc., Columbus, Ohio, 1968-84; dir. Washington ops. Am. Chem. Soc., 1984-86; chief exec. officer, dir. Chem. Abstracts Svc., Am. Chem. Soc., Columbus, 1986-91; dir. info. tech. Am. Chem. Soc., Columbus, 1991-94; chmn. bd. Online Computer Libr. Ctr., Dublin, Ohio, 1985-87, trustee, 1978-92. Contbr. articles to profl. jours. Pres., various positions PTA Prince George's County, Md., 1966-68; moderator, treas. Community Assn. Upper Arlington (Ohio), 1970-74; mem. Upper Arlington Civic Orch., 1970-84, pres., 1973, 76; bd. dirs. Nat. Fedn. Abstracting and Info. Svcs., 1979-84, pres. 1982-83; bd. dirs. Ohio Ctr. of Sci. and Industry, 1988-93; trustee Health Coalition of Cen. Ohio, Columbus, 1991—, treas., 1994—. Served with U.S. Army, 1954-56. Summerfield scholar U. Kans., 1949; recipient Nat. Capital award D.C. Council Engring. and Archtl. Socs., 1967, Meritorious Civilian Service award Dept. Defense, 1967. Mem. IEEE (sr.), Am. Chem. Soc., Internat. Coun. Sci. and Tech. Info. (exec. bd. 1986-94, treas. 1992-94), Material Property Data Network (bd. dirs. 1987-94), Sigma Xi. Avocations: gardening, music. Home: 2470 Wimbledon Rd Columbus OH 43220

WIGLER, MICHAEL H., molecular biologist; b. N.Y.C., Sept. 3, 1947. BA, Princeton U., 1970; MMS, Rutgers U., 1972; PhD in Microbiology, Columbia U., 1978. Head Mammalian Cell Genetics Sect. Cold Spring Harbor Lab., 1978—; adj. prof. Columbia Univ. Dept. of Genetics, N.Y.C., 1988—. Recipient Pfizer Biomed. Rsch. award, 1986, G.H.A. Clowes Meml. award for cancer rsch. Am. Assn. for Cancer Rsch., 1991; Am. Bus. Cancer Found. grantee. Mem. NAS. Office: Cold Spring Harbor Lab PO Box 100 Cold Spring Harbor NY 11724*

WIGMORE, BARRIE ATHERTON, investment banker; b. Moose Jaw, Sask., Can., Apr. 11, 1941; came to U.S., 1970; s. Fred Henry and Pauline Elizabeth (Atherton) W.; m. Deedee Dawson, Aug. 24, 1964. B. Edn., U. Sask., Can., 1962, B.A., 1963; M.A., U. Oreg., 1964; D.A., Oxford U., Eng., 1966, M.A., 1971. Investment banker A.E. Ames & Co. Ltd., Toronto, Ont., Can., 1966-70; investment banker Goldman, Sachs & Co., N.Y.C., 1970—.; bd. dirs. Potash Corp. Sask. Author: The Crash and Its Aftermath, A History of U.S. Securities Markets 1929-33, 1985. Trustee Progressive Policy Inst., Dem. Leadership Coun., Am. Friends of Worcester Coll. (U. Oxford) Inc. Democrat. Avocations: politics, financial history. Home: 1 W 72rd St New York NY 10023 Office: Goldman Sachs & Co 85 Broad St New York NY 10004-2434

WIGMORE, JOHN GRANT, lawyer; b. L.A., Mar. 14, 1928; s. George Theodore and Mary (Grant) W.; m. Dina Burnaby, July 27, 1968 (dec. 1994); children: Alexander Trueblook, Adam Trueblood, John B. Jr., Mary. BS in Geology, Stanford U., 1949; JD, UCLA, 1958. Geologist Western Geophys., Calif., Colo., Mo., 1953-55; assoc. Lawler, Felix & Hall, L.A., 1958-62, ptnr., 1963-86; ptnr. Pillsbury, Madison & Sutro, L.A., 1986—; lectr. in field. Contbr. articles to profl. jours. Trustee, gov. L.A. County Mus. Natural History, 1970—; participant various local & state election campaigns, 1965-75. Officer USN, 1950-53. Fellow Am. Coll. Trial Lawyers, Am. Bar Found.; mem. ABA (chair litigation com. antitrust sect. 1970-74), Calif. State Bar (L.A. County bar del. 1965-75), L.A. County Bar Assn. (exec. com. trial sect. 1965-68), L.A. County Bus. Trial Lawyers (exec. com. 1984-87), Barristers (exec. com. 1960-65). Home: 870 Neptune Ave Encinitas CA 92024 Office: Pillsbury Madison & Sutro Citicorp Plz 725 S FIgueroa St Ste 1200 Los Angeles CA 90071

WIGTON, PAUL NORTON, steel company consultant, former executive; b. Linesville, Pa., Aug. 13, 1932; s. Charles and Viola Grace (Dennis) W.; m. Janet Ohl, July 11, 1953; children: Bruce, Douglas. BS in Chemistry, Youngstown State U., 1957a; postgrad. exec. mgmt. program, MIT, 1974; hon. doctorate, Youngstown State U., 1980. Gen. supt. metal services Republic Steel Corp., Warren, Ohio, 1971-73, asst. to dist. mgr., 1973-75, dist. mgr., 1975-78; asst. v.p. ops. Republic Steel Corp., Cleve., 1978-80, v.p. steel ops., 1980-83, v.p., gen. mgr. flat rolled product group, 1983-84; pres. tubular products LTV Steel, 1984-91, ret., 1991; mem. Sr. Cons. Network Co., Inc., Beachwood, Ohio, 1991-92; prin. Paul N. Wigton & Assocs. Consultants, Sarasota, Fla., 1992—. Served to cpl. U.S. Army, 1953-54. Scholar Henry Roemer Found., 1957; scholar Am. Chem. Soc., 1957; named Industrialist of Yr. Mahoning Valley Econ. Devel. Corp., 1981, Mgr. of Yr. Mahoning Valley Econ. Devel. Corp., 1992. Mem. AIME, Am. Iron and Steel Inst., Assn. Iron and Steel Engrs. (nat. pres. 1988). Presbyterian. Clubs: Tournament Players (Prestancia-Sarasota, Fla.). Home: 3826 Torrey Pines Way Sarasota FL 34238-2839 Office: Paul N Wigton & Assocs Consultants 3826 Torrey Pines Way Sarasota FL 34238-2839

WIIG, ELISABETH HEMMERSAM, audiologist, educator; b. Esbjert, Denmark, May 22, 1935; came to U.S., 1957, naturalized, 1967; d. Svend Frederick and Ingeborg (Hemmersam) Nielsen; m. Karl Martin Wiig, June 10, 1958; children—Charlotte E., Erik D. B.A., Statsseminariet Emdrupborg, 1956; M.A., Western Res. U., 1960; Ph.D., Case Western Res. U., 1967; postgrad., U. Mich., 1967-68. Clin. audiologist Cleve. Hearing and Speech Center, 1959-60; instr. dept. phonetics Bergen (Norway) U., 1960-64; asst. prof., dir. aphasia rehab. program U. Mich., 1968-70; asst. prof. Boston U., 1970-73, asso. prof., chmn. dept., 1973-77, prof. dept. communication disorders, 1977-87, prof. emerita, 1987—; v.p. EDUCOM Assocs. Inc., 1992-93. Author: Language Disabilities in Children and Adolescents, 1976, Language Assessment and Intervention for the Learning Disabled, 1980, 84, CELF Screening Tests: Elementary and Secondary Levels, 1980, Clinical Evaluation of Language Fundamentals, revised, 1987, Test of Language Competence, 1985, expanded edit., 1989, Test of Word Knowledge, 1992, Clinical Evaluation of Language Fundamentals Preschool, 1992; editor: Human Communication Disorders: An Introduction, 1982, 86, 90, 94; contbr. articles to profl. jours. Recipient Metcalf Cup and Prize for excellence in teaching Boston U., 1967. Fellow Am. Speech and Hearing Assn. (cert. clin. competence in speech pathology and audiology); mem. Coun. for Learning Disabilities, Coun. for Exceptional Children, Internat. Assn. for Rsch. on Learning Disabilities, Am. Psychol. Soc. Address: 5211 Vicksburg Arlington TX 76017-4941

WIIN-NIELSEN, AKSEL CHRISTOPHER, meteorologist educator; b. Juelsminde, Denmark, Dec. 17, 1924; emigrated to U.S., 1959; s. Aage Nielsen and Marie Christophersen; m. Bente Havsteen Zimsen, Dec. 5, 1953; children: Charlotte, Barbro Marianne, Karen Margrete. BS in Math, U. Copenhagen, Denmark, 1947, MS in Math, 1950; Fil. Lic. in Meteorology, U. Stockholm, Sweden, 1957, PhD in Meteorology, 1960; DSc (h.c.), U. Reading, 1981; DSc (honoris causa), U. Copenhagen, 1986. Staff meteorologist Danish Meteorol. Inst., 1952-55; research meteorologist Internat. Meteorol. Inst. U. Stockholm, 1955-58, asst. prof. Internat. Meteorol. Inst., 1957-58, exec. editor publ. Internat. Meteorol. Inst., Tellus, 1957-58; research meteorologist Air Weather Service, USAF; also staff mem. joint numerical weather prediction unit and lectr. George Washington U., 1959-61; research staff mem. Nat. Center Atmospheric Research, 1961-62, asst. dir., 1962-63; prof., chmn. dept. meteorology and oceanography U. Mich., 1963-71; prof. theoretical meteorology U. Bergen, Norway, 1971-72, U. Mich., 1972-74; dir. European Centre for Medium-Range Weather Forecasts, 1974-79; sec. gen. World Meteorol. Orgn., 1980-83; dir. Danish Meteorol. Inst., 1984-87; prof. U. Copenhagen, 1988-94; pres. Internat. Commn. for Dynamic Meteorology, 1971-79; chmn. working group on numerical experimentation, also mem. joint organizing com. Global Atmospheric Research Program, 1973-79; chmn. working group on earth scis., sci. adv. com. European Space Agy., 1977-79; sci. adv. com. Max Planck Inst. Meteorology, Hamburg, W. Ger.; v.p. Eumetsat Council, 1986-87; v.p. Council for European Ctr. for Medium-Range Weather Forecasts, 1985-86, pres., 1986-87; vis. scientist Nat. Ctr. Atmosphere Res., 1987; vis. prof. U. Mich., 1988; chmn. NATO-Panel on The Sci. of Global Environ. Changes, 1990-92. Recipient Ohridski medal Sofia (Bulgaria) U., 1980; Buys-Ballot medal Acad. Sci., Netherlands, 1981; Wihuri prize, Finland, 1983; Rossby prize Swedish Geophys. Soc., 1985, Friedman Rescue award, 1993. Fellow Am. Meteorol. Soc. (hon.); mem. Am. Geophys. Union, Swedish Geophys. Soc., Norwegian Geophys. Soc., Royal Swedish Acad. Sci., Royal Meteorol. Soc. (hon.), Finnish Acad. Arts and Scis., European Geophys. Soc. (pres. 1988-90), Danish Acad. Tech. Scis. (v.p. 1989-92), Royal Danish Soc. Scis., Tau Beta Pi. Home: Solbakken 6, 3230 Grasted Denmark

WIKANDER, LAWRENCE EINAR, librarian; b. Pitts., Dec. 16, 1915; s. Oscar Ragnar and Mary Edna (Gerdes) W.; m. Ethel Marie Whitlow, Nov. 23, 1940; children: Frederick Whitlow, Matthew Hays. B.A., Williams Coll. 1937; B.S. in Library Sci, Columbia U., 1939; M.A., U. Pa., 1949. Gen. asst. Carnegie Library, Pitts., 1939-40; supr. circulation Mt. Pleasant Br., D.C. Public Library, Washington, 1940-42; asst. librarian Temple U., Phila., 1946-50; librarian Forbes Library, Northampton, Mass., 1950-68; librarian Williams Coll., Williamstown, Mass., 1968-82, librarian emeritus, 1982—; curator Calvin Coolidge Meml. Room Forbes Library, Northampton, Mass., 1982-93. Author: Disposed to Learn, 1972, Completing a Century: History of the Northampton Social and Literary Club, 1962, Calvin Coolidge: A Chronological Summary, 1957; editor: The Hampshire History, 1962, The Northampton Book, 1954, A Guide to the Personal Files of Calvin Coolidge, 1986, (with Robert H. Ferrell) Grace Coolidge: An Autobiography, 1992. Pres. Northampton Community Chest, 1958-60; bd. dirs. Calvin Civil Liberties Union Mass., Hampshire, 1957-68; trustee Calvin Coolidge Meml. Found., 1969—; dir. South Mountain Concert Assn., 1975—; clk. Northampton Hist. Soc., 1955-68; dir. Hampshire Inter-Library Center, 1956-68. Served to capt. AUS, 1942-46. Mem. Am. Library Assn. (mem. council 1962-68), New Eng. Library Assn. (pres. 1967-68), Mass. Library Assn. (pres. 1960-61), Western

Mass. Library Club (pres. 1953-55). Home: 21 Cluett Dr Williamstown MA 01267-2804

WIKENHAUSER, CHARLES JOSEPH, zoological park director; b. Bloomington, Ill., Dec. 3, 1948; s. Clift J. Wikenhauser and Mary K. Krug.; m. Patricia M. Byerly; children: Amy, Sarah, Erica. BS in Zoology, U. Ill., 1971. Zoo keeper Niabi Zoo, Rock Island, Ill., 1973; dir. Glen Oak Zoo, Peoria, Ill., 1973-81, John Ball Zoo, Grand Rapids, Mich., 1981-83, Pitts. Zoo, 1986-89, Milwaukee County Zoo, Milw., 1990—; cons. Whittle Communication, Knoxville, Tenn., 1991—. Fellow Am. Assn. Zool. Pks. and Aquariums; mem. Rotary. Roman Catholic. Avocations: travel, bird watching, swimming. Office: Milwaukee County Zool Gardens 10001 W Bluemound Rd Milwaukee WI 53226*

WIKSTEN, BARRY FRANK, communications executive; b. Seattle, June 23, 1935; s. Frank Alfred and Alice Gertrude (Ensor) W.; m. Madeleine Schmeil, Nov. 23, 1979; children: Karen Anne, Eric Marshal, Kurt Edward. BA, Miami U., Oxford, Ohio, 1960; MA, Fletcher Sch. Law and Diplomacy, 1961. Dir. econ. programs U.S. Council, Internat. C. of C., N.Y.C., 1962-63; with TWA, N.Y.C., 1964-79, dir. fin. relations, 1972, v.p. pub. affairs, 1973, v.p. pub. rels., 1973-76, sr. v.p. pub. affairs, mem. airline policy bd., 1976-79; v.p. corp. adminstrn. Trans World Corp., 1979-82, also sec. corp. policy com., mem. consumer affairs com. and corp. compensation com.; sr. v.p. communications CIGNA Corp., Phila., 1982-84, sr. v.p. pub. affairs, 1984—; bd. dirs. Sta. WHYY, Phila. Served with USMC, 1954-57. Mem. Bus. Roundtable (pub. info. com.), Conf. Bd. (pub. affairs rsch. coun.), Pub. Rels. Seminar, Wisemen, Ind. Hall Assn. (bd. dirs.), Union League Club (N.Y.), The Athenaeum (Phila.). Office: CIGNA Corp 1650 Market St 1 Liberty Pl Philadelphia PA 19192-1550

WILBANKS, JAN JOSEPH, philosopher; b. Lynchburg, Ohio, Dec. 17, 1928; s. James Odell and Bernice Elizabeth (Daugherty) W.; m. Alice Ramona Pacheco, Nov. 14, 1953; children—Elise, Anita, Jennifer. B.S., Cin. Coll. Pharmacy, 1951; P.h.D. in Philosophy, Ohio State U., 1964. Instr. Purdue U., 1961-64; mem. faculty Marietta (Ohio) Coll., 1964-89, prof. philosophy, 1973-89. Author: Hume's Theory of Imagination, 1968, also articles. With AUS, 1951-53. Home: 122 High St Marietta OH 45750-2636

WILBER, CHARLES GRADY, forensic science educator, consultant; b. Waukesha, Wis., June 18, 1916; s. Charles Bernard and Charlotte Agnes (Grady) W.; m. Ruth Mary Bodden, July 12, 1944 (dec. 1950); children: Maureen, Charles Bodden, Michael; m. Clare Marie O'Keefe, June 14, 1952; children: Thomas Grady (dec.), Kathleen, Aileen, John Joseph. BSc, Marquette U., 1938; MA, Johns Hopkins U., 1941, PhD, 1942. Asst. prof. physiology Fordham U., 1945-49; assoc. prof. physiology, dir. biol. labs. St. Louis U., 1949-52; leader Arctic expdns., 1943-44, 48, 50, 51; physiologist Chem. Corps, U.S. Army, 1952-61; assoc. physiology and pharmacology U. Pa., 1953-61, chief comparative physiology, 1956-61; profl. lectr. biol. scis. Loyola Coll., Balt., 1957-61; dir. Loyola Coll. (In-Service Inst. Sci. Schrs.), 1958-61; prof. biol. scis., univ. rsch. coord., dean Grad. Sch. Kent State U., 1961-64; dir. marine laboratories U. Del., 1964-67; chmn., prof. dept. zoology Colo. State U., 1967-73, prof., 1967-87, emeritus prof. and chmn., 1987—; dir. forensic sci. lab., 1965—; dep. coroner Larimer County, Colo., 1968-78; pres. Manrasa Co., 1978—; mem. Ctr. for Human Identification; expert witness fed. and state cts. on poisons, firearms, others; life mem. Marine Biol. Lab., Woods Hole, Mass., 1947—; mem. U.S. Army Panel Environ. Physiology, 1952-61; mem. study group Nat. Acad. Scis.-USAF, 1958-61; Wellcome vis. prof. basic med. scis. Ohio U. Med. Sch., 1983-84; vis. lectr. Am. Inst. Biol. Scis., 1957—. Author: Biological Aspects of Water Pollution, 2d edit, 1971, Japanese edit., 1970, Forensic Biology for the Law Enforcement Officer, 1975, Contemporary Violence, 1975, Ballistic Science for the Law Enforcement Officer, 1977, Medicolegal Investigation of The President John F. Kennedy Murder, 1978, Chemical Trauma from Pesticides, 1979, Forensic Toxicology, 1980, Beryllium, 1980, Agent Orange, 1980; Author: Turbidity, 1983, Selenium, 1983; contbr. articles to profl. jours.; exec. editor: Adaption to the Environment, vol. in series, 1962; editor: Am. Lecture Series in Environ. Studies; mem. editorial bd.: Am. Jour. Forensic Medicine and Pathology; contbr.: Harper Ency. Nat. Capt. USAAF, 1942-46; col. USAF, ret. Disting. scholar in criminal justice Albany State Coll., 1993. Fellow N.Y. Acad. Scis., Am. Acad. Forensic Sci.; mem. Am. Physiol. Soc., Cosmos Club (Washington), Phi Beta Kappa, Sigma Xi, Phi Sigma, Gamma Alpha. Republican. Roman Catholic. Home: 900 Edwards St Fort Collins CO 80524-3824 Office: Colo State U Dept Biology Fort Collins CO 80523 *The accident of history which has enabled me to study as I wished, work at what I enjoyed, and live as I chose is a mystery for which I must be eternally thankful.*

WILBER, LAURA ANN, audiologist; b. Memphis, May 26, 1934; d. Leon Austin and Ivah Edith (Ostrander) W. B.S. in Speech Correction, U. So. Miss., 1955; M.S. in Deaf Edn. (grad. fellow), Gallaudet Coll., 1958; Ph.D. in Audiology (grad. fellow), Northwestern U., 1964. Tchr. hard of hearing and deaf McKinley Elem. Sch., Bakersfield, Calif., 1955-57; speech therapist, coordinator spl. edn. U.S. Army Dependent Sch. System, Heidelberg, Ger., 1958-61; audiology research asst. Northwestern U., Evanston, Ill., 1961-64; asst. research audiologist UCLA, 1964-70; dir. Audiology Clinic, UCLA Hosp., 1968-69; assoc. prof. dept. otorhinolaryngology, dir. hearing and speech services Albert Einstein Coll. Medicine, Bronx, N.Y., 1970-77; asst. prof. dept. rehab. medicine Albert Einstein Coll. Medicine, 1971-77; prof. audiology, dir. hearing clinics dept. communicative disorders Northwestern U., 1978-81, acting chmn. dept., head program audiology, 1981—; lectr., mem. faculty State U., Los Angeles, U. So. Calif., 1964-71; mem. working groups Am. Nat. Standards Inst., 1970—, chmn. com. on bioacoustics, 1984; noise expert N.Y.C. Environ. Control Bd., 1972-78, mem. steering com. on noise subcom., 1971-78; U.S. rep. working groups in techniques for audiometry and threshold of hearing Internat. Standards Orgn., 1973—; chmn. Clinic Sch.-Council N.Y., 1972-73. Author: (with Feldman) Acoustic Impedance and Admittance; contbr. articles to profl. publs., chpts to books. Fellow Am. Speech-Lang.-Hearing Assn. (com. audiologic standards 1971—, subcom. electroacoustic characteristics 1973—, v.p. standards and ethics 1978-80, pres.-elect 1981, pres. 1982); mem. N.Y. State Speech and Hearing Assn. (v.p. hosp. and agys. 1975-76, pres. 1977-78), Calif. Speech and Hearing Assn., Acoustical Soc. Am., N.Y. Audiology Study Group (chmn. 1973-74), Dirs. Hosp. Speech and Hearing Programs Assn., Soc. Ear, Nose and Throat Advances in Children, Acad. Rehab. Audiology (pres. 1987), Am. Auditory Soc. (pres. 1980). Home: 422 Skokie Blvd Wilmette IL 60091-3003 Office: Northwestern U Searle Bldg Audiology and Hearing Impair Prog 2299 N Campus Dr Evanston IL 60208-3550

WILBER, ROBERT EDWIN, corporate executive; b. Boston, Dec. 15, 1932; s. Charles Edwin and Mary Gwen (Gay) W.; m. Bonnie Marilyn Jones; children: Debra, Kathleen, Robert Jr., Thomas, Jeffrey, Mark, Matthew. BSBA in Acctg., Bowling Green State U., 1954. CPA, Mass., Tex. Sr. acct. Peat, Marwick, Mitchell and Co., Boston, 1954-58; gen. mgr. Door Controls Inc., Boston, 1958-59; asst. controller MKM Knitting Mills Inc., Manchester, N.H., 1959-63; internal audit supr. Raytheon Co., Lexington, Mass., 1963; asst. treas. Glens Falls (N.Y.) Ins. Co., 1963-66; controller Pnobscott Co., Boston, 1966-67; v.p. fin. and adminstrn. S.S. Pierce Co., Boston, 1967-73, Samson Ocean Systems Inc., Boston, 1973-79; v.p., chief acctg. officer Enserch Corp., Dallas, 1979-88; pres. Trade U.S.A., 1990—. Mem. Rep. Nat. Com. Mem. AICPAs, Fin. Execs. Inst., Tex. Soc. CPAs, Mass. Soc. CPAs, Pres.'s Club (Bowling Green, Ohio). Home: 5804 Goliad Ave Dallas TX 75206-6818 Office: 5740 Prospect Ave Dallas TX 75204

WILBOURN, EDGAR SHERMAN, III, construction company executive, consultant; b. Blytheville, Ark., Aug. 1, 1945; s. Edgar S. Jr. and Darris V. (Maxwell) W.; m. Sara E. Wilson, Sept. 2, 1967; children: Michael Paul, Dawn Marie. AA, Purdue U., 1972, BS, 1972. Owner Wilbourne Devel., Modesto, Calif., 1972-85, Winnamuca, Nev., Colorado Springs, Colo.; owner F&W Farms and Cal Vada Produce, Winnamuca, 1979-86; ptnr. Magnum Devel., Colorado Springs, 1981-85; project exec. Hardage Enterprises, Wichita, Kans., 1985-86; project mgr. A.S. McGaughan Co., Inc., Bethesda, Md., 1986-87, sr. project mgr., 1987-88, contract mgr., 1989-90, v.p. project administration, 1991—; apptd. mem. by Richard Lugar's adminstrn. Indpls. Model Cities Project Team, 1970; pres. Citizens Action Com., 1989-90; lectr. Risk Mgmt. seminar, 1992; owner Cal Vada Farms, Winnamuca, Nev., 1978-

84; ptnr. Magnum Devel., Inc., Colorado Springs, 1983-85; vice chmn. Prince William Citizens' Devel. Task Force, 1994—, chairperson econ. devel. com., mem. codes and regulations com. 1994—. Pres. Citizen's Action Com., Manassas, Va., 1989. Mem. Am. Contract Bridge, KC (dep. grand knight 1974-77, knight of yr. 1977). Avocation: tournament bridge. Office: AS McGaughan Co Inc 4550 Montgomery Bethesda MD 20814-3304

WILBOURN, GORDON GENE, investment banker; b. Little Rock, Feb. 8, 1933; s. Walter Blann and Maude (Moore) W.; m. Meredith Ann Miller, June 19, 1955; children: Gordon, Melanie. BA, Hendrix Coll., 1954; MS in Edn., U. Cen. Ark., 1957. Coach, instr. Clinton (Ark.) Sch. Dist., 1954-55, Little Rock Sch. Dist., 1955-56; coach, instr. adminstr. Hendrix Coll., Conway, Ark., 1956-70; mgr. investment banking Stephens, Inc., Little Rock, 1971—. Bd. dirs. Florence Crittenton Home for Girls, Little Rock, 1982-88, Bapt. Health Found. Bd., Little Rock, 1987—. With USNR, 1951-55. Mem. Nat. Assn. Security Dealers, Ark. Assn. Security Dealers, Pub. Securities Assn. Methodist. Office: Stephens Inc PO Box 3507 111 Center St Little Rock AR 72201-4402

WILBUR, BRAYTON, JR., distribution company executive; b. San Francisco, Oct. 2, 1935; s. Brayton and Matilda (Baker) W.; m. Judith Flood, June 29, 1963; children: Jennifer, Edward, Claire, Michael. B.A., Yale U., 1957; M.B.A. Stanford U., 1961. With Arthur Young & Co., San Francisco, 1962-63; v.p. Wilbur-Ellis Co., San Francisco, 1963-74, exec. v.p., 1974—, also dir.; dir. Chronicle Pub. Co., San Francisco, 1983-89; pres. Wilbur-Ellis Co., San Francisco, 1989—; bd. dir. Safeway Stores, 1977-86. Pres. San Francisco Symphony, 1980-87; v.p. Sponsors for Performing Arts Ctr., San Francisco, 1975—; trustee Fine Art Mus. of San Francisco, 1978-81, Asia Found., 1972—, chmn. 1990—. Served with USAR, 1958-63. Mem. Council on Fgn. Relations, Bohemian Club, Pacific Union Club, Cypress Point Club, Burlingame Country Club. Republican. Home: 821 Irwin Dr Burlingame CA 94010-6327 Office: Wilbur-Ellis Co 320 California St San Francisco CA 94104-1403

WILBUR, COLBURN SLOAN, foundation administrator, chief executive officer; b. Palo Alto, Calif., Jan. 20, 1935; s. Blake Colburn and Mary (Sloan) W.; m. Maria Grace Verburg, Sept. 1, 1961; children: Marguerite Louise, Anne Noelle. BA in Polit. Sci., Stanford U., 1956, MBA, 1960. Asst. cashier United Calif. Bank, San Francisco, 1960-65; v.p. Standata, San Francisco, 1965-68; adminstrv. mgr. Tab Products, San Francisco, 1968-69; exec. dir. Sierra Club Found., San Francisco, 1969-76, David and Lucile Packard Found., Los Altos, Calif., 1976—; bd. dirs., mem. adv. bd. Coun. Founds., Washington, Found. Ctr., 1977-67. Former bd. dirs., mem. adv bd Global Fund Women, Palo Alto, Calif.; past bd. dirs. Big Bros. San Francisco, Calif. Confederation Arts, Peninsula Grantmakers, Women's Fund Santa Clara; former bd. dirs., pres. Big Bros. Peninsula, North Fork Assn., Peninsula Conservation Ctr.; past bd. dirs., chmn. No. Calif. Grantmakers; bd. dirs., mem. adv. bd. Sierra Club Found., Stanford Theater Found., Palo Alto, U. San Francisco/Inst. Nonprofit Orgn. Mgmt. With U.S. Army, 1957-58. Office: David and Lucile Packard Found 300 2d St Los Altos CA 94022

WILBUR, DAVID E., JR., chemicals executive; b. 1942. With Lever Bros. Co., N.Y.C., 1967-72, Mobil Chem. Co., Macedon, N.Y., 1972-76; v.p. polytech divsn. U.S. Industries, Inc., Mlps., 1976-84; pres. Poly-Tech Inc., Mlps., 1984-90, pres., chief operating officer, 1992—; pres. Wilbur & Assocs., Mlps., 1990-92. Office: Poly-Tech Inc 1401 W 94th St Minneapolis MN 55431*

WILBUR, E. PACKER, investment company executive; b. Bridgeport, Conn., Sept. 9, 1936; s. E. Drumheller and Elizabeth (Wells) W.; m. Laura Mary Ferrier, Sept. 17, 1965; children—Alison Mary, Andrew Packer, Gillian Elizabeth. B.A., Yale U., 1959; M.B.A., Harvard U., 1965. Cons. McKinsey & Co. Inc., N.Y.C., 1964-67; dir. corp. planning Am. Express Co., N.Y.C., 1967-69; v.p. Van Alstyne Noel & Co., N.Y.C., 1969-70; exec. v.p., dir., mem. exec. com. Newburger Loeb & Co. Inc., N.Y.C., 1970-73; pres. E.P. Wilbur & Co., Inc., Southport, Conn., 1973—, Southport Fin. Corp., 1986—; chmn. bd. Criterion Mgmt., Inc., Lafayette, Ind., Trend Mgmt., Inc., Tampa, Fla., Fairfield Advisors, Inc., Southport, EPW Securities, Inc., Southport; gen. ptnr. Grandland Realty Assos., English Oaks Apts., Embankment Properties Ltd., London, Pepper Hill Townhouses, Kemar Townhouse Assos., Autumn Woods Assos., Country Villa Assos., others; former allied mem. N.Y. Stock Exchange. Contbr. articles to fin. jours. Past bd. dirs. Inst. Govt. Assisted Housing, Washington; Mus. Art, Sci., Industry, Bridgeport, Wakeman Meml. Boys' Club, Southport, Greater Bridgeport Jr. Hockey League, Pequot Library, Southport, Bridgeport U., Northfield-Mt. Hermon Sch. Served with AUS, 1959-60. Clubs: Pequot Yacht (Southport), Pequot Running (Southport) (chmn.); Country Club of Fairfield; Yale (N.Y.C.). Home: 648 Harbor Rd Southport CT 06490-1321 Office: 2507 Post Rd Southport CT 06490-1259

WILBUR, HENRY MILES, zoologist; b. Bridgeport, Conn., Jan. 25, 1944; s. Robert Leonard and Martha (Miles) W.; m. Dorothy Spates, Jan. 27, 1967 (div. Dec. 1980); 1 child, Sarah; m. Rebecca Burchell, May 22, 1981; children: Helen, Lindsay. BS, Duke U., 1966; PhD, U. Mich., 1971. Asst. prof. Duke U., Durham, N.C., 1973-77, assoc. prof., 1977-81, prof., 1981-91, chmn., 1990-91; prof. U. Va., Charlottesville, 1991—; dir. Mt. Lake Biol. Sta., Charlottesville, 1991—. Assoc. editor Ecol. Soc. Am., Soc. Study of Evolution, Soc. Am. Naturalists. Recipient Disting. Herpetologist Herpetologists League, 1990. Mem. Am. Soc. Icthologists and Herpetologists, Am. Soc. Naturalists (treas.), Ecol. Soc. Am., Soc. of Study of Evolution, Herpetologists League, British Ecol. Soc. Office: U Va Dept Biology Gilmer Hall Charlottesville VA 22903-2477

WILBUR, JAMES BENJAMIN, III, philosopher, educator; b. Hartford, Conn., Feb. 21, 1924; s. James Benjamin, Jr. and Martha (Shekosky) W.; m. Margie Mattmiller, July 9, 1949; children: James Benjamin IV, Ann Elizabeth. B.A., U. Ky., 1948; postgrad., Harvard, 1948-50; M.A., Columbia, 1951, Ph.D., 1954. Mem. faculty Adelphi U., Garden City, N.Y., 1952-64; chmn. philosophy dept. Adelphi U., 1954-64, asst. prof., 1954-59, assoc. prof., 1959-64; assoc. prof. U. Akron, Ohio, 1964-66; prof. U. Akron, 1966-68, chmn. philosophy dept., 1964-68; prof. philosophy SUNY Coll. Arts and Sci., Geneseo, 1968-90; chmn. philosophy dept. SUNY Coll. Arts and Sci., 1968-78; founder, co-dir. Confs. on Value Inquiry, 1967—; vis. prof. U. Kent, Canterbury, Eng., spring 1971; faculty adviser Empire State Coll., 1972-74. Author: (with H.J. Allen) The Worlds of Hume and Kant, 1967, 2d rev. edit., 1981, The Worlds of Plato and Aristotle, 1962, 2d rev. edit., 1979, The Worlds of the Early Greek Philosophers, 1979, The Moral Foundations of Business Practice, 1992; editor, contbr.; (with B. Magnus) Cartesian Essays (M. Nijhoff), 1969, Spinoza's Metaphysics (Van Gorcum), 1976; co-editor; (with E. Laszlo) Human Values and Natural Science, 1970, Values and the Mind of Man, 1971, Value Theory in Philosophy and Social Science (Gordon and Breach), 1971, Value and the Arts, 1978, The Dynamics of Value Change, 1978; editor: Human Value and Economic Activity, 1979, The Life Sciences and Human Values, 1979, Human Values and the law, 1980, Values in the Law, 1980, Ethics and Management, 1983, Integration of Ethics into Business Education, 1984, Integrating Ethics into Business Education, 1983; contbn. Self-interest Dictionary of Business Ethics, 1995, others. Served with AUS, 1943-45. SUNY grantee, 1969, 70; NEH grantee, 1981; Western Electric Fund awardee, 1983. Mem. AAUP, Am. Metaphys. Soc., L.I. Philos. Soc. (founder 1963), Creighton Club (pres. 1970-72), Rochester Oratorio Soc., Am. Soc. Value Inquiry (sec.-treas. 1971, pres. 1973-74, founder Jour. Value Inquiry 1967, exec. editor 1967-90, assoc. editor 1990—), Vt. Hist. Soc., Manchester Hist. Soc. (pres. 1991-94), Hudson (Ohio) Country Club (founding trustee, hon. life mem.), Ekwanok Country Club (Manchester), Harvard Club (N.Y.C.). Home: PO Box 376 Manchester VT 05254-0376

WILBUR, KARL MILTON, zoologist, educator; b. Binghamton, N.Y., May 7, 1912; married, 1946; 2 children. B.A., Ohio State U., 1935, M.A., 1936; Ph.D., U. Pa. 1940. Asst. zoologist Ohio State U., 1935-36, instr. zoology, 1941-42; instr. U. Pa., 1939-40; Rockefeller fellow NYU, 1940-41; asst. prof. physiology Dalhousie U. Med. Sch., 1942-44; assoc. prof. Duke U., Durham, N.C., 1946-50, prof., from 1950, now James B. Duke emeritus prof. zoology; physiologist AEC, 1952-53; vis. prof. U. de Sao Paulo, 1965, OAS, Guayaquil, Ecuador, 1973; program advisor Ford Found., Caracas, Venezuela, 1967-69; adv. panel com. on biology ORNL, 1950-56; mem. vis.

com. Woods Hole Oceanographic Inst., 1966-67; cons. Ford Found., 1969-70, Nat. Coun. Marine Resources and Engring. Devel., 1969, Fgn. Area Fellowship Program, 1969; mem. sci. rev. com. U. N.C., 1970-80; mem. adv. com. Coun. for Internat. Exch. of Scholars, 1977-80. Recipient dedication of Mechanisms of Biomineralization in Animals and Plants Biomineralization Symposium, 1980, Mechanisms of Calcification in Biol. Systems Symposium, 1983. Mem. Am. Physiol. Soc., Am. Soc. Naturalists, Soc. Gen. Physiology, Am. Soc. Zoologists (chmn. div. comparative physiology and biochemistry 1967-79), Phi Beta Kappa. Office: Duke U Dept Zoology 239 Biol Sci Durham NC 27706*

WILBUR, LESLIE CLIFFORD, mechanical engineering educator; b. Johnston, R.I., May 12, 1924; s. Clifford Elwood and Isabel (Winsor) W.; m. Gertrude Monica Widmer, Sept. 9, 1950; children—Clifford Leslie, Kenneth Charles, Ted Winsor, Christopher Francis. B.S. in Mech. Engring, U. R.I., 1948; M.S., Stevens Inst. Tech., 1949. Registered profl. engr., Mass. Instr., then asst. prof. Duke, 1949-57; mem. faculty Worcester Poly. Inst., 1957—; prof. mech. engring., 1961—, dir. nuclear reactor facility, 1959-86, prof. emeritus, 1987—; Mem. N.E. adv. council Atomic Indsl. Forum, 1972—. Editor-in-chief: Handbook of Energy Systems. Served with AUS, 1943-46, ETO. Mem. Am. Nuclear Soc. (mem. at large exec. com. Northeastern sect. 1961-62, 66-67, chmn. Northeastern sect. 1968-69), ASME (vice chmn. Eastern N.C. sect. 1956-57), Am. Soc. Engring. Edn., AAAS, Sigma Xi, Tau Beta Pi, Phi Kappa Phi, Pi Tau Sigma. Baptist (deacon 1962-65). Home: PO Box 105 Sebasco Estates ME 04565-0105 Home (winter): 94 Parkway N Brewer ME 04412-1235 Office: Worcester Poly Inst Worcester MA 01609

WILBUR, LYMAN DWIGHT, consulting engineering executive; b. L.A., Apr. 27, 1900; s. Curtis Dwight and Olive (Doolittle) W.; m. Henrietta Shattuck, July 6, 1925 (dec.May 1984); 1 child, Olive Gamble Waugh; m. Pauline Jordan, Apr. 26, 1985 (dec. Mar. 1995). AB, Stanford U., 1921; LLD (hon.), Coll. Idaho, 1962; DSc (hon.), U. Idaho, 1967. Field engr. Hetch Hetchy Project, City of San Francisco, 1921-24; designer Merced (Calif.) Irrigation Dist., 1924-26; asst. to chief cons. engr. Mid. Asia Water Economy Svc., Tashkent, USSR, 1929-31; from engr. to dist. mgr. Morrison-Knudsen Co. Inc., L.A., 1932-47; chief engr. Morrison-Knudsen Co. Inc., Boise, 1947-52, v.p., 1950-70; constrn. mgr. Morrison-Knudsen-Ford Twaits Cos., Camp Roberts, Calif., 1939-40, Morrison-Knudsen-Peter Kiewit Cos., Camp White, Oreg., 1942; resident ptnr. Atlas Constructors, Casablanca, 1952-54, RMK-BRJ, Saigon, Republic of Vietnam, 1965-66; exec. v.p. Internat. Engring. Co. Inc., San Francisco, 1956-58, pres.-chmn., 1958-70; pvt. practice cons. engr., Boise, 1971—. Chmn. Blue Cross Idaho, Boise, 1977; pres. Good Samaritan League Inc., Boise, 1982-91; trustee Coll. of Idaho, Caldwell, 1981-92; bd. dirs. St. Alphonsus Med. Ctr. Found., Boise, 1980-88. Recipient Golden Beaver award The Beavers, L.A., 1962, Constrn. Man of Yr. award Engring. News Record, N.Y.C., 1966, John Fritz medal Five Founder Engring. Socs., 1973, Moles award The Moles, N.Y.C., 1974, Ann. award NSPE, 1975. Fellow ASCE (hon., chmn. exec. com. constrn. divsn. 1960, chmn. Pacific N.W. coun. 1973), Idaho Soc. Profl. Engrs. (sec./treas. 1972-74), Soc. Am. Mil. Engrs., Arid Club, Hillcrest Club, Rotary Internat. Republican. Presbyterian. Avocations: philately, photography. Address: 4502 Hillcrest Dr Boise ID 83705-2857

WILBUR, RICHARD PURDY, writer, educator; b. N.Y.C., Mar. 1, 1921; s. Lawrence L. and Helen (Purdy) W.; m. Mary Charlotte Hayes Ward, June 20, 1942; children: Ellen Dickinson, Christopher Hayes, Nathan Lord, Aaron Hammond. AB, Amherst Coll., 1942, AM, 1952, DLitt (hon.), 1967; AM, Harvard U., 1947; LHD (hon.), Lawrence Coll., Washington U., Williams Coll., U. Rochester, SUNY, Potsdam, 1986, Skidmore Coll., 1987, U. Lowell, 1990; DLitt (hon.), Clark U.; DLitt, Am. Internat. Coll., Marquette U., Wesleyan U., Carnegie-Mellon U.; D.Litt. (hon.), Lake Forest Coll., 1982. Jr. fellow Harvard U., Cambridge, Mass., 1947-50, asst. prof. English, 1950-54; assoc. prof. Wellesley Coll., 1955-57; prof. Wesleyan U., 1957-77; writer in residence Smith Coll., 1977-86. Author: The Beautiful Changes, 1947, Ceremony, 1950, A Bestiary, 1955, reprint, 1993, Things of This World, 1956, Poems 1943-56, 1957, Advice to a Prophet, 1961, Poems of Richard Wilbur, 1963, Walking to Sleep, 1969, The Mind-Reader, 1976, Seven Poems, 1981, The Whale, 1982, New and Collected Poems, 1988 (Pulitzer prize for poetry 1989); (children's books) Loudmouse, 1963, Opposites, 1973, More Opposites, 1991, A Game of Catch, 1994, Runaway Opposites, 1995; (criticism) Responses, 1976; co-author: (comic opera, with Lillian Hellman) Candide, 1957, (cantata, with William Schuman) On Freedom's Ground, 1986; translator: (Moliere) The Misanthrope, 1955, Tartuffe, 1963 (co-recipient Bollingen Translation prize 1963), The School for Wives, 1971, The Learned Ladies, 1978, Four Comedies, 1982, (Racine) Andromache, 1982, Phaedra, 1986, Molière's The School for Husbands, 1992, Imaginary Cuckold, 1993, Molière's Amphitryon, 1995; editor: Complete Poems of Poe, 1959, Poems of Shakespeare, 1966, Selected Poems of Witter Bynner, 1978. Decorated chevalier Ordre des Palmes Academiques; recipient Harriet Monroe prize Poetry mag., 1948, Oscar Blumenthal prize, 1950, Prix de Rome, Am. Acad. Arts and Letters, 1954, Edna St. Vincent Millay Meml. award, 1957, Nat. Book award, 1957, Pulitzer prize, 1957, Sarah Josepha Hale award, 1968, Bollingen prize, 1971, Brandeis U. Creative Arts award, 1971, Prix Henri Desfeuilles, 1971, Shelley Meml. award, 1973, Harriet Monroe Poetry award, 1978, St. Botolph's Club Found. award 1983, Drama Desk award, 1983, Aiken-Taylor award, 1988, Bunn award, 1988, Washington Coll. Lit. award, 1988, St. Louis Lit. award, 1989, Grand Master award Birmingham-So. Coll., 1989, Gold Medal for Poetry, Am. Acad. Inst. Arts and Letters, 1991, Edward MacDowell medal, 1992, Nat. Arts Club Medal of Honor for Lit., 1994, PEN/Manheim Medal for Translation, 1994; Guggenheim fellow, 1952-53, 63, Ford fellow, 1960-61, Camargo Found. fellow, 1985; named U.S Poet Laureate, Libr. Congress, 1987, Nat. Medal of the Arts, 1994. Fellow MLA (hon.); mem. AAAL (pres. 1974-76, chancellor 1976-78, 80-81), ASCAP, PEN (Transl. award 1983), Am. Acad. Arts and Scis., Acad. Am. Poets (chancellor), Dramatists Guild, Century Club. Home: 87 Dodwells Rd Cummington MA 01026 also: 715R Windsor Ln Key West FL 33040

WILBUR, RICHARD SLOAN, physician, foundation executive; b. Boston, Apr. 8, 1924; s. Blake Colburn and Mary Caldwell (Sloan) W.; m. Betty Lou Fannin, Jan. 20, 1951; children: Andrew, Peter, Thomas. BA, Stanford U., 1943, MD, 1946; JD, John Marshall Law Sch., 1990. Intern San Francisco County Hosp., 1946-47; resident Stanford Hosp., 1949-51, U. Pa. Hosp., 1951-52; postgrad. tng. U. Mich. Hosp., 1957, Karolinska Sjukhuset, Stockholm, 1960; mem. staff Palo Alto (Calif.) Med. Clinic, 1952-69; dep. exec. v.p. AMA, Chgo., 1969-71, 73-74; asst. sec. for health and environment Dept. Def., 1971-73; sr. v.p. Baxter Labs., Inc., Deerfield, Ill., 1974-76; exec. v.p. Council Med. Splty. Socs., 1976-91, sec. accreditation council for continuing med. edn., 1979-91; asso. prof. medicine Georgetown U. Med. Sch., 1971-77, Stanford Med. Sch., 1952-69; pres. Nat. Resident Matching Plan, 1991-92; mem. bd. Calif. Med. Assn., 1968-69, Calif. Blue Shield, 1966-68, Am. Medico-Legal Found., 1987—; chmn. bd., CEO Inst. for Clin. Info. 1994—; CEO Medic Alert, 1992-94; pres. Am. Bd. Med. Mgmt., 1992; mem. Am. Bd. Electrodiagnostic Medicine, 1993—. Contbr. articles to med. jours. Vice chmn. Republican Cen. Com. Santa Clara County, Calif., 1966-89; bd. govs. ARC; chmn. bd. dirs. Medic Alert Found.; bd. dir. Nat. Adv. Cancer Coun., Nat. Health Coun., 1993—; bd. visitors Drew U. Postgrad. Med. Sch.; chmn. Mid-Am. Blood Svcs. Bd. Served with USNR, 1942-49. Recipient Disting. Svc. medal Dept. Def., 1973, scroll of merit Nat. Med. Assn., 1971. Fellow ACP, Am. Coll. Legal Medicine, Am. Coll. Physician Execs. (bd. regents 1985-89, pres.-elect 1987, pres. 1988-89), Internat. Coll. Dentistry (hon.); mem. Inst. Medicine, Ill. Med. Assn., Lake County Med. Soc., Am. Gastroent. Assn., Pacific Interurban Clin. Club, Am. Soc. Integral Medicine, Santa Clara County Med. Soc. (hon.), Cedars Club (Soda Springs, Calif.), Union League Phila., Phi Beta Kappa, Alpha Omega Alpha. Home: 985 Hawthorne Pl Lake Forest IL 60045-2217 Office: 207 Westminster Rd Lake Forest IL 60045-1885

WILBUR, ROBERT LYNCH, botanist, educator; b. Annapolis, Md., July 4, 1925; s. Ralph Sydney and Elizabeth Ellen (Lynch) W.; m. Jeanne Marie Doucette; children: Martha, Ralph, Ellen, Mark, Margaret, Lenore. BS, Duke U., 1946, MA, 1947; PhD, U. Mich., 1952. Asst. prof. botany U Ga., Athens, 1952-53, N.C. State U., Raleigh, 1953-57; asst. prof. botany Duke U., Durham, N.C., 1957-63, assoc. prof., 1963-70, prof. botany, systematic botanist, 1970—. Roman Catholic. Home: 2613 Stuart Dr Durham NC 27707-2835 Office: Duke U Dept Of Botany Durham NC 27707

WILBURN, L. THOMAS, JR., health facility administrator; b. Pocahontas, Va., Dec. 20, 1928. Grad., Va. Poly. Inst. and State U., 1951. Asst. dir. plant ops. Community Hosp., Indpls., 1964, dir. adminstrv. svcs., 1964-65, assoc. dir., v.p., 1965-71; v.p. Bethesda Hosp. Inc., Cin., 1971-72, v.p., mgr., 1972-76, pres., from 1976, now chmn., pres., chief exec. officer. Office: Bethesda Hosp Inc 619 Oak St Cincinnati OH 45206

WILBURN, MARION TURNER, library and information scientist educator, consultant; b. Hamilton, Ont., Can., Aug. 30, 1946; d. Albert Gordon and Lilian (Heywood) Turner; m. Eugene Richard Wilburn, Nov. 27, 1971; 1 child, Trevor Michael. BA in English, History, McMaster U., 1969, MA in English, 1970; BEd in English and Theatre Arts, Queen's U., 1971; MEd in Adult Edn., Ont. Inst. Studies in Edn., 1977; MLS, U. Toronto, Ont., 1981. Cert. permanent high sch. specialist Eng., Ont.; permanent cert. theatre arts, Ont.; diploma life skills coaches. Asst. head English dept. W. Humber Collegiate Inst., Etobicoke, Ont., 1971-75; project leader asst. program for instrnl. devel. Coun. Ont. Univs., Toronto, 1977-80; dir. office teaching and learning Ont. Univs., Toronto, 1980-81; sr. mktg. rep. Utlas Internat., Toronto, 1981-83; coord. libr. and info. technician program Sheridan Coll., Oakville, Ont., 1983-94, ednl. techs. facilitator, 1994—; v.p. Wilburn Comm. Ltd., Mississauga, Ont. Author: Automation in Libraries, various workbooks; contbr. articles profl. jours.; presented over 150 workshops, courses, seminars in field. Mem. Ont. Assn. Libr. Technician Instrs. (chair), Can. Libr. Assn., Ont. Libr. Assn., Spl. Librs. Assn., Can. Assn. Adult Edn., Ont. Genealogical Assn., Manchester and Lancashire Family Hist. Soc. Avocations: genealogy, microcomputers, bird watching, mystery fiction. Office: Sheridan Coll Applied Arts, 1430 Trafalgar Rd, Oakville, ON Canada L6H 2L1

WILBURN, MARY NELSON, lawyer, writer; b. Balt., Feb. 18, 1932; d. David Alfred and Phoebe Blanche (Novotny) Nelson; m. Adolph Yarbrough Wilburn, Mar. 5, 1957; children: Adolph II, Jason David. AB cum laude, Howard U., 1952; MA, U. Wis., 1955, JD, 1975. Bar: Wis. 1975, U.S. Supreme Ct 1981. Lectr. U. Wis. Law Sch., 1975-77, 83, 84, 85; atty. adv. Bur. Prisons, Dept. Justice, 1977-82; chmn. Wis. State Parole Bd., Madison, 1986-87; gen. counsel CC. Bd. Parole, 1987-89; commr. The Commn. to Restructure the Interstate Compact, 1988-89; mgr. Bethune Mus.-Archives, Inc., 1990; asst. regional counsel mid-atlantic region Fed. Bur. Prisons, 1990-93, atty. Affirmative Action Programs, 1993—; mem. Wis. Sentencing Commn., 1986-87. Mem. Madison Met. Sch. Dist. Bd. Edn., 1975-77; assoc. mem. Schutz Am. Sch. Bd., Alexandria, Egypt, 1983-85; commr. Nat. Coun. of Negro Women Commn. on Edn., 1986—; treas. Women's Strategies for 21st Century, Inc.; v.p. Leadership Greater Washington, 1995—; vol. One Ch. One Addict, 1995—. Mem. Internat. Assn. Paroling Authorities (exec. v.p. 1987-89), Nat. Assn. Black Women Attorneys (pres. Rolark chpt. 1989-93), Fedn. Internat. de Abogadas, Howard U. Alumni Assn., Links, Inc., Leadership (Am. Class 1991, bd. dirs. Greater Washington 1992-94, v.p. 1995—), Alpha Kappa Alpha. Office: 320 1st St NW Rm 437 Washington DC 20534

WILBURN, ROBERT CHARLES, institute executive; b. Latrobe, Pa., July 1, 1943; s. Robert Charles and Annabel Grace (McWherter) W.; m. Patricia Ellen Zuidema, May 18, 1968; children: Jason, Rae, Jesse, Benjamin. BS, U.S. Air Force Acad., 1965; MPA, Princeon U., 1967, PhD, 1970; LLD (hon.), U. Scranton, Pa., 1983, Hahneman U., 1984, Duquesne U., 1985. Econometrician Dept. of Def., Washington, 1967-69, policy analyst, 1970-72; economist The White House, Washington, 1969-70; v.p. Chase Manhattan Bank, N.Y.C., 1972-75; pres. Indiana U. of Pa., Indiana, 1975-79; sec. of budget Commonwealth of Pa., Harrisburg, 1979-83, sec. edn., 1983-84; pres. Carnegie Inst., Pitts., 1984-92, Colonial Williamsburg (Va.) Found., 1992—; bd. dirs. Harsco Corp., Wormleysburg, Pa., Dravo Corp., Pitts. Trustee Carnegie Mellon U., 1985-92, Shadyside Hosp., Pitts., 1985-92; sec. Allegheny Conf. on Community Devel., Pitts. Capt. USAF, 1965-72. Named Man of Yr., Pitts. Vectors, 1992. Mem. ALA, Am. Mus. Assn. (bd. dirs. 1989-92), Urban Librs. Coun. Chgo. (pres. 1991-93), World Affairs Coun. (bd. dirs. 1988-92), Duquesne Club (bd. dirs. 1990-92), Pitts. Athletic Assn. Republican. Roman Catholic. Office: Colonial Williamsburg Found PO Box 1776 Williamsburg VA 23187-1776

WILBY, WILLIAM LANGFITT, international portfolio manager, economist; b. New Orleans, May 10, 1944; s. Langfitt Bowditch and Routh (Trowbridge) W.; m. Cynthia Warren Pike, Mar. 19, 1982; 1 child, Molly. BS in Engring., U.S. Mil. Acad., 1967; MA in Econs., U. Colo., 1978, PhD in Econs., 1980. Commd. lt. U.S. Army, 1967, advanced through grades to capt., 1969, served in Europe, Vietnam, Washington, resigned, 1974; internat. economist Fed. Res. Bank Chgo., 1980-81; v.p., economist No. Trust Bank, Chgo., 1981-86; mng. dir. AIG Global Investors, N.Y.C., 1986—; vis. prof. Am. Grad. Sch. Internat. Mgmt., Glendale, Ariz., 1978-79, Kellogg Grad. Sch. Bus. Northwestern U., Evanston, Ill., 1981-84. Mem. Nat. Assn. Bus. Economists, Am. Econ. Assn. Profl. ski instr. Austria and Colo., 1975-76. Office: AIG Global Investors 1 World Fin Ctr 200 Liberty St New York NY 10281-1003 also: Oppenheimer Mgmt 34 th Flr 2 World Trade Ctr New York NY 10048

WILCAUSKAS, EUGENE, chemicals executive. Pres. Akzo Rsch. Lab., Dobbs Ferry, N.Y. Office: Akzo Am Inc Akzo Rsch Lab 1 Livingston Ave Dobbs Ferry NY 10522-3401

WILCHA, JOHN SAMUEL, food products company executive; b. Yonkers, N.Y., Aug. 31, 1942; s. Samuel and Mary (Panko) W.; m. Margaret Patricia Swift, Mar. 21, 1943; children: Jennifer, Christopher. BS, Fordham U., 1964; MBA, Okla. State U., 1965. V.p. mktg., planner Standard Brands Inc., N.Y.C., 1966-76; corp. v.p. Gallo Wine Co., Modesto, Calif., 1976-77; v.p. mktg. and sales Bordens divsn. Drake Bakery, N.J., 1978-81, CPC Internat., N.J., 1986-87; v.p. group exec. Oroweat Foods Co., Greenwich, Conn., 1981-86; pres. Arnold Bakers Inc., Greenwich, 1986-88; pres., CEO Wilds Bakery Co., N.J., 1988-92; chmn., pres. Amerifoods Cos. Inc., Paramus, N.J., 1992—; bd. dirs. BHL Inc., Greenwich, Anderson Baking Co., Lancaster, Pa., U.S.A. Foods, Paramus, N.J., York (Pa.) Snacks, Harrison (N.J.) Baking Co., Allied Baking Co., Westbury, L.I., Cabana Foods, Inc., Detroit. Fund raiser Fordham U., Bronx, N.Y., 1982—, chmn. fedn. bd., 1985—; dir. sesquicentennial com., 1987—; dir. Nat. Advt. Rev. Bd., 1983—; Soc. Religious Leadership, Orlando, Fla., 1982-86. Named Man of the Yr., Fordham U. 1986. Mem. Assn. Nat. Advertisers, Am. Bakers Assn. (bd. dirs.), Young Bakery Exec. Com., Privy Coun., Explorers Club, Alpha Kappa Psi. Republican. Roman Catholic. Club: Sales Execs. Avocations: travel, paddle-tennis, stamps, coins, art. Office: Amerifoods Companies Inc 80 E Rt 4 Paramus NJ 07652

WILCHER, LAJUANA SUE, lawyer; b. Danville, Ky., Sept. 16, 1954; d. Dwain LaRue and Juanita (Tungate) W. BS magna cum laude, Western Ky. U., 1977; postgrad., U. Louisville, 1978; JD, No. Ky. U., 1980. Bar: Ky. 1980, U.S. Dist. Ct. (we. dist.) Ky. 1980. Assoc. Reynolds Catron & Johnston, Bowling Green, Ky., 1980-83; spl. asst. to gen. counsel USDA, Washington, 1983; spl. asst. to gen. counsel EPA, Washington, 1983-85, asst. to dep. adminstr., 1985-86; assoc. Bishop Cook Purcell & Reynolds, Washington, 1986-88, ptnr., 1988-89; asst. adminstr. for water U.S. EPA, Washington, 1989-93; ptnr. Winson & Strawn, Washington, 1993—. Mem. ABA, Ky. Bar Assn. Republican. Presbyterian. Avocations: horseback riding, sailing, caving. Office: Winston & Strawn 1400 L St NW Washington DC 20005-3509

WILCHER, LARRY KEITH, lawyer; b. Lebanon, Ky., July 19, 1950; s. Dwain LaRue and Juanita (Tungate) W.; m. Mary Jo Hayden, Aug. 21, 1971; children: Emily Jane, Joseph Keith. BS in Pharmacy, St. Louis Coll. Pharmacy, 1973; JD, No. Ky. U., 1983; program of instrn. for lawyers, Harvard U., 1987, 91, 94. Pharmacist Wood Drugs, Princeton, Ky., 1973-74; pharmacist SuperX Drugs Corp., Cin., 1975-81, real estate supr., 1981-84; dir. real estate, real estate counsel Dollar Gen. Corp., Scottsville, Ky., 1984-85, gen. counsel, 1985—, asst. sec., 1988—; chmn., chief exec. officer John Doran & Assocs. Ltd., 1991—. Chmn. Warren County Young Reps., Bowling Green, Ky., 1977-79; sec., dir. Scottsville-Allen County Leasing Corp., 1992—; dir. Scottsville-Allen County Indsl. Devel. Authority, Inc., 1991—; dir. Leadership Ky., 1994—. Named to Hon. Order Ky. Cols., 1968, One of Outstanding Young Men of Am., U.S. Jaycees, 1978; recipient Johnson & Johnson award St. Louis Coll. Pharmacy, 1973, Thurston B.

Morton Leadership award Ky. Young Rep. Fedn., 1979. Mem. ABA, Nat. Assn. Corp. Dirs., Ky. Bar Assn. (recognition award 1987), Louisville Bar Assn., Def. Rsch. Inst., Am. Corp. Counsel Assn., The Federalist Soc. Republican. Baptist. Avocations: gardening, reading. Office: Dollar Gen Corp 427 Beech St Scottsville KY 42164-1698

WILCHER, SHIRLEY J., lawyer; b. Erie, Pa., July 28, 1951; d. James S. Wilcher and Jeanne (Evans) Cheatham. AB cum laude, Mt. Holyoke Coll., 1973; MA, New Sch. Social Research, 1976; JD, Harvard U., 1979. Bar: N.Y. 1980. Assoc. Proskauer Rose Goetz and Mendelsohn, N.Y.C., 1979-80; staff atty. Nat. Women's Law Ctr., Washington, 1980-85; assoc. counsel Com. on Edn. and Labor U.S. Ho. Reps., Washington, 1985-90; dir. state rels., gen. counsel Nat. Assn. Ind. Colls. and Univs., Washington, 1990-94; dep. asst. sec. Office Fed. Contract Compliance Programs, U.S. Dept. Labor, Washington, 1994—. Editor Harvard U. Civil Rights/Civil Liberties Law Rev., 1978-79; contbr. articles to profl. jours. Nat. bd. dirs. Nat. Polit. Congress of Black Women, Washington, 1985-87; convenor Black Women's Roundtable on Voter Participation, Washington, 1984-85. Mem. ABA, Nat. Bar Assn., Nat. Conf. Black Lawyers (local bd. dirs. 1980-87, nat. bd. dirs. 1986-87). Democrat. Buddhist. Avocations: music, Oriental art. Office: US Dept Labor Fed Contract Compliance Programs FPB 200 Constitution Ave NW Washington DC 20210-1531

WILCHINS, SIDNEY A., gynecologist; b. Paterson, N.J., Feb. 2, 1940; s. Philip Aaron and Esther (Blake) W.; m. Carole Diane Brill, June 23, 1963, (div. Mar. 1985); children: Joan Helen, Edward Victor; m. Estelle Angel, Mar. 15, 1985; children: Jacqueline, Susan. BA in Biol. Scis., Rutgers U., 1961; MD, Georgetown U., 1965. Diplomate Am. Bd. Ob Gyn. Clin. instr. N.J. Med. Sch., Newark, N.J., 1971-73; clin. asst. prof. N.J. Med. Sch., Newark, 1973-78, clin. assoc. prof., 1978—; adj. rsch. prof. N.J. Inst. Tech., Newark, 1978—; assoc. dir. Pilgrim Med. Ctr., Montclair, N.J., 1982-93; med. dir. Ultrasound Diagnostic Sch., Union, N.J., 1989-91, N.J. Menopause Found., 1992—; gynecol. cons. Organon/Akzo, 1991—; med. dir. Gynchoices of Cen. Jersey, 1994—; pres. Soc. of Forensic Obstetricians & Gynecologists, 1994—. Author, editor: Cryosurgery and Medicine, 1990; contbr. articles to profl. jours. Lt. USNR, 1965-69. Fellow ACOG, ACS, N.Y. Acad. Medicine; mem. N.Y. Acad. Scis., Forensic Soc. Ob-Gyn. (pres. 1994-95), Colonia Country Club. Achievements include patent pending on Intraperitoneal Hyperthermia Device, pregnancy conducto for labor software copyright; application of chaost level to analysis of labor physiology. Home: 154 Devon Rd Colonia NJ 07067-3205 Office: 14 E Westfield Ave Roselle Park NJ 07204-2208

WILCOCK, DONALD FREDERICK, mechanical engineer; b. Bklyn., Sept. 24, 1913; s. Frederick and Jennie Marie (Young) W.; m. Marjorie Ellen Ferris, Sept. 3, 1938; 1 son, Donald Everett. B.S. in Civil Engring, Harvard U., 1934; D.Engring. Sci., U. Cin., 1939. Research chemist Sherwin Williams Co., Chgo., 1939-42; with Gen. Electric Co., 1942-65; mgr. tribology dept. Mech. Tech., Inc., Latham, N.Y., 1965-78; pres. Tribolock Inc., Schenectady, 1978—. Inst. for Innovation Through Tribology, 1980-82. Author: Bearing Design and Application, 1957. Fellow ASME (Nat. Hersey award), Am. Soc. Lubrication Engrs. Patentee. Home and Office: 40 Autumn Dr Apt 200 Slingerlands NY 12159

WILCOCK, JAMES WILLIAM, corporation executive, retired capital equipment manufacturing company executive; b. Dayton, Ohio, Sept. 2, 1917; s. Lewis Floyd and Blanche Irene (Conner) W.; m. Catherine Crosby, July 19, 1941; 1 child, Tod C. B.S., U. Mich., 1938; postgrad., Ohio Wesleyan U., 1938-41. With 3M Co., 1948-52, Oliver Iron and Steel Co., 1952-56; mktg. mgr., then mgr. Sturtevant div. Westinghouse Elec. Corp., 1956-62; pvt. cons., 1962-65; with Joy Mfg. Co., Pitts., 1965—, sr. v.p., 1967, pres., chief exec. officer, 1967-76, chmn. bd., chief exec. officer, 1976-82, ret., 1982, chmn. exec. com., 1982-87; assoc. Kolberg, Kravis and Roberts Co., 1983—; chmn., pres., chief exec. officer Pace Industries, 1984-89; chmn., pres. Pace Industries, Inc., 1989—; bd. dirs. Copperweld Corp., Michael Baker Corp.; chmn., bd. dirs. L.B. Foster Co., 1990—; chmn., CEO Monitor Group, Inc., 1991—; adj. prof. Grad. Bus. Sch. U. Pitts. Served as officer AUS, 1942-46. Republican. Episcopalian. Clubs: Duquesne, Allegheny Country, John's Island, Rivers. Office: LB Foster Co PO Box 2806 Pittsburgh PA 15220-2806

WILCOX, ARTHUR MANIGAULT, newspaper editor; b. Phila., May 2, 1922; s. John Walter and Caroline (Manigault) W.; m. Katharine Moore McMurray, Nov. 25, 1944; children: Margaret Moore, Arthur Manigault, Priscilla McMurray, Robert Manigault. B.S., Ga. Inst. Tech., 1943. Reporter Charleston (S.C.) Eve. Post, 1946-52, city editor, 1952-57, editor, 1968-74; asst. editor Charleston News and Courier, 1957-68, editor, 1974-90; sec., cons. Evening Post Pub. Co., pubs. Post-Courier, 1990—. Curator S.C. Hist. Soc., 1957-60; trustee Hist. Charleston Found., 1985-94; trustee Charleston Mus., 1967—, pres. bd., 1971-81; mem. bd. visitors Winthrop Coll., Rock Hill, S.C., 1984-87; chmn. Nat. Com. To Save Ft. Sumter Flags, 1983-89; vestryman Protestant Episcopal Ch., 1954-59, 62-69, 68-72, 79-82, sr. warden, 1981. Lt. (j.g.) USN, 1943-46; rear adm. USNR. Mem. Am. Soc. Newspaper Editors, Nat. Conf. Editorial Writers, New Eng. Soc., St. Cecilia Soc., Soc. Colonial Wars (registrar 1991—), Caroline Art Assn., U.S. Naval Inst., Audubon Soc., Nat. Trust, Huguenot Soc. S.C. (v.p. 1990-91, pres. 1991—), Charleston Club, Carolina Yacht Club, Tennis Club, Army and Navy Club (Washington), Wild Dunes Club (Isle of Palms, S.C.), Rotary. Home: 26 St Augustine Dr Charleston SC 29407-6018 Office: 171 Church St Ste 300 Charleston SC 29401-3165

WILCOX, BENSON REID, cardiothoracic surgeon, educator; b. Charlotte, N.C., May 26, 1932; s. James Simpson and Louisa (Reid) W.; m. Lucinda Holderness, July 25, 1959; children: Adelaide, Alexandra, Melissa, Reid. BA, U.N.C., 1953, MD, 1957. Diplomate Am. Bd. Surgery, Am. Bd. Thoracic Surgery (chmn. 1991-93). Resident Barnes Hosp., St. Louis, 1958-59, N.C. Meml. Hosp., Chapel Hill, 1959-60, 62-64; clin. assoc. Nat. Heart Inst., Bethesda, Md., 1960-62; instr. U.N.C., Chapel Hill, 1963-65, asst. prof., 1965-68, assoc. prof., 1968-71, chief divsn. of cardiothoracic surgery, 1969—, prof., 1971—; cons. NIH Grant Com., Bethesda, 1986-89. Contbr. articles to profl. jours.; author (with others) Surgical Anatomy of the Heart, 1992. Pres. Atlantic Coast Conf., Greensboro, N.C., 1980-81; dir. Am. Bd. Thoracic Surgery, 1983-93, chmn., 1991-93. Markle scholar John and Mary Markle Found., 1967; recipient Hadassah Myrtle Wreath award, 1979. Mem. Am. Assn. Thoracic Surgery, Am. Surg. Assn., Soc. Thoracic Surgeons (treas. 1980-86, pres. 1994-95), Soc. Univ. Surgeons, So. Surg. Assn., Thoracic Surgery Dirs. Assn. (pres. 1985-87), Womack Soc. (pres. 1991-93). Democrat. Presbyterian. Avocations: medical history, tennis, golf, hiking. Office: U NC Med Sch Div Cardiothoracic Surgery 108 Burnett-Womack CB-7065 Chapel Hill NC 27599-7065

WILCOX, BRUCE GORDON, publisher; b. Boston, Sept. 3, 1947; s. Edward Teed and Maud (Eckert) W.; m. Greta Green, Apr. 7, 1974; children—Sarah M., Thor E., Hilary A. BA, Harvard U., 1969; postgrad., Peace Corps, Senegal, 1969-70, NYU, 1972-75. Asst. sales mgr. U. Wash. Press, Seattle, 1971-72, editor, 1975-82; program officer Franklin Book Programs, N.Y.C. and Dacca, Bangladesh, 1972-75; dir. U. Mass. Press, Amherst, 1983—; editorial adv. bd. Scholarly Publ., 1992—; cons. NEH, Washington, 1983, 85, NEA, Washington, 1991. Bd. dirs. Mass. Rev., 1987—. Mem. Assn. Am. Univ. Presses (del. to USSR and Ea. Europe 1977, to China 1985, to Estonia and CSFR 1992, bd. dirs. 1990—, pres. 1994-95). Home: 191 Lincoln Ave Amherst MA 01002-2009

WILCOX, CALVIN HAYDEN, mathematics educator; b. Cicero, N.Y., Jan. 29, 1924; s. Calvin and Vara (Place) W.; m. Frances I. Rosekrans, May 29, 1947; children: Annette Faye, Victor Hayden, Christopher Grant. Student, Syracuse U., 1947-48; A.B. magna cum laude, Harvard U., 1951, A.M., 1952, Ph.D., 1955. Inst. math. faculty Calif. Inst. Tech., Pasadena, 1955-61; asst. prof. math. Calif. Inst. Tech., 1957-60, asso. prof., 1960-61; prof. U. Wis.-Madison, 1961-66; prof., head dept. U. Ariz., Tucson, 1966-69; prof. U. Denver, 1969-70, U. Utah, Salt Lake City, 1971—; vis. prof. U. Geneva, 1970-71, U. Liege, Belgium, 1973, U. Stuttgart, Fed. Republic Germany, 1974, 76-77, Kyoto (Japan) U., 1975, Ecole Polytechnique Fédérale, Lausanne, Switzerland, 1979, U. Bonn (W. Ger.), 1980. Author: Lectures on Scattering Theory for the d'Alembert Equation in Exterior Domains, 1975; monograph Scattering Theory for Diffraction Gratings, 1983, Sound Propa-

gation in Stratified Fluids, 1983; Editor: Asymptotic Solutions of Differential Equations and Their Applications, 1964, Perturbation Theory and its Application in Quantum Mechanics, 1966. Served with AUS, 1945-47. NSF predoctoral fellow, 1952-53; Sr. U.S. Scientist award Alexander von Humboldt Found., W. Ger., 1976-77. Mem. AAAS, Soc. Indsl. and Applied Math., Am. Math. Soc., Math. Assn. Am. Office: Univ Utah Dept Math Salt Lake City UT 84112

WILCOX, CHARLES JULIAN, geneticist, educator; b. Harrisburg, Pa., Mar. 28, 1930; s. Charles John and Gertrude May (Hill) W.; m. Eileen Louise Armstrong, Aug. 27, 1955; children: Marsha Lou, Douglas Edward. BS, U. Vt., 1950; MS, Rutgers U., 1955, PhD, 1959. Registered profl. animal scientist. Dairy farm owner, operator Charlotte, Vt., 1955-56; prof. U. Fla., Gainesville, 1959—; cons. in internat. animal agrl. various orgns., Great Britain, France, Sudan, Can., Mex., El Salvador, Ecuador, Brazil, Bolivia, Peru, Columbia, Venezuela, Dominican Republic, Sweden, Norway, 1965—. Author: (with others) Animal Agriculture, 1973, 2d edit., 1980, Improvement of Milk Production in Tropics, 1990; editor: Large Dairy Herd Management, 1978, 93. 1st Lt. U.S. Army, 1951-53, Korea. Recipient Disting. Svc. award Fla. Purebred Dairy Assn., 1986; jr. faculty award Gamma Sigma Delta, 1968, sr. faculty award, 1984, internat. award for disting. svc. to agr., 1987; sr. rsch. scientist award Sigma Xi, 1994. Mem. Am. Dairy Sci. Assn., Am. Soc. Animal Sci., Brazilian Soc. Genetics (editorial bd. 1979—), Am. Registry Profls. Animal Sci. (examining bd. 1987—), Fla. Holstein Assn. (pres. 1979), Fla. Guernsey Cattle Club (pres. 1974-76). Republican. Avocations: spectator sports (baseball, football, basketball, tennis). Office: Univ Fla Dairy Sci Dept Gainesville FL 32611-0920

WILCOX, COLLIN M., author; b. Detroit, Sept. 21, 1924; s. Harlan Collin and Lucile Armina (Spangler) W.; m. Beverley Buchman, Dec. 20, 1954; children—Christopher, Jeffrey. B.A., Antioch Coll., 1948. Tchr., 1949-51, copywriter, 1951-53; partner Amthor & Co., 1953-54; propr. Collin Wilcox Lamps, San Francisco, 1955-72; mystery and suspense novelist, 1967—. Mystery and suspense novelist: works include The Black Door, 1967; The Third Figure, 1968, The Lonely Hunter, 1969, The Disappearance, 1970, Dead Aim, 1971, Hiding Place, 1972, Long Way Down, 1972, Aftershock, 1973, The Faceless Man, 1974; pseudonym Carter Wick: works include The Third Victim, 1975; Doctor, Lawyer, 1975, The Watcher, 1976, (with Bill Pronzini) Twospot, 1977, Power Plays, 1978, Mankiller, 1980, Spellbinder, 1981, Stalking Horse, 1982, Swallow's Fall, 1983, Victims, 1985, Night Games, 1986, The Pariah, 1988, Bernhardt's Edge, 1988, A Death Before Dying, 1990, Silent Witness, 1990, Except for the Bones, 1991, Hire a Hangman, 1991, Find Her a Grave, 1993, Switchback, 1993, Full Circle, 1994. Served with USAAF, 1943-44. Mem. Mystery Writers Am. (dir.), Sierra Club (com. 1975-76), Aircraft Owners and Pilots Assn. Democrat. Home: 4174 26th St San Francisco CA 94131-1915

WILCOX, DAVID ERIC, educational consultant; b. Cortland, N.Y., Sept. 4, 1939; s. James A. and Lucille (Fiske) C.; B.S. in Elec. Engring., U. Buffalo, 1961; postgrad. Syracuse U., 1965, Marist Coll.; M.S., U. Bridgeport, 1977; Ed.D. candidate Rutgers U.; m. Phyllipa Ann Wilcox, Jan. 23, 1977; children: Terri L., Cindy A., Jana L. Research engring. mgr. input/output devices Rome (N.Y.) Air Devel. Center, 1966-70; dir. sales Mercon Inc., Winsooki, Vt., 1970-73, dir., 1972—; pres. Wilcox Tng. Systems, Newburgh, N.Y., 1973—; prin. Exec. Effectiveness, Inc., N.Y.C.; instr. Dale Carnegie courses. Pres. N.Y. State Jaycees, 1972-73, chmn. bd., 1973-74; dir. U.S. Jaycees, 1970-71; bd. dirs., v.p. N.Y. State Spl. Olympics, 1972-73; bd. dirs., treas. Family Counseling Service, Inc.; mem. Orange County Pvt. Industry Coun.; mem. N.Y. State Excelsior Examiner, 1995. Served to 1t. USAF, 1961-65. Registered profl. engr., N.Y. Mem. Soc. Info. Display, IEEE, N.Y., State Soc. Profl. Engrs., Internat. Transactional Analysis Assn., Internat. Platform Assn., Am. Soc. Quality Control. Methodist. Author: Information System Sciences, 1965; also articles. Patentee in field. Home: 511 River Rd Newburgh NY 12550-1304 Office: Rock Cut Rd Newburgh NY 12550 also: 30 W 60th St New York NY 10023

WILCOX, HARRY HAMMOND, retired medical educator; b. Canton, Ohio, May 31, 1918; s. Harry Hammond and Hattie Estelle (Richner) W.; m. D. June Freed., June 21, 1941; children: Joyce L. Wilcox Graff, Margaret J. (Mrs. Grayson S. Smith), James Hammond. B.S., U. Mich., 1939, M.S., 1940, Ph.D., 1948. Asso. prof. biology Morningside Coll., Sioux City, Iowa, 1947-48; asso. in anatomy U. Pa., 1948-52; mem. faculty U. Tenn. Center for Health Scis., 1952-83, Goodman prof. anatomy, 1966-83, emeritus prof. anatomy, 1983—. Assoc. editor: Anat. Record, 1968-83. Served with AUS, 1945-46. Mem. AAAS, Am. Assn. Anatomists, Am. Soc. Zoologists, Sigma Xi. Home: 1031 Marcia Rd Memphis TN 38117-5513

WILCOX, HARRY WILBUR, JR., retired corporate executive; b. Phila., Feb. 13, 1925; s. Harry Wilbur and Justine Elizabeth (Doolittle) W.; m. Colleen Ann Cerra, Apr. 6, 1946; children: Justine, Harry Wilbur III. B.S., Yale U., 1949. With Gen. Electric Co., N.Y.C., 1949-50; mfg. supt. Sylvania Electric Products, 1951-67; v.p., gen. mgr. Granger Assocs. (electronics), Palo Alto, Calif., 1967-70; gen. mgr. ITT-Cannon Electric Co., Phoenix, 1970-72; pres. Hills McCanna Co., Carpentersville, Ill., 1972-75; pres. VSI, and group v.p. IU Internat. Corp., 1975-78; exec. v.p. ITT-Grinnell, 1978-85; pres. ITT Valve Div, Lancaster, Pa., 1985-88; dir. Meyer Industries, Nat. Temperature Control Centers, Paul N. Howard Co.; former chmn. VSI, VSI-UK. Mem. adv. com. Town of Sherborn, Mass. Served with U.S. Army, 1943-46. Decorated Bronze star. Mem. R.I. Country Club, Yale Club of Vero Beach, Grand Harbor Golf and Beach Club (Vero Beach). Patentee in electroluminescence. Home: 31 Sea Breeze Ln Bristol RI 02809-1520 also: 4818 Wood Duck Circle Vero Beach FL 32967

WILCOX, HARVEY JOHN, lawyer; b. Elyria, O., Nov. 1, 1937; s. Hubbard Clyde and Sylvia (Wahter) W.; m. Leslie Louise Coleman, Apr. 11, 1970. B.A. cum laude, Amherst Coll., 1959; LL.B., Yale U., 1962. Bar: Ohio 1962, Va. 1994. Mem. firm Wilcox & Wilcox, 1962-78; with office gen. counsel Dept. Navy, Washington, 1966-94; asst. to gen. counsel Dept. Navy, 1969-72, counsel Naval Air Systems Command, 1972-76, dep. gen. counsel, 1976-94; guest lectr. U. Army Logistics Mgmt. Center; mem. Navy Contract Adjustment Bd., 1968-72. Designed Arlington County (Va.) flag, 1983. Bd. dirs. Navy Fed. Credit Union, 1974-77, sec.-treas., 1974-75, 2d v.p., 1975-77; mem. Def. Adv. Panel on Streamlining Acquisition Laws, 1991-92. Lt. USNR, 1963-66. Recipient Meritorious Exec. rank 1990, Disting Exec. rank, 1981, 89, Navy Disting. Civilian Svc. award, 1989, Defense Disting. Civilian Svc. award, 1994. Mem. Ohio Bar Assn., Va. Bar Assn., Nat. Trust Hist. Preservation, Nature Conservancy. Home: PO Box 338 Turner Mountain Rd Ivy VA 22945-0338

WILCOX, JERRY COOPER, architect; b. June 8, 1938; m. Nancy K. Wilcox; children: Lance Cooper, Kevin Morris. BArch, U. Ark., 1962. With Erhart, Eichenbaum, Rauch & Blass, 1964-76, Blass Chilcote Carter & Wilcox, 1976-89; pres. Wilcox Group, Little Rock, 1989—. Mem. adminstrv. bd. U. Ark. Sch. Arch., Asbury United Meth. Ch., Little Rock, 1983—, trustee, 1990—; mem. Little Rock Bicentennial Com., 1975-76; chmn. archs. and engrs. divsn. United Way Campaign, 1981; mem. Pulaski county bd. dirs. Am. Heart Assn., 1986-91; bd. dirs. Camp Aldersgate, 1987—. Capt. U.S. Army Corps of Engrs., 1962-64, USAR, 1964-66. Mem. AIA (bd. dirs. Ark. chpt. 1970-72, 77, treas. 1972-74, v.p. 1975, pres. 1976; com. arch. for the arts and recreation 1973-80, vice chmn. 1976, chmn. 1977, ednl. endowment fund pres. 1985—, steering com. 1978, nat. nominating com. 1980; co-chmn. Gulf States regional conv. 1979), Coun. Ednl. Facility Planners. U. Ark. Alumni Assn., Little Rock C. of C. (econ. devel. com. 1979-85, bd. dirs. 1981-86), Rotary (Little Rock Downtown chpt.), Pi Kappa Alpha. Office: Wilcox Group Riverside Bldg 2228 Cottondale Ln Apt 100 Little Rock AR 72202-2037

WILCOX, JOANN ROSE COURT, hospital administrator; b. Detroit, Apr. 6, 1940; d. Harry Clement and Rose Martha (Seide) Court; children from previous marriage: Andrea, Julie, Grant IV. BS in Nursing, U. Mich., 1963; MS in Nursing, Wayne State U., Detroit, 1979. Cert. advanced nurse administr. Nurse U. Mich. Hosp., Ann Arbor, 1963; Borgess Hosp., Wayne, Mich., 1964, Annapolis Hosp., Wayne, Mich., 1964-66, Mt. Carmel Mercy Hosp., Detroit, 1966-71; nurse Pontiac (Mich.) Gen. Hosp., 1971-78, dir. nursing, 1978-81, v.p. nursing, 1981-86, v.p. adminstrn., 1986—. Mem. Am.

Orgn. Nurse Execs., Mich. Nurses Assn. (pres. 1985—), U. Mich. Alumni Orgn., Wayne State Alumni Orgn., Sigma Theta Tau. Episcopalain. Home: 5539 Lessandro St Saginaw MI 48603-3627 Office: Pontiac Gen Hosp Seminole At W Huron Pontiac MI 48053

WILCOX, JOHN CAVEN, lawyer, corporate consultant; b. N.Y.C., Nov. 12, 1942; s. Daniel A. and Jessie Alexandra (Caven) W.; m. Vanessa Guerrini-Maraldi, Sept. 30, 1983; children: Daniel D.G., William G.M., Julia G.M. BA magna cum laude, Harvard U., 1964, JD, 1968; MA, U. Calif., Berkeley, 1965; LLM, NYU, 1981. Bar: N.Y. 1973. Account exec. Georgeson & Co. Inc., N.Y.C., 1973-79, mng. dir., 1979-90, chmn. 1990—; trustee Family Dynamics, Inc., N.Y.C., 1979—. With U.S. Army, 1968-70, Vietnam. Woodrow Wilson fellow, 1965. Mem. ABA, NYSE (mem. shareholders comm. com. 1989—), N.Y. State Bar Assn., Am. Soc. Corp. Secs. (mem. securities industry com. 1987—), Nat. Assn. Security Dealers (mem. issuer affairs com. 1990—), Downtown Assn., Harvard Club (N.Y.C.), Phi Beta Kappa. Democrat. Home: 580 W End Ave New York NY 10024-1723 Office: Georgeson & Co Inc Wall Street Plz New York NY 10005

WILCOX, JON P., judge; b. Berlin, Wis., Sept. 5, 1936; m. Jane Ann; children: Jeffrey, Jennifer. AB in Polit. Sci., Ripon Coll., 1958; JD, U. Wis., 1965. Pvt. practice Steele, Smyth, Klos and Flynn, LaCrosse, Wis., 1965-66, Hacker and Wilcox, Wautoma, Wis., 1966-69, Wilcox, Rudolph, Kubasta & Rathjen, Wautoma, 1969-79; elected judge Waushara County Cir. Ct., 1979-92; apptd. Wis. Supreme Ct., 1992; apptd. family ct. commnr. Waushara County, 1977-79, vice-chairperson, chairperson Wis. Sentencing Commn., 1984-92; apptd. chief judge by Wis. Supreme Ct., 6th Jud. Dist., 1985-92, to State-Fed. Jud. Coun., 1992, to Jud. Coun. Wis., 1993; mem. prison overcrowding task force, 1988-90, numerous coms. Wis. State Judiciary; with faculty Wis. Jud. Coll., 1986—; elected chairperson Wis. Chief Judges Com., 1990-92; lectr. in field. Author: (with others) Wisconsin News Reporters Handbook; Wisconsin Courts and Court Procedures, 1987. Lt. U.S. Army, 1959-61. Recipient Outstanding Jaycee award 1974, Disting. Alumni award Ripon Coll., 1993. Fellow ABA; mem. Am. Judicature Soc., Nat. Coun. Juvenile and Family Ct. Judges, Wis. State Bar Assn., Dane County Bar Assn., Tri-County Bar Assn., Rotary, Trout Unlimited, Ruffed Grouse Soc., Ducks Unlimited, Phi Alpha Delta. Office: Supreme Court State Capitol PO Box 1688 Madison WI 53701-1688

WILCOX, MARK DEAN, lawyer; b. Chgo., May 25, 1952; s. Fabian Joseph and Zeryle Lucille (Tase) W.; m. Catherine J. Wertjes, Mar. 12, 1983; children: Glenna Lynn, Joanna Tessie, Andrew Fabian Joseph. BBA, U. Notre Dame, 1973; JD, Northwestern U., 1976; CLU, Am. Coll., 1979, ChFC, 1992. Bar: Ill. 1976, U.S. Dist. Ct. (no. dist.) Ill. 1976, Trial Bar 1982, U.S. Ct. Appeals (7th cir.) 1987, U.S. Supreme Ct. 1989. Staff asst. Nat. Dist. Attys. Assn., Chgo., 1974-75; trial asst. Cook County States Atty., Chgo., 1975; intern U.S. Atty. No. Dist. Ill., Chgo., 1975-76; assoc. Lord, Bissell & Brook, Chgo., 1976-85, ptnr., 1986—. Bd. mgrs. YMCA Metropolitan Chgo., Internat. Spl. Olympics. Mem. ABA (tort and ins. practice sect.), Am. Soc. CLU and ChFC, Nat. Assn. Life Underwriters, Chgo. Bar Assn. (ins. law com.), Def. Rsch. Inst., Trial Lawyers Club Chgo., Union League Club (Chgo.). Office: Lord Bissell & Brook 115 S La Salle St Chicago IL 60603-3801

WILCOX, MAUD, editor; b. N.Y.C., Feb. 14, 1923; d. Thor Fredrik and Gerda (Ysberg) Eckert; m. Edward T. Wilcox, Feb. 9, 1944; children: Thor (dec.), Bruce, Eric, Karen. A.B. summa cum laude, Smith Coll., 1944; A.M., Harvard U., 1945. Teaching fellow Harvard U., 1945-46, 48-51; instr. English Smith Coll., Northampton, Mass., 1947-48, Wellesley Coll., Mass., 1951-52; exec. editor Harvard U. Press, 1958-66, humanities editor, 1966-73, editor-in-chief, 1973-89, ret.; freelance editorial cons. Cambridge, 1989—; cons., panelist NEH, Washington, 1974-76, 82-84; cons. Radcliffe Pub. Course, 1991. Mem. MLA (com. scholarly edits. 1982-86), Assn. Am. Univ. Presses (chair com. admissions and standards 1976-77, v.p. 1978-79, chair program com. 1981-82), Phi Beta Kappa. Democrat. Episcopalian. Home and Office: 63 Francis Ave Cambridge MA 02138-1911

WILCOX, MICHAEL WING, lawyer; b. Buffalo, July 21, 1941; s. Paul Wing and Barbara Ann (Bauter) W.; m. Diane Rose Dell, June 18, 1966; children: Timothy, Katherine, Matthew. AB, UCLA, 1963; JD, Marquette U., 1966. Bar: Wis. 1966, U.S. Ct. Appeals (7th cir.) 1967. Law clk. to judge U.S. Ct. Appeals (7th cir.), Chgo., 1966-67; with firm Boardman, Suhr, Curry & Field, Madison, Wis., 1967-83; ptnr. Quarles & Brady, Madison, Wis., 1983-90, Stolper, Koritzinsky, Brewster & Neider, Madison, 1990-94, Stolper, Wilcox & Hughes, Madison, 1995—; lectr. in field. Author: (with others) Marital Property Law in Wisconsin, 1986. Bd. dirs. Meriter Found. Mem. ABA (chmn. marital property com. of real property probate and trust law sect. 1986-89), Wis. State Bar Assn. (chmn. taxation sect. 1983-84), Am. Coll. Trust and Estate Counsel, Rotary (bd. dirs. Madison West chpt.). Club: The Madison. Home: 6318 Keelson Dr Madison WI 53705-4367 Office: Stolper Wilcox & Hughes 6510 Grand Teton Plz Madison WI 53744-6010

WILCOX, PHILIP CONNACHER, JR., foreign service officer; b. Denver, Feb. 1, 1937; m. Cynda R. Buxton, Sept. 10, 1965; children: Elizabeth, Andrew. BA, Williams Coll., 1958; LLB, Stanford U., 1961; student, Nat. War Coll. Tchr. Sierra Leone, 1961-65; joined Fgn. Svc., Dept. State, Washington, 1966; press officer U.S. Info. Svc., Vientiane, 1967-69; spl. asst. Office Under Sec. Mgmt. Dept. State, Washington, 1969-71; polit. and econ. officer U.S. Embassy, Jakarta, Indonesia, 1972-76; U.S. Embassy Dept. State, Dhaka, 1977-79; dep. dir. Office UN Polit. Affairs Dept. State, Washington, 1981-83; dir. Office Regional Affairs, Bur. Near East and South Asian Affairs, 1983-84, dir. Office Israeli and Arab-Israeli Affairs, 1984-87, dep. asst. sec. state, Bur. Near East and South Asian Affairs, 1987-88; U.S. consul gen. Jerusalem, 1988-91; prin. dep. asst. sec., Bur. Intelligence and Rsch. Dept. State, Washington, 1991-94; amb. coord. for counterterrorism Dept. State., Washington, 1994—. Office: US State Dept 2201 C St NW Rm 2507 Washington DC 20520-0001

WILCOX, RHODA DAVIS, elementary education educator; b. Boyero, Colo., Nov. 4, 1918; d. Harold Francis and Louise Wilhelmina (Wilfert) Davis; m. Kenneth Edward Wilcox, Nov. 1945 (div. 1952); 1 child, Michele Ann. BA in Elem. Edn., U. No. Colo., 1941; postgrad., Colo. Coll., 1955-65. Life cert. tchr., Colo. Elem. tchr. Fruita (Colo.) Pub. Sch., 1938-40, Boise, Idaho, 1940-42; sec. civil service USAF, Ogden, Utah, 1942-43, Colorado Springs, Colo., 1943-44; sec. civil service hdqtrs. command USAF, Panama Canal Zone; sec. Tech. Libr., Eglin Field, Fla., 1945-46; elem. tchr. Colorado Springs Sch. Dist. 11, 1952-82, mem. curriculum devel. com., 1968-69; lectr. civic, profl. and edn. groups, Colo.; judge for Excellence in Literacy Coldwell Bankers Sch. Dist. 11, Colo. Coun. Internat. Reading. Assn. Author: Man on the Iron Horse, 1959, Colorado Slim and His Spectackler, 1964, (with Jean Pierpoint) Changing Colorado (Social Studies), 1968-69, Founding Fathers and Their Friends, 1971, The Bells of Manitou, 1973, (with Ben Froisland) In the Footsteps of the Founder, 1993. Mem. hist. adv. bd. State Colo., Denver, 1976; mem. Garden of the Gods master plan rev. com. City of Colorado Springs, 1987—; mem. cemetery adv. bd. City of Colorado Springs, 1988-91; mem. adv. bd. centennial com. 1971; mem. steering com. Spirit of Palmer Festival, 1986; judge Nat. Hist. Day, U. Colo. Colorado Springs and Colo. Coll., Colorado Springs; hon. trustee Palmer Found., 1986—; mem. Am. the Beautiful Centennial Celebrations, Inc., 1992-93. Named Tchr. of the Yr., Colorado Springs Sch. Dist. 11, 1968. Mem. AAUW (Woman of Yr. 1987), Colo. Ret. Educators Assn., Colorado Springs Ret. Educators Assn., Helen Hunt Jackson Commemorative Coun. Avocations: lecturing, conducting tours and writing tour scripts, volunteering in Pioneers Mus. Archives, Ecumenical Social Ministries, Garden of the Gods. Home: 1620 E Cache La Poudre St Colorado Springs CO 80909-4612

WILCOX, RICHARD, grain company executive; b. 1952. BS, Phillips U., 1974. With Cargill Inc., Cin. 1974-80, Con Agra, Inc., St. Louis 1980-82; v.p. Zen-Noh Grain Corp., Metairie, La., 1982-91; active with subsidiary, 1991—; with CGB Enterprises, Inc., Covington, La., 1993—, pres., chief exec. officer; also pres. Consolidated Grain at N. Bend, Cin. Office: CGB Enterprises Inc 1001 Service Rd E Covington LA 70433*

WILCOX, RICHARD HOAG, information scientist; b. Wooster, Ohio, Sept. 23, 1927; s. Raymond Boorman and Hazel (Hoag) W.; m. Jean Balderston, May 13, 1950; children: Linda, Kathryn. BS in Elec. Engring., Lafayette Coll., Easton, Pa., 1951, Elec. Engr., 1955; M Engring. Adminstrn., George Washington U., Washington, 1964. Enlisted USN, 1945-47; commd. ensign USNR, 1951, advanced through grades to comdr., 1969; electronic scientist, ops. rsch. analyst U.S. Naval Rsch. Lab., Washington, 1951-58; ops. rsch. analyst, electronic engr. Office Naval Rsch., Washington, 1958-62, head info. systems br., acting dir. math. scis. div., 1961-68; head resource evaluation div. Exec. Office of Pres., Office Emergency Preparedness, Washington, 1968-69, head info. systems div., 1969-74; chief mil. affairs div. U.S. Arms Control and Disarmament Agy., Washington, 1974-75, chief arms transfer div., 1975-78, sr. scientist, 1978-93; pvt. cons. Info. Systems Mgmt. Sci., Temple Hills, Md., 1993—; commr., dir. Commn. on Profls. in Sci. and Tech., Washington, 1967-92; asst. dir. computers and comm. Fed. Emergency Mgmt. Agy., Washington, 1981; vis. scholar Ctr. for Strategic and Internat. Studies, Georgetown U., Washington, 1983-84. Co-editor: Redundancy Techniques for Computing Systems, 1962, Computer and Information Sciences, 1964, Research Program Effectiveness, 1965; contbr. articles to profl. jours, chpts. to books. Recipient Superior Civiliam Svc. award Office Naval Rsch., 1966, Citation Pres. U.S., 1973, Superior Honor award U.S Arms Control and Disarmament Agy., 1993. Mem. AAAS, George Washington U. Club, Herrington Harbour Sailing Assn., Sigma Xi, Tau Beta Pi. Achievements include patent for microwave multiplier device; devising info.-theoretic measure of randomness of human performance; mgmt. devel. and operation of first operational computer conferencing system; creation a variety of novel info. systems. Home: 5702 Cedar Bluff Pl Temple Hills MD 20748-4809

WILCOX, RONALD BRUCE, biochemistry educator, researcher; b. Seattle, Sept. 23, 1934; s. Howard Bruce and Edna Jane (McKeown) W.; m. Susan Lenore Folkenberg, May 15, 1937; children: Deanna Marie, Lisa Suzanne. B.S., Pacific Union Coll., 1957; Ph.D. U. Utah, 1962. Research fellow Harvard Med. Sch., Boston, 1962-65; asst. prof. Loma Linda U., Calif., 1965-70, assoc. prof., 1973-77, prof., 1973—, chmn. dept. biochemistry, 1973-83. Mem. gen. plan rev. com. City of Loma Linda, 1981-92; bd. dirs. East Valley United Way, 1990—. Fellow Danforth Found., St. Louis, 1957; fellow Bank Am. Giannimni Found. San Francisco, 1965. Mem. Am. Thyroid Assn., Endocrine Soc. Democrat. Seventh-day Adventist. Home: 25516 Lomas Verdes St Loma Linda CA 92354-2417 Office: Loma Linda U Dept Biochemistry Loma Linda CA 92350

WILCOX, WAYNE F., plant pathologist, educator, researcher; b. Newman, Calif., July 1, 1950; s. Donald Franklin and Sara Jane W.; m. Linda Theresa Pembroke, Nov. 16, 1969; children: Miranda Corrina, Holly Carolyn. BS in Plant Pathology (Pomology), U. Calif., Davis, 1977, MS in Plant Pathology, 1978, PhD, 1982. Asst. extension prof. U. Ky., Princeton, 1982-84; asst. prof. Cornell U., N.Y. State Agrl. Expt. Sta., Geneva, 1984-90, assoc. prof., 1990—; dept. extension leader Cornell U., 1984-93; state liaison rep. Nat. Impact Assessment Program, 1992—, mem. statewide fruit competitiveness and profitability com., 1991—, IPM commodity com. fruit, 1984—; researcher in field. Contbr. numerous articles to profl. jours. Recipient Ciba-Geigy award Am. Phytopathological Soc., 1993. Mem. Am. Phytopathological Soc. (sec. deciduous tree fruit disease workers 1984-85, chmn. 1985-86, editor jours. 1985-92, extension com. 1988-90), Am. Soc. Hort. Sci. Achievements include patents in biological control of phytophthora by trichoderma and by gliocladium; notable findings include elucidation of role of phytophthora species as casual agents of root rot of fruit crops, particularly their interaction with soil water status as it effects pathogenesis. Office: Cornell U NY State Agrl Expt Sta Dept Plant Pathology Geneva NY 14456

WILCOX, W(EBSTER) WAYNE, forest products pathologist, educator; b. Berkeley, Calif., Oct. 28, 1938; s. Webster Williamson and Edith Jeanette (La Belle) W.; m. Margaret Ruth Starkweather, Aug. 7, 1960; children: Melissa Margaret, Wynn William. BS in Forestry, U. Calif., Berkeley, 1960; MS in Plant Pathology, U. Wis., 1962, PhD in Plant Pathology, 1965. Plant pathologist U.S. Forest Products Lab., Madison, Wis., 1960-64; from asst. to assoc. forest products pathologist, lectr. U. Calif. Forest Products Lab., Richmond, Calif., 1964-77, forest products pathologist, prof., 1977—; mem. Structural Pest Control Bd., Sacramento, Calif., 1979-81; cons. in field. Contbr. numerous articles to profl. jours. Fulbright-Hays sr. postdoctoral fellow, Fed. Republic Germany, 1973-74. Fellow Internat. Acad. Wood Sci.; mem. Forest Products Soc. (Wood award 1965), Soc. Wood Sci. and Tech., Internat. Assn. Wood Anatomists, Am. Inst. Biol. Scis., Sigma Xi, Xi Sigma Pi. Avocations: sailing, vocal music, backpacking. Office: U Calif Forest Products Lab 1301 S 46th St Richmond CA 94804-4603

WILCOXSON, ROY DELL, plant pathology educator and researcher; b. Columbia, Utah, Jan. 12, 1926; m. Iva Wall, 1949; children: Bonnie, Paul, Karren, John. BS, Utah State U., 1953; MS, U. Minn., 1955, PhD in Plant Pathlogy, 1957. Asst. prof. U. Minn., 1957-66; prof. plant pathology U. Minn., St. Paul, 1966—; spl. staff mem. Rockefeller Found.; vis. prof. Indian Agrl. Rsch. Inst., New Delhi; dir. Morocco Project U. Minn., 1983-87; adj. prof. Inst. Agron & Vet Medicine, Hassan II, Rabat, Movac, 1985—. Fellow Am. Phytopath Soc., Indian NAS, Indian Phytopath Soc., AAAS. Research in diseases of forage crops and cereal crops; cereal rust diseases. Office: 4200 West Lake Ave Apt 205B Glenview IL 60025 Address: Dept Plant Path U Minn Saint Paul MN 55101*

WILCZEK, FRANK ANTHONY, physics educator; b. Mineola, N.Y., May 15, 1951; s. Frank John and Mary Rose (Cona) W.; m. Elizabeth Jordan Devine, July 3, 1973; children: Amity, Mira. BS in Math., U. Chgo., 1970; MA in Math., Princeton U., 1971, PhD in Physics, 1973. Instr. Princeton (N.J.) U., 1973-74, asst. prof., 1974-76, assoc. prof., 1978-79, prof., 1980-81; prof. Inst. for Theoretical Physics, Santa Barbara, Calif., 1981-88, Inst. for Advanced Study, Princeton, 1989—; vis. fellow Inst. for Advanced Study, Princeton, 1977-78; vis. prof. Harvard U., 1987-88. Author: Longing for the Harmonies, 1988, Fractional Statistics and Anyon Superconductivity, 1990; contbr. articles to profl. jours. Recipient J.J. Sakurai prize Am. Phys. Soc., 1986, Dirac medal UNESCO, 1994; A.P. Sloan fellow, 1975-77, MacArthur fellow, 1982-87, Huttenback prof. U. Calif., Santa Barbara, 1984-88. Mem. NAS, Am. Acad. Arts & Scis. Avocations: chess, music, logic puzzles. Home: 112 Mercer St Princeton NJ 08540-6827 Office: Inst Advanced Study Dept Natural Scis Olden Ln Princeton NJ 08540-4920

WILCZEK, JOHN FRANKLIN, history educator; b. San Francisco, Jan. 9, 1929; s. Leonard Matthew and Teresa Edith (Silvey) W.; m. Kuniko Akabane, Nov. 14, 1966; 1 child, Mary Theresa Wilczek. BA in History with honors, U. Calif., Berkeley, 1952; MA, U. Calif., 1953; PhD, Pacific Western U., Encino, Calif., 1978. Cert. secondary tchr., Calif. Instr. history and polit. sci. City Coll. of San Francisco, 1956-94; retired, 1995; instr. Kobe (Japan) Women's Coll., 1979-81; instr. Seido Lang. Inst., Kobe, 1979-81; sec.-treas. Tokyo TV Broadcasting Corp., San Francisco 1975—. Author: The Teaching of Japanese History on the Community College Level, 1978. Sgt. U.S. Army, 1953-55. Mem. U. Calif. Alumni Assn. Republican. Roman Catholic. Avocations: art, numismatics, philately, classical music, photography. Home: 5 Windsor Dr Daly City CA 94015-3257 Office: City Coll of San Francisco 50 Phelan Ave San Francisco CA 94112-1821

WILCZEK, JOSEPH, health facilities administrator. Sr. v.p., COO Caritas Christi Inc. Office: Caritas Christi Inc 125 Technology Dr Waltham MA 02154*

WILCZEK, ROBERT JOSEPH, lawyer; b. Chgo., Jan. 8, 1944; s. Andrew J. and Anne (Danielczak) W.; m. Shirley Pfenning, Oct. 2, 1976; 1 child, Meghan R. BA, U. Dayton, 1965; LLB, U. Notre Dame, 1968. Bar: Ill. 1968, U.S. Supreme Ct. 1974. Ptnr. Gardner, Carton & Douglas, Chgo., 1971—; bd. dirs. Pacific Dunlop Holdings Inc., Chgo. Note and book rev. editor Notre Dame Law Rev., 1967-68; contbr. articles to profl. jours. Trustee St. Patrick High Sch., Chgo., Chgo. Cultural Found.; mem. adv. coun. Coll. Arts & Scis. U. Dayton. Capt. U.S. Army, 1968-70, Vietnam. Decorated Bronze Star. Mem. ABA, Chgo. Bar Assn., Law Club Chgo., Australian-Am. C. of C. (bd. dirs. Chgo. chpt.). Office: Gardner Carton & Douglas Quaker Tower Ste 3400 321 N Clark St Chicago IL 60610-4714

WILD, HARRY E., engineering company executive; b. Province, R.I., Sept. 25, 1940; s. Harry Edward and Lula Elizabeth (Johnson) W.; m. Marjorie D. Dompe, Nov. 26, 1981; children: Elizabeth Ann, Eric Johnson. BCE, U. Fla., 1966, MS, 1967. Registered profl. engr. Fla., Ga., Maine. Draftsman, inspector, surveyor Briley Wild & Assocs., Ormond Beach, Fla., 1959-65; treatment plant operator U. Fla., Gainesville, 1965-66; design engr. Metcalf & Eddy, Boston, 1966-68, project engr., 1968-71; v.p. Briley, Wild & Assocs., Ormond Beach, 1971, pres., chief exec. officer, 1972—; peer reviewer in field. Contbr. articles to profl. jours. Served with U.S. Army. Recipient Harrison P. Eddy award, Water Pollution Control Fedn., 1972. Fellow Fla. Engring. Soc. (v.p. 1977-78, 81-83), Am. Cons. Engrs. Council; mem. ASCE, Am. Water Works Assn., Fla. Inst. Cons. Engrs. (officer 1974-80, pres. 1979-80, Ormond Beach C. of C. (bd. govs.). Presbyterian. Club: Halifax (Daytona Beach, Fla.). Home: 110 Knollwood Estate Dr Ormond Beach FL 32174-4223 Office: Briley Wild & Assocs Inc PO Box 607 Ormond Beach FL 32175-0607

WILD, JAMES ROBERT, biochemistry and biophysics educator; b. Sedalia, Mo., Nov. 24, 1945; s. Robert Lee and Frances Elleta (Wheeler) W.; m. Ann Lynn Brenner, Aug. 1, 1973; 1 child, Kalli Ann. BA in Zoology, U. Calif., Davis, Calif., 1967; PhD in Cell Biology, U. Calif., Riverside, 1971; post doctoral fellow, U. Calif., 1972. Rsch. microbiologist NMR Inst., Active Duty USN, Bethesda, Md., 1972-75; from asst. to assoc. prof. genetics and plant sci. Tex. A&M U., Coll. Sta., Tex., 1975-84; prof., chair genetics faculty Tex. A&M U., Coll. Sta., 1984-87, prof. biochemistry & genetics, 1984—, head biochemistry and biophysics dept., 1986-90; exec. assoc. dean Coll. Agriculture & Life Scs., Tex. A&M U., Coll. Sta., 1987-92; prof., head dept. biochemistry and biophysics, 1994—. Recipient Incentive in Excellence award Ctr. for Teaching Excellence, 1984-85, Outstanding Youth Educator, Tex. Conf., United Meth. Ch., 1984, So. Regional award for excellence in coll. and univ. teaching in food and agrl. scis. Higher Edn. program USDA, 1992. Methodist. Office: Tex A&M U Biochemistry Bldg Rm 339 College Station TX 77843-2128

WILD, JOHN JULIAN, physician, director medical research institute; b. Sydenham, Kent, Eng., Aug. 11, 1914; came to U.S., 1946; s. Ovid Frederick and Ellen Louise (Cuttance) W.; m. Nancy Wallace, Nov. 14, 1949 (div. 1966); children: John O., Douglas J.; m. Valerie Claudia Grosenick, Aug. 9, 1968; 1 child, Ellen Louise. BA, U. Cambridge, Eng., 1936, MA, 1940, MD, 1942, PhD, 1971. Intern, resident U. Coll. Hosp., London, 1938-42; intern U. College Hosp., London, 1938-42; staff surgeon Miller Gen., St. Charles and North Middlesex Hosps., London, 1942-44; venereologist Royal Army Med. Corps, 1944-45; rsch. fellow, instr. depts. surgery and elec. engring., prin. investigator U. Minn., Mpls., 1946-51; dir. rsch. Medico-Technol. Rsch. Dept. St. Barnabas Hosp., Mpls., 1953-60; dir. Medico-Technol. Rsch. Unit Minn. Found., St. Paul, 1960-63; pvt. practice Mpls., 1966—; dir. Medico-Technol. Rsch. Inst. Mpls., St. Louis Park, Minn., 1965—; lectr. in field of medical instruments, ultrasound. Contbr. articles to jours. in field; patentee in field; originator ultrasonic med. imaging instruments and diagnostic techniques. Recipient Japan prize in Medical Imaging, Sci. and Tech. Found. Japan, 1991. Fellow Am. Inst. Ultrasound in Medicine (Pioneer award 1978); mem. AMA, World Fedn. Ultrasound in Medicine and Biology, Minn. State Med. Assn., Hennepin County Med. Soc., N.Am. Alvis Owners Club; hon. mem. British Inst. of Radiology, Japan Soc. of Ultrasound in Medicine. Avocations: automobile restoration, antiques collecting and restoration. Home and Office: Medico-Technol Rsch Inst 4262 Alabama Ave S Minneapolis MN 55416-3105

WILD, NELSON HOPKINS, lawyer; b. Milw., July 16, 1933; s. Henry Goetseels and Virginia Douglas (Weller) W.; m. Joan Ruth Miles, Apr. 12, 1969; children: Mark, Eric. A.B., Princeton U., 1955; LL.B., U. Wis., 1961. Bar: Wis. 1962, Calif. 1967; cert. specialist in probate, estate planning and trust law State Bar of Calif. Research assoc. Wis. Legis. Council, Madison, 1955-56; assoc. Whyte, Hirschboeck, Minahan, Harding & Harland, Milw., 1961-67, Thelen, Marin, Johnson & Bridges, San Francisco, 1967-70; sole practice law San Francisco, 1970—; mem. State Bar Calif. Client Trust Fund Commn., 1983, mem. exec. com. conf. dels., 1985-88. Contbr. articles to legal jours. Bd. dirs. Neighborhood Legal Assistance Found., San Francisco, 1974-85, chmn. bd., 1978-81. Served with USAF, 1956-58. Mem. ABA, Calif., San Francisco bar assns., Am. Bar Found. Club: Lawyers of San Francisco (gov. 1975, treas. 1981, v.p. 1982, pres.-elect 1983, pres. 1984). Office: 220 Montgomery St San Francisco CA 94104-3402

WILD, RICHARD P., lawyer; b. N.Y.C., Aug. 13, 1947; s. Alfred P. and Harriet C. (Hoffman) W.; m. Deirdre L. Felbin, June 15, 1969; children: Nicholas B., Daniel M. AB, Columbia U., 1968; JD, Yale U., 1971. Bar: Pa. 1971, U.S. Dist. Ct. (ea. dist.) Pa. 1971, U.S. Tax Ct. 1973, U.S. Claims Ct. 1977. Assoc. Dechert Price & Rhoads, Phila., 1971-78, ptnr., 1978—; bd. dirs. Penn Fuel Gas Co., Inc. Mem. Phila. Bar Assn. (mem. tax sect.). Office: Dechert Price & Rhoads 4000 Bell Atlantic Tower 1717 Arch St Philadelphia PA 19103-2713

WILD, ROBERT LEE, physics educator; b. Sedalia, Mo., Oct. 9, 1921; s. Alwin Bernard and Nellie Marie (Nowlin) W.; m. Frances Elleta Wheeler, Oct. 7, 1943; children: James Robert, Janet Gayle, Margaret Nell. B.S., Central Mo. State U., 1943; M.A., U. Mo., 1948, Ph.D., 1950. Asst. prof. physics U. N.D., Grand Forks, 1950-52; prof. U. Calif., Riverside, 1953-88, prof. emeritus, 1988; Fulbright lectr. U. Philippines, 1981-82; mem. adv. com. Calif. Project, 1967-69—. Contbr. articles profl. jours. Served with AUS, 1943-45. NSF fellow, 1959-60; recipient Disting. Teaching award U. Calif., Riverside, 1973, Faculty of the Yr. award U. Calif.-Riverside Alumni, 1993. Pub. Svc. award Citizens U. Com., 1994. Mem. Am. Phys. Soc., Am. Assn. Physics Tchrs. (v.p. sect. 1983-84, pres. So. Calif. sect. 1985-86, pres. 1986-87, award 1966), Sigma Xi. Baptist. Home: 5709 Durango Rd Riverside CA 92506-3216 Office: U Calif Dept Physics Riverside CA 92521

WILD, ROBERT WARREN, lawyer; b. Syracuse, N.Y., Mar. 25, 1942; s. Robert Sumner and Evelyn I. (Yorman) W.; m. Elizabeth Trowbridge, Sept. 5, 1965; children: Robert Mason, Alexander Lewis, Elizabeth Anne. BS, MIT, 1964; JD, Cornell U., 1970. Bar: N.Y. 1971, D.C. 1973. Engr. Smithsonian Astrophysical Obs., Cambridge, Mass., 1965-67; atty., advisor U.S. Dept. Justice, Washington, 1970-72; law clk. to Hon. Justice William H. Rehnquist U.S. Supreme Ct., Washington, 1972-73; ptnr. Nixon, Hargrave, Devans & Doyle, Rochester, N.Y., 1973—; dir. N.Y. Employee Benefit Conf., Rochester. Trustee Rochester Police Benevolent Assn., 1994—. Mem. Monroe County Bar Assn. (trustee 1990-91, 92-94, treas. 1992—; counsel 1994—). Office: Nixon Hargrave Devans & Doyle Clinton Sq PO Box 1051 Rochester NY 14603

WILDE, CARLTON D., lawyer; b. Houston, Apr. 11, 1935; s. Henry Dayton and Louise (Key) W.; m. Martha Cloyes, July 26, 1958; children: Carlton D. Jr., Jennifer. Student, Coll. of William and Mary, 1953-55; B.A., U. Tex., 1957, J.D., 1959. Assoc. Bracewell & Patterson, Houston, 1959-62, ptnr., 1962-67, 85—, mng. ptnr., 1967-85. Trustee Presbyn. Sch., So. Tex. Coll. Law. Fellow Am. Bar Found., Tex. Bar Found., Houston Bar Found.; mem. ABA, State Bar Tex., Houston Club, River Oaks Country Club, Ramada Club (Houston), Biltmore Forest Country Club (Asheville, N.C.). Republican. Home: 3105 Reba Dr Houston TX 77019-6209 Office: Bracewell & Patterson 2900 S Tower Pennzoil Pl 711 Louisiana St Ste 2900 Houston TX 77002-2721

WILDE, DANIEL UNDERWOOD, computer engineering educator; b. Wilmington, Ohio, Dec. 27, 1937; s. Arthur John and Ruby Dale (Underwood) W. BSEE, U. Ill., 1960; MS, M.I.T., 1962, Ph.D., 1966. Research instr. medicine Boston U. Med. Sch., 1964-65; assoc. adminstrn. U. Conn., 1966-69, assoc. prof., 1970-75, prof., 1976-85; assoc. dir. New Eng. Rsch. Application Ctr., Storrs, Conn., 1966-72, dir., 1973-85; dir. NASA Indsl. Application Ctr., 1972-91; pres. NERAC, Inc., Tolland, Conn., 1985—; trustee Engring. Index, Inc.; cons. Am. Soc. Metals, 1973—. Author: Introduction to Computing: Problem Solving, Algorithms and Data Structures, 1973; contbr. articles to profl. jours. Served with USAF. Recipient NASA Public Service award, 1975. Mem. IEEE, Am. Soc. Info. Sci., Assn. Computing Machinery, Assn. Info. and Dissemination Centers (sec.-treas. 1976-79, pres. 1979-81). Office: Nerac Inc 1 Technology Dr Tolland CT 06084-3902

WILDE, DAVID GEORGE, electrical engineer, consultant; b. Rock Springs, Wyo., Aug. 26, 1928; s. David George and Mayme Elizabeth (Savela) W.; m. Mildred Marie Levar, June 20, 1954; children: David Levar, Diane L. Wilde Duhl, Wade Wallace, Deborah Lynn. BSEE, U. Wyo., 1950. Registered profl. engr., Wyo. Engr. Bur. Reclamation, Rock Springs, 1952-55, supervising engr., 1955-61, chief office engring., 1961-64; chief Dixie project Bur. Reclamation, St. George, Utah, 1964-66; Wyo. rep. Bur. Reclamation, Cheyenne, 1966-78; project mgr. Bur. Reclamation, Grand Island, Nebr., 1978-80, Casper, Wyo., 1980-88; cons. Dept. Justice, Casper, 1988—; pvt. practice cons., Casper, 1988—. Lt. U.S. Army, 1950-52, Korea. Decorated Silver Star, Purple Heart; named Outstanding Engr. Wyo., Wyo. Engring. Soc., 1985. Fellow ASCE (pres. Wyo. sect. 1972); mem. DAV, NSPE (pres. Cheyenne chpt. 1974), Am. Water Resource Assn., Am. Legion, Soil and Water Conservation Soc., Elks. Democrat. Methodist. Avocations: camping, fishing. Home: 4731 S Center St Casper WY 82601-6304

WILDE, EDWIN FREDERICK, mathematics educator; b. Lombard, Ill., Jan. 14, 1931; s. Edwin Frederick and Carrie Belle (Hammond) W.; m. Connie Mae Rawlings, Aug. 23, 1952; children—Brad Alan, Bruce Ramon, Elizabeth Lynn. B.S., Ill. State U., 1952, M.S., 1953; M.A., U. Ill., 1955, Ph.D., 1959; postgrad., U. Wis., part time, 1955-58, Stanford U., 1964-65. With Beloit (Wis.) Coll., 1955-76, prof. math., dean faculty, 1969-71, v.p. for planning, 1971-75; dean Roger Williams Coll., Bristol, R.I., 1976-80; provost, dean of faculty U. Tampa, Fla., 1980-86; vice chancellor U. S.C., Spartanburg, 1986-91, prof. math., 1991—; cons. AID insts., India, 1964, Insts. Internat. Edn., East Pakistan, 1969. NSF Sr. Sci. Faculty fellow, 1964-65. Mem. Math. Assn. Am. (bd. govs. 1968-69, 72-75). Home: 275 James Rd Gaffney SC 29341-4013 Office: U SC Spartanburg SC 29303

WILDE, GARY KEZERIAN, hospital administrator, business educator; b. L.A., Sept. 9, 1955; s. Virgil Justin and Lydia (Kezerian) W.; m. Cheryl Anne Harp, Dec. 28, 1978; children: Jaron, Kyrsten, Daniel, John, Aricka. BA, Brigham Young U., 1979; M Health Svcs. Adminstrn., Ariz. State U., 1982. Pharm. rep. Bristol Labs., Syracuse, N.Y., 1979-80; fin. asst. St. Luke's Hosp., Phoenix, 1981; adminstrv. resident Santa Barbara (Calif.) Cottage Hosp., 1982, assoc. dir. nursing, 1982-83, asst. adminstr., 1984-87, v.p., 1988-92, sr. v.p., 1992—; instr. bus., La Verne, Calif., 1985—. Chmn. allocations panel United Way Santa Barbara, 1985—. Fellow Am. Coll. Healthcare Execs. Republican. Mem. LDS Ch. Avocations: French horn, making furniture, water sports. Home: 9626 Oneida St Ventura CA 93004 Office: Santa Barbara Cottage Hosp PO Box 689 Santa Barbara CA 93102

WILDE, HAROLD RICHARD, college president; b. Wauwatosa, Wis., May 14, 1945; s. Harold Richard and Winifred (Wiley) W.; m. Benna Brecher, Feb. 4, 1970; children: Anna, Henry, Elizabeth Ty. BA, Amherst Coll., 1967; MA, PhD, Harvard U., Cambridge, Mass., 1973. Spl. asst. to gov. Office of Gov., State of Wis., Madison, 1972-75; ins. commr. Office of Commr. of Ins., State of Wis., Madison, 1975-79; spl. asst. to pres. U. Wis. System, Madison, 1979-81; v.p. for external affairs Beloit (Wis.) Coll., 1981-91; pres. North Cen. Coll., Naperville, Ill., 1991—. Bd. dirs. Ctr. for Pub. Representation, Inc., Madison, 1981-87, Beloit Community Found., 1988-91, Budget Funding Corp., 1993—. Mem. Phi Beta Kappa. Home: 329 S Brainard St Naperville IL 60540-5401 Office: North Cen Coll 30 N Brainard St Naperville IL 60540-4690

WILDE, JOHN, artist, educator; b. Milw., Dec. 12, 1919; s. Emil F. and Mathilda (Lotz) W.; m. Helen Ashman, July 1943 (dec. Dec. 1966); children: Jonathan, Phoebe; m. Shirley Miller, 1969. B.S., U. Wis., 1942, M.S., 1948. Mem. faculty U. Wis., 1948—, prof. art, 1960—, chmn. dept. art and art edn., 1960-62, Alfred Sessler Distinguished prof. art, 1969-82, prof. emeritus, 1982—; elected mem. Nat. Acad. Design, 1994. Works exhibited Met. Mus. Art, Mus. Modern Art, Whitney Mus. Am. Art, Corcoran Mus. Art, Mpls. Art Mus., San Francisco Mus. Art, Whitney Mus. Am. Art, 1978-80, Nat. Portrait Gallery, Smithsonian Instn., 1980, Nat. Gallery, Washington, 1988; retrospective Elvehjem Mus. Art, U. Wis., 1984-85; 3-man retrospective, Milw. Art Mus., 1982, others; represented in permanent collections, Pa. Acad. Art, Detroit Inst. Fine Art, Worcester Art Mus., Wadsworth Atheneum, Whitney Mus. Am. Art, Carnegie Inst., Nat. Collection Art, Smithsonian Instn., Yale U. Art Gallery, Butler Inst. Am. Art, Art Inst. Chgo., Sheldon Meml. Art Gallery, U. Nebr., Zimmerli Mus. Art, Rutgers U., N. Brunswick, N.J., Mus. Contemporary Art, Chgo., others, also extensive exhbns. abroad. Recipient numerous awards for painting and drawing in regional and nat. exhbns. including, Childe Hassam purchase award Am. Acad. and Inst. Arts and Letters, 1981, 87. Office: U Wis 6221 Humanities Bldg Madison WI 53706

WILDE, NORMAN TAYLOR, JR., investment banking company executive; b. Phila., Sept. 13, 1930; s. Norman Taylor and Elizabeth (Duthie) W.; m. Ruth Nancy Osterndorf, Sept. 26, 1959; children: Karen, Suzanne, Norman Taylor III. B.S., U. Pa., 1953. Vice pres. Janney, Montgomery, Scott, Inc., Phila., 1966-69; pres. Janney, Montgomery, Soctt, Inc., Phila., 1969—; trustee Penn Mutual Life Ins. Co. Served to lt. USN, 1953-55. Mem. Nat. Assn. Security Dealers (chmn. 1983—), Securities Industries Assn. (gov. 1979-82), Pine Valley Golf Club, Phila. Cricket Club. Office: Janney Montgomery Scott Inc 1801 Market St Philadelphia PA 19103-1628

WILDE, PATRICIA, artistic director; b. Ottawa, Ont., Can., July 16, 1928; m. George Bardyguine; children: Anya, Youri. Dancer Am. Concert Ballet, Marquis de Cuevas Ballet Internat., N.Y.C., 1944-45, Ballet Russe de Monte Carlo, N.Y.C., 1945-49, Roland Petit's Ballet Paris, Met. Ballet Britain, London, 1949-50; prin. ballerina N.Y.C. Ballet, 1950-65; dir. Harkness Sch. Ballet, N.Y.C., 1965-67; ballet mistress, tchr. Am. Ballet Theatre, N.Y.C., 1969-77; dir. Am. Ballet Theatre Sch., N.Y.C., 1977-82; artistic dir. Pitts. Ballet Theatre, 1982—; tchr. Am. Ballet Theatre, 1969-77, Joffrey scholarship program, N.Y.C. Ballet, 1968-69; established Sch. of Grand Theatre of Geneva, 1968-69; adjudicator Regional Ballet in Am. S.E. and S.W., 1969-82; choreographer N.Y. Philharmonic; guest tchr. various ballet cos. and colls.; trustee Dance U.S.A.; panelist Nat. Choreographic Project. Recipient Leadership award in Arts and Letters YWCA, 1990, Pitts. Woman of Yr. in Arts award, 1993. Office: Pitts Ballet Theatre 2900 Liberty Ave Pittsburgh PA 15201-1511

WILDE, PAUL K., computer company executive. BS in Acctg., Brigham Young U. With Prive Waterhouse and Co., L.A., 1974-78; chief fin. officer Infomatics, 1978-85; chief fin. officer, v.p. internat. ops. Candle Corp., 1985-89; chief fin. officer Viasoft, Inc., 1989-90; with Synon Corp., Larkspur, Calif., 1991—, v.p., sec., chief fin. officer. Office: Synon Corp 1100 Larkspur Landing Cir Larkspur Ca 94939*

WILDE, WILLIAM KEY, lawyer; b. Houston, May 3, 1933; s. Henry Dayton and Louise (Key) W.; m. Ann Jennine Austin, Aug. 3, 1957; children—William Key, Austin, Adrienne, Michael. A.B., Coll. William and Mary, Williamsburg, Va., 1955; J.D., U. Tex., Austin, 1958. Bar: Tex. 1958. Assoc. Bracewell & Patterson, Houston, 1958-61, ptnr., 1961—; dir. Nat. Convenience Stores, Inc., 1959—. Bd. dirs. Goodwill Industries Houston, 1972—; elder 1st Presbyn. Ch.; trustee Presbyn. Found. U.S.A., Ky., 1983-391, Schriener Coll., 1991— Fellow ABA, Am. Bar Found., Am. Coll. Trial Lawyers; mem. Tex. Bar Assn. (bd. dirs. 1984-87), Houston Bar Assn. (pres. 1982-83), Houston Club (pres. 1981-82), Houston Country Club (bd. dirs., pres. 1989-90). Republican. Avocations: golf; tennis; skiing; scuba diving. Home: 6206 Woods Bridge Way Houston TX 77007 Office: Bracewell & Patterson 2900 S Tower Pennzoil Place Houston TX 77002

WILDE, WILSON, insurance company executive; b. Hartford, Conn., Sept. 24, 1927; s. Philip Alden and Alice Augusta (Wilson) W.; m. Joanne Gerta Menzel, June 19, 1953; children—Stephen W., David W. Elizabeth L., Richard A. Student, Swarthmore Coll., 1945-46; BA, Williams Coll., 1949. Sales agt. Conn. Gen. Life Ins. Co., Hartford, 1949-53; with Hartford Steam Boiler Inspection & Ins. Co., 1953—, exec. v.p., 1970-71, pres., CEO, 1971—, chmn., CEO, 1993-94, chmn. exec. com., 1994—; bd. dirs. Shawmut Nat. Corp., Radian Corp., Phoenix Home Life Mut. Ins. Co., PXRe Corp. Corporator Inst. Living, Hartford; hon. bd. dirs. Hartford Stage Co., 1973—; Jr. Achievement, Old State House Assn., 1976—; trustee Loomis-Chaffee Sch., 1974—, chmn. bd., 1988—. Served with USNR, 1945-47, 51-53. Club: Hartford (pres. 1974). Office: Hartford Steam Boiler PO Box 5024 1 State St PO Box 5024 Hartford CT 06102-5024

WILDENTHAL, BRYAN HOBSON, university administrator; b. San Marcos, Tex., Nov. 4, 1937; s. Bryan and Doris (Kellam) W.; m. Joyce Lockhart; children: Rebecca, Bryan, Lora; m. Adele Sutton; children: Kerry, Andrea. BA, Sul Ross State Coll., 1958; PhD, U. Kans., 1964. Rsch. assoc. Rice U., Houston, 1964-66; AEC postdoctoral fellow Oak Ridge (Tenn.) Nat. Lab., 1966-68; asst. prof. physics Tex. A&M U., College Station, 1968-69; assoc. prof. physics Mich. State U., East Lansing, 1969-72, prof. physics, 1972-83; head physics and atmospheric sci. Drexel U., Phila., 1983-87; dean arts and scis. U. N.Mex., Albuquerque, 1987-92; v.p. acad. affairs U. Tex., Dallas, 1992-94; provost, v.p. acad. affairs, 1994—; cons. Los Alamos (N.Mex.) Nat. Lab., 1987-92; sr. U.S. prof. Humboldt Found., Germany, 1973. Fellow J.S. Guggenheim Found., 1977. Mem. Phi Beta Kappa. Home: 3002 Cross Timbers Ln Garland TX 75044 Office: U Tex at Dallas Office Academic Affairs Richardson TX 75083

WILDENTHAL, C(LAUD) KERN, physician, educator; b. San Marcos, Tex., July 1, 1941; s. Bryan and Doris (Kellam) W.; m. Margaret Dehlinger, Oct. 15, 1964; children—Pamela, Catharine. B.A., Sul Ross Coll., 1960; M.D., U. Tex. Southwestern Med. Ctr., Dallas, 1964; Ph.D., U. Cambridge, Eng., 1970. Intern Bellevue Hosp., N.Y.C., 1964-65; resident in medicine, fellow cardiology Parkland Hosp., Dallas, 1965-67; research fellow Nat. Heart Inst., Bethesda, Md., 1967-68; vis. research fellow Strangeways Research Lab., Cambridge, 1968-70; asst. prof. to prof. internal medicine and physiology U. Tex. Southwestern Med. Ctr., Dallas, 1970-76, prof., dean grad. sch., 1976-80, prof., dean Southwestern Med. Sch., 1980-86, prof., pres., 1986—; hon. fellow Hughes Hall, U. Cambridge, 1994—; bd. dirs. Westcott Comm. Inc. Author: Regulation of Cardiac Metabolism, 1976, Degradative Processes in Heart and Skeletal Muscle, 1980; contbr. articles to profl. jours. Bd. dirs. Dallas Symphony, Dallas Opera, Dallas Mus. Art, S.W. Mus. Sci. and Tech., Dallas Citizen's Coun.; Am. Friends Cambridge U. Recipient rsch. career devel. award NIH, 1972; spl. rsch. fellow USPHS, 1968-70; Guggenheim fellow, 1975-76. Mem. AMA, Am. Soc. Clin. Investigation, Am. Coll. Cardiology, Royal Soc. Medicine Gt. Britain, Am. Physiol. Soc., Internat. Soc. Heart Rsch. (past pres. Am. sect.), Am. Fedn. Clin. Rsch., Assn. Am. Med Colls., Assn. Am. Physicians, Am. Heart Assn. (past chmn. sci. policy com.), Assn. Acad. Health Ctrs. (past chmn. sci. policy com.). Home: 4001 Hanover Ave Dallas TX 75225-7010 Office: U Tex Southwestern Med Ctr 5323 Harry Hines Blvd Dallas TX 75235-7200

WILDER, BILLY, motion picture director, writer, producer; b. Vienna, Austria, June 22, 1906; came to U.S., 1934; m. Audrey Young. Reporter Berlin. Began: film writing with People On Sunday, produced in, Berlin; followed by Emil and the Detectives; now in, Mus. Modern Art, went to, Paris; writer, dir.: Mauvaise Graine; placed under contract as writer, Paramount Studios; writer: (in collaboration) screenplays Bluebeard's Eighth Wife, 1938, Midnight, 1939, Ninotchka, 1939, Arise My Love, 1940, Hold Back the Dawn, 1941; dir., writer: (in collaboration) Five Graves to Cairo, 1943, Double Indemnity, 1944, The Lost Weekend (Acad. award Best Dir.), 1945 (co-award with Charles Brackett for screenplay), The Emperor Waltz, 1948, A Foreign Affair, 1948, Sunset Boulevard, 1950 (Acad. award co-award best story, screenplay); producer, dir., writer: (in collaboration) The Big Carnival (Ace in the Hole), 1951, Stalag 17, 1953, Sabrina, 1954, Love in the Afternoon, 1957, Some Like It Hot, 1959, The Apartment, 1960 (Acad. awards best direction, best picture, co-award best story and screenplay); co-producer, dir., writer: (in collaboration) The Seven Year Itch, 1959; dir., collaborator: The Spirit of St. Louis, 1957, Witness for the Prosecution, 1957, Buddy, Buddy, 1981; producer, dir., writer: One, Two, Three, 1961, Irma la Douce, 1963, Kiss Me, Stupid, 1964, The Fortune Cookie, 1966, The Private Life of Sherlock Holmes, 1970, Avanti, 1972, Fedora, 1979; dir., author: screenplay The Front Page, 1974. Head Intel sect. Psychol. Warfare div. U.S. Army, 1945. Recipient Poses Creative Art medal for film Brandeis U., 1983, Irving G. Thalberg award Motion Picture Acad., 1988, D.W. Griffith Dirs. award, 6 Acad. awards, 2 Laurel awards Screen Writers Guild. Address: care Equitable Investment Corp PO Box 93877 Hollywood CA 90093*

WILDER, DAVID RANDOLPH, materials engineer, consultant; b. Lorimor, Iowa, June 11, 1929; s. Rex Marshall and Ethel Marie (Busch) W.; m. Donna Jean Moore, June 17, 1951; children: Susan, Michael, Margaret, Bruce. BS, Iowa State U., 1951, MS, 1952, PhD, 1958. Registered profl. engr., Iowa. Engr. Ames Lab., 1951-81; faculty mem. dept. materials sci. and engring Iowa State U., Ames, 1955—, prof. engring., chmn. dept., 1961-89, prof. engring., 1989-91, prof. emeritus, 1991—; cons. to various industries, fed. agys, 1955—. Contbr. numerous tech. paper to profl. lit.; patentee in field. Fellow Am. Ceramic Soc., Accreditation Bd. for Engring. and Tech.; mem. Nat. Inst. Ceramic Engrs., Am. Soc. for Engring. Edn., Keramos. Republican. Methodist. Home: 1214 Ridgewood Ave Ames IA 50010-5208

WILDER, DONNY, state legislator, retired newspaper publisher; b. Woodruff, S.C., Mar. 9, 1932; s. Robert Perry and Shadie (Skinner) W.; m. Gene Marshall, Aug. 28, 1954; 1 child, Robert Perry II. BA, Furman U., 1954. Sports writer Spartanburg (S.C.), 1954-55; assoc. editor Evening Herald, Rock Hill, S.C., 1955-60; asst. mng. editor Herald-Tribune, Sarasota, Fla., 1961-63; mng. editor The Daily Star, Shelby, N.C., 1963-67; editor-pub. The Chronicle, Clinton, S.C., 1967-87; pres. Chronicle Pub. Co., Clinton, 1967-87, Laurens County Comms., Clinton, 1985-93; mem. S.C. Ho. of Reps., Columbia, 1992—; pres. S.C. Press Assn., 1974; mem. econ. task force State of S.C., 1979-83; mem. bd. visitors Presbyn. Coll., Clinton, 1986-87. Democrat. Presbyterian.

WILDER, GENE, actor, director, writer; b. Milw., June 11, 1935; s. William J. and Jeanne (Baer) Silberman; m. Mary Joan Schutz, Oct. 27, 1967 (div. 1974); 1 child, Katharine Anastasia; m. Gilda Radner, 1984 (dec.); m. Karen Boyer, Sept. 8, 1991. BA, U. Iowa, 1955; postgrad., Bristol Old Vic Theatre Sch., 1955-56. Appeared in Broadway play: The Complaisant Lover, 1962 (Clarence Derwent award); appeared in motion pictures: Bonnie and Clyde, 1966, The Producers, 1967 (Acad. award nomination), Start the Revolution Without Me, 1968, Quackser Fortune Has a Cousin in the Bronx, 1969, Willy Wonka and the Chocolate Factory, 1970, Everything You Always Wanted to Know About Sex, 1971, Rhinoceros, 1972, Blazing Saddles, 1973, The Little Prince, 1974, Silver Streak, 1976, The Frisco Kid, 1979, Stir Crazy, 1980; Hanky Panky, 1982, See No Evil, Hear No Evil, 1989, Funny About Love, 1990, Another You, 1991; dir., writer, actor film: The Adventures of Sherlock Holmes' Smarter Brother, 1975, The World's Greatest Lover, 1977, Sunday Lovers, 1980, The Woman in Red, 1984, Haunted Honeymoon, 1986; actor, co-writer film: Young Frankenstein, 1974 (Acad. award nomination); TV appearances include: The Trouble With People, 1973, Marlo Thomas Spl., 1973, The Scarecrow, 1972, Thursday's Games, 1973, (series) Something Wilder, 1994—. Campaigned with Elaine May and Rene Taylor for Eugene McCarthy, Allard Lowenstein and Paul O'Dwyer, 1968. Served with U.S. Army, 1956-58. Office: 1511 Sawtelle Blvd # 155 Los Angeles CA 90025-3262*

WILDER, JOHN SHELTON, lieutenant governor, president senate; b. Fayette City, TN, June 3, 1921; s. John Chamblee and Martha (Shelton) W.; m. Marcelle Morton, Dec. 31, 1941; children: John Shelton, David Morton. Student, U. Tenn.; LL.B., Memphis Law U., 1957. Bar: Tenn. 1957. Engaged in farming Longtown, Tenn., 1943—; supr. mgmt. Longtown Supply Co.; judge Fayette County Ct.; mem. Tenn. Senate, 1959—; lt. gov. Tenn., 1971—; past pres. Nat. Assn. Soil Conservation Dists., Tenn. Soil Conservation Assn., Tenn. Agrl. Council; exec. com. So. Legis. Conf., Conf. Lt. Govs.; dir. Oakland Deposit Bank, Tenn., Somerville Bank and Trust Co., Tenn. Served with U.S. Army, 1942-43. Mem. Tenn. Cotton Ginners Assn. (past pres.), Delta Theta Phi. Democrat. Methodist. Club: Shriners. Office: Legislative Pl Ste 1 Nashville TN 37243

WILDER, MARGARET T., bank holding company executive; b. 1926. With Trustmark Corp., Jackson, Miss., 1968—, asst. sec. Office: Trustmark Corp 248 E Capitol St Jackson MS 39201*

WILDER, MICHAEL STEPHEN, insurance company executive; b. New Haven, Conn., Sept. 8, 1941. BA, Yale U., 1963; JD, Harvard U., 1966. Bar: Conn. 1966. Atty. Hartford (Conn.) Fire Ins. Co., 1967-69, asst. gen. counsel, 1969-71, assoc. gen. counsel, 1971-75, gen. coun., sec., 1975-87, sr. v.p., gen. counsel, sec., 1987—. Mem. ABA, Conn. Bar Assn. Office: Hartford Fire Insurance Co Hartford Plz Hartford CT 06115

WILDER, PELHAM, JR., chemist, pharmacologist, educator; b. Americus, Ga., July 20, 1920; s. Pelham and Hattie (Wilder) W.; m. Alma Sterly Lebey, Mar. 20, 1945; children: Alma Ann, Pelham III, Sterly Lebey. A.B. Emory U., 1942, M.A., 1943; M.A., Harvard U., 1947, Ph.D., 1950. Teaching fellow Harvard U., 1943-44, 46-49; instr. chemistry Duke U., 1949-52, asst. prof., 1952-58, assoc. prof., 1958-62, prof., 1962-67, prof. chemistry and pharmacology, 1967-87, Univ. Disting. Svc. prof. chemistry and pharmacology, 1987-90, Univ. Disting. Svc. prof. emeritus, 1990—, univ. marshal, chief of protocol, 1977—; cons. NSF, Washington, 1960-68; Research Triangle Inst., Durham, 1965—, I.I. duPont deNemours & Co., 1966-69; Mem. advanced placement com. Coll. Entrance Exam. Bd., N.Y., 1967-75, chmn. chemistry com., 1969-75, cons., 1975—; mem. exec. com. Gov. N.C. Sci. Advisory Com., 1962-64. Author: (with W.C. Vosburgh) Laboratory Manual of Fundamentals of Analytical Chemistry, 1956, Laboratory Manual of Physical Chemistry of Aqueous Solutions, 1967; Contbr. articles to profl. jours. Bd. dirs. Durham Acad., chmn., 1970-72; chmn. Exptl. Study of Religion and Soc., Raleigh, N.C., 1966-69. Served with USNR, 1944-46. Recipient 1st annual Alumni Distinguished Undergrad. Teaching award Duke, 1971, Disting. Pub. Svc. award USN, 1989. Mem. Am. Chem. Soc. (chmn. N.C. sect. 1956, com. on profl. tng.), Assn. Naval ROTC Colls. and Univs. (pres. 1982-88), Chem. Soc. London, Phi Beta Kappa (chpt. pres. 1974-75), Sigma Xi, Omicron Delta Kappa. Democrat. Presbyn. (ruling elder; exec. com. Ednl. Instns. Synod of N.C. 1966-72). Lodge: Rotary. Club: Univ. (Durham, N.C.). Home: 2514 Wrightwood Ave Durham NC 27705-5830 Office: Duke U Dept Chemistry PO Box 90357 Durham NC 27708-0357

WILDER, ROBERT GEORGE, advertising and public relations executive; b. Hornell, N.Y., Mar. 27, 1920; s. George Reuben and Laura (Nolan) W.; m. Annabel D. Heritage, Feb. 21, 1953; children: Loraine Wilder Powell, Gordon Heritage. B.A., Coll. Wooster, 1942. Propr. Robert G. Wilder & Co., Inc. (public relations), Phila., 1945-50; dir. public relations Lewis & Gilman (advt.-public relations), Phila., 1950-55; v.p. Lewis & Gilman (advt.-public relations), 1955-59, exec. v.p., 1959-64, pres., from 1964; chmn. Lewis, Gilman & Kynett (merger with Foote, Cone & Belding), 1983-90, chmn. emeritus, 1990—; bd. dirs. Rittenhouse Trust Co.; dir. emeritus Round Hill Devel. Co. Ltd., Montego Bay, Jamaica. Trustee emeritus Franklin Inst., Lankenau Hosp., Phila.; bd. dirs. Independence Hall Assn.; life trustee emeritus Coll. of Wooster, Ohio. Served to lt. comdr. USNR, 1942-46. Recipient award Charles M. Price Sch., 1971, Bus. and Industry award Opportunities Industrialization Ctr., 1971, Disting. Alumni award Coll. Wooster, 1971, Area Council Econ. Edn. Enterprise award, 1980, Gold Liberty Bell award TV, Radio & Advt. Club Phila., 1982, Vol. of Yr. award Leukemia Soc. Eastern Pa., 1983, Silver medal Phila. Club of Advt. Women, 1984, ann. achievers award Wheels, 1985, Good Scout award Phila. coun. Boy Scouts Am., 1986, Heart of Phila. award Am. Heart Assn., 1989, Great Am. award Poor Richard Club Phila., 1990; named to Bus./Profl. Advt. Assn. Hall of Fame, 1988; inducted into First Annual Hall of Fame of Broadcast Pioneers, Phila. chpt., 1992. Mem. Res. Officers Assn. (past pres. Pa.), Greater Phila. C. of C. (past chmn., bd. dirs., William Penn award 1991); Clubs: Union League (past pres.), Penn, Bachelors Barge (chmn.), Phila. Country, Merion Cricket, Sunday Breakfast. Home: Grays Ln House 100 Grays Ln Haverford PA 19041 Office: FCB 200 S Broad St Philadelphia PA 19102-3803

WILDER, RONALD PARKER, economics educator; b. Freeport, Tex., Jan. 15, 1941; s. J Barton and Lois (Parker) W.; m. Charlotte D. Pearson, Sept. 4, 1965; children: Erika, Rachel, David. BA, Rice U., 1963, MA, 1964; PhD, Vanderbilt U., 1969. Asst. prof. econs. U. S.C., Columbia, 1970-75, assoc. prof., 1975-80, prof., 1980—, chmn. dept. econs., 1987—. Co-author: Stock Life Insurance Profitability, 1986; mem. editorial bd. So. Econ. J., 1978-80; contbr. articles to profl. jours. Capt. U.S. Army, 1968-70. Fellow Ford Found., Vanderbilt U., 1964-65. Mem. Am. Econ. Assn., So. Econ. Assn., Omicron Delta Epsilon. United Methodist. Avocations: hiking, canoeing. Office: U of SC Dept of Econs Columbia SC 29208

WILDER, VALERIE, ballet company director; b. Pasadena, Calif., Aug. 5, 1947; d. Douglas Wilder and Helen Marie (Wilson) Morrill; m. Geoffrey Duer Perry. Nov. 24, 1973; children: Stuart Whittier, Sabina Woodman. Student, Butler U., Indpls., 1966-68, U. Toronto, 1969-75. Dancer Nat. Ballet Can., Toronto, 1970-78; ptnr. Perry & Wilder Inc., Toronto, 1976-83; artistic adminstr. Nat. Ballet Can., Toronto, 1983-86, assoc. artistic dir., 1986-87, co-artistic dir., 1987-89, assoc. dir., 1989—; adv. bd. Dancer Transition Ctr., Toronto, 1986—; dance adv. panel Can. Coun., 1984-89; dance adv. com. Ont. Arts. Coun., 1985-90. Bd. dirs. Toronto Arts Coun., 1990-94. Mem. Dance in Can. Assn., Can. Assn. Profl. Dance Orgns. (bd. dirs.). Avocations: competitive running, triathlon. Office: Nat Ballet of Can, 157 King St E, Toronto, ON Canada M5C 1G9

WILDERMUTH, GORDON LEE, architect; b. Lima, Ohio, Nov. 13, 1937; s. Oliver and Margery (Mason) W.; B.S. in Architecture, U. Cin., 1961; m. Patricia Williams, June 1, 1963 (dec. 1983); m. Hannelore Brauning, Aug. 10, 1993. With Skidmore, Owings & Merrill, Architects/Engrs., 1963—, assoc., 1967-70, assoc. ptnr., 1970-73, ptnr., 1973-87, ret. ptnr., 1987-90, cons. ptnr., 1991—. Bd. dirs. Police Athletic League N.Y., 1974-81, N.Y. Poly. Inst., 1975-77, Founders Council, Field Mus. Natural History. Served with Spl. Forces, U.S. Army, 1962-1963. Recipient Aga Khan award for architecture, 1983. Fellow AIA. Home: 175 E Delaware Pl Chicago IL 60611 Office: Skidmore Owings & Merrill 224 S Michigan Ave Chicago IL 60604

WILDERMUTH, ROGER GREGORY, publishing company executive; b. Sandwich, Ill., 1944. Degree, U. Ill., 1966. Pres. pub. group Rand McNally & Co., Skokie, Ill.; v.p., dir. Rand McNally-Internat., Inc.; chmn. Rand McNally Map Svcs. Co., Rand McNally-Infomap, Inc. Office: Rand McNally & Co 8255 Central Park Ave Skokie IL 60076-2908

WILDEROTTER, JAMES ARTHUR, lawyer; b. Newark, July 25, 1944; s. Arthur Walter and Dorothy Theresa (King) W.; m. Cheryl Lynn Clifford; children: James, Kristin Kathryn. B.A., Georgetown U., 1966; J.D., U. Ill., 1969. Bar: D.C. 1969, U.S. Supreme Ct. 1974. Assoc. Covington & Burling, Washington, 1969-71; spl. asst. to Under Sec. Commerce, Washington, 1971-73; exec. asst. to Sec. HUD, Washington, 1973-74; assoc. dept. atty. gen. U.S. Washington, 1974-75, assoc. counsel to Pres. U.S., 1975-76; gen. counsel U.S. Energy Research and Devel. Adminstrn., Washington, 1976-77; of counsel Morgan, Lewis & Bockius, Washington, 1977-78; ptnr. Jones, Day, Reavis & Pogue, Washington, 1978-91; v.p., gen. counsel Internat. Paper Co., Purchase, N.Y., 1991—. Editor in chief: U. Ill. Law Rev., 1968-69. Gen. counsel rules com. Rep. Nat. Conv., 1980; sec. James S. Brady Presdl. Found., 1982-88; gen. counsel Nat. Sudden Infant Death Syndrome Found., 1986-90, sec. Sudden Infant Death Syndrome Alliance, 1990-93. Served with USN, 1962-68. Mem. ABA. Republican. Roman Catholic. Home: 60 Hampshire Rd Bronxville NY 10708-5820 Office: Internat Paper Co 2 Manhattanville Rd Purchase NY 10577-2118

WILDEROTTER, MAGGIE, cable television executive; b. Neptune, N.J., Feb. 9, 1955; d. Denis James and Constance Rosemary (Shields) Sullivan; m. Philip Jay Wilderotter; children: Christopher, Daniel. BA in Econs., Holy Cross Coll., 1977. Accts. receivable supr. CableData, Sacramento, 1979-80; mgr. acctg. svcs. CableData 1980-82, mgr. reg. support, 1982, mktg. mgr., 1982-83, dir. mktg., 1983, dir. nat. accts., 1983-85, v.p., 1985—; bd. dirs. Phoenix Cable Ptnrs., San Rafael, Calif., 1988—, Satellite Video Ctr., Rancho Cordova, Calif., 1988—, CableData Europe Ltd., Leeds, Eng., 1989—. Mem. Nat. Cable TV Assn. (bd. dirs. 1987—), Women in Cable (exec. mem.), Cable TV Adminstrn. & Mktg. Soc., Calif. Cable TV Assn., Nat. Acad. Cable Programming. Republican. Roman Catholic. Office: CableData 11020 Sun Center Dr Rancho Cordova CA 95670-6184

WILDES, LEON, lawyer, educator; b. Scranton, Pa., Mar. 4, 1933. BA magna cum laude, Yeshiva U., 1954; JD, NYU, 1957, LLM, 1959. Bar: N.Y. 1958, U.S. Dist. Ct. (so. dist.) N.Y. 1960, U.S. Supreme Ct. 1961. Ptnr. Wildes and Weinberg, N.Y.C., 1960—; adj. prof. law Benjamin N. Cardozo Sch. Law, N.Y.C., 1981—. Contbr. numerous articles to law revs. Mem. ABA, Assn. of Bar of City of N.Y. (com. immigration and nationality law 1975-78, 88-91), Am. Immigration Lawyers Assn. (nat. pres. 1970-71, bd. govs. 1971—, editor Immigration and Nationality Law Symposium 1983,

co-chair ethics com. 1993—). Office: 515 Madison Ave New York NY 10022-5403

WILDHACK, WILLIAM AUGUST, JR., lawyer; b. Takoma Park, Md., Nov. 28, 1935; s. William August and Martha Elizabeth (Parks) W.; m. Martha Moore Allston, Aug. 1, 1959; children: William A. III, Elizabeth L. B.S., Miami U., Oxford, Ohio, 1957; J.D., George Washington U., 1963. Bar: Va. 1963, D.C. 1965, Md. 1983, U.S. Supreme Ct. 1967. Agt. IRS, No. Va., 1957-65; assoc. Morris, Pearce, Gardner & Beitel, Washington, 1965-69; sole practice Washington, 1969; v.p., corp. counsel B.F. Saul Co. and affiliates, Chevy Chase, Md., 1969-87, Chevy Chase Bank, F.S.B. and affiliates, 1987-90; atty. pvt. practice, Arlington, Va., 1991—; sec. B.F. Saul Real Estate Investment Trust, Chevy Chase, 1972-87. Mem. Arlington Tenant Landlord Commn., 1976-91. Mem. ABA, Md. Bar Assn., D.C. Bar, Va. Bar, Arlington County Bar Assn., Nat. Acad. Elder Law Attys., Am. Soc. Corp. Secs., Phi Alpha Delta. Presbyterian.

WILDIN, MAURICE WILBERT, mechanical engineering educator; b. Hutchinson, Kans., June 24, 1935; s. John Frederick and Mildred Minerva (Dawson) W.; m. Mary Ann Brovan Christiansen, Aug. 9, 1958; children: Molly, Mildred. AA, Hutchinson Jr. Coll., 1955; BSME, U. Kans., 1958; MSME, Purdue U., 1959, PhD, 1963. Grad. asst. and instr. mech. engring. Purdue U., West Lafayette, Ind., 1958-61; from asst. prof. to assoc. prof. mech. engring. U. N.Mex., Albuquerque, 1961-73, prof., 1973, dept. chair, 1968-73; mem. tech. staff Sandia Nat. Labs., Albuquerque, 1984-85; cons. several domestic and fgn. firms on stratified thermal storage, 1985—. Contbr. articles to profl. jours. Mem. ASME, ASHRAE, Am. Solar Energy Soc. Office: U NMex Dept Mech Engring Albuquerque NM 87131

WILDING, DIANE, marketing, financial and information systems executive; b. Chicago Heights, Ill., Nov. 7, 1942; d. Michael Edward and Katherine Surian; m. Manfred Georg Wilding, May 7, 1975 (div. 1980). BSBA in Acctg. magna cum laude, No. Ill. U., 1963; postgrad., U. Chgo., 1972-74; cert. in German lang., Goethe Inst., Rothenburg, Germany, 1984; cert. in internat. bus. German, Goethe Inst., Atlanta, 1994. Lic. cosmetologist. Systems engr. IBM, Chgo., 1963-68; data processing mgr. Am. Res. Corp., Chgo., 1969-72; system rsch. and devel. project mgr. Continental Bank, Chgo., 1972-75; fin. industry mktg. rep. IBM Can., Ltd., Toronto, Ont. 1976-79; regional telecommunications mktg. exec. Control Data Corp. Atlanta, 1980-84; gen. mgr. The Plant Plant, Atlanta, 1985-92; IBM; sys. engr. IBM, Atlanta, 1993—; pioneer installer on-line Automatic Teller Machines, Pos Equipment. Author: The Canadian Payment System: An International Perspective, 1977. Mem. Chgo. Coun. on Fgn. Rels.; bd. dirs. Easter House Adoption Agy. Chgo., 1974-76. Mem. Internat. Brass Soc., Goethe Inst., Mensa. Clubs: Ponte Verde (Fla.); Royal Ont. Yacht, Libertyville Racquet. Avocations: horticulture, travel, dancing, gourmet cooking, foreign languages. Home: 1948 Cobb Pky #28J Smyrna GA 30080

WILDING, JAMES ANTHONY, airports manager; b. Washington, Dec. 22, 1937; s. Anthony Warwick and Dorothy (Lauten) W.; m. Marcella Anne Gibbons, Aug. 5, 1961; children: Matthew, William, Patricia, Marcella. B.S. in Civil Engring., Catholic U., 1959. With planning dept. Bur. Nat. Capital Airports, Washington, 1959-63, with civil engring. dept., 1963-72, acting dir., 1974; chief engring. staff Met. Washington Airports, 1972-75, dep. dir., 1975-79, dir., 1979-87; gen. mgr. Met. Washington Apts. Authority, Alexandria, Va., 1987—; chmn. Airports Coun. Internat. N.A. Recipient Sr. Exec. Service Performance award Dept. Transp., 1981, Meritorious Exec. award Pres. of U.S., 1982, Outstanding Achievement award Sec. Transp., 1985. Roman Catholic. Home: 1805 Crystal Ln Silver Spring MD 20906-2102 Office: Met Washington Airports Authority 44 Canal Center Plz Alexandria VA 22314-1563

WILDING, LAWRENCE PAUL, pedology educator, soil science consultant; b. Winner, S.D., Oct. 1, 1934; s. William Kasper and Ruth Inez (Root) W.; m. Gladys Dora Milne, Nov. 25, 1956; children: Linda Kay, Doris Bertha, Charles William, David Lawrence. BSc, S.D. State U., 1956, MSc, 1959; PhD, U. Ill., 1962. Asst. in agronomy S.D. State U., Brookings, 1956-59; rsch. fellow U. Ill., Urbana, 1959-62; prof. agronomy Ohio State U., Columbus, 1962-76; prof. pedology Tex. A&M U., College Station, 1976—; vis. prof. U. Guelph, Ont. Can., 1971-72; mem. NATO Advanced Rsch. Workshop on Expansive Soils, Cornell U., 1990-91. Author or/and editor 3 books; assoc. editor Catena Verlag, 1989, Geoderma, 1988-92; contbr. over 130 articles to profl. jours., chpts. to books. Sgt. S.D. N.G., 1956-59. Recipient Mem. award Sigma XI, 1988, Superior Svc. Group award sci. rsch. USDA, 1993; Campbell Soup fellow, 1992-93; grantee USDA, AID, 1986—. Fellow Am. Soc. Agronomy (cert.), Soil Sci. Soc. Am. (Soil Sci. Rsch. award 1987, opportunities in soil sci. com., chmn. subcommun. B 1989-92, chmn. divsn. S-5, bd. dirs. rep., mem. steering com. 1990-91, pres. elect 1992-93, pres. 1993-94, pst pres. 1994-95), Am. Inst. Chemists; mem. Soil Scientists Assn. Tex., Soil and Water Conservation Soc. Am., Tex. A&M Faculty Club, Gamma Sigma Delta. Democrat. Presbyterian. Avocations: golf, woodworking, travelling, sports, antiques. Office: Texas A&M U Dept Soil and Crop Scis College Station TX 77843

WILDMAN, GARY CECIL, chemist; b. Middlefield, Ohio, Nov. 25, 1942; s. Gerald Robert and Frances Jane (Swager) W.; m. Nancy Jackson, June 5, 1965; children: Debbie, Eric. A.B. in Chemistry, Thiel Coll., 1964; Ph.D. in Chemistry, Duke U., 1970. Research asst. B.F. Goodrich Research, Brecksville, Ohio, summer 1964; instr. Duke U., 1966-67; research chemist Hercules Research Center, Wilmington, Del., 1968-71; assoc. prof. polymer sci. U. So. Miss., Hattiesburg, 1971-76; prof. U. So. Miss., 1976-83, chmn. dept., 1971-76, dean Coll. Sci. and Tech., 1976-83; v.p. research and devel. Schering Plough, Memphis, 1983—. Mem. Am. Chem. Soc., So. Soc. Coatings Tech., Soc. Plastics Engrs., Am. Crystallographic Assn., Phi Beta Kappa, Sigma Xi, Phi Lambda Upsilon, Sigma Pi Sigma, Omicron Delta Kappa. Republican. Methodist. Club: Rotary. Home: 8857 Aldershot Dr Memphis TN 38139-6522 Office: PO Box 377 Memphis TN 38151-0002

WILDMAN, MAX EDWARD, lawyer; b. Terre Haute, Ind., Dec. 4, 1919; s. Roscoe Ellsworth and Lena (Shaw) W.; m. Joyce Lenore Smith, Sept. 25, 1948; children: Leslie, William. B.S., Butler U., 1941; J.D., U. Mich., 1947; M.B.A., U. Chgo., 1952. Bar: Ill., Ind. Ptnr. Kirkland & Ellis, Chgo., 1947-67; mng. ptnr. Wildman, Harrold, Allen & Dixon, Chgo., 1967-89; dir. Colt Industries, N.Y., Nat. Blvd. Bank, Ill. Contbr. articles to profl. jours. Trustee Butler U., Indpls., Lake Forest Hosp., Ill., Lake Bluff Library Bd., Ill.; chmn. Lake Bluff Zoning Bd. Served to lt. col. USAF, 1943-46; PTO. Fellow Am. Coll. Trial Lawyers; mem. Soc. Trial Lawyers, Law Club, Legal Club, Trial Lawyers Club of Chgo. Presbyterian. Clubs: Anglers (Chgo.), Pere Marquette Rod and Gun (Baldwin, Mich.), Shoreacres (Lake Bluff), Univ. of Chgo. Office: Wildman Harrold Allen & Dixon 225 W Wacker Dr Chicago IL 60606-1224

WILE, JULIUS, former corporate executive, educator; b. N.Y.C., Apr. 17, 1915; s. Irwin and Harriet (Brussel) W.; m. Ruth Miller, June 26, 1941 (dec. Feb. 1992); children: Barbara Miller Wile Schwarz, Andrew Brussel. B.S. in Mech. Engring. and Aeronautics, NYU, 1936; DFA (hon.), Culinary Inst. Am., 1994. With Julius Wile Sons & Co. Inc., N.Y.C., 1936-41, 45-76, v.p., 1955-66, sr. v.p., 1967-76; prodn. engr. Brewster Aero. Corp., LI City, N.Y. 1942-44, Greer Hydraulics Inc., Bklyn., 1944-45; trustee Culinary Inst. Am., Hyde Park, N.Y., 1970-79, 81-90, chmn. bd. trustees, 1981-83; vis. lectr. Sch. Hotel Adminstrn. Cornell U., Ithaca, N.Y., 1953-82; wines and spirits lectr.; v.p. New Eng. Distillers Inc., Teterboro, N.J., 1955-72. Contbr. Brit. Book of Yr, 1957-75; editor: Frank Schoonmaker's Encyclopedia of Wine, 7th edit., 1979. V.p. Spain-U.S. C. of C., N.Y.C., 1972; bd. dirs. Scarsdale Family Counseling Service, N.Y., 1973-79; chmn. ann. drive ARC, Scarsdale, 1976. Decorated Ordre de l'Economie Nationale France, Ordre National du Merite France, Membre d'Honneur Academie du Vin de Bordeaux. Mem. Commanderie de Bordeaux (gov. 1959—, dep. grand maitre 1978-88, grand chancelier 1988—); Soc. Wine Educators (bd. dirs. 1980—, treas. 1986-93), Wine and Food Soc. N.Y. (bd. dirs. 1971-73, 77-83), Nat. Assn. Beverage Importers (chmn. table wine com. 1965-76). Republican. Jewish. Clubs: Explorers, Quaker Ridge Golf (Scarsdale); Daniel Gray Fishing. Home and Office: 27 Grand Park Ave Scarsdale NY 10583-7611 *Fifteen years of Prohibition led to public ignorance of fine wines and spirits. Education of myself, employees, the trade and the public has been an important part of my career. It was and still is both a duty and a pleasure to pass on* *what I have learned and enjoyed. My tenet is that 'there is no premium for good taste.'*

WILENSKY, ALVIN, real estate investment trust executive; b. Scranton, Pa., Nov. 3, 1921; s. Isaac and Sarah (Barnett) W.; m. Ruth L. Gross, June 3, 1945; children: I. David, Robert B. A.A., Keystone Jr. Coll., 1941; B.A., Pa. State U., 1943. C.P.A., Pa. Sr. acct. Alberts, Kahn & Levess, N.Y.C., 1945-48; prin. Alvin Wilensky, CPA, Scranton, Pa., 1948-72; v.p. then pres. Century Village Inc., West Palm Beach, Fla., 1973-81; pres. CV Reit, Inc. (formerly Cenvill Investors, Inc.), N.Y. Stock Exch., West Palm Beach, Fla., 1981—; instr. Keystone Jr. Coll., La Plume, Pa., 1949-50. Mem. Dist. Dirs. IRS Profl. Adv. Com., Scranton, 1961-62; mem. Mayor's Tax Study Commn. City of Scranton, 1963-65; pres. Keystone Jr. Coll. Alumni Assn., 1966; v.p. Jewish Fedn. Palm Beach County, 1983-87, bd. dirs., 1987-94. 1st lt. USAF, 1943-45. Decorated Air medal with 5 oak leaf clusters, 1945; recipient Spl. award Jewish War Vets, 1960, Humanitarian award Mid-County Med. Ctr., West Palm Beach, 1981. Mem. AICPA, N.E. chpt. Pa. Inst. CPAs (pres. 1967-68, pres's award), Fla. Inst. CPAs, Nat. Assn. Real Estate Investment Trust (bd. govs. 1983-86). Republican. Jewish. Clubs: Forum of the Palm Beaches; President Country (West Palm Beach). Home: 2480 Presidential Way West Palm Beach FL 33401-1355 Office: CV Reit Inc 100 Century Blvd West Palm Beach FL 33417

WILENSKY, GAIL ROGGIN, economist; b. Detroit, June 14, 1943; d. Albert Alan and Sophia (Blitz) Roggin; AB with honors, U. Mich., 1964, MA in Econs., 1965, PhD in Econs., 1968; hon. degree Hahnemann U., 1993; m. Robert Joel Wilensky, Aug. 4, 1963; children: Peter Benjamin, Sara Elizabeth. Economist, President's Commn. on Income Maintenance Programs, exec. dir. Md. Council of Econ. Advisors, 1969-71; sr. researcher Urban Inst., Washington, 1971-73; assoc. research scientist, public policy and public health U. Mich., Ann Arbor 1973-75, vis. asst. prof. econs., 1973-75; sr. research mgr. Nat. Center for Health Services Research, Hyattsville, Md., 1975-83; assoc. profl. lectr. George Washington U., 1976-78; v.p. div. health affairs Project HOPE, Millwood, Va., 1983-90; adminstr. Health Care Fin. Adminstrn., Washington, 1990-92, dep. asst. to the pres. for policy devel., White House, 1992-93; sr. fellow Project Hope, Bethesda, Md. Vol. Am. Heart Assn., 1980-85; mem. health adv. com. Compt. Gen. U.S., 1987-90, 93—; bd. dirs. United Healthcare Corp., Adv.Tiss Sci., Coram, St. Jude Med., Syncor Internat., Marion Merrill Dow. Mem. vis. com. med. sch. U. Mich., 1993—; trustee United Mine Workers Am. Retirement Fund, 1993—. Flinn Found. disting. scholar, 1985; recipient Dean Conley award Am. Coll. Healthcare Execs. 1989. Mem. NAS (mem. inst. medicine 1989—), Am. Econ. Assn. (women's com. 1982-84), Fedn. Orgns. of Profl. Women (chmn. econ. task force 1981-83), Am. Statis. Assn., Nat. Tax Assn., Washington Women Economists, Assn. Health Svcs. Rsch. (bd. dirs. 1984-87), Found. Health Svcs. Rsch. (bd. dirs. 1987-90, commr. physician payment rev. com. 1989-90). Contbr. 90 articles in field to profl. jours. Mem. Cosmos Club (Washington). Home: 2807 Battery Pl NW Washington DC 20016-3439

WILENSKY, HAROLD L., political science and industrial relations educator; b. New Rochelle, N.Y., Mar. 3, 1923; s. Joseph and Mary Jane (Wainsten) W.; children: Stephen David, Michael Alan, Daniel Lewis. Student, Goddard Coll., 1940-42; AB, Antioch Coll., 1947; MA, U. Chgo., 1949, PhD, 1955. Asst. prof. sociology U. Chgo., 1951-53, asst. prof. indsl. relations, 1953-54; asst. prof. sociology U. Mich., Ann Arbor, 1954-57, assoc. prof., 1957-61, prof., 1961-62; prof. U. Calif., Berkeley, 1963-82, prof. polit. sci., 1982—; research sociologist Inst. Indsl. Relations, 1963—; project dir. Inst. Internat. Studies, 1970-90; project dir. Ctr. for German and European Studies, Berkeley, 1994—; mem. research career awards com. Nat. Inst. Mental Health, 1964-67; cons. in field. Author: Industrial Relations: A Guide to Reading and Research, 1954, Intellectuals in Labor Unions: Organizational Pressures on Professional Roles, 1956, Organizational Intelligence: Knowledge and Policy in Government and Industry, 1967, The New Corporatism, Centralization, and the Welfare State, 1976, (with C.N. Lebeaux) Industrial Society and Social Welfare, 1965, (with others) Comparative Social Policy, 1985, (with L. Turner) Democratic Corporatism and Policy Linkages, 1987; editor: (with C. Arensberg and others) Research in Industrial Human Relations, 1957, (with P.F. Lazarsfeld and W. H. Sewell) The Uses of Sociology, 1967; contbr. articles to profl. jours. Recipient aux. award Social Sci. Rsch. Coun., 1962, Book award McKinsey Found., 1967; fellow Ctr. for Advanced Study in Behavioral Scis., 1956-57, 62-63, German Marshall Fund, 1978-79; Harry A. Millis rsch. awardee U. Chgo., 1950-51. Fellow AAAS; mem. Internat. Sociol. Assn., Internat. Polit. Sci. Assn., Indsl. Relations Research Assn. (exec. com. 1965-68), Soc. for Study Social Problems (chmn. editorial com.), Am. Polit. Sci. Assn., Am. Sociol. Assn. (exec. council 1969-72, chmn. com. on info. tech. and privacy 1970-72), Council European Studies (steering com. 1980-83), AAUP, ACLU. Democrat. Jewish. Avocations: music, trumpet, skiing. Office: U Calif Dept Polit Sci 210 Barrows Hall Berkeley CA 94720

WILENSKY, JULIUS M., publishing company executive; b. Stamford, Conn., Oct. 10, 1916; s. Joseph and Mary (Wainstein) W.; m. Dorothy T. Jobrack, July 2, 1939; children—Joseph L. (dec.), Nancy L. Jamie, Martha J. Hansen. Student, Rensselaer Poly. Inst., 1934-36. Methods engr. Yale & Towne Mfg. Co., Stamford, 1939-49; prodn. mgr. Yale & Towne Mfg. Co., 1953-57; dir. purchasing lock and hardware div. Eaton Yale & Towne, Rye, N.Y., 1957-67; mayor of Stamford, 1969-73; dir. materials, arms operations Winchester div. Olin Corp., New Haven, 1973-78; pres. Wescott Cove Pub. Co., 1978—; lectr. in field. Author guide books on cruising L.I. Sound, Cape Cod, Windward Islands, Bay Islands of Honduras and Abacos; contbr. articles to boating mags. and newspapers; contbg. editor: Rudder, 1970-77; author cruising columns Ea. and So. edits. Sea mag., 1978-80, Rudder mag., 1981-83; editor cruising guides to Tahiti, French Soc. Islands, Maine (2 vols.), Turkey, Belize, Mexico's Caribbean Coast, I Don't Do Portholes, Lights and Legends, Beachcombing and Beachcrafting, Pacific Wanderer, Irma Quarterdeck Reports, Inside American Paradise, Beachcruising and Coastal Camping. Bd. dirs. Stamford Ctr. for Arts, 1981-90; trustee Lifeline, 1983-85; first v.p. Met. Regional Coun., 1973; mem. Tri-State Regional Planning Commn., 1971-73, Stamford Bd. Fin., 1965-69, Stamford Planning Bd., 1963-65; chmn. Coun. Rep. Clubs, Stamford, 1961-62. With USAAF, 1943-46. Named Republican of Yr. Stamford Reps., 1962. Mem. Am. Mgmt. Assn., Stamford Power Squadron, Stamford Good Govt. Assn. (dir., treas. 1949-57), Stamford Chamber Residences (pres. 1953-55). Home: 51 Barrett Ave Stamford CT 06905-3212 *To be productive in fields or enterprises which are useful to other people has been my aspiration, and it's a high one. It's important to set goals early in life, then follow a plan to obtain the education and experience required to achieve these goals. Courage, honesty, objectivity, determination, hard work, and consideration for others will enable one to become outstanding in any field.*

WILENTZ, ROBERT NATHAN, state supreme court justice; b. Perth Amboy, N.J., Feb. 17, 1927; children: James Robert, Amy, Thomas Malino. Student, Princeton U., 1944-45; AB, Harvard U., 1949; LLB, Columbia U., 1952. Bar: N.J. 1952. Ptnr. Wilentz, Goldman & Spitzer, Perth Amboy, 1952-79; mem. N.J. legislature, 1966-69; chief justice N.J. Supreme Ct., 1979—. With USN, 1945-46. Office: NJ Supreme Ct 257 Monmouth Rd Oakhurst NJ 07755-1586

WILENTZ, ROBERT SEAN, history educator, author; b. N.Y.C., Feb. 20, 1951; s. Elias and Jeanne Marie (Campbell) W.; m. Mary Christine Stansell, Jan. 30, 1980; children: James Thomas Farrell, Hannah Cady Rose. BA, Columbia U., 1972, Oxford U., 1974; PhD, Yale U., 1980. Asst. prof. history Princeton (N.J.) U., 1979-85, assoc. prof., 1985-87, prof., 1987—. Author: Chants Democratic, 1984; co-author: The Kingdom of Matthias, 1994; contbg. editor The New Republic, 1995—. John Simon Guggenheim Meml. Found. fellow, 1990; recipient A.J. Beveridge award Am. Hist. Assn., 1984, Ann. Book award Soc. for History of Early Republic, 1984, F.J. Turner award Orgn. Am. Historians, 1985. Home: 7 Edgehill St Princeton NJ 08540-6801 Office: Princeton U Dept History Princeton NJ 08544

WILES, ANDREW J., mathematician, educator; b. England, 1952; married; children. BS in Math., Oxford U., England; PhD in Math., Cambridge U., England. Lecturer Inst. Advanced Studies, Princeton, N.J.; asst. assoc. prof. math. Harvard U., Cambridge, Mass.; prof. math. Princeton U., Princeton, N.J., 1982—. Achievements include solving (with Richard Taylor) Pierre de Fermat's last theory of 1637. Office: Princeton U Dept Math Princeton NJ 08544

WILES, CHARLES PRESTON, minister; b. Frederick, Md., Aug. 5, 1918; s. Charles Wesley and Nellie (Burgess) W.; m. Mary Margaret; children: Charles Preston, Wade Burgess. A.B., Washington Coll., 1939; postgrad., U. Va., 1940; M.A., Duke U., 1945, Ph.D. (Univ. fellow 1947-51, Kearns Honor fellow 1949-50), 1951; B.D., Va. Theol. Sem., 1947. Ordained to ministry Episc. Ch., 1947. Priest-in-charge St. Joseph's Ch., Durham, N.C., 1947-51; rector St. Mary's Episcopal Ch., Burlington, N.J., 1951-64; pres., trustee Burlington Coll., 1951-64, faculty cons., 1956-64; mem. faculty Phila. Div. Sch., 1959-62, lectr. ch. history, 1960-62; dean St. Matthew's Episcopal Cathedral, Dallas, 1964-87, dean emeritus, 1989; assoc. priest St. Luke's, Dallas, 1987—; dep. gen. Conv. from Diocese Dallas, 1967, 69, 70, 73, 76, 79; del. Provincial Synod from Diocese Dallas, 1966, 69, 72, 75, 78; mem. exec. council Diocese Dallas, 1967-77, 84-86, pres. mem. standing com., 1970-73, pres., 1971-73, mem. bd. missions, 1967-69, chmn. dept. coll. work, 1965-71, mem. bd. examing chaplains, 1965-71; mem. standing liturgical commn.; dean, warden Cathedral Center for Continuing Edn. and Pastoral Concern, 1971-87, Commn. Ministry, 1971-76; dean Dallas Deanery, 1965-69, 84-86, Bicentennial preacher, 1975; pres. convocation and clericus Diocese of N.J., 1961-64; examining chaplain, mem. bd. missions, mem. bd. Christina edn., dean Burlington-Trenton convocation; instr., dean Drew Conf. for Adults in N.J., 1952-56; retreat conductor St. Martin's House, Bernardsville, N.J., St. John Bapt. Convent, Mendhan, N.J.; dean Diocesan Sch. Religion, N.J., 1962-63; parish life lab. and weekend conductor Nat. Dept. Christian Edn., 1962; co-founder, dean Princeton (N.J.) Conf., 1956-64; mem. Goals for Dallas Com.; co-chmn. N.Am. Cathedral Deans' Conf., 1980-81. Author: Sacrament and Sacrifice, 2d edit., 1973, Lancelot Andrews, Caroline Divine, 1951, Lift Up Your HEarts, 1956, A Manual of Prayers, 1975, The Holy Eucharist: Word and Sacrament, 1993, The Gate of Heaven, 1993. Trustee Gen. Theol. Sem., 1968-80; bd. dirs. Evergreen Home for Aging, St. Philip's Community Center, Overseas Mission Soc. Named Priest of Yr. 1969. Mem. Navy League, Ch. Hist. Soc. (dir. 1960-68), Kiwanian Club (Disting. Svc. award 1951, Disting. Citizen award Brunswick, Md. 1986), Dallas Athletic club, (Chaparral, Vesper (Phila.) Club, Burlington County Country Club. Home: 7023 Northwood Rd Dallas TX 75225-2439

WILES, DAVID MCKEEN, chemist; b. Springhill, N.S., Can., Dec. 28, 1932; s. Roy McKeen and Olwen Gertrude (Jones) W.; m. Valerie Joan Rowlands, June 8, 1957; children: Gordon Stuart, Sandra Lorraine. B.Sc. with honors, McMaster U., 1954, M.Sc., 1955; Ph.D. in Chemistry, McGill U., 1957. Research officer chemistry div. Nat. Research Council of Can., Ottawa, 1959-66; head textile chemistry sect. chemistry div. Nat. Research Council of Can., 1966-75, dir. chemistry div., 1975-90; pres. Plastichem Cons., Victoria, B.C., Can., 1990—; chmn. Can. High Polymer Forum, 1967-69; v.p. N.Am. Chem. Congress, Mexico City, 1975. Contbr. articles to profl. jours.; mem. editorial adv. bd. numerous profl. jours. Can. Ramsay Meml. fellow, 1957-59. Fellow Chem. Inst. Can. (chmn. bd. dirs. 1972-74, pres. 1975-76, Dunlop Lectr. award 1981), Royal Soc. Chem. London, Royal Soc. Can.; mem. Am. Chem. Soc. (Polymer Chem. div.). Patentee in field. Home and Office: 3965 Juan de Fuca Terr, Victoria, BC Canada V8N 5W9

WILES, PAUL MARTIN, hospital administration executive; b. Takoma Park, Md., May 11, 1947; married. BA, St. Michael's Coll., 1969; MHA, Duke U., 1971. Adminstrv. asst. Fanny Allen Hosp., Winooski, Vt., 1968-69; adminstrv. resident Forsyth Meml. Hosp., Winston-Salem, N.C., 1970-71, asst. adminstr., 1971; asst. adminstr. USAF Hosp., Kincheloe AFB, Mich., 1972-73; med. squad comdr. USAF Regional Hosp., Hampton, Va., 1973-74; asst. to pres. Forsyth County Hosp. Authority, Winston-Salem, 1974-75, v.p., 1975-79, sr. v.p., 1979-84; pres., CEO Carolina Medicorp Inc., Winston-Salem, 1985—; also adminstr. Forsyth Meml. Hosp., Winston-Salem. Contbr. articles to profl. jours. Mem. N.C. Hosp. Assn. (bd. dirs., chmn. regional adv. bd.). Office: Forsyth Meml Hosp 3333 Silas Creek Pkwy Winston Salem NC 27103-3090

WILETS, LAWRENCE, physics educator; b. Oconomowoc, Wis., Jan. 4, 1927; s. Edward and Sophia (Finger) W.; m. Dulcy Elaine Margoles, Dec. 21, 1947; children—Ileen Sue, Edward E., James D.; m. Vivian C. Wolf, Feb. 8, 1976. B.S., U. Wis., 1948; M.A., Princeton, 1950, Ph.D., 1952. Research asso. Project Matterhorn, Princeton, N.J., 1951-53, U. Calif. Radiation Lab., Livermore, 1953; NSF postdoctoral fellow Inst. Theoretical Physics, Copenhagen, Denmark, 1953-55; staff mem. Los Alamos Sci. Lab., 1955-58; mem. Inst. Advanced Study, Princeton, 1957-58; mem. faculty U. Wash., Seattle, 1958—; prof. physics U. Wash., 1962—; cons. to pvt. and govt. labs.; vis. prof. Princeton, 1969, Calif. Inst. Tech., 1971. Author: Theories of Nuclear Fission, 1964, Nontopological Solitons, 1989; contbr. over 170 articles to profl. jours. Del. Dem. Nat. Conv., 1968. NSF sr. fellow Weizmann Inst. Sci., Rehovot, Israel, 1961-62; Nordita prof. and Guggenheim fellow Lund (Sweden) U., also Weizmann Inst., 1976—; Sir Thomas Lyle rsch. fellow U. Melbourne, Australia, 1989; recipient Alexander von Humboldt sr. U.S. scientist award, 1983. Fellow Am. Phys. Soc., AAAS; mem. Fedn. Am. Scientists, AAUP (pres. 1969-70, 73-75, pres. state conf. 1975-76), Phi Beta Kappa, Sigma Xi. Club: Explorers. Research on theory of nuclear structure and reactions, nuclear fission, atomic structure, atomic collisions, many body problems, subnuclear structure and elementary particles. Office: U Washington Dept Physics FM 15 Seattle WA 98195

WILEY, BARRY HOLLAND, marketing executive; b. Iola, Kans., Sept. 18, 1936; s. William G. and Kathryn (Holland) W.; m. Leanna M. Hauder, June 15, 1963; children: Ann-Kristina, Timothy H., Michael C. BA in Physics, U. Calif., Berkeley, 1958; MA in Physics, U. So. Calif., L.A., 1965; MBA, Harvard U., 1967. Plant mgr. RF power TRW Semiconductor, Lawndale, Calif., 1967-72; pres. Tympanium Corp., Woburn, Mass., 1972-80; mgr. strategic mktg. Unitrode Corp., Lexington, Mass., 1980-85; v.p. mktg. and sales Cherry Semiconductor Corp., East Greenwich, R.I., 1985—. Capt. USMCR, 1958-61. Mem. Am. Phys. Soc., Magic Circle (London), T.E. Lawrence Soc. (London), Internat. Brotherhood Magicians. Office: Cherry Semiconductor Corp 2000 S County Trl East Greenwich RI 02818-1530

WILEY, BONNIE JEAN, journalism educator; b. Portland, Oreg.; d. Myron Eugene and Bonnie Jean (Galliher) W. BA, U. Wash., 1948; MS, Columbia U., 1957; PhD, So. Ill. U., 1965. Mng. editor Yakima (Wash.) Morning Herald; reporter, photographer Portland Oregonian; feature writer Seattle Times; war correspondent AP, San Francisco; reporter Yakima Daily Republic; journalism tchr. U. Wash., Seattle, Cen. Wash. U., Ellensburg, U. Hawaii, Honolulu; mem. grad. faculty Bangkok U., Thailand, 1991; mem. faculty journalism program U. Hawaii, Honolulu, 1992—; adminstr. Am. Samoa Coll., Pago Pago; news features advisor Xinhua News Agy., Beijing. Mem. Women in Communications (Hawaii Headliner award 1985, Nat. Headliner award 1990), Theta Sigma Phi. Home: 1434 Punahou St Apt 722 Honolulu HI 96822-4729

WILEY, CARL ROSS, timber company executive; b. Astoria, Oreg., Apr. 17, 1930; s. Hamilton Ross and Ada Ellen (Smith) W.; m. Dolores Eileen Brice, Dec. 19, 1953; children: Susan, Steven, Kenneth. BS in Indsl. Engring., Oreg. State U., 1958; grad. exec. ing. program, MIT, 1974. Quality control engr. Oreg. Metall. Corp., 1958-59; indsl. engr. Osborne Electronics Corp., Portland, Oreg., 1959-62; v.p. timber and mfg. Boise Cascade Corp., Idaho, 1962-80; exec. v.p. Roseburg (Oreg.) Lumber Co., 1980-85; chief exec. officer Puget Sound Plywood, Tacoma, 1986-93; pres., CEO Lane Plywood, Eugene, Oreg., 1993—. Bd. dirs. Boise YMCA, 1975-78. With AUS, 1951-53. Mem. Am. Plywood Assn. (trustee), Western Wood Products Assn. (bd. dirs., chmn. econ. svcs. 1974-80). Lutheran. Office: Lane Plywood 65 N Bertelsen Rd Eugene OR 97402-5301

WILEY, DAVID OWEN, public relations executive; b. Philipsburg, Pa., Jan. 26, 1935; s. Franklin Williams and Mary (Owens) W.; divorced; children: Bethalee Dawn Jones, Jeffrey Brian. Student, Mich. State U., 1959-62. Editor Ford Motor Co., Dearborn, Mich., 1966-70; pubs. specialist Goodyr. Tire and Rubber Co., Akron, Ohio, 1970-74; mgr. communication services Wean United Inc., Warren, Ohio, 1974-78; dir. pub. relations The Patton Agy., Phoenix, 1978-79; pres. Petroglyph Communications, Inc., Phoenix, 1979-86; prin. Cook, Riggs & Wiley, Inc., Phoenix, 1986-87, David C. Wiley Assocs. Inc., Phoenix, 1987—. Mem. speakers bur. New Detroit Inc., 1969; bd. dirs. West Side Neighborhood Inc., Akron, 1971-72, Phoenix City Club,

1987—, Valley Citizens League, 1988—; chmn. state pub. info. Ariz. Chpt. Nat. Cancer Soc., Phoenix, 1980. Served as sgt. USMC, 1955-59. Mem. Pub. Relations Soc. Am. (bd. dirs. Phoenix chpt. 1979—, pres. 1988), Internat. Assn. Bus. Communicators (pres. Phoenix chpt. 1979-80, dist. v.p., bd. dirs. 1975-77, Gold Quill award 1973). Democrat. Episcopalian. Club: Phoenix City. Avocations: hiking, photography, reading, writing. Office: David O Wiley Assocs Inc 2700 N Central Ave Ste 600 Phoenix AZ 85004-1139

WILEY, DEBORAH E., publishing executive; b. 1946. AA, Pine Manor Coll., 1966; BA, Boston U., 1968; Harvard U., 1983. Vice chmn. bd. John Wiley & Sons, Inc., 1977—. Office: John Wiley & Sons Inc 605 3rd Ave New York NY 10158-0001

WILEY, DON CRAIG, biochemistry and biophysics educator; b. Akron, Ohio, Oct. 21, 1944; s. William Childs and Phyllis Rita (Norton) W.; m. Katrin Valgeirsdottir; 1 child, William Valgeir; children from previous marriage: Kristen D., Craig S. BS in Physics and Chemistry, Tufts U., 1966; PhD in Biophysics, Harvard U., 1971. Asst. prof. dept. biochemistry and molecular biology Harvard U., Cambridge, Mass., 1971-75, assoc. prof., 1975-79, prof. biochemistry and biophysics, 1979—, chmn. dept. molecular and cellular biology, 1992—, investigator Howard Hughes Med. Inst., 1987—; mem. biophys. chemistry study sect. NIH, 1981-85; Shipley Symposium lectr. Harvard Med. Sch., 1985, Peter A. Leermakers Symposium lectr. Wesleyan U., 1986, K.F. Meyer lectr. U. Calif., San Francisco, 1986, John T. Edsall lectr. Harvard U., 1987, Washborn lectr. Boston Mus. Sci., 1987, Harvey lectr. N.Y. Acad. Sci., 1988, XVI Linus Pauling lectr. Stanford U., 1989; rsch. assoc. in medicine Children's Hosp., Boston, 1990—. Contbr. numerous articles to profl. jours. Recipient Ledlie prize Harvard U., 1982, Louisa Gross Horwitz prize Columbia U., 1990, William B. Coley award Cancer Rsch. Inst., 1992, V.D. Mattia award, 1992, Passano Found. Laureate award, 1993, Emil von Behring prize, 1993, Gairdner Found. Internat. award 1994; European Molecular Biology fellow, 1976. Fellow NAS (lectr. 1988); mem. AAAS, Am. Acad. Arts and Scis., Am. Chem. Soc. (Nichol's Disting. Symposium lectr. N.E. sect. 1988), Am. Crystallographic Assn., Am. Soc. for Chemistry and Molecular Biology, Am. Soc. for Virology, Biophys. Soc. (Nat. lectr. 1989), Protein Soc. Office: Harvard U Dept Molecular and Cellular Biology 7 Divinity Ave Cambridge MA 02138-2092 also: Children's Hosp Lab of Molecular Medicine 320 Longwood Ave Boston MA 02115-5746

WILEY, EDWIN PACKARD, lawyer; b. Chgo., Dec. 10, 1929; s. Edwin Garnet and Marjorie Chastina (Packard) W.; m. Barbara Jean Miller, May 21, 1949; children: Edwin Miller, Clayton Alexander, Stephen Packard. BA, U. Chgo., 1949, JD, 1952. Bar: Wis. 1952, Ill. 1952, U.S. Dist. Ct. (ea. dist.) Wis. 1953, U.S. Supreme Ct. 1978. Assoc. Foley & Lardner, Milw., 1952-60, ptnr., 1960—; bd. dirs. Badger Meter, Inc., Genetic Testing Inst., Inc., Nat. Rivet and Mfg. Co., Shaler Co., Waukesha Cutting Tools, other corps. and founds. Co-author: Bank Holding Companies: A Practical Guide to Bank Acquisitions and Mergers, 1988, Wisconsin Uniform Commercial Code Handbook, 1971; author: Promotional Arrangements: Discrimination in Advertising and Promotional Allowances, 1976; editor in chief U. Chgo. Law Rev., 1952; contbr. articles to legal jours. Bd. dirs. Blood Ctr. of Southeastern Wis., pres., 1978-82; pres. Blood Ctr. Rsch. Found., Inc., 1983-87; v.p. Friends of Schlitz Audubon Ctr., Inc., 1975-87; active United Performing Arts Fund of Milw.; pres. Wis. Conservatory of Music, 1968-74; pres. First Unitarian Soc. Milw., 1961-63; v.p. Mid-Am. Ballet Co., 1971-73, Milw. Ballet Co., 1977-82; pres. Florentine Opera Co., 1983-86; bd. dirs. Milw. Symphony Orch., pres., 1993—; bd. dirs. Milw. Pub. Mus., Inc. sec. 1992—. Mem. ABA, State Bar of Wis., Milw. Bar Assn., Am. Law Inst., Order of Coif, Milw. Club, Univ. Club, Phi Beta Kappa (pres. Greater Milw. assn. 1962-63). Unitarian-Universalist. Home: 929 N Astor St #2101 Milwaukee WI 53202-3499 Office: Foley & Lardner Firstar Ctr 777 E Wisconsin Ave Milwaukee WI 53202-5302

WILEY, GREGORY ROBERT, publisher; b. Mpls., Sept. 21, 1951; s. William Joseph and Terese (Kunz) W.; m. Sheila Francis, May 25, 1979; children: Kathleen, Mary Glennon. BA in Personnel Adminstrn., U. Kans., 1972-74. Dist. sales mgr. Reader's Digest, St. Louis, 1976-80, regional sales dir., Chgo., 1980-82; nat. sales mgr. retail div. Rand McNally & Co., Chgo., 1982-83, nat. sales mgr. premium incentive div., 1983-86, nat. sales mgr. bookstore and mass market sales, 1986-88; book publisher, The Sporting News, St. Louis, 1988-90, v.p. mktg. Marketmakers Internat., St. louis, 1990-93; v.p. mktg. Sofsource Inc., 1993—. Mem Nat. Premium Sales Execs., 93; v.p. mktg. Sofsource Inc., 1993—. Mem Nat. Premium Sales Execs., Promotional Mktg. Assn. Am. Roman Catholic. Avocations: pvt. pilot, historic restoration, golf. Home: 1867 Ironstone Rd Saint Louis MO 63131-3804 Office: Sofsource Inc 14615 Manchester Rd Ste 203 Saint Louis MO 63105

WILEY, JASON LARUE, JR., neurosurgeon; b. Canandaigua, N.Y., Dec. 2, 1917; s. Jason LaRue and Eva Althea (Moore) W.; m. Alma Williams, Jan. 4, 1944 (div. Feb. 1956); children: Robert W., Richard L.; m. Ann Valentine Gerrish, Apr. 14, 1956 (div. July 1979); children: Martha V., Pamela M., Catherine A. Student, Antioch Coll., 1934-37; MD, Harvard U., 1941. Diplomate Am. Bd. Surgery, Am. Bd. Neurol. Surgery. Intern Kings County Hosp., Bklyn., 1941-42; asst. resident surgery Ellis Hosp., Schenectady, N.Y., 1948-49; from asst. to assoc. resident surgery Rochester (N.Y.) Gen. Hosp., 1949-51; from asst. to assoc. to chief resident neurosurgery Yale U. and Hartford Hosp., New Haven and Hartford Conn., 1951-54; practice medicine specializing in neurosurgery Kansa City, Mo., 1954-56, Rochester, 1956—; chief neurosurgery Rochester Gen. Hosp., 1959-71, emeritus neurosurgeon, 1989—; clin. asst. prof. neurosurgery U. Rochester, 1961-88. Mem. Bd. for Profl. Med. Conduct, N.Y. State Dept. Health, Albany, N.Y., 1985—. Served to lt. comdr. USN, 1942-47, PTO. Mem. Med. Soc. County Monroe, Med. Soc. State N.Y., N.Y. State Neurosurg. Soc. (bd. dirs. 1972-77, 93—), Congress Neurol. Surgeons, Am. Assn. Neurol. Surgeons, Canandaigua Yacht Club. Republican. Episcopalian. Avocations: sailing, skiing, fishing, genealogy. Office: 1445 Portland Ave Rochester NY 14621-3008

WILEY, JAY D., lawyer; b. Anderson, Ind., June 13, 1945. BBA, U. Mich., 1967, JD, 1971. Bar: Ariz. 1972. Ptnr. Snell & Wilmer, Phoenix, 1971—; instr. legal writing Ariz. State U., 1971, 72. Mem. ABA. Office: Snell & Wilmer One Arizona Ctr Phoenix AZ 85004

WILEY, RICHARD ARTHUR, lawyer; b. Bklyn., July 18, 1928; s. Arthur Ross and Anna Thorsen (Holder) W.; m. Carole Jean Smith, Aug. 13, 1955; children: Kendra Elizabeth, Stewart Alan, Garett Smith. AB, Bowdoin Coll., Brunswick, Maine, 1948; BCL, Oxford (Eng.) U., 1951; LLM, Harvard U., 1959; LLD, Bowdoin Coll., 1994. Bar: Mass. 1954, U.S. Ct. Mil. Appeals 1954, U.S. Dist. Ct. Mass. 1962, U.S. Supreme Ct. 1985. Atty. John Hancock Mut. Life Ins. Co., Boston, 1956-58; from atty. to mng. ptnr. Bingham, Dana & Gould, Boston, 1959-76; gen. counsel, asst. sec. Dept. Def., 1976-77; v.p. counsel First Nat. Bank Boston, 1977-78, exec. v.p., 1978-85; exec. v.p. Bank of Boston Corp., 1985; ptnr. Csaplar & Bok, Boston, 1986-90, mem. exec. com., 1987-90, chmn., 1989-90, of counsel, 1990; of counsel Gaston & Snow, Boston, 1990-91; dir. Powers and Hall P.C., 1991-94, of counsel, 1994—; bd. dirs., chmn. Am. Student Assistance Corp.; bd. dirs. Nomadic Structures, Inc., Nypro, Inc., Mupac Corp., R.F. Group Inc., Edn. Resources Inst., World Shelters, Inc., Mass. Higher Edn. Assistance Corp.; lectr. Boston U. Law Sch., 1961-64; past vice chmn. New Eng. Conf. on Doing Bus. Abroad; trustee New Eng. Legal Found., chmn., 1980-83; adj. lectr. Dept. Govt. and Legal Studies, Bowdoin Coll., 1995—. Author: Cases and Materials on Law of International Trade and Investment, 1961; contbr. articles to profl. jours. Bd. overseers Bowdoin Coll., 1966-81, pres., 1977-80, trustee, 1981-93, trustee emeritus, 1993—; mem. Mass. Edn. Financing Authority, 1986-91, chmn., 1987-91; mem. Wellesley (Mass.) Town Meeting, 1975-78, mem. fin. adv. com., 1973-74; chmn. Mass. Bd. Regents of Higher Edn., 1991; bd. regents Task Force on Student Fin. Aid, 1987; active Mass. Higher Edn. Coordinating Coun., 1991—, vice chmn., 1991-93, chmn., 1993—; chmn. lawyers div. United Way Mass. Bay, 1975; mem. devel. com., trustees of donations Episcopal Diocese Mass., 1975; trustee, exec. com. North Conway Inst. mem. 1980-92, chmn. 1988-92; bd. trustees Internat. Coun. Trust, Boston; trustee, mem. exec. com. (chmn. 1989-92) Mass. Taxpayers Found.; chmn. bd. trustees World Peace Found., Boston; corporator Schepens Eye Rsch. Inst.; dep. chmn. planning Mass.

Rep. State Com., 1971, vice chmn. Mass. Rep. State Fin. Com., 1971-72. Served as officer USAF, 1953-56. Decorated Air Force Commendation medal; recipient Dep. Def. Disting. Pub. Svc. medal, 1977; Rhodes scholar, 1949. Mem. ABA (vice chmn. fgn. and internat. bus. law com. 1967-69), Boston Bar Assn. (exec. com., antitrust com. 1965-68), Council on Fgn. Relations, Boston Com. on Fgn. Relations (mem. exec. com., chmn. 1980-83), Phi Beta Kappa.

WILEY, RICHARD EMERSON, lawyer; b. Peoria, Ill., July 20, 1934; s. Joseph Henry and Jean W. (Farrell) W.; m. Elizabeth J. Edwards, Aug. 6, 1960; children: Douglas S., Pamela L. B.S. with distinction, Northwestern U., 1955, J.D., 1958; LL.M., Georgetown U., 1962. Bar: Ill. 1958, D.C. 1972. Pvt. practice Chgo., 1962-70; gen. counsel FCC, Washington, 1970-72, mem., 1972-74, chmn., 1974-77, chmn. FCC's adv. com. on advanced TV svc., 1987—; mng. ptnr. Wiley, Rein & Fielding, Washington, 1983—; prof. law John Marshall Law Sch., U. Chgo., 1963-70. Chmn. adv. bd. Inst. for Tele-Info., Columbia U., 1989—. Capt. AUS, 1959-62. Fellow Am. Bar Found.; mem. ABA (mem. ho. of dels. 1969-71, 77-84, chmn. young lawyers sect., 1977-84, chmn. Forum com. on communications 1969, chmn. bd. editors ABA Jour. 1984-89, chmn. com. on scope and correlation of work 1989, chmn. adminstrv. law and regulatory practice 1993-94), Fed. Bar Assn. (pres. 1977), Fed. Communications Bar Assn. (pres. 1987), Ill. Bar Assn., Chgo. Bar Assn., Adminstrv. Conf. U.S. (coun., sr. fellow), Phi Delta Phi, Phi Delta Kappa. Methodist. Home: 3818 N Woodrow St Arlington VA 22207-4345 Office: Wiley Rein & Fielding 1776 K St NW Ste 1100 Washington DC 20006-2304

WILEY, RICHARD GORDON, electrical engineer; b. Wind Ridge, Pa., Aug. 25, 1937; s. Asa Gordon and Mildred Louise (Fisher) W.; m. Jane Bradley Wilmes, Oct. 15, 1960; children: Richard Bradley, John Gordon, Laura Jane, Timothy Scott, Martha Anne, James Robert. BS, Carnegie-Mellon U., 1959, MS, 1960; PhD, Syracuse U., 1975. Rsch. engr. Syracuse (N.Y.) Rsch. Corp., 1960-67, staff cons. engr., 1975-86; asst. dir. applied rsch. Lab. Microwave Sciences, Inc., Syracuse, 1967-75; v.p., chief scientist Rsch. Assocs. Syracuse, Inc., 1986—. Author: Electronic Intelligence: The Analysis of Radar Signals, 1982, 2d edit. 1993, Electronic Intelligence: The Interception of Radar Signals, 1985; co-author: Radar Vulnerability to Jamming, 1990; co-inventor pulse train analysis using personal computer, 1987. 1st lt. U.S. Army, 1961-63. Fellow IEEE; mem. Assn. Old Crows. Republican. Office: Rsch Assocs Syracuse Inc 510 Stewart Dr N Syracuse NY 13212-3451

WILEY, RICHARD HAVEN, chemist, educator; b. Mattoon, Ill., May 10, 1913; s. John Frederick and Mary Frances (Moss) W.; m. Marybeth Signaigo, Dec. 28, 1940; children: Richard Haven, Frank Edmund. A.B., U. Ill., 1934, M.S., 1935; Ph.D., U. Wis., 1937; LL.B., Temple U., 1943. Fellow Wis. Alumni Research Found., 1935-37; research chemist E.I. duPont de Nemours & Co., Wilmington, Del., 1937-45; assoc. prof. chemistry U. N.C., 1945-49; prof. chemistry, chmn. dept. U. Louisville, 1949-65; NSF sr. postdoctoral fellow Imperial Coll., London, 1957-58; vis. prof. grad. div. CUNY, 1963-64, exec. officer chemistry, 1965-68; prof. chemistry Hunter Coll., 1965-79, prof. emeritus, 1979—; vis. scholar Stanford U., 1978-80; vol. employee San Jose State U., 1980-85. Author: (with P.F. Wiley) Pyrazolones, Pyrazolidones and Derivatives, 1963; Editor: (with P.F. Wiley) Five and Six Membered Compounds with Nitrogen and Oxygen, 1963, Pyrazoles, Pyrazolines, Pyrazolidine and Condensed Ring Systems, 1967; asso. editor: Jour. Chem. and Engring. Data, 1966-71; past mem. editorial bd.: Jour. Polymer Sci., Jour. Macromolecular Chemistry; Contbr. to textbook articles on organic and polymer chemistry sci. jours. Fellow AAAS, Am. Inst. Chemists, N.Y. Acad. Scis.; mem. Am. Chem. Soc. (Midwest award St. Louis sect. 1965), N.Y. Acad. Scis., Phi Beta Kappa, Sigma Xi, Phi Eta Sigma, Phi Lambda Upsilon, Phi Kappa Psi. Patentee in field. Home: Apt 115C 23500 Cristo Rey Dr Cupertino CA 95014

WILEY, ROBERT ALLEN, pharmaceutical educator; b. Ann Arbor, Mich., Sept. 5, 1934; married, 1955; 3 children. BS, U. Mich., 1955; PhD in pharm. chemistry, U. Calif., San Francisco, 1962. From asst. prof. to prof. med. chemistry U. Kans., Lawrence, 1962-84; dean Coll. Pharmacy U. Iowa, Iowa City, 1984-91; prof. Coll. Pharmacy U. Iowa, 1991—. Mem. Am. Chem. Soc., Am. Pharm. Soc., Soc. Toxicology. Office: U Iowa Coll Pharmacy Iowa City IA 52242*

WILEY, RONALD LEROY, financial executive; b. Malta, Ohio, Dec. 17, 1936; s. Milford LeRoy and Freda Alice (Bowman) W.; m. Georgia Mae Johnson, Sept. 17, 1960 (div. Jan. 1963); m. Barbara Anne Harkins, Nov. 28, 1964; children: Michael Lane, Ronald Joseph. Grad., Ohio State U. 1963. CPA, Ohio, Iowa, Nebr. Auditor to audit mgr. Cooper & Lybrand, Columbus, Ohio, 1963-74; audit mgr. Cooper & Lybrand, Dayton, Ohio, 1974-78; treas. Consumers Coal Co., Dayton 1978-81; corp. controller Iowa Beef Processors, Inc., Dakota City, Nebr., 1981-84; asst. v.p., controller IBP, Inc., Dakota City, 1984-88, v.p., controller, 1988-91; chief fin. officer Gibbon Packing Co., Inc., 1992—. Sgt. U.S. Army, 1956-60. Mem. AICPAs, Iowa Soc. CPAs, Nebr. Soc. CPAs, Ohio Soc. CPAs, Jaycees (treas. 1966-67). Republican. Home: 1 Pony Express Dr Kearney NE 68847 Office: Gibbon Packing Co Inc PO Box 730 East Hwy 30 Gibbon NE 68840

WILEY, THOMAS GLEN, retired investment company executive; b. Salt Lake City, Feb. 1, 1928; s. Thomas J. and Juanita (Dean) W.; children: Jana Lynn, Jill, Tina Elizabeth, Tova Suzanne. B.B.A. cum laude, U. Wash., 1951, postgrad., 1954. With Shell Chem. Co., 1954-61; fin. analyst Shell Chem. Co., N.Y.C., 1960-63; mgr. fin. analysis and pricing Lear Siegler, Los Angeles, 1963-72; v.p. finance, treas. Electronic Memories & Magnetics Corp., Los Angeles, 1963-72; exec. v.p. Hale Bros. Assocs., San Francisco, 1972-80; pres. Computer Election Systems, Berkeley, Calif., 1980-84, Texport, Inc., Anaheim, Calif., 1988-89; dir. NetVantage, Santa Monica, Calif., 1994—, Osmotics, Denver, 1994—. 1st lt. AUS, 1951-53. Home: 1765 Broadway St San Francisco CA 94109-2425

WILEY, WILLIAM RODNEY, microbiologist, administrator; b. Oxford, Miss., Sept. 5, 1931; s. William Russell and Edna Alberta (Threlkeld) W.; m. Myrtle Louise Smith, Nov. 10, 1952; 1 child: Johari. B.S., Tougaloo Coll., Miss., 1954; M.S., U. Ill., Urbana, 1960; Ph.D., Wash. State U., Pullman, 1965. Instr. electronics and radar repair Keesler AFB-U.S. Air Force, 1956-58; Rockefeller Found. fellow U. Ill., 1958-59; research assoc. Wash. State U., Pullman, 1960-65; research scientist dept. biology Battelle-Pacific N.W. Labs., 1965-69, mgr. cellular and molecular biology sect. dept. biology, 1969-72, inst. coordinator, life scis. program, assoc. mgr. dept. biology, 1972-74, mgr. dept. biology, 1974-79, dir. research, 1979-84; dir. Pacific Northwest Lab., Richland, Wash., 1984-94; sr. v.p. for sci. & tech. policy Battelle Meml. Inst., Richland, Wash., 1994—; adj. assoc. prof. microbiology Wash. State U., Pullman, 1968—; found. assoc. Pacific Sci. Ctr., Seattle, 1989—; bd. dirs. Sta. KCTS Channel 9, Seattle, 1990-94; trustee Oreg. Grad. Inst. Sci. and Tech., 1990—; cons. and lectr. in field. Contbr. chpts. to books, articles to profl. jours. Co-author book in microbiology. Bd. dirs. Wash. Tech. Ctr., 1984-85, sci. adv. panel Wash. Tech. Ctr., 1984-88, Fed. Res. Bank of San Francisco (Seattle br.) 1991—; mem. adv. com. U. Wash. Sch. Medicine, 1976-79; trustee Gonzaga U., 1981-89; bd. regents, 1968-81; bd. dirs. MESA program U. Wash., Seattle, 1984; United Way of Benton & Franklin Counties, Wash., 1984—; Tri-City Indsl. Devel. Coun., 1984-94; mem. Wash. Coun. Tech. Advancement, 1984-85; bd. dirs. Forward Wash., The Voice for Statewide Econ. Vitality, 1984-95. N.W. Coll. and Univ. Assn. for Sci., 1985—; mem. Tri-City Univ. Ctr. Citizens Adv. Coun., 1985—; apptd. Wash. State Higher Edn. Coord. Bd., 1986-89, Wash. State U. Found., 1986—; mem. Wash. State U. bd. Regents, 1989—; bd. dirs. Washington Roundtable, 1989—, Goodwill Games, 1989-90; mem. adv. coun. Mont. State Sci. and Tech., 1990-91; mem. bd. overseers Whitman Coll., 1990—; mem. external adv. bd. Clark Atlanta U., 1991—; mem. Ctrl. Wash. U. Inst. for Sci. and Soc. Bd. of Advisors, 1991—, Engring. exec. com. S.U., Baton Rouge, La., 1992—; mem. Coun. Govt. Univ. Industry Rsch. Roundtable, 1993—; trustee Fred Hutchinson Cancer Rsch. Ctr., 1992—; engring. exec. com. Southern U., 1992—. With U.S. Army, 1954-56. Named Black Engr. of Yr., 1994. Mem. Am. Soc. Biol. Chemists, Am. Soc. Microbiology, AAAS, Soc. Exptl. Biology and Medicine, Sigma Xi. Office: Battelle Meml Inst Pacific NW Divsn Battelle Blvd Richland WA 99352

WILEY, WILLIAM T., artist; b. Bedford, Ind., Oct. 21, 1937; s. Sterling P. and Mary (Abel) W.; m. Dorothy Ann Wiley, Sept. 8, 1959; children: Ethan J., Zane J. B.F.A., San Francisco Art Inst., 1960, M.F.A., 1961. Tchr. U. Nev., spring 1967, Wash. State Coll., 1967, San Francisco Art Inst., fall 1966, U. Calif. at Berkeley, 1967, Sch. Visual Arts, N.Y.C., 1968, U. Colo., 1968. One-man shows include San Francisco Mus. Art, 1960, 81, Staempfli Gallery, N.Y.C., 1962-64, Carnegie Inst., 1962, 2d Biennale Ann. Art, Cordoba, S.Am., 1964, Hansen Fuller Gallery, San Francisco, 1968, 69, 71, 72-80, 83, Allan Frumkin Gallery, N.Y.C., 1968-81, 83, Allan Frumkin Gallery, Chgo., 1969-79, L.A. Louver, Venice, Calif., 1984, 87, Fuller Goldeen Gallery, 1986, Moore Coll., 1986, Natsoulas Novelozo Gallery, Davis, Calif., 1988, Marsha Mateyka Gallery, Washington, 1988, Max Potech Gallery, 1988, Newport Harbor Art Mus. with traveling to Palm Springs (Calif.) Desert Mus., Boise Art Gallery, San Francisco Mus. Art, 1984-85, Studio Marconi, Milan, Italy, 1971, Margo Leavin Gallery, Los Angeles, 1972, 75, 76, Gallerie Odyssia, Rome, 1976, Stedelijk van Abbemuseum, Netherlands, 1973, Mus. Modern Art, N.Y.C., 1976, Balt. Mus. Art, 1979, Inst. Modern Art, Brisbane, Australia, 1980, Fla. State U., Tallahasse, 1981, Dallas Mus. Fine Arts, 1980-81, Denver Art Mus., 1981, Phoenix Art Mus., 1981, Corcoran Gallery, Washington, 1991; nat. exhbns. include Whitney Mus. Am. Art, 1960, Art Inst. Chgo., 1961-66, U. Ill., 1961; regional exhbns. include, Calif. Palace Legion Honor, 1961, 62, Oakland (Calif.) Mus., 1961; group shows include Staempfli Gallery, N.Y.C., 1960, U. Nebr., 1961, San Francisco Mus. Art, 1962, 63, 64, 4th ann. painting and sculpture, La Jolla, Calif., 1963, Stanford Mus., 1964, Whitney Mus. Am. Art, 1966, 67, 68, 76, 81, 83, Mus. Fine Arts, Boston, 1968, Found. Maeght, Paris, 1970, Albright-Knox Art Gallery, Buffalo, 1972, 78-79, Documenta V, Kassel, Ger., 1972, Corcoran Gallery Art, Washington, 1975, Mus. Modern Art, N.Y.C., 1976, 84, Art Inst. Chgo., 1977, Walker Art Ctr., Mpls., 1980, Wadsworth Atheneum, Hartford, Conn., 1981, Hirshorn Mus., 1984; rep. permanent collections. San Francisco Mus., Whitney Mus., Oakland Mus.; author film Man's Nature. Recipient painting prize San Francisco ann., 1959, 1st prize painting San Francisco Art Festival, New Talent award Art in Am. Mag., 1961, painting prize Art Inst. Chgo., 1962, sculpture prize Los Angeles County Mus., 1962, purchase prize Whitney Mus. Am. Art, N.Y.C., 1968, William Bartels prize Art Inst. Chgo., 1976, Am. Acad. and Inst. of Arts and Letters award, 1991; grantee Australian Arts Council, 1980. Address: care of Brian Gross Fine Art 250 Sutter St Ste 370 San Francisco CA 94108

WILFORD, DAN SEWELL, hospital administrator; b. Memphis, June 11, 1940; married. BA, U. Miss., 1962; MA, Washington U., 1966. Adminstrv. resident Hillcrest Med. Ctr., Tulsa, 1965-66, asst. adminstr., 1966-69, sr. assoc. adminstr., 1969-74; adminstr. North Miss. Med. Ctr., Tupelo, Miss., 1974-82; pres. North Miss. Health Svcs., Tupelo, Miss., 1982-84, Meml. Healthcare System, Houston, 1984—. With Armed Forces, 1962-64. Home: 730 Chevy Chase Cir Sugar Land TX 77478 Office: Meml Hosp System Meml Hosp SW 7600 Beechnut Houston TX 77074

WILFORD, JOHN NOBLE, JR., news correspondent; b. Murray, Ky., Oct. 4, 1933; s. John Noble and Pauline (Hendricks) W.; m. Nancy Everett Watts, Dec. 25, 1966; 1 child, Nona. Student, Lambuth Coll., 1951-52; BS, U. Tenn., 1955; MA, Syracuse U., 1956; Internat. Reporting fellow, Columbia, 1961-62; DHL (hon.), R.I. Coll., 1987; DSc (hon.), Middlebury Coll., 1991. Reporter Comml. Appeal, Memphis, summers 1954-55; reporter Wall St. Jour., N.Y.C., 1956, 59-61; contbg. editor Time mag., N.Y.C., 1962-65; sci. reporter N.Y. Times, 1965-73, asst. nat. editor, 1973-75; dir. sci. news, 1975-79, sci. corr., 1979—; vis. journalist Duke U. 1984; McGraw lectr. Princeton U., 1985; Disting. prof. journalism, U. Tenn., Knoxville, 1989-90; mem. Am. Mus. - Mongolian Gobi Expdn., 1991; dir.'s vis. Inst. for Advanced Study, 1995. Author: We Reach The Moon, 1969, The Mapmakers, 1981, The Riddle of the Dinosaur, 1985, Mars Beckons, 1990, The Mysterious History of Columbus, 1991; co-author: The New York Times Guide to the Return of Halley's Comet, 1985, (with William Stockton) Spaceliner, 1981; editor: Scientists at Work, 1979. With CIC AUS, 1957-59. Recipient Book award Aviation/Space Writers, 1970, Writing award Aviation/Space Writers, 1983; G.M. Loeb Achievement award U. Conn., 1972; Press award Nat. Space Club, 1974; AAAS-Westinghouse Sci. Writing award, 1983; Pulitzer prize nat. reporting, 1984; mem. N.Y. Times Pulitzer Prize Winning Team, 1987. Mem. Nat. Assn. Sci. Writers, Authors Guild, Soc. Profl. Journalists, Am. Geog. Soc. (councilor 1994—), Century Assn., Sigma Chi, Phi Kappa Phi. Home: 232 W 10th St New York NY 10014-2976 Office: 229 W 43rd St New York NY 10036

WILFORD, WALTON TERRY, economics educator; b. Murray, Ky., Sept. 27, 1937; s. Jasper Dekalb and Rebecca (Sykes) W. B.B.A., So. Meth. U., 1958, Ph.D., 1964. Asst. prof. econs U. Ga., Athens, 1962-63; asst. prof. econs U. Idaho, Moscow, 1963-65; vice adv. State Dept. AID, Bolivia and Guatemala, 1965-68; assoc. prof. econs. and fin. U. New Orleans, 1968-73, prof., 1973-93, prof. emeritus, 1993—, chmn. dept. econs. and fin., 1973-88, acting dean Coll. Bus. Adminstrn., 1984; vis. prof. Calif. State U-San Jose, 1972, U. Western Australia, fall 1989; econ. adviser to El Salvador, 1975. Author: Essays in Latin American Economic Issues, 1970; editor Rev. Fin. Econs., 1991—; contbr. numerous articles to profl. jours. Recipient H. M. Cotton Disting. Faculty award La. State U. System, 1982; Ford Found. fellow, 1964. Mem. Am. Econ. Assn., So. Econ. Assn., N. Am. Econs Fin. Assn. (pres. 1985), Western Econ. Assn., Fin. Mgmt. Assn., Omicron Delta Epsilon. Home: 404 Eden Isles Blvd Slidell LA 70458-5572 Office: U New Orleans Dept Econs And Fin New Orleans LA 70148

WILFRIED, GRAU, hotel executive officer. Pres. c.e.o. Ramada Internat. Hotels and Resorts (sub. New World Hotels Inc.), Phoenix, Ariz. Office: Ramada Internat Hotels 3838 E Van Buren St Phoenix AZ 85008-6906

WILGIS, HERBERT E., JR., corporate executive; b. Balt., Apr. 30, 1935; s. Herbert E. and Margaret S. (Shaw) W.; m. Jane VandeGrift; children—Jeffery, Herbert, Edward. A.B. in History, Princeton U., 1957. Foreign service officer U.S. Dept. State, numerous countries, 1958-86; counselor Am. embassy, Budapest, 1977-80; minister-counselor Am. embassy, Warsaw, Poland, 1981-83; consul gen. U.S. consulate gen., Barcelona, Spain, 1983-86; pres., chief exec. officer Penniman and Browne, Balt., 1986—. Served with U.S. Army, 1957. Recipient Superior and Meritorious Honor awards Dept. State, 1978, 86. Mem. Am. Fgn. Service Assn. Office: Penniman and Browne Inc 6252 Falls Rd Baltimore MD 21209-2126

WILHARM, JOHN H., JR., lawyer; b. Pitts., May 19, 1932. BA, Amherst Coll., 1954; JD, Western Reserve U., 1960. Bar: Ohio 1960. Ptnr. Baker & Hostetler, Cleve.; mem. bd. bar examiners Supreme Ct., 1967-71. Editor: Western Reserve Law Review, 1959-60. Mem. bd. edn. Chagrin Falls Village, 1974-81. Mem. Phi Delta Phi. Office: Baker & Hostetler 3200 Nat City Ctr 1900 E 9th St Cleveland OH 44114-3485

WILHELM, DAVID C., political organization administrator; m. Degee Wilhelm; 1 child, Luke. Grad., Ohio U., Harvard U. Campaign mgr. Senator Paul Simon, 1984, Senator Joseph Biden for Pres., Iowa, 1987, Richard M. Daly for Mayor, Chgo., 1989, 91, Gov. Bill Clinton for Pres., 1991-92; chmn. Nat. Dem. Com., 1993-94; sr. mng. dir. investment banking Kemper Securities, Inc., Chgo., 1994—. Exec. dir. Citizens for Tax Justice. Mem. AFL-CIO (dir. pub. policy, pub. employee dept.). Office: Kemper Securities Inc 77 W Wacker Dr Ste 3100 Chicago IL 60601

WILHELM, GAYLE BRIAN, lawyer; b. Springfield, Mass., Sept. 1, 1936; s. William E. and Margaret (Koerber) W.; m. Emogene Chase, Sept. 1, 1957; children: Gayle Barrett, Erica Chase Fotta, Laura Elizabeth. BA, Harvard U., 1957, LLB, 1964. Bar: Conn. 1964. Sr. ptnr. Cummings & Lockwood, Stamford, Conn., 1964—. Author: Connecticut Estates Practice, 6 vols., 1970—, The Executor's Handbook, 1985, The Connecticut Living Trust, 1993. 1st lt. USAF, 1957-61, Japan. Fellow Am. Coll. Trust and Estate Counsel. Avocations: tennis, bicyclig, fishing. Office: Cummings & Lockwood 4 Stamford Plaza Stamford CT 06901-3202

WILHELM, HARLEY A(LMEY), chemist, educator, mechanical engineer, retired; b. Ellston, Iowa, Aug. 5, 1900; s. Bert C. and Anna B. (Glick) W.; m. Orpha E. Lutton, May 29, 1923; children: Lorna Wilhelm Livingston, Max Gene, Myrna Wilhelm Elliott, Gretchen. BA, Drake U., 1923; PhD, Iowa State U., 1931, LLD, 1961; LLD, Drake U., 1961. Fellow in

chemistry, 1924-25; postdoctoral work U. Mich., Ann Arbor, 1941; tchr. Mapleton (Iowa) H.S., 1923-24, Guthrie Center (Iowa) H.S., Helena, Mont., 1925-26; prof., coach Intermountain Union Coll., Helena, Mont., 1926-27; semi-pro baseball pitcher Ames (Iowa) Mchts. team, 1930-42; grad. asst. dept. chemistry Iowa State U., Ames, 1927-28, from instr. to prof. chemistry, 1928-45, prof. chemistry, 1945-71, prof. metallurgy, 1963-71; assoc. dir. Ames Lab. of U.S. AEC (now Dept. Energy), 1942-66; prof. emeritus Iowa State U., 1971—; Manhattan Dist. engr., 1942-66, prin. scientist, 1966—; AEC del. to Eng., 1949, to Eng. and Europe, 1953, to Argentina and Brazil, 1957; cons. desalinization of water Dept. Interior, 1967; cons. licensing of reactors AEC, Washington, 1968; vis. prof. U. Waterloo, Kitchener, Ont., Can., 1969; presenter, cons. in field. Author more than 100 published articles; holder more than 75 patents. Decorated Army-Navy E Flag with 4 stars; recipient Gold medal ASME, 1990, Alumni Disting. Svc. award Drake U., 1959, Double D award Nat. D Club Drake U., 1968, Centennial award for svc. Drake U. Nat. Alumni Assn., 1981; metallurgy bldg. Ames Lab. U.S. Dept. Energy named Harley A. Wilhelm Hall, Iowa State U., 1986, Centennial Recognition as one of 100 all time great athletes in Bulldog history Drake U., 1991, Chgo. Alumni award Iowa State U., 1949, faculty citation Iowa State U. Alumni, 1969. Fellow Am. Soc. Metals (nat. trustee 1957-60, William Hunt Eisenman award 1962); mem. SAR, Am Chem. Soc. (gold medal Iowa sect. 1954), Iowa Acad. Sci. (Centennial citation 1975), Rotary Club, Phi Beta Kappa, Sigma Xi, Phi Lambda Upsilon, Phi Kappa Phi. Home: 513 Hayward Ave Ames IA 50014

WILHELM, JOSEPH LAWRENCE, archbishop; b. Walkerton, Ont., Can., Nov. 16, 1909; s. John and Magdalena (Uhrich) W. J.C.L., Ottawa U., 1948. Ordained priest Roman Cath. Ch., 1934. Asst. bishop's sec. Hamilton, Ont., 1934-40; chaplain Canadian Army, 1940-45; pastor St. Peter & Paul Ch., Hamilton, 1948-63; aux. bishop of Calgary, Alta., 1963-67; archbishop of Kingston, Ont., 1967-82, ret., 1982. Apptd. col. comdt. Canadian Chaplain Corps., 1982-88. Decorated Mil. Cross.

WILHELM, KATE (KATY GERTRUDE), author; b. Toledo, June 8, 1928; d. Jesse Thomas and Ann (McDowell) Meredith; m. Joseph B. Wilhelm, May 24, 1947 (div. 1962); children: Douglas, Richard; m. Damon Knight, Feb. 23, 1963; 1 child, Jonathan. Writer, 1956—; co-dir. Milford Sci. Fiction Writers Conf., 1963-76; lectr. Clarion Fantasy Workshop Mich. State U., 1968-94. Author: (novels) More Bitter Than Death, 1962, (with Theodore L. Thomas) The Clone, 1965, The Nevermore Affair, 1966, The Killer Thing, 1967, Let the Fire Fall, 1969, (with Theodore L. Thomas) The Year of the Cloud, 1970, Abyss: Two Novellas, 1971, Margaret and I, 1971, City of Cain, 1971, The Clewiston Test, 1976, Where Late the Sweet Birds Sang, 1976, Fault Lines, 1976, Somerset Dreams and Other Fictions, 1978, Juniper Time, 1979, (with Damon Knight) Better Than One, 1980, A Sense of Shadow, 1981, Listen, Listen, Listen, 1981, Oh! Susannah, 1982, Welcome Chaos, 1983, Huysman's Pets, 1986, (with R. Wilhelm) The Hills Are Dancing, 1986, The Hamlet Trap, 1987, Crazy Time, 1988, Dark Door, 1988, Smart House, 1989, Children of the Wind: Five Novellas, 1989, Cambio Bay, 1990, Sweet, Sweet Poison, 1990, Death Qualified, 1991, And the Angels Sing, 1992, Seven Kinds of Death, 1992, Naming the Flowers, 1992, Justice for Some, 1993, The Best Defense, 1994, (multimedia space fantasy) Axoltl, U. Oreg. Art Mus., 1979, (radio play) The Hindenburg Effect, 1985; editor: Nebula Award Stories #9, 1974, Clarion SF, 1976; contbr. short stories to anthologies and periodicals. Mem. PEN, Nat. Writers Union, Mystery Writers Am., Sci. Fiction Writers Am., Authors Guild. Address: 1645 Horn Ln Eugene OR 97404-2957

WILHELM, MARILYN, private school administrator. Founder-dir. The Wilhelm Sch., Houston. Office: The Wilhelm Sch 3003 Richmond Ave Houston TX 77027-6839

WILHELM, MORTON, surgery educator; b. Roanoke, Va., June 22, 1923; s. Walter LeRoy and Della Mae (Turner) W.; m. Jean Osborne, June 3, 1949; children: Melissa, Christina. BS, Va. Mil. Inst., 1944; MD, U. Va., 1947. Diplomate Am. Bd. Surgery. Intern, resident in surgery VA Mason Hosp., Seattle, 1947-51, 52-53; fellow, instr. surgery Med. Ctr. U. Va., Charlottesville, 53-54, 56-66, assoc. prof. surgery Med. Ctr., 1966-80, prof. surgery Med. Ctr., 1980-93, chief dept. surg. oncology Med. Ctr., 1990-93, Joseph Farrow prof. surg. oncology Med. Ctr., 1990-93. Pres. Va. Am. Cancer Soc., Meritorious Svc. award, Horsley award, Nat. Teresa Lasser award. Lt. U.S. Army, 1951-53. Fellow Am. Coll. Surgeons (vice chmn. commn. on cancer 1989-90, pres. Va. chpt.); mem. Am. Soc. Clin. Oncology, So. Surg. Assn., So. Soc. Clin. Surgeons, Soc. Surg. Oncology. Avocations: tennis, golf, woodworking. Office: U Va Med Ctr Box 334 Cancer Ctr Charlottesville VA 22908

WILHELM, RALPH VINCENT, JR., electronics company executive, ceramics engineer; b. Corpus Christi, Tex., Jan. 22, 1944; s. Ralph Vincent and Kathryn (Krug) W.; m. Katharine Elizabeth Foote, Aug. 26, 1967; children: Heidi, Peter. BSEE, Cornell U., 1967; PhD in Ceramic Engring., Rutgers U., 1972; postgrad., U. Ill., 1985; MBA, U. Mich., 1987. Project engr. Allis Chalmers Mfg. Corp., Boston, 1966-67; rsch. assoc. ceramics dept. Rutgers U., New Brunswick, N.J., 1967-71; sr. rsch. ceramist GM Rsch. Labs., GM, Warren, Mich., 1971-78; supr. thin film devel. AC Spark Plug div. GM, Flint, Mich., 1978-80, dept. head advanced devel., 1980-84; staff engr. advanced instrumentation GM-Delco Electronics Corp., Flint, 1984-87; staff engr. advanced instrumentation GM-Delco Electronics Corp., Kokomo, Ind., 1987-88, dir. tech. strategies, 1988-89, dir. advanced engr., 1989-94; v.p. dir. engring. GM-Delco Electronics Asia/Pacific Pte Ltd., Singapore, 1995—; trained visitor for ceramics Accreditation Bd. for Engring. and Tech., 1982-94; coord. univ. rels. team GM and Cornell U., Detroit and Ithaca, N.Y., 1985-93; mem. indsl. adv. bd. dept. elec. engring. Northwestern U., Evanston, Ill., 1989-94; mem. bd. mgrs. Mecel AB, Amål, Sweden, 1990-94; lectr. in field. Contbr. numerous articles to profl. jours.; patentee in thin film materials and processes field. Mem. Delco Electronics-Kokomo Sch. Partnership, 1989-94; mem. coun. Cornell U., 1990-94. Fellow Am. Ceramic Soc.; mem. IEEE, Soc. Automotive Engrs. (Vincent Bendix Automotive Elec. Engring. award 1978, Arch. T. Colwell merit award 1978), Sigma Xi, Keramos. Presbyterian. Avocations: tennis, sailing, gardening. Office: Delco Electronics Asia/Pacific, 501 Orchard Rd, 18-00 Ln Crawford Pl Singapore 0923, Singapore

WILHELM, ROBERT OSCAR, lawyer, civil engineer, developer; b. Balt., July 7, 1918; s. Clarence Oscar and Agnes Virginia (Grimm) W.; m. Grace Sanborn Luckie, Apr. 4, 1959. B.S. in Civil Engring., Ga. Tech. Inst., 1947, M.S.I.M., 1948; J.D., Stanford U., 1951. Bar: Calif. 1952. U.S. Supreme Ct. Mem. Wilhelm, Thompson, Wentholt and Gibbs, Redwood City, Calif., 1952—; gen. counsel Bay Counties Gen. Contractors; pvt. practice civil engring., Redwood City, 1952—; pres. Bay Counties Builders Escrow, Inc., 1972-88. With C.E. AUS, 1942-46. Mem. Bay Counties Civil Engrs. (pres. 1957), Peninsula Builders Exchange (pres. 1958-71, dir.), Calif. State Builders Exchange (tres. 1971). Clubs: Mason, Odd Fellows, Eagle, Elks. Author: The Manual of Procedures for the Construction Industry, 1971, Manual of Procedures and Form Book for Construction Industry, 8th edit., 1987; columnist Law and You in Daily Pacific Builder, 1955—; author: Construction Law for Contractors, Architects and Engineers. Home: 134 Del Mesa Carmel Carmel CA 93923-7950 Office: 600 Allerton St Redwood City CA 94063-1504

WILHELM, WILLIAM JEAN, civil engineering educator; b. St. Louis, Oct. 5, 1935; s. Maurice Ferdinand and Eileen Winifred (McClintock) W.; m. Patricia Jane Zietz, Aug. 17, 1957; children—William, Robert, Andrew, Mary, David. B.M.E., Auburn U., 1958, M.S., 1963; Ph.D., N.C. State U., 1968. Registered profl. engr., Kans., W.Va. Structural engr. Palmer & Baker Engrs., Mobile, Ala., 1958-60; instr. engring. graphics Auburn U., 1960-64; asst. prof. civil engring. W.Va. U., Morgantown, 1967-72; assoc. prof. W.Va. U., 1972-76, prof. 1976-79, chmn., 1974-79; dean engring., prof. Wichita State U., 1979—; dir. Ctr. for Productivity Enhancement, 1984-86, exec. dir. Ctr. for Tech. Application, 1988-91. Contbr. articles to profl. jours. Served with C.E. U.S. Army, 1959, 62. Recipient Recognition award Wichita State U. Alumni Assn., 1993. Fellow ASCE, Am. Concrete Inst. (Joe W. Kelley award 1986, Henry L. Kennedy award 1994); mem. NSPE, Soc. Women Engrs. (sr.), Am. Soc. Engring. Edn., Kans. Engring. Soc. (Outstanding Engr. of Yr. award 1989, pres. 1994-95), Precast/Prestressed Concrete Inst., Order of the Engr., Sigma Xi, Phi Kappa Phi, Tau Beta Pi, Pi

Tau Sigma Chi Epsilon (chpt. hon. W.Va. U. 1979). Roman Catholic. Home: 2500 Banbury Cir Wichita KS 67226-1046 Office: Wichita State U Coll Engring Wichita KS 67260-0044

WILHELMSEN, HAROLD JOHN, accountant, operations controller; b. Kansas City, Mo., July 13, 1928; s. Karl John and Cora Irene (Reynolds) W.; m. Audrey Loraine Woodard, Oct. 14, 1950. BBA, U. Wis., 1950. CPA, Wis. With S.C. Johnson & Son Inc., Racine, Wis., 1953-90, dir. fin. South Pacific, 1970-72, mgr. overseas fin. svcs., 1972-76, contr. U.S. ops., 1976-78, v.p., contr. internat. ops., 1978-90, ret., 1990. Pres. Racine Symphony Orch. Assn., 1957-60; trustee Carthage Coll., Kenosha, Wis., 1984-91, dir., sec. Pinnacle Peak Country Club Estates, 1992-95; dir., treas. Pinnacle Peak Country Club; treas. Christ the Lord Luth. Ch. Served with U.S. Army, 1950-52. Republican. Lutheran. Clubs: Pinnacle Peak Country (Scottsdale, Ariz.); Am. Nat. (Sydney, Australia). Avocations: golf, squash, bridge, reading, music.

WILHELMY, ODIN, JR., insurance agent; b. New Kensington, Pa., Oct. 9, 1920; s. Odin and May (Hazeltine) W.; m. Betty M. Rollins, Nov. 23, 1945; children: Ann Leslie, Margaret Linn, Janet Lee. BA with honors, U. Cin., 1941; PhD, Cornell U., 1950. CLU, ChFC. Asst. prof. Cornell U., Ithaca, N.Y., 1949-52; div. chief Battelle Meml. Inst., Columbus, Ohio, 1952-70; sr. agt. Prin. Mut. Life Ins. Co., Columbus, 1970--. Scoutmaster Boy Scouts Am., Ithaca, N.Y., Columbus, Ohio, 1946-74. Sgt. U.S. Army, 1942-46, Aleutian Islands. Recipient Silver Beaver award Boy Scouts Am. Mem. Phi Beta Kappa, Phi Kappa Phi, Pi Kappa Alpha, Omicron Delta Kappa. Presbyterian. Avocations: church work, scouting, gardening. Home: 2942 North Star Rd Columbus OH 43221

WILHITE, CLAYTON EDWARD, advertising executive; b. Saginaw, Mich., Aug. 9, 1945; s. Clayton Robson and Ruth Margaret (Westendorf) W.; m. Anne Denise Douglass, June 27, 1970. BA in Polit. Sci., U. Mich., 1967, MBA, 1969. Account exec., account supr. Foote, Cone & Belding, Chgo. and Sydney, Australia, 1969-75; v.p., account supr. McCann-Erickson, N.Y.C., 1975-77; exec. v.p., dir. Ammirati & Puris Inc., N.Y.C., 1977-83; mktg. dir. Young & Rubicam Ltd., London, 1983-85; chief exec., mng. dir. D'Arcy, Masius, Benton & Bowles (formerly D'Arcy, MacManus, Masius, Inc.), St. Louis, 1985-88; pres. D'Arcy, Masius, Benton & Bowles/USA, N.Y.C., 1988-91, DMB&B/N.Am., N.Y.C., 1991--; bd. dirs. DMB&B Inc. Mem. Exec. Campaign 1976 In-House Advt. Agy. for Pres. Ford Re-election Com., Washington; pres. Nov. Co. Bush Re-election Advt. Agy., 1992, Young Pres Orgn., 1986--; bd. dirs. vis. com. White Burkett Miller Ctr., U.Va.; mem. pres.'s adv. group U. Mich. Mem. River Club (N.Y.C.), Phi Beta Kappa. Republican. Lutheran. Avocations: photography; overseas travel; rock climbing; tennis; skiing. Office: D'Arcy Masius Benton & Bowles Inc 1675 Broadway New York NY 10019-5865

WILHITE, COLBERT ROLAND, chemical and oil company executive; b. Mangum, Okla., Sept. 29, 1931; s. Clarence Calvin and Margaret (Baker) W.; m. Carol Jenkins, Mar. 22, 1958; 1 child, Lisa Gayle. B.A. in Bus. Adminstrn., U. Okla., 1957, M.B.A. 1958. Various positions pipeline dept. Conoco, Inc., Ponca City, Okla., 1958-68, mgr. transp. dept., 1968-72; mgr. Western Hemisphere planning Conoco Inc., Houston, 1972-73; mgr. investor relations Conoco, Inc., Stamford, Conn., 1973-77; v.p. external affairs E.I. DuPont de Nemours and Co., Wilmington, Del., 1977-86; v.p. state affairs E.I. DuPont de Nemours and Co., Wilmington, 1987--. Mem. adminstrv. bd. Aldersgate United Methodist Ch., Wilmington, 1985--; bd. dirs. Keep Am. Beautiful, N.Y.C., Students in Free Enterprise, Bolivar, Mo.; adv. coun. State Legis. Leaders Found., Council of State Govts'. Policy Assn. Group. With USN, 1951-55, PTO. Mem. Am. Petroleum Inst. (chmn. gen. com. state relations 1985-86), Chem. Mfrs. Assn. (state affairs com.). Club: University (Washington). Office: E I du Pont de Nemours & Co External Affairs Dept 1007 N Market St Wilmington DE 19898

WILHOIT, CAROL LYNN, physician; b. Pasco, Wash., Nov. 15, 1951; d. Raymond Francis and Alice Blanche (Mc Neely) Collins; m. James C. Wilhoit; children: Elizabeth, Juliana. BS, Stanford U., 1973; MD, U. Washington, 1977. Cert. bd. Internal Medicine, 1980. Instr. U. Ill., 1980-82; intern Glen Ellyn Clinic, 1981--. Office: Glen Ellyn Clinic 454 Pennsylvania Ave Glen Ellyn IL 60137-4496

WILHOIT, HENRY RUPERT, JR., federal judge; b. Grayson, Ky., Feb. 11, 1935; s. H. Rupert and Kathryn (Reynolds) W.; m. Jane Horton, Apr. 7, 1956; children: Mary Jane, H. Rupert, William. LLB, U. Ky. 1960. Ptnr. Wilhoit & Wilhoit, 1960-81; city atty. City of Grayson, Ky., 1962-66; county atty. Carter County, Ky., 1966-70; judge U.S. Dist. Ct. (ea. dist.) Ky., 1981--. Recipient Disting. Service award U. Ky. Alumni Assn., 1980. Mem. ABA, Ky. Bar Assn. Office: US Dist Ct 320 Fed Bldg 1405 Greenup Ave Ashland KY 41101-7542

WILKE, CHET, real estate executive; b. Chgo., Dec. 10, 1942; m. Beverly J. Galuska, July 11, 1981; children: Lisa Michelle, Rebecca Ann, Christa Leann. BA in Comm., Columbia Coll. L.A., 1970. Cert. real estate mktg. cons. Sta. mgr. dir. TV news, personality Armed Forces Radio & TV, 1965-69; acct. exec. Sta. KALI, L.A., 1970-72; sr. acct. exec. HR/Stone Radio Reps., L.A., 1972-75; gen. sales mgr. Sta. KYXY-FM, San Diego, 1975-77; pres., founder Wilke Enterprises Inc., San Diego and Houston, 1977-81; gen. sales mgr. Sta. KEYH, Houston, 1982; gen. sales mgr., acting mgr. Sta. KYST, Houston, 1982-85; mgr., mktg./creative dir. Advt. Concepts Inc., Houston, 1985-88; exec. v.p. First Hanover Real Estate/Mortgage, Houston and Sugar Land, Tex., 1988-89; pres., real estate broker Ameristar Group Corp., Plano, Tex., 1989--. With USAF, 1964-69. Mem. Nat. Assn. Realtors, Tex. Assn. Realtors, Greater Dallas Assn. Realtors, Collin County Assn. Realtors, Lions. Republican. Methodist. Home: 2312 Cardinal Dr Plano TX 75023 Office: Ameristar Group Corp PO Box 260115 Plano TX 75026

WILKE, CONSTANCE REGINA, elementary education educator; b. Camden, N.J., Mar. 20, 1944; d. Matthew Stanley Sr. and Regina Rita (Przeradzki) Wojtkowiak; m. Alvin Frank Wilke Jr., Apr. 20, 1968; children: Joseph Alvin, Suzanne Renee. BA in Elem. Edn., Glassboro State U., 1967, MA in Reading and Supervision, 1979. Cert. tchr. and reading speicalist, N.J. Tchr. 5th grade Bellmawr (N.J.) Bd. Edn., 1967-70; tchr. 2d grade Ethel M. Burke Sch., Bellmawr, N.J., 1970--. Author: Wojtkowiak Family History, 1992. Vol. Gloucester (N.J.) City Libr., 1972-75; sec. E.M. Burke Sch. PTA, Bellmawr, 1973-78, publicity person, 1980-85, pres., 1982-85, author and editor publicity book, 1980-81, 82-83; advisor Community Edn. Bd., Gloucester City, 1973-74; eucharistic minster St. Mary's Ch., Gloucester City, 1990--; dir. and founder of Internat. Day at E.M. Burke Sch. Named Citizen of Yr., Polish-Am. Congress, 1993. Mem. NEA, N.J. Epilepsy Found., N.J. Edn. Assn., Bellmawr Edn. Assn. (faculty rep.), Asthma Assn. Roman Catholic. Avocations: needle crafts, reading, gardening, family historian. Office: E M Burke Sch 112 S Black Horse Pike Bellmawr NJ 08031-2309

WILKE, LEROY, church administrator. Exec. dir. Bd. for Youth Svcs. Luth. Ch.-Mo. Synod, St. Louis, St. Louis. Office: 1333 S Kirkwood Rd Saint Louis MO 63122

WILKE MONTEMAYOR, JOANNE MARIE, patient care coordinator; b. Jerome, Ariz., Sept. 10, 1941; d. Karl Nickolas and Anna Linda (Worgt) Wilke; m. Casimiro L. Montemayor, Oct. 8, 1978. BS in Nursing, U. Colo., 1965; M in Nursing, U. Washington, 1974. Patient care coord. Vesper Hospice, San Leandro, Calif., 1989--. With USNR, 1959-79. Mem. Nat. Hospice Orgn. Democrat. Methodist. Avocations: music, gardening, cooking, silk flower arranging.

WILKEN, CLAUDIA ANN, judge; b. Mpls., Aug. 17, 1949; d. Claudius W. and Dolores Ann (Grass) W.; m. John M. True, 1984; 1 child, Peter William True. BA with honors, Stanford U., 1971; JD, U. Calif., Berkeley, 1975. Bar: Calif. 1975, U.S. Dist. Ct. (no. dist.) Calif. 1975, U.S. Ct. Appeals (9th cir.) 1976, U.S. Supreme Ct. 1981. Asst. fed. pub. defender U.S. Dist. Ct. (no. dist.) Calif., San Francisco, 1975-78, U.S. magistrate judge, 1983-93, dist. judge, 1993--; ptnr. Wilkin & Leverett, Berkeley, Calif., 1978-84; adj. prof. U. Calif., Berkeley, 1978-84; prof. New Coll. Sch. Law, 1980-85; mem.

jud. br. com. Jud. Conf. U.S.; mem. edn. com. Fed. Jud. Ctr. Magistrate Judges, 9th Cir. Magistrate Judges; chair 9th cir. Magistrates Conf., 1987-88. Mem. ABA (mem. jud. adminstrn divsn.), Calif. State Bar Assn., Alameda County Bar Assn. (judge's membership), Fed. Magistrates Judges Assn. (sec.), Nat. Assn. Women Judges, Order of Coif, Phi Beta Kappa. Office: US Dist Ct No Dist PO Box 36060 450 Golden Gate Ave San Francisco CA 94102*

WILKEN, ROBERT LOUIS, historian, theologian; b. New Orleans, Oct. 20, 1936; s. Louis Frederick and Mabel (Rayl) W.; m. Carol Weinhold, June 4, 1960; children: Gregory, Jonathan. BA, Concordia Sem., 1957, BD, 1960; MA, U. Chgo., 1961, PhD, 1963. Asst. prof. Luth. Theol. Sem., Gettysburg, Pa., 1964-67; Fordham U., N.Y.C., 1967-72; from assoc. prof. to prof. U. Notre Dame, Ind., 1972-85; William R. Kenan prof. of history of Christianity, U. Va., Charlottesville, 1985--; Lady Davis prof. Hebrew U., 1982. Author: The Christians as the Romans Saw Them, John Chrysostom & The Jews, The Myth of Christian Beginnings, Judaism and The Early Christian Mind. NEH research grantee, 1981-82. Mem. Am. Soc. Ch. History, Am. Acad. Religion (v.p. 1986-87, pres. 1988-89, Am. Hist. Assn., N.Am. Patristics Soc. (pres. 1985-86). Lutheran. Home: 1630 Brandywine Dr Charlottesville VA 22901-2802 Office: U Va Dept Religious Studies Locke Hall Charlottesville VA 22903

WILKENING, LAUREL LYNN, university official, planetary scientist; b. Richland, Wash., Nov. 23, 1944; d. Marvin Hubert and Ruby Alma (Barks) W.; m. Godfrey Theodore Sill, May 18, 1974. BA, Reed Coll., 1966; PhD, U. Calif., San Diego, 1970. Asst. prof. to assoc. prof. U. Ariz., Tucson, 1973-80, dir. Lunar and Planetary Lab., head planetary scis., 1981-83, vice provost, prof. planetary scis., 1983-85, v.p. rsch., dean Grad. Coll., 1985-88; div. scientist NASA Hdqrs., Washington, 1980; prof. geol scis., adj. prof. astronomy, provost U. Washington, Seattle, 1988-93; chancellor U. Calif., Irvine, 1993--; dir. Seagate Tech., Inc., 1993--, Rsch. Corp., 1991--; vice chmn. Nat. Commn. on Space, Washington, 1984-86, Adv. Com. on the Future of U.S. Space Program, 1990; chair Space Policy Adv. Bd., Nat. Space Coun., 1991-92; co-chmn. primitive bodies mission study team NASA/European Space Agy., 1984-85; chmn. com. rendezvous sci. working group NASA, 1983-85; mem. panel on internat. cooperation and competition in space Congl. Office Tech. Assessment, 1982-83. Author: (monograph) Particle Track Studies and the Origin of Gas-Rich Meteorites, 1971; editor: Comets, 1982. U. Calif. Regents fellow, 1966-67; NASA trainee, 1967-70. Fellow Meteoritical Soc. (councilor 1976-80), Am. Assn. Advanced Sci.; mem. Am. Astron. Soc. (chmn. div. planetary scis. 1984-85), Am. Geophys. Union, AAAS, Planetary Soc. (dir. 1994--), Phi Beta Kappa. Democrat. Avocations: gardening, camping, swimming. Office: U Calif Chancellors Office 501 Adminstrn Bldg Irvine CA 92717

WILKENS, LEONARD RANDOLPH, JR. (LENNY WILKENS), professional basketball coach; b. Bklyn., Oct. 28, 1937; s. Leonard Randolph Sr. and Henrietta (Cross) W.; m. Marilyn J. Reed, July 28, 1962; children: Leesha Marie, Leonard Randolph III, Jamée McGregor. BS in Econs., Providence Coll., 1960, HHD (hon.), 1980. Counselor Jewish Employment Vocat. Services, 1962-63; salesman packaging div. Monsanto Co., 1966; profl. basketball player St. Louis Hawks, 1960-68; player-coach Seattle SuperSonics, 1969-72, head coach, 1977-85, gen. mgr., 1985-86; profl. basketball player Cleve. Cavaliers, 1972-74, player NBA All-Star Game, 1973, head coach, 1986-93; player-coach Portland (Oreg.) Trail Blazers, 1974-76; head coach Atlanta Hawks, 1993--; coach 4 NBA All-Star Teams including Ea. Conf. team All-Star game, Mpls., 1994, World Champion basketball team, 1979, NBA Coach of the Year, 1994; winningest coach of all time, 1995. Author: The Lenny Wilkens Story, 1974. Bd. regents Gonzaga U., Spokane; bd. dirs. Seattle Cir., Big Bros. Seattle, Bellevue (Wash.) Boys Club, Seattle Opportunities Industrialization Ctr., Seattle U.; co-chmn. UN Internat. Yr. of Child program, 1979; organizer Lenny Wilkens Celebrity Golf Tournament for Spl. Olympics. 2d lt. U.S. Army, 1961-62. Recipient Whitney Young Jr. award N.Y. Urban League, 1979, Disting. Citizens award Boy Scouts Am., 1980; named MVP in NBA All-Star Game, 1971, Man of Yr., Boys High Alumni chpt. L.A., 1979, Sportsman of Yr., Seattle chpt. City of Hope, 1979, Congl. Black Caucus Coach of Yr., 1979, CBA Coach of Yr., 1979, Coach of Yr., Black Pubs. Assn., 1979, NBA Coach of Yr., 1994; named to NIT-NIKE Hall of Fame, 1988; named to 9 NBA All-Star Teams. *

WILKENS, ROBERT ALLEN, utilities executive, electrical engineer; b. Esmond, S.D., Jan. 3, 1929; s. William J. and Hazel C. (Girch) W.; m. Barbara M. Davis, Apr. 15, 1952; children—Bradley Alan, Beth Ann, Bonnie Sue, William Frank. B.S.E.E., S.D. State U., 1951. Dispatcher, engr. G.O., Northwestern Pub. Service Co., Huron, 1953-55, div. engr., Huron 1955-58, div. elec. supt., 1958-59, div. mgr., 1959-66, asst. to pres., 1966-69, vice pres. ops., G.O., 1969-80, pres., chief operating officer, 1980-90, pres., chief exec. officer, 1990-94, chmn. bd. dirs. 1994—, also dir.; v.p., past pres. N. Cen. Electric Assn., past dir. Midwest Gas Assn.; dir. Farmers & Mchts. Bank Huron; past adminstrv. chmn., treas. Mid-Continent Area Power Pool. Mem. Salvation Army Adv. Bd., 1962-87; S.D. State R.R. Bd., 1982-87; past pres. Huron United Way. Served to capt. USAF, 1951-53. Named Disting. Engr., S.D. State U., 1977. Mem. North Central Elec. Assn., Midwest Gas Assn., S.D. Engring. Soc., Huron C. of C. (pres. 1963). Republican. Methodist. Lodges: Kiwanis, Masons, Shriners. Office: Northwestern Pub Svc Co 33 3rd St SE Huron SD 57350

WILKERSON, CHARLES EDWARD, architect; b. Essex County, Va., Apr. 1, 1921; s. John Pullen, Jr. and Eva Lee (Eubank) W.; m. Sallie Ray Bowers, Feb. 14, 1959; children: Judith Gardner, Ann Hunter, Edward Ray. B.Arch., Va. Poly. Inst. and State U., 1943. Registered architect, Va. Bookkeeping clk. Crawford Mfg. Co., Richmond, Va., 1937-39; draftsman Dixon & Norman Architects, Richmond, 1946-47, John S. Efford Architect, Richmond, 1947-49; draftsman Walford & Wright Architects, Richmond, 1949-54, ptnr., 1955-60; ptnr. Wright, Jones & Wilkerson, Richmond, 1961-91. Pres., sec.-treas., bd. dirs Va. Found. Architecture, 1964-86. Served to sgt. C.E., U.S. Army, 1943-46, PTO. Fellow AIA (Va. chpt., sec. Va. chpt. 1959-61, dir. James River chpt. 1979-82, William C. Noland award Va. Soc.). Baptist.

WILKERSON, ISABEL, journalist. With The N.Y. Times, N.Y.C.; now bureau chief The N.Y. Times, Chgo. Bureau, Chgo. Recipient Pulitzer Prize for feature writing, 1994. Office: The New York Times Chicago Bureau 122 S Michigan Ave Ste 1916 Chicago IL 60603*

WILKERSON, JOHN LEE, telecommunications executive; b. Ft. Worth, Aug. 5, 1945; s. Leonard E. and Francis (Lee) W.; m. Muffie Daugherty, Aug. 3, 1984; children: John Jr., Mitchell, Leana, Tonia. BA, U. Tex., 1967. Gen. mgr. TeleMktg. Comm., Columbus, Ohio, 1981-86; midwest dir. ITT Comm., Secaucus, N.J., 1986-88; pres. CEO TeleCom Network Solutions, Inc., Orlando, Fla., 1988--; CEO Cash Card Sys. Inc., Orlando, 1993--. Chmn. com. Columbus (Ohio) C. of C., 1982. Mem. Nat. Interm Housing Network, Moose. Avocations: flying, men's senior baseball, bowling. Office: Telecom Network Inc 3660 Maguire Blvd Ste 210 Orlando FL 32803-3062

WILKERSON, KENNETH L., retail department stores executive. Chmn. Famous-Barr Co., St. Louis. Office: Robinson's 600 W 7th St Los Angeles CA 90017

WILKERSON, PINKIE CAROLYN, state legislator, lawyer; b. L.A., Feb. 8, 1948; d. Calvin and Dora (Garner) W.; 1 child, John David Barabin Jr. BA cum laude, Grambling (La.) State U., 1968; MA with honors, Ohio U., 1971; JD with honors, So. U., 1979; LLM, Tulane U., 1989. Bar: La., N.Y., U.S. Tax Ct., U.S. Supreme Ct. Asst. dist. counsel IRS, L.A.; asst. prof. law So. U. Sch. Law, Baton Rouge; asst. atty. gen. La. Dept. Justice, Baton Rouge; with Merrill Lynch, Pierce, Fenner & Smith, N.Y.C.; asst. dist. atty. for Lincoln and Union Parishes, 3d Jud. Dist., La.; pvt. practice, Baton Rouge; mem. La. Ho. of Reps., Grambling State U., 1992--. Mem. U.S. Law Rev., 1978-79. Mem. adv. bd. Grambling State U.; bd. dirs. Phillips Sch. Theology, Atlanta; past pres. United League Voters; past v.p. Ruston-Grambling LWV. Named to Hall of Fame, Grambling State U., 1993; recipient Significant Achievement award World U., 1994. Mem. Nat. Bar Assn. (bd. dirs. 1985-89), La. Bar, N.Y. State Bar Assn., Grambling State U. Alumni Assn. (life), So. U. Alumni Assn. (life), Delta Sigma Theta.

Democrat. Methodist. Home: 611 E Grand Ave Grambling LA 71245 Office: PO Box 893 Grambling LA 71245

WILKERSON, WILLIAM HOLTON, banker; b. Greenville, N.C., Feb. 16, 1947; s. Edwin Cisco and Agnes Holton (Gaskins) W.; m. Ellen Logan Tomskey, Oct. 27, 1973; 1 child, William Holton Jr. AB in Econs., U. N.C. 1970. Asst. v.p. First Union Nat. Bank, Greensboro, N.C., 1972-77; v.p. Peoples Bank & Trust Co., Rocky Mount, N.C., 1977-79; sr. v.p. Hibernia Nat. Bank, New Orleans, 1979-86; exec. v.p. Peoples Bank and Trust Co., 1987-89, pres., 1989-90; sr. exec. v.p., bd. dirs. Centura Banks, Inc., 1990—; chmn., pres. Centura Ins. Svcs., Inc., 1995; chmn. Centura Securities, Inc., 1995--; bd. dirs. Peoples Bancorp. Bd. advisor Jr. League, New Orleans, 1986; bd. dirs. Trinity Episc. Sch., New Orleans, 1986, Cmty. Ministries Inc., 1989, Cities in Schs., 1995. Mem. Robert Morris Assoc., Rocky Mount C. of C. (bd. dirs. 1989—, vice chmn. 1992-94, chmn.-elect 1994, chmn. 1995), Benvenue Country Club, Kiwanis, Omicron Delta Epsilon, Chi Beta Phi, Phi Sigma Pi. Republican. Home: 336 Iron Horse Rd Rocky Mount NC 27804-2118

WILKES, BRENT AMES, management consultant; b. Melrose, Mass., Sept. 30, 1952; s. Gordon Borthwick and Frances (Ames) W.; m. Betsy Timmerman, May 26, 1973; 1 child, Erin. Bachelor, U. Mass., 1974; M of Pub. Affairs, U. Conn., 1977. Adminstrv. asst. Town of Tolland, Conn., 1975-76; mgmt. specialist Mass. Dept. Community Affairs, Boston, 1976-79; adminstrv.. asst. to mayor City of Gloucester, Mass., 1979-80; assoc. dir., adminstrv. asst. to mayor City of Gloucester, Mass., 1979-80; v.p., treas. Mass. dir. of field svcs. Mass. Mcpl. Assn., Boston, 1980-89; v.p., treas. Mass. Interlocal Ins. Assn., Boston, 1984-89; pres. MMA Consulting Group, Inc., Boston, 1989-94, MMA Mgmt. Svcs. Inc., Boston, 1995—; v.p., treas. Pub. Employer Risk Mgmt. Assn., Albany, N.Y., 1989—; adj. prof. Suffolk U. Grad. Sch. Mgmt., Boston, 1980-82; lectr. numerous regional and nat. trade assns. Author and editor: Managing Small Towns, 1986; contbr. articles to profl. jours. Mem. fin. com. Town of Acton, Mass., 1977-79; mem. town meeting Town of Reading, Mass., 1987-89; pres. Unitarian Universalist Ch. of Reading, 1990-93. Mem. Internat. City Mgmt. Assn. (cert. in mgmt.), Mass. Mcpl. Mgmt. Assn. Democrat. Unitarian Universalist. Avocations: golf, tennis, volleyball, reading. Office: MMA Mgmt Svcs Inc 60 Temple Pl Boston MA 02111

WILKES, JAMES E., telecommunications industry executive; b. 1937. BA, Mich. State U., 1959, MBA, 1962. With Ameritech Corp. and/or related cos., 1962—; pres., chief exec. officer Mich. Bell Telephone, Detroit, 1993—. Office: Mich Bell Tel Co 444 Michigan Ave Detroit MI 48226*

WILKES, JOSEPH ALLEN, architect; b. N.Y.C., Aug. 14, 1919; s. Abraham P. and Rose W.; m. Margaret Wilcoxson, Dec. 7, 1946; children—Jeffrey, Roger. B.A., Dartmouth Coll., 1941; M.Arch., Columbia U., 1949. Registered architect, N.Y., Fla., Md., D.C., Va. Assoc. prof. architecture U. Fla., Gainesville, 1952-59; project dir. Bldg. Research Adv. Bd. Nat. Acad. Sci., Washington, 1959-62; assoc. architect Keyes, Lethbridge & Condon, Washington, 1962-66; ptnr. Wilkes & Faulkner, Washington, 1966-82, Wilkes Faulkner Jenkins & Bass, Washington, 1983-90; lectr. architecture U. Md., 1971-85. Editor: Ency. of Architecture, 5 vols., 1988-89; chmn. editorial rev. bd.: Architectural Graphic Standards, 7th edit., 1980; archtl. works include: bldgs. Nat. Zool. Park; (bldg. renovation) Fed. Res. Bd. Bldg., Washington. Pres. Nat. Ctr. for a Barrier Free Environment, Washington, 1978; mem. profl. adv. council Nat. Easter Seals Soc. for Crippled Children, 1977-80; mem. Pres. Com. for Employment of Handicapped, Washington, 1976-82. Served to capt. AC U.S. Army, 1942-45; ETO. Fellow AIA; mem. Alpha Rho Chi. Home: 1720 Winchester Rd Annapolis MD 21401-5851

WILKES, L. A., oil industry executive; b. 1937. BS in Chem. Engring., Ga. Inst. Tech., 1960. With Texaco Inc., 1960-88, regional mgr. USA's Tulsa region, 1985—; v.p. ops. Star Enterprise, Houston, 1988—, pres., chief exec. officer. Office: Star Enterprise 12700 Northborough Dr Houston TX 77067-2508*

WILKES, ROBERT EDMOND, bank executive; b. Norwalk, Conn., Jan. 21, 1933; s. Howard Ranke and Helen (Edmond) W.; m. Carol Virginia Conron, Feb. 3, 1933; children: Robert E. Jr., W. Blake, Howard P., Kimberly C. BA, Williams Coll., 1955; postgrad., NYU, 1960-69. From trainee to v.p. First National City Bank (now CitiBank), N.Y.C., 1969-70; asst. treas. Magnavox Corp., N.Y.C., 1970-73; v.p. Morgan Guaranty Trust Co., N.Y.C., 1973-81; sr. v.p. Nat. Mkt. Affiliates Corp., Balt., 1981-83; exec. v.p. Nat. Westminster Bank N.J. (formerly First Jersey Nat. Bank), Jersey City, 1983—; pres., COO First Valley Bank, Bethlehem, Pa., 1990—; exec. v.p. First Valley Corp., 1990—. Trustee St. Luke's Hosp., Bethlehem, 1992—; bd. dirs., chmn. Northampton C.C. Found., 1991—; bd. dirs. Bethlehem Econ. Devel. Corp., 1991—, Lehigh Valley Indsl. Park Inc., 1994—. Mem. Bethlehem Area C. of C. (bd. dirs. 1991—), Saucon Valley Country Club, Baltusrol Golf (Springfield, N.J.), ElkRidge (Balt.). Republican. Episcopalian. Avocations: tennis, golf, paddle tennis. Office: First Valley Bank 1 Bethlehem Plz Bethlehem PA 18018-5781

WILKEY, MALCOLM RICHARD, retired ambassador, former federal judge; b. Murfreesboro, Tenn., Dec. 6, 1918; s. Malcolm Newton and Elizabeth (Gilbert) W.; m. Emma Seul Depolo, Dec. 21, 1959. AB, Harvard U., 1940, LLB, 1948; LLD (hon.), Rose-Hulman Inst. Tech., 1984. Bar: Tex. 1948, N.Y. 1963, U.S. Supreme Ct. 1952. U.S. atty. So. Dist. Tex., 1954-58; asst. atty. gen. U.S., 1958-61; ptnr. Butler Binion Rice & Cook, 1961-63; gen. counsel, sec. Kennecott Copper Corp., 1963-70; judge U.S Ct. Appeals D.C. Circuit, 1970-85; U.S. amb. to Uruguay, 1985-90; official in charge fed. forces at Little Rock Sch. Crisis, Dept. Justice, 1958; mem. U.S.-Chile Arbitration Commn., 1991—; lectr. internat. constl. and adminstrv. law London Poly., 1979, 80; lectr. Tulane U. Law Summer Sch., Grenoble, France, 1981, 83, San Diego Law Summer Sch., Oxford, Eng., 1983, Brigham Young Law Sch., 1984, 93; vis. fellow Wolfson Coll., Cambridge U., 1985; chmn. Pres.'s Commn. on Revision Fed. Ethics Laws, 1989; spl. counsel to Atty. Gen. for inquiry into the House Banking Facility, 1992. Del. Republican Nat. Conv., 1960. Served from 2d lt. to lt. col. AUS, 1941-45. Hon. fellow Wolfson Coll., Cambridge. Mem. Am. Bar Found.; mem. Am. Law Inst. (adv. com. restatement fgn. rels. law of U.S.), Jud. Conf. U.S. (com. on standards for admission to fed. cts. 1976-79), Phi Beta Kappa, Delta Sigma Rho, Phi Delta Phi (hon.). Address: Av El Bosque 379, Providencia, Santiago Chile

WILKIE, DONALD WALTER, biologist, aquarium museum director; b. Vancouver, B.C., Can., June 20, 1931; s. Otway James and Jessie Margaret (McLeod) W.; m. Patricia Ann Archer, May 18, 1980; children: Linda, Douglas, Susanne. B.A., U. B.C., 1960, M.Sc., 1966. Curator Vancouver Pub. Aquarium, 1961-63, Phila. Aquarama, 1963-65; exec. dir. aquarium-mus. Scripps Instn. Oceanography, La Jolla, Calif., 1965-93, ret., 1993; aquatic cons. Author books on aquaria and marine ednl. materials; contbr. numerous articles to profl. jours. Fellow San Diego Mus. Natural History.; mem. Am. Soc. Ichthyologists and Herpetologists, San Diego Zool. Soc. (animal health and conservation com.). Home: 4548 Cather Ave San Diego CA 92122-2632 Office: U Calif San Diego Scripps Instn Oceanography Libr 9500 Gilman Dr La Jolla CA 92093-0207 *As a biologist and teacher my major goal has been to increase public interest in learning about our environment and promoting wise use of the earth's resources for the long term good of mankind and the plants and animals with which we share the planet.*

WILKIE, EVERETT CLEVELAND, JR., librarian; b. Kinston, N.C., June 27, 1947; s. Everett Cleveland, Sr. and Nancy Frances (Stroup) W.; m. Barbara Lande Turman, Feb., 1986; 1 child, Lauren Llewellyn. Student, Campbell Coll., 1965-67; BA in English, Wake Forest U., 1969, MA in English, 1970; PhD in Comparative Lit., U. S.C., 1977, M Librarianship, 1978. Instr. dept. English McDowell Tech. Inst., Marion, N.C., 1970-71, Anderson (S.C.) Coll., 1971-72; adminstrv. asst. office dean freshmen U. S.C., Columbia, 1973-74; adminstrv. asst. office dean Coll. Humanities and Social Scis., 1976-78; rsch. assoc. dept. comparative lit. Brown U., Providence, 1978-80; bibliographer John Carter Brown Libr., 1981-84; reference libr. Lilly Libr. U. Bloomington, 1980-81; head libr., Crofut curator rare books and manuscripts, editor Bulletin Conn. Hist. Soc., Hartford, 1985—; mem. publ. adv. com. Conn. Jewish History; mem. state Hist.

Records Adv. Bd., 1994, subcom. on membership, 1994; mem. RBMS Security & Seminars Com.; presenter papers in field. Contbr. 29 articles to profl. jours. McClean fellow Libr. Co. Phila., 1989, Mellon fellow, 1992; Travel to Collections grantee NEH, 1992. Mem. ALA, Bibliographical Soc. Am., Am. Printing History Assn., Soc. Am. Archivists, New England Printing History Assn., New England Archivists. Office: Conn Hist Soc 1 Elizabeth St Hartford CT 06105-2213

WILKIE, VALLEAU, JR., foundation executive; b. Summit, N.J., July 3, 1923; s. Valleau and Amelia Wilkie (Parry) W.; m. Donna Hartwell, Oct. 28, 1985; children: Janice, Robert. A.B., Yale U., 1948; M.A., Harvard U., 1954. Instr. history Phillips Acad., 1948-59; headmaster Gov. Dummer Acad., Byfield, Mass., 1959-72; mem. bd. trustees Gov. Dummer Acad., 1960-72, dir. devel., 1972-73; exec. v.p. Sid W. Richardson Found., Ft. Worth, 1973—; bd. dirs. Nat. Charities Info Bureau;. Bd. dirs. S.W. Ednl. Devel. Lab., 1976-82, pres. 1981-82; mem. Council on Founds., Inc., 1980—; bd. dirs., 1981-87, chmn. bd., 1985-87; bd. dirs. Conf. of S.W. Founds., 1977-82, pres., 1981-82; bd. dirs. Found. Ctr., 1982-91, Nat. Charities Info. Bur., 1991—. Served to 1st lt. USAAF, 1942-45. Mem. Headmasters Assn., N.E. Assn. Schs. and Colls. (chmn. commn. on ind. secondary schs. 1967-70, pres. 1972-73), Delta Kappa Epsilon. Episcopalian. Office: Sid W Richardson Found 309 Main St Fort Worth TX 76102-4006

WILKIN, RICHARD EDWIN, clergyman, religious organization executive; b. nr. Paulding, Ohio, Nov. 3, 1930; s. Gaylord D. and Beulah E. (Tarlton) W.; m. Barbara A. Zehender, Aug. 10, 1952; children:—Richard Edward, James Lee, Deborah Ann. Student, Giffin Jr. Coll., 1948-49; B.S., Findlay Coll., 1952, D.D., 1975; postgrad., Ind. U., 1959-60. Ordained to ministry Churches of God Gen. Conf., 1953; pastor Neptune Ch. of God, Celina, Ohio, 1952-59, Wharton (Ohio) Ch. of God, 1959-64, Anthony Wayne Ch. of God, Ft. Wayne, Ind., 1964-70; administr., chief exec. Chs. of God Gen. Conf., Findlay, Ohio, 1970-87; supr. mission work India, Bangladesh, Haiti, 1970-85; dir. field edn. and Inst. for Biblical Studies, faculty mem. Winebrenner Theol. Sem., Findlay, 1987-92; interim sr. pastor Celina 1st Ch. of God, Findlay, 1992-93, sr. pastor, 1992-93; Dir. summer youth camps, sec., mem. exec. com. Ohio Conf., 1952-59, state clk., pres., 1959-64; chmn. Commn. on Edn., mem. exec. com. Ind. Conf., 1964-70; adv. com. Am. Bible Soc.; steering com. U.S. Ch. Leaders, 1979; pres. Ft. Wayne Ministerial Assn.; bd. dirs. Associated Chs. of Ft. Wayne and Allen County, 1966-70; tchr. Center Twp. Jr. High Sch., Celina, Mendon (Ohio) Union High Sch., Van Del High Sch., Van Wert, Ohio, 1954-59; interim pastor Shawnee First Ch. of God, Lima, Ohio, 1987-88, ch. cons., 1987—. Vice pres. bd. trustees Winebrenner Haven, mem. adv. com. in race relations regarding sch. reorgn. and busing, Ft. Wayne, 1967-69; trustee Winebrenner Theol. Sem., 1980-87, sec. bd. trustees; trustee U. Findlay, 1985—, chmn. of com. on trustees of bd. of trustees; sec. Bd. of Pensions of Ch. of God, Gen. Conf., 1986—. Recipient Outstanding Tchr. award, 1958; Disting. Alumnus award Findlay Coll., 1973, Outstanding Leadership award Ohio Conf. Chs. of God, 1986, Disting. Assoc. award U. Findlay, 1992; named Hon. Alumnus Winebrenner Theol. Sem., 1978. Mem. NEA, Ohio Edn. Assn., NAACP, Farm Bur. Home: 1806 Greendale Ave Findlay OH 45840-6918

WILKINS, (GEORGE) BARRATT, librarian; b. Atlanta, Nov. 6, 1943; s. George Barratt and Mabel Blanche (Brooks) W. B.A., Emory U., 1965; M.A., Ga. State U., 1968, U. Wis., 1969. Reference libr. S.C. State Libr., Columbia, 1969-71; instl. libr. cons. Mo. State Libr., Jefferson City, 1971-73; asst. state libr. State. Fla., Tallahassee, 1973-77; state libr. State Libr. Fla., 1977—; dir. div. Libr. and Info. Svcs. State of Fla., Tallahassee, 1986—, acting asst. sec. state, 1987; abstractor Hist. Abstracts, 1967-71; dir. survey project Nat. Ctr. Edn. Statistics, 1976-77; del. The White House Conf. on Libr. and Info. Svcs., 1991; mem. planning com. Fla. Gov.'s Conf. on Libraries and Info. Svcs.; bd. dirs. Southeastern Libr. Network, Inc., 1979-82, treas., 1980-81, vice chmn., 1981-82; mem. adv. coun. U.S. Pub. Printer, 1983-86, Southeastern/Atlantic Regional Med. Libr. Svcs. 1986-89 (mem. planning com., Fla. Automated Edn. Common., 1989—); cons. in field. Contbr. articles to profl. jours. Mem. adv. com. statewide jail project Mo. Assn. Social Welfare, 1971-73, bd. dirs. central div., 1971-73; mem. State Univ. System Interinstl. Library Com., 1977—; bd. dirs. Fla. Ctr. Libr. Automation, 1984—, Fla. Ctr. for the Book, 1984—, Fla. Coll. Ctr. for Libr. Automation, 1990—. Recipient Exceptional Achievement award Assn. Specialized and Coop. Libr. Agys., 1991, Outstanding Pub. Svc. award Gov. of Fla., 1991; U. Wis. fellow, 1969. Mem. ALA (coun. 1981-85, legis. com. 1982-86, com. on orgn. 1988-90, planning com., 1993—), Assn. State Libr. Agys. (pres. 1976-77), Assn. Hosp. Instl. Librs. (bd. dirs. 1973-74), Am. Correctional Assn. (instn. libr. com.), Southeastern Libr. Assn. (pres. 1982-84), Chief Officers of State Libr. Agys. (bd. dirs. 1980-82, pres. 1990-92, chair legis. com. 1992—), Beta Phi Mu, Phi Alpha Theta. Democrat. Episcopalian. Office: Dept State Divsn Libr Svcs RA Gray Bldg Tallahassee FL 32399-0250

WILKINS, BURLEIGH TAYLOR, philosophy educator; b. Bridgetown, Va., July 1, 1932; s. Burleigh and Helen Marie (Taylor) W.; children: Brita Taylor, Carla Cowgill, Burleigh William. BA summa cum laude, Duke U., 1952; MA, Harvard U., 1954, Princeton U., 1963; PhD, Princeton U., 1965. Instr. MIT, Cambridge, 1957-60, Princeton U., 1960-61, 63; asst. prof. Rice U., Houston, 1965-66, assoc. prof., 1966-67; assoc. prof. U. Calif., Santa Barbara, 1967-68, prof., 1968—. Author: Carl Becker, 1961, The Problem of Burke's Political Philosophy, 1967, Hegel's Philosophy of History, 1974, Has History Any Meaning?, 1978, Terrorism and Collective Responsibility, 1992. Mem. Phi Beta Kappa. Office: Univ of Calif Dept of Philosophy Santa Barbara CA 93106

WILKINS, C. HOWARD, JR., diplomat; b. Wichita, Kans., 1938. BA, Yale U., 1960. Franchise dir., then v.p. Pizza Hut, Inc., 1968-70; founder, pres. Pizza Hut Corp. of Am., 1970-74, also chmn. bd.; founder, pres. Maverick Devel. Corp., 1975—; amb. to The Netherlands U.S. Dept. State, 1989—; chmn. bd. Maverick Restaurant Corp. Office: Comml Sect Am Embassy APO AE 09159 also: Am Embassy, Lange Voorhout 102, The Hague Netherlands

WILKINS, CAROLINE HANKE, consumer agency administrator, political worker; b. Corpus Christi, Tex., May 12, 1937; d. Louis Allen and Jean Guckian Hanke; m. B. Hughel Wilkins, 1957; 1 child, Brian Hughel. Student, Tex. Coll. Arts and Industries, 1956-57, Tex. Tech. U., 1957-58; BA, U. Tex., 1961; MA magna cum laude, U. Ams., 1964. Instr. history Oreg. State U., 1967-68; administr. Consumer Svcs. divsn. State of Oreg., 1977-80, Wilkins Assoc., 1980—; mem. PFMC Salmon Adv. sub-panel, 1982-86. Author: (with B. H. Wilkins) Implications of the U.S.-Mexican Water Treaty for Interregional Water Transfer, 1968. Dem. precinct committeewoman, Benton County, Oreg., 1964-90; publicity chmn. Benton County Gen. Election, 1964; chmn. Get-Out-the-Vote Com., Benton County, 1966; vice chmn. Benton County Dem. Cen. Com., 1966-70; vice chmn. 1st Congl. Dist., Oreg., 1966-68, chmn.; vice chmn. Dem. Party Oreg., 1968-69, chmn. 1969-74; mem. exec. com. Western States Dem. Conf., 1970-72; vice chmn. Dem. Nat. Com., 1972-77, mem. arrangements com., 1972, 76, mem. charter commn., 1973-74; mem. Dem. Nat. Com., 1972-77, 85-89, mem. size and composition com., 1987-89, rules com. 1988; mem. Oreg. Govt. Ethics Commn., 1974-76; del., mem. rules com. Dem. Nat. Conv., 1988; 1st v.p. Nat. Fedn. Dem. Women, 1983-85, pres., 1985-87, parliamentarian, 1993—; mem. Kerr Libr. Bd. Oreg. State U., 1989—, pres., 1994—, Corvallis-Benton County Libr. Found., 1991—, sec., 1993, v.p., 1994—. Named Outstanding Mem., Nat. Fedn. Dem. Women, 1992. Mem. Nat. Assn. Consumer Agy. Administrs., Soc. Consumer Affairs Profls., Oreg. State U. Folk Club (pres. faculty wives 1989-90), Zonta (vice area bd. dirs. dist. 8 1992-94, area dir., bd. dist. 8 1994—). Office: 3311 NW Roosevelt Dr Corvallis OR 97330-1169

WILKINS, CHARLES L., chemistry educator; b. Los Angeles, Calif., Aug. 14, 1938; s. Richard and Lenore M. (McKean) W.; m. Susan J., Oct. 17, 1966; 1 child, Mark R. BS, Chapman Coll., 1961; PhD, U. Oreg., 1966. Prof. chemistry U. Nebr., Lincoln, 1967-81; prof. U. Calif., Riverside, 1981—. Office: Univ of Calif-Riverside Dept Of Chemistry Riverside CA 92521

WILKINS, CHRISTOPHER PUTNAM, conductor; b. Boston, May 28, 1957; s. Herbert Putnam and Angela (Middleton) W. BA, Harvard U.,

1978; MusM, Yale U., 1981. Condr.-in-residence SUNY, Purchase, 1981-82; asst. condr. Oreg. Symphony, Portland, 1982-83, Cleve. Orch., 1983-86; assoc. condr. Utah Symphony, Salt Lake City, from 1986; condr. Colo. Springs Symphony Orch., 1989—; condr. Exxon Arts Endowment, 1982-86. Home: 168 Nashawtuc Rd Concord MA 01742-1617 Office: Colo Springs Symphony Orch PO Box 1692 Colorado Springs CO 80901-1692*

WILKINS, DAVID GEORGE, fine arts educator; b. Battle Creek, Mich., Sept. 12, 1939; s. George Henry and Marjorie Ewing (Pierce) W.; m. Ann Thomas, June 25, 1966; children: Rebecca Louise, Katherine May. BA, Oberlin Coll., 1961; MA, U. Mich., 1963, PhD, 1969. Instr. U. N.H., Durham, 1963-64; prof. dept. history of art and arch. U. Pitts., 1967—, chair, 1989-92; dir. univ. art gallery, 1976-92; faculty mem. summer sessions Sarah Lawrence Coll.-U. Mich., Florence, Italy, 1975-81. Author: (with Bernard Schultz and Kathryn M. Linduff) Art Past/Art Present, 2d edit., 1994, (with Bonnie A. Bennett) Donatello, 1984, Maso di Banco, 1985, (with K.J. Arbitman) The Illustrated Bartsch, Vol. 53, Pre-Rembrandt Etchers, 1985, Paintings and Sculpture of the Duquesne Club, 1986 (with Mark M. Brown and Lu Donnelly) The History of the Duquesne Club, 1989; revising editor: Hartt History of Italian Renaissance Art, 4th edit., 1994. Bd. dirs. Pitts. Ctr. for Arts, 1979-93—; bd. dirs. Mendelssohn Choir of Pitts., 1979-84; mem. Pa. Humanities Coun., 1984-88; mus. adv. panel Pa. Coun. on Arts, 1985-87. William E. Suida fellow Kress Found., Kunsthistorisches Inst., Florence, 1966-67; recipient Chancellor's Disting. Teaching award U. Pitts., 1987. Mem. Coll. Art Assn., Italian Art Soc., Renaissance Soc. Am. Democrat. Home: 1217 Shady Ave Pittsburgh PA 15232-2811 Office: U Pitts Dept History Art & Arch 104 Frick Fine Arts Pittsburgh PA 15260-7610

WILKINS, (JACQUES) DOMINIQUE, professional basketball player; b. Paris, Jan. 12, 1960; s. John and Geraldine Wilkins; m. Nicole Berry, Sept. 26, 1992; 1 d.: Iyisha. Student, U. Ga., 1979-82. Basketball player Atlanta Hawks, 1982-94, Los Angeles Clippers, 1994, Boston Celtics, 1994—. Mem. NBA All-Star team, 1986-91, 93-94; NBA scoring leader, 1986; mem. All-NBA first team, 1986; mem. NBA All-Rookie team, 1983; Sporting News NCAA All-American, 1981, 82; mem. Dream Team II; slam dunk champion NBA, 1985, 90. Holds single game record for most free throws without a miss-23, 1992. Office: Boston Celtics 151 Merrimac St Boston MA 02114*

WILKINS, EARLE WAYNE, JR., surgery educator emeritus; b. Albany, N.Y., Aug. 17, 1919; s. Earle Wayne and Mildred Anna (Dana) W.; m. Suzanne Porter, Aug. 26, 1944; children: Clinton Porter, Wendy Dana Wilkins Hopkins, Wayne Lawrence. AB, Williams Coll., 1941; MD, Harvard U., 1944. Diplomate Am. Bd. Surgery, Am. Bd. Thoracic Surgery. Surg. resident Mass. Gen. Hosp., Boston, 1944-46, 48-51, mem. staff, 1952—, vis. surgeon, 1968—; mem. staff Harvard Med. Sch., Boston, 1953—, clin. prof. surgery, 1979-89, prof. emeritus, 1989—; Fulbright vis. prof. Allgemeines Krankenhaus, Vienna, Austria, 1964-65; vis. prof. Nat. Def. Med. Ctr., Taipei, Taiwan, 1989; surgeon Boston Bruins Hockey Club, 1969-85; physician tech. advisor div. of Emergency Med. Svcs., Washington, 1977-81, med. dir. Mass. Region IV, Boston, 1980-82; chmn. bd. Boston Med. Flight, 1985-87. Editor: Current Therapy in Cardiothoracic Surgery, 1989, Esophageal Cancer, 1988, Emergency Medicine: Scientific Foundations and Current Practice, 1989; contbr. numerous articles to profl. jours. Trustee Williams Coll., Williamstown, Mass., 1971-89, pres. Soc. of Alumni, 1967-69. Lt. (j.g.) USNR, 1946-48. Recipient Sports Illustrated Silver Anniversary award All-American Time Inc., N.Y.C., 1965, Commonwealth award Commonwealth Mass., 1986, Disting. Alumnus award Albany Acad., 1988, Rogerson Cup Williams Coll., 1991, Bicentennial Medal Williams Coll., 1993. Fellow ACS, Am. Surg. Assn.; mem. AMA, Mass. Med. Soc., Boston Surg. Soc., Am. Assn. Thoracic Surgery (councillor 1984-88), Soc. Thoracic Surgeons, New Eng. Surg. Soc. (pres. 1980-81), Taconic Golf Club (pres. 1990-95). Republican. Avocations: golf, tennis, skiing, travel, stamps. Home: 240 South St Williamstown MA 01267-2822

WILKINS, FLOYD, JR., retired lawyer, consultant; b. Fowler, Calif., Sept. 8, 1925; s. Floyd and Kathryn (Springborg) W.; m. Holly Blee, June 18, 1949 (div. Jan. 1964); children: Douglas B., Janet H., Steven B., Kevin D.; m. Sybil Ann Perrault, Feb. 22, 1964. BS, U. Calif., Berkeley, 1946; LLB, Harvard U., 1952. Bar: N.Y. 1953, Calif. 1959. Assoc. Dwight, Royall, Harris, Koegel & Caskey, N.Y.C., 1952-58; v.p., trust officer San Diego Trust & Savs. Bank, 1958-63; assoc., then prin., prin. Seltzer Caplan Wilkins & McMahon, P.C. and predecessors, San Diego, 1963-91; lectr. U. So. Calif. Tax Inst., L.A., 1975, Title Ins. and Trust Co. L.A. and Santa Ana, Calif., 1973, 78, 83, Trust Svcs. of Am. Tax Forum, San Diego, U. Calif. Continuing Edn. of Bar, San Diego, 1977-91. Bd. dirs., pres. San Diego County Citizens Scholarship Found. Served with USNR, 1944-46. Mem. ABA, State Bar Calif., San Diego County Bar Assn. Republican. Avocations: travel, photography, wine, gardening. Home: 2005 Soledad Ave La Jolla CA 92037

WILKINS, HERBERT PUTNAM, judge; b. Cambridge, Mass., Jan. 10, 1930; s. Raymond Sanger and Mary Louisa (Aldrich) W.; m. Angela Joy Middleton, June 21, 1952; children: Douglas H., Stephen M., Christopher P., Kate W. McManus. A.B., Harvard U., 1951, LL.B. magna cum laude, 1954; LL.D., Suffolk U., 1976; J.D., New Eng. Sch. Law, 1979. Bar: Mass. 1954. Assoc. firm Palmer & Dodge, Boston, 1954-59; ptnr. Palmer & Dodge, 1960-72; assoc. justice Mass. Supreme Jud. Ct., 1972—. Editor: Harvard U. Law Rev, 1953-54. Bd. overseers Harvard U., 1977-83, pres. bd., 1981-83; trustee Milton Acad., 1971-76, Phillips Exeter Acad., 1972-78; mem. Concord (Mass.) Planning Bd., 1957-60; selectman Town of Concord, 1960-66, town counsel, 1969-72; town counsel Town of Acton, Mass., 1966-72. Mem. Am. Law Inst. (council), Am. Coll. Trial Lawyers (jud. fellow). Republican. Unitarian-Universalist. Office: Mass Supreme Jud Ct Pemberton Sq 1300 New Courthouse Boston MA 02108

WILKINS, J. ERNEST, JR., mathematician; b. Chgo., Nov. 27, 1923; s. J. Ernest and Lucille B. (Robinson) W.; m. Gloria Louise Stewart, June 22, 1947 (dec.); children: Sharon Wilkins Hill, J. Ernest III; m. Maxine G. Malone, June 2, 1984. BS, U. Chgo., 1940, MS, 1941, PhD, 1942; BME, NYU, 1957, MME, 1960. Mathematician Am. Optical Co., Buffalo, 1946-50; mgr. R&D United Nuclear Corp., White Plains, N.Y., 1950-60; assoc. dir. lab. Gen. Atomic Co., San Diego, 1960-70; Disting. prof. applied math. physics Howard U., Washington, 1970-77; vis. scientist Argonne (Ill.) Nat. Lab., 1976-77, fellow, 1984-85; v.p., dep. gen. mgr. EG & G Idaho, Idaho Falls, 1977-84; Disting. prof. Clark Atlanta U., 1990—; mem. Army Sci. Bd. Dept. Army, 1978-81; mem. Adv. Com. on Reactor Safeguards, Washington, 1990-94, chmn., 1993-94. Contbr. articles to profl. jours. With AUS, 1946-47. Recipient Outstanding Civilian Svc. medal U.S. Army, 1980. Mem. Am. Nuclear Soc. (pres. 1974-75, cons. 1987-90), Am. Math. Soc., Math. Assn. Am., Oak Ridge Assn. Univs. (coun. 1990—). Office: Clark Atlanta U Box J Atlanta GA 30314

WILKINS, JOHN WARREN, physics educator; b. Des Moines, Mar. 11, 1936; s. Carl Daniel and Ruth Elizabeth (Warren) W. B.S. in Engring. Northwestern U., 1959; M.S., U. Ill., 1960, Ph.D, 1963; D.Tech. (hon.), Chalmers Tekniska Hogskola, Göteborg, 1990. NSF postdoctoral fellow U. Cambridge, Eng., 1963-64; asst. prof. physics Cornell U., 1964-68, assoc. prof., 1968-74, prof., 1974-88; Ohio Eminent scholar, prof. physics Ohio State U., 1988—; vis. prof. H. C. Ørsted Inst., Copenhagen, 1968, Nordita, Copenhagen, 1972-73, 75-76, 79-81; cons. Los Alamos Nat. Lab., 1984—; mem. computational/theoretical techniques panel Naval Rsch. Lab., 1994—. Assoc. editor Physica Scripta, 1978-85, Phys. Rev. Letters, 1982-85, Rev. Modern Physics, 1983—, Phys. Rev. B, 1991—; coord. Comments on Condensed Matter Physics, 1985-90. Guggenheim fellow Inst. Theoretical Physics, U. Calif.-Santa Barbara, 1985-86; Sloan fellow, 1966-68. Fellow AAAS, Am. Phys. Soc. (divisional councillor, div. condensed matter physics 1989—, exec. com. div. biol. physics 1973-77); mem. European Phys. Soc. Office: Ohio State U Dept Physics 174 W 18th Ave Columbus OH 43210-1168

WILKINS, LUCIEN SANDERS, gastroenterologist; b. Sanford, N.C., Mar. 30, 1942; s. Alexander Betts and Olive Elizabeth (Pittman) W.; m. Freda Barry Hartness, July 16, 1966; children: Lucien Sanders Jr., Elise Perryman. BA, Duke U., 1963; MD, Med. Coll. Va., 1967. Diplomate Am. Bd. Internal Medicine. Intern Medical Coll. Va., Richmond, 1967-68, re-

sident in internal medicine, 1970-72, gastroenterology fellow, 1972-73; clin. gastroenterologist Wilmington (N.C.) Health Assoc., 1973—; vis. physician Hopital STE. Croix, Leogane, Haiti, 1984; founder Divsn. Gastrointestinal Edoscopy Hopital STE. Croix, Leogane, Haiti, 1988, First Endoscopic Ambulatory Surgery Facility in the State of Haiti, 1990;chmn. dept. medicine New Hanover Regional Med. Ctr., Wilmington, N.C., 1990-92, pres. med. staff, 1985, bd. trustees, 1984-87, exec. com. 1994—; pres. Wilmington Health Assoc., 1988-92; asst. prof. clin. medicine U. N.C., Chapel Hill, 1974—; bd. dirs. Br. Banking and Trust, Wilmington, 1991—; physician adv. Nat. Found. Ileitis and Colitis, 1976-78. Author: Progeny, 1994. Bd. dirs. Cape Fear Coun. for the Arts, Wilmington, 1976-77, New Hanover Regional Med. Ctr. Found., Wilmington, 1993—, Com. of 100, Wilmington, 1992—. Lt. comdr. M.C., USN, 1968-70. Paul Harris fellow Rotary, 1986; winner GTP-L Al Holbert Meml. Race, Sebring, Fla., 1995. Mem. ACP, New Hanover-Pender County Med. Soc. (pres. 1980), Cape Fear Country Club, Surf Club, Hist. Stock Car Racing Group, Figure Eight Island Yacht Club(charter). Presbyterian. Avocations: vintage automobile racing, tennis, sailing, skiing, outdoors. Home: 2215 Lynnwood Dr Wilmington NC 28403-8026 Office: Wilmington Health Assoc 1202 Medical Center Dr Wilmington NC 28401-7307

WILKINS, ORMSBY, music director, conductor, pianist; b. Sydney, Australia. Student, Sydney Conservatory Music, Melbourne (Australia) Conservatory Music. Joined Australian Ballet, 1973, condr., 1976-82, resident condr., 1982-83, guest condr. tour USSR and Eng., 1988, guest condr. tour Am., 1990; formerly condr. Sadler's Wells Royal Ballet (now Birmingham Royal Ballet); music dir., prin. condr. Nat. Ballet Can., Toronto, Ont., Can., 1990—; condr. Royal Swedish Ballet, Royal Opera House Orch. at Covent Garden, Opera Ballet de Lyon, Philharmonic Orch. London, Royal Philharm. Orch. Lodon, Hong Kong Philharmonic Orch., Winnipeg Symphony Orch. Performances include Swan Lake, Sleeping Beauty, Coppelia, Raymonda, Petrouchka, Rite of Spring, premiere of Hobson's Choice. Office: Nat Ballet Can, 157 King St East, Toronto, ON Canada M5C 1G9*

WILKINS, PHILIP CHARLES, judge; b. Jan. 27, 1913; student Sacramento Jr. Coll.; LL.B., U. Calif. San Francisco, 1939; m. Sue Wilkins, Aug. 9, 1941. Bar: Calif. 1939. Mem. firm A.D. McDougall, Sacramento, 1940-42, Rowland & Craven, Sacramento, 1946-54; individual practice law, Sacramento, 1954-59; ptnr. firm Wilkins, Little & Mix, Sacramento, 1959-65, Wilkins & Mix, Sacramento, 1966-69; judge U.S. Dist. Ct., Eastern Dist. Calif., Sacramento, 1969—, now sr. judge. Served to lt. USNR, 1942-46. Office: US Dist Ct 2028 US Courthouse 650 Capitol Mall Sacramento CA 95814-4708

WILKINS, RITA DENISE, researcher, multimedia design consultant; b. Detroit, June 21, 1951; d. William H. and Alice L. (Hayes) Smith. Student, George Peabody Coll., 1969-70, Cleveland (Tenn.) State Community Coll. 1973-75. Mgmt. coord., legal coord. Arlen Realty and Devel. Corp., Chattanooga, Tenn., 1973-76; asst. v.p., office mgr. Newburger Andes & Co., Atlanta, 1976-78, asst. v.p., project mgr., 1978-79; project mgr. Robinson-Humphrey, Atlanta, 1979-80; dept. head Office Properties Group Merrill Lynch Realty Comml. Svcs., Atlanta, 1980-83; acquisition devel. mgmt. rep. Cardinal Industries, Inc., Atlanta, 1983-86; pres., sr. cons. CPC/Foresite, Charleston, S.C., 1986—; guest lectr. Ga. State U. Contbr. articles to profl. jours. Mem. Indsl. Devel. Rsch. Coun. (devel. and edn. coms.), S.C. Real Estate Broker, S.C. Econ. Developers Assn., Am. Real Estate Soc., Comml. Real Estate Women of Ga. (founder), Charleston World Trade Ctr. (steering com., growth strategy sub-com., facility sub-com.), Comml. Real Estate Women, Goodlettsville C. of C. (econ. devel. com.). Office: CPC/Foresite 115 Dorris Ave Goodlettsville TN 37072

WILKINS, ROBERT HENRY, neurosurgeon, editor; b. Pitts., Aug. 18, 1934; s. George H. and Mary M. (Lemon) W.; m. Gloria A. Kohl, Dec. 28, 1957; children: Michael I., Jeffrey K., Elizabeth A. BS, U. Pitts., 1955, MD, 1959. Diplomate Am. Bd. Neurol. Surgery. Intern, resident gen. surgery Duke U. Med. Ctr., Durham, N.C., 1959-61, resident neurosurgery, 1963-68, asst. prof. neurosurgery, 1968-72, prof., chief div. neurosurgery, 1976—; clin. assoc. surgery br. Nat. Cancer Inst., Bethesda, Md., 1961-63; chmn. dept. neurosurgery Scott and White Clinic, Temple, Tex., 1972-75; assoc. prof. neurosurgery U. Pitts., 1975-76; lectr. Cook County Grad. Sch. Medicine, Chgo., 1976—; attending neurosurgeon Durham VA Hosp., 1978—; mem. Nat. Adv. Coun., Nat. Inst. Neurol. Disorders and Stroke, 1989-92. Co-editor: Neurosurgery, 2d edit., 5 vols., 1995, Neurosurgery Updates I and II, 1990, 91, Neurosurgery Operative Atlas, 1991—, Principles of Neurosurgery, 1994; editor Clin. Neurosurgery, 1972-75; assoc. editor Surg. Neurology, 1975-76; founding editor Neurosurgery, 1977-82; mem. editl. bd. Jour. Neurosurgery, 1987-96, chmn., 1996-97; neurosurgery editor Key Neurology and Neurosurgery, 1993—, Yr. Book of Neurology and Neurosurgery, 1994—. Recipient Travel award Copenhagen, Nat. Inst. Neurol. Diseases and Blindness, Royal Australasian Coll. Surgeons, Found. lectr. Adelaide 1986. Mem. Congress Neurol. Surgeons (pres. 1979-80), Am. Assn. Neurol. Surgeons (treas. 1989-92), So. Neurosurg. Soc. (sec. 1988-91, pres. 1992-93), Am. Bd. Neurological Surgery (dir. 1991—), Phi Beta Kappa, Alpha Omega Alpha. Democrat. Episcopalian. Avocations: medical writing and editing. Office: Duke U Med Ctr PO Box 3807 Durham NC 27702-3807

WILKINS, ROBERT PEARCE, lawyer; b. Jesup, Ga., Sept. 10, 1933; s. Ransom Little and Sarah (Pearce) W.; m. Rose Truesdale, Jan. 7, 1956; children: Robert Pearce, Chisolm Wallace (dec.), Sarah Ruth Weiss, Rose Anne Brooks. B.A., U. S.C., 1953, J.D., 1956; LL.M., Georgetown U., 1957. Bar: S.C. 1954. Atty. Office Gen. Counsel, Sec. Army, Washington, 1956; trust officer First Nat. Bank S.C., Columbia, 1957-60; practice law Columbia, 1960-64; ptnr. McLain, Sherrill & Wilkins, Columbia, 1964-68, McKay, Sherrill, Walker, Townsend & Wilkins, Columbia, 1969-75; sole practice law Columbia and Lexington, S.C., 1975-88; of counsel Nelson, Mullins, Riley & Scarborough, Lexington, 1988—; pres. Sandlapper Press, Inc., 1967-72, pub. Sandlapper Mag. S.C., 1968-72; editor Sandlapper Mag. S.C., 1968-72, 89—; editor, pub. S.C. History Illustrated, 1970; pres. R.P.W. Pub. Corp.; mem., chmn. S.C. Splty. Adv. Bd. Estate Planning and Probate, 1982-85; lectr. in law U. S.C., 1971-78. Author: Drafting Wills and Trust Agreements in South Carolina, 1971, Drafting Wills and Trust Agreements in Michigan, 1978, Wills and Trust System (Arkansas), 1978, Drafting Wills and Trust Agreements: A Systems Approach, 1988, 2d edit., 1989, software edit.; (with others) Word Processing for a Law Office, 1979; also articles; editor: The Lawyer's Microcomputer, 1982-85, The Lawyer's PC, 1983—. What a Lawyer Needs to Know to Buy and Use a Computer, 1984, The Perfect Lawyer, 1990—, The Lawyer's Word, 1991, Shepard's ElderCare/Law Newsletter, 1991—. Del., Spl. Liaison Tax. Com. Southeastern Region, 1967-70; exec. com. Richland County Republican Com., 1960-64; sec.-treas. Richland County Rep. Club, 1960; bd. dirs. Central Tb-RD Assn.; trustee Sch. Dist. 1, Lexington County, S.C., 1971-78, sec., 1972-75, chmn., 1975-78; mem. S.C. Commn. on Higher Edn., 1978-80, S.C. Commn. on Lawyer Competence, 1980-82; bd. dirs. Crime Stoppers of the Midlands, 1983-85, RPW Learning Ctr., 1987—, Mt. Hope Cemetary, 1991—, also v.p., 1992—; v.p. 11th cir. Alumni Coun. U. S.C., 1993-95; mem. commn. Riverbanks Zoo., 1986—, sec., 1991—. Served with AUS, 1954-55. Fellow Am. Bar Found., Am. Coll. Trust and Estate Counsel (publs. com. 1984-87, bd. regents 1986-87, mem. tech. com. 1989—), Am. Coll. Tax Counsel, Coll. Law Practice Mgmt. (charter, trustee), S.C. Bar (tax coordinating com. 1968-70, chmn. legal econs. com. 1973-75, ho. of dels. 1978-80, editor S.C Lawyer 1989-91, mem. alternative dispute resolution sect. 1993—), S.C. Bar Found. (life, bd. dirs. 1984-88, v.p. 1986-87, pres. 1987-88); mem. ABA (ho. of dels. 1986-87, chmn. valuation subcom., estate and gift tax com., taxation sect. 1967-73, vice chmn. svc. and assistance to law student div. com. gen. practice sect. 1971-72, vice chmn. corp. counsel com. gen. practice sect. 1972-74, editor econs. of law practice sect. legal econs. 1974-78, sec. 1977-78, vice chmn. 1978-79, chmn. 1980-81, mem. standing com. assn. comm. 1981-84, real property, probate and trust law, mem. publs. com. 1985-89, editor Probate and Property, 1986-89), Richland County Bar Assn. (chmn. probate sect. 1973-74, unauthorized practice of law com. 1976, Columbia Jaycees (sec.-treas. 1958-59), Columbia Estate Planning Coun. (pres. 1964-65), Am. Y-Flyer Yacht Racing Assn. (area v.p. 1971, internat. dir. 1972-73), Omicron Delta Kappa, Sigma Chi. Clubs: Columbia Sailing (dir. 1968-71), Columbia Tip Off (dir. 1968-73), Columbia (pres. 1971-72). Home: PO Box 729 Lexington SC 29071-0729 Office: 334 Old Chapin Rd Lexington SC 29072-8801

WILKINS, ROGER CARSON, retired insurance company executive; b. Houlton, Maine, June 9, 1906; s. George W. and Amanda (Carson) W.; m. Evelyn McFadden, Aug. 23, 1933; 1 child, Susan J. Student, Ricker Classical Inst., 1919-24; B.A., U. Maine, 1929; LL.D., U. Hartford, 1966, Ricker Coll., 1970, Trinity Coll., 1973. With Travelers Ins. Companies, Hartford, from 1929; beginning as mgr. mortgage loan dept. for Travelers Ins. Companies, Tex., 1930; successively asst. mgr. home office, mgr., sec. v.p. Travelers Ins. Companies, 1953-65, sr. v.p., 1965-69, pres., 1969-71, chmn. bd., from 1971; also chief exec. officer; chmn. bd. Travelers Corp., 1971-73, chmn. exec. com., from 1974; former dir. Allis-Chalmers Corp., United Tech., Conn. Bank and Trust Co., Conn. Natural Gas Co.; former trustee Wells Fargo Mortgage Investor. Bd. dirs. U.S. C. of C. Corporator Hartford Hosp.; pres. Hartford Inst. Living; trustee St. Joseph Coll. Clubs: Hartford, Hartford Golf; Gulf Stream Golf (Fla.); Ekwanok Country (Manchester, Vt.).

WILKINS, WILLIAM WALTER, JR., federal judge; b. Anderson, S.C., Mar. 29, 1942; s. William Walter and Evelyn Louise (Horton) W.; m. Carolyn Louise Adams, Aug. 15, 1964; children: Lauren, Lyn, Walt. B.A., Davidson Coll., 1964; J.D., U.S.C., 1967. Bar: S.C., 1967, U.S. Dist. Ct. S.C. 1967, U.S. Ct. Appeals (4th cir.) 1969, U.S. Supreme Ct. 1970. Law clk. to judge U.S. Ct. Appeals 4th Cir., 1969; legal asst. to U.S. Senator Strom Thurmond, 1970; ptnr. Wilkins & Wilkins, Greenville, S.C., 1971-75; solicitor 13th Jud. Cir., 1974-81; judge U.S. Dist. Ct., Greenville, 1981-86, U.S. Ct. Appeals (4th cir.), 1986—; lectr. Greenville Tech. Coll.; chmn. U.S. Sentencing Commn., 1985-94. Editor-in-chief S.C. Law Rev., 1967; contbr. articles to legal jours. Served with U.S. Army, 1967-69. Named Outstanding Grad. of Yr. U. S.C. Sch. Law, 1967. Mem. S.C. Bar Assn., Wig and Robe. Republican. Baptist. Office: US Cir Ct 4th Ct PO Box 10857 Greenville SC 29603-0857

WILKINSON, ALBERT MIMS, JR., lawyer; b. Nashville, June 29, 1925; s. Albert Mims and Mary Nelle (Derryberry) W.; m. Edythe Bush, Mar. 27, 1953 (div.); children: William Terry, Elizabeth Ann, David Bush; m. Dolores Jean Attard, Oct. 22, 1971 (div.); 1 child, Mary Dolores. Student, Emory U., 1942-43; JD, U. Ga., 1949. Bar: Ga. 1948. Pvt. practice law Atlanta, 1950-85; gen. counsel GEC-Marconi Avionics Inc., Atlanta, 1985—; hon. legal adviser to Brit. Consul Gen. at Atlanta. Author: The Winning of the Revolutionary War in the South, 1976, The Rights of Unsecured Creditors-The Law in Georgia, 1979. Mem. DeKalb County Bd. Elections, 1966-72; chmn. 4th Congl. Dist. Republican Exec. Com., 1964-65, Ga. State Rep. Exec. Com., 1968-74; 1st vice chmn. Ga. Rep. Party, 1972-74, asst. gen. counsel, 1974-75; vice chmn., trustee Atlanta Counseling Center, Inc., 1960-83. Served with USCGR, 1943-46. Fellow Comml. Law Found.; mem. Atlanta, ABA, Ga. Bar Assn., Ga. Soc. (pres. 1962-63), SAR, Southeastern Mem.'s Assn. (pres. 1960-61), Comml. Law League Am., Ga. Soc. Colonial Wars, Old Guard of Gate City Guard (commandant 1986), N.C. Soc. of Cincinnati, Order British Empire, Commerce Club, Civitan, Masons. Baptist. Home and Office: 333 Sky Valley Dillard GA 30537 *By precept and example my parents pointed out the upward way in life, on a foundation of religious faith. "To do justly, to love mercy, to walk humbly with thy God." Later a beloved teacher taught the lines from Ulysses as he prepared to set sail, "To strive, to seek, to find and never yield." Their inspiration has continued throughout my life.*

WILKINSON, BEN, chancellor, evangelist, ministry organizer, writer; b. Gloster, Miss., July 6, 1932; s. Thomas Lamar and Evie (Quackenbush) W.; m. Mary Pittman; children: Evangeline Patricia Wilkinson Light, William Dwight, Manford Leighton, Glen Calvin. BA in Pub. Speaking, U. So. Miss., 1954; MDiv, Columbia Theol. Sem., Decatur, Ga., 1957, postgrad., 1964-65; DD, Whitefield Theol. Sem., 1992. Pastor Trinity Presbyn. Ch., Huntsville, Ala., 1955-62, Ga. Ave Presbyn. Ch., Atlanta, 1962-66; evangelist, exec. dir. Presbyn. Evangelistic Fellowship, Decatur, 1966—; founder, dean, 1971-74; pres. Atlanta Sch. Bibl. Studies, 1974-85, chancellor, 1986—; bd. dirs. Atlanta Sch. Bibl. Studies, Westminster Bibl. Missions, World Harvest Missions, Lords Day Alliance. Founder, server Synod Planting Ch. in Inner City. Avocations: sports, writing, reading, family life. Home: 214 Inman Dr Decatur GA 30030-3833 Office: Presbyn Evangelistic Fellowship 4211 Flat Shoals Pky Decatur GA 30034-4203

WILKINSON, BRUCE W., corporate executive, lawyer; b. Dallas, 1944; married. BA, U. Okla., 1966, JD, 1969; LLM, U. London, 1970. Gen. counsel Dresser Industries, Inc., Dallas, 1970-78; v.p., treas. CRS Sirrine, Inc. (now CRSS Inc.), Houston, 1978-79, sr. v.p., treas., 1979-82, pres., chief exec. officer, 1982—, chmn., 1989—; also bd. dirs. Annual bd. dirs., CEO. Office: CRSS Inc 1177 W Loop S Ste 800 Houston TX 77027*

WILKINSON, CHRISTOPHER FOSTER, toxicologist, educator; b. Driffield, Yorkshire, Eng., Feb. 9, 1938; came to U.S., 1961; s. Joseph Kemp and Winifred Margaret (Foster) W.; m. Maria Luisa, Aug. 6, 1976; 1 son, Paul Christopher. B.S., U. Reading, 1961; Ph.D., U. Calif.-Riverside, 1965. Sr. research fellow Agrl. Research Council, Pest Infestation Lab., Slough, Bucks, Eng., 1965-66; asst. prof. Cornell U., Ithaca, N.Y., 1966-71, assoc. prof., 1971-78, prof. insecticide chemistry and toxicology, 1978-88; dir. Inst. Comparative and Environ. Toxicology, Cornell U., 1982-85; toxicology cons. Versar, Inc., Springfield, Va., 1988-91; dir. div. toxicology, v.p. Tech. Scis. Group, Inc., Washington, 1991—; mem. adv. com. NIH, Nat. Acad. Sci.; mem. Fed. Insecticide, Fungicide and Rodenticide Act sci. adv. panel EPA, 1983-85. Editor: Insecticide Biochemistry and Physiology, 1976, Effect of Pesticides on Human Health, 1990; contbr. over 120 articles to profl. publs. Mem. AAAS, Am. Chem. Soc., Soc. Toxicology. Office: Tech Scis Group Inc 1101 17th St NW Washington DC 20036-4704

WILKINSON, DAVID TODD, physics educator; b. Hillsdale, Mich., May 13, 1935; s. Harold Arba and Thelma Ellen (Todd) W.; m. Sharon E. Harper, June 14, 1958 (div. June 1979); children: Wendy, Kenton; m. Eunice H. Dowell, Oct. 13, 1984. BS in Engring. Physics, U. Mich., 1957, MS in Nuclear Engring., 1959, PhD in Physics, 1962. Lectr. physics U. Mich., Ann Arbor, 1962-63; instr. Princeton U., N.J., 1963-65; asst. prof. Princeton U., 1965-68, assoc. prof., 1968-71; prof. Princeton U., N.J., 1971—, chmn. dept., 1987-90; cons. NASA. Contbr. articles to profl. jours. Alfred P. Sloane fellow, 1965-67, John Simon Guggenheim fellow, 1977-78. Mem. NAS. Office: Princeton U Jadwin Hall PO Box 708 Dept Princeton NJ 08544

WILKINSON, DONALD MICHAEL, JR., lawyer; b. Detroit, Apr. 22, 1931; s. Donald Michael and Martha Mary (Dursek) W.; m. Minette Yoshimoto, Oct. 26, 1963; children: Phoebe, Donald, Heidi, Genevieve. B.A., U. Mich., 1951, J.D., 1954. Bar: Mich. 1954, N.Y. 1957. Assoc. White & Case, N.Y.C., 1957-68, ptnr., 1968—; resident ptnr. White & Case, London, 1979-83. Editor: Mich. Law Rev., 1954; contbr. articles to legal periodicals. Trustee Village of Laurel Hollow, N.Y., 1969-79, dep. mayor, 1976-79. Served to 1st lt. U.S. Army, 1955-57. Mem. ABA, N.Y. State Bar Assn., Assn. Bar City N.Y., Order of Coif. Democrat. Roman Catholic. Clubs: Huntington Country (N.Y.); Princeton (N.Y.C.); Wentworth (Virginia Lake, Eng.). Office: White & Case 1155 Ave Of The Americas New York NY 10036-2711

WILKINSON, DORIS YVONNE, medical sociology educator; b. Lexington, Ky., June 13, 1936; d. Howard Thomas and Regina Wilkinson. BA, U. Ky., 1958; MA, Case Western Res. U., 1960, PhD, 1968; MPH, Johns Hopkins U., 1985. Asst. prof. U. Ky., Lexington, 1968-70; assoc. prof., then prof. Macalester Coll., St. Paul, 1970-77; exec. assoc. Am. Sociol. Assn., Washington, 1977-80; prof. medical sociology Howard U., Washington, 1980-84; vis. prof. U. Va., 1984-85; prof. sociology U. Ky., Lexington, 1985—; chmn. panel women in sci. program NSF, Washington, 1976; rev. panelist Nat. Inst. Drug Abuse, Washington, 1978-79; mem. bd. sci. counselors Nat. Cancer Inst., Bethesda, Md., 1980-84; vis. scholar Harvard U., Cambridge, Mass., 1989-90, vis. prof., summers 1992, 93, 94; Rapoport vis. prof. social theory Smith Coll., summer 1995. Author: Wookbook for Introductory Sociology, 1968; editor: Black Revolt: Strategies of Protest, 1969; co-editor: The Black Male in America, 1977, Alternative Health Maintenance and Healing Systems, 1987, Race, Gender and the Life Cycle, 1991; social history photographic exhbn. "The African American Presence in Medicine" Harvard Med. Libr., 1991, Pearson Mus.- So. Ill. U. Med. Sch., 1992, N.J. Coll. Medicine and Dentistry, 1993, Louisville Mus. History and Sci., 1994, U Cin. Med. Sch. Libr., 1994, Albert Einstein Coll. of Medicine, 1995; contbr.

articles to profl. jours. Bd. overseers Case Western Res. U., Cleve., 1982-87. Recipient Pub. Humanities award U. Ky., 1990, Midway Coll. Women's History Month award, 1991, Great Tchr. award Nat. Alumni Assn. U. Ky., Disting. Scholar award Assn. Black Sociologists, 1993; inducted into Hall of Disting. Alumni, U. Ky., 1989; fellow Woodrow Wilson Found. 1959-61, Ford Found.; grantee Social Sci. Rsch. Coun., 1975, Nat. Inst. Edn., 1978-80, Nat. Cancer Inst., 1986-88, Ky. Humanities Coun., 1988, Am. Coun. Learned Soc., 1989-90, NEH, 1991; Disting. Prof. in Coll. Arts and Scis. U. Ky., 1992-93. Mem. So. Sociol. Soc. (honors com. 1993-94), Am. Sociol. Assn. (exec. assoc., budget com. 1985-88, v.p. 1991-92, mem. coun. 1994—, Dubois-Johnson-Frazier award 1988), D.C. Sociol. Soc. (pres. 1982-83), Soc. for Study Social Problems (v.p. 1984-85, pres. 1987-88), Ea. Sociol. Soc. (v.p. 1983-84, pres. 1992-93, I. Peter Gellman award 1987), N.Y. Acad. Scis., Phi Beta Kappa, Alpha Kappa Delta. Unitarian.

WILKINSON, EDWARD ANDERSON, JR., retired naval officer, business executive; b. Selma, Ala., Sept. 21, 1933; s. Edward Anderson and Alice Margaret (Moorer) W.; m. Barbara Anne Parker, June 4, 1955 (dec. June 1991); children: Daryl Edward, Daniel Bryan, Edward Anderson III, David Park; m. Sondra Marie Moore, Oct. 2, 1994. B.S., U.S. Naval Acad., 1955; M.S. in Mech. Engring., 1964; grad., Nat. War Coll., 1972. Commd. ensign U.S. Navy, 1955, advanced through grades to rear adm., 1979; dir. Anti-Submarine Warfare Systems Program Office, Washington, 1978-79; dep. dir. Def. Mapping Agy., Washington, 1979-81; cmdr. Patrol Wings, U.S. Atlantic Fleet, Brunswick, Maine, 1981-83; dir. Def. Mapping Agy., Washington, 1983-85; ret., 1985; exec. v.p. Internat. Fed. Systems Intergraph Corp., Reston, Va. Decorated Legion Merit, D.S.M. (Dept. Def.). Presbyterian. Home: 1155 Regatton Ln Reston VA 22094 Office: Intergraph Corp Reston VA

WILKINSON, EUGENE PARKS, nuclear engineer; b. Long Beach, Calif., Aug. 10, 1918; s. Dennis William and Daisy Amelia (Parks) W.; m. Janice Edith Thuli, Mar. 28, 1942; children: Dennis Eugene, Stephen James, Marian Lynn, Rodney David. AB in Chemistry, San Diego State U., 1938. Instr. chemistry San Diego State U., 1938-39; commd. ensign U.S. Navy, 1940, advanced through grades to vice adm., 1970; served various locations including 1st comdg. officer USS Nautilus (1st nuclear-powered submarine), 1953-57; 1st comdg. officer USS Long Beach, 1959-63, 1st nuclear-powered surface ship; ret., 1974; exec. v.p. Data Design Labs., Cucamonga, Calif., 1977-80; pres., chief exec. officer Inst. Nuclear Power Ops., Atlanta, 1980-84, pres. emeritus, 1984—; bd. dirs. Data Design Labs.; emeritus bd. dirs. Advanced Resource Devel. Corp. Columbia, Md., MDM Engring. Corp., San Clemente, Calif., chmn. bd. Decorated Legion of Merit, Silver Star, D.S.M. with three oak leaf clusters, others, Second Order Sacred Treasure Japan; recipient George Westinghouse Gold medal ASME, 1983, Oliver Townsend medal Atomic Indsl. Forum, 1984, Gold medal Uranium Inst., 1989. Mem. Am. Soc. Naval Engrs., Am. Nuclear Soc. (Henry DeWolf Smyth Nuclear Statesman medal 1994), Navy League, Submarine League, Nat. Acad. Engring. Avocations: tennis, bridge. Home: 1449 Crest Rd Del Mar CA 92014-2530

WILKINSON, G. THOMAS, gas and oil industry executive; b. 1937. BSE, St. Louis U., 1959. With AMOCO, ARCO, Seagull Energy S&P; pres. Ashland Exploration, Inc., 1990—; v.p. Ashland Oil, Inc., 1990-91, sr. v.p., 1992—. Office: Ashland Exploration Inc 14701 St Mary's Ln Houston TX 77079*

WILKINSON, HAROLD ARTHUR, neurosurgeon; b. Wake Forest, N.C., June 17, 1935; s. Charles T. and Ursula (Bernstein) W.; m. Alice D. Speas, June 22, 1957; children: Arthur, Edward. BS, Wake Forest Coll., 1955; MD, Duke U., 1959, PhD, 1962. NIH postdoctoral rsch. fellow Duke U. Med. Ctr., Durham, N.C., 1959-61, intern, 1961-62; resident in neurosurgery Mass. Gen. Hosp., Boston, 1962-66; mem. faculty Harvard U. Med. Ctr., Cambridge, Mass., 1966-78; mem. staff Boston City Hosp., 1966-71, Beth Israel Hosp., Boston, 1971-78; prof. neurosurgery, chmn. div. U. Mass. Med. Ctr., Worcester, 1979—, prof. anatomy cell biology program, 1985—, residency program dir., 1991—. Contbr. articles to profl. jours.; inventor intracranial pressure monitoring cup catheter. Med. Found. fellow, 1966-69. Mem. AMA, ACS, Am. Assn. Neurol. Surgery, Congress of Neurosurgery, New Eng. Neurol. Soc. Office: U Mass Med Ctr Div Neurosurgery 55 Lake Ave N Worcester MA 01655-0002

WILKINSON, HARRY EDWARD, management educator and consultant; b. Richmond Heights, Mo., June 30, 1930; s. Harry Edward and Virginia Flo (Shelton) W.; m. Sara Beth Kikendall, Aug. 30, 1958; children: Linda Beth, Cheryl Susan. BA in Physics, Princeton U., 1952; MBA, Washington U., St. Louis, 1957; D Bus. Adminstrn., Harvard U., 1964. Lic. psychologist, Mass. Staff engr. Southwestern Bell Tel. Co., St. Louis, 1954-57; traffic engr. New Eng. Tel. & Telegraph Co., Boston, 1957-60; sr. mgmt. cons. Harbridge House Inc., Boston, 1961-65; dean bus. adminstrn., dir. Mgmt. Inst., Northeastern U., Boston, 1965-67; pres., chmn. bd. Univ. Affiliates Inc., North Port, Fla., 1967—; vis. prof. mgmt. Rice U., Houston, 1990-94, prof. office of exec. devel., 1994—; cons. to various industries and govt., 1961—. Author: Influencing People in Organizations, 1993; contbr. articles to mgmt. jours. Lt. (j.g.) USN, 1952-54, Korea. Mem. APA, Acad. Mgmt., N.Am. Case Rsch. Assn., S.W. Case Rsch. Assn., Harvard Bus. Sch. Assn. Office: Jones Grad Sch Rice U 6100 Main St Houston TX 77005

WILKINSON, HARRY J., technical company executive; b. Phila., Nov. 15, 1937; s. Frank and Annie Wilkinson; children: Tracey, Todd, Betsey. BS in Indsl. Engring., Temple U., 1965. Mktg. mgr. aerospace div. SPS Techs., Jenkintown, Pa., 1969-75; mng. dir. Unbrako, Ltd. div. SPS Techs., Coventry, Eng., 1975-79; pres. Unbrako, Ltd. div. SPS Techs., Jenkintown, 1979-82; pres. aerospace and indsl. products div., group v.p. domestic ops. SPS Techs., Newtown, Pa., 1984-86, pres., chief operating officer, 1986—; also bd. dirs.; bd. dirs. Drexelbrook Engring., Horsham, Pa., Flexible Circs., Inc., Warrington, Pa. Served to 1t. U.S. Army, 1957-59. Office: SPS Techs Inc Box 1000 Rte 332 Newtown PA 18940

WILKINSON, HOWARD R., association administrator; b. Jackson, Mich., May 3, 1925; m. Glennis D. Sillaway, 1944; 6 children. Student, Mich. State U., 1946. Sales and mgmt. exec. various cos., 1947-54; sales supt. southeastern dist. Crowell-Collier Pub. Co., 1953-55; founder, pres., CEO Nat. Child Safety Coun., Jackson, 1955-93; cons., fundraiser Jackson, 1993—. Pres. Missing Children HELP Ctr. Mem. Greater Jackson C. of C., Am. Security Coun. (nat. adv. bd.), Internat. Coun. Prevention Practitioners, Arbor Hills Country Country Club, Jackson Town Club. Home: 1301 Wilkinson Dr Jackson MI 49203 Office: Nat Child Safety Coun PO Box 1368 4065 Page Ave Jackson MI 49204

WILKINSON, JAMES HARVIE, III, federal judge; b. N.Y.C., Sept. 29, 1944; s. James Harvie and Letitia (Nelson) W.; m. Lossie Grist Noell, June 30, 1973; children: James Nelson, Porter Noell. B.A., Yale U., 1963-67; J.D., U. Va., 1972. Bar: Va. 1972. Law clk. to U.S. Supreme Ct. Justice Lewis F. Powell, Jr., Washington, 1972-73; asst. prof. law U. Va., 1973-75, assoc. prof., 1975-78; editor Norfolk (Va.) Virginian-Pilot, 1978-81; prof. law U. Va., 1981-82, 83-84; dep. asst. atty. gen. Civil Rights div. Dept. Justice, 1982-83; judge U.S. Ct. Appeals (4th cir.), 1984—. Author: Harry Byrd and the Changing Face of Virginia Politics, 1968, Serving Justice: A Supreme Court Clerk's View, 1974, From Brown to Bakke: The Supreme Court and School Integration, 1979. Bd. visitors U. Va., 1970-73; Republican candidate for Congress from 3d Dist. Va., 1970. Served with U.S. Army, 1968-69. Mem. Va. State Bar, Va. Bar Assn., Am. Law Inst. Episcopalian. Home: 1713 Newton Dr Charlottesville VA 22901-3035 Office: US Ct Appeals 255 W Main St Rm 230 Charlottesville VA 22902-5058

WILKINSON, JOEL, oil company executive. Office: LL & E Petroleum Mktg 909 Poydras St New Orleans LA 70112

WILKINSON, JOHN BURKE, former government official, novelist, biographer; b. N.Y.C., Aug. 24, 1913; s. Henry and Edith (Burke) W.; m. Frances I. Proctor, June 11, 1938; children: Eileen B. Wilkinson Wirta, Charles P. Student, St. George's Sch.; B.A. magna cum laude, Harvard U., 1935; Lionel Harvard studentship, Cambridge (Eng.) U., 1936. Copy writer Lord & Thomas (advt.), 1936-38; asst. advt. mgr. Reynal & Hitchcock, 1938-

39; advt. mgr. Little, Brown & Co., 1939-41; free lance writer, 1946-50, 52-54, spl. asst. to asst. sec. state for pub. affairs, 1954-56, dep. asst. sec. state pub. affairs, 1956-58; pub. affairs adviser SHAPE, Paris, 1958-62; dir. U.S. Nat. Tennis Hall of Fame, v.p., 1962-81. Author: Proceed at Will, 1948, Run, Mongoose, 1950, Last Clear Chance, 1954, By Sea and By Stealth, 1956, Night of the Short Knives, 1964, The Helmet of Navarre, 1965, Cardinal in Armor, 1966, The Adventures of Geoffrey Mildmay (trilogy of 1st 3 novels), 1969, Cry Spy!: Anthology, 1970, Young Louis XIV, 1970, Francis in All His Glory, 1972, Cry Sabotage!, 1972, The Zeal of the Convert, 1976, re-issued, 1985, Uncommon Clay, the Life and Works of Augustus Saint Gaudens, 1985 (Pulitzer Prize nominee, Trustees' medal of St. Gaudens Hist. Site); Contbr. to: nat. mags. Christian Sci. Monitor. Trustee Corcoran Gallery of Art, 1973-88. Comdr. USNR, 1941-46, 51-52. Decorated Commendation Ribbon; commendatore Italian Order of Merit. Mem. Public Members Assn. of Fgn. Service (pres. 1979-83), Phi Beta Kappa; hon. mem. Internat. Lawn Tennis Club France Gt. Britain (chmn. Prentice Cup com. 1956-57). Clubs: Metropolitan (Washington), National Press (Washington); Chevy Chase (Md.), Tavern (Boston). Home: 3210 Scott Pl NW Washington DC 20007 *My life as a writer has been a running battle with the English language. My own 14 books have been in the nature of experimentation in style and language, and this has also held true in doing reviews and magazine articles. Whether novel or article or biography, the purpose has been the same: to try to make the style carry the content as effectively and as clearly as possible. I don't know how well I have succeeded so far, but as Hemingway truly said authors are apprentices all their lives.*

WILKINSON, JOHN HART, lawyer; b. Newton, Mass., Dec. 31, 1940; s. Roger Melvin and Margaret (Carter) W.; children: Heather, Carter. BA, Williams Coll., 1962; LLB, Fordham U., 1965. Bar: N.Y. 1965, U.S. Dist. Ct. (so. and ea. dists.) 1968, U.S. Ct. Appeals (2d cir.) 1981, U.S. Ct. Appeals (11th cir.) 1982, U.S. Ct. Appeals (3d cir.) 1984, U.S. Ct. Appeals (5th cir.) 1987. Assoc. Donovan, Leisure, Newton & Irvine, N.Y.C., 1965, 67-73, ptnr., 1973—, editor, contbg. author to firm's ADR Practice Book, 1990; law clk. to presiding justice U.S. Dist. Ct. N.Y. (so. dist.), 1967-68; frequent speaker on litigation. Contbr. numerous articles to profl. jours. Bd. dirs., pres. Childfind of Am., Inc., 1993-94; v.p. bd. dirs. Pelham (N.Y. Family Svc., 1982-85; vol. learning disabled children Chelsea Neighborhood, N.Y.C., 1965-67; bd. dirs. Catskill Ctr. for Conservation and Devel., 1993—. Recipient Am. Jurisprudence award Fordham U. Mem. ABA (litigation, econs. of law, anti-trust sects., ADR com. 1989—), N.Y. State Bar Assn. (alt. dispute resolution com. 1989—), Fed. Bar Coun., Assn. Bar of City of N.Y. (profl. responsibility com. 1987-89, Pub. Assistance Com. 1991—). Avocation: woodworking, flyfishing, biking, camping. Office: Donovan Leisure Newton & Irvine 30 Rockefeller Plz New York NY 10112-0001

WILKINSON, LOUISE CHERRY, psychology educator, dean; b. Phila., May 15, 1948; m. Alex Cherry Wilkinson; 1 child, Jennifer Cherry. B.A. magna cum laude with honors, Oberlin Coll., 1970; Ed.M., Ed.D., Harvard U., 1974. Prof., chmn. dept. ednl. psychology U. Wis., Madison, 1976-85; prof., exec. officer Grad. Sch. Ph.D. Program CUNY, N.Y.C., 1984-86; prof. II, dean Grad. Sch. Edn. Rutgers U., 1986—; mem. Nat. rev. bd. Nat. Inst. Edn., 1977, 85, 87; cons. Nat. Ctr. for Bilingual Research, 1982, 84; adv. bd. Nat. Reading Rsch Ctr., 1992—. Co-author: Communicating for Learning, 1991; editor: Communicating in Classroom, 1982, Social Context of Instruction, 1984, Gender Influences in the Classroom; mem. editorial bds. and contbr. articles to profl. jours. Fellow Am. Psychol. Assn., Am. Psychol. Soc., Soc. for Rsch. Child Devel., Internat. Assn. for Study Child Lang., Am. Edn. Rsch. Assn. (v.p. 1990-92). Home: 3 Andrews Ln Princeton NJ 08540 Office: Rutgers U Grad Sch Edn 10 Seminary Pl New Brunswick NJ 08901-1183

WILKINSON, MICHAEL KENNERLY, physicist; b. Palatka, Fla., Feb. 9, 1921; s. Robert Ridley and Henrietta Lucille (Kennerly) W.; m. Virginia Sleap, June 18, 1944; children: Robert Warren, William Michael, Lucille Elizabeth. B.S., The Citadel, 1942; Ph.D., M.I.T., 1950. Research asso. M.I.T., 1948-50; research scientist Oak Ridge Nat. Lab., 1950-64, assoc. dir. Solid State div., 1964-72, dir. Solid State div., 1972-86, sr. advisor Solid State div., 1986-91; cons., 1991—; vis. prof. physics Ga. Inst. Tech., 1961-62, adj. prof., 1962-91; mem. adv. com. div. materials research NSF.; mem. council on materials sci. Dept. Energy. Contbr. articles on solid state physics to profl. jours. Served with AUS, 1942-46. Fellow Am. Phys. Soc., AAAS; mem. Am. Crystallog. Assn., Tenn. Acad. Sci., Sigma Xi, Sigma Pi Sigma. Episcopalian. Home: 124 Morningside Dr Oak Ridge TN 37830-8320 Office: Oak Ridge Nat Lab Oak Ridge TN 37831

WILKINSON, RICHARD FRANCIS, JR., marketing executive; b. L.A., Jan. 25, 1944; s. Richard Francis and Doris Louise (Courtion) W.; m. Judith Anne Polodna, Sept. 13, 1966; children: Michael Francis, Mark William, Misty Anne, Michelle Louise. AA in Sci., Pasadena (Calif.) City Coll., 1965; BS in Microbiology, Calif. State Polytech. U., 1968; MS in Biology, Utah State U., 1972, PhD in Genetics, 1974. Microbiologist Space Gen. Corp., El Monte, Calif., 1967-68; rsch. fellow U. Wash. Marine Labs., Friday Harbor, 1972; post doctoral fellow, instr. Harvard Med. Sch., Boston, 1974-76; asst. prof. U. So. Calif., L.A., 1976-77; tech. mgr. N. Am. Sci. Assocs., Irvine, Calif., 1977-79; mgr., biol. scis. Am. Pharmaseal Corp., Irwindale, Calif., 1979-81; self employed - agr., 1981-84; rsch. assoc. U. Tex. Med. Sch., Houston, 1984-85; tech. dir. LifeCell Corp., Woodlands, Tex., 1986-87; sales mgr. Hyclone Labs., Inc., Logan, Utah, 1987-89, dir. mktg., 1989-92, sr. tech. dir., 1992—. Contbr. articles to profl. jours. Asst. scoutmaster Boy Scouts Am., El Toro, Calif., 1980, scoutmaster, Rupert, Idaho, 1984, dist. chmn., Houston, 1985, cubmaster, Hyde Park, Utah, 1991. Mem. World Trade Assn. Utah, Acad. Model Aeros., Utah Pilots Assn., Aircraft Owners Pilots Assn., Cache Anglers. Republican. Mem. LDS Ch. Avocations: private pilot, fly fishing, photography, hiking, model aviation. Office: HyClone Labs Inc 1725 Hyclone Rd Logan UT 84321-8209

WILKINSON, ROBERT EUGENE, plant physiologist; b. Oilton, Okla., Oct. 24, 1926; s. Olney Samuel and Grace Elma (Curry) W.; m. Evalyn Dolores Smith, Jan. 31, 1951; children: Olney Thomas, Randall David. BS in Botany, U. Ill., Champaign, 1950; MS in Plant Physiology, U. Okla., 1952; PhD in Plant Physiology, U. Calif., Davis, 1956. Plant physiologist USDA, Clarkdale, Ark., 1957-62, Los Lunas, N.Mex., 1962-65; assoc. agronomist U. Ga. Agrl. Ext. Sta., 1965-74; agronomist U. Ga., 1974-94; ret., 1994; cons. U. Sao Paulo, Piricicaba, Brazil, 1978. Contbr. articles to profl. jours. With USNR, 1944-45; to lt. USAFR, 1950-58. Sr. Fulbright grantee, Turku, Finland, 1974-75, Teaching Rsch. Fulbright grantee, Nova Sad, Yugoslavia, 1975. Fellow Am. Inst. Chemistry; mem. Weeds Sci. Soc. Am., Am. Soc. Plant Physiologists, Kiwanis. Home: 655 Laura Dr Griffin GA 30223-5315

WILKINSON, RONALD STERNE, science administrator, environmentalist, historian; b. Chgo., Feb. 16, 1934; s. Maurice Sterne and Florence Marie (Colby) W.; m. Karen Ensinger, June 14, 1969 (div. 1976). BA, Mich. State U., 1960, PhD, 1969. Chemist Berry Bros., Detroit, 1955-57; mem. faculty Mich. State U., East Lansing, 1960-70; sci. specialist Libr. of Congress, Washington, 1970-90, sr. sci. specialist, 1990—; assoc. in bibliography Am. Mus. Nat. History, N.Y.C., 1976-82; trustee William T. Hornaday Conservation Trust, La Jolla, Calif., 1985—. Author: John Winthrop, Jr. and the Origins of American Chemistry, 1969, Benjamin Wilkes, The British Aurelian, 1982; editor-in-chief The Mich. Entomologist (later The Great Lakes Entomologist), 1966-71; contbr. more than 160 articles to sci. and history of sci. publs. Ryder scholar Mich. State U., U. London, 1960, Woodrow Wilson Found. fellow Harvard U. 1960-61, Fulbright scholar Univ. Coll., London, 1965-66. Fellow Linnean Soc. London, Geol. Soc. London, Royal Entomol. Soc. London; mem. Grolier Club (N.Y.C., asst. editor 1979-82). Democrat. Home: 228 9th St NE Washington DC 20002-6110 Office: Libr of Congress Washington DC 20540

WILKINSON, SIGNE, cartoonist; b. Phila. BA in English, 1972. Reporter West Chester (Pa.) Daily Local News, Academy of Natural Scis. Phila.; organizer for housing project Cyprus, 1974; freelance cartoonist Phila. and N.Y. publs.; cartoonist San Jose (Calif.) Mercury News, 1982-85, Phila. Daily News, 1985—. Recipient Pulitzer Prize for editorial cartooning, 1992. Avocation: gardening. Office: Phila Daily News PO Box 8263 400 N Broad St Philadelphia PA 19101

WILKINSON, STANLEY RALPH, agronomist; b. West Amboy, N.Y., Mar. 28, 1931; s. Ralph Ward and Eva Goldie (Perkins) W.; m. Jean Saye; children—Rachael, Stanley R. Jr., Augusta J. B.S., Cornell U., 1954; M.S., Purdue U., 1956, Ph.D., 1961. Soil scientist U.S. Regional Pasture Research Lab., University Park, Pa., 1960-64, So. Piedmont Conservation Research Ctr., Watkinsville, Ga., 1965—. Past advance chmn. Boy Scouts Am. Served to capt. USAF, 1955-57. Recipient 3d prize Freedoms Found., 1956. Fellow Soil and Water Conservation Soc. Am., Am. Soc. Agronomy; mem. Am. Soc. Agronomy, Soil Sci. Soc. Am., Soil and Water Conservation Soc., Sigma Xi. Methodist. Contbr. 18 chpts. to books and 140 tech. articles to profl. jours.

WILKINSON, WARREN SCRIPPS, manufacturing company executive; b. Detroit, Feb. 2, 1920; s. Almadus DeGrasse and Harriet Gertrude (Whitcomb) W.; m. Joan Todd, June 14, 1941; m. Mireille De Bary, Dec. 17, 1966. Grad., Hotchkiss Sch., Lakeville, Conn., 1937; BS in Math, Harvard U., 1941; student, Calif. Inst. Tech., 1941-42. With U.S. Rubber Co., Detroit, 1942-43, Hanson Van Winkle-Munning Co., Matawan, N.J., 1946-64; pres. Hanson Van Winkle-Munning Co., 1961-64; v.p., gen. mgr. Hanson-Van Winkle-Munning div. M & Chems. Inc., 1964-66; chmn. RPI Designs, Marlette, Mich., 1966—. Pres. Detroit Hist. Commn., 1994, City of Grosse Pointe Found., 1993—. Home: 2 Woodland Pl Grosse Pointe MI 48230-1920

WILKINSON, WILLIAM DURFEE, museum director; b. Utica, N.Y., Sept. 2, 1924; s. Winfred Durfee and Edith (Lockwood) W.; m. Dorothy May Spencer, Apr. 2, 1966. B.S., Harvard U., 1949; postgrad., Munson Inst. Am. Maritime History, Mystic, Conn., 1961-62. Group ins. underwriter Home Life Ins. Co., N.Y.C., 1949-59; adminstr., marine curator Mus. City of New York, 1960-63; registrar Met. Mus. Art, N.Y.C., 1963-71; assoc. dir. Mariners Mus., Newport News, Va., 1971-73, dir., 1973-94, dir. emeritus, 1994—; ret., 1994. Mem. Sec. of Navy Adv. Com. on Naval History, 1986-88, 91-94, Exec. Coun. Internat. Congress Maritime Mus., 1989-93; chmn. sec. Navy Adv. Com. on Naval History 1991-94; bd. dirs. Coun. Am. Maritime Mus., 1975-79, pres., 1978-79; bd. dirs. Mus. Computer Network, Inc., 1972-83, Assn. for Rescue at Sea, Inc., 1977—, Coast Guard Acad. Found., Inc., 1981-87. With C.E. AUS, 1943-45. Mem. Am. Assn. Museums, Nat. Trust Hist. Preservation (maritime preservation com. 1978-80). Home: 747 W Springfield Rd Springfield PA 19064

WILKINSON, WILLIAM SHERWOOD, lawyer; b. Williston, N.D., Sept. 6, 1933; s. John Thomas and Evelyn (Landon) W.; m. Carol Ann Burns, Aug. 20, 1960; children—Leslie Ann, Richard Sherwood, Greta Diann. B.S. in Bus, U. Idaho, 1955; J.D., U. Denver, 1960. Bar: Colo. bar 1960, Mich. bar 1966. Practiced in Canon City, Colo., 1960-66; asst. dist. atty. 11th Jud. Dist., Colo., 1961-65; gen. counsel, sec. Mich. Farm Bur. and affiliate cos., Lansing, 1966—; Lectr. Pre-Parole Release Center, Colo. State Penitentiary, 1961-65; instr. adult edn., Canon City, 1965; counsel Canon City Recreation Dist., 1964-65. Mem. lay adv. bd. St. Thomas More Hosp., Canon City, 1963-66; Del., county, dist. and congl. convs. Republican party, 1964. Served to capt. USAF, 1955-58. Recipient Community Distinguished Service award Canon City Jr. C of C, 1964; named one of Outstanding Young Men of Am., 1965. Mem. ABA, Colo. Bar Assn., Mich. Bar Assn., Am. Judicature Soc., Am. Corp. Counsel Assn., Phi Delta Phi, Tau Kappa Epsilon. Methodist (lay leader, mem. ch. ofcl. bd.). Home: 1707 Foxcroft Rd East Lansing MI 48823-2131 Office: Mich Farm Bur 7373 W Saginaw Hwy Lansing MI 48917-1124

WILKNISS, PETER E., foundation administrator, researcher; b. Berlin, Germany, Sept. 28, 1934; U.S. citizen.; s. Fritz and Else (Stueber) W.; m. Edith P. Koester, May 25, 1963; children: Peter F., Sandra M. MS in Chemistry, Tech. U., Munich, Ger., 1958, PhD in Radio and Nuclear Chemistry, 1961. Rsch. chemist, radiological protection officer U.S. Naval Ordnance Sta., 1961-64, head nuclear chemistry branch, 1964-66; rsch. oceanographer U.S. Naval Rsch. Lab., 1966-70, head chemical oceanography branch, 1970-75; mgr. Nat. Ctr. Atmospheric Rsch. Program NSF, Washington, 1975-76, mgr. Internat. Phase of Ocean Drilling/Ocean Sediment Coring Program, 1976-80, mgr. Ocean Drilling Project Team, AAEO Directorate, 1980, dir. divsn. Ocean Drilling Programs, 1980-81, sr. sci. assoc. Office of Dir., 1981-82, dep. asst. dir. Sci, Tech., Internat. Affairs Directorate, 1982-84, dir. divsn. Polar Programs, 1984-93, sr. sci. assoc. Geoscis. Directorate, 1993—; liaison mem. NRC, NAS, Marine Bd., 1978-81, Polar Rsch. Bd., 1984-93; mem. atmospheric chemistry and radioactivity com. Am. Meteorological Soc., 1975-78; mem. interagy. com. atmospheric scis., 1975-76, space station adv. com., NASA, 1988-93. Contbr. 61 articles to sci., tech. jours., USN reports; over 100 formal presentations nat., internat. sci. confs., symposia, meetings; participant 16 nat., internat. workshops. Presdl. citation AIA, 1993; Wilkniss mountain Antarctic named in his honor Sec. Interior, U.S. Bd. Geographic Names, 1992. Mem. AAAS, Am. Geophysical Union, Antarctican Soc., Sigma Xi. Episcopalian. Avocations: soccer, swimming, skiing. Home: 8814 Stockton Pky Alexandria VA 22308-2360 Office: Nat Sci Found 4201 Wilson Blvd Arlington VA 22230

WILKS, ALAN DELBERT, chemical research and technology executive, researcher; b. Liberal, Kans., Sept. 4, 1943; s. Delbert Elvado and Mabel Ida (Howell) W.; m. Irvana Sue Keagy, June 11, 1967; 1 child, Jolin Rai. BS in Chemistry, U. Kans., 1965; PhD in Analytical Chemistry, U. Iowa, 1970. Chemist UOP Rsch. Ctr., Des Plaines, Ill., 1969-76, group leader catalysis div., 1976-77, mgr. catalysis rsch., 1977-84; dir. phys. chemistry and surface sci. Allied-Signal Inc., Des Plaines, 1984-88, v.p rsch. & tech., 1988-93, v.p., dir. rsch. & tech., 1993-94; pres. The Wilks Group, Inc., Mount Prospect, Ill., 1994—; cons. Los Alamos (N.Mex.) Nat. Lab., 1990-94. Contbr. articles to profl. jours.; holder 5 patents. Mem. Am. Chem. Soc., Am. Vacuum Soc., Rsch. Dirs. Assn. Chgo., Chgo. Catalyst Club, Alpha Chi Omega. Office: The Wilks Group Inc 1201 W Cleven Mount Prospect IL 60056

WILKS, CHARLES E., chemicals executive; b. 1944. BS in Chem. Engring., Auburn U. With Amoco Chem. Co., Chgo., Chgo., 1966—, exec. v.p. Office: Amoco Chem Co 200 E Randolph Dr Chicago IL 60601*

WILKS, IVOR GORDON HUGHES, historian, educator; b. Coventry, Warwickshire, Eng., July 19, 1928; came to U.S., 1965; s. Gordon Wilfred and Lilian Mary (Hughes Bates) W.; m. Grace O. Amanor, 1956 (div. 1972); children: Sebastian Amanor-Wilks, Anne Amanor-Wilks, Compton Amanor-Wilks, Margaret Amanor-Wilks; m. Nancy Ellen Lawler, 1989. BA with 1st class honors, U. Wales, 1951, MA, 1958; PhD, U. Cambridge, Eng., 1971. Lectr. in philosophy U. Gold Coast, Ghana, 1953-55; resident tutor Inst. Extra-Mural Studies U. Ghana, Africa, 1955-61, prof., dep. dir. Inst. African Studies, 1961-66; prof. history Northwestern U., Evanston, Ill., 1966-68, 70—, Herskovits prof. African studies, 1984—; asst. dir. research Faculty History, U. Cambridge, Eng., 1968-70; vis. prof. Ind. U., Bloomington, 1965-70—, U. Wales, winter 1989; sr. mem. Centre for Rsch. and Scholarship, St. David's U. Coll., U. Wales, 1990—; hon. prof. history and Welsh history U. Coll. of Wales, Aberystwyth, 1993—; cons. Ency. Brit., 1972—. Author: Asante in the 19th Century, 1975, 2d edit., 1989, South Wales and the Rising of 1839, 1984, Wa and the Wala, 1989; sr. author: Chronicles from Gonja, 1986; contbr. articles to profl. jours. Served to lt. Brit. Army, 1946-48. Recipient Herskovits award African Studies Assn., 1976, Non-fiction prize Welsh Arts Council, 1985. Office: Northwestern U Dept History 202 Harris Evanston IL 60201-5032

WILL, CLIFFORD MARTIN, physicist, educator; b. Hamilton, Ont., Can., Nov. 13, 1946; m. Leslie Saxe, June 26, 1970; children: Elizabeth, Rosalie. BS, McMaster U., Hamilton, 1968; PhD, Calif. Inst. Tech., 1971. Enrico Fermi fellow U. Chgo., 1972-74; asst. prof. physics Stanford U., Palo Alto, Calif., 1974-81; assoc. prof. physics Washington U., St. Louis, 1981-85, prof. physics, 1985—, chmn. dept. physics, 1991—; chmn. com. on time transfer in satellite systems Air Force Studies Bd., Washington, 1984-86. Assoc. editor Physical Rev. Letters, 1989-92; author: Theory and Experiment in Gravitational Physics, 1981, rev. edit., 1993, Was Einstein Right?, 1986, rev. edit., 1993. Recipient Sci. Writing award Am. Inst. Physics, 1987; Alfred P. Sloan Found. fellow, 1975-79. Fellow Am. Phys. Soc. (exec. com. astrophysics div. 1988-90); mem. Am. Astron. Soc., Am. Assn. Physics Tchrs. (Richtmyer Meml. Lectr. 1987), Internat. Soc. Gen. Relativity and Gravitation. Office: Washington U Dept Physics Campus Box 1105 1 Brookings Dr Saint Louis MO 63130-4899

WILL, EDWARD EDMUND, oil company executive; b. Elizabeth, N.J., July 4, 1952; m. Patricia Susan Granat. BA, Reed Coll., 1975; MBA, Harvard U., Boston, 1980; dipl., U. Paris, 1972. Mgr. strategic planning NL Shaffer/NL Industries, Houston, 1980-82; v.p. mktg. and internat. ops. NL Acme Tool Inc./NL Industries, Inc., Houston, 1982-87; v.p. internat. ops. Western Petroleum Svcs./Western Co. of N.Am., Houston, 1987-88; v.p Western Co. N.Am., 1988; pres. Western Petroleum Svcs., 1988—; adj. prof bus. policy U. Houston, 1981-82. Contbr. articles to profl. jours. Mem. Phi Beta Kappa. Office: Western Petro Svc Internat Co 515 Post Oak Blvd Houston TX 77027

WILL, ERIC JOHN, state senator; b. Omaha, Nebr., Apr. 16, 1959; s. John Babcock and Patricia Elaine (Propst) W.; m. Laurie Ann Beber, Oct. 19, 1984. BA in Polit. Sci., U. So. Calif., 1981; postgrad., Creighton U., 1993—. Legis. researcher Nebr. State Legis., Omaha, 1981-90, senator, 1991—; chmn. enrollment and rev. com., 1991-93, rules com., 1993—; vice chmn. gen. affairs com., 1991—; mem. revenue and urban affairs com., 1991—. Mem. Phi Beta Kappa. Democrat. Presbyterian. Avocations: softball, bowling, volleyball. Home: 2349 N 50th Ave Omaha NE 68104 Office: Nebr State Capitol District 8 Lincoln NE 68509

WILL, GEORGE FREDERICK, editor, political columnist, news commentator; b. Champaign, Ill., May 4, 1941; s. Frederick L. and Louise (Hendrickson) W.; children: Jonathan, Geoffrey, Victoria. BA, Trinity Coll., 1962, Oxford (Eng.) U., 1964; MA, Ph.D., Princeton U., 1967; LLD (hon.), U. San Diego, 1977; LittD (hon.), Dickinson Coll. and Georgetown U., 1978; hon. degree, U. Ill., 1988. Prof. polit. philosophy Mich. State U., 1967-68, U. Toronto, 1968-70; mem. staff of Sen. Gordon Allott U.S. Senate, Washington, Can., 1970-72; editor The Nat. Rev., Washington, 1973-76; contbg. editor Newsweek mag., 1976—; syndicated columnist Washington Post, 1974—; TV news analyst ABC-Capitol Cities, 1981—; bd. dirs. Ctr. for Strategic Internat. Studies, Washington, Balt. Orioles. Author: The Pursuit of Happiness and Other Sobering Thoughts, 1979, The Pursuit of Virtue and Other Tory Notions, 1982, Statecraft as Soulcraft: What Government Does, 1983, The Morning After: American Successes and Excesses, 1986, The New Season: A Spectator's Guide to the 1988 Election, 1987, Men at Work, 1990, Suddenly: The American Idea at Home and Abroad 1988-89, 1990, Restoration: Congress, Term Limits and the Recovery of Deliberate Democracy, 1992, The Leveling Wind: Politics, the Culture and Other News, 1994; participant This Week With David Brinkley, ABC-TV, 1981—; commentator World News Tonight, 1984—. Recipient Pulitzer prize for Commentary, 1977; named Young Leader Am. Time mag., 1974. Mem. Coun. Fgn. Rels.; The Trilateral Commn., The Emil Verban Soc. Avocation: baseball. Address: ABC Pub Rels 1330 Avenue Of The Americas New York NY 10019-5422 Office: The Washington Post Writers Group 1150 15th St NW Washington DC 20071-0001

WILL, HUBERT LOUIS, federal judge; b. Milw., Apr. 23, 1914; s. Louis E. and Erna (Barthman) W.; m. Phyllis Nicholson, July 23, 1938; children: Jon Nicholson, Wendy (dec.), Nikki, Ami Louise; m. Jane R. Greene, Dec. 20, 1969. A.B., U. Chgo., 1935, J.D., 1937; L.L.D. (hon.), John Marshall Law Sch., 1973. Bar: Wis. 1937, Ill. 1946, U.S. Supreme Ct. 1941. Mem. gen. counsel's staff SEC, Washington, 1937-38; sec. U.S. Senator Robert F. Wagner, 1939; spl. asst. to atty. gen. U.S., 1940-41; asst. to gen. counsel OPA, 1942; tax counsel Alien Property Custodian, 1943; atty. firm Pope & Ballard, Chgo., 1946-48, Nelson, Boodell & Will, Chgo., 1949-61; U.S. dist. judge No. Dist. Ill., 1961—; Mem. Commn. on Bankruptcy Laws of U.S., 1971-73; mem. com. to consider standards for admission to practice in fed. cts. U.S. Jud. Conf., 1976-79. Contbr. articles legal publs. Chmn. Chgo. Com. Youth Welfare, 1957-61. Served as capt. OSS AUS, 1944-45, chief counterespionage br., ETO. Decorated Bronze Star. Mem. ABA, Fed. Bar Assn., Chgo. Bar Assn., Am. Judicature Soc., Am. Vets. Com., World Vets Fedn. (v.p. coun. U.S.A.). Office: US Dist Ct 2578 US Courthouse 219 S Dearborn St Chicago IL 60606-7206

WILL, JAMES FREDRICK, steel company executive; b. Pitts., Oct. 12, 1938; s. Fred F. and Mary Agnes (Ganter) W.; m. Mary Ellen Bowser, Dec. 19, 1964; children: Mary Beth, Kerry Ann. BSEE, Pa. State U., 1961; MBA, Duquesne U., 1972. Works mgr. Kaiser Steel Corp., Fontana, Calif., 1976-78, v.p. ops., 1978-80, v.p. planning, 1980-81, exec. v.p., 1981, pres., 1981-82; exec. v.p., pres. indsl. group Cyclops Corp., Pitts., 1982-86, pres., chief operating officer Cyclops Corp., Pitts., 1986-88, pres., chief exec. officer, 1989-92; pres., chief oper. officer Armco, Inc., Parsippany, NJ, 1992-93; pres., chief exec. officer Armco, Inc., Pitts., 1994—; vice-chmn. 1994, chmn. 1995, Specialty Steel Industry of N.Am. Office: Armco Inc 1 Oxford Ctr Pittsburgh PA 15219-1415

WILL, JOANNE MARIE, food and consumer services executive, communications consultant, writer; b. Mpls., Mar. 18, 1937; d. Lester John and Dorothea Amelia (Kuenzel) W. BS in Home Econs. and Journalism, Iowa State U., 1959. Food writer, editor food guide Chgo. Tribune, 1959-67; account supr., home econs. coordinator J. Walter Thompson Co., Chgo., 1967-73; assoc. food editor, then food editor Chgo. Tribune, 1973-81; dir. food and consumer services Hill and Knowlton, Inc., Chgo., 1981-87; dir., group mgr. food and consumer svcs. Selz, Seabolt & Assocs., Inc., Chgo. Mem. bd. govs. Iowa State U. Found., past mem. home econs. adv. bd.; bd. dirs., officer Sr. Ctrs. Met. Chgo. Recipient Alumnae Recognition medal Iowa State U., 1994; named Outstanding Young Alumnus Iowa State U., 1968. Mem. Home Econs. in Bus., Am. Home Econs. Assn., Ill. Home Econs. Assn. (past pres. dir.), Chgo. Nutrition Assn. (pres.-elect 1993-94, pres. 1994-95), Dames d'Escoffier (bd. dirs. Chgo. chpt., past v.p.).

WILL, MARI MASENG, communications consultant; b. Chgo., Mar. 15, 1954; d. Leif Eric and Betty (Hagen) Maseng; m. George F. Will. B.A., U. S.C., 1975. Reporter Charleston Evening Post, S.C., 1976-78; press sec. Reelect Thurmond Com., Columbia, S.C., 1978; staff dir. Dole for Pres. Com., Alexandria, Va., 1979-80; spl. asst. to chmn. Reagan-Bush Com., Arlington, Va., 1980; press officer Office of Pres.-Elect, Washington, 1980-81; presdl. speechwriter The White House, Washington, 1981-83; asst. sec. for pub. affairs Dept. Transp., Washington, 1983-85; v.p., dir. corp. rels. Beatrice Cos. Inc., Chgo., 1985-86; dep. asst to the pres., dir. Office of Public Liaison The White House, Washington, 1986-87; press sec. Dole for Pres. Campaign, Washington, 1987-88; pub. affairs cons. Washington, 1988; asst. to Pres. for communications White House, 1988-89; prin. Maseng Communications, cons., Washington, 1989—. Active Nat. Coun. on Vocat. Edn., 1989-91, Def. Adv. Com. on Women in Svcs., 1992—. Recipient Alumna Achievement award U.S.C., Columbia, 1984. Mem. Soc. Profl. Journalists, U. S.C. Alumni Assn., Nat. Press Club, Chi Omega. Republican. Presbyterian. Avocation: photography.

WILL, ROBERT ERWIN, economics educator; b. Dousman, Wis., Mar. 8, 1928; s. Erwin and Gena (Luedtke) W.; m. Barbara Anne Couture, Dec. 22, 1956; children: Jonathan (dec.), Leslie Anne, Jennifer. B.A. cum magna laude, Carleton Coll., 1950; M.A., Yale U., 1951, Ph.D., 1965. Mem. faculty Yale, 1951-54, U. Mass., 1954-57; mem. faculty econs. Carleton Coll., Northfield, Minn., 1957—; prof. Carleton Coll., 1968-73, W.A. Williams prof., 1973-82, Plank prof., 1982—, chmn. dept. econs., dir. First Bank System execs. seminars, 1971-80; dir., treas. Community Electronics Corp., Mpls.; vis. prof. U. Minn., 1965; vis. fellow Inst. Devel. Studies, U. Sussex, Eng., 1970-71, H.H. Humphrey Inst., 1981-82; John de Quedville Briggs lectr., St. Paul Acad., 1966-70; dir. Kings' Coll. seminar in econs. Cambridge (Eng.) U., 1990. Author: Poverty in Affluence: The Social, Political and Economic Dimensions of Poverty in the United States, 1965, Scalar Dimensions and Urban Service Requirements, 1965, also articles and research on manpower, tourism, and devel. Mem. Minn. Dept. Manpower Services Adv. Council, 1966-80; mem. Wilton Park, Brit. Fgn. Office Study Ctr., 1970—; dir., chief fin. officer Community Electronics Corp., Mpls., 1968-91; dir. Minn. World Affairs Ctr., 1972-90, Minn. Internat. Ctr., 1979-86, UN Rally Bd., 1978-85, 92—; bd. dirs. Minn. World Trade Week, 1978—, pres., 1983-86; mem. policy com. United Shareowners Am., 1960-80; mem. Northfield Heritage Preservation Commn., 1982—, Northfield Sister Cities Commn., 1991—, Mpls. Inst. Art, Walker Art Ctr., Northfield Arts Guild; bd. visitors Am. Grad. Sch. Internat. Mgmt., 1980-90; bd. dirs. Northfield United Way, 1983-86, Lutheran Home Cannon Valley, Northfield Manor, Northfield Parkview, 1993—; exec. dir. Northfield Hist. Soc. Endowment Fund, 1993—. Served with USNR, 1945-46. Ford Found. Faculty fellow,

1962-63, NSF Faculty fellow, 1970-71; Interuniv. Ctr. for European Studies fellow, 1975-85; Mellon grantee, Mex., 1976, Spain, 1981; Devel. Fund grantee, France, 1985, World Tourism grantee, Eng., 1990. Mem. World Future Soc., Assn. for Third World Studies, Soc. for Internat. Devel., Bus. and Econ. History Soc., Assn. Cultural Econs., Assn. Comparative Econ. Studies, Am. Friends Wilton Park, Assn. for Pvt. Enterprise Edn., Nat. Assn. Bus. Economists, Assn. Evolutionary Econs., History Econ. Assn., Caribbean Studies Assn., N.Am. Econ. and Fin. Assn., Population Action Coun. (nat. com.), Minn. Econ. Assn., Midwest Econ. Assn., Chactonbury Ring Club (Sussex), Rotary, Phi Beta Kappa. Democrat. Episcopalian. Home: 708 3rd St E Northfield MN 55057-2311

WILL, TREVOR JONATHAN, lawyer; b. Ashland, Wis., Aug. 11, 1953; s. William Taylor and Geraldine Sue (Trevor) W.; m. Margaret Ann Johnson, Aug. 28, 1976; children: Tyler William, Alexandra Marie, Jennifer Catherine. BA summa cum laude, Augustana Coll., 1975; JD cum laude, Harvard U., 1978. Bar: Wis. 1978, U.S. Dist. Ct. (ea. dist.) Wis. 1978, U.S. DIst. Ct. (we. dist.) Wis. 1980, U.S. Ct. Appeals (7th cir.) 1983, U.S. Supreme Ct. 1984, U.S. Dist. Ct. (ea. dist.) Mich. 1985. Assoc. Foley & Lardner, Milw., 1978-87, ptnr., 1987—; adj. law prof. Marquette U. Law Sch., 1994. Mem. ABA, State Bar Wis., Milw. Bar Assn., Def. Rsch. Inst. Home: 10011 N Waterleaf Dr Thiensville WI 53092-6146 Office: Foley & Lardner 777 E Wisconsin Ave Milwaukee WI 53202-5302

WILLARD, A. KEITH, chemicals executive; b. 1941. With Sun Life Assurance Co. Can., 1964-81, Wardair Internat., 1981-88, ICI Can. Inc. 1988-93; with Zeneca Holdings, Inc., Wilmington, Del., 1993—, now chmn. bd. Office: Zeneca Holdings Inc 1800 Concord Pike Wilmington DE 19803*

WILLARD, LOUIS CHARLES, librarian; b. Tallahassee, Fla., Sept. 28, 1937; s. Bert and Rose (De Milly) W.; m. Nancy Booth, June 22, 1963. BA, U. Fla., 1959; BD, Yale, 1965, MA, 1967, PhD, 1970. Tchr. Tripoli (Lebanon) Boys' Sch., 1959-62; ordained to ministry Presbyn. Ch., 1965; acting librarian Princeton Theol. Sem., 1968-69, librarian, 1969-86; librarian, mem. faculty Harvard Div. Sch., 1986—. Mem. A.L.A., Theol. Library Assn., Soc. Bibl. Lit., Am. Acad. Religion, Phi Beta Kappa, Chi Phi. Home: 24 Concord Greene Unit 8 PO Box 1250 Concord MA 01742-1250 Office: Andover-Harvard Theol Libr Div Sch 45 Francis Ave Cambridge MA 02138-1994

WILLARD, NANCY MARGARET, writer, educator; b. Ann Arbor, Mich.; d. Hobart Hurd and Margaret (Sheppard) W.; m. Eric Lindbloom, Aug. 15, 1964; 1 child, James Anatole. B.A., U. Mich., 1958, Ph.D., 1963; M.A., Stanford U., 1960. Lectr. English Vassar Coll., Poughkeepsie, N.Y., 1965—. Author: (poems) In His Country: Poems, 1966; Skin of Grace, 1967; A New Herball: Poems, 1968, Testimony of the Invisible Man: William Carlos Williams, Francis Ponge, Rainer Maria Rilke, Pablo Neruda, 1970, Nineteen Masks for the Naked Poet: Poems, 1971, The Carpenter of the Sun: Poems, 1974, A Visit to William Blake's Inn: Poems for Innocent and Experienced Travelers, 1981 (Newbery Medal 1982), Household Tales of Moon and Water, 1983, Water Walker, 1989, The Ballad of Biddy Early, 1989; (short stories) The Lively Anatomy of God, 1968, Childhood of the Magician, 1973; (juveniles) Sailing to Cythera and Other Anatole Stories, 1974, All on a May Morning, 1975, The Snow Rabbit, 1975, Shoes Without Leather, 1976, TOe Well-Mannered Balloon, 1976, Night Story, 1986, Simple Pictures are Best, 1977, Stranger's Bread, 1977, The Highest Hit, 1978, Papa's Panda, 1979, The Island of the Grass King, 1979, The Marzipan Moon 1981, Uncle Terrible, 1982, (adult) Angel in the Parlor: Five Stories and Eight Essays, 1983, The Nightgown of the Sullen Moon, 1983, Night Story, 1986, The Voyage of Ludgate Hill, 1987, The Mountains of Quilt, 1987, Firebrat, 1988; (novel) Things Invisible To See, 1984, Sister Water, 1993; (play) East of the Sun, West of the Moon, 1989, The High Rise Glorious Skittle Skat Roarious Sky Pie Angel Food Cake, 1991, A Nancy Willard Reader, 1991, Pish Posh Hieronymus Bosch, 1991, Beauty and the Beast, 1992; illustrator: The Letter of John to James and Another Letter of John to James, 1982, The Octopus Who Wanted to Juggle (Robert Pack), (novel) Sister Water, 1993, (essays) Telling Time, 1993, (juvenile) A Starlit Somersault Downhill, 1993, (juvenile) The Sorcerer's Apprentice, 1993; author, illustrator: An Alphabet of Angels, 1994. Recipient Hopwood award, 1958, Devins Meml. award, 1967; Woodrow Wilson fellow, 1960; NEA grantee, 1987. Mem. The Lewis Carroll Soc., The George MacDonald Soc. Office: Vassar Coll Dept English Raymond Ave Poughkeepsie NY 12601

WILLARD, RALPH LAWRENCE, surgery educator, physician, former college president; b. Manchester, Iowa, Apr. 6, 1922; s. Hosea B. and Ruth A. (Hazelrigg) W.; m. Margaret Dyer Dennis, Sept. 26, 1969; children: Laurie, Jane, Ann, H. Thomas. Student, Cornell Coll., 1940-42, Coe Coll., 1945; D.O., Kirksville Coll. Osteo. Medicine, 1949; EdD (hon.), U. North Tex., 1985; ScD (hon.), W.Va. Sch. Osteo. Medicine, 1993. Intern Kirksville Osteo. Hosp., 1949-50, resident in surgery, 1954-57; chmn. dept. surgery Davenport Osteo. Hosp., 1957-68; dean, prof. surgery Kirksville Coll. Osteo. Medicine, 1969-73; assoc. dean acad. affairs, prof. surgery Mich. State U. Coll. Osteo. Medicine, 1974-75; dean Tex. Coll. Osteopathic Medicine, 1975-76, pres., 1981-85, prof. surgery, 1985-87; v.p. med. affairs North Tex. State U., Denton, 1976-81; assoc. dean W.Va. Sch. Osteo. Medicine, Lewisburg, 1988-91; mem. Nat. Adv. Council Edn. for Health Professions, 1971-73, Iowa Gov.'s Council Hosps. and Health Related Facilities, 1965-68; chmn. council deans Am. Assn. Colls. Osteo. Medicine, 1970-73, pres., 1979-80. Served with USAAF, 1942-45; Served with USAF, 1952-53; col. USAFR, ret. Decorated D.F.C., Air medal with 4 oak leaf clusters, Meritorious Svc. medal, Legion of Merit; recipient Robert A. Kistner Educator award Am. Assn. Colls. Osteo. Medicine, 1989. Fellow Am. Coll. Physician Execs., Am. Coll. Osteo. Surgeons; mem. Am. Osteo. Assn. (Disting. Svc. cert. 1992), Tex. Osteo. Assn., W.Va. Soc. Osteo. Medicine, Am. Acad. Osteopathy, Acad. Osteo. Dirs. Med. Edn., Aerospace Med. Assn., Flying Physicians Assn., Quiet Birdmen, Rotary, Masons, Shriners, Order of Daedalions. Democrat. Episcopalian. Home: PO Box 749 Lewisburg WV 24901-0749 Office: WVa Sch Osteo Medicine 400 N Lee St Lewisburg WV 24901-1128 *The wise man has faith, the fool is he who betrays that faith.*

WILLARD, RICHARD KENNON, lawyer; b. Houston, Sept. 1, 1948; s. Fair McDaniel Willard and Elsbeth Rowe (Kennon) Willard Armistead; m. Leslie Harral Hopkins, July 10, 1976; children: Stephen Hopkins, Lauren Suzanne. B.A., Emory U., 1969; J.D., Harvard U., 1975. Bar: D.C. 1988, Tex. 1978, Ga. 1975. Law clk. U.S. Ct. Appeals San Francisco, 1975-76, U.S. Supreme Ct., Washington, 1976-77; atty. Baker & Botts, Houston, 1977-81; counsel for intelligence policy U.S. Dept. Justice, Washington, 1981-82, dep. asst. atty. gen. civil div., 1982-83, asst. atty. gen., 1983-88; ptnr. Steptoe & Johnson, Washington, 1988—; adj. prof. Georgetown U. Law Ctr., 1991—. Note editor: Harvard U. Law Rev. 1974-75. Gen. counsel Republican Party of Tex., Austin, 1980-81. Served to 1st lt. U.S. Army, 1969-72. Episcopalian. Office: 1330 Connecticut Ave NW Washington DC 20036-1704

WILLARD, ROBERT EDGAR, lawyer; b. Bronxville, N.Y., Dec. 13, 1929; s. William Edgar and Ethel Marie (Van Ness) W.; m. Shirley Fay Cooper, May 29, 1954; children: Laura Marie, Linda Ann, John Judson. B.A. in Econs., Wash. State U., 1953; J.D., Harvard U., 1958. Bar: Calif. 1959. Law clk. to U.S. dist. judge, 1958-59; pvt. practice L.A., 1959-82; assoc. firm Flint & Mackay, 1959-61; pvt. practice, 1962-64; mem. firm Willard & Baltaxe, 1964-65, Baird, Holley, Baird & Galen, 1966-69, Baird, Holley, Galen & Willard, 1970-74, Holley, Galen & Willard, 1975-82, Galvin & Willard, Newport Beach, Calif., 1982-86; pvt. practice Newport Beach, 1987-89; mem. firm Davis, Punelli Keathley & Willard, Newport Beach, 1990—; Dir. various corps. Served with AUS, 1946-48, 50-51. Mem. ABA, Los Angeles County Bar Assn., State Bar Calif., Assn. Trial Lawyers Am., Am. Judicature Soc., Acacia Frat. Congregationalist. Club: Calcutta Saddle and Cycle. Home: 1840 Oriole Dr Costa Mesa CA 92626-4758 Office: Ste 1000 610 Newport Center Dr Newport Beach CA 92660-6462

WILLAUER, WHITING RUSSELL, systems integration company executive; b. Boston, May 24, 1931; s. Whiting and Louise Knapp (Russell) W.; m. Julie Matheson Arnold, July 11, 1959 (div.); children—Whiting Russell, Jr., William Arnold. B.S., Princeton U., 1955, M.S., 1959; Ph.D., Georgetown U., 1964. Research assoc. joint research com. Dept. Def., 1951-52; ops. mgr. Civil Air Transport Airline Taiwan, 1952-53; scientist Analytic Services, Inc.,

1958-61; asst. prof. astronomy Georgetown U., 1965-68; mgr. TRW Systems Group support to chief Naval ops., McLean, Va., 1968-73, TRW Antisubmarine projects, 1973-79, TRW Ship Acquisition project, 1979-85; advanced systems mgr. TRW Systems Integration Group, 1985-90, cost estimating mgr., 1990-95; sr. cons., 1995—; cons. Nat. Geog. Soc., 1961-65, U. Tex., 1962, NSF, 1963, Booz-Allen & Hamilton, 1966-67. Mng. editor: Jour. Astronautical Scis, 1969-71; Designer: Orrery (planetarium) on permanent exhibit, New Explorers Hall, Nat. Geog. Soc. Asst. chief steward Alpine Venue XIII Olympic Winter Games, Lake Placid, 1980; mem. U.S. Olympic Com., bd. dirs., 1987-94, sec. nat. governing bodies, 1989-92, mem. membership svcs. com., 1988-92, mem. athletic devel. com., 1992—; chef de mission Winter Pan Am. Games, Las Lenas, Argentina, 1990; asst. chief de mission XVI Winter Olympics, Albertville, France, 1992; U.S. Olympic Com. liaison to VI Paralympic Winter Games, Lillehammer, Norway, 1994. Research fellow Georgetown U., 1961-65. Fellow AAAS (council); mem. Am. Astronautical Soc. (v.p. fin.), Blue Ridge Ski Coun. (pres. 1976-78), U.S. Ski Assn. (pres. 1982-87, Julius Blegan award 1988), U.S. Skiing (vice chmn. 1994—), Internat. Ski Fedn. (chmn. U.S. del. 1983, 85, chmn. recreational skiing com. 1987—, eligibility com. 1988—), Ea. Ski Assn. (treas. 1980-82), Pan Am. Sports Orgn. (winter games adv. com. 1988—), Sigma Xi, Chevy Chase Club (Md.), Nantucket Yacht Club (Mass.) (commodore 1981-83, bd. govs. 1957-59, 68—). Home: 4201 Cathedral Ave NW Apt 701W Washington DC 20016-4606 Office: TRW Systems Integration Grp One Federal Systems Park Dr Fairfax VA 22033-3810

WILLCOTT, MARK ROBERT, III, chemist, educator, researcher; b. Muskogee, Okla., July 23, 1933; s. Mark Robert Willcott Jr. and Josephine Oliver; m. Earline Faye Hinkle, June 4, 1955; children: Julie, June Elinor, Mark Robert IV, Ashley. BA, Rice U., 1955; MS, Yale U., 1959, PhD, 1963. Asst. prof. chemistry Emory U., Atlanta, 1962-64; asst. prof. chemistry U. Houston, 1965-68, assoc. prof., 1968-73, prof., 1973-83; head biomed. Nuc. Magnetic Resonance lab. Baylor Coll. Medicine, Houston, 1982-83; pres., chmn. bd. Nuc. Magnegic Resonance Imaging, Inc., Houston, 1983-88; prof. chemistry and radiology Vanderbilt U., Nashville, 1989-94; prof. radiology, vice chmn. rsch. med. br. U. Tex., Galveston, 1994—; cons. Codman & Shurtleff, Inc., Randolph, Mass., 1991—, Advanced NMR Systems, Andover, Mass., 1994—, Cooper and Dunham, N.Y.C., 1994—. Author patents for magnetic resonance imaging, 1988-94. Lt. (j.g.) USN, 1955-58. John Simon Guggenheim fellow Guggenheim Found., 1972; recipient Alexander von Humboldt Sr. Scientist prize Humboldt Found., 1978. Mem. Am. Chem. Soc., Am. Assn. Physicists in Medicine, Soc. Magnetic Resonance. Democrat. Presbyterian. Avocations: mountaineering, photography, philately. Home: 1807 Orchard Country Ln Houston TX 77062-2336 Office: U Tex Med Br Dept Radiology Houston TX 77555-0793

WILLCOXON, SAM RANDOLPH, communications executive; b. Oberlin, Kans., Jan. 13, 1931; s. Samuel Randolph and Bernice (Barr) W.; m. Kathleen Holthus, Aug. 22, 1953; children—Samuel Randolph, Kimberly Ann, Dan Wesley, Kerri Kathleen. B.S.E.E., U. Kans.; M.S., M.I.T. Vice pres. Eastern Area AT&T Long Lines, Washington, 1970-75; dir. mktg. AT&T, Basking Ridge, N.J., 1975-78; exec. v.p. mktg.-bus. PT&T, San Francisco, 1978-80; exec. v.p. network ops. AT&T Long Lines, Bedminster, N.J., 1980-81; v.p. mktg. AT&T, Basking Ridge, N.J., 1981-84; exec. v.p. mktg. AT&T Communications, Basking Ridge, N.J., 1984-85; pres. Bus. Markets Group, from 1986; dir. AT&T Long Lines, 1980-83, Pacific N.W. Bell, 1981-83, AT&T Communications, 1984—. Contbr. articles to profl. jours. Served to 1st. Lt. USAF, 1952-54. Recipient award for Best Promotions of 1984, Advertising Age, 1984. Republican. Presbyterian. Avocations: Golf; tennis. Home: 64 Falcon Hills Dr Littleton CO 80126-2900 Office: AT&T Communications 295 N Maple Ave Basking Ridge NJ 07920-1002

WILLE, KARIN L., lawyer; b. Randolph, Minn., Dec. 14, 1949; d. James Virginia Wille. BA summa cum laude, Macalester Coll., 1971; JD cum laude, U. Minn., 1974. Bar: Minn. 1974, U.S. Dist. Ct. Minn. 1974. Atty. Dresselhuis & Assoc., Mpls., 1974-75; assoc. Dorsey & Whitney, Mpls., 1975-76; atty. Dayton-Hudson Corp., Mpls., 1976-84; gen. counsel B. Dalton Booksellers, Edina, Minn., 1985-87; assoc. Briggs & Morgan, Mpls., 1987-88; shareholder Briggs and Briggs, 1988—. Co-author: MN Real Estate-Vol. II, 1982. Pres. 1st Universalist Ch., Mpls., 1988-90, bd. dirs. 1984-88. Mem. Minn. State Bar Assn. (labor and employment sect., corp. counsel sect., dir. 1989-91), Hennepin County Bar Assn. (labor and employment sect.), Minn. Women Lawyers, Phi Beta Kappa. Office: Briggs & Morgan 2400 IDS Ctr Minneapolis MN 55402

WILLE, LOIS JEAN, retired newspaper editor; b. Chgo., Sept. 19, 1931; d. Walter and Adele S. (Taege) Kroeber; m. Wayne M. Wille, June 6, 1954. B.S., Northwestern U., 1953, M.S., 1954; Litt.D. (hon.), Columbia Coll., Chgo., 1980, Northwestern U., 1990, Rosary Coll., 1990. Reporter Chgo. Daily News, 1958-74, nat. corr., 1975-76, assoc. editor charge editorial page, 1977; assoc. editor charge editorial and opinion pages Chgo. Sun-Times, 1978-83; assoc. editor editorial page Chgo. Tribune, 1984-87, editor editorial page, 1987-91, ret., 1991. Author: Forever Open, Clear and Free: the Historic Struggle for Chicago's Lakefront, 1972. Recipient Pulitzer prize for public svc., 1963, Pulitzer prize for editorial writing, 1989, William Allen White Found. award for excellence in editorial writing, 1978, numerous awards Chgo. Newspaper Guild, numerous awards Chgo. Headline Club, numerous awards Nat. Assn. Edn. Writers, numerous awards Ill. AP, numerous awards Ill. UPI. Home: 120 Charmont Dr Radford VA 24141-4205

WILLE, WAYNE MARTIN, retired editor; b. Des Plaines, Ill., Nov. 17, 1930; s. Clarence Louis and Lois Naomi (Martin) W.; m. Lois Jean Kroeber, June 6, 1954. B.S.J., Northwestern U., 1952, M.S.J., 1953. Reporter Chgo. Sun Times, 1956-57; dir. press info. WBBM-TV and CBS-TV, Chgo., 1957-58; feature editor Sci. and Mechanics mag., 1958-60, mng. editor, 1960-62; news editor Nat. Safety Council, Chgo., 1962-64, asst. dir. pub. info., 1964-67; mng. editor World Book Year Book, Chgo., 1967-69; exec. editor World Book Yr. Book, 1969-83; mng. editor World Book Yr. Book and Sci. Yr. and Health & Med. Ann., 1983-91. Served with AUS, 1953-55. Mem. Chgo. Headline Club (pres. 1967-68), Soc. Profl. Journalists. Clubs: La Salle Street Rod and Gun.

WILLEKE, GENE E., environmental engineer, educator; b. Dola, Ohio, Sept. 5, 1934; s. Gale Charles and Mildred Elizabeth (Marling) W.; m. Carol Ann Blomquist, Sept. 8, 1962; children: Andrew Gerhard, Jonathan Christopher. AB in Math., Ohio No. U., 1956, BS in Civil Engring., 1957; MS in Civil Engring., Stanford U., 1960, PhD in Civil Engring., 1969. Registered profl. engr., Ohio. Civil engr. Madison Engring. Assn., Mansfield, Ohio, 1957; hydraulic rsch. engr. U.S. Bur. Pub. Rds., Washington, 1960-62; supr. sanitary engring. USPHS, Chgo., 1962-65; acting asst. prof. Stanford (Calif.) U., 1968-70; prof. Ga. Inst. Tech., Atlanta, 1970-77; dir. and prof. Inst. of Environ. Sci., Oxford, Ohio, 1977—; cons. in field. Treas. Boy Scouts Am., Oxford, 1988-90. With U.S. Army, 1957-59. Hwy. Rsch. Bd. awardee, 1971. Mem. ASCE, Nat. Assn. Environ. Profls., Nat. Soc. Profl. Engrs., Am. Geophys. Union, Am. Meteorol. Soc., Assn. Am. Geographers, Am. Soc. Engring. Edn. Democrat. Lutheran. Home: 1007 Cedar Dr Oxford OH 45056-2416 Office: IES Miami Univ 102 Boyd Hall Oxford OH 45056

WILLEMS, CONSTANCE CHARLES, lawyer; b. Zuilen, Utrecht, Netherlands, Oct. 31, 1942; came to U.S., 1967, naturalized, 1975; d. Anton Henri and Maria (Van der Meys) Charles; m. Cornelis Franciscus Willems, May 25, 1965; 1 son. Maurice. BA in Sociology magna cum laude, U. New Orleans, 1974; J.D. with honors, Tulane U., 1977. Bar: La. 1977, U.S. Dist. Ct. (ea. dist.) La. 1977, U.S. Ct. Appeals (5th cir.) 1977, U.S. Supreme Ct. 1983. Assoc. McGlinchey, Stafford, Mintz, Cellini, and Lang, New Orleans, 1977-81, ptnr., 1982—. Mem. Task Force on Municipalization. Mem. ABA, La. Assn. Women Attys. (pres. 1983-85, 86-87), La. State Bar Assn. (mem. ho. of dels. 1984-85, chair internat. law sect. 1994—), New Orleans Bar Assn. Club: Holland (pres. 1980). Office: McGlinchey Stafford Lang 643 Magazine St New Orleans LA 70130

WILLENBECHER, JOHN, artist; b. Macungie, Pa., May 5, 1936; s. John George and Geneva (Bacon) W. B.A., Brown U., 1958; postgrad., N.Y. U., Inst. Fine Arts, 1958-61. sculptor-mem. N.Y.C. Art Commn., 1980-92;

mem. commn. for plaza and pavillion, Mpls. Inst. Arts, 1991. Exhibited in one-man shows including Hamilton Gallery Contemporary Art, N.Y.C., 1977, 80, U. Mass. Art Gallery, Amherst, 1977, Wright State U. Art Gallery, Dayton, Ohio, 1977, Jaffe-Friede Gallery, Dartmouth Coll., Hanover, N.H., 1977, Fine Arts Ctr., U. R.I., Kingston, 1978, Neuberger Mus., SUNY at Purchase, 1979, Allentown (Pa.) Art Mus., 1979; exhibited in numerous group shows including Albright-Knox Art Gallery, Buffalo, 1963, Whitney Mus. Am. Art, N.Y.C., 1964-68; represented in permanent collections including Solomon R. Guggenheim Mus., N.Y.C., Met. Mus., N.Y.C., Whitney Mus. Am. Art, N.Y.C., Albright-Knox Art Gallery, Phila. Mus. Art, Centre d'Art et Culture Georges Pompidou, Paris, Hirshhorn Mus. and Sculpture Garden, Washington, Art Inst. Chgo. Nat. Endowment for Arts grantee, 1977, Esther and Adolph Gottlieb Found. grantee, 1994. Subject of profl. articles and catalogues.

WILLENBROCK, FREDERICK KARL, engineer, educator; b. N.Y.C., July 19, 1920; s. Berthold Daniel and Anna Marie (Koniger) W.; m. Mildred Grace White, Dec. 20, 1944. Sc.B., Brown U., 1942; M.A., Harvard U., 1947, Ph.D., 1950. Research fellow, lectr. and asso. dean Harvard U., Cambridge, Mass., 1950-67; provost, prof. faculty engring. and applied sci. SUNY, Buffalo, 1967-70; dir. Inst. Applied Tech., Nat. Bur. Standards, Washington, 1970-76; dean Sch. Engring. and Applied Sci., So. Meth. U., Dallas, 1976-81; Cecil and Ida Green prof. engring. Sch. Engring. and Applied Sci., So. Meth. U., 1976-86; exec. dir. Am. Soc. for Engring. Edn., Washington, 1986-89; asst. dir. Sci., Technol. and Internat. Affairs NSF, Washington, 1989-91; sr. scientist Tech. Adminstrn. Dept. of Commerce, 1992-93; cons. Washington, 1993—; vis. prof. engring. and pub. policy Carnegie-Mellon U., 1991-92. Contbr. articles to profl. jours. With USNR, 1943-46. Recipient Disting. Engring. award Brown U., 1962; Gold medal U.S. Dept. Commerce, 1975. Fellow IEEE, AAAS; mem. NAE, Sigma Xi, Tau Beta Pi. Office: Unit E 1740 New Hampshire Ave NW Washington DC 20009-2535

WILLENS, ALAN RUSH, management consultant; b. Detroit, Jan. 14, 1936; s. Gerald Lionel Willens and Gertrude Virginia Rush; m. Harriet Lois Sinclair (June 30, 1958 (div. 1985); children: Beth Willens Hollander, Scott Sinclair Willens, Lori Helen Willens. BBA, U. Mich., 1957, MBA, 1958. Project dir. United Rsch., Inc., Cambridge, Mass., 1958-61; sr. assoc. Systems Analysis and Rsch. Corp., Boston, 1961-64; sr. cons. Regional and Urban Planning Implementation, Inc., Cambridge, 1964-65; v.p. Charles River Assocs., Inc., Boston, 1965-87, exec. v.p., 1987-92, pres., 1992—, also bd. dirs. Chmn. com. Ellis Neighborhood Assn., Boston, 1985-88; trustee Dartmouth Sq. Condo. Assn., Boston, 1992—, chmn., 1994. Mem. Profl. Svcs. Mgmt. Assn. (bd. dirs. 1977-80, treas. 1978-80, First Fellow 1979). Avocations: sailing, skiing, photography, personal computers, tennis. Home: 130 Appleton St # 1G Boston MA 02116 Office: Charles River Assocs Inc John Hancock Tower 200 Clarendon St T-33 Boston MA 02116

WILLENSON, KIM JEREMY, publisher, journalist, author; b. Milw., Feb. 10, 1937; s. Lawrence Alvin and Miriam Hannah W.; m. Keiko Okubo, Dec. 1964 (div. Aug. 1977); m. Ayako Doi, Oct. 10, 1981. BS, U. Wis., 1960; MS, Columbia U., 1962. Reporter Wis. State Jour., Madison, 1959-61, Washington Post, 1962-63; corr. UPI, Tokyo, 1963-65, Asia div. news editor, 1965-66; chief S.E. Asia corr. UPI, Bangkok, Thailand, 1966-69; corr. UPI, Saigon, Republic of Vietnam, 1970-72; chief nat. security reporting team UPI, Washington, 1972-74, internat. mng. editor, 1987; assoc. editor fgn. and mil. affairs Newsweek, N.Y.C., 1974-78; corr. Newsweek, Washington, 1978-80, Tokyo bur. chief, 1980-83, nat. security corr., Washington, 1983-86; pub. The Daily Japan Digest, 1990—. Author: The Bad War, 1987. Served with U.S. Army, 1957-59. Recipient Best War Corr. award Overseas Press Club, N.Y., 1977, Best Mag. Fgn. Affairs Article award Overseas Press Club, N.Y., 1981. Mem. Nat. Press Club. Jewish. Avocation: sailing. Office: Japan Digest Ste 207 5510 Columbia Pike Arlington VA 22204

WILLERDING, MARGARET FRANCES, mathematician; b. St. Louis, Apr. 26, 1919; d. Herman J. and Mildred F. (Icenhower) W. A.B., Harris Tchrs. Coll., 1940; M.A., St. Louis U., 1943, Ph.D., 1947. Tchr. (Pub. Schs.), St. Louis, 1940-46; instr. math. Washington U., St. Louis, 1947-48; asst. prof. Harris Tchrs. Coll., St. Louis, 1948-56; mem. faculty San Diego State Coll., 1956—, asso. prof., 1959-65, prof. math., 1966-76, prof. emeritus, 1976—. Author: Intermediate Algebra, 1969, Elementary Mathematics, 1971, College Algebra, 1971, College Algebra and Trigonometry, 1971, Arithmetic, 1968, Probability: The Science of Chance, 1969, Mathematics Around the Clock, 1969, Mathematical Concepts, 1967, From Fingers to Computers, 1969, Probability Primer, 1968, Mathematics: The Alphabet of Science, 1972, 74, 77, A First Course in College Mathematics, 1973, 77, 80, Mathematics Worktext, 1973, 77, Business and Consumer Mathematics for College Students, 1976, The Numbers Game, 1977. Mem. Nat. Council Tchrs. Math., Assn. Tchrs. Sci. and Math., Am. Math. Soc., Math. Assn. Am., Greater San Diego Math. Council (dir. 1963-65), Sigma Xi, Pi Mu Epsilon. Home: 10241 Vivera Dr La Mesa CA 91941-4370 Office: Dept Math San Diego State Coll San Diego CA 92085

WILLERMAN, LEE, psychologist, educator; b. Chgo., July 26, 1939; s. Israel and Anna Willerman; m. Benne Secter, Jan. 21, 1962; children: Raquel, Amiel. BA, Roosevelt U., Chgo., 1961, MA, 1964; PhD, Wayne State U., 1967. Research psychologist NIH, Bethesda, Md., 1967-70; NIH postdoctoral fellow dept. human genetics U. Mich. Med. Sch., Ann Arbor, 1970-71; asst. prof. psychology U. Tex., Austin, 1971-74, assoc. prof., 1974-81, prof., 1981—, Sarah M. and Charles E. Seay Regents prof. clin. psychology, 1985—; vis. Scheinfeld prof. Hebrew U. Jerusalem, 1983. Author: Psychology of Individual and Group Differences, 1979; co-author: Psychopathology, 1990. Fellow Am. Psychol. Assn., Internat. Soc. Twin Studies; mem. AAAS, Soc. Study Social Biology, Behavior Genetics Assn. Jewish. Home: 3415 Ledgestone Dr Austin TX 78731-5124 Office: U Tex at Austin Dept Psychology Austin TX 78712-1189*

WILLERT, SISTER ST. JOAN, health care corporation executive; b. Wheeling, W.Va., June 13, 1924; d. Arthur Edgar and Viola (Fitzsimmons) W. BA, Mt. St. Mary's Coll., 1946; human relations cert., Loyola U., L.A., 1951; MS, Mt. St. Mary's Coll., 1953; health care adminstrn., St. Louis U., 1975. Cert. health care adminstrn., elem. sch. adminstrn., secondary sch. adminstrn. Elem. sch. tchr. Diocese of San Francisco, L.A., and Fresno, 1945-54; elem. sch. prin. several cities, 1954-65; secondary sch. prin. Queen of the Valley Acad., Fresno, Calif., 1965-67, Salpointe Catholic High Sch., Tucson, 1967-70; regional superior Sisters of St. Joseph, L.A., 1970-74, Washington, Idaho, 1974-77; with health care adminstrn. Daniel Freeman Hosp., Inglewood, Calif., 1977-79; pres., chief exec. officer Health Care Corp. Ariz., Tucson, 1979—; bd. dirs. Freeman Health Ventures, St. John of God, L.A.; bd. sec. Downtown Devel. Corp., Tucson, 1986—; bd. dirs. Our Lady of Lourdes Health Ctr., Pasco, Wash., 1975-81, 85—; bd. chairperson Health Care Corp., St. Louis, 1986—. Contbr. articles to MSMC, 1966, Health Progress, 1982. Chairperson state campaign Arizonans to Protect Quality Health Svc., Phoenix, Tucson, 1984-85. Named for Outstanding Svc. to Community Una Noche Plateada, Tucson, 1982; honoree Tucson Diocesan Found. Mem. Ariz. Hosp. Assn. (bd. dirs. 1979—, sec. 1988, chairpersonelect 1989-90, Salisbury Leadership award 1985), Cath. Health Assn. (bylaws com. 1985-86, nominating com. 1984-85), Health Care Corp. Sisters of St. Joseph (chairperson 1985—). Democrat. Roman Catholic. Avocations: reading, tennis, writing. Office: Carondelet St Mary's Hosp 1601 W St Mary's Rd Tucson AZ 85745

WILLERTSEN, STEVEN, food products executive. With Cargill Corp., Wayzata, Minn.; pres. Rocco Turkeys, Inc., Dayton, Va. Office: Rocco Turkeys Inc Huffman Dr RR 42 Dayton VA 22821*

WILLES, MARK HINCKLEY, food industry executive; b. Salt Lake City, July 16, 1941; s. Joseph Simmons and Ruth (Hinckley) W.; m. Laura Fayone, June 7, 1961; children: Wendy Anne, Susan Kay, Keith Mark, Stephen Joseph, Matthew Bryant. AB, Columbia U., 1963, PhD, 1967. Mem. staff banking and currency com. Ho. of Reps., Washington, 1966-67; asst. prof. fin. U. Pa., Pitts., 1967-69; economist Fed. Res. Bank, Phila., 1967, sr. economist, 1969-70; dir. research, 1970-71, v.p. dir. research 1971, 1st v.p., 1971-77; pres. Fed. Res. Bank of Mpls., 1977-80; exec. v.p. chief fin. officer Gen. Mills, Inc., Mpls., 1980-85, pres., chief oper. officer, 1985—, vice chmn., 1992—. Office: Gen Mills Inc 1 General Mills Blvd Minneapolis MN

55426-1347 *My success is based on adherence to principles I learned in the home, which is the most basic and important organizational unit in the world. Three of those principles stand out in my mind: Be just, honest and moral—do things not only because they are required, but because they are right. Have mercy—care enough about others to be fair and kind. Be humble—you can get more done effectively with the help of others than you can do on your own.*

WILLET, RICHARD A., engineering company executive; b. Oceanside, N.Y.; s. Robert H. and Ruth (Woodcock) W.; m. Connie Dupler, 1973; children: Bryan, Bonnie, Kenneth, Brooks. BS in Engring., Duke U., 1973; MS in Engring., George Washington U., 1978. Registered profl. engr., Va., N.C., Ohio, Md., Tenn., W.Va., Pa.; registered environ. profl.; cert. environ. auditor. Project engr. City of Alexandria, Va., 1974-79; town engr. Town of Blacksburg, Va., 1979-86; president pres. Brightwaters Engring., Salem, Va., 1986—; past adj. prof. Va. Tech. Sch. Engring. Author several technical manuals. Address: 4836 Warrior Dr Salem VA 24153-5816

WILLET, EDWARD FARRAND, JR., lawyer; b. Takoma Park, Md., Jan. 30, 1933; s. Edward Farrand and Fern Leona (Hawkins) W.; m. Anita Joan McComas, Dec. 26, 1954; children—Jeffrey Dean, Gary Louis, Deborah Ann. B.A., Andrews U., Berrien Springs, Mich., 1954; J.D., George Washington U., 1957. Bar: D.C. 1958. Atty. advisor U.S. Civil Service Commn., Washington, 1958-69, legis. counsel, 1969-70; asst. law revision counsel U.S. Ho. of Reps., Washington, 1970-73, law revision counsel, 1973—. Editor: U.S. Codes, 1973—. Mem. ABA, D.C. Bar Assn. Home: 11320 Country Club Rd New Market MD 21774 Office: Law Revision Counsel 304 Ford House Office Bldg Washington DC 20515

WILLET, ROBERT LEE, health care administrator; b. Takoma Park, Md., Aug. 28, 1935; s. Edward Farrand and Fern Leona (Hawkins) W.; m. Crystal May Wery, June 28, 1959; children: Jesse Allen, Gregory Dean. B.S., Columbia Union Coll., Washington, 1957; M.B.A., George Washington U., 1964. Acct. Hadley Meml. Hosp., Washington, 1960-62; dir. patient service Kettering Med. Ctr., Dayton, Ohio, 1963-66, asst. adminstr., 1966-69, assoc. adminstrn., 1969-72, v.p., 1972-79, pres., 1979—. Developer: system for healthcare outpatient services Verticare. Fellow Am. Coll. Healthcare Execs.; mem. Greater Dayton Area Hosp. Assn. (chmn. 1982-83), Seventh-Day Adventist Hosp. Assn. (pres. 1982), Am. Coll. Hosp. Adminstrs., Am. Hosp. Assn., Montgomery County Med. Soc. (assoc.), Kettering C. of C. (dir. 1983—), Dayton C. of C., Rotary. Adventist. Home: 3350 Winding Way Dayton OH 45419-1242 Office: Kettering Med Ctr 3535 Southern Blvd Dayton OH 45429-1217

WILLET, THOMAS EDWARD, lawyer; b. N.Y.C., Nov. 8, 1947; s. Oscar Edward and Alice (Fleming) W.; m. Marilyn Kenney, Dec. 28, 1969; children: Thomas Justin, Christopher Joseph. BS, USAF Acad., Colo., 1969; JD with distinction, Cornell U., 1972. Bar: N.Y. 1973, U.S. Ct. Claims 1973, U.S. Supreme Ct. 1977. Judge advocate USAF, Syracuse, N.Y., 1973-75, Kincheloe AFB, Mich., 1975-77; judge advocate USAF Hdqs., Washington, 1977-79; assoc. Harris, Beach & Wilcox, Rochester, N.Y., 1979-84, ptnr., 1985—. Pres. Monroe County Legal Assistance Corp., Rochester, 1983-89. Capt. USAF, 1969-79. Mem. ABA, N.Y. State Bar Assn., Monroe County Bar Assn., Order of Coif. Office: Harris Beach & Wilcox Granite Bldg 130 Main St E Rochester NY 14604-1687

WILLEY, DARRELL S., education educator; b. Farmington, Utah, May 9, 1925; s. R.C. Willey and Helen (Swaner) Barber; m. Velma Roush, June 7, 1947 (dec. May 1971); children: Randie Carol Boldra, Trica L. Hazelton, Jacqui I, Monninger; m. Irene Knox Mayfield, May 30, 1972; 1 foster child, Roger E. Mayfield III. AB, Denver U., 1948; MS, Utah State U., 1949; EdD, U. Utah, 1953; postdoctoral, U. So. Calif., 1957. Cert. sch. mgmt., Utah, Colo., N.Mex. Prin. Wendover (Utah) Sch., 1949-50, West Sch., Littleton, Colo., 1952-53; from asst. prof. to assoc. prof. edn. mgmt. and devel. N.Mex. State U., Las Cruces, 1953-61, prof., 1962-89; prof. emeritus, 1989—; dir. edn. research ctr. N.Mex. State U., Las Cruces, 1969-82, head dept. edn. mgmt. and devel., 1962-70, dir. ERIC-CRESS program, 1966-68, dir. edn. research tng. program, 1966-72; cons. NIH, NSF, U.S. Dept. Edn., U.S. Civil Rights Commn., 1963—. Author N.Mex. Survey Vocat. Tech. Ednl. Needs, 1963-64, numerous other publications. Senator's del. White House Conf. on Children, 1970. Staff sgt. USAAF, 1943-45, CBI, commd., 1948-68. Mem. AAAS, Am. Assn. Sch. Adminstrs., Am. Edn. Rsch. Assn., Hump Pilots Assn. 7th Bombardment Group Assn., Phi Delta Kappa. Democrat. Mormon. Lodge: Elks. Avocations: travel, color photography, coins. Home: PO Box 486 Mesilla NM 88046-0486

WILLEY, FRANK PATRICK, lawyer, insurance company executive; b. Albany, N.Y., July 15, 1953; m. Katie Kroskob, Sept., 1988. BS in Acctg., LeMoyne Coll., 1975; JD, Union U., 1978. Bar: Ariz. 1978. Assoc. T. M. Shumway, Scottsdale, Ariz., 1978-80, Foley, Clark & Nye, Phoenix, 1980-83; gen. counsel, v.p. Land Resources Corp., Scottsdale, 1983-84; gen. counsel, exec. v.p. Fidelity Nat. Title Ins., Irvine, Calif., 1984—. Office: Fidelity Nat Title Ins Co 2100 S E Main St Ste 400 Tustin CA 92714*

WILLEY, GORDON RANDOLPH, retired anthropologist, archaeologist, educator; b. Chariton, Iowa, Mar. 7, 1913; s. Frank and Agnes Caroline (Wilson) W.; m. Katharine W. Whaley, Sept. 17, 1938; children: Alexandra, Winston. AB, U. Ariz., 1935, AM, 1936, LittD (hon.), 1981; PhD, Columbia U., 1942; A.M. honoris causa, Harvard U., 1950; Litt.D. honoris causa, Cambridge U., 1977, U. N.Mex., 1984. Archaeol. asst. Nat. Pk. Svc., Macon, Ga., 1936-38; archaeologist La. State U., 1938-39; archaeol. field supr. Peru, 1941-42; instr. anthropology Columbia U., 1942-43; anthropologist Bur. Am. Ethnology, Smithsonian Instn., 1943-50; Bowditch prof. archaeology Harvard U., 1950-83, sr. prof. anthropology, 1983-87, chmn. dept. anthropology, 1954-57; vis. prof. Am. archaeology Cambridge (Eng.) U., 1962-63; mem. expdns. to Peru, Panama, 1941-52, Brit. Honduras, 1953-56, Guatemala, 1958, 60, 62, 64, 65, 66, 67, 68, Nicaragua, 1959, 61, Honduras, 1973, 75-77. Author: Excavations in the Chancay Valley, Peru, 1943, Archaeology of the Florida Gulf Coast, 1949, Prehistoric Settlement Patterns in the Viru Valley, Peru, 1953, Introduction to American Archaeology, 2 vols, 1966-71, The Artifacts of Altar de Sacrificios, 1972, Excavations of Altarde Sacrificious, Guatemala: Summary and Conclusions, 1973, Das Alte Amerika, 1974, The Artifacts of Seibal, Guatemala, 1978, Essays in Maya Archaeology, 1987, Portraits in American Archaeology, 1988, New World Archaeology and Culture History, 1990, Excavations at Seibal: Summary and Conclusions, 1990; co-author: Early Ancon and Early Supe Cultures, 1954, The Monagrillo Culture of Panama, 1954, Method and Theory in American Archaeology, 1958, Prehistoric Maya Settlements in the Belize Valley, 1965, The Ruins of Altar de Sacrificios, Department of Peten, Guatemala: An Introduction, 1969, the Maya Collapse: An Appraisal, 1973, A History of American Archaeology, 1974, 3d edit., 1993, The Origins of Maya Civilization, 1977, Lowland Maya Settlement Patterns: A Summary View, 1981, the Copan Residential Zone, 1994; co-editor: Courses Toward Urban Life, 1962, Precolumbian Archaeology, 1980, A Consideration of the Early Classic Period in the Maya Lowlands, 1985; editor: Prehistoric Settlement Patterns of the New World, 1956, Archaeological Researches in Retrospect, 1974. Overseas fellow Churchill Coll., Cambridge U., 1968-69; decorated Order of Quetzal Guatemala; recipient Viking Fund medal, 1953; Gold medal Archaeol. Inst. Am., 1973; Alfred V. Kidder medal for achievement in Am. Archaeology, 1974; Huxley medal Royal Anthrop. Inst., London, 1979; Walker prize Boston Mus. Sci., 1981; Drexel medal for archaeology Univ. Mus., Phila., 1981, Golden Plate award Am. Acad. Achievement, 1987. Fellow Am. Anthrop. Assn. (pres. 1961), Am. Acad. Arts and Sci., London Soc. Antiquaries, Soc. Am. Archaeology (pres. 1968, Disting. Svc. award 1980); mem. Nat. Acad. Sci., Am. Philos. Soc., Royal Anthrop. Inst. Gt. Britain and Ireland, Cosmos Club (Washington), Tavern Club (Boston), Phi Beta Kappa, Brit. Acad. (corr.).

WILLEY, JOHN DOUGLAS, retired newspaper executive; b. Melrose, Mass., June 4, 1917; s. Arthur Peach and Lillian (Holden) W.; m. Marilynn Miller, July 3, 1943; children: Margery Lynn Willey Marshall (dec.), John Douglas, James Campbell, David Spencer, Peter Whitney. LLD (hon.), U. Toledo, 1972. Sec. Boston & Maine R.R., Boston, 1935-40, Jones & Lamson Machine Co., Springfield, Vt., 1940-41; reporter The Blade, Toledo, 1946-49, asst. to pub., 1949-51, city editor, 1952-54, asst. mng. editor, 1954-56, dir. pub. rels., 1956-58, treas., 1962-69, assoc. pub., 1965-81, pres., 1969-81, also bd. dirs.; pres. Clear Water, Inc., 1966-89; bd. dirs. Buckeye Cablevision, Inc., Monterey Peninsula Herald; v.p., dir. Lima Communications Corp., 1971-81, Red Bank Register, 1975-81; mem. Ohio adv. bd. Liberty Mut. Ins. Co., 1976-82. Mem. exec. com. of bd. trustees, treas. Toledo Area Med. Coll. and Edn. Found., 1960-75, hon. trustee, 1975—; mem. adv. bd. St. Vincent Hosp., 1961-75; trustee Maumee Valley Country Day Sch., 1974-77, Med. Coll. Ohio, 1982-91; treas. Amateur Athletic Union Task Force Com., 1976-82, Ohio chmn. U.S. Olympic Commn. 1979-80; mem. Inter-Univ. Coun., Ohio, 1988-91. Capt. A.C., U.S. Army, 1942-46. Recipient Disting. Citizen award Med. Coll. Ohio, 1994. Mem. Belmont Country Club, Med. Coll. Ohio Faculty Club, Sigma Delta Chi. Home: 3534 River Rd Toledo OH 43614-4326

WILLEY, PAUL WAYNE, financial executive; b. Independence, Kans., Jan. 19, 1938; s. Warren Frederick and Alice (Jenista) W.; m. V. Diane Peavy, June 18, 1965; children: P. Wayne Jr., Warren Leon. BS in Acctg., U. Kans., 1960; MBA in Fin., Ind. U. 1961; student, So. Meth. U., 1962-63. CPA, Tex.; cert. real estate broker. Treas. and various other fin. positions Dresser Industries, Inc., Dallas, 1962—. Treas., chmn. ARC, Dallas, 1980—, MD Anderson Cancer Hosp., Houston. Mem. Fin. Execs. Inst. (bd. dirs. 1986, pres. 1990), Tex. Soc. CPA's (bd. dirs. 1986—), Nat. Assn. Treas., Dallas Chpt. CPA's (v.p. 1986), Alpha Tau Omega, Beta Gamma Sigma. Republican. Presbyterian. Club: City (Dallas). Lodge: Toastmasters (bd. dirs., v.p.). Avocations: skiing, boating, farming. Office: Dresser Industries Inc PO Box 718 Dallas TX 75221-0718

WILLGING, PAUL RAYMOND, trade association executive; b. New Rochelle, N.Y., Feb. 14, 1942; s. Herbert Martin and Pauline Mary (Mast) W.; m. Monika Guenther, Aug. 25, 1967; children: Kirsten, Birgit. BA, U. St. Thomas, 1963; M in Internat. Affairs, Columbia U., 1966, PhD, 1973. Assoc. administr. Health Services Administrn., Parklawn, Md., 1973-75; dep. commr. Med. Services Administrn., Washington, 1975-80; dep. administr. Health Care Fin. Adminstrn., Balt., 1980-82; asst. v.p. Blue Cross/Blue Shield Greater N.Y., N.Y.C., 1982-83; exec. v.p. Am. Health Care Assn. Washington, 1983—. Contbr. articles to profl. jours. Bd. dirs. Nat. Health Coun., Washington, 1986—, Howard County Gen. Hosp., Columbia, 1987—. Fulbright scholar, 1964; fellow Woodrow Wilson Found., 1965, Ford Found., 1966. Avocations: skiing, jogging. Home: 10366 Crossbeam Circle Columbia MD 21044-3819 Office: Am Health Care Association 1201 L St NW Washington DC 20005-4024

WILLHAM, RICHARD LEWIS, animal science educator; b. Hutchinson, Kans., May 4, 1932; s. Oliver S. and Susan E. (Hurt) W.; m. Esther B. Burkhart, June 1, 1954; children: Karen Nell, Oliver Lee. B.S., Okla. State U., 1954; M.S., Iowa State U., 1955, Ph.D., 1960. Asst. prof. Iowa State U. Ames, 1959-63, assoc. prof., 1966-71, prof. dept. animal sci., 1971-78, Disting. prof., 1978—; assoc. prof. Okla. State U., Stillwater, 1963-66; cons. in field; tchr. livestock history; guest curator exhbn. Art About Livestock, 1990. Recipient Svc. award Beef Improvement Fedn., 1974, Edn. and Rsch. award Am. Polled Herefore Assn., 1979, Rsch. award Nat. Cattlemen's Assn., 1986, 91, Disting. Alumnus award Okla. State U., 1978, Regents Faculty Excellence award Iowa State U., 1993; named to Hall of Fame Am. Hereford Assn., 1982, Am. Angus Assn., 1988. Fellow Am. Soc. Animal Sci. (animal breeding and genetics award 1978, industry service award 1986). Home: 316 E 20th St Ames IA 50010-5563 Office: Iowa State U Dept Animal Sci Ames IA 50011

WILLIAM, DAVID, director, actor; b. London, Eng., June 24, 1926; arrived in Can., 1986; s. Eric Hugh Williams and Olwen (Roose) Kerr. BA, U. Coll., Oxford, Eng., 1950. Artistic dir. Glasgow Citizen's Theatre, The Nottingham Playhouse, The New Shakespeare Co., London, The National Theatre of Israel, Stratford Festival, Can., 1989-93; instr. U.S., Can., Britain; founder, 1st artistic dir. Ludlow Festival. Theatre directing credits include: Bacchae, The Importance of Being Earnest, The Tempest, Entertaining Mr. Sloane. Love Letters, Treasure Island, Hamlet, Love for Love, The Shoemaker's Holiday, Murder in the Cathedral, Troilus and Cressida, The Winter's Tale, She Stoops to Conquer, Antigone, Separate Tables, Romeo and Juliet, Othello, King Lear, Volpone, Albert Herring, The Merry Wives of Windsor, Twelfth Night; directing world premieres of operas include: Therese, Royal Opera House Covent Garden, The Lighthouse, Edinburgh Festival, Iphigenie en Tauride, The Fairy Queen, Lisbon, La Traviata, Scottish Opera, Il Re Pastore, Camden Festival, Albert Herring, Aldeburgh Festival; he appeared in Uncle Vanya as Serebryakov, As You Like It as Jaques, Twelfth Night as Malvolio, Hamlet as Rosencrantz to Richard Burton's (Hamlet); he appeared in numerous TV productions most notably as Richard the Second in the BBC series An Age of Kings.

WILLIAMS, ABIODUN, international relations educator; b. Freetown, Sierra Leone, Dec. 24, 1961; s. George L.V. and Rebecca Lucinda O. (Pabs-Garnon) W. MA in English with honors, U. Edinburgh, 1983; MALD, Tufts U., 1986, PhD in Internat. Rels., 1987. Teaching asst. dept. polit. sci., dept. history Tufts U., 1984-86, rsch. asst. Fletcher Sch. Law and Diplomacy, 1984-86, lectr. dept. polit. sci., 1987; asst. prof. internat. rels. Sch. Fgn. Svc. Georgetown U., Washington, 1988—; vis. asst. prof. dept. polit. sci., Frederick Douglass Inst. African and African-Am. Studies, U. Rochester, 1987-88; cons. William Greaves Film and TV Prodns., Inc., N.Y.; lectr. Royal Viking Line, 1993; grant application reviewer Fund for Improvement Postsecondary Edn. U.S. Dept. Edn., Washington; mem. grants rev. panel U.S. Inst. Peace, Washington, 1992; speaker, presenter in field. Editor: Many Voices: Multilateral Negotiations in the World Arena, 1992; contbr. articles to profl. jours., encys. Bd. dirs. Jesuit Internat. Vols. Pew faculty fellow internat. affairs JFK Sch. Govt. Harvard U., 1990-91, Joseph Harrison-Francis H. Russell fellow The Fletcher Sch., 1986-87, Fletcher scholar Fletcher Sch. Law and Diplomacy, 1983-87; Fletcher rsch. assistantship, 1984-87. Mem. Internat. Studies Assn., African Studies Assn. Office: Georgetown University School Of Foreign Serv Washington DC 20057

WILLIAMS, ALBERT PAINE, economist; b. Elgin, Tex., Mar. 5, 1935; s. Albert Paine and Mary Dempes (Hudler) W.; m. Elizabeth Ann Whitaker, June 22, 1957; children: Albert, Robert, John. B.S., U.S. Naval Acad., 1957; M.A., Fletcher Sch., Tufts U., 1963; M.A.L.D., Tufts U., 1964, Ph.D., 1967. Budget examiner, internat. economist Bur. Budget, Washington, 1965-67; adv. on fgn. assistance strategy and econ. policy White House Staff, Washington, 1967-68; economist RAND, Santa Monica, Calif., 1968-72, sr. economist, 1972—; dir. health scis. program, 1976-90; dir. RAND/UCLA Ctr. for Health Policy Study, 1982—, corp. rsch. mgr., social policy, 1990—; prof. RAND Grad. Sch., 1971—; mem. adv. bd., 1975—. Trustee Santa Monica Hosp. Med. Ctr., 1992—, Ednl. Commn. for Fgn. Med. Grads., 1993—; scoutmaster Great Western coun. Boy Scouts. Am., 1971-78, 82-88. With USN, 1957-62. Recipient Profl. Achievement award Exec. Office of Pres., 1967. Mem. AAAS, Am. Econ. Assn., Am. Pub. Policy Analysis and Mgmt., Assn. for Health Svcs. Rsch., Sierra Club. Unitarian. Office: 1700 Main St Santa Monica CA 90401-3208

WILLIAMS, ANDY, entertainer; b. Wall Lake, Iowa, Dec. 3, 1930; s. Jay Emerson and Florence (Finley) W.; m. Claudine Longet, Dec. 15, 1961 (div.); children: Noelle, Christian, Robert; m. Debbie Haas, May 3, 1991. pres. Barnaby Records, Barnaby Prodns., Barnaby Sports; owner Moon River Enterprises; host Andy Williams San Diego Golf Open, 1969-89. Worked with 3 brothers as Williams Brothers Quartet, on radio stations in Des Moines, Chgo., Cin. and Los Angeles, 1938-47, Williams Brothers, (teamed with Kay Thompson); worked for night clubs, U.S. and Europe, 1947-52; regular performer: Steve Allen Tonight TV show, 1953-55; star: Andy Williams TV Show, 1962-71; night club and concert entertainer, rec. artist for Columbia Records; recordings include Moon River, Love Story, theme from The Godfather, Can't Get Used to Losing You, Days of Wine and Roses, Born Free, Hawaiian Wedding Song, Butterfly. Named Number One Male Vocalist Top Artist on Campus Poll, 1968; recipient 17 gold albums, 3 Emmy awards, 6 Grammy awards. Office: Moon River Theatre 2500 W Highway 76 Branson MO 65616

WILLIAMS, ANN CLAIRE, federal judge; b. 1949; m. David J. Stewart. BS, Wayne State U., 1970; MA, U. Mich., 1972; JD, U. Notre Dame, 1975. Asst. U.S. atty. U.S. Dist. Ct. (no. dist.) Ill., Chgo., 1976-85; faculty mem. Nat. Inst. for Trial Advocacy, 1979—; judge U.S. Dist. Ct. (no. dist.) Ill., Chgo., 1985—; chief Crime Drug Enforcement Task Force North

Ctrl. Region, 1983-85; chair ct. adminstrn. and case mgmt. com. Jud. Conf. U.S., 1993—; adj. prof., lectr. Northwestern U. Law Sch., Chgo., 1979—. Trustee U. Chgo. Lab Sch.; sec. bd. trustees U. Notre Dame, Mus. Sci. and Industry. Mem. Fed. Bar Assn. (treas.), Fed. Judges Assn., Women's Bar Assn. of Ill. Office: US Dist Ct 219 S Dearborn St Chicago IL 60604-1702

WILLIAMS, ANNE M., diplomat, lawyer; b. Mpls., Dec. 20, 1940; d. Kenneth P. and Bette Jane (Linne) Martin; m. James Williams (div.); children: K. Malaika, Earl L. BA, Mt. Holyoke Coll., 1962; grad. diploma of edn., Makerere U., Kampala, Uganda, 1963; MLS, SUNY, Buffalo, 1972, JD, 1975. Bar: N.Y. Tchr. Murray H.S., Wusi, Kenya, 1963-65; atty. Phillips, Lytle et al, Buffalo, 1975-78; regional legal advisor USAID, Washington, 1979-88, AID rep. USAID Couinea Bissau, 1988-90, sr. democracy advisor, 1991-92, AID rep. USAID Chad, 1992-94, dir. USAID Senegal, 1994—; prof. English U. N'Djamena, Chad, 1992-94. Office: Ave Felix Eboue BP 413, N'Djamena Chad

WILLIAMS, ANNETTE POLLY, state legislator; b. Belzoni, Miss., Jan. 10, 1937. Student, Milw. Area Tech. Coll.; BS, U. Wis. Mem. Wis. State Assembly, Milw. 1980—; attendee African-Am. Leadership summit, New Orleans; organizer Com. 21, 1985, Black Ribbon Commn. to study forced busing, Milw., 1989; panelist Nat. Conf. State Legislators, 1989; active parental sch. choice legislation; lectr. numerous colls. and univs. T.V. appearances include 60 Minutes, ABC World News, This Week with David Brinkley, McNeil Lehrer Report, The British Broadcasting Company, Great Lakes Watch on Washington, CBS This Morning, Both Sides with Rev. Jesse Jackson, CNN News; contbr. articles to profl. jours. Dem. adminstrv. and exec. com.; state chairperson Wis. Jesse Jackson for Pres. campaign; del. Nat. Dem. Conv., 1984, 88; mem. Nat. Dem. Platform Com., 1984; bd. dirs. Rainbow Coalition; founder, chmn. bd. dirs. Milw. Parental Assistance Ctr. Recipient Carrie Chapman Catt award as Nat. Women's Bus. Advocate of Yr., Outstanding Leadership award Dem. party Wis., Harambee Martin Luther King Jr. award for Outstanding Accomplishment and Svc. Am. Legis. Exchange Coun., 1991, Nat. Human Rights award Nat. Cath. Ednl. Assn., 1992, Seton award Career Youth Devel., 1992, Image award for Excellence in Community Svc. and Love of Youth Gamma Phi Delta, 1992, Community Leadership award Libertarian Party Wis., 1992, Liberty award, 1993, Martin Luther King Jr. Community Svc. award Lydell Comm., 1994; named Legislator of Yr. Freedom Mag., 1992; vis. fellow Auckland (New Zealand) Inst. Tech., 1993. Mem. Nat. Black Caucus State Legislators (bd. dirs.). Home: 3927 N 16th St Milwaukee WI 53206-2918 Office: Wis State Assembly State Capital Madison WI 53702

WILLIAMS, ANTHONY, lawyer; b. N.Y.C., Jan. 12, 1946; s. Patrick and Palma (Leone) W. AB in Govt. cum laude, Harvard U., 1968; JD, NYU, 1973. Bar: N.Y. 1974, U.S. Supreme Ct. 1976, Calif. 1977. Assoc. Coudert Bros., N.Y.C., 1973-75, San Francisco, 1976-79; ptnr. Coudert Bros., N.Y.C., 1981—, adminstrv. ptnr., 1982-85; chmn. exec. com. Coudert Bros. 1993—. Served with U.S. Army, 1968-70. Mem. ABA, N.Y. Bar Assn., Assn. Bar of City of N.Y., Calif. Bar Assn. Avocations: reading, baseball, golf. Office: Coudert Bros 1114 Avenue Of The Americas New York NY 10036-7701

WILLIAMS, ARTHUR BENJAMIN, JR., bishop; b. Providence, R.I., June 25, 1935; m. Lynette Rhodes, 1985. AB, Brown U., 1957; MDiv, Gen. Theol. Sem., 1964, DD, 1986. Clarence Horner fellow Grace Ch. Providence, 1964-65; asst. St. Mark, Riverside, R.I., 1965-67; sub-dean St. John Cathedral, Providence, 1967-68; assoc. & interim rector Grace Ch., Detroit, 1968-70; asst. to bishop Diocese of Mich., 1970-77; archdeacon Ohio Cleve., 1977-85; suffragan bishop Episcopal Diocese of Ohio, Cleve., 1986—; v.p. Ho. of Bishops, 1995—. Chair editl. com. Lift Every Voice and Sing II, 1993. Office: Diocese of Ohio 2230 Euclid Ave Cleveland OH 44115-2405

WILLIAMS, ARTHUR COZAD, broadcasting executive; b. Forty Fort, Pa., Feb. 12, 1926; s. John Bedford and Emily Irene (Poyck) W.; m. Ann Cale Bragan, Oct. 1, 1955; children: Emily Williams Van Hoorickx, Douglas, Craig. Student, Wilkes U., 1943-44; B.A. cum laude, U. So. Calif., 1949. With Kaiser Aluminum, 1949, Sta. KPMC, 1950-51; v.p., mgr. KFBK and KFBK-FM Radio Stas., Sacramento, 1951-80; with public relations dept. Sacramento Bee, McClatchy Newspapers, 1981-86; dir.-treas. Norkal Opportunities, Inc.; pres. Sacramento Bee Credit Union. Served with AUS, 1944-46. Mem. Sigma Delta Chi. Clubs: Rotary, Sutter, Valley Hi Country, Masons, Shriners. Home: 1209 Nevis Ct Sacramento CA 95822-2532 Office: 1125 Brownwyk Dr Sacramento CA 95822-1028

WILLIAMS, ARTHUR E., federal agency administrator; b. Watertown, N.Y.; m. Carol Waite; children: Scott, Christina, Cheryl. BA in Math., St. Lawrence U., Canton, N.Y., 1960; BSCE, Rensselaer Poly. Inst., 1962; M in Civil Engring./Econ. Planning, Stanford U., 1969; grad., U.S. Army Comd. and Gen. Staff Coll., U.S. Naval War Coll.; D in Engring. (hon.), Rensselaer U., 1994. Registered profl. engr., Minn. Comdr. various assigments U.S. Army Corps Engrs.; chief engrs., comdr. U.S. Army Corps Engrs., Washington, 1992—. Office: Dept of the Army Chief of Engineers 20 Massachusetts Ave NW Washington DC 20314

WILLIAMS, ARTHUR T., JR., gas, oil industry executive; b. 1927. With Winston Salem (N.C.) Tobacco Bd. of Trade, 1949-57, Taylor Oil Co., Inc., Winston Salem, N.C., 1957-63; with A T Williams, Winston Salem, N.C., 1963—, now CEO. Office: A T Williams Oil Co 5446 University Pkwy Winston Salem NC 27105*

WILLIAMS, ARTHUR T., III, oil, gas industry executive; b. 1957. Graduate, U. N.C., 1979. With A. T. Williams, Winston-Salem, N.C., 1979—; now pres. Office: A T Williams Oil Co 5446 University Pkwy Winston Salem NC 27105*

WILLIAMS, AUBREY WILLIS, anthropology educator; b. Madison, Wis., July 31, 1924; s. Aubrey Willis and Anita (Schreck) W.; m. Alice Rebecca Williams, Sept. 20, 1950 (div. June 1972); children: Jonathan Goree, Nancy Clark; m. Graceanne Adamo, Dec. 21, 1974 (div. June 1992); 1 child, Aubrey Ralph Rhys. BA, U. N.C., 1955, MA, 1957; PhD, U. Ariz., 1964. Circulation mgr. So. Farmer Inc., Montgomery, Ala., 1950-53, pub. rep., 1953-55; research asst. dept. anthropology U. N.C., Chapel Hill, 1956; field camp dir. Am. Friends Service Com., San Salvador el Verde, Puebla, Mex., 1957-58; teaching asst. U. Ariz., Tucson, 1958-60; ethnologist Navajo Tribe, Window Rock, Ariz., 1961-62; asst. prof. U. Md., College Park, 1962-66, assoc. prof., dir. div. of anthropology, 1967-71, full prof., 1971—; research assoc. Smithsonian Instn., Washington, 1966-67; Fulbright prof., USSR, 1982, Fulbright-Hays prof., Mex., 1984, USIA prof. Tampere (Finland) U., 1990-91. Mem. Am. Anthrop. Assn., Soc. for Applied Anthropology. Democrat. Office: U Md Dept Anthropology College Park MD 20472

WILLIAMS, B. JOHN, JR., lawyer, former federal judge; b. Lancaster, Pa., Dec. 13, 1949; s. Bernard John and Sarah Elizabeth (Sykes) W.; m. Martha Caroline Roberts, Aug. 6, 1977; children: Robert, Sarah, Anne, Bernard. BA, George Washington U., 1971, JD, 1974. Bar: D.C., Pa., U.S. Ct. Appeals (fed. cir.). Law clk. to judge U.S. Tax Ct., Washington 1974-76; assoc. Ballard, Spahr, Andrews & Ingersoll, Phila., 1976-81; spl. asst. to chief counsel IRS, Washington, 1981-83; dep. asst. atty. gen. Tax Div. Dept. Justice, Washington, 1983-84; ptnr. Morgan, Lewis & Bockius, Washington, 1984-85; judge U.S. Tax Ct., Washington, 1985-90; ptnr. Morgan, Lewis & Bockius, Washington, 1990—; mem. adv. com. U.S. Tax Ct. Appeals, Fed. Cir. Fellow Am. Coll. Tax Counsel; mem. ABA (adv. com.), Am. Law Inst., Phi Beta Kappa, Omicron Delta Kappa. Republican. Office: Morgan Lewis & Bockius 1800 M St NW Washington DC 20036-5802

WILLIAMS, BARBARA ANNE, college president; b. Camden, N.J., Oct. 14, 1938; d. Frank and Laura Dorothy (Szweda) W. BA cum laude, Georgian Court Coll., 1963; MLS, Rutgers U., 1965; MA, Manhattan Coll., 1973; postgrad., NYU, 1976-81, 93—. Cert. English tchr., N.J.; joined Sisters of Mercy, 1957. Sec. Camden Cath. High Sch., 1956-57; registrar Georgian Ct. Coll., Lakewood, N.J., 1960-66, dir. libr. svcs., 1966-74, dean acad. affairs, 1974-80, pres., 1980—; bd. dirs. N.J. Natural Gas Co., 1986-91. Mem. editorial bd. N.J. Woman mag. Bd. dirs., mem. ednl. adv. coun. Diocese of Trenton, N.J., 1983-90; mem. adv. bd. Ocean County Ctr. for Arts,

Lakewood, N.J., 1983-91; mem. Ocean County Pvt. Industry Coun. 1983-92; bd. dirs. Monmouth/Ocean Devel. Coun., 1981-84; mem. State of N.J. Student Assistance Bd., 1995—. Named Outstanding Woman N.J. Assn. Women Bus. Owners, 1983; recipient Humanitarian award Monmouth/ Ocean Devel. Coun., 1985, Salute to Policymakers award Exec. Women N.J., 1986, Woman in Leadership award Monmouth Coun. Girl Scouts, 1987, Citizen of Yr. Alcoholism & Drug Abuse Coun. Ocean County, 1993, Brotherhood/Sisterhood award Monmouth/Ocean County chpts. NCCJ, 1994. Mem. Assn. of Mercy Colls. (pres. 1981-83), Mercy Higher Edn. Colloquium (mem. exec. com. 1980-87), Ocean County Bus. Assn. (trustee 1982-84), Nat. Assn. Inc. Colls. and Univs. (secretariat 1981-83, 87-91). Home and Office: Georgian Ct Coll 900 Lakewood Ave Lakewood NJ 08701-2600

WILLIAMS, BARBARA JEAN MAY, state official; b. Alphoretta, Ky., June 5, 1927; d. Andrew Jackson and Bess (Salisbury) May. A.B. in Spanish, Centre Coll., 1949; postgrad., Columbia U., 1957; M.S. in L.S., U. Ky., 1963. Librarian Midway Jr. Coll., 1960-62, Ky. Dept. Libraries, Frankfort, 1965-68; planning librarian Ky. Program Devel. Office, Frankfort, 1968-71, Ky. Exec. Dept. for Fin. and Adminstrn., Frankfort, 1972-76; asst. state librarian Ky. Dept. Libraries and Archives, Frankfort, 1976; state librarian Ky. Dept. Libraries and Archives, 1977-80; adminstr. Ky. suggestion system program Dept. Personnel, div. employee services State of Ky., Frankfort, 1980-91; retired; mem. Depository Library Council to Public Printer. Mem. ALA, Southeastern Library Assn., Ky. Library Assn. (sec. spl. library sect. 1976, chmn. sect. 1976), Chief Officers State Library Agys. (liaison com. office Edn. 1979-80), Assn. State Library Agys. (Index State Library Activities 1979-80), Council Planning Librarian (treas.), Ky. Council Archivists, Ky. Hist. Soc., J. B. Speed Museum Guild. Presbyterian. Clubs: Democratic Woman's, Filson, La Jardiniere Garden Club.

WILLIAMS, BEN FRANKLIN, JR., mayor, lawyer; b. El Paso, Tex., Aug. 12, 1929; s. Ben Franklin and Dorothy (Whitaker) W.; m. Daisy Federighi, June 2, 1951; children: Elizabeth Lee, Diane Marie, Katherine Ann, Benjamin Franklin III. BA, U. Ariz., 1951, JD, 1956. Bar: Ariz. 1956. With Bd. Immigration Appeals, Dept. Justice, 1957, ICC, 1959; pvt. practice Tucson, Ariz., 1956—; city atty. Douglas and Tombstone, 1962; atty. Mexican consul, 1960; mayor of Douglas, 1980-88; bd. dirs. Ariz. Pub. Service Co. Pres. Ariz. League Cities and Towns, pres. Douglas Sch. Bd., 1963, 69, 70; mem. bd. Ariz. Dept. Econ. Planning and Devel.; bd. dirs. Ariz.-Mex. Commn., Ariz. Acad. (Town Hall), Merabank & Ariz. Pub. Service Co.; ward committeeman Douglas Republican Com., 1962. Served to 1st lt. AUS, 1951-53. Mem. ABA, Internat. Bar Assn., Ariz. Bar Assn. (treas. 1963), Cochise County Bar Assn. (pres. 1959), Pima County Bar Assn., Am. Judicature Soc., U. Ariz. Law Coll. Assn. (dir.), Ariz. Hist. Soc. (dir.), Sigma Nu, Phi Delta Phi, Blue Key. Episcopalian. Lodge: Elks. Home: 6555 N St Andrews Dr Tucson AZ 85718-2615 Office: 3773 E Broadway Blvd Tucson AZ 85716

WILLIAMS, BERTHA ELIZABETH GRIFFIN, elementary education educator; b. Maxton, N.C., Nov. 27, 1942; d. John Wright and Mary Azerlee Williams. BA in Bibl. Lit., Northwestern Bible Coll., Essex Fells, N.J., 1984; postgrad., New Brunswick Theol. Sem., 1985. Cert. elem. tchr., N.J.; ordained elder A.M.E. Ch., 1983. Accounts receivable, collections, billings clk., bookkeeper Newark Beth Israel Med. Ctr., 1964-74; outpatient and impatient billing clk., receptionist Overlook Hosp., Summit, N.J., 1975-86; elem. tchr. Newark Bd. Edn., 1985—; asst. tchr. Headstart program Broadway Jr. High Sch., Newark, summer 1967-68; staff chaplain Hagedon Ctr. for Geriatrics, Glen Gardner, N.J., 1984—; pastor Mt. Pisgah A.M.E. Ch., Washington, N.J., 1990-93, Mt. Zion A.M.E. Ch., Princeton, N.J., 1993—; former assoc. min. St. James A.M.E., Ch., Newark; dir. Newark Dist. Bd. Christian Edn.; evangelist Newark Dist.; mem. Newark and No. N.J. Com. Churchmen; chmn. edn. com. St. James Credit Union; chmn. local bd. Christian edn. Mem. Newark Dist. Mins. Alliance (sec.), Zeta Phi Beta. Democrat. Office: Mt Zion AME Ch RFD # 4 Old Rd Princeton NJ 08540

WILLIAMS, BILL, academic administrator. Pres. Grand Canyon U. Office: Grand Canyon U 3300 W Camelback Rd Phoenix AZ 85017-1097

WILLIAMS, BILLY DEE, actor; b. N.Y.C., Apr. 6, 1937. Student (Hallgarten scholar), Nat. Acad. Fine Arts and Design; student acting, Paul Mann, Sidney Poitier, Actor's Workshop in Harlem. Child actor; Broadway adult debut The Cool World, 1961; other stage appearances include A Taste of Honey, 1961, I Have a Dream, 1976, Hallelujah, Baby, Fences, 1988; films The Last Angry Man, 1959, The Out-of-Towners, 1970, The Final Comedown, Lady Sings the Blues, 1972, Hit!, 1973, Mahogany, 1975, The Bingo Long Travelling All-Stars and Motor Kings, 1976, Scott Joplin, 1977, The Empire Strikes Back, 1980, Nighthawks, 1981, Return of the Jedi, 1983, Marvin and Tige, 1983, Fear City, 1985, Number One with a Bullet, 1987, Batman, 1989, Driving Me Crazy, 1991; TV films Carter's Army, 1970, Brian's Song, 1971, The Glass House (Emmy nomination), The Hostage Tower, 1980, Children of Divorce, 1980, Shooting Stars, 1983, Chiefs, 1983, Time Bomb, 1984; Dangerous Passion, 1990, The Jacksons: An American Dream, 1992, Marked for Murder, 1993; guest appearances: TV series The Jeffersons, The Interns, The FBI, Mission Impossible, Mod Squad, Police Woman, Dynasty, In Living Color; appeared in TV movie Scott Joplin: King of Ragtime, 1978. Office: David Shapiro and Assocs 15301 Ventura Blvd Ste 345 Sherman Oaks CA 91403*

WILLIAMS, BILLY LEO, professional baseball coach; b. Whistler, Ala., June 15, 1938; m. Shirley Ann Williams; children: Valarie, Nina, Julia, Sandra. Profl. baseball player Chgo. Cubs, Nat. League, 1959-74, coaching staff, 1978-82, hitting instr., from 1986; profl. baseball player Oakland (Calif.) Athletics, Am. League, 1975-76, coaching staff, 1983-85. Named to Nat. League All-Star Team, 1962, 64-65, 68, 72-73, to Baseball Hall of Fame, 1987, Ala. Sport Hall of Fame, Mobile Sport Hall of Fame; named Nat. League Rookie of Yr., 1961, Nat. League and Maj. Leagues Player of Yr., Sporting News, 1972, Nat. Batting Champ., 1972. Mem. Chgo. Sports Hall of Fame. Nat. League record holder for consecutive games played, 1963-70; maj. league record holder for most games by an outfielder in a season, 1965. Office: Chicago Cubs Wrigley Field 1060 W Addison St Chicago IL 60613-4397*

WILLIAMS, BOBBY See EVERHART, ROBERT PHILLIP

WILLIAMS, BROWN F, television media services company executive; b. Evanston, Ill., Dec. 22, 1940; s. Jack Kermit Williams and Virginia Helen (Benjamin) Likar; m. Linda Francee Ludt, Sept. 1961 (div. 1968); 1 child, Eden Carol Williams McCarthy; m. Sandra Ann Matkowski, Jan. 1984; 1 child, Bronwyn Emily. BA in Math. and Physics, U. Calif., Riverside, 1962, MA in Physics, 1964, PhD in Physics, 1966. Mgr. Electro-Optics Lab., Princeton, N.J., 1969-75; dir. RCA Labs., Princeton, 1976-82, v.p.-1982-87; pres. Williams Cons. Group, Princeton, 1988-90; pres. Princeton Electronic Billboard, 1990—. Fellow IEEE; mem. Am. Phys. Soc., Sigma Xi. Avocations: skiing, ocean sailing, tennis. Office: 47 Hulfish St Princeton NJ 08542

WILLIAMS, CAMILLA, soprano, voice educator; b. Danville, Va.; d. Booker and Fannie (Cary) W.; m. Charles T. Beavers, Aug. 28, 1950. BS, Va. State Coll., 1941; postgrad., Ph.L. U., Pa., 1942; studies with Mme. Marian Szekely-Freschl, 1943-44, 1952, Berkowitz and Cesare Sodero 1944-46, Rose Dirman, 1948-52, Sergius Kagen, 1958-62; MusD (hon.), Va. State U., 1986, D. (hon.), 1985. Prof. voice Bronx Coll., N.Y.C., 1970, Bklyn. Coll., 1970-73, Queens Coll., N.Y.C., 1974, Ind. U., Bloomington, 1977—; 1st black prof. voice Cen. Conservatory Music, Beijing, People's Republic China, 1983. Created role of Madame Butterfly as 1st black contract singer, N.Y.C. Ctr., 1946, 1st Aida, 1948; 1st N.Y. performance of Mozart's Idomeneo with Little Orch. Soc., 1950; 1st Viennese performance Menotti's Saint of Bleecker Street, 1955; 1st N.Y. performance of Handel's Orlando, 1971; other roles include Nedda in Pagliacci, Mimi in La Boheme, Marguerite in Faust; major tours include Alaska, 1950, London, 1954, Am. Festival in Belgium, 1955, tour of 14 African countries for U.S. Dept. State, 1958-59, Israel, 1959, concert for Crown Prince of Japan as guest of Gen. Eisenhower, 1960, tour of Formosa, Australia, New Zealand, Korea, Japan, Philippines, Laos, South Vietnam, 1971, Poland, 1974; appearances with orchs. including Royal Philharm., Vienna Symphony, Berlin Philharm., Chgo. Symphony, Phila.

Orch., BBC Orch., Stuttgart Orch., many others; contract with RCA Victor as exclusive Victor Red Seal rec. artist, 1944—. Recipient Marian Anderson award (1st winner), 1943, 44, Newspaper Guild award as First Lady of Am. Opera, 1947, Va. State Coll. 75th anniv. cert. of merit, 1957, NYU Presdl. Citation, 1959, Gold medal Emperor of Ethiopia and Key to City of Taiwan during Pres. Johnson's Cultural Exchange Program, 1962, Art, Culture and Civic Guild award, 1962, Negro Musician's Assn. plaque, 1963, Harlem Opera and World Fellowship Soc. award, 1963; named Disting. Virginian Gov. of Va., 1972; inducted Danville (Va.) Mus. Fine Arts and History Hall of Fame, 1974; Camilla Williams Park designated in her honor, Danville, 1974; honored by Ind. U. Sch. Music Black Music Students' Orgn., 1979; named to Hon. Order Ky. Cols., 1979; honored by Phila. Pro Arte Soc., 1982; Disting. award of Ctr. for Leadership and Devel., 1983; Taylor-Williams student residence hall at Va. State U. named in Billy Taylor's and her honor, 1985. Mem. NAACP (hon. life), Internat. Platform Assn., Alpha Kappa Alpha. Office: Ind U Sch Music Bloomington IN 47401 *Years of travel have given me the chance to meet people of every race, kind, and condition. I have been a witness to the brotherhood and sisterhood of mankind, for we are all children of God. The most important lesson of my life is the value of giving. When you give of yourself you receive the blessings of your talents.*

WILLIAMS, CARL CHANSON, oil company executive; b. Cin., Oct. 16, 1937; s. Charles J. and Alcie (Brazile) W.; m. Clare Bathé, May 26, 1985; 1 child, Michelle. A.S., U. Cin., 1965; B.S., SUNY-Brockport, 1974; M.B.A., U. Rochester, 1975. Mgr. fin. systems Xerox Corp., Rochester, N.Y., 1972-77; dir. info. mgmt. Am. Can Co., Greenwich, Conn., 1977-79, mng. dir. info. mgmt., 1979-80, mng. dir. ops. control, 1980-82; sr. v.p., dir. mgmt. info. systems DDB Needham Worldwide, N.Y.C., 1982-90; pres. The Intertechnology Group, Inc., N.Y.C., 1990-91; v.p. infosystems and tech. Macmillan Pub. Co., N.Y.C., 1991-93; gen. mgr. info. tech. Amoco Corp., Chgo., 1993-94, v.p. info. tech., 1994—; cons. Stamford (Conn.) Bd. Edn., 1981-82; lectr. U. Rochester, N.Y., 1975-77; adj. prof. Fordham U., 1991—. Exec. dir. Concerned Assn. Rochester, N.Y., 1971-75 bd. dirs. Stamford Community Arts Council, 1983-84. Mem. Soc. Info. Mgmr. (exec. coun. 1980-83, pres. 1985, pres. coun. 1986—), Exec. Leadership Coun. Office: Amoco Corp 200 E Randolph Dr Chicago IL 60601

WILLIAMS, CARL E., SR., bishop. Presiding bishop Ch. of God in Christ, Internat., N.Y.C., 1977—. Office: Ch of God in Christ Internat 170 Adelphi St Brooklyn NY 11205

WILLIAMS, CARL HARWELL, utilities executive; b. Mansfield, Ga., Oct. 22, 1915; s. John Horace and Mary Ruby (Harwell) W.; m. Diane Barnes, June 25, 1967; children: Edward Vincent, Lesa Anne. Student, U. Fla., 1934-35; B.S., Ga. Sch. Tech., 1939; postgrad., Harvard Advanced Mgmt. Program, U. Hawaii, 1956. Registered profl. engr., Hawaii. Engr. Fla. Power & Light Co., Miami, 1939-41; with Hawaiian Electric Co., Inc., Honolulu, 1945-80; mgr. engring. Hawaiian Electric Co., Inc., 1955-62, v.p., 1962-71, exec. v.p., 1971-72, pres., 1972-80, dir., 1970-85, chmn. exec. com., 1980-85; chmn. bd., dir. Maui Electric Co. (subsidiary), 1972-80, Hawaii Electric Light Co. (subsidiary), 1972-80; dir. Bank of Hawaii, Hawaiian Electric Industries, Inc., Bancorp Hawaii, Inc. Bd. dirs. Aloha United Way, 1973-79; bd. dirs. Oahu Devel. Conf., 1972-81, chmn., 1979-80; bd. visitors Coll. Bus. Administrn., Hawaii, mem. adv. com. advanced mgmt. program, 1969-75, mem. adv. com. Hawaii geothermal project, 1973-78; mem. State Energy Policy Task Force, 1974-78, Hawaii Energy Conservation Council, 1978-80, Gov.'s Com. Alt. Energy Devel., 1978-80; bd. dirs. Am.-Samoa Power Authority, 1981-83. Served to lt. col., Signal Corps AUS, 1941-45. Decorated Legion of Merit. Fellow IEEE; mem. Hawaii C. of C. Engring. Assn. Hawaii, Nat. Soc. Profl. Engrs. (past dir.), Hawaii Soc. Profl. Engrs. (past dir. pres.), Pacific Coast Elec. Assn. (dir. 1972-81, pres. 1979-80), AIEE (past chmn. Hawaii sect.). Clubs: Pacific, Outrigger Canoe. Home: 2969 Kalakaua Ave Apt 501 Honolulu HI 96815-4620

WILLIAMS, CARLTON HINKLE, dentist; b. St. Louis, Sept. 16, 1914; s. Thomas A. and Lillian (Hinkle) W.; m. Evelyn Stewart, Dec. 31, 1934; children: Lynn Williams Martin, Gayle Williams Culbertson. Student, S.D. State U., 1932-33; D.D.S., U. So. Calif., 1937. Pvt. practice dentistry San Diego, 1937-89; vice chmn. bd. First La Mesa Bank; dir. Dental Service Plans Ins. Co. Chmn. med. instns. commn. for San Diego County, 1949-70. Served to maj. AUS, 1953-55. Fellow Am. Coll. Dentists, Internat. Coll. Dentists, Am. Inst. Oral Biology, Acad. Dentistry Internat.; mem. ADA (speaker Ho. of Dels. 1966-72, pres. 1973-74), Am. Acad. Restorative Dentistry, Am. Acad. Periodontology, Acad. Gen. Dentistry, San Diego County Dental Soc. (pres. 1946), So. Calif. Dental Assn., Calif. Dental Assn. (pres. 1959), Calif. Dental Service (pres. 1961-62), Fedn. Dentaire Internationale (speaker gen. assembly 1975-85, pres.-elect 1985-87, pres. 1987-89), Los Angeles County Dental Soc. (hon.), German Dental Assn. (hon.), Dutch Dental Assn. (hon.), Kiwanis (hon.), Psi Omega. Home: 10840 Melva Rd La Mesa CA 91941-5754 *I have always felt confident that I could accomplish whatever goals I set for myself, and I have always set goals.*

WILLIAMS, CAROL JOAN, foreign correspondent; b. Pawtucket, R.I., July 20, 1955; d. Paul Vincent and Joan Carol (Sawyer) W.; m. Kenneth Gordon Olsen, June 16, 1979. BA, U. Wash., 1977. Reporter Bremerton (Wash.) Sun, 1977-79; news editor Fournier Newspapers, Kent, Wash., 1979-80; writer, editor AP, Seattle, 1980-83; fgn. desk copy editor AP, N.Y.C., 1983-84; Moscow corr. AP, 1984-88, Bonn (Germany) corr., 1988-90; bur. chief Ea. Europe, L.A. Times, Vienna, Austria, 1990—. Recipient Hal Boyle award Overseas Press Club, 1988, Bob Consadine award, 1991; award for internat. affairs writing Soc. Profl. Journalists, 1992. Avocations: hiking, skiing, boating.

WILLIAMS, CAROLYN ELIZABETH, manufacturing executive; b. L.A., Jan. 24, 1943; d. George Kissam and Mary Eloise (Chamberlain) W.; m. Richard Terrill White, Apr. 9, 1972; children: Sarah Anne, William Daniel. BS, Ga. Inst. Tech., 1969; MM, Northwestern U., 1988. Saleswoman Ea. Airlines, Atlanta, Montreal (Can.) and Seattle, 1964-69; job analyst Allied Products Corp., Atlanta, 1969-70; mgr. Allied Products Corp., Frankfort, Mich., 1970-71; planning analyst, sr. planning analyst Allied Products Corp., Chgo., 1972-74 dir. planning, 1974-76, staff v.p. planning, 1976-79, v.p. planning and bus. research, 1979-86, v.p. corp. devel., chief planning officer, 1986-93; pres. White, Williams & Daniels, 1993—. Mem. adv. bd. Ga. Inst. Tech. Mem. Winnteka Yacht Club (dir. jr. sailing), Midwest Youth Sailing Assn. (bd. dirs., treas.).

WILLIAMS, CATHLENE ANN, association executive, researcher; b. Waterloo, Iowa, Apr. 17, 1945; d. Harold Stanley and Martha Elizabeth (Loonan) Nation; m. Jan Adrian DeYoung, June 10, 1967 (div. Feb. 20, 1976); 1 child: Laura Elizabeth; m. Clyde Roydon Williams, Jan. 3, 1977. BS, Iowa State U., 1967; MA, U. N. Iowa, 1971; PhD, George Washington U., 1995. Tchr. Oak Park (Ill.) Pub. Schs., 1967-69, Cedar Falls (Iowa) Pub. Schs., 1969-75; adminstrv. asst. Sys. Rsch. Inc./Ednl. Methods, Washington, 1975-77; adminstrv. asst. to exec. dir. Nat. Assn. State Bds. Edn., Alexandria, Va., 1985-86, project specialist, 1978-80, project dir., 1980-82, dir., 1985-86; communications mgr. Nat. Soc. Fund Raising Execs., Alexandria, Va., 1987-88, dir. external affairs, 1989-91, dir. libr. and rsch. svcs., 1991-94, dir. edn. and rsch. programs, 1994—. Author: (with others) Manual on State Policies Related to Adolescent Parenthood, 1980, A Guide to Employment and Training Programs for Adolescent Parents, 1981; editor: The Journal, 1987-92, Nat. Soc. Fund Raising Execs. News, 1987-91, The State Bd. Connection, 1981-86. Vestry Ch. of the Resurrection Episcopal Ch. (register 1988, jr. warden 1989, 93, assoc. sr. warden 1990, lay ordination com. 1990, cmty. concerns com. 1993—, stewardship com.). Mem. Am. Soc. Assn. Execs., PRSA, Internat. Soc. for 3d Sector Rsch., AAUW (newsletter editor 1986-87, treas. 1986-87, v.p. mem. 1984-85, pres. Alexandria br. 1988-89), Assn. Rsch. on Nonprofit Orgns. and Voluntary Action, Phi Gamma Delta, Phi Upsilon Omicron, Omicron Delta Kappa. Office: Nat Soc Fund Raising Execs 1101 King St Ste 700 Alexandria VA 22314-2944

WILLIAMS, CHARLES D., bishop. Bishop of Alaska Ch. of God in Christ, Anchorage. Office: Ch of God in Christ 2212 Vanderbilt Cir Anchorage AK 99508-4563

WILLIAMS, CHARLES DAVID, oil and steel company executive; b. Mineola, Tex., July 16, 1935; s. Floyd L. and Audie N. (Hall) W.; m. Shirley R. Dodd, Jan. 31, 1954; children: Jan, Charles D. Jr. BS in Petroleum Engring., Tex. A&M U., 1957, MS in Petroleum Engring., 1959; MBA in Fin., So. Meth. U., 1971. Asst. to exec. v.p. Atlantic Richfield Co., N.Y.C., 1971-72; dir. planning Atlantic Richfield Co., Dallas, 1972-76; mgr. investor relations Atlantic Richfield Co., L.A., 1976-79; v.p. investor affairs Tex. Oil and Gas Corp., Dallas, 1979-86; v.p. investor relations USX Corp., Pitts., 1986—. Mem. Soc. Petroleum Engrs., N.Y. Soc. Security Analysts, Republican. Baptist. Avocations: golf, fishing. Office: USX Corp 600 Grant St Pittsburgh PA 15219-2749

WILLIAMS, C(HARLES) FRED, history professor; b. Allen, Okla., Dec. 24, 1943; s. Charley Howard and Willie Mae (Brooks) W.; m. Glenda Belcher, June 6, 1963 (dec. Oct. 1970); 1 child, Laura; m. Janet Hamm, Dec. 27, 1971; children: Brad, Libby. BE, East Cen. State U., Ada, Okla., 1965; MA, Wichita State U., 1966; PhD, U. Okla., 1970. Asst., then assoc. prof. History Univ. Ark., Little Rock, 1969-73, dept. chmn., 1973-80, assoc. dean Coll. Liberal Arts, 1980-83, assoc. vice chmn. Edn. Program, 1983-88; prof. history, dir. Ctr. Ark. Studies U. Ark., Little Rock, 1988—. Author: A History of Pharmacy in Arkansas, 1982, Arkansas: An Illustrated History, 1986; editor: A Documentary History of Arkansas, 1984, A Cartoon History of Arkansas. Bd. dirs. Old State House Assocs., Little Rock, 1981-85, Ark. Hist. Preservation Alliance, 1985-86; pres. Vol. in Pub. Schs., Little Rock, 1986—. Recipient Cert. of Merit State of Ark., 1976, Supt.'s Citation Little Rock Sch. Dists., 1984; named Humanist of Yr. Ark. Endowment for the Humanities, Little Rock, 1988. Mem. Orgn. Am. Historians, Agriculture History Soc., Western History Assn., Ark. Hist. Assn., Phi Delta Kappa (pres. 1987-88). Home: 8214 Reymere Dr Little Rock AR 72207-3942 Office: U Ark Dept Edn 2801 S University Ave Little Rock AR 72204-1000

WILLIAMS, C(HARLES) K(ENNETH), poet, literature and writing educator; b. Newark, N.J., Nov. 4, 1936; s. Paul Bernard and Dossie (Kasdin) W.; m. Sarah Dean Jones, June, 1966 (div. 1975); 1 child, Jessica Anne; m. Catherine Justine Mauger, Apr. 15, 1975; 1 child, Jed Mauger. BA, U. Pa., 1958. Vis. prof. lit. Beaver Coll., Jenkintown, Pa., 1975, Drexel U., Phila., 1976, U. Calif., Irvine, 1978, Boston U., 1979-80, Bklyn. Coll., 1982-83; Mellon vis. prof. lit. Franklin and Marshall Coll., Lancaster, Pa., 1977; prof. writing Columbia U., N.Y.C., 1981-85; prof. lit. George Mason U., Fairfax, Va., 1982—; Halloway lectr. U. Calif., Berkeley, 1986. Author: A Day for Anne Frank, 1968, Lies, 1969, I Am the Bitter Name, 1972, With Ignorance, 1977, The Lark, The Thrush, The Starling, 1983, Tar, 1983, Flesh and Blood, 1987, Poems, 1963-1983, 1988, The Bacchae of Euripides, 1990, Helen, 1991, A Dream of Mind: Poems, 1992, Selected Poems, 1994; contbr. editor Am. Poetry Rev., 1972—; translator: Women of Trachis (Sophocles), 1978. Sponsor People's Fund, Phila., 1967—. Recipient Nat. Book Critics Circle award in poetry, 1987, Morton Dauwen Zabel prize Am. Acad. of Arts and Letters, 1989, Harriet Monroe prize, 1993; fellow Guggenheim Found., 1975, Nat. Endowment for Arts, 1985, 93; Lila Wallace-Reader's Digest grantee, 1993—. Mem. PEN, Poetry Soc. Am. Avocations: piano, guitar, drawing. Home: 82 Rue d'Hauteville, 75010 Paris France

WILLIAMS, CHARLES LAVAL, JR., physician, international organization official; b. New Orleans, Jan. 19, 1916; s. Charles Laval and Lewise (McLaurine) W.; m. Ellen Clendenin Ustick, Dec. 14, 1946; children: Ellen Clendenin, Katherine McLaurine. Student, U. Va., 1933-35; M.D., Tulane U., 1940; M.P.H., U. Mich., 1945. Diplomate: Am. Bd. Preventive Medicine and Pub. Health. Intern U.S. Marine Hosp., New Orleans, 1941; with USPHS, 1941-67; assigned N.C. State Health Dept., 1941-44, USPHS States Relations div., 1944, U. Mich., 1944-45, Am. Acad. Pediatrics Nat. Study Child Health Services, 1945-47; chief planning unit, asst. chief div. commd. officers, 1947-51; with US/AID Div. Pub. Health, 1951-62; chief pub. health adviser AID Mission to Peru, 1959-62; assoc. dir. internat. relations Office Internat. Health, 1962-64; chief Office Internat. Research, NIH, Bethesda, Md., 1965-66; dep. dir., then dir. Office Internat. Health, Office Surgeon General, USPHS, Washington, 1966-67; dep. dir. Pan Am. Health Orgn., 1967-79; ret.; exec. v.p. Am. Assn. World Health, 1980-84. Fellow Am. Pub. Health Assn.; mem. U.S.-Mexico Border Pub. Health Assn., Phi Kappa Phi, Delta Omega. Home: 5600 Wisconsin Ave Apt 1009 Chevy Chase MD 20815-4411

WILLIAMS, CHARLES LINWOOD (BUCK WILLIAMS), professional basketball player; b. Rocky Mount, N.C., Mar. 8, 1960; s. Moses and Betty Williams. Student, U. Md. Basketball player New Jersey Nets, NBA, 1981-89, Portland Trail Blazers, 1989—. Mem. U.S. Olympic Team, 1980, NBA All-Rookie Team, 1982; player NBA All-Star Games, 1982, 83, 86; named NBA Rookie of Yr., 1982; named to NBA All-Defensive Team, 1990, 91. Office: Portland Trail Blazers Port of Portland Bldg 700 NE Multnomah St Ste 600 Portland OR 97232*

WILLIAMS, CHARLES MARVIN, commercial banking educator; b. Romney, W. Va., Apr. 20, 1917; s. W. Marvin and Lula H. (Taylor) W.; m. Elizabeth Huffman, Oct. 19, 1946; children: Holland H., Andrea L. AB, Washington and Lee U., 1937; MBA, Harvard U., 1939, DCS, 1951; LLD, Washington and Lee U., 1966. Credit trainee Mfrs. Trust Co., N.Y.C., 1939-41; asst. prof. finance Harvard Grad. Sch. Bus. Adminstrn., 1947-51, assoc. prof., 1951-56, prof. bus. adminstrn., 1956-60, Edmund Cogswell Converse prof. banking and finance, 1960-66, George Gund prof. comml. banking, 1966-86, prof. emeritus, 1986—; pres. Charles M. Williams Assocs.; bd. dirs. Horace Mann Educators Corp.; adv. dir. ORIX USA Corp., Keystone Group Funds. Author: Cumulative Voting for Directors, 1951, (P. Hunt) Basic Case Problems in Finance, 1949, (with P. Hunt and G. Donaldson) Basic Business Finance, 1958. Served to lt. comdr., Supply Corps USNR, 1941-47. Mem. Inst. Fin. Mgmt. (bd. dirs.), Phi Beta Kappa, Kappa Alpha. Clubs: Harvard (N.Y.C.); Weston Golf. Home: 50 Cherry Brook Rd Weston MA 02193-1306 Office: Soldiers Field Boston MA 02163

WILLIAMS, CHARLES MURRAY, computer information systems educator, consultant; b. Ft. Bliss, Tex., Dec. 26, 1931; s. Robert Parvin and Barbara (Murray) W.; m. Stanley Bright, Dec. 31, 1956; children: Margaret Allen Williams Becker, Robert Parvin, Mary Linton Williams Bondurant. BS, Va. Mil. Inst., 1953; MS, Stanford U., 1964; PhD, U. Tex., 1967. Physicist USAF, Kirtland AFB, N.Mex., 1956-58; staff mem. Sandia Labs., Albuquerque, 1958-62; programmer analyst Control Data Corp., Palo Alto, Calif., 1962-63; mathematician Panoramic Rsch., Inc., Palo Alto, 1963-64; mem. tech. staff Thomas Bede Found., Los Altos, Calif., 1964-65; rsch. scientist assoc. U. Tex., Austin, 1965-67; asst. prof. Computer Sci. Pa. State U., State College, 1967-72, Va. Poly. Inst. and State U., Blacksburg, 1972-75; assoc. prof. Computer Info. Systems Ga. State U., Atlanta, 1975-83, prof. Computer Info. Systems, 1983—; cons. Visicon Inc., State Coll., 1970-72, Broomall (Pa.) Industries Inc., 1973-79, Bausch & Lomb Inc., Rochester, N.Y. 1981, Bell South Media Techs. Inc., Atlanta, 1987-90; mem. tech. staff Bell Labs., Whippany, N.J., 1979; textbook reviewer various publs. including Harper & Row, Prentice Hall, Simon & Schuster, 1976—. Contbr. articles to profl. computer graphics and image processing publs. Bd. dirs. Ga. Striders, 1993—; presenter Walking and Running to the Fountain of Youth seminar, 23 municipalities in 4 states, 1992—. Grantee Xerox Corp., 1985, Ga. Rsch. Alliance Telemedicine Project, 1993; recipient Silver medals in 1500-meter and 3000 meter runs 60-64 age divsn. Athletic Congress (now U.S.A. Track & Field) Nat. Masters Indoor Track and Field Championships, 1992, Gold medals in 5000-meter and 10,000-meter runs, Bronze medal in 1500-meter run, 1992, Gold medals in 1500-meter and 3000-meter runs U.S.A. Track & Field Indoor Championships, 1993, Gold medals in 5000-meter and 10,000 meter runs, Bronze medal in 1500-meter run U.S. Track and Field Outdoor Championships, 1993, Bronze medal in 5000-meter run and 10,000-meter runs U.S.A. Track & Field Outdoor Championships, 1994, Gold medal in 3000-meter run U.S.A. Track & Field Indoor Championships, 1994; ranked 3d nationally in road racing Running Times, 1992; ranked 5th, (2nd honorable mention) 1993. Mem. Nat. Computer Graphics Assn. (hon., Ga. bd. dirs. 1979-85, bd. dirs. Ga. chpt. 1985-89, sec. 1988-89), Computer Graphics Pioneers, Upsilon Pi Epsilon, Omicron Delta Kappa. Republican. Episcopalian. Avocation: competitive road running (recipient numerous gold and silver medals). Home: 316 Argonne Dr NW Atlanta GA 30305-2814 Office: Ga State U University Pla Atlanta GA 30303

WILLIAMS, CHARLES WESLEY, technical executive, researcher; b. Palestine, Ark.; s. Fredrick Charles and Fannie Rochet (Southall) W.; m. Nancy Sue Rhea, Sept. 5, 1959; children: Brent L., Brian E. B.S.E.E., U. Tenn.-Knoxville, 1959, M.S., 1963. Registered profl. engr., Ohio. Devel. engr. Mead Research Lab., Chillicothe, Ohio, 1959-60, Oak Ridge Nat. Lab., 1960-63; tech. mgr. EG & G Ortec, Oak Ridge, 1963-76, tech. dir. phys. and life sci., 1976-81; mgr. Assay Inst. EG & Ortec, Oak Ridge, 1981-85; phys. Autograffix Inc., Knoxville, Tenn., 1985—. Contbr. articles to tech. jours., chpt. to book. Fellow IEEE (v.p. Nuclear and Plasma Sci. Soc. 1979); mem. Tau Beta Pi, Eta Kappa Nu. Baptist.

WILLIAMS, CHESTER ARTHUR, JR., insurance educator; b. Blakely, Pa., Mar. 6, 1924; s. C. Arthur and Alice (Robinson) W.; m. Roberta Riegel, Sept. 1, 1951; children—Robert Arthur, Bruce Allan. A.B., Columbia U., 1947; A.M., 1949, Ph.D., 1952. Lectr. ins. U. Buffalo, N.Y., 1950-52; asst. prof. U. Minn., 1952-55, asso. prof., 1955-58, Ford Found. faculty fellow, 1957-58, prof., 1958-80, acting dean, 1971-72, dean, 1971-72, 1972-78, Minn. Ins. Industry chair prof., 1980-92, prof. emeritus, 1992—; vis. prof. U. Pa., 1960-61, Keio U., Tokyo, 1984. Author: Price Discrimination in Property and Liability Insurance, 1959, Economic and Social Security, 1957, Risk Management and Insurance, 1964, Insurance Arrangements under Workmen's Compensation, 1969, Insurance Principles and Practices: Property and Liability, 1976, Principles of Risk Management and Insurance, 1978, Insurance and Risk Management, 1980, Ocean Marine Insurance, 1988, An International Comparison of Workers' Compensation, 1991; editor Jour. of Risk and Ins., 1981-86. Contbr. articles to profl. jours. Bd. dirs. State Capitol Credit Union, 1965-68, pres., 1967-68; bd. dirs. Consumers Union, 1972-75; bd. dirs. Minn. State Coun. on Econ. Edn., 1973-78, chmn., 1975-77; bd. dirs. St. Paul Cos., Inc., 1975-90. Served to 1st lt. USAF, 1943-46. Recipient Gold medal Internat Ins. Soc., 1993, Elizur Wright award Am. Risk and Ins. Assocs., 1993; laureate Ins. Hall of Fame. Mem. Am. Risk Ins. Assn. (dir. 1960-65, 81-86, pres. 1965), Am. Acad. Actuaries, Decision Sci. Inst., Am. Statis. Assn., Am. Finance Assn., AAUP, Phi Beta Kappa, Beta Gamma Sigma. Episcopalian. Home: 1984 Shryer Ave W Saint Paul MN 55113-5415

WILLIAMS, CHRISTOPHER PEELE, architect; b. Denver, Apr. 21, 1947; s. Arnold H. and Margaret A. (Keith) W.; m. Ann Hulley, Oct. 26, 1975; 1 child, Mae H. BArch, Carnegie Mellon U., 1972. Registered architect, N.H., Maine, Mass., Vt. Architect in tng. Architect's Workshop, Campton, N.H., 1973-75; architect WM Design Group, Center Harbor, N.H., 1975-84; prin. arch. Christopher P. Williams Architects, Meredith, N.H., 1984—. Bd. dirs. Lakes Region Planning Commn., Meredith, 1980-88, Percent for Arts Program, Concord, 1979-84; bd. dirs. Ctr. Harbor Planning Bd., 1976-83; bd. dirs. vice chmn. Ctr. Harbor Bd. Adjustment, 1983—; bd. dirs., chair Waukewan Shore Owners Assn., Meredith 1989—; chmn. bd. dirs. Inherit N.H., Cooncord, 1985—. Recipient Builder's Gold award N.H. Home Builder's Assn., 1991, 93, 94, Citation Urban Design award progressive Architecture, 1980. Mem. AIA (N.H. chpt., v.p. 1984—), bd. dirs. 1990—, Excellence in Architecture award 1990, 94), New Eng. Solar Energy Assn., Nat. Trust for Hist. Preservation, N.H. Coun. Sch. Architects. Avocations: hiking, music, reading, travel. Office: PO Box 656 Meredith NH 03253-0656

WILLIAMS, CLYDE E., JR., lawyer; b. Niagara Falls, N.Y., Dec. 17, 1919; s. Clyde E. and Martha (Barlow) W.; m. Ruth Van Aken, Oct. 16, 1948; children: Clyde E. III (dec.), Mark Van Aken, Sara. AB, Denison U., Granville, Ohio, 1942; LLB, Harvard U., 1945. Bar Ohio 1945. Practice corp. and real estate law, 1945—; v.p. Spieth, Bell, McCurdy & newell Co., L.P.A., Cleve., 1964—; also bd. dirs. Spieth, Bell, McCurdy & Newell Co.; gen. counsel Growth Cos., Inc., Phila., 1950-55; pres., dir. Williams Cleve.; gen. counsel Growth Cos., Inc., Phila., 1950-55; pres., dir. Williams Investment Co., Cleve., 1954—; sec., dir. Williams Internat. Corp., Walled Lake, Mich., 1954—; gr. dir. Gen. Counsel Techno-fund, Inc., Columbus, Ohio, 1960-67; dir. rAdio Seaway, Inc. (Sta. WCLV-FM), 1962—; mem. faculty Fenn Coll. and Cleve. Coll. divsn. Western Res. U., 1945-50. Trustee, mem. exec. com., v.p. Cleve. Soc. for Blind, 1979—, pres., 1985-87, mem. adv. council, 1987—. Mem. ABA, Ohio Bar Assn., Cleve. Bar Assn., Union Club, Skating Club. Office: Spieth Bell McCurdy & Newell Co 2000 Huntington Bldg Cleveland OH 44115

WILLIAMS, DARRYL MARLOWE, medical educator; b. Denver, Apr. 3, 1938; s. Archie Malvin and Dorothy Merle (Grapes) W.; m. Susan Arlene Moore, June 24, 1966; children: Carol Ruth, Peter Todd, Sarah Elizabeth. Student, U. Colo., 1956-58; BS, Colo. State U., 1993; MD, MS in Anatomy, Baylor U., 1964. Diplomate Am. Bd. Internal Medicine, Am. Bd. Hematology. Intern and resident Baylor Affiliated Hosps., Houston, 1964-66, 67-68; resident U. Utah, Salt Lake City, 1966-67, fellow in hematology, 1968-73, asst. prof., 1973-77; assoc. prof. La State U., Shreveport, 1977-81, prof., 1981-90, chief hematology sect., 1977-85, asst. dean/rsch., 1981-85, dean Sch. Medicine, 1985-90; prof. medicine, dean Sch. Medicine Tex. Tech U. Health Scis. Ctr., Lubbock, 1990—; mem. hemophilia adv. com. La. Legislature, Baton Rouge, 1977-83; vice chair La. Lung and Cancer Bd., New Orleans, 1984-90; pres. N.W. La. AIDS Task Force, Shreveport, 1987. Mem. Am. Heart Assn. Lubbock chpt., Shreveport Biracial Commn., 1988, Lubbock Indigent Health Care Coalition Task Force, 1991-92, Health Professions Edn. Adv. Com., Lubbock Friends of Pub. Radio; vice chair health profls. edn. advisory com. Tex. Coord. Bd. Higher Edn., 1992—. Recipient award Nat. Ski Patrol System, Salt Lake City, 1975. Fellow ACP, Am. Coll. Nutrition; mem. AMA, Am. Soc. Hematology, Am. Inst. Nutrition, Am. Soc. Clin. Nutrition, Tex. Med. Assn. (physicians oncology edn. com.), Royal Soc. Medicine, Alpha Omega Alpha. Office: Health Scis Ctr Tex Tech U Lubbock TX 79409

WILLIAMS, DAVE HARRELL, investment executive; b. Beaumont, Tex., Oct. 5, 1932; s. George Davis and Mary (Hardin) W.; m. Reba White, Mar. 15, 1975. B.S. in Chem. Engring. U. Tex., 1956; M.B.A. (Baker scholar, Teagle fellow), Harvard U., 1961. Chartered fin. analyst. Chem. engr. Exxon Corp., Baton Rouge, 1959; security analyst deVegh & Co., N.Y.C., 1961-64; dir. research Waddell & Reed, Kansas City, Mo., 1964-67; exec. v.p. Mitchell Hutchins, Inc., N.Y.C., 1967-77; chmn. bd. Alliance Capital Mgmt. Corp., N.Y.C., 1977—; bd. dirs. The Equitable Cos., Inc. Contbr.: articles to Fin. Analysts Jour. Trustee Am. Fedn. of Art, Fgn. Policy Assn., Metropolitan Mus. of Art. Served with USNR, 1956-59. Mem. Fin. Analysts Fedn. (past officer, dir.), N.Y. Soc. Security Analysts (past pres.), Bond Club N.Y., Econ. Club N.Y., Knickerbocker Club, Down Town Assn., Century Assn., Grolier Club. Presbyterian. Office: Alliance Capital Mgmt Corp 1345 Ave Of The Americas New York NY 10105-0099

WILLIAMS, DAVID ARTHUR, marketing professional; b. Lima, Ohio, Jan. 22, 1953; s. Arthur Henry and Jane Elenor (Davisson) W. AA Bus., Coll. DuPage, 1973; BA Mktg., Columbia Coll., Chgo., 1976. Dir. mktg. Breckenridge (Colo.) Ski Corp., 1976-81; pres. Williams & Assocs., Denver, 1981-84; dir. real estate advt. Kohler (Wis.) Co., 1984-89; v.p. mktg. and advt. Abbey Group, Ltd., Oakbrook Terrace, Ill., 1989—. Office: Abbey Group Ltd 1901 S Meyers Rd Ste 520 Villa Park IL 60181

WILLIAMS, DAVID BENTON, advertising agency executive; b. Chgo., May 18, 1920; s. Howard D. and Margaret (Clark) W.; m. Edith Chapin Huntington, Aug. 24, 1943; children—David Huntington, Deborah Benton, Howard Chapin. A.B. magna cum laude, Harvard, 1942. Service detail, media, prodn. Erwin Wasey, Chgo., 1946-47; copy contact Erwin Wasey, Los Angeles, 1947-48, account exec., v.p., 1948-49; v.p. mgmt. Erwin Wasey, N.Y.C., 1949-54; exec. v.p. gen. mgr. Erwin Wasey, 1954-56, pres., 1956; pres. Erwin Wasey, Ruthrauff & Ryan (merger of Erwin Wasey & Co. and Ruthrauff & Ryan), N.Y.C., 1957-65; v.p., dir. Interpub. Group of Cos., Inc., 1965-68, now dir.; exec. v.p. Interpub. S.A., 1966-68; sr. v.p. Wilson Haight & Welch (advt.), Hartford, Boston, Greenwich, N.Y.C., Phila., Tampa and Houston, 1969-72; exec. v.p., dir. Wilson Haight & Welch (advt.), 1972-78, pres., dir. 1974-78; dir. Howard Swink Advt. (now Fahlgren & Swink), 1978-84; pres., dir. 1035 Fifth Ave Corp., 1973—. Served with CIC, U.S. Army. Mem. Apartment Owners Assn. (bd. dirs.), Phi Beta Kappa. Clubs: University, Union (N.Y.C.); Preston Mountain (Kent, Conn.); American (London). Home: 1035 Fifth Ave New York NY 10028-0135 *Always hire people as able, or better yet, more able than yourself. Trust them. Support them. Their success will be your own. Take intelligent risks.*

Always bet on people - as the right ones are the magic that makes business work.

WILLIAMS, DAVID BERNARD, educator; b. Leeds, Yorkshire, Eng., July 25, 1949; came to U.S. 1976, naturalized 1985; s. Joseph Edward and Catherine (Tull) W.; m. Margaretha Johanna Louwers, June 12, 1976; children—Matthew John, Bryn Joseph, Stephen David. B.A., Cambridge U., Eng., 1970, M.A., 1973, Ph.D., 1974. Chartered engr., U.K. Postdoctoral research fellow Cambridge U., Eng., 1974-76; asst. prof. Lehigh U., Bethlehem, Pa., 1976-79, assoc. prof., 1979-82, prof. materials sci. engring., 1982—; steering com. Argonne Nat. Labs Electron Microscope Group, Ill., 1984-86. Assoc. editor Jour. Microscopy, Oxford, Eng., 1984-92, editor, 1990-95, Jour. Electron Microscopy Technique, N.Y.C., 1983-91. Author: Practical Analytical Electron Microscopy in Materials Science, 1984. Recipient Burton medal Electron Microscopy Soc. Am., 1984; Robinson award Lehigh U., 1979, William J. Priestly Disting. professorship, 1984. Fellow Inst. Metals, Royal Microscopical Soc., Am. Soc. Metals; mem. Metall. Soc. of AIME, Electron Microscopy Soc. Am., Microbeam Analysis Soc. (dir., pres. 1991-92, pres. internat. union 1994—). Roman Catholic. Avocations: rugby; running; piano; reading. Office: Lehigh U Dept Material Sci and Engring Whitaker Lab 5 E Packe Ave E Bethlehem PA 18015

WILLIAMS, DAVID FULTON, industrial distribution company executive; b. Columbus, Ohio, Oct. 28, 1926; s. William Wallace and Marion Fulton W.; m. Velma Sater, June 30, 1951; children—William S., Patricia Williams French, Elizabeth. BS, Ohio State U., 1950. Chmn., W. W. Williams Co., Columbus, 1963—, also dir.; bd. dirs. Bank One of Columbus, 1978—. Bd. dirs. Riverside Meth. Hosp., Columbus. Served with USAAF, 1944-45. Methodist. Home: 3750 Hillview Dr Columbus OH 43220-4734 Office: W W Williams Co 835 Goodale Blvd Columbus OH 43212-3824

WILLIAMS, DAVID HOWARD, lawyer; b. Las Vegas, Nev., Sept. 21, 1945; s. Howard Cummins and Alice Emma (Taufenbach) W.; m. Kathleen Graham, Sept. 2, 1967; children: David Howard Jr., Jonathan Graham. BA in History cum laude, Denison U., 1967; MA in Polit. Sci., Columbia U., 1969; JD cum laude, Ohio State U., 1973. Bar: Ohio 1973, Ga. 1980. Assoc. Vorys, Sater, Seymour & Pease, Columbus, Ohio, 1973-79; from assoc. to ptnr. Powell, Goldstein, Frazer & Murphy, Atlanta; ptnr. Hunton & Williams, Atlanta; adj. prof. U. Ga. Sch. Law, 1994—; lectr. workshop ann. conv. Ohio League of Savs. Assns., others. Former mem. profl. adv. bd. Ohio Assn. for Children with Learning Disabilities; bd. dirs. Northside Youth Orgn., Atlanta, 1985—; active Peachtree Presbyn. Ch., Atlanta, 1982—. Served to 1st lt. Ohio NG, 1969-75. Mem. ABA (state compensation com. corp. sect., taxation and employee benefits sects.), Ga. Bar Assn. (taxation sect.), Atlanta Bar Assn., So. Pension Conf., Midwest Pension Conf. (cen. Ohio chpt. organizer, former vice chmn.). Republican. Office: Hunton & Williams NationsBank Plz 600 Peachtree St NE Atlanta GA 30326-2216

WILLIAMS, DAVID PERRY, manufacturing company executive; b. Detroit, Nov. 16, 1934; s. M.S. Perry and Virginia (Hayes) W.; m. Jill Schneider, July 27, 1972; children: Tracy, Perry, David, William, Nell. B.A., Mich. State U., 1956, M.B.A., 1964. V.p. sales Automotive div. Kelsey Hayes Co., Romulus, Mich., 1958-71; v.p., mgr. automotive product line ITT, N.Y.C., 1971-76; v.p., dir. Budd Co, Troy, Mich., 1976-79; sr. v.p. ops., dir., 1979-80, sr. v.p., chief ops. officer, 1980-86, pres., chief operating officer, dir., 1986—; dir. Standard Fed. Bank, Troy, Mich., 1990—, SPX Corp., Muskegon, Mich., 1992—, Budd Canada, Inc., Kitchener, Ont., 1981—, Thyssen Prodn. Systems, 1994. Served to 1st lt. USAF, 1956-58. Mem. Soc. Automotive Engrs., Engring. Soc. Detroit, Soc. Jfg. Engrs., Bloomfield Hills Country Club, Country of Detroit, Yondotega, PGA Nat. Club (Fla.), Tournament Players Club (Mich.), Question Club, Royal and Ancient Golf Club of St. Andrews (Scotland), Beta Gamma Sigma. Republican. Episcopalian. Home: 333 Lincoln Rd Grosse Pointe MI 48230-1604 Office: Budd Co PO Box 2601 3155 Big Beaver Rd Troy MI 48084

WILLIAMS, DAVID ROGERSON, JR., engineer, business executive; b. Tulsa, Oct. 20, 1921; s. David Rogerson and Martha Reynolds (Hill) W.; m. Pauline Bolton, May 28, 1944 (dec. Feb. 4, 1988); children: Pauline B. Williams Lampshire, David Rogerson III, Rachel K. Williams Zebrowski; m. Anne W. Kerr, Jan. 5, 1990. B.S., Yale U., 1943. Constrn. foreman, supt. Williams Bros. Corp., 1939-49; co-founder, v.p. Williams Bros. Co., 1949-56, exec. v.p., 1956-66, chmn. exec. com., 1966-70; chmn. bd. Resource Scis. Corp., Tulsa, 1970-83, Williams Techs. Inc., Carbon Resources, Inc.; chmn. Integrated Carbons Corp., Tulsa; co-founder, dir. Patagonia Corp., Tucson; dir. The Williams Cos., Tulsa. Trustee Hudson Inst., Indpls. Served to capt. USAAF, World War II. Fellow ASCE; mem. Am. Petroleum Inst., Alta. Assn. Profl. Engrs. Am. Gas Assn., Yale Engring. Assn., Ind. Natural Gas Assn., Royal Soc. Arts, Duke of Edinburgh's World Fellowship, Chagrin Valley Hunt Club (Gates Mill, Ohio), Ranchmen's Club (Calgary), Springdale Hall (Camden, S.C.), Racquet and Tennis Club, Yale Club, Golf Club of Okla. (Tulsa), Rolling Rock Club (Ligonier, Pa.), So. Hills (Tulsa). Office: 320 S Boston Ave Ste 831 Tulsa OK 74103-3728

WILLIAMS, DAVID RUSSELL, music educator; b. Indpls., Oct. 21, 1932; s. H. Russell and Mary Dean (Whitmer) W.; m. Elsa Bühlmann, Jan. 30, 1960. AB, Columbia U., 1954, MA, 1956; PhD, U. Rochester, 1965. Dir. music Windham Coll., Putney, Vt., 1959-62; opera coach Eastman Sch. Music, Rochester, N.Y., 1962-65, assoc. prof. theory, adminstr. of MusM program, 1965-80; prof., chmn. dept. music Memphis State U., 1980-87, prof. music, 1980—; bd. dirs. Memphis Youth Symphony, Memphis Symphony, 1984-90; mem. exec. bd. Opera Memphis, 1980-87, Salute to Memphis Music, 1980-87. Author: Bibliography of the History of Music Theory, 1971, Conversations with Howard Hanson, 1988, Music Theory from Zarlino to Schenker: A Bibliography and Guide, 1990; producer: Highwater Records album 8201 featuring John Stover, classical guitar, 1983; composer Suite for Oboe, Clarinet and Piano, 1968, Five States of Mind, 1970. Bd. dirs., sec. Rochester Philharm. Orch., 1976-78; v.p., bd. dirs. Rochester Chamber Orch., 1974-78; pres., bd. dirs. Opera Theatre of Rochester, 1973-74; bd. dirs., chmn. Am. Ritual Theatre, 1979-80; bd. sponsors Met. Opera Mid. South Region, Memphis, 1983—. Served as cpl. U.S. Army, 1957-59. Recipient Eastman Sch. Music Pub. award, 1970. Mem. NARAS (treas. Memphis chpt. 1986-87), Coll. Music Soc. (sec. 1973-83), Music Tchrs. Nat. Assn. (state chmn. 1971-74), Nat. Assn. Schs. of Music (chmn. region 8 1989-92), Tenn. Assn. Music Execs. in Colls. and Univs. (pres. 1986-87), Southeastern Composers League (composer mem.), Pi Kappa Lambda (pres. Memphis State chpt. 1988-90), Phi Beta Kappa, Phi Mu Alpha (hon.), Sigma Alpha Iota (hon.). Clubs: Rochester, Univ., Summit. Avocations: stock market study, language study, word puzzles. Home: 273 W Central Park St Apt 1 Memphis TN 38111-4570 Office: U Memphis Dept Music Memphis TN 38152 *Having had a family background that was superior in so many ways has helped me to sharpen my purpose in life, in that it has made me realize to what an extent affirmative action is necessary in order to provide a milieu in which truly equal opportunity can exist. Many doors of opportunity have been held open for me; those of disadvantaged access are often not aware that these doors exist. The more individuals I can lead to these portals, the more I will have achieved in my lifetime.*

WILLIAMS, DAVID SAMUEL, insurance company executive; b. Purcell, Okla., Oct. 16, 1926; s. David Skelton and Mattie Carolyn (Kimberlin) W.; m. Gloria Jean Trudgeon, Jan. 14, 1951; children: Mellanie K., David R., Gary B., Kimberly R. BA, U. Okla., 1950; LLB, LaSalle U., 1968. With U.S. Fidelity & Guaranty Cos., various locations, 1952-74; asst. mgr. U.S. Fidelity & Guaranty Cos., Albuquerque, 1963-66; mgr. U.S. Fidelity & Guaranty Cos., San Jose, Calif., 1966-74; v.p. Eldorado Ins. Co., Palo Alto, Calif., 1974-77, exec. v.p., chief operating officer, 1977-78; v.p. Eldorado Mgmt. Co., Palo Alto, Calif., 1973-78, chief operating officer, exec. v.p., 1978; mng. dir. Eldorado Service Corp., 1974-76, exec. v.p., 1976-78; ptnr. Williams Ranch Co., 1977—; owner David S. Williams and Assocs. L.C., 1988—; chmn. bd., pres. Homeland Gen. Corp., Homeland Ins. Co. and Homeland Indsl. Corp., San Jose, Calif., 1978-87; pres. Homeland Mgmt. Corp. (Cayman) Ltd., 1980-87, Homeland Internat. (Bermuda) Ltd., 1982-87; chmn. bd. On Line Ins. Systems, Inc., 1982-92; underwriting mem. Lloyds of London, 1979—; adv. bd. Pacific Valley Bank, 1975-87; tchr. Albuquerque U., 1957-58, N.Mex. U., 1958-59, bd. dirs. Fin. Guardian Group, Inc., Kansas City, Mo., Kestrel Aircraft Co. Mem. indsl. panel

Stanford Research Inst., 1968; mgmt. cons. County Santa Clara Edn. Dept., 1968-73; mem. Calif. adv. com. Ins. Services Office; bd. dirs. ins. council City of Hope, Los Angeles; committeeman pioneer council Boy Scouts Am., 1968; pres. Immanuel Luth. Ch., Saratoga, Calif., 1989-90. Served to lt. col. AC U.S. Army, 1944-46, 50-52. Recipient Outstanding Fieldman's award for N.Mex., N.Mex. Insurors Assn., 1959. Mem. Internat. Bar Assn., Cen. Coast Fieldmen's Assn., Calif. Ins. Cos. (dir.), Sigma Alpha Epsilon. Lutheran. Clubs: San Jose Athletic, Rotary (pres. 1974, Paul Harris fellow 1976); Univ. San Jose, British-Am., Center., San Francisco Comml. Home: 4220 Ridgeline Cir Norman OK 73072-1731

WILLIAMS, DAVID VANDERGRIFT, organizational psychologist; b. Balt., Feb. 5, 1943; s. Laurence Leighton and Mary Duke (Warfield) W.; m. Diane M. Gayeski, Aug. 23, 1980; 1 child, Evan David Williams. BA, Gettysburg (Pa.) Coll., 1965; MA, Temple U., 1967; PhD, U. Pa., 1971. Asst. prof. psychology Ithaca (N.Y.) Coll., 1970-75, assoc. prof. psychology, 1975—; ptnr. OmniCom Assocs., Ithaca, 1979—; co-dir. Inst. Behavior-Econs., Ithaca, 1993—; cons. and speaker in field. Co-author: Interactive Media, 1985, (multimedia comms.) interactive multimedia software, 1979—; contbr. to books and articles to profl. jours. Bd. dirs. Ctr. for Religion, Ethics and Social Policy, Cornell U., 1975-77, Eco-Justice Task Force, Ithaca, 1975-78; trustee Montessori Sch., Ithaca, 1993—; Alternatives Fed. Credit Union, Ithaca, 1994—. Rsch. fellow U.S. Office of Edn., 1967-70; recipient various grants. Mem. APA, Nat. Soc. for Performance and Instrn., Am. Montessori Soc., Welsh Nat. Gymanfa Ganu Assn., Ithaca Yacht Club, Tau Kappa Epsilon. Avocations: singing, sailing, sign language, geneology, travel. Office: OmniCom Assocs 407 Coddington Rd Ithaca NY 14850

WILLIAMS, DAVID WELFORD, federal judge; b. Atlanta, Mar. 20, 1910; s. William W. and Maude (Lee) W.; m. Ouida Maie White, June 11, 1939; children: David Welford, Vaughn Charles. A.A., Los Angeles Jr. Coll., 1932; A.B., UCLA, 1934; LL.B., U. So. Calif., 1937. Bar: Calif. 1937. Practiced in Los Angeles, 1937-55; judge Mcpl. Ct., Los Angeles, 1956-62, Superior Ct., Los Angeles, 1962-69, U.S. Dist. Ct. (cen. dist.) Calif., Los Angeles, 1969—; now sr. judge U.S. Dist. Ct. (cen. dist.) Calif.; judge Los Angeles County Grand Jury, 1965. Recipient Russwurm award Nat. Assn. Newspapers, 1958; Profl. Achievement award UCLA Alumni Assn., 1966. Mem. ABA, Los Angeles Bar Assn., Am. Judicature Soc. Office: US Dist Ct 255 E Temple St Rm 7100 Los Angeles CA 90012-3334

WILLIAMS, DELWYN CHARLES, telephone company executive; b. Idaho Falls, Idaho, Apr. 27, 1936; s. Charles H. and Vonda (Wood) W.; m. Marlene Grace Nordland, Feb. 29, 1964; children—Stephen, Kirstin, Nicole. B.S. in Bus., U. Idaho, 1959. C.P.A. Calif. Accountant Peat, Marwick, Mitchell & Co. (C.P.A.s), San Francisco, 1960-65; treas. Dohrmann Instruments Co., Mountain View, Calif., 1965-68; with Continental Telephone Co. of Calif., Bakersfield, 1968-84; controller Continental Telephone Co. of Calif., 1969-70, v.p., treas., 1970-77, v.p., gen. mgr., 1977-79, pres., 1977-84, also dir.; pres. J.H. Evans, Inc., and subs., 1984-95; CEO J.H. Evans, Inc., and sbus., 1995—. Mem. Am. Inst. C.P.A.s, Calif. Soc. C.P.A.s. Home: 10052 Oak Branch Cir Carmel CA 93923 Office: 4918 Taylor Ct Turlock CA 95380-9579

WILLIAMS, DONALD CLYDE, lawyer; b. Oxnard, Calif., Oct. 12, 1939; s. Leslie Allen and Elizabeth Esther (Orton) W.; m. Miriam Arline, Oct. 5, 1966; children—Erin K., Nikki Dawn. B.A. in Gen. Bus, Fresno State Coll. 1963; J.D., Willamette U., 1967. Bar: Oreg. 1967. Practice in Grants Pass, 1967-70; ptnr. Myrick, Seagraves, Williams & Nealy, 1968-70, Carlsmith, Ball, Wichman, Murray & Ichiki, 1977—; asst. atty. gen. Am. Samoa, 1970-71, atty. gen., 1971-75; assoc. justice High Ct. Trust Ter. of Pacific Islands, 1975-77. Served with USCGR, 1958-59. Mem. ABA, Calif. Bar Assn., Oreg. Bar Assn., Am. Samoa Bar Assn., Guam Bar Assn., Hawaii Bar Assn., Commonwealth No. Mariana Islands Bar Assn., Fed. States of Micronesia Bar Assn., Guam C. of C., Young Lawyers of C. of C. Office: Carlsmith Ball Wichman & Ichiki 301 E Ocean Blvd Ste 700 Long Beach CA 90802-4828

WILLIAMS, DONALD HERBERT, psychiatric education administrator; b. Chgo., Oct. 29, 1936; s. Herbert George and Theresa Elizabeth (Pratt) W.; m. Beverly Joann Wagner, Oct. 11, 1968 (div. 1981); 1 child, David; m. Sharon Rebecca Hobbs, June 18, 1983; children: Jonathan, Rebecca. BA cum laude, U. Ill., Urbana, 1957; MD, U. Ill., Chgo., 1962. Intern U. Ill. Research and Ednl. Hosps., Chgo., 1962-63, resident in anesthesiology, 1963-64, resident in psychiatry, 1964-67; instr., then asst. prof. psychiatry U. Chgo., Chgo., 1967-71; asst. prof. psychiatry Yale U., New Haven, Conn., 1971-77, assoc. prof., 1977-84; prof. Mich. State U., East Lansing, 1984—, chmn. dept. psychiatry, 1984-89; chief mental health sect. Woodlawn Mental Health Ctr., Chgo., 1967-70; chief inpatient service Hill-West Haven div. Conn. Mental Health Ctr., New Haven, 1971-73, head med. evaluation com., 1973-78, chief community support services, 1973-79, asst. dir. out-patient div., 1979-84; staff, liaison psychiat. services West Haven VA Hosp. 1971-80; head liason team Conn. Valley Hosp., 1973-79; med. dir. Eaton, Clinton and Ingham Community Mental Health Ctr., Lansing, 1984-87; cons. psychiatry edm br., faculty NIMH, Rockville, Md., 1971-81; mem. task panel Pres.' Commn. on Mental Health, Washington, 1978; speaker in field. Referee Archives Gen. Psychiatry, Am. Jour. Psychiatry, Soc. Psychiatry, Hosp. and Community Psychiatry; contbr. articles to profl. jours. Served to capt. M.C. U.S Army, 1963-68. Recipient Ill. Psychiat. Soc. award, 1968. Fellow Am Psychiat. Assn.; mem. Black Psychiatrists Am. (treas. 1978-80), Am. Orthopsychiat. Assn., Nat. Med. Assn., AMA, Omega Beta Pi. Democrat. Episcopalian. Office: Mich State U Dept Psychiatry East Fee Hall East Lansing MI 48824

WILLIAMS, DONALD JOHN, research physicist; b. Fitchburg, Mass., Dec. 25, 1933; s. Toivo John and Ina (Kokkinen) W.; m. Priscilla Mary Gagnon, July 4, 1953; children: Steven John, Craig Mitchell, Eino Stenroos. B.S., Yale U., 1955, M.S., 1958, Ph.D., 1962. Sr. staff physicist Applied Physics Lab., Johns Hopkins U., 1961-65; head particle physics br. Goddard Space Flight Center, NASA, 1965-70; dir. Space Environ. Lab., NOAA, Boulder, Colo., 1970-82; prin. investigator Energetic Particles expt. NASA Galileo Mission, 1977—; prin. staff physicist Johns Hopkins U. Applied Physics Lab., 1982-89; dir. Milton S. Eisenhower Rsch. Ctr., 1990—; mem. nat. and internat. sci. planning coms.; chmn. NAS com. on solar-terrestrial rsch., 1989-93; mem. sci. adv. bd. USAF, 1993—. Author: (with L.R. Lyons) Quantitative Aspects of Magnetospheric Physics, 1983; assoc. editor: Jour. Geophys. Research, 1967-69, Revs. of Geophysics and Space Research, 1984-86; editor: (with G.D. Mead) Physics of the Magnetosphere, 1969, Physics of Solar-Planetary Environments, 1976; mem. editorial bd.: Space Sci. Revs., 1975-85; contbr. articles to profl. jours. Mem. USAF Sci. Adv. Bd., 1994—. Lt. USAF, 1955-57. Recipient Sci. Research award, 1974; Disting. Authorship award, 1976, 85. Fellow Am. Geophys. Soc.; mem. Am. Phys. Soc., Internat. Assn. Geomagnetism and Aeronomy (pres. 1991—), Sigma Xi. Home: 14870 Triadelphia Rd Glenelg MD 21737-9408

WILLIAMS, DONALD MAXEY, dancer, singer, actor; b. Chgo., June 23, 1959; s. Arlandus Maxey and Florida (Jelks) W. Student, pub. schs., Chgo. Prin. dancer Dancer Theatre of Harlem, N.Y.C., 1977—. Dancer in movie Cotton Club, 1983-84. Mem. Am. Guild Mus. Artists, Screen Actors Guild. Baptist. Club: The Sevens (co-founder). Avocations: basketball; bowling; table tennis. Office: Dance Theatre of Harlem 466 West 152nd St New York NY 10031*

WILLIAMS, DOUGLAS H., lawyer; b. South Bend, Ind., Mar. 2, 1948. BA with high distinction, U. Mich., 1970; MBA, U. Chgo., 1977, JD, 1977. Bar: Ill. 1977. Ptnr. Sidley & Austin, Chgo. Office: Sidley & Austin 1 First National Plz Chicago IL 60603-0001

WILLIAMS, DOYLE Z., university dean, educator; b. Shreveport, La., Dec. 18, 1939; s. Nuell O. and Lurline (Isbell) W.; m. Maynette Derr, Aug. 20, 1967; children: Zane Derr, Elizabeth Marie. B.S., Northwestern State U., 1960; M.S. in Acccy., La. State U., 1962, Ph.D., 1965. CPA, Tex. Mgr. spl. edn. projects AICPA, N.Y.C., 1967-69; assoc. prof. Tex. Tech. U., Lubbock, 1969-71, prof. accrg., 1972-73, prof. area accrg., coord., 1973-78; prof. accrg. U. So. Calif., L.A., 1979, dean Sch. Accrg., 1979-87, interim dean Sch. Bus., 1986-88; dean U. Ark. Coll. Bus. Adminstrn., Fayetteville, 1993—; vis. prof. U. Hawaii, Honolulu, 1971-72. Author over 40 jour. articles and books. Chmn. Accrg. Edn. Change Commn., 1989-93. Named Mem. of Yr.

N.Y. chpt. Nat. Assn. Accts., 1967, Outstanding Acctg. Educator Beta Alpha Psi, 1982; recipient Disting. Faculty award Calif. CPA Found., 1983, Outstanding Acctg. Educator award AICPA, 1990, Nat. Leadership award Acad. Bus. Adminstrs., 1995. Mem. AICPA (coun. 1983-91, v.p. 1987-88, bd. dirs. 1987-91), Am. Acctg. Assn. (dir. edn. 1973-75, pres. 1984-85), Fedn. Schs. Accountancy (pres. 1982, Faculty Merit award 1993), Adminstrs. Acctg. Programs (pres. 1977-78). Home: 2447 Boston Mountain Vw Fayetteville AR 72701-2802 Office: Coll Bus Adminstrn U Ark Fayetteville AR 72701

WILLIAMS, DREW DAVIS, surgeon; b. San Augustine, Tex., Jan. 18, 1935; s. Floyd Everett and Villamae (Morehead) W.; m. Marilyn Raus, June 27, 1958; children: Leslie, Cynthia, Matthew, Jennifer, Amelia. BS, Tex. A&M Coll., 1957; MD, U. Tex., 1960; grad., naval flight surgeon, U.S. Naval Sch. Aviation Medicine, Jan.-June, 1963. Diplomate Am. Bd. Surgery, Am. Bd. Quality Assurance and Utilization Rev. Physicians. Intern USPHS Hosp., Seattle, 1960-61; resident in gen. surgery U. Tex. Med. Br., Galveston, 1961-62, 64-68; resident pulmonary svc. M.D. Anderson Hosp., Houston, 3 months, 1968; pvt. practice gen. surgery Baytown, Tex., 1968—; active staff mem. San Jacinto (Tex.) Meth. Hosp., 1968—, chief surgery, 1972, 73, pres. med. staff, 1976; mem. courtesy staff Bay Coast Hosp., Baytown, 1968—; cons. staff Baytown Med. Ctr. Hosp., 1972—; 1st chmn. surgery dept. in devel. family practice residency program affiliated with Tex. Med. Sch., Houston, 1977; mem. Tex. State Bd. Med. Examiners, 1983-89, sec.-treas., 1984-88, pres., 1988-89. Author articles in field. Flight surgeon USN, 1962-64; lt. comdr. USNR, ret., 1967. Am. Cancer Soc. clin. fellow, 1966-67. Fellow ACS, AMA (Physicians Recognition award), Tex. Med. Assn.; mem. Tex. Med. Found. (fed. peer rev. group), Houston Surg. Soc. (pres. 1993), Southwestern Surg. Congress, Tex. Surg. Soc., Singleton Surg. Soc. (past pres.), Harris County Med. Soc. (chmn. coun. med. splty., mem. exec. bd. 1994), East Harris County Med. Soc. (pres. 1982), Baytown Surg. Soc., Sir William Osler Soc., Am. Cancer Soc. (pres. Baytown chpt. 1970-71), Sons of Republic Tex. (at large life), SAR (past pres. local chpt.), Soc. Descendents of Colonial Clergy, Magna Carta Barons (Somerset chpt.), Colonial Order of the Crown, Sovereign Colonial Soc.-Ams. of Royal Descent, Masons (32 degree), Shriners, KT, Gideons Internat., Phi Beta Pi. Democrat. Mem. Ch. of Christ. Avocations: gardening, hunting, fishing, geneology, golf. Home: 1217 Kilgore Rd Baytown TX 77520-3912 Office: 4201 Garth Rd Ste 309 Independence Plaza Baytown TX 77521

WILLIAMS, EARLE CARTER, retired professional services company executive; b. Selma, Ala., Oct. 15, 1929; s. Henry Earle and Nora Elizabeth (Carter) W.; m. June Esther Anson, Sept. 7, 1951; children: Gayle Marie, Carol Patrice, Sharon Elaine. B.E.E., Auburn U., 1951; postgrad., U. N.Mex., 1959-62; DSc (hon.), Auburn U., 1991. Registered profl. engr., N.Mex. Utilities design engr. Standard Oil Co. Ind., Whiting, 1954-56; mem. tech. staff Sandia Corp., Albuquerque, 1956-62; sr. engr. BDM Internat., Inc., El Paso, Tex., 1962-64, spl. projects dir., 1964-66, dir. ops., 1966-68; v.p., gen. mgr. BDM Internat., Inc., Vienna, Va., 1968-72; pres., CEO, BDM Internat., Inc., Vienna and McLean, Va., 1972-92, bd. dirs., 1972—; ret. as CEO, BDM Internat. Inc., Vienna and McLean, Va., 1992; bd. dirs. Parsons Corp., Nortel Fed. Systems, Inc., GTS Duratek, Inc., Gamma-A Techols., Inc., Med. Scis. Rsch. Inst.; mem. Naval Rsch. Adv. Com., 1984-90, chmn., 1986-90; dir. Am. Bus. Conf., 1985-88. Exec. com., steering com. El Paso Community Coll., 1968-69, trustee, 1969-70; commr. Fairfax County Econ. Devel. Authority, 1976-80, chmn., 1978-80; mem. Va. State Bd. for Community Colls., 1980-87; bd. dirs. Cen. Va. Ednl. TV Corp., 1978-87, The Atlantic Coun. of the U.S., 1987—; chmn. George Mason Inst. Indsl. Policy Bd., 1982-91; bd. dirs. Wolf Trap Found., 1984-92, vice chmn., 1985-87, chmn. 1988-90, emeritus dir., 1992—; trustee Va. Found. for Ind. Colls., 1984-87, 90-94, Flint Hill Sch., Oakton, Va., 1990—, George Mason U. Found., 1987—, Auburn U. Found., 1991—. With AUS, 1951-53. Recipient Engr. of Yr. award Va. Soc. Profl. Engrs., 1989, Superior Pub. Svc. award Dept. Navy, 1990; named to Ala. Engring. Hall of Fame, 1994. Mem. NSPE, Profl. Svcs. Coun. (bd. dirs. 1974-92, emeritus bd. dirs. 1992—, pres. 1976-79), Armed Force Comm. and Electronics Assn. (bd. dirs. 1978-82, 86-87, permanent dir. 1990, internat. v.p. 1979-82, 84-85, chmn. 1988-90, Disting. Svc. award 1987), Coun. on Fgn. Rels., Fairfax County C. of C. (bd. dirs. 1978-86), City Club (D.C.), Met. Club (D.C.), Tower Club (Vienna, Va.), Bay Colony Club (Naples, Fla.), Eta Kappa Nu. Presbyterian.

WILLIAMS, EDDIE NATHAN, research institution executive; b. Memphis, Aug. 18, 1932; s. Ed and Georgia Lee (Barr) W.; m. Jearline F. Reddick, July 18, 1981; children: Traci Lynne, Edward Lawrence, Terence Reddick. BS, U. Ill., 1954; postgrad., Atlanta U., 1957, Howard U., 1960; LLD (hon.), U. D.C., 1986; DHL, Bowie State Coll., 1980, Chgo. State U., 1994. Reporter Atlanta Daily World Newspaper, 1957-58; staff asst. U.S. Senate Com. on Fgn. Relations, Washington, 1959-60; fgn. service res. officer U.S. Dept. State, Washington, 1961-68; v.p. U. Chgo., 1968-72; pres. Joint Ctr. for Polit. and Econ. Studies, Washington, 1972—; sec.-treas. Black Leadership Forum, 1993; bd. dirs. The Promus Cos., The Riggs Nat. Bank Washington, Blue Cross Blue Shield Nat. Capital Area; advisor Ctrs. for Disease Control, 1992—. Editorial columnist: Chgo. Sun Times, 1970-72; contbr. articles to profl. jours. Bd. dirs. Nat. Opinion Rsch. Ctr., 1992—, Inst. for Ednl. Leadership, 1987—; past chmn. bd. dirs. Nat. Coalition on Black Voter Participation, 1982—; chmn. Pew Partnerships for Civic Change, 1993—. Am. Polit. Sci. Assn. fellow, 1958, MacArthur Found. fellow, 1988, Nat. Acad. Pub. Adminstrn. fellow, 1993; recipient Adam Clayton Powell Award Congl. Black Caucus, 1981, Washingtonian of Yr. award Washingtonian Mag., 1991, Nation Builder award Nat. Black Caucus of State Legislators, 1993, Outstanding Leadership award Korean Am. Alliance, 1994. Mem. Am. Polit. Sci. Assn. Coun., Coun. Fgn. Rels., Overseas Devel. Coun., Kappa Tau Alpha, Omega Psi Phi, Sigma Phi Phi. Office: Joint Ctr for Polit & Econ Studies 1090 Vermont Ave NW Ste 1100 Washington DC 20005-4905

WILLIAMS, EDGAR GENE, university administrator; b. Posey County, Ind., May 4, 1922; s. Noley Wesley and Anna Lena (Wilsey) W.; m. Joyce Ellen Grigsby, May 7, 1944; children: Cynthia Ellen Williams Mahigian, Thomas Gene. A.B., Evansville Coll., 1947; M.B.A., Ind. U., 1948, D.B.A., 1952. Instr. Ind. U., Bloomington, 1948-52; asst. prof. Ind. U., 1952-55, assoc. prof., 1955-58, prof. bus. adminstrn., 1958—, assoc. dean, 1965-69, v.p., 1974-88, now emeritus. Bd. dirs. Found. for Sch. of Bus., Ind. U., Bloomington, 1966—, Bloomington Community Found. Served with U.S. Army, 1943-46. Mem. Beta Gamma Sigma. Democrat. Methodist. Clubs: Masons, Bloomington Country. Home: 1126 E 1st St Bloomington IN 47401-5076

WILLIAMS, EDSON POE, retired automotive company executive; b. Mpls., July 31, 1923; s. Homer A. and Florence C. Williams; m. Irene Mae Streed, June 16, 1950; children: Thomas, Louise, Steven, Linnea, Elisa. B.S.M.E. cum laude, U. Minn., 1950. Spl. purpose machinery operator, 1946-50; mfg. engr., project engr. Crestliner div. Bigelow Sanford Inc., 1950-53, v.p., mgr. mfg. and engring., 1953-58, pres. 1958-63; with Ford Motor Co., 1963-87, mgr. customer svc. div. 1973; gen. mgr. Ford Motor Co. (Ford Mexico), 1973-75; pres. Ford Motor Co. (Ford Mid-East & Africa), 1975-79, Ford Motor Co. (Ford Asia-Pacific Inc.), 1979-87; v.p. Ford Motor Co., 1979-82, v.p.-gen. mgr. N.Am. truck ops., 1982-86, v.p. Ford Diversified Products ops., 1986-87. Served with USAAF, 1942-46. Mem. Collier Athletic Club, Naples Yacht and Sailing Club. Home: 32808 Outland Trl Bingham Farms MI 48025 also: 606 21st Ave S Naples FL 33940

WILLIAMS, EDWARD, textile executive; b. 1943. With E & B Carpet Mills, 1964-70; western divsnl. mgr. Galaxy Carpet Mills, 1970-73; pres., owner N.Am. Carpet Corp. (acquired by Galaxy Carpet Mills in 1986) 1973-89; officer Galaxy Carpet Mills, Chatsworth, Ga., 1986—, pres., chief operating officer. Office: Galaxy Carpet Mills Inc 101 Industrial Blvd Chatsworth GA 30705*

WILLIAMS, EDWARD DAVID, consulting executive; b. Scranton, Pa., June 20, 1932; s. David Thomas and Mabel (Sims) W. m. Natalie Imnadze, Oct. 18, 1952; children: Denise, Claudia. BBA, Hofstra U., 1960; postgrad. in Bus. Adminstrn., Fairleigh Dickenson U., 1979. Cons. Cresap, McCormick and Paget, N.Y.C., 1964-65; sr. mgmt. cons. Union Carbide Corp., N.Y.C., 1965-67; asst. contr. data processing Western Union, N.Y.C.,

1967-69; v.p. mgmt. info. systems ABC, Hackensack, N.J., 1970-86; v.p., chief info. officer Blue Cross Blue Shield of N.J., Newark, 1986-88; v.p. Chantico Pub. Co., Carrellton, Tex., 1989-90; pres. SMC-BIS Inc., Basking Ridge, N.J., 1990-93; pres., CEO Strategic Outsourcing Svcs. Inc., Mountain Lakes, N.J., 1993—; v.p., bd. dirs. GBM-Servicios de Informacion Tecnologicos. Speaker in field. Mem. adv. bd. YMCA. With U.S. Army, 1948-52. Decorated Silver Star with oak leaf cluster, Bronze Star with V, Purple Heart with 2 oak leaf clusters. Mem. Soc. Mgmt. Info. Systems, N.J. C. of C., Profit Oriented Systems Planning Bd. (bd. dirs.), Masons. Republican. Office: Strategic Outsourcing Svcs 49 Old Bloomfield Ave Mountain Lakes NJ 07046

WILLIAMS, EDWARD EARL, JR., entrepreneur, educator; b. Houston, Aug. 21, 1945; s. Edward Earl and Doris Jewel (Jones) W.; m. Susan M. Warren, June 28, 1983; children: Laura Michelle, David Brian. BS, U. Pa., 1966; PhD, U. Tex., 1968. Asst. prof. econs. Rutgers U., New Brunswick, N.J., 1968-70; assoc. prof. fin. McGill U., Montreal, Que., Can., 1970-73; v.p., economist Service Corp. Internat., Houston, 1973-77; prof. adminstrv. sci. Rice U., Houston, 1978-82, Henry Gardiner Symonds prof., 1982—; prof. stats., 1995—; chmn. bd. Edward E. Williams & Co., Houston, 1976-92; chmn. bd., pres. Tex. Capital Investment Co., 1979—; chmn. bd. First Tex. Venture Capital Corp., 1983-92; mng. dir. First Tex. Venture Capital, LLC, 1992—; dir. Equus Capital Corp., Equus II Inc., Video Rental of Pa. Inc., Svc. Corp. Internat., Park Nat. Bank.; Benjamin Franklin scholar, Jesse Jones scholar, U. Pa., 1966, Tex. Savs. and Loan League fellow, NDEA fellow, U. Tex., 1968. Mem. Am. Statis. Assn., Coll. Innovation Mgmt. and Entrepreneurship, Fin. Mgmt. Assn., Beta Gamma Sigma, Alpha Kappa Psi. Author: Prospects for the Savins and Loan Industry, 1968, An Integrated Analysis for Managerial Finance, 1970; Investment Analysis, 1974; Business Planning for the Entrepreneur, 1983; contr. articles to profl. jours. Home: 7602 Wilton Park Dr Spring TX 77379-4672 Office: Rice U Jesse H Jones Grad Sch Adminstrn Houston TX 77251

WILLIAMS, EDWARD F(OSTER), III, environmental engineer; b. N.Y.C., Jan. 3, 1935; s. E. Foster Jr. and Ida Frances (Richards) W.; m. Sue Carol Osenbaugh, June 5, 1960; children: Cecile Elizabeth, Alexander Harmon. BS in Engring., Auburn U., 1956; MA in History, U. Memphis, 1974. Registered profl. engr., Tenn. Engr. Buckeye Cellulose Corp. (subs. of Procter & Gamble), Memphis, 1957, process safety engr., 1960; resident constrn. engr. Buckeye Cellulose Corp. (subs. of Procter & Gamble), Perry, Fla., 1960-61; staff engr. Buckeye Cellulose Corp. (subs. of Procter & Gamble), Memphis, 1961-70; chief engr., v.p. Enviro-trol, Inc., Memphis, 1970-73; v.p., then pres. Ramcon Environ. Corp., Memphis, 1973-80; pres. E.F. Williams & Assocs., Inc., Memphis, 1980—; EFW Comml. Ventures Inc., 1990—; bd. dirs. Mobile Process Tech. Inc., Memphis; v.p. Environ. Testing and Consulting, Inc., Memphis, 1985-94. Author: Fustest with the Mostest, 1968, Early Memphis and Its River Rivals, 1969; editor Environ. Control News for So. Industry, 1971—. State rep. Tenn. Gen. Assembly, 1970-78; mem. Shelby County Bd. Commrs., Memphis, 1978-94, chmn., 1987-88, 90-92; mem. Shelby County Records Commn., 1978—, chmn., 1993—; environ. coord. Shelby County Mayor's staff, 1995—; trustee Bolton Coll., 1982—; chmn. 1987-88, 90-92; del. Rep. Nat. Conv. 1988, 92, Rep. state exec. com., 1994—; state chmn. Nat. Conf. Rep. County Ofcls., 1993—; vice-chmn. Memphis-Shelby Local Emerg. Planning Com., 1986—. Capt. USAF, 1957-60. Named Tenn. Water Conservationist of the Yr. Tenn. Conservation League, 1973, Tenn. Legis. Conservationist of the Yr. Nat. Wildlife Fedn., 1974, Memphis Outstanding Engr. Memphis Joint Engrs. Coun., 1980. Mem. NSPE, ASME, Am. Acad. Environ. Engrs. (diplomate), Water Environ. Fedn., Am. Indsl. Hygiene Assn. (chpt. pres.), Am. Soc. Safety Engrs., Air and Waste Mgmt. Assn., Engrs. Club Memphis (bd. dirs. 1979-80), Rotary, C. of C. (environ. coun. chmn. 1988—), Tenn. Hist. Soc. (v.p. 1972), Tenn. Hist. Commn. (vice chmn. 1987—), West Tenn. Hist. Soc. (pres. 1983-85), Am. Hist. Assn. Republican. Presbyterian. Avocation: history. Home: 148 Perkins Ext Memphis TN 38117-3127 Office: EF Williams & Assocs 751 E Brookhaven Cir Memphis TN 38117-4501 also: PO Box 241813 Memphis TN 38124-1813

WILLIAMS, EDWARD GILMAN, retired banker; b. Ware, Mass., Apr. 11, 1926; s. Carl Emmons and Susan Helen (Gilman) W.; m. Barbara Thompson Russell, June 19, 1959; children: Thomas Clarke, Susan Gilman. B.A., Trinity Coll., Conn., 1950. With Union Trust Co., New Haven, 1951-89; asst. trust officer Union & New Haven Trust Co., 1956-59, trust officer, 1959-64, v.p., 1964-65, v.p., sr. adminstrv. officer, 1965-69; sr. v.p. Union Trust Co., 1969-72, exec. v.p. 1972-89; v.p. Northeast Bancorp., Inc., 1972-89. Former treas. Leila Day Nurseries, Inc., New Haven; treas., pres. Ridge Rd. PTA, Hamden Hall Country Day Sch. Parents Assn.; bd. dirs. Vis. Nurse Assn., New Haven, 1963-86, pres., treas., 1970-75; trustee New Eng. Sch. Banking, 1971-74, 81-88, vice chmn., 1985-86, chmn. 1986-88; trustee Shubert Performing Arts Ctr., New Haven, 1985-90; bd. dirs. New Haven Colony Hist. Soc., 1987-89; trustee, deacon, chmn. music. com., Ch. of Redeemer, New Haven; treas. Edgerton Garden Ctr., 1992—. With USNR, 1944-46. Mem. Am. Inst. Banking, English-Speaking Union (treas. New Haven chpt. 1994—), New Haven Lawn Club (pres. 1979-82), Masons. Home: 900 Mix Ave # 17 Hamden CT 06514-9999 Office: 3074 Whitney Ave # 3-10 Hamden CT 06518

WILLIAMS, EDWARD JOSEPH, banker; b. Chgo., May 5, 1942; s. Joseph and Lillian (Watkins) W.; m. Johnnita E. Daniel, June 29, 1967; children: Elaine, Paul. BBA, Roosevelt U., 1973. Owner Mut. Home Delivery, Chgo., 1961-63; exec. v.p. Harris Trust and Savs. Bank, Chgo., 1964—; mem. Consumer Adv. Council, Washington, 1986—. Trustee Adler Planetarium, Chgo., 1982; chmn. Provident Med. Ctr., Chgo., 1986; bd. dirs. Voices for Ill. Children, Chgo. Coun. on Urban Affairs; pres. Neighborhood Housing Svcs. Recipient Disting. Alumni award Clark Coll., Atlanta, 1985. Mem. Nat. Bankers Assn., Urban Bankers Forum (Pioneer award 1986), Econ. Club. Chgo. Methodist. Clubs: Metropolitan, Union League (Chgo.). Office: Harris Trust & Savs Bank 111 W Monroe St Chicago IL 60603-4003

WILLIAMS, EDWARD VINSON, music history educator; b. Orlando, Fla., July 12, 1935. B.M., Fla. State U., 1957; M.M., Ind. U., 1962; M.A., Yale U., 1966, Ph.D., 1968. Prof. music history dept. music U. Kans., Lawrence, 1969-90, chmn. dept. music history, 1975-84; assoc. dean rsch. and grad. studies Coll. Arts and Architecture, prof. music Pa. State U., University Park, Pa., 1990—. Author: The Bells of Russia: History and Technology, 1985. Served with U.S. Army, 1957-60. Recipient Chancellor's award for Excellence in Teaching, U. Kans., 1975; Kennan Inst. fellow Wilson Ctr., Washington, 1985; fellow Nat. Humanities Ctr., Research Triangle Park, N.C., 1980-81. Mem. Am. Musicological Soc., Am. Assn. for Advancement Slavic Studies, Assn. Bell Art (Moscow). Home: 330 Toftrees Ave Apt 149 State College PA 16803-2043 Office: Pa State U Coll Arts and Architecture 115 Arts Bldg University Park PA 16802

WILLIAMS, EDWIN NEEL, newspaper editor; b. Rives, Mo., Jan. 14, 1942; s. Carl Edwin and Vina Marie (Edmonston) W.; m. Marylyn Lentine, 1973; 1 child, Jonathan Lentine. BA in History, U. Miss., 1965. Reporter Clarksdale (Miss) Press-Register, 1965; reporter, editor Delta Dem.-Times, Greenville, Miss., 1967-72; Nieman fellow Harvard U., Cambridge, Mass., 1972-73; writer, researcher Ford Found., N.Y.C., 1973; editorial writer Charlotte (N.C.) Observer, 1973-76, editor of editorial pages 1976-80, 87—. Chmn. KinderMourn, Charlotte, 1988, N.C. Harvest, 1993-94; bd. dirs. N.C. Ctr. for Pub. Policy Rsch., Raleigh, 1992—. With U.S. Army, 1965-67. Baptist. Home: 916 Mount Vernon Ave Charlotte NC 28203-4845 Office: Charlotte Observer PO Box 30308 Charlotte NC 28230-0308

WILLIAMS, EDWIN WILLIAM, publisher; b. N.Y.C., May 3, 1912; s. William and Amelia W.; m. Doris O. Smith, June 3, 1953 (div.); children: Edwina, Andrew; m. Alma Davies Kaye, June 22, 1985. Student, Columbia U., 1930. Publisher Quick Frozen Foods Internat. mag., N.Y.C., 1938—; Pvt. Label mag., 1979—; PL Internat. and PL Directories and Newsletter; pres. Pioneer Assocs., Inc., North Bergen, N.J., 1972—, E.W. Pubdns. Co., N.Y.C., 1940—; Williams Electric Co., Shelby, N.C., 1970—; owner Columbia Pub. Co. N.Y., 1995—; organizer frozen food industry directories and convs., speaker in field. Author: Frozen Foods, Biography of an Industry, 1969; co-author: Private Labels. Chmn. Dept. Commerce mission to Eastern countries. Recipient award ICA, 1956, award Internat. Assn. Refrigerated Warehouses, 1960, Presdl. E award 1962, Man of Yr. award Food Divsn. Nat. Conf. Christians and Jews, 1995. Mem. Am. Frozen Food Inst., Pvt. Label Mfrs. Assn. (founder), Advt. Club N.Y.C., Oversees Press Club (N.Y.C.), Princeton Club. Republican. Home: 8200 Boulevard E North Bergen NJ 07047-6039 Office: 2125 Center Ave Fort Lee NJ 07024-5858 *If a man early in his career carves his dream like a sculptor on the unyielding stone of life, with many a sharp incision, he is bound to reach his goal; he has caught the angel vision.*

WILLIAMS, ELEANOR JOYCE, government air traffic control specialist; b. College Station, Tex., Dec. 21, 1936; d. Robert Ira and Viola (Ford) Toliver; m. Tollie Williams, Dec. 30, 1955 (div. July 1978); children: Rodrick, Viola Williams Smith, Darryl, Eric, Dana Williams Jones, Sheila Williams Watkins, Kenneth. Student Prairie View A&M Coll., 1955-56, Anchorage Community Coll., 1964-65, U. Alaska-Anchorage, 1976. Clk./stenographer FAA, Anchorage, 1965-66, adminstrv. clk., 1966-67, pers. staffing asst., 1967-68, air traffic control specialist, 1968-79; air traffic contr. supr., San Juan, P.R., 1979-80, Anchorage, 1983-85, airspace specialist, Atlanta, 1980-83; with FAA, Washington, 1985-87; area mgr. Kansas City Air Rt. Traffic Control Ctr., Olathe, Kans., 1987-89, asst. mgr. quality Assurance, 1989-91, supr. traffic mgmt., 1991-93; supr. system effectiveness section, 1991-93, asst. air traffic mgr., 1993-94; air traffic mgr. Cleve. Air Route Traffic Control Ctr., FAA, Oberlin, Ohio, 1994—. Sec. Fairview Neighborhood Coun., Anchorage, 1967-69; mem. Anchorage Bicentennial Commn., 1975-76; bd. dirs. Mt. Patmos Youth Dept., Decatur, Ga., 1981-82; mem. NAACP; del. to USSR Women in Mgmt., 1990; mem. citizens amb. program People to People Internat. Recipient Mary K. Goddard award Anchorage Fed. Exec. Assn. and Fed. Women's Program, 1985, Sec.'s award Dept. transp., 1985, Pres. VIP award, 1988, C. Alfred Anderson award, 1991, Disting. Svc. award Nat. Black Coalition of Fed. Aviation Employees, 1991, Paul K. Bohr award FAA, 1994; A salute to Her Name in the Congl. Record 104th Congress, 1995. Mem. Nat. Coun. Negro Women, Bus. and Profl. Women U.S.A. Inc. (North to the Future club, charter pres. 1975-76), Blacks in Govt., Nat. Black Coalition of Fed. Aviation Employees (pres. cen. region chpt. 1987-92, Over Achievers award, 1987, Disting. Svc. award 1988), Profl. Women Contrs. Orgn., Air Traffic Contrs. Assn., Fed. Mgrs. Assn., Internat. Platform Assn., Women in Mgmt. (del. Soviet Union), Gamma Phi Delta. Democrat. Baptist. Avocations: singing; sewing. Home: 5770-D2 Great Northern Blvd North Olmsted OH 44070 Office: FAA 326 East Lorain St Oberlin OH 44074

WILLIAMS, EMILY ALLEN, English language educator; b. Nottoway, Va., Aug. 14, 1955; d. Joseph Robert and Cornelia (Scott) Allen; m. Kenneth Jerome Williams, Feb. 29, 1992. BA, St. Paul's Coll., 1977; MA, Va. Commonwealth U., 1979; DA, Clark Atlanta U., 1993—. Instr. adult edn. Med. Coll. Va./Va. Commonwealth U. Richmond, 1977-79; instr. English Richmond Bus. Coll., 1979-80; regional grants coord. Va. Commn. for Arts, Richmond, 1980-83; grants program coord. Ga. Coun. for Arts, Atlanta, 1986-87; grants dir. City of Atlanta Bur. Cultural Affairs, 1987-91; prof. English Clark Atlanta U., 1991-92, Morehouse Coll., Atlanta, 1992—; continuing edn. prof. Spelman Coll.; adj. instr. English Reynolds C.C., Richmond, 1983-85; site reviewer NEA, Washington, 1990-91; panelist Nat. Black Arts Festival, Atlanta, 1991, Ga. Coun. Arts, Atlanta, 1987-90; cons. Fulton County Arts Coun., Atlanta, 1991-92, African Am. Philarmonic Arch., Atlanta, 1991-92. Author of poems. Advisor student newspaper Morehouse Coll., 1992-93, grant com. chmn. English dept., 1992-93; speaker arts sem. Va. Commonwealth U., Richmond, 1982; cons. The APEX Mus., Atlanta, 1992-93. E. Bradlee Watson scholar, St. Paul's Coll., 1976. Mem. Delta Sigma Theta, Alpha Kappa Mu. Avocations: writing, backgammon, travel. Home: 6196 Spring Lake Walk Lithonia GA 30038-3467 Office: Morehouse Coll 830 Westview Dr SW Atlanta GA 30314

WILLIAMS, EMMA LOUISE, elementary education educator; b. Warrenton, N.C., Apr. 18, 1945; d. John Henry and Irene (Williams) W. BA, CUNY, 1986, MS in Elem. Edn., 1993. Asst. student-mentoring project Bklyn. Coll., CUNY, 1985-88; reading tutor Bklyn., 1986-87; elem. tchr. Wibecan Sch., Pub. Sch. 309, Bklyn., 1987—. Mem. Assn. Black Educators of N.Y., United Fedn. of Tchrs., Am. Fedn. of Tchrs., ASCD. Avocations: missionary, nature appreciation, Sunday Sch. tchr., writing, decorating, art. Home: PO Box 70088 Brooklyn NY 11207-0088

WILLIAMS, EMORY, former retail company executive, banker; b. Falco, Ala., Oct. 26, 1911; s. William Emory and Nelle (Turner) W.; m. Janet Hatcher Allcorn, May 15, 1943; children: Nelle (Mrs. Gilbert Brown), Janet (Mrs. Edwin Harrison), Bliss (Mrs. Howell Browne), Carol (Mrs. James Schroeder), Emory III. A.B. Emory U., 1932. With Sears, Roebuck & Co., 1933-75; pres. Sears, Roebuck (S.A.), Brazil, 1958-60, Homart Devel. Co., 1960-67; treas. parent co.; 1962-64, v.p., treas., 1964-75; chmn. bd., chief exec. officer Sears Bank & Trust Co., 1975-81, also dir.; chmn. bd. dirs., pres. Chgo. Milw. Corp., 1981-85; ptnr. Williams Realty Co.; chmn. Williams & Nichols Co.; bd. dirs. Ft. Dearborn Income Securities Inc. Div. chmn. Chgo. Crusade of Mercy, 1962-64, gen. chmn., 1966, pres, 1976-78; chmn. Ill. Health Edn. Commn., 1968-70; pres. Adler Planetarium, 1972-75, Ravinia Festival Assn., 1972-78; ptrs. bd. dirs. Community Fund, 1970-73; trustee Emory U., Chgo. Community Trust, Northwestern Meml. Hosps., Episcopal Diocesan Found., Kellstadt Found.; chmn. Chgo. Chamber Musicians. Lt. col. C.E., U.S. Army, World War II, CBI. Mem. Piedmont Driving Club (Atlanta); Chgo. Club, Old Elm Club (Chgo.), Commercial Club; Indian Hill Club (Winnetka, Ill.), Loblolly Bay Yacht Club, Loblolly Pines Golf Club (Hobe Sound, Fla.), Seminole Golf Club (North Palm Beach). Home: 1630 Sheridan Rd Wilmette IL 60091 Also: 7760 SE Lake Shore Dr Hobe Sound FL 33455-3833

WILLIAMS, ERIK GEORGE, professional football player; b. Phila., Sept. 7, 1968. Student, Ctrl. State U. Offensive tackle Dallas Cowboys, 1991—; mem. Superbowl Championship team, 1993, 94. Named to Pro Bowl Team, 1993; named offensive tackle on The Sporting News NFL All-Pro Team, 1993. Office: Dallas Cowboys 1 Cowboys Pky Irving TX 75063-4999*

WILLIAMS, ERNEST GOING, paper company executive; b. Macon, Miss., Sept. 24, 1915; s. Augustus Gaines and Mary (Sanford) W.; m. Cecil Louise Butler, Aug. 18, 1951; children: Ernest Butler, Turner Butler, Elizabeth Cecil. BS in Commerce and Bus. Adminstrn., U. Ala., 1938, LLD, 1987. Asst. to treas. U. Ala., 1938-42, 45-48, treas., 1948-56; v.p. First Nat. Bank Tuscaloosa, Ala., 1956-58; dir. First Nat. Bank Tuscaloosa, 1956-84; v.p., dir. Gulf States Paper Corp., Tuscaloosa, 1958-77; chmn. bd., dir. Affiliated Paper Cos., Inc., Tuscaloosa, 1977-94; bd. dirs., chmn. Southland Nat. Ins. Corp.; past pres. Associated Industries Ala. Trustee emeritus U. Ala., David Warner Found.; past chmn. Tuscaloosa County chpt. ARC; past pres. DCH Found.; mem. Tuscaloosa Indsl. Devel. Bd. With USNR, 1942-45. Named Tuscaloosa Citizen of Year Civitan Club, 1974. Mem. Greater Tuscaloosa C. of C., Newcomen Soc. N.Am., Ala. Acad. of Honor, Univ. Club, River Club, Indian Hills Country Club, North River Yacht Club (vice commodore), Exch. Club (past pres.), Kappa Alpha, Omicron Delta Kappa, Beta Gamma Sigma. Presbyterian. Home: 156 The Highlands Tuscaloosa AL 35404-2900 Office: Affiliated Paper Co Inc 1806 6th St Tuscaloosa AL 35401-1721

WILLIAMS, ERNEST WILLIAM, JR., economist, educator; b. Scranton, Pa., Oct. 27, 1916; s. Ernest William and Kathryn (Winterstein) W.; m. Thelma Foxwell Kelcher, Dec. 7, 1957 (dec. 1984). B.S., Columbia U., 1938, M.S., 1939, Ph.D., 1951. Economist Nat. Resources Planning Bd., 1940-42, WPB, 1942-44; chief transp. div. U.S. Strategic Bombing Survey, 1944-45; fiscal analyst U.S. Bur. Budget, 1945-46; lectr. transp. Grad. Sch. Bus. Columbia, 1947-52, assoc. prof., 1952-58, prof. transp., 1958-86, prof. emeritus, 1987—, vice dean, 1977-79; vis. prof. mgmt. U. Ariz., 1972, 74; cons. ODM, 1951-60; dir. transp. study Dept. Commerce, 1959-60; dir. ACF Industries, Inc., N.Y.C., 1960-84; mem. N.Y.-N.J. Met. Rapid Transit Commn., 1955-58; mem. task force Pres.'s Adv. Com. Transp. Policy and Orgn., 1954-55; mem. task force on regulatory agencies First Hoover Commn., 1948. Author: (with Marvin L. Fair) Economics of Transportation, rev. edit, 1959, The Regulation of Rail-Motor Rate Competition, 1958, Freight Transportation in the Soviet Union, 1962, The Future of American Transportation, 1971, Economics of Transportation and Logistics, 1974, rev. edit., 1981, (with G.K. Sletmo) Liner Conferences in the Container Age, 1981; contr. articles to profl. publs. Trustee TAA Research Fund, 1962-65; bd. visitors U.S. Army Transp. Sch., 1963-66. Recipient Medal for Freedom,

Mem. Am. Econ. Assn., Am. Soc. Transp. and Logistics. Home: 415 Janes Stamford CT 06903

WILLIAMS, ERVIN EUGENE, religious organization administrator; b. Corning, N.Y., Feb. 25, 1923; s. Douglas Lewis and Mina P. (Barnes) W.; m. Ruth Evelyn Snyder, June 12, 1945; children: Roger Eugene, Virginia Ruth. Student, Toccoa Falls (Ga.) Bible Coll., 1939, Cornell U., 1942; BA, Pa. State U., 1949; MA, Mich. State U., 1961, PhD in Communications, 1971. Ordained to ministry Ind. Bapt. Ch., 1950. Acad. dean Greensburg (Pa.) Bible Inst., 1949-51; min. Bapt. Ch., New Kensington, Pa., 1951-53; instr. Pa. State U., 1953-55; sr. min. East Lansing (Mich.) Trinity Ch., 1955-71; vis. prof. Trinity Evang. Div. Sch., Deerfield, Ill., 1968-71; prof. communication and practical theology, 1971-77, dir. D Ministry program, 1975-76; gen. dir. Am. Missionary Fellowship, Villanova, Pa., 1977-92; exec. min. Ch. of the Apostles, Atlanta, 1993—; chaplain Mich. State U., East Lansing, 1955-71; cons. Haggai Inst. for Advanced Leadership Tng., Atlanta, 1969—; lectr. Calvary Bapt. Coll., Kansas City, Mo., 1962, Haggai Inst. Third World Leaders, Singapore, 1970—; Staley lectr. Robert Wesleyan Coll., North Chili, N.Y., 1973, Judson Coll., Elgin, Ill., 1977-79; cons. to mission bds., 1967-76; assoc. dir. Camp of Woods, Speculator, N.Y., 1971-77. Contbr. numerous articles to religious periodicals, also monographs. Trustee Dorothy H. Theis Meml. Found., Sierra Vista, Ariz., 1987—; trustee Gospel Vols., Speculator, N.Y., 1963-93; mem. bd. regents Owosso (Mich.) Coll., 1971-73. Pilot USAAF, 1942-45, prisoner of war, ETO, 1945. Mem. Nat. Sunday Sch. Assn., Christian Assn. Psychol. Studies, Mich. Acad. Arts and Scis., Aircraft Owners and Pilots Assn., Phi Beta Kappa, Pi Gamma Mu, Pi Kappa Phi, Alpha Kappa Delta. Office: Ch of Apostles 3585 Northside Pky NW Atlanta GA 30327 *It is much more difficult to conceal ignorance and prejudice than it is to acquire knowledge and fairness.*

WILLIAMS, FORMAN ARTHUR, engineering science educator, combustion theorist; b. New Brunswick, N.J., Jan. 12, 1934; s. Forman J. and Alice (Pooley) W.; m. Elsie Vivian Kara, June 15, 1955 (div. 1978); children: F. Gary, Glen A., Nancy L., Susan D., Michael S., Michelle K.; m. Elizabeth Acevedo, Aug. 19, 1978. BSE, Princeton U., 1955; PhD, Calif. Inst. Tech., 1958. Asst. prof. Harvard U., Cambridge, Mass., 1958-64; prof. U. Calif.-San Diego, 1964-81; Robert H. Goddard prof. Princeton U., N.J., 1981-88; prof. dept. applied mechs. and engring. scis. U. Calif., San Diego, 1988—. Author: Combustion Theory, 1965, 2d edit., 1985; contbr. articles to profl. jours. Fellow NSF, 1962; fellow Guggenheim Found., 1970; recipient U.S. Sr. Scientist award Alexander von Humboldt Found., 1982, Silver medal Combustion Inst., 1978, Bernard Lewis Gold medal Combustion Inst., 1990. Fellow AIAA (Pendray Aerospace Lit. award 1993); mem. Am. Phys. Soc., Combustion Inst., Soc. for Indsl. and Applied Math., Nat. Acad. Engring., Nat. Acad. Engring Mex. (fgn. corr. mem.), Sigma Xi. Home: 8002 La Jolla Shores Dr La Jolla CA 92037-3230 Office: U Calif San Diego Ctr Energy & Combustion Rsch 9500 Gilman Dr La Jolla CA 92093-5003

WILLIAMS, FRANK JAMES, JR., department store chain executive, lawyer; b. St. Louis, July 2, 1938; s. Frank James and Alberta Klaus Williams; children by previous marriage: Kimberly, Andrew, Renee; m. Sandra M. Garbe, Feb. 13, 1988. B.S.B.A., Washington U., St. Louis, 1960; J.D., Washington U., 1963; postgrad., U. Mo., 1960-61. Bar: Mo. 1963. Asst. gen. counsel May Dept. Stores, St. Louis, 1964-66, v.p.-labor relations, 1970-75, v.p.-labor relations and govt. affairs, 1975-80, v.p.-pub. affairs, 1980—; atty. Pet, Inc., St. Louis, 1966-67; lectr. various trade, profl. orgns. Treas. May Dept. Stores Polit. Action Com., St. Louis, 1981—. Mem. ABA, Mo. Bar Assn., St. Louis Bar Assn., Nat. Retail Merchants Assn. (chmn. employee relations com. 1977-78 Silver plaque), Am. Retail Fedn. (chmn. employee relation com. 1973-76). Roman Catholic. Club: Mo. Athletic (1st v.p. and treas. 1980-81) (St. Louis). Home: 2907 Bayberry Ridge Dr Saint Louis MO 63129-6422 Office: May Dept Stores 611 Olive St Saint Louis MO 63101-1721

WILLIAMS, FRANKLIN CADMUS, JR., bibliographer; b. Palestine, Tex., July 30, 1941; s. Franklin Cadmus and Cathryn Lucille (Pessoney) W. BA, Baylor U., 1963; MA, Stephen F. Austin State U., 1965; PhD, U. Wis., 1975. Cert. in secondary edn. English and History. Teaching fellow Stephen F. Austin State U. Nacogdoches, Tex., 1964-65, U. Wis., Madison, 1965-68; instr. English Austin Peay State U., Clarksville, Tenn., 1970-71; adj. asst. prof. East Tex. State U., Commerce, 1975; asst. prof. English Jarvis Christian Coll., Hawkins, Tex., 1976-78, 79-81; ind. scholar Palestine, Tex., 1981—; owner, bibliographer Goldsmith Archive, Palestine, 1981—; cons. Diocese of Galveston-Houston, 1977-84, Tex. State Hist. Assn., Austin, 1988; speaker, editor Jarvis Christian Coll., Hawkins, Tex., 1976-78, 79-81; nat. teaching fellow Office Edn., Washington, 1976-77; del. to Baylor U., U. Wis. System, Madison, 1981. Contbr. articles to profl. jours. Mem. Modern Lang. Assn., Tex. State Hist. Assn., Tex. Cath. Hist. Soc., Baylor Alumni Assn. (life), Wis. Alumni Assn. (life), Sigma Tau Delta. Avocations: reading, record collecting, historical genealogy, tennis, swimming. Office: PO Box 96 Palestine TX 75802-0096

WILLIAMS, FREDERICK, statistics educator; b. Middlesbrough, Eng., Feb. 9, 1922; came to U.S., 1926; s. Frederick William and Violet (Taylor) W.; m. Frances Marian Sacks, July 7, 1945. B.S.E., U. Mich., 1947, M.A. with distinction, 1948; Ph.D., Northwestern U., 1958. Teaching asst. statistics U. Mich., 1947-48; instr. statistics Northwestern U., 1948-54; instr., then asst. prof. statistics U. Ill., 1954-58; assoc. prof. statistics U. Mo., 1958-61, prof., 1961—, chmn. dept., 1966-71, 1973-76, acting chmn., 1980-81, tchr. exec. devel. program, 1959-65, dir. grad. studies statistics, 1971-72; prof. emeritus, 1992—; cons., lectr. in field. Co-author: An Introduction to Probability, 1965. Served with USNR, 1943-46. Mem. Am. Statis. Assn. (pres. Mid-Mo. chpt. 1982, 93-94, 95, mem. nat. coun. 1982-83, 85-95), Ops. Rsch. Soc. Am., Beta Gamma Sigma, Phi Kappa Phi. Home: 2501 N Leisurely Way Columbia MO 65202-2204

WILLIAMS, GARTH MONTGOMERY, illustrator; b. N.Y.C., Apr. 16, 1912; married; 6 children. Studied, Westminster Sch. Art, Royal Coll. Art, London. Illustrator numerous children's books, including Charlotte's Web, Little House on Prairie series, Cricket in Times Square series, Miss Bianca Books, Stuart Little; writer, illustrator Rabbits' Wedding, Adventures of Benjamin Pink, also others. Recipient Brit. Prix de Rome for sculpture, 1936. Address: care Richard M Ticktin 1345 Avenue Of The Americas New York NY 10105-0010

WILLIAMS, GARY ALAN, management consultant; b. Houston, May 24, 1950; s. Jesse W. and Bertha M. (Collins) W.; m. Valerie A. Newman, Aug. 25, 1973; children: Jordan P., Jacqueline Blair. BBA, U. Tex., 1972. Mktg. rep. IBM, Houston, 1973-75, project leader, 1975-78; mktg. mgr. IBM, Dallas, 1978-80; mgr. Coopers & Lybrand, Dallas, 1980-82, dir., 1982-84, ptnr., 1984—; adv. coun. U. Tex. Info. Systems, Austin, Tex., 1985—. Bd. dirs. U.S.A. Film Festival, Dallas, 1988. Democrat. Methodist. Avocations: golf, skiing. Office: Coopers & Lybrand 1999 Bryan St Ste 3000 Dallas TX 75201-3185

WILLIAMS, GARY MURRAY, medical researcher, pathology educator; b. Regina, Sask., Can., May 7, 1940; s. Murray Austin and Selma Ruby (Domstad) W.; m. Julia Christine Lundberg; children: Walter, Jeffrey, Ingrid. BA, Washington and Jefferson Coll., 1963; MD, U. Pitts., 1967. Diplomate Am. Bd. Pathology, Am. Bd. Toxicology. Assoc. prof. pathology Temple U., Phila., 1971-75; mem. Fels Rsch. Inst., Phila. 1971-75; rsch. prof. N.Y. Med. Coll., Valhalla, 1975—; dir. med. scis., chief pathology and toxicology div. Am. Health Found., Valhalla, 1975—; mem. toxicology study sect. NIH, Bethesda, Md., 1985-87; mem. working groups Internat. Agy. Rsch. on Cancer, Lyon, France, 1976, 80, 82, 83, 87, 89, 91. Editor: Sweeteners: Health Effects, 1988; co-editor: Cellular Systems for Toxicity Testing, 1983; editor-in-chief Cell Biology and Toxicology, 1984—, Antioxidants: Chemical, Physiological, Nutritional and Toxicological Aspects, 1993; author more than 370 sci. papers; featured Cancer Rsch. Jour. for contbns. to understanding mechanisms of carcinogenesis, 1995. Lt. comdr. USPHS, 1969-71. Recipient Sheard-Sanford award Am. Soc. Clin. Pathologists U. Pitts., 1967. Mem. Am. Assn. Cancer Rsch., Soc. Toxicology (Arnold J. Lehman award 1982), Phi Beta Kappa, Alpha Omega Alpha. Home: 8 Elm Rd Scarsdale NY 10583-1410 Office: Am Health Found 1 Dana Rd Valhalla NY 10595-1549

WILLIAMS, GAYLEN EUGENE, accountant; b. Marlow, Okla., June 24, 1940; s. Gaylen Lafayette and Myrtle Francis (Sage) W.; m. Janice Ladean Moore, July 19, 1958; children: Mark, Gayla, Leland, Charm. Assoc. degree, Cameron Coll., Lawton, Okla., 1960. With Whiteway Grocery, Marlow, 1950-60; store mgr. Pratt Foods, Marlow, 1960-67; sales mgr. Jewel Co., Chgo., 1967-76; pvt. practice acct. Midwest City, Okla., 1976—.

WILLIAMS, GEORGE EARNEST, engineer, retired business executive; b. Bartow, Fla., Nov. 27, 1923; s. Earnest Roscoe and Ruby Barnett (Mathews) W.; m. Muriel Theodorsen, June 9, 1949. BS in Engring. with honors, USCG Acad., 1944; postgrad., Harvard U., 1945-46; SM in Mgmt., MIT, 1949. Registered profl. engr. 2 states. Project engr., bus. cons. Ebasco, N.Y.C.; design engr., prodn. supr. Minute Maid Corp., Orlando, Fla.; asst. contr., div. contr., group contr., corp. dir. fin. planning and analysis United Technologies Corp., Hartford, 1957-76, v.p., 1977-82; sr. v.p. Kensington Mgmt. Cons., 1982-84; sr. v.p. fin. Otis Elevator Co., N.Y.C., 1976-77; Mem. exec. com. Conn. Commerce Services and Expenditures, 1971. Contbr. articles to fin. jours., chpts. to books. Served with USCG, 1941-47. Mem. AIAA, Fin. Execs. Inst.; Army and Navy Club (Washington), Naples Yacht Club, Port Royal Club. Originator pricing system purchase of Fla. oranges for concentrate mfg.; avocation: yachtsman. Home: 1325 7th St S Naples FL 33940-7354

WILLIAMS, GEORGE HOWARD, lawyer, association executive; b. Hempstead, N.Y., Feb. 12, 1918; s. George R. and Marcella (Hogan) W.; m. Mary Celeste Madden, Nov. 23, 1946; children—Mary Beth Williams Barritt, Stephen, Kevin, Jeanne Marie. A.B., Hofstra Coll., 1939, LL.D. (hon.), 1969; J.D., N.Y. U., 1946, LL.D. (hon.), 1969; postgrad., Inst. Advanced Legal Studies, U. London, 1959. Bar: N.Y. 1946. Adminstrv. asst. to dean NYU Law Sch., N.Y.C., 1946-48, instr. law, 1948-50, asst. prof., 1950-52, assoc. prof., 1952-55, prof., 1956-62, v.p. univ. devel., 1962-66, exec. v.p. planning and devel., 1966-68; pres. Am. U., Washington, 1968-75; exec. v.p. dir. Am. Judicature Soc., Chgo., 1976-87. Author: (with A.T. Vanderbilt and L.L. Pelletier) Report on Liberal Adult Education, 1955; (with K. Sampson) Handbook for Judges, 1984. Bd. dirs. Nat. Ctr. Edn. Politics, 1948-58, trustee, 1958-65; trustee Hofstra U., 1961-64; chmn. bd. trustees Trinity Coll., Vt., 1978-86; bd. dirs. Ctr. for Conflict Resolution, 1988—; Univ. Support Svcs. Served to lt. col., inf. AUS, World War II. Decorated Legion of Merit, Silver Star. Mem. Am. Polit. Sci. Assn., ABA Assn. Bar City N.Y., Alpha Kappa Delta, Phi Delta Phi. Clubs: N.Y. U. (N.Y.C.); Nat. Lawyers (Washington). Home: 1322 Judson Ave Evanston IL 60201-4720 Office: Am Judicature Soc 25 E Washington St Ste 1600 Chicago IL 60602-1805

WILLIAMS, GEORGE HUNTSTON, church historian, educator; b. Huntsburg, Ohio, Apr. 7, 1914; s. David Rhys and Lucy Adams (Pease) W.; m. Marjorie Louise Derr, July 27, 1941; children: Portia, Jeremy, Jonathan, Roger. Student, U. Munich, 1934-35; AB, St. Lawrence U., 1936; BDiv, U. Chgo., 1939, LittD (hon.), 1965; postgrad., U. Strasbourg, 1939-40, U. Calif. 1943-45; ThD, Union Theol. Sem., 1946; DD (hon.), Meadville Theological Sch., 1954; DHL (hon.), Loyola U., 1980, St. Anselm Coll., 1984; DCnL (hon.), King's Coll. U., 1986; DD, U. Edinburgh, Scotland, 1987. Ordained to ministry Unitarian and Congl. Chs., 1940. Asst. minister Ch. of Christian Union, Rockford, Ill., 1940-41; mem. faculty Starr King Sch. for Ministry, Pacific Sch. Religion, Berkeley, Calif., 1941-47; assoc. prof. ch. history Starr King Sch. for Ministry, Pacific Sch. Religion, 1946-47; lectr. ch. history, head dept. Harvard Div. Sch., 1947-53, assoc. prof., acting dean, 1953-55, prof., 1955—, Winn prof. ecclesiastical history, 1956, Hollis prof. div., 1963-81, emeritus, 1981—; Fulbright lectr. U. Strasbourg, 1960-61; Gunning lectr. U. Edinburgh, Scotland, 1987. Author: The Church and the Democratic State and the Crisis in Religious Education, 1948, An Examination of the Thought of Frederic Henry Hedge, 1949, The Norman Anonymous of ca. 1100, 1951, Public Aid to Parochial Education, 1951, Christology and ChurchState Relations in the Fourth Century, 1951, Church History in the U.S 1900-1950, 1951, Church, State and Society in John Paul II, 1983; editor, contbr. Harvard Divinity School History, 1954, Ministry in the Patristic Period, 1956, Golden Priesthood and the Leaden State1, 1957, Anabaptist and Spiritual Writers, 1957, Anselm, 1960, The Radical Reformation, 1962 (enlarged Spanish edit. 1983, 2d English edit. 1992), Wilderness and Paradise, 1962, Camillo Renato, 1965, Georges Florovsky, 1965, Sacred Condominium in American Debate on Abortion, 1970, The Last Catholic Modernist, 1973, Two Social Strands Italian Anabaptism, 1973, The Stancarist Schism, 1980; co-editor: Writings of Thomas Hooker before 1633, 1976, Polish Brethren, 1601-85, 1980, Protestantism in The Ukraine, 1550-1701, 1978, The Mind of John Paul II, 1981; translator, editor Lubieniecki's History of the Polish Reformation, 1995, Divinings: Religion at Harvard, 1636-1992, 1993; mem. editorial bd. or co-editor: Harvard Theol. Rev. and Studies, Church History, Greek, Roman, and Byzantine Studies, Jour. Church and State, Studies in Romanticism, Mennonite Quar. Rev., Reflections, Bibliotheca Unitariorum. Decorated knight Order of St. Gregory the Great (John Paul II); Guggenheim fellow and IREX scholar U. Lublin, Poland, 1972-73; NEH 1980. Fellow Deputazione di Storia Patria per le Venezie (hon.); mem. Am. Soc. Reformation Research (pres. 1967), Patristic Soc., Am. Acad. Arts and Scis., Mediaeval Acad. Am., Am. Soc. Ch. History (pres. 1958), Cath. Hist. Assn., Société Européenne de Culture, Civil Liberties Union Mass. (adv. com.), Americans United for Life (pres. 1971-77), Mass. Hist. Soc., Phi Beta Kappa. Decorated by jubilee vol. Continuity in Church History, 1979. Home: 58 Pinehurst Rd Belmont MA 02178-1504 Office: Widener Libr K Cambridge MA 02138

WILLIAMS, GEORGE LEO, retired secondary education educator; b. N.Y.C., June 29, 1931; s. Leo Dominick and Cathryn Margaret (Schellderfer) W.; m. Adelia Gilda Musa, Feb. 26, 1958; children: Adelia, Marina, Gilda. BA, CUNY, 1953, MA, 1955; PhD, NYU, 1966. Tchr. Port Washington (N.Y.) Pub. Schs., 1953, chairperson integrated studies, 1960-65, coord. Amherst project, 1968-69, chairperson English dept., 1970-90; adminstrv. asst. secondary and higher edn. dept. NYU, N.Y.C., 1965-66; adj. prof. NYU, 1966-74, Adelphi U., Garden City, N.Y. 1966-68, Hofstra U., Hempstead, N.Y., 1967-74; chmn. profl. growth and devel. com. Port Washington Pub. Schs., 1973-90, chmn. bicentennial com. 1989-90, mem. policy bd. Port Washington Tchr. Ctr., 1987-90. Co-author: (play) The Triumph of the Constitution, 1988; author: (play) Remembrances of the First Colonial Settlement, 1993, (book) Fascist Thought and Totalitarianism in Italy's Secondary Schools: Theory and Practice, 1922-1943, 1993; editor Port Arrow Community Newsletter, 1973-84, Cow Neck Peninsula Hist. Soc. Newsletter, 1974-77; contbg. editor Long Island Forum, 1985—. Chairperson landmarks com. Cow Neck Peninsula Hist. Soc., Port Washington, 1980—, trustee, 1974-77; commr. landmarks com. Village of Port Washington North, 1983—, chmn., 1991; chair Hist. Landmark Preservation Commn., North Hempstead, N.Y., 1984—; Port Washington Continuing Edn. Advr. Coun. Recipient environ. award Residents for a More Beautiful Port Washington, 1994. Mem. ASCD, Nat. Coun. Tchrs. English, Soc. for Preservation L.I. Antiquities, Port Washington Tchrs. Assn. (v.p. 1963-64, bd. dirs. 1966-74, founder ret. tchrs. chpt. 1991, newsletter editor 1990-92), Am. Hist. Assn. (cert. recognition 1988), Friends for L.I.'s Heritage, Roslyn Landmark Soc., N.Y. Geneal./Biog. Soc., N.Y. State Hist. Assn., Fulbright Assn., Hofstra Univ. Club, Residents for a More Beautiful Port Washington (1994 Environ. award), Phi Beta Kappa, Phi Alpha Theta, Pi Sigma Alpha. Home: 84 Radcliff Ave Port Washington NY 11050-1600

WILLIAMS, GEORGE MASAYASU, religious organization administrator, editor; b. Seoul, Korea, June 16, 1930; came to U.S. 1957; naturalized, 1973; s. Masao and Yae (Yoshimoto) Sadanaga; m. Virginia K. Sueta, Mar. 17, 1961; children: Andrew, Monica, David. BA in Law, Meiji U., Tokyo, 1954, Phd in Hist. Sci., 1988; MA in Polit. Sci., U. Md., 1962. Organizer, gen. dir. Soka Gakkai Internat. - U.S.A., Santa Monica, Calif., 1960—; v.p. Soka Gakkai Internat., 1980—, organizer, gen. dir. emeritus, 1992—; founding editor, pub. World Tribune, newspaper, 1964—; editor, pub. Seikyo Times mag., 1981—; condr. Buddhist seminars at 80 univs. Author: An Introduction to True Buddhism, Freedom and Influence: The Role of Religion in America, 1985. Named Disting. Alumnus U. Md., 1974; fellow Soka U., Tokyo, 1975—. Office: Soka Gakkai Internat - USA 525 Wilshire Blvd Santa Monica CA 90401-1497

WILLIAMS, GEORGE RAINEY, surgeon, educator; b. Atlanta, Oct. 25, 1926; s. George Rainey and Hildred (Russell) W.; m. Martha Vose, June 16,

1950; children: Bruce, Alden, Margaret, Rainey. Student, U. Tex., 1944-46; B.S., Northwestern U., 1948; M.B., 1950, M.D., 1950. Intern Johns Hopkins Hosp., 1950-51, William Stewart Halsted fellow surgery, 1951-52, asst. resident surgery, 1952-53, asst. resident surgeon, 1955-57, resident surgeon, 1957-58; practice medicine specializing in gen. and thoracic surgery Oklahoma City, 1958—; asst. prof. surgery U. Okla. Health Scis. Center, Oklahoma City, 1958-61; assoc. prof. U. Okla. Health Scis. Center, 1961-63; prof. surgery U. Okla. Health Scis. Center Coll. of Medicine, 1963—, chmn. dept. surgery, 1974—; interim dean U. Okla. Coll. Medicine, 1981-82, 85-86, 88-89; dir. Am. Bd. Surgery, 1975-81, vice chmn., 1979-81. Contbr. articles on gen. and thoracic surgery to profl. jours. Served lt., MC, 3d Inf. Div. AUS, 1953-55. Recipient Disting. Service citation U. Okla., 1982; named to Okla. Hall of Fame, 1986. Fellow ACS (sec. bd. govs. 1985-87, 1st v.p. 1989-90), Soc. Univ. Surgeons, Am. Assn. Thoracic Surgery, So. Surg. Assn., Am. Surg. Assn., Phi Beta Kappa, Delta Kappa Epsilon, Phi Beta Pi, Alpha Epsilon Delta, Alpha Omega Alpha, Pi Kappa Epsilon. Home: 6722 Country Club Dr Oklahoma City OK 73116-4706 Office: U Okla Dept Surgery PO Box 26307 Oklahoma City OK 73126-0307

WILLIAMS, GEORGE WALTON, English educator; b. Charleston, S.C., Oct. 10, 1922; s. Ellison Adger and Elizabeth Simonton (Dillingham) W.; m. Harriet Porcher Simons, Nov. 28, 1953; children: George Walton Jr., Ellison Adger II, Harriet Porcher Stoney. B.A., Yale U., 1947; M.A., U. Va., 1949, Ph.D., 1957. Asst. cashier Carolina Savs. Bank, Charleston, 1949-54; asst. prof. English, Duke U., 1957-63, asso. prof., 1963-67, prof., 1967, chmn. dept. English, 1982-86, prof. emeritus, 1993—; dir. summer inst. Commn. on English, Coll. Entrance Exam. Bd., 1962; pres. Durham Savoyards, Ltd., 1966-68, 81-82; sr. fellow Coop. Program in Humanities, Duke-U. N.C. 1969; Historiographer, Diocese of S.C., 1960-78; vis. prof. U.S. Mil. Acad., 1982-83. Author: St. Michael's, Charleston, 1751-1951, 1951, Image and Symbol in the Sacred Poetry of Richard Crashaw, 1963, The Craft of Printing and the Publication of Shakespeare's Plays, 1985; editor: Romeo and Juliet, 1964, Complete Poetry of Richard Crasahw, 1970, Jacob Eckhard's Choirmaster's Book, 1971, Shakespeare's Speech-Headings, 1995; contbg. editor: Dramatic Works of Beaumont and Fletcher, 1966-96. Served with inf. U.S. Army, 1943-45, ETO. Decorated Combat Inf. badge; recipient Outstanding Civilian Service medal Dept. Army, 1983; Guggenheim Found. fellow, 1977-78; Huntington Library fellow, 1981. Mem. MLA (com. on new varioum 1980-92, chmn. Shakespeare div. 1990), South Atlantic MLA (pres. 1980-81), Southeastern Renaissance Conf. (editor 1960-70, 91-95, pres. 1973), Bibliog. Soc. U. Va., Royal Soc. Arts London, S.C. Hist. Soc., Carolina Yacht Club (Charleston), St. Cecilia Soc. (Charleston), Elizabethan Club Yale U., Phi Beta Kappa, Phi Kappa Phi. Home: 6 Sylvan Rd Durham NC 27701-2849 Office: Duke U Dept English Durham NC 27708

WILLIAMS, GERTIE BOOTHE, retired home school coordinator; b. Smithfield, Va.; d. Claiborne and Elnora Mae (Brown) Boothe; m. Jesse Cary Williams, June 14, 1949; children: Linda, Jesse Cary, Sharon. BS, Va. State Coll., 1945; postgrad., U. Va., 1971; MS, Va. State Coll., 1980. Technician Norfolk (Va.) Naval Base, 1942-43; filing clk. IRS, Bronx, N.Y., 1945-46; tchr. Sussex County, Waverly, Va., 1946-57; supervising tchr. Va. State U., Petersburg, 1957-59; tchr. Petersburg Pub. Schs., 1957-75, coordinator home sch., 1976-86; mentor Students in Upward Bound, Va. State U., 1992. Mem. Petersburg Commn. on Community Rels. Affairs, 1993—; mem. Women for Robb for Gov. of Va., Petersburg, 1979, MADD; area chmn. Am. Heart Assn., 1993; mem. women's com. Petersburg Symphony Orch.; mentor Links Inc. Project Children Learning About Self and Sch., 1994—. Recipient vol. svc. award Cystic Fibrosis Found., 1979, cert. of appreciation for mental health project Ctrl. State Hosp., 1980, Alumnus of Yr. award Petersburg chpt. Va. State U., 1978, Dir.'s award 1978, Nat. Alumna of Yr. award 1991, Disting. Alumna Citation of Yr. award Nat. Assn. Equal Opportunity in Higher Edn., 1992. Mem. NEA, Va. Edn. Assn., Va. State U. Nat. Assn. (v.p. 1984), Internat. Platform Assn., Wives Beaux-Twenty (reporter 1985-93), Jack and Jill Am. Ptnrs. (journalist 1957), Nat. Coun. Negro Women (local chmn. 1975), Order Ea. Star (worthy matron 1949-50), Nat. Alumni Assn. Va. State U. (life), Links (pres. 1977-79, coord. Just Say No 1986-87), Phi Delta Kappa (treas., historian 1978), Kappa Delta Pi (v.p., historian 1981-84), Delta Sigma Theta (pres. 1968-70, mentor Links, Inc. Project CLASS, 19. Democrat. Baptist. Avocations: reading, sewing, music, keeping scrapbooks. Home: 920 Shields St Petersburg VA 23803

WILLIAMS, GLEN MORGAN, federal judge; b. Jonesville, Va., Feb. 17, 1920; s. Hughy May and Hattie Mae W.; m. Jane Slemp, Nov. 17, 1962; children: Susan, Judy, Rebecca, Melinda. A.B. magna cum laude, Milligan Coll., 1940; J.D., U. Va., 1948. Bar: Va. 1947. Pvt. practice law Jonesville, 1948-76; judge U.S. Dist. Ct. (we. dist.) Va., 1976-88, sr. judge, 1988—; commonwealth's atty. Lee County, Va., 1948-51; mem. Va. Senate, 1953-55. Mem. editorial bd.: Va. Law Rev, 1946-47. Mem. Lee County Sch. Bd., 1972-76; trustee, elder First Christian Ch., Pennington Gap, Va. Lt. USN, 1942-46, MTO. Recipient Citation of Merit Va. Def. Lawyers Assn., Outstanding Alumnus award Milligan Coll., 1980. Mem. ABA, Va. State Bar (citation of merit), Va. Bar Assn. (citation of merit), Fed. Bar Assn., Va. Trial Lawyers Assn. (Meritorious Svc. award 1986, Disting. Svc. award), Am. Legion, 40 and 8. Republican. Clubs: Lions, Lee Players, Masons, Shriners. Office: US Dist Ct Fed Bldg PO Box 339 Abingdon CA 24212

WILLIAMS, GORDON BRETNELL, construction company executive; b. Phila., Apr. 3, 1929; s. Thomas W. and Helen (Berryman) W.; m. Susan M. Cunningham, June 20, 1953 (div. 1980); children: Lucy Chase, Marcus Bretnell. B.S., Yale, 1951. Registered profl. engr., Mich., Ohio, Tex. Chief indsl. engr. Chrysler Corp., Detroit, 1954-57; pres., dir. Cunningham-Limp Co., Birmingham, Mich., 1957-76; v.p.-mktg. H.K. Ferguson Co., Cleve., 1976-78; pres. H.K. Ferguson Co., 1979-85, vice chmn., 1986-91; exec. v.p. indsl. mfg. divsn. Morrison Kindsen Corp., 1992—. Bd. dirs. St. Vincent Charity Hosp. and Health Ctr., Cleve.; adv. bd. engring. sch. U. Akron. Served as ensign, ordnance USNR, 1952-54. Mem. Phi Gamma Delta. Clubs: Union (Cleve.); Yale of Ohio. Home: 12700 Lake Ave Cleveland OH 44107-1576 Office: MK-Ferguson Co 1500 W 3rd St Cleveland OH 44113-1453

WILLIAMS, GORDON HAROLD, medical educator, researcher; b. Denver, Colo., May 23, 1937; s. Freeman Royal and Vonda Lerne (Olsen) W.; m. Dorrell Deen Ward, June 11, 1963; children: Jeffrey Scott, Christopher Shawn, Jonathan Sylvan, TarrynSue, Megan Suzanne, Brenya Shannon. BA, Harvard U., 1959, MD, 1963. Diplomate Am. Bd. Internal Medicine, 1970, endocrinology, 1975, 93. Intern U. Chicago Hosps., 1963-64; resident Peter Bent Brigham Hosp., Boston, Mass., 1966-67; fellow, endocrinology, 1967-70; sr. physician Brigham Women's Hosp., Boston, Mass., 1981—; asst. prof. medicine Harvard U., Boston, 1970-73, assoc. prof., 1973-80, prof., 1980—; dir. endocrine and hypertension unit Brigham and Women's Hosp., Boston, 1973—; chief svc., 1980—. Lt. USN, 1964-66. Fellow ACP, Coun. High Blood Pressure Rsch.; mem. Endocrine Soc., Am. Soc. Clin. Investigation, Am. Physiol. Soc., Am. Assn. Physicians. Mem. LDS Ch. Office: Brigham and Womens Hosp Dept Endocrinology/Hypertension 221 Longwood Ave Boston MA 02115-5817*

WILLIAMS, GORDON L, aircraft manufacturing executive; b. 1932. BS, U. Colo. Dir. aircraft components program Martin Marietta Corp., Balt., 1959-85; group v.p. LTV Aerospace and Defense Co., Inc., Dallas, 1985-92; pres. Aircraft Products Group, Dallas, 1989; pres., CEO Vought Aircraft Co., Dallas, 1992—. Office: Vought Aircraft Co 9314 W Jefferson Blvd Dallas TX 75211-9302

WILLIAMS, GORDON ROLAND, librarian; b. Ontario, Oreg., July 26, 1914; s. Herbert Harrison and George Lola (Davis) W.; m. Jane Margaret Smith, Apr. 25, 1942; 1 dau., Megan Davis. AB, Stanford U. 1936; AM, U. Chgo., 1952. Vice pres. Brentano's Inc., Calif., 1945-49; chief asst. librarian UCLA, 1952-59; dir. Center for Research Libraries, Chgo., 1959-80; bd. dirs. Napa Valley Wine Libr., 1984-95; Mem. 1st Japan-U.S. Conf. on Libraries in Higher Edn., Tokyo, 1969, 2d Japan-U.S. Conf. on Libraries in Higher Edn., Wingspread, 1972, Internat. Conf. on Library Automation, Brasenose Coll., Oxford U., 1966; mem. archives and library com. Nat. Conservation Advisory Council, 1973—; Trustee, vice chmn. Bioscis. Info. of Biol. Abstracts, 1977-83; chmn. Conf. Cataloging and Info. Sers. for Machine-readable Data Files, 1978; mem. Study Com. Libraries and Archives Nat. Conservation Advisory Council, 1973—; chmn. adv. com. McCune Rare Book

Collection, 1989—. Author: Ravens and Crows, 1966, Bewick to Dovaston, Letters 1824-1828, 1968, Cost of Owning vs. Borrowing Serials, 1969; hon. editorial adv. Interlending Rev., Eng. Served with USNR, 1942-45. Decorated Commendation medal. Mem. ALA (chmn. com. nat. union catalogue 1960-85), Internat. Inst. Conservation Historic and Artistic Works, Assn. Research Libraries (com. on preservation of research library materials 1960-68, dir. 1964-67), Soc. Am. Archivists (chmn. com. on paper preservation 1970-77). Clubs: Caxton (Chgo., hon.); Rounce and Coffin, Zamorano (Los Angeles); Roxburghe (San Francisco).

WILLIAMS, GREGORY HOWARD, lawyer, educator; b. Muncie, Ind., Nov. 12, 1943; s. James Anthony Williams; m. Sara Catherine Whitney, Aug. 29, 1969; children: Natalia Dora, Zachary Benjamin, Anthony Bladimir, Carlos Gregory. B.A., Ball State U., 1966; M.A., U. Md., 1969; Ph.D., George Washington U., 1982, M.Ph., 1977, J.D., 1971. Bar: Va. 1971, D.C. 1972. Dep. sheriff Delaware County, Muncie, Ind., 1963-66; tchr. Falls Ch. Public Sch., Va., 1966-70; legis. asst. U.S. Senate, Washington, 1971-73; dir. exptl. programs George Washington U., 1973-77; prof. law U. Iowa Coll. Law, Iowa City, 1977-93; assoc. v.p. Acad. Affairs U. Iowa, 1991-93; dean, prof. law Ohio State U., Columbus, 1993—. Author: Law and Politics of Police Discretion, 1984, Iowa Guide to Search and Seizure, 1986, Life on the Color Line: The True Story of a White Boy Who Discovered He Was Black, 1995. Mem. Iowa Adv. Commn. to U.S. Commn. on Civil Rights, Washington, 1978-86; chmn., mem. Iowa Law Enforcement Acad., Camp Dodge, 1979-85. Recipient cert. of appreciation Black Law Students Assn., Iowa City, 1984, GW Edn. Opportunity Program, Washington, 1977, Disting. Alumnus award George Washington U., Nat. Law Ctr., 1994. Office: Ohio State U Coll of Law 55 W 12th Ave Columbus OH 43210-1338

WILLIAMS, H. RANDOLPH, lawyer; b. Miami, Okla., Oct. 11, 1942. AB, U. Kans., 1964; JD, So. Meth. U., 1968; LLM, NYU, 1971. Bar: Tex. 1967, Kans. 1970, Ill. 1978. Ptnr. Baker & McKenzie, Chgo. Office: Baker & McKenzie 1 Prudential Plz 130 E Randolph St Chicago IL 60601

WILLIAMS, HANK, JR., country music singer, songwriter; b. Shreveport, La., May 26, 1949; s. Hank and Audrey W.; 1 son, Shelton Hank; m. 2d Beck White (div.); children: Hilary, Holly; m. Mary Jane Thomas, July 1990. Performer throughout U.S.; recorded song Ain't Misbehavin'; latest albums include: Montana Cafe, 1986, Hank Live, 1987, Born to Boogie, 1987, Wild Streak, 1988, Greatest Hits III, Lone Wolf, 1990, Pure Hank, 1991, (with Clink Black) Maverick, 1992, Out of Left Field, 1993, A Tribute to My Father, 1993, (with Waylon Jennings and Ray Charles) Greatest Hits, vol. 2, 1994; composer All My Roudy Friends, 1993. Recipient 18 Gold albums, 5 Platinum/1 Double Platinum album; voted Entertainer of Yr. Acad. Country Music, 1987, 88, 89, Entertainer of Yr. Country Music Assn., 1987, 88, Video of Yr. award Acad. Country Music, 1987-88, best music video Acad. Country Music, 1989, Album of Yr. Acad. Country Music, 1989, Music Video of Yr. Country Music Assn., 1987, Grammy award, 1990. Office: Hank Williams Jr Enterprises PO Box 850 Paris TN 38242-0850 Office: Warner/Curb Records 10585 Santa Monica Blvd # 300 Los Angeles CA 90025-4921*

WILLIAMS, HAROLD, geology educator; b. St. John's, Nfld., Can., Mar. 14, 1934; s. Alexander and Catherine (Snow) W.; m. Emily Jean King, Sept. 19, 1958; children—Alexander, David, Steven. B.Sc., Meml. U., 1956, diploma in engring., 1956, M.Sc., 1958; Ph.D., U. Toronto, 1961. Research scientist Geol. Survey Can., Ottawa, Ont., 1961-68; prof. geology Meml. U., St. John's, 1968—, Alexander Murray prof., 1990—. Contbr. numerous articles and geol. maps to profl. jours. Killam scholar Can. Council, 1977-81, Miller medal Royal Soc. Can., 1987, Gov. Gen.'s medal Meml. U. Fellow Royal Soc. Can., Geol. Assn. Can. (Past Pres. medal 1976, Logan medal 1988), Geol. Soc. Am., Can. Soc. Petroleum Geologists (Douglas medal 1981). Avocation: folk musician. Office: Meml Univ Dept Earth Sci, SJ Carew Bldg, Saint John's, NF Canada A1B 3X5

WILLIAMS, HAROLD ANTHONY, retired newspaper editor; b. Milw., Apr. 22, 1916; s. Harold Ambrose and Helen Theresa (Schmitt) W.; m. Ruth Edna Smith, Oct. 17, 1942; children—Anne Meredith Williams Gibson, Mary Helen Williams Winter, Sara B. Williams Cherner, Julie C. Williams Stewart. A.B., U. Notre Dame, 1938. Editor Towson (Md.) Union News, 1938-40; mem. staff Balt. Sunpapers, 1940-81; fgn. corr. Balt. Sunpapers, Europe, 1949-50; asst. to exec. editor, then city desk editor Balt. Sunpapers 1950-54, Sunday editor, 1954-79, asst. mng. editor, 1979-81; sr. instr. Towson (Md.) State U., 1982-89; chmn. Newspaper Comics Coun., 1970-72, mem. exec. com., 1972-81; chmn. curriculum com., lectr. Renaissance Inst., Coll. Notre Dame of Md., 1989-92; discussion leader Am. Press Inst.; lectr. Towson State U. Elderhostel, 1993—. Author: A History of the Western Maryland Railway, 1952, Baltimore Afire, 3d edit. 1990, Guide to Baltimore and Annapolis, 1957, History of the Hibernian Society of Baltimore, 1957, A History of Eudowood, 1964, Robert Garrett and Sons, 1965, Bodine, A Legend in His Time, 1971; The Baltimore Sun, 1837-1987. Chmn. Friends Coun., Albin O. Kuhn Libr. and Gallery, U. Md., Balt. County, 1990—; mem. adv. coun. Friends of the Johns Hopkins U. Librs., 1990—, pres., 1993—. With CIC, AUS, 1942-46. Named Marylander of Yr., Md. Colonial Soc., 1989. Mem. Am. Assn. Sunday and Feature Editors, Wine and Food Soc. Balt. (pres. 1979-81), Balt. Bibliophiles (pres. 1978-79, exec. com.), Md. Hist. Soc., 14 W Hamilton St. Club (Balt.), Johns Hopkins Club. Democrat. Roman Catholic. Home: 307 Cedarcroft Rd Baltimore MD 21212-2520

WILLIAMS, HAROLD MARVIN, foundation official, former government official, former university dean, former corporate executive; b. Phila., Jan. 5, 1928; s. Louis W. and Sophie (Fox) W.; m. Nancy Englander; children: Ralph A., Susan J., Derek M. AB, UCLA, 1946; JD, Harvard U., 1949; postgrad. U. So. Calif. Grad. Sch. Law, 1955-56; DHL (hon.), Johns Hopkins U., 1987. Bar: Calif. 1950; practiced in Los Angeles, 1950, 53-55; with Hunt Foods and Industries, Inc., Los Angeles, 1955-68, v.p. 1958-60, exec. v.p., 1960-66, pres., 1968; gen., mgr. Hunt-Wesson Foods, 1964-66, pres., 1966-68; chmn. finance com. Norton Simon, Inc., 1968-70, chmn. bd., 1969-70, dir., 1959-77; dir. Times-Mirror Corp., SunAmerica; prof. mgmt., dean Grad. Sch. Mgmt., UCLA, 1970-77; pres., dir. Special Investments & Securities Inc., 1961-66; chmn. SEC, Washington, 1977-81; pres., chief exec. officer J. Paul Getty Trust, 1981—; regent U. Calif., 1983-94. Mem. Commn. for Econ. Devel. State of Calif., 1973-77; energy coordinator City of Los Angeles, 1973-74; public mem. Nat. Advt. Review Bd., 1971-75; co-chmn. Public Commn. on Los Angeles County Govt.; mem. Coun. on Fgn. Rels., Com. for Econ. Devel.; commn. to rev. Master Plan for Higher Edn., State of Calif., 1985-87; trustee Nat. Humanities Ctr. Served as 1st lt. AUS, 1950-53. Mem. State Bar Calif. Office: J Paul Getty Trust 401 Wilshire Blvd Ste 900 Santa Monica CA 90401

WILLIAMS, HAROLD ROGER, economist, educator; b. Arcade, N.Y., Aug. 22, 1935; s. Harry Alfred and Gertrude Anna (Scharf) W.; m. Lucia Dorothy Preuschoff, Apr. 23, 1955; children: Theresa Lynn, Mark Roger. B.A., Harpur Coll., SUNY, Binghamton, 1961; M.A., Pa. State U., 1963; Ph.D., U. Nebr., 1966; postgrad., Harvard U., 1969-70. Instr., Pa. State U., 1962-63; Instr. U. Nebr., 1965-66; mem. faculty Kent (Ohio) State U., 1966-68; prof. econs. and internat. bus., 1971—, chmn., dept., 1974-81, dir. Internat. Bus. Program, Grad. Sch. Mgmt., 1980-86, chmn. faculty senate, 1988-89; assoc. dean Grad. Sch. Mgmt., 1994—; econ. cons. and adv. to numerous govt., bus. and internat. orgns. Author over 100 books and articles in field. Served with AUS, 1954-57. Grantee NSF. Mem. Am. Econ. Assn., Internat. Econs. Assn., Acad. Internat. Bus., Midwest Econ. Assn. (v.p. 1969-70), So. Econ. Assn., Phi Gamma Mu, Omicron Delta Epsilon, Beta Gamma Sigma. Home: 415 Suzanne Dr Kent OH 44240-1933 Office: Dept Econs Kent State U Kent OH 44242

WILLIAMS, HARRY GEORGE, minister; b. Kokomo, Ind., Aug. 9, 1925; s. Thomas Ralph and Marguerite Ann (Bergman) W.; m. Mary Virginia Carroll, Aug. 25, 1952 (dec. 1972); children: Barbara, Thomas, Kathleen, Mary Beth, Harry, Timothy; m. Trudy Anne Sly, June 17, 1980. BFA in Broadcast Edn., Cin. Coll. Music, 1949; MDiv, Gen. Theol. Sem., N.Y.C., 1978. Ordained priest Episcopal Ch., 1979. Tchg. asst., reading Gen. Theol. Seminary, 1976-77; canon residentiary St. Peter's Cathedral, St. Petersburg, Fla., 1978-80; rector/vicar St. Luke's Ch./Our Savior Ch., Lincolnton, N.C., 1980-83; founding rector St. Anne of Grace Ch., Seminole, Fla., 1983-92;

ret., 1992; mem. Diocesan Coun. St. Luke's Ch., Lincolnton, 1981-83, St. Anne of Grace Ch., Seminole, 1986-89; founding dir. Mission 4 Consortium of Small Chs., 1981-83; dean Shelby Deanery, 1982-83; founding legis. del. Episc. Synod of Am., Ft. Worth, 1989—. With USN, 1943-45. Mem. Soc. Holy Cross, Evang. and Cath. Mission, Nat. Orgn. Episcs. for Life. Republican. Home: 8021 Bayhaven Dr Largo FL 34646-3320

WILLIAMS, HENRY STRATTON, radiologist, educator; b. N.Y.C., Aug. 26, 1929; m. Frances S. Williams; children: Mark I, Paul S. BA HS, CCNY, 1950; MD, Howard U., 1955. Diplomate Nat. Bd. Med. Examiners. Intern Brooke Army Hosp., San Antonio, 1956; resident in radiology Letterman Army Hosp., San Francisco, 1957-60; pvt. practice radiology L.A., 1963—; assoc. clin. prof. radiology Charles R. Drew Med. Sch., L.A.; chmn. bd. Charles Drew U. Medicine and Sci. Found.; interim pres. Charles R. Drew U. of Medicine and Sci. Mem. ad hoc adv. com. Joint Commn. Accreditation Hosps. Served to maj. U.S. Army, 1960-63. Fellow Am. Coll. Radiology; mem. Calif. Physicians Service (bd. dirs. 1971-77), Calif. Med. Assn. (counselor, mem. appeals bd., del., chmn. urban health com.), Los Angeles County Med. Assn.

WILLIAMS, HENRY THOMAS, retired banker, real estate agent; b. Worton, Md., Mar. 27, 1932; s. Henry Thomas W. and Ivy Lorraine (Urie) Francis; m. Marion Dwyer, Aug. 1953 (div. 1954); m. Laura Lynne Davis, Sept. 13, 1958; children: Lisa C. Ross, Henry Thomas III, Davis F. Student, Washington Coll., 1951-52; grad., ABA Nat. Installment Credit Sch. at U. Chgo., 1968, Va.-Md. Sch. Bank Mgmt. at U. Va., 1972. Teller Chestertown Bank Md., 1960-61, note teller, 1961-63, asst. cashier, 1963-68, mgr. installment loans, 1968-73, v.p.; sr. loan officer, sec., 1973-85; v.p. br. mgr. Chestertown Bank Md., Rock Hall, 1985-88; now associate broker Wm. Norris Clark, Realtor, Chestertown; mem. Kent County Real Estate Bd., Chestertown. Past dir. United Way Kent County, Chestertown; past vestryman, past chmn. budget com. St. Paul's Ch., Chestertown. Mem. Bank Adminstrn. Inst. (past sec., past chmn. Ea. Shore Chpt.), Md. Bankers Assn. (past v.p., past chmn. group 5), Md. Young Bankers Com., Chester River Yacht and Country Club, Lions (bd. dirs., past sec., past v.p.). Democrat. Home: 21139 Green Ln Rock Hall MD 21661-0161 Office: Wm Norris Clark Realtor Rt 213 N 801 Washington Ave Chestertown MD 21620

WILLIAMS, HERBERT J., bishop. Bishop of N. Cen. Mich. Ch. of God in Christ, Saginaw. Office: Ch of God in Christ 1600 Cedar St Saginaw MI 48601-2837

WILLIAMS, HIBBARD EARL, medical educator, physician; b. Utica, N.Y., Sept. 28, 1932; s. Hibbard G. and Beatrice M. W.; m. Sharon Towne, Sept. 3, 1982; children: Robin, Hans. AB, Cornell U., 1954, MD, 1958. Diplomate Am. Bd. Internal Medicine. Intern Mass. Gen. Hosp., Boston, 1958-59, resident in medicine, 1959-60, 62-64, asst. physician, 1964-65; clin. assoc. Nat. Inst. Arthritis and Metabolic Diseases, NIH, Bethesda, MD, 1960-62; instr. medicine Harvard U., Boston, 1964-65; asst. prof. medicine U. Calif., San Francisco, 1965-68, assoc. prof., 1968-72, prof., 1972-78, chief divsn. med. genetics, 1968-70, vice chmn. dept. medicine, 1970-78; prof., chmn. dept. medicine Cornell U. Med. Coll., N.Y.C., 1978-80; physician-in-chief N.Y. Hosp.-Cornell Med. Ctr., N.Y.C., 1978-80; dean Sch. Medicine U. Calif., Davis, 1980-92, prof. internal medicine, 1980—; mem. program project com. NIH, Nat. Inst. Arthritis and Metabolic Diseases, 1971-73. Editor med. staff confs. Calif. Medicine, 1966-70; mem. editl. bd. Clin. Rsch., 1968-71, Am. Jour. Medicine, 1978-88; cons. editor Medicine, 1978-86; assoc. editor Metabolism, 1970-80; mem. adv. bd. physiology in medicine New Eng. Jour. Medicine, 1970-75; contbr. articles to med. jours. With USPHS, 1960-62. Recipient Career Devel. award USPHS, 1968; recipient award for excellence in teaching Kaiser Found., 1970, Disting. Faculty award U. Calif. Alumni-Faculty Assn., 1978; John and Mary R. Markle scholar in medicine, 1968. Fellow ACP; mem. AAAS, Am. Fedn. Clin. Rsch., Am. Soc. Clin. Investigation (sec.-treas. 1974-77), Assn. Am. Physicians, Assn. Am. Med. Colls. (adminstrv. bd., coun. deans 1989-92, exec. coun. 1990-92), Calif. Acad. Medicine (pres. 1984), San Francisco Diabetes Assn. (bd. dirs. 1971-72), Western Assn. Physicians (v.p. 1977-78), Western Soc. Clin. Rsch., Calif. Med. Assn. (chmn. coun. sci. affairs 1990-95, bd. dirs. 1990-95), Am. Clin. and Climatol. Soc., St. Francis Yacht Club, Alpha Omega Alpha. Office: U Calif Sch Medicine Davis CA 95616

WILLIAMS, HIRAM DRAPER, artist, educator; b. Indpls., Feb. 11, 1917; s. Earl Boring and Inez Mary (Draper) W.; m. Avonell Baumunk, July 7, 1941; children—Curtis Earl, Kim Avonell. B.S., Pa. State U., 1950, M.Ed., 1951. Tchr. art U. So. Calif., 1953-54, UCLA, summer 1959, U. Tex., 1954-60; mem. faculty and pres's. coun. U. Fla., Gainesville, 1960—; Disting. Service prof. U. Fla., until 1982, prof. emeritus, 1982; Mem. chancellor's council U. Tex. System. Exhibited, Pa. Acad. Fine Arts anns., Whitney Mus. Am. Art bi-anns., Corcoran Gallery Bi-anns., U. Ill. bi-anns., Mus. Modern Art anns., also Nordness Gallery, N.Y.C.; represented in permanent exhbns., Mus. Modern Art, Wilmington Art Center, Whitney Mus. of Am. Art, N.Y.C., Sheldon Meml. Art Mus., Milw. Art Center, Guggenheim Mus., Smithsonian Inst., Harn Art Mus., U. Fla., Yale; also pvt. collections; author: Notes for a Young Painter, 1963, rev., 1985; contbr. articles to mags. Served to capt. C.E. U.S. Army, World War II, ETO. Tex. Rsch. grantee, 1968; Guggenheim fellow, 1967-68; inducted into Fla. Artists Hall of Fame, 1994. Address: 2804 NW 30th Terr Gainesville FL 32605 *My desire as a painter is to animate material with imagery that strikes conjunctions of art and life.*

WILLIAMS, HOWARD RUSSELL, lawyer, educator; b. Evansville, Ind., Sept. 26, 1915; s. Clyde Alfred and Grace (Preston) W.; m. Virginia Merle Thompson, Nov. 3, 1942; 1 son, Frederick S.T. AB, Washington U., St. Louis, 1937; LLB, Columbia U., 1940. Bar: N.Y. 1941. With firm Root, Clark, Buckner & Ballantine, N.Y.C., 1940-41; prof. law, asst. dean U. Tex. Law Sch., Austin, 1946-51; prof. law Columbia U. Law Sch., N.Y.C., 1951-63; Dwight prof. Columbia Law Sch., 1959-63; prof. law Stanford U., 1963-85, Stella W. and Ira S. Lillick prof., 1968-82, prof. emeritus, 1982, Robert E. Paradise prof. natural resources, 1983-85, prof. emeritus, 1985—; Oil and gas cons. President's Materials Policy Commn., 1951; mem. Calif. Law Revision Commn., 1971-79, vice chmn., 1976-77, chmn., 1978-79. Author or co-author: Cases on Property, 1954, Cases on Oil and Gas, 1956, 5th edit., 1987, Decedents' Estates and Trusts, 1968, Future Interests, 1970, Oil and Gas Law, 8 vols., 1959-64 (with ann. supplements/rev. 1964-95), abridged edit., 1973, Manual of Oil and Gas Terms, 1957, 9th edit., 1994. Bd. regents Berkeley Baptist Divsn. Sch., 1966-67; trustee Rocky Mountain Mineral Law Found., 1964-66, 68-85. Maj. U.S. Army, 1941-46. Recipient Clyde O. Martz Tchg. award Rocky Mountain Mineral Law Found., 1994. Mem. Phi Beta Kappa. Democrat. Home: 360 Everett Ave Apt 4B Palo Alto CA 94301-1422 Office: Stanford U Sch Law Nathan Abbott Way Stanford CA 94305

WILLIAMS, HUGH ALEXANDER, JR., retired mechanical engineer, consultant; b. Spencer, N.C., Aug. 18, 1926; s. Hugh Alexander and Mattie Blanche (Megginson) W.; BS in Mech. Engring., N.C. State U., 1948, MS in Diesel Engring. (Norfolk So. R.R. fellow), 1950; postgrad. Ill. Benedictine Coll. Inst. Mgmt., 1980; m. Ruth Ann Gray, Feb. 21, 1950; children: David Gray, Martha Blanche Williams Heidengren. Jr. engr.-field service engr. Baldwin-Lima Hamilton Corp., Hamilton, Ohio, 1950-52, project engr., 1953-55; project engr. Electro-Motive div. Gen. Motors Corp., La Grange, Ill., 1955-58, sr. project engr., 1958-63, supr. product devel. engine design sect., 1963-86, staff engr., advanced mech. tech., 1986-87. Trustee Downers Grove (Ill.) San. Dist., 1965-92, pres., 1974-91, v.p., 1992-91; pres. Ill. Assn. San. Dists., 1976-77, bd. dirs., 1977-89; mem. statewide policy adv. com. Ill. EPA, 1977-79; mem. DuPage County Intergovtl. Task Force Com., 1988-92; elder Presbyn. Ch. Served with USAAC, 1945. Registered profl. engr., Ill. Recipient Trustee Svc. award Ill. Assn. San. Dists., 1986, Citizens award Downers Grove Evening chpt. Kiwanis, 1991. Fellow ASME (chmn. honors and awards com. 1993—, Diesel and Gas Engine Power Div. Speaker awards 1968, 84, Div. citation 1977, Internal Combustion Engine award 1987, exec. com. Internal Combustion Engine div. 1981-87, ASME chmn. 1985-86, sec. 1988-92); mem. Soc. Automotive Engrs. (life), ASME (chmn. Soichiro Honda medal com. 1987-92), Ill. Assn. Wastewater Agys. (Outstanding Mem. award 1990, hon. mem. 1992), Lions, Masons (32 degree), Sigma Pi. Republican. Editor: So. Engr., 1947-48; contbr. articles to profl. jours. Patentee in field. Home: 2108 Weybridge Dr Raleigh NC 27615-5562

WILLIAMS, HULEN BROWN, former university dean; b. Lauratown, Ark., Oct. 8, 1920; s. Ernest Burdett and Ann Jeanette (Miller) W.; m. Virginia Anne Rice, June 20, 1942 (dec. June 1970); children: James Browning, Virginia Jean; m. Michaela Galasso, Mar. 20, 1971. BA, Hendrix Coll., 1941; MS, La. State U., 1943, PhD, 1948; postgrad., Cornell U., summer 1950, U. Calif., Berkeley, 1953. Instr. through assoc. prof. La. State U., Baton Rouge, 1947-56; prof., head chemistry dept. La. State U., 1956-68, dean Coll. Chemistry and Physics, 1968-82; ret., 1982; Cons. to chem. and legal professions. Co-author books on chemistry; contbr. articles to profl. jours. Served to lt. (j.g.) USNR, 1944-46. Mem. Am. Chem. Soc., Sigma Xi, Sigma Pi Sigma, Phi Lambda Upsilon, Phi Kappa Phi, Omicron Delta Kappa. Home: 470 Castle Kirk Dr Baton Rouge LA 70808-6011

WILLIAMS, IRVING LAURENCE, physics educator; b. Newport, R.I., Dec. 3, 1935; s. Leroy Payton and Alberta Helen (Troy) W.; m. Carrie Mae Graves, Aug. 26, 1967; children: Cheryl Anita, Carla Chantrase. EdB, R.I. Coll., 1957; MA in Teaching, Brown U., 1962; PhD, NYU, 1975. Cert. teaching, R.I. Classroom tchr. Newport (R.I.) Sch. Dept., 1962-63; prof. physics Morgan State U., Balt., 1963-67; prof. physics Nassau Community Coll., Garden City, N.Y., 1967—, asst. to pres., 1980-85; adj. prof. Hofstra U., Hempstead, N.Y., 1980-87; dist. clk. Roosevelt (N.Y.) Sch. Bd., 1989-91. Co-author: (lab. workbook) Meterology Lab. Exercises, 1975, 76. Treas. Econ. Opportunity Commn., Nassau County, N.Y., 1984; trustee Grace Lutheran Ch., Malverne, N.Y., 1987, Roosevelt Bd. Edn., 1988; active Roosevelt Rep. Club, 1989; mem. sch. bd. Grace Lutheran Sch., Malverne, 1991. With U.S. Army, 1957-60. Recipient Chancellor's award SUNY, 1975, Citizen's award EOC Nassau County, Hempstead, 1987, Roosevelt Educator's award, Roosevelt Coun., 1989; NSF Weather Svc. grantee, Washington, 1989. Mem. AAUP, Nat. Sci. Tchrs. Assn., Am. Assn. Physics Tchrs., Soc. Coll. Sci. Tchrs., N.Y. Acad. Sci., Am. Assn. Higher Edn., N.Y. Assn. Two Yr. Colls. Republican. Avocation: piano. Home: 220 Beechwood Ave Roosevelt NY 11575-1634 Office: Nassau C C Physical Sciences Dept Garden City NY 11530

WILLIAMS, J. BRYAN, lawyer; b. Detroit, July 23, 1947; s. Walter J. and Maureen June (Kay) W.; m. Jane Elizabeth Eisele, Aug. 24, 1974; children: Kyle Joseph, Ryan Patrick. AB, U. Notre Dame, 1969; JD, U. Mich., 1972. Bar: Mich. 1972, U.S. Dist. Ct. (ea. dist.) Mich. 1972. Exec. ptnr. Dickinson, Wright, Moon, Van Dusen & Freeman, Detroit, 1972—. Mem. Mich. Bar Assn., Detroit Bar Assn. (bd. dirs.), Notre Dame Club (Detroit pres. 1984), Oakland Hills Country Club, Nat. Club Assn. (bd. dirs.), Greater Detroit C. of C. (bd. dirs.). Roman Catholic. Home: 993 Suffield Ave Birmingham MI 48009-1242 Office: 500 Woodward Ave Ste 4000 Detroit MI 48226-3425

WILLIAMS, J. VERNON, lawyer; b. Honolulu, Apr. 26, 1921; s. Urban and W. Amelia (Olson) W.; m. Malvina H. Hitchcock, Oct. 4, 1947 (dec. May 1970); children—Carl H., Karin, Frances E., Scott S.; m. Mary McLellan, Sept. 6, 1980. Student, Phillips Andover Acad., 1937-39; B.A. cum laude, Amherst Coll., 1943; LL.B., Yale, 1948. Bar: Wash. 1948. Assoc. Riddell, Riddell & Hemphill, 1948-50; ptnr. Riddell, Williams, Bullitt & Walkinshaw (and predecessor firms), 1950—; lectr. Wash. Bar Rev. Assos., 1949-63; Sec., dir. Airborne Freight Corp., 1968-79, gen. counsel, 1968—. Chmn. March of Dimes, Seattle, 1954-55; Mem. Mayor's City Charter Rev. Com., 1968-69; chmn. Seattle Bd. Park Commrs., 1966-68; co-chmn. parks and open space com. Forward Thrust, 1966-69; dir. bd. and commrs br. Nat. Recreation and Parks Assn., 1968-69; chmn. Gov.'s adv. com. Social and Health Services, 1972-75; Bd. dirs. Seattle Met. YMCA, 1965—, pres., 1976-79; trustee Lakeside Sch., 1971-79; mem. alumni council Phillps Andover Acad., 1970-73, Yale Law Sch., 1969-77; chancellor St. Mark's Cathedral, Seattle, 1964—. Served with USAAF, 1943-45. Mem. Univ. Club, Seattle Tennis Club, Birnam Wood Golf Club. Home: 1100 38th Ave E Seattle WA 98112-4434 Office: 4400 1001 4th Ave Plaza Seattle WA 98154

WILLIAMS, JACK MARVIN, chemist; b. Delta, Colo., Sept. 26, 1938; s. John Davis and Ruth Emma (Gallup) W. B.S. with honors, Lewis and Clark Coll., 1960; M.S., Wash. State U., 1964, Ph.D., 1966. Postdoctoral fellow Argonne (Ill.), Nat. Lab., 1966-68, asst. chemist, 1968-70, assoc. chemist, 1970-72, chemist, 1972-77, sr. chemist, group leader, 1977—; vis. guest prof. U. Mo., Columbia, 1980, 81, 82, U. Copenhagen, 1980, 83, 85; chair Gordon Rsch. Conf. (Inorganic Chemistry), 1980. Bd. editors: Inorganic Chemistry, 1979—, assoc. editor, 1982-93. Crown-Zellerbach scholar, 1959-60; NDEA fellow, 1960-63; recipient Disting. Performance at Argonne Nat. Labs. award U. Chgo., 1987, Centennial Disting. Alumni award Wash. State U., 1990. Mem. Am. Crystallographic Assn., Am. Chem. Soc. (treas. inorganic div. 1982-84), Am. Phys. Soc., AAAS. Office: Chemistry Div 9700 Cass Ave Lemont IL 60439-4803

WILLIAMS, JAMES A., principal. Prin. Gulliver Prep. Sch., Miami, Fla. Recipient Blue Ribbon award U.S. Dept. Edn., 1990-91. Office: Gulliver Prep Sch 6575 N Kendall Dr Miami FL 33156-1899

WILLIAMS, JAMES ALEXANDER, lawyer; b. Pine Bluff, Ark., Oct. 30, 1929; s. Absalom Alexander and Kyle (Baggarly) W.; m. Janet L. Bray, Nov. 27, 1953; children: Laura Kay, Victoria Lynn, Diana Leigh. Student, U. Ark., 1948; B.A., So. Methodist U., 1951, J.D., 1952, M.L.A., 1971. Bar: Tex. 1952. Since practiced in Dallas; mem. firm Touchstone, Bernays & Johnston, 1955-57; partner firm Bailey and Williams, 1957—. Bd. dirs. Spl. Care Sch.; bd. mgmt. YMCA; chmn. adminstrv. bd. Univ. Park United Meth. Ch., 1973; bd. dirs. Dallas Opera. Lt. USNR, 1952-55. Mem. ABA, Dallas Bar Assn., State Bar Tex., Dallas, Tex. Assn. Def. Counsel, Internat. Assn. Def. Counsel, Fedn. Ins. and Corp. Counsel, Am. Bd. Trial Advocates, Acad. Hosp. Attys., Trial Attys. Am., So. Meth. U. Law Alumni Assn. (pres. 1970-72), Exch. Club (pres. 1967), Dallas Club, Northwood Club, Crescent Club, Giraud Club (San Antonio), Chapperal Club (Dallas), Lambda Chi Alpha, Phi Alpha Delta. Democrat. Home: 4630 Northaven Rd Dallas TX 75229-4225 Office: Maxus Energy Bldg 717 N Harwood St Ste 1650 Dallas TX 75201-9999 *Honesty and fair dealing with one's fellow man are essential to real success.*

WILLIAMS, JAMES ARTHUR, retired army officer, information systems company executive; b. Paterson, N.J., Mar. 29, 1932; s. Charles M. and Elsie (Kretszchmar) W.; m. Barbara Widnall, June 26, 1959; children: Steven, Karen. BS, U.S. Mil. Acad.; MA in Latin Am. Studies, U. N.Mex. Commd. 2d lt. U.S. Army, 1954, advanced through grades to lt. gen.; asst. army attache U.S. Def. Attache Office, Caracas, Venezuela, 1966-72; exch. officer State-Def. Exch. Program Office of Sec. Def., Washington, 1972-74; comdr. 650th MI Group, Shape, 1974-76; dir. prep. def. estimates Def. Intelligence Agy., Washington, 1977-80; dep. chief staff for intelligence U.S. Army, Europe, 1980-81; dir. Def. Intelligence Agy., Washington, 1981-85; ret., 1985; v.p. PSC Corp., 1986; pres. Direct Info. Access Corp., Annandale, Va., 1987—. Decorated Legion of Merit, Bronze Star with oak leaf cluster, Air medals, D.S.M., Nat. Intelligence D.S.M., Army Commendation medal, French Legion of Honor; Dist. Mem. Mil. Intelligence Hall of Fame. Mem. Assn. U.S. Army, Nat. Mil. Intelligence Assn. (chmn. bd. 1987—). Methodist. Home: 8928 Maurice Ln Annandale VA 22003-3914 Office: Direct Info Access Corp PO Box 721 Annandale VA 22003-0721

WILLIAMS, JAMES B., retail electronics company executive; b. Toronto, Ont., Can., Oct. 16, 1945; s. Norman James and Marie (McBride) W.; m. Kathleen Mary Fitzgerald, May 10, 1969; children: Jason Lawrence, Laura Marie. BA, U. Toronto, Ont., Can., 1967; MBA, U. Toronto, 1969. Sr. v.p. fin. and adminstrn., CFO Dominion Stores Ltd., Toronto, 1969-85; exec. v.p. fin. and adminstrn., CFO Gt. Atlantic & Pacific Tea Co. Can. Inc., Toronto, 1985-86; exec. v.p. fin. and adminstrn., CFO Can. Tire Corp. Ltd., Toronto, 1986-92, exec. v.p. mktg., real estate, constrn. and distbn., 1988-91, pres. mdse. bus. group, corp. exec. v.p. dealer rels., 1992-91; pres., CEO InterTAN Inc., Mississauga, 1992—. Office: InterTAN Inc., 2700 Matheson Blvd E Ste 401, Mississauga, ON Canada L4W 4V9

WILLIAMS, JAMES BRYAN, banker; b. Sewanee, Tenn., Mar. 21, 1933; s. Eugène G. and Ellen (Bryan) W.; m. Betty G. Williams, July 11, 1980; children: Ellen, Elizabeth, Bryan. AB, Emory U., 1955. Chmn., chief exec. officer SunTrust Banks, Inc., Atlanta, 1991—; bd. dirs. The Coca-Cola Co., Genuine Parts Co., Rollins Inc., Ga.-Pacific Corp., RPC Energy Svcs., Inc.

(all Atlanta), Sonat Inc., Birmingham, Ala. Trustee Emory U.; chmn. bd. trustees Robert W. Woodruff Health Scis. Ctr. Lt. USAF, 1955-57. Mem. Bankers Roundtable. Presbyterian. Clubs: Piedmont Driving (Atlanta), Capital City (Atlanta), Commerce (Atlanta), Augusta Country. Office: SunTrust Banks Inc 25 Park Pl NE Atlanta GA 30303-2900

WILLIAMS, JAMES CASE, metallurgist; b. Salina, Kans., Dec. 7, 1938; s. Luther Owen and Clarice (Case) W.; m. Joanne Rufener, Sept. 17, 1960; children: Teresa A., Patrick J. B.S. in Metall. Engring, U. Wash., 1962, M.S., 1964, Ph.D., 1968. Rsch. engr., lead engr. Boeing Co., Seattle, 1961-67; tech. staff N.Am. Rockwell Corp., Thousand Oaks, Calif., 1968-74; mgr. interdivisional tech. program N.Am. Aerospace group, 1974, program devel. mgr. structural materials, 1974-75; prof. metallurgy, co-dir. Ctr. for Joining of Materials, Carnegie-Mellon U., Pitts., 1975-81; pres. Mellon Inst., Pitts., 1981-83; dean Carnegie Inst. Tech., Carnegie-Mellon U., Pitts., 1983-88; gen. mgr. materials dept. GE Aircraft Engines, 1988—; chmn. Nat. Materials Adv. Bd., materials and structures comm. NASA Aero. Adv. Com.; mem. Materials Sci. and Engr. Study; mem. adv. bd. Engring. Sch. U. Va.; bd.dirs. Minorities in Math., Sci. and Engring., Wheeling-Pitts. Steel, 1987-91; bd. govs. Inst. for Mechs. & Materials, U. Calif., San Diego. Co-editor: Scientific and Technological Aspects of Titanium and Titanium Alloys, 1976; contbr. numerous articles to tech. jours. Trustee Oreg. Grad. Inst. Sci. and Tech., 1988-94; cons. Cubmaster Boy Scouts Am., 1976-77. Recipient Ladd award Carnegie Inst. Tech.; Adams award Am. Welding Soc.; Boeing doctoral fellow. Fellow Am. Soc. Metals (Gold medal 1992); mem. NAE, ASM, AIME (Leadership award 1993), ARPA Materials Rsch. Coun., Alpha Sigma Mu. Republican. Episcopalian. Home: 3307 Brinton Trl Cincinnati OH 45241-4814 Office: GE Aircraft Engines Md H85 Cincinnati OH 45215

WILLIAMS, JAMES E., food products manufacturing company executive; married. With Golden State foods Corp., 1961—; pres., chief exec. officer Golden State foods Corp., Pasadena, Calif., 1978—. Office: Golden State Foods Corp Ste 1100 18301 Von Karman Ave Irvine CA 92715

WILLIAMS, JAMES EUGENE, JR., management consultant; b. Macon, Ga., June 23, 1927; s. James Eugene and Margaret Elizabeth (Tinker) W.; m. Linda K. Magnuson, June 23, 1984; children: Paul David, Lisa Jane Williams Robertson, Philip Alan, Gail Ellen Williams Feeney, Amanda Allen Thompson, Jason Douglas Allen, Joel Winston Allen. BS in Aero. Engring., Iowa State Coll., 1950. Engr. Robins AFB, Ga., 1950-54, Hqdrs. USAF, Washington, 1954-61; dep. asst. sec. Office Asst. Sec. Air Force, Washington, 1961-85; dir. govt. bus. policy Northrop Corp., Washington, 1986-88; mgmt. cons. Chandler, Ariz., 1988—. Recipient Presdl. Meritorious Exec. award, 1981, Presdl. Disting. Exec. award, 1982. Home: 5747 W Del Rio St Chandler AZ 85226-1802

WILLIAMS, JAMES FRANKLIN, II, university dean, librarian; b. Montgomery, Ala., Jan. 22, 1944; s. James Franklin and Anne (Wester) W.; m. Madeline McClellan, Jan. 1966 (div. May 1988); 1 child, Madeline Marie; m. Nancy Allen, Aug. 1989; 1 child, Audrey Grace. BA, Morehouse Coll., 1966; MLS, Atlanta U., 1967. Reference libr. Wayne State U. Sci. Libr., Detroit, 1968-69; document delivery libr. Wayne State U. Med. Libr., Detroit, 1969-70, head of reference, 1971-72, dir. med. libr. and regional med. libr. network, 1972-81, regional dir., 1975-82; assoc. dir. of librs. Wayne State U., 1981-88; dean librs. U. Colo., Boulder, 1988—; bd. regents Nat. Libr. Medicine, Bethesda, Md., 1978-81. Contbr. articles to profl. jours., chpts. to books; book editor and author. Subject of feature interview in centennial issue Am. Librs. jour., 1976. Mem. ALA (Visionary Leader award 1988), Colo. Libr. Assn., Assn. Rsch. Librs. (bd. dirs. 1994—). Avocations: cycling, travel, fishing. Office: U Colo Office of Dean Librs Campus Box 184 Boulder CO 80309-0184

WILLIAMS, JAMES HENRY, JR., mechanical engineer, educator, consultant; b. Newport News, Va., Apr. 4, 1941; s. James H. Williams and Margaret L. (Holt) Mitchell; children: James Henry III, Sky Margaret Melodie. Mech. designer (Homer L. Ferguson scholar), Newport News Apprentice Sch., 1965; S.B., MIT, 1967, S.M., 1968; Ph.D., Trinity Coll., Cambridge U., 1970. Sr. design engr. Newport News Shipyard, 1960-70; asst. prof. mech. engring. M.I.T., 1970-74, assoc. prof., 1974-81, prof., 1981—; duPont prof., 1973. Edgerton prof., 1974-76; cons. engring. to numerous cos. Contbr. numerous articles on stress analysis, vibration, fracture mechanics, composite materials and nondestructive testing to profl. jours. Recipient Charles F. Bailey Bronze medal, 1961, Charles F. Bailey Silver medal, 1962, Charles F. Bailey Gold medal, 1963, Baker award M.I.T., 1973, Den Hartog Disting. Educator award, 1981; named prof. teaching excellence Sch. Engring., 1991; C.F. Hopewell faculty fellow, 1993—. Mem. ASME, Am. Soc. Nondestructive Testing, Nat. Tech. Assn. Subspecialties: Theoretical and applied mechanics; Composite materials. Office: MIT Room 3-360 77 Massachusetts Ave Cambridge MA 02139

WILLIAMS, JAMES HOWARD, sociologist, research agency executive; b. Wheat, Tenn., Dec. 19, 1920; s. William Wess and Sallie (Shelton) W.; AB, Carson-Newman Coll., 1942; MA, George Peabody Coll., 1947; PhD, Vanderbilt U., 1956; m. Mary Helen Mewshaw, Aug. 31, 1946; children: James Howard, Edward Robert, Nancy Jean. Instr. dept. sociology U S.C., 1950-55; asst. dir. Nat. Inst. Mental Health Project, Vanderbilt U., 1956-58; asst. prof. social welfare and sociology Fla. State U., 1958-61; rsch. dir. Fla. Bur. Alcoholic Rehab., Avon Park, 1961-75; rsch. assoc. Fla. Aging and Adult Svcs., 1975-76; planner, evaluator Fla. Alcoholic Rehab. Program, Tallahassee, 1976—. Social sci. cons. City of Columbia (S.C.) Planning Comm., 1950-55. Lt. USNR, 1942-46. Mem. N.Am. Assn. Alcohol Programs, So. Sociol. Soc., Soc. Study Social Problems, Am. Sociol. Assn., Nat. Rehab. Assn., Population Assn. Am. Fla. Acad. Sci. Kiwanian (pres. Avon Park club 1970-71, 74-75). Contbr. articles to profl. jours. Home: 1537 Woodgate Way Tallahassee FL 32312-3228 Office: 1323 Winewood Blvd Tallahassee FL 32399-6567

WILLIAMS, JAMES KELLEY, diversified resources company executive; b. Bentonia, Miss., Mar. 29, 1934; s. James C. and Katheryn (Kelley) W.; m. Jean Pittman, June 16, 1956; children: James Kelley Jr., George P., Clifford C. B.S. in Chem. Engring. Ga. Inst. Tech., 1956; M.B.A., Harvard U., 1962. Asst. to pres. Tyrone Hydraulics, Corinth, Miss., 1962-67; mgr. corp. planning and devel. First Miss. Corp., Jackson, 1967-69, v.p., 1969-71, pres., CEO, 1971-88, chmn., pres., CEO, 1988—, also chmn. exec. com., bd. dirs.; chmn. B.C. Rogers Poultry, Inc., Morton, Miss., 1981—; mem. adv. coun. Degussa Corp.; dir. Deposit Guaranty Corp., Deposit Guaranty Nat. Bank. Dirs. Miss. Econ. Coun., Com. for Econ. Devel., Washington; deacon Northminster Bapt. Ch.; trustee Miss. Found. Ind. Colls., Nature Conservancy; chmn. Inst. Tech. Devel. for Miss. With USAR, 1957-60. Mem. Fertilizer Inst., Chief Execs. Orgn., Mfg. Chemists Assn., Agribus Promotion Coun., World Bus. Coun., Hundred of Jackson. Clubs: Jackson Country, River Hills, Hundred of Jackson. Office: First Miss Corp PO Box 1249 700 North St Jackson MS 39215-1249 also: BC Rogers Poultry Inc 121 Old Hwy 80 E Morton MS 39117*

WILLIAMS, JAMES KENDRICK, bishop. Ed., St. Mary's Coll., St. Mary's, Ky., St. Maur's Sch. Theology, South Union, Ky. Ordained priest Roman Catholic Ch., 1963; ordained titular bishop Catula and aux. bishop of Covington, 1984; ordained first bishop of Lexington, Ky., installed 1988. Office: Bishop of Lexington PO Box 12350 1310 Leestown Rd Lexington KY 40582-2350

WILLIAMS, JAMES LEE, financial industries executive; b. Tampa, Fla., Nov. 5, 1941; s. Donald Clark and Nell (Medlin) W.; m. Linda Taylor, Dec. 28, 1968; children: Donald Clark II, Taylor Lee. AA, St. Petersburg (Fla.) Jr. Coll., 1965; BS, Fla. State U., 1967. Mgmt. Ryder Truck Lines, Jacksonville, Fla., 1967-69; dist. mgr. underwriting div. U.S. Leasing Corp., Dallas, 1969-73; area v.p. Mfrs. Hanover Leasing Corp., Houston and London, 1973-79; v.p. corp. fin. Underwood Neuhause & Co. Inc., Houston, 1979-81; chmn., chief exec. officer 1st City Leasing Corp., Houston, 1981-85; mng. dir. capital markets 1st City Bancorp., Houston, 1985-89; mng. dir. fin. svcs. M.P.S.I. Systems Inc., Dallas, 1989-90; pres., chief exec. officer Strategic Decisions Holdings Corp., Dallas, 1990-92; sr. mng. dir. Williams and Assocs., 1992; pres. Global Svcs. Capital Corp., Houston, 1993—. Served with USN, 1959-62. Mem. Am. Assn. Equipment Lessors (fed. govt.

relations com. 1984-88), Tex. Assn. Equipment Lessors (bd. dirs. 1985-89), Houston C. of C. Republican. Presbyterian. Clubs: Houston Ctr. (bd. dirs. 1985-89), Lakeside Racquet (athletic com. 1986-89), Forum (Houston). Avocations: tennis, jogging, swimming. Office: Global Svcs Capital Corp 2902 W 12th St Houston TX 77008-6114

WILLIAMS, JAMES ORRIN, university administrator, educator; b. New Orleans, Jan. 8, 1937; married, 1956; 3 children. BS, Auburn U., 1960, MEd, 1963, EdD, 1967; postgrad., Tchrs. Coll., Columbia U., summer 1964. Tchr. social sci., coach Columbus High Sch. Ga., 1960-61; tchr., coach Eufaula High Sch. Ala., 1961-63; prin. Troy Jr. High Sch., 1963-65; grad. asst. Sch. Edn. Auburn U., 1965-66, interim dir. field service, 1966-67; asst. prof. edn. adminstrn. U. Fla., 1967-68; asst. prof. Columbus Coll., 1968-69; assoc. prof., chmn. div Auburn U., Montgomery, 1969-73, vice chancellor acad. affairs, 1973-80, chancellor, 1980—. Contbr. articles to profl. jours. Phi Delta Kappa grantee, 1967. Mem. Am. Assn. State Colls. and Univs., Am. Assn. Coll. Tchr. Edn., Assn. Tchr. Edn., So. Regional Council Edn. Adminstrn., Phi Delta Kappa (v.p. 1965), Phi Kappa Phi. Office: Auburn U-Montgomery Office of Chancellor 7300 University Dr Montgomery AL 36117-3596

WILLIAMS, JAMES P., JR. (JAY WILLIAMS), broadcasting executive; b. Harvey, Ill., Oct. 19, 1944; s. J Paul and Lucille (Larson) W. A.B., Wabash Coll., 1966; postgrad., Ind. U. Sch. Law, 1966-67. Morning personality, music dir. Sta. WAVI, Dayton, Ohio, 1967-68; afternoon personality, music dir. Sta. WXLW, Indpls., 1968-70; account exec. Sta. WNAP, Indpls., 1970-71; local sales mgr. Sta. WVBF, Framingham and Boston, 1971-73; gen. sales mgr. Sta. WVBF, 1973-75, v.p. and gen. mgr., 1975-82; chmn. The Fifth Estate, Inc., Sta. WLKZ-FM, Wolfeboro, N.H., 1982—; COO Sta. WXLO, Fitchburg-Worcester, Mass., 1985—; chief oper. officer Sta. WIZN-FM, Burlington, Vt., 1985—; pres. Broadcasting Unltd., cons., 1979—; CEO Direct Mktg. Results, 1988—; frequent speaker Nat. Assn. Broadcasters, Radio Advt. Bur., seminars. Adv. Lakes Region Conservation Trust, Meredith, N.H. Republican. Methodist. Home: 16 Coltsway Wayland MA 01778-3905 Office: 35 Main St Wayland MA 01778-5037

WILLIAMS, JAMES RICHARD, human factors engineering psychologist; b. Chgo., Apr. 16, 1932; s. James Henry and Margaret Lucille (Keefer) W.; m. Jonetta Rae Gilbert, Dec. 19, 1959; children: Janise Rebecca, Jason Richard. BS in Psychology, Purdue U., 1958, MS in Human Factors/Indsl. Psychology, 1960; PhD in Edn., NYU, 1971. Bd. cert. in profl. ergonomics. Technical asst. Sci. Rsch. Assocs., Chgo., 1960-61; sr. systems cons. System Devel. Corp., Paramus, N.J., 1961-64; human factors engr. Kollsman Instrument Corp., Elmhurst, N.Y., 1964-66; project mgr. System Devel. Corp., Paramus, 1966-69; supr. tng. and standards Bell Labs., Piscataway, N.J., 1969-74; dist. mgr. AT&T, Basking Ridge, N.J., 1975-80; mem. technical staff Bell Labs., Piscataway, 1981-83; learning technologist Bell Communications Rsch., Piscataway, 1984—; cons. NYU, N.Y.C., 1968-70; chair U.S. Tech. Adv. Group, to internat. orgn. for standardization in ergonomics of human system interaction, 1988—. Editor: International Standards for Menu Dialogues, Command Dialogues and Form-fill Dialogues with Computer Systems. Cub master Boy Scouts, Watchung, N.Y., 1973-74, asst. scout master, 1975-78. With USAF, 1951-55. Mem. Am. Psychol. Soc. (charter), Assn. for Computing Machinery (spl. interest group on computer-human interaction), Human Factors and Ergonomics Soc. (rep. 1986—), Delta Rho Kappa, Kappa Delta Pi. Avocations: winemaking-co-owner Del Vista Vineyards, astronomy, body bldg. Home: 137 County Rd 513 Frenchtown NJ 08825-3727 Office: Bell Comm Rsch 6 Corporate Pl Piscataway NJ 08854-4120

WILLIAMS, JOBETH, actress; b. Houston, 1953; m. John Pasquin; children: Nick, Will. Student, Brown U. Appeared in plays A Coupla White Chicks Sitting Around Talking, 1980, Gardenia, 1982, Idiot's Delight, 1986, Cat on a Hot Tin Roof, 1993; films include Kramer vs. Kramer, 1979, The Dogs of War, 1980, Stir Crazy, 1980, Poltergeist, 1982, Endangered Species, 1982, The Big Chill, 1983, American Dreamer, 1984, Teachers, 1984, Desert Bloom, 1986, Poltergeist II, 1986, Memories of Me, 1988, Welcome Home, 1989, Switch, 1991, Dutch, 1991, Stop! Or My Mom Will Shoot, 1992, Me, Myself and I, 1993, Wyatt Earp, 1994; TV movies include Fun and Games, 1980, The Big Black Pill, 1981, Adam, 1983 (Emmy award nominee, Golden Globe award nominee), The Day After, 1983, Kids Don't Tell, 1985, Adam: His Song Continues, 1986, Murder Ordained, 1987, Baby M, 1988 (Emmy award nominee, Golden Globe award nominee), My Name is Bill W., 1989, Child in the Night, 1990, Victim of Love, 1991, Jonathan: The Boy Nobody Wanted, 1992, Sex, Love and Cold Hard Cash, 1993, Chantilly Lace, 1993, Voices from Within, 1994, Lemon Grove, 1994, Parallel Lives, 1994, Voices from Within, 1994, Season of Hope, 1994; TV series include The Guiding Light, Somerset, John Grisham's The Client; contbr. voice to Fish Police; co-exec. prodr.: (TV movie) Bump in the Night, 1991; dir. film: On Hope, 1994 (Acad. award nominee for Best Live Action Short Film 1995). Office: William Morris Agy Inc 151 El Camino Beverly Hills CA 90212

WILLIAMS, JOE, jazz and blues singer; b. Cordele, Ga., Dec. 12, 1918. Founder singing group, The Jubilee Boys, Chgo., 1930's, numerous nightclub appearances, Chgo.; appeared with Jimmie Noone Band, Les Hite Band, Coleman Hawkins Band, Lionel Hampton Band, Red Saunders Band, blues singer, Count Basie Orch., 1954-61, also appeared, with Duke and Mercer Ellington Orchs.; appeared in concerts with Buddy Rich, Harry Edison, Junior Mance and frequent reunions with Count Basie Orch.; numerous jazz festivals including regular appearances Newport Jazz Festival; film Moonshine War, 1969; video Joe Williams: A Song Is Born with George Shearing, 1992; recs. include Joe Williams and his Count Basie Orch., 1993, (with the Robert Farnon Orch.) Here's To Life, 1994; actor Bill Cosby Show, 1987. Winner Downbeat Readers Poll, 1955-56. Downbeat Internat. Critics Poll, 1955, 74, 75, 76, 77, 78, D.J. Poll, Billboard mag., 1959; recipient Top award Rhythm and Blues Mag., 1956, Grammy award for Best Jazz Vocal, 1984. Office: Thomas Cassidy Inc 366 Horseshoe Dr Basalt CO 81621-9104*

WILLIAMS, JOHN A. (JACK WILLIAMS), newspaper publishing executive; b. Springfield, Ill., May 1, 1950; m. Judy Williams; children: Suzanne, Michel. BBA, U. Ill., 1972. Part-time employee Ill. State Jour. & Register, Springfield, 1968-72; bus. mgr. San Francisco Progress, 1972-74; gen. mgr. Yakima (Wash.) Herald Republic, 1975-80, Modesto (Calif.) Bee, 1980-85; v.p. sales & mktg. Seattle Times Co., 1985-89, exec. v.p., 1989—; dir., 1st v.p. Direct Mktg. Puget Sound, Inc., Times Communications Co., Inc, Times Distribution, Inc., Times Info. Svcs., Inc.; v.p., dir. Yakima Herald-Republic, Inc., Rotary Offset Press, Inc., Times Community Newspapers, Inc. Chmn. bd. Leadership Tomorrow, bd. dirs., 1987—; mem. strategic planning com. United Way, 1991—; bd. dirs. Corp. Coun. Arts, 1989—. Mem. Newspaper Assn. Am. (dir.), Newspapers First (dir., exec. com.), Glendale Country Club, The Lakes Club, The Rainier Club, Washington Athletic Club, Bellevue Athletic Club. Office: Seattle Times Co PO Box 70 Fairview Ave N & John Seattle WA 98111-0070*

WILLIAMS, JOHN A., English language educator, author; b. Jackson, Miss., 1925; m. Lorrain Isaac; 1 son, Adam; children by previous marriage: Gregory, Dennis. Grad., Syracuse U., Nat. Inst. Arts and Letters, 1962; LL.D., U. Mass., Dartmouth, 1978; Lit.D, Syracuse U., 1995. With Am. Com. on Africa, N.Y.C.; Disting. prof. English La Guardia Community Coll., 1973-74, 74-75; prof. English Rutgers U., 1979—, Paul Robeson prof. English, 1990—; Bard Ctr fellow Bard Coll., 1994-95; lectr. CCNY; guest writer Sarah Lawrence Coll.; Regents lectr. U. Calif., Santa Barbara 1972, U. Hawaii, 1974, Nat. Endowment for the Arts, 1977; vis. prof. Boston U., 1978-79, NYU, 1986-87. Started writing poetry during World War II, in Pacific; Author: (novels) The Angry Ones, 1960; novels Night Song, 1961, Sissie, 1963, The Man Who Cried I Am, 1967, Sons of Darkness, Sons of Light, 1969, Captain Blackman, 1972, Mothersill and the Foxes, 1975, The Junior Bachelor Society, 1976, (plays) Last Flight from Ambo Ber, 1981, The Berhama Account, 1983, Jacob's Ladder, 1987, also 8 vols. of non-fiction, vol. of poems: !Click Song, 1982 (Before Columbus Found. Am. Book award 1983); 7 anthologies. Recipient Centennial medal for outstanding achievement Syracuse U., 1970, Lindback award for Disting. Teaching Rutgers U., 1982. Home: 693 Forest Ave Teaneck NJ 07666-2042 *I've tried to adhere to the philosophies of W.E.B. DuBois. He never quit.*

WILLIAMS, JOHN A., real estate developer, property manger. Chmn. bd, dirs., CEO Post Properties, Inc., Atlanta, Ga. Office: Post Properties Inc 3350 Cumberland Cir NW Atlanta GA 30339*

WILLIAMS, JOHN ANDREW, physiology educator, consultant; b. Des Moines, Aug. 3, 1941; s. Harold Southall and Marjorie (Larsen) W.; m. Christa A. Smith, Dec. 26, 1965; children: Rachel Jo, Matthew Dallas. BA, Cen. Wash. State Coll., 1963; MD, U. Wash., Seattle, 1968, PhD, 1968. Staff fellow NIH, Bethesda, Md., 1969-71; research fellow U. Cambridge, Eng., 1971-72; from asst. to prof. physiology U. Calif., San Francisco, 1973-87; prof. physiology, chair dept. physiology, prof. internal medicine U. Mich., Ann Arbor, 1987—; mem. gen. medicine study sect. NIH, Bethesda, 1985-88, DDK-C study sect., 1991-95. Contbr. numerous articles to profl. jours.; editor Am. Jour. Physiology: Gastrointestinal Physiology, 1985-91. Trustee Friends Sch. in Detroit, 1992—. NIH grantee, 1973—. Mem. Am. Physiol. Soc. (Hoffman LaRoche prize 1985), Am. Soc. of Cell Biology, Am. Soc. for Clin. Investigation, Am. Gastroenterology Assn., Am. Pancreatic Assn. (pres. 1985-86). Democrat. Home: 1115 Woodlawn Ave Ann Arbor MI 48104-3956 Office: Dept Physiology Univ of Mich Med Sch Ann Arbor MI 48109

WILLIAMS, JOHN CHRISTOPHER RICHARD, bishop; b. Sale, Cheshire, Eng., May 22, 1936; arrived in Can., 1960; s. Frank Harold and Ceridwen Roberts (Hughes) W.; m. Rona Macrae Aitken, Mar. 18, 1964; children: Andrew David, Judith Ann. BA in Commerce, Manchester U., Eng., 1958; diploma in Theology, Cranmer Hall, Durham, Eng., 1960. Ordained deacon Anglican Ch. of Can., 1960, priest, 1962. Missionary in charge Anglican Ch. Can., Sugluk, Que., Can., 1961-72, Cape Dorset, N.W.T., Can., 1972-75, Baker Lake, N.W.T., 1975-78; archdeacon of the Keewatim Anglican Ch. Can., 1975-87; rector Holy Trinity Anglican Ch. Can., Yellowknife, N.W.T., 1978-87; bishop suffagan Diocese of the Arctic, Can., 1987-90, diocesan bishop, 1990—; trustee Can. Churchman, Anglican Ch. Can., 1976-82, mem. nat. exec. com., 1976-79, 92—. Coord., trans. into Eskimo Inukkitut New Testament, 1992. Avocations: reading, skiing, swimming. Office: Diocese of the Arctic, Box 89, Iqaluit, NT Canada X0A 0H0

WILLIAMS, JOHN COBB, lawyer; b. Chgo., June 11, 1930; s. Ralph Milton and Mary Mason (Cobb) W.; m. Helen Gilbert, Aug. 19, 1955; children: Holly Montague, Nancy Morrison, Sarah M. B.A., Wesleyan U., 1951; LL.B., Yale U., 1954. Bar: Ill. 1955, Fla. 1974. Assoc. firm Sidley & Austin, Chgo., 1954-63; ptnr. Sidley & Austin, 1964—. Trustee Village of Northbrook, Ill., 1965-69, village pres., 1969-73, mem. plan commn. zoning bd. appeals, 1965-69; mem. police pension fund bd. Village of Glencoe, Ill., 1980-82; chmn. pub. safety commn. Village of Gencoe, 1982—; bd. dirs. North Suburban Assn. Health Resources, 1973, pres., 1974-75; bd. dirs. North Suburban Blood Ctr., 1973-75. Fellow Am. Coll. Probate Counsel; mem. ABA, Ill. Bar Assn. (chmn. on legis. 1975-76, chmn. estate planning, probate and trust sec. council 1984-85), Chgo. Bar Assn. (chmn. legis. com. 1969-71, chmn. com. on probate practice 1972-73). Clubs: Skokie Country (Glencoe); University, Econ, Law, Legal (Chgo.). Home: 486 Greenleaf Ave Glencoe IL 60022-1768 Office: Sidley & Austin 1 First Nat Plz Chicago IL 60603

WILLIAMS, JOHN CORNELIUS, lawyer; b. Lee Valley, Tenn., Jan. 24, 1903; s. Hugh and Kitty (Lawrence) W.; 1 son by former marriage, John Cornelius; m. Darthey I. Black, Aug. 12, 1954; 1 dau., Kitty. A.B., Wofford Coll., 1927; LL.B., U. S.C., 1931. Bar: S.C. bar 1931. Prin. Campobello High Sch., Spartanburg County, S.C., 1927-28; practiced in Spartanburg, 1931-61; U.S. atty. Western Dist. S.C., 1951-54, 61-68; partner law firm Williams and Williams, Spartanburg, 1968—; Mem. S.C. Legislature, 1931-32, 49-50. Served to col. U.S. Army, 1940-46. Mem. S.C. Bar Assn., Spartanburg County Bar Assn. (past pres.), 4th U.S. Jud. Conf., V.F.W. (past comdr. S.C.), Am. Legion, 40 and 8, Blue Key, Pi Kappa Delta, Phi Kappa Sigma, Phi Alpha Delta. Democrat. Baptist. Club: Masons (32 degree). Home: 318 S Park Dr Spartanburg SC 29302-3244

WILLIAMS, JOHN EDWARD, lawyer; b. Atlanta, May 21, 1946; s. Edward Carl and Mary E. (Griffin) W.; m. Kristin Forsberg, May 22, 1976; children: Alexandra, Courtney, Charles. BA, Yale U., 1968; JD, U. Va., 1974; LLM in Taxation, Georgetown U., 1977. Bar: Va. 1974, D.C. 1975, U.S. Dist. Ct. D.C. 1975, U.S. Tax Ct. 1975, U.S. Ct. Appeals (D.C. cir.) 1975, U.S. Supreme Ct. 1977. Law clk. to Judge Charles R. Richey U.S. Dist. Ct. (D.C. dist.), 1974-75; assoc. Patton, Boggs & Blow, Washington, 1975-78, Cadwalader, Wickersham & Taft, Washington, 1978-81; asst. to the commr. IRS, Washington, 1981-84; tax counsel Ropes & Gray, Washington, 1984-86; ptnr. David & Hagner, P.C., Washington, 1986-90, Winston & Strawn, Washington, 1990—. With U.S. Army, 1968-74. Mem. ABA (tax sect., chmn. tech. subcom., adminstrv. practice com. 1988-89), Met., Yale N.Y.C., Chevy Chase Club. Home: 4526 36th St NW Washington DC 20008-4250 Office: Winston & Strawn 1400 L St NW Washington DC 20005-3509

WILLIAMS, JOHN EDWIN, psychology educator; b. Bluefield, W.Va., June 12, 1928; s. Marvin Glenn and Kathleen Virginia (Stinson) W.; m. Doris Jean Crawford, July 6, 1948 (div. 1971); children: Kathleen Diane, James Taylor, Thomas Crawford, Jeannette Kiser; m. Kathryn Lee Bond, June 19, 1971 (div. 1995); stepchildren: Kimberly Lyn Himan, Brock Eugene Himan. Student, Bluefield Coll., 1945-46, 48-49; B.A., U. Richmond, 1951; M.A., U. Iowa, 1953, Ph.D., 1954. Instr. Yale U., 1954-55; asst. prof., then assoc. prof. U. Richmond, 1955-59; prof. psychology Wake Forest U., 1959—, Disting. prof., 1992—, chmn. dept., 1960-94; editor Jour. of Cross-Cultural Psychology, 1991—. Author: (with J.K. Morland) Race, Color and the Young Child, 1976, (with D.L. Best) Measuring Sex Stereotypes—A 30-Nation Study, 1982, Sex and Psyche: Gender and Self Viewed Cross-Culturally, 1990; contbr. articles to profl. jours. Served with AUS, 1946-48. Recipient research grants Nat. Inst. Child Health and Human Devel., 1967-73, research grants NIMH, 1977-79. Fellow APA, Am. Psychol. Soc., N.Y. Psychol. Assn. (pres. 1964-65); mem. AAUP, Soc. Exptl. Social Psychology, Southeastern Psychol. Assn. (pres. 1991-92), Internat. Assn. Cross-Cultural Psychology, Coun. Grad. Depts. of Psychology (chair 1984-85), Phi Beta Kappa, Sigma Xi, Phi Theta Kappa, Psi Chi. Office: Wake Forest U Box 7778 Dept Psychology Winston Salem NC 27109

WILLIAMS, JOHN ELBERT, JR., library services director; b. Rogers, Tex., Mar. 9, 1948; s. John Elbert and Delma Ruth (McDaniel) W.; m. Cynthia Ann Bonds, Nov. 23, 1977; children: Lary Don Whitten, Christy Lynn Whitten, John Matthew Williams. BS, U. Tex., Arlington, 1970; MLS, U. North Tex., 1973; MS, East Tex. State U., 1976. Cert. secondary tchr. Tex. Adult libr. Mesquite (Tex.) Pub. Libr., 1971-73, supr. pub. svcs., 1973-74, supr. tech. svcs., 1979-91, dir. libr. svcs., 1991—; sci. tchr. Mesquite High Sch., 1974-79. Mem. ALA, Tex. Libr. Assn., Tex. Mcpl. Libr. Dirs. Assn., Pub. Libr. Adminstrs. of North Tex. Avocations: antique collecting, genealogy, reading, cooking. Office: Mesquite Pub Libr 300 W Grubb Mesquite TX 75149

WILLIAMS, JOHN HORTER, civil engineer, oil, gas, telecommunications and allied products distribution company executive; b. Havana, Cuba, Aug. 17, 1918; s. Charles P. and Alice Magruder (Dyer) W.; m. Emily Alice Ijams, June 6, 1942 (div.); children—John H., Burch I., S. Miller; m. Joanne Harwell Simpson., Feb. 1, 1975. B.S., Yale U., 1940. Registered profl. engr., Okla., Minn. With The Williams Cos. Inc., Tulsa, 1940-42, 46-50, pres., dir. 1950-70, chmn., chief exec. officer, 1971-78, now hon. dir.; bd. dirs. Apco Argentina, Inc., Unit Corp. Served with USAR, 1942-46. Decorated Order of Condor of Andes (Bolivia); named Okla. Hall of Fame, 1977; recipient Outstanding Okla. Oil Man awad Okla.-Kans. Oil and Gas Assn., 1982, Disting. Svc. award Nat. Petroleum Hall of Fame, 1985; inducted into Okla. Commerce and Industry Hall of Honor, 1986, Tulsa Hall of Fame, 1993. Mem. ASCE, Yale Engring. Assn. Office: The Williams Cos Inc 1 Williams Ctr 49th Fl Tulsa OK 74172-0101

WILLIAMS, JOHN LYLE, lawyer; b. Saginaw, Mich., Oct. 2, 1944; s. John Lyle and Jean Elizabeth (Cleary) W.; m. Jane Farmer Edwards, Apr. 19, 1969; children: Jennifer Leigh, Benjamin Winn. BA, Mich. State U., 1965; LLB Stanford U., 1968. Assoc. Hall, Henry, Oliver & McReary, San Francisco, 1970-72; atty. Santa Clara County Pub. Defender, San Jose, Calif.,

1972-79; ptnr. Manchester & Williams, San Jose, 1979—; dir. Advanced Criminal Practitioners Seminar, San Jose, Hawaii, 1980-87; lectr. Calif. Continuing Edn. of Bar, 1985—; lectr. law Stanford U. Sch. Law, 1994—. Capt. U.S. Army, 1968-70. Mem. Calif. Attys. for Criminal Justice, Santa Clara County Bar Assn., State Bar Calif., Inns. of Ct. Santa Clara U. (bencher 1990—). Avocations: reading, biking. Office: Manchester & Williams 100 Park Center Plz # 525 San Jose CA 95113

WILLIAMS, JOHN PATTISON, JR., association executive, lawyer; b. Cin., Feb. 14, 1941; s. John P. Williams and Anne (Sawyer) Greene; m. Janie Pepper, Nov. 20, 1971. BA in Religion, Princeton U., 1963; JD, U. Cin., 1966; postgrad. Naval Justice, Newport, R.I., 1967. Bar: Ohio 1966, U.S. Dist. Ct. (so. dist.) Ohio 1966. Assoc., Taft, Stettinius & Hollister, Cin., 1966, 71-77, ptnr., 1977-90; pres. Greater Cin. C. of C., 1984—; bd. dir. Kennedy Mfg. Co., Van Wert, Ohio, Portman Equipment Co. Capt. USMCR, 1966-69; Vietnam. Mem. Cin. Bar Assn., Commonwealth Club, Queen City Club, Cin. Country Club, Bankers Club, Bohemian Club, Princeton Club (N.Y.C.). Episcopalian. Avocations: jogging, travel, social golf, motorcycles. Home: 3 Resor Pl Cincinnati OH 45220-1615 Office: Greater Cin C of C 300 Carew Tower 441 Vine St Cincinnati OH 45202-2806

WILLIAMS, JOHN RODMAN, theologian, educator; b. Clyde, N.C., Aug. 21, 1918; s. John Rodman and Odessa Lee (Medford) W.; m. Johanna SerVaas, Aug. 6, 1949; children: John, Lucinda Lee, David Bert. AB, Davidson Coll., 1939; BD, Union Theol. Sem., 1943, ThM, 1944; PhD, Columbia U., 1954. Ordained to ministry Presbyn. Ch., 1943. Chaplain USNR, 1944-46; chaplain, assoc. prof. philosophy Beloit Coll., 1949-52; pastor First Presbyn. Ch., Rockford, Ill., 1952-59; prof. systematic theology and philosophy of religion Austin Presbyn. Theol. Sem., 1959-72; prof. Christian doctrine, pres. Melodyland Sch. Theology, Anaheim, Calif., 1972-82; prof. Christian theology Regent U., Virginia Beach, Va., 1982—. Author: Contemporary Existentialism and Christian Faith, 1965, The Era of the Spirit, 1971, The Pentecostal Reality, 1972, Ten Teachings, 1974, The Gift of the Holy Spirit Today, 1980, Renewal Theology, Vol. 1, 1988, Vol. 2, 1990, Vol. 3, 1992, God, the World and Redemption, 1988, Salvation, the Holy Spirit, and Christian Living, 1990, The Church, the Kingdom, and the Last Things, 1992. Home: 4105 Ace Ct Virginia Beach VA 23462-4829 Office: Regent U Virginia Beach VA 23464 *There is only one ultimate "Who", Jesus of Nazareth, in whose light all the rest of us are but dimly burning candles.*

WILLIAMS, JOHN TAYLOR, lawyer; b. Cambridge, Mass., June 19, 1938; s. Paul Merchant Taylor and Audrey Arlene Dowling; m. Leonora Hall; children: Caleb, Jared, Nathaniel. AB, Harvard U., 1960; LLB, U. Pa., 1965. Bar: Mass. 1965, U.S. Dist. Ct. Mass., U.S. Ct. Appeals (1st cir.), U.S. Supreme Ct. Corp. loans officer State St. Bank & Trust Co., Boston, 1960-62; from assoc. to ptnr. Haussermann, Davison & Shattuck, Boston, 1965-83; ptnr. Palmer & Dodge, Boston, 1983—; bd. dirs. Blackwell Sci. Inc.; lectr. on 1st amendment, copyright, pub. and intellectual property law for Practicing Law Inst., Mass. CLE/New Eng. Law Inst., Nat. Assn. Archivists, Boston Patent Lawyers Assn., others; apptd. mem. U.S. Courthouse Arts Comm., U.S. Publ. Del. to China, 1993; mem. lit. panel Nat. Endowment for the Arts, 1990, 91, 94. Author: (screenplay) Rolf in the Woods, 1987, (screenplay) Toussaint L'Overture, 1989, (with E. Gabriel Perle) The Publishing Law Handbook, 2 vols. (revised annually); contbg. author: Legal Problems in Book Publishing, 1981, 84, 86; contbg. editor: Small Voices and Great Trumpets: Minorities and the Media, 1980. Bd. dirs. City of Cambridge Arts Coun., 1973-83, chmn., 1981-83; bd. dirs. Ploughshares Inc., 1988-89; trustee Arthur Fiedler Meml. Inc., 1983—, Boston Philharm Orch., 1983-85, Petra Found., 1988—; trustee, gen. counsel Inst. Contemporary Art, 1970-92; mem. corp. Mass. Gen. Hosp., 1985—; mem. Patent and Tech Conflicts Comm., 1985-91; clk. John F. Kennedy Meml. Commn. Inc., 1986—; mem. adv. bd. Provincetown Fine Arts Work Ctr., 1992—. Mrm. ABA (sect. patent, trademark, copyright law, chmn. com. on authors 1978-81, communications and entertainment law forum coms.), Boston Bar Assn. (former chmn. com. on delivery of legal svcs. to indigent), Lawyers' Com. for Civil Rights under Law (chmn. steering com. 1988-91), Mass. Bar Assn. (bus. law and computer law sects.), Nat. Lawyers' Com. for Civil Rights (bd. dirs. 1989—), Tavern Club (Boston). Home: 9 Orchard St Cambridge MA 02140-1321 Office: Palmer & Dodge 1 Beacon St Boston MA 02108-3106

WILLIAMS, J(OHN) TILMAN, insurance executive, real estate broker, city official; b. Detroit, Feb. 26, 1925; s. Aubrey and Martha (Lou) W.; m. Sally Jane Robinson, Aug. 22, 1947; children: Leslie Ann, Martha Lou. B.S. in Agr. Mich. State U., 1951. Pres. Satellite Ins. Brokerage, Garden Grove, Calif., 1959—; pres. Satellite Real Estate, Satellite Mortgage & Loan Co. Mayor Garden Grove, 1976-78, re-elected, 1987, mem. coun., 1980-92, apptd. vice mayor, 1989—; mem. Ad Hoc Com. on Property Tax to Limit Govt. Spending with Spirit of 13 Initiative; past pres. Garden Grove High Sch. Band Boosters. With USAAF, World War II, PTO. Mem. Bd. Realtors, Ind. Ins. Agts. Assn., Orange County Esperanto Assn. (pres. 1985—), Am. Legion, VFW. Democrat. Methodist. Clubs: Toastmasters (Anaheim, Calif.), Fifty-Plus Sr. Citizens of Garden Grove (pres. 1986—). Lodges: Lions, Elks. Home: 11241 Chapman Ave Garden Grove CA 92640-3301 Office: 12311 Harbor Blvd Garden Grove CA 92640-3809 *Service to one's fellowman and community is the greatest avocation and pleasure one can follow.*

WILLIAMS, JOHN TOWNER, composer, conductor; b. Flushing, N.Y., Feb. 8, 1932. Student, UCLA; pvt. studies with Mario Castelnuovo-Tedesco, Los Angeles; student, Juilliard Sch.; pvt. studies with Madame Rosina Lhevinne, N.Y.C.; hon. degree, Berklee Coll. Music, Boston, Northeastern U., Boston, Tufts U., U. So. Calif., Boston U., New Eng. Conservatory Music, Providence Coll.; others. Condr. Boston Pops Orch., 1980—. Composer: (film scores) I Passed for White, 1960, Because They're Young, 1960, The Secret Ways, 1961, Bachelor Flat, 1962, Diamond Head, 1962, Gidget Goes to Rome, 1963, The Killers, 1964, John Goldfarb, Please Come Home, 1964, None But the Brave, 1965, How to Steal a Million, 1966, The Rare Breed, 1966, Not With My Wife, You Don't, 1966, The Plainsman, 1966, Penelope, 1966, A Guide for the Married Man, 1967, Valley of the Dolls, 1967 (nominated Acad. award), Fitzwilly, 1968, Sergeant Ryker, 1968, The Reivers, 1969 (nominated Acad. award), Daddy's Gone A-Hunting, 1969, Goodbye, Mr. Chips, 1969 (nominated Acad. award), The Story of A Woman, 1970, Fiddler on the Roof, 1971 (Acad. award for musical adaptation 1971), The Cowboys, 1972, The Poseidon Adventure, 1972 (nominated Acad. award), Images, 1972 (nominated Acad. award), Pete 'n' Tillie, 1972, The Paper Chase, 1973, The Long Goodbye, 1973, The Man Who Loved Cat Dancing, 1973, Cinderella Liberty, 1973 (nominated Acad. award), Tom Sawyer, 1973 (nominated Acad. award), Sugarland Express, 1974, Earthquake, 1974, The Towering Inferno, 1974 (nominated Acad. award), Conrack, 1974, Jaws, 1975 (Acad. award 1976, Grammy award, Golden Globe award), The Eiger Sanction, 1976, Family Plot, 1976, Midway, 1976, The Missouri Breaks, 1976, Raggedy Ann and Andy, 1977, Black Sunday, 1977, Star Wars, 1977 (Acad. award, 3 Grammy awards, Golden Globe award), Close Encounters of the Third Kind, 1977 (2 Grammy awards, nominated Acad. award), The Fury, 1978, Jaws II, 1978, Superman, 1978 (2 Grammy awards), Meteor, 1979, Quintet, 1979, Dracula, 1979, "1941", 1979, The Empire Strikes Back, 1980 (2 Grammy awards, nominated Acad. award), Raiders of the Lost Ark, 1981 (Grammy award, nominated Acad. award), Heartbeeps, 1981, E.T., 1982 (Acad. award for best original score, 3 Grammy awards, Golden Globe award), Monsignor, 1982, Yes, Giorgio, 1982 (nominated Acad. award), Superman III, 1983, Return of the Jedi, 1983 (nominated Acad. award), Indiana Jones and the Temple of Doom, 1984 (nominated Acad. award), The River, 1984 (nominated Acad. award), Space Camp, 1986, Emma's War, 1986, The Witches of Eastwick, 1987 (nominated Acad. award), Empire of the Sun, 1987 (nominated Acad. award), Jaws: The Revenge, 1987, Superman IV: The Quest for Peace, 1987, The Secret of My Success, 1987, The Accidental Tourist, 1988 (nominated Acad. award), Indiana Jones and the Last Crusade, 1989 (nominated Acad. award), Always, 1989, Born On The Fourth of July, 1989 (nominated Acad. award), Stanley and Iris, 1990, Presumed Innocent, 1990, Home Alone, 1990 (nominated Acad. award), Hook, 1991 (nominated Acad. award), JFK, 1991 (nominated Acad. award), Far and Away, 1992, Home Alone II, 1992, Jurassic Park, 1993, Schindler's List, 1993 (Academy award best original score 1993); composer: (TV programs) Heidi, 1969 (Emmy award), Jane Eyre, 1971

(Emmy award), others; composer numerous concert pieces and symphonies including Jubilee 350 Fanfare for the Boston Pops, 1980, theme to the 1984 Summer Olympic Games, Liberty Fanfare, 1987; recorded numerous albums with Boston Pops Orch. including Pops in Space, That's Entertainment (Pops on Broadway), Pops on the March, Pops Around the World (Digital Overtures), Aisle Seat, Pops Out of This World, Boston Pops on Stage, America, the Dream Goes On; collaborator: (with Jessye Norman) With A Song in My Heart, Swing, Swing, Swing, Unforgettable; guest condr. major orchs. including London Symphony Orch., Cleve. Orch., Phila. Orch., Toronto Orch., Montreal Orch. Served with USAF. Recipient several gold and platnum records Rec. Industry Assn. Am. Office: Gorfaine & Schwartz care of Michael Gorfaine 3301 Barham Blvd Ste 201 Los Angeles CA 90068-1477*

WILLIAMS, JOHN TROY, librarian, educator; b. Oak Park, Ill., Mar. 11, 1924; s. Michael Daniel and Donna Marie (Shaffer) W.; B.A., Central Mich. U., 1949; M.A. in Libr. Sci., U. Mich., 1951, M.A., 1954; Ph.D., Mich. State U., 1973. Reference libr. U. Mich., Ann Arbor, 1955-59; instr. Bowling Green (Ohio) State U., 1959-60; reference librarian Mich. State U., East Lansing, 1960-62; 1st asst. reference dept. Flint (Mich.) Pub. Library, 1962-65; head reference svcs., Purdue U., West Lafayette, Ind., 1965-72; head pub. svcs. No. Ill. U., Dekalb, 1972-75; asst. dean, asst. univ. libr. Wright State U., Dayton, Ohio, 1975-80; vis. scholar U. Mich., Ann Arbor, 1980—; cons. in field. Served with U.S. Army, 1943-46. Mich. State fellow, 1963-64; HEW fellow, 1971-72. Mem. Am. Libr. Assn., Spl. Libraries Assn., Am. Soc. for Info. Scis., Am. Sociol. Assn., AAUP, Coun. on Fgn. Rels. Contbr. articles to profl. jours. Home: PO Box 7531 Ann Arbor MI 48107-7531

WILLIAMS, JOHN WESLEY, fine arts educator; b. Memphis, Feb. 25, 1928; s. Wesley Alfred and Anna Belle (Curtis) W.; m. Mary Ellen Schmidt, Dec. 26, 1955; children: Maxwell, Katherine, Sarah, Cyril, Elena, Amelia. Student, Duke U., 1948-50; B.A., Yale U., 1952; M.A., U. Mich., 1953, Ph.D., 1960. Instr., assoc. prof. Swarthmore Coll., Pa., 1960-72; prof. fine arts U. Pitts., 1972—, Disting. Svc. prof., 1993—; dir. Internat. Center Medieval Art, N.Y.C., 1982-85. Author: Early Spanish Illum, 1977, Apocalypse in Spain, 1991, The Illustrated Beatus, 1994. Served with USMC, 1946-48. Guggenheim fellow, 1984-85, Inst. for Advanced Study member, 1991-92. Home: 749 S Linden Ave Pittsburgh PA 15208-2814 Office: Univ Pitts Pittsburgh PA 15260

WILLIAMS, JOHN YOUNG, merchant banker; b. Cordele, Ga., Apr. 13, 1943; s. George Wilmer and Minnie Converse (Roberts) W.; m. Julian Perdue Boykin; m. Joyce, Isabel. BS in Indsl. Engring., Ga. Inst. Tech., 1965; MBA in Fin., Harvard U., 1969. CFA, Ga. Assoc. Kuhn, Loeb & Co., N.Y.C., 1969-71; asst. v.p. Stone & Webster Securities Corp., N.Y.C., 1971-74, Chem. Bank, N.Y.C., 1974-75; mng. dir. Dean Witter Reynolds, Inc., Atlanta, 1975-84; sr. v.p., ltd. ptnr. Bear Stearns & Co., Atlanta, 1984-85; mng. dir. Robinson Humphrey Co., Atlanta, 1985-87; mng. dir., co-founder Grubb & Williams, Ltd., Atlanta, 1987—, Equity South Ptnrs., 1995—; bd. dirs. Tech Data Corp., Clearwater, Fla., Consol. Engring. Corp., Atlanta, CCS Tech. Group, Inc., Orlando, Fla. 1st lt. U.S. Army, 1965-67, Korea. Fellow Soc. Internat. Bus. Fellows (sec. 1988-89); mem. Assn. for Investment Mgmt. and Rsch. (CFA), Assn. for Corp. Growth (pres. 1983-84), Harvard Bus. Sch. Club (pres. 1982-83), Phi Delta Theta (alumni pres. 1980-81). Episcopalian. Avocation: military history. Home: 750 Arden Close Atlanta GA 30327 Office: Equity South Advisors, LLC 3399 Peachtree Rd Ste 1790 Atlanta GA 30326

WILLIAMS, JOSEPH DALTON, pharmaceutical company executive; b. Washington, Pa., Aug. 15, 1926; s. Joseph Dalton and Jane (Day) W.; m. Mildred E. Bellaire, June 28, 1973; children: Terri, Daniel. BS in Pharmacy, U. Nebr., 1950; DSc (hon.), Union U., 1991, U. Nebr., 1989; LHD (hon.), Albany Coll. Pharmacy, Union U., 1980, Rutgers U., 1987, Long Island U., 1988; DSc (hon.), Phila. Coll. Pharmacy and Sci., 1988, Long Island U., 1988, Albany Coll. Pharmacy of Union U., 1991; D Human Svcs. (hon.), Caldwell Coll., 1989; LLD (hon.), Bethune-Cookman Coll., 1990, Coll. St. Elizabeth, 1990, Seton Hall U., 1990, U. Md., 1991, St. Augustine Coll., 1992. Pres. Parke-Davis Co., Detroit, 1973-76; pres. pharm. group Warner-Lambert Co., Morris Plains, N.J., 1976-77; pres. Internat. Group, 1977-79; pres., dir. Warner-Lambert Corp., 1979-80, pres., chief operating officer, 1980-84, chmn., CEO, 1985-91, chmn. exec. com., 1991—; bd. dirs. AT&T, J.C. Penney & Co., Exxon Corp., Rockefeller Fin. Svcs., Inc., Rockefeller and Co., Inc., Thrift Drug Inc., The Wyatt Co. Bd. dirs. People to People Health Found., United Negro Coll. Fund; trustee Columbia U.; chmn. Commn. on Higher Edn. for State of N.J. With USNR, 1943-46. Mem. Am. Pharm. Assn., N.J. Pharm. Assn., Somerset Hills Country Club, Links Club, Pine Valley Golf Club, Baltusrol Golf Club, Mid Ocean Club, Robert Trent Jones Internat. Golf Club. Office: Warner-Lambert Co 201 Tabor Rd Morris Plains NJ 07950-2693

WILLIAMS, JOSEPH HILL, retired diversified industry executive; b. Tulsa, June 2, 1933; s. David Rogerson and Martha Reynolds (Hill) W.; children: Joseph Hill Jr., Peter B., James C.; m. Terese T. Ross, May 7, 1977; stepchildren: Margot Ross, Jennifer Ross. Diploma, St. Paul's Sch., 1952; B.A., Yale U., 1956, M.A. (hon.), 1977; postgrad., Sch. Pipeline Tech. U. Tex., 1960. Field employee div. domestic constrn. The Williams Cos., Inc., Tulsa, 1958-60; project coord. div. engring. The Williams Cos. Inc., Tulsa, 1960-61; project supt. Iran, 1961-62, asst. resident mgr., 1962-64; project mgr., 1964-65, resident mgr., 1965-67; exec. v.p. Tulsa Corp., 1968—, pres., chief operating officer, 1971-78; chmn., chief exec. officer The Williams Cos., Inc., Tulsa, 1979-93; chmn. bd. The Williams Cos., Inc., 1994; now chmn. & CEO The Williams Co., Inc., Tulsa, O.K. Former fellow, trustee Yale Corp. Served with AUS, 1956-58. Mem. (hon.) Am. Petroleum Inst. (hon. bd. dirs.), Met. Tulsa C. of C. (past chmn.), Okla. State C. of C. and Industry (past. chmn.), Bus. Coun., Nature Conservancy (chmn. bd. govs.). Episcopalian. Clubs: Southern Hills Country, Tulsa; Springdale Hall (Camden, S.C.); Augusta (Ga.); Grandfather Golf and Country (Linville, N.C.); Old Baldy Club, (Saratoga, Wyo). Office: Williams Cos Inc 1 Williams Ctr PO Box 2400 Tulsa OK 74102-2400

WILLIAMS, JOSEPH R., newspaper publishing executive; b. Detroit, May 15, 1931; s. George E. and Helen Marie (Kennedy) W.; m. Joan Baumann, June 15, 1956; children—Cathy Jean, Joseph R. B.A., U. Miami, 1956. Dir. advt. All Fla. Mag., Jacksonville, 1960-61; mgr. gen. advt., salesman Knoxville News Sentinel, Tenn., 1961-66, dir. advt., 1966-60; mgr. bus. Cin. Post, 1971-74; v.p., gen. mgr. Memphis Pub. Co., 1975—. Past pres. Liberty Bowl, Memphis, 1984; bd. dirs. Future Memphis, Inc., 1975—; Fed Express St. Jude Memphis Classic, 1976—; Memphis Zool. Soc.; trustee Scripps Howard Found., 1987—. With USN, 1951-54, Korea. Recipient silver medal for outstanding svc. to industry and community Memphis Advt. Fedn., 1991. Mem. Am. Newspaper Pubs. Assn., So. Newspaper Pubs. Assn., Internat. Newspaper Advt. Execs., Tenn. Press Assn., Colonial Country Club, Tournament Players Club at Southwind. Avocation: golf. Home: 8354 Countrywood Fwy Cordova TN 38018-4528 Office: Memphis Pub Co 495 Union Ave Memphis TN 38103-3242

WILLIAMS, JOSEPH THEODORE, oil and gas company executive; b. Oklahoma City, June 19, 1937; s. Roland Leslie and Mary Virginia (Maloy) W.; m. Marilyn Kay Hansen, Sept. 3, 1948; children: Joseph Kent, John Kevin, Katharine Ann, Jennifer Lyn. BS in Petroleum Engring., U. Tex., 1960. Engr. Chevron Corp., New Orleans and Brookhaven, Miss., 1960-65; engr. mgr. Arabian Am. Oil Co., Dhahran, Saudi Arabia, 1965-70, Chevron Corp., Denver and San Francisco, 1970-74; gen. mgr. ops. Chevron Petroleum (U.K.) Ltd., London, 1974-78; sr. v.p. Mitchell Energy and Devel. Corp., Houston, 1978-81; pres., chmn. Sovran Energy Corp., Houston, 1981-83; v.p. Lear Petroleum Corp., Dallas, 1983-85, pres., chief exec. officer, 1985-89, also chmn. bd. dirs.; pres., CEO DALEN Resources Corp. (formerly PG&E Resources Co.), Dallas, 1989-95; vice chmn., CEO Enserch Exploration, Inc., 1995—. Mem. AIME, Soc. Petroleum Engrs., Tex. Ind. Producers and Royalty Owners Assn., Ind. Petroleum Assn. Am., Domestic Petroleum Coun., Dallas Petroleum Club, Northwood Club. Avocations: golf, tennis, bridge, music.

WILLIAMS, JUDITH L., library administrator; b. Jacksonville, Fla., Sept. 3, 1948; d. Herman D. and Lucille T. (Jaskowiak) W. BA, Fla. State U., 1970, MLS, 1971. From librarian to sr. librarian to asst. dir. to dir. Jack-

sonville Pub. Libraries, 1971—. Active Jacksonville Community Council. Mem. ALA, Fla. Library Assn., Southeastern Library Assn., League of Women Voters, Jacksonville C. of C. Office: Jacksonville Pub Librs 122 N Ocean St Jacksonville FL 32202-3314*

WILLIAMS, JUDY CAROL, teacher; b. Fort Worth, Tex., Jan. 4, 1946; d. Wells Wallis and Hazel (Nunn) W. BEd, Tex. Christian U., 1968; cert. English as 2d Lang., Tex. Western U., 1985; postgrad., U. Calif., Irvine, 1985-87, Calif. State U. Long Beach, 1987, Chapman Coll., 1989. Tchr. Dallas Ind. Sch. Dist., 1968-85, Calif. Elem. Sch., Orange, 1987—. Named Tchr. of Yr. at Lakewood Sch., Dallas Ind. Sch. Dist., 1984-85. Mem. Internat. Reading Assn., NEA, Classroom Tchrs. Dallas, Calif. Tchrs. Orange, Unified Tchrs. Avocations: snow skiing, crewel embroidery, sailing. Home: 3405 S Plaza Dr Apt D Santa Ana CA 92704-7222 Office: Office of Supt 507 Luther Cir Billings MT 59102

WILLIAMS, JULIE BELLE, psychiatric social worker; b. Algona, Iowa, July 29, 1950; d. George Howard and Leta Maribelle (Durschmidt) W. BA, U. Iowa, 1972, MSW, 1973. Lic. psychologist, ind. clin. social worker marriage and family therapist, Minn.; lic. social worker, Iowa. Social worker Psychopathic Hosp., Iowa City, 1971-72; OEO counselor YOUR, Webster City, Iowa, 1972; social worker Child Devel. Clinic, Iowa City, 1973; therapist Mid-Eastern Iowa Community Mental Health Ctr., Iowa City, 1973; psychiat. social worker Mental Health Ctr. No. Iowa, Mason City, 1974-79, chief psychiat. social worker, 1979-80; asst. dir. Community Counseling Ctr., White Bear Lake, Minn., 1980-85, dir., 1985—; lectr., cons. in field. NIMH grantee, 1972-73. Mem. NASW (Acad. Cert. Social Workers, Qualified Clin. Social Workers, diplomate), NOW, Am. Orthopsychiat. Assn., Am. Assn. Sex Educators, Counselors and Therapists, Minn. Women Psychologists, Minn. Lic. Psychologists, Phi Beta Kappa. Democrat. Office: 1280 N Birch Lake Blvd White Bear Lake MN 55110-6708

WILLIAMS, JULIE FORD, mutual fund specialist; b. Long Beach, Calif., Aug. 7, 1948; d. Julious Hunter and Bessie May (Wood) Ford; m. Walter Edward Williams, Oct. 20, 1984; 1 child, Andrew Ford. BA in Econs., Occidental Coll., 1970. Legal sec. Kadison, Pfaelzer, Woodard, Quinn & Rossi, L.A., 1970-71, 74-77; legal sec. Fried, Frank, Harris, Shriver & Jacobson, N.Y.C., 1971-72, Pallot, Poppell, Goodman & Shapo, Miami, Fla., 1973-74; adminstrv. asst. Capital Research-Mgmt., Los Angeles, 1978-82; corp. officer Cash Mgmt. Trust Am., 1982—, Bond Fund Am., 1982—, Tax-Exempt Bond Fund Am., 1982—, AMCAP Fund, 1984—, Am. Funds Income Series, 1985—, Am. Funds Tax-Exempt Series II, 1986—, Capital World Bond Fund, 1987—, Am. High-Income Trust, 1987—, Intermediate Bond Fund Am., 1987—, Tax-Exempt Money Fund Am., 1989—, U.S. Treasury Money Fund Am., 1991—, Fundamental Investors, 1992—, Ltd. Term Tax-Exempt Bond Fund Am., 1993—, Am. High-Income Mcpl. Bond Fund, 1994—; v.p. fund bus. mgmt. group Capital Rsch. Mgmt., 1986—. Mem. alumni bd. govs. Occidental Coll., 1994—. Democrat. Episcopalian. Avocations: scuba diving, RVing, theatre. Office: Capital Rsch and Mgmt Co 333 S Hope St Los Angeles CA 90071-1406

WILLIAMS, JUSTIN W., government official; b. N.Y.C., Jan. 4, 1942; s. Louis P. and Edith W. Williams. BA, Columbia U., 1963; LLB, U. Va., 1967. Bar: Va. 1967. Atty. Dept. Justice, 1967-68; asst. commonwealth atty. Arlington County, Va., 1968-70; asst. U.S. atty. Ea. Dist. Va., 1970-78, 1st asst. U.S. atty., 1978-79; U.S. atty. Alexandria, Va., 1979-81; asst. U.S. atty., 1981-86; U.S. atty. Ea. dist. Va., 1986; asst. U.S. atty., chief criminal divsn. Ea. dist. Va., Alexandria, Va., 1986—. Episcopalian. Office: US Atty's Office 1101 King St Ste 502 Alexandria VA 22314-2944

WILLIAMS, KAREN HASTIE, lawyer; b. Washington, Sept. 30, 1944; d. William Henry and Beryl (Lockhart) Hastie; m. Wesley S. Williams, Jr.; children: Amanda Pedersen, Wesley Hastie, Bailey Lockhart. Cert., U. Neuchatel, Switzerland, 1965. BA, Bates Coll., 1966; MA, Tufts U., 1967; JD, Cath. U. Am., 1973. Bar: D.C. 1973. Staff asst. internat. gov. relations dept. Mobil Oil Corp., N.Y.C., 1967-69; staff asst. com. Dist. Columbia U.S. Senate, 1970, chief counsel com. on the budget, 1977-80; law clk. to judge Spottswood Robinson III U.S. Ct. Appeals (D.C. Cir.), Washington, 1973-74; law clk. to assoc. justice Thurgood Marshall U.S. Supreme Ct., Washington, 1974-75; assoc. Fried, Frank, Harris, Shriver & Kampelman, Washington, 1975-77, 1975-77; adminstr. Office Mgmt. and Budget, Washington, 1980-81; of counsel Crowell & Moring, Washington, 1982, ptnr., 1982—; Bd. dirs. Crestar Fin. Services Corp., Fannie Mae, Washington Gas Light Co., Continental Airlines, SunAmerica, Inc. Chair, trustee Greater Washington Research Ctr., chair. Mem. ABA (pub. contract law sect., past chair), Nat. Bar Assn., Washington Bar Assn., Nat. Contract Mgmt. Assn., NAACP (bd. dirs. legal defense fund). Office: Crowell & Moring Ste 1200W 1001 Pennsylvania Ave NW Washington DC 20004-2595

WILLIAMS, KAREN JOHNSON, federal judge; b. Orangeburg, S.C., Aug. 4, 1951; d. James G. Johnson and Marcia (Reynolds) Johnson Dantzler; m. Charles H. Williams, Dec. 27, 1968; children: Marian, Ashley, Charlie, David. BA, Columbia Coll., 1972; postgrad., U. S.C., 1973, JD cum laude, 1980. Bar: S.C. 1980, U.S. Dist. Ct. S.C. 1980, U.S. Ct. Appeals (4th cir.) 1981. Tchr. Irmo (S.C.) Mid. Sch., 1972-74, O-W High Sch., Orangeburg, 1974-76; assoc. Charles H. Williams P.A., Orangeburg, 1980-92; circuit judge U.S. Ct. Appeals (4th cir.), 1992—; mem. exec. bd. grievance commn. S.C. Supreme Ct., Columbia, 1983-92. Mem. child devel. bd. First Baptist Ch., Orangeburg; bd. dirs. Orangeburg County Mental Retardation Bd., 1986—; Orangeburg-Calhoun Hosp. Found; bd. visitors Columbia Coll., 1988-92; dir. Reg. Med. Ctr. Hosp. Found., 1988-92; mem. Orangeburg-Calhoun Tech. Coll. Adv. Bd., 1987-92; mem. Rotary Club Orangeburg, 1989—. Mem. ABA, S.C. Bar Assn., Orangeburg County Bar Assn. (co-chairperson Law Day 1981), Assn. Trial Lawyers Am., S.C. Trial Lawyers Assn., Bus. and Profl. Women Assn., Order of Wig and Robe, Order of Coif, Jr. Service League. Home: RR 2 Box 110 Orangeburg SC 29115-9604 Office: US Courthouse PO Box 2087 Orangeburg SC 29116-2087*

WILLIAMS, KARMEN PETERSEN, secondary school educator; b. Kansas City, Mo., Sept. 19, 1942; d. Hans Jorgen and Rosella Petersen; m. James Emmett Williams, Aug. 28, 1965; children: Jan Elizabeth Williams Parks, James Jorgen. BA in English, Okla. Bapt. U., 1964; MS in Edn., Ouachita Bapt. U., 1983. Cert. secondary tchr., reading specialist, K-12, Ark. Instr. English/reading Fern Creek H.S., Louisville, 1966-69; dir. kindergarten 1st Bapt. Ch., Texarkana, Ark., 1970-73; staff devel. specialist Divsn. Children & Family Svc., Pine Bluff, Ark., 1974-85; instr. English speech, drama White Hall (Ark.) High Sch., 1985—, chairperson English dept., 1989—. Vol. Casa Women's Shelter, Pine Bluff, 1992—. Mem. MLA, Nat. Fedn. Interscholastic Speech & Debate Assn., Nat. Coun. Tchrs. English. Democrat. Southern Baptist. Avocations: calligraphy, cake decorating, pastel artist, speech consultant, tutor. Home: 517 E 7th St Little Rock AR 72202

WILLIAMS, KEITH ROY, museum director; b. Sunnyside, Wash., Sept. 5, 1958; s. Charles N. Williams and Ruth Arlene (Plank) Hicks; m. Nancy Maxson, 1980 (div. 1984); m. Deanna Lynn Murphy, Oct. 26, 1987; children: Steven, Jeremy. AA in Gen. Studies, Columbia Basin C.C., Pasco, Wash., 1979; BA in Anthropology, Wash. State U., 1981, MA in History/Pub. History, 1984, PhD in History, 1991. Interpretive ranger Nez Perce Nat. Hist. Pk. Nat. Pk. Svc., 1984; vis. prof. historian Alaska regional office Nat. Pk. Svc., Anchorage, 1986; dir. North Ctrl. Wash. Mus., Wenatchee, 1987—; cons. Office Archaeology and Hist. Preservation, 1985, Batelle N.W. DOSE Reconstruction Project, Hanford, 1987, 88; instr. Wenatchee Valley C.C. 1988, 93—; speaker in field. Author: (video, booklet) Wash. State Heritage Coun., Olympia, 1988-90, Wash. Centennial Com., Wenatchee, 1989; mem. design com. Wenatchee Downtown Assn., 1993—; bd. dirs. Wash. Friends Humanities, Seattle, 1990—, Wenatchee Centennial Com., 1992. Grantee Assn. Humanities Idaho, Wash. Commn. Humanities, various other founds. Mem. Wash. Mus. Assn. (bd. dirs. 1988-90, 94—), Kiwanis (bd. dirs.). Avocations: boating, gardening, hunting, camping, reading. Office: North Central Washington Museum 127 S Mission Wenatchee WA 98801

WILLIAMS, KENNETH OGDEN, farmer; b. Clarksdale, Miss., Jan. 18, 1924; s. Peter Fairley and Robbie (Casey) W.; m. Frances Dyer Lott, June 14, 1969; 1 child, Frances. BS, Vanderbilt U., 1949. Ptnr. P.F. Williams

and Sons, Clarksdale, 1949-88, Swan Lake Farms, Clarksdale, 1989—. Mem. Miss. Ho. of Reps., Jackson, 1960-84, Miss. Senate, 1988-92. Sgt. U.S. Army, 1942-46. Decorated Bronze Star. Republican. Baptist. Home: 1505 Holly St Clarksdale MS 38614-2912

WILLIAMS, KENNETH SCOTT, entertainment company executive; b. Tulsa, Okla., Dec. 31, 1955; s. David Vorhees Williams and Mary Louise (Newell) Rose; m. Jann Catherine Wolfe, May 20, 1989; children: Catherine Eloise, Michael Holbrook. BA, Harvard Coll., 1978; MS, Columbia U., 1985. Bank officer Chase Manhattan Bank, N.Y.C., 1978-82; asst. treas. Columbia Pictures Entertainment, N.Y.C., 1982-84, v.p.; treas., 1984-89; sr. v.p. fin. and adminstrn. Columbia Pictures Entertainment, Burbank, Calif., 1990-91; sr. v.p. corp. ops. Sony Pictures Entertainment, Culver City, Calif., 1991—. Mem. Blue Hill Troupe, N.Y.C., 1979—; vice chmn. Graphic Arts Coun., L.A. County Mus., 1993—. Mem. N.Y. Soc. Securities Analysts, Fin. Execs. Inst., Beta Gamma Sigma. Home: 966 Stone Canyon Rd Los Angeles CA 90077-2914 Office: Sony Pictures Entertainment 10202 Washington Blvd Culver City CA 90232-3119

WILLIAMS, LARRY BILL, university president; b. Cushing, Okla., June 9, 1945; s. Louis Albert and Morene Ruth (Cox) W.; m. Pam Bryan, May 1, 1993; children: Natalie Michelle, Nicole Diane, Louis Bradley. BS, Cen. State U., Edmond, Okla., 1967, MBA, 1972; PhD, U. Okla., 1985. Office mgr. Okla. State U., Stillwater, 1967-69; asst. comptroller Cen. State U., Edmond, 1969-71, dir. affirmative action, 1971-72, assoc. dir. univ. personnel services, 1971-72, dir. affirmative action, 1972-80, dir. univ. personnel services, 1972-80, asst. v.p. adminstrn., 1980-84, v.p. adminstrn., 1984-87; interim pres. Southeastern Okla. State U., Durant, 1987, pres., 1987—; managerial cons. various municipalities; mktg. cons. State of Okla.; arbitrator Met. Fraternal Order of Police. Bd. dirs. Bryan County Econ. Devel. Corp., 1989—, Bryan County United Way, 1988—; mem. adv. bd. Med. Ctr. Southeastern Okla., 1987-92; bd. dirs. Bryan County Retired Sr. Vol. Program, 1990-92, Leadership Okla. Class IV, 1991; mem. exec. bd. Boy Scouts Am., 1991; com. mem. Okla. Ctr. for the Advancement Sci. and Tech. Long Range Planning Task Force, Most Eminent Scholars and Rsch. Equipment, 1990—; mem. higher edn. alumni coun. Okla. State Regents for Higher Edn. Tuition Com., 1989-90, outreach com. 19-91, chmn.; budget com., 1990-91; mem. adv. coun. Ea. Okla. Schs., 1987—; trustee Southeastern Found., 1990—; Kickingbird Golf Course Mgmt. Bd. past pres., Edmond; bd. dirs. Edmond C. of C., 1984; mem. Okla. State Regents for Higher Edn. Coun. of Pres.; Choctaw Nation of Okla JTPA Adv. Coun; vice chmn. Diamond Jubilee Commn., Edmond; mem. found. bd. trustees Cen. State U., Edmond; mem. adv. com. Curant Airport. With USNG. 1962-70. Named One of Outstanding Young Men of Am., Edmond Jaycees, 1971, 74, 79; recipient Presdl. Leadership award Nat. U.S. Jaycee Pres., 1971, Presdl. Leadership, Achievement and Honor awards Nat. Jaycees, 1972, Nat. Presdl. award of Honor Nat. Coll. and Univ. Pers. Assn., 1973, Disting. Svc. award City of Edmond, 1974, Dwight F. Whelan Meml. award for Outstanding Leadership, Edmond, 1972; named to Cushing Alumni Hall of Fame, 1988, recipient Nat. Order Omega (charter hon. mem), 1991. Mem. Okla. Assn. Coll. and Univ. Personnel Adminstrs. (founder, bd. dirs., chmn.), Nat. Coll. and Univ. Personnel Assn., Okla. Assn. Affirmative Action (co-founder, pres., bd. dirs.), Okla. Assn. Coll. and Univ. Bus. Officers (bd. dirs., pres.), Acad. Cert. Adminstrv. Mgrs., Durant C. of C. (past pres., bd. dirs.), Okla. State C. of C. (bd. dirs. 1991-92), Blue Key (hon.), Nat. Order Omega (charter hon. mem.). Democrat. Presbyterian. Lodge: Rotary (sec. Edmond club 1986-87). Avocation: golf. Office: Southeastern Okla State U Office of Pres Durant OK 74701

WILLIAMS, LARRY EMMETT, oil company executive; b. Chickasha, Okla., July 11, 1936; s. J. Emmett and Zella M. (Venrick) W.; m. Xan Z. Hart, Sept. 7, 1957; children—Jesslyn, Jon. BS in Mech. Engring., U. N.Mex., 1958, MS in Mech. Engring., 1959. Various positions Cities Svc. Co., 1959-74; v.p. Cities Svc. Co., Tulsa, 1974-83; pres., chief exec. officer Nat. Coop. Refinery Assn., McPherson, Kans., 1983—; bd. dirs. Bank IV Kansas, Jayhawk Pipeline Co., Wichita, Kans., Osage Pipeline Co., Denver, Kaw Pipeline Co., Denver, Farmers Alliance Mut. Ins. Co., McPherson; pres., bd. dirs. Clear Creek, Inc., McPherson. Mem. Nat. Petroleum Refiners Assn. (bd. dirs.), Nat. Coun. Farmer Coops. (bd. dirs., energy policy com.), Nat. Coop. Bus. Assn., McPherson Healthcare Found., Country Club of McPherson, Petroleum Club (Wichita). Office: Nat Coop Refinery Assn PO Box 1404 2000 S Main St Mc Pherson KS 67460-9402*

WILLIAMS, LAWRENCE FLOYD, conservation organization official; b. Eugene, Oreg., Mar. 26, 1937; s. Carroll Parven and Catherene (Dorris) W.; m. Patricia Ann Pride. Student, Portland State U. Advt. staff asst. Omark Industries, Portland, Oreg., 1963-67; internat. advt. liaison Hyster Co., Portland, 1968; exec. dir. Oreg. Environ. Coun., Portland, 1969-78; policy analyst pub. land mgmt. White House Coun. on Environ. Quality, Washington, 1978-81; spl. cons. Sierra Club, Portland, 1969; Washington rep. Sierra Club, 1981-85; dir. internat. program Sierra Club, Washington, 1985—; Former mem. dist. adv. bd. Bur. Land Mgmt.; former mem. Adv. Com. on Forest Mgmt. Policy; former cons. Coun. on Econ. Priorities; former mem. acv. com. Bonneville Power Adminstrn.; mgr. N.W. Workshops for Conservation Found. on Implementation Clean Air Act, 1972, Clean Water Act, 1975, U.S. Energy Policy, 1976; former mem. Western Forest Environ.-Industry Policy Discussion Group. Author: with (Raymond Mikesell) International Banks and the Environment, from Growth to Sustainability: An Unfinished Agenda, 1992; mng. editor: Bankrolling Disasters, International Development Banks and the Global Environment, 1986. Past mem. bd. dirs. Inst. for Transp. and Devel. Policy, N.W. Environ. Def. Ctr.; past chmn. Nat. Coalition for Clean Water; past chmn. Pacific N.W. chpt. Sierra Club, founder, past 1st chmn. Portland group; past v.p. Fedn. Western Outdoor Clubs; past pres. Trails Club Oreg.; past assembly pres. Inst. Ecology; organizer, past chmn. Com. for Volcanic Cascades Study, People Against Nerve Gas; organizer Oreg. League Conservation Voters. With USAF, 1956-70. Recipient Richard L. Neuberger award Oreg. Environ. Coun., 1988. Democrat. Home: 4607 Van Ness St NW Washington DC 20016 Office: Sierra Club 408 C St NE Washington DC 20002-5818

WILLIAMS, LAWRENCE SOPER, photographer; b. Balt., July 8, 1917; s. Lawrence S. and Ida (Exall) W.; m. Avilda Leyshon Williams, Nov. 21, 1940; children: Jay Stephen, Wendy Lauren. Student, Md. Inst. Wirephoto operator AP, Balt., 1937-38; news photographer Balt. Sun Papers, 1938-40, Harris and Ewing News Photos, Washington, 1940-41; war corr. photographer Bur. Info. U.S. War Dept., Washington, 1941-45; picture editor Holiday mag., Phila., 1945-48; freelance photographer Havertown, Pa., 1949-59; pres. Lawrence S. Williams, Inc., Upper Darby, Pa., 1959-83, chmn., 1983-93. Pres. Archtl. Photographers Assn., N.Y.C., 1960-70, Paoli (Pa.) Woods Homeowner's Assn., 1985-86. Recipient Gold medal Artist Guild of Phila., 1965, Silver medal Artist Guild of Pa., 1964, George W. Berry trophy Soc. Comml. Photographers Del. Valley, 1961, 66, 78, 79, 82, Best of Show trophy Am. Mus. Photography, Phila., 1966, 71, 77, 79, 82, Best Comml. Print trophy Guild of Profl. Photographers Del. Valley, 1971, 70, Award of Excellence Am. Advtg. Assn. Pa., 1978, Pres.'s Cup Profl. Photographers Assn. Pa., 1971, numerous archtl., comml., indsl., pictorial awards. Fellow Am. Soc. Photographers; mem. Soc. Comml. Photographers Del. Valley (life), Profl. Photographers Assn. Pa. (life), Profl. Photographers Am., Inc. (life, master photography degree 1966, craftsman photography degree 1968), Overbrook Golf Club (Bryn Mawr, Pa.), Shriners. Republican. Lutheran. Avocation: traveling. Home: 305 Paoli Woods Paoli PA 19301-1538 Office: PO Box 694 Kimberton PA 19442

WILLIAMS, LEA EVERARD, history educator; b. Milw., July 25, 1924; s. William Everard and Paula Herndon (Pratt) W.; m. Daisy Shen, Sept. 15, 1949; children—Adrienne Paula Covington, William Herndon. BA, Cornell U., 1950; M.A., Harvard U., 1952, Ph.D., 1956. With U.S. Fgn. Service, Chungking, China, 1944-45; Am. vice consul U.S. Fgn. Service, Shanghai, 1945-48; with Brown U., 1956—, prof. Asian history, 1969-76, prof. history, 1976-89, prof. history emeritus, 1989—; dir. East Asia Lang. and Area Ctr., 1969-84; vis. prof. history U. Singapore, 1961-63; vis. prof. Asian affairs Fletcher Sch., 1964-65; lectr. Fgn. Svcs. Inst., U.S. Dept. State, staff lectr. spl. expeditions, 1993—. Author: Overseas Chinese Nationalism, 1960, The Future of the Overseas Chinese in Southeast Asia, 1966, Southeast Asia: A History, 1976; editor, transl.: The Origins of the Modern Chinese Movement in Indonesia, 1969. Served with U.S. Army, 1943. Social Sci.

Research fellow, 1957; Fulbright-Hays fellow, 1966-67; Am. Council Learned Socs. fellow, 1969; Nat. Sci. Council vis. scholar Taiwan, 1980; Gulbenkian Found. travel grantee, 1980, 82, 85, 89. Mem. The South Seas Soc., Assn. Asian Studies, Royal Asiatic Soc. (Malayan br.), Koninklijk Instiuut voor Taal, Land-en Volkenkunde, Hakluyt Soc., Providence Athenaeum, Phi Beta Kappa. Clubs: Bristol Yacht (R.I.); Catboat Assn., Am. Club (Singapore); Royal Singapore Yacht, U.S. Coast Guard Aux. Home: 73 Transit St Providence RI 02906-1022 Office: Brown U History Dept Providence RI 02912

WILLIAMS, LESLIE PEARCE, history educator; b. Harmon-on Hudson, N.Y., Sept. 8, 1927; s. George and Addie Adelia (Williams) Greenberg; m. Sylvia Irene Alessandrini, Sept. 3, 1949; children: David Rhys, Alison Ruth, Adam Jonathan, Sarah Lucille. B.A., Cornell U., 1949, Ph.D., 1952. Instr. history Yale U., 1952-56; asso. historian Nat. Found. for Infantile Paralysis, N.Y.C., 1956-57; asst. prof. U. Del., 1956-59; asst. prof. history Cornell U., 1960-62, assoc. prof., 1962-65, prof., 1965-71, John Stambaugh prof. history of sci., 1971-94, prof. emeritus, 1994—, chmn. dept. history, 1969-74, dir. program in history and philosophy sci. and tech., 1984-91. Author: Michael Faraday, A Biography, 1965, The Origins of Field Theory, 1967, Album of Science: The Nineteenth Century, 1978, (with Henry John Steffens) A History of Science in Western Civilization, 3 vols, 1978; editor: The Selected Correspondence of Michael Faraday, 2 vols, 1972, Relativity Theory: Its Origin and Impact on Modern Thought, 1968, (with B. Tierney and D. Kagan) Great Issues in Western Civilization, 2 vols., 1968; cons. editor Italian jour. Physis, Rivista della Storia della Scienza. Served with USNR, 1945-46. NSF fellow, 1959-60; 1st degree black belt Hayashi-ha Shito-ryu Karate. Mem. History Sci. Soc., Royal Institution of Great Britain, Academie internationale d'histoire des sciences, French Acad. Scis. (comite Lavoisier), Phi Beta Kappa. Independent. Home and Office: 207 Iradell Rd Ithaca NY 14853 Office: Cornell Univ Dept Sci And Studies Ithaca NY 14853

WILLIAMS, LOUIS CLAIR, JR., public relations executive; b. Huntington, Ind., Nov. 7, 1940; s. Louis Clair and Marian Eileen (Bowers) W.; children—Terri Lynn, L. Bradley, Lisa C.; m. Mary Clare Moster. B.A., Eastern Mich. U., 1963. Copywriter, Rochester (N.Y.) Gas and Electric Co., 1963-65, editor RG&E News, 1965-66; employee info. specialist Gen. Ry. Signal Co., Rochester, 1966-67; supr. employment and employee rels., 1967-69; supr. pub. rels. Heublein, Inc., Hartford, Conn., 1969-70; dir. corp. communications Jewel Cos., Inc., Chgo., 1970-71; account exec. Ruder & Finn of Mid-Am., Chgo., 1971-73, v.p., 1973-76, sr. v.p., 1976-78; cons. Towers, Perrin, Forster & Crosby, Los Angeles, 1978-79; exec. v.p., gen. mgr. Harshe-Rotman & Druck, Inc., Chgo., 1979, pres. midwest region, 1979-80; v.p. Hill & Knowlton, Inc., Chgo. 1980-81, sr. v.p., 1981-83; pres. Savlin Williams Assocs., Evanston, Ill., 1983-85, L.C. Williams & Assocs., Chgo., 1985—. Recipient Clarion award Women in Communications, 1978, award of Excellence, Internat. Coun. Indsl. Editors, 1969, Bronze Oscar-of-Ind., Fin. World, 1974. Mem. Internat. Assn. Bus. Communicators (pres. 1979-80), Chgo. Assn. Bus. Communicators (pres.), Publicity Club Chgo., Pub. Rels. Soc. Am.

WILLIAMS, LOUIS STANTON, glass and chemical manufacturing executive; b. Honolulu, Oct. 7, 1919; s. Urban and Amelia (Olson) W.; m. Dorothy Webster Reed, June 12, 1943; children: Eric Reed, Timothy Howell, Steven Neil, Deborah Reed Sawin. A.B., Amherst Coll., 1941, LL.D., 1981; M.B.A., Harvard U., 1943; D.H.L., Thiel Coll., 1985. With PPG Industries (formerly Pitts. Plate Glass Co.), 1946-84, various acctg. positions, 1946-56, became controller, 1956, v.p. finance, 1963-75, dir., 1975-90, exec. v.p., 1975-76, vice chmn., 1976-78, chmn., chief exec. officer, 1979-84; chmn. Fed. Home Loan Bank, Pitts. 1971-73; bd. dirs. Duplate Can. 1976-84, Rubbermaid Inc., 1977-90, Dravo Corp., 1978-91, Prudential Ins. Co. Am., 1981-89, Mellon Bank Corp, 1981-92, Texaco Inc., 1988-92. Trustee Family and Children's Service, Pitts., 1955-61; bd. dirs. YMCA, Pitts., 1959-93, pres., 1975-77, mem. YMCA nat. bd., 1973-88, chmn., 1983-85; trustee YMCA Retirement Fund, 1989-94; pres. exec. com. Allegheny Conf. on Community Devel., 1982-83, chmn., 1983-85; bd. dirs. Pa. Economy League, 1978-83, Community Chest Allegheny County, 1961-67, Pitts. Symphony Soc., 1978-90; chmn. United Way Campaign of Southwestern Pa., 1981; bd. dirs. United Way of Allegheny County, 1978—, pres., 1984-86; trustee St. Margaret's Meml. Hosp., Pitts., 1969-83, Carnegie-Mellon U., 1978-95, Carnegie Inst., 1977-95, Com. Econ. Devel., 1981-84, Tax Found., 1980-84, Pitts. Cultural Trust, 1984-93. Lt. USNR, 1943-46. Mem. Financial Execs. Inst. (pres. Pitts. 1965-66, nat. dir. 1968-73, nat. v.p. 1972-73), Bus. Roundtable (Policy Com. 1982-84), Phi Beta Kappa. Presbyn. Clubs: Duquesne, Fox Chapel Golf (Pitts.); Laurel Valley Golf, Rolling Rock (Ligonier, Pa.); Iron City Fishing (Can.); John's Island, Bent Pine Golf (Fla.). Home: 5 The Trillium Pittsburgh PA 15238 Office: PPG Industries 1 PPG Pl Pittsburgh PA 15272

WILLIAMS, LOWELL CRAIG, lawyer, employee relations executive; b. Tehachapi, Calif., Dec. 3, 1947; s. Lyndon Williams and Gertrude (White) Sievert; m. Marsha Mendelssohn; children: John S., Jeffrey A. Bescheinigungeschichte, Georg August U., Germany, 1968; BA, U. Calif., Santa Barbara, 1969; JD, Columbia U., 1972. Bar: N.Y. 1973, U.S. Ct. Appeals (2nd cir.) 1974, U.S. Supreme Ct. 1974. Assoc. Sullivan & Cromwell, N.Y.C., 1972-75; sr. v.p., chief adminstrv. officer, gen. counsel, dir. Elf Aquitaine Inc. and Texasgulf Inc., N.Y.C., 1976—; bd. dirs. Am. Natural Soda Ash Co. Pres. Scarsdale Synagogue. Mem. Internat. Bar Assn., German Law Assn. (dir.). Home: 37 Paddington Rd Scarsdale NY 10583-2321 Office: Elf Aquitaine Inc 280 Park Ave 36th FL New York NY 10017-1216

WILLIAMS, LUCINDA, country musician; b. Lake Charles, La., 1953; d. Miller W.; m. Greg Sowders (div.). Albums include: Ramblin' On My Mind, 1979, Happy Woman Blues, 1980, Lucinda Williams, 1988, Passionate Kisses, 1989 (Grammy award Best Country Song 1994), (EP, Sweet Old World, 1992; contbr. songs to: Sweet Relief, 1993, Born to Choose, 1993. Office: c/o Chameleon Records 23rd Floor 1740 Broadway New York NY 10019*

WILLIAMS, LUTHER STEWARD, biologist, federal agency administrator; b. Sawyerville, Ala., Aug. 19, 1940; s. Roosevelt and Mattie B. (Wallace) W.; m. Constance Marie Marion, Aug. 23, 1963; children: Mark Steward, Monique Marie. B.A. magna cum laude, Miles Coll., 1961; M.S., Atlanta U., 1963; Ph.D., Purdue U., 1968, D.Sc. (hon.), 1987. NSF lab asst. Spelman Coll., 1961-62; NSF lab. asst. Atlanta U., 1962-63, instr. biology, faculty research grantee, 1963-64, asst. prof. biology, 1969-70, prof. biology, 1984-87, pres., 1984-87; grad. teaching asst. Purdue U., West Lafayette, Ind., 1964-65, grad. research asst., 1965-66, asst. prof. biology, 1970-73, assoc. prof., 1973-79, prof., 1979-80, NIH Career Devel. awardee, 1971-75, asst. provost, 1976-80; dean Grad. Sch., prof. biology Washington U., St. Louis, 1980-83; v.p. acad. affairs, dean Grad. Sch. U. Colo., Boulder, 1983-84; Am. Cancer Soc. postdoctoral fellow SUNY-Stony Brook, 1968-69; assoc. prof. biology MIT, 1973-74; spl. asst. to dir. Nat. Inst. Gen. Med. Scis., NIH, Bethesda, Md., 1987-88; dep. dir. Nat. Inst. Gen. Med. Scis. NIH, Bethesda, Md., 1988-89; sr. sci. advisor to dir. NSF, Washington, 1989-90, asst. dir. for edn. and human resources, 1990—; chmn. rev. com. MARC Program, Nat. Inst. Gen. Med. Scis., NIH, 1972-76; grant reviewer NIH, 1971-73, 76, NSF, 1973, 76-80, Med. Research Council of N.Z., 1976; mem. life scis. screening com. recombinant DNA com. HEW, 1979-81; mem. nat. adv. gen. med. sci. council NIH, 1980-85; mem. adv. com. Office Tech. Assessment, Washington, 1984-87; chmn. fellowship adv. com. NRC Ford Found., 1984-85; mem.-at-large Grad. Record Exam. Bd., 1981-85, chmn. minority grad. edn. com., 1983-85; mem. health, safety and environ. affairs. com. Nat. Labs., U. Calif., 1981-87; mem. adv. panel Office Tech. Assessment, U.S. Congress, 1985-86; mem. fed. task force on women, minorities and the handicapped in sci. and tech., 1987-91; mem. adv. panel to dir. sci. and tech. ctrs. devel. NSF, 1987-88; mem. nat. adv. com. White House Initiative on Historically Black Colls. and Univs. on Sci. and Tech., 1986-89; numerous other adv. bds. and coms. Contbr. sci. articles to profl. jours. Vice chmn. bd. advisors Atlanta Neighborhood Justice Ctr., 1984-87; bd. dirs. Met. Atlanta United Way, 1986-87, Butler St. YMCA, Atlanta, 1985-87; trustee Atlanta Zool. Assn., 1985-87, Miles Coll., 1984-87, Atlanta U., 1984-87, 90—; mem. nominating com. DANA Found. NIH predoctoral fellow Purdue U., 1966-68. Fellow AAAS, Am. Acad. Microbiology; mem. Am. Soc. Microbiology, Am. Chem. Soc., Am. Soc. Biol. Chemists (mem. ednl. affairs com. 1979-82,

com. on equal opportunities for minorities 1972-84), AAAS, N.Y. Acad. Scis. Home: 11608 Split Rail Ct Rockville MD 20852-4423 Office: NSF Education & Human Resources 4201 Wilson Blvd Arlington VA 22203-0001

WILLIAMS, LYNN RUSSELL, labor union official; b. Springfield, Ont., Can., July 21, 1924; came to U.S., 1977; s. Waldemar and Emma Elizabeth (Fisher) W.; m. Audrey Hansuld, Sept. 12, 1946; children—Judith Williams Hocking, David, Barbara, Brian. BA, McMaster U., Hamilton, Ont., 1944, LLD (hon.), 1978; LittD, Brock U., St. Catherines, Ont., 1985. Organizer Can. Congress of Labour (now Can. Labour Congress), 1947-55; staff rep. United Steelworkers Am., Toronto, Ont., Can., 1956-57; area supr. United Steelworkers Am., Niagara Peninsula, 1958-62; asst. dir. Dist. 6 United Steelworkers Am., Toronto, 1963-73, dir. Dist. 6, 1973-77; internat. sec. United Steelworkers Am., Pitts., 1977-83, internat. pres., 1983—; mem. exec. council AFL-CIO, Washington, 1983, mem. exec. council Ind. Union Dept., 1983; mem. exec. com. Metalworkers Fedn., Geneva, 1983; dir. Am. Arbitration Assn., 1983; bd. dirs. African-Am. Labor Ctr., Am. Productivity Ctr., Citizen/Labor Energy Coalition, Com. for Nat. Health Ins., Work in Am. Inst.; trustee Am. Inst. for Free Labor Devel.; mem. exec. com. Can.-Am. Com.; mem. panel Econ. Policy Council; mem. adv. com. Labor Desk, USYC; trustee Labor Heritage Found.; v.p. Labor-Industry Coalition for Internat. Trade; mem. ad hoc com. Nat. Planning Assn.; mem. adv. bd. Niagara Inst. Vice pres. Ams. for Democratic Action; bd. dirs. Am. Open U., 1983—; mem. steering group Council on Fgn. Relations; bd. dirs. Pitts. Symphony Soc., 1978—, United Way of Allegheny County, 1984—, World Affairs Council of Pitts.; bd. govs. United Way, 1984—; mem. Aspen Inst., 1983—, Econ. Policy Council of UN, USA, 1982—; trustee Brother Brothers Found., 1983—; mem. Can.-Am. Commn., 1983— Served with Can. Navy, 1944-45. Avocations: running; jogging; reading; skiing. Office: United Steelworkers Am 5 Gateway Ctr Pittsburgh PA 15222*

WILLIAMS, MARGARET, federal official. Asst. to Pres., chief of staff to First Lady The White House, Washington, 1993—. Office: Office of the First Lady The White House 1600 Pennsylvania Ave NW Washington DC 20500

WILLIAMS, MARK, food products executive; b. 1949. With Safeway Corp., L.A., 1966-67, Fred Meyer Corp., Seattle, 1967-75; exec. v.p., COO Carr-Gottstein Foods Co., Anchorage, 1975—. Office: Carr-Gottstein Foods Co 6411 A St Anchorage AK 99518

WILLIAMS, MARK H., advertising agency executive; b. Omaha, Apr. 30, 1959; s. Perry T. and Donna M. (Hodges) W. BA in Communications, Loyola U., Chgo., 1981. Asst. account exec. Bozell & Jacobs, Omaha, 1981-82, account exec., 1982-86; account supr. Bozell, Jacobs, Kenyon & Eckhardt, Omaha, 1986-88, v.p., 1987—; sr. v.p. client svcs. and bus. devel. Bozell Worldwide, Chgo., 1988—; speaker Creighton U., 1985-87, U. Nebr., 1985, Harvard U., 1989-90, Northwestern U., 1990-95. Mem. Am. Advt. Fedn. Home: 910 Lake Shore Dr Chicago IL 60611-1540 Office: Bozell Worldwide Inc 625 N Michigan Ave Chicago IL 60611-3110

WILLIAMS, MARSHALL HENRY, JR., physician, educator; b. New Haven, July 15, 1924; s. Marshall Henry and Henrietta (English) W.; m. Mary Butler, Aug. 27, 1948; children: Stuart, Patricia, Marshall, Frances, Richard. Grad., Pomfret Sch., 1942; B.S., Yale, 1945, M.D., 1947. Diplomate Nat. Bd. Med. Examiners, Am. Bd. Internal Medicine. Intern Presbyn. Hosp., N.Y.C., 1947-48; asst. resident medicine Presbyn. Hosp., 1948-49; asst. resident medicine New Haven Hosp., 1949-50, asst. in medicine, 1950; trainee Nat. Heart Inst., 1950; practice medicine, specializing in internal medicine Bronx, N.Y.; chief respiratory sect., dept. cardiorespiratory diseases Army Med. Service Grad. Sch., Walter Reed Army Med. Center, 1953-55; dir. cardiorespiratory lab. Grasslands Hosp., Valhalla, N.Y., 1955-59; dir. chest svc. Bronx Mcpl. Hosp. Ctr., 1959-94; vis. asst. prof. physiology Albert Einstein Coll. Medicine, Bronx, 1955-59, assoc. prof. medicine and physiology, 1959-66, prof. medicine, 1966—; dir. pulmonary div. Montefiore Med. Ctr., Albert Einstein Coll. Medicine, 1981-94. Author: Clinical Applications of Cardiopulmonary Physiology, 1960, Essentials of Pulmonary Medicine, 1982, Consultation in Chest Medicine, 1985; contbr. articles to profl. jours. Served from 1st lt. to capt. U.S. Army, 1950-52. Mem. Am. Physiol. Soc., AAAS, Am. Heart Assn., Westchester Heart Assn (past pres.), Am. Thoracic Soc., Am. Fedn. Clin. Research, N.Y. Acad. Sci., N.Y. Trudeau Soc. (past pres.), Am. Soc. Clin. Investigation, Soc. Urban Physicians (past pres.), N.Y. Tb. and Health Assn. (past dir.), Alpha Omega Alpha. Home: 103 Fox Meadow Rd Scarsdale NY 10583-2301 Office: Albert Einstein Coll Medicine Bronx NY 10461

WILLIAMS, MARTHA ETHELYN, information science educator; b. Chgo., Sept. 21, 1934; d. Harold Milton and Alice Rosemond (Fox) W. B.A., Barat Coll., 1955; M.A., Loyola U., 1957. With IIT Rsch.Inst., Chgo., 1957-72, mgr. info. scis., 1962-72, mgr. computer search ctr., 1968-72; adj. assoc. prof. sci. info. Ill. Inst. Tech., Chgo., 1965-73, lectr. chemistry dept., 1968-70, rsch. prof. info. sci., coordinated sci. lab. Coll. engring.; also dir. info. retrieval research lab. U. Ill., Urbana, 1972—; affiliate, computer sci. dept., 1979—; chmn. large data base comf. Nat. Acad. Sci./NRC, 1974, mem. ad hoc panel on info. storage and retrieval, 1977, numerical data adv. bd., 1979-82, computer sci. and tech. bd., nat. rsch. network rev. com., 1987-88, chmn. utility subcom., 1987-88; mem. task force on sci. info. activities NSF, 1977; U.S. rep. review com. for project on broad system of ordering, UNESCO, Hague, Netherlands, 1974; vice chmn. Gordon Rshc. Conf. on Sci. Info. Problems in Rsch., 1978, chmn., 1980; mem. panel on intellectual property rights in age of electronics and info. U.S. Congress, Office of Tech. Assessment; program chmn. Nat. Online Meeting, 1980—; cons. to numerous cos., govt. agys. and rsch. founds.; invited lectr. Commn. European Communities, Industrial R&D adv. com., Brussels, 1992. Editor in chief Computer-Readable Databases Directory and Data Sourcebook, 1976-89, founding editor, 1989-92; editor Ann. Rev. Info. Sci. and Tech., 1976—, Online Rev., 1979-92, Online and CDROM Rev., 1993—, procs. nat. online meeting, 1981—; contbg. editor column on databases to Bull. Am. Soc. Info. Sci., 1974-78; mem. editorial adv. bd. Database, 1978-88; mem. editorial bd. Info. Processing and Mgmt., 1982-89, The Reference Libr.; contbr. more than 200 articles to profl. jours. Trustee Engring. Info., Inc., 1974-87, bd. dirs., 1976-91, chmn. bd. dirs., 1982-91, v.p., 1978-79, pres., 1980-81; regent Nat. Libr. Medicine, 1978-82, chmn. bd. regents, 1981; mem. task force on sci. info. activities NSF, 1977-78; mem. nat. adv. com. ACCESS ERIC, 1989-91. Recipient best paper of year award H. W. Wilson Co., 1975; NSF travel grantee Luxembourg, 1972; NSF travel grantee Honolulu, 1973; NSF travel grantee Tokyo, 1973; NSF travel grantee Mexico City, 1975; NSF travel grantee Scotland, 1976. Fellow AAAS (elected, computers, info. and communication mem.-at-large 1978-81, nominating com. 1983, 85); hon. fellow Inst. Info. Sci., 1985; mem. Am. Chem. Soc., Am. Soc. Info. Sci. (councilor 1971-72, 87-89, chmn. networks com. 1973-74, chmn. spl. interest group on SDI 1974-75, pres. elect 1986-87, pres. 1987-88, past pres. planning com. 1988-89, chmn. 1989, nominations com. 1989, chmn. budget and fin. com. 1987-89, Award of Merit 1984, Pioneer Info. Sci. 1987), Assn. for Computing Machinery (pub. bd. 1972-75), Assn. Sci. Info. Dissemination Ctrs. (v.p. 1971-73, pres. 1975-77), Nat. Acad. Sci. (joint com. with NRC on chem. info 1971-73), U.S. Nat. Com. for Internat. Fedn. for Documentation. Home: RR 1 Monticello IL 61856-9801 Office: U Ill 1308 W Main St Urbana IL 61801-3005

WILLIAMS, MARTHA SPRING, psychologist; b. Dallas, Oct. 5, 1951; d. Thomas Ayers and Emma Martha (Felmet) Spring; m. James Walter Williams, June 30, 1979; children: Dane Ayers, Jake Austin. BA, East Tex. State U., 1972, MEd, 1974, EdD, 1978. Cert. and lic. psychologist, Tex.; lic. profl. counselor, marriage and family therapist. Tchr. Dallas Ind. Sch.; grad. asst. to dean Coll. Edn. East Tex. State U., 1975-77; intern Terrell State Hosp. Outreach Clinic and Hunt County Clinic, Greenville, Tex., 1975-76, Univ. Counseling Ctr., East Tex. State U., 1976-77; learning dir. Man and His Environ. Program, 1978-85; pvt. practice psychology Dallas, 1981—; adolescent group therapist in-patient psychiat. facility, 1986-91; mem. staff Baylor/Richardson (tex.) Med. Ctr., clin. dir. allied mental health profls., 1992—; mem. staff Green Oaks Psychiat. Hosp. Author: (with others) The Role Innovative Woman and Her Positive Impact on Family Functioning, 1981, Women and Intimacy, 1982, Permenstral Syndrome: A Family Affair, 1984, The Expanding Horizons of Traditional Private Pracitce: High Tech High/Touch, 1986, Adolescent Suicide: Consequences of an Anti-Child

Society, 1986, Therapist as a Partner, 1987. Nat. del. Dem. Conv., San Francisco, 1984; Dem. county chair Kaufman County, 1993—; mem. state Dem. Exec. Com. 1993—. Mem. APA, Am. Assn. Marriage and Family Therapists, Am. Soc. Clin. Hypnosis. Lutheran. Avocations: snow skiing, travel, politics, tap dancing. Home: PO Box 1119 Terrell TX 75160-1119 Office: 4835 LBJ Fwy Ste 825 Dallas TX 75244-6079 In this increasingly complex mobile and hurried world, it is vital that people seek out and nurture healthy relationships to maintain a sense of connection which in times past flowed more naturally from extended family and communities.

WILLIAMS, MARY IRENE, college administrator; b. Hugo, Okla., June 30, 1944; d. Primer and Hyler B. (Tarkington) Jackson; m. Lee A. Williams (div. June 1981); 1 child, Monica Ariane. BS in Bus. Edn., Langston U., 1967; MS in Bus. Emporia (Kans.) State U., 1973; EdS, U. Nev., Las Vegas, 1977; D of Bus. Adminstrn. in Internat. Bus., U.S. Internat. U., 1992. Instr. Spokane (Wash.) C.C., 1967-70; tchr. bus. Topeka Pub. Schs., 1970-73; instr. Clark County C.C., Las Vegas, Nev., 1973—; assoc. dean of bus. Clark County C.C., Las Vegas, 1978-93; dean acad. support svcs. C.C. So. Nev., 1993—. Named Educator of Yr. Nucleus Plaza Assn., 1985, New Visions, Inc., 1986. Mem. NAFE, AAUW, Internat. Assn. Bus. Communicators, Nat. Bus. Edn. Assn., Nat. Coun. on Black Affairs, Am. Assn. Cmty. and Jr. Colls., Nat. Assn. Instrnl. Adminstrs., Nat. Rainbow Coalition. Avocations: exercise, studying langs., reading. Office: CC So Nev 3200 E Cheyenne Ave North Las Vegas NV 89030-4228

WILLIAMS, MARY JANE, fundraiser; b. Phila., Dec. 4, 1943; d. Herbert S. and Constance (Clements) W. BA in History, U. Pa., 1965; MEd, Temple U., 1968, MBA in Mktg., 1981. Advt. prodn. asst. N.W. Ayer Inc., Phila., 1965-66; auto and personal liability claims adjuster Reliance Ins. Co., Phila., 1966-67; asst. dir. ann. giving U. Pa., Phila., 1967-71, dir. individual gifts, 1982-86, asst. v.p. devel. and alumni rels., 1986-88; assoc. dir. devel. Haverford (Pa.) Coll., 1971-73; dir. devel. Med. Coll. Pa., Phila., 1973-77; asst. v.p. devel. Temple U., Phila., 1977-80; v.p. devel. NYU Med. Ctr., N.Y.C., 1988-90; mem. women's athletic bd. U. Pa.; mem. adv. bd. Fund-Raising Inst., 1981-94. Mem. Coun. Penn Women (assoc. trustee), Nat. Soc. Fund Raising Execs. (Fund Raising Exec. of Yr. 1993), Assn. for Healthcare Philanthropy, Cosmopolitan Club. Office: Schultz & Williams Inc 421 Chestnut St Fl 400 Philadelphia PA 19106-2419

WILLIAMS, MARY PEARL, judge, lawyer; b. Brownsville, Tex., Jan. 12, 1928; d. Marvin Redman and Theo Mae (Kelley) Hall; m. Jerre Stockton Williams, May 28, 1950; children—Jerre Stockton, Shelley Hall, Stephanie Kethley. B.A., Tex., 1948, J.D., 1949. Bar: Tex. 1949, U.S. Supreme Ct. 1955, U.S. Dist. Ct. (we. dist.) Tex., 1987. Asst. atty. gen. State of Tex. Austin, 1949-50, relief judge Municipal Ct., summer 1964; asst. instr. dept. govt. U. Tex., Austin, 1966-67; atty. Office of Emergency Preparedness, Exec. Office of Pres., Washington, 1968-70; labor arbitrator, mem. arbitration panel Am. Arbitration Assn., 1972-73; judge County Ct. at Law 2, Travis County, Tex., 1973-80, 53d Judicial Dist. Ct., 1981—; cons. Dept. HEW, 1966-67. Mem. adv. com. Juvenile Bd. of Travis County, 1964-67; trustee United Way, 1974-78. Named Outstanding Woman, Austin Am.-Statesman, 1974, Austin Citizen, 1978; named Woman of Yr. Austin dist. Bus. and Profl. Women, 1977. Mem. ABA, State Bar Tex., Coll. State Bar Tex., Tex. Bar Found., Am. Bar Found., Travis County Bar Assn., Am. Law Inst., Am. Judicature Soc., Inst. Jud. Adminstrn., Jr. League Austin, Kappa Alpha Theta, Delta Kappa Gamma (hon.). Democrat. Methodist. Office: Travis County Courthouse PO Box 1748 Austin TX 78767-1748

WILLIAMS, MATT (MATTHEW DERRICK WILLIAMS), professional baseball player; b. Bishop, Calif., Nov. 28, 1965. Student, U. Nev., Las Vegas. With San Francisco Giants, 1986—; player Nat. League All-Star Team, 1990, 94. Recipient Gold Glove award, 1991, 93, 94, Silver Slugger award, 1990, 93-94; named to Sporting News Nat. League All-Star team, 1990, 93-94, Coll. All-Am. team Sporting News, 1986; Nat. League RBI Leader, 1990. Office: San Francisco Giants Candlestick Park San Francisco CA 94124*

WILLIAMS, MAURICE JACOUTOT, development organization executive; b. New Brunswick, Can., Nov. 13, 1920; s. Alfred Jacoutot and Yvonne (Theberge) W.; m. Betty Jane Bath, Dec. 18, 1943; children: Jon, Peter, Stephen. Student, Northwestern U., 1940-42, U. Manchester, Eng., 1945; M.A., U. Chgo., 1949. Research fellow London Sch. Econs., summer 1948; Dir. U.S. student program U. Fribourg, Switzerland, 1946; prin. examiner Chgo. Civil Service Commn., 1949; economist Office Internat. Trade Policy, Dept. State, Washington, 1950-53; econ. officer Am. embassy, London, 1953-55; chief Econ. Def. Coordination, 1955-58; asst. dir. U.S. Operations Mission to Iran, ICA, 1958-60, dep. dir., 1961-63; dep. dir. USAID/Pakistan, 1963-65, dir., 1965-67; chief program div. Near East-South Asia, 1961; asst. adminstr. Nr. East-South Asia AID/W, 1967-70; dep. adminstr. AID, 1970-74; chmn. Devel. Assistance Com. OECD, Paris, 1974-78; exec. dir. UN World Food Council, 1978-86; sec.-gen., pres. emeritus Soc. Internat. Devel., 1986—; Presdl. coordinator Fgn. Disaster Relief, Bangladesh, Peru, Philippines, Managua, Sahel, 1971-74; chief U.S. del. U.S.-N. Vietnam Joint Econ. Commn., 1974—. Recipient Nat. Civil Service award, 1971, AID Distinguished Honor award, 1974, Rockefeller Pub. Service award, 1974. Club: Cosmos. Address: Overseas Devel Council 1875 Connecticut Ave NW Washington DC 20009-5728 The principles guiding me have been those of middle-America at mid-century, namely that integrity and concentrated efforts yield their own reward. Implicit are beliefs in democratic values, equity in opportunities for social and economic progress, and the need to build up institutions for their realization. The challenge of our time has been to extend these goals worldwide. They are best pursued in cooperative endeavors through the United Nations. A decent standard of food, health and personal security is possible for all people and nations. Endeavors to these ends have been personally rewarding.

WILLIAMS, MAXINE ELEANOR, elementary education educator; b. Birmingham, Ala., Nov. 8, 1940; d. Ocie and Annie Bell (McCants) Easter; m. Ardre Dell Williams, Aug. 3, 1968 (div. 1988); children: Andrea Babett, Roxanne Denise, John Ashley. BS, Tuskegee Inst., 1963; MA, Mich. State U., 1970. Elem. tchr. Chester A. Moore Elem. Sch., Ft. Pierce, Fla., 1963-64, R.J. Wallis Elem. Sch., Kincheloe AFB, Mich., 1964-66, Alexander Elem. Sch., Grand Rapids, Mich., 1966-67, Brown St. Elem. Sch., Milw., 1967-68, Jefferson T.P.L.L., Milw., 1968-78; team leader Twenty First Sch., Milw., 1978-80; reading tchr. Bryant & Parkview Sch., Milw., 1980-81; reading resource tchr. Morse Mid. Sch., Milw., 1981-93, Parkman Mid. Sch., 1993—. Census ctr. vol. Morse Mid. Sch., 1990. Recipient Excellence Pin Milw. Pub. Schs., 1983. Mem. ACA, NAACP, Milw. Tchrs. Edn. Assn., Wis. State Reading Assn. Democrat. Avocations: bowling, reading. Home: 11706 N Silver Ave Thiensville WI 53092-3620

WILLIAMS, MELVIN JOHN, sociologist, educator; b. Stovall, N.C., Feb. 13, 1915; s. John Presley and Mary Jenera (Wilkerson) W.; m. Frances Clark, Oct. 15, 1936; children—Kay Frances (Mrs. Bradley Yount), Dorothy Virginia (dec.), Melvin John, Deborah Susan (Mrs. Monte F. Little), Steven Clark, Eric Stanton. A.B., Duke, 1936, B.D., 1939, Ph.D., 1941. From instr. to asst. prof. sociology Albion (Mich.) Coll., 1941-44; prof. sociology, head dept. Wesleyan Coll., Macon, Ga., 1944-47; assoc. prof. sociology Fla. State U., Tallahassee, 1947-52; prof. sociology, head dept. Stetson U., De Land, Fla., 1952-60; prof. sociology, chmn. social work Stetson U., 1960-63; prof. sociology. East Carolina U., Greenville, 1963—; chmn. dept. sociology East Carolina U., 1963-71; vis. prof. summers Mich. State Normal Coll., 1943, Whittier Coll., 1957, U. N.C., 1970; With Duke Found., summer 1936. Author: with others Contemporary Social Theory, 1940, Catholic Social Thought, Its Approach to Contemporary Social Problems, 1950, Social Norms of Adolescents, A Study in Social Guidance, 1959, Moral and Spiritual Values in Education, 1955; Contbr. articles to profl. pubs. Co-dir. Addison project Kresge Found., 1942-44; dir. YWCA Community Survey, Macon, Ga., 1944; dir., family counselor Children's Center, Macon, 1946-47; dir. Adolescent Research project Wesleyan Coll., 1944-46, East Carolina U., 1963; research and social. cons., 1946—; dir. NSF Inst. in Sociology, 1967. Fellow Am. Sociol. Assn.; mem. AAAS, AAUP, Am. Acad. Polit. and Social Sci., So. Sociol. Soc. (sec. treas. 1953-55, 1st v.p. 1955-56), Groves Conf., Nat. Council Family Relations, S.A.R., Omicron Delta Kappa, Alpha Kappa Delta, Pi Gamma Mu. Methodist. Club: Lion (pres. DeLand, Fla. 1960). Home: 103 Poplar Dr Greenville NC 27834-6435

WILLIAMS, MICHAEL ANTHONY, lawyer; b. Mandan, N.D., Sept. 14, 1932; s. Melvin Douglas and Lucille Ann (Gavin) W.; m. Marjorie Ann Harrer, Aug. 25, 1962 (div. 1989); children: Ann Margaret, Douglas Raymond, David Michael; m. Dorothy Ruth Rand, 1989. B.A., Coll. of St. Thomas, 1954; LL.B., Harvard U., 1959. Bar: Colo. 1959, U.S. Dist. Ct. Colo. 1959, U.S. Ct. Appeals (10th cir.) 1959, U.S. Supreme Ct. 1967. Assoc. Sherman & Howard and predecessor Dawson, Nagel, Sherman & Howard, Denver, 1959-65, ptnr., 1965-91; pres. Williams, Youle & Koenigs, P.C., Denver, 1991—. Served as 1st lt. USAF, 1955-57. Mem. Am. Coll. Trial Lawyers, Am. Bd. Trial Advs., Colo. Bar Found., Am. Law Inst., ABA, Colo. Bar Assn., Denver Bar Assn., Arapahoe County Bar Assn. Office: Williams Youle & Koenigs PC 1200 17th St Ste 1420 Denver CO 80202-5814

WILLIAMS, MICHAEL ROY, marketing research, management educator; b. Altus, Okla., Apr. 14, 1946; s. Roy L. and Goldie L. (Smith) W.; m. Marilyn Kay Henry, Oct. 5, 1968; children: Aimee Lynn, Kerri Nicole. BBA, U. Okla., 1968, MBA, 1970; PhD, Okla. State U., 1992. Teaching assoc. Coll. Bus. U. Okla., Norman, 1968-69, dean's rsch. assoc., 1969-70; nat. rsch. dir. Doric Corp., Oklahoma City, 1970-71, asst. to pres., 1971-73; gen. mgr. A&W Sales and Leasing Corp., Lawton, Okla., 1973-78, pres., 1978-87; rsch. assoc. Bus. Devel. Svcs., Inc., Lawton, 1978—, Sales Promotion Cons., Inc., Englewood, Colo., 1986-90, Ctr. for Values Rsch., Dallas; prof. Cameron U., Lawton, 1987-91, Ill. State U., Normal, 1991—; mem. undergrad. curriculum com. Ill. State U., 1992-93; rsch. assoc. Ctr. for Values Rsch. Internat., Inc., Dallas; cons. in field; reviewer for nat. conf. in sales and sales mgmt.; lectr. Internat. Bus. Inst., 1994, 95. Author: Project Evaluation, 1988, The Political Futures Game, 1993, other manuscripts; reviewer European Journal of Marketing, 1994, Southern Marking Association, 1995, Am. Marketing Association National Educators Conference, 1995, Academy of Marketing Science, 1995. Mem. adminstrv. bd. Centenary meth. Ch., Lawton, 1985-90; mktg. advisor Comanche Indian Nation, Lawton, 1986-88; advisor Leadership Lawton Found., 1990; mem. undergrad. curriculum com., Coll. of Bus., Ill. State U. Grantee Kellogg Found. 1987, Ill. State U., 1992, 93, 94, 95, Old Republic Rsch. Program, 1993, 94; Nat. Consortium fellow, 1990; Richard D. Irwin Found. fellow, 1991, IBM-U. Toronto Inst. Market Driven Quality Rsch. Consortium, 1993; Old Republic Corp. rsch. scholar, 1993, 94, 95; recipient Outstanding Manuscript award S.W. Bus. Symposium, 1990, Hon. Mention award Mktg. Sci. Inst., Alden G. Clayton Competition, 1992, Innovation in Leadership of Bus. Edn. award MidContinent Am. Assembly Collegiate Schs. of Bus., 1993, Outstanding Rsch. Manuscript award Nat. Conf. Sales Mgmt., 1994, 95. Fellow Alpha Mu Alpha, Beta Gamma Sigma, Phi Kappa Phi; mem. Am. Mktg. Assn. (Nat. Faculty Consortium fellow 1992, 94), So. Mktg. Assn., Acad. Mktg. Sci. (presentor spl. panel 1993, 94; discussant 1994), Acad. Bus. Adminstrn., Kiwanis (pres. Lawton chpt. 1983), Beta Theta Pi, Pi Sigma Epsilon (charter mem., faculty adv.), Phi Kappa Phi. Republican. Avocations: flying, scuba diving instructing, writing. Home: 5 Haylott Rd Bloomington IL 61704 Office: Ill State U Dept Mktg Williams Hall Normal IL 61761

WILLIAMS, MILLER, poet, translator; b. Hoxie, Ark., Apr. 8, 1930; s. Ernest Burdette and Ann Jeanette (Miller) W.; m. Lucille Day, Dec. 29, 1951 (div.); m. Rebecca Jordan Hall, Apr. 11, 1969; children: Lucinda, Robert, Karyn. BS, Ark. State Coll., 1951; MS, U. Ark., 1952; postgrad., La. State U., 1951, U. Miss., 1957; HHD (hon.), Lander Coll., 1983. Instr. in English La. State U., 1962-63, asst. prof., 1964-66; vis. prof. U. Chile, Santiago, 1963-64; assoc. prof. Loyola U., New Orleans, 1966-70; Fulbright prof. Nat. U. Mex., Mexico City, 1970; co-dir. grad. program in creative writing U. Ark., 1970-84, assoc. prof., 1971-73, prof. English and fgn. langs., dir. program in transl., 1973-87, univ. prof., 1981—; dir. poetry-in-the-prisons programs div. continuing edn., 1974-79, chmn. program in comparative lit., 1978-80; dir. U. Ark. Press, 1980—, Bank of Elkins, Ark. 1988—; fellow Am. Acad. in Rome, 1976—, mem. advisor coun. Classical Studies, 1985-91; first U.S. del. Pan Am. Conf. Univ. Artists and Writers, Concepcion, Chile, 1964; invited del. Internat. Assembly Univ. Press Dirs., Guadalajara, Mex., 1991; mem. poetry staff Bread Loaf Writers Conf., 1967-72; founder, exec. dir. Ark. Poetry Cir., 1975; participant Assn. Am. Univ. Presses Soviet Mission, 1989. Author: (poems) A Circle of Stone, 1964, Recital, 1965, So Long At the Fair, 1968, The Only World There Is, 1971; (criticism) The Achievement of John Ciardi, 1968, The Poetry of John Crowe Ransom, 1971; (with John Ciardi) (criticism) How Does a Poem Mean?, 1974; (poems) Halfway From Hoxie: New & Selected Poems, 1973, Why God Permits Evil, 1977, Distractions, 1981, The Boys on Their Bony Mules, 1983; translator: (poems) Poems & Antipoems (Nicanor Parra), 1967, Emergency Poems (Nicanor Parra), 1972, Sonnets of Giuseppe Belli, 1981; editor: (poems) 19 Poetas de Hoy en Los Estados Unidos, 1966, (with John William Corrington) Southern Writing in the Sixties: Poetry, 1967, Southern Writing in the Sixties: Fiction, 1966, Chile: An Anthology of New Writing, 1968, Contemporary Poetry in America, 1972, (with James A. McPherson) Railroad: Trains and Train People in American Culture, 1976, A Roman Collection: An Anthology of Writing about Rome and Italy, 1980, Ozark, Ozark: A Hillside Reader, 1981, (criticism) Patterns of Poetry, 1986, (poetry) Imperfect Love, 1986, Living on the Surface: New and Selected Poems, 1989, Adjusting to the Light, 1992, Points of Departure, 1995; poetry editor La. State U. Press, 1966-68; contbr. articles to profl. publs. Mem. ACLU. Recipient Hanry Bellaman Poetry award, 1957, award in poetry Arts Fund, 1973, Prix de Rome, Am. Acad. Arts and Letters, 1976, Acad. award for lit., 1995, Nat. Poets' prize, 1990, Charity Randall citation Internat. Poetry Forum, 1993, John William Corrington award for excellence in lit. Centenary Coll., Shreveport, La., 1994; Bread Loaf fellow in poetry, 1963. Mem. MLA, PEN, AAUP, South Ctrl. MLA, Am. Lit. Translators Assn. (v.p. 1978-79, pres. 1979-81), Authors' Guild, Soc. Benemerito dell'Assn. Centro Romanesco Trilussa (Rome). Home: 1111 Valley View Dr Fayetteville AR 72701-1603 Office: U Ark Press 201 Ozark St McIlroy House Fayetteville AR 72701

WILLIAMS, MILTON A., bishop. Bishop 12th Episcopal dist. A.M.E. Zion Ch., Greensboro, N.C. Office: AME Zion Ch PO Box 7441 Greensboro NC 27417

WILLIAMS, MILTON LAWRENCE, judge, educator; b. Augusta, Ga., Nov. 14, 1932; s. Richard and Helen (Riley) W.; m. Rose King, Oct. 22, 1960; children: Milton Lawrence, Darrie T. BS, NYU, 1960; LLB, N.Y. Law Sch., 1963. Bar: N.Y. 1965, U.S. Dist. Ct. (so. and ea. dists.) N.Y. 1967, U.S. Supreme Ct. 1968, U.S. Customs Ct. 1971. Regional counsel SBA, N.Y.C., 1966-68; assoc. gen. counsel Knapp Commn., N.Y.C., 1970-71; exec. dir. McKay Commn., N.Y.C., 1972; judge N.Y.C. Criminal Ct., 1977-84; acting justice N.Y. State Supreme Ct., N.Y.C., 1978-84, adminstrv. judge Criminal Term, N.Y. State Supreme Ct., 1st Jud. Dist., 1983-85, justice, 1985—; dep. chief adminstrv. judge N.Y.C. Cts., 1985-93; assoc. justice appellate divsn. 1st Dept., 1994—; mem. N.Y. State Commn. on Sentencing Guidelines, N.Y.C., 1983-86, bd. trustees Edwin Gould Found. for Children, St. Patrick's Cathedral, Inner City Scholarship Fund, Cath. Charities of N.Y., New York Law Sch. with USN, 1951-55. Fellow Am. Bar Found.; mem. Assn. of Bar of City of N.Y., Am. Bar Assn. (bd. dirs.), Sigma Pi Phi, Zeta Boule, Knight of Malta. Roman Catholic. Office: Assoc Justice Appellate Divsn First Dept 27 Madison Ave New York NY 10010

WILLIAMS, MORGAN LLOYD, retired investment banker; b. N.Y.C., Mar. 30, 1935; s. John Lloyd and Adelaide Veronica (Patchell) W.; m. Margaret Patricia Rooney, May 13, 1961; children: Morgan Lloyd Jr., John Graham, Christine Joyce. BS in Econs., Wharton Sch., U. Pa., 1957; MBA, Columbia U., 1961. V.p., stockholder Kidder, Peabody & Co., N.Y.C., 1970-90, mng. dir., 1985-87. Trustee Inc. Village of Plandome, N.Y., 1982-86, mayor, 1986-87. Lt. USN, 1957-59. Mem. Nassau Country Club (Glen Cove, N.Y.). Republican. Roman Catholic. Office: 2040 Broadway # 403 San Francisco CA 94115-3516

WILLIAMS, N. THOMAS, gas company executive; b. 1933; married. Student, Vanderbilt U.; BS, Ga. Inst. Tech., 1955; MS, Harvard U., 1959. Project engr. Rust Engring. Co., 1960-68; with So. Natural Gas Co. Birmingham, Ala., 1968—, various mgmt. positions, 1968-79, v.p. engring., 1979-85, exec. v.p., 1985—, also bd. dirs. Served to lt. USN, 1955-58. Office: So Natural Gas Co First National So Birmingham AL 35203

WILLIAMS, NEIL, JR., lawyer; b. Charlotte, N.C., Mar. 22, 1936; s. Lyman Neil and Thelma (Peterson) W.; m. Sue Sigmon, Aug. 23, 1958; children: Fred R., Susan S. AB, Duke U., 1958, JD, 1961. Bar: Ga. 1962, U.S. Dist. Ct. (no. dist.) Ga. 1977, U.S. Ct. Appeals (11th cir.) 1977. Assoc. Alston & Bird (and predecessor firm), Atlanta, 1961-65, ptnr., 1966—, mng. ptnr., 1984—; bd. dirs. Nat. Data Corp., Atlanta, Printpack, Inc., Atlanta, Atty's Liability Assurance Soc., Inc., Chgo. Chmn. bd. trustees Duke U. 1983-88, trustee, 1980-93; chmn. bd. trustees Vasser Woolley Found., Atlanta, 1975—; Leadership Atlanta, 1976-80; trustee Brevard Music Ctr., 1977-86, 91—, Presbyn. Ch. USA Found, Jeffersonville, Ind., 1983-90, Research Triangle Inst., 1983-88; bd. dirs. Atlanta Symphony Orch., 1970-76, 84-93, 95—, pres. 1988-90; Woodruff Arts Ctr., 1987—; bd. counsellors The Carter Ctr., Atlanta, 1987—; Cen. Atlanta Progress, 1984—; bd. dirs. Am. Symphony Orch. League, Washington, 1990—, vice chmn., 1991—. Recipient Disting. Alumni award Duke U., 1991. Mem. ABA, Am. Bar Found., State Bar Ga., Am. Law Inst. Atlanta C. of C. (bd. dirs.), 1994—, vice chmn. 1994-95), Phi Beta Kappa, Omicron Delta Kappa. Clubs: Piedmont Driving, Commerce (Atlanta); University (N.Y.C.). Home: 3 Nacoochee Pl NW Atlanta GA 30305 Office: Alston & Bird 1 Atlantic Ctr 1201 W Peachtree St NW Atlanta GA 30309-3424

WILLIAMS, NEVILLE, international development organization executive; b. Muncie, Ind., Mar. 28, 1943; s. Donald Charles and Rose Eileen (Boughton) W. Student, U. Colo., 1964-66, U. Neuchatel, Switzerland, 1967. Freelance corr. Vietnam, 1968-69; freelance journalist Montreal, Que., Can., 1970-71, London, 1971-73; writer, producer Sta. WNBC-TV News, N.Y.C., 1973-74; freelance writer Telluride, Colo., 1975-79; media liaison Office of Solar Energy U.S. Dept. Energy, Washington, 1979-80; dir. of mktg. Telluride Ski Resort, Inc., 1981-83; owner, operator Hist. Sheridan Opera Ho., Telluride, 1983-85; nat. media dir. Greenpeace U.S.A., Washington, 1987-89; founder, pres., chmn. Solar Electric Light Fund, Washington, 1990—; also bd. dirs.; pres. Williams & Assocs., Telluride and Washington, 1983-90. Author: The New Exiles, 1971, (monograph) Great Telluride Strike, 1977; contbr. articles to N.Y. Times mag., Penthouse, Outside, New Times, The Nation, The New Republic, Nature, others. Apptd. mem. Adv. Com. for Commerce and Devel., State of Colo., 1980-85; apptd. mem. Gov.'s Motion Picture & TV Commn., 1981-85. Fellow Am. Solar Energy Soc., Internat. Solar Energy Soc. Avocations: mountaineering, hiking, history, metaphysics. Office: Solar Electric Light Fund 1734 20th St NW Washington DC 20009

WILLIAMS, NORMAN, law educator, city planner; b. Chgo., Dec. 26, 1915; s. Norman and Joan (Chalmers) W.; m. Jeanne Tedesche, Nov. 27, 1947; children: Norman Jr., Joan Chalmers, Roger Sidney, Sarah Dorothy. BA, Yale U., 1938, LLB, 1943; postgrad., Corpus Christi Coll., Cambridge, 1938-39, Yale U., 1939-40. Bar: N.Y. 1944. Practice N.Y.C., 1943-48; sr. analyst The Plan for Rezoning N.Y., N.Y.C., 1948-50; from acting dir. to dir. div. of planning, acting chief to chief office of master planning N.Y.C. Dept. of Planning, 1950-60; cons. Outdoor Recreation Resources Rev. Commn., 1961; dir. Guyana Project Joint Ctr. for Urban Studies, Caracas, Venezuela, 1961-62; exec. dir. Gov.'s adv. commn. on transp. State of N.J., 1964-65; mem., vice chmn. Princeton (N.J.) Borough Planning Bd. and Princeton Regional Planning Bd., 1965-75; prof. Vt. Law Sch., 1976—; prof. urban planning and law U. Ariz., 1978-86; vis. lectr. city planning Columbia U. Architecture Sch., 1951-61, Yale U. Architecture Sch., 1952-61; vis. prof. city planning MIT, 1960, U. Va., 1973; vis. prof. law Rutgers-Newark U., 1965-75, U. Ariz., 1976-78, 87-91, Vt. Law Sch., 1975; prof. urban planning Rutgers U., 1969-75. Note editor, editor-in-chief Yale U. Law Jour., 1942; author: (with others) Vermont Townscape, 1986, American Land Planning Law, 5 vols., 1974-75, 2d edit., 8 vols., 1984-88; contbr. numerous articles to profl. jours. Pres. Citizens Housing and Planning Council N.Y., N.Y.C. 1950; mem. Billings Park Commn., Woodstock, Vt., 1985-92. Mem. Am. Planning Assn. (Disting. Leadership award 1991), Am. Inst. of Cons. Planners. Democrat. Clubs: Yale (N.Y.C.); Lakota (Barnard, Vt.) (bd. dirs. 1977-80, 82-85), Elizabethan, Yale U. (bd. govs. 1937-38). Avocations: hiking, stamp collecting. Home: 26 River St Woodstock VT 05091-1022 Office: Vt Law Sch South Royalton VT 05068

WILLIAMS, NORMAN DALE, geneticist, researcher; b. Roca, Nebr., Nov. 4, 1924; s. John Alva and L. Carrie (Crawford) W.; m. Elaine Elizabeth Kuster, Aug. 7, 1947; children: David N., Curtis A. BS, U. Nebr., 1951, MS, 1954, PhD, 1956. Assoc. internat Argonne Nat. Lab., Lemont, Ill., 1954-56, rsch. assoc., 1956; rsch. geneticist USDA Agrl. Rsch. Svc., Fargo, N.D., 1956-72, rsch. leader, 1972—; adj. prof. N.D. State U., Fargo, 1972—. Contbr. articles to profl. jours. With U.S. Army, 1945-47. Fellow AAAS, Am. Soc. Agronomy, Crop Sci. Soc. Am.; mem. Am. Genetics Assn., Genetics Soc. Am., Coun. for Agrl. Sci. and Tech., Masons, Sigma Xi (pres., pres.-elect N.D. chpt. 1976-78). Presbyterian. Avocations: golf, fishing, bowling, woodworking, gardening. Home: 809 South Dr Fargo ND 58103-4933 Office: USDA Agrl Rsch Svcs State University Sta PO Box 5677 Fargo ND 58105-5677

WILLIAMS, NORMAN F., geologist, researcher; b. Norman, Okla., Oct. 3, 1916; s. Arthur James and Carolyn Maria (Hill) W.; m. Geneva West, July 20, 1942; children: Norman F. Jr., Geneva, Carolyn Sue. BS in Geol. Engring., U. Okla., 1939. Geology instr. U. Okla., Norman, 1946-47; field geologist Geology div. Ark. Resources and Devel. Commn., Little Rock, 1947-51, state geologist, 1951-56; state geologist Ark. Geol. and Conservation Commn., Little Rock, 1956-63, Ark. Geol. Commn., Little Rock, 1963—. Lt. col. U.S. Army, 1940-46. Home: 8490 N Rodney Parham Rd Little Rock AR 72205-2423 Office: Ark Geol Commn 3815 W Roosevelt Rd Little Rock AR 72204-6369

WILLIAMS, NORRIS HAGAN, JR., biologist, educator, curator; b. Birmingham, Ala., Mar. 31, 1943; s. Norris Hagan Sr. and Ernestyne Edna (Brown) W.; m. Nancy Jane Fraser, June 26, 1970; children: Matthew Ian, Luke Fraser. BS, U. Ala., 1964, MS, 1967; PhD, U. Miami, 1971. Asst. prof. Fla. State U., Tallahassee, 1973-78, assoc. prof., 1978-81; assoc. curator U. Fla., Gainesville, 1981-83, curator, 1983—; dept. chmn., 1985—. Co-author: Orchid Genera of Costa Rica, 1986, Identification Manual for Wetland Plant Species of Florida, 1987; author: (chpt.) Orchid Biology II, 1982, Handbook of Experimental Pollination Biology, 1983; contbr. article to Biol. Bull., 1983. Mem. Assn. for Tropical Biology, Bot. Soc. Am., Soc. for Study Evolution, Linnean Soc. of London. Democrat. Office: U Fla Fla Mus Natural History Gainesville FL 32611

WILLIAMS, OMER S. J., lawyer; b. Rushville, Ind., June 20, 1940; s. John Thomas and Dorothy June (Jackson) W.; m. Gail Duff Shute, July 17, 1965; children: James Jackson, John Wesley. BA, Yale U., 1962, LLB, 1965. Assoc. Thacher Proffitt & Wood, N.Y.C., 1965-71, ptnr., 1971—, chmn. exec. com., mng. ptnr., 1992—. Dir. Greater N.Y. Coun. Boy Scouts Am., coun. commr.; dir. Downtown Lower Manhattan Assn. Mem. ABA (coms. new devels. bus. financing, banking law), N.Y. State Bar Assn., Assn. of the Bar of the City of N.Y. (coms. savings instns., banking law), The Downtown Assn. Club. Mem. Christian Ch. Avocations: tennis, genealogy, civil war history. Home: 206 N Franklin Tpke Ho Ho Kus NJ 07423-1425 Office: Thacher Proffitt & Wood 2 World Trade Ctr New York NY 10048-0203

WILLIAMS, PARHAM HENRY, JR., law educator; b. Lexington, Miss., June 8, 1931; s. Parham Henry and Mary Gladys (Hoover) W.; m. Polly Fay Franklin, Sept. 5, 1954; children: Mary Martha, Parham Henry III, John Franklin, Daniel Dickson. BA, U. Miss., 1953, JD, 1954; LLM (Sterling fellow), Yale U., 1965. Bar: Miss. 1954, U.S. Supreme Ct., 1966. Dist. atty. 4th Jud. Dist. Miss., 1957-63; assoc. prof. Law U. Miss., University, 1963-65, prof., 1966-71, dean, 1971-85; commr. to Nat. Conf. Commrs. on Uniform State Laws, 1972-85; chmn. Ala. Humanities Found., 1990-91; v.p., dean Cumberland Sch. of Law Samford U. Law adminstrn. fellow NYU, 1968, Sterling fellow Yale U., 1965. Fellow Am. Bar Found.; mem. ABA, Miss. Bar Assn. Office: Samford U Cumberland Sch of Law 800 Lakeshore Dr Birmingham AL 35209-6717

WILLIAMS, PAT, congressman; b. Helena, Mont., Oct. 30, 1937; m. Carol Griffith, 1965; children: Griff, Erin, Whitney. Student, U. Mont., 1956-57, William Jewell U.; BA, U. Denver, 1961; postgrad., Western Mont. Coll., LLD (hon.), Carroll Coll., Montana Coll. of Mineral Sci. and Tech. Mem. Mont. Ho. of Reps., 1967, 69; exec. dir. Hubert Humphrey Presdl. campaign, Mont., 1968; exec. asst. to U.S. Rep. John Melcher, 1969-71; mem. Gov.'s Employment and Tng. Council, 1972-78, Mont. Legis. Reapportionment Commn., 1973; co-chmn. Jimmy Carter Presdl. campaign, Mont., 1976; mem. 96th-102nd Congresses from 1st Mont. dist., 1979—; ranking mem. postsecondary edn. subcom. Coordinator Mont. Family Edn. Program, 1971-78. Served with U.S. Army, 1960-61; Served with Army N.G., 1962-69. Mem. Mont. Fedn. Tchrs. Democrat. Lodge: Elks. Office: House of Representatives 2329 Rayburn Ho Office Bldg Washington DC 20515

WILLIAMS, PATRICK MOODY, composer; b. Bonne Terre, Mo., Apr. 23, 1939; s. Wilson Moody and Jean (Murphy) W.; m. Catherine Greer, Apr. 7, 1962; children: Elizabeth, Greer, Patrick. B.A., Duke U., 1961; hon. doctorate, U. Colo., 1983. vis. prof. U. Utah, 1970-71, U. Colo., 1975-77. Composer, N.Y.C., 1961-68, Los Angeles, 1968—; composer 60 film scores, music for TV series; artist 11 record albums; works include An American Concerto, 1977, (for jazz quartet and symphony orch.) Rhapsody (for concert band, jazz ensemble), 1975, (for solo cello and orch.) The Silent Spring, 1974, (for narrator and orch.) Gulliver, 1985 (for symphony orch. and narrator) Romances, (jazz soloist, orch.) 1986, Theme For Earth Day, 1990, An Overture To A Time, 1990. Served with U.S. Army. Acad. award nominee, 1980, nominee for Grammy 10 times, winner, 1974, 86, Pulitzer Prize music nominee, 1977, nominee for Emmy 17 times, winner, 1979, 81, 93, nominee for Cable ACE award 2 times, winner 1994. Mem. Acad. Motion Picture Arts and Scis., Acad. TV Arts and Scis., Acad. Recording Arts and Scis., Broadcast Music, Inc. Democrat. *I am a convinced believer in the apprenticeship system of learning. There were a few people in my life that taught me many things, and I will be forever grateful that I had the opportunity to know them and learn from them. What they knew about music was invaluable to me, and what they were as people was even better.*

WILLIAMS, PAUL, federal agency administrator; b. Jacksonville, Ill., Aug. 6, 1929; s. Russell and Bernice (Wheeler) W.; m. Ora B. Mosby; 1 child, Reva Williams. BA, Ill. Coll., 1956, LHD, 1980. Dir. fin. City of Chgo., 1956-63; assoc. dir. fin. United Planning Orgn., Washington, 1964-65; internat. adminstrv. officer Dept. State, Washington, 1965-68; dir. of office mgmt. Dept. Housing and Urban Devel., Washington, 1968-93, gen. deputy dept. fair housing and equal opportunity, 1993-94, dep. ops. and mgmt., 1994—. Author: Questionnaire on Execution of Urban Renewal Programs, 1959. Pres. Bel Pre Civic Assn., Wheaton, Md., 1978; bd. dirs. Bel Pre Civic Assn., Wheaton, Md., 1971, 79; pres. Bel Pre PTA, Wheaton, Md., 1973. Served as sgt. U.S. Army, 1948-52. Recipient Cert. Superior Svc. Dept. Housing and Urban Devel., 1979, Sr. Exec. Svc. Performance award, 1983, 93-94, Cert. Spl. Achievement, Com. Fraud Waste and Mismanagement Dept. Housing and Urban Devel., 1984, Cert. Recognition, Nat. Assn. Black and Minority C. of C., 1997. Methodist. Avocations: racquetball, jogging. Home: 14009 Blazer Ln Silver Spring MD 20906-2321 Office: Dept Housing and Urban Devel 451 7th St SW Rm 5100 Washington DC 20410

WILLIAMS, PAUL H., textile executive; b. Clarksdale, Miss., Jan. 4, 1938; s. Henry Wall and Thelma G. (McKeithen) W.; m. Judy Kelly, Mar. 14, 1959; children: Kathy, Kelly. B in Chem. Engr., Ga. Inst. Tech., 1960. With R & D dept. Celanese Fibers Co., Charlotte, N.C., 1960-64; with Fibers Industries Inc., Greenville, S.C. and Salisbury, N.C., 1964-73; mfg. tech. dir. Fibers Industries Inc., Charlotte, 1973-76, mfg. dir. then v.p. mfg., 1976-81; v.p. mktg. tech. Celanese Fibers Mktg. Co., Charlotte, 1981-82; dir. textiles, tech. Celanese Textile Fibers, Charlotte, 1982-86; exec. v.p. Celanese Can. Inc., Montreal, 1986-87, exec. v.p., pres. textile group, 1987-88, pres., pres. textile group, 1988—; mem. Can. adv. bd. Allendale Ins. Co.; mem. nat. adv. bd. chem. engr. Ga. Tech.; bd. dirs. Monterey Textiles, Inc., Can. Textiles Inst. Past trustee Textile Rsch. Inst.; past dir. N.C. State U. Engring. Found.; past bd. dirs. Jr. Achievement, Charlotte. Avocations: golf, skiing, travel. Office: Hoechst Celanese Corp 1211 Ave Of The Americas New York NY 10036-8701 also: Celanese Can Inc, 800 Dorchester Blvd W Box 617, Montreal, PQ Canada H3C 3K8

WILLIAMS, PAUL HAMILTON, composer, singer; b. Omaha, Sept. 19, 1940; s. Paul Hamilton and Bertha Mae (Burnside) W.; m. Hilda Keenan Wynn, Apr. 16, 1993. Grad. high sch. asso. A & M Records, 1970—; pres. Hobbitron Enterprises, 1973—. Songwriter: (with Roger Nichols) Out in the Country, 1969, Talk it Over in the Morning, 1970, We've Only Just Begun, 1970, (with Craig Doerge) Cried Like A Baby, 1970, (with Jack S. Conrad) Family of Man, 1971, Rainy Days and Mondays, 1971, An Old Fashioned Love Song, 1972, Family of Man, 1972, Let Me Be the One, 1972, (with John Williams) You're So Nice to Be Around, 1973 (Acad. award nomination best song), The Hell of It, 1974, (with Barbara Streisand) Evergreen, 1976 (Acad. award best song) 1976, Golden Globe award 1977, Grammy award 1977), (with Michael Colombier) Wings, 1977, (with Charles Fox) My Fair Share, 1977, (with Kenny Ascher) The Rainbow Connection, 1979; film appearances include The Loved One, 1964, The Chase, 1966, Planet of the Apes, 1967, Watermelon Man, 1970, The Phantom of the Paradise, 1974 (also score 1974, Acad. award nomination best score 1974), Smokey and the Bandit, 1977, The Cheap Detective, 1978, The Muppet Movie, 1979, Stone Cold Dead, 1980, Smokey and the Bandit II, 1980, Smokey and the Bandit III, 1983, The Chill Factor, 1990, The Doors, 1991, A Million to Juan, 1994, Headless Body in Topless Bar, 1995; wrote songs for: The Getaway, 1972, (with John Williams) The Man Who Loved Cat Dancing, 1973, (with Williams) Cinderella Liberty, 1973, (with John Barry) The Day of The Locust, 1975; wrote scores for: (with Ascher) A Star is Born, 1976 (Golden Globe award best score 1976), Bugsy Malone, 1976, One on One, 1977, The End, 1978, (with Ascher) The Muppet Movie, 1979, Agatha, 1979, (with Jerry Goldsmith) The Secret of Nihm, 1982, Ishtar, 1987, The Muppet Christmas Carol, 1992; TV scores include (series) The McLean Stevenson Show, 1976-77, (with Charles Fox) The Love Boat, 1977-86, Sugar Time!, 1977-78, It Takes Two, 1982-83, (movies) No Place to Run, 1972, Emmet Otter's Jug Band Christmas, 1980; numerous TV appearances including 4 NBC Midnight spls; co-host on: numerous TV appearances including Mike Douglas show; other TV appearances including, Merv Griffin, Jonathan Winters, others; albums include Someday Man: Just An Old-Fashioned Love Song, 1971, Life Goes On, 1972, A Little Bit of Love, 1974, Here Comes Inspiration, 1974, Ordinary Fools, 1975, Classics, 1977, A Little on the Windy Side, 1979, Crazy For Loving You, 1981. Co-recipient Best Songwriter Grammy award, 1977. Mem. ASCAP, Nat. Acad. Rec. Arts and Scis. (trustee). Office: Robert Light Agency 6404 Wilshire Blvd Ste 900 Los Angeles CA 90048 also: Tugboat Prodns Lazy Creek Prodns 4508 Noeline Ave Encino CA 91436-3336

WILLIAMS, PAULETTE W., state agency administrator; b. Moulton, Ala., Oct. 21, 1944; d. Paul Price and Sallie Davis (Bass) Wiley; m. Robert Thomas Williams, Oct. 11, 1968; 1 child, Shannon Thomas. Student, Florence State Coll., 1963-64. Planning and ops. officer civil def Decatur (Ill.)/Morgan Co., 1964-74, planning and ops. officer emergency mgmt., 1975-77; planning and ops. officer, dep. dir. emergency mgmt. Mobile (Ala.) Co., 1977-89; emergency mgmt. area coord. I State of Ala., Clanton, 1989-94; dir. Ala. Emergency Mgmt. Agy., Clanton, 1994—; observer nuc. power plant Dept. Def., Romania, 1994; mem. gov. cabinet State of Ala., Clanton, 1994—. Mem. cmty. advisor coun. Occidental Chem. Co., Muscle Shoals, Ala., 1993—; mem. state disaster svcs. com. ARC, Ala., 1993—. Recipient Spl. Recognition award Ala. Police Acad., 1986, Appreciation cert. Mobile (Ala.) Police Acad., 1986, Outstanding Svc. and Dedication cert. and flag, 1988, Hon. Adm. cert. Mayor of Decatur, 1988, Outstanding Svc. and Contbns. Appreciation cert. Nat. Coordinating Coun. on Emergency Mgmt., 1988, Appreciation plaque Greater Mobile Indsl. Assn., 1989, Appreciation for Profl. Assistance plaque Kerr McGee Chem. Corp., 1989, Appreciation plaque City of Mobile, 1989, Meritorious Svc. cert. City of Mobile, 1989, Appreciation for Help and Support plaque City of Mobile Police Dept. Hazardous Materials Unit, 1989, Outstanding Dedication and Svc. plaque Mobile County Local Emergency Planning Com., 1989, Appreciation cert. FEMA-Floods of 1990, 1990, Pub. Svc. award U.S. Dept. Commerce, NOAA, 1994. Mem. Ala. Emergency Mgmt. Coun. (pres., Sec.-treas. plaque 1986, Appreciation cert. 1986, Legis. Chmn. plaque 1987), Nat. Emergency Mgmt. Assn. (mem. recovery com.). Episcopal. Home: 2224 Marietta Ave Muscle Shoals AL 35661 Office: Ala Emergency Mgmt 5898 Co Rd 41 Clanton AL 35045

WILLIAMS, PEGGY RYAN, academic administrator; b. Montreal, Que., Can., May 27, 1947; d. Fred Smith and Carol (Kennedy) Ryan; m. David A.

Williams, May 30, 1970. BA, U. Toronto, Can., 1968; MEd, U. Vt., 1976; EdD, Harvard U., 1983. Caseworker Monroe County Dept. Social Svcs., Rochester, N.Y., 1968-72; med. social worker Med. Ctr. Hosp. of Vt., Burlington, 1972; coord. instruction, project dir. Community Coll. of Vt., Lamoille County, 1973-75, 75-76; regional dir. Community Coll. of Vt., Montpelier, Vt., 1976-82; asst. to the pres. Johnson (Vt.) State Coll., summer 1981; dir. ednl. and pers. svcs. Vt. State Coll., Waterbury, 1982-85; dir. bus. programs Trinity Coll., Burlington, 1985-88, assoc. acad. dean, 1988-89; pres. Lyndon State Coll., Lyndonville, Vt., 1989—; bd. dirs. Vt. Community Found., Blue Cross/Blue Shield of Vt., Alumni Coun. Grad. Sch. Edn. Harvard U., Lyndon State Coll. Found.; past chair Am. Coun. on Edn. Commn. on Women. Mem. Am. Assn. Higher Edn., Am. Assn. State Colls. and Univs., Vt. Higher Edn. Coun., Am. Coun. on Edn. Office: Lyndon State Coll Office of the President Vail Hill Lyndonville VT 05851

WILLIAMS, PERCY DON, lawyer; b. Dallas, Sept. 19, 1922; s. Percy Don and Frances (Worrill) W.; m. Helen Lucille Brunsdale, Aug. 4, 1954; children—Anne Lucy, Margaret Frances, Elizabeth Helen. B.A. with honors, So. Methodist U., 1942, M.A., 1943; LL.B. magna cum laude, Harvard U., 1946. Bar: Tex. 1951. Instr. So. Meth. U. Law Sch., 1946-47; asst. prof. then assoc. prof. U. Tex. Law Sch., Austin, 1947-49; lectr. U. Va. Law Sch. 1951; law clk. to Justice Tom C. Clark U.S. Supreme Ct., 1949-51; pvt. practice Houston, 1952—; master dist. ct. Harris County, Tex., 1980-95. Contbr. articles to legal jours. Decorated Order of Sacred Treasure Gold Rays, Rosette, Japan. Fellow Tex. Bar Found.; mem. ABA, State Bar Tex. (col.), Fed. Bar Assn., Houston Bar Assn., Am. Law Inst., Am. Judicature Soc., Order of Coif, Phi Beta Kappa, Phi Eta Sigma, Pi Sigma Alpha, Tau Kappa Alpha, Kappa Sigma. Clubs: Houston, Houstonian. Home: 31 Briar Hollow Ln Houston TX 77027-9301 Office: 5685 1st Interst Bank Plz Houston TX 77002

WILLIAMS, PHILLIP ADGER, insurance company executive; b. Greensboro, N.C., Mar. 31, 1928; s. John Wesley and Lila Lee (Darnell) W.; m. Joan Jeanette Morel, Oct. 26, 1958; children: Paige Leigh, Gail Darnell, Christopher Steven. Student, Guilford Coll., 1946; BA, U. N.C., 1951. V.p. The Travelers Ins. Co., Hartford, Conn., 1967-72; v.p. and actuary The Travelers Corp., Hartford, 1972-84; sr. v.p. and actuary The Travelers Corp., The Travelers Ins. Co. and subs., Hartford, 1984—; pres. Constn. Plaza Corp., Hartford, 1970-71, pres. Tabco, Inc., Hartford, 1971-76; bd. dirs. Constn. State Ins. Co., Hartford. Editor: Automobile Insurance Ratemaking, 1961. Mem. exec. bd. gov.'s com. on services and expenditures, Hartford, 1971. Served as sgt. U.S. Army, 1946-48. Mem. (fellow) Casualty Actuarial Soc. (pres. 1977-78, bd. dirs. 1972-80), (charter mem.) Am. Acad. Actuaries (pres. 1982-83, bd. dirs. 1975-85), Actuarial Standards Bd. Republican. Congregationalist. Club: Hartford. Home: 3089 Brookhill Dr Birmingham AL 35242-3701

WILLIAMS, PHILLIP L., newspaper publishing executive; married. BA, Harvard U., MBA. Mgr. Mach devel. Owens-Corning Fiberglas Corp., 1948-60; dir. spl. ventures Starwood Corp., 1960-62; pres., treas., dir. Westland Capital Corp., 1962-64; chmn. bd., treas., dir. Grove Mortgage Corp., 1964-65; v.p., asst. to pres. Beneficial Standard Corp., 1965-68; formerly v.p. corp. programs, v.p. fin., group v.p. newspapers and TV Times Mirror Co., L.A., sr. v.p. newspapers and TV, exec. v.p., from 1980, now vice chmn. bd., also bd. dirs. Lt. comdr. USN. Mem. L.A. C. of C. (bd. dirs.). Office: Times Mirror Co Times Mirror Sq Los Angeles CA 90053*

WILLIAMS, PHYLLIS CUTFORTH, retired realtor; b. Moreland, Idaho, June 6, 1917; d. William Claude and Kathleen Jessie (Jenkins) Cutforth; m. Joseph Marsden Williams, Jan. 21, 1938 (dec. 1986); children: Joseph Marlis, Bonnie L. Williams Thompson, Nancy K. Williams Stewart, Marjorie Williams Karren, Douglas Claude, Thomas Marsden, Wendy K. Williams Clark, Shannon I. Williams Ostler. Grad., Ricks Coll., 1935. Lic. realtor, Idaho. Tchr. Grace (Idaho) Elem. Sch., 1935-38; realtor Williams Realty, Idaho Falls, Idaho, 1972-77; mem. Idaho Senate, Boise, 1977; owner, mgr. river property. Compiler: Idaho Legisladies Cookbook, Cookin' Together, 1981. With MicroFilm Ctr., LDS Ch. Mission, Salt Lake City, 1989-90; block chmn. March of Dimes Soc.; active Idaho State Legisladies Club, 1966-84, v.p., 1982-84. Republican. Avocations: genealogy, cooking, music, politics, photography, travel. Home: 1950 Carmel Dr Idaho Falls ID 83402-3020

WILLIAMS, PRESTON NOAH, theology educator; b. Alcolu, S.C., May 23, 1926; s. Anderson James and Bertha Bell (McRae) W.; m. Constance Marie Willard, June 4, 1956; children—Mark Gordon, David Bruce. A.B., Washington and Jefferson Coll., 1947, M.A., 1948; B.D., Johnson C. Smith U., 1950; S.T.M., Yale, 1954; Ph.D., Harvard, 1967. Ordained to ministry Presbyn. Ch., 1950. Martin Luther King. Jr. prof. social ethics Boston U. Sch. Theology, 1970-71; Houghton prof. theology and contemporary change Harvard U. Div. Sch., Cambridge, Mass., 1971—; acting dean Harvard U. Div. Sch., 1974-75; acting dir. W.E.B. DuBois Inst., 1975-77. Editor-at-large: Christian Century, 1972—; contbr. articles to profl. jours. Mem. Am. Acad. Religion (pres. 1975—), Am. Soc. Christian Ethics (dir. pres. 1974-75), Phi Beta Kappa. Home: 36 Fairmont St Belmont MA 02178 Office: 45 Francis Ave Cambridge MA 02138-1994

WILLIAMS, QUENTIN CHRISTOPHER, geophysicist, educator; b. Wilmington, Del., Jan. 1, 1964; s. Ferd Elton and Anne Katherine (Lindberg) W.; m. Elise Barbara Knittle, Dec. 19, 1987; children: Byron Frederick, Alanna Katherine. AB, Princeton U., 1983; PhD, U. Calif., Berkeley, 1988. Rsch. geophysicist Inst. of Tectonics, U. Calif., Santa Cruz, 1988-91; asst. prof. dept. earth sci. U. Calif., Santa Cruz, 1991-95, assoc. prof. dept. earth sci., 1995—. Contbr. articles to profl. jours. Presdl. Faculty fellow, 1993—. Mem. Am. Geophys. Union, Am. Phys. Soc. Office: U Calif Santa Cruz Dept Earth Sciences Santa Cruz CA 95064

WILLIAMS, QUINN PATRICK, lawyer; b. Evergreen Park, Ill., May 6, 1949; s. William Albert and Jeanne Marie (Quinlan) W.; children: Michael Ryan, Mark Reed, Kelly Elizabeth. BBA, U. Wis., 1972; JD, U. Ariz. 1974. Bar: Ariz. 1975, N.Y. 1984, U.S. Dist. Ct. Ariz. 1976. Vice pres., sec., gen. counsel Combined Comm. Corp., Phoenix, 1975-80; v.p., sec., gen. counsel Swensen's Ice Cream Co., Phoenix, 1980-83; sr. v.p. legal and adminstrn. Swensen's Inc., Phoenix, 1983-86; of counsel Winston & Strawn, Phoenix, 1985-87, ptnr., 1987-89, ptnr. Snell & Wilmer, Phoenix, 1989—. Vice chmn., treas. Combined Comm. Polit. Action Com., Phoenix, 1976-80; chmn. Ariz. Tech. Inventor, Ariz. Tech. Incubator, Ariz. Venture Capital Conf.; co-chair Gov. Small Bus. Advocate Exec. Coun., 1993—. Served with USAR, 1967-73. Mem. ABA, Maricopa County Bar Assn., N.Y. Bar Assn., State Bar Ariz., Internat. Franchise Assn., Paradise Valley Country Club, Phi Alpha Delta. Republican. Roman Catholic. Home: 8131 N 75th St Scottsdale AZ 85258-2781 Office: Snell & Wilmer One Arizona Ctr Phoenix AZ 85004

WILLIAMS, RALPH CHESTER, JR., physician, educator; b. Washington, Feb. 17, 1928; s. Ralph Chester and Anne (Perry) W.; m. Mary Elizabeth Adams, June 23, 1951; children—Cathy, Frederick, John (dec.), Michael, Ann. AB with distinction, Cornell U., 1950, MD, 1954; MD (hon.), U. Lund, Sweden, 1991. Diplomate: Am. Bd. Internal Medicine. Intern Mass. Gen. Hosp., Boston, 1954-55; asst. resident internal medicine Mass. Gen. Hosp., 1955-56; resident internal medicine N.Y. Hosp., 1956-57; chief resident Mass. Gen. Hosp., Boston, 1959-60; guest investigator Rockefeller Inst., N.Y.C., 1961-63; practice medicine specializing in internal medicine (subspecialty rheumatology), 1963—; asso. prof. U. Minn. at Mpls., 1963-68, prof., 1968-69; chmn. dept. medicine U. N.Mex., Albuquerque, 1969-88; Schott prof. rheumatology and medicine U. Fla., Gainesville, 1988—; mem. study sect. allergy and immunology NIH. Asso. editor: Jour. Lab. and Clin. Medicine, 1966-69; editorial bd.: Arthritis and Rheumatism, 1968—; Contbr. numerous articles to profl. jours. Served to capt. USAF, 1957-59. Fellow A.C.P.; mem. Am. Assn. Immunology, Am. Rheumatism Assn., Assn. Am. Physicians, Am. Fedn. Clin. Research, Am. Soc. Clin. Investigation, Central Soc. Clin. Research, Western Soc. Clin. Research, Am. Thoracic Soc., Alpha Omega Alpha, Phi Beta Kappa. Research in immunologic processes and connective tissue diseases. Home: 2516 NW 20th St Gainesville FL 32605-2981

WILLIAMS, RALPH WATSON, JR., retired securities company executive; b. Atlanta, July 2, 1933; s. Ralph Watson and Minnie Covington (Hicks) W.;

m. Nancy Jo Morgan, Mar. 19, 1955 (dec. Dec. 1989); children: Ralph Watson III, Nancy Jane, John Martin Hicks; m. Almonese Brown Clifton, Nov. 24, 1990. Student, Davidson Coll., 1951; B.B.A., U. Ga., 1955. Trainee banking Trust Co. Ga., Atlanta, 1955; mcpl. sales staff Courts & Co., Atlanta, 1955-57; v.p., salesman securities First Southeastern Corp., Atlanta, 1957-60; br. mgr. Francis I. duPont & Co., 1960-69; spl. partner duPont Glore Forgan Inc., N.Y.C., 1969-70; gen. partner Glore Forgan Inc., 1970, exec. v.p., 1971—, sr. v.p., 1972—; also dir.; sr. v.p., dir., mem. exec. com. duPont-Walston Inc., 1973-74; sr. v.p. E.F. Hutton & Co. Inc., 1974-81; exec. v.p., dir. E.F. Hutton & Co. Inc., 1981-88; exec. v.p. Shearson Lehman Hutton Inc., Atlanta, 1988-89; ret., 1989. Mem. Nat. Assn. Security Dealers (chmn. dist. com. 7), Benedicts Atlanta, Phi Delta Theta. Methodist. Clubs: Commerce (Atlanta), Capital City (Atlanta), Piedmont Driving (Atlanta). Home: 3504 Dumbarton Rd NW Atlanta GA 30327-2614

WILLIAMS, RAYMOND CRAWFORD, veterinary anatomy educator; b. Kansas City, Mo., Sept. 22, 1924; s. Raymond Montrose and Alice Viola (Crawford) W.; m. Shirley Walton, July 25, 1959; 1 child, Sherelle Rae. DVM, Kans. State U., Manhattan, 1946; MS, Cornell U., 1955, PhD, 1961. Instr. vet. medicine Tuskegee (Ala.) U., 1946; asst. veterinarian UN Relief and Rehab. Adminstrn., Newport News, Va., 1946; instr. to prof. Sch. Vet. Medicine Tuskegee (Ala.) U., 1946-92, prof. emeritus, 1992—; external examiner anatomy faculty vet. medicine U. Ibadan (West Nigeria), 1976, 77; cons. neuro svc. VA Hosp., Tuskegee, 1972-74; vis. prof. anatomy Coll. Vet. Medicine, Cornell U., Ithaca, 1975; mem. life sci. adv. com. Coun. Internat. Exch. Scholars, Washington, 1982-85. Served with U.S. Army, 1943-44. Recipient Disting. Tchr. award Norden Labs. Mem. Am. Assn. Vet. Anatomists (pres. 1969-70), World Assn. Vet. Anatomists, Am. Vet. Med. Assn. (rsch. scholar 1959), AAAS, Ala. Vet. Med. Assn., Sigma Xi, Phi Kappa Phi. Avocations: photography, bowling, jazz record collecting, gardening, reading.

WILLIAMS, RAYMOND F., regigious organization executive. Gen. sec. of evangelism, missions and human concerns Christian Meth. Episcopal Ch. Office: 909 Shanon Bradley Rd Gastonia NC 28052

WILLIAMS, REDFORD BROWN, medical educator; b. Raleigh, N.C., Dec. 14, 1940; s. Redford Brown Sr. and Annie Virginia (Betts) W.; m. Virginia Carter Parrott, August 9, 1967; children: Jennifer Betts, Lloyd Carter. AB, Harvard U., 1963; MD, Yale U., 1967. Diplomate Am. Bd. Internal Medicine. Intern, then resident Yale-New Haven Med. Ctr., 1967-70; sr. surgeon USPHS, Bethesda, Md., 1970-72; asst. prof. Duke U. Med. Ctr., Durham, N.C., 1972, prof. psychiatry, 1977—, prof. psychology, 1990—, dir. behavioral medicine rsch. ctr., 1985—; cons. NIH Nerv. coms., Bethesda, 1977—. Author: The Trusting Heart, 1989, Anger Kills, 1993; contbr. articles to profl. jours. Dir. N.C. Heart Assn., Chapel Hill, 1980-83. Recipient Rsch. Scientist award NIMH, 1974—; NIH grantee, 1986—. Fellow Soc. Behavioral Medicine (pres. 1984-85, Upjohn Disting. Scientist award 1992), Acad. Behavioral Medicine Rsch. (pres. 1995—); mem. Am. Psychosomatic Soc. (bd. dirs. 1978-81, pres. 1992). Unitarian Universalist. Avocation: tennis. Office: Duke U Med Ctr Box 3926 Durham NC 27710

WILLIAMS, REGINA MARION, nursing educator; b. Sandusky, Ohio; d. Charles Louis and Cora Nell (Collier) Sallee; m. Robert M. Williams; children: Michael N., Peter M., Regina M. BS, Ohio State U., 1955; MSN, Wayne State U., 1974; PhD in Edn., U. Mich., 1986; diploma, Mt. Carmel Sch. Nursing, Columbus, Ohio. Instr. Grant Hosp. Sch. Nursing, Columbus, Ohio, 1957-64; organizer, coord. Nurse Refresher Program, Columbus Bd. Edn., 1965-66; instr. Mercy Sch. Nursing, Detroit, 1966-73; asst. dir. health careers Schoolcraft Coll., Livonia, Mich., 1974-77; asst. prof. Wayne State U., Detroit, 1977-81, dir. outreach BSN program, 1981-84, interim asst. dean, 1989-90; prof., head dept. nursing Ea. Mich. U., Ypsilanti, 1990—; mem. Mich. State Bd. Nursing, 1987—, vice chair, 1993-95; bd. dirs. Wellness Networks Inc., Ferndale, Mich., 1991—. Contbr. articles to profl. jours. 1st lt. U.S. Army, 1954-57. Fellow Nightingale Soc.; mem. NAACP, ANA (chairperson nominating com. 1986-87, mem. cabinet on nursing edn. 1988-89, cabinet chairperson 1989-90), Mich. Nurses Assn. (bd. dirs. 1980-83, 1st v.p. 1982-83, pres. 1983-85, Bertha Lee Culp Human Rights award 1989), Assn. Black Nurse Faculty in Higher Edn. (editorial bd. Jour. of Black Nurse Faculty 1990—), Nat. Coun. Negro Women, Detroit Black Nurses Assn. (Disting. Nurse Achiever award 1992, 94), Sigma Theta Tau (pres. Lambda chpt. 1989-90, Disting. Leadership award 1995), Chi Eta Phi (Outstanding Svc. award 1990). Home: 17312 Woodingham Detroit MI 48221 Office: Ea Mich U 228 King Hall Ypsilanti MI 48197

WILLIAMS, REGINALD VICTOR, III, marketing communications company executive; b. Buffalo, June 20, 1956; s. Reginald Victor and Sodonie (Triepel) W.; m. Michele Mason, June 27, 1981; children: Lauren, Reginald IV. BA, Bowdoin Coll., 1978. Pres. Action Plan Travel, Buffalo, 1978; account exec. Faller, Klenk & Quinlan Inc., Buffalo, 1978-83, dir. fin. and adminstrn., 1983-84, exec. v.p., gen. mgr., 1984-87, pres., 1987-90; pres. Vickers & Benson/Faller Klenk & Quinlan Inc., Buffalo, 1987—; pres. FSI/Computer Mktg. Svcs., Inc., Buffalo, 1990—, also bd. dirs.; bd. dirs. Slipper Lake Mgmt. Inc., Buffalo, Williams Charter Inc., Buffalo. Bd. dirs., vol. fundraiser YMCA, Buffalo, 1986-87. Recipient 100 Best & Brightest USA award Ad Age mag., 1985. Mem. Profl. Communicators, Country Club of Buffalo, The Buffalo Club, Tennis and Squash Club, Holimont Ski Club. Republican. Episcopalian. Avocations: flying, tennis. Office: 2401 N Forest Rd PO Box 50 Buffalo NY 14226

WILLIAMS, REX ENOCH, international union representative; b. Kansas City, Mo., July 20, 1925; s. George and Ruth Elizabeth (Coons) W.; m. Barbara Lee Haynes, Mar. 8, 1987. Grad. high sch., Altamont, kans. Sec., treas. San Diego Typographical Union, 1970-74; headqtrs. staff Internat. Typographical Union, Colo. Springs., Colo., 1974-79; field rep. Internat. Typographical Union, San Diego, 1979-86, Joplin, Mo., 1986-92; owner-operator Nutri-Best Vending System, Joplin, Mo. Author: Intenat. Union Typographers Review, 1978. With U.S. Army, 1943-46, PTO. Mem. Kans. City Musician's Union. Democrat. Home: 1208 Duquesne Joplin MO 64801

WILLIAMS, RHYS, minister; b. San Francisco, Feb. 27, 1929; s. Albert Rhys and Lucita (Squier) W.; m. Eleanor Hoyle Barnhart, Sept. 22, 1956; children: Rhys Hoyle, Eleanor Pierce. AB, St. Lawrence U., 1951, BD, MDiv, 1953, DD, 1966; postgrad., Union Sem., summer 1956; LLD (hon.), Emerson Coll., 1962. Ordained to ministry Unitarian Ch., 1954. Min. Unitarian Ch., Charleston, S.C., 1953-60, 1st and 2d Ch., Boston, 1960—; mem. faculty, field edn. supr. Harvard U., 1969—; Russell lectr. Tufts U., 1965, Minns lectr., 1986. Pres. Edward Everett Hale House, 1987—, Soc. Cin., State N.H., 1986-89; v.p. Franklin Inst., 1981—; Benevolent Fraternity Unitarian Universalist Chs., 1982-92; pres. Unitarian Universalist Urban Ministries, 1991—; sec. bd. trustees Emerson Coll., 1962-94, trustee, 1994—; chaplain General Soc. Cin., Washington, 1977—, New Eng. coun. Navy League, 1980—; Founders & Patriots of Mass., SR; chmn. Festival Fund, Inc., Am.-Soviet Cultural Exch., 1989-91; trustee Opera Co. Boston, 1970—; trustee Meadville Lombard Theol. Sch., Chgo., 1971-77, ministerial fellowship com., 1961-69, chmn., 1968-71; dir. chmn. Ch. Larger Fellowship, 1968-86.; bd. dirs. Peter Faneuil Housing Corp., 1992—; trustee Franklin Square House, 1993—. Mem. Unitarian Universalist Mins. Assn. (pres. 1968-70), Unitarian Hist. Soc. (pres. 1960-75), Evang. Missionary Soc. (pres. 1965-80, v.p. 1980—), Soc. for Propagation Gospel Among Indians and Others in N.Am. (v.p. 1975—), Unitarian Svc. Pension Soc. (pres. 1973—), Soc. Ministerial Relief (pres. 1973—, mem. com. for ch. staff fin.), Mass. Hist. Soc., Colonial Soc. Mass., Union Club (Boston), Union Boat Club (Boston), Beta Theta Pi (pres. New Eng. 1964-66). Office: 1st and 2d Church in Boston 66 Marlborough St Boston MA 02116-2007

WILLIAMS, RICHARD, JR., animal scientist; b. Centerville, Miss., Jan. 31, 1947; s. Richard Sr. and Effie Etherine Williams; m. Voletta Ann Polk, Mar. 8, 1981; children: Sharon, TeAndrea, Orland, DeVeron. BS, Alcorn State U., 1970; MS, Miss. State U., Starkville, 1976; postgrad., Wayne State U., U. Wash., U. Minn. Cert. tchr. in agrl. edn., math. and sci. Forestry specialist Oreg. State U., Portland, 1966-67; instr., animal scientist Alcorn State U., Lorman, Miss., 1970—, instr. coop. ext., 1989—. Contbr. to Jour. Animal Sci., Miss. Acad. of Sci. Symposiums; co-author 6 MAFES

publs. Deacon Holly Grove M.B. Ch., 1989—; active Future Farmers Am. Mem. Kiwanis (pres. 1989, v.p. 1993, judging team 4-H club 1991, Outstanding Kiwanian 1990), Omega Psi Phi (pres. 1989-91, Omega Man of Yr. 1991), Alpha Tau Alpha, Gamma Sigma Delta, Masons. Democrat. Baptist. Office: Alcorn State University PO Box 330 Lorman MS 39096

WILLIAMS, RICHARD CLARENCE, retired librarian; b. Guide Rock, Nebr., Apr. 9, 1923; s. Lyall Wesley and Elsie Marie (Guy) W. Student, Southwestern U., Georgetown, Tex., 1944-45; student, U. Tex., Austin, 1945-46; BA, U. Idaho, Moscow, 1948; BA in Librarianship, U. Wash., Seattle, 1949; MLS, U. Mich., Ann Arbor, 1952. Sec. Schaefer-Hitchcock Co., Sandpoint, Idaho, 1941-42; asst. librarian Willamette U. Library, Salem, Oreg., 1949-51; cataloger U. Mich. Library, Ann Arbor, 1951-59; serials cataloger N.Y.C. Pub. Library, 1959-66, asst. dir. for cataloging, 1967-88, Astor fellow for library research, 1988-89; mem. subcom. on cataloging standards Research Libraries Group, Palo Alto, Calif., 1978-88. Contbr. poetry to coll. publs., 1944-48; bibliographer for Mexicon, 1986—. Bd. dirs Eugene James Dance Co., N.Y.C., 1978—. Served with USN, 1943-46. Mem. ALA, Soc. Am. Archaeology, Am. Anthrop. Assn., Archeol. Inst. Am., John Bartram Assn., Bot. Soc. Am., Coun. on Botanical and Horticultural Librs., Pre-Columbian Art Rsch. Inst., Phi Beta Kappa (U. Idaho chpt.). Avocations: New World archeology, Black studies, botany.

WILLIAMS, RICHARD DAVID, III, naval officer; b. Memphis, May 4, 1942; s. Richard David Jr. and Lucille Sue (Sequin) W.; m. Sherryl Cooper; children: Deborah Lea, Richard David IV. BS in Naval Sci., U.S. Naval Acad., 1964; MS in Physics, Naval Postgrad. Sch., 1972. Commd. ensign USN, 1964, advanced through grades to rear adm., 1992; commdg. officer USS Clark (FFG 11), 1982-84, USS California (CGN 36), 1985-88, Naval Ship Weapon Sys. Engrng. Sta., Port Hueneme, Calif., 1990-92; DUINS Surface Warfare Officers Sch. Command, 1985; DUINS naval reactors activity Dept. Energy, Washington, 1985; chief staff for Surface Combatants Directorate, Naval Sea Sys. Command, 1988-90; dir. warfare sys. architecture and engring. Space and Naval Warfare Sys. Command, 1992; program exec. officer for mine warfare Office Asst. Sec. Navy, Arlington, Va., 1992—. Mem. edn. partnership com. Oxnard (Calif.) Sch. Dist., 1990-92. Decorated Legion of Merit with two gold stars. Avocations: rare books, sports memorabilia. Home: Quarters Washington Navy Yd Washington DC 20374 Office: 2531 Jefferson Davis Hwy Arlington VA 22242-5167

WILLIAMS, RICHARD DONALD, retired wholesale food company executive; b. Audubon, Iowa, Feb. 19, 1926; s. Walter Edward and Olga M. (Christensen) W.; m. Carol Francis, June 17, 1950; children: Gayle, Todd, Scott. B.A., Ohio Wesleyan U., 1948; M.B.A., Northwestern U., 1949. Dir. indsl. and pub. rels. Gardner div. Diamond Nat. Corp., Middletown, Ohio, 1949-61; with Fleming Cos., Inc., 1961-89; v.p. pers. Fleming Cos., Inc., Oklahoma City, 1972-76; sr. v.p. human resources Fleming Cos., Inc., 1976-80, exec. v.p. human resources, 1980-89, ret., 1989. Pres. Jr. Achievement, Topeka, Kans., 1972; v.p. Last Frontier council Boy Scouts Am., Oklahoma City, 1980; campaign chmn. United Way Greater Oklahoma City, 1980, pres., 1985-87; bd. dirs. Community Council Central Okla., Oklahoma City chpt. ARC, Support Ctr. Okla., Better Bus. Bur., Okla. City Beautiful. Served with USN, 1944-46. Mem. Am. Soc. Personnel Adminstrn., Soc. Advancement Mgmt., Am. Mgmt. Assn., Phi Gamma Delta. Clubs: Quail Creek Country (Oklahoma City), Petroleum (Oklahoma City); Baille 'd Oklahoma (hon.), La Chaine des Rotisseurs. Home: 2940 Brush Creek Rd Oklahoma City OK 73120

WILLIAMS, RICHARD DWAYNE, physician, educator; b. Wichita, Kans., Oct. 7, 1944; s. Errol Wayne and Roseanna Jane (Page) W.; m. Beverly Sue Ferguson, Aug. 29, 1964; 1 child, Wendy Elizabeth. BS, Abilene Christian U., 1966; MD, Kans. U., 1970. Diplomate Am. Bd. Urology, Nat. Bd. Med. Examiners. Intern, then resident in gen. surgery U. Minn., Mpls., 1970-72, resident in urology, 1972-76, asst. prof., 1976-79; asst. prof. U. Calif., San Francisco 1979-84; prof., chmn. dept. urology U. Iowa, Iowa City, 1984—; chief urology VA Med. Ctr., San Francisco, 1979-84, VA Med. Ctr., Iowa City, 1984-88; mem. task force on bd. exams Am. Bd. Urology, 1981-85, guest examiner Oral exams, 1984—, trustee, 1994—; Rubin H. Flocks chair in urology U. Iowa, 1994; mem. nat. adv. coun. NIDDK, NIH. Author: (with others) Advances in Urologic Oncology, 1987, Genitourinary Cancer: Basic and Clinical Aspects, 1987, Adult and Pediatric Urology, 1987, General Urology, 1988, Textbook of Medicine, 1988, also others; editor: Advances in Urologic Oncology, 1987; guest editor Seminars in Urology, 1985, Problems in Urology: Prostate Cancer, 1989; bd. editors Jour. Urology, 1980-88; mem. editorial bd. Urology, Jour. Urology; also articles. Bd. dirs. Iowa chpt. Nat. Kidney Found., bd. sci. advisors 1989—. Major USAR, 1971-77. Bordeau scholar Kans. U. Med. Ctr., 1968-69; NIH, VA, Am. Cancer Soc. grantee. Fellow ACS (chmn. urology sect. No. Calif. chpt. 1980-82, chmn. ann. meeting programs 1988, mem. residency rev. com. urology 1993—, vice chair 1995); mem. AAAS, Iowa Med. Soc., Iowa Urologic Soc., Am. Urologic Assn. (dir. seminar on residency evaluation 1987, bd. editors alt. 1988—, rep. North Ctrl. sect., prodr. slide presentations 1988, recipient prizes 1982, 87, mem. various coms. 1987—), Am. Assn. for Cancer Rsch., Am. Soc. Clin. Oncology, Am. Assn. GU Surgeons, Clin. Soc. Genitourinary Surgeons, Soc. Internat. D'Urologie (U.S. sect.), Soc. Univ. Urologists (chmn. com. on residency evaluation 1986-88, councillor 1987—, pres. 1993), Soc. Surg. Oncology, Soc. Urologic Oncology (chmn. membership com. 1987-90, sec. 1990-91, 91—), Johnson County Med. Soc., Flock's Soc., Western Urologic Forum, Nat. Urologic Forum, Surgeons Club, Alpha Omega Alpha. Republican. Office: U Iowa Dept Urology 200 Hawkins Dr Iowa City IA 52242-1009

WILLIAMS, RICHARD F., banker; b. Oak Park, Ill., Sept. 9, 1941; s. Harvey B. and Marie (Gallery) W.; m. Barbara Ann Zdon, Aug. 8, 1964; children: Ann Marie, Richard Lewis. Grad., DePaul U., 1964. Various positions CNA Ins., Chgo., 1964-80; 2asst. v.p. Zurich Ins. Co., Chgo., 1980-84; pres., CEO, Empire Fire & Marine, Omaha, 1984-93, Fidelity & Deposit Co. Md., Balt., 1993—. Republican. Roman Catholic. Home: 15404 Duncan Hill Rd Sparks MD 21152 Office: Fidelity & Deposit Co Md 300 St Paul Pl Baltimore MD 21203

WILLIAMS, RICHARD LEROY, federal judge; b. Morrisville, Va., Apr. 6, 1923; s. Wilcie Edward and Minnie Mae (Brinkley) W.; m. Eugenia Kellogg, Sept. 11, 1948; children: Nancy Williams Davies, R. Gregory, Walter L., Gwendolyn Mason. LLB, U. Va., 1951. Bar: Va. 1951. Ptnr. McGuire, Woods & Battle and predecessor firms, 1951-72; judge Cir. Ct. City of Richmond, 1972-76; ptnr. McGuire, Woods & Battle, 1976-80; dist. judge U.S. Dist. Ct., Richmond, Va., 1980—, sr. judge, 1992—. Served to 2d lt., USAAF, 1940-45. Fellow Am. Coll. Trial Lawyers; mem. Va. State Bar, Va. Bar Assn., Richmond Bar Assn. Office: US Dist Ct PO Box 630 Richmond VA 23205-0630

WILLIAMS, RICHARD LLEWELLYN, diplomat; b. Chgo., Dec. 28, 1929; s. David Walter and Clara Elma (Petersen) W.; m. Jane Xuezhen Khuo, Mar. 25, 1961; children: Marc, Maria Cypher. AB in Liberal Arts, U. Chgo., 1948; BS in Mech. Engring., Purdue U., 1951; MBA, Harvard U., 1953. V.p. Williams Bros. & Miller Inc., East Chicago, Ind., 1960-62; spl. asst. to v.p. Commonwealth Edison, Chgo., 1962-65; with Dept. State, Washington, 1965-66, 65—, dep. for Micronesian negotiations, 1978-79; consul gen. Dept. State, Guangzhou, China, 1979-81; dir. Chinese affairs Dept. State, Washington, 1981-88; amb. to Mongolia Dept. State, Ulaan Baatar, 1988-90; consul gen. Dept. State, Hong Kong, 1990-93; sr. Asian specialist Dept. State, Washington, 1993-94; adj. prof. Columbia U. and NYU, N.Y.C., 1994—. With U.S. Army, 1953-55. Mem. Am. Club (Hong Kong), Royal Hong Kong Jockey Club. Avocations: walking, reading, mah jong, bridge. Office: Dept State Washington DC 20520

WILLIAMS, RICHARD LUCAS, III, electronics company executive, lawyer; b. Evanston, Ill., Oct. 30, 1940; s. Richard Lucas Jr. and Ellen Gene (Munster) W.; m. Karen Louise Carmody, Nov. 11, 1967. A.B., Princeton U., 1962; LL.B., U. Va., 1965. Bar: Ill. 1965, D.C. 1968, U.S. Supreme Ct. 1968. Assoc. Winston & Strawn, Chgo., 1968-74; ptnr. Winston & Strawn, 1974-79; sr. v.p., gen. counsel Gould Inc., Rolling Meadows, Ill., 1979-81; sr. v.p., adminstrn., gen. counsel Gould Inc., 1981-90, also bd. dir., 1985-88; ptnr. Smith Williams and Lodge, Chgo., 1990—; bd. dirs. GNB Batteries, Inc., 1984-86, ULINE Inc., Lake Bluff, Ill, Branca, Inc., Chgo. Bd. dirs.

Internat. Tennis Hall of Fame, Newport, R.I.; v.p. Chgo. Dist. Tennis Assn., 1968-70; vice chmn. Am. Cancer Soc., Chgo., 1984; bd. dirs., pres. Lake Shore Found. for Animals, Chgo., 1990-94. With JAGC USNR, 1965-68. Mem. ABA, Ill. Bar Assn., Chgo. Bar Assn., Meadow Club (Rolling Meadows) (gov. 1979—, chmn. 1985-90). Home: 1200 N Lake Shore Dr Chicago IL 60610-2301 Office: Smith Williams & Lodge 1800 Zerox Ctr 55 W Monroe Chicago IL 60603

WILLIAMS, RICHARD T., hospital administrator; b. 1931. With Dow Chem. Corp., Midland, Mich., 1958-88, Janis Pacific Inc., San Luis Obispo, Calif., 1988-90, Long Beach Meml. Health Ctr., Calif., 1990-93; with Childrens Hosp. L.A. Inc., 1993—, pres., chief exec. officer. Office: Childrens Hosp Los Angeles Inc 4650 W Sunset Blvd Los Angeles CA 90027*

WILLIAMS, RICHARD THOMAS, lawyer; b. Evergreen Park, Ill., Jan. 14, 1945; s. Raymond Theodore and Elizabeth Dorothy (Williams) W. AB with honors, Stanford U., 1967, MBA, JD, 1972. Bar: Calif. 1972, U.S. Supreme Ct. 1977. Assoc., then ptnr. Kadison Pfaelzer Woodard Quinn & Rossi, L.A., 1972-87; ptnr. Whitman & Ransom, 1987-93, Whitman Breed Abbott & Morgan, L.A., 1993—. Contbg. editor Oil and Gas Analyst, 1978-84. Mem. ABA, L.A. County Bar Assn. Office: Whitman Breed Abbott & Morgan 633 W 5th St Los Angeles CA 90071

WILLIAMS, RICHMOND DEAN, library appraiser, consultant; b. Reading, Mass., Dec. 10, 1925; s. Theodore Ryder and Anabel Lee (Hutchison) W.; m. Eleanor Davidson Washbourne, Sept. 26, 1953; children—Richmond Lyttleton, Eleanor Davidson, Anne Ryder. AB cum laude, Williams Coll., 1950; MA, U. Pa., 1952, PhD, 1959. Instr., asst. dean Williams Coll., Williamstown, Mass., 1954-56; dir. Wyo. Hist. and Geol. Soc., Wilkes-Barre, Pa., 1956-60; asst. dir. Am. Assn. State and Local History, Madison, Wis., 1960-61; dir. libraries Eleutherian Mills-Hagley Found., Wilmington, Del., 1962-87; cons. archivist M.S. Hershey Found., Pa., 1981—, Md. Dept. Housing and Community Devel., 1993-94; bd. dirs. Scholarly Resources Inc. Co-author: A Look at Ourselves, 1962; author: They Also Served, 1965; compiler: Directory of Historical Records in Delaware, 1995. Sec., U. Del. Library Assocs., Wilmington, 1972-86; mem. adv. bd. Del. Hist. Records, Dover, 1982—; mem. Del. Humanities Forum, Wilmington, 1984-87; trustee Conservation Ctr. Phila., 1984-86. Served to lt. AUS, 1943-47. Pennfield fellow U. Pa., 1953. Mem. Econ. History Assn. (sec.-treas. 1975-88), Soc. Am. Archivists, Am. Assn. State and Local History (pres. 1974-76), Am. Antiquarian Soc., Phi Beta Kappa. Avocations: golf; sailing; book collecting. Home and Office: 202 Brecks Ln Wilmington DE 19807-3011

WILLIAMS, ROBERT AUGUSTUS, manufacturing company executive; b. Macon, Ga., June 11, 1936; s. John Herbert and Mary Dean (Pritchett) W.; m. Antionette Caruso, Feb. 14, 1959; children: Robert A. Jr., Ronald M. Student, Syracuse (N.Y.) U. Salesperson Mobile Paint Mfg. Co. Inc., Theodore, Ala., 1954-70, sales mgr., 1970-75, v.p. sales, 1975-78, exec. v.p., 1978-84, pres., 1984—; pres. Spetromatic Assocs., Ill., 1974-76, Nat. Paint Distbrs., Park Ridge, Ill., 1984-86. Chmn. Goodwill Industries, Mobile, Ala., 1987—; bd. dirs. Vols. of Am., Mobile, 1986-87, Jr. Achievement, Mobile, Better Bus. Bur., Mobile. Mem. Sales and Mktg. Execs. of Mobile (past pres.). Democrat. Baptist. Club: Country Club of Mobile. Lodge: Rotary (sec. 1986-88). Avocation: golf. Home: 601 Shenandoah Rd W Mobile AL 36608-3354 Office: Mobile Paint Mfg Co Inc PO Box 717 Theodore AL 36590-0717

WILLIAMS, ROBERT C., paper company executive; b. 1930. BSME, U. Cin.; MBA, Xavier U.; postgrad., Inst. Paper Chemistry, Rochester Inst. Tech. Various tech. and supervisory positions Gardner div. Diamond Internat. Corp., 1947-59; with research and devel. dept. Albermarle Paper Co., 1963-68; co-founder James River Corp. of Va., Richmond, 1969—, formerly pres., COO, chmn., pres., CEO; bd. dirs. Sovran Fin. Corp. Office: James River Corp Va PO Box 2218 Richmond VA 23217-2218*

WILLIAMS, ROBERT CHADWELL, history educator; b. Boston, Oct. 14, 1938; s. Charles Reagan and Dorothy (Chadwell) W.; m. Ann Bennett Kingman, Aug. 27, 1960; children: Peter, Margaret, Katharine. B.A., Wesleyan U., 1960; A.M., Harvard U., 1962, Ph.D., 1966. Asst. prof. history Williams Coll., Williamstown, Mass., 1965-70; prof. history Washington U., St. Louis, 1970-86; dean of faculty Davidson Coll., N.C., 1986—; pres. Central Slavic Conf., 1971-72; v.p. History Assocs. Inc., Gaithersburg, Md., 1980—; sr. research assoc. St. Antony's Coll., Oxford, 1985. Author: Culture in Exile, 1972, Artists in Revolution, 1976, Russian Art and American Money, 1980 (Pulitzer nominee), The Other Bolsheviks, 1986, Klaus Fuchs, Atom Spy, 1987; co-author: Crisis Contained, 1982; mem. editorial bd.: Slavic Rev., 1979-82. Fellow Kennan Inst., 1976-77; fellow Am. Council Learned Socs., 1973-74, W. Wilson Found., 1960-61. Mem. Am. Assn. for Advancement of Slavic Studies, Phi Beta Kappa, Sigma Xi. Presbyterian. Office: Davidson Coll Office VP Acad Affairs Davidson NC 28036

WILLIAMS, ROBERT D., cable television advertiser; b. Grand Rapids, Mich., Mar. 22, 1947; s. Robert and Betty (Berthold) W.; m. Linda Williams. BA, Western Reserve U., 1969. With Nat. Cable Advt., N.Y.C.; bd. dirs. New Eng. Broadcasting. Recipient Carl Weinstein award Cable Ad Bur., 1986. Office: Nat Cable Advt 137 Newbury St Boston MA 02116-2903

WILLIAMS, ROBERT DANA, lawyer; b. Hyannis, Mass., Feb. 21, 1939; s. Harold Warren and Winifred Josephine (Shores) W.; m. Gaye Carol Gorringe, May 30, 1964 (div. 1974); children: Sarah Ann, Amy Alden; m. Barbara Ellen Bruce, Aug. 7, 1976; children: Dana Ariana Brix, Nathaniel Shepard. AB magna cum laude, Harvard U., 1961, LLB, 1964. Bar: Mass. 1965. Rsch. asst. Am. Law Inst., Cambridge, Mass., 1964-65; assoc. Warner & Stackpole, Boston, 1965-71; ptnr. Warner & Stackpole, 1971-85; of counsel Hinckley, Allen, Tobin & Silverstein, Boston, 1985-87; ptnr. Hinckley, Allen, Snyder & Comen, Boston, 1987-90, Wayne, Lazares & Chappell, Boston, 1990-95, Masterman, Culbert & Tully, Boston, 1995—; firm rep. New Eng. Entrepreneurship Coun., Inc. Boston, 1986-89. Bd. govs., exec. com. Concord (Mass.) Mus., 1980-86, capital campaign steering com., 1990-92; bd. dirs. Found. of Mass. Eye and Ear Infirmary, Boston, 1980-91; trustee, sec. Guidance Camps, Inc., 1968-86; trustee Mass. Eye and Ear Infirmary 1971—, bd. mgrs., 1980-91, chmn nominating com., 1984-91; dir., sec. Napoleonic Soc. of Am., Clearwater, Fla., 1985—; bd. dirs. Psychomotor Inst., Inc., Cambridge, Mass., 1979—. Mem. Orgn. Am. Historians, Am. Soc. Legal History (com. on documentary preservation 1980-88), Phi Beta Kappa. Congregationalist. Avocations: history, antiquarian books. Home: 41 Monument St Concord MA 01742-5516 Office: Masterman Culbert & Tully One Lewis Wharf Boston MA 02110-3985

WILLIAMS, ROBERT DELAND, lawyer; b. Montclair, N.J., Nov. 15, 1924; s. Robert Warren and Katharine (Wing) W.; m. Frances Keyes Wickham, Jan. 18, 1952; children: Priscilla, Katharine. B.A., Haverford Coll., 1948; J.D., Yale U., 1951. Bar: Pa. 1953, U.S. Supreme Ct. 1961. With Dechert Price & Rhoads, Phila., 1951—, ptnr., 1959—. Bd. govs. Pa. Economy League, Phila.; active Met. bd. Phila. YMCA. Served with U.S. Army, 1943-45. Mem. ABA, Phila. Bar Assn., Pa. Bar Assn. Republican. Clubs: Merion Cricket (Haverford, Pa.); Racquet (Phila.). Home: Swedesford Rd Paoli PA 19301 Office: Dechert Price & Rhoads 3400 Ctr Sq W 1500 Market St Philadelphia PA 19102-2189

WILLIAMS, ROBERT EUGENE, astronomer; b. Dunsmuir, Calif., Oct. 14, 1940; s. Francis Henry and Lois Evangeline (Youde) W.; m. Elaine Carolyn Eckwall, Dec. 29, 1961; 1 child, Scott Francis. AB, U. Calif. Berkeley, 1962; PhD, U. Wis., 1965. Rsch. asst. U. Calif., Berkeley, 1960-62; Wis. Alumni Rsch. Found. fellow U. Wis., 1962-65; from asst. prof. to assoc. prof. U. Ariz., Tucson, 1965-79, prof., 1977-83; vis. rsch. assoc. European So. Obs., Garching, 1983-84; NRC sr. rsch. fellow NASA-Ames Rsch. Ctr., 1984-85; dir. Cerro Tololo Inter-Am. Obs., La Serena, Chile, 1985-93, Space Telescope Sci. Inst.; mem. exec. com. Aspen (Colo.) Ctr. for Physics, 1983-88, trustee/treas., 1982-88; adj. prof. The Johns Hopkins U., 1993—; Sr. Fulbright prof. Univ. Coll. London, 1972-73; mem. NSF Minority Grad. Fellowship Panel, 1982-85, CTIO Users Com., 1978-81, KPNO Telescope Allocation Com., 1978-80, CTIO Telescope Allocation Com., 1976-78; chmn. U.S. Nat. Fulbright Com., Astronomy, 1974-78. Author 100 profl. papers.

Recipient Alexander von Humboldt award German Govt., 1991; named Fulbright prof. U. London, 1971-72. Mem. Internat. Astron. Union (U.S. nat. commn. 1990-92), Am. Astron. Soc. (com. on astronomy and pub. policy 1994-96, edn. adv. bd. 1981-83), Astron. Soc. of the Pacific. Avocation: running. Office: Space Telescope Science Institute 3700 San Martin Dr Baltimore MD 21218

WILLIAMS, ROBERT JENE, lawyer, rail car company executive; b. Darby, Pa., Oct. 30, 1931; s. Joslyn Justus and Dolores Marie (Dugan) W.; m. Shirley Geraldine Fiedler, Aug. 8, 1953; children: Robin Jeanne, Sara Ann. B.S., Ursinus Coll., 1953; J.D., U. Pa., 1956. Bar: N.J. 1957, Pa. 1959, Ill. 1973. Asso. firm Bleakly, Stockwell & Zink, Camden, N.J., 1956-58; atty., asst. gen. atty. Reading Co., Phila., 1958-69; gen. counsel, sec. Trailer Train Co., Phila., 1969-71, Trailer Train Co. (now TTX Co.), Chgo., 1971-94; v.p. Trailer Train Co., 1975-94; ret., 1994. Mem. Ill. Bar Assn. Home: 1349 Woodland Dr Deerfield IL 60015-2017

WILLIAMS, ROBERT JOSEPH, museum director, educator; b. Bennington, Vt., June 21, 1944; s. Joseph and Ruthe Allison (Moody) W. BS in Edn., U. Vt., 1970; MA in Interdisciplinary Social Sci., San Francisco State U., 1981. Tchr. adult edn. Mt. Anthony Union High Sch., Bennington, Vt., 1972-74; columnist Bennington Banner, 1972-77; tchr. San Francisco State U., 1976-79; founder, dir. NORRAD Drug Rehab. Ctr., San Francisco, 1986-88; museum curator Shaftsbury (Vt.) Historical Soc., 1989—; founder, dir. Bennington Tutorial Ctr., 1971-74. Author: Toward Humanness in Education, 1981, Chalice of Leaves: Selected Essays and Poems, 1988, Modern Salvation: Guidelines from Cosmology, 1994; author: (with others) Intimacy, 1985. Recipient Edmunds Essay medal Vt. Historical Soc., Montpelier, 1961, award of the League of Vt. Writers, 1972, Golden Poet award World of Poetry, Sacramento, Calif., 1990. Democrat. Avocation: cosmology. Home: 102 Putnam St Bennington VT 05201-2348 Office: Shaftsbury Hist Soc PO Box 401 Shaftsbury VT 05262-0401

WILLIAMS, ROBERT JOSEPH, SR., automotive executive; b. Dec. 14, 1926; s. Michael Paul and Eullalia Claire (Buschell) W.; m. margaret R. Williams (dec. 1985); children: Robert, Michael, Roger, Mary Ellen, Claire Ann; m. Anne J. Long, Feb. 15, 1986. BS in Aero. Engring., U. Notre Dame, 1949. Prodn. engr., prodn. mgr., v.p., gen. mgr. Cadillac Products, Inc., Sterling Heights, Mich., 1950-62, pres., 1962-89, chief exec. officer, 1989—; mem. Nat. Def. Exec. Res.; trustee Packaging Found. Mem. libr. coun. U. Notre Dame, Ind.; bd. dirs. Boys Hope, Phoenix. Recipient Flexible Packaging Converter of Yr. award Package, Printing and Converting, 1991. Mem. Flexible Packaging Assn. (pres. 1972), Flexographic Tech. Assn., Soc. Plastics Industry. Avocations: tennis, golf, skiing, hunting. Office: Cadillac Products Inc 7000 15 Mile Rd Utica MI 48315

WILLIAMS, ROBERT L., pharmaceutical executive; b. 1946. Undergrad. degree, Ind. U., 1968, JD, 1971. With Price Waterhouse, N.Y.C., 1971-75; with Pfizer, Inc., N.Y.C., 1975—, treas., 1993—. Office: Pfizer Corp 235 E 42nd St New York NY 10017*

WILLIAMS, ROBERT LEON, psychiatrist, neurologist, educator; b. Buffalo, July 22, 1922; s. Leon R. and L. Paulyne (Ingraham) W.; m. Shirley Glynn Miller, Feb. 5, 1949; Karen, Kevin. B.A., Alfred U., 1944; M.D., Albany Med. Coll., Union U., 1946. Chief neurology and psychiatry Lackland AFB Hosp., USAF, San Antonio, 1952-55; cons. neurology and psychiatry to USAF Surgeon Gen., 1955-58; faculty Coll. Medicine, U. Fla., Gainesville, 1958-72, prof., chmn. dept. psychiatry, 1964-72; prof. psychiatry Baylor Coll. Medicine, Houston, 1972-92, chmn. dept., 1972-90, prof. neurology, 1976-92, acting chmn. dept., 1976-77, prof. emeritus psychiatry and neurology, 1992—; mem. faculty various univs., part time 1949-58 including Albany Med. Coll. at Union U., Columbia Coll. Physisicans and Surgeons, Boston U., U. Tex., Georgetown U. Author: (with W.B. Webb) Sleep Therapy: A. Bibliography and Commentary, 1966, (with others) EEG of Human Sleep: Clinical Applications, 1974; editor: (with Ismet Karacan and Carolyn J. Hursch) Psychopharmacology of Sleep, 1976, Sleep Disorders: Diagnosis and Treatment, 1978, 2d edit., 1988; (with others) Phenomenology and Treatment of Anxiety, 1979, of Alcoholism, 1980, of Psychophysiological Disorders, 1982, of Psychosexual Disorders, 1983, of Psychiatric Emergencies, 1984. Served from 1st lt. to lt. col. USAF, 1949-58; col. Res., ret. Recipient Cert. Profl. Achievement USAF Surgeon Gen., 1967. Mem. Am. Psychiat. Assn., Am. Electroencephalographic Soc., Am. Coll. Psychiatrists (pres. 1982-83), Am. Acad. Neurology, AMA, Group for Advancement of Psychiatry, Benjamin Rush Soc. (pres. 1986-88), Accreditation Coun. for grad. Med. Edn. (residency rev. com. for psychiatry 1985-93), Alpha Omega Alpha. Research and publs. on basic psychophysiology of human sleep.

WILLIAMS, ROBERT LUTHER, city planning consultant; b. Porterville, Calif., June 24, 1923; s. Luther Esco and Mary (Lyon) W.; children: Jeffrey Robert, Derrick Paul, Gail Diane. Student, Utah State Coll., 1944; A.B., U. Calif.-Berkeley, 1949, M.C.P., 1951. Asst. planning dir. Stockton, Calif., 1951-54; planning dir. Alameda, Calif., 1954-57, Alameda County, 1957-63; exec. dir. Am. Inst. Planners, Washington, 1963-69; v.p. Hill Devel. Corp., Middletown, Conn., 1969-71; dir. land mgmt. dept. Gulf Oil Corp., Reston, Va., 1971-74; pres. Coleman-Williams, Inc., Greenbrae, Calif., 1975-78, Robert Williams Assocs., Inc., San Rafael, Calif., 1978-87; mem. community affairs panel KQED-TV, San Francisco, 1991-94; lectr. U. Calif. at Berkeley extension, 1956-59; tech. adviser regional planning Assn. Bay Area Govts., Calif., 1961-63; vis. prof. U. R.I., 1969-71; pres. G.I.F.T. Inst., Inc., 1991-94. Bd. dirs. Planning Found., Inc., 1965-70, Communities Found., Inc., 1973-77. Served to 1st lt. AUS, 1943-46, 52, ETO. Named Young Man of Year Alameda, 1956. Mem. Am. Inst. Cert. Planners (pres. Calif. chpt. 1960), Am. Planning Assn., World Future Soc., Lambda Alpha, Lambda Chi Alpha. Presbyterian. Home: Box 379 Pitcher Pond Rd RR # 2 Lincolnville ME 04849

WILLIAMS, ROBERT LYLE, corporate executive, consultant; b. Nowata, Okla., June 22, 1942; s. Clifford Lyle and Eula Mae (Barnes) W.; m. Lorene Linnet Dillahunty, June 12, 1965; 1 child, Eleanor Lynn. B.S., Okla. State U., 1964; M.B.A., Baylor U., 1965. Acctg. supr. Southwestern Bell Telephone Co., Houston, 1965-66; fin. exec. Ford Motor Co., Dearborn, Mich., 1969-80; treas. Ford Brazil, Sao Paulo, 1976-79, Agrico Chem. Co., Tulsa, 1980-82; v.p., chief fin. officer Texas City Refining, Inc., Tex., 1983-88; sr. v.p. Furnishings 2000, Inc., San Diego, 1988-89; pvt. cons. Houston, 1990—; chmn. Galveston County Taxpayers Research Council, 1987-88. Served to lt. USN, 1966-69. Republican. Presbyterian. Avocation: travel.

WILLIAMS, ROBERT MARTIN, economist, consultant; b. N.Y.C., May 4, 1913; s. Joseph Tuttle and Mary Adeline (Johnson) W.; m. Vera Jean Bobsene, July 31, 1956; 1 son, Kenneth Martin. B.A., Pomona Coll., 1934; M.A., UCLA, 1942; Ph.D., Harvard U., 1950. Teaching fellow physics Dartmouth Coll., 1935-36; mgmt. trainee Western Electric Co., Inc., Los Angeles, 1936-40; lectr. UCLA, 1947-51, asst. prof., 1951-56, assoc. prof., 1956-63, prof. bus. econs. and statis. Grad. Sch. Mgmt., 1963-83, prof. emeritus, 1983—, vice chmn. dept. mgmt., 1961-67, dir. bus. forecasting project, 1952-81, consulting, 1981—; dir. Imperial Corp. Am., 1975-86, prof. emeritus dir., 1986—; dir. Am. Savs. and Loan Assn. Kans., 1982-86, Silver State Savs. and Loan Assn. Colo., 1982-86; mem. coun., dir. Imperial Savs. and Loan Assn. Calif., 1978-82; econ. cons. Fed. Res. Bank Kansas City, Lockheed Aircraft Corp., others, also state and fed. agys. Editor, contbr. The UCLA Business Forecast for the Nation and California, 1961-88; contbr. numerous articles on bus. forecasting and regional econ. devel. Served to lt. comdr. USNR, 1942-46. Resources for Future, Inc. Research grantee, 1962; NSF grantee, 1965. Mem. Am. Econ. Assn., Am. Statis. Assn., Nat. Assn. Bus. Economists, World Future Soc., Centre for Internat. Rsch. on Econ. Tendency Surveys, Ostomy Assn. L.A. (exec. v.p 1989—). Home: 750 Enchanted Way Pacific Palisades CA 90272-2818 Office: UCLA John E Anderson Grad Sch Mgmt Bus Forecasting Project Los Angeles CA 90024

WILLIAMS, ROBERT WALTER, physics educator; b. Palo Alto, Calif., June 3, 1920; s. Philip S. and Louise (Brown) W.; m. Erica Lehman, Sept. 23, 1969; children: Paul, David, Eric. AB, Stanford U., 1941; MA, Princeton U., 1943; PhD, MIT, 1948. Assoc. physicist Los Alamos Lab., 1943-46; rsch. assoc. MIT, 1946-48, asst. prof., 1948-52; assoc. prof., 1952-59; prof.

physics U. Wash., Seattle, 1959-90, prof. emeritus, 1990—; cons. Boeing Co., Seattle, 1961-64; vis. scientist CERN (European Orgn. Nuclear Rsch.) Lab., Geneva, 1967, 74, 81, 88—; trustee Univs. Rsch. Assn., 1978-84. Contbr. articles to profl. jours. Fellow Am. Phys. Soc., Am. Acad. Arts and Scis. Research on properties of fundamental particles. Home: 3413 E Laurelhurst Dr NE Seattle WA 98105-5357 Office: Univ Wash Dept Physics Mail Stop FM 15 Seattle WA 98195

WILLIAMS, ROBERTA GAY, pediatric cardiologist, educator; b. Rocky Mount, N.C., Oct. 23, 1941. BS, Duke U., 1963; MD, U. N.C. 1968. Diplomate Am. Bd. Pediats. (mem. com. ofcl. examiners 1985—, bd. dirs. and rep. sub-bd. chmn. com. 1992—, mem. exec. com. 1993—), Am. Bd. Pediat. Cardiology (chmn. 1991-92, cons. 1993). Med.-pediat. intern N.C. Meml. Hosp., Chapel Hill, 1968-69; pediat. resident Columbia Presbyn. Med. Ctr., N.Y., 1969-70; fellow in cardiology Children's Hosp. Med. Ctr., Boston, 1970-73, from asst. in cardiology to assoc. in cardiology, 1973-75, sr. assoc. in cardiology, 1976-82; from instr. pediats. to asst. prof. pediats. Harvard Med. Sch.-Children's Hosp., Boston, 1973-82; assoc. prof. pediats. UCLA Med. Ctr., 1982-86, chief divsn. pediat. cardiology, 1982-95, prof. pediats., 1986-95; chair pediatrics U. N.C. Sch. Medicine, Chapel Hill, 1995—; attending physician Cardiac Med. Svcs., Children's Hosp. Med. Ctr., Boston, 1974, cardiology cons. Cardiothoracic Surgery Svc., 1974, med. dir. Cardiovasc. Surgery ICU, 1974-79, dir. Cardiac Graphic Lab. and Cost Ctr., 1977-82, mem. com. neonatal ICU, 1978-79, v.p. med. staff, 1980-81; guest lectr., invited spkr., seminar leader in field. Mem. editl. bd.: Pediat. Cardiology, 1979, Circulation, 1983-91, Am. Jour. Cardiology, 1984-91, Jour. Applied Cardiology, 1985, Clin. Cardiology, 1988, Internat. Jour. Cardiology, 1992-95, Archives of Pediats. and Adolescent Medicine, 1994—; editl. cons. Jour. of Am. Coll. of Cardiology, 1992-94. Mem. exec. coun. cardiovasc. disease in the young Am. Heart Assn., 1979-85, mem. subcom. on genital cardiac defects, 1980-82, subcom. nominating com., 1982-83; mem. Am. Heart Assn.-Greater L.A. affiliate, 1983—, exec. com. and rsch. com., 1984—, judge young investigator competition, 1984, mem. program com., 1986-90, v.p. med.-exec. com., 1991-92, pres.-elect, 1992-93, and numerous other coms. Fellow Am. Coll. Cardiology (allied health profls. com. 1984-87, mem. physician workforce adv. com. 1988-94, mem. manpower adv. com. 1988—, mem. extramural continuing edn. com. Heart House 1990—, cochmn. Bethesda conf. 1993, gov. So. Calif. chpt. 1994—, pres. Calif. chpt. 1994—), Am. Acad. Pediats. (sec. exec. com. sect. on cardiology 1985-87, mem. com. on fetus and newborn 1985-88, mem. exec. com. sect. on cardiology 1989—, chmn. program com. 1988-89, mem. subcom. Am. Heart Assn. task force on assessment of diagnosis and therapeutic cardiovascular procedures 1989, chairperson sec. cardiology 1989, mem. credentials com. 1991—, mem. coun. on sects. mgmt. com. 1995—); mem. Soc. for Pediat. Rsch., Am. Pediat. Soc., Am. Soc. Echocardiography (mem. exec. com. 1975-78, com. on guidelines for technician tng. 1975-78, bd. dirs. 1976-80, treas. exec. coun. com. 1981-83). Avocations: photography, hiking. Office: U No Calif Sch Medicine Dept Pediatrics CB 7220 Chapel Hill NC 27599

WILLIAMS, ROBIN, actor, comedian; b. Chgo., July 21, 1951; s. Mr. and Mrs. Robert W.; m. Valerie Velardi, June 4, 1978 (div.); 1 child, Zachary; m. Marsha Garces, Apr. 30, 1989; children: Zelda, Cody. Attended, Claremont Men's Coll., Marin Coll., Juilliard Sch., N.Y.C. Started as stand-up comedian in San Francisco clubs, including Holy City Zoo, The Boardinghouse; later became regular at Comedy Store, Los Angeles; appeared in TV series Laugh-In, The Richard Pryor Show, America 2-Night, Happy Days, Homicide: Life on the Streets, 1993 (Emmy nomination, Guest Actor - Drama Series, 1994); star of TV series Mork and Mindy, 1978-82 (People's Choice award), (cable) Robin Williams: An Evening at the Met, 1986 (Grammy award), host of HBO's Shakespeare: The Animated Tales, 1993 (CableAce Award, Best Entertainment Host); film appearances include: Popeye, 1980, The World According to Garp, 1982, The Survivors, 1983, Moscow on the Hudson, 1984, Club Paradise, 1986, Good Morning Vietnam, 1987 (Golden Globe award 1988, Acad. Award nominee for best actor), The Adventures of Baron Munchausen, 1989, Dead Poets Society, 1989 (Best Actor nomination Golden Globe award, 1994, nominated best actor Acad. award), Cadillac Man, 1990, The Fisher King, 1991 (Golden Globe award, Acad. award nominee for best actor 1991), Dead Again, 1991, Hook, 1991, Aladdin (voice) (Spl. Achievement award Hollywood Fgn. Press, Nat. Bd. Rev. 1992), 1992, Toys, 1992, Mrs. Doubtfire, 1993 (Best Picture, Best Actor in a Musical or Comedy, Golden Globe, 1994, Best Picture, Best Actor, People's Choice award), Nine Months, 1995; theatre: Waiting for Godot, 1988; recorded albums: Reality, What a Concept, 1979 (Grammy award), Throbbing Python of Love, A Night at the Met (Grammy award); host Comic Relief, 1986; appeared in TV variety programs, ABC Presents a Royal Gala, 1988 (Emmy award, 1988), Carol, Carl, Whoopi & Robin, 1987 (Emmy award). Recipient Golden Apple award Hollywood Women's Press Club; Golden Globe award; ACE award; Am. Comedy award, 1987, 88; Grammy award for best comedy rec., 1987. Office: PO Box 480909 Los Angeles CA 90048-9509*

WILLIAMS, ROBIN MURPHY, JR., sociology educator; b. Hillsborough, N.C., Oct. 11, 1914; s. Robin Murphy and Mabel Claire (Strayhorn) W.; m. Marguerite York, July 29, 1939; children: Robin Murphy III, Nancy, Susan. B.S., N.C. State Coll., 1933, M.S., 1935; postgrad., Cornell U., 1935-36; Ph.D. (Austin fellow, 1938-39), Harvard U., 1943; D.Sc. (hon.), U. N.C., Greensboro, 1989. Various research positions govtl. agys., 1933-37; asst. rural sociologist N.C. Agrl. Expt. Sta., 1936-38; instr., research asst. U. Ky., 1939-42; research analyst and statistician, research br. U.S. War Dept., 1942-45; prof. sociology Cornell U., Ithaca, N.Y., 1946-67; Henry Scarborough prof. social sci. Cornell U., 1967-85, prof. emeritus, 1985—, chmn. dept. sociology and anthropology, 1956-61; dir. Soc. Research Center, 1949-54; Cons. Nat. Inst. Mental Health, 1949-67; mem. sci. adv. bd. USAF, 1950-54; adv. com. for social scis. NSF, 1967-69; com. on life sci. and social policy NRC, 1968-74; vis. scholar Russell Sage Found., 1968-69; vis. fellow Center for Creative Leadership, 1974-75; Center for Advanced Study Behavioral Scis. fellow, 1961-62, NSF Sr. postdoctoral fellow; chmn. NRC Com. on Status of Black Ams., 1985-89. Author: The Reduction of Intergroup Tension, 1947, (with others) The American Soldier, vols. I and II, 1949, American Society, 1951, 60, 70, What College Students Think, 1960, Strangers Next Door, 1964, Mutual Accomodation, 1977; editor: (with Margaret W. Ryan) Schools in Transition, 1954, Sociol. Forum, 1984-92, (with Gerald David Jaynes) A Common Destiny, 1989. Mem. Am. Sociol. Soc. (council, 1st v.p. 1956, pres. 1958, sec. 1965-68), Eastern Sociol Soc. (pres. 1966), Am. Philos. Soc., Am. Acad. Arts Scis., Nat. Acad. Scis., Sociol. Research Assn. (pres. 1958), Rural Sociol. Soc. Am. Office: Cornell U 342 Uris Hall Ithaca NY 14853-7601

WILLIAMS, ROGER LAWRENCE, historian, educator; b. Boulder, Colo., June 22, 1923; s. Raymond Ustick and Mabel (Woolf) W. BA, Colo. Coll., 1947; MA, U. Mich., 1948, PhD, 1951. Asst. prof. history State Coll., Mankato, 1950-52, MIT, Cambridge, 1952-55; vis. prof. Mich. State U., East Lansing, 1955-56; assoc. prof. Antioch Coll., Yellow Springs, Ohio, 1956-65; prof. U. Calif., Santa Barbara, 1965-71; prof. U. Wyo., Laramie, 1971-78, Disting. prof., 1978-88. Author: French Revolution of 1870-71, 1969, The Mortal Napoleon III, 1971, The Horror of Life, 1980, Aven Nelson of Wyoming, 1984, Gérard and Jaume: Two Neglected Figures in the History of the Jussiaean Classification, 1988, Napoleon III and the Stoffel Affair, 1993; co-author: How Modernity Came to a Provençal Town, 1993; author Handbook of Rocky Mountain Plants, 1992; mem. editorial bd. Antioch Rev., 1958-64. Vol. Rocky Mountain Nat. Park, Estes Park, Colo., 1986-87. Mem. French Hist. Studies (life), History Sci. Soc. (life), Nat. Coun. for History Edn., N.Y. Bot. Soc., Denver Bot. Soc. Home: 1701 S 17th St Laramie WY 82070-5406

WILLIAMS, ROGER STEWART, physician; b. San Diego, Feb. 15, 1941; s. Manley Samuel and Ethelyn Mae W.; children: Roger S., Karen E., David G., Sarah E. M.D., Emory U. 1966. Diplomate Am. Bd. Psychiatry and Neurology. Intern, Grady Hosp., Atlanta, 1966-67. Med. resident Emory U., Atlanta, 1966-68; resident neurology Mass. Gen. Hosp., Boston, 1970-73, neurologist, 1973-87; asst. prof. neurology Harvard Med. Sch., Boston, 1977-87; asst. dir. Pathology Labs.; asst. dir. Shriver Ctr., Waltham, 1983-87; neurologist Billings (Mont.) Clinic, 1987—; prof. medicine Mont. State U., Bozeman. Contbr. articles to profl. jours. Served to lt. comdr. USN, 1968-70. Kennedy fellow Kennedy Found., Washington, 1973-75; NIMH grantee, Bethesda, Md., 1979-87. Mem. Am. Acad. Neurology, Mont. Med. Assn., AMA, Alpha Omega Alpha.

WILLIAMS, ROGER WRIGHT, public health educator; b. Great Falls, Mont., Jan. 24, 1918; s. Elmer Howard and Mary (Stuart-Davidson) W.; m. Marjorie Madeline Jones, May 9, 1943; children: Barbara, Stuart Roger. B.S., U. Ill., 1939, M.S., 1941; postgrad., Cornell U., U. N.C. Sch. Pub. Health; Ph.D., Columbia Sch. Pub. Health, 1947; cert. applied parasitology and entomology, U. London, 1957. Mem. faculty Columbia Sch. Pub. Health, N.Y.C., 1944-83, prof. med. entomology, 1966-82, prof. emeritus, 1983, acting head div. tropical medicine, 1970; cons. USPHS, Alaska, 1949, Newton, Ga., 1952, Therapeutic Research Found. of Phila. Inc., 1949, Jackson Hole Preserve Inc., Govt. V.I., U.S. Nat. Park Service, 1959-61, Rockefeller Found., Trinidad, W.I. and Brazil, 1963; filariasis research project WHO, Rangoon, Burma, 1966-70; mem. arbovirus field staff Rockefeller Found., Nigeria, 1964-65; mem. Corp. Bermuda Biol. Sta. for Rsch., 1955-80. Contbr. articles on arthropods of med. importance and diseases they transmit to profl. jours. and books. Mem. Tenafly (N.J.) Cmty. Orch., 1960-63; mem. Tenafly Town-Wide Com., 1970; mem. Boys Activities Com., 1968-72, trustee, 1969-72, pres., 1970-72; chmn. dads' com. troop 140 Boy Scouts Am., Tenafly, 1968-69, merit badge councilor, 1965-83, 88-92; mem. Ocean County Coun., 1991-92; dist. coord. Manchester Township, N.J., 1989-91; trustee Tenafly Nature Ctr., 1967-71, v.p., 1968-71; adv. bd. Am. Christian Coll., 1971-78; deacon Tenafly Presbyn. Ch., 1968-74, elder, 1974-79, 81-82; deacon Lakehurst Presbyn. Ch., 1984-87, elder, 1988-93, chmn. Vesper com., mem. chapel com. and exec. com. Crestwood Manor, 1993—; vol. Meals on Wheels program, 1989-92. Officer USNR, 1943-46. Recipient commendation Boy Scouts Am., 1990; Rockefeller traveling fellow, 1947; Childs Frick fellow Bermuda, 1955, 57; NSF sr. postdoctoral fellow U. London (Eng.) Sch. Hygiene and Tropical Medicine, 1956-57; La. State U. Sch. Medicine fellow in tropical medicine Central Am., 1957. Fellow AAAS; mem. Internat. Coll. Tropical Medicine, Internat. Filariasis Assn., Am. Wash. Entomol. Socs., Am. Mosquito Control Assn., Am. Soc. Parasitologists, Am. Royal Socs. Tropical Medicine and Hygiene, Elisha Mitchel Sci. Soc., N.Y. Soc. Tropical Medicine (pres. 1969-70), Tenafly Swim Club (trustee 1972-74, v.p. 1973, pres. 1974), Travel Club of Leisure Village West (bd. dirs. 1983-89, v.p. 1988), Nature Club (pres. 1989), Kiwanis (pres. elect Leisure Village West chpt. 1985-86, pres. 1986-87, Dist-ing. past pres. 1987-88), Mens Club Crestwood Manor, 1993—, Phi Sigma. Co-discoverer West African arbovirus, Dugbe virus. Home: 50 Lacey Rd Ste B105 Whiting NJ 08759-2954 *Success is living in peace and contentment with one's self. I have attempted to achieve this by leading what I consider to be a Christian Life and helping others to do the same, by giving some of my time to help improve the world around us for others, and by giving a little more effort to a task than the minimum necessary to just get it done.*

WILLIAMS, RONALD L., pharmaceutical association executive; b. Akron, Ohio, July 30, 1935; s. Reuben and Thelma W. B.S. in Pharmacy, Ohio No. U., 1957. Pharmacist, pharmacy owner Akron, 1957-66; exec. sec. Student Am. Pharm. Assn., Washington, 1968-71, 77-81; asst. exec. sec. Am. Pharm. Assn. Acad. Pharm. Practice, Washington, 1971-72; exec. sec. Am. Pharm. Assn. Acad. Pharm. Practice, 1972-83, Am. Pharm. Assn. Acad. Pharm. Sci., 1978-83; dir. liaison and state relations Am. Pharm. Assn., 1983-85, dir. profl. affairs, 1985-86, dir. communications, 1986-90, exec. dir. planning, exec. officer ops., 1990-95, dir. comm., strategic planning, 1995—, coord. pharm. recovery program, 1984—; mem. nat. high blood pressure coordinating com., 1977-86, Interdisciplinary Task Force on Provider Roles, 1979-80, U.S. Drug Enforcement Adminstrn./Pharmacy Working Com., 1974-86; co-chmn. Nat. Conf. on High Blood Pressure Control, 1979-80, bd. dirs., 1982-86; mem. ann. meeting planning com. Nat. Council on Patient Info. and Edn., 1985-86; mem. Medic Alert Nat. Pharmacy Task Group, 1985-92; mem. informal steering Com. on Prescription Drug Abuse, 1982-86; leader pharmacists sect. U. Utah Sch. Alcohol and Other Drug Dependencies, 1984—; mem. adv. bd. Ohio No. U. Coll. Pharmacy, 1987-94, Campbell U. Coll. Pharmacy, 1993—; mem. planning com. Nat. Conf. on Impaired Health Profl., 1986-88; mem. Poison Prevention Week Coun., 1988—. Editor: Pharmacy Practice, 1971-86, Pharmacy Student, 1977-82, Acad. Reporter, 1978-83. Mem. AMA (affiliate), Am. Pharmacy Assn., Washington Pharm. Assn., Planning Forum, Am. Soc. Assn. Execs., Cuyahoga Falls Schs. Found., Am. Legion, Kappa Psi. Democrat. Methodist. Office: Am Pharm Assn 2215 Constitution Ave NW Washington DC 20037-2975

WILLIAMS, RONALD OSCAR, systems engineer; b. Denver, May 10, 1940; s. Oscar H. and Evelyn (Johnson) W. BS in Applied Math., U. Colo. Coll. Engring., 1964, postgrad. U. Colo., U. Denver, George Washington U. Computer programmer Apollo Systems dept., missile and space divsn. Gen. Electric Co., Kennedy Space Ctr., Fla., 1965-67, Manned Spacecraft Ctr., Houston, 1967-68; computer programmer U. Colo., Boulder, 1968-73; computer programmer analyst def. systems divsn. System Devel. Corp. for NORAD, Colorado Springs, 1974-75; engr. def. systems and command-and-info. systems Martin Marietta Aerospace, Denver, 1976-80; systems engr. space and comm. group, def. info. systems divsn. Hughes Aircraft Co., Aurora, Colo, 1980-89; rsch. analyst, 1990—. Vol. fireman Clear Lake City (Tex.) Fire Dept., 1968; officer Boulder Emergency Squad, 1969-76, rescue squadman, 1969-76, liaison to cadets, 1971, pers. officer, 1971-76, exec. bd., 1971-76, award of merit, 1971, 72, emergency med. technician 1973—; spl. police officer Boulder Police Dept., 1970-75; spl. dep. sheriff Boulder County Sheriff's Dept., 1970-71; nat. adv. bd. Am. Security Coun., 1979-91, Coalition of Peace through Strength, 1979-91. Served with USMCR, 1958-66. Decorated Organized Res. medal; recipient Cost Improvement Program award Hughes Aircraft Co., 1982, Systems Improvement award, 1982, Top Cost Improvement Program award, 1983. Mem. AAAS, AIAA, Math. Assn. Am., Am. Math. Soc., Soc. Indsl. and Applied Math., Math. Study Unit of the Am. Topical Assn., Armed Forces Comm. and Electronics Assn., Assn. Old Crows, Am. Def. Preparedness Assn., Marine Corps Assn., Air Force Assn., U.S. Naval Inst., Nat. Geog. Soc., Smithsonian Instn., Soc. Amateur Radio Astronomers, Met. Opera Guild, Colo. Hist. Soc., Hist. Denver, Inc., Historic Boulder, Inc., Hawaiian Hist. Soc., Denver Botanic Gardens, Denver Mus. Natural History, Denver Zool. Found., Inc., Mensa. Lutheran.

WILLIAMS, RONALD PAUL, lawyer; b. Tulsa, June 28, 1947; s. Donald Paul and Reon Bessie (Thomason) W.; m. Judy Ann Seivers, May 25, 1968 (div. Apr. 1984); children: Heather Ann, Brian Paul; m. Barbara Susan Wehby, Nov. 9, 1984; children: Amy Katherine Williams, Marianne Christine Williams. BA in Polit. Sci., Southwestern Coll., Winfield, Kans., 1974; JD, Washburn U., 1977. Bar: Kans. 1977, U.S. Dist. Ct. Kans. 1977, U.S. Dist. Ct. (we dist.) Mo. 1986, U.S. Ct. Appeals (10th cir.) 1980. Assoc. Shaw, Hergenreter, Quarnstrom & Wright, Topeka, 1977-80, McDonald, Tinker, Skaer, Quinn & Herrington, Wichita, Kans., 1980-84, Morrison & Hecker, Wichita, 1984—; instr. Nat. Inst. for Trial Advocacy, 1982—, Kans. Coll. Advocacy, Topeka, 1980—. Served with USAF, 1965-69. Mem. Nat. Transp. and Safety Bd. Bar Assn. (regional v.p. 1986—), Def. Rsch. Inst., Kans. Bar Assn. (pres. aviation sect. 1984, 85), Kans. Assn. Def. Counsel (pres. 1988-89). Republican. Avocations: flying, golf. Home: 9408 Wyncroft St Wichita KS 67205-1404 Office: Morrison & Hecker 150 N Main St Ste 600 Wichita KS 67202-1320

WILLIAMS, ROY, university athletic coach. Head coach U. Kansas Jayhawks, 1988—. Named Nat. Rookie Coach of Yr., Basketball Times, 1989, Coach of Yr., Basketball Writers Assn., 1990, Big 8 Coach of Yr., AP and UPI, 1990, Big 8 Coach of Yr., AP, 1992, Nat. Coach of Yr., 1992. 1991 NCAA Tournament runner-up. Office: Univ Kansas Allen Fieldhouse Lawrence KS 66045*

WILLIAMS, RUSSELL, II, production sound mixer; b. Oct. 14, 1952. BA in Film Prodn., Art History, Lit., Am. U., Washington, 1974; student, Rec. Inst. Am., Silver Spring, Md., 1974; student in Basic Electronics, U. Sound Arts, Hollywood, Calif., 1979. Studio engr. rec. lab. Libr. Congress, Washington, 1971-73; vol. co-dir. Spirits Radio Workshop, WAMU-FM radio, Am. U., Washington, 1972-79; engr. WRC/NBC TV, Washington, 1973, 77; documentary sound recordist, transfer engr. WMAL TV, Washington, 1974-76; workshop leader radio vol. activity com. Corp. for Pub. Broadcasting, Washington, 1976; engr., editor WMAL/ABC radio, Washington, 1978-79; motion picture sound mixer, 1979—; founder, owner Sound Is Ready, 1979—; guest lectr. U.D.C., 1973, 77; vis. prof. dept. film and TV, UCLA, 1991. Productions include (feature films) The Distinguished Gentleman, Boomerang, Mo Money, True Identity, Jungle Fever, Dances with Wolves (Acad. award 1991, Brit. Acad. nomination 1992), Glory (Acad. award 1990), Field of Dreams, (movies for TV) Heatwave, The Women of Brewster

Place, Inherit the Wind, Billionaire Boys Club, Terrorist on Trial (Prime Time Emmy award), (documentary and indsl. films) Eyes on the Prize I, The Making of JoJo Dancer, Return to Iwo Jima. Mem. IATSE, Acad. Motion Picture Arts and Scis., Acad. Television Arts and Scis., Cinema Audio Soc. (3 awards).

WILLIAMS, S. LINN, lawyer; b. St. Louis, July 1, 1946; s. Sidney Duane and Elizabeth Gertrude (Relfe) W.; m. Noriko Kurosawa, Sept. 13, 1975. B.A., Princeton U., 1968, J.D., Harvard U., 1971, postgrad. Cambridge U., 1972-74. Bar: Mass. 1971, D.C. 1972, Pa. 1987. Law clk. to Hon. I.L. Goldberg, U.S. Ct. Appeals 5th Cir., Dallas, 1971-72; assoc. Blakemore & Mitsuki, Tokyo, 1974; assoc., then ptnr. Leva, Hawes, Symington, Martin & Oppenheimer, Washington, 1975-81; v.p., gen. counsel Overseas Pvt. Investment Corp., Washington, 1981-84; v.p., gen. counsel Sears World Trade, Inc., 1984-85; ptnr. Gibson Dunn and Crutcher, Washington and Tokyo, 1985-89, 92-93, Jones Day Reavis & Pogue, Washington, 1993-94; sr. v.p., gen. counsel Mission Energy Co., Irvine, Calif., 1995—; Japanese fgn. legal cons. Tokyo Dainibengoshikai, 1987-89; dep. U.S. trade rep., amb., Washington, 1989-91; mem. bd. adv. Coun. Competitiveness, CEO Inst., Inst. Asian Law and Policy Studies Georgetown U., Washington, U.S. Com. of Pacific Econ. Coop. Coun., European Inst.; sr. fellow Ctr. Strategic and Internat. Studies, Washington. Fulbright scholar, 1972, NEH fellow, 1972, McConnell fellow, 1967, Ford Found. fellow, 1972. Mem. Inst. Internat. Commercial Law (trustee), United Oxford & Cambridge Club (London), Met. Club (Washington). Author: Developing an Export Trading Business, 1989; contbr. chpts. in book, also numerous articles on trade and investments. Office: Mission Energy Co 18101 Von Karman Ave Irvine CA 92715

WILLIAMS, SANDRA, insurance company executive; b. 1947. Law degrees, U. Madison, U. Conn. With Farmington Casualty Co., Hartford, 1979—, sec. Office: Farmington Casualty Co 151 Farmington Ave Hartford CT 06156*

WILLIAMS, SANDRA KELLER, postal service executive; b. Bethesda, Md., Oct. 3, 1944; d. Park Dudley and Julia Mildred (Hunter) Keller; m. Tommy Allen Williams, Dec. 24, 1970; children: Chris Allen, Wakenna, Barbara. BA, U. Colo., 1966; MBA, U. Mo., Kansas City, 1971; MS, Ga. Inst. Tech., 1973. Mathematician Colo. State U., Ft. Collins, 1966; sr. scientist Booz-Allen Applied Rsch., Kansas City, Mo., 1967-68; computer sci. instr. Mo. Western Coll., St. Joseph, 1968-71; systems planning analyst Decatur (Ga.) Fed. Savs. and Loan Assn., 1972-73; planning analyst Fed. Res. Bank, Atlanta, 1974-75; indsl. engr. so. region hdqrs. U.S. Postal Svc., Memphis, 1975-79; nat. mgr. quality control U.S. Postal Svc., Washington, 1979-86; dir. city ops. so. Md. div. U.S. Postal Svc., Capital Heights, 1986-87, dir., oper. supt. so. Md. div., 1987-88; postmaster U.S. Postal Svc., Reading, Pa., 1988—; cons. Personal Bus., St. Joseph, 1968-69; grad. teaching asst. Ga. Inst. Tech., Atlanta, 1971-73; adj. faculty Dekalb C.C., Clarkston, Ga., 1973-75, Memphis State U., 1976-78; owner Custom Florals, 1995—. Chmn. Combined Fed. Campaign, Reading, 1988-95, U.S. Postal Svc.-Berks County Savs. Bond Program, 1988-95, United Way's Govt. divsn., 1989-90; bd. dirs. YWCA, Reading and Berks County, treas., 1990, pres., 1991. Mem. Nat. League Postmasters (legis. officer 1988-91), Berks County Women's Network (bd. dirs. 1994-95, treas. 1995). Avocations: interior design, gardening, investment portfolio management. Home: 1514 Hill Rd Reading PA 19602-1410

WILLIAMS, SANKEY VAUGHAN, health services researcher, internist; b. San Antonio, Apr. 15, 1944; s. James Sankey and Helen (Long) W.; m. Constance Hess, June 27, 1972; children: Elizabeth Helen, Jennifer Lee. AB, Princeton U., 1966; MD, Harvard U., 1970. Diplomate Am. Bd. Internal Medicine. Intern Hosp. of U. Pa., 1970-71, jr. resident, 1971-72, chief med. resident, 1974-75; assoc. dir. clin. rsch. Ctr. for Study of Aging, U. Pa., 1982-86; assoc. dir. for med. affairs Leonard Davis Inst. for Health Econs., U. Pa., 1978-90; dir. clin. scholars program U. Pa., Phila., 1988—; prof. health care systems Wharton Sch., U. Pa., Phila., 1989—; prof. medicine U. Pa., Phila., 1989—, chief div. gen. internal medicine, 1992—, Sol Katz prof. medicine, 1992—; commr. Prospective Payment Assessment Commn., U.S. Congress, Washington, 1988-91; chairman health svcs. rsch. devel. grants study sect. Agy. for Health Care Policy and Rsch., 1991-94; counselor for med. affiars to the pres. U. Pa., 1990-92. Co-editor: The Physician's Practice, 1980; author 14 revs, chpt. or editorials; contbr. 35 articles to various sci. jours. Lt. comdr. USPHS, 1972-74. Recipient Career Devel. award Henry S. Kaiser Family Found., 1981-86. Mem. ACP (diplomate, chmn. clin. privileges com. 1989-93, Am. Fedn. for Clin. Rsch. (program chmn. health svcs. rsch. 1985), Soc. for Med. Decision Making (pres. 1985-86), Soc. for Gen. Internal Medicine (coun. 1979-84, editor Jour. Gen. INternal Medicine 1995—). Office: Hosp Univ of Pa Divsn Gen Internal Medicine Silverstein 3 Philadelphia PA 19104

WILLIAMS, SOLOMON, Indian organization executive; b. Mekoryuk, Alaska, Aug. 29, 1943; s. Jack Uyohitch and Susie (Brown) W.; m. Alice Marie Mathlaw, Oct. 29, 1969; children: Claudine Jo Williams Davis, Patricia Renae. Grad. edn. diploma, Juneau (Alaska)-Douglas C.C., 1971. Notary pub., Alaska. Warehouseman Native Village of Mekoryuk, 1957-66; store mgr., 1972-73; acctg. clk. Bur. Indian Affairs, Juneau, 1966-72; realty specialist Bur. Indian Affairs, Bethel, Alaska, 1974-81; land law examiner Bur. Indian Affairs, Anchorage, 1987-89; mgr. Bering Sea Reindeer Products, Mekoryuk, 1981-84; city clk. City of Mekoryuk, 1984-85; pres.-supr. Indian Reorgn. Act Coun., Meyoryuk, 1989-95, exec. officer, 1995—. Recipient 10-Yr. Svc. award Bur. Indian Affairs, 1985. Avocations: hunting, commercial fishing. Office: Indian Reorgn Act Coun 1st Chase St Mekoryuk AK 99630

WILLIAMS, SPENCER M., federal judge; b. Reading, Mass., Feb. 24, 1922; s. Theodore Ryder and Anabel (Hutchison) W.; m. Kathryn Bramlage, Aug. 20, 1943; children: Carol Marcia (Mrs. James B. Garvey), Peter, Spencer, Clark, Janice, Diane (Mrs. Sean Quinn). AB, UCLA, 1943; postgrad., Hastings Coll. Law, 1946; JD, U. Calif., Berkeley, 1948. Bar: Calif. 1949, U.S. Supreme Ct. 1952. Assoc. Beresford & Adams, San Jose, Calif., 1949, Rankin, O'Neal, Center, Luckhardt, Bonney, Marlais & Lund, San Jose, Evans, Jackson & Kennedy, Sacramento; county counsel Santa Clara County, 1955-67; adminstr. Calif. Health and Welfare Agy., Sacramento, 1967-69; judge U.S. Dist. Ct. (no. dist.) Calif., San Francisco, from 1971, now sr. judge; County exec. pro tem, Santa Clara County; adminstr. Calif. Youth and Adult Corrections Agy., Sacramento; sec. Calif. Human Relations Agy., Sacramento, 1967-70. Chmn. San Jose Christmas Seals Drive, 1953, San Jose Muscular Dystrophy Drive, 1953, 54; team capt. fund raising drive San Jose YMCA, 1960; co-chmn. indsl. sect. fund raising drive Alexian Bros. Hosp., San Jose, 1964; team capt. fund raising drive San Jose Hosp.; mem. com. on youth and govt. YMCA, 1967-68; Candidate for Calif. Assembly, 1954, Calif. Atty. Gen., 1966, 70; Bd. dirs. San Jose Better Bus. Bur., 1955-66, Boys City Boys' Club, San Jose, 1965-67; pres. trustees Santa Clara County Law Library, 1955-66. Served with USNR, 1943-46; to lt. comdr. JAG Corps USNR, 1950-52, PTO. Named San Jose Man of Year, 1954. Mem. ABA, Calif. Bar Assn. (vice chmn. com on publicly employed attys. 1962-63), Santa Clara County Bar Assn., Sacramento Bar Assn., Internat. Assn. Trial Judges (pres. 1995-96), Calif. Dist. Attys. Assn. (pres. 1963-64), Nat. Assn. County Civil Attys. (pres. 1963-64), 9th Cir. Dist. Judges Assn. (pres. 1981-83), Fed. Judges Assn. (pres. 1982-87), Kiwanis, Theta Delta Chi. Office: US Dist Ct 280 S 1st St San Jose CA 95113-3002

WILLIAMS, STANLEY, ballet dancer and teacher; b. Chappel, Eng., 1925. guest tchr. Sch. Am. Ballet, N.Y.C. Ballet Co., 1960-62; mem. faculty Sch. Am. Ballet, N.Y.C., 1964—, now co-chmn. faculty; guest instr. Royal Danish Ballet, 1966-80; sr. faculty chair The Brown Found., Inc., 1987. Staged: Bournonville Divertissement for, N.Y.C. Ballet (Dance Mag. award 1981); studied at school, Royal Danish Ballet, also in, Paris; accepted into the company, 1943, became solo dancer, 1949, tchr.. 1950—, guest artist, Iceland, 1947, Brussels and Stockholm, 1948, ballet master, leading dancer with, George Kirsta's Ballet Colombe in Eng., 1953-54; repertoire in Denmark includes leading roles in Coppelia, others. Knighted by King of Denmark; recipient Mae L. Simon silver knigen award, 1992. Address: Sch Am Ballet 70 Lincoln Center Plz New York NY 10023-6548

WILLIAMS, STEPHEN, anthropologist, educator; b. Mpls., Aug. 28, 1926; s. Clyde Garfield and Lois (Simmons) W.; m. Eunice Ford, Jan. 6, 1962; children: Stephen John, Timothy. BA, Yale U., 1949, PhD, 1954; MA

(hon.), U. Mich., 1950; MA, Harvard, 1962. Asst. anthropology dept. Peabody Mus., Yale U., 1950-52; mem. faculty Harvard U., Cambridge, Mass., 1958—, prof. anthropology, 1967-72, Peabody prof., 1972-93, prof. emeritus, chmn. dept., 1967-69; rsch. fellow Peabody Mus., Harvard U., Cambridge, Mass., 1954-57, mem. staff, 1954—, dir. mus., 1967-77; curator N.Am. Archaeology, 1962-93, hon. curator 1993—; dir. rsch. of Peabody Mus.'s Lower Miss. Survey, 1958-93. Author books and articles on N.Am. archaeology and "Fantastic" archaeology. Home: 1017 Foothills Trail Santa Fe NM 87505 Office: PO Box 22354 Santa Fe NM 87502-2354

WILLIAMS, STEPHEN FAIN, federal judge; b. N.Y.C., N.Y., Sept. 23, 1936; s. Charles Dickerman and Virginia (Fain) W.; m. Faith Morrow, June 11, 1966; children: Susan, Geoffrey Fain, Sarah Margot Nu, Timothy Dwight, Nicholas Morrow. B.A., Yale U., 1958; J.D., Harvard U., 1961. Bar: N.Y. 1962, Colo. 1977. Assoc. Debevoise, Plimpton, Lyons & Gates, N.Y.C., 1962-66; asst. U.S. atty. So. Dist. N.Y., 1966-69; asst. prof. law U. Colo., Boulder, 1969-77; prof. U. Colo., 1977-86; judge U.S. Ct. Appeals (D.C. cir.), Washington, 1986—; vis. prof. UCLA, 1975-76; vis. prof., fellow in law and econs. U. Chgo., 1979-80; vis. William L. Hutchison prof. energy law So. Meth. U., 1983-84; cons. Adminstrv. Conf. U.S., 1974-76, FTC, 1983-85; mem. Boulder Area Growth Study Commn., 1972-73. Contbr. articles to law revs., mags. Served with U.S. Army, 1961-62. Mem. Am. Law Inst. Office: US Courthouse 3rd Constitution Ave NW Washington DC 20001

WILLIAMS, STERLING LEE, electronics executive; b. Spokane, Wash., July 29, 1943; s. Henry Sterling and Alma (Whitaker) W.; m. Sharolyn Snow, Aug. 23, 1963 (div. Nov. 5, 1971); children: Brett, Lance; m. Barbara Gattis, Nov. 22, 1971; 1 child, Tiffany Nicole. BS, East Central U., Ada, Okla., 1967; postgrad. studies, Tex. Christian U., 1967-69. Sales rep. RCA computer systems div., Dallas, 1969-71; gen. mgr. computer services div. University Computing Co., Dallas, 1971-78; v.p. domestic ops. Inforex, Burlington, Mass., 1978-79; pres. numerical control div. Mfg. Data Systems Inc., Ann Arbor, Mich., 1979-81; pres., chief exec. officer Sterling Software Inc., Dallas, 1981—, also bd. dirs. Mem. Assn. Data Processing Services Orgns., Sigma Pi Sigma. Republican. Avocations: reading, traveling. Office: Sterling Software Inc 8080 N Cen Expressway St #1100 LB53 Dallas TX 75206

WILLIAMS, STEVEN A., hospital administrator. With Livingston County Hosp., Salem, Ky., 1972-79, Norton-Children's Hosp., Louisville, 1977-79, Caldwell County Hosp., Princeton, Ky., 1979-84; officer N.K.C. Mgmt., Inc., Louisville, 1984-85; with Alliant Hosp., Inc., Louisville, 1986—, pres., chief exec. officer. Office: Alliant Hosp Inc 200 E Chestnut St Louisville KY 40202*

WILLIAMS, SUE DARDEN, library director; b. Miami, Fla., Aug. 13, 1943; d. Archie Yelverton and Bobbie (Jones) Eagles; m. Richard Williams, Sept. 30, 1989. B.A., Barton Coll., Wilson, N.C., 1965; M.L.S., U. Tex., Austin, 1970. Cert. librarian, N.C.. Va. Instr. Chowan Coll., Murfreesboro, N.C., 1966-68; libr.'s asst. Albemarle Regional Libr., Winston, N.C., 1968-69; br. libr. Multnomah County Pub. Libr., Portland, Oreg., 1971-72; asst. dir. Stanly County Pub. Libr., Albemarle, N.C., 1973-76; dir. Stanly County Pub. Libr., 1976-80; asst. dir. Norfolk (Va.) Pub. Libr., 1980-83; dir., 1983-94. Mem. ALA (orientation com. 1990-92, chair 1991), Libr. Adminstrv. and Mgmt. Assn. (pub. rels. sec. 1985-87), Southeastern Libr. Assn. (staff devel. com. 1986-88, Rothrock award com. 1984-86, sec. pub. libr. sect. 1982-84), Va. Libr. Assn. (SELA rep. 1993—, coun. 1984, 88-91, 93—, ad hoc conf. guidelines com. 1985-86, chmn. conf. program 1984, awards and recognition com. 1983), Pub. Libr. Assn. (bd. dirs.-at-large Met. area 1986-89), Va. State Libr. (coop edn. com. 88-89). Home: 3534 Brest Ave Norfolk VA 23509-2143

WILLIAMS, SYLVIA HILL, museum director; b. Lincoln University, Pa., Feb. 10, 1936; m. Charlton E. Williams. AB, Oberlin Coll., 1957; Cert. de Francais Paris, Ecole Pract. de l'Alliance Francaise, Paris, 1963; MA in Primitive Art, NYU Inst. of Fine Arts, 1975; LHD honoris causa, Amherst Coll., 1989. Program cons. Nat. Assembly for Social Policy and Devel., N.Y.C., 1963-68; account exec. Harry L. Oram, Inc., N.Y.C., 1968-71; Mellon research fellow The Bklyn. Mus., 1971-73, asst. curator, 1973-76, assoc. curator, 1976-78, curator, 1978-83; dir. Nat. Museum of African Art, Smithsonian Inst., Washington, 1983—; lectr. African art New Sch. for Social Rsch., N.Y.C., 1979-80; adj. asst. prof. NYU, 1980; mem. vis. com. Allen Meml. Art Mus. Oberlin Coll. Author: Black South Africa: Contemporary Graphics, 1976, Mohammad Omer Khalil, Etchings/Amir I. M. Nour, Sculpture, 1994; contbg. author: African Art as Philosophy, 1974; contbr. articles to Apollo mag., African Arts, also others; curator, organizer major exhbns. Bklyn. Mus., Nat. Mus. African Art. Trustee Oberlin Coll., 1990—; mem. pvt. sect. arts com. USIA, 1990-92. Nat. Mus. Act grantee (Paris, Tervuren, London), 1974. Mem. Assn. Art Mus. Dirs. (pres. 1994-95), Am. Assn. Museums. Office: Smithsonian Instn Nat Mus African Art 950 Independence Ave SW Washington DC 20560-0001

WILLIAMS, T. RAYMOND, lawyer; b. Meridian, Miss., Aug. 26, 1940. BS, U. Ala., 1962, LLB, 1964. Bar: Ala. 1964, Tex. 1979, U.S. Supreme Ct. 1980, D.C. 1983. Ptnr. McDermott, Will & Emery, Washington. Mem. D.C. Bar Assn., Ala. State Bar Assn., State Bar Tex. Office: McDermott Will & Emery 1850 K St NW Washington DC 20006-2213

WILLIAMS, TED (THEODORE SAMUEL WILLIAMS), former baseball player, former manager, consultant; b. San Diego, Aug. 30, 1918; s. Samuel Steward and May m. Doris Soule; 3 children. Played with Boston Red Sox, 1939-42, 46-60; now cons. and spring tng. instr.; mgr. Washington Senators, 1969-71, Tex. Rangers, 1972; sports cons. Sears, Roebuck & Co. Author: (with John Underwood) My Turn at Bat: The Story of My Life, 1968, The Science of Hitting, 1972. Served to 2d lt. USMCR, 1942-45. Named to Am. League All-Star Team, 1940-42, 46-51, 54-60; named Sporting News Player of Year, 1941, 42, 47, 49, 57, Am. League Most Valuable Player, 1946, 49, Am. League Mgr. of Year, 1969; inducted to Baseball Hall of Fame, 1966. *

WILLIAMS, TEMPLE WEATHERLY, JR., internist, educator; b. Wichita Falls, Tex., Apr. 19, 1934; s. Temple Weatherly and Dorothy (Coleman) W.; married; children: Holly Clare, Temple Weatherly III; m. Joan Loos, Apr. 6, 1991. Student, Midwestern U., 1951-53; B.S., So. Meth. U., 1955; M.D., Baylor U., 1959. Intern, resident in internal medicine Duke U. Hosp., Durham, N.C., 1959-60, 62-63; fellow in infectious disease Baylor U., 1960-62; clin. assoc. infectious disease NIH, Bethesda, Md.; prof. medicine and microbiology/immunology Baylor Coll. Medicine, Houston, 1974—. Contbr. 100 articles on infectious diseases to profl. jours., chpts. to books. Served with USPHS, 1963-65. Fellow ACP, Infectious Disease Soc. Am.; mem. AMA. Republican. Methodist. Office: 6565 Fannin MS 910 Houston TX 77030

WILLIAMS, THEODORE EARLE, industrial distribution company executive; b. Cleve., May 9, 1920; s. Stanley S. and Blanche (Albaum) W.; m. Rita Cohen, Aug. 28, 1952; children: Lezlie, Richard Atlas, Shelley, William Atlas, Wayne, Marsha, Patti Blake, Jeff Blake. Student, Wayne U., 1937-38; BS in Engring, U. Mich., 1942, postgrad. in bus. adminstrn, 1942. Pres. Wayne Products Co., Detroit, 1942-43, L.A., 1947-49; pres. Williams Metal Products Co., Inglewood, Calif., 1950-69; chmn. bd., pres., chief exec. officer Bell Industries, L.A., 1969-; instr. U. Mich. 1942. Patentee in field. Served to 1st lt. AUS, 1943-46. Recipient Humanitarian award City of L.A., 1977. Democrat. Home: 435 N Layton Way Los Angeles CA 90049-2022 Office: Bell Industries Inc 11812 San Vicente Blvd Los Angeles CA 90049-5022 *It seems to me that many of our current problems in this world originate from the drift away from concern for other people to the emphasis on self. We are reluctant to get involved, and as this spaceship gets smaller, we become more interdependent all the time. If we don't learn to live together, I'm afraid we may all perish together.*

WILLIAMS, THEODORE JOSEPH, engineering educator; b. Black Lick, Pa., Sept. 2, 1923; s. Theodore Finley and Mary Ellen (Shields) W.; m. Isabel Annette McAnulty, July 18, 1946; children: Theodore Joseph, Mary Margaret, Charles Augustus, Elizabeth Ann. B.S.Ch.E., Pa. State U., 1949,

M.S.Ch.E., 1950, Ph.D., 1955; M.S. in Elec. Engring., Ohio State U., 1956. Research fellow Pa. State U., University Park, 1947-51; asst. prof. Air Force Inst. Tech., 1953-56; technologist Monsanto Co., 1956-57, sr. engring. supr., 1957-65; prof. engring. Purdue U., Lafayette, Ind., 1965-94, prof. emeritus, 1995—, dir. control and info. systems lab., 1965-66; dir. Purdue Lab. Applied Indsl. Control, 1966-94, dir. emeritus, 1995—; cons., 1964—; vis. prof. Washington U., St. Louis, 1962-65. Author: Systems Engineering for the Process Industries, 1961, Automatic Control of Chemical and Petroleum Processes, 1961, Progress in Direct Digital Control, 1969, Interfaces with the Process Control Computer, 1971, Modeling and Control of Kraft Production Systems, 1975, Modeling, Estimation and Control of the Soaking Pit, 1983, The Use of Digital Computers in Process Control, 1983, Analysis and Design of Hierarchical Control Systems - With Special Reference to Steel Plant Operations, 1985, A Reference Model for Computer Integrated Manufacturing (CIM) - A Description from the Viewpoint of Industrial Automation, 1989, The Purdue Enterprise Reference Architecture, 1992; editor: Computer Applications in Shipping and Shipbuilding, 6 vols., 1973-79, Proceedings Advanced Control Confs., 19 vols., 1974-93. Served to 1st lt. USAAF, 1942-45; to capt. USAF, 1951-56. Decorated Air medal with 2 oak leaf clusters. Fellow AAAS, Instrument Soc. America (pres. 1968-69, Albert F. Sperry medal 1990), Am. Inst. Chemists, Am. Inst. Chem. Engrs., Inst. Measurement and Control (London, Sr. Harold Hartley Silver medal 1975); sr. mem. IEEE; mem. Am. Chem. Soc., Am. Automatic Control Council (pres. 1965-67), Am. Fedn. Info. Processing Socs. (pres. 1976-78), Sigma Xi, Tau Beta Pi, Phi Kappa Phi, Phi Lambda Upsilon. Home: 208 Chippewa St West Lafayette IN 47906-2123 Office: Purdue U Potter Rsch Ctr Inst Interdisciplinary Engring Studies West Lafayette IN 47907-1293

WILLIAMS, THOMAS ALLISON, lawyer; b. Port Chester, N.Y., Dec. 19, 1936; s. Howard Hunter and Mary Katharine (Covell) W.; m. Anne Lamson Bell, Sept. 7, 1961; children: Thomas Allison, Laura L., James C., David D. BA in Econs., Yale U., 1959, LLB, 1962. Bar: N.Y. 1963. Assoc. Milbank, Tweed, Hadley & McCloy, N.Y.C., 1962-70, ptnr., 1971-94, pres., dir., The Depository Trust Co., N.Y.C., 1994—. Trustee Rye Free Reading Room (N.Y.), 1965-85, pres., 1978-85; trustee Rye Presbyn. Ch., 1972-75; trustee, chmn. planning com. United Hosp., Port Chester, N.Y., 1978-86, chmn. bd., 1986—; trustee Westchester Libr. System, Westchester, N.Y., 1968-73, pres., 1972-73. Mem. ABA, N.Y. State Bar Assn., Assn. of Bar of City of N.Y., Am. Yacht Club (vice commodore), N.Y. Yacht Club, Apawamis Club. Republican. Presbyterian. Office: The Depository Trust Co 55 Water St New York NY 10041

WILLIAMS, THOMAS ARTHUR, biomedical computing consultant, psychiatrist; b. Racine, Wis., May 11, 1936; s. Robert Klinkert and Marion Anne (Wisneski) W.; m. Rexanne Louise Smith, Aug. 8, 1988; children: Jennifer, Thomas, Ted, Susan. BA, Harvard Coll., 1958; MD, Columbia U., 1963; postgrad., NIH, 1967-68. Diplomate Nat. Bd. Med. Examiners, Am. Bd. Psychiatry and Neurology. Intern in surgery Presbyn. Hosp., N.Y.C., 1963-64; resident in psychiatry N.Y. State Psychiat. Inst., N.Y.C., 1964-67; chief depression sect. NIMH, Bethesda, Rockville, Md., 1967-71; asst. prof. U. Pitts., 1969-70; assoc. prof. U. Utah, Salt Lake City, 1971-77; prof., chmn. dept. psychiatry Eastern Va. Med. Sch., Norfolk, Va., 1977-78; clin. dir. Sheppard & Enoch Pratt Hosp., Towson, Md., 1978-80; prof. U. South Fla., Tampa, 1980-83; practitioner psychiat. medicine, med. dir. St. Augustine (Fla.) Psychiat. Ctr., 1983-89, 89-90; prin. Williams & Assocs., Tampa, 1990—. Chief editor: Psychobiology of Depression, 1972, Mental Health in the 21st Century, 1979; contbr. numerous articles to profl. jours. and chpts. to books. Mem. Gov.'s Adv. Com. on Mental Health, Salt Lake City, 1971-77, Gov.'s Adv. Com. on Penal Code, Richmond, Va., 1978, Dist. Mental Health Bd., Tampa, 1980-83; sponsor, coach Forest Hills Little League Baseball, Tampa, 1980-83. Sr. surgeon USPHS, 1958-67. Recipient Predoctoral fellowship NIMH, 1960-61, Alumni Rsch. award N.Y. State Psychiat. Inst., 1964, Rush Bronze Medal award Am. Psychiat. Assn., 1973, Rsch. grants VA, 1971-77. Mem. AMA, Fla. Med. Assn., Hillsborough County Med. Assn. Avocations: personal computing, classical music, opera, profl. basketball. Home: 831 S Delaware Ave Tampa FL 33606 Office: Williams & Assocs 831 S Delaware Ave Tampa FL 33606

WILLIAMS, THOMAS FFRANCON, chemist, educator; b. Colwyn Bay, Wales, Jan. 30, 1928; came to U.S., 1961; s. David and Margaret (Williams) W.; m. Astra Silvia Birins, Jan. 31, 1959; children: Ifor Rainis, Gwyn David. B.Sc., Univ. Coll., London, Eng., 1949; Ph.D., U. London, 1960. Sci. officer U.K. Atomic Energy Authority, Harwell, Eng., 1949-55; sr. sci. officer U.K. Atomic Energy Authority, 1955-61, prin. sci. officer, 1961; research scientist Ill. Inst. Tech. Research Inst., Chgo., 1961; asst. prof. chemistry U. Tenn., Knoxville, 1961-63; assoc. prof. U. Tenn., 1963-67, prof., 1967—; Alumni Distinguished Service prof., 1974—; teaching, research assoc. Northwestern U., Evanston, Ill., 1957-58; NSF vis. scientist Kyoto (Japan) U., 1965-66; coordinator U.S.-Japan Sci. Sem., Hakone, Japan, 1969; chmn. Gordon Research Conf. on Radiation Chemistry, New Hampton, N.H., 1971, Gordon Research Conf. Radical Ions, Wolfeboro, N.H., 1984; John Simon Guggenheim Meml. Found. fellow, Swedish Research Councils' Lab., Studsvik, Nykoping, 1972-73; vis. scientist Royal Inst. Tech., Stockholm, Sweden, 1972-73; chmn. 10th Southeastern Magnetic Resonance Conf., 1978; mem. chemistry div. rev. com. Argonne (Ill.) Nat. Lab., 1988, 91, 95. Contbg. author: Fundamental Processes in Radiation Chemistry, 1968, Radiation Chemistry of Macromolecules, 1972; mem. editorial bd. Radiation Rsch., 1993-97; contbr. numerous articles on chem. effects of high energy radiation to profl. jours. AEC, ERDA, Dept. Energy grantee, 1962—. Mem. Am. Chem. Soc. (program chmn. sect. 1968-69, exec. com. 1986-88), Brit. Chem. Soc., Radiation Rsch. Soc., Phi Beta Kappa (hon.), Sigma Xi (U. Tenn. chpt. 1993-94). Home: 3117 Montlake Dr Knoxville TN 37920-2836 Office: U Tenn Dept of Chemistry Knoxville TN 37996

WILLIAMS, THOMAS FRANKLIN, architect; b. Atlanta, Aug. 14, 1944; s. George and Annie Grace (Stansell) Feckoury; m. Sandra Jean Harris Williams, July 12, 1966; children: Leigh Ann, Andrew Thomas. A in Engring., So. Tech. Coll., Marietta, Ga., 1966. Registered architect; cert. Nat. Coun. Archtl. Registration Bds. Architect Philip B. Windsor Co., Atlanta, 1964-75; v.p. Diedrich Architects & Assocs., Atlanta, 1976—. Trustee Christian City, Union City, Ga., 1992—. Served with U.S. Army, 1966-68.; Mem. AIA, Constrn. Specifications Inst. (Dan Bodin Meml. award Atlanta chpt. 1981, Citation S.E. Region 1980, Cert. of Appreciation Atlanta chpt. 1983). Avocations: hunting, fishing. Home: 6326 Saddlewood Dr Lithonia GA 30058-6122 Office: Diedrich Architects & Assocs Inc 3399 Peachtree Rd Ste 820 Atlanta GA 30326

WILLIAMS, THOMAS FRANKLIN, physician, educator; b. Belmont, N.C., Nov. 26, 1921; s. T.F. and Mary L. (Deaton) W.; m. Catharine Carter Catlett, Dec. 15, 1951; children: Mary Wright, Thomas Nelson. BS, U. N.C., 1942; MA, Columbia U., 1943; MD, Harvard U., 1950; DSc (hon.), Med. Coll. Ohio, 1987, U. N.C., 1992. Diplomate Am. Bd. Internal Medicine. Intern Johns Hopkins, Balt., 1950-51; asst. resident physician Johns Hopkins, 1951-53; resident physician Boston VA Hosp., 1953-54; research fellow U. N.C., Chapel Hill, 1954-56; instr. dept. medicine and preventive medicine U. N.C., 1956-57, asst. prof., 1957-61, assoc. prof., 1961-68, prof., 1968; attending physician Strong Meml. Hosp., Rochester, N.Y., 1968—; cons. physician Genesee Hosp., Rochester, N.Y., 1973—, St. Mary's Hosp., Rochester, N.Y., 1974-83, Highland Hosp., Rochester, N.Y., 1973; prof. medicine, preventive medicine and community health U. Rochester, 1968-92, also prof. radiation biology and biophysics, 1968-91, on leave, 1983-91, prof. emeritus, 1992—; mem. adv. bd. U. Rochester (Sch. Medicine and Dentistry), 1968-91; clin. prof. medicine U. Va., 1983-89; lectr. medicine Johns Hopkins U., 1983-89; clin. prof. depts family medicine and medicine Georgetown U., 1983-91; dir. Nat. Inst. on Aging NIH, 1983-91; asst. surgeon gen. USPHS, 1983-91, ret., 1991; attending physician Monroe Community Hosp., Rochester, 1991—, vice chmn. Cmty. Coalition for Long Term Care, 1991—; disting. physician VA Med. Ctr., N.Y., 1995—; med. dir. Monroe Cmty. Hosp., Rochester, 1968-83; mem. rev. coms. Nat. Ctr. for Health Svcs. Rsch., 1991—; mem. adv. bd. St. Ann's Home; mem. gov. bd. NRC, 1981-83; sci. dir. Am Fedn. Aging Rsch., 1992—; bd. dirs. Kirkhaven, Nat. Coun. on Aging. Contbr. articles on endocrine disorders, diabetes, health care delivery in chronic illness and aging to profl. publs. Served with USNR, 1943-46. USPHS fellow, 1966-67; Markle scholar, 1957-61. Fellow Am. Pub. Health Assn., ACP; mem. AAAS, Inst. Medicine, NAS (coun. 1980-83, governing bd. 1981-83), Assn. Am. Physicians, N.Y. State Med. Soc.,

Monroe County Med. Soc., Am. Diabetes Assn. (bd. dir. 1974-80), Am. Fedn. Clin. Rsch., Soc. Exptl. Biology and Medicine, Am. Geriatrics Soc., Am. Gerontol. Soc., Rochester Regional Diabetes Assn. (pres. 1977-79), N.C. Coun. for Human Rels. (chmn. 1963-66), Am. Clin. Climatol. Assn. Episcopalian. Home: 287 Dartmouth St Rochester NY 14607-3202 Office: Monroe Community Hosp Office Med Dir Rochester NY 14620

WILLIAMS, THOMAS LLOYD, psychiatrist; b. Mt. Carmel, Pa., May 8, 1925; s. Thomas Lloyd and Anna (Roberts) W.; m. Lucille H. Held, June 23, 1989; children: Scott, Michael. BS, U. Pitts., 1949, MD, 1952. Diplomate Am. Bd. Neurology and Psychiatry. Intern Allegheny Gen. Hosp., Pitts., 1952-53; family practice Gilbert, Pa., 1953-59; resident Mental Health Hosp. affiliated with U. Iowa, Cherokee, 1959-62, mem. staff, 1962-63; pvt. practice Bethlehem, Pa., 1963—; chief of psychiatry St. Lukes Hosp., Bethlehem, Pa., 1976-88, mem. staff emeritus, 1988—. 1st lt. navigator, U.S. Army Air Corps, 1943-45, ETO. Decorated 7 Battle Stars, Air medal with 3 clusters, Disting. Flying Cross. Fellow Am. Psychiat. Assn. (life). Republican. Avocations: hunting, fishing, carving.

WILLIAMS, THURMON, retail company executive. Pres. Mex. Corp. Sears. Office: Sears Roebuck & Co Sears Towers Chicago IL 60684

WILLIAMS, TIMOTHY JAMES, sanctuary administrator, naturalist; b. Covington, Ky., Sept. 22, 1950; s. Carl Henry and Marcella Virginia (Neff) W.; m. Deborah Louise LeForce, Feb. 15, 1975. B.S. in Biology, No. Ky. State U., 1974. Waiter various restaurants in No. Ky.; park aide Mammoth Cave Nat. Park, 1971; sanctuary mgr. Nat. Audubon Soc.'s Clyde E. Buckley Wildlife Sanctuary, Frankfort, Ky., 1975—. Mem. Nat. Audubon Soc., Assn. of Interpretive Naturalists, Ky. Assn. Environ. Edn. (bd. dirs.)

WILLIAMS, TIMOTHY WAYNE, finance company executive; b. Knoxville, Tenn., Oct. 3, 1955; s. Ladonval and Ouida Faye (Welch) W.; m. Judy Katherine Mize, Dec. 5, 1974; children: Timothy Wayne II, Jennifer Kaye. BSBA, U. Tenn., 1986, MBA, 1993. V.p. Clayton Homes, Knoxville, 1982-88; exec. v.p. Clayton Homer, Knoxville, 1988-93; pres. Vanderbilt Mortgage subs. Clayton Homer, Knoxville, 1993—; bd. dirs. Credit Bur. Knoxville, Bank First, Knoxville, Manufactured Housing Inst. Mem. Knoxville Track Club, YPO. Republican. Baptist. Avocation: tennis. Office: Vanderbilt Mortgage & Fin Inc 4131 Alcoa Hwy Louisville TN 37777-5333

WILLIAMS, TOD CULPAN, architect, educator; b. Detroit, May 11, 1943; s. Richard Jamison and Bettina Joy (Culpan) W.; m. Patricia Jones, June 21, 1966 (div. Mar. 1975); children: Rachel, Tod C.; m. Billie Tsien, Feb. 14, 1983; 1 child, Kai Tsien. B.A., Princeton U., 1965, M.F.A., 1967; postgrad. Cambridge U., 1966. Registered architect, N.Y., Conn., Mass., N.J., Mich., Tex. Assoc. Richard Meier & Assocs., N.Y.C., 1967-74; owner, prin. Potters/Williams, N.Y.C., 1975-78; prin. Tod Williams/Billie Tsien and Assocs., Architects, N.Y.C., 1978—; prof. architecture Cooper Union, N.Y.C. 1974—; advisor Princeton Sch. Architecture, 1983—. Author, curator: (book/exhbn.) Window Room Furniture, 1982-83; contbr. to various archtl. jours. Advanced fellow Am. Acad. in Rome (Graham Found.), 1983. Mem. AIA (Disting. Architecture award 1982, 86, 87), Nat. Coll. Architects Registration Bds. Office: Tod Williams/Billie Tsien 222 Central Park S New York NY 10019-1408

WILLIAMS, TONY, jazz drummer; b. Chgo., Dec. 12, 1945. Played with Sam Rivers, Boston, Jackie McLean, N.Y.C., 1963; mem. Miles Davis quintet, 1963-69, founder group Lifetime (with John McLaughlin and Larry Young), re-formed Lifetime (with Miles Davis), 1975; albums include: Nefertiti, Believe It, Emergency, Turn It Over, Ego, Million Dollar Legs, The Joy of Flying, Foreign Intrigue, Old Burn's Rush, Miles Smiles, Sorcerer, Nefertiti, Civilization, 1987, Angel Street, 1988, Native Heart, 1990; albums include (with Gil Evans) There Comes a Time, Spring, 1985, Tokyo Live, 1993. Office: care Manhattan Records 1370 Ave Of The Americas New York NY 10019-4602*

WILLIAMS, TREAT (RICHARD WILLIAMS), actor; b. Stamford, Conn., Dec. 1, 1951; s. Richard Norman and Marion (Andrew) W. B.A., Franklin and Marshall Coll., 1973. Appeared in Broadway plays Over There, Grease; films include Deadly Hero, Eagle Has Landed, Hair, 1941, 1978, Why Would I Lie, 1979, Pursuit, 1980, Prince of the City, 1980, Once Upon a Time in America, 1982, Flashpoint, 1984, Smooth Talk, 1986, The Heart of Dixie, 1989, Russicum, 1989, Where the Rivers Run North, 1994; repertory plays Servant of Two Masters, Ohio, Claptrap, Cambridge, Mass., 1985, Pirates of Penzance at N.Y. Shakespeare Festival, Glass Menagerie, Long Wharf, New Haven, 1986, Bobby Gould in Hell, 1989; TV movies Jack Dempsey Story, 1982, Streetcar Named Desire, 1983, Some Men Need Help, 1983, Hoover, Sweet Lies, 1986; TV appearances Faerie Tale Theatre, 1984, Men's Club, 1985, Third Degree Burn, 1989, Max and Helen, 1990, Drug Wars: The Enrico Campaniera Story, 1990, Bonds of Love, 1993; TV series include Good Advice, 1993-94. Mem. AFTRA, SAG, Actors Equity Assn. Episcopalian. Office: UTA 9560 Wilshire Blvd 5th Fl Beverly Hills CA 90212*

WILLIAMS, VANESSA, recording artist, actress; b. Millwood, N.Y., 1963; m. Ramon Hervey II, 1988; children: Melanie, Jillian, Devin. Recording artist, 1988—. Stage appearances include: (Broadway) Kiss of the Spider Woman, 1994; film appearances include Another You, 1991, Harley Davidson and the Marlboro Man, 1991, The Drop Squad, 1994; albums: The Right Stuff, 1988, The Comfort Zone, 1991, The Sweetest Days, 1994; # 1 hit single Save the Best for Last. Recipient 8 Grammy award nominations; named one of 50 Most Beautiful People, People Mag. First Black to be named Miss America, 1983 (resigned title 1983). Office: Polygram Records Worldwide Plaza 825 8th Ave New York NY 10019-7416

WILLIAMS, VAUGHN CHARLES, lawyer; b. L.A., Mar. 2, 1945; s. David Welford and Ovida M. (White) W.; m. Joan M. Maddox, May 1, 1971 (div. June 1975). AB, Harvard U., 1966; JD, Stanford U., 1967. Bar: Calif. 1969, Washington 1971, N.Y. 1977, U.S. Supreme Ct. 1981. Law clk. to Hon. Carl McGowan U.S. Ct. of Appeals (D.C. cir.), Washington, 1969-70; counsel U.S. Senate, Dist. Col. Comm., Washington, 1970-71; assoc. Wilmer Cutler & Pickering, Washington, 1971-74; gen. counsel U.S. Coun. on Wage-Price Stability, Washington, 1975-76; assoc. Skadden Arps Slate Meagher & Flom, N.Y.C., 1977-79, ptnr., 1979—; dir. N.Y.C. Campaign Fin. Bd. Dir. Lincoln Ctr. for Performing Arts, N.Y.C., Bklyn. Acad. Music; vice chmn. Fund for the City of N.Y. Mem. Assn. Bar of City of N.Y. (Bainbridge-Smith com., com. for future), University Club. Office: Skadden Arps Slate Meagher & Flom 919 3rd Ave New York NY 10022-3903

WILLIAMS, VERGIL LEWIS, criminal justice educator; b. Crosbyton, Tex., Sept. 29, 1935; s. Albert Lewis W. and Neola Belle (Bass) Pinkston; m. Vergnel Campbell, June 8, 1956 (div. 1967); 1 son, Sheldon Victor; m. Velma Arlene Minor, Dec. 23, 1974; 1 stepdau., Colleen Angela Jeffries. B.A. in Econs., West Tex. State J., 1966; Ph.D. in Bus. Adminstrn., U. Ala.-Tuscaloosa, 1972. Patrolman Amarillo Police Dept., Tex., 1960-64, police patrol sgt., 1964-66; instr. fin. U. Ala., University, 1968-71, asst. prof. Sch. Social Work, 1971-75, assoc. prof., 1975-77, prof., chmn. dept. criminal justice, 1977—; rsch. cons. Police Dept., Birmingham, Ala., 1977-79. Co-author: Convicts, Codes and Contraband, 1974, Introduction Criminal Justice, 1982; author: Dictionary American Penology, 1979 (Outstanding Reference Book ALA 1979). Mem. Ala. Assn. Criminal Justice Educators (pres. 1981-82), Nat. Assn. Vols. in Criminal Justice (bd. gids. 1983—). Bahai. Home: 2633 47th Ave E Tuscaloosa AL 35404-5234 Office: Dept Criminal Justice U Ala PO Box 870320 Tuscaloosa AL 35487-0320

WILLIAMS, VICKI, mortgage company executive; b. 1949. With Colonial Mortgage, Montgomery, Ala., 1970-76, Bank Boston, Montgomery, 1976-83, Window Fashions, Montgomery, 1983-84, Aronov Realty, Montgomery, 1984-86, Century Mortgage, Montgomery, 1986-88; with Anchor Mortgage Svcs Inc, Montgomery, 1988—, pres. Office: Anchor Mortgage Svcs Inc 4260 Carmichael Ct N Montgomery AL 36106*

WILLIAMS, W. CLYDE, religious organization administrator. Exec. sec. Christian Meth. Episcopal Ch., Atlanta, 1987—. Office: Christian Meth

Episcopal Ch 2805 Shoreland Dr SW Atlanta GA 30331-6714 Office: 201 Ashby St NW Ste 212 Atlanta GA 30314-3422

WILLIAMS, W. GENE, architect; b. Oklahoma City, Okla., Nov. 20, 1928; s. James Lacy and Beulah Mar (Tuggle) W.; m. Mary Eleanor Edwards, Apr. 1, 1955; children: Randall Gene, Suzanne Eleanor Williams Bennett. BArch, U. Okla., 1953. Registered architect. Architect intern Coston-Franfurt-Short Architects, Oklahoma City, 1952-56, Jack Nusbaum, Architect, Oklahoma City, 1956-58; architect Wright & Selby, Architects, Oklahoma City, 1958-65; prin. W. Gene Williams, Architect, Oklahoma City, 1965-67; prin. Mansur-Steele-Williams, Architects/Engrs., Oklahoma City, 1967-72, Tulsa, 1967-72; prin. W. Gene Williams & Assocs. Inc., Oklahoma City, 1972—, Houston, 1972—; bd. dirs. Nat. Coun. Archtl. Registration Bd., 1967—. Author: (book) Human Response to Tall Buildings, 1975; author archtl. handbooks. 1st lt. USAF, 1953-55. Fellow AIA (pres. 1975, chmn. speakers bureau 1975-86, chmn. nat. pub. rels. com. 1975-76, chmn. nat. architecture for justice com. 1985); mem. Am. Correctional Assn., Tex. Correctional Assn., Houston C. of C., Woodlands (Tex.) Round Table. Avocations: aviation, golf, travel. Home: 2506 Blackjack Oak Pl The Woodlands TX 77380 Office: W Gene Williams & Assoc Inc 2506 Blackjack Oak Pl The Woodlands TX 77380-1708

WILLIAMS, WALTER ABNER, JR., healthcare administrator, realtor; b. Gadsden, Ala., Nov. 23, 1947; s. Walter Abner and Mildred Elaine (Dillard) W.; m. Donna Mae Culbertson, June 6, 1970 (div. Sept. 1984); m. Melinda Darlene Ford, Nov. 25, 1988; children: Beth, Michael. BS in Biology, U. Ala., Tuscaloosa, 1970; MBA, Jacksonville (Ala.) State U., 1981; cert. in health care adminstrn., U. Ala., Birmingham, 1984. Adminstv. asst. Gadsden (Ala.) Regional Med. Ctr. (former Bapt. Med. Hosp.), 1978-93, v.p., 1993, asst. adminstr.,, 1993—; mem. adv. bd. GRMC Home Health, Gadsden, 1993—; bd. dirs. Bapt. Health Svc. Found., Gadsden, 1993—. Maj. U.S. Army, 1970-78. Fellow Am. Coll. Healthcare Execs.; mem. Am. Assn. Healthcare Risk Mgrs., Birmingham Regional Health Exec. Forum, Assn. Mil. Surgeons U.S., Naval Res. Assn. (v.p. for health affairs), Assn. Med. Svc. Corps Officers of Navy, Gadsden-Etowah C. of C. (leadership Etowah group, mil. affairs com., Coosa Capital Club, Partnership 2000), Briarmeade Golf Club, Masons. Avocations: golf, weightlifting, martial arts. Home: PO Box 2146 Gadsden AL 35903 Office: Gadsden Regional Med Ctr 1007 Goodyear Ave Gadsden AL 35999

WILLIAMS, WALTER BAKER, mortgage banker; b. Seattle, May 12, 1921; s. William Walter and Anna Leland (Baker) W.; m. Marie Davis Wilson, July 6, 1945; children: Kathryn Williams-Mullins, Marcia Frances Williams Swanson, Bruce Wilson, Wendy Susan. BA, U. Wash., 1943; JD, Harvard U., 1948. With Bogle & Gates, Seattle, 1948-63, ptnr., 1960-63; pres. Continental Inc., Seattle, 1963-91, chmn., 1991—; bd. dirs. United Graphics Inc., Seattle, 1973-86, Fed. Nat. Mortgage Assn., 1976-77; chmn. Continental Savings Bank, 1991—. Rep. Wash. State Ho. of Reps., Olympia, 1961-63; sen. Wash. State Senate, Olympia, 1963-71; chmn. Econ. Devel. Council of Puget Sound, Seattle, 1981-82; pres. Japan-Am. Soc. of Seattle, 1971-72; chmn. Woodland Park Zoo Commn., Seattle, 1984-85. Served to capt. USMC, 1942-46, PTO. Recipient Brotherhood Citation, NCCJ, Seattle, 1980. Mem. Mortgage Bankers Assn. Am. (pres. 1973-74), Wash. Mortgage Bankers Assn., Fed. Home Loan Mortgage Corp. (adv. com.), Wash. Savs. League (bd. dirs., chmn 1991-92), Rotary (pres. local club 1984-85), Rainier Club Seattle (pres. 1987-88). Republican. Congregationalist. Office: Continental Inc 2000 Two Union Sq Seattle WA 98101

WILLIAMS, WALTER FRED, steel company executive; b. Upland, Pa., Feb. 7, 1929; s. Walter James and Florence (Stott) W.; m. Joan B. Carey, Aug. 26, 1950; children: Jeffrey F., Richard C., Douglas E. B. in Civil Engring. summa cum laude, U. Del., 1951; postgrad., Harvard, 1969; D (hon.), Allentown Coll., 1983, Leigh U., 1990. With Bethlehem Steel Corp., Pa., 1951—, asst. chief engr. on staff v.p operations, 1965-66, chief engr. constrn., 1966-67, chief engr. projects group engring. dept., then mgr. engring. in charge projects, design and constrn., 1967-68, asst. to v.p. engring., 1968, asst. v.p. shipbldg., 1968-70, v.p. shipbldg., 1970-75, v.p. steel operations, 1975-77, sr. v.p. steel operations, 1978-80, pres., chief operating officer, 1980-85, chmn., chief exec. officer, 1986-92, also dir.; bd. dirs. Gen. Re Corp. 1st lt. U.S. Army, 1951-53. Mem. Bus. Coun., Saucon Valley Country Club, Hobe Sound Golf Club. Methodist. Home: Saucon Valley Rd Bethlehem PA 18015-9333 Office: Bethlehem Steel Corp 1170 8th Ave Bethlehem PA 18016

WILLIAMS, WALTER JACKSON, JR., electrical engineer, consultant; b. Elkhart, Ind., Jan. 17, 1925; s. Walter Jackson and Mary (Delcamp) W.; m. Helen L. Evans, July 20, 1944 (dec. Aug. 1980); children—David, Eileen, Valerie; m. Evelyn M. Bowyer, May 26, 1984 (dec. Oct. 1990). B.S. in Elec. Engring., Purdue U., 1948, M.S., 1950; Ph.D., 1954. From grad. asst. to instr. Purdue U., Layfayette, Ind., 1948-54; jr. engr. Argonne Nat. Lab., Ill., 1950, Naval Ordnance Plant, Indpls., 1951; engr. Internat. Tel. & Tel. Co., Ft. Wayne, Ind., 1954-60, cons., 1961-63; sr. tech. advisor Internat. Tel. & Tel. Co. (Aerospace Optical div.), 1975-80, tech. dir., 1980-87, ret., 1987, cons., 1987—; chmn. dept. elec. engring. Ind. Inst. Tech., Ft. Wayne, 1961-65, dean engring., 1963-67, v.p., acad. dean, 1967-75, interim pres., 1970-72; cons. in field, 1960—. Patentee in field. Bd. dirs. Assoc. Chs., Ft. Wayne, 1965-67. Served with AUS, 1943-46. Mem. IEEE (com. on accreditation activities com. 1984-89), NSPE, Am. Soc. Engring. Edn., Accreditation Bd. for Engring. and Tech. (engring. accreditation commn. 1990—), Ind. Soc. Profl. Engrs. (Ft. Wayne 1968-70), Ft. Wayne Engrs. Club (pres. 1967-68, dir. 1969-71), Sigma Xi, Tau Beta Pi, Eta Kappa Nu. Home: 6518 Dumont Dr Fort Wayne IN 46815-7841

WILLIAMS, WALTER JOSEPH, lawyer; b. Detroit, Oct. 5, 1918; s. Joseph Louis and Emma Geraldine (Hewitt) W.; m. Maureen June Kay, Jan. 15, 1944; 1 child, John Bryan. Student, Bowling Green State U., 1935-36; B.S.B.A., Ohio State U., 1940; J.D., LL.B., U. Detroit, 1942. Bar: Mich. bar 1942. Title atty. Abstract & Title Guaranty Co., 1944-47; corp. atty. Ford Motor Co., 1947-51, Studebaker-Packard Corp., 1951-56; asst. sec., house counsel Am. Motors Corp., Am. Motors Sales Corp., Am. Motors Pan-Am. Corp., Evart Products Co., Ltd., 1956-65, corp. sec. house counsel, 1965-72; Corp., Evart Products Co., Ltd., corp. sec.; dir. Evart Products Co., 1959-72; dir., corporate sec., house counsel Jeep Corp., Jeep Sales Corp., Jeep Internat. Corp., 1968-72; partner Gilman and Williams, Southfield, Mich. 1972-74; atty. Detroit Edison Co., 1974-75; asst. sec., sr. staff atty. Burroughs Corp. (and subsidiaries), 1975-84; pvt. practice, pres. Walter J. Williams P.C., Bloomfield Hills, Mich., 1984—. Charter commr., city of Dearborn Heights, Mich., 1960-63; dir. Detroit Met. Indsl. Devel. Corp., 1962-72, also asst. sec. Served to capt. U.S. Army, 1942-46. Mem. ABA, Detroit Bar Assn. (chmn. corp. gen. counsel com. 1965-68), Fed. Bar Assn., State Bar Mich., Ohio State U. Alumni Assn. (pres. Detroit 1961-63), U. Detroit Law Alumni, Delta Theta Phi. Club: Oakland Hills Country. Home and Office: 3644 Darcy Dr Bloomfield Hills MI 48301-2125

WILLIAMS, WALTER W., consumer products manufacturing executive. With GE, 1956-87, v.p. gen. mgr. housewares and audio products div., 1979-83; chmn., pres. Gen. Electric Info. Svcs. Co., 1983-86; v.p. mktg. and sales GE, 1986-87; pres., chief oper. officer Rubbermaid Inc., Wooster, Ohio, 1987-90, vice chmn., pres., chief oper. officer, 1990-91, chmn. bd., chief exec. officer, 1991—. Office: Rubbermaid Inc 1147 Akron Rd Wooster OH 44691-2501

WILLIAMS, WALTER WAYLON, lawyer, pecan grower; b. Gause, Tex., Nov. 12, 1933; s. Jesse Nathaniel and Lola Fay (Matthews) W.; m. Velmalene Von Gonten, Mar. 6, 1953; children—Diana Lee, Virginia Marie. B.B.A. with honors, U. Tex., 1959, J.D. with honors, 1960. Bar: Tex. bar 1960. Since practiced in Houston; mem. firm Fulbright, Crooker, Freeman, Bates & Jaworski, 1960-63, Bates & Brock, 1964-66, Brock, Williams & Boyd, 1966-79, Williams & Boyd, 1979-88; pres. Nat. Pecan Growers Coun., 1976-78; Tex. Pecan Growers Assn. Served with AUS, 1953-55. Named Outstanding Soldier of Second Army, 1955. Mem. ABA, Houston Bar Assn., State Bar Tex., Tex. Trial Lawyers Assn. (dir. 1972-76), Houston Trial Lawyers Assn. (dir. 1969), Assn. Trial Lawyers Am., Chancellors, Beta Gamma Sigma, Phi Delta Phi. Home: RR 3 Box 101 Yoakum TX 77995-9726

WILLIAMS, WAYNE DE ARMOND, lawyer; b. Denver, Sept. 24, 1914; s. Wayne Cullen and Lena Belle (Day) W.; m. Virginia Brinton Deal, Sept. 9, 1937; children—Marcia Lee, Daniel Deal. A.B., U. Denver, 1936; J.D., Columbia U., 1938. Bar: Colo. 1938. Pvt. practice Denver, 1938-43, 46-58; ptnr. firm Williams & Erickson (and predecessors), Denver, 1958-77; gen. counsel Denver Water Dept., 1977-91; asst. city atty. Denver, 1939-43, spl. asst. city atty., 1946-49; chmn. Denver County Ct. Nominating Commn., 1968-69; mem. Denver Dist. Ct. Nominating Commn., 1969-75; lectr. in field U. Denver, 1947-60. Contbr. articles to legal jours. Chmn. Denver Mcpl. Airport Adv. Commn., 1963-65; chancellor Rocky Mountain Meth. Ann. Conf., 1978-86; former mem. governing bd. Colo. chpt. English Speaking Union, Colo. Tuberculosis Assn., Colo. Soc. for Prevention Blindness; mem. adv. bd. Anchor Ctr. for Blind Children. Capt. JAGD U.S. Army, 1943-46. Mem. ABA (Ross Essay prize 1944), Colo. Bar Assn. (gov. 1974-77), Denver Bar Assn. (pres. 1974-75), Sigma Alpha Epsilon, Phi Delta Phi, Omicron Delta Kappa. Democrat. Methodist. Clubs: Lions, Masons. Home: 625 S Alton Way Apt 3A Denver CO 80231-1752

WILLIAMS, WILLIAM ARNOLD, agronomy educator; b. Johnson City, N.Y., Aug. 2, 1922; s. William Truesdall and Nellie Viola (Tompkins) W.; m. Madeline Patricia Moore, Nov. 27, 1943; children—David, Kathleen, Andrew. B.S., Cornell U., 1947, M.S., 1948, Ph.D., 1951. Prof. emeritus U. Calif., Davis, 1993—. Editor agr. sect. McGraw-Hill Ency. Sci. & Tech.; contbr. articles to profl. jours. Mem. Nat. Alliance for Mentally Ill. Served to lt. U.S. Army, 1943-46. Grantee NSF, 1965-82, Kellogg Found., 1963-67; Fulbright scholar, Australia, 1960, Rockefeller Found. scholar, Costa Rica, 1966. Fellow AAAS, Am. Soc. Agronomy, Crop Sci. Soc. Am.; mem. Soil Sci. Soc. Am., Soc. Range Mgmt., Am. Statis. Assn., Assn. for Tropical Biology, Fedn. Am. Scientists, Am. Math. Soc., Math Assn. Am. Democrat. Home: 718 Oeste Dr Davis CA 95616-3531 Office: Univ California Dept Agronomy And Rang Davis CA 95616

WILLIAMS, WILLIAM COREY, Old Testament educator, consultant; b. Wilkes-Barre, Pa., July 12, 1937; s. Edward Douglas and Elizabeth Irene (Schooley) W.; m. Alma Simmenroth Williams, June 27, 1959; 1 child, Linda. Diploma in Ministerial Studies, NE Bible Inst., 1962; BA in Bibl. Studies, Cen. Bible Coll., 1963, MA in Religion, 1964; MA in Hebrew and Near Ea. Studies, NYU, 1966, PhD in Hebrew Lang. and Lit., 1975; postgrad., Hebrew U., 1977-78, Inst. Holyland Studies, 1986. Ref. libr. Hebraic section Libr. of Congress, Washington, 1967-69; prof. Old Testament So. Calif. Coll., Costa Mesa, 1969—; adj. prof. Old Testament Melodyland Sch. Theology, Anaheim, Calif., 1975-77; vis. prof. Old Testament Fuller Theol. Sem., Pasadena, Calif., 1978-81, 84, Asian Theol. Ctr. for Evangelism and Missions, Singapore and Sabah, E. Malaysia, 1985, Continental Bible Coll., Saint Pieters-Leeuw, Belgium, 1985, Mattersey Bible Coll., Eng., 1985, Inst. Holy Land Studies, Jerusalem, 1986, Regent U., 1994; transl. cons. and reviser New Am. Standard Bible, 1969-94; transl. cons. The New Internat. Version, New Century Version, 1991, A New Translation, 1992—, New Internat. Version, Simplified, 1993-94; transl. cons. and editor Internat. Children's Version, 1985-86; transl. editor: Everyday Bible, 1990. Author: (books, tapes) Hebrew I: A Study Guide, 1986, Hebrew II: A Study Guide, 1986; transl. editor: Everyday Bible, 1990; contbr. articles to International Standard Bible Encyclopedia, New International Dictionary of Old Testament Theology and Evangelical Dictionary of Biblical Theology; contbr. articles to profl. jours.; contbr. notes to Spirit Filled Life Study Bible. Nat. Def. Fgn. Lang. fellow NYU, 1964-67; Alumni scholar N.E. Bible Inst., 1960-61; NEH fellow, summer 1992. Mem. Soc. Bibl. Lit., Evang. Theol. Soc. (exec. office 1974-77), Am. Acad. Religion, Nat. Assn. Profs. of Hebrew, Inst. Bibl. Rsch., The Lockman Found. (hon. mem. bd. dirs. 1992-94, mem. editorial bd. 1974-94). Home: 1817 Peninsula Pl Costa Mesa CA 92627-4591 Office: So Calif Coll 55 Fair Dr Costa Mesa CA 92626-6597

WILLIAMS, WILLIAM EARLE, artist, educator, curator; b. Vicksburg, Miss., Apr. 19, 1950; s. Willie and Estella (Steele) W.; m. Mary Katherine Meermans, Aug. 19, 1978; children: Emily Katherine, Daniel Earle. BA, Hamilton Coll., Clinton, N.Y., 1973; MFA, Yale U., 1978. Prof. art Haverford (Pa.) Coll., 1978—; bd. dirs. Midtown Y Gallery, N.Y.C., 1988; nat. cons. in photography Ctr. for Study So. Culture, U. Miss., Oxford, 1981—; mem. com. Visual Arts Hamilton Coll., 1989; mem. adv. bd. Inst. of Contemporary Art U. Pa., 1993—. Author: Pictures, 1985; author, editor: Photographers of Sculpture, 1988; editor: Japanese Wood Block Prints, 1987; one-man show include Cleve. Mus. of Art., 1990; exhibited in group shows Allentown Mus. Art, 1995, Phila. Mus. Art, 1988, Pa. Acad. Fine Arts, 1984, Bardini Mus., Florence, Italy, 1990; represented in permanent collections Phila. Mus. Art, Met. Mus. Art, also others. Mem. Soc. Photographic Edn. (bd. dirs. 1987—, chmn. Mid-Atlantic region), Print Club Phila. (Elinor Williams purchase award 1986), Yale Club, Philobiblian Club, Athenaeum, Franklin Inn Club. Avocations: running, bicycling, walking. Home: 753 College Ave Haverford PA 19041-1301 Office: Haverford Coll 370 Lancaster Ave Haverford PA 19041-1392

WILLIAMS, WILLIAM H., food products executive, retail executive; b. 1948. BS, Okla. State U., 1970. Pres., CEO Neiman-Marcus Inc., Dallas, 1970-88; pres. Bear Creek Corp., Medford, Oreg., 1988—; pres., CEO Harry & David Co., Medford, Jackson & Perkins Co., Medford. Office: Bear Creek Corp 2518 S Pacific Hwy Medford OR 97501*

WILLIAMS, WILLIAM HARRISON, retired librarian; b. Seattle, Apr. 18, 1924; s. William E. and Letah M. (Hollenback) W.; m. Mary Helen Sims, Apr. 19, 1945; children: Linda Lee, Dee Ann. B.S., Brigham Young U., 1969, M.L.S., 1970. Dir. Provo Pub. Library, Utah, 1969-70; Wyo. State Librarian, 1970-78; dir. Wyo. state Archives and Hist. dept., 1971-78; exec. sec. Wyo. Hist. Soc., 1971-78; sr. research analyst Wyo. Taxpayers Assn., 1978-84. Served to lt. col. USAAF, 1943-64. Decorated USAF commendation with oak leaf cluster. Mem. Beta Phi Mu, Phi Alpha Theta. Home: 21607 N 123rd Dr Sun City West AZ 85375-1950

WILLIAMS, WILLIAM JAMES, electrical engineering educator; b. Rio Grande, Ohio, May 9, 1935; s. David Hansen and Thelma (Lackey) W.; m. Carol Fay Gibson, Sept. 10, 1961; children: Gwen Ellen, Sarah Elizabeth. BEE, Ohio State U., 1958; MSEE, U. Iowa, 1961, PhD, 1963; MS in Physiology, U. Mich., 1966. Rsch. engr. Battelle Meml. Inst., Columbus, Ohio, 1958-60; sr. engring. specialist Emerson Electric, St. Louis, 1963-64; from asst. prof. to assoc. prof. U. Mich., Ann Arbor, 1966-74, prof., 1974—; area chair Biosys., 1989—; cons. Ford Motor Co., Dearborn, Mich., 1981—; vis. scientist Johns Hopkins U., 1974; rsch. engr. Rackhan Sch. Grad. Studies, U. Mich., 1981—; guest investigator Woods Hole Oceanographic Inst., 1991—; developer of reduced inference time-frequency analysis concept. Patentee in field; contbr. numerous articles to profl. jours., 1964—. William Clay Ford fellow Ford Rsch., 1991; rsch. grantee NSF, NIH, Office of Naval Rsch., ONR. Mem. IEEE (guest editor procs. 1977, co-chair Internat. Conf. on acoustics, speech and signal proc. 1995), Soc. for Neurosci. Methodist. Avocations: gardening, bicycling, walking, music, reading. Office: Univ Mich 4230 Eecs Ann Arbor MI 48109

WILLIAMS, WILLIAM JOHN, JR., lawyer; b. New Rochelle, N.Y., Feb. 6, 1937; s. William John and Jane (Gormley) W.; m. Barbara Reuter. B.A., Holy Cross Coll., Worcester, Mass., 1958; LL.B., NYU, 1961. Bar: N.Y. 1961. Practiced in N.Y.C., 1962—; ptnr. firm Sullivan & Cromwell, 1969—. Trustee NYU Law Ctr. Found., 1977—, Holy Cross Coll., 1988—. Fellow Am. Bar Found.; mem. Am. Law Inst., ABA, N.Y. State Bar Assn., Assn. Bar City N.Y., U.S. Golf Assn. (exec. com. 1978-87, sec. 1980-81, v.p. 1982-85, pres. 1986-87). Democrat. Roman Catholic.

WILLIAMS, WILLIAM JOSEPH, physician, educator; b. Bridgeton, N.J., Dec. 8, 1926; s. Edward Carlaw and Mary Hood (English) W.; m. Margaret Myrick Lyman, Aug. 12, 1950 (dec. Aug., 1985); children: Susan Lyman, William Prescott, Sarah Robb; m. Karen A. Hughes, Feb. 18, 1989. Student, Bucknell U., 1943-45; MD, U. Pa., 1949. Diplomate: Am. Bd. Internal Medicine. (hematology com. 1976-80). Intern U. Pa. 1949-50, Am. Cancer Soc. research fellow in Biochemistry, 1950-52, resident medicine, 1954-55, assoc. to asst. prof. medicine, 1955-58, assoc. prof. to prof. medicine, chief hematology, 1961-69; sr. instr. microbiology Case Western Res. U., 1952; asst. prof. medicine Washington U., St. Louis, 1959-60; research fellow Oxford U., Eng., 1960-61; mem. hematology tng. com. Nat. Inst. Arthritis and Metabolic Disease, 1964-68, research career program

com., 1968-72; chmn. dept. medicine SUNY Health Sci. Ctr., Syracuse, N.Y., 1969-92, prof. medicine, 1969—; interim dean Coll. Medicine SUNY Health Sci. Ctr., Syracuse, 1991-92; vis. scientist Walter and Eliza Hall Inst., Melbourne, Australia, 1980; vis. prof. Monash U., Melbourne, 1980; mem. thrombosis adv. com. Nat. Heart and Lung Inst., 1969-73, chmn., 1971-73; adv. coun. Nat. Arthritis, Metabolism and Digestive Diseases, 1975-79; mem. residency rev. com. internal medicine Accreditation Coun. Grad. Med. Edn., 1983-89, mem. bd. appeals panel for internal medicine, 1989—; mem. N.Y. State Coun. Grad. Med. Edn., 1987-89. Editor-in-chief: Hematology, 1972, 3d edit., 1983, 4th edit., 1989; contbr. articles to med. lit. Trustee Everson Mus. Art, 1975-81, 83-89. With USNR, 1944-46, 52-54. Recipient Research Career Devel. award Nat. Heart Inst., 1963-68; Daland fellow Am. Philos. Soc., 1955-57; Markle scholar, 1957-62. Mem. AMA, ACP (gov. Upstate N.Y. 1976-81), Am. Soc. Biol. Chemists, Am. Soc. Clin. Investigation, Assn. Am. Physicians, Am. Clin. and Climatol. Assn., Am. Heart Assn. (council on thrombosis exec. com. 1977-81), Internat. Soc. Thrombosis and Haemostasis, Assn. Profs. Medicine, Am. Soc. Hematology, Interurban Clin. Club (sec. 1964-70), Internat. Hematology Soc., Alpha Omega Alpha. Mem. Soc. Friends. Home: 5160 Peck Hill Rd Jamesville NY 13078-9724 Office: 750 E Adams St Syracuse NY 13210-2306

WILLIAMS, WILLIAM JOSEPH, insurance company executive; b. Cin., Dec. 19, 1915; s. Charles Finn and Elizabeth (Ryan) W.; m. Helen DeCourcy, May 26, 1941; children—Mary Frances Williams Clauder, William Joseph, Richard Francis, Carol Ann Williams Jodar, Sharon Mary Williams Frisbie, Thomas Luke. AB, Georgetown U., 1937; postgrad. in bus., Harvard U., 1938. With Western-So. Life Ins. Co., Cin., 1939-54, chmn. bd., 1979-84, pres., chief operating officer, 1984-88; pres., chief exec. officer, 1988-89, chmn. bd., pres., chief exec. officer, 1989, chmn. bd., chief exec. officer, 1989—; bd. dirs. Western-So. Life Ins. Co., Cin.; pres. N.Am. Mgmt. & Devel. Co., Cin., 1954-84; chmn. Cin. Reds Baseball Club, 1966-85; dir. Cin. Bengals, Columbus Life Ins., Ohio. Chmn. bd. Good Samaritan Hosp., Cin., 1984-86, Taft Mus., Cin., 1984-87; trustee, v.p. Cin. Art Mus.; trustee Cin. Inst. Fine Arts; bd. dirs. Georgetown U. Served to capt. U.S. Army, 1941-45. Decorated knight Order Knights of Malta, knight comdr. Holy Sepulchre; honored by NCCJ, 1979. Roman Catholic. Clubs: Queen City (pres. 1982-84), Commercial (pres. 1983), Cin. Country (Cin.); Camargo; Royal Poinciana Golf (Naples, Fla.). Home: 7801 Ayers Rd Cincinnati OH 45255-4610 Office: Western & So Life Ins Co 400 Broadway St Cincinnati OH 45202-3312

WILLIAMS, WILLIAM LANE, university administrator, anatomist; b. Rock Hill, S.C., Dec. 23, 1914; s. Oscar Kell and Cora Robertson (Mobley) W. B.S., Wofford Coll., 1935; M.A., Duke U., 1939; Ph.D., Yale U., 1941. Instr. anatomy U. Rochester, N.Y., 1941-42, Yale U., 1942-43; asst. prof. anatomy La. State U., New Orleans, 1943-45; asst. prof. U. Minn., Mpls., 1945-49; asso. prof. U. Minn., 1949-58; prof. U. Miss. Med. Center, Jackson, 1958-80; chmn. dept. anatomy U. Miss. Med. Center, 1958-79, asst. vice chancellor, 1975-80, emeritus, 1980—. Asso. editor: Anat. Record, 1959-75. Donner Found. fellow, 1942-43; NIH grantee, 1949-73. Mem. Am. Assn. Pathologists, Am. Physiol. Soc., Endocrine Soc., Histochem. Soc., Soc. Exptl. Biology and Medicine, Inst. Nutrition, Am. Assn. Anatomists. Presbyterian. Home: 3975 I55N Apt J2 Jackson MS 39216

WILLIAMS, WILLIAM MAGAVERN, headmaster; b. Niles, Mich., Dec. 22, 1931; s. Errol Edwin and Mary Elizabeth (Magavern) W.; m. Linda Carol Grush, June 15, 1958; children: Diana, William Jr., Sarah. BA, Williams Coll., 1953, LHD (hon.), 1984; postgrad. in Philosophy, Columbia U., 1954-58, MA in Ednl. Psychology, 1966. Tchr. elem. English, history, phys. edn. McTernan Sch., Waterbury, Conn., 1953-54; head guidance, boarding and humanities depts., instr. English, coach varsity wrestling Riverdale Country Sch., Bronx, N.Y., 1955-66; headmaster Doane Acad., Burlington, N.J., 1966-70, Poly. Prep. Country Day Sch., Bklyn., 1970—. Trustee Bklyn Inst. Arts and Scis., 1972-79, Bklyn. Ctrl. YMCA, 1974-78, Profl. Children's Sch., 1976-79, Bklyn. Children's Mus., 1979-82, Plymouth Ch. Pilgrims, 1979-86, N.Y. State Assn. Ind. Schs., 1980-86. Mem. Headmasters' Assn., Country Day Sch. Headmasters' Assn., Cum Laude Soc. (regent dist. III 1971-87, pres. gen. 1981-87, pres. gen. 1987—), Guild Ind. Schs. N.Y. (pres. 1986-88). Avocations: skiing, chess, travel, Civil War history. Home: 195 Amity St Brooklyn NY 11201 Office: Poly Prep Country Day Sch 92d St and 7th Ave Brooklyn NY 11228

WILLIAMS, WILLIAM RALSTON, retired bank and trust company executive; b. Hattiesburg, Miss., Jan. 20, 1910; s. William Ralston and Beulah (Smith) W.; m. Renée M. Marsh, May 8, 1936; chiildren—Mary J. (Mrs. Charles W. Cargill, Jr.), Julie D. Sher. Student, Central State Coll., Edmond, Okla., 1929-32, Okla. State U., 1933. Dist. mgr. Oklahoma City area Internat. Harvester Co., 1935-43; owner Stipes-Williams Co., Altus, Okla., 1943-55, Williams Investment and Ins. Co., Altus, 1955-69; sr. v.p. Fidelity Nat. Bank & Trust Co., Oklahoma City, 1968-83; ret., 1983; Regent A. and M. Colls. Okla., 1952-69, chmn., 1957-67; v.p. Am. Assn. Gov. Bds. Colls. and Univs. Am., 1958. Mem. Altus City Council, 1948-52. Served to lt. USNR, 1944-46. Mem. Oklahoma City C. of C., Am. Legion, Beta Theta Pi. Democrat. Episcopalian. Clubs: Kiwanis (pres. Altus 1947, lt. gov. 1952), Masons (33 deg., K.T., Jester), Elks; Quail Creek Country (Oklahoma City). Home: 3012 Thorn Ridge Rd Oklahoma City OK 73120-1924

WILLIAMS, WILLIAM STANLEY COSSOM, physics educator and researcher; b. Margate, Kent, England, Aug. 4, 1929; s. Stanley Charles and Winifred Florence (Cossom) W.; m. Mary E. Marsh, Sept. 5, 1956; children: Claire, Matthieu. BSc, U. Coll. London, 1950, PhD, 1953. Univ. lectr. U. Glasgow, 1955-61; sr. rsch. officer dept. nuclear physics U. Oxford, 1961-90, re-designated lectr. physics, 1990—; fellow and tutor St. Edmund Hall, Oxford, 1963—. Author: Introduction to Elementary Particle Physics, 1961, 2d edit. 1971, Nuclear and Particle Physics, 1991; contbr. articles to profl. jours. Mem. Inst. Physics London, Am. Phys. Soc. Office: Nuclear and Astrophys Lab Dept Physics, 1 Keble Rd, Oxford OX1 3RH, England

WILLIAMS, WILLIAM THOMAS, artist, educator; b. Cross Creek, N.C., July 17, 1942; s. William Thomas and Hazel (Davis) W.; m. Patricia Ayn Deweese; children—Nila Winona, Aaron Thomas. B.F.A., Pratt Inst., 1966; M.F.A., Yale U., 1968. Mem. faculty Sch. Visual Arts, Pratt Inst., 1969-70; mem. faculty dept. art Bklyn. Coll., City U., N.Y., 1970—; prof. art Bklyn. Coll., City U., 1977—. Home: 654 Broadway New York NY 10012-2301

WILLIAMS, WILLIE, protective services official; b. 1943; m. Evelina; children: Lisa, Willie Jr., Eric. AS, Phila. Coll. Textiles and Sci., 1982; postgrad., St. Joseph U., 1991. Police officer City of Phila., 1964-72, police detective, 1972-74, police sgt., 1974-76, police lt. juvenile aid div., 1976-84, police capt. 22nd and 23rd dists., 1984-86, police inspector, head tng. bur., civil affairs div., North police div., 1986-88, dep. commr. adminstrn., 1988, police commr., 1988-92; chief of police L.A. Police Dept., 1992—; lecture, instr. Temple U., Univ. Pa., Univ. Del. Former scoutmaster Boy Scouts Am.; mem. Pa. Juvenile Officers' Assn., Southeastern Pa. Chiefs of Police, West Angeles Ch. of God in Christ; past bd. dirs. Rebuild L.A. Mem. Nat. Orgn. Black Law Enforcement Execs. (past nat. pres.), Internat. Assn. Chiefs of Police, Alpha Sigma Lambda. Office: Office of Police Chief 150 S Los Angeles St Los Angeles CA 90012

WILLIAMS, WILLIE, JR., physicist, educator; b. Independence, La., Mar. 24, 1947; s. Willie Sr. and Lee Anner (Booker) W. B.S., So. U., 1970; M.S., Iowa State U., 1972, Ph.D., 1974. Mem. faculty Lincoln U., Lincoln University, Pa., 1974—, assoc. prof. physics, 1979-84; prof. physics Lincoln U., Lincoln University, 1984—, chmn. dept., 1976—; chmn. sci. and math. div., 1978-80, 83—, founder, dir. Lincoln Advance Sci. and Engring. Reinforcement (LASER) Program, 1980—, dir. pre-engring., 1976—, dir., prin. investigator Early Alert-Young Scholars Program, 1992—; bd. dirs. women tech. program Lincoln U. Urban Ctr., Phila.; vis. prof. Ctr. for Teaching Innovation, Drexel U., 1975; liaison officer Nat. Assn. for Equal Opportunity in Higher Edn., Dept. Def. Program, 1987—; mem. steering com. NSF Comprehensive Ctr. for Minorities, Phila.; bd. dirs. Prime Inc., Phila. Contbr. articles to profl. jours. Chmn. Cheyney Lincoln Temple Cluster, 1974-78; pres. The Men Fedn., So. U., 1968-69. Recipient Lindback award for Outstanding Teaching, 1976, Outstanding Scientist award White House Initiative, 1988; named one of Outstanding Young Men of Am.

1979; fellow NASA, 1979, Mobil Oil Corp., 1977, Nat. Bur. Standards, 1979, Dept. Def., 1980-81, Navy fellow, 1982. Mem. AAAS, AAUP, Am. Assn. Physics, N.Y. Acad. Scis., Math. Assn. Am., Am. Phys. Soc., Nat. Soc. Black Physicists, Nat. Geog. Soc., Iowa State Alumna Assn., Sigma Xi, Sigma Pi Sigma. Baptist. Home: 1454 Church Hill Pl Reston VA 22094-1228 Office: Lincoln U Dept Physics Lincoln University PA 19352 *Throughout my life I have always striven to achieve the very best and have held on to the belief that wherever possible improve upon today, so that everyone might have a better tomorrow! I have been guided by the the principle of being selective in my endeavors, having specific objectives, followed by detailed analysis, concise actions and intense work with continous review.*

WILLIAMS, WINTON HUGH, civil engineer; b. Tampa, Fla., Feb. 14, 1920; s. Herbert DeMain and Alice (Grant) W.; m. Elizabeth Walser Seelye, Dec. 18, 1949; children: Jan, Dick, Bill, Ann. Grad. Adj Gens. Sch., Gainesville, Fla., 1943; student U. Tampa, 1948; grad. Transp. Sch., Ft. Eustis, Va., 1949; BCE, U. Fla., 1959; grad. Command and Gen. Staff Coll., Ft. Levenworth, Kans., 1964, Engrs. Sch., Ft. Belvoir, 1965, Indsl. Coll. Armed Forces, Washington, 1966, Logistics Mgmt. Center, Ft. Lee, Va., 1972. Registered profl. engr., Fla., N.C. Constrn. engr. air fields C.E., U.S. Army, McCoy AFB, Fla., 1959-61, Homestead AFB, Miami, Fla., 1961-62; civil engr. C.E., Jacksonville (Fla.) Dist. Office, 1962-64, chief master planning and layout sect., mil. br., engring. div., 1964-70; chief master planning and real estate div. Hdqrs. U.S. Army So. Command, Ft. Amador, C.Z., 1970-75, spl. asst. planning and mil. constrn. programming Marine Corps Air Bases Eastern Area, Marine Corps Air Sta., Cherry Point, N.C., 1975-82; cons. engr., Morehead City, N.C., 1982—. Mem. Morehead City Planning Bd., 1982-94; mem. Carteret County N.C. Health Bd., 1990—; active Boy Scouts, C.Z.; mem. nat. council U. Tampa. Served with AUS, World War II, ETO, Korean War; col. Res. Decorated Breast Order of Yun Hi (Republic of China); presdl. citation, Meritorious Service medal (Republic of Korea); eagle scout with gold palm. Fellow ASCE (life); mem. NSPE (life), Res. Officers Assn. (life, v.p. C.Am. and S.Am.), Profl. Engrs. N.C., Am. Soc. Photogrammetry, Prestressed Concrete Inst. (profl.), Soc. Am. Mil. Engrs. (life, engr.), Nat. Eagle Scout Assn., Nat. Rifle Assn. Am., Am. Legion (life), Order Arrow, Theta Chi. Presbyterian. Home and Office: 4322 Coral Point Morehead City NC 28557-2745

WILLIAMS-ASHMAN, HOWARD GUY, biochemistry educator; b. London, Eng., Sept. 3, 1925; came to U.S., 1950, naturalized, 1962; s. Edward Harold and Violet Rosamund (Sturge) Williams-A.; m. Elisabeth Bächli, Jan. 25, 1959; children—Anne Clare, Christian, Charlotte, Geraldine. B.A., U. Cambridge, 1946; Ph.D., U. London, 1949. From asst. prof. to prof. biochemistry U. Chgo., 1953-64; prof. pharmacology and exptl. therapeutics, also prof. reproductive biology Johns Hopkins Med. Medicine, 1964-69; prof. biochemistry Ben May Inst., U. Chgo., 1969—, Maurice Goldblatt prof., 1973-91, prof. emeritus, 1991. Contbr. numerous articles in field to pubs. Recipient Research Career award USPHS, 1962-64. Fellow Am. Acad. Arts and Scis. (Amory prize 1975); mem. Am. Soc. Biochemistry and Molecular Biology. Home: 5421 S Cornell Ave Chicago IL 60615-5608 Office: Ben May Inst U Chgo Chicago IL 60637

WILLIAMSON, ALAN BACHER, English literature educator, poet, writer; b. Chgo., Jan. 24, 1944; s. George and Jehanne (Bacher) W.; m. Anne Winters, Oct. 12, 1968 (div. Feb. 1988); 1 child, Elizabeth Kilner. BA, Haverford Coll., 1964; MA, Harvard U., 1965, PhD, 1969. Asst. prof. U. Va., Charlottesville, 1969-75; Briggs-Copeland lectr. Harvard U., Cambridge, Mass., 1977-80; Fannie Hurst lectr. Brandeis U., Waltham, Mass., 1980-82; prof. English, U. Calif., Davis, 1982—; poetry panelist Nat. Endowment for Arts, 1989. Author: (criticism) Pity the Monsters, 1974, Introspection and Contemporary Poetry, 1984, Eloquence and Mere Life, 1994, (poetry) Presence, 1983, The Muse of Distance, 1988, Love and the Soul, 1995. Poetry fellow Nat. Endowment for Arts, 1973; Guggenheim fellow, 1991. Mem. MLA (exec. com. div. on poetry 1987-91). Democrat. Zen Buddhist. Office: U Calif Dept English Davis CA 95616

WILLIAMSON, CHRISTINE WILDER, educational consultant, small business owner; b. Sylvester, Ga., Jan. 1, 1929; d. Thomas Herman and Irene (Beverly) Wilder; m. James Bryant Williamson, Aug. 10, 1947; children: James Robert, Joseph Nathan, Janet Marie. BS, Tift Coll., Forsyth, Ga., 1972; MEd, Mercer U., 1973; D Ministry, Luther Rice Sem., Jacksonville, Fla., 1983. Tchr. Houston County Bd. Edn., Warner Robins, Ga., 1947-50, Kathleen Pape Kindergarten, Macon, Ga., 1963-66, Vineville Bapt. Kindergarten, Macon, 1966-71; elem. dir. Vineville Bapt. Ch., 1971-80; presch. specialist, cons. Ga. Bapt. and So. Bapt. Conv., 1970—; instr. Macon Tech. Inst., 1980-85; owner, founder Splendid Difference Ent., 1990—. Author: I Can Do It Myself, 1983, Creative Art Activities for Children, 1991. Fund raiser Ga. Cancer Assn., Macon, 1970-88; dir. Mission Friends, Macon Bapt. Women's Missionary Union, 1989—; dir. Royal Ambassadors. Mem. Nat. Assn. Edn. Young Children, So. Assn. Children under Six, Ga. Assn. Young Children, Ga. Presch. Assn. (pres. 1984-86, chaplain 1990—), Bibb County Presch. Assn. (pres. 1975-77, chaplain, treas. 1988—), MADD. Democrat. Avocations: walking, aerobics, watching sports events, travel, reading. Home and Office: 577 Old Lundy Rd Macon GA 31210-4305

WILLIAMSON, CLARENCE KELLY, microbiologist, educator; b. McKeesport, Pa., Jan. 19, 1924; s. James Frederick and Loretta (McDermott) W.; m. Dorothy Birgit Ohlsson, Aug. 18, 1951; children: Lisa Ann, Erik James. B.S., U. Pitts., 1949, M.S., 1951, Ph.D., 1955. Bacteriologist E.S. Magee Hosp., Pitts., 1951; instr. bacteriology U. Pitts., 1951-55, Pa. State U. summer 1953; mem. faculty Miami U., Oxford, Ohio, 1955—, chmn. dept. microbiology, 1962-72, prof., 1963-85, dean Coll. Arts and Sci., 1971-82, prof. emeritus, 1985—, exec. v.p. acad. affairs, provost, 1982-85, provost, exec. v.p. acad. affairs emeritus, 1985—; cons. Warren-Teed Products Co., Columbus, Ohio, 1953-62; cons. editor microbiology World Pub. Co., Cleve., 1965-68. Sec.-treas. McCullough-Hyde Meml. Hosp., 1968-70, trustee, bd. dirs., 1967-77, vice chmn., 1970-71, 72-74, chmn., 1974-76; trustee Hospice of The Miami Valley, 1984-92; mem. common on arts and scis. Nat. Assn. State Univs. and Land-Grant Colls., 1974-80; bd. govs. Am. Inst. Biol. Scis., 1977-83; bd. dirs. Council Colls. of Arts and Scis., 1975-79, pres., 1977-78; trustee SW Ohio and No. Ky. chpt. Nat. Multiple Sclerosis Soc., 1981-89; trustee Lakeside Assn., Chautauqua, Lakeside, Ohio, 1990—. Served with USNR, 1943-46. Recipient Benjamin Harrison medallion, 1982. Fellow Am. Acad. Microbiology, Ohio Acad. Sci. (v.p. med. sci. sect. 1970-71); mem. Am. Soc. Microbiology, Sigma Xi, Beta Gamma Sigma, Phi Kappa Phi, Omicron Delta Kappa, Rho Chi, Phi Sigma (nat. v.p. 1975-77, pres. 1977-83). Club: Torch (pres. Butler County 1969-70). Lodge: Rotary (pres. Oxford 1967-68). Spl. research poststreptococcal glomerulonephritis, classification of viridans streptococci, dissociation of Pseudomonas aeruginosa. Home: 104 Mckee Ave Oxford OH 45056-9025

WILLIAMSON, DON, newspaper columnist; b. St. Louis. Attended, Wichita State U. Editor, pub. 67214 Mag., Wichita, Kans., 1973-74; prodr., cons. As We See It Series Chgo. Pub. TV, 1974-76; gen. assignment reporter Wichita (Kans.) Eagle-Beacon, 1977-78, news, pub. affairs dir., 1978-79, editorial writer, columnist, 1979-83; edn. writer San Diego Union, 1983-85; assoc. editor, columnist, editorial pages Phila. Daily News, 1985-89; columnist, editorial bd. Seattle Times, 1989—; instr. Inst. Journalism Edn.; dir. Urban Newspaper Workshop High Sch. Students; minority profl. in-residence program Am. Soc. Newspaper Editors. Recipient William Allen White Found. Kans. News Enterprise award, AP Sports Editors Investigative Reporting award, Outstanding Reporting award Nat. Headliners, Washington Gov.'s Child Abuse Prevention award, Outstanding Govtl. News Reporting award Seattle Mcpl. League, Journalism award Kans. NAACP, Investigative Reporting award Kans. Press Women, Proficiency in Eng. Program Vol. award, Seattle Pub. Schs. Vol. award, Community Svc. award Royal Esquire Club Seattle, Community Svc. award Atlantic St. Ctr., Benefit Guild Seattle Children's Svc. award; John S. Knight Stanford U. fellow. Mem. Nat. Conf. Editorial Writers, Nat. Assn. Black Journalists (Leadership award, Region 10 Mem. of Yr. award), Soc. Profl. Journalists, Sigma Delta Chi. Office: The Seattle Times PO Box 70 Fairview Ave N & John St Seattle WA 98111

WILLIAMSON, DONALD RAY, retired career Army officer; b. Amarillo, Tex., Oct. 13, 1943; s. Floy Edwin and Dorothy Lorene (Orr) W.; m. Beverly

WILLIAMSON, DOUGLAS, Aug. 31, 1963; children: Rebecca Ann, Catherine Paige. BS in Econs., W. Tex. State U., 1966; MA in Bus., Cen. Mich. U., 1977; degree, Dept. Def. Program Mgrs., 1982, U.S. Army Command and Gen. Staff Coll., 1980. Commd. 2d lt. U.S. Army, 1966, advanced through grades to lt. col., 1982, retired, 1986; comdg. officer combat support co. U.S. Army, Ft. Hood, Tex., 1973-74; comdg. officer 2d aviation co. U.S. Army, Ft. Hood, 1974-75; dep. insp. gen. U.S. Army, Ft. Leavenworth, Kans., 1975-78; comdg. officer 213th aviation co. U.S. Army, Rep. of Korea, 1978-79; asst. program mgr. advanced scout helicopter program U.S. Army, 1981-86; owner Witan Group, Chesterfield, Mo., 1986-88; pres. Sys. Test Evaluation Inc., St. Louis, Mo., 1988—. Contbr. articles to profl. jours. Decorated Bronze Star, 37 Air medals with "V" device, D.F.C. with oak leaf cluster, Legion of Merit. Mem. Army Aviation Assn. Am., Assn. U.S. Army, Lansing Jaycees (past pres.), Mensa. Avocations: flying, reading, tennis. Home: 50 Orange Hills Chesterfield MO 63017 Office: 4433 Woodson Rd Saint Louis MO 63134

WILLIAMSON, DOUG, data processing executive. V.p. Caribbean Data Svcs. Ltd., Ft. Worth. Office: Caribbean Data Svcs Ltd 4255 Amon Carter Blvd Fort Worth TX 76155*

WILLIAMSON, DOUGLAS FRANKLIN, JR., lawyer; b. Anniston, Ala., Mar. 23, 1930; s. Douglas Franklin and Elizabeth Louise (Connor) W.; m. Barbara Tuerk, Dec. 28, 1957; children: Mary Leyden, Douglas Franklin III, Bruce Reynolds. AB summa cum laude, Amherst Coll., 1952; LLB, Yale U., 1955. Bar: N.Y. 1958, Fla. 1976. Assoc. Breed, Abbott & Morgan, N.Y.C., 1957-63, ptnr., 1963-72; ptnr. Williamson & Hess and predecessor firm, N.Y.C., 1972-79; of counsel Winthrop, Stimson, Putnam & Roberts, N.Y.C., 1979-81, ptnr., 1982—. Bd. dirs. World Wildlife Fund, Washington, 1979-88, treas., 1986-88, mem. nat. coun., 1988-94; bd. dirs. The Conservation Found., Washington, 1985-88, treas., 1986-88; bd. dirs. Lower Hudson chpt. Nature Conservancy, Mt. Kisco, N.Y., 1976-87, 93—, sec., 1976-87, hon. dir., 1987—, chmn., 1993-94; bd. dirs. Oblong Land Conservancy, Pawling, N.Y., 1990—; Quaker Hill Civic Assn., Pawling, 1974—, past pres.; chmn. Pawling Assessment Rev. Bd., 1976—. With U.S. Army, 1955-57. Fellow Am. Coll. Trust and Estate Counsel, N.Y. State Bar Found.; mem. ABA, N.Y. State Bar Assn., Assn. Bar City N.Y. (com. on trusts, estates and surrogate cts. 1973-78, chmn. 1975-78), Everglades Club, Quaker Hill Country Club (pres. 1980-81), Down Town Assn., Phi Beta Kappa, Phi Beta Kappa Assocs. (sec. 1975-77, v.p. 1977-79). Office: Winthrop Stimson Putnam & Roberts One Battery Park Plz New York NY 10004

WILLIAMSON, EDWIN DARGAN, lawyer, former federal official; b. Florence, S.C., Sept. 23, 1939; s. Benjamin F. and Sara (Dargan) W.; m. Kathe Gates, July 12, 1969; children: Samuel Gates, Edwin Dargan Jr., Sara Elizabeth. BA cum laude, U. of the South, 1961, DCL (hon.), 1992; JD, NYU, 1964. Bar: N.Y. 1965, D.C. 1988. Assoc. Sullivan & Cromwell, N.Y.C., 1964-70, ptnr., 1971-76; ptnr. Sullivan & Cromwell, London, 1976-79, N.Y.C., 1979-88, Washington, 1988-90, 93—; legal adviser U.S. Dept. State, Washington, 1990-93, Permanent Ct. of Arbitration, 1991—; bd. dirs. Triton Energy Corp. Regent U. of the South, Sewanee, Tenn., 1981-87, chmn., 1985-87; bd. dirs. Nat. Dance Inst., N.Y.C.; bd. dirs. BB&T Episcopal Ch. Found., N.Y.C., 1984-86-94; vestryman St. James Episcopal Ch., N.Y.C., 1984-88. Mem. ABA (coun. internat. law sect. 1993—), Assn. Bar City N.Y. (com. on internat. arms control and security affairs 1993—), U.S. Coun. Internat. Bus. and Bus.and Industry Adv. Coun. to OECD (vice chmn. coms. on multinat. enterprises and investment 1993—), Internat. Rep. Inst. (rule of law adv. bd. 1993—), Down Town Assn. (N.Y.C.), Racquet and Tennis Club (N.Y.C.), Met. Club. Republican. Office: Sullivan & Cromwell 8th Fl 1701 Pennsylvania Ave NW Washington DC 20006-5805

WILLIAMSON, ERNEST LAVONE, petroleum company executive; b. Perryton, Tex., Sept. 10, 1924; s. Ernest and Mabel Robert (Donnell) W.; m. Gertrude Florence Watkins, Dec. 2, 1950; children: Richard Dean, Judith Watkins, Mary Nan, David Ernest. BSEE, U. Okla., 1950; student, Hill's Bus. Coll., 1943. Sales and svc. rep. Hughes Tool Co., 1950-52; with land dept. Phillips Petroleum Co., 1952-54; with La. Land & Exploration Co., New Orleans, 1954—, exec. v.p., 1967-74, pres., 1974-84, COO, 1982-83, CEO, 1984-88, chmn., 1985-88, also dir.; bd. dirs. Hibernia Nat. Bank, New Orleans, Halliburton Co., Cen. La. Electric Co. Mem. adv. bd. Salvation Army, 1971—; bd. visitors U. Okla.; bd. dirs. New Orleans Jr. Achievement. With U.S. Army, 1943-46. Mem. Am. Assn. Petroleum Landmen, Ind. Petroleum Assn. Am., Mid-Continent Oil and Gas Assn. (chmn. 1980-81), Am. Petroleum Inst., Petroleum Club, Tchefuncta Country Club. Presbyterian. Office: La Land & Exploration Co 909 Poydras St PO Box 60350 New Orleans LA 70160

WILLIAMSON, FLETCHER PHILLIPS, real estate broker; b. Cambridge, Md., Dec. 16, 1923; s. William Fletcher and Florence M. (Phillips) W.; student U. Md., 1941, 42; m. Betty June (Stoker), Apr. 6, 1943; 1 son, Jeffrey Phillips; m. 2d, Helen M. Stumberg, Aug. 28, 1972. Test engr. Engring. Lab., Glen Martin Co., 1942-43; salesman Corkran Ice Cream Co., Cambridge, 1946-50; real estate broker, 1950—; chmn. bd. Williamson Real Estate, Dorchester Corp., 1963-72; bd. dirs. WCEM, Inc., 1966-75; vice chmn. bd., dir. Nat. Bank of Cambridge, 1979—; dir. Cam-Storage Inc., Dorchester Indsl. Devel. Corp., Delmarva Bank Data Processing Ctr.; co-receiver White & Nelson, Inc. Bd. dirs Delmarva council Boy Scouts Am.; past pres. Cambridge Hosp., United Fund of Dorchester County; bd. dirs. Del. Mus. Natural History, Dorchester County Pub. Library; bd. dirs., v.p. Game Conservation Internat.; v.p. Del. Mus. Natural History. Served as ordnance tech. intelligence engr. AUS, 1943-46; ETO. Mem. Md. Real Estate Assn. (gov. 1956-66), Outdoor Writers Assn., Nat. Rifle Assn., Nat. Def. Preparedness Assn., Cambridge Dorchester C. of C. (dir. 1955—), Power Squadron (comdr. 1954-56), Dorchester County Bd. Realtors (pres.), Scandinavian Atlantic Salmon Group, Explorers Club, Soc. of S. Pole. Methodist. Clubs: Rolling Rock, Shikar Safari, Anglers, Chesapeake Bay Yacht, Camp Fire, Md., Georgetown. Lodges: Masons, Shriners.

WILLIAMSON, FREDERICK BEASLEY, III, rubber company executive; b. Balt., June 21, 1918; s. Frederick Beasley and Virginia Ogden (Ranson) W.; m. Katherine Stryker, Apr. 19, 1941; children—Katherine L., Frederick Beasley IV, Marsha R. Student, Princeton, 1937-40. With Goodall Rubber Co., Trenton, N.J., 1940-41, 46-88, pres., chmn. bd., 1957-85, dir., 1950-89; bd. dirs. N.J. Nat. Bank. Bd. dirs. Mercer Med. Center, Trenton, N.J, 1965-89, New Jobs, 1962-91; campaign chmn. Delaware Valley United Way, 1964. Served to capt., 5th Armored Div. U.S. Army, 1942-46. Mem. Rubber Mfrs. Assn. (dir. 1958-86), Nat. Assn. Mfrs. (bd. dirs. 1981-82), N.J. Mfrs. Ins. Co. (bd. dirs. 1965-90, dir. emeritus 1990—, chmn. 1977-79), N.J. Bus. Industry Assn. (dir. emeritus 1990—). Clubs: Princeton (N.Y.C.); Trenton Country; Hartwood (Port Jervis, N.Y.); Pine Valley Golf. Home: 1265 Eagle Rd New Hope PA 18938-9221

WILLIAMSON, HANDY, JR., agricultural economist, educator; b. Louin, Miss., Oct. 24, 1945; s. Handy and Lilla (Nobles) W.; m. Barbara Jean Herndon, Dec. 28, 1968; 1 child, Lilla-Marie J. BS in Agrl. Edn., Alcorn State U., 1967; MS in Agrl. Edn., Tenn. State U., 1969; MS in Agrl. Econs., U. Mo., 1971, PhD in Agrl. Econs., 1974. Asst. prof., assoc. dir. Tuskegee U., Tuskegee Institute, Ala., 1974-77; rsch. dir., assoc. prof. Tenn. State U., Nashville, 1977-85; dep. administr. AID, Washington, 1985-88; prof., head dept. agrl. econs. U. Tenn., Knoxville, 1988—; cons. AID, TVA, USDA, other orgns. and ednl. instns., 1975—. Author, co-author rsch. monographs, articles; co-author: Small Farms in Tennessee, 1985, Diversity in Agricultural Economics, 1994. Mem. U.S. Joint Coun. Food and Agriscis., 1984-85, White House Com. on HBCU's, 1985-88, NASULGC Internat. Affairs Com., 1981-84, Knoxville Men's Club, 1990—; mem. bd. dirs. So. Rural Devel. Ctr., 1993—, Va. Bus. Devel. Ctr., 1989-92, United Methodist Found. 1993—; mem. com. pub. svc. U. Tenn. Bd. Trustees, 1992-93. Recipient Outstanding Svc. award, AID, 1986, Tenn. State U., Nashville, 1985-87, Disting. Alumni award Alcorn State U., 1987, U. Mo., 1993. Mem. Am. Agrl. Econs. Assn., So. Agrl. Econs. Assn., Assn. Rsch. Dirs. (sec.-treas. 1977-85), Tenn. Coun. Ag. Deans (chmn. 1984), Assn. Internat. Dirs. (bd. dirs. 1982-87), So. Dept. Heads Assn. (sec.-treas.), Kiwanis Club (bd. dirs., v.p. Knoxville chpt. 1993—), Optimist Club, Phi Beta Sigma, Gamma Sigma Delta. Avocations: travel, woodworking, gardening, fishing, tennis. Home: 12108 E Ashton Ct Knoxville TN 37922-1526 Office: U Tenn Dept Agrl Econs Rural Knoxville TN 37901

WILLIAMSON, HARWOOD DANFORD, utility company executive; b. Waimea, Kauai, Hawaii, 1932. Grad., Stanford U., 1956. Pres., CEO Hawaiian Electric Co., Inc., Honolulu, also bd. dirs.; bd. dirs. Hawaiian Electric Industries, Inc.; chmn. Hawaii Electric Light Co., Inc., Maui Electric Co., Ltd. Office: Hawaiian Electric Co Inc PO Box 2750 900 Richards St Honolulu HI 96813

WILLIAMSON, HENRY GASTON, JR., banker; b. Whiteville, N.C., Aug. 18, 1947; s. Henry Gaston and Elizabeth Lee (Brittain) W.; m. Nancy Thomas Williamson, Aug. 30, 1969; children: Leigh, Clay. BSBA, East Carolina U., 1969, MBA, 1972; grad. bus. adminstrn., U. N.C., 1979. Mgr. bus. loans Branch Banking & Trust Co., Fayetteville, N.C., 1973-77; v.p., regional loan adminstr. Branch Banking & Trust Co., Wilson, N.C., 1977-80; v.p., city exec. Branch Banking & Trust Co., Tarboro, N.C., 1980; exec. v.p., mgr. ops./human resources div. Branch Banking & Trust Co., Wilson, N.C., 1981-83, sr. exec. v.p., adminstrv. group mgr., 1983-89, pres., 1989—, COO, 1991—; bd. dirs. BB&T Fin. Corp., BB&T; bd. dirs. BB&T Ctr. for Leadership Devel. Author: American Antiques: A Case Study, 1973 (First Place award Robert Morris Assocs.). Bd. dirs. Wilson County chpt. ARC, 1984—, East Carolina U. 1985—, N.C. Med. Soc. Found., Inc., 1991; mem. exec. com., bd. dirs. East Carolina coun. Boy Scouts Am., 1985—; bd. dirs. Wilson Heart Fund Assn., 1983-87, pres., 1985-86. East Carolina faculty scholar, 1969; recipient Outstanding Alumni award East Carolina U., 1988. Mem. Omicron Delta Epsilon, Beta Gamma Sigma. Club: Wilson Country. Lodge: Kiwanis (pres. Wilson club 1984-85). Avocation: skiing. Home: 1210 Cambridge Rd NW Wilson NC 27896-1458 Office: BB&T Fin Corp 223 Nash St W Wilson NC 27893-3880

WILLIAMSON, JACK (JOHN STEWART WILLIAMSON), writer; b. Bisbee, Ariz., Apr. 29, 1908; s. Asa Lee and Lucy Betty (Hunt) W.; m. Blanche Slaten Harp, Aug. 15, 1947 (dec. Jan. 1985); stepchildren: Keigh Harp (dec.), Adele Harp Lovorn. BA, MA, Eastern N.Mex. U., 1957, LHD (hon.), 1981; PhD, U. Colo., 1964. Prof. English Eastern N.Mex. U., Portales, 1960-77. Author numerous sci. fiction books including The Legion of Space, 1947, Darker Than You Think, 1948, The Humanoids, 1949, The Green Girl, 1950, The Cometeers, 1950, One Against the Legion, 1950, Seetee Shock, 1950, Seetee Ship, 1950, Dragon's Island, 1951, The Legion of Time, 1952, (with Frederik Phhl) Star Bridge, 1955, Dome Around America, 1955, The Trial of Terra, 1962, Golden Blood, 1964, The Reign of Wizardry, 1965, Bright New Universe, 1967, Trapped in Space, 1968, The Pandora Effect, 1969, People Machines, 1971, The Moon Children, 1972, H.G. Wells: Critic of Progress, 1973, Teaching SF, 1975, The Early Williamson, 1975, The Power of Blackness, 1976, The Best of Jack Williamson, 1978 Brother to Demons, Brother to Gods, 1979, Teaching Science Fiction: Education for Tomorrow, 1980, The Alien Intelligence, 1980, The Humanoid Touch, 1980, Manseed, 1982, The Queen of a Legion, 1983, Wonder's Child: My Life in Science Fiction, 1984 (Hugo award 1985), Lifeburst, 1984, Firechild, 1986, Mazeway, 1990; (with Frederik Pohl) Undersea Quest, 1954, Undersea Fleet, 1955, Undersea City, 1956, The Reefs of Space, 1964, Starchild, 1965, Rogue Star, 1969, The Farthest Star, 1975, Wall Around a Star, 1983, Land's End, 1988, Mazeway, 1990; (with Frederik Pohl) The Singers of Time, 1991, Beachhead, 1992, Demon Moon, 1994; (with Miles J. Breuer) The Birth of an New Republic, 1981. Served as staff sgt. USAAF, 1942-45. Mem. Sci. Fiction Writers Am. (pres. 1978-80, Grand Master Nebula award 1976), Sci. Fiction Research Assn. (Pilgrim award 1968), World Sci. Fiction, Planetary Soc. Avocations: travel, astronomy, photography. Home: PO Box 761 Portales NM 88130-0761 Office: Ea NMex U Golden Libr Portales NM 88130

WILLIAMSON, JERRY DEAN, radio station executive; b. Appleton City, Mo., Mar. 14, 1934; s. Charles Murry and Eunice Lee (Davis) W.; m. Joan Hawkes, Apr. 22, 1955; children: Kirk Dean, Vicky Lynn, Kimberly Dawn, Gregory Alan, Robert Todd. Student, Idaho State U., 1952-56, Ea. Wash. U., 1956-57. Radio announcer Sta. KOSI, Denver, 1957-61; sales mgr. Sta. KLAK-AM-FM, Denver, 1961-76; gen. mgr. Stas. KIRO, Seattle, 1976-78; gen. mgr. Stas. KIDO, KIDQ, Boise, Idaho, 1978-80, Sta. KART/KFMA, Twin Falls, Idaho, 1980-82; gen. sales mgr. Sta. KUTV-TV, Salt Lake City, 1982-85; nat. sales mgr. Stas. KLTQ, KUTR, Salt Lake City, 1985; sta. mgr. Sta. KGHL/KIDX, Billings, Mont., 1985—; sales cons. Sta. KART/KFMA, Twin Falls, 1982—. Mem. Mont. Broadcasters Assn., Billings Advt. Club., Rotary. Republican. Mormon. Avocations: hunting, photography, genealogy. Home: 2589 Granite St Idaho Falls ID 83402-1400 Office: Sta KGHL 2070 Overland Ave Ste 103 Billings MT 59102-7429

WILLIAMSON, JOEL RUDOLPH, humanities educator; b. Anderson County, S.C., Oct. 27, 1929; s. James Henry and Carrie Mae (Sweany) W.; m. Marie Ahern, Nov. 17, 1953 (div. May 1983); children: Joelle, William, Alethea; m. Anna Woodson, Oct. 16, 1986. AB, U. S.C., 1949, MA, 1951; PhD, U. Calif., 1964. Instr. dept. history U. N.C., Chapel Hill, 1960-64, asst. prof., 1964-66, assoc. prof., 1966-69, prof., 1969-85, Lineberger prof. in humanities, 1985—; resident fellow Rockefeller Ctr., Bellagio, Italy, 1988; Eudora Welty prof. in so. studies Millsaps Coll., 1984; disting. vis. prof. Rhodes Coll., 1984; vis. prof. dept. history, assoc. Lowell House Harvard U., 1981-82. Author: After Slavery: The Negro in South Carolina During Reconstruction, 1861-1877, 1965, The Origins of Segregation, 1968, New People: Miscegenation and Mullatoes in the United States, 1980, The Crucible of Race, 1984 (Francis Parkman prize Soc. Am. Historians, Ralph Waldo Emerson award Phi Beta Kappa, Mayflower Cup, Frank L. and Harriet C. Owsley award 1985, Robert Francis Kennedy Book award), William Faulkner and Southern History, 1993 (Pulitzer prize in History nomination), also articles. Lt. USN, 1951-55. Fellow Guggenheim Found., 1970-71, NEH, 1987-88, Ctr. for Advanced Study in Behavioral Scis., Stanford, Calif., 1977-78, summer 1979, 80, 91, So. fellow, 1961-62, Charles Warren Ctr. Avocation: travel. Home: 211 Hillsborough St Chapel Hill NC 27514 Office: U NC Dept History 567 Hamilton # 070A Chapel Hill NC 27599

WILLIAMSON, JOEL V., lawyer; b. Akron, Ohio, May 26, 1945. BA, Davidson Coll., 1967; JD, U. Ky., 1970. Bar: Ky. 1970, Ill. 1986, U.S. Supreme Ct., U.S. Ct. Appeals (6th, 7th, 8th, 9th and 11th cirs.), U.S. Dist. Ct. (no. dist.) Ill., U.S. Tax Ct., U.S. Ct. Fed. Claims. Ptnr. Mayer, Brown & Platt, Chgo. Mem. Ky. Bar Assn., Chgo. Bar Assn., Internat. Fiscal Assn. Office: Mayer Brown & Platt 190 S La Salle St Chicago IL 60603-3410

WILLIAMSON, JOHN PRITCHARD, utility executive; b. Cleve., Feb. 22, 1922; s. John and Jane (Russell) W.; m. Helen Morgan, Aug. 3, 1945; children: John Morgan, James Russell, Wayne Arthur. BBA, Kent State U., 1945; postgrad., U. Toledo, 1953-56, U. Mich., 1956. CPA, Ohio. Sr. acct Arthur Andersen & Co., Detroit and Cleve., 1945-51; dir. methods and procs. Toledo Edison Co., 1951-59, asst. treas., 1959-60, sec., 1960-62, sec.-treas., 1962-65, v.p. finance, 1965-68, sr. v.p., 1968-72, pres., chief exec. officer, 1972-79, chmn., chief exec. officer, 1979-86; chmn. Centerior Energy Corp., 1985; chmn. emeritus Toledo Edison Co., Centerior Energy Corp., 1986—; chmn. N.Am. Electric Reliability Coun., 1984-87. Pres. Ohio Electric Utility Inst., 1972; chmn. East Cen. Area Power Coordination Pool, 1971-72, mem. exec. com. Edison Electric Inst., 1981-85; trustee Assn. Edison Illuminating Cos., 1982-84; trustee Toledo Symphony Orch., pres., 1985-86; trustee Toledo Mus. Art, Toledo Hosp., Kent State U. Found.; vice chmn. Greater Toledo Corp., 1984-86; trustee, treas. Rio Verde Community Ch., 1989-92; elder Presbyn. Ch.; mem. Toledo Comm. Chest (pres. 1972), Area United Way (chmn. 1971). Named Toledo Outstanding Citizen, 1976; recipient Kent State U. medallion, 1992; Williamson Alumni Ctr. named in his honor, 1991. Mem. Fin. Analysts Soc. Toledo (pres. 1968-69), Systems and Procs. Assn. (internat. treas. 1960), Inst. Pub. Utilities (chmn. exec. com. 1969-70), Toledo C. of C. (pres. 1970), Ohio C. of C. (chmn. 1979-81, life dir.), Toledo Boys Club (Echo award 1974), Kent State U. Alumni Assn. (pres. 1971-72, outstanding alumnus 1974), Belmont Country Club, Rio Verde Country Club, Rio Verde Saddle Club (past pres.), Kiwanis (past pres. Toledo, Disting. Svc. award 1977), Blue Key, Delta Sigma Pi, Beta Alpha Psi, Delta Upsilon. Republican. Home: 10661 Cardiff Rd Perrysburg OH 43551-3404 also: 18524 Poco Vista Dr Rio Verde AZ 85253

WILLIAMSON, LAIRD, stage director, actor; b. Chgo., Dec. 13, 1937; s. Walter B. and Florence M. (Hemwell) W. B.S. in Speech, Northwestern U., 1960; M.F.A. in Drama, U. Tex., 1965. Dir. Am. Conservatory Theatre, San Francisco, 1974—; stage dir. A Christmas Carol, 1976-81, The Matchmaker (tour of Soviet Union), 1976, A Month in the Country, 1978, The Visit, 1979, Pantagleize, 1980, Sunday in the Park, 1986, End of the World, 1988, Imaginary Invalid, 1990; dir. Oreg. Shakespearean Festival, Ashland, 1972-74, Western Opera Theatre, San Francisco, 1976-77, Theater Fest, Santa Maria, Calif., 1971-84, Denver Theater Ctr., 1981, Bklyn. Acad. Music, 1981, Denver Ctr. Theatre Co., 1985-94, Seattle Repertory Theatre, 1990, Old Globe Theatre, San Diego, 1977, 92, 94; artistic dir. Theater Fest, Solvang, Calif., 1981-83, Intiman Theatre, 1986, 88, Seattle Repertory Theatre, 1990, Berkeley Shakespeare Festival, 1990, Guthrie Theatre, 1991, 93, The Shakespeare Theatre, Washington, 1995; actor in Othello, 1973, Twelfth Night, 1974, Cyrano, 1974, Enrico IV, 1977, Judas, 1978, Hamlet, 1979, The Bacchae, 1981. Mem. Soc. Stage Dirs. Actors Equity Assn., Screen Actors Guild. *Learn from the multitude of wonderful teachers that life provides. Keep it fun, and work from your heart.*

WILLIAMSON, MARILYN LAMMERT, English educator, university adminstrator; b. Chgo., Sept. 6, 1927; d. Raymond Ferdinand and Edith Louise (Eisenbies) Lammert; m. Robert M. Williamson, Oct. 28, 1950 (div. Apr. 1973); 1 child, Timothy L.; m. James H. McKay, Aug. 15, 1974. BA, Vassar Coll., 1949; MA, U. Wis., 1950; PhD, Duke U., 1956. Instr. Duke U., Durham, N.C., 1955-56, 58-59; lectr. N.C. State U., Raleigh, 1957-58, 61-62; asst. prof. Oakland U., Rochester, Mich., 1965-68, assoc. prof., 1968-72; prof. English Wayne State U., Detroit, 1972-90, Disting. prof. English, 1990—, chmn. dept. English, 1972-74, 81-83, assoc. dean Coll. Liberal Arts, 1974-79; dir. women's studies Wayne State U., 1976-87; dep. provost Wayne State U., Detroit, 1987-91, sr. v.p. for acad. affairs, provost, 1991—; pres. Assn. Depts. English, 1976-77. Author: Infinite Variety, 1974, Patriarchy of Shakespeare's Comedies, 1986, British Women Writers 1650-1750, 1990; editor: Renaissance Studies, 1972, Female Poets of Great Britain, 1981; contbr. articles to profl. jours. Pres. LWV, Rochester, 1963-65. Recipient Detroit Disting. Svc. award, 1986, Faculty Recognition award Bd. Govs., Wayne State U., 1991; Bunting Inst. fellow, 1969-70, AAUW fellow, 1982-83, J.N. Keal fellow, 1985-86. Mem. MLA (exec. coun. 1977-80, mem. editorial bd. 1992-94), Renaissance Soc. Am., Coll. English Assn., Mich. Acad. (pres. 1978-79), Shakespeare Assn. Am., Mich. Coun. Humanities (chair 1991-93), Fed. State Humanities Coun. (bd. dirs. 1994—). Democrat. Home: 2275 Oakway Dr West Bloomfield MI 48324-1855 Office: Wayne State Univ Dept of English Detroit MI 48202

WILLIAMSON, MICHAEL, writer. Author: (with Dale Maharidge) And Their Children After Them, 1989 (Pulitzer prize for gen. non-fiction 1990), The Last Great American Hobo, 1993. *

WILLIAMSON, MYRNA HENRICH, retired army officer, lecturer, consultant; b. Gregory, S.D., Jan. 27, 1937; d. Walter Ferdinand and Alma Lillian (Rajewich) H. BS with highest honors, S.D. State U., 1960; MA, U. Okla., 1973; grad., U.S. Army Command and Gen. Staff Coll., 1977, Nat. War Coll., 1980. Commd. 2d lt. U.S. Army, 1960, advanced through grades to brig. gen., 1985; bn. comdr. Mil. Police Sch. U.S. Army, Fort McClellan, Ala., 1977-79; chief plans policy and service div. Jl 8th Army U.S. Army, Korea, 1980-81; chief mgmt. support Office Dep. Chief Staff for Research, Devel. and Acquisition U.S. Army, Washington, 1981-82; brigade comdr. U.S. Army, Fort Benjamin Harrison, Ind., 1983-84; comdg. gen. 3d ROTC Region U.S. Army, Fort Riley, Kans., 1984-87; dep. dir. mil. personnel mgmt. U.S. Army, Washington, 1987-89, ret., 1989; U.S. del. com. on women in NATO Forces, 1986-89. Pres. S.D. State U. Found.; bd. dirs. Women in Mil. Svc. to Am. Found.; mem. bd. adv. Safe Streets. Recipient Disting. Alumnus award S.D. State U., 1984. Mem. Internat. Platform Assn., Assn. U.S. Army (trustee), United Svcs. Automobile Assn. (bd. dirs.), Exec. Women in Govt., Phi Kappa Phi.

WILLIAMSON, OLIVER EATON, economics and law educator; b. Superior, Wis., Sept. 27, 1932; s. Scott Gilbert and Lucille S. (Dunn) W.; m. Dolores Jean Celeni, Sept. 28, 1957; children: Scott, Tamara, Karen, Oliver, Dean. SB, MIT, 1955; MBA, Stanford U., 1960; PhD, Carnegie-Mellon U., 1963; PhD (hon.), Norwegian Sch. Econs. and Bus. Adminstrn., 1986; PhD in Econ. Sci. (hon.), Hochschule St. Gallen, Switzerland, 1987, Groningen U., 1989. Project. engr. U.S. Govt., 1955-58; asst. prof. econs. U. Calif., Berkeley, 1963-65; assoc. prof. U. Pa., Phila., 1965-68, prof., 1968-83, Charles and William L. Day prof. econs. and social sci., 1977-83; Gordon B. Tweedy prof. econs. law and orgn. Yale U., 1983-88; Transam. prof. of bus., econs. and law U. Calif., Berkeley, 1988-94, Edgar F. Kaiser prof. bus. adminstrn., prof. econs. and law, 1994—; spl. econ. asst. to asst. atty. gen. for antitrust Dept. Justice, 1966-67; dir. Ctr. for Study of Organizational Innovation, U. Pa., 1976-83; transam. prof. of bus., econs. and law U. Calif., Berkeley, 1988—; on. in field. Author: The Economics of Discretionary Behavior, 1964, Corporate Control and Business Behavior, 1970, Markets and Hierarchies, 1975, The Economic Institutions of Capitalism, 1985, Economic Organization, 1986, Antitrust Economics, 1987; assoc. editor: Bell Jour. Econs., 1973-74, editor, 1975-82; co-editor: Jour. Law, Econs., and Orgn., 1983—. Fellow Ctr. for Advanced Study in Behavioral Scis., 1977-78; Guggenheim fellow, 1977-78; Am. Acad. Arts and Scis. fellow, 1983; recipient Alexander Henderson award Carnegie-Mellon U., 1962, Alexander von Humboldt Rsch. prize, 1987, Irwin award Acad. of Mgmt., 1988. Fellow Econometric Soc.; mem. NAS, Am. Econ. Assn. Office: U Calif Dept Econs Berkeley CA 94720

WILLIAMSON, PETER DAVID, lawyer; b. Houston, Oct. 13, 1944; s. Sam and Sophie Ann (Kaplan) W.; m. Patricia Golemon; children: Heather, Amber, Asia, Ginger. B.A., U. Ill., 1966; J.D., U. Tex., 1969. Bar: Tex. 1969, U.S. Supreme Ct. 1974, U.S. Ct. Appeals (4th, 9th, 5th, 8th, 10th, 11th and D.C. cirs.); lic. comml. pilot. Pvt. practice Houston, 1971—; founder IMMLAW, The Nat. Consortium of Immigration Law Firms. Mem. Am. Immigration Lawyers Assn. (pres. 1994-95). Home: 2417 Branard St Houston TX 77098-2213 Office: 1111 Fannin St Ste 1360 Houston TX 77002-6923 *I do not believe in the existence of national boundaries. The philosophy of my practice of the law is to help my clients achieve the ability to pass freely through such artificial political borders.*

WILLIAMSON, RICHARD CARDINAL, physicist; b. Minocqua, Wis., Sept. 10, 1939; s. Lyman Olaf and Edna (Cardinal) W.; m. Christine Bauer, Sept. 2, 1961; children—Kari, Meagan, Heidi, Ryan. B.S. in Physics, MIT, 1961, Ph.D. in Physics, 1966. Staff physicist NASA Electronics Research Ctr., Cambridge, Mass., 1965-70; staff mem. and assoc. group leader MIT Lincoln Lab., Lexington, Mass., 1970-80, group leader applied physics, electrooptic device rsch., 1980—. Contbr. articles to jours., chpts. to books; patentee in field. Fellow IEEE (Centennial award 1984, Sonics and Ultrasonics Achievement award 1985); mem. Am. Phys. Soc., Optical Soc. Am., Sigma Xi. Methodist. Home: 21 Pendleton Rd Sudbury MA 01776-1612 Office: MIT Lincoln Lab PO Box 73 Room C-317 Lexington MA 02173-9108

WILLIAMSON, RICHARD HALL, association executive; b. Canton, N.C., July 29, 1940; s. James Eustace and Gwendolyn (Hall) W.; m. Julia Draper Brown, Nov. 7, 1965 (div. Jan. 1981); children: Shawn Nicol, Kevin Carson. BS in Physics, N.C. State U., 1962, MS in Nuclear Engring., 1970, PhD in Econs., 1972. Instr. N.C. State U., Raleigh, 1972-75; chief, energy systems analysis AEC, Washington, 1972-75; asst. dir., energy analysis U.S. Energy R & D Adminstrn., Washington, 1975-77; dir., program analysis U.S. Dept. Energy, Washington, 1977-80, dir., policy devel., 1980-84, dep. asst. sec. for internat. affairs, 1984-94; dep. exec. dir. U.S. Energy Assn., Washington, 1995—. Author: A Group Strategy for Energy Research, Development and Demonstration, 1980; contbr. articles to jours. in field. Football ofcl. Atlantic Coast Conf., Greensboro, N.C., 1980—, Rose Bowl, Pasadena, Calif., 1995. 1st lt. U.S. Army, 1962-64; col. USAR, 1964-93. NSF fellow, 1964-65; AEC fellow, 1965-68; recipient Outstanding alumnus award IFC, N.C. State U., 1971, Presdl. Rank award U.S. Dept. Energy, 1990. Mem. Sigma Alpha Mu (nat. pres. 1984-86), Tau Beta Pi, Phi Kappa Phi, Omicron Delta Kappa, Sigma Pi Sigma, Phi Mu Epsilon. Republican. Methodist. Avocations: stamp collecting, tennis, golf, skiing. Home: Apr 1107-S 3705 S George Mason Dr Falls Church VA 22041-3720 Office: US Energy Assn 1620 I St NW Ste 1000 Washington DC 20006

WILLIAMSON, RICHARD SALISBURY, lawyer; b. Evanston, Ill., May 9, 1949; s. Donald G. and Marion (Salisbury) W.; m. Jane Thatcher, Aug.

25, 1973; children: Elizabeth Jean, Craig Salisbury, Richard Middleton. A.B. with honors, Princeton U., 1971; J.D., U. Va., 1974. Bar: Ill. bar 1974, D.C. bar 1975. Legis. counsel, adminstrv. asst. to Congressman Philip M. Crane of Ill., 1974-76; assoc. firm Winston & Strawn, Washington, 1977-80; ptnr. Winston & Strawn, 1980; asst. to Pres. for intergovtl. affairs, Washington, also assoc. dir. President's Task Force on Regulatory Relief, 1981-83; U.S. ambassador Vienna, Austria, 1983-85; sr. v.p. corp. and internat. relations Beatrice Cos., Inc., Chgo., 1985-86; ptnr. Mayer, Brown & Platt, Chgo., 1986-88, 89—; asst. sec. of state internat. orgn. affairs Dept. of State, Washington, 1988-89; rep. UN Orgns., Vienna, 1983-85; dep. ref. with rank of ambassador IAEA. Co-editor: (with Paul Laxalt) A Changing America: Conservatives View the 80's From the United States Senate, 1980, Reagan's Federalism: His Efforts to Decentralize Government, 1990, The United Nations: A Place of Promise and of Mischief, 1991; editor: Trade & Economic Growth, 1993. Republican. Office: Mayer Brown & Platt 190 S La Salle St Chicago IL 60603-3410

WILLIAMSON, ROBERT CHARLES, marketing executive; b. West Chester, Pa., Jan. 3, 1925; s. Herman Gideon and Grace (Faddis) W.; m. Frances Yvonne Ishmael, Apr. 10, 1945 (div. July 1969); children: Robert C. Jr., Edward H., Richard F., Kathryn G.; m. Mary Elizabeth Bogle, Oct. 1, 1983. BS, Naval Sci. Sch., Monterey, Calif., 1959; postgrad. in Internat. Rels., Naval War Coll., Newport, R.I., 1960. Commd. ensign, designated naval aviator USN, 1944, advanced through grades to comdr., 1963, ret., 1966; gen. mgr. Springfield (Va.) Assocs., 1966-69; v.p. CCC Corp., Rosslyn, Va., 1969-70; pres. WILCO Assocs., Mt. Vernon, Va., 1970-73; dir. mktg. Documail Systems, Lenexa, Kans., 1973-80; N.Am. mktg. mgr. Leigh Instruments, Waterloo, Ont., Can., 1981-83; v.p. Tabs Assocs., Abingdon, Md., 1983-87; pres. WILLMAR Assocs. Internat., Brandon, Fla., 1987—. Mem. Nat. Assn. Presort Mailers (exec. dir. 1984—), Ret. Officers' Assn., Assn. Former Intelligence Officers, Assn. Naval Aviation. Club: Army and Navy. Home and Office: 3906 Butternut Ct Brandon FL 33511-7961

WILLIAMSON, ROBERT ELMORE, agricultural engineering educator; b. York County, S.C., Nov. 8, 1937; s. Charles Edward Jr. and Margaret Gladys (Elmore) W.; m. Eva Evelyn Simpson, June 27, 1964; children: Margaret Edye, Robert Elmore Jr. BS, Clemson U., 1959, MS, 1964; PhD, Miss. State U., 1972. Registered profl. engr., Ga. Rsch. assoc. Miss. State U., Starkville, 1966-71; asst. prof. agrl. engring. U. Ga., Tifton, 1971-78; assoc. prof. Clemson (S.C.) U., 1978-81, prof. agrl. engring., 1981—. Co-inventor bulb, root and leafy vegetable harvester, improved harvesting machinery, multi-purpose horticultural transplanter; contbr., co-contbr. over 54 articles to scholarly jours.; contbr., co-contbr. over 24 articles to sci. jours. Asst. scoutmaster Clemson area Boy Scouts Am., 1972-78, 80—. 1st lt. USAF, 1959-62. Mem. Am. Soc. AGrl. Engrs., Phi Kappa Phi, Gamma Sigma Delta, Alpha Zeta, Sigma Xi. Presbyterian. Avocations: hunting, camping, backpacking, woodworking. Home: 303 Princess Grace Ave Clemson SC 29631-1215 Office: Agrl Engring McAdams Hall Clemson U Clemson SC 29631

WILLIAMSON, RONALD FRANK, banker, former national guard official; b. Huron, S.D., Dec. 31, 1941; s. Thomas Jefferson and Alice Evelyn (Hauck) W.; m. Elisabeth White, Nov. 14, 1964; children—Michael, Stephen, Wendy; m. Paula Dorsey, Sept. 6, 1986; children: Jacelyn, Heidi. Student, Augustana Coll., Sioux Falls, S.D., 1960; BS, U.S. Mil. Acad., 1964; MA, U. S.D., 1989. Mem. staff S.D. Legis. Research, 1970-71; exec. dir. S.D. Mcpl. League, 1971-78; chief of staff to Gov. of S.D., 1979-83; adjutant gen. S.D. Nat. Guard, Pierre, 1983-87; chief of staff Citibank, Sioux Falls, S.D., 1987-88, v.p., dir. svc. quality, Tng. and Corp. Svcs., 1989-90, pres., chief exec. officer, 1990—, also bd. dirs.; mem. exec. bd. Nat. League of Cities, 1973-75; gov.'s rep. Old West Regional Commn., 1979-81. Pres., Little League, Pierre, S.D., 1973; chmn. Republican State Conv., Rapid City, S.D., 1976; bd. dirs. S.D. Symphony, S.D. Industry and Commerce Assn., McKennan Hosp., Sioux Empire United Way. Capt. U.S. Army, 1964-70. Named Master Aviator, U.S. Army, 1979; fellow HUD, 1970. Mem. Nat. Guard Assn. (fin. com., chmn. aviation com. 1985), Air Force Assn., VFW, Am. Legion. Episcopalian. Lodges: Masons, Elks. Avocations: flying; water skiing; tennis.

WILLIAMSON, SAM, lawyer; b. Detroit, Aug. 15, 1910; s. Solomon and Minnie (Nichamin) W.; m. Sophie Ann Kaplan, May 6, 1943; children: Peter D., Jane Williamson Kessler, Marianne Williamson. B.A., U. Ill., 1937, J.D., 1940. Bar: Ill. 1940, Tex. 1946. Since practiced in Houston. Maj. U.S. Army, 1942-46. Mem. ABA, Fed. Bar Assn. (pres. Houston chpt. 1956), Houston Bar Assn., Am. Immigration Lawyers Assn. (past chmn. Tex.), State Bar Tex., Am. Soc. Internat. Law, Nat. Lawyers Guild, Am.-Arab Anti-Discrimination Com. Home: 3616 Tartan Ln Houston TX 77025-2520 Office: 1320 Americana Bldg Houston TX 77002

WILLIAMSON, SAMUEL RUTHVEN, JR., historian, university administrator; b. Bogalusa, La., Nov. 10, 1935; s. Samuel Ruthven and Frances Mitchell (Page) W.; m. Joan Chaffe Andress, Dec. 30, 1961; children: George Samuel, Treeby Andress, Thaddeus Miller. BA, Tulane U., 1958; AM, Harvard U., 1960, PhD, 1966, grad. advanced mgmt. program, 1986; hon. degrees, Furman U. Va. Theol. Sem. Asst. prof. U.S. Mil. Acad., 1963-66; instr. history Harvard U., 1966-68, asst. prof., 1968-72, Allston Burr sr. tutor, 1968-72, asst. to dean of Harvard Coll., 1969-70; rsch. assoc. Inst. Politics, faculty assoc. Ctr. for Internat. Affairs, 1971-72; mem. faculty J.F. Kennedy Sch. Govt., 1971-72; assoc. prof. history U. N.C., Chapel Hill, 1972-74; prof. U. N.C., 1974-88, dean Coll. Arts and Scis., 1977-85, provost univ., 1984-88; pres. vice chancellor The U. of the South, Sewanee, Tenn., 1988—; cons. Historian's Office, Office of Sec. Def., 1974-76; vis. fellow Churchill Coll., 1976-77; mem. vis. com. Harvard Coll., 1986-92; dir. Research Triangle Inst., 1984-88; trustee N.C. Sch. Sci. and Math., 1985-88, Day Found., 1990-93; mem. bd. visitors Air U., 1994—. Author: The Politics of Grand Strategy: Britain and France Prepare for War, 1904-1914, 1969, 2d edit., 1990; co-author: The Origins of U.S. Nuclear Strategy, 1945-53, 1993; editor: The Origins of a Tragedy: July 1914, 1981; co-editor: Essays on World War I: Origins and Prisoners of War, 1983, Austria-Hungary and the Origins of the First World War, 1991; am. editor: War and Soc. Newsletter, 1973-88. Mem. cen. com. Morehead Found., 1978-93. Capt. U.S. Army, 1963-66. Fulbright scholar U. Edinburgh, 1958-59; Woodrow Wilson fellow, 1958-63; Danforth fellow, 1958-63; Nat. Endowment Humanities fellow, 1976-77; Ford Found. grantee, 1976; fellow Nat. Humanities Ctr., 1983; recipient George Louis Beer prize for best book on internat. history Am. Hist. Assn., 1970. Mem. Am. Hist. Assn., Internat. Inst. Strategic Studies, Nat. Assn. Ind. Colls. and Univs. (chairperson bd. dirs. 1994-95). Democrat. Episcopalian. Home: PO Box 837 Sewanee TN 37375-0837 Office: U of the South Office of Pres Sewanee TN 37375-4013

WILLIAMSON, THOMAS ARNOLD, publishing company executive; b. Sagamore, Pa., Oct. 4, 1939; s. Thomas and Mabel (Kennedy) W.; m. Kathryn Steiner White, Mar. 1, 1980; 1 child, Thomas J. Grad., Phillips Exeter Acad., 1957; A.B., Harvard U., 1961. With Harcourt Brace & Co., N.Y.C., 1962-95, editor-in-chief coll. dept., 1971-76, dep. dir. coll. dept., 1976-77, sr. v.p. Academic Press, Inc., 1977-80, exec. v.p. Academic Press, Inc., 1981-82; pres. The Psychol. Corp., San Antonio, 1982-88; v.p. Harcourt Brace & Co., Orlando, Fla., 1986-88, sr. v.p., 1988; v.p. Holt Rinehart & Winston Harcourt Brace, 1989-95, pres. Sch. Pubs., 1989-93, pres. Ednl. Devel. Group, 1993-94; pres. The Initiative for Better Learning Inc., Orlando, 1994—, T. Williamson Assocs., Inc., Windermere, Fla., 1995—. Bd. dirs. Quality Edn. for Minorities Network. Mem. AAAS, Internat. Reading Assn., Nat. Staff Devel. Coun., Japan Soc., The Nature Conservancy, Harvard Club, Bay Hill Club. Home: 10522 Down Lakeview Cir Windermere FL 34786-7906 Office: Initiative for Better Learning 6277 Sea Harbor Dr Orlando FL 32887

WILLIAMSON, THOMAS GARNETT, nuclear engineering and engineering physics educator; b. Quincy, Mass., Jan. 27, 1934; s. Robert Burwell and Elizabeth B. (McNeer) W.; m. Kaye Darlan Love, Aug. 16, 1961; children: Allen, Sarah, David. BS, Va. Mil. Inst., 1955; MS, Rensselaer Poly. Inst., 1957; PhD, U. Va., 1960. Asst. prof. nuclear engring. and engring. physics dept. U. Va., Charlottesville, 1960-62, assoc. prof., 1962-69, prof., 1969-90, prof. emeritus, 1990—, chmn. dept., 1977-90; sr. scientist Westinghouse Savannah River Labs., Aiken, S.C., 1990—; with Gen. Atomic (Calif.), 1965, Combustion Engring., Windsor, Conn., 1970-71, Los Alamos

Sci. Lab., 1969, Nat. Bur. Standards, Gaithersburg, Md., 1984-85; cons. Philippine Atomic Energy Commn., 1963, Va. Power Co., 1975-90, Babcock & Wilcox, Lynchburg, Va., 1975-90. Vestryman Ch. of Our Savior, Charlottesville, St. Thaddeus, Aiken, S.C. Fellow Am. Nuclear Soc.; mem. AAAS, Am. Soc. Engring. Edn., Sigma Xi, Tau Beta Pi. Episcopalian. Home: 217 Colleton Ave Aiken SC 29801 Office: Westinghouse Savannah River Labs Aiken SC 29806

WILLIAMSON, THOMAS SAMUEL, JR., lawyer; b. Plainfield, N.J., July 14, 1946; s. Thomas Samuel and Winifred (Hall) W.; married; 2 children. BA, Harvard U., 1968; postgrad., Oxford U., Eng. 1968-69; JD, U. Calif., Berkeley, 1974. Bar: D.C. 1975, Calif. 1975, U.S. Dist. Ct. D.C. 1977. Dir. tng. div. Alem Pub. Relations, Addis Ababa, Ethiopia, 1970-71; assoc. Covington & Burling, Washington, 1974-78, 81-82, ptnr., 1982-93; dep. inspector gen. U.S. Dept. Energy, Washington, 1978-81; solicitor U.S. Dept. Labor, Washington; ptnr. Covington & Burling, Washington; mem. exec. com. Washington Lawyers for Civil Rights Under Law, 1983-93, co-chair, 1990-92. Mem. vis. com. to dept. of athletics Harvard U., 1985-87. Rhodes scholar, 1968. Mem. ABA, Nat. Bar Assn., Coun. of Fgn. Rels., Washington Coun. Lawyers (bd. dirs. 1975-90). Avocations: camping, cycling. Home: 1663 Primrose Rd NW Washington DC 20012-1117 Office: US Dept Labor Solicitor Office 200 Constitution Ave NW Washington DC 20210

WILLIAMSON, WALKER KENDRICK, insurance executive; b. Ft. Worth, Tex., May 14, 1924; s. Mertz Kendrick and Bertie Hearn (Carson) W.; m. Nancy Jane Wilson, May 1, 1948 (dec. 1969); children: Blake Kendrick, Jane Elise; m. Laura Mary McKee, Jan. 29, 1972. BS in Econs., Tex. A & M U., 1947. Mgr., ptnr. Williamson Ins. Agy., Okla. City, Okla., 1947-55; spl. agt. No. British Ins. Group, OKla. City, 1955-58; mgr. No. British Ins. Group, Dallas, 1958-60; asst. mgr. Commi. Union, Dallas, 1960-61; spl. agt. Hartford Ins. Group, Okla. City, 1961-62; sr. spl. agt. Hartford Ins. Group, Dallas, 1962-72, asst. agy. mgr., 1972-76, mktg. mgr., 1976-82, mktg. adminstr., 1982-90. Hon. dep. commr. Okla. Ins. Commn., Oklahoma City, 1956; active Dallas Mus. Art, 1989—, Dallas Hist. Soc., 1989—, Dallas County Heritage Soc., 1989—, Highland Park Community League, Dallas, 1989—, Dallas Symphony Assn., 1989—. Capt. U.S. Army, 1943-46. Decorated Asiatic-Pacific Campaign medal with battle star, Am. Campaign medal, Army of Occupation medal with Japan clasp, World War II Victory medal. Mem. North Tex. Fieldmen's Assn. (pres. 1965-66), Okla. Fire Underwriters Assn. (pres. 1965-66), Okla. Fire Underwriters Assn. (pub. rels. dir. 1956-58), Dallas Country club (bd. govs. 1988-91, 93-96, chmn. ins. com. 1988-91, 94-96, ins. com. mem. 1981-82, 88-95, ho. com. mem. 1979-80, 84-85, 86-87, 91-95, interview com. mem. 1993-95), Masons (master). Republican. Presbyterian. Avocations: golf, sports. Home: 4205 Arcady Ave Dallas TX 75205-3701

WILLIAMSON, WILLIAM A., JR., medical products executive; b. 1936. BSBA, U. Ala. With Durr-Fillaner Med. Inc., Montgomery, Ala., 1958—, sec., treas., 1961-70, v.p., 1970-72, exec. v.p., 1972-74, now chmn. bd. dirs., chief exec. officer, 1974—. Office: Durr-Fillauer Med Inc 218 Commerce St. Montgomery AL 36104*

WILLIAMSON, WILLIAM FLOYD, JR., architect; b. Baton Rouge, Dec. 20, 1924; s. William Floyd and Georgie (Perkins) W.; m. Adele Redditt, Aug. 24, 1946; children: Adele Redditt Williamson Scielzo, Nancy Scott Williamson Cadwallader. B.S. in Architecture, Tulane U., 1947. Lic. architect, La. Treas., gen. mgr. La. Agrl. Supply Co., Inc., Baton Rouge, 1947-69; owner W.F. Williamson, Jr., Architect, Baton Rouge, 1970-74; pres., ptnr. Williamson-Carroll Architect, Inc., Baton Rouge, 1974—; chmn. Polit. Com. for Design Profls., La., 1975-83; chmn. Benefit Ins. Trust, 1981-82; trustee, vice-chmn. Architects Nat. Employers Trust, 1986—. Architect chmn. United Givers Fund Drive, Baton Rouge, 1978; bd. dirs. First United Meth. Ch., 1968-82. With USN, 1943-45. Fellow AIA (pres. Baton Rouge chpt. 1978, chmn. chpt. govt. affairs com. 1973-75, nat. trustee Benefit Ins. Trust 1978-83); mem. La. Inst. Bldg. Scis. (founding), La. Architects Assn. (pres. 1981, chmn. govtl. affairs com. 1973-78 commendation outstanding service), Delta Tau Delta. Republican. Club: Baton Rouge Country. Home: 920 N Foster Dr Baton Rouge LA 70806-1807 Office: Williamson & Carroll Architects PO Box 843 Baton Rouge LA 70821-0843

WILLIAMSON, WILLIAM PAUL, journalist; b. Des Moines, Mar. 30, 1929; s. William Paul and Florence Alice (Dawson) W.; m. Vania Torres Nogueira, Nov. 27, 1959; children—Mary Liz (Mrs. Omar Fernandez), Jon Thadeus, Margaret Ann(Mrs. Cesar Rocha). Student, Mex. City Coll., 1952, U. Havanna, 1955; B.A., U. No. Iowa, 1953; M.A., U. Iowa, 1954. Editor Brazilian Bus., Rio de Janeiro, 1958-60; mng. ptnr. Editora Mory Ltd., Rio de Janeiro, 1960-79; editor Brazil Herald, Rio de Janeiro, 1960-80; exec. dir. Inter Am. Press Assn., Miami, Fla., 1981-94, hon. life mem., mem. adv. coun., 1994—; dir. Inter Am. Press Assn., 1966-80, chmn. awards com. 1975-80; solo navigator 1st passage Madeira Island, Portugal-Madeira Island, Brazil, 1994-95. Editor for Brazil, Fodor's South America, 1970-79; contbr. articles to various newspapers and mags. Pres. Am. Soc., Rio de Janeiro, 1968; bd. dirs. Instituto Brasil-Estados Unidos, Rio de Janeiro, 1977-80, Am. C. of C. for Brazil, Rio de Janeiro, 1964-68. Served with USMC, 1946-48. Decorated Order of.Rio Branco (Brazil); recipient Citizen of Rio de Janeiro award State Legislature, 1975; Hon. Carioca award O Globo Newspaper, Rio de Janeiro, 1972; Ralph Greenburg award Am. Soc. Rio de Janeiro, 1977; Outstanding Svc. to Freedom of Expression and Newspapers awards Internat. Fedn. of Newspaper Pubs. and Internat. Assn. of Broadcasting, 1994; Benemeritous Citizen award Mcpl. Legislature, Itaquai, Brazil, 1995. Mem. Am. Soc. Assn. Execs., South Fla. Soc. Assn. Execs. (pres. 1987), Soc. Profl. Journalists, Overseas Press Club Am., Rio Yacht Club, Ilha da Madeira Yacht Club, Kappa Tau Alpha. Home: 2600 Castilla Is Fort Lauderdale FL 33301-1594 Office: Inter Am Press Assn 2911 NW 39th St Miami FL 33142-5148

WILLIE, CHARLES VERT, sociology educator; b. Dallas, Oct. 8, 1927; s. Louis James and Carrie (Sykes) W.; m. Mary Susannah Conklin, Mar. 31, 1962; children: Sarah Susannah, Martin Charles, James Theodore. BA, Morehouse Coll., 1948, DHL (hon.) 1983; MA, Atlanta U., 1949; PhD, Syracuse U., 1957, DHL (hon.), 1992; DD (hon.), Gen. Sem., 1974; DHL (hon.), Berkeley Div. Sch., Yale U., 1972, R.I. Coll., 1983, Johnson C. Smith U., Charlotte N.C. 1991; MA (hon.), Harvard U., 1974; DL (hon.), Framingham (Mass.) State Coll., 1992. Instr. to asst. prof. sociology Syracuse (N.Y.) U., 1952-63, assoc. prof., 1964-67, prof., 1968-74, chmn. dept. sociology, 1967-71, v.p., 1972-74; prof. edn. and urban studies Grad. Sch. Edn. Harvard U., 1974—; instr. dept. preventive medicine SUNY Upstate Med. Center, Syracuse, 1955-60; research dir. Washington Action for Youth delinquency prevention project, Pres.' Com. on Juvenile Delinquency and Youth Crime, Washington, 1962-64; vis. lectr. Lab. Community Psychiatry, Harvard U. Med. Sch., Boston, Mass., 1966-67; vis. lectr. edn. and soc. Episcopal Div. Sch., Cambridge, Mass., 1966-67; res's Commn. on Mental Health, 1977-78; mem. tech. adv. bd. Maurice Falk Med. Fund, 1968—; bd. dirs. Social Sci. Rsch. Coun., 1969-75; master Boston Sch. Desegregation case, Fed. Dist. Ct., 1975. Author: Church Action in the World, 1969, Black Students at White Colleges, 1972, Race Mixing in the Public Schools, 1973, Oreo, 1975, A New Look at Black Families, 1976, 2d edit., 1981, 3d edit., 1988, 4th edit., 1991, The Sociology of Urban Education, 1978, The Caste and Class Controversy on Race and Poverty, 1979, 2d edit., 1989, The Ivory and Ebony Towers, 1981, Race, Ethnicity and Socioeconomic Status, 1983, School Desegregation Plans That Work, 1984, Black and White Families, 1985, Five Black Scholars, 1986, (with Michael Grady) Metropolitan School Desegregation, 1986, Effective Education, 1987, (with Michael Grady and Richard Hope) African-Americans and the Doctoral Experience, 1991, Theories of Human Social Action, 1994; editor: The Family Life of Black People, 1970, (with B. Brown and B. Kramer) Racism and Mental Health, 1973, Black/Brown/White Relations, 1977, (with R. Edmonds) Black Colleges in America, 1978, (with S. Greenblatt) Community Politics and Educational Change, 1981, (with Inabeth Miller) Social Goals and Educational Reforms, 1988, (with A. Garibaldi and W. Reed), The Education of African-Americans, 1991, (with P. Rieker, B. Kramer and B. Brown) Mental Health, Racism and Sexism, 1995. Hon. trustee Episcopal Div. Sch., Cambridge, Mass.; mem. United Negro Coll. Fund, 1983-90; mem. nat. exec. coun. Episcopal ch., 1967-74, v.p. gen. conv., 1970-74; host Inner City Beat nat. pub. affairs weekly television program, monitor channel, 1991-92; mem. Maxwell Sch. Adv. bd. of Syracuse U.,

1992—. Recipient faculty svc. award Nat. Univ. Ext. Assn., 1969, 50th Anniversary Disting. Alumnus award Syracuse U. Maxwell Sch., 1974; Lee-Founders award Soc. for Study Social Problems, 1983, Disting. Family Scholar award, 1986; Disting. Career Contbn. award com. on role and status minorities in ednl. R & D, Am. Ednl. Rsch. Assn., 1990, Benjamin E. Mays Svc. award Morehouse Coll., 1994, Father John LaFarge, S.J. award Catholic Intergroup Rel. Coun., 1994. Mem. Am. Ednl. Rsch. Assn., Am. Sociol. Assn. (coun. 1980-83, DuBois-Johnson-Frazier award 1994), Ea. Sociol. Soc. (pres. 1974-75, Robin Williams Jr. Disting. Lectureship award 1994), Boston Mus. Sci. (overseer), Sociol. Rsch. Assn., Urban League (bd. dirs. Ea. Mass. 1975-77, trustee emeritus), Greeley Found. for Peace and Justice (bd. dirs. chmn. bd. 1989-92), Phi Beta Kappa, Alpha Phi Alpha. Episcopalian. Home: 41 Hillcrest Rd Concord MA 01742-4615 Office: Harvard U Grad Sch Edn 457 Gutman Libr 6 Appian Way Cambridge MA 02138-3704

WILLIFORD, DONALD BRATTON, accounting company executive; b. York, S.C., Sept. 20, 1936; s. Thomas Leslie and Florence Odessa (Brown) W.; m. Linda Craven, June 12, 1959; 1 child, Linda Sharon. BSBA, U. S.C., 1958. CPA, N.C. Jr. acct. J. P. Stevens, Charlotte, N.C., 1959; staff acct. Haskins & Sells, CPAs, Charlotte, 1959-62; with audit and tax div. Belk Stores Svcs., Inc., Charlotte, 1962-69; corp. sec. Ruddick Corp., Charlotte, 1969—. Mem. AICPA, N.C. Assn. CPA, Am. Soc. Corp. Secs., Risk and Ins. Mgmt. Soc., Employee Stock Ownership Plans Assn. (chair 1991-93), River Hills Country Club. Avocation: golf. Office: Ruddick Corp 2000 Two 1st Union Ctr Charlotte NC 28282

WILLIFORD, LAWRENCE HARDING, public relations company executive; b. Oakland, Calif., June 12, 1929; s. Albert Walter and Dorothy Katherine (Thompson) W.; m. Nancy Marbach; children—Laura, Jeffrey, Robert, Julie. B.S. in Bus. Adminstrn., Northwestern U., 1952. With All-state Ins. Co., Northbrook, Ill., 31 yrs., sr. v.p. corp. reis.; sr. v.p., bd. dirs. Hill and Knowlton, San Francisco; bd. dirs. Nat. Safety Council, Chgo., 1981—; mem. Nat. Commn. Against Drunk Driving, Washington, 1983—. Dep. trustee Neighborhood Housing Services of Am., Washington, 1982—; trustee Found. for Am. Communications, 1978—, Nat. Coll. Edn., Evanston, Ill., 1978—. Mem. Insurers Pub. Relations Council, Nat. Assn. Ind. Insurers, Pub. Relations Soc. Am., Am. Council Life Ins. Info. Inst. Republican. Lodge: Masons. Office: Hill and Knowlton Inc 177 Post St Ste 400 San Francisco CA 94108-4758

WILLIFORD, RICHARD ALLEN, oil executive, flight simulator company executive; b. Galveston, Tex., Dec. 24, 1934; s. Walter Hamilton and Marian Lela (Heartfield) W.; m. Mollie Marie Blansett, Feb. 16, 1957; children: Richard Allen Jr., Monica Marie Williford Powell. BS in Petroleum Engring., Tex. A&M U., 1956, BS in Geol. Engring., 1956. Registered profl. engr., Tex. Petroleum/reservoir engr. Gulf Oil Co., La., Tex., 1956-61; mgr. prodn. Tenneco Oil Co., Lafayette, La., and Denver, 1961-73; exec. v.p. Samson Resources Co., Tulsa, 1973-79; owner, chmn. Williford Energy Co., 1979—; chmn., CEO Williford, Inc., Tulsa, 1986—; Safety Tng. Systems, Inc., Tulsa, 1984—, Williford Bldg. Corp., Tulsa, 1990—; chmn. Engineered Equipment Systems, Tulsa, 1989—; past bd. dirs. Samson Resources Co., Tulsa, Tilco, Inc., Tulsa, Intersci. Capital Mgmt. Corp., Tulsa, W.R Leasing Co., Fourth Nat. Bank Tulsa, Sun Belt Bank & Trust Tulsa, Union Nat. Bank Tulsa. Patentee in field. Bd. dirs. Inst. Nautical Archaeology, 1993—, 12th Man Found., College Station, Tex., 1983-94; Tex. A&M Assn. Former Students, College Station, 1985-91, pres., 1989; bd. dirs., sr. v.p. Tulsa Opera, Inc., 1985—, Thomas Gilcrease Mus. Assn., Tulsa, 1987-93; trustee River Parks Authority, Tulsa, 1987-93, chmn. bd. trustees, 1993-94; trustee, chmn. Tex. A&M Devel. Found., 1991—, Verde Valley Sch., Sedona, Ariz., 1983-86; pres. exec. bd. Indian Nations coun. Boy Scouts Am. Recipient Disting. Achievement medal Geoscis. and Resource Coun., Tex. A&M U., 991, Humanitarian award Nat. Jewish Ctr. for Immunology, 1994. Mem. Ind. Petroleum Assn. Am., Soc. Petroleum Engrs., Okla. Ind. Producers Assn., Tex. Ind. Producers & Royalty Owners Assn., Masons, Shriners, Royal Order Jesters, So. Hills Country Club, The Golf Club Okla., Philcrest Tennis Club, The Summit Club, Plaza Club, Tex. A&M Faculty Club, Tau Beta Pi. Republican. Methodist. Avocations: golf, hunting, fishing, flying, scuba diving. Home: 6730 S Evanston Ave Tulsa OK 74136-4509 Office: Williford Cos 5314 S Yale St 770 Tulsa OK 74135

WILLIG, KARL VICTOR, computer firm executive; b. Idaho Falls, Idaho, June 4, 1944; s. Louis Victor and Ethel (McCarty) W.; m. Julianne Erickson, June 10, 1972; 1 son, Ray. BA magna cum laude, Coll. of Idaho, 1968; MBA (Dean Donald Kirk David fellow), Harvard U., 1970. Pres. Ariz. Beef, Inc., Phoenix, 1971-73; group v.p. Ariz.-Colo. Land & Cattle Co., Phoenix, 1973-76; v.p. Rufenacht, Bromagen & Hertz, Inc., Chgo., 1976-77; pres. Sambo's Restaurants, Inc., Santa Barbara, Calif., 1977-79; ptnr. Santa Barbara Capital, 1979-85; pres. EURUSA Equities Corp., 1985-86; pres., chief exec. officer InfoGenesis, 1986—; trustee Am. Bapt. Sem. of West, 1977-85. Named one of Outstanding Young Men of Am., 1972; recipient Assn. of U.S. Army award, 1964.

WILLIG, ROBERT DANIEL, economics educator; b. Bklyn., Jan. 16, 1947; s. Jack David and Meg W.; m. Virginia Mason, July 8, 1973; children: Jared Mason, Scott Mason, Brent Mason, Alexandra Mason. BA, Harvard U., 1967; MS in Ops. Rsch., Stanford U., 1968, PhD in Econs, 1973. Lectr. Stanford U., Palo Alto, Calif. 1971-73; mem. tech. staff Bell Labs., Holmdel, N.J., 1973-77; supr. dept. econs. rsch. Bell Labs., 1977-78; prof. econs. and pub. affairs Princeton U., 1978—; mem. Aspen Inst. Task Force on Future of Postal Svc., 1978-80; dep. asst. atty. gen. U.S. Dept. Justice, Washington, 1989-91; cons. in field; rsch. fellow U. Warwick, Eng., 1977; mem. organizing com. Telecomm. Policy Rsch. Conf., 1977-78; mem. rsch. adv. bd. Am. Enterprise Inst., 1980-88; mem. N.J. Gov.'s Task Force on Market-Based Pricing of Electricity, 1987; bd. dirs. Cons. in Industry Econs., Inc., 1983—; mem. Def. Sci. Bd. Task Force on Antitrust for the Def. Industry, 1993-94. Author: Welfare Analysis of Policies Affecting Prices and Products, 1973, Contestable Markets and the Theory of Industry Structure, 1982; editor: Handbook of Industrial Organization, 1986; contbr. articles to profl. jours. mem. editorial bd.: M.I.T. Press Series on Govt. Regulation, 1978—, Am. Econ. Rev., 1980-83, Jour. Indsl. Econs., 1985-89, Utility Policy, 1989—. Mem. adv. bd. B'nai B'rith Hillel Found., Princeton U., 1978—. NSF grantee, 1979-85. Fellow Econometric Soc. (program com. 1978-81); mem. Am. Econ. Assn. (nominating com. 1980-81). Office: Princeton U Princeton NJ 08540

WILLIMON, WILLIAM HENRY, minister, educator; b. Greenville, S.C., May 15, 1946; s. Robert Charles and Ruby (Steer) W.; m. Patricia Parker, June 7, 1969; children: William Parker, Harriet Patricia. BA, Wofford Coll., 1968, DLitt (hon.), 1994; MDiv, Yale U., 1970; STD, Emory U., 1972; DD (hon.), Westminster Coll., New Wilmington, Pa., 1990, Lehigh U., 1995. Ordained to ministry United Meth. Ch., 1972. Pastor Level Creek/Trinity United Meth. Chs., Buford, Ga., 1970-71; assoc. pastor Broad St. United Meth. Ch., Clinton, S.C., 1971-73; pastor Trinity United Meth. Ch., North Myrtle Beach, S.C., 1973-76; assoc. prof. Duke Divinity Sch., Durham, N.C., 1976-80; pastor Northside United Meth. Ch., Greenville, S.C., 1980-84; minister to univ., prof. Duke U., Durham, 1984-89, dean of chapel, prof., 1989—. Author: Why I Am a United Methodist, 1990, Clergy and Laity Burnout, 1988, Acts of the Apostles, Interpretation, A Commentary for Teaching and Preaching, 1988, The Promise of Marriage, 1988, Preaching About Conflict in the Local Church, 1987, Rekindling the Flame, 1987, With Glad and Generous Hearts, 1986, The Laugh Shall Be First, 1986, Sighing for Eden, 1985, What's Right With the Church, 1984, Handbook on Preaching and Worship, 1984, On A Wild and Windy Mountain, 1984, many other books. 1st lt. U.S. Army, 1969-70. Fellow N.Am. Acad. of Liturgy; mem. Phi Beta Kappa. Home: 3104 Doubleday Pl Durham NC 27705-5412 Office: Dean Chapel Duke U Durham NC 27706

WILLINGHAM, CLARK SUTTLES, lawyer; b. Houston, Nov. 29, 1944; s. Paul Suttles and Elsie Dell (Clark) W.; m. Jane Joyce Hitch, Aug. 16, 1969; children: Meredith Moores, James Barrett. BBA, Tex. Tech U., 1967; JD, So. Meth. U., 1971, LLM, 1984. Bar: Tex. 1971. Ptnr. Kasmir, Willingham & Krage, Dallas, 1972-86, Finley, Kumble et al, Dallas, 1986-87, Mankoff, Hill, Held & Metzger and predecessor, Dallas, 1988—; mem. Tex. Bd. Vet. Med. Examiners, 1991-95, pres., 1994. Contbr. articles to profl. jours. Mem. exec. com. Dallas Summer Musicals, 1979-93, pres., 1994—). Mem. ABA (chmn. agrl. com. tax sect. 1984-86), Dallas Bar Assn., State Bar Tex.

(chmn. agrl. tax com. 1985-87), Am. Law Inst., Nat. Cattlemen's Assn. (bd. dirs., pres.-elect 1995), Tex. Cattle Feeders Assn. (bd. dirs., pres. 1987-88), U.S. Meat Export Fedn. (bd. dirs., exec. com. 1991-93), Beef Industry Coun. (bd. dirs., exec. com. 1990-91, promotion chmn. 1992-94), Dallas Country Club. Republican. Episcopalian. Home: 3824 Shenandoah St Dallas TX 75205-1702 Office: Mankoff Hill Held & Metzger One Turtle Creek Village Ste 400 Dallas TX 75219

WILLINGHAM, JEANNE MAGGART, dance educator, ballet company executive; b. Fresno, Calif., May 8, 1923; d. Harold F. and Gladys (Ellis) Maggart. student Tex. Woman's U., 1942; student profl. dancing schs., worldwide. dance tchr. Beaux Arts Dance Studio, Pampa, Tex., 1948—; artistic dir. Pampa Civic Ballet, 1972—. Mem. Tex. Arts and Humanities, Tex. Arts Alliance, Pampa C. of C. (fine arts com.), Pampa Fine Arts Assn. Office: Pampa Civic Ballet Beaux Arts Dance Studio 315 N Nelson St Pampa TX 79065-6013

WILLINGHAM, WARREN WILLCOX, psychologist, testing service executive; b. Rome, Ga., Mar. 1, 1930; s. Calder Baynard and Eleanor (Willcox) W.; m. Anna Michal, Mar. 17, 1954; children: Sherry, Judith, Daniel. Student, Ga. Inst. Tech., 1952; PhD, U. Tenn., 1955. Rsch. assoc. World Book Co., N.Y.C., 1959-60; dir. evaluation studies Ga. Inst. Tech., Atlanta, 1960-64; dir. rsch. Coll. Bd., N.Y.C., 1964-68; dir. access rsch. office Coll. Bd., Palo Alto, Calif., 1968-72; asst. v.p., disting. rsch. scientist Ednl. Testing Svc., Princeton, N.J., 1972—; vis. prof. U. Minn., 1988; mem. adv. bd. on ednl. requirements on Sec. Navy, 1968; cons. to numerous schs., colls. U.S. Office Edn. Author: Free Access Higher Education, 1970, Source Book for Higher Education, 1973, College Placement and Exemption, 1974, Assessing Experiential Learning, 1977, Selective Admissions in Higher Education, 1977, Personal Qualities and College Admissions, 1982, Success in College, 1985, Testing Handicapped People, 1988, Predicting College Grades, 1990; editor: Measurement in Education, 1969-72; mem. editorial bds.: Jour. Ednl. Measurement, 1971-75, Alternate Higher Education, 1976-80, Am. Ednl. Research Jour, 1968-71; contbr. articles, tech. reports to profl. jours. Served to lt. USNR, 1955-59. Recipient Ann. award So. Soc. Philosophy and Psychology, 1958. Fellow Am. Psychol. Assn., AAAS; mem. Nat. Council on Measurement in Edn. (dir.), Am. Ednl. Research Assn., Sigma Xi. Office: Edn Testing Svc Princeton NJ 08540

WILLIS, BEVERLY ANN, architect; b. Tulsa, Feb. 17, 1928; d. Ralph William and Margaret Amanda (Porter) W. BFA, U. Hawaii, 1954; PhD in Fine Arts (hon.), Mt. Holyoke Coll., 1983. Prin. Willis Atelier, Honolulu, 1954-66, Willis & Assocs., Inc., San Francisco, 1966-80, Beverly Willis Architects, N.Y.C., 1990—; dir., Architecture Rsch. Inst., Inc., N.Y.C. 1993—. Prin. works include Union St. Stores (Merit award San Francisco chpt. AIA, Award Distinction State of Calif.), Nob Hill Cts. (Merit award AIA), 1970, Margaret Hayward Park (Grand and Merit awards Pacific Coast Bldg. Conf., Hon. award Design Internat.), 1983, San Francisco Ballet bldg., 1984; contbr. articles to profl. jours. and chpts. to books. Trustee Nat. Bldg. Mus., Washington, 1976—; bldng. rsch. adv. bd. Nat. Acad. Sci., 1971-79, chair Fed. Construction Coun., 1976-79. Recipient Phoebe Hearst Gold Medal award, 1969. Fellow AIA; mem. Achievement Rewards for Coll. Scientists, Internat. Women's Forum, Lambda Alpha Internat. (pres. San Francisco chpt. 1981-82). Club: Villa Taverna (San Francisco). Avocations: poetry, sketching, walking. Office: 119 East 35th St New York NY 10016 also: PO Box 669 Stockbridge MA 01262

WILLIS, BRUCE WALTER, actor, singer; b. Fed. Republic of Germany, Mar. 19, 1955; came to U.S., 1957; s. David and Marlene Willis; m. Demi Moore; children: Rumer Glenn, Scout Larve, Tallulah Belle. Student, Montclair State Coll.; studied with Stella Adler. mem. First Amendment Comedy Theatre. Actor: (off-Broadway prodns.) Heaven and Earth, 1977, Fool for Love, 1984, The Bullpen, The Bayside Boys, The Ballad of Railroad William, (TV film) Trackdown, (feature films) Prince of the City, 1981, The Verdict, 1982, Blind Date, 1987, Sunset, 1988, Die Hard, 1988, In Country, 1989 (Golden Globe nomination 1990), Look Who's Talking (voice), 1989, Die Hard 2: Die Harder, 1990, Bonfire of the Vanities, 1990, Mortal Thoughts, 1991, Hudson Hawk, 1991, Billy Bathgate, 1991, The Last Boy Scout, 1991, Death Becomes Her, 1992, Striking Distance, 1993, Color of Night, 1994, North, 1994, Pulp Fiction, 1994, Nobody's Fool, 1994, Color of Night, 1994, Die Hard With a Vengeance, 1995; guest star (TV series) Miami Vice, The Twilight Zone; regular (TV series) Moonlighting, 1985-89 (People's Choice award 1986, Emmy award 1987, Golden Globe award 1987), musician (TV spl.) The Return of Bruno, 1986; rec. artist (album) The Return of Bruno, 1987, If It Don't Kill You, It Just Makes You Stronger, 1989; appeared in numerous commls. Named Internat. Broadcasting Man of Yr. Hollywood Radio and TV Soc. *

WILLIS, CLAYTON, broadcaster, corporation executive, former government official, educator, arts consultant, photojournalist, lecturer; b. Washington, Aug. 11, 1933; s. William H. and Elizabeth Carl (Keferstein) W. Student, The Sorbonne, Paris, 1953-54; BA, George Washington U., 1957; student, U. Oslo, 1953; grad., N.Y. Inst. Fin., 1966, Assn. Commodities Exch. Firms Inc., 1966. Spl. assignment Am. Embassy, London, 1957; writer NBC Network radio show Tex and Jinx, 1958; spl. corr. NBC News, La Paz, Bolivia, 1959; spl. Washington corr. Fin. News TV Network (now CNBC), N.Y.C., 1988; contbr., corr. Saudi Arabian TV, Newsweek mag., Philips News Svc. The Hope (Ark.) Star, Christian Sci. Monitor, L.A. Times-Mirror Syndicate, The Palm Beach (Fla.) Post, The Greenwich (Conn.) Time, The Bar Harbor (Maine) Times, Info-Explo Mining Jour., Rouyn-Noranda, Que., Can., Fin. News TV Network, New York, The Mainichi, Tokyo, The China Post, Taipei, Taiwan, Chattanooga Times, The Nashville Tennesseean, the Daily Nation of Kenya, The Khartoum Echo, Sudan, The Washington Daily News, Washington Post, Cape Argus of Capetown, South Africa, Bangkok Post, Irish Times, Dublin; reporter, movie, art critic Albuquerque Tribune, 1959-61; asst. editor Newsweek Mag., N.Y.C., 1961-62; TV broadcaster-writer UPI Newsfilm, N.Y.C., 1962; White House, Washington corr., chief bur., anchor World Radio News, Houston; White House, Washington corr. WAVA Radio Sta., Washington, 1963-65; editorial writer, corr. Hearst Newspapers, N.Y.C., 1965; press officer UN, N.Y.C., 1965-66; spl. assignment Am. Embassys, Reykjavik, Iceland, 1967; editorial writer, critic, reporter N.Y. Amsterdam News, N.Y.C., 1967-68; cons. Ford Found., N.Y.C., 1968-69; dir. pub. affairs U.S. EEOC, Washington, 1969-70; cons. OEO, Washington, 1970, Pres.'s Nat. Coun. on Indian Opportunity, Washington, 1970-71, Community Rels. Svc., U.S. Dept. Justice, Washington, 1970-73, Cabinet Com. on Opportunities for Spanish-Speaking People, 1971-72, Fed. Energy Adminstrn., Washington, 1973-74; dir. pub. affairs Office Petroleum Allocation U.S. Dept. Interior, 1973-74; dir. Congl. rels., dir. pub. affairs Pres.'s Nat. Commn. on Fire Prevention and Control, 1971-73; pub., editor, owner Four Corners Chieftain, Ignacio and Durango, Colo., 1972-73; lectr. Sch. of Bus., U. D.C., Washington, 1973-74; owner, White House corr., photojournalist Willis News Svc., Washington, 1974—; pub. affairs dir. Inaugural Vets. Com., 1976-77; White House corr., photojournalist Washington Life mag., 1993—; anchor Channel 33, Arlington, Va., 1991—; adviser to Fernando E.C. de Baca, spl. asst. to the Pres., White House, 1974-76; lectr. nat., internat. affairs, Haiti, art, communications, strategic and precious metals, diamond, nickel, copper, and cobalt mining, energy; corr.-broadcaster Sta. KTEN-TV, Ada, Okla., 1985; mem. staff presdl. transition office U.S. Pres. Bush, 1988-89, 90; anchor, pres. 30 minutes with Clayton Willis, 2000 Today With Clayton Willis; pres., anchor, exec. producer TV show 30 Minutes with Clayton Willis, PBS, 1990; dir. L. Clayton Willis Art Collection, Washington; anchor, corr. Channel 33 Arlington, Va., 1991—; pres., White House corr., congressional corr., photojournalist, Evening News Broadcasting Co., Washington and Willis World TV Show Ltd. with Clayton Willis, Alexandria, 1991—, 30 Mins. with Clayton Willis, and Willis News Service; prodr., anchor documentary programs Saudi Arabian TV, 1992—; exec. prodr., anchor Glimpses of the World documentaries, 1993; White House corr., photojournalist Hope (Ark.) Star, 1994—. Contbg. author: Capital Fare; contbr. articles to Daily Mail, London, London Sunday Express, Umtali Post, Zimbabwe, Gwelo (Zimbabwe) Times, To the Point news mag., Johannesburg, The Citizen, Johannesburg, Hartford Courant, Sacramento Union, Chattanooga Times, UPI Radio Networks, Washington Post, The Hope (Ark.) Star, Phillpis News Svc., also other mags. and newspapers. Broadcaster with Bush/Quayle Nat. Campaign Hdqrs., Won, 1988; adviser Presdl. Transition Office of Pres. George Bush, 1988-89; loaned Haitian paintings for spl. exhbn. to Haitian Embassy, Washington, 1991, Milw. Art Mus., 1992. Recipient Outstanding Svc. award Harlem Prep. Sch., Johannes

Gutenberg medal, 1984, Letters of Cert. Appreciation Pres. of U.S., 1989. Mem. Monterey Country Club, Blue Ridge Summit, Penna. Club: Overseas Press of Am.; Monterey Country Club, Blue Ridge Summit, Pa. Covered Vietnam, Congo, Mid. East, Rhodesian and South African wars; visited 150 countries; specialist gold, diamond, energy, silver, platinum, nickel, copper, and cobalt mining and strategic minerals; covered Clarence Thomas and Robert Gates U.S. Senate confirmation hearings, 1991. Home and Office: Evening News Broadcasting Co PO Box 25617 Washington DC 20007

WILLIS, CLIFFORD LEON, geologist; b. Chanute, Kans., Feb. 20, 1913; s. Arthur Edward and Flossie Duckworth (Fouts) W.; m. Serreta Margaret Thiel, Aug. 21, 1947 (dec.); 1 child, David Gerard. BS in Mining Engring., U. Kans., 1939; PhD, U. Wash., 1952. Geophysicist The Carter Oil Co. (Exxon), Tulsa, 1939-42; instr. U. Wash., Seattle, 1946-50, asst. prof., 1950-54; cons. geologist Harza Engring. Co., Chgo., 1952-54, 80-82, chief geologist, 1954-57, assoc. and chief geologist, 1957-67, v.p., chief geologist, 1967-80; pvt. practice cons. geologist Tucson, Ariz., 1982—; cons. on major dam projects in Iran, Iraq, Pakistan, Greece, Turkey, Ethiopia, Argentina, Venezuela, Colombia, Honduras, El Salvador, Iceland, U.S. Lt. USCG, 1942-46. Recipient Haworth Disting. Alumnus award U. Kans., 1963. Fellow Geol. Soc. Am., Geol. Soc. London; mem. Am. Assn. Petroleum Geologists, Soc. Mining, Metallurgy and Exploration Inc., Assn. Engring. Geologists, Sigma Xi, Tau Beta Pi, Sigma Tau. Republican. Roman Catholic. Avocations: travel, reading. Home: 4795 E Quail Creek Dr Tucson AZ 85718-2630

WILLIS, CONNIE (CONSTANCE E. WILLIS), author; b. 1945. Tchr. elem. and jr. high schs. Branford, Conn., 1967-69. Author: short stories/ novels) Letter from the Clearys (Nebula award 1982, Hugo award 1983), Lincoln's Dreams, 1987, Doomsday Book (Nebula award 1992, Hugo award 1993), Impossible Things, 1993, Uncharted Territory, 1994, Even the Queen (Nebula 1992, Hugo 1993), (novelette) Fire Watch (Nebula 1982, Hugo 1983), At the Rialto (Nebula 1990), The Last of the Winnebagos (Nebula 1988, Hugo 1989), Death on the Nile (Hugo 1994), (novel) Uncharted Territory, 1994, Remake, 1995; (with Cynthia Felice) Water Witch, 1982, Light Raid, 1989. Address: 1716 13th Ave Greeley CO 80631-5418

WILLIS, CRAIG DEAN, university president; b. Cambridge, Ohio, Mar. 21, 1935; s. John Russell and Glenna (Stevens) W.; m. Marilyn Elaine Foster, June 9, 1956; Mark Craig, Bruce Dean, Todd Laine, Garth John. B.A., Ohio Wesleyan U, 1957; M.A., Ohio State U., 1960, Ph.D., 1969. Registrar Ohio Wesleyan U., 1964-69; dir. admissions Wright State U., 1970-72, dean, 1971-77; v.p. acad. affairs Concord Coll., 1977-82; pres. Lock Haven U., Pa., 1982—; vice chmn. Clinton region Mellon Bank Cen., 1987, chmn., 1988, also bd. dirs.; bd. dirs. Lock Haven U., Lock Haven Hosp.; chmn. Lock Haven Hosp. Health Fund; cons. Ellis Assocs., Princeton, W.Va., 1980-82. Chmn. bd. Kirkmont Preschool, Beavercreek, Ohio, 1974-77, Beavercreek Library, 1976-77, Regional Edn. Service Agy., Beckley, W.Va., 1978-82; mem. N.E.-Midwest leadership Coun., 1989—. Recipient Disting. Alumnus award dept. edn. Ohio Wesleyan U., 1991; scholar Sohio Oil, 1953, Govt. of France, Paris, 1964, Shell Oil Co., 1967. Mem. Commn. State Coll. and Univ. Pres., Assn. State Colls. and Univs., Rotary (Citizen of Yr. award Lock Haven 1989), Ohio Wesleyan U. Alumni Assn. (Disting. Sesquicentennial Alumnus of the Edn. 1992), Phi Kappa Phi, Kappa Kappa Psi, Phi Delta Kappa, Kappa Delta Pi. Presbyterian. Office: Lock Haven U North Fairview St Lock Haven PA 17745

WILLIS, DAVID EDWIN, retired geophysicist; b. Cleve., Mar. 13, 1926; s. Russell E. and Eleanor Marie (Himebaugh) W.; m. Martha Louise Mumma, Jan. 3, 1948; children: Karen, Mark, Marta, Seth. B.S., Case Western Res. U., 1950; M.S. (U. Mich. Engring. Research Inst. fellow), U. Mich., 1957, Ph.D., 1968. Party chief, asst. supr. Keystone Exploration Co., Houston, 1950-55; research geophysicist, geophysics lab. head U. Mich., Ann Arbor, 1955-70; assoc. prof. U. Mich., 1968-70; prof. dept. geol. sci. U. Wis., Milw., 1970-82; chmn. dept. U. Wis., 1972-76; v.p. Geo-Aid Corp., 1975-80; sr. geophysicist UNOCAL, Los Angeles, 1982-92; geophysical cons. Richmond, Tex., 1992-93. Contbr. articles to profl. jours. Served with USNR, 1944-46. NSF grantee, 1964-79; Air Force Office Sci. Research grantee, 1958-76; AEC grantee, 1971-74; ERDA grantee, 1974-77. Fellow Geol. Soc. Am.; mem. Seismol. Soc. Am., Soc. Exploration Geophysicists, Am. Assn. Petroleum Geologists, L.A. Basin Geol. Soc., Phi Beta Kappa, Sigma Xi, Phi Kappa Phi. Home: 1311 Woodfair Dr Richmond TX 77469-6650

WILLIS, DAVID LEE, radiation biology educator; b. Pasadena, Calif., Mar. 15, 1927; s. Olan Garnet and Ida May (Lott) W.; m. Earline L. Fleischman, Dec. 26, 1950; children: David Lee, Paul J., Daniel N. B.Th., Biola Sem., Los Angeles, 1949; B.A., Biola U., 1951; B.S., Wheaton (Ill.) Coll., 1952; M.A., Calif. State U., Long Beach, 1954; Ph.D., Oreg. State U., 1963. Tchr. sci. various high schs., Calif., 1952-57; instr. biology Fullerton (Calif.) Coll., 1957-61; mem. faculty Oreg. State U., Corvallis, 1962—, prof. radiation biology, 1971-87, prof. emeritus, 1987—, chmn. dept. gen. sci., 1969-85; mem. Hanford Health Effects Panel, 1986; cons. in radioecology. Co-author: Radiotracer Methodology in Biological Science, 1965, Life in the Laboratory, 1965, Radiotracer Methodology in the Biological, Environmental and Physical Sciences, 1975. Mem. Am. Sci. Affiliation (pres. 1975), Health Physics Soc., Radiation Research Soc. Republican. Baptist. Home: 3135 NW McKinley Dr Corvallis OR 97330-1139 Office: Oreg State Univ Radiation Ctr Corvallis OR 97331-5901

WILLIS, DOYLE HENRY, state legislator, lawyer; b. Kaufman, Tex., Aug. 18, 1908; s. Alvin and Eliza Jane (Phillips) W.; m. Evelyn McDavid, 1942; children: Doyle Jr., Dan, Dina, Dale. BS, BA, U. Tex., 1934; LLB, Georgetown U., 1938. Bar: D.C. 1937, Tex. 1938, U.S. Supreme Ct. 1942. Mem. coun. City of Fort Worth, 1963-64; mem. Tex. Ho. of Reps., Austin, 1946-52, 1969—, Tex. State Senate, Austin, 1952-62. Maj. USAF, 1941-46, PTO. Decorated Bronze Star, 4 battle stars, USAF. Mem. KP Club, Masons (life), Shriners (life), Ind. Order Odd Fellows., Lions Club. Democrat. Methodist. Avocations: golf, fishing, reading. Home: 3316 Browning Ct Fort Worth TX 76111 Office: Sinclair Bldg Fort Worth TX 76102

WILLIS, EDWARD CHARLES, legislator; b. Barstow, Calif., Nov. 29, 1923; s. Charlie Brice and Mary Elizabeth (Indihar) W.; m. Joyce Houtz, June 23, 1949; children: Steve (dec.), Rodney, Charles, Linda, Marla. Student, San Bernadino C.C., 1941-42. Lessee, operator svc. sta. Barstow, 1948-49; power plant engr. Dept. of Army, Alaska, 1950-74; maintenance worker State of Alaska, 1979-84. Rep. Alaska Ho. of Reps., 1993—; senator Alaska State Senate, 1975-78; assemblyman Anchorage Borough Assembly, 1966-74, pres., 1973-74, 69-70; mem. Chugiak (Alaska) Adv. Sch. Bd., 1961-63; co-chair Operation Chugiak High Sch., 1961-63. With USCG/Merchant Marines, 1944-47, PTO. Decorated Mcht. Marine emblem Pacific War Zone Bar; recipient Bear Paw award Chugiak-Eagle River C. of C., 1970, Appreciation honor Alaskan VFW, 1993. Mem. NRA, Mothers Against Drunk Driving, Alaska Retarded Citizens Assn., Am. Legion (life) Alaska Legionnaire of Yr. (1994), Alpine Alternatives (bd. dirs. 1990), Am. Assn. Ret. Persons, Ret. Officers Assn. (hon.), Elks. Office: 11940 Business Blvd Eagle River AK 99577

WILLIS, EVERETT IRVING, lawyer; b. Canadian, Tex., Oct. 28, 1908; s. Newton Percy and Lena (Powers) W.; m. Margaret Virginia Wilson, Dec. 25, 1935; children: Everett Irving, Robert Frampton. Student, Austin Coll., Sherman, Tex., 1924-26; AB, U. Mo., 1928; LLB magna cum laude, Harvard U., 1932. Bar: N.Y. 1933. With firm Dewey Ballantine (and predecessors), N.Y.C., 1932—; ptnr., 1944—. Mem. Bd. of Edn., Rye, N.Y., 1946-52, pres., 1951-52. Recipient drug industry Man of Year award, 1964. Mem. ABA (council pub. utilities sect. 1966-69), N.Y. State Bar Assn., Assn. Bar City N.Y., N.Y. County Lawyers Assn., Phi Beta Kappa, Sigma Nu, Alpha Pi Zeta. Republican. Presbyterian. Clubs: Univ. (N.Y.C.), City Midday (N.Y.C.); Manursing Island (Rye, N.Y.), Apawamis (Rye, N.Y.). Home: 59 Hillandale Rd Rye Brook NY 10573-1704 Office: 1301 Avenue Of The Americas New York NY 10019-6022

WILLIS, FRANK EDWARD, retired air force officer; b. Clinton, Ill., June 19, 1939; s. William Edward and Bernardine (Saveley) W.; m. Clarice Marie Hull, June 7, 1961; children: Michael, Steven, William. BS in Engring., USAF Acad., Colorado Springs, Colo., 1961; MA in Bus. Mgmt., U. Nebr.,

1973. Commd. 2d lt. USAF, 1961, advanced through grades to maj. gen., 1989; dep. comdr. 314th Tactical Airlift Group, Little Rock AFB, 1978-79, comdr., 1979-80; vice comdr. 374th Tactical Airlift Wing, Clark Air Base, The Philippines, 1980-81, comdr., 1981-83; comdr. 317th Tactical Airlift Wing, Pope AFB, N.C., 1983-84; vice comdr. Air Force Manpower and Pers. Ctr., Randolph AFB, Tex., 1984-85; comdr. Air Command and Staff Coll., Maxwell AFB, Ala., 1985-88; vice comdr. 22d Air Force, Travis AFB, Calif., 1988-89; dir. and dep. chief of staff for requirements Air Mobility and Mil. Airlift Command, Scott AFB, Ill., 1989-93; ret., 1993. Decorated D.S.M. (2), Legion of Merit (2), Air medal (7), Meritorious Svc. medal (2). Presbyterian. Avocations: electronics, computers, model railroading. Home: 1901 Mistflower Glen Ct Chesterfield MO 63005-4317

WILLIS, FRANK ROY, history educator; b. Prescot, Lancashire, Eng., July 25, 1930; s. Harry and Gladys Reid (Birchall) W.; m. Mary K. Willis, Oct. 2, 1959; children: Jane, Clare, Geoffrey. BA, Cambridge (Eng.) U., 1952, cert. in edn., 1955, diploma in devel. econs., 1974; PhD, Stanford U., 1959. Instr. Stanford (Calif.) U., 1959-60; from instr. to assoc. prof. history U. Wash., Seattle, 1960-64; assoc. prof. then prof. U. Calif., Davis, 1964—. Author: The French in Germany, 1962, France, Germany and the New Europe, 1945-1967, 1968, Europe in the Global Age, 1968, Italy Chooses Europe, 1971, Western Civilization: An Urban Perspective, 1973, World Civilizations, 1982, Western Civilization, 1982, Western Civilization: A Brief Introduction, 1987. Fellow Rockefeller Found., Paris, 1962-63, Guggenheim Found., 1966-67, Social Scis. Research Council, Cambridge, 1973-74. Avocation: travel. Office: Univ of Calif Davis Dept Of History Davis CA 95616

WILLIS, FRANKLIN KNIGHT, lawyer, environmental services company executive; b. Detroit, Aug. 26, 1942; s. Edgar Ernest and Zella Carrine (Nobles) W. BA magna cum laude, Harvard U., 1966; JD cum laude, U. Mich., 1969. Staff atty. Dept. of State, Washington, 1969-75, asst. legal adviser African affairs, 1975-76; asst. legal adviser Inter-Am. affairs Dept. of State, 1976-78, asst. legal adviser econ. and bus. affairs, 1978-80, asst. legal adviser Near Eastern and South Asian affairs, 1980-81, dep. asst. sec. transp. and telecommunications, 1983-85; dep. asst. sec. for policy and internat. affairs Dept. of Transp., 1981-83; chmn. bd., chief exec. officer Rollins Environ. Svcs. (LA) Inc., Baton Rouge, 1986-89; v.p. legal and environ. affairs Rollins Environ. Svcs. (DE) Inc., Wilmington, Del., 1986-91; group v.p. legal, environ. affairs Rollins Environ. Svcs. (DE) Inc., Wilmington, 1992—. Mem. editorial bd. Mich. Law Rev., 1967-69. Baptist. Home: 14 Cinnamon Dr Hockessin DE 19707-1349 Office: Rollins Environ Svcs Inc 1 Rollins Plz Wilmington DE 19899

WILLIS, GARY K., computer company executive; b. 1946. With Foxboro (Mass.) Corp., nat. sales mgr., 1979-82, gen. mgr., 1982-84, now pres., dir. Office: The Foxboro Co 38 Neponset Ave Foxboro MA 02035-2098

WILLIS, GEORGE EDMUND, chemical processing and electrical manufacturing executive; b. Newmarket, Ont., Can., July 16, 1920; came to U.S., 1925; s. George Clarence and Marion Romer (Gillespie) W.; m. Dorothy Anne Rice, June 7, 1943; children: Dorothy Anne, Jacqueline Pamela, Marion Jean, George Patterson Rice, James Edmund, Lorna Isabel; m. Rolande Germaine deLipowski Hastings, July 23, 1983; stepchildren: Julian Martin, Marianne Frances. BSchemE cum laude, Mich. State U., 1942; MBA, Harvard U., 1947; DHL (hon.), Lake Erie Coll., 1984. Engr. Lincoln Electric Co., Cleve., 1947-51, supt., 1951-59, v.p., 1959-69, exec. v.p., 1969-72, pres., 1972-87, chief exec. officer, 1987—; also chmn. bd.; bd. dirs. Lincoln Big Three, Inc., Baton Rouge, Big Three Lincoln Alaska, Inc., Anchorage, Big Three Lincoln (U.K.) Ltd., Ross-Shire Scotland, Lincoln Electric Co. (Europe) S.A., Grand-Quevilly, France, Lincoln Electric Co. Can., Ltd., Toronto, Ont., Lincoln Electric Co. (Australia) Pty., Ltd. Chmn. bd. trustees, treas. Camp Ho Mita Koda; bd. govs. Geauga County YMCA; bd. trustees Lake Erie Coll.; trustee, exec. com. Cleve. Council World Affairs, active Cleve. Com. Fgn. Relations. Served to maj. AUS, 1942-46, ETO. Decorated Bronze Star with oak leaf cluster. Mem. Am. Welding Soc., Wire Assn., Greater Cleve. Growth Assn., Cleve. Engring. Soc., Elec. Mfrs. Club, Alpha Chi Sigma, Tau Beta Pi, Phi Kappa Phi. Clubs: Fifty, Harvard Bus. Sch. (Cleve.); Chagrin Valley Hunt, St. Christopher's-by-the-River, The Hangar. Avocations: fencing, riding, tennis, canoeing. Home: 11661 Sperry Rd Chesterland OH 44026-1617 Office: Lincoln Electric Co 22801 St Clair Ave Cleveland OH 44117-1199

WILLIS, GORDON, cinematographer; m. Helen Willis. Cinematographer: (films) including End of the Road, 1970, Loving, 1970, The Landlord, 1970, Little Murders, 1970, Klute, 1971, The Godfather, 1972, Up the Sandbox, 1972, Bad Company, 1972, The Paper Chase, 1973, The Godfather, Part II, 1974, The Parallax View, 1974, The Drowning Pool, 1975, All the President's Men, 1976, Sept 30, 1955, 1977, Annie Hall, 1977, Comes a Horseman, 1978, Interiors, 1978, Manhattan, 1979 Stardust Memories, 1980, Pennies from Heaven, 1981, A Midsummer Night's Sex Comedy, 1982, Zelig, 1983, Broadway Danny Rose, 1984, Purple Rose of Cairo, 1985, Perfect, 1985, The Money Pit, 1986, The Pick-Up Artist, 1987, Bright Lights, Big City, 1988, Presumed Innocent, 1989, The Godfather, Part III, 1990, Damages, 1992; cinematographer, dir. (film) Windows, 1980. Office: care Ron Taft 18 W 55th St New York NY 10019-5315

WILLIS, GUYE HENRY, JR., soil chemist; b. L.A., July 1, 1937; s. Guye Henry and Esther Mae (Bloomer) W.; m. Phyllis Joy Payne, Dec. 27, 1960; children: Michael Guye, Mark Charles. BS, Okla. State U., 1961; MS, Auburn U., 1963, PhD, 1965. Soil chemist USDA Agrl. Rsch. Svc., Baton Rouge, 1965—. Contbr. over 70 articles to profl. jours. Mem. Am. Soc. Agronomy, Am. Chem. Soc., Am. Soc. Agrl. Engrs. Achievements include discovery that less than 5% of applied pesticides are lost in surface runoff; volatile loss to atmosphere is pathway of greatest loss of surface applied pesticides; rainfall amount more important than rainfall intenisty in washing pesticides from plant foliar surfaces. Office: USDA Agrl Rsch Svc 4115 Gourrier Ave Baton Rouge LA 70808

WILLIS, JOHN ALVIN, editor; b. Morristown, Tenn., Oct. 16, 1916; s. John Bradford and George Ann (Myers) W.; m. Claire Olivier, Sept. 25, 1960 (div.); m. Marina Sarda, Jan. 26, 1978 (div.). BA cum laude, Milligan Coll., 1938; MA, U. Tenn., 1941; postgrad., Ind U., Harvard U. Asst. editor Theatre World, N.Y.C., 1945-65, editor, 1965—; asst. editor Screen World, N.Y.C., 1948-65, editor, 1965—; tchr. pub. high schs., N.Y.C., 1950-76; editor Dance World, 1966-80; asst. editor Opera World, 1952-54, Great Stars of Am. Stage, 1952, Pictorial History of Silent Screen, 1953, Pictorial History of Opera in America, 1959, Pictorial History of the American Theatre, 1950, 60, 70, 80, 85; mem. Tony Theatre Awards Com. Nat. bd. dirs. U. Tenn. Theatre; mem. com. to select recipients for Mus. Theatre Hall of Fame, NYU. Lt. USNR, 1943-45. Recipient Lucille Lortel Lifetime Achievement award, 1993, Drama Desk Lifetime Achievement award, 1994; high sch. auditorium renamed John Willis Performing Arts Ctr. in his honor, Morristown, 1993. Mem. Actors Equity Assn., N.Y. Drama Desk, Nat. Bd. Rev. Motion Pictures (past bd. dirs.). Home and Office: 190 Riverside Dr New York NY 10024-1008

WILLIS, JOHN RANDOLPH, hospital administrator; b. Farmville, N.C., June 6, 1929; married. BA, Wake Forest U., 1955. Adminstrv. intern Rex Hosp., Raleigh, N.C., 1955-57, adminstrv. asst., 1957-58, asst. dir. purchasing, 1959-62, asst. dir. pers., 1962-64, asst. dir., 1965-67, sr. asst. dir. 1967-74, assoc. dir., 1974-77, adminstrv. dir., 1977-79, exec. dir., 1979-84, pres., 1984—. Mem. Am. Hosp. Assn. (del. 1986-88), N.C. Hosp. Assn. (bd. dirs. 1982-84, chmn.-elect 1983-84, chmn. 1984). Office: Rex Hosp 4420 Lake Boone Trl Raleigh NC 27607-6599

WILLIS, KEVIN ALVIN, professional basketball player; b. L.A., Sept. 6, 1962. Student. Jackson C.C., Mich., Mich. State U. Basketball player Atlanta Hawks, 1984-94; with MiamiHeat, 1994—. Named NBA All-Star, 1992. Office: Miami Heat The Miami Arena Miami FL 33136*

WILLIS, MARY CATHERINE, brigadier general; b. Balt., Jan. 31, 1940. BS in Elem. Edn., Salisbury State Tchrs. Coll., 1962; MS in Pub. Adminstrv., Shippensburg State Coll., 1982. Supply and tng. officer Hdqs. Co. U.S. WAC, Ft. Myer, Va., 1964-66; S-1, adminstrv. svcs. officer, S-2 20th Gen. Support Group U.S. Army, Korea, 1966-67; WAC recruiting officer, selection officer, pers. officer U.S. Army 5th Recruiting Dist., Chgo., 1967-68; chief Pers. Actions Br. U.S. Army Air Def. Command, Ent AFB, Colo., 1969-70; staff officer Enlisted Br., Mil. Pers. Ops. Divsn. Office of the Dep. Chief of Staff for Pers., Ft. Monroe, Va., 1970-71; pers. mgmt. officer, exec. officer WAC br. U.S. Army Mil. Personnel Ctr., Alexandria, Va., 1971-73; exec. officer Basic Trn. Bn. 2d U.S. WAC, Ft. McClellan, Ala., 1974-76; ops. officer, spl. asst. to Supt. for Policy and Planning, Staff and Fac. U.S. Mil. Acad., West Point, N.Y., 1976-79; comdt. 90th Pers. and Adminstrn. Bn. 21st Support Command, Europe, 1979-81; dir., pers. services directorate, pers. activities directorate USAR Component Pers. Adminstrn. Ctr., St. Louis, 1982-85; dep. chief staff USAR Component Personnel Adminstrn. Ctr., St. Louis, 1982-85; dir., commdt. The Adjutant Gen. Sch. U.S. Army Soldier Support Ctr., Ft. Benjamin Harrison, Ind., 1985-86, comdr. Troop Brigade, 1986-88; dep. dir. Pers. Svc. Support Directorate U.S. Total Army Personnel Command, Alexandria, Va., 1988-89; dir. J-1 The Joint Staff, Washington, 1991—. Decorated Legion of Merit with oak leaf cluster. Office: Jt Chiefs of Staff Manpower & Personnel The Pentagon Washington DC 20301

WILLIS, PAUL ALLEN, librarian; b. Floyd County, Ind., Oct. 1, 1941; s. Clarence Charles and Dorothy Jane (Harritt) W.; m. Barbara Marcum, June 15, 1963; children: Mark, Sally. A.B., U. Ky., 1963, J.D. 1969; M.L.S., U. Md., 1966. Cataloger, Library of Congress, Washington, 1963; head descriptive cataloging br. Sci. and Tech. Info. Facility NASA, College Park, Md., 1963-66; law librarian, prof. law U. Ky., Lexington, 1966-73; dir. libraries U. Ky., 1973—, acting dean Coll. Library Sci., 1975-76, 88; exec. sec. Ky. Jud. Retirement and Removal Commn., 1977-81; mem. adv. com. Center for Jud. Conduct Orgns., Am. Judicature Soc., Chgo., 1979-81; bd. dirs. Southeastern Library Network, Atlanta, 1980-83; mem. exec. com. Ky. Hist. Soc., 1984-88; mem. Ky. Adv. Coun. on Libraries, 1985—, adv. com. Online Computer Library Ctr., 1986-90; cons. S.E. Consortium for Internat. Devel., U. Sriwijaya, Palembang, Sumatera, Indonesia, 1987-88. Sr. fellow UCLA, summer 1982. Mem. Assn. Southeastern Research Libraries (chair 1986-88). Home: 2055 Bridgeport Dr Lexington KY 40502-2615 Office: U Ky Libr Office of Dir Lexington KY 40506

WILLIS, RALPH HOUSTON, mathematics educator; b. McMinnville, Tenn., Dec. 26, 1942; s. Carl Houston and Carrie Lee (Hill) W.; m. Gayle Catherine Celestin, June 29, 1973 (div. Apr. 1985); m. Velma Inez Church, Aug. 10, 1985; stepchild, Bobbie Lynn White. BS in Math., Mid. Tenn. State U., 1964, MA in Math., 1966. Cert. secondary edn. Instr. math. dept. Western Carolina U., Cullowhee, N.C., 1968-73, asst. prof. math. dept., 1973-83, assoc. prof. math. dept., 1983—. Editor: (newsletters) Abelian Grapevine-Secondary Math, 1970-88, The Child of Mathematics-Elementary-Middle Grade Math., 1972-78; contbr. articles to profl. jours. Dir., coord. Western Carolina U. High Sch. Math. Contest, Cullowhee, 1970—; solicitor-coord. Math. Contest Scholarship Program, Cullowhee, 1971-82; initiator-coord. Math. Dept.'s Vis. Speaker Program, Western Carolina U., Cullowhee, 1974-77; faculty sponsor N.C. Coun. Tchrs. Math. Student Affiliate, Cullowhee, 1988—. 1st lt. U.S. Army, 1966-68. Recipient Paul A. Reid Disting. Svc. award Western Carolina U., 1991, hon. mention N.C. Gov.'s Award for Excellence, 1991, Innovator award N.C. Coun. Tchrs. in Math., 1994. Mem. Nat. Coun. Tchrs. Math., N.C. Coun. Tchrs. Math. (state historian 1993—, Innovator award 1994), Phi Kappa Phi, Kappa Mu Epsilon. Avocations: genealogy, gardening, military history, model building, carpentry. Office: Western Carolina U Math Dept Stillwell Bldg Cullowhee NC 28723

WILLIS, RAYMOND EDSON, strategic management and organization educator; b. Winthrop, Mass., June 9, 1930; s. Raymond Edson and Mollie (Murtagh) W.; m. Elizabeth Frances Monaghan, Aug. 24, 1957; children: Peter, Brian, Kevin, Garth. BS in Physics, Rensselaer Poly. Inst., 1951; MBA, Boston U., 1956; PhD in Econs., MIT, 1964. Prof. strategic mgmt. and orgn. U. Minn., Mpls., 1959—, chmn. dept. mgmt., 1984-87, prof. emeritus, 1995—. Co-author: Statistical Analysis and Modeling for Management Decision Making, 1974; author: A Guide to Forecasting for Planners and Managers, 1987; contbr. articles to profl. jours. Served to lt. (j.g.) USN, 1951-54, PTO. Fulbright-Hays fellow, 1981. Mem. Alliance Francais. Avocations: bicycling, cross country skiing, bookbinding. Home: 2267 Commonwealth Ave Saint Paul MN 55108-1602 Office: U Minn Carlson Sch Mgmt 271 19th Ave S Minneapolis MN 55455-0430

WILLIS, THORNTON WILSON, painter; b. Pensacola, Fla., May 25, 1936; s. Willard Wilson and Edna Mae (Hall) W.; m. Peggy Jean Whisenhant, June, 1960; 1 son, David Shaw.; m. Vered Lieb, 1983; 1 dau., Rachel Elizabeth. B.S., U. So. Miss., 1962; M.A., U. Ala., 1966. vis. artist-in-residence La. State U., New Orleans, 1971-72. Represented in U.S. by Douglas Drake Gallery, N.Y., in Europe by Galerie Nordenhake, Stockholm.; assoc. editor: Re-View, 1978—; one-man exhbns. include: Henri Gallery, Washington, 1968, Paley and Lowe, N.Y.C., 1970, New Orleans Mus. Art, 1972, 55 Mercer St. Gallery, 1979, Galerie Nordenhake, Sweden, 1980, Oscarsson Hood Gallery, N.Y.C., 1980-84, Gloria Luria Gallery, Miami, 1985, Pensacola Mus. retrospective, 1988, Galerie Nordenhake retrospective, Stockholm, 1988, 89, Twining Gallery retrospective, 1990, André Zarre Gallery, N.Y.C. 1993; group exhbns. include: Phila. Civic Center, 1970, Whitney Mus., 1971, Contemporary Art Mus., Houston, 1980, 81, Sidney Janis Gallery, N.Y.C., 1980, 81, Johnson Mus., Ithaca, N.Y., 1981, Mus. Modern Art, N.Y.C., 1981, 84, 85-86, Galerie Arnesen, Copenhagen, 1981, ARS '83, Helsinki, André Emmerich Gallery, N.Y.C., 1992, Anita Shapolsky Gallery, N.Y.C., 1993; represented in permanent collections, Whitney Mus., N.Y.C., Mus. Modern Art, N.Y.C., New Orleans Mus. Art, Denver Mus. Fine Art, Rochester Meml. Gallery, Albright-Knox Mus., Phillips Collection, Washington, Herbert F. Johnson Mus., Cornell U., Chase Manhattan Collection, William Paley Collection, CBS, Power Collection, Sidney, Australia, Solomon R. Guggenheim Mus., N.Y.C., various collections, museums Europe, Scandanavia. With USMC, 1954-57. Recipient award Adolph & Esther Gottlieb Found., 1991; John Simon Guggenheim fellow, 1978-79; Nat. Endowment Arts grantee, 1980-81. Mem. Am. Golf Assn. Avocation: golf. Home: 85 Mercer St New York NY 10012-4438 Office: 87 Mercer St New York NY 10012-4438

WILLIS, WESLEY ROBERT, college administrator; b. Rahway, N.J., Mar. 16, 1941; s. Meachen William and Mildred (Sisco) W.; m. Elaine Stanislaw, May 22, 1965; children: Mark, Kevin, Nathan. BS, Phila. Coll. Bible, 1963; ThM, Dallas Theol. Sem., 1967; EdD, Ind. U., 1978. Prof. dept. chmn. Washington Bible Coll., 1967-70; minister edn. Forcey Meml. Ch., Washington, 1967-71; prof., acad. v.p. Ft. Wayne (Ind.) Bible Coll., 1971-78; exec. v.p. Scripture Press Ministries, Wheaton, Ill., 1978-80; sr. v.p. Scripture Press Publs., Inc., Wheaton, 1980-90; v.p. acad. affairs Phila. Coll. Bible, Langhorne, Pa., 1990—; bd. dirs. Scripture Press Publs., Ltd., Whitby, Ont., Can.; bd. dirs., chmn. bd. Christian Svc. Brigade, Wheaton, 1972-88. Author: 200 Years and Still Counting, 1981, Make Your Teaching Count, 1984, Developing the Teacher in You, 1990, also 6 others; ocntbr. over 150 articles to religious publs. Sunday sch. tchr., elder Coll. Ch., Wheaton; bd. regents Dallas Theol. Sem., 1987—. Recipient Disting. Edn. Alumnus award Phila. Coll. Bible, 1988, Gold Medallion award Evang. Pubs. Assn., 1990. Mem. Nat. Assn. Profs. Christian Edn., Nat. Assn. Dirs. Christian Edn., Evang. Theol. Soc. Office: Phila Coll Bible 200 Manor Ave Langhorne PA 19047-2990

WILLIS, WILLIAM DARRELL, JR., neurophysiologist, educator; b. Dallas, July 19, 1934; s. William Darrell and Dorcas (Chamberlain) W.; m. Jean Colette Schini, May 28, 1960; 1 child, Thomas Darrell. B.S., B.A., Tex. A&M U., 1956; M.D., U. Tex. Southwestern Med. Sch., 1960; Ph.D., Australian Nat. U., 1963. Postdoctoral research fellow Nat. Inst. Neurol. Diseases and Blindness, Australian Nat. U., 1960-62, Istituto di Fisiologia, U. Pisa, Italy, 1962-63; from asst. prof. to prof. anatomy, chmn. dept. U. Tex. Southwestern Med. Sch., Dallas, 1963-70; chief lab. comparative neurobiology Marine Biomed. Inst., prof. anatomy and physiology U. Tex. Med. Br., Galveston, 1970—, dir. Marine Biomed. Inst., 1979—, chmn. dept. anatomy and neurosci., 1986—, Ashbel Smith prof., 1986— Cecil and Ida Green prof., 1995—; mem. neurology B study sect. NIH, 1968-72, chmn., 1970-72, mem. neurol. disorders Program Poject rev. com., 1972-76, Nat. Adv. Neurol. and Communicative Disorders and Stroke Coun., 1987-90; tng. grant com. Nat. Inst. Neurol. Diseases and Stroke, 1994—. Mem. editl. bd.

Neurosci., Exptl. Neurology, 1970-90, Archives Italienne Biologie, Neurosci. Letters, 1976-92; chief editor Jour. Neurophysiology, 1978-83, Pain, 1986-89; chief editor Jour. Neurosci., 1986-89, editor-in-chief, 1993-94; sect. editor Exptl. Brain Rsch., 1990-92, 95—. Mem. AAAS, Am. Assn. Anatomists (exec. com. 1980-86), Am. Pain Soc. (pres. 1982-83), Internat. Assn. Study Pain (coun. 1984-90), Am. Physiol. Soc., Soc. Exptl. Biol. Medicine, Soc. Neurosci. (pres. 1984-85), Internat. Brain Rsch. Orgn., Cajal Club, Sigma Xi, Alpha Omega Alpha. Home: 2925 Beluche Dr Galveston TX 77551-1511 Office: U Tex Med Br Marine Biomed Inst Dept Anatomy and Neurosci Galveston TX 77550-2711

WILLIS, WILLIAM ERVIN, lawyer; b. Huntington, W.Va., Oct. 11, 1926; s. Asa Hannon and Mae (Davis) W.; m. Joyce Litteral, Sept. 1, 1949; children: Kathryn Cunningham, Anne Dresser, William. Student, Ind. U., 1944, NYU, 1945; AB, Marshall U., 1948; JD, Harvard, 1951. Bar: N.Y. 1952. Pvt. practice N.Y.C., 1951—; ptnr. Sullivan & Cromwell, 1960—; lectr. Practising Law Inst., 1963—; trustee Fed. Bar Council, 1968-72; mem. 2d Circuit Commn. on Reduction Burdens and Costs Civil Litigation, 1977-82. Co-author Doing Business in America; contbr. Edn. Civil Practice Law Rev. Forms and Guidance for Lawyers, also articles to legal jours. Mem. panel arbitrators Pub. Resources. With AUS, 1944-46. Fellow Am. Coll. Trial Lawyers, Am. Bar Found.; mem. ABA (standing com. on fed. judiciary 1987-93, chair 1992-93, exec. com. 1976-83), N.Y. Bar Assn. (chmn. antitrust sect. 1976-77, exec. com. 1976-83), Assn. Bar City N.Y. (chmn. profl. discipline com. 1983-86), Fed. Bar Coun. (trustee 1969-72), Am. Judicature Soc., Am. Arbitration Assn. (panel arbitrators), N.Y. Law Inst., N.Y. County Lawyers, Ins. Judicial Adminstrn., India House, World Trade Ctr. Home: 190 Tekening Dr Tenafly NJ 07670-1219 also: Otterhole Rd West Milford NJ 07480 Office: Sullivan & Cromwell 125 Broad St New York NY 10004

WILLIS, WILLIAM HAROLD, JR., management consultant, executive search specialist; b. Harrisburg, Pa., Dec. 19, 1927; s. William Harold and Elizabeth Tilford (Keferstein) W.; BA, Yale U., 1949; m. Pauline Sabin Smith, Oct. 15, 1955; children: Wendell Willis Livingston, Christopher, Gregory. Mktg. mgr. Owens-Corning Fiberglas Corp., N.Y.C., 1956-62; div. mgr. AMF, Inc., Greenwich, Conn., 1962-65; ptnr. Devine, Baldwin & Willis, N.Y.C., 1965-70; pres. William Willis Worldwide Inc., Greenwich, Conn., 1970—. Bd. dirs. Girls Inc. (formerly Girls Clubs Am., Inc.), N.Y.C., 1962-80, treas., chmn. fin. com., 1961-76, chmn. devel. com., 1976-77; expdn. leader Am. Mus. Nat. History Davison-Willis Expdn. to Madagascar; vestryman St. Barnabas Episcopal Ch., Greenwich, Conn., 1978-81; bd. dirs. Greenwich Hosp. Corp.; human resources com. YMCA of Greater N.Y.; del. People to People Citizen Amb. Program, del. traveling to Peoples Republic of China. With U.S. Army, 1950-52. Named to Exec. Search Hall of Fame, 1992. Mem. Assn. Exec. Search Cons. (dir. 1979-82), Internat. Assoc. of Corp. and Profl. Recruiters, Inc., Yale Club. Republican. Home: 55 Zaccheus Mead Ln Greenwich CT 06831-3716 Office: 164 Mason St Greenwich CT 06830-6611

WILLIS, WILLIAM HENRY, marketing executive; b. Canton, Ohio, Mar. 15, 1951; s. William Lincoln and Gwendolyn Ann (Wasem) W.; m. Rebecca Ann Klinker, June 16, 1973; children: Kristen Ann, Patrick Michael, Susan Kathleen. BSBA, Ohio State U., 1973; M of Mgmt., Northwestern U., 1974. Assoc. product mgr. H.J. Heinz Co., Pitts., 1974-76; product mgr. Pillsbury Co., Mpls., 1976-77, mktg. mgr., 1977-79, group mktg. mgr., 1979-81; dir. bus. planning Pepsico, Inc., Purchase, N.Y., 1981-82, dir. mktg., 1982-85; exec. v.p. mktg. Ogden Svcs. Corp., N.Y.C., 1985-87, exec. v.p. indsl. svcs., 1987-93; pres. spl. mkts. divn. Reader's Digest Inc., Pleasantville, N.Y., 1994—. Exec. fundraiser Minn. Orch. Guaranty Fund, Mpls., 1979; United Way chmn. Pillsbury Co., Mpls., 1980. Named Advertiser of Yr. Aviation mag., 1986. Republican. Roman Catholic. Avocations: real estate management, renovating old homes. Office: Reader's Digest Inc Reader's Digest Rd Pleasantville NY 10570

WILLIS, WILLIAM J., lawyer; b. Rhinelander, Wis., July 22, 1927; s. Ray Milford and Grace Luella (Miller) W.; m. Doris Mae Albert, June 13, 1949; children: Nancy J. Willis Burrows, Sarah J. Willis Snowden, David A., Rebeccah A. Willis Cram, Deborah J. Willis Koster. BA, U. Wis., 1950, LLB, 1952. Assoc. Foley & Lardner, Milw., 1952-61, ptnr., 1961—. Bd. dirs. Planned Parenthood of Wis., Milw., 1960-87, pres., 1963-65; bd. dirs. Planned Parenthood Fedn. of Am., N.Y.C., 1965-73, Fairhaven Corp., Whitewater, Wis., 1960—. Named Dir. of Yr., Council for Health & Human Services, United Ch. of Christ, 1987. Mem. ABA, State Bar Wis. Mem. United Ch. of Christ. Home: W57n524 Hilbert Ave Cedarburg WI 53012-2013 Office: Foley & Lardner 777 E Wisconsin Ave Milwaukee WI 53202-5302

WILLISCROFT, BEVERLY RUTH, lawyer; b. Conrad, Mont., Feb. 24, 1945; d. Paul A. and Gladys L. (Buck) W.; m. Kent J. Barcus, Oct. 1984. BA in Music, So. Calif. Coll., 1967; JD, John F. Kennedy U., 1977. Bar: Calif. 1977. Elem. tchr., Sunnyvale, Calif., 1968-72; legal sec., legal asst. various law firms, Bay Area, 1972-77; assoc. Neil D. Reid, Inc., San Francisco, 1977-79; sole practice, Concord, Calif., 1979—; exam. grader Calif. Bar, 1979—; real estate broker, 1980-88; tchr. real estate King Coll., Concord, 1979-80; lectr. in field; judge pro-tem Mcpl. Ct., 1981—. Bd. dirs. Contra Costa Musical Theatre, Inc., 1978-82, v.p adminstrn., 1980-81, v.p. prodn., 1981-82; mem. community devel. adv. com. City of Concord, 1981-83, vice chmn., 1982-83, mem. status of women com., 1980-81, mem. redevel. adv. com., 1984-86, planning commnr. 1986-92, chmn., 1990; mem. exec. bd. Mt. Diablo coun. Boy Scouts Am., 1981-85; bd. dirs. Pregnancy Ctrs. Contra Costa County, 1991—, chmn., 1993—. Recipient award of merit Bus. and Profl. Women, Bay Valley Dist., 1981. Mem. Concord C. of C. (bd. dir., chmn. govt. affairs com. 1981-83, v.p. 1985-87, pres. 1988-89, Bus. Person of Yr. 1986), Calif. State Bar (chmn. adoptions subcom. north, 1994), Contra Costa County Bar Assn., Todos Santos Bus. and Profl. Women (co-founder, pres. 1983-84, pub. rels. chmn. 1982-83, Woman of Achievement 1980, 81), Soroptimists (fin. sec. 1980-81). Office: 3018 Willow Pass Rd Ste 205 Concord CA 94519-2570

WILLISON, BRUCE GRAY, banker; b. Riverside, Calif., Oct. 16, 1948; s. Walter G. and Dorothy (Phillips) W.; m. Gretchen A. Illig; children: Patrick, Bruce G., Kristen, Jeffery, Geoffrey, Lea. B.A. in econs., UCLA, 1970; M.B.A., U. So. Calif., 1973. With Bank of Am., Los Angeles 1973-79; dir. mktg. First Interstate Bancorp, Los Angeles, 1981; sr. v.p. corp. banking group First Interstate Bank, L.A., 1982, mgr. trust divsn., 1983; exec. v.p. world banking group First Interstate Bank, Los Angeles, 1983-85; pres., chief exec. officer First Interstate Bank Ltd., 1985-86; chmn., chief exec. officer First Interstate Bank Oreg., Portland, 1986-91; chmn., pres., chief exec. officer First Interstate Bank of Calif., L.A., 1991—. Served to lt. USN, 1970-72. Office: First Interstate Bank Calif 707 Wilshire Blvd Los Angeles CA 90017

WILLITS, EILEEN MARIE, medical/surgical nurse, health facility administrator; b. Euclid, Ohio, 1953; d. John Francis and Geraldine Alice (Denoyer) Donohoe; m. Gary Eugene W., May 24, 1986; 1 child, William. Diploma, Providence Hosp. Sch. Nursing, 1974; BS in Human Svcs., U. Detroit, 1979; MS in Nursing Adminstrn., U. Mich., 1984. From nurse to head nurse, then to adminstrv. asst. St. John Hosp., Detroit, 1974-84; v.p. patient svcs. E.L. Bixby Med. Ctr., Adrian, Mich., 1984-89; v.p. nursing Grandview Hosp. and Med. Ctr., Dayton, Ohio, 1989—. Mem. Am. Orgn. Nurse Execs., Ohio Orgn. Nurse Execs., Soc. Ambulatory Care Profls., Am. Hosp. Assn. Office: Grandview Hosp & Med Ctr 405 W Grand Ave Dayton OH 45405-4796

WILLKE, THOMAS ALOYS, university official, statistics educator; b. Rome City, Ind., Apr. 22, 1932; s. Gerard Thomas and Marie Margaret (Wuennemann) W.; m. Geraldine Ann Page, Dec. 28, 1954; children: Richard, Susan, Donald, Jeanne, Mary, Kathleen. AB, Xavier U., 1954; MS, Ohio State U., 1956, PhD, 1960. Sr. engr. N.Am. Aviation, Columbus, Ohio, 1959-60; instr. math. Ohio State U., Columbus, 1960-61, assoc. prof., 1966-70, assoc. prof. statistics, 1970-72, prof., 1972—; dir. stats. lab., 1971-73, vice provost Arts and Scis., 1973-86, acting dean Univ. Coll., 1983-85; dean undergrad. studies Arts and Scis., 1987; prof. math. scis. Otterbein coll., Westerville, Ohio, 1987—, chmn. dept. math. scis., 1988—; rsch. mathematician U.S. Nat. Bur. Standards, Washington, 1961-66; asst. prof. math. U. Md., College Park, 1963-66. Contbr. articles on statis. non

parametric methods and robustness to profl. jours. Mem. Am. Statis. Assn., Math. Assn. Am. Roman Catholic. Home: 4375 Mumford Dr Columbus OH 43220-4438 Office: Otterbein Coll Dept Of Math Scis Westerville OH 43081

WILLKIE, WENDELL LEWIS, II, lawyer; b. Indpls., Oct. 29, 1951; s. Philip Herman Willkie and Rosalie (Heffelfinger) Hall; m. Carlotta Fendig, June 27, 1987; children: Alexandra Elizabeth, Diana Fendig. AB, Harvard U., 1973; BA, Oxford (Eng.) U., 1975, MA, 1983; JD, U. Chgo., 1978. Bar: N.Y. 1979. Assoc. Simpson Thacher and Bartlett, N.Y.C., 1978-82; gen. counsel NEH, Washington, 1982-84; assoc. counsel to Pres. The White House, Washington, 1984-85; chief of staff, counselor to Sec. U.S. Dept. Edn., Washington, 1985, gen. counsel, 1985-88; counsel Office of the Pres.-elect, Washington, 1988-89; gen. counsel Dept. of Commerce, Washington, 1989-93; v.p. Westvaco Corp., N.Y.C., 1995—; vis. fellow Am. Enterprise Inst., Washington, 1993-94. Co-author, editor: (with J.R. Lilley) Beyond MFN: Trade with China and American Interests, 1994. Harvard U. scholar, 1969-73, Rhodes scholar, 1973-75. Republican. Episcopalian. Home: 4826 Drummond Ave Bethesda MD 20815-5429 Office: Westvaco Corp 299 Park Ave New York NY 10171

WILLMAN, ARTHUR CHARLES, healthcare executive; b. N.Y.C., Oct. 25, 1938; s. Arthur Charles Willman and Irene (Lamb) Meyer; m. Mary McHugh, Dec. 30. 1961; children: Jean, Susan, Brian, Kevin. BS in Pharmacy, St. Johns U., 1960; MS, Columbia U., 1968. Staff pharmacist St. Vincent's Hosp., S.I., N.Y., 1960-61, Valentine Pharmacy, S.I., 1961; commd. ensign USPHS, 1962, advanced through grades to capt.; 1982; chief pharmacist USPHS Hosp., Kotzebue, Alaska, 1962-63, adminstr., 1963-66; svc. unit dir. USPHS Hosp., Sitka, Alaska, 1971-86; ret. USPHS Hosp., 1991; adminstrv. resident So. Nassau Communities Hosp., Oceanside, N.Y., 1967-68; exec. officer Gallup (N.Mex.) Indian Med. Ctr., 1968-71; dir. Phys. Asst. Tng. Program, Gallup, N.Mex., 1971; v.p. S.E. Alaska Regional Health Corp., Sitka, 1986—; chmn. bd. dirs. S.E. Alaska Health Systems Agy., Ketchikan, 1980-83; instr. mgmt. U. Alaska, Sitka, 1975-85. Active Ad hoc Com. on Diversification, Sitka, 1993. Fellow APHA, Am. Coll. Healthcare Execs.; mem. Sitka Rotary Club (v.p., chmn.). Roman Catholic. Avocations: boating, running, mechanics, computers. Home: 1203 Seward Ave Sitka AK 99835-9418 Office: SE Alaska Regional Health Corp 222 Tongass Dr Sitka AK 99835-9416

WILLMAN, JOHN NORMAN, management consultant; b. St. Joseph, Mo., Jan. 19, 1915; s. John N. and Frances (Potter) W.; m. Victoria King, May 9, 1941; 1 dau., Victoria. Student, St. Benedict's Coll., 1936; B.A., St. Louis U., 1979. With Am. Hosp. Supply Corp., 1940-59, v.p., 1954-59; with Brunswick Corp., St. Louis, 1959-68; v.p. Brunswick Corp., 1961-68, pres. Health and Sci. div., 1961-68; v.p. Sherwood Med. Industries, Inc., St. Louis, 1961-67; pres. Sherwood Med. Industries, Inc., 1967-72, vice chmn. bd., 1972-73, also dir.; pres., chief exec. officer, dir. IPCO Corp., White Plains, N.Y., 1973-78; mgmt. cons., 1978—. Mem. Old Warson Country Club (St. Louis), St. Louis Club, Noonday Club (St. Louis), Univ. Club (St. Louis). Home: 530 N Spoede Rd Saint Louis MO 63141-7754

WILLMAN, VALLEE LOUIS, physician, surgery educator; b. Greenville, Ill., May 4, 1925; s. Philip L. and Marie A. (Dall) W.; m. Melba L. Carr, Feb. 2, 1952; children: Philip, Elizabeth, Susan, Stephen, Mark, Timothy, Jane, Vallee, Sarah. Student, U. Ill., 1942-43, 45-47; MD, St. Louis U., 1951. Diplomate Am. Bd. Surgery (sr. examiner 1976—), Am. Bd. Thoracic Surgery. Intern Phila. Gen. Hosp., 1951-52; intern, resident St. Louis U. Group Hosps., 1952-56; Ellen McBride fellow in surgery St. Louis U., 1956-57, sr. instr. surgery, 1957-58, asst. prof. surgery, 1958-61, assoc. prof., 1961-63, prof., 1963—; C. Rollins Hanlon prof. surgery, chmn. dept., 1969—, vice chmn. dept., 1967-69; attending physician St. Louis U. Hosp., 1969—; chief of surgery, 1969—; mem. staff Cardinal Glennon Children's Hosp., 1969—; cons. St. Louis VA Hosp., 1969—. Mem. editorial bd. Jour. Thoracic and Cardiovascular Surgery, 1976-86, Archives of Surgery, 1977-87, Jour. Cardiovascular Surgery, 1982-87, N.Am. editor, 1987—; contbr. over 250 articles to profl. jours. With USN, 1943-45. Recipient Merit award St. Louis Med. Soc., 1973, Health Care Leadership award Hosp. Assn. Met. St. Louis, 1988. Fellow Am. Surg. Assn., Am. Assn. Thoracic Surgery, Cen. Surg. Assn. (pres., mem. ad hoc com. on coronary artery surgery 1971-72); mem. ACS (Disting. Svc. award 1987), Soc. for Vascular Surgery, Internat. Soc. for Cardiovascular Surgery (pres. N.Am. chpt. 1985-87), Phi Beta Kappa, Phi Eta Sigma, Alpha Omega Alpha. Roman Catholic. Office: St Louis U Hosp 3635 Vista Ave Saint Louis MO 63110-2500

WILLMARTH, WILLIAM WALTER, aerospace engineering educator; b. Highland Park, Ill., Mar. 25, 1924; s. Sinclair Anson and Dorothy (Cox) W.; m. Nancy Robinson, Nov. 20, 1959; children—Robert, Deborah, Elizabeth, Kathleen. B.S. in Mech. Engring, Purdue U., 1949; M.S. in Aero. Engring, Calif. Inst. Tech., 1950, Ph.D., 1954. Research fellow, then sr. research fellow Calif. Inst. Tech., 1954-58; mem. faculty U. Mich., Ann Arbor, 1958—; prof. aerospace engring. U. Mich., 1961-90, prof. emeritus aerospace engring., 1990—; cons. to industry, 1952—. Author papers, reports. Served with AUS, 1943-46. Vis. fellow Joint Inst. Lab. Astrophysics, Boulder, Colo., 1963-64; fellow Max Planck Inst. für Stromungsforschung, Göttingen, Fed. Republic Germany, summer 1975. Fellow AIAA, Am. Phys. Soc. (Fluid Dynamics prize 1989); mem. AAUP, Sigma Xi, Tau Beta Pi, Tau Sigma. Home: 765 Country Club Rd Ann Arbor MI 48105-1034

WILLMORE, ROBERT LOUIS, lawyer; b. Ramstein AFB, Fed. Republic Germany, July 16, 1955; s. Wendell James and Theresia (Galler) W. BS in Econs., MIT, 1977; JD, Yale U., 1980. Bar: D.C. 1981, U.S. Ct. Appeals (D.C. cir.) 1985. Legis. asst. Senator Carl T. Curtis, Washington, 1977-78; law clk. to presiding judge U.S. Dist. Ct. (no. dist.) Tex., Dallas, 1980-81; assoc. Shaw, Pittman, Potts & Trowbridge, Washington, 1981-82; asst. gen. counsel Office of Mgmt. and Budget, Exec. Office of the Pres., Washington, 1982-85; dep. asst. atty. gen. civil div. U.S. Dept. Justice, Washington, 1985-88; of counsel Arent, Fox, Kintner, Plotkin & Kahn, Washington, 1988-93; exec. sec. Cabinet Council Tort Policy Working Group, Washington, 1985-88; chmn. task force on liability ins. availability, Washington, 1985-88. Editor Yale Law Jour., 1979-80. Mem. ABA, D.C. Bar Assn. Republican. Roman Catholic. Home: 6879 St Albans Rd Mc Lean VA 22101-2810 Office: Crowell & Moring 1001 Pennsylvania Ave NW Washington DC 20004-2505

WILLMOTT, PETER SHERMAN, retail executive; b. Glens Falls, N.Y., June 1, 1937. B.A., Williams Coll., 1959; M.B.A., Harvard U., 1961. Sr. fin. analyst Am. Airlines, N.Y.C., 1961-63; mgr. cons. Booz, Allen & Hamilton, N.Y.C., 1964-66; treas. Continental Baking Co., Rye, N.Y., 1966-69, v.p., 1969-74; v.p. fin. Fed. Express Corp., Memphis, 1974-77, exec. v.p. fin. and adminstrn., 1977-80, pres., chief operating officer, 1980-83, now bd. dirs.; pres., chief exec. officer Carson Pirie Scott & Co., Chgo., 1983—, chmn., 1984—, also bd. dirs. Office: Pic N Save Corp 2430 E Del Amo Blvd Compton CA 90220-6300

WILLNER, ALAN ELI, electrical engineer, educator; b. Bklyn., Nov. 16, 1962; s. Gerald and Sondra (Bernstein) W.; m. Michelle Frida Green, June 25, 1991. BA, Yeshiva U., 1982; MS, Columbia U., 1984, PhD, 1988. Summer tech. staff David Sarnoff Rsch. Ctr., Princeton, N.J., 1983, 84; grad. rsch. asst. dept. elec. engring. Columbia U., N.Y.C., 1984-88; postdoctoral mem. tech. staff AT&T Bell Labs., Holmdel, N.J., 1988-90; mem. tech. staff Bell Communications Rsch., Red Bank, N.J., 1990-91; assoc. prof. U. So. Calif., L.A., 1992—, assoc. dir. Ctr. Photonic Tech., 1994—; head del. Harvard Model UN Yeshiva U., 1982; instr. Columbia U., 1987; rev. panel mem. NSF, Washington, 1992, 93, 94; invited optical comm. workshop NSF, Washington, 1994, chair panel on optical info. and comm., 1994. Author 1 book; contbr. articles to IEEE Photonics Tech. Letters, Jour Lightwave Tech., Jour. Optical Engring., Jour. Electrochem. Soc., Electronics Letters, Applied Physics Letters, Applied Optics; assoc. editor Jour. Lighwave Tech., guest editor. Mem. faculty adv. bd. U. So. Calif. Hillel Orgn., 1992. Grantee NSF, Advanced Rsch. Projects Agy., Packard Found., Powell Found.; fellow Semiconductor Rsch. Corp., 1986, NATO/NSF, 1985, Sci. and Engring. fellow David and Lucile Packard Found., 1993, Presdl. faculty fellow NSF, 1994; recipient Armstrong Found. prize Columbia U., 1984, Young Investigator award NSF, 1992. Mem. IEEE (sr. mem.), IEEE Lasers and Electro-Optics Soc. (mem. optical comm. tech. com., bd. govs., chmn.

optical comm. tech. com., chmn. optical comm. subcom. ann. meeting 1994, mem. optical networks tech. com.), Optical Soc. Am. (vice-chair optical comm. group, symposium organizer ann. meeting 1992, 95, panel organizer ann. meeting 1993, 95, program com. for conf. on optical fiber commn. 1996), Soc. Photo-Instrumentation Engring. (program chair telecomm. engring. photonics west 1995, chmn. conf. on emerging technologies for all-optical networks, photonics west, 1995, program com. for Conf. on Optical Fiber Comm., 1996, conf. program com. components for WDM), Sigma Xi. Achievements include patents for localized photochemical etching of multi-layered semiconductor body, optical star coupler utilizing fiber amplifier technology, and one-to-many simultaneous optical WDM 2-dim. plane interconnections. Home: 1200 S Shenandoah St Apt 201 Los Angeles CA 90035-2265 Office: U So Calif Dept Elec Engring EEB 538 Los Angeles CA 90089-2565

WILLNER, ANN RUTH, political scientist, educator; b. N.Y.C., Sept. 2, 1924; d. Norbert and Bella (Richman) W. B.A. cum laude, Hunter Coll., 1945; M.A., Yale U., 1946; Ph.D., U. Chgo., 1961. Lectr. U. Chgo., 1946-47, research assoc. Ctr. for Econ. Devel. and Cultural Change, 1954-56, 61-62; advisor on orgn. and tng. Indonesian Ministry for Fgn. Affairs, Jakarta, 1952-53; expert for small scale indsl. planning Indonesian Nat. Planning Bur., Jakarta, 1953-54; fgn. affairs analyst Congl. Reference Service, Library of Congress, 1960; asst. prof. polit. sci. Harpur Coll., Binghamton, N.Y., 1962-63; postdoctoral fellow polit. sci. and Southeast Asian studies Yale U., New Haven, 1963-64; research assoc. Ctr. Internat. Studies, Princeton U., 1964-69; assoc. prof. polit. sci. U. Kans., Lawrence, 1969-70, prof., 1970—; vis. prof. polit. sci. CUNY, 1975; cons. govt. agys. and pvt. industry. Polit. sci. editor Ency. of the Social Scis., 1961; mem. editorial bd. Econ. Devel. and Cultural Change, 1954-57, Jour. Comparative Adminstrn., 1969-74, Comparative Politics, 1977—; author: The Neotraditional Accomodation to Political Independence, 1966, Charismatic Political Leadership: A Theory, 1968, The Spellbinders, 1984; also monographs, articles, chpts. to books. Grantee Rockefeller Found., 1965, Social Sci. Research and Am. Council Learned Socs., 1966. Mem. Am. Polit. Sci. Assn. (gov. council 1979-81). Home: 2112 Terrace Rd Lawrence KS 66049-2733

WILLNER, DOROTHY, anthropologist, educator; b. N.Y.C., Aug. 26, 1927; d. Norbert and Bella (Richman) W. Ph.B., U. Chgo., 1947, M.A., 1953, Ph.D., 1961; postgrad., Ecole Pratique des Hautes Etudes, U. Paris, France, 1953-54. Anthropologist Jewish Agy., Israel, 1955-58; tech. asst., adminstrn. expert in community devel. UN, Mexico, 1958; asst. prof. dept. sociology and anthropology U. Iowa, Iowa City, 1959-60; research assoc. U. Chgo., 1961-62; asst. prof. dept. sociology and anthropology U. N.C., Chapel Hill, 1962-63, Hunter Coll., N.Y.C., 1964-65; assoc. prof. anthropology U. Kans., Lawrence, 1967-70; prof. U. Kans., 1970-90; professorial lectr. Johns Hopkins U. Sch. Advanced Internat. Studies, 1992. Author: Community Leadership, 1960, Nation-Building and Community in Israel, 1969. Contbr. numerous articles to profl. publs. Fellow Am. Anthrop. Assn.; mem. Soc. Applied Anthropology, Royal Anthrop. Inst.; mem. Cen. States Anthrop. Soc. (past pres.), Assn. Polit. and Legal Anthropology (past pres.). Home: 5480 Wisconsin Ave Bethesda MD 20815-3530

WILLNER, JAY R., consulting company executive; b. Aurora, Ill., Sept. 22, 1924; s. Charles R. and Ida (Winer) W.; m. Suzanne Wehmann, July 17, 1958; 1 child, Adam. Student U. Calif., Los Angeles, 1946-48; BS, MIT, 1950; MBA, Rutgers U., 1959. Researcher Andrew Brown Co., Los Angeles, 1950-52; tech. salesman Glidden Co., Los Angeles, 1952-54; market researcher Roger Williams Inc., N.Y.C., 1954-59; sr. market analyst Calif. Chem. Co., San Francisco, 1959-63; mgr. planning chem. coatings div. Mobil Chem. Co., N.Y.C., 1963-68; pres. WEH Corp., San Francisco, 1968—; lectr. U. Calif., Berkeley, 1962—; adj. faculty U. San Francisco, 1977—; U.S. corr. German mag. Farbe & Lack. Contbg. editor Jour. Protective Coatings and Linings; editor The WEH Report. Served to 2d lt. A.C., AUS, 1943-46. Mem. Am. Chem. Soc., San Francisco Comml. Club, Chemists Club (N.Y.C.), MIT Club No. Calif. Home: 700 Presidio Ave San Francisco CA 94115 Office: WEH Corp PO Box 470038 San Francisco CA 94147-0038

WILLNER, ROBERT FRANKLIN, health administrator; b. Cobleskill, N.Y., Aug. 13, 1942; s. Charles Benjamin and Catherine Spencer (McNeil) W.; m. Marie Angela Muchiarone, Apr. 15, 1972; children: Karen Marie, Stephanie Agnes. A.B., Franklin and Marshall Coll., 1964; M.H.A. Med. Coll. Va., 1966; D.Minn., Chgo. Theol. Sem., 1979. Adminstrv. resident Washington (Pa.) Hosp., 1965-66; asst. adminstrv. officer USPHS Hosp., Carville, La., 1966-68; asst. adminstr./acting adminstr. Nat. Orthopedic and Rehab. Hosp., Arlington, Va., 1968-69, adminstr., 1969-72; assoc. adminstr. Cook County Hosp., Chgo., 1972, Oak Forest (Ill.) Hosp., 1973-79; pres. Billings (Mont.) Deaconess Hosp., 1979-82; pres. United Meth. Assn. of Health and Welfare Ministries, Dayton, Ohio, 1983—; vice chmn. South Suburban Adv. Council, Suburban Cook County, Dupage County Health Systems Agy., 1977-79; bd. dirs. South Suburban Council on Aging, 1977-79; community profl. Sch. Health Scis., Governors State U., 1978-79; chmn. Big Sky Hospice, Billings, from 1980; bd. dirs. Dist. 6 Learning Ctr. Mem. health and fitness com. Billings YMCA, 1981-82; mem. exec. com., chmn. Christian Action com. Leighton Ford Billings Crusade, 1982; mem. health and welfare com. Yellowstone Conf., United Methodist Ch.; vice chmn. diaconal minister, W. Ohio Conf., United Meth. Ch.; bd. dirs., chmn. worship for worship planning Grace United Meth. Ch., Billings. Served with USPHS, 1966-68. Recipient spl. appreciation recognition med. staff of Oak Forest Hosp., 1979, cert. and recognition for services rendered in field of rehab., 1979; lic. nursing home adminstr., Ill. Fellow Am. Coll. Hosp. Adminstrs. (regent); mem. Am. Hosp. Assn., United Wesleyan Hosp. Assn. Dist. 6 Hosp. Assn. (vice chmn.), Mont. Hosp. Assn., Am. Protestant Hosp. Assn. (health and religious values council, govt. relations council and fin. com.), Commd. Officers Assn. USPHS, Woman Line (bd. dir.) (Dayton, Ohio), Lodge: Rotary. Office: McKendree Village 4343-47 Lebanon Rd Hermitage TN 37076

WILLOCK, MARCELLE MONICA, medical educator; b. Georgetown, Guyana, Mar. 30, 1938; came to U.S. 1954; d. George and Renee (Dumanoir) W. BA, Coll. New Rochelle, 1958; MD, Howard U., 1962; MA, Columbia U., 1982; MBA, Boston U., 1989. Diplomate Am. Bd. Anesthesiology. Asst. clin. prof. med. ctr. NYU, 1968-72, assoc. clin. prof. med. ctr., 1972-74; asst. prof. clin. anesthesiology Columbia U., N.Y.C., 1978-82; prof., chmn. dept. anesthesiology Boston U., 1982—; sec. The Med. Found., Boston, 1991—. Contbr. articles to profl. jours. Pres. Louis and Marthe Deveaux Found., Panama, 1965—; trustee Coll. New Rochelle, N.Y., 1976-82. Mem. Am. Soc. Anesthesiologists (del. 1986-, alt. dir. 1990-94, dir. 1994—), Mass. Soc. Anesthesiologists (pres. 1988-89), Soc. Acad. Anesthesia Chairs (sec.-treas. 1989-91, pres.-elect 1993-94, pres. 1994—), Alpha Omega Alpha. Roman Catholic. Office: Boston U Med Ctr 75 E Newton St Boston MA 02118-2340

WILLOCKS, ROBERT MAX, retired librarian; b. Maryville, Tenn., Oct. 1, 1924; s. Willis Lemuel and Hannah (Emert) W.; m. Neysa Nerene Ferguson, May 23, 1947; children—Margret Sharon, Samuel David, Mark Timothy, Robert Daniel, Kent Max. B.A., Maryville Coll., 1949; B.D., Golden Gate Bapt. Theol. Sem., 1951, Th.M., 1962; M.A. in Library Sci, Peabody Coll., 1962. Ordained to ministry Bapt. Ch., 1950; pastor in Calif., 1950-56; missionary to Korea So. Bapt. Fgn. Mission Bd., Taejon, 1956- 65; assoc. dir. library Heidelberg Coll., Tiffin, Ohio, 1965-67; dir. library Columbia (S.C.) Coll., 1967-70; asst. dir. libraries Syracuse (N.Y.) U., 1970-76; assoc. dir. libraries U. Fla., Gainesville, 1976-83, acting dir. libraries, 1983-84, dep. dir. libraries, 1984-89, ret., 1989; pastor Northwood Bapt. Ch., Gainesville, 1981-92; libr. Bapt. Theol. Sem., Lusaka, Zambia, 1994—; mem. Choong Chung Nam Province Library Assn., Korea, 1962-65; dir. Korea Bapt. Press, 1959-61; prof. ch. history Korea Bapt. Sem., 1957-65, acting pres., 1958-59, librarian, 1959-65; Vice chmn. Korea Bapt. Mission, 1962-64; del. Fla. Gov.'s Conf. on Libraries, 1978. Editor: Korean translations Thus it is Written, 1963, The Progress of Worldwide Missions, 1965. Chmn. trustees Wallace Meml. Bapt. Hosp., Pusan, Korea, 1964-65; pres. bd. dirs. Phoenix Homeowners Assn., 1980-88. With USNR, 1943-46. Mem. ALA (chmn. telefacsimile com. 1976-78, tech. com. 1980-84, chmn. standards com. 1985-88), Fla. Libr. Assn., Southeastern Library Assn., AAUP, Peabody Coll. Alumni Assn. (pres. S.C. 1968-69). Home: 1930 NW 12th Rd Gainesville FL 32605-5338

WILLOME, JOHN, construction executive. Mng. ptnr. Rayco Ltd., San Antonio. Office: Rayco Ltd 4800 Fredericksburg Rd San Antonio TX 78229-3628*

WILLOUGHBY, ANTHONY R., satellite support services executive; b. 1942. Graduate, Coll. Electronics, U.K.; MBA, Loyola Coll., 1972. Jr. engr. Bendix I. L. S. D., Davenport, Iowa, 1967; with Allied Signal Tech. Svcs., Columbia, Md., 1967—; now v.p., asst. sec. Office: Allied Signal Tech Svcs 1 Bendix Rd Columbia MD 21045*

WILLOUGHBY, CARROLL VERNON, retired motel chain executive; b. Toms River, N.J., Nov. 8, 1913; s. Cleveland Carroll and Margaret Vernia (Ely) W.; m. Jo Evelyn Williams, Aug. 3, 1944; children: Charles Carroll, Jon Michael (dec.). Cert. in aero. engring, Balt. Vocat. Sch., 1933; student, Johns Hopkins U., 1939-42. Asso. Booz Allen & Hamilton, 1952-58; v.p., gen. mgr. Lawrence L. Frank Enterprises, 1958-60; real estate broker, v.p. Felger Constrn. Co., 1960-66; asst. to chmn. bd. Ky. Fried Chicken, Inc., 1966-70; sr. group v.p. Ramada Inns, Inc., Phoenix, 1970-81, also bd. dirs.; bd. dirs. Aztar Corp. Elder Presbyterian Ch. Served to capt. USAAF, 1942-45. Mem. San Fernando Valley Symphony Assn. (pres. 1962-66). Republican. Home: 4801 N 72nd Way Scottsdale AZ 85251-1301

WILLOUGHBY, JOHN WALLACE, former college dean, provost; b. Brumanna, Lebanon, July 30, 1932; s. James Wallace and Ida Cecilia (Frost) W.; m. Joanne Arnoldt DeWitt, Sept. 2, 1959; children—James Wallace, David Frost. B.A., Yale U., 1952; B.A., M.A., Oxford U., Eng., 1954; Ph.D., U. Rochester, 1959. Instr. English U. N.Mex., Albuquerque, 1959-60; instr. U. Chgo., 1960-63; from asst. prof. to prof., dean faculty Southampton Coll. Long Island, N.Y., 1963-73; v.p. for acad. affairs S.W. Minn. State Coll., Marshall, 1973-74, St. Francis Coll., Loretto, Pa., 1974-83; provost, dean of faculty, dir. continuing edn. Southwestern Coll., Winfield, Kans., 1983-92; distributor Success Motivation Inst., 1988—. Editor: English: Selected Readings, 1963; asst. editor Brownings Correspondence Wedgestone Press, 1993—; dcontbr. articles to profl. jours. Treas. Cambria-Somerset Coun. for Health Edn., Johnstown, Pa., 1976-83; v.p. for scouting Penns Woods Coun. Boy Scouts Am., 1978-82; mem. com. on preparation for ministry South Kans. Presbyn., 1989—; staff devel. and history writer Ctr. for Improvement of Human Functioning, Wichita, 1991—; v.p Winfield (Kans.) Lions Club, 1994—. With U.S. Army, 1956-58. Rhodes scholar, Oxford, 1952-54. Mem. Am. Assn. Rhodes Scholars. Democrat. Presbyterian. Avocations: bicycling; camping; philately; gardening; singing. Home: 518 E 15th St Winfield KS 67156-3604

WILLOUGHBY, RODNEY ERWIN, retired oil company executive; b. Dallas, July 24, 1925; s. Charles V. and Juanita (Jones) W.; m. Marie J. Johnston, Feb. 27, 1954; five children. B.B.A., Tulane U., 1945; M.B.A., Harvard U., 1947. Mem. dean's staff Harvard Bus. Sch., 1947-48; with ECA, Paris, France, 1948-49; petroleum attache Am. embassy, London, Eng., 1949-52; concession mgr. Gulf Oil Corp., N.Y.C., 1952-55; mem. fgn. staff Standard Oil Co. Calif., San Francisco, 1955-65; pres. Refineria Conchan Chevron, Peru, 1965-69, Chevron Oil Co. Latin Am., 1969-71; v.p., treas. Chevron Corp. (formerly Standard Oil Co.), Calif., San Francisco, 1971-84; v.p. fgn. Chevron Corp. (formerly Standard Oil Co.), 1984-89. Trustee San Francisco, Fine Arts Mus. San Francisco. Served to lt. (j.g.) USNR, 1943-46. Clubs: Pacific Union, Burlingame Country. Office: 55 Newplace Rd Hillsborough CA 94010-6446

WILLOUGHBY, STEPHEN SCHUYLER, mathematics educator; b. Madison, Wis., Sept. 27, 1932; s. Alfred and Elizabeth Frances (Cassell) W.; m. Helen Sali Shapiro, Aug. 29, 1954; children: Wendy Valentine (Mrs. Peter Gallen), Todd Alan. AB (scholar), Harvard U., 1953, AM in Teaching, 1955; EdD (Clifford Brewster Upton fellow), Columbia U., 1961. Tchr. Newton (Mass.) Pub. Schs., 1954-57, Greenwich (Conn.) Pub. Schs., 1957-59; instr. U. Wis., Madison, 1960-61, asst. prof. math. edn. and math., 1961-65; prof. math. edn. and math. NYU, 1965-87, dir. math. edn. dept., 1967-83, chmn. math., sci. and stats. edn. dept., 1970-80, 86-87, chmn. Univ. Faculty Council, 1981-82; prof. math. U. Ariz., Tucson, 1987—; mem. nat. bd. advisors Sq. One TV, 1983—; U.S. Commn. on Math. Instrn., 1984—, chmn., 1991—; math. adv. com. Nat. Tchr. Exam. Successor (Praxis), 1989—; edn. panel New Am. Schs. Devel. Corp., 1991—; U.S. Nat. rep. Internat. Commn. on Math. Instrn., 1991—. Author: Contemporary Teaching of Secondary School Mathematics, 1967, Probability and Statistics, 1968, Teaching Mathematics: What Is Basic, 1981, Mathematics Education for a Changing World, 1990, Real Math, 1981, 85, 87, 91—; contbr. articles to profl. jours. and encys., chpts. to yearbooks and anthologies. Recipient Leadership in Math. Edn. Trust Lifetime Achievement medal, 1995. Mem. Nat. Coun. Tchrs. Math. (dir. 1968-71, pres. 1982-84, Lifetime Achievement award for Leadership in Math. Edn. 1995), Coun. Sci. Soc. Pres. (exec. bd. 1984, 85, 86, 87, chmn. 1988). Home: 5435 Gleneagles Dr Tucson AZ 85718-1805 Office: U Ariz Dept Math Tucson AZ 85721

WILLOUGHBY, WILLIAM, II, retired nuclear engineer; b. Birmingham, Ala., Jan. 14, 1933; s. William and Marion Louise (Hart) W.; m. Doris Jean Lindsey, Oct. 16, 1954; 1 child, William III. BSChemE, MIT, 1954; MS in Nuclear Engring., U. Calif., Berkeley, 1960. Registered profl. engr., S.C. Physicist U. Calif. Lawrence Livermore (Calif.) Lab., 1957-61; tech. support supr. Carolina Va. Nuclear Power Assocs., Parr, S.C., 1962-67; mgr. nuclear engr. S.C. Elec. & Gas, Columbia, 1967-76; sr. project mgr., consulting engr. Stone & Webster Engring., N.Y.C., 1976-93; ret., 1993; mem. S.C. Nuclear Adv. Coun., Columbia, 1974-76; instr. Bridgeport Engring. Inst., Fairfield, Conn., 1994, Midlands Tech. Coll., Columbia, S.C., 1994-95. Contbr. articles to profl. jours. Commodore Columbia Sailing Club, 1974. 1st lt. U.S. Army, 1955-57. Mem. AAAS, Am. Nuclear Soc., Sigma Xi, Tau Beta Pi. Episcopalian. Home: 506 Killington Ct Columbia SC 29212

WILLOUGHBY, WILLIAM FRANKLIN, II, physician, researcher; b. Washington, Feb. 4, 1936; s. William Westel and Patricia (DeZychlinska) W.; m. Mary Scott Fishburne, 1963 (div. 1974); children: Westel Woodbury, William Franklin III, Laura Fishburne, Mary Scott; m. Judith Eleanor Barbaras, Oct. 25, 1975; 1 child, Robert Alexander Willoughby. AB, Johns Hopkins U., 1957, MD, 1965, PhD in Microbiology, 1965; grad. with distinction, USAF War Coll., 1985. Diplomate Am. Bd. Pathology. Intern then resident in pathology Johns Hopkins Hosp., 1965-67; asst. prof. depts. pathology and microbiology Case Western Res. U., Cleve.; dir. Virginia Mason Rsch. Ctr., Seattle, 1972-75; assoc. prof. dept. pathology Sch. Medicine, Johns Hopkins U., Balt., 1975-87; prof., chmn. dept. pathology Sch. Medicine, U. S.C., Columbia, 1987-92; prof. dept. pathology Rush U. Coll. Medicine, 1994—; dir. labs. Cook County Hosp., Chgo., 1992—; interim med. dir., 1994—; prof. dept. pathology Rush Med. Coll., Chgo., 1994—; cons. NIH, Bethesda, Md., 1979—, mem. pathology A study sect., 1982-86; cons. NRC, Washington, 1981-84; mem. Res. Component Med. Coun., Dept. Def., Pentagon, 1991-93; dept. surgeon gen. for res. affairs USAF, Bolling AFB, D.C., 1991—; asst. surg. gen. USAF, Desert Storms/Desert Shield, 1990-91. Mem. editorial bd. Am. Rev. Respiratory Disease, 1978-84; contbr. articles to profl. jours., reviewer numerous sci. manuscripts. Vestryman Trinity Episcopal Ch., Long Green, Md., 1984-87; bd. dirs. Ctrl. S.C. chpt. ARC, Columbia, 1989-92; bd. fellow Norwich U., 1992—. Maj. USAFR, 1975-95, advanced through grades to maj. gen., 1992—; asst. surgeon gen. USAF, 1990-91, Desert Storm. Decorated Legion of Merit; recipient Edwin E. Osgood prize Va. Mason Rsch. Ctr., 1973; Arthritis Found. fellow Scripps Clinic and Rsch. Found., 1967-69; Poncine scholar Poncine Found., 1972-74; NIH rsch. grantee, 1976-91. Fellow Coll. Am. Pathologists; mem. AAAS, Am. Soc. Investigative Pathology, Am. Assn. Immunologists, Am. Soc. Cell Biologists, Internat. Acad. Pathology, Assn. Pathology Chmns., Aerospace Med. Assn., Soc. USAF Flight Surgeons (bd. govs. 1993—), Soc. Cons. to Armed Forces, Am. Thoracic Soc., Assn. Mil. Surgeons U.S. Avocations: aviation, music, tennis. Home: 1416A S Federal St Chicago IL 60605-2710 Office: Cook County Hosp Hektoen Inst 627 S Wood St Chicago IL 60612-3810

WILLOWS, ARTHUR OWEN DENNIS, neurobiologist, zoology educator; b. Winnipeg, Man., Can., Mar. 26, 1941; came to U.S., 1959; s. Danby and Laura Beatrice (Bumstead) W.; m. Karen Dunkelbarger, June 14, 1987; children by previous marriage: Kurt Danby, Keith Stratton, Amy Margaret. B.S., Yale U., 1963; Ph.D., U. Oreg., 1967. Asst. prof. U. Wash., Seattle, 1969-72, assoc. prof., 1972-75, prof. zoology, 1975—, chmn. dept.,

1979—; dir. Friday Harbor Labs., Wash., 1973—. Editor: Invertebrate Learning, 2 vols., 1973, Neurobiology and Behavior, 2 vols., 1985, Marine Behavior and Physiology. Guggenheim fellow, 1976. Mem. Soc. for Neurosci., Am. Soc. Zoologists, Western Soc. Naturalists, Am. Soc. Physiologists. Home: Friday Harbor Labs Friday Harbor WA 98250 Office: U Wash Dept Zoology 620 University Rd Friday Harbor WA 98250-9218

WILLRICH, MASON, utility company executive, consultant; b. L.A., 1933; m. Patricia Rowe, June 11, 1960; children: Christopher, Stephen, Michael, Katherine. BA magna cum laude, Yale U., 1954; JD, U. Calif., Berkeley, 1960. Atty. Pillsbury Madison and Sutro, San Francisco, 1960-62; asst. gen. coun. U.S. Arms Control and Disarmament Agy., 1962-65; assoc. prof. law U. Va., 1965-68, prof. law, 1968-75, John Stennis prof. law, 1975-79; dir. internat. rels. Rockefeller Found., N.Y.C., 1976-79; v.p. Pacific Gas & Electric, San Francisco, 1979-84, sr. v.p., 1984-88, exec. v.p., 1988-89; CEO, pres. PG&E Enterprises, San Francisco, 1989-94; exec. Pacific Gas and Electric Co., San Francisco, 1979-94; cons., 1994—. Author: Non-Proliferation Treaty, 1969, Global Politics of Nuclear Energy, 1971, (with T.B. Taylor) Nuclear Theft, 1974, Administration of Energy Shortages, 1976 (with R.K. Lester) Radioactive Waste Management and Regulation, 1977. Trustee, past chmn. bd. dirs. World Affairs Coun. No. Calif.; pres. Midland Sch.; mem. Resources for the Future, Atlantic Coun. U.S. Guggenheim Meml. fellow, 1973. Mem. Phi Beta Kappa, Order of Coif. Office: 1452 Hamilton Ave Palo Alto CA 94301

WILLS, CHARLES FRANCIS, former church executive, retired career officer; b. Avalon, N.J., July 26, 1914; s. Charles H. and Anna Margaret (Diemand) W.; m. Charlotte Emily Robson, Aug. 22, 1936; children: C. Frederic, Emily, Sally and Larry (twins). B.S., Wheaton (Ill.) Coll., 1935; B.D., Eastern Bapt. Theol. Sem., 1938, Th.M., 1941; grad., Air War Coll., 1961. Commd. 1st lt. U.S. Army, 1941; advanced through grades to col. U.S. Air Force, 1963; chaplain AUS, 1941-49, U.S. Air Force, 1949-67; ret., 1967; exec. dir. chaplaincy services Am. Bapt. Chs., Valley Forge, Pa., 1969-75; exec. dir. profl. services Am. Bapt. Chs., 1975-78; assoc. sec. Bapt. World Alliance, Washington, 1978-80; treas. Bapt. World Alliance, 1980-81; mem. Commn. on Doctrine and Interchurch Cooperation, 1980-90. Decorated Legion of Merit, Bronze Star, Purple Heart. Mem. Mil. Chaplains Assn., Smithsonian Assos.

WILLS, DAVID WOOD, minister, educator; b. Portland, Ind., Jan. 25, 1942; s. Theodore Oscar Mitchell and Elizabeth Lochore (Wood) W.; m. Carolyn Reynolds Montgomery, Aug. 22, 1964; children: John Brookings, Theodore Worcester, Thomas Churchill. BA, Yale U., 1962; BD, Princeton Theol. Sem., 1966; PhD, Harvard U., 1975. Ordained to ministry Presbyn. Ch., 1970. Asst. prof. Sch. of Religion, U. So. Calif., 1970-72; asst. prof. dept. of religion Amherst Coll., Mass., 1972-78, assoc. prof. 1978-83, prof., 1983-90, prof. religion and Black studies, 1990-94, Winthrop H. Smith '16 prof. Am. history and Am. studies, dept. religion and Black studies, 1994—, also dir. Luce Program in Comparative Religious Ethics 1978-88. Editor (with Richard Newman) Black Apostles at Home and Abroad, 1982, (with Albert Raboteau) Afro-American Religion: A Documentary History Project, 1987—. Kent fellow Danforth Found., 1966-70, 75, Ford Found. fellow, 1972, Inst. for Ecumenical and Cultural Rsch. fellow, 1972, Nat. Humanities Ctr. fellow, 1980-81, 94, NEH fellow for Coll. Tchrs., 1988-89, W. E. B. DuBois Inst. for Afro-Am. Rsch. fellow, 1989-91. Mem. Am. Acad. Religion (chair Afro-Am. religious history group 1975-78), Am. Hist. Assn., Am. Soc. Ch. History, Am. Studies Assn., Orgn. Am. Historians, So. Hist. Assn., Phi Beta Kappa. Home: 100 Woodside Ave Amherst MA 01002-2526 Office: Amherst Coll Dept Religion Amherst MA 01002

WILLS, EDGAR W. (BILL), newspaper editor; b. Urbana, Ill., Oct. 27, 1943; s. Edgar and Laura Loretta (McDermott) W.; m. Phyllis A. Robinson, Jan. 21, 1962; children: Teresa, Richard, Michael. Graduate, Mahomet H.S. From reporter to mng. editor/editorial The Pantagraph, Bloomington, Ill., 1962—. Dir. Four Seasons Assn., Bloomington, 1990-91; advisor Students for Free Enterprise Ill. State U., Normal, 1990-91; mem. adv. bd. Centrillo Girl Scout Coun., Bloomington, 1990—; v.p. St. Joseph Med. Ctr. Cmty. Bd., Bloomington, 1987—; dir. McLean County Assn. for Retarded Citizens. Mem. AP Mng. Editors, Ill. AP Editors (bd. dirs., former pres.), Mid-Am. Press Inst. (dir.), Bloomington Rotary Club. Avocation: woodworking. Home: 126 Ginger Creek Bloomington IL 61704 Office: The Pantagraph 301 W Washington Bloomington IL 61701

WILLS, GARRY, journalist, educator; b. Atlanta, May 22, 1934; s. John and Mayno (Collins) W.; m. Natalie Cavallo, May 30, 1959; children: John, Garry, Lydia. Student St. Louis U., 1957; MA, Xavier U., Cin., 1958, Yale U., 1959; PhD, Yale U., 1961; LittD (hon.), Coll. Holy Cross, 1982, Columbia Coll., 1982, Beloit Coll., 1988, Xavier U., 1993, St. Xavier U., 1993, Union Coll., 1993, Bates Coll., 1995, Macalester Coll., 1995. Fellow Center Hellenic Studies, 1961-62; assoc. prof. classics Johns Hopkins U., 1962-67, adj. prof., 1968-80; Henry R. Luce prof. Am. culture and public policy Northwestern U., 1980-88, adj. prof., 1988—; newspaper columnist Universal Press Syndicate, 1970—. Author: Chesterton, 1961, Politics and Catholic Freedom, 1964, Roman Culture, 1966, Jack Ruby, 1967, Second Civil War, 1968, Nixon Agonistes, 1970, Bare Ruined Choirs, 1972, Inventing America, 1978, At Button's, 1979, Confessions of a Conservative, 1979, Explaining America, 1980, The Kennedy Imprisonment, 1982, Lead Time, 1983, Cincinnatus, 1984, Reagan's America, 1987, Under God, 1990, Lincoln at Gettysburg, 1992 (Pulitzer Prize for gen. non-fiction 1993), Certain Trumpets: The Call of Leaders, 1994, Witches and Jesuits: Shakespeare's Macbeth, 1994. Recipient Pulitzer prize, 1993, Merle Curti award Orgn. Am. Historians, Nat. Book Critics Circle award (2), Wilbur Cross medal Yale U., Peabody award. Mem. AAAL, Am. Acad. Arts and Scis., Am. Antiquarian Soc., Mass. Hist. Soc. Roman Catholic. Office: Northwestern U Dept History Evanston IL 60201

WILLS, J. ROBERT, academic administrator, drama educator, writer; b. Akron, Ohio, May 5, 1940; s. J. Robert and Helen Elizabeth (Lapham) W.; m. Barbara T. Salisbury, Aug. 4, 1984. B.A., Coll. of Wooster, 1962; M.A. U. Ill., 1963; Ph.D., Case-Western Res. U., 1971; cert. in arts adminstrn, Harvard U., 1976. Instr. to asst. prof., dir. theatre Wittenberg U., Springfield, Ohio, 1963-72; assoc. prof., dir. grad. studies, chmn. dept. theatre U. Ky., Lexington, 1972-77; prof. theatre, dean U. Ky. (Coll. Fine Arts), 1977-81; prof. drama, dean Coll. Fine Arts, U. Tex., Austin, 1981-89; Effie Marie Cain Regents chair in Fine Arts, 1986-89; provost, prof. theatre Pacific Luth. U., Tacoma, Wash., 1989-94; prof. theatre, dean coll. fine arts Ariz. State U., Tempe, 1994—; cons. colls., univs., arts orgns., govt. agencies. Author: The Director in a Changing Theatre, 1976, Directing in the Theatre: A Casebook, 1980, rev. edit., 1994; dir. 92 plays; contbr. articles to profl. jours. Bd. dirs. various art orgns., Ky. Tex. and Wash. Recipient grants public and pvt. agencies. Mem. Nat. Assn. State Univs. and Land-Grant Colls.(chmn. common. on arts 1981-83), Coun. Fine Arts Deans (exec. com. 1984-89, sec. 1986-89), Univ. and Coll. Theatre Assn. (pres. 1981-82), Assn. for Communication Adminstrn. (pres. 1986-87), Ky. Theatre Assn. (pres. 1976). Office: Ariz State U Coll Fine Arts Tempe AZ 85287-2101

WILLS, JOHN ELLIOT, JR., history educator, writer; b. Urbana, Ill., Aug. 8, 1936; s. John Elliot and George Anne (Hicks) W.; m. Carolin Connell, July 19, 1958; children: Catherine, Christopher John, Jeffrey David, Joanne, Lucinda. BA in Philosophy, U. Ill., 1956; MA in East Asian Studies, Harvard U., 1960, PhD in History and Far Ea. Langs., 1967. History instr. Stanford (Calif.) U., 1964-65; history instr. U. So. Calif., L.A., 1965-67, asst. prof., 1967-72, assoc. prof., 1972-84, prof., 1984—, acting chair East Asian Langs. and Cultures, 1987-89; dir. East Asian Studies Ctr. USC-UCLA Joint East Asian Studies Ctr., L.A., 1990-94; rsch. abroad in The Netherlands, Taiwan, China, Japan, Macao, Philippines, Indonesia, India, Italy, Spain, Portugal, Eng. Author: Pepper, Guns, and Parleys: The Dutch East India Company and China, 1662-1681, 1974, Embassies and Illusions: Dutch and Portuguese Envoys to K'ang-hsi, 1666-1687, 1984, Mountain of Fame: Portraits in Chinese History, 1994; co-editor: (with Jonathan D. Spence) From Ming to Ch'ing: Conquest, Region, and Continuity in Seventeenth-Century China, 1979; contbr. articles to profl. jours. Grantee Nat. Acad. Scis., 1985, Am. Coun. Learned Socs., 1979-80; Younger Humanist fellow NEH, 1972-73. Mem. Assn. for Asian Studies, Am. Hist. Assn., Phi Beta Kappa, Phi Kappa Phi (Recognition award 1986, 95). Avocation: travel. Office: U So Calif Dept History Los Angeles CA 90089-0034

WILLS, MICHAEL RALPH, medical educator; b. Bath, Somerset, Eng., May 4, 1931; came to U.S., 1977; s. Ralph Herbert and Una Read (Hearse) W.; m. Margaret Christine Lewis, Sept. 12, 1955; children: Matthew, Catherine, Sarah, Benjamin, Thomas. M.B., Ch.B., U. Bristol, Eng., 1954, M.D., 1964, Ph.D., 1978. Intern Bristol Royal Infirmary, 1954-55, fellow, resident, 1957-64; sr. lectr. Royal Free Hosp. and Med. Sch., London, 1964-70, reader, 1970-74, prof., 1974-77; dir. clin. labs. U. Va., Charlottesville 1977—. Author books, films; contbr. articles to profl. jours. Lt. comdr. Royal Naval Res., Eng. NIH rsch. fellow, 1967-68. Fellow ACP, Royal Coll. Physicians, Royal Coll. Pathologists. Roman Catholic. Avocations: reading, wood carving, gardening, military modelling. Home: 236 Rookwood Dr Charlottesville VA 22903 Office: U Va Dept Pathology Charlottesville VA 22908

WILLS, ROBERT HAMILTON, newspaper executive; b. Colfax, Ill., June 21, 1926; s. Robert Orson and Ressie Mae (Hamilton) W.; m. Sherilyn Lou Niersthemer, Jan. 16, 1949; children: Robert L., Michael H., Kendall J. B.S., M.S., Northwestern U., 1950. Reporter Duluth (Minn.) Herald & News-Tribune, 1950-51; reporter Milw. Jour., 1951-59, asst. city editor, 1959-62; city editor Milw. Sentinel, 1962-75, editor, 1975-91; exec. v.p. Jour./Sentinel, Inc., Milw., 1991-92, pres., 1992-93; vice-chmn., 1993; also bd. dirs. Jour./Sentinel, Inc., Milw.; pub. Milw. Jour.; sr. v.p., bd. dirs. Jour. Communications; pres. Wis. Freedom of Info. Council, 1979-86; Pulitzer Prize juror, 1982, 83, 90. Mem. media-law rels. com. State Bar Wis.; chmn. Wis. Privacy Coun., 1994. Served with USNR, 1944-46. Recipient Leadership award Women's Ct. and Civic Conf. Greater Milw., 1987, Freedom of Information award, 1988; named Wis. Newsman of Yr. Milw. chpt. Sigma Delta Chi, 1973. Mem. Wis. Newspaper Assn. (pres. 1985-86, Disting. Svc. award 1992), Wis. AP (pres. 1975-76, Dion Henderson award Svc. 1993), Am. Soc. Newspaper Editors. Internat. Press Inst., Milw. Press Club (Media Hall Fame, 1993), Soc. Profl. Journalists (pres. Milw. chpt. 1979-80, nat. pres. 1986-87). Home: 17965 Maple Tree Ln Brookfield WI 53045-2624 Office: Jour/Sentinel Inc 333 W State St PO Box 661 Milwaukee WI 53201

WILLS, WALTER JOE, agricultural marketing educator; b. Beecher City, Ill., Oct. 8, 1915; s. Joe J. and Lillian L. (Buzzard) W.; m. Mary E. Triffet, May 22, 1942 (dec. 1981); m. Martha Jane Smith Peck, June 12, 1982. Student, Blackburn Coll., Carlinville, Ill., 1934; B.S. in Agr, U. Ill., 1936, M.S. in Agrl. Econs, 1937, Ph.D., 1952. Credit bureau Prodn. Credit Corp., St. Louis, 1937-47; asst. prof. U. Ill., 1947-52; dir. farm relations Am. Trucking Assn., 1953-54; extension marketing specialist Wash. State Coll., 1954-56; prof. agrl. marketing So. Ill. U., Carbondale, 1956-83, chmn. agrl. industries dept., 1957-72, cons., 1983—; Fulbright lectr. Ege U., Izmir, Turkey, 1969-70. Author: Introduction to Grain Marketing, 1972, Introduction to Agribusiness Management, 1973, (with Michael E. Newman) Agribusiness Management and Entrepreneurship, 3d edit., 1993, Introduction to Agricultural Sales, 1982. Served to capt., ordnance dept. U.S. Army, 1941-46. Recipient Outstanding Coop. Educator award Am. Inst. Cooperation, 1978; Great Tchr. award So. Ill. U., 1984, Disting. Svc. award, 1992. Mem. Goldern Key, Phi Kappa Phi, Gamma Sigma Delta, Alpha Zeta. Club: Rotarian. Home: 904 S Valley Rd Carbondale IL 62901-2421

WILLS, WILLIAM RIDLEY, II, former insurance company executive, historian; b. Nashville, June 19, 1934; s. Jesse Ely and Ellen (Buckner) W.; m. Irene Weaver Jackson, July 21, 1962; children: William Ridley III, Morgan Jackson, Thomas Weaver. BA, Vanderbilt U., 1956. Agt., staff mgr. Nat. Life & Accident Ins. Co., Nashville, 1958-62, supr., 1962-64, asst. sec., 1964-67, asst. v.p., 1967-70, 2d v.p., 1970-75, v.p., 1975-81, sr. v.p., 1981-83; sr. v.p. Am. General Services Co., 1982-83; dir. Nat. Life & Accident Ins. Co., Nashville, 1976-83; pres. Tenn. Hist. Soc., 1985-87; bd. dirs. Nat. Trust for Hist. Preservation, 1988-91. Author: History of Belle Meade: Mansion, Plantation and Stud, 1991. Nat. chmn. Living Endowment Drive Vanderbilt U., 1974; pres. Cumberland Mus. and Sci. Ctr., Nashville, 1977; gen. chmn. campaign United Way, Nashville and Middle Tenn., 1978; pres. YMCA of Met. Nashville, 1984; trustee Ladies Hermitage Assn., 1981-90; mem. Tenn. Hist. Commn.; chmn. bd. Montgomery Bell Acad., 1988—; bd. dirs. Vanderbilt U., 1988—. Lt. USN, 1956-58. Recipient awards YMCA, 1977, 1983, United Way De Tocqueville award, 1989, Tenn. History Book award Tenn. Lib. Assn. and Tenn. Hist. Comm., 1991. Fellow Life Office Mgmt. Assn.; mem. Assn. Preservation Tenn. Antiques (pres. Nashville chpt. 1987-89), Belle Meade Country Club, YMCA Athletic Club, Coffee House Club, Round Table Literary Club. Presbyterian.

WILLSE, JAMES PATRICK, newspaper editor; b. N.Y.C., Mar. 17, 1944; s. Sherman Stokes and Katherine (Mackey) W.; m. Sharon Margaret Stack, Sept. 15, 1973; 1 child, Elizabeth Ruth. BA, Hamilton Coll., 1967; MS, Columbia U., 1968. Nat. editor AP, N.Y.C., 1969-74; news editor AP, San Francisco, 1975-78; city editor San Francisco Examiner, 1978-82, mng. editor, 1982-84; mng. editor N.Y. Daily News, 1984-89, editor, pub., 1989-95; editor Star Ledger, Newark, 1995—. Fellow Stanford U., 1975. Mem. Am. Soc. Newspaper Editors, AP Mng. Editors. Office: Star Ledger 1 Star Ledger Plz Newark NJ 07102*

WILLSON, ALAN NEIL, JR., engineering educator, dean; b. Balt., Oct. 16, 1939; s. Alan Neil and Dorothy Sybil (Evert) W.; m. Frances Elizabeth Beneze, Oct. 6, 1962 (div. Dec. 1986); children: Catherine Elizabeth, Deborah Frances, David Alan. BEE, Ga. Inst. Tech., 1961; MSEE, Syracuse U., 1965, PhD, 1967. Assoc. engr. IBM, Poughkeepsie, N.Y., 1961-64; instr. Syracuse (N.Y.) U., 1965-67; mem. tech. staff Bell Labs., Murray Hill, N.J., 1967-72; assoc. prof. UCLA, 1972-76, prof., 1976—, asst. dean for grad. studies, 1977-81, assoc. dean engring., 1987—. Editor: Nonlinear Networks, 1974; contbr. articles to profl. jours. Bd. dirs. Nat. Consortium for Grad. Degrees for Minorities in Engring. Inc., 1979-81. Recipient George Westinghouse award Am. Soc. Engring. Edn., 1982, Disting. Faculty award UCLA Engring. Alumni Assn., 1982, Myril B. Reed award Midwest Symposium on Cirs. and Systems, 1984, Engring. Merit award San Fernando Valley Engrs. Coun., 1985. Fellow IEEE (pres. Cirs. and Systems Soc. 1984, editor Transactions and Cirs. and Systems Jour., 1977-79, Guillemin-Cauer award 1979, W.R.G. Baker prize 1985, 94), Sigma Xi, Eta Kappa Nu, Tau Beta Pi. Libertarian. Avocations: bridge, skiing. Office: UCLA Dept Electrical Engineering 405 Hilgard Ave Los Angeles CA 90024-1301*

WILLSON, C. GRANT, chemistry educator, engineering educator; b. Vallejo, Calif., Mar. 30, 1939; s. Carlton P. and Margaret Ann (Cosner) W.; m. Deborah Jeanne Merritt, Dec. 13, 1975; children: William, Andrew. BS in Chemistry, U. Calif., Berkeley, 1962, PhD in Organic Chemistry, 1973; MS in Organic Chemistry, San Diego State U., 1969. With propellent rsch. Aerojet Gen. Corp., Sacramento, 1962-64; tchr., coach Fairfax High Sch., L.A., 1964-67; prof. Calif. State U., Long Beach, 1973-74, U. Calif., San Diego, 1974-78; mgr. polymer sci. and tech. IBM Almaden Rsch. Ctr., San Jose, Calif., 1978-93; prof. chemistry, chem. engring. U. Tex., Austin, 1993—. Contbr. articles to profl. jours.; patentee in field. Mem. NAE, AAAS, Am. Soc. Photographic and Instrumentation Engrs., Am. Phys. Soc., Am. Chem. Soc. (Arthur K. Doolittle award 1986, award Chemistry of Materials 1991, Carouthers award 1994, Coop. Rsch. award in Polymer Sci. 1993), St. Francis Yacht Club, Sigma Xi. Avocations: sailing, skiing. Office: U Tex Dept Chem Engring CPE3 474 Austin TX 78712

WILLSON, JAMES DOUGLAS, aerospace executive; b. Edinburgh, Scotland, May 24, 1915; came to U.S., 1921; s. George William and Margaret (Douglas) W.; m. Genevieve Best, Nov. 11, 1939; children: James Douglas, Stephen J., Wendy. B.S. with honors, Ohio State U., 1937, M.B.A., 1938. C.P.A., N.Y. Sr. auditor Arthur Andersen & Co. (C.P.A.'s), N.Y.C., 1938-42; controller Stinson div. Consol. Vultee Aircraft Corp., 1946-48, Plaskon div. Libbey-Ownes-Ford Glass Co., 1948-53; treas. Affiliated Gas Equipment Co., Cleve., 1953; v.p. finance, treas. Norris-Thermador Corp., Los Angeles, 1957-59; controller, mgr. finance Tidewater Oil Co., Los Angeles, 1959-60; v.p. finance Tidewater Oil Co., 1960-66, Northrop Corp., Los Angeles, 1966-70; sr. v.p. finance, treas. Northrop Corp., 1970-80, also dir. Author: Controllership, 1952, 63, 81, 90, Business Budgeting and Control, 1956, 57, Internal Auditing Manual, 1983, 89, Budgeting and Profit Planning, 1983, 89, 92, Fin. Info. Systems, 1986. Served to lt. comdr. USNR, 1942-46. Mem. Nat. Assn. Accts. (Lybrand Gold medal 1960), Am. Inst. C.P.A.s, Controllers Inst. Am. Home: 1715 Chevy Chase Dr Beverly Hills CA 90210-2709

WILLSON, JOHN MICHAEL, mining company executive; b. Sheffield, England, Feb. 21, 1940; s. Jack Desmond and Cicely Rosamond (Long Price) W.; m. Susan Mary Partridge, Aug. 26, 1942; children: Marcus J., Carolyn A. BSc in Mining Engring. with honors, Imperial Coll., London, 1962, MSc in Mining Engring., 1985. With Cominco Ltd., 1966-74; v.p. No. Group Cominco Ltd., Vancouver, B.C., Can., 1981-84; pres. Garaventa (Canada) Ltd., Vancouver, 1974-81; pres. CEO Western Can. Steel Ltd., Vancouver, 1985-88, Pegasus Gold Inc., Spokane, Wash., 1989-92, Placer Dome Inc., Vancouver, B.C., Can., 1993—; chmn. bd. dirs. Placer Pacific Ltd., Sydney, Australia, Placer Dome U.S., San Francisco, Placer Dome Can. Ltd., Placer Dome Latin Am. Pres. N.W.T. Chamber Mines, Yellowknife, Can., 1982-84; chmn. bd. dirs. Western States Pub. Lands Coalition, Pueblo, Colo., 1990-91; bd. dirs. World Gold Coun. Mem. AIME, Can. Inst. Mining and Metallurgy, Inst. Mining and Metallurgy (London), Assn. Profl. Engrs. B.C., Assn. Profl. Engrs. and Geologists N.W.T., N.W. Mining Assn. (bd. dirs. Corp. Leadership award 1991), Am. Mining Congress (bd. dirs.), World Gold Coun. (bd. dirs.). Avocations: cycling, tennis, squash, sailing, skiing. Home: 4722 Drummond Dr, Vancouver, BC Canada V6T 1B4 Office: Placer Dome Inc, 1055 W Dunsmuir St Ste 1600, Vancouver, BC Canada V7X 1P1

WILLSON, MARY F., ecology researcher, educator; b. Madison, Wis., July 28, 1938; d. Gordon L. and Sarah (Loomans) W.; m. R.A. von Neumann, May 29, 1972 (dec.). B.A. with honors, Grinnell Coll., 1960; Ph.D., U. Wash., 1964. Asst. prof. U. Ill., Urbana, 1965-71, assoc. prof., 1971-76, prof. ecology, 1976-90; rsch. ecologist Forestry Scis. Lab., Juneau, Alaska, 1989—; adj. prof. zoology and botany Wash. State U., Pullman; prin. rsch. scientist, affiliate prof. biology Inst. Arctic Biology U. Alaska, Fairbanks; faculty assoc. divsn. biol. scis. U. Mont., Missoula. Author: Plant Reproductive Ecology, 1983, Vertebrate Natural History, 1984; co-author: Mate Choice in Plants, 1983. Fellow AAAS, Am. Ornithologists Union; mem. Soc. for Study Evolution, Am. Soc. Naturalists (hon.), Ecol. Soc. Am., Brit. Ecol. Soc. Office: Forestry Scis Lab 2770 Sherwood Ln Juneau AK 99801-8545

WILLSON, PRENTISS, JR., lawyer; b. Durham, N.C., Sept. 20, 1943; s. Prentiss and Lucille (Giles) W.; m. Ellen Borgersen, May 22, 1982. AB, Occidental Coll., 1965; JD, Harvard U., 1968. Bar: Calif. 1969, U.S. Dist. Ct. (no. dist.) Calif. 1971, U.S. Ct. Appeals (9th cir.) 1971, U.S. Tax Ct. 1971, U.S. Supreme Ct. 1975. Instr. law Miles Coll., Birmingham, Ala., 1968-70; ptnr. Morrison & Foerster, San Francisco, 1970—; prof. Golden Gate U., 1971-84; lectr. Stanford U. Sch. Law, 1985-88. Contbr. articles to legal publs. Mem. ABA, Calif. Bar Assn. Democrat. Office: Morrison & Foerster 345 California St San Francisco CA 94104

WILLSON, ROBERT (WILLIAM), glass sculpture and watercolor artist; b. Mertzon, Tex., May 28, 1912; s. James Thomas and Birdie Alice (Blanks) W.; m. Virginia Lambert, Aug. 12, 1941 (div. 1977); 1 child, Mark Joseph; m. Margaret Pace, May 30, 1981. BA, U. Tex., 1934; MFA, U. Bellas Artes, Mex., 1941. Pub. sch. tchr. various small Tex. towns, 1936-40; chmn. art dept. Tex. Wesleyan Coll., Ft. Worth, 1940-48; owner Nob Hill Tourist Resort, Winslow, Ariz., 1948-52; prof. art U. Miami, 1952-77, ret., 1977; represented by Sol Del Rio Gallery, San Antonio, Galleria d'Arte Moderna Ravagnan, Venice, Italy, Lyons-Martrix Gallery, Austin, Tex., Sandra Ainsley Gallery, Toronto, Stein Gallery, Portland, Maine, Bryant Galleries, Jackson, New Orleans, Atlanta, Palm Beach, Guy Lyons Gallery, Houston, Painted Horse Gallery, Aspen, Colo.; tchr. U. Mex., 1935; dir. Nob Hill Art Gallery, Ark. Ozarks, 1948-52; dir. Tex. Wesleyan Coll. Art Gallery, 1940-48; cons.-dir. Peoria Art Mus., Ill., 1969. One-man shows include U. Tex., Austin, 1980, McNay Art Mus., San Antonio, 1982, Art Inst. of the Permian Basin, Odessa, Tex. 1985, Tulane U., New Orleans, 1986, San Antonio Mus. Art, 1986, San Angelo (Tex.) Mus. of Art, 1989, Lyons-Matrix Gallery, Austin, 1989, 92, 95, Mus. of Modern Art, Venice, Italy, 1984, Galleria d'Arte Sant'Apollonia, 1989, Galleria d'Arte Moderna, San Marco, Venice, 1984-89, Martin Mus. of Art, Baylor U., Waco, Tex., 1991-92, N.Mex. Mus. of Fine Art, Santa Fe, 1993; exhibited in group shows at Internat. Glass Art 982 Show, Venice, Italy, 1994; juried shows include San Francisco Mus. Art, 1971, Mus. Modern Art, Mexico City, Adria Gallery, N.Y.C., Harmon Gallery, Naples, Fla., Lowe Art Mus., Fucina degli Angeli Internat. Glass Sculpture Exhbns., Venice, 1966-88, La Biennale di Venizia, 1972; permanent collections include Museo Correr, Venice, Victoria and Albert Mus., London, Nat. Italian Glass Mus., Murano, Italy, Auckland Nat. Art Mus., New Zealand, U. Tex., Austin, Corning Mus. Glass, N.Y., Witte Art Mus., San Antonio, San Antonio Mus. Art, Phila. Mus. Art, Little Rock Ctr., Ark., Ft. Lauderdale (Fla.) Art Mus., Peoria Art Mus., Lowe Art Mus., Miami, Fla., Columbus (Ga.) Art Mus., Duke U. Art Mus., N.C., Oxford (Eng.)-Wilson-Willson Glass Collection, New Orleans Mus. Art, New Mex. Mus. Fine Art, Santa Fe, others; contbr. articles to profl. jours. Capt. USMCR, 1942-45. Tex. Regents scholarship U. Tex., 1930-34, Farmer Internat. fellowship to Mex., 1935; Nat. study grant Corning Mus. of Glass, 1956, rsch. grant U. Miami, 1964, 66, Feldman Found., 1976, Internat. rsch. grant U.S. Office of Edn., 1966-68, Coll. grants Shell Co. Found., 1971, 73. Mem. AAUP, Coun. of Ozark Artists and Craftsmen (founder), Fla. Craftsmen, Coll. Art Assn., Am. Assn. Mus., Fla. Sculptors, Tex. Sculptors, Tex. Watercolor Soc., others. Avocations: collecting ancient glass, Indian poetry. Home: 207 Terrell Rd San Antonio TX 78209

WILLSON, WARRACK G., physical chemist. BA in Chemistry & Math., U. No. Colo., 1965; PhD in Phys. Chemistry, U. Wyo., 1970. Rsch. scientist Nat. Resources Rsch. Inst. U. Wyo., Laramie, 1971-73; rsch. engr. div. reactor engring. Engring. Tech. Ctr. E. I. DuPont Nemours Co., Wilmington, Del., 1973-76; group leader coal chem. devel. Occidental Rsch. Corp., La Verne, Calif., 1976-78; mgr. br. gasification and liquefaction Grank Forks (N.D.) Energy Tech. Ctr. Dept. of Energy, 1978-83; dir. Fuels and Process Chemistry Rsch. Inst. and Energy and Environ. Rsch. Ctr. U. N.D., Grand Forks, 1983—; bd. dirs. Internat. Pitts. Coal Conf., 1987-88; tech. dir. Internat. Opportunities in the Synfuels Industry Biennial Symposium, 1988—; vis. prof. coal sci. and tech. Mineral Industry Rsch. Lab. U. Alaska, Fairbanks, 1988-89, adj. prof. coal tech., 1988—; adj. prof. chem. engring. U. N.D., 1980—. Contbr. over 75 articles to profl. jours. Mem. Am. Inst. Chem. Engrs., Am. Chem. Soc., Sigma Xi, Lambda Sigma Tau. Achievements include research and development of fuels production and utilization, of environmental control systems, and of process chemistry. Office: U ND Energy & Environ Rsch Ctr PO Box 8213 Grand Forks ND 58202-8213

WILLUMSON, GLENN GARDNER, curator, art educator; b. Glendale, Calif., June 22, 1949; s. Donald Herbert and Aileen Ann (Gardner) W.; m. Margaret Julia Moore, June 20, 1970; children: Erik Ryan, Ashley Aileen. BA, St. Mary's Coll., 1971; MA, U. Calif., Davis, 1984; PhD in Art History, U. Calif., Santa Barbara, 1988. Asst. curator Nelson Art Gallery, Davis, Calif., 1982-83; with collection devel. Getty Ctr. for History of Art and Humanities, Santa Monica, Calif., 1988-92; curator Palmer Mus. of Art, University Park, Pa., 1992—; fellow Nat. Writing Project, 1987; vis. prof. U. Calif., Irvine, 1990; adj. prof. art history Pa. State U., University Park, 1994—. Author: W. Eugene Smith and the Photo-Essay, 1992 (grantee J. Paul Getty Trust 1991), Collecting With a Passion, 1993; mem. editl. bd. History of Photography mag., London, 1991-94, Cambridge Univ. Press, N.Y.C., 1993—. Mem. Am. Studies Assn. (Annette K. Baxter prize 1987), Coll. Art Assn., Soc. Photog. Edn. (mem. governing bd. Mid-Atlantic region), Assn. Historians Am. Art. Office: Palmer Mus Art Curtin Rd University Park PA 16802

WILMERDING, JOHN, art history educator, museum curator; b. Boston, Apr. 28, 1938; s. John Currie and Lila Vanderbilt (Webb) W. A.B., Harvard U., 1960, A.M., 1961, Ph.D., 1965. Asst. prof. art Dartmouth Coll., 1965-68, assoc. prof., 1973-83, prof. art, 1973-77, chmn. dept. art, 1968-72, chmn. humanities div., 1971-72; sr. curator Am. art Nat. Gallery of Art, 1977-83, dep. dir., 1983-88; Sarofim prof. Am. art Princeton (N.J.) U., 1988—, chmn. dept. art and archeology, 1992—; vis. lectr. history of art Yale U., 1972; vis. prof. fine arts Harvard U., 1976; vis. prof. art U. Md., 1979; vis. prof. art history U. Del., 1982; hon. curator painting Peabody Mus., Salem, Mass.; vis. curator Met. Mus., 1988—. Author: Fitz Hugh Lane, American Marine Painter, 1964, A History of American Marine Painting, 1968, Pittura Americana dell' Ottocento, 1969, Robert Salmon, Painter of Ship and Shore, 1971, Fitz Hugh Lane, 1971, Winslow Homer, 1972, Audubon, Homer, Whistler and 19th Century America, 1972, The Genius of American Painting, 1973, American Art, 1976, American Light, The Luminist Movement, 1980, American Masterpieces from the National Gallery of Art, 1980, An American Perspective, 1981, Important Information Inside, 1982, Andrew Wyeth, The Helga Pictures, 1987, American Marine Paintings, 2d edit., 1987, Paintings by Fitz Hugh Lane, 1988; American Views: Essays on American Art, 1991, The Artist's Mount Desert: American Painters on the Maine Coast, 1994. Trustee Shelburne Mus., Vt.; Guggenheim Mus., N.Y.C., Lewis Walpole Libr., Hartford, Conn., N.E. Harbor Libr., Maine, Wendell Gilley Mus., S.W. Harbor, Maine, Wyeth Endowment for Am. Art, Wilmington, Del. Guggenheim fellow, 1973-74. Fellow Phila. Atheneum (hon.). Mem. Coll. Art Assn., Am. Studies Assn. Office: Princeton U Dept Art and Archaeology 105 McCormick Hall Princeton NJ 08544-1018

WILMERS, ROBERT GEORGE, banker; b. N.Y.C., Apr. 20, 1934; s. Charles K. and Cecilia (Eitingon) W.; children: Robert George, Christopher C. B.A., Harvard U., 1956; postgrad., Harvard Bus. Sch., 1958-59. Dep. fin. adminstr. City of N.Y., 1966-70; v.p. Morgan Guaranty Trust Co., N.Y.C. and Belgium, 1970-80; owner Robert G. Wilmers Assocs., N.Y.C., 1980—; chmn., pres., chief exec. officer, dir. First Empire State Corp., Buffalo, 1982—; chmn. bd. pres., chief exec. officer, dir. Mfrs. & Traders Trust Co., Buffalo, 1983—; bd. dirs. Fed. Res. Bank N.Y., The Bus. Coun. N.Y. State, A/Knox Art Gallery, ENY Savs. Bank, Greater Buffalo Partnership; mem. gov. coun. N.Y. State Bankers Assn. Bd. dirs. Buffalo Found., 1986. Decorated officer de l'Ordre de la Couronne (Belgium). Mem. Coun. Fgn. Rels. Home: 800 W Ferry St Buffalo NY 14222-1660 also: 1 W 64th St New York NY 10023-6734 Office: Mfrs & Traders Trust Co 1 M&T Plz Buffalo NY 14211-1638

WILMETH, DON BURTON, theater arts educator, theater historian, administrator; b. Houston, Dec. 15, 1939; s. Perry Davis and Pauline Wilmeth; m. Judy Eslie Hansgen, June 10, 1963; 1 child, Michael Tyler. BA, Abilene Christian U., 1961; MA, U. Ark., 1962; Ph.D. U. Ill., 1964; MA Ad Eundem (hon.), Brown U., 1970. Teaching asst. U. Ark., Fayetteville, 1961-62, U. Ill., Urbana, 1962-64; asst. prof., head drama dept. Eastern N.Mex. U., Portales, 1964-67; from asst. to prof. theatre arts, dept. chmn. Brown U., Providence, 1967—; curator H. Adrian Smith Collection of Conjuring Books and Magicana, 1988—; cons. Internat. Exchange of Scholars (Fulbright), Washington, 1982-84, Am. memory Libr. Congress, 1992-94, Am. Theatre series Sta, WNET-TV, N.Y.C.; bd. dirs. Inst. Am. Theatre Studies, Bloomington, Ind., 1981-84; juror George Freedley Theatre Book Award com., 1971-93, 94, Barnard Hewitt Book Award com., 1985-89; mem. Theatre Hall of Fame Com. Hist. Figures, 1993—; O.R. and Eva Mitchell Vis. Disting. prof. Trinity U., Providence, 1995. Dir. numerous theatrical prodns. including (Brown U. prodns.) Carousel (Rodgers and Hammerstein, 1968, The Devils, 1969, The Night of the Iguana (Tennesee Williams), 1970, Much Ado About Nothing (Shakespeare), 1971, Too True to be Good, 1972, Dial "M" for Murder, 1972, The Beggar's Opera (John Gay), 1973, Company (Stephen Sondheim), 1974, Look Homeward, Angel, 1975, Secret Service, 1976, Romeo and Juliet (Shakespeare), 1977, The Hostage (Brendan Behan), 1978, The Seagull (Chekhov), 1979, The Importance of Being Earnest (Oscar Wilde), 1980, The Playboy of the Western World (J.M. Synge), 1982, The Rivals (Sheridan), 1983, Our Town (Thorton Wilder), 1985, Philadelphia Story, 1987, Mrs. Warren's Profession (Shaw), 1989, The Duchess of Malfi (John Webster), 1992, The Illusion, 1994, also numerous prodns. at other venues; acting roles include Twelfth Night (Colo. Shakespeare Festival 1960), The Tempest (Champlain Shakespeare Festival 1962), The Passion of Dracula, 1979, The Runner Stumbles, 1984, Follies, 1991; author: The American Stage to World War I, 1978, American and English Popular Entertainment, 1980, George Frederick Cooke, 1980 (Hewitt award 1981), The Language of American Popular Entertainment, 1981, Variety Entertainment and Outdoor Amusements, 1982; co-editor: Plays by Augustin Daly, 1984, Plays by William Hooker Gillette, 1983, Mud Show, American Tent Circus Life, 1988, Cambridge Guide to America Theatre, 1993; editor (book series) Cambridge Studies Am. Theatre and Drama, 1992—; contbg. editor: Cambridge Guide to World Theatre, 1988; contbr. articles to profl. jours., chpts. to books and reviewer of books; adv. editor of 6 jours; contbr. articles to World Book Encyclopedia, Dictionary of Am. Biography and other reference material. Corp. mem. Providence Pub. Library, 1983—; bd. mgrs. The Players of Providence, 1968-80; mem. adv. bd. East Lynne Theatre Co., Secaucus, N.J., 1981—; Langston Hughes Cultural Arts Ctr., Providence, 1982-92; Actors Theatre of Louisville, 1987—; grants panelist R.I. State Council on the Arts, Providence, 1981—; cons. Libr. of Congress, 1992—. Union Simon Guggenheim fellow, 1982. Fellow Am. Theatre Assn. (chmn. publs. 1975-77); mem. Theatre Library Assn. (v.p. 1981-84), Internat. Fed. Theatre Research, Theatre Hist. Soc., Am. Soc. Theatre Research (exec. com. 1976-78, 80-83, 85-88, pres. 1991-94, sec. 1995—), Soc. for Advancement of Edn.-N.Y.C. (bd. trustees 1977-91), Coll. Fellows of Am. Theatre (bd. dirs. 1995—, dean elect 1995), Nat. Theatre Conf. Avocations: reading, collecting theatre books and memorabilia, bookbinding. Home: 525 Hope St Providence RI 02906-1630 Office: Brown U Dept Theatre Speech and Dance PO Box 1897 Providence RI 02912-1897

WILMOT, IRVIN GORSAGE, former hospital administrator, educator, consultant; b. Nanking, China, June 30, 1922; s. Frank Alonzo and Ethel (Ranney) W.; m. Dorothy Agnes Mohlfeld, Feb. 6, 1943; children: Marcia Beth, David Michael. BS, Northwestern U., 1955; MBA, U. Chgo., 1957. With Internat. Register Co., Chgo., 1946-47; buyer U. Chgo., 1947-49; adminstrv. asst., then asst. supt. U. Chgo. Clinics, 1949-61; adminstr. NYU Med. Center-Univ. Hosp., 1961-68, exec. v.p., 1968-81; exec. v.p. Blue Cross-Blue Shield Greater N.Y., 1981-83, dir., 1977-81; exec. v.p., chief operating officer Montefiore Hosp. and Med. Ctr., N.Y.C., 1984-85; healthcare cons., 1985—; instr. then asst. prof. U. Chgo., 1957-61; assoc. prof. NYU, 1961-68; prof., 1968—; assoc. dir. U. Chgo. Grad. Program Hosp. Adminstrn., 1959-61; mem. hosp. rev. and planning council State of N.Y., 1979-87. Bd. dirs. N.Y. Blood Center, 1978-81. With USN, 1940-46. Fellow Am. Coll. Hosp. Adminstrs. (chmn. central. com. insts. 1959-65, regent N.Y. State and P.R. 1974—); mem. Assn. U. Programs Hosp. Adminstrs. (exec. sec. 1959-61), Am. Hosp. Assn. (mem. council research and planning 1965-68, council on mgmt. 1979-80, council on fin. 1981-84, trustee 1979-81), Assn. Am. Med. Colls. (chmn. council teaching hosps. 1970-71), Greater N.Y. Hosp. Assn. (bd. govs., pres. 1973-74), Hosp. Assn. N.Y. State (trustee, chmn. 1976-71). Home: 34 Helen Ave Rye NY 10580-2447 Office: PO Box 672 Rye NY 10580-0672

WILMOT, LOUISE C., charitable organization executive; b. Wayne, N.J., Dec. 31, 1942; d. W.J. Currie and Dorothy Murphy; m. James E. Wilmot. BA in History, Coll. St. Elizabeth, Convent Sta., N.J., 1964; student, Naval War Coll., Newport, R.I., 1977; M in Legis. Affairs, George Washington U., 1978. Commd. ensign USN, 1964; advanced through grades to rear adm., 1991; comm. watch officer, registered pubis. custodian, women's barracks officer Naval Air Sta., Pensacola, Fla.; with NATO staff Allied Forces, So. Europe, 1966-68; officer recruiter Recruiting Area Seven, Dallas; Naval Senate liaison officer Office Legis. Affairs, Washington; head women's equal opportunity br. Bur. Naval Pers., 1974-76; exec. officer Navy Recruiting Dist., Montgomery, Ala., 1977-79; command of Navy Recruiting Dist., Omaha, 1979-82; dep. dir accession policy Asst. Sec. Def. for Manpower, Installations, and Logistics, Washington, 1982-85; comdr. Navy Recruiting Area Five, Gt. Lakes, Ill., 1985-87; exec. asst., Naval aide Asst. Sec. Navy for Manpower and Reserve Affairs, Washington, 1987-89; comdr. Naval Tng. Ctr., Orlando, Fla., 1989-91; vice chief Naval Edn. and Tng., Pensacola, 1991-93; comdr. Naval Base, Phila., 1993-94; ret. U.S. Navy, 1994; dep. exec. dir. Cath. Relief Svcs., Balt., 1994—. Decorated DSM, Def. Superior Svc. medal, Legion of Merit with 3 gold stars. Office: Cath Relief Svcs Baltimore MD 21201-3443

WILMOUTH, ROBERT K., commodities executive; b. Worcester, Mass., Nov. 9, 1928; s. Alfred F. and Aileen E. (Kearney) W.; m. Ellen M. Boyle, Sept. 10, 1955; children: Robert J., John J., James P., Thomas G., Anne Marie. BA, Holy Cross Coll., 1949; MA, U. Notre Dame, 1950, LLD, 1984. Exec. v.p., dir. 1st Nat. Bank Chgo., 1972-75; pres., chief adminstrv. officer Crocker Nat. Bank, San Francisco, 1977; pres., chief exec. officer Chgo. Bd. Trade, 1977-82; chmn. LaSalle Nat. Bank, 1982—; pres., chief exec. officer Nat. Futures Assn., 1982—; dir. Pvt. Export Funding Corp. Trustee U. Notre Dame, chmn. investment com.; mem. adv. coun. Kellogg Grad. Sch. Mgmt., Northwestern U. 2d lt. USAF, 1951-53. Mem. Chicago Club, Barrington Hill Country Club, Economic Club (dir.). Home: 429 Caesar Dr

Barrington IL 60010-4029 Office: Nat Futures Assn 200 W Madison St Ste 1600 Chicago IL 60606-3415

WILMUT, CHARLES GORDON, environmental engineer; b. Dallas, Apr. 13, 1947; s. Charlie Ephram and Cathryn (Chapman) W.; m. Janet Gayle Machicek, Jan. 25, 1969; children: Bryan Gregory, Lauren Gabrielle. BS in Aerospace Engring., U. Tex., 1970; MS in Environ. Engring., U. Tex., Arlington, 1977. Registered profl. engr., Tex. Engr. Designers and Planners, Galveston, Tex., 1970-71; project engr. U.S. EPA, Dallas, 1971-73; Contbr. pres. Gutierrez, Smouse, Wilmut & Assocs., Inc., Dallas, 1973—. Contbr. articles to profl. jours. Active Planning and Zoning Commn., Colleyville, Tex., 1990—. Mem. ASCE, NSPE, Water Pollution Control Fedn., Tex. Soc. Profl. Engrs. (bd. dirs. 1989-92, chmn. environ. coun. 1990-92), Tex. Water Pollution Control Assn. (sect. rep. 1991-93), Oak Cliff C. of C. (dir. 1989-91). Methodist. Home: 6913 Westcoat Dr Colleyville TX 76034-6511 Office: Gutierrez Smouse Wilmut & Assocs Inc 11117 Shady Trl Dallas TX 75229-4646

WILNER, JUDITH, journalist; b. Framingham, Mass., Mar. 30, 1943; d. John C. and Marjorie E. (Devonshire) Earley; m. David Alan Wilner, Aug. 27, 1964 (div. Aug. 1968); 1 child, Erica Susan; m. Fred Karp, July 28, 1991. BA in Letters, U. Okla., 1964. Wire editor, copy editor The Norman (Okla.) Transcript, 1967-72; news editor Loveland (Colo.) Reporter-Herald, 1972-73; editor of editl. page The Albuquerque Tribune, 1974-76, city editor, 1974-76; copy editor The Denver Post, 1976-77, copy desk chief, 1977-80, mgr. editl. sys., 1980-84; dep. tech. editor N.Y. Times, 1984-86, tech. editor, 1986—; women's editor The Norman Transcript, 1964-66. Mem. Newspaper Assn. of Am. (tech. com., chmn. wire svc. guidelines com. 1992—).

WILNER, MORTON HARRISON, retired lawyer; b. Balt., May 28, 1908; s. Joseph A. and Ida (Berkow) W.; m. Zelda Dunkelman, Nov. 3, 1940; children: James D., Thomas B., Lawrence J., Theodora. B.S. in Econs, U. Pa., 1930; J.D., Georgetown U., 1934. Bar: D.C. 1933. Gen. counsel emeritus Armed Forces Benefit Assn.; vice chmn. AFBA Indsl. Bank; bd. dirs. Armed Forces Benefit Svcs., Inc.; mem. emeritus Giant Food, Inc. Past pres. Jewish Community Center of Greater Washington.; Emeritus life trustee U. Pa.; past pres. Nat. Child Research Center; bd. govs. St. Albans Sch., 1968-72. Served to maj. USAAF; dep. dir. aircraft div. WPB 1942-45. Decorated Legion of Merit; recipient Ourisman Meml. award for civic achievement, 1970; Ben Franklin award U. Pa., 1973; alumni award of merit, 1975; Friar of Yr. award U. Pa., 1976; Wharton Sch. Club Joseph Wharton award, 1980. Mem. Fed. Bar Assn., ABA (ho. dels. 1971-73), D.C. Bar Assn., Internat. Bar Assn., Fed. Communications Bar Assn. (pres. 1969-70). Clubs: Army and Navy, Woodmont Country. Home: 2701 Chesapeake St NW Washington DC 20008-1042 Office: AFBA 909 N Washington St Alexandria VA 22314-1556

WILNER, PAUL ANDREW, journalist; b. N.Y.C., Feb. 12, 1950; s. Norman and Sylvia (Rubenstein) W.; m. Alyson Paula Bromberg, June 3, 1980; children: Anne Charlotte, Daniel Joseph. Student, U. Calif., Berkeley, 1968; BA, CUNY, 1976. Copy clk. N.Y. Times, 1976-80; reporter L.A. Herald Examiner, 1980-85; mng. editor Hollywood Reporter, L.A., 1985-87; asst. mng. editor features San Francisco Examiner, 1987—; sr. instr. U. So. Calif., L.A., 1983-85. Author: (poetry) Serious Business, The Paris Rev., 1977. Office: San Francisco Examiner Mags. 110 5th St San Francisco CA 94103-2918

WILNER, THOMAS BERNARD, lawyer; b. Toronto, Ont., Can., July 7, 1944; came to U.S., 1944; s. Morton H. and Zelda (Dunkelman) W.; m. Jane Ten Broeck; children: Amanda, Adam, David. BA, Yale U., 1966; LLB, U. Pa., 1969. Clk. U.S. Ct. Appeals, Phila., 1969-70; assoc. Debevoise Plimpton, N.Y.C., 1970-72; counsel Amtrak, Washington, 1972-73; ptnr. Arnold & Porter, Washington, 1973-89, Shearman & Sterling, Washington and Tokyo, 1989—.

WILPON, FRED, real estate developer, baseball team executive; b. Bklyn., Nov. 22, 1936; s. Nathan and Frances (Altman) W.; m. Judith Anne Kessler, Sept. 27, 1958; children: Jeffrey Scott, Robin Lynn, Bruce Nathan. B.A., U. Mich., 1958. Vice pres. Hanover Equities Corp., N.Y.C., 1959-69, Peter Sharp & Co., N.Y.C., 1969-71; chmn. bd. Sterling Equities, Inc., Manhasset, N.Y., 1971—; pres. N.Y. Mets Profl. Baseball Team, 1980—, now also chief exec. officer. Mem. Vol. Urban Cons. Group, Mayor N.Y.C. Housing Task Force; trustee Jewish Inst. Geriatric Care, New Hyde Park, N.Y., 1976—, Green Vale Sch., Glen Head, N.Y., 1977—. Served with USAF, 1959. Mem. Young Pres. Orgn. Club: KP. Office: NY Mets Roosevelt Ave & 126th St Flushing NY 11368

WILSDON, THOMAS ARTHUR, product development engineer, administrator; b. Waterbury, Conn., Aug. 18, 1942; s. Arthur and Ruth (Wellington) W.; m. Yvonne Jeanne Pettit, June 19, 1964 (div. Apr. 1986); children: Thomas Charles, Beth Jeanne; m. Sharon Diann Culbertson, Feb. 14, 1988; children: Vandee Hyder, Jacklynn Hyder. BSEE, U. Conn., 1964; MBA, SUNY, Buffalo, 1978. Product design engr. Westinghouse Gen. Control Divsn., Buffalo, 1964-78; mgr. product devel. Westinghouse Control Divsn., Asheville, N.C., 1978-87; mgr. advantage engring. Westinghouse Elec. Components Divsn., Asheville, 1987-94; mgr. control components engring. Eaton/Cutler Hammer, Milw., 1994—. Mem. IEEE, NSPE, Am. Mgmt. Assn. Methodist. Achievements include development of low voltage AC and DC motor starters, Ampgard 7200V motor starter components, solid state controlled Advantage motor starters. Home: PO Box 250 Pewaukee WI 53072 Office: Eaton/Cutler Hammer 4201 N 27th St Milwaukee WI 53216

WILSKE, KENNETH RAY, internist, rheumatologist, researcher; b. American Falls, Idaho, Jan. 4, 1935; s. Emil and Emelia (Levi) W.; m. Edna Janean Walsh, June 23, 1958; children: Lisa Janean, Ashley Renee, Kendell Colleen. BA in Biology, Coll. Idaho, 1955; MD with honors, U. Wash., Seattle, 1959. Diplomate Am. Bd. Internal Medicine, Am. Bd. Rheumatology. Intern in medicine Columbia Presbyn. Hosp., N.Y.C., 1959-60, asst. resident in medicine, 1960-61; asst. resident in medicine U. Wash., Seattle, 1961-62, postdoctoral rsch. fellow in arthritis, 1962-64; with Virginia Mason Clinic, Seattle, 1968—, chmn. continuing med. edn. com., 1968-78, head section allergy, immunology and rheumatic diseases 1969—, dep. chief of medicine, staff physician, 1976—, mem. clin. pharmacology com., 1983—, co-chmn. ad hoc com. on establishment Ctr. for Asian & Internat. Memdine, 1984—; pres. bd. trustees and chmn. exec. com. Virginia Mason Rsch. Ctr., 1978-82, mem. long range planning com., other coms., 1979—; mem. pub. rels. and devel. com. Virginia Mason Med. Found., 1978—, bd. dirs., 1979—, v.p., 1984-86; clin. assoc. prof. medicine U. Wash., 1970; cons. arthritis Pub. Health Svc. Hosp., Seattle, VA Hosp., Seattle; cons. staff physician Univ. Hosp., Seattle; staff physician Harborview Hosp., St. Francis Xavier Hosp., Drs. Hosp., all Seattle; clin. prof. medicine U. Wash., Seattle; mem. nat. teaching faculty Merck, Sharp & Dohme, 1984-86; mem. arthritis adv. com. FDA, 1979; speaker, presenter, vis. lectr. numerous profl. orgns., symposia, confs. and hosps. U.S.A., Can., Buenos Aries, Prague, Czechoslovakia, Eng., Indonesia, Japan. Author: (with L.A. Healy, B.H. Hansen) Beyond the Copper Bracelet, 1972, (with Healey), Systemic Manifestation of Temporal Arteritis, 1978; contbr. numerous articles , revs. to profl. jours. Recipient Physicians Recognition award AMA, 1969. Fellow ACP, Am. Coll. Rheumatologists; mem. N.W. Soc. Clin. Rsch. (pres. 1972), N.W. Rheumatism Soc. (pres. 1970), N.W. Med. Assn., N. Pacific Soc. Internal Medicine (prgram com. 1977-79), Am. Rheumatism Assn. (program com., chmn. local arrangements Western sect. 1983, mem. nat. exec. com. 1974-76), Am. Group Practice Assn. (continuing med. edn. com. 1971-76), Am. Soc. Clin. Rheumatology, Am. Soc. Rheumatology, Wash. State Med. Assn. (various coms. 1974-78, liaison sub-com. Bd. Med. Axaminers 1978, Aesculapius award 1967), Seattle Acad. Internal Medicine, King County Med. Soc. (trustee 1979-81, jud. coun. 1984), Arthritis Found. (bd. dirs. and exec. com. 1974-76, bd. dirs. Western Wash. chpt. 1965—; mem. med. and sci. com. 1965—, Disting. Svc. award 1966), Pacific Interurban Clin. Club, U. Wash. Med. Alumni Assn. (sec./treas. 1977, exec. com. 1977-79, pres. 1978). Home: 6529 NE Windermere Rd Seattle WA 98105-2057 Office: Virginia Mason Clinic 1000 9th Ave Seattle WA 98104-1227

WILSNACK, ROGER E., medical association administrator. Dir. Becton Dickinson Rsch. Ctr., Research Triangle Park, N.C. Office: Becton Dick-

inson & Co Becton Dickinson Rsch Ctr PO Box 12016 Research Triangle Park NC 27709-2016

WILSON, AARON MARTIN, religious studies educator, college executive; b. Bazette, Tex., Sept. 30, 1926; s. John Albert and Myrtle (Hulsey) W.; m. Marthel Shoults, Jan. 31, 1947; children: Gloria Dallis, John Bert. BA, So. Bible Coll., 1963, DD (hon.), 1980; MA, Pitts. State U., 1972; PhD, Valley Christian U., 1980. Pastor various chs., 1947-58; pastor Pentacostal Ch. of God, Houston, 1958-64, Modesto, Calif., 1985-88; nat. dir. Christian edn. Pentecostal Ch. of God, Joplin, Mo., 1964-79, 88-93; pres. Evang. Christian Ch., Fresno, Calif., 1979-85; v.p. devel. Messenger Coll., Joplin, 1993—; treas. Evang. Curriculum Commn., 1988-93; prof. So. Bible Coll., Houston, 1962-64. Author: Basic Bible Truth, 1988, Studies on Stewardship, 1989. Republican. Home: 4701 Connecticut Ave Joplin MO 64804-5147 Office: Messenger Coll PO Box 4050 300 E 50th St Joplin MO 64804-4909

WILSON, ADDISON GRAVES (JOE WILSON), lawyer, state senator; b. Charleston, S.C., July 31, 1947; s. Hugh deVeaux and Wray Smart (Graves) W.; m. Roxanne Dusenbury McCrory, Dec. 30, 1977; children—Michael Addison Graves, Julian Dusenbury, Hunter Taylor. B.A., Washington and Lee U., 1969; J.D., U. S.C.-Columbia, 1972. Bar: S.C. 1972. Staff mem. Sen. Strom Thurmond, Washington, 1967, Congressman Floyd Spence, Columbia, S.C., 1970-72; atty./ptnr. Kirkland, Wilson, Moore, Allen & Taylor, West Columbia, S.C., 1972—; dep. gen. counsel U.S. Energy Sec. Jim Edwards, Washington, 1981-82; bd. dirs. NationsBank, Lexington, S.C.; senator State of S.C., Columbia, 1984—; presdl. appointee to Intergovtl. Adv. Coun. on Edn., 1990-91; mem. Internat. Observation Del. for 1990 Bulgarian parliamentary election. Campaign mgr. Congressman Floyd Spence, Columbia, 1974, 78, 80, 82; dist. campaign mgr. Gov. Carroll Campbell, 1986; vice chmn. S.C. Republican Party, 1972-74 . Served to lt. col. USNG, 1975—. Mem. ABA, Am. Judicature Soc. Presbyterian. Lodges: Rotary, Masons, Shriners. Home: 2825 Wilton Rd West Columbia SC 29170-2601 Office: Kirkland Wilson Moore Allen & Taylor 1700 Sunset Blvd West Columbia SC 29169-5940 also: PO Box 5709 West Columbia SC 29171-5709

WILSON, ALBERT EUGENE, retired nuclear engineering educator; b. Glenwood Springs, Colo., Jan. 17, 1927; s. Albert V. and Iva D. (Lape) W. B.S., U. Colo., 1950; M.S., U. N.Mex., 1959; Ph.D., U. Okla., 1964. Registered profl. engr., Idaho. Engr. Nat. Bur. Standards, 1950-54, Los Alamos Sci. Lab., 1954-59; instr. U. Okla., 1959-66; mem. faculty Idaho State U. Sch. Engring., Pocatello, 1966-95; prof. nuclear engring. Idaho State U. Sch. Engring., 1966-95, dean, 1975-83; sabatical leave Nebr. Pub. Power Dist., 1984-85; bd. govs. Argonne Nat. Lab. 1982-85, also mem. sci. and tech. adv. com.; bd. dirs. Associated Western Univs., 1978-82; vice chmn. Idaho Nuclear Energy Commn., 1968-78. Served with USNR, 1945-46. Mem. Am. Nuclear Soc. (chmn. Eastern Idaho sect. 1981-82), Am. Soc. Engring. Edn., Nat. Soc. Profl. Engrs., Idaho Soc. Profl. Engrs. Office: Idaho State U PO Box 8060 Pocatello ID 83209-8060

WILSON, ALEXANDER ERWIN, JR., lawyer, management consultant; b. Atlanta, Aug. 26, 1910; s. Alexander Erwin Wilson and Evelyn Smith; m. Constance Dinkler, June 10, 1932; children: Mrs. H.S.B. Treloar, Alexander Erwin III. AB, Emory U., 1930. Bar: Ga., 1931, D.C., 1942. Regional atty. Nat. Labor Relations Bd., Atlanta, Washington, 1933-42; ptnr. Wilson & Wilson, Atlanta, 1942-85; pvt. practice Atlanta, 1985—. Bd. dirs Metro Atlanta Boys Club, 1958—; mem. bd. visitors Emory U., Atlanta, 1964—; state chair Cystic Fibrosis Rsch Found., 1954-56; founding trustee Canterbury Ct., 1956-58. Mem. ABA, Ga. Bar Assn., Atlanta Bar Assn., Lawyers Club of Atlanta, Commerce Club, Sigma Pi (nat. pres. 1956-58). Republican. Episcopalian. Clubs: Atlanta Athletic, Piedmont Driving, Peachtree Golf, Capital City. Avocations: golf, hunting, all sports. Home: 358 King Rd NW Atlanta GA 30342-4050 Office: 305 Buckhead Ave NE Atlanta GA 30305-2305

WILSON, ALLAN BYRON, graphics company executive; b. Jackson, Miss., Aug. 19, 1948; s. Allen Bernice Wilson and Mary Pickering (Levereault) W.; m. Ines Ghinato, May 19, 1975; 1 child, Lucas Ghinato. B.S., Rice U., 1970, M.S. in Elec. Engring., 1971. Systems adminstr. Max Planck Institut für Kohlenforschung, Mülheim Ruhr, Fed. Republic Germany, 1971; systems programmer Digital Equipment Corp., Maynard, Mass., 1972-74, mktg. specialist, 1974-75, mktg. mgr., 1976-79; internat. ops. dir. Intergraph Corp., Huntsville, Ala., 1980-82, v.p. corp. and internat. ops., 1982-83, exec. v.p., 1983—. Contbr. articles to profl. jours. Mem. Assn. for Computing Machinery, IEEE. Home: 52 Revere Way Huntsville AL 35801-2846 Office: Intergraph Corp Huntsville AL 35894-0001

WILSON, ALMA, state supreme court justice; b. Pauls Valley, Okla.; d. William R. and Anna L. (Schuppert) Bell; m. William A. Wilson, May 30, 1948 (dec. Mar. 1994); 1 child, Lee Anne. AB, U. Okla., 1939, JD, 1941, LLD (hon.), 1992. Bar: Okla. 1941. Sole practice Muskogee, Okla., 1941-43; sole practice Oklahoma City, 1943-47, Pauls Valley, 1948-69; judge Pauls Valley Mcpl. Ct., 1967-68; apptd. spl. judge Dist. Ct. 21, Norman, Okla., 1969-75, dist. judge, 1975-79; justice Okla. Supreme Ct., Oklahoma City, 1982—. Mem. alumni bd. dirs. U. Okla.; mem. Assistance League; trustee Okla. Meml. Union. Recipient Guy Brown award, 1974, Woman of Yr. award Norman Bus. and Profl. Women, 1975, Okla. Women's Hall of Fame award, 1983, Pioneer Woman award, 1985, Disting. Svc. Citation U. Okla., 1985. Mem. AAUW, Garvin County Bar Assn. (past pres.), Okla. Bar Assn. (co-chmn. law and citizenship edn. com.), Okla. Trial Lawyers Assn. (Appellate Judge of Yr. 1986, 89), Altrusa, Am. Legion Aux. Office: Okla Supreme Ct State Capitol Rm 245 Oklahoma City OK 73105

WILSON, ALMON CHAPMAN, surgeon, educator, retired naval officer; b. Hudson Falls, N.Y., July 13, 1924; s. Almon Chapman and Edith May (Truesdale) W.; m. Sofia M. Bogdans, Jan. 24, 1945; 1 child, Geoffrey Peter. B.A., Union Coll., Schenectady, 1946; M.D., Albany Med. Coll., 1952; M.S., George Washington U., 1969; student, Naval War Coll., Newport, R.I., 1968-69. Diplomate: Am. Bd. Surgery. Served as enlisted man and officer U.S. Navy, 1943-46, lt. j.g., M.C., 1952, advanced through grades to rear adm., 1976; intern U.S. Naval Hosp., Bremerton, Wash., 1952-53; resident VA Hosp., Salt Lake City, 1954-58; chief of surgery Sta. Hosp. Naval Sta., Subic Bay, Philippines, 1959-61; staff surgeon Naval Hosp., San Diego, 1961-64; asst. chief surgery Naval Hosp., Chelsea, Mass., 1964-65; comdg. officer 3d Med. Bn., 3d Marine Div. Fleet Marine Force, Pacific, Vietnam, 1965-66; chief surgery Naval Hosp., Yososuka, Japan, 1966-68; assigned Naval War Coll., 1968-69; fleet med. officer, comdr. in chief U.S. Naval Forces, Europe; sr. med. officer Naval Activities London, 1969-71; dep. dir. planning div. Bur. Medicine and Surgery Navy Dept., Washington, 1971-72; dir. planning div. Navy Dept., 1972-74; with additional duty as med. adv. to dep. chief naval ops. (logistics) and personal physician to chmn. Joint Chiefs of Staff, 1972-74; comdg. officer Naval Hosp., Great Lakes, Ill., 1974-76; asst. chief for material resources Bur. Medicine and Surgery Navy Dept., Washington, 1976-79; comdg. officer (Navy Health Scis. Edn. and Tng. Command), 1979-80; the med. officer U.S. Marine Corps., 1980-81, project mgr. Fleet Hosp. Programs, 1981-82; dir. Resources Div., 1982-83; dep. dir. naval medicine, dep. surgeon gen. Dept. Navy, 1983-84; ret., 1984; mem. grad. med. edn. adv. group; chmn. Bur. Def. Decorated Legion of Merit with gold V (2 stars), Meritorious Service medal, Joint Service Commendation medal. Fellow ACS (gov.); mem. Assn. Mil. Surgeons U.S.

WILSON, ANTHONY VINCENT, business executive, mechanical engineer; b. Harrow, Eng., June 30, 1936; came to U.S., 1966; s. Maurice William and Betty (Hodgson) W.; m. Jennifer Margaret Braund, Dec. 12, 1959; children: Claire Margaret, Neil Geoffrey. B.S.M.E., London U., 1957; M.S.M.E., Purdue U., 1973; AMP, Harvard U., 1985. Engring. mgr. Rolls Royce, 1957-66; program mgr. Cummins Engine, Columbus, Ind., 1966-76; dir. research, design and devel. Onan Corp., Mpls., 1978-80, v.p. tech. and new product mgmt., 1980-82, v.p. div. gen. mgr., 1982-86; pres., chief oper. officer Churchill Inds., 1987-91; pres., chief exec. officer LB White Co., 1992—. Mem. Soc. Automotive Engrs., ASME, Inst. Mech. Engrs. Home: 5250 Brackenwood Ct La Crosse WI 54601 Office: LB White Co W6636 LB White Rd Onalaska WI 54650

WILSON, AUGUST, playwright; b. Pitts., Pa., 1945; s. David Bedford (stepfather) and Daisy Wilson; 1 child, Sakina Ansari. Founder Black

Horizons Theatre Co., Pitts., 1968; script writer Sci. Mus. of Minn., 1979. Author: (playwright) The Homecoming, 1979, The Coldest Day of the Year, 1979, Fullerton Street, 1980, Black Bart and the Sacred Hills, 1981, Jitney, 1982, Ma Rainey's Black Bottom, 1984 (N.Y. Drama Critics Circle award for best play 1985, Tony award nomination for best play 1985, Whiting Writers' award 1986), Fences, 1985 (Am. Theatre Critics Outstanding Play award 1986, Drama Desk award for outstanding new play 1986, N.Y. Drama Critics' Circle award for best play 1986, Pulitzer Prize for drama 1987, Tony award for best play 1987, Outer Critics' Circle award for best play 1987), Joe Turner's Come and Gone, 1986 (N.Y. Drama Critics Circle award for best play 1988, Tony award nomination for best play 1988), The Piano Lesson, 1987 (Drama Desk award for outstanding new play 1990, N.Y. Drama Critics' Circle award for best play 1990, Pulitzer Prize for drama 1990, Tony award nomination for best play 1990, Am. Theatre Critics Outstanding Play award 1990), Two Trains Running, 1990 (Am. Theatre Critics Assn. award 1992, Tony award nomination for best play 1992), Seven Guitars, 1995. Recipient John Gassner Best Am. Playwright award Outer Critics Circle, 1987; named Artist of Yr., Chgo. Tribune, 1987, Literary Lion award N.Y. Pub. Libr., 1988. Office: care John Breglio Paul Weiss Rifkind Wharton & Garrison 1285 Ave of the Americas New York NY 10019*

WILSON, BARBARA LOUISE, communications executive; b. Bremerton, Wash., Aug. 3, 1952; d. Algernon Frances and Dorothy Virginia (Martin) W.; m. Ashby A. Riley III, Feb. 7, 1979 (div. Dec. 1983). BA in Fin. and Econs., U. Puget Sound, 1974; MBA, U. Wash., Seattle, 1985. With Pacific N.W. Bell, Seattle and Portland, Oreg., 1974-86, divsn. mgr. pub. comm., 1983-85, asst. v.p., exec. dir. number svcs. mktg., 1985-86; v.p. implementation planning US West, Inc., Englewood, Colo., 1986-87; pres. US West Info. Systems, Englewood, 1987-89; v.p. govt. and edn. svcs. US West Comm., Englewood, 1989; v.p. human resources U.S. West, Denver, 1989-92; v.p., chief exec. officer Idaho state U.S. West Communications, Boise, 1992—; bd. dirs. U.S. West New Vector Group, Bellevue, Wash., 1988-90, U.S. Bank Idaho, Idaho Bus. Coun.; audit com. chair U.S. Bank; chair nat. adv. com. Tel. Pioneers Am., N.Y.C., 1989; chair adv. bd. Coll. Bus. and Boise State U. Sch. Bus., mem. exec. com. Wash. Coun. for Edn., Seattle, 1985-86; team capt. major gifts com. Boys and Girls Club, Seattle, 1986; chairperson co. campaign United Way, Seattle, 1985; bd. dirs. Denver Arts Ctr. Found., 1989-91; bd. advisors U. Wash. Exec. MBA Program, 1991-93; mem. adv. bd. Boise State U. Sch. Bus.; mem. bd. Boise State U. Found. Bd. dirs., mem. exec. com. Wash. Coun. for Edn., Seattle, 1985-86; team capt. major gifts com. Boys and Girls Club, Seattle, 1986; chairperson co. campaign United Way, Seattle, 1985; bd. dirs. Denver Arts Ctr. Found., 1989-91; bd. advisors U. Wash. Exec. MBA Program, 1991-93; mem. adv. bd. Boise State U. Sch. Bus.; bd. mem. Mountain States Med. Rsch. Inst.; Bd. dir. Boise State U Found. Mem. Idaho Bus. Coun. (bd. dirs., chair-elect), Idaho Assn. Commerce and Industry (vice chmn. bd. dirs. 1992—), Boise C. of C. (bd. dirs. 1992—), Arid Club Boise. Roman Catholic. Avocations: golf, snow skiing, travel, boating. Office: US West Communications 999 Main St Fl 11 Boise ID 83702-9001

WILSON, BARRY WILLIAM, biology educator; b. Bklyn., Aug. 20, 1931; s. Albert Abraham Wilson and Ethel (Lubart) Bedsow; m. Joyce Ann Sisson, June 7, 1957; 1 child, Sean. BA, U. Chgo., 1950; BS, MS, Ill. Inst. Tech., 1957; PhD, UCLA, 1962. Asst. prof. biology U. Calif., Davis, 1962-1972, prof. avian sci. and environ. toxicology, 1972—, chmn. dept. Avian scis., 1991—; mem. drug task force Muscular Dystrophy Assn., N.Y.C., 1980—; councilor NeuroToxicology subsect. Soc. Toxicology, Washington, 1985-86; pres. Calif. br. Tissue Culture Assn., Washington, 1978; mem. editorial bd. NeuroToxicology, Little Rock, 1986-91; ad hoc mem. NIH Toxicology Study Sect., Washington, 1985; mem. EPA sci. adv. panel Cholinesterase, 1989—; chair EPA Cholinesterase Methodologies Workshop, 1991. Editor: Birds: Readings From Science American, 1980; assoc. editor Bulletin Environ. Contamination and Toxicology, 1990—; contbr. numerous articles to profl. jours. Mem. Am. Physiol. Soc., Am. Soc. Cell Biology, Am. Ornithologists Union, Soc. Neurosci., Soc. Toxicology, Soc. Environ. Toxicology and Chemistry, Tissue Culture Assn., Soc. Devel. Biology, Am. Chem. Soc., Soc. for In Vitro Biology. Avocations: bird watching, photography, music. Office: U Calif Dept Avian Scis Davis CA 95616

WILSON, BASIL WRIGLEY, oceanographic engineering consultant, artist, author; b. Cape Town, Cape, Republic South Africa, June 16, 1909; came to U.S., 1952, naturalized, 1956; s. George Hough and Sarah Anne (Hearn) W.; m. Elizabeth Mary Davenport, Feb. 27, 1941; children—Mary Douglas, Richard Lyman, Gerald Hearn, Derek Wrigley. BS in Civil Engring., U. Cape Town, 1931; M.S. in Ry. Engring., U. Ill., 1939, C.E., 1940; D.Sc. in Engring., U. Cape Town, 1953. Registered profl. engr., South Africa, Tex. Asst. research engr. South African Rys. & Harbours, Johannesburg, Republic South Africa, 1932-52; prof. engring. oceanography Nat. Engring. Sci. Co., Pasadena, Calif., 1961-64; dist. dir. engring. oceanography Nat. Engring. Sci. Co., Pasadena, Calif., 1964-68; cons. oceanographic engr. Basil W. Wilson D.Sc., Pasadena, Calif., 1968—. Editor, author: Berthing and Mooring of Ships, 1970, Two Frogs of Olde Japan, 1986; also over 120 papers in engring. jours. and books. Bd. dirs. Pasadena Artist Assocs., 1966. Commonwealth Fund Service fellow, Harkness Found. N.Y., U. Ill., 1938-39, Disting. Alumnus award U. Ill. Alumni Assn., 1987. Fellow Instn. Civil Engrs. (overseas premium 1968), ASCE (A.M. Wellington prize 1952, Norman medal 1969, Moffat-Nichol award 1983, hon. mem. 1988), South African Instn. Civil Engrs. (instn. award 1959, meritorious rsch. award 1984); mem. NAE (emeritus mem. 1984), Am. Geophys. Union, Sigma Xi. Avocations: art, poetry, writing.

WILSON, BEN, elementary school principal. Prin. Ingleside Sch., Athens, Tenn. Recipient Elem. Sch. Recognition award U.S. Dept. Edn., 1989-90. Office: Ingleside Sch Guille St Athens TN 37303

WILSON, BERTHA, Canadian justice; b. Kirkcaldy, Scotland, Sept. 18, 1923; d. Archibald Wernham and Christina Noble; m. John. Wilson, 1945. MA, Aberdeen (Scotland) U., 1944; parchment, Tng. Coll. Tchrs., Aberdeen, 1945; LLB, Dalhousie U., Halifax, N.S., 1957, LLD (hon.), 1980; LLD (hon.), Queen's U., Kingston, 1983, U. Calgary, 1983, U. Toronto, 1984, U. Alta, 1985, York U., 1986, U. B.C., 1988, U. Aberdeen, 1989; LHD (hon.), Mt. St. Vincent U., Halifax, 1984, Mt. St. Vincent U., Halifax, N.S., 1984, Chatham Coll., 1990; DCL (hon.), U. Windsor, 1985, U. Western Ont., 1985; DLitt (hon.), U. Victoria, U. Toronto, 1990; D.Univ. (hon.), U. Ottawa, 1990; LLD (hon.), Law Soc. Upper Can., 1991, Mount Allison U., Ottawa, 1990; LLD (hon.), Law Soc. Upper Can., 1991, Mount Allison U., 1991, Carleton U., Can., 1991. Bar: N.S. 1957, Ont. 1959. Assoc. Osler, Hoskin & Harcourt, Toronto, 1958-68, ptnr., 1968-75; created Queen's Council Can., 1973; judge Can. Ct. Appeals, Ont., 1975-82, Supreme Ct. of Can., Ottawa, Ont., 1982-91; mem. Can. Permanent Ct. Arbitration, 1984-90. Trustee Clarke Inst. of Psychiatry, 1972-75; trustee Toronto Sch. Theol., 1975-81, mem. exec. com., 1977-81; chmn. Rhodes Scholarship Selection Com., Ont., 1980-84; bd. govs. Carleton U., 1983-85; bd. dirs. Can. Ctr. for Philanthropy, 1981—; mem. jud. com. United Ch. Can., 1985—. Fellow Royal Soc. Can. Mem. Can. Bar Assn. (mem. nat. council, mem. Ont. council 1970-73). Mem. United Ch. Can. Home: 147 Rideau Terr, Ottawa, ON Canada K1M 0Z4

WILSON, BETTY MAY, finance company executive; b. Moberly, Mo., Mar. 13, 1947; d. Arthur Bunyon and Martha Elizabeth (Denham) Stephens; m. Ralph Felix Martin, Aug. 22, 1970 (div. May 1982); m. Gerald Robert Wilson Sr., Mar. 3, 1984; stepchildren: Gerald Robert Jr., Heather Lynn, Jeffrey Michael. BS in Acctg. and Bus. Adminstrn., Colo. State U., 1969. CPA, Mo. Tax mgr. Arthur Andersen and Co., St. Louis, 1969-75; v.p., asst. sec., dir. taxes ITT Fin. Corp., St. Louis, 1975—; sr. v.p., bd. dirs. Lyndon Ins. Co., St. Louis, 1977—, ITT Lyndon Life Ins. Co., ITT Lyndon Property Ins. Co., St. Louis, 1977—. Mem. AICPA, Mo. Soc. CPA's (chmn. family issues com. 1994-95), Tax Execs. Inst. Inc. (chair corp. tax mgmt. com. 1993—, regional v.p., 1995—, bd. dirs. St. Louis chpt., past sec., past pres.), Mo. Girls Racing Assn. (pres. 1977-82). Baptist. Avocations: country western dancing, horses. Office: ITT Fin Corp 645 Maryville Ctr Dr Saint Louis MO 63141-5832

WILSON, BLENDA JACQUELINE, university chancellor; b. Woodbridge, N.J., Jan. 28, 1941; d. Horace and Margaret (Brogsdale) Wilson; m. Louis Fair Jr. AB, Cedar Crest Coll., 1962; AM, Seton Hall U., 1965; PhD,

Boston Coll., 1979; DHL (hon.), Cedar Crest Coll., 1987, Loretto Heights Coll., 1988, Colo. Tech. Coll., 1988, U. Detroit, 1989; LLD (hon.), Rutgers U., 1989, Ea. Mich. U., 1990, Cambridge Coll., 1991, Schoolcraft Coll., 1992. Tchr. Woodbridge Twp. Pub. Schs., 1962-66; exec. dir. Middlesex County Econ. Opportunity Corp., New Brunswick, N.J., 1966-69; exec. asst. to pres. Rutgers U., New Brunswick, N.J., 1969-72; assoc. dean Grad. Sch. Edn. Harvard U., Cambridge, Mass., 1972-82; v.p. effective sector mgmt. Ind. Sector, Washington, 1982-84; exec. dir. Colo. Commn. Higher Edn., Denver, 1984-88; chancellor and prof. pub. adminstrn. & edn. U. Mich., Dearborn, 1988-92; pres. Calif. State U., Northridge, 1992—; Am. del. U.S./U.K. Dialogue About Quality Judgments in Higher Edn.; adv. bd. Mich. Consolidated Gas Co., Stanford Inst. Higher Edn. Rsch., U. So. Col. Dist. 60 Nat. Alliance, Nat. Ctr. for Rsch. to Improve Postsecondary Teaching and Learning, 1988-90; bd. dirs. Alpha Capital Mgmt.; mem. higher edn. colloquium Am. Coun. Edn., vis. com. Divsn. Continuing Edn. in Faculty of Arts & Scis., Harvard Coll., Pew Forum on K-12 Edn. Reform in U.S.; trustee Children's TV Workshop. Dir. U. Detroit Jesuit High School, Northridge Hosp. Med. Ctr., Arab Community Ctr. for Econ. & Social Svcs., Union Bank, J. Paul Getty Trust, Internat. Found. Edn. and Self-Help, Achievement Coun., L.A.; dir., vice-chair Met. Affairs Corp.; exec. bd. Detroit area coun. Boy Scouts Am.; bd. dirs. Commonwealth Fund, Henry Ford Hosp.-Fairlane Ctr., Henry Ford Health System, Met. Ctr. for High Tech., United Way for Southeastern Mich.; mem. Nat. Coalition 100 Black Women, Detroit, Race Rels. Coun. Met. Detroit, Women & Founds. (corp. philanthropy), Greater Detroit Interfaith Round Table NCCJ, Adv. Bd. Valley Cultural Ctr., Woodland Hills; trustee assoc. Boston Coll., trustee emeritus Cambridge Coll., trustee emeritus/bd. dirs. Travel Cts.; trustee Henry Ford Mus. & Greenfield Village, Sammmy Davis Jr. Nat. Liver Inst. Mem. AAUW, Assn. Governing Bds. (adv. coun. of pres.'s), Edn. Commn. of the States (student minority task force), Am. Assn. Higher Edn. (chairelect), Am. Assn. State Colls. & Univs. (com. on policies & purposes, acad. leadership fellows selection com.), Assn. Black Profls. and Adminstrs., Assn. Black Women in Higher Edn., Women Execs. State Govt., Detroit. Women's Forum, Mich. Women's Forum, Women's Econ. Club Detroit, Econ. Club, Rotary. Office: Calif State Univ Office of President 18111 Nordhoff St Northridge CA 91330-8230

WILSON, BRANDON LAINE, writer, advertising and public relations consultant, explorer; b. Sewickley, Pa., Oct. 2, 1953; s. Edgar C. and Mary Beth (Tuttle) W.; m. Cheryl Ann Keefe, June 23, 1989. BA, U. N.C., 1973; Cert. Am. Acad. Dramatic Arts, 1974. Asst. acct. exec. Hill & Knowlton Pub. Rels., Pitts., 1973; dir. video Seattle Repertory Theatre, 1975-76; asst. dir., cameraman Pub. Broadcasting Network, Chapel Hill, 1976-77; dir. advt. and TV Prodn. N.Am. Films, Eugene, Oreg., 1977-79; gen. mgr. Boulder Community Coops., 1980-81; pub. info. officer, asst. to mayor City of Barrow, Alaska, 1981-82; dir. advt. and promotion Anchorage Conv. and Visitors Bur., Anchorage, 1983-85; mgr. mktg. communications GTE, Honolulu, 1986-87; v.p., sr. copywriter, producer Peck, Sims, Mueller Advt. (NW Ayer affiliate), Honolulu, 1987-89; pres., creative dir. Wilson & Assoc., Inc., Hawaii, 1987—, pres. Brandon Wilson Lit. Svcs., 1991—. Author: Dead Men Don't Leave Tips, A Couple's Trans-African Odyssey, 1991 Yak Butter Blues, 1994; prin. works (TV) include The General Assembly Today, 1976-77, (films) Sasquatch, Mystery of the Sacred Shroud, Buffalo Rider; contbr. articles to nat. mags. and newspapers. Named Eagle Scout Boy Scouts Am., one of Exceptionally Able Youth, 1970, Literary award U. Pitts., 1970, one of Outstanding Young Men in Am., 1986, Men of Achievement award U.K., 1987, 93, Dict. of Internat. Biography, U.K., 1993; recipient Order of the Arrow, two Ike Pono Gold awards Internat. TV Assn., 6 creative advt. awards, (AAF). Mem. Am. Advt. Fedn., (accreditation), PRSA, Soc. of Friends, Mensa, Internat. Campaign for Tibet, Amnesty Internat. Journeyed length of Africa overland (Ceuta to Cape Town), 1990; half of first western couple to cross Himalayas from Lhasa, Tibet to Kathmandu, Nepal, 1992; climbed Mt. Nyaragongo, Mt. Kilimanjaro, Mt. Olympus, Mt. Everest Base Camp, Tibet, Mt Miyajima, Crough Patrick, Te Rua Manga; rafted down the Zambezi River; tracked mountain gorillas in Zaire; journeyed overland across C.Am.; explored Eastern Europe, 1989. Home and Office: 32 Wailea Alanui Dr Ste 705 Kihei HI 96753

WILSON, BRIAN DOUGLAS, recording artist, composer, record producer; b. Inglewood, Calif., June 20, 1942; s. Murry Gage and Audree Neva (Korthof) W.; m. Marilyn Sandra Rovell, Dec. 7, 1964; children: Carnie, Wendy. Student, El Camino Coll. Mem. musical group, The Beach Boys, 1961—; also composer; albums include Surfin Safari, 1962, Surfin' USA, 1963, Surfer Girl, 1963, Little Deuce Coupe, 1963, All Summer Long, 1964, Christmas Album, 1964, Beach Boys Party, 1965, Pet Sounds, 1966; solo album: Brian Wilson, 1988, Sire, 1988, Sweet Insanity, 1991; author: (autobiography) Wouldn't It Be Nice, 1991. Named to Rock and Roll Hall of Fame, 1988. Address: 1317 Club View Dr Los Angeles CA 90024-5303 also: 151 S El Camino Dr Beverly Hills CA 90212-2704*

WILSON, BRUCE BRIGHTON, transportation executive; b. Boston, Feb. 6, 1936; s. Robert Lee and Jane (Schlotterer) W.; m. Elizabeth Ann MacFarland, Dec. 31, 1958; children: Mabeth, Mary, Bruce Robert, Caroline Daly. AB, Princeton U., 1958; LLB, U. Pa., 1961. Bar: Pa. 1962. Assoc. Montgomery, McCracken, Walker & Rhoads, Phila., 1962-69; atty. U.S. Dept. Justice, Washington, 1969-79; dep. asst. atty. gen. antitrust div. U.S. Dept. Justice, 1971-76; spl. counsel Consol. Rail Corp., Phila., 1979-81, gen. counsel litigation and antitrust, 1981-82, v.p., gen. counsel, 1982-84, v.p. law, 1984-87, sr. v.p. law, 1987—; bd. dirs. Concord Resources Group, Inc., Princeton, N.J., Phila. Indsl. Devel. Corp.; mem. mgmt. com. Concord Resources Group, 1989-91. Fellow Salzburg Seminar in Am. Studies (Austria), 1965; fellow Felz Inst. State and Local Govt., 1967. Mem. ABA, Phila. Bar Assn. Clubs: Corinthian Yacht, Pyramid. Home: 224 Chamounix Rd Wayne PA 19087-3606 Office: Consol Rail Corp PO Box 41417 2001 Market St 17th Flr Philadelphia PA 19101-1417

WILSON, BRUCE G., lawyer; b. Iowa City, Dec. 17, 1949. BS, Iowa State U., 1972; MBA with distinction, U. Mich., 1974; JD with distinction, U. Iowa, 1977. Bar: Ill. 1977. Ptnr. Jenner & Block, Chgo. Mem. ABA, Ill. State Bar Assn. Office: Jenner & Block 1 IBM Plz Chicago IL 60611

WILSON, C. DANIEL, JR., library director; b. Middletown, Conn., Nov. 8, 1941; s. Clyde D. and Dorothy M. (Neal) W.; m. M. April Jackson, Apr. 1986; children: Christine, Cindy, Clyde, Ben. BA, Elmhurst Coll., 1967; MA, Rosary Coll., 1968. Trainee Chgo. Pub. Libr., 1967-68; instr. U. Ill., 1968-70; asst. dir. Perrot Meml. Libr., Greenwich, Conn., 1970-76; dir. Wilton Pub. Libr., Wilton, Conn., 1976-79; assoc. dir. Birmingham Pub. Libr., Birmingham, Ala., 1979-83; dir. Davenport Pub. Libr., Davenport, Iowa, 1983-85, New Orleans Pub. Libr., 1985—. With USMC, 1962-65. Mem. Am. Libr. Assn., La. Libr. Assn., Am. Soc. Pub. Adminstrs., Pi Gamma Mu, Rotary. Episcopalian. Office: New Orleans Pub Libr Simon Heinsheim & Fisk Libe 219 Loyola Ave New Orleans LA 70140-1016

WILSON, C. NICK, health educator, consultant, researcher, lecturer; b. Balt., Feb. 18, 1942; s. Anna May (Gallion) W.; m. Nancy Ann King, Sept. 17, 1966 (div. Apr. 1976); children: Anna Nicole, Tara Stacia; m. Linda Persons, Feb. 25, 1984; children: Melissa Lauren, Kristin Marie. BS, U. Hartford, 1966; MHA, George Washington U., 1972; PhD, U. Miss., 1983. Dir. ops. Health M. Louisville, 1976-79. So. Health Svcs., Marks, Miss., 1979-81; rsch. and teaching asst. U. Miss., Oxford, 1981-83; asst. prof. U. Tex., Galveston, 1983-85, U. Okla., Oklahoma City, 1987-91; pres. Shriners Burn Hosp., Galveston, 1985-87; assoc. prof. health, cons., sr. lectr. U. North Fla., Jacksonville, 1991—; cons., Jacksonville, 1991—. Author: Health Care Management, 1983; also over 125 articles. Bd. dirs., treas. First Coast Healthcare Execs. Group, Jacksonville, 1991—. Lt. USAF, 1966-69. Fellow Am. Coll. Healthcare Execs. (various offices, faculty advisor student chpt. Jacksonville 1991—), Royal Soc. Health; mem. APHA (various offices), Am. Hosp. Assn. (various offices). Republican. Episcopalian. Avocations: golf, tennis, hunting, fishing, sailing. Office: U North Fla Coll Health 4567 St Johns Bluff Rd S Jacksonville FL 32224

WILSON, CARL WELDON, JR., construction company executive, civil engineer; b. Norfolk, Va., Sept. 4, 1933; s. Carl Weldon and Janie Marie (Ludford) W.; m. Jean Roberts, Feb. 13, 1960; children: Lisa Ann, Carl Weldon III. BCE, Tex. A&M U., 1954. Registered profl. engr., Tex. Engr. Magnolia Petroleum Co., Morgan City, La., 1954-55, Brown & Root,

Houston, 1957-60; project mgr. Claude Everett Constrn. Co., Houston, 1960-62; pres. Falcon Constrn. Co., Houston, 1962-63; pres., owner Wilson Engring. and Constrn. Co., Houston, 1963-68; v.p. Divcon, Inc., Houston, 1968-71, Wilson Industries, Inc., Houston, 1971-81; pres., prin. owner BS&B Engring. Co., Inc., Houston, 1981-86; chmn., majority shareholder Task Internat., Inc., Houston, 1986—. Served to 1st lt. U.S. Army, 1955-57. Republican. Episcopalian. Avocations: tennis, running, painting. Home: 750 Bison Dr Houston TX 77079-4401 Office: Task Internat Inc PO Box 218327 Houston TX 77218-8327

WILSON, CAROLYN ROSS, school administrator; b. Lake Charles, La., June 25, 1941; d. Charles Wesley and Lucille Gertrude (Payne) Ross; m. James David Wilson, Apr. 10, 1971; 1 child, Charlise. BS in Music Edn. cum laude, Xavier U., 1962; MMus in Music Edn., Cath. U., Washington, 1968; postgrad., U. D.C., 1985-86, George Washington U., 1987-88, Harvard U., 1989. Tchr. Xavier U. Jr. Sch. Music, New Orleans, 1960-61, Orleans Parish Schs., New Orleans, 1962-63; tchr. D.C. Pub. Schs., Washington, 1964-87, curriculum writer, summer 1984, 85, adminstrv. intern Ea. High Sch., 1987-88, asst. prin. Cardozo High Sch., 1988-89, asst. prin. Duke Ellington Sch. of Arts, 1989-93; acting prin. Duke Ellington Sch. Arts, Washington, 1993—; curriculum writer music dept. D.C. Pub. Schs., Washington, 1984-85, dir. All City High Sch. Chorus, 1973. Composer: A Dedication to Federal City Alumnae Chapter of Delta, Sigma Theta Sorority, Inc., 1973. Lector Immaculate Conception Ch., Washington, 1986—; named D.C. Tchr. of Yr., 1987. Recipient Cert. of Merit-Outstanding Tchr. and Prin. award D.C. Govt., 1994; U.S. Dept. Edn. Effective Schs. grantee, Washington, 1992. Mem. ASCD, Instn. for Devel. Ednl. Activities (6th yr. fellow, session chair 1988, seminar leader 1991, 92, 93, 94), Delta Sigma Theta (Fed. City Alumnae chpt.). Roman Catholic. Avocations: reading, travel, bowling, musical arranging, playing the piano. Office: Duke Ellington Sch Arts 35th And R St NW Washington DC 20912

WILSON, CHARLES (CHARLIE WILSON), congressman; b. Trinity, Tex., June 1, 1933. Student, Sam Houston State U., Huntsville, Tex., 1951-52; B.S., U.S. Naval Acad., 1956. Commd. ensign U.S. Navy, 1956, advanced through grades to lt.; ret., 1960; mem. Tex. Ho. of Reps., 1960-66, Tex. Senate, 1966-72, 93rd-104th Congresses from 2d Tex. dist., Washington, D.C., 1973—; ranking minority mem. appropriations subcom. on fgn. ops., export financing & related programs; mgr. lumber yard, 1962-72. Democrat. Office: US Ho of Reps 2256 Rayburn House Office B Washington DC 20515*

WILSON, CHARLES B., neurosurgeon, educator; b. Neosho, Mo., Aug. 31, 1929; married; 3 children. BS, Tulane U., 1951, MD, 1954. Resident pathologist Tulane U., 1955-56, instr. neurosurgery, 1960-61; resident Ochsner Clinic, 1956-60; instr. La. State U., 1961-63; from asst. prof. to prof. U. Ky., 1963-68; prof. neurosurgery U. Calif., San Francisco, 1968—. Mem. Am. Assn. Neurol. Surgery, Soc. Neurol. Surgery. Achievements include research in brain and pituitary tumors. Office: U Calif Med Ctr 505 Parnassus Ave San Francisco CA 94143-0350 Office: U Calif Sch Medicine Dept Neurol Surgery San Francisco CA 94143

WILSON, CHARLES BANKS, artist; b. Springdale, Ark., Aug. 6, 1918; s. Charles Bertram and Bertha Juanita (Banks) W.; m. Edna Frances McKibben, Oct. 10, 1941; children—Geoffrey Banks, Carrie Vee. Student, Art Inst. Chgo., 1936-41. Mag. and book illustrator, 1943-60; head art dept. N.E. Okla. A. & M. Coll., Miami, Okla., 1947-61; painter, printmaker. Executed mural, Okla. State Capitol, 1975; represented in permanent collections, Met. Mus., N.Y.C., Library of Congress, Washington, U.S. Capitol Bldg., D.C. Corcoran Gallery, Smithsonian Inst., Will Rogers Meml. Mus., Philbrook Art Center, Tulsa, Nat. Cowbow Hall of Fame, Oklahoma City.; Illustrator numerous books. Bd. dirs. Thomas Gilcrease Mus. History and Art, Tulsa, 1957-61; chmn. Pub. Libr. Bd., Miami, Okla., 1954-59. Named to Okla. Hall of Fame; recipient Western Heritage award Cowboy Hall of Fame, D.C.S., U. Okla.; subject of books The Lithographs of Charles Banks Wilson, 1989, Search for the Purebloods, 1989, An Oklahoma Portrait, 1989. Mem. Internat. Inst. Arts and Letters (Geneva). Democrat. Presbyterian. Office: 1611 Mission Blvd Fayetteville AR 72703-3043

WILSON, CHARLES EDWARD, lawyer; b. Indpls., May 26, 1937; s. Paul John and Margaret Mary (Burns) W.; m. Judy Ann Scotten, June 17, 1961 (div. 1986); children: Ann, Mary, Kathleen; m. Karen Lynn Schmidt, July 15, 1986; stepchildren: Tonya Grace Root. BA, St. Joseph Coll., 1959; JD, Ind. U., 1965. Bar: Ind. 1965. Law clk. Lawyers Title Ins. Corp., Indpls., 1960-65; assoc. Ice Miller Donadio & Ryan, Indpls., 1965-71, ptnr., 1972—. Bd. dirs. St. Francis Hosp., Beech Grove, Ind., 1975—; chmn., pres. Metro Indpls. Pub. Broadcasting, 1981-89. Mem. Am. Coll. Real Estate Lawyers, Order of Coif. Roman Catholic. Avocations: tennis, boating. Home: 8632 Trails Run Rd Indianapolis IN 46217 Office: Ice Miller Donadio & Ryan 1 American Sq PO Box 82001 Indianapolis IN 46282

WILSON, CHARLES GLEN, zoo administrator; b. Clinton, Okla., Aug. 24, 1948; s. Claude Lee and Alva Dean (Gaskins) W.; m. Susan Elizabeth Mosher, Nov. 21, 1975; children: Erica Dean, Grant Mosher. BS, Okla. State U., 1972, MS, 1980. Dir. Memphis Zool. Gardens and Aquarium, 1976—. Contbr. articles to profl. jours. Served with U.S. Army, 1968-70. Recipient Ark. Traveler award, 1977. Profl. fellow Am. Zool. Parks and Aquariums. Office: Memphis Zoo & Aquarium 2000 Galloway Ave Memphis TN 38112-5099

WILSON, CHARLES REGINALD, real estate executive; b. Bear Lake, Pa., Nov. 7, 1904; s. Earl Ayling and Edith (Finch) W.; m. Josephine Harrison, Sept. 8, 1927; children—Charles Reginald, Jacquelyn Ann. Student, U. Pitts., 1927. Asst. dean mem Pitts., 1927-29; bus. promotion mgr. Hotel Schenley, Pitts., 1929-35; sales mgr. William Penn Hotel, Pitts., 1935-39; v.p., gen. mgr. William Penn Hotel, 1952; mgr. Roosevelt Hotel, Pitts., 1939-52; sr. v.p. Union Nat. Bank of Pitts. (formerly Commonwealth Bank & Trust Company), 1952-71, Realty Growth Corp., Pitts., 1972—; pres. Commonwealth Real Estate Co., 1957-64. Pres. Panther Found., U. Pitts.; exec. com. Pitts. Conv. and Visitors Bur. Mem. Pitts. Athletic Assn., Soc. Indsl. Realtors, Delta Tau Delta, Omicron Delta Kappa. Clubs: Mason, Pittsburgh Field, Duquesne. Home: 4601 5th Ave Pittsburgh PA 15213-3666 Office: Roosevelt Bldg Sixth St and Penn Ave Pittsburgh PA 15222

WILSON, CHARLES ZACHARY, JR., newspaper publisher; b. Greenwood, Miss., Apr. 21, 1929; s. Charles Zachary and Ora Lee (Means) W.; m. Doris J. Wilson, Aug. 18, 1951 (dec. Nov. 1974); children: Charles III, Joyce Lynne, Joanne Catherine, Gary Thomas, Jonathan Keith; m. Kelly Freeman, Apr. 21, 1986; children: Amanda Fox, Walter Bremond. BS in Econs., U. Ill., 1952, PhD in Econs. and Stats., 1956. Asst. to v.p. Commonwealth Edison Co., Chgo., 1956-59; asst. prof. econs. De Paul U., Chgo., 1959-61; assoc. prof. bus. SUNY, Binghamton, 1961-67, prof. econs. and bus., 1967-68; prof. mgmt. and edn. UCLA, 1968-84, vice chancellor acad. programs, 1985-87; CEO, pub., pres. Cen. News-Wave Publs., L.A., 1987—; pres. Czamd Assoc., Pacific Palisades, Calif., 1994—; mem. adv. council Fed. Res. Bank, San Francisco, 1986-88, 2001 com. Office of Mayor of Los Angeles, 1986-89. Author: Organizational Decision-Making, 1967; contbr. articles on bus. to jours. Bd. dirs. Los Angeles County Mus. Art, 1972-84; com. on Los Angeles City Revenue, 1975-76, United Nations Assn. panel for advancement of U. and Japan Relations, N.Y.C. 1972-74; chmn. Mayor's task force on Africa, 1979-82. Fellow John Hay Whitney, U. Ill., 1955-56, Ford Found., 1960-61, 81-82, 84, Am. Council of Edn., UCLA, 1967-68, Aspen Inst. for Human Studies; named one of Young Men of Yr., Jaycees, 1965. Mem. AAAS, Am. Econ. Assn., Nat. Newspaper Pub. Assn., Am. Mgmt. Assn., Alpha Phi Alpha (pres., pledgemaster 1952-54), Phi Kappa Phi, Order of Artus (pres.). Avocations: tennis, jogging, collecting old bus. texts. Home: 1053 Tellem Dr Pacific Palisades CA 90272-2243 Office: Cen Newspaper Publs 2621 W 54th St Los Angeles CA 90043-2614

WILSON, CLARENCE IVAN, banker; b. Kerrville, Tex., Sept. 16, 1927; s. Jesse Leroy and Ruby Jewel (Longley) W.; m. Lola Jean Tiner, Jan. 30, 1954; children: Alan, Dale, Greg, Mark. Student, Freed Hardeman Coll., 1944-46, Abilene Christian U., 1947-48; BS in Math., S.W. Tex. State U., 1949; banking degree, So. Meth. U., 1967. Bank systems specialist Burroughs Corp., San Antonio, 1954-64; v.p., cashier First City Tex., Corpus Christi, 1964-70, pres., 1971-75, chief exec. officer, 1975-91, chmn. bd., 1975-

92; chmn., chief exec. officer First City Tex., Alice, 1988-90, Houston, 1991-92; chmn., chief exec. officer 1st City Bankcorp. Tex., Inc., Houston, 1991—. Trustee Driscoll Found., Corpus Christi, 1982—; pres. United Way Coastal Bend, Corpus Christi, 1972; pres. bd. regents Del Mar Coll., 1982-83; bd. dirs. Univ. System South Tex., 1986-89. Sgt. USAF, 1950-53. Named civic salesman of yr. Sales and Mktg. Club Corpus Christi, 1974; recipient Eleanor Roosevelt award for humanitarian service State of Israel, 1977, brotherhood award NCCJ, 1980. Mem. Am. Bankers Assn. (chmn. edn. policyand devel. coun., Tex. rep. to govt. rels. com.), Conf. State Bank Suprs. (state rep. 1981-91), Tex. Bankers Assn. (chmn. 1989, chmn. govt. rels. com. 1986, past chmn. state bank divsn., past chmn. com. bank taxation task force), Corpus Christi Bankers Assn. (pres. 1981), Tex. Assn. Taxpayers (area v.p. 1976, pres.-elect 1983, pres. 1985), Tex. Rsch. League (bd. dirs. 1981, exec. com.), Corpus Christi C. of C. (pres. 1974). Lodges: Rotary; Kiwanis (pres. 1972). Home: HC 1 Box 2565 Sandia TX 78383-9403 Office: First City Bancorp of Texas 1021 Main St Ste 2600 Houston TX 77002-6606

WILSON, CLAUDE RAYMOND, JR., lawyer; b. Dallas, Feb. 22, 1933; s. Claude Raymond and Lottie (Watts) W.; 1 dau., Deidra Nicole Frazier. BBA, So. Meth. U., 1954, JD, 1956. Bar: Tex. 1956; CPA, Calif., Tex. Asso. firm Cervin & Melton, Dallas, 1956-58; atty. Tex. & Pacific R.R. Co., Dallas, 1958-60; atty. office regional counsel IRS, San Francisco, 1960-63; sr. trial atty. office chief counsel IRS, Washington, 1963-65; ptnr. Wilson, White & Copeland, Dallas, 1965—; chmn., Dallas dist. dir. IRS Adv. Commn., 1990-91. ABA, AICPA (coun. 1989-93), State Bar Tex., Dallas Bar Assn. (pres. sect. taxation 1969-70), Tex. Soc. CPAs (bd. dirs. 1979—, sec. 1978-79, exec. com. 1980-81, v.p. 1985-86, pres. 1989-90, pres. Dallas chpt. 1983-84) Greater Dallas C. of C. (chmn. apprpriations and tax com. 1990-91), Dallas Gun Club, Crescent Club, Masons, Shriners, Jesters, Delta Sigma Phi, Delta Theta Phi. Republican. Episcopalian. Office: 2300 Tower II Republic Towers 325 N Saint Paul St Dallas TX 75201-3801

WILSON, CLEALYN BULLOCK, elementary education educator; b. Phila., Mar. 25, 1950; d. Clinton Nathaniel Bullock and Odaris (Wilson) Jeter; s. Thomas A. Jeter Jr. (stepfather); m. Cecil Charles Wilson, Mar. 19, 1989. BS in Elem. Edn., Morgan State U., 1972; postgrad., We. Wash. U., 1976, Berry Coll., 1978; MEd in Early Childhood Edn., West Ga. Coll., 1980; postgrad., U. New Orleans, 1981, Wilmington Coll., 1991—. Cert. tchr. elem. and early childhood, Del.; cert. elem. tchr. La., Ga. Tchr. 2nd grade Schaeffer Elem. Sch., Pitts., 1972-74; tchr. 1st grade Friends Lower Sch., Balt., 1974-75; follow through tchr. 1st grade Roosevelt Elem. Tacoma, Wash.; open space tchr. 2nd grade Boze. Elem Sch., Tacoma, 1976-77; title 1 tchr. reading resource North Heights Elem. Sch., Rome, Ga., 1977-80; tchr. 2nd grade Main Elem. Sch., Rome, 1980-81; tchr. 4th grade Nelson Elem. Sch., New Orleans, 1981; tchr. 1st and 3rd grades, resource tchr. lang. and early acad. program. Joseph A. Craig Elem. Sch., New Orleans, 1981-88; tchr. 1st grade, 1st and 2nd grade split Towne Point Elem. Sch., Dover, Del., 1988-90; tchr. first grade Willards (Md.) Elem. Sch., 1990-91, East Dover Elem. Sch., 1991—; tchr. homework Community Edn. Program, New Orleans, 1982, high potential tchr., 1983-84; team tchr. Capital Sch. Dist. Summer Reading Camp, Dover, 1992, coord., 1993; creator art projects The Edn. Ctr., Inc., 1992; cons. district-wide writing workshops; mem. district-wide English Lang. Arts Review and Selection Com.; chairperson Del. Tchrs. Forum. Youth coord., MYF co-leader, coun. on ministries, chancel choir, active aerobics programs, altar guild, tchr. Sunday sch. Whatcoat United Meth. Ch., chair Christian Edn., 1992—; layspeaker United Meth. Comm. Com.; active United Meth. Women.; counselor Camp Pe-Co-Meth, Centreville, Md., 1969, mgr. dining room, 1971; mem. choir, brownie leader, nominating com., chair Women's Day observance, instr. aerobics program Bethany United Meth. Ch., New Orleans; program aide Nat. Youth Sports Program; counselor Camp George. Recipient Tchr. of Yr. award State of Del., 1992-93, Capital Sch. Dist., Dover, 1992-93, Appreciation award Whatcoat United Meth. Ch. Winterim Summer Day Camp; named High Potential Tchr., Orleans Parish Cmty. Ctr., 1983-84. Mem. NEA, ASCD, Assn. for Childhood Learning Internat., Del. State Edn. Assn., Diamond State Reading Assn., Capital Educators Assn., Kent Coun. for Reading, Alpha Kappa Alpha (sub-debutantes, assist with youth awareness activities, project lead), Phi Delta Kappa, Kappa Delta Pi, Alpha Delta Kappa. Democrat. Avocations: aerobics, dance, cooking, doll collecting, writing poetry. Home: 130 Brandywine Dr Dover DE 19904 Office: East Dover Elem Sch 852 South Little Creek Rd Dover DE 19901

WILSON, COLIN HENRY, writer; b. Leicester, Eng., June 26, 1931; s. Arthur and Anetta W.; m. Joy Stewart; children: Sally, Damon, Rowan; 1 child from previous marriage, Roderick. writer in residence Hollins (Va.) Coll., 1966-67; vis. prof. U. Wash., Seattle, 1967, Rutgers U., New Brunswick, N.J., 1974. Author (numerous books including novels): The Glass Cage, 1967, The Occult, 1971, The Black Room, 1971, The Space Vampires, 1975, Mysteries, 1978; 6 critical studies in the Outsider series; non-fiction: Access to Inner Worlds, 1982, The Criminal History of Mankind, 1983, (with Donald Seaman) Modern Encyclopedia of Murder, 1983, The Essential Colin Wilson, 1984, The Personality Surgeon, 1986, (with Damon Wilson) Encyclopedia of Unsolved Mysteries, 1987, Spiderworld, 1987, The Misfits, 1988, Beyond The Occult, 1988, Written in Blood, 1989, (with Donald Seaman) The Serial Killers, 1990; (play) Mozart's Journey to Prague, 1991, Spiderworld: The Magician, 1992, The Strange Life of P.D. Ouspensky, 1993, Unsolved Mysteries Past and Present (with Damon Wilson), 1993. Club: Savage.

WILSON, DAVID CARTWRIGHT, headmaster; b. N.Y.C., May 27, 1941; s. Sturgis Starbuck and Margaret (Gould) W.; m. Martha Smith Wood, Mar. 21, 1970; children: Christine, Sara, Kenneth. BA, Williams Coll., 1963; EdM, Harvard U., 1965. Tchr., coach The Pingry Sch., Martinsville, N.J., 1969-77, asst. head, 1977-80, headmaster, 1980-87; headmaster Upland Country Day Sch., Kennett Square, Pa., 1987—. Rep. committeeman, Birmingham Township, Pa., 1990-92. 1st lt. U.S. Army, Vietnam, 1966-68. Decorated bronze star. Avocations: fly fishing, tennis. Home: 1065 Country Club Rd West Chester PA 19382-8060 Office: Upland Country Day Sch 420 W Street Rd Kennett Square PA 19348-1193

WILSON, DAVID EUGENE, magistrate judge; b. Columbia, S.C., Jan. 12, 1940; s. David W. and Emma (Moseley) W.; m. Nancy Ireland, Sept. 5, 1964; children: Amy R., Cara S. BA, U.S.C., 1962, JD, 1966; MA, Boston U., 1971. Bar: Vt. 1972, D.C. 1973, Wash. 1980, U.S. Dist. Ct. Vt. 1972, U.S. Dist. Ct. (we. dist.) Wash. 1976. Asst. atty. gen. State of Vt., Montpelier, 1972-73; asst. U.S. atty. U.S. Dist. Ct. D.C., Washington, 1973-76; asst. U.S. atty. U.S. Dist. Ct. (we. dist.) Wash., Seattle, 1976-89, U.S. atty., 1989, asst. U.S. atty., chief criminal div., 1989-92; U.S. magistrate judge Seattle, 1992—; mem. faculty Atty. Gen.'s Advocacy Inst., Washington, 1979—, Nat. Inst. Trial Advocacy, Seattle, 1987—. Capt. U.S. Army, 1966-71, col. USAR. Recipient Disting. Community Svc. award B'nai Brith, 1987. Fellow Am. Coll. Trial Lawyers; mem. Fed. Bar Assn., Wash. State Bar, Seattle-King County Bar Assn. Avocations: hunting, fishing, skiing, books. Office: 304 US Courthouse Seattle WA 98104

WILSON, DAVID GORDON, mechanical engineering educator; b. Sutton Coldfield, Warwick, UK, Feb. 11, 1928; s. William and Florence Ida (Boulton) W; m. Anne Ware Sears, July 18, 1963 (div. May 1988); children: John M.B., Erica Sears, m. Ellen Cecilia Warner, Dec. 30, 1988. Postgrad., MIT, Harvard U., 1955-57; BS with honors, U. Birmingham, UK, 1948; PhD, U. Nottingham, UK, 1953. Brush fellow, rsch. asst. Nottingham U., 1950-53; ship's 7th engr. officer Donaldson Line, Glasgow, UK, 1953; engr. Brush Elec. Engring. Co., Ltd., UK, 1953-55; sr. gas-turbine designer Ruston & Hornsby, Lincoln, UK, 1957-58; sr. lectr., mech. engring. U. London, Zaria, Nigeria, 1958-60; v.p., tech. dir. No. Rsch. and Engring. Corp., Cambridge, Mass. and U.S.A., 1960-66; assoc. prof. mech. engring. MIT, Cambridge, 1966-71, prof., 1971-94; prof. emeritus, 1994—; vis. engr., Boeing Airplane Co., 1956-57; vis. fellow MIT and Harvard U., 1955-56; cons., lectr. in field. Author: The Design of Gas-Turbine Engines, 1991, The Design of High-Efficiency Turbomachinery and Gas Turbines, 1984; co-author: (with Frank Rowland White) Bicycling Science, 1974, 2d rev. edit., 1982, (with Douglas Stephen Beck) Gas-Turbine Regenerators, 1995, (with Richard Wilson et al) The Health Effects of Fossil-Fuel Burning, 1981; co-editor: (with Allan V. Abbott) Human-Powered Vehicles, 1995; editor: Solid Waste-Management Handbook, 1977, The Treatment and Management of Urban Solid Waste, 1972. Recipient T. Bernard Hall prize Inst. Mech.

Engrs., 1954, Lord Weir 1st prize Inst. Mech. Engrs., 1955, Indsl. Rsch. IR-100 award, 1974, Reclamation Industries Internat. prize, 1974; Power-Jets Sch. scholar, 1954; Commonwealth Fund fellow MIT and Harvard U., 1955-57. Avocations: human power, biking, hiking, tennis, music. Office: MIT/Mech Engring Rm 3-455 Cambridge MA 02139

WILSON, DAVID JAMES, chemistry educator; b. Ames, Ia., June 25, 1930; s. James Calmar and Alice Winona (Olmsted) W.; m. Martha Carolyn Mayers, Sept. 6, 1952; children: John Wesley, Charles Steven, William David, Andrew Lyman, Joyce Ballin. B.S. in Chemistry, Stanford U., 1952; postgrad., 1952-53, 55-57; Ph.D., Calif. Inst. Tech., 1958. Faculty U. Rochester, N.Y., 1957-69; asso. prof. U. Rochester, 1963-67, prof. phys. chemistry, 1967-69; prof. Vanderbilt U., Nashville, 1969—; prof. chemistry and environ. engring. Vanderbilt U., 1977-95, Alexander Heard disting. service prof., 1983-84; prof. emeritus Vanderbilt U., Nashville, 1995—; sr. rsch. fellow Eckenfelder, Inc., 1995—; vis. sr. lectr. chemistry U. Ife, Nigeria, 1964-65; vis. prof. chem. engring. U. Malaga, Spain, 1993-94; mem. Rochester Com. for Sci. Info., 1960-69, v.p., 1966-69; prin. chemist Nashville Com. for Sci. Info., 1971-74; sr. rsch. assoc. Eckenfelder, Inc., 1988-95. Pres. Tenn. Environ. Council, 1985-87. Served with AUS, 1953-55. Recipient award Monroe County Conservation Council, 1967, Conservation League, 1971; Alfred P. Sloan Found. fellow, 1964-66. Mem. AAAS, Am. Chem. Soc., Tenn. Acad. Sci., Sigma Xi, Phi Beta Kappa. Home: 3600 Wilbur Pl Nashville TN 37204-3829

WILSON, DAVID LEE, clinical psychologist; b. Mooresville, N.C., July 5, 1941; s. William John Mack and Joyce Evelyn (Evans) W.; m. Barbara Ann Klepfer, Apr. 22, 1960 (div. Jan. 1982); children: Cheryl, Lisa, David; m. Cheryl Andersen, May 22, 1983 (div. Jan. 1992). Student, Auburn U., 1959-60; AB in Psychology, Davidson Coll., 1963; PhD in Clin. Psychology, U. N.C., 1967. Teaching fellow U. N.C., Chapel Hill, 1964; psychology intern Letterman Hosp., San Francisco, 1966-67, supr., 1967-70; sr. psychologist Kaiser Hosp., Hayward, Calif., 1972-74; pvt. practice psychology San Francisco, 1970-72; mem. staff Far No. Regional Ctr., Redding, Calif., 1970-74; dir. Redding Psychotherapy Group, 1974—, Vietnam Vets. Readjustment Program, Shasta and Tehama, 1984—; cons. in field. Author: play The Moon Cannot Be Stolen, 1985; contbr. articles to profl. jours. Chmn. Shasta Dam P.U.D. Com., Shasta County, 1981-82, Shasta County Headstart Bd., 1982-85, Criminal Justice Adv. Bd. Shasta County, 1982-87, Youth and Family Counseling Ctr., Shasta County, 1986-89. Capt. U.S. Army, 1965-70. Recipient Danforth award Danforth Found., 1959; Woodrow Wilson Found. fellow, 1963; Smith Fund grantee, 1966; Dana scholar, 1960-63. Fellow Am. Bd. Med. Psychotherapy; mem. APA, Calif. State Psychol. Assn.(chpt. rep. 1990—, bd. dirs. 1990—, chair membership com. 1993—, exec. com. 1993-95, chair publs. com. 1994—, Silver PSI award 1995), Shasta Cascade Psychol. Assn.(pres. 1990-91, mem. bd. dirs. 1990—, Outstanding Psychologist 1993), Am. Assn. Advancement of Behavior Therapy, Eye Movement Desensitization and Reprocessing Network (Outstanding Rsch. award 1994). Democrat. Avocations: fly fishing, backpacking, camping, white water rafting. Office: Redding Psychotherapy Group 616 Azalea Ave Redding CA 96002-0217

WILSON, DEBRA, oil, gas industry executive. Mgr. devel., adminstr. United Aviation Fuels Corp., Arlington Heights, Ill., 1985—. Office: United Aviation Fuels Corp 1200 E Algonquin Rd Arlington Heights IL 60005*

WILSON, DELANO DEE, consulting company executive; b. Great Falls, Mont., Apr. 15, 1934; s. William McKinley and Alvina Henrietta (Beck) W.; m. Marilyn Ann Harant, Nov. 14, 1959; children: Robin David, Leslie Ann Wilson, Christian William. BSEE, Mont. State U., 1959. Analytical engr. GE, Schenectady, N.Y., 1960-69, sr. engr., 1964-69, mgr. alternating current studies, 1969-72; mgr. engring. projects GE, Phila., 1972-74; prin. engr. Power Techs., Inc., Schenectady, 1974-82; v.p., prin. engr. Power Techs., Inc.-Tech. Assessment Group, Schenectady, 1980-85; pres., CEO Power Techs. Inc., Schenectady, 1986-95, chmn. bd. dirs., 1989-95; expert eyewitness, cons. Internat. Conf. on High Voltage Systems, Paris, 1974-90. U.S. rep., 1986-92. Author, co-author 6 books; contbr. numerous tech. papers to profl. jours.; patentee in field. Bd. dirs. Ellis Hosp., Schenectady, 1987—; trustee Capital Dist. YMCA, 1989—. With U.S. Army, 1954-56. Fellow IEEE (mem. transp. and dist. com., exec. bd. Power Engring. Soc. 1988-94, Disting. Svc. award 1988); mem. Am. Nat. Standards Inst., Nat. Fedn. Indsl. Bus., Schenectady C. of C. (bd. dirs.), Bone Marrow Resource Found. (bd. dirs.), Rotary. Avocations: skiing, fishing, amateur auto rebuilding. Office: Power Techs Inc 1482 Erie Blvd PO Box 1058 Schenectady NY 12301

WILSON, DELBERT RAY, publisher, author; b. Riverdale, Calif., Jan. 16, 1926; s. Elmer Ray and Hanna Marie (Pelto) W.; m. Beatrice Joy Daffer, Oct. 5, 1947; children: Jeri Rae, Vicky Joy, Julianne, Margaret Erin. A.A., A.S., Elgin (Ill.) Community Coll., 1975; B.S., No. Ill. U., 1980; Litt.D. (hon.), Judson Coll., 1985. Editor The Reporter, McCook, Nebr., 1949-50; co-pub. The Reporter, Times-Republican (Hayes Center, Nebr.), Pioneer-Press (Palisade, Nebr.), News (Haigler, Nebr.), 1951-52; advt. mgr. Daily Telegram, Norton, Kans., 1952-53; mgr. The Star, Dos Palos, Calif., 1953-54; gen. mgr. Tribune, Holtville, Calif., 1954-57; bus. mgr. Desert Newspapers, Glendale, Ariz., 1957-59; advt. sales rep. Union Tribune Pub. Co., San Diego, 1959-60, merchandising mgr., 1961-65; gen. advt. mgr. Union Tribune Pub. Co., 1966; editor, pub. Evening Star-News, Culver City, Calif., 1966-70, Daily Courier-News, Elgin, Ill., also, Daily Jour., Wheaton, Ill., 1970-91; CEO Crossroads Communications, Carpentersville, Ill., 1991—, AmTec Learning Corp., Elgin, Ill., 1992—. Author: The Folks, 1974, Fort Kearny on the Platte, 1980, Episode on Hill 616, 1981, Nebraska Hist. Guide, 1983, Wyoming Hist. Guide, 1984, Iowa Hist. Tour Guide, 1985, Kansas Hist. Guide, 1987, Missouri Hist. Tour Guide, 1987, Greater Chicago Hist. Tour Guide, 1989, Colorado Hist. Guide, 1989, Illinois Hist. Tour Guide, 1990; editor Oklahoma Hist. Tour Guide, 1991, Indiana Hist. Tour Guide, 1993, Organizing the Organization, 1993. Founder, chmn. bd. VIP Friendship Council, Inc. of Ill., 1972—, DuPage County Heritage Gallery, Wheaton, 1976—; bd. govs. State Colls. and Univs., Ill., 1981-91; trustee Judson Coll., Elgin, 1971—, Elgin Acad., 1973-78; chmn. bd. Elgin Sesquicentennial Inc.; bd. mgrs. Sherman Hosp., Elgin, 1971—; active Boy Scouts Am. (Silver Beaver award 1977); chmn. bd. Christian Coll. So. Africa, Harare, Zimbabwe, 1983-87; bd. govs. Luth. Social Services of Ill., 1983-89; mem. Ill. Vets. Adv. Council, 1983—; bd. dirs. Cornerstone Found., 1984—, Wheaton Eye Found., 1985-93, Elgin Community Coll. Found., 1986—, Summit Sch. Found., 1987—, Ill. C.C. Coll. System Found., 1992—, Elgin United Way, 1988—; bd. dirs. western div. Jr. Achievement Chgo., 1991—; mem. No. Star Publs. Bd. No. Ill. U., 1988—; pres. Council on America's Mil. Past, Dept. Ill.; mem. nat. adv. com. Ednl. Assistance, Ltd., Glen Ellyn, Ill., 1989—; bd. dirs. Sherman Health Systems, Elgin, 1989, Elgin Symphony, 1989—, Elgin Devel., Inc., 1989-91; chmn. nat. adv. bd. Lincoln Train Project, Ill. Benedictine Coll., Lisle, 1991—; consulting dir. Sister Cities Assn. of Elgin, Russian dept., 1992—, v.p., bd. dirs. Ill. Chpt. Sister Cities Internat., 1993—; mem. ch. coun. Metro Synod Evang. Luth. Ch. in Am., 1993—. With USN, 1943-45, USAF, 1946-49. Mem. Am. Soc. Newspaper Editors, Nebr. Hist. Soc. (life mem.), DAV (Man of Yr. 1978, comdr. Ill. 1980-82, editor and pub. Ill. DAV News 1977-87), Am. Legion, Sigma Delta Chi. Republican. Lutheran. Home: 1507 Laurel Ct Dundee IL 60118-1708 Office: 35 N Western Ave Carpentersville IL 60110-0007

WILSON, DON WHITMAN, archivist, historian; b. Clay Center, Kans., Dec. 17, 1942; s. Donald J. Wilson and Lois M. (Sutton) Walker; m. Patricia Ann Sherrod, July 9, 1983; children—Todd, Jeffrey, Michael, Denise. AB, Washburn U., Topeka, 1964; MA, U. Cin., 1965, PhD, 1972, LittD (hon.), 1988. Archivist Kans. State Hist. Soc., Topeka, 1967-69; instr. history Washburn U., 1967-69; historian, dept. dir. Dwight D. Eisenhower Library, Abilene, Kans., 1969-78; assoc. dir. State Hist. Soc. Wis., Madison, 1978-81; dir. Gerald R. Ford Library and Mus., Ann Arbor, Mich., 1981-87; lectr. history U. Mich., 1982-87; Archivist of the U.S. Washington, 1987-93; rsch. prof. Tex. A&M U.; College Station, 1993—, exec. dir. George Bush libr. ctr., 1993—. Author: Governor Charles Robinson of Kansas, 1975; editor: D-Day: The Normandy Invasion, 1971; bd. editors: Teaching History Jour., 1975—. Mem. Abilene Library Bd., 1973-76; mem. Abilene City Commn., 1976-78; pres. Dickinson County Hist. Soc., Abilene, 1976-77. NDEA fellow, 1964-67; recipient Pub. Service award Gen. Services Adminstrn., 1973. Mem. Am. Hist. Assn. (mem. Beveridge Book Prize com. 1979-82), Am. Assn. State and Local History, Kans. Hist. Soc. (bd. dirs. 1987—), Am.

Antiquarian Soc., Soc. Am. Archivists. Republican. Baptist. Home: 209 Chimney Hill Dr College Station TX 77840 Office: Tex A&M U George Bush Libr Ctr College Station TX 77843-1145

WILSON, DONALD EDWARD, physician, educator; b. Worcester, Mass., Aug. 28, 1936; s. Rivers Rivo and Licine (Bradshaw) W.; m. Patricia C. Littell, Aug. 27, 1977; children: Jeffrey D.E., Sean D., Monique, Sheila L. A.B., Harvard U., 1958; M.D., Tufts U., 1962. Diplomate Am. Bd. Internal Medicine. Intern St. Elizabeth Hosp., Boston, 1962-63; resident in medicine, research fellow in gastroenterology VA Hosp. and Lemuel Shattuck Hosp., Boston, 1963-66; assoc. chief gastroenterology Bklyn. Hosp., 1968-71; instr. medicine SUNY Downstate Med. Center, Bklyn., 1968-71; asst. prof. medicine U. Ill., Chgo., 1971-73; asso. prof. U. Ill., 1973-75, prof., 1975-80, acting head dept. medicine, 1976-77; dir. div. gastroenterology U. Ill. Hosp., Chgo., 1971-80; chief of gastroenterology U. Ill. Hosp., 1973-80, physician-in-chief, 1976-77; prof., chmn. dept. medicine SUNY Downstate Med. Center, Bklyn., 1980-91; physician-in-chief State U. and Kings County Hosp., 1980-91; dean, prof. medicine U. Md.Sch. Medicine, Balt., 1991—; mem. Part II test com. Nat. Bd. Med. Examiners, 1985-88; mem. gen. clin. rsch. ctrs. com. NIH, 1987—; mem. nat. digestive disease adv. bd. NIH, 1985-87, chmn., 1986-87; vis. prof. medicine U. London, Kings Coll. Med. Sch., 1977-78; mem. gastrointestinal drugs adv. bd. FDA, 1985-87, chmn., 1986-87; mem. nat. adv. com. Agy. for Health Care Policy and Rsch., Dept. HHS, 1991—, chmn., 1992—; mem. nat. com. fgn. med. edn. and accreditation U.S. Dept. Edn., 1994—. Contbr. articles to med. jours. Bd. vis. Harvard Sch. of Pub. Health, 1992-94. Served to capt. M.C., USAF, 1966-68. Recipient Rsch. award HEW, 1971, 74, Rsch. award John A. Hartford Found., Inc., 1972-79, Rsch. award Distilled Spirits Coun. U.S., 1972-74, Rsch. award VA, 1974. Master ACP; mem. NAS, AAAS, Am. Gastroent. Assn., Am. Fedn. Clin. Rsch., Am. Assn. Study Liver Disease, Accreditation Coun. Grad. Med. Edn. (rev. com. internal medicine), Central Soc. Clin. Rsch., Central Rsch. Club, Chgo. Soc. Gastroenterology (pres. 1978-79), Digestive Disease Found., Midwest Gut Club, Soc. Exptl. Biology and Medicine, N.Y. Acad. Scis., N.Y. Acad. Medicine, N.Y. Soc. Gastroenterology, Chgo. Soc. Gastrointestinal Endoscopy (pres. 1979-80), Assn. Am. Physicians, Assn. for Acad. Minority Physicians (sec./treas. 1986—), Nat. Med. Assn., Am. Clin. and Climatological Assn., 1994—, Assn. Profs. Medicine (sec.-treas. 1990-91), Inst. of Medicine, Med. Club Bklyn., Sigma Phi Phi (grand boule). Club: Harvard (Chgo., N.Y.C.), 14 West Hamilton St. Club (Balt.), The Ctr. Club, (Balt.). Home: Kawiya Manor Owings Mills MD 21117-4338 Office: U Md Sch Medicine 655 W Baltimore St Baltimore MD 21201-1559

WILSON, DONALD GREY, management consultant; b. Bridgeport, Conn., Sept. 20, 1917; s. William Gray and Jeannetta McAvoy (Kerr) W.; m. Elizabeth Jean Lanning, Apr. 24, 1943 (dec. Mar. 1971); children: Kirk Lanning, Craig Gardner, William Grey. B.S. in Elec. Engring. Rensselaer Poly. Inst., 1938; S.M., Harvard U., 1939, M.E.S., 1947, Ph.D., 1948. Mgr. automatic fire alarm div. Sealand Corp., Bridgeport, Conn., 1939-40; instr. elec. engring. Rensselaer Poly. Inst., 1940-42; staff mem. Radiation Lab. Mass. Inst. Tech., 1942-45; with dept. elec. engring. U. Kan., Lawrence, 1947-55; prof. U. Kan., 1950-55, chmn. dept., 1948-55; cons. U.S. Naval Ordance Test Sta., China Lake, Calif., 1953-54; assoc. dir. rsch. dept. Stromberg-Carlson Co., San Diego, 1955-59, gen. mgr., 1959, asst. v.p., 1959-60; v.p. rsch. P.R. Mallory & Co., Indpls., 1960, v.p. rsch. and engring., 1961-71, v.p. rsch., engring. and environ. affairs, 1971-75; alt. dir. Mallory Metal. Products, Eng., 1967; pres. Contemporary Custom Cabinets, San Diego, 1975-76; v.p. Continental Resources and Minerals Corp., Dayton, Ohio, 1978-79; sr. v.p. Ranzi Mergers/Acquisitions, San Diego, 1983-86; mgmt. cons., 1976—; sr. lectr. U. Rochester, 1956-57; lectr. dept. elec. engring. San Diego State U., 1981-92, adj. dean coll. engring., 1987, prof. emeritus, 1992—; mng. dir., exec. bd. nat. Bur. Prof. Cons., 1988-94, sr. counsel, 1994—. Contbr. articles to profl. jours. Bd. dirs. Speech and Hearing Clinic, Indpls., 1960-66; bd. dirs. Washington Twp. Sch. Dist., 1964-88, pres., 1966-67. Recipient Outstanding Acad. Advisor award San Diego State U., 1992. Fellow AAAS; mem. IEEE (sr., Internat. Outstanding Br. Counselor award 1992), Affiliation Profl. Cons. Orgns. (chmn. bd. govs. 1991-93), Sigma Xi, Sigma Phi Epsilon, Tau Beta Pi, Eta Kappa Nu, Mensa, Intertel. Home: 3110 Levante St Carlsbad CA 92009-8332

WILSON, DONALD MALCOLM, publishing executive; b. Glen Ridge, N.J., June 27, 1925; s. Robert and Adelaide (Streubel) W.; m. Susan M. Neuberger, Apr. 6, 1957; children: Dwight Malcolm, Katherine Loudon, Penelope. Grad., Deerfield (Mass.) Acad., 1943; B.A., Yale U., 1948. Reporter Life mag., 1949-53, chief Far Ea. corr., 1953-56, chief Washington corr., 1956-60, asso. chief, 1968-69; gen. mgr. Time- Life Internat., 1965-68; v.p. corporate and pub. affairs Time, Inc., 1969-81, corp. v.p. pub. affairs, 1981-89; pub. New Jersey's Bus. Newspapers, New Brunswick, 1989—; dep. dir. USIA 1961-65; mem. adv. council Edward R. Murrow Ctr., Tufts U., The Nat. Council of La Raza, 1985-89; mem. Pub. Broadcasting Authority of N.J., 1969-73, 76-79. Trustee Vassar Coll., 1971-79, The Brearley Sch., 1977-86; bd. dirs. Solomon R. Guggenheim Mus., The Schumann Fund for N.J., Ctr. for Analysis of Pub. Issues. Decorated Air medal. Mem. Council on Fgn. Relations. Clubs: Federal City (Washington); Century Assn. (N.Y.C.). Home: 4574 Province Line Rd Princeton NJ 08540-2212 Office: NJ Bus Newspapers 391 George St New Brunswick NJ 08901

WILSON, DONALD WALLIN, university president, educator; b. Poona, India, Jan. 9, 1938; s. Nathaniel Carter and Hannah Myrtle Wilson; m. Kathleen, Dec. 28, 1965; children: Carrie, Jennifer, Gregory, Andrew. B.A., So. Missionary Coll., 1959; M.A., Andrews U., 1961; Ph.D., Mich. State U. 1966. Dean applied arts and tech. Ont. (Can.) Colls., North Bay, 1968-73; acad. dean Olivet Coll., 1973-76; pres. Castleton State Coll., 1976-79; pres. Southampton Coll., 1979-83, profl. communications and history, 1973-83; pres., prof. Pittsburg State U. (Kans.), 1983—. Author: The Untapped Source of Power in the Church, 1961, Long Range Planning, 1979, The Long Road From Turmoil to Self Sufficiency, 1989, The Next Twenty-Five Years: Indonesias Journey Into The Future, 1992, The Indispensable Man: Sudomo, 1992. Mem. Kans. Adv. Coun. of C.C.'s; bd. dirs. Internat. U. Thailand; pres. Internat. Univ. Found.; recipient Outstanding Alumni award Mich. State U., 1984. Mem. Speech Communication Assn., Assn. Asian Studies, Internat. Univ. Found. (pres.), Rotary. Methodist. Home: 515 E Ford St Pittsburg KS 66762-6311 Office: Pittsburg State U Office of President Pittsburg KS 66762

WILSON, DOROTHY CLARKE, author; b. Gardiner, Maine, May 9, 1904; d. Lewis Herbert and Flora Eva (Cross) Clarke; m. Elwin L. Wilson, Aug. 31, 1925; adopted children: Joan S., Harold Elwin (dec.). A.B., Bates Coll., 1925, Litt.D., 1947; L.H.D., U. Maine, 1984. Author of: about seventy religious plays, vol. religious plays Twelve Months of Drama for the Average Church, 1934; novels The Brother, 1944, The Herdsman, 1946, Prince of Egypt, 1949 (winner Westminster $7500 award for best religious novel), House of Earth, 1952, Fly With Me to India, 1954, Jezebel, 1955, The Gifts, 1957, Dr. Ida: A Biography Dr. Ida S. Scudder of India, 1959, The Journey, 1962, Take My Hands: Biography Dr. Mary Verghese, 1963, The Three Gifts, 1963, Ten Fingers for God: Biography Dr. Paul Brand, 1965, Handicap Race: The Story of Roger Arnett, 1967, Palace of Healing, The Story of Dr. Clara Swain, 1968, Lone Woman: Biography of Dr. Elizabeth Blackwell, 1970, The Big-Little World of Doc Pritham, 1971, Hilary, The Brave World of Hilary Pole, 1973, Bright Eyes, the Story of Susette La Flesche-an Omaha Indian, 1974, Stranger and Traveler, The Story of Dorothea Dix, American Reformer, 1975, Climb Every Mountain, 1976, Granny Brand, Her Story, 1976, Twelve Who Cared: My Adventures with Christian Courage, 1977, Apostle of Sight, Story of Dr. Victor Rambo, 1980, Lincoln's Mothers: A Story of Nancy and Sally Lincoln, 1981, Lady Washington, 1984, Queen Dolley: A Story of Dolley Madison, 1987, Alice and Edith: The Wives of Theodore Roosevelt, 1989, Union in Diversity: The Story of Our Marriage, 1993; lectr. on India, Middle East. Trustee Bates Coll. Recipient Woman of Distinction award Alpha Delta Kappa, 1971, New Eng. United Meth. award, 1975, Distinguished Achievement award U. Maine, 1977, achievement citation AAUW, 1988, MaryAnn Hartman award U. Maine, 1989, Deborah Morton award Westbrook Coll., 1989. Mem. Phi Beta Kappa. Home: 117 Bennoch Rd Orono ME 04473-1765

WILSON, DWIGHT LISTON, former military officer, investment advisor; b. Hereford, Tex., Oct. 30, 1931; s. Liston Oscar and Pauline (Smart) W.; m.

WILSON, EARLE LAWRENCE, church administrator; b. Rensselaer, N.Y., Dec. 8, 1934; s. Lawrence Wilbur Wilson and Wilhelaminia Knapp; m. Sylvia M. Beck; children: Deborah, Stephen, Colleen. B in Theology, United Wesleyan Coll., 1956, BS, 1961; M of Divinity, Evang. Sch. of Theology, 1965; M of Theology, Princeton Theol. Sem., 1967; D of Divinity, Houghton Coll., 1974. Sr. pastor Wesleyan Church, Gloversville, N.Y., 1956-61; gen. supt. Wesleyan Church, Indpls., 1984—; sr. pastor First Wesleyan Church, Bethlehem, Pa., 1961-72; pres. United Wesleyan Coll., Allentown, Pa., 1972-84. Author: When You Get Where You're Going, 1966, Within a Hair's Breadth, 1989. Mem. chaplain Rotary. Republican. Home: 11697 Pompano Dr Indianapolis IN 46236-8819 Office: Wesleyan Ch PO Box 50434 Indianapolis IN 46250-0434

WILSON, EDGAR BYRON, business executive; b. Albany, N.Y., May 13, 1931; s. Harold Edgar and Marie Elizabeth (Brush) W.; m. Mary Beth Weilbacher, Aug. 2, 1956. BA, St. Lawrence U., 1953; MBA, Harvard U., 1955. Mkt. dir. Richardson-Vicks, Inc., N.Y.C., Paris, Manila, 1957-64; chief exec. officer Japan Kimberly-Clark Corp., Neenah, Wis., 1964-68, France, 1968-71; v.p. internat. div. Pillsbury Co., Mpls., 1971-76; exec. v.p. Shaklee Corp., San Francisco, 1976-79; pres., chief exec. officer Almay Cosmetics, Inc., N.Y.C., 1979-84, Hathaway Group of Warnaco, N.Y.C., 1984-86; chmn. Global Brands, Inc., N.Y.C., 1986—; chmn., chief exec. officer Sero Co., Branford, Conn., Mortin Jonap, Ltd., Hauppauge, N.Y.; bd. dirs. William Schneider, Inc., Miami. Trustee St. Lawrence U., Canton, N.Y., 1986—, San Francisco Ballet, 1978; devel. dir. Cen. Park Conservancy, N.Y.C., 1983—. With USAR, 1955-57. Mem. Eastward Ho Club (gov. 1986—). Republican. Avocations: perennial gardening, golfing, cooking, reading. Home: 39 E 79th St New York NY 10021-0230 Office: Global Brands Inc 1090 Ave Of The Americas New York NY 10036-6711

WILSON, EDWARD CONVERSE, JR., oil and natural gas production company executive; b. Cambridge, Mass., Jan. 1, 1928; s. Edward Converse and Jean (McLean) W.; m. Patricia Ann Cairns, Sept. 10, 1953; children—Amy Cairns, Sarah Converse. A.B., Harvard U., 1949. Brokerage trainee Estabrook & Co., Boston, 1951; Midwest Stock Exchange cle. Paul H. Davis & Co., Chgo., 1951-52; mem. Chgo. Bd. Trade, 1952-78, dir., 1966-67, chmn., 1970-71; partner Nolan & Wilson Co. (specialists on Midwest Stock Exchange), 1965-72; sr. partner Wilson Prodn. Co., Ft. Smith, Ark., 1972-74; dir. Rutledge Assos., Wakefield, Mass., 1965-74, Paul H. Robinson Inc., Chgo., 1972-81. Mem. devel. com. Chgo. chpt. Nat. Multiple Sclerosis Soc., 1970; mem. vis. com. on univ. resources Harvard, 1971-74, 76-81; Bd. dirs. Franklin Blvd. Community Hosp., 1970-74. Served with USAAF, 1946-47. Mem. Racquet Club (Chgo.). Home: 11114 Wickwood Dr Houston TX 77024-7523 Office: 1770 St James Pl Houston TX 77056-3402

WILSON, EDWARD NATHAN, mathematician, educator; b. Warsaw, N.Y., Dec. 2, 1941; s. Hugh Monroe and Margaret Jane (Northrup) W.; m. Mary Katherine Schooling, Aug. 19, 1976; children: Nathan Edward, Emily Katherine. BA, Cornell U., 1963; MS, Stanford U., 1965; PhD, Washington U., St. Louis, 1971. Instr. Ft. Valley (Ga.) State Coll., 1965-67, Washington U. St. Louis, 1968-69, U. Calif., Irvine, 1970-71, Brandeis U., Waltham, Mass., 1971-73; asst. prof. Washington U., St. Louis, 1973-77, assoc. prof., 1977-87, dean grad. sch., 1983-93, dean univ. coll., 1986-88, prof., 1987—; mem. Grad. Record Exams. Bd., Princeton, N.J., 1986-90; sec.-treas. Assn. Grad. Schs. Contbr. articles to profl. jours. Mem. Brentwood Sch. Bd., Mo., 1984. Woodrow Wilson fellow, 1963; NSF fellow, 1963-65; NDEA fellow, 1967-70. Mem. Am. Math. Soc., Math. Assn. of Am. Democrat. Office: Washington U Campus Box 1146 1 Brookings Dr Saint Louis MO 63130-4862

WILSON, EDWARD OSBORNE, biologist, educator; b. Birmingham, Ala., June 10, 1929; s. Edward Osborne and Inez (Freeman) W.; m. Irene Kelley, Oct. 30, 1955; 1 dau., Catherine Irene. BS, U. Ala., 1949, MS, 1950; PhD, Harvard U., 1955; DS (hon.), Duke U., Grinnell Coll., Lawrence U., U. West Fla., Oxford U., Fitchburg State Coll., U. Conn., Ripon Coll., Macalester Coll., U. Mass., Ripon Coll.; DPhil, Uppsala U.; LHD (hon.), U. Ala., Hofstra U.; Pa. State U.; LLD (hon.), Simon Fraser U., Pa. State U.; D.h.c., U. Madrid Complutense, 1995. Jr. fellow Soc. Fellows, Harvard U., 1953-56, mem. faculty, 1956—, Baird prof. sci., 1976-94, Pellegrino prof., 1994—, Pellegrino univ. prof., curator entomology, 1971—; fellow Guggenheim Found., 1978, mem. selection com., 1982-89; bd. dirs. World Wildlife Fund, 1983-94, Organ. Tropical Studies, 1984—, N.Y. Bot. Gardens, 1991—; Am. Mus. Natural History, 1992—, Am. Acad. Liberal Edn., 1993—. Author: The Insect Societies, 1971, Sociobiology: The New Synthesis, 1975, On Human Nature, 1978 (Pulitzer Prize for non-fiction 1979), Promethean Fire, 1983, Biophilia, 1984, (with Bert Holldobler) The Ants, 1990 (Pulitzer Prize for non-fiction 1991), Success and Dominance in Ecosystems, 1990, The Diversity of Life, 1991 (Nat. Wildlife Assn. award, Conservation 1992), (with Bert Holldobler) Journey to the Sir Peter Kent Conservation prize), (with Bert Holldobler) Journey to the Ants, 1994, Naturalist, 1994. Recipient Cleve.-AAAS rsch. prize, 1967, Nat. Medal Sci., 1976, Leidy medal Acad. Natural Sci., Phila., 1979, Disting. Svc. award Am. Inst. Biol. Scis., 1976, Mercer award Ecol. Soc. Am., 1971, Founders Meml. award and L.O. Howard award Entomol. Soc. Am., 1972, 85, Archie Carr medal U. Fla., 1978, Disting. Svc. award Am. Humanist Soc., 1982, Tyler ecology prize, 1984, Silver medal Nat. Zool. Park, German Ecol. Inst. prize, 1987, Weaver award scholarly letters Ingersoll Found., 1989, Crafoord prize Royal Swedish Acad. Scis., 1990, Prix d'Inst. de la Vie, Paris, 1990, Revelle medal, 1990, Gold medal Worldwide Fund for Nature, 1990, Achievement award Nat. Wildlife Fedn., 1992, Shaw medal Mo. Botanical Garden, 1993, Internat. prize Biology Govt. of Japan, 1993, Audubon medal Audubon Soc., 1995, John Hay award Orion Soc., 1995, others. Fellow Am. Acad. Arts and Scis., Am. Phil. Soc., Deutsche Akad. Naturforsch; mem. NAS, Am. Genetics Assn. (hon. life), Brit. Ecol. Soc. (hon. life), Entomol. Soc. Am. (hon. life), Zool. Soc. London (hon. life), Am. Humanist Soc. (hon. life), Acad. Humanism (hon. life), Netherlands Entomol. Soc. (hon. life), Royal Soc. London, Finnish Acad. Sci. and Letters, Russian Acad. Nat. Sci., Royal Soc. Sci. Uppsala (Sweden). Home: 9 Foster Rd Lexington MA 02173-5505 Office: Harvard U Mus Comparative Zoology Cambridge MA 02138

WILSON, EDWIN GRAVES, university official. BA, Wake Forest U.; AM, Harvard U., PhD; Litt.D., U. N.C. Mem. faculty dept. English Wake Forest U., Winston-Salem, N.C., 1951—; prof. English, 1959—, asst. dean, 1957-58, acting dean, 1958-60, dean, 1960-67, provost, 1967-90; v.p. spl. projects Wake Forest U., 1990—. Author: (with David B. Green) Keats, Shelley, Byron, Hunt and Their Circles, 1964. Bd. trustees Belmont Abbey Coll., 1979—; mem. N.C. Humanities Coun., 1977-80; bd. visitors Winston-Salem State U., 1993-94. Mem. Phi Beta Kappa, Omicron Delta Kappa, Alpha Phi Omega, Kappa Sigma. Office: Wake Forest U Office of Provost Winston Salem NC 27109

WILSON, EUGENE ROLLAND, foundation executive; b. Findlay, Ohio, Jan. 14, 1938; s. Clair and Ethel Bernice (Cryer) W.; m. Mary Ann Dalton; children: Jeff, Andy. B.A., Bowling Green State U., 1960; M.S., Syracuse U., 1961. Dir. devel., asst. to pres. Bowling Green (Ohio) State U., 1964-66; mgr. radio-TV advt. Columbia Gas of Ohio, Inc., Columbus, 1964-66; assoc. dir. devel. Calif. Inst. Tech., Pasadena, 1971-77, v.p. for instl. relations, 1979-80; assoc. dir. ARCO Found., Los Angeles, 1977-79, exec. dir., 1980-83, pres., 1984-94; pres. youth devel. Ewing Marion Kauffman Found., Kansas City, Mo., 1995—; chmn. contbns. coun. Conf. Bd.; mem. corp. grant makers com. Coun. of Founds. Nat. bd. of visitors Ctr. on Philanthropy; founding trustee Arcadia (Calif.) Edn. Found.; elder trustee Presbyn. Ch. Named Outstanding Young Man Bowling Green Jaycees, 1967; recipient hon. service award Hugo Reid Sch. PTA, 1977, Corp. Social Responsibility award Mex.-Am. Legal Def. and Edn. Fund, 1989, Nat. Leadership award in edn. Inst. for Ednl. Leadership, 1992. Mem. Bowling Green State U. Alumni Assn. (pres. 1965), Gnome and Athenaeum Clubs of Caltech, Omicron Delta Kappa. Home: 14117 W 56th Ct Shawnee KS 66216 Office: 4900 Oak St Kansas City MO 64112-2776 *Our values and judgments are shaped by our roots. The special relationships developed in small-town rural America, and the many opportunities to enjoy a variety of leadership experiences, prove invaluable later in life to cope with the broader, more vexing problems of pluralistic society. Later sophistication—tempered by the humility of those early roots—then becomes more meaningful.*

WILSON, EWEN MACLELLAN, economist; b. Nairobi, Kenya, July 29, 1944; came to U.S., 1969; s. Walter Maclellan and Barbara (Gange) Maclellan W.; m. Kay Stephens, May 31, 1969; children: Libby, Cindy, Riara. BS, U. London, 1965; MS, W.Va. U., 1970; PhD, N.C. State U., 1973. With conservation and extension dept. Ministry of Agrl., Banket, Rhodesia, 1965-68; research fellow U. Rhodesia, Salisbury, 1973-74; asst. prof. Va. Tech. Inst., Blacksburg, 1975-77; dir. econs. and stats. Am. Meat Inst., Arlington, Va., 1977-83, v.p., 1983-85; apptd. dep. asst. sec. U.S. Dept. Agrl., Washington, 1985-87, asst. sec., 1987-89; pres. Wilson Agribus. Analysis, 1989-90; exec. dir. Commodity Futures Trading Commn., Washington, 1990-94; chief agriculture and fin. statistics div. Bur. of Census, Washington, 1994—; bd. dirs. Nat. Cooperative Bank, 1988-90, Commodity Credit Corp, 1987-89. Mem. Am. Agrl. Econs. Assn. Republican. Episcopalian. Office: Bur of Census 437 Iverson AGFS Washington DC 20233

WILSON, F(RANCIS) PAUL, novelist; b. Jersey City, May 17, 1946; s. Frank P. and Mary (Sullivan) W.; m. Mary Murphy, Aug. 23, 1969. Grad., Georgetown U., 1968. With Cedar Bridge Med. Group, Bricktown, N.Y., 1974—. Author: Healer, 1976, 2d edit., 1992, Wheels Within Wheels, 1978, 2d edit., 1992, An Enemy of the State, 1980, 2d edit., 1992, The Keep, 1981 (N.Y. Times bestseller list), 2d edit., 1982, The Tomb, 1984 (N.Y. Times bestseller list, Porgie award West Coast Rev. Books 1984), The Touch, 1986, Black Wind, 1988, Soft and Others, 1989, Dydeetown World, 1989, The Tery, 1990, Reborn, 1990, Reprisal, 1991, Sibs, 1991, Nightworld, 1991; editor: Freak Show, 1992, The Select, 1994; also numerous short stories. Office: care Albert Zuckerman Writers House 21 W 26th St New York NY 10010-1003

WILSON, FRANKLIN LEONDUS, III, political science educator; b. L.A., Feb. 7, 1941; s. Franklin Leondus II and Ruth (Elieson) W.; m. Carol Ann West, Feb. 16, 1968; children: Erin, Sara, John, Marc. BA in Internat. Rels., UCLA, 1964, MA in Polit. Sci., 1965, PhD in Polit. Sci., 1969. Teaching asst. UCLA, 1966-67, lect., 1969-70; asst. prof. Iowa State U., Ames, 1970-71; assoc. prof. Purdue U., West Lafayette, Ind., 1971-83, prof., head dept. polit. sci., 1987—; vis. scholar Ctr. for European Studies, Harvard U., 1993; vis. asst. prof. Calif. State Coll., Long Beach, 1969-70; vis. prof. UCLA, summers 1984-86, Brigham Young U., Provo, Utah, 1986; chmn. advanced placement test devel. in govt. and politics Coll. Bd., N.Y.C., 1988-93. Author: French Political Parties under the Fifth Republic, 1982, Interest Group Politics in France, 1987, (co-author) Comparative Politics, 1986, 3rd edit., 1995, The Failure of West European Communism, 1993, West European Politics Today, 2nd edit., 1994, Concepts and Issues in Comparative Politics, 1995. Ct. apptd. spl. advocate Tippecanoe County Superior Ct. No. 3, Lafayette, 1988—. Named Frederick Hovde Outstanding Faculty Fellow, Purdue U., 1989; Spencer Found. grantee, Chgo., 1989; Japan Found. grantee, N.Y.C., 1990-93. Fellow Am. Philos. Soc.; mem. Am. Polit. Sci. Assn., Midwest Polit. Sci. Assn., French Politics and Soc. (exec. com.), Coun. European Studies, Phi Beta Kappa (pres. Purdue chpt. 1991-92). Home: 423 Jennings St West Lafayette IN 47906-1147 Office: Purdue U Dept Polit Sci 1363 LAEB West Lafayette IN 47907-1363

WILSON, FRED C., manufacturing company executive; b. 1932. MBA, U. Chgo., 1976. With Caterpillar Tractor Co., East Peoria, Ill., 1950-53, 56-60; with Ingersoll Milling Machine Co., Rockford, Ill., 1960—, project mgr., 1965, chief engr., 1967-71, dir. mktg., 1971-80, gen. mgr. prodn. machinery, 1980-81, v.p., gen. mgr. prodn. machinery, 1981-84, pres., 1984—. Office: Ingersoll Milling Machine Co 707 Fulton Ave Rockford IL 61103-4069*

WILSON, FRED M., II, ophthalmologist, educator; b. Indpls., Dec. 10, 1940; s. Fred Madison and Elizabeth (Fredrick) W.; m. Karen Joy Lyman, Sept. 10, 1959 (div. June 1962); 1 child, Teresa Wilson Kulick; m. Claytonia Leigh Pemberton, Aug. 28, 1964; children: Yvonne Wilson Hacker, Jennifer, Benjamin James. AB in Med. Scis., Ind. U., 1962, MD, 1965. Cert. Am. Bd. Ophthalmology. Intern Sacred Heart Hosp., Spokane, Wash., 1965-66; resident in ophthalmology Ind. U., Indpls., 1968-71, fellow in ophthalmology, 1971-72; fellow in ophthalmology F.I. Proctor Found., San Francisco, 1972-73; from asst. prof. to assoc. prof. ophthalmology Ind. U., Indpls., 1972-76, prof. ophthalmology, 1981—; med. dir. Ind. Lions Eye Bank, Inc., Indpls., 1973—; cons. surgeon Ind. U., Indpls., 1973—. Author or editor numerous sci. articles, book chpts. and books on ophthalmology. Lt. comdr. USNR, 1966-68, PTO. Mem. Am. Acad. Ophthalmology (assoc. sec. 1988-93, Sr. Teaching award 1989), Assn. Proctor Fellows, Soc. Heed Fellows, Am. Ophthalmol. Soc., Am. Bd. Ophthalmology (bd. dirs. 1993—), Ill. Soc. Ophthalmology (hon.), Mont. Acad. Ophthalmology (hon.), Pacific-Coast Ophthalmol. Soc. (hon.). Republican. Methodist. Avocations: photography, guitar, history, language, natural history. Home: 12262 Crestwood Dr Carmel IN 46033 Office: Ind U Sch Medicine Dept Ophthalmolgy 702 Rotary Cir Indianapolis IN 46202

WILSON, FREDERIC SANDFORD, pharmaceutical company executive; b. Schenectady, NY, Mar. 28, 1944; s. Robert Omer and Isabel May (Sandford) W.; children: Amy Kathleen, Adrienne Ann; m. Judith Ann Goettsche, Feb. 7, 1973; children: Marla Ann, Brian Bennett, Jessica Lee, Jennifer Lynn. BS, Syracuse U., 1968. Acct. exec. Mastropaul Design Inc., Syracuse, N.Y., 1969-70; copy editor Norwich Eaton Pharms., Norwich, N.Y., 1970-72; sales rep. Norwich Eaton Pharms., Gary, Ind., 1972-73; asst. product mgr. Norwich Eaton Pharms., Norwich, 1974-75, mktg. svcs. mgr., 1975-76, product mgr., 1977-81, bus. devel. mgr., 1981-83, sr. product mgr., 1983-85, mgr. med. foods, 1986-89; assoc. mktg. mgr. P&G Pharms., Norwich, 1989-92; dir. profl. rels. P & G Pharms., Cin., 1993—; cons. Sandoz Nutrition Corp., Mpls., 1992. Inventor Jejunostomy Kit, 1981, Vivonex T.E.N. med. food, 1983, Tolerex med. food, 1987. Bd. dirs. Syracuse U. Minority Access Program, 1989-91; active Nat. Osteo. and Physician Asst. Found. Mem. Am. Acad. Nurse Practitioners (Pharm. healthcare industry adv. bd.), Pharms. Assn. for Continuing Med. Edn. (treas., membership chmn.). Office: P&G Pharms Sharon Woods Tech Ctr 11520 Reed Hartman Hwy Cincinnati OH 45241

WILSON, FREDERICK ALLEN, medical educator, medical center administrator, gastroenterologist; b. Winchester, Mass., Aug. 22, 1937; s. Warren Archibald and Alice Jane (Springall) W.; m. Lynne Stewart Cantley, Feb. 24, 1962; children: Douglas, Victoria. A.B., Colgate U., 1959; M.D. Albany Med. Coll., 1963. Intern Hartford Hosp., Conn., 1963-64, resident in medicine, 1964-66; fellow in gastroenterology Albany Med. Coll., N.Y., 1966-67; USPHS postdoctoral fellow in gastroenterology U. Tex. Southwestern Med. Sch., Dallas, 1969-72; asst. prof. medicine Vanderbilt U. Sch. Medicine, Nashville, 1972-76, assoc. prof., 1976-82, mem. adv. com. clin. research ctr., 1978-81; prof. medicine, chief div. gastroenterology Milton S. Hershey Med. Ctr., Pa. State U., Hershey, 1982-90; prof. medicine, dir. div. gastroenterology Med. U. S.C., Charleston, 1990-94; mem. ACP Med. Knowledge Self-assessment Program VI, 1980-81; mem. gastroenterology and clin. nutrition rev. group Nat. Inst. Arthritis, Diabetes, Digestive and Kidney Disease, NIH, Bethesda, Md., 1985-89. Contbr. numerous articles, abstracts, chpts. to profl. publs.; reviewer for sci. jours. Served to maj. M.C., U.S. Army, 1967-69. Recipient Clin. Investigator award VA Med. Ctr., Nashville, 1972-75; recipient Investigator award Howard Hughes Med. Inst., Vanderbilt U., 1975-78; NIH Fogarty Internat. Ctr. sr. internat. fellow Max Planck Inst. for Biophysics, Frankfurt, W.Ger., 1979-80. Mem. Am. Fedn. Clin. Research, Central Soc. Clin. Research, Am. Gastroenterology Assn., Am. Assn. Study Liver Diseases, Am. Soc. Clin. Investigation, N.Y. Acad. Scis., Eastern Gut Club, Pa. Soc. Gastroenterology. Office: Med U SC Div Gastroenterology 171 Ashley Ave Charleston SC 29425-0001

WILSON, FREDRIC WOODBRIDGE, musicologist, library curator; b. Point Pleasant, N.J., Sept. 8, 1947; s. Fredric Woodbridge and Ruth Elaine (Chapman) W. BA in Music, Lehigh U., 1969; MS in Musicology, N.Y.U.,

1978. Conductor Wall Chamber Choir, Wall, N.J., 1969-81, Allaire Singers Spring Lake, N.J., 1981—, editor Allaire Music Pubs., Spring Lake, 1980—; curator Gilbert and Sullivan Collection, Pierpont Morgan Library, 1981—; musician, textural cons. Ky. Opera, 1984—, D'Oyly Ark Opera Co., London, 1987—; chmn. 19th Century Musical Theatre in English Conf., 1985. Author and editor books on opera and musical theatre, also exhbn. catalogues; contbr. articles to profl. jours.; pub. over 50 musical editions. Mem. N.E. Assn. Computing in Humanities (pres. 1985—), Am. Textual Scholarship (exec. com. 1985—), Am. Musicol. Soc., Music Library Assn., Theatre Library Assn., Assn. Profl. Vocal Ensembles, Music Pubs. Assn. (bd. dirs. 1987—), Am. Choral Dirs. Assn. Office: Pierpont Morgan Library 29 E 36th St New York NY 10016-3490

WILSON, GAHAN, cartoonist, author; b. Evanston, Ill., Feb. 18, 1930; s. Allen Barnum and Marion (Gahan) W.; m. Nancy Dee Midyette ((Nancy Winters)), Dec. 30, 1966; stepchildren—Randy Winters, Paul Winters. Graduate, Art Inst. Chgo., 1952. Commentator, Nat. Public Radio. Collections include Gahan Wilson's Graveyard Manner, 1965, The Man In the Cannibal Pot, 1967, I Paint What I See, 1971, Weird World of Gahan Wilson, 1975, Gahan Wilson's Cracked Cosmos, 1975, First World Fantasy Collection Anthology, 1977, Gahan Wilson's Favorite Tales of Horror, 1977, And Then We'll Get Him, 1978, Nuts, 1979, Chog: A Gothic Fable, 1980, Is Nothing Sacred, 1982, Wilson's America, 1985, Eddy Deco's First Case, 1987, Playboy's Gahan Wilson, 1980, Eddy Deco's Last Caper, 1989, Still Weird, 1994; juvenile works: Harry, The Fat Bear Spy, 1973, The Bang Bang Family, 1974, Harry and the Sea Serpent, 1976, Harry and the Snow Melting Ray, 1980; editor: First World Fantasy Awards, 1977, The Raven & Other Poems, 1990; illustrator: Matthew Looney & the Space Pirates, 1972, Catch Your Breath: A Book of Shivery Poems, 1973, Granny's Fish Story, 1975, Maria Looney & The Cosmic Circus, 1978, Maria Looney & The Remarkable Robot, 1979, Bob Fulton's Amazing Soda-Pop Stretcher, 1982, Plots & Pans, 1989, How To Be A Guilty Parent, Murder For Christmas, Passport to World Band Radio, 1992, The Keep of Two Moons, 1992, The Keep of Two Moons, 1992, A Night in the Lonesome October, 1993, Credo!: The Game of Dueling Dogmas, 1993, A Night in the Lonesome October, 1993, Spooky Stories For A Dark & Stormy Night, 1994; co-editor: Animals, Animals, Animals, 1979; co-author: The Upside-Down Man, 1977, Hairticklers, 1989, The Devil's Dictionary & Other Works; author: Everybody's Favorite Duck, 1989; animator (movie): Gahan Wilson's Diner, 1993; contbr. to Nat. Lampoon, New Yorker, Collier's, Look, Playboy, Punch, Esquire, Fantasy and Sci. Fiction, Paris Match, Pardon. Mem. Mystery Writers Am., Sci. Fiction Writers Am., Soc. Illustrators, Wolfe Pack, Cartoonists Assn. Commentator, Horror Writers Am. (Life Achievement award 1992), Writers Guild East, Authors Guild, Nat. Public Radio. Office: HMH Pubs care Readers Svc 919 N Michigan Ave Chicago IL 60611-1601*

WILSON, GARY DEAN, lawyer; b. Wichita, Kans., June 7, 1943; s. Glenn E. and Roe Zella (Mills) W.; m. Diane Kay Williams, Dec. 29, 1965; children: Mark R., Matthew C., Christopher G. BA, Stanford U., 1965, LLB, 1968. Bar: D.C. 1970, U.S. Dist. Ct. D.C. 1970, U.S. Ct. Appeals (D.C. cir.) 1972, U.S. Ct. Appeals (7th cir.) 1979, U.S. Ct. Appeals (2d cir.) 1983. Law clk. U.S. Ct. Appeals, 2d cir., N.Y.C., 1968-69, U.S. Supreme Ct., Washington, 1969-70; assoc. Wilmer, Cutler & Pickering, Washington, 1970-75, ptnr., 1976—; acting prof. law Stanford (Calif.) Law Sch., 1981-82. Bd. visitors Stanford Law Sch., 1990-92. Democrat. Home: 4636 30th St NW Washington DC 20008-2127 Office: Wilmer Cutler & Pickering 2445 M St NW Washington DC 20037-1435

WILSON, GARY LEE, airline company executive; b. Alliance, Ohio, Jan. 16, 1940; s. Elvin John and Fern Helen (Donaldson) W.; children: Derek, Christopher. BA, Duke U., 1962; MBA, U. Pa., 1963. V.p. fin. dir. Trans-Philippines Investment Co., Manila, 1964-70; exec. v.p. dir. Checchi & Co., Washington, 1971-73; exec. v.p. Marriott Corp., Washington, 1973-85; exec. v.p., chief exec. officer, dir. The Walt Disney Co., Burbank, Calif., 1985-89, dir., 1990; co-chmn. bd. Northwest Airlines, Inc., St. Paul, Minn., 1990—. *

WILSON, GEORGE LARRY, computer software company executive; b. Greensboro, N.C., July 31, 1946; s. George Thomas and Charlcie (Worrell) W.; m. Patricia Ervin, Jan. 19, 1966; children: Christopher Chadwick, Elizabeth Burns. BS, U. S.C., 1968, MBA, 1970. CPCU; cert. data processor. Sr. v.p. Seibels, Bruce & Co., Columbia, S.C., 1966-81, bd. dirs., 1975—; pres. Policy Mgmt. Systems Corp., Columbia, 1981-85, chmn., 1985—, also bd. dirs.; bd. dirs. LEGENT Corp., Vienna, Va. Bd. dirs. Gov.'s Sch. for Arts, Greenville, S.C., 1988—, Cen. Carolina Community Found., Columbia, 1990—, Cities in Schs., Columbia, 1990—; chmn. Enterprise Devel., Inc., Columbia, 1991—; mem. bd. visitors Heathwood Hall, 1980-85. Recipient Disting. Alumnus award U. S.C. Coll. Bus. Adminstrn., 1985, 5 ann. awards as one of top 3 chief exec. officers in computer software and svcs. industry Wall Street Transcript. Mem. Soc. CPCU's, Summit Club. Republican. Methodist. Avocations: sport fishing, vintage cars. Office: Policy Mgmt Systems Corp PO Box 10 Columbia SC 29202-0010

WILSON, GEORGE MACKLIN, history educator, cultural studies center administrator; b. Columbus, Ohio, Apr. 27, 1937; m. Joyce DeCoster Klain, June 11, 1960; children: George David, Elizabeth Adeline. AB in Politics and Russian Studies, Princeton U., 1958; AM in East Asian Regional Studies, Harvard U., 1960, PhD in History and Far Ea. Langs., 1965. From instr. to asst. prof. history U. Ill., Urbana-Champaign, 1964-67; assoc. prof. history Ind. U., Bloomington, 1967-76, assoc. prof. East Asian langs. and cultures, 1975-76, prof., 1976—; dir. East Asian studies program, 1970-71, 72-73, assoc. dean rsch. and advanced tudies, assoc. dean internat. programs, 1972-75, dean internat. programs office of pres., 1975-78, dir. grad. studies dept. history, 1980-83, acting chair dept. history, 1983-84, summer 1981, summer 1982, dir. East Asian studies ctr., 1987—, dir. Title VI nat. resource ctr. East Asian studies, 1991—; vis. lectr. Japanese history U. Mich., Ann Arbor, 1963-64, summer 1964; vist. asst. prof. history summer sch. arts and scis. Harvard U., 1966, assoc. prof. history summer sch., 1975, rsch. assoc. East Asian rsch. ctr., 1966, 75, 78-79; rsch. assoc. faculty letters Kyoto U., 1971-72, vis. research faculty edn., 1985; mem., chair various coms. Ind. U., mem. bd. advisors East Asian summer lang. inst., 1985—, chair Japan forum, 1990—; cons. internat. divsn. Ford Found., 1974-77, cons. history Midwest univs. consortium internat. activities, 1979-80; mem. rev. panel divsn. pub. programs NEH, 1978-80; mem. adv. screening com. Japan Coun. Internat. Exch. Scholars, 1978-81, chair, 1980-81; mem. adv. panel Annenberg Sch. Comm. and Corp. Pub. Broadcasting, 1982-84; cons. East Asian history Am. Rev., 1985-91; mem. Gov. Robert Orr's Higher Edn. Del. to Ind.'s Sister State, Zhejiang Province, China, 1988; chair U.S.-Japan Bus. Forum, 1988-90; bd. dirs. Ind. Consortium Internat. Programs, 1972-78; Ind. U. mem. bd. dirs. Interuniversity Ctr. Japanese Lang. Studies in Yokohama, 1988—; presenter in field. Author: Radical Nationalist in Japan: Kita Ikki, 1883-1937, 1969, Japanese edit., 1971, Patriots and Redeemers in Japan: Motives in the Meiji Restoration, 1992; editor, contbg. author: Crisis Politics in Prewar Japan: Institutional and Ideological Problems of the 1930s, 1970; Editl. advisor for Japanese and Korean history Encyclopaedia Britannica, 1969—; book manuscript reader U. Hawaii Press, Ind. U. Press, Princeton U. Press; article manuscript evaluator Am. Hist. Rev., Comparative Studies Soc. and History, Jour. Asian History, Jour. Asian Studies; contbr. articles and book revs. to profl. jours. Grantee U. Ill., 1965, Harvard U., 1966, 75, Ind. U., 1967, 68, 72, Am. Philos. Soc., 1968, Am. Coun. Learned Socs., 1971; Grad. Sch. Arts and Scis. fellow Harvard U., 1959-60, Fgn. Area Tng. fellow Ford Found., 1960-63, Fulbright-Hays Sr. fellow, 1971-72, Profl. fellow Japan Found., 1985. Mem. Am. Hist. Assn. (convener 1984 and 1988 ann. meetings, chair conf. Asian history 1989—), Midwest Conf. Asian Affairs (mem. nominating com. 1990-91), Midwest Univs. Consortium Internat. Activities (lic. liaison officer for Ind. U. 1973-78, bd. dirs. 1974-78, sec. corp. 1974-78), Assn. Asian Studies (mem. program com., Japan rep. 1985 ann. meeting), Japan-Am. Soc. Ind., Inc. (founding, mem. steering com. 1987-88, bd. dirs. 1988-93), Hudson Inst. (pub.). Office: Indiana University East Asian Studies Ctr Memorial Hall W Rm 207 Bloomington IN 47405

WILSON, GEORGE PETER, engineer, educator; b. Truro, N.S., Can., Dec. 8, 1939; s. George W. and Madlyn (Merriam) W.; m. Rose Derry Blount, Mar. 17, 1967; children—David, Ian, James, Chris. B.Engring., N.S. Tech. Coll., 1962; diploma engring., Dalhousie U., 1960; M.S., U. Birmingham, Eng., 1964. Registered profl. engr., N.S. Indsl. engr. Can. Nat. Rys., Mon-

treal, Que., 1965-67; dir. Atlantic Indsl. Research Inst., Halifax, N.S., 1972—; prof., head dept. indsl. engring. Tech. U. N.S., Halifax, 1967—; pres. Wilson Fuel Co. Ltd., Truro, N.S., 1976—, Applied Computer Systems Ltd., Truro, 1974—, Wentworth Valley Devels. Ltd, 1987—; bd. dirs. Kerr Controls Ltd., Truro. Contbr. articles on indsl. engring. to profl. jours. Served to lt. Royal Can. Navy Res., 1957-67. Fellow Engring. Inst. Can.; mem. Inst. Indsl. Engrs. (pres. chpt.), Can. Ops. Research Soc., Assn. Profl. Engrs. N.S. Liberal Anglican. Clubs: Wentworth Valley Ski (Halifax) (pres. 1978-80); Shortas Lake Yacht (N.S.) (commodore 1980-82). Office: Atlantic Indsl Rsch Inst, PO Box 1000, Halifax, NS Canada B3J 2X4

WILSON, GEORGE PETER, association executive; b. Perth, Scotland, July 6, 1935; came to U.S., 1985; s. Alan Johnson and Doris L. (Allan) W.; m. Sandra Graham, Feb. 6, 1960 (div. 1984); 1 child, Iain; m. Robbyn Dee LaCroix, Nov. 18, 1984; 1 stepchild, Orion. Diploma in Hotel Mgmt., Scottish Coll. Commerce, Glasgow, 1954. Chartered acct., 1965, cert. internal auditor, 1985. Hotel mgr., auditor Can. Nat. Rys., Ottawa and Montreal, 1956-65; fin. officer Treasury Bd. Can., asst. sec. to Cabinet, dir. Pub. Service Commn., counsellor external affairs Govt. of Can., Ottawa, Geneva, 1965-78; dir. gen. audit UN, N.Y.C., 1978-80; dep. auditor gen. of Can. Govt. of Can., Ottawa, 1980-85; pres. Inst. Internal Auditors, Orlando, Fla., 1985-92; dir. audit FAO UN, Rome, 1992—. Contbr. articles to profl. jours. Mem. Can. Inst. Chartered Accts. (com. mem.), Inst. Internal Auditors (com. mem.), Can. Comprehensive Audit Found. (gov. 1985-88), Internat. Consortium on Govt. Fin. Mgmt. (bd. dirs. 1983-92), Inst. for Fin. Crime Prevention. Home: Via Giulia 98 # 9, 00186 Rome Italy Office: FAO HQ, Viale delle Terme di Caraca, 00100 Rome Italy

WILSON, GEORGE WHARTON, newspaper editor; b. Phila., Feb. 22, 1923; s. Joshua Wharton and Eva (Frear) W.; m. Neva Jean Gossett, Nov. 18, 1950; children: Guy Richard, Lee Robert. B.A., Western Md. Coll., 1947; postgrad., U. Pa., 1948. Reporter, city editor News-Chronicle, Shippensburg, Pa., 1945-46; asst. news dir. Sta. WILM-Radio, Wilmington, Del., 1947-48; sports editor Evening Chronicle, Uhrichsville, Ohio, 1948-49, editor, 1949-50; editor Daily Record, Morristown, N.J., 1950-54; chief editorial writer Standard-Times, New Bedford, Mass., 1954-59; editorial writer Phila. Inquirer, 1959-64, chief editorial writer, 1964-87. Author: Yesterday's Philadelphia, 1975. Served with USAAF, 1942-45. Recipient George Washington honor medal Freedoms Found., 1961, 67, 72; Phila. Press Assn. award editorial writing, 1967, 68; award for editorial writing Pa. Press Assn., 1972, 79; award for editorial writing U.S. Indsl. Council, 1975, 77; Disting. Service award Sigma Delta Chi, 1977; Disting. Journalism award Citizens Com. on Public Edn. in Phila., 1978; Public Service award Phila. Convention and Visitors Bur., 1980; award for column writing N.J. Soc. Profl. Journalists, 1981; Elm award Fishtown Civic Assn., 1982. Mem. Am. Acad. Polit. and Social Sci., Franklin Inst., Acad. Natural Sci., Hist. Soc. Pa., Soc. Profl. Journalists, Phila. Mus. Art, Phila. Maritime Mus., Phila. Writers Orgn., Phila. Zool. Soc., Pa. Soc., Friends of Independence Nat. Hist. Park, Huguenot Hist. Soc., Pa. Acad. Fine Arts, Pen and Pencil Club (Phila.), Elks, Am. Legion. Republican. Congregationalist. Club: Pen and Pencil (Phila.). Home: PO Box 617 Albrightsville PA 18210-0617

WILSON, GEORGE WILTON, economics educator; b. Winnipeg, Man., Can., Feb. 15, 1928; came to U.S., 1952, naturalized, 1970; s. Walter and Ida (Wilton) W.; m. I. Marie McKinney, Sept. 6, 1952 (dec. July 1986); children: Ronald Leslie, Douglas Scott, Suzanne Rita; m. Joan Murdock, May 16, 1988. B.Commerce, Carleton U., Ottawa, Can., 1947-50; M.A., U. Ky., 1951; Ph.D., Cornell U., 1955. Economist Bd. Transp. Commrs., Ottawa, 1951-52; teaching fellow Cornell U., 1952-55; asst. prof. econs. Middlebury (Vt.) Coll., 1955-57; prof. transp. Ind. U., Bloomington, 1957-66; prof. bus. econs., chmn. dept. Ind. U., 1966-70, dean Coll. Arts and Scis., 1970-73, disting. prof. bus. econs., 1978-92, disting. prof. emeritus bus. econs., prof. emeritus econs., 1992; Collaborator study South Asia 20th Century Fund, 1962-65, dir. research Can.'s needs and resources, 1964-65; dir. case studies role transp. in econ. devel. Brookings Instn., 1964, study transport and econ. devel. of Indochina, 1974; mem. Presdl. Task Force Transp., 1964, 68; dir. Transp. Res. Ctr., Ind. U., 1990-92. Author: Essays on Some Unsettled Questions in the Economics of Transportation, 1962, Economic Analysis of Intercity Freight Transportation, 1980, Inflation: Causes, Consequences and Cures, 1982, U.S. Intercity Passenger Transportation Policy, 1930-91, An Interpretive Essay, 1992; co-author: Mathematical Models and Methods in Marketing, 1961, Canada: An Appraisal of Its Needs and Resources, 1965, The Impact of Highway Investment on Development, 1966, Growth and Change at Indiana U, 1966, Transportation on the Prairies, 1968, Asian Drama, 1968, Essays in Economic Analysis and Policy, 1970, Southeast Asian Regional Transport Survey, 1972, Regional Study of the Impact of the Energy Situation on Transport Development, 1983; Editor: Classics of Economic Theory, 1964, Technological Development and Economic Growth, 1971. Recipient A. Davidson Dunton Alumni award Carleton U., Salzberg Hon. Medallion Syracuse U., 1992. Mem. Am. Econ. Assn. (Disting. Mem. award 1986), Transp. Rsch. Forum (pres. 1969, Transp. Rsch. award 1990), Gamma Sigma. Address: RD 3 Box 1132 Butternut Ridge Rd Middlebury VT 05753-8744

WILSON, GERALD EINAR, mechanical and industrial engineer, business executive; b. Newhill, Alta., Can., Mar. 20, 1922; s. Robert E. and Cecelia (Stephenson) W.; m. Helen M. Martens, June 9, 1945. B.A.Sc., U. Toronto, 1950. Registered profl. engr., 8 provinces. Asst. brewmaster John Labatt Ltd., London, Ont., Can., 1950-62; v.p. prodn. Labatt Ont. Breweries, 1962-64; v.p. engring. John Labatt Ltd., 1964-69, v.p. engring. services, 1969-85, v.p., 1986-87, retired; pres. Carpools Environ. Protection Services Ltd., 1977—. Patentee solar quilt, continuous separator, others. Bd. dirs. Ont.a Environ. Assessment Bd., 1977-83; chmn. Boys and Girls Club Found., London; bd. dirs. Boys and Girls Clubs, Can., Heritage London Found. Served to 1st lt. RCAF, 1942-45. Decorated D.F.C., others. Mem. Assn. Profl. Engrs., Engring. Inst. Can., Master Brewers Assn., Internat. C. of C. Conservative. Anglican. Clubs: London Hunt (London); Union (Victoria, B.C.). Lodge: Royal Can. Legion (pres. 1981-82). Home: Sir Adam Beck Suite, 240 Sydenham St, London, ON Canada N6A 1W5

WILSON, GERALD LOOMIS, electrical engineer, college dean; b. Springfield, Mass., Apr. 29, 1939; s. Benjamin J. and Theresa Wilson; m. Marian Saunders, June 11, 1958; children: Daniel Scott, Karen Elizabeth, Marjorie Ruth, David Owen. BS, MIT, 1961, MS, 1963, ScD, 1965. Asst. prof. MIT, Cambridge, Mass., 1965-70, assoc. prof., 1970-76, dir. electric power systems engring. lab., 1971-78, Philip Sporn prof. energy processing, 1973-81, Vennevar Bush prof. engring., 1982—, prof., 1976—, head dept. elec. engring. and computer sci., 1978-81, dean Sch. Engring., 1981-91; cons. in field. Ford Found. fellow, 1965-67. Fellow IEEE (Hickernell award 1971); mem. NAE, Am. Nat. Standards Inst., Am. Phys. Soc., Sigma Xi. Office: MIT 4-405 Cambridge MA 02139

WILSON, GLEN PARTEN, association administrator; b. Waco, Tex., Dec. 10, 1922; s. Glen P. and Hazel (Parnell) W.; m. Alice B. Groves, Dec. 19, 1982. BS in Aero. Engring., U. Tex., Austin, 1943, MA in Psychology, 1948, PhD in Psychology, 1952. Engr. Lockheed Aircraft Co., Burbank, Calif., 1943-44; teaching fellow, rsch. asst., instr. U. Tex., Austin, 1946-52; rsch. psychologist USAF, Lackland AFB, Tex., 1952-53; gen. mgr. Tex. Ednl. Devices Co., Austin, 1953-54; asst. to Senator Lyndon B. Johnson Washington, 1955-57; staff Senate Preparedness Investigating Subcom. and Senate Spl. Com. on Space and Astronautics, Washington, 1957-59; chief clk., profl. staff mem. Senate Com. on Aero. and Space Scis., Washington, 1959-77; cons. Washington, 1977-79; spl. asst. for student activities NASA, Washington, 1979-80, acting dir. acad. affairs div., 1980-82; pres. Marie D. and Glen P. Wilson Found., Washington, 1982-87; exec. dir. Nat. Space Soc., Washington, 1984-88, exec. dir. emeritus, 1988—; lectr. on aero. and space programs, Senate orgn.; sci. policy, tech. assessment, student activities, space activism. Participant as staff passage of Nat. Aeros. and Space Act, 1958, Communications Satellite Act, 1962, NASA Authorization Acts, 1958-77; editor Policy Planning for Aeronautical Rsch. and Devel., Senate Document 90, 89th Congress, 1966; developer NASA shuttle student involvement program, 1980, space edn. prog., 1984—. With USN, 1944-46. Recipient Exceptional Svc. medal NASA, 1981; Nat. Space Soc. Hdqrs. renamed The Glen P. Wilson Internat. Space Ctr., 1988. Mem. AIAA (spl. presdl. citation 1976), Am. Astro. Soc., AAAS, Nat. Space Soc., Internat. Acad. of Astronautics, Sigma Xi, Nat. Space Club, Cosmos Club. Home: 433 New Jersey Ave SE Washington DC 20003-4034 Office: 922 Pennsylvania Ave SE Washington DC 20003-2140

WILSON, GLENN, economist, educator; b. East St. Louis, Ill., Feb. 4, 1929; s. Herschel and Regina (Hayes) W.; m. Helen Janice O'Dell, Jan. 28, 1951; children—David, Thomas, Ann. B.A., U. Okla., 1951; M.A., 1952. Administr., Welfare and Retirement Fund United Mine Workers, Pitts., Knoxville, Tenn., 1952-58; dir. med. care research Nationwide Ins. Co. Columbus, 1958-62; exec. dir. Community Health Found., Cleve., 1962-68; exec. v.p. Kaiser Community Health Found., Cleve., 1968-69; assoc. dean U. N.C. Med. Sch., Chapel Hill, 1970-88, prof. dept. social medicine, 1977—, chmn. dept., 1977-89; cons. Sault Ste. Marie and Dist. Group Health Assn.; health adv. Mayor Stokes, Cleve., 1967-69. Contbr. articles to profl. jours. Home: 214 Glandon Dr Chapel Hill NC 27514-3816 Office: U NC Med Sc Dept Social Medicine Chapel Hill NC 27514

WILSON, GRAHAM MCGREGOR, energy company executive; b. Kilwinning, Scotland, Aug. 2, 1944; s. Peter and Jessie (Scott) W.; m. Josee Perrault; children: Stefanie, Richard, Patrick. BS, McGill U., Montreal, Que., Can., 1967; MBA, U. Western Ont., London, Can., 1969. Investment analyst Greenshields Inc., 1969-72; asst. treas. Genstar, 1972-74; various fin. positions, v.p. fin. MacMillan Bloedel Ltd., Vancouver, B.C., Can., 1974-83; v.p. fin. and adminstrn. Petro-Can. Inc., Calgary, Alta., 1983-88; exec. v.p., CFO Westcoast Energy Inc., Vancouver, 1988—; bd. dirs. Foothills Pipe Lines Ltd., Calgary, Pacific No. Gas Ltd., Vancouver, Pacific Coast Energy Corp., Vancouver, Westcoast Power Inc., Vancouver, Westcoast Gas Svcs., Calgary, Centra Gas Inc., Toronto, Ont., Centra Gas Alta., Inc., Leduc Contra Gas B.C. Inc., Victoria, Itron Inc., Spokane, Wash., Union Gas Ltd., Chatham, Ont., Union Energy Inc., Chatham, Westcoast Energy Internat. Inc., B.C. Internat. Power Group, Lake Superior Power Inc., Can. China Bus. Coun., Ottawa, ICS Internat. Avocations: squash, golf. Office: Westcoast Energy Inc Park Pl, 666 Burrard St Ste 3400, Vancouver, BC Canada V6C 3M8

WILSON, H(AROLD) FRED(ERICK), chemist, research scientist; b. Columbiana, Ohio, Aug. 15, 1922; s. Lloyd Ralph and Erma Rebecca (Frederick) W.; m. Alice Marjorie Steer, Aug. 20, 1949; children: Janice, Deborah, James, Kathleen. B.A., Oberlin Coll., 1947; Ph.D., U. Rochester, 1950. With Rohm & Haas Co., Phila., 1950-83; beginning as rsch. scientist, successively lab. head, rsch. supr., asst. dir., assoc. dir., dir. rsch. Rohm & Haas Co., 1950-74, v.p., 1974-83, chief sci. officer, from 1981; now with Wilson Assocs., Cape May, N.J.; mem. U.S. nat. com. IUPAC, 1977-84, vice chmn., 1980-82, chmn., 1982-84, fin. com., 1979-89, chmn., 1981-89; chmn. I.R.I. Research Corp., 1980-82, dir., 1979-82. Served to 1st lt. USAAF, 1942-46. Decorated Air Medal. Mem. Am. Chem. Soc., AAAS, Soc. Chem. Industry, Dirs. Indsl. Research. Patentee in field. Home: 214 Gilmore Ave Merchantville NJ 08109-2531 Office: Wilson Assocs 24 Congress St Cape May NJ 08204-5308

WILSON, HARRY BURGOYNE, retired public relations company executive; b. St. Louis, Mar. 17, 1917; s. H. Burgoyne and Margaret (Drew) W.; m. Helen Cain, July 27, 1940 (dec. Oct. 1983); children: Margaret Wilson Pennington, Harry B., Andrew B., Daniel B. Josephine Wilson Havlak, Julie Wilson Sakellariadis, Ellen Wilson Shumway; m. Mary Virginia Peisch, Apr. 7, 1984. Ph.B., St. Louis U., 1938. Mng. editor Sedalia (Mo.) Capital, 1939-40; reporter Kansas City Star; also state capital bur. chief St. Louis Globe-Democrat, 1940-42, polit. writer, columnist, 1946-52; corr. Business Week mag., 1948-52; with Fleishman-Hillard Inc., St. Louis, 1953; sr. ptnr. Fleishman-Hillard Inc., 1964-70, pres., 1970-74, chmn. bd., 1974-88, sr. ptnr., 1989-92. Bd. dirs. St. Louis Family Support Network. With USNR, 1942-46. Home: # 901 625 S Skinker Saint Louis MO 63105-2340

WILSON, HARRY COCHRANE, clergyman; b. St. John, N.B., Can., May 31, 1945; s. Harry Shepherd and Gertrude (Cochrane) W.; m. Gloria Lea Trites, Oct. 8, 1965; children: Troy Spurgeon, Kristi Lea. BA, Bethany Bible Coll., 1972, DD (hon.), 1988; DD (hon.), Cen. Wesleyan Coll., S.C., 1989. Br. exec. Can. Permanent Trust Co., Monton, N.B., 1965-70; pastor Wesleyan Ch., Blacks Harbor, N.B., 1971-74, Dartmouth, N.S., Can., 1974-80; dist. supt. Delta dist. Wesleyan Ch., Jackson, Miss., 1981-88; bd. adminstr. Wesleyan Ch., Indpls., 1988—; Sunday schs. Wesleyan Ch. World Hdqrs., Marion, Ind., 1980-81; gen. supt. Wesleyan Ch. Internat. Ctr., Indpls., 1988—. Author: The Wesleyan Advocate, 1992, Seize the Day-Your Church Can Thrive, 1992. Active A.D. 2000, Heritage USA. Recipient Pastor's award Atlantic Dist., 1975, 77. Mem. Nat. Assn. Evangs., World Meth. Coun. Office: Internat Ctr Wesleyan Ch 6060 Castleway West Dr Indianapolis IN 46250-1969

WILSON, HARRY L., lawyer; b. Hutchinson, Kans., Dec. 13, 1942. BA summa cum laude, Mich. State U., 1970; JD, U. Mich., 1973. Bar: Ill. 1973. Ptnr. Clausen Miller Gorman Caffrey & Witous P.C., Chgo. Office: Clausen Miller Gorman Caffrey & Witous PC 10 S LaSalle St Chicago IL 60603-1098

WILSON, HENRY ARTHUR, JR., management consultant; b. Detroit, June 12, 1939; s. Henry Arthur and Ruth (Scott) W.; m. Mildred Rendell, June 17, 1961; 1 child, Suzanne. B.S., Mich. Luth. Coll., 1968; M.A., U. Detroit, 1976. Police officer Grosse Pointe Park Police Dept., Mich., 1960-68; v.p. Uniflight, Inc., St. Clare Shore, Mich., 1968-73; coordinator Criminal Justice Inst., Detroit, 1973-76; ptnr. Grant Thorton (formerly Alexander Grant & Co.), Detroit, 1976-92, BW Assocs., 1992—. Author: Michigan Harbors/Ports 1985, 1985; Masonic Etiquette and Protocol, 1985. Sponsor Ebenhardt re-election, Detroit, 1984—; usher St. Columba Episcopal Ch., Detroit, 1976—. Served with USAF, 1957-60. Mem. Certified Data Processing Auditors Assn., Masons (grand master Mich. 1984-85). Republican. Avocation: boating. Office: 1022 Nottingham Rd Grosse Pointe MI 48230-1332

WILSON, HERMAN T., JR., agricultural products supplier; b. 1941. Food divsn. mgr. Granada Corp., Houston, 1986-88; chmn., co-founder Western Farm Svc. Inc., Fresno, Calif., 1988—. Office: Western Farm Svc Inc 3705 W Beechwood Fresno CA 93711*

WILSON, HUGH SHANNON, retired manufacturing company executive, consultant; b. Bklyn., July 1, 1926; s. Matthew and Margaret (Shannon) W.; m. Rita Vigliarolo, Feb. 14, 1953; children: Noel C. Wilson Fillers, Hugh V., Hugh S., Hugh T. BSChemE, Pratt Inst., 1951. Registered profl. engr., Calif., chartered engr., Eng. With Moore Products Co., 1951—; br. mgr. Moore Products Co., Chgo., 1953-55, Wilmington, Del., 1955-62; mgr. chem. internat. Moore Products Co., 1966-72, internat. sales mgr., 1972-78, v.p. internat. ops., 1979-92; founder Wilcon Internat. Consultants, 1992. Served with USAAF, 1945. Fellow Instrument Soc. Am. (hon., pres. 1978-79), Inst. Measurement Control. Home: 903 Parkview Dr A 303 King of Prussia PA 19406

WILSON, HUGH STEVEN, lawyer; b. Paducah, Ky., Nov. 27, 1947; s. Hugh Gipson and Rebekah (Dunn) W.; m. Clare Maloney, Apr. 28, 1973; children: Morgan Elizabeth, Zachary Hunter, Samuel Gipson. BS, Ind. U., 1968; JD, U. Chgo., 1971; LLM, Harvard U., 1972. Bar: Calif. 1972, U.S. Dist. Ct. (cen. dist.) Calif. 1972, U.S. Dist. Ct. (so. dist.) Calif. 1973, U.S. Ct. Appeals (9th cir.) 1975, U.S. Dist. Ct. (no. dist.) Calif. 1977, U.S. Dist. Ct. (ea. dist.) 1980. Assoc. Latham & Watkins, Los Angeles, 1972-78, ptnr., 1978—. Trustee Greater L.A. Zoo Assn. Recipient Jerome N. Frank prize U. Chgo. Law Sch., 1971. Mem. ABA, L.A. County Bar Assn., Order of Coif, Calif. Club, Jonathan Club. Republican. Avocations: lit., zoology.

WILSON, IAN EDWIN, cultural organization administrator, archivist; b. Montreal, Que., Can., Apr. 2, 1943; s. Andrew and Marion (Mundy) W.; m. Ruth Dyck, Mar. 24, 1979. BA, Queen's U., Kingston, Ont., 1968, MA History, 1974. Archivist Queen's U., Kingston, Ont., Can., 1966-76; provincial archivist Sask. (Can.) Archives, 1976-86; archivist of Ont. Ont. Govt., Toronto, 1986—; dir. gen. info. resource mgmt. divsn. Ministry Culture, Tourism and Recreation, Toronto, 1990-93; sec. Kingston Hist. Soc. 1967-72, v.p., 1972-76; chair cons. group Social Sci. and Humanities Rsch. Coun. Can., Ottawa, 1979-80; adj. prof. Faculty Info. Studies U. Toronto, 1993—; spkr. in field. Author: (with J. Douglas Stewart) Heritage Kingston,

1973, (with J. William Brennan) Regina Before Yesterday, 1978; editor Kingston City Hall, 1975; contbr. articles to profl. jours., encys. Chmn. congregation Mennonite Ch., Regina, 1981-84; mem. Sask. Award Merit Selection com., 1985-86; chair Sask. Heritage adv. bd., 1978-83, mem. 1983-86. Recipient Queen Elizabeth II silver jubilee medal, 1977, W.G. Leland cert. commendation Soc. Am. Archivists, 1981, W. Kaye Lamb prize Assn. Can. Archivists, 1983; Woodrow Wilson hon. fellow, 1967. Mem. Assn. Can. Archivists (various com., editl. bd. 1986-88), Ont. Hist. Soc. (exec. coun. 1970-73, v.p. 1973-75, pres. 1975-76), Can. Hist. Assn. (past chmn., vice chmn., pres. archives sect. 1982-84), Champlain Soc. (bd. dirs., v.p. 1989-95, pres. 1995—), Sask. Mus. Assn., Sask. History and Folklore Soc., Sask. Geneal Soc., Soc. Hist. de Sask. (bd. dirs., spkr.). Home: 249 Woburn Ave, Toronto, ON Canada M5M 1L1 Office: Archives of Ontario, 77 Grenville St, Toronto, ON Canada M7A 2R9

WILSON, IAN HOLROYDE, management consultant, futurist; b. Harrow, England, June 16, 1925; came to U.S., 1954; s. William Brash and Dorothy (Holroyde) W.; m. Page Tuttle Hedden, Mar. 17, 1951 (div. Dec. 1983); children: Rebecca, Dorothy, Ellen, Holly, Alexandra; m. Adrianne Marcus, July 12, 1992. MA, Oxford U., 1948. Orgn. cons. Imperial Chem. Industries, London, 1948-54; various staff exec. positions in strategic planning, mgmt. devel. Gen. Electric Co., Fairfield, Conn., 1954-80; sr. cons. to maj. U.S. and internat. cos. SRI Internat., Menlo Park, Calif., 1980-93; prin. Wolf Enterprises, San Rafael, Calif., 1993—; exec. in residence Va. Commonwealth U., Richmond, 1976. Author: Planning for Major Change, 1976, The Power of Strategic Vision, 1991, Rewriting the Corporate Social Charter, 1992, Managing Strategically in the 1990s, 1993; mem. editorial bd. Planning Rev., Oxford, Ohio, 1973-81; Am. editor Long Range Planning Jour., London, 1981-89; sr. editor Planning Review, 1993—. Mem. adv. bd. Technol. Forecasting and Social Change, 1989—; chmn. Citizen's Long Range Ednl. Goals Com., Westport, Conn., 1967-70; mem. strategic process com. United Way of Am., Alexandria, Va., 1985-94. Capt. Brit. Army, 1943-45, ETO. Mem. AAAS, Planning Forum, World Future Soc. Unitarian. Avocations: camping, writing, photography. Office: 79 Twin Oaks Ave San Rafael CA 94901-1915

WILSON, IAN ROBERT, food company executive; b. Pietermaritzburg, South Africa, Sept. 22, 1929; s. Brian J. and Edna C. W.; m. Susan Diana Lasch, Jan. 14, 1970; children: Timothy Robert, Christopher James, Diana Louise, Jason Luke. B.Commerce, U. Natal, South Africa, 1952; postgrad., Harvard U. Bus. Sch., 1968. With Coca-Cola Export Corp., Johannesburg, South Africa, 1956-74; mgr. Coca-Cola Export Corp., 1969-72, v.p., regional mgr., 1972-73, area mgr., 1973; pres., chief exec. officer Coca-Cola Ltd., Toronto, Ont., Can., 1974-76; chmn. bd. Coca-Cola Ltd., 1976-81; exec. v.p. Coca-Cola Co., Atlanta, 1976-79; vice chmn. Coca-Cola Co., 1979-81, pres. Pacific group; dir. Coca-Cola Export Corp., Atlanta, 1976-81; pres., chief exec. officer, dir. Castle & Cooke, Inc., San Francisco, 1983-84, Wyndham Foods, Inc., 1985-89; chmn. bd., chief exec. officer Windmill Corp., San Francisco, 1989-94; mng. ptnr. Dartford Partnership and Induna Ptnrs., San Francisco, 1993—; also bd. dirs. Dartford Partnership and Induna Ptnrs.; bd. dirs. Novell Inc., Golden State Foods, Inc., Egoli Ptnrs., New Age Beverages Ltd., U.S./Asean Coun., East-West Ctr. Mem. Church of Eng. Clubs: Durban Country and Johannesburg Country, Inanda Hunt and Polo, Atlantic Salmon, San Francisco Golf, Pacific Union, Burlingame Country. Home: 945 Green St San Francisco CA 94133-3639 Office: Dartford Partnership 801 Montgomery St Ste 400 San Francisco CA 94133-5162

WILSON, J. PARRISH, religious organization administrator. Chmn. Education Bd. of the Nat. Baptist Convention, USA, Saginaw, Mich. Office: Education Bd 19 Commons West Ct Saginaw MI 48603

WILSON, J. STEVEN, lumber company executive; b. 1943. BS, U. N.C. 1966; MBA, Ga. State U., 1970. With First Nat. Bank, Atlanta, 1968-73, The Charter Co., 1973-80; pres., chmn. CEO Riverside Group Inc., 1979—; pres. Wilson Fin. Co., 1989—; CEO Wickes Lumber, Vernon Hills, Ill., 1991—. Office: Wickes Lumber 706 Deerpath Dr Vernon Hills IL 60061

WILSON, J. TYLEE, business executive; b. Teaneck, N.J., June 18, 1931; s. Eric J. and Florence Q. W.; m. Patricia F. Harrington, July 17, 1970; children: Jeffrey J., Debra L., Christopher F. A.B., Lafayette Coll., 1953. Group v.p., dir. Chesebrough-Pond's Inc., 1960-74; pres., chief exec. officer RJR Foods, Inc., 1974-76; chmn., chief exec. officer R.J. Reynolds Tobacco Internat. Inc., Winston-Salem, N.C., 1976-78; exec. v.p. RJR Nabisco, Inc. (formerly R.J. Reynolds Industries Co., Inc.), Winston-Salem, N.C., 1976-79; pres. R.J. Reynolds Tobacco Internat., Inc., Winston-Salem, 1979-83; chmn., chief exec. officer RJR Nabisco Inc. (formerly R.J. Reynolds Industries. Co., Inc.), Winston-Salem, 1984-87; bd. dirs. Bell South Corp., Carolina Power & Light Co. With U.S. Army, 1954-56. Mem. Piedmont Club, Old Town Club, River Club, Marsh Landing Country, Epping Forest Yacht Club, Ponte Vedra Club, Elk River Club. Office: PO Box 2057 Ponte Vedra Beach FL 32004

WILSON, JACK, aeronautical engineer; b. Sheffield, Yorkshire, Eng., Jan. 5, 1933; came to U.S., 1956; s. George and Nellie (Place) W.; m. Marjorie Reynolds, June 3, 1961 (div. Jan. 1991); children: Tanya Ruth, Cara. BS in Engring., Imperial Coll., London, 1954; MS in Aero. Engring., Cornell U. 1958, PhD in Aero. Engring., 1962. Sr. scientific officer Royal Aircraft Establishment, Farnborough, Eng., 1962-63; prin. rsch. sci. Avco-Everett Rsch. Lab., Everett, Mass., 1963-72; vis. prof. Inst. de Mecanique des Fluides, Marseille, France, 1972-73; sr. scientist U. Rochester (N.Y.), 1973-80; sr. rsch. assoc. Sohio/BP Am., Cleve., 1980-90; sr. engring. specialist Sverdrup Tech. Inc., Cleve., 1990-93, NYMA, Brook Park, 1994—. Author: (chpt.) "Gas Lasers" of Applied Optics in Engineering VI, 1980, "Laser Sources" of Techniques in Chemistry XVII, 1982; contbr. articles to profl. jours. Mem. AIAA (sr., mem. tech. com. 1991-92). Achievements include first to demonstrate gas-dynamic laser; patent in application of high speed flow to gas laser media; patent in devel. of antimony dopant sources; measurement of air ionization rate at very high speeds. Office: NYMA 2001 Aerospace Pkwy Brook Park OH 44142

WILSON, JACK FREDRICK, retired federal government official; b. Salt Lake City, Apr. 2, 1920; s. John Lorimer and Mayme J. (James) W.; m. Gwendolyn Gwynn, Nov. 20, 1947; children—Wendy, Elaine, Barbara Ann, Laurel, John F. Jr., James C. B.S., Brigham Young U., 1942; postgrad., Mont. State U., 1962, Pa. State U., 1965. Range conservationist Bur. Land Mgmt., Rawlins, Wyo., 1949-57; dist. mgr. Bur. Land Mgmt., Burley, Idaho, 1957-67; dist. and land office mgr. Bur. Land Mgmt., Riverside, Calif., 1967-72; dir. Boise Interagy. Fire Ctr., Idaho, 1972-81; dir. Office Aircraft Services U.S. Dept. Interior, Boise, 1981-87; dir. Boise Interagy. Fire Ctr., 1987-92, ret., 1992. Contbr. articles to profl. jours. Dir. county disaster com. ARC, 1982-88. Maj. USAF, 1942-47. Recipient Meritorious award U.S. Dept. Interior, 1976, Disting. Service award, 1981, EEO Performance award, 1985; Outstanding Contbn. to Fire Mgmt. award U.S. Dept. Agr. Forest Service, 1976. Mem. Soc. Am. Foresters (chmn. fire com. 1980-82), Am. Soc. Range Mgmt. (sec. pres. 1967), So. Calif. Assn. Foresters and Fire Wardens, Lions (sec. 1954-57), Rotary. Mem. Ch. of Jesus Christ of Latter-day Saints. Avocations: long range weather forecasting, reading, golf. Home: 1820 Sunrise Rim Rd Boise ID 83705-5138

WILSON, JACK MARTIN, university administrator, scientific association executive, physics educator; b. Camp Atterbury, Ind., June 29, 1945; s. Jack Maurer and Ruth L. (Leiseder) W.; m. Judi Chang, Aug. 18, 1990; children: John, Jessica; children from previous marriage: Erika, Gretchen. A.B., Thiel Coll., Greenville, Pa., 1967; M.A., Kent State U., 1970, Ph.D., 1972. Assoc. prof. physics Sam Houston State U., Huntsville, Tex., 1972-80; chmn. dept. physics Sam Houston State U., Huntsville, 1980-81, chmn. div. chemistry and physics, 1981-82; prof. physics U. Md., College Park, 1984-90, co-dir. univ. project in physics and ednl. tech.; dir. Anderson Ctr. for Innovation in Undergrad. Edn. Rensselaer Poly. Inst., Troy, N.Y., 1990—, dean undergrad. cont. edu., 1995—; mem. U.S. com. Internat. Union Pure and Applied Physics, Washington, 1984-90, IBM consulting schlar., 1992—; dir. U.S. team in Internat. Physics Olympia, 1985-90. Editor: Teacher Institutes and Workshops, 1984, The Education of the Physicist, 1985; also articles in field. Recipient Computers in Physics award Dept. Edn., Washington, 1985; Physics Teaching Resource Agents award NSF, 1985; Developing Student

Confidence award Exxon Edn. Found., 1983; grantee various fed. agys. and pvt. founds. Mem AAAS, Am. Assn. Physics Tchrs. (exec. officer 1982-90), Am. Phys. Soc. (edn. com. 1982—), Am. Inst. Physics (governing bd. 1984-91), Sigma Xi (del., rsch. award 1972). Office: Rensselaer Poly Inst Undergrad Cont Edn CII 4011 Troy NY 12180

WILSON, JAMES ERNEST, petroleum consultant, writer; b. McKinney, Tex., Apr. 19, 1915; s. James Ernest and Agnes (Neill) W.; m. Elloie Barkely, Apr. 4, 1940; children: Judith Wilson Grant, Elizabeth Wilson. BS, Tex. A&M U., 1937. Surface geologist Shell Oil Co., Tex., 1938-41, various positions, 1945-59, v.p., Houston, New Orleans and Denver, 1959-73; cons., Denver, 1973—. Trustee and chmn. Am. Assn. Petroleum Geologists Found., 1975-79; trustee Children's Hosp. Denver, 1970-83, Denver Symphony, 1968-82, Inst. Internat. Edn., Denver, 1968-82; mem. Bd. University Park Meth. Ch., 1968—. Maj. U.S. Army, 1941-45; ETO. Recipient Geosciences and Earth Resources medal Tex. A&M, 1986, Disting. Alumnus, 1991. Fellow Geol. Soc. Am., Soc. Petroleum Engrs., Am. Assn. Petroleum Geologists (hon., recipient Sidney Powers Meml. medal, 1988). Republican. Methodist. Clubs: Cherry Hill Country (Denver); Confrerie des Chevaliers du Tastevin (pres. 1983-93, grand officier honoraire). Home: 4248 S Hudson Pky Englewood CO 80110-5015

WILSON, JAMES F., pharmaceutical executive; b. 1943. BA, U. Ariz., 1966, MBA, 1968. With Syntex USA Inc., Palo Alto, Calif., 1968-82, pres., CEO, 1992—; CEO Lifescan, Inc., Milpitas, Calif., 1989—; chmn, CEO Neurex Corps., Menlo Park, Calif., 1989-91. Office: Syntex USA Inc 3401 Hillview Ave Palo Alto CA 94304-1320*

WILSON, JAMES HARGROVE, JR., lawyer; b. Oliver, Ga., Nov. 26, 1920; s. James Hargrove and Louise (Sealy) W.; m. Frances Audra Schaffer, Dec. 24, 1942 (dec. Nov. 1990); children: Susan Frances, James Hargrove. A.B. with honors, Emory U., 1940; LL.B. summa cum laude, Harvard U., 1947. Bar: Ga. 1947, D.C. 1951. Assoc. firm Sutherland, Tuttle & Brennan (now Sutherland, Asbill & Brennan), Atlanta and Washington, 1947-53, ptnr., 1953—; lectr. Emory U., 1959, chmn. bd. visitors, 1967-68; trustee The Northwestern Mut. Life Ins. Co., Milw., 1972-91; mem. advisory group Commr. of Internal Revenue, 1963-64. Pres.: Harvard Law Review, 1946-47. Chmn. bd. trustees Met. Atlanta Crime Commn., 1970-71; mem. Harvard U. Overseers Com. to Visit Law Sch., 1959-65; trustee Emory U., 1983-90, trustee emeritus, 1990—. Served to lt. comdr. USNR, 1942-46. Fellow Am. Bar Found., Am. Coll. Tax Counsel; mem. ABA, State Bar Ga., D.C. Bar, Atlanta Bar Assn., Am. Law Inst. (coun. 1974—), Lawyers Club Atlanta (pres. 1960-61), Am. Judicature Soc., Harvard Law Sch. Assn. (coun. 1981-85), Emory U. Alumni Assn. (pres. 1966-67), Capital City Club, Piedmont Driving Club, Commerce Club, Peachtree Club, Phi Beta Kappa, Omicron Delta Kappa, Kappa Alpha. Methodist. Home: 3171 Marne Dr NW Atlanta GA 30305-1931 Office: Sutherland Asbill & Brennan 999 Peachtree St NE Ste 2300 Atlanta GA 30309-3996

WILSON, JAMES L., superintendent. Supt. Cape Henlopen Sch. Dist., Lewes, Del. Recipient State Finalist for Nat. Supt. of Yr. award, 1992. Office: Cape Henlopen Sch Dist Adminstry Office 1270 Kings Hwy Lewes DE 19958

WILSON, JAMES LAWRENCE, chemical company executive; b. Rosedale, Miss., Mar. 2, 1936; s. James Lawrence and Mary Margaret (Klingman) W.; m. Barbara Louise Burroughs, Aug. 30, 1958; children: Lawrence Burroughs, Alexander Elliott. B.Mech. Engring., Vanderbilt U., 1958; M.B.A., Harvard, 1963. Vice pres. Naugatuck Properties, Inc., Phila., 1963-65; staff assoc. Rohm & Haas Co., Phila., 1965-67; exec. asst. to pres. Rohm & Haas Co., 1971-72, treas., 1972-74; regional dir. Rohm & Haas Co., Europe, 1974-77; group v.p. Rohm & Haas Co., 1977-86, vice-chmn., 1986-88, chmn., CEO, 1988—; treas. Warren-Teed Pharms., Inc., Columbus, Ohio, 1967-68, v.p., 1969; pres. Consol. Biomed. Labs., Inc., Dublin, Ohio, 1970-71; bd. dirs. Rohm and Haas Co., Vanguard Group Investment Cos., Cummins Engine Co., Inc. Co-author: Creative Collective Bargaining, 1964. Trustee Vanderbilt U., 1987—, Culver Ednl. Found., 1988—; chmn. Phila. High Sch. Acads., 1989—. Office: Rohm & Haas Co 100 Independence Mall W Philadelphia PA 19106

WILSON, JAMES LEE, retired geology educator, consultant; b. Waxahachie, Tex., Dec. 1, 1920; s. James Burney and Hallie Christine (Hawkins) W.; m. Della I. Moore, May 8, 1944; children: James Lee Jr., Burney Grant, Dale Ross (dec.). Student, Rice U., 1938-40; BA, U. Tex., 1942, MA, 1944; PhD, Yale U., 1949. Geologist Carter Oil Co., Tulsa, 1943-44; asst. and assoc. prof. U. Tex., Austin, 1949-52; rsch. geologist Shell Devel. Co., Houston, 1952-66; prof. Rice U., Houston, 1966-79, U. Mich., Ann Arbor, 1979-86; geol. cons. New Braunfels, Tex., 1986—; cons. Erico Corp., London, 1985-88, Masera Corp., Tulsa, 1988—, Coyote Geol. Svcs., Boulder, Col., 1990—; adj. prof. Rice U., 1986—. Author: Carbonate Facies in Geologic History, 1975; contbr. articles to tech. jours. With C.E., U.S. Army, 1944-46, Italy. Grantee NSF. Mem. Am. Assn. Petroleum Geologists (hon.), Internat. Sedimentological Soc., Soc. Econ. Paleontology and Minerology (pres. 1972-73, field trip guide books 1989), Paleontological Soc. West Tex. Geol. Soc., South Tex. Geol. Soc., Can. Soc. Petroleum Geologists. Avocations: piano, languages. Home and Office: 1316 Patio Dr New Braunfels TX 78130-8505

WILSON, JAMES MILTON, III, bank executive; b. Newport News, Va., Feb. 17, 1934; s. James Milton, Jr. and Pearle (Forrest) W.; m. Jacqueline Rose Willingham, Aug. 19, 1962 (div. 1969); 1 child, James Milton IV; m. Peggy Ann Lowell, Nov. 21, 1992. B.A., U. Richmond, 1955, M.S., 1963. Sales rep. Met. Life Ins., Newport News, 1956-58; personnel officer Crestar Fin Corp, Richmond, 1959-70, sr. v.p., human resources dir., 1970-85; exec. v.p., human resources dir. Crestar Fin Corp, 1985—; adj. faculty U. Richmond, 1969-92. Bd. dirs. St. John's Hosp., Inc., Richmond, 1983-89, pers. com., planning com., 1983-89; bd. dirs. Family and Children's Service, Richmond, 1975-82; mem. Rector's Club, U. Richmond, 1982—, human resources com. St. Mary' Health Corp., 1988-89; chmn. Va. Banker's Assn. Sch. Bank Mgmt., 1989-90. 2d lt. USAF, 1955-56. Williams fellow, 1958. Mem. Richmond Met. C. of C. (chmn. edn. com. 1984-85), Internat. Transactional Analysis Assn., Soc. for Human Resources Mgmt. (bd. dirs. 1983, chmn. region IV conf. 1983), Nat. Speakers Assn., Pers. Accreditation Inst. (sr. profl. in human resources), Bull and Bear Club. Baptist. Office: Crestar Fin Corp 919 E Main St Richmond VA 23219-4625

WILSON, JAMES NEWMAN, retired laboratory executive; b. San Diego, Aug. 28, 1927; s. Jack Alexander and Irene (Newman) W.; m. Alice Ann Gorcie, Sept. 19, 1954 (div. July 1979); children: Patricia Ann Brugman, Martin James; m. Sibyl Winslow-Bloom, Dec. 14, 1993. BS, U. Calif., Berkeley, 1951; SM, MIT, 1952. With Calif. Inst. Tech. Jet Propulsion Lab., Pasadena, 1952-89; asst. spacecraft system mgr. Mariner Venus Mercury 1973 Project, 1970-74; project mgr. Calif. Inst. Tech. Jet Propulsion Lab., Pasadena, 1985-89. Author: An Arm and a Leg or Two, 1989. Ednl. officer U.S. Power Squadron, Pasadena, 1982-84. With U.S. Army, 1945-46. Recipient Exceptional Svc. medal NASA, 1974, Presidential award Gerald R. Ford, 1974. Mem. Los Angeles Yacht Club. Avocations: classical guitarist, yachtsman. Home: 3200 Alta Laguna Laguna Beach CA 92651

WILSON, JAMES QUINN, government, management educator; married; 2 children. Henry Lee Shattuck prof. govt. Harvard U., 1961-86; now James Collins prof. mgmt., UCLA; bd. dirs. Am. Enterprise Inst., New Eng. Electric Sys., Rand Corp. Author: Negro Politics, 1960, Political Organizations, 1961, Varieties of Police Behavior, 1968, The Amateur Democrat, 1973, The Investigators, 1978, Thinking About Crime, 1983; (with R.J. Herrnstein) Crime and Human Nature, 1985, (with Roberta Wilson) Watching Fishes, 1985; Bureaucracy: What Government Agencies Do and Why They Do It, 1989, American Government: Institutions and Policies, 1991, The Moral Sense, 1993. Former chmn. Nat. Adv. Coun. for Drug Abuse Prevention, Police Found.; former mem. com. on rsch. on law enforcement and the adminstrn. of justice NRC, Pres.'s Fgn. Intelligence Adv. Bd.; former mem. U.S. Atty. Gen.'s Task Force on Violent Crime; former mem. Commn. on Presdl. Scholars, Sloan Commn. on Cable Comms.; former dir. Joint Ctr. for Urban Studies MIT and Harvard. Fellow Am. Acad. Arts and Scis.; mem. Am. Philos. Soc., Am. Polit. Sci. Assn. (pres., James Madison award). Office: UCLA Grad Sch Mgmt 405 Hilgard Ave Los Angeles CA 90024-1301

WILSON, JAMES RAY, international business educator; b. Hamilton, Ohio, Mar. 7, 1930; s. Ray Crawford and Ruth Lee (Walthers) W.; B.A. (U.S. Navy Coll. Tng. Program scholar), Miami U., Oxford, Ohio, 1952, postgrad., 1967-68; M.A., Ohio State U., 1956; Ph.D., U. Minn., 1984; m. Carolyn Dempsey, Feb. 1, 1952; children—Robin E., Victoria, Mark, Jamie. Grad. asst. Ohio State U., 1955-56; grain mcht. Cargill Inc., Balt., 1956-58; pres. Granexport Corp., Manila, Philippines, 1959-66; mng. dir. Tradax Graanhandel B.V., Amsterdam, 1966-67; instr. in geography Miami U., 1967-68; pres. Cargill Agricola S.A., Sao Paulo, Brazil, 1968-78; dir. indsl. div. Tradax Geneve S.A., Geneva, 1978-80; corp. v.p. Cargill Inc., Mpls., 1980-83; pres. Cargill Southeast Asia, Ltd., Singapore, 1984-88; internat. bus. prof. Miami U., Oxford, Ohio, 1988-92, prof. mgmt. dept., 1994-95; chmn. Cargill Tech. Svcs., Ltd., Thame, Eng., 1992-94. Served with USN, 1952-55. Fellow Royal Geog. Soc.; mem. Assn. Am. Geographers. Congregationalist. Home: 6533 Buckley Rd Oxford OH 45056

WILSON, JAMES RIGG, aircraft manufacturing company executive; b. 1941. BA, Coll. Wooster, 1963; MBA, Harvard U., 1965. V.p. Textron, Providence, 1967-76; with Fairchild Industries Inc., Chantilly, Va., 1977-80, 82-87, chief fin. officer, 1977—, v.p., 1977-80, sr. v.p., 1982-85, exec. v.p., 1985—; chief fin. officer, sr. v.p. Wickes Cos., San Diego, 1980-82; exec. v.p., CFO Thiokol Corp., Ogden, Utah, 1989-93, pres., CEO, 1993—. Office: Thiokol Corp 2475 Washington Blvd Ogden UT 84401-2300

WILSON, JAMES ROBERT, lawyer; b. Meade, Kans., Dec. 3, 1927; s. Robert J. and Bess O. (Osborne) W.; m. Marguerite Jean Reiter, Nov. 27, 1960; 1 son, John Ramsey. B.A., Kans. U., 1950, LL.B., 1953. Bar: Kans. 1953, Nebr. 1961, Colo. 1981. Pvt. practice Meade, Kans., 1953-57, Lakewood, Colo., 1989-93; county atty. Meade County, 1954-57; city atty. Meade, 1954-57; asst. gen. counsel Kans. Corp. Commn., 1957-59, gen. counsel, 1959-61, mem., 1961; atty. KN Energy, Inc., 1961-75, personnel dir., 1964-67, v.p., treas., 1968-75, exec. v.p., 1975-78, pres., chief operating officer, 1978-82, pres., chief exec. officer, 1982-85, chmn., pres., chief exec. officer, 1985-88, chmn., 1988-89; bd. dirs. Alliance Ins. Cos. With USNR, 1945-46. Mem. Phi Kappa Sigma. Home: 1725 Foothills Dr S Golden CO 80401-9167

WILSON, JAMES WILLIAM, lawyer; b. Spartanburg, S.C., June 19, 1928; s. James William and Ruth (Greenwaldt) W.; m. Elizabeth Clair Pickett, May 23, 1952; children: Susan Alexandra Wilson Albright, James William. Student, Tulane U., 1945-46; BA, U. Tex., Austin, 1950, LLB, 1951. Bar: Tex. 1951. Practiced in Austin, 1951-79; ptnr. McGinnis, Lochridge & Kilgore (and predecessors), 1960-76; of counsel Stubbeman, McRae, Sealy, Laughlin & Browder, 1976-79; sr. v.p. and gen. counsel Brown & Root, Inc., Houston, 1980-93, also dir.; of counsel Sewell & Riggs, Houston, 1993—; asst. atty. gen., 1957-58; legis. asst. to senate majority leader Lyndon B. Johnson, 1959-60; adj. prof. U. Tex. Law Sch., 1962-63, 95. Lt. (j.g.) USNR, 1952-55. Fellow Tex. Bar Found., Houston Bar Found.; mem. ABA, Tex. Bar Assn., Harris County Bar Assn., Am. Law Inst., Order of Coif, Phi Beta Kappa. Home: 3218 Reba Dr Houston TX 77019-6212 Office: Ste 800 333 Clay Ave Houston TX 77002-4086

WILSON, JANE, artist; b. Seymour, Iowa, Apr. 29, 1924; d. Wayne and Cleone (Marquis) W.; m. John Gruen, Mar. 28, 1948; 1 dau., Julia. B.A., U. Iowa, 1945, M.A., 1947. Mem. fine arts faculty Parsons Sch. Design, 1973-83, 89-90; vis. artist U. Iowa, 1974; adj. assoc. prof. painting and drawing Columbia U., 1975-85, assoc. prof., 1985-86, prof., 1986-88, acting chair, 1986-88; Andrew Mellon vis. prof. painting Cooper Union, 1977-78. Exhibited one-man shows include. Hansa Gallery, N.Y.C., 1953, 55, 57, Stuttman Gallery, N.Y.C., 1958, 59, Tibor de Nagy Gallery, N.Y.C., annually, 1960-66, Graham Gallery, N.Y.C., 1968, 69, 71, 73, 75, Fischbach Gallery, N.Y.C., 1978, 81, 84, 88, 90, 91, 93, Munson-Williams-Proctor Inst., 1980, Utica, N.Y., Cornell U., Ithaca, N.Y., 1982, Compass Rose Gallery, Chgo. 1988, Am. U., Washington, 1989; U. Richmond, Va., 1990, Earl McGrath Gallery, L.A., 1990-91, 93, Dartmouth Coll., Hanover, N.H., 1991, Arnot Mus., Elmira, N.Y., 1993-94; represented in permanent collections. Met. Mus., Mus. Modern Art, Whitney Mus., Wadsworth Atheneum, Heron Art Mus., NYU, Rockefeller Inst., Vassar Coll., Pa. Acad. Fine Arts, Hirschhorn Mus., Washington.; (Recipient Purchase prize Childe Hassam Fund 1971, 73, Ranger Fund Purchase prize 1977, award in art Am. Acad. and Inst. of Arts and Letters 1981). Ingram-Merrill grantee, 1963; Louis Comfort Tiffany grantee, 1967, Eloise Spaeth award The Guild Hall, East Hampton, N.Y., 1988. Mem. Am. Acad. of Arts and Letters (treas. 1992—), Nat. Acad. Design (pres. 1992-94), Phi Beta Kappa.

WILSON, JANIE MENCHACA, nursing educator, researcher; b. Lytle, Tex., Mar. 15, 1936; m. Patrick W. Wilson; 1 child, Kathryn Lynn Kohlleppel. BSN, Incarnate Word Coll., San Antonio, 1958; MSN, U. Tex., San Antonio, 1973; PhD in Nursing, U. Tex., Austin, 1978. RN. Oper. rm. nurse Santa Rosa Hosp., San Antonio, 1958-59; instr. Brackenridge Hosp. Sch. Nursing, Austin, 1963-66; staff nurse Med. Coll. Ga., Augusta, 1967-68; instr. dept. nursing San Antonio Coll., 1968-72, prof. dept. nursing edn., 1976—; counselor Project GAIN Tex. Nurses Assn., Austin, 1973-76; rsch. assoc. Ctr. for Health Care Rsch. and Evaluation, U. Tex. System, Austin, 1974-75; cons. Nurse Aide Competency Evaluation Program, San Antonio, 1989—; mem. manuscript rev. panel Nursing Rsch., N.Y.C., 1989-91. Contbr. chpts. to books, articles to profl. jours. Bd. dirs. Ctr. for Health Policy Devel., San Antonio, 1988-92; mem. Nat. Adv. Coun. on Nurse Edn. and Practice, 1995—. 1st lt. USAF, 1960-63. Mem. AAUP, ANA (coun. nurse rschrs., coun. cultural diversity, fellow program for ethnic minorities 1975-77), Am. Acad. Nursing, Nat. League Nursing, Nat. Assn. Hispanic Nurses, Sigma Theta Tau. Roman Catholic. Avocations: music, reading, fishing, dancing, sewing. Home: 4126 Longvale Dr San Antonio TX 78217-3525 Office: San Antonio Coll 1300 San Pedro Ave San Antonio TX 78212-4299

WILSON, JEAN DONALD, endocrinologist, educator; b. Wellington, Tex., Aug. 26, 1932; s. J.D. and Maggie E. (Hill) W. BA in Chemistry, U. Tex., 1951, MD, 1955. Diplomate: Am. Bd. Internal Medicine. Intern, then resident in internal medicine Parkland Meml. Hosp., Dallas, 1955-58; clin. assoc. Nat. Heart Inst., Bethesda, Md., 1958-60; instr. internal medicine U. Tex. Southwestern Med. Sch., Dallas, 1960-61; prof. U. Tex. Southwestern Med. Sch., 1968—. Editor: Jour. Clin. Investigation, 1972-77. Served as sr. asst. surgeon USPHS, 1958-60. Recipient Amory prize Am. Acad. Arts and Scis., 1977, Fuller prize Am. Urol. Assn., 1983, Lita Annenberg Hazen award, 1986, Dale medal Soc. for Endocrinology, 1991, Pincus medal Worchester Found., 1992. Fellow Royal Clin. Physicians; mem. NAS, Inst. Medicine, AAAS, Am. Fedn. Clin. Rsch., Am. Soc. Clin. Investigation, Assn. Am. Physicians, Soc. Exptl. Biology and Medicine, Am. Soc. Biochemistry and Molecular Biology, Am. Soc. Neurochemistry, Endocrine Soc. (Oppenheimer award 1972, Koch award 1993). Office: U Tex Southwestern Med Ctr Dept Internal Medicine 5323 Harry Hines Blvd Dallas TX 75235-8857

WILSON, JIMMY, computer service company executive. CFO Fiserv Basis, Inc., Atlanta, 1990—. Office: Fiserv Basis Inc 3 Corporate Sq NE Ste 500 Atlanta GA 30329*

WILSON, JOAN EMILY, nursing education administrator; b. Plainfield, N.J., May 15, 1937; d. Walter William and Julia (Leahy) W.; m. Charles Morris, Apr. 26, 1968 (dec. Apr. 1977); m. James Wright, Feb. 14, 1981 (dec. Aug. 1981). Diploma, Jersey City Med. Ctr., 1958; BS in Nursing, Ohio State U., 1965, M in Nursing, 1966. Staff nurse Overlook Hosp., Summit, N.J., 1958-63, Dr.'s Hosp., Columbus, Ohio, 1963-64; instr. U. Wash., Seattle, 1966-68, Everett (Wash.) Community Coll., 1968-72; dir. nursing program Tacoma Community Coll., 1972—; mem. Wash. State Bd. Nursing, 1982-87. Trustee Lakewood Hosp., Tacoma, 1986—. Mem. Am. Nurses Assn., Nat. League for Nursing, Fedn. Tchrs., Sigma Theta Tau. Home: 6018 Hillcrest Dr SW Tacoma WA 98499-1112

WILSON, JOHN, artist; b. Boston, Apr. 14, 1922; s. Reginald and Violet (Caesar) W.; m. Julia Kowitch, June 25, 1950; children—Rebecca, Roy, Erica. Diploma with highest honors, Boston Mus. Sch. (Paige fellow for European study), 1944; B.S. in Edn, Tufts U., 1947; student, Fernand Leger's Sch., Paris, France, 1948-49; student (John Hay Whitney fellow), Esmeralda Sch. of Art, Mex. Instr. Boston Mus. Sch., 1949-50, Bd. Edn., N.Y.C., 1959-64; prof. Boston U., 1964-86, prof. emeritus, 1986—. Exhib-

ited at, Atlanta U., Smith Coll., Carnegie Inst. Annual Art Show, Library of Congress Print Nationals, Mus. Modern Art, at N.Y.C. Met. Mus. Art, N.Y.C., Rose Art Mus., Brandeis U., Detroit Inst. Arts, Mus. Fine Arts, Boston; represented in permanent collections, Boston Pub. Library, Smith Coll., Mus. Modern Art, Atlanta U., Carnegie Inst., Bezalel Mus., Jerusalem, Rose Art Mus., Brandeis U., Howard U., Tufts U., Dept. Fine Arts, French govt., Mus. Nat. Ctr. Afro-Am. Artists, Boston; winner competitions for monument, Statue of Martin Luther King, Jr., Buffalo, 1983, U.S. Capitol, Washington, 1986, monument, Roxbury Community Coll., Boston, 1985. Illustrator: children's books Spring Comes to the Ocean (Jean Craighead George), 1965, Becky (Julia Wilson), 1970, Striped Ice Cream (Joan Lexau), 1968, Malcolm X (Arnold Adoff), 1970. Bd. dirs. Elma Lewis Sch. Fine Arts, Boston, 1970-75. Sculpture fellow Mass. Arts and Humanities Found., 1976. Home: 44 Harris St Brookline MA 02146-4933

WILSON, JOHN, protective services official. Police chief Montgomery, Ala. Office: Office of Police Chief PO Box 1111 Montgomery AL 36192

WILSON, JOHN ABRAHAM ROSS, academic administrator; b. Trout Lake, B.C., Can., Aug. 25, 1911; s. Henry and Grace Ellen (Ross) W.; m. Nora Margaret (Mains) June 28, 1940; children: John Richard Meredith, Douglas Gordon. BA, U. B.C., 1932, MA, 1939; EdD, Oreg. State U., 1951; LLD with honors, U. Santa Barbara, 1979. Tchr., counselor various schs., B.C., 1934-51; prof. U. Calif., Santa Barbara, 1951-79; prof., adminstr. U. Santa Barbara, 1979—; chmn. bd. Acoustic Mktg. of Can. Ltd., Vancouver, Can., 1979—. Author: (with others) Psychological Foundation of Learning and Teaching, 1969, Kind Evaluation of Learning Potential, 2d edit. 1967, Psychology of Reading, 1974; editor; Diagnosis of Learning Difficulties, 1971. Mem. Calif. Ednl. Research Assn. (pres. 1968-69), Nat. Edn. Assn., Nat. Assn. for Study Edn., Phi Delta Kappa. Club: Cosmopolitan (Santa Barbara). Home: 2665 Tallant Rd N286 Santa Barbara CA 93105 Office: Univ Santa Barbara 4050 Calle Real # 200 Santa Barbara CA 93110-3413

WILSON, JOHN BENEDICT, office supplies company executive; b. Wethersfield, Conn., July 18, 1959; s. Thomas Frederick and Jeanette Faith Wilson; m. Leslie Ann Quartermain, Aug. 18, 1990. BSchE magna cum laude, Rensselaer Poly. Inst., 1981; MBA, Harvard U., 1983. Mgr., analyst Treas.' Office, GM, N.Y.C., 1983-86; v.p., mgr. cons. Bain & Co., Boston, 1986-90; sr. v.p. corp. planning N.W. Airlines Inc., Eagan, Minn., 1990-92; CFO, exec. v.p. fin. and strategy Staples Inc., Framingham, Mass., 1992—. Mem. Fin. Execs. Inst., Harvard Club, Tau Beta Pi, Theta Xi. Office: Staples PO Box 9328 100 Pennsylvania Ave Framingham MA 01701

WILSON, JOHN D., university president; b. Lapeer, Mich., Aug. 17, 1931; s. Myron John and Helen (O'Conner) W.; m. Anne Veronica Yeomans, Sept. 21, 1957; children: Stephen, Anthony, Patrick, Sara. BA, Mich. State U., 1953, PhD, 1965; BA with honors, Oxford (Eng.) U., 1955, MA with honors, 1955. Asst. to v.p. acad. affairs Mich. State U., East Lansing, 1958-59, assoc. dir. Honors Coll., 1963-65, dir. Honors Coll., 1965-67, dir. undergrad. edn., 1967-68; asst. to pres. SUNY, 1959-63; pres. Wells Coll., Aurora, N.Y., 1969-75; v.p. acad. affairs Va. Poly. Inst. and State U., Blacksburg, 1975-83, univ. provost, 1976-83; pres. Washington and Lee U., Lexington, Va., 1983—. Served with USAF, 1955-57. Mem. Assn. Am. Rhodes Scholars, Phi Beta Kappa, Phi Kappa Phi. Home: 2 University Pl Lexington VA 24450-2114 Office: Washington & Lee U Office of the President Lexington VA 24450*

WILSON, JOHN DONALD, banker, economist; b. McKeesport, Pa., Feb. 8, 1913; s. John Johnston and Katherine A. (Hollerman) W.; m. Myriam Rohr, Mar. 10, 1942 (div. Feb. 18, 1950); 1 dau., Nina Marie; m. Danesi Matthews Hilton, Nov. 3, 1951; children: John Douglas, David Matthews, Mary Danesi. B.A. magna cum laude, U. Colo., 1935; M.A. in Econs. (Braker teaching fellow), Tufts Coll., 1937; M.A. in Econs., Harvard U., 1940. Instr. econs. Harvard U., 1937-40; editor Survey of Current Bus., U.S. Dept. Commerce, 1940-42; economist Editor and Publisher McGraw-Hill Pub. Co., 1946-50; established McGraw-Hill Am. Letter; mem. research and devel. staff N.Y. Life Ins. Co., 1950-51; v.p. charge ops. Inst. Internat. Edn., 1951-53; with Chase Manhattan Bank, 1953-81, successively bus. cons., v.p. and dir. econ. research, group exec. econ. research, pub. relations and market research, 1961-63, sr. v.p., dir. bank's corp. plans, 1963-69, sr. v.p., dir. econ. group, 1969-72, sr. v.p., chief economist, dir. econs., 1972-81, econ. cons., 1981-84; cons. U.S. Govt. Intelligence Svcs., 1984-92; dir. Chase Econometric Assos., 1971-81, chmn., 1971-75. Author: The Chase—The Chase Manhattan Bank, N.A., 1945-1985, 1986. Bd. dirs. United Neighborhood Houses, N.Y.C., 1955-68; treas., organizing trustee Found. Libr. Ctr., 1956-63; dir. Associated Alumni U. Colo., 1959-63; trustee Inst. Internat. Edn., N.Y.C., 1964-85. Lt. (j.g.) USNR, 1943-46, OSS. Mem. Council Fgn. Relations, Internat. C. of C. (exec. com. U.S. council internat. bus. 1969—, sr. trustee), Am. Econ. Assn., Am. Statis. Assn., Phi Beta Kappa, Sigma Chi. Presbyn. Club: Harvard (N.Y.C.), Field (Bronxville, N.Y.). Home: 6 Sunset Ave Bronxville NY 10708-2215

WILSON, JOHN ERIC, biochemistry educator; b. Champaign, Ill., Dec. 13, 1919; s. William Courtney and Marie Winette (Lytle) W.; m. Marion Ruth Heaton, June 7, 1947; children—Kenneth Heaton, Douglas Courtney, Richard Mosher. S.B., U. Chgo., 1941; M.S., U. Ill., Urbana, 1944; Ph.D., Cornell U., 1948. Research asst. Pyroxylin Products, Inc., Chgo., summers 1941-42, Gen. Foods Corp., Hoboken, N.J., summer, 1943; asst. in chemistry U. Ill., 1944-44; asst. in biochemistry Cornell U. Med. Coll., N.Y.C., 1944-48, research asso., 1948-50; asst. prof. biochemistry U. N.C., Chapel Hill, 1950-60, asso. prof., 1960-65, prof., 1965-90, prof. emeritus, 1990—, dir. grad. studies, dept. biochemistry, 1965-71, acting dir. neurobiology program, 1968-69, asso. dir., 1969-72, dir., 1972-73; Kenan prof. U. Utrecht, Netherlands, 1978. Mem. editl. bd. Jour. Neurochemistry, 1987-94; contbr. numerous articles on biochemistry and neurochemistry to profl. publs. Scoutmaster Occoneechee council Boy Scouts Am., 1959-66; mem. Chapel Hill Twp. Adv. Council, 1978-85, Orange County (N.C.) Planning Bd., 1979-85. Fellow AAAS; mem. Am. Chem. Soc., Am. Soc. for Biochemistry and Molecular Biology, Am. Soc. Neurochemistry, N.C. Acad. Sci., Internat. Soc. for Neurochemistry, Internat. Brain Rsch. Orgn., Soc. Neurosci (coun. 1969-70, chmn. fin. com. 1973-78, organizer and mem. exec. com. N.C. chpt. 1974-75), Harvey Soc., Sigma Xi, Phi Lambda Upsilon, Alpha Chi Sigma, Beta Theta Pi. Home: 214 Spring Ln Chapel Hill NC 27514-3540 Office: U NC Sch Medicine Dept Biochemistry Chapel Hill NC 27599-7260

WILSON, JOHN FRANCIS, religion educator; b. Springfield, Mo., Nov. 4, 1937; s. Frederick Marion and Jesse Ferrel (Latimer) W.; m. L. Claudette Faulk, June 9, 1961; children: Laura, Amy, Emily. BA, Harding U., Searcy, Ark., 1959; MA, Harding U., Memphis, 1961; PhD, U. Iowa, 1967. Dir. Christian Student Ctr., Springfield, 1959-73; prof. religious studies S.W. Mo. State U., Springfield, 1961-83; prof. of religion, dean Seaver Coll. Arts, Letters and Scis. Pepperdine U., Malibu, Calif., 1983—. Author: Religion: A Preface, 1982, 2d edit., 1989; co-author: Discovering the Bible, 1986, Excavations at Capernaum, 1989; contbr. articles, revs. to profl. publs. Mem. Archaeol. Inst. Am., Am. Schs. of Oriental Rsch., Soc. Bib. Lit., Am. Numismatic Soc., Am. Coun. Acad. Deans. Mem. of Christ. Office: Pepperdine U Seaver Coll 24255 Pacific Coast Hwy Malibu CA 90263-0001

WILSON, JOHN GROVER, securities trader; b. Chattanooga, June 7, 1945; s. Minos Fletcher and Marguerite (Church) W.; m. Michele Harbrook, Apr. 12, 1946; children: Christopher J., Brooke E., Ashley R.; stepchildren: Bradley B. Lance, Meredith B. Lance. BS, U. Tenn., 1967; MPA, U. No. Colo., 1977. Registered rep. and reg. investment advisor. Commd. 2nd lt. USAF, 1968, advanced through grades to lt. col., resigned, 1977; broker Merrill Lynch Pierce Fenner and Smith, Knoxville, Tenn., 1977-78; broker, v.p., mem. Pacesetter coun. PaineWebber, Knoxville, 1978-82; 1st v.p. investments, mem. partnership coun. Prudential Securities, Inc., Knoxville, 1988—. Pres. bd. dirs. Knoxville Cerebral Palsy Ctr., 1984-88; scoutmaster handicapped troop Boy Scouts Am., Knoxville, 1979-84. With USAFR, 1977-93, lt. col. ret. Decorated D.F.C., Air medal with 2 oak leaf clusters. Mem. Sigma Phi Epsilon (mem. fin. com. U. Tenn. chpt.). Republican. Methodist. Home: 12226 Brighton Ct Knoxville TN 37922 Office: Prudential Securities Inc Plaza Tower 800 S Gay St Ste 2605 Knoxville TN 37929

WILSON, JOHN HILL TUCKER, investment banker; b. Charlotte, N.C., May 24, 1934; s. Millard Thomas and Catharine Chevasse (Tucker) W.; m. Sandra Scudder Wilson, July 14, 1962; children—Tucker, William, Emily, David. B.A. in History, Princeton U., 1956; M.B.A., Harvard U., 1960. Assoc. Morgan Stanley & Co. Inc., N.Y.C., 1960-69, mng. dir., 1969-92, adv. dir., 1993—. Chmn. Settlement Coll. Readiness, N.Y.C. Morgan Stanley Found., N.Y.C.; bd. dirs. Union Settlement Assn., N.Y.C., Environ. Def. Fund, Classroom, Inc., N.Y.C.; trustee Greenwich Hosp. Assn.; mem. bd. visitors U. N.C. Bus. Sch., Links Club, Round Hill Club. Office: Morgan Stanley & Co Inc 1251 Avene Of The Americas New York NY 10020

WILSON, JOHN JAMES, federal judge; b. Boston, Dec. 23, 1927; s. John J. and Margaret (Thomas) W.; m. Joan Ellen Bostwick, Sept. 1, 1951 (div. Sept. 1975); children: Jeffrey, John, Julie; m. Elizabeth Brower, Dec. 4, 1975; 1 child, Stephane. AB, Tufts U., 1951; LLB, Stanford U., 1954. Bar: Calif. 1954, Mass. 1954, Oreg. 1982, U.S. Dist. Ct. (no., cen., ea. and so. dists.) Calif., U.S. Dist. Ct. Oreg. Asst. U.S. atty. L.A., 1958-60; ptnr. Hill, Farrer & Burrill, L.A., 1960-85; bankruptcy judge U.S. Dist. Ct. Calif., San Bernardino, 1985-88, Santa Ana, Calif., 1989—. 1 child, Stephane. Seventh Day Adventist. Office: US Bankruptcy Ct 506 Fed Bldg PO Box 12600 34 Civic Center Plz Santa Ana CA 92701-4025

WILSON, JOHN LEWIS, university official; b. Columbus, Ohio, Mar. 18, 1943; s. John Robert and Betty Marie (Barker) W.; m. Linda Patricia Kiernan, Apr. 23, 1966; 1 child, Heidi Annette. BA in Internat. Rels., Am. U., 1963, MA in Econs., 1973, PhD, 1977. Staff asst. Congressman Paul N. McCloskey, Washington, 1968-72; sr. assoc. Govt. Affairs Inst., Washington, 1973-77; pres. Experience Devel., Inc., Tucson, 1978-85; from asst. to assoc. dean faculty sci. U. Ariz., Tucson, 1985-93, acting asst. to sr. v.p. adminstrn. and fin., 1988-89, dir. decision and planning support, 1994—; instr. U. Phoenix, Tucson, 1980-83. Author: (with others) Managing Planned Agricultural Development, 1976. 1st lt. U.S. Army, Vietnam, 1964-68. Decorated Bronze Star with oak leaf cluster and V device. Mem. Am. Econ. Assn., Am. Soc. Quality Control, Assn. for Instnl. Rsch., Tucson Met. C. of C. Democrat. Avocations: walking, computers, reading, dancing. Home: 8030 E Garland Rd Tucson AZ 85715-2830 Office: U Ariz Adminstration 116 Tucson AZ 85721

WILSON, JOHN OLIVER, economist, educator, banker; b. St. James, Mo., May 22, 1938; s. John Riffie and Jacquetta Ruth (Linck) W.; B.A. in Math., Northwestern U., 1960; Ph.D. in Econs., U. Mich., 1967; m. Beclee Newcomer, Jan. 28, 1961; children—Beth Anne, Benjamin Duncan. Asst. prof. Yale U., 1967-70; asst. office Econ. Opportunity, Washington, 1969-71; asst. sec. HEW, 1972; dir. North Star Research Inst., Mpls., 1972-74; exec. v.p., chief economist Bank of Am., San Francisco 1975—, chief economist, 1982—; prof. Grad. Sch. Pub. Policy and Haas Sch. Bus. U. Calif., Berkeley, 1979-92. bd. dirs. Nat. Bur. Econ. Rsch., Cambridge, Mass. Bd. visitors Joint Center for Urban Studies, Harvard U.-M.I.T., 1978-87; trustee Grad. Theol. Union, Berkeley, Calif. Served with U.S. Navy, 1960-63. Ford Found. fellow, 1966-67. Mem. Am. Econ. Assn., Western Econ. Assn., Nat. Assn. Bus. Economists. Republican. Presbyterian. Author: After Affluence, Economics to Meet Human Needs 1980, Middle Class Crisis: The American and Japanese Exprience, 1983, The Power Economy, Building An Economy That Works, 1985; contbr. articles to profl. jours. Office: Bank of America Ctr 555 California St San Francisco CA 94104-1502

WILSON, JOHN ROSS, retired law educator; b. Memphis, Aug. 8, 1920; s. Charles Monroe and Lida Scott (Christenberry) W.; m. Anne Woodruff Talley, Feb. 7, 1944; children—Margaret Anne, Andrew Ross. B.B.A., So. Meth. U., 1943, LL.B., 1948; student, U. Tex., Austin, 1939-41. Bar: Tex. bar 1948. Mem. faculty Baylor U. Law Sch., Waco, Tex., 1948-86; assoc. prof. law Baylor U. Law Sch., 1951-55, prof., 1955-86, prof. emeritus, 1986; cons. on bankruptcy and judicial remedies. Author: Cases and Materials on Judicial Remedies, 1966; contbr. articles to profl. jours. Served to lt. USNR, 1943-46. Mem. Am. Judicature Soc., Tex. Bar Assn., Am. Bar Assn., Waco-McLennan County Bar Assn., Tex. Trial Lawyers Assn., Delta Theta Phi, Sigma Alpha Epsilon. Republican. Methodist. Office: Baylor Law Sch Waco TX 76703

WILSON, JOSEPH CHARLES, IV, ambassador; b. Bridgeport, Conn., Nov. 6, 1949; s. Joseph Charles III and Phyllis (Finnell) W.; m. Susan Dale Otchis, Apr. 27, 1973 (div. 1986); children: Sabrina Cecile, Joseph Charles; m. Jacqueline Marylene Giorgi, July 1, 1986. BA in History, U. Calif., Santa Barbara, 1972. Fgn. svc. officer Dept. of State, Washington, 1976—; congl. fellow Am. Polit. Sci. Assn., Washington, 1985-86; dep. chief of mission Am. Embassy, Bujumbura, Burundi, 1982-85, Brazzaville, Congo, 1986-88, Baghdad, Iraq, 1988-91; amb. Dept. of State Am. Embassy, Libreville, Gabon, Sao Tome and Principe, 1992—. Recipient Disting. Alumni award U. Calif. Santa Barbara, 1991; named hon. adm. County Commr., El Paso, Tex., 1991. Mem. Am. Polit. Sci. Assn., Am. Fgn. Svc. Assn. (William R. Rivkin award 1987), U. Calif. Santa Barbara Alumni Assn. (Disting. Alumni award 1991), San Onofre Surfing Club. Avocations: golf, bicycling, weight lifting. Home and Office: Am Embassy Gabon Libreville # 2270 Washington DC 20521

WILSON, JOSEPH MORRIS, III, lawyer; b. Milw., July 26, 1945; s. Joseph Morris Jr. and Phyllis Elizabeth (Cresson) W.; children: Elizabeth J., Eric M.; m. Dixie Lee Brock, Mar. 23, 1984. BA, Calif. State U., Chico, 1967; MA, U. Washington, 1968; JD summa cum laude, Ohio State U., 1976. Bar: Alaska 1976, U.S. Dist. Ct. Alaska 1976, U.S.Ct. Appeals (9th cir.) 1986. Recruiter and vol. U.S. Peace Corps, People's Republic of Benin, 1969-73; legal intern U.S. Ho. of Reps., Washington, 1975; ptnr. Guess & Rudd P.C., Anchorage, 1976-88, chmn. comml. dept., 1981-82, ptnr. compensation com., 1982-84; mgr. Alaska taxes, sr. tax atty. BP Exploration Inc., Alaska, 1990—; bus. law instr. U. Alaska, Anchorage, 1977-78. Counsel Tanaina Child Devel. Ctr., Anchorage, 1982-84, Alaska Child Passenger Safety Assn., Anchorage, 1983-86; bd. dirs. Alaska Alcohol Safety Action Program, Anchorage, 1977-79. Mem. ABA, Alaska Bar Assn. (taxation sect.), Anchorage Bar Assn. Democrat. Club: UAA Basketball Boosters, World Affairs Coun. Avocations: music, sports, travel. Home: 1779 Morningtide Ct Anchorage AK 99501-5722 Office: MB6-4 PO Box 196193 Anchorage AK 99519-6193

WILSON, JUDY VANTREASE, publishing executive; b. Old Hickory, Tenn., Apr. 8, 1939; d. Luther Benjamin and Ethel (Shepherd) Vantrease; m. Robert Roland Wilson, May 4, 1968; children: Robert Roland Jr., Hilary Shepherd. Ba, Smith Coll., 1961. Project mgr. Ency. Britannica, Palo Alto, Calif., 1961-62; prodn. mgr. AICPA, N.Y.C., 1962-63; successively editorial asst., assoc. editor, editor, mgr. programmed instrn., editor profl. group, pub. John Wiley & Sons, N.Y.C., 1963-85; v.p., gen. mgr. Macmillan Pub. Co., N.Y.C., 1985-88, pres., gen. mgr., 1988-94. Recipient Presdl. citation Nat. Soc. for Programmed Instrn., 1985; named to Acad. Women Achievers, YWCA, 1983. Mem. Women in Comm., Assn. Booksellers for Children, Soc. Childrens Book Writers, Am. Assn. Pubs. (exec. coun. 1979-82, childrens pub. com. 1988-93, gen. pub. divsn. coun. 1993-94).

WILSON, KAREN LEE, museum curator; b. Somerville, N.J., Apr. 2, 1949; d. Jon Milton and Laura Virginia (Van Dyke) W.; m. Paul Ernest Walker, 1980; 1 child, Jeremy Nathaniel. AB, Harvard U., 1971; MA, NYU, 1973, PhD, 1985. Rsch. assoc., dir. excavation at Mendes, Egypt Inst. Fine Arts, NYU, 1979-81; coord. exhbn. The Jewish Mus., N.Y.C., 1981-82, adminstrv. cataloguer, 1982-83, coord. curatorial affairs, 1984-86; curator Oriental Inst. Mus. U. Chgo., 1988—. Author, editor: Mendes, 1982; contbr. articles to profl. jours. Mem. Am. Oriental Soc., Am. Rsch. Ctr. in Egypt. Office: Oriental Institute Museum 1155 E 58th St Chicago IL 60637

WILSON, KENNETH GEDDES, physics research administrator, educator; b. Waltham, Mass., June 8, 1936; s. E. Bright and Emily Fisher (Buckingham) W.; m. Alison Brown, 1982. A.B., Harvard U., 1956, DSc hon., 1981; Ph.D., Calif. Tech. Inst., 1961; Ph.D. (hon.), U. Chgo., 1976. From asst. prof. to prof. physics Cornell U., Ithaca, N.Y., 1963—; James A. Weeks prof. in phys. sci., 1974—; Hazel C. Youngberg Trustees Disting prof. The Ohio State U., Columbus, 1988—. Recipient Nobel prize in Physics, 1982, Dannie Heinemann prize, 1973, Boltzmann medal, 1975, Wolf prize, 1980, A.C. Eringen medal, 1984, Franklin medal, 1982, Aneesur Rahman prize,

1993. Mem. NAS, Am. Philos. Soc., Am. Phys. Soc., Am. Acad. Arts and Scis.

WILSON, KENNETH JAY, writer; b. Oklahoma City, Aug. 25, 1944; s. Kenneth J. and Betty Wallace (Bleakmore) W. B.A. magna cum laude, Yale U., 1966, M.Phil., 1969; postgrad. Queen's Coll., Oxford U., Eng., 1969-70; Ph.D., Yale U., 1973. From instr. to assoc. prof. English U. Rochester, N.Y., 1970-83; assoc. Clare Hall, Cambridge U., Eng., 1977; vis. assoc. prof. English Coll. William and Mary, Williamsburg, Va., 1983; editor in chief Peter Lang Pub. N.Y.C., 1983-87; dir. of rights and permissions Princeton U. Press, 1987-88; commissioning editor polit. sci. and psychology Routledge, N.Y.C., 1988-90; adminstrv. dir. HIV Clin. Rsch. Ctr. Mt. Zion Med. Ctr./U. Calif., San Francisco, 1994—; cons. USIA, 1985. Editor: Letters of Sir Thomas Elyot, 1976, English Works of Thomas More, 1978; author: Incomplete Fictions, 1985, Pope John Paul II, 1992; contbr. articles to profl. jours. Woodrow Wilson fellow, 1966, 83; sr. fellow Folger Shakespeare Library, Washington, 1976; Am. Philos. Soc. grantee, 1976; Am. Council Learned Soc. fellow, 1977. Mem. Mory's Club, Elizabethan Club (New Haven), Yale Club (N.Y.C.), Palm-Aire Country Club, Phi Beta Kappa. Democrat. Roman Catholic. Home: 5570 Country Club Way Sarasota FL 34243-3759 Office: Mt Zion Med Ctr/U Calif HIV Clin Rsch Ctr 2300 Sutter St Ste 202 San Francisco CA 94115

WILSON, KIRK GEORGE, medical service executive; b. Great Falls, Mont., Apr. 1, 1951; s. Floyd Daniel and Lorna (Stark) W.; m. Monica Jane Moline, Aug. 17, 1975; 1 child, Bret Michael. BABS, Concordia Coll., Moorhead, Minn., 1972; MA in Hosp. Adminstrn., U. Iowa, 1975. Adminstrv. asst. Columbus Hosp., Great Falls, 1975-78, asst. adminstr., 1978-80; asst. adminstr., profl. services St. Anthony Hosp., Oklahoma City, Okla., 1981-83, St. Vincent Med. Ctr., Portland, Oreg., 1983-86; adminstr. Meml. Women's/Childrens Hosp., Meml. Med. Ctr., Long Beach, Calif., 1987-88; pres., chief exec. officer Mont. Deaconess Med. Ctr., Great Falls, 1988—; Bd. dirs. Mountain States VHA Regional Bd., Denver, Bank of Mont. Co-author: (monograph) Mental Health Care Systems, 1975. Bd. dirs. Symphony Assn. Bd., Great Falls, 1988—; mem. pres.'s coun. Coll. Great of Falls. Fellow Am. Coll. Healthcare Execs., Mont. Hosp. Assn. (bd. dirs. Dist. II), Mont. Amb., Great Falls C. of C. (bd. dirs., Leadership award 1981), Rotary. Republican. Congregationalist. Home: 520 Fox Ct Great Falls MT 59404-3874 Office: Mont Deaconess Med Ct PO Box 5014 Great Falls MT 59403-5014

WILSON, LANFORD, playwright; b. Lebanon, Mo., Apr. 13, 1937; s. Ralph E(ugene) and Violetta (Tate) W. Student, San Diego State Coll., 1955-56; PhD in Humanities, U. Mo., 1985, Grinnell Coll., 1994; Southampton Coll., 1987. Playwright, 1962—; resident playwright, dir. Circle Repertory Co., N.Y.C., 1969-95. Author: (plays) So Long at the Fair, 1963, Home Free, 1964, No Trespassing, 1964, Sandcastle, 1964, The Madness of Lady Bright, 1964, Ludlow Fair, 1965, Balm in Gilead, 1965, This is the Rill Speaking, 1965, Days Ahead, 1965, Sex is Between Two People, 1965, The Gingham Dog, 1966, The Rimers of Eldritch, 1966, Wandering, 1966, Days Ahead, 1967, Lemon Sky, 1969, Serenading Louie, 1970, The Great Nebula in Orion, 1970, The Hot L Baltimore, 1972, The Family Continues, 1972, The Mound Builders, 1975, Fifth of July, 1978, Brontasaurus, 1978, Talley's Folly, 1979, A Tale Told, 1981, Angels Fall, 1983, A Betrothal, 1984, Talley & Son, 1985, Burn This, 1987, A Poster of the Cosmos, 1987, The Moonshot Tape, 1990, Redwood Curtain, 1991; translator Three Sisters, 1984, Uncle Vanya, 1995; author: (books) Balm in Gilead and Other Plays, 1966, The Rimers of Eldritch and Other Plays, 1968, The Gingham Dog, 1969, Lemon Sky, 1970, The Hot L Baltimore, 1973, The Mound Builders, 1976, Fifth of July, 1979, Talley's Folly, 1980, Angels Fall, 1983, Serenading Louie, 1985, Talley & Son, 1986, Burn This, 1988, Redwood Curtain, 1992, 21 Short Plays, 1994. ABC Yale fellow, 1969; Rockefeller grantee, 1967, 73; Guggenheim grantee, 1970, NEA grantee, 1990; recipient Vernon Rice award, 1966-67, Inst. Arts and Letters award, 1970, Obie award, 1972, 75, 84, Outer Critics Circle award, 1973, Drama Critics Circle award, 1973, 80, Pulitzer prize, 1980, Brandeis award, 1981, John Steinbeck award, 1990, Edward Albee Last Frontier award, 1994. Mem. Dramatists Guild Council.

WILSON, LAUREN ROSS, academic administrator; b. Yates Center, Kans., May 4, 1936; s. Roscoe C. and Margaret D. W.; m. Janie Haskin, Jan. 25, 1959; children—Lance Kevin, Keela Lynn. B.S., Baker U., Baldwin, Kans., 1958; Ph.D., U. Kans., 1963. Mem. faculty Ohio Wesleyan U., Delaware, 1963-87; prof. chemistry Ohio Wesleyan U., 1971-87, Homer Lucas U. prof., dean acad. affairs, 1978-86, acting provost, 1985-86, asst. to pres., 1986, 87; vice chancellor for acad. affairs U. N.C., Asheville, 1987-95, prof. chemistry, 1987-95, interim chancellor, 1993-94; pres. Marietta Coll., 1995—; vis. prof. Ohio State U., 1968, 74; vis. research assoc. Oak Ridge Nat. Lab., 1972-73. Recipient Outstanding Tchr. award Ohio Wesleyan U., 1968. Mem. AAAS, AAUP, Am. Chem. Soc., Am. Assn. Higher Edn., Coun. Undergrad. Rsch., Sigma Xi. Office: Univ NC Phillips Hall Asheville NC 28804

WILSON, LAWRENCE ALEXANDER, construction company executive; b. Nashville, 1935. Grad., Vanderbilt U., 1957. With H.C. Beck Co., Inc., Dallas, 1959-80, pres., COO, 1976-80; chmn., CEO Beck Co., Inc., Dallas, 1980—; pres., CEO HCB Contractors, Dallas, 1980—. Office: HCB Contractors 1401 Elm St Dallas TX 75202-2910

WILSON, LAWRENCE FRANK (LARRY WILSON), professional football team executive; b. Rigby, Idaho, Mar. 24, 1938; m. Nancy Drew, Apr. 15, 1980. Student, U. Utah, 1956-60. Defensive back St. Louis Cardinals, NFL, 1960-72, dir. profl. scouting, 1973-76, dir. profl. pers., 1977-88; v.p., former gen. mgr. Ariz. Cardinals, NFL, 1988—. Mem. All-NFL Team, 1963, 66, 67, 68, 69; player Pro Bowl, 1962-63, 65-70; inducted Pro Football Hall of Fame, 1978; led in interceptions NFL, 1966. Office: Ariz Cardinals PO Box 888 Tempe AZ 85284*

WILSON, LELAND EARL, petroleum engineering consultant; b. Ft. Recovery, Ohio, Oct. 28, 1925; s. John Huffman and Matilda Caroline (Sunderhaus) W.; m. Marian Ruthetta Trygstad, Nov. 27, 1948; children: Kathleen Ann, Linda Kay, Mary Lee, John Russell. BS in Petroleum Engring., Tulsa U., 1950. Registered profl. engr., Alaska, Tex. Drilling engr. Atlantic Refining Co., Tex., Ark., and La., 1950-56; drilling supr. Atlantic Refining Co., La., Tex., 1956-65; drilling supt. Atlantic Richfield, Anchorage, 1965-67; prodn. and drilling supt., 1967-72; ops. mgr. ARCO Oil Prodn. Co., London, 1972-75; resident mgr. ARCO Greenland, Copenhagen, 1975-78; pres. ARCO Indonesia, Inc., Jakarta, 1978-82; v.p. ARCO China, Hong Kong, 1982-85; petroleum cons. Lindale, Tex., 1985—; bd. dirs. Houma Oil Treaters, Inc., DPM Non-Destructive Testing, Odessa, Tex. Contbr. articles to profl. jours; inventor in field. Aviation cadet AUS, 1943-45. Mem. NSPE, Tex. Soc. Profl. Engrs., Tyler Petroleum Club, Soc. Petroleum Engrs., Petroleum Club (pres. Anchorage 1971-72), Indonesian Petroleum Assn. (pres. 1981-82). Republican. Roman Catholic. Avocations: genealogy, golf, travel. Home: PO Box 893 428 Lonestar Ln Lindale TX 75771 Office: PO Box 893 2715 S Main Lindale TX 75771

WILSON, LENNOX NORWOOD, aeronautical engineering educator; b. Quebec, Que., Can., Feb. 15, 1932; s. William Scott and Thelma Caroline (Myers) W.; m. Mary Joan Stephenson, Nov. 15, 1958; children—Robert, Catherine, Paul. B.A.Sc., U. Toronto, Ont., Can., 1953, M.A.Sc., 1954, Ph.D., 1959. Head Aerochemistry group Gen. Motors Corp., Santa Barbara, Calif., 1962-66; mgr. fluid mechanics and acoustics IIT Research Inst., Chgo., 1966-71; prof. mech. and aerospace engring. U. Mo., Columbia, 1971-73; prof. aerospace engring. Iowa State U., Ames, 1973—; chmn. dept. aerospace engring., 1981-87; pres. Engring. Devel. Corp., Ames, 1989—; cons. Gen. Motors Corp., Santa Barbara, 1973-78; v.p. Engring. Analysis, Inc., Ames, 1978-81. Contbr. articles to profl. jours. Gordon N. Patterson lectr. Inst. for Aerospace Studies, Toronto, 1984. Fellow AIAA (assoc.); mem. Am. Soc. Engring. Edn., Aerospace Dept. Chmn.'s Assn. (chmn. 1985-87). Home: 3621 Woodland St Ames IA 50014-3467 Office: Iowa State Univ Aerospace Engring Dept Ames IA 50011

WILSON, LEONARD GILCHRIST, history of medicine educator; b. Orillia, Ont., Can., June 11, 1928; s. George Edward and Mary Agnes (MacPhee) W.; m. Adelia Katherine Hans, June 7, 1969; 1 child, George

Edward Hans. B.A., U. Toronto, Can., 1949; M.Sc., U. London, 1955; Ph.D., U. Wis., Madison, 1958. Lectr. Mount Allison U., Sackville, N.B., Can., 1950-53; vis. instr. U. Calif., Berkeley, 1958-59; asst. prof. Cornell U., Ithaca, N.Y., 1959-60; asst. prof. Yale U., New Haven, 1960-65, assoc. prof., 1965-67; prof., head dept. history of medicine U. Minn., Mpls., 1967—. Author: Charles Lyell: The Years to 1841: The Revolution in Geology, 1972, Medical Revolution in Minnesota, 1989; editor: Benjamin Silliman and His Circle, 1979, Sir Charles Lyell's Scientific Journals on the Species Question, 1971; editor Jour. History Medicine and Allied Scis., 1973-82; co-editor: Readings in History of Physiology, 1966; mem. bd. mgrs. Jour. Hist. Medicine, 1962—. Fellow AAAS; mem. Am. Assn. History of Medicine, Am. Hist. Assn., History of Sci. Soc., Minn. Acad. Medicine (pres. 1984-85, sec.-treas. 1989—), Brit. Soc. for the History of Sci., Soc. for the History of natural History. Home: 797 Goodrich Ave Saint Paul MN 55105-3344 Office: U Minn Dept History of Medicine 420 Delaware St SE Minneapolis MN 55455-0374

WILSON, LEROY, retired glass manufacturing company executive; b. Indpls., July 15, 1928; s. Paul Allison and Lula (Berry) W.; m. Claudie Leenaert, Aug. 9, 1968; children: Paul Neil, Daniel Stuart, Benjamin, Antoine, Virginie. B.S. in Mech. Engring, Purdue U., 1950. With Corning Glass Works, N.Y., 1950-87; v.p. gen. mgr. electronic products div. Corning Glass Works, 1975-80; pres. Corning Europe Inc., Neuilly, France, 1980-87. Mem. dean's adv. council Krannert Sch., Purdue U. Served with AUS, 1954-56. Named Disting. Engring. Alumnus, Purdue U., 1981. Fellow Inst. Dirs.; mem. Royal Automobile Club (London). Ch. of Eng. Home: Egypt House, Rushlake Green, Heathfield, East Sussex TN21 9QT, England

WILSON, LESLIE, biochemist, cell biologist, biology educator; b. Boston, June 29, 1941; s. Samuel Paul Wilson and Lee (Melniker) Kamerling; m. Carla Helena Van Wingerden, Sept. 9, 1989; children from previous marriage: Sebastian A. Michael, Naomi Beth. BS, Mass. Coll. Pharmacy and Allied Health Scis., 1963; PhD, Tufts U., 1967; postdoctoral study, U. Calif at Berkeley, 1967-69. Asst. prof. dept. pharmacology Stanford U. Sch. Medicine, 1969-74; assoc. prof. dept. biol. scis. U. Calif., Santa Barbara, 1975-78, prof. biochemistry, 1979—, chmn. dept. biol. scis., 1987-91, head divsn. molecular, cellular, devel. biol., 1992-93; sci. adv. panel mem. cell and devel. biology Am. Cancer Soc., Atlanta, 1984-88; cons. Eli Lilly & Co., Indpls., 1980—. Editor: (book series) Methods in Cell Biology, 1987—; assoc. editor Biochemistry; contbr. over 100 rsch. papers to profl. publs. Bd. dirs. Cancer Found. Santa Barbara. Rsch. grantee NIH, 1970—, Am. Cancer Soc., 1986—. Mem. AAAS, Am. Soc. Cell Biology (chmn. sci. program 1977), Am. Soc. Biol. Chemistry and Molecular Biology, Am. Soc. Pharmacology and Exptl. Therapeutics. Democrat. Jewish. Office: Univ of Calif Dept Biol Scis Santa Barbara CA 93106

WILSON, L(ETITIA) ALEXANDRA, elementary school educator; b. Ft. Bragg, N.C., Aug. 17, 1943; d. Frank Grant and Elizbeth L. (Campbell) Schnerr; m. J.T. Lewis Wilson, June 18, 1966; children: John T.L. Jr., Mary Elizabeth. BS, Moore Coll. of Art, Phila., 1966; MEd, Millersville U., 1985. Cert. tchr., S.C. Kindergarten tchr. Private Sch., Santa Monica, Calif., 1966-68; layout artist Cooke Pub. Co., St. Davids, Pa., 1972-77; adminstr. Head Start Lancaster County, Pa., 1977-84; elem. art tchr. Florence (S.C.) Sch. Dist., 1985—; mem. curriculum writing com. Florence Sch. Dist., 1986-91, mem. grant writing com., 1990-92, mem. 1st summer inst. Winthrop Coll. DBAE curriculum devel., 1989; pvt. art tutor, Florence, 1987—; mem. S.C. Curriculum Congress. Editor (newsletter) Episcopal Diocese of S.C. Mem. Florence Fine Arts Coun., MacDowell Evening Music Club, 1986—. Grantee Pee Dee Edn. Found., Florence, 1989. Mem. NEA, S.C. Art Educators Assn. (ea. region coord., youth art month coord. 1992—), Nat. Art Educators Assn. (program standards award), S.C. Edn. Assn., Pee Dee Artisans Guild (mem. organizing bd.). Episcopalian. Home: 4008 Foxturn Rd Florence SC 29501 Office: Royall Elem Sch 1400 Woods Rd Florence SC 29501

WILSON, LINDA, librarian; b. Rochester, Minn., Nov. 17, 1945; d. Eunice Gloria Irene Wilson. BA, U. Minn., Morris, 1967; MA, U. Minn., 1968. Libr. rsch. svcs. U. Calif., Riverside, 1968-69, head dept. phys. scis. catalog, 1969-71; city libr. Belle Glade (Fla) Mcpl. Libr., 1972-74; instr. part-time Palm Beach Jr. Coll., Belle Glade, 1973; head adult-young adult ext. Kern County Libr. Sys., Bakersfield, Calif., 1974-80; dir. dist. libr. Lake Agassiz Regional Libr. System, Crookston, Minn., 1980-85; supervising libr. San Diego County Libr., 1985-87; county libr. Merced (Calif.) County Libr., 1987-93; learning network mgr. Merced Coll., 1994-95; libr. Monterey Park (Calif.) Bruggemeyer Meml. Libr., 1995—. Active Leadership Merced, 1987-88; mem. East Site Based Coordinating Coun., Merced, 1990-92, Merced Gen. Plan Citizens Adv. Com., 1992—, Sister City Com., Merced, 1992—. Recipient Libr. award Eagles Aux., 1984, Woman of Achievement award Commn. on the Status of Women, 1990, Libr. award Calif. Libr. Trustees and Commrs., 1990, Woman of Yr. award Merced Bus. and Profl. Women, 1987. Mem. ALA (sec. pub. libr. systems sect. 1988-89), Calif. Libr. Assn. (sec. govt. rels. com. 1991-92, continuing edn. com. 1993-94), Minn. Libr. Assn. (pres. pub. libr. div. 1985), Merced County Mgmt. Coun. (pres. 1989), Bus. and Profl. Women (pres. 1988-89). Democrat. Lutheran. Avocations: travel, walking, reading, swimming, stamp collecting. Home: 1000 E Newmark Ave # 22 Monterey Park CA 91754

WILSON, LINDA SMITH, university administrator; b. Washington, Nov. 10, 1936; d. Fred M. and Virginia D. (Thompson) Smith; m. Paul A. Wilson, Jan. 22, 1970; 1 dau. by previous marriage: Helen K. Whatley, a stepdau., Beth A. Wilson. B.A., Newcomb Coll., Tulane U., 1957; Ph.D., U. Wis., 1962; HLD (hon.), Tulane U., 1993; DLitt, U. Md., 1993. Postdoctoral rsch. assoc. U. Md., College Park, 1962-64, rsch. assoc., 1964-67; vis. asst. prof. U. Mo.-St. Louis, 1967-68; asst. to vice chancellor for rsch., asst. vice chancellor for rsch., assoc. vice chancellor for rsch. Washington U., St. Louis, 1968-75; assoc. vice chancellor for rsch. U. Ill., Urbana, 1975-85; assoc. dean Grad. Coll., U. Ill., Urbana, 1978-85; v.p. for rsch. U. Mich., Ann Arbor, 1985-89; pres. Radcliffe Coll., Cambridge, Mass., 1989—; chmn. adv. com. office sci. and engring. pers. NRC, 1990—; mem. dir.'s adv. coun. NSF, Washington, 1980-89, adv. com. edn. and human resources, 1990—; mem. Nat. Commn. on Rsch., Washington, 1978-80; mem. com. on govt.-univ. relationships NAS, 1981-83, mem. coun. for govt.-univ.-industry rsch. roundtable, 1984-89; mem. rsch. resources adv. coun. NIH, Bethesda, Md., 1978-82, energy rsch. adv. bd. DOE, 1987-90; mem. sci., tech. and the states task force Carnegie Commn. on Sci., Tech. and Govt., 1991-92. Author book chpts.; contbr. articles to profl. jours. Bd. govs. YMCA, Champaign-Urbana, Ill., 1980-83; mem. adv. bd. Nat. Coalition for Sci. and Tech., Washington, 1983-87; trustee Mass. Gen. Hosp., 1992—. Recipient Centennial award Newcomb Coll., 1986; named One of 100 Emerging Leaders Am. Coun. Edn. and Change, 1978. Fellow AAAS (bd. dirs. 1984-88); mem. Am. Chem. Soc. (bd. coun. com. on chemistry and pub. affairs 1978-80), Soc. Rsch. Adminstrs. (Disting. Contbn. to Rsch. Adminstrn. award 1984), Nat. Coun. Univ. Rsch. Adminstrs., Assn. for Biomed. Rsch. (bd. dirs. 1983-86), Inst. Medicine (mem. coun. 1986-89), Nat. Acad. Scis. (coord. coun. for edn. 1991-93), Am. Coun. Edn. (commn. on women in higher edn. 19919-93, chair 1993), Phi Beta Kappa, Sigma Xi, Alpha Lambda Delta, Phi Delta Kappa, Phi Kappa Phi. Home: 76 Brattle St Cambridge MA 02138-3452 Office: Radcliffe Coll Office of Pres Fay House 10 Garden St Cambridge MA 02138*

WILSON, LLOYD LEE, organization administrator; b. Elkton, Md., Sept. 14, 1947; s. Clifton Laws and Betty Raye (Bare) W.; m. Susan Sieg Wilson, 1992; children: Asa, Ryan, Morgan, Daniel. BS in Mgmt., MIT, 1969, MS in Mgmt., 1977. Bus. mgr. med. clinics Mass. Gen. Hosp., Boston, 1970-73; ptnr. Willow Co. mgmt. cons., Cambridge, Mass., 1974-77; dir. community relations Wilson Neuropsychiat. Hosp., Charlottesville, Va., 1977-78; exec. dir. Jefferson Area United Transp. Inc., Charlottesville, Va., 1978-80, Va. Mountain Housing Inc., Blacksburg, 1980-82; gen. sec. Friends Gen. Conf. Religious Soc. Friends, Phila., 1982-85; dir. rsch. and devel. Va. Mountain Housing, Inc., Christiansburg, 1985-88, dir. multifamily housing, 1989-91, regional dir., 1991-92; pres. Friendly Mgmt. Svcs. Corp., 1992—; pres., dir. Va. Housing Coalition, Inc., 1981-82; treas., bd. dirs. Fiddle Hill Farm, Inc., Barboursville, Va., 1982-89; bd. mgrs. Bible Assn. Friends in Am., Phila., 1983-85; mem. com. rec. ministers Balt. Yearly Meeting Friends, Sandy Spring, Md., 1984-86; asst. sec.-treas. Friends Meeting House Fund, Inc., Phila., 1984-85; asst. presiding clk. Communications Commn. of Friends

United Meeting, Richmond, Ind., 1987-88; recorded minister of the gospel, Soc. of Friends, 1989— (presiding clk. Va. Beach monthly meeting 1990-92); dir. coordinating cabinet Va. Coun. Chs., 1988; presiding clk. N.C. Yearly Meeting of Friends, 1991-92. Author: Essays on the Quaker Vision of Gospel Order, 1993; contbr. articles to profl. jours. Treas., bd. dirs. Norfolk (Va.) Quaker House, Inc., 1995—; bd. dirs. New Dominion Housing, Inc., Norfolk, 1992-94; vice chmn. Montgomery County Cmty. Svc. Commn., Christianburg, Va., 1980-82; mem. edn. coun. MIT, 17777-89; bd. dirs. Am. Friends Svc. Com., Inc., Phila., 1980-83; bd. dirs. Interfaith Housing Corp. Cambridge, Inc., 1975-77, treas., 1975-77, also numerous others. Home: 536 Carnaby Ct Virginia Bch VA 23454 Office: Friendly Mgmt Svcs Corp 2517 Lafayette Blvd Norfolk VA 23509-2511

WILSON, LOIS M., minister; b. Winnipeg, Man., Can., Apr. 8, 1927; d. Edwin Gardiner Dunn and Ada Minnie (Davis) Freeman; m. Roy F. Wilson, June 9, 1950; children: Ruth, Jean, Neil, Bruce. BA, United Coll., Winnipeg, 1947, BDiv, 1969; Diploma in TV prodn., Ryerson Tech. Inst., 1974; DDiv (hon.), Victoria U., Toronto, 1978, United Theol. Coll., Montreal, 1978, Wycliff Coll., 1983, Queens U., Kingston, 1984, U. Winnipeg, 1986, Mt. Allison U., 1988; LLD (hon.), Trent U., Peterborough, 1984, Dalhousie U., 1989, Dalhousie U., 1989, Ripon Coll., Wis., 1992; DCL (hon.), Acadia U., 1984, DHuml (hon.), Mt. St. Vincent, Halifax, 1984. Ordained to ministry United Church of Can., 1965. Minister Thunder Bay, 1965-69, Hamilton, 1969-78, Kingston, 1978-80; moderator United Church of Can., Kingston, 1980-82; McGeachy sr. scholar United Church of Can., 1989-91; pres. Can. Council of Chs., Toronto, Ont., 1976-79; co-dir. Ecumenical Forum Can., Toronto, Ont., 1983-89; pres. World Council of Chs., Geneva, 1983-91; chancellor Lakehead U., Thurder Bay, Ont., 1990—; mem. adv. coun. internt. devel. studies U. Toronto, 1987-93; spokesperson Project Ploughshares, 1st and 2d UN Conf. on Disarmament, N.Y.C., 1978-82; lectr. Vancouver Sch. Theology, 1980, Queens Theol. Coll., 1982-83, 92, Chancellor's lectr., 1992; officer Human Rights Commn., Ont., 1973; mem. bd. regents Victoria U., 1990—; chief Can. Fact finding Mission to Sri Lanka, 1992; team mem. Ctrl. Am. Monitoring Group to El Salvador and Guatemala, 1993. Author: Like a Mighty River, 1980, Turning the World Upside Down, 1989, Miriam, Mary and Me, 1992, Telling Her Story, 1992; mem. adv. bd. Can. Woman Studies Jour., York U., 1993—; contbr. articles to profl. publs. Pres. Social Planning Coun., Thunder Bay, 1967-68, Can. Com. for Scientists and Scholars, Toronto, 1982; bd. dirs. Elizabeth Fry Soc., Hamilton, 1976-79, Amnesty Internat., 1970-80, Can. Inst. for Internat. Peace and Security, 1984-88, Energy Probe, 1981-86; active Refugee Status Adv. Com., 1985-89; bd. dirs. Can. Univ. Svc. Overseas, 1983-85; chmn. Urban Rural Mission, Can., 1990—; mem. Environ. Assessment Panel Govt. Can., Nuclear Fuel Waste Mgmt. and Disposal Concept, 1989—; trustee Nelson Mandela Fund 1990-92. Decorated Order of Can., 1984, Order of Ont., 1991; recipient Queens Jubilee medal, Commemorative medal for 125th Anniversary of Confederation of Can., 1992, World Federalist Peace award, 1985, Pearson Peace medal UN Assn. of Can., 1985; named hon. pres. Student Christian Movement of Can., Toronto, 1976. Mem. CAW (pub. rev. bd. 1986—), Can. Assn. Adult Edn. (bd. dirs. 1986-90), Friends Can. Broadcasting (bd. dirs. 1986—, v.p.), Civil Liberties Assn. (v.p. 1986—), UNIFEM (v.p 1993—, mem. CCIC team to monitor El Salvador election 1994), Parliament of World's Religions (del. 1993), Christian-Jewish Dialogue Jerusalem (keynote speaker 1994). Home and Office: 482 Markham St, Toronto, ON Canada M6G 2L3

WILSON, LORRAINE M., medical, surgical nurse, nursing educator; b. Mich., Nov. 18, 1931; d. Bert and Frances Fern (White) McCarty; m. Harold A. Wilson, June 9, 1953; children: David Scott, Ann Elizabeth. Diploma in Nursing, Bronson Meth. Sch. Nursing, Kalamazoo, Mich., 1953; BS in Chemistry, Siena Heights Coll., 1969; MSN, U. Mich., 1972; PhD, Wayne State U., Detroit, 1985. RN, Mich. Staff nurse U. Mich. Med. Ctr., Ann Arbor, 1953-54, Herrick Meml. Hosp., Tecumseh, Mich., 1954-69; asst. prof. nursing U. Mich., Ann Arbor, 1972-78, Wayne State U., Detroit, 1978-79; assoc. prof. nursing Sch. of Nursing Oakland U., Rochester, Mich., 1986-89; assoc. prof. nursing Ea. Mich. U., Ypsilanti, Mich., 1989—; researcher in field; bd. advs. Profl. Fitness Systems, Warren, Mich., 1986—; cons. wellness and exercise program General Motors CPC Hdqs., Warren, 1986; cons. and faculty liaison nurse extern program in critical care Ea. U. Catherine McAuley Health Ctr., 1989—. Co-author (with Sylvia Price) Pathophysiology: Clinical Concepts of Disease Processes, 4th ed., 1992; contbr. articles to profl. jours. Vol. Community Health Screening Drives, Tecumseh, 1960-70, leader Girl Scouts U.S., Tecumseh, 1960; sunday sch. tchr. Gloria Dei Luth. Ch., Tecumseh, 1960; mem. PTA. Grantee Mich. Heart Assn., 1984, 88, R.C. Mahon Found., 1988. Mem. ANA (various offices and com. chairs), Midwest Nursing Rsch. Soc. (v.p., sec.-treas., bd. dirs.), Mich. Nurses Assn. (del.), Nat. League Nursing, Nat. Orgn. Women, Sigma Theta Tau. Lutheran. Avocations: traveling, theatre, jogging. Home: 1010 Red Mill Dr Tecumseh MI 49286-1145 Office: Ea Mich U 53 W Michigan Ave Ypsilanti MI 48197-5436

WILSON, LUCY JEAN, librarian; b. Cin., Dec. 27, 1938; d. Gregory Girard and Harriet Elsa (Wiggers) Wright; m. Paul Robert Wilson, Aug. 25, 1962 (div. 1968); 1 child, Ellen Field; m. William Carl Schutzius, Dec. 12, 1976; stepchildren: Christopher Matthew, Catharine Alexander, John Benedict, Margaret Elizabeth. BA in French, Middlebury (Vt.) Coll., 1960; MS in Libr. Sci., U. Ill., 1963. Tech. libr. Chanute AFB, Rantoul, Ill., 1963-65; libr. Coll. Prep. Sch., Cin., 1969-74; pub. svcs. libr. Raymond Walters Coll., Cin., 1974-79, dir. libr., 1979-92, sr. libr., 1988—; dir. libr. and instructional media program Raymond Walters Coll., U. Cin., 1979-92; dir. media profl. cert. program, 1989-93; access svcs. libr. U. Cin. Coll. Engring., 1992—; bd. dirs. Ohio-Ky. Cooperating Librs., Union List of Serials, 1984-87; sec. instrn. and trng. coun. Ohionet, 1981-82. Mem. ALA, AAUP, Am. Soc. Info. Sci. (sec. 1980-81), Midwest Federating of Libr. Assn. (registration com. 1983), Acad. Libr. Assn. Ohio (nominating com. 1985), Greater Cin. Libr. Consortium (bd. dirs. 1979-92), Am. Soc. for Profl. Sci., Spl. Librs. Assn., Libr. Guild U. Cin. Home: 3444 Stettinius Ave Cincinnati OH 45208-1204 Office: U Cin Engring Coll Libr 880 Baldwin Hall U Cin Cincinnati OH 45221-0018

WILSON, LYNTON RONALD, telecommunications company executive; b. Port Colborne, Ont., Can., Apr. 3, 1940; s. Ronald Alfred and Blanche Evelyn (Matthews) W.; m. Brenda Jean Black, Dec. 23, 1968; children: Edward Ronald, Margot Jean, Jennifer Lyn. BA, McMaster U., 1962; MA, Cornell U., 1967. Dep. minister Ministry Industry and Tourism, Ont., 1978-81; pres., chief exec. officer Redpath Industries, Ltd., Toronto, Ont., 1981-88; mng. dir. N.Am. Tate & Lyle, PLC, London, 1986-89; chmn. bd. Redpath Industries, Ltd., Toronto, Ont., 1988-89; vice chmn. Bank of Nova Scotia, 1989-90; pres., chief operating officer BCE, Inc., Montreal, 1990-92; pres., CEO BCE Inc., Montreal, Can., 1992-93, chmn., pres. CEO, 1993—; bd. dirs. Tate & Lyle plc, London, Stelco Inc., BCE, Inc., Bell Can., No. Telecom, Teleglobe Inc., C.W. Howe Inst., Bell Can. Internat., BCE Mobile Comm., Inc., Chrysler Can. Ltd., Chrysler Corp., Bell-Northern Rsch. Ltd. Bd. govs. Olympic Trust of Can.; gov. McGill U., Can., 1992—; mem. internat. coun. J.P. Morgan & Co., N.Y., British-N.Am. Com.; mem. policy com. Bus. Coun. on Nat. Issues; mem. The Trilateral Commn.; bd. trustees Montreal Mus. of Fine Arts Found. Mem. The Mount Royal Club of Montreal, York Club, Toronto Club, Toronto Golf Club, Rideau Club, Univ. Club of Montreal, Royal Montreal Golf Club, Mount Bruno Country Club. Home: 1321 Sherbrooke St W Apt A-110, Montreal, PQ Canada H3G 1J4 Office: BCE Inc / Ste 3700, 1000 Rue de la Gauchetière O, Montreal, PQ Canada H3B 4Y7

WILSON, MARC FRASER, art museum administrator and curator; b. Akron, Ohio, Sept. 12, 1941; s. Fraser Eugene and Pauline Christine (Hoff) W.; m. Elizabeth Marie Fulder, Aug. 2, 1975. BA, Yale U., 1963, MA, 1967. Departmental asst. Cleve. Mus. Art, 1964; translator, project cons. Nat. Palace Mus., Taipei, Taiwan, 1968-71; assoc. curator of Chinese art Nelson Gallery-Atkins Mus., Kansas City, Mo., 1971-73, curator of Oriental art, 1973—, interim dir., 1982, dir. and curator Oriental art, 1982—; mem., rapporteur Indo-US Subcom. on Edn. and Culture, Washington, 1976-79; mem. adv. coun. Asia Soc. Galleries, N.Y.C., 1984—, China Inst. in Am., 1985—. Mem. adv. com. Muni-Art Commn. on Urban Sculpture, Kansas City, 1984-87; com. mem. Kansas City-Xi'an, China, Sister City program, 1986—; mem. humanities coun. Johnson County Community Coll., 1976-79; commr. Japan-U.S. Friendship Commn., Washington, 1986-88; panelist Japan-U.S. Cultural and Edn. Cooperation, Washington, 1986-88. Mem.

Assn. Art Mus. Dirs. (treas., trustee 1988-90, chmn. works of art com. 1986-90), Mo. China Coun., Fed. Coun. Arts and Humanities (chmn. arts and artifacts indemnity adv. panel 1986-89). Office: Nelson-Atkins Mus Art 4525 Oak St Kansas City MO 64111-1818

WILSON, MARGARET BUSH, lawyer, civil rights leader; b. St. Louis, Jan. 30, 1919; married; 1 child, Robert Edmund. B.A. cum laude, Talladega Coll., 1940; LL.B., Lincoln U., 1943. Ptnr. Wilson & Wilson, St. Louis, 1947-65; now with firm Wilson & Assocs.; asst. dir. St. Louis Lawyers for Housing, 1969-72; asst. atty. gen. Mo., 1961-62; atty. Rural Electrification Adminstrn., Dept. Agr., St. Louis, 1943-45; instr. civil procedure St. Louis U. Sch. Law, 1971; chmn. St. Louis Land Reutilization Authority, 1975-76; mem. Mo. Coun. Criminal Justice, 1972—; chmn. Intergroup Corp., 1985-87; bd. dirs. Mut. of N.Y. Mem. gen. adv. com. ACDA, 1978-81; trustee emeritus Washington U., St. Louis; chmn. bd. trustees Talladega Coll., Ala., 1988-92; nat. bd. dirs. ARC, 1975-81, United Way, 1978-84, Police Found., 1976-93; treas. NAACP Nat. Housing Corp., 1971-84, chmn. nat. bd., 1975-84; dep. dir./acting dir. St. Louis Model City Agy., 1968-69; adminstr. Mo. Commn. Svc. and Continuing Edn., 1967-68. Recipient Bishop's award Episcopal Diocese Mo., 1962; Juliette Derricotte fellow, 1939-40. Mem. ABA (chmn. youth edn. for citizenship 1991-94), Nat. Bar Assn., Mo. Bar Assn., Mound City Bar Assn., St. Louis Bar Assn., Alpha Kappa Alpha. Office: Wilson & Assocs 4054 Lindell Blvd Saint Louis MO 63108-3202

WILSON, MARGARET DAULER, philosophy educator; b. Pitts., Jan. 29, 1939; d. Lee Van Voorhis and Margaret (Hodge) D.; m. Emmett Wilson, Jr., June 12, 1962. A.B., Vassar Coll., 1960; A.M., Harvard U., 1963, Ph.D., 1965; postgrad., Oxford U., 1963-64. Asst. prof. philosophy Columbia U., 1965-67; asst. prof. Rockefeller U., 1967-70; asso. prof. philosophy Princeton (N.J.) U., 1970-75, prof., 1975—, acting chmn. dept. philosophy, 1987-88; dir. Summer Inst. Early Modern Philosophy, Bristol, R.I., 1974; vis. asst. prof. Barnard Coll., part-time 1969-70. Author: Descartes, 1978; editor: The Essential Descartes, 1969. Mem. Planning Bd. Franklin Twp., N.J., 1988-92, Environ. Commn., 1988—. Recipient Centennial medal Harvard Grad. Sch. Arts and Scis., 1989, Behrman prize for distinction in humanities Princeton U., 1994; Japan Soc. for Promotion of Sci. fellow, 1990, Guggenheim fellow, 1977-79, Am. Coun. Learned Socs. fellow, 1982-83; visitor Inst. Advanced Study, spring 1973. Fellow Am. Acad. Arts and Scis.; mem. Am. Philos. Assn. (v.p. ea. divsn. 1993-94, pres. ea. divsn. 1994-95), Leibniz Soc. N.Am. (pres. 1986-90), Internat. Berkeley Soc. Home: 943 Canal Rd Princeton NJ 08540-8509 Office: Princeton U Dept Philosophy 1879 Hall Princeton NJ 08544

WILSON, MARJORIE PRICE, physician, medical commission executive. Student, Bryn Mawr Coll., 1942-45; M.D., U. Pitts., 1949. Intern U. Pitts. Med. Ctr. Hosps., 1949-50; resident Children's Hosp. U. Pitts., 1950-51, Jackson Meml. Hosp., U. Miami Sch. Medicine, 1954-56; chief residency and internship dir. edn. svc. Office of Rsch. and Edn., VA, Washington, 1956, chief profl. tng. div., 1956-60, asst. dir. edn. svc., 1960; chief tng. br. Nat. Inst. Arthritis and Metabolic Disease NIH, Bethesda, Md., 1960-63, asst. to assoc. dir. for tng. Office of Dir., 1963-64, assoc. dir. program devel. OPPD, 1967-69, asst. dir. program planning and evaluation, 1969-70; assoc. dir. extramural programs Nat. Libr. Medicine, 1964-67; dir. dept. instl. devel. Assn. Am. Med. Colls., Washington, 1970-81; sr. assoc. dean U. Md. Sch. Medicine, Balt., 1981-86; vice dean, 1986-88, acting dean, 1984; pres., chief exec. officer Edl. Commn. Fgn. Med. Grads., Phila., 1988—; mem. Inst. Medicine Nat. Acad. Scis.,1974—; bd. visitors U. Pitts. Sch. Medicine, 1974—; mem. Nat. Bd. Med. Examiners, 1980-87, 89—; mem. adv. bd. Fogarty Internat. Ctr., 1991—. Contbr. articles to profl. jours. Mem. adv. bd. Robert Wood Johnson Health Policy Fellowships, 1975-87; trustee Analytic Services, Inc., Falls Church, Va., 1976—. Fellow Am. Coll. Physician Execs., AAAS; mem. Assn. Am. Med. Colls., Am. Fedn. Clin. Research, IEEE. Office: Ednl Commn Fgn Med Grads 3624 Market St Philadelphia PA 19104-2614

WILSON, MARY ELIZABETH, physician; b. Indpls., Nov. 19, 1942; d. Ralph Richard and Catheryn Rebecca (Kurtz) Lausch; m. Harvey Vernon Fineberg, May 16, 1975. AB, Ind. U., 1963; MD, U. Wis., 1971. Diplomate Am. Bd. Internal Medicine, Am. Bd. Infectious Diseases. Tchr. of French and English Marquette Sch., Madison, Wis., 1963-66; intern in medicine Beth Israel Hosp., Boston, 1971-72, resident in medicine, 1972-73, fellow in infectious diseases, 1973-75; physician Albert Schweitzer Hosp., Deschapelles, Haiti, 1974-75, Harvard Health Svcs., Cambridge, Mass., 1974-75; asst. physician Cambridge Hosp., 1975-78; hosp. epidemiologist Mt. Auburn Hosp., Cambridge, 1975-79, chief of infectious diseases, 1978—; adv. com. immunization practices Ctrs. for Disease Control, Atlanta, 1988-92; acad. adv. com. Nat. Inst. Pub. Health, Mex., 1989-91; cons. Ford Found., 1988; instr. in medicine Harvard Med. Sch., Boston, 1975-93, asst. clin. prof., 1994—; asst. prof. depts. epidemiology and population and internat. health Harvard Sch. Pub. Health, 1994—; lectr. Sultan Qaboos U., Oman, 1991; chair Woods Hole Workshop, Emerging Infectious Diseases. Author: A World Guide to Infections: Diseases, Distribution, Diagnosis, 1991; co-editor: (with Richard Levins and Andrew Spielman) Disease in Evolution: Global Changes and Emergence of Infectious Diseases, 1994; mem. editl. bd. Current Issues in Pub. Health. Mem. Cambridge Task Force on AIDS, 1987—, Earthwatch, Watertown, Mass., Cultural Survival, Inc., Cambridge; bd. dirs. Horizon Communications, West Cornwall, Conn., 1990. Recipient Lewis E. and Edith Phillips award U. Wis. Med. Sch., 1969, Cora M. and Edward Van Liere award, 1971, Mosby Scholarship Book award, 1971. Fellow ACP, Infectious Diseases Soc. Am., Royal Soc. Tropical Medicine and Hygiene; mem. Am. Soc. Microbiology, N.Y. Acad. Scis., Am. Soc. Tropical Medicine and Hygiene, Mass. Infectious Diseases Soc., Peabody Soc., Internat. Soc. Travel Medicine, Wilderness Med. Soc., Soc. for Vector Ecology, Internat. Union Against Tuberculosis and Lung Disease, Soc. for Epidemiol. Rsch., Sigma Sigma, Phi Sigma Iota, Alpha Omega Alpha. Avocations: playing the flute, hiking, reading, travel. Office: Mt Auburn Hosp 330 Mt Auburn St Cambridge MA 02138-5502

WILSON, MARY LOUISE, learning systems company executive; b. Chgo., June 29, 1940; d. John Baptiste and Marion Margaret (Coveney) Sweig; m. John Paul Wilson, June 7, 1969; 1 son, Devin Sweig. Student, U. Toronto, 1960-61; B.A., Smith Coll., 1962; M.A., Emerson Coll., 1965; Ph.D., Northwestern U., 1968. Assoc. prof. speech pathology California (Pa.) State Coll., 1968-69; prof. communication scis. and disorders U. Vt., Burlington, 1969-94, prof. emerita, 1994—, dir. program in communication sci. and disorders, 1971-77, acting chmn., 1977-80; dir. E. M. Luse Center for Communication Disorders, 1971-81; disting. vis. scholar Worcester State Coll., Mass., 1984; pres. Laureate Learning Systems, Inc., 1982—; mem. Vt. State Adv. Com. on Spl. Edn., 1974; project dir. Bur. Edn. of Handicapped, 1971-83. Author: Wilson Initial Syntax Program, 1972, Wilson Expanded Syntax Program, 1976, Syntax Remediation: A Generative Grammar Approach to Language Development, 1977, Prescriptive Analysis of Language Disorders, 1979, Expressive Syntax Assessment, 1979, Sequential Software for Language Intervention, 1991; co-author: First Words, 1982, 3d edit., 1989, Speak Up, 1983, First Categories, 1983, Microcomputer Language Assessment and Development System, 1984, 2d edit., 1988, First Verbs, 1985, 2d edit., 1989, Fast Access Scan Talker, 1985, First Words II, 1986, 2d edit., 1989, Twenty Categories, 1986, 2d edit., 1989, Talking Series, 1987, Creature Antics, 1987, Creature Chorus, 1987, Creature Capers, 1988, Words and Concepts, 1989, Concentrate! On Words and Concepts, 1989, Early Emergins Rules, 1990, Creature Features, 1992, Exploring Vocabulary, 1994, Simple Sentence Structure, 1994. Mem. Am. Speech and Hearing Assn., Am. Assn. Mental Retardation (pres. Region X), Council Exceptional Children, Vt. Speech and Hearing Assn. Home: RR 2 Box 355 Hinesburg VT 05461-9409 Office: Laureate Learning Systems Inc 110 E Spring St Winooski VT 05404-1837

WILSON, M(ATHEW) KENT, retired chemist, researcher, educator; b. Salt Lake City, Dec. 22, 1920; s. Mathew Bytheway and Helen Marie (Marsh) W.; m. Gladys E. Acevedo, Oct. 25, 1944; 1 son, Mathew K. BS, U. Utah, 1943; PhD, Calif. Inst. Tech., 1949. Instr. Harvard U., 1948- 51, asst. prof., 1951-56; prof. chemistry, chmn. Tufts U., 1956-66, Robinson prof., 1957-66; head chemistry sect. Nat. Sci. Found., 1966-74; head office Energy Related Gen. Rsch., 1974-75, dep. asst. dir. math. and phys. scis. and engring. directorate, 1975-77, sr. sci. assoc. office of the dir., 1977, dir. office of planning and resource mgmt., 1977-83, exec. officer math. and phys. sci., 1983-92, acting asst. dir. math and phys. sci., 1989-90; acting divsn. dir.

math., 1992, divsn. dir. astronomy, 1992-93. Author: General Chemistry: A Topical Introduction, 1954; Contbr. articles profl. jours. Fulbright research scholar, 1954-55; Guggenheim fellow, 1954-55. Fellow Am. Acad. Arts and Scis.; mem. Am. Chem. Soc.

WILSON, MATTHEW FREDERICK, newspaper editor; b. San Francisco, May 10, 1956; s. Kenneth E. and Verna Lee (Hunter) W. BA in Philosophy, U. Calif., Berkeley, 1978. Copy person San Francisco Chronicle, summers 1975, 76, 77, copy editor, 1978-82, editorial systems coord., 1982-84; budget analyst San Francisco Newspaper Agy., 1984085; asst. news editor San Francisco Chronicle, 1985-87, asst. to exec. editor, 1987-88, mng. editor, 1988-95, exec. editor, 1995—. Mem. Am. Soc. Newspaper Editors, AP Mng. Editors, Calif. Soc. Newspaper Editors. Office: San Francisco Chronicle 901 Mission St San Francisco CA 94103-2988*

WILSON, MICHAEL ALAN, health facility administrator; b. Springfield, Mo., Aug. 18, 1947; s. Allen and Harold (Hudson) W.; m. Alla L. Sachowicz, Feb. 14, 1985; children: Shawn, Cara. B, Baylor U., 1970; M, Chapman Coll., 1973; MBA, S.W. Mo. State U., 1975. Asst. adminstr. Nicollet Clinic, Mpls., 1976-80; exec. dir. Colorado Springs (Colo.) Med. Ctr., 1980-84; exec. v.p. LaSalle Clinic, Neenah, Wis., 1984-90; pres., chief adminstrv. officer Dean Med. Ctr., Madison, Wis., 1990—; bd. dirs. Dean Med. Ctr. and Dean Care HMO, Madison, Physician Ins. Co. Wis., Madison. Bd. dirs. Edgewood High Sch., Madison 1991-93, Physician Ins. Co. of Wis., 1991—; SMS Holdings, 1990-91; mem. cabinet United Way, Madison, 1991—, chmn. ptnrs. in prevention, 1992—. With USN, 1970-76. Mem. Wis. Med. Group Mgmt. Assn. (pres. 1989-90), Med. Group Mgmt. Assn. (2d v.p. Midwest sect. 1991-92, 1st v.p. Midwest sect. 1992-93, pres. Midwest sect. 1994—), Rotary Club. Presbyterian. Avocations: golf, literature, sports. Office: Dean Med Ctr 1313 Fish Hatchery Rd Madison WI 53715-1991

WILSON, MILNER BRADLEY, III, banker; b. Spartanburg, S.C., Nov. 17, 1933; s. Milner Bradley and Margaret (Nash) W.; m. Nancy Brock, Aug. 18, 1956; children—Margaret, Julia, Bradley. A.B., Duke U., 1955; LL.B., U. S.C., 1961; A.M.P., Harvard U., 1973. C.L.U., CTFA. With Citizens & So. Nat. Bank S.C., Charleston, 1961-84, gen. trust officer, 1971-72; sr. v.p., 1972-84; v.p. Barnett Banks Trust Co. N.A., Hallandale, Fla., 1984-86; regional v.p. Barnett Banks Trust Co. N.A., Tampa, Fla., 1986-87; sr. v.p. Barnett Banks Trust Co. N.A., Jacksonville, Fla., 1987-89; v.p. No. Trust Bank of Fla., Miami, 1989—. Served with USMC, 1955-58. Mem. ABA. Home: 337 Bedford Ave Fort Lauderdale FL 33326-2977 Office: 700 Brickell Ave Miami FL 33131-2804

WILSON, MINTER LOWTHER, JR., retired officers association executive; b. Morgantown, W.Va., Aug. 19, 1925; s. Minter Lowther and Mary Mildred (Friend) W.; m. Helen Hope Sauerwein, June 18, 1946; children—Mary Florence, Barbara Ann, Karen Lee, Stephen David. B.S. in Mil. Sci. and Engring., U.S. Mil. Acad., 1946; M.S. in Journalism, U. Wis., Madison, 1963; diploma, NATO Def. Coll., Rome, 1969, U.S. Army War Coll., 1971. Commd. officer U.S. Army, 1946, advanced through grades to col., comdg. officer 1st Brigade, 1st Armored Div., 1968-69; chief of pub. info. Supreme Hdqrs. Allied Powers, Europe, 1969-72; editor Ret. Officer Mag., Alexandria, Va., 1972-88; dir. communications Ret. Officers Assn., Alexandria, 1972-88. Contbr. articles to profl. jours. Chmn. bd. deacons Ch. of the Covenant, Arlington, 1974-77, elder, 1977-80, 88-93, clk. of session, 1991-94, chmn. bd. trustees, 1982-86; mem. troop com. Boy Scouts Am., 1972-78. Decorated Commendation medal, Legion of Merit (2); recipient George Washington Honor medal Freedoms Found., 1975, 76, 77, George Washington Honor medal encased Freedoms Found., 1979, Honor cert. Freedoms Found., 1973, 74, 78. Mem. West Point Soc. of D.C. (life, bd. govs. 1978-81), Army Distaff Found. (bd. dirs. 1980-83), Assn. U.S. Army, Ret. Officers Assn. (life). Presbyterian. Club: Army Navy Country. Avocations: photography; golf; skiing; tennis; racquetball. Home: 3116 N Thomas St Arlington VA 22207-4120

WILSON, MIRIAM GEISENDORFER, physician, educator; b. Yakima, Wash., Dec. 3, 1922; d. Emil and Frances Geisendorfer; m. Howard G. Wilson, June 21, 1947; children—Claire, Paula, Geoffrey, Nicola, Marla. B.S., U. Wash., Seattle, 1944, M.S., 1945; M.D., U. Calif., San Francisco, 1950. Mem. faculty U. So Calif. Sch. Medicine, L.A., 1965—, prof. pediatrics, 1969—. Office: U So Calif Med Ctr 1129 N State St Los Angeles CA 90033-1069

WILSON, MIRIAM JANET WILLIAMS, publishing executive; b. London, Ont., Can., July 13, 1939; d. Ralph George and Lillian Conn Williams; m. Carson Winnette, Nov. 20, 1960 (div. 1971); children: Barrie Carson Winnette, Rebecca Lynn Winnette; m. Charles Lindsay Wilson, Dec. 14, 1973; 1 child, Charles William Wilson; stepchildren: Kenneth M., Carol Ann, Catherine S., Nancy L., Patrick L. Diploma in nursing, Glendale (Calif.) Sanitarium & Hosp., 1960. RN, Calif., Va., Ohio, Md., W.Va. Head nurse emergency and med. fls. Glendale Sanitarium and Hosp., 1960-65; psychometrist Harding Hosp., Worthington, Ohio, 1969-73; biofeedback specialist in assn. Dr. Randolph P. Johnston, Winchester, Va., 1980-84; dir. Stress Ctr. for Children and Adults, Shepherdstown, W.Va., 1985-87; pres. Rocky River Pubs., Shepherdstown, 1987—; lectr. ednl., profl. and civic groups, 1984—. Author: Help For Children, 6 edits., 1987-95, Stress Stoppers, 2 edits., 1987-89; contbr. articles to profl. publs. Active Shepherdstown Women's Club, 1986-95. Mem. NAFE, Internat. Platform Assn., Am. Booksellers Assn., N.Y. Acad. Scis. Avocations: gardening, music, reading. Office: Rocky River Pubs PO Box 1679 Shepherdstown WV 25443-1679

WILSON, MYRON ROBERT, JR., former psychiatrist; b. Helena, Mont., Sept. 21, 1932; s. Myron Robert Sr. and Constance Ernestine (Bultman) W. BA, Stanford U., 1954, MD, 1957. Diplomate Am. Bd. Psychiatry and Neurology. Dir. adolescent psychiatry Mayo Clinic, Rochester, Minn., 1965-71; pres. and psychiatrist in chief Wilson Ctr., Faribault, Minn., 1971-86; ret., 1986; chmn. Wilson Ctr., 1986-90; ret., 1990; assoc. clin. prof. psychiatry UCLA, 1985—. Contbr. articles to profl. jours. Chmn., chief exec. officer C.B. Wilson Found., L.A., 1986—; mem. bd. dirs. Pasadena Symphony Orchestra Assn., Calif., 1987. Served to lt. comdr., 1958-60. Fellow Mayo Grad. Sch. Medicine, Rochester, 1960-65. Fellow Am. Psychiat. Assn., Am. Soc. for Adolescent Psychiatry, Internat. Soc. for Adolescent Psychiatry (founder, treas. 1985-88, sec. 1985-88, treas. 1988-92); mem. Soc. Sigma Xi (Mayo Found. chpt.). Episcopalian. Office: Wilson Found 8033 W Sunset Blvd # 4019 West Hollywood CA 90069-1925

WILSON, NANCY, singer; b. Chillicothe, Ohio, Feb. 20, 1937; d. Olden and Lillian (Ryan) W.; m. Kenneth C. Dennis (div. 1969); 1 child, Kenneth C.; m. Wiley Burton, 1974; children: Samantha, Sheryl. Ed., Columbus (Ohio) schs. Began career as singer with local groups, then joined Rusty Bryant band, 1956, toured Midwest and Can., until 1958, singing independently, 1959—; rec. artist Capitol Records, EMI Records, Japan, Nippon Columbia, Japan, Interface, Japan, Columbia Records, USA, Epic/Sony Japan; ablums include (with Heart): Dreamboat Annie, 1976, Little Queen, 1977, Magazine, 1978, Dog and Butterfly, 1978, Beb La Strange, 1980, Greatest Hits Live, 1980, Private Audition, 1982, Passionwroks, 1983, Heart, 1985, Bad Animals, 1987; recs. include I'll Be a Song, Just To Keep You Satisfied, Forbidden Lover, Nancy Now, Lady With A Song, With My Lover Beside Me, 1991; internat. concert tours, U.S., Japan, Europe, Indonesia, Australia; rec. artist; TV appearances include Police Story, Hawaii Five-O, 1974-75, Red Hot & Cool (syndicated), 1990—; appeared in film: The Big Score. Recipient Grammy award for Best R&B Vocal Nat. Acad. Rec. Arts and Scis., Best Female Vocalist award Playboy and Down Beat Jazz Polls, Image award NAACP, 1986, award Nat. Med. Assn., Equitable (17th Black Achievement) award, Urban Network Lifetime Achievement award, 1990, Whitney Young awd., Los Angeles Urban League, Essence awd., Essence Magazine, 1992; Star on Hollywood Walk of Fame, 1990. *

WILSON, NANCY LINDA, church officer; b. Mineola, N.Y., July 13, 1950. Grad., Allegheny Coll.; student, Boston U.; MDiv, SS, Cyril and Methodius Sem. Ordained to ministry Universal Fellowship of Met. Cmty. Chs. Dist. coord. N.E. dist. Universal Fellowship of Met. Cmty. Chs; clk. bd. of elders Fellowship hdqrs. Universal Fellowship of Met. Cmty. Chs., L.A., 1979-86; sr. pastor Met. Comty. Ch. UFMCC, L.A., 1986—, vice-moderator, 1993—; bd. trustees Samaritan Coll.; founder, chief ecumenical

officer Ecumenical Witness and Ministry. Co-author: Amazing Grace; prodr.: (brochure) Our Story Too. Rockefeller scholar. Office: UFMCC PO Box 388 Culver City CA 90232

WILSON, NORA D., nursing administrator; b. Rio Grande City, Tex., Oct. 2, 1942; d. Luis and Ana (Martinez) Saenz; m. James W. Wilson, Feb. 27, 1971; 1 child, Coy. BSN, Incarnate Word Coll., San Antonio, 1965; MS, SW Tex. State U., 1978. RN, Tex. Assoc. adminstr. Med. Ctr. Hosp., San Antonio, St. Rose Hosp., San Antonio. Recipient Patty L. Hawken award. Mem. ANA (cert. advanced nurse adminstr.), Tex. Nurses Assn. Home: 8039 Callaghan Rd # 611 San Antonio TX 78230-4718

WILSON, NORMAN GLENN, church administrator, writer; b. Rensselaer, N.Y., Nov. 3, 1936; s. Lawrence Wilbur and Wilhelmena Augusta (Knapp) W.; m. Nancy Ann Deyo, Nov. 17, 1956; children: Beth, Lawrence, Jonathon. BRE in Religious Edn., United Wesleyan Coll., 1958, DD (hon.), 1986; MA in Biblical Studies, Winona Lake Sch. Theology, 1968. Pastor The Wesleyan Ch. 1958-76, Gloversville, N.Y., 1963-66, North Lakeport, Mich., 1966-70, Owosso, Mich., 1970-76; dir. comm. The Wesleyan Ch., Indpls., 1992—; program prodr., speaker The Wesleyan Hour, Indpls., 1975—; mem. gen. bd. adminstrn. The Wesleyan Ch., Indpls., 1992—; disting. lectr. Staley Found., 1986. Author: How to Have a Happy Home, 1976, Christianity in Shoe Leather, 1978, The Constitution of the Kingdom, 1989, People Just Like Us, 1994; editor The Wesleyan Advocate, 1992—. Mem. Nat. Religious Broadcasters (bd. dirs. 1984—, Merit award 1984). Avocations: oil painting, antique cars. Home: 304 Scarborough Way Noblesville IN 46060

WILSON, NORMAN LOUIS, psychiatrist, educator; b. Buffalo, Oct. 4, 1937; s. Norman Louis and Martha (Aiken) W.; m. Phien Ly Thi, Aug. 22, 1988; 1 child, Daniel. BS in Biophysics summa cum laude, Yale U., 1959; MD, Harvard U., Boston, 1963. Diplomate Am. Bd. Psychiatry and Neurology. Med. intern Rush-Presbyn.-St. Luke's Med. Ctr., Chgo., 1963-64; resident in psychiatry, tchg. fellow Mass. Mental Health Ctr.-Harvard U., Boston, 1964-66, Peter Bent Brigham Hosp.-Harvard U., 1966-67; pvt. practice, Washington, 1969—; condr. workshops on use of hypnosis in treatment of multiple personality disorder, mood disorders, psychopharmacology; asst. clin. prof. dept. psychiatry and behavioral sci. George Washington U. Sch. Medicine, Washington, 1973—; founding mem., mem. faculty Washington Psychotherapy Tng. Inst., 1989—; staff psychiatrist Cmty. Psychiat. Clinic, Bethesda, Md., 1969-71, D.C. Forensic Psychiat. Adminstrn., 1974-89; psychiatrist NIH Employee Health Svc., 1971-74, John Howard Pavilion, St. Elizabeth's Hosp., Washington, 1987-89; cons. Clin. Ctr., NIH, 1974-80, Mental Health Assocs., Adelphi, Md., 1983-92, Luth. Social Svcs., Washington, 1990-93, occupl. med. svc. NIH, 1989-93; chmn. dept. psychiatry Washington Hosp. Ctr., 1987-92, admitting privileges; admitting privileges George Washington U. Hosp., Psychiat. Inst. Washington, Dominion Hosp.; mem. mktg. com. Nat. Capital Reciprocal Ins. Co. Capt. M.C., USAF, 1967-69. Fellow Am. Psychiat. Assn.; mem. Am. Group Therapy Assn., Am. Coll. Forensic Examiners, Am. Acad. Psychiat. and Law, Internat. Soc. for Study Multiple Personality and Dissociation, Washington Psychiat. Soc. (former mem. coms. on liaison with non-psychiatry mental health workers, forensic psychiatry, pub. rels.), Med. Soc. D.C. (past mem. alcohol com. and mental health com.), Amnesty Internat., Physicians for Social Responsibility, Am. Coalition for Abuse Awareness, Phi Beta Kappa. Avocations: scuba diving, backpacking, canoe tripping, movies, classical and folk music. Office: 4025 Connecticut Ave NW Washington DC 20008-1148

WILSON, OWEN MEREDITH, JR., lawyer; b. Oakland, Calif., Dec. 22, 1939; s. Owen Meredith Sr. and Marian (Wilson) W.; children: Ann, Melissa, Jennifer; m. Theodora Anne Dusa, May 1, 1984; children: Amanda Louise, Lisa Christine. AB, Harvard U., 1961; LLB, U. Minn., 1965. Bar: Oreg. 1965, U.S. Dist. Ct. Oreg. 1965, U.S. Ct. Appeals (9th cir.) 1968, U.S. Supreme Ct. 1971, Wash. 1985. Assoc. McColloch, Dezendorf & Spears, Portland, Oreg., 1965-69; ptnr. Spears, Lubersky, Bledsoe, Anderson, Young & Hilliard, Portland, 1969-90, Lane Powell Spears Lubersky, Portland, 1990—. Mem. ABA, Oreg. Bar Assn., Wash. Bar Assn., Am. Arbitration Assn. Office: Lane Powell Spears Lubersky 520 SW Yamhill St Ste 800 Portland OR 97204-1383

WILSON, PATRICIA POTTER, library science and reading educator, educational and library consultant; b. Jennings, La., May 3, 1946; d. Ralph Harold and Wilda Ruth (Smith) Potter; m. Wendell Merlin Wilson, Aug. 24, 1968. BS, La. State U., 1967; MS, U. Houston-Clear Lake, 1979; EdD, U. Houston, 1985. Cert. tchr., learning resources specialist (librarian), Tex. Tchr., England AFB (La.) Elem. Sch., 1967-68, Edward White Elem. Sch., Clear Creek Ind. Schs., Seabrook, Tex., 1972-77; librarian C.D. Landolt Elem. Sch., Friendswood, Tex., 1979-81; instr./lectr. children's lit. U. Houston 1983-86; with U. Houston/Clear Lake, 1984-87, asst. prof. libr. sci. and reading, 1988-94, assoc. prof. learning resources and reading edn., 1994—, mem. faculty senate, 1992-93, 95—; cons. Hermann Hosp., Baywood Hosp., 1986-87, Bedford Meadows Hosp., 1989-90, Wetcher Clinic, 1989; v.p., sec. Potter Farms, Inc., 1994—. Trustee, Freeman Meml. Library, Houston, 1982-87, v.p., 1985-86, pres., 1986-87; trustee Evelyn Meador Libr., 1993-94; adv. bd. Evelyn Meador Libr., 1994—; mem. adv. bd. Bay Area Soc. Prevention Cruelty Animals, 1994—; mem. Armand Bayou Nature Ctr., Houston, 1980—, bd. dirs. 1989-94; bd. dirs. Sta. KUHT-TV, 1984-87; mem. Bay Area Houston Symphony League. Editor A Rev. Sampler, 1985-86, 89-90; dir. Learning Resources Book Rev. Ctr., 1989-90. Author: HAPPENINGS: Developing Successful Programs for School Libraries, 1987; contbg. editor Tex. Library Jour., 1988-94; contrib. articles to profl. jours. Recipient Rsch. award Tex. State Reading Assn., 1993, Pres. award Tex. Coun. Tchrs. of English; grantee Tex. Libr. Assn., 1993. Mem. ALA, Am. Assn. Sch. Librarians, Internat. Reading Assn., Nat. Council Tchrs. English, (Books for You review com. 1985-88, Your Reading review com., 1993—), Tex. Council Tchrs. English, Antarctican Soc., Phi Delta Kappa. Methodist. Club: Lakewood Yacht (Seabrook). Home: 629 Bay Vista Dr Seabrook TX 77586-3001 Office: U Houston Clear Lake 2700 Bay Area Blvd Houston TX 77058-1002

WILSON, PAUL EDWIN, lawyer, educator; b. Quenemo, Kans., Nov. 2, 1913; s. Dale Edwin and Clara (Jacobs) W.; m. Harriet Eileen Stephens, June 16, 1941; children: Elizabeth, Mary Paulette, Eileen, David. BA, U. Kans., 1937, MA, 1938; LLB, Washburn U., 1940. Bar: Kans. 1940, U.S. Supreme Ct. 1952, U.S. Ct. Appeals 1950. Pvt. practice law Ashland, Kans., 1941-42, Lyndon, Kans., 1946-50; atty. County of Osage, Kans., 1947-50; gen. counsel dept. social welfare State of Kans., 1950-51, asst. atty. gen., 1951-53, 1st asst. atty. gen., 1953-57; assoc. prof. law U. of Kans., 1957-62, prof., 1962-68, Kane prof., 1968-81, prof. emeritus, 1981—; assoc. dir. Inst. Judicial Adminstrn., 1964-65; vis. prof. The Menninger Found. 1972; cons. in field. Author: (with Reams) Segregation and the Fourteenth Amendment in the States, 1975, Pattern Rules of Court and Code Provisions, 1975, Judicial Education in the United States, 1965; Editor: American Criminal Law Quarterly, 1963-70; contbr. articles in field to profl. jours. Mem. Lawrence (Kans.) Planning Commn., 1962-65; chmn. Bd. Zoning Appeals, Lawrence, 1966-67; mem. Kans. Hist. Sites Bd. Rev., 1973-77; trustee Ft. Burgwin (N.Mex.) Rsch. Ctr., 1976-79, Task Force for Hist. Preservation, Lawrence, Kans. (Disting. Svc. citation 1991), 1987-89. With U.S. Army, 1942-46. Recipient Justice award Kans. Supreme Ct., 1992; cited for Disting. Service to Bar and Pub., Kans. Bar Assn., 1987, Gov. Kans., Ho. Reps., Kans. Mem. Am. Bar Assn., Kans. Bar Assn. (chmn. com. criminal law 1960-68), Am. Law Inst., Am. Bar Found., Selden Soc., Nat. Trust Historic Preservation (bd. advisors 1972-78), Kans. State Hist. Soc. (v.p. 1987-89, pres. elect 1990, pres. 1990-91f, Phi Alpha Delta. Republican. Methodist. Office: U Kans 410 Green Hall Lawrence KS 66045 *Few things in my life have happened according to a preconceived plan. My admonition to the young is "Don't plan, just live." Perhaps I should add "also let live," by which I mean a concern for humanity, contemporary and prospective.*

WILSON, PAUL HOLLIDAY, JR., lawyer; b. Schenectady, N.Y., Sept. 4, 1942; s. Paul H. and Sarah Elizabeth (MacLean) W.; m. Elaine Hawley Griffin, May 30, 1964; children: Hollace, Paul, Kirsten, Katherine. AB, Brown U., 1964; LLB, MBA, Columbia U., 1967. Bar: N.Y. 1967, U.S. Dist. Ct. (so. dist.) 1968. Law clk. U.S. Dist. Ct. (so. dist.) N.Y., N.Y.C. 1967-68; assoc. Debevoise & Plimpton, N.Y.C., 1968-75, ptnr., 1976—, fin.

ptnr., 1980-88, 91-93, dep. presiding ptnr., 1993—. Vice-chmn., trustee St. Michael's Montessori Sch., N.Y.C., 1977-79, chmn. bd. trustees, 1979-81. Mem. ABA, Assn. Bar City N.Y. (mem. commn. on securities regulations 1985-88). Club: Vineyard Haven Yacht (Mass.) (vice-commodore 1985, commodore 1986-87). Avocations: sailing, reading, music. Office: Debevoise & Plimpton 875 3rd Ave New York NY 10022-6225

WILSON, PEGGY HENICAN, city official; b. New Orleans, June 24, 1937; d. C. Ellis and Elizabeth (Cleveland) Henican; m. Gordon Francis Wilson Jr., Dec. 10, 1932; children: Gordon, Alice, Peter, Carter. BA cum laude, Barat Coll., Lake Forest, Ill., 1959; postgrad., Tulane and Dominican Coll., 1960-75. Cert. tchr. Tchr. Mercy Acad., New Orleans, 1961-62, Acad. Sacred Heart, New Orleans, 1959-72; mgr. polit. campaigns Campaign Specialists, 1978-80; ptnr. Mason, Glickman, Wilson, New Orleans, 1981-82; owner Trolley Tours, 1975-85; pres. Peggy Wilson & Assocs., New Orleans, 1980-87; mem. city council dist. A New Orleans, 1986-94, coun. mem.-at-large, 1994—; chmn. fin. com. S&WB, mem. bd. liquidations. Author: Trolley Tours, 1982. Chmn. Alcoholic Beverage Control Bd., 1984-86; sec.-treas. Warehouse Dist. Devel. Assn., 1982-84, pres., 1984; bd. dirs. Carrollton-Hollygrove Community Ctr.; bd. dirs. YWCA, 1984-87; bd. dirs. City Park, New Orleans Mus. Art, Preservation Action; mem. mktg. com. City of New Orleans; mem. Cox Cable Com.; chmn. Hist. Dist. Landmarks Commn., 1981, 82; mem. bd., exec. com. St. George's Episcopal Sch., 1980-82; mem. Housing Task Force, 1978-80; mem. Police Chief Selection Com., 1978-79. Inst. Politics fellow Loyola U., 1978. Mem. Alliance for Good Govt., LWV, Upper St. Charles Civic Assn., Warehouse Dist. Devel. Assn., AARP. Office: Office City Council City Hall Rm 2E09 1300 Perdido St New Orleans LA 70112-2114

WILSON, PETE, governor of California; b. Lake Forest, Ill., Aug. 23, 1933; s. James Boone and Margaret (Callaghan) W.; m. Betty Robertson (div.); m. Gayle Edlund, May 29, 1983. B.A. in English Lit., Yale U., 1955; J.D., U. Calif., Berkeley, 1962; LL.D., Grove City Coll., 1983, U. Calif., San Diego, 1983, U. San Diego, 1984. Bar: Calif. 1962. Mem. Calif. Legislature, Sacramento, 1966-71; mayor City of San Diego, 1971-83; U.S. Senator from Calif., 1983-91; gov. State of Calif., 1991—. Trustee Conservation Found.; mem. exec. bd. San Diego County council Boy Scouts Am.; hon. trustee So. Calif. Council Soviet Jews; adv. mem. Urban Land Inst., 1985-86; founding dir. Retinitis Pigmentosa Internat.; hon. dir. Alzheimer's Family Ctr., Inc., 1985; hon. bd. dirs. Shakespeare-San Francisco, 1985. Recipient Golden Bulldog award, 1984, 85, 86, Guardian of Small Bus. award, 1984, Cuauhtemoc plaque for disting. svc. to farm workers in Calif., 1991, Julius award for outstanding pub. leadership U. So. Calif., 1992, award of appreciation Nat. Head Start, 1992; named Legislator of Yr., League Calif. Cities, 1985, Man of Yr. N.G. Assn. Calif., 1986, Man of Yr. citation U. Calif. Boalt Hall, 1986; ROTC scholar Yale U., 1951-55. Mem. Nat. Mil. Family Assn. (adv. bd.), Phi Delta Phi, Zeta Psi. Republican. Episcopalian. Office: State Capitol Office Of Governor Sacramento CA 95814*

WILSON, R. DALE, marketing educator, consultant; b. Ironton, Ohio, July 16, 1949; s. Robert J. and Treva L. (Shively) W.; m. Emily J. Ray, June 19, 1971; 1 child, Travis Ray. BBA cum laude, Ohio U., 1971; MBA, U. Toledo, 1972; PhD, U. Iowa, 1977. Asst. prof. mktg. Pa. State U., University Park, 1976-80; v.p. dir. mktg. scis. Batten, Barton, Durstine & Osborn, Inc., N.Y.C., 1980-83; vis. prof. Cornell U., Ithaca, N.Y., 1983-84; assoc. prof. Mich. State U., East Lansing, 1984-87, prof., 1987—; cons. in field. Contbr. articles to profl. jours. Treas., bd. dirs. So. Age Child Care, East Lansing, 1988-89. Faculty research grantee Pa. State U., Mich. State U. Mem. Am. Acad. Advt., Am. Mktg. Assn., Inst. Mgmt. Scis. (assoc. editor Interfaces, cert. recognition 1983), Assn. Consumer Research, Product Devel. and Mgmt. Assn., Beta Gamma Sigma. Home: 859 Audubon Rd East Lansing MI 48823-3003 Office: Mich State U Eli Broad Grad Sch Mgmt Dept Mktg and Logistics N322 N Business Complex East Lansing MI 48824-1122

WILSON, R. MERINDA D., lawyer; b. Pitts., Feb. 24, 1952. BA magna cum laude, Pa., 1973; JD, Harvard U., 1976. Bar: Ga. 1976, D.C. 1978. Ptnr. Sidley & Austin, Washington; chair bd. trustees Pub. Defender Svc., Washington, 1985-89. Mem. Nat. Bar Assn. (chair legal edn. com. 1989-91). Office: Sidley & Austin 1722 I St NW Washington DC 20006-3705

WILSON, RALPH EDWIN, lawyer, justice; b. Osceola, Ark., Sept. 28, 1921; s. Emmett A. and Lillie (Simmons) W.; m. Mary Ann Murray, Apr. 23, 1949; children: Ralph Edwin, Teresa Ann, Don Alan. Student, U.S. Naval Acad., 1943; A.B., Union U., 1946; J.D., Vanderbilt U., 1949. Bar: Tenn. 1948, Ark. 1948. Practice in Osceola, 1949—; city atty. Osceola, 1949; dep. pros. atty. 2d Jud. Dist. Ark., 1950-53; spl. asst. to atty. gen. Ark. 1956-60, spl. assoc. justice Supreme Ct. Ark., 1984; pres. Liberal State Bank, Gt. Eastern Assurance Co., North Little Rock; sec. Farmers Agri Export, Inc.; dir. Allied Cos., Inc., Does-More Products Corp., Allied Real Estate Investment Trust, Osceola Land Devel. Co.; Mem. adv. council Nat. Pub. Works Week, 1964. Alderman Osceola City Council, 1958-61. Served as lt. U.S. Mcht. Marines USNR, 1943-45. Recipient Ark. House and Senate Concurrent Resolutions Commendation, 1971. Mem. Ark. Bar Assn. (past mem. exec. com.), Osceola Bar Assn. (pres.), Am. Trial Lawyers Assn., U.S. Bar (Supreme Ct.), Am. Legion, Phi Alpha Delta, Alpha Tau Omega, Tau Kappa Alpha. Democrat. Methodist. Club: Kiwanian (internat. v.p. 1970-71, trustee 1966-70, life fellow internat. found.). Home: 903 W Hale Ave Osceola AR 72370-2428 Office: 109 N Maple St Osceola AR 72370-2537 *I believe it is man's highest achievement to reach far and find truth. The adversary system in law is this searching and finding truth. The drama of the courtroom involves all that is precious—life, liberty, property, dominion over children. These interacting forces play against each other, but if all facts are before the court, truth invariably prevails.*

WILSON, RAMON B., agricultural economics educator, administrator; b. Ogden, Utah, Sept. 22, 1922; s. Benjamin Andrew and Hannah Josephine (Browning) W.; m. Ruth G. Worlton, July 27, 1945; children: Lynn, William Scott, Bruce Ramon, JoAnne, Kathleen. B.S., Utah State U., 1947; M.S., Purdue U., 1948, Ph.D., 1950; postgrad., U. Calif., Berkeley, 1972, Georgetown U., 1976. Extension economist Utah State U., Logan, 1950-53; mktg. economist Calif. Dept. Agr., Sacramento, 1953-55; asst. prof. Purdue U., West Lafayette, Ind., 1955-57; assoc. prof. Purdue U., 1957-63, prof. agrl. econs., 1963-78, prof. emeritus, 1978—; market service dir., 1960-68; asst. dir. Ind. Coop. Extension Service, 1963-74, assoc. dir. agrl. expt. sta., asst. to dean agr., 1968-74; from asst. to assoc. dir. Benson Agrl. Food Inst. Brigham Young U., Provo, Utah, 1979-82; asst. to sec. U.S. Dept. Agr., Washington, 1974-76; pres. Nat. Assn. State Depts. Agr., 1966; cons., lectr. Served with U.S. Army, 1943-46. Republican. Mem. Ch. Jesus Christ of Latter-day Saints. Home: 435 E 2200 N Provo UT 84604-1725

WILSON, RAYMOND CLARK, former hospital executive; b. Birmingham, Ala., July 8, 1915; s. Raymond Clyde and Lida (Gay) W.; m. Sara Elizabeth Paris, Feb. 17, 1940; children: Margery Jo, Richard Clark, Sara Elizabeth, Raymond Paul. Student, Oglethorpe U., 1933-34, U. Ga., 1934-37; Tulane U., 1948; D.Bus. Adminstrn. (hon.), William Carey Coll. Office mgr. firm C.R. Justi (contractor), Atlanta, 1933-42; paymaster J.A. Jones Constrn. Co., Brunswick, Ga., 1942-45; asst. supt. So. Bapt. Hosp., New Orleans, 1946-53; adminstr. So. Bapt. Hosp., 1953-68, exec. dir., 1969-77; pres. Affiliated Bapt. Hosps., Inc., 1977-80, Health Care Cons. & Mgmt. Services, Inc., 1977-80; ret., 1980; exec. dir. Bapt. Meml. Hosp., Jacksonville, Fla., 1973-77; dir., chmn. La. Health and Indemnity Co.; dir. New Orleans Area Health Planning Council, 1969-74. Bd. dirs. Bapt. Hosp. Found., 1970-78; bd. trustees Crosby Meml. Hosp., 1992-94, chmn., 1993-94. With USAAF, 1945-46. Paul Harris fellow Rotary Found. Fellow Am. Coll. Healthcare Execs. (bd. regents 1972-75); mem. Hosp. Svc. Assn. (bd. dirs., treas. 1953-74), Am. Hosp. Assn. (ho. dels. 1972-75), La. Hosp. Assn. (pres. 1956), New Orleans Hosp. Coun. (pres. 1954-55), Southeastern Hosp. Conf. (pres. 1963), Bapt. Hosp. Assn. (pres. 1964-65). Baptist (trustee, deacon). Home: 200 W Sunnybrook Rd Carriere MS 39426-7831

WILSON, RAYMOND P., communications systems marketing professional; b. 1954. BA, MA, Merrimack Coll. 1981; MA, MBA, Bentley Coll., 1986. With Chaffin Co., Cambridge, Mass., 1975-79, Lexidata Corp., Billerica, Mass., 1979-85; with Scitex Am Corp., Bedford, Mass., 1985—, now v.p.

fin., treas., CFO. Office: Scitex Am Corp 8 Oak Park Dr Bedford MA 01730*

WILSON, RICHARD A., oil/gas industry support services executive; b. 1938. BS in Petroleum Engring., U. Wyo. Pres. Energy Svc. Co. Inc., Dallas, 1988-89, sr. v.p.- ops., 1989—; formerly with ESSO Exploration; past v.p. Global Marine Drilling Co.; various positions, then exec. v.p. Schlumberger Tech. Corp. Office: Energy Service Co Inc 1445 Ross Ave Ste Dallas TX 75202-2711*

WILSON, RICHARD ALEXANDER, career officer; b. San Francisco, Apr. 5, 1941; s. William Alexander and Myrlin Francis (Ralph) W.; m. Elizabeth Ray Esleeck, Feb. 24, 1962; children: Richard Scott, David Alexander. BS in Naval Sci., U.S. Naval Academy, 1963; MS in Systems Acquisition, Navy Postgrad. Sch., 1975; grad., USN Test Pilot Sch. Commd. ensign USN, advanced through grades to rear adm.; commdg. officer Fighter Squadron 154, Miramar, Calif., 1976-78; comdr. Carrier Airwing 14, Miramar, 1981-82; chief of staff Comfitaewing PAC, Miramar, 1982-84; commdg. officer USS Camden, Bremerton, Wash., 1984-86; with OPNAV Staff, Pentagon, Washington, 1986-87; commdg. officer USS Midway, Yokosuka, Japan, 1987-89; with Joint Staff, Pentagon, Washington, 1989-91; comdr. Carrier Group 7, San Diego, 1991-92; dep. chief staff ops. and plans CINCPACFLT, Pearl Harbor, Hawaii, 1993—. Named Outstanding Young Man of Am., Jaycees, 1970. Mem. Naval Inst. Procs. (life), Assn. Naval Aviation (life), Naval Aviation Mus. Found. (life), U.S. Naval Acad. Alumni Assn. (life), Order Daedalians.

WILSON, RICHARD ALLAN, landscape architect; b. Chgo., Feb. 5, 1927; s. Edgar Allan and Lois Helena (Hearn) W.; m. Lisabet Julie Horchler, May 31, 1958; children: Gary Allan, Carl Bruce. BS, U. Calif., Berkeley, 1952. Engring. draftsman Freeland Evanson & Christenson, San Diego, 1952-53; designer, estimator Blue Pacific Nursery & Landscape Co., San Diego, 1955-59; prin. Richard A. Wilson, FASLA and Assocs., San Diego, 1959—; sec. Calif. Coun. Landscape Architects, 1982-85; expert witness for law firms, 1983—. Designer Phil Swing Meml. Fountain, 1967. Mem. landscape com. Clairemont Town Coun., San Diego, 1955. With U.S. Army, 1944-46, Korea. Recipient First Pl. award for landscape So. Calif. Expdn., Del Mar, 1963. Fellow Am. Soc. Landscape Architects (del. coun. 1982-85), Am. Inst. Landscape Architects (treas. 1970, 2d v.p. 1971). Republican. Home and Office: 2570 Tokalon Ct San Diego CA 92110-2232

WILSON, RICHARD CHRISTIAN, engineering firm executive; b. Bethlehem, Pa., July 17, 1921; s. Christian and Laura Barrows (Langham) W.; m. Jean M. Avis, July 16, 1949; children—Richard A., Christy. B.S. Carnegie-Mellon U., 1943; M.S., Lehigh U., 1947; Ph.D., U. Mich., 1961. Mfg. engr. Westinghouse Electric Corp., East Pittsburgh, 1943; instr. mech. engring. Carnegie-Mellon U., Pitts., 1943-44; vacuum test engr. Kellex Corp., N.Y.C., 1944; area supr. Carbide & Carbon Chem. Co., Oak Ridge, 1945-46; apparatus engr. Westinghouse Electric Corp., Jackson, Mich., 1947-55; instr. indsl. and operation engring. U. Mich., 1955-61, asst. prof., 1961-63, assoc. prof., 1963-66, prof., 1966-85, chmn. dept., 1973-77, assoc. dean Coll. Engring., 1968-72; pres. Techware, Inc., 1985-86, ret., 1986; dir. Cascade Data Corp., 1969-72. Contbr. articles to profl. jours. Bd. dirs. Ecumenical Assn. Internat. Washington, 1970-87, pres., 1975-76, 86-87. Mem. IEEE, Inst. Mgmt. Sci., Am. Inst. Indsl. Engrs., Ops. Research Soc. Am., Sigma Xi, Beta Theta Pi, Phi Kappa Phi. Club: Rotary. Home: 805 Mt Pleasant Ave Ann Arbor MI 48103-4776 Office: U Mich Dept Indsl Engring Ann Arbor MI 48109

WILSON, RICHARD DALE, executive training, consulting company; b. L.A., July 22, 1933; s. Wayne Merle and June Lillian (Buys) W.; m. Nancy Irene Colby, 1974; children: Christopher, Jennifer, Janie, Matthew, Dixie, Tracey, Mark, Mysti, Tiffany. BA, San Jose Coll., 1964, MTH; LLB, Blackstone Law Sch., 1974; postgrad., Harvard U., 1987; PhD, Kennedy Western U., 1993. Cert. profl. cons. TV news anchor, overseas correspondent, investigative reporter numerous TV stas., 1964-75; legis. services dir. Utah State Legis., Salt Lake City, 1976; sr. cons. The Co. Cons., 1981—; pres. Nat. Inst. for Sales Tng. and Cons. Author: Handwriting 12 Keys to Every Personality, 1968, 10 Basic Habits Superstar Salesperson, 1986, 10 Critical Steps to Building a Powerful and Profitable Sales Organization, 1987, 10 Basic Habits of A Superstar Sales Manager, 1989, Do It Right The First Time: Finding, Assessing and Selecting the Best Sales Force For The 90's, 1991; editor, pub. The Co. Cons. Newsletter, 1985—; contbr. articles to profl. jours. Media planner Rep. Conv., N.D., 1972; organizer Rep. Conv., Calif., 1964; del. Utah State Conv., 1976. Sgt. USMC, 195-57, Korea. Recipient Gavel award ABA, 1973; named Regional Dir. Yr. Westworld Services, Inc., 1981. Mem. Soc. Profl. Cons., Am. Handwriting Analysis Found., Nat. Assn. Realtors, Realtors Nat. Mktg. Inst., Nat. Speakers Assn. Mormon. Avocation: certified handwriting expert. Home: 1736 S 320 W Orem UT 84058 Office: Nat Inst Tng & Consulting Inc PO Box 0817 2696 N University Ave Provo UT 84603-0817

WILSON, RICHARD EDWARD, composer, pianist, music educator; b. Cleve., May 15, 1941; s. James F. and Edith Ann (Zingler) W.; m. Adene Stevenson Green, May 15, 1971; children: Katherine Blanca, James Graham. A.B. magna cum laude, Harvard U., 1963; M.A., Rutgers U., 1966. Asst. prof. music Vassar Coll., Poughkeepsie, N.Y., 1966-70, assoc. prof. music, 1970-76, prof. music, 1976—, chmn. dept. music, 1979-82, 85-88; Mary Conover Mellon Chair Vassar Coll., Poughkeepsie, 1988—. Composer: Music for Violin and Violoncello, 1969, Eclogue for Piano Solo, 1974 (Burge prize 1979), Figuration 1980, String Quartet No. 3, 1982, two symphonies, 1984, 87; Opera: Aethelred the Unready, 1994. Recipient 23 ann. awards for profl. distinction ASCAP, 1970—, Walter Henrichsen award Am. Acad. Inst. Arts and Letters, 1986, Cleve. Arts prize, 1988, Exec.'s award Dutchess County, 1989, Stoeger prize Chamber Music Soc. Lincoln Ctr., 1994; named Guggenheim fellow, 1992, composer-in-residence Am. Symphony Orch., 1992—. Mem. Am. Music Ctr., Am. Soc. Composers, ASCAP, Phi Beta Kappa. Club: Harvard (N.Y.C.). Home: 8 Vassar Lake Dr Poughkeepsie NY 12601-3021 Office: Vassar Coll Dept Music Raymond Ave Poughkeepsie NY 12601

WILSON, RICHARD FERROL, plant physiologist, educator; b. Macomb, Ill., July 6, 1947; s. Elmer Ferrol and Velma Lucille (Swartzbaugh) W.; m. Pamela Ann Hanback, Aug. 28, 1971. BS, Western Ill. U., 1970; MS, U. Ill., 1973, PhD, 1975. Plant physiologist USDA Agrl. Rsch. Svc., Raleigh, N.C., 1975—; prof. crop sci. N.C. State U., Raleigh, 1975—. Recipient Arthur S. Fleming award Downtown Jaycees, D.C., 1986, Alumni Achievement award Western Ill. U., 1989, Merit award Gamma Sigma Delta, 1989, Disting. Svc. award USDA, 1989, Utilization Rsch. award Am. Soybean Assn., 1990, Soybean Team Rsch. award Am. Soybean Assn., 1991; named Disting. Scientist of Yr., USDA Agrl. Rsch. Svc., 1987. Fellow Am. Soc. Agronomy, Crop Sci. Soc. Am.; mem. Am. Oil Chemists Soc., Am. Soc. Crop Sci., N.Y. Acad. Sci., Am. Soc. Plant Physiologists, Kiwanis, Sigma Xi, Alpha Zeta (chancellor 1969-70, Outstanding Alumni award 1991). Republican. Methodist. Avocations: bicycling, bowling, golf. Home: 110 Chattel Close Cary NC 27511-9745 Office: USDA Agrl Rsch Svc PO Box 7620 Raleigh NC 27695

WILSON, RICHARD HAROLD, government official; b. Waterloo, Iowa, July 15, 1930; s. Clarence Hough and Mary (Dillon) W.; m. Elaine Elizabeth Aniol., June 14, 1957; children: Elizabeth Aniol Wilson Adams, Andrew Edward. B.A., U. Ill., 1952; M.P.A., U. Kans., 1958. Lic. real estate broker, Tex.; lic. police ct. clk., Kans. Adminstrv. asst. to city mgr. San Antonio, 1956-58; budget analyst Kansas City, Mo., 1959; research asso. Internat. Union Local Authorities, The Hague, 1959-60; city mgr. Nevada, Mo., 1960-65; asst. to city mgr. Ft. Worth, 1965-67; asst. city mgr. Albuquerque, 1967-68, city mgr., 1968-72; dir. housing and urban rehab. Dallas, 1972-82; sr. v.p. Metroplex R&D Cons., Dallas, 1982-83; regional dir. comty. planning and devel. HUD Region V, Chgo., 1983-94; sr. advisor HUD, Chgo., 1994—; lectr. real estate U. Tex.-Arlington; instr. govt. Dallas County Community Coll. Dist.; exec. v.p. Designs for Worship, Inc., Dallas, 1982-83. Bd. dirs. Neighborhood Housing Svcs. Am., Inc., 1974-82; chmn. Housing Task Force of North Cen. Tex. Coun. Govts., 1974-80, chmn. human resources com., 1981-82; active Boy Scouts Am. Lt. (j.g.) USN, 1952-55; naval intelligence comdr. Res., 1955-82, ret. Fulbright fellow

Leiden (The Netherlands) U., 1959-60, Kennedy Sch., Harvard U., 1981, Fed. Exec. Inst., 1995. Mem. Nat. Assn. Housing and Redevel. Ofcls. (v.p. Tex. chpt. 1975-80, mem. S.W. regional coun. 1975-82), Internat. City/County Mgmt. Assn., Am. Soc. Pub. Adminstrn. (pres. N.Mex. 1968-69, v.p. North Tex. 1976-77, pres. North Tex. 1977-78, mem. nat. coun. 1979-82, Greater Chgo. chpt. coun. 1987-93), Naval Res. Assn., Chgo. Arch. Found. (docent 1990—), Phi Gamma Delta, Pi Sigma Alpha, Alpha Phi Omega. Episcopalian. Club: Rotary (Chicago). Home: 300 N State St Apt 2833 Chicago IL 60610-4805 Office: HUD 77 W Jackson Blvd 24th Floor Chicago IL 60604-3507

WILSON, ROBERT, food products executive. Vice chmn. Affiliated Food Coop., Inc., Norfolk, Nebr., also bd. dirs. Office: Affiliated Food Coop Inc 13th St Omaha Ave Norfolk NE 68701

WILSON, ROBERT ALLEN, religion educator; b. Geff, Ill., Oct. 7, 1936; s. Perry Arthur and Eva Mae (Dye) W.; m. Patsy Ann Jarrett, June 1, 1957; children: Elizabeth Ann, Angela Dawn, Christine Joy. AB, Lincoln (Ill.) Christian Coll., 1958, Hanover Coll., 1961; MRE, So. Bapt. Seminary, 1965, EdD, 1972. Ordained to ministry Ch. of Christ, 1958. Minister Fowler (Ind.) Christian Ch., 1955-59, Zoah Christian Ch., Scottsburg, Ind., 1959-64; minister of edn. and youth Shively Christian Ch., Louisville, 1964-69; prof. minister of edn. and family life Lincoln (Ill.) Christian Seminary, 1969—; pres. Christian Marriage and Family Enrichment Services, Lincoln, 1980—. Contbr. articles to profl. jours. Mem. Nat. Assn. Profs. Christian Edn. (editor newsletter 1975-79, pres. 1979-80), Religious Edn. Assn. Lodge: Rotary (bd. dirs. Lincoln chpt. 1988—, pres. 1993-94). Home: 330 Campus View Dr Lincoln IL 62656-2106 Office: Lincoln Christian Coll & Seminary 100 Campus View Dr # 178 Lincoln IL 62656-2167

WILSON, ROBERT BURTON, veterinary and medical educator; b. Salt Lake City, June 29, 1936; s. Stanley Burton and Jessie Adelia (Hassell) W.; m. Janet Diane McMurdie, June 1, 1962; children: Robert Burton Jr., Janet Diane. BS, Utah State U., 1958; DVM with highest honors, Wash. State U., 1961; PhD, U. Toronto, Ont., Can., 1967. Lic. veterinarian, Mass., Wash., Utah. Intern Angell Meml. Animal Hosp., Boston, 1962-63; asst. prof. Brigham Young U., Provo, Utah, 1963-64; asst. scientist Hosp. for Sick Children, Toronto, 1964-69; assoc. prof. MIT, Cambridge, 1969-73; prof. vet. medicine U. Mo., Columbia, 1973-76; prof., chmn. vet. micro. and pathology Wash. State U., Pullman, 1976-83, dean coll. vet. medicine, 1983-88; vet. cons. Forsyth Dental Inst., Boston, 1972-73; mem., chmn. adv. com. NIH, Bethesda, Md., 1976-80, 89-93. Contbr. over 100 articles to profl. jours. Recipient Mary Mitchell award Mass. Soc. Prevention Cruelty to Animals, 1964, Tchr. of Yr. award MIT, 1971, Tchr. of Yr. award W.A.M.I. Med. Program, 1992, 94. Fellow Am. Heart Assn. (coun. of arteriosclerosis); mem. Am. Vet. Med. Assn., Am. Inst. Nutrition. Mem. LDS Ch. Avocations: genealogy, history, golf, fishing. Home: 505 SE Crestview St Pullman WA 99163-2212 Office: Wash State U Coll Vet Medicine Bustad Hall Pullman WA 99164-7040

WILSON, ROBERT FOSTER, lawyer; b. Windsor, Colo., Apr. 6, 1926; s. Foster W. and Anne Lucille (Svedman) W.; m. Mary Elizabeth Clark, Mar. 4, 1951 (div. Feb. 1972); children: Robert F., Katharine A.; m. Sally Anne Nemec, June 8, 1982. BA in Econs., U. Iowa, 1950, JD, 1951. Bar: Iowa 1951, U.S. Dist. Ct. (no. and so. dists.) Iowa 1956, U.S. Ct. Appeals (8th cir.) 1967. Atty., FTC, Chgo., 1951-55; sole practice, Cedar Rapids, Iowa, 1955—; pres. Lawyer Forms, Inc.; dir. Appollo Computer Tech.; pres. S.E. Asia Trading Corp., Lawyers Forms, Inc. Democratic state rep. Iowa Legislature, Linn County, 1959-60; mem. Iowa Reapportionment Com., 1968; pres. Linn County Day Care, Cedar Rapids, 1968-70; del. to U.S. and Japan Bilateral Session on Legal and Econ. Rels. Conf., Tokyo, 1988, Moscow Conf. on Law and Bilateral Rels., Moscow, 1990; U.S. del. to Moscow conf. on legal and econ. rels., 1990. Served to sgt. U.S. Army, 1944-46. Mem. Am. Arbitration Assn. (panel arbitrators), Am. Legion (judge advocate 1970-75, 1987-93), Iowa Trial Lawyers Assn., Assn. Trial Lawyers Am., Iowa Bar Assn., Linn County Bar Assn., Delta Theta Phi. Club: Cedar View Country. Lodges: Elks, Eagles. Home: 100-1st Ave NE Cedar Rapids IA 52401 Office: 810 Dows Rd SE Cedar Rapids IA 52403-7010

WILSON, ROBERT GOULD, management consultant; b. Springfield, Mass., July 29, 1929; s. George Winthrop Wilson and Clara Margret (Smyth) Turnbull; m. Jane Seaman, Sept. 14, 1952; children: Roberta Wilson DiBlasi, Richard Jan. BA in Eng., Bates Coll., 1951. Various positions Gen. Electric Co., Bridgeport, Conn., 1953-64; v.p. planning Warnco, Inc., Bridgeport, 1964-76; pres. Hathaway Can., Prescott, Ont., 1976-79; sr. mgmt. cons. Arthur D. Little, Cambridge, Mass., 1979-84; pres. Northeast Cons., Boston, 1984—. Co-author: Business Strategy, 1983. Trustee Bates Coll., Lewiston, Maine, 1984-89. Office: NE Cons Resources Inc One Liberty Sq Boston MA 02109

WILSON, ROBERT HENRY, English educator; b. Gary, Ind., Apr. 5, 1909; s. Joseph Henry and Nell (Cox) W.; m. Lucille Bridgers, May 28, 1936 (dec. Apr. 1994); 1 dau., Edith Margaret Wilson Miles. Student, Kenyon Coll., 1924-25; A.B., Stanford U., 1928, M.A., 1929; Ph.D., U. Chgo., 1932. Instr. English U. Tex., Austin, 1934-36, 37-38; asst. prof. U. Tex., 1947-52, asso. prof., 1952-63, prof., 1963-79, prof. emeritus, 1980—; instr. La. State U., 1944-47. Contbr. to: A Manual of the Writings in Middle English, 1972; Contbr. articles in field to profl. jours. Mem. MLA, Modern Humanities Research Assn., Internat. Arthurian Soc., Phi Beta Kappa. Episcopalian. Home: 4201 Shoal Creek Blvd Austin TX 78756-3518

WILSON, ROBERT JAMES MONTGOMERY, investment company executive; b. Millbrook, N.Y., Feb. 8, 1920; s. Albert James Montgomery and Charlotte (Kaye) W.; m. Yvette Laneres, May 10, 1952; children—Robert James Montgomery, Olivia Laneres Wilson Welbourn, Geoffrey Laneres. Grad., Choate Sch., 1938; A.B., Yale U., 1942. Securities analyst buying dept. Union Securities Corp., N.Y.C., 1946-49; securities analyst Union Service Corp., N.Y.C., 1949-59; v.p. Union Service Corp., 1959-63; pres., dir. Surveyor Fund, Inc. (formerly Gen. Public Service Corp.), N.Y.C., 1963-71; with Rockefeller Family and Assos., 1972-75; pres. Adams Express Co., N.Y.C., 1975-86, also bd. dirs. 1975—; pres. Petroleum & Resources Corp. (formerly Petroleum Corp. Am.), N.Y.C., 1975-86, also bd. dirs., 1975—; mem. adv. investment com. Md. State Retirement Systems, 1979-82; bd. dirs. Assn. Publicly Traded Investment Cos., 1968-71, chmn., 1969-71. Mem. 1940 Fahnestock Expdn. of Am. Mus. Natural History to South Seas. Served to capt. AUS, World War II. Mem. Md. Club, Sea Oaks Beach and Tennis Club.

WILSON, ROBERT M., theatrical artist; b. Waco, Tex., Oct. 4, 1941; s. D.M. and Loree Velma (Hamilton) W. Student, U. Tex., 1962; BFA, Pratt Inst., 1966, DFA (hon.), 1991. Artistic dir. Byrd Hoffman Found., N.Y.C., 1969—; lectr. Internat. Sch., Paris, 1971, Atelje Festival, Belgrade, Yugoslavia, Internat. Theater Inst. of UNESCO, Durdan, France, 1971, Skowhegan Art Sch., Maine, 1977, Harvard U., 1982; condr. seminars U. Calif.-Berkeley, 1970, George Sch., New Hope, Pa., 1970, U. Iowa, 1970, Newark State Coll., 1971; condr. workshops Royaumont, France, 1972, Boulder, Colo., 1973; condr. workshops Ohio State U., 1973, Centre de Development du Potential Humain, Paris, 1973, 74, NEA, Seattle, 1982, UCLA, 1985. Theatrical and operatic performances U.S and Europe include: Deafman Glance, 1970 (Best Fgn. Play award Le Syndicat de la Critique Dramatique et Musicale, Paris 1970, Drama Desk award for best direction 1971), The Life and Times of Joseph Stalin (Obie Spl. Citation award for direction 1974), A Mad Man A Mad Giant A Mad Dog A Mad Urge A Mad Face, 1974, The Life and Times of Dave Clark, 1974, A Letter for Queen Victoria, 1974 (Maharam Found. award for scenic design 1975, nominee Tony award for best score and libretto 1975, Best Lyric Theatre award Le Syndicat de la Critique Dramatique et Musicale Paris, 1977), The $ Value of Man, 1974, Dialog, 1974, Einstein on the Beach, 1976, 84 (Best Play award Theatre of Nations, Belgrade, Yugoslavia, 1977, Lumen award, 1977), I Was Sitting on my Patio This Guy Appeared I Thought I Was Hallucinating, 1977, Dialog/Network, 1978, Death, Destruction and Detroit, 1979 (German Critics award 1979, German Press award 1979), Edison, 1979, Dialog/Curious Product, 1980, The Man in the Raincoat, 1981, Prologue to Fourth Act of Deafman Glance, 1982, Medea, 1984, Great Day in the Morning, 1982, The Golden Windows, 1982, 85 (Der Rosenstrauss award 1982), The Civil Wars, 1983-85 (Pulitzer prize nominee for drama 1986),

Hamletmachine, 1986 (Obie award for direction Village Voice 1986), Alceste, 1986, Salome, 1987, Parzival, 1987, Quartett, 1987, Death, Destruction and Detroit, 1987, The Martyrdom of St. Sebastian, 1988, Cosmopolitan Greetings, 1988, The Forest, 1988, DeMaterie, 1989, Doktor Faustus, 1989 (Best Prodn. award Italian Theatre Critics, 1989), Swan Song, 1989, Orlando, 1989, The Black Rider, 1990, (German Theater Critics award for Best Prodn. of Yr.), King Lear, 1990, When We Dead Awaken, 1991, Parsifal, 1991, The Magic Flute, 1991, Lohengrin, 1992, Dr. Faustus Lights the Lights, 1992, Alice, 1993, Alice in Bed, 1993, Madame Butterfly, 1993, The Black Rider, 1993, Orlando, 1993, Der Mond im Gras, 1994, Hanjo/ Hagoromo, 1994, T.S.E., 1994, The Meek Girl, 1994, Hamlet, Bluebeard's Castle, 1995; author (plays): Two Conversations with Edwin Denby, 1973, A Letter for Queen Victoria, 1974, I Was Sitting on my Patio This Guy Appeared I Thought I Was Hallucinating, 1977, Death, Destruction and Detroit, 1979, The Golden Windows, 1981, The Civil Wars, 1983, Death, Destruction and Detroit II, 1987; contbg. author: (anthology) New American Plays Vol. III, 1970; films include: Overture for a Deafman, Murder; video works include: Spaceman, 1976, 84, Video 50, 1978, Deafman Glance, 1981, Stations, 1982, La Femme a la Cafeterie, 1989 (Grand Prize Biennale Festival of Cinema Art, Barcelona), The Death of King Lear, 1989, Mr. Bojangles' Memory, 1991, La Mort de Moliere, 1993; exhibited drawings and sculpture one-man shows: Iolas Gallery, N.Y.C., Palazzi Gallery, Milan, Galerie Fred Lanzenberg, Brussels, Paula Cooper Gallery, N.Y.C., Musée Galliera, Paris, 1972, 74, Multiples/Goodman Gallery, 1977, 79, Neuberger Mus., Purchase, N.Y., 1980, Contemporary Art Ctr., Cin., 1980, Castelli Feigen Corcoran, N.Y.C., Portia Harcus Gallery, Cambridge, Mass., Alpha Gallery, Cambridge, Richard Kunlenschmidt Gallery, Los Angeles, Hewlet Gallery, Pitts., Lehman Coll. Arts Gallery, Bronx, Walker Art Ctr., Mpls., 1984, Rhona Hoffman Gallery, 1986, Galerie der Stadt Stuttgart, 1987, Galerie Herald Behm, Hamburg, 1988, AnneMarie Verna Galerie, Zurich, 1989, Galerie Ha Galerie Yvon Lambert, 1989, Feigen Gallery, Chgo., 1990, Mus. Fine Arts, Boston, 1991, Centre Georges Pompidou, Paris, 1991, Galerie Fred Jahn, Munich, 1991, Hiram Butler Gallery, Houston, 1992, Laura Carpenter Gallery, Sante Fe, 1992, IVAM, Valencia, 1992, Produzenentengalerie, Hamburg, 1992, Deichtorhallen, Hamburg, 1993, Mus. Boymans-van Beuningen, Rotterdam, 1993, Akira Ikeda Gallery, N.Y.C., 1994; exhibited numerous other maj. galleries, U.S. and abroad, including: Willard Gallery, N.Y.C., 1971, Marian Goodman Gallery, 1982, Pavillion des Arts, Paris, 1983, Otis-Parsons, Los Angeles, 1984, Inst. Contemporary Art, Boston, 1985, Galeria Gamarra y Garrigues, Madrid, 1992, Kamakura Gallery, Tokyo, 1992, Galerie van Rijsbergen, Rotterdam, 1993; works represented in permanent collections: Mus. Modern Art, N.Y.C., Boston Mus. Fine Arts, Australian Nat. Gallery, Canberra, Kunst Mus., Bern, Lannan Mus., L.A., Mus. Modern Art, Paris, Mus. Art, R.I. Sch. Design, Providence, The French Govt., Paris, Mus. Contemporary Art, Los Angeles, Boymans Mus., Rotterdam, Stedelijk Mus., Amsterdam, Menil Mus., Houston, Tex., Centre Georges Pompidou, Paris, Art Inst., Chgo., Huntington Art Mus. U. Tex., Austin, Met. Mus. Art, N.Y.C., Phila. Mus. Art. Recipient Chgo. Art Inst. Skowhegan medal for drawing Skowhegan Sch. Painting, 1987, Inst. Honor award AIA, 1988, Mondello award, Palermo, 1988, Brandeis Univ. Poses Creative Arts award, 1991, Golden Lion award in sculpture, Venice Bienniale, 1993; named Most Outstanding Theater Designer of the Seventies, U.S. Inst. Theater Tech., Washington, 1977; Rockefeller grantee, 1970, 77-80; Guggenheim fellow, 1971, 80. Mem. Nat. Inst. Music Theatre (trustee), Am. Repertory Theatre (hon. bd. dirs.), The Dramatists Guild, Soc. des Auteurs et Compositeurs Dramatiques, Soc. Stage Dirs. and Choreographers, PEN Am. Ctr., I.C.A. Boston (bd. overseers). Office: Byrd Hoffman Found 131 Varick St Rm 908 New York NY 10013-1410

WILSON, ROBERT NEAL, sociologist, educator; b. Syracuse, N.Y., Nov. 15, 1924; s. Robert Marchant and May Eloise (Neal) W.; m. Arleene Eleanor Smith, Aug. 21, 1948 (div. 1973); children—Lynda Lee, Deborah Eloise; m. Joan Wallace, Aug. 1, 1973. B.A., Union Coll., 1948; Ph.D., Harvard U., 1952. Research assoc. Cornell U., Ithaca, N.Y., 1951-53; staff Social Sci. Research Council, Washington, 1953-56; lectr. Harvard U., Cambridge, Mass., 1957-60; assoc. prof. Yale U., New Haven, 1960-63; prof. sociology U. N.C., Chapel Hill, 1963—; trustee Easter Seal Research Found., Chgo., 1966-72; cons. NIMH, Washington, 1968-72, Nat. Inst. Child Health and Human Devel., Washington, 1970-77; reviewer NEH, Washington, 1977—. Author: Man Made Plain, 1958, Sociology of Health, 1970, The Writer as Social Seer, 1979, Experiencing Creativity, 1986; author, editor: The Arts in Soc., 1964. Served to sgt. U.S. Army, 1943-46, ETO. Ctr. for Advanced Study Behavioral Scis. fellow, 1956-57; Fulbright scholar, 1975. Fellow Am. Sociol. Assn., Am. Pub. Health Assn., Social Sci. Soc. Democrat. Episcopalian. Avocation: poetry. Home: 103 Springvalley Rd Carrboro NC 27510-1246 Office: Univ NC Chapel Hill NC 27514

WILSON, ROBERT R. H., airline company executive; b. 1937. Joined TWA, Mt. Kisco, N.Y., 1964, various mgmt. positions, 1964-85, co-CEO, 1992—; with Burlington Air Express, Inc., 1986-88, GPA Group plc, 1989-92. Office: TWA Inc 100 S Bedford Rd Mount Kisco NY 10549-3432

WILSON, ROBERT RATHBUN, retired physicist; b. Frontier, Wyo., Mar. 4, 1914; s. Platt Elvin and Edith (Rathbun) W.; m. Jane Inez Scheyer., Aug. 20, 1940; children—Daniel, Jonathan, and Rand. AB, U. of Calif., 1936; PhD, 1940; PhD (hon.), Notre Dame U.; PhD hon. degree, U. Bonn; PhD (hon.), Harvard U., 1986, Wesleyan U., 1987. Instr. Princeton U., 1940-42, asst. prof., 1942-45; head rsch. divsn. Los Alamos Lab., 1944-45, 1944-45; assoc. prof. physics Harvard, 1946-47; prof. physics and dir. Lab Nuclear Studies Cornell U., 1947-67; prof. physics U. Chgo., 1967-78, Peter B. Ritzma prof., 1978-80; dir. Fermi Nat. Accelerator Lab., Batavia, Ill., 1967-78; Michael Pupin prof. Columbia U., 1980-83; now ret. Contbr. articles to Physics Rev. Recipient Elliott Cresson medal Franklin Inst., 1964; Nat. medal sci., 1973; Enrico Fermi award, 1984, The Wright prize, 1986, del Regato medal, 1989. Fellow NAS, Am. Phys. Soc. (pres. 1985), Am. Acad. Arts and Scis., Fedn. Am. Scientists (chmn. 1946, 63), Am. Philos. Soc., Sigma Xi. Address: 916 Stewart Ave Ithaca NY 14850-2123

WILSON, ROBERT SPENCER, magazine editor; b. Bolling Field, D.C., Feb. 21, 1951; s. Joseph Griswold and Helen (Hodnett) W.; m. Martha Elaine Ritchie, Oct. 19, 1974; children—Matthew Spencer, Cole Ritchie, Robert Samuel. B.A., Washington and Lee U., 1973; M.A., U. Va., 1977. Lectr. U. Va., Charlottesville, 1977-80; asst. editor Washington Post, 1977-83; book editor, book columnist USA Today, Washington, 1983-94; lit. editor Civilization mag., Washington, 1994—. Office: Civilization Mag 666 Pennsylvania Ave SE Washington DC 20003

WILSON, ROBERT WOODROW, radio astronomer; b. Houston, Tex., Jan. 10, 1936; s. Ralph Woodrow and Fannie May (Willis) W.; m. Elizabeth Rhoads Sawin, Sept. 4, 1958; children—Philip Garrett, Suzanne Katherine, Randal Woodrow. B.A. with honors in Physics, Rice U., 1957; Ph.D., Calif. Inst. Tech., 1962. Research fellow Calif. Inst. Tech., Pasadena, 1962-63; mem. tech. staff AT&T Bell Labs., Holmdel, N.J., 1963-76; head wireless tech. rsch. dept. AT&T Bell Labs., 1976-94; sr. sci. Harvard-Smithsonian Ctr. for Astrophysics, Cambridge, Mass., 1994—. Discoverer 3 deg. k microwave background radiation, 1965; discoverer CO and other molecules in interstellar space using their millimeter wavelength radiation. Recipient Henry Draper medal Royal Astron. Soc., London, 1977, Herschel medal Nat. Acad. Scis., 1977; named Fairchild Disting. scholar Caltech., 1987; Nobel prize in physics, 1978; NSF fellow, 1958-61, Cole fellow, 1957-58. Mem. Am. Astron. Soc., Internat. Astron. Union, Am. Phys. Soc., Internat. Sci. Radio Union, Nat. Acad. Scis., Phi Beta Kappa, Sigma Xi. Home: 9 Valley Point Dr Holmdel NJ 07733-1320 Office: Harvard-Smithsonian Ctr Astrophysics 60 Garden St MS-42 Cambridge MA 02138

WILSON, ROBIN SCOTT, university president, writer; b. Columbus, Ohio, Sept. 19, 1928; s. John Harold and Helen Louise (Walker) W.; m. Patricia Ann Van Kirk, Jan. 20, 1951; children: Kelpie, Leslie, Kari, Andrew. B.A., Ohio State U., 1950; M.A., U. Ill., 1951, Ph.D., 1959. Fgn. intelligence officer CIA, Washington, 1959-67; prof. English Clarion State Coll., (Pa.), 1967-70; assoc. dir. Com. Instnl. Cooperation, Evanston, Ill., 1970-77; assoc. provost instrn. Ohio State U., Columbus, 1977-80; univ. pres. emeritus Calif. State U., Chico, 1980—. Author: Those Who Can, 1973; short stories, criticism, articles on edn. Lt. USN, 1953-57. Mem. AAAS, Phi Kappa Phi. Office: Calif State U Monterey Bay 915 Hilby Ave Seaside CA 93955-5339

WILSON, ROBLEY CONANT, JR., English educator, editor, author; b. Brunswick, Maine, June 15, 1930; s. Robley Conant and Dorothy May (Stimpson) W.; m. Charlotte A. Lehon, Aug. 20, 1955 (div. 1991); children: Stephen, Philip; m. Susan Hubbard, June 17, 1995. B.A., Bowdoin Coll., 1957, D.Litt (hon.), 1987; M.F.A., U. Iowa, 1968. Reporter Raymondville Chronicle, Tex., 1950-1951; asst. publicity dir. N.Y. State Fair Syracuse, 1956; instr. Valparaiso U., Ind., 1958-63; asst. prof. English U. No. Iowa, Cedar Falls, 1963-69, assoc. prof., 1969-75, prof., 1975—, editor N.Am. Rev., 1969—. Author: The Pleasures of Manhood, 1977, Living Alone, 1978, Dancing for Men, 1983 (Drue Heinz Lit. prize 1982), Kingdoms of the Ordinary, 1987 (Agnes Lynch Starrett award 1986), Terrible Kisses, 1989, A Pleasure Tree, 1990 (Soc. Midland Authors Poetry award 1990), The Victim's Daughter, 1991. Bd. dirs. Associated Writing Programs, Norfolk, Va., 1983-86; pres. Iowa Woman Endeavors, Inc., 1986-90. With USAF, 1951-55. Guggenheim fellow, 1983-84. Mem. Am. Soc. Mag. Editors, Authors' Guild. Home: PO Box 527 Cedar Falls IA 50613-0527 Office: North American Review University of Northern Iowa Cedar Falls IA 50614

WILSON, ROGER B., lieutenant governor, school administrator; b. Columbia, Mo., Oct. 10, 1948; m. Patricia O' Brien; children: Erin, Drew. BA, Ctrl. Methodist Coll.; MA in Edn., U. Mo.; grad., Harvard U., 1990. Asst. prin. Russell Blvd. Elem. Sch., Columbia, Mo.; real estate broker; collector Boone County, Mo., 1976-79; mem. Mo. State Senate from Dist. 19, 1979-92; lt. gov. State of Mo., 1993—; chmn. senate appropriations com., apportionment com., vice chmn. tourism commn.; mem. Mo. bus. and edn. partnership commn., transportation devel. commn., gov.'s adv. coun. physical fitness. Bd. dirs. United Way, Columbia; mem. Mo. Assn. Community Arts Agencies, Boone County Hist. Soc.; mem. com. Mo. Parents as Tchrs. Recipient Everett award MSTA, Boss of the Yr. award Am. Businesswomen's Assn., Disting. Legis. award NCSL, Horace Mann award MNEA, Outstanding Legis. of Yr. award MSTA, 1991 Pub. Official of Yr. award Mo. Assn. Homes for Aging, M.U. Alumni award, 1991. Mem. Columbia C. of C., Cosmopolitan Internat. Office: PO Box 563 Jefferson City MO 65102

WILSON, ROGER GOODWIN, lawyer; b. Evanston, Ill., Sept. 3, 1950; s. G. Turner Jr. and Lois (Shay) W.; m. Giovinella Gonthier, Mar. 7, 1975. AB, Dartmouth Coll., 1972; JD, Harvard U., 1975. Bar: Ill. 1975, U.S. Dist. Ct. (no. dist.) Ill. 1976, U.S.C.t. Appeals (7th cir.) 1977, U.S. Dist. Ct. (no. dist.) Ind. 1985. Assoc. Kirkland & Ellis, Chgo., 1975-81, ptnr., 1981-86; sr. v.p., gen. counsel, corp. sec. Blue Cross/Blue Shield, 1986—; speaker Nat. Healthcare Inst., U. Mich., 1987-93, Am. Law Inst.-ABA Conf. on Mng. and Resolving Domestic and Internat. Bus. Disputes, N.Y.C., 1988, Washington, 1990; cert. health cons. program Purdue U., 1993-94, Inst. for Bus. Strategy Devel., Northwestern U., 1993-94. Advisor Constl. Rights Found., Chgo., 1982-87; mem. So. Poverty Law Ctr., Montgomery, Ala., 1981—. Mem. ABA, Nat. Health Lawyers Assn. (spkr. 1984), Chgo. Coun. Lawyers (bd. govs. 1988-92), Sinfonietta (bd. dirs. 1987—), Univ. Club, Phi Beta Kappa. Avocations: French lang. and culture. Home: 2800 N Lake Shore Dr Apt 1917 Chicago IL 60657-6246 Office: Blue Cross/Blue Shield 676 N St Clair St Chicago IL 60611-2927

WILSON, RONALD D., soft drink bottling company executive; b. Mesa, Ariz., May 16, 1949; s. William Wayne and Theresa (Mallin) W.; m. Kathleen Jean Wilson, May 10, 1975; children: Christopher, Erin. BA in History U., Rutgers U., New Brunswick, N.J., 1971, postgrad., 1973-74; postgrad., Rutgers U., Camden, N.J., 1971-72. Route. mgr. Pepsi-Cola Met. Bottling Co., North Brunswick, N.J., 1974-75; ter. mgr. Pepsi-Cola Met. Bottling Co., Boston, 1975-77; fin. analyst N.J. div Coca-Cola Bottling Co. N.Y., N.Y.C., 1977-79, div. mgr. Conn. div., 1977-79, v.p., gen. mgr. New Eng. div., 1979-81, v.p., gen. mgr. N.J.-Upstate N.Y. div., 1981-84; exec. v.p., gen. mgr. Phila. Coca-Cola Bottling Co., 1984-85, pres., COO, 1985—; bd. dirs. Coca-Cola Co. Trustee Suburban Gen. Hosp., Norristown, Pa., mem. adv. bd., 1994-95; bd. dirs. United Negro Coll. Fund, Phila., Chestnut Hill Acad., Phila.; mem. adv. bd. Rutgers U. Sch. Bus., Camden. Recipient chmn.'s award United Negro Coll. Fund, 1992, bd. recognition Suburban Gen. Hosp., 1992, Chestnut Hill Acad., 1994. Mem. Pa. and N.J. Soft Drink Assn., Cedarbrook Country Club. Republican. Roman Catholic. Avocations: basketball, golf, reading. Office: Phila Coca-Cola Bottling Co 75 E Erie Ave & G St Philadelphia PA 19134*

WILSON, ROOSEVELT LEDELL, secondary education educator; b. Baton Rouge, La., Aug. 8, 1941; m. Barbara Batiste; 1 child, Janile. BS, So. U., 1964, MEd, 1970; MS, U. Okla., 1973; PhD, U. Iowa, 1975. Cert. tchr. math. and sci. La. Tchr. East Baton Rouge Parish Sch. Bd., 1964-75, 81—; teaching asst. U. Iowa, Iowa City, 1974; asst. prof. Jackson (Miss.) State U., 1976-81; tchr. math. and sci. Baton Rouge Prep. Acad., 1994—; club sponsors, dept. chairperson McKinley Mid. Magnet, Baton Rouge, 1981—; dir. workshops E. Baton Rouge Parish Schs., 1983, 85; coord. after-sch. tutorial program Jordan United Meth. Ch., Baton Rouge, 1992—; participant adminstrv. internship program E. Baton Rouge Parish, 1993-94. Contbr. articles to profl. jours. Mem. male chorus Jordan United Meth. Ch., Baton Rouge. Fellow Nat. Fellowship Fund; grantee NSF. Mem. NEA, Nat. Sci. Tchrs. Assn., La. Assn. Educators, Phi Delta Kappa. Methodist. Avocations: golf, tennis, fishing. Home: 21253 Old Scenic Hwy Zachary LA 70791 Office: Baton Rouge Prep Acad 5959 Cadillac St Baton Rouge LA 70811

WILSON, ROSE EATON, elementary education educator; b. Monroe, La., July 7, 1941; d. Wyatt and Olivia (Walker) Eaton; m. Elvin Gene Wilson Sr., July 30, 1989; stepchildren: Karen Patricia, Elvin Jr. BS, Grambling Coll., 1966; MEd, Northeast La. U., 1977, postgrad., 1984. Cert. tchr., supr., La. Tchr. Monroe City Schs., 1966—; tchr. gifted program 1980-86, assessment tchr., 1986—; liaison mem. spl. edn. adv. bd., 1988—. Mem. beautification bd. City of Monroe, 1985-87; mem. Mayor's Commn. for Women, Monroe, 1989-90; commr. Franklin Parish Voter Registration, 1992—. Mem. La. Edn. Assessment Tchrs. Assn. (region rep. 1992—), Delta Sigma Theta (v.p. 1982-83). Democrat. Baptist. Avocations: basketball, reading, cooking, shopping. Home: 1202 Gum St Apt C Winnsboro LA 71295-2855

WILSON, ROY GARDINER, real estate developer; b. Coronation, Alta., Can., May 4, 1932; s. Forest Archibald and Florence Mabel (Gardiner) W.; m. Leila Erma Graham, 1956; children: Keith, Shannon. Salesman, broker, 1951-71; dir. Carma Developers Ltd., Calgary, Alta., 1958—, pres., 1971-85, chmn., 1985-86; dir., pres. Devstar Properties Ltd., Calgary, 1987-90; dir. URBCO Inc., 1988—, chmn., 1990—; dir., chmn. Mortgage Properties Inc., 1991-93. Chmn. Residential Devel. Council, 1977, 78; Mem. Legis. Assembly Alta., 1971-75; mem. Calgary Police Commn., 1976-80. Named to Hall of Fame Olds Coll., 1988.

WILSON, ROY KENNETH, retired education association executive, consultant; b. Charleston, Ill., July 9, 1913; s. George William and Ruth (Woody) W.; m. Ruth June Royce, Aug. 19, 1939; 1 child, Robert Royce (dec.). B.Ed., Eastern Ill. State Coll., 1936; A.M., U. Ill., 1943; Litt. D. (hon.), Glassboro (N.J.) State Coll., 1959. Asso. editor Nat. Printer Journalist, The Printing Industry, Springfield, Ill., 1935-37; dir. pub. relations Eastern Ill. U., Charleston, 1937-42; asst. dir. div. press and radio relations N.E.A., Washington, 1946-57; dir. div. press, radio and TV relations N.E.A., 1957-68; sec-treas., staff dir. Nat. Sch. Pub. Relations Assn., 1950-68, exec. dir., 1968-76; cons. Ednl. Research Service, 1977—. Editorial dir.: Edn. U.S.A, 1958-76. Served to lt. comdr. USNR, World War II. Mem. NEA, Pub. Rels. Soc. Am., Am. Sch. Admnstrs., Am. Assn. Sch. Admnstrs., Houndslake and Woodside Plantation (S.C). Methodist. Home: Brandon Wilde # 414 4275 Owens Rd Evans GA 30809-8600 Office: 2000 Clarendon Blvd Arlington VA 22201-2908

WILSON, RUBY LEE, nurse, director; b. Chgo., Sept. 3, 1935; d. Henry Lee Jernigan and Ruby Nettie Frances (Wilborn) Chavis; m. Franklin Tyson (div.); children: Franklin Delanor, Anthony DeWayne, Derek Alan; m. Alonzo Wilson, July 31, 1959. AA, Amundsen-Mayfair, Chgo., 1967; BS, Coll. of St. Francis, Joliet, Ill., 1976; MEd, U. Ill., 1980. Cert. registered psychiat. and mental health nurse. Lic. practical nurse Rush Presbyn.-St. Luke's Hosp. Med. Ctr., Chgo., 1962-65, staff nurse, 1969-70, head nurse, 1970-81, program dir., 1981—; health coordinator Project Upgrade, Chgo., 1967-69; mem. adv. bd. Issac Ray Ctr. Rush U., Chgo., 1986—, bd. dirs., 1987; dir. nursing bd. St. Stephen A.M.E. Ch., 1986—, also pres. Missionary Soc.; presenter numerous workshops psychiatry, forensic and stress issues.

Recipient Merit cert. Chgo. Merit Employment of Assn. of Commerce and Industry and Vice-Presdl. Task Force on Youth Motivation, 1967-68, Cert. of Appreciation George Williams Coll., plaque for Outstanding Performance Amundsen Nursing Class, 5 Tertiary Care Victim Witness Recovery Program grants Atty. Gen. Violent Crime Victims Assistance Program, 5 consecutive yrs., Cert. of Merit, Chgo. Merit Employment Community of Chgo. Assn Commerce and Industry and the V.P.'s Task Force Youth Motivation. Mem. Am. Nursing Assn. (cert.), Ill. Nursing Assn. (first chairperson commn. on human rights), Peer Assistance Network For Nurses, Nat. Black Nurses Assn., Chgo. Black Nurses Assn. Orthopsychiatric Assn., Am. Assn. Suicidology, Ill. Assn. Suicidology, Lambda Pi Alpha (pres. bd. dirs. 1982—, Was Basileus 1979-81, Outstanding Contbr. plaque 1986). African Methodist Episcopalian. Avocation: church choir singing. Home: 2319 W 80th Pl Chicago IL 60620-5914 Office: Issac Ray Ctr Rush Presbyn-St Luke's Med Ctr 1720 W Polk St Chicago IL 60612-4315

WILSON, RUBY LEILA, nurse, educator; b. Punxsutawney, Pa., May 29, 1931; d. Clark H. and Alda E. (Armstrong) W. BS in Nursing Edn., U. Pitts., 1954; MSN, Case Western Res. U., 1959; EdD, Duke U., 1969. Staff nurse, asst. head nurse Allegheny Gen. Hosp., Pitts., 1951-52; night clin. instr., adminstrv. supr. Allegheny Gen. Hosp., 1951-55; staff nurse, asst. head nurse Fort Miley VA Hosp., San Francisco, 1957-58; instr. nursing Duke U. Sch. Nursing, Durham, N.C., 1955-57; asst. prof. med. surg. nursing Duke U. Sch. Nursing, 1959-66, assoc. in medicine, 1963-66, prof. nursing, 1971—, dean sch. nursing., 1971-84, asst. to chancellor for health affairs, 1984—; asst. prof. dept. community and family medicine Duke U. Sch. Medicine, 1971—; cons., vis. prof. Rockefeller Found., Thailand, 1968-71; vis. prof. Case Western Res. U., 1982-84; mem. Gov.'s Commn. on Health Care Reform in N.C., 1994. Contbr. articles to profl. jours. Active N.C. Med. Care Commn., Gov.'s Commn. on N.C. Health Care Reform, 1994—. Fellow Am. Acad. Nursing, Inst. Medicine; mem. ANA, Am. Assn. Colls. Nursing, Am. Assn. Higher Edn., Nat. League Nursing, Assn. for Acad. Health Ctrs. (mem. inst. planning com.), Women's Forum N.C. (bd. dirs. 1984-88, 95—), N.C. Found. for Nursing (pres. 1990-94). Office: Duke U Med Ctr PO Box 3243 Durham NC 27715-3243

WILSON, SAM N., transportation services executive; b. 1935. Grad., North Tex. State U., 1958. Mgr. internat. distbn. Tex. Instruments, Inc., Dallas, 1958-75; v.p. Circle Airfreight Corp., DFW Internat. Airport, Dallas, 1975-80; chmn., CEO Intertrans Corp., Irving, Tex., 1978—. Office: Intertrans Corp 125 E John Carpenter Fwy Irving TX 75062*

WILSON, SAMUEL GRAYSON, federal judge; b. So. Richmond, 1971; JD cum laude, Wake Forest U., 1974. Asst. commonwealth atty. City of Roanoke, Va., 1974-76; asst. U.S. atty. Western Dist. Va., 1976; U.S. magistrate U.S. Dist. Ct. for Western Dist. Va., 1976-81; mem. Woods, Rogers & Hazlegrove, Roanoke, 1981-90; dist. judge U.S. Dist. Ct. for Western Dist. Va., Abingdon, Va., 1990—. Mem. staff Wake Forest Law Rev., 1973-74. Mem. law bd. visitors Wake Forest U. Mem. Va. State Bar, Fed. Bar Assn., Va. Bar Assn. Roanoke Bar Assn., Supreme Ct. Hist. Soc. Methodist. Office: US Dist Ct PO Box 749 180 W Main St Abingdon VA 24210-0749

WILSON, SAMUEL V., academic adminstrator. Pres. Hampden-Sydney (Va.) Coll. Office: Hampden-Sydney Coll Office of Pres PO Box 128 Hampden Sydney VA 23943-0128*

WILSON, SARA REDDING, lawyer; b. Washington, Feb. 20, 1950; d. Lawrence James III and Jane Elizabeth (Smith) Redding; m. Steven L. Myers, June 21, 1969 (div. 1979); children: Blythe Ann, Robert Lawrence; m. Claude Watson Wilson, May 24, 1986; stepchildren: David B., Jessica Leigh. BA, Hamilton Coll., 1972; JD, U. Richmond, 1977; postgrad., Columbia U., Duke U. Bar: Va. 1978, U.S. Dist. Ct. (ea. dist.) Va. 1980. Mgmt. cons. Bankers Trust Co., N.Y.C., 1972-75; corp. atty. Signet Banking Corp. (formerly Bank of Va.), Richmond, 1977-79, assoc. corp. atty., 1979-83, corp. counsel, 1983-84, sr. corp. counsel, 1984-93, exec. v.p., gen. counsel, 1994, exec. v.p., gen. counsel, corporate sec., 1995—; mem. bank counsel unit Am. Bankers Assn., 1985-94. Bd. dirs. Bank of Va. Vol. Orgn., Richmond, 1984-86, Dispute Resolution Ctr., 1989—; chmn. U. Richmond Law Alumni Fund, 1985-86; trustee Hamilton Coll., 1993—, U. Richmond, 1994—; bd. mgrs. Jackson-Feild Home for Girls. Mem. ABA, Va. Bar Assn., Richmond Bar Assn., Am. Corp. Counsel Assn., Va. Bankers Assn. (chmn. legal affairs 1986-88), U. Richmond Law Alumni Assn. (bd. dirs. 1986-94), Bull and Bear Club. Episcopalian. Home: 8857 River Rd Richmond VA 23229-7801 Office: Signet Banking Corp 7 N 8th St Richmond VA 23219-3301

WILSON, SHERYL J., state agency administrator; b. Shelton, Wash., May 23, 1936; d. Kenneth F. and Bernice (Angell) Sturdevant; m. Daniel I. Stuckey, Sept. 8, 1956 (div. June 1967); children: Mark, Ann, David, Noni; m. Donald R. Wilson, Aug. 9, 1968. Student, Wash. State U., 1954-57; BA, Evergreen State Coll., 1985. Rsch. analyst Wash. Pub. Pension Commn., Olympia, 1967-75; budget analyst Wash. State Senate, Olympia, 1975-80; retirement and ins. officer U. Wash., Seattle, 1980-83; asst. dir. Wash. Dept. Retirement Sys., Olympia, 1983-89, dir., 1993—; exec. dir. Oreg. Pub. Employees Retirement Sys., Portland, 1989-93; mem. exec. com. Nat. Coun. Tchr. Retirement, Austin, 1992—; pres., mem. exec. com. Nat. Preretirement Edn. Assn., 1985-91; vice chair Wash. State Investment Bd., Olympia, 1993—; mem. steering com. cert. employee benefit specialist program U. Wash., 1983—. Chair Interagy. Com. Status of Women, Olympia, 1987-88. Mem. Nat. Assn. State Retirement Admnstrs. (legis. com. 1989—), Women in Pub. Adminstrn. (founder Oreg. chpt. 1990), Govt. Fin. Officers (retirement and benefits adminstrn. com. 1992—), Zonta Internat. Avocations: photography, travel, hiking, snorkeling.

WILSON, SLOAN, author, lecturer; b. Norwalk, Conn., May 8, 1920; s. Albert F. and Ruth (Dannehower) W.; m. Elise Pickhardt, Feb. 4, 1941 (div.); children—Lisa, Rebecca, David Sloan; m. Betty Stephens; 1 dau. Jessica. Grad., Fla. Adirondack Sch., 1938; AB, Harvard, 1942; LHD (hon.), Rollins Coll., 1982. Writer, contbr. New Yorker and other mags.; with Providence Jour., 1946-47, Time, Inc., 1947-49, Nat. Citizens Commn. for Pub. Schs., 1949-53; dir. information services, asst. prof. English Buffalo U., 1953-55; asst. dir. White House Conf. on Edn., 1955-56; Disting. writer-in-residence Rollins Coll., Winter Park, Fla., 1981-82; dir. Winter Park Artists Workshop, 1983-85; cons. Philip Crosby Assocs., Winter Park, 1984-87; lectr. Va. Commwealth U., 1990. Author: Voyage to Somewhere, 1946, The Man in the Gray Flannel Suit, 1955, A Summer Place, 1958, A Sense of Values, 1960, Georgie Winthrop, 1962, Janus Island, 1966, Away From It All, 1969, All The Best People, 1970, What Shall We Wear to This Party, 1976, Small Town, 1978, Ice Brothers, 1979, The Greatest Crime, 1980, Pacific Interlude, 1982, The Man in the Gray Flannel Suit II, 1983. Served to lt. USCGR, World War II. *Although some of my books have been widely read, I of course am not as successful as a writer as I would like to be. Almost all writers, after all, must, if they are honest, suspect that their triumphs are temporary. This is no cause for lament, for the same happens to almost everybody in all walks of life. I am lucky to have a wife who makes my private life a joy and three daughters and a son who with my ten grandchildren give me a kind of immortality. Much like the characters in most of my books, I find my family the only part of my life which does not disappoint. My children and my wife always give me excellent reviews which never yellow in a scrapbook. I sometimes lecture on the topic of 'Success.' Nowadays that word seems to me to be much more complex than it did when I was young. As I grow old I love life more and more.*

WILSON, SONJA MARY, secondary education educator, consultant, poet; b. Lake Charles, La., Mar. 28, 1938; d. Albert Ronald and Annelia (DeVille) Molless; m. Willie McKinley Williams, Apr. 28, 1956 (div. May 1969); children: William P., Dwayne L., Rachelle A., Devon A., Lisa M., Ricardo Soto; m. Howard Brooks Wilson, Nov. 12, 1982; stepchildren: Howard N. Wilson, Yvonne Wilson. AA in Social and Behavioral Scis., Mt. St. Jacinto Jr. Coll., 1992; cert. U. Calif., San Bernardino, 1983; student, Calif. State Poly. U., 1986, Laverne U., 1984-85; BS, So. Ill. U., 1995; student, Riverside (Calif.) City Coll., 1988-89, 94. Prin.'s sec. Elsinore (Calif.) H.S., Elsinore Jr. H.S., 1974-83; tchr. bus. and adult vocat. edn., 1979-84, notary pub. 1981-85, coord. vocat. edn., 1983-84, class adviser, 1983-88; long-term substitute tchr. Perris H.S. Dist., 1991-94. Clk., v.p., pres. Lake Elsinore Unified Sch. Dist. Bd., 1988—; pres., clk., mem. Lake Elsinore Elem. Sch. Bd., 1979-88, v.p., 1988-89; pres., sec., treas., v.p. Riverside County Sch. Bds. Assn., 1979—; assoc. sponsor, advisor Black Student Union/Future Leaders of Am., 1984-90; svc. unit rep., leader Girl Scouts U.S.; den mother Boy Scouts Am.; mem. Ctrl. Dem. Com., 1989-91; del. PTSA, 1991-93. Tribute in her honor Black Student Union/Future Leaders Am., 1989; recipient Excellence in Edn. award Hilltop Community Ctr. Club, 1989, Leadership award Black Art and Social Club, 1989, Svc. award Sojourner Truth Media Network, 1989, Proclamation award City of Elsinore, 1989, County of Riverside, 1989; named Outstanding Poet, Nat. Libr. of Congress, 1994, 95. Mem. NAACP (Lake Elsinore affiliate, plaque), Calif. Sch. Bds. Assn. (regional dir. 1988-92, conf. planning com. 1989, legis. com. 1981—, nominations com. 1988, media com., dir. at large block 1993-95, audit com. 1993, dir./del. trainer 1993, alt. del., sgt. at arms 1994, 95, FRN rep. 1995), Calif. Elected Women Ofcls. Assn., Calif. Sch. Employees Assn. (pres., treas., regional rep. assn., state negotiation com., del. to conf.), Internat. Soc. Poets, Lake Elsinore C. of C., Calif. Coalition Black Sch. Bd. Members (v.p. 1989, pres. 1990, program liaison 1989), Nat. Coun. Negro Women (charter, Willa Mae Taylor sect.), Black Art and Social Club, Hilltop Community Club (plaque), Sojourner Truth Media Network (plaque), Eta Phi Beta (treas., sec. Gamma Alpha chpt., plaque, pres. 1992—). Avocations: travel, writing poetry, winemaking, childcare, reading. Home: 21330 Waite St Lake Elsinore CA 92530-9503

WILSON, STANLEY P., retired lawyer; b. Hamlin, Tex., Sept. 1, 1922; s. Milton Young and Ethel M. (Patterson) W.; m. Claudie Park, Sept. 23, 1944; children: Stanley P., Russell Park, Marianne. BS, U. North Tex., Denton, 1943; LLB, U. Tex., Austin, 1948. Bar: Tex. 1948. Ptnr. McMahon, Smart, Wilson, Surovik & Suttle, Abilene, Tex., 1948-81; sr. v.p., gen. counsel Central and S.W. Corp., Dallas, 1981-86; exec. v.p., gen. counsel Central and S.W. Corp., 1986-88, ret., 1988. Lt. (j.g.) USN, 1943-46, PTO. Mem. ABA, State Bar Tex., Am. Coll. Trial Lawyers, Abilene Bar Assn., Abilene Country Club, Preston Trail Club. Methodist. Home: 1921 Elmwood Dr Abilene TX 79605-4802 Office: Ste 800 First Nat Bank Bldg Abilene TX 79601

WILSON, STEPHEN RAY, fertilizer manufacturing company executive; b. DuBois, Pa., Oct. 20, 1948; s. Richard C. and Marilyn J. (Stewart) W.; m. Susan K. Condon, Sept. 5, 1970; children: Jeffrey M., Elizabeth A. BA in Sociology, Northwestern U., 1970, MBA in Fin. and Acctg., 1974. CPA, Ill. Various positions Inland Steel Industries, Chgo., 1974-91, asst. treas., 1985-88; contr., treas. James T. Ryerson & Son, Chgo., 1988-89; v.p. info. mgmt. and fin. Joseph T. Ryerson & Son, Chgo., 1989-90; gen. mgr. corp. planning Inland Steel Industries, Inc., Chgo., 1990-91; sr. v.p., CFO, CF Industries, Inc., Long Grove, Ill., 1991—. Bd. dirs. Northwestern Club Chgo., 1982-84; bd. trustees Chgo. Found. for Edn., 1993—. With U.S. Army, 1970-72. Mem. AICPA, Fin. Execs. Inst., Econ. Club Chgo. Avocations: running, golf, travel. Office: CF Industries Inc 1 Salem Lake Dr Long Grove IL 60047-8402

WILSON, STEPHEN VICTOR, federal judge; b. N.Y.C., Mar. 26, 1942; s. Harry and Rae (Ross) W. B.A. in Econs., Lehigh U., 1963; J.D., Bklyn. Law Sch., 1967; LL.M., George Washington U., 1973. Bars: N.Y. 1967, D.C. 1971, Calif. 1972, U.S. Ct. Appeals (9th cir.) U.S. Dist. Ct. (so., cen. and no. dists.) Calif. Trial atty. Tax div. U.S. Dept. Justice, 1968-71; asst. U.S. atty., L.A., 1971-77, chief spl. prosecutions, 1973-77; ptnr. Hochman, Salkin & Deroy, Beverly Hills, Calif., from 1977; judge U.S. Dist. Ct. (cen. dist.) Calif., L.A., 1985—; adj. prof. law Loyola U. Law Sch., 1976-79; U.S. Dept. State rep. to govt. W.Ger. on 20th anniversary of Marshall Plan, 1967; del. jud. conf. U.S. Ct. Appeals (9th cir.), 1982-86. Recipient Spl. Commendation award U.S. Dept. Justice, 1977. Mem. ABA, L.A. County Bar Assn., Beverly Hills Bar Assn. (chmn. criminal law com.), Fed. Bar Assn. Jewish. Contbr. articles to profl. jours. Home: 9100 Wilshire Blvd Beverly Hills CA 90212-3403 Office: US Dist Ct 312 N Spring St Los Angeles CA 90012-4701

WILSON, STEVE, metal products executive; b. 1943. BSME, Northwestern U., Evanston, Ill., 1966; MBA, U. Chgo., 1973. With Vapor Corp., Niles, Ill., 1966-69, Electro Products Co., Niles, 1969-71, Signode Corp., Lincolnshire, Ill., 1971-89; with Duo-Fast Corp., Franklin Park, Ill., 1991—, v.p. engring. Office: Duo-Fast Corp 3702 River Rd Franklin Park IL 60131*

WILSON, TED LEWIS, educator, former mayor; b. Salt Lake City, May 18, 1939; s. Robert L. and Eva (Simpson) W.; m. Kathryn Carling, June 10, 1963; children—Benjamin, Jennifer, Melissa, Jessica, Joseph. B.S., U. Utah, 1964; M.Ed. (NSF fellow), U. Wash., 1969. Tchr. Granite Sch. Dist., Salt Lake City, 1966-73; adminstrv. asst. to a congressman, 1973-75; social services dir. Salt Lake County, Utah, 1975-76; mayor of Salt Lake City, from 1976; now dir. Hinckley Inst. U. Utah. Contbr. articles to profl. jours. Bd. dirs. Intermountain Health Care, Inc.; bd. advs. Mountain Bell. Served with Army NG, 1957-62. Recipient Valor award Dept. Interior, 1968. Mem. U.S. Conf. of Mayors (dir.), Nat. League Cities and Towns, Am. Soc. Pub. Adminstrs., Common Cause. Democrat. Mormon. Office: Univ Utah Hinckley Inst Pol 253 Orson Spencer Hall Salt Lake City UT 84112-1103

WILSON, TERRENCE RAYMOND, manufacturing executive; b. St. Louis, July 1, 1943; s. Raymond Lemuel and Eula Ellen (Sutton) W.; m. Judy Marie Coleman, May 23, 1964; children: John Scott, Dustin Marint. Student, Drury Coll., 1961-62, St. Louis Jr. Coll., 1962-64, Mo. U., 1965-67. Program control planning adminstr. McDonnell Aircraft, St. Louis, 1962-65, 67; mgmt. control mgr. Vitro Labs., Silver Spring, Md., 1966; mgr. customer svc. Teledyne Wis. Motor, Milw., 1968-69, dir. ops., 1970-71, dir. mktg., 1972-73; gen. mgr. Teledyne Still-Man, Cookeville, Tenn., 1973-74; pres. multiplant div. Teledyne Still-Man, Cookeville, 1975-78; group exec. Teledyne, Inc., 1979-84; pres. Teledyne Indsl. Engines, 1984-87; pres., chief exec. officer Morgan Corp., Morgantown, Pa., 1987-92; pres. Magnatech Internat. Inc., Sinking Spring, Pa., 1992—. Bd. dirs. Tenn. Tech. U. Coll. Bus. Found.; mem. exec. bd. Hawk Mountain Coun. Boy Scouts Am.; bd. trustees Cmty Gen. Hosp., Kutztown U. Found.; mem. pres. adv. com. Mem. Beta Gamma Sigma. Roman Catholic. Home: 411 Green Ln Reading PA 19601-1009 Office: Magnatech Internat Inc 796 Fritztown Rd Sinking Spring PA 19608-1522

WILSON, THEODORE HENRY, retired electronics company executive, aerospace engineer; b. Eufaula, Okla., Apr. 23, 1940; s. Theodore V. and Maggie E. (Buie) W.; m. Barbara Ann Tassara, May 16, 1958 (div. 1982); children: Debbie Marie, Nita Leigh, Wilson Axten, Pamela Ann, Brenda Louise, Theodore Henry II, Thomas John; m. Colleen Fagan, Jan. 1, 1983 (div. 1987); m. Karen L. Lerohl, Sept. 26, 1987. BSME, U. Calif., Berkeley, 1962; MSME, U. So. Calif., 1964, MBA, 1970, MSBA, 1971. Sr. tech. engr. N.Am. Aviation Co. div. Rockwell Internat., Downey, Calif., 1962-65; propulsion analyst, supr. div. applied tech. TRW, Redondo Beach, Calif., 1965-67; mem. devel. staff systems group, 1967-71; sr. fin. analyst worldwide automotive dept. TRW, Cleve., 1971-72; contr. systems and energy group TRW, Redondo Beach, 1972-79; dir. fin. control equipment group TRW, Cleve., 1979-82, v.p. fin. control indsl. and energy group, 1982-85; mem. space and def. group TRW, Redondo Beach, 1985-93, ret., 1993; lectr., mem. com. acctg. curriculum UCLA Extension, 1974-79. Mem. Fin. Execs. Inst. (com. govt. bus.), Machinery and Allied Products Inst. (govt. contracts coun.), Nat. Contract Mgmt. Assn. (bd. advisors), Aerospace Industries Assn. (procurement and fin. coun.), UCLA Chancellors Assocs., Tau Beta Pi, Beta Gamma Sigma, Pi Tau Sigma. Republican. Avocations: golf, bridge. Home: 3617 Via La Selva Palos Verdes Peninsula CA 90274-1115

WILSON, THOMAS ARTHUR, economics educator; b. Vancouver, B.C., Canada, Aug. 5, 1935; s. Victor and Estel Christina (Grange) W.; m. Julia Ann Dillon, Feb. 8, 1958; children: Christine Diana, Arthur Dillon. B.A., U. B.C., 1957; Ph.D., Harvard U., 1961. Instr. Harvard U., 1961-62, asst. prof., 1962-67; assoc. prof. U. Toronto, 1967-68, prof., 1968—, dir. Inst. for Policy Analysis, 1969-75, dir. econs., 1979-82, chmn. econs. dept., 1982-85, dir. policy and econ. analysis program, 1987—, area coord. bus. econs. Faculty of Mgmt., 1989—; cons. various govtl. depts. Author: Advertising and Market Power, 1974, Canadian Competition Policy, 1979, Fiscal Policy in Canada, 1993. Fellow Royal Soc. Can.; mem. Am. Econs. Assn., Canadian Econ. Assn. (pres. 1984-85). Office: 140 St George St, Toronto, ON Canada M5S 1A1

WILSON, TOM, cartoonist, greeting card company executive; b. Grant Town, W.Va., Aug. 1, 1931; s. Charles Albert and Hazel Marie W.; m. Carol; children: Tom, Ava. Grad., Art Inst. Pitts., 1955. Advt. layout man Uniontown Newspapers Inc., Uniontown, PA, 1950-53; designer Am. Greetings Corp., Cleveland, OH, 1955-56; creative dir. Am. Greetings Corp., 1957-78, v.p. creative devel., 1978-81; pres. Those Characters from Cleve., 1981—; former mem. faculty Cooper Sch. Art. Cartoonist: Ziggy, 1971—; syndicated in newspapers across U.S. by Universal Press Syndicate, Kansas City; collections include: Life is Just a Bunch of Ziggys, 1973, It's a Ziggy World, 1974, Ziggy Coloring Book, 1974, Never Get Too Personally Involved with Your Own Life, 1975, Promises to Myself: Ziggy's Thirty-Day Ledger of I Owe Me's, 1975, Plants are Some of My Favorite People, 1976, Ziggys of the World Unite!, 1976, Pets Are Friends You Like Who Like You Right Back, 1977, The Ziggy Treasury, 1977, This Book is for the Birds, 1978, Encore! Encore!, 1979, Ziggy's Love Notes, 1979, Ziggy's Thinking of You Notebook, 1979, Ziggy's Fleeting Thoughts Notebook, 1979, A Ziggy Christmas, 1980, Ziggy's Door Openers, 1980, Ziggy Faces Life, 1981, One Thing You Can Say About Living Alone...There's Never Any Question About Who Didn't Jiggle the Handle on the John, 1981, Short People Arise, 1981, A Word to the Wide is Sufficient, 1981, Ziggy's Sunday Funnies, 1981, Ziggy & Friends, 1982, Ziggy Faces Life...Again!, 1982, Ziggy's For You With Love, 1982, Ziggy's Gift, 1982, Ziggy's Big Little Book, 1983, Ziggy and Friends, 1983, Ziggy's Funday Sunnies, 1983, Alphabet Soup Isn't Supposed to Make Sense, 1984, Ziggy Weighs In, 1984, Ziggy's Ship Comes In, 1984, Ug! The Original Hunk, 1985, Ziggy In the Rough, 1985, Ziggy's Ins and Outs, 1985, Ziggy's Ups and Downs, 1985, Ziggy In the Fast Lane, 1987, Ziggy's Follies, 1988, Ziggy's Star Performances, 1989, Ziggy's School of Hard Knocks, 1989, Ziggy On the Outside Looking In, 1990, (also illustrator) Ziggy's Christmas Book Levels 1, 2, 1991, (also illustrator) Ziggy's Play Today Guitar Method, 1991, Look Out World...Here I Come! Ziggy's Own Down-to-Earth Humor: A Look At the Environment and Ourselves, 1991, Ziggy...A Rumor in His Own Time, 1992, The Ziggy Cookbook: Great Food From Mom's Diner, 1993, A Day in the Life of Ziggy, 1993, One-Eight Hundred-Ziggy, 1994, My Life As a Cartoon: A Ziggy Collection, 1995, Ziggy's Place. Served with U.S. Army, 1953-55. Recipient Purchase award Butler Mus. Nat. Painting Competition, Emmy award for best animated spl., 1982. Developer Soft Touch line of greeting cards. Office: Universal Press Syndicate PO Box 419149 Kansas City MO 64141-6149 *My objective and chief motivation has always been . . ."to bring something about that wasn't there before.".*

WILSON, TRISHA, interior architectural designer; b. Augusta, Ga.; d. Lemuel Edward Wilson and Doris (Howard) Gray. BS in Interior Archtl. Design, U. Tex., 1969. Interior designer Titche-Goettinger Allied Stores, Dallas, 1969-72; ptnr. Merrill/Wilson and Assocs., Dallas, 1972-75; chmn., chief exec. officer Wilson and Assocs., Dallas, N.Y.C., L.A., Singapore and Johannesburg, South Africa, 1975—; Bd. dirs. Shelby Williams Industries, Exec. Travel Svc., SPCA of Tex.; mem. found. adv. coun. U. Tex. Sch. Architecture; mem. devel. bd. U. Tex. Adv. dir. Susan G. Komen Found.; bd. dirs. State Fair of Tex., Dallas; mem. Rep. Nat. Com., Friend of Kennedy Ctr. Found. Dallas Assembly; past chmn. bd. dirs. Tex. bus. Hall Fame Found., corp. com. Dallas Mus. Art; trustee Dallas Mus. Art; past mem. adv. bd. dept. home econs. U. Tex., Austin. Recipient numerous bus. and profl. awards. Mem. Am. Soc. Interior Designers (state chpt. bd. dirs. 1978-80), Ins. bus. Designers, Tex. Women's Forum, Dallas Women's Found., Internat. Women's Forum, Soc. Partially Sighted, U. Tex. Ex-Students' Assn. (adv. bd., at-large rep. exec. council), Young Pres. Orgn. Avocations: travel, fine art and antiques. Office: Wilson and Assocs 3811 Turtle Creek Blvd 15th Fl Dallas TX 75219-4419 also: Wilson and Assocs 415 E 54th St Ste 15D New York NY 10022 also: 8342 1/2 Melrose Ave Los Angeles CA 90046

WILSON, VINCENT JOSEPH, JR., writer, historian, publisher; b. Cleve., Apr. 24, 1921; s. Vincent Joseph and Genevieve Margaret (Vleck) W.; m. Mary Jo Cavender, Sept. 30, 1944; children: Nicholas Cavender, Lisa Jane. Student, Georgetown U., 1939-41; AB with honors, Ariz. State U., 1948; MA, Claremont Grad. Sch., 1949; postgrad., Harvard U., 1949-50. Instr. English dept. Mitchell Coll., New London, Conn., 1950-53, chmn. English dept., 1953-55; corr. New London Day, 1952-55; editor Nat. Security Agy., Fort Meade, Md., 1956-62, sr. staff writer, 1963-71, chief historian, sr. editor, 1972-81; pub. Am. History Rsch. Assn., 1962—; lectr. English, U. Md., 1959-67, George Washington U., 1963-65. Author: The Book of the Presidents, 1962, 11th edit., 1993, The Book of Great American Documents, 1967, 76, 3rd edit., 1993, The Book of States, 1972, 79, 3rd edit., 1992, The Book of the Founding Fathers, 1974, 86, 93, The Book of Distinguished American Women, 1983, 2nd edit., 1992; editor: The Pocket Guide to Wines, 1970; pub. Brooke Meadow Press, 1970—; contbr. articles to various publs. 1st lt. USAAF, 1943-46. Recipient Freedoms Found. at Valley Forge Washington medal, 1968, Honor award, 1974, Nat. Security Agy. Meritorious Svc. award, 1975. Mem. Cosmos Club (Washington). Home and Office: PO Box 140 1711 Gold Mine Rd Brookeville MD 20833

WILSON, W. STEPHEN, mathematics educator; b. Iowa City, Iowa, Nov. 11, 1946; s. Charles William and Frances Preshia (Stephenson) W.; m. Norma Jean Kriger, June 9, 1990; 1 child, Saul Kriger. SB in Math., MIT, 1968, SM in Math., 1969, PhD in Math., 1972. Instr., then asst. prof. Princeton (N.J.) U., 1972-78; assoc. prof. math. Johns Hopkins U., Balt., 1977-80, prof., 1980—, chair dept., 1993—; mem., Inst. Advanced Study, Princeton, 1974-75, 77-78. Contbr. articles on algebraic topology to math. jours. Alfred P. Sloan Found. fellow, 1977-79. Mem. Am. Math. Soc. Office: Johns Hopkins U Dept Math 34th and Charles Sts Baltimore MD 21218

WILSON, WALLACE, art educator, artist; b. Dallas, June 10, 1947; s. William Wallace and Zoe (Naylor) W.; m. Mary Claire Straw, Apr. 3, 1982; 1 child, Erin Rebecca. Student, Tex. Tech. U., 1965-67; B.A., U. Tex., 1970; M.A., Sch. of Art Inst. Chgo., 1975. Asst. prof. U. Ky., Lexington, 1970-75, U. Del., Newark, 1975-79; assoc. prof. U. Fla., Gainesville, 1979-90, prof., 1990-94; prof., chmn. art dept. U. South Fla., Tampa, 1994—; vis. prof. U. Gothenburg, Sweden, 1984, 86, London Study Ctr. Fla. State U., 1988. One-man shows O.K. Harris Gallery, N.Y.C., 1977, 87, Photopia, Mancini Gallery, Phila., 1977, Balt. Mus. Art, 1977, Images Gallery, New Orleans, 1979, U. Ala., Birmingham, 1983, Francesca Anderson Gallery, Boston, 1986, Marcuse Pfeifer Gallery, N.Y.C., 1987, 89, Tartt Gallery, Washington, 1987, 90, 92, The Photographers Gallery, London, 1989, Robert Klein Gallery, Boston, 1991, Southeast Mus. Photography. Fla., 1993; group exhbns. include U. Nebr., Lincoln, 1972, Galerie Zabriskie, Paris, 1978, Boston Visual Arts Union, 1981, Santa Barbara Mus. Art, Calif., 1982, Robert Freidus Gallery, N.Y.C., 1983, N.Mex. State U. Gallery, Las Cruces, 1987, Spl. Photographers Co., London, 1989, Douglas Drake Gallery, N.Y.C., 1992, Art Network, Atlanta, 1993, The Art Inst. Chgo., 1994; represented in permanent collections Mus. Modern Art, N.Y.C., Art Inst. Chgo., Oakland Mus., Calif., New Orleans Mus. Art, Balt. Mus. Art, City Mus. Munich, Houston Mus. Fine Arts, The Bklyn. Mus. Recognized in various publs. including Village Voice, N.Y.C., 1977, 87, 89, Le Figaro, Paris, 1978, Art Voices, Palm Beach, Fla., 1981, Art Papers, Atlanta, 1982, Miami Herald, 1989, 90, The Sunday Times, 1989, Photo Metro, San Francisco, 93, Washington Post, 1987, 92; recipient U. Del. Faculty research award, 1978, 20x24 Camera award Polaroid, 1985; fellow Swedish Found., Stockholm, 1986; U. Fla. Faculty research grantee, 1980, 88, 93; Individual Artist fellow State of Fla. Div. Cultural Affairs, 1982, 88. Mem. Soc. for Photog. Edn. (vice chmn. S.E. region 1982-85). Office: U South Fla Art Dept Tampa FL 33620-7350

WILSON, WARNER RUSHING, psychology educator; b. Jackson, Miss., July 27, 1935; s. William Enouch and Ruby (Goyne) W. A.B., U. Chgo., 1956; M.A., U. Ark., 1958; Ph.D., Northwestern U., 1960. Teaching asst. Northwestern U., 1957-60; research psychologist E.I. duPont de Nemours & Co., Wilmington, Del., 1960; asst. prof. U. Hawaii, 1960-65; asso. prof. U. Ala., 1965-73; prof. Wright State U., Dayton, Ohio, 1973-93; pvt. practice Las Vegas, Nev., 1993—; Cons. Bryce State Hosp., Tuscaloosa, Ala., 1966, Ednl. Testing Service, 1968, Tuscaloosa VA Hosp., 1968-74, H.R.B. Singer Co., 1972; Trainee Downey (Ill.) VA Hosp., summer 1959. Contbr. articles to profl. jours. spl. summer fellow in evaluation research Northwestern U., 1973-74, NSF grantee, 1976-78, Johnson Assocs. Postdoctoral Clin. fellow, 1981-82; Research grantee DuPont Co., 1961-62; Research grantee NIMH, 1965, 68-70; Research grantee NSF, 1966-68; Named Outstanding

Psychology student U. Ark., 1956-57. Mem. Soc. Exptl. Social Psychology. Home: 2117 Flower Ave N Las Vegas NV 89109 Office: 3376 S Eastern Ave Las Vegas NV 89109-3367

WILSON, WARREN SAMUEL, clergyman, bishop; b. New Orleans, May 15, 1927; s. Charlie Price and Warnie (Heart) W.; m. Lillie Pearl Harvey, Mar. 31, 1949; 1 child, Barbara LaJoyce. BA, So. U., Baton Rouge, 1950; DDiv, Moody Coll., Chgo., 1952; DDiv (hon.), Trinity Hall Coll. and Sem., Springfield, Ill., 1975. Ordained to ministry Ch. of God in Christ, 1952, crowned bishop, apptd. state bishop, Calif., 1970. Min. St. Bernard St. Church of God in Christ, New Orleans, until 1960, Fresno (Calif.) Temple Ch. of God in Christ, 1960—. Served with USN, 1942-46, PTO. Mem. NAACP (life). Avocations: bass fishing, boating. Office: Fresno Temple Ch of God in Christ 1137 F St Fresno CA 93706-3314

WILSON, WILLIAM JULIUS, sociologist, educator; b. Derry Twp., Pa., Dec. 20, 1935; s. Esco and Pauline (Bracy) W.; m. Mildred Marie Hood, Aug. 31, 1957; children—Carter, Paula. BA, Wilberforce U., 1958; MA, Bowling Green State U., 1961; PhD, Wash. State U., 1966; LHD (hon.), U. Mass., 1982, L.I. U., 1982, Columbia Coll., Santa Clara U., Loyola Coll., 1988, De Paul U., 1989; LLD (hon.), Marquette U., Mt. Holyoke Coll., 1989; LHD (hon.), New Sch. for Social Rsch., 1991, Bard Coll., 1992, John Jay Sch. Criminal Justice, 1992, U. Pa., 1993, So. Ill. U., 1993, Northwestern U., 1993, Bowling Green State U., 1994, SUNY, Binghamton, 1994, Princeton U., 1994. Asst. prof. U. Mass., Amherst, 1965-69; assoc. prof. U. Mass., 1969-71; vis. asso. prof. U. Chgo., 1971-72, assoc. prof. dept. sociology, 1972-75, prof., 1975—, chmn. dept. sociology, 1978—, Lucy Flower prof. urban sociology, 1980-84, Lucy Flower disting. service prof., 1984—; Lucy Flower Univ. prof., 1990—; mem. bd. univ. publs. U. Chgo. Press, 1975-79; bd. dirs. Ctr. for Nat. Policy, 1988—, Ctr. for Advanced Study of Behavioral Scis., 1988—, Twentieth Century Fund, 1992—, Jerome Levy Inst., 1992—, Manpower Demonstration Rsch. Corp., 1993—; mem. domestic strategy group Aspen Inst., 1992—; bd. dirs. Pub./Private Ventures, Phila. Author: Power, Racism and Privilege, 1973, Through Different Eyes, 1973, The Declining Significance of Race, 1978, The Truly Disadvantaged, 1987, The Ghetto Underclass, 1993, Sociology and the Public Agenda, 1993. Bd. dirs. Social Sci. Research Council, 1979-84, Chgo. Urban League, 1983—, Spencer Found., George M. Pullman Found., Russell Sage Found., 1989—, Ctr. for the Advanced Study of the Behaviorial Scis., 1989—, Nat. Humanities Ctr., 1990; mem. Environment, Devel., and Public Policy, 1980—; nat. bd. dirs. A. Philip Randolph Inst., Inst. Research on Poverty, 1983—; trustee Spelman Coll., 1989—; mem. Pres. Commn. on White House Fellowships, 1994—; mem. Pres. Com. Nat. Medal Sci., 1994—. Served with U.S. Army, 1958-60. Recipient Disting. Tchr. of Year award U. Mass., Amherst, 1970, Regents Disting. Alumnus award Wash. State U., 1988, Burton Gordon Feldman award Brandeis U., 1991, Frank E. Seidman disting. award in polit. econ., 1994; MacArthur Prize fellow, 1987. Fellow AAAS, Am. Acad. Arts and Scis.; mem. NAS, Am. Philos. Soc., Am. Sociol. Assn. (pres. 1989-90, Sydney M. Spivack award 1977, DuBois, Johnson, Frazier award 1990), Soc. for Study Social Problems (C. Wright Mills award 1988), Sociol. Rsch. Assn. (pres. 1987-88), Consortium Of Social Sci. Assn. (pres. 1993-94), Internat. Sociol. Assn. Chgo. Urban League (Beautiful People award 1994). Democrat. Home: 1031 E 48th St Chicago IL 60615-1803 Office: U Chgo Dept Sociology 1126 E 59th St Chicago IL 60637

WILSON, WILLIAM PRESTON, psychiatrist, emeritus educator; b. Fayetteville, N.C., Nov. 6, 1922; s. Preston Puckett and Rosa Mae (VanHook) W.; m. Dorothy Elizabeth Taylor, Aug. 21, 1950; children: William Preston, Benjamin V., Karen E., Tammye E., Robert E. B.S., Duke U., 1943, M.D., 1947. Diplomate: Am. Bd. Psychiatry and Neurology (examiner). Intern Gorgas Hosp., Ancon, C.Z.; then resident psychiatry Duke U. Med. Center, later resident neurology, 1949-54; asst. prof. psychiatry Duke U. Med. Sch., 1955-58; asso. prof. psychiatry, dir. psychiat. research U. Tex. Med. Br., Galveston, 1958-60; asso. prof. psychiatry Duke U. Med. Center, 1961-64, head div. clin. neurophysiology, 1961-83, prof. psychiatry, head div. biol. psychiatry, 1964-84, emeritus prof. psychiatry, 1985—; dir. Inst. Christian Growth, Burlington, N.C., 1985—; chief neurophysiol. labs. VA Hosp., Durham, N.C., 1961-76; sec. Am. Bd. Qualification in Electroencephalography, 1971-77; mem. N.C. Gov.'s Task force on Diagnosis and Treatment; mem. med. adv. com. N.C. Found. Mental Health Rsch.; bd. dirs. nat. div. Contact Teleministry USA, also mem. internat. commn. healing; cons. numerous area hosps.; Finch lectr. Fuller Theol. Sem., Pasadena, Calif., 1974; vis. prof. psychiatry Marshall U. Sch. Medicine, Huntington, W.Va., 1985-89. Co-author: The Grace to Grow; editor: Applications of Electroencephalography in Psychiatry; co-editor: EEG and Evoked Potentials in Psychiatry and Behavioral Neurology; Contbr. med. jours. Mem. ofcl. bd. Asbury United Methodist Ch., Durham; mem. program and curriculum com. United Meth. Ch., 1973-81; trustee Meth. Retirement Home, Durham, N.C.; pres. United Meth. Renewal Services, Inc., 1978-82. Served with AUS, 1943-46. Recipient Ephraim McDowell award Christian Med. Found., 1982, Pioneer in Christian Psychiatry award Congress on Christian Counseling, 1988; EEG Montreal Neurol. Inst. fellow, 1954-55, postdoctoral fellow NIMH. Mem. Am. Psychiatric Assn., So. Psychiatric Assn. (pres. 1977-78), AMA, So. Med. Assn. (chmn. sect. neurology and psychiatry 1970), Med. Soc. N.C., Durham-Orange County Med. Soc. (chmn. student recruitment com. 1965), Soc. Biol. Psychiatry, Am. EEG Soc. (councillor), So. EEG Soc. (pres. 1964), Assn. Research Nervous and Mental Diseases, Am. Epilepsy Soc., AAAS, Am. Acad. Neurology, Sigma Xi, Alpha Omega Alpha. Republican. Club: U.S. Power Squadron (comdr. Durham 1971). Home: 1209 Virginia Ave Durham NC 27705-3263 Office: PO Box 2347 Burlington NC 27216-2347

WILSON, WILLIAM R., JR., judge; b. 1939. Student, U. Ark., 1957-58; BA, Hendrix Coll., 1962; JD, Vanderbilt U., 1965. Atty. Autrey & Goodson, Texarkana, Ark., 1965-66, Wright, Lindsey & Jennings, Little Rock, 1969-72, Wilson & Hodge, Little Rock, 1972-74; prin. William R. Wilson Jr., P.A., Little Rock, 1974-80, Wilson & Engstrom, Little Rock, 1980-83, Wilson, Engstrom & Vowell, Little Rock, 1984, Wilson, Engstrom, Corum & Dudley, Little Rock, 1984-93; judge U.S. Dist. Ct. (ea. dist.) Ark., Little Rock, 1993—; chair Ark. Supreme Ct. Com. on Model Criminal Jury Instrns., 1978—; active Ark. Supreme Ct. Com. on Civil Practice, 1982—. Lt. USN, 1966-69. Named Disting. Alumnus, Hendrix Coll., 1993, Outstanding Lawyer, Pulaski County Bar Assn., 1993. Mem. ABA, ATLA, Am. Bd. Trial Advocates (Nat. Civil Justice award 1992), Am. Coll. Trial Lawyers, Internat. Acad. Trial Lawyers, Internat. Soc. Barristers, Ark. Bar Assn. (Outstanding Lawyer 1991), S.W. Ark. Bar Assn., Ark. Trial Lawyers Assn. (pres. 1982, Outstanding Trial Lawyer 1988-89). Office: US Dist Ct Ark 600 W Capitol St Rm 153 Little Rock AR 72203-0869

WILSON, WILLIAM STANLEY, oceanographer; b. Alexander City, Ala., June 5, 1938; s. Norman W. and Helen C. (Hackemack) W.; m. Anne M. Stout; children: Lauren, Jonathan (dec.). BS, William & Mary Coll., 1959, MA, 1965; PhD, Johns Hopkins U., 1972. Marine biol. collector Va. Inst. Marine Sci., Gloucester Point, 1959-62, computer systems analyst, 1964-65; computer systems analyst Chesapeake Bay Inst., Balt., 1965-66; phys. oceanography program mgr. Office of Naval Rsch., Washington, 1972-78; chief oceanic processes program NASA, Washington, 1979-89, program scientist earth observing system, 1989-92; asst. adminstr. for ocean svcs. and coastal zone mgmt. NOAA, Washington, 1992—. Recipient Antarctica Svc. medal NSF, 1961, Superior Civilian Svc. award USN, 1979, Exceptional Sci. Achievement medal NASA, 1981, Disting. Achievement award MTS and Compass Publs., 1989, award Remote Sensing Soc., 1992, medal French Space Agy., 1994. Mem. Am. Meteorol. Soc., Am. Geophys. Union (Ocean Scis. award 1984), Oceanography Soc. (com. chmn. 1989-92), The Oceanography Soc., Sigma Xi. Avocations: bicycling, hiking, gardening. Home: 219 Tunbridge Rd Baltimore MD 21212-3423 Office: N SSMC4 Sta 13632 1305 East West Hwy Silver Spring MD 20910

WILSTED, JOY, elementary education educator, reading specialist, parenting consultant; b. St. Marys, Pa., Aug. 12, 1935; d. Wayne and Carrie (Neiger) Furman; m. Richard William Wilsted, Feb. 14, 1982; 2 children. BA, Fla. Atlantic U., 1970; MS in Edn., Old Dominion U., Norfolk, Va., 1975. Cert. reading specialist, elem. tchr., N.J.; cert. permanent tchr., N.Y. Tchr. creative dramatics Hillsboro Country Day Sch., Pompano Beach, Fla., 1966-68; tchr. PTA Kindergarten, Boca Raton, Fla., 1968-69;

tchr. creative dramatics Wee-Wisdom Montessori Sch., Delray Beach, Fla., 1969-70; elem. tchr. Birmingham (Mich.) Pub. Schs., 1970-72; classroom and reading resource tchr. Chesapeake (Va.) Pub. Schs., 1972-79; reading coord. Harrisonville (Mo.) Pub. Schs., 1979-81; Chpt. I reading tchr., reading improvement tchr. North Kansas City Pub. Schs., Kansas City, Mo., 1981—; instr. continuing edn. U. Mo., Kansas City, 1980-87, Ottawa U., Overland Park, Kans., 1990—; cons. Young Authors' Conf., Oakland U., Rochester, Mich., 1971; coord. fine arts Alpha Phi Alpha Tutorial Project, Chesapeake, 1973-75; presenter Chpt. I Summer Inst., Tech. Assistance Ctr., Mo., 1984; cons. on parenting Reading Success Unltd., Gallatin, Mo., 1987—; mem. adv. bd. Parents & Children Together, Ind. U. Family Literacy Ctr., Bloomington, 1990-93; keynote speaker ann. conf. Nat. Coalition. Author: Dramatics for Self-Expression, 1967, Now Johnny CAN Learn to Read, 1987, Reading Songs and Poems of Joy, 19o87, Character-Building Poems for Young People. Mem. Internat. Reading Assn. (mem. coun., pres. local coun. 1986-88, state chmn. parents and reading com. 1988-89, mem. nat. parents and reading com. 1989-92, Local Literacy award 1989). Office: Reading SUCCESS Unltd PO Box 215 Gallatin MO 64640-0215

WILT, ALAN FREESE, history educator; b. Nappanee, Ind., May 14, 1937; s. Lisle and Helen (Freese) W.; m. Maureen Gilmore, Aug. 3, 1963; children: Karen, Rachel. BA, DePauw U., 1959; MA, U. Mich., 1960, PhD, 1969. Part-time instr. history Midwestern U., Wichita Falls, Tex., 1961-62; from instr. to prof. Iowa State U., Ames, 1967-81, prof., 1981—; vis. prof. mil. history Air War Coll., Maxwell AFB, Ala., 1982-83. Author: The Atlantic Wall: Hitler's Defenses in the West, 1941-44, 1975, The French Riviera Campaign of August 1944, 1981, War from the Top: German and British Military Decision Making during World War II, 1990, Nazi Germany, 1994. 1st lt. USAF, 1960-63, Korea. Mem. Am. Hist. Assn., Soc. for Military History, German Studies Assn. Democrat. Presbyterian. Home: 4203 Arizona Cir Ames IA 50014-3612 Office: Iowa State U Dept History 643 Ross Hall Ames IA 50011

WILT, JEFFREY LYNN, pulmonary and critical care physician; b. Fairmont, W.Va., Nov. 15, 1963; s. Paul Lynn and Linda (Amos) W. BA, U. Mich., 1986, MD, 1988. Diplomate Am. Bd. Internat. Medicine, subspecialty pulmonary diseases, Am. Bd. Med. Examiners; cert. ACLS. Resident in internal medicine Blodgett/St. Mary's Hosp., Grand Rapids, Mich. 1988-91, chief med. resident in internal medicine, 1990-91; asst. dir. internal medicine residency St. Mary's Hosp., Grand Rapids, 1992; fellow sect. pulmonary and critical care W.Va. U., Morgantown, 1992-95. Mem. ACP (Nat. Clin. Vignette winner 1991), AMA, Am. Thoracic Soc. (assoc.), Am. Coll Chest Physicians (Young Investigators award 1993). Republican. Avocations: bicycling, karate, magic, reading, swimming. Home: 1510 Buckhannon Ave Morgantown WV 26505 Office: W Va U Sect Pulm & Critical Care PO Box 9166 Morgantown WV 26506-9166

WILT, LAWRENCE J.M., librarian; b. Buffalo, June 2, 1948; s. Cecil J.W. and Bernice M. (Yaeck) W.; m. Jane Maienscheim, Mar. 10, 1974 (div. 1981); m. Pamela Gail Nase, May 15, 1982; 1 child, Tori Lauren. BA in Humanities, SUNY, Binghamton, 1970; MA in Philosophy, Ind. U., 1974, MLS, 1977, PhD in Philosophy, 1980. Assoc. faculty Ind. U./Purdue U., Indpls., 1976-77; asst. prof. libr. resources Dickinson Coll., Carlisle, Pa., 1977-79, head reference dept., 1979-81; collection mgmt. libr. U. Md. Baltimore County, Catonsville, 1981-86, assoc. dir for collections and info. svcs., 1986-90, dir libr., 1990—. Contbr. articles to profl. jours. Mem. ALA (chair Assn. of Coll. and Rsch. Libraries publs. com. 1979-81, mem. Assn. of Coll. and Rsch. Libraries acad. status com. 1988-91). Home: 4 N Beechwood Ave Catonsville MD 21228 Office: U Md Baltimore County Albin O Kuhn Libr & Gallery Catonsville MD 21228

WILT, SONYA ANNE MUGNANI, speech and language pathologist; b. Charleroi, Pa., Mar. 7, 1937; d. Carl E. and Emilie A. (Erickson) Mugnani; m. Roy W. Wilt, Aug. 6, 1960; children: Roy Jr., Rod E. AB summa cum laude, Muskingum Coll., 1959; MS with highest honors, U. Pitts., 1962, PhD, 1975. Grad. fellow, teaching asst. U. Pitts., 1959-62; speech pathologist-in-tng. Children's Hosp. Pitts., 1960-62; instr., asst. prof., assoc. prof. prof. English and comm. Thiel Coll., Greenville, Pa., 1965-94, dir. forensics and debate, 1965-75, coord. undergrad. major in speech and hearing sci., 1975-94; pvt. practice speech pathology Greenville, 1966—; teaching asst. U. Pitts., 1974-75; speech pathologist Greenville Regional Hosp. Home Care Agy., White Cliff Nursing Home, Greenville, Outpatient Rehab. Facility, Greenville Regional Hosp., Med. Assocs., Greenville Regional Hosp., Shenango Valley Med. Ctr., Horizon Health System; rsch. cons. Bethesda/Luth. Social Svcs., Bethesda Home for Children, Meadville, Pa., 1978; leader various workshops and presentations. Recipient award for continuing edn. Am. Speech-Hearing-Lang. Assn., award for teaching excellence Sears-Roebuck Co. Republican. Lutheran. Avocations: piano, needlework, writing. Home: 262 Leech Rd Greenville PA 16125

WILTBANK, JOSEPH KELLEY, lawyer, university counsel, sports association executive; b. Albuquerque, June 5, 1950; s. William J. and Joyce I. (Jones) W.; m. Antonia Louise Urquidi, Aug. 5, 1978; children: Mitch, Drew, Jay, Neeley. BA in History, U. Fla., 1972; JD, Gonzaga U., 1977; BA in French with high honors, Idaho State U., 1990. Bar: Idaho 1977, U.S. Dist. Ct. Idaho 1977, U.S. Ct. Appeals (9th cir.) 1979. Adminstrv. asst. to mayor Mountain Home, Idaho, 1977-79; dep. prosecuting atty. Ada County, Boise, Idaho, 1979-83; univ. counsel, counsel to pres. Idaho State U., Pocatello, 1983-94, gen. counsel, dir. Intercollegiate Athletics, 1995—; interim dir. athletics Idaho State U., 1989-90. Editor: The Practical Aspects of Technology Transfer, 1990. Ex officio bd. dirs. Idaho State U. Found., 1983—; bd. dirs. First Security Games of Idaho, 1991—, pres. 1992-94, Bannock Boys Baseball, Pocatello, 1989-91, Real Dairy Bowl (formerly Centennial Bowl), 1987-94, exec. dir., 1991-94; advisor Mortar Bd. Idaho State U., 1988-91. Mem. Nat. Assn. Coll. and Univ. Attys. (bd. dirs. 1990-93), Rotary (bd. dirs. 19994—). Avocations: sports, music.

WILTROUT, ANN ELIZABETH, foreign language educator; b. Elkhart, Ind., Aug. 3, 1939; d. F. LeRoy and Margaret Elizabeth (Williams) W.; m. Joseph Alli, Aug. 25, 1990. BA, Hanover Coll., 1961; MA, Ind. U., 1964, PhD, 1968. Vis. asst. prof. Ind. U., Bloomington, 1968-69; asst. prof. Miss. State U., Mississippi State, 1969-71, assoc. prof., 1971-87, prof. Miss. State U., NEH fellow in residence Duke U., 1977-78. Author: A Patron and a Playwright in Renaissance Spain, 1987; contbr. articles to profl. publs. Recipient Disting. Svc. cert. Nat. Internat. Edn., 1986. Mem. AAUP, MLA (del. to assembly 1975-78), Assn. Internat. Hispanitas, Cervantes Soc. Am., Am. Assn. Tchrs. of Spanish and Portuguese, Assn. Hispanic Classical Theater, Soc. Scholars in Arts and Scis., Phi Kappa Phi, Sigma Delta Pi. Avocations: Shakespeare, travel, reading, roses. Office: Miss State U Dept Fgn Langs Drawer FL Mississippi State MS 39762

WILTSE, JAMES CLARK, civil engineer; b. Dearborn, Mich., Apr. 14, 1927; s. Cecil C. and Mary G. (Brashear) W.; m. Marlyn R. Glatus, Feb. 14, 1953; children: Richard, Mary, Michael. BSCE, U. Mich., 1953. Registered profl. engr., Mass. Civil engr. U.S. Army C.E., Detroit, 1954-67; project engr. USAF Civil Engring., London, 1968-72; civil engr. USN Facilities Engring. Command, Norfolk, Va., 1973-75; chief engr. USN Resident Office, Keflavik, Iceland, 1976-81; staff civil engr. USAF Electronic Systems Div., Kaiserslautern, Germany, 1982-91; spl. asst. ROICC Norfolk, Lantnavfac Eng Com, Norfolk, Va., 1992-93, Lantnavfac Eng Com, Norfolk, Va., 1993-94; quality assurance engr. HQ Lantnavfac; ret., 1994. Sgt. U.S. Army, 1946-47, Japan. Fellow ASCE; mem. Soc. Am. Mil. Engrs. Home: 8555 Lawson Ave Norfolk VA 23503-5220

WILTSHIRE, RICHARD WATKINS, SR., insurance company executive; b. Richmond, Va., July 17, 1921; s. William Ernest and Essie (Watkins) W.; m. Jean Watkins Betts, Sept. 5, 1942; children: Mrs. Henry M. Massie, Jr., Richard Watkins, Jr., William Betts, Virginia Betts McGurn. B.A., U. Va., 1943. With Home Beneficial Life Ins. Co., Richmond, Va., 1946—; dir. agy. tng. Home Beneficial Life Ins. Co., 1947, asst. supr. agys., 1947-50, asst v.p., 1950-52, dir., 1949—, v.p., 1952-66, exec. v.p., gen. mgr., 1966-68, pres., 1968—, chmn., 1983—. Trustee The Collegiate Schs., Richmond Meml. Hosp., Children's Hosp.; bd. dirs. Union Theol. Sem. Served with USMCR, 1942-45. Presbyterian (elder). Office: Home Beneficial Life Ins Co 3901 W Broad St Richmond VA 23230-3962

WILTSHIRE, RICHARD WATKINS, JR., insurance company executive; b. Richmond, Va., July 24, 1945; s. Richard W. and Jean (Betts) W.; m. Barbara Griffin; children: Richard III, Andrew, Anne. BA, Hampden-Sydney Coll., 1968. With agy. dept. Home Beneficial Life Ins. Co., Richmond, 1969-71, with securities dept., 1972-74, mgr. securities dept., 1975-87, v.p., 1979, exec. v.p., 1985, pres., 1988, also bd. dirs.; mem. exec. com. Life Insurers Conf., Atlanta, 1979-82, 87—; bd. dirs. Mut. Assurance Soc. Va., Richmond. Mem. investment com. Union Theol. Sem., Richmond, 1989—; pres.-elect Children's Hosp., Richmond, 1989—. Mem. Richmond Soc. Fin. Analysts. Presbyterian. Office: Home Beneficial Corp 3901 W Broad St Richmond VA 23230

WILVER, WAYNE R., electronics executive; b. 1933. BA, Rutgers U., 1955. Various positions, then chief fin. exec. GE, Lynchburg, Va., 1955-83; mem. U.S. Com. Energy Awareness, Washington, 1983-86; v.p., CFO, sec., treas. Comdial Corp., Charlottesville, Va., 1986—. Office: Comdial Corp 1180 Seminole Trl Charlottesville VA 22901*

WILZACK, ADELE, state health official; Student Loyola Coll., R.N. diploma Mercy Hosp. Sch. Nursing, Balt., 1957; B.S. in Nursing, Mt. St. Agnes coll., 1959; .M.S. in Nursing, U. Md., 1960; postgrad. in pub. adminstrn. U. So. Calif., 1976. Staff nurse Mercy Hosp., Balt., 1957-60, supr. non-profl. personnel, 1961-63, asst. dir. nursing services, 1963-65; project nurse operation REASON, Community Action Agy., Health and Welfare Council, Balt., 1965-67; asst. dir. bur. spl. home services Balt. City Health Dept., 1967-72, dir. bur. spl. home services, 1972-74, dir. health services for aging, 1974-76, asst. commr. health services for aging and med. care, 1976-79; asst. sec. for med. care programs Md. Dept. Health and Mental Hygiene, Balt., 1979-83, sec. dept., 1983—; mem. Gov.'s Drug and Alcohol Commn., chairperson, treatment subcom. Children and Youth Subcabinet; assoc. faculty mem. U. Md. Sch. Nursing; vis. faculty mem. U. Mich. Inst. Gerontology, Ann Arbor; past mem. Md. Gov.'s Task Force on Med. Malpractice Ins., Md. Gov.'s Task Force on Health Care Cost Containment; mem. Gov.'s Commn. on Black and Minority Health, Gov.'s Council on Adolescent Pregnancy, Gov.'s Adv. Bd. for Justice Assistance; past com. mem. and chmn. Central Md. Health Systems Agy.; past com. mem., past subcom. chmn. Md. Med. Assistance Adv. Com.; past chmn. Balt. City Sub-Area Adv. Council; past mem. regional adv. task force Johns Hopkins Hosp., task force on aging U. Md. Recipient award for outstanding contbns. to intergroup relations and dedicated humanitarian service to citizens of Balt. City, Balt. Community Relations Commn., 1978, Alumna of Yr. award Loyola Coll., 1978, Woman Mgr. of Yr., Conf. for Women in State Service, 1981; Merit scholar U. Md. Sch. Nursing. Mem. Md. Pub. Health Assn. (past mem. exec. com.), Am. Pub. Health Assn. (past mem. governing council state affiliate), Balt. City Med. Soc. (past mem. long-term care com.), Sigma Phi Sigma, Sigma Theta Tau. Office: Md Dept Health and Mental Hygiene 201 W Preston St Baltimore MD 21201-2323 Office: Hlth Facilities Assn of MD 229 Hanover St Annapolis MD 21401-1621

WIMBERLY, GEORGE JAMES, architect; b. Ellensburg, Wash., Jan. 16, 1915; s. George Welch and Eurma (Bezdechek) W.; m. Janet Harrietta Brebner, July 7, 1939 (div. Sept. 1969); 1 child, Heather Mary; m. Walton Jeffords, Dec. 12, 1969. B.Arch., U. Wash., 1937; student in, Mex., 1938. Draftsman, designer Seattle, Los Angeles, Phoenix, 1938-40; architect U.S. Civil Service, Pearl Harbor, 1940-45; practice architecture Honolulu, 1945—; partner Wimberly & Cook, 1945-59; pres., dir. Wimberly, Whisenand, Allison, Tong & Goo, Architects, Ltd., 1959-87; con.s Wimberly, Allison, Tong & Goo, Inc., 1987—; cons. for tourist facilities, Western Samoa, 1967-69, Ceylon, 1968, New Zealand, 1968, Australia, 1969, Singapore, 1970, 85, Taiwan, 1971, Malaysia, 1971, Fiji, 1972, India, 1972, Nepal, 1975; mem. Hawaii Bd. Registration Profl. Architects and Engrs., 1959-67; pres. Waikiki Assn., 1951-53. Prin. works include Keelikolani State Bldg., Honolulu, 1950, Canlis Restaurant, Seattle, 1951, Coco Palms Hotel, Kauai, Hawaii, 1952, First Nat. Bank, Waikiki, 1953, Canlis Restaurant, Honolulu, 1954, Honolulu Gas Co. Bldg., 1955, Hawaiian Trust Co. Bldg., Honolulu, 1956, Windward City Shopping Ctr., Kaneohe, Hawaii, 1957, First Nat. Bank, Kapiolani Jr., Honolulu, 1958, Fin. Factors home office bldg., Honolulu, 1958, Home Ins. Bldg., Honolulu, 1959, Princess Kaiulani Hotel Waikiki, 1960, Hotel Tahiti, 1960, 3019 Kalakaua Ave. Apt., 1961, Sheraton Maui Hotel, 1962, Civic Auditorium, American Samoa, 1963, Pago Pago Intercontinental Hotel, American Samoa, 1965, Bank of Hawaii Bldg., Waikiki, 1967, Visitor Ctr., Mt. Rainier Nat. Park, 1967, Kona-Hilton Hotel, 1968, Taharaa's Intercontinental Hotel, Tahiti, 1968, Fijian Hotel, Nadi, Fiji, 1968, Sheraton Kauai Hotel, Kauai, 1968, Mauna Kea Beach Hotel South Wing, Kamuela, Hawaii, 1968, New Surfrider Hotel, Waikiki, 1969, Royal Hawaiian Diamond Head Wing, Waikiki, 1969, Tokyu Djakarta Hotel, Indonesia, 1971, Sheraton Waikiki Hotel, Honolulu, 1971, Hawaiian Telephone Office Bldg., Honolulu, 1972, Ibusuki Kanko Hotel, Tokyo, 1972, Maui Land and Pineapple Co. Bldg., 1972, Mauna Kea Beach Hotel Addition, Kamuela, 1972, First Hawaiian Bank, Waianae, Oahu, 1972, Hayashida Onsen Hotel, Japan, 1973, Iwasaki Hotel, Japan, 1973, Wailea Golf Clubhouse, Maui, 1973, Hanalei Beach and Racquet Club, 1975, Hyatt Regency at Hemmeter Ctr., Waikiki, 1976, Aloha Towers Condominium, Waikiki, 1977, Sheraton Molokai Hotel, 1977, Tangjong Jara Beach Hotel, Malaysia, 1978, Shangri-La Hotel Addition, Singapore, 1978, Hyatt Maui Hotel, 1980, Hilton Tapa Tower, 1982, Bangkok Peninsula Hotel, 1983, Arcadia Condominiums, Singapore, 1984, Ritz-Carlton Hotel, Laguna Niguel, Calif., 1985, Four Seasons Hotel, Newport Beach, Calif., 1986. Bd. dirs. Honolulu Community Theatre, 1961-64, 80-84, Honolulu Theatre for Youth, 1960-63; mem. Hawaii Visitors Bur., 1952—; bd. dirs., 1973-77; mem. U.S. Dept. Commerce Hawaii/Pacific Dist. Export Council, 1979-83. Recipient Institutions Mag. Design awards; Holiday Mag. Design award; White Cement award of excellence Portland Cement Assn., 1972; Aga Kahn award for architecture Tanjong Jara Beach Hotel and Rantau Abang Visitor Ctr., 1983; Platinum Circle award Restaurant and Hotel Design mag., 1989. Fellow AIA (pres. Hawaii 1953, hon. awards Hawaii chpt. 1955, 60 (3), 1962, 64, 66, 68 (2), 1972, 73-75, 79, 82, 84); mem. Pacific Area Travel Assn. (life mem., contbg. mem., alt. dir. 1972-77, chmn. Devel. Authority 1979-81, award of merit 1979), Honolulu C. of C., Waikiki Improvement Assn., Tau Sigma Delta (pres. 1936). Clubs: Sports Car Club Am, Les Chevaliers du Deuxième Hemisiècle, Le Grand Chevalier Intérimaire (sr. steward); Pacific (Waikiki), Outrigger Canoe (Waikiki). Office: Wimberly Allison Tong & Goo 1000 Quail St # 190 Newport Beach CA 92660 also: 2260 University Dr Newport Beach CA 92660

WIMPRESS, GORDON DUNCAN, JR., corporate consultant, foundation executive; b. Riverside, Calif., Apr. 10, 1922; s. Gordon Duncan and Maude A. (Waldo) W.; m. Jean Margaret Skerry, Nov. 30, 1946; children—Wendy Jo, Victoria Jean, Gordon Duncan III. B.A., U. Oreg., Eugene, 1946, M.A., 1951; Ph.D., U. Denver, 1958; LL.D., Monmouth Coll., Ill., 1970; L.H.D., Tusculum Coll., Greenville, Tenn., 1971. Lic. comml. pilot. Dir. pub. relations, instr. journalism Whittier (Calif.) Coll., 1946-51; asst. to pres. Colo. Sch. Mines, Golden, 1951-59; pres. Monticello Coll., Alton, Ill., 1959-64, Monmouth Coll., Ill., 1964-70, Trinity U., San Antonio, 1970-77; vice chmn. S.W. Found. for Biomed. Rsch., San Antonio, 1977-82, pres., 1982-92, also bd. govs., pres. Duncan Wimpress & Assocs., Inc., San Antonio, 1992—; commr. Burlington No. R.R. scholarship selection com.; chmn. Valero Energy Corp. scholarship commn.; bd. dirs. Southwest Rsch. Inst. Author: American Journalism Comes of Age, 1950. Bd. dirs. Am. Inst. Character Edn., ARC, Am. Heart Assn., Cancer Therapy and Rsch. Found.; trustee San Antonio Med. Found., Eisenhower Med. Ctr., Rancho Mirage, Calif.; mem. San Antonio Fiesta Commn.; ruling elder United Presbyn. Ch., U.S.A.; mem. adv. bd. Alamo Area chpt. Am. Diabetes Assn. 1st lt. AUS, 1942-45, ETO. Decorated Bronze Star. Mem. Aircraft Owners and Pilots Assn., Am. Acad. Polit. and Social Sci., Am. Assn. Higher Edn., MENSA, Nat. Pilots Assn., Pilots Internat. Assn., Inc., Quiet Birdmen, Greater San Antonio C. of C. (bd. dirs.), North San Antonio C. of C. (bd. dirs.), Assn. Former Intelligence Officers, Confederate Air Force, Pi Gamma Mu, Sigma Delta Chi, Sigma Delta Pi, Sigma Phi Epsilon (trustee found.), Sigma Upsilon, Newcomen Soc. N.Am. Clubs: Argyle, St. Anthony, San Antonio Country, the Dominion (bd. govs.), City , Plaza, San Antonio Golf Assn. Lodge: Rotary (dist. gov. 1983-84, San Antonio). Avocations: golf, skiing, flying. Office: PO Box 780818 San Antonio TX 78278-0818

WIN, KHIN SWE, anesthesiologist; b. Rangoon, Burma, Sept. 27, 1934; came to U.S., 1962; d. U Mg and Daw Aye (Kyin) Maung; m. M. Shein Win, May 28, 1959; children: Tha Shein, Thwe Shein, Maw Shein, Thet Shein, Htoo Shein. Intermediate of Sci. Degree, U. Rangoon, 1954, MB, BS, 1962. Intern Waltham (Mass.) Hosp., 1962-63; resident anesthesiology Boston City Hosp., 1963-65; fellow pediatric anesthesiology New Eng. Med. Ctr. Hosps., Boston, 1965-66; fellow anesthesiology Martin Luther King Jr. Gen. Hosp., L.A., 1978-79; pvt. practice anesthesiology Apple Valley, Calif., 1984—; asst. prof. anesthesiology Martin Luther King Jr./Charles R. Drew Med. Ctr., L.A., 1979-84. Republican. Buddhist. Avocations: gardening, meditation. Home: 13850 Pamlico Rd Apple Valley CA 92307-5400 Office: St Mary Desert Valley Hosp Dept Anesthesiology 18300 Us Highway 18 Apple Valley CA 92307-2206

WINAHRADSKY, MICHAEL FRANCIS, drug company executive; b. Syracuse, N.Y., Oct. 21, 1948; s. Frank F. and Genelle M. (Charmley) W.; m. Linda L. Peters, Oct. 10, 1981; children: Kevin M., Kari M. Distbn. ctr. supr. Fay's Inc., Liverpool, N.Y., 1967-76, distbn. ctr. mgr., 1976-81; asst. v.p. distbn. Fay's Drug Co. Inc., Liverpool, N.Y., 1981-82, v.p. distbn., 1982—; guest speaker Syracuse (N.Y.) U., 1984. Participant Cen. N.Y. chpt. Cystic Fibrosis Bowl for Breath, 1987-93. Mem. Warehouse Edn. and Rsch. Coun., Nat. Fire Protection Assn., Boat Owners U.S., Moose, Elks, Lakeshore Yacht & Country Club, Nat. Assn. Chain Drug Stores (co-chmn. distbn. and logistics com. 1995). Avocations: power boating, fishing, cross-country skiing, cruising, golf. Home: 4320 Lazybrook Cir Liverpool NY 13088 Office: Fay's Inc 7245 Henry Clay Blvd Liverpool NY 13088-3523

WINAWER, SIDNEY JEROME, physician, clinical investigator, educator; b. N.Y.C.; s. Nathan and Sally Winawer; children: Daniel, Jonathan, Joanna. BA, NYU, 1952; MD, SUNY, N.Y.C., 1956. Asst. in medicine Harvard Med. Sch., Boston, 1962-66; asst. physician Harvard Med. Svc. Boston City Hosp., 1964-66; with Meml. Sloan-Kettering Cancer Ctr., N.Y.C., 1978—, head lab for gastroent. cancer rsch., 1988—, chief gastroent. and nutrition svc., 1988—, mem. with tenure of title, 1988—, Paul Sherlock chair, 1991—; prof. medicine Cornell U. Coll. Medicine, N.Y.C., 1980—; head Ctr. for Prevention Colon Cancer WHO, Geneva, 1985; liason rep. Nat. Cancer Adv. Bd., Washington, 1984-89; mem. adv. com. on cancer prevention Am. Cancer Soc., 1988-90; mem. sci. adv. bd. ICRF; cons. various rev. coms., Nat. Cancer Inst., Washington. Editor: Prevention Colorectal Cancer, 1980, Basic and Clinical Perspectives of Colorectal Polyps and Cancer, 1988, Lar Bowel Cancers: Policy, Prevention, Research and Treatment, 1991, Management of Gastrointestinal Disease, 1992, Gastrointestinal Cancer, 1992, Cancer of the Colon, Rectum and Anus, 1994, Cancer Free, 1995; contbr. chpts. to books, articles to profl. jours. Capt. USAF, 1959-61. Nat. Cancer Inst. grantee 1974, 77, 80 (2), 85, 88 , 90. Fellow ACP, Am. Coll. Gastroenterology (pres. 1979-80, Disting. Sci. Achievement award 1982, Baker Presdl. lectr. 1992, Master 1993); mem. Am. Soc. Gastrointestinal Endoscopy (bd. dirs. 1974-78, disting. lectr. 1985, Schindler award 1994), Am. Gastroent. Assn. (nat. chmn. cancer sect. 1989-91), Am. Soc. Clin. Oncology, Am. Assn. Cancer Rsch., N.Y. Soc. Gastrointestinal Endoscopy (founder, pres. 1978-79, ann. lectr. 1985). Jewish. Avocations: opera, modern art, biking, cross-country skiing, sailing. Office: Meml Sloan-Kettering Cancer Ctr 1275 York Ave New York NY 10021-6094

WINBORN, TERRY LEE, lawyer; b. Jennings, La., Mar. 25, 1950; s. Stephen A. and Phyllis B. (Brownnell) W.; m. Linda L. Johnson. BA in Social Sci., Houston Baptist U., 1973; JD, So. Meth. U., 1976. Bar: Tex. 1976, U.S. Dist. Ct. (no. dist.) Tex., U.S. Tax Ct. Assoc. Johnson & Cravens, Dallas, 1976-82, ptnr., 1982-88; ptnr. Hopkins & Sutter. Bd. dirs., innovators Dallas Symphony Orch. Assn., 1983-84; mem. exec. bd. Coun. Ten Boy Scouts Am., 1992—; pres. Wadley Found., 1991—. Mem. ABA, Tex. Bar Assn., Dallas Bar Assn., Tex. Assn. Bank Counsel, Tower Club. Office: Tuttle & Graber 1220 Maxus Energy Tower 717 N Harwood St Dallas TX 75201-6501

WINCENC, CAROL, concertizing flutist, educator; b. Buffalo, June 29, 1949; d. Joseph and Margaret (Miller) Wincenc; m. Douglas Webster; 1 child, Nicola Wincenc-Webster. Grad., Santa Cecilia Acad., Rome, 1967, Chigiana Acad., Siena, Italy, 1968; MusB, Manhattan Sch. Music, N.Y.C., 1971; MusM, Juilliard Sch. Music, N.Y.C., 1972. Concertizing flutist recs. with Deutsche, Gramaphon, Nonesuch, New World, Music Masters, and Decca records; soloist with major symphony orchs.; artist faculty Juilliard Sch., 1988—. Bd. dirs., v.p. Chamber Music Am., N.Y.C., 1990-91, 91—. Recipient Naumburg award, 1978. Mem. Nat. Flute Assn. (life). Home: 875 W End Ave Apt 14E New York NY 10025-4954 Office: The Juilliard Sch Lincoln Ctr New York NY 10023

WINCER, SIMON, film director. Films include Harlequin, 1980, The Day After Halloween, 1981, Phar Lap, 1984, D.A.R.Y.L., 1985, The Lighthorsemen, 1987, Quigley Down Under, 1990, Harley Davidson and the Marlboro Man, 1991, Free Willy, 1993, Operation Dumbo Drop, 1995; exec. prodr.: The Man From Snowy River, 1982, One Night Stand, 1983; TV dir.: Prisoner: Cell Block H, 1980, The Girl Who Spelled Freedom, 1986, The Last Frontier, 1986, Bluegrass, Lonesome Dove, 1989 (Outstanding Direction Emmy award 1989); cons. The Adventures of the Black Stallion, 1990. Office: c/o Creative Artists Agency 9830 Wilshire Blvd Beverly Hills CA 90212*

WINCE-SMITH, DEBORAH L., federal agency administrator; m. Michael B. Smith; 2 children. Grad. magna cum laude, Vassar Coll., 1972; Master's, Cambridge (Eng.) U., 1974. Former program mgr. internat. programs NSF; asst. dir. internat. affairs and global competitiveness Office of Sci. and Tech. Policy The White House, 1984-89; asst. sec. tech. policy Dept. Commerce, Washington, 1989-93; sr. fellow Coun. on Competitiveness, Washington, 1993—; sr. fellow Congl. Econ. Leadership Inst., Washington, 1993—. Office: Coun on Competitiveness 1401 H St NW Ste 650 Washington DC 20005

WINCOR, MICHAEL Z., psychopharmacology educator, clinician, researcher; b. Chgo., Feb. 9, 1946; s. Emanuel and Rose (Kershner) W.; m. Emily E.M. Smythe; children: Meghan Heather, Katherine Rose. SB in Zoology, U. Chgo., 1966; PharmD, U. So. Calif., 1978. Rsch. project specialist U. Chgo. Sleep Lab., 1968-75; psychiat. pharmacist Brotman Med. Ctr., Culver City, Calif., 1979-83; asst. prof. U. So. Calif., L.A., 1983—; cons. Fed. Bur. Prisons Drug Abuse Program, Terminal Island, Calif., 1978-81, Nat. Inst. Drug Abuse, Bethesda, Md., 1981, The Upjohn Co., Kalamazoo, 1982-87, 91-92, Area XXIV Profl. Stds. Rev. Orgn., L.A., 1983, Brotman Med. Ctr., Culver City, Calif., 1983-88, SmithKline Beecham Pharms., Phila., 1990-93, Tokyo Coll. of Pharmacy, 1991, G. D. Searle & Co., Chgo., 1992—. Contbr. over 30 articles to profl. jours., chpts. to books, papers presented at nat. and internat. meetings and reviewer. Mem. adv. coun. Franklin Ave. Sch., 1986-89; bd. dirs. K.I. Children's Ctr., 1988-89; trustee The Sequoyah Sch., 1992-93; mem. tech. com. Ivanhoe Sch., 1993—. Recipient Cert. Appreciation, Mayor of L.A., 1981, Bristol Labs Award, 1978; Faculty scholar U. So. Calif. Sch. Pharmacy, 1978. Mem. Am. Coll. Clin. Pharmacy (chmn. constn. and bylaws com. 1983-84, mem. credentials com. 1991-95, mem. ednl. affairs com. 1994), Am. Assn. Colls. Pharmacy (focus group on liberalization of profl. curriculum), Am. Soc. Hosp. Pharmacists (chmn. edn. and tng. adv. working group 1985-88), Am. Pharm. Assn. (del. ann. meeting ho. dels. 1989), Sleep Rsch. Soc., Am. Sleep Disorders Assn., U. So. Calif. Sch. Pharmacy Alumni Assn. (bd. dirs. 1979—), Rho Chi. Avocation: photography. Office: U So Calif 1985 Zonal Ave Los Angeles CA 90033-1058

WIND, HERBERT WARREN, writer; b. Brockton, Mass., Aug. 11, 1916; s. Max E. and Dora O. Wind. BA, Yale U., 1937; MA, Cambridge U., Eng., 1939. Staff writer New Yorker mag., N.Y.C., 1947-54, 62-90, Sporting Scene; editor, writer Sports Illustrated mag., N.Y.C., 1954-60; cons. writer, assoc. producer TV series Shell's Wonderful World of Golf, 1961-62; tchr. seminar on lit. of sports, Yale U., 1973. Author: The Story of American Golf, 1948, revised 1956, 75, (with Ben Hogan) The Modern Fundamentals of Golf, 1957, (with Jack Nicklaus) The Greatest Game of All, 1969, Game, Set, and Match, collection of tennis articles, 1979, Following Through, collection of golf articles, 1985; editor The Classics of Golf reprint series, 1983—. With USAAF, 1942-46, PTO. Mem. Oxford and Cambridge Golfing Soc., Yale Golf Assn., Royal and Ancient Golf Club of St. Andrews. Home: 32 Jericho Rd Weston MA 02193-1210

WINDEL, ROBERT EUGENE, school system administrator; b. New York Mills, Minn., Mar. 2, 1944; s. Adolph H. and Dora Ellen (Ramsay) W.; children from previous marriage: Jonathan, Jill; m. Patricia Dianne Tschetter, July 1, 1977; children: Pamela, Timothy, Robert J. BS, Concordia Coll., 1966; MS, Mankato State U., 1973; EdS, Tri-Coll. U., 1981; EdD, Mont. State U., 1991. Cert. adminstr., Mont., tchr. elem. edn., adminstr., Minn. Tchr. Prior Lake (Minn.) Elem. Sch., 1966-69; team leader Sweeney Elem. Sch., Shakopee, Minn., 1969-70, 71-73; tchr. sci. Grant Elem. Sch., Duluth, Minn., 1970-71; team leader, asst. prin. William Byrne Elem. Sch., Burnsville, Minn., 1973-77; elem. prin. Lake PArk (Minn.) Elem. Sch., 1977-79; asst. supt. Lake Park Pub. Schs., 1979-81; adminstrv. asst. supt. West Fargo (N.D.) Pub. Schs., 1981-86; supt. Havre (Mont.) Pub. Schs., 1986—; keynote speaker Ann. Regional Adminstrv. Conf., Saskatchewan, Can., 1987; chmn. sch. adminstrn. Cert./Aspiring Prins., Mont, 1991-93; pres. Vanguard Paradigm, Inc., 1992—, corp. pres. sch. reform initiative, 1992. Bd. dirs. No. Mont. Health Care, Havre; pres. Hi Line Sch. Adminstrn. Assn., 1989-91. Mem. Am. Assn. Sch. Adminstrs. (reader, evaluator conf. proposals 1992), Internat. Reading Assn. (presenter nat. convention 1990), Minn. Assn. Elem. Sch. Prins. (presenter confs. 1977-81), Mont. Conf. Edn. Leadership (sectional leader 1988, 89, 91, 92), Active Corp. Execs., Rotary, Havre C. of C. Avocation: hunting. Office: Havre Pub Schs 425 6th St Havre MT 59501-4032

WINDELS, PAUL, JR., lawyer; b. Bklyn., Nov. 13, 1921; s. Paul and Louise E. (Gross) W.; m. Patricia Ripley, Sept. 10, 1955; children: Paul III, Mary H., James H.R., Patrick D. AB, Princeton U., 1943; LLB, Harvard U., 1948. Bar: N.Y. 1949. Spl. asst. counsel N.Y. State Crime Commn., 1951; asst. U.S. atty. Ea. Dist. N.Y., 1953-56; N.Y. regional adminstr. SEC, 1956-61, also spl. asst, U.S. atty. for prosecution securities frauds, 1956-58; lectr. law Am. Inst. Banking, 1950-57; mem. Windels, Marx, Davies & Ives and predecessor firms, 1961-88, of counsel, 1988—. Author: Our Securities Markets-Some SEC Problems and Techniques, 1962. Trustee, chmn. Bklyn. Law Sch., Lycée Francais N.Y.; trustee Princeton U. Rowing Assn., Knox Sch., Garta Charitable trust; past pres. Fed. Bar Coun.; mem. adv. bd. NYU Inst. French Studies, SUNY Marine Scis. Rsch. Sta.; bd. dirs. Horticulture Soc. N.Y. Capt. F.A., AUS, 1943-46, ETO; maj. USAR. Recipient Flemming award for fed. svc.; decorated chevalier Order French Acad. Palms; officer Nat. Order Merit France. Fellow Am. Bar Found.; mem. ABA, N.Y. State Bar Assn., Assn. of Bar of City of N.Y., N.Y. County Lawyers Assn. Republican. Presbyterian. Office: Windels Marx Davies & Ives 156 W 56th St New York NY 10019-3800

WINDER, ALVIN ELIOT, public health educator, clinical psychologist; b. N.Y.C., Feb. 17, 1923; s. Martin Winder and Frances (Erdrick) Isaacson; m. Barbara Ina Dietz, July 19, 1949; children: Mark, Joshua, Sarah, Susan. BA, CUNY, 1947; MS, U. Ill., 1948; PhD, U. Chgo., 1952; MPH, U. Calif., Berkeley, 1980. Lic. clin. psychologist, Mass. Chief psychologist VA Hosp., Downey, Ill., 1953-56; rsch. asst., asst. prof. Clark U., Worcester, Mass., 1956-58; chief psychologist VA Clinic, Springfield, Mass., 1958-61; assoc. prof. psychology Springfield Coll., 1961-63; chmn. psychology dept. Westfield (Mass.) State Coll., 1963-65; assoc. prof. counseling edn. Sch. Edn., U. Mass., Amherst, 1965-69, prof., dir. grad. program div. nursing, 1969-78, prof. Sch. Pub. Health, 1978-93; dir. planning, cons. Springfield (Mass.) Pub. Health Dept., 1993-95; adj. prof. Sch. Pub. Health, Boston U., 1995—; assoc. to exec. sec. Asian Pacific Assn. for Control of Tobacco, 1988—. Author: Introduction to Health Education, 1984, Solid Waste Education Recycling Directory, 1989; editor: Adolescence Contemporary Studies, 1974; guest editor Jour. Applied Behavior, 1970; co-editor: Internat. Quar. of Cmty. Health Edn., 1992—. Sr. selectman Town of Leverett, Mass., 1988-90; Lilly Found. mentor U. Mass., 1989. Grantee U.S. Childrens Bur., 1966, 67, Dexter Found., 1969, NIMH, 1974, Nat. Cancer Inst., 1986-96. Mem. APHA, APA. Avocations: dressage, handball, tennis. Home: 84 Booth Rd Dedham MA 02026-5702 Office: Springfield Dept Pub Health Springfield MA 01109

WINDER, CLARENCE LELAND, psychologist, educator; b. Osborne County, Kans., June 16, 1921; s. Clarence McKinley and Edna (Ikenberry) W.; m. Elizabeth Jane Jacobs, Aug. 14, 1943; children—David William, Christina Louise. Student, Santa Barbara State Coll., 1941; A.B. with honors, U. Calif. at Los Angeles, 1943; M.A., Stanford U., 1946, Ph.D., 1949. From instr. to asso. prof. Stanford, 1949-61; dir. Psychol. Clinic, 1953-61; prof., dir. Psychol. Clinic, Mich. State U., 1961-62, prof. psychology, 1961-91, prof. emeritus, 1991—, chmn. dept., 1963-67; dean Coll. Social Sci. Mich. State U., 1967-74, assoc. provost, 1974-77, provost, 1977-86, provost emeritus, 1991—; prof., dir. Psychol. Services Center, U So. Calif., 1962-63; spl. research psychol. aspects schizophrenia, parent-child rels., personality devel., and higher edn. adminstrn. Served to 1st lt. USAAF, 1943-45. Decorated Air medal with 7 clusters, D.F.C. Fellow APA, AAAS; mem. Sigma Xi. Home: 1776 Hitching Post Rd East Lansing MI 48823-2144

WINDER, DAVID KENT, federal judge; b. Salt Lake City, June 8, 1932; s. Edwin Kent and Alma Eliza (Cannon) W.; m. Pamela Martin, June 24, 1955; children: Ann, Kay, James. BA, U. Utah, 1955; LLB, Stanford U., 1958. Bar: Utah 1958. Calif. 1958. Assoc. firm Clyde, Mecham & Pratt Salt Lake City, 1958-66; law clk. to chief justice Utah Supreme Ct., 1958-59; dep. county atty. Salt Lake County, 1959-63; chief dep. dist. atty., 1965-66; asst. U.S. atty. Salt Lake City, 1963-65; partner firm Strong & Hanni, Salt Lake City, 1966-77; from judge to chief judge U.S. Dist. Ct., Dist. Utah, Salt Lake City, 1979—; examiner Utah Bar Examiners, 1975-79, chmn., 1977-79. Served with USAAF, 1951-52. Mem. Am. Bd. Trial Advocates, Utah State Bar (Judge of Yr. award 1978), Salt Lake County Bar Assn., Calif. State Bar. Democrat. Office: US Dist Ct 350 S Main St Salt Lake City UT 84111-2321

WINDER, ROBERT OWEN, retired mathematician, computer engineer executive; b. Boston, Oct. 9, 1934; s. Claude V. and Harriet O. W.; m. Kathleen C. Winder; children by previous marriage: Katherine, Amy. A.B., U. Chgo., 1954; B.S., U. Mich., 1956; MS., Princeton U., 1958, Ph.D., 1962. With RCA, 1957-78; group head RCA, Princeton and Somerville, N.J., 1969-75; dir. microprocessors RCA, 1975-77, dir. systems, 1977-78; mgr. workstation devel. Exxon Enterprises, Inc., Princeton, 1978-85; v.p. Syntex Computer Systems Inc., Bordentown, N.J., 1985-88; mgr. product engring., Princeton Operation Intel Corp., 1988-93; mgr. engring. ops. Video Products Div., Intel, Chandler, Ariz., 1993-95; ret., 1995. Contbr. articles to profl. jours.; patentee in field. NSF fellow, 1956-57; Recipient David Sarnoff award RCA, 1975. Fellow IEEE.

WINDHAGER, ERICH ERNST, physiologist, educator; b. Vienna, Austria, Nov. 11, 1928; came to U.S., 1954; s. Maximilian and Bertha (Feitzinger) W.; m. Helga A. Rapant, June 18, 1956; children: Evelyn Ann, Karen Alice. MD, U. Vienna, 1954. Research fellow in biophysics Harvard Med. Sch., Boston, 1956-58; instr. in physiology Cornell U. Med. Coll., N.Y.C., 1958-61; vis. scientist U. Copenhagen, 1961-63; asst. to prof. physiology Cornell U. Med. Coll., N.Y.C., 1963—; Maxwell M. Upson prof. physiology and biophysics, 1978—, chmn. dept. physiology, 1973—. Recipient Homer W. Smith award N.Y. Heart Assn., 1978. Office: Cornell U Med Coll Dept Physiology 1300 York Ave New York NY 10021-4805

WINDHAM, CUYLER LARUE, state narcotics agent; b. Lamar, S.C., Nov. 29, 1936; s. Raymond Baxter and Zeloise (Parnell) W.; m. Mary Frances Dowling, Aug. 24, 1955; children: Cuyler LaRue Jr., David Baxter. Student, Ben Franklin U., 1956. With fingerprint divsn. FBI, Washington, 1955-57; night security clk. Charlotte (N.C.) divsn. FBI, 1957-62; condr. investigations resident agy. FBI, Fayetteville, N.C., 1962-67; spl. agt. N.C. State Bur. Investigation, Fayetteville & Kannapolis, 1967-72; supr. inter-agy. narcotics squad N.C. State Bur. Investigation, Fayetteville, 1968-72; asst. supr. Fayetteville divsn. N.C. State Bur. Investigation, 1972-73, asst. dir., 1974-85; sr. asst. dir. N.C. State Bur. Investigation, Fayetteville, 1985-94 (ret.); major, chief of detectives Cumberland County Sheriff Office, Fayetteville, N.C., 1994—; speaker on law enforcement, violent crimes and narcotics problems, N.C. and southeastern U.S.; chmn. drug subcom. Law Enforcement Coord. Com., Ea. Dist. N.C. Pres. Christian Peace Officers Assn., Cumberland County chpt., Fayetteville, 1991-92; deacon Southview Bapt. Ch., Hope Mills, N.C. Named Outstanding Young Law Enforcement Officer Cumberland County, Cape Fear Jaycees, 1970-71; recipient 1st place award for outstanding young law enforcement officer N.C., N.C. Jaycees,

1971. Mem. Law Enforcement Officers Assn. (com. mem. statewide violent crimes task force, violent crimes com.), Law Enforcement Officers Alumni Assn. (pres. nat. tng. inst. drug enforcement adminstrn. 1977), Gamecock Club. Democrat. Baptist. Home: 3722 Hillcrest St Hope Mills NC 28348

WINDHORST, JOHN WILLIAM, JR., lawyer; b. Mpls., July 6, 1940; s. John William and Ardus Ruth (Bottge) W.; m. Diana Margarita Aranda, Feb. 15, 1975; 1 child, Diana Elizabeth. AB, Harvard U., 1962; LLB, U. Minn., 1965. Bar: Minn. 1965, U.S. Tax Ct., U.S. Ct. Appeals (8th cir.) 1965, U.S. Dist. Ct. Minn. 1967, U.S. Supreme Ct. 1975. Law clk. to Hon. H.A. Blackmun U.S. Cir. Ct., Rochester, Minn., 1965-66; assoc. Dorsey & Whitney, Mpls., 1966-70; with office of Revisor of Statutes State of Minn., 1967, 69; ptnr. Dorsey & Whitney, 1971—. Bd. dirs. St. Paul Chamber Orch., 1980-86. Mem. ABA, Minn. State Bar Assn., Hennepin County Bar Assn., Mpls. Athletic Club, Skylight Club, Harvard Club of Minn. (pres. 1977-78). Home: 4907 Lakeview Dr Minneapolis MN 55424-1525 Office: Dorsey & Whitney Pillsbury Ctr S 220 S 6th St Minneapolis MN 55402-1498

WINDLE, JOSEPH RAYMOND, bishop; b. Ashdad, Ont., Can., Aug. 28, 1917; s. James David and Bridget (Scollard) W. Student, St. Alexander's Coll., Limbour, Que., 1936-39; D.D., Grand Sem., Montreal, 1943; D.C.L., Lateran U., Rome, 1953. Ordained priest Roman Catholic Ch., 1943; asst. priest, later parish priest and vice-chancellor Pembroke Diocese, 1943-61; titular bishop of Ugita and aux. bishop of Ottawa, 1961-69; coadjutor bishop of Pembroke, 1969-71; bishop, 1971—. Club: K.C. Office: Chancery Office, 188 Renfrew St PO Box 7, Pembroke, ON Canada K8A 6X1

WINDMAN, ARNOLD LEWIS, retired mechanical engineer; b. N.Y.C., Oct. 17, 1926; s. Raphael and Anna (Wexler) W.; m. Patricia Foley, Dec. 13, 1967; children—Richard, Marjorie, Kevin, Colleen, Sean, JoAnn, Brian, William. B.M.E., Coll. City N.Y., 1947. Bar: registered profl. engr., N.Y., 13 other states. Project engr. F.E. Sutton, N.Y., 1947-50; with Syska & Hennessy, Inc., N.Y.C., 1950-90, pres., 1976-86, vice chmn., 1986-90, also bd. dirs.; pres. Am. Cons. Engrs. Coun., 1985-86; chmn. N.Y. State Bd. Engring. and Land Surveying, 1982-84; bd. dirs. Sea Pines Plantation. Bd. dirs. Phelps Meml. Hosp., Tarrytown, N.Y., 1974-82. Mem. Am. Soc. Heating, Refrigerating and Air Conditioning Engrs., chpt. pres. (1965), N.Y. Assn. Cons. Engrs. (pres. 1981-82, dir. 1977), ASME, Tau Beta Pi, Pi Tau Sigma. Democrat. Jewish. Home: 1919 S Beach Club Vl Hilton Head Island SC 29928-4068 *Professional integrity, enthusiasm, and a continuing effort to train younger people for advancement are three key ingredients of a successful career.*

WINDMULLER, JOHN PHILIP, industrial relations educator, consultant; b. Dortmund, Germany, Dec. 4, 1923; came to U.S., 1942; s. Solomon and Bertha (Kahn) W.; m. Ruth Heilbrun, Aug. 15, 1947; children: Betsey, Thomas. B.A., U. Ill., 1948; Ph.D., Cornell U., Ithaca, N.Y., 1951; postgrad., Grad. Inst. Internat. Studies, U. Geneva, 1957-58. Elections examiner NLRB, St. Louis, 1949; asst. prof. indsl. and labor relations Cornell U., 1951-54, assoc. prof., 1954-61, prof., 1961-83, dir. internat. activities N.Y. State Sch. Indsl. and Labor Relations, 1961-64, assoc. dean sch., 1975-77, Martin P. Catherwood prof. indsl. and labor relations, 1983—; vis. prof. Free U., Amsterdam, Netherlands, 1964-65; sr. staff mem. ILO, Geneva, 1971-72, ILO Dir. Gen.'s rep. in Netherlands, 1984; vis. lectr. Dept. State, Germany, Austria, Netherlands, 1957-58, U. Istanbul, Turkey, 1958, Dept. State, Germany, 1964-65. Author: American Labor and the International Labor Movement, 1954, Labor Relations in the Netherlands, 1970, Collective Bargaining in Industrialized Market Economies: A Reappraisal, 1987, The International Trade Secretariats, 1991, rev., 1995; co-author: Convergence and Diversity in International and Comparative Industrial Relations, 1995; editor: Industrial Democracy in International Perspective, 1977; co-editor: Employers Associations and Industrial Relations, 1984; mem. editl. bd. Indsl. and Labor Relations Rev., 1953—; bd. editors Cornell U. Press, 1981-84, Labour (Rome), 1987-94. Recipient Silver medal Gov. Netherlands Minister Social Affairs, 1970; Fulbright sr. research fellow U.S. Commn. on Internat. Exchange, Netherlands, 1964-65; Ford Found. internat. relations fellow, 1957-58. Mem. Indsl. Relations Research Assn., Conseil Scientifique Institut de Travail, U. Bordeaux, Phi Beta Kappa, Phi Kappa Phi. Office: Cornell U NY State Indsl & Labor Rels Ithaca NY 14853-3901

WINDOM, STEPHEN RALPH, lawyer; b. Florence, S.C., Nov. 6, 1949; s. Ralph and Connie (Hinds) W.; children: Robert Stephen, Thomas Patrick. BS, U. Ala., 1971, JD, 1974. Bar: Ala. 1974, U.S. Supreme Ct. 1980. Assoc. McDermott, Slepian, Kittrell & Fleming, Mobile, Ala., 1974-77; ptnr. McDermott, Slepian, Windom & Reed, Mobile, Ala., 1974-86, Sirote & Permutt, P.C., 1984—; mem. Ala. State Senate, 1989—; lectr. in field, 1985—. Pres. Greater Gulf State Fair, Mobile, 1981, Cystic Fibrosis Found., Mobile, 1981. Capt. USAFR, 1971-82. Mem. Ala. State Bar Assn., Mobile Bar Assn., Am. Bankruptcy Inst., Comml. Law League, Jaycees, Shriners, Masons, Phi Delta Phi. Democrat. Avocations: hunting, water sports. Office: Sirote Permutt PO Box 2025 Mobile AL 36652-2025

WINDSOR, JAMES THOMAS, JR., printing company executive, newspaper publisher; b. Blakely, Ga., July 30, 1924; s. James Thomas and Mary Alice (Blitch) W. Student, Emory Jr. Coll., Valdosta, Ga., 1941-42, Cardiff (Wales) U., 1945-46; BA, Emory U., 1947. Insp./scientist U.S. Argl. Rsch. Adminstrn., San Augustine, Tex., 1948; pres. J.T. Windsor & Co., McRae, Ga., 1949-65; v.p. McRae Industries, Inc., 1963-64; pres. dir. Sunbeam Corp., McRae, 1965-71; editor, pub. The Laurens County News, 1973-74; editor, publisher The Soperton (Ga.) News, 1971—, The Wheeler County Eagle, Alamo, Ga., 1975—, The Montgomery Monitor, Mt. Vernon, Ga., 1987—; pres. The Mulberry Bush, Inc., Soperton, 1985-89, Suburban Printing Corp., Higgston, Ga., 1972—. Editor: Blueprint for Progress, 1963 (Washington Model award); also cookbooks and hist. books; area newspaper columnist, 1971—. Mayor City of McRae, 1962-70; adminstr. Telfair County, McRae, 1965; pres. Telfair Redevel. Corp., 1963-64; former coun. bd. dirs. Boy Scouts Am., Macon, Ga.; bd. dirs. Million Pines Festival, Soperton, 1973-87, Ga. Mcpl. Assn., Atlanta, 1963-66; dir. Eastman (Ga.) Planning and Devel. Commn., 1965-70; supt. sch. McRae Meth. Ch., 1951-71; active Eagle Scouts Am. With AUS, 1943-46, ETO. Recipient 20 yrs. perfect attendance award McRae Meth. Ch. Sch. Mem. Ga. Press Assn. (numerous awards 1972—), Nat. Newspaper Assn., Montgomery County C. of C., Soperton-Treutlen C. of C., Telfair County C. of C. (pres.), Jaycees (editor jour. 1959, 1st place Jour. in Nation award, Rebel Corps col. 1991—), One of 5 Ga. Outstanding Young Men award 1961), VFW, Am. Legion (post comdr. 1957-58), Treutlen County Sportsman Club, McRae Rotary Club (pres.), Toastmasters, Lions (pres. Soperton 1975-76, 15 yrs. perfect attendance award). Avocations: photography, reading, walking, writing, graphic arts. Home: 308 3rd St # 537 Soperton GA 30457 Office: Suburban Printing Corp RR 1 Ailey GA 30410-9801

WINDSOR, LAURENCE CHARLES, JR., publishing executive; b. Bronxville, N.Y., July 4, 1935; s. Laurence Charles and Margaret (Phalen) W.; m. Ruth Ester Lindstrom, 1977. Disting. grad., St. John's Mil. Acad., 1953; student, Grinnell Coll., 1953-55, U.S. Mil. Acad., 1957-58. V.p., dir. promotion Conover-Mast, 1960-67; assoc. promotion dir. Life mag., N.Y.C., 1967-70; merchandising dir. Life mag., 1970—; v.p., dir. advt. and pub. relations Sterling Communications subsidiary Time-Life; exec. v.p. Calderhead, Jackson, Inc., 1974-78; sr. v.p. dir. promotion Young and Rubicam Army Group, N.Y.C., 1978—; pub. relations cons. Penobscot Charitable Trust, 1966; spl. asst. to postmaster gen. U.S., 1972-74. Appeared in motion picture The D.I., 1957. Mem. pub. edn. com. N.Y. Gov.'s Conf. on Alcohol Problems; mem. coun. Episcopal Ch. Found., pres.'s coun. Phoenix House; mem. adv. bd. Army ROTC. With USMC, 1955-61. Decorated Commemorative War Cross Royal Yugoslav Army; recipient citation of merit Wis. Res. Officers Assn., Am. Spirit Honor medal Citizen's Com. for Army, Navy, and Air Force, Inc., 1956. Mem. U.S. Sales Promotion Exec. Assn. (dir., named Promotion Exec. of Yr. 1969), Marine Corps Combat Corr. Assn. (sec.), West Point Soc. N.Y. (gov. 1967—), Publicity Club N.Y., Publicity Club Chgo., Nat. Acad. TV Arts and Scis., Internat. Radio and TV Soc., Am. Inst. Plant Engrs., Order Vet. Corps Arty. (lt. col., aide-de-camp, comdg. gen., coun. of adminstrn., Disting. Expert pistol award, 1st Provincial Regtl. medal, Order Centennial Legion), 7th Regt. Rifle Club, Marine Corps Pub. Affairs Unit, U.S. Darting Assn., Nat. Sci. Tchrs. Assn., Assn. U.S. Army (v.p. N.Y. chpt.), Am. Def. Preparedness Assn., Kosciuszko Assn., Marine Corps League, Employer Support of the

Guard and Res. (N.Y. State Exec. Com.), Army-Navy Union, NRA, Conn. AAU of U.S., Nat. Jogging Assn., New Eng. Soc., Ends of Earth Assn. (chaplain), English Speaking Union, Sovereign Mil. Order of the Temple of Jerusalem, Time-Life Alumni Soc., Nat. Com. for Responsible Patriotism, St. Georges Soc., Nat. Eagle Scout Assn., Old Boys Assn., Nat. Fedn. Breeders of Giant Flemish Rabbits, Soc. Colonial Wars, Soc. Colonial Clergy, Order Descs. Colonial Govs., Order Colonial Acorn, SAR, Soc. Descs. Founders of Hartford, Order of St. Vincent, Soc. of 1812, Order Crown of Charlemagne in U.S.A., Order Lafayette, Sons and Daus. of Pilgrims, The Pilgrims, Sons of Colonial New England, N.Y. Geneal. and Biog. Soc., Met. Squash Racquets Assn., Church Club N.Y., Union League (v.p., bd. govs., chmn. pub. and mil. affairs), Manhattan Club, Bedford Bicycle Polo Club, Bombay Bicycle Club, Squadron A Club, Soldiers, Sailors and Airmens Club (bd. advisors), Road Runners Club, Alpha Phi Omega. Republican. Episcopalian (vestryman, lay reader). Office: Union League Club Box 7 38 E 37th St New York NY 10016-3095

WINDSOR, PATRICIA (KATONAH SUMMERTREE), author, educator, lecturer; b. N.Y.C., Sept. 21, 1938; d. Bernhard Edward and Antoinette (Gaus) Seelinger; m. Laurence Charles Windsor, Jr., Apr. 3, 1959 (div. 1978); children: Patience Wells, Laurence Edward; m. Stephen E. Altman, Sept. 21, 1986 (div. 1989). Student, Bennington Coll., 1956-58, Westchester Community Coll.; A.A., NYU. V.p. Windsor-Morehead Assocs. N.Y.C., 1960-63; info. mgr. Family Planning Assn., London, 1974-76; faculty mem. Inst. Children's Lit. Redding Ridge, Conn., 1976-94; editor-in-chief AT&T, Washington, 1978-80; instr. U. Md. Writers Inst., Open Univ., Washington, 1980-82; creative developer, faculty mem. Long Ridge Writer's Group, Danbury, Conn., 1988—; dir. Summertree Studios, Savannah, Ga., 1992—; dir. Wordspring Lit. Cons., 1989—; dir. Devel. Writing Worshops, Katonah, N.Y., 1976-78; judge Internat. Assn. Bus. Communicators, Washington, 1979, 89; lectr. L.I. U., Jersey City State Coll., Skidmore Coll., others, 1987—. Author: The Summer Before, 1973 (ALA Best Book award 1973, transl. 1980 Austrian State prize 1980, also Brit., Norwegian, German edits.), Something's Waiting for You, Baker D, 1974 (starred selection Lib. Jour., Brit., Japanese edits.), Home Is Where Your Feet Are Standing, 1975, Diving for Roses, 1976 (N.Y. Times Outstanding Book for Young Adults award, starred selection Lib. Jour.), Mad Martin, 1976, Killing Time, 1980, Demon Tree, 1983 (pen name Colin Daniel), The Sandman's Eyes, 1985 (Edgar Allan Poe Best Juvenile Mystery award Mystery Writers Am.), How a Weirdo and a Ghost Can Change Your Life, 1986, The Hero, 1988 (highest rating Voice of Youth Advocate), Just Like the Movies, 1990, The Christmas Killer, 1991 (Edgar nominee, Brit., Danish, French edits.), Two Weirdos and a Ghost, 1991, A Weird and Moogly Christmas, 1991; columnist The Blood Review, 1990-92, Savannah Parent, 1990-92; also short stories in anthologies and mags.; actress The Haunting of Hill House, City Lights Theatre Co., 1991. Mem. City Lights Theatre Co., Savannah, Ga., 1991. Mem. Children's Book Guild, Authors Guild, Poetry Soc. Ga., Savannah Storytellers. Avocations: skiing, painting, modern dance. Office: Writers House 21 W 26th St New York NY 10010

WINE, DONALD ARTHUR, lawyer; b. Oelwein, Iowa, Oct. 8, 1922; s. George A. and Gladys E. (Lisle) W.; m. Mary L. Schneider, Dec. 27, 1947; children: Mark, Marcia, James. B.A., Drake U., 1946; JD, State U. Iowa, 1949. Bar: Iowa 1949, D.C. 1968. Pvt. practice in Newport and Wine, 1949-61; U.S. atty. So. Dist. Iowa, 1961-65; of counsel Davis, Hockenberg, Wine, Brown, Koehn & Shors. Bd. dirs. Des Moines YMCA, 1963-75; bd. dirs. Salvation Army, 1969—, chmn., 1971; bd. dirs. Davenport YMCA, 1961; bd. dirs. Internat. Assn. Y's Men, 1957-59, area v.p., 1961; bd. dirs. Polk County Assn. Retarded Persons, 1992-95; mem. internat. com. YMCA's U.S. and Can., 1961-75; v.p. Iowa Council Chs.; pres. Des Moines Area Religious Council, 1975; chmn. Des Moines Area Religious Coun. Found., 1992—; chmn. bd. trustees First Bapt. Ch., 1975; trustee U. Osteo. Medicine and Health Scis., 1980-95; Organizer Young Dems., Iowa, 1946; co-chmn. Scott County Citizens for Kennedy, 1960. Served to capt., navigator USAAF, 1943-45. Decorated D.F.C. Mem. ABA (chmn. com. jud. adminstrn. jr. bar sect. 1958), Iowa Bar Assn. (pres. jr. bar sect. 1957), Polk County Bar Assn. (sec. 1973-74), Des Moines C. of C. (chmn. city-state tax com. 1978-79, chmn. legis. com. 1979-84, bd. dirs. 1981), Des Moines Club, Masons, Kiwanis (pres. Downtown club 1969), Order of Coif, Sigma Alpha Epsilon. Office: 2500 Financial Ctr 666 Walnut St Des Moines IA 50309-3904

WINE, L. MARK, lawyer; b. Norfolk, Va., Apr. 16, 1945; s. Melvin Leon and Mildred Sylvia (Weiss) W.; m. Blanche Weintraub, June 8, 1969; children—Kim, Lara, Dana. B.A. with high honors, U. Va., 1967; J.D., U. Chgo., 1970. Bar: D.C. 1970, U.S. Supreme Ct. 1977. Assoc., Kirkland, Ellis & Rowe, Washington, 1970-72; trial atty. land and natural resources div. Dept. of Justice, Washington, 1972-78; ptnr. Kirkland & Ellis, Washington, 1978—. Mem. ABA. Office: Kirkland & Ellis 655 15th St NW Ste 1200 Washington DC 20005-5701

WINE, MARK PHILIP, lawyer; b. Iowa City, Jan. 6, 1949; s. Donald Arthur and Mary Lepha (Schneider) W.; children: Nicholas, Meredith Kathryn; m. Kathryn Bouquet Arneson, May 31, 1986. AB, Princeton U., 1971; JD, U. Iowa, 1974. Bar: Iowa 1974, Minn. 1976, U.S. Dist. Ct. Minn. 1976, U.S. Ct. Appeals (8th cir.) 1976, U.S. Supreme Ct. 1984, U.S. Ct. Appeals (4th cir.) 1985, U.S. Ct. Appeals (7th and Fed. cirs.) 1992. Law clk. to judge U.S. Ct. Appeals (8th cir.), St. Louis, 1974-76; ptnr. Oppenheimer Wolff & Donnelly, Mpls., 1976—. Mem. ABA, Minn. Bar Assn., Internat. Assn. Def. Counsel, Town and Country Club, Princeton Club N.W. Democrat. Congregationalist. Avocations: cooking, reading, biking, golf. Home: 5404 Larada Ln Edina MN 55436-1025 Office: Oppenheimer Wolff & Donnelly 3400 Plaza VII 45 S 7th St Minneapolis MN 55402-1607

WINE, SHERWIN THEODORE, rabbi; b. Detroit, Jan. 25, 1928; s. William Harry and Tillie (Israel) W. B.A., U. Mich., 1950, A.M., 1952; B.H.L., Hebrew Union Coll., Cin., M.H.L., 1956, rabbi, 1956. Rabbi Temple Beth El, Detroit, 1956-60, Windsor, Ont., Can., 1960-64; Rabbi Birmingham (Mich.) Temple, 1964—; cons. editor Humanistic Judaism, 1966—. Author: A Philosophy of Humanistic Judaism, 1965, Meditation Services for Humanistic Judaism, 1977, Humanistic Judaism-What Is It?, 1977, Humanist Haggadah, 1980, High Holidays for Humanists, 1980, Judaism Beyond God, 1985, Celebration, 1988. Bd. dirs. Ctr. for New Thinking, Birmingham, 1977—; founder Soc. Humanistic Judaism, 1969; pres. N.Am. Com. for Humanism, 1982-93. Chaplain U.S. Army, 1956-58. Mem. Conf. Liberal Religion (chmn. 1985—), Leadership Conf. Secular and Humanistic Jews (chmn. 1983-93), Internat. Inst. Secular Humanistic Judaism (co-chmn. 1986—), Internat. Assn. Humanist Educators, Counselors and Leaders (pres. 1988-93), Internat. Fedn. Secular Humanistic Jews (co-chmn. 1993—). Home: 362 Southfield Rd Birmingham MI 48009-3739 Office: 28611 W 12 Mile Rd Farmington MI 48334-4225

WINE-BANKS, JILL SUSAN, lawyer; b. Chgo., May 5, 1943; d. Bert S. and Sylvia Dawn (Simon) Wine; m. Ian David Volner, Aug. 21, 1965; m. Michael A. Banks, Jan. 12, 1980. BS, U. Ill.-Champaign-Urbana, 1964; JD, Columbia U., 1968; LLD (hon.), Hood Coll., 1975. Bar: N.Y. 1969, U.S. Ct. Appeals (4th cir.) 1969, U.S. Ct. Appeals (6th and 9th cirs.) 1973, U.S. Supreme Ct. 1974, D.C. 1976, Ill. 1980. Asst. press. and pub. rels. dir. Assembly of Captive European Nations, N.Y.C., 1965-66; trial atty. criminal div. organized crime and racketeering sect. and labor racketeering sect. U.S. Dept. Justice, 1969-73; asst. spl. prosecutor Watergate Spl. Prosecutor's Office, 1973-75; lectr. law seminar on trial practice Columbia U. Sch. Law, N.Y.C., 1975-77; assoc. Fried, Frank, Harris, Shriver & Kampelman, Washington, 1975-77; gen. counsel Dept. Army, Pentagon, Washington, 1977-79; ptnr. Jenner & Block, Chgo., 1980-84; solicitor gen. State of Ill. Office of Atty. Gen., 1984-86, dep. atty. gen., 1986-87; exec. v.p., chief oper. officer ABA, Chgo., 1987-90; pvt. practice law, 1990-92; bd. dirs. Cenvill Devel. Corp., 1991-92; v.p. Motorola Wireless Network Ventures Ltd. and sr. mgr. bus. devel. Network Ventures Divsn., Motorola, 1992—; mem. EEC disting. vis. program European Parliament, 1987; bd. dirs. Cenvill Devel. Corp., 1991-92; mem. bd. assocs. program for the study of cultural values & ethics U. Ill. Recipient Spl. Achievement award U.S. Dept. Justice, 1972, Meritorious award, 1973, Cert. Outstanding Svc., 1975; decoration for Disting. Civilian Svc., Dept. Army, 1979; named Disting. Visitor to European Econ. Community. Mem. Internat. Women's Forum, The Chgo. Network, Econ. Club. Address: 425 N Martingdale Rd 18th fl Schaumburg IL 60173

WINECKI, WILLIAM, food products executive; b. 1944. With Cargill Inc., Mpls., 1968-78; with Premier Edible Oils Corp., Portland, Oreg. 1978—, exec. v.p. sales/trading. Office: Premier Edible Oils Corp 12005 N Burgard St Portland OR 97203*

WINEGAR, ALBERT LEE, computer systems company executive; b. Beloit, Wis., Apr. 23, 1931; s. Albert Richard and Theo Rayneta (Hubbell) W.; m. Phyllis M. Everill, June 21, 1953; children: Bradford, Steven, Kristine, Kathleen. B.B.A., U. Wis., 1954; Stanford Sloan Exec. fellow, Stanford U., 1970. With IBM Corp., 1956-79, div. dir. mgmt. services, 1977-79; v.p. corp. planning, then group v.p. field ops. Olivetti Corp., Tarrytown, N.Y., 1979-80; pres. Olivetti Corp., 1980-81; v.p. field ops. NBI Inc., Boulder, Colo., 1981-84; pres., chief exec. officer Sensory, Inc., Santa Clara, Calif., 1984-85; pres., chief exec. officer VICOM Systems, Inc., Fremont, Calif., 1985-91, ret., 1991; bd. dirs. JRL Systems, Inc. V.p. bd. trustees Valley Hosp., Ridgewood, N.J., 1978-81; pres. N.J. Bus. Arts Found., 1977-78; Estates of Barton Creek Homeowners Assn., 1992-94. Capt. AUS, 1954-56. Mem. Computer and Bus. Equipment Mfrs. Assn. (dir. 1980-81), Barton Creek Country Club, Beta Theta Pi. Republican. Home: 8401 Hickory Creek Dr Austin TX 78735-1530

WINEGARDNER, ROSE MARY, special education educator; b. Granite City, Ill., Feb. 4, 1933; d. Arthur Udell and Margaret Helen (Brown) Barco; m. Carl Norman Winegardner, July 23, 1954; children: Laura Helen, Thelma Rose Winegardner Czajkowski, Jacob Harrison. BS in Edn., Mo. U., Columbia, 1954; MA in Edn. Adminstrn., Wyo. U., 1977; edn. specialist, Nebr. U., 1988. Cert. tchr., Nebr., Iowa, Mo. Tchr. Elem. Sch. Grandview & Belton, Mo., 1957-64; tchr. mid. sch. Schleswig (Iowa) Community Schs., 1978-82; spl. edn. resource tchr. Ednl. Svc. Unit #4, Auburn, Nebr., 1982-94, Kans. U. Inst. Rsch. Learning Disabilities strategy implementation model trainer, 1989—; spl. edn. resource tchr. Dawson-Verdon Consol. Schs., 1990—. Grantee Nebr. Dept. Edn., 1990-93. Mem. Internat. Reading Assn., Coun. for Exceptional Children (v.p. S.E. Nebr. chpt. 1990-92, pres. 1992-94, 94—), DAR, Phi Delta Kappa. Lutheran. Home: 2100 23d St Auburn NE 68305

WINEGRAD, ALBERT IRVIN, immunologist, educator; b. Phila., 1926. Intern Hosp. U. Pa., Phila., 1952-53, resident in immunology, 1953-55, resident, 1957—; resident in endocrinology Peter Bent Brigham Hosp., Boston, 1955-57; prof. medicine U. Pa. Home: 3400 Spruce St Philadelphia PA 19104 Office: George S Cox Med Rsch Institute 36th Hamilton Walk Philadelphia PA 19104

WINEGRAD, GERALD WILLIAM, lawyer, state senator, educator; b. Balt., Sept. 9, 1944; s. Benjamin Bernard and Eleanor D. (Messick) W.; m. Madeline Frost Powers, Dec. 10, 1970; children: Pamela Leah, Susan Frost, Rebecca Ann. B.A., Western Md. Coll., 1966; J.D., U. Md., 1969. Bar: Md. 1969. Assoc. revisor Gov.'s Commn. to revise the code, Annapolis, Md., 1974-78; cons. Friends of the Earth, Washington; mem. Md. Senate, 1982—; instr. pub. policy, environ. Grad. Sch. U. Md., 1988. Bd. dirs. Md. Environ. Trust, Balt., 1983—; mem. Chesapeake Bay Commn.; mem. Md. Ho. of Dels., 1978-82; del. Dem. Nat. Conv., 1984. Lt. JAGC, USN, 1970-74, comdr. Res. Recipient Outstanding Conservation Legislator award Md. Wildlife Fedn., 1981, Cert. of Merit, Common Cause of Md., 1984, Outstanding Conservation Legislator award Clean Water Action Project, 1985, Outstanding Environmentalist award Sierra Club, 1985. Mem. Nat. Conf. State Legislators (energy com.), Sierra Club, of Md., Am. Legion, Optimists. Democrat. Roman Catholic. Office: 314 James Senate Off Bldg 110 College Ave Annapolis MD 21401-1676

WINEKE, WILLIAM ROBERT, reporter, clergyman; b. Madison, Wis., Apr. 4, 1942; s. Edward Ervin and Jennie Mae (Lanigan) W.; m. Susan L. Detering, Dec. 9, 1964 (div. June 1975); children: Gregory, Andrew; m. Jacqueline Cone, Mar. 18, 1990. BS, U. Wis., 1965; BDiv, chgo. Theol. Sem., 1969. Reporter Wis. State Jour., Madison, 1963-65; writer United Ch. of Christ, N.Y.C., 1966-68; pub. rels. dir. Chgo. (Ill.) Theol. Sem., Chgo., 1968-69; reporter Wis. State Jour., Madison, 1969—; chaplain Wis. Rescue Mission, Madison, 1977—; bd. rev. Wis. Health Policy Network, Madison, 1994—. Fellow Religions Pub. Rels. Soc., 1974; recipient Disting. Svc. award State Med. Soc. Wis., 1992, Disting. Svc. award LWV, Madison, 1994. Democrat. Home: 1024 Ridgewood Dr Stoughton WI 53589 Office: Wis State Jour 1901 Fish Hatchery Rd Madison WI 53713

WINEMAN, ALAN STUART, mechanical engineering and applied mechanics educator; b. Wyandotte, Mich., Nov. 17, 1937; s. Meyer Michael and Sophia Ethel (Cohen) W.; m. Carol Sue Frank, Dec. 20, 1964; children—Lara, Daniel. B.S.E., U. Mich., 1959; Ph.D., Brown U., 1964. Asst. prof. mech. engring. and applied mechanics U. Mich., Ann Arbor, 1964-69, assoc. prof. mech. engring. and applied mechanics, 1969-75, prof. mech. engring. and applied mechanics, 1975—. Contbr. articles to profl. jour. NSF grantee. Mem. Soc. Rheology, Am. Acad. Mechanics, Soc. Natural Philosophy, ASME. Avocations: singing; appearing in amateur musical productions. Office: U Mich Dept Mech Engring & Applied Mech Ann Arbor MI 48109

WINER, WARD OTIS, mechanical engineer, educator; b. Grand Rapids, Mich., June 27, 1936; s. Mervin Augustus and Ina Katherine (Wood) W.; m. Mary Jo Wielinga, June 15, 1957; children: Mathew Owen, James Edward, Paul Andrew, Mary Margaret. Asso., Grand Rapids Jr. Coll., 1956; B.S., U. Mich., 1958, M.S., 1959, Ph.D., 1961; Ph.D. (Cavendish Lab. fellow), Cambridge (Eng.) U., 1961-63. Asst. prof. dept. mech. engring. U. Mich., Ann Arbor, 1963-66, assoc. prof., 1966-69; assoc. prof. mech. engring. Ga. Inst. Tech., 1969-71, prof., 1971-84, Regents' prof., 1984—, dir. George W. Woodruff Sch. Mech. Engring., 1988—; mem. exec. bd., 1983-88, chmn., 1984-86; chmn. Gordon Research Conf. on Friction, Lubrication and Wear, 1980; mem. NRC, 1980-88; chmn. Com. on Recommendations for U.S. Army Basic Sci. Research, 1985-87; mem. div. mech., structural, materials engring. adv. bd. NSF Engring. Directorate, 1984-89. Co-editor: Wear Control Handbook, 1980; tech. editor: Jour. Lubrication Tech., 1980-84, Jour. of Tribology, 1984-87; contbr. articles to profl. jours. Democratic precinct chmn., 1967-68; Mem. exec. bd. Horace H. Rackham Sch. Grad. Studies, U. Mich., 1968. Recipient Disting. Faculty Svc. award Coll. Engring. U. Mich., 1967, Cert. Recognition, NASA, 1977, Clarence E. Earle Meml. award Nat. Grease Lubricating Inst., 1979, Disting. Prof. award Ga. Inst. Tech., 1987. Fellow AAAS, ASME (bd. comms. 1987-81, v.p. rsch. 1989-93, Melville medal 1975, Centennial medallion 1980, Mayor D. Hersey award 1986, Charles Russ Richards Meml. award 1988), Soc. Tribologists and Lubrication Engrs. (bd. dirs. 1983-86), Brit. Tribology Trust (gold medal 1987); mem. Am. Soc. Engring. Educators (Benjamin Carver Lamme award 1995), NAE, Metro Atlanta Engring. Soc. (Engr. of Yr. 1989), Am. Acad. Mechanics, Soc. Rheology, Soc. Engring. Sci. (dir. 1980-84), AAUP (pres. Ga. Tech. chpt. 1972-74, v.p. state conf. 1973-75), Sigma Xi (chpt. pres. 1982-83, Sustained Rsch. in Engring. award 1975), Tau Beta Pi, Pi Tau Sigma, Phi Kappa Phi. Home: 1025 Mountain Creek Trl NW Atlanta GA 30328-3535

WINER, WARREN JAMES, insurance executive; b. Wichita, Kans., June 16, 1946; s. Henry Charles and Isabel (Ginsburg) W.; m. Mary Jean Kovacs, June 23, 1968 (div. Feb. 1973); m. Jo Lynn Sondag, May 5, 1975; children: Adam, Lauren. BS in Math., Stanford U., 1968. With Gen. Am. Life Ins. Co., St. Louis, 1968-73, dir. retirement plans, 1973-76, 2d v.p., 1976-80; v.p. sr. actuary Powers, Carpenter & Hall, St. Louis, 1980-84, sr. v.p., dir. pension div., 1984-85, pres., chief operating officer, 1985-86, lobbyist, commentator, 1985—, pres., chief exec. officer, 1986—; pres. W F Corroon, 1988-93; prin. William M. Mercer, 1993—, mng. dir., 1994—; mem. Actuarial Exam. Com., Chgo., 1973-74. Contbr. articles to profl. jours. Bd. dirs. Lucky Lane Nursery Sch. Assn., St. Louis, 1978-93, pilot divsn. United Way, 1986-87; co-pres. Conway Sch. Parent Assn., 1986-87; bd. dirs. Paraquad, 1991—, chmn., 1994—; bd. dirs. ATD, 1992—. Fellow Soc. Actuaries; mem. Am. Acad. Actuaries, Enrollment of Actuaries (joint bd.), Am. Life Ins. Assn. (small case task force 1979-80), Life Office Mgmt. Assn. (ICPAC com. 1975-80), St. Louis Actuaries Club. Jewish. Clubs: St. Louis, Clayton (St. Louis). Avocations: bridge, wine tasting, swimming, weight tng. Office: Wm M Mercer 10 S Broadway Saint Louis MO 63102-1712

WINETT, SAMUEL JOSEPH, manufacturing company executive; b. Chgo., June 15, 1934; s. Maurice and Ruby (Caplan) W.; m. Susan Carol Finkel, Apr. 24, 1957; children: Bradley, William, James. BS in Acctg., U. Ill., 1956; MBA, U. Chgo., 1970. CPA, Ill. Staff auditor Arthur Young & Co., Chgo., 1958-63; with Outboard Marine Corp., Waukegan, Ill., 1963-91, asst. controller, 1974-78, controller ops., 1978-86, v.p. fin., 1986-91; cons. QED Ptnrs., Chgo., 1993—. Served as 1st lt. U.S. Army, 1956-58. Mem. Am. Inst. CPA's, Ill. CPA Soc., Fin. Execs. Inst. Home: 3128 Mapleleaf Dr Glenview IL 60025-1123

WINFIELD, DAVID MARK, professional baseball player; b. St. Paul, Oct. 3, 1951. Student, U. Minn.; LL.D.(hon.), Syracuse U., 1987. Player San Diego Padres (Nat. League), 1973-80, N.Y. Yankees (Am. League), 1980-90, Calif. Angels (Am. League), 1990-91; with Toronto Blue Jays (Am. League), 1991-92, Minnesota Twins (Am. League), 1992-94, Cleve. Indians, 1994—; mem. Nat. League All-Star team, 1977-80, Am. League All-Star team, 1981-88; led Nat. League in total bases, 1979; played in World Series, 1981. Author (with Tom Parker) autobiography Winfield: A Player's Life, 1988. Recipient Golden glove, 1979-80, 82-85, 87, Silver Slugger award, 1981-85, 92; named top Sporting News All-Star Team, 1979, 82-84, 92; named Sporting News Am. League Comeback Player of Yr., 1990. Office: Cleve Indians 2401 Ontario St Cleveland OH 44115*

WINFIELD, JOHN BUCKNER, rheumatologist, educator; b. Kentfield, Calif., Mar. 19, 1942; s. R. Buckner and Margaret G. (Katterfelt) W.; m. Patricia Nichols (div. 1968); 1 child, Ann Gibson; m. Teresa Lee McGrath, 1969; children: John Buckner III, Virginia Lee. BA, Williams Coll., 1964; MD, Cornell U., 1968. Diplomate Am. Bd. Internal Medicine. Intern in medicine N.Y. Hosp., N.Y.C., 1968-69; staff assoc. LI/Nat. Inst. Allergy and Infectious Diseases NIH, Bethesda, Md., 1969-71; resident in medicine, fellow in rheumatology U. Va. Sch. Medicine, Charlottesville, 1971-73; fellow in immunology Rockefeller U., N.Y.C., 1973-75; asst. prof. medicine U. Va. Sch. Medicine, Charlottesville, 1975-76, assoc. prof. medicine, 1976-78; assoc. prof. medicine U. N.C., Chapel Hill, 1978-81, prof. medicine, 1981—, chief div. rheumatology and immunology, 1987—; dir. Thurston Arthritis Rsch. Ctr. U. N.C. Sch. Medicine, Chapel Hill, 1982—; Smith prof. medicine U. N.C. Sch. Med., Chapel Hill, 1987—; adv. coun. Nat. Inst. Arthritis and Musculoskeletal and Skin Diseases, NIH, 1988-92; chmn. edn. com. Am. Rheumatism Assn., Atlanta, 1980-84; immunol. scis. study sect. NIH, 1979-83, Arthritis Musculoskeletal and Skin study sect., 1992—; vice-chair fellowship com. Arthritis Found., 1982; med. coun. Lupus Found. Am., 1987—. Author more than 100 med. and sci. articles in peer reviewed rheumatology and immunology jours.; mem. editorial bd. Arthritis and Rheumatism, Bull. Rheumatic Diseases, Rheumatology Internat., Clin. Exptl. Rheumatology. Sr. asst. surgeon with USPHS, NIH, Bethesda, Md., 1968-71. Recipient Borden prize Cornell U. Med. Coll., 1964, numerous rsch. grants NIH and Arthritis Found., 1975—, Sr. Investigator award Arthritis Found., 1976-79, Kenan award U. N.C., 1985, NIH merit award, 1992. Fellow ACP; mem. Am. Assn. Immunologists, Am. Coll. Rheumatology, Am. Fedn. Clin. Rsch., Am. Soc. Clin. Investigation, Assn. Am. Physicians, Am. Clin. Climatol. Assn., Chapel Hill Country Club. Republican. Episcopalian. Avocations: golf, off-road motorcycling, scuba diving instructor. Home: 801 Kings Mill Rd Chapel Hill NC 27514-4920 Office: U NC Sch Medicine Thurston Arthritis Rsch Ctr 3330 Thurston Bldg Chapel Hill NC 27599

WINFIELD, MICHAEL D., engineering company executive; b. 1939. BS in Chem. Engring., Ohio State U.; MBA, U. Chgo. Chem. engr. UOP, Des Plaines, Ill., 1962-74, mgr. refinery projects, 1974-76, asst. dir. tech. svcs., 1976-81, dir. bus. devel., 1981-83, v.p. tech. svcs., 1983-84, v.p. process svcs., 1984-92, pres., CEO, 1992—. Office: UOP 25 E Algonquin Rd Des Plaines IL 60016-6101*

WINFIELD, NOVALYN L., federal bankruptcy judge; b. 1950. BA, Coll. St. Elizabeth; JD, N.Y. Law Sch. Bar: N.J. 1981. Bankruptcy judge U.S. Dist. Ct. N.J., Newark. Office: US Bankruptcy Court Martin Luther King Jr Fed Bldg 50 Walnut St Newark NJ 07102

WINFIELD, PAUL EDWARD, actor; b. Los Angeles, May 22, 1941. Student, U. Portland, 1957-59, Stanford U., 1959, Los Angeles City Coll., 1959-63, UCLA, 1962-64. artist-in-residence Stanford U., 1964-65, U. Hawaii, 1965, U. Calif., Santa Barbara, 1970-71. Films include Gordons War, 1973, Huckleberry Finn, 1974, Conrack, 1974, Guess Who's Minding the Mint, 1969, Sounder, 1972 (Acad. Award nomination 1973), Hustle, 1975, Twilights Last Gleaming, 1976, A Hero Ain't Nothing But A Sandwich, 1978, Carbon Copy, 1981, White Dog, 1981, Star Trek II, 1982, Mike's Murder, 1982, On the Run, 1982, The Terminator, 1985, Blue City, 1986, Death Before Dishonor, 1987, The Serpent and the Rainbow, 1988, Presumed Innocent, 1990, Cliff Hanger, 1993, Dennis the Menace (The Movie), 1993, Kingdom of The Blind, 1994, The Mike Tyson Story, 1994, Fluke, 1994; TV appearances include Green Eyes, 1976, All Deliberate Speed, 1976, King, 1978 (Emmy nomination), Backstairs at the White House, 1979, The Blue and the Gray, 1982, Star Trek: Next Generation, 1992; guest star: TV appearances include Roots II (Emmy nomination), Angel City, 1980, Sisters, 1981, Sophisticated Gents, 1981, Go Tell It on the Mountain, 1983, Queen (miniseries), 1993, Scarlett (miniseries), 1994, Picket Fences; theatrical appearances include Checkmates, 1988, nat. tour A Few Good Men, 1992, Othello, Guthrie Theatre, 1993. Office: Ste 590 5750 Wilshire Blvd Los Angeles CA 90036

WINFIELD, SUSAN REBECCA, judge; b. East Orange, N.J., June 13, 1948; children: Jessica, Heather. BA in Math., U. Pa., 1970; JD, Boston Coll., 1976. Assoc. atty. Law Office of Salim Shakur, Boston, 1976-77; staff atty. U.S. Dept. of Justice, Washington, 1978-79; asst. U.S. atty. U.S. Atty.'s Office, Washington, 1979-84; assoc. judge D.C. Superior Ct., 1984—; chair Benchbook Com., Washington, 1991—, Amenities & Misfortune Com., Washington, 1992—, Family Divsn. Rules Com., Washington, 1993—, Justice Systems Coord. Com., Washington, 1993—. Boston Coll. scholar, 1973-76; recipient letter of commendation Met. Police Dept., Washington, 1981. Mem. District of Columbia Bar, Bar Assn. D.C., Washington Bar Assn., Women's Bar Assn. Avocations: reading, jogging, taichi. Office: DC Superior Ct 500 Indiana Ave NW Washington DC 20001

WINFREE, ARTHUR TAYLOR, biologist, educator; b. St. Petersburg, Fla., May 15, 1942; s. Charles Van and Dorothy Rose (Scheb) W.; m. Ji-Yun Yang, June 18, 1983; children: Rachael, Erik from previous marriage. B.Engring. in Physics, Cornell U., 1965; Ph.D. in Biology, Princeton U., 1970. Lic. pvt. pilot. Asst. prof. theoretical biology U. Chgo., 1969-72; assoc. prof. biology Purdue U., West Lafayette, Ind., 1972-79; prof. Purdue U., 1979-86; prof. ecology and evolutionary biology U. Ariz., Tucson, 1986-88, Regents' prof., 1989—, pres., dir. research Inst. Natural Philosophy, Inc., 1979-88. Author: The Geometry of Biological Time, 1980, When Time Breaks Down, 1986, The Timing of Biological Clocks, 1987. Recipient Career Devel. award NIH, 1973-78, The Einthoven award Einthoven Found. and Netherlands Royal Acad. Scis., 1989; NSF grantee, 1966—; MacArthur fellow, 1984-89, John Simon Guggenheim Meml. fellow, 1982. Home: 1210 E Placita De Graciela Tucson AZ 85718-2834 Office: Univ Ariz 326 Bsw Tucson AZ 85721

WINFREY, CAREY WELLS, journalist, magazine editor; b. N.Y.C., Aug. 1, 1941; s. William Colin and Mary (Robinson) W.; m. Laurie Beardsley Platt, July 30, 1972 (div. 1980); m. Jane Elizabeth Keeney, Feb. 13, 1982; children—Graham William, Wells Millar. AB, Columbia U., N.Y.C., 1963, MS in Journalism, 1967. With Pub. Broadcasting Lab. NET; assoc. editor Time Inc., N.Y.C., 1968-71; exec. producer Ednl. Broadcast Corp., N.Y.C., 1971-77; reporter, fgn. corr. for Africa N.Y. Times, N.Y.C., 1977-80; mag. editor CBS Mags., N.Y.C., 1981-90, dir. video devel., 1981-83, editor Cuisine mag., 1983-84, v.p., editorial dir., 1985-87; v.p. Diamandis Communications, Inc. (formerly mag. div. CBS), N.Y.C., 1987-90; editor in chief Memories mag. Diamandis Communications, Inc., N.Y.C., 1987-90; editor in chief Am. Health mag. Reader's Digest Publs., N.Y.C., 1990—; cons. Ford Found., N.Y.C., 1976. Author: Starts and Finishes, 1975; exec. producer: (TV programs) Behind the Lines, 1971-75 (Emmy award 1973-74, NYU Don Hollenback award 1974), Assignment America, 1975, WNET Reports, 1976-77; columnist: "Eye on Books" for Book of the Month Club News, 1980, Parenting mag., 1986-89; producer Mixed Bag, twice-weekly video arts mag.

for CBS Cable; contbr. articles to numerous publs. including The N.Y. Times Mag., Harpers, N.Y. Mag. Served to capt. USMC, 1963-66. Pulitzer Travelling fellow, 1967; recipient Meyer Berger award for Disting. Reporting Columbia U., 1978. Home: 340 Riverside Dr New York NY 10025 also: Dutchess County NY Office: Reader's Digest Publs 28 W 23rd St New York NY 10010-5204

WINFREY, DORMAN HAYWARD, scientific society executive; b. Henderson, Tex., Sept. 4, 1924; s. Luke Abel and Linnie (Fears) W.; m. Ruth Carolyn Byrd, June 12, 1954; children: Laura Madge Gould, Jennifer Ruth Leisure. B.A., U. Tex., 1950, M.A., 1951, Ph.D., 1962. Social sci. research asso. research in Tex. history Tex. State Hist. Assn. U. Tex., 1946-58, archivist, 1960-61; state archivist Tex., 1958-60; librarian, dir. Tex. State Library, 1962-86; sec. Philos. Soc. Tex., Austin, 1975—; chmn. State Bd. Library Examiners, 1962-81, State Records Preservation Adv. Com., 1965-87; mem. Tex. Travel Trails Com. Author: Arturo Toscanini in Texas: The 1950 NBC Symphony Orchestra Tour, 1967, also articles; editor: Texas Indian Papers, 1825-43, 1959, Texas Indian Papers, 1844-45, 1960, Texas Indian Papers, 1846-1859, 1960, A History of Rusk County, Texas, 1961 (award of merit Am. Assn. State and Local History), Julien Sidney Devereux and His Monte Verdi Plantation, 1964 (award merit Am. Assn. State and Local History); hist. coordinator: Six Missions of Texas, 1965; editor: Indian Papers of Texas and the Southwest, 1825-1916, 5 vols. 1966, Seventy-Five Years of Texas History: The Texas State Historical Association, 1897-1972, 1974, History of the Philosophical Society of Texas, 1837-1987, 1987; staff writer: Handbook of Texas, 1952; asso. editor: Jr. Historian of the Texas State Hist. Assn, 1951-58; spl. editor for: Tex., Ency. for Young People, 1962. Bd. dirs. Internat. Festival, Inst. at Round Top; vice chmn. Tex. 1986 Sesquicentennial Commn. Served with Armed Forces, 1943-46. Decorated knight Order San Jacinto; recipient Outstanding Ex-Student award Henderson High Sch., 1967; named Tex. Pub. Administr. of Yr. Austin Soc. for Pub. Adminstrs., 1985; Clara Driscoll scholar for rsch. in Tex. history, 1952-54. Fellow Soc. Am. Archivists (internat. archival affairs com. council), Tex. Hist. Assn. (pres., mem. council), East Tex. Hist. Assn.; mem. Tex. Library Assn., Philos. Soc. Tex. (sec., editor procs. 1976—), Tex. Inst. Letters, Bicentennial Assn. Tex., Sons of Republic of Tex. (hon.), Phi Alpha Theta, Pi Sigma Alpha. Mem. Disciples of Christ Ch. Club: Austin Town and Gown. Home: 6503 Willamette Dr Austin TX 78723-2108

WINFREY, JOHN CRAWFORD, economist, educator; b. Somerville, Tenn., July 2, 1935; s. Arthur Peter and Frances (Crawford) W.; m. Barbara Ann Strickland, July 20, 1957; 1 child, Mae Millicent. A.B., Davidson Coll., 1957; Ph.D., Duke U., 1965. Asst. dir. data processing Hanes Hosiery, Winston Salem, N.C., 1959-62; research asst. in econs. Duke U., Durham, N.C., 1963-64; asst. prof. econs. Washington and Lee U., Lexington, Va., 1965-68, assoc. prof., 1969-73, prof., 1974—; vis. prof. Vanderbilt U., Nashville, 1966, Tufts U., Boston, 1975, UCLA, 1978, U. Ill., 1982, U. Va., 1986, Duke U., 1989, U. Calif., Berkeley, 1993. Co-author: The Motion Commotion, 1972; author: Public Finance, Public Choice and the Public Sector, 1973. Bd. dirs. Lexington Tennis Clinic, Va., 1968-72, Rockridge Area Conservation Council, 1982-84; pres. Rockbridge Arts Guild, 1986-88. Recipient Comunity Svc. Lexington Jaycees, 1971; NEH fellow, 1975, 78, 82, 86, 89, 93; vis. fellow U. Coll. Oxford U., Eng., 1979, 95. Fellow Soc. for Values in Higher Edn.; mem. Am. Econ. Assn., So. Econ. Assn., History of Econs. Soc., Eastern Econ. Assn. Democrat. Presbyterian. Club: High Wheelers (Lexington). Home: 628 Stonewall St Lexington VA 24450-1933 Office: Washington and Lee U Dept Econs Lexington VA 24450

WINFREY, MARION LEE, television critic; b. Knoxville, Tenn., July 7, 1932; s. Charles Houston and Norma Elsa (Wesenberg) W.; m. Mary Anne Hight, Sept. 5, 1958 (div. 1977); 1 son, David Dylan; m. Kiki Olson, Aug. 24, 1978 (div. 1982). B.S., U. Tenn., 1966; M.F.A., U. Iowa, 1968. Reporter Nashville Tennessean, 1957-58, Knoxville News-Sentinel, 1958-60, Miami bur. UPI, 1960-62, Miami Herald, 1962-63, Washington bur. Knight Newspapers, 1963-66, Detroit Free Press, 1968-71; reporter Phila. Inquirer, 1972-74, TV critic, 1974—; instr. journalism U. Iowa, 1966-68; Bernard Kilgore journalism counselor DePauw U., 1971. Author: Kent State Report, The President's Commission on Campus Unrest, 1970. Served with U.S. Army, 1954-56. Nieman fellow Harvard U., 1971-72. Mem. TV Critics Assn. (founding pres. 1978-79), Sigma Delta Chi, Phi Gamma Delta. Baptist. Clubs: Harvard (Phila.); Pen and Pencil; Nat. Press (Washington). Home: 1700 Benjamin Franklin Pky Philadelphia PA 19103 Office: 400 N Broad St Philadelphia PA 19130-4015

WINFREY, OPRAH, television talk show host, actress, producer; b. Kosciusko, Miss., Jan. 29, 1954; d. Vernon Winfrey and Vernita Lee. BA in Speech and Drama, Tenn. State U. News reporter Sta. WVOL Radio, Nashville, 1971-72; reporter, news anchorperson Sta. WTVF-TV, Nashville, 1973-76; news anchorperson Sta. WJZ-TV, Balt., 1976-77, host morning talk show People Are Talking, 1977-83; host talk show A.M. Chgo. Sta. WLS-TV, 1984; host The Oprah Winfrey Show, Chgo., 1985—; nationally syndicated, 1986—; host series of celebrity interview spls. Oprah: Behind the Scenes, 1992; owner, prodr. Harpo Prodns., 1986—. Appeared in films The Color Purple, 1985 (nominated Acad. award and Golden Globe award), Native Son, 1986, Throw Momma From the Train, 1988, Listen Up: The Lives of Quincy Jones, 1990; prodr., actress ABC-TV mini-series The Women of Brewster Place, 1989, also series Brewster Place, 1990, movie There Are No Children Here, 1993; exec. prodr. (ABC Movie of the Week) Overexposed, 1992; host, supervising prodr. celebrity interview series Oprah: Behind the Scenes, 1992, ABC Aftersch. Spls., 1991-93; host, exec. prodr. Michael Jackson Talks...to Oprah-90 Prime-Time Minutes with the King of Pop, 1993. Recipient Woman of Achievement award NOW, 1986, Emmy award for Best Daytime Talk Show Host, 1987, 91, 92, America's Hope award, 1990, Industry Achievement award Broadcast Promotion Mktg. Execs./ Broadcast Design Assn., 1991, Image awards NAACP, 1989, 90, 91, 92, Entertainer of Yr. award NAACP, 1989, CEBA awards, 1989, 90, 91; named Broadcaster of Yr. Internat. Radio and TV Soc., 1988. Office: Harpo Prodns 110 N Carpenter St Chicago IL 60607-2101

WING, DAVID ALLAN, biochemistry educator; b. Chgo., Sept. 19, 1948; s. Richard Wallace and Darlene (Cross) W.; m. Ruth Ellyn Anderson, June 6, 1970; children: Emily, Rebecca, Daniel, Matthew. BS in Chemistry, Wheaton (Ill.) Coll., 1970; PhD in Chemistry, Northwestern U., 1977. Postdoctoral fellow St. Louis U. Med. Sch., 1978, Washington U. Med. Sch., St. Louis, 1979-80; asst. prof. Grand Canyon U., Phoenix, 1980-82, assoc. prof., 1983-85, prof. biochemistry and chemistry, 1985—. Contbr. articles to profl. jours. Served to capt. U.S. Army, 1975-77. Fellow Mo. Heart Assn., 1979-80, sabbatical fellow Sammuel R. Noble Found., 1987-88. Mem. Am. Chem. Soc. Baptist. Avocation: music. Office: Grand Canyon U PO Box 11097 Phoenix AZ 85061-1097

WING, ELIZABETH SCHWARZ, museum curator, educator; b. Cambridge, Mass., May 5, 1932; d. Henry F. and Maria Lisa (Gutherz) (dec.) Schwarz; m. James E. Wing, Apr. 18, 1957; children: Mary Elizabeth Wing-Berman, Stephen R. BA, Mt. Holyoke Coll., 1955; MS, U. Fla., 1957, PhD, 1962. Interim asst. curator Fla. Mus. Natural History, U. Fla., Gainesville, 1961-69, asst. curator, 1969-73, assoc. curator, 1973-78, curator, 1978—; chmn. dept. anthropology U. Fla., Fla. Mus. Natural History, Gainesville, 1990-92; U.S. rep. Internat. Congress Archaeozoology, 1981—. Author: (with A.B. Brown) Paleonutrition, 1979; editor (with J.C. Wheeler) Economic Prehistory of the Central Andes, 1988; contbr. articles to profl. jours. NSF grantee, 1961-64, 68-70, 70-73, 79-80, 84-85, 89-91. Mem. Soc. Ethnobiology (pres. 1991-99, trustee 1991—). Office: U Fla Fla Mus Natural History PO Box 117800 Museum Rd Gainesville FL 32611-7800

WING, JOHN ADAMS, financial services executive; b. Elmira, N.Y., Nov. 9, 1935; s. Herbert Charles and Clara Louise (Stewart) W.; m. Joan Cook Montgomery, June 19, 1964; children: Lloyd Montgomery, Elizabeth Montgomery, Mary Ellen. B.A. in Econs., Union Coll., 1958; LL.B., George Washington U., 1963. Bar: Va. 1963, D.C. 1965, Ill. 1968. Fin. analyst SEC, Washington, 1960-63; trial atty. SEC, 1963-65; asst. to pres. Investors Diversified Services, Inc., Mpls., 1966-67; v.p., gen. counsel A.G. Becker & Co., Chgo., 1968-71, sr. v.p., 1971-74, pres., 1974-80, also dir.; pres., chief exec. officer Chgo. Corp., 1981—, now chmn. bd. dirs.; bd. dirs. Chgo. Bd. Options Exch., Am. Mut. Life. Bd. dirs. Ill. Inst. Tech., Risk Mgmt. Ctr. Chgo. With U.S. Army, 1958-60. Mem. Ill. Bar Assn., Va. Bar Assn., Ill.

State C. of C. (bd. dirs. capital fund). Episcopalian. Clubs: Chgo., Economics, Civic, Mid-Day, Bond, Saddle & Cycle. Office: Chgo Corp 208 S La Salle St Chicago IL 60604-1003

WING, JOHN RUSSELL, lawyer; b. Mt. Vernon, N.Y., Jan. 20, 1937; s. John R. and Elinore (Smith) W.; m. Mary Zeller, Aug. 24, 1963 (div. June 1975); children: Ethan Lincoln, Catherine Dorothy; m. Audrey Strauss, Aug. 12, 1979; children: Carlin Elinore, Matthew Lawrence. BA, Yale U., 1960; JD, U. Chgo., 1963. Bar: N.Y. 1964. Assoc. Sherman & Sterling, N.Y.C., 1963-66; asst. U.S. atty. So. Dist. N.Y., N.Y.C., 1966-78; chief fraud unit U.S. Dist. Atty. So. Dist. N.Y., 1971-78; ptnr. Weil, Gotshal & Manges, N.Y.C., 1978—. Contbr. articles to profl. jours. Fellow Am. Coll. Trial Lawyers; mem. ABA (white collar crime com. criminal justice sect. 1978—, environ. task force com. 1983-85), Assn. Bar of City of N.Y. (criminal advocacy com. 1985-88), Fed. Bar Coun. (2d cir. cts. com 1982-84), N.Y. Coun. Def. Lawyers (bd. dirs. 1986-90). Republican. Episcopalian. Avocation: sailing. Home: 52 Livingston St Brooklyn NY 11201-4813 Office: Weil Gotshal & Manges 767 5th Ave New York NY 10153-0001

WINGARD, RAYMOND RANDOLPH, transportation products executive; b. Goshen, Ala., Nov. 6, 1930; s. Raymond T. and Mary (Sanders) W.; student So. Meth. U., 1948-49, Birmingham-So. Coll., 1949-50, Harvard, 1973; m. Gainnell Harris, June 2, 1951; children: Renee, Kay, Beckie, Robin, Randy. With Koppers Co. Inc., 1951-62, area mgr., Montgomery, Ala., 1963-64, mgr. R.R. sales and plannning Western region, Chgo., 1964-71, div. mgr., asst. v.p. R.R. sales and planning, 1971-74, asst. v.p., mktg. mgr., Pitts., 1974-75, v.p. mgr. human resources, 1975-80, v.p. mgr. mktg. dept., 1981-85, v.p. mgr. adminstrv. svcs. and corp. planning, 1985-88; agy. mgr. Ala. Farm Bur. Svc., Andalusia, 1962-63; exec. dir. Railway Tie Assn., 1988—. Chmn., R-1 Sch. Dist. Adv. Coun., Independence, Mo., 1960; pres. Independence Suburban Community Improvement League, 1959-60; mem. dist. 58 Bd. Edn., 1969-71; trustee Pitts. Coll. Internat. Visitors, 1978-84, pres., 1982-83; pres. Minority Engring. Edn. Effect, Inc., 1977-80; bd. dirs. Allegheny coun. Boy Scouts Am., Blue Cross of Pa., vice-chmn., 1986-89; bd. dirs. Diversified Benefits Svc., Inc., 1990—. With AUS, 1950-51. Mem. Am. Wood Preservers Assn., Japan Mgmt. Assn., Railway Tie Assn., Western Ry. Club. Methodist. Duquesne Club, Harvard-Yale-Princeton Club. Home: 15300 State Hwy 180 Gulf Shores AL 36542-8242 Office: PO Box 1039 140 Cove Ave Gulf Shores AL 36547

WINGATE, C. KEITH, legal educator; b. Darlington, S.C., May 12, 1953; s. Clarence L. and Lilly (Frazier) W.; m. Gloria Farley. BA in Polit. Sci., U. Ill., 1974, JD cum laude, 1978. Bar: Calif., 1978. Assoc. litigation dept. Morrison & Foerster, San Francisco, 1978-80; from asst. to assoc. prof. law U. Calif.-Hastings, San Francisco, 1980-86, prof., 1986—; dir. Coun. Legal Edn. Opportunity Region I Inst., 1989; vis. prof. law Stanford (Calif.) Law Sch., fall 1990, 94; cahir Minority law Tchrs.' Conf. Com., 1990; mem. acad. assistance work group, law sch. admissions coun. U. Calif.-Hastings, 1991. Author: (with David I. Levine and William R. Slomanson) Cases and Materials on California Civil Procedure in a Nutshell, 1994 (with Donald L. Doernberg) Federal Courts, Federalism and Separation of Powers, 1994. Bd. dirs. Community Housing Devel. Corp., North Richmond. Recipient 10 Outstanding Persons award U. Ill. Black Alumni Assn., 1980; Harno fellow U. Ill., Coll. of Law, 1976. Mem. Assn. Am. Law Schs. (chair sect. minority groups 1990, exec. com. mem. sect. civil procceedure 1991), Charles Housing Bar Assn., Phi Sigma Alpha. Office: U Calif Hastings Coll Law 200 McAllister St San Francisco CA 94102

WINGATE, DAVID AARON, manufacturing company executive; b. Tel Aviv, Jan. 6, 1921; came to U.S., 1950, naturalized, 1955; s. Israel Winograd and Hanna Glick; m. Shoshanna L. Abrams, June 16, 1943; children—Bathsheva Wingate Ostrow, Ealan J. Student, Grad. Sch. Law and Econs., Tel Aviv, 1938-42. Mem. War Supply Bd., Jerusalem, 1943-47; pres. Yale Mfg. Co., Tel Aviv, 1947-50, Corona Internat. Corp., N.Y.C., 1951-55; v.p. Reynolds Atlantic Corp., N.Y.C., 1956-58; pres., chief exec. Midwood Industries, Inc., North Hills, N.Y., 1959-77; chmn., chief exec. officer Hi-Shear Industries Inc., North Hills, 1977—. Clubs: Glen Oaks (Old Westbury); Mission Hills Country (Palm Springs, Calif.); Govs. and Palm Beach Country (Palm Beach, Fla.). Home: 33 Applegreen Dr Old Westbury NY 11568-1202 Office: Hi-Shear Industries Inc 3333 New Hyde Park Rd New Hyde Park NY 11042-1204

WINGATE, HENRY TAYLOR, JR., foundation administrator, fundraiser; b. Opelika, Ala., Mar. 2, 1929; s. Henry T. and Dorothy Inez (Mathews) W.; m. Mary Frances Grimes, Sept. 17, 1949; children: Frances, Kenneth, Mathew. BS in Agrl. Sci., Auburn U., 1950. Field rep. agrl. chems. div. Swift Co., Birmingham, Ala., 1953-57; regional dir. Muscular Dystrophy Assn. Am., Birmingham, 1958-64; dir. state crusade Am. Cancer Soc., Atlanta, 1964-65; regional fund raising rep. Nat. Assn. Retarded Citizens, Atlanta, 1965-69; regional dir. Nat. Multiple Sclerosis Soc., Atlanta, 1969-77; asst. dir. field services Epilepsy Found. Am., Washington, 1977-78; group v.p. fin. devel. Nat. Arthritis Found., Atlanta, 1978-89. Vol. counselor Svc. Corp. Retired Execs., 1991—. 1st lt. U.S. Army, 1951-53. Named to Gov.'s com. on employment of handicapped Gov. of Ga., 1977, Col. Aide de Camp, Gov. of Tenn., 1982, 86. Mem. Nat. Soc. Fund Raising Execs. (bd. dirs. 1971-72, cert.), Arthritis Found. Staff Assn., Nat. Vol. Health Agys. (chmn. 1981-82), Combined Health Appeals Am. (bd. dirs. 1985-88). Republican. Baptist. Avocations: photography, fishing. Home: 4860 Mountain West Ct Stone Mountain GA 30087-1038

WINGATE, HENRY TRAVILLION, federal judge; b. Jackson, Miss., Jan. 6, 1947; s. J.T. and Eloise (Anderson) W.; m. Turner Arnita Ward, Aug. 10, 1974. BA, Grinnell Coll., 1969; JD, Yale U., 1973; LLD (hon.), Grinnell Coll., 1986. Bar: Miss. 1973, U.S. Dist. Ct. (so. dist.) Miss. 1973, U.S. Ct. Appeals (5th cir.) 1973, U.S. Mil. Ct. 1973. Law clk. New Haven (Conn.) Legal Assistance, 1971-72, Community Legal Aid, Jackson, 1972-73; spl. asst. atty. gen. State of Miss., Jackson, 1976-80; asst. dist. atty. (7th cir.), Jackson, 1980-84; asst. U.S. atty. U.S. Dist. Ct. (so. dist.), Jackson, 1984-85; judge U.S. Dist. Ct. (so. dist.) Miss., Jackson, 1985—; lectr. Miss. Prosecutors Coll., 1980-84, Law Enforcement Tng. Acad., Pearl, Miss., 1980-84, Miss. Jud. Coll., 1980-84, Nat. Coll. Dist. Attys., 1984-85; adj. prof. law Golden Gate U., Norfolk, Va, 1975-76, Tidewater Community Coll., 1976, Miss. Coll. Sch. Law, 1978-84. Former mem. adv. bd. Jackson Parks and Recreation Dept.; former mem. bd. dirs. SCAN Am. of Miss., Inc., Jackson Arts Alliance, Drug Rsch. and Edn. Assn. in Miss., Inc., United Way Jackson; mem. exec. com. Yale U. Law sch., 1989—; chmn. bd. dirs. YMCA, 1978-80. Racquetball State Singles Champion Jr. Vets. Div., 1981, State Singles Champion Srs. Div., 1982, Outstanding Legal Service award NAACP (Jackson br. and Miss. br.), 1982, Civil Liberties award Elks, 1983, Community Service award Women for Progress Orgn., 1984. Mem. ABA (cochmn. sect. litigation liaison with judiciary 1989-91), Miss. Bar Assn., Hinds County Bar Assn., Fed. Bar Assn., Yale Club Miss. Avocations: reading, theater, racquetball, jogging, bowling. Home: 6018 Huntview Dr Jackson MS 39206-2130 Office: James D Eastland Courthouse 245 E Capitol St Ste 109 Jackson MS 39201-2411

WINGATE, ROBERT LEE, JR., internist; b. Columbia, S.C., May 28, 1936; s. Robert Lee and Helen (Owen) W.; m. Ritanne Cooper, Apr. 19, 1962 (div. 1965); 1 child, Elizabeth Anne Butterfield-Wingate; m. Jeannette DeLatte, Mar. 27, 1968 (div. 1980); children: Laura Owen, Charlotte Talbot. BS, U. S.C., 1957; MD, Med. Coll. S.C., 1961. Intern Cin. Gen. Hosp., 1961-62, jr. resident internal medicine, 1964-65; asst. resident in internal medicine Med. Coll. of Va., Richmond, 1965-66; resident in internal medicine Charity Hosp. of La., New Orleans, 1966-67, resident in neurology, 1967-68; pvt. practice Columbia, 1968-78; PruCare physician Memphis, 1983-85; med. dir. M. Lowenstein and Celanese Corps., Rock Hill, S.C. 1978-80; med. dir. nursing home care unit Dorn VA Hosp., Columbia, 1980-82; med. cons. disability determination div. Vocat. Rehab. S.C., Columbia, 1982-83; cons. Student Health Ctr. U.S.C., Columbia, 1985-86; cons. Urgent Care Ctrs. S.C., 1986-87; pvt. practice Pelion, S.C., 1987-92; cons. internal medicine Western Mental Health Inst., Western Institute, Tenn., 1992—; med. dir. Forest Hills Nursing Ctr., Columbia, 1968-78; med. cons. S.C. Commn. for Blind, Columbia, 1970-78, Mid-Carolina Coun. on Alcoholism, Columbia, 1970-74; instr. internal medicine U. S.C. Sch. Medicine, 1980-82; cons. internal medicine and urgent care Pelion Cmty. Care Ctr., 1989-92; med. dir. Nursing, Med. Coll. S.C., Winthrop divsn., 1978-80; lectr. in field.

Contbr. articles to newspapers. Ofcl. physician Peanut Party S.C., 1990-92. Lt. comdr. M.C., USNR, 1958-66. Grantee Burroughs-Wellcome Co., 1958, Med. Coll. S.C., 1960, Congress of U.S. 1987. Mem. ACP, AMA (physician's recognition award 1969, 74, 79, 85, 86, 94-96), Am. Soc. Internal Medicine, Am. Occupational Med. Assn., So. Med. Assn., S.C. Med. Assn., Lexington County Med. Assn., Ruritan, Phi Rho Sigma. Avocations: chess, hunting, fishing, movie making, collecting stamps and coins. Office: Western Mental Health Inst Western Institute TN 38074

WINGENBACH, GREGORY CHARLES, minister, religious-ecumenical agency director; b. Washington, Feb. 1, 1938; s. Charles Edward and Pearl Adeline (Stanton) W.; m. MaryAnn Pearce, Sept. 16, 1961; children: Mary-Adele, Karl Eduard, John Clair, Evgenia Kisa Maria. Student, Georgetown U., 1958-62; BA, Goddard Coll., 1972; postgrad., U. Thessalonike, Greece, 1973-74; MDiv, Louisville Presbyn. Theol. Sem., 1976, D of Ministry in Pastoral and Ecumenical Theology, 1982. Ordained to ministry Greek Orthodox Archdiocese North and South Am. as deacon, 1971, assoc. priest, 1973. Editl. asst. mem. staff Washington Star and N.Y. Herald-Tribune, 1957-62; rsch. and legis. asst. U.S. Senator Clair Engle, Calif., 1962-63; mgr. community rels. programs U.S. Exec. Office Econ. Opportunity, Washington, 1965-69; regional program devel. officer AEC-Oak Ridge (Tenn.) Assn. Univs., 1970-73; assoc. St. George's Ch., Knoxville, Tenn., 1971-73; chaplain St. John Chrysostomos Ch. and Vlatadon Monastery, Thessalonike, 1973-74; named steward/oikonomos, preacher Met. Archdiocese of Thessalonike, 1974; pastor Assumption of Virgin Mary Ch., Louisville, 1974-79, Holy Trinity Ch., Nashville, 1979-82; named father confessor Greek Orthodox Archdiocese North and South Am., 1980; pastor St. Spyridon's Ch., Monessen, Pa., 1983-86; nat. dir. family life/pastoral ministries Greek Orthodox Archdiocese North and South Am., N.Y.C. and Brookline (Mass.), 1986-90; exec. dir. Kentuckiana Interfaith Community, Louisville, 1990—; Orthodox del. Louisville Area Interch. Coun. and Ecumedia Com., 1974-79; pres., exec. adminstr. LAIOS-Kentuckiana Interfaith Coun., 1977-79; diocesan rep. Archdiocese Nat. Presbyters Coun., 1982-85; archdiocese del. Nat. Coun. Chs., Orthodox/Luth. Dialogues Consultation, 1986—, Orthodox Nat. Missions Bd., 1981-90. Author: The Peace Corps, 1961, Guide to the Peace Corps, 1965, Broken...Yet Never Sundered: The Ecumenical Tradition, 1987; editorial researcher: Richard Nixon, 1979, Duel at the Brink, 1960, The Floating Revolution, 1962. Mem. Fellowship St. Alban and St. Sergius, Orthodox Theol. Soc. Am. (exec. bd.), N.Am. Acad. Ecumenists (exec. bd.). Office: Kentuckiana Interfaith Community 1115 S 4th St Louisville KY 40203-3101

WINGER, DEBRA, actress; b. Cleve., 1955; d. Robert and Ruth W.; m. Timothy Hutton, March 16, 1986 (div.); 1 child, Emanuel Noah. Student, Calif. State U., Northridge. Made 1st profl. appearance in Wonder Woman TV series, 1976-77; appeared TV film Spl. Olympics, 1977; appeared in films Thank God It's Friday, 1978, French Postcards, 1979, Urban Cowboy, 1980, Cannery Row, 1982, An Officer and a Gentleman, 1982, Terms of Endearment, 1983, Mike's Murder, 1984, Legal Eagles, 1986, Black Widow, 1987, Made in Heaven, 1987, Betrayed, 1988, Everybody Wins, 1990, The Sheltering Sky, 1990, Leap of Faith, 1992, Wilder Napalm, 1992, Shadowlands, 1993 (Academy award nominee, Best Actress, 1993), A Dangerous Woman, 1993, Forget Paris, 1995. Office: care John West PMK Pub Rels Inc 955 S Carrillo Dr # 200 Los Angeles CA 90048*

WINGER, DENNIS LAWRENCE, medical products company executive; b. Niagara Falls, N.Y., Nov. 24, 1947; s. James W. and Millicent Rose (McCabe) W.; m. Barbara Lee Waldman, May 19, 1984. BA, Siena Coll., 1969; MBA, Columbia U., 1974. Various fin. positions Continental Can Co., N.Y.C., 1974-77; v.p. fin. Continental Can Brazil, Sao Paulo, 1977-80; gen. mgr. Latin Am. ops. Continental Can Internat., Stamford, Conn., 1980-81, gen. mgr. fin., 1981-82; v.p. Cooper Devel. Co., Palo Alto, Calif., 1982-87, controller, 1982-83, treas., 1983-87; v.p. fin. and adminstrn., chief fin. officer Cooper Cos. Inc., Palo Alto, 1987-89; sr. v.p. fin. and adminstrn., chief fin. officer Chiron Corp., Emeryville, Calif., 1989—; bd. dirs. Advance Polymer Systems. Home: 2828 Jackson St San Francisco CA 94115-1146 Office: Chiron Corp 4560 Horton St Emeryville CA 94608-2900

WINGER, HOWARD WOODROW, library educator; b. Marion, Ind., Oct. 29, 1914; s. Joseph Pendleton and Amanda Ellen (Shoemaker) W.; m. Helen Margaret Gray, Dec. 25, 1941; children—John, Michael, Philip, Elizabeth, Robert. A.B. with high distinction, Manchester Coll., 1936, LL.D., 1975; B.S., George Peabody Coll., 1945; M.S., U. Ill., 1948, Ph.D., 1953. Tchr. Swayzee High Sch., Ind., 1936-37; copy writer Crowell Pub. Co., Springfield, Ohio, 1937-38; tchr. Jefferson Twp. High Sch., Warren, Ind., 1940-42; asst. librarian U. Ill. at Urbana, 1943-50; asst. prof. U. Wis.-Madison, 1950-53; asst. prof. Grad. Library Sch., U. Chgo., 1953-59, assoc. prof., 59-68, prof., 1968-81, prof. emeritus, 1981—, dean, 1972-77; Bd. library dirs. Park Forest Pub. Library, Ill., 1955-61. Author: Iron Curtains and Scholarship, 1959, Seven Questions About the Profession' of Librarianship, 1962, The Medium Sized Public Library, 1964, Area Studies and the Library, 1966, Deterioration and Preservation of Library Materials, 1970, Printers and Publishers Devices, 1976, American Library History: 1876-1976, 1976, At This Point in Time (verse), 1976; mng. editor Library Quar, 1961-72, editor, 1979-84. Served with U.S. Army, 1942-44. Mem. ALA (mem. council 1956-60), Assn. of Am. Library Schs. (sec. 1953-56), Beta Phi Mu (internat. pres. 1977), Tau Kappa Alpha. Mem. United Protestant Ch. (chmn. bd. elders 1966-68). Club: Quadrangle (Chgo.). Home: 310 Hickory Ln North Manchester IN 46962-9606 Office: 1100 E 57th St Chicago IL 60637-1596

WINGER, RALPH O., lawyer; b. Keokuk, Iowa, July 8, 1919; s. Ralph O. and Mary Ellen (Lee) W.; m. Irene L. Sutton, Apr. 5, 1941; children: Ralph O. (dec.), Allen, Louise, Robert. BA, State U. Iowa 1940; LLB, Harvard U., 1947. Bar: N.Y. 1948. Assoc. Cahill Gordon & Reindel and predecessor firms, N.Y.C., 1947-60, ptnr., 1960-91, sr. counsel, 1992—. Lt. USNR, 1942-46, PTO. Mem. ABA, N.Y. State Bar Assn. (chmn. tax sect. 1973-74, ho. of dels. 1974-75), Bay Terrace Country Club (N.Y.). Republican. Home: 25908 28th Rd Flushing NY 11360-2413 Office: Cahill Gordon & Reindel 80 Pine St New York NY 10005-1702

WINGER, ROGER ELSON, church administrator; b. Fisherville, Ont., Can., Dec. 25, 1933; s. Elson Clare and Bertha Caroline (Schwer) W.; m. Della Bertha Lebien, June 7, 1958; children: Jeffrey, Karen Mohr, David, Thomas, Susan. AA, Concordia Jr. Coll., Ft. Wayne, Ind., 1953; BA, Concordia Sem., St. Louis, 1955, theol. diploma, 1958; DD (hon.), Concordia Luth. Sem., Edmonton, Alta., Can., 1991. Ordained to ministry, Luth. Ch., 1958. Pastor Holy Trinity Luth. Ch., London, 1958-64, Good Shepherd Luth. Ch., Coventry, Eng., 1964-69, Luth. Mission, Liverpool, Eng., 1969-72, Faith Luth. Ch., Dunnville, Ont., 1972-78, St. Matthew Luth. Ch., Smithville, Ont., 1972-78, St. Paul's Luth. Ch., Kitchener, Ont., 1978-91; pres. ea. dist. Luth. Ch.-Can., Kitchener, 1991—; v.p. East Ont. dist. Luth. Ch.-Can., 1982-88; sec. Luth. Ch.-Can., Winnipeg, Man., Can., 1988-91; bd. regents Concordia Luth. Sem., Edmonton, Alta., 1984-88, Concordia Luth. Theol. Sem., St. Catharines, Ont., 1991—. Avocations: photography, golf, woodworking. Home: 76 Deerwood Crescent, Kitchener, ON Canada N2M 1R3 Office: Luth Ch Can East Dist, 275 Lawrence Ave, Kitchener, ON Canada N2M 1Y3

WINGET, CARL HENRY, science administrator, forest ecologist; b. Noranda, Quebec, Can., Sept. 28, 1938; m. Madelein Roy, 1964; children: Julie, Marian, Jeffrey. BScF, U. N.B., 1960; MSc, U. Wis., 1962, PhD in Forestry, Botany, 1964. Prof. forestry and geod. Laval U., 1967-73; dir. Laurentian Forestry Rsch. Ctr., 1978-82; dir. gen. Rsch. and Tech. Svcs., 1982-88; dir. gen. Ont. region Can. Forest Svc., 1988—. Mem. Can. Inst. Forestry. Achievements include forest resource mgmt., silviculture of tolerant northern hardwoods. Office: Canadian Forest Svc/ON Region, 1219 Queen St E, Sault Sainte Marie, ON Canada P6A 5M7*

WINGET, CLIFFORD, oil industry executive. Pres. Astra Oil Co., Inc., Long Beach, Calif. Office: Astra Oil Co Inc 100 Ocean Ave Ste 1120 Long Beach CA 90802

WINHAM, GEORGE KEETH, mental health nurse; b. Plain Dealing, La., Nov. 25, 1934; s. Henderson and Lula Mae (Kelly) W.; m. Patricia Annie Weise, Nov. 7, 1959; children: Adrian Keeth, George Kevin, Karla Ann. ADN, La. State U., 1974; BS in Health Care, Carolina Christian U.,

1986. Cert. chem. dependency nurse specialist; RN, La. Staff nurse preceptor ward 10 VAMC, Shreveport, La., 1972-76, staff nurse ward 10, 1976-88; guest speaker in field. With RSAFR, 1982-95, ret. Mem. DANA, ASPMN, Nat. Fedn. Fed. Employees (local treas. 1956, Nurse of Yr. 1989), Air Force Sgts. Assn., Nat. Consortium Chem. Dependency Nurses, Consol. Assn. Nurses in Substance Abuse, Masons. Baptist. Avocations: repairing antique furnitures, framing pictures. Home: 106 Lancashire Dr Bossier City LA 71111-2023 Office: Overton Brooks VAMC 510 E Stoner Ave Shreveport LA 71101-4243

WINICK, ALFRED ZELL, data services corporation executive; b. Des Moines, June 27, 1941; s. Sam and Ida (Booth) W.; m. Barbara Marie Fischer, July 8, 1962; children: Jeffrey Howard, Stacy Helene, Susan Renee, Mark Richard. B.A., U. Iowa, 1963, J.D., 1966. Bar: Iowa 1966. Asst. counsel Dial Corp., Des Moines, 1966-72; asst. to pres. Dial Corp., 1972-73, corp. sec., 1973-80, v.p., sec., 1980-84; pres. Norwest Fin. Info. Services Group, Des Moines, 1984—. Bd. dirs. Des Moines Children's Home, Orchard Pl. Found., 1977—; Tifereth Israel Synagogue, 1984—; trustee Jewish Welfare Fedn., 1976-79; sect. chmn. Greater Des Moines United Way, 1975, 85; pres. Bur. for Jewish Living, 1979-81. Mem. Am. Bar Assn., Iowa State Bar Assn., Am. Fin. Services Assn. Home: 7819 Luin Ln Windsor Hts IA 50322-5744 Office: Norwest Financial Svcs 206 8th St Des Moines IA 50309-3805

WINICK, CHARLES, sociologist, educator; b. N.Y.C., Aug. 4, 1922; s. David and Sadie (Brussel) W.; m. Mariann Pezzella, July 2, 1961; children—Elizabeth, Laura, Raphael. B.A., City Coll. N.Y., 1941; M.A., N.Y.U., 1949; Ph.D., 1950. Asst. prof. U. Rochester, 1951-53; research dir. Anti- Defamation League, 1953-55; lectr. Queens Coll., 1953-56; vis. prof. Mass. Inst. Tech., 1956-57, Columbia, 1957-58, 61-63, 75-80, N.Y. U., 1975-76, New Sch., 1974-76; dir. basic research J. Walter Thompson Co., 1959-61; research dir. N.Y. State Narcotics Commn., 1957-59; cons. Am. Social Health Assn., 1961-73; research dir. group therapy dept. Postgrad. Center Mental Health, 1957-66; cons. Central Labor Rehab. Council N.Y., 1977—; prof. sociology City Coll. and grad. center of CUNY, 1966—; assoc. univ. seminar Columbia, 1963—; Cons. subcom. juvenile delinquency U.S. Senate, 1955-57, Joint Commn. Mental Health Children, 1968-69, Commn. on Obscenity and Pornography, 1969-70, Commn. on Marihuana and Drug Abuse, 1972-73, N.Y. State Commn. on Violence in Criminal Justice, 1986-87. Author: Trends in Human Relation Research, 1955, Dictionary of Anthropology, 1956, Taste and Censor, 1959, Insights into Pricing from Behavioral Science and Operations Research, 1961, For the Young Viewer, 1962, Practicum of Group Psychotherapy, 1963, 2d edit., 1974, Outer Space Humor, 1963, U.S.S.R. Humor, 1964, Group Psychotherapy Today, 1965, The New People, 1968, The Narcotic Addiction Problem, 1968, The Glue Sniffing Problem, 1968, The Lively Commerce, 1971, Children's Television Commercials, 1973, Sociological Aspects of Drug Dependence, 1974, Deviance and Mass Communications, 1978, The Television Experience, 1979, A Labor Approach to Alcohol Problems, 1982, Starting an Employee Assistance Program, 1984, Desexualization in American Life, 1994; editor: Yearbook of Drug Dependence, 1978—, Annual Rev. of Research in Deviance, 1978—. Served with AUS, 1942-46. Recipient Flowerman award Postgrad. Center Mental Health, 1960; Edn. Press Assn. award Edinl. Press Assn., 1963; Peabody award, 1964; Progressive Architecture award, 1979, Ctrl. Labor Rehab. Coun. of N.Y. award, 1993. Mem. Am. Sociol. Assn., Am. Psychol. Assn., Brit. Soc. Study Addiction, Am. Assn. Pub. Opinion Research, Soc. Study Social Problems, Soc. Psychol. Study Social Issues. Office: City Coll Convent Ave New York NY 10027

WINICK, MYRON, educator, physician; b. N.Y.C., May 4, 1929; s. Charles B. and Ruth E. (Gesser) W.; m. Elaine L. Lasky, Sept. 19, 1964; children: Jonathan, Stephen. A.B., Columbia U., 1951; M.S., U. Ill., 1952; M.D., SUNY, 1956. Intern U. Pa., Phila., 1956-57; asst. resident pediatrics Cornell U. Med. Coll., N.Y.C., 1957-59; chief resident Cornell U. Med. Coll., 1959-60; attending pediatrician Stanford U. Hosp., 1963-64; asst. prof. pediatrics Cornell U. Med. Coll., N.Y.C., 1964-68, assoc. prof. pediatrics and nutrition, 1968-70, prof., 1970-71; dir. Inst. Human Nutrition Columbia U. Inst. Human Nutrition, 1972-87, prof. pediatrics, 1972-89, R.R. Williams prof. nutrition, 1973-89, R.R. Williams prof. emeritus, 1990—; pres. U. Health Scis./Chgo. Med. Sch., North Chgo., Ill., 1990-93; dir. Ctr. for Nutrition, Genetics and Human Devel., 1975-87; vis. prof. pediatrics U. Chile, Santiago, 1967; asst. attending pediatrician N.Y. Hosp., N.Y.C., 1964-68, asso. attending pediatrician, 1968-70, attending pediatrician, 1970-71; attending pediatrician Presbyn. Hosp., N.Y.C., 1972-89; cons. Pan Am. Health Orgn., 1966—. Author: Malnutrition and Brain Development, 1976; textbook Nutrition in Health and Disease, 1980; Growing Up Healthy; A Parent's Guide to Good Nutrition, 1982; For Mothers and Daughters: A Guide to Good Nutrition for Women, 1983; Your Personalized Health Profile: Choosing the Diet That's Right for You, 1985; Nutrition, Pregnancy and Early Infancy, 1989; The Fiber Prescription, 1992; editor: textbook Current Concepts in Nutrition, 1972—; Nutrition: Pre- and Postnatal Development, Vol. I, Human Nutrition: A Comprehensive Treatise, 1979, Columbia Ency. of Nutrition, 1988; contbg. editor Nutrition Revs., 1969-76; mem. editorial bd. Jour. Nutrition, 1972-76, 82-86, The Year in Metabolism (now Contemporary Metabolism), 1975—; assoc. editor Growth, 1984—; nutrition editor Cancer Prevention, 1994—. Trustee Found. for Internat. Child Health; mem. nutrition interdisciplinary cluster Pres.' Biomed. Research Panel, 1975; mem. panel on infants and children Pres.' Commn. on Mental Health, 1977; cons. Office of Tech. Assessment, U.S. Congress, 1976-78; mem. Food and Nutrition Bd. NRC, 1982-88. With USNR, 1960-62. Bank of Am.-Gianini Found. fellow Stanford, 1962; NIH Spl. fellow, 1963; recipient NIH Career Devel. award, 1968-71; E. Mead Johnson award pediatric research, 1970; Osborne and Mendel award Am. Inst. Nutrition, 1976; Agnes Higgins award March of Dimes Found., 1983. Fellow Royal Soc. Health, Am. Acad. Pediatrics; mem. AAAS, Am. Soc. Cell Biology, Soc. Developmental Biology, Harvey Soc., Soc. Pediatric Research, Royal Soc. Medicine, Brit. Nutrition Soc., Am. Inst. Nutrition, Am. Soc. Clin. Nutrition, N.Y. Acad. Scis., N.Y. Acad. Medicine, (cons.), Soc. for Exptl. Biology and Medicine, Soc. for Neurosci., Internat. Soc. for Devel. Neurosci. Office: Columbia U Inst Human Nutrition New York NY 10027

WINIK, JAY B., writer, political scientist, consultant; b. New Haven, Feb. 8, 1957; s. Herbert Edward Winik and Marilyn Joan (Fishman) Abrams; m. Lyric Wallwork, Nov. 17, 1991. BA in Psychology cum laude, Yale U., 1980, PhD in Polit. Sci., 1993; MS in Internat. Rels. with distinction, London Sch. Econs., 1981. Arms control cons. Rand Corp., Santa Monica, Calif., 1983; chief speechwriter Ambassador Benjamin Netanyahu, N.Y.C., 1984; sr. profl. staff mem. House Com. on Armed Svcs., Washington, 1985-88; vis. fellow Ctr. for Strategic and Internat. Studies, Washington, 1988; dep. exec. dir. Def. Sec.'s Commn. on Base Realignment and Closure, Washington, 1988; legis. assoc. for def. and fgn. policy Office of Sen. Charls S. Robb & Senate Com. on Fgn. Rels., Washington, 1989-91; sr. fellow Sch. Pub. Affairs U. Md., College Park, 1991—; advisor to Sec. Defense, 1993; prin. advisor for def. and fgn. policy, 1986 policy commn. Dem. Nat. Com.; assoc. staff mem. select com to investigate covert arms transactions with Iran, 1987. Editorial contbr. Wall Street Jour., N.Y. Times, Washington Post, other pubs., 1981—; dep. editor Millenium, Jour. Internat. Studies, 1981; contbr. articles to profl. jours. including Fgn. Policy, The Washington Quarterly, others. Grantee U.S. Inst. Peace, 1987; fellow Bradley Found. Fellow Ctr. for Strategic and Internat. Studies (adj.); mem. Coun. on Fgn. Rels. (term mem.), Coalition for Dem. Majority (bd. dirs.). Jewish. Avocation: tennis. Home: 4628 Hunt Ave Chevy Chase MD 20815 Office: U Md CISSM Sch Pub Affairs College Park MD 20740

WINIKOFF, BEVERLY, physician; b. N.Y.C., Aug. 26, 1945; d. Harry and Blanche (Tepper) W.; m. Michael Charles Alpert, July 15, 1973; children: Hilary Winikoff A., Lindsay Winikoff A. AB magna cum laude, Harvard U., 1966; MD, NYU, 1971; MPH, Harvard U., 1973, rsch. fellow Sch. Pub. Health, 1973-74. Diplomate Nat. Bd. Med. Examiners. Tchr. history, social studies Escola Americana do Rio de Janeiro, 1966-67; intern in mixed medicine Gen. Rose Meml. Hosp., Denver, 1971-72; physician East Side Neighborhood Health Ctr. Denver Dept. Health, 1972, Boston Evening Clinic, 1973-74; med. writer ambulatory care project Beth Israel Hosp., Boston, 1973-74; asst. dir. health scis. Rockefeller Found., N.Y.C., 1974-78; med. assoc. The Population Coun., N.Y.C., 1978-82, sr. med assoc., 1982—; cons. Congl. Office Tech. Assessment, 1976-77, 78, Senate Select Com. Nutrition and Human Needs, 1976-77, Internat. Vitamin A Consultative Group,

1977, Internat. Nutritional Anemia Consultative Group, 1978—, Nat. Inst. Aging Consultancy, 1977-78, NAS, 1978, 78-79, Rockefeller Found., 1978; lectr. to numerous profl. groups. Co-author, editor: Nutrition and National Policy, 1978, Feeding Infants in Four Societies: Causes and Consequences of Mothers' Choices, 1988, (with S. Wymelenberg) The Contraceptive Handbook, 1992; guest editor spl. issue Social Sci. and Medicine, 1980; editor spl. issue Studies in Family Planning, 1981, mem. editorial bd., 1978—; contbr. articles to profl. jours., chpts. to books. Mem. White House Spl. Task Force on Internat. Health, 1977, Mayor's Emergency Med. Svcs. Adv. Com., 1978—, Steering Com. to Promote Breastfeeding in N.Y.C. Office Pub. Health, N.Y. State Health Dept., 1982—. Recipient scholarships Radcliffe Coll., 1962-66, GM, NYU, 1967; fellowship USPHS, 1967. Mem. Harvard U. Sch. Pub. Health Alumni Assn. (councillor 1983-85, pres. 1989-91), Harvard U. Alumni Assn. (bd. dirs. 1991—). Office: Population Coun 1 Dag Hammarskjold Plz New York NY 10017-2201

WINKEL, FRED MICHAEL, marketing professional; b. N.Y.C., July 5, 1944; s. Leon Woodruff and Lillian (Altman) W.; m. Barbara Dorothy Winkel, June 25, 1967; children: Jason (dec.), Sam, John, Sue Mee. BS, Tex. A&M U., 1966. Sr. v.p., dir. Audits & Surveys Inc., N.Y.C.; statistician Census Bur., Suitland, Md., 1966-69; with Audits & Surveys Inc., N.Y.C., 1969—, sr. v.p., 1992—. Recipient Co-author of Yr. award Shell Oil, 1992, 93, Supplier of Excellence award NCR Corp., 1994. Mem. Am. Mktg. Assn., Am. Assn. Pub. Opinion Rsch. Avocation: triathlon. Home: 8 Woodstock Ct Oyster Bay NY 11771 Office: Audit & Surveys Inc 650 Ave of Americas New York NY 10011

WINKEL, JUDY KAY, lawyer; b. Sibley, Iowa, Mar. 14, 1947; d. Harold Ralph and Hazel (Johnson) W. BBA, U. Iowa, 1969, JD, 1972. Bar: Iowa 1972. Govt. affairs counsel Assocs. Corp. N.Am., South Bend, Ind., 1972-76; asst. v.p. govt. affairs Assocs. Corp. N.Am., Dallas, 1976-79, v.p., 1979-89, sr. v.p., 1989—. Methodist. Avocations: piano, theatre. Office: Assocs Corp N Am PO Box 660237 250 Carpenter Frwy Dallas TX 75266-0237

WINKEL, RAYMOND NORMAN, avionics manufacturing executive, retired naval officer; b. Flint, Mich., Dec. 8, 1928; s. Norman Martin and Evelyn Matilda (Hylen) W.; m. Ellen Stefula, Dec. 29, 1955; children: Raymond Norman, Ann, Maryellen. B.S., U.S. Naval Postgrad. Sch., Monterey, Calif., 1964; M.S., Villanova (Pa.) U., 1967; grad., Advanced Mgmt. Program, Harvard U., 1973. Enlisted in U.S. Navy, 1948, commd. ensign, designated naval aviator, 1951, advanced through grades to rear adm., 1979; service in Far East; comdg. officer Naval Electronics Systems Test and Evaluation Facility St. Inigoes, Md., 1969-71; dir. avionics U.S. Navy, 1973-76; project mgr. Navy/Marine Corps heavy lift helicopter, 1976-78; gen. mgr. Navy/industry team to develop new ship/aircraft weapon system for anti-submarine warfare LAMPS Mark III, 1978-81; ret. U.S. Navy, 1981; v.p. Washington ops. Telephonics Corp., Huntington, N.Y., 1981-82; v.p. programs and contracts Astronautics Corp. Am., Milw., 1982-94; aerospace industry cons. Heathsville, Va., 1994—. Decorated Legion of Merit, Meritorious Service medal, Air medal, Navy Achievement medal. Mem. Am. Helicopter Soc., Armed Forces Comms. and Electronics Assn., Navy Helicopter Assn., Exptl. Aircraft Assn., U.S. Naval Inst., Assn. Naval Aviation, Ret. Officers Assn., Kiwanis, Milw. Yacht Club. Republican. Roman Catholic. Home and Office: Island Point Rd RR 2 Box 123 Heathsville VA 22473

WINKELMAN, JAMES WARREN, hospital administrator, pathology educator; b. Bklyn., Oct. 29, 1935; s. Charles Winkelman and Augusta Spiselman; m. Sidra Levi, Sept. 1, 1957 (div. Sept. 1972); children: Elizabeth, Claudia, Recha; m. Rina Lavie, Sept. 20, 1977; 1 child, Zev. AB, U. Chgo., 1955; MD, Johns Hopkins U., 1959; MA (hon.), Harvard U., 1990. Diplomate Am. Bd. Pathology. Intern in medicine Johns Hopkins Hosp., 1959-60; resident in pathology NYU Hosp., Bellevue Hosp., 1962-65; asst. prof. pathology NYU, 1965-67; assoc. clin. prof. UCLA, 1969-80; asst. dir. Bio-Sci. Labs. Van Nuys, Calif., 1967-70, v.p., 1970-72, pres., 1972-77; bd. dirs., 1970-77; exec. v.p. Nat. Health Labs., La Jolla, Calif., 1977-80; prof. pathology SUNY Health Sci. Ctr., Syracuse, 1980-86, Harvard U. Med. Sch., Boston, 1986—; v.p., dir. clin. labs. Brigham and Women's Hosp., Boston, 1986—; cons. to numerous govt. agys. and industry; vis. prof. Soroka Med. Ctr., Beersheva, Israel, 1982. Author: Clinical Chemistry, 1974; also over 100 articles; patentee in field lab. sci. Capt. USPHS, 1960-62. Mem. Coll. Am. Pathologists, Acad. Clin. Lab. Scientists, Am. Soc. Clin. Pathology, Clin. Lab. Mgmt. Assn., Alpha Omega Alpha. Republican. Jewish. Avocations: tennis, golf, travel, classical music. Office: Brigham and Women's Hosp 75 Francis St Boston MA 02115-6195

WINKELSTERN, PHILIP NORMAN, financial executive; b. N.Y.C., Aug. 1, 1930; s. Philip and Lydia Mae (Kaiser) W.; m. Bette Louise Grugett, June 15, 1956; children: Philip J., Kristen N. B.A., Mich. State U., 1956. Fin. analyst Gen. Electric, Schenectady, 1956-61; div. controller Ford Motor Co., Dearborn, Mich., 1961-75; sr. v.p. Comml. Inertech, Youngstown, Ohio, 1975—; dir. Comml. Inertech, 1984—, McDonald Steel Co. Chmn. Better Bus. Bur., Youngstown, 1977; trustee Western Res. Care Assn., Cin., 1987—. Served with USMC, 1951-53. Mem. Fin. Execs. Inst., Am. Mgmt. Assn., Machinery and Allied Products Inst., C. of C. Office: Comml Intertech PO Box 239 Youngstown OH 44501-0239

WINKHAUS, HANS-DIETRICH, chemicals executive; b. 1937. Degree, U. Munich, U. Muenster, Germany, 1937. Dep. pres. Henkel KGaA, King Of Prussia, Pa., 1967—; now CHB Henkel of Am., Inc., King Of Prussia, Pa., 1992—. Office: Henkel Corp 2200 Renaissance Blvd King Of Prussia PA 19406*

WINKIN, JUSTIN PHILIP, engineering executive; b. Englewood, N.J., July 14, 1922; s. John Quirin and Cora (Senner) W.; widowed; children: Justin, John, Susan. BSME, Rensselaer Polytech. Inst., 1944; postgrad., NYU, 1951-53. Registered profl. engr., N.J. Student engr. Babcock & Wilcox, N.Y.C., 1946-47; field service engr., 1947-50, staff engr., 1950-58; ops. engr. Jersey Cen. Power and Light, Morristown, N.J., 1958-63; staff engr., dir., v.p. engring. Foster Wheeler Energy Corp., Livingston, N.J., 1963-77, sr. v.p., 1979-82; v.p., cons. Foster Wheeler Energy Corp., Clinton, N.J., 1987—; cons. Foster Wheeler Corp., Foster Wheeler Ltd., Can., 1987—; pres. Foster Wheeler Ltd., St. Catherines, Can., 1979-82, also bd. dirs., 1972-87; v.p. group exec. Foster Wheeler Corp., Livingston, 1982-87; bd. dirs. Generadores De Vapor, S.A., Madrid, Spain, Belco Pollution Corp., Livingston, Foster Wheeler Energy Applications, Livingston; cons. for power plants and energy, 1982—. Contbr. articles to profl. jours; patentee in field. Mem. Radburn Assn., Fair Lawn, N.J., 1950—; pres. Radburn Theater, Fair Lawn, 1975-77. Lt. USN, 1944-46, PTO. Fellow ASME. Republican. Presbyterian. Avocations: swimming, tennis, hiking, golf, theater. Home: 19-12 Radburn Rd Fair Lawn NJ 07410-4540 Office: Foster Wheeler Corp Perryville Corp Park PO Box 4000 Clinton NJ 08809-4000

WINKLE, SHARON LOUISE, library administrator; b. Cin., Nov. 29, 1950; d. John F. and Marguerite T. (Platt) W.; m. Clifford J. Smith, June 16, 1979. BS, Findlay Coll., 1972; MLS, U. Ky., 1973; MPA, U. Denver, 1984. Libr. Findlay (Ohio)-Hancock County Pub. Libr., 1973-74; deputy dir. Sandusky (Ohio) Libr., 1974-76, dir., 1976-79; libr. dir. Englewood (Colo.) Pub. Libr., 1979-89; dir. libr. and recreation svcs. City of Englewood, 1989-90; libr. dir. Mead Pub. Libr., Sheboygan, Wis., 1991—. Ohio State U. scholar, 1972; named Mktg. Student of Yr., Findlay Coll., 1972, Outstanding MPA Student U. Denver, 1984, Woman of Yr. Englewood Bus and Profl. Women, 1989. Mem. ALA, Wis. Libr. Assn., Sheboygan Rotary, Altrusa Club Sheboygan, Sheboygan C. of C. Home: 1810 N 5th St Sheboygan WI 53081-2840 Office: Mead Pub Library 710 N 8th St Sheboygan WI 53081-4505

WINKLER, ALLAN MICHAEL, history educator; b. Cin., Jan. 7, 1945; s. Henry Ralph and Clare (Sapadin) W.; div.; children: Jennifer, David; m. Sara Penhale, May 2, 1992. BA, Harvard U., 1966; MA, Columbia U., 1967; PhD, Yale U., 1974. Vol. Peace Corps, The Philippines, 1967-69; instr., asst. prof. history Yale U., New Haven, 1973-78; asst. prof., assoc. prof. U. Oreg., Eugene, 1979-86; prof. history Miami U., Oxford, Ohio, 1986—, chmn. dept., 1986—; prof. Helsinki U., 1978-79, U. Amsterdam (Netherlands), 1984-85. Author: The Politics of Propaganda, 1978, Modern America, 1985, Home Front, U.S.A., 1986, The American People, 1986, The Recent Past, 1989,

Life Under a Cloud, 1993, America: Pathways to the Present, 1994, Cassie's War, 1994. Fulbright grantee, 1978-79, 84-85, NEH grantee, 1981-82. Mem. Am. Hist. Assn., Orgn. Am. Historians, Am. Studies Assn., Harvard Club (Cin.). Avocations: running, bicycling, squash, tennis, golf. Home: 925 Cedar Dr Oxford OH 45056-2416 Office: Miami U Dept History Oxford OH 45056

WINKLER, HENRY FRANKLIN, actor; b. N.Y.C., Oct. 30, 1945; s. Harry Irving and Ilse Anna Maria (Hadra) W.; m. Stacey Weitzman, May 5, 1978; 1 dau., Zoe Emily. Student, Emerson Coll., 1963-67, D.H.L., 1978; student, Yale Sch. Drama, 1967-70. With Yale Repertory Theatre, 1970-71; founder New Haven Free Theatre, 1968, Off The Wall N.Y., improvisation co., 1972; tchr. drama UCLA Adult Extension. Off-Broadway shows, 1972-73; Cin. Playhouse, 1973; films include The Lords of Flatbush, 1972, Crazy Joe, 1974, Heroes, 1977, The One and Only, 1977, Night Shift, 1983; starred in TV series Happy Days, 1973-84, Monty, 1994; appeared on ABC-TV movie An American Christmas Carol, 1979, CBS movie Absolute Strangers, 1991, ABC movie Grounds for Murder, 1994; exec. producer TV program Who Are the Debolts and Where Did They Get Nineteen Kids, TV series for ABC Ryan's Four, 1983, NBC-TV movie When Your Lover Leaves, 1983, TV movie Scandal Sheet, 1984, MacGyver, 1985, producer, host home video Strong Kids, Safe Kids, 1985, PBS animated spl. Happy Ever After, 1985, Two Daddies to Love Me, 1988; producer ABC After Sch. Spl. Losing a Sister, 1988; pres. Fair Dinkum Prodns., Hollywood, Calif., 1979—, Winkler-Daniels Prodns., Hollywood, 1987-91; producer TV program Run, Don't Walk for own co. JZM Prodns., 1981; dir. TV movie A Smokey Mountain Christmas, 1986, feature film Memories of Me, 1988, Cop and a Half, 1992. Named Best Actor in Comedy Series, Photoplay mag. 1976-77, recipient Golden Globe award 1976, 77, 78; named King of Baccus, Mardi Gras, New Orleans 1977, Emmy nominee 1975, 76, 77; recipient Golden Plate award Am. Acad. Achievement 1980, Daytime Emmy nomination best dir. All The Kids Do It, produced for JZM Prodns., 1985; Sorrisi e Canzoni Telegato award (Italian TV award) 1980; nat. spokesperson United Friends of the Children, 1982—. Recipient Humanitarian award Women in Film, 1988; named hon. youth chmn. Epilepsy Found.; chmn. Toys for Tots, 1977. Mem. AFTRA, Screen Actors Guild, Actors Equity. Office: care Richard Grant & Assoc 8484 Wilshire Blvd Ste 500 Beverly Hills CA 90210-9999*

WINKLER, HENRY RALPH, retired university president, historian; b. Waterbury, Conn., Oct. 27, 1916; s. Jacob and Ethel (Rieger) W.; m. Clare Sapadin, Aug. 18, 1940; children—Allan Michael, Karen Jean; m. Beatrice Ross, Jan. 28, 1973. A.B., U. Cin., 1938, M.A., 1940; Ph.D., U. Chgo., 1947; hon. degrees, Lehigh U., 1974, Rutgers U., 1977, No. Ky. U., 1978, St. Thomas Inst., 1979, Hebrew Union Coll., 1980, Xavier U., 1981, U. Akron, 1984, U. Cin., 1987, Thomas More Coll., 1989. Instr. U. Cin., 1939-40; asst. prof. Roosevelt Coll., 1946-47; mem. faculty Rutgers U., 1947-77, prof. history, 1958-77, chmn. dept., 1960-64; dean Faculty Liberal Arts, 1967, vice provost, 1968-70, acting provost, 1970, v.p. for acad. affairs, 1970-72, v.p. for acad. affairs, 1972-76, exec. v.p., 1976-77; exec. v.p. U. Cin., 1977, pres., 1977-84, pres. emeritus, 1984—; Univ. prof. history, 1977-86, prof. emeritus, 1986—; mng. editor Am. Hist. Rev., 1964-68; vis. prof. Bryn Mawr Coll., 1959-60, Harvard, summer 1964, Columbia, summer 1967; faculty John Hay Fellows Inst. Humanities, 1960-65; bd. overseers Hebrew Union Coll., 1984—. Author: The League of Nations Movement in Great Britain, 1914-19, 1952, Great Britain in the Twentieth Century, 1960, 2d edit., 1966; editor: (with K.M. Setton) Great Problems in European Civilization, 1954, 2d edit., 1966, Twentieth-Century Britain, 1977, Paths Not Taken: British Labour and International Policy in the Nineteen Twenties, 1994; mem. editorial bd. Historian, 1958-64, Liberal Edn., 1986—; mem. adv. bd. Partisan Rev., 1972-79; contbr. articles to jours., revs. Nat. chmn. European history advanced placement com. Coll. Entrance Exam. Bd., 1960-64; mem. Nat. Commn. on Humanities in Schs., 1967-68, Am. specialist Eastern Asia, 1968; exec. com. Conf. on Brit. Studies, 1968-75; chmn. bd. Nat. Humanities Faculty, 1970-73; chmn. adv. com. on history Coll. Entrance Exam. Bd., 1977-80; mem. council on acad. affairs, mem. bd. trustees, chmn., 1982-84; pres. Highland Park (N.J.) Bd. Edn., 1962-63; mem. exec. com. Nat. Assn. State Univs. and Land-Grant Colls., 1978-81, mem. Cin. Lit. Club, 1978—, pres., 1993—; bd. dirs. Am. Council on Edn., 1979-81; trustee Seasengood Good Govt. Found., 1979—, pres., 1991-93; trustee Thomas More Coll., 1986-93; mem. Ohio Indsl. Tech. and Enterprise Bd., 1983-89; bd. dirs. Nat. Civic League, 1986—, Planning Accreditation Bd., 1988—; mem. adv coun. Clin. Valley State Coll., Ohio Humanities Coun., 1994—. With USNR, 1943-46. Recipient Rutgers U. medal, 1977, William H. Taft medal U. Cin., 1984, Disting. Alumnus award Coll. Arts and Scis., U. Cin., 1990; Winkler Residence Hall, Rutgers U. named in his honor, 1989. Mem. Am. Hist. Assn., Phi Beta Kappa, Tau Kappa Alpha, Phi Alpha Theta. Clubs: Comml., Bankers, Cin., Lit. Office: U Cin 571 Langsam Library Cincinnati OH 45221

WINKLER, HOWARD LESLIE, investment banker, stockbroker, business consultant; b. N.Y.C., Aug. 16, 1950; s. Martin and Magda (Stark) W.; m. Robin Lynn Richards, Sept. 12, 1976; 1 child, David Menachem. AA in Mktg., Los Angeles City Coll., 1973, AA in Bus. Data Processing, 1977, AA in Bus. Mgmt., 1981. Sr. cons. Fin. Cons. Inc., Los Angeles, 1972-81; asst. v.p. Merrill Lynch, Inc., Los Angeles, 1981-83; v.p. Drexel, Burnham, Lambert, Inc., Beverly Hills, Calif., 1983-84; pres. Howard Winkler Investments, Beverly Hills, Calif., 1984-90, Landmark Fin. Group, L.A., 1990—; ptnr. N.W.B. Assocs., L.A., 1988-91; chmn. bd. United Cmty. and Housing Devel. Corp., L.A., 1986—; bd. dirs. Earth Products Internat., Inc., Kansas City, Kans., 1992, Fed. Home Loan Bank of San Francisco, 1991-93. Nat. polit. editor B'nai B'rith Messenger, 1986-95. Mem. Calif. Rep. Cent. Com., 1985-93; mem. L.A. County Rep. Cent. Com., 1985-92, chmn. 45th Assembly Dist., 1985-90; mem. Rep. Senatorial Inner Circle, 1986—, Rep. Presdl. Task Force, 1985— (Legion of Merit award 1992); mem. Rep. Eagles, 1988-92; Nat. Rep. Senatorial Com., 1986—, Golden Circle Calif., 1986-92, GOP Platform Planning Com. at Large del., 1992; del. to GOP nat conv., Houston, 1992; Calif. chmn. Jack Kemp for Pres., 1988, mem. nat. steering com. Bush-Quayle '88, 1987, nat. Exec. com. Bush-Quayle '92, 1991; mil. adminstrv. supr. CID US Army, 1969-72, SE Asia; legis. and civic action Agudath Israel Calif., 1985—; mem. L.A. County Narcotics and Dangerous Drugs Commn., 1988—; trustee, sec.-treas. Minority Health Professions Edn. Found., 1989-94; program chmn. Calif. Lincoln Clubs Polit. Action Com., 1987-88; state chmn. Pete Wilson for Gov. Campaign, 1989, John Seymour for Lt. Gov. Campaign, 1989-90; chpt. pres. Calif. Congress of Reps., 1989-93; chmn. Claude Parrish for Bd. of Equalization, 1989-90; founder, dir. Community Rsch. & Info. Ctr.; mem. fin. com. John Seymour for Senate '92, 1991. Decorated Legion of Merit; recipient Cmty. Svc. award Agudath Israel Calif., 1986, Pres.'s Cmty. Leadership award, 1986, Disting. Cmty. Svc. U.S Senator Pete Wilson, 1986, Calif. Gov.'s Leadership award, 1986, Cmty. Svc. award U.S. Congresswoman Bobbi Fiedler, 1986, Resolution of Commendation Calif. State Assembly, 1986, Outstanding Cmty. Svc. Commendation Los Angeles County Bd. Suprs., 1986, 90, Outstanding Citizenship award City of Los Angeles, 1986, 90, Cmty. Leadership award Iranian-Jewish Community L.A., 1990, Resolution of Commendation, State of Calif., 1992, Cmty. Svc. Commendation, 1993, Rep. Senatorial Medal of Freedom award, Sentorial Inner Circle, 1994, Commendation L.A. County Bd. Suprs., 1994. Mem. Calif. Young Reps., Calif. Rep. Assembly, VFW, Jewish War Veterans. Jewish. Avocations: philanthropy, family time. Office: PO Box 480454 Los Angeles CA 90048

WINKLER, IRWIN, motion picture producer; b. N.Y.C., May 28, 1931; s. Sol and Anna Winkler. BA, NYU, 1955. Mailroom messenger William Morris Agy., N.Y.C., 1955-62; motion picture producer, owner Winkler Films, Culver City, Calif., 1992—; pres., Chartoff-Winkler Prodns., 1966—. Producer: Rocky, 1976 (10 Acad. award nominations, winner 3 including Best Picture, Los Angeles Film Critics award for best picture), They Shoot Horses Don't They, 1969 (9 Acad. award nominations), Nickelodeon, 1976, The Gambler, 1974, Up the Sandbox, 1972, The New Centurions, 1972, Point Blank, 1967, Double Trouble, 1967, Leo the Last, 1970 (Best Dir. award Cannes Film Festival, Belgrade Film Festival), The Strawberry Statement, 1970 (Jury prize Cannes Film Festival), The Split, 1968, Breakout, 1975, Believe in Me, 1972, The Gang That Couldn't Shoot Straight, 1971, The Mechanic, 1972, Busting, 1974, S.P.Y.S. 1974, Peeper, 1975, New York, New York, 1977, Valentino, 1977, Uncle Joe Shannon, 1978, Comes a Horseman, 1978, Rocky II, 1979, Raging Bull, 1980 (8 Acad. award nominations, winner 2, Los Angeles Film Critics award for best picture), Rocky III, 1981, True Confessions, 1981, Author, Author, 1982,

The Right Stuff, 1983 (8 Acad. award nominations), Rocky IV, 1984, Revolution, 1985, 'Round Midnight, 1986 (2 Acad. award nomiations, Acad. award Best Original Score), Betrayed, 1988 (Chgo. Film Festival Lifetime Irwin Achievement award 1987), Goodfellas, 1990 (6 Acad. award nominations, winner 1, Brit. Acad. award Best Picture, N.Y. Film Critics Best Picture, L.A. Film Critics Best Picture), Rocky V, 1990, Music Box, 1990 (Golden Bear award for best film Berlin Film Festival); writer/dir.: Guilty by Suspicion, 1991 (U.S. selection Cannes Film Festival); producer/dir.: Night and the City, 1992 (N.Y. Film Festival, London Film Festival), The Net, 1995; retrospectives Brit. Film Inst., 1989, Chgo. Film Festival, 1989, Mus. Modern Art, N.Y.C., 1990, L.A. County Mus. Art, 1992. Served with U.S. Army, 1951-53. Named Commander d'Artes et de Lettres, French Govt. Minister of Culture, 1985. Mem. Am. Film Inst. (bd. govs.), Prodrs. Guild Am. (bd. dirs.). Office: Winkler Films 211 S Beverly Dr #200 Beverly Hills CA 90212 Office: CAA 9830 Wilshire Blvd Beverly Hills CA 90212*

WINKLER, JAMES B., health care consultant; b. Jersey City, N.J., Dec. 26, 1945; m. Mary Ann DiMola; children: James C., Craig M., Jessica, Kaitlin. AA, Harriman Coll., 1976; BSN, Hunter Coll., 1978; MSN, Columbia U., 1981. RN, Fla., Tex.; cert. infection control practitioner. Firefighter City of N.Y., 1969-78; head nurse, staff nurse, float nurse N.Y. Hosp., N.Y.C., 1977-80; asst. grant adminstr., clin. instr. in nursing Mount St. Mary Coll., Newburgh, N.Y., 1980-81; cons., dir. nurses Nat. Med. Enterprises, Santa Monica, Calif., 1981-82; chief of nursing Shriners Burns Inst., Galveston, Tex., 1982-87; v.p. for nursing Univ. Med. Ctr., Jacksonville, Fla., 1987-91; assoc. prof., asst. dean for clin. affairs U. Fla. Coll. of Nursing, 1987-91; health care cons. Matrix Group, Jacksonville, Fla., 1991—; presenter in field. Contbr. chpts. to books and articles to profl. jours; mem. editorial bd. Critical Care Quar., 1983—. Active Dem. Com. Town of Warwick, N.Y., 1978, Bd. Edn. Greenwood Lake Union-Free Sch. Dist., 1977. Named Boss of Yr. Am. Bus. Women's Assn., 1985. Mem. NLN, Am. Orgn. Nurse Execs., Fla. Orgn. Nurse Execs. (exec. bd.), N.E. Fla. Orgn. Nurse Execs. Home: 9718 Whitley Park Pl Bethesda MD 20814

WINKLER, JOSEPH CONRAD, former recreational products manufacturing executive; b. Newark, May 20, 1916; s. Charles and Mollie (Abrams) W.; m. Geraldine M. Borok, Sept. 20, 1953; children: Charles H., David J. B.S., NYU, 1941. Gen. mgr. Ideal. Washing Machine Corp., New Brunswick, N.J., 1941-48; controller Mojud Corp., N.Y.C., 1948-52; controller, asst. treas. Barbizon Corp., N.Y.C., 1952-57; controller Ideal Toy Corp., N.Y.C., 1957-58; dir. fin. and adminstrn. Ideal Toy Corp., 1960-62, v.p. fin., 1962-68, sr. v.p. fin., 1968-78, exec. v.p., chief operating officer, dir., 1978-81, pres., dir., 1981-83; exec. in residence, mem. bus. adv. coun. Sch. Bus. Adminstrn., Montclair (N.J.) State U., 1983-90; controller McGregor-Doniger, Inc., N.Y.C., 1958-59; dir. Ideal of Australia Ltd., Melbourne, 1963-82, Ideal of Canada Ltd., Toronto, 1963-82, Ideal of Japan Ltd., Tokyo and Kiowa, 1963-80, Ideal Toy Co. Ltd., High Wycombe and Wokingham, Eng., 1966-82, Arxon Spiel & Freizeit GmbH, Rotgau, Germany, 1968-82, Perfekta Ltd. and Hollis Industries Ltd., Hong Kong, 1970-74, Ideal Loisirs S.A., Paris, 1972-82. Mem. editorial rev. bd. Issues in Internat. Bus., 1985—. Committeeman, troop treas. Boy Scouts Am., Tenafly, N.J., 1965-71; bd. dirs. N.Y. League Hard of Hearing, 1982-88; active Nat. Roster Sci. and Splized. Pers., War Manpower Commn., 1941-46. Served with Office Statis. Control USAAF, 1945. Mem. Fin. Execs. Inst. Home: 3546 S Ocean Blvd Apt 605 Palm Beach FL 33480-5720

WINKLER, LEE B., business consultant; b. Buffalo, Dec. 31, 1925; s. Jack W. and Caroline (Marienthal) W.; children: James, Cristina Ehrlich, Richard Ehrlich Jr.; m. Maria Mal Verde. B.S. cum laude, NYU, 1945, M.S. cum laude, 1947. Mgr. LBW, Inc. (formerly Winkler Assocs. Ltd.), N.Y.C., 1948-58; pres. Winkler Assocs. Ltd., Beverly Hills, Calif., and N.Y.C., 1958—; exec. dir. Global Bus. Mgmt. Inc., Beverly Hills, 1967—; v.p. Bayly Martin & Fay Inc., N.Y.C., 1965-68, John C. Paige & Co., N.Y.C., 1968-71; cons. Albert G. Ruben Co., Beverly Hills, 1971—. Served with AUS, 1943-45. Decorated chevalier comdr. Order Holy Cross Jerusalem, also spl. exec. asst., charge d'affaires, 1970; chevalier comdr. Sovereign Order Cyprus, 1970. Mem. Nat. Acad. TV Arts and Scis., Nat. Acad. Recording Arts and Scis., Beverly Hills C. of C., Phi Beta Kappa, Beta Gamma Sigma, Mu Gamma Tau, Psi Chi Omega. Office: 15250 Ventura Blvd Sherman Oaks CA 91403 *In the final analysis, the bottom line, if you will—the only thing that truly matters in life are those friends and family that hold you dear to them. Success, and its attendant monies, rise and fall like the tides, and even vanish at times, but earned love is as constant as the earth's rotation is independent of the tides.*

WINKLER, PAUL FRANK, JR., astrophysicist, educator; b. Nashville, Nov. 10, 1942; s. Paul Frank and Estelle (Pye) W.; m. Janet Pippitt Beers, June 25, 1983; children—Katharine Estelle, Johanna Pye; stepchildren—Sarah Creighton Beers, Nathan Pippitt Beers. B.S., Calif. Inst. Tech., 1964; A.M., Harvard U., 1965, Ph.D., 1970. From instr. to prof. physics Middlebury Coll., Vt., 1969—, chmn. dept., 1980-88, William R. Kenan Jr. prof. physics, 1984-87, chmn. nat. scis. div., 1988-93, asst. to pres. for sci. planning, 1993—; vis. scientist MIT, Cambridge, 1973-74, 78-80; sr. vis. fellow Inst. Astronomy U. Cambridge, 1985-86; vis. resident astronomer Cerro Tololo InterAm. Observatory, La Serena, Chile, 1990-91; vis. fellow Joint Inst. for Laboratory Astrophysics, U. Colo., Boulder, 1991. Contbr. articles to profl. jours. NSF fellow, 1965-69, Alfred P. Sloan Found. fellow, 1976-80. Mem. Am. Phys. Soc., Am. Astron. Soc., Internat. Astron. Union, Coun. on Undergraduate Rsch. Office: Middlebury Coll Dept Physics Middlebury VT 05753

WINKLER, ROBERT LEWIS, statistics educator, researcher, author, consultant; b. Chgo., Feb. 12, 1943; s. Roy Henry and Catherine Pauline (Fleming) W.; m. Dorothy Marie Hespen, June 13, 1964; children: Kevin Mark, Kristin Lynne. B.S., U. Ill., 1963; Ph.D., U. Chgo., 1966. Asst. prof. Ind. U., Bloomington, 1966-69, assoc. prof., 1969-72, prof., 1972-80, Disting. prof. quantitative bus. analysis, 1980-84; vis. assoc. prof. U. Wash., Seattle, 1970-71; vis. scientist Nat. Ctr. Atmospheric Rsch., Boulder, Colo., 1972; rsch. scientist internat. Inst. Applied Systems Analysis, Laxenburg, Austria, 1973-74; vis. prof. Stanford U., 1974, Institut Européen d'Administration des Affaires, Fontainebleau, France, 1980-81, 90-91; IBM rsch. prof. Duke U., 1984-85, Calvin Bryce Hoover prof., 1985-89, James B. Duke prof., 1989—, sr. assoc. dean for faculty and rsch., 1991—; cons. in field, 1970—. Author: Statistics, 1970, Introduction to Bayesian Inference and Decision, 1972; contbr. numerous articles to profl. jours.; departmental editor Mgmt. Sci., 1981-89; assoc. editor 7 profl. jours., 1970—. Fellow Am. Inst. Decision Scis., Am. Statis. Assn.; mem. Inst. Mgmt. Sci. (v.p. publs. 1982-85), Internat. Inst. Forecasters (pres. 1989-90). Home: 225 Huntington Dr Chapel Hill NC 27514-2419 Office: Duke U Dept Mgmt Durham NC 27708-0120

WINKLER, SHELDON, dentist, educator; b. N.Y.C., Jan. 25, 1932; s. Ben and Lillian (Barsh) W.; m. Sandra M. Cohen, Aug. 13, 1961; children: Mitchell, Lori. BA, Washington Sq. Coll., 1953; DDS, NYU, 1956. Asst. prof. denture prosthesis NYU Coll. Dentistry, N.Y.C., 1958-61, 66-68, rsch. asst. prof., 1962-63; dir. materials rsch. Consol. Metal Products Industries Inc., Albany, N.Y., 1963-65, cons. materials rsch., 1966-68; asst. prof. removable prosthodontics sch. dentistry SUNY, Buffalo, 1968-70; assoc. prof. SUNY, 1970-79; prof., chmn. dept. prosthodontics Temple U. Sch. Dentistry, Phila., 1979-86, 94—, asst. dean for advanced studies, continuing edn./rsch., 1987-89, acting asst. dean, 1993—; asst. dir., vis. dentist, dental dept. N.Y. U. Med. Center, Goldwater Meml. Hosp., N.Y.C., 1966-89; attending in prosthodontics E.J. Meyer Meml. Hosp., Buffalo, 1975-79; postgrad. instr. First Dist. Dental Soc. N.Y., N.Y.C., 1963—; cons. Coe Labs., Chgo., 1967-87, Harkness Center, Buffalo, Rosa Coplon Home and Infirmary, Buffalo, 1970-79, Erie Community Coll., Buffalo, 1979—, Lever Bros. Co., N.Y.C., 1981—, VA Hosp., Phila., 1989—; lectr. dept. dental hygiene N.Y.C. Community Coll., 1967-68. Author: (with A. Davidoff and M.H.M. Lee) Dentistry for the Special Patient: The Aged, Chronically Ill and Handicapped, 1972, Essentials of Complete Denture Prosthodontics, 1979, 2d edit., 1988; editor: Resins in Dentistry, 1975, Complete Dentures, 1977, Removable Prosthodontics, 1984; editor Jour. Implant Dentistry, 1990—; contbr. articles to profl. lit.; co-designer McGowan-Winkler complete denture trays. Served as capt. AUS, 1956-58, 61-62. Recipient Outstanding Layman award Vocat. Tech. Alumni and Student Assn., SUNY, Buffalo, 1974, Internat. Edn. award Internat. Congress Oral Implantologists, 1992, journalism award Internat. Coll. Dentists, 1993. Fellow Am. Coll.

Dentists, Greater N.Y. Acad. Prosthodontics; mem. ADA, Internat. Assn. Dental Rsch., Am. Assn. Dental Schs., Am. Acad. Implant Prosthodontics, Sci. Rsch. Soc. Am., Acad. Plastics Rsch., Am. Prosthodontic Soc., Am. Soc. Geriatric Dentistry, Internat. Congress of Oral Implantologists, Sigma Xi, Sigma Epsilon Delta, Omicron Kappa Upsilon. Home: 1224 Liberty Bell Dr Cherry Hill NJ 08003-2759 Office: Sch Dentistry Temple U Philadelphia PA 19140

WINKS, ROBIN WILLIAM, history educator; b. West Lafayette, Ind., Dec. 5, 1930; s. Evert McKinley and Jewell (Sampson) W.; m. Avril Flockton, Sept. 27, 1952; children: Honor Leigh, Eliot Myles. BA magna cum laude, U. Colo., 1952, MA, 1953; PhD with distinction, Johns Hopkins U., 1957; MA (hon.), Yale U., 1967; DLitt (hon.), U. Nebr., 1976, U. Colo., 1987; MA (hon.), Oxford U., 1992; Westminster Coll., 1995. From instr. to Randolph W. Townsend prof. history Yale U., New Haven, 1957—; dir. office of spl. projects and founds., 1974-76, master Berkeley Coll., 1977-90; Eastman prof. Oxford U., 1992-93, chair studies in environment, 1993—. Author: Canada and the U.S., 1960, The Cold War, 1964, Historiography of the British Empire-Commonwealth, 1966, History of Malaysia, 1967, Age of Imperialism, 1969, Pastmasters, 1969; The Historian as Detective, 1969, A Forty-Year Minuet, 1970, The Blacks in Canada, 1971, Slavery, 1972, An American's Guide to Britain, 1977, Other Voices, Other Views, 1978, Relevance of Canadian History, 1979, Western Civilization, 1979, Detective Fiction, 1980, Modus Operandi, 1982, History of Civilization, 1984, Cloak and Gown, 1987, Asia in Western Fiction, 1990, Frederick Billings, 1991, The Imperial Revolution, 1994. Cultural attache U.S. Embassy, London, 1969-71; chair Nat. Park System Adv. Bd., Washington, 1981-83, bicentennial com. for internat. Confs. of Americanists Dept. State, 1974-77. Smithsonian Mundt prof. U. Malaya, 1962; Inst. Commonwealth Studies at U. London fellow, 1966-67; Guggenheim fellow, 1976-77; grantee Social Sci. Rsch. Coun., 1959, 75; Resident scholar Sch. Am. Rsch., 1985, 91, 94. Fellow Royal Hist. Soc., Explorers Club; mem. Am. Hist. Assn., Can. Hist. Assn., Royal Commonwealth Soc. (life), Yale Club (N.Y.C.), Athenaeum, Spl. Forces Club. Office: Yale U Dept History PO Box 1504 A New Haven CT 06506-1504

WINN, ALBERT CURRY, clergyman; b. Ocala, Fla., Aug. 16, 1921; s. James Anderson and Elizabeth (Curry) W.; m. Grace Neely Walker, Aug. 29, 1944; children: Grace Walker (Mrs. Stewart E. Ellis), James Anderson, Albert Bruce Curry, Randolph Axson. A.B., Davidson Coll., 1942, LL.D., 1968; B.D., Union Theol. Sem., Va., 1945, Th.D., 1956; Th.M., Princeton Theol. Sem., 1949; LL.D., Stillman Coll., 1975. Ordained to ministry Presbyn. Ch., 1945; asst. prof. Davidson Coll., 1946-47; pastor Potomac Rural Parish, Va., 1948-53; prof. Bible Stillman Coll., 1953-60; prof. theology Louisville Presbyn. Theol. Sem., 1960-73, pres., 1966-73; pastor 2d Presbyn. Ch., Richmond, Va., 1974-81, N. Decatur Presbyn. Ch., Decatur, Ga., 1981-86; Moderator Presbyn. Synod Ala., 1958, Presbyn. Synod Ky., 1969, Gen. Assembly, Presbyn. Ch. U.S., 1979; vis. prof. Union Theol. Sem. in Va., 1987, Columbia Theol. Sem., 1987, Louisville Presbyn. Theol. Sem., 1988; interim pastor Cen. Presbyn. Ch., Atlanta, 1989-90, St. Andrews Presbyn. Ch., Tucker, Ga., 1993-94. Author: Layman's Bible Commentary on Acts, 1960, The Worry and Wonder of Being Human, 1966, Where Do I Go From Here, 1972, Proclamation Two: Epiphany, 1980, A Sense of Mission, 1981, Christ the Peacemaker, 1982, Plain Talk about the Apostles' Creed, 1985, The Christian Primer, 1990, Ain't Gonna Study War No More, 1993. Chmn. trustees Stillman Coll., 1965-70. Served as chaplain USNR, 1945-46. Mem. Phi Beta Kappa, Beta Theta Pi, Omicron Delta Kappa. Office: 2425 Harrington Dr Decatur GA 30033-4903

WINN, EDWARD BURTON, lawyer; b. Dallas, Sept. 23, 1920; s. Edward Frost and Verdie Catherine (Robbins) W.; m. Conchita Elisa Hassell, June 1, 1945; children—Edward Arthur, David Burton, William Hassell, Richard Wellington, Alan Randolph. B.A., U. Tex., 1942; LL.B., Yale, 1948. Bar: Tex. bar 1948. Since practiced in Dallas; ptnr. Lane, Savage, Counts & Winn., 1958-81, Winn, Beaudry & Virden, 1981-91, Winn, Beaudry & Winn, L.L.P., 1992—; Pres. Dallas Jr. Bar Assn., 1951, Jr. Bar Tex., 1953, Dallas Estate Council, 1954-55; adv. council Dallas Community Chest Trust Fund, 1965-68; mem. staff armed forces preparedness subcom U.S. Senate, 1951; chmn. Inst. on Wills and Probate, Southwestern Legal Found., 1966—. Coauthor: Texas Estate Administration, How to Live and Die with Texas Probate, 1985; Contbr. articles to profl. jours. Chmn. Dallas County Profl. and Bus. Men for Kennedy-Johnson, 1960; vice chmn. Dallas County Democratic Exec. Com., 1964-66; Bd. dirs. Operation LIFT, 1962-82; trustee Nat. Pollution Control Found., Southwestern Legal Found., 1986—. Served to lt. USNR, 1942-46, ETO. Decorated with the Admirals' Commendations, 1943; recipient William W. Treat award Nat. Coll. Probate Judges, 1985. Fellow Am. Coll. Probate Counsel (pres. 1974-75), Am. Coll. of Trust and Estate Council; mem. ABA (bd. govs. 1985-88, council 1955-84, sect. chmn. 1963-64, sect. real property probate and trust law, bd. of dels. 1965-66, 78-84, 85-90, conf. of sect. and div. dels. 1982-84), Dallas Bar Assn. (dir. 1959-61), Dallas UN Assn. (pres.), UN Assn. of U.S. (gov. 1980-84, dir., pres. Tex. div. 1967-71), State Bar Tex. (chmn. sect. real estate, probate and trust law 1962-63), Am. Bar Found., Tex. Bar Found., Dallas Council World Affairs (pres. young execs. group 1959-60, bd. dirs. 1958-73), Yale Law Sch. Alumni Assn. N. Tex. (pres. 1962-66, regional rep. 1966-72), U. Tex. Ex-Students Assn. Dallas (pres. 1963-64), Dallas Club, Dallas Knife and Fork Club (pres. elect 1994-95, bd. dirs.), Calyx Club, Rotary (Park Cities club, pres. elect 1995—), Phi Kappa Sigma (pres. Sigma chpt. 1941-42), Phi Eta Sigma. Home: 6712 Prestonshire Ln Dallas TX 75225-2712 Office: Winn Beaudry & Winn Thanksgiving Tower 1601 Elm St Ste 4200 Dallas TX 75201-7203

WINN, ELWOOD F., consumer product company executive; b. 1951; married. BS, Wayne State U., 1977; MBA, De Paul U., 1990. With Deloitte, Haskins & Sells, Detroit, 1977-82; divsn. contr. Allied Super Markets, Detroit, 1982-85; sec., treas., CFO Certified Grocers Midwest, Inc., Hodgkins, Ill., 1985—, pres., CEO, 1992—. With USAF, 1970-74. Office: Certified Grocers Midwest Inc 1 Certified Dr Hodgkins IL 60525-4836

WINN, GEORGE MICHAEL, electrical equipment company executive; b. Victoria, Can., 1944. Student U. Wash., 1968. Pres., chief oper. officer, John Fluke Mfg. Co., Everett, Wash., 1988— Office: John Fluke Mfg Co Inc PO Box C9090 6920 Seaway Blvd Everett WA 98203-5829

WINN, HARRY L., food products financial executive; b. Edgerton, Wis., Aug. 11, 1944; s. Harry Lee and Margaret Ann (Dickerson) W.; m. Dorothy M. House, May 24, 1969; children: Amy, Brannon. BBA, U. Wis., 1966; MBA, Northwestern U., 1973. CPA, Ill. 2d v.p. bank investments Am. Nat. Bank, Chgo., 1966-74; mgr. banking Am. Hosp. Supply Corp., Evanston, Ill., 1974-76, dir. banking, 1976-80, treas., 1980-85; v.p., treas. Baxter Travenol Labs. Inc., Deerfield, Ill., 1985-86; v.p., treas. Squibb U.S., Princeton, N.J., 1987-88, v.p., controller, 1988-89; sr. v.p., CFO, mem. strategic issue coun. UtiliCorp United, Kansas City, Mo., 1990-93; mng. sr. v.p. UtiliCorp United Inc., Kansas City, Mo., 1993; exec. v.p., CFO, mem. strategic issue com. Fleming Cos., Inc., Oklahoma City, 1994—; bd. dirs. Aquila Gas Pipeline Corp., San Antonio; chmn. bd. Am. Employees Fed. Credit Union, McGaw Park, Ill., 1982-87. Mem. Bd. Ethics City of Evanston, 1983-87, chmn., 1985-87. Served to sgt. USMCR, 1966-72. Mem. Nat. Assn. Corp. Treasurers, Soc. Internat. Treasurers, Fin. Execs. Inst., Am. Inst. CPAs, Ill. Soc. CPA's. Home: 12304 Kingsbrook Rd Oklahoma City OK 73142

WINN, JAMES JULIUS, JR., lawyer; b. Colon, Panama, Nov. 7, 1941; came to U.S., 1941; s. James Julius and Molly (Brown) W.; m. Elizabeth Kokernot Lacy, Aug. 15, 1970; children: Mary Ann, Elizabeth Lacy, James Julius VI. AB, Princeton U., 1964; JD cum laude, Washington & Lee U., 1970. Bar: Md. 1970, U.S. Dist. Ct. Md. 1971, U.S. Dist. Ct. D.C. 1982. Assoc. Piper & Marbury L.L.P., Balt., 1970-78; ptnr. Piper & Marbury, Balt., 1978—. Assoc. editor, contbr. author Washington & Lee U. Law Rev., 1968-70. Counselor St. John's Ch., Western Run Parish, Glyndon, Md., 1974—; mem. com. on canons and other bus. Episc. Diocese Md., 1986—; dir. Ctr. for Ethics and Corp. Policy, 1988—, chmn., 1991—; dir. Ctr. Stage, 1986—, chmn. fin. com.; dir. Oldfields Sch., 1991—; v.p., dir. Ruxton Country Sch., 1988-91. Mem. ABA (chmn. subcom. on tech. and devel. of com. on devels. in investment svcs., chmn. subcom. on publs., mem. com. on law and acctg. of sect. of bus. law), Md. State Bar Assn. (com. on corp. law of sect. of bus. law). Office: Piper & Marbury LLP 36 S Charles St Baltimore MD 21201-3020

WINN, JULIE, state representative; b. Tucson, Ariz., Sept. 6, 1956; d. George Richard and Mary Kay (Behnke) W. AS, U. Maine, BS, MBA. Home: RR 4 Box 570 Bangor ME 04401-9512 Office: Maine House of Reps State House Augusta ME 04330

WINN, KENNETH HUGH, archivist, historian; b. Seattle, June 27, 1953; s. John Hugh and Elaine (Spoor) W.; m. Karen Anderson, June 13, 1981; children: Alice Anderson, David Dysart. BA, Colo. State U., 1975, MA, 1977; AM, Washington U., 1979, PhD, 1985. Resident historian Mo. Hist. Soc., St. Louis, 1987-90, jour. editor, 1987-91, dir. publications, 1989-91; state archivist Sec. State, Jefferson City, Mo., 1991—; vis. asst. prof. Washington U., St. Louis, 1984-87, adj. asst. prof., 1987-90, adj. prof., 1991—; cons. St. Louis Art Mus., 1989-90; dep. coord. Mo. Hist. Records adv. bd., 1991—; adv. bd. Mo. Ctr. for Book, 1993—; bd. dirs. Mo. Conf. History, 1991—, pres. 94-95. Author: Exiles in a Land of Liberty, 1989; co-author Differing Visions, 1994; contbr. chpt. to ency. Charlotte W. Newcombe fellow Woodrow Wilson Found., 1981-82; grantee Richard S. Brownlee Fund, 1992-93, 93-94. Mem. Nat. Assn. Govt. Archives and Records Adminstrs., Am. Hist. Assn., Orgn. Am. Historians, Coun. State Hist. Records Coords., Soc. Historians Early Am. Republic. Home: 814 Primrose Ln Jefferson City MO 65109-1888 Office: Mo State Archives 600 W Main St Jefferson City MO 65101-1532

WINN, OTIS HOWARD, English educator; b. Poughkeepsie, N.Y., June 28, 1925; s. Arthur Howard and Ruth Martina (Collins) W.; children: Martin, Bruce, Katherine, Martha. BA, Vassar Coll., 1950; MA, Stanford U., 1953; postgrad., U. Calif., San Francisco, 1955, NYU, 1960, 64. Tchr. Petaluma (Calif) Sch. Dist., 1955-58; prof. Eng., dept. head Dutchess Community Coll., Poughkeepsie. Author: Four Picture Sequence, 1978, Bridges, 1988. Council mem. Dutchess County Arts Council, Poughkeepsie, 1984. Newhouse Honors fellow Stanford U., Palo Alto, 1952-53. Mem. Nat. Council Tchrs. English, Council Writing Adminstrs., MLA, Assn. Chairpersons English Depts. Avocation: photography, hiking. Home: 22 Sheldon Dr # A Poughkeepsie NY 12603-4818 Office: Dutchess Community Coll 53 Pendell Rd Poughkeepsie NY 12601

WINN, PAUL T., electronics executive; b. 1944. With IBM, Stamford, Conn.; pres., CEO, dir. Genicom Corp., Chantilly, Va., 1990. Office: Genicom Corp 14800 Conference Ctr Chantilly VA 22021*

WINN, STEVEN JAY, critic; b. Phila., Apr. 25, 1951; s. Willis Jay and Lois (Gengelbach) W.; m. Katharine Weber, Sept. 15, 1979 (div. Dec. 1985); m. Sally Ann Noble, July 22, 1989; 1 child, Phoebe Ann. BA, U. Pa., 1973; MA, U. Wash., 1975. Staff writer, editor Seattle Weekly, 1975-79; staff critic San Francisco Chronicle, 1980—. Co-author: Ted Bundy: The Killer Next Door, 1980; contbr. articles to various publs. Wallace Stegner fellow Stanford U., 1979-80. Office: San Francisco Chronicle 901 Mission St San Francisco CA 94103-2905

WINNEFELD, JAMES ALEXANDER, defense analyst, former naval officer, author; b. Paterson, N.J., Jan. 1, 1929; s. Carl Herbert and Helen Dorothy (Rienecker) W.; m. Fredda Coupland, Mar. 15, 1952; children: Lea Winnefeld Sandman, James Alexander. Student, Drew U., 1946-47; B.S., U.S. Naval Acad., 1951; M.A. in Internat. Affairs, Stanford U., 1960. Commd. ensign U.S. Navy, 1951, advanced through grades to rear adm., 1977; ops. officer for comdr. Carrier Div. Six, 1971-72; exec. asst. and sr. aide to Chief Naval Personnel, 1972-74; comdg. officer U.S.S. Trenton, 1974-75; comdr. Amphibious Squadron Two, 1975-76; comdt. of midshipmen U.S. Naval Acad., 1976-78; dir. Office Chief Naval Ops Total Force Programming div., from 1978, ret.; now def. analyst Rand Corp., Washington. Contbr. articles to jours. Decorated Bronze medal with Combat V, Legion of Merit, Meritorious Service medal (3), Air medal (2), Navy Commendation medal (2). Mem. U.S. Naval Inst. Presbyterian. Clubs: Naval Acad. Sailing Assn, Athletic Assn, Ends of Earth. Office: Rand Corp 2100 M St NW Washington DC 20037-1207

WINNER, KARIN, newspaper editor. Editor San Diego Union-Tribune. Office: Copley Press Inc 350 Camino De La Reina San Diego CA 92108-3003

WINNER, LESLIE JANE, state legislator, lawyer; b. Asheville, N.C., Oct. 24, 1950; d. Harry and Julienne (Marder) W.; m. Kenneth L. Schorr, Dec. 20, 1987. AB, Brown U., 1972; JD, Northeastern U., Boston, 1976. Bar: N.C. 1976, U.S. Dist. Ct. (we. dist.) N.C. 1976, U.S. Ct. Appeals (4th cir.) 1976, U.S. Dist. Ct. (ea. and mid. dists.) 1981, U.S. Supreme Ct. 1985. Clk. to presiding judge U.S. Dist. Ct., Charlotte, N.C., 1976-77; mng. atty. Legal Services of So. Piedmont, Charlotte, 1977-81; ptnr. Ferguson, Stein, Watt, Wallas, Adkins and Gresham, P.A., Charlotte, 1981-92; mem. N.C. Senate, Raleigh, 1993—. Pres. N.C. Women's Employment Law Ctr., 1989-90; past chmn. Mecklenburg County Dispute Resolution Ctr., Charlotte, 1985-86; coun. mem. So. Regional Coun., Atlanta, 1989—; trustee Temple Israel, Charlotte, 1980-81; pres. Elizabeth Community Assn., Charlotte, 1980-81. Mem. U.S. Ct. Appeals (4th cir.) Advr. Com. (N.C. rep. 1989—), N.C. Assn. Women Attys. (pres. 1982-83, pub. service award 1985), N.C. Acad. Trial Lawyers (legis. com.), N.C. Bar Assn. (litigation sect. coun.), Mecklenburg County Bar Assn. (grievance com.). Democrat. Jewish. Avocations: hiking, jogging, cooking. Office: NC Senate Legis Office Bldg Rm 409 Raleigh NC 27611-2808

WINNER, MICHAEL ROBERT, film director, writer, producer; b. London, Oct. 30, 1935; s. George Joseph and Helen (Zloty) W. Degree in law and econs. with honors, Cambridge (Eng.) U., 1956. Writer Fleet St. (newspapers), London, 1956-58; columnist London Sunday Times, 1990—, London News of the World, 1995—. Engaged in film prodn., 1956—; dir. films Play it Cool, 1962, West 11, 1963, The Mechanic, 1972, Death Wish II, 1981; dir. writer The Cool Mikado, 1962, You Must be Joking, 1965, The Wicked Lady, 1982; producer, dir. The System, 1963, I'll Never Forget What's 'isname, 1967, The Games, 1969, Lawman, 1970, The Nightcomers, 1971, Chato's Land, 1971, Scorpio, 1972, The Stone Killer, 1973, Death Wish, 1974, Won Ton Ton The Dog Who Saved Hollywood, 1975, Firepower, 1978, Scream for Help, 1983, Death Wish III, 1985; producer, writer, dir. films The Jokers, 1966, Hannibal Brooks, 1968, The Sentinel, 1976, The Big Sleep, 1977, Appointment With Death, 1987, A Chorus of Disapproval, 1988, Bullseye!, 1989, Dirty Weekend, 1992; producer plays Nights at the Comedy, Comedy Theatre, London, 1960, The Silence of St. Just, Gardner Centre, Brighton, 1971, The Tempest, Wyndhams Theatre, London, 1974, A Day in Hollywood, A Night in the Ukraine, Mayfair Theatre, London, 1978, (TV series London Weekend TV) Michael Winner's True Crimes, 1990, 91, 92, 93, 94. Founder, chmn. Police Meml. Trust, 1984. Mem. Dirs. Guild Gt. Britain (coun., trustee, chief censorship officer 1983). Office: Scimitar Films Ltd, 6-8 Sackville St, London W1X 1DD, England

WINNER, THOMAS G., foreign literature educator; b. Prague, Czechoslovakia, May 4, 1917; came to U.S., 1939, naturalized, 1950; s. Julius and Franziska (Grünhutová) Wiener; m. Irene Portis, Sept. 25, 1942; children: Ellen, Lucy Franziska. Student, Charles U., Prague, 1936-38, U. Lille, France, 1936; B.A., Harvard U., 1942, M.A., 1943; Ph.D., Columbia U., 1950; M.A. (hon.), Brown U., 1966; PhD (hon.), Masaryk U., 1995. With OWI, 1943-46; vis. fellow Johns Hopkins, 1947-48; from instr. Russian to asso. prof. Duke, 1948-58; asso. prof., then prof. Slavic langs. and lits. U. Mich., 1958-65; prof. Slavic langs. and comparative lit. Brown U., 1965-82, chmn. dept. Slavic langs., 1968-72, prof. emeritus, 1982—; dir. Center for Research in Semiotics, 1977-83; dir. Program in Semiotic Studies Boston U., 1984—; Fulbright lectr. Sorbonne, Paris, 1956-57, Ruhr Univ., Bochum, Fed. Republic Germany, 1989; exchange prof. U. Warsaw, 1972-73, U. Zagreb, spring 1973; mem. seminar theory lit. Columbia, 1968—. Author: Oral Art and Literature of the Kazakhs of Russian Central Asia, 1958, Chekhov and his Prose, 1965; editor: Brown U. Slavic Reprints; editor Am. Jour. Semiotics, 1980-85; spl. interests Russian lit., Czech lit., semiotics and poetics. Ford Found. sr. fellow, 1951-52, NEH sr. fellow, 1972, 92-93; Rockefeller grantee, 1977, IREX grantee, 1972, 78, 79, 90, 92, Fulbright-Hayes, 1973. Mem. MLA, Am. Com. Slavists, Internat. Assn. for Semiotic Studies, Semi-

otics Soc. Am. (pres. 1977-78), Czech Semiotic Soc. (hon.), Czechoslovak Soc. for Arts and Scis. (v.p. 1982-85), Am. Assn. Tchrs. Slavic and East European Langs., Comparative Lit. Assn., Internat. Assn. Slavists, Am. Assn. Advancement of Slavic Studies, Karel Teige Soc. (Czech Republic), F.X. Salda Soc. (Czech Republic). Address: 986 Memorial Dr Apt 404 Cambridge MA 02138

WINNERMAN, ROBERT HENRY, home building company executive; b. Newark, Mar. 25, 1921; s. Henry W. and Katherine (Richter) W.; children: Lawrence J., Sanford B., Henry W.; m. Lilli Burg Winnerman. Student, U. Md., 1940-41, Rutgers U., 1945-48. Founder U.S. Home Corp., N.Y.C., 1954—, chmn. bd. dirs.; founder Internat. Am. Co., 1980, Internat. Am. Homes, 1983. Lt. col. USAAF. Mem. Builders Assn. of Metro N.J., Nat. Assn. Home Builders, Cedar Hill, Town Club Found., High Ridge. Jewish. Avocations: golf, reading, philanthropy. Home: 2000 S Ocean Blvd Apt 402S Palm Beach FL 33480-5214 Office: Internat Am Co 412 Harrison Ave Harrison NJ 07029-1741

WINNIE, ALON PALM, anesthesiologist, educator; b. Milw., May 16, 1932; s. Russell Griffith and Evelyn Dorothy (Olson) W.; m. June Patton Bethune, July 16, 1960; children: Alon Palm, Russell, Debra. B.A., Princeton U., 1954; M.D., Northwestern U., 1958. Diplomate Am. Bd. Anesthesiology. Mem. teaching staff Cook County Hosp., Chgo., 1963-72; assoc. dir. anesthesia Cook County Hosp., 1968-72; prof. anesthesiology, head dept. U. Ill. Coll. Medicine, 1972-89; dir. Pain Control Ctr., U. Ill. Hosp., Chgo., 1989-92; chmn. dept. anesthesiology & critical care Cook County Hosp., Chgo., 1992—. Author: Plexus Anesthesia (Book of Yr. award Anesthesia Found. 1983). Served as 1st lt. M.C. USAF. Recipient Humanitarian award Mil. Soc. Anesthesiologists, 1980, Gillespie award Faculty of Anesthetists of Royal Australasian Coll. Surgery, 1986, Nils Lofgren award Astra Pharmm. Products inc., 1987. Fellow Am. Coll. Anesthesiologists, Royal Australasian Coll. Surgeons (faculty anaesthetists sect.), Coll. Anaesthetists of Royal Coll. Surgeons of Eng. (faculty anaesthetists sect.); mem. AMA, Am. Soc. Regional Anesthesia (pres. 1976-80, Gaston Labat award 1982), Am. Soc. Anesthesiologists, Ill. Soc. Anesthesiologists (pres. 1971-72, Disting. Svc. award 1974, McQuiston award, 1983), Ill. Med. Soc., Chgo. Soc. Anesthesiologists (pres. 1968-74). Republican. Episcopalian. Office: 1835 W Harrison St Chicago IL 60612-3701

WINNINGHOFF, ALBERT C. M., advertising company executive. Vice chmn. Leo Burnett Co., Inc., Chgo. Office: Leo Burnett Co Inc 35 W Wacker Dr Chicago IL 60601

WINNOWSKI, THADDEUS RICHARD (TED WINNOWSKI), bank executive; b. Albany, N.Y., Feb. 20, 1942; s. Thaddeus Walter and Harriet Frances (Witko) W.; m. Sheila Margaret Neary, June 15, 1968; children: Dona, Paul. BS in Econs., Siena Coll., 1963. Adminstrv. v.p. Key Bank N.A., Albany, 1978-80; pres. Key Bank L.I., Sayville, N.Y., 1980-85; pres., CEO Key Bank of Oreg., Woodburn, 1985-86, chmn., CEO, Portland, 1986—. Bd. dirs. Blue Cross/Blue Shield Oreg; bd. regents U. Portland, Oreg. 1st lt. U.S. Army, 1964-66. Mem. Oreg. SBA (mem. adv. coun.), Oreg. Bankers Assn. (mem. exec. coun.), Portland Met. C. of C. (chmn. elect.). Roman Catholic. Home: 11333 SW Northgate Ct Portland OR 97219-8328

WINOGRAD, AUDREY LESSER, advertising executive; b. N.Y.C., Oct. 6, 1933; d. Jack J. and Theresa Lorraine (Elkind) Lesser; m. Melvin H. Winograd, Apr. 29, 1956; 1 child, Hope Elise. BA, U. Conn., 1953. Asst. advt. mgr. T. Baumritter Co., Inc., N.Y.C., 1953-54; asst. dir. pub. rels. and creative merchandising Kirby, Block & Co., Inc., N.Y.C., 1954-56; divsn. mdse. mgr., dir. advt. and sales promotion Winograd's Dept. Store, Inc., Point Pleasant, N.J., 1956-73, v.p., 1960-73, exec. v.p., 1973-86; pres. AMW Assocs., Ocean Twp., N.J., 1976—. Editor bus. newsletters. Bd. dirs. Temple Beth Am, Lakewood, N.J., 1970-72. Mem. NAFE, Jersey Pub. Rels. and Advt. Assn. (past pres., bd. dirs.), Retail Advt. and Mktg. Assn. Internat., Monmouth Ocean Devel. Coun., Monmouth County Bus. Assn. (bd. dirs. 1985—, pres. 1988-90, woman of yr. 1992-93), N.J. Assn. Women Bus. Owners, Am. Soc. Advt. and Promotion, Ocean C. of C. (bd. dirs. 1994—, award 1993, 94), Retail Advt. Conf., Soc. Prevention Cruelty to Animals, Animal Protection Inst. Am., Human Soc., United Animal Nation U.S., Internat. Fund Animal Welfare, World Wildlife Fund, Friends of Animals, Animal Protection Inst., Defenders of Wildlife, Nat. Humane Edn. Soc. Avocations: collecting animal paintings, figurines, gourmet cooking, skiing, exercise. Office: AMW Assocs 10 Pine Ln Ocean NJ 07712-7242

WINOGRAD, BERNARD, financial adviser; b. Detroit, Dec. 31, 1950; s. Daniel and Lillian (Walder) W.; m. Carol Leslie Snodgrass, Mar. 8, 1974; children: Simon James Bartholomew, Christina Lynn. B.A., U. Chgo., 1970. Pub. affairs mgr. Bendix Corp., Southfield, Mich., 1975; exec. asst. to W.M. Blumenthal, 1975-77, dir. corp. communications, 1977-79, treas., 1979-83; exec. v.p. Taubman Investments, 1983-84; pres. Taubman Investment Co., 1984—; exec. asst. to W. Michael Blumenthal, U.S. Sec. Treasury, Washington, 1977. Mem. Fin. Mgmt. Assn., Fin. Execs. Inst., Econ. Club of Detroit. Home: 841 N Glengarry Rd Bloomfield Hills MI 48301-2227 Office: Taubman Investment Co 200 E Long Lake Rd Bloomfield Hills MI 48304-2314

WINOGRAD, NICHOLAS, chemist; b. New London, Conn., Dec. 27, 1945; s. Arthur Selig Winograd and Winifred (Schaefer) Winograd Mayes; m. Barbara J. Garrison. BS, Rensselaer Poly. Inst., 1967; PhD, Case Western Reserve U., 1970. Asst. prof. chemistry Purdue U., West Lafayette, Ind., 1970-75, assoc. prof. chemistry, 1975-79; prof. chemistry Pa. State U., University Park, 1979-85, Evan Pugh prof. chemistry, 1985—; cons. Shell Devel. Co., Houston, 1975—; mem. chemistry adv. bd. NSF, Washington, 1987-90, analytical chemistry adv. bd., 1986-89. Contbr. articles to profl. jours. A.P. Sloan Found. fellow, 1974; Guggenheim Found. fellow, 1977; recipient Founder's prize Tex. Instruments Found., 1984, Faculty Scholar's Pa. State U., 1985, Bennedetti Pichler award Am. Microchem. Soc., 1991, Outstanding Alumnus award Case Western Res. U., 1991. Fellow AAAS (Sect. award); mem. Am. Chem. Soc. Home: 415 Nimitz Ave State College PA 16801-6412 Office: Pa State U Dept of Chemistry 152 Davey Lab University Park PA 16802-6300

WINOGRAD, SHMUEL, mathematician; b. Tel Aviv, Jan. 4, 1936; came to U.S., 1956, naturalized, 1965; s. Pinchas Mordechai and Rachel Winograd; m. Elaine Ruth Tates, Jan 5, 1958; children: Daniel H., Sharon A. BSEE, MIT, MSEE; PhD in Math., NYU, 1968. Mem. research staff IBM, Yorktown Heights, N.Y., 1961-70, dir. math. sci. dept., 1970-74, 81-94; IBM fellow, 1972—; permanent vis. prof. Technion, Israel. Author: (with J.D. Cowan) Reliable Computations in the Presence of Noise; research on complexity of computations and algorithms for signal processing. Fellow IEEE (W. Wallace McDowell award 1974), Assn. Computing Machinery, N.Y. Acad. Scis.; mem. NAS, Am. Math. Soc., Math. Assn. Am., Am. Philos. Soc., Soc. Indsl. and Applied Math., Am. Acad. Arts & Scis. Home: 235 Glendale Rd Scarsdale NY 10583-1533 Office: IBM Research PO Box 218 Yorktown Heights NY 10598-0218

WINOGRAD, TERRY ALLEN, computer science educator; b. Takoma Park, Md., Feb. 24, 1946; m. Carol Hutner; children: Shoshana, Avra. BA in Math., Colo. Coll., 1966, DSc (hon.), 1986; postgrad. U. Coll., London, 1967; PhD in Applied Math., MIT, 1970. Instr. math. MIT, 1970-71, asst. prof. elec. engring. 1971-74; vis. asst. prof. computer sci. and linguistics Stanford (Calif.) U., 1973-74, from asst. prof. to assoc. prof., 1974-79, assoc. prof. computer sci., 1979-89; prof. computer scis., 1989—; cons. Xerox Palo Alto (Calif.) Rsch. Ctr., 1972-85, Hermenet Inc., San Francisco, 1981-83, Action Techs., 1983—; lectr. in field; mem. adv. bd. Ctr. for Teaching and Learning Stanford U., 1979-83, mem. acad. coun. com. on info. tech., 1981-83, mem. undergrad. coun. Sch. Engring., 1985—; adviser State of Calif., 1983. Bd. dirs. Live Oak Inst., Berkeley, Calif., 1980—, pres., 1984—. Grantee Advanced Rsch. Project Agys., 1969-75, NSF, 1975-77, 82-85, Xerox, 1975-80, System Devel. Found., 1982-83; Hon. Woodrow Wilson fellow, 1966, Hon. NSF fellow, 1966, 90-93, Fulbright fellow, 1966-67, Danforth fellow, 1967-70, Mellon Jr. Faculty fellow, 1977. Mem. Computer Profls. for Social Responsibility (mem. nat. exec. com. 1983—, mem. nat. bd. dirs. 1984—, pres. 1987-90), Am. Assn. Artificial Intelligence, Union of Concerned Scientists, Assn. for Computing Machinery. Home: 746 Esplanada Way Palo Alto CA 94305-1013 Office: Stanford U Dept Computer Sci Stanford CA 94305-2140

WINOKUR, GEORGE, psychiatrist, educator; b. Phila., Feb. 10, 1925; s. Louis and Vera P. Winokur; m. Betty Stricklin, Sept. 15, 1951; children: Thomas, Kenneth, Patricia. A.B., Johns Hopkins U., 1944; M.D., U. Md. 1947. Intern Church Home and Hosp., Balt., 1947-48; asst. resident Seton Inst., Balt., 1948-50; assoc. in neuropsychiatry Washington U., St. Louis, 1950-51; resident in neuropsychiatry Barnes Hosp., St. Louis, 1950-51; asst. prof. psychiatry Washington U., St. Louis, 1955-59, assoc. prof., 1959-66, prof., 1966-71; assoc. psychiatrist Barnes Hosp., 1963-71; cons. in psychiatry Homer G. Phillips Hosp., 1954-64; instr. psychiatry Meharry Med. Coll., Nashville, 1954-55; prof. U. Iowa, Iowa City, 1971—, head dept. psychiatry, 1971-90; dir. Iowa Psychiat. Hosp. Author: Manic Depressive Illness, 1969, Depression: The Facts, 1981, Mania and Depression, A Classification of Syndrome and Disease, 1991; mng. editor European Archives of Psychiatry and Neurol. Scis.; chief Am. editor Jour. Affective Disorders, 1979—; mem. editorial bd. 8 profl. jours.; contbr. numerous articles on clin. genetics of affective disorders, alcoholism and schizophrenia to profl. jours. Served to capt. M.C. USAF, 1952-54. Recipient Anna-Monika 1st prize award, 1973, Hofheimer prize, 1972, Samuel W. Hamilton award, 1977, Leonard Crammer Meml. award, 1980, Paul Hoch award, 1981, Vol. Svc. award Nat. Coun. Alcoholism, 1974, Achievement award Am. Acad. Clin. Psychiatrists, 1987, Nelson Urban Rsch. award Mental Health Assn., Iowa, 1988, Lifetime Rsch. award Nat. Depressive and Manic Depressive Assn., 1990, Lifetime Achievement award Internat. Soc. Psychiat. Genetics, 1993, Regents award U. Iowa, 1994, Paul Huston award Iowa Psychiat. Soc., 1994, Gold medal Soc. Biol. Psychiatry, 1984, Lapinlahti medal Helsinki Finland Lapinlahti Hosp. Fellow Am. Psychiat. Assn. (life), Royal Coll. Psychiatrists (hon.); mem. Am. Psychopath. Assn. (pres. 1975-77, Joseph Zubin award 1992), Am. Soc. Human Genetics, Am. Physicians (hon.), Internat. Group Study of Affective Disorders, Psychiat. Rsch. Soc., Am. Fedn. Clin. Rsch., Assn. Rsch. in Nervous and Mental Disorders, Am. Coll. Neuropsychopharmacology, Societat Catalana de Psiquiatra, Sigma Xi, Tudor and Stewart Club (Balt.). Office: U Iowa Psychiatry Rsch MEB Iowa City IA 52242-1000

WINOKUR, HERBERT SIMON, JR., transportation company executive; b. Columbus, Ga., Dec. 30, 1943; s. Herbert Simon and Marjorie (Lipman) W.; m. Deanne Howard, Mar. 13, 1971; children: Annick, Andra. A.B. cum laude, Harvard U., 1964, A.M., 1965, Ph.D. in Decision & Control Theory, 1967. Vice pres. Penn. Co., 1976-78; chief exec. officer Pinehurst, Inc., N.C., 1978-80; v.p. Victor Palmieri & Co., Los Angeles, 1978-80; sr. v.p. Pacific Holding Corp., Los Angeles, 1981-83; sr. exec. v.p., dir. Penn Central Corp., Greenwich, Conn., from 1983; co-founder, bd. dirs. Ursa Oil Co.; bd. dirs. U.S. Leasing Internat., Inc., Enron Corp. Bd. advisors UCLA Med. Ctr. Served to capt. U.S. Army, 1967-69. Office: The NY Hist Society 170 Central Park W New York NY 10024-5102 also: Dyncorp 2000 Edmund Halley Dr Reston VA 22091-3400

WINOKUR, ROBERT M., lawyer; b. N.Y.C., Oct. 28, 1924; s. Harry S. and Katherine S. W.; m. Diane R. Kramer, June 21, 1953; children: Hugh R., Andrew S., Douglas B. B.S., CUNY, 1947; S.J.D., Columbia U., 1949. Bar: Calif., N.Y., U.S. Supreme Ct. Sr. partner firm Winokur, Maier & Zang (and predecessors), San Francisco, 1954-85; of counsel Crosby, Heafey, Roach & May, Oakland, 1985—; guest lectr. Hastings Coll. Law, U. Calif., NYU Tax Inst., U. So. Calif. Tax Inst., Practising Law Inst.; mem. adv. group to U.S. Commr. Internal Revenue, 1967-68. Contbr. articles to legal jours. Served to lt. U.S. Army, 1943-46. Decorated Bronze Star. Mem. Am., Calif., San Francisco bar assns., Am. Law Inst., San Francisco Tax and City Club. Democrat. Home: 645 Stockton St Apt 1100 San Francisco CA 94108-2353 Office: 1999 Harrison St Oakland CA 94612-3515

WINSHIP, DANIEL HOLCOMB, medicine educator, university dean; b. Houston, July 4, 1933; m. Winnifred Jeneanne Rowold; children: Charles Dwayne, Nancy Ellen, David Rhoads, Rebecca Susan, Molly Beth. BA, Rice U., 1954; MD, U. Tex., Galveston, 1958. Diplomate Am. Bd. Internal Medicine. Intern in internal medicine Ochsner Found. Hosp., New Orleans, 1958-59; asst. resident U. Utah Coll. Medicine, Salt Lake City, 1969-61; fellow in gastroenterology Yale U. Sch. Medicine, New Haven, 1961-63, rsch. fellow med. ethics, fellow law, sci.-medicine program, 1977; asst. prof., then assoc. prof. medicine Marquette U. Sch. Medicine, Milw., 1963-69; assoc. prof., then prof. U. Mo. Sch. Medicine, Columbia, 1969-84, assoc. dean for VA affairs, 1982-84; prof. U. Kans. Sch. Medicine, Kansas City, 1984-87; assoc. dep. chief med. dir. dept. medicine and surgery VA Ctrl. Office, Washington, 1987-90; prof. medicine, dean Loyola U. Stritch Sch. Medicine, Maywood, Ill., 1990—; gastroenterologist Harry S. Truman Meml. Vets. Hosp., Columbia, 1974-79, chief med. svc., 1979-82, chief staff, 1982-84; chief staff VA Med. Ctr., Kansas City, 1984-86, dir., 1986-87; attending physician Loyola U. Med. Ctr., 1990—, Edward Hines (Ill.) Med. Ctr., 1990—; mem. adv. bd. Greater Chgo. Alliance for Mentally Ill, 1991; pres., bd. dirs. gastroenterology adv. com. VA, 1982-85, chmn. clin. and programs adv. coun., 1988-90; mem. rev. com. Mo. Dept. Mental Health, 1981-82; numerous others. Mem. editl. bd. Clin. Rsch., 1970-73, Annals Clin. Gastroenterology, 1978-83, Gastroenterology: A Weekly Update, 1978-81; assoc. editor Jour. Lab. and Clin. Medicine, 1980-83; contbr. numerous articles and abstracts to med. jours. Bd. dirs. John H. Walters Hospice Ctrl. Mo., 1982-84, chmn., 1983-84. Recipient Outstanding Clin. Tchr. in Medicine award Milwaukee County Hosp. Housestaff, 1964, Golden Apple award Student AMA, 1972, Disting. Svc. medal and award VA, 1990, Ashbel Smith Disting. Alumnus award U. Tex. Med. Br., 1992. Mem. Am. Gastroent. Assn. (com. on rsch. 1975-78, com. on tng. and edn. 1978-81, dir. clin. tchg. project 1990-82, program chmn. motility sect. 1987), Gastroenterology Rsch. Group, Ctrl. Soc. for Clin. Rsch., So. Soc. for Clin. Investigation, Am. Fedn. for Clin. Rsch., Midwest Gut Club (presiding pres. 1980-83), Soc. for Health and Human Values, Inst. Society, Ethics and Life Scis., Sigma Xi, Alpha Omega Alpha (vis. prof. U. Mo. Sch. Medicine 1991, Med. Coll. Wis. 1993). Office: Loyola U Med Ctr 2160 S 1st Ave Maywood IL 60153-3304

WINSHIP, FREDERICK MOERY, journalist; b. Franklin, Ohio, Sept. 24, 1924; s. Wilbur William and Edna B. (Moery) W.; m. Joanne Tree Thompson, Aug. 29, 1967. A.B., DePauw U., 1945; M.S., Columbia, 1946. Corr. UPI, 1946—; assigned UN, 1947-49; editorial staff N.Y.C., 1950-60, cultural affairs editor, 1960-72, sr. editor, 1972-75, asst. mng. editor, 1975-80; sr. editor arts/theater N.Y.C., 1980—; Broadway critic, 1985—. Contbr. articles mags. Pres. Letters Abroad, Inc., 1962-83; chmn. Easter Seal Soc. N.Y.C., 1964-73, Governor Assoc. N.Y., 1965-75, N.Y. Conf. Patriotic Socs., 1967-72; Bd. dirs. Odell House-Rochambeau Hdgrs., 1965-75, N.Y. State Easter Seal Soc., 1969-72, Mus. of City of N.Y., 1974—, Am. Philharm. Orch., 1981-82, Friends of the Am. Theater Wing, 1990—. Recipient Am. Legion Journalism award, 1955; Whitelaw Reid Journalism fellow india, 1958; Creative Club Journalism award, 1962. Mem. S.A.R. (sec. N.Y. chpt. 1963-68), St. Nicholas, Founders and Patriots, Mayflower Descs., Soc. Colonial Wars (bd. dirs.), S.R., Soc. Cincinnati, Sigma Delta Chi. Republican. Episcopalian. Home: 417 Park Ave New York NY 10022-4401 Office: UPI 2 Penn Plz New York NY 10001

WINSHIP, WADLEIGH CHICHESTER, holding company executive; b. San Francisco, Oct. 3, 1940; s. Henry Dillon and Anne Eliza (Chichester) W.; m. Lynne McPherson, Dec. 28, 1970; children: Wadleigh Chichester, Kelly McPherson. BA, U. Ga., 1964. Trainee Ga. Hwy. Express, Inc., Atlanta, 1964-68 v.p., dir., mem. exec. com., 1968-78; v.p., dir., mem. exec. com. Transus, Inc., Atlanta, 1978-84, pres., chief exec. officer, mem. exec. com., 1984-88, chmn. bd. SurfAir div., 1970—; pres., chief exec. officer Winship Group Inc., Atlanta, 1988—; past chmn. Regional and Dist. Carriers Conf.; bd. govs. Regular Common Carriers Conf., 1970-88. Chmn. transp. com. Atlanta chpt. ARC, 1968; life bd. dirs.; past mem. exec. com. Alliance Theatre Co., Atlanta; bd. dirs., past chmn. Goodwill Industries Atlanta; bd. dirs., past chmn. Ga. Soc. to Prevent Blindness; past bd. dirs. Pace Acad., Darlington Sch. Mem. Am. Trucking Assn. (v.p. exec. com. 1982-88), Ga. Bus. and Industry Assn. (bd. dirs. 1972-78), World Pres. Orgn., Peachtree Golf Club, The Nine O'Clocks, Piedmont Driving Club, Highlands Country Club, Chi Phi. Libertarian. Episcopalian. Home: 3296 Rilman Rd NW Atlanta GA 30327-1551 Office: Winship Group Inc 4751 Best Rd Ste 190 Atlanta GA 30337-5609

WINSKILL, ROBERT WALLACE, manufacturing executive; b. Tacoma, Oct. 30, 1925; s. Edward Francis William and Margaret Eyre (Myers) W. BA, Coll. Puget Sound, Tacoma, 1947. Field rep. Ray Burner Co., San Francisco, 1954-57, nat. sales mgr., 1960-69; v.p. sales Western Boiler Co., L.A., 1957-60; gen. sales mgr. Ray Burner Co., San Francisco, 1973-82; v.p., chief exec. officer Orr & Sembower, Inc., Middletown, Pa., 1969-73; pres. Combustion Systems Assocs., Inc., Mill Valley, Calif., 1982—; bd. dirs. Sino-Am. Boiler Engring. Co., Shanghai, China, S. T. Johnson Co., Oakland, Calif. Contbr. articles to profl. jours.; columnist Marin Scope, Mill Valley Herold, 1991—. With U.S. Army, 1943-44. Mem. ASME, Olympic Club (San Francisco), Rotary. Avocation: vineyard. Office: Combustion Systems Assocs Inc PO Box 749 Mill Valley CA 94942-0749

WINSLOW, DAVID ALLEN, chaplain, naval officer; b. Dexter, Iowa, July 12, 1944; s. Franklin E. and Inez Maude (McPherson) W.; m. Frances Lavinia Edwards, June 6, 1970; children: Frances, David. BA, Bethany Nazarene Coll., 1968; MDiv, Drew U., 1971, STM, 1973. Ordained to ministry United Meth. Ch., 1969. Clergyman, 1969—; assoc. minister All Sts. Episcopal. Ch., Millington, N.J., 1969-70; asst. minister Marble Collegiate Ch., N.Y.C., 1970-71; min. No. N.J. Conf., 1971-75; joined chaplain corps USN, 1974, advanced through grades to lt. comdr., 1980, ret., 1995; exec. dir. Marina Ministries, 1995—. Author: The Utmost for the Highest, Epiphany: God Still Speaks, Be Thou My Vision, Evening Prayers at Sea, The Utmost, 1993, Epiphany, 1994, Be Thou My Vision, 1994, Evening Prayers, 1995, Wisemen Still Adore Him, 1995, (with Walsh) A Year of Promise: Meditations, 1995; editor: The Road to Bethlehem: Advent, 1993, Preparation for Resurrection: Lent, 1994, God's Promise: Advent, 1994, The Way of the Cross: Lent, 1995; contbr. articles to profl. jours. Bd. dirs. disaster svcs. and family svcs. ARC, Santa Ana, Calif., 1988-91, Child Abuse Prevention Ctr., Orange, Calif., 1990-91; bd. dirs. Santa Clara County Coun. Chs., 1993-94, del., 1995—. Mem. ACA, Internat. Soc. Traumatic Stress Studies, Mil. Chaplain Assn. USA, Commonwealth Club Calif., USN League (hon.), Sunrise Exch. Club (chaplain 1989-91), Dick Richards Breakfast Club (chaplain 1988-91), Masons (charter) Shriners, Scottish Rite. Avocations: golf, skiing, sailing. Home: 20405 Via Volante Cupertino CA 95014

WINSLOW, PAUL DAVID, architect; b. Phoenix, June 12, 1941; s. Fred D. and Thelma E. (Ward) W.; m. Carole Lynn Walker, June 13, 1964; 1 child, Kirk David. B.Arch., Ariz. State U., 1964. Lic. architect, Ariz.; Calif. Ptnr. The Orcutt/Winslow Partnership, Phoenix, 1972—; speaker solar energy workshops, Phoenix, 1986-89; adjunct prof. Ariz. State Univ., 1991. Mem. profl. adv. council Ariz. State U. Coll. Architecture, Tempe, 1970—, bd. dirs. Architecture Found., 1972-76; mem. adv. com. City of Phoenix Bldg. Safety Bd., 1981. Bd. dirs. Central Ariz. Project Assn., Phoenix, 1971-74, Ariz. Ctr. for Law in the Pub. Interest, Phoenix, 1979-86; chmn. Encanto Village Planning Com., Phoenix, 1981-86; mem. council City of Phoenix, chmn. adv. com. Indian Sch. Citizens adv. com. Ind. Sch. Land Use Planning Team; lectr. on planning Ariz. State Univ. planning dept., 1989, city of Prescott, Phoenix and Tempe, 1988-89. Mem. AIA (bd. dirs. Central Ariz. chpt. also sec., treas. and pres.), Ariz. Soc. Architects (bd. dirs. 1970-71, 78-82), Bldg. Owners and Mgrs. Assn. Greater Phoenix (pres. 1985-91), Boar Valley Forward Assn. (exec. com. 1994—). Methodist. Club: Plaza (Phoenix). Home: 816 E Circle Rd Phoenix AZ 85020-1107 Office: The Orcutt.Winslow Partnership 1130 North 2nd St Phoenix AZ 85004

WINSLOW, ROBERT ALBERT, gas, oil industry executive; b. Carthage, Ind., Feb. 5, 1922; s. William Howard and Ione (Morris) W.; m. Totsye Harper, June 14, 1944; children: A. Robert, M. Craig, Judith Winslow Huchton. B.S. in Chem. Engring, Purdue U., 1943; Chinese Acad. Scis. Various engring. and managerial positions Exxon Co., USA, 1946-66; sr. v.p. Esso Chemicals Europe, 1966-68, pres., 1968-70; pres. Exxon Chemicals USA, 1970-74; exec. v.p. Exxon Chemicals, Inc., 1974-79; v.p. Exxon Corp., 1974-79, 81-85; pres. Exxon Enterprises, Inc., N.Y.C., 1979-85. Served with USN, 1943-46. Fellow Am. Acad. Optometry; mem. AAAS, Assn. for Rsch. in Vision and Ophthalmology, Human Factor and Ergonomics Soc., Sigma Xi. Presbyterian. Home: 5555 Del Monte Dr Apt 1605 Houston TX 77056-4119

WINSLOW, WALTER WILLIAM, psychiatrist; b. Lacombe, Alta., Can., Nov. 23, 1925; came to U.S. 1959, naturalized, 1964; s. Floyd Raymond and Lily Evangeline (Palmer) W.; m. Barbara Ann Spiker; children: Colleen Denise, Dwight Walter, Barbara Jean, Wendi Jae. BS, La Sierra Coll., 1949; MD, Loma Linda U., 1952. Diplomate: Am. Bd. Psychiatry and Neurology. Intern Vancouver Gen. Hosp., 1952; psychiat. resident Provincial Mental Hosp., Essondale, B.C., 1957-59, Harding Hosp., Worthington, Ohio, 1959-60; instr. dept. psychiatry and indsl. medicine U. Cin., 1960-66, dept. preventive medicine, 1964-66; asst. prof. psychiatry U.N.Mex., Albuquerque, 1966-68, assoc. prof. psychiatry, 1969-74, prof., chmn. dept. psychiatry, 1974-91, dir. mental health programs, 1976-91; med. dir. Charter Hosp. of Albuquerque, 1991—; assoc. prof. psychiatry Georgetown U., Washington, 1968-69; dir. bernalillo County Mental Health/Mental Retardation Ctr., 1970-78, 81-91. Contbr. articles to profl. jours. Recipient N.Mex. Gov.'s Commendation for 10 yrs. service in mental health, 1979. Fellow Am. Psychiat. Assn. (life, area VII rep. 1981-85, Assembly Speaker's award 1984), Am. Coll. of Psychiatrists, Am. Assn. Community Psychiatrists (hon.); mem. AMA, Am. Assn. Psychiatry and the Law, N.Mex. Psychiat. Assn. (pres. 1974-75). Republican. Office: 5901 Zuni SE Albuquerque NM 87108

WINSOR, JACKIE, artist; b. St. John's, Nfld., Can., 1941. Student, Yale Summer Sch. Art and Music, 1964; BFA, Mass. Coll. Art, 1965; MFA, Rutgers U., 1967. instr. Douglass Coll., New Brunswick, N.J., 1967, Middlesex County Coll., 1968-69, Newark State Tchrs. Coll., 1968-69, Mills Coll. Edn., 1968, 71, Greenwich House Pottery Sch., 1969-72, Loyola Univ., New Orleans, 1969, Sch. Visual Arts, N.Y.C., 1971, 75, Hunter Coll., 1972-75; lectr. N.Y. Studio Sch. Drawing, Painting, and Sculpture, 1987. One-person exhbns. include Douglass Coll. Gallery, New Brunswick, N.J., 1968, Nova Scotia Coll. Art and Design, Halifax, Can., 1971, Paula Cooper Gallery, N.Y.C., 1973, 76, 82, 83, 86, 89, Contemporary Arts Ctr., Cin, 1976, Portland Ctr. for Visual Arts, 1976-77, San Francisco Mus. Modern Art, 1977, Wadsworth Atheneum, Hartford, Conn., 1978, Mus. Modern Art, N.Y.C., 1979, Art Gallery Ont., Toronto, Can., 1979, Fort Worth Art Mus, 1979, Va. Mus., Richmond, 1981, Akron (Ohio) Art Mus., 1982, 92, Margarete Roeder Fine Arts, N.Y.C., 1985, Margo Leavin Gallery, L.A., 1987, Centre d'Art du Domaine de Kerguehennec Bignan, Locmine, France, 1988, Milw. Art Mus., 1991-92, Newport Harbor Art Mus., 1992, N.C. Mus. Art, Raleigh, 1992, Mus. Fine Arts, Boston, 1992; group exhbns. include Am. Fedn. Artists, 1968, Galerie Ricke, Cologne, Germany, 1970, 71, Vassar Coll. Art Gallery, Poughkeepsie, N.Y., 1971, Rutgers U., New Brunswick, 1972, 75, 77, Whitney Mus. Am. Art, N.Y.C., 1973, 74, 77, 78, 79, 82, 83, 85, 88, 89, Mus. Modern Art, N.Y.C., 1973, 74, 79, 84, 86, Musée d'Art Moderne, Paris, 1973, Art Inst. Chgo., 1974, Hayward Gallery, London, 1975, Aarhus Mus. Art, Copenhagen, 1976, U. Chgo., 1977, Mus. Contemporary Art, Chgo., 1977, 85, Stedelijk Mus., Amsterdam, 1978, Cleve. Mus. Art, 1981, Hayden Gallery MIT, Cambridge, 1983-84, Solomon R. Guggenheim Mus., N.Y.C., 1985, Contemporary Arts Ctr., Cin., 1987, Univ. Gallery U. Mass., Amherst, 1988, Cin. Art Mus., 1989, Mus. Contemporary Art, L.A., 1989, Holly Solomon Gallery, 1990-91, Wexner Ctr. Arts, Columbus, Ohio, 1991, Cleve. Ctr. Contemporary Art, 1991, Rubin Spangle, N.Y.C., 1992, Horodner Romley Gallery, N.Y.C., 1992, Philippe Staib Gallery, N.Y.C., 1992, Feigen Inc., Chicago, 1992, Locks Gallery, Philadelphia, 1992; included in numerous pub. collections including Mus. Fine Arts, Boston, Detroit Inst. Arts, Mus. Modern Art, N.Y.C., Whitney Mus. Am. Art, Solomon R. Guggenheim Mus., Fonds Nat. d'Art Contemporain, Paris, Mus. Modern Art, San Francisco, Australia Nat. Gallery, Canberra, Musée d'Art Moderne, Paris, Tehran Mus. Contemporary Art, Iran, Albright-Knox Art Gallery, Buffalo. Grantee NEA, 1974, 77, 84, Louis Comfort Tiffany, 1977, John Simon Guggenheim Meml. Found., 1978; recipient award N.Y. State Coun. Arts, 1973, Mather award Art Inst. Chgo., 1974, Creative Artist's award Brandeis U., 1979. Office: care Paula Cooper Gallery 155 Wooster St New York NY 10012*

WINSOR, KATHLEEN, writer; b. Olivia, Minn., Oct. 13, 1919; d. Harold Lee and Myrtle Belle (Crowder) W.; m. Robert John Herwig, 1936 (div. 1946); m. Arty Shaw (div.); m. Paul A. Porter, June 26, 1956 (dec. Nov. 1975); m. Arnold Robert Krakower. AB, U. Calif., 1938. Author: Forever

Amber, 1944, Star Money, 1950, The Lovers, 1952, America, With Love, 1957, Wanderers Eastward, Wanderers West, 1965, Calais, 1979, Jacintha, 1984, Robert and Arabella, 1986; story cons.: (TV series) Dreams in the Dust, 1971. Mem. Authors Guild. Democrat. Presbyterian. Office: care Roslyn Targ Lit Agy Inc 105 W 13th St New York NY 10011-7851*

WINSPEAR, WILLIAM W., home improvement company executive; b. Edmonton, Alta., Can., Oct. 1933; s. Francis George and Bessie Brooks (Watchorn) W.; B.Commerce, U. Alta., 1954; m. Margot Macleod, May 30, 1955; children—Deborah Jean, Donald William, Malcolm George, Barbara Louise, Robert Lloyd. Partner, Winspear, Higgins, Stevenson & Co., Edmonton, 1958-64; pres. TPL Industries Ltd. Vancouver, B.C., Can., 1964-70; pres. Lake Ont. Steel Co. Ltd., Whitby, Ont., 1970-75; pres., chief exec. officer Chaparral Steel Co., Midlothian, Tex., 1975-82; chief exec. officer Associated Materials Inc., Dallas, 1983—. Pres. Tex. Arts Alliance; trustee Dallas Opera, 1982-84, chmn., 1984-86; pres. Dallas Civic Music Assn.; trustee, exec. com. Dallas Arboretum. Home: 4815 Brookview Dr Dallas TX 75220-3915 Office: Assoc Materials Inc 2200 Ross Ave Ste 4100E Dallas TX 75201

WINSTEAD, JOY, journalist, consultant; b. Washington, May 31, 1934; d. Purnell Judson and Mellie Richardson (Winstead) W.; m. David Boyd Propert, Jul. 28, 1956 (div. June 1980); children: Kathleen Joy, David Bruce. BA in pol. sci., U. Richmond, 1955. Reporter Richmond (Va.) Times-Dispatch, 1955-56; staff writer, pub. rels. U. Pa., Phila., 1956-58; dir. publicity Children's Hosp., Washington, 1958-59; staff writer Richmond News Leader, 1972-77; features editor Columbia (S.C.) Record, 1977-81; asst. editor lifestyles Richmond Times-Dispatch, 1981-83, fashion editor, 1983-92; coord. pub. rels. Sci. Mus. Va., Richmond, 1992-93; dir. communications Medical Soc. Va., Richmond, 1993—; guest lectr. U. Richmond, Va. Commonwealth U., U. S.C.; book reviewer Richmond Times-Dispatch. Contbg. author: Richmond Reader; contbg. editor: A Gem of a Coll. History of Westhampton Coll.; author (introduction): University of Richmond, A Portrait. Co-chmn. alumni weekend U. Richmond, 1968, alumnae fund chmn., 1989, chmn. lectr. series, 1992-94, mem. 75th Anniversary com. Recipient 1st pl. award for spl. articles Nat. Fedn. Press Women, 1975, 95, Va. Press Women, 1975, Va. Press Assn., 1978. Mem. Soc. Profl. Journalists (bd. dirs. 1975), Va. Press Women (hospitality chmn. 1993), Soc. Profl. Journalists Found. (bd. dirs. 1987-91), Va. Assn. Med. Soc. Execs. (assoc.), Am. Assn. Med. Soc. Execs., Richmond Pub. Rels. Assn., Fashion Editors and Reporters Assn. (bd. dirs. 1985-91, nominating com. chmn. 1991). Presbyterian. Avocations: theater, music, travel. Home: 109 N Crenshaw Ave Richmond VA 23221 Office: Medical Soc Va 4205 Dover Rd Richmond VA 23221

WINSTEAD, NASH NICKS, university administrator, phytopathologist; b. Durham County, N.C., June 12, 1925; s. Nash L. and Lizzy (Featherston) W.; m. Geraldine Larkin Kelly, Sept. 17, 1949; 1 dau., Karen Jewell. B.S., N.C. State U., 1948, M.S., 1951; Ph.D., U. Wis., 1953. Asst. prof. plant pathology Raleigh, 1953-58; assoc. prof. N.C. State U., Raleigh, 1958-61; prof. N.C. State U., 1961-90, prof. emeritus, 1991—, dir. inst. biol. scis., 1965-67, asst. dir. agrl. exptl. sta., 1965-67, asst. provost, 1967-73, assoc. provost, 1973-74, provost and vice chancellor, 1974-90, acting chancellor, 1981-82; Phillip Found. intern acad. adminstrn. Ind. U., 1965-66; bd. trustees N.C. Sch. Sci. and Math., 1985-90. Contbr. articles profl. jours. Mem. N.C. Council on Higher Edn. for Adults, 1967-75; inst. rep. So. Assn. for Colls. and Schs., 1965-74; mem. Cooperating Raleigh Colls., 1968-90, pres., 1971-73, 83-85; chmn. interaction between protoplasm and toxicants com. So. Regional Edn. Bd., 1964-65; Bd. dirs. N.C. State U. YMCA, 1963-65; trustee Meth. Home for Children, 1980-88, pres., 1983-84, N.C. Wesleyan Coll., 1987— Served with USAAF, 1943-46. Recipient Sigma Xi research award, 1960. Fellow AAAS; Mem. Am. Phytopath. Soc. (chmn. disease, pathogen physiology com.), Am. Inst. Biol. Scis., N.C. Assn. Colls. and Univs. (exec. com. 1974-80, pres. 1978-79), Nat. Assn. State Univs. and Land Grant Colls. (edn. telecommunications com. 1980-85, equal opportunity com. 1985-88), Acad. Deans for So. States, N.C. Assn. of Acad. Officers (exec. com. 1986-89, v.p., pres. 1987-88), Sigma Xi, Phi Kappa Phi, Omicron Delta Kappa. Club: Torch Internat. (sec.). Home: 1109 Glendale Dr Raleigh NC 27612-4709 Office: NC State U Box 7111 Raleigh NC 27695-7101

WINSTEN, ARCHER, retired newspaper and movie critic; b. Seattle, Sept. 18, 1904; s. Harry Jerome and Nell (Archer) W.; m. Sheila Raleigh, Feb. 6, 1931 (div.); children: Kezia, Stephen, Martha. Student, Augusta Mil. Acad., 1916-18, Univ. Sch., Cleve., 1918-22; A.B., Princeton U., 1926. Reporter Phila. Evening Pub. Ledger, 1928, New Yorker mag., 1930; columnist (In the Wake of the News) New York Post, 1933-35, motion picture critic, 1936-86, also ski editor, 1947-86; motion picture documentary script writer Princeton Film Center, 1944-48, for R.K.O. Pathe, 1946; lectr., asso. in journalism Columbia U., 1946, 47. Recipient 1st prize Harper's 1st Intercollegiate Short Story prize contest, 1926. Mem. Am. Newspaper guild. Home: Wittenberg Rd RR 1 Box 263 Queensbury NY 12804 Having learned in the course of more than seven decades of varied living that I am neither a physical marvel nor a mental giant, I have adjusted to my limitations but have resisted complete rejection of either competition in sports, which I enjoy, or independent thinking, which keeps my mind out of total desuetude. I try to do unto others as I would be done by, at the same time resisting the temptation to control others (for their good) or be controlled (for my good). This has enabled me to regard life, in success or failure, as rather fascinating. The past is remembered, the future a suspense story proceeding to a known destination. I am moderately content. Postscript: Approaching 90, I sleepless nights, which provide a necessary re-evaluation of my life downward. It started so well athletically and literarily, but ended a flap.

WINSTEN, I. W., lawyer, law educator; b. Flint, Mich., Sept. 10, 1952; s. Stanley Dean and Harriet (Solomon) W.; m. Beth Tanenhaus, Dec. 18, 1982. BA with honors, Wayne State U., 1976, JD magna cum laude, 1979. Bar: Mich. 1979, U.S. Dist. Ct. (ea. dist.) Mich. 1979, U.S. Dist. Ct. (we. dist.) Mich. 1980, U.S. Ct. Appeals (6th cir.) 1980, U.S. Ct. Appeals (9th cir.) 1984, U.S. Ct. Appeals (11th, D.C. and 4th cirs.) 1985. Assoc. Honigman, Miller, Schwartz & Cohn, Detroit, 1979-83, ptnr., 1984—; chmn. pro bono involvement com. Mich. State Bar, 1991—; trustee Hist. Soc. for U.S. Dist. Ct. for Ea. Dist. Mich., 1994—. Bronze Key scholar Wayne State U., 1977-79. Mem. ABA (instr. trial advocacy Am. Law Inst. 1986—), Nat. Inst. Trial Advocacy (instr. 1987—), Fed. Bar Assn. (instr. trial advocacy 1985—, chmn. membership com. 1985-86), Mich. Bar Assn., Detroit Bar Assn., ACLU (cooperating atty. 1983—), Detroit Inst. of Arts Founders Soc., Wayne State Alumni Assn., Jaycees (named one of Outstanding Young Men of Am. 1984). Democrat. Jewish. Office: Honigman Miller Schwartz & Cohn 2290 1st National Bldg Detroit MI 48226

WINSTEN, SAUL NATHAN, lawyer; b. Providence, Feb. 23, 1953; s. Harold H. and Anita E. Winsten; m. Patricia J. Miller, Aug. 8, 1977; children: David A., J. Benjamin, Jennifer M. BA with honors, Beloit Coll., 1976; JD, Drake U., 1980. Ptnr. Michael, Best & Friedrich, Milw., 1988—. Contbr. articles to profl. jours. Mem. legal com. Jewish Community Ctr., Milw., 1983—. Mem. ABA (com. young lawyers div. 1989-90, governing coun., rep. antitrust law sect.), Wis. Bar Assn., Internat. Bar Assn., Japan-Am. Soc. Wis. (pres. 1993-94, co-founder 1990, sec. 1990-92), Nat. Assn. Japan-Am. Socs. (bd. dirs. 1991—, mem exec. com. 1993—), mem. Devel. Comm., Milw. Sch. of Engring, Am. Soc. Assn. Execs. (legal sect.), Wis. Found. Ind. Colls. (bd. dirs.), Order of Barristers. Office: Michael Best & Friedrich 100 E Wisconsin Ave Milwaukee WI 53202-4107

WINSTON, BENTE, academic administrator. Dir. Sussex Sch. Office: Sussex Sch 1800 S 2d W Missoula MT 59801

WINSTON, CHARLES DAVID, transportation company executive; b. N.Y.C., Mar. 15, 1941; s. Louis and Sylvia W.; children—Amy Rebecca, Gregory Charles. B.S. in Physics, CUNY, 1962; M.S. in Physics, Rutgers U., 1964; M.B.A. in Mktg., U. So. Calif., Los Angeles, 1969. Research physicist Bausch & Lomb Inc., Rochester, N.Y., 1964-65; research physicist Aerojet Gen. Corp., Azusa, Calif., 1967-69; various mktg. mgmt. positions Xerox Corp., Rochester, 1969-78; v.p. mktg. mgr. AM Internat., Chgo., 1978-81; v.p. network systems Federal Express, Memphis, 1981-83; sr. v.p. electronics products Federal Express, 1983—. Bd. dirs. Memphis Mus.,

1984—, Memphis Orchestral Soc., 1984—. Avocations: sailing; skiing; reading.

WINSTON, GEORGE, keyboardist, recording company executive; b. Hart, Mich., 1949. Ind. musician, 1966—; founder Dancing Cat Productions, Santa Cruz, CA, 1983—. Premier rec. artist for Windham Hill Records, 1980—; albums include Ballads and Blues, 1972, Autumn, 1980, December, 1982, Winter into Spring, 1982, Summer, 1991, Variations on the Kanon by Pachelbel; (with others) An Evening with Windham Hill Live, 1983; audiobook soundtracks: (with Meryl Streep) The Velveteen Rabbit, 1985, The Night Before Christmas, 1992, (with Liv Ullman) Sadako and the Thousand Paper Cranes, 1992. Office: care Dancing Cat Productions PO Box 639 Santa Cruz CA 95061*

WINSTON, GORDON CHESTER, economic educator, former academic administrator; b. San Francisco, Feb. 9, 1929; s. Chester Parker and Lois Genevieve (Warner) W.; m. Mary Primrose Wales, June 13, 1953 (div. 1975); children: Victoria, Gordon Parker, Pamela; m. Mary Burner Lamb, May 16, 1985. A.B., Whitman Coll., Walla Walla, Wash., 1950; postgrad., U. Wash., 1950-51; M.A., Stanford U., 1961, Ph.D., 1964. Salesman Internat. Paper Co., 1953-56, W.Va. Pulp and Paper Co., 1956-60; instr. Stanford U., 1962-63; asst. prof. econs. William Coll., Williamstown, Mass., 1963-67; sr. research advisor Yale U. Pakistan Project, Karachi, Pakistan, 1966-67, 70-71; fellow Nuffield Coll. and Queen Elizabeth House Oxford U., 1971; prof. econs. Williams Coll., 1967-73, Orrin Sage prof. polit. economy, 1974—, chmn. econs. dept., 1981-84, provost, 1988-90; mem. Sch. Social Sci. Inst. Advanced Study, Princeton, N.J., 1978-79; vis. scholar Yale U., 1984-85; Murphy Inst. Disting. vis. prof. Tulane U., 1985; vis. scholar Inst. for Internat. Econ. Studies, Stockholm U., 1979-80; cons. in field. Author: The Timing of Economic Activities, 1982; Contbr. articles in field to profl. jours. Served with C.E. U.S. Army, 1951-53. Ford Found. grantee, 1971-73; Edna McConnell Clark Found. grantee, 1977-78; grantee Inst. Internat. Economic Studies, Stockholm, 1979-80; Nat. Sci. Found. grantee, 1985-87. Mem. Am. Econ. Assn., Royal Econ. Soc., Western Econ. Assn. Home: 4 Greylock Vlg Williamstown MA 01267 Office: Williams Coll Dept Econs Williamstown MA 01267

WINSTON, JUDITH ANN, lawyer; b. Atlantic City, Nov. 23, 1943; d. Edward Carlton and Margaret Ann (Goodman) Mariunno; B.A. magna cum laude, Howard U., Washington, 1966; J.D., Georgetown U., 1977; m. Michael Russell Winston, Aug. 10, 1963; children: Lisa Marie, Cynthia Eileen. Dir. EEO Project, Council Great City Schs., Washington, 1971-74; legal asst. Lawyers Com. for Civil Rights Under Law, Washington, 1975-77; admitted to D.C. bar, 1977, U.S. Supreme Ct. bar; spl. asst. to dir. Office for Civil Rights, HEW, Washington, 1977-79; exec. asst., legal counsel to chair U.S. EEO Commn., Washington, 1979-80; asst. gen. counsel U.S. Dept. Edn., 1980-86; dep. dir. Lawyers Com. for Civil Rights Under Law, 1986-88; dep. dir. pub. policy Women's Legal Def. Fund, Washington, 1988-90, chair employment discrimination com., 1979-88; edml. cons., 1974-77; asst. prof. law Washington Coll. Law of Am. U., 1990-93. assoc. prof. law, 1993—; gen. counsel U.S. Dept. Edn., Washington, 1993—. Pres. bd. dirs. Higher Achievement Program. Mem. ACLU (pres. Nat. Capital Area, bd. dirs.), D.C. Bar Assn., Washington Council Lawyers, Washington Bar Assn., Nat. Bar Assn., Lawyers' Com. for Civil Rights Under Law (treas., bd. dirs.), Links Inc., Alpha Kappa Alpha, Phi Beta Kappa, Delta Theta Phi. Democrat. Episcopalian. Author: Desegregating Schools in the Great Cities: Philadelphia, 1970, Chronicle of a Decade 1961-1970, 1970, Desegregating Urban Schools: Educational Equality/Quality, 1970; contbr. articles to profl. jours. Home: 1371 Kalmia Rd NW Washington DC 20012-1444 Office: Dept Edn 600 Independence Ave SW Washington DC 20202-2100

WINSTON, JUDITH ELLEN, marine biologist, curator; b. Haverhill, Mass., Mar. 11, 1945; d. John Leo and Ruth Arline (Noyes) W.; m. Stephen A. Dudley, May 16, 1970 (div. July 1977); 1 child, Elica Catherine. AB, Brown U., 1966; MS, U. N.H., 1970; PhD, U. Chgo., 1974. Postdoctoral fellow Smithsonian Marine Sta., Ft. Pierce, Fla., 1974-75; asst. prof. Indian River Community Coll., Ft. Pierce, 1976-77; assoc. rsch. scientist The Johns Hopkins U., Balt., 1977-80; asst. curator Am. Mus. Natural History, N.Y.C., 1980-85, assoc. curator, 1985-91, curator, chairwoman, 1991—; mem. publ. com. Columbia Univ. Press, N.Y.C., 1988-91. Contbr. 11 revs. and 37 articles to Bull. Marine Sci., Jour. Exptl. Marine Biol. Ecology, Biol. Bull., others. Rsch. grantee NSF, 1977-91, Nat. Geog. Soc., 1983, 87; travel grantee Smithsonian Instn., 1988. Fellow AAAS; mem. Am. Assn. Mus., Am. Soc. Zoologists, Internat. Bryozoology Assn. Achievements include rsch. on ecology and systematics of marine bryozoans. Home: 340 W 87th St Apt 8C New York NY 10024-2631 Office: Dept Invertebrates Am Mus Natural History Central Pk West at 79th St New York NY 10024-5192

WINSTON, KRISHNA RICARDA, foreign language professional; b. Greenfield, Mass., June 7, 1944; d. Richard and Clara (Brussel) W.; 1 child, Danielle Billingsley. BA, Smith Coll., 1965; MPhil, Yale U., 1969, PhD, 1974. Instr. Wesleyan U., Middletown, Conn., 1970-74, asst. prof., 1974-77; assoc. prof. Wesleyan U., Middletown, 1977-84, prof., 1984—, acting dean, 1993-94; coord. Mellon Minority Undergrad. Program, 1993—. Author: O. v. Horváth: Close Readings of Six Plays, 1975; translator: O. Schlemmer, Letters and Diaries, 1972, S. Lenz, The Heritage, 1981, G. Grass, Two States, One Nation, 1990, C. Hein, The Distant Lover, 1989, G. Mann, Reminiscences and Reflections, 1990, W. v. Goethe, Wilhelm Meister's Journeyman Years, 1989, C. v. Krockow, The Hour of the Women, 1991, E. Heller, With the Next Man Everything Will be Different, 1992, R.W. Fassbinder, The Anarchy of the Imagination, 1992, G. Reuth, Goebbels, 1994, E. Lappin, editor, Jewish Voices, German Words, 1994, P. Handke, Essay on the Jukebox, 1994. Vol. Planned Parenthood, Middletown, 1972-77; mem. Recycling Task Force, Middletown, 1986-87; chmn. Resource Recycling Adv. Coun., Middletown, 1989—. Recipient Schlegel-Tieck prize for translation, 1994; German Acad. Exch. Svc. fellow. Mem. MLA, NEMLA, Soc. for Exile Studies, Am. Lit. Translators' Assn., Am. Assn. Tchrs. German, Phi Beta Kappa (pres. Wesleyan chpt. 1987-90). Home: 655 Bow Ln Middletown CT 06457-4808 Office: Wesleyan Univ German Studies Dept Middletown CT 06459

WINSTON, MICHAEL RUSSELL, foundation executive, historian; b. N.Y.C., May 26, 1941; s. Charles Russell and Jocelyn Anita Prem Das Winston; m. Judith Ann Marianno, Aug. 10, 1963; children: Lisa Marie, Cynthia Eileen. BA magna cum laude, Howard U., 1962; MA, U. Calif.-Berkeley, 1964, PhD, 1974. Instr. dept. history Howard U., Washington, 1964-66, asst. dean Coll. Liberal Arts, 1968-69, asst. prof. dept. history, 1970-73, v.p. acad. affairs, 1983-90, prof. emeritus, 1990—; assoc. dir. Inst. Svcs. to Edn., Washington, 1966; fellow Haus. Hof-und Staatsarchiv, Vienna, Austria, 1969; dir. Moorland Spingarn Rsch. Ctr., 1973-83; v.p., bd. dirs. Alfred Harcourt Found., Silver Spring, Md., 1992-93, pres., 1993—; cons. Smithsonian Instn., 1979—; nat. Inst. Edn., 1978-85, NSF, 1985—. Author: (with R.W. Logan) The Negro in the United States, 1970, The Howard University Department of History, 1913-73, 1973; editor: (with R.W. Logan) Dictionary of American Negro Biography, 1982, (with G.R. McNeil) His-torical Judgements Reconsidered, 1988; mem. editorial bd. Washington Historical Judgements Reconsidered, 1988; mem. editorial bd. Washington Historical History, 1993—. Trustee spl. contbn. fund NAACP, 1980-82; trustee D.C. Pub. Defender Svc., 1985-88; mem. exec. bd. Nat. Capital Area coun. Boy Scouts Am., 1988-90; bd. mgrs. Hist. Soc. Washington; bd. dirs. Harcourt Brace Jovanovich, 1980-91, D.C. Pub. Libr. Found., 1994—, pres., 1995—, Nat. Coun. for History Standards; mem. Commn. on Coll. and Univ. Nonprofl. Studies, ABA; mem. Nat. Ctr. for History in the Schs., UCLA/NEH; mem. nat. adv. com. and coun. of scholars Libr. of Congress, nat. adv. bd. Protect Historic Am. Moten fellow U. Edinburgh, 1962, Wilson fellow U. Calif., 1962, Ford fellow, 1969-70, Woodrow Wilson Internat. Ctr. Scholars fellow, 1979-80. Mem. Am. Hist. Assn., Orgn. Am. Historians, Am. Antiquarian Soc., Hist. Soc. Washington, Atlantic Coun. U.S., Coun. on Fgn. Rels., Nat. Coun. for History Standards, Epsilon Boule, Sigma Pi Phi. Democrat. Episcopalian. Club: Cosmos (Washington). Home: 1371 Kalmia Rd NW Washington DC 20012-1444 Office: Alfred Harcourt Found 8401 Colesville Rd Silver Spring MD 20910-3352

WINSTON, MORTON MANUEL, equipment executive; b. N.Y.C., Dec. 9, 1930; s. Myron Hugh and Minna (Schneller) W.; m. Katherine Tupper Winn, Feb. 3, 1979; 1 child, Kate Winston; children by previous marriages: Gregory Winston, Livia Winston; stepchildren—Wesley Hudson, Laura Hud-

son. A.B., U. Vt., 1951; M.A., U. Conn., 1953; LL.B. magna cum laude, Harvard U., 1958. Bar: D.C. 1961. Law clk. to Justice Frankfurter, Supreme Ct. U.S., 1959-60; asso. firm Cleary, Gottlieb, Steen & Hamilton, N.Y.C., Washington, 1960-67; v.p. Tosco Corp., N.Y.C., 1964-67; exec. v.p. Tosco Corp., 1967-71, pres., 1971-83, chief exec. officer, 1976-83, chmn., 1983-84, dir., 1984-86; pres., chmn. Stamet Inc., Gardena, Calif., 1987—; chmn. Norad Corp., 1986—; dir. Stamet Inc. and Norad Corp, 1986—; bd. dir. Baker Hughes Corp. trustee George C. Marshall Research Found., Lexington, Va. Mus. Contemporary Art, L.A.; chmn. Station KLON-FM, Long Beach, Calif.; trustee Calif. State Summer Sch. for the Arts Found. Served to lt. (j.g.) USCGR, 1953-55. Office: Stamet Inc 17244 S Main St Gardena CA 90248-3101

WINSTON, ROLAND, physicist, educator; b. Moscow, USSR, Feb. 12, 1936; s. Joseph and Claudia (Goretskaya) W.; m. Patricia Louise LeGette, June 10, 1957; children—Joseph, John, Gregory. A.B., Shimer Coll., 1953; B.S., U. Chgo., 1956, M.S., 1957, Ph.D., 1963. Asst. prof. physics U. Pa., 1963-64; mem. faculty U. Chgo., 1964—, prof. physics, 1975—, chmn. physics dept., 1989—; physicist Argonne (Ill.) Nat. Lab., 1974-78. Sloan fellow, 1968-70; Guggenheim fellow, 1977-78. Fellow AAAS, Am. Phys. Soc., Am. Optical Soc.; mem. Internat. Solar Energy Soc. (Abbot award 1987). Achievements include patent for ideal light collector for solar concentrators. Home: 5217 S University Ave # C Chicago IL 60615-4405 Office: Physics Dept U Chgo 5630 S Ellis Ave Chicago IL 60637-1433

WINT, DENNIS MICHAEL, museum director; b. Macon, Ga., Mar. 17, 1943; s. Paul Kenneth and Mary (McClure) W.; m. Patricia McLaughlin, Dec. 27, 1970; 1 child, Laurel Julia. B.S., U. Mich., 1965; tchr.'s cert., Lake Erie Coll., 1970; Ph.D., Case Western Res. U., 1977. Dir. environ. edn. Wiloughby Eastlake City Schs., 1968-70; dir. Ctr. Devel. Environment Curriculum, 1970-75; cons. Ohio Dept. Edn., 1975-77; dir. mus. and edn. Acad. Natural Scis., Phila., 1977-79; v.p., dir. natural history mus. Acad. Natural Scis., 1979-82; dir. Cranbrook Inst. Sci., Bloomfield Hills, Mich., 1982-86; pres. St. Louis Sci. Ctr., 1986-95; adj. asst. prof. Temple U.; past chmn. edn. and human resources adv. com. NSF, 1991-92; immediate past pres. St. Louis Area Mus. Collaborative, 1991-92, mem. exec. com. Grantee in field. Mem. Am. Assn. Mus. (mem. accreditation commn., ethics com.), Assn. Sci.-Tech. Ctrs. (mem. nominating com., v.p. 1993—). Home: 8205 Ardmore Ave Wyndmoor PA 19038

WINTER, ALAN, retired publishing company executive; b. Rogate, Sussex, Eng., Oct. 14, 1937; came to U.S., 1982; s. George Adolph and Muriel (Burton) W.; m. Anne Claire, Sept. 22, 1962; children: Mark, Paul. B.S., U. Wales, 1959, Ph.D, 1963; M.A., U. Cambridge, Eng., 1972. Instr. Harvard U., Cambridge, Mass., 1964-65; lectr. U. York, Eng., 1965-68; editor Cambridge U. Press, 1968-82; dir. Cambridge U. Press, N.Y.C., 1982-93. Contbr. numerous articles to sci. jours. Chmn. Govs. of Newnham Croft Sch., Cambridge, Eng., 1975-81. Clubs: Athenaeum (London); Century Assn. (N.Y.C.).

WINTER, ANDREW J., ambassador; b. N.Y.C., May 9, 1946; s. Ernest and Ilona (Robicek) W.; m. Christine Bo Yuan, Apr. 11, 1987; 1 child, Joanna Ning. B.A., Dartmouth Coll., 1968; M.B.A., Columbia Univ., 1970; student, Nat. War Coll., 1983-84. Sr. advisor U.S. mission UN, N.Y.C., 1975-77; adminstrv. officer Am. Embassy, Helsinki, Finland, 1977-80, Am. Consulate Gen., Rio de Janeiro, 1980-81; exec. asst. to dir. gen. of fgn. svc. Dept. State, 1981-83; chief adminstrv. sect. Am. Inst., Taipei, Taiwan, 1984-87; counselor for adminstrv. affairs Am. Embassy, Pretoria, South Africa, 1987-90; exec. dir., Bur. of African Affairs Dept. State, 1990-93; U.S. amb. to Gambia Banjul, 1993—. Office: Dept of State Washington DC 20521-2070

WINTER, ARCH REESE, architect; b. Mobile, Ala., Sept. 13, 1913; s. Augustus Reese and Winona (Battson) W.; m. Mary, June 2, 1938; children: Augustus Reese and Winona (Battson). BArch, Auburn U., 1935; MArch, Cath. U. Am., 1937; postgrad., Cranbrook Acad. Art, Bloomfield Hills, Mich., 1939-41. Cons. Nat. Resources Planning Bd., Washington, 1941-43; practice architecture city planning firm as Arch R. Winter, Mobile, 1945-84. City plans include Natchez and Gulfport, Miss., Shreveport and Monroe, La., Old Louisville, Ky., restoration area archtl. includes YWCA Youth Center and Residence, Isle Dauphine Country Club, Dauphin Island (Gulf States region AIA Honor award, 1957). Cons. Mobile Planning Commn. Recipient medal of merit Tenn. Soc. Architects, 1971, Thomas Jefferson medal selection com U. Va. Sch. Architecture, 1976-79, cert. of commendation Mobile Historic Devel. Commn., 1981. Fellow AIA (pres. Ala. chpt. 1955, nat. AIA engrs. joint coun. 1957-59, urban design com. 1959-64, chmn., del to commn. d'Urbanisme, 1962, design com. 1972-78, bd. dirs. 1968-71, chmn. Honor award, 1969, chmn. environ. commn. 1970-71, Citation for Excellence in Community Architecture 1965); mem. Am. Planning Assn. (Disting. Svc. Plaque Ala. chpt. 1984). Address: 9 Bienville Ave Mobile AL 36606-1463

WINTER, CHESTER CALDWELL, physician, surgery educator; b. Cazenovia, N.Y., June 2, 1922; s. Chester Caldwell and Cora Evelyn (Martin) W.; m. Mary Antonia Merullo, Oct. 22, 1983; children by previous marriage: Paul, Ann, Jane. B.A., U. Iowa, 1943, M.D., 1946. Diplomate: Am. Bd. Urology. Intern Meth. Hosp., Indpls., 1946-47; med. resident St. Luke's Hosp., Cedar Rapids, Iowa, 1947; resident gen. surgery VA Hosp., Los Angeles, 1952-53; resident urology VA Hosp.-U. Calif. at Los Angeles Med. Center, 1953-57; physician Mentone, Calif., 1950-51; clin. asst. surgery UCLA, 1954-57, instr. surgery and urology, 1957-58, asst. prof. surgery and urology, 1958-59, asst. prof. Step II, 1959-60; prof. surgery and urology Ohio State U., 1960-88, prof. emeritus surgery and urology, 1988—, Louis Levy prof. urology, 1980-88; dir. urology Ohio State U. Hosp., Columbus, 1960-78; cons. urology VA, Air Force hosps., Dayton. Author: Radioisotope Renography, 1963, Correctable Renal Hypertension, 1964, Nursing Care of Patients with Urologic Diseases, 4th edit, 1977, Practical Urology, 1969, Vesicoureteral Reflux, 1969; Editorial cons.: Exerpta Medica: Nuclear Medicine, Jour. AMA; editorial bd.: Andrology, Jour. Urology; Contbr. articles to med. jours. Served to capt. M.C. U.S. Army, 1943-46, 48-49. Fellow Am. Acad. Pediatricians, Am. Coll. Surgeons; mem. Am. Assn. Genitourinary Surgeons, Am. Urol. Assn., Soc. Univ. Surgeons, Soc. Pediatric Urology, Soc. Univ. Urologists, Internat. Soc. Urology, Urol. Investigators Forum, Ohio State Med. Assn., Columbus Surg. Soc., Central Ohio Urology Soc., Columbus Acad. Medicine, Ohio State U. Med. Soc., York Country Club (Worthington, Ohio), Kiwanis. Home: 6425 Evening St Worthington OH 43085-3054

WINTER, DAVID FERDINAND, electrical engineering educator, consultant; b. St. Louis, Nov. 9, 1920; s. Ferdinand Conrad and Annie (Schaffer) W.; m. Bettie Jeanne Turner; children: Suzanne, Sharie Winter Chappeau. BSEE, Washington U., St.Louis, 1942; MSEE, MIT, 1948. Registered profl. engr., Mo. Staff mem. radiation lab. MIT, Cambridge, 1942-45, rsch. assoc. electronics lab., 1945-48; prof. elec. engring. Washington U., 1948-55, affiliate prof. elec. engring., 1955-67; v.p. engring. and rsch. Moloney Elec. Co., St. Louis, 1955-74; v.p. rsch. and engring. Blackburn div. IT&T, St. Louis, 1974-82; dir. advanced tech. devel., 1982-86; pvt. practice cons. St. Louis, 1986—; tech. expert on effects of stray voltage on dairy cattle for Wis. Pub. Svc. Commn.; cons. Naval Ordanance Lab. of Ind., Indpls., 1950-53, other industries, St. Louis, 1979—. Contbr. articles to profl. jours; holder 28 patents. Elder, pastor Maplewood Bible Chapel, St. Louis. Fellow IEEE (life), Inst. Radio Engrs.; mem. NSPE, Am. Soc. Agrl. Engrs., Mo. Soc. Profl. Engrs., Sigma Xi, Tau Beta Pi, Eta Kappa Nu. Avocations: cabinet maker, photography, music instruments. Home and Office: 629 Meadowridge Ln Saint Louis MO 63122-3021

WINTER, DAVID LOUIS, systems engineer, human factors scientist, retired; b. Pitts., July 30, 1930; s. Louis A. and Gladys M. (Quinn) W.; m. Nancy L. Tear, July 1, 1952; children: Leeson, Blaise, Gregory, Lauren. BA, U. Pitts., 1952; MA, Columbia U., 1960; cert. computer sci., Northeastern U., 1971. Assoc. rsch. scientist Am. Insts. Rsch., Washington, 1961-66; sr. rsch. scientist Am. Insts. Rsch., Bedford, Mass., 1966-71, prin. rsch. scientist, 1976-95, retired, 1995; sr. systems analyst RCA Corp.-Sarnoff Labs., Princeton, N.J., 1971-73; mgr. systems engring. Codon Corp., Bedford, 1973-76; computer systems cons. Mass. Dept. Mental Health, 1971-73. Pres. Mayo Peninsula Civic Assn., Edgewater, Md., 1964-65; v.p. Bedford Human Rels. Coun., 1992-94. Capt. USAF, 1952-64. Mem. Am. Acad. Polit. Sci., Human Factors Soc. (dir. New Eng. chpt.), Soc. Ednl. Tech. Democrat.

Roman Catholic. Achievements include development of 35 programs physics for computer; design and human factors test for eight USAF electronic, intelligence and backscatter radar systems; design of four computer-assisted training systems (CATS) for E3 AWACS radar, computer displays, communications and navigation subsystems. Home: 27 Gould Rd Bedford MA 01730

WINTER, DONALD FRANCIS, lawyer; b. Hackensack, N.J., June 11, 1941; s. Frank Joseph and Ina Beulah (Swanson) W.; m. Katherine C. Blodgett, Nov. 30, 1963 (div. 1974); children: Andrew Blodgett, Matthew Francis, Anthony Reed. AB, Harvard U., 1963, JD, 1966. Bar: Mass. 1966, U.S. Dist. Ct.Mass. 1966. Assoc. Palmer & Dodge, Boston, 1966-73, ptnr., 1973—; bd. dirs. Ellis Meml. Assn. Chmn. Back Bay Archtl. Commn., 1969-82; trustee Boston Ballet Co., 1969—; mem. Park Pla. Civic Adv. Com.. Mem. ABA, Mass. Bar Assn., Boston Bar Assn., Nat. Assn. Bond Lawyers, Somerset Club, Harvard Club. Lutheran. Home: 2 Clarendon St Boston MA 02116-6139 Office: Palmer & Dodge 1 Beacon St Boston MA 02108-3106

WINTER, DOUGLAS E., lawyer, writer; b. St. Louis, Oct. 30, 1950; s. William E. and Dorothy E. (Schuster) W.; m. Lynne G.Turner, July 9, 1977; children: John, Stephen. BS, U. Ill., 1971, MS, 1972, JD, Harvard U., 1975; postgrad., Judge Advocate Gen.'s Sch., 1977. Bar: Mo. 1975, Ill. 1976, D.C. 1976. Clk. to Hon. William H. Webster U.S. Ct. Appeals (8th cir.), St. Louis, 1975-76; assoc. Covington & Burling, Washington, 1976-84; ptnr. Bryan Cave, Washington, 1985—; vis. prof. U. Iowa, Iowa City, 1980-81. Author or editor: Stephen King, 1982, Shadowings: The Reader's Guide to Horror Fiction, 1983, Stephen King: The Art of Darkness, 1984, Faces of Fear, 19885, Black Wine, 1986, Splatter: A Cautionary Tale, 1987, Prime Evil, 1988, Darkness Absolute, 1991, Black Sun, 1994, American Zombie, 1995; contbr. articles and short stories to popular mags. and newspapers. Capt. U.S. Army, 1973-77. Recipient World Fantasy award World Fantasy Conv., 1986, award Internat. Horror Critics Guild, 1995. Mem. Nat. Book Critics Circle, Horror Writers Assn. (chmn. grievance com. 1989—). Office: Bryan Cave 700 13th St NW Washington DC 20005-3960

WINTER, FREDERICK ELLIOT, fine arts educator; b. Barbados, W.I., June 19, 1922; s. Edward Elliot and Constance Mabel (Gill) W.; m. Joan Elizabeth Hay, June 9, 1951; children: Elizabeth, Penelope, Mary, Michael. B.A., McGill U., 1945; Ph.D., U. Toronto, 1957. Instr. U. Toronto, 1947-49, 50-51, lectr., 1951-57, asst. prof., 1957-61, asso. prof., 1961-68, prof., 1968-90, prof. emeritus, 1990—, chmn. dept. fine art, 1971-77, grad. coordinator history of art, 1978-81; chmn. U. Toronto Assn. Teaching Staff, 1968-69; mem. mng. com. Am. Sch. Classical Studies, Athens, Greece; mem. programme com. Can. Archaeol. Inst. at Athens, 1990-94; dir. Can. Acad. Inst., Athens, 1994—. Author: (with G.S. Vickers, P.H. Brieger) Art and Man, Vol. I, 1963, Greek Fortifications, 1971; contbr. articles Jour. Classical Assn. Can., Am. Jour. of Archaeology, Echos du Moude Classique/Classical Views. Recipient Gold medal in classics McGill U., 1945; Flavelle fellow U. Toronto, 1947-48; White fellow Am. Sch., Athens, 1949-50; spl. research fellow, 1977-78, 87-88; sr. assoc. fellow, 1982, 83-84, 86, 91; Am. Philos. Soc. grantee, 1957; grantee Soc. Scis. Humanities Rsch. Coun. Can., 1962, 68, 71, 75, 77-78, 82, 83-84, 86, 87-88, 91; grantee U. Toronto Humanities and Social Scis. Rsch. Com., 1993. Mem. Classical Assn. Can., Archeol. Inst. Am. (editorial adv. bd. Am. Jour. Archaeology 1981-85). Home: 164 Highgate Ave, Willowdale, ON Canada M2N 5G8 Office: Dept Fine Art, U Toronto, Toronto, ON Canada

WINTER, HARVEY JOHN, government official; b. New Albion, N.Y., Apr. 6, 1915; s. George J. and Irene (Harvey) W.; m. Virginia M. Shaw, Sept. 2, 1939; 1 child, Jeffrey S. BA. magna cum laude, U. Buffalo, 1938, M.A., 1939; teaching fellow, George Washington U., 1939-40. Historian U.S. Nat. Park Service, 1940-42; archivist U.S. Nat. Archives, 1942-43; with U.S. Office Alien Property Custodian, 1943-51, chief reports and stats. sect., 1948- 51; with State Dept., 1951—, chief internat. bus. practices div., 1959-61, asst. chief, 1961-70, chief bus. practices div., 1970-71, dir. office bus. protection, 1971-73, dir. office bus. practices, 1973-90; dir. office intellectual property and competition, 1991-92; U.S. del. European Productivity Agy. cartel meetings, Paris, 1958-60; mem. U.S. del. diplomatic confs. Internat. Design Agreement, The Hague, 1960, 17th session GATT, Geneva, Switzerland, 1960; U.S. alt. rep. 5th session Intergovtl. Copyright Com., London, 1960, 6th session, Madrid, 1961, 7th session, New Delhi, 1963; U.S. alt. rep. Interunion Coordinating Com., Geneva, 1963-69; U.S. observer African Seminar on Indsl. Property, Brazzaville, Congo, 1963; U.S. alt. observer Latin Am. Indsl. Property Seminar, Bogota, Colombia, 1964, Asian Indsl. Property Seminar, Colombo, Ceylon, 1966, Com. of Experts on Inventors' Certificates, Geneva, 1965, Com. of Experts on Adminstrv. Agreement, Geneva, 1965, Intellectual Property Diplomatic Conf., Stockholm, 1967, Diplomatic Conf. on Agreement for Classification of Indsl. Designs, Locarno, Switzerland, 1968, Diplomatic Conf. on Patent Cooperation Treaty, Washington, 1970, Diplomatic Conf. on Agreement for Internat. Patent Classification, Strasbourg, France, 1971, Diplomatic Conf. on Universal Copyright Conv., Paris, 1971; U.S. alt. rep. Diplomatic Conf. on Phonogram Conv., Geneva, 1971, Diplomatic Conf. on Indsl. Property, Vienna, 1973; U.S. rep. Com. Experts on Type Face Agreement, Geneva, 1972, Com. Experts on Communications Satellites Problems, Nairobi, Kenya, 1973; U.S. del. Diplomatic Conf. on Communications Satellites Conv., Brussels, 1974, Diplomatic Conf. on Treaty for Deposit Microorganisms, Budapest, Hungary, 1977, Diplomatic Conf. on Plant Protection Conv., Geneva, 1978, World Intellectual Property Orgn. Governing Bodies, Geneva, 1979-82; alt. del. World Intellectual Property Orgn. Governing Bodies, 1983-91; alt. U.S. del. Diplomatic Conf. on Revision of Paris Conv., Geneva, 1980, 82, 83, 84 Nairobi, 1981; U.S. del. UNESCO Experts on Rental of Videograms, Paris, 1984, Com. Govtl. Experts on Audiovisual Works and Phonograms, Paris, 1986, Com. Govtl. Experts on Internat. Register of Audiovisual Works, Geneva, 1988, Diplomatic Conf. on Treaty for Internat. Registration of Audiovisual Works, Geneva, 1989, Com. Experts on Disputes Steelement Treaty on Intellectual Property, 1990; chmn. Internat. Patent Classification Assembly, 1992. Recipient Superior Honor award Dept. State, 1971, 75, 89, 92, 50-Yr. Svc. award, 1990, Jefferson meda. N.J. Patent Law Assn., 1982; honoree Copyright Soc. U.S.A., 1989. Mem. Phi Beta Kappa. Episcopalian (vestry). Home: 1019 S 22d St Arlington VA 22202 Office: Dept of State Washington DC 20520

WINTER, JOHN DAWSON, III, blues guitarist, singer; b. Beaumont, Tex., Feb. 23, 1944; s. John Dawson II and Edwina (Holland) W. Grad. high sch. Organizer, performer numerous rock and blues bands, rec. artist, CBS Records, Inc., 1969—; TV and concert appearances through, U.S. and Europe, 1969—; albums include Johnny Winter, 1969, Second Winter, 1969, Johnny Winter-And, 1970, Live, 1971 (Gold Record award 1974), Still Alive and Well, 1973, Saints and Sinners, 1974, John Dawson Winter III, 1974, Nothin' But the Blues, 1977, White Hot and Blue, 1978, The Johnny Winter Story, 1980, Raisin' Cain, Serious Business, 1985, 3rd Degree, 1986, The Winter of '88, 1988, Winter Scene, 1990, Let Me In, 1991, Scorchin' Blues, 1992, A Rock n' Roll Collection, 1994; producer recs. by Muddy Waters; albums include Still Hard (Artist of Yr., Rolling Stone mag. 1969). Mem. Broadcast Music Inc., Musicians Union. *

WINTER, MIRIAM THERESE (GLORIA FRANCES WINTER), nun, religious education educator; b. Passaic, N.J., June 14, 1938; d. Mathias William and Irene Therese (Marton) W. BMus, Cath. U. Am., 1964; M in Religious Edn., McMaster Divinity Coll., Hamilton, Ont., Can., 1976; PhD in Liturgical Studies, Princeton Theol. Sem., 1983; LHD (hon.), Albertus Magnus Coll., 1991, St. Joseph Coll., 1993. Joined Med. Mission Sisters, Roman Cath. Ch., 1955. Dir. liturgy and liturgical music Med. Mission Sisters, Phila., 1960-76, pub. rels. dir. coord., 1963-72; assoc. prof. liturgy, worship and spirituality Hartford (Conn.) Sem., 1980-85, prof., 1985—, prof. liturgy, worship, spirituality, and feminist studies, 1994—; mem. faculty St. Therese's Inst., Phila., 1964-68, acad. dir., 1968-72, Immaculate Conception Sem. Summer Program, Mo., 1969, Cath. U. Summer Grad. Program, Washington, 1970, Hope Ecumenical Inst., Jerusalem, summer 1974, 75, 76, McMaster Divinity Coll. Grad. Program, 1976, Continuing Edn. Program, 1976, N.Y. Archdiocesan Sch. Liturgical Music, summer 1980, 82, Vancouver Sch. Theology, summer 1982, USN Chaplains through Auburn Theol. Sem., 1990; mem. adj. faculty Union Inst., Cin., 1992-94; with emergency relief work Internat. Rescue Com., Cambodia, 1979-80, Malteser-

Hilfsdienst Auslandsdienst, Germany, 1984, Med. Mission Sisters, Ethiopia, 1985; lectr., instr., performer, worship leader, song leader for various groups by invitation, nat. and internat., 1967—. Author: Preparing the Way of the Lord, 1978, God-With-Us: Resources for Prayer and Praise, 1979, An Anthology of Scripture Songs, 1982, Why Sing? Toward a Theology of Catholic Church Music, 1984, WomanPrayer, Woman Song: Resources for Ritual, 1987, WomanWord: A Feminist Lectionary and Psalter, 1990, WomanWisdom: A Feminist Lectionary and Psalter, Women of the Hebrew Scriptures, Part I, 1992 (First Place award for books on liturgy Cath. Press. Assn. 1992), WomanWitness: A Feminist Lectionary and Psalter, Women of the Hebrew Scriptures, Part II, 1992 (First Place award for books on liturgy Cath. Press Assn. 1993), The Gospel According to Mary: A New Testament for Women, 1993; co-author: Defecting in Place: Women Claiming Responsibility for Their Own Spiritual Lives, 1994, The Chronicles of Noah and Her Sisters: Genesis and Exodus According to Women, 1995; author numerous songs included in albums EarthSong, WomanSong, Remember Me, Sandstone, Songs of Promise, RSVP: Let Us Pray, Gold, Incense and Myrrh, In Love, Seasons (Christian Oscar award Nat. Evang. Film Found. 1971), Knock, Knock, Praise the Lord in Many Voices (live recording of Mass of A Pilgrim People premired at Carnegie Hall, 1967), I Know the Secret, Joy is Like the Rain (Gold album in USA and Australia), Mass of A Pilgrim People (live recording premiered at Carnegi Hall 1967); contbr. articles to profl. jours. Bd. dirs. Capitol Region Conf. Chs., 1984-91, v.p., 1986-88, pres. bd. dirs., 1988-90, past. pres., 1990-91, Archdiocesan Office Urban Affairs, 1986-95; mem. Christian Conf. Conn. ann. event WINFEST, 1986, 87; mem. small christian communities design team Archdiocese of Hartford, 1987-91; mem. major events design team RENEW, 1988; subcommn. chair Archdiocesan Office of Synod, 1991; mem. New Eng. team Ministry of Money, 1984-90, 93; mem. hymnal editl. com. United Ch. of Christ, 1993; active Ho. of Bread, Pediats. AIDS Unit Yale-New Haven Hosp., Covenant to Care, Voices of Joy Gospel Choir women imprisoned at Niantic. Grantee Lilly Endowment, 1989-90, 91-93; recipient Ho. of Reps. citation Commonwealth of Pa., 1968, Women in Leadership Edn. award YWCA Conn., 1989, Convenant to Care award for ministry to children, 1993; named to McMaster U. Alumni Gallery, 1982, Celebration of 120 Women in Leadership, 1987, Bayley-Ellard H.S. Hall of Fame, 1993. Mem. ASCAP (Popular Awards list 1968—), Nat. Assn. Pastoral Musicians, N.Am. Acad. of Liturgy, Societas Liturgica. Avocations: photography, calligraphy. Office: Hartford Sem 77 Sherman St Hartford CT 06105

WINTER, PAUL THEODORE, musician; b. Altoona, Pa., Aug. 31, 1939; s. Paul Theodore and Beaulah (Harnish) W. B.A., Northwestern U., 1961. Leader: Paul Winter Sextet, 1961-65, Winter Consort, 1967—; performed concerts in, 26 countries and throughout U.S., 1st jazz group to perform at, White House, 1962, recorded numerous albums; pres. Living Music Records Inc. Founder Living Music Found., 1976. Fellow Lindisfarne Assn., 1977; recipient Global 500 award UN, 7 Grammy nominations, Best New Age Album Grammy Award, 1994 for Spanish Angel, 1995 for Prayer for the Wild Things. Address: Living Music Records Inc PO Box 72 Litchfield CT 06759-0072

WINTER, PETER MICHAEL, physician, anesthesiologist, educator; b. Sverdlovsk, Russia, Aug. 5, 1934; came to U.S., 1938, naturalized, 1944; s. George and Anne Winter; m. Michelle Yakopec, Dec. 28, 1991; children: Karin Anne, Christopher George. Lia Lynn. B.A., Cornell U., 1958; M.D., U. Rochester, 1962. Intern U. Utah, Salt Lake City, 1962-63; resident in anesthesiology, pharmacology and respiratory physiology Mass. Gen. Hosp., Boston, 1963-65; USPHS fellow Harvard U. Med. Sch., 1964-66; Buswell fellow dept. physiology, asst. prof. SUNY, Buffalo, 1966-69; assoc. prof. dept. anesthesiology Sch. Medicine, U. Wash., Seattle, 1969-74; prof. Sch. Medicine, U. Wash., 1974-79; prof., chmn. dept. anesthesiology and critical care medicine U. Pitts. Sch. Medicine, 1979—, Peter and Eva Safar prof. anesthesiology/critical care med.; anesthesiologist in chief Univ. Health Ctr. Hosps., Pitts. Editorial cons. Anesthesiology; contbr. chpts. to books, papers and abstracts on anesthesia, environ. phys. pharmacology and med. edn. to publs. Served with U.S. Army, 1953-56. Recipient NIH career devel. award, 1971. Mem. AMA, Am. Coll. Chest Physicians, Am. Soc. Anesthesiologists, Royal Soc. Medicine, N.Y. Acad. Scis., Undersea Med. Soc. Internat. Anesthesia Research Soc., Soc. Acad. Anesthesia Chairmen, Assn. Univ. Anesthetists. Club: Alt. Alpine. Office: U Pitts Sch Medicine 1385 Scaife Hall Pittsburgh PA 15261-2013

WINTER, RALPH KARL, JR., federal judge; b. Waterbury, Conn., July 30, 1935; married. B.A., Yale U., 1957, J.D., 1960. Bar: Conn. 1973. Research assoc., lectr. Yale U., 1962-64, asst. prof. to assoc. prof. law, 1964-68, prof. law, 1968-82; spl. cons. subcom. on separation of powers U.S. Senate Com. on Judiciary, 1968-72; sr. fellow Brookings Inst., 1968-70; adj. scholar Am. Enterprise Inst., 1972-82; judge U.S. Ct. Appeals (2d cir.), New Haven, 1982—; vis. prof. law U. Chgo., 1966; mem. Adv. Com. Civil Rights, 1987-92; chair Adv. Com. Rules Evidence, 1993. Contbr. articles to profl. jours. Office: US Ct Appeals 55 Whitney Ave New Haven CT 06510-1300*

WINTER, ROBERT BRUCE, orthopaedic surgeon, educator; b. Cedar Rapids, Iowa, June 21, 1932; s. Fred Aldrich and Mildred Elizabeth (Cavin) W.; m. Jane Havenhill, Aug. 31, 1957; children: Catherine, Sarah, David, Andrew, Karin. BA, Grinnell Coll., 1954; MD, Washington U., 1958. Intern Mpls. Gen. Hosp., 1958-59; resident in orthopedic surgery U. Minn., Mpls., 1959-63, asst. prof. orthopaedic surgery, 1971-76, prof., 1976-86, clin. prof., 1986—; pvt. practice specializing in orthopaedic surgery St. Paul, 1963-71; ret., 1995; dir. med. edn. Gillette Children's Hosp., St. Paul, 1968-80. Author: Textbook of Congenital Deformities of the Spine, 1983; co-author: Textbook of Scoliosis, 3rd edit. 1994; co-editor: Pediatric Orthopaedics, 1978. Mem. AMA, Minn. Med. Assn., Pediatric Orthopaedic Soc. (sec. 1974-79), Scoliosis Rsch. Soc. (pres. 1974), Am. Acad. Orthopaedic Surgeons, Am. Orthopaedic Assn. Office: 606 24th Ave S Minneapolis MN 55454-1439

WINTER, ROGER PAUL, government official; b. Hartford, Conn., July 13, 1942; s. Raymond Gustav and Marion Nellie (Stafford) W.; m. Delorise Allen, Aug. 22, 1966; children: Jonathan, Raymond Todd, Nicole. B.A. in Psychology, Wheaton Coll., 1964; LLD (hon.), Holy Family Coll., 1993. Asst. sec. Md. Dept. Human Resources, Balt., 1970-79, Md. Dept. Budget and Fiscal Planning, Annapolis, 1979-80; dir. Office of Refugee Resettlement, HHS, Washington, 1980-81, U.S. Com. for Refugees, Washington, 1981—; exec. dir. Immigration and Refugee Svcs. Am., Washington, 1994—; cons. on refugee affairs Women's Refugee Project, Washington, 1981-84; adv. bd. Refugee Policy Group, 1981-86; mem. bd. Refugee Voices, 1988—; mem. exec. com. Coun. Washington Reps. on UN, 1989-91. Recipient Disting. Service Cambodian Assn. Am., 1982, Disting. Service award Indochina Resource Action Ctr., 1988. Mem. Nat. Ry. Hist. Soc.-Balt., Sudan Relief and Rehab. Assn. (bd. dirs., sec. 1991-93). Lodge: Eagles. Home: 6328 Departed Sunset Ave Columbia MD 21044-2562 Office: US Com for Refugees 1717 Massachusetts Ave NW Washington DC 20036

WINTER, RUTH GROSMAN (MRS. ARTHUR WINTER), journalist; b. Newark, May 29, 1930; d. Robert Delmas and Rose (Rich) Grosman; m. Arthur Winter, June 16, 1955; children: Robin, Craig, Grant. B.A., Upsala Coll., 1951; MS, Pace U., 1989. With Houston Press, 1955-56; gen. assignment Newark Star Ledger, 1951-55, sci. editor, 1956-69; columnist L.A. Times Syndicate, 1973-78, Register and Tribune, syndicate, 1981-85; contbr. to consumer mags.; instr. St. Peters Coll., Jersey City; vis. lectr. mag. writing Rutgers U. Author: Poisons in Your Food, rev. edits., 1971, 91, How to Reduce Your Medical Bills, 1970, A Consumers Dictionary of Food Additives, 1972, 3d rev. edit., 1994, Vitamin E: The Miracle Worker, 1972, So You Have Sinus Trouble, 1973, Ageless Aging, 1973, So You Have a Pain in the Neck, 1974, A Consumers Dictionary of Cosmetic Ingredients, 1974, 4th rev. edit., 1994, Don't Panic, 1975, The Fragile Bond: Marriage in the '70's, 1976, Triumph Over Tension, 1976, The Smell Book: Scent, Sex and Society, 1976 (N.J. Press Women's Book award), Scent Talk Among Animals, 1977, Cancer Causing Agents: A Preventive Guide, 1979, The Great Self-Improvement Sourcebook, 1980, The Scientific Case Against Smoking, 1980, People's Guide to Allergies and Allergens, 1984; co-author: The Lean Line One Month Lighter Program, 1985, Thin Kids Program, 1985, Build Your Brain Power, 1986, Eat Right! Be Bright, 1988, A Consumer's Dictionary of Household, Yard and Office Chemicals, 1992, A Consumer's Guide to Free Medical Information By Phone and By Mail, 1993, A

Consumer's Dictionary of Medicines: Prescription, Over-the Counter and Herbal, 1994. Recipient award of merit ADA, 1966, Cecil award Arthritis Found., 1967, Am. Soc. Anesthesiologists award, 1969, Arthritis Found. award, 1978; named Alumnus of Year Upsala Coll., 1971, Woman of Year N.J. Daily Newspaper Women, 1971, Woman of Achievement Millburn Short Hills Profl. and Bus. Women's Assn., 1991. Mem. Soc. Mag. Writers, Authors League, Nat. Assn. Sci. Writers, Am. Med. Writers Assn. (Eric Martin Meml. award), N.J. Daily Newspaper Women (awards news series 1958, 70, named Woman of Achievement 1971, 83), Am. Soc. Journalists and Authors (pres. 1977-78, spl. service award 1983), N.J. Press Women (pres. 1982-84). Home and Office: 44 Holly Dr Short Hills NJ 07078-1318

WINTER, THOMAS SWANSON, editor, newspaper executive; b. Teaneck, N.J., Dec. 28, 1937; s. Frank J. and Beulah (Swanson) W.; m. Dawne Cina, Mar. 28, 1978; children—Victoria Ruth, Abigail Swanson. A.B., Harvard U., 1959, M.B.A., 1961. Asst. editor Human Events newspaper Human Events, Inc., Washington, 1961-64, editor, 1964—, co-owner, pres., 1966—; pres. Fund for Objective News Reporting. Treas. Conservative Victory Fund, Washington, 1975—; 1st vice chmn. Am. Conservative Union, 1972—. Lutheran. Clubs: Nat. Press, Capitol Hill. Home: 16 4th St SE Washington DC 20003-3804 Office: Human Events 422 1st St SE Washington DC 20003-1803

WINTER, WILBURN JACKSON, JR., financial executive; b. Savannah, Ga., June 23, 1944. BSBA, U. N.C., 1966. Asst. v.p. Nations Bank, Charlotte, N.C., 1969-74; v.p. 1st Nat. Bank Chgo., Atlanta, 1974-86; prin. Acorn Fin. Svcs., Inc., Atlanta, 1986-88; v.p. Greyhound Fin. Corp., Atlanta, 1988-89; mng. dir. LBO Capital Corp., Atlanta, 1989-90; sr. v.p., CFO, Rosser Internat., Inc., Atlanta, 1990—. Lt. USN, 1966-69; capt. USNR, 1969—. Mem. Assn. for Corp. Growth, Soc. Am. Mil. Engrs., Constrn. Fin. Mgmt. Assn., Atlanta Venture Forum, S.R. Home: No 8 3050 Margaret Mitchell Dr Atlanta GA 30327 Office: Rosser Internat Inc 524 W Peachtree St NW Atlanta GA 30308-3512

WINTER, WILLIAM EARL, mayor, retired beverage company executive; b. Granite City, Ill., Sept. 21, 1920; s. William M. and Ada M. (Compton) W.; m. Dorothy E. Schuster, Feb. 20, 1944 (dec. 1976); children: William C., Douglas E.; m. Mildred E. Stiebel, Mar. 18, 1977. A.B, U. Ill., 1942. With Seven-Up Co., St. Louis, 1946-81; v.p., dir. mktg. Seven-Up Co., 1969-71, exec. v.p., 1971-74, pres., chief operating officer, 1974-76, pres., chief exec. officer, 1976-79, chmn. bd., 1979-81, also former dir., cons.; mayor City of Creve Coeur, Mo. Bd. dirs. Combined Health Appeals Am., YMCA Greater St. Louis, U. Ill. Found., Deaconess Hosp. Found.; mem. exec. bd. St. Louis Area coun. Boy Scouts Am. Capt. U.S. Army, 1942-46. Named to Promotion Mktg. Hall of Fame, 1979, Beverage World Hall of Fame, 1986. Mem. Am. Mktg. Assn., Sales and Mktg. Execs. St. Louis, Promotion Mktg. Assn. Am. (chmn. bd. 1971-72), Phi Beta Kappa, Phi Eta Sigma, Omicron Delta Gamma. Home: 12310 Boothbay Ct Saint Louis MO 63141-8119 Office: Seven-Up Co 8900 Page Ave Saint Louis MO 63114-6103

WINTER, WILLIAM FORREST, former governor, lawyer; b. Grenada, Miss., Feb. 21, 1923; s. William Aylmer and Inez (Parker) W.; m. Elise Varner, Oct. 10, 1950; children: Anne, Elise, Eleanor. BA, U. Miss., 1943, LLB, 1949; LLD, William Carey Coll., 1980, Millsaps Coll., 1983, Troy State U., 1988. Bar: Miss. 1949. Practice in Grenada, 1949-58; practice in Jackson, Miss., 1968—; ptnr. Watkins, Pyle, Ludlam, Winter and Stennis, 1968-80; sr. ptnr. Watkins, Ludlam & Stennis, 1985—; mem. Miss. Ho. of Reps., 1948-56; state tax collector, 1956-64, state treas., 1964-68; lt. gov. State of Miss., 1972-76; gov., 1980-84; Eudora Welty prof. So. studies Millsaps Coll., 1989, Jamie Whitten prof. law U. Miss., 1989; chmn. So. Growth Policies Bd., 1981, So. Regional Edn. Bd., 1982, Adv. Commn. on Intergovtl. Rels., 1993—; bd. dirs. MDC, Inc. Pres. bd. trustees Miss. Dept. Archives and History; chmn. Kettering Found., 1990-93, Appalachian Regional Commn., 1983, Commn. on Future of South, 1986, Nat. Civic League, 1987-88, Nat. Commn. on State and Local Pub. Svc., Stennis Ctr. for Pub. Svc., Found. for the Mid South. With AUS, 1943-46, 51. Harvard U. Inst. Politics fellow, 1985. Mem. Am., Miss., Hinds County bar assns., U. Miss. Alumni Assn. (pres. 1976), Phi Delta Phi, Omicron Delta Kappa, Phi Delta Theta. Democrat. Presbyterian. Club: Univ. (Jackson). Office: 633 N State St Jackson MS 39202-3304

WINTER, WINTON ALLEN, JR., lawyer, state senator; b. Ft. Knox, Ky., Apr. 19, 1953; s. Winton A. and Nancy (Morsbach) W.; m. Mary Boyd, July 28, 1978; children: Kate, Molly, Elizabeth. BA, U. Kans., 1975, JD, 1978. Bar: Kans. 1978. Ptnr. law firm Stevens, Brand, Lungstrum, Golden & Winter, Lawrence, Kans., 1978—; pres. Corp. for Change; mem. Kans. Senate, 1982-92. Bd. dirs. Lawrence United Fund, Boys Club of Lawrence. Mem. ABA, Kans. Bar Assn., Douglas County Bar Assn. Kans. U. Law Soc. Republican. Roman Catholic. Club: Rotary. Note and comment editor Kans. Law Rev., 1977-78. Office: PO Box 189 502 Mercantile Bank Tower Lawrence KS 66044-0189

WINTERER, PHILIP STEELE, lawyer; b. San Francisco, July 8, 1931; s. Steele Leland and Esther (Hardy) W.; m. Patricia Dowling, June 15, 1955; children: Edward J., Amey C. BA, Amherst Coll., 1953; LLB, Harvard U., 1956. Bar: N.Y. 1957, Republic of Korea 1958. Assoc. Debevoise & Plimpton, N.Y.C., 1956-65, ptnr., 1966-93, of counsel, 1994—; dir. Am. Savs. Bank, 1972-92. Contbr. articles to profl. publs. Trustee Amherst Coll.; bd. dirs., past pres. Am. Italy Soc.; chmn. exec. com. Phipps Houses; chmn. Austen Riggs Ctr.; vice chmn. N.Y. State Bd. Nature Conservancy; bd. dirs. Phi Beta Kappa Assocs. Recipient Amherst Coll. medal for Eminent Service, 1980. Mem. Assn. of Bar of City of N.Y., Coun. on Fgn. Rels., Am. Law Inst. (tax adv. group), Citizens Housing and Planning Coun. N.Y., N.Y. Sci. Policy Assn., N.Y. Acad. Scis., Tax Forum, Am. Coll. Tax Counsel. Home: 1165 Fifth Ave New York NY 10029 Office: Debevoise & Plimpton 875 3rd Ave New York NY 10022-6225

WINTERHALTER, DOLORES AUGUST (DEE WINTERHALTER), art educator; b. Pitts., Mar. 22, 1928; d. Joseph Peter and Helen August; m. Paul Joseph Winterhalter, June 21, 1947 (dec.); children: Noreen, Audrey, Mark; m. Marvin Bernard Hoeing, Mar. 26, 1988 (div. dec. 1995). Student, Yokohama, Japan, 1963-64, Paris, 1968-70. Cert. tchr. Japanese Flower Arranging, Kamakuri Wood Carving. Tchr. YWCA, Greenwich, Conn., 1978-84, Friends of the Arts and Scis., Sarasota, Fla., 1992—; lectr. Sarasota Art Assn., 1984—; tchr., workshop presenter, Bangkok, 1971; mem. staff Hilton Leech Art Studio and Gallery, Sarasota; events chmn. State of Fla. Watercolor Exhbn., Sarasota, 1995. Numerous works in watercolor, ink, oriental brushwork; paintings in numerous corp. collections. Pres. Am. Women's Club, Genoa, Italy, 1962; participant to help raise money for scholarships Collectors and Creators Tour of Fine ARts Soc. of Sarasota, 1994. Recipient numerous awards Old Greenwich (Conn.) Art Assn., 1971-84, Sarasota, 1985, Collectors and Creators Tour award Fine Arts Soc. Sarasota, 1994; named Artist of Yr., Fine Arts Soc. Sarasota, 1994. Mem. Nat. League Am. Pen Women (pres. Sarasota br. 1994—), Suncoast Fla. Watercolor Soc. (life), Fla. Watercolor Soc., Long Boat Key Art Assn., Sarasota Art Assn., Sumi-e Soc. Am. Democrat. Roman Catholic. Avocations: wood carving, travel, bridge, creative design in crochet and fashion. Home and Office: 5773 Whistlewood Cir Sarasota FL 34232

WINTERMANS, JOSEPH JACK GERARD FRANCIS, financial services executive; b. Eindhoven, North Brabant, The Netherlands, Oct. 4, 1946; arrived in Can., 1973; s. Joseph J.F.G. and Catherine (Van Dijk) W.; m. Eileen Simon, Oct. 30, 1972. LLB, Leyden, The Netherlands, 1967, LLM, 1972; MBA, Queens, Kingston, Ont., Can., 1972. V.p. Bristol Myers Can., Toronto, Ont. 1981-82; sr. v.p. Am. Express Can., Markham, Ont., 1982-87; pres. Can. Tire Acceptance Ltd., Welland, Ont., 1988—; sr. v.p. diversified bus. Can. Tire Corp., 1995—. Hon. fellow Ryerson Poly. Univ., Toronto, 1993. Mem. Am. Mktg. Assn. (pres. Toronto chpt. 1981-82). Office: Can Tire Acceptance Ltd, 555 Prince Charles Dr, Welland, ON Canada L3C 6B5

WINTERMUTE, MARJORIE MCLEAN, architect, educator; b. Great Falls, Mont., Sept. 15, 1919; d. Allan Edward and Gladys Pearl (Pelton) McLean; m. Charles Richard Wintermute, June 14, 1947 (div.); children: Lynne Wintermute, Lane. BA, U. Oreg., 1941; postgrad. Portland State U., 1969-72. Registered architect, Oreg. Archtl. draftsman Def. Projects, Portland and San Francisco, 1941-43; architect Pietro Belluschi, Portland, 1943-

47; free-lance architect, Portland, 1948—; architect-in-residence Edn. Service Dist., Portland, 1978-91, ret.; instr. Portland State U., 1973—; architect-in-residence Dept. Def. Dependents Sch. Asian Region Hdqrs. Japan, 1981-83; with Upshur Group Collaborative, 1976-87; architect-in-residence program coord. Oreg. Arts Commn., 1987—, AIA; leader archtl. tours to Europe, 1969, 71, 73, Greece and Turkey, 1989, 91. Author: Students, Structures, Spaces, 1983, Blueprints: A Built Environment Education Program, 1984, Architecture As A Basic Curriculum Builder, 1987-90; editor: Pitter Patter (Gold medal 1965), 1960-69. Prin. archtl. works include comml. and residential bldgs. and restoration and mus. installation Timberline Lodge, Oreg., 1983, 2d Timberline Restoration project, 1993. Bd. dirs. Oreg. Heart Assn., Portland, 1960-70, pres. 1968-69; bd. dirs. Friends of Timberline, Creative Arts Community, pres. 1993—; program devel. cons. Am. Heritage Assn., Lake Oswego, Oreg., 1969-83, Mt. Angel Abbey, St. Benedict, Oreg., 1970-73; bd. dirs., com. chmn. Environ. Edn. Assn., Portland, 1978-85. Recipient Disting. Citizen award Environ. Edn. Assn., 1983; role model award area coun. Girl Scouts, 1994; Woman of Achievement award Inst. Profl. and Managerial Women, 1984; Woman of Distinction award Women in Arch., 1993, named Disting. Citizen Portland Hist. Landmarks Commn., 1988, fellowship in The Am. Inst. of Architects, 1978. Fellow AIA (pub. edn. com. 1970-80, chair 1972-73); mem. Women's Archtl. League (bd. dirs., com. chmn. 1980—), Fashion Group Internat. (facilitator 1983-84), Ednl. Futures Inc. (Western rep. 1978-83), Oreg. State Dept. Edn. (adv. bd. 1980-83). Republican. Presbyterian. Home: 6740 SW Canyon Ln # 1 Portland OR 97225-3606

WINTEROWD, WALTER ROSS, English educator; b. Salt Lake City, Jan. 24, 1930; s. Harold Ross and Henrietta Ethel (Fike) W.; m. Norma Graham, Aug. 2, 1952; children: Geoffrey Ross, Anderson Gordon. B.S., Utah State U., 1952; Ph.D., U. Utah, 1960. Asst. prof. U. Mont., Missoula, 1962-66; assoc. prof. U. So. Calif. Los Angeles, 1966-71, prof. English, 1971-79; McElderry prof. English U. So. Calif., 1979—. Author: Rhetoric: A Synthesis, 1967, Contemporary Rhetoric, 1975, The Contemporary Writer, 1975, Composition/Rhetoric: A Synthesis, 1986, The Culture and Politics of Literacy, 1989, The Rhetoric of the "Other" Literature, 1990, (with Geoffrey Winterowd) The Critical Reader, Thinker, and Writer, 1992. Served with U.S. Army, 1953-55. Mem. Nat. Council Tchrs. English, AAUP. Democrat. Home: 17551 San Roque Ln Huntington Beach CA 92647-6641 Office: Dept English U So Calif Los Angeles CA 90089-0354

WINTERROND, WILLIAM J., bishop. Bishop Diocese of Colo., Denver, 1991—. Office: Diocese of Colo PO Box M 1300 Washington Denver CO 80203

WINTERS, ARTHUR RALPH, JR., chemical and cryogenic engineer, consultant; b. Mercer, Pa., May 17, 1926; s. Arthur Ralph and Rebecca Grace (McLaughry) W.; m. Elizabeth Colt Burgess, Oct. 4, 1952; children: Philip, Andrew, Paul. BSChemE summa cum laude, Lafayette Coll., Easton, Pa., 1948; SM, MIT, 1952. Registered profl. engr., Pa. Devel. engr. Allied Chem. Corp., Morristown, N.J., 1948-50; process engr. Monsanto Co., Boston and St. Louis, 1952-55; specialist Gen. Electric Co., Hudson Falls, N.Y., 1955-62; process mgr. Air Products and Chems. Inc., Trexlertown, Pa., 1963-86; sr. cons. Cryogenic Cons. Inc., Allentown, Pa., 1986—. Contbr. articles to profl. jours. Pres. Saucon Assn. for a Viable Environ., Coopersburg, Pa., 1981-86, other offices, 1976-92. Mem. NSPE, AIChE (chairperson 1980-81), Am. Chem. Soc., Phi Beta Kappa, Tau Beta Pi. Republican. Presbyterian. Achievements include patents; design and construction of nuclear off-gas clean-up systems for use in some 50 nuclear plants worldwide. Home: 4584 Pleasant View Dr Coopersburg PA 18036 Office: CCI Cryogenics Inc 1176 N Irving St Allentown PA 18103

WINTERS, BARBARA JO, musician; b. Salt Lake City; d. Louis McClain and Gwendolyn (Bradley) W. AB cum laude, UCLA, 1960, postgrad., 1961; postgrad., Yale, 1960. Mem. oboe sect. L.A. Philharm., 1961-94, prin. oboist, 1972-94; ret.; clinician oboe, English horn, Oboe d'amore. Recs. movie, TV sound tracks. Avocation: painting in oils and mixed media. Home: 3529 Coldwater Canyon Ave Studio City CA 91604-4060 Office: 135 N Grand Ave Los Angeles CA 90012-3013

WINTERS, DONALD, finance company executive. Pres. Farm Cr. Svcs. Mid. Am. An. Acad., Louisville, 1970—. Office: Farm Cr Svcs Mid Am An Aca 700 Hilliard Lyons Ctr Louisville KY 40202*

WINTERS, HAROLD FRANKLIN, physicist; b. Renton, Wash., May 19, 1932; s. Walter Wade and Ruth Elizabeth (Meyer) W.; m. Marjorie Ann Neiswender, June 9, 1956; children: Kathie Nee, David Winters, John Winters, Janice Assadi, Judy Ahlquist. Attended, Biola Coll., 1950-51; BS, Whitworth Coll., 1958; PhD, Washington State U., 1963. Rsch. staff mem. IBM Almaden Rsch. Ctr., San Jose, Calif., 1963-93; emeritus IBM Almaden Rsch. Ctr., San Jose, 1993—; vis. prof. Odense U., Denmark, 1979-80; past N.Am. rep. Subcom. on Plasma Chemistry, Internat. Union Pure and Applied Chemistry; past lectr. numerous major nat. and internat. confs. throughout the world. Mem. editorial bd. Plasma Materials Interactions; contbr. numerous articles to sci. jours. Corp. U.S. Army, 1952-54. Recipient (with John Coburn) Thinkers award Tegal Corp., 1983, Disting. Alumni Achievement award Wash. State U., 1992, John A. Thornton Meml. award and lectr. Am. Vacuum Soc., 1993, honored by plasma sci. divsn. of Am. Vacuum Soc. with naming of John Coburn and Harold Winters Student Award, 1994. Mem. AAAS, Am. Sci. Affiliation. Achievements include patents for plasma processing, ion sources and ion pumps; scientific contributions in the fields of plasma science, surface science, thin films, ion bombardment of solids, dissociation of gases by electron impact. Home: 632 Lanfair Dr San Jose CA 95136-1947 Office: IBM Almaden Rsch Ctr 650 Harry Rd San Jose CA 95120-6099

WINTERS, J. OTIS, oil industry consultant; b. Tulsa, Nov. 6, 1932; s. John McAfee, Jr. and Marian Dunn (McClintock) W.; m. Ann Allene Varnadow, Oct. 18, 1958; children: John, Richard, David. Paul. MS in Petroleum Engring., Stanford U., 1955; MBA, Harvard U., 1962. Registered profl. engr., Okla. V.p. Warren Am. Oil Co., Tulsa, 1962-65; pres. Ednl. Devel. Corp., Tulsa, 1965-73; exec. v.p. dir. Williams Cos., Tulsa, 1973-77, First Nat. Bank of Tulsa, 1978-79; pres. Zephyr Corp., Tulsa, 1980-90; chmn. Pate Winters & Stone Inc., 1990—; bd. dirs. Triton Energy Corp., NGC Corp., Hat Brands, Inc., Liberty Bancorp Inc., United Medicorp Inc. Chmn. bd. First United Meth. Ch., 1977-79; pres. Downtown Tulsa Unltd., 1977; former vice chmn. bd. Oral Roberts U.; bd. dirs. Jr. Achievement; commr. Tulsa Urban Renewal Authority; 1st v.p. Ark. Basin Devel. Assn. Served as 1st lt., C.E. U.S. Army, 1955-57. Recipient various pub. service awards. Mem. Tulsa C.C. (bd. dirs.), Square Hills Club (Tulsa), Pine Valley Club, Augusta Golf Club, Cypress Point Club, Royal and Ancient Club, St. Andrews Club. Home: 4616 Christopher Pl Dallas TX 75204-1611 Office: Pate Winters & Stone Inc 5956 Sherry Ln Ste 2001 Dallas TX 75225

WINTERS, J. SAM, lawyer, federal official; b. Amarillo, Tex., July 7, 1922; m. Dorothy Jean Rushing, Dec. 21, 1947; 1 child, Leila Winters Mischer. BA, U. Tex., 1944, JD, 1948. Bar: Tex. 1948. Briefing atty. Supreme Ct. Tex., Austin, 1948-49; chief Charter div. Sec. of State, State of Tex., Austin, 1949-50; ptnr. Bagby & Winters, Austin, 1950-57; shareholder Clark, Thomas, & Winters, Austin, 1957—; bd. govs. U.S. Postal Svc., Washington, 1991-95; chmn. bd. govs. U.S. Postal Svc., 1994-96; mem. stds. com. Nat. Flood Inst. Program, Washington, 1990-93, dir. 1990-94. Bd. dirs. Tex. Assn. Taxpayers; mem. devel. bd. U. Tex., Austin, 1988—, mem. Pres.'s Assocs., 1981—; mem. chancellor's coun. U. Tex. Sys., 1983—; mem. symposium planning com. Lyndon B. Johnson Sch. Pub. Affairs, Austin, 1987—. Mem. ABA (chair-elect, sect. pub. utility comm. and transp. law), State Bar Tex., Travis County Bar Assn., Tex. Bar Found., Internat. Assn. Def. Counsel. Tex. Assn. Def. Counsel, Fedn. Ins. and Corp. Counsel, Tex. Rsch. League (past chair), Tex. Coun. Econ. Edn., Tex. Hist. Soc., Panhandle Plains Hist. Soc., SAR. Democrat. Episcopalian. Office: Clark Thomas & Winters PO Box 1148 Austin TX 78767

WINTERS, JONATHAN, actor; b. Dayton, Ohio, Nov. 11, 1925; s. Jonathan H. and Alice Kilgore (Rodgers) W.; m. Eileen Ann Schauder, Sept. 11, 1948; children: Jonathan IV, Lucinda Kelley. Student, Kenyon Coll., 1946; B.F.A., Dayton Art Inst., 1950. With radio sta. WING, Dayton, 1949; disc jockey sta. WBNS-TV, Columbus, Ohio, 1950-53. Appeared on:

Garry Moore Show, 1954-63, Steve Allen Show, 1954-61, Omnibus, 1954, NBC Comedy Hour, 1956, Jonathan Winters Show, 1956-57, Jack Paar Show, 1963-64, Andy Williams Show, 1966-67, Dean Martin Show, 1966-67, Jonathan Winters Show, CBS-TV, 1968-69, Wacky World of Jonathan Winters, 1972-73; numerous appearances NBC Monitor show, 1963—. Hollywood Squares, 1975—; TV series include Mork & Mindy, 1982-83, Davis Rules, (Emmy award for best supporting actor) 1991-92, 5 spls. Showtime Cable TV; night club appearances, 1953-60; motion picture appearances: It's a Mad, Mad, Mad World, 1963, The Loved One, 1964, The Russians Are Coming, The Russians Are Coming, 1966, Penelope, 1967, The Midnight Oil, 1967, 8 On the Lam, 1967, Oh Dad, Poor Dad, 1968, Viva Max, 1969, The Fish That Saved Pittsburgh, 1979, The Longshot, 1986, Say Yes, 1986, Moon Over Parador, 1988, The Flintstones, 1994, The Shadow, 1994; rec. artist, Columbia Records.; author: Mouse Breath, Conformity and Other Social Ills, 1965, Winter's Tales, 1987, Hang-Ups, 1990; voice numerous cartoon characters. Served with USMCR, 1943-46, PTO. Named to Comedy Hall of Fame U.S., 1993, Comedy Hall of Fame Can., 1994.

WINTERS, SISTER MARY ANN, religious organization administrator; b. Paterson, N.J., Nov. 15, 1937; d. Russell Lewis and Nellie Marie (Cramer) W. BA, Seton Hill Coll., 1967; PhD, U. Pitts., 1972. Tchr. various cath. schs., Pa., Ariz., 1957-67; from instr. to chmn. chemistry dept. Seton Hill Coll., Greensburg, Pa., 1967-68, 72-81; councilor Sisters Charity Seton Hill, Greensburg, Pa., 1981-85, major superior, 1985—; mem. task force Leadership Conf. Women Religious, Silver Springs, Md. 1986-88; retreat dir. Sisters of Charity Seton Hill, Greensburg, Pa., 1977-81. Trustee Seton Hill Coll., Greensburg, Pa., Jeannette Dist. Meml. Hosp., Jeannette, Pa., DePaul Inst., Pitts.; mem. Ethics Task Force Forbes Regional, Pitts. Named Teacher of Yr., Seton Hill Coll., Greensburg, Pa., 1981. Mem. Am. Chem. Soc., Tri-Diocesan Sisters' Leadership Coun. (pres. 1988—), Elizabeth Seton Fedn. (exec. com. 1989—). Avocations: walking, handwork, listening to music, cooking. Office: Sisters Charity Seton Hill De Paul Ctr Mt Thor Rd Greensburg PA 15601-1233

WINTERS, NOLA FRANCES, food company executive; b. Achilles, Kans., Aug. 27, 1925; d. Edward Earl and Mary Ruby (Mikesell) Ginther; divorced. Student, U. Kans., 1943-45; BA, U. Colo., 1972. Exec. sec. Holly Sugar Corp., Colorado Springs, Colo., 1953-66, asst. sec., 1966-84, dir. corp rels., asst. sec., 1981-84, dir. corp. and pub. rels. asst. sec. 1984-90; asst. sec. HSC Export Corp., Colorado Springs, 1980-90, Imperial Holly Corp., Colorado Springs, 1988-90. Mem. Phi Beta Kappa. Republican. Methodist.

WINTERS, RALPH E., film editor. Films include Gaslight, Little Women, King Solomon's Mines, Quo Vadis (Acad. award nomination), Kiss Me Kate, Executive Suite, Seven Brides for Seven Brothers (Acad. award nomination), High Society, Jailhouse Rock, Ben-hur (Acad. award), Butterfield 8, Soldier in the Rain, The Pink Panther, The Great Race (Acad. award nomination), Fitzwilly, How to Succeed in Business without Really Trying, The Party, The Thomas Crown Affair, The Hawaiians, Kotch (Acad. award nomination), The Front Page, Mr. Majestyk, King Kong, 10, S.O.B., Victor Victoria, Curse of the Pink Panther, Big Trouble, Let's Get Harry, Moving, Tagget. Office: The Mirisch Agy 10100 Santa Monica Blvd Ste 70 Los Angeles CA 90067

WINTERS, ROBERT CHARLES, architect; b. Cleve., July 18, 1946; s. Charles J. Winters and Grace (Campbell) Patchin; m. Janis Jaclyn Robison, Aug. 31, 1968; children: Jason Andrew, Aaron Robert. BArch, Kent State U., 1971. Project architect, designer Forest City-Dillon/Hecky and Yee Architects, Akron, Ohio, 1971-73; assoc., project architect Fletcher Properties Inc., Jacksonville, Fla., 1973-75; designer, architect Richard L. Bowen and Assoc., Cleve., 1975-76; v.p. design Hass and Reed Architects Inc., Jacksonville, 1976-78; archtl. mgr. Structures Med. East Corp., Jacksonville, 1978-81; owner Winterstudio, Jacksonville, 1980—; ptnr., exec. v.p. Manss and Winters Architects and Planners Inc., Jacksonville, 1983-86; pvt. practice architecture Jacksonville, 1986—. Mem. AIA, Constrn. Specification Inst., Nat. Council Archtl. Registration Bds., Jacksonville C. of C. (com. 100 1986—), Epsilon Delta Rho. Avocations: photography, art, music. Office: 420 Wharfside Way Ste A Jacksonville FL 32207-8104

WINTERS, ROBERT CUSHING, insurance company executive; b. Hartford, Conn., Dec. 8, 1931; s. George Warren and Hazel Keith (Cushing) W.; m. Patricia Ann Martini, Feb. 10, 1962; children: Sally, Beth. BA, Yale U., 1953; MBA, Boston U., 1963. With Prudential Ins. Co. Am., 1953—, v.p. actuary, 1969-75, sr. v.p. Can. Atlantic home office, 1975-78, exec. v.p., Newark, 1978-84, vice chmn., 1984-86, chmn., CEO, 1987-94, chmn. emeritus, pres., CEO Prudential Ins. Co. Am., Newark, 1995—; bd. dirs. Allied-Signal Inc. Trustee Mayo Found. With U.S. Army, 1954-56. Fellow Soc. Actuaries; mem. Am. Acad. Actuaries (past pres.), Am. Coun. Life Ins. (chmn. bd. dirs. 1990-91), Bus. Coun., Trilateral Commn., Sigma Xi. Office: Prudential Ins Co Am 751 Broad St Newark NJ 07102-3777

WINTERS, ROBERT W., medical educator, pediatrician; b. Evansville, Ind., May 23, 1926; s. Frank and Clara (Flentke) W.; m. Madoris, Sept. 5, 1948 (div. Feb. 1992); children: Henry N., R. George. m. Agnete Thomsen, Feb. 11, 1992; children: Charlotte, Anne. AB magna cum laude, Indiana U., 1948; MD cum laude, Yale U., 1952. Diplomate Am. Bd. Pediatrics. Intern, resident, and fellow U.N.C., Chapel Hill, 1954-58; asst. prof. U. Pa., Phila., 1959-61; prof. Columbia U., N.Y.C., 1962-81; CEO HNS-Healthdyne, Parsippany, N.J., 1985-89; cons., 1989—. Contbr. to profl. jour.; author 5 books. 2nd lt. cav. U.S. Army, 1944-46. Recipient Mead Johnson award Am. Acad. Pediatrics, 1966, Borden award, 1972. Office: HNS-Healthdyne 600 Lamdex Pl Parsippany NJ 07054

WINTERS, SHELLEY (SHIRLEY SCHRIFT), actress; b. St. Louis, Aug. 18, 1922; m. Vittorio Gassman (div.); 1 child, Vittoria; m. Anthony Franciosa, 1957 (div. Nov. 1960). Student, Wayne U. Began acting career in vaudeville, later played roles on legitimate stage; motion pictures include The Diary of Anne Frank, 1958 (Acad. award best supporting actress), Odds Against Tomorrow, Let No Man Write My Epitaph, Matter of Convictions, Lolita, 1962, Wives and Lovers, 1963, The Balcony, 1964, A House Is Not a Home, 1964, Patch of Blue, 1966 (Acad. award best supporting actress), Time of Indifference, 1965, Alfie, 1965, The Moving Target, 1965, Harper, 1966, Enter Laughing, 1967, The Scalp Hunters, 1968, Buona Sera Mrs. Campbell, 1968, Wild in the Streets, 1968, The Mad Room, 1969, How Do I Love Thee, 1971, What's the Matter with Helen, 1971, The Poseidon Adventure, 1972, Blume in Love, 1973, Cleopatra Jones, 1973, Something to Hide, 1973, Diamonds, 1975, Next Stop Greenwich Village, 1976, The Tenant, 1976, An Average Man, 1977, Tentacles, 1977, Pete's Dragon, 1977, King of the Gypsies, 1978, The Visitor, 1980, Looping, 1981, S.O.B., 1981, My Mother, My Daughter, 1981, Over the Brooklyn Bridge, Ellie, Deja Vu, 1985, The Delta Force, 1986, Marilyn Monroe: Beyond the Legend, 1987, Purple People Eater, 1988, An Unremarkable Life, 1989, Touch of a Stranger, 1990, Stepping Out, 1991, The Pickle, 1993; appeared in: TV films Revenge!, 1971, The Devil's Daughter, 1973, Double Indemnity, 1974, The Sex Symbol, 1974, Elvis, 1978, Alice in Wonderland; plays A Hatfull of Rain, 1955, Girls of Summer, 1957, Night of the Iguana, Cages, Who's Afraid of Virginia Wolf?, Minnie's Boys; TV miniseries The French Atlantic Affair, 1979; Author: play One Night Stands of a Noisy Passenger, 1971; autobiography Shelley: Also Known As Shirley, 1980, Shelley II: The Middle of My Century, 1989. Recipient Annual award Best Actress, 1964, Monte Carlo Golden Nymph award, 1964, Internat. TV award as best actress Cannes Festival, 1965.

WINTERS, SUZANNE, biomedical scientist, researcher; b. Cleve., Feb. 10, 1954; d. William Ebersole and Mary Louise (Stough) W.; m. Robert Howard Ramsey, Mar. 15, 1986; 1 child, Robert William Ramsey. BS, Ohio Wesleyan U., 1976; PhD, U. Utah, 1986. Rschr. Battelle Columbus (Ohio) Labs., 1976-81; sr. sci. Symbion Inc., Salt Lake City, 1986-90; dir. biomatris/membranes CardioPulmonics, Inc., Salt Lake City, 1986-90; cons. Membrane & Coatings Cons., Salt Lake City, 1990-93; state sci. advisor State of Utah, Salt Lake City, 1993—. Office: Planning & Budget Office 116 State Capitol Bldg Salt Lake City UT 84114

WINTERS, WENDELL DELOS, microbiology educator, researcher, consultant; b. Herrin, Ill., Sept. 24, 1940; s. Charles D. and Juanita (Burness) W.; m. Bonnie Tomlinson (div. Mar. 1990); children: Timothy, Amma Jean,

Craig. BS, U. Ill., 1962; MS, U. Ill., Chgo., 1966, PHD, 1968. Teaching asst. U. Ill. Med. Sch., 1963-68; postdoctoral researcher Mat. Inst. Med. Rsch., London, 1968-70; resarcher Nat. Cancer Inst., NIH, Washington, 1970-71; asst. prof. UCLA Sch. Medicine, 1971-76; assoc. prof. microbiology U. Tex. Health Sci. Ctr., San Antonio, 1977—; cons. Royal Navy, USAF, Nat. Cancer Inst., 1976-82 Am. Med., Kinetic Concepts, Phytotherapeutics, 1983—; chmn. sci. bd., Aloe Rsch. Found., Dallas, Tex., 1989—, pres., 1992—; lectr. Burroughs Wellcome Fund, Cambridge, Eng., 1977, Beckman Rsch., Japan, Australia, 1978, Tomlinson-Burness Fund, Fed. Republic Germany, France, 1980-91, Japan, 1990; rsch. vis. prof. Damon Runyon Cancer Fund, London, 1969-71, NAS, Paris, 1974. Contbr. articles to sci. jours. Mem. West L.A. Housing Bd., 1972-76; mem. scouting com. Boy Scouts Am., San Antonio, 1978-82. Fellow Am. Acad. Microbiology; mem. Bioelec. Repair and Growth Soc. (program chmn. bd. dirs. 1990-92), Tissue Culture Assn. (chmn. meetings 1972—, v.p. Calif. chpt. 1974-76), Am. Soc. Microbiology, Am. Assn. Cancer Rsch., Am. Assn. Immunologists. Achievements include research in immunotherapy as adjunct in cancer treatment, in vitro assembly of human viruses, bioeffects induced by environmental electromagnetic fields, plant substances as phytotherapeutic agents. Office: U Tex Health Sci Ctr Dept Microbiology 7703 Floyd Curl Dr San Antonio TX 78284-6200

WINTERSHEIMER, DONALD CARL, state supreme court justice; b. Covington, Ky., Apr. 21, 1932; s. Carl E. and Marie A. (Kohl) W.; m. Alice T. Rabe, June 24, 1961; children: Mark D., Lisa Ann, Craig P., Amy T., Blaise Q. BA, Thomas More Coll., 1953; MA, Xavier U., 1956; JD, U. Cin., 1959. Bar: Ky. 1960, Ohio 1960. Pvt. practice Covington, Ky., 1960—; city solicitor City of Covington, 1962-76; judge Ky. Ct. Appeals, Frankfort, 1976-83; justice Ky. Supreme Ct., Frankfort, 1983—, chmn. criminal rules com., 1988-94, chmn. continuing jud. edn. com., 1983—, chmn. rules com., 1994—; del. Foster Parent Rev. Bd., 1985—; mem. adv. bd. Sta. WNKU-FM, 1984-94, Am. Soc. Writers on Legal Subjects. Trustee Sta. WNKU-FM. Recipient Cmty. Svc. award Thomas More Coll., 1968; recipient Disting. Alumnus award Thomas More Coll., 1982; named Disting. Jurist Chase Coll. Law, 1983, Outstanding Jurist Phi Alpha Delta Law Frat., 1990. Mem. ABA, Am. Judicature Soc., Ky. Bar Assn., Ohio Bar Assn., Cin. Bar Assn., Inst. Jud. Adminstrn. Democrat. Roman Catholic. Home: 224 Adams Ave Covington KY 41014-1712 Office: Ky Supreme Ct Capitol Building Rm 201 Frankfort KY 40601

WINTERS-MALONEY, CAROL EMERSON, nursing educator, academic administrator; b. Logan, W.Va., Sept. 2, 1949; d. Carmi Emerson and Mary Louise (Stallings) W.; children: Heather, Chapin, Claire. BA cum laude, Greensboro Coll., 1971; BSN magna cum laude, U. N.C. Greensboro, 1974, MSN with honors, 1978; PhD, U. Pitts., 1985. Dir. religious edn. Elon (N.C.) Coll. and Elon Coll. Community Ch., 1971-72; primary nurse Moses H. Cone Meml., Greensboro, 1973-81, Children's Hosp. Pitts., 1981; asst. prof. Allegheny Community Coll., Pitts., 1981-82, U. Pitts., 1982-85, U. Rochester, N.Y., 1986; instr. U. N.C., Greensboro, 1978-81, asst. prof., 1986-90; asst. dir. nursing and health care studies Hawaii Loa Coll, Kaneohe, 1990; dean Nursing and Acad. Adminstrn. Hawaii Loa Campus/ Hawaii Pacific U., Kaneohe, 1990—. Contbr. articles to med. jours. Active PTA, Kaneohe, 1990—. Mem. ANA (Hawaii cabinet on profl. nursing edn., Hawaii cabinet on nursing rsch. 1992), Am. Orgn. Nurse Execs., Epilepsy Found. Am. (bd. dirs.), Sigma Theta Tau (charter, 1st pres. Gamma Zi chpt. 1976-78, counselor 1987-89). Mem. Soc. of Friends. Avocations: Scottish country dance, hula, ukelele and guitar, reading, sailing. Office: Hawaii Pacific U Hawaii Loa Campus 45-045 Kamehameha Hwy Kaneohe HI 96744-5221

WINTHROP, JOHN, investment company executive; b. Boston, June 22, 1936; s. Nathaniel Thayer and Serita Bartlett (Harwood) W.; m. Elizabeth Goltra; children: John, H. Grenville, Bayard, Edward Field Winthrop. BA, Harvard U., 1958; MBA, Columbia U., 1962. With Wood, Struthers & Winthrop, N.Y.C., 1964-79; former chmn. Mgmt. Co. (subs. DJL); pres. de Vegh Fund, 1973-79, dir., 1973—; founder, pres. John Winthrop & Co., N.Y.C.; dir. Alliance Capital Reserves, N.Y.C., Nat. Utilities & Industries, N.J., Ivanhoe Plantation, Inc., S.C., Pioneer Funds, Boston; bd. dirs. Am. Farmland Trust, Washington. Author: Book of Bad Verse, 1972, Animal Sketches, 1980, Letters to a Son, 1989; also articles for Wall St. Jour., N.Y. Times, others. Past bd. dirs. Brookdale Found., N.Y.C.; past bd. dirs. Nat. Audubon Soc.; former mem. vis. coms. history dept. Harvard U.; former bd. govs. Investment Co. Inst., Washington. With USNR, 1958-60. Mem. N.Y. Soc. Security Analysts, Mass. Hist. Soc., Harvard Alumni Assn. (bd. dirs.), Pilgrims. Republican. Clubs: Harvard (past bd. mgrs. N.Y.C. club), Knickerbocker (N.Y.C.). Home: 9 Ladson St Charleston SC 29401-2703 Office: One North Adger's Wharf Charleston SC 29401-2571

WINTHROP, JOHN, real estate executive, lawyer; b. Salt Lake City, Apr. 20, 1947; m. Marilyn MacDonald, May 17, 1975; children: Grant Gordon, Clayton Hanford. AB cum laude, Yale U., 1969; JD magna cum laude, U. Tex., 1972. Bar: Calif. 1972. Law clk. 9th cir. U.S. Ct. Appeals, L.A., 1972-73; conseil juridique Coudert Freres, Paris, 1973-75; v.p. gen. counsel MacDonald Group, Ltd., L.A., 1976-82; pres., CEO MacDonald Mgmt. Corp. and MacDonald Group Ltd., L.A., 1982-86; pres., chief exec. officer MacDonald Corp. (gen. contractors), L.A., 1982-86; chmn., CEO Comstock Mgmt. Co., L.A., 1986—; pres., CEO Winthrop Investment Properties, Los Angeles, 1986—; bd. dirs. Plus Prods., Tiger's Milk Prods., Irvine, Calif., 1977-80. Bd. dirs. sec. L.A. Sheriff's Dept. Found.; bd. dirs. L.A. Opera. Mem. Calif. Bus. Properties Assn. (mem. bd. advisors 1981-87), Internat. Coun. Shopping Ctrs., Nat. Eagle Scout Assn. (life), French-Am. C. of C. (bd. dirs. 1982-87), Urban Land Inst., Nat. Realty Bd., Regency Club, Yale Club N.Y., Calif. Club, The Beach Club, Elizabethan Club. Republican. Office: Comstock Mgmt Co Penthouse 9460 Wilshire Blvd Beverly Hills CA 90212

WINTHROP, LAWRENCE FREDRICK, lawyer; b. Los Angeles, Apr. 18, 1952; s. Murray and Vauneta (Cardwell) W.; BA with honors, Whittier Coll., 1974; JD magna cum laude, Calif. Western Sch., 1977. Bar: Ariz. 1977, Calif. 1977, U.S. Dist. Ct. Ariz. 1977, U.S. Dist. Ct. (so. dist.) Calif. 1981, U.S. Ct. Appeals (9th cir.) 1981, U.S. Dist. Ct. (cen. dist.) Calif. 1983, U.S. Supreme Ct. 1983. Assoc. Snell and Wilmer, Phoenix, 1977-83, ptnr., 1984-93, Doyle, Winthrop, Oberbillig & West, P.C., Phoenix, 1993—. judge pro tem Maricopa County Superior Ct., 1987—, Ariz. Ct. Appeals, 1992—; lectr. Ariz. personal injury law and practice and state and local tax law Tax Exec. Inst., Nat. Bus. Inst., Profl. Edn. Systems, Inc., Ariz. Trial Lawyers Assn., Maricopa County Bar Assn.; chmn. bd. dirs. Valley of the Sun Sch., 1989—; mem. Vol. Lawyers Program, Phoenix, 1980—. Fellow Ariz. Bar Found.; Maricopa Bar Found.; mem. ABA, Calif. Bar Assn., Ariz. Bar Assn., Ariz. Tax Rsch. Assn. (bd. dirs. 1989-93), Maricopa County Bar Assn., Ariz. Assn. Def. Counsel (bd. dirs., pres. 1988-89, chmn. med.-malpractice com. 1993—). Republican. Methodist. Clubs: Fairfield Flagstaff, LaMancha Racquet. Avocations: music, golf, tennis. Editor-in-chief Calif. Western Law Rev., 1976-77. Home: 6031 N 2nd St Phoenix AZ 85012-1210 Office: Doyle Winthrop Oberbillig & West PC PO Box 10417 2800 N Central Ave Ste 1550 Phoenix AZ 85016-4666

WINTON, JAMES C., lawyer; b. Ft. Worth, Oct. 8, 1952. AB cum laude, U. So. Calif., 1974; JD magna cum laude, Southwestern U., 1977. Bar: Calif. 1977, U.S. Ct. Military Appeals 1979, D.C. 1980, U.S. Dist. Ct. (no. dist.) Calif. 1980, U.S. Dist. Ct. (ctrl. dist.) Calif. 1981, U.S. Dist. Ct. (so. dist.) Calif. 1983, U.S. Ct. Appeals (9th cir.) 1985, Tex. 1988, U.S. Dist. Ct. (so. dist.) Tex. 1989, U.S. Ct. Appeals (5th cir.) 1991, U.S. Dist. Ct. (no. dist.) Tex. 1992. Ptnr. Baker & Hostetler, Houston. Mem. ABA, State Bar Calif., D.C. Bar, State Bar Tex., Maritime Law Assn. U.S., Houston Bar Assn. Office: Baker & Hostetler 1000 Louisiana Ste 2000 Houston TX 77002

WINTOUR, ANNA, editor; b. Eng., Nov. 3, 1949; came to U.S., 1976; d. Charles and Elinor W.; m. David Shaffer, Sept. 1984; children: Charles, Kate. Student, Queens Coll., 1963-67. Deputy fashion editor Harper's and Queen Mag., London, 1970-76; fashion editor Harper's Bazaar, New York, 1976-77; fashion and beauty editor Viva Mag., New York, 1977-78; contbg. editor fashion and style Savvy Mag., New York, 1980-81; editor N.Y. Mag., 1981-83; creative dir. U.S. Vogue, N.Y., 1983-86; editor-in-chief British Vogue, London, 1986-87, House and Garden, N.Y., 1987-88, Vogue,

N.Y., 1988—. Office: Vogue Mag Conde Nast Bldg 350 Madison Ave New York NY 10017-3704*

WINTRISS, LYNN, lawyer; b. Canandaigua, N.Y., Apr. 16, 1954; d. George V. and Ann L. (Wheeler) W.; m. E.H. Richardson III, Aug. 1, 1981. BA cum laude, Union Coll., Schenectady, 1975; JD, Cornell U., 1978; LLM in Taxation, Georgetown U., 1982. Bar: Md. 1978, D.C. 1986. Assoc. Semmes, Bowen & Semmes, Balt., 1978-86, ptnr., 1986-93; lawyer, v.p. Mercantile-Safe Deposit and Trust Co., Balt., 1993—. Mem. ABA, Am. Coll. Trust and Estate Coun., Md. State Bar Assn., D.C. Bar, Balt. City Bar Assn., Women's Bar Assn. Office: Mercantile-Safe Deposit and Trust Co PO Box 2257 Baltimore MD 21203

WINTRODE, RALPH CHARLES, lawyer; b. Hollywood, Calif., Dec. 21, 1942; s. Ralph Osborne and Maureen (Kavanagh) W.; m. Leslie Ann O'Rourke, July 2, 1966 (div. Feb. 1994); children: R. Christopher, Patrick L., Ryan B. BS in Acctg., U. So. Calif., 1966, JD, 1967. Bar: Calif. 1967, N.Y. 1984, Japan 1989, Washington 1990. From assoc. to ptnr. Gibson, Dunn & Crutcher, Tokyo, L.A., Newport Beach and Irvine, Calif., 1967—. Sec. Music Ctr. Los Angeles County, 1986-88; bd. dirs. Coro Found., L.A. County, 1986-89. Mem. Newport Harbor Club, Am. Club Tokyo. Avocations: sailboat racing, car racing, flying. Office: Gibson Dunn & Crutcher 4 Park Plz Irvine CA 92714-8557 also: Gibson Dunn & Crutcher 333 S Grand Ave Los Angeles CA 90071

WINTROL, JOHN PATRICK, lawyer; b. Wichita, Kans., Feb. 13, 1941; s. Clarence Joseph and Margaret (Gill) W.; m. Janet Lee Mitchell; children: John Howard, Joanna Lee. BA, Rockhurst Coll., 1963; JD, Georgetown U., 1969. Bar: U.S. Supreme Ct., U.S. Ct. Appeals (4th, 11th, D.C. cirs.), U.S. Dist. Ct. Md., D.C. Law clk. to Hon. Howard Corcoran U.S. Dist. Ct., Washington, 1969-71; assoc. Howrey & Simon, Washington, 1971-77; mng. ptnr. Perito, Duerk & Pinco, Washington, 1978-85; ptnr. Finley Kumble, Washington, 1985-87, Laxalt, Washington, Perito & Dubuc, Washington, 1987-91, McDermott, Will & Emery, Washington, 1991—; mem. jud. conf. U.S. Ct. Appeals (D.C. cir.) Mem. ABA, D.C. Bar Assn. Democrat. Roman Catholic. Office: McDermott Will & Emery 1850 K St NW Washington DC 20006-2296

WINTROUB, BRUCE URICH, dermatologist, educator, researcher; b. Milw., Nov. 8, 1943; s. Ernest Bernard and Janet (Zien) W.; m. Marya Kraus, Jan. 20, 1973; children: Annie, Ben, Molly. AB, Amherst Coll., 1965; MD, Washington U., St. Louis, 1969. Diplomate Am. Bd. Internal Medicine, Am. Bd. Dermatology. Intern in medicine Peter Bent Brigham Hosp., Boston, 1969-70, jr. asst. resident in medicine, 1970-71, jr. assoc. in medicine, 1976-80, asst. then attending physician, 1976-81; resident in dermatology Harvard Med. Sch., Boston, 1974-76, instr., 1976-78, asst. prof., 1978-82; assoc. prof. dermatology Sch. Medicine, U. Calif., San Francisco, 1982-85, attending physician med. ctr., 1982—, prof., chmn., mem. exec. com., vice chmn. dept. dermatology, 1985—, mem. dean's adv. com., governing bd. continuing med. edn., other coms., 1986—; assoc.dean Sch. Medicine, U. Calif., Mount Zion, 1990—; dir. Dermatology Assocs., San Francisco, 1982-85; cons. in dermatology Mass. Gen. Hosp., Boston, 1976-82, Beth Israel Hosp. and Children's Hosp. Med. Ctr., Boston, 1978-82, Parker Hill Med. Ctr., Boston, 1980-82; attending physician Robert B. Brigham Hosp. dir. Brigham and Women's Hosp., Boston, 1980-81, assoc. 1980-82; chief dermatology svc. Brockton (Mass.) VA Med. Ctr., 1980-82; asst. chief dermatology VA Med. Ctr., San Francisco, 1982-85, mem. space com., 1984-85, dean's adv. com., 1985—, chmn. budget com., 1987—; clin. investigator Nat. Inst. Allergy, Metabolism and Digestive Disease, NIH, 1978. Author: (with others) Biochemistry of the Acute Allergic Reactions, Fifth International Symposium, 1988; contbr. numerous articles, abstracts to profl. jours. NIH clin. fellow and grantee, 1967-69. Fellow Am. Acad. Dermatology (com. evaluations 1985—, coun. govt. liaison 1987—, congress on tech. plannning commn. 1988—, assoc. editor Dialogues in Dermatology jour. 1982-85, Stellwagon prize 1976); mem. Soc. Investigative Dermatology (chmn. pub. rels. com 1987-88), Assn. Profs. Dermatology (chmn. program com. 1987—, bd. dirs.), Pacific Dermatol. Assn. (chmn. program com. 1987—), San Francisco Dermatol. Soc., Am. Fedn. Clin. Rsch. (chmn. dermatology program 1988-89), Am. Assn. Immunology, Dystrophic Epidermolysis Bullosa Rsch. Am. (bd. dirs. 1981), Internat. Soc. Dermatology, Internat. Soc. Cutaneous Pharmacology (founding mem.), Am. Soc. Clin. Investigation, Skin Pharmacology Soc., Calif. Med. Soc., San Francisco Med. Soc., Clin. Immunology Soc., Dermatology Found., (bd. dirs., exec. com.), AAAS, Am. Assn. Physicians, Calif. Acad. Medicine, Am. Dermatol. Assn., Sigma Xi, Alpha Omega Alpha. Avocation: golf. Office: U Calif Dept Dermatology 515 Spruce St Box 1214 San Francisco CA 94143-1214

WINWOOD, STEPHEN LAWRENCE, musician, composer; b. Birmingham, England, May 12, 1948; s. Lawrence Samuel and Lillian Mary (Saunders) W.; m. Eugenia Crafton, Jan. 17, 1987; children: Mary Clare, Elizabeth Dawn, Stephen Calhoun. Rec. artist Spencer Davis Group, 1964-67, Blind Faith, 1970, Traffic, 1967-74; solo artist N.Y.C. and in England, 1974—; dir. F.S. Ltd. Albums include: Arc of a Diver, 1980, Talking Back to the Night, 1982, Back in the High Life, 1986, Roll With It, 1988 (Grammy 1989), Chronicles, Refugees of the Heart, 1991, Traffic: Far From Home, 1994. Recipient 14 Gold Record awards, 4 Platinum Record awards, 2 Grammy awards.

WINZENRIED, JESSE DAVID, retired petroleum executive; b. Byron, Wyo., June 13, 1922; s. Fritz and Margaret Smith W.; m. Marion Suzan Jacobson, Mar. 15, 1945 (dec. 1984); children: Suzan Winzenried Carlston, Jay Albert, Keith Frederic; m. Lela Madsen, Mar. 12, 1988. B.S., U. Wyo., 1945; M.S., U. Denver, 1946; Ph.D., NYU, 1955. Dir. research Tax Found., N.Y.C.; 1947-56; sr. v.p. Husky Oil Ltd., Cody, Wyo., 1956-65, Calgary, Alta., Can., 1965-67; v.p. firm Booz, Allen & Hamilton, Cleve., 1968-69; v.p. Coastal States Gas Corp., Houston, 1969-74; group v.p., dir. Crown Central Petroleum Corp., Balt., 1974-81; vice chmn., dir. Securities Investor Protection Corp., Washington, 1988—; lectr. mgmt. NYU, 1955-56. Contbr. articles to profl. jours. Served with US Air Corps, 1942-43. Republican. Mem. Ch. Jesus Christ of Latter-day Saints. Office: Securities Investor Protection Corp 805 15th St NW Ste 800 Washington DC 20005-2207

WION, J. MIKE, oil industry executive; b. 1944. With Shell Oil Co., Inc., Anacortes, Wash.. 1968-93; with Atlas Processing Co., Shreveport, La., 1993—, pres. Office: Atlas Processing Co 3333 Midway St Shreveport LA 71109*

WIOT, JEROME FRANCIS, radiologist; b. Cin., Aug. 24, 1927; s. Daniel and Elvera (Weisgerber) W.; m. Andrea Kockritz, July 29, 1972; children—J. Geoffrey, Jason. M.D., U. Cin., 1953. Diplomate: Am. Bd. Radiology (trustee, pres.). Intern Cin. Gen. Hosp., 1953-54, resident, 1954-55, 58-59; gen. practice medicine Wyoming, Ohio, 1955-57; mem. faculty U. Cin., 1959-67, 68—, prof., chmn. radiology, 1973-93, acting sr. v.p., provost for med. affairs, 1985-86; practice medicine specializing in radiology Tampa, Fla., 1967-68. Contbr. articles to med. jours. Bd. dirs. Ruth Lyons Fund. Served with USN, 1945-46. Fellow Am. Coll. Radiology (pres. 1983-84, chmn. commn. on diagnostic radiology); mem. Radiol. Soc. N.Am., Am. Roentgen Ray Soc. (pres. 1986-87), Am. Bd. Radiology (pres. 1982-84), Ohio Med. Assn., Cin. Acad. Medicine, Radiol. Soc. Greater Cin., Ohio Radiol. Soc., Am. Thoracic Soc., Ohio Thoracic Soc., Fleischner Soc., Soc. Gastrointestinal Radiologists. Office: U Cin Med Ctr 234 Goodman St Cincinnati OH 45267-0001

WIPKE, W. TODD, chemistry educator; b. St. Charles, Mo., Dec. 16, 1940; s. M. Mo., Columbia, 1962; PhD, U. Calif., Berkeley, 1965. Research chemist Esso Research and Engring. Co., Baton Rouge, 1962; postdoctoral research fellow Harvard U., 1967-69; asst. prof. Princeton U., 1969-75; assoc. prof. chemistry, U. Calif., Santa Cruz, 1975-81, prof. chemistry, 1981—; founder, cons. Molecular Design Ltd., San Leandro, Calif., 1978-91, Ciba-Geigy, Basle, Switzerland, 1978-82, BASF, Ludwigshafen, Fed. REpublic Germany, 1974-78, Squibb, Princeton, N.J., 1976-81; advr. EPA, 1984—. Editor: Computer Representation and Manipulation of Chemical Information, 1973, Computer-Assisted Organic Synthesis, 1977 ; editor in chief: (jour.) Tetrahedron Computer Methodology, 1987-92; editor Tetrahedron and Tetrahedron Letters, 1987-92; contbr. articles to profl. jours. Served to capt. U.S. Army, 1966-67. Recipient Eastman Kodak Research award, 1964, Texaco Outstanding Research award, 1962; Alexander von Humboldt Sr. Scientist award, 1987; Merck Career Devel. grantee, 1970; NIH, fellow, 1964-65. Mem. NAS, Am. Chem. Soc. (assoc., Computers in Chemistry award 1987, Herman Skolnik award 1991), Assn. Computing Machinery, Chem. Soc., Am. Assn. Artificial Intelligence (charter), Chemical Structure Assn. (charter), Internat. Soc. Study Xenobiotics. Office: U Calif Dept Chemistry Santa Cruz CA 95064

WIRE, WILLIAM SHIDAKER, II, retired apparel and footwear manufacturing company executive; b. Cin., Jan. 5, 1932; s. William Shidaker and Gladys (Buckmaster) W.; m. Alice Dumas Jones, Aug. 31, 1957; children: Alice Wire Freeman, Deborah Wire Suber. Student, U. of South, 1950; AB, U. Ala., 1954, JD, 1956; LLM, NYU, 1957. Bar: Ala. 1956. Atty. Hamilton, Denniston, Butler & Riddick, Mobile, 1959-60; with Talladega Ins. Agy., Ala., 1961-62; with Genesco, Inc., Nashville, 1962-94, former chmn. and CEO; bd. dirs. Genesco Inc., 1st Am. Corp., 1st Am. Nat. Bank Nashville, Dollar Gen. Corp. Bd. dirs. in Roads-Nashville, Inc.; chmn. Pub. Edn. Nashville Citizens Involved in Leadership Found., Nashville. Mem. Belle Meade Contry Club (Nashville), University Club (N.Y.), Shoal Creek (Ala.) Club, Golf Club Tenn., Kappa Alpha. Presbyterian. Home: 6119 Stonehaven Dr Nashville TN 37215-5613

WIREMAN, BILLY OVERTON, college president; b. Jackson, Ky., Oct. 7, 1932; s. William and Emily (Bach) W.; m. Katie Marie Coomer, Mar. 3, 1955; children: James, Gary, Emily Kay Crigler. B.A., Georgetown Coll. (Ky.), 1954, LHD, 1987; M.A., U. Ky., 1957; Ed.D., Peabody Coll., Vanderbilt U., 1960; L.H.D., U. Tampa, 1970, Eckerd Coll., 1977. Mem. faculty Eckerd Coll., St. Petersburg, Fla., 1960-63, v.p. devel., 1963-68, pres., 1968-77; pres. Queens Coll., Charlotte, N.C., 1978—; guest lectr. People's U. Beijing (China), 1982, also Hong Kong, Taiwan, Philippines; pub. interviews with polit. leaders in Phillipines and S. Korea, 1988, 89; rsch. work in USSR, 1989; speaker fundraising panel So. Assn. Colls. and Schs., 1989; past v.p. Ormond Beach Pier, Inc., Fla. Co-author: Getting It All Together: The New American Imperative, 1973, Dangerous Grace, 1992; contbr. over 150 articles to profl. publs. Chmn. edn. div. St. Petersburg United Fund, 1966-67; del. White House Conf. Children and Youth, 1970, White House Conf. Youth, 1971; trustee, chmn. devel. cabinet United Bd. Christian Higher Edn. in Asia, 1974-83; chmn., trustee Bd. for Need-Based Med. Student Loans, State of N.C., 1982; past bd. dirs. Coll. Found Pinellas County; mem. internat. adv. bd. Han Nam U., Korea, 1987-92, OALS Coll. Bd.; rep. Charlotte C. of C. in China; chair Charlotte-Mecklenburg Community Rels. Com., 1989, bd. dirs. Friendship Trays, Charlotte World Affairs Coun.; vice chair Multiple Sclerosis Dinner of Champions Hope Award event, 1988; chmn. Charlotte-Mecklenburg Community Rels. Com. Recipient Liberty Bell award St. Petersburg Bar Assn., 1971, Univ. Medal of Honor Han Nam U., South Korea, 1988, Dinner of Champions Hope award Multiple Sclerosis Soc., Charlotte, 1989. Mem. AAUP, Am. Acad. Polit and Social Sci., Am. Mgmt. Assn. (dir.), Club of Rome, Am. Coun. Edn. (Internat. Commn.), Young Pres. Orgn., Univ. Club of N.Y.C., N.C. Soc. of N.Y., Charlotte Squires, Tower Club, City Club of Charlotte, Goodfellows, Phi Delta Kappa. Office: Queens Coll 1900 Selwyn Ave Charlotte NC 28274-0002

WIRKLER, NORMAN EDWARD, architectural, engineering, construction management firm executive; b. Garnavillo, Iowa, Apr. 1, 1937; s. Herbert J. and Irene (Kregel) W.; m. Margaret Anne Gift, Oct. 16, 1959; children: Chris Edward, Scott Norman, Elizabeth Anne. BArch, Iowa State U., 1959. Designer The Durrant Group Inc., Dubuque, Iowa, 1959-64, assoc., 1964-67, prin., 1967-82; pres. The Durrant Group Inc., Denver, 1982—; co-owner Wirkler Property Mgmt. Snowmass Co., 1993; pres. Foresite Capital Facilities Corp., Denver County, 1993—; commr., mem. exec. com. Commn. on Accreditation on Corrections, 1985-91; archtl. cons. to Am. Correctional Assn. Standards Program; mem. Am. Correctional Assn. Standards Com., 1992-98; v.p. Garnavillo (Iowa) Bank Corp. Co-author: Design Guide for Secure Adult Correctional Facilities, 1983; Bd. dirs. United Way, Dubuque, 1984. Fellow AIA (pres. Iowa chpt. 1977; mem. nat. com. on arch. for justice 1974—, chmn. 1979; chmn. AIA Ins. Trust 1985-87, mem. Colo. chpt. 1987—); mem. ASTM (detention component standards com. 1982-84), Dubuque C. of C. (legis. com. 1978-83, chmn. 1979; v.p. 1984, exec. com. 1982-85), Iowa State U. Devel. Coun. Club. Republican. Avocations: flying, skiing, jogging, golf, hunting. Office: The Durrant Group Inc 3773 Cherry Creek N Dr #240 Denver CO 80209

WIRSCHING, CHARLES PHILIPP, JR., brokerage house executive, investor; b. Chgo., Oct. 26, 1935; s. Charles Philipp and Mamie Ethel (York) W.; m. Beverly Ann Bryan, May 28, 1966. BA, U. N.C. 1957. Sales rep. Adams-Millis Corp., Chgo., 1963-67; ptnr. Schwartz-Wirsching, Chgo., 1968-70; sec., dir. Edwin H. Mann, Inc., Chgo., 1971-74; stockbroker Paine Webber, Inc., Chgo., 1975-85, account v.p., 1986—. Trustee Wirsching Charitable Trust, 1987—. Republican. Episcopalian. Avocation: foreign travel. Home: 434 Clinton Pl River Forest IL 60305-2249 Office: Paine Webber Inc 181 W Madison St Chicago IL 60602-4510

WIRSIG, WOODROW, magazine editor, trade organization executive, business executive; b. Spokane, Wash., June 28, 1916; s. Otto Alan and Beulah Juliet (Marohn) W.; m. Jane Barbara Dealy, Dec. 11, 1942; children: Alan Robert, Gary Rodney, Paul Harold. Student, Kearney (Nebr.) State Tchrs. Coll., Los Angeles City Coll., UCLA, 1933-39; B.A., Occidental Coll., 1941; M.S., Columbia Grad. Sch. Journalism, 1942. Dir. Occidental Coll. News Bur., 1939-41; radio newswriter WQXR, N.Y.C., 1941-42; news writer, propaganda analyst CBS, 1942-43; rewrite man Los Angeles Times, 1943-44; asst. editor This Week mag., 1944-45; staff writer Look mag., 1946, asst. mng. editor, 1946-49, exec. editor, 1950-52; mng. editor Quick mag., 1949-50; asso. editor Newsweek mag., Ladies' Home Jour., 1952; editor Woman's Home Companion, 1952-56; editorial cons. Ednl. Testing Service, Princeton, 1957-67; TV cons. NBC-TV, ABC-TV; creator Nat. Daytime Radio Programs, 1957-60; radio documentary Companion; pres. communications firm Wirsig, Gordon and O'Connor, Inc., 1956-58; editor Printers' Ink mag., N.Y.C., 1958-65, Salesweek mag., 1959-60; editorial dir. Overseas Press Club ann. mag. Dateline, 1961, 62; creator, editorial dir. Calif. Life mag.; pres. Better Bus. Bur. Met. N.Y., Inc., 1966-77; also pres. Edn. Research Found.; pres. Bus. Advocacy Center, Inc., 1977—; creator Corp. Social Accountability Audit and Customer Services/Consumer Affairs Audit.; Cons. to Office Sec. HEW, 1965-66. Author: I Love You, Too., 1990; editor, contbr.: Your Diabetes (Dr. Herbert Pollack), 1951; editor: Advertising: Today-Yesterday-Tomorrow; New Products Marketing; cons. editor: Principles of Advertising; contbr. nat. mags.; lectr.; syndicated columnist: other newspapers L.A. Times, 1964-65. Recipient gold medal Benjamin Franklin Mag. Awards, 1956. Mem. Soc. Consumer Affairs Profls. (pres. 1983), Newcomen Soc., Archons, Players Club, Overseas Press Club, Nat. Press Club, N.Y. Advt. Club, N.Y.C. Club, Springdale Country Club, Evergreen Country Club (v.p.), Nassau Club, Century Assn., Families for Alzheimers Rights Assn. (pres. 1994—), Univ. Club, Sigma Delta Chi, Phi Gamma Delta, Gamma Delta Upsilon. Democrat. Presbyterian. Home and Office: Sandhill Cove 1459 SW Shoreline Dr Palm City FL 34990

WIRSZUP, IZAAK, mathematician, educator; b. Wilno, Poland, Jan. 5, 1915; came to U.S., 1949, naturalized, 1955; s. Samuel and Pera (Golomb) W.; m. Pola Ofman, July 19, 1940 (dec. 1943); 1 son Vladimir (dec. 1943); m. Pera Poswianska, Apr. 23, 1949; 1 dau., Marina (Mrs. Arnold M. Tatar). Magister of Philosophy in Math, U. Wilno, 1939; Ph.D. in Math, U. Chgo., 1955. Lectr. math. Tech. Inst. Wilno, 1939-41; dir. Bur. d'Études et de Statistiques Spéciales, Société Centrale d'Achat-Société Anonyme des Monoprix, Paris, 1946-49; mem. faculty U. Chgo., 1949—, prof. math., 1965-85, prof. math. emeritus, 1985—, prin. investigator U. Chgo. Sch. Math. Project (sponsored by Amoco Found., also dir. resource devel. component), 1983—, dir. Internat. Math. Edn. Resource Ctr., 1988—; dir. NSF Survey Applied Soviet Rsch. in Math. Edn., 1985-91; cons. Ford Found., Colombia, Peru, 1965-66, Sch. Math Study Group, 1960, 61, 66-68; participant, writer tchr. tng. material African Math. Program, Entebbe, Uganda, summer 1964, Mombasa, Kenya, summers 1965-66; assoc. dir. Survey Recent Ea. European Math. Lit., 1956-68, dir., 1968-84; dir. NSF program application computers to mgmt., 1976-83; cons. NSF-AID Sci. Edn. Program, India, 1969; mem. U.S. Commn. on Math. Instn., 1969-73. Contbr. articles to profl. jours.; Editor Math. books, transls., adaptions from Russian; Adviser math.: Ency. Brit., 1971—. Recipient Lewelyn John and Harriet Manchester Quantrell

award U. Chgo., 1958, Univ. Alumni Svc. medal, U. Chgo., 1994; resident master Woodward Ct., U. Chgo., 1971-85; endowed Wirszup Lecture Series, U. Chgo., 1986. Mem. N.Y. Acad. Scis., Am. Math. Soc., Math. Assn. Am., AAAS, Nat. Council Tchrs. Math. (chmn. com. internat. math. edn. 1967-69). Home: 5750 S Kenwood Ave Chicago IL 60637-1744 Office: U Chgo Dept Math 5734 S University Ave Chicago IL 60637-1546

WIRT, FREDERICK MARSHALL, political scientist; b. Radford, Va., July 27, 1924; s. Harry Johnson, Sr. and Goldie (Turpin) W.; m. Elizabeth Cook, Sept. 6, 1947; children: Leslie Lee, Sandra Sue, Wendy Ann. B.A., DePauw U., 1948; M.A., Ohio State U., 1949, Ph.D., 1956. Instr. to prof. polit. sci. Denison U., Granville, Ohio, 1952-66; vis. prof., lectr. U. Calif., Berkeley, 1966-68, 69-72; dir. policy scis. grad. program U. Md. Balt. County, 1972-75; prof. polit. sci. U. Ill., Urbana, 1975—; dir. Inst. for Desegregation Problems, U. Calif.-Berkeley, 1970-72; cons. Motion Picture Assn. Am., Rand Corp., Nat. Inst. Edn., SUNY Sch. Edn. Albany; vis. prof. U. Rochester, Nova U., U. Melbourne; acad. visitor London Sch. Econs. Author: Politics of Southern Equality, 1970 (honorable mention for best book 1972), Power in the City, 1974; (with others) The Polity of the School, 1975, Political Science and School Politics, 1977, Education, Recession, and the World Village, 1986, (with others) Culture and Education Policy in the American States, 1992. Mem. Granville City Charter Commn., 1964. Am. Philos. Soc. grantee, Denison Rsch. Assn. grantee, U. Ill. Rsch. Bd. grantee, NEH grantee, Ford Found. grantee, Ctr. Advanced Studies grantee; U. Ill. fellow, Dept. Edn. fellow, Spencer Found. fellow; recipient Lifetime Achievement awards Am. Ednl. Rsch. Assn., 1975, Am. Polit. Sci. Assn., 1994. Mem. Am. Polit. Sci. Assn. (nat. council, Career Achievement award 1993), Midwestern Polit. Sci. Assn., Am. Ednl. Rsch. Assn., Policy Studies Orgn. Home: 2007B Eagle Ridge Ct Urbana IL 61801-8617 Office: U Ill Dept of Polit Sci Urbana IL 61801

WIRT, JOHN STEPHEN, journalist; b. Richmond, Aug. 21, 1955; s. Emmett Edward Jr. and Aileen (Kenny) W. MusB, Va. Commonwealth U., 1979, MusM, 1982. Freelance writer articles and revs. various nat., regional, local mags., Richmond, 1983—; spl. corr. Richmond Times-Dispatch, 1983—. Roman Catholic. Home: 2702 Hanover Ave Apt 2 Richmond VA 23220-4042

WIRT, MICHAEL JAMES, library director; b. Sault Ste. Marie, Mich., May 21, 1947; s. Arthur James and Blanche Marian (Carruth) W.; m. Barbara Ann Hallesy, Aug. 12, 1972; 1 child, Brendan. BA, Mich. State U., 1969; MLS, U. Mich., 1971; postgrad. U. Wash., 1990. Cert. librarian, Wash. Acting librarian Univ. Mich., Ctr. for Research on Econ. Devel., Ann Arbor, 1971-72; instnl. services librarian Spokane County Library Dist., Wash., 1972-76, asst. dir., 1976-79, acting dir., 1979, dir., 1980—. Mem. Adv. com. Partnership for Rural Improvement, Spokane, 1982-85, Wash. State Libr. Planning and Devel. Com., 1984-85, Ea. Wash. U. Young Writers Project Adv. Bd., 1988-89; mem. issues selection com. Citizens League of Greater Spokane, 1991-93, City of Spokane Indian Trail Specific Plan Task Force, 1992-95; mem. comm. com. United Way Spokane County, 1994. Mem. Wash. Libr. Assn. (2d v.p. 1984-86, Merit award 1984, dir. 1989-91, legis. planning com., 1991—, pub. rels. com. 1993—), Wash. Libr. Network (rep. Computer Svc. Coun. 1983-86, v.p., treas. State Users Group 1986-87), Am. Libr. Assn. (Pub. Libr. Affiliates Network 1990-93, PLA Bus. Coun. 1990-94, chmn. 1991-94), Spokane Valley C. of C. (local govt. affairs com. 1987—), Spokane Area C. of C. (local govt. com 1990-94, human svcs. com. 1990-92, chmn. 1991-92, govt. reorgn. task force 1995—), Momentum (local govt. strategy com. 1992-94). Office: Spokane Ct Libr Dist 4322 N Argonne Rd Spokane WA 99212-1853

WIRTA, RAY, real estate developer; b. 1944. MBA in Internat. Mgmt., Golden Gate U. With various cos., Calif., 1966-81; with Koll Co., Newport Beach, Calif., 1982—, now pres., CEO. Office: Koll Co 4343 Von Karman Ave Newport Beach CA 92660-2005*

WIRTH, FREMONT PHILIP, neurosurgeon, educator; b. Nashville, July 23, 1940; s. Fremont P. and Willa (Dean) W.; m. Penelope Simpson, July 25, 1964; children: Fremont Philip II, Andrew Simpson, Carolyn Howe. BA with honors in History, Williams Coll., 1962; MD, Vanderbilt U., 1966. Diplomate Am. Bd. Neurol. Surgery (guest examiner 1988, bd. dirs. 1992—), Nat. Bd. Med. Examiners; cert. advanced trauma life support ACS. Surg. intern Johns Hopkins Hosp., Balt., 1966-67, resident and fellow in surgery, 1967-68; asst. resident in neurosurgery Barnes Hosp., Washington U., St. Louis, 1970-72, fellow in neurosurgery, 1972-74; pvt. practice, Savannah, Ga., 1974—; asst. clin. prof. neurosurgery Med. Coll. Ga., Augusta, 1991—; vis. prof., 1978, 79, 86, 87; mem. staff, neurosurg. ICU, St. Joseph's Hosp., 1974—, dir. 1978—; mem. staff Meml. Med. Ctr., 1974—, dir. rehab., 1983; mem. staff Candler Gen. Hosp., 1974—; med. dir. Head and Spinal Cord Injury Prevention Project for Ga., 1984—; presenter in field, 1970—; vis. prof. U. Md., Balt., 1981, Tufts New Eng. Med. Ctr., Boston, 1982. Series editor (with R.A. Ratcheson) Concepts in Neurosurgery, 1986-93; editor: (with Ratcheson) Neurosurgical Critical Care, Concepts in Neurological Surgery, Vol. 1, 1987, Ruptured Cerebral Aneurysms, Concepts in Neurological Surgery, Vol. 6, 1994; contbr. articles and book revs. to med. jours., chpts. to books. Elder Skidaway Island Presbyn. Ch., 1981-83; mem. pack 57 com. Cub Scouts Am., Savannah, 1979-84; mem. troop 57 com. Boy Scouts Am., Savannah, 1980-85, mem. fin. com. Coastal Empire coun., 1987-90, mem. adv. bd., 1990—; chmn. physicians' solicitation United Way Coastal Empire, 1987; bd. dirs. Think First Found., 1990—. With USPHS, 1968-70. Fellow ACS (bd. govs. 1984-90, sr. mem. trauma com. 1991—); mem. AMA (physician's recognition award 1973-76, 77-79, 80-82, 83-85, 88-91, 91-94, 95—), Congress Neurol. Surgeons (profl. conduct com. 1989—, Disting. Svc. award 1989), Neurol. Soc. Am., Am. Assn. Neurologic Surgeons, Brain Surgery Soc., Ga. Med. Soc., Med. Assn. Ga. (editl. bd. 1987-93), pres. 1995, Ga. Neurosurg. Soc. (exec. com. 1981-88, pres. 1988-89), So. Neurosurg. Soc. (exec. com. 1982-91, pres. 1988-89), Am. Heart Assn. (fellow stroke coun.). Avocations: golf, fly fishing, hunting. Office: Neurol Inst Savannah 4 E Jackson Blvd Savannah Ga 31405-5810

WIRTH, LAWRENCE, chemicals executive; b. 1935. With prodn. Reynolds Consumer Products, Appleton, Wis., 1964-73, v.p.prodn., 1973-83, pres., CEO, 1983—. Office: Reynolds Consumer Products 670 N Perkins St Appleton WI 54914*

WIRTH, PETER, lawyer; b. Halgehausen, Germany, July 17, 1950; came to U.S., 1956; BA, U. Wis., 1972; JD, Harvard U., 1975. Bar: Mass. 1975. Assoc. Palmer & Dodge, Boston, 1975-81, ptnr., 1982—; lectr. Boston U. grad. tax program, 1982-85; chmn. Tech. Practice Group, 1986—; chmn. Mass. Continuing Legal Edn. bus. and coml. law curriculum adv. com. Mem. ABA, Mass. Bar Assn., Boston Bar Assn., Phi Beta Kappa. Office: Palmer & Dodge 1 Beacon St Boston MA 02108-3106

WIRTH, SANDRA LEE, real estate company owner; b. Buffalo, June 8, 1945; d. Dominic A. and Santina (Lopez) Liberatore; 1 child, H. William III. Prin. Metro Sandra Lee Wirth Robshaw Gallery of Homes, Tonawanda, N.Y.; regional mgr. Paul Robshaw Galler of Homes, Tonawanda, N.Y.; mgr. line Paul Robshaw Galler of Homes, Cheektowaga, N.Y.; broker assoc. B.W. Morris and Son Realtors, Buffalo. Past chmn. West Seneca Druga Abuse Prevention Coun. Mem. Nat. Assn. Realtors (cert.), N.Y. Assn. Realtors (state dir.), Greater Buffalo Bd. Realtors (1st v.p. 1988, treas. 1989, pres. elect 1990), Buffalo and West Seneca C. of C. Office: Office County Legislature 25 Delaware Ave Buffalo NY 14202

WIRTH, TIMOTHY ENDICOTT, federal official, former senator; b. Santa Fe, Sept. 22, 1939; s. Cecil and Virginia Maude (Davis) W.; m. Wren Winslow, Nov. 26, 1965; children: Christopher, Kelsey. B.A., Harvard U., 1961, M.Ed., 1964; Ph.D., Stanford U., 1973. White House fellow, spl. asst. to sec. HEW, Washington, 1967; asst. to chmn. Nat. Urban Coalition, Washington, 1968; dep. asst. sec. for edn. HEW, Washington 1969; v.p. Great Western United Corp., Denver, 1970; mgr. Rocky Mountain office Arthur D. Little, Inc. (cons. firm), Denver, 1971-73; mem. 94th-99th Congresses from 2d Colo. Dist., 1975-87, mem. energy and commerce com., sci. and tech. com., budget com., chmn. subcom. telecommunications, fin. and consumer protection; U.S. senator from Colo., 1987-92, mem. armed services com., energy and natural resources com., budget com., banking com., housing and urban affairs com.; counselor U.S. Dept. State, Washington, 1993—. Mem. Gov.'s Task Force

on Returned Vietnam Vets., 1970-73; mem. bd. visitors U.S. Air Force Acad., 1978—; advisor Pres.'s Commn. on the 80's, 1979-80; trustee Planned Parenthood, Denver Head Start. Recipient Disting. Service award HEW, 1969; Ford Found. fellow, 1964-66. Mem. White House Fellows Assn. (pres. 1968-69), Denver Council Fgn. Relations (exec. com. 1974-75). Office: Dept of State The Counselor 2201 C St NW Washington DC 20520-0004

WIRTHLIN, DAVID BITNER, hospital administrator; b. Salt Lake City, Sept. 19, 1935; s. Joseph L. and Madeline (Bitner) W.; m. Anne Goalen, Apr. 25, 1961; children: Kimberly, Jennifer, David, Deborah, John, Marianne. B.S. in Bus. Adminstrn. cum laude, U. Utah, 1960; M.H.A., U. Minn., 1963. Asst. adminstr. Idaho Falls (Idaho) Latter Day Saints Hosp., 1963-66; asst. to adminstr. Latter Day Saints Hosp., Salt Lake City, 1966-67; 1st asst. adminstr. Latter Day Saints Hosp., 1967-70, assoc. adminstr., 1970-73 adminstr., 1973-85; regional v.p. IHC Hosps., Inc., 1985—, Primary Children's Med. Ctr., 1973-75; v.p. cen. region Intermountain Health Care, Salt Lake City, 1984—; trustee Utah State Hosps.; mem. rev. com. Great Salt Lake Health Planning Agy., 1974; mem. Comprehensive Health Planning Rev. Com., 1975; chmn. Met. Hosp. Coun., 1975; mem. bd. Utah Profl. Rev., 1985-89; adv. com. Robert Wood Johnson Found.'s Hosp.-based Rural Health Care Program. Active with Mission for the LDS Ch., 1989-92, exec. dir. Inc Fund Devel., 1992—, exec. dir. LDS desert Hosp. found., 1992. Fellow Am. Coll. Hosp. Adminstrs. (regent, editoral bd. 1989, Gold Com. Mem. award 1989); mem. Am. Hosp. Assn., Utah Hosp. Assn. (past pres.), Western Assn. Hosps. (del. from Utah Hosp. Assn.), Coun. Teaching Hosps., Rotary, Timpanogos Club, Bonneville Knife and Fork Club. Republican. Mormon. Home: 2757 St Marys Way Salt Lake City UT 84108-2071 Office: Intermountain Health Care 36 S State St Ste 2200 Salt Lake City UT 84111-1401

WIRTHLIN, JOSEPH B., church official; b. Salt Lake City, June 11, 1917; s. Joseph L. and Madeline (Bitner) W.; m. Elisa Young Rogers, May 26, 1941; 8 children. Degree in Bus. Adminstrn., U. Utah. Ordained apostle LDS Ch., 1986. Served a mission to Germany, Austria and Switzerland LDS Ch., 1930s, served in stake and ward aux. positions, counselor, bishop to mem. stake presidency, until 1971, 1st counselor Sunday Sch. Gen. Presidency, 1971-75, asst. to coun. of 12 apostles, 1975-76, gen. authority area supr. Europe area, 1975-78, mem. 1st Quorum of Seventy, 1976-86, exec. adminstr. to S.E. area U.S. and Caribbean Islands, 1978-82, mng. dir. Melchizedek Priesthood Com., Relief Soc. and Mil. Rels. Com., 1978-84; exec. adminstr. LDS Ch., Brazil, 1982-84; pres. Europe area of ch. LDS Ch., 1984-86, mem. presidency of 1st Quorum of Seventy, exec. dir. curriculum dept., editor ch. mags., 1986, apostle, 1986—, mem. missionary exec. coun., mem. gen. welfare svcs. com., ch. bd. edn. and bd. trustees, 1986—. Office: LDS Ch Joseph Smith Meml Bldg 15 E South Temple St Salt Lake City UT 84150

WIRTHS, THEODORE WILLIAM, public policy consultant; b. Ansonia, Conn., June 23, 1924; s. Theodore Eugene and Elizabeth (McLean) W.; m. Claudine Turner Gibson, Dec. 28, 1945; children: William M., David G. B.A., Yale, 1947; M.A., U. Ky., 1949; postgrad., U. N.C., 1948-51. Teaching fellow U. N.C., 1949-50, field dir. urban studies, 1951-53; with AEC, 1953-66; chief reports and emergency planning Savannah River Ops., Aiken, S.C., 1960-62; real estate officer Washington, 1962-64; planning officer, 1964-65, Congl. fellow, 1965-66; congl. liaison officer NSF, Washington, 1966-70, dep. for govt. liaison, 1970-73, dir. Office of Govt. and Pub. Programs, 1973-76, dir. Office Small Bus. R&D, 1976-83; cons. in sci. and pub. policy, 1983—. Author: (with Chapin, Gould and Denton) In the Shadow of a Defense Plant, 1954. Chmn. Aiken Zoning Bd. Adjustment, 1956-62; vol. Hospice of Frederick County, 1986— (Hospice Vol. of Yr. 1994). With AUS, 1943-45, ETO. Recipient Meritorious Service award NSF, 1970, Disting. Service award NSF, 1983. Mem. AAAS. Episcopalian. Home: 6608 Jefferson Blvd PO Box 335 Braddock Heights MD 21714-0335

WIRTZ, ARTHUR MICHAEL, JR., professional hockey team executive; m. Sunny Wirtz; children: Laura, Arthur III, Jimmy. BS, U. Pa. V.p. Chgo. Black Hawks, 1958—. Office: Consol Enterprises 680 N Lake Shore Dr 19 Chicago IL 60611 also: Chgo Black Hawks 1901 W Madison St Chicago IL 60612*

WIRTZ, VIRGINIA HAYNES, nursing educator. Diploma in nursing, St. Anthony Hosp., Louisville, 1951; BSN, Spalding Coll., 1962; MSN, U. Fla., 1967; EdD, E. Tex. State U., 1976. RN, Mass., Ky., Fla., Tex., Okla., Ill., La., Md.; cert. advanced adminstrn., ANA. Nurse various med. orgns. and instns., Ky., Ill., and Mass., 1951-66; nursing educator various hosps. and univs., Ky., Fla., La., and Tex., 1952-75; DON women's clinic, prof. nursing Johns Hopkins Hosp. Coll. of Medicine, Balt., 1975-77; prof., chair baccalaureate nursing Ea. Ky. U., Richmond, 1977-78; asst. adminstr. patient care Prince Georges Hosp., Cheverly, Md., 1978-79, Suburban Hosp., Bethesda, Md., 1979-80, Citizens Meml. Hosp., Victoria, Tex., 1980-81; prof. grad. program U. Okla. Coll. Nursing, Oklahoma City, 1981-86; mgmt. cons. The ALPHA Group, 1986-89; prof., chair dept. nursing Assumption Coll., Worcester, Mass., 1989-93; prof., asst. dir. nursing U. So. Miss., 1993-95; prof., chair dept. nursing Edgewood Coll., Madison, Wis., 1995—; cons., lectr. in field, 1982—. Author: (book) Introduction to Budgeting: A Self-Paced Program, 1989, Advanced Budgeting: A Self-Paced Program, 1989; contbr. articles to profl. jours. Active Phoenix Players of Worcester. Grantee Internat. Edn. in Gyn.-Ob., 1975. Mem. Nat. League Nursing, New Eng. Orgn. Nursing, Mass. Assn. Colls. of Nursing, Mass. Orgn. BS Programs for RNs, Mass. and R.I. League for Nurses (bd. dirs.), Excellence in Nursing for Worcester, Phi Delta Kappa, Sigma Theta Tau. Baptist. Office: Edgewood Coll 855 Woodrow St Madison WI 53711

WIRTZ, WILLEM KINDLER, garden and lighting designer, public relations consultant; b. N.Y.C., Jan. 8, 1912; s. Carel Augustus Marie and Wilhelmina Johanetta (Kindler) W. Ed., Ethical Culture Sch., N.Y.C., also Inst. Musical Art, N.Y.C. Dir. exhibits svc. Pa. Art Program, 1937-42, pub. rels. dir., 1937-42; ptnr. Campbell-Wirtz Assos., Phila., 1942-51; pres. Willem Wirtz Assos., Phila., 1952—; founder, 1961, since pres. Willem Wirtz Garden Assos., Inc., and Willem Wirtz Assocs., mfrs. of Ribbonlite; design assoc. Am. Soc. Interior Decorators; Am. Jour. Nursing Co.; also chmn. Pa. bull. award com., 1964; guest lectr. Charles Morris Price Sch., Phila.; pres. Phila. chpt. Am. Pub. Relations Assn., 1954-56, nat. sec., 1955-57, Eastern v.p., 1960. Inventor (with Isaiah Roossine): Ribbonlite. Mem. Nat. Assn. Pub. Relations Counsel (dir.), Pub. Relations Soc. Am. (v.p. 1961, assembly dir. 1961-63), Pa. Hort. Soc., Phila. Art Alliance, Zool. Soc. Palm Beaches (sec. 1971), Netherlands-Am. Soc., Soc. of Four Arts. Club: Pen and Pencil (Phila.). Office: 228 Phipps Plz Palm Beach FL 33480-4241

WIRTZ, WILLIAM WADSWORTH, real estate and sports executive; b. Chgo., Oct. 5, 1929; s. Arthur Michael and Virginia (Wadsworth) W.; m. Joan Roney, Dec. 15, 1950 (dec. May 1983); children: William R., Gail W., Karen K., Peter R., Alison M.; m. Alice Pirie Hargrave, Dec. 1, 1987. A.B., Brown U., 1950. Pres. Chgo. Blackhawk Hockey Team, Inc., 1966—; mgr. Stadium Corp., 1966—; Consol. Enterprises, Inc., Chgo., 1966—; Forman Realty Corp., Chgo., 1965—, 333 Bldg. Corp., Chgo., 1966—; Wirtz Corp., Chgo., 1964—; chmn. bd. govs. Nat. Hockey League. Inducted into NHL Hall of Fame, 1976; recipient Lester Patrick trophy, 1978. Clubs: Saddle and Cycle (Chgo.), Racquet (Chgo.), Mid-America (Chgo.); Fin and Feather (Elgin, Ill.); Sunset Ridge Country (Northbrook, Ill.). Office: Consol Enterprises 680 N Lake Shore Dr 19 Chicago IL 60611 also: Chgo Stadium 1800 W Madison St Chicago IL 60612-2620 also: Nat Hockey Leage, 1155 Metcalfe St Ste 960, Montreal, PQ Canada H3B 2W2

WIRTZ, WILLIAM WILLARD, lawyer; b. DeKalb, Ill., Mar. 14, 1912; s. William Wilbur and Alfa Belle (White) W.; m. Mary Jane Quisenberry, Sept. 8, 1936; children—Richard, Philip. Ed., No. Ill. State Teachers Coll., DeKalb, Ill., 1928-30, U. Calif. at Berkeley, 1930-31; A.B., Beloit Coll., 1933; LL.B., Harvard, 1937. Instr. Kewanee (Ill.) High Sch., 1933-34, U. Iowa, 1937-39; asst. prof. Sch. Law, Northwestern U., 1939-42; asst. gen. counsel Bd. Econ. Warfare, 1942-43; with War Labor Bd., 1943-45, gen. counsel and pub. mem., 1945; chmn. Nat. Wage Stblzn. Bd., 1946; prof. law Northwestern U., 1946-54; engaged law practice, 1955-61; sec. of labor Dept. Labor, 1962-69; prof. law U. San Diego; mem. Ill. Liquor Control Commn. 1950-56. Mem. Am., D.C., Ill. bar assns., Phi Beta Kappa, Beta

Theta Pi, Delta Sigma Rho. Office: 1211 Connecticut Ave NW Washington DC 20036-2701

WIRZ, GEORGE O., bishop; b. Monroe, Wis., Jan. 17, 1929. Student, St. Francis Sem., Milw., Marquette U., Milw., Cath. U. Ordained priest Roman Cath. Ch., 1952. Appointed titular bishop of Municipa Roman Cath. Ch., Madison, Wis., 1978—; aux. bishop Roman Cath. Ch., Madison, 1978—. Office: St Patrick Church 404 E Main St Madison WI 53703-2891 Office: Box 11 15 E Wilson St Madison WI 53701*

WIRZ, PASCAL FRANCOIS, trust company executive; b. Paris, Dec. 26, 1943; came to U.S., 1971; s. Boris and Armande (Martini) W.;m. Sharon T. Oller, Aug. 16, 1968; children: Matthieu, Benoit, Colette, Severin. BA in Econs., U. Paris, 1966; MBA in Bus., Hautes Etudes Commerciales, Paris, 1965; MBA in Fin., Lehigh U., 1968. Audit traine Peat Marwick & Mitchell, N.Y.C., 1968-69; tchr. auditing CESA (HEC), Jouy en Josas, France, 1969-71; security analyst European-Am. Econ. Corp., N.Y.C., 1971-82; sr. v.p. Fiduciary Trust Internat., N.Y.C., 1982—. Trustee Corlette Glorney Found. Served with French Air Force, 1969-70. Mem. India House, Paris-Am. Club. Home: 186 Christopher St Montclair NJ 07042-4206 Office: Fiduciary Trust Internat 2 World Trade Ctr New York NY 10048-0203

WISBAUM, WAYNE DAVID, lawyer; b. Niagara Falls, N.Y., May 29, 1935; s. Franklin C. and Elizabeth (Boff) W.; m. Janet Katz, July 3, 1960; children—Karen, Wendy, Deborah. B.A., Cornell U., 1956; LL.B., Harvard U., 1959. Bar: N.Y. 1960. Assoc. Kavinoky & Cook, Buffalo, 1960-66; sr. ptnr. Kavinoky & Cook, 1966—; mem. adv. com. Ticor Title Co.; bd. dirs., pres., chmn. bd. Kleinhans Music Hall Mgmt. Inc. Pres. Buffalo Coun. on World Affairs, 1968-70; mem. Young Leadership Cabinet Nat. United Jewish Appeal, 1967-73; mem. com. on leadership devel. Nat. Coun. Jewish Fedn. and Welfare Funds, 1967—; mem. Mayor's Com. on Youth Opportunity; bd. dirs. Anti-Defamation League; mem. Coun. Internat. Studies, SUNY, Buffalo; chmn. Buffalo chpt. Am. Jewish Com.; treas. Buffalo Fedn. Jewish Philanthropies; bd. govs. United Jewish Fedn., Buffalo; chmn. bd. dirs. Buffalo Philharm. Orch. Soc.; bd. dirs., mem. exec. com. Burchfield Art Ctr.; bd. dirs., pres. Jewish Family Service of Erie County. Served to capt. U.S. Army, 1964. Recipient United Jewish Fedn. Buffalo Leadership award, 1967, Community Relations award Am. Jewish Com., 1985, Abram Pugash award Jewish Family Service, 1985; named Harvard Alumnus of Yr., 1990. Mem. ABA, N.Y. State Bar Assn. (chmn. com. lawyers title guaranty funds), Erie County Bar Assn., Am. Law Inst., Harvard Law Sch. Assn. Western N.Y. (sec.), Zool. Soc. Buffalo (dir., mem. exec. com.), Harvard Club (pres. Buffalo chpt., mem. N.Y.C. chpt.), Buffalo Club, Cornell Club (N.Y.C. chpt.), Zeta Beta Tau. Home: 180 Greenaway Rd Buffalo NY 14226-4166 Office: Kavinoky & Cook 120 Delaware Ave Buffalo NY 14202-2704

WISDOM, JACK LEACH, physicist, educator; b. Lubbock, Tex., Jan. 28, 1953; s. Woodrow Wilson and Oleta (Leach) W.; m. Cecile Helene Herold, June 19, 1981; children: William Woodrow, Edward Thomas, Thomas Ambrose, John Francis. BA in Physics, Rice U., 1976; PhD in Physics, Calif. Inst. Tech., 1981. NATO postdoctoral fellow Observatoire de Nice, France, 1981-82; rsch. assoc. U. Calif., Santa Barbara, 1982-84; rsch. scientist MIT, Cambridge, 1984-85, asst. prof. planetary sci., 1985-88, assoc. prof. tenure planetary sci., 1988-91, prof. planetary sci., 1991—; cons. Internat. Astron. Union. Contbr. numerous sci. articles to profl. jours. Recipient Helen B. Warner prize, 1987, Presdl. Young Investigator award NSF, 1988; John D. and Catherine T. MacArthur fellow, 1994. Fellow Am. Acad. Arts and Scis.; mem. Am. Astron. Soc. (divsn. for planetary sci., divsn. dynamical astronomy, Helen B. Warner award 1984, Harold C. Urey prize divsn. for planetary sci. 1986). Roman Catholic. Avocation: music. Office: MIT Dept Earth Scis 77 Massachusetts Ave Cambridge MA 02139-3594*

WISDOM, JOHN MINOR, federal judge; b. New Orleans, May 17, 1905; s. Mortimer Norton and Adelaide (Labatt) W.; m. Bonnie Stewart Mathews, Oct. 24, 1931; children: John Minor (dec.), Kathleen Mathews, Penelope Stewart Wisdom Tose. AB, Washington and Lee U., 1925; LLB, Tulane U., 1929, LLD (hon.), 1976; LLD (hon.), Oberlin Coll., 1963, San Diego U., 1979, Haverford Coll., 1982, Middlebury Coll., 1987, Harvard U., 1987, So. Meth. U., 1994. Bar: La. 1929. Mem. Wisdom, Stone, Pigman & Benjamin, New Orleans, 1929-57; judge U.S. Ct. Appeals (5th cir.), 1957—, now sr. judge; mem. Multi-Dist. Litigation Panel, 1968-78, chmn., 1975-78; mem. Spl. Ct. Regional Reorgn. of R.R.s, 1974, presiding judge, 1986—; adj. prof. law Tulane U., 1938-57; faculty IJA Appellate Judges Seminar, 1961-70; vis. coms. law schs. U. Chgo., Harvard U., U. Miami, U. San Diego. Mem. Pres.'s Com. on Govt. Contracts, 1953-57; past pres. New Orleans Council Social Agys.; Republican nat. committeeman for La., 1952-57; trustee Washington and Lee U., 1953—. Served from capt. to lt. col. USAAF, 1942-46. Decorated Legion of Merit, Army Commendation medal; recipient 1st Disting. Jurist award La. Bar Found., 1986, St. Thomas More Medallion, Loyola U. of L.A., 1987, Devitt Disting. Svc. to Justice award, 1989, Tulane Disting. Alumnus award, 1989, Alfred E. Clay award Children's Bur., 1992, Strength in Aging award (with Mrs. Wisdom) LSU Geriatric Ctr., 1992, LPB Living Legends award, 1993, Trumpet award Turner Broadcasting, 1994. Mem. ABA (chmn. appellate judges conf. 1966-67, 1st recipient John Minor Wisdom pub. svc. and profl. award sect. litigation 1990, Am. Inns of Ct. Lewis F. Powell Jr. award 1991, Fellows award young lawyers div. 1991, Pres.'s medal of Freedom 1993), Am. Acad. Arts and Scis., La. Bar Assn., New Orleans Bar Assn., La. Bar Found., Am. Law Inst. (coun. mem. 1961), La. Law Inst., Am. Judicature Soc., Order of Coif, Delta Kappa Epsilon, Phi Alpha Delta (Tom C. Clark Equal Justice under Law award 1982), Omicron Delta Kappa. Episcopalian. Clubs: Boston (New Orleans), Louisiana (New Orleans); Metropolitan (Washington). Office: John Minor Wisdom US Ct of Appeals Bldg 600 Camp St New Orleans LA 70130-3479

WISE, ALLEN FLOYD, insurance executive; b. Wichita, Kans., Aug. 20, 1942; s. Woodrow and Constance (Weber) W.; m. Hanna Jo Dunlap, June 6, 1964; children: Marc, Brian. BA in Econs., Wichita State U., 1964. Regional mgr. Travelers Ins., Hartford, Conn., 1964-78; sr. v.p. Union Fidelity Life, Phila., 1978-85; exec. v.p. U.S. Health Care, Phila., 1985-88, pres., 1988-89; pres. Corp. Health Adminstrs., Moorestown, N.J., 1989—; bd. dirs. Mo. Blue Cross, St. Louis. Home: 2841 Furlong Rd Doylestown PA 18901-1605 Office: US Healthcare Inc 980 Jolly Rd Box 1109 Blue Bell PA 19422

WISE, CHARLES CONRAD, JR., educator, past government official, author; b. Washington, Apr. 1, 1913; s. Charles Conrad and Lorena May (Sweeney) W.; m. Ruth Miles Baxter, Nov. 19, 1938; children: Gregory Baxter, Charles Conrad III, Jenifer; m. Norma Lee Clasbey, Apr. 28, 1984. A.B., George Washington U., 1938, J.D., 1936; M. Fiscal Adminstrn., Columbus U., 1943. Bar: D.C. 1935. Clk. U.S. Dept. Agr., 1933-36; adminstrv. asst. Bur. Accounts, Treasury Dept., 1936-39; atty. R.R. Retirement Bd., 1939-41; claims atty. Q.M.C., C.E., U.S. War Dept., 1941-43; asst. counsel Office Gen. Counsel, U.S. Navy Dept., 1946-47; gen. counsel War Contracts Price Adjustment Bd., 1948-51; mem., 1950-51; legislative counsel R.F.C., 1951-53; exec. sec. Subversive Activities Control Bd., 1953-61; dept. counsel indsl. personnel security Dept. Def., 1962-71, chief dept. counsel, 1971-73; instr. thanatology, religion and philosophy Blue Ridge C.C., 1973—; assoc. English dept. George Washington U., 1960, Am. U., 1961. Author: Windows on the Passion, 1967, Windows on the Master, 1968, Ruth and Naomi, 1971, Mind Is It: Meditation, Prayer, Healing and the Psychic, 1978, Picture Windows on the Christ, 1979, The Magian Gospel, 1979, Thus Saith the Lord: The Autobiography of God, 1984, The Holy Families, 1990; various articles for mags. Served as lt. USNR, 1944-46. Mem. Fed. Bar Assn., Delta Theta Phi, Phi Beta Kappa. Home: PO Box 117 Penn Laird VA 22846-0117

WISE, DAVID, author, journalist; b. N.Y.C., May 10, 1930; s. Raymond L. and Karena (Post) W.; m. Joan Sylvester, Dec. 16, 1962; children: Christopher James, Jonathan William. BA, Columbia Coll., 1951. Reporter N.Y. Herald Tribune, 1951-66, N.Y. city hall bur. chief, 1953-57; bur. chief N.Y. Herald Tribune, Albany, N.Y., 1956-57; mem. Washington bur. N.Y. Herald Tribune, 1958-66, chief Washington bur., 1963-66; fellow Woodrow Wilson Internat. Center for Scholars, 1970-71; lectr. in polit. sci. U. Calif. at Santa Barbara, 1977-79. Author: (with Thomas B. Ross) The U-2 Affair, 1962, (with Ross) The Invisible Government, 1964, (with Ross) The Espionage Establishment, 1967, (with Milton C. Cummings, Jr.) Democracy Under Pressure: An Introduction to the American Political System, 1971, The Politics of Lying: Government Deception, Secrecy, and Power, 1973 (George Polk Meml. award 1974), The American Police State: The Government Against the People, 1976, Spectrum, 1981, The Children's Game, 1983, The Samarkand Dimension, 1987, The Spy Who Got Away, 1988, Molehunt: The Secret Search for Traitors that Shattered the CIA, 1992, Nightmover: How Aldrich Sold the CIA to the KGB for 4.6 Million Dollars, 1995; contbg. author: The Kennedy Circle, 1961, None of Your Business, 1974, The CIA File, 1976; contbr. articles to nat. mags. Recipient Page One award Newspaper Guild N.Y., 1969. Mem. Washington Ind. Writers, Am. Polit. Sci. Assn. Clubs: Fed. City (Washington), Gridiron (Washington). Office: Sterling Lord Literistic Inc One Madison Ave New York NY 10010

WISE, DOUG, retail executive; b. 1942. With Citizens State Bank, Cameron, Tex., 1961—; with Winn's Stores, Inc., San Antonio, Tex., 1963—, now pres. Office: Winn's Stores Inc 4342 N Panam Expy San Antonio TX 78218-5285*

WISE, GEORGE EDWARD, lawyer; b. Chgo., Feb. 26, 1924; s. George E. and Helen L. (Gray) W.; m. Patricia E. Finn, Aug. 3, 1945; children: Erich, Peter, Abbe, Raoul, John. J.D., U. Chgo. Bar: Calif. 1949, U.S. Dist. Ct. (no. dist.) Calif. 1948, U.S. Ct. Appeals (9th cir.) 1948, U.S. Dist. Ct. (cen. dist.) 1950, U.S. Supreme CT. 1955. Law clk. Calif. Supreme Ct., 1948-49; sr. ptnr. Wise, Wiezorek, Timmons & Wise, Long Beach, 1949—. With USNR, 1943-45. Fellow Am. Coll. Trial Lawyers; mem. ABA, Los Angeles County Bar Assn., Long Beach Bar Assn. (pres. 1970, Atty. of Yr. 1990), Calif. State Bar. Home: 5401 E El Cedral St Long Beach CA 90815-4112 Office: Wise Wiezorek Timmons & Wise 3700 Santa Fe Ave Ste 300 Long Beach CA 90810-2171

WISE, GEORGE URBAN, botanic garden administrator, horticulturist, entomologist; b. Balt., Apr. 20, 1945; s. Raymond August and Helen Catharine (Miller) W.; m. Susan Patricia Doud, May 26, 1968; children: John, G. Thomas. B.S., Loyola Coll., Balt., 1967; M.S., N.C. State U., 1970, U. Del., 1977. Cert. Am. Registry Profl. Entomologists. Sr. entomologist Naval Facilities Engring. Command, Phila., 1969-76; dir. Awbury Arboretum, Phila., 1977-78; supt. Shaw Arboretum, Mo. Botanic Garden, St. Louis, 1979-83; dir. Memphis Botanic Garden, 1983-94, also bd. dirs.; exec. v.p. Agricenter Internat., 1994—; hon. dir. Nature Inst., Alton, Ill., 1981-82; chmn. adv. com. Dept. Horticulture, Union, Mo., 1979-82; rev. inst. Mus. Svcs., 1984-88, panelist, 1990-92. Author: The Role of Labeling in Botanical Gardens, 1979, The Path to Self Governance, 1993; project mgr. prairie recreation Shaw Arboretum, 1980. Leader Boy Scouts Am., Memphis, 1984-92; bd. dirs. Memphis Conv. and Visitors Bur., 1989; hon. councilman City of Memphis, 1994; mem. task force Memphis State U., 1994. USPHS grantee, 1969; Longwood program fellow, 1975-77; recipient Disting. Employee award City of Memphis, 1987. Mem. Am. Botanic Gardens and Arboreta (coord. SE sect. 1991-94), Am. Assn. Mus. (mus. assessment surveyor), Memphis Metro Attractions Assn. Avocations: sculpture, dancing, woodcarving, hiking. Office: Agricenter Internat. 7777 Walnut Grove Rd Memphis TN 38120-2100

WISE, JIM PRICE, energy company executive; b. Houston, Dec. 11, 1943; s. Sherwood Price and Rebecca (Cook) W.; m. Jane Anette Briggs, June 27, 1964; children—Kenneth Price, Tiffany Nicole. BBA, U. Houston, 1966. C.P.A., Tex. Acct. Deloitte Haskins & Sells, Houston, 1965-69; v.p., treas. Houston Natural Gas Co., 1971-81; sr. v.p., chief fin. officer Templeton Energy, Inc., Houston, 1981-82; exec. v.p., chief fin. officer Transco Energy Co., Houston, 1982—; bd. dirs. Team Bank, Transco Energy Co. Bd. dirs. Tex. Bus. Hall of Fame, Greater Houston Area YMCA, Salvation Army; mem. dean's exec. adv. bd. U. Houston; mem. adv. bd. Am. Heart Assn. Mem. Tex. Soc. CPAs; Houston Soc. CPAs, U. Houston Alumni Assn., Lakeside Country Club.

WISE, JOHN AUGUSTUS, lawyer; b. Detroit, Mar. 30, 1938; s. John Augustus and Mary Blanche (Parent) W.; m. Helga M. Bessin, Nov. 27, 1965; children: Monique Elizabeth, John Eric. Student, U. Vienna, 1957-58; AB cum laude, Coll. Holy Cross, 1959; JD, U. Mich., 1962; postgrad., U. Munich, 1962-63. Bar: Mich. 1963, D.C. 1966. Assoc. Dykema, Gossett, Detroit, 1962-64; asst. to pres. Internat. Econ. Policy Assn., Washington, 1964-66; assoc. Parsons, Tennent, Hammond, Hardig & Ziegelman, Detroit, 1967-70; pres. Wise & Marsac P.C., 1970—; dir. Peltzer & Ehlers Am. Corp., 1975-80, Colombian Am. Friends Inc., 1974-89. Mem. Detroit Com. on Fgn. Rels.; bd. dirs. Huyde Park Coop., 1974-77; trustee Friends Sch., Detroit, 1977-81, Brighton Health Svcs. Corp., 1991—, Brighton Hosp., 1994—. Ford Found. grantee U. Munich, 1962-63. Mem. ABA, Mich. Bar Assn., Detroit Bar Assn., Internat. Bar Assn., Detroit Athletic Club, Detroit Econ. Club. Roman Catholic. Home: 1221 Yorkshire Rd Grosse Pointe MI 48230-1105 Office: BUHL Bldg 11th Fl Detroit MI 48226

WISE, JOHN JAMES, oil company executive; b. Cambridge, Mass., Feb. 28, 1932; s. Daniel and Alice E. (Donlon) W.; m. Rosemary S. Bishop, Mar. 4, 1967; children: Susannah, Jean. BS, Tufts U., 1953; PhD, MIT, 1966. Rsch. scientist Mobil R & D Corp., Paulsboro, N.J., 1953-76, mgr. process R & D, 1976-77, sect. mgr., 1976-77; v.p. planning Mobil R & D Corp., N.Y.C., 1977-81; mgr. exploration and producing rsch. Mobil R & D Corp., Dallas, 1981-82; v.p. planning Mobil R & D Corp., N.Y.C., 1982-84; mgr. process and products R & D Mobil R & D Corp., Paulsboro, N.J., 1984-87, v.p. rsch., 1987—. Patentee in field (25); contbr. articles to profl. jours. Mem. NAE, Am. Inst. Chem. Engrs., Indsl. Research Inst., World Petroleum Congress, Sigma Xi. Office: Mobil Res & Devel Corp PO Box 1031 Princeton NJ 08543-1031

WISE, KELLY, private school educator, photographer, critic; b. New Castle, Ind., Dec. 1, 1932; s. John Kenneth W. and Geraldine (Kelly) Edwards Wise; m. Sybil Anahid Zulalian, Aug. 15, 1959; children: Jocelyn Anne, Adam Kelly, Lydia Louise. B.S., Purdue U., 1955; M.A., Columbia U., 1959. Instr. English Mt. Hermon Sch., Gill, Mass., 1960-66; instr. English Phillips Acad., Andover, Mass., 1966—, chmn. dept., 1978-82, acting dean faculty, 1982-83, dean faculty, 1985-90; founder, dir. Inst. for Recruitment of Tchrs., Andover, Mass., 1989—; photography critic The Boston Globe, 1982-93; art commentator Nat. Pub. Radio, 1987-89; photography and English cons. Nat. Humanities Faculty, Concord, Mass., 1970-83; mem. Pub. Art Adv. Bd. of Mass. Coun.; cons. editor Addison House Pubs., Danbury, N.J., 1974-79. Author: (with Kalkstein and Regan) English Competence Handbook, 1972; editor: The Photographers' Choice, 1975, Lotte Jacobi, 1978, Portrait: Theory, 1981, Photo Facts and Opinions, 1981; author, photographer: Still Points, 1977, A Church, A People, 1979; editor photographer: City Limits, 1987; assoc. editor: Views, Jour. Photography, 1980-81; works included in anthologies, one-man shows, Portland Museum Art, Maine, 1974, Silver Image Gallery, Columbus, Ohio, 1975, Canon Photo Gallery, Amsterdam, Holland, 1977, Focus Gallery, San Francisco, 1977, Art Mus., U. Mass., Amherst, 1978, Neikrug Gallery, N.Y.C., 1979, Sheldon Gallery, U. Nebr., Lincoln, 1980, Yuen Lui Gallery, Seattle, 1980, Rose Art Mus., Brandeis U., Waltham, Mass., 1981, Blixt Gallery, Ann Arbor, Mich., 1981, Snite Art Gallery, U. Notre Dame, 1981, Jeb Gallery, Providence, 1981, Currier Gallery Art, Manchester, N.H., 1985, Addison Gallery Am. Art, Andover, Mass., 1985, Art Ctr., DePauw U., 1986, Art Gallery, Conn. Coll., 1986, Yuen Lui Gallery, Seattle, 1986, Kresge Art Mus., Mich. State U., 1987, Brockton Art Mus., 1987; group shows include Inst. Contemporary Art, Boston, 1972, Mus. Fine Arts, Boston, 1974, Fogg Art Mus., Cambridge, 1976, Sidney Janis Gallery, N.Y.C., 1977, The Photographer's Gallery, London, 1979, Il Diaframma, Milan, Italy, 1979, Iisalmen Kamera, Helsinki, Finland, 1984, Archive Gallery, N.Y., 1987, Mass. Coll. Art, 1988, Martin Schweig Gallery, St. Louis, 1988, Satellite Gallery, Cultural Affairs Dept., Los Angeles; works included in book Flesh and Blood: Photographers' Images of Their Own Families. Served with USN, 1955-57, PTO. Office: Phillips Acad Andover MA 01810

WISE, LESLIE, surgeon, educator; b. Budapest, Hungary, May 3, 1932; came to U.S., 1967; s. Emil and Jolan Weisz; m. Jan Buchanan (div.); children: Nicholas, Julian, Tania. BSc in Medicine, U. Sydney, Australia, 1955; MB, BS, U. Sydney, 1958. Diplomate Am. Bd. Surgery. Intern Royal Newcastle Hosp., New South Wales, Australia, 1958-59; jr. house surgeon, 1959-60, sr. house surgeon, 1960-61; proctor in anatomy Royal Coll.

Surgeons, London, 1961-62; surg. resident Hammersmith Hosp., London, 1962-63, St. James Hosp., London, 1963-64; surg. registrar St. Helier Hosp., London, 1964-65; sr. surg. registrar St. Helier Hosp. and St. Mark's Hosp., London, 1965-67; fellow in surgery Johns Hopkins U. Sch. Medicine, Balt., 1967-68; asst. prof. surgery, dir. surg. rsch. labs. Washington U. Sch. Medicine, St. Louis, 1968-69, 1969-71, assoc. prof., 1971-75; attending surgeon Barnes and Allied Hosps., St. Louis, 1969-75, Homer G. Phillips Hosp., John Cochran VA Hosp., St. Louis Children's Hosp., St. Louis County Hosp., 1971-75; prof. surgery SUNY, Stony Brook, 1975-89, Albert Einstein Coll. Medicine, Bronx, N.Y., 1989—; chmn. dept. surgery L.I. Jewish Hosp., New Hyde Park, N.Y., 1975-93; surgeon-in-chief Queens Hosp. Ctr., Jamaica, N.Y., 1975-92; prof. Med. Coll. Cornell U., 1993—; program dir. dept. surgery LaGuardia Hosp., Forest Hills, N.Y., 1992-93. Editor 3 books; contbr. over 380 articles and abstracts to profl. jours. Mem. senate exec. com. Albert Einstein Coll. Medicine, 1992-93. Fellow ACS, Royal Coll. Surgeons (Eng., Hunterian Prof. 1970-71), Royal Soc. Medicine, Collegium Internationale Chirurgiae Digestivae, Internat. Soc. Surgery; mem. AMA, AAUP, Am. Surg. Assn., Am. Soc. Clin. Oncology, Assn. Acad. Surgery, Am. Fedn. Clin. Rsch., Am. Gastroent. Assn., Am. Surg. Assn., Ctrl. Surg. Assn., Soc. Surg. Oncology, Assn. Surgery Alimentary Tract, Am. Gastroent. Assn., Soc. Am. Gastrointestinal Endoscopic Surgeons, Soc. Program Dirs. Surgery, Soc. Laparoendoscopic Surgeons, Soc. Univ. Surgeons, N.Y. Surg. Soc. (pres. elect 1991-92, pres. 1992-93)., N.Y. State Soc. Surgeons, N.Y. State Med. Soc., N.Y. Cancer Soc., N.Y. Met. Breast Cancer Group, Inc., Bklyn. Surg. Soc., Nassau County Med. Soc. Home: 721 5th Ave Apt 38E New York NY 10022-2523 Office: NY Meth Hosp Dept Surgery 506 Sixth St Brooklyn NY 11215

WISE, MARVIN JAY, lawyer; b. San Antonio, Apr. 6, 1926; s. Philip and Anna Edith (Corman) W.; m. Gloria Marian Johnston, Sept. 19, 1954; children: Philip Johnston, Jennifer Lea, Amelia Ann. B.A. magna cum laude, U. Tex., 1945; LL.B. cum laude, Harvard U., 1949; diploma comparative legal studies, U. Cambridge, Eng., 1950. Bar: Tex. 1949. Assoc. Thompson & Knight, Dallas, 1950-57; ptnr. Wise and Stuhl, Dallas, 1957-88; of counsel Baskin & Novakov, Dallas, 1988—. Bd. dirs. Dallas Assn. Mental Health, Isthmus Inst., Dallas Home Jewish Aged, Dallas Civic Ballet Soc., Walden Prep. Sch. Served with AUS, 1945-46. Fulbright scholar, 1949-50. Fellow Tex. Bar Found.; mem. ABA, Tex. Bar Assn., Dallas Bar Assn. (chmn. probate, trusts and estates sect. 1981-82), Am. Coll. Probate Counsel, UN Assn. (dir. Dallas chpt.), Phi Beta Kappa, Alpha Phi Omega, Phi Eta Sigma, Pi Sigma Alpha. Jewish. Club: Crescent. Home: 3444 University Blvd Dallas TX 75205-1834 Office: 2000 St Paul Pl 750 N Saint Paul St Dallas TX 75201-3236

WISE, PATRICIA, lyric coloratura; b. Wichita, Kans.; d. Melvin R. and Genevieve F. (Dotson) W.; 1 child, Jennifer. B. Music Edn., U. Kans., Lawrence, 1966. Debut as Susanna in Marriage of Figaro, Kansas City, 1966; prin. roles include Lucia, Gilda, Micaela, Juliette, Zerbinetta, Pamina, Musetta, Lulu, Violetta, Nedda, numerous others; appeared with leading Am. opera cos. including, Chgo., Santa Fe, N.Y.C., San Francisco, Houston, San Diego, Miami, Balt., Phila., Pitts.; European appearances, 1971-76, London Royal Opera, Glyndebourne Festival, Vienna Volksoper, Geneva Opera; guest artist with Vienna, Hamburg, Munich, Cologne, Frankfurt, and Berlin State Operas; guest appearances in Madrid, Barcelona, Rome, La Scala Milan, Nice, Paris Chatelet, Zurich, Dresden, Salzburg Festival, Theatro Colon, Buenos Aires; appeared with orchs. including, Chgo. Symphony Orch., Los Angeles Symphony Orch., N.Y. Handel Soc., Israel Philharm. Orch., Vienna Philharm. Orch., N.Y. Philharm., Cleve. Orch., Berlin Symphonic Orch., BBC Orch., Nat. Orch. France; Angel Recordings; internat. TV, film appearances. Recipient Morton Baum award N.Y.C. Ctr., 1971, Dealey Meml. award Dallas Symphony, 1966, Naftzger young Artist award Wichita Symphony, 1966, Midland Young Artist award Midland (Tex.) Symphony Orch., 1966; M.B. Rockefeller Fund grantee, 1967-70; Sullivan Found. grantee, 1967-68; named Kammersänger Vienna Staatsoper, 1989.

WISE, PAUL SCHUYLER, insurance company executive; b. Pratt, Kans., July 16, 1920; s. George Warren and Bess Grace (Cossairt) W.; m. Frances H. Christie, Oct. 26, 1975; children by previous marriage: Schuyler, David, Betsy. Student, U. Kans., 1938-40; BA, Washburn U., 1942, JD, 1947; student, U. Mich., 1945-46. Bar: Kans. Atty. Kans. Ins. Dept., 1947, asst. commr. ins., 1948-51, commr. workmen's compensation, 1951-52; atty.-ins. legislation Alliance of Am. Insurers, Chgo., 1952-56, mgr. legis. bur., 1956-61, asst. mgr., 1961-62, gen. mgr., 1962-68, pres., chief exec. officer, 1968-84, chmn. bd., 1984-85; dir. Ins. Inst. for Hwy. Safety, Coll. of Ins.; bd. overseers Inst. for Civil Justice; lectr. in field; bd. dirs. United Funds, Kansas City, Mo., Potash Corp. of Sask., Can. Contbr. articles to profl. jours. Co-founder, bd. dirs. Hospice of North Shore; bd. dirs. Sr. Net. Lt. USN. Recipient Man of Yr. award Fedn. Ins. Counsel, 1982; inducted into Hall of Fame, Kans. Ins. Ednl. Found., 1983. Home: 8648 Silver Saddle Dr PO Box 5248 Carefree AZ 85377-5248

WISE, ROBERT, film producer, director; b. Winchester, Ind., Sept. 10, 1914. Student, Franklin Coll., D.F.A. (hon.), 1968. Staff cutting dept. R.K.O., 1933, became sound cutter, asst. editor, film editor, 1939-43, dir., 1943-49; with 20th Century-Fox, 1949-52, M.G.M., 1954-57; free-lance, 1958—, ptnr. ind. films co. 1970—; Past mem. Nat. Council of Arts. Ind. producer/dir. various studios; motion pictures include The Curse of the Cat People, 1944, Mademoiselle Fifi, 1944, The Body Snatcher, 1945, A Game of Death, 1945, Criminal Court, 1946, Born to Kill, 1947, Mystery in Mexico, 1948, Blood on the Moon, 1948, The Set-Up, 1949, Two Flags West, 1950, Three Secrets, 1950, The House on Telegraph Hill, 1951, The Day the Earth Stood Still, 1951, The Captive City, 1952, Something For the Birds, 1952, The Desert Rats, 1953, Destination Gobi, 1953, So Big, 1953, Executive Suite, 1954, Helen of Troy, 1955, Tribute to a Bad Man, 1956, Somebody Up There Likes Me, 1957, This Could Be the Night, 1957, Until They Sail, 1957, Run Silent, Run Deep, 1958, I Want to Live, 1958, Odds Against Tomorrow, 1959, West Side Story (Acad. awards best dir., best picture), 1961, Two For the Seasaw, 1962, The Haunting, 1963, The Sound of Music, 1965 (Acad. award best dir., best picture), The Sand Pebbles, 1966, Star!, 1968, The Andromeda Strain, 1971, Two People, 1973, The Hindenburg, 1975, Audrey Rose, 1977, Star Trek-The Motion Picture, 1979, Rooftops, 1989. Recipient Nat. Medal of Arts award, 1992. Mem. Dirs. Guild (pres. 1971-74), Acad. Motion Picture Arts and Scis. (pres. 1985-87). Office: Robert Wise Prodns 315 S Beverly Dr Ste 214 Beverly Hills CA 90212-4322

WISE, ROBERT, computer services company executive. CEO US Connect, Inc., Stamford, Conn. Office: US Connect Inc 72 Cummings Point Rd Stamford CT 06902*

WISE, ROBERT EDWARD, radiologist; b. Pitts., May 21, 1918; s. Joseph Frank and Victoria Rose (Conley) W.; m. Yvonne Burkhard, Mar. 27, 1943; children: Lynne Dailey, Robert Edward, John Burkhard. B.S., U. Pitts., 1941; M.D., U. Md., 1943. Intern U.S. Naval Hosp., Phila., 1943-44; fellow in radiology Cleve. Clin. Found., 1947-49; radiologist Cleve. Clinic, 1949-52; practice medicine specializing in radiology Pitts., 1952-53; CEO, chmn. bd. govs., 1975-91; chmn. bd. Lahey Clinic Found., 1986—; instr. radiology U. Pitts., 1952-53; clin. prof. radiology Sch. Medicine, Boston U.; dir. Bay State Skills Corp., Boston. Author: Intravenous Cholangiography, 1962, Accessory Digestive Organs, 1973, Radiology, Gallbladder and Bile Ducts. Trustee Eleanor Naylor Dana Charitable Trust, Lahey Clinic Hosp., Boston Ballet Co., Lahey Clinic Found.; bd. dirs. Boston Pub. Libr. Found.; corporator New Eng. Deaconess Hosp., Boston Opera Assn., Lahey-Hitchcock Clinic; chmn. Robert E. Wise M.D. Rsch. and Edn. Inst. of Lahey Clinic Found. Lt. Med. Corp USN, 1943-47. Mem. Am. Coll. Radiology (pres. 1975), Radiol. Soc. N.Am. (pres. 1974), New Eng. Roentgen Ray Soc. (pres. 1963), AMA, Mass. Med. Soc., Mass. Radiol. Soc. (pres. 1973), Eastern Radiol. Soc. (pres. 1965), N. Suburban C. of C. (dir.). Roman Catholic. Clubs: Algonquin (Boston) (dir.); Brae Burn Country (West Newton, Mass.); Webhannet Golf (Kennebunk Beach, Maine), Kennebunk River (Kennebunkport), Atlantis Golf (Atlantis, Fla.), La Coquille (Manalapan, Fla.), Beach (Palm Beach). Home: 1545 Lands End Rd Manalapan FL 33462 also: Marshalls Point Rd Kennebunkport ME 04014 Office: Lahey Clinic Found 41 Mall Rd Burlington MA 01805-0002

WISE, ROBERT ELLSWORTH, JR. (BOB ELLSWORTH), congressman; b. Washington, D.C., Jan. 6, 1948; m. Sandra Casber, 1984. BA, Duke U., 1970; JD, Tulane U., 1975. Bar: W.Va. 1975. Sole practice Charleston, W.Va., 1975-80; atty., legis. council for judiciary com. W.Va. Ho. of Dels., 1977-78; mem. W.Va. Senate, 1980-82, 97th-103rd Congresses from 2nd W.Va. dist., Washington, D.C., 1982—; whip at large Congress from W.Va., 1986—. Dir. West Virginians for Fair and Equitable Assessment of Taxes, Inc. Mem. ABA, W.Va. State Bar Assn. Democrat. Avocations: physical fitness, bluegrass music. Office: US Ho of Reps 2434 Rayburn House Office Bldg Washington DC 20515

WISE, ROBERT F., lawyer; b. Bronxville, N.Y., Oct. 1, 1947; m. Alison Bell; children: Katherine B., Robert A. BA, U. Va., 1969; JD, Yale U., 1972. Bar: N.Y. 1973, U.S. Dist. Ct. (so. and ea. dists.) N.Y. 1973, U.S. Ct. Appeals (2d cir.) 1973, U.S. Supreme Ct. 1980. Ptnr. Davis Polk & Wardwell, N.Y.C., 1972—. Pres. Purchase (N.Y.) Environ. Protective Assn., 1988-92. 1st lt. USAFR, 1969-73. Mem. ABA, Fed. Bar Coun., N.Y. Bar Assn. (chmn. fed. procedure com. 1991—), N.Y.C. Bar Assn., Westchester Country Club (bd. govs. 1993—). Office: Davis Polk & Wardwell 450 Lexington Ave New York NY 10017-3911

WISE, ROBERT LESTER, utilities executive; b. Curwensville, Pa., Oct. 4, 1943; s. Robert Lester Wise and Kathryn Elizabeth (Riddle) Husak; m. Sandra Lee Leonard, June 12, 1965; 1 child: Robert L. III. BSME, Lafayette Coll., 1965. Registered profl. engr., Pa. Cadet engr., jr. engr. Pa. Electric Co., Johnstown, 1965-68, stat. supr. prodn., sta. supt. ops., 1968-71, sta. supt., mgr. generating stas., 1971-79, asst. v.p. ops., v.p. ops., 1979-82, v.p. generation engrng. and support, 1982-83, v.p. ops., 1984-86, pres., bd. dirs., 1986-94; pres. fossil generation GPU Svc. Corp., Johnstown, Pa., 1994—; bd. dirs. GPU Svc. Corp., GPU Nuclear Corp., Energy Intiatives, Inc., Parsippany, U.S. nat. bank, USBANCORP, Inc., USBANCORP Trust Co., Johnstown Area Regional Industries, High Speed Rail Assn., 1990, Pa. Chamber Bus. and Industry, 1991; mem. Pa. Bus. Roundtable, 1990. Bd. dirs. Johnstown Symphony Orch., 1988; mem. adv. coun. of exec. bd. Penn's Woods coun. Boy Scouts Am., 1980—; mem. exec. com. Greater Johnstown Com., 1987, Pa. Electric Assn., Harrisburg, 1987, Cambria-Somerset Labor Mgmt. Com., 1987; mem. exec. adv. com. Johnstown Bus. Coun. on Health Care, 1987; trustee United Way Greater Johnstown, 1991. Mem. Sunnehanna Country Club. Republican. Avocations: sailing, racquet sports, golf. Office: GPU Svc Corp 1001 Broad St Johnstown PA 15906-2437

WISE, SHERWOOD WILLING, lawyer; b. Hazlehurst, Miss., Aug. 13, 1910; s. Joseph Sherwood and Myra (Willing) W.; m. Elizabeth Carter Powell, July 28, 1937; children: Elizabeth Wise Copeland, Sherwood Willing, Joseph Powell, Robert Powell and Louise Wise Hardy (twins). BA, Washington and Lee U., 1932, J.D., 1934. Bar: Miss. 1934. Practiced law Jackson; counsel Wise Carter Child & Caraway, 1941-86; commr. Miss. Bar, 1958-60; gen. counsel Miss. Power & Light Co., 1961-80. Author: Wise Carter Child & Caraway, One Mississipi Law Firm, 1883-1986, 1988, The Cathedral of St. Andrew, 1839-1989, 1989. Co-founder Jackson Symphony Orch., 1944; pres. Jackson Cmty. Chest, 1950; Miss. chmn. Ducks Unlimited, Inc., 1961-71; mem. exec. com. Episcopal Diocese Miss., 1941, past mem. dept. missions and standing com., also trustee, 1958-88; del. Episc. Gen. Conv., 1952, 64, 67, 69, 70, 79; mem. joint commn., ecumenical rels. Episc., Ch., 1967-73; co-founder, chmn. St. Mark's Ednl. Day care Ctr., 1967; a founder, organizer St. Andrew's Episc. Day Sch., Jackson, 1947, trustee, 1947-72, 78-82; trustee Nat. Cathedral Assn., 1975-77; del. Democratic Nat. Conv., 1940; trustee State Dept. Archives and History, 1964, King Jackson Jr. League Carnival Ball, 1971. Served to lt. comdr. USNR, 1942-46. Recipient Disting. Alumnus award Washington and Lee U., 1983. Fellow Am. Coll. Trial Lawyers, Am. Inns of Ct. (Charles Clark chpt.). Magna Charta Barons, Gen. Soc. of War of 1812 (pres. Miss. 1992-94), The Sovereign Colonial Soc., Am. of Royal Descent, Order First Families of Miss. 1699-1817, SCV; mem. ABA (com. on civil rights and racial unrest 1962, standing com. fed. judiciary 1969-75, Miss. state del. to ho. of dels. 1981-87), Nat. Conf. Lawyers and Environ. Design Profls. (chmn. 1979-85), Nat. Soc. SAR, Sons of the Revolution, Miss. Bar Assn. (pres. 1961-62), Hinds County Bar Assn. (pres. 1958-59), Edison Electric Inst. (legal com. 1962-80), Nat. Assn. R.R. Trial Counsel, Am. Judicature Soc., Scribes, Jackson C. of C. (past v.p., dir.), Newcomen Soc., Cum Laude Soc., Kappa Sigma, Omicron Delta Kappa, Phi Delta Phi. Clubs: Rotary (past dir., Paul Harris fellow), Jackson Country (past bd. govs.), Capital Club, Jackson Yacht (past gov.). Home: 3839 Eastover Dr Jackson MS 39211-6731 Office: PO Box 651 Jackson MS 39205-0651

WISE, WARREN ROBERTS, lawyer; b. Beaver City, Nebr., Oct. 8, 1929; s. Harold Edward and Doris Lorene (Roberts) W.; m. Marcia Hench, Oct. 14, 1961; children: Debra, David, Susan. BS, U. Nebr., 1950, LLB, 1953; LLM, Georgetown U., 1960. Atty. U.S. Dept. Justice Lands Div., Washington, 1955-61, U.S. Dept. Justice Tax Div., Washington, 1961-63; assoc. counsel Mass. Mut. Life Ins. Co., Springfield, 1963-67, asst. gen. counsel, 1967-72, 2d v.p., assoc. gen. counsel, 1972-74, v.p., assoc. gen. counsel, 1974-85, sr. v.p., assoc. gen. counsel, 1985-88, exec. v.p., gen. counsel, 1988-93; ret., 1993. Author: Business Insurance Agreements, 1970, 80, 91; editor; Massachusetts Life Insurance Law, 1980. Chmn. bd. East Coast Conf. Evang. Covenant Ch., 1987-89, chmn. pension bd., 1984-86. Served with U.S. Army, 1953-55. Mem. ABA (chmn. life ins. law com. torts and ins. sect. 1992-93), Assn. Life Ins. Counsel (bd. dirs. 1987-92, pres. 1992-93), Colony Club, Longmeadow Country Club. Republican. Avocation: golf. Home: 37 W Colonial Rd Wilbraham MA 01095-2117

WISE, WILLIAM ALLAN, oil company executive, lawyer; b. Davenport, Iowa, July 10, 1945; s. A. Walter and Mary Virginia (Kuhl) W.; m. Marie Figge, Sept. 27, 1969; children—Vivian Marie, Genevieve Marie, Mary Elizabeth. B.A., Vanderbilt U.; J.D., U. Colo. Bar: Colo. 1970. Prin. counsel El Paso Natural Gas, Tex., 1970-80, sr. v.p. mktg., 1985-87, exec. v.p. mktg., 1987-89; pres., chief oper. officer El Paso Natural Gas, 1989-90, pres., chief exec. officer, 1990-93, chmn., pres., CEO, 1994—; asst. gen. counsel in Houston The El Paso Co., 1980-82, v.p., gen. counsel, 1983, sr. v.p., gen. counsel and sec., 1983-85; bd. dirs. Am. Gas Assn., Arlington, Va., El Paso Natural Gas Co., The El Paso Co., Mojave Pipeline Oper. Co., Bakersfield, Calif., Tex. Commerce Bank, El Paso, Tex. Commerce Bancshres, Inc., Houston, Interstate Natural Gas Assn. Am., Washington; mem. N.Y. Merc. Exch., Tri-Regional Com. Contbr. articles to profl. jours. Bd. dirs. Battle Mountain Gold Co., U. Colo. Found., Boulder, Gas Industry Stds., Natural Gas Coun., Tex. Gov.'s Bus. Coun.; mem. bus. adv. coun. and devel. bd. U. Tex., El Paso; bd. visitors M.D. Anderson Cancer Ctr. Mem. Nat. Petroleum Coun. (bd. dirs.), Colo. Bar Assn., Tex. C. of C. (bd. dirs.), El Paso Country Club, George Town Club (Washington), River Oaks Country Club (Houston), Old Baldy Club (Saratoga, Wyo.). Republican. Roman Catholic. Avocations: golf, running. Home: 5605 Westside Dr El Paso TX 79932-2921 Office: El Paso Natural Gas Co 100 N Stanton One Paul Kayser Cen El Paso TX 79901

WISE, WILLIAM JERRARD, lawyer; b. Chgo., May 27, 1934; s. Gerald Paul and Harriet Muriel (Rosenblum) W.; m. Peggy Spero, Sept. 3, 1959; children: Deborah, Stephen, Betsy, Lynne. B.B.A., U. Mich., 1955, M.B.A., 1958, J.D. with distinction, 1958. Bar: Ill. 1959. Spl. atty. Office Regional Counsel, IRS, Milw., 1959-63; with firm McDermott, Will & Emery, Chgo., 1963-70, Coles & Wise, Ltd., 1971-81, Wise & Stracks, Ltd., 1982—; Lectr., contbr. Ill. Inst. Continuing Legal Edn.; arbitrator Cir. Ct. Cook County Ill., 1990—. Mem. Village of Winnetka (Ill.) Caucus, 1974-75; Bd. dirs. Blind Service Assn., Chgo., 1964-74; dir., treas. Suzuki Orff Sch. for Young Musicians, Chgo., 1981-91. Served with AUS, 1958-59. Mem. Chgo. Bar Assn. Home: 1401 Tower Rd Winnetka IL 60093-1629 Office: Wise & Stracks Ltd 20 N Clark St Ste 1000 Chicago IL 60602-4160 I believe that one succeeds best in our society if one gives as little thought as possible to one's personal well being.

WISEHART, ARTHUR MCKEE, lawyer; b. Evanston, Ill., July 3, 1928; s. Arthur J. and Dorothy H. (Rice) W.; m. Mary Elizabeth Dodson, 1953; children: William, Ellen, Arthur, Charles. B.A., Miami U., Oxford, Ohio, 1950; M.P.A., Wayne State U., 1953; J.D., U. Mich., 1954. Bar: N.Y. 1955. With firm Chadbourne, Parke, Whiteside & Wolff, N.Y.C., 1954-59; with Am. Airlines, Inc., 1959-69, corp. sec., asst. gen. counsel, 1968-69; sr. v.p., gen. counsel, sec. REA Express, 1969-74; dir., sec. REA Holding Corp.,

1969-74; sr. partner Law Offices of Arthur M. Wisehart, 1974-75, Wisehart & Koch, 1975—, 1981—; dir. Hoover Co., 1975-76. Author articles. Mem. ABA, Assn. of Bar of City of N.Y., Order of Coif, Delta Chi. Presbyterian. Clubs: Princeton. Office: Wisehart & Koch Ste 412 19 W 44th St New York NY 10036

WISEHART, MARY RUTH, academic administrator; b. Myrtle, Mo., Nov. 2, 1932; d. William Henry and Ora (Harbison) W. BA, Free Will Baptist Bible Coll., 1955; BA, George Peabody Coll. Tchrs., 1959, MA, 1960, PhD, 1976. Tchr. Free Will Bapt. Bible Coll., Nashville, 1956-60, chmn. English dept., 1961-85; exec. sec.-treas. Free Will Bapt. Women Nat. Active for Christ, 1985—. Author: Sparks Into Flame, 1985; contbr. poetry to jours. Mem. Nat. Coun. Tchrs. English, Christian Mgmt. Assn., Religious Conf. Mgmt. Assn., Scribbler's Club. Avocations: photography, music, drama. Office: Women Nat Active for Christ Free Will Bapt PO Box 5002 Antioch TN 37011-5002

WISELEY, RICHARD EUGENE, securities corporation executive; b. Tulsa, Oct. 20, 1945; s. Jess Porter and Gussie (Wright) W.; m. March McCoy, May 29, 1965; children: Jessica, March Elizabeth, Katherine. B.S. in Econs., U. Tulsa, 1970. Stock broker Bache & Co., Tulsa, 1972-75; resident mgr. Bache, Halsey, Stuart, Shields, Inc., Ft. Worth, 1975-78; regional dir., sr. v.p. Prudential-Bache Securities Inc., Ft. Lauderdale, Fla., 1978-84; with Oppenheimer & Co. Inc., N.Y.C., 1984—; gen. ptnr. Oppenheimer & Co. Inc., 1985—. Author book on recruiting, 1975. Mem. Securities Industry Assn., Nat. Assn. Security Dealers. Republican. Presbyterian. Club: Safari Club Internat. (pres. Carolinas). Office: Oppenheimer & Co Inc 10880 Wilshire Blvd Los Angeles CA 90024

WISEMAN, ALAN M(ITCHELL), lawyer; b. Long Branch, N.J., July 6, 1944; s. Lincoln B. and Gertrude (Gorcey) W.; m. Paula Wiseman, July 8, 1965; children—Steven, David, Julie. B.A., Johns Hopkins U., 1965; J.D., Georgetown U., 1968. Bar: Md. 1968, Ill. 1970, D.C. 1973. Law clk. to Hon. William J. McWilliams Md. Ct. Appeals, 1968-69; assoc. Schiff Hardin & Waite, Chgo., 1970-74; ptnr. Howrey & Simon, Washington, 1976—. Editor Georgetown Law Jour., 1967-68. Mem. U.S. C. of C. (council on antitrust policy). Office: 1299 Pennsylvania Ave NW Washington DC 20004-2400

WISEMAN, DENNIS GENE, college dean; b. Anderson, Ind., Aug. 25, 1947; s. Harold Leslie and Lillian Loetta (Woods) W.; m. Susan Jean Reidenbach, June 10, 1971; children: Matthew Benjamin, Andrew Joseph. BA, U. Indpls., 1969; MA, U. Ill., 1970, PhD, 1974; postgrad., Ind. U., 1970-71. Tchr. Indpls. Pub. Schs., 1970-71; rsch. asst. U. Ill., Urbana, 1971-74, clinician, supr., 1972-74, coord. Office for Profl. Svc., 1973-74; dir., tchr. Champaign (Ill.) pub. schs., 1972-73; asst. prof. U. S.C. Coastal Carolina Coll., Conway, 1974-77, assoc. prof., 1977-84, prof., 1984—, dean Sch. Edn., 1982-93; dean Sch. Edn. and Grad. Studies, 1993—; field disseminator Social Sci. Edn. Consortium, Boulder, Colo., 1979-81; reviewer Ethnic Heritage Studies Program, U.S. Office Edn., Washington, 1980-81; cons. S.C. State Dept. Edn., Columbia, 1986—; dir. Oxford program U.S.C. Coastal Carolina Coll., summer, 1990; evaluator So. Assn. Colls. and Schs., Atlanta, 1991. Co-author: Effective Teaching, 1st edit., 1984, 2d edit. 1991, Wondering about Thinking, 1988; contbr. articles to jours. in field. Mem. Horry County Human Rels. Coun., Conway, 1990-93; mem. curriculum frameworks rev. panel S.C. Dept. Edn., 1993—. Named Tchr. of Yr., U. S.C. Coastal Carolina Coll., 1980; S.C. Com. for the Humanities grantee, 1984, S.C. Com. on Higher Edn. grantee, 1985, 86; Japan Study Program scholar U.S. Office Edn., 1980. Mem. Nat. S.C. Assn. Colls. for Tchr. Edn. (pres. elect 1989, pres. 1989-91), Coun. Edn. Deans (pres. 1986-90), Nat. Coun. for the Social Studies, Am. Assn. Colls. for Tchrs. Edn. (instl. rep. 1980—), Assn. Tchr. Educators, Phi Delta Kappa (pres. Coastal Carolina chpt. 1984-85). Methodist. Avocations: reading, travel, tennis, writing. Office: Coastal Carolina U Office Dean & Grad Studies PO Box 1954 Conway SC 29526-1954

WISEMAN, FREDERICK, filmmaker; b. Boston, Jan. 1, 1930; s. Jacob Leo and Gertrude Leah (Kotzen) W.; m. Zipporah Batshaw, May 29, 1955; children: David B., Eric T. BA, Williams Coll., 1951; LLB, Yale U., 1954; LHD (hon.), U. Cin., 1973, Williams Coll., 1976; John Jay Coll. Crim. Justice, 1994; DFA (hon.), Lake Forest Coll., 1991; postgrad., Princeton U., 1994. Bar: Mass. 1955. Lectr. law Boston U. Law Sch., 1958-61; research assoc. Brandeis U., Waltham, Mass., 1962-66; treas. Orgn. for Social and Tech. Innovation, 1966-70; filmmaker Zipporah Films, Cambridge, Mass., 1970—; vis. lectr. numerous schs. Filmmaker: Titicut Follies, 1967, High School, 1968, Law and Order, 1969, Hospital, 1970, Basic Training, 1971, Essene, 1972, Juvenile Court, 1973, Primate, 1974, Welfare, 1975, Meat, 1976, Canal Zone, 1977, Sinai Field Mission, 1978, Manoeuvre, 1979, Model, 1980, Seraphita's Diary, 1982, The Store, 1983, Racetrack, 1985, Deaf, 1986, Blind, 1986, Multi-Handicapped, 1986, Adjustment and Work, 1986, Missile, 1987, Near Death, 1989, Central Park, 1989, Aspen, 1991, Zoo, 1993, High School II, 1994, Ballet, 1995; dir. theatre Tonight We Improvise, 1986-87, Life and Fate, 1988, Hate, 1991, Am. Repertory Theatre, Welfare: The Opera, Am. Music Theater Festival, 1992. Served with U.S. Army, 1955-56. Fellow Russell Sage Found., 1961-62, NATAS fellow, 1991; Guggenheim Found., 1980-81; recipient MacArthur prize, 1982-87, The Peabody award, Personal award, 1991. Fellow Am. Acad. Arts and Scis. Office: 1 Richdale Ave # 4 Cambridge MA 02140-2627

WISEMAN, JAMES RICHARD, classicist, archaeologist, educator; b. North Little Rock, Ark., Aug. 29, 1934; s. James Morgan and Bertie Lou (Sullivan) W.; m. Margaret Lucille Mayhue, Aug. 20, 1954; children—James Alexander, Stephen Michael. B.A., U. Mo., Columbia, 1957; M.A., U. Chgo., 1960, Ph.D., 1966; postgrad., Am. Sch. Classical Studies, Athens, Greece, 1959-60. Instr. U. Tex., Austin, 1960-64; asst. prof. classics U. Tex., 1964-66, asso. prof., 1966-70, prof., 1970-73; dir. archaeol. excavations at Ancient Corinth, Greece, 1965-72; chmn. archaeol. studies program, 1969-73; prof. classics Boston U., 1973—, prof. art history, 1975—, prof. archeology 1980—, chmn. dept. classical studies, 1974-82, chmn. dept. archeology, 1982—, dir. archaeol. studies program, 1975-76, 79-82, dir. Ctr. Archeol. Studies, 1980—; dir. summer program in Greece, 1976-77, 81, 92; vis. assoc. prof. classics U. Colo., Boulder, 1970; Am. prin. investigator, co-dir. Am.-Yugoslav Archaeol. Excavations at Stobi, Yugoslavia, 1970-81; project supr. Boston U. Archaeol. Excavations in Temple, N.H., 1975-76; vis. research prof. Am. Sch. Classical Studies, Athens, 1978-79; cons. archaeology; chmn. exec. com. Ctr. Remote Sensing; dir. Boston U. Nikopolis Project in N.W. Greece. Author: Stobi, A Guide to the Excavations, 1973, The Land of the Ancient Corinthians, 1978, (with Thomas Sever) Remote Sensing and Archaeology: Potential for the Future, 1985; contbr. numerous articles on ancient history, epigraphy, classical studies, archaeology to profl. jours.; editor, contbg. author: Studies in the Antiquities of Stobi I, 1973, II, 1975, III, 1981; founding editor: Jour. Field Archaeology, 1974—. Trustee Am. Schs. Oriental Research, 1985-89. Served with USN, 1952-55. Recipient Bromberg award U. Tex., 1964, Bronze Plaque award City of Titov Veles, SR Makedonija, Yugoslavia; disting. alumnus award Coll. Arts and Sci. U. Mo. Columbia, 1989; Am. Council Learned Socs. fellow, 1967-68, 78-79, 90-91; Guggenheim fellow, 1971-72; U. Tex. Research Inst. grantee, summers 1961, 66, 67, and 1968-71, 71-72; NEH grantee, 1968, 69, 76-80; Ford Found. grantee, 1968-72; Smithsonian Instn. grantee, 1970-75, 79-81; Dumbarton Oaks fellow, 1983-84; NGS grantee, 1984, 92; NASA grantee, 1984, 91; W.M. Keck Found. grantee, 1985, 86, 88, 92; NEH fellow, 1990; Mellon fellow Inst. Advanced Study, Princeton U., 1990-91. Fellow Soc. Antiquaries of London, Explorers Club; mem. Archaeol. Inst. Am. (nat. pres. 1985-88, exec. com 1973-77, 81—, prse. Ctrl. Tex. Soc. 1962-64, pres. Boston Soc. 1979-81, Gold Seal award 1989, Chase Eliot Norton lectr.), Am. Philol. Assn., Am. Sch. Classical Studies at Athens (exec. com. 1973-76), Am. Acad. at Rome, Assn. Ancient Historians, Assn. Field Archaeology (exec. com. 1970-85), Am. Inst. Nautical Archaeology, Internat. Assn. Archaeology, Ctr. Materials Rsch. in Archaeology and Ethnology (exec. com. 1975-78, 79-83), Soc. Am. Archaeology, Soc. Hist. Archaeology, Am. Coun. Learned Soc. (del. 1985-89), German Archeol. Inst. (corr.). Democrat. Office: Boston U Dept Archaeology 675 Commonwealth Ave Boston MA 02215-1406

WISEMAN, JAY DONALD, photographer, mechanical designer and contractor; b. Salt Lake City, Dec. 23, 1952; s. Donald Thomas and Reva (Stewart) W.; m. Barbara Helen Taylor, June 25, 1977; children: Jill Reva,

Steve Jay. Ed. Utah State U., Logan, U. Utah. Cert. profl. photographer. Pvt. practice photography; owner, pres. JB&W Corp. Recipient Grand prize Utah State Fair, 1986, Kodak Crystal for Photographic Excellence, 1986, 87, Master of Photography degree, 1989, Best of Show award, 1991-92; Profl. Photographer Mag. cover photo, 1988; numerous photos inducted for permanent collection Internat. Photographic Hall of Fame, 1989; photo named one of World's Greatest, Kodak, 1987-88; 2 photos named among World's Best, Walt Disney World and Profl. Phototgraphers Assn., 1988, 2 prints tied for Best of Show award RMPPA Regional contest, 1991; recipient Gold Medallion award Best in Show (world wide). Mem. Profl. Photographers Assn. Am. (one of top 10 scores internat. photo contest), Rocky Mountain Profl. Photographers (Best of Show, highest score ever 1987, Master Photographer of Yr. 1991, Ct. of Honour 1981-91), Inter-Mountain Profl. Photographers Assn. (Master's Trophy Best of Show 1982, 86, 88, Photographer of Yr. award 1986, Ct. of Honour 1981-91), Photographers Soc. Am (Best of Show award Utah chpt. 1986). Latter Day Saints. Represented in Salt Lake City Internat. Airport permanent photo exhibit, various traveling loan collections, U.S. and Europe, 1988, loan collection Epcot Ctr., 1988-91; photographs published numerous profl. jours.

WISEMAN, LAURENCE DONALD, foundation executive; b. Washington, Feb. 24, 1947; s. Leon Robert and Marion (Zuckerman) W.; m. Robin Lynn Jeweler, May 29, 1978; children: Justin J., David B. AB with highest distinction, Dartmouth Coll., 1969; M in Pub. Affairs, Princeton U., 1971. Exec. producer Sta. WQED-TV (pub. broadcasting), Pitts., 1971-75; prin. Moses, Epstein and Wiseman, Washington, 1975-78; v.p. Yankelovich, Skelly and White, N.Y.C., 1978-81; v.p. Am. Forest Council, Washington, 1981-84, pres., 1984—; pres. Am. Forest Coun., 1984-92, Am. Forest Found., 1993—. Author: Coalition Building, 1977. Bd. dirs. Cystic Fibrosis Found., N.Y.C., 1979-80, Urban Philharmonic, Washington, 1980-83, Sasha Bruce House, Washington, 1980-82; adv. com. Soc. for Profl. Journalists, Washington, 1984; hon. trustee Nat. Arbor Day Found., Nebraska City, Nebr., 1984—. Mem. Am. Forestry Assn., Soc. Am. Foresters, Pub. Rels. Soc. Am. Home: 10621 Democracy Ln Potomac MD 20854-4016 Office: Am Forest Found 1111 19th St NW Washington DC 20036-3603

WISEMAN, THOMAS ANDERTON, JR., federal judge; b. Tullahoma, Tenn., Nov. 3, 1930; s. Thomas Anderton and Vera Seleta (Poe) W.; m. Emily Barbara Matlack, Mar. 30, 1957; children: Thomas Anderton III, Mary Alice, Sarah Emily. B.A., Vanderbilt U., 1952, LL.B., 1954; LLM, U. Va., 1990. Bar: Tenn. Pvt. practice Tullahoma, 1956-63; ptnr. Haynes, Wiseman & Hull, Tullahoma and Winchester, Tenn., 1963-71; treas. State of Tenn., 1971-74; ptnr. Chambers & Wiseman, 1974-78; judge U.S. Dist. Ct. (mid. dist.) Tenn., Nashville, 1978—, chief judge, 1984-91; mem. Tenn. Ho. of Reps., 1964-68; adj. prof. law Vanderbilt U. Sch. Law. Asso. editor: Vanderbilt Law Rev., 1953-54. Democratic candidate for gov., Tenn., 1974; chmn. Tenn. Heart Fund, 1973, Middle Tenn. Heart Fund, 1972. Served with U.S. Army, 1954-56. Fellow Tenn. Bar Found.; mem. Masons (33 deg.), Shriners, Amateur Chefs Soc. Presbyterian. Office: US Dist Ct 824 US Courthouse 801 Broadway Nashville TN 37203

WISER, J. W., engineering company executive, construction executive. Sr. v.p. Bechtel Savannah River Inc., North Augusta, S.C. Office: Bechtel Savannah River Inc 802 E Martintown Rd North Augusta SC 29841*

WISER, JAMES LOUIS, political science educator; b. Detroit, Mar. 4, 1945; s. Louis Bernard and Nita Pauline (Neff) W.; m. Bethany Marie Goodall, Dec. 27, 1967; children: Steven Louis, Michael James. B.A., U. Notre Dame, 1967; M.A., Duke U., 1968, Ph.D., 1971. Asst. prof. Loyola U., Chgo., 1971-74, assoc. prof., 1974-81, prof., 1981—, chmn. dept. polit. sci., 1980-84, dean Coll. Arts and Scis., 1987-89, sr. v.p., dean of faculties, 1989—. Author: Political Philosophy: A History of the Search for Order, 1983; Political Theory: A Thematic Inquiry, 1986. Bd. dirs. Am. Cancer Soc., Chgo., 1982-84. Recipient dissertation award Woodrow Wilson Found., 1970; Fulbright-Hayes grantee, 1969; NEH grantee, 1979. Mem. Am. Polit. Sci. Assn., Conf. for Study of Polit. Thought (chmn. 1975-77), Internat. Seminar for Philosophy and Polit. Theory. Democrat. Roman Catholic. Home: 6725 N Wildwood Ave Chicago IL 60646-1306 Office: Loyola U 820 N Michigan Ave Chicago IL 60611-2103

WISHARD, DELLA MAE, state legislator; b. Bison, S.D., Oct. 21, 1934; d. Ervin E. and Alma J. (Albertson) Preszler; m. Glenn L. Wishard, Oct. 18, 1953; children: Glenda Lee, Pamela A., Glen Ervin. Grad. high sch., Bison. Mem. S.D. Ho. of Reps., Pierre, 1984—. Columnist County Farm Bur., 1970—. Committeewoman state Rep. Cen. Com., Perkins County, S.D., 1980-84. Mem. Am. Legis. Coun. (state coord. 1985-91, state chmn. 1991—), Fed. Rep. Women (chmn. Perkins County chpt. 1978-84), S.D. Farm Bur. (state officer 1982). Lutheran. Avocations: writing, gardening. Home and office: PO Box 139 HC 1 Prairie City SD 57649-0367

WISHARD, GORDON DAVIS, lawyer; b. Indpls., Jan. 7, 1945; s. William Niles Jr. and Caroline (Davis) W.; m. Anne Emison; children: Claire Clark, Gordon Davis Jr. BA, Williams Coll., 1966; JD, Ind. U., 1969. Bar: Ind. 1969, U.S. Dist. Ct. (so. dist.) Ind. 1969, U.S. Ct. Appeals (7th cir.) 1976, U.S. Supreme Ct. 1980, U.S. Tax Ct. 1983. Ptnr. Ice Miller Donadio & Ryan, Indpls. Mem. Am. Coll. Trust and Estate Coun. (Ind. chmn. 1990-95). Avocations: hunting, fishing. Office: Ice Miller Donadio & Ryan 1 American Sq Indianapolis IN 46282

WISHART, ALFRED W., JR., foundation administrator; b. Pitts., Dec. 21, 1931; s. Alfred W. and Corrinne C. (Bell) W.; m. Barbara J. Scott, June 30, 1956; children: Scott S., Kathryn A., Craig C. BA, Coll. Wooster, 1953; MDiv, Union Theol. Seminary, 1956; DHL (hon.), Waynesburg U., 1976; DD (hon.), Washington and Jefferson Coll., 1983. Asst. min. Shadyside Presbyn. Ch., Pitts., 1956-60; sr. min. Arlington Ave. Presbyn. Ch., East Orange, N.J., 1961-70; exec. dir. Howard Heinz Endowment, Pitts., 1970-92, Vira I. Heinz Endowment, Pitts., 1985-92; sec. H.J. II Charitable and Family Trust, Pitts., 1970-89; exec. sec. Pitcairn-Crabbe Found., Pitts., 1970—; pres., CEO Pitts. Edn. Found., Pitts., 1970—. Mem. Duquesne Club (bd. dirs. 1983-86), Fox Chapel Golf Club, Rolling Rock Club. Republican. Avocations: tennis, golf, squash, shotting, fishing. Home: 408 Buckingham Rd Pittsburgh PA 15215-1555 Office: Howard Heinz Endowment 30 CNG Tower 625 Liberty Ave Pittsburgh PA 15222-3110 also: Pitts Found One PPG Pl 30th Fl Pittsburgh PA 15222

WISHART, LEONARD PLUMER, III, army officer; b. Newark, Sept. 24, 1934; s. Leonard Plumer and Mabel Dorothea (Womsley) W.; m. Sandra Frances De Vito, Apr. 12, 1958; children: Leonard Plumer IV, Scott Brian. Student, Va. Mil. Inst., 1952-53; BS in Engring., U.S. Mil. Acad., 1957; M.S. in Nuclear Physics, U. Va., 1966. Commd. 2d lt. U.S. Army, 1957, advanced through grades to lt. gen., 1988; served in Germany and Vietnam; tactical officer U.S. Mil. Acad., West Point, N.Y., 1971-73; sr. mil. asst. to Sec. of Army, 1975-76; comdr. 1st Brigade, 24th Inf. Div., Ft. Stewart, Ga., 1977-78; chief of staff 24th Inf. Div., 1979, VII Corps in Germany, 1981-83; asst. div. comdr. 1st Armored Div., 1983, 85; comdr. CACDA, Ft. Leavenworth, Kans., 1983-86; comdr. 1st Inf. Div., Ft. Riley, Kans., 1986-88, Combined Arms Command, Ft. Leavenworth, Kans., 1988-91; dep. comdr. TRADOC, Ft. Leavenworth, Kans., 1988-91, ret., 1991; assoc. Burdeshow Assocs. Ltd. Bethesda, Md., 1991-92, 94—; apptd. 1st dir. non-legis. and fin. svcs. U.S. Ho. of Reps., Washington, 1992-94. Active in scouting and other community activities. Decorated Disting. Service Medal (2), Legion of Merit (2), D.F.C., Bronze Star medal (2), Army Commendation medal, Air medals. Mem. Assn. U.S. Army, Assn. Grads. U.S. Mil. Acad., Alumni Assn. U. Va., VFW, Soc. of the First Div. Methodist. Office: Burdeshaw Assocs Ltd 4701 Sangamore Rd Bethesda MD 20816-2508

WISHART, RONALD SINCLAIR, retired chemical company executive; b. Bklyn., Mar. 1, 1925; s. Ronald Sinclair and Elizabeth Lathrop (Phillips) W.; m. Betty B. Burnup, Sept. 14, 1951 (dec. Dec. 1973); children—Michael Sinclair, James Ronald; m. Eleanor Dorothy Parrish Dooley, Jan. 11, 1975; step children—Donna Dooley Willix, Arthur D. Dooley. BChemE, Rensselaer Poly. Inst., 1948. Engr., chemist Linde air div. Union Carbide Corp., Tonawanda, N.Y., 1948-51; sales rep. Chgo., Cleve., 1951-56; region mgr. Chgo., 1956-57; product mgr. mktg. mgr. Silicones div. N.Y.C. 1957-64, gen. mgr., pres., 1964-66, pres. devel. and coating materials divs., 1966-71, corp. dir. energy and transp. policy, 1972-82, v.p. fed. govt. regulations, 1983-85; v.p. pub. affairs Danbury, Conn., 1985-90; chief of staff to chmn. of corp. Union Carbide, N.Y.C., 1984-85; mem. adv. coun. Gas Rsch. Inst., Energy Modeling Ctr., Stanford U., 1979-83, Environ. and Energy Policy Ctr., John F. Kennedy Sch. Pub. Policy, Harvard U., 1980-87; energy com. Aspen Inst., 1976-88; chmn., exec. dir. Electricity Consumers Resource Coun., Washington, 1976-79. Author: The Marketing Factor, 1966; contbr. chpts. to books and articles to profl. jours.; patentee silicone formulas. Vol. Am. Field Svc., Burma, 1944-45; pres., trustee, elder White Plains (N.Y.) Presbyn. Ch.; treas., bd. dirs. Ct. Christopher's Jenni Clarkson Home, 1968-91; mem. exec. bd. Westchester Putnam coun. Boy Scouts Am., White Plains, 1985-91; v.p. Carbide Retiree Corps. Mem. Am. Mgmt. Assn. (v.p. 1966-69), Chem. Mfrs. Assn. (chmn. energy com. 1974-78), Nat. Petroleum Refiners Assn. (v.p. 1972-76, issues com. chmn. 1985-89), Internat. Fedn. Ind. Energy Users (chmn. 1978), Am. Chem. Soc., Soc. Chem. Industry, NAM (energy com.), U.S. C. of C. (energy com.), Whipporwill Club, Met. Club Washington, Harbor Ridge Yacht and Country Club. Republican. Presbyterian. Avocations: golf, skiing, reading. Home: 1329 Lancewood Terr Palm City FL 34990

WISHNER, MAYNARD IRA, finance company executive, lawyer; b. Chgo., Sept. 17, 1923; s. Hyman L. and Frances (Fisher) W.; m. Elaine Loewenberg, July 4, 1954; children: Ellen (Mrs. Tom Kenemore), Jane, Miriam. B.A., U. Chgo., 1944, J.D., 1947. Bar: Ill. 1947. Exec. dir. Chgo. Commn. on Human Relations, 1947-52; chief ordinance enforcement div. Law Dept., City of Chgo., 1952-55; mem. law firm Cole, Wishner, Epstein & Manilow, Chgo., 1955-63; with Walter E. Heller & Co., Chgo., 1963-86, pres., 1974-86; of counsel Rosenthal and Schanfield, Chgo., 1986-95; dir. Walter E. Heller Internat. Corp., Am. Nat. Bank & Trust Co., and br. cos., Chgo. Pres. Jewish Fedn. Met. Chgo., 1987-89; chair adv. coun. Nat. Jewish Community Rels., 1992-94, pres. Coun. Jewish Fedn., 1993—; chmn. nat. exec. coun. Am. Jewish Com., 1973-76, chmn. bd. govs., 1977-80, nat. pres. 1980-83, hon. pres., recipient Human Rights medallion, 1975; bd. dirs. Nat. Found. for Jewish Culture; chmn. Ill. Humanities Coun.; commr. Nat. Hillel Found.; mem. vis. com. U. Chgo. Sch. Social Svc. Adminstrn.; chair Ill. Humanities Coun., 1991-93. Served with AUS, 1943. Home: 1410 Sheridan Rd Wilmette IL 60091-1840 Office: Rosenthal & Schanfield 55 E Monroe St Chicago IL 60603-5855

WISHNER, STEVEN R., retail executive; b. N.Y.C., Mar. 21, 1950; s. Jerome and Florence (Wanger) W.; m. Lauri Ruth Berkson, June 5, 1977; children: Andrew R., Sara M. BA, Colgate U., 1972; MBA, Cornell U., 1976. 2nd v.p. Chase Manhattan Bank, N.Y.C., 1976-78; functional v.p. Chase Manhattan Bank, 1978; dir. fin. svcs. Gen. Instrument Corp., Clifton, N.J., 1978-79; asst. to treas. Gen. Instrument Corp., 1979-81; dir. fin. svcs. Viacom Internat. Inc., N.Y.C., 1981-82; asst. treas. Viacom Internat. Inc., 1982-86; v.p., treas. Zayre Corp., Framingham, Mass., 1987-89; v.p. fin., treas. The TJX Cos., Inc., Framingham, 1987—; mem. ea. adv. bd. Protection Mut. Ins. Co., 1987-91. Vice chmn. fin. com. Town of Sudbury, Mass. Mem. Fin. Execs. Inst., Nat. Assoc. Corp. Treas., Nat. Investor Rels. Inst., Cornell U. Alumni Assn. (co-chmn. admissions com., alumni exec. coun. 1987-90), Masons. Home: 92 Fox Run Rd Sudbury MA 01776-2768 Office: The TJX Companies Inc 770 Cochituate Rd Framingham MA 01701-9117

WISHNICK, MARCIA MARGOLIS, pediatrician, geneticist, educator; b. N.Y.C., Oct. 10, 1938; d. Hyman and Tillie (Stoller) Margolis; m. Stanley Wishnick, June 12, 1960; 1 child, Elizabeth Anne. BA, Barnard Coll., 1960; PhD, NYU, 1970, MD, 1974. Diplomate Am. Bd. Pediatrics, Nat. Bd. Med. Examiners. Rsch. technician Lederle Labs./Am. Cyanamid, Pearl River, N.Y., 1960-66; postdoctoral fellow N.Y. Pub. Health Lab., N.Y.C., 1970-71; resident in pediatrics Bellevue Med. Ctr. NYU-Bellevue Med. Ctr., N.Y.C., 1974-77; asst. prof. pediatrics Bellevue Med. Ctr. NYU Med. Ctr., N.Y.C., 1977-82, clin. assoc. prof. pediatrics Bellevue Med. Ctr., 1982-87, clin. prof. pediatrics Bellevue Med. Ctr., 1987—; pvt. practice, N.Y.C., 1977—. Contbr. articles to profl. jours. Fellow Am. Acad. Pediatrics; mem. AMA, Am. Soc. Human Genetics, N.Y. Pediatric Soc., N.Y. Med. Soc., N.Y. Women's Med. Assn. Office: 157 E 81st St New York NY 10028-1844

WISKIND, MILTON I., wholesale distribution executive, chemicals executive; b. 1925. BS, Wharton Sch. Commerce, 1947. With Myers Industries, Inc., Akron, Ohio, 1957—, v.p., 1963; v.p., sec. Myers Industries, Inc., Akron, 1971, now sr. v.p. With USN, USNR, 1947-67. Office: Myers Industries Inc 1293 S Main St Akron OH 44301*

WISKOWSKI, EUGENE, health facility administrator. CFO Eisenhower Med. Ctr., Rancho Mirage, Calif. Office: Eisenhower Med Ctr 39000 Bob Hope Dr Rancho Mirage CA 92270*

WISLER, CHARLES CLIFTON, JR., retired cotton oil company executive; b. Oklahoma City, June 6, 1926; s. Charles Clifton and Lucille Sunshine (McCormick) W.; m. Frances Joan Higgins, Sept. 21, 1946; children: Karen Lynn Collins-Eiland, Gary Clifton, David Charles. Student, Oklahoma City U., 1945-47. Bookkeeper Magnolia Petroleum Co., Oklahoma City, 1947-51; cotton buyer C.S. Higgins Co., Lubbock, Tex., 1951-52; office mgr. Sharp & Glover, Harlingen, Tex., 1952; with Toyo Cotton Co., Dallas, 1952-81; pres. Toyo Cotton Co., 1972-81; pres. Chickasha Cotton Oil Co., Ft. Worth, Tex., 1981-86, chmn., 1983-88; advisor to bd. dirs. Nat. Cotton Coun., 1985-91. Bd. dirs. Nat. Kidney Found., Dallas, 1976-83, Granbury Opera House Assn., 1992-94; mem. Agr. Policy Adv. Com. for Trade Negotiations, Washington, 1975-77. With USAAF, 1944-45. Mem. Tex. Cotton Assn. (dir. 1971-75, 79-80, pres. 1974), Am. Cotton Shippers Assn. (dir. 1972, 74-75, 77). Republican. Methodist. Home: 6115 Belvidere Cir Granbury TX 76049

WISLER, DAVID CHARLES, aerospace engineer, educator; b. Pottstown, Pa., Apr. 21, 1941; s. Lloyd William and Ruth Georgiana (Enos) W.; m. Judith Ann Caleen, Aug. 22, 1964 (dec. Mar. 1979); children: Scott David, Cheryl Lynn; m. Beth Ellen Howard, Jan. 5, 1980; 1 child, Daniel James. BS in Aero Engring., Pa. State U., 1963; MS in Aero. Engring., Cornell U., 1965; PhD in Aero. Engring., U. Colo, 1970. Rsch. engr. GE R & D Ctr., Schenectady, 1965-67; mgr. aero tech. labs. GE Aircraft Engines, Evendale, Ohio, 1985—; adj. prof. Iowa State U., Ames, 1987—. Contbr. articles to profl. jours.; patentee in sloped trenches in compressors. Fellow AIAA (assoc.); mem. ASME (chmn. turbomachinery com. 1993—, Melville medal for best tech. paper 1989, Gas Turbine award 1990, 92). Avocation: photography. Home: 1895 Doral Dr Fairfield OH 45014-4759 Office: GE Aircraft Engines 1 Neumann Way # A323 Cincinnati OH 45215-1915

WISLER, WILLARD EUGENE, health care management executive; b. Cliffside Park, N.J., May 31, 1933; s. Willard Walter and Doris Alice (McGlone) W.; m. Carol M. Askey, Aug. 19, 1966; children: Diana Marie, Jennifer Lee. BBA, U. Fla., 1955; MBA, The George Washington U., 1963. Asst. adminstr. Halifax Dist. Hosp., Daytona Beach, Fla., 1963-64; CFO Waterman Meml. Hosp., Eustis, Fla., 1964-67, COO, 1967-72; COO Suburban Hosp., Louisville, 1972-73; exec. dir. Gen. Hosp. of Fort Walton Beach, Fla., 1973-77; pres. Winter Pk. (Fla.) Meml. Hosp., 1977-91, Park Health Corp., Winter Pk., 1985-91, The Tampa Bay Hosp. Assn., St. Petersburg, Fla., 1991—; bd. dirs. Village on the Green, Winter Pk. Mem. bd. mem. ho of dels. Am. Hsp. Assn., Chgo., 1985-88; regent State of Fla. Am. Coll. Healthcare Execs., Chgo., 1988-93. Adv. council mem. Hamilton Holt Sch., Rollins Coll., Winter Pk., 1986-89, Orlando Bus. Jour., 1989, Pioneer Savings Bank, Winter Pk., 1986-88. Sgt. U.S. Army, 1955-59. Fellow Am. Coll. Healthcare Execs, Citrus Club, Winter Park Racquet, Interlachen Country. Democrat. Home: 3414 W Mullen Ave Tampa FL 33609 Office: The Tampa Bay Hosp Assn 9455 Koger Blvd N Ste 118 Saint Petersburg FL 33702

WISNE, ANTHONY E., metal products executive; b. 1918. With Prog Tool & Indsl. Co., Southfield, Mich., 1939—, now chmn. Office: Prog Tool & Inds Co 21000 Telegraph Rd Southfield MI 48034*

WISNE, LAWRENCE A., metal products executive; b. 1947; s. Anthony E. W. With Prog Tool & Indsl. Co., Southfield, Mich., v.p., 1977-79, pres., 1979—. Office: Prog Tool & Inds Co 21000 Telegraph Rd Southfield MI 48034*

WISNER, FRANK GEORGE, ambassador; b. N.Y.C., July 2, 1938; s. Frank Gardiner W. and Mary Knowles (Fritchey) W.; m. Genevieve de Virel, July, 1969 (dec. 1974); 1 dau., Sabrina; m. Christine de Ganay, June, 1976; 1 son, David; stepchildren: Caroline Sarkozy, Olivier Sarkozy. BA, Princeton U., 1961. With Fgn. Svc. Dept. Dept. State, Algiers, Morocco, 1962-64; from staff aide to sr. advisor Vietnamese province Tuyen Duc Agy. Internat. Devel., Vietnam, 1964-68; officer-in-charge Tunisian affairs Dept. State, Washington, 1968-71; chief econ.-comml. sect. Am. Embassy, Tunis, Tunisia, 1971-73; chief polit. sect. Am. Embassy, Dacca, Bangladesh, 1973-74; dir. plans and mgmt. Bur. Pub. Affairs, Washington, 1974-75; spl. asst. to dir., then dep. dir. Pres.' Interagy. Task Force Refugee Resettlement, Washington, 1975; spl. asst. to undersec. polit. affairs, 1975-76; dir. office So. African affairs Dept. State, Washington, 1976-77, dep. exec. sec., 1977-79; U.S. amb. to Zambia Lusaka, 1977-82; dep. asst. sec. African affairs Dept. State, Washington, 1982-86; U.S. amb. to Egypt Cairo, 1986-91; U.S. amb. to Philippines Manila, 1991-92; under sec. of state for internat. security affairs Washington, 1992-93; under sec. of def. for policy Dept. Def., Washington, 1993-94; U.S. amb. to India, 1994—. Recipient meritorious honor award Dept. State, 1973, superior honor award, 1992; recipient Mil. Medal of Honor Govt. Vietnam, 1968, Social Welfare medal of honor, 1968. Mem. Council on Fgn. Relations, Metropolitan Club (Washington), Ivy Club (Princeton, N.J.), Knickerbocker Club (N.Y.). Episcopalian. Office: Shanti Path, Chanakyapuri, New Delhi 110021, India

WISNER, ROSCOE WILLIAM, JR., human resources executive; b. Beatrice, Nebr., Mar. 17, 1926; s. Roscoe William Sr. and Genevieve M. (McVey) W.; m. Louise Jackson, Mar. 15, 1952; children: Jacqueline Louise, Valerie Joyce. BA, Lincoln U., Oxford, Pa., 1950; MEd, Temple U., 1963. Accredited profl. in human resource mgmt. Sr. personnel examiner Phila. Personnel Dept., 1954-64; supr. testing and rsch. Port Authority of N.Y. and N.J., N.Y.C., 1964-76; coord. spl. programs for people with disabilities, 1976-91; ret.; instr., adj. faculty LaGuardia Community Coll. Author: Performance Test Procedures and Problems, 1964; contbr. articles to profl. jours. Adv. coun. Industry-Labor Coun., Albertson, N.Y., 1976—, Kessler's Rehab. Inst., East and West Orange, N.J., 1979—, Rusk Rehab. Inst., N.Y.C., 1980—, Mayor's Office People with Disabilities, N.Y.C., 1980, Internat. Ctr. for Disabled, N.Y.C., 1980—, N.Y.C. Bd. Edn. Spl. Edn. Project Future, 1986—; exec. dir. Cmty. Action Program, Westbury, 1965; mem. Watchful Eye Civic Assn., Roosvelt, N.Y., 1983—; life mem. NAACP. Sgt. U.S. Army, 1944-46. Recipient Exec. Dir. Unit citation Port Authority N.Y. and N.J., 1984, Disting. Svc. award, 1990, Profl. Achievement award Ea. Region/Pub. Pers. Assn. Conf., 1969. Mem. APA (assoc.), NAACP (life), Internat. Pers. Mgmt. Assn., Soc. Human Resource Mgmt. (life), Am. Soc. Pub. Adminstrn., Masons, Alpha Phi Alpha. Home: 266 E Greenwich Ave Roosevelt NY 11575-1205

WISNESKI, MARY JO ELIZABETH, reading specialist, educator; b. Saginaw, Mich., Dec. 18, 1938; d. Walter Frank and Hedwig Josephine (Borowicz) W. BS, Cen. Mich. U., 1961; MS, So. Ill. U., 1969; EdD, U. No. Colo., 1979; postdoctoral, U. Calif., Berkeley, 1980-81. Cert. elem. educator, elem. adminstr., reading specialist, Calif.; reading recovery tchr. Elem. educator various schs., 1960-75; instr. U. No. Colo., Greeley, 1976-78, 79; reading specialist Vacaville (Calif.) Unified Sch. Dist., 1980—; instr. San Francisco State U., 1983-86; prof. Chapman Coll., Travis AFB, Calif., 1986-90; cons. in field. Author: Clifford Books Teacher Manual, 1991, Reading Recovery Position Paper, 1995. Vol. ARC, Travis Air Mus., Travis AFB; bd. dirs. Polish Arts and Culture Found., San Francisco, 1988-91, Vistula Dancers; mem. Reading Del. to Vietnam, People-to-People Internat. Amb. Program, 1995. Recipient Tchr. in Space Certificate NASA, 1986, Outstanding Tchr. Commendation Dept. of Defense, 1973. Mem. AAUW, Nat. Women's Polit. Caucus, Nat. Reading Conf., Internat. Reading Assn., Western Coll. Reading Assn., Calif. Profs. Reading (v.p., treas.), Calif. Edn. Assn., Solano County Reading Assn. (pres., v.p., sec.), Lowiczanie Folk Dance Ensemble (pres. pro tem, treas.), Polish Am. Congress, Phi Delta Kappa, Phi Kappa Phi, Kappa Delta Pi, Pi Lambda Theta. Avocations: modeling, travel, skiing, gardening, nature. Home: 314 Creekview Ct Vacaville CA 95688-5318

WISNIEWSKI, HENRY GEORGE, wholesale distribution executive; b. Chgo., Feb. 26, 1940; s. Henry John and Jeanette A. (Wawrylska) W.; m. Joyce Anne Kennedy, May 28, 1966; children: Mark, Paul. BSc, Loyola U., Chgo., 1961; MBA, Northwestern U., 1981. CPA, Ill. Ptnr. Arthur Andersen & Co., Chgo., 1961-76; pres. JMPH Enterprises, Chgo., 1977-82, Robank & Co., Chgo., 1982-89; exec. v.p., CFO Tash Inc., Des Plaines, Ill., 1989-92; sr. v.p. fin. Tuthill Corp., Hinsdale, Ill., 1992—; bd. dirs. Quality Control Corp., Chgo., Paragon Die Casting, Chgo. Bd. dirs. Chgo. Youth Ctrs., 1966—, past pres., 1971. Sgt. USMCR, 1962-67. Mem. AICPAs, Ill. Soc. CPAs, Fin. Execs. Inst. Roman Catholic. Office: Tuthill Corp 908 N Elm Hinsdale IL 60521

WISNIEWSKI, HENRYK MIROSLAW, pathology and neuropathology educator, research facility administrator, research scientist; b. Luszkowko, Poland, Feb. 27, 1931; came to U.S., 1966; s. Alexander and Ewa (Korthals) W.; m. Krystyna Wylon, Feb. 14, 1954; children: Alexander (dec.), Thomas. MD, Med. Sch., Gdansk, Poland, 1955; PhD in Exptl. Neuropathology. Med. Sch., Warsaw, Poland, 1960; DSc (hon.), Med. Sch., Gdansk, Poland, 1991, Coll. of Staten Island, 1992. From asst. to assoc. prof., head. lab. exptl. neuropathology, assoc. dir. Inst. Neuropathology Polish Acad. Sci., Warsaw, 1958-66; rsch. assoc. from asst. prof. to prof. Albert Einstein Coll. Medicine, N.Y.C., 1966-75; dir. MRC Demyelinating Diseases Unit, Newcastle upon Tyne, Eng., 1975-76; prof. neuropathology SUNY Health Sci. Ctr., Bklyn., 1976—; dir. N.Y. State Inst. Basic Rsch. in Devel. Disabilities, S.I., 1976—; vis. neuropathologist U. Toronto, Ont., Can., 1961-62; vis. scientist Lab. of Neuropathology Nat. Inst. Neurol. and Communicative Diseases and Stroke, NIH, 1962-63; docent Med. Sch., Warsaw, 1965; past mem. Neuology B study sect. NIH; past mem. mental retardation com. Nat. Inst. Child Health and Human Devel. Contbr. over 561 articles to profl. jours. and symposia proceedings; mem. editorial bd. Acta Neuropathologica, Neurotoxicology, Jour. Neuropathology and Exptl. Neurology, Devel. Neurosci., Internat. Jour. Geriatric Psychiatry, Alzheimer Disease and Associated Disorders Internat. Jour., Brain Dysfunction, Dementia; mem. editorial adv. bd. Neurobiology of Aging. Recipient N.Y.C. Chpt. award Assn. for Help of Retarded Children, 1984, Welfare League award letchworth Village chpt. Assn. for Help of Retarded Children, 1985, Staten Island Chpt. award Benevolent Soc. for Retarded Children, 1986; named Career Scientist, Health Rsch. Coun. of City of N.Y., Honoris Causa Doctor of Sci., Med. Sch., Gdansk, Poland, 1992, Honoris Causa, Doctor of Sci., Coll. of Staten Island, 1992. Fellow AAAS; mem. Am. Assn. Neuropathologists (pres. 1984, Weil award 1969, Moore award 1972), British Soc. Neuropathology, Can. Assn. Neuropathologists, Am. Assn. Retarded Citizens, Assn. Rsch. in Nervous and Mental Disease, Am. Assn. Mental Deficiency, Internat. Soc. Devel. Neurosci., Soc. Exptl. Neuropathology, World Fedn. Neurology, Sigma Xi. Democrat. Roman Catholic. Achievements include research of developmental disabilities, aging, Alzheimer disease, Down syndrome, amyloidosis, neuronal fibrous protein pathology; demyelinating diseases. Office: NY State Inst Basic Rsch Devel Disabilities 1050 Forest Hill Rd Staten Island NY 10314-6330

WISNIEWSKI, JOHN WILLIAM, mining engineer, bank engineering executive; b. Portage, Pa., Jan. 22, 1932; S. John and Agnes (Ease) W.; m. Joan Smith, Aug. 24, 1957; children: John Andrew, Jean Marie, Maria. BS in Mining Engring., U. Pitts., 1954, postgrad., 1967-68. Mining engr. Bethlehem Mines Corp., Johnstown, Pa., 1956-61, Fairmont, W.Va., 1961-62; mining and gen. engr. IRS, Pitts., 1962-69; mining engr., then coordinating engr. IRS, Washington, 1969-72, supervisory gen. engr., chief rsch., planning and studies sect., 1972-76; mining engr., then dep. chief engr. Export-Import Bank U.S. Washington, 1976-82, chief engr., 1982, v.p. engring., 1982-94; v.p. engring. and environ. Inc., 1994—. With U.S. Army, 1954-56; Korea. AIME scholar U. Pitts., 1950. Home: 9308 Ironhorse Ln Gaithersburg MD 20879-2161 Office: Export-Import Bank US 811 Vermont Ave NW Washington DC 20571-0002

WISNIEWSKI, JOSEPH MICHAEL, engineering executive; b. Grand Rapids, Mich., Sept. 7, 1954; s. Victor Chester Sr. and Clara (Wiewiora) W.; m. Barbara Alice Berry, May 4, 1974; children: Michele, Michael. BS in Mech. Engring., Western Mich. U., 1980; MBA in Fin., U. Notre Dame,

1988. Product engr. Steelcase, Grand Rapids, 1973-80; sr. project engr. Haworth, Holland, Mich., 1980-85, dir. engring., 1985-87; v.p. engring. Shaw-Walker, Muskegon, Mich., 1987—; exec. v.p., gen. mgr. Harpers, Torrance, Calif., 1988-93; pres. Gunlocke, Wayland, N.Y., 1993—. Patentee in field. Recipient Welded Steel Tubing Inst. Design award 1980. Mem. Soc. Plastic Engrs., Soc. Mfg. Engrs. Avocations: small game and waterfowl hunting, archery hunting, fishing, golf. Home: 12 Crownwood Circle Pittsford NY 14534 Office: The Gunlocke Co 1 Gunlocke Dr Wayland NY 14572

WISNIEWSKI, RICHARD, dean. Dean dept. edn. U. Tenn., Knoxville. Office: U Tenn Office of Dean Coll of Edn Knoxville TN 37996-0230

WISNIEWSKI, STEPHEN ADAM, professional football player; b. Rutland, Vt., Apr. 7, 1967. Student, Pa. State U. Offensive guard L.A. Raiders, 1989—. Named All-Pro Team Guard by Sporting News, 1990-93, Coll. All-Am. Team, 1987, 88. Played in Pro Bowl, 1990-91, 93. Office: L A Raiders 332 Center St El Segundo CA 90245*

WISNIEWSKI, THOMAS JOSEPH, music educator; b. Chgo., Sept. 17, 1926; s. George Wisniewski and Rose (Jelewski) W.; children: Dieter, Lisa Ann, Ericka. B.Mus., Am. Conservatory of Music, Chgo., 1948; M.Mus., No. Ill. U., 1964. Instr. string instrument Sch. Dist. 89, Maywood, Ill., 1950-55; orch. dir. Sch. Dist. 44, Lombard, Ill., 1955-67; dir. orchs. Glenbard East High Sch., Lombard, 1959-67; prof. music U. Ill., Urbana, 1967-94, emeritus prof., 1994—, chair music edn. div., 1988-92; music cons. Webster Internat. Illustrated Dictionary, 1993. Producer: (films) Playing the String Bass, 1967, Playing the Cello, 1968; author: Learning Umlimited String Program Vols. 1, 1975, Learning Unlimited String Program, Vols. II, 1976; editor Orch. Pubis., 1990; music editor: Webster International Illustrated Dictionary, 1994. Mem. Am. String Tchrs. Assn. (Disting. Svc. award Ill. unit 1991, Disting. Svc. award Tenn. unit 1993), Ill. Music Educators Assn., Music Educators Nat. Conf., Ill. String Tchrs. Assn. (editor 1967, 87, pres. 1970), Nat. Jazz Educators Assn. (nat. orch. chmn. 1976), Kappa Kappa Lambda, Phi Mu Alpha. Office: U Ill 1114 W Nevada St Urbana IL 61801-3859

WISS, MARCIA A., lawyer; b. Columbus, Ohio, May 15, 1947; d. John William and Margaret Ann (Cook) W.; m. Donald Gordon MacDonald, Nov. 18, 1921; children: Christopher C. Wiss, Joan Merle. BS in Fgn. Svc., Georgetown U., 1969, JD, 1972. Bar: D.C. 1972. Econ. analyst World Bank, Washington, 1969; atty. U.S. Dept. Justice, Washington, 1972-73; atty. office gen. counsel Overseas Pvt. Investment Corp., Washington, 1973-78; assoc. Stroock & Stroock & Lavan, Washington, 1978-79; gen counsel-designate Inst. for Sci. and Tech. Cooperation, Washington, 1979; affiliate Curtis, Mallet-Prevost, Colt & Mosle, Washington, 1979-80; ptnr. Anderson & Pendleton, Chartered attys., Washington, 1980-87; with Kaplan Russin & Vecchi, Washington, 1987-92; ptnr. Whitman, Breed, Abbott & Morgan, Washington, 1992—; gen. counsel Washington chpt., Soc. Internat. Devel., 1980—; gen. counsel, Assn. for Women in Devel., 1982—; bd. advisers Procedural Aspects of Internat. Law Inst., 1985—. Author: Third World Debt and Relative Financial Arrangements, 1978, Multinationals and Third World Issues..., 1984, Renewal of Generalized Systems of Preferences, 1984; editor, Georgetown Law Ctr. Jour. Law and Policy in Internat. Bus.; 1971-72. Chairperson Holy Trinity Parish Coun., Washington, 1976; mem. bd. advisers Trees for Life, Wichita, Kans., 1984—. Mem. Am. Fedn. Govt. Employees (chmn. 1975-76), D.C. Bar (steering com. div. 12, 1985-88, co-chmn. fin. and banking com. 1985), Am. Soc. Internat. Law (v.p. 1991—, coun. 1987-90), Washington Fgn. Law Soc. (pres. 1983-84). Roman Catholic. Office: Whitman Breed Abbott & Morgan 1215 17th St NW Washington DC 20036-3008

WISSBRUN, KURT FALKE, chemist, consultant; b. Brackwede, Westphalia, Germany, Mar. 19, 1930; came to the U.S., 1939; s. Hermann and Bertha (Falke) W. BS, U. Pa., 1952; PhD, Yale U., 1956. Rsch. chemist Hoechst-Celanese (formerly Celanese Corp.), Summit, N.J., 1957-60; group leader Hoechst-Celanese, Summit, N.J., 1960-62; rsch. assoc. Hoerst-Celanese (formerly Celanese Corp.), Summit, N.J., 1966-70, sr. rsch. assoc., 1970-90; polymer cons. Summit, 1990—; adj. prof. U. Del., Newark, 1974—; mem. governing bd., mem. exec. com. Am. Inst. Physics, College Park, Md., 1981-93. Author: Melt Rheology and Plastics Processing, 1989, (with others) Blow Molding Handbook, 1988; contbr. articles to profl. jours.; patentee, inventor in field. Mem. Am. Chem. Soc., Soc. Rheology (v.p. 1993—, Bingham medal 1992), British Soc. Rheology, Sigma Xi. Jewish. Avocations: golf, opera, travel. Home: 1 Euclid Ave Apt 4E Summit NJ 07901

WISSLER, EUGENE HARLEY, chemical engineer, educator; b. Cherokee, Iowa, Dec. 18, 1927; s. Lloyd L. and Gertrude F. (Holmes) W.; m. Patricia A. Nygren, July 29, 1951; children: Gerhardt E., Konrad P., Neysa L. BS, Iowa State Coll., 1950; PhD, U. Minn., 1955. Registered profl. engr., Tex. Prof. chem. engring. U. Tex., Austin, 1957—, assoc. dean, 1968-74, 81-93; cons. Naval Coastal Sys. Ctr., Panama City, Fla., 1975-80; cons. NUTEC, Bergen, Norway, Brooks AFB Sch. Aerospace Medicine, San Antonio, SINTEF, Trondheim, Norway, McDonnell Douglas, St. Louis. With AUS, 1955-57. NSF Sci. Faculty fellow, 1961-62. Fellow ASME; mem. AIChE, Aerospace Med. Assn., Rotary (pres. 1976-77). Home: 4704 Ridge Oak Dr Austin TX 78731-4724 Office: U Tex Dept Chem Engring Austin TX 78712 *A desire to do something unique probably accounts for my choosing an academic career and for my research in human physiology, even though my formal education was in engineering. My mathematical models describing human response to exercise and thermal stress represent an application of physical principles to living systems. They also embody the engineering philosophy that certain questions must be answered using the best information currently available; it is satisfying that they have found application in the design of life support systems for astronauts, aircrew members and divers.*

WISSMAN, JACK PAUL, financial executive; b. Sidney, Ohio, Apr. 9, 1952; s. Paul Kenneth and Alice Carol (Schmidt) W.; m. Elizabeth Ann Duffell, Aug. 21, 1984; children: Danielle, Jack Paul, Jr. BSBA, Bowling Green U., 1974. CPA, Fla. Successively audit staff mem., audit sr., audit mgr. Arthur Andersen & Co., Tampa, Fla., 1974-81; v.p. fin. and adminstrn. Lamalie Assocs., Inc., Tampa, 1981—. Mem. AICPA, Fla. Inst. CPAs, Carrollwood Village Country Club (Tampa). Office: Lamalie Assocs Inc 13920 N Dale Mabry PO Box 273260 Tampa FL 33688-3260

WISSNER, GARY CHARLES, motion picture art director, production designer; b. N.Y.C., Feb. 9, 1964; s. Sidney and Penina (Gologor) W.; m. Tambre Hemstreet, Nov. 13, 1993. BFA, NYU, 1986. Scenic artist Cape Code Melody Tent, Hyannas, Mass., 1983; prodn. technician Imero Fiorentino Assocs., N.Y.C., 1984-86; asst. scenic designer Radio City Music Hall, N.Y.C., 1986; art dir. MTV Networks, N.Y.C., 1987-88; asst. art dir. Country Music Awards, L.A., 1987; asst. art dir. TV show Young and the Restless, L.A., 1987; asst. art dir. Patty Hearst Atlantic Entertainment, L.A., 1987. Art dir.: (commls) Chrysler, Laser Tag, Michelob, (theme parks/indsls.) Tomorrowland, 1990, Korean World Expo, 1991, AT&T Futurecom, 1993, (TV) Road to Daytona (MTV segment), 1987, Superbowl in San Diego (MTV spl.), 1988, Family of Spies (CBS mini-series), 1989, In Living Color, 1991, (feature films) Teenage Mutant Ninja Turtles, 1989, Another 48 Hours, 1990, Hoffa, 1992, Wyatt Earp, 1993, Junior, 1994, Seven, 1995; prodn. designer: (comml.) Balance Health Foods, 1993, (feature film) Stephen King's Graveyard Shift, 1990, Gundown, 1995; asst. art dir.: (feature films) Warlock, 1988, The Abyss, 1988. Mem. Acad. Motion Picture Arts and Scis. (voting mem.), Soc. Motion Picture Art Dirs. (voting mem.), United Scenic Artists (voting mem.). Avocations: computers, sculpture, sports, fitness. Office: care Art Directors Guild 11365 Ventura Blvd #315 Studio City CA 91604

WISSNER, SETH ERNST, gynecologist, educator; b. St. Louis, June 7, 1922; s. Henry William and Cora Mary (Husman) W.; m. Ruth Mary Waters, June 18, 1955; children—Seth Paul, Mark David, Sarah Ann. A.B., Washington U., St. Louis, 1942, M.D., 1945. Diplomate Am. Bd. Ob-Gyn. Intern Deaconess Hosp., St. Louis, 1945-46; resident ob-gyn Barnes Hosp., St. Louis, 1948-52; asst. prof., surg. pathologist Washington U. Med. Sch., St. Louis, 1952-79; practice medicine specializing in gynecology St. Louis,

1952—; chief of staff Deaconess Hosp., 1964-67; mem. staff Mo. Baptist Hosp., St. Joseph Hosp.; med. dir. St. Louis Planned Parenthood, 1970—. Contbr. articles to profl. jours. Cons. for internat. edn. in ob-gyn, Balt., Nigeria, Caribbean Islands area. Served to capt. U.S. Army, 1946-48, PTO. Recipient 25 yr. award Barnes Hosp. and Deaconess Hosp. 1977. Fellow Am. Coll. Ob-Gyn (triennial awards 1977, 80, 83, 86, 89, 92, 95); mem. St. Louis Gynecol. Soc., St. Louis Med. Soc., Mo. Med. Soc. (awards), Assn. Planned Parenthood, Chaine des Rotisseurs, Ordre Mondiale. Avocation: playing piano duets. Home: 844 Audubon Dr Saint Louis MO 63105-2912 Office: 9147 Watson Rd Saint Louis MO 63126-2239

WISTISEN, MARTIN J., agricultural business executive; b. Bancroft, Idaho, May 30, 1938; s. Raoul and Cora (Johnson) W.; m. Katherine Callister, Dec. 28, 1960; children: Kevin, Diane, Kaeleen, Janette, Richard, Michelle, R. Brent, N. Greg. BS, Brigham Young U., 1962; MBA, Northwestern U., 1964; PhD, Columbia U., 1976. Fin. analyst Esso Internat., Inc., N.Y.C., 1964-65; dir. fin. analysis, mgr. econ. analysis TWA, N.Y.C., 1967-70; dir. bus. and econs., prof. bus. mgmt. and bus. econs., dir. MBA program, asst. dean Grad. Sch. Mgmt. Brigham Young U., Provo, Utah, 1971-80; v.p. sales and mktg. U & I, Inc., Kennewick, Wash., 1980-82; exec. v.p., chief oper. officer UI Group, Kennewick, 1982-86; pres., chief exec. officer AgriNorthwest, Kennewick, 1986—. Pres. Blue Mountain Coun. Boy Scouts Am., Kennewick, 1987-89; bd. dirs. Wash. State Potato Commn., Moses Lake, 1990-93; mem. strategy commn. Wash. State Energy Adv. Bd., 1991-92. Mem. Assn. Wash. Bus. (bd. dirs. 1986—), Beta Gamma Sigma, Phi Kappa Phi. Republican. Mem. LDS Ch. Office: AgriNorthwest 2810 W Clearwater Ave Kennewick WA 99336-2963

WISWALL, FRANK LAWRENCE, JR., lawyer, educator; b. Albany, N.Y., Sept. 21, 1939; s. Frank Lawrence and Clara Elizabeth (Chapman) W.; m. Elizabeth Curtiss Nelson, Aug. 9, 1975; children by previous marriage: Anne W. Kowalski, Frank Lawrence III. BA, Colby Coll., 1962; JD, Cornell U., 1965; PhD in Law, Cambridge U., 1967. Bar: Maine 1965, N.Y. 1968, U.S. Supreme Ct. 1968, D.C. 1975; lic. master near coastal steam and motor vessels, 1960—. Assoc. Burlingham, Underwood, Barron, Wright & White, N.Y.C., 1967-73; maritime legal adviser Rep. of Liberia, 1968-88; mem. legal com. Internat. Maritime Orgn., London, 1972-74, vice chmn. 1974-79, chmn., 1980-84; tutorial supr. internat. law Clare Coll., Cambridge, Eng., 1966-67; vis. lectr. Cornell Law Sch., 1969-76, 82; lectr. U. Va. Law Sch. and Ctr. for Oceans Law and Policy, 1978-82; prof. law Cornell U., 1984; Johnsen prof. maritime law Tulane U., 1985; prof. law World Maritime U., Malmo, Sweden, 1986—; prof. Internat. Maritime Law Inst., Malta, 1991—, mem. governing bd., 1992—; prof. admiralty law Maine Maritime Acad., 1993-94; del. Internat. Conf. Marine Pollution, London, 1973; del., chmn. drafting com. Internat. Conf. Carriage of Passengers and Luggage by Sea, Athens, 1974; del. Internat. Conf. on Safety of Life at Sea, London, 1974, 3d UN Conf. on Law of Sea, Caracas, Venezuela, 1974, 3d UN Conf. on Law of Sea (all subsequent sessions); del., chmn. com. final clauses Internat. Conf. on Limitation of Liability for Maritime Claims, London, 1976; del. UN Conf. Carriage of Goods by Sea, Hamburg, 1978, XIII Diplomatic Conf. on Maritime Law, Brussels, 1979; chmn. com. of the whole Internat. Conf. Carriage of Hazardous Substances by Sea, 1984; del. internat. conf. on Maritime Terrorism, Rome, 1988; counsel various marine casualty bds. of investigation, 1970—; harbormaster, Port of Castine, 1960-62; ofcl. prin. Diocese of the Mid-Atlantic States Anglican Cath. Ch., 1988—, chancellor, Missionary Diocese of N.E., 1993—. Author: The Development of Admiralty Jurisdiction and Practice Since 1800, 1970; editor-in-chief Benedict on Admiralty, Vols. 6, 6A-6C (treaties and convs.), 1992—; contbr. articles to profl. jours. Recipient Yorke prize U. Cambridge, 1968-69. Fellow Royal Hist. Soc.; mem. Titulaire of the Comité Maritime Internat. (exec. councillor 1989—), Maritime Law Assn. U.S. (chmn. com. on intergovtl. orgns. 1983-87, chmn. com. on CMI 1987-95), Ecclesiastical Law Soc., Selden Soc., Am. Soc. Legal History, U.K. Assn. Average Adjusters, U.S. Assn. Average Adjusters, Maine Bar Assn., United Oxford and Cambridge U. Club (London), Century Assn., Alpha Delta Phi, Phi Delta Phi. Office: PO Box 201 Castine ME 04421-0201

WIT, DANIEL, international consultant; b. N.Y.C., June 8, 1923; s. Benjamin and Stella (Bloom) W.; m. Phyllis J. Citron, June 15, 1947; children: Pamela S., Frederick W. AB, Union Coll., N.Y., 1943; postgrad., Yale U. Italian program, Paris, 1943-44, Institut d'Etudes Politiques, Paris, 1945-46; AM, Princeton U., 1948, PhD, 1950. Mem. dept. polit. sci. Ohio State U., 1948-50, U. Cin., 1950-54, U. Mich., 1954-56, U. Miss., 1956-58; mem. dept. polit. sci. George Washington U., 1959-61; head dept. polit. sci. No. Ill. U., DeKalb, 1961-69; dir. internat. programs No. Ill. U., 1969-77, dean internat. and spl. programs, 1977-92, acting v.p., provost, 1986-87; internat. mgmt. cons., 1992—; internat. mgmt. cons., 1992—; co-dir. Ctr. S.E. Asian Studies and Tng., 1962-69; Fulbright prof. pub. adminstrn., master's degree dir. Inst. Social Studies, The Hague, The Netherlands, 1966-67; vis. prof. pub. adminstrn., adv. Ind. U.-ICA program, Thailand, 1956-58; dir. internat. studies Govt. Affairs Inst., Washington, 1959-61; project dir. Thai Labor Law and Practice, 1960, Brazilian Labor-A Mgmt. Survey, 1960, Indonesian Labor-A Mgmt. Survey, 1961; cons. tng. programs Peace Corps S.E. Asia, Thai Dept. Interior; prof. fgn. affairs Nat. War Coll., 1963-64. Author: Comparative Political Institutions, 1953, A Comparative Survey of Local Government and Administration, 1958, Local Government in Thailand, 1958, Manpower Problems in Southeast Asia, 1960, Labor Conditions in Thailand, 1960, Labor Law and Practice in Thailand, 1964, Thailand: Another Vietnam?, 1968; co-author: Our American Government and Political System, 1972, 77, 82; contbr. articles to profl. jours. Inst. Am. Univs. fellow, France, 1981. Mem. Am. Polit. Sci. Assn. (nat. coun. 1967-69), Phi Beta Kappa. Home: 222 Fairmont Dr De Kalb IL 60115-2332

WIT, HAROLD MAURICE, investment banker, lawyer, investor; b. Boston, Sept. 6, 1928; s. Maurice and Martha (Bassist) W.; m. Judith Haworth, Apr. 1989; children from previous marriage: David Edmund, Hannah Edna. A.B. magna cum laude, Harvard, 1949; J.D. (editor law jour.), Yale, 1954. Bar: N.Y. 1954. Assoc. Cravath, Swaine & Moore, N.Y.C., 1954-58; asst. sec. One William St. Fund, Inc., N.Y.C., 1958-59; v.p., sec. One William St. Fund, Inc., 1959-60; assoc. Allen & Co., 1960-70; assoc Allen & Co., Inc., 1965—, v.p., 1965-70, exec. v.p., 1970—, mng. dir., mem. exec. com., dir.; mem. exec. com., chmn. audit com., chmn. nominating com. Toys-R-Us, Inc.; dir. Allen Investments, Inc., dir. mem. exec. com., chmn. audit com. Allegheny & Western Energy Corp. Co-founder Group for South Fork; mem. Panel on Future of Govt. in N.Y., 1979-80; mem. vis. coms. Harvard U. Div. Sch.; mem. nat. adv. bd. project on being with dying Upaya Found. With Mass. N.G., 1947-50; lt. (j.g.) USNR, 1951-53, Korea. Mem. VFW, Am. Legion, Korean War Vets. Assn., University Club (N.Y.C.), Harvard Club (N.Y.C.), Phi Beta Kappa, Phi Delta Phi. Home: 160 East 65th St New York NY 10021-6691 also: Cross Hwy East Hampton NY 11937 Office: Allen & Co 711 Fifth Ave New York NY 10022

WITCHER, DANIEL DOUGHERTY, retired pharmaceutical company executive; b. Atlanta, May 17, 1924; s. Julius Gordon and Myrtice Eleanor (Daniel) W.; divorced; children: Beth S., Daniel Dougherty Jr., J. Wright, Benjamin and m. Betty Lou Middaugh, Oct. 30, 1982. Student, Mercer U., 1946-47, Am. Grad. Sch. Internat. Mgmt., 1949-50. Regional dir. Sterling Drug Co., Rio de Janeiro and Sao Paulo, Brazil, 1951-56; gen. mgr. Mead Johnson & Co., Sao Paulo, 1956-60; area mgr. Upjohn Internat., Inc., Sao Paulo, 1960-64; v.p. Upjohn Internat., Inc., Kalamazoo, 1964-70, group v.p., 1970-73; pres., gen. mgr. Upjohn Internat., 1973-86; v.p. Upjohn Co., 1973-86, sr. v.p., 1986-89, asst. to pres., 1988-89; chmn. Upjohn Healthcare Svcs., 1982-87; ret., 1989; bd. dirs. Upjohn Co.; trustee Am. Grad. Sch. Internat. Mgmt., 1981—. With USNR, 1943-46. Mem. Pharm. Mfrs. Assn. (chmn. internat. sect. 1981-82, 85-86), Am. Grad. Sch. Internat. Mgmt. Alumni Assn. (pres. 1989-91). Republican. Episcopalian. Avocations: tennis, golf.

WITCHER, ROBERT CAMPBELL, bishop; b. New Orleans, Oct. 5, 1926; s. Charles Swanson and Lily Sebastian (Campbell) W.; m. Elisabeth Alice Cole, June 4, 1957; 2 children. BA, Tulane U., 1949; MDiv, Seabury-Western Theol. Sem., 1952, DD, 1974; MA, La. State U., 1960, PhD, 1968; DCL (hon.), Nashotah House, 1984. Ordained priest Episc. Ch., 1953; consecrated bishop, 1975. Priest-in-charge St. Andrew Ch., Linton, La. and St. Patrick Ch., Zachary, La., 1953-56; priest-in-charge St. Augustine Ch., Baton Rouge, La., 1953-54; rector St. Augustine Ch., 1954-61; canon pastor Christ Ch. Cathedral, New Orleans, 1961-62; rector St. James Ch., Baton Rouge, 1962-

75; coadjutor bishop L.I., 1975-77; bishop, 1977-91; prof. ch. history Mercer Sch. Theology, 1975-91; interim bishop of Armed Forces, 1989-90; bishop in residence Baton Rouge, New Orleans, 1991-92; pres. Mercer Scholarship Fund; trustee Ch. Pension Fund, 1991-92; pres. bd. trustees estate belonging to Diocese of L.I., 1975-91; pres. Anglican Soc. N.Am., 1980-83; chmn. pastoral com. House of Bishops, 1980-90, Com. to Revise Title III, 1980-90; chmn. Com. on Developing Guidelines for Theol. Edn.; cons. Episc. Health Fund L.I. Author: The Episcopal Church in Louisiana, 1801-1861. Trustee U. of South, 1963-69, Seabury-Western Theol. Sem., 1963-82, Gen. Theol. Sem., 1979-88, Ch. Pension Fund, 1985-91, Bch. Reins. Corp.; pres. Episc. Health Svcs.; bd. dirs. Nat. Coun. Alcoholism, L.I. Coun. Alcoholism, Alcohol and Drug Abuse Coun., Baton Rouge, St. Mary's Hosp. for Children, Baton Rouge Green, La. Urban Forestry Coun., United Way; bd. dirs., trustee St. James Place; active NCCJ (Baton Rouge chpt.). Capt. USNR, ret. Mem. N.Y. State Coun. Chs., L.I. Coun. Chs. (com. social justice), Am. Legion, Mil. Order of World Wars. Address: 1934 Steele Blvd Baton Rouge LA 70808-1673

WITCOFF, SHELDON WILLIAM, lawyer; b. Washington, July 10, 1925; s. Joseph and Zina (Ceppos) W.; m. Margot Gail Hoffner, Sept. 6, 1953; children: Lauren Jill, David Lawrence, Lisa Ann, Julie Beth. B.S. in Elec. Engring. U. Md., 1949; J.D., George Washington U., 1953. Bar: D.C. 1953, N.Y. 1955, Ill. 1956. Patent examiner Patent Office, Dept. Commerce, 1949-53; patent lawyer Bell Telephone Labs., Murray Hill, N.J., 1953-55; ptnr. Bair, Freeman & Molinare, Chgo., 1955-69, Allegretti, Newitt, Witcoff & McAndrews, Chgo., 1970-88, Allegretti & Witcoff, LTD, Chgo., 1988—; v.p. Art Splty. Co., 1987—; v.p. Caspian Fur Trading Co., N.Y.C.; dir. Child Abuse Unit for Studies, Edn. and Svcs., Chgo. Fire and police commr., Skokie, Ill. 1960-63. Served with USNR, 1943-46. Mem. Am. Bar Assn., Bar Assn. 7th Circuit, Chgo. Patent Law Assn., Order of Coif, Tau Epsilon Phi, Phi Delta Phi., B'nai B'rith. Home: 235 Maple Hill Rd Glencoe IL 60022-1257 Office: 10 S Wacker Dr Chicago IL 60606-7407

WITCOVER, JULES JOSEPH, newspaper columnist, author; b. Union City, N.J., July 16, 1927; s. Samuel and Sarah (Carpenter) W.; m. Marian Laverty, June 14, 1952 (div. Oct. 1990); children: Paul, Amy, Julie. AB, Columbia Coll., 1949, MS in Journalism, 1951. Reporter Hackensack (N.J.) Star-Telegram, 1949-50, Providence Jour., 1951-52, Newark Star-Ledger, 1953, Washington br. Newhouse Newspapers, 1954-69, L.A. Times, Washington, 1970-72, Washington Post, 1973-76; columnist Washington Star and Tribune Media Svcs., 1977-81, Balt. Sun, Washington, 1981—. Author: 85 Days: The Last Campaign of Robert Kennedy, 1969, The Resurrection of Richard Nixon, 1970, White Knight: The Rise of Spiro Agnew, 1972, (with Richard M. Cohen) A Heartbeat Away: The Investigation and Resignation of Vice President Spiro T. Agnew, 1974, Marathon: The Pursuit of the Presidency, 1972-76, 1977, (novel) The Main Chance, 1978, (with Jack W. Germond) Blue Smoke and Mirrors: How Reagan Won and Why Carter Lost the Election of 1980, 1981, (with Germond) Wake Us When It's Over: Presidential Politics of 1984, 1985, (with Germond) Whose Broad Stripes and Bright Stars?: The Trivial Pursuit of the Presidency 1988, 1989, Sabotage at Black Tom: Imperial Germany's Secret War in America, 1914-1917, 1989, Crapshoot: Rolling the Dice on the Vice Presidency, 1992, (with Germond) Mad as Hell: Revolt at the Ballot Box 1992, 1993. With USN, 1945-46. Recipient Washington Corr. award Sigma Delta Chi, 1963, Alumni award Columbia Grad. Sch. Journalism, 1972; Reid Found. fellow, Europe, 1958. Roman Catholic. Home: 3042 Q St NW Washington DC 20007-3080 Office: Washington Bur Balt Sun 1627 K St NW Washington DC 20006-1702

WITEK, JAMES EUGENE, public relations executive; b. LaPorte, Ind., Sept. 14, 1932; s. Stanley and Victoria (Peret) W.; m. Mary Carolyn Hood, June 18, 1955; children: James Jay, Janet Marie, Jeffrey Patrick, Jean Theresa. A.B., Ind. U., 1954; M.A., U. Mo., 1970. Joined U.S. Army, 1954, commd. 2d lt., 1954, advanced through grades to lt. col., 1968; editor, pub. Infantry Mag., Fort Benning, Ga., 1967-70; advisor to Vietnamese Mil. Region IV Ranger Comdr., 1970-71; plans officer CINCPAC, Hawaii, 1971-75; exec. editor Soldiers, Washington, 1975-77; editor in chief Soldiers, 1977-79; dir. public affairs Nat. Com. for Employer Support Guard and Res., Arlington, Va., 1979-82, ret., 1982; dep. dir. pub. relations Am. Legion, Washington, 1982-86; mgr. pub. rels. Dowty Aerospace, Sterling, Va., 1986—. Decorated Legion of Merit, Bronze Star, Air Medal, Purple Heart, Vietnamese Cross of Gallantry with Silver Star. Mem. Assn. U.S. Army, Am. Legion, Ret. Officers Assn., Phi Beta Kappa, Tau Kappa Alpha, Pi Kappa Phi. Roman Catholic. Home: 3240 Atlanta St Fairfax VA 22030-2128 Office: Dowty Aerospace PO Box 5000 Sterling VA 20167-1050

WITHAM, BARRY BATES, drama educator; b. Newcastle, Maine, Dec. 11, 1939; s. Cecil Leroy Witham and Afton Eloise Bates; m. Sheila Ann McNamara, Dec. 28, 1964 (div. June 1972); children: Michael Bates, Drake Sean; m. Margaret Ann Thomas, Aug. 13, 1977. BA in English magna cum laude, Tufts U., 1961; MA in Drama, U. Iowa, 1964; PhD in Theatre, Ohio State U., 1968. Asst. prof. drama Miami U., Oxford, Ohio, 1968-72, assoc. prof., 1972-78, prof., 1978-80; assoc. prof. U. Wash., Seattle, 1980-92, prof., 1993—, exec. dir. Sch. of Drama, 1988-94; dramaturge Seattle Repertory Theatre, 1983-87. Co-author: Uncle Sam Presents, 1982; contbr. numerous articles to profl. and scholarly jours. Vol. Big Bros., Inc., Seattle, 1984—. Grantee NEA, 1982; named Outstanding Tchr. Miami U., 1978. Mem. Am. Soc. Theatre Rsch. (exec. com. 1982-84, 93—), Am. Theater Assn. (chmn. commn. theater rsch. 1982), Nat. Theatre Conf. Democrat. Avocations: golf, running. Home: 11909 80th Pl NE Kirkland WA 98034-5810 Office: U Wash Dept Drama Seattle WA 98195

WITHERELL, MICHAEL S., physics educator; b. Toledo, Sept. 22, 1949; s. Thomas W. and Marie (Savage) W.; m. Elizabeth Hall. BS, U. Mich., 1968; MS, U. Wis., 1970, PhD, 1973. Instr. Princeton (N.J.) U., 1973-75, asst. prof., 1975-81; asst. prof. U. Calif., Santa Barbara, 1981-83, assoc. prof., 1983-86, prof., 1986—; mem. high energy physics adv. panel U.S. Dept. Energy, Washington, 1990-93; chmn. physics adv. com. Fermi Nat. Accelerator Lab., Batavia, Ill., 1987-89. Guggenheim fellow John S. Guggenheim Found., 1988; recipient W. K. H. Panofsky prize Am. Phys. Soc., 1990. Fellow AAAS. Office: U Calif Dept Physics Santa Barbara CA 93106

WITHERS, ALTON MERRILL, retail store executive; b. San Antonio, Nov. 17, 1926; s. Walter Weyland Withers and Norma L. (Smith) Stendebach; m. Marion Ruth Guthrie, Apr. 20, 1947; children: Alton M. Jr., Deborah R. Withers Flannery. BA in Acctg., Tex. A&M U., 1949. Contr. Sears Roebuck and Co., 1949-57; staff acct. Sears Roebuck and Co., Chgo., 1957-59; comptr. Sears Roebuck S.A., Sao Paolo, Brazil, 1959-63; group contr. Sears Roebuck and Co., Denver, 1964-66; catalog order contr. Sears Roebuck and Co., Phila., 1966-68, regional contr., 1968-76; v.p. Spiegel Inc., Oak Brook, Ill., 1976-84, exec. v.p., chief fin. officer, 1985—; pres. acceptance corp. Spiegel Inc., 1988—; bd. dirs. Oak Brook Bank, First Oak Brook Bancshares, Eddie Bauer, Inc., Honeybee, Inc. Served as corp. USAF, 1945-47. Republican. Baptist. Clubs: DuPage (Oak Brook Terr., Ill.), Monroe (Chgo.). Lodge: Masons. Avocations: gardening, photography, sports. Office: Spiegel Inc Regency Towers 1515 W 22nd St Hinsdale IL 60521-2007

WITHERS, RAMSEY MUIR, government consultant, former government official; b. Toronto, Ont., Can., July 28, 1930; s. William Muir and Alice Smith Hope (Hannah) W.; m. Jean Alison Saunders, May 8, 1954; children—James Scott, Leslie Susan, Deidre Ann. BSc, Royal Mil. Coll. Can., Kingston, Ont., 1952, DEng (hon.), 1994; BSc in Elec. Engring., Queen's U., Kingston, 1954; D Mil. Sci. honoris causa, Royal Roads Mil. Coll., Victoria, B.C., 1992. Registered profl. engr., Ont. Commd. officer Can. Army, 1948, advanced through grades to gen., 1980; sta. in Can., Republic of Korea, Fed. Republic of Germany and U.K., 1952-94; comdr. Can. Forces Europe, Fed. Republic of Germany, 1976-77; vice chief def. staff Can. Forces, 1977-80, chief def. staff, 1980-83, ret., 1983; dep. minister transport Dept. of Transp., Ottawa, Ont., 1983-88; pres., chief oper. officer Govt. Cons. Internat., Ottawa, 1988-93; dir. Can. Inst. Strategic Studies, 1990—, ATS Aerospace Inc., 1993—; chmn. Industry Govt. Rels. Group Inc. (IGRG Inc.), Ottawa, 1993—. V.p., sec. nat. coun. Boy Scouts Can., 1977-84, internat. commr., 1985-90, hon. v.p., 1990—; chmn. Can. War Mus. Com., 1988—; trustee Can. Mus. Civilization, 1990—. Decorated comdr. Order of Mil. Merit, comdr. Order of St. John, Can. Forces Decoration with two bars; Georgian Coll. fellow, 1987; recipient Outstanding Achievement Pub. Svc. award,

1986, Silver Wolf award Boy Scouts Can., 1990. Mem. Assn. Profl. Engrs. Ont., Rideau Club. Avocations: boating; cycling. Home: 150 Waverly St Apt 2C, Ottawa, ON Canada K2P OV4

WITHERS, W. RUSSELL, JR., broadcast executive; b. Cape Girardeau, Mo., Dec. 10, 1936; s. Waldo Russell Sr. and Dorothy Ruth (Harrelson) W.; 1 child, Dana Ruth. BA, S.E. Mo. State U., 1958. Disc jockey Sta. KGMO Radio, Cape Girardeau, 1955-58; account exec. Sta. WGGH Radio, Marion, Ill., 1961-62; v.p. LIN Broadcasting Corp., Nashville, 1962-69; exec. v.p., dir. Laser Link Corp., Woodbury, N.Y., 1970-72; owner Withers Broadcasting of Hawaii, 1975-79, Withers Broadcasting of Minn., 1974-79, Withers Broadcasting Cos., Iowa, 1981—, Mood Music Ill., Mt. Vernon, 1973—, Mood Music, Inc., Cape Girardeau, 1972—, Royal Hawaiian Radio Co., Inc., others; owner various radio and TV stas. including KREX-TV, Grand Junction, Colo., KREY-TV, Montrose, Colo., KREG-TV, Glenwood Springs, Colo., KREZ-TV, Durango, Colo., KAVU-TV, Victoria, Tex., 1990, Page Ins. and Real Estate, Mt. Vernon, Ill.; bd. dirs., chmn. bd. chief exec. officer Withers Beverage Corp., Mobile, Ala., 1973-79; chmn. adv. bd. Mut. Network; dir. Theatrevision, Inc., Turneffe Island Lodge, Ltd., Belize, Sta. WDTV, Clarksburg, W.Va., WMIX/AM-FM, Mt. Vernon, KGMO/KAPE, Cape Girardeau, KOKX AM-FM, Keokuk, Iowa; pres. Ill. Pub. Airports Assn.; co-chair TARPAC. Bd. dirs., chmn. bd. Mt. Vernon Tourism and Conv. Bur.; chmn. Mt. Vernon Airport Authority. With U.S. Army, 1957-58. Mem. Mt. Vernon C. of C. (bd. dirs.), Nat. Assn. Broadcasters, Ill. Broadcasters Assn., Stadium Club, Mo. Athletic Club, Elks, Moose, Sigma Chi. Christian Scientist. Home: 1 Sleepy Hollow Mount Vernon IL 62864 Office: PO Box 1508 Mount Vernon IL 62864-1508

WITHERS, W. WAYNE, lawyer; b. Enid, Okla., Nov. 4, 1940; s. Walter O. and Ruby (Mackey) W.; m. Patricia Ann Peppers, Dec. 12, 1974; children: Jennifer Lynn, Whitney Lee. BA, U. Okla., 1962; JD, Northwestern U., 1965. Bar: Okla. 1965, Mo. 1970, U.S. Ct. Appeals (8th cir.) 1972, U.S. Supreme Ct. 1972, U.S. Ct. Appeals (fed. cir.) 1984, U.S. Ct. Appeals (D.C. cir.) 1985, U.S. Ct. Claims, 1988. Staff atty. FTC, Washington, 1965-68; co. atty. Monsanto Co., St. Louis, 1968-78, asst. gen. counsel, 1978-85; gen. counsel Monsanto Agrl. Co., St. Louis, 1985-87, v.p., gen. counsel, 1987-89; sr. v.p., sec., gen. counsel Emerson Electric Co., St. Louis, 1989—; v.p. Internat. Food Biotech. Coun., Washington, 1989-90; bd. dirs. Internat. Life Scis. Inst., Washington, 1989-90. Contbr. articles to profl. jours. Mem. ABA (sec. corp. law. dept.), Am. Law Inst., Assn. Gen. Counsels, Bar Assn. Met. St. Louis, Indsl. Biotech. Assn. (chmn. law com. 1983-85), CLO Roundtable, The Conf. Bd's. Coun. for Gen. Counsels (vice chmn. 1992—), MAPI Law Coun. Home: 608 Claymont Estate Dr Chesterfield MO 63017-7060 Office: Emerson Electric Co 8000 W Florissant Ave Saint Louis MO 63136-1414

WITHERSPOON, CAROLYN BRACK, lawyer; b. Little Rock, Mar. 29, 1950; d. Gordon Paisley and Mildred Louise (Lemon) Brack; m. Joseph Roger Armbrust, July 25, 1970 (div. 1976); 1 child, Catherine Paisley; m. John Leslie Witherspoon, June 15, 1979. Student, U. Ark., 1968-70, So. Meth. U., 1970; BA, U. Ark., 1972, JD with honors, 1978. Bar: Ark. 1978, U.S. Dist. Ct. (ea. and we. dists) Ark. 1978, U.S. Ct. Appeals (8th cir.) 1979, U.S. Supreme Ct. 1981. Asst. atty. City of Little Rock, 1978, chief dep. atty., acting city atty., 1984-85; assoc. House, Wallace & Jewell, Little Rock, 1985-87, ptnr., 1987-90; dir. McGlinchey Stafford Lang, Little Rock, 1990—; co-chmn. Fed. Ct. Orientation Seminar, 1983-85; mem. com. Fed. Ct., 1988-91, Ark. Supreme Ct., 1989—; chair adv. com. Civil Justice Reform Act, 1993-95. Contbr. articles to profl. jours. Commr. Ark. Real Estate Commn., 1978-81; chmn. Little Rock Housing Authority Bd. of Comm., past pres., bd. dirs. Advs. for Battered Women; past bd. dirs., pub. rels. chmn. LWV; past pres. Ark. Women's History Inst.; del. Dem. Committeewoman for Pulaski County; vol. PTA, United Way, March of Dimes, Heart Found., Am. Cancer Soc. Recipient Am. Jurisprudence labor law award, 1977. Mem. Am. Law Inst., Ark. Bar Assn. (pres.-elect 1994-95, exec. coun., house of dels., jud. nominating com., chmn. civil procedure com., chair, labor law sect., Golden Gavel award 1989, 93, award Ark. Inst. for Continuing Legal Edn. 1991), Ark. Assn. Women Lawyers (pres. 1982-83), Pulaski County Bar Assn. (pres. 1989-90), Nat. Inst. Mcpl. Law Officers (v.p. 1987-89, state chmn. 1985-87), William R. Overton Inn of Ct. (pres. 1992-93). Avocations: hunting, fishing, reading, traveling. Office: McGlinchey Stafford Lang 425 E Capitol Ave Ste 3900 Little Rock AR 72201-3439

WITHERSPOON, JAMES DONALD, biology educator; b. Springfield, Mo., Dec. 19, 1933; s. Harry H. and Lucy Catherine (Applegate) W.; m. Rebecca Jane Hutto, Jan. 24, 1958; children: Sarah Jane, John Edward. BS, Purdue U., 1955, MS, 1960, PhD, 1963. From instr. to asst. prof. biology Western Md. Coll., Westminster, 1960-68; assoc. prof. Southwestern at Memphis Coll., 1968-76; free-lance writer Phoenix, 1976-82; adj. prof. Grand Canyon Coll., Phoenix, 1982-84, prof., 1984—, chmn. dept. scis., 1985-92, acting chmn. dept. math. and computer scis., 1988-89; coord. allied health Grand Canyon U. (formerly Grand Canyon Coll.), Phoenix, 1992-94, assoc. dean Coll. Sci. and Applied Health, 1994—; cons. Doubleday & Co., Garden City, N.Y., 1960-62, Narco Bio-Systems, Houston, 1972-76; assoc. coord. med. edn. S.W. Kirksville Coll. Osteo. Medicine, 1990-94; leader Am. tchr. Eszterhazy Karoly Tchrs. Tng. Coll., Hungary, summers 1991-93. Author: The Functions of Life, 1970, Human Physiology, 1984, From Field to Lab, 1993; co-author: The Living Laboratory, 1960; co-author numerous tapes and computer programs, 1973-87. Grantee Grass Found., 1962-72, Ariz. Commn. for Postsecondary Edn., 1985-87. Mem. AAAS, Am. Inst. Biol. Scis., Ariz. Alliance for Sci. (bd. dirs. 1986-88), Sigma Xi. Republican. Presbyterian. Achievements include rsch. on relation of hypoxia to body temperature, innovative methods for biological education. Home: 17122 E Grande Blvd Fountain Hls AZ 85268-3224 Office: Grand Canyon U 3300 W Camelback Rd Phoenix AZ 85017-1097

WITHERSPOON, JERE WARTHEN, foundation executive; b. Shepherdstown, W.Va., June 24, 1932; m. Ellen L. Wheby, Oct. 5, 1957; children: Jere W. Jr., Jean Katherine, James A. BS, Davidson Coll., 1954; MHA, Washington U., 1961. Adminstrv. asst. Meml. Mission Hosp., Asheville, N.C., 1960-63; asst. adminstr. Meml. Hosp., Charleston, W.Va., 1963-67; adminstr. Cape Fear Valley Hosp., Fayetteville, N.C., 1967-69; dir. adminstr. svc. The Duke Endowment, Charlotte, N.C., 1969-77, assoc. dir., 1977-89, asst. to exec. dir., 1989-90, dep. exec. dir., 1990-92, exec. dir., 1992—. Bd. deacons, chmn., elder, chmn. endowment coun. Myers Park Presbyn. Ch.; pres., bd. dirs. Hospice at Charlotte; v.p., bd. dirs. Hospice of N.C.; mem. study com. on AIDS United Way; com. chmn. Mecklenburg County Area Mental Health Bd.; trustee Southeastern Coun. Founds.; bd. dirs. Grantmakers in Health, Presbyn. Home at Charlotte; bd. vis. Davidson Coll.; adv. bd. Kate B. Reynolds Charitable Trust; mem. N.C. Med. Care Commn. With USAF, 1954-58. Fellow Am. Coll. Healthcare Execs.; mem. Am. Hosp. Assn. (life). Office: Duke Endowment 100 N Tryon St Ste 3500 Charlotte NC 28202

WITHERSPOON, JOHN KNOX, JR., investment banking executive; b. Chattanooga, May 3, 1928; s. John Knox and Helen (Newell) W.; m. Norma Cofer, Sept. 28, 1957; children: Laura, Alice, Mark, Eric, Cary, Clay. BA, Princeton U., 1950. CLU. Pension analyst Provident Life and Accident Ins. Co., Chattanooga, 1953-57, asst. mgr. pension div., 1957-60, agy. sec., 1960-64, asst. v.p., 1964-69, v.p., 1969-84, sr. v.p., 1984-90; mng. dir. Crownpoint Fin. Group, Chattanooga, 1990-92; v.p. Porter, White & Co., Inc., Chattanooga, 1993—. Chmn. Hamilton County Bd. Edn., Chattanooga, 1984-85; pres. Met. Council Community Services, Chattanooga, 1977; v.p. Family and Children's Services, Chattanooga, 1978-80. Served as cpl. U.S. Army, Korea. Mem. Am. Med. Care and Rev. Assn., Am. Soc. CLU's, Assn. for Corp. Growth, Phi Beta Kappa. Presbyterian. Presbyterian. Lodge: Kiwanis. Office: Porter White & Co 651 E 4th St Ste 100 Chattanooga TN 37403-1924

WITHERSPOON, JOHN MARSHALL, advertising executive; b. San Antonio, June 25, 1945; s. Claude Leland and Bettie (McDavid) W.; 1 child, Jason. BBA, U. Tex., 1967. Ptnr., designer Sosart, Inc., San Antonio, 1969-73; pres. Texican Graphics, San Antonio, 1976-77; v.p. mktg. Westport, Inc., Houston, 1977-78; pres. Hayes Broadcasting, Inc., San Antonio, 1978-84; dir. animation Hayes Prodns., Inc., San Antonio, 1973-76, v.p. mktg., creative svcs., 1984—; pres. Witherspoon & Assocs., animation/design and creative svcs., San Antonio, 1987—; guest instr. U. Tex., San Antonio, 1985; speaker regional advt. groups, Tex., Okla., La., 1984-87. Author, editor: Remember San Antonio, 1973; artist, designer many graphic and animation awards. Polit. cons. various campaigns, 1984-87. Mem. San Antonio Advt. Fed., Order of the Alamo. Avocations: sailing, music, writing. Home: 260 E Edgewood San Antonio TX 78209

WITHERSPOON, PAUL ADAMS, JR., geological engineer, petroleum engineer; b. Pitts., Feb. 19, 1919. BS, U. Pitt., 1941; MS, U. Kans., 1951; PhD in geol. phys. chmn., U. Ill., 1957. Prof. petrol. engr. U. Calif. Berkeley, 1957-65, prof.; 1965; head earth divsn., assoc. dir. Lawrence Berkeley Lab, 1977—. Recipient Robert E. Horton award Am. Geophys. Union, 1990, O.E. Meinzer award Geol. Soc. Am., 1976. Am. Geophys.Union, Geol. Soc. Am., Am. Assn. Petrol. Geol., Am. Inst. Mining, Metall & Petrol Engrs., Sigma Xi. Flow of fluids in porous and fractured rocks, regional groundwater flow, well hydraulics, underground storage of fluids, radioactive waste isolation, geothermal systems. Home: 1824 Monterey Ave Berkeley CA 94707-2544*

WITHERSPOON, SHARON, lawyer; b. Detroit, Apr. 8, 1955; d. James Paul and Iola (Washington) W. BA magna cum laude, Mich. State U., 1977; JD, Harvard U., 1980; MLT, Georgetown U., 1983. Bar: D.C. 1980, Md. 1994, U.S. Supreme Ct. 1991. Atty., advisor SEC, Washington, 1980-83; assoc. Hamel & Park, Washington, 1983, Hogan & Hartson, Washington, 1983-86; assoc. Dechert Price & Rhoads, Washington, 1986-88, ptnr., 1988-94; of counsel Christian Wadsworth & Smith, Washington, 1994—. Tutor Washington Literacy Coun., 1990-95; bd. dirs. Fairfax Village Cmty. Assn., Washington, 1990-93. Mem. ABA (del. for D.C. Bar 1992-94), Fed. Bar Assn., Nat. Bar Assn., Nat. Assn. Securities Profls., Phi Beta Kappa, Phi Kappa Phi. Avocations: reading, walking. Home: 3824 V St SE Washington DC 20020

WITHERSPOON, WILLIAM, investment economist; b. St. Louis, Nov. 21, 1909; s. William Conner and Mary Louise (Houston) W.; student Washington U. Evening Sch., 1928-47; m. Margaret Telford Johanson, June 25, 1938; children: James Tomlin, Jane Telford, Elizabeth Witherspoon Vodra. Rsch. dept. A. G. Edwards & Sons, 1928-31; pres. Witherspoon Investment Co., 1931-34; head rsch. dept. Newhard Cook & Co., 1934-43; chief price analysis St. Louis Ordnance Dist., 1943-45; head rsch. dept. Newhard Cook & Co., 1945-53; owner Witherspoon Investment Counsel, 1953-64; ltd. ptnr. Newhard Cook & Co., economist, investment analyst, 1965-68; v.p. rsch. Stifel, Nicolaus & Co., 1968-81; lectr. on investments Washington U., 1948-67. Mem. Clayton Bd. of Edn., 1955-68, treas., 1956-68, pres., 1966-67; mem. Clayton Park and Recreation Comm., 1959-60; trustee Ednl. TV, KETC, 1963-64; mem. investment com. Gen. Assembly Mission Bd. Presbyn. Ch. (USA), Atlanta, 1976-79, mem. permanent com. ordination exams, 1979-85; cons. to investment com. Ctr. Theol. Inquiry, Princeton, N.J., 1990—. Served as civilian Ordnance Dept., AUS, 1943-45. Chartered fin. analyst. Mem. St. Louis Soc. Fin. Analysts (pres. 1949-50). Club: Mo. Athletic (St. Louis). Home: 6401 Ellenwood Ave Saint Louis MO 63105-2228 *Many of the current social and ethical problems of today might be partially resolved if theology would be influenced by the 4th dimension of spacetime plus the 5th dimension of the mind, the 6th dimension of the spirit and the 7th dimension of God the Father.*

WITHROW, MARY ELLEN, treasurer of United States; b. Marion, Ohio, Oct. 2, 1930; d. Clyde Welsh and Mildred (Stump) Hinamon; m. Norman David Withrow, Sept. 4, 1948; children: Linda Rizzo, Leslie Legge, Norma, Rebecca. Mem. Elgin Local Bd. Edn., Marion, Ohio, 1969-73, pres., 1972; safety programs dir. ARC, Marion, 1968-72; dep. registrar State of Ohio, Marion, 1972-75; dep. county auditor Marion County, Ohio, 1975-77, county treas., 1977-83; treas. State of Ohio, Columbus, 1983-94; treas. of the U.S. Dept. Treasury, Washington, 1994—; chmn. Ohio Bd. Deposits, 1983—, Anthony Commn. on Pub. Fin. Mem. exec. com. Ohio Dem. Com., mem. exec. com. women's caucus; mem. Dem. Nat. Com.; mem. Met. Women's Ctr.; pres. Marion County Dem. Club, 1976; participant Harvard U. Strategic Leadership Conf., 1990.; mem. Dem. Leadership Coun. Inducted Ohio Women's Hall of Fame, 1986; named Outstanding Elected Dem. Woman Holding Pub. Office, Nat. Fedn. Dem. Women, 1987, Advocate of Yr., SBA, 1988, Most Valuable State Pub. Ofcl., City and State newspaper, 1990; recipient Donald L. Scantlebury Meml. award, 1991, Women of Achievement award YWCA of Met. Columbus, 1993; fellow Women Execs. in State Govt., Harvard U., 1987. Mem. LWV (dem. leadership coun.), State Assn. County Treas. (legis. com. 1979-83, treas. 1982), Nat. Assn. State Treas. (pres. 1992, Jesse Unruh award 1993, chair long range planning com., mem. exec. com.), Nat. Assn. State Auditors Comtps. and Treas. (pres. 1990, strategic planning com., intergov. rels. com., chair state and mcpl. bonds com.), Coun. State Govts. (exec. com., internat. affairs com., orgnl. planning and coord. com., strategic planning task force), Women Execs. in State Govt. (chair fund devel. com.). Club: Bus. and Profl. Women's. Office: Dept Treasury 1500 Pennsylvania Ave NW Rm 2134 Washington DC 20220

WITIAK, DONALD THEODORE, medicinal chemistry educator; b. Milw., Nov. 16, 1935; s. Theodore and Elvi (Dahlbacka) W.; m. Deanne Beth Knapton, Dec. 16, 1958; children—Mark Donald, Elizabeth Jane. B.S. in Pharmacy, U. Wis.-Madison, 1958, postgrad., 1959-60, Ph.D. in Medicinal Chemistry, 1961; postgrad., U. Kans., 1960-61. Asst. prof. U. Iowa, Iowa City, 1961-66, assoc. prof., 1966-67; assoc. prof. Ohio State U., Columbus, 1967-71, prof. medicinal chemistry, 1971-93, chmn. div. medicinal chemistry, 1973-82, dir. basic rsch. univ. Comprehensive Cancer Ctr., 1987-93; prof. med. cheistry, dean sch. pharmacy U. Wis. Madison, 1993-95; mem. study sect. NIH, 1980-83; U.S. rep. to provisional sect. com. Internat. Union Pure and Applied Chemistry, 1986-88; mem. Can. Govt. internat. multidisciplinary peer-rev. com. for networks of Ctr. Excellence; mem. drug. devel., hematology and pathology study sect. Am. Cancer Soc., 1995—. Editor: Calcium Regulation, 1982, Antilipidemic Drugs Medicinal, Chemical and Biochemical Aspects, vol. 17, 1991; mem. editorial bd. Jour. Medicinal Chemistry, 1971-75, European Jour. Med. Chemistry, 1986—; Pharmacochemistry Libr., 1987—; assoc. editor Current Medicinal Chemistry, 1994—; contbr. numerous articles toprofl. jours., chpts. to books; holder 15 patents in field. Mem. Columbus Biotech. Adv. Com., 1985, Columbus Tech. Roundtable, 1983. Served with USNR, 1955-63. Recipient Kimberly prof. rsch. award, 1985, Apha Found./Acad. Pharm. Scis. Rsch. Achievement award, 1985, Taito O. Soine Meml. award U. Minn., 1988; grantee NIH 1971—, EPA, 1984—. Fellow Am. Pharm. Assn., Acad. Pharm. Scis., Am. Assn. Pharm. Scis.; mem. Am. Chem. Soc. (com. nomenclature 1984-85, chmn. com. to rev. Jour. Medicinal Chemistry 1983, councilor div. med. chem. 1990-92), Am. Cancer Soc. (supported rsch. 1987—). Ohio div. 1988, bd dirs. 1991-93). Home: 3046 Bosshard Dr Fitchburg WI 53711 Office: U Wis Madison 425 N Charter St Madison WI 53706-1515

WITKE, DAVID RODNEY, newspaper editor; b. Council Bluffs, Iowa, Mar. 24, 1937; s. Arnold and Rosamond Louise (Storer) W.; m. Priscilla Bill Smith, Oct. 8, 1960; 1 son, Carl. B.S. in Journalism, Northwestern U., 1959. Reporter, editor The Courier, Champaign-Urbana, Ill., 1962-66; copy editor The Register, Des Moines, 1966-70, city editor, 1970-73, asst. mng. editor adminstrn., 1973-74, asst. mng. editor electronics, 1974-75, mng. editor, 1975-83, dir. ops., 1983-85, dep. editor, 1985-87, exec. sports editor, 1987—; rep. Iowa Freedom of Info. Coun., Des Moines, 1973—, pres., 1986-88; vis. lectr. Drake U., 1986—, Iowa State U., 1990—; juror Pulitzer Prize, 1989-91. Served to lt. (j.g.) USN, 1959-62, PTO. Mem. Assoc. Press Mng. Editors Assn., Mid-Am. Newspaper Assn., AP Sports Editors Assn., The Prairie Club, Sigma Delta Chi. Unitarian. Home: 2521 48th Pl Des Moines IA 50310-2506 Office: Des Moines Register and Tribune Co 715 Locust St Des Moines IA 50309-3724

WITKIN, EVELYN MAISEL, geneticist; b. N.Y.C., Mar. 9, 1921; d. Joseph and Mary (Levin) Maisel; m. Herman A. Witkin, July 9, 1943 (dec. July 1979); children—Joseph, Andrew. AB, NYU, 1941; MA, Columbia U., 1943, PhD, 1947; DSc honoris causa, N.Y. Med. Coll., 1978. Mem. staff genetics dept. Carnegie Inst., Washington, 1950-55; mem. faculty State U. N.Y. Downstate Med. Center, Bklyn., 1955-71; prof. medicine State U. N.Y. Downstate Med. Center, 1968-71; prof. biol. scis. Douglass Coll., Rutgers U., 1971-79, Barbara McClintock prof. genetics, 1979-83; Barbara McClintock prof. genetics Waksman Inst. Microbiology, 1983-91; Barbara McClintock prof. emerita Waksman Inst. Microbiology, Rutgers U., 1991—.

Author articles; mem. editorial bds. profl. jours. Postdoctoral fellow Am. Cancer Soc., 1947-49; fellow Carnegie Instn., 1957; Selman A. Waksman lectr., 1960; Phi Beta Kappa vis. scholar, 1980-81; grantee NIH, 1956-89; recipient Prix Charles Leopold Mayer French Acad. Scis., 1977, Lindback award, 1979. Fellow AAAS, Am. Acad. Microbiology; mem. NAS, Am. Acad. Arts and Scis., Environ. Mutagen Soc., Am. Genetics Soc., Am. Soc. Microbiology. Home: 1 Firestone Ct Princeton NJ 08540-5220 Office: Rutgers U Waksman Inst Microbiology Piscataway NJ 08854

WITKIN, GEORGIA HOPE, clinical psychologist, lecturer, author. Student Wellesley Coll., 1961-63; BA in Sociology, Barnard Coll., 1965; postgrad. in elem. edn. Hunter Coll., 1967-69; MA in Psychology, New Sch. for Social Rsch., 1970, PhD in Psychology, 1977; postgrad. Psychiat. Inst., 1979. Lic. clin. psychologist, N.Y. Asst. producer Grey Advt., N.Y.C., 1966-68; teaching asst. New Sch. for Social Rsch., 1968-69; adj. lectr. Lehman Coll., CUNY, 1971-72; assoc. prof. dept. social and behavioral sci. SUNY-Valhalla, 1972-86, mem. vis. faculty criminal justice dept., 1978; supr. residency program human sexuality program Mt. Sinai Sch. Medicine, N.Y.C., 1982—, asst. clin. prof. psychiatry, 1985—; staff psychologist dept. ob-gyn. and reproductive sci. Mt. Sinai Med. Ctr., N.Y.C., 1990—; former mem. vis. faculty U. Conn., NYU Coll. Dentistry, also others; former assoc. prof. psychology Westchester Community Coll., Valhalla; presenter at profl. confs., also papers; pvt. practice clin. psychology, N.Y.C.; appeared on various TV shows including Donahue, Today Show, Hour Mag.; host TV program Between the Sexes, CNBC-TV; reporter TV program The Real Story, CNBC-TV; contbr. Today In N.Y., WNBC-TV, Live at Five, WNBC-TV. Author: Human Sexuality, 1982, The Female Stress Syndrome, 1984 (also Dutch, Japan, German, English, Spanish and Australian edits.), rev. edit., 1991, Coping with Stress, 1984, The Male Stress Syndrome, 1986, Quick Fixes and Small Comforts, 1986, Beyond Quick Fixes, 1991, Passions, 1992; columnist Your Emotional Best, Health Mag., also mem. editorial adv. bd.; mem. editorial adv. bd. Jour. Preventive Psychiatry; contbr. articles to profl. publs., mags. and newspapers. Mem. steering com. Westchester Community Coll. Found., 1973-75. NSF fellow, 1978. Mem. AAAS, Soc. for Sex Therapy and Research, Westchester County Psychol. Assn., N.Y. Acad. Scis., Am. Assn. Sex Educators, Counselors and Therapists (cert. sex educator; mem. regional bd., exec. com.), Am. Assn. for Profl. Law Enforcement, Mensa, Criminal Justice Educators Assn. N.Y. State, Am. Soc. Criminology, World Future Soc., N.Y. State United Tchrs., Eastern Psychol. Assn., Am. Med. Writers Assn. Home: 8 E 83rd St Apt 3A New York NY 10028-0418 Office: Mt Sinai Med Coll Dept Psychiatry New York NY 10053

WITKIN, JOEL-PETER, photographer; b. Bklyn., Sept. 13, 1939; s. Max and Mary (Pellegrino) W.; m. Cynthia Jean Bency, June 30, 1978; one child, Kersen Ahanu. B.F.A., Cooper Union, 1974; M.F.A., U. N.Mex., 1986; student (fellow), Columbia U., 1973-74. Exhibited in Projects Studio One, N.Y.C., 1980, Galerie Texbraun, Paris, 1982, Kansas Ctiy Art Inst., 1983, Stedelijk Mus.. Amsterdam, 1983, Fraenkel Gallery, 1983-84, 87, 91, 93, 95, Pace/MacGill Gallery, N.Y.C., 1983, 84, 87, 89, 91, 93, 95, San Francisco Mus. Modern Art, 1985, Bklyn. Mus., 1986, Galerie Baudoin Lebon, Paris, 1987, 89, 91, 95, Centro de Arte Reina Sofia Mus., Madrid, 1988, Palais de Tokyo, Paris, 1989, Fahey/Klein Gallery, L.A., 1989, 92, 93, Mus. Modern Art, Haifa, Israel, 1991, Photo Picture Space Gallery, Osaka, Japan, 1993, Guggenheim Mus., N.Y.C., 1995, Interkamera, Prague, 1995; group shows: Mus. Moder Art, N.Y.C., 1959, San Francisco Mus. Moder Art, 1981, Whitney Biennial, 1985, Palais de Tokyo, Paris, 1986; represented in permanent collections, Mus. Modern Art, N.Y.C., San Francisco Mus. Modern Art, 1980, Nat. Gallery Art, Washington, Victoria and Albert Mus., London, George Eastman House, N.Y., The Getty Collection, Moder Museet, Stockholm, Sweden, Whitney Mus., N.Y.C., The Guggenheim Mus.; represented by Pace/MacGill, N.Y.C., Fraenkel Gallery, San Francisco, Baudoin Lebon Gallery, Paris; subject of monographs: Joel-Peter Witkin, 1985, 88, 89, 91, 93, 95; editor: Masterpieces of Medical Photography, 1987, Harms Way, 1994. Served with U.S. Army, 1961-64. Decorated Chevalier Des Arts et de Letters (France), 1990; recipient Disting. Alumni award The Cooper Union, 1986, Internat. Ctr. Photography award, 1988; Ford Found. grantee, 1977, 78, Nat. Endowment in Photography grantee, 1980, 81, 86, 92. Address: 1707 Five Points Rd SW Albuquerque NM 87105 *My need is to understand existence. That need becomes art when it reaches into the extreme limit of the possible.*

WITKIN, MILDRED HOPE FISHER, psychotherapist, educator; b. N.Y.C.; d. Samuel and Sadie (Goldschmidt) Fisher; children: Georgia Hope, Roy Thomas, Laurie Phillips, Kimberly, Nicole, Scott, Joshua, Jennifer; m. Jorge Radovic. Aug. 26, 1983. AB, Hunter Coll., MA, Columbia U., 1968; PhD, NYU, 1973. Diplomate Am. Bd. Sexology, Am. Bd. Sexuality; cert. supr. Head counselor Camp White Lake, Camp Emanuel, Long Beach, N.J.; tchr. econs., polit. sci. Hunter Coll. High Sch.; dir., group leader follow-up program Jewish Vacation Assn., N.Y.C.; investigator N.Y.C. Housing Authority; psychol. counselor Montclair State Coll., Upper Montclair, N.J., 1967-68; mem., lectr. Creative Problem-Solving Inst., U. Buffalo, 1968; psychol. counselor Fairleigh Dickinson U., Teaneck, N.J., 1968, dir. Counseling Center, 1969-74; pvt. practice psychotherapy, N.Y.C., also Westport, Conn.; sr. faculty supr., family therapist and psychotherapist Payne Whitney Psychiat. Clinic, N.Y. Hosp., 1973—; clin. asst. prof. dept. psychiatry Cornell U. Med. Coll., 1974—; assoc. dir. sex therapy and edn. program Cornell-N.Y. Hosp. Med. Ctr., 1974—; sr. cons. Kaplan Inst. for Evaluation and Treatment of Sexual Disorders, 1981—; supr. master's and doctoral candidates, NYU, 1975-82; pvt. practice psychotherapy and sex therapy, N.Y.C., also Westport, Conn.; cons. counselor edn. tng. programs N.Y.C. Bd. Edn., 1971-75; cons. Health Info. Systems, 1972-79; vis. prof. numerous colls. and univs.; chmn. sci. com. 1st Internat. Symposium on Female Sexuality, Buenos Aires, 1984. Exhibited in group shows at Scarsdale (N.Y.) Art Show, 1959, Red Shutter Art Studio, Long Beach, 1968. Edn. legislation chmn. PTA, Yonkers, 1955; publicity chmn. United Jewish Appeal, Scarsdale, 1959-65; Scarsdale chmn. mothers com. Boy Scouts Am., 1961-64; mem. Morrow Assn. on Correction N.J., 1969-91; bd. dirs. Girl Scouts of Am. Recipient Bronze medal for svcs. Hunter Coll.; United Jewish Appeal plaque, 1962; Founders Day award N.Y. U., 1973, citation N.Y. Hosp./ Cornell U. Med. Ctr., 1990. Fellow Internat. Coun. Sex Edn. and Parenthood of Am. U., Am. Acad. Clin. Sexologists; mem. AAUW, APA, ACA, Assn. Counseling Supervision, Am. Coll. Personnel Assn., Internat. Assn. Marriage and Family Counselors, Am. Coll. Sexuality (cert.), Women's Med. Assn. N.Y.C., N.Y. Acad. Sci., Am. Coll. Pers. Assn. (nat. mem. commn. II 1973-76), Nat. Assn. Women Deans and Counselors, Am. Assn. Sex Educators, Counselors and Therapists (regional bd., nat. accreditation bd., cert. internat. supr.), Soc. for Sci. Study Sex Therapy and Rsch., Eastern Assn. Sex Therapists, Am. Assn. Marriage and Family Counselors, N.J. Assn. Marriage and Family Counselors, Ackerman Family Inst., Am. Personnel and Guidance Assn., Am., N.Y., N.J. psychol. assns., Creative Edn. Found., Am. Assn. Higher Edn., Assn. Counselor Supervision and Edn. Profl. Women's Caucus, LWV, Am. Assn. counseling and Devel., Am. Women's Med. Assn., Nat. Coun. on Women in Medicine, Argentine Soc. Human Sexuality (hon.), Am. Assn. Sexology (diplomate), Pi Lambda Theta, Kappa Delta Pi, Alpha Chi Alpha. Author: 45-And Single Again, 1985, Single Again, 1994; contbr. articles to profl. jours. and textbooks; lectr. internat. and nat. workshops, radio and TV. Home: 9 Sturges Commons Westport CT 06880-2832 Office: 35 Park Ave New York NY 10016-3838

WITKOP, BERNHARD, chemist; b. Freiburg, Baden, Fed. Republic Germany, May 9, 1917; came to U.S., 1947, naturalized, 1953; s. Philipp W. and Hedwig M. (Hirschhorn) W.; m. Marlene Prinz, Aug. 8, 1945; children: Cornelia Johanna, Phyllis, Thomas. Diploma, U. Munich, 1938, PhD, 1940, Golden Dr. Diploma, 1990; ScD, Privat-Dozent, 1947. Minister T. Mellon research fellow Harvard U., 1947-48, mem. faculty, 1948-50; spl. USPHS fellow Nat. Heart Inst., NIH, 1950-52; vis. scientist Nat. Inst. Arthritis and Metabolic Diseases, 1953, chemist, 1954-55, chief sect. metabolites, 1956-87, chief lab. chemistry, 1957-87, scholar, 1987-92, hon. scholar emeritus, 1993; vis. prof. U. Kyoto, Japan, 1961, U. Freiburg, Fed. Repubic Germany, 1962; adj. prof. U. Md. Med. Sch., Balt.; Nobel symposium lect. Stockholm-Karlskoga, 1981; mem. bd. Internat. Sci. Exchange, 1974; mem. exec. com. NRC, 1975; mem. Com. Internat. Exchange, 1977, Paul Ehrlich Award Com., Frankfurt, 1980. Editor: Fedn. European Biochem. Soc. Letters, 1979-90. Recipient Superior Service award USPHS, 1967; Paul Karrer gold medal U. Zurich, 1971; Kun-ni-to (medal of sci. and culture 2d class) Emperor of Japan, 1975; Alexander von Humboldt award for U.S. scien-

tists, 1978. Mem. NAS, Am. Chem. Soc. (Hillebrand award 1958), Am. Acad. Arts and Sci., Acad. Leopoldina (fgn.), Pharm. Soc. Japan (hon.), Chem. Soc. Japan (hon.), Japanese Biochem. Soc. (hon.). Office: Nat Inst of Health Dept of Health Educ & Welfare Nat Institute Rm B1a-11 Bethesda MD 20892 *A career between two worlds and two wars, spanning 50 years of research aims changing from structural to dynamic aspects, may be considered epigonal in the sense that my teacher H. Wieland (Nobel Prize 1928) always considered biochemistry as a neglected area of organic chemistry. In a small way I tried to follow his example and interests, such as oxidation mechanisms, natural products and highly active toxins.*

WITKOWSKY, GIZELLA, dancer; b. Toronto, Ont., Can.. Student, Nat. Ballet Sch. With Nat. Ballet Can., 1975—, 2nd soloist 1977, 1st soloist, 1978, prin. dancer, 1985—; dancer David Allan's Italian Tour, 1985. Performances include Swan Queen/Black Queen in Swan Lake, Snow Queen/ Sugar Plum Fairy in Nutcracker, Queen of the Wilis in Giselle, Swanild in Coppélia, Hanna in Merry Widow, Tatiana in Onegin, others; lead roles in Sphinx, Alice, Voluntaries, Rite of Spring; other roles include Serenade, Four Temperaments, Les Sylphides, Paquita, La Bayadere Act II, Offenbach in the Underworld, Elite Syncopations; created roles Pastorale, Compenents, L'Ile Inconnue, Oiseaux Exotiques, Concerto for the Elements, Lostin Twilights; guest performances include inaugural Huntsville Festival of Arts, 1993, Hungarian Nat. Ballet, Budapest, 1992, Bermuda Festival, 1991, 93, Annual Nijinsky Gala, Hamburg, 1991, Stars and Soloists of Can. Ballet, Italy, 1985. Office: National Ballet of Canada, 157 King St East, Toronto, ON Canada M5C 1G9*

WITMER, G. ROBERT, retired state supreme court justice; b. Webster, N.Y., Dec. 26, 1904; s. George H. and Lillian (Woodhull) W.; m. Marian P. Costello, June 27, 1936; children: George Robert, John R., Thomas W., Sylvia Witmer Bissell. A.B., U. Rochester, N.Y., 1926; LL.B., Harvard U., 1929. Bar: N.Y. 1929. Pvt. practice Rochester, 1929-45; ptnr. Easton & Witmer, 1931-45; surrogate Monroe County, 1946-53; justice N.Y. State Supreme Ct., 1954-81; assoc. justice appellate div. 1st dept., 1963-67, appellate div. 4th dept., 1968-81; jud. adminstrv. officer, appellate div. N.Y. State Supreme Ct. (4th dept.), 1981-94; adminstrv. judge N.Y. State Supreme Ct. (7th Jud. Dist.), 1962-68; ret., 1994; town atty., Webster, 1934-35; served on N.Y. State Ct. Appeals, 1974. Co-author: N.Y. Pattern Jury Instructions-Civil, Vol. 1, 1965, rev. edit., 1974, Vol. 11, 1968; co-chmn. pub. com. Practitioner's Handbook for Appeals Appellate Divs. N.Y., 1979, Practitioner's Handbook for Appeals to the Court of Appeals of New York, 1981. Supr. Town of Webster and County of Monroe, 1936-45; chmn. Webster Republican Com., 1933-45, mem. exec. com. of Monroe County Republican Com., 1933-45. Mem. Am., N.Y. State, Monroe County Bar Assns., Am. Law Inst., Webster Grange, Univ. Club (Rochester), Masons, Theta Chi. Home: 45 Corning Park Webster NY 14580-3503

WITMER, GEORGE ROBERT, JR., lawyer; b. Rochester, N.Y., Mar. 23, 1937; s. George Robert and Marian Pauline (Costello) W.; m. Nancy Rosetta Wenner, Dec. 28, 1968; children: Wendy Lynn, Heidi Dawn, George Robert, III, Frank David. A.B., U. Rochester, 1959; LL.B., Harvard U., 1962. Bar: N.Y. 1962, U.S. Dist. Ct. (we. dist.) N.Y. 1963, U.S. Supreme Ct. 1967, U.S Dist. Ct. (no. dist.) N.Y. 1977. Assoc. Nixon, Hargrave, Devans & Doyle, Rochester, 1962-70; ptnr. Nixon, Hargrave, Devans & Doyle, 1970—; instr. in bus. law U. Rochester, 1965-66; mem. com. to advise and cons. Jud. Conf. State N.Y. on Civil Practice Law and Rules, 1970-77. Mem. N.Y. State Rep. Com., 1976-93; trustee Eastman Dental Ctr. Rochester, 1977—, pres. bd. trustees, 1989-90; trustee U. Rochester, 1979—, chmn. exec. com., 1992—. Fellow N.Y. Bar Found. (dir. 1991—), ABA Found.; mem. ABA, Monroe County (N.Y.) Bar Assn., N.Y. State Bar Assn. (ho. of dels. 1978—, v.p. 1984-88, sec. 1989-90, pres.-elect 1993-94, pres. 1994-95, exec. com. environ. law sect. 1981-93, environ. law sect. Disting. Svc. award), Am. Law inst., Rochester Rotary Club (dir. local chpt. 1977-79), Masons (master 1971), Phi Beta Kappa. Republican. Lutheran. Home: 892 Lake Rd Webster NY 14580-9008 Office: Nixon Hargrave Devans & Doyle PO Box 1051 Clinton Sq Rochester NY 14604-1729

WITMER, JOHN ALBERT, librarian; b. Lancaster, Pa., Nov. 29, 1920; s. Albert Franklin and Mary Esther (Conrad) W.; m. Doris May Ferry, June 10, 1943; children: Marilyn May Witmer Custis, John Richard, Deborah Witmer Redd. AB, Wheaton Coll., 1942, AM, 1946; ThM, Dallas Theol. Sem., 1946, ThD, 1953; MS in L.S., E. Tex. State U., 1969; cert. Archival Adminstrn., U. Tex., Arlington, 1988. Grad. fellow Wheaton Coll., 1942-44; mng. editor Child Evanglism mag., Dallas, 1944-46; instr. Child Evangelism Inst., Dallas and Chgo., 1945-47; instr. systematic theology Dallas Theol. Sem., 1947-54, asst. prof., 1954-86, assoc. prof., 1986-87, assoc. prof. emeritus, 1987—; librarian Mosher Library, 1964-86, archivist, 1987—; cert. instr. Dale Carnegie Course, 1956-92, instr. emeritus, 1992—. Contbr. articles to profl. jours., essays; editor: The Christian Librarian, 1972-74. Treas. Evang. Communications Research Found., 1970-73; bd. dirs. Dallas Bible Coll., 1972-83, chmn., 1974-77, sec., 1979-82; bd. dirs. Evang. Projects, 1975-92. Mem. Assn. Christian Librs., Evang. Philos. Soc., Evan. Theol. Soc., Soc. Am. Archivists, Soc. Southwest Archivists, Grace Evang. Soc. Home: 6630 Westlake Ave Dallas TX 75214-3441

WITMER, JOHN HARPER, JR., lawyer; b. Phila., May 5, 1940; s. John Harper and Jane Carolyn (Lentz) Witmer; m. Arlene Marie Rosipal, June 9, 1962; 1 dau., Tara Leah. BA, Pa. State U., 1962; JD, George Washington U., 1969. Bar: Md. 1969, D.C. 1970, Ill. 1979, Colo. 1991. Mgmt. analyst Nat. Security Agy., Ft. Meade, Md., 1963-66; mem. Sidley & Austin, Washington, 1969-78; sr. v.p., gen. counsel DEKALB Energy Co., 1978—, DEKALB Genetics Corp., 1978—. Mem. ABA, Ill. State Bar Assn., Md. State Bar Assn., D.C. Bar Assn. Home: 2575 Greenwood Acres Dr De Kalb IL 60115-4916 Office: DEKALB Genetics Corp 3100 Sycamore Rd De Kalb IL 60115-9621 also: DeKalb Energy Co, Calgary, PQ Canada

WITSCHEY, WALTER ROBERT THURMOND, science museum administrator, archaeologist, computer systems consultant; b. Charleston, W.Va., June 19, 1941; s. Robert E. and Sarah Elizabeth (Thurmond) W.; m. Joan DuRelle Vincent, July 19, 1980; children: Anne Elizabeth, Schon Roberts Parris, Sarah C. Brauner, Walter Robert Thurmond II, Benjamin Hart Vincent. BA in Physics, Princeton U., 1963; MBA in Ops. Rsch., U. Va., 1965; MA in Anthropology-Maya Archaeology, Tulane U., 1989, PhD in Anthropology-Maya Archaeology, 1993. Systems engr. IBM Corp., Richmond, Va., 1965-67, mktg. rep., 1967-69; v.p. The Computer Co., Richmond, Va., 1969-70, pres., CEO, 1970-84, cons., pub., proprietorship Gatewood Co., Richmond, Va., 1978—; dir., CEO Sci. Mus. Va., Richmond, Va., 1992—; bd. dirs. Highland Data Svcs., 1982-85; vis. instr. computer systems U. Va., 1985-86; instr. word processing, Delgado Community Coll., 1989; lectr. microcomputer applications, Our Lady Of Holy Cross Coll., 1989-92; lectr. dept. Anthropology, Tulane U., 1987—, asst. to the dir., 1987-88, lectr.; curriculum cons., 1988-92, adj. instr. A.B. Freeman Sch., 1991; adj. faculty dept. Sociology, Anthropology and Mathematical Scis., Va. Commonwealth U., 1992—. Contbr. articles to profl. jours. Pres., dir. Richmond-on-the-James, Richmond, 1984-85; dir. Sci. Mus. Va. Found., Richmond, 1981-90, La. Sci. Ctr., New Orleans, 1985-90; sec., dir. Richmond Community High Sch. Policy Bd.; cons. Federated Arts Coun., Richmond. Tinker Found. archaeol. rsch. grantee (3), Middle Am. Rsch. Inst. archaeol. grantee, Mesoam. Ecology Inst. archaeol. rsch. grantee (3), Middle Am. Rsch. Inst. archaeol. grantee (3), pvt. archaeol. rsch. grantee. Mem. AAAS, Am. Assn. Mus., Am. Anthrop. Assn., Assn. Sci.-Tech. Ctrs., Soc. Am. Archaeology, Va. Acad. Sci., Va. Assn. Mus., Va. Space Grant Consortium, Assn. Computing Machinery, Sigma Xi. Presbyterian. Avocation: field archaeology. Office: Sci Mus Va 2500 W Broad St Richmond VA 23220-2057

WITT, BUFORD RANDOLPH, air force officer; b. Memphis, June 6, 1946; s. Buford Witt; m. Margaret Ann Witt, Aug. 9, 1969; children: Ann, Rudolph. Comdr. Comm. Squadron 50th Bomb Wing, Pease AFB, N.H., 1980-82; comms. staff officer hdqs. USAF, Washington, 1982-84; exec. officer to comdr. Air Force Comms. Command, Scott AFB, Ill. 1984-86; comdr. 3d Combat Comms. Group, Tinker AFB, Okla., 1986-88; dep. chief of staff C4 Sys. Hdqs. 9th AF and U.S. Cen. Command, Shaw AFB, S.C., 1989-92; asst. dep. dir. Unified and Command Support, Joint Staff Pentagon, Washington, 1992-93; dir. plans, policy, dep. chief of staff C4 Hdqs. USAF, Washington, 1993-94; dir. command, control comm. sys. Hdqs. U.S.

European Command, Stuttgart, Germany, 1994—. Editor: AF Tactical Communications in War, 1991. Mem. Armed Forces Comms. Electronics Assn., Washington Citadel Club (pres. 1993-94). Avocation: flying. Home: Box 741 HQ USEUCOM Unit 30400 APO AE 09128 Office: HQ USEUCOM/ECJ6 Unit 30400 Box 1000 APO AE 09128

WITT, CHARLES E., coal company executive; b. Jenkins, Ky., Sept. 24, 1917; s. L. L. and Dez (Litton) W.; m. Jane Reed, Sept. 11, 1940; children—Cordella Witt Carrico, Susan Witt Beam, Amy Witt Shook. A.B., W.Va. U., 1939. Purchasing agt. Fairmont Supply Co. (subs. Consolidation Coal Co.), Washington, Pa., 1946-57; br. mgr. Fairmont Supply Co. (subs. Consolidation Coal Co.), 1956-57; dir. purchases parent co. Fairmont Supply Co. (subs. Consolidation Coal Co.), Pitts., 1957-62; v.p. purchasing Fairmont Supply Co. (subs. Consolidation Coal Co.), 1962-72; chmn. bd. Fairmont Supply Co., 1972-77; sr. v.p. Consolidation Coal Co., 1972-77; dir. Nat. Mine Service Co.; mgmt. cons.; dir. B.P. Tracy Co., 1977—; bd. dirs. Perma-Cote Industries. Home: 8 Deer Path Farmington PA 15437 Office: PO Box 235 Farmington PA 15437-0235

WITT, DAVID L., curator, writer; b. Kansas City, Mo., Nov. 3, 1951; s. Lloyd Vernon and Dean W. B.S. in Polit. Sci., Kans. State U., 1974. Naturalist Naish Nature Ctr., Edwardsville, Kans., summers 1967-70; asst. curator Seton Mus., Cimarron, N.Mex., summers 1972-74; curatorial asst. Riley County Hist. Mus., Manhattan, Kans., 1973-74; mus. asst. Millicent Rogers Mus., Taos, N.Mex., 1976-77; curator The Gaspard House Mus., Taos, N.Mex., 1978-79, The Harwood Found., Taos; 1979—; Author: The Taos Artists, 1984, Taos Moderns: Art of the New, 1992 (Southwest Book award Border Regional Libr. Assn. 1993); contbr. articles to profl. jours. Organizer first N.Mex. Art History Conf., 1986; founder Southwest Art History Coun., 1990. Mem. PEN, Mountain-Plains Mus. Assn. (council mem. 1983-85), N.Mex. Assn. Mus. (pres. 1986-88). Democrat. Home: PO Box 317 Taos NM 87571-0317 Office: PO Box 4081 Taos NM 87571

WITT, ELIZABETH NOWLIN (BETH WITT), special education educator; b. Columbus, Miss., Apr. 11, 1941; d. Mervyn Davis and Elizabeth (Moody) Smith; m. Lawrence V. Witt Jr., Feb. 10, 1963; children: Lawrence V. III, Ben, John, Catherine, Elizabeth. BS in Journalism and English, Miss. U. for Women, Columbus, 1963; MA in Spl. Edn., La. Tech. U., Ruston, 1979; postgrad., La. State U., 1990—. Cert. in English, learning disabilities, mental retardation, presch. handicapped severe/profound, also prin., ednl cons., ednl. diagnostician, La. Tchr. spl. edn. Caddo-Bossier Assn. for Retarded Citizens, Shreveport, La., 1976-79; tchr presch. handicapped Bossier Parish Schs., Bossier City, La., 1979-83; ednl. diagnostician Caddo Parish Schs., Shreveport, 1983—; ednl. cons. Ruston (La.) State Sch., summer 1981; instr. La. Tech. U., 1990—; mem. author adv. bd. Comm. Skill Builders, Tucson, 1986-88; ex officio mem. Region VII Infant Coun., Shreveport, 1990-92; bd. dirs. Childcare of N.W. La., Shreveport, 1986-90, Head Start, Shreveport, 1984-85. Mem. editorial adv. bd. JCCD, DCCD; author lang. activity kits and programs. Vol. ednl. cons. Lighthouse Presch. Program, Vols. of Am., Shreveport, 1986—; elder First Presbyn. Ch., Bossier City, 1989-91. Mem. Am. Speech and Hearing Assn., Coun. for Exceptional Children (editor newsletter La. Fedn. 1988-90, pres. La. div. early childhood 1989-90, pres. La. div. mental retardation 1986-87, coun. for children with commun. disorders 1986—). Avocations: reading, collecting quilts, country decorating, travel. Office: Caddo Parish Sch Spl Edn Ctr 5948 Union Ave Shreveport LA 71108-3928

WITT, HUGH ERNEST, technology consultant; b. Winchester, Ky., Nov. 18, 1921; s. Hugh E. and Louella (Milliken) W.; m. Janie Bryan (dec. Oct. 1990); m. Evelyn Chapman, Apr. 22, 1993. Student, Transylvania U., 1941-43; BS, U. Ky., 1945; MS, MIT, 1957. Asst. to dep. asst. sec. Dept. of Air Force, Washington, 1954-61, dep. asst. sec., 1961-70; dep. asst. sec. Dept. of Navy, Washington, 1970-73; prin. dep. asst. Sec. of Def., Washington, 1973-74; fed. procurement policy adminstr. Office Mgmt. and Budget, Washington, 1974-77; dir., govtl. liaison United Techs. Corp., Washington, 1977-81, v.p., govt. liaison, 1981-87, cons. to United Techs. Corp., 1987—. Pres. Old Town Civic Assn., Alexandria, Va., 1963; bd. dirs. Alexandria Hist. Found.; mem. Alexandria Bd. Archtl. Rev., 1964-77; trustee Alexandria Hosp. Found., 1992—. Alfred P. Sloan fellow MIT, Cambridge, Mass., 1956-57. Fellow Nat. Contract Mgmt. Assn.; mem. Aerospace Industries Assn., Nat. Security Indsl. Assn., MIT Alumni Assn., Soc. Sloan Fellows, Kappa Alpha.

WITT, JAMES LEE, federal agency administrator; b. Dardanelle, Ark., 1944; m. Lea; children: Jimmy, Michael. Founder Witt Constrn. Co.; county judge Yell County, Ark.; state dir. Office Emergency Svcs., Ark.; dir. Fed. Emergency Mgmt. Agy., Washington, 1993—. Chmn. bd. Child Devel., Inc., charter; Gov.'s rep. state disasters, Presdl. disasters. Recognized for outstanding efforts Nat. Assn. Counties. Office: Federal Emergency Mgmt Agency Office of Dir 500 C St SW Washington DC 20472

WITT, RAYMOND BUCKNER, JR., lawyer; b. Lenoir City, Tenn., Apr. 20, 1915; s. Raymond Buckner and Gertrude (Jackson) W.; m. Florence Elder Bagley, Sept. 14, 1943; children—Florence Elder, Mary Alice, George Evans. A.B., U. Chattanooga, 1937; LL.B., U. N.C., 1939. Bar: Tenn. 1939. Since practiced in Chattanooga; with Witt, Gaither, Whitaker and predecessor firms, 1945—, partner, 1946—; dir., gen. counsel Dixie Yarns, Inc., 1947-92. Pres. Met. Council Community Services, 1966-68; mem. Chattanooga Bd. Edn., 1953-65, vice chmn., 1963-65; chmn. Chattanooga Bicentennial Religious Com., 1976; chmn. bd. Chattanooga-Hamilton County Bicentennial Library, 1976-78; trustee Westend Found.; mem. U. Chatanooga Found. Inc., 1969—, trustee, sec., gen. counsel, chmn. 1988-90; pres. Chattanooga YMCA, 1986-87; chmn. United Way Fund campaign, 1987; chmn. bd. trustees 1st Centenary United Methodist, 1989, chmn. adminstrv. bd., 1993, 94. Served to lt. comdr. USNR, 1942-45, PTO. Recipient Distinguished Service award Chattanooga Kiwanis, 1963, Tenn. Sch. Bds. Assn., 1963. Mem. ABA, Tenn. Bar Assn. Methodist (chmn. commn. on Christian edn. 1953-55, ch. sch. supt. 1955-60). Home: 1615 Minnekahda Rd Chattanooga TN 37405-2411 Office: American Nat Bank Bldg Chattanooga TN 37402

WITT, ROBERT CHARLES, finance educator; b. Tyndall, S.D., Aug. 24, 1941; s. Emmanuel M. and Hilda Veronica (Link) W.; m. Laura Gutierrez, May 21, 1974; 1 child, Kristina Monique. BA cum laude, BS with honors, U. S.D., 1964; MS in Actuarial Sci., U. Wis., 1966; MA in Econs., U. Pa., 1968, PhD in Bus. and Applied Econs., 1972. CLU. Teaching asst. U. Wis., Madison, 1965; instr. econs. Augustana Coll., Sioux Falls, S.D., 1965-66; instr. bus. stats. Temple U., Phila., 1969-70; prof. fin. U. Tex., Austin, 1970—, CBA Found. prof., 1980-82, Blades prof., 1982-86, Gus Wortham chaired prof., 1986—, chmn. fin. dept., 1984-88; vis. prof. fin. U. B.C., Vancouver, Can., 1979; advisor U.S. Senate Subcom. on Antitrust and Monopoly, 1969-70, Ill. Ins. Laws Study Commn., 1975-78, Tex. Legis., 1973—, Atty. Gen.'s Office, State of Tex., 1984, Tex. Gov.'s Office, 1989, Ins. Info. Inst., 1982-86, Houston Power and Light, 1989-90, State Bd. of Ins., 1990, 93, U.S. Justice Dept., 1991—, Constrn. Industry Inst., 1989—, Nat. Assn. Ind. Insurers, 1992-93, Tex. Pub. Policy Found., 1994—, also various ins. cos. Assoc. editor Jour. Risk and Ins., 1976-86, 90—, Benefits Quar., 1985-90, Jour. Fin. Svcs. and Rsch., 1989-94; contbg. editor Ins. Abstracts and Revs., 1982—; mem. rsch. and pub. adv. bd., referee Jour. Ins. Issues and Practices, 1977-88; contbr. articles to profl. jours. Bd. govs. Internat. Ins. Soc., 1981—, chmn. rsch. roundtable, 1984-89, chmn. acad. directorate, 1989-91, chmn. bd. moderators, 1991; mem. rsch. bd. S.S. Huebner Found. for Ins. Edn., Wharton Sch., U. Pa., 1983-90; chmn. doctoral awards coms. in bus. and ins. State Farm Cos. Found., 1989—; mem. bd. dirs. Tex. Property and Casualty Ins. Guaranty Assn., 1991-92. Grantee S.S. Huebner Found., Law Found. U. Tex., Ill. Legis., Grad. Sch. Bus. U. Tex., Tex. Atty. Gen., Tex. Legis., Tex. Gov.'s Office, 1989, Nat. Assn. Ind. Insurers, Constrn. Industry Inst., Tex. Pub. Policy Found., 1993-94, Texand for Lawsuit Reform, 1994. Mem. Am. Risk and Ins. Assn. (pres., bd. dirs. 1980-87, Outstanding Feature Aticle award 1974, 76, 85, 86, 93), S.S. Huebner Found. (adminstrv. bd. 1987—), Am. Fin. Assn., Am. Econ. Assn., Fin. Mgmt. Assn., Risk Theory Seminar (chmn. 1977), Fin. Execs. Inst. (bd. dirs. 1992—). Avocations: basketball, bicycling, running. Office: U Tex Dept Fin CBA 6-222 Austin TX 78712

WITT, ROBERT LOUIS, materials manufacturing and sales company executive, lawyer; b. Vallejo, Calif., Feb. 22, 1940; s. Charles Louis and Encie Lyndell (Bates) W.; m. Myrna Doreen Harvey; 1 child, Mark Louis. A.A., Solano Coll., 1959; student, Oreg. State U., 1959-61; J.D., San Francisco Law Sch., 1968. Sec., corp. counsel Hexcel Corp., San Francisco, 1969-76, v.p., sec., 1976-80, v.p. adminstrn., 1980-82, sr. v.p. internat., 1982-84, exec. v.p., 1984-85, pres., 1985—, CEO, 1986—, chmn. bd. dirs., 1986. Office: Hexcel Corp 11555 Dublin Blvd Dublin CA 94568-2854

WITT, ROBERT WAYNE, English educator; b. Scottsville, Ky., Mar. 26, 1937; s. Aubrey G. Witt and Nina Loyce (Cook) Jackson. BA, Georgetown Coll., 1959; MA, U. Miss., 1961, PhD, 1970. Instr. U. Miss., Oxford, 1965-70; asst. prof. Ea. Ky. U., Richmond, 1970-75, assoc. prof., 1975-80, prof., 1980—. Author: Mirror-within, 1975, Shakespeare's Sonnets, 1979, Rocking Chair, 1987, Combining Modes, 1992, Hour in Paradise, 1993. Mem. MLA, South Atlantic Modern Lang., Dramatists Guild, Automatic Musical Instruments Collectors. Avocations: playing piano, collecting antique automatic musical instruments. Home: PO Box 419 Richmond KY 40476-0419

WITT, THOMAS POWELL, lawyer; b. Pitts., Nov. 11, 1946; s. Fabian J. and Blanche (Powell) W.; m. Loretta Jean Cooper, June 27, 1970; children: John, Christopher, Susan. BA magna cum laude, LaSalle U., Phila., 1968; MA, Harvard U., 1969; JD cum laude, Temple U., 1975. Bar: Pa. 1975, U.S. Dist. Ct. (ea. dist.) Pa. 1976. Adminstrv. asst. Phila. Housing Devel. Corp., 1969-72; supr. loan processing Firstrust Savs. Bank, Phila., 1972-75; atty. Morgan, Lewis & Bockius, Phila., 1975-83; ptnr. Wolf, Block, Schorr & Solis-Cohen, Phila., 1983—. Dir., pres. S. W. Germantown Assn. Fed. Credit Union, Phila., 1982-89, bd. dirs. Women Against Abuse, Inc., Phila., 1988-89, Juvenile Justice Ctr. Pa., Phila, 1989—, Regional Housing Legal Svcs., 1989—, The Pa. Prison Soc., 1994—. Fellow Woodrow Wilson Found., Princeton, N.J., 1968. Mem. Bicycle Club Phila. (pres. 1992—). Democrat. Avocation: bicycle touring. Home: 5127 Pulaski Ave Philadelphia PA 19144-4021 Office: Wolf Block Schorr & Solis- Cohen 12th Fl Packard Bldg SE Corner 15 & Chestnut Sts Philadelphia PA 19122

WITT, WALTER FRANCIS, JR., lawyer; b. Richmond, Va., Feb. 18, 1933; s. Walter Francis and Evelyn Virginia (Riggleman) W.; m. Rosemary Winter, Sept. 5, 1964; children: Leslie Anne, Walter Francis III. BS, U. Richmond, 1954, JD, 1966. Bar: Va. 1966, D.C. 1974. Assoc. Hunton and Williams, Richmond, 1966-74, ptnr., 1974—. Contbr. articles to profl. jours. 1st lt. U.S. Army, 1955-57. Mem. ABA (chmn. real property com. sect. of gen. practice 1994—, dep. chair urban, state and local govt. com., sect. gen. practice), Va. Bar Assn., Richmond Bar Assn., D.C. Bar Assn., Phi Beta Kappa, Phi Delta Phi. Home: 8901 Tresco Rd Richmond VA 23229-7725 Office: Hunton & Williams Riverfront Plaza East Twr 951 East Byrd St Richmond VA 23219-4074

WITTBRODT, EDWIN STANLEY, consultant, former bank executive, former air force officer; b. Flint, Mich., Aug. 13, 1918; s. Stanley Frank and Marie (Ross) W.; m. Joan Helen Miller, Apr. 22, 1950; children: Stephanie Rita, Candace Lee, Edwin Stanley. Student, Gen. Motors Inst. Tech., 1936-38, Grad. Sch. Dept. Agr., 1950-51, Indsl. Coll. Armed Forces, 1961-62, George Washington U., 1962, U. So. Calif., 1963-64. Joined U.S. Army, 1941, commd. 2d lt., 1942; advanced through grades to brig. gen. USAF, 1968; various assignments U.S., 1941-49; budget officer Hdqrs. USAF, 1949-53, 56-61; dir. budget and acctg. Hdqrs. N.E. Air Command, Nfld., 1953-56; comptroller space systems div. Los Angeles, 1962-64; comptroller aero., systems div. Wright-Patterson AFB, 1964-66; asst. comptroller USAF, 1966-67; dir. acctg. and fin. Hdqrs. USAF, 1967-68; asst. comptroller air force for acctg. and fin., comdr. Bank Force Acctg. and Fin. Ctr., Denver, 1968-71; v.p. systems Cen. Bank Denver, 1971-81, v.p. info. resources mgmt., 1981-84; dir. Computer Congenerics Corp. Colo., Hasa Corp. Co-chmn. Combined Fed. Campaign, Denver, 1968-87; Hon. dir. USO, Denver, 1968-71; mem. council, 1971-87 . Decorated D.S.M., Legion of Merit, Soldier's medal, Commendation medal with oak leaf cluster; Air Force recipient Gen. Jimmy Doolittle Disting. Fellow award, Flint No. Alumni Assn. Disting. Fellow award, 1990. Mem. Am. Soc. Mil. Comptrollers (past pres. Washington chpt., nat. v.p. 1968-70, pres. Denver chpt. 1971-72), Assn. Govt. Accountants, Assn. Mil. Banks (dir. 1974-84), Am. Inst. Banking, Denver C. of C. (chmn. mil. affairs com. 1979-82), Aurora C. of C. (mil. affairs coun. 1987—), Air Force Assn. (v.p. N. Colo. 1971-72, pres. Silver and Gold chpt. 1972-73, state treas. 1976-83, pres. Mile High chpt. 1987-88). Club: Columbine Country. Home: 10 Niblick Ln Columbine Valley CO 80123-6622 *I have adopted two attitudes that I believe assisted me in all of my undertakings: (1)—that of being what I call a "responsible non-conformist" and (2)—"no problems—just opportunities."*

WITTCOFF, HAROLD AARON, chemist; b. Marion, Ind., July 3, 1918; s. Morris and Bessie (Pruss) W.; m. Dorothy Brochin, 1946; 2 sons. A.B. magna cum laude, DePauw U., 1940; Ph.D., Northwestern U., 1943; grad., Advanced Mgmt. Program, Harvard U., 1964. With Gen. Mills, Inc., Mpls., 1943-79; head chem. research dept. Gen. Mills, Inc., 1952-56, Dir. chem. research, 1956-67, v.p. dir. chem. research and devel., 1967-69, v.p., dir. corp. research, 1969-79; dir. research and devel. Koor Chems., Beer Sheva, Israel, 1979-82; dir. process evaluation and research planning Chem Systems, Tarrytown, N.Y., 1982-85; sci. adviser Chem. Systems Internat., Tarrytown, N.Y., 1985—; adj. prof. chemistry U. Minn., 1973-82. Author: The Phosphatides, 1951, Industrial Organic Chemistry: A Perspective, 2 vols., 1980, The Pharmaceutical Industry: Chemistry and Perspectives, 1989; contbr. articles to profl. jours. Recipient Minn. award Am. Chem. Soc., 1976. Mem. Phi Beta Kappa, Sigma Xi, Phi Eta Sigma. Patentee in field. Home: Box 307 Scarborough Manor Scarborough NY 10510

WITTE, MERLIN MICHAEL, oil company executive; b. Los Angeles, Mar. 28, 1926; s. Anthony A. and Julia (Macke) W.; m. Donna Patricia Hurth, Jan. 22, 1949; children: James Anthony, Daniel Michael, Catherine Ann, Michael Leon, Robert Joseph, Joseph William, Anne Marie, William Benson, Janet Mary. B.A., Loyola U., Los Angeles, 1949. With IRS, U.S. Treasury Dept., 1949-51; investment, tax mgr. McCulloch Motors Corp., also Robert P. McCulloch, 1951-55; pres., gen. mgr., dir. McCulloch Oil Corp., Los Angeles, 1956-80; pres. dir. Merlin Assocs., Inc., Los Angeles, 1980—, M.M. Witte & Assocs., Inc., Los Angeles, 1980—; mgr., chief exec. United Oil Producers, Los Angeles, 1984-86; bd. dirs. Kent Fin. Svcs., Inc., Search Exploration, Inc.; bd. dirs., chmn. McCulloch Energy, Inc., 1991—. Mem. bd. regents Loyola Marymount U., L.A., 1991—. Served with USAAF, 1944-45. Mem. Ind. Oil and Gas Producers Assn., Ind. Petroleum Assn., Western, West Cen. Tex. oil and gas assns., Town Hall, Bel-Air Country Club (pres. 1990-91), PGA West Golf Club.

WITTEN, DAVID MELVIN, radiology educator; b. Trenton, Mo., Aug. 16, 1926; s. Buford Isom and Mary Louise (Melvin) W.; m. Netta Lee Watkins, Dec. 23, 1950; children—David Melvin, II, Michael Lee. Student, Trenton Jr. Coll., 1943-44, 46-47; A.B., Washington U., St. Louis, 1950, M.D., 1954; M.S. in Radiology, Mayo Grad. Sch. Medicine, U. Minn., 1960. Diplomate: Am. Bd. Radiology. Intern Virginia Mason Hosp., Seattle, 1954-55; practice medicine specializing in family medicine Trenton, Mo., 1955-57; fellow in radiology Mayo Clinic/Mayo Found., Rochester, Minn., 1957-60; cons. in diagnostic roentgenology Mayo Clinic, 1960-70; instr. Mayo Grad. Sch. Medicine, Rochester, 1960-66; asst. prof. radiology Mayo Grad. Sch. Medicine, 1966-70; pvt. practice medicine specializing in radiology Aberdeen, Wash., 1970-71; clin. assoc. prof. U. Wash., 1970-71; prof. diagnostic radiology, chmn. dept. diagnostic radiology U Ala., Birmingham, 1971-82; diagnostic radiologist in chief Univ. Hosp., Birmingham, 1971-82; prof., chmn. dept. radiology U. Mo., Columbia, 1982-87, prof. emeritus, 1987—; mem. U. Ala. Health Services Found., 1973-75. Author: Atlas of Tumor Radiology-The Breast, 1969, Clinical Urography, 1977; contbr. articles on radiology of breast cancer, urologic and gastrointestinal disease to profl. jours.; mem. editorial bd. Am. Jour. Roentgenology, 1976-87, Applied Radiology, 1978-87, Urologic Radiology, 1979-87, Radiographics, 1983-87. Served with USNR, 1944-46. Fellow Am. Coll. Radiology; mem. Radiol. Soc. N. Am., Am. Roentgen Ray Soc., AAAS, Soc. Genitourinary Radiology (pres. 1981-82), Assn. Univ. Radiologists, AMA, Mo. Radiol. Soc. (pres. 1988-89), Mo. State Med. Assn., Canadian Assn. Radiologists (hon.), Audubon Soc. (editor The Bluebird, Mo. chpt. 1990—). Home: 601 Covered Bridge Rd Columbia MO 65203-9562 Office: Univ Mo Health Scis Ctr 1 Hospital Dr Columbia MO 65201-9972

WITTEN, EDWARD, mathematical physicist; b. 1951; s. Louis W.; m. Chiara Nappi; 3 children. Grad. in history, Brandeis U., 1971; Ph.D., Princeton U., 1976. Prof. physics Princeton Univ., 1980-87; prof. natural scis. Inst. for Advanced Study, Princeton, N. J., 1987—. Contbr. articles to mags. and profl. jours. MacArthur fellow; recipient Einstein medal Einstein Soc. Berne, Switzerland, 1985, Phys. and Math. Sci. award N.Y. Acad. Sci., 1985, Dirac medal Internat. Ctr. Theoretical Physics, 1985, Alan Waterman award NSF 1986, Fields Medal, 1990. Mem. NAS. Office: Inst for Advanced Study Sch Natural Scis Olden Ln Princeton NJ 08540-4920*

WITTEN, LOUIS, physics educator; b. Balt., Apr. 13, 1921; s. Abraham and Bessie (Perman) W.; m. Lorraine Wollach, Mar. 27, 1949 (dec. 1987); children: Edward, Celia, Matthew, Jesse; m. Francis L. White, Jan. 2, 1992. B.E., Johns Hopkins U., 1941, Ph.D., 1951; B.S., NYU, 1944. Research assoc. Princeton U., N.J., 1951-53; research assoc. U. Md., College Park, 1953-54; staff scientist Lincoln Lab., MIT, 1954-55; assoc. dir. Martin Marietta Research Lab., Balt., 1955-68; prof. physics U. Cin., 1968—; trustee Gravity Research Found. Editor: Gravitation: An Introduction to Current Research, 1962, Relativity: Procs. of Relative Conf. in Midwest of 1969, 1970, Symposium on Asymptotic Structure of Space-Time, 1976; patentee in field; contbr. numerous articles to sci. jours. Served to 1st lt. USAF, 1942-46. Fulbright lectr. Weismann Inst. Scis., Rehovot, Israel, 1963-64. Fellow Am. Phys. Soc.; mem. Am. Math. Soc., Internat. Astron. Union, AAAS. Office: Univ Cincinnati Dept Physics Cincinnati OH 45221

WITTEN, THOMAS JEFFERSON, JR., mathematics educator; b. Welch, W.Va., Feb. 10, 1942; s. Thomas Jefferson and Gladys Marium (McMeans) W.; m. Barbara Phyllis Honaker, Feb. 20, 1965; children: Thomas Jefferson III, Rebecca A. Dye, Timothy A., Stephanie L. Dye. BS in Edn., Concord Coll., Athens, W.Va., 1965; MA in Edn., W.Va. U., Morgantown, 1971. Cert. tchr., W.Va. Tchr. math. McDowell County Schs., Gary (W.Va.) High Sch., 1965-71, asst. prin., 1971-73; asst. prin. math. Tazewell County Schs., Richlands (Va.) High Sch., 1973-87; secondary supr. Jackson County Schs., Ripley, W.Va., 1987-88; asst. prof. math. Southwest Va. Community Coll., Richlands, 1988—; math. cons. S.W. Va. C.C. Computer Math. Grant Project, Richlands, 1988-90; coord. S.W. Va. Tech. Prep Consortium, 1992—. Mem. sch. bd. Tazewell (Va.) County Schs., 1990-91; faculty senate pres. South Va. Community Coll., 1992-94. Recipient K-8 Tchr. Improvement grant, 1992-93. Mem. Va. C.C. Assn., Mountain Math Alliance (chmn. 1909—), PTA (life, pres. 1979-81), Richlands Rotary (pres. 1989-91), Masons (jr. deacon 1966-68), Shriners. Democrat. Methodist. Avocations: painting, reading, computers, old cars, writing. Home: 737 Terry Dr Richlands VA 24641-2616 Office: SW Va C C Box SVCC Richlands VA 24641

WITTER, RICHARD LAWRENCE, veterinarian, educator; b. Bangor, Maine, Sept. 10, 1936; s. John Franklin and Verna Harriet (Church) W.; m. Joan Elizabeth Denny, June 30, 1962; children—Jane Katherine, Steven Franklin. B.S., Mich. State U., 1958, D.V.M., 1960; M.S., Cornell U., 1962, Ph.D., 1964. Rsch. veterinarian Agrl. Rsch. Svc., U.S. Dept. Agr., East Lansing, Mich., 1964-75; dir. Avian Disease and Oncology Lab., 1975—; clin. prof. pathology Mich. State U. East Lansing, 1965—. Contbr. articles to profl. jours. Recipient Disting. Alumni award Coll. Vet. Medicine, Mich. State U., 1985, Disting. Service award USDA, 1985. Mem. AVMA, Am. Assn. Avian Pathologists (P.P. Levine award 1967, 81, 88, 92, Upjohn Achievement award 1992), Poultry Sci. Assn. (CPC Internat. award 1976), Mich. Vet. Med. Assn., World Vet. Poultry Assn. (B. Rispens rsch. award 1983). Lodge: Kiwanis. Avocations: piano, hunting, fishing, gardening. Home: 3880 Sheldrake Ave Okemos MI 48864-3646 Office: Avian Disease and Oncology Lab 3606 E Mt Hope Rd East Lansing MI 48823-5338

WITTHUHN, BURTON ORRIN, university official; b. Allentown, Pa., Aug. 22, 1934; s. Ray Arthur and Mae Marcella (Kline) W.; m. Patricia King, June 24, 1961; children: Jonathan, Andrew. BS, Kutztown (Pa.) U., 1956; MEd, Pa. State U., 1962, PhD, 1968. Tchr. Allentown (Pa.) Pub. Schs., 1956-63; teaching asst., assoc. Pa. State U., University Park, 1963-66, research asst., 1965-66; asst. prof. Ohio State U., Columbus, 1967-70; prof., chmn. dept. geography Edinboro (Pa.) State Coll., 1970-79, assoc. v.p. acad. affairs, 1980-83; provost, v.p. acad. affairs Edinboro Univ. of Pa., 1984-88; provost, v.p. acad. affairs Western Ill. U., Macomb, 1988-93, acting pres., 1993, provost, v.p. acad. affairs, 1994—; vis. rsch. prof. Nat. Taiwan Normal U., 1978; cons. Project Africa/Carnegie-Mellon U., Pitts., 1967-70; mem. mid. states evaluation team Grifis AFB, Utica, N.Y., 1987, Cortland (N.Y.) U., 1962; mem. mid. states periodic rev. team, Phila., 1986; mem. mid. states evaluation tewam in connuction with Am. Optometric Assn. accreditation visit SUNY Sch. Optometry, 1987; mem. evaluation team Pa. Dept. Edn., U. Pitts., 1988; mem. accreditation team U. Calif. Coll. Optometry, Berkeley, 1990, Ferris State U., Big Rapids, Mich., 1991, U. Houston, 1992; cons., core evaluator North Ctrl. Assn., 1994—; vice chmn. Quad Cities Grad. Ctr., 1991—. Author: Discovery in Geography, 1976; mem. editl. bd. Pa. Geographer, Chronicle of CQI; contbr. chpts. to books in field. Mem. Edinboro Planning & Zoning Commn., 1973-77. Recipient Disting. Alumnus award Kutztown U., 1990; Fulbright Hays fellow, Ethiopia, Kenya, Uganda, 1965. Mem. Nat. Coun. Geog. Edn. (exec. bd. 1977-80, mem. award com. for region IV 1981—), Pa. Coun. Geog. Edn. (exec. sec. 1976-79, pres. 1975-76, Outstanding Prof. award 1978), Bishops Com. Democrat. Episcopalian. Lodge: Rotary (pres. Edinboro club 1972-73). Avocations: reading, golf, photography, model constrn. Home: 1106 Bayberry Ln Macomb IL 61455 Office: Western Ill U Sherman Hall Adams St Macomb IL 61455

WITTICH, BRENDA JUNE, religious organization executive, minister; b. Muncie, Ind., Dec. 19, 1946; d. Plano Brentie and Norma June (Huggins) Gossett; m. Chester Edward Wittich, Dec. 24, 1980; 1 child, September Leigh Noonan. Lic., Morris Pratt Inst. Assn., 1979, postgrad., 1983-86. Ordained minister Nat. Spiritualist Assn. of Churches, 1986. Pastor Fifth Spiritualist Ch., St. Louis, 1988—. Co-author, editor: National Spiritualist Association Churches Public Relations Handbook, 1992; co-author booklet: Spiritualism - Pathway of Light, 1992; contbr. articles to Nat. Spiritualist Mag. Mem. St. Louis Pub. Sch. Clergy Leaders Forum, 1991-92, Tchrs. for Nat. Spiritualist Assn. of Chs. Ednl. Ctr.-Psychology and Parlimentary Procedures. Mem. Nat. Hemlock Soc., Nat. Spiritualist Assn. of Chs. (trustee 1990-92, supt. pub. rels. 1990-94, v.p. bd. trustees 1992-94, pres. bd. trustees 1994), Inst. Noetic Scis. Avocations: travel, reading. Home: 3903 Connecticut St Saint Louis MO 63116 Office: Nat Spiritualist Assn Chs 13 Cottage Row PO Box 217 Lily Dale NY 14752

WITTICH, JOHN JACOB, retired college president, educational administrator, corporation consultant; b. Huntley, Ill., Nov. 13, 1921; s. John and Eva (Karl) W.; m. Leah Elliott, Apr. 2, 1944; children: Karen Ann Zvonar, Jane Ellen Tock, John Elliott. B.A., DePauw U., 1943, LL.D. (hon.), 1971; M.A., U. N.Mex., 1949; Ph.D., Stanford U., 1952; L.H.D. (hon.), Ill. Coll., 1979; D.P.S. (hon.), MacMurray Coll., 1980. Tchr. Albuquerque High Sch., 1948-49; teaching asst. Stanford, 1949-51; asst. prof. psychology Coll. of Pacific, Stockton, Calif., 1951-52; dean of admissions, dir. scholarships, assoc. prof. DePauw U., Greencastle, Ind., 1952-61; exec. dir. Coll. Center of Finger Lakes, Corning, N.Y., 1961-63, Coll. Student Personnel Inst., Claremont, Calif., 1963-68; grad. studies in student pers. Claremont Grad. Sch., 1963-68; pres. MacMurray Coll. Jacksonville, Ill., 1968-80; program dir. Fla. Assn. Colls. and Univs., 1980-84; dir. higher edn. program Stetson U., 1981-88; v.p. Capital Formation Counselors, Inc., Belleaire Bluffs, Fla., 1983—. Contbr. articles to popular and profl. jours. Mem. exec. com. Divsn. Higher Edn., Ctrl. Ill. Coun. of United Meth. Ch., 1968-80; mem. exec. com. Fedn. Independent Ill. Colls. and Univs. and Assoc. Colls. Ill.; mem. non-pub. adv. com. Ill. Bd. Higher Edn., 1972-78; mem. Nat. Merit Scholarship Selection Com., 1956, 61; cons. Calif. Gov.'s Conf. on Edn., 1965, on Youth, 1966; trustee Fla. Endowment for Humanities, 1982-85; presdl. counsellor Stetson U., 1987—; bd. dirs. DeLand House Next Door, 1990-94; adv. com. West Volusia County Hosps., 1992—. With USMC, 1943-46, PTO. Recipient Alumni citation DePauw U., 1994; Rockefeller fellow Aspen Inst. for Humanistic Studies, 1979. Mem. AAUP, APA, Am. Coll. Pers. Assn. (commn. chmn.), Nat. Assn. Coll. Admissions Counselors (exec. bd. 1955-58), Cen. States Coll. Assn. (exec. com. 1969-77, sec.-treas. 1970-77), 4th Marine Divsn. Assn., Sigma Chi.

WITTLER, SHIRLEY JOYCE, former state official, state commissioner; b. Ravenna, Nebr., Oct. 10, 1927; d. Earl William and Minnie Ethel (Frink)

Wade; m. LeRoy F. Wittler, Dec. 31, 1946; children: Julie Diane, Barbara Liane. Student, U. Nebr., 1944-47. Real estate saleswoman Harrington Assocs., Lincoln, Nebr., 1965-69; real estate broker Tom Searl Realty, Inc., Cheyenne, Wyo., 1970-76; dep. state treas. Wyo., 1976-78; state treas., 1979-83; chmn. state tax commn. and bd. equalization State of Wyo., 1985-90; ret., 1990. Pres. LWV, Lincoln, 1965-69; bd. dirs. LWV Wyo., 1970-72; fin. chmn. Republican Central Com. Laramie County, Wyo., 1974-76; chmn. Laramie County Pres. Ford Com., 1976; Rep. precinct committeewoman, 1972-77; mem. Laramie County Library Bd., 1976, Community Devel. Adv. Bd., 1974-77. Mem. Cheyenne Bd. Realtors (pres. 1976, Cheyenne Realtor of Yr. 1974), Women's Civic League (treas. 1974, legis. chmn. 1975-76). Lutheran. Home: 5022 Hoy Rd Cheyenne WY 82009-4850

WITTLICH, GARY EUGENE, music theory educator; b. Belleville, Ill., Dec. 3, 1934; s. Marvin Oscar W. and Erma Carrie (Garlich) Jackson Wittlich; m. Barbara L. Casey, Jan. 4, 1958 (div. Feb. 1969); children: M. Kent, Kristi L.; m. Mildred Elizabeth Read, Mar. 17, 1971. B.M.Ed., So. Ill. U., 1957, M.Mus., 1959; Ph.D., U. Iowa, 1969. Asst. prof. music Upper Iowa U., Fayette, 1959-63; prof. music, grad. studies in music theory Ind. U., Bloomington, 1975-94, assoc. dean Office of Info. Tech., 1995—, coord. of computing, 1989-95; Meadows disting. vis. prof. music So. Meth. U., Dallas, 1982-83; vis. prof. N. Mich., Ann Arbor, 1974; dir. Ctr. for Profl. Devel. in Music Tech., CMS/ATMI, 1995—; cons. videodisc project NEH, U. Del., 1982-85; mem. advanced music exam. com. Ednl. Testing Service, Princeton, N.J., 1983-85, chmn., 1986-90; mem. IBM Music Adv. Group, 1990—. Author: (with C. Lee Humphries) Ear Training: An Approach Through Music Literature, 1974, (with others) Aspects of Twentieth-Century Music, 1975, (with J. Schaffer and L. Babb) Microcomputers and Music, 1986, (with D. Martin) Tonal Harmony for the Keyboard, 1988. Served with U.S. Army, 1957, 61-62. NSF grantee Ind. U., 1970; fellow Inst. for Acad. Tech., 1992. Mem. Assn. for Tech. in Music Instrn. (founding), Coll. Music Soc. (bd. mem. for theory 1987-89), Soc. Music Theory (exec. bd. 1982-85, pres. 1988-91). Home: 3101 David Dr Bloomington IN 47401-4472 Office: Sch Music Ind U Bloomington IN 47405

WITTLINGER, TIMOTHY DAVID, lawyer; b. Dayton, Ohio, Oct. 12, 1940; s. Charles Frederick and Dorothy Elizabeth (Golden) W.; m. Diane Cleo Dominy, May 20, 1967; children: Kristine Elizabeth, David Matthew. BS in Math., Purdue U., 1962; JD with distinction, U. Mich., 1965. Bar: Mich. 1966, U.S. Dist. Ct. (ea. dist.) Mich. 1966, U.S. Ct. Appeals (6th cir.) 1968, U.S. Supreme Ct. 1971. Assoc. Hill Lewis (formerly Hill, Lewis, Adams, Goodrich & Tait), Detroit, 1965-72, ptnr., 1973—, head litigation dept., 1976—; mem. profl. assistance com. U.S. Dist. Ct. (ea. dist.) Mich. 1981-82. Mem. house of deps. Episc. Ch., N.Y.C., 1979—; vice chmn. Robert Whitaker Sch. Theology, 1983-87; sec. bd. trustees Episc. Ch., Diocese of Mich., Detroit, 1983—, sec. conv. Episc. Diocese Mich., 1990—, mem., sec. Episcopal nat. econ. justice implementation com., 1988—, mem. Episc. nat. exec. coun., 1991—; active Nat. Episc. Jubilee Minstry Com., Nat. Episc. Coalition for Social Witness and Justice, Fifth Province Episc. Ecclesiastical Ct. Appeal; bd. dirs. Episc. Student Found., U. Mich., 1990-93; chair Grubb Inst. Behavioral Studies Ltd., Washington, 1986—. Mem. ABA, State Bar Mich., Nat. Bd. Trial Advocacy (cert.), Engring. Soc. Detroit. Home: 736 N Glenhurst Dr Birmingham MI 48009-1143 Office: Hill Lewis 255 S Woodward Birmingham MI 48009

WITTMANN, OTTO, art museum executive; b. Kansas City, Mo., Sept. 1, 1911; s. Otto and Beatrice Knox (Billingsley) W.; m. Margaret Carlisle Hill, June 9, 1945; children—William Hill, John Carlisle. Student, Country Day Sch., Kansas City; A.B., Harvard U., 1933; postgrad., 1937-38, postgrad. Carnegie scholar, summer 1937; LL.D., U. Toledo; D.F.A., Hillsdale Coll., Bowling Green State U., U. Mich., Kenyon Coll., Skidmore Coll. Curator prints Nelson Gallery Art, Kansas City, 1933-37; instr. history of art Emerson Sch., Boston, 1937-38; curator Hyde Collection, Glens Falls, N.Y., 1938-41; instr. history of art Skidmore Coll., Saratoga Springs, N.Y. 1938-41; asst. dir. Portland (Oreg.) Mus. Art, 1941; asso. dir. Toledo Mus. Art, 1946-59, trustee, 1958—, dir. 1959-76, dir. emeritus, 1977—; v.p., cons., art advisor, 1977—; trustee, cons. Los Angeles County Mus. Art, 1977-78; vice chmn., trustee, cons. J. Paul Getty Trust, 1977—; organizer exhbns. art activities Am. museums USIA, 1953-55; editorial cons. Gazette des Beaux Arts; vice chmn. Nat. Collection Fine Arts Commn.; bd. dirs. Toledo Trust Co.; cons. Clark Art Inst., 1990—. Editorial chmn. Toledo Mus. Catalogue of European Paintings and Guide to Collections; writer numerous museum catalogues, profl. articles. Founding mem. Nat. Council Arts; mem. mus. panel NEH; chmn. adv. panel Nat. Found. Arts and Humanities; mem. art adv. panel IRS; mem. nat. arts accessions com. U.S. embassies; mem. U.S.-ICOM Nat. Com.; former sec. gen. com. pour Musées du Verre, ICOM; founding mem. Ohio Arts Council; sponsor Nat. Trust Sch., Attingham, Shropshire, Eng. Served to maj. AUS, USAAF, OSS, 1941-46. Decorated officer Legion of Honor, France, officer Order Orange Nassau, Netherlands, comdr. Arts and Letters France; comdr. Order of Merit Italy). Fellow Museums Assn. (Eng.); mem. Intermus. Conservation Assn. (pres. 1955-56, trustee), Harvard Soc. Contemporary Art (co-dir. 1931-33), Assn. Art Mus. Dirs. (pres. 1961-62, 71-72), Am. Assn. Museums (former v.p., Disting. Service to Mus. award 1987), Coll. Art Assn., Archeol. Inst. Am., Internat. Inst. for Conservation of Hist. and Artistic Works, Soc. Archtl. Historians, Verien der Freunde Antiker Kunst, Am. Soc. French Legion Honneur, Alliance Francaise de Toledo (trustee), Phi Kappa Phi. Episcopalian (vestryman). Clubs: Traveller's (London); Century Assn. (N.Y.C.); Toledo, Harvard (pres. 1956-57), Rotary (pres. 1963-64). Home: 300 Hot Springs Rd #163 Montecito CA 93108 Office: Toledo Mus Art PO Box 1013 Toledo OH 43697-1013 also: J Paul Getty Mus PO Box 2112 Santa Monica CA 90406

WITTMER, JAMES FREDERICK, preventive medicine physician, educator; b. Carlinville, Ill., Dec. 30, 1932; s. Franklin Benjamin and Eva Caroline (Zihlman) W.; m. Juanita Lou Wilkey, June 29, 1962; children: Ellen, Carol, Nancy. MD, Washington U., St. Louis, 1957; MPH, Harvard U., 1961. Diplomate Am. Bd. Preventive Medicine. Intern U. Va. Hosp., Charlottesville, 1857-58; commd. capt. USAF, 1958, advanced through grades to col., 1971; ret., 1979; dean allied health U. Tex. Health Sci. Ctr., San Antonio, 1979-80; asst. med. dir. Conoco Oil Co. Ponca City, Okla., 1980-81; assoc. med. dir. Mobil Oil Corp., N.Y.C., 1981-83; dir. health, environ. and safety ITT, N.Y.C., 1983-95, corp. v.p., 1990-95; clin. prof. medicine Cornell U. Med. Coll., N.Y.C., 1984—; lectr. environ. medicine NYU, N.Y.C., 1984—; adj. prof. U. Tex. Sch. Pub. Health, Houston, 1987—; nat. coord. com. on clin. preventive svcs. USPHS, 1994—. Mem. med. and ins. com. Pres.'s Com. on Employment People with Disabilities, Washington, 1986-94, chmn., 1986-90. Fellow ACP, Am. Coll. Occupational and Environ. Medicine (bd. dirs. 1990—, sec. 1992-94), Am. Coll. Preventive Medicine, Aerospace Med. Assn., N.Y. Acad. Medicine; mem. AMA, Tex. Occupational Med. Assn., Physicians Sci. Soc. Avocations: running, skiing, boating. Home and Office: 159 Sabine Rd Boerne TX 78006-6217

WITTNER, LOREN ANTONOW, lawyer, former public relations executive; b. N.Y.C., May 2, 1938; s. Monte Warren and Miriam Margo (Antonow) W.; m. Judith Ginsberg, June 21, 1959 (div. Sept. 1972); children: Jennifer Leslie, Elizabeth Anne; m. Dianna Marks, Apr. 2, 1975. AB, Columbia U., 1958; JD, Harvard U., 1961. Bar: N.Y. 1961, Ill. 1966. Assoc. O'Dwyer & Bernstien, N.Y.C., 1961-62, Emil & Kobrin, N.Y.C., 1962-66; assoc. Antonow & Fink, Chgo., 1966-70, ptnr., 1970-77; rep. of Sec. U.S. Dept. Commerce, Chgo. and Washington, 1977-81; exec. v.p. Daniel J. Edelman, Inc., Chgo., 1981-90; ptnr. Winston & Strawn, Chgo., 1990-94; dir. client svcs. Lewis and Roca, Phoenix, 1994—; chmn. Midwest region Fed. Regional Council, 1978-79. Served with USAR, 1961-65. Mem. ABA. Avocation: classical music.

WITTREICH, JOSEPH ANTHONY, JR., English language educator, author; b. Cleve., July 23, 1939; s. Joseph Anthony and Mamie (Puchl) W. BA, U. Louisville, 1960. MA, 1961; PhD, Western Res. U., 1966. Faculty U. Wis., 1966-78; prof. English U. Md., 1978-88; disting. prof. English The Grad. Ctr. CUNY, 1988—, exec. officer English program, 1990—; vis. prof. Calif. State U., L.A., 1972, U. Md., 1977, Brown U., 1978, Brandeis U., 1981, Grad. Ctr. CUNY, 1987, Queens Coll. CUNY, 1992, Hunter Coll. CUNY, 1994, Inst. Renaissance and Eighteenth-Century Studies, Folger Shakespeare Library, 1979. Author: The Romantics on Milton, 1970, Calm of Mind, 1971, Milton and the Line of Vision, 1975,

Angel of Apocalypse, 1975, Visionary Poetics, 1979, Composite Orders, 1983, Image of That Horror, 1984, Interpreting Samson Agonistes, 1986, Feminist Milton, 1987. Nat. Endowment for Humanities grantee, 1974, 86; Nat. Endowment for Humanities-Huntington Library grantee, 1976; Guggenheim fellow, 1978. Mem. MLA, Renaissance Soc. Am., Milton Soc. Am. (pres. 1979, honored Miltonist 1993), Internat. Assn. Profs. English. Democrat. Roman Catholic. Home: 25 Central Park W Apt 2D New York NY 10023-7206 Office: CUNY Grad Ctr 33 W 42d St New York NY 10036

WITTROCK, MERLIN CARL, educational psychologist; b. Twin Falls, Idaho, Jan. 3, 1931; s. Herman C. and Mary Ellen (Baumann) W.; m. Nancy McNulty, Apr. 3, 1953; children: Steven, Catherine, Rebecca. BS in Biology, U. Mo., Columbia, 1953, MS in Ednl. Psychology, 1956; PhD in Ednl. Psychology, U. Ill., Urbana, 1960. Prof. grad. sch. edn. UCLA, 1960—, founder Ctr. Study Evaluation, div. ednl. psychology; univ. com. on disting. teaching; chmn. faculty, exec. com., univ. com. on disting. tchg. UCLA; fellow Ctr. for Advanced Study in Behavioral Scis., 1967-68; vis. prof. U. Wis., Ill., Ind. U., Monash U., Australia; bd. dirs. Far West Labs., San Francisco, 1989—; chmn. com. on evaluation and assessment L.A. Unified Sch. Dist.; mem. nat. adv. panel for math. scis. NRC of NAS, 1988-89; chmn. nat. bd. Nat. Ctr. for Rsch. in Math. Scis. Edn., 1991—; chmn. charges com. UCLA. Author, editor: The Evaluation of Instruction, 1970, Changing Education, 1973, Learning and Instruction, 1977, The Human Brain, 1977, Danish transl. 1980, Spanish transl., 1982, The Brain and Psychology, 1980, Instructional Psychology: Education and Cognitive Processes of the Brain, Neuropsychological and Cognitive Processes of Reading, 1981, Handbook of Research on Teaching, 3d edit., 1986, The Future of Educational Psychology, 1989, Research in Learning and Teaching, 1990, Testing and Cognition, 1991, Generative Science Teaching, 1994, Metacognition, 1995. Capt. USAF. Capt. USAF. Recipient Thorndike award for outstanding psychol. rsch., 1987, Disting. Tchr. of Univ. award UCLA, 1990; Ford Found. grantee. Fellow AAAS, APA (pres. divsn. ednl. psychology 1987-88, assn. coun. 1988-91, Award for Outstanding Svc. to Ednl. Psychology 1991, 93), Am. Psychol. Soc. (charter fellow), Am. Ednl. Rsch. Assn. (chmn. ann. conv., chmn. publs. 1980-83, assn. coun. 1986-89, bd. dirs. 1987-89, chmn. com. on ednl. TV 1989—, Outstanding Contbns. award 1986, Outstanding Svc. award 1989); mem. Phi Delta Kappa. Office: UCLA 321 Moore Hall Los Angeles CA 90095

WITTRUP, RICHARD DERALD, health care executive; b. Marne, Iowa, Oct. 2, 1926; s. Otis Kermit and Ruby Beatrice (Olsen) W.; m. Marilyn Eleanor Sorensen, June 7, 1949; children: Kenton Lawrence, Alan Scott, Eleanor Elizabeth. BA in Econs., U. Mo., 1951; MBA, U. Chgo., 1955. Adminstrv. asst. U. Chgo. Hosp., 1952-57; adminstr. U. Ky. Hosp., Lexington, 1957-68; asst. exec. v.p. Brigham Women's Hosp., Boston, 1968-69, exec. v.p., 1970-78; adminstr. Herman Smith Assocs. Internat., Jeddah, Saudia Arabia, 1978-80, mng. dir., 1981-88, v.p. profl. affairs, 1980-88; asst. to pres. and CEO Henry Ford Health System, Detroit, 1988-93, corp. v.p., 1993—. Sgt. U.S. Army, 1945-47, Italy. Fellow ACHE; mem. Am. Hosp. Assn., Healthcare Execs. Study Soc. Baptist. Office: Henry Ford Health System 1 Ford Pl Detroit MI 48202-3450

WITTRY, DAVID BERYLE, physicist, educator; b. Mason City, Iowa, Feb. 7, 1929; s. Herman Joseph and Edna Pearl (Filbey) W.; m. Mildred Elizabeth DuBois, July 1, 1955; children—James David, Robert Andrew, Kristopher Lee, Diane Marie, Linda Beryle. B.S., U. Wis., 1951; M.S., Calif. Inst. Tech., 1953, Ph.D., 1957. Research fellow Calif. Inst. Tech., Pasadena, 1957-59; asst. prof. U. So. Calif., Los Angeles, 1959-61; assoc. prof. dept. elec. engring. U. So. Calif., 1961-69, prof. dept. materials sci. and elec. engring., 1969—; cons. Hughes Semiconductors, 1958-59, Applied Research Labs., Inc., 1958-83, Exptl. Sta., E.I. du Pont de Nemours & Co., 1962-71, Gen. Telephone and Electronics Research Labs., 1966-72, Autonetics div. N. Am. Aviation, 1961-63, Electronics Research div. Rockwell Internat., 1976-81, Atlantic Richfield Co. Corp. Tech. Lab., 1981-87, Jet Propulsion Lab., 1985-88, Hitachi Instruments, 1989-90; vis. scientist Japan Soc. Promotion of Sci., U. Osaka Prefecture, 1974. Editor 3 proceedings of com. Contbr. articles to profl. jours. Patentee in field. Recipient first award essays on gravity, Gravity Research Found., 1949, Disting. Scientist award phys. scis. Microscopy Soc. Am., 1995; Guggenheim fellow, 1967-68; Knapp scholar U. Wis., 1949-51. Mem. IEEE, Electron Microscopy Soc. Am. (dir. phys. scis. 1979-81, pres. 1983), Microbeam Analysis Soc. (sec. organizing com. 1966, exec. council 1970-72, pres. 1988, Presdl. award 1980, Birks award 1987, 89, hon. mem.), Am. Phys. Soc., Sigma Xi. Methodist. Office: U So Calif Dept Materials Sci Los Angeles CA 90089-0241

WITTSTEIN, EDWIN FRANK, stage and film production designer; b. Mt. Vernon, N.Y., Apr. 7, 1929; s. Nathan Harry and Miriam (Goldman) W. Student, Parsons Sch. Design, 1946-50; BS, NYU, 1950; postgrad., Cooper Union, 1950-52. Stage designer Dramatic Workshop prodn. The Inspector General, 1947; set designer Gertrude Stein's Yes Is for a Very Young Man; set and costume designer Ounga Opera, Phila., 1950, (opera) The Celebrated Jumping Frog of Calaveras County, Venice, Italy, 1953, The Transposed Heads, 1958, The Fantasticks, 1960 (still running); designer Broadway prodn. Kean, 1961; set and costume designer The Gondoliers, N.Y.C. Opera, 1963, The Knack (directed by Mike Nichols), 1964, The Marriage of Figaro, N.Y.C. Opera, 1965, The Amen Corner, 1965, Happy Birthday Wanda June, Enter Laughing, 1965, The Room, A Slight Ache, 1965, The Yearling, 1965, Serjeant Musgrave's Dance, 1966 (Obie award 1966), You Know I Can't Hear You When the Water's Running, 1967, set designer Merchant of Venice, Shakespeare Festival Conn., 1967, As You Like It, Richard II, Shakespeare Festival Conn., 1968, The Man in the Glass Booth, 1968, The Basement, The Tea Party, Celebration, 1969, (for Cin. Playhouse) The Miser, Volpone, The Good Woman of Setzuan, Angel Street, He Who Gets Slapped, 1968-70, The Country Wife, Shakespeare Theatre, Conn., 1973, Ulysses in Nightown, 1974 (Tony award nomination 1974, Maharam award 1974), The Torchbearers, 1978, The Aspern Papers, 1978, Love's Labors Lost, 1983, Berkshire Theatre Festival, 1988, Tusitala, 1988, Tete a Tete, 1989, The Hasty Heart, 1990, Trains, 1991, (sets, costumes 30th anniversary tour) The Fantasticks, 1990, Sarah, Plain and Tall, 1991 (Emmy nomination 1991), Colette Collage, 1991, March of the Falsettos, 1991, Falsettoland, 1991, (prodn. designer Hallmark Hall of Fame TV) An American Story, 1992, (prodn. designer Hallmark Hall of Fame TV) A Place for Annie, 1993, (prodn. designer Hallmark Hall of Fame TV) A Place for Annie, 1993; designer TV shows Armstrong Circle Theatre, The Tonight Show with Steve Allen, NBC operas Cosi Fan Tutte, La Traviata, La Boheme, Boris Godounov, Cavalleria Rusticana, Blithe Spirit, The Diary of Anne Frank, Camino Real, The Royal Family, The Prince of Homburg; prodn. designer TV series The Adams Chronicles (Emmy nomination 1977); designer TV films A Memory of Two Mondays, 1971, For Ladies Only, 1982, Legs, 1982, Samson and Delilah, 1983, Heartsounds, 1984; designer TV spl. Echoes in the Darkness, 1987; designer films Bananas, 1971, Play It Again Sam, 1971, The Seven-Ups, 1972; art dir. films Smile, 1975, Fame, 1979; prodn. designer film Endless Love, 1981; set and costume designer (ballet) Coppelia, 1992. Home: 339 E 87th St New York NY 10128-4801

WITWER, SAMUEL WEILER, SR., lawyer; b. Pueblo, Colo., July 1, 1908; s. Samuel W. and Lulu (Richmond) W.; m. Ethyl L. Wilkins, Aug. 14, 1937; children: Samuel Weiler III, Michael Wilkins, Carole Ann Witwer Dalton, David R. PhB, Dickinson Coll., 1930, LLD, 1970; JD, Harvard, 1933; LLD, Simpson Coll., 1955, U. Ill., 1971, John Marshall Law Sch., 1976; LHD, DePaul U., 1971; JD, Lake Forest Coll., 1971. Bar: Ill. 1933. Since practiced in Chgo.; now mem. firm Witwer, Burlage, Poltrock & Giampietro; spl. asst. Ill. Atty. Gen., 1971; dir. Harvard Law Soc. Ill.; state laureate Lincoln Acad. Ill., 1974, vice chancellor, 1984—. Contbr. articles on constl. law and govt. to legal publs. Ill. chmn. U.S.O., 1958-63; citizens com. U. Ill.; mem. Bd. Social and Econ. Relations, Methodist Ch. (gen.), 1954-60, Council World Service and Fin., 1960-64; mem. jud. council Supreme Ct. of United Methodism, 1964-72; Chmn. Ill. Com. Constl. Revision, 1950-55; pres. 6th Ill. Constnl. Conv., 1969-70; State chmn. Ill. Citizens for Eisenhower-Nixon, 1956; v.p. United Republican Fund of Ill.; Rep. candidate U.S. senate, Ill., 1960; Pres. bd. trustees Dickinson Coll., 1964-79, hon. pres. bd., 1980—; trustee Northwestern Meml. Hosp. Recipient 1st Disting. Svc. medal of Ill., 1970, Citizen Fellow award Inst. Medicine Chgo., 1973; named A Chicagoan of Yr., Chgo. C of C., 1954, 68, The Chicagoan of Yr., 1970; Chicagoan of Yr., Chgo. Press Club, 1971, Ill. Man of Yr., Ill. News Broadcasters; 1970; subject of biographies A Political Biography of Samuel W. Witwer of Illinois (Gertz and Gilbreth), 1984, Quest for a Constitution,

1984. Mem. Am. Law Inst. (dir.), ABA, Ill. Bar Assn. (citation civic service 1972), Chgo. Bar Assn. (bd. mgrs. 1944-46), Chgo. Council on Fgn. Relations (past dir.), Chgo. Urban League (past dir.), Chgo. Sunday Evening Club (trustee emeritus), Union League (1st Disting. Pub. Svc. award 1955), Legal Club (Chgo.), Comml. Club, Law Club, Omicron Delta Kappa, Sigma Chi (Significant Sig award). Republican. Methodist. Home: 111 Abingdon Ave Kenilworth IL 60043-1201 Office: 125 S Wacker Dr Ste 2700 Chicago IL 60606-4501

WITZGALL, CHRISTOPH JOHANN, mathematician; b. Hindelang, Bavaria, Germany, Feb. 25, 1929; came to U.S., 1959; s. Otto and Hanna (Schulte-Liese) W.; m. Elizabeth Bingham, Oct. 10, 1964; children: John Chandler, Hanna Elizabeth, George Matheus. PhD in Maths., Universitat Munich, 1958. Rsch. assoc. Princeton (N.J.) U., 1959-61, U. Mainz, Germany, 1961; postdoctoral RAND Corp., Santa Monica, Calif., 1961, Argonne Nat. Lab., Joliet, Ill., 1962; mathematician Nat. Bur. of Stds., Washington, 1962-66, Boeing Scientific Rsch. Labs., Seattle, 1966-73, Nat. Inst. Stds. and Tech., Gaithersburg, Md., 1973—; acting chief ops. rsch. div. Nat. Inst. Standards and Tech., Gaithersburg, Md., 1979-82; vis. prof. U. Tex., Austin, 1971, Universitat Wurzburg, Germany, 1972, U. Md., College Park, 1977, Johns Hopkin's U., Balt., 1985. Co-author: Convexity and Optimization in Finite Dimensions, 1970. Mem. AAAS, Ops. Rsch. Soc. Am., Soc. for Indsl. and Applied Maths., Am. Math. Soc. Office: Nat Inst Stds and Tech Gaithersburg MD 20899

WITZIG, WARREN FRANK, nuclear engineer, educator; b. Detroit, Mar. 26, 1921; s. Arthur Judson and Mary (Bender) W.; m. Bernadette Sullivan, Mar. 31, 1942; children: Eric, Leah, Marc, Lisa Witzig Davidson. B.E.E., Rensselaer Poly. Inst., 1942; M.S., U. Pitts., 1944, Ph.D., 1952. Registered profl. engr., Pa., Washington. Research engr. Westinghouse Research, Pitts., 1942-48; mgr. reactor physics, engr. Bettis Atomic, Pitts., 1948-60; co-founder, sr. v.p., dir. NUS Corp., Washington, 1960-67; head dept. nuclear engring. Pa. State U., 1967-87, emeritus, 1987—; cons. nuclear engr. utilities industry; chmn. Pa. Gov.'s Com. on Atomic Energy Devel., 1970-80; mem. waste com. Atomic Indsl. Forum, 1971-73; mem. adv. com. Dept. Energy, 1980-82; mem. ops. rev. com. Tex. Utility; mem. nuclear safety and compliance com. GPU, 1983-92;mem. nuclear oversight com. PSE&G, 1983-91; mem. accrediting bd. Inst. Nuclear Power Ops., 1992—; mem. safety rev. bd. TVA, 1986-91; chmn. Westinghouse Nuclear Safety and Environ. Commn., 1988-93; chmn. safety audit bd. Centichem., 1989. Designer S5W submarine reactor, 1956-60. Mem. bd. mgmt. YMCA, 1955-64. Fellow AAAS, Am. Nuclear Soc. (mem. exec. com. edn. div., past chmn. nat. com. on public info., chmn. nuclear engring. dept. head com. 1980); mem. Am. Phys. Soc., IEEE (past chmn. nuclear eng. and plasma div.), Sigma Xi, Eta Kappa Nu, Pi Kappa Alpha, Sigma Pi Sigma (Power Engring. Educator spl. citation). Presbyterian (elder). Achievements include design of S5W submarine reactor. Home: 1330 E Park Hills Ave State College PA 16803-3244 Office: Pa State U 231 Sackett Bldg University Park PA 16802

WIWCHAR, MICHAEL, bishop; b. Komarno, Manitoba, Canada, May 9, 1932. ordained priest June 28, 1959. Pastor St. John the Baptist Church, Newark, NJ, 1990-93; bishop Diocese of St. Nicholas of Chicago for the Ukrainians, 1993—. Office: Chancery Office 2245 W Rice St Chicago IL 60622*

WIXOM, WILLIAM DAVID, art historian, museum administrator, educator; b. Phila., July 17, 1929; s. Clinton Wood and Beatrice Rachel (Hunt) W.; BA, Haverford (Pa.) Coll., 1951; MA, Inst. Fine Arts NYU, 1963; m. Nancy Coe, Aug. 8, 1959; 3 children. Asst. curator to curator medieval and renaissance decorative arts Cleve. Mus. Art, 1958-78, chief curator early western art, 1979; chmn. dept. medieval art and The Cloisters, Met. Mus. Art, N.Y.C., 1979—; adj. assoc. prof. history of art Case Western Res. U., Cleve., 1967-78, adj. prof., 1978; adj. prof. N.Y.U., 1981-82; mem. adv. council for Snite Mus. Art Notre Dame U., 1974—. Bd. dirs. Internat. Ctr. Medieval Art, N.Y.C., 1971-82, pres., 1971-74. Belgium-Am. Ednl. Found. fellow, 1962; Nat. Endowment Arts grantee, 1973; fellow Pierpont Morgan Library, 1979—. Fellow Soc. of Antiquaries of London; mem. Coll. Art Assn. (dir. 1979-83), Medieval Acad. Am., Internat. Center Medieval Art. Quaker. Author: Treasures from Medieval France, 1967; Renaissance Bronzes from Ohio Collections, 1975; contbg. author The Royal Abbey of Saint Denis in the Time of Abbot Suger, 1981, The Treasury of San Marco, 1985; Gothic and Renaissance Art in Nuremberg, 1986, Festschrift Gerhard Bott, 1987, Hommage à Hubert Landais, 1987, The Cloisters, Studies in Honor of the Fiftieth Anniversary, 1992, Festschrift Gerhard Schmidt, 1994; contbr. articles in field to profl. jours. Office: Cloisters Fort Tryon Park New York NY 10040

WIXON, RUFUS, retired accounting educator; b. Cherokee County, Iowa, Nov. 27, 1911; s. Rufus and Stella Maude (Mathews) W.; m. Doris Elizabeth Hunter, Oct. 28, 1939; children: Marjorie Jeanne, Joanne Elizabeth, Kathryn Ann. B.S.C., U. Iowa, 1933, M.A., 1935; Ph.D., U. Mich., 1945. Staff accountant I.B. McGladrey & Co., Cedar Rapids, Iowa, 1933-34; instr. accounting U. N.D., 1935-36; staff accountant Edward Gore & Co., Chgo., 1936-37; instr. accounting Wayne U., 1937-41; lectr. econs. U. Mich., 1941-45, asst. prof. econs., 1945-47; prof. accounting, chmn. dept. U. Buffalo, 1947-49, U. Pa., 1949-65; prof. accounting U. Pa., Phila., 1966-80, emeritus prof., 1980—; assoc. chief, specialist accounting U. Pa.-U. Karachi Project, Karachi, Pakistan, 1955-57; Cons. Office Asst. Sec. Def. (comptroller) 1958-60; prof. IMEDE, Mgmt. Devel. Inst., Lausanne, Switzerland, 1961-62; accounting editorial bd. Found. Press. Author: (with W.A. Paton, H.L. Dixon) Problems and Practise Sets for Essentials of Accounting, 1949, Budgetary Control, 1952, rev., 1961, Principles of Accounting, (with R.G. Cox), 1961, 2nd edit., 1969; Editor: Accountant's Handbook, 5th edit, 1970. Mem. Am. Acad. Polit. and Social Sci., Am. Accounting Assn. (chmn. com. standards accounting instrn., v.p. 1959), mem. Am. Econ. Assn., Controllers Inst. Am., Order of Artus, Beta Gamma Sigma, Beta Alpha Psi. Phi Kappa Phi, Alpha Kappa Psi, Alpha Tau Omega. Club: Springhaven. Home: 1343 W Baltimore Pike D-116 Granite Farms Estates Wawa PA 19063 Office: Wharton Sch U Pa Philadelphia PA 19104

WIZMUR, JUDITH H., federal judge; b. 1949. BA, Rutgers U., 1971, JD, 1974. Law clk. Camden County Ct., 1974-75; mcpl. prosecutor Twp. of Berlin, N.J., 1976-78; atty. Lewis Katz, P.A., Cherry Hill, N.J., 1976-78; asst. dir. N.J. Div. Motor Vehicles, 1978-81; adminstrv. law judge State of N.J., 1982-85, worker's compensation judge, 1985; bankruptcy judge U.S. Dist. Ct. N.J., Camden, 1985—. Mem. ABA, N.J. Bar Assn., Camden County Bar Assn., Burlington County Bar Assn., Nat. Assn. Women Judges, Nat. Conf. Bankruptcy Judges, Tri-State Women Lawyers Assn. Office: US Dist Ct 15 N 7th St Camden NJ 08102-1104

WIZNER, STEPHEN, law educator; b. Jan. 19, 1938. AB, Dartmouth Coll., 1959; JD, U. Chgo., 1963. Bar: D.C. 1964, U.S. Dist. Ct. 1964, U.S. Ct. Appeals (D.C. cir.) 1964, N.Y. 1967, U.S. Dist. Ct. (so. dist.) N.Y. 1970, Conn. 1971, U.S. Dist. Ct. Conn. 1971, U.S. Ct. Appeals (2d dist.) 1971, U.S. Tax Ct. 1974, U.S. Supreme Ct. 1975. Trial atty. criminal divsn. U.S. Dept. Justice, Washington, 1963-66; staff atty. ctr. social welfare policy and law Columbia U., N.Y.C., 1966-67; staff atty. Mobilization Youth Legal Svcs., N.Y.C., 1967-68, assoc. dir., 1968-70; instr.-in-law Yale Law Sch., New Haven, 1970-73, lectr.-in-law, 1973-77, adj. prof., 1977-88, clin. prof., 1989-91, William O. Douglas clin. prof. law, 1989—, supervising atty., 1970-81, dir. clin. studies, 1981-91; mem. child placement conflict consulting group Yale Child Study Ctr., 1980—; instr. psychiat. residency trng. program Conn. Valley Hosp., Middletown, 1984—. Author: (with Keller) Connecticut Mental Health Law Practice Manual, 1978; contbr. articles to profl. jours. Former mem. long range planning and budget and allocation coms. New Haven Jewish Fedn.; bd. dirs. Hill Coop. Youth Svcs., Inc., New Haven, 1987—, Conn. Legal Rights Project, Middletown, 1990—, pres., chmn. 1990-92; Congregation Beth El Keser Israel, New Haven, 1990—, fin. sec., 1991-92. Recipient Richard S. Jacobson Trial Advocacy Teaching award Roscoe Pound Am. Trial Lawyers Found., 1985, Charles J. Parker Legal Svcs. award Conn. Bar Assn., 1988. Mem. Nat. Bd. Trial Advocacy (examiner 1981— bd. dirs. 1987—), New Haven County Bar Assn. (com. devel. opportunities minority lawyers 1990—, pro bono com. 1990—), Soc. Am. Law Tchrs. (bd. govs. 1990—). Office: Yale Law Sch PO Box 9688 New Haven CT 06536-0688

WLEUGEL, JOHN PETER, manufacturing company executive; b. Hoyanger, Sogn, Norway, July 1, 1929; s. Johan and Helga (Faye) W.; m. Leonor Abaroa, Dec. 1959; children—Jan Andrew, Cecilia Maria. B.A., U. Copenhagen, 1953; M.B.A., U. Toronto, 1957. With Belgium Machine Tool Assn., 1953-54; with Massey-Ferguson Ltd., Toronto, 1954-71, treas., 1968-71, also dir. several subs.; s.v.p. Bata Ltd., Toronto, also bd. dirs.; dir. officer several subsidiaries (Bata Shoe Orgn.), Don Mills, Ont., Can., 1972-89; exec.-in-residence faculty of adminstrv. studies York U., Toronto, Can., 1990—; bd. dirs. Internat. UNP Holdings Ltd., Toronto, Ont. Can., Advanced Material Resources Ltd., The Canadian Coun. for the Americas. Mem. Financial Execs. Inst. Club: University (Toronto). Home: 5 Campbell Crescent, North York, ON Canada M2P 1P1 Office: York U Faculty Adminstrv Studies, 4700 Keele St, North York, ON Canada M3J 1P3

WOBST, FRANK GEORG, banker; b. Dresden, Germany, Nov. 14, 1933; came to U.S., 1958, naturalized, 1963; s. Robert Georg and Marianne (Salewsky) W.; m. Joan Shuey Firkins, Aug. 24, 1957; children: Franck Georg, Ingrid, Andrea. Student, U. Erlangen, 1952-54, U. Goettingen, 1954-58, Rutgers U., 1964. With Fidelity American Bankshares, Inc., Lynchburg, Va., 1958-74, exec. v.p., dir., 1974-85; chmn., chief exec. officer, dir. Huntington Nat. Bank, 1974-85, chmn. exec. com., 1986—; chmn., chief exec. officer, dir. Huntington Bancshares, Inc., 1974—. Mem. Greater Columbus C. of C., Am. Inst. Banking, Assn. Res. City Bankers, Robert Morris Assos., Newcomen Soc. Club: Scioto Country. Home: 129 N Columbia Ave Columbus OH 43209-1414 Office: Huntington Bancshares Inc 41 S High St PO Box 1558 Columbus OH 43287*

WOBUS, REINHARD ARTHUR, geologist, educator; b. Norfolk, Va., Jan. 11, 1941; s. Reinhard Schaffer and Oral (Phares) W.; m. Sheridan Whitcher, Mar. 18, 1967; children: Erik Reinhard, Cameron Wright. BA, Washington U., St. Louis, 1962; MA, Harvard U., 1963; PhD, Stanford U., 1966. Asst. prof. geology Williams U., Williamstown, Mass., 1966-72, assoc. prof., 1972-78, prof., 1978-85, Edna McConnell Clark prof. geology, 1985—; dept. chmn., 1988—; geologist U.S. Geol. Survey, Denver, 1967-86; vis. prof. Colo. Coll., Colorado Springs, 1976, 82-83, Colo. State U., Ft. Collins, summers 1977-84; staff geologist Colo. Outdoor Edn. C., Florissant, Colo., 1983; co-founder Keck Twelve-Coll. Geol. Consortiums, 1986. Contbr. maps and articles on Precambrian geology of So. Rocky Mountains to profl. jours. Danforth fellow, 1962, Woodrow Wilson felow, 1962, NSF fellow, 1962-66. Fellow Geol. Soc. Am.; mem. Am. Geophys. Union, Nat. Assn. Geology Tchrs., Coun. on Undergrad. Rsch., Colo. Sci. Soc., Mineral Soc. Am., Phi Beta Kappa, Sigma Xi. Current work: Petrology and geochronology of Precambrian igneous and metamorphic rocks and mid-Tertiary volcanic rocks, so. Rocky Mountains. Subspecialties: Petrology, Geology. Home: 20 Grandview Dr Williamstown MA 01267-2528 Office: Williams Coll Dept Geology Williamstown MA 01267

WODARCZYK, FRANCIS JOHN, chemist; b. Chgo., Dec. 11, 1944; s. Sigmund Frank and Josephine Aurelia (Boblak) W. BS, Ill. Inst. Tech., 1966; AM, Harvard U., 1967, PhD, 1971. Postdoctoral U. Calif., Berkeley, 1971-73; rsch. chemist Cambridge Rsch. Labs., Hanscom AFB, Mass., 1973-77; program mgr. Office of Sci. Rsch., Bolling AFB, D.C., 1977-78; mem. tech. staff Rockwell Internat. Sci. Ctr., Thousand Oaks, Calif., 1978-85; program mgr. Office of Sci. Rsch., Bolling AFB, 1985-90; program dir. NSF, Washington, 1990—. Recipient scholarship, George M. Pullman Found., 1962, Ill. Inst. Tech., 1962-66, Ill. State scholarship, 1962-66, NSF fellowship, 1966-71, 71-72. Mem. AAAS, Am. Chem. Soc., Sigma Xi, Alpha Chi Sigma (chpt. v.p. 1965-66, chpt. award 1964). Achievements include development of radio frequency-microwave double resonance spectroscopy; first demonstration cw optically pumped molecular laser; laser-excited electronic to vibrational energy transfer studies. Office: NSF 4201 Wilson Blvd Arlington VA 22230-0001

WODLINGER, ERIC W., lawyer; b. New Rochelle, N.Y.; s. D. B. and G. L. G. Wodlinger; m. H. C. Wodlinger. BA, Amherst Coll., 1970; JD, Harvard U., 1973. Bar: Mass. 1974, U.S. Dist. Ct. Mass. 1974. From assoc. to ptnr. Choate, Hall & Stewart, Boston, 1973—. Bd. trustees Comty. Music Ctr., Boston, 1987-90, pres., 1990-95. Mem. Boston Bar Assn. Office: Choate Hall & Stewart Exchange Pl 53 State St Boston MA 02109

WODLINGER, MARK LOUIS, broadcast executive; b. Jacksonville, Fla., July 13, 1922; s. Mark H. and Beatrice Mae (Boney) W.; m. Marilyn Stone-Birk; children: Kevin, Michael, Stephen, Mark. BS, U. Fla., 1943. Salesman Sta. WQUA, Moline, Ill., 1948; mgr. Sta. WOC-AM-FM-TV, Davenport, Iowa, 1949-58; v.p. Sta. WMBD-TV, Peoria, Ill., 1959-61; v.p., gen. mgr. Sta. WZZM-TV, Grand Rapids, Mich., 1962-63, Sta. KMBC-TV, Kansas City, Mo., 1963-69; pres. Intermedia, Kansas City, 1969-73; builder, owner comml. radio stas. Swaziland, Africa; operator Radio Malawi, Blantyre, and Marknews TV and Radio News Bur., Nairobe, Kenya, 1971-74; owner, pres. Sta. KBEQ, Kansas City, 1973-77; owner Sta. WCJX-FM, Miami, 1985-86, Sta. WIXI-FM, Naples and Ft. Myers, Fla., 1986-95, Sta. KKLO-AM, Leavenworth, Kans., 1982-92, Sta. KCWV, Kansas City, Mo., 1982-90, TV-5, Hit Video USA, Satellite Music Network, Houston, 1985-88; owner SMR-2-way radio/telephone, Naples, Fla., 1993—, San Francisco, 1993—; chmn. bd. dirs. Wodlinger Broadcasting Co., Naples, 1978—; ptnr. Wireless Cable, Naples, Fla., 1990—; owner, chmn. bd. dirs. KABELTEL KFT, Budapest, Hungary, Sopron, Hungary, Nagykanizsa, Hungary, Pap Hungary, Szombathely, Hungary, Kecskemet, Kaposvar, Hungary, 1991—; comml. FM Radio Ikva, Sopron, 1993—, Hungary comml. FM Radio Zalaegerszeg, Hungary, 1995, comml. FM Radio Kecskemet, Hungary, 1995—; comml. RM Love Radio 97.8, Tallinn, estonia, 1993—, comml. FM Love Radio 67.07, Riga, Latvia, 1994—; ptnr., chmn. bd. dirs. wireless cable TV Ukrainian-Am. Broadcasting, Kiev, Ukraine, 1990—, comml. TV Channel 7, 1990—, comml. FM Radio 69.89, Kiev, 1992—; owner, ptnr. comml. FM Radiocentras, Vilnius, Lithuania, 1992—; ptnr. joint mktg. AT&T Paradyne, Largo, Fla., 1992—, Advanced Rsch. tEch. Inc., N.Y.C., 1993—, Bellcore, Morristown, N.J., 1995—; owner, ptnr., chmn. bd. dirs. real estate devel., Croatia, 1991—; owner outdoor advt., billboards, Tallinn, estonia, 1993—; owner, ptnr. real estate devel., Hungary, 1991—. Bd. dirs. Kansas City Philharm., Kansas City Civic Coun., Naples YMCA; mem. Conservancy, Naples Civic Assn. Served to lt. USN, 1941-45. Mem. Nat. Assn. Broadcasters, Mo. Assn. Broadcasters, Broadcast Pioneers. Republican. Episcopalian. Clubs: Kansas City, Univ., Vanguard, Carriage, Port Royal, Naples Yacht, Houston Yacht, White Lake Yacht (Whitehall, Mich.). Lodge: Rotary. Home: 800 Galleon Dr Naples FL 33940-7646 Office: 3355 Tamiami Trl N Naples FL 33940-4165

WOELFEL, JAMES WARREN, philosophy educator; b. Galveston, Tex., Aug. 16, 1937; s. Warren Charles and Mary Frances (Washinka) W.; m. Sarah Chappell Trulove, Nov. 24, 1982; children by previous marriages: Skye Caitlin, Allegra Eve, Sarah Judith; stepchildren: Ann Marie and Paul Trulove. BA, U. Okla., 1959; MDiv, Episcopal Div. Sch., Cambridge, Mass., 1962; MA, Yale U., 1964; PhD, U. St. Andrews, Scotland, 1967. Asst. prof. philosophy and religion U. Kans., Lawrence, 1966-70, asst. prof. philosophy, 1970-71, assoc. prof. philosophy and religion, 1971-75, prof. philosophy and religious studies, 1975-88, prof. philosophy, 1988—, acting chmn. dept. religious studies, 1983-84, dir. Western civilization program, 1985—; manuscript reader for various presses, jours. Author Bonhoeffer's Theology, 1970, Borderland Christianity, 1973, Camus: A Theological Perspective, 1975 (republished as Albert Camus on the Sacred and the Secular, 1987), Augustinian Humanism, 1979, The Agnostic Spirit as a Common Motif in Liberal Theology and Liberal Scepticism, 1990; editor (with Sarah Chappell Trulove) and contbr.: Patterns in Western Civilization, 1991; assoc. editor Am. Jour. Theology and Philosophy; contbr. numerous articles, essays, revs. to profl. publs. Danforth grad. fellow Episcopal Div. Sch., Cambridge, Mass., 1959-62, U. St. Andrews, 1962-63, 65-66, Yale U., New Haven, 1963-65; Fulbright scholar U. St. Andrews, 1962-63; grantee NEH, Exxon Found., Mellon Found., Menninger Found., Inst. for Ecumenical and Cultural Research. Mem. Am. Acad. Religion, Highlands Inst. for Am. Religious Thought, Phi Beta Kappa. Democrat. Avocations: piano; walking. Home: 808 Alabama St Lawrence KS 66044-3942 Office: U Kans Western Civilization Program 2106 Wescoe Hall Lawrence KS 66045-2178

WOELFFER, EMERSON SEVILLE, artist; b. Chgo., July 27, 1914; s. George K. and Marguerite (Seville) W.; m. Diane Anderson, Dec. 7, 1945. Student, Art Inst. Chgo., 1935-38; B.F.A., Inst. Design, Chgo., 1949;

PhD (hon.), New Sch. for Social Rsch., 1991, Otis Parsons Sch. Design, L.A., 1993, Otis Parson's Art Inst., 1993. head painting dept. Otis Art Inst., Los Angeles, 1974—; artist in residence. One-man shows include Paul Kantor Gallery, Beverly Hills, Calif., 1953, 60, Poindexter Gallery, N.Y.C., 1958, 61, Primus-Stuart Gallery, L.A., 1961, Santa Barbara (Calif.) Mus. Art, 1964, Quay Gallery, San Francisco, 1967, Honolulu Acad. Arts, 1970, Jodi Scully Gallery, L.A., 1972, 73, Newport Harbour Art Mus., Newport Beach, Calif., 1974, Phillips Collection, Washington, 1975, Gruenebaum Gallery, N.Y.C., 1978, New Orleans Mus. Art, 1987, Wenger Gallery, L.A., Manny Silverman Gallery, L.A., 1991, 93, Parsons Sch. Design, L.A., 1992, Otis Art Inst., James Corcoran Gallery, 1993, Hyundai Art Gallery, Seoul, Korea, 1995; traveling exhbn. at Modern Art Mus., New Delhi, India, 1988, collages of 1987-89 Manny Silverman Gallery, L.A.; two-person show Harcourt Gallery, San Francisco, 1990; exhibited in group shows at UCLA, 1987-88; represented in permanent collections British Mus., Art Inst. Chgo., Whitney Mus. Am. Art, Mus. Modern Art, N.Y.C., L.A. County Mus. Art, Washington Gallery Modern Art, Wight Galleries of UCLA, San Francisco Mus. Art, Bauhaus Archives, Berlin, Smithsonian Archives Am. Art, Washington, Santa Fe Mus. Art, Seattle Art Mus., Biblioteque Nationale, Paris, Acad. Arts and Sci., N.Y., also numerous others. Grantee Guggenheim Found., 1968-69, NEA, 1974, Pollock Krasner, 1986, Greenburger Found., 1988. Home: 475 Dustin Dr Los Angeles CA 90065-5023

WOELFLEIN, KEVIN GERARD, banker; b. Haverhill, Mass., Feb. 9, 1933; s. John Henry and Helen Margaret (Hoar) W.; m. Ann Buckley, Sept. 9, 1957; children: Karl G., Luise A., Andrew B., Peter H. B.S., MIT, 1954; M.B.A., U. Pa., 1958, postgrad., 1959-65. Venture analyst Atlas Chem. Industries, Wilmington, Del., 1959-66; economist Fed. Res. Bank Phila., 1966-67; asst. v.p. 1st Nat. Bank Chgo., 1967-70, v.p., 1970-72; v.p., gen. mgr. (Tokyo br.), 1972-75; pres., chief exec. officer, dir. UBAF Arab Am. Bank, N.Y.C., 1975-81; pres., chief operating officer, dir. Am. Security Bank, Washington, 1981-83; pres., dir. Mass. Co., Inc., Boston, 1983-86; pres. U.S. Capital Investments Co., Greenwich, Conn., 1983—; chmn. bd. Conn. Bancorp, Inc., also bd. dirs.; chmn. bd. Norwalk (Conn.) Bank, 1990-92, also bd. dirs. Bd. dirs. Small Bus. High Tech. Inst., 1982-85; mem. exec. com. MIT Enterprise Forum, Washington, 1982-85; mem. MIT Corp. vis. com. Ctr. for Internat. Studies; mem. adv. council U.S.-Japan Study Ctr., Johns Hopkins U. Sch. Advanced Internat. Studies, 1982-85; trustee Convent of Sacred Heart, Greenwich, Conn., 1977-81; mem. U.S.-Saudi Arabian Joint Commn. on Econ. Cooperation, 1982-84. Served to lt. U.S. Army, 1954-56. Recipient Corp. Leadership award MIT, 1980; Knight of Malta, Fed. Assns., 1984. Mem. Riverside Yacht Club, Columbia Country Club. Office: US Capital Investments Co 2 Greenwich Plz Ste 100 Greenwich CT 06830

WOERNER, PETER KURT, architect, builder; b. Phila., Feb. 7, 1942; s. Kurt and Berenice (Scheuer) W.; m. Anne Love Woodhull, June 21, 1971 (div. Feb. 1975). Student, U. Paris, 1964; BA, Yale Coll., 1966, MArch, 1970. With Heat Wave Constrn. Co., South Londonderry, Vt., 1970-71; architect Warren Platner Architects, New Haven, Conn., 1973, Meyers-Gravino Architects, New Haven, 1974, Russell Gibson von Dohlen, Hartford, Conn., 1974; architect, pres. Peter Kurt Woerner & Assocs., New Haven, 1975—; pres. Woerner Assocs., Inc., New Haven, 1978—; dir. Istituto di Tanelle, Radicondoli, Siena, Italy, 1989; cons. Bruno Internat., South Kent, Conn., 1990—. Fellow AIA (Design Honor award 1976, 80, (2) 85); mem. Saint Anthony Hall, Nat. Assn. Realtors, Ducks Unltd. Avocations: demolition derby, driver, hunting, fishing, rebuilding farmhouse in Tuscany. Office: Peter Kurt Woerner & Assocs 44 Kendall St New Haven CT 06512

WOERNER, ROBERT LESTER, landscape architect; b. Rochester, N.Y., Jan. 31, 1925; s. William John and Loretta Bertha (Hettel) W.; m. Mary Jane Warn, May 12, 1952; children: Jane Marie, Anne Louise. B.S., SUNY Coll. Forestry, Syracuse, 1949. Cert. landscape architect, Wash., Idaho. Draftsman N.A., Rotunno Landscape Architects, Syracuse, 1947-49; landscape architect Park Dist., Plan Common., Yakima, Wash., 1949-50; asst. supt. parks Spokane Park Dept., Spokane, Wash., 1950-56; dir. Denver Bot. Gardens, 1956-58; pvt. practice landscape architect Spokane, 1959—; chmn. bd. registration Landscape Architects State of Wash., 1976-78; pres. Council Landscape Archtl. Registration Bds., 1978-79. Mem. Zoning Bd. Adjustment, Spokane, 1983; mem. Urban Design Com., 1983; mem. Capitol Campus Design Adv. Com., 1982-94. Cpl. U.S. Army, 1943-45, ETO. Recipient Indsl. Landscaping Award Am. Assn. Nurserymen, Lincoln Bldg., Spokane, 1966; recipient Cert. of Merit Wash. Water Power, 1967, State Indsl. Landscaping award Wash State Nurserymen's Assn., Wash. Water Power, 1968. Fellow Am. Soc. Landscape Architects (pres. 1979-80, Disting. Svc. award 1976). Republican. Roman Catholic. Lodge: Kiwanis.

WOESTE, JOHN THEODORE, academic administrator; b. Alexandria, Ky., June 28, 1934; s. Theodore John and Ruth Elizabeth (Kinstler) W.; m. Martha Helen Messmer, Aug. 11, 1956; children: Shan, Keith, Lori, John, Jennifer, Troy. BS, U. Ky., 1956; MS, U. Wis., 1963, PhD, 1967. Asst. county agt. Ky. Coop. Extension Service, Owen County, 1956-57; county extension agt. Ky. Coop. Extension Service, Richmond, 1959-62; area adminstr. Ky. Cooperative Extension Service, Lexington, 1966-69; dist. extension dir. U. Wis., Madison, 1969-72; asst. dir. Wis. Coop. Extension Service, Madison, 1972-76; dean, dir. of extension U. Fla. Inst. Food and Agrl. Scis., Gainesville, 1976—. Mem. sch. bd. Middleton (Wis.)-Cross Plains Dist., 1973; supr. Alacua Soil and Water Conservation Dist., Gainesville, 1980; bd. dirs. Fla. State Fair, Tampa, 1976—, Fla. 4-H Found., Gainesville. Recipient Disting. Service award USDA, Washington, 1987; named Outstanding Citizen Middleton-West Towne Rotary, Middleton, 1974. Mem. Nat. Assn. Nat. Assn. State Colls. and Land Grant Univs. (chmn. extension section 1984-85, senator 1988-91), Nat. Extension Com. (joint coun. 1991-94, strategic planning coun. 1992-96), Epsilon Sigma Phi (State Disting. Service award), Gamma Sigma Delta, Alpha Gamma Rho. Democrat. Roman Catholic. Lodge: Kiwanis, Rotary. Avocations: fishing, coaching youth basketball, baseball, lector. Home: 4410 NW 16th Pl Gainesville FL 32605-3408 Office: U Fla Agriculture Extension 1038 McCarty Hall Gainesville FL 32611

WOESTENDIEK, (WILLIAM) JOHN, JR., reporter; b. Winston-Salem, N.C., Sept. 5, 1953; s. William John Sr. and Josephine (Pugh) W.; m. Jennifer Ann Swartz, Sept. 1, 1979; 1 child, Joseph Yoon Tae. BJ, U.N.C., 1975. Reporter Ariz. Daily Star, Tucson, 1975-78; reporter, asst. city editor, city editor Lexington (Ky.) Herald-Leader, 1978-81; reporter Phila. Inquirer, 1981-90; nat. corr. West Coast bur. Phila. Inquirer, Newport Beach, Calif., 1990-93; reporter Phila. Inquirer. Recipient Paul Tobenkin Meml. award Columbia U., 1984, Nat. Headliners award Press Club Atlantic City, 1987, Pulitzer Prize for Investigative Reporting Columbia U., 1987, Ernie Pyle award, 1994, Best Feature Story award Ky. Press Assn., 1978, Best Investigative Story award Ky. Press Assn., 1979, Nat. Arc of Excellence Nat. Assn. Retarded Citizens, 1984, Best News Reporting First Place award AP Mng. Editors Pa., 1985, Sigma Delta Chi award for Feature Writing, 1994; John S. Knight fellow Stanford U., 1988-89. Office: The Phila Inquirer PO Box 8263 Philadelphia PA 19101

WOETZEL, DAMIAN ABDO, ballet dancer, educator; b. Newton, Mass., May 17, 1967; s. Robert Kurt and Sheila Marilyn (Barry) W. Grad. high sch., Hollylwood, Calif., 1983. Prin. dancer L.A. Ballet, 1983-85; mem. corps de ballet N.Y.C. Ballet, 1985-88, soloist, then prin. dancer, 1989—; Dir. ballet program New York State Summer School for the Arts, Saratoga Springs, N.Y., 1994—; dancer, choreographer New York City Opera, 1994-95. Performed in Jerome Robbins' Four Seasons Dance at a Gathering: Goldberg Variations, Glass Pieces, Interplay, Other Dances; Balanchine's La Sonnambula, Stars and Stripes, Mozariana, Ballo della Regina, Tarantella, The Nutcracker, La Source, Coppelia, Donizetti Variations, Raymonda Variations, Martin's the Sleeping Beauty, Jeu de Cartes, Musical Offering, Paulenc Sonata, Les Petits Riens, The Waltz Project; also Tschaikovsky's Pas de Deux; danced in N.Y.C. Ballet's Balanchine Celebration, 1993, danced in film George Balanchine's The Nutcracker, 1993; choreographed Ebony Concerto, 1994, Glazounov Pas de Deux, 1994; danced in Alexander Borodin's opera Prince Igor, 1994. Recipient 1st prize Commemorative award Nat. Ballet Achievement Fund, Phila., 1984. Avocations: carpentry, gardening, guitar playing, surfing. Office: NYC Ballet Inc NY State Theater Lincoln Ctr Plz New York NY 10023*

WOFFORD, HARRIS LLEWELLYN, former senator, lawyer; b. N.Y.C., Apr. 9, 1926; s. Harris Llewellyn and Estelle (Gardner) W.; m. Emmy Lou Clare Lindgren, Aug. 14, 1948; children: Susanne, Daniel, David. B.A., U. Chgo., 1948; study fellow, India, 1949, Israel, 1950; LL.B., Yale U., 1954, Howard U., 1954. Bar: D.C. 1954, U.S. Supreme Ct. 1958, Pa. 1978. Asst. to Chester Bowles, 1953-54; law assoc. Covington & Burling, Washington, 1954-58; legal asst. to Rev. Theodore Hesburgh, Commn. on Civil Rights, 1958-59; assoc. prof. Notre Dame Law Sch., 1959-60, on leave, 1961-66; asst. to Sen. Kennedy, 1960; spl. asst. to Pres. Kennedy, 1961-62; spl. rep. for Africa, dir. Ethiopian program U.S. Peace Corps, 1962-64; assoc. dir. Peace Corps, Washington, 1964-66; pres. Coll. at Old Westbury, SUNY, 1966-70, Bryn Mawr (Pa.) Coll., 1970-78; counsel firm Schnader, Harrison, Segal and Lewis, Phila. and Washington, 1979-86; chmn. Pa. Dem. State Com., 1986; sec. labor and industry Commonwealth of Pa., 1987-91; U.S. senator from Pa., 1991-95; vis. lectr. Howard Law Sch., 1956. Author: It's Up to Us, 1946, (with Clare Wofford) India Afire, 1951, Of Kennedys and Kings, 1980; editor: Embers of the World, 1970; co-editor: Report of the U.S. Commission on Civil Rights, 1959. Mem. Coun. Fgn. Rels., 1968—; co-chmn. Com. for Study of Nat. Svc., 1977-80; mem. U.S. Adv. Com. on Nat. Growth Policy Processes, 1975-76; trustee The Am. Coll., Bryn Mawr, 1975-83; mem. coun. U.S.-South Africa Leader Exch. Program, 1971-87; bd. dirs. Internat. League for Human Rights, 1979—, pres., 1980—; bd. dirs. Pub. Interest Law Ctr. Phila., 1978-87; trustee Martin Luther King Ctr. for Nonviolent Social Change, 1983-87; governing coun. Wilderness Soc., 1983-87. With USAF, 1944-45. Mem. ABA. Roman Catholic.

WOGAN, GERALD NORMAN, toxicology educator; b. Altoona, Pa., Jan. 11, 1930; s. Thomas B. and Florence E. (Corl) W.; m. Henrietta E. Hoenicke, Aug. 24, 1957; children—Christine F., Eugene E. B.S., Juniata Coll., 1951; M.S., U. Ill., 1953, Ph.D., 1957. Asst. prof. physiology Rutgers U., New Brunswick, N.J., 1957-61; asst. prof. toxicology MIT, Cambridge, 1962-65, assoc. prof., 1965-69, prof. toxicology, 1969—; head dept. applied biol. scis. MIT, 1979-88; dir. div. toxicology Whitaker Coll. Health Scis. and Tech. MIT, Cambridge, 1988—; prof. chemistry MIT, 1989—; cons. to nat. and internat. govt. agys., industries. NIH grantee, 1963—. Mem. editorial bd.: Cancer Research, 1971-79, Applied Microbiology, 1971-79, Chem.-Biol. Interactions, 1975-78, Toxicology, Environ. Health, 1974-84, Jour. Nat. Cancer Inst., 1988—; Contbr. articles and revs. to profl. jours. Recipient Disting. Alumni award U. Ill.; NSF grantee, 1965-68. Fellow Inst. of Medicine, Am. Acad. of Microbiology; mem. AAAS, Nat. Acad. Scis. U.S., Am. Assn. Cancer Rsch., Am. Soc. Pharmacology and Exptl. Therapeutics, Am. Soc. Microbiology, Soc. Toxicology, Am. Inst. Nutrition, Sigma Xi. Office: MIT Divsn of Toxicology 77 Massachusetts Ave Rm 16-333 Cambridge MA 02139-4307

WOGAN, ROBERT, broadcasting company executive; b. N.Y.C., Oct. 13, 1925; s. Robert and Johanna (Hilderbrandt) W.; m. Phyllis Jayn Volz, Nov. 21, 1965 (div. 1991); children—Robert, Stephen. Grad. pub. schs. Page NBC, 1943, asst. mgr. guest relations, 1945-46, night announcer, sec., 1946, asst. supr. announcing, 1946-47; asst. supr. announcing NBC (prodn. div.), 1947-48, night adminstrv. asst., 1948-50, supr. network program operations, 1950-55, Eastern radio program and prodn. mgr., 1955-63, exec. producer "Monitor" program, 1963-65, v.p. radio network programs, 1965-73; exec. producer spl. programs NBC Radio Network, 1973-75, regional mgr. affiliate relations, 1975-81, regional dir. affiliate relations, 1981-89; regional mgr. Westwood One Cos., 1989—, Mut. Broadcasting System, 1989—, NBC Radio Network, 1989—, Talknet Programs, 1989—; exec. producer conv. entertainment, coordinator NBC/Mus. of Broadcasting to preserve history radio data. Exec. producer X Minus One radio program, 1974-75. Mem. Nat. council Boy Scouts Am., 1970—; chmn. Radio com. United Hosp. Fund, 1972. Served with AUS, 1944-45. Recipient Radio-TV All-Am. of Year award for Experiment in Drama, 1963, Gabriel award for pub. service programming, 1967, Freedoms Found. award, 1972, Peabody awards for "Monitor", 1972, for "Project I Experiment", 1973. Mem. Broadcast Pioneers, Internat. Radio and TV Soc. Home: 360 W 22nd St New York NY 10011-2600 Office: 30 Rockefeller Plz New York NY 10112-0001 also: 1700 Broadway New York NY 10019-5905 also: 1775 S Jefferson Davis Hwy Arlington VA 22202

WOGEN, WARREN RONALD, mathematics educator; b. Forest City, Iowa, Feb. 19, 1943; s. Milford N. and Olive A. (Sime) W.; m. Sherry D., Aug. 23, 1969; children—Shannon, Lori. A.B., Luther Coll., 1965; M.A. in Math., Ind.U., 1967, P.h.D. in Math., 1969. Prof. math. U. N.C., Chapel Hill, 1969—. Contbr. articles to profl. jours. Mem. Am. Math. Soc., Math. Assn. Am. Office: U NC Math Dept. Chapel Hill NC 27599-3250

WOGLOM, ERIC COOKE, lawyer; b. Bklyn., Mar. 14, 1943; s. Joseph F. and Rita Mary (Cooke) W.; m. Joshan Robin Levitsky, May 11, 1968; children—Peter Douglas, Brian Stewart. B.A., Yale U., 1964; LL.B., U. Pa. 1967. Bar: N.Y. 1968, U.S. Patent and Trademark Office 1970, U.S. Ct. Appeals (9th cir.) 1972, U.S. Ct. Appeals (2d cir.) 1973, U.S. Dist. Ct. (so. and ea. dist.) N.Y. 1974, U.S. Supreme Ct. 1974, U.S. Ct. Appeals (7th cir.) 1980, U.S. Ct. Appeals (Fed. cir.) 1982. With Fish & Neave, N.Y.C., 1967—, sr. ptnr., 1976—. Served with U.S. Army, 1967. Mem. ABA. Am. Intellectual Property Law Assn., Assn. Bar City N.Y. (chair com. on patents), N.Y. Law Inst., N.Y. Intellectual Property Law Assn. (past chair com. on econ. matters effecting the profession), N.Y. State Bar Assn. Republican. Roman Catholic. Clubs: Yale of N.Y.C.; Shelter Island Yacht. Home: 430 North St Harrison NY 10528-1118 Office: Fish & Neave 1251 Ave of the Americas New York NY 10020-1104

WOGSLAND, JAMES WILLARD, retired heavy machinery manufacturing executive; b. Devils Lake, N.D., Apr. 17, 1931; s. Melvin LeRoy and Mable Bertina (Paulson) W.; m. Marlene Claudia Clark, June 1957; children: Karen Lynn, Steven James. BA in Econs., U. Minn., 1957. Various positions fin. dept. Caterpillar Tractor Co., Peoria, Ill., 1957-64, treas., 1976-81; mgr. fin. Caterpillar Overseas S.A., Geneva, 1965-70, sec.-treas., 1970-76; prin.-pres. Caterpillar Brasil S.A., São Paulo, 1981-87; exec. v.p. Caterpillar, Inc., Peoria, 1980-90, also bd. dirs., vice-chmn., 1990-95; bd. dirs. First of Am. Bank Corp., Kalamazoo, Protection Mut. Ins. Co., Park Ridge, Ill., Cipsco, Inc., Springfield, Ill. Mem. adv. bd. St. Francis Hosp., Peoria, 1987-95; bd. dirs. Peoria Area Cmty. Found., 1986-92; trustee Eureka Coll., 1987-95. Sgt. USAF, 1951-55. Mem. Hayden Lake Golf & Country Club, Peoria. Republican. Presbyterian. Home: 9675 Easy St Hayden ID 83835

WOHL, DAVID, humanities educator, theatre director; b. Washington, Nov. 28, 1950; s. Joseph Gene and Carol (Weiss) W.; m. Diana Bradshaw Bowman, Aug. 31, 1974; children: Isaac, Gabriele. BA, Clark U., 1972; MA, U. Conn., 1975; PhD, Kent State U., 1988. Staff asst. Am. Theatre Assn., Washington, 1975-76; prof. W.Va. State Coll., Institute, 1976-79; chmn. dept. communications, 1979-88, chmn. div. arts and humanities, 1988—; artistic dir. Charleston (W.Va.) Stage Co., 1991—; gen. mgr. Porthouse Theatre Festival, Cuyahoga Falls, Ohio, 1984-85; cons. U. South Ala., Mobile, 1988; bd. dirs., treas., pres.-elect Southeastern Theatre Conf., 1993—; co-dir. W.Va. Great Tchrs. Stage dir. Kanawha Players, 1978—, Nutmeg Summer Playhouse, 1975-76, W.Va. Theatre Festival, Charleston Playhouse; prodr.: (films) Chillers, 1985, Strangest Dreams, 1990, Paradise Park, 1992 (Gold medal Houston Internat. Film Festival 1992, 1st place award Chgo. Film Festival 1992); contbr. articles to theatre jours. Bd. dirs. Kanawha Arts Alliance, Charleston, W.Va., 1979-81, Kanawha Players, 1982-85; pres. W.Va. Theatre Conf., 1987-89. NEH Fellow, 1977, 80; Dept. Edn. teaching fellow, 1976-77. Mem. Am. Soc. for Theatre Rsch., Assn. for Theatre in Higher Edn., Southeastern Theatre Conf. (treas.), Speech Comm. Assn. Home: 1411 Summit Ln Charleston WV 25302-2512 Office: WVa State Coll PO Box 28 Institute WV 25112-0028

WOHL, RONALD GENE, lawyer; b. N.Y.C., Dec. 10, 1934; s. Arthur and Bernice (Deutch) W.; m. Linda Susan Meltsner, May 2, 1965; children: Allison Brooke Wohl George, Arthur Evan, Amanda Kate. AB, Syracuse U., 1956, LLB, 1961; LLM, Bklyn. Law Sch., 1967. Bar: N.Y. 1962, U.S. Dist. Ct. (so. and ea. dists.) N.Y. 1963, U.S. Ct. Appeals (2d cir.) 1964, U.S. Supreme Ct. 1965, U.S. Dist. Ct. (no. dist.) N.Y. 1977, U.S. Tax Ct. Conn. 1980, U.S. Tax Ct. 1986. Law clk. to judge Jacob Mishler U.S. Dist. Ct. (ea. dist.) N.Y., N.Y.C., 1963-64; assoc. Edward Gettinger & Peter Gettinger, N.Y.C., 1962-63, 68-70; asst. U.S. atty. U.S. Dept. of Justice, N.Y.C., 1964-68; ptnr. Squadron, Gartenberg, Ellenoff & Pleasant, N.Y.C., 1970-71; pvt.

practice N.Y.C., 1971-74; sr. ptnr. Finkelstein, Bruckman, Wohl, Most & Rothman, N.Y.C., 1974—. Trustee Roslyn (N.Y.) Union Free Sch. Dist. 1981-93. Mem. N.Y. Bar Assn., N.Y. Dist. Attys. Assn., Assn. of Bar of City of N.Y., Nassau County Bar, Fed. Bar Coun., Soc. of Med. Jurisprudence. Avocation: photography. Home: 70 The Intervale Roslyn Est NY 11576 Office: Finkelstein Bruckman Wohl Most & Rothman 575 Lexington Ave New York NY 10022-6102

WOHL, RONALD H., management consultant, readability expert; b. Washington, Sept. 3, 1942; s. Bernard Carl and Martha (Aberbach) W.; m. Myrna Zelda Chevelier, June 27, 1965; children: Jennifer Lynn, Amy Beth. Student, Fla. State U., 1960-62; BA in Anthropology, George Washington U., 1965, postgrad., 1965-67; postgrad., Am. U., Washington, 1969-74. Cert. mgmt. cons. Asst. to regional credit mgr. Sears, Roebuck & Co. Bethesda, Md., 1966-67; supr. payroll & ins. Montgomery Coll., Rockville, Md., 1967-71; supr. program info. & analysis Nat. Rural Elec. Coop. Assn. Washington, 1971-74; employee benefits comms. cons. Wyatt Co., Washington, 1974-77; pres. R.H. Wohl & Assocs./In Plain English, Gaithersburg, Md., 1977—; columnist Gazette Newspapers, Gaithersburg, 1987, Montgomery Jour., Rockville, 1989-90. Mem. editorial bd.; author: Employers Guide to Managed Health Care, 1994. Citizen mem. Community Policing Steering Com., Montgomery County, Md., 1992—; chmn. Commn. on Humanities Montgomery County Md., 1987—; dir. North Potomac (Md.) Citizens Assn., 1988—; Dem. candidate for Md. Ho. of Dels., Annapolis, 1986; precinct chair Montgomery County Dem. Party, 1978—; tchr. Am. Jewish history & comparative religion; bd. dirs. Temple Beth Ami Brotherhood, Rockville, 1981-95, pres. 1990-92. Mem. Am. Assn. Home Based Bus. (nat. bd. dirs.), Inst. for Mgmt. Cons. (v.p. mem. Washington D.C. chpt. 1994-95). Home: 14501 Antigone Dr North Potomac MD 20878-2484 Office: R H Wohl & Assocs In Plain English PO Box 3300 Gaithersburg MD 20885-3300

WOHLER, JEFFERY WILSON, newspaper editor; b. Eugene, Oreg., Dec. 30, 1947; s. Benjamin Otto and Mildred Martha (Wilson) W.; m. Kandis Brewer, May 4, 1974 (div. 1985); m. Mary Lou Fletcher, Aug. 30, 1986; 1 child, Kennedy Read. BS in Journalism, U. Oreg., 1970. Staff writer Oreg. Jour., Portland, 1970-76, suburban editor, 1976-78, asst. city editor, 1978-80, city editor, 1980-82; dep. metro. editor The Oregonian, Portland, 1982-84, sports editor, 1984-92, editor, voice info. svcs., 1992—. Mem. Assoc. Press Sports Editors (v.p. 1989-91, pres. 1991-92), City Club of Portland (com. chair). Avocations: golf, reading. Home: 7610 NE Sacramento St Portland OR 97213-6043 Office: Oregonian 1320 SW Broadway Portland OR 97201-3499

WOHLETZ, LEONARD RALPH, soil scientist, consultant; b. Nekoma, N.D., Oct. 22, 1909; s. Frank and Anna (Keifer) W.; m. Jane Geisendorfer, Sept. 1, 1935; children: Mary Jane, Leonard Ralph Jr., Elizabeth Ann, Catherine Ellen, Margaret Lee. BS, U. Calif., Berkeley, 1931, MS, 1933. Jr. soil expert USDA Soil Erosion Svc., Santa Paula, Calif., 1934; asst. regional chief soil surveys USDA Soil Conservation Svc., Santa Paula, Calif., 1935; asst. regional chief soil surveys USDA Soil Conservation Svc., Berkeley, 1939-42, soil survey supr., 1942-45, state soil scientist, 1945-68, asst. to state conservationist, 1969-71; cons. soil scientist Berkeley, 1973—. Author: Survey Guide, 1948; contbr. articles to profl. publs. including Know Calif. Land, Soils and Land Use Planning, Planning by Foresight and Hindsight. Mem. Waste Mgmt. Commn., Berkeley, 1981; chmn. com. Rep. for Congress, 8th Dist. Calif., 1980; pres. State and Berkeley Rep. Assembly, 1985—. Recipient Soil Conservationist of Yr., Calif. Wildlife Fedn., 1967. Mem. Soil and Water Conservation Soc. (chmn. organic waste mgmt. com. 1973—, sect. pres., Dist. Svc. award, charter and life mem., Disting. Svc. award 1971, Outstanding Svc. award 1983), Soil Sci. Soc. Am. (emeritus), Internat. Soc. Soil Sci., Profl. Soil Sci. Assn. Calif., Commonwealth Club Calif., San Francisco Farmers Club. Roman Catholic. Achievements include expedition of soil surveys, interpretations, funding and publications in California, improvement of methods of conveying technical soils interpretations, land use, waste management information. Home: 510 Vincente Ave Berkeley CA 94707-1522

WOHLGELERNTER, BETH, organization executive; b. N.Y.C., Jan. 30, 1956; d. Maurice Nathaniel and Esther Rachel (Feinerman) W. BA, Barnard Coll., 1977. Exec. aide to pres. Barnard Coll., N.Y.C., 1977-80; spl. asst. to pres. The Commonwealth Fund, N.Y.C., 1980-81; asst. to chief exec. officer/pres. Mary McFadden, Inc., N.Y.C., 1981-84; exec. administr. The Donna Karan Co., N.Y.C., 1984-90; exec. dir. Hadassah, The Women's Zionist Orgn. Am., Inc., N.Y.C., 1990—; comm. adv. coun. AT&T, 1992—. Bd. dirs., v.p. N.Am. Conf. on Ethiopian Jewry, N.Y.C., 1981-85, bd. advisors, 1985—; bd. govs. Lincoln Sq. Synagogue, N.Y.C., 1988-94, bd. trustees, 1994—; bd. govs. United Israel Appeal, 1991—. Office: Hadassah The Women's Zionist Orgn Am Inc 50 W 58th St New York NY 10019-2590

WOHLGEMUTH, JOHN HAROLD, solid state physicist; b. N.Y.C., Dec. 20, 1946; s. Harold V. and Joan G. (Purvey) W.; m. Bethany H. Hubbard, June 23, 1973; children: Edward J., Robert B. BA, Rensselaer Poly. Inst., 1968; PhD, Rensselaer Poly. Inst., 1973. Post-doctoral rsch. U. Waterloo, Ont., Can., 1973-75, U. Pa., Phila., 1975-76; mgr. advanced devel. Solarex Corp., Rockville, Md., 1976-83; mgr. solid state group Cabot Corp., Billerica, Md., 1983-86; dir. rsch. & devel. Solarex Corp., Frederick, Md., 1986—; U.S. del. Internat. Electrotechnical Commn., Geneva, 1986—. Author IEEE Photovoltaic Specialist Conference, 1988, 90, 91, 93, 94. Mem. IEEE, Am. Physical Soc., Materials Rsch. Soc. Methodist. Home: 5215 Fairgreen Way Ijamsville MD 21754-9634 Office: Solarex Corp 630 Solarex Ct Frederick MD 21701-8624

WOHLGENANT, RICHARD GLEN, lawyer; b. Porterville, Calif., Dec. 2, 1930; s. Carl Ferdinand and Sara Alice (Moore) W.; m. Teresa Joan Bristow, Dec. 27, 1959; children: Mark Thomas, Tracy Patrice, Timothy James. B.A., U. Mont., Missoula, 1952; LL.B., Harvard U., Cambridge, Mass., 1957. Bar: Colo. 1957, U.S. Dist. Ct. Colo. 1957. Assoc. Holme Roberts & Owen LLC, Denver, 1957-62; ptnr./mem. Holme Roberts & Owen, Denver, 1962—. Bd. dirs. Adopt-A-Sch., Denver, 1976-80, St. Joseph Found., Denver, 1990-93, Denver Com. Coun. Fgn. Rels., Japanese-Am. Soc. Colo., Rocky Mountain chpt. U.S. Mex. C of C. Mem. ABA, Colo. Bar Assn., Denver Bar Assn., Am. Coll. Real Estate Lawyers, Univ. Club, Law Club, City Club. Republican. Roman Catholic. Home: 300 Ivy St Denver CO 80220-5855 Office: Holme Roberts & Owen LLC 1700 Lincoln St Denver CO 80203-1014

WOHLSCHLAG, DONALD EUGENE, zoologist, marine ecologist, educator emeritus; b. Bucyrus, Ohio, Nov. 6, 1918; s. Herman Albert and Agnes Mae (Canode) W.; m. Elsie Marjorie Baker, June 5, 1943; children: William Eugene, Nancy Sue, Sarah Ann. BS, Heidelberg Coll., 1940; PhD, Ind. U., 1949. Research assoc. in zoology U. Wis., 1948-49; asst. prof. biol. scis. Stanford U., 1949-56, asso. prof., 1956-64, prof., 1964-65; prof. zoology and marine scis. U. Tex., Aransas, 1965-86; prof. emeritus zoology and marine scis. U. Tex., Port Aransas, 1986—; dir. Marine Sci. Inst., 1965-70; mem. U.S. Marine Subcom. for Internat. Biol. Program, 1966-71; mem. com. on ecol. research interocean-canal Nat. Acad. Scis., 1969-70; mem. Tundra Biome Panel, NSF, 1971-74; mem. water ecosystems com. Inst. Ecology, 1974-76. Contbr. numerous articles on arctic, antarctic and Gulf Coast fish ecol. research to profl. publs.; editor: Contbns. in Marine Sci, 1974-88. Served to 1st lt. USAAF, 1942-46. Recipient Antarctic medal NSF, 1965; NSF grantee, 1955-70; NOAA grantee, 1976-79; Office Naval Research grantee, 1952-54; Tex. Dept. Water Resources grantee, 1975-79. Fellow AAAS, Am. Inst. Fisheries Research Biologists, Arctic Inst. N. Am., Explorers Club; mem. Am. Fisheries Soc., Am. Soc. Limnology and Oceanography, Am. Soc. Zoologists, Am. Soc. Ichthyology and Herpetology, Ecol. Soc. Am. (pres. Western sect. 1965), Estuarine Research Fedn. (dir. 1976-78), Gulf Estuarine Research Soc. (pres. 1976-78), Sigma Xi. Home: 625 E Ave C Port Aransas TX 78373 Office: U Tex Port Aransas Marine Lab Port Aransas TX 78373 *Maintain the habitat; preserve the species, humans included.*

WOHLSTETTER, CHARLES, telephone company executive; b. 1910; married. With Charles R. Hammerslough & Co., N.Y.C., 1929-32, Theodore Prince Co., N.Y.C., 1932-33; ptnr. Rubinger, Wohlstetter & Co., 1933-38; with investment dept. Allen & Co., 1938-40; pres. Cyclohm Motor Corp.,

1940-48; ptnr. F.L. Rossman & Co., 1949-50, Seskis & Wohlstetter, 1950-71; past chmn. bd. Continental Telephone Corp. (now Contel Corp.), Atlanta; now dir. Continental Telephone Corp. (now GTE), Atlanta; bd. dirs. 5th Dimension Inc.; chmn. bd. dirs. Tesoro Petroleum Corp.; vice chmn. GTE Corp. Chmn. Billy Rose Found.; vice chmn. bd. trustees Nat. Symphony, Kennedy Center; trustee Am. Enterprise Inst.; chmn. Inst. Ednl. Affairs; active adv. council Rockefeller U., Council of World Communications; chmn. adv. panel Internat. Cultural and Edn. Exchange for U.S. Info. Agy.; regional chmn. Pres.' Commn. on White House Fellowships.; nat. ambassador Salk Inst.; adj. prof. Ala. Sch. Bus. Adminstrn. Mem. Am. Ent. Inst., (trustee), French Acad. of Wine. Office: Contel Corp 375 Park Ave Ste 2405 New York NY 10152-0184

WOHLTMANN, HULDA JUSTINE, pediatric endocrinologist, diabetologist; b. Charleston, S.C., Apr. 10, 1923; d. John Diedrich and Emma Lucia (Mohrmann) W. B.S., Coll. Charleston, 1944; M.D., Med. U. S.C., 1949. Diplomate Am. Bd. Pediatrics. Intern Louisville Gen. Hosp., 1949-50; resident in pediatrics St. Louis Children's Hosp., 1950-53; mem. faculty Washington U. Sch. Medicine, St. Louis, 1953-65, instr., 1953-58, asst. prof., 1958-65, postdoctoral fellow biochemistry, 1961-63; assoc. prof. pediatrics, head pediatric endocrinology Med. U. S.C., Charleston, 1965-70, prof., 1970-90, prof. emeritus, 1990—. Bd. dirs. Franke Home, Charleston, 1975—, treas., 1989-91; mem. adv. bd. for ethics ctr. Newberry (S.C.) Coll., 1989—; trustee Luth. Theol. So. Sem., 1991—. Mem. Am. Pediatric Soc., Ambulatory Pediatric Assn., Endocrine Soc., Am. Diabetes Assn., Am. Acad. Pediatrics, Am. Fedn. Clin. Rsch., Midwest Soc. Pediatric Rsch., So. Soc. Pediatric Rsch., S.C. Diabetes Assn. (bd. dirs. 1970-86, pres. 1970-73, 84-85, v.p., 1982-83, Profl Svc. award 1977), Lawson Wilkins Endocrine Soc., Sugar Club. Lutheran. Contbr. articles to sci. jours. Home: 280 N Hobcaw Dr Mount Pleasant SC 29464-2562

WOIT, ERIK PETER, corporate executive, lawyer; b. Riga, Latvia, Mar. 10, 1931; s. Walter E. and Sigrid (Radzins) W.; m. Bonnie Jean Ford, June 16, 1953; children: Peter Gordon, Steven Ford. A.B., Allegheny Coll., 1953; J.D., Harvard U., 1956. Bar: N.Y. 1959, U.S. Supreme Ct., 1971. Asso. firm Mudge, Stern, Baldwin & Todd, N.Y.C., 1956-57, 60-62; asst. sec., internat. counsel Richardson-Merrell, Inc., 1962-71; sec., gen. counsel Amerace Corp., N.Y.C., 1971-73, v.p., group exec., 1973-74, pres. ESNA div., 1974-77, sr. v.p. adminstrn., chief adminstrv. and chief fin. officer, 1977-83; sr. v.p. Orient Express Hotels, Inc., N.Y.C., 1983—, also bd. dirs.; chmn. Sea Containers Am. Inc., 1984—; sr. v.p. Sea Containers Ltd., 1987—; participant Dept. Def. Joint Civilian Orientation Conf., 1994. Served to capt. USMCR, 1957-60. Mem. Assn. Bar City N.Y., Am. Bar Assn., Sigma Alpha Epsilon. Clubs: Harvard, Sky (N.Y.C.). Home: 559 West Rd New Canaan CT 06840-2512 Office: 1155 Avenue Of The Americas New York NY 10036-2711

WOITACH, RICHARD, conductor, pianist; b. Binghamton, N.Y., July 27, 1935; s. Peter T. and Ester L. (Karkula) W.; m. Theresa Ballester, June 29, 1957 (div.); children—Paul, Karl; m. Jeryl E. Metz, Apr. 16, 1976. B.M., Eastman Sch. Music, 1956. Asst. condr. Met. Opera, N.Y.C., 1959-68; assoc. condr. Met. Opera, 1973—; guest lectr. in music Ind. U., 1972; music dir. Wolf Trap Opera Co., 1981-87; mem. faculty Juilliard Sch. Music, 1987; pres. New Artists Coalition Inc., 1986-87. Recs. with London Symphony for Saturn, 1980, with Regina Reshik for Epic, 1969, with Theresa Stratas for Nonesuch, 1982, with Jon Vickers for Centre discs, 1985; solo piano recs. on Opus One Label, 1967, 71; contbg. editor Opera Quar., 1983-89. Home: 697 West End Ave New York NY 10025-6823 Office: care Met Opera Lincoln Center New York NY 10023*

WOJAHN, R. LORRAINE, state legislator; b. Tacoma, Wash.; m. Gilbert M. Wojahn (dec.); children: Mark C, Gilbert M. Jr. (dec.). Mem. Wash. State Ho. of Reps., 1969-76, Wash. State Senate, 1977—, pres. pro tempore; vice chmn. rules, health and human svcs. com.; mem. labor and commerce, ways and means coms. Bd. dirs. Allenmore Hosp.; trustee Comsumer Credit Counseling Svcs., Inc., Tacoma-Pierce County; active, past pres. mem. Eastside Boys' and Girls' Club, Tacoma-Pierce County; active Wash. State Hist. Soc. Democrat. Office: State Senate State Capital Olympia WA 98504 Other: 2515 S Cedar St Tacoma WA 98405-2323

WOJCICKI, ANDREW ADALBERT, chemist, educator; b. Warsaw, Poland, May 5, 1935; s. Franciszek Wojcicki and Janina (Kozlowa) Hoskins; m. Marba L. Hart, Dec. 21, 1968; children: Katherine, Christina. BS, Brown U., 1956; PhD, Northwestern U., 1960; postdoctoral fellow, U. Nottingham, Eng., 1960-61. Asst. prof. chemistry Ohio State U., Columbus, 1961-66, assoc. prof., 1966-69, prof., 1969—, acting chmn., 1981-82; assoc. chmn. Ohio State U., 1982-83, 84-86; vis. prof. Case Western Res. U., 1967, U. Bologna, Italy, 1988; vis. researcher U. Coll. London, 1969; sr. U.S. scientist Alexander von Humboldt Found., Mulheim/Ruhr, Germany, 1975-76; vis. scholar U. Calif.-Berkeley, 1984. Contbr. articles to profl. and scholarly jours. Guggenheim fellow U. Cambridge (Eng.), 1976; recipient Disting. Teaching award Ohio State U., 1968, Humboldt Sr. award Humboldt Found., 1975, 76. Mem. Am. Chem. Soc. (Columbus sect. award 1992), Royal Chem. Soc., Sigma Xi, Phi Lambda Upsilon. Home: 825 Greenridge Rd Columbus OH 43235-3411 Office: Ohio State U 120 W 18th Ave Columbus OH 43210-1106

WOJCICKI, STANLEY GEORGE, physicist, educator; b. Warsaw, Poland, Mar. 30, 1937; came to U.S., 1950; s. Franciszek and Janina (Kozlow) W.; m. Esther Denise Hochman, Nov. 17, 1961; children: Susan Diane, Janet Maia, Anne Elizabeth. A.B., Harvard U., 1957; Ph.D., U. Calif., Berkeley, 1962. Physicist Lawrence Radiation Lab., Berkeley, 1961-66; asst. prof. physics Stanford U., 1966-68, assoc. prof., 1968-74, prof., 1974—, chmn. dept., 1982-85, dep. dir. Superconducting Supercollider Central Design Group, 1984-89; chmn. Stanford Linear Accelerator Center Exptl. Program Adv. Com., 1979-81; chmn. High Energy Physics Adv. Panel, 1990—. Assoc. editor Phys. Rev. Letters for Exptl. High Energy Physics, 1978-80. Recipient Alexander von Humboldt Sr. Am. Scientist award, 1981; NSF fellow, 1964-65; Sloan Found. fellow, 1968-72; Guggenheim fellow, 1973-74. Fellow Am. Phys. Soc. Office: Stanford U Physics Dept Stanford CA 94305

WOJCIK, ANTHONY STEPHEN, computer science educator; b. Chgo., Sept. 18, 1945; s. Casimir Anthony and Elizabeth Anne (Hudak) W.; m. Paula Jean Valaitis, Aug. 16, 1969; children: Laura Anne, Jeffrey Anthony. BS in Math., U. Ill., 1967, MS in Math., 1968, PhD in Computer Sci., 1971. Asst. prof. dept. computer sci. Ill. Inst. Tech., Chgo., 1971-76, assoc. prof. dept. computer sci., 1976-81, chmn. dept. computer sci., 1978-84, prof. dept. elec. and computer engring., 1984-86, prof. dept. computer sci., 1981-86; mem. tech. staff Bell Labs., Naperville, Ill., 1974; scientist in residence Argonne (Ill.) Nat. Lab., 1981, resident assoc., 1982-85, 86—, vis. scientist, 1985-86; prof., chmn. dept. computer sci. Mich. State U., East Lansing, 1986—. Named Outstanding Young Man of Am., 1981-82. Mem. IEEE (chmn. midwestern area com. 1975-78), Assn. Computing Machinery. Roman Catholic. Office: Mich State U Dept Computer Sci East Lansing MI 48824

WOJCIK, KATHLEEN LOUISE, state representative; b. Chgo., July 15, 1936; d. George Frederick and Anna Marie (Nowak) Zorger; m. Norbert Robert Wojcik Sr., Aug. 25, 1956; children: Norbert Robert Jr., Noreen Wojcik Gallagher. Student, William Rainey Harper Coll. Exec. sec. E.L. Reibold Sales Promotion Agy., Chgo., 1956-60; twp. clk., mgr. office Schaumburg Twp., Hoffman Estates, 1968-83; broker Quinlin & Tyson Realty, Schaumburg, Ill., 1970-75; owner, broker Kathleen L. Wojcik Realty, Schaumburg, 1976—; state rep. Ill. Gen. Assembly, Springfield, 1983—. Active Republican Orgn. Schaumbrug Twp., 1960—; twp. coordinator Women for Reagan, Women for Percy, Schaumburg, 1984; co-chmn. Small Businessmen for Reagan/Bush, Cook and DuPage Counties, Ill, 1984. Named Best Legislator of Yr. Ill Small Bus. Adminstrn., 1985, Legislator of Yr. Ill Assn. Homes for the Aging, 1985; recipient Superior Rating Taxpayers' Fedn. Ill, 1985, Cert. Appreciation Chgo. Bar Assn., 1986, Meritorious and Disting. Service award VFW, 1987. Mem. DAR, VFW, Am. Legion, Nat. Conf. State Legislators, Am. Legis. Exchange Council (membership co-chair 1983), NW Suburban Assn. Commerce and Industry, Ill. Realtors Assn. (legis. chmn.), Twp. Clks. Assn. Ill. (pres. 1979), Twp. Clks. Assn. Cook County (bd. dirs. 1973-82, past pres.). Lodge: Moose.

Avocation: golf. Home: 411 Redwood Ln Schaumburg IL 60193-2747 Office: 514 W Wise Rd Schaumburg IL 60193-3815

WOJCIK, LAWRENCE A., lawyer; b. Chgo., Apr. 4, 1951. BS with high honors, De Paul U., 1973, LLM in Taxation, 1981; JD, Northwestern U., 1977. Bar: Ill. 1977; CPA., Ill. Ptnr. Keck, Mahin & Cate, Chgo. Mem. ABA, AICPA, Ill. Soc. CPA, Chgo. Bar Assn., Ill. State Bar Assn., Fed. Cir. Bar Assn., Seventh Cir. Bar Assn. Office: Keck Mahin & Cate 77 W Wacker Dr Ste 4900 Chicago IL 60601

WOJCIK, MARTIN HENRY, foundation development official; b. Chgo., May 10, 1948; s. Henry Martin and Mary Lorraine (Naughton) W. B.S., Ill. Inst. Tech., 1970; M. in Humanities, Bonn U., W. Ger., 1975. Price adminstr. R.R. Donnelley & Sons., Chgo., 1970-72; dir. devel. Citizens for a Better Environment, Milw., 1976-79; pres. Citizens for a Better Environment, Chgo., 1979-85, bd. dirs., 1979-85, 89—; chmn. bd. dirs. Citizens for a Better Environment, 1990-91; dir. found. relations Northwestern U., Evanston, Ill., 1987-89; dir. corp. and found. rels. Mayo Found., Rochester, Minn., 1989—; mem. policy adv. com. Ill. EPA, Springfield, 1980-82. Bd. dirs. Rochester Civic Theatre, 1991—, pres. bd. dirs. 1994-95; mem. adv. panel Minn. State Arts Bd., 1995. Mem. Ill. Inst. Tech. Alumni Assn. Roman Catholic. Home: 535 19th St NW Rochester MN 55901-4901 Office: Mayo Found Med Edn and Rsch Rochester MN 55905

WOJEWODSKI, STAN, JR., artistic director, dean. MFA, Cath. U. of Am. Artistic dir. Ctr. Stage, Balt., 1977-91, Yale Repertory Theatre, 1991—; dean Yale Sch. of Drama, 1991—; tchr. Hammerstein Ctr. for Theater Studies, Columbia U.; advisor Theater Cornell; bd. dirs. Theatre Comms. Group; mem. theater panel Nat. Endowment for Arts. Dir.: Hamlet, The Baltimore Waltz, On the Verge, Edward the Second (Yale Repertory Theatre), The Countess Cathleen (Abbey Theatre, Dublin, Ireland), On the Verge, Volpone (Guthrie Theater), Don Quixote de la Jolla, The Heliotrope Bouquet by Scott Joplin and Louis Chauvin (La Jolla Playhouse), Much Ado About Nothing (Settle Repertory Theatre); staged David Mamet's Oleanna; dir. Williamstown Theatre Festival, Old Globe Theatre, San Diego, Hudson Guild Theatre, N.Y., Berkshire Theatre Festival. Office: Yale Repertory Theatre Box 208244 Yale Sta 222 York St New Haven CT 06520-8244

WOJNILOWER, ALBERT MARTIN, economist; b. Vienna, Austria, Feb. 3, 1930; came to U.S., 1939; s. Theodore and Lissy (Koppel) W.; m. Sue Freudenfels, Apr. 6, 1952; children: Daniel, Michael, Joel, Samuel. A.B., Columbia U., 1951, A.M., 1951, Ph.D, 1960. Economist Fed. Res. Bank of N.Y., N.Y.C., 1951-62; assoc. economist First Nat. City Bank of N.Y.C., N.Y.C., 1962-63; chief economist The First Boston Corp., N.Y.C., 1964-86, sr. advisor, 1986—; cons. Rep. Nat. Bank of N.Y., N.Y.C., 1980—; adj. prof. fin. NYU Grad. Sch. Bus. Adminstrn., N.Y.C., 1961-66. Author: The Quality of Business Loans, 1960; co-author: Financial Institutions and Markets, 1970, 2d edit., 1981. Recipient A.A. Green prize Columbia Coll., 1951. Mem. Am. Fin. Assn. (bd. dirs. 1979-81), Am. Econ. Assn., Phi Beta Kappa. Democrat. Jewish. Office: Clipper Asset Mgmt Investment Mgmt Corp 12 E 49 St New York NY 10017

WOJTAL, STEVEN FRANCIS, geology educator, researcher; b. Albany, N.Y., Oct. 3, 1952; s. Francis Joseph and Shirley Aileen (Ditzel) W.; m. Wendy Kozol, July 20, 1985. ScB in Geology, Brown U., 1974; MA in Geology, Johns Hopkins U., 1976, PhD in Geology, 1982. From instr. to assoc. prof. Oberlin (Ohio) Coll., 1979-88, prof., 1988—, chmn. geology dept., 1989-93. Author: (with others) Basic Methods in Structural Geology, Thrust Tectonics, Structural Geology of Fold and Thrust Belts; editor: Geometries and Mechanisms of Thrusting with special reference to the Appalachians, 1988; assoc. editor Jour. Structural Geology, 1990—. Mem. Am. Geophys. Union, Geol. Soc. Am., Internat. Assn. Structural/Tectonic Geologists, Sigma Xi. Avocations: hiking, bird watching, squash. Office: Oberlin Coll Dept Geology 52 W Lorain St Oberlin OH 44074-1044

WOJTYLA, KAROL JOZEF See JOHN PAUL II, HIS HOLINESS POPE

WOLANDE, CHARLES SANFORD, corporate executive; b. Chgo., July 25, 1954; s. Sam C. and Marie Helene (Riccio) W.; m. Marian Helene Gillespie, Nov. 10, 1985; children: Eric, Jill, Patrick. B. St. Mary's Coll., Winona, Minn., 1976. Lab. tech. Jefferson Electric, Bellwood, Ill., 1976-73; pres. Comark, Inc., Glendale Heights, Ill., 1978—; also CFO Comark, Inc., Bloomingdale, Ill. Named High Tech. Enterpreneur of the year Peat, Marwick, Mitchell, Chgo., 1987. Mem. C. of C. Glendale Heights. Republican. Roman Catholic. Avocations: golf, bowling, skiing. Home: 132 Triple Crown Ct Wheaton IL 60187-1027 Office: Comark Inc 471 Brighton Dr # 600 Bloomingdale IL 60108-3102*

WOLANER, ROBIN PEGGY, magazine publisher; b. Queens, N.Y., May 6, 1954; d. David H. and Harriet (Radlow) W.; m. Steven J. Castleman, 1992; 1 child, Terry David. BS in Indsl. and Labor Rels., Cornell U., 1975. Sr. editor Viva Mag., N.Y.C., 1975-76; editor Impact Mag., N.Y.C., 1976-77; circulation mgr. Runner's World Mag., Mountain View, Calif., 1977-79; cons. Ladd Assocs., San Francisco, 1979-80; gen. mgr. Mother Jones Mag., San Francisco, 1980-81, pub., 1981-85; founder, pub. Parenting Mag., San Francisco, 1985-91, pres., 1991-92; v.p. Time Pub. Ventures, 1990—; pres. CEO Sunset Pub. Corp. 1992—; trustee Muir Investment Fund, 1991-94. Mem. bd. advisors Grad. Sch. Journalism, U. Calif., Berkeley, 1991—; bd. dirs. Bay Area Coun., 1991—. Jewish. Office: Sunset Pub Corp 80 Willow Rd Menlo Park CA 94025-3661

WOLANIN, BARBARA ANN BOESE, art curator, art historian; b. Dayton, Ohio, Dec. 12, 1943; d. William Carl and Elisabeth Cassell (Barnard) Boese; m. Thomas R. Wolanin, June 11, 1966 (div. 1980); children: Peter Michael, Andrew Thomas. AB, Oberlin Coll., 1966, AM, 1969; MAT, Harvard U., 1967; PhD, U. Wis., 1981. Dir. children's art classes Allen Art Mus., Oberlin, Ohio, 1967-68; art tchr. Lorain (Ohio) Pub. Schs., 1968-69, Newton (Mass.) Pub. Schs., 1969-71; teaching asst. U. Wis., Madison, 1972-74; asst. prof. art history Trinity Coll., Washington, 1978-83, James Madison U., Harrisonburg, Va., 1983-85; curator U.S. Capitol, Architect of the Capitol, Washington, 1985—; guest curator Pa. Acad. of Fine Arts, Phila, 1980-83. Author exhbn. catalog Arthur B. Carles, 1983, others; contbr. articles to profl. jours. Woodrow Wilson fellow, 1967, Kress fellow U. Wis., 1974, Smithsonian fellow, 1976; recipient Faculty Devel. award James Madison U., 1985. Mem. Women's Caucus for Art, Am. Assn. Mus., Coll. Art Assn., Am. Inst. for Conservation, Phi Beta Kappa (pres. Trinity Coll. 1982-83). Democrat. Episcopalian. Home: 4347 Brandywine St NW Washington DC 20016-4542 Office: US Capitol Office Capitol Architect Washington DC 20515

WOLANIN, SOPHIE MAE, civic worker, tutor, scholar, lecturer; b. Alton, Ill., June 11, 1915; d. Stephen and Mary (Fijalka) W. Student Pa. State Coll., 1943-44; cert. secretarial sci. U. S.C., 1946, BSBA cum laude, 1948; PhD (hon.), Colo. State Christian Coll., 1972. Clk. stenographer, sec. Mercer County (Pa.) Tax Collector's Office, Sharon, 1932-34; receptionist, social sec., nurse-technician to doctor, N.Y.C., 1934-37; coil winder, assembler Westinghouse Electric Corp., Sharon, 1937-39, duplicator operator, typist, stenographer, 1939-44, confidential sec., Pitts., 1949-54; exec. sec., charter mem. Westinghouse Credit Corp., Pitts., 1954-72, hdqrs. sr. sec., 1972-80; reporter WCC News, 1967-68, asst. editor, 1968-71, asso. editor, 1971-76; student office sec. to dean U. S.C. Commerce, 1944-46, instr. math., bus. adminstrn., secretarial sci., 1946-48. Publicity and pub. relations chmn., corr. sec. South Oakland Rehab. Council, 1967-69; U. S.C. official del. Univ. Pitts. 200th Anniversary Bicentennial Convocation, 1986; mem. nat. adv. bd. Am. Security Council; mem. Friends Winston Churchill Mem. and Library, Westminster Coll., Fulton, Mo.; active U. S.C. Ednl. Found. Fellow; charter mem. Rep. Presdl. Task Force, trustee; sustaining mem. Rep. Nat. Com.; permanent mem. Nat. Rep. Senatorial Com.; patron Inst. Community Service (life), U. S.C. Alumni Assn. (Pa. state fund chmn. 1967-68, pres. council 1972-76, ofcl. del. rep. inauguration Bethany Coll. 1973); mem. Allegheny County Scholarship Assn. (life), Allegheny County League Women voters, AAUW (life), Internat. Fedn. U. Women, N.E. Historic Geneal. Soc. (life), Hypatian Lit. Soc. (hon.), Acad. Polit. Sci. (Columbia) (life), Bus. and

Profl. Women's Club Pitts. (bd. dirs. 1963-80, editor Bull. 1963-65, treas. 1965-66, historian 1969-70, pub. relations 1971-76, Woman of Year 1972), Met. Opera Guild, Nat. Arbor Day Found., Kosciuszko Found. (assoc.), World Literary Acad., Missionary Assn. Mary Immaculate Nat. Shrine of Our Lady of Snows; charter mem. Nat. Mus. Women in Arts, Statue Liberty Ellis Island Found. Inc., Shenago Conservancy (life); supporting mem. Nat. Woman's Hall of Fame; Recipient numerous prizes Allegheny County Fair, 1951-56; citation Congl. Record, 1969; medal of Merit, Pres. Reagan, 1982; named WPIC Sweetheart-of-the-Day Mercer County's Info. and Entertainment Radio Sta. 730, 1991. Fellow Internat. Inst. Community Service (founder); mem. World Inst. Achievement (rep.), Liturgical Conf. N. Am. (life), Westinghouse Vet. Employees Assn., Nat. Soc. Lit. and Arts, Early Am. Soc., Am. Acad. Social and Polit. Sci., Societe Commemorative de Femmes Celebres, Nat. Trust Historic Preservation, Am. Counselors Soc. (life), Am. Mus. Natural History (asso.), Nat. Hist. Soc. (founding mem.), Anglo-Am. Hist. Soc. (charter), Nat. Assn. Exec. Secs., Internat. Platform Assn., Smithsonian Assos., Asso. Nat. Archives, Nat., Pa., Fed. bus. and profl. women's clubs, Mercer County Hist. Soc. (life), Am. Bible Soc., Polish Am. Numismatic Assn., Polonus Philatelic Soc., UN Assn. U.S., Polish Inst. Arts and Scis. Am. (vice assoc.), N.Y. Acad. Scis. (assoc.), Am. Council Polish Cultural Clubs Inc. Roman Catholic (mem. St. Paul Cathedral Altar Soc., patron organ recitals). Clubs: Jonathan Maxcy of U. S.C. (charter); Univ. Catholic of Pitts.; Key of Pa., Fedn. Bus. and Profl. Women (hon.); Coll. (hon.) (Sharon). Contbr. articles to newspapers. Home: 5223 Smith Stewart Rd Girard OH 44420-1341

WOLANIN, THOMAS RICHARD, federal government official; b. Detroit, Dec. 1, 1942; s. Chester Richard and Helen Theresa (Luszki) W.; children: Peter, Andrew. BA magna cum laude, Oberlin Coll., 1965; MA, Harvard U., 1970, PhD, 1972. Staff dir. subcom. on labor-mgmt. rels. House Edn. and Labor Com., 1975-77, dep. staff dir. subcom. on select edn., 1977-78; exec. asst. to pres. NYU, 1981-82; analyst Senate Budget Com., 1982-83; staff dir. subcom. on investigations House P.O. and Civil Svc. Com., 1983-85, 87-91; staff dir. subcom. on postsecondary edn. House Edn. and Labor Com., 1978-81, 85-87;; 91-93; dep. asst. sec. legis. and congl. affairs U.S. Dept. Edn., Washington, 1993—; instr. govt. Oberlin Coll. 1967-69; teaching fellow in govt. Harvard U., 1969-70; asst. prof. polit. sci. U. Wis., Madison, 1971-78; congl. fellow Office of Congressman Frank Thompson, Jr., 1971-72; rsch. specialist Spl. Com. on Labor, House Edn. and Labor Com., 1972; cons. Nat. Commn. on Student Fin. Assistance, ERIC Clearinghouse on Higher Edn., Antioch U.; mem. Task Force on Student Loan Options, Nat. Assn. Ind. Colls. and Univs., adv. com. Nat. Study Debt Study, Lilly Found., Am. Coun. Edn. Author: Presidential Advisory Commissions: Truman to Nixon, 1975; co-author: Congress and the Colleges: Higher Education in National Politics, 1976; contbr. articles to profl. jours. Woodrow Wilson Fellow, 1965-66, Harvard Grad. prize fellow, 1965-67, 69-71; guest scholar The Brookings Instn., 1970, Congl. fellow, 1971-72, Ford Found. travel and student grantee, 1972-73, 73-74, Spencer fellow Nat. Acad. Edn., 1975-81, acad. specialist grantee USIA, 1990. Mem. Am. Polit. Sci. Assn., Polish Am. Arts Assn. Washington, Polish Am. Congress, Congl. Fellowship Alumni Assn., Phi Beta Kappa. Democrat. Roman Catholic. Avocations: military history, Polish history, literature. Office: Legis & Congl Affairs Office US Dept Edn 600 Independence Ave Washington DC 20202

WOLAS, HERBERT, lawyer; b. Bronx, N.Y., June 27, 1933; s. Irving and Mary (Kessner) W.; m. Annette Rudolph, Aug. 20, 1957; children: Cherise, Collette, Claudine. AA, UCLA, 1953, BA, 1954, JD, 1960. Bar: Calif. 1961. Since practiced in L.A. Served with F.A. AUS, 1955-56. Office: 1875 Century Pk E Ste 2000 Los Angeles CA 90067

WOLBRINK, DONALD HENRY, landscape architect, city planner; b. Ganges, Mich., May 13, 1911; s. Isaac M. and Ruby (Payne) W.; m. Florence Theresa Stack, Dec. 24, 1938; 1 child, Gretchen. B.A., U. Mich., 1932, M. Landscape Design, 1933. Landscape architect Nat. Park Service, Washington, 1934-41; landscape architect C.E., Omaha, 1941-44; assoc. Bartholomew Assocs., Honolulu, 1946-58, ptnr., 1958-64; pres. Donald Wolbrink, Honolulu, 1964-87, ret., 1989; dir. emeritus First Fed. Savs. and Loan, Honolulu; chmn. bd. Hawaii Architects and Engrs., Honolulu, 1979-84 (project dir. Melbourne strategy plan 1972-73); dir. Interplan, Melbourne, Australia, 1972-80. Co-author Hawaii State Law (land use law), 1961, socio-physical planning process, 1980; dir. (book) Tourism Standards, 1972. Bd. dirs. Oahu Devel. Conf., Honolulu, 1975-86 (project dir. 9 prin. Micronesian Islands 1961-75), C. of C., Honolulu, 1971-73, Downtown Improvement Assn., Honolulu, 1973-79; pres. Foresight, Inc., Honolulu, 1972-85. Served to lt. USN, 1944-46. Recipient Victorian Archtl. award Royal Australian Inst., 1977, Disting. Service award Engring. Assn. Hawaii, 1983, Spl. Achievement award Am. Plan Assn., 1990. Fellow ASCE, Am. Soc. Landscape Architects (trustee 1960-66, 77-78, merit award Hawaii chpt. 1983); mem. Am. Inst. Cert. Planners, Nat. Hist. Planning Pioneer Am., Inst. Consulting Planners. Club: Pacific (Honolulu). Avocations: photography; hiking. Home: 900 W Alpine Way Shelton WA 98584

WOLBRINK, JAMES FRANCIS, real estate investor; b. Charles City, Iowa, Sept. 8, 1942; s. Richard William and Anna (Butt) W.; m. Karen Ann Dunkerly, June 18, 1966. B.S. in Indsl. Engring. Iowa State U., 1966, postgrad., 1968-72. Cert. assn. exec. Tech. writer/editor Lawrence Radiation Lab., Livermore, Calif., 1966-67; editor, head engring. publs. Engring. Research Inst., Iowa State U., Ames, 1967-70; mng. dir., edn. and publs. Am. Inst. Indsl. Engrs., Norcross, Ga., 1971-83; commodities broker Clayton Brokerage, 1983-85; now pres. Wolbrink Properties, 1983—. Named Outstanding Young Alumnus Iowa State U., 1977. Mem. Sandy Springs Optimist Club (pres. 1989-90), Optimist Internat. (gov. Ga. dist. 1994-95), Delta Chi. Home and Office: 4520 Northside Dr NW Atlanta GA 30327-4548

WOLCK, WOLFGANG HANS-JOACHIM, linguist, educator; b. Koenigsberg, Germany, Sept. 19, 1932; came to U.S., 1963; s. Walter Erich and Margarete (Brettschneider) W.; m. Carolyn Ann Burch, June 18, 1966. Student, Birkbeck Coll., London, 1956; Staatsexamen, Christian Albrecht U., Kiel, Germany, 1960; Ph.D., J.W. Goethe U., Frankfurt, Germany, 1963. Instr. German and Latin Liverpool (Eng.) Inst., 1957-58; instr. Albert Ludwig U., Freiburg, Germany, 1964-65; asst. prof. Ind. U., Bloomington, 1966-69; assoc. prof. linguistics SUNY-Buffalo, 1970-74, prof., 1975—, chmn. dept., 1977-87, 89-91, dir. Latin Am. Studies program, 1972-76; research fellow Instituto de Estudios Peruanos, Lima, Peru, 1976-77; advisor Ministry of Edn., Lima, 1972, 82-83; rsch. prof. Belgian Nat. Sc. Found., 1991—; cons. Fischer-Price Toys, Inc., East Aurora, N.Y., 1980—; hon. prof. San Marcos Nat. U., Lima, 1972; mem. Fulbright Nat. Screening Com., 1993—; E.C. Scientific Com. Linguistic Minorities, 1993—. Author: Phonematische Analyse der Sprache von Buchan, 1965, Pequeño Breviario Quechua, 1987; co-author: Interkulturelle Mehrsprachigkeit, 1991; editor: The Social Dimension of Dialectology, 1976, The Fifth LACUS Forum, 1979, International Handbook on Contact Linguistics, 1990. Founding mem. Peru Earthquake Relief Com., Washington, 1972; field rep. United Way Campaign, Buffalo, 1977-81. Recipient Bronze medal Mazaryk U., Brno, Czechoslovakia, 1971; Fulbright Commn. grantee, 1963-64. Mem. Am. Dialect Soc., Linguistic Soc. Am., Societas Linguistica Europea, Linguistic Assn. Can. and U.S., Am. Assn. Applied Linguistics, Ctr. for Cognitive Sci., Centre for Multilingual Rsch., Sociedad Boliviana de Linguistica (hon.), Ellicottville Ski Club (dir. 1988-94). Home: 611 Skinnersville Rd Buffalo NY 14228-2505 Office: SUNY 685 Baldy Hall Buffalo NY 14260-1030

WOLCOTT, JOHN WINTHROP, III, corporate executive; b. Balt., Dec. 3, 1924; s. John Winthrop, Jr. and Dorothy C. (Fraser) W.; m. Elizabeth Thelin Hooper, Apr. 24, 1948 (div. 1985); children: John Winthrop IV, Elizabeth T., Katherine C.; m. Karen E. Jones, Oct. 1, 1985; 1 child, Oliver Lund. B.Indsl. Engring., Gen. Motors Inst., 1951. Registered profl. engr., Ohio. With Gen. Motors Corp., 1946-53, Weatherhead Co., Cleve., 1957-60; v.p. H.K. Porter Co., Inc., Pitts., 1960-64; pres., dir., CEO Ametek, Inc., N.Y.C., 1964-66; v.p. Am. Machine & Foundry Co., 1966-77, group exec.; process equipment group, 1967-70; exec. v.p. ops., dir. AMF, Inc., 1970-77; pres., chief exec. officer, dir. Transway Internat. Corp., N.Y.C., 1978-86, chmn. bd., 1982-86; bd. dirs. Burlington Motor Carriers, Inc., Fleet Aerospace Inc. Served with USCGR, 1943-46. Mem. Soc. Colonial Wars, Mary-

land Club (Balt.), Brook Club (N.Y.C.), The Rainier Club (Seattle). Episcopalian. Home: 210 Carrsbrook Dr Charlottesville VA 22901

WOLCOTT, OLIVER DWIGHT, international trading company executive; b. Marshfield, Oreg., Oct. 17, 1918; s. Dwight Oliver and Agnes Beatrice (Kunkel) W.; m. Valborg K. Rasmussen, Mar. 22, 1942; 1 child, John Oliver. B.S., U. Calif., 1940; M.B.A., Stanford U., 1942. With Chemurgic Corp., 1943-50, pres., 1947-50; with subs. W.R. Grace & Co., 1950-60, v.p., 1958-60; with Balfour Guthrie & Co., San Francisco, 1961-64; v.p. Balfour Guthrie & Co., 1964-65, exec. v.p., 1966, pres., 1967-77; dir. Barclays Bank Calif., 1974-88, chmn., 1979-85; dir. Wilson & Geo., Meyer & Co., 1981-92, Bd. Trade San Francisco, 1969-77. Club: Pacific-Union. Address: 662 Terra California Dr #3 Walnut Creek CA 94595

WOLCOTT, ROBERT WILSON, JR., consulting company executive; b. Phila., Nov. 20, 1926; s. Robert Wilson and Alice (Huston) W.; m. Margaret Hoopes, June 24, 1949; children: Allyn M., Anne H. BSCE, Princeton U., 1948. V.p., gen. mgr. Internat. Mill Service div. IU Internat. Corp., Phila., 1963-65, pres., 1965-70; group v.p. IU Internat. Corp., Phila., 1970-82, exec. v.p., 1982-88; cons. Phila., 1988—; bd. dirs. Echo Bay Mines Ltd., Edmonton, Alta., The Nature Conservancy, Pa. chpt., 1990—. Bd. dirs. The Church Farm. Sch., Exton, Pa., 1981—, Zool. Soc. Phila., 1983—. Mem. Am. Iron & Steel Inst., AIME. Clubs: Merion Cricket (Haverford, Pa.); Gulph Mills Golf (King of Prussia, Pa.); Phila. Home: 236 Atlee Rd Wayne PA 19087-3836 Office: 125 Strafford Ave Ste 130 Wayne PA 19087

WOLCOTT, SAMUEL H., III, investment banker; b. Boston, June 1, 1935; s. Samuel H. and Mary (Weld) W.; m. Nora Bradley, Dec. 28, 1960; 1 child, Natalie. A.B., Harvard U. 1957. Ptnr. J. Barth & Co., San Francisco, 1961-70; exec. v.p. Dean Witter Reynolds, N.Y.C., 1970-87, E.F. Hutton, 1987-88, Dean Witter Reynolds, N.Y.C., 1988—. Office: Dean Witter Reynolds 2 World Trade Ctr Fl 65 New York NY 10048-0002

WOLD, DAVID C., bishop. Bishop of Southwestern Wash. Evang. Luth. Ch. in Am., Tacoma. Office: Synod of Southwestern Washington 420 121st St S Tacoma WA 98444-5218

WOLD, FINN, biochemist, educator; b. Stavanger, Norway, Feb. 3, 1928; came to U.S., 1950, naturalized, 1957; s. Sverre and Herdis (Rasmussen) W.; m. Bernadine Moe, June 13, 1953; children—Eric Robert, Marc Sverre. Student, U. Oslo, 1946-50; M.S., Okla. State U., 1953; Ph.D., U. Calif. at Berkeley, 1956. Research asso. U. Calif. at Berkeley, 1956-57; asst. prof. biochemistry U. Ill., Urbana, 1957-62; asso. prof. U. Ill., 1962-66; prof. biochemistry U. Minn. Med. Sch., Mpls., 1966-74; prof. biochemistry U. Minn., St. Paul, 1974-81, head dept., 1974-79; Robert A. Welch prof. chemistry U. Tex. Med. Sch., Houston, 1981—; vis. prof. Nat. Taiwan U., 1971, Rice U., 1974, Academia Sinica, Taiwan, 1990, U. Tromso, Norway, 1991—; cons. in field. Author, contbg. author books; contbr. articles profl. publs.; mem. editorial bd.: Jour. Biol. Chemistry, 1974-79, 81-86, Biochemistry, 1974-83,. Fulbright fellow, 1950; John Simon Guggenheim fellow, 1960-61; recipient Lalor Found. Research award, 1958, NIH research career devel. award, 1961-66. Mem. AAAS, Am. Soc. Biochemistry and Molecular Biology (councilor 1978-81, sec. 1992—), Am. Chem. Soc. (councilor 1980-83, chmn. divsn. biol. chemistry 1985-86), Protein Soc. (pres. 1989-91), Biochem. Soc. (London). Office: U Tex Med Sch PO Box 20708 Houston TX 77225-0708

WOLD, JOHN SCHILLER, geologist, former congressman; b. East Orange, N.J., Aug. 31, 1916; s. Peter Irving and Mary (Helff) W.; m. Jane Adele Pearson, Sept. 28, 1946; children: Peter Irving, Priscilla Adele, John Pearson. AB, St. Andrews U., Scotland and Union Coll., Schenectady, 1938; MS, Cornell U., 1939; LLD (hon.), U. Wyo., 1991. Dir. Fedn. Rocky Mountain States, 1966-68; v.p. Rocky Mountain Oil and Gas Assn., 1967, 68; mem. Wyo. Ho. of Reps., 1957-59; Wyo. Republican candidate for U.S. Senate, 1964, 70; mem. 91st Congress at large from, Wyo.; chmn., CEO Wold Trona Co., Inc.; pres., chmn. Wold Oil & Gas Co.; ret. Wold Nuclear Co., Wold Mineral Exploration Co., Casper, Wyo.; founding pres. Wyo. Heritage Soc.; founder Central Wyo. Ski Corp.; chmn. Wyo. Natural Gas Pipeline Authority, 1987-91; chmn. bd. Nuclear Exploration and Devel. Corp., Mineral Engring. Co. Contbr. articles to profl. jours. Chmn. Wyo. Rep. Com., 1960-64, Western State Rep. Chmns. Assn., 1963-64; mem. exec. com. Rep. Nat. Com., 1962-64; chmn. Wyo. Rep. State Fin. Com.; Active Little League Baseball, Boy Scouts Am., United Fund, YMCA, Boys Clubs Am.; former pres. bd. trustees Casper Coll.; trustee Union Coll. Served to lt. USNR, World War II. Named Wyo. Man of Yr. AP-UPI, 1968; Wyo. Mineral Man of Yr., 1979, Wyo. Heritage award, 1992; named Benefactor of Yr., Nat. Coun. for Resource Devel., 1993. Mem. Wyo. Geol. Assn. (hon. life, pres. 1956), Am. Assn. Petroleum Geologists, Ind. Petroleum Assn. Am., AAAS, Wyo. Mining Assn., Sigma Xi, Alpha Delta Phi. Episcopalian (past vestryman, warden). Home: 1231 W 30th St Casper WY 82604-4738 Office: Mineral Resource Ctr 139 W 2d St Casper WY 82601

WOLD, ROBERT LEE, architect, engineer; b. Oak Park, Ill., Oct. 20, 1931; s. Leaman A. and Helen (Mengel) W.; m. Susan J. Olmstead, Dec. 18, 1954; children: Kyle, Eric, Karla. MArch with high honors, U. Ill., 1954. Registered architect, Ill., Mich., Fla., Pa., S.C., Mass. Designer DeLeuw Cather Co., Chgo., 1949-53; architect Perkins & Will, Chgo., 1954-55, Donker Assocs., Grand Rapids, Mich., 1957-59, Wold, Bowers, De Shane & Covert, Grand Rapids, 1960-76; prin. Robert Lee Wold & Assocs., Grand Rapids, 1976—. Prin. works include Walker City Ctr., Kent Community Hosp. (AIA Design award 1972), Grand Valley State U. Campus Ctr. (AIA Design award 1975), First of Am. Bank Bldg. (AIA Design award 1983), Grand Valley State Downtown Campus (AIA Design award 1989). 1st lt. Corps of Engrs., U.S. Army, 1955-56. Recipient Gold medal Mich. Soc. Architects, 1982. Fellow AIA; mem. Rotary. Home: 5970 Parview SE Grand Rapids MI 49546 Office: Tower Pinkster Titus Wold Inc 678 Front Ave NW Grand Rapids MI 49504-5323

WOLDEGABRIEL, GIDAY, research geologist; b. Mai Misham/Adwa, Tigray, Ethiopia, Sept. 3, 1955; came to U.S., 1982; s. Giday WoldeGabriel and Mislal Mesfin; m. Almaz Berhane Tesfamichael, Jan. 15, 1994. BS in Geology with honors, Addis Ababa (Ethiopia) U., 1978, MS in Geology, 1980; PhD in Geology, Case Western Res. U. 1987. Lectr. geology Addis Ababa U., 1980-82; dir.'s postdoctoral fellow Los Alamos (N.Mex.) Nat. Lab., 1987-90, contractor/collaborator, 1990-92, mem. tech. staff, 1992—. Author: (with others) Water Rock Interaction: Low-Temperature Environments, 1992; contbr. articles to profl. jours. Mem. Am. Geophysical Union. Avocations: running, camping, skiing, body building, swimming. Home: 45 Paige Cir Los Alamos NM 87544 Office: Los Alamos Nat Lab EEES-1/MS D462 Los Alamos NM 87545

WOLDT, HAROLD FREDERICK, JR., newspaper publishing executive; b. Atlanta, July 4, 1947; s. Harold Frederick and Dorothy R. (Lansdowne) W.; m. Lisa Diane Neves; children: Lauren Rae, Katherine Neves. BS in Journalism, So. Ill. U., 1969. Classified advt. rep. Chgo. Tribune, 1969-70, classified automobile staff mgr., 1970-72; nat. advt. sales rep. Chgo. Tribune newspapers, N.Y.C., 1972-74, city circulation mgr., 1974-77; nat. circulation mgr. Chgo. Tribune, 1977-80, circulation dir., 1980-84; v.p., circulation dir. News & Sun Sentinel Co., Ft. Lauderdale, Fla., 1985; circulation mgr. Newsday, Inc., L.I., N.Y., 1985-86; circulation dir. Newsday, Inc., Melville and L.I., N.Y., 1986-88, v.p., circulation dir., 1988—; with Distbn. Systems. Am. subs. of Newsday, Inc., 1988-94; v.p. circulation Newsday and Distbn. Systems Am., subs. Newsday, Inc., Melville, 1994—; speaker, participant Am. Press Inst.; bd. dirs. Abilities Health and Rehab. Svcs. (Nat. Ctr. for Disability Svcs.), Albertson, L.I., N.Y., 1992—. Bd. dirs. Robert R. McCormick Boys Club, Chgo., 1980-81; chmn. United Way campaign, Chgo. Tribune, 1980. Mem. Am. Pubs. Newspaper Assn. (circulation and readership com 1988-93), Internat. Circulation Mgrs. Assn. (pres. 1991-92), Alpha Delta Sigma, Tau Kappa Epsilon. Office: Newsday Inc 235 Pinelawn Rd Melville NY 11747-4226*

WOLENSKY, MICHAEL K., lawyer; b. Chattanooga, Aug. 16, 1946; s. Gabriel Albert and Irene (Northcutt) W.; m. Sandra Joy Silverman, Aug. 10, 1969; 1 child, David G. BME, Ga. Inst. Tech., 1967; JD, Am. U., 1971. Bar: Va. 1971, Fla. 1972, D.C. 1972, Ga. 1981, U.S. Supreme Ct. 1974.

Patent examiner U.S. Patent Office, Washington, 1968-71; trial atty. SEC, Miami, Fla., 1971-75; chief enforcement atty. SEC, San Francisco, 1975-77; asst. gen. counsel SEC, Washington, 1977-82; regional adminstr. SEC, Atlanta, 1982-87; of counsel Kilpatrick & Cody, Atlanta, 1987-90; ptnr., chmn. litigation dept. Kutak Rock, Atlanta, 1990—; arbitrator Nat. Assn. Securities Dealers, N.Y.C., 1987—, Am. Arbitration Assn., Atlanta, 1988—. Contbr. articles to profl. publs. Mem. ABA, Atlanta Bar Assn. Avocations: tennis, coaching youth sports. Office: Kutak Rock 4400 Ga-Pacific Ctr 133 Peachtree St Atlanta GA 30303

WOLF, ALFRED, rabbi; b. Eberbach, Germany, Oct. 7, 1915; came to U.S., 1935, naturalized, 1941; s. Hermann and Regina (Levy) W.; m. Miriam Jean Office, June 16, 1940; children: David B., Judith C. (dec.), Dan L. BA, U. Cin., 1937; MHL, Hebrew Union Coll., 1941; DD, 1966; PhD, U. So. Calif., 1961; DHL, U. Judaism, 1987, Loyola Marymount U., 1990. Ordained rabbi, 1941. Rabbi Temple Emanuel, Dothan, Ala., 1941-46; S.E. regional dir. Union Am. Hebrew Congregations, 1944-46; Western regional dir. Union Am. Hebrew Congregations, Los Angeles, 1946-49; rabbi Wilshire Blvd. Temple Los Angeles, 1949-85, rabbi emeritus, 1985—; dir. Skirball Inst. on Am. Values of Am. Jewish Com., 1985—; lectr. U. So. Calif., 1955-69, Hebrew Union Coll., Jewish Inst. Religion, Calif., 1963-65, 74; lectr. religion Seven Seas div. Chapman Coll., 1967; adj. prof. theology Loyola U. Los Angeles, 1967-74; lectr. sociology Calif. State U., Los Angeles, 1977; cochair First Nationwide Conf. for Cath. Jewish and Protestant seminiaries, Chgo., 1993. Author: (with Joseph Gaer) Our Jewish Heritage, 1957, (with Monsignor Royale M. Vadakin) Journey of Discovery - A Resource Manual for Catholic-Jewish Dialogue, 1989; editor Teaching About World Religions: A Teacher's Supplement, 1991. Mem. camp commn. adminstrv. com. Camp Hess Kramer, 1951—; mem. L.A. Com. on Human Rels., 1956-72, mem. exec. bd., 1960—, chmn., 1964-66, hon. mem., 1972—; pres. Anytown U.S.A., 1964-66; mem. Universal Way Planning Coun. Bd., chmn., 1974-78; mem. youth adv. com. NCCJ, 1968-72, exec. bd., 1972-93; founding pres. Interreligious Coun. So. Calif., 1970-72; chmn. clergy adv. com. L.A. Sch. Dist., 1971-81; chmn. Nat. Workshop on Christian-Jewish Rels., 1978; bd. govs. Hebrew Union Coll., bd. alumni overseers, 1972—; mem. L.A. 2000 Com., 1986-89, The 2000 Partnership, 1989-95, Berlin Sister City Com., L.A., 1987-89; bd. dirs. Jewish Fedn. Coun., 1978-85, bd. govs., 1985—; bd. dirs. Jewish Family Svc. L.A., sec., 1978-88. Recipient Samuel Kaminer award as Jewish educator of year Western Assn. Temple Educators, 1965, John Anson Ford Human Relations award County Commn. on Human Relations, 1972, 90, Harry Hollzer Meml. award Los Angeles Jewish Fedn. Council, 1978, Volpert Community Service award, 1986, Community Service award United Way of Los Angeles, 1980, Leadership award Los Angeles Bd. Edn., 1981, Service to Edn. award Associated Adminstrs. Los Angeles, 1983, Pub. Service award Jewish Chautauqua Soc., 1986, N.Am. Interfaith Leadership award Nat. Workshop for Christian-Jewish Rels., 1990. Mem. Bd. Rabbis So. Calif. (pres.), Am. Jewish Com. (exec. com. Los Angeles chpt., Max Bay Meml. award 1986), Central Conf. Am. Rabbis (exec. bd., mem. commn. on Jewish edn. 1970-72, treas. 1975-79, chmn. interreligious activities com. 1975-79, hon. mem. 1991—), Pacific Assn. Reform Rabbis (pres.), So. Calif. Assn. Liberal Rabbis (pres.), Synagogue Council Am. (mem. com. interreligious affairs), Alumni Assn. Hebrew Union Coll., Jewish Inst. Religion, Town Hall, Los Angeles World Affairs Council, U. So. Calif. Alumni Assn. Home: 3389 Ley Dr Los Angeles CA 90027-1315 Office: Skirball Inst on Am Values 635 S Harvard Blvd Los Angeles CA 90005-2586

WOLF, ALFRED PETER, chemist, educator; b. N.Y.C., Feb. 13, 1923; s. Josef and Margarete (Kunst) W.; m. Elizabeth H. Gross, June 15, 1946; 1 child, Roger O. B.A., Columbia U., 1944, M.A., 1948, Ph.D., 1952; Ph.D. (hon.), U. Uppsala, (Sweden), 1983, U. Rome, 1989. Chemist Brookhaven Nat. Lab., Upton, N.Y., 1951, chemist with tenure, 1957-64, sr. chemist, 1964—, chmn. chemistry dept., 1982-87; adj. prof. chemistry Columbia U., N.Y.C., 1953-83; vis. lectr. U. Calif., Berkeley, 1964; cons. Philip Morris, Inc., Richmond, Va., 1966-91, NIH, Bethesda, Md.; cons. advisor IAEA, Vienna, Austria; advisor Italian NRC, Rome, 1959—, Atomic Rsch. Inst., Julich, Germany, 1981-90; rsch. prof. psychiatry NYU, 1988—. Author: Synthesis of 11C, 18F and 13N Labelled Radiotracers for Biomedical Application, 1982; contbr. numerous articles to profl. jours.; patentee in field; editor: Jour. Labelled Compounds and Radiopharms., Radiochimica Acta. Served with AUS, 1943-46. Recipient JARI award, Pergamon Jours., 1986, The Javits Neurosci. Investigator award, 1986, Georg V. Hevesy Meml. Medal, Georg V. Hevesy Found. of Nuclear Medicine, 1986,. Mem. NAS, Am. Chem. Soc. (Nuclear Applications in Chemistry award 1971, Esselen award 1988), Chem. Soc. (U.K.), Soc. Nuclear Medicine (1982 Paul Aebersold award, pres. radiopharm. council 1980, George Hevesy award 1991), German. Chem. Soc. Home: PO Box 1043 Setauket NY 11733-0803 Office: Brookhaven Nat Lab Dept Chemistry Upton NY 11973

WOLF, BARRY, genetics, pediatric educator; b. Chgo. June 19, 1947; s. Bert D. and Toby E. (Urkoff) W.; m. Gail Harriet Ross, Oct. 2, 1971; children: Michael Loren, Bryan Phillip. BS, U. Ill., 1969; MD, U. Ill. Coll. Medicine, 1974; PhD, U. Ill., 1974. Diplomate Am. Bd. Pediatrics, Med. and Biochem. Genetics. Intern, resident in pediatrics Childrens Meml. Hosp., Northwestern U., Chgo., 1974-76; fellow Yale U. Sch. Medicine, New Haven, Conn., 1976-78; prof. human genetics Med. Coll. Va., Richmond, 1978—. Author 100 jour. articles and book chpts. dealing with inherited disorders of metabolism and biochm. genetics, specifically disorders of biotin metabolism. Recipient E. Mead Johnson award for pediatric rsch. Am. Acad. Pediatrics, 1988, Borden award in nutrition Am. Inst. Nutrition, 1987, Outstanding Scientist of Va. award Va. Sci. Mus., 1986, Ounce of Prevention award Action for Prevention of Va., 1985. Mem. Am. Soc. Clin. Investigation, Soc. Pediatric Rsch., Soc. for Inherited Metabolic Diseases (bd. dirs.), Am. Soc. Clin. Nutrition, Am. Inst. Nutrition, Soc. for the Study of Inborn Errors of Metabolism, Am. Soc. Human Genetics. Avocations: oriental cloisonne. Office: Med Coll Va Dept Human Genetics PO Box 980033 Richmond VA 23298

WOLF, CHARLES, JR., economist, educator; b. N.Y.C., Aug. 1, 1924; s. Charles and Rosalie W.; m. Theresa van de Wint, Mar. 1, 1947; children: Charles Theodore, Timothy van de Wint. B.S., Harvard U., 1943, M.P.A., 1948, Ph.D. in Econs., 1949. Economist, fgn. service officer U.S. Dept. State, 1945-47, 49-53; mem. faculty Cornell U., 1953-54, U. Calif., Berkeley, 1954-55; sr. economist The Rand Corp., Santa Monica, Calif., 1955-67; head econs. dept. The Rand Corp., 1967-81; dean The Rand Grad. Sch., 1970—; sr. economist, 1981—; sr. fellow Hoover Inst., 1988—; bd. dirs. Fundamental Investors Fund, Capital Income Builder Fund, Am. Capital Fund, Capital World Growth Fund; mem. exec. com. Rand-UCLA Health Policy Ctr.; mem. adv. com. UCLA Clin. Scholars Program; mem. exec. com. Rand Ctr. for Russian and Eurasian Studies; lectr. econs. UCLA, 1960-72; mem. adv. bd. grad. sch. pub. policy Carnegie-Mellon U., 1992—. Author: The Costs and Benefits of the Soviet Empire, 1986, Markets or Governments: Choosing Between Imperfect Alternatives, 1988, 93, (with others) The Impoverished Superpower: Perestroika and the Soviet Military Burden, 1990, Linking Economic Policy and Foreign Policy, 1991, Promoting Democracy and Free Markets in Eastern Europe, 1992, Defense Conversion and Economic Reform in Russia and Ukraine, 1994; contbr. articles to profl. jours. Mem. Assn. for Public Policy Analysis and Mgmt. (pres. 1980-81), Am. Econs. Assn., Econometric Soc., Coun. on Fgn. Rels., Internat. Inst. Strategic Studies London. Clubs: Cosmos (Washington); Riviera Tennis (Los Angeles); Harvard (N.Y.). Office: RAND Grad Sch Policy Studies 1700 Main St Santa Monica CA 90401-3208

WOLF, CHARLES BENNO, lawyer; b. Chgo., Apr. 16, 1950; s. Ludwig and Hilde (Mandelbaum) W.; m. Sarah Lloyd, Sept. 1, 1973; children: Walter Ludwig, Peter Baron. AB, Brown U., 1972; JD, U. Chgo. 1975. Bar: Ill. 1975, U.S. Dist. Ct. (no. dist.) Ill. 1975, U.S. Ct. Appeals (4th, 5th, 6th, 7th, 8th, 9th and 11th cir.) 1985, U.S. Supreme Ct. 1985. Ptnr. Vedder, Price, Kaufman & Kammholz, Chgo., 1975—. Co-author: ERISA Claims and Litigation (fed. pub. 9th edit. 1994); contbr. articles to profl. jours. Mem. ABA, Chgo. Bar Assn., Internat. Found. Employee Benefit Plans. Office: Vedder Price Kaufman & Kammholz 222 N La Salle St Ste 2600 Chicago IL 60601-1194

WOLF, CHARLOTTE ELIZABETH, sociologist; b. Boulder, Colo., Sept. 14, 1926; d. Marion Guy and Ethel Eugenia (Thomas) Rosetta; m. René A. Wolf, Sept. 3, 1952; children: Christopher Robin, Michele Renee. B.A., U.

Colo., 1949, M.A., 1959; Ph.D., U. Minn., 1968. Lectr. sociology U. Md., Tokyo, 1959-62, Turkey, 1965-67; instr. St. Mary Coll., Leavenworth, Kans., 1962-63; teaching asst. U. Minn., 1963-65; asst. prof. Colo. State U., 1968-69, Colo Woman's Coll., 1969-74; assoc. prof. sociology Ohio Wesleyan U., Delaware, 1974-80, prof., 1980, chmn. dept. sociology and anthropology, 1974-83; prof., chairperson dept. sociology and social work Memphis State U., 1983-92, prof. emeritus, 1992—. Author: Garrison Community: A Study of an Overseas American Military Colony, 1969, Southern Town/Two Communities, 1993; adv. editor Sociological Inquiry, 1988—, mem. bd. editors, 1990— ; contbr. chpts. to books and social sci. encys., articles to profl. jours.; mem. editorial bd. dirs. Sociological Spectrum, 1989-92. Recipient Ohio Wesleyan Outstanding Rsch. award, 1982, Faculty Devel. Leave Memphis State U., 1987-88; Mellon rsch. grantee, 1977, Shell Oil Co. grantee, 1978; Memphis State Ctr. for Humanities fellow, 1990. Mem. ACLU (bd. dirs Memphis chpt. 1988—), Am. Sociol. Assn. (chmn. com. status women 1974-76, nominations com. 1982-84), Soc. Study Social Problems (chair budget, audit and fin. com. 1975-79, treas. 1979-81), Western Social Sci. Assn. (exec. council 1974-77), Pacific Sociol. Assn., So. Sociol. Soc. (nominating com. 1987—, membership com. 1986-87), Mid South Sociol. Assn. (chair local arrangements 1986-87, awards com.), Sociologists Women in Soc. (chair nomination com. 1971-73, chair nominations com. South 1987-88c), Soc. for Study Symbolic Interaction (C.H. Cooley award com. 1985-86, publs. com. 1989-92, chair George Herbert Mead publs. com., 1989-92, award com. 1988-89, North Cen. Sociol. Assn. (v.p. 1983-84), AAUP (chpt. pres.), NOW (pres. Denver 1970-71, nat. dir. 1971-73 Woman of Yr. Denver chpt., chair nat. rsch. com. 1971-74), Memphis Bus. and Profl. Women's Network (exec. bd. 1991-93). Democrat. Home: Rock Creek Ranch Mc Coy CO 80463

WOLF, CYNTHIA TRIBELHORN, librarian, library educator; b. Denver, Dec. 12, 1945; d. John Baltazar and Margaret (Kern) Tribelhorn; m. H.Y. Rassam, Mar. 21, 1969 (div. Jan. 1988); children: Najma C., Yousuf J.; adopted children: Leonard Joseph Lucero, Lakota E. Rassam-Lucero. BA, Colo. State U., 1970; MLS, U. Denver, 1985. Cert. permanent profl. librarian, N.Mex. Elem. tchr. Sacred Heart Sch., Farmington, N.Mex., 1973-78; asst. prof. library sci. edn. U. N.Mex., Albuquerque, 1985-90, dir. libr. sci. edn. divsn., 1989-90; pres. Info. Acquisitions, Albuquerque, 1990—; libr. dir. Southwestern Coll., Santa Fe, 1992-94; mem. youth resources Rio Grande Valley Libr. Sys., Albuquerque, 1994—; fine arts resource person for gifted edn. Farmington Pub. Schs., 1979-83; speaker Unofficial Mentorships & Market Research, 1992—. Mem. Farmington Planning and Zoning Commn., 1980-81; bd. dirs. Farmington Mus. Assn., 1983-84; pres. Farmington Symphony League, 1978. Mem. ALA, N.Mex. Library Assn., LWV (bd. dirs. Farmington, 1972-74, 75, pres.). Avocations: mixed media graphics design, market research, personal journals. Office: Rio Grande Valley Libr Sys Albuquerque NM 87000

WOLF, DALE EDWARD, state official; b. Kearney, Nebr., Sept. 6, 1924. BSc, U. Nebr., 1945; PhD in Agronomy and Weed Control, Rutgers U., 1949. With Dept. Agr., 1946; assoc. prof. agronomy Rutgers U., 1949; with E.I. duPont de Nemours & Co., Inc., from 1950, dir. agrichem. mktg., then gen. mgr. biochem. dept., 1972-79; v.p. biochems., also chmn. bd. subs. Endo Labs., Inc., Wilmington, Del., from 1979; group v.p. Agrl. Products, Wilmington, Del., from 1983; dir. Del. Devel. Office, Dover, 1987-89; lt. gov. of Del. Dover, 1989-93; gov. State of Del., Dover, 1993. Co-author: Principles of Weed Control, 1951. Bd. dirs. Del. chpt. ARC, 1975; gen. campaign chmn. United Way Del., 1978, also bd. dirs.; gen. campaign chmn. Girls Club Del., 1987. Served to 1st. lt. AUS, 1943-46. Decorated Bronze Star, Purple Heart. Mem. Nat. Agrl. Chem. Assn. (chmn 1981-83), Pharm. Mfrs. Assn. (dir.), Masons, Sigma Xi, Alpha Zeta.

WOLF, DAVID, lawyer; b. Boston, July 11, 1927; s. Ezekiel and Ray (Cohen) W.; m. Maxine Laura Bunnin, June 29, 1963; children—Eric E., Douglas R., James A. BA, U. Mass., 1949; LLB, Harvard U., 1952; postgrad., Northeastern U., 1952-55. Bar: Mass. 1952, U.S. Patent Office 1952, U.S. Ct. Customs and Patent Appeals 1955, U.S. Supreme Ct. 1958, U.S. Ct. Appeals (fed. cir.) 1983. Ptnr. Wolf, Greenfield & Sacks, P.C., Boston, 1952—; Watercolor artist; exhibited various local shows; holder of 13 U.S. letters patents in various arts. Watercolor artist; exhibited various local shows; holder of 12 U.S. letters patents in various arts. Bd. dirs. Newton Country Players, 1964-67, Killington East Homeowners Assn., pres. 1992—; mem. Com. for Accuracy in Mid. East Reporting in Am., 1989—; bd. dirs., 1990, gen. counsel, 1993—; mem. Am. Jewish Congress, 1990-92. Recipient various awards for art. Mem. Am. Patent Law Assn. (lectr. trademark trial adv. programs 1986-89), Lic. Execs. Soc., U.S. Trademark Assn., Mass. Bar Assn., Boston Bar Assn., Harvard Law Sch. Alumni Assn., Boston Patent Law Assn. (pres. 1976), New Eng.-Israel C. of C. (v.p., bd. dirs. 1984-95), Hadassah Men's Assn., B'nai B'rith, Free Sons Israel, Alpha Epsilon Pi. Office: Wolf Greenfield & Sacks PC Fed Res Plz 600 Atlantic Ave Boston MA 02210-2211

WOLF, DON ALLEN, hardware wholesale executive; b. Allen County, Ind., June 18, 1929; s. Ellis Adolphus and Bessie Ruth (Fortman) W.; m. Virginia Ann Lunz, Oct. 8, 1949; children—Rebecca, Donna, Richard, Lisa. Student exec. course, Ind. U., 1969. With Hardware Wholesalers Inc., Fort Wayne, Ind., 1947—; purchasing mgr. Hardware Wholesalers Inc., 1957—, v.p., gen. mgr., 1967-80, pres., 1980-92; ret., 1992; bd. dirs. Group Dekko Co., Fort Wayne Nat. Bank, Clarcor. Pres., bd. dirs. Big Brothers, Fort Wayne, 1973-74; nat. pres. Big Brothers Soc. Am., 1977-80. Mem. Nat. Wholesale Hardware Assn. (dir. 1977—, pres. 1984-85, named Hardware Wholesaler of Year 1973, 85), Ind. State C. of C. (dir.). Republican. Lutheran. Office: Hardware Wholesalers Inc PO Box 868 Fort Wayne IN 46801-0868 also: 6502 Nelson Rd Fort Wayne IN 46803-1920

WOLF, DUANE CARL, microbiologist; b. Forsyth, Mo., Apr. 7, 1946; s. Deward Carl and Mary Catherine (Collins) W. BS, U. Mo., 1968; PhD, U. Calif., Riverside, 1973. Asst. prof. dept. agronomy U. Md., College Park, 1973-78; assoc. prof. dept. agronomy U. Ark., Fayetteville, 1979-81; prof. dept. agronomy U. Ark., 1981—; presenter in field at nat. meetings. Contbr. articles to profl. jours.; author, co-author rsch. reports at regional meetings; co-author 5 book chpts. Fellow Am. Soc. Agronomy (chair environ. quality sect. 1988), Soil Sci. Soc. Am. (chair microbiol. biochem. sect. 1994); mem. AAAS, Am. Soc. Microbiology, Vietnam Vets. Am., Sigma Xi, Gamma Sigma Delta. Office: U Ark Dept Agronomy Fayetteville AR 72701

WOLF, EDWARD DEAN, electrical engineering educator; b. Quinter, Kans., May 30, 1935; s. Ezra Lawrence and Zora Blanche (Jamison) W.; m. Marlene Kay Simpson, Aug. 12, 1955; children: Julie Christine, LeAnn Cynthia, Shelly Diane. Student, Kans. State U., 1953; BS magna cum laude, McPherson Coll., 1957; PhD, Iowa State U., 1961; postgrad., Princeton U., 1961-62, U. Calif.-Berkeley, 1968. Mem. tech. staff Rockwell Internat. Sci. Ctr., Thousand Oaks, Calif., 1963-65; mem. tech. staff, sr. mem. tech. staff Hughes Research Labs., Malibu, Calif., 1965-67, 67-72, sect. head, 1972-78, sr. scientist, 1974-78; dir. Nat. Nanofabrication Facility, Cornell U., Ithaca, N.Y., 1978-88, prof. elec. engring., 1978-90, prof. emeritus, 1991—; dir. Office Technology Access and Bus. Assistance Cornell U., Ithaca, N.Y., 1995—; co-owner, pres. Biolistics, Inc., 1989-89; cons. Dept. Def., 1978, 81-82, various indsl. cos., 1978—; mem. univ. adv. com. Semiconductor Rsch. Corp., Research Triangle, N.C., 1982-84, ad hoc com. NAS, 1977-79, steering com. European Microcircuits Engring. Conf., 1976-78; guest prof. Tech. U., Vienna, 1987; vis. fellow Trinity Coll, Cambridge (Eng.) U., 1986-87; fgn. fellow Erwin Schrodinger Soc., Vienna, 1987; bd. dirs. Phyton, Inc., Cornell Rsch. Found. Editorial bd.: IEEE Spectrum, 1983-85; contbr. numerous articles on microminiaturization to profl. jours.; patentee in field. Named outstanding young man of Am., 1966. Fellow Am. Inst. Chemists, IEEE; mem. Bohmische Phys. Soc. (sci. me.), Am. Phys. Soc., Am. Vacuum Soc., Electron Microscopy Soc. Am., Sigma Xi, Phi Lambda Upsilon. Republican. Home: 1691 Taughannock Blvd Trumansburg NY 14886-9120 Office: Cornell U Phillips Hall Ithaca NY 14853

WOLF, EDWARD LINCOLN, physics educator; b. Cocoa, Fla., Nov. 22, 1936; s. Norman Lincoln and Harriet (Burgess) W.; m. Carol Joyce Euwema, June 15, 1958; children: Douglas Wakefield, David Lincoln. BA, Swarthmore Coll., 1958; PhD, Cornell U., 1964. Postdoctoral fellow U. Ill. Dept. Physics, Urbana, 1964-66; research assoc. Eastman Kodak Co. Rochester, N.Y., 1967-75; prof. physics Iowa State U., Ames, 1975-85; head

dept. physics, prof. Polytechnic U., Bklyn., 1986—; sr. vis. fellow Cavendish Lab. U. Cambridge, U.K., 1973-74; vis. prof. U. Pa., Phila., 1982. Author: Principles of Electron Tunneling Spectroscopy, 1985; editor: Materials and Mechanisms of Superconductivity, 1985. Fellow Am. Phys. Soc.; mem. Phi Beta Kappa, Sigma Xi. Presbyterian. Avocations: jogging, cycling, music. Office: Polytechnic U Dept Physics Six Metrotech Ctr Brooklyn NY 11201-2990

WOLF, EMIL, physics educator; b. Prague, July 30, 1922; naturalized U.S. citizen, 1967; BSc, U. Bristol, Eng., 1945, PhD, 1948; DSc, U. Edinburgh, Scotland, 1955; D. honoris causa, U Groningen, 1989, U. Edinburgh, 1990, Palacky U., Czechoslovakia, 1992. Rsch. asst. observatory Cambridge U., Eng., 1948-51; rsch. asst., lectr. math. and physics U. Edinburgh, 1951-54; rsch. fellow theoretical physics U. Manchester, Eng., 1954-59; vis. rsch. scientist Courant Inst. NYU, 1957; assoc. prof. optics U. Rochester, N.Y., 1959-61; prof. physics U. Rochester, 1961—, prof. optics, 1978—, Wilson prof. optical physics, 1987—; Guggenheim fellow, vis. prof. U. Calif. at Berkeley, 1966-67; vis. prof. U. Toronto, 1974-75. Author: (with M. Born) Principles of Optics, 1959; editor: Progress in Optics, Vol. I-XXXIII, 1961-94, (with L. Mandel) Selected Papers on Coherence and Fluctuations of Light, 2 vols., 1970, Coherence and Quantum Optics, 3d conf., 1973, 4th conf., 1978, 5th conf., 1983, 6th conf., 1990; contbr. articles to profl. jours. Recipient Marconi medal Italian Nat. Rsch. Coun., 1987, Gold medal Czechoslovak Acad. Scis., 1991, medal Union of Czechoslovak Mathematicians and Physicists, 1991, Gold medal Palacky U., Olomouc, Czechoslovakia, 1991. Fellow Optical Soc. Am. (Frederic Ives medal 1977, Max Born award 1987, dir.-at-large 1972-74, v.p 1976, pres. 1978, hon. mem.), Am. Phys. Soc., Brit. Inst. Physics, Am. Inst. Physics (governing bd. 1977-78), Franklin Inst. (Albert A. Michelson medal 1980), Optical Soc. India (hon.), Optical Soc. Australia (hon.). Office: U Rochester Dept Physics and Astronomy Rochester NY 14627

WOLF, ERIC ROBERT, anthropologist, educator; b. Vienna, Austria, Feb. 1, 1923; came to U.S., 1940, naturalized, 1943; s. Arthur George and Maria (Ossinovski) W.; m. Kathleen Bakeman, Sept. 24, 1943; children: John David, Daniel Jacob; m. Sydel Finfer Silverman, Mar. 18, 1972. B.A., Queens Coll., 1946; Ph.D. (Viking Fund fellow), Columbia U., 1951; DL (hon.), U. Mich., 1992; D.h.c., U. Vienna, 1993. Asst. prof. U. Ill., 1952-55, U. Va., 1955-58; vis. asst. prof. Yale U., 1958-59; assoc. prof. U. Chgo., 1959-61; prof. U. Mich., Ann Arbor, 1965-71, chmn. dept. anthropology, 1970-71; disting. prof. Herbert H. Lehman Coll. and Grad. Ctr., CUNY, 1971-92, disting. prof. emeritus, 1992—; field work, P.R., 1948-49, Mexico, 1951-52, Italy, 1960-61. Author: Sons of the Shaking Earth, 1958, Peasants, 1968, Peasant Wars of the Twentieth Century, 1969, Europe and the People Without History, 1982. Served with AUS, 1943-45. Decorated Silver Star; recipient Career award NIH, 1964-69, J.S. Staley prize Sch. for Am. Rsch., Santa Fe 1988, Kevin Lynch award MIT, 1989; Guggenheim fellow, 1960-61; sr. fellow NEH, 1973-74; MacArthur Found. fellow, 1990. Fellow Am. Acad. Arts and Scis.; mem. Am. Anthrop. Assn. Home: 4 Blueberry Hl Irvington NY 10533-1402

WOLF, ERVING, oil company executive; b. Kimball, Nebr., Mar. 6, 1926; s. Leon and Dora W.; m. Joyce Mandel, Sept. 16, 1951; children: Diane, Daniel, Mathew. B.S., Notre Dame U., 1947, Northwestern U., 1947; J.D., Northwestern U., 1950. Owner, mgr. Wolf Land Co., Cheyenne, Wyo., and Denver, 1950-67; chmn., pres. Inexco Oil Co., 1967-86, La. Land Exploration Co. (merged with Inexco), 1986; owner, mgr. Wolf Exploration Co., 1986—. Home: 2200 Willowick Rd Houston TX 77027-3950 Office: Wolf Exploration Co 1001 Fannin St Ste 2000 Houston TX 77002-6709

WOLF, FRANK R., congressman, lawyer; b. Philadelphia, Pa., Jan. 30, 1939; m. Carolyn Stover; children: Frank, Virginia, Anne, Brenda, Rebecca. B.A., Pa. State U., 1961; LL.B., Georgetown U., 1965. Bar: Va., D.C. Legis. asst. former Congressman Edward G. Biester, Jr., 1968-71; asst. to Sec. of Interior Rogers B. Morton, 1971-74; dep. asst. sec. for Congl. and Legis. Affairs, Dept. Interior, 1974-75; mem. 97th-104th Congresses from 10th Va. dist., Washington, 1981—; mem. appropriations com., chmn. transp. subcom., mem. TPS and fgn. affairs subcom. Served with USAR. Republican. Presbyterian. Office: US Ho of Reps 241 Cannon Hse Office Bldg Washington DC 20515-4610

WOLF, FRED, III, lawyer; b. Phila., Jan. 18, 1946; s. Fred and Margery (Stern) W.; m. Peggy Kaufman, June 12, 1968; children: Rachel K., Matthew S. BA, Dartmouth Coll., 1968; JD, George Washington U., 1972. Bar: Md. 1972. Law clk. Hon. Francis I. Van Dusen, U.S. Ct. Appeals, 3d Cir., Phila., 1972-73; assoc./ptnr. Frank, Bernstein, Conaway & Goldman, Balt., 1973-80; asst. atty. gen. of Md. and counsel Dept. Econ. and Community Devel. of Md., Annapolis, 1980-82; ptnr. Frank, Bernstein, Conaway & Goldman, Balt., 1982-92, Ballard Spahr Andrews & Ingersoll, Balt., Balt., 1992—. Chmn. bd. Mt. Washington Pediatric Hosp., Balt., 1980-83; prs. Jewish Family Svcs., Inc., Balt., 1990-92; bd. dirs. Assoc. Jewish Community Fedn. of Balt., 1990-92, 93—, exec. com., 1993—. With U.S. Army, 1968-74. Mem. Am. Coll. Real Estate Lawyers. Avocations: hiking, travel. Office: Ballard Spahr et al 300 E Lombard St Ste 1900 Baltimore MD 21202

WOLF, G. VAN VELSOR, JR., lawyer; b. Balt., Feb. 19, 1944; s. G. Van Velsor and Alice Roberts (Kimberly) W.; m. Ann Holmes Kavanagh, May 19, 1984; children: George Van Velsor III, Timothy Kavanagh (dec.), Christopher Kavanagh, Elisabeth Huxley. BA, Yale U., 1966; JD, Vanderbilt U., 1973. Bar: N.Y. 1974, Ariz. 1982, U.S. Dist. Ct. (so. dist.) N.Y. 1974, U.S. Dist. Ct. Ariz. 1982, U.S. Ct. Appeals (2d cir.) 1974, U.S. Ct. Appeals (9th cir.) 1982. Agrl. advisor U.S. Peace Corps, Tanzania and Kenya, 1966-70; assoc. Milbank, Tweed, Hadley & McCloy, N.Y.C., 1973-75; vis. lectr. law Airlangga U., Surabaya, Indonesia, 1975-76, U. Ariz. 1990, Vanderbilt U., 1991, U. Md., 1994; editor in chief Environ. Law Reporter, Washington, 1976-81; cons. Nat. Trust for Historic Preservation, Washington, 1981; assoc. Lewis & Roca, Phoenix, 1981-84, ptnr., 1984-91; ptnr. Snell & Wilmer, Phoenix, 1991—. Bd. dirs. Ariz. div. Am. Cancer Soc., 1985—, sec. 1990-92, vice chmn. 1992-94, chmn., 1994—. Editor: Toxic Substances Control, 1980; contbr. articles to profl. jours. Bd. dirs. Phoenix Little Theater, 1983-90, chmn., 1986-88. Mem. ABA (vice chmn. SONREEL commn. state and regional environ. coop.), Assn. Bar City N.Y., Ariz. State Bar Assn. (com. environ. & nat. res. law sect. 1988-93, chmn. 1991-92), Maricopa County Bar Assn., Ariz. Acad., Union Club (N.Y.C.), Univ. Club (Phoenix). Office: Snell & Wilmer 1 Arizona Ctr Phoenix AZ 85004-0001

WOLF, GARY HERBERT, architect; b. Lansing, Mich., July 15, 1950; s. Herbert C. and Margaret Wolf; m. Bonnie L. Grad, June 21, 1980; children: Alexander, Theodore. BA, Cornell U., 1972; M Archtl. History, U. Va., 1974; MArch, Princeton U., 1978. Assoc. Graham Gund Archs., Inc., Cambridge, Mass., 1983-87; prin. Adams & Wolf Archs., Inc., Belmont, Mass., 1987-91, Gary Wolf Archs., Inc., Boston, 1991—; dir. design Heliotrope, Providence, R.I., 1993—; mem. other archtl. firms, preservation orgns. and other instns. including constrn. mgmt. dept. Harvard U., Michael Graves Arch., Nat. Register Historic Places, 1974-83; vis. critic Harvard U. Grad. Sch. Design, Cambridge, Mass.; thesis advisor Boston Archtl. Ctr.; guest juror R.I. Sch. Design, Providence, Mass. Inst. Tech., Cambridge. Prin. archtl. works include Tree-House Porch, Brookline, Mass., 1987-88, 66 Leonard St., Belmont, Mass., 1988, Grad-Wolf House, Weston, Mass., 1988-94, Ibis Hair and Skin Care Salon, Boston, 1989-90, Synectics Bldg. Restoration, Cambridge, Mass., 1987-88, 90-91, Synectics Corp. Offices, Cambridge, 1992-93, Mus. of Our Nat. Heritage Renovations, Lexington, Mass., 1993-94, Brookline Music Sch., 1991-94; contbr. articles to profl. jours. Recipient Thomas Jefferson Meml. Found. Scholarship U. Va., 1972-74, Merit award Internat. Conceptual Furniture Competition, Progressive Architecture Mag., 1980, 1st pl. Great Am. Facades Design Competition, 1990, Builder's Choice Design awards, 1991, 92, 93, Good Design Disting. Product award Chgo. Athenaeum: Mus. Architecture and Design, 1994, Gold Indsl. Design Excellence award Bus. Week/Indsl. Design award, 1994, Best Products award Time Mag., 1994. Mem. AIA, Am. Assn. Mus., Nat. Trust Historic Preservation, Boston Soc. Archs (past chair membership com.). Office: Gary Wolf Archs 145 Hanover St Boston MA 02108

WOLF, GARY WICKERT, lawyer; b. Slinger, Wis., Apr. 19, 1938; s. Leonard A. and Cleo C. (Wickert) W.; m. Jacqueline Weltzin, Dec. 17, 1960; children: Gary, Jonathan. B.A.A., U. Minn., 1960, J.D. cum laude, 1963.

Bar: N.Y. 1964, U.S. Ct. Appeals (2d cir.) 1969, U.S. Dist. Ct. (so. dist.) N.Y. 1969, U.S. Supreme Ct. 1971. Assoc. Cahill, Gordon & Reindel, N.Y.C., 1963-70, ptnr., 1970—; dir. Southwestern Pub. Svc. Co. Trustee Newark Acad. Livingston (N.J.). Mem. N.Y. State Bar Assn. (com. on securities regulation), Anglers Club (N.Y.C.), Downtown Assn. (N.Y.C.), Mashomack Fish and Game Club (Pine Plains, N.Y.). Home: Pleasantville Rd New Vernon NJ 07976 Office: Cahill Gordon & Reindel 80 Pine St New York NY 10005-1701

WOLF, HANS ABRAHAM, retired pharmaceutical company executive; b. Frankfurt, Fed. Republic Germany, June 27, 1928; came to U.S., 1936, naturalized, 1944; s. Franz Benjamin and Ilse (Nathan) W.; m. Elizabeth J. Bassett, Aug. 2, 1958; children: Heidi Elizabeth, Rebecca Anne, Deborah Wolf Streeter, Andrew Robert. AB magna cum laude, Harvard U., 1949, MBA, 1955; PhB, Oxford U., 1951. Math instr. Tutoring Sch., 1946-47; statis. research Nat. Bur. Econ. Research, N.Y.C., 1948-49; researcher Georgetown U., 1951-52; confidential aide Office Dir. Mut. Security, Washington, 1952; analyst Ford Motor Co., Dearborn, Mich., summer 1954; foreman prodn. M&C Nuclear Inc., Attleboro, Mass., 1955-57; asst. supt. prodn. Metals & Controls Corp., Attleboro, 1957-59, mgr. product dept., 1959-62, controller, 1962-67; asst. v.p., controller materials and services group Tex. Instruments Inc., Dallas, 1967-69, treas., v.p., 1969-75; v.p., fin., chief fin. officer Syntex Corp., Palo Alto, Calif., 1975-78, exec. v.p., 1978-86, vice chmn., chief adminstrv. officer, 1986-92, vice chmn., 1992-93, also bd. dirs., 1986-93; bd. dirs. Clean Sites, Inc., Alexandria, Va., Tab Products Co., Palo Alto, Calif., chmn. 1995—; bd. dirs. Network Equipment Techs., Redwood City, Calif., Satellite Dialysis Ctrs., Inc., Redwood City, Hyal Pharms., Toronto, Ont. Author: Motivation Research—A New Aid to Understanding Your Markets, 1955. Mem. Norton (Mass.) Sch. Bd., 1959-62, chmn., 1961-62; pres., bd. dirs. Urban League Greater Dallas, 1971-74; bd. dirs. Dallas Health Planning Coun., mem. community adv. com., 1973-75; bd. dirs., pres. Children's Health Coun. of the Mid Peninsula; cubmaster Boy Scouts Am., 1976-78; elder United Ch. Christ, 1970-73, vice chmn. gen. bd., 1970-71, moderator, 1978-80; trustee Pacific Sch. Religion, 1986-94, chmn., 1990-94; trustee World Affairs Coun. San Francisco, 1986-92, 94—; dir. Tech Mus. San Jose. With USAF, 1952-53. Mem. Am. Mgmt. Assn. (planning council fin. div. 1970-76), Phi Beta Kappa.

WOLF, HAROLD ARTHUR, finance educator; b. Lind, Wash., Feb. 10, 1923; s. Edward and Olga (Limert) W.; March 23, 1961; children: Mark, Suellen. B.A., U. Oreg., 1951; M.A., U. Mich., 1952, Ph.D., 1958. Instr. Lehigh U., 1955-56; economist Prudential Life Ins. Co., Newark, 1957-58; asst. prof. fin., money, banking U. Colo., 1958-60, assoc. prof., 1961-64, prof., 1965-68; prof. fin. U. Tex., Austin, 1969—; pvt. practice consulting for fin. instns., 1960—. Author: Personal Finance, 1978, 8th edit., 1989, Managing Your Money, 1977, Personal Financial Planning, 8th edit., 1989, alternate edit., 1991, 2nd alternate edit., 1992. Served with U.S. Navy, 1941-47. Mem. Am. Economic Assn., Am. Fin. Assn., So. Fin. Assn. Home: 7004 Edgefield Dr Austin TX 78731-2926 Office: Dept Finance University of Texas Austin TX 78712

WOLF, HAROLD HERBERT, pharmacy educator; b. Quincy, Mass., Dec. 19, 1934; s. John I. and Bertha F. (Sussman) W.; m. Joan Z. Silverman, Aug. 11, 1957; children: Gary Jerome, David Neal. B.S., Mass. Coll. Pharmacy, 1956; Ph.D., U. Utah, 1961; LLD (hon.), U. Md., 1994. Asst. prof. pharmacology Coll. Pharmacy Ohio State U., 1961-64, assoc. prof., 1964-69, prof., 1969-76, Kimberly prof., 1975-76, chmn. div. pharmacology, 1973-76; dean Coll. of Pharmacy, U. Utah, Salt Lake City, 1976-89, prof. pharmacology, 1989—; dir. Anticonvulsant Drug Devel. Program, 1989—; vis. prof. U. Sains Malaysia, 1973-74; mem. Nat. Joint Commn. on Prescription Drug Use, 1976-80; mem. NIH rev. com. Biomed. Research Devel. Grant Program, 1978-79; external examiner U. Malaya, 1978, 92, U. Sains Malaysia, 1980. Contbr. articles in field of central nervous system pharmacology and field of pharm. edn. Recipient Alumni Achievement award Mass. Coll. Pharmacy, 1978, Disting. Faculty award U. Utah, 1989, Rosenblatt prize, 1989, Disting. Alumnus award Coll. Pharmacy, U. Utah, 1991. Fellow Acad. Pharmaceutical Scis., AAAS; mem. Am. Soc. Pharmacology and Exptl. Therapeutics, Am. Pharm. Assn. (task force on edn. 1982-84), Am. Assn. Colls. of Pharmacy (pres. 1977, Disting. Pharmacy Educator award 1988, scholar in residence, 1989, chmn. commn. on implementing change in pharmacy edn. 1989-92), Am. Soc. Hosp. Pharmacists (Commn. on Goals 1982-84), Am. Council on Pharm. Edn. (bd. dirs. 1985-88), Sigma Xi. Jewish. Home: 4512 Bruce St Salt Lake City UT 84124-4720 Office: Coll Pharmacy U Utah Salt Lake City UT 84112

WOLF, IRVING, clinical psychologist; b. New Haven, Aug. 7, 1924; s. Samuel and Annie W.; m. Elizabeth Pennington Haughey, Aug. 1, 1949; children: Susan, Richard, Robert, William. A.B., Boston U., 1949, A.M., 1951, Ph.D., 1954. Diplomate Am. Bd. Profl. Psychology. Clin. psychologist VA Hosp., Brockton, Mass., 1954-57; clin. psychologist Mass. Gen. Hosp., Boston and research assoc. Harvard Med. Sch., 1957-59; prof. psychology, chmn. doctoral program clin. psychology, dir. fed. relations Boston U., 1959-75; vis. Fulbright prof. U. Philippines, Manila, 1965-66; dir. Nat. Ctr. Alcohol Edn., Washington, 1974; div. dir., sr. exec. Nat. Inst. Alcohol Abuse and Alcoholism, HEW, 1976-80; prof. psychology, sr. exec. Fed. Exec. Inst. Charlottesville, Va., 1981-85; pvt. practice, 1986-88; clin. dir. Devereux Found., Rutland, Mass., 1989-92; clin. assoc. Am. Geriatric Svcs., Rockland, Mass., 1992—. Author articles in field. Served with AUS, 1943-46. Named Disting. Alumnus Boston U. Coll. Liberal Arts, 1974. Fellow Am. Psychol. Assn.; mem. Eastern Psychol. Assn., Sr. Exec. Assn., Phi Beta Kappa. Home: 20 Pickwick Way Wayland MA 01778-3800

WOLF, JACK KEIL, electrical engineer, educator; b. Newark, Mar. 14, 1935; s. Joseph and Rosaline Miriam (Keil) W.; m. Toby Katz, Sept. 10, 1955; children—Joseph Martin, Jay Steven, Sarah Keil. B.S., U. Pa., 1956; M.S.E., Princeton, 1957, M.A., 1958, Ph.D., 1960. With R.C.A., Princeton, N.J., 1959-60; assoc. prof. N.Y. U., 1963-65; from assoc. prof. to prof. elec. engring. Poly. Inst. Bklyn., 1965-73; prof. dept. elec. and computer engring. U. Mass., Amherst, 1973-85; chmn. dept. U. Mass., 1973-75; Stephen O. Rice prof. Ctr. Magnetic Rec. Research, dept. elec. engring. and computer sci. U. Calif.-San Diego, La Jolla, 1985—; Mem. tech. staff Bell Telephone Labs., Murray Hill, N.J., 1968-69; engring. assoc. Qualcomm Inc., San Diego, 1985—. Editor for coding I.E.E.E. Transactions on Information Theory, 1969-72. Served with USAF, 1960-63. NSF sr. postdoctoral fellow, 1971-72; Guggenheim fellow, 1979-80. Fellow IEEE (pres. info. theory group 1974, co-recipient info. theory group prize paper award 1975, co-recipient Comm. Soc. prize paper award 1993), Nat. Acad. Engring.; mem. AAAS, Sigma Xi, Sigma Tau, Eta Kappa Nu, Pi Mu Epsilon, Tau Beta Pi. Achievements include research on information theory, communication theory, computer/communication networks, magnetic recording. Home: 8529 Prestwick Dr La Jolla CA 92037

WOLF, JAMES ANTHONY, insurance company executive; b. Washington, May 10, 1945; s. Arthur William and Marie Antoinette (Dalton) Wolf; m. Sheila Marie Regan, June 27, 1968; children: Jayne Ann, Elizabeth. BS in Fin. cum laude, Boston Coll., 1967. Mktg. rep. IBM, Newark, N.J., 1967-68, Boston, 1970-78; mktg. mgr. IBM, N.Y.C., 1978-81; 2nd v.p. Tchrs. Ins. & Annuity Assn., N.Y.C., 1981-82, v.p., 1982-85, sr. v.p., 1985—. Served to sgt. U.S. Army, 1968-70, Vietnam. Mem. Am. Mgmt. Assn. Republican. Roman Catholic. Home: 233 Ridge Common Fairfield CT 06430-7010 Office: Tchrs Ins & Annuity Assn Am 730 3rd Ave New York NY 10017-3206

WOLF, JOHN S., ambassador; b. Sept. 12, 1948. BA, Dartmouth Coll., 1970; postgrad., Princeton U., 1978-79. Fgn. svc. officer, 1970—; amb. to Malaysia Kuala Lumpur. Office: Am Embassy KL APO AP 96535

WOLF, JOSEPH ALBERT, mathematician, educator; b. Chgo., Oct. 18, 1936; s. Albert M. and Goldie (Wykoff) W. BS, U. Chgo., 1956, MS, 1957, PhD, 1959. Mem. Inst. for Advanced Study, Princeton, 1960-62, 65-66; asst. prof. U. Calif., Berkeley, 1962-64, assoc. prof., 1964-66, prof., 1966—, Miller research prof., 1972-73, 83-84; prof. honorario Universidad Nacional de Cordoba, Argentina, 1989; vis. prof. Rutgers U., 1969-70, Hebrew U., Jerusalem, 1974-76, Tel Aviv U., 1974-76, Harvard U., 1979-80, 86. Author: Spaces of Constant Curvature, 1967, 72, 74, 77, 84, Unitary Representations on Partially Holomorphic Cohomology Spaces, 1974, Unitary Representations of Maximal Parabolic Subgroups of the Classical Groups, 1976, Classification and Fourier Inversion for Parabolic Subgroups with Square Integrable Nilradical, 1979; co-editor, author: Harmonic Analysis and Representations of Semisimple Lie Groups, 1980, The Penrose Transform and Analytic Cohomology in Representation Theory, 1993; editor Geometriae Dedicata, Math Reports, Journal of Mathematical Systems, Estimation and Control, Nova Journal of Algebra and Geometry, Letters in Mathematical Physics, Journal of Group Theory in Physics; contbr. articles to profl. jours. Alfred P. Sloan rsch. fellow, 1965-67, NSF fellow, 1959-62; recipient Médaille de l'Université de Liège, 1977. Mem. Am., Swiss math. socs. Office: Dept Math U Calif Berkeley CA 94720

WOLF, JULIUS, medical educator; b. Boston, Aug. 15, 1918; s. Herman and Rose (Kurgan) W.; m. Irene H. Bechtloff, May 4, 1945; children—Maritja Ann, Miriam Jeanne, Brenda Joyce. S.B., Boston U., 1940, M.D., 1943. Intern L.I. Coll. Hosp., 1943-44, resident, 1944-45; resident Bronx VA Hosp., 1947-48, sect. chief medicine, chief gastroenterology sec., chief med. service, 1948-72, chief staff, 1970-90; assoc. dean Mt. Sinai Med. Ctr., N.Y.C., 1974-90; assoc. prof. medicine Columbia Coll. Phys. and Surg., 1961-67; prof. medicine Mt. Sinai Sch. Medicine, 1968—. Chmn. VA Lung Cancer Group, 1962-75. Served to capt. AUS, 1943-45. Fellow A.C.P.; mem. Am. Soc. Clin. Endoscopy, Harvey Soc., Am. Soc. Clin. Oncology. Home: 315 Covert Ave New Hyde Park NY 11040-5436

WOLF, KARL EVERETT, aerospace and communications corporation executive; b. Hartford, Conn., Aug. 19, 1921; s. Carl Fred and Anna (Voss) W.; m. Lola Sue Stoner, Aug. 1, 1948; children: Paula R., Gloria J., Glenn K. B.S., U.S. Mil. Acad., 1943; J.D., U. Pa., 1953; S.J.D., George Washington U., 1963. Bar: D.C. 1953, Conn. 1953, U.S. Supreme Ct. 1960, Calif. 1971, Mich. 1975. Commd. 2d lt. U.S. Army, 1943, advanced through grades to lt. col., 1959, ret., 1963; assoc. counsel Philco. Corp., Phila., 1963-73; v.p., gen. counsel Ford Aerospace Corp., Detroit, 1973-88; ret., 1988; mem. adv. bd. Bur. Nat. Affairs, Fed. Contract Reports, Washington, 1963-73. Author: State Taxation of Government Contractors, 1964. Decorated Silver Star, Bronze Star; Croix de Guerre (Belgium). Mem. ABA, Fed. Bar Assn., Calif. Bar Assn. Home: 535 Dunnegan Dr Laguna Beach CA 92651-1432

WOLF, KATIE LOUISE, state legislator; b. Wolcott, Ind., July 9, 1925; d. John H. and Helen Munsterman; m. Charles W. Wolf, 1945; children: Mark, Marcia. Grad., Ind. Bus. Coll., 1944. Registration officer County of White, Ind., 1960, mgr. lic. bur., 1960-68; clk. 39th Jud. Cir. Ct., 1968-78; mem. Ind. Ho. of Reps., 1985-86, Ind. State Senate, 1987—; mem. Dem. Nat. Com., 1968-90; del. Dem. nat. convs., 1972, 76, 80, 84. Recipient Athens award, 1987; named Woman of Yr. Bus. and Profl. Women's Club, 1984, Outstanding Freshman Legislator, 1985. Lutheran. Home: PO Box 766 Monticello IN 47960-0766 also: State Senate State Capitol Indianapolis IN 46204

WOLF, LESLEY SARA, lawyer; b. N.Y.C., Jan. 15, 1953; d. Herbert and Ardelle (Brush) W.; m. Dhiya El-Saden; children: Jordan, Evan. BA, Sarah Lawrence Coll., 1975; JD, U. Va., 1978. Bar: Calif. 1978. Assoc. Gibson, Dunn & Crutcher, L.A., 1978-86, ptnr., 1987—. Bd. dirs. L.A. Arts Coun., 1990-91, Franciscan Health Ctr., 1992-94. Office: Gibson Dunn & Crutcher 333 S Grand Ave Los Angeles CA 90071-1504

WOLF, MARK LAWRENCE, federal judge; b. Boston, Nov. 23, 1946; s. Jason Harold and Beatrice (Meltzer) W.; m. Lynne Lichterman, Apr. 4, 1971; children: Jonathan, Matthew. BA cum laude, Yale U., 1968; JD cum laude, Harvard U., 1971; hon. degree, Boston Latin Sch., 1990. Bar: Mass. 1971, D.C. 1972, U.S. Supreme Ct. 1976. Assoc. Surrey, Karasik & Morse, Washington, 1971-74; spl. asst. to dep. atty. gen. U.S. Dept. Justice, Washington, 1974-75; spl. asst. to atty. gen., 1975-76; dep. U.S. atty. U.S. Dept. Justice, Boston, 1981-85; from assoc. to ptnr. Sullivan & Worcester, Boston, 1977-81; judge U.S. Dist. Ct. Mass., Boston, 1985—; lectr. Harvard U. Law Sch., Cambridge, Mass., 1990—; adj. prof. Boston Coll. Law Sch., 1992. Bd. dirs. Albert Schweitzer Fellowship, Boston, 1974—, pres., 1989—; chmn. John William Ward Fellowship, Boston, 1986—. Recipient cert. appreciation U.S. Pres., 1975, Disting. Service award U.S. Atty. Gen., 1985. Mem. Boston Bar Assn. (council 1982-85), Am. Law Inst. Office: US Dist Ct McCormack PO & Courthouse Rm 1900 Boston MA 02109

WOLF, MILTON ALBERT, economist, former U.S. ambassador, investor; b. Cleve., May 29, 1924; s. Sam and Sylvia (Davis) W.; m. Roslyn C. Zehman, June 23, 1948; children: Leslie Eric, Caryn Sue, Nancy Gail, Sherri Hope. BA in Chemistry and Biology, Ohio State U., 1948; BS in Civil Engring. summa cum laude, Case Inst. Tech., 1954; MA in Econs., Case Western Res. U., 1973, PhD in Econs., 1993, LHD (hon.), 1980; LLD (hon.), Cleve. State U., 1980. Pres. Zehman-Wolf Constrn. Co., Cleve., 1948-76; U.S. ambassador to Austria, 1977-80; Disting. professorial lectr. in econs. Case Western Res. U., 1981-87; chmn. Milton A. Wolf Investors, 1980—; bd. dirs. Am. Greetings Corp., Huntington Bancshares Inc., Town and Country Trust; U.S. del. UN Conf. on Sci. and Tech. for Devel., 1979; U.S. del. dedication of UN Internat. Ctr., Vienna, 1979; host Salt II Summit, Vienna, 1979; trustee Cleve. Clinic; chmn. Fulbright Commn. for Austria, 1977-80. Trustee, chair Ohio State U.; trustee Case Western Res. U., Cleve. Orch.; vice chmn. Coun. Am. Ambs.; chmn. Am. Austrian Found.; pres. Am. Jewish Joint Distbn. Com.; life trustee Mt. Sinai Med. Ctr., Cleve.; mem. econ. adv. task force Carter Presdl. Campaign, 1976; mem. Carter Inauguration Com.; nat. fin. chmn. John Glenn Presdl. Coampaign, 1983-84; dir. transition Gov. Celeste, State of Ohio, 1982-83; nat. trustee United Israel Appeal, United Jewish Appeal, Coun. Jewish Fedns.; trustee United Way Svcs.; life trustee Park Synagogue, Cleve.; past pres., life trustee Jewish Community Fedn., Cleve. With USAAF 1943-48. Recipient Gt. Golden medal of honor with sash Republic of Austria, 1980, Gt. Golden medal of State Province of Salzburg, Republic of Austria, 1979, Eisenman award Jewish Cmty. Fedn. Cleve., 1990, Internat. Humanitarian award Raoul Wallenberg Com., 1995. Mem. Am. Econ. Assn., Cleve. Engring. Soc., Cleve. Com. World Affairs, UN Assn.-U.S. (bd. govs.), Tau Beta Pi. Jewish. Home: 19200 S Park Blvd Shaker Heights OH 44122 Office: Landmark Ctr Ste # 350 25700 Science Park Dr Beachwood OH 44122

WOLF, NAOMI, writer; b. San Francisco, Nov. 12, 1962; d. Leonard and Deborah W.; m. David Shipley, Sept. 1993. BA, Yale U., 1984. Author: The Beauty Myth: How Images of Beauty Are Used Against Women, 1990, Fire With Fire: The New Female Power and How It Will Change the 21st Century, 1993; contbr. to periodicals including New Republic, N.Y. Times, Wall Street Journal. Rhodes scholar, 1986. Office: care Royce Carlton Inc 866 UN Plz New York NY 10017*

WOLF, NEAL LLOYD, lawyer; b. Chgo., Feb. 8, 1949; s. Ira and Bettye (Brainin) W.; m. Caren Ellen Mirsky, June 11, 1972 (div. Apr., 1995); children: Michael Elliot, Brian Martin. AB magna cum laude, Princeton U., 1970; JD, U. Chgo., 1974. Bar: Ariz. 1974, U.S. Dist. Ct. Ariz. 1974, U.S. Ct. Appeals (9th cir.) 1975, Ill. 1983, U.S. Dist. Ct. (no. dist.) Ill. 1983, U.S. Ct. Appeals (7th cir.) 1983, U.S. Ct. Appeals (8th cir.) 1985, U.S. Supreme Ct., 1985, U.S. Dist. Ct. (no. dist.) Tex., 1990. Ptnr. Lewis and Roca, Phoenix, 1974-83, Winston & Strawn, Chgo., 1983-86, 89—; Ross & Hardies, Chgo., 1986-89. Mem. ABA. Avocations: golf, reading, movies, tennis. Office: Winston & Strawn 35 W Wacker Dr Chicago IL 60601-1614

WOLF, PETER MICHAEL, investment and land planning consultant, educator, author; b. New Orleans, Dec. 6, 1935; s. Morris and Ruth (New) W.; m. Alessandra Cantey, July 3, 1967; children—Phelan Godchaux, Alexis Ambler. B.A., Yale U., 1957; M.A., Tulane U., 1963; Ph.D., NYU, 1968. Ptnr. Wolf and Co., New Orleans, 1958-62; assoc. Wilbur Smith & Assocs., N.Y.C., 1968-70; faculty mem. NYU, 1966-67, Pratt Inst., N.Y.C., 1968-70; adj. prof. Cooper Union, N.Y.C., 1971-87; chmn. bd. fellows and mem. faculty Inst. Architecture and Urban Studies, N.Y.C., 1972-82; prin. Peter Wolf Assocs., N.Y.C., 1970—; organizer of exhbns. Mus. Modern Art, N.Y.C., 1969; writer exhbns. Whitney Mus. Art, N.Y.C., 1970; contbr. exhbns. Mus. Modern Art, N.Y.C., 1973, Albany Inst Art, 1975. Author: Land in America: Its Value, Use and Control, 1981; On Streets, 1979; The Future of the City: New Directions in Urban Planning, 1974; The Evolving

City, Urban Design Proposals by Ulrich Franzen and Paul Rudolph, 1974. Trustee Guild Hall, East Hampton, N.Y., 1981-86, Nat. Inst. Archtl. Edn., 1993—. NEA Fellow, 1979; Graham Found. Fellow, 1967-68, 93-94; Fulbright Fellow, 1965-66; Ford Found. grantee, 1971-74. Recipient Charles B. Shattuck award Nat. Research and Edn. Trust Fund, 1983. Mem. Am. Inst. Cert. Planners. Avocation: tennis. Home: 325 West End Ave New York NY 10023 Office: 7 W 36th St New York NY 10018

WOLF, ROBERT B., lawyer; b. Phila., Aug. 18, 1914; s. Morris and Pauline (Binswanger) W.; children—Edwin David, Virginia. B.A. Haverford Coll., 1936; LL.B., Harvard, 1939. Bar: Pa. 1939. Ptnr. Wolf, Block, Schorr & Solis-Cohen, 1940-43, 46-56, 57-85, of counsel, 1985—; gen. counsel FHA, Washington, 1956-57; instr. humanities Haverford Coll., 1948-49, 71-72. Chmn. mayor's coordinated housing improvement program, Phila., 1951, Phila. Youth Svcs. Coordinating Com., 1948-84; past chmn. Pa. Com. Crime and Delinquency; mem. juvenile adv. com. Pa. Commn. on Crime and Delinquency, 1976-86; ct. master Phila. Youth Study Ctr., 1976-89; trustee Benjamin Franklin Found., Berlin, Germany, 1955-56. 1st lt. inf. AUS, 1943-45; office Asst. Sec. War, 1945-46. Mem. Am., Pa., Phila. bar assns., Phi Beta Kappa. Home: 2101 Harts Ln Conshohocken PA 19428-2416 Office: Wolf Block Schorr & Solis-Cohen Packard Bldg Philadelphia PA 19102

WOLF, ROBERT HOWARD, advertising executive, marketing consultant; b. N.Y.C., Feb. 11, 1942; s. Charles and Dorothy (Goldstein) W.; m. Rebecca Helene Beck, Feb. 26, 1978; children—Jessica Leigh, Caroline Beth. B.A., Long Island U., 1964; M.B.A., Adelphi U., 1967. Mktg. mgr. Lever Bros, N.Y.C., 1967-70; mgmt. supr Wells, Rich, Greene, N.Y.C., 1971-77, sr. v.p., mng. dir., 1978-81; sr. v.p., gen. mgr. Kenyon & Eckhardt, Los Angeles, 1981-83; exec. v.p., gen. mgr. Chiat/Day Advt., N.Y.C., 1983-87, pres., chief exec. officer, vice chmn., 1987-89, bd. dirs.; chmn., chief exec. officer Chiat/Day/Mojo N.Am.; mem. world bd. Chiat/Day/Mojo; bd. dirs. Chiat/Day Mktg. Communications. Mem. Am. Mktg. Assn. Advt. Agys. (bd. govs.), Western States Assn. Advt. Agys., N.Y. Advt. Club, L.A. Advt. Club, Riviera Tennis Club, Mountaingate Country Club (L.A.), Tennisport Tennis Club (N.Y.C.). Home: 9817 Hythe Ct Beverly Hills CA 90210-1016 Office: Chiat/Day Inc Advt 340 Main St Venice CA 90291-2524

WOLF, ROBERT THOMAS, lawyer; b. N.Y.C., Apr. 14, 1936; s. Simon and Rose (Salzhauer) W.; divorced; 1 child, Lisa Eve. BS in Econs., U. Pa., 1955; LLB, Bklyn. Law Sch., 1963. Bar: N.Y. 1964. Asst. corp. counsel City of N.Y., 1970-80; ptnr. Weinberger & Wolf, Bronx, N.Y., 1980-83, Weinberger, Wolf, Rodrigues & Malach, Bronx, 1983-87, Weinberger, Wolf & Malach, Bronx, 1987-88, Wolf & Malach, Bronx, 1988-90; sole practice Bronx, 1990—. With U.S. Army, 1957-59. Mem. N.Y. State Bar Assn., Bronx County Bar Assn., Assn. Trial Lawyers Am., N.Y. State Trial Lawyers Assn. Avocations: sports, reading, swimming, Spanish literature and conversation. Office: 327 E 149th St Bronx NY 10451-5601

WOLF, ROSALIE JOYCE, financial executive; b. Southampton, N.Y., May 8, 1941; d. Saul and Anne W.; m. Milton Stern, May 15, 1979; 1 dau., Dina G. Pruzansky. A.B., Wellesley Coll., 1961; M.A. in Math, Northwestern U., 1962. With Mobil Oil Corp., N.Y.C., 1962-77; asst. treas. internat. Mobil Oil Corp., to 1977; v.p. venture capital group Donaldson, Lufkin, Jenrette, N.Y.C., 1977-79; asst. corp. contrl. Internat. Paper Co., N.Y.C., 1979—, treas., 1981-86; prin., chief fin. officer Aldrich, Eastman & Waltch Inc., Boston, 1986-89; mng. dir. pvt. equity Merchant Banking Group, Bankers Trust Co., N.Y.C., 1989-93; treas., chief investment officer The Rockefeller Found., N.Y.C., 1994—; dir., mem. compensation com. Narragansett Capital Corp., 1983-86. Durant scholar Wellesley Coll., 1961. Mem. Fin. Women's Assn. N.Y., Women's Forum, Phi Beta Kappa.

WOLF, STEPHEN M., airline executive; b. Oakland, Calif., Aug. 7, 1941. BA, San Francisco State U., 1965. Various positions Am. Airlines, Los Angeles, 1965-79, v.p. western div., 1979-81; sr. v.p. mktg. Pan Am. World Airlines, N.Y.C., 1981-82; pres., chief operating officer Continental Airlines, Houston, 1982-83; pres. Republic Airlines, Mpls., 1984-85, pres. chief exec. officer, 1985-86; chmn., pres., chief exec. officer Tiger Internat., Los Angeles, 1986-87; chmn., pres., chief exec. officer UAL Corp. and United Airlines, Chgo., 1987-92, chmn., CEO, 1992-94, former pres. dir.; adviser Air France, 1994—; bd. dirs. Air Transport Assn., Bus. Roundtable, Washington, conf. bd. N.Y. Internat. Air Transport Assn., Geneva, World Travel and Tourism Coun., London. Bd. dirs. Alzheimer's Disease and Related Disorders Assn., Chgo., Art Inst., Chgo., Chgo. Symphony Orch., Muscular Dystrophy Assn., Rush-Presbyn.-St. Luke's Med. Ctr., Chgo., J.L. Kellogg Sch. Bus. Adv. Coun., Northwestern U. Trustee Northwestern U. mem. bus. adv. com. Transportation Ctr. Office: United Airlines PO Box 66100 Chicago IL 60666 also: UAL Corp 1200 E Algonquin Rd Elk Grove Village IL 60007

WOLF, STEWART GEORGE, JR., physician, medical educator; b. Balt., Jan. 12, 1914; s. Stewart George and Angeline (Griffing) W.; m. Virginia Danforth, Aug. 1, 1942; children: Stewart George III, Angeline Griffing, Thomas Danforth. Student, Phillips Acad., 1927-31, Yale U., 1931-33; A.B., Johns Hopkins U., 1934, M.D. 1938; M.D. (hon.), U. Göteborg, Sweden, 1968. Intern N.Y. Hosp., 1938-39, resident medicine, 1939-42, NRC fellow, 1941-42; rsch. fellow Bellevue Hosp., 1939-42, clin. assoc. vis. neuropsychiatrist, 1946-52; rsch. head injury and motion sickness Harvard neurol. unit Boston City Hosp., 1942-43; asst., then assoc. prof. medicine Cornell U., 1946-52; prof., head dept. medicine U. Okla., 1952-67, Regents prof. medicine, psychiatry and behavioral scis., 1967—, prof. physiology, 1967-69; dir. Marine Biomed. Inst., U. Tex. Med. Br., Galveston, 1969-78; dir. emeritus Marine Biomed. Inst., U. Tex. Med. Br., 1978—, prof. medicine univ.; also prof. internal medicine and physiology med. br., 1970-77; prof. medicine Temple U., Phila., 1977—; dir. Totts Gap Inst., Bangor, Pa., 1958—; supr. clin. activities Okla. Med. Rsch. Found., 1953-55, head psychosomatic and neuromuscular sect., 1952-67, head neuroscis. sect., 1967-69; adv. com. Space Medicine and Behavioral Scis., NASA, 1960-61; cons. internal medicine VA Hosp., Oklahoma City, 1952-69; cons. (European Office), Paris, Office Internat. Rsch., NIH, 1963-64; mem. edn. and supply panel Nat. Adv. Commn. on Health Manpower, 1966-67; mem. Nat. Adv. Heart Coun., 1961-65, U.S. Phamacologic Scope Panel on Gastroenterology, Regent Nat. Libr. Medicine, 1965-69; chmn. Health Scis. Adv. Com. Nat. Adv. Environ. Health Scis. Coun., 1978-82; exec. v.p. Frontiers Sci. Found., 1967-69; mem. sci. adv. bd. Muscular Dystrophy Assns. Am., Inc., 1974-91, chmn., 1980-89; mem. gastrointestinal drug adv. com. FDA, 1974-77; bd. Internat. Cardiology Fedn.; mem. bd. visitors dept. biology Boston U., 1978-88; mem. vis. com. Ctr. for Social Rsch., Lehigh U., 1980-90; chmn. adv. com. Wood Inst. on History of Medicine, Coll. Physicians, Phila., 1980-90; mem. program com. Coll. Physicians, 1990-91; dir. Inst. for Advanced Studies in Immunology and Aging, 1988—. Author: Human Gastric Function, 1943, The Stomach, 1965, Social Environment and Health, 1981, others; adv. editor Internat. Dictionary Biology and Medicine, 1978—; editor in chief Integrative Physiol & Behavioral Sci.: The Official Jour. of Pavlovian Soc., 1990—. Pres. Okla. City Symphony Soc., 1956-61; mem. Okla. Sch. of Sci. and Math. Found., 1961—. Recipient Disting. Svc. Citation U. Okla., 1968, Dean's award for disting. med. svc., 1992; Horsley Gantt medal Pavlovian Soc., 1987, Hans Selye award Am. Inst. Stress, 1988, Rsch. award Carolinska Inst., Stockholm, 1994, Wilém Laufberger medal Acad. Scis. of Czech Republic, Citation for sci. and humanitarian achievement The J.E. Purkyně Bohemian Med. Assn. Fellow Am. Psychiat. Assn. (disting., trustee 1992—); Hofheimer prize for rsch. 1952); mem. AMA (coun. mental health 1960-64), Am. Soc. Clin. Investigation, Am. Clin. and Climatol. Assn. (pres. 1975-76), Assn. Am. Physicians, Am. Psychosomatic Soc. (pres. 1961-62), Am. Gastroent. Assn. (rsch. award 1943, pres. 1969-70), Am. Heart Assn. (chmn. com. profl. edn., com. internat. program, award), Coll. Physicians Phila., Collegium Internat. Activitas Nervosae Superioris (exec. com. 1992—, pres. 1994), Philos. Soc. Tex., Sigma Xi, Alpha Omega Alpha, Omicron Delta Kappa. Club: Cosmos (Washington). Home: RR 1 Box 1120G Bangor PA 18013-9716 Office: Totts Med Rsch Labs Bangor PA 18013

WOLF, WERNER PAUL, physicist, educator; b. Vienna, Austria, Apr. 22, 1930; came to U.S., 1963, naturalized, 1977; s. Paul and Wilhelmina Wolf; m. Elizabeth Eliot, Sept. 23, 1954; children: Peter Paul, Mary-Anne Githa. BA, Oxford (Eng.) U., 1951, DPhil, 1954, MA, 1954; MA (hon.),

Yale U., 1965. Rsch. fellow Harvard U., 1956-57; Fulbright travelling fellow, 1956-57; Imperial Chem. Industries rsch. fellow Oxford U., 1957-59, univ. demonstrator, lectr., 1959-62; lectr. New Coll., 1957-62; faculty Yale U., 1963—, prof. physics and applied sci., 1965-76, dir. grad. studies dept. engring. and applied sci., 1973-76, Becton prof., 1976-84, chmn. dept. engring. and applied sci., 1976-81, chmn. council engring., 1981-84, Raymond J. Wean prof. engring. and applied sci., prof. physics, 1984—, dir. undergrad. studies dept. applied physics, 1987-94, dir. grad. studies coun. engring., 1989, chmn. dept. applied physics, 1990—, chair commn. on econ. status of faculty, 1990-92; dir. ednl. affairs, 1994—; cons. Dupont Exptl. Sta., Wilmington, Del., 1957, Hughes Aircraft, Culver City, Calif., 1957, GE Rsch. Lab., Schenectady, N.Y., 1960, Mullard Rsch. Labs., Salfords, England, 1961, IBM, Yorktown Heights, N.Y., 1962-66, Brookhaven Nat. Lab., 1966-80, GE R & D Ctr., Schenectady, 1966—; vis. prof. Technische Hochschule, Munich, Germany, 1969; Sci. Research Council sr. vis. fellow Oxford U., 1980, 84; vis. fellow Corpus Christi Coll., 1984, 87; mem. program com. Conf. Magnetism and Magnetic Materials, 1963, 65, 86, chmn., 1968, mem. adv. com., 1964-65, 70-76, 85-88, chmn., 1972, steering com., 1970-71, conf. gen. chmn., 1971; mem. organizing, program coms. Internat. Congress on Magnetism, 1967, internat. program com., 1978-79, planning com., 1979-85; vis. physicist Brookhaven Nat. Lab., 1966, 68, vis. sr. physicist, 1970, research collaborator, 1972, 74, 75, 77, 80; mem. vis. com. dept. phys./sci. U. Del., 1980, 84, 86; mem. NATO Advanced Study Inst. Program Com., 1983, 85, internat. adv. bd. Yamada Conf. XXV on Magnetic Phase Transitions, 1990. Editor: CASE Reports, 1988-90; contbr. papers on magnetic materials and low temperature physics. Alexander von Humboldt Found. sr. U.S. scientist awardee, 1983; vis. guest fellow Royal Soc. London, 1987. Fellow IEEE, Am. Phys. Soc. (edn. com. 1977-80, program dir. Indsl. Grad. Intern Program 1978-79, chmn. fellowship com., Div. Condensed Matter Physics 1981-83); mem. Conn. Acad. Sci. and Engring., Yale Sci. and Engring. Assn. (Meritorious Svc. award 1985). Home: 37 Apple Tree Ln Woodbridge CT 06525-1258 Office: Yale U Dept Applied Physics PO Box 208284 New Haven CT 06520-8284

WOLF, WILLIAM MARTIN, computer company executive, consultant; b. Watertown, N.Y., Aug. 29, 1928; s. John and Rose (Emrich) W.; m. Eileen Marie Jolly, Aug. 19, 1952 (div. 1974); children: Rose, Sylvia, William. BS, St. Lawrence U., 1950; MS, U. N.H., 1951; postgrad., U. Pa., 1951-52, MIT, 1952-55. Programmer digital computer lab. MIT, Cambridge, Mass., 1952-54; pres. Wolf R & D Corp., Boston, 1954-69, Wolf Computer Corp., Boston, 1969-76, Planning Systems Internat., Boston, 1976-81, Micro Computer Software Inc., Cambridge, 1981-88, Tech. Acquisition Corp., Boston, 1989-91, Planning Internat., Inc., Boston, 1989-94, Wolfsort Corp., Boston, 1989—; dir., exec. dir. Tech. Capital Network MIT, 1992-94; co-founder, pres. Assn. Internat. Software Cos., Washington, 1965-67, Design Sci. Inst., Phila., 1969-73, Nat. Coun. Profl. Svc. Firms, Washington, 1970-75; seminar leader MIT Sloan Sch., Cambridge, 1970; co-founder, bd. dirs. Harbor Nat. Bank, Boston. Author computer program; inventor management system, orbit calculator, sorting method. Co-founder X-10 Orgn., Boston, 1962; trustee Addison Gilbert Hosp., Gloucester, Mass., 1963; v.p. Young Pres. Orgn., Boston, 1970; overseer Mus. Sci., Boston, 1989—; mem. Computer Mus. Named Outstanding Young Man in Boston, Jaycees, 1962; recipient Speaker's award Data Processing Mgmt. Assn., 1966. Mem. World Bus. Coun., MIT Club (Alumni award 1991), Boston Computer Soc., Forty-Niners.

WOLFART, H. C., linguistics scholar, author, editor; b. Lindau im Bodensee, Germany, 1943. Grad. (BA equivalent), Albert-Ludwigs-U., Freiburg im Breisgau, Fed. Republic Germany, 1964; MA, Cornell U., 1967, Yale U., 1966, M.Phil., Yale U., 1967, PhD, 1969. Lectr. U. Alta., Edmonton, Can., 1967-68; asst. prof. U. Man., Winnipeg, Can., 1969-72; assoc. prof. U. Manitoba, Winnipeg, Can., 1972-77, prof., head anthropology dept., 1977-78, prof., coord. linguistics program, 1978-87, prof., head linguistics dept., 1987-93, U. Disting. Prof. head linguistics dept., 1993—. Author: Plains Cree: A Grammatical Study, 1973, (with F. Pardo) Computer-Assisted Linguistic Analysis, 1973, (with J.F. Carroll) Meet Cree: A Guide to the Cree Language, 2d edit., 1981, (with D.H. Pentland) Bibliography of Algonquian Linguistics, 1982; editor: Essays in Algonquian Bibliography in Honour of V.M. Dechene, 1984; editor and translator: (told by L. Beardy) pisiskiwak ká-pîkiskwêcik/Talking Animals, 1988, (told by Nêhiyaw/Glecia Bear, co-edited and co-translated with F. Ahenakew) wanisinwak iskwêsisak/Two Little Girls Lost in the Bush, 1991; Linguistic Studies Presented to John L. Finlay, 1991, (told by Nêhiyaw/Glecia Bear and others, co-edited and co-translated with F. Ahenakew) kôhkominawak otâcimowiniwâwa/Our Grandmothers' Lives as Told in their own Words, 1992, (co-edited and co-translated with F. Ahenakew) kinêhiyâwiwininaw nêhiyawêwin/The Cree Language is Our Identity: The LaRonge Lectures of Sarah Whitecalf, 1993; mem. editorial bd. Actes du Congrès des Algonquinistes, 1982—; Revue canadienne de linguistique, 1983-86; assoc. editor (supplements) Algonquian and Iroquoian Linguistics, 1985—; assoc. editor Société d' Edition de textes algonquiens, 1985—. recipient Rh Inst. award in the humanities, 1980; fellow Studienstiftung des deutschen Volkes, 1963-67, Can. Coun./Social Scis. and Humanities Rsch. Coun., 1975-76, 82-83, s. Fellow Philol. Soc., Algonquian Text Soc.; mem. Assn. canadienne de linguistique, Societas Linguistica Europaea, Linguistic Assn. Gt. Britain, Linguistic Soc. Am., Soc. for Study of Indigenous Languages of Ams., Soc. for Mesopotamian Studies, Rupert's Land Rsch. Ctr., British Assn. Can. Studies, Oxford Bibliog. Soc., Friends of Bodleian, Henry Sweet Soc. Office: Linguistics Dept, U Manitoba, Winnipeg, MB Canada R3T 2N2

WOLFBEIN, SEYMOUR LOUIS, economist, educator; b. Bklyn., Nov. 8, 1915; s. Samuel and Fanny (Katz) W.; m. Mae Lachterman, Mar. 1, 1941; children: Susan Lois, Deeva Irene. B.A., Bklyn. Coll., 1936; M.A., Columbia U., 1937, Ph.D, 1941. Research assoc. U.S. Senate Com. on Unemployment and Relief, 1938; economist, div. research WPA, 1939-42; economist Bur. Labor Statistics, Dept. Labor, 1942-45, chief occupational outlook div., 1946-49, chief div. manpower and productivity, 1949-50, chief div. manpower and employment, 1950-59, dep. asst. sec. labor, 1959-67; dir. Office Manpower, Automation and Tng., 1962-67, spl. asst. to sec. labor for econ. affairs, 1965-67; dean Sch. Bus. Adminstrn., Temple U., Phila., 1967-78; Joseph A. Boettner prof. bus. adminstrn. Sch. Bus. Adminstrn., Temple U., 1978-85; dean Temple U. in Japan, 1983-85; pres. T/W/O, 1986—; prof. econs. Am. U., Washington; dir. Lincoln Bank of Phila. Author: Decline of a Cotton Textile City, 1942, The World of Work, 1951, Employment and Unemployment in the U.S.—A Study of American Labor Force, 1964, Employment, Unemployment and Public Policy, 1965, Education and Training for Full Employment, 1967, Occupational Information: A Career Guidance View, 1968, Emerging Sectors of Collective Bargaining, 1970, Work in American Society, 1971, Manpower Policy: Perspectives and Prospects, 1973, Labor Market Information for Youth, 1975, Men in the Pre-Retirement Years, 1977, Establishment Reporting in the U.S, 1978, The New Labor Force, 1988, The Changing Geography of America, 1988, America's Service Economy, 1988, The Older Worker, 1988, Working and Not Working in the U.S.A., 1989, Part Time Work in the U.S.A., 1989, The Temporary Help Supply Industry, 1989, In The Year 2000: A New Look, 1990, Our Industrial Future, 1990, Our Occupational Future, 1990, To the Year 2000—and Beyond: The World of Work, 1992, The Job Outlook in the U.S.A., 1994; contbr. numerous articles to tech. and profl. jours. Mem. commn. on human resources Nat. Acad. Scis.; mem. adv. com. NSF; bd. mgrs. Springarden Coll.; v.p. World Trade Council; mem. Mayor's Adv. Council on Employment, Phila.; bd. dirs. Jewish Employment and Vocat. Service. Served with U.S. Army, 1944-45. Recipient alumni award of honor Bklyn. Coll., 1954; Distinguished Service award Dept. Labor, 1955, 61. Fellow Am. Statis. Assn., AAAS; mem. Nat. and Civic Assn. (pres. Bannockburn 1957-59), Washington Statis. Soc. (pres.), Data Mgmt. Processing Assn. (hon. life), Am. Statis. Assn. (chmn. social statistics sect. 1956-57), Nat. Vocational Guidance Assn. (Eminent Career award 1970, chmn. occupational research com.), D.C. Guidance and Personnel Assn. (trustee). Home: E 706 Parktowne 2200 Benjamin Franklin Pky Philadelphia PA 19130 *Every year that goes by underscores the major common denominator to successful career development in America: the need to be responsive to social and economic change.*

WOLFBERG, MELVIN DONALD, company executive, optometrist, former college president, consultant; b. Altoona, Pa., June 24, 1926; s. Max Alex and Claire (Schiffman) Wolfberg; m. Audrey Iris Koch, Apr. 26, 1952; children: Debra Lynn, Michael Alex, Daniel Ben; m. Linda Diane Machesic,

Dec. 4, 1979. OD, Pa. Coll. Optometry, Phila., 1951; D of Ocular Sci. (hon.), New England Coll. Optometry, 1989, Ill. Coll. Optometry, 1990. Lic. optometrist, Pa. Pvt. practice and ptnr. optometric practice Selinsgrove, Pa., 1951-79; pres. Pa. Coll. Optometry, Phila., 1979-89; chmn. bd., 1976-79; v.p. profl. rels. Bausch and Lomb, Rochester, N.Y., 1991-95; pres. In Vision Inst., Boston, 1991-95; cons. to sec. HEW, Washington, 1970-77; dir. Better Vision Inst., N.Y.C., 1960-80. Mem. Selinsgrove City Coun., 1961-62; pres. Selinsgrove Community Chest, 1957; chmn. Optometrists Rep. Nat. Com. 1972, 76; chmn. Nat. Inter-Profl. Health Coun., Washington, 1972-77; dir. Univ. City Sci. Ctr., Phila., 1980-87; adv. com. Coun. Higher Edn., Commonwealth Pa., 1980-89. Served with U.S. Army, 1944-46, ETO. Decorated Purple Heart, Bronze Star, Silver Star; named Man of Yr. Central Pa. Optometric Soc., 1964, Alumnus of Yr. Pa. Coll. Optometry, 1970; recipient Carel C. Koch Meml. medal, 1989. Fellow Am. Acad. Optometry (pres. 1985-86); mem. Pa. Assn. Colls. and Univs. (exec. com. 1982-89, sec.-treas. 1985-88, vice chmn. 1988-89), Pa. Optometric Assn. (pres. 1959-61, Optometrist of Yr.), Am. Optometric Assn. (pres. 1969-70, Disting. Svc. award 1994), Pa. Coll. Optometry Alumni Assn. (pres. 1957), Beta Sigma Kappa.

WOLFCALE, ARTHUR DALE, lawyer; b. Youngstown, Ohio, July 12, 1929; s. Arthur Dale and Linnea T.A. (Larson) W.; m. Helen Louise Davies, July 8, 1960; children: Amy Louise, Nils Barthel. BA, Youngstown U., 1952; LLB, Western Res. U., 1954. Bar: Ohio 1954, U.S. Dist. Ct. (no. dist.) Ohio 1957. Dep. clk. Mahoning County Probate Ct., Youngstown, 1956-59; pvt. practice Youngstown, 1959-61; sec., asst. counsel Edward J. DeBartolo Corp., Youngstown, 1961-81, v.p., sec., 1981—. Bd. dirs. Youngstown Symphony Soc., 1987—. With U.S. Army, 1954-56, Fed. Republic Germany. Mem. Masons, Elks. Democrat. Methodist. Home: 6460 Leffingwell Rd Canfield OH 44406-9108 Office: Edward J DeBartolo Corp 7620 Market St Youngstown OH 44512-6078

WOLFE, AL, marketing and advertising consultant; b. Wyo., May 3, 1932; s. Clyde A. and Margaret V. (Joyce) W.; m. F. Carilouise, 1957 (div. 1994); children: Kirk, Kelley, Alison. B.A. in Psychology, U. Wyo., 1958. Product mgr., merchandising mgr. Gen. Mills, Mpls., 1958-62; asst. mktg. dir., v.p., account supr. Compton Advt., Chgo. and N.Y.C., 1963-66; v.p., account supr., exec. v.p., gen. mgr. Wells Rich Greene, N.Y.C., 1967-76; exec. v.p., dir. N.W. Ayer ABH Internat., N.Y.C., 1976-81; mng. dir., pres., bd. dirs. DDB Needham Worldwide, Chgo., 1981-87, pres. U.S. Div., 1987-88; pres. Al Wolfe Assocs., Inc., Mktg. and Advt. Cons., Sedona, Ariz., 1989—; bd. dirs. Clorox Co., Oakland, Calif., Dolphin Software, Inc., Lake Oswego, Oreg. Bd. dirs. U. Wyo. Found., pres., 1993-94; past pres. bd. dirs. U. Wyo. Art Mus.; chmn. Sedona Med. Ctr. Found.; bd. dirs Sedona Acad.; trustee Heard Mus., Phoenix; bd. dirs. Sedona Cultural Park. Recipient Disting. Alumnus award U. Wyo. 1981. Mem. Econ. Club (Chgo.), Sedona 30 Club. Home: 405 Manzanita Dr Sedona AZ 86336 Office: Al Wolfe Assocs Inc PO Box 2367 Sedona AZ 86339

WOLFE, ALBERT BLAKESLEE, lawyer; b. Parkersburg, W.Va., Apr. 6, 1909; s. William Henry and Katharine (White) W.; m. Beatrice Ewan, Oct. 23, 1942 (dec. Nov. 1986); children: Katharine Ward, Diana Ewan Wolfe Larkin. Grad., Hill Sch., 1927; A.B., Princeton U., 1931; LL.B., Harvard U., 1934. Bar: Mass., W.Va. 1934. Assoc. Rackemann, Sawyer & Brewster, Boston, 1934-40; partner Rackemann, Sawyer & Brewster, 1940-74, of counsel, 1974—; pres. Parkersburg Property Mgmt. Co., 1956-78. Chmn. Cambridge Hist. Commn., 1963-73; mem. Mass. Hist. Commn., 1963-73; pres. Keystone Fund (charitable fund), W.Va., 1951-89; trustee Marietta Coll., 1961-74, life emeritus, 1974—; trustee Nat. Trust for Historic Preservation, 1970-79; dir. Longfellow's Wayside Inn, 1972-89. Served to lt. comdr. USNR, 1942-45. Fellow Am. Bar Found. (life), Mass. Bar Found. (life); mem. ABA (chmn. real property, probate and trust law sect. 1968-69), Mass. Bar Assn., W.Va. Bar Assn., Am. Law Inst. (adviser model land devel. code 1963-76), Mass. Hist. Soc., Soc. Colonial Wars, Colonial Soc. Mass., Harvard Club Boston, Abstract Club Boston, pres. 1963-730, Harvard Faculty Club. Home: Old Harrisville Rd PO Box 97 Dublin NH 03444-0097 *Conservation of resources—natural, cultural, and human, can, since space explorations have held a mirror to earth, be seen as the greatest challenge humankind has ever faced. We need more than ever before to understand all facets of human history, and to transcend allegiances to territory, home, country, ideology, religious sect, and even family, and to see all earth as home, and each and every man and woman, no matter how different from us, as a fellow sharer of the human experience. Building bridges of mutual understanding becomes ever more important.*

WOLFE, BARBARA AHMAJAN, stock brokerage company executive, administrator; b. Providence, Aug. 1, 1943; d. Michael Ashod and Liberty (Hagopian) A.; m. Thomas Francis Wolfe, Apr. 7, 1984. B.A., Mills Coll., 1965. Mktg. analyst Calif. Blue Shield, San Francisco, 1967-70; research analyst Pacific Maritime Assn., San Francisco, 1970-73; corp. administr. Lawrence Systems, Inc., San Francisco, 1973-75; analyst Stanford Research Inst., Calif., 1975; exec. v.p., administr. Charles Schwab & Co., San Francisco, 1976—; dir.; corp. sec. Charles Schwab & Co., 1976—. Bd. govs. Mills Coll., Oakland, Calif., 1977-80. Home: 1221 Jones St # 3hc San Francisco CA 94109-4228 Office: Charles Schwab & Co Inc 101 Montgomery St San Francisco CA 94104-4122

WOLFE, CAMERON WITHGOT, SR., federal judge; b. San Francisco, Aug. 14, 1910; s. Frederick Lee and Edythe (Turnor) W.; m. Jean Brown, Aug. 15, 1936; children: Cameron Jr., Bruce McLaren, Robert Reese. AB, Stanford U., 1931; LLB, U. Calif., Berkeley, 1934. Bar: Calif. 1934, U.S Dist. Ct. (no. dist.) Calif. 1934, U.S.C.t. Appeals (9th cir.) 1934. Dep. dist. atty. Alameda County, Oakland, Calif., 1936-42; ptnr. Feruhoff & Wolfe, Oakland, 1946-75; bankruptcy judge U.S. Cts., Oakland, 1975—; adj. prof. U. Calif., Berkeley, 1946-51. Lt. commdr. USN, 1942-46. Mem. Nat. Conf. Bankruptcy Judges, Calif. State Bar Assn., Alameda County Bar Assn., Phi Beta Kappa. Avocations: teaching, gardening, golf, boating. Home: 522 Blair Ave Piedmont CA 94611 Office: Bankruptcy Ct PO Box 2070 Oakland CA 94604

WOLFE, CAMERON WITHGOT, JR., lawyer; b. Oakland, Calif., July 7, 1939; s. Cameron W. and Jean (Brown) W.; m. Frances Evelyn Bishopric, Sept. 2, 1964; children: Brent Everett, Julie Frances, Karen Jean. AB, U. Calif.-Berkeley, 1961, JD, 1964. Bar: Calif. 1965, U.S. Dist. Ct. (no. dist.) Calif. 1965, U.S.C.t. Appeals (9th cir.) 1965, U.S. Tax Ct. 1966, U.S. Ct. Claims 1977, U.S. Ct. Appeals (3d cir.) 1980, U.S. Ct. Appeals (fed. cir.) 1983, U.S. Supreme Ct. 1986 . Assoc., then ptnr. Orrick, Herrington & Sutcliffe, San Francisco, 1964—; bd. dirs. Crowley Maritime Corp.; mem. steering com. Western Pension Conf. Pres. League to Save Lake Tahoe, 1979, 80; chmn. League to Save Lake Tahoe Charitable Trust, 1966-91, Piedmont Ednl. Fund Campaign, 1982-83; pres. Piedmont Ednl. Found., 1986-90; bd. dirs. Yosemite Fund, 1993—. Served with U.S. Army, 1957, with USAR, 1957-65. Mem. ABA (mem. taxation com.), Calif. State Bar, San Francisco Bar Assn., Order of Coif, Phi Beta Kappa. Clubs: Pacific Union (San Francisco); Claremont Country (Oakland, Calif.). Home: 59 Lakeview Ave Piedmont CA 94611-3514 Office: Orrick Herrington & Sutcliffe 400 Sansome St San Francisco CA 94111

WOLFE, CHARLES MORGAN, electrical engineering educator; b. Morgantown, W.Va., Dec. 21, 1935; s. Slidell Brown and Mae Louise (Maness) W.; children—David Morgan, Diana Michele. B.S.E.E., W.Va. U., Morgantown, 1961, M.S.E.E., 1962; Ph.D., U. Ill., 1965. Research assoc. U. Ill., Urbana, 1965; mem. staff MIT Lincoln Lab., Lexington, Mass., 1965-75; prof. elec. engring Washington U., St. Louis, 1975—; Samuel C. Sachs prof., 1982-90, dir. semicondr. research lab., 1979-90; cons. MIT Lincoln Lab., 1975-76, Fairchild Semicondr., Palo Alto, Calif., 1975-76, Air Force Avionics Lab., Dayton, Ohio, 1976-79, U. Ill., 1983-85. Author: Physical Properties of Semiconductors, 1989; editor: Gallium Arsenide and Related Compounds, 1979; contbr. articles to profl. jours., chpts. to books. Served as sgt. USMC, 1955-58. Fellow IEEE (field awards com. 1984-87, Jack A. Morton award 1990); mem. NAE, AAAS, AAUP, Electrochem. Soc. (Electronics divsn. award 1978). Office: Washington U Campus Box 1127 Saint Louis MO 63130-1127

OLFE, DAVID LOUIS, lawyer; b. Kankakee, Ill., July 24, 1951; s. ...st Christian and Irma Marie (Nordmeyer) W.; m. Gail Lauret Fritz,

Aug. 25, 1972; children: Laura Beth, Brian David, Kaitlin Ann. BS, U. Ill., 1973; JD, U. Mich., 1976. Bar: Ill. 1976, U.S. Dist. Ct. (no. dist.) Ill. 1976. Assoc., Gardner, Carton & Douglas, Chgo., 1976-82, ptnr., 1983—; lectr. estate planning Aid Assn. for Lutherans SMART Program, Chgo., 1980-84; lectr. Ill. Inst. Continuing Legal Edn., Chgo. Bar Assn., Lake Shore Nat. Bank, Ill. State Bar Assn. Contbr. articles to legal publs. Recipient Recognition award Ill. Inst. Continuing Legal Edn., 1981-84. Mem. ABA (sects. on taxation, corp. banking and bus. law 1981—, chmn.), NFL Players Assn. (cert. contract advisor 1983—), NCAA (cert. contract advisor), Chgo. Assn. Commerce and Industry (employee benefit subcom. 1983—), Ill. State Bar Assn. (employee benefits sect. council, 1986—, recognition award 1983), Phi Kappa Phi, Beta Alpha Psi, Beta Gamma Sigma, Sigma Iota Lambda, Phi Eta Sigma. Office: Gardner Carton & Douglas 321 N Clark St Ste 3300 Chicago IL 60610-4717

WOLFE, DEBORAH CANNON PARTRIDGE, government education consultant; b. Cranford, N.J.; d. David Wadsworth and Gertrude (Moody) Cannon; 1 son, Roy Partridge. BS, N.J. State Coll.; MA, EdD, Tchrs. Coll., Columbia U.; postgrad., Vassar Coll., U. Pa., Union Theol. Sem., Jewish Sem. Am.; hon. doctorates, Seton Hall U., 1963, Coll. New Rochelle, 1963, Morris Brown U., 1964, Glassboro/Rowan Coll., 1965, Bloomfield Coll., 1988, Monmouth Coll., 1988, William Paterson Coll., 1988; LLD (hon.), Kean Coll., 1981; LHD (hon.), Stockton State Coll., 1982; LLD (hon.), Jersey City State Coll., 1987, Centenary Coll., William Paterson Coll., 1989, Tuskegee U., 1989, Glassboro State Coll., 1985, Tuskegee U., 1989, St. Peter's Coll., 1989, Rider Coll., 1989, Georgian Court Coll., 1990; DSc (hon.), Stevens Inst. Tech., 1991; LLD (hon.), Rutgers U., 1992, Thomas Edison Coll., 1992; DSc, U. Med. and Dentistry N.J. Former prin., tchr. pub. schs. Cranford, also Tuskegee, Ala.; faculty Tuskegee Inst., Grambling Coll., NYU, Fordham U., U. Mich., Tex. Coll., Columbia U.; supervision and adminstrn. curriculum devel., social studies U. Ill., summers; prof. edn., affirmative action officer Queens Coll.; prof. edn. and children's lit. Wayne State U.; edn. chief U.S. Ho. of Reps. Com. on Edn. and Labor, 1962—; Fulbright prof. Am. lit. NYU; U.S. rep. 1st World Conf. on Women in Politics; chair non-govtl. reps. to UN (NGO/DPI exec. com.), 1983—; editl. cons. Macmillan Pub. Co.; cons. Ency. Brit.; adv. bd. Ednl. Testing Svc.; mem. State Bd. Edn., 1964-94; chairperson N.J. Bd. Higher Edn., 1967-94; mem. nat. adv. panel on vocat. edn. HEW; mem. citizen's adv. com. to Bd. Edn., Cranford; mem. Citizen's Adv. Com. on Youth Fitness, Pres.'s Adv. Com. on Youth Fitness, White House Conf. Edn., 1955, White House Conf. Aging, 1960, White House Conf. Civil Rights, 1966, White House Conf. on Children, 1970, Adv. Coun. for Innovations in Edn.; v.p. Nat. Alliance for Safer Cities; cons. Vista Corps, OEO; vis. scholar Princeton Theol. Sem., 1989—; active Human Rels. Coun., N.J., 1994—; vis. prof. U. Ill., U. N.C., Wayne State U.; theologian-in-residence Duke U.; mem. trustee bd. Sci. Svc. Contbr. articles to ednl. publs. Bd. dirs. Internat. Welfare Assn., Cmty. Ctr., 1st Bapt. Ch., Cranford Cmty. Ctr. Migratory Laborers, Hurlock, Md.; trustee Sci. Svc., Seton Hall U.; mem. Pub. Broadcasting Authority; bd. regents Seton Hall U.; sec. Kappa Delta Pi Ednl. Found.; mem. adv. com. Elizabeth and Arthur Schlesinger Libr., Radcliffe Coll.; trustee Edn. Devel. Ctr., Sci. Svc., 1965—; assoc. min. First Bapt. Ch.; mem. Tuskegee Sci. Alumni, 1995, N.J. Conv. of Progressive Baptists, 1995. Recipient Woman of Yr. award Delta Beta Zeta, Woman of Yr. award Morgan State Coll., Medal of Honor, DAR, 1990, Disting. Svc. medal Nat. Top Ladies of Distinction, 1991, Disting. Svc. award Nat. Assn. State Bds. Edn., 1992, Disting. Svc. to Edn. award N.J. Commn. on Status of Women, 1993, Svc. to Children award N.J. Assn. Sch. Psychologists, 1993, U. Medicine and Dentistry of N.J. Disting. Svc. award Nat. Assn. State Bd. Edn., 1994, Disting. Medal award U. Medicine and Dentistry N.J., Union Coll., citation N.J. State Coun. on Vocat. Edn., 1994, citation N.J. State Bd. Edn., 1994. Mem. NEA (life), ASCD (rev. coun.), AAAS (chmn. tchr. edn. com.), LWV, NCCJ, AAUW (nat. edn. chmn.), AAUP, NAACP (Medal of Honor 1994), Coun. Nat. Orgns. Children and Youth, Am. Coun. Human Rights (v.p.), Nat. Panhellenic Coun. (dir.), Nat. Assn. Negro Bus. and Profl. Women (chmn. speakers bur., Nat. Achievement award 1958), Nat. Assn. Black Educators (pres.), N.Y. Tchrs. Assn., Am. Tchrs. Assn., Fellowship So. Churchmen, Internat. Reading Assn., Comparative Edn. Soc., Am. Acad. Polit. and Social Sci., Internat. Assn. Childhood Edn., Nat. Soc. Study Edn., Am. Coun. Edn. (commn. fed. rels.), Nat. Alliance Black Educators (pres.), Internat. Platform Assn., Ch. Women United (UN rep., mem. exec. com.), UN Assn.-U.S.A. (exec. com.), N.J. Fedn. Colored Women's ClDelta Kappa Gamma (chmn. world fellowship com.), Kappa Delta Pi (chmn. ritual com., mem. ednl. found., 1980—, laureate 1990, scholarship named in her honor, citation 1994), Pi Lambda Theta, Zeta Phi Beta (internat. pres. 1954, chmn. edn. found. 1974—, Achievement award Atlantic region). Home: 326 E Nantucket Ln Jamesburg NJ 08831 Office: NJ State Bd Higher Edn 20 W State St Trenton NJ 08608-1206 *I feel I am extremely fortunate to have been born into a family where love of God and love of knowledge have been major concerns. The knowledge we have sought has not been 'knowledge for knowledge's sake' but 'knowledge to improve society and the world'. I have always felt that 'God power' linked with 'Brain power' was the greatest force in the world and I knew that in order to achieve such strength one must work diligently and constantly. Because knowledge changes so rapidly this quest for wisdom must be eternal. Hence I hope I'm still learning and growing for education must be involved from 'the womb to the tomb'.*

WOLFE, ETHYLE RENEE (MRS. COLEMAN HAMILTON BENEDICT), college administrator; b. Burlington, Vt., Mar. 14, 1919; d. Max M. and Rose (Saiger) W.; m. Coleman Hamilton Benedict, Dec. 4, 1954. B.A., U. Vt., 1940, M.A., 1942; postgrad., Bryn Mawr Coll., 1942-43; Ph.D., N.Y. U., 1950; LHD (hon.), CUNY, 1989; LLD (hon.), Iona Coll., 1989. Teaching fellow U. Vt., 1940-42; research fellow Latin Bryn Mawr (Pa.) Coll., 1942-43; instr. classics Bklyn. Coll., 1947-49, instr. classical langs., 1949-54, asst. prof., 1954-59, assoc. prof., 1960-68, prof., 1968—, acting chmn. dept. classics and comparative lit., 1962-63, chmn. dept., 1967-72; dean Bklyn. Coll. (Sch. Humanities), 1971-78; exec. officer Humanities Inst. Bklyn. Coll., 1980-89, provost and v.p. for acad. affairs, 1982-88, provost emeritus, 1989—; mem. exec. com., chmn. com. on undergrad. affairs, com. on univ.-wide programs CUNY faculty senate; mem. study group AAAS, 1987-89; dir. Fund for Improvement of Postsecondary Edn.-funded Ctr. for Core Students, 1987-88; co-chair senate report, Chancellor's Coll. Prep. Initiative, 1991; mem. exec. com for publ.: The Liberal art of science: Agenda for Action:, dir. Nat. Core Visitors Programs, 1985-89. Asso. editor: Classical World, 1965-71; co-editor: The American Classical Review, 1971-76. Ethyle R. Wolfe Inst. for the Humanities Bklyn. Coll. named in honor, 1989; mem. Columbia U. Seminar in Classical Civilization. Recipient Kirby Flower Smith award, 1939, Goethe prize U. Vt., 1940, Alumni Achievement award U. Vt., 1985, Charles Frankel prize NEH, 1990; named to Hall of Honor U. Vt., 1991; named Disting. U. Faculty Sen. Emeritus, CUNY, 1992; NEH grantee, 1971, 1982-84, Andrew W. Mellon Found. grantee, 1984-88. Mem. Am. Philol. Assn., Archeol. Inst. Am., Vergilian Soc. Am., Classical Assn. Atlantic States (exec. com.), Am. Soc. Papyrologists, N.Y. Classical Club (past pres.), Phi Beta Kappa (past pres. Rho chpt., pres. 1988-90). Home: 360 W 22nd St New York NY 10011-2600 Office: Bklyn Coll Bedford Ave # H Brooklyn NY 11222

WOLFE, GARY JOHNSON, financial executive; b. Wilmington, N.C., Sept. 13, 1937; s. Vivian Earcelle (Johnson) W.; m. Carolyn Wilson; children: Kimberly L., Steven G. AA, Wilmington Coll., 1957; BS, U. N.C. 1959. CPA, N.C., S.C, Ga. Acct. A.M. Pullen & Co., Danville, Va., 1959-62; with Cherry, Bekaert & Holland, Charlotte, N.C., 1962—; ptnr. Cherry, Bekaert & Holland, Charlotte, 1967—; ptnr. in charge Cherry, Bekaert & Holland, Beaufort, N.C., 1967-70; ptnr. in charge Cherry, Bekaert & Holland, Atlanta, 1970-78, mem. exec. com., 1973—, ptnr. regional ops., 1974-78; mng. ptnr., chief exec. officer Cherry, Bekaert & Holland, Charlotte, 1978—; exec. bd. dirs. Summit Internat., Inc. Contbr. articles to jours. and chpts. to books. Mem. AICPA (com. Group B), N.C. Assn. CPAs, S.C. Assn. CPAs, Ga. Soc. CPAs, Nat. Assn. Accts., Civitan Club, Exchange Club, Rotary. Avocations: golf, hiking, outdoor activites. Office: Cherry Bekaert & Holland 3100 One First Union Ctr Charlotte NC 28202

WOLFE, GEORGE B., lawyer; b. Columbia, S.C.; s. Oliver Jordan and Marie (Ulmer) W.; m. Virginia Earl Wilson Short, Feb. 5, 1983; 1 child, Oliver. BA cum laude, Washington & Lee U., 1973; JD cum laude, U. Pa., 1977. Bar: S.C. 1977, D.C. 1978. Clerk to Donald Russell U.S. Ct. Appeals (4th cir.), 1977-78; lawyer Wilmer, Cutler & Pickering, Washington, 1978-81, Zuckerman, Spaeder, Taylor & Kolker, Washington, 1981-83; with econ.

devel. transition team Gov. Campbell, 1987; mem. Investment Policy Adv. com. U.S. Trade Rep., 1990-94; del. Southeast-U.S. confs. Tokyo, Seoul, 1989; mem. East Asian Trade mission Gov. Carroll Campbell, 1989; private sector mem. S.C. Gov. Carroll Campbell's Trade mission Europe, 1990; ptnr. Nelson, Mullins, Riley & Scarborough, Columbia, S.C., 1992—. Bd. dirs. Greater Columbia C. of C., 1987-91, chmn. Govtl. Affairs Coun.; chmn. Com. of 100, 1987, chmn. Internat. com., 1988-93; mem. Gov.'s Coun. Competitiveness, 1987-91, vice chmn., 1988-91, co-chmn. S.C Lawyers for Bus, 1988, 92; S.C. steering com., bus. adv. coun., legal counsel George Bush for Pres.; bd. dirs. S.C. C. of C., 1993—. Participant Internat. Bus. Fellows program, Atlanta, London, Paris, 1991. Mem. ABA, Am. Immigration Lawyers Assn., S.C. Bar Assn. (chair corp., banking, securities law sect., securities law com.), Richland County Bar Assn. Order of Coif. Republican. Avocations: tennis, history, government, reading. Office: Nelson Mullins et al 1330 Lady St Columbia SC 29201-3300

WOLFE, GEORGE C., theater director, producer, playwright; b. 1954. Writer, lyricist Paradise!, 1985; writer, dir. The Colored Museum, 1986 (Elizabeth Hull-Kate Warriner award Dramatists Guild 1986); librettist Queenie Pie, 1987; scene contbr. Urban Blight, 1988; adaptor, dir. Spunk, 1990 (Obie award best dir. 1990), writer, dir. Jelly's Last Jam, 1992 (Joe A. Callaway award Stage Dirs. and Choreographers Found. 1993); dir. Angels in America (Tony award best dir. play 1993), Millennium Approaches, Twilight: Los Angeles, 1992, 1994, Perestroika, 1994, Blade to the Heat, 1994; prodr. N.Y. Shakespeare Festival, Broadway, 1990-91, assoc. dir. 1993—. Office: NY Shakespeare Festival Joseph Papp Pub Theater 425 Lafayette St New York NY 10003

WOLFE, GREGORY BAKER, international relations educator; b. Los Angeles, Jan. 27, 1922; s. Harry Norton and Laura May (Baker) W.; m. Mary Ann Nelson, June 15, 1946; children: Gregory Nelson, Laura Ann, Melissa Helene. A.B., Reed Coll., 1943; M.A., Fletcher Sch. Law and Diplomacy, 1947, Ph.D., 1961; Dr. honoris causa, U. Autonoma de Guadalajara, Mex., 1984; D.H.L., Southeast Coll. Osteo. Medicine, Miami, Fla., 1985. With internat. div. Arthur D. Little, Inc., Cambridge, Mass., 1951-57; dir. Greater Boston Econ. Study Com., 1957-61; dir. Latin Am. program Com. Econ. Devel., 1961-64; dir. intelligence and rsch. for Am. republics State Dept., 1964-68; pres. Portland State U. 1968-74; dean Sch. Internat. Svc. Am. U., Washington, 1975-79; pres. Fla. Internat. U., Miami, 1979-86; prof. internat. rels. Fla. Internat. U., 1979—; vis. scholar Cambridge U., Eng., 1986-87; sr. cons. Orion Comml. Realty Inc., 1991—; fed. negotiator Joint Transp. Com. Washington 1962-66. Contbr. articles to profl. jours. Chmn. bd. trustees Internat. Fine Arts Coll., 1993—; bd. dirs. Chopin Found. U.S., Inc., 1988—; Concert Assn. Fla., Inc., 1988—, Am. Coll. Madrid, 1994—; chmn. Brickell Avenue Lit. Soc., 1988—. Recipient Fla. Internat. Ctr. award, 1980, Leonard Abess award, 1984, Orden del Merito Civil, King of Spain, 1986, Fulbright lectr., Ecuador, 1989.

WOLFE, HAROLD JOEL, lawyer, business executive; b. Toronto, Ont., Can., July 21, 1940; s. Max and Beatrice Irene (Albert) W.; m. Carole S. Wolfe, Aug. 17, 1967; 3 children. B.Commerce, U. Toronto, 1963, LL.B., 1966. Mem. firm Goodman & Carr (Barristers), Toronto, 1968-69; with Oshawa Group Ltd., Toronto, 1970—; corp. v.p. real estate, sec. Oshawa Group Ltd., 1971—, also dir. Mem. Law Soc. Upper Can. Office: Oshawa Group Ltd, 302 East Mall, Toronto, ON Canada M9B 6B8

WOLFE, J. W., newspaper publishing executive. Chmn. bd. Dispatch Newspapers, Columbus, Ohio. Office: Columbus Dispatch PO Box 1289 34 S 3rd St Columbus OH 43215

WOLFE, JAMES RONALD, lawyer; b. Pitts., Dec. 10, 1932; s. James Thaddeus and Helen Matilda (Corey) W.; m. Anne Lisbeth Dahle Eriksen, May 28, 1960; children: Ronald, Christopher, Geoffrey. B.A. summa cum laude, Duquesne U., 1954; LL.B. cum laude, NYU, 1959. Bar: N.Y. 1959. Assoc. Simpson Thacher & Bartlett, N.Y.C., 1959-69, ptnr., 1969—. Co-editor: West's McKinney's Forms, Uniform Commercial Code, 1965. Served to 1st lt. U.S. Army, 1955-57. Mem. ABA, N.Y. State Bar Assn., Assn. of Bar of City of N.Y., Am. Judicature Soc., N.Y. Law Inst. Republican. Roman Catholic. Home: 641 King St Chappaqua NY 10514-3807 Office: Simpson Thacher & Bartlett 425 Lexington Ave New York NY 10017-3903

WOLFE, JANICE E., government executive; b. Racine, Ohio, Aug. 25, 1939; d. Donald Clark and Erline (Sargent) W. A.B. in Govt., Ohio U., 1961; J.D., Ohio State U., 1964. Bar: Ohio 1964. Atty. examiner Ohio Dept. Liquor Control, Columbus, 1964; asst. atty. gen., Columbus, Ohio, 1965-72; dist. counsel SBA, 1972-80, dep. dist. dir., Chgo., 1980-83, dist. dir., Washington, 1983-87, dep. assoc. adminstr. bus. devel., 1987—. Recipient SBA awards. Office: SBA 1441 L St NW Washington DC 20005-3512

WOLFE, JEAN ELIZABETH, medical illustrator, painter; b. Newark, N.J., Oct. 3, 1925; d. Arthur Howard and Ethel (Harper) Wolfe; B.S., Russell Sage Coll., 1947; student Pratt Inst., 1949-50; grad. diploma U. Rochester Sch. Medicine and Dentistry, 1955; postgrad. (W.B. Saunders fellow), U. Pa., 1955-56, U. Pa., 1980; M.F.A. in Painting, U. Pa., 1974, M.A. (hon.), 1973. Cert. Med. Illustrator. Exhibitor, Pratt Inst. Galleries, Bklyn., 1958, N.Y. Med. Coll., 1958, Assn. Med. Illustrators, 1961-86, 90, AMA, N.Y.C., 1965, Phila., 1965, A.C.S., Atlantic City, 1965, Rsch. Study Club L.A., 1966, Phila. Art Alliance, 1967, 73, U. Pa. Alumni Ophthal. Assn., 1967-68, N.J. Med. Soc., 1968, Cayuga Mus. History and Art, 1968, Pensacola Art Ctr., 1969, FAA Aero. Center, Oklahoma City, 1970, Scheie Eye Inst., 1972-75, Assn. Med. Illustrators Traveling Salon, 1978, Moore Coll. Art, 1985, Mus. of Am. Illustration Soc. of Illustrators, 1986, Mutter Mus., Phila. Coll. of Physicians, 1990-92; represented in permanent collections Archives of Med. Visual Resources, Francis A. Countway Med. Libr., Harvard Univ., Mutter Mus., Phila. Coll. Physicians; collection of work donated by Scheie Eye Inst., life history and papers housed in The Arthur and Elizabeth Schlesinger Libr. on the History of Women in Am., Radcliffe Coll.; contbg. illustrator Adler's Textbook Ophthalmology, 8th edit., 1969; illustrations in med. books, jours., pharm. house pubs.; instr. Pembroke Coll. Brown U., 1947-49; mem. faculty Kimberley Sch., Upper Montclair, N.J., 1950-52; free lance med. illustration Studio N.Y. Med. Coll., 1956-60; instr. Pratt Inst., 1958-59; assoc. in med. illustration U. Pa. Sch. Medicine, 1960-72, tenured sole artist in the hist. of the sch. of medicine, research asst. prof. med. art in ophthalmology, 1972-85, rsch. asst. prof. emeritus, 1985—; independent studio (fine art) painting and medical illustration, 1985—; guest lectr. Johns Hopkins Med. Sch., 1973, NIH; guest artist USAF, Air Force Acad. and NORAD, 1971. Recipient Merit certificate AMA; Appreciation certificate ACS; 1st prize Pensacola Art Center, Am. Heart Assn., 1969, Gold medal Graphic Arts Soc. of Del. Valley, 1973. Fellow Assn. Med. Illustrators (emeritus); mem. Assn. Med. Illustrators (Ralph Sweet, Tom Jones awards, gov. 1970—, chmn. nominating com. 1972-73, vice chmn. bd. govs. 1973-74, chmn. bd. 1974-75, selection com., Lifetime Achievement award 1989—, adv. coun. Vesalius Trust 1990—), Soc. Illustrators (cert. merit 1986), Coll. Art Assn., Women's Caucus for Art, Faculty Club of U. Pa.

WOLFE, JOHN THOMAS, JR., university president; b. Jackson, Miss., Feb. 22, 1942; s. John Thomas Sr. and Jeanette (Wallace) W.; children: Wyatt Bardouille, John Thomas Dantzler, David Andrew Dantzler. BEd, Chgo. Tchrs. Coll., 1964; MS, Purdue U., 1972, PhD, 1976. Tchr. English Englewood High Sch., Chgo., 1965-67; linguistics prof. Cuttington Coll., Liberia, West Africa, 1967-69; asst. mgr. residence hall Purdue U., West Lafayette, Ind. 1971-75, employee relations mgr., 1975-77; asst. prof. English Fayetteville (N.C.) State U., 1977-82, coordinator of English and dramatic arts, 1978-83, head div. humaities and fine arts 1979-84; acad. dean. Ft. Bragg U. Ctr., 1983-85; provost, v.p. for acad. affairs Bowie (Md.) State Coll., 1985-90; pres. Ky. State U., Frankfort, 1990—; lectr. Krannert Sch. Mgmt., 1976; mem. N.C. Humanities Commn., 1981-85. Contbr. articles in field. Active N.C. Humanities Com., Greensboro, 1979-83, Arts Council Fayetteville, Cumberland, N.C., 1979-85, Minority Bus. Resource Inst. Bd., Landover, Md., 1986—; bd. dirs. Entrepreneurial Devel. Program, Landover, 1986—. NEH grantee, 1979; Am. Council on Edn. fellow, 1982-83; recipient award Fayetteville Human Relations Commn., 1981. Mem. Nat. Coun. Tchrs. English (pres. Black Caucus 1981-88), Conf. Coll. Composition and Communication (chmn. resolutions com. 1982—), Assn. Tchr. Educators, Am. Assn. Higher Edn., Am. Assn. Univ. Adminstrs., Am. Coun. Edn., Am. Assn. Tchr. Educators, Maledicta

Soc., Kappa Delta Pi, Omega Psi Phi, Alpha Kappa Mu (hon.). Roman Catholic. Avocations: poetry, reading, golfing, long distance motoring. Home: 263 Meadowview Dr # B Frankfort KY 40601-4128 Office: Ky State U Office of Pres Frankfort KY 40601

WOLFE, JONATHAN A., food wholesaler, retailer. Pres., COO Oshawa Group Ltd., Toronto, Ont., Can. Office: The Oshawa Group Ltd, 302 E Mall, Toronto, ON Canada M9B 6B8

WOLFE, JONATHAN JAMES, pharmacy educator; b. Little Rock, Ark., Mar. 13, 1944; s. Jonathan Edwards and Mary Anne (Murphy) W.; m. Donna Jean Manley, Aug. 13, 1966; 1 child, Robert Jonathan. AB in History and Polit. Sci with honors, Hendrix Coll., 1966; MA in History, U. Va., 1968, PhD in U.S. History, 1971; post grad., Ark. Tech. U., 1973-74; BS in Pharmacy, U. Ark., 1977. Lic. pharmacist. Asst. prof. history and polit. sci Ark. Tech. U., Russellville, Ark., 1970-73; instr. dept. history U. Ark., Little Rock, 1974-85; staff pharmacist The Doctor's Hosp., Little Rock, 1976-78, pharmacy supr., 1978-81; supr. intravenous admixtures Ark. Children's Hosp., Little Rock, 1981-82, pharmacy supr.intensive care satellite, 1982-85; pharmacist Caremark Homecare, Divsn. of Baxter Internat., Little Rock, 1985-88; asst. prof. of pharmacy practice U. Ark. for Med. Sci., Little Rock, 1986-91; pharmacist Little Rock Ambulatory Care Pharmacy, Little Rock, 1989-91; asst. prof. history U. Ark., Little Rock, 1991—; asst. prof. pharmacy practice U. Ark for Med. Sci., Little Rock, 1991—; del. USP Conv., 1995; adv. bd. gov. Winthrop Rockefeller Lectureship, 1990—, chmn., 1994—; state coord. Ark. State Cancer Pain Initiative, 1993. Contbr. to profl. jours. Coun. mem. for liberal arts U. Ark., Little Rock, 1983-86; bd. dir., v.p. Little Rock Chamber Mus. Soc., 1992—. Recipient Nat. Achievement award Am. Soc. Hosp. Pharmcists Rsch. and Edn. Found., 1993; Woodrow Wilson fellow Woodrow Wilson Nat. Fellowship Found., 1966, Va.-Wilson fellow U. Va. and Woodrow Wilson Nat. Fellowship Found., 1967, Va.-Danforth fellow U. Va., 1967-70, Summer fellow NEH, 1972; Woodrow Wilson Nat. Fellowship Found. affiliated scholar U. Ark. at Little Rock, 1991. Mem. Ark. Assn. Hosp. Pharmacists (program com. 1987-88, Staff Pharmacist of the Yr. award 1984), History of Medicine Assocs. (bd. dirs. 1991—), Ark. Pharmacists Assn. (ethical affairs com. 1991—, com. chmn.), U. Ark. for Med. Sci. (alumni adv. coun. 1984-93, coun. mem., Meyer Bros. award 1976). Democratic. Roman Catholic. Avocations: chamber music, travel. Home: PO Box 250043 Little Rock AR 72225 Office: U Ark Coll of Pharmacy 4301 W Markham - Slot 522 Little Rock AR 72205-7122

WOLFE, KENNETH L., food products manufacturing company executive; b. 1939; married. B.A., Yale U., 1961; M.B.A., U. Pa., 1967. With Bankers Trust Corp., 1961-62; with Hershey Foods Corp., Pa., 1968—, asst. treas., 1968-70, budget dir., 1970-76, treas., 1976-80, v.p. fin. adminstrn. Hershey Chocolate Co., from 1980, v.p., chief fin. officer, 1981-84, sr. v.p., chief fin. officer, 1984-85, pres., chief operating officer, 1985-93, chmn., CEO, 1994—, also dir. Office: Hershey Foods Corp PO Box 810 Hershey PA 17033-0810*

WOLFE, LESLIE R., think-tank executive. Exec. dir. Ctr. for Women Policy Studies, Washington, D.C. Office: Ctr Women Policy Studies 2000 P St NW Ste 508 Washington DC 20036

WOLFE, MARGARET RIPLEY, historian, educator, consultant; b. Kingsport, Tenn., Feb. 3, 1947; d. Clarence Estill and Gertrude Blessing Ripley; m. David Earley Wolfe, Dec. 17, 1966; 1 child, Stephanie Ripley. BS magna cum laude, East Tenn. State U., 1967, MA, 1969; PhD, U. Ky., 1974. Instr. history East Tenn. State U., 1969-73, asst. prof., 1973-77, assoc. prof., 1977-80, prof., 1980—. Author: Lucius Polk Brown and Progressive Food and Drug Control, Tennessee and New York City, 1908-1920, 1978, An Industrial History of Hawkins County, Tennessee, 1983, Kingsport, Tennessee: A Planned American City, 1987, Daughters of Canaan: A Saga of Southern Women, 1995; contbg. author: Appalachia: Family Patterns in Transition, 1975, The United States and Italy: The First Two Hundred Years, 1977, Research in Social Policy: Historical and Contemporary Perspectives, 1987, The Future South: An Historical Perspective for the Twenty-First Century, 1991, Tennessee in American History, 1991; contbr. articles to profl. jours. Mem. Tenn. Com. for Humanities, 1983-85, exec. coun. mem., 1984-85; mem. Women's Symphony Com., Kingsport; exec. com. Tenn. Commemorative Woman's Suffrage Commn., 1994—. Haggin fellow U. Ky., 1972-73; recipient Disting. Faculty award East Tenn. State U., 1977; East Tenn. State U. Found. rsch. award, 1979, Alumni cert. merit, 1984. Mem. AAUP, ACLU (exec. com. Tenn. 1991-92), NOW, Tenn. State Employees Assn., Am. Studies Assn. (John Hope Franklin Prize com. 1992), Am. Hist. Assn., Orgn. Am. Historians, So. Assn. Women Historians (pres. 1983-84, exec. com. 1984-86), So. Hist. Assn. (com. on the status of women 1987, program com. 1988, interim chair of program com. 1988, mem. com. 1993, 94, 95, nominating com. 1994, chair nominating com. 1995), Smithsonian Assocs., Tenn. Hist. Soc. (editorial bd., 1995—), Coordinating Com. for Women in Hist. Profession, East Tenn. Hist. Soc. (mem. editorial bd. Jour. East Tenn. History), Phi Kappa Phi. Office: ETSU/UT at Kingsport Kingsport TN 37660 also: East Tenn State U Dept History Johnson City TN 37614

WOLFE, MARTHA, elementary education educator; b. Centralia, Ill., Apr. 16, 1944; d. Elmer A. and Dorothy L. (Stonecipher) Krietemeyer; children: Kimberly S., Debora L. BS, So. Ill. U., 1967, MS, 1973, adminstrv. cert., 1987. Cert. elem. tchr., K-12 adminstrn., Ill. Tchr. Chpt. 1 reading, dir. Cobden (Ill.) Unit Sch. Dist.; presenter in field. Recipient Master Tchr. award Gov. of Ill., 1984. Mem. NEA, Internat. Reading Assn., So. Ill. Reading Assn. (pres., v.p., bd. dirs.), Delta Kappa Gamma (Lambda State scholar 1986). Home: 301 South St Anna IL 62906-1528

WOLFE, RALPH STONER, microbiology educator; b. Windsor, Md., July 18, 1921; s. Marshall Richard and Jennie Naomi (Weybright) W.; m. Gretka Margaret Young, Sept. 9, 1950; children: Daniel Binns, Jon Marshall, Sylvia Suzanne. Mem. faculty U. Ill., Urbana, 1953—, prof. microbiology, 1961—; cons. USPHS, Nat. Inst. Gen. Med. Scis. Contbr. microbial physiology rsch. papers to profl. jours. Guggenheim fellow, 1961, 75, USPHS spl. postdoctoral fellow, 1967; recipient Pasteur award Ill. Soc. for Microbiology, 1974. Mem. NAS (Selman Waksman award in microbiology 1995), Am. Acad. Arts and Scis., Am. Soc. Microbiology (Carski Disting. Teaching award 1971, hon. mem.), Am. Soc. Biol. Chemists. Office: U Ill Dept Microbiology 335 Burrill Hall Urbana IL 61801

WOLFE, RICHARD RATCLIFFE, lawyer; b. Palmyra, Mo., Nov. 29, 1933; s. Francis Dunnan and Marie Ann (Ratcliffe) W.; m. Marilyn Jean McPheron, May 22, 1965; children: Richard Jr., Marie, John, Anne. BS in Engring., Okla. State U., 1955; JD, U. Mich., 1957. Patent atty. Cherry Burrell Corp., Chgo., 1958; designer rocket engring. NASA; tech. asst. U.S. Senate Com. on Aero. and Space Scis., Washington, 1961-64; adminstrv. asst. dir. revenue State of Ill., Springfield, 1964-67, adminstrv. asst. sec. of state, 1967-69; atty. Taylor, Miller, Magner, Sprowl & Hutchings, Chgo., 1969-81, Quinn, Jacobs, Barry & Miller, Chgo., 1981-86, Murchie, Calcutt & Boynton, Traverse City, Mich., 1986—. Author senate report on manned spaced flight program NASA. Dem. nominee 20th dist. U.S. Congress, Ill., 1966. With U.S. Army, 1958-60. Mem. Grand Traverse Yacht Club. Roman Catholic. Avocation: sailing. Home: 9781 Avondale Ln Traverse City MI 49684 Office: Murchie Calcutt & Boynton 109 E Front St Traverse City MI 49684

WOLFE, ROBERT RICHARD, bioresource engineer, educator; b. Chippewa Falls, Wis., Nov. 9, 1937; s. Lewis Samuel and Bernice (Quale) W.; m. Carol Abrams, June 23, 1974; children: Laura Allene, Richard Kevin. B.S., U. Wis., 1960, M.S., 1961; Ph.D., Purdue U., 1964. Research engr. A.O. Smith Corp., Milw., 1961; research asst. Purdue U., Lafayette, Ind., 1963; asst. prof. U. Wis., Madison, 1964-70; asso. prof. Rutgers U., New Brunswick, N.J., 1970-77; prof. Rutgers U., 1977—. Contbr. numerous articles to profl. jours. NSF grad. fellow, 1962. Mem. Am. Soc. Engring. Edn., Assn. Environ. Engring. Profs., ASME Machine Vision Soc., IEEE Computer Soc., Am. Soc. Agrl. Engrs. (Jour. Article award 1973, 77, 84, 86), Water Environ. Fedn., Inst. Food Technologists, Instruments Soc. Am., AAUP, Sigma Xi, Tau Beta Pi, Phi Kappa Phi, Alpha Epsilon, Alpha Zeta, Delta Theta Sigma. Home: 31 Wagner Rd Stockton NJ 08559-1413 Office: Rutgers U Dept Bioresource Engri New Brunswick NJ 08903

WOLFE, SHEILA A., journalist; b. Chgo.; d. Leonard M. and Rena (Karn) W. B.A., Drake U. Reporter Chgo. Tribune, 1956-73, asst. city editor, 1973-75, day city editor, 1975-79, city editor, 1979-81, met. coordinator, 1981-83, adminstrv. asst. to mng. editor, 1983—; pres. City News Bur. Chgo. 1986-88, 94—. Recipient Beck award for outstanding profl. performance Chgo. Tribune, 1979; recipient Disting. Service award Drake U., 1982. Mem. Phi Beta Kappa. Home: 71 E Division St Chicago IL 60610-2367 Office: 435 N Michigan Ave Chicago IL 60611-4001

WOLFE, STANLEY, composer, educator; b. N.Y.C., Feb. 7, 1924; s. Bert S. and Dorothy (Sanders) W.; m. Marguerite Wiberg, Aug. 10, 1960; children: Jeffrey, Madeline. Student, Stetson U., 1946-47, Henry St. Music Sch., 1947-48; B.S. in Composition, Juilliard Sch. Music, 1952, M.S. in Composition, 1955. Faculty Juilliard Sch., N.Y.C., 1955—; dir. extension div. Juilliard Sch., 1956-89; adj. prof. music Lincoln Ctr. campus Fordham U., 1969-73; lectr. N.Y. Philharmonic Pre-Concert Series, 1985—. Prin. compositions include King's Heart; dance score, 1956, Canticle for Strings, 1957, Lincoln Square Overture, 1958, Symphony Number 3, 1959, String Quartet, 1961, Symphony Number 4, 1965, Symphony Number 5 (Lincoln Center Commn.), 1970, Symphony Number 6, 1981; Violin Concerto, 1987. Served with AUS, 1943-46. Recipient award Am. Acad. and Inst. Arts and Letters, 1990; Guggenheim fellow in composition, 1957; Nat. Endowment for Arts grantee, 1969, 70, 77. Mem. ASCAP, Am. Music Center, Am. Symphony Orch. League (Alice Ditson award 1961), U.S. Chess Fedn. Home: 32 Ferndale Dr Hastings On Hudson NY 10706

WOLFE, THAD ALLISON, military officer; b. Coulee Dam, Wash., Oct. 26, 1942; s. Clyde Allison and Leona (Ruffner) W.; m. Jill Ann Strathern, June 4, 1964; children: Thori, Christian, Molly. BS in Mil. Sci., USAF Acad., 1964; MSEE, U. Wyo., 1969; grad., Squadron Officer Sch., 1972, Air Command and Staff Coll., 1978, Nat. War Coll., 1985; grad. sr. exec. program in nat. and internat. security, Harvard U., 1992. Commd. 2nd lt. USAF, 1964, advanced through grades to lt. gen., 1993; ops. flight comdr. 6950th Security Wing, RAF Sta. Chicksands, Eng., 1965-66; signals intelligence ops. officer 6994th Security Squadron, Pleiku, South Vietnam, 1966-67; devel. engr. Def. Intelligence Agy., Va., 1969-70; instr. pilot, flight comdr., asst. sect. comdr. Vance AFB, Okla., 1970-74; aircrew tng. Castle AFB, Calif., 1974-75; crew comdr., ops. officer 325th Bombardment Squadron, Fairchild AFB, Wash., 1975-77; readiness analyst, chief of pers. and adminstrn., exec. officer to dir., directorate ops. and readiness Hdqs. USAF, Washington, 1978-81; comdr. 9th Bombardment Squadron, Carswell AFB, Tex., 1981; dep. comdr. for standardization and evaluation 1st Combat Evaluation Group, Barksdale AFB, La., 1982; command ctr. sr. contr. Hdqs. Strategic Air Command, Offutt AFB, Nebr., 1982-84, spl. asst. to comdr. for officer profl. devel., 1988, dep. dir. nat. strategic target list, joint strategic target planning staff, 1988-90; vice comdr., then comdr. 509th Bombardment Wing, Pease AFB, N.H., 1985-88; comdr. Strategic Warfare Ctr., Ellsworth AFB, S.D., 1990-92; asst. dep. dir. for ops. Nat. Security Agy., Ft. George G. Meade, Md., 1992-93; vice comdr. Air Combat Command, Langley AFB, Va., 1993—; chmn. profl. mil. edn. bd. dirs. Air Combat Command, Langley AFB, 1993—, chief environ. leadership coun., 1993—; bd. dirs. Air U., Maxwell AFB, Ala., Inst. Environ. and Natural Resources, Rsch. and Policy, U. Wyo., Laramie. Chmn. membership Boy Scouts Am., Rapid City, S.D., 1991. Decorated D.D.S.M., D.S.S.M., Legion of Merit, Bronze Star, Meriorious Svc. medal with three oak leaf clusters, Air medal, Air Force Commendation medal, Vietnam Svc. medal with svc. star, Republic of Vietnam Campaign medal. Mem. USAF Acad. Assn. of Grads., U. Wyo. Alumni Assn., Air Force Assn., Daedalians. Avocations: reading, sports, antiques, gardening. Office: Air Combat Command 205 Dodd Blvd Ste 207 Langley AFB VA 23665-2788

WOLFE, THOMAS KENNERLY, JR., writer, journalist; b. Richmond, Va., Mar. 2, 1931; s. Thomas Kennerly and Helen (Hughes) W.; m. Sheila Berger; children: Alexandra, Thomas. AB, Washington and Lee U., 1951, DLitt (hon.), 1974; PhD in Am. Studies, Yale U., 1957; DFA (hon.), Mpls. Coll. Art, 1971, Sch. of Visual Arts, 1987; LHD (hon.), Va. Commonwealth U., 1983, Southampton Coll. (N.Y.), 1984, Randolph-Macon Coll., 1988, Manhattanville Coll., 1988, Longwood Coll., 1989; DLitt (hon.), St. Andrews Presbyn. Coll., 1990, Johns Hopkins U., 1990, U. Richmond, 1993. Reporter Springfield (Mass.) Union, 1956-59; reporter, Latin Am. corr. Washington Post, 1959-62; city reporter N.Y. Herald Tribune, 1962-66; mag. writer N.Y. World Jour. Tribune, 1966-67; contbg. editor New York mag., 1968-76, Esquire Mag., N.Y.C., from 1977; writer N.Y. Sunday Mag., 1962-66; contbg. artist Harper's Mag., N.Y.C., 1978-81. One-man show of drawings include Maynard Walker Gallery, N.Y.C., 1965, Tunnel Gallery, N.Y.C., 1974; Author: The Kandy-Kolored Tangerine-Flake Streamline Baby, 1965, The Electric Kool-Aid Acid Test, 1968, The Pump House Gang, 1968, Radical Chic and Mau-mauing the Flak Catchers, 1970, The Painted Word, 1975, Mauve Gloves and Madmen, Clutter and Vine and Other Short Stories, 1976, The Right Stuff, 1979 (Am. Book award 1980, Nat. Book Critics Circle award 1980), In Our Time, 1980, From Bauhaus to Our House, 1981, The Purple Decades: A Reader, 1982, The Bonfire of the Vanities, 1987; editor, contbr.: The New Journalism, 1973; contbr. articles to Esquire Mag., others. Recipient Front Page awards for humor and fgn. news reporting Washington Newspaper Guild, 1961, Soc. Mag. Writers award for excellence, 1970, Frank Luther Mott Rsch. award, 1973, Harold D. Vursell Meml. award Am. Acad. and Inst. Arts and Letters, 1980, Columbia Journalism award, 1980, Nat. Sculpture Soc. citation for art history, 1980, John Dos Passos award, 1984, Gari Melchers medal, 1986, Benjamin Pierce Cheney medal Ea. Wash. U., 1986, Washington Irving Medal St. Nicholas Soc., 1986, Theodore Roosevelt medal Theodore Roosevelt Assn., 1990, Wilbur Cross medal Yale Grad. Sch. Alumni Assn., 1990, St. Louis Literary award Quinnipiac Coll., 1990, pres. award 1993; named Va. Laureate for Lit., 1977. Office: Farrar Straus & Giroux Inc 19 Union Sq W New York NY 10003-3304*

WOLFE, TOWNSEND DURANT, III, art museum director, curator; b. Hartsville, S.C., Aug. 15, 1935; m. Jane Rightor Lee; 1 child, Zibilla Lee; children (by previous marriage): Juliette Elizabeth, Mary Bryan, Townsend Durant. BFA, Atlanta Art Inst., 1958; MFA, Cranbrook Acad. Art, 1959; postgrad. Harvard Inst. Arts Adminstrn., 1970. Instr. Atlanta Art Assn., 1956-59, Memphis Acad. Art, 1959-64, Scarsdale Studio Workshop and Seamen Inst., N.Y.C., 1964-65; dir. Ford Found. Fund for Advancement of Edn. Wooster Community Art Ctr., Danbury, Conn., 1965-68; lectr. art U. Ark., Little Rock, 1969—; dir., chief curator The Ark. Arts Ctr., Little Rock, 1968—; sec. Ark. Arts Ctr. Found., 1973—; pres. Ark. Copnsortium Arts, 1976-80; pres. Ark. Arts in Edn. Adv. Coun., 1977-79; bd. dirs. Mid-Am. Arts Alliance, 1982-89; mem. adv. bd. Ark. Artists Registry, 1986—, Ark. Repertory Theatre, 1976-84; reviewer Inst. Mus. Svcs., 1984-87, examiner mus. assessment program, 1985-87; overview panel Nat. Endowment for Arts, 1986-88, rev. panel utilization of mus. resources, 1986, grant rev. panel conservation and collection maintenance, 1987. One-man shows include Madison Gallery, N.Y.C., 1961, U. Miss., 1963, Soutwestern U. Memphis, 1964, Ark. State U., Jonesboro, 1964, 70; group shows include Ball State Tchrs. Coll., Muncie, Ind., 1959, 63,65, 67, Ann. New Eng. Exhbn., 1966-67, Wadsworth Atheneum, Hartford, Conn., 1967, Audubon Artists, N.Y.C., 1968; represented in permanent collections Ark. State U., Union Planters Nat. Bank, Memphis, Mint Mus. Art, Charlotte, N.C., East Tenn. State U., others; author: Trustee Handbook, 1978, Appraiser Handbook, 1979, Selections from the Permanent Collection of the Arkansas Arts Center Foundation catalogue, 1983, Twentieth Century American Drawings from the Arkansas Arts Center Foundation Collection, 1984, American Drawings, 1986, National Drawings Invitational, 1986, 87, 88, 91, 92, 93, 94, National Objects Invitational, 1987, 88, 89, 91, National Crafts Invitational, 1987, Picasso: The Classical Years 1917-1925, 1987, Carroll Cloar Arkansas Collections, 1987, Revalations Drawing/America catalogue, 1988, The Face, 1988, 90, American Abstract Drawings, 1989, The Figure, 1990, Will Barnet Drawings: 1930-90, 1991, Silverpoint Etc., 1992, Edward Faiers Retrospective, 1994, exhbn. catalogue Memphis Coll. Art. Recipient 20 awards for painting, 1958-68, Winthrop Rockefeller Meml. award, 1973, James R. Short award Southeastern Mus. Conf., 1981, Individual Achievement award Ark. Mus. Assn., 1984, Ark. Art Edn. Advocacy award, 1985, Promethean award for excellence in the arts March of Dimes, 1986, Chevalier dans l'ordre des Arts et Lettres, 1988. Mem. Assn. Art Mus. Dirs., Assn. Am. Museums (membership com. 1982-88, accreditation com., sr. examiner 1972—). Democrat. Episcopalian. Office: The Ark Arts Ctr MacArthur Park 9th and Commerce Little Rock AR 72202

WOLFE, VERDA NELL, pension consultant, financial planner; b. Sulphur Springs, Tex., Jan. 31, 1927; d. Marvin Alvin and Winnie Davis (Bass) Hamiter; m. James Braddy Wolfe, May 3, 1947; children: James Gordon, William Gregory, Charles Gary. Student, Baylor U., 1948-52, Tex. Tech U., 1974-76. CLU, CFP; cert. pension cons. Estate analyst Estate Fin. Planning Svc., Lubbock, Tex., 1973-76, Planning Conns., Lubbock, 1977-81; pres. DDRW Fin. Svcs., Lubbock, 1982-85, Pension Concepts and Administration, Lubbock, 1986—. Mem. Am. Soc. CLU and ChFC (chpt. pres. 1988-89), Inst. Cert. Fin. Planners, Am. Soc. Pension Actuaries and Cons. Avocations: music, oil painting, gardening. Home: 2125 57th St Lubbock TX 79412 Office: Pension Concepts & Adminstn 2811A 74th St Lubbock TX 79423

WOLFE, WILLIAM JEROME, librarian, English language educator; b. Chgo., Feb. 24, 1927; s. Fred Wiley and Eleanor (Brady) W.; m. ViviAnn Lundin O'Connell, June 25, 1960 (div. 1982); 1 child, Lund. AB, U. Chgo., 1948; BA, Roosevelt U., Chgo., 1953; MEd, Chgo. State U., 1963; AA with high honors, Pima C.C., 1992; BAA magna cum laude, U. Ariz., 1994. Tchr. English John Marshall High Sch., Chgo., 1956-60; libr. Safford Jr. High Sch., Tucson, Ariz., 1961-71, Santa Rita High Sch., Tucson, 1971-75, Tucson High Sch., 1975-87; tutor Eastside Ctr., Tucson Adult Lit. Vols., 1988—, supr., 1993—. Co-founder Tucson Classic Guitar Soc., 1969-72; docent U. Ariz. Mus. Art, Tucson, 1989—; singer U. Ariz. Collegium Musicum, Sons of Orpheus Male Chorus. With U.S. Army, 1945-46, ETO. Mem. Norsemen's Fedn., Sons of Norway, U. Chgo. Century Club, Roosevelt U. Sparling Soc., U. Ariz. Pres. Club, U. Ariz. Hon. Fellows Soc., Tucson Post Card Exch. Club, Nat. Assn. Scholars, Assn. Literary Scholars & Critics, Phi Kappa Phi. Republican. Mem. Ch. of Christ Scientist. Avocations: poetry writing, drawing, singing, piano, photography. Home: 8460 E Rosewood Tucson AZ 85710

WOLFE, WILLIAM LOUIS, optics educator; b. Yonkers, N.Y., Apr. 5, 1931; s. William Louis and Louise Helene (Becker) W.; m. Mary Lou Bongort; children: Carol, Barbara, Douglas. BS in Physics, Bucknell U., 1953; MS in Physics, U. Mich., 1956, MSEE, 1966. Research engr. U. Mich., Ann Arbor, 1953-66; dept. mgr., chief engr. Honeywell Radiation Ctr., 1966-69; prof. Optical Sci. U. Ariz., Tucson, 1969—. Author: (with others) Fundamentals of Infrared Technology, 1962; (with George J. Zissis) The Infrared Handbook, 1979; series editor: Optical Physics and Engineering; editor: Handbook of Military Infrared Technology; editor-in-chief Infrared Physics; contbr. articles to profl. jours. Fellow Optical Soc. Am. (many bds. and coms.), Soc. Photo-optical Instrumentation Engrs. (pres., bd. govs., chmn. symposia, exec. com.); mem. IEEE (sr. mem.), Nat. Acad. Sci. (many coms.), Infrared Info. Symposia, Naval Intelligence Adv. Bd. (sci. adv. bd.), Air Force Ad Hoc Electro-Optics Com., Army Research Office Adv. Com., Army Scientific Adv. Bd., Am. Men of Sci., Leaders in Am. Sci., Phi Beta Kappa, Sigma Xi, Omicron Delta Kappa, Pi Mu Epsilon, Sigma Pi Sigma, Phi Eta Sigma. Avocations: fishing, travel. Office: U Ariz Tucson AZ 85721

WOLFEN, WERNER F., lawyer; b. Berlin, May 15, 1930; came to U.S., 1939; s. Martin and Ruth Eva (Hamburger) W.; m. Mary Glasier, July 1, 1956; children: Richard, James, Lawrence (dec.). BS, U. Calif., Berkeley, 1950, JD, 1953. Bar: Calif. 1953. Assoc. Irell & Manella, L.A., 1953-57, ptnr., 1957—; co-chmn. exec. com. Irell & Manella; bd. dirs. Mercantile Nat. Bank, L.A. Trustee UCLA Found.; pres. L.A. Goal. Irell & Manella, J.A. Bill Honig for Supt. of Pub. Schs., 1982, 86, 90. Mem. ABA. Democrat. Jewish. Office: Irell & Manella 1800 Ave of the Stars Ste 900 Los Angeles CA 90067-4276

WOLFENDEN, RICHARD VANCE, biochemistry educator; b. Oxford, Eng., May 17, 1935; s. John Hulton and Josephine (Vance) W.; m. Anita Gaunitz, May 25, 1965; children: Peter, John. BA, Princeton U., 1956, Exeter Coll., Oxford U., Eng., 1958; MA, Exeter Coll., Oxford U., Eng., 1958; PhD, Rockefeller Inst., 1964. Asst. prof. chemistry Princeton U., N.J., 1964-70; assoc. prof. biochemistry U. N.C., Chapel Hill, 1970-73, prof. biochemistry, 1973-83, alumni disting. prof., 1983—; vis. fellow Exeter Coll., Oxford, 1969; vis. prof. U. Montpellier, France, 1976; mem. molecular biology panel NSF, Washington, 1973-76; mem. bio-organic and natural products study sect. NIH, Washington, 1981-86; cons. Burroughs-Wellcome Co., Research Triangle Park, N.C., 1989—. Mem. editorial bd. Bioorganic Chemistry, 1983—, Biomed. Chem. Letters, 1993—. Fellow AAAS; mem. Am. Chem. Soc., Am. Soc. Biol. Chemists. Democrat. Home: 1307 Mason Farm Rd Chapel Hill NC 27514-4609 Office: U North Carolina Dept Biochemistry Chapel Hill NC 27514

WOLFENSOHN, JAMES DAVID, bank executive; b. Sydney, Australia, Dec. 1, 1933; naturalized, 1980; s. Hyman and Dora (Weinbaum) W.; m. Elaine Ruth Botwinick, Nov. 26, 1961; children: Sara, Naomi, Adam. BA, U. Sydney, 1954, LLB, 1957; MBA, Harvard U., 1959. Bar: Supreme Ct. of Australia 1957. Ptnr. Ord Minnett (brokers), Australia, 1963-65; mng. dir. Darling & Co. (investment bankers), Australia, 1965-67, J. Henry Schroder Wagg, London, 1968-70; pres. J. Henry Schroder Banking Corp., N.Y.C., 1970-76; exec. dep. chmn. dir. Schroders Ltd., London; prin. exec. officer Schroder Group, London, 1974-77; exec. ptnr. Salomon Bros., N.Y.C., 1977-81; chmn. Salomon Bros. Internat., London, 1977-81; pres., CEO James D. Wolfensohn, Inc., 1981—; pres. World Bank, 1995—; vis. lectr. fin. U. New South Wales, 1963-66; bd. dirs. CBS Inc. Contbr. articles to profl. jours. Mem. Australian Olympic team, 1956; chmn. bd. dirs. John F. Kennedy Ctr. for the Performing Arts, Washington, 1990-95, chmn. emeritus, 1995—; bd. dirs. Met. Opera Assn., 1977-93, Joint Ctr. for Polit. Studies, 1978-88, mem. emeritus, 1988—; trustee Rockefeller Found., 1979-85, Population Coun., 1977-84; trustee Inst. for Advanced Study, Princeton, N.J., 1978—, chmn., 1986—; trustee Brookings Inst., 1983-90, hon., 1990—; trustee Rockefeller U., 1985-94, Howard Hughes Med. Inst.; steering com. Bilderberg meeting, treas. Am. Friends of Bilderberg, Inc., 1985—; pres. Internat. Fedn. Multiple Sclerosis Socs., 1977-83, Carnegie Hall, 1972—, bd. dirs. chmn., 1980-91, chmn. emeritus, 1991; bd. dirs. Nat. Multiple Sclerosis Soc., 1977—. Served with Royal Australian Air Force, 1952-57. Recipient Business Committee for the Arts Leadership award, 1994. Fellow Am. Acad. Arts and Scis.; mem. Coun. on Fgn. Rels., Century Assn., Harvard Club (N.Y.C.), Australian Club (Sydney). Office: James D Wolfensohn Inc 599 Lexington Ave New York NY 10022-6030 also: JFK Ctr for Performing Arts New Hampshire Ave & F St NW Washington DC 20566

WOLFENSON, AZI U., electrical, mechanical and industrial engineer, consultant; b. Rumania, Aug. 1, 1933; came to Peru, 1937; s. Samuel G. and Polea S. (Ulanowski) W.; m. Rebeca Sterental, Jan. 10, 1983; 1 child, Michael Ben; children by previous marriage: Ida, Jeannette, Ruth, Moises, Alex. Mech., Elec. Engr., Universidad Nacional de Ingenieria, Peru, 1955; MSc in Indsl. Engring., U. Mich., 1966; Indsl. Engr., U. Nacional de Ingenieria, Peru, 1967; PhD in Engring. Mgmt. Pacific Western U., 1983, PhD in Engring. Energy, Century U., 1985, D in Philosophy of Engring. (hon.) World U. Roundtable, Ariz., 1987. Power engr. Peruvian Trading Co., 1956-57; gen. mgr. AMSA Ingenieros S.A., 1957-60; prof. Universidad Nacional de Ingenieria, Peru, 1956-72, dean mech. and elec. engring., 1964-66, dean indsl. engring., 1967-72; dir. SWSA Automotive Parts, Peru, 1954-77; project mgr. Nat. Fin. Corp., Cofide, 1971-73; Peruvian dir. Corporacion Andina de Fomento, CAF, 1971-73; rep. in Peru, CAF, 1973-74; pres. DESPRO cons. firm, 1973-76; exec. pres. Electricity, 1976-80; cons. engr., 1964—; dir. Tech. Transference Studies, 1971-72. Mem. Superior Coun. Electricity, 1964-66; metal mech. expert for andean group, 1970-71; Nat. Coun. Fgn. Investment and Tech. Transfer, 1972-73; councilman at the Concejo Provincial De Lima, 1969-75; mem. Consultive Coun. Ministry Economy and Fin., 1973-74; pres. Peruvian Economic Community, 1966-70, Peruvian Hebrew Sch., 1976-78; promoter, co-founder, gen. mgr. La Republica Newspaper, Peru, 1981; pres. PROA project promotion AG, Switzerland, 1982—; chmn. Inst. for the Devel. of the Americas, Inc., Fla., 1993—; co-founder La Republica, 1981, El Popular, 1983, El Nacional, 1985, Todo Sport, 1993, El Chino, 1994, pres. bd. dirs., newspapers; chmn. Inst. Devel. Ams., Inc., Fla., 1993—; chmn. editorial bd. Sport Peru, 1994—. Recipient awards Order Merit for Disting. Svcs., Peru, 1980, Disting. by City Coun. of Huancayo, 1968, Trujillo, 1978, Huaral, 1979, Piura, 1980, Disting. Contbn. award City of Lima, 1970, 71, Disting. Contbn. to Elec. Devel. in Peru, 1979; others; named 1979 Exec., Gente mag., recognition Israel Govt., 1967, Disting. Comision Integracion Electrica Regional, CIER, medal, 1984.

Fellow Inst. Prodn. Engrs., Brit. Inst. Mgmt.; mem. Colegio Ingenieros Peru, Instituto Peruano de Ingenieros Mecanicos (pres. 1965-66, v.p. 1967, dir. 1969, 70, 76), Asociacion Electrotechnica del Peru, ASME, AIIE (sr.), MTM Assn., Am. Soc. Engring. Edn., Am. Inst. Mgmt. Sci., AAAS, Assn. Mgmt. Sci. (dir. 1968), Asociacion Peruana Avance Ciencia, Inst. Adminstrv. Mgmt., British Inst. Mgmt., Am. Nuclear Soc. (vice chmn. 1988, 90, chmn. Swiss sect. 1991-93), Alumni Assn. of the Mich., Pacific Western and Century U., United Writers Assn., Swiss Soc. Writers, Swiss Sect. PEN Club Internat., others. Author: Work Communications, 1966, Programmed Learning, 1966, Production Planning and Control, 1968, Transfer of Technology, 1971, National Electrical Development, 1977, Energy and Development, 1979, El Gran Desafio, 1981, Hacia una politica economica alternativa, 1982, The Power of Communications: The Media, 1987. Contbr. articles to newspapers and jours. Clubs: Club der 200, FCL, Hebraica. Home: 3781 NE 208th Ter Miami FL 33180-3835

WOLFENSON, MARV, professional basketball team executive; m. Sandy Wolfenson; children: Ellyn, Ernie, David. Owner Minn. Timberwolves, The N.W. Racquet, Swim & Health Club, 1963—. Office: Minn Timberwolves Target Ctr 600 1st Ave N Minneapolis MN 55403-1416*

WOLFF, ALAN WILLIAM, lawyer; b. Malden, Mass., June 12, 1942; s. Louis K. and Etta (Bernstein) W.; m. Helene N. Novick, Mar. 3, 1965; children: Anna, Jeremy, Ewan. AB, Harvard U., 1963; LLB, Columbia U., 1966. Bar: Mass. 1967, N.Y. 1966, U.S. Supreme Ct. 1971, D.C. 1972, U.S. Ct. Appeals (fed. cir.) 1982, Ct. Internat. Trade 1993. Atty., office of gen. counsel U.S. Treasury Dept., Washington, 1968-73; dep. gen. counsel Spl. Trade Rep. (now U.S. Trade Rep.), Washington, 1973-74, gen. counsel, 1974-76, dep. spl. trade rep. (with rank of ambassador), 1977-79; ptnr. Verner, Liipfert et al, Washington, 1979-85; ptnr. Dewey, Ballantine, Bushby, Palmer & Wood (now Dewey Ballantine), Washington, 1985-92, mng. ptnr., 1992—; counsel Labor-Industry Coalition for Internat. Trade, 1979—, Semiconductor Industry Assn., 1980—, Bethlehem Steel, USX, 1980—, Nat. Forest Products Assn., 1988—; mem. Pres.'s Adv. Com. for Trade Negotiations, 1980-82, U.S. Trade Rep.'s Svcs. Policy Adv. Com. 1980-86 (all located in Washington, D.C.); mem. adv. bd. Inst. for Internat. Econs., 1981—, Econ. Strategy Inst., 1990—; adv. trade panel Atlantic Coun., 1979-86; nat. adv. bd. Ctr. for Nat. Policy, 1988—; mem. 20th Century Fund's Task Force Future Internat. Trade Policy, 1989, Coun. Fgn. Rels., 1979—, Overseas Devel. Coun., 1989—; mem. def. indsl. strategy task force Def. Mfg. Bd., 1989—. Co-author: The Microelectronics Race, 1987, Steel and the State, 1988, Conflict Among Nations: Trade Policy for the 1990s, 1992; contbr. articles to profl. jours. Mem. Nat. Planning Assn. (com. changing internat. realities 1982—), Japan-Am. Soc. Washington (trustee 1983-89). Democrat. Unitarian. Office: Dewey Ballantine 1775 Pennsylvania Ave NW Washington DC 20006-4605 also: 1301 Ave of Americas New York NY 10019

WOLFF, CHRISTIAN, composer, music and classics educator; b. Nice, France, Mar. 8, 1934. A.B., Harvard U., 1955, M.A., 1957, Ph.D. 1963. Instr. classics Harvard U., 1962-65, asst. prof., 1965-71; assoc. prof. classics, comparative lit. and music Dartmouth Coll., Hanover, N.H., 1971-78, prof. classics and music, 1978-80, Strauss prof. music and classics, 1980—; vis. composer Deutscher Akademischer Austauschdient, Berlin, 1974; vis. prof. classics Harvard U., 1980. Author: Ueber form, 1960, Orestes, In Euripides: A Collectin of Critical Essays, 1968, On Political Texts and New Music, SONUS, 1980, Euripides in Ancient Writers: Greece and Rome, 1982; contbr. to profl. jours. Loeb bequest grantee Harvard U., 1967-68; fellow Ctr. Hellenic Studies, Washington, 1970-71; recipient Music award Am. Acad. and Nat. Inst. Arts and Letters, 1974. Office: Dept of Classics Dartmouth College Hanover NH 03755

WOLFF, CHRISTOPH JOHANNES, music historian, educator; b. Solingen, Germany, May 24, 1940; came to U.S., 1970; s. Hans Walter and Annemarie (Halstenbach) W.; m. Barbara Mahrenholz, Aug. 28, 1964; children: Katharina, Dorothea, Stephanie. Ed., U. Berlin, 1960-63, U. Freiburg, Germany, 1963-65; Dr. Phil., U. Erlangen, Germany, 1966. Lectr. U. Erlangen, 1966-69; asst. prof. U. Toronto, Ont., Can., 1968-70; assoc. prof. musicology Columbia U., 1970-73, prof., 1973-76; prof. musicology Harvard U., 1976—; William Powell Mason prof., 1985—, dept. chmn., 1980-88, 90-91; vis. prof. Princeton U., 1973, 75; hon. prof. U. Freiburg, Germany, 1990—; acting dir. Harvard U. Libr., 1991-92; dean Grad Sch. Arts and Scis., 1992—. Author: Der Stile Antico in der Musik J.S. Bachs, 1968, The String Quartets of Haydn, Mozart, and Beethoven, 1980, Bach Compendium, 7 vols., 1986-89, Bach: Essays on His Life and Music, 1991, Mozart's Requiem, 1991; contbr. numerous articles to profl. jours.; editor: Bach-Jahrbuch, 1974—; critical edits. of music by, Scheidt, Buxtehude, Bach, Mozart, and Hindemith. Recipient Dent medal Royal Mus. Assn., London, 1978. Fellow Am. Acad. Arts and Scis.; Mem. Internat. Musicol. Soc., Am. Musicol. Soc., Gesellschaft fuer Musikforschung. Home: 182 Washington St Belmont MA 02178-3560 Office: Harvard U Univ Hall 18 Cambridge MA 02138

WOLFF, CHRISTOPHER See KENDALL, CHRISTOPHER

WOLFF, CYNTHIA GRIFFIN, humanities educator, author; b. St. Louis, Aug. 20, 1936; d. James Thomas and Eunice (Heyn) Griffin; m. Robert Paul Wolff, June 9, 1962 (div. 1986); children—Patrick Gideon, Tobias Barrington; m. Nicholas J. White, May 21, 1988. B.A., Radcliffe Coll., 1958; Ph.D., Harvard U., 1965. Asst. prof. English Manhattanville Coll., Purchase, N.Y., 1968-70; asst. prof. English U Mass., Amherst, 1971-74, assoc. prof., 1974-76, prof., 1976-80; prof. humanities MIT, Cambridge, 1980-85, Class of 1922 prof. lit. and writing, 1985—; mem. exec. com. for Am. lit. MLA, 1979-81; mem. selection bd. Literary Classics Am., 1981—; mem. exec. bd. for fgn. grants Am. Council Learned Socs., 1981-84. Author: (literary criticism) Samuel Richardson, 1972, (literary biography) A Feast of Words: The Triumph of Edith Wharton, 1977, 2d edit. 1994, Emily Dickinson, 1986; bd. editors Am. Quar., 1979-84. AAUW grantee, 1964-65; NEH grantee, 1975-76, 1983-84; Am. Council Learned Socs. grantee, 1984-85. Mem. Am. Studies Assn. Home: Apt 619 416 Commonwealth Ave Boston MA 02215-2812 Office: MIT Dept Humanities 14N-226 Cambridge MA 02139

WOLFF, DEBORAH H(OROWITZ), lawyer; b. Phila., Apr. 6, 1940; d. Samuel and Anne (Manstein) Horowitz; m. Morris H. Wolff, May 15, 1966 (div.); children: Michelle Lynn, Lesley Anne; m. Walter Allan Levy, June 7, 1987. BS, U. Pa., 1962, MS, 1966; postgrad., Sophia U., Tokyo, 1968; JD, Villanova U., 1979; LLM, 1988. Tchr. Overbrook High Sch., Phila., 1962-68; homebound tchr. Lower Merion Twp., Montgomery County, 1968-71; asst. dean U. Pa., Phila., 1975-76; law clk. Stassen, Kostos and Mason, Phila., 1977-78; assoc. Spencer, Sherr, Moses and Zuckerman, Norristown, Pa., 1980-81; ptnr. Wolff Assocs., 1981—; lectr. law and estate planning, Phila., 1980—; Recipient 3d Ann. Community Svc. award Phila. Mayor's Com. for Women, 1984; named Pa. Heroine of Month, Ladies Home Jour., July 1984. Founder Take a Brother Program; bd. dirs. Germantown Jewish Ctr.; high sch. sponsor World Affairs Club, Phila., 1962-68; mem. exec. com., sec. bd. Crime Prevention Assn., Phila., 1965—; bd. dirs. U. Pa. Alumnae Bd., Phila., 1965—, v.p. organized classes; chmn. urban conf. Boys Club Am., 1987; active Hahnaman Brain Tumor Rsch. Bd. Mem. ABA, Pa. Bar Assn., Phila. Bar Assn., Montgomery County Bar Assn., Phila. Women's Network, Bus. Women's Network (pres.), Crime Prevention Assn. (sec. bd. dirs., v.p. of bd.), Cosmopolitan Club (membership com. Phila.), Lions Club (mem. chmn.). Home and Office: 422 W Mermaid Ln Philadelphia PA 19118-4204

WOLFF, DERISH MICHAEL, economist, company executive; b. Boston, May 14, 1935; s. Nathan and Ruth Mae (Derish) W.; m. Maureen Robinson; children: Jeffrey Scott, Hayley Beth. BA, U. Pa., 1957; MBA, Harvard U., 1959. Adminstrv. asst. Sigmund Werner, Inc., Belleville, N.J., 1959-61; devel. economist Louis Berger, Inc., East Orange, N.J., 1961-65, chief economist, 1965-67, v.p., 1968-74, exec. v.p., 1975-82, pres., CEO, 1982—; dir. Louis Berger Internat., Inc., internat. devel. firm, Brokonsult AB, CHELBI, Ammann & Whitney; guest lectr. Fgn. Svc. Inst., Newark Inst. Tech., U. Nev., MIT; mem. Bretton Woods Coms., 1987—. Mem. editorial ... dern Engring. Tech., 1978-80, Nat. Devel.-Modern Govt. mag., 1972- ... trn. Bus. Review, 1991—. Class chmn. U. Pa. Ann. Giving, 1975- ... pres., 1982-92; mem. U.S. Presdl. Trade Del. to Japan, 1986; mem.

indsl. sector adv. com. Dept. of Commerce, 1988-92; mem. adv. com. U.S. Trade and Devel. Program, 1989-92. Mem. Am. Cons. Engrs. Coun. (chmn. internat. engring. com., 1983-85, vice chmn. 1986-93), Internat. Engring. and Constrn. Industries Coun. (del. 1986, 87, chmn. 1988-90, bldg. futures coun. 1990—), Ctr. for Strategic and Internat. Studies (steering group/GATT negotiations 1989), Phi Beta Kappa. Jewish. Clubs: Harvard, Penn. Office: Louis Berger Group 100 Halsted St East Orange NJ 07018-2699

WOLFF, EDWARD A., electronics engineer; b. Chgo., Oct. 31, 1929; s. Samuel S. and Lillian P. W.; m. Anna Lee Tishk, June 19, 1951; children: David Steven, Elliot Marvin, Susan Toby. B.S.E.E., U. Ill., 1951; M.S., 1953; Ph.D., U. Md., 1961. Electronic scientist Naval Research Lab., Washington, 1951-54; project engr. Md. Electronic Mfg. Corp., Litton Industries, College Park, Md., 1956-59, Electromagnetic Research Corp., College Park, Md., 1959-61; engring. mgr. Aero Geo Astro-Keltec Industries/Aiken Industries, Alexandria, Va., 1961-67; v.p. Geotronics, Inc., Falls Church, Va., 1967-71; supervisory electronics engr. NASA Goddard Space Flight Ctr., Greenbelt, Md., 1971—; system mgr. Network TDRS System, 1981-89, MRJ, Inc., Oakton, Va., 1989—; instr. Tex. A&M U., 1962. Author: Spacecraft Technology, 1962, Antenna Analysis, 1966, 2d edit. 1988, Geoscience Instrumentation, 1974, Urban Alternatives, 1975, Microwave Engineering and Systems Applications, 1988. Mem. Md. Gov.'s Sci. Resources Adv. Bd., 1963-67; pres. U.S. Environment and Resources Council, 1972-75; treas. World Evironment and Resources Council, 1975-81. Served with U.S. Army, 1954-56. Fellow IEEE (dir. 1971-72), Washington Acad. Scis.; mem. AIAA, Nat. Soc. Profl. Engrs., Eta Kappa Nu, Sigma Tau, Phi Eta Sigma. Home: 1021 Cresthaven Dr Silver Spring MD 20903-1602 Office: MRJ Inc Oakton VA 22124 *Everything I have done has been with the help of others. In return, as I have acquired management responsibilities, a primary objective has been to help others achieve their goals.*

WOLFF, ELEANOR BLUNK, actress; b. Bklyn., July 10, 1931; d. Sol and Bessie (Schultz) Blunk; m. William Howard Wolff, June 19, 1955; children: Ellen Jill, Rebecca Louise. BA in Edn., Speech and Theatre, Bklyn. Coll., 1972, MS in Spl. Edn., 1975; postgrad. Adelphi U., 1980-81. Cert. tchr., N.Y. Fashion model Garment Ctr., N.Y.C., 1949-50; sec. to v.p. out-of-town/export sales Liebmann Breweries Inc., Bklyn., 1950-58; tchr. N.Y.C. Bd. Edn., Bklyn., 1971-76; sec. to dir. environ. programs, pub. affairs officers, speakers bur. project leader Power Authority State of N.Y., N.Y.C., 1976-85; tchr. Hewlett-Woodmere (N.Y.) Sch. Dist., 1986-89; instr. adult edn. County of Nassau, N.Y., 1986—; actress/model, N.Y.C., 1992—. V.p. program devel. for youth ctr. Wavecrest Gardens Community Assn., Far Rockaway, N.Y., 1959-63; teen leader Far Rockaway Jewish Ctr. Youth Coun., 1965-68; pres. Parents Assn. P.S. 215Q, Far Rockaway, 1966-67; tutor N.Y. C. Bd. Edn. Sch. Vol. Program, Far Rockaway, 1969-71; chair civic affairs Dem. Club, Far Rockaway, 1961-63; committeewoman Dem. Ctrl. Com., Queens County, N.Y., 1963-64; v.p. membership, mem. constn. com. Nassau County Dem. Women's Caucus, 1988, 89; awards com. Bklyn Coll. Named Mother of Yr. Congregation Shaaray Tefila, Far Rockaway, 1968; recipient Merit award Wavecrest Gardens Community Assn., 1960, Theater Arts Trophy for disting. svc. Bklyn. Coll. Alumni, 1992. Mem. NAFTRA, Nassau Assn. Cmty./Continuing Edn., Alumni Assn. Bklyn. Coll. (life), Nat. Audubon Soc. Avocations: painting, piano. Home: 29 Princeton Ave Hewlett NY 11557

WOLFF, ELROY HARRIS, lawyer; b. N.Y.C., May 20, 1935; s. Samuel and Rose Marian (Katz) W.; children: Ethan, Anna Louise. A.B., Columbia U., 1957, LL.B. 1963. Bar: N.Y. 1963, D.C. 1969. Assoc. Kaye, Scholer, Fierman, Hays & Handler, N.Y.C., 1963-65; atty.-adviser to commr. FTC, Washington, 1965-67; sr. trial atty. Dept. Transp., 1967-69; assoc. Leibman, Williams, Bennett, Baird & Minow, Washington, 1969-70, ptnr., 1970-72; ptnr. Sidley & Austin, Washington, 1972—; mem. adv. com. on practice and procedure FTC, 1969-71; chmn. adv. com. on procedural reform CAB, 1975. Served to 1st lt. USAF, 1957-60. Mem. ABA (chmn. FTC com. antitrust sect. 1989-91, chmn. spring meeting program antitrust sect. 1992-94), Union Internat. des Advocats (chmn. comm. on competition 1994—), Monroe Club, Fed. City Club. Office: Sidley & Austin 1722 I St NW Washington DC 20006-3705

WOLFF, FERIDA, author; b. Bklyn., July 7, 1946; d. Sam and Shirley J. (Gootrad) Mevorach; m. Michael L. Wolff, Feb. 3, 1965; children: Stephanie E., Russell S. BA, Queens Coll., Flushing, N.Y., 1967, MS in Edn., 1970; cert. holistic studies, Rosemont (Pa.) Coll., 1992. Tchr. N.Y.C. Bd. Edn., Queens, 1967-68; head tchr. Happy Time Nursery Sch., Queens, 1968-70; freelance writer, 1972-87; instr. yoga adult schs. Camden County (N.J.) Coll., 1990-95; spkr., 1989—; panelist Phila Writer's Conf., 1990, workshop leader, 1993; workshop leader Teen Arts Festival, Camden, N.J., 1993. Author: Pink Slippers, Bat Mitzvah Blues, 1989 (Sydney Taylor honor book), The Woodcutter's Coat, 1992, Danish edit., 1993, French edit., 1993, Seven Loaves of Bread, 1993, The Emperor's Garden, 1994; (with Dolores Kozielski) The Toothless Vampire and 99 Other Howl-oween Riddles, 1992, The Halloween Grab Bag, 1993, On Halloween Night, 1994, Spitballs and Spaghetti, 1995; contbr. articles to profl. jorus. Bd. mem., v.p. Friends of the Cherry Hill (N.J.) Free Pub. Libr., 1991-92; scouting coord., troop com. mem. troop 167 Boy Scouts Am., Cherry Hill, 1985-90; libr. vol. coord. Joe D. Sharp Elem. Sch., Cherry Hill, 1979-87. Mem. Authors Guild, Soc. Children's Book Writers and Illustrators, Penn Laurel Poets, Phila. Children's Reading Round Table (steering com.). Home: 21 Candlewyck Way Cherry Hill NJ 08003

WOLFF, FRANK PIERCE, JR., lawyer; b. St. Louis, Feb. 27, 1946; s. Frank P. and Beatrice (Stein) W.; m. Susan Scalet, May 11, 1984; children: Elizabeth McLane, Victoria Hancox. BA, Middlebury Coll., 1968; JD, U. Va., 1971. Bar: Mo. 1971, U.S. Ct. Appeals (5th cir.) 1974, U.S. Ct. Appeals (8th cir.) 1975, U.S. Supreme Ct. 1975. Ptnr. Lewis, Rice & Fingersh, St. Louis, 1971-90; Bryan Cave, St. Louis, 1990—; bd. dirs. Wood Ceilings, Inc. Bd. dirs. Leadership St. Louis, 1985-88, Washington U. Child Guidance Clinic, St. Louis, 1976-79, Jewish Family and Children's Svc., St. Louis, 1981-83, John Burroughs Sch., 1995—; gen. counsel Mo. Bot. Garden, St. Louis, 1981—, Mo. History Mus. Subdist., St. Louis, 1987—; spl. counsel St. Louis Symphony Soc., 1989—. Capt. USAR, 1968-76. Mem. ABA, Mo. Bar Assn., Bar Assn. Met. St. Louis (chmn. corp. sect. 1984-85), Noonday Club, Westwood Country Club (chmn. fin. com. 1988-91, treas. 1989-91, v.p. 1991-93, pres. 1993—, exec. com. 1989—). Jewish. Home: 21 Westwood Country Clb Saint Louis MO 63131-2411 Office: Bryan Cave 1 Metropolitan Sq Saint Louis MO 63102-2750

WOLFF, GEOFFREY ANSELL, novelist, critic, educator; b. L.A., Nov. 5, 1937; s. Arthur Saunders III and Rosemary (Loftus) W.; m. Priscilla Bradley Porter, Aug. 21, 1965; children: Nicholas Hinckley, Justin Porter. Grad., Choate Sch., 1955; student, Eastbourne (Eng.) Coll., 1955-56; BA summa cum laude, Princeton U., 1961; postgrad., Churchill Coll., Cambridge U., Eng., 1961-64. Lectr. in comparative lit. Robert Coll., Istanbul, Turkey, 1961-63; lectr. in Am. civilization Istanbul U., 1962-63; lectr. aesthetics Md. Inst. Coll. Art, 1965-69; vis. lectr. creative arts Princeton (N.J.) U., 1970-71, Ferris prof., 1980, 92; writer-in-residence Brandeis U., Waltham, Mass., 1982—; lectr. English lit. Middlebury (Vt.) Coll., 1976, 78; vis. lectr. Columbia U., N.Y.C., 1979, Brown U. Providence, 1981, 88, Boston U., 1981; mem. policy panel in lit. NEA; book critic Esquire mag., 1979-81; founder Golden Horn lit. mag., 1962. Author: Bad Debts, 1969, The Sightseer, 1974, Black Sun, 1976, Inklings, 1978, The Duke of Deception, 1979, Providence, 1986; editor: Best American Essays, 1989, The Final Club, 1990, A Day at the Beach, 1992; book editor Washington Post, 1964-69, Newsweek mag., 1969-71, New Times mag., 1974-79; contbr. to mags. Recipient R.I. Gov.'s Arts award, 1992; Woodrow Wilson fellow, 1961-62, 63-64, Fulbright fellow, 1963-64, Guggenheim fellow, 1972-73, 77-78, NEH sr. fellow, 1974-75, NEA fellow, 1979-80, 86-87, Am. Coun. Learned Socs. fellow, 1983-84, Lila Wallace Writing fellow, 1990-95. Mem. PEN, Princeton Club (N.Y.C.), Colonial CLub (Princeton), Dunes Club. Home: 175 Narragansett Ave Jamestown RI 02835-1147

WOLFF, GUNTHER ARTHUR, physical chemist; b. Essen, Germany, Mar. 31, 1918; came to U.S., 1953; s. Joseph and Anna (Breidecker) W.; m. Gertrude Anna Stolte, Feb. 27, 1945; children: Christine, Francis. B.S., Berlin U., 1944, M.S., 1945; Sc.D., Berlin Tech. U., 1948. Research assoc. Fritz Haber Inst., Berlin, 1944-50, sci. head, dep. chief crystal kinetics dept.,

1950-53; cons. sr. scientist, team leader Signal Corps Research and Devel. Lab. U.S. Army, Fort Monmouth, N.J., 1953-60; sr. group leader material research Harshaw Chem. Co., Cleve., 1960-63; dir. material research Erie Tech. Products Co., Pa., 1963-64; prin. scientist Tyco Labs., Inc., Waltham, Mass., 1964-70; cons. chemist Lamp Phenomena Research Lab., Lamp Envelope Materials Research Lab. Gen. Electric Co., Cleve., 1970-77; sr. staff engr. Nat. Semicondr. Corp., Hawthorne, Calif., 1977-81, indsl. cons., 1981-83; indsl. cons. G.A. Cons. NPO, 1983—; chmn. Gordon Research Conf. on Chemistry and Metallurgy of Semicondrs., 1965; mem. crystal growth com. Internat. Union Crystallography, 1967-75; mem. Am. com. for crystal growth, 1967-72. Fellow Am. Inst. Chemists, Mineral Soc. Am.; mem. N.Y. Acad. Sci., Am. Chem. Soc., Electrochem. Soc., Am. Crystallographic Assn., Am. Ceramic Soc., Assn. for Crystal Growth, AAAS. Home and Office: 3776 Northampton Rd Cleveland OH 44121-2027

WOLFF, HERBERT ERIC, banker, former army officer; b. Cologne, Germany, May 24, 1925; s. Hugo and Juanna Anna (Van Dam) W.; m. Alice (Billy) Rafael, Nov. 13, 1946 (dec. July, 1987); children: Karen (dec. Jan., 1992), Herbert E., Allen R. B.A., Rutgers U., 1953; B.S., U. Md., 1957; M.A., George Washington U., 1962; grad., U.S. Army War Coll., 1962, Harvard U., 1979. Commd. 2d lt. U.S. Army, 1945, advanced through grades to maj. gen.; served in Fed. Republic of Germany, Greece, Iran, Republic of Korea, Australia, New Guinea, The Phillipines, Japan and Socialist Republic of Vietnam; dep. dir. ops. NSA-CSS, Ft. Meade, Md., 1973-75; dep. corps. comdr. V. Corps U.S. Army, Frankfurt, Germany, 1975-77; comdr. gen. U.S. Army Western Command U.S. Army, Hawaii, 1977-81; with First Hawaiian Bank, Honolulu, 1981—, sr. v.p., corp. sec.; hon. consul gen. (Dató) U.S. Pacific region Govt. of Malaysia, Honolulu, 1985—. Author: The Man on Horseback, 1962, The Tenth Principle of War, 1964, Public Support, 1964, The Military Instructor, 1968. Mem. exec. bd. Aloha coun. Boy Scouts Am.; bd. dirs. USO, ASYMCA, Girl Scouts of U.S., Hawaii; v.p. Hawaii Com. Fgn. Rels.; pres. Pacific Asian Affairs Coun.; pres. Hawaii Army Mus. Soc. Decorated Bronze Star with V and 3 oak leaf clusters U.S. Army, Air medal (24) U.S. Army, Joint Services commendation medal U.S. Army, Army Commendation medal U.S. Army, Purple Heart, Gallantry Cross with 2 palms, Gallantry Cross with palm and silver star Nat. Order 5th class S. Vietnam, Order Nat. Security Merit Choen-Su S. Korea, D.S.M. with oak leaf clusters (2), U.S. Army, Silver Star with oak leaf cluster U.S. Army, Legion of Merit with 3 oak leaf clusters U.S. Army, D.F.C. U.S. Army, Combat Infantry Badge with two stars; named Citizen of Yr. Fed. Exec. Bd., 1987. Mem. Am. Bankers Assn., Am. Soc. Corps. Secs., Assn. U.S. Army (trustee), 1st Inf. Divsn. Assn., 1st Cav. Divsn. Assn., U.S. Army Mus. Soc. (trustee), Plaza Club (bd. dirs.), Honolulu Country Club, Waialae Country Club, Rotary, Phi Kappa Phi. Office: First Hawaiian Bank PO Box 3200 Honolulu HI 96847

WOLFF, HOWARD KEITH, computer science educator, consultant; b. L.A., Mar. 28, 1948; s. Fred and Yvonne (Primock) W.; m. Anna Bornino, Dec. 6, 1966 (div. June 1971); children: Francesea, Jeffrey; m. Cindy Brattan, June 4, 1981; children: Jeffrey, Mariya. BA, Calif. State U., Dominguez Hill, 1969; MPA, U. So. Calif., 1971, PhD, 1973; MS, Calif. State U., Chico, 1992. Prin. investigator U. Simon Fraser, Vancouver, B.C., Can., 1970-71; prof. U. So. Calif., L.A., 1971-73, Tribhuvan (Nepal) U., 1974-75, Calif. State U., Chico, 1976-85, 87—, Colo. State U., Ft. Collins, 1985-87; evaluation cons. Nat. Planning Commn., Kathmandu, Nepal., 1973-75; statis. cons. Nat. Population Commn., Kathmandu, 1983-87; cons. Butte Canyon Rsch. Assocs., Chico, 1979—; evaluator migrant edn. program Calif. State Dept. Edn., 1992—. Author: Social Science and Thesis Handbook, 1974; contbr. articles to profl. jours. Research grantee Can. Govt., Vancouver, 1970. Mem. IEEE, Am. Assn. Computing Machinery, Am. Soc. Pub. Adminstrn., Soc. Computer Simulations. Democrat. Club: Gears (Chico). Avocations: skiing, biking, hiking, travel, flying. Home: 1966 Honey Run Rd Chico CA 95928-8835 Office: Calif State U Dept Computer Sci/Dept Polit Sci Chico CA 95929

WOLFF, IVAN LAWRENCE, venture capitalist; b. Bklyn., Oct. 9, 1944; s. Zachary Henry and Gertrude (Abramowitz) W.; m. Susan R. Joseph, June 18, 1967; 1 child, Adam Gregory. B.A., Cornell U., 1966; M.B.A. with distinction, Harvard U., 1968. Cert. fin. analyst. Mktg. mgr. Hughes Aircraft Co., Culver City, Calif., 1968-74; mktg. mgr. M-A Com, Burlington, Mass., 1974-76; div. mgr. customer strategy AT&T, Basking Ridge, N.J., 1976-81; v.p., securities analyst Donaldson, Lufkin, & Jenrette, N.Y.C., 1981-84; sr. v.p., prin. Rothschild, Inc. (Rothschild Venture), N.Y.C., 1984-87, mng. dir., 1987-91; mng. dir. Wolff Assocs., Mountain Lakes, N.J., 1991—. Pres. Cornell Alumni Class, Ithaca, 1981-86, v.p., 1986—; bd. dirs. Smugglers' Notch Condominium Assn., Jeffersonville, Vt., 1982-85. Mem. Inst. Cert. Fin. Analysts. Republican. Office: Wolff Assocs 174 Laurel Hill Rd Mountain Lakes NJ 07046-1217

WOLFF, JESSE DAVID, lawyer; b. Mpls., Aug. 26, 1913; s. Maurice I. and Annalee (Weiskopf) W.; m. Elizabeth Hess, Nov. 22, 1939; children: Nancy Nicholas, Paula, Daniel Jesse. B.A. summa cum laude, Dartmouth Coll., 1935; J.D., Harvard U., 1938. Bar: N.Y. 1938. Practiced in N.Y.C., 1938—; assoc., then ptnr., to counsel Weil, Gotshal & Manges, 1938-88, 88—, sr. mng. ptnr., 1966-86; past dir., dep. chmn. Sotheby Parke Bernet Group (Eng.); past mem. adv. bd. Sotheby's Inc. Trustee, exec. com. Greatery N.Y. ARC; past mem. exec. com. Salvation Army, N.Y.C. Served with AUS, 1942-45. Mem. ABA, Judge Adv. Gen. Assn. Office: Weil Gotshal & Manges 767 5th Ave New York NY 10153-0002

WOLFF, KURT JAKOB, lawyer; b. Mannheim, Fed. Republic of Germany, Mar. 7, 1936; s. Ernest and Florence (Marx) W.; m. Sanda Lynn Dobrick, Dec. 28, 1958; children: Tracy Ellin, Brett Harris. AB, NYU, 1955; JD, U. Mich., 1958. Bar: N.Y. 1958, U.S. Supreme Ct. 1974, Hawaii 1985, Calif. 1988. Sole practice, N.Y.C., 1958—; assoc. Hays, Sklar & Herzberg, 1958-60; sr. assoc. Nathan, Mannheimer, Asche, Winer and Friedman, 1960-65; sr. assoc. Otterbourg, Steindler, Houston & Rosen, 1965-68, sr. ptnr., 1968-70, dir., treas. 1970—, chmn. bd., 1978-82, chief exec. officer, 1982—; spl. master N.Y. Supreme Ct., 1977-85; vol. master U.S. Dist. Ct. (so. dist.) N.Y., 1978-82. Lectr., U. Mich. Law Sch.; mem. com. of visitors U. Mich. Law Sch., 1993—; spl. mediator Dept. Disciplinary Com. Appellate Divsn. First Judical Dept., 1991—. Mem. N.Y. State Bar Assn. (lectr.), Am. Arbitration Assn. (arbitrator), N.Y.C. Bar Assn. (arbitration com. 1979-83, state cts. of superior jurisdiction com. 1983-86, mem. com. on legal edn. and admission to the bar, 1991-94), ABA (chmn. ins. com. econs. sect. 1980-82, editor arbitration newsletter, arbitration com. sect. of litigation), Hawaii State Bar Assn., Calif. State Bar Assn., Gen. Arbitration Council Textile Industry N.Y.C., Fed. Bar Council. Contbr. articles to legal jours. Home: 9 Sunset Dr N Chappaqua NY 10514-1633 also: 48-641 Torrito Ct Palm Desert CA 92260 Office: 230 Park Ave New York NY 10169-0004

WOLFF, LARRY F., dental educator, researcher; b. Mankato, Minn., May 25, 1948; m. Charles Harold and Madelyn Catherine (Burns) W.; m. Elizabeth Spencer Thompson, Aug. 7, 1976; children: Adam, Ryan, Sara. BA in Biology, Mankato State U., 1970, M in Biology and Chemistry, 1971; PhD in Microbiology, Northwestern U., 1974; DDS, U. Minn., 1978; M in Periodontology, NYU, 1980; cert. in dentistry, Aarhus (Denmark) Dental Coll., 1979. Rsch. fellow Northwestern U., Chgo., 1972-74; asst. prof. dentistry U. Minn., Mpls., 1980-85, assoc. prof., 1985—, assoc. prof. periodontology, 1985-94. Contbr. articles to profl. jours. Grantee Nat. Inst. Dental Rsch. NIH, 1982—; numerous corps., 1988—. Mem. Am. Acad. Periodontology, Am. Dental Assn., Internat. Assn. Dental Rsch., Internat. Assn. Periodontists, Minn. Dental Assn., Minn. Assn. Dental Rsch. Office: U Minn Sch Dentistry 515 Delaware St SE Minneapolis MN 55455-0348

WOLFF, MANFRED ERNST, medicinal chemist, pharmaceutical company executive; b. Berlin, Germany, Feb. 14, 1930; s. Adolph Abraham and Kate (Fraenkel) W.; m. Helen S. Scandalis, Aug. 1, 1953 (div. 1971); children: Stephen Andrew, David James, Edward Allen; m. Susan E. Hurbert, Jan. 19, 1973 (div. 1975); m. A. Gloria Johnson, Dec. 25, 1982. B.S., U. Calif. at Berkeley, 1951, M.S., 1953, Ph.D, 1955. Research fellow U. Va., 1955-57; sr. medicinal chemist Smith, Kline & French Labs., Phila., 1957-60; mem. faculty U. Calif. at San Francisco, 1960-82, prof. medicinal chemistry, 1965-82, chmn. dept. pharm. chemistry, 1970-82; dir. discovery research Allergan Labs, Irvine, Calif., 1982-84; v.p. discovery rsch. Allergan Pharms., Irvine, Calif., 1984-89; v.p. R & D Immunopharmaceutics Inc., San Diego, 1989-91, sr. v.p. R & D, 1991-95; pres. Technipharm Cons., 1995—; adj. prof. medicinal chemistry U. So. Calif., 1982—; elected mem. U.S. Pharm. Conv. Com. of Revision, 1990—. Editor: Burger's Medicinal Chemistry and Drug Discovery, 5th edit, vol. 1-5, 1995-96; asst. editor: Jour. Medicinal Chemistry, 1968-71; mem. editorial bd. Medicinal Chemistry Rsch., 1991-94; contbr. articles to profl. jours.; discoverer Tazaratene, 1987, Brimonidine, 1988. Fellow AAAS, Am Assn. Pharm. Scientists; mem. Am. Chem. Soc., Licensing Execs. Soc. Patentee in field.

WOLFF, PETER ADALBERT, physicist, educator; b. Oakland, Calif., Nov. 15, 1923; s. Adalbert and Ruth Margaret W.; m. Catherine C. Carroll, Sept. 11, 1948; children: Catherine Mia, Peter Whitney. AB in Physics, U. Calif., Berkeley, 1945, PhD in Physics, 1951. Rsch. scientist Lawrence Radiation Lab., 1951-52; staff scientist Bell Telephone Lab., Murray Hill, N.J., 1952-63; dept. head, dir. electronic rsch. lab. Bell Telephone Lab., 1964-70; prof. physics U. Calif., San Diego, 1963-64; prof. physics, head solid state and atomic physics div., assoc. dir. Material Sci. Ctr. MIT, Cambridge, 1970-76, prof. physics, 1976-89, prof. emeritus, 1994—; dir. rsch. lab. of electronics MIT, 1976-81; dir. Francis Bitter Nat. Magnet Lab., 1981-87; dir. Draper Lab. Contbr. articles to profl. jours. Served with C.E. U.S. Army, 1945-46. Fellow Nippon Electric Co. Rsch. Inst., Princeton, 1989-94. Mem. Am. Phys. Soc., Am. Acad. Arts and Scis.

WOLFF, ROBERT PAUL, philosophy educator; b. N.Y.C., Dec. 27, 1933; s. Walter Harold and Charlotte (Ornstein) W.; m. Cynthia Griffin, June 9, 1962 (div. 1986); children: Patrick Gideon, Tobias Barrington; m. Susan Gould, Aug. 25, 1987. AB, Harvard U., 1953, MA in Philosophy, 1954, PhD, 1957. Instr. Harvard U., 1958-61; asst. prof. philosophy U. Chgo., 1961-63; vis. lectr. Wellesley Coll., 1963-64; assoc. prof. philosophy Columbia, 1964-69, prof., 1969-71; prof. philosophy U. Mass., Amherst, 1971-92, prof. Afro-Am. studies and philosophy, 1992—. Author: Kant's Theory of Mental Activity, 1963, A Critique of Pure Tolerance, 1965, Political Man and Social Man, 1966, Kant: A Collection of Critical Essays, 1967, Poverty of Liberalism, 1968, The Ideal of the University, 1969, In Defense of Anarchism, 1970, Philosophy: A Modern Encounter, 1971, The Autonomy of Reason, 1973, About Philosophy, 1975, 6th edit., 1995. Exec. dir. Harvard-Radcliffe Alumni/ae Against Apartheid, 1988-90; pres., exec. dir. Univ. Scholarships for South African Students, 1990—; co-dir. inst. advanced study in humanities U. Mass., 1992—. Home: 107 Buffam Rd Amherst MA 01002-9723

WOLFF, SANFORD IRVING, lawyer; b. Chgo., Apr. 13, 1915; s. Herbert Barron and Libby (Levey) W.; m. Ann Barry, Mar. 21, 1970; children—Paul, David, Laura. BA, Knox Coll., 1936; grad., John Marshall Law Sch., U. Chgo., 1940. Bar: Ill. 1940, N.Y. 1973. Pvt. practice Chgo. and N.Y.C., 1945—; chief exec. AFTRA, AFL-CIO, N.Y.C., 1968-85; of counsel Becker, London & Kossow, N.Y.C., 1985—; chief exec. and counsel Am. Guild of Musical Artists, AFL-CIO, 1988-93. Trustee Harris Sch., Chgo. Served with AUS, 1940-45. Decorated Combat Inf. badge, Purple Heart, Bronze Star with cluster, Silver Star. Mem. ABA, Chgo. Bar Assn. Office: 1841 Broadway New York NY 10023-7603

WOLFF, SHELDON, radiobiologist, educator; b. Peabody, Mass., Sept. 22, 1928; s. Henry Herman and Goldie (Lipchitz) W.; m. Frances Faye Farbstein, Oct. 23, 1954; children: Victor Charles, Roger Kenneth, Jessica Raye. B.S. magna cum laude, Tufts U., 1950; M.A., Harvard U., 1951, Ph.D., 1953. Teaching fellow Harvard U., 1951-52; sr. research staff biology div. Oak Ridge Nat. Lab., 1953-66; prof. cytogenetics U. Calif., San Francisco, 1966—, dir. Lab. Radiobiology and Environ. Health, 1983—; vis. prof. radiation biology U. Tenn., 1962, lectr., 1953-65; cons. several fed. sci. agys.; chmn. U.S. Dept. Energy's Health and Environ. Rsch. Adv. Com., 1987—, co-chmn. Joint NIH/Dept. Energy Subcom. on Human Genome, 1989-94. Editor: Chromosoma, 1983—; assoc. editor: Cancer Research, 1983—; Editorial bd.: Radiation Research, 1968-72, Photochemistry and Photobiology, 1962-72, Radiation Botany, 1964-86, Mutation Research, 1964—, Caryologia, 1967—, Radiation Effects, 1969-81, Genetics, 1972-85; Contbr. articles to sci. jours. Recipient E.O. Lawrence meml. award U.S. AEC, 1973. Mem. Genetics Soc. Am., Radiation Rsch. Soc. (counselor for biology 1968-72, Failla lectr. 1992, medal 1992), Am. Soc. Cell Biology, Environmental Mutagen Soc. (coun. 1972—, pres. 1980-81, award 1982), Internat. Assn. Environ. Mutagen Socs. (treas. 1978-85), Sigma Xi. Democrat. Home: 41 Eugene St Mill Valley CA 94941-1717 Office: U Calif Lab Radiobiology San Francisco CA 94143

WOLFF, SIDNEY CARNE, astronomer, observatory administrator; b. Sioux City, Iowa, June 6, 1941; d. George Albert and Ethel (Smith) Carne; m. Richard J. Wolff, Aug. 29, 1962. BA, Carleton Coll., 1962, DSc (hon.), 1985; PhD, U. Calif., Berkeley, 1966. Postgrad. research fellow Lick Obs, Santa Cruz, Calif., 1969; asst. astronomer U. Hawaii, Honolulu, 1967-71, assoc. astronomer, 1971-76; astronomer, assoc. dir. Inst. Astronomy, Honolulu, 1976-83, acting dir., 1983-84; dir. Kitt Peak Nat. Obs., Tucson, 1984-87, Nat. Optical Astronomy Observatories, 1987—; dir. Gemini Project Gemini 8-Meter Telescopes Project, 1992-94. Author: The A-Type Stars—Problems and Perspectives, 1983, (with others) Exploration of the Universe, 1987, Realm of the Universe, 1988, Frontiers of Astronomy, 1990; contbr. articles to profl. jours. Trustee Carleton Coll., 1989—. Rsch. fellow Lick Obs. Santa Cruz, Calif., 1967; recipient Nat. Meritorious Svc. award NSF, 1994. Mem. Astron. Soc. Pacific (pres. 1984-86, bd. dirs. 1979-85), Am. Astron. Soc. (coun. 1983-86, pres.-elect 1991, pres. 1992-94). Office: Nat Optical Astronomy Obs PO Box 26732 950 N Cherry Ave Tucson AZ 85719-4933

WOLFF, STEVEN ALEXANDER, arts and entertainment consultant; b. N.Y.C., July 18, 1957; s. Joel Charles and Joan (Mittlemark) W.; m. Gail English Loflin, June 12, 1988; children: Jessica Sadye, Ian Charles. BA in Econs., SUNY, Brockport, 1978; MFA in Theatre Adminstrn., Yale U. 1981. Cert. mgmt. cons. Cons. Artec Cons., N.Y.C, 1981-83; mgr. Theatre Projects Cons., N.Y.C., 1983-88; sr. v.p., prin. Hill Arts & Entertainment/ AMS/ArtSoft Mgmt. Svcs., Guilford, Conn., 1988-91; pres. AMS Planning & Rsch. Corp., Fairfield, Conn., 1991—; lectr. in field. Major projects include Ohio Ctr. for Arts, Cin., Calif. Ctr. for Arts, Escondido, Metro-Dade Arts Ctr., Miami; contbr. articles to profl. jours. Recipient Cert. of Honor, ARC (nat. chpt.), 1978. Mem. Internat. Soc. Performing Arts Adminstrs., Internat. Downtown Assn., Assn. Performing Arts Presenters. Avocation: competitive offshore sailing. Office: AMS Planning & Rsch Corp 2150 Post Rd Fairfield CT 06430-5669

WOLFF, THOMAS JOHN, insurance company executive, consultant, author; b. Berlin, Aug. 1, 1928; naturalized U.S citizen, 1940; s. Kurt and Eva (Hermann) W.; m. Mary Elizabeth Granberg, May 1, 1949; children—Gregory, Gary, Debra. Cert., N.Y. Tech. Inst., 1948; B.A. cum laude, U. Conn., 1956. C.L.U.; chartered fin. cons. Author, pres. Vernon-Longman Pub., Conn., 1966—; chmn. bd. dirs. Wolff-Zackin & Assocs., Vernon, Conn., 1967—, chmn. bd. dirs. emeritus; instr. Life Underwriting Tng. Council, 1958-59, trustee, Washington, 1983-85, sec., 1985-86, chmn. 1987-88; mem. faculty Capital Need Analysis Tng. Schs., 1960—, Am. Coll. Life Underwriters, 1976—; mem. faculty C.L.U. Inst., 1970-84; mem. com. Nat. C.L.U. Devel. Fund. Inventor capital need analysis, 1966, fin. need analysis, 1980; author: Life Insurance in Action, 1967, Life Insurance A 9% Investment, 1967, Business Estate Asset Review (BEAR), 1986. Past v.p. Town of Vernon Bd. Edn., 1960-66; mem. city council Town of Vernon, 1966-75, mem. charter rev. com., 1977; chmn. Citizens Com. for Edn., Vernon, 1973;corporatore Rockville Gen. Hosp., Conn., 1980, Am. Coll. of CLU and Chartered Fin. Cons., 1990—; chmn. parent's com. Westminster Sch.; past chmn. sch. devel. com. Rumsey Hall Sch. Recipient John Newton Russell award, 1982, Disting. Alumni award U. Conn., 1981,So. New Eng. Entrepreneur of Yr. award, 1990, UConn Club award U. Conn., 1991; Founders Gold medal Internat. Ins. Soc., 1991; named one of top 20 life ins. agents in U.S., Leaders Mag. Mem. Nat. Assn. Life Underwriters (nominating com. 1972, chmn. nat. membership com. 1973-74, trustee 1973-75, sec. 1977-78, pres. 1979-80, 33 nat. quality awards), Internat. Assn. Fin. Planning (Am. Salesmaster award 1970), Assn. for Advanced Life Underwriters, Am. Soc. CLUs (sec. Hartford chpt. 1967), Million Dollar Round Table (charter, life, mem. Top of the Table). Hartford Assn. Life Underwriters (past pres. 1960-61, v.p. 1969), Conn. Assn. Life Underwriters (pres. 1970-71), Million Dollar Round Table Found. (pres.), Rockville C. of C.

(v.p. 1958-59), Ellington Ridge Country Club (pres. 1961-62, 69-70), Rotary (past pres.). Mem. United Ch. of Christ. Home: 45 Valley View Ln Vernon Rockville CT 06066-4135 Office: Wolff Zackin & Assocs One Executive Pk E Vernon Rockville CT 06066

WOLFF, TOBIAS (JONATHAN ANSELL WOLFF), author; b. Birmingham, Ala., June 19, 1945; s. Arthur Saunders and Rosemary (Loftus) W.; m. Catherine Dolores Spohn, 1975; children: Michael, Patrick, Mary Elizabeth. BA, Oxford Univ., 1972, MA, 1975; MA, Stanford Univ., 1978. Mem. faculty Stanford (Calif.) U., Goddard Coll., Plainfield, Vt., Ariz. State U., Tempe, Syracuse (N.Y.) U.; reporter Washington Post. Author: In the Garden of the North American Martyrs, 1981 (St. Lawrence award for fiction 1982), The Barracks Theif, 1984 (PEN/Faulkner award for fiction 1985), Back in the World, 1985, This Boy's Life: A Memoir, 1989 (L.A. Times Book prize 1989), In Pharaoh's Army: Memories of the Lost War, 1994; editor: Matters of Life and Death: New American Stories, 1983, The Stories of Anton Chekhov, 1987, Best American Short Stories, 1994, The Vintage Book of Contemporary American Stories, 1994. Recipient Wallace Stegner fellowship in creative writing, 1975-76; Nat. Endowment for the Arts fellowship in creative writing, 1978, 85; Mary Roberts Rinehart grant, 1979; Ariz. Coun. on Arts and Humanities fellowship in creative writing, 1980, Guggenheim fellowship, 1982; Rea award, 1989; Whiting Writer's award, 1989, Lila-Wallace-Reader's Digest award, 1993, Lyndhurst Found. award, 1994. Office: Syracuse Univ Dept of English Syracuse NY 13244-0002

WOLFF, VIRGINIA EUWER, writer, secondary education educator; b. Portland, Oreg., Aug. 25, 1937; d. Eugene Courtney and Florence Evelyn (Craven) Euwer; m. Art Wolff, July 19, 1959 (div. July 1976); children: Anthony Richard, Juliet Dianne. AB, Smith Coll., 1959; postgrad., Goddard Coll., Warren Wilson Coll., L.I. U., Portland State U., Lewis & Clark Coll. Cert. tchr., Oreg. Tchr. The Miquon Sch., Phila., 1968-72, The Fiedel Sch., Glen Cove, N.Y., 1972-75, Hood River Valley (Oreg.) H.S., 1976-86, Mt. Hood Acad., Govt. Camp, Oreg., 1986—; 2d violinist Quartet con brio, Portland, 1989—. Author: Probably Still Nick Swansen, 1988, The Mozart Season, 1991, Make Lemonade, 1993. Violinist Mid-Columbia Sinfonietta, Hood River, 1976—, Oreg. Sinfonietta, Portland, 1988—. Recipient Child Study Children's Book award Bank St. Coll., 1994, Young Adult Book award Internat. Reading Assn., 1989, PEN U.S.A. Ctr. West, 1989, Oreg. Book award Oreg. Lit. Arts, 1994. Mem. Soc. Children's Book Writers/ Illustrators (Golden Kite 1994), Chamber Music Soc. Oreg. Avocations: chamber music, swimming, hiking, playing violin, gardening. Office: Curtis Brown Ltd care Marilyn E Marlow 10 Astor Pl New York NY 10003

WOLFF, WILLIAM F., III, investment banker; b. N.Y.C., Apr. 12, 1945; s. William F. Jr. and Nancy (Wimpfheimer) W.; m. Phyllis Fox, June 1, 1969; children: Kenneth, Jonathan, Gillian. BA, U. Mich., 1967; JD, Columbia U., 1970, MBA, 1971. Bar: N.Y. 1970. V.p. Salomon Bros., Inc., N.Y.C. 1971-78; prin. Morgan Stanley & Co., N.Y.C., 1978-83; mng. dir. Lehman Brothers, N.Y.C., 1983—. Trustee St. David's Sch., N.Y.C., 1985—, Nat. Glaucoma Trust, 1992—. Mem. Univ Club (N.Y.), Ocean Beach Club (Elberon, N.J.) (trustee 1985-89). Office: Lehman Bros Three World Fin Ctr New York NY 10285

WOLFF, WILLIAM I., surgeon, educator; b. N.Y.C., Oct. 24, 1916; s. Julius Louis and Matilda (Brick) W.; m. Lillian Myrick, June 30, 1952 (div. 1967); children: Richard, Deborah, David, Alan, Lisa, Mitchell, George Rebecca, Barbara; m. Rita T. Smith, Feb. 15, 1972. BS, NYU, 1936; MD, U. Md., 1940. Diplomate Am. Bd. Surgery, Am. Bd. Thoracic Surgery. Intern Bellevue Hosp., 1940-42, resident specializing in chest surgery, 1942-43; resident, chief Bronx Vets. Hosp., 1946-48; chief thoracic surgery Deshon Vets. Hosp., 1949; practice medicine specializing in surgery N.Y.C., 1950—; assoc. prof. surgery NYU, N.Y.C., 1960—; dir. surgery Beth Israel Med. Ctr., N.Y.C., 1962-76; prof. surgery Mt. Sinai Sch. Medicine, N.Y.C., 1965—; 1st ann. lectr. Am. Soc. for Gastrointestinal Endoscopy, 1987. Early contbr. to subject of cardiac resuscitation by cardiac massage; originator of sci. procedure of colonoscopy and removal of colonic polyps; contbr. over 100 articles to leading sci. jours. Served to maj. M.C. AUS, 1943-46, ETO. Named Disting. Lectr., Soc. Am. Gastrointestinal Endoscopic Surgeons, 1987, Univ. Prize Gold Medal winner. Mem. Am. Coll. Gastroenterology (bd. govs.), N.Y. Surg. Soc. (pres. 1980-81), N.Y. Acad. Medicine (chmn. sect. on surgery), Assn. Alumni Bellevue Hosp. (pres. 1982). Club: Aspetuck Valley Country (Weston, Conn.). Avocations: gardening, ballet, tennis, theatre. Office: 44 Gramercy Park N New York NY 10010-6310

WOLFFE, ALAN PAUL, molecular embryologist, molecular biologist; b. Burton-on-Trent, Staffordshire, Eng., June 21, 1959; s. Ronald and Mildred (Hasbury) W.; m. Elizabeth Jane Hall, Aug. 21, 1982. BA with honors in Biochemistry, Oxford U., 1981; PhD, MRC London, 1983. Postdoctoral fellow Carnegie Instn., Balt., 1984-86, prin. investigator, 1987; prin. investigator, asst. prof. Nat. Inst. Diabetes and Digestive and Kidney Diseases, Bethesda, Md., 1988-90; assoc. prof. Nat. Inst. Diabetes and Digestive and Kidney Diseases, Bethesda, 1990; chief lab. molecular embryology Nat. Inst. Child Health and Human Devel., Bethesda, 1990—, prof., 1992—; ad hoc reviewer NSF, 1989-92, molecular biology study sect. NIH, 1990; mem. biological scis. study sect. NIH, 1991—; mem. biochemistry program panel NSF, 1992-93; chmn. meeting Chromatin Structure and Transcription Fedn. Am. Socs. Exptl. Biology, 1993. Author: Chromatin: Structure and Function, 1992; contbr. articles. Fellow Rsch. Coun. Predoctoral Rsch., 1981-84, European Molecular Biology Orng., 1984-86; grantee Am. Cancer Soc., 1987, Fogarty Internat. Ctr., 1991, NIH, 1992, NSF, 1993. Mem. AAAS, Am. Assn. Cancer Rsch., Am. Soc. Microbiology, Am. Soc. Cell Biology, Brit. Soc. Devel. Biology, Biochemical Soc. (U.K.). Achievements include major contributions to elucidating role of nucleic acid packaging proteins (histones for DNA, Y-box proteins for RNA) in regulating gene expression (transcription of DNA, translation of RNA). Office: Nat Inst Child Health & Human Devel Molecular Embryol Lab Rm B1A13 9000 Rockville Pike Bldg 6 Bethesda MD 20892

WOLFGANG, BONNIE ARLENE, musician, bassoonist; b. Caribou, Maine, Sept. 29, 1944; d. Ralph Edison and Arlene Alta (Obetz) W.; m. Eugene Alexander Pridonoff, July 3, 1965 (div. Sept. 1977); children: George Randall, Anton Alexander, Stephan Eugene. MusB, Curtis Inst. Music, Phila., 1967. Soloist Phila. Orch., 1966; soloist with various orchs. U.S., Cen. Am., 1966-75; prin. bassoonist Phoenix Symphony, 1976—, with Woodwind Quintet, 1986—. Home: 9448 N 106th St Scottsdale AZ 85258

WOLFGANG, MARVIN EUGENE, sociologist, criminologist, educator; b. Millersburg, Pa., Nov. 14, 1924; s. Charles T. and Pauline (Sweigard) W.; m. Lenora D. Poden, June 1, 1957; children: Karen Eleanor, Nina Victoria. B.A., Dickinson Coll., Carlisle, Pa., 1948; M.A., U. Pa., 1950, Ph.D., 1955. Instr., asst. prof. Lebanon Valley Coll., 1948-52; instr. to prof. sociology U. Pa., Phila., 1952—; chmn. dept. U. Pa., 1968-72, prof. sociology and law, 1972—; also dir. Sellin Ctr. for Studies in Criminology and Criminal Law; vis. prof., fellow Churchill Coll., U. Cambridge, Eng., 1968-69; cons. Rand Corp.; Chmn. rev. com. on crime and delinquency NIMH, 1971-73; rsch. dir. Nat. Commn. on Causes and Prevention of Violence, 1968-69; commr. Nat. Commn. on Obscenity and Pornography, 1968-70. Author: Patterns in Criminal Homicide, 1958, Crime and Race, 1964, (with T. Sellin) The Measurement of Delinquency, 1964, (with F. Ferracuti) The Subculture of Violence, 1967, Crime and Culture, 1968, (with L. Radzinowicz) Crime and Justice, 3 vols, 1971, rev. edit., 1977, (with T. Sellin, R. Figlio) Delinquency in a Birth Cohort, 1972, (with R. Figlio, T. Thornberry) Criminology Index, 2 vols, 1975, Evaluating Criminology, 1978, (with N. Weiner) Criminal Violence, 1981, (with R. Figlio et al) National Survey of Crime Severity, 1986, (with T.Thornberry and R. Figlio) From Boy to Man: From Delinquency to Crime, 1987, (with N. Weiner) Violent Crime, Violent Criminals, Pathways to Criminal Violence, 1988, (with P. Tracy and R. Figlio) Delinquency Careers in Two Birth Cohorts, 1990, (with D. Nevares and P. Tracy) Delinquency in Puerto Rico: The 1970 Birth Cohort Study, 1991. Chmn., bd. dirs. Thomas Skelton Harrison Found.; chmn. Eisenhower Found. With AUS, 1943-45, ETO. Recipient Fulbright rsch. award, 1957-58, Hans von Hentig award World Soc. Victimology, 1988; Guggenheim fellow, 1957-58, 68-69. Mem. Am. Philos. Soc., Am. Acad. Arts and Scis., Internat. Soc. Criminology, Am. Soc. Criminology (past pres., rsch. award 1960, Edwin Sutherland award 1989), Am. Acad. Polit. and Social Sci.

(pres.), Pa. Prison Soc. (bd. dirs., past pres.). Home: 4106 Locust St Philadelphia PA 19104-3509 Office: Am Acad Polit & Social Sci 3937 Chestnut St Philadelphia PA 19104-3110

WOLFINGER, RAYMOND EDWIN, political science educator; b. San Francisco, June 29, 1931; s. Raymond Edwin and Hilda (Holm) W.; m. Barbara Kaye, Aug. 8, 1960; 1 son, Nicholas Holm. A.B., U. Calif.-Berkeley, 1951; M.A., U. Ill., 1955; Ph.D., Yale U., 1961. Asst. prof. polit. sci. Stanford U., 1961-66, assoc. prof., 1966-70, prof., 1970-71; prof. U. Calif.-Berkeley, 1971—; dir. U. Calif. Data Archive and Tech. Assistance, 1980-92; chmn. bd. overseers Nat. Election Studies, Ann Arbor, Mich., 1982-86. Author: The Politics of Progress, 1974, (with others) Dynamics of American Politics, 1976, 80, (with Steven J. Rosenstone) Who Votes, 1980, (with others) The Myth of the Independent Voter, 1992; mem. editorial bd. Brit. Jour. Polit. Sci., 1980-84, Am. Polit. Sci. Rev., 1985-88. Bd. dirs. S.W. Voter Rsch. Inst. Inc., San Antonio, 1988—; Consortium of Social Sci. Assns., 1987-93, pres., 1988-90. 1st lt. U.S. Army, 1951-53. Fellow Ctr. for Advanced Study in Behavioral Scis., 1960-61; Guggenheim fellow, 1965; Ford Found. faculty research fellow, 1970-71. Fellow Am. Acad. Arts and Scis.; mem. Am. Polit. Sci. Assn. (sec. 1981-82), AAUP (council 1981-84), Western Polit. Sci. Assn. (v.p 1988-89, pres. 1989-90). Democrat. Office: U Calif Dept Polit Sci Berkeley CA 94720

WOLFLE, DAEL LEE, public affairs educator; b. Puyallup, Wash., Mar. 5, 1906; s. David H. and Elizabeth (Pauly) W.; m. Helen Morrill, Dec. 28, 1929 (dec. July 1988); children: Janet Helen (Mrs. Peter M. Baumgartner), Lee Morrill, John Morrill. B.S., U. Wash., 1927, M.S., 1928; postgrad., U. Chgo., summers 1929, 30; Ph.D., Ohio State U., 1931, D.Sc., 1957; D.Sc., Drexel U., 1956, Western Mich. U., 1960. Instr. psychology Ohio State U., 1929-32; prof. psychology U. Miss., 1932-36; examiner in biol. scis. U. Chgo., 1936-39, asst. prof. psychology, 1938-43, assoc. prof., 1943-45; on leave for war work with Signal Corps, 1941-43; with OSRD, 1944-45; exec. sec. Am. Psychol. Assn., 1946-50; dir. commn. on human resources and advanced tng. Assoc. Research Councils, 1950-54; exec. officer AAAS, 1954-70; editor Sci., 1955, pub., 1955-70; prof. pub. affairs U. Wash., Seattle, 1970-76; prof. emeritus U. Wash., 1976—; mem. sci. adv. bd. USAF, 1953-57; mem. def. sci. bd. Dept. Def., 1957-61; mem. adv. council on mental health NIMH, 1960-64; mem. nat. adv. health council USPHS, 1965-66; mem. commn. on human resources NRC, 1974-78; mem. adv. bd. Geophys. Inst., Fairbanks, Alaska., 1970-93, chmn. adv. bd., 1972-81. Author: Factor Analysis to 1940, 1941, Science and Public Policy 1959, The Uses of Talent, 1971, The Home of Science, 1972, Renewing a Scientific Society, 1989; editor: America's Resources of Specialized Talent, 1954. Trustee Russell Sage Found., 1961-78, Pacific Sci. Cent. Found., 1962-80, Biol. Scis. Curriculum Study, 1980-85; chmn. bd. J. McK. Cattell Fund, 1962-82. Named Alumnus Summa Laude Dignatus, U. Wash., 1979. Mem. AAAS (pres. Pacific div. 1991-92), AAUP, Am. Psychol. Assn., Am. Acad. Arts and Scis. (exec. com. western sect. 1985-92), Sigma Xi. Home: 4545 Sand Point Way NE #805 Seattle WA 98105-3926 Office: U Wash Grad Sch Public Affairs Seattle WA 98195

WOLFLEY, ALAN, corporate executive; b. Rockford, Ill., Dec. 23, 1923; s. Chester E. and Lois (Karlson) W.; m. Joanne Higgins, Jan. 6, 1945; children: C. Alan, Susan (Mrs. Peter M. Baumgartner), E. William. B.A. cum laude, Middlebury (Vt.) Coll., 1947; M.B.A., Harvard U. 1949. Budget supr. Merck & Co., Rahway, N.J., 1949-52; asst. to treas. Standard Vacuum Oil Co., 1952-59; asst. treas. Parke-Davis & Co., 1959-64; v.p. finance Cardorundum Co., 1964-68; v.p. finance, dir. Scovill Mfg. Co., 1968-71; exec. v.p., mem. exec. com., dir. Cerro Corp., N.Y.C., 1971-73; dir. Southern Peru Copper Co., N.Y.C., 1973-77, Marmon Group, Inc., Chgo., 1977-86; pres., dir. Greenley Energy Corp., 1978-88; U.S.A. rep. Coenco Corp., 1989—. Mem. nat. council Salk Inst., 1979-86. Served to capt. USAAF, World War II. Decorated Silver Star, D.F.C., Air medal, Purple Heart. Mem. Harvard (N.Y.C.), Wee Burn Country Club (Darien, Conn.), Pine Valley Golf Club (Clementon, N.J.), Landsdowne Club (London, Eng.), Chi Psi. Republican. Methodist. Home: 22 Canaan Close New Canaan CT 06840-4928 Office: Coenco Corp PO Box 218 New Canaan CT 06840-0218

WOLFMAN, BERNARD, lawyer, educator; b. Phila., July 8, 1924; s. Nathan and Elizabeth (Coff) W.; m. Zelda Bernstein, Dec. 25, 1948 (dec. Oct. 1973); children: Jonathan L., Brian S., Dina A.; m. Toni A. Grotta, June 12, 1977. AB, U. Pa., 1946, JD, 1948; LLD (hon.), Jewish Theol. Sem., 1971, Capital U., 1990. Bar: Pa. 1949, Mass. 1976. Mem. law firm Wolf, Block, Schorr & Solis-Cohen, Phila., 1948-63; prof. law U. Pa. Law Sch., 1963-76, dean, 1970-75, Kenneth W. Gemmill prof. tax law and tax policy, 1973-76, chmn. Faculty Senate, 1969-70; Fessenden prof. law Harvard U., 1976—; vis. prof. Stanford Law Sch., summer 1966, U. Mich. Law Sch., summer 1982, NYU Law Sch., 1987-88; Irvine lectr. Cornell U. Law Sch., 1980; Halle lectr. Case Western Res. U. Law Sch., 1983, Cleve. State U. Sch. Law, 1983; Sugarman lectr. Case Western Res. U. Law Sch., 1989; Altheimer lectr. U. Ark. at Little Rock Sch. Law, 1994; mem. tax adv. bd. Little, Brown & Co., Tax Practice Series, Commerce Clearing House, Inc., 1983-94; mem. editl. bds. law divsn. Little Brown & Co., Jour. Corp. Taxation; gen. counsel AAUP, 1966-68, mem. coun., 1979-82; cons. to intl. counsel Lawrence E. Walsh (Iran/Contra prosecution), 1987-89; mem. adv. group to commr. internal revenue, 1966-67; cons. tax policy U.S. Treasury Dept., 1963-68, 77-80; chmn. Task Force U. Governance, U. Pa., 1968-70; mem. steering com. IRA project Adminstrv. Conf. U.S. 1974-80; vice chmn. bd. advs. NYU/IRS Continuing Profl. Edn. Project, 1981-85; mem. legal activities policy bd. Tax Analysts, 1974—; exec. com. Fed. Tax Inst. New Eng., 1976—. Author: Federal Income Taxation of Corporate Enterprise, 1971, 3d edit., 1990; (with J. Holden and D. Schenk) Ethical Problems in Federal Tax Practice, 1981, 3d edit., 1995; (with J. Holden and K. Harris) Standards of Tax Practice, 1991, 2d edit., 1995; sr. author: Dissent Without Opinion: The Behavior of Justice William O. Douglas in Federal Tax Cases, 1975; contbr. articles to profl. jours. Adv. com. Commn. Philanthropy and Pub. Needs, 1973-75; mem. Phila. regional council Pa. Gov.'s Justice Commn., 1973-75; trustee Found. Center, N.Y.C., 1970-76, Fedn. Jewish Agys. Greater Phila., 1968-74; bd. dirs. Phila. Lawyers Com. Civil Rights Under Law, 1970-74, Phila. Defender Assn., 1955-69; mem. Nat. Lawyers Adv. Council of Earl Warren Legal Tng. Program. Served with AUS, 1943-45. Fellow Am. Bar Found., Am. Coll. Tax Counsel (regent); mem. ABA (past chmn. com. on taxation, coun. sect. individual rights and responsibilities 1978-82, coun. sect. taxation 1982-85), Am. Law Inst. (cons. fed. income tax project 1974—), ACLU (nat. dir. 1973-75, bd. dirs. Phila. chpt. 1964-76, pres. 1972-75), Order of Coif (exec. com. 1982-91, v.p. 1986-89, pres. 1989-91), Phi Beta Kappa. Home: 229 Brattle St Cambridge MA 02138-4623 Office: Law Sch Harvard U Cambridge MA 02138

WOLFMAN, BRUNETTA REID, education educator; b. Clarksdale, Miss., Sept. 4, 1931; d. Willie Orlando and Belle Victoria (Allen) Reid Griffin; m. Burton Wolfman, Oct. 4, 1952; children: Andrea, Jeffrey. BA, U. Calif., Berkeley, 1957, MA, 1968, PhD, 1971; DHL (hon.), Boston U., 1983; DP (hon.), Northeastern U., 1983; DL (hon.), Regis Coll., 1984, Stonehill Coll., 1985; DHL, Suffolk U., 1985; DET (hon.), Wentworth Inst., 1987; AA (hon.), Roxbury Community Coll., 1988. Asst. dean faculty Dartmouth Coll., Hanover, N.H., 1972-74; asst. v.p. acad. affairs U. Mass., Boston, 1974-76; acad. dean Wheelock Coll., Boston, 1976-78; cons. Arthur D. Little, Cambridge, Mass., 1978; dir. policy planning Dept. Edn., Boston, 1978-82; pres. Roxbury Community Coll., Boston, 1983-88, ACE sr. assoc., 1988—; assoc. v.p. acad. affairs George Washington U., Washington, 1989-92, prof. edn., 1992—; pres. bd. dirs. Literacy Vols. of Capitol Region; bd. dirs. Am. Coun. Edn., Harvard Community Health Plan. Author: Roles, 1983. Bd. overseers Wellesley (Mass.) Coll., 1981; bd. dirs. Boston-Fenway Program, 1977, Freedom House, Boston, 1983, Boston Pvt. Industry Coun., 1983, NCCJ, Boston, 1983; bd. overseers Boston Symphony Orch.; trustee Mus. Fine Arts, Boston; councilor Coun. on Edn. for Pub. Health. Recipient Freedom award NAACP No. Calif., 1971, Amelia Earhart award Women's Edn. and Indsl. Union, Boston, 1983; Sr. scholar Nat. Assn. Women in Edn. Mem. Am. Sociol. Assn., Assn. Black Women in Higher Edn., D.C. Sociol. Soc., Greater Boston C. of C. (edn. com. 1982), Cosmos Club (Washington), Pi Lambda Theta, Alpha Kappa Alpha (Humanitarian award 1984), Phi Delta Kappa (pres. GW chpt.), Nat. Assn. Women in Edn. (sr. scholar). Home: 2022 Columbia Rd NW Washington DC 20009-1352 Office: George Washington U 2134 G St NW Washington DC 20052-0001

WOLFMAN, EARL FRANK, JR., surgeon, educator; b. Buffalo, Sept. 14, 1926; s. Earl Frank and Alfreda (Peterson) W.; m. Lois Jeannette Walker, Dec. 28, 1946; children—Nancy Jeannette, David Earl, Carol Anne. BS cum laude, Harvard U., 1946; M.D. cum laude, U. Mich., 1950. Diplomate Am. Bd. Surgery. Intern U. Mich., Ann Arbor, 1950-51, asst. resident in surgery, 1951-52, resident in surgery, 1954-55, jr. clin. instr. surgery, 1955-56, sr. clin. instr., 1956-57, instr., 1957-60, asst. prof., 1960-63, assoc. prof., 1963-66, asst. to dean, 1960-61, asst. dean, 1961-64; practice medicine specializing in surgery, 1957—, Sacramento, 1966—; prof. surgery Sch. Medicine, U. Calif., Davis, 1966—, chmn. dept. surgery, 1968-78, assoc. dean, 1966-76; mem. staff, chief surg. svcs. Sacramento (Calif.) Med. Ctr., 1966—. Contbr. articles to profl. jours. Served to lt. M.C. USNR, 1952-54. Fellow ACS; mem. AMA (del. 1987—), Ctrl. Surg. Soc., Western Surg. Soc., Sacramento Surg. Soc., Pacific Coast Surg. Soc., Calif. Acad. Medicine, Frederick A. Coller Surg. Soc., Pan Am. Med. Assn., Soc. Surgery Alimentary Tract, Am. Assn. Endocrine Surgeons, Sacramento Med. Soc., Yolo Med. Soc., Calif. Med. Assn. (trustee 1991—), Am. Soc. Gen. Surgeons, Comstock Club. Methodist. Home: 44770 N El Macero Dr PO Box 3086 El Macero CA 95618 Office: U Calif-Davis Sch Medicine Dept Surgery 4301 X St Sacramento CA 95817-2214

WOLFMAN, IRA JOEL, editor, writer; b. Oct. 7, 1950; s. Aaron and Beatrice Ruth (Perlo) W.; m. Julia Diamant, June 24, 1979 (dec. 1982); m. Ronda Small, Dec. 20, 1991. B.A. cum laude, SUNY, Albany, 1971. News editor Washington Park Spirit, Albany, N.Y., 1971-73; sr. editor Smash mag., N.Y.C., 1975-76; Circus mag., N.Y.C., 1976-79; assoc. editor 3-2-1 Contact mag., N.Y.C., 1979-80; editor Sesame St Parents' Newsletter, N.Y.C., 1980-83; editor in chief Enter mag., N.Y.C., 1983-85, Sesame St. mag., Parents Guide, 1990—; v.p., editor-in-chief Adult Consumer mags., Children's TV Workshop, N.Y.C., 1994—; newsletter editor Found. for Grandparenting, Mt. Kisco, N.Y., 1984-87; editor Am. Writer, 1988-89; freelance writer and editor, contbr. to Travel & Leisure, Architectural Record, Metropolis, N.Y. Daily News, Ms., Spy, 1985—. Author: Do People Grow on Family Trees? Genealogy for Kids and Other Beginners, 1991, My World and Globe, 1991. N.Y. State Legis. Corrs. scholar, 1970. Jewish.

WOLFMAN JACK (ROBERT WESTON SMITH), radio personality; b. Bklyn., Jan. 21, 1938; s. Anson Weston and Rosmond (Small) S.; m. Lou Lamb, May 5, 1961; children: Joy Rene, Tod Weston. Grad. high sch., L.I., N.Y.; 1st class lic., Nat. Acad. Broadcasting, Washington. Radio personality, salesman, sta. mgr. Universal Broadcasting, Shreveport, La. and Mpls.; radio personality, salesman, owner U.S. rights Sta. XERF, Del Rio, Tex., 1961-65; radio personality, sta. mgr., owner U.S. rights Sta. XERB, Rosarito Beach, Calif., 1966-71; radio personality Armed Forces Radio, 1970-86, Sta. KDAY, Los Angeles, 1971-73, Sta. WNBC, N.Y.C., 1973-74, 1976-77; first English-speaking radio personality in Japan Sta. FM-Tokyo, 1975-77; radio personality syndicated on 2,177 stations in 53 fgn. countries, 1973—; tv personality-host The Midnight Special, L.A., 1973-82, The Wolfman Jack Show, 24 countries and U.S., 1978-79, The Disco Awards Special, 1979; appears as actor 26 U.S. network tv shows, 1974—; tv personality-host The Rock'N' Roll Palace, 1984—. Appeared in films American Graffiti, 1973, Hanging on a Star, 1976, Dead Man's Curve, 1977, Motel Hell, 1980, Mortuary Academy, 1987; author: Have Mercy!, 1995. Mem. AFTRA, Screen Actors Guild, AGVA, Alliance Can. Cinema, TV and Radio Artists. Republican. Episcopalian. Subject of 18 U.S. pop/rock songs including Clap for the Wolfman by The Guess Who, Living on the Highway by Freddie King, and Wolfman Jack by Todd Rundgren. Died July 1, 1995.

WOLFORD, PATRICIA WEBER, management company executive; b. Bowling Green, Ky., July 31, 1940; d. James Freeman and Selina Grace (McLin) Jones; m. Bruce Dennis Weber, Aug. 8, 1959 (div. Aug. 1980); children: Tod Alan, Scott David; m. Joseph Theodore Wolford Sr., Mar. 5, 1981. Student, Bryant Bus. Coll., 1959; mgmt. cert., Columbia U., 1981. Adminstrv. asst. U. Louisville Engring. Sch., 1959-60; asst. dir. Louisville Urban Renewal Agy., 1960-64; bus. relocation advisor Nashville Housing Authority, 1964-69; adminstr. S.E. Washington County Health Svcs., Keedysville, Md., 1976-80; exec. dir. Hancock (Md.) Health Care Corp, 1980-88; coord. property mgmt. Magnolia Mgmt., Inc., Hagerstown, Md., 1988-94; pres. AB Profls., Inc., Hagerstown, Md., 1995—; pres. Md. Primary Care Assn., Annapolis, 1984-86; chairperson Md. Health Systems Agy. Com., Cumberland, 1978; bd. dirs. The Maryland Theatre. Author: Standard Performance Maintenance Manual, 1994, Standard Performance Housekeeping Manual, 1994, Standard Performance Safety and Health Manual, 1994. Pres. Washington County Cmty. Action Coun. Bd., Hagerstown, 1974-77, Washington County Coun. PTA, Hagerstown, 1976-78; chairperson/commr. Washington County San. Com., 1980-84; dist. chairperson United Way Area Campaign, Hancock, Md., 1983, United Way Hagerstown, 1992, 93; mem. bd. Am. Heart Assn., Hagerstown, 1984-87; mem. dist. staff Dist. 10 Little League, Hagerstown, 1976-78; mem. Correctional Instn. Citizens Adv. Com., 1994—; mem. outreach com. First Christian Ch., 1993-94; ch. rep. Wash. County Habitat for Humanity, 1993-94; gov. appointed mem. citizens adv. com. Correctional Instn., 1994—, chairperson, 1994—; mem. transition com. Gov. P. Glendening, State of Md., 1994-95. Recipient Spirit award United Way of Washington County, 1992, Gov.'s Citation Com. to Children and Youth, Annapolis, 1979, Cert. of Appreciation, Am. Lung Assn., Hagerstown, 1985. Mem. NAFE, LWV, Md. Congress PTA, Am. Legion Aux. Christian. Avocations: theater, music, flower gardening, travel. Home: 13023 Lance Cir Hagerstown MD 21742-2939

WOLFRAM, STEPHEN, physicist, computer company executive; b. London, Aug. 29, 1959; came to U.S., 1978; Degree, Eton Coll., 1976, Oxford U., 1976; PhD in Theoretical Physics, Calif. Inst. Tech., 1979. With Calif. Inst. Tech., Pasadena, 1979-82, Inst. for Advanced Study, Princeton, N.J., 1983-86; prof. physics, math, computer sci. U. Ill., Champaign, 1986—; pres., chief exec. office Wolfram Rsch. Inc., Champaign, 1987—. Author: Mathematica, 1988, Theory and Applications of Cellular Automata, 1986; editor jour. Complex Systems, 1987—. Fellow MacArthur Found., 1981. Office: Wolfram Rsch Inc PO Box 6059 Champaign IL 61826-6059*

WOLFRAM, THOMAS, physicist; b. St. Louis, July 27, 1936; s. Ferdinand I. and Audrey H. (Calvert) W.; m. Eleanor Elaine Burger, May 22, 1965; children: Michael, Gregory, Melanie, Susan, Steven. BA, U. Calif., Riverside, 1959, PhD in Physics, 1963; MA in Physics, UCLA, 1960. Engr. Atomics Internat., Canoga Park, Calif., 1960-63; mem. tech. staff N.Am. Aviation Corp. Sci. Ctr., Thousand Oaks, Calif., 1963-68; group leader in solid state physics Rockwell Internat. Sci. Ctr., Thousand Oaks, 1968-72, dir. div. physics and chemistry, 1972-74; prof. physics, chmn. dept. physics and astronomy U. Mo., Columbia, 1974-83; dir. phys. tech. div. AMOCO Corp., 1983-87; v.p., gen. mgr. AMOCO Laser Co., 1987—; cons. in field. Editor: Inelastic Electron Tunneling Spectroscopy, 1978, research, numerous publs. in field. Recipient Disting. Prof. award Argonne Univs. Assn., 1977. Fellow Am. Phys. Soc. Office: Amoco Laser Co 1251 Frontenac Rd Naperville IL 60563-1750 Crisis is the catalyst for constructive change.

WOLFSBERG, MAX, chemist, educator; b. Hamburg, Germany, May 28, 1928; came to U.S., 1939, naturalized, 1945; s. Gustav and Ida (Engelmann) W.; m. Marilyn Lorraine Fleischer, June 23, 1957; 1 dau., Tyra Gwendolen. A.B., Washington U., St. Louis, 1948, Ph.D., 1951. Asso. chemist Brookhaven Nat. Lab., Upton, N.Y., 1951-54; chemist Brookhaven Nat. Lab., 1954-63, sr. chemist, 1963-69; prof. chemistry SUNY, Stony Brook, 1966-69; vis. prof. chemistry Ind. U., Bloomington, 1965, Cornell U., Ithaca, N.Y., 1963; prof. chemistry U. Calif., Irvine, 1969—, chmn. dept., 1974-80; Deutsche Forschungs Gemeinschaft guest prof. U. Ulm, Fed. Republic Germany, 1986; Forchheimer vis. prof. Hebrew U., 1993. Assoc. editor: Jour. Chem. Physics, 1968-70; editor: Comments on Chemical Physics, 1986-89; mem. editorial bd. Isotopenpraxis, 1987—; contbr. articles to profl. jours. AEC fellow, 1950-51; NSF sr. postdoctoral fellow, 1959; Alexander von Humboldt awardee, 1977, reinvitations 1982, 93. Mem. Am. ~~~. Soc., Phi Beta Kappa, Sigma Xi. Jewish. Home: 4533 Gorham Dr ~~~ Del Mar CA 92625-3111 Office: U Calif Dept Chemistry Irvine CA

WOLFSHEIMER, RONALD MILTON, financial services executive; b. Washington, July 24, 1952; s. Frank and Lois (Baer) W.; m. Janet Rosen; children: Chad, Jacob. BS, Ind. U., 1974. Audit staff Arthur Andersen & Co., Washington, 1974-76; audit supr. Alexander Grant & Co., Washington, 1976-79; sr. v.p. Calvert Group, Ltd., Bethesda, Md., 1979—; bd. dirs. Calvert Adminstrv. Svcs. Co., Bethesda, 1980—. Home: 11402 Duryea Dr Potomac MD 20854 Office: Calvert Group Ltd 4550 Montgomery Ave Ste 1000N Bethesda MD 20814-3343

WOLFSON, FREDA L., judge; b. Vineland, N.J., May 20, 1954; d. Samuel and Ida (Vetter) Linsenbaum; m. Douglas Wolfson, June 8, 1975; children: Brian Samuel, Matthew Bradley. BA, Douglass Coll., 1976; JD, Rutgers Law Sch., 1979. Bar: N.J. 1979, U.S. Ct. Appeals (3rd cir.). With Sullivan & Cromwell, N.Y.C., 1978; assoc. Lowenstein, Sandler, Brochin, Kohl, Fisher & Boylan, 1979-81, Clapp & Eisenberg, Newark, 1981-86; magistrate judge U.S. Dist. Ct. N.J., 1986—. Recipient Profl. Achievement award N.J. Bar Assn. Young Lawyers Div. Mem. Middlesex County Bar Assn. Avocations: golf, tennis. Office: US Post Office & Courthouse 402 East State St Rm 436 Trenton NJ 08608-0515

WOLFSON, HAROLD, corporate executive; b. Pawtucket, R.I., Oct. 3, 1926; s. Samuel and Dora (Kasindorf) W.; m. Marian A. Granrud, Oct. 9, 1953; children: Nancy C., Peter G. BA, Yale U., 1949. Feature writer N.Y. Jour.-Am., N.Y.C., 1949-55; v.p. Ruder & Finn Inc., N.Y.C., 1955-63; pres. Rubenstein, Wolfson & Co., N.Y.C., 1963—. Served with USN, 1944-46. Mem. Pub. Relations Soc. Am. (chmn. pub. relations com. N.Y. chpt. 1984-86). Home: 20 Iselin Ter Larchmont NY 10538-2631 Office: Rubenstein Wolfson & Co Inc 220 E 42nd St New York NY 10017-5806

WOLFSON, IRWIN M., insurance company executive; b. Bronx, N.Y., May 29, 1937; s. Herman M. and Kate (Greenstein) W.; m. Pauline S. Frechtel, Dec. 25, 1962; children: Fran M., Lisa G. BS in Econs., NYU, 1960. Owner/CEO Wolfson Agency, Yonkers, N.Y., 1973—; instr., owner Successful Adult Fin. Seminars, Yonkers, 1990—. Mem. operating bd. Child Abuse Prevention Ctr., White Plains, N.Y., 1990—. Sgt. U.S. Army, 1960-66. Recipient Achievement award Congressman Elliot Engel, 1992, proclamation from T. Zaleski (Mayor) City of Yonkers, 1992, letter of Recognition from M. Cuomo (Governor) N.Y. 1992; Irwin M. Wolfson Day proclaimed by A. O'Rourk (County Exec.) N.Y. 1992. Mem. Yonkers Nat. Exchange Club (pres. 1990-91, N.Y. dist. dir., 1991-95, N.Y. dist. pres.-elect 1995—). Home: 11-4 Jackson Ave Scarsdale NY 10583 Office: Wolfson Agency 475 Tuckahoe Rd Yonkers NY 10710-0250

WOLFSON, LARRY A., lawyer; b. Springfield, Ill., June 12, 1947; m. Cynthia Sherwood, 1972; children: Sharon Eve, Rachel Beth, Anna Faye. BSBA, Northwestern U., 1969; JD cum laude, U. Mich., 1974. Bar: Ill. 1974. Ptnr. Jenner & Block, Chgo. Mem. ABA, Ill. State Bar (lectr. Commercial Banking and Bankruptcy Law Edn. Series 1990), Chgo. Bar Assn., Chgo. Coun. Lawyers, Commercial Law League Am. Office: Jenner & Block 1 E Ibm Plz Chicago IL 60611-3608

WOLFSON, LAWRENCE AARON, hospital administrator; b. Chgo., July 11, 1941; s. Norman William and Doris D. (Brownstein) W.; m. Cheryl Jean Vogel, Feb. 6, 1987; children: Marc David, Sara Elizabeth, Aaron Michael, Ryan Anthony, Ashley Michelle. BA in Biology, Ind. U., South Bend, 1973, MBA, 1980. Sales rep. Gen. Med. Corp., South Bend, 1973-75, Hoechst-Roussel Pharmaceuticals, Somerville, N.J., 1975-79; purchasing agt. Simon Bros., Inc., South Bend, 1979-81; purchasing mgr. Ingalls Meml. Hosp., Harvey, Ill., 1981-83; dir. purchasing Community Hosp., Munster, Ind., 1983-86; corp. purchasing mgr. Columbus-Cuneo-Cabrini Med. Ctr., Chgo., 1986-88; materials mgmt. cons. South Western Med. Ctr., Chgo., 1988-91; asst. dir. materials mgmt. Michael Reese Hosp. and Med. Ctr., Chgo., 1989-91; dir. material mgmt. Regional Med. Ctr. at Memphis, 1991—; mem. editorial bd. Hosp. Material Mgmt. Quarterly, Aspens Pubs. Editorial bd. Hosp. Material Mgmt. Quar. Cubmaster Cub Scouts, South Bend, 1976-78. With USN, 1961-71. Mem. Am. Soc. Hosp. Materials Mgmt., Healthcare Materials Mgmt. Soc. (regional rep. 1984), Nat. Assn. Purchasing Mgmt., Am. Soc. Clin. Pathologists (affiliate), Am. Legion, B'nai Brith (pres. 1980-81). Jewish.

WOLFSON, MARK ALAN, accounting and finance educator; b. Chgo., Sept. 25, 1952; s. Jack and Maribelle (Simen) W.; m. Sheila Rae Aronesti, Aug. 3, 1975; children: Laura Rachel, Charles Michael. BS in Acctg. and Fin., U. Ill., 1973, M Acctg. Sci., 1974; PhD in Acctg., U. Tex., 1977. Asst. prof. Stanford (Calif.) U., 1977-81, assoc. prof., 1981-85, assoc. prof. 1985-87, Joseph McDonald prof., 1987-92, assoc. dean, 1990-93; Dean Witter prof., 1992—; Ford Found. vis. assoc. prof. U. Chgo., 1981-82; Thomas Henry Carroll vis. prof. Harvard U., Boston, 1988-89; cons. Fin. Acctg. Stds. Bd., Norwalk, Conn., 1985, 89-92; mem. adv. bd. Cornerstone Rsch., Menlo Park, Calif., 1989—; rsch. assoc. Nat. Bur. Econ. Rsch., Cambridge, Mass., 1988—; mem. steering com. Ctr. Econ. Policy Rsch., Stanford, 1990—; mem. task force Fed. Home Loan Bank Bd., 1989; bd. dirs. Investment Tech. Group, Jefferies Group, L.A., New Am. Holdings (Robert M. Bass Group). Mem. editorial bd. Jour. Acctg. and Econs., Jour. Acctg. Rsch., Jour. Acctg. Auditing and Fin., Jour. Corp. Fin., Rev. Acctg. Studies; contbr. articles to profl. jours. Recipient Pomerance prize Chgo. Bd. Options Exch., 1981, Disting. Tchg. award Stanford U., 1990, Notable Contbn. to Lit. award AICPA-Am. Acctg. Assn., 1990, 92, Wildman award, 1991; named Disting. Accountancy Alumnus, U. Ill., 1989. Mem. Acctg. Rschrs. Internat. Assn., Am. Acctg. Assn., Am. Fin. Assn., Am. Econ. Assn., Am. Taxation Assn. Jewish. Office: Stanford U Grad Sch of Bus Stanford CA 94305

WOLFSON, MICHAEL GEORGE, lawyer; b. Chgo., Sept. 1, 1938; s. A. Lincoln M. Weingarten and Brina (Nelson) W.; m. Rita Sue Parsont, Sept. 11, 1966; children: Bethany Lynne, Sara Wynne, Deborah Kay. Student, MIT, 1956-58; BA, U. Chgo., 1961, JD, 1964, postdoctoral, 1964-65. Bar: Ill. 1964, N.Y. 1969. Assoc. Cravath, Swaine & Moore, N.Y.C., 1965-71, Brown, Wood, Fuller, Caldwell & Ivey, N.Y.C., 1971-73; ptnr. Brown & Wood (and predecessor firm Brown, Wood, Fuller, Caldwell & Ivey), N.Y.C., 1974—. Woodrow Wilson fellow, 1961; Ford Found. fellow in internat. trade and devel., 1965. Fellow Am. Bar Found.; mem. ABA. Avocations: reading, photography, running, cross-country skiing. Office: Brown & Wood 1 World Trade Ctr New York NY 10048-0557

WOLFSON, SUSAN JEAN, English literature educator; b. Seattle, May 16, 1948; d. Andrew Tobias and Janet (Spencer) W.; m. Ronald Levao, Sept. 1, 1978. Student, Brown Univ., 1966-68; BA, Univ. Calif., 1970, MA, 1972, PhD, 1978. Teaching assoc. Univ. Calif., Berkeley, Calif., 1973-78; asst. prof. Rutgers Univ., New Brunswick, N.J., 1978-84, assoc. prof., 1984-90, prof., 1990-91; prof. Princeton Univ., Princeton, N.J., 1991—. Author: The Questioning Presence, 1986; contbr. articles to profl. jours.; bd. of editors Keats-Shelly Jour., 1988—, Romanticism, 1994—, Nineteenth-Century Contexts, 1994—. John Solomon Guggenheim fellow Guggenheim Found., 1990-91, fellow for rsch. in humanities Am. Coun. Learned Socs., 1986-87, NEH fellow, 1995-96. Mem. N.Am. Soc. for Study of Romanticism (bd. advisors 1990—), MLA (divsn. on Romanticism exec. com. 1988-92), Keats-Shelley Assn., Wordsworth-Coleridge Assn. Office: Princeton Univ Dept English 22 McCosh Hall Princeton NJ 08544-1016

WOLFSON, WARREN DAVID, lawyer, specialty retail store company executive; b. Syracuse, N.Y., Mar. 2, 1949; s. Isaiah Wolfson and Rosalind (Rothman) Gingold; separated; children: Scott E., Tara N., Lynn T. BSBA, Boston U., 1970; JD, Syracuse U., 1974. Bar: N.Y. 1975, U.S. Tax Ct. 1975, U.S. Ct. Claims 1975, U.S. Ct. Appeals (2d cir.) 1975. Assoc.; Hancock & Estabrook, Syracuse, 1974-80; sec. Fay's Inc., Liverpool, N.Y., 1980—, gen. counsel, 1981—, v.p., 1983-89, sr. v.p., 1989—; bd. dirs. Syracuse Label Co. Inc; bd. dirs. Drug Quiz Show, Inc. Bd. dirs., sec., treas. Fay's Found. Liverpool, 1982—; mem. adv. coun. Inst. for Sensory Rsch., Syracuse U., 1991—; bd. dirs. Jewish Home of Ctrl. N.Y. Mem. ABA, Am. Corp. Counsel Assn., Nat. Assn. Chain Drug Stores (mem. govtl. affairs com.), Lafayette Country Club. Office: Fay's Inc 7245 Henry Clay Blvd Liverpool NY 13088-3523

WOLGIN, DAVID LEWIS, psychology educator; b. Elizabeth, N.J., Oct. 17, 1945. BA, Rutgers U., 1967; MA, Vanderbilt U., 1968; PhD, Rutgers U., 1973. Postdoctoral fellow Inst. for Neurological Sci., U. Pa., Phila., 1973-74; rsch. assoc. U. Ill., Urbana, 1974-75; asst. prof. Fla. Atlantic U., Boca Raton, 1975-79, assoc. prof., 1979-85, prof., 1985—, dir. Inst. for the Study of Alcohol and Drug Dependence, 1986—. Author: (with others) Hunger: Basic Mechanisms and Clinical Implications, 1976, The Expression of Knowledge, 1982, Psychoactive Drugs: Tolerance and Sensitization, 1989; contbr. articles to profl. jours. Pres. Synagogue Inverrary-Chabad, Lauderhill, Fla., 1981-92; dir. Boca Raton Synagogue, 1995—. Rsch. grantee Nat. Inst. on Drug Abuse, 1990—. Mem. Soc. for Neurosci., N.Y. Acad. Sci., Soc. for Stimulus Properties Drugs, Soc. for the Study Ingestive Behavior, European Behavioural Pharmacology Soc., Ea. Psychol. Assn., Internat. Behaviorial Neurosci. Soc. (charter). Office: Fla Atlantic U Dept Psychology Boca Raton FL 33431

WOLICKI, ELIGIUS ANTHONY, nuclear physicist, consultant; b. Buffalo, May 10, 1927; s. Karol Thaddeus and Katarzyna (Garbus) W.; m. Wilma Pitsenbarger, Aug. 28, 1954; children: Karol, Ann, Stasia, Stefanie. BS magna cum laude, Canisius Coll., 1946; PhD in Nuclear Physics, U. Notre Dame, 1950. Postdoctoral rsch. assoc. in nuclear physics, dept. physics State U. Iowa, Iowa City, 1950-52; rsch. physicist Van de Graaff Br. Naval Rsch. Lab., Washington, 1952-55, head charged particles reactions sect. Van de Graaff Br., 1955-66, assoc. div. supt. nuclear sci. and tech. div., 1966-84; program area reviewer for hardness assurance Dept. Def. Nuclear Agy., Washington, 1976-84, program area reviewer for single event upsets, 1981-84; chmn. Air Force NASA Hardness Assurance Com., 1979-90; pres. Wolicki Assocs. Inc., Alexandria, Va., 1984-94. Contbr. articles to jours., chpts. to books; patentee in field. Recipient Centennial award U. Notre Dame, 1965, Meritorious Civilian Svc. award Naval Rsch. Lab., 1971. Fellow IEEE (best paper award conf. on nuclear and space radiation effects 1987), Am. Phys. Soc. Roman Catholic. Achievements include early research on ion beam analysis of surfaces; ion implantation; radiation effects in electronic devices, SDI neutral particle beams; early work on single event upsets of microcircuits by cosmic rays in space. Avocations: travel, tennis, theater, music composition. Home and Office: Wolicki Assocs Inc 1310 Gatewood Dr Alexandria VA 22307-2032

WOLIN, ALFRED M., federal judge; b. Orange, N.J., Sept. 17, 1932; s. George and Juliet (Rosenstock) W.; m. Jane Zapiekov, Mar. 27, 1960; children: Roger, Marc. BA, U. Mich., 1954; LLB, JD, Rutgers U., 1959. Pvt. practice Elizabeth, N.J., 1960-80; judge Union County Dist. Ct., Elizabeth, N.J., 1980-85, Union County Superior Ct., Elizabeth, N.J., 1985-87, U.S. Dist. Ct., Newark, N.J., 1987—; atty. Roselle Bd. Adjustment, 1965-74; legis. aide to Senator Matthew J. Rinaldo, N.J. Senate, 1970-72; spl. asst. prosecutor Union County, 1970; congl. field rep. 12th congl. dist., 1972-79; mcpl. prosecutor Town of Westfield, N.J., 1973-74. Chief staff atty. Union County Legal Aid Soc., 1964-74; mem. Union County Ethics Com., sec., 1970-78, exec. com. Statewide Speedy Trial Com., Conf. Presiding Criminal Judges, Criminal Practice Com.; active Temple Emanuel, Jewish Fedn. Cen. N.J. SPC 2 U.S. Army, 1954-56, Germany. Mem. ABA, Am. Judicature Soc., N.J. Bar Assn. (judicial selection, discipline of the bar, lawyer referral coms.), Union County Bar Assn. (sec. 1970-74, pres. elect 1975, pres. 1976, judicial appointments com.), Fed. Judges Assn. Jewish. Office: US Dist Ct 367 US Courthouse Newark NJ 07101 Notable cases include: (as judge) presided over trademark rights suit involving Procter & Gamble vs. Revlon, 1990, which alleged that Revlon's creation of Ivory Coast shampoo infringed on name of Procter & Gamble's Ivory soap. The suit was settled for an undisclosed amount.

WOLIN, JEFFREY ALAN, artist. AB, Kenyon Coll., 1972; MFA, Rochester Inst. Tech., 1977. Represented by Catherine Edelman Gallery, Chgo.; photographer City of Kalamazoo (Mich.) Police Dept., 1973-74; asst. prof. photography Ind. U., Bloomington, 1980-86, assoc. prof. photography, 1986-92, prof., 1993—; head photographics svcs. George Eastman House, Rochester, 1976-80; adj. instr. photography U. Rochester, 1978-80. Exhbns. include Ryerson Photog. Are Ctr., Toronto, Can., 1978, New Eng. Sch. Photography, Boston, 1979, Northlight Gallery, Tempe, Ariz., 1980, 88, Israel Mus., Jerusalem, 1980, George Eastman House, Rochester, 1981, 82, Boston Visual Arts Union, 1983, Ind. State Mus., Indpls., 1985, Seattle Arts Mus., 1986, Chgo. Cultural Ctr., 1986, 87, J.B. Speed Art Mus., Louisville, 1987, Silver Image Gallery, Columbus, Ohio, 1987, Marianne Deson Gallery, Chgo., 1988, Burden Gallery, N.Y., 1988, Nexus Contemporary Art Ctr., Atlanta, 1988, 89, Exposure Gallery, Orleans, Mass., 1988, Images Gallery, Cin., 1989, New Harmony (Ind.) Gallery Contemporary Art, 1989, Catherine Edelman Gallery, Chgo., 1989, 91, 92, 93, 94, San Francisco Camerawork, 1990, U. Oreg. Mus. Art, Eugene, 1990, 92, Sol Mednick Gallery, Phila., 1991, Mus. Contemporary Photography, Chgo., 1991, 92, Blue Sky Gallery, Oreg. Ctr. for Photog. Arts, Portland, 1992, Mus. Fine Arts, Houston, 1992, L.A. County Art Mus., 1992, Opsis Gallery, N.Y.C., 1992, Mus. Modern Art, N.Y.C., 1992, Ctr. Creative Photography, Tucson, 1993, Robert Klein Gallery, Boston, 1994, Fuller Mus. Art, Brockton, Mass., 1994, Nelson-Atkins Mus. Art, Kansas City, 1994, Mpls. Mus. Am. Art, St. Paul, 1995, others; permanent collections include Seattle Arts Mus., San Francisco Mus. Modern Art, Northlight Gallery, Mus. Modern Art, N.Y., Mus. Contemporary Photography, Chgo., Mus. Fine Arts, Houston, L.A. County Art Mus., Kalamazoo (Mich.) Inst. Art, Internat. Mus. Photography at George Eastman House, Ctr. Creative Photography, Tucson, Can. Ctr. for Architecture, Montreal, others. Visual Artist fellow NEA, 1988, 92, Master Artist fellow Ind. Arts Commn., 1991, John Simon Guggenheim fellow, 1991, ArtsLink fellow to Czechoslovakia, 1994, U.S./France fellow Cité Internationale des Arts-Paris, 1994. Subject of books and articles. Home: 2504 Poplar Ct Bloomington IN 47401

WOLINS, JOSEPH, artist; b. Atlantic City, Mar. 26, 1915; s. Morris and Rebecca (Katerinska) W.; m. Selma Polikoff Lazaar, Dec. 7, 1957; children: Richard Lazaar, David Lazaar, John Wolins, Sarah Wolins. Student, Nat. Acad. Design, 1931-35. Painter with Fed. art projects, 1934-41; tchr. South Shore Art Sch., Rockville Center, N.Y., 1950-55, 92d St. YMHA, N.Y.C., 1960, Bklyn. Mus. Art Sch., 1961-62, Long Beach (N.Y.) High Sch., 1962-68; pvt. classes, 1961—. One-man exhbns. include, Contemporary Arts Gallery, N.Y.C., Bodley Gallery, N.Y.C., Silvermine Guild, Norwalk, Conn., Slater Mus., Norwich, Conn., Agra Gallery, Washington, Everson Mus., Syracuse, N.Y.; group exhbns. include, World's Fair, N.Y.C., 1939, J.B. Neumann Gallery, N.Y.C., Toledo Mus., Corcoran Art Gallery, U. Ill. Mus., Pa. Acad. Fine Art, Whitney Mus., Sao Paolo Mus. Modern Art, Norfolk (Va.) Mus., Smithsonian Instn., Butler Art Inst., Youngstown, Ohio, Met. Mus. Art, N.Y.C.; rep. permanent collections, Met. Mus. Art, Norfolk Mus., Albert Gallery at St. Joseph's (Mo.) U., Ball State Mus. of Art, Muncie, Ind., Fiske U. Art Gallery, Mobile, Mus. in Ein Horod, Israel, Butler Art Inst., Nat. Mus. Am. Art, Washington, Slater Mem. Mus., Norwich, Conn., Wichita (Kans.) Art Mus., Everson Mus. of Art, Syracuse, N.Y., New Brit. Mus. Art (Conn.), Boca Raton Art Mus., Fla., also pvt. collections. Grantee Mark Rothko Found., 1971; recipient Painting award Audubon Artists, 1976, Painting award Nat. Inst. Arts and Letters, 1976, Painting award Am. Soc. Contemporary Artists, 1976. Mem. Audubon Artists, Am. Soc. Contemporary Artists. Address: 463 West St New York NY 10014

WOLINSKY, DAVID, metal processing company executive. Exec. v.p. Metall. Inc., N.Y.C. Office: Metall Inc 25 E 39th St New York NY 10016-0903

WOLINSKY, EMANUEL, physician, educator; b. N.Y.C., Sept. 23, 1917; s. Jacob and Bertha (Siegel) W.; m. Marjorie Claster, Nov. 15, 1946; children: Douglas, Peter. B.A., Cornell U., 1938, M.D., 1941. Diplomate Am. Bd. Med. Microbiology. Intern, resident medicine N.Y. Hosp., 1943-45; bacteriologist Trudeau Lab., Saranac Lake, N.Y., 1947-56; mem. faculty Case Western Res. U. Sch. Medicine, 1956—, prof. medicine, 1968-88, prof. pathology, 1981-88, prof. emeritus, 1988—; dir. microbiology Cleve. Met. Gen. Hosp., 1959-91, acting dir. dept. pathology, 1980-86, chief div. infectious diseases, 1961-83. Co-editor Textbook of Pulmonary Diseases, 5th edit., 1993; assoc. editor: Am. Rev. Respiratory Diseases, 1973-79; Contbr. articles to profl. jours., textbooks. Mem. Tb panel U.S.-Japan Co-op. Med. Sci. Program, 1969-75. Mem. Am. Soc. Microbiology, Am. Thoracic Soc. (Trudeau medal 1986), Infectious Diseases Soc. Am., Phi Beta Kappa, Alpha Omega Alpha. Home: 24761 S Woodland Rd Cleveland OH 44122-3327

Office: Met Health Med Ctr 2500 Metro Health Dr Cleveland OH 44109-1998

WOLINSKY, LEO C., newspaper editor. BA in Journalism, U. So. Calif., 1972. Journalist, 1972—; staff writer L.A. Times, 1977-86, chief Sacramento bur., 1987-89, city editor, 1990, Calif. polit. editor, 1991, metro editor, 1994—. Office: Los Angeles Times Times Mirror Sq Los Angeles CA 90053

WOLINTZ, ARTHUR HARRY, physician, neuro-ophthalmologist; b. Bklyn., May 30, 1937; s. Louis and Celia (Ragofsky) W.; m. Carol Sue Bergstein, Nov. 28, 1963; children: Robyn Joy, Ellen Sharon. Student, NYU, 1955-58; MD summa cum laude, SUNY, Bklyn., 1962; postgrad., Columbia U., 1967-68. Diplomate Am. Bd. Psychiatry and Neurology, Am. Bd. Ophthalmology; licensee Nat. Bd. Med. Examiners, U. State of N.Y. Intern Maimonides Hosp., Bklyn., 1962-63, jr. resident in medicine, 1963-64; resident Nat. Inst. Neurol. Diseases and Blindness, Bethesda, Md., 1964-66; chief resident Mt. Sinai Hosp., N.Y.C., 1966-67; clin. asst. prof. neurology Downstate Med. Ctr. SUNY, Bklyn., 1968-69, resident in ophthalmology, 1969-71, from asst. prof. to prof., 1971—, prof. clin. ophthalmology and clin. neurology, 1977—, interim chief ophthalmology, 1983, acting regional chmn. dept. ophthalmology, 1984, prof., chmn. dept ophthalmology, 1987—; asst. neurologist Presbyn. Hosp., N.Y.C., 1967-68; instr. neuropathology Coll. Physicians and Surgeons Columbia U., N.Y.C., 1967-68; instr. neurology Mt. Sinai Sch. Medicine, N.Y.C., 1967-68; assoc. dir neurology Maimonides Med. Ctr., Bklyn., 1968-69; asst. neurologist Coney Island Hosp., Bklyn., 1968-69; vis. neurologist Kings County Hosp. Ctr., Bklyn, 1968-69; chief div. ophthalmology and neuro-ophthalmology Kingsbrook Jewish Med. Ctr., Bklyn., 1971, sec. med. and dental staff 1976-77, v.p. 1978-79, pres. 1980-81, dir. ophthalmology 1981; attending physician State Univ. Hosp., Bklyn., 1971, Kings County Hosp. Ctr., Bklyn., 1971; cons. Luth. Med. Ctr., Beth Israel Med. Ctr., Brookdale Hosp. Med. Ctr., Bklyn., L.I. Coll. Hosp., Bklyn., Maimonides Med. Ctr., Cath. Med. Ctr. Bklyn. and Queens, Bklyn. VA Hosp. Author: Essentials of Clinical Neuro-Ophthalmology, 1976; contbr. chpts. to sci. textbooks and handbooks, articles to profl. jours. Treas. Flatbush Jewish Ctr., Bklyn. With USPHS 1964-66. Recipient J. Eugene Chalfin Meml. Lecture award Alumni Assn. State Univ.-Kings County, 1981, Tchr. of Yr. award dept. ophthalmology Interfaith Med. Ctr., 1988. Fellow ACP, ACS, Am. Acad. Ophthalmology and Otolaryngology, Am. Acad. Neurology; mem. AMA, Med. Soc. County Kings, Med. Soc. State N.Y., Bklyn. Ophthal. Soc., N.Y. Acad. Medicine, AAAS, Am. Acad. Neurology, Alumni Assn. SUNY (Master Tchr. award 1987, pres.-elect 1989, pres. 1990-91), Oddfellows, Alpha Omega Alpha. Avocations: Torah reader, cantor. Home and Office: 100 Ocean Pky Brooklyn NY 11218

WOLITARSKY, JAMES WILLIAM, securities industry executive; b. Tarrytown, N.Y., Feb. 19, 1946; s. Edward and Beulah (Kemmet) W.; divorced; children: James Jr., Matthew. BA, Franklin & Marshall Coll., 1968; MBA, NYU, 1973. Auditor Hertz, Herson & Co., N.Y.C., 1970-73; comml. loan officer The Phila. Nat. Bank, 1973-76; chief fin. officer Almo Electronics Corp., Phila., 1976-80; dir. budget and control Paine Webber Inc., N.Y.C., 1981-82, dir. mktg. adminstrn., 1982-83, dir. mut. funds and asset mgmt., 1983-84; sr. v.p., dir. product mgmt. Phila. Nat. Bank, 1984-86; exec. v.p., chief fin. officer The Moseley Holding Corp., N.Y.C., 1986-87; pres., chief exec. officer Moseley Securities Corp., N.Y.C., 1987-88; exec. v.p. Gruntal Fin. Corp., N.Y.C., 1988-91; chief fin. officer, bd. dirs. Janney Montgomery Scott Inc., Phila., 1991—; bd. dirs. Phila. Depository Transfer Corp., Addison Capital Shares, Inc., treas.; treas. Addison Capital Mgmt. Corp. Bd. dirs. Cliveden of Nat. Hist. Trust, Inc. Sgt. U.S. Army, 1968-70. Decorated Bronze Star, Vietnam Cross of Gallantry. Mem. Securities Industry Assn. Episcopalian. Club: Phila. Racquet, Phila. Country. Avocations: fishing, skiing, tennis, golf. Home: 49 Oak Knoll Dr Berwyn PA 19312 Office: Janney Montgomery Scott Inc 1801 Market St Philadelphia PA 19103

WOLITZER, STEVEN BARRY, investment banker; b. Bklyn., Mar. 14, 1953; s. Philip and Regina (Wurm) W.; m. Joyce Sue Lindower, Dec. 7, 1985; children: David Joel, Scott Richard, Rachel. BS, NYU, 1973; MBA, Harvard U., 1977. CPA, N.Y. Mng. dir. Lehman Bros. Inc., N.Y.C., 1977—. Home: 250 E 87th St Apt 21B New York NY 10128-3120 Office: Lehman Bros Inc 3 World Fin Ctr New York NY 10285

WOLK, BRUCE ALAN, law educator; b. Bklyn., Mar. 2, 1946; s. Morton and Gertrude (Bayne) W.; m. Lois Gloria Krepliak, June 22, 1968; children: Adam, Daniel. BS, Antioch Coll., 1968; MS, Stanford U., 1972; JD, Harvard U., 1975. Bar: D.C. 1975. Assoc. Hogan & Hartson, Washington, 1975-78; prof. U. Calif. Sch. Law, Davis, 1978—, acting dean, 1990-91, dean, 1993—. Danforth Found. fellow, 1970-74, NSF fellow, 1970-72, Fulbright sr. research fellow, 1985-86. Mem. ABA, Am. Law Inst. Office: U Calif Sch Law Davis CA 95616

WOLK, MARTIN, electronic engineer, physicist; b. Long Branch, N.J., Jan. 13, 1930; s. Michael and Tillie (Barron) W.; 1 child, Brett Martin. BS, George Washington U., 1957, MS, 1968; PhD, U. N.Mex., 1973. Physicist Naval Ordnance Lab., White Oak, Md., 1957-59, Nat. Oceanic and Atmospheric Adminstrn., Suitland, Md., 1959-66; solid state physicist Night Vision Lab., Fort Belvoir, Va., 1967-69; rsch. asst. U. N.Mex., Albuquerque, 1969-73; electronics engr. Washington Navy Yard, 1976-83, TRW, Inc., Redondo Beach, Calif., 1983-84; physicist Metrology Engring. Ctr., Pomona, Calif., 1984-85; electronics engr. Naval Aviation Depot North Island, San Diego, 1985—; cons. Marine Corps Logistics Base, Barstow, Calif., 1985—, Naval Weapons Station, Fallbrook, Calif., 1987-89, Naval Weapons Support Ctr., Crane, Ind., 1989—. Contbr. articles to Jour. Quantitative Spectroscopy and Radiative Transfer, Monthly Weather Rev., Proceedings of SPIE. Cpl. U.S. Army, 1946-49, Japan. Mem. IEEE, Soc. Photo-Optical Instrumentation Engring., Sigma Pi Sigma, Sigma Tau. Achievements include development of first Tiros meteorological satellites; research on electron-beam for micro-circuit device fabrication. Home: 740-91 Eastshore Ter Chula Vista CA 91913

WOLKEN, JEROME JAY, biophysicist, educator; b. Pitts., Mar. 28, 1917; s. Abraham I. and Dina (Lando) W.; m. Dorothy O. Mallinger, June 19, 1945 (dec. 1954); children: Ann Alex, A. JOnathan; m. Tobey J. Holestein, Jan. 26, 1956; children: H. Johanna, Erik Andrew. Student, Pa. State U., 1935-36, Duquesne U., 1937-39; B.S., U. Pitts., 1946, M.S., 1948, Ph.D., 1949. Rsch. fellow Mellon Inst., 1943-47, Rockefeller Inst., 1950-51, Princeton U., 1951; asst. prof. U. Pitts. Sch. Medicine, 1953-57, assoc. prof., 1957-61, prof. biophysics physiology, 1962-66; head dept. bioscis. Carnegie Inst. Tech., Pitts., 1964-67; prof. biophysics and bioscis. Carnegie-Mellon U., 1964—, head biophys. research lab., 1964-76; head biophys. research lab. Eye and Ear Hosp., Pitts., 1953-64; rsch. assoc. Carnegie Mus.; guest prof. Pa. State U., 1963, U. Paris, 1967-68, U. Miami (Fla.) Inst. Theoretical Studies, 1966, Univ. Coll., London, 1971, Pasteur Inst. Paris, 1972, AEC, Saclay, France; rsch. fellow Princeton U., 1978; U.S. rsch. fellow Tohoku U., Sendai, Japan, 1988. Author 9 books; editor 2 books; contbr. 120 articles to profl. jours. Served with USNR, 1941-43. Recipient Career award USPHS, 1962-65. Fellow N.Y. Acad. Scis., AAAS, Optical Soc. Am. (pres. Pitts. sect. 1964-65), Am. Inst. Chemists, Explorers Club; mem. Am. Chem. Soc., Chemists Club N.Y., Am. Inst. Biol. Sci., Biophys. Soc., Soc. Gen. Physiologists, Am. Soc. Cell Biology, Am. Photobiol. Sci., Sigma Xi, Phi Sigma. Achievements include 2 patents for Light Concentrating Lens System. Home: 5817 Elmer St Pittsburgh PA 15232-1915 Office: Carnegie Mellon U Mellon Coll of Sci 4400 5th Ave Pittsburgh PA 15213-2617

WOLKIN, PAUL ALEXANDER, lawyer, former institute executive; b. Phila., Oct. 14, 1917; s. Alex and Anna (Friedman) W.; stepson Rebecca (Likalter) W.; m. Martha Kessler, June 25, 1944 (dec. 1992); children: Rachel, Adam; m. Diana S. Burgwyn, Dec. 23, 1994. B.A., U. Pa., 1937, M.A., 1938, J.D., 1941. Bar: Pa. 1942, U.S. Supreme Ct. 1947. Law clk. U.S. Ct. Appeals (3d Cir.), Phila., 1942-44; atty. Fgn. Econ. Adminstrn., Washington, 1944-45; asso. counsel French Supply Council, Washington, 1945-46; asst. legal adviser Dept. State, 1946-47; legis. draftsman Phila. Charter Commn., 1948-51; spl. asst. to Phila. Solicitor, 1951; partner firm Wolkin, Sarner & Cooper, Phila., 1951-66; counsel Sarner, Cooper & Stein, Phila., 1966-69, Hudson, Wilf & Kronfeld, Phila., 1947-77, Rawle & Henderson, 1980-81; asst. dir. Am. Law Inst., Phila., 1947-77, exec. v.p. 1977-93, sec., 1979-92, exec. v.p. emeritus, coun., 1993—; exec. dir. com. on continuing profl. edn. Am. Law Inst.-ABA, 1963-93; sec. permanent editorial

bd. Uniform Comml. Code, 1962-93, sec. emeritus, 1993—; mem. com. specialized pers. Dept. Labor, 1964-69; dir. Pub. Svc. Satellite Consortium, 1980-84. Editor: The Practical Lawyer, 1955-92, founding editor, 1993—; contbr. articles to profl. jours. Pres. Phila. Child Guidance Center, 1966-72. Recipient Rawle award, 1993. Fellow Am. Bar Found. (life); mem. ABA (spl. com. on standards and codes 1974-80), Am. Law Inst. (coun. 1992—), Am. Judicature Soc., Jud. Conf. 3d Cir. U.S., Pa. Bar Assn., Phila. Bar Assn. (chair sr. lawyers com. 1994-95), Pa. Bar Inst. (bd. dirs. 1967-75), Order of Coif, Scribes (past pres.). Home and Office: 1610 N 72nd St Philadelphia PA 19151-2308

WOLKING, JOSEPH ANTHONY, publishing company executive; b. Morris, Minn., May 7, 1934; s. Lawrence William and Tecla Catherine (Loegering) e7W.); m. Kathleen Marie Poehling, Apr. 18, 1959; children: Christopher, Lisbeth, Gregory, Rebecca, Eric. Student, Fordham U., 1952-54; B.A., U. Minn., 1957. With Ojibway Press Inc., Duluth, Minn., 1958-69; asst. to pres. Petroleum Pub. Co. (name changed to PennWell Pub. Co. 1980), Tulsa, 1969; pub. Dental Econs., 1972-75, group v.p., 1975-82, sr. v.p., chief operating officer, 1982-84, exec. v.p., chief operating officer, 1985—, also dir., pres., 1987—. Office: PennWell Pub Co 1421 S Sheridan Rd Tulsa OK 74112

WOLKOFF, EUGENE ARNOLD, lawyer; b. N.Y.C., June 9, 1932; s. Oscar and Jean (Zablow) W.; m. Judith Gail Edwards, Oct. 15, 1967; children—Mandy, Elana, Alexa, Justine. A.B., Bklyn. Coll., 1953; LL.B., St. John's U., 1961. Bar: N.Y. 1962, N.Mex. 1994. Practiced in N.Y.C and Santa Fe; mem. firm Callahan & Wolkoff, N.Y.C., 1965—; bd. dirs. Babylon Enterprises, Inc., Hist. Newspaper Archives, Inc., Data Image Processing Corp.; mem. nat. panel arbitrators Am. Arbitration Assn. Served to lt. col. USAFR, 1953-75. Mem. N.Y. State Bar Assn., N.Mex. Bar Assn., Pi Beta Gamma. Office: 17 Battery Pl New York NY 10004-1101 also: 330 Garfield St Santa Fe NM 87501

WOLL, HARRY J., electrical engineer; b. Farmington, Minn., Aug. 25, 1920; s. Henry L. and Clara M. (Fredrickson) W.; m. Mary V. Cowan, Feb. 15, 1947; children: Daniel, Alice. B.S.E.E., N.D. State U., 1940; postgrad., Ill. Inst. Tech., 1940-41; Ph.D., U. Pa., 1953. With RCA Corp., 1941-85; chief engr. aerospace systems div. RCA Corp., Burlington, Mass., 1963-69; div. v.p. govt. engring. RCA Corp., Moorestown, N.J., 1969-75; div. v.p., gen. mgr. RCA Automated Systems, Burlington, 1975-81; staff v.p., chief engr. RCA Electronic Products and Labs., Princeton, N.J., 1981-85. Chmn. bd. trustees Moore Sch. Elec. Engring., U. Pa., 1976-90; trustee U. Pa., 1989-91. Recipient 50th Anniversary gold medal Moore Sch. Elec. Engring., U. Pa., 1973. Fellow AAAS, IEEE (past chmn. Phila. sect., past chmn. fellow com.), Aerospace Industries Tech. Council (past chmn.); mem. Sigma Phi Delta, Phi Kappa Phi. Roman Catholic. Patentee in field. Home: PO Box 679 Concord MA 01742-0679

WOLLE, CHARLES ROBERT, federal judge; b. Sioux City, Iowa, Oct. 16, 1935; s. William Carl and Vivian (Down) W.; m. Kerstin Birgitta Wennerstrom, June 26, 1961; children: Karl Johan Knut, Erik Vernon, Thomas Dag, Aaron Charles. AB, Harvard U., 1959; JD, Iowa Law Sch., 1961. Bar: Iowa 1961. Assoc. Shull, Marshall & Marks, Sioux City, 1961-67, ptnr., 1968-80; judge Dist. Ct. Iowa, Sioux City, 1981-83; justice Iowa Supreme Ct., Sioux City and Des Moines, 1983-87; chief judge, 1992—; judge U.S. Dist. Ct. (so. dist.) Iowa, Des Moines, 1987-92, chief judge, 1992—; faculty Nat. Jud. Coll., Reno, 1983—, chief judge 1992—. Editor Iowa Law Rev., 1960-61. Vice pres. bd. dirs. Sioux City Symphony, 1972-77; sec., bd. dirs. Morningside Coll., Sioux City, 1977-81. Fellow Am. Coll. Trial Lawyers; mem. ABA, Iowa Bar Assn., Sioux City C. of C. (bd. dirs. 1977-78). Avocations: sports, art, music, literature. Home: 1601 Pleasant View Dr Des Moines IA 50315 Office: US Dist Judge 103 US Courthouse 123 E Walnut Des Moines IA 50309-2039

WOLLE, WILLIAM DOWN, foreign service officer; b. Sioux City, Iowa, Mar. 11, 1928; s. William Carl and Vivian Lucille (Down) W.; m. Zanie L. Donahue, Feb. 7, 1992; children from previous marriage: Laila Jean, William Nicholas. B.A., Morningside Coll., 1949; M.Internat. Affairs, Columbia U., 1951. Joined U.S. Fgn. Service, 1951; consular officer Baghdad, Iraq, 1951-52; econ. officer, 1952-53; consular officer Manchester, Eng., 1954-56; trainee Arab lang. and area Beirut, Lebanon, 1957-58; fgn. service officer gen. Aden, So. Yemen, 1958-59; econ. officer Jidda, Saudi Arabia, 1959-62; internat. economist Washington, 1962-64; internat. relations officer, 1964-65; officer in charge Arab-Israeli affairs, 1965-67; detailed Nat. War Coll., 1967-68; counselor polit. affairs Kuwait City, Kuwait, 1968-70; econ. officer, dir. AID, Amman, Jordan, 1970-73; econ. officer Nairobi, 1973-74; ambassador to Oman, Muscat, 1974-78; dir. Middle Eastern/South Asian Research Office, Dept. State, 1978-79; ambassador to United Arab Emirates, 1979-81; adviser internat. affairs Indsl. Coll. Armed Forces, 1982-84; chief sr. officer assignments, Washington, 1984-86. Served with AUS, 1946-47. Recipient Superior Service award Dept. State, 1974, Outstanding Civilian Service award Dept. Def., 1984. Home: 12 Flewellen Dr Stafford VA 22554

WOLLEN, W. FOSTER, lawyer; b. Union City, N.J., Dec. 24, 1936; s. Ross and Grace (Foster) W.; m. Sheila M. Culkin, Oct. 3, 1964; children: W. Foster, John Ross, Evan, Gillian. AB, Holy Cross Coll.; 1958; LLB, U. Va., 1961. Bar: N.Y. 1962, D.C. 1990. Assoc. Shearman & Sterling, N.Y.C., 1962-70, ptnr., 1970-90, mng. ptnr., Washington, 1990-94, sr. v.p., dir. and gen. counsel Bechtel Group, Inc., 1994—. Served with U.S. Army, 1961-62. Fellow Am. Coll. Trial Lawyers (N.Y. chmn. 1987-88); mem. ABA, Bar Assn. City of N.Y. Roman Catholic. Note editor U. Va. Law Rev. Office: Bechtel Group Inc 50 Beale St PO Box 193965 San Francisco CA 94105

WOLLENBERG, J. ROGER, lawyer; b. N.Y.C., May 1, 1919; s. Harry Lincoln and Gertrude (Arnstein) W.; m. Patricia S. Albright, Jan. 2, 1948; children: Christopher, Meredith, Pamela, Peter, Edward. B.A., U. Calif. at Berkeley, 1939, LL.B., 1942. Bar: Calif. 1946, D.C. 1954. Law clk. U.S. Supreme Ct. Justice William O. Douglas, 1946; with Dept. Justice, 1947-52; asst. gen. counsel FCC, 1952-54; pvt. practice, 1954—; ptnr. Wilmer, Cutler & Pickering, Washington, 1962-91, sr. counsel, 1992—. Mem. Falls Church (Va.) Sch. Bd., 1960-71, chmn., 1962-70; mem. city council City of Falls Church, 1982-88; chmn. adv. com. on procedures, U.S. Ct. Appeals, D.C. Cir., 1988-90. Served to lt. USNR, 1942-46. Mem. FCC Bar Assn. (pres. 1965-66), Am. Bar Assn. (ho. of dels. 1967-71). Home: 508 Lincoln Ave Falls Church VA 22046-2621 Office: Wilmer Cutler & Pickering 2445 M St NW Washington DC 20037-1420

WOLLENBERG, RICHARD PETER, paper manufacturing company executive; b. Juneau, Alaska, Aug. 1, 1915; s. Harry L. and Gertrude (Arnstein) W.; m. Leone Bonney, Dec. 22, 1940; children: Kenneth Roger, David Arthur, Keith Kermit, Richard Harry, Carol Lynne. BSME, U. Calif., Berkeley, 1936; MBA, Harvard U., 1938; grad. study, Army Indsl. Coll., 1941; D in Pub. Affairs (hon.), U. Puget Sound, 1977. Prodn. control Bethlehem Ship, Quincy, Mass., 1938-39; with Longview (Wash.) Fibre Co., 1939—, safety engr., asst. chief engr., chief engr., mgr. container operations, 1951-57, v.p., 1953-57, v.p. ops., 1957-60, v.p., 1960-69, pres., 1969-78, pres., chief exec. officer, 1978-85, pres., chief exec. officer, chmn. bd., 1985—, also bd. dirs.; mem. Wash. State Council for Postsecondary Edn., 1969-79, chmn., 1970-73; mem. western adv. bd. Allendale Ins. Bassoonist SW Washington Symphony. Trustee Reed Coll., Portland, 1962—, chmn. bd. 1982-90. Served to lt. col. USAAF, 1941-45. Recipient Alumni Achievement award Harvard U., 1994. Mem. NAM (bd. dirs. 1981-86), Pacific Coast Assn. Pulp and Paper Mfrs. (pres. 1981-92), Inst. Paper Sci. and Tech. (trustee), Wash. State Roundtable, Crabbe Huson (bd. dirs.). Home: 1632 Kessler Blvd Longview WA 98632-3633 Office: Longview Fibre Co PO Box 606 Longview WA 98632-7391

WOLLERSHEIM, JANET PUCCINELLI, psychology educator; b. Anaconda, Mont., July 24, 1936; d. Nello J. and Inez Marie (Ungaretti) Puccinelli; m. David E. Wollersheim, July 1, 1959 (div. June 1972); children: Danette Marie, Tod Neil; m. Daniel J. Smith, July 17, 1976. AB, Gonzaga U., 1958; MA, St. Louis U., 1960; PhD, U. Ill. 1968. Lic. psychologist, Mont. Asst. prof. psychology, asst. dir. testing and counseling ctr. U. Mo., 1968-71; prof. psychology U. Mont., Missoula, 1971—, dir. clin. psychology, 1980-87; chair Mont. Bd. Psychologists, 1977-78; cons. Mont. State Prison, 1971-85, Trapper Creek Job Corps, 1973—; pvt. practice, Mis-

soula, 1971—. Author numerous rsch. articles. Bd. dirs. Crisis Ctr., Missoula, 1972-73; mem. profl. adv. bd. Head Start, Missoula, 1972-79. Recipient Disting. scholar award U. Montana, 1991. Fellow Am. Psychol. Assn. (bd. dirs. div. clin. psychology 1990-92); mem. Rocky Mountain Psychol. Assn. (pres. 1983-84), Nat. Council Univ. Dirs. Clin. Psychology (bd. dirs., 1982-88). Roman Catholic. Catholic. Home: 105 Greenwood Ln Missoula MT 59803-2401 Office: 900 N Orange St Ste 201 Missoula MT 59802-2998

WOLLERT, GERALD DALE, retired food company executive, investor; b. LaPorte, Ind., Jan. 21, 1935; s. Delmar Everette and Esther Mae W.; m. Carol Jean Burchby, Jan. 26, 1957; children—Karen Lynn, Edwin Del. B.S., Purdue U., 1957. With Gen. Foods Corp., 1959-89; dir. consumer affairs Gen. Foods Corp., White Plains, N.Y., 1973-74; mng. dir. Cottee Foods div. Gen. Foods Corp., Sydney, Australia, 1974-76; gen. mgr. Mexico div. Gen. Foods Corp., Mexico City, 1978-79; pres. Asia/Pacific ops. Gen. Foods Corp., Honolulu, corp. v.p. worldwide coffee and internat. div., 1979-89; ret., 1989; dir. Gen. Foods cos., Japan, Peoples Republic China, Korea, India, Taiwan, Singapore, Philippines. Webelos leader Boy Scouts Am., Mexico City, 1978-79; co. gen. chmn. United Fund campaign, Battle Creek, Mich., 1964-65, White Plains, N.Y., 1972-73. Served with U.S. Army, 1958. Mem. Asian-U.S. Bus. Coun., Oahu Country Club (Hawaii), Venice Golf and Country Club (Fla.), Beacon Hills and Beechwood (Ind.) Club.

WOLLMAN, HARRY, medical educator; b. Bklyn., Sept. 26, 1932; s. Jacob and Florence Roslyn (Hoffman) W.; m. Anne Carolyn Hamel, Feb. 16, 1957; children: Julie Ellen, Emily Jane, Diana Leigh. AB summa cum laude, Harvard Coll., 1954, MD, 1958. Diplomate Am. Bd. Anesthesiology. Intern U. Chgo. Clinics, 1958-59; resident U. Pa., 1959-63, assoc. in anesthesia, 1963-65, mem. faculty, 1965-87, prof. anesthesia, 1970-87, prof. pharmacology, 1971-87, Robert Dunning Dripps prof., chmn. dept. anesthesia, 1972-87; prin. investigator Anesthesia Rsch. Ctr., 1972-78; program dir. Anesthesia Rsch. Tng. Grant, 1972-87; sr. v.p., chief acad. officer, dean Sch. Medicine Hahnemann U., Phila., 1987-92, prof. anesthesiology, 1987-92, prof. pharmacology, 1987-92, univ. prof., 1992—; Mem. anesthesia drug panel, drug efficacy study, com. on anesthesia Nat. Acad. Scis.-NRC, 1970-71, com. on adverse reactions to anesthesia drugs, 1971-72; mem. pharm. and toxicology tng. grants com. NIH, 1966-68, anesthesia tng. grants com., 1971-73, surgery, anesthesia and trauma study sect., 1974-78; chmn. com. on studies involving human beings U. Pa., 1972-76, chmn. clin. practice exec. com., 1976-80. Assoc. editor for revs.: Anesthesiology, 1970-75; Contbr. and editor books. Hon. John Harvard scholar Harvard Coll., 1950-53, Harvard Coll. scholar, 1953-54, Detur award, 1951; NIH rsch. traineeship fellow, 1959-63, Pharm. Mfg. Assn. fellow, 1960-61. Mem. Pa. Soc. Anesthesiologists (pres. 1972-73), Am. Physiol. Soc., Assn. U. Anesthetists (exec. com. on fin. resources 1973-77, pres. 1977-78), Am. Soc. Anesthesiologists, Phila. Soc. Anesthesiologists, AMA, Pa. Med. Soc., Phila. County Med. Soc., Am. Dental Soc., Anesthesiology (adv. bd. 1985-90), Assn. Med. Coll., Coll. Physicians Phila., Phi Beta Kappa, Sigma Xi. Home: Mus Towers 1801 Buttonwood St Apt 1020 Philadelphia PA 19130 Office: Hahnemann Univ 3508 Market St Ste 201 Philadelphia PA 19104-3316

WOLLMAN, LEO, physician; b. N.Y.C., Mar. 14, 1914; s. Joseph and Sara (Samrick) W.; m. Eleanor Rakow, Aug. 16, 1936 (dec. 1953); children: Arthur Lee, Bryant Lee; m. Charlotte Kornberg Seidman, Oct. 6, 1954 (div. 1969); m. Ellen Hershenson, Mar. 25, 1985. BS, Columbia U., 1934; MS, NYU, 1938; MD, Royal Coll. Edinburgh, 1942; PhD (hon.), Rochdale, 1972; DSc (hon.), U. Mich., 1973. Diplomate Am. Bd. Hypnosis in Ob-Gyn, Nat. Bd. Acupuncture Medicine, Am. Acad. Pain Mgmt., Am. Bd. Psychiatry and Neurology, Am. Bd. Sexology. Intern Cumberland Hosp., Bklyn., 1942-43; resident Leith Gen. Hosp., 1942; practice medicine specializing in ob-gyn Bklyn., 1944-72; in psychiatry, 1972—; mem. staff Maimonides, Coney Island hosps., Bklyn. Hosp. Ctr., Bklyn., Park East, Mt. Sinai hosps., N.Y.C. Author: Write Yourself Slim, 1976, Eating Your Way to a Better Sex Life, 1983, numerous articles in profl. jours.; editor-in-chief: Jour. Am. Soc. Psychosomatic Dentistry and Medicine, 1968-83; editor newsletter: Soc. Sci. Study Sex; editor: News Bull. of Inst. for Comprehensive Medicine; assoc. editor: Jour. Sex Research; internat. editor: Latin Am. Jour. Clin. Hypnosis; films I Am Not This Body, 1970, StrangeHer, 1971, Let Me Die a Woman, 1978. Pres. Jewish Com. Coun. Greater Coney Island, 1989—. Recipient Jules Weinstein Ann. Pioneer in Modern Hypnosis award, 1964. Fellow Am. Geriatrics Soc., N.Y. Acad. Scis. (life), Acad. Psychosomatic Medicine (sec. 1965), Soc. Clin. and Exptl. Hypnosis (life), Am. Soc. Clin. Hypnosis (life), Soc. Sci. Study Sex (pres. Eastern region 1979-81), Am. Soc. Psychical Research (life), Am. Med. Writers Assn. (life), Internat. Soc. Comprehensive Medicine, Am. Acad. Psychiatry and Neurology, Am. Coll. Sexology; mem. Nat. Geog. Soc. (life), AAAS (council 1971-73), Am. Assn. Social Psychiatry, Am. Soc. Abdominal Surgeons, Internat. Soc. Nonverbal Psychotherapy, N.Y. State Soc. Med. Research, Royal Medico-Psychol. Assn. (Eng.), N.Y. Soc. for Gen. Semantics, Nat. Assn. on Standard Med. Vocabulary (sec. 1964—), Am. Assn. History Medicine, Am. Assn. Study Headache, Am. Acad. Dental Medicine, Am. Assn. Marriage Counselors, Soc. Med. Jurisprudence, Bklyn. Psychol. Assn., Canadian Soc. for Study Fertility, Am. Fertility Soc. (life), Internat. Fertility Assn., Internat. Soc. for Clin. and Exptl. Hypnosis (life), Am. Soc. Psychosomatic Dentistry and Medicine (pres. 1969-72, exec. dir. 1973-83), Assn. Advancement Psychotherapy, Pan-Am. Med. Assn., Andalusian Soc. Sophrology and Psychosomatic Medicine, Brit. Med. Assn., Bklyn. Acad. Medicine, Internat. Soc. Psychoneuroendocrinology, L.I. Hist. Soc.; also hon. mem. numerous fgn. orgns. Address: 3813 Poplar Ave Brooklyn NY 11224-1301 *I have learned that to be busily occupied doing the work I like is to be happy. Doing what you like to do usually results in a job well done. To take pride in one's work is a virtue.*

WOLLMAN, NATHANIEL, economist, educator; b. Phila., May 15, 1915; s. Leon and Rose (Schimmel) W.; m. Lenora Levin, Dec. 25, 1939 (dec. Dec. 1994); children: Stephen, Eric. A.B., Pa. State U., 1936; Ph.D., Princeton U., 1940; LL.D., Colo. Coll., 1972. Instr., asst. prof. Colo. Coll., 1939-48; asso. prof., prof. econs. U. N.Mex., 1948-81, prof. emeritus, 1981—, chmn. dept. econs., 1960-69; dean Coll. Arts and Scis., 1969-81; economist Resources for the Future, 1959-60, 64-65; Chmn. Internat. Environ. Problems Com., 1976-79. Author: (with others) Water Supply and Demand, 1960, Value of Water in Alternative Uses, 1962, Water Resources of Chile, 1968, (with Gilbert Bonem) The Outlook for Water: Quality, Quantity and National Growth, 1971, (with others) Man, Materials and Environment, 1973. Served with USNR, World War II. Mem. Am. Econs. Assn. Home: 7010 Phoenix Ave NE Apt 713 Albuquerque NM 87110-3562

WOLLMAN, ROGER LELAND, federal judge; b. Frankfort, S.D., May 29, 1934; s. Edwin and Katherine Wollman; m. Diane Marie Schroeder, June 21, 1959; children: Steven James, John Mark, Thomas Roger. BA, Tabor Coll., Hillsboro, Kans., 1957; JD magna cum laude, U. S.D., 1962; LLM, Harvard U., 1964. Bar: S.D. 1964. Sole practice, Aberdeen, 1964-71; justice S.D. Supreme Ct., 1971-85, chief justice, 1978-82; judge U.S. Ct. Appeals (8th cir.), 1985—; states atty. Brown County, Aberdeen, 1967-71. Served with AUS, 1957-59. Office: US Ct Appeals 311 Fed Bldg and US Courthouse 400 S Phillips Ave Sioux Falls SD 57102-0961*

WOLLNER, THOMAS EDWARD, manufacturing company executive; b. Rochester, Minn., Dec. 30, 1936; s. Clarence E. and Grace W. (Day) W.; m. Marlene A. Hanson, July 12, 1958; children: Mark R., Jill M. BA, St. John's U. Collegeville, Minn. 1958; PhD, Wash. State U. 1964. Sr. research chemist tape research 3M Co., St. Paul, 1964-66, research supr., mgr. comml. tape div. lab., 1966-73, mgr. Cen. Research Labs., 1973-77, dir. Chem. Research Lab., 1977-81, dir. Indsl. and Consumer Sector Research Lab., 1981-84, exec. dir. research and devel. indsl. and consumer sector, 1984-86, v.p. research and devel. indsl. and consumer sector, 1987, staff v.p. Corp. Research Labs., 1987—. Served to lt. U.S. Army, 1960. Mem. Am. Chem. Soc., Tech. Assn. Pulp and Paper Industry (alt. rep.). Office: 3M Co 3M Ctr Bldg 220 4E 01 Saint Paul MN 55144-1000

WOLLUM, ARTHUR GEORGE, II, microbiologist, researcher, educator; b. Chgo., Sept. 26, 1937; s. Arthur George and Hertha (Christensen) W.; m. Karen Hanson, June 18, 1960; children: Steven Arthur, Mark Hanson. BS, U. Minn., 1959; MS, Oreg. State U., 1963; PhD, 1965. Rsch. assoc. Oreg. State U., Corvallis, 1965-67; asst. prof. microbiology N.Mex. State U., Las

Cruces, 1967-71; assoc. prof. N.C. State U., Raleigh, 1971-76, prof., 1976—, head oncology program, 1984-89; vis. prof. Ohio State U., Columbus, 1978-79. Author over 90 articles and book chpts. on biological nitrogen fixation, microbial ecology, bioremediation. Fellow Soil Sci. Soc. Am., Am. Soc. Agronomy (div. chair, assoc. editor, coms.); mem. Am. Soc. Microbiology, Soc. Am. Forest (assoc. editor Forest Sci.), Soil Sc. Soc. Am., Sigma Xi, Gamma Sigma Delta. Achievements include advances in the understanding of stress ecology of Bradyrhizobium japonicum and its genetic diversity in soil environments. Office: NC State U Dept Soil Sci Box 7619 Raleigh NC 27695-7619

WOLMAN, J. MARTIN, retired newspaper publisher; b. Elizabeth, N.J., Mar. 8, 1919; s. Joseph D. and Dora (Baum) W.; m. Anne Paley, Sept. 12, 1943; children: Natalie, Jonathan, Ruth Ellen, Lewis Joel. Student, U. Wis., 1937-42. With Wis. State Jour., Madison, 1936-84; pub. Wis. State Jour., 1968-84; pres. gen. mgr Madison Newspaper, Inc., 1969-84, ret., 1984, dir., 1969—; dir. Lee Enterprises, Inc., 1971-74; treas. Lee Endowment Trusts, 1988—; sec.-treas. Madison Improvement Corp., 1958-62. Treas. Wis. State Jour. Empty Stocking Club, 1948, Children and Youth Services Inc., 1962—; mem. Mayor Madison Adv. Com., 1965; bd. dirs. United Givers Fund, 1960-64, trustee, 1980—; ex-officio Roy L. Matson Scholarship Fund, 1961, Central Madison Com., Madison Art Assn.; trustee Edgewood Coll., Madison, U. Wis. Hosp. and Clinic; chmn. Madison Area Arts Coalition, 1984-85; bd. dirs. Univ. Health Sci. Center, 1975; chmn. U.S. Savs. Bond Met. Wis., 1983; coordinator Barneveld Disaster Fund, Wis., 1985-86; mem. U. Wis. Found., 1968—; bd. dirs. Wisc. Clin. Cancer Ctr., 1986—; Dir. Wisc. Newspaper Found., 1986-88; v.p., treas. Lee Endowment Found., 1989—. Served with AUS, 1942-46. Named Advt. Man of Year Madison Advt. Club, 1969, Madison Man of Achievement, 1976, Man of Yr. Salvation Army, 1993; recipient Disting. Service award Wis. Newspaper Assn., 1982, Community Service award Inland Daily Press Assn., 1983, Ralph D. Casey Minn. award for Disting. Service in Journalism, 1987, First Ringling Bros. Silver Smile award, 1993. Mem. Madison C. of C. (dir. 1966-70, 74-84), Inland Daily Press Assn. (dir. 1961-65), Wis. Daily Newspaper League (dir. 1961-65), Wis. Newspaper Assn. (dir. 1977-84). Clubs: B'nai B'rith, Madison. Office: 1901 Fish Hatchery Rd Madison WI 53713-1248

WOLMAN, M. GORDON, geography educator; b. Balt., Aug. 16, 1924; s. Abel and Anna (Gordon) W.; m. Elaine Mielke, June 20, 1951; children: Elsa Anne, Abel Gordon, Abby Lucille, Fredericka Jeannette. Student, Haverford Coll.; A.B. in Geology, Johns Hopkins U., 1949; M.A. in Geology, Harvard U., 1951, Ph.D., 1953. Geologist U.S. Geol. Survey, 1951-58, part-time, 1958—; assoc. prof. geography Johns Hopkins U., Balt., 1958-62; prof. Johns Hopkins, 1962—; chmn. dept. geography and environ. engring., 1958-90, Interim Provost, 1987, 1990; Mem. adv. com. geography U.S. Office Naval Rsch.; mem. exec. com. Div. Earth Sci. NRC; mem. com. internat. environ. programs, mem. environ. studies bd.; mem. com. water, mem. exec. com. Earth Sci. div., mem. com. mineral resources and environment, chmn. nat. commn. water quality policy NAS; chmn. NRC Com. Adv. U.S. Geol. Survey; chmn. NAS Commn. Geoscis., Environment and Resources; cons. in field to City of Balt., Baltimor County, State of Md., fed. govt. and industry. Author: Fluvial Processes in Geomorphology, 1964; Editorial bd.: Science mag. Pres. bd. trustees Park Sch., Balt., Md. Acad. Scis., Sinai Hosp., Balt.; pres. bd. dirs. Resources for Future, 1980-87; mem. adv. com. Inst. Nuclear Power Ops., 1982-85; mem. Balt. City Charter Revision Commn., Community Action Com., Balt. With USNR, 1943-46. Recipient Meritorious Contbn. award Assn. Am. Geographers, 1972, Disting. Career award Geomorphology, 1993. Fellow Am. Acad. Arts and Scis.; mem. ASCE, NAS, Am. Geophys. Union (chmn. subcom. sedimentation, pres. hydrol. sect.), Geol. Soc. Am. (v.p. 1983, pres. 1984), Am. Geog. Soc. (councillor 1965-70, Cullum Geog. medal 1989), Washington Geol. Soc., Agrl. Hist. Soc., Md. Acad. Scis. (exec. com. 1970-75), Phi Beta Kappa, Sigma Xi. Home: 2104 W Rogers Ave Baltimore MD 21209-4553 Office: Johns Hopkins U Dept Geography/Environ Engr Baltimore MD 21218

WOLMAN, MARTIN, lawyer; b. Albany, N.Y., Feb. 2, 1937; s. Benjamin S. and Sonya (Kogan) W.; children: Koren M. Wolman-Tardy, Barton T., William B., Brandon S. AB, Brown U., 1958; LLB, U. Calif., Berkeley, 1964. Bar: Calif., 1964, Conn., 1965. Atty. Conn. Bank & Trust Co., Hartford, 1964-67; assoc. Day, Berry & Howard, Hartford, 1967-72, ptnr., 1972—; mem. Conn. Law Revision Commn. Trustee Russell-Sage Coll., Troy, N.Y., 1990, Wadsworth Atheneum, 1994; trustee Kingswood-Oxford Sch., West Hartford, Conn., 1980-93, chmn., 1986-89; bd. dirs. Hartford Hosp., 1991, Inst. of Living, 1994; mem. bd. govs. Hill-Stead Mus., Farmington, Conn., 1990—. Lt. (j.g.) USN, 1958-61. Fellow Am. Coll. Trust and Estate Counsel (chmn. chpt. 1981-86); mem. Conn. Bar Assn. (chmn. exec. com. probate sect. 1979-82). Office: Day Berry & Howard City Place Hartford CT 06103

WOLMAN, WILLIAM, economist, journalist, broadcaster; b. Montreal, Que., Can.; s. Nathan and Toba (Wexler) W.; m. Ann Livia Colamosca, Jan. 7, 1982; children: John, Flora. BA, McGill U., 1948; PhD, Stanford U., 1957. Asst. prof. econs. Wash. State U., Pullman, 1954-60; v.p. Citicorp, N.Y.C., 1969-71, Argus Rsch. Corp., N.Y.C., 1971-74; chief economist CNBC, Ft. Lee, N.J., 1989—; econs. editor Bus. Week, N.Y.C., 1960-69, sr. editor, 1974-83, editor, 1984-89, exec. editor, 1983-84; chief economist Bus. Week, N.Y.C., N.J., 1989—. Avocations: skiing, photography. Office: Bus Week 1221 Ave of Americas New York NY 10020-1001

WOLNER, RENA MERYL, publisher; b. Boston, Feb. 22, 1945; d. Samuel and Gertrude (Leaman) Tannenbaum. B.S., U. Bridgeport, 1967. Spl. asst. to pres. Bantam Books, N.Y.C., 1968-78; v.p. Berkley Books, N.Y.C., 1978-84, pres., 1985; pres., pub. Avon Books, N.Y.C., 1985-88; cons. Putnams Pub. Group., N.Y.C., 1989-94. Bd. dirs. Am. Book Awards, 1981-83. Mem. MS Soc. (bd. dirs. So. N.Y. chpt. 1889—).

WOLOTSKY, HYMAN, retired college dean; b. N.Y.C., Nov. 27, 1918; s. Max and Bessie (Davis) W.; m. Ruth Schaffel, Mar. 31, 1946; children: Eugene, Paul. BA, CCNY, 1947; MA, Columbia U., 1948, doctoral studies, 1975-80. Cert. social worker. Program dir. Jewish Community Ctr., Portland, Maine, 1949-51; asst. exec. dir. Montgomery County Jewish Community, Chevy Chase, Md., 1951-53; exec. dir. Jewish Community Ctr. of Revere, Mass., 1953-59, YM-YWHA of Brockton, Mass., 1959-61, Mid-Westchester YM & YWHA, Eastchester, N.Y., 1961-65; exec. dir. early childhood ctr. Bank St. Coll. of Edn., N.Y.C., 1965-70, assoc. to provost, 1970-81, assoc. dean, 1981-84; cons. Assn. Mgmt. Svcs., New Rochelle, N.Y., 1984—; field instr. U. Md., College Pk., 1951-53, Boston U. Sch. Social Work, 1954-56, NYU Sch. Social Work, 1965-66, Hunter Coll. Sch. of Social Work, N.Y.C., 1967-70. Co-author: Career Development in Head Start, 1970, Brace Program of Systematic Observation, 1976; producer of videotapes including Experiencias Pre-escolares en Venezuela, 1978; contbr. articles to profl. jours. Trustee Fleetwood Synagogue, Mount Vernon, N.Y., 1963—, Clinton Child Care Assn., N.Y.C., 1970-80, Eastchester Youth Bd., 1961-64. Corp. U.S. Army, 1941-46. Mem. AAUP, Faculty Club Columbia U., Fleetwood Synagogue (pres. 1971-74). Democrat. Jewish. Avocations: travel, film/theatre, literature, museums. Office: Assn Mgmt Svcs 1270 North Ave New Rochelle NY 10804-2629

WOLOWITZ, STEVEN, lawyer; b. Chgo., June 27, 1952; s. Myron and Rose (Gaines) W.; m. Allison Josephy, June 15, 1974; children: Ashley Rose, Jordan Michael. BA with distinction, George Washington U., 1974, JD with honors, 1977. Bar: N.Y. 1978, U.S. Dist. Ct. (so. and ea. dists.) N.Y. 1979, U.S. Ct. Appeals (2d and 7th cirs.) 1984, U.S. Ct. Appeals (5th cir.) 1988, U.S. Supreme Ct. 1988. Assoc. Rosenman & Colin, N.Y.C., 1977-85, ptnr., 1986-88; ptnr. Mayer, Brown & Platt, N.Y.C., 1988—; arbitrator Nat. Futures Assn., 1988—. Contbr. articles to profl. jours. Mem. Phi Eta Sigma, Phi Beta Kappa. Office: Mayer Brown & Platt 787 7th Ave Ste 2400 New York NY 10019-6018

WOLPER, ALLAN L., journalist, educator; b. N.Y.C.; s. Sydelle Wolper; m. Joanna Birnbaum; children: Jill, Richard, Kim. BS, NYU, 1965. Reporter Providence Jour., 1965-67; polit. writer AP, N.Y.C., 1967-69, N.Y. _____, 1970-63; writer, producer WABC Eyewitness News, N.Y.C., _____; columnist Soho Weekly News, N.Y.C., 1974-82; host, writer, _____ditor, Right to Know Suburban Cablevision and N.J. Network, Sta. _____ V, N.Y.C., Newark and Avenel, N.J., 1982-89; host, producer

series on media Right to Know Right to Know syndicated pub. radio series on the media, Newark, 1989—; prof. journalism Newark campus Rutgers U., 1978-92; assoc. prof. hournalism Rutgers U., Newark, 1992—. Host, producer, writer documentary The Marielitos, 1984, Hillside: Desegration, 1985, Impact, 1988, TV spl. The First Amendment, 1989; columnist Sports Media, Washington Journalism Rev., 1980-82, media N.J. Reporter, Princeton, N.J., 1982-85; editor, pub. Campus Journalism, 1987—; contbr. articles to profl. jours. With U.S Army, 1961-63. Recipient best pub. affairs program award Internat. TV and Video Festival, 1985, Nat. Cable TV Assn., 1986, award for cable excellence, 1986, 3 Aces award Nat. Cable TV, 1985, 86, Lowell Mellett award Pa. State U., 1985, Alfred I. DuPont award Columbia U., 1985, award in broadcast journalism (1st cable prodr. to win) N.J. Press Assn., 1987, N.J. Bell Enterprise award for best radio documentary, 1992, Best Radio Commentary and Media Nat. Headliner award 1993. Mem. AAUP, Soc. Profl. Journalists (chmn. freedom of info. com. Dedline Club N.Y.C. br. 1980, Outstanding Broadcast Journalism award 1984, 87, Disting. Svc. award 1st Place Bicentennial Broadcast Competition 1989, spl. award N.J. Chpt., spl. award N.J. chpt. media criticism 1991, 1st Place Pub. Svc. award Mag. N.J. chpt. 1994, radio documentary 1992, investigative report 1992). Home: 327 Central Park W New York NY 10025-7631 Office: Rutgers U Hill Hall Newark NJ 07102

WOLPER, DAVID LLOYD, motion picture and television executive; b. N.Y.C., Jan. 11, 1928; s. Irving S. and Anna (Fass) W.; m. Margaret Dawn Richard, May 11, 1958 (div.); children: Mark, Michael, Leslie; m. Gloria Diane Hill, July 11, 1974. Student, Drake U., 1946, U. So. Calif., 1948. V.p., treas. Flamingo Films, TV sales co., 1948-50, v.p. West Coast Ops., 1954-58; chmn., pres. Wolper Prodns., L.A., 1958—; cons., exec. producer Warner Bros., Inc., 1976—. TV prodns. include Race for Space, Making of the President 1960, 64, Biography series, Story of... series, The Yanks are Coming, Berlin: Kaiser to Khrushchev, December 7: Day of Infamy, The American Woman in the 20th Century, Hollywood and The Stars, March of Time Specials, The Rise and Fall of the Third Reich, The Legend of Marilyn Monroe, Four Days in November, Krebiozen and Cancer, National Geographic, Undersea World of Jacques Cousteau, China: Roots of Madness, The Journey of Robert F. Kennedy, Say Goodbye, George Plimpton, Appointment With Destiny, American Heritage, Smithsonian, They've Killed President Lincoln, Sandburg's Lincoln, Primal Man, The First Woman President, Chico and the Man, Get Christie Love, Welcome Back, Kotter!, Collison Course, Roots, Victory at Entebbe, Roots: The Next Generations, Moviola, The Thorn Birds, North and South Books I, II, III, Napoleon and Josephine, Alex Haley's Queen, Men Of The Dragon, Unwed Father, The Morning After; feature films include The Hellstrom Chronicle, Devil's Brigade, The Bridge at Remagen, If It's Tuesday, This Must Be Belgium, Willy Wonka and The Chocolate Factory, Visions of Eight, This is Elvis, Nurder in the First; live spl. events include Opening and Closing Ceremonies 1984 Olympic Games, Liberty Weekend July 3-6, 1986. Trustee Los Angeles County Mus. Art, Am. Film. Inst., L.A. Thoracic and Cardiovascular Found., The Boys and Girls Clubs of Am., U.S. Golf Assn. Found.; bd. dirs. Amateur Athletic Assn. L.A., L.A. Herat Inst., Acad. TV Arts and Scis. Found., So. Calif. Com. for Olympic Games, U.S. Golf. Cinema/TV Dept.; bd. govs. Cedars Sinai Med. Ctr.; com. mem. U.S. Olympic Team Benefit; mem. adv. com. Nat. Ctr. Jewish Film. Recipient award for documentaries San Francisco Internat. Film Festival, 1960, 7 Golden Globe awards, 5 George Foster Peabody awards, Disting. Service award U.S. Jr. C. of C.; 40 Emmy awards, 145 Emmy nominations Acad. TV Arts and Scis.; Monte Carlo Internat. Film Festival award, 1964, Cannes Film Festival Grand Prix for TV Programs, 1964; Oscar award, 11 Oscar nominations, Jean Hersholt Humanitarian award Acad. Motion Picture and TV Scis., medal of Chevalier The French Nat. Legion of Honor, 1990; named to TV Hall of Fame, 1988. Mem. Nat. Acad. TV Arts and Scis., Acad. Motion Picture Arts and Scis., Producers Guild Am., Caucus for Producers, Writers and Dirs. Office: care Warner Bros Inc 4000 Warner Blvd Burbank CA 91522-0001

WOLPER, MARSHALL, insurance and financial consultant; b. Chgo., Nov. 19, 1922; s. Harry B. and Bessie (Steiner) W.; m. Thelma R. Freedman, April 15, 1957 (div. Oct. 1968); m. Jacqueline N. Miller, Sept. 19, 1969 (div. Jan. 1976); m. Lucee I. G. Lee, Mar. 20, 1985; stepchildren—Robert Insinga, Cyndi Wolper. B.A. in Polit. Sci. and Econs., U. Ill., 1942. Chartered fin. cons. With Kent Products, Chgo., 1946; pres. Marshall Industries, Chgo., 1947-52; with Equitable Life Assurance Soc., 1953-89, nat. honor agt., 1966, nat. sales cons., 1967—; sr. ptnr. Wolper & Katz, 1958—; ptnr. Wolper and Katz Thoroughbred Racing Stable, 1977-86; instr. life underwriting and pensions U. Miami, 1959—; pres. Marshall Wolper Co., 1953—; chmn. bd. M.W. Computer Systems, Inc., 1971-80; pres. Marshall Wolper Pension Sers. Inc., 1978-80, Wolper Ross & Co., 1980-87; lectr. life ins., employee benefit plans, pensions, estate planning to various univs. and spl. meetings; pres. Greater Miami Tax Inst., 1963, Estate Planning Coun. Greater Miami, 1969-70; faculty Practicing Law Inst., 1967—; mem. adv. com., lectr. Inst. on Estate Planning. Author: Medical Entities Taxed as Corporations, 1961, Tax and Business Aspects of Professional Corporations and Associations, 1968; contbr. articles to profl. jours. Bd. dirs. Dade County chpt. ARC, Profl. Selling Inst. Served to 1st lt. AUS, Parachute Infantry, World War II, ETO. Decorated Bronze Star, Purple Heart; recipient Paragon award Equitable Life Assurance Soc., 1972; C.L.U. Mem. Am. Soc. CLUs (pres. Miami chpt. 1963, inst. faculty 1963-65, dir. 1966-67, regional v.p. 1968), The Am. Coll. (joint com. on continuing edn. 1965—), Nat. Assn. Life Underwriters (lectr. 1963, 66, 81), Million Dollar Round Table (life mem., speaker 1962-81, exec. com. 1974-78, pres. 1977), Assn. Advanced Life Underwriting (lectr. 1966, pres. 1972), Am. Soc. Pension Actuaries (dir.), Nat. Assn. Pension Consultants and Adminstrs. (treas.). Office: The Marshall Wolper Co 1546 NE Quayside Terr Miami FL 33138

WOLPERT, EDWARD ALAN, psychiatrist; b. Chgo., Apr. 22, 1930; s. Sol and Dorothy (Greenwald) W.; m. Gloria Adele Yanoff, Mar. 23, 1958; children: Seth Isaac, Andrew Oxman, Edward Greenwald. B.A., U. Chgo., 1950, M.A., 1954, Ph.D., 1959, M.D., 1960. Diplomate: Am. Bd. Neurology and Psychiatry. Intern medicine U. Ill. Research Hosp., 1960-61; resident psychiatry Michael Reese Hosp., 1961-64; dir. clin. services Psychosomatic and Psychiat. Inst., 1966-79, dir. of hosp., 1979-83; clin. assoc. prof. psychiatry U. Chgo. Sch. Medicine, 1972-76, clin. prof. psychiatry, 1976-90; clin. prof. psychiatry U. Ill. Sch. Medicine, 1990-93; prof. psychiatry Rush Med. Coll., 1993—; sr. rsch. scholar Rush Inst. Mental Well-Being, 1993—; cons. Sonia Shankman Orthogenic Sch., 1973—. Contbr. articles to profl. jours. Fellow Am. Psychiat. Assn.; mem. AMA, Ill., Chgo. med. socs., Ill. Psychiat. Soc. (pres. 1982-83), AAAS, Am. Psychoanalytic Assn. (certified in psychoanalysis), Assn. for Psychophysiol. Study of Sleep, Am. Psychol. Assn., N.Y. Acad. Scis., George S. Klein Meml. Psychoanalytic Research Forum, Am. Soc. for Clin. Pharmacology and Therapeutics, Chgo. Psychoanalytic Soc., Inst. Medicine Chgo., Wis. Acad. Arts, Letters and Scis. Home: 680 N Lake Shore Dr Apt 1004 Chicago IL 60611 Office: Rush Inst Mental Well Being 1725 W Harrison Chicago IL 60612

WOLPOFF, MILFORD HOWELL, paleoanthropologist, educator, author; b. Chgo., Oct. 28, 1942; s. Ben and Ruth (Silver) W.; m. Sheila Dunn, Apr. 10, 1966 (div. Sept. 4, 1985); 1 child, Michael. B.A., U. Ill., 1964, Ph.D., 1969. Prof. anthropology Case Western Res. U., Cleve., 1969-71; prof. anthropology U. Mich., Ann Arbor, 1971—, curator Mus. Anthropology, 1976—. Author: Metric Trends in Hominid Dental Evolution, 1971, Paleoanthropology, 1980. Research grantee, NSF, 1976-79, NSF, 1981. Mem. Am. Assn. Phys. Anthropologists, Am. Anthropol. Assn. (biol. anthropology div.). Democrat. Office: U Mich Dept Anthropology Ann Arbor MI 48109

WOLRICH, PETER M., lawyer; b. N.Y.C., Sept. 4, 1946. AB magna cum laude, Temple U., 1968; student, U. London, 1966-67; AM Philosophy, Brown U., 1969; JD, Georgetown U., 1973. Bar: N.Y. 1974; cert. avocat Cr. Paris 1984. Lectr. Regional and Local Activities Am. Soc. Internat. Law, 1974-76; assoc. Curtis, Mallet-Prevost, Colt & Mosle, N.Y.C., 1973-76, 80-82, Curits Mallet-Prevost, Colt & Mosle, Paris, 1976-80; ptnr. Curtis, Mallet-Prevost, Colt & Mosle, N.Y.C., 1982-84; mng. ptnr. Paris Office, Curtis, Mallet-Prevost, Colt & Mosle, Paris, 1984—; arbitrator internat. cases; lectr. in field in I.S., France, West Africa. Editor Georgetown Law Jour. Pres'. scholar Temple U., 1968; Woodrow Wilson fellow Brown U., 1969. Office: Curtis Mallet-Prevost et al, 8 Ave Victor Hugo, 75116 Paris France

WOLSIFFER, PATRICIA RAE, insurance company executive; b. Indpls., Aug. 15, 1933; d. Charles L. and Dorothy M. (Smith) Bohlsen; m. Edward C. Wolsiffer, Oct. 5, 1956; children: John M., Anderson, Sherry L. Anderson Cooney, Edward J. Wolsiffer. Student, Ind. Central U., 1974-75. Various secretarial positions, 1964-71; with Blue Cross/Blue Shield Ind. (Associated Ins. Cos., Inc.), Indpls., 1971-88, supr. personnel, 1973-76, exec. asst. to pres., 1976-79, corp. sec., 1979-85, exec. asst. to chmn. bd., chief exec. officer, 1985-88, ret. Vol. Hancock Meml. Hosp. Guild. Republican. Presbyterian. Clubs: Order Eastern Star, Daus. of Nile, Ladies Oriental Shrine. Home: 5550 E 100 N Greenfield IN 46140 Office: 120 Monument Cir Indianapolis IN 46204-4906

WOLSKY, ALBERT, costume designer. Costume designer: (films) The Heart is a Lonely Hunter, 1968, Popi, 1969, Lovers and Other Strangers, 1970, Loving, 1970, Where's Poppa (also known as Going Ape), 1970, Little Murders, 1971, Born to Win, 1971, Lady Liberty, 1972, The Last of the Red Hot Lovers, 1972, The Trial of the Catonsville Nine, 1972, Up the Sandbox, 1972, Lenny, 1974, Harry and Tonto, 1974, The Gambler, 1974, Next Stop, Greenwich Village, 1976, Thieves, 1977, The Turning Point, 1977, Fingers, 1977, An Unmarried Woman, 1977, Grease, 1978, Moment by Moment, 1978, Meteor, 1979, Manhattan, 1979, All That Jazz, 1979 (Acad. award best costume design 1979), Willie and Phil, 1980, The Jazz Singer, 1980, All Night Long, 1981, Paternity, 1981, Temptest, 1982, Still of the Night, 1982, Sophie's Choice, 1982 (Acad. award nomination best costume design 1982), To Be or Not To Be, 1983, Star 80, 1983, Moscow on the Hudson, 1984, The Falcon and the Snowman, 1985, The Journey of Natty Gann, 1985 (Acad. award nomination best costume design 1985), Crimes of the Heart, 1986, Down and Out in Beverly Hills, 1986, Legal Eagles, 1986, Nadine, 1987, Moon Over Parador, 1988, Chances Are, 1989, Cookie, 1989, Enemies, a Love Story, 1989, She-Devil, 1989, Funny About Love, 1990, Bugsy, 1991 (Acad. award best costume design 1991), Scenes From a Mall, 1991, Toys, 1992 (Acad. award nomination best costume design 1992), The Pickle, 1993, Fatal Instinct, 1994, The Pelican Brief, 1994, (TV movie) Beauty and the Beast, 1976 (Emmy award nomination best costume design for a drama spl. 1976), (theatre) Generation, 1964, 66-67, Your Own Thing, 1968-70, Little Murders, 1969, The White House Murder Case, 1970, The Trial of the Catonsville Nine, 1971, The Sunshine Boys, 1972-75, The Jockey Club Stakes, 1973, All Over Town, 1974-75, Hamlet, 1975, 27 Wagons Full of Cotton, 1976, A Memory of Two Mondays, 1976, Sly Fox, 1976-77, Wine Untouched, 1979, Tricks of the Trade, 1980, Wally's Cafe, 1981, One More Song/One More Dance, 1983, Ann Reinking...Music Moves Me, 1984-85, Oliver Oliver, 1985. Address: c/o Friedman & LaRosa 747 Third Ave New York NY 10017*

WOLSKY, MURRAY, corporation executive; b. Bklyn., Dec. 16, 1931; s. Meyer and Rose (Schissel) W.; m. Doris Shapiro, Aug. 29, 1953; children: Susan Robin, Frederick Craig. BIE, NYU, 1953; JD, Bklyn. Law Sch., 1962. Bar: N.Y. 1963; cert. profl. engr. Vt. 1964. With Sperry Gyroscope, Great Neck, N.Y., 1957-70; supervising buyer Consol. Edison N.Y., N.Y., 1970-71; with Foster Wheeler Corp., Livingston, N.J., 1971—, dir. contract adminstrn., 1971-78, corp. dir. procurement, 1978-93, v.p., 1979-87; also chmn. bd. Foster Wheeler Real Estate Devel. Corp., Clinton, N.J., 1985-94; v.p., group exec. real estate and adminstrn. Foster Wheeler Corp., Clinton, N.J., 1987-94, sr. v.p. adminstrn., 1994, ret., cons., 1994—. 1st Lt. U.S. Army, 1954-56. Mem. IEEE, Nat. Assn. Corp. Real Estate Execs. Jewish. Office: Foster Wheeler Corp Perryville Corp Park Clinton NJ 08809

WOLSON, CRAIG ALAN, lawyer; b. Toledo, Feb. 20, 1949; s. Max A. and Elaine B. (Cohn) W.; m. Janis Nan Braun, July 30, 1972 (div. Mar. 1986); m. Ellen Carol Schulgasser, Oct. 26, 1986; children: Lindsey, Michael and Geoffrey (triplets). BA, U. Mich., 1971, JD, 1974. Bar: N.Y. 1975, U.S. Dist. Ct. (so. and ea. dists.) N.Y. 1975, U.S. Ct. Appeals (2d cir.) 1975, U.S. Supreme Ct. 1978. Assoc. Shearman & Sterling, N.Y.C., 1974-81; v.p., asst. gen. counsel Thomson McKinnon Securities Inc., N.Y.C., 1981-85; v.p., sr. gen. counsel J.D. Mattus Co., Inc., Greenwich, Conn., 1985-88; also bd. dirs. J.D. Mattus Co., Inc. and affiliated cos., Greenwich; v.p., asst. gen. counsel Chem. Bank, N.Y.C., 1988-94; of counsel Williams & Harris, N.Y.C., 1995—; dep. clk. Lucas County Courthouse, Toledo, 1968-69, 71-72. Articles and administrv. editor U. Mich. Law Rev., 1973-74. Mem. ABA, N.Y. State Bar Assn., Assn. of Bar of City of N.Y. (securities regulation com. 1994—), Corp. Bar. Assn. of Westchester and Fairfield, Phi Beta Kappa, Phi Eta Sigma, Pi Sigma Alpha. Avocations: reading, playing piano, fine dining, theater. Home: 41 Bonnie Brook Rd Westport CT 06880-1507 Office: Williams & Harris Wall St Tower 20 Exchange Pl New York NY 10005

WOLSONOVICH, NICHOLAS, school system administrator. Supt. schs. Diocese of Youngstown, Ohio. Office: Office Supt Schs 144 W Wood St Youngstown OH 44503-1030

WOLTER, DUANE ROLAND, retail executive; b. Milw., July 18, 1948; s. Roland Arthur and Haroldean (Tegge) W.; m. Gail M. Kieckhefer (div. 1980); m. Margaret Shelton, June 27, 1981; children: Sean Zachary, Megan Meinhart. BS in Bus. Adminstrn., Marquette U., 1971. CPA. Staff auditor Arthur Andersen and Co., Milw., 1971-72, sr. auditor, 1972-74, audit mgr., 1974-76; dir. acctg. May Dept. Stores Inc., St. Louis, 1976-79; v.p., corp. controller H.J. Wilson Co. Inc., Baton Rouge, 1979-84; v.p. fin. Home Depot Inc., Atlanta, 1984-86; sr. v.p., chief fin. officer McCrory Stores, York, Pa., 1986-87; exec. v.p., chief fin. officer Ames Dept. Stores Inc., Hartford, Conn., 1987-90; sr. v.p. fin. Hecht's Dept. Stores, Arlington, Va., 1990-93; sr. v.p., CFO Luria's, Miami Lakes, Fla., 1994—. Mem. pres. coun. Marquette U. Sgt. USAR, 1966-72. Mem. AICPA, Am. Fin. Assn., Fin. Execs. Inst., Wis. Soc. CPAs. Roman Catholic. Avocations: golf, softball, racketball, tennis, jogging. Office: Luria's 5770 Miami Lakes Dr Miami Lakes FL 33014

WOLTER, JOHN AMADEUS, librarian, government official; b. St. Paul, July 25, 1925; s. Amadeus Frank and Marjorie (Wears) W.; m. Joan Patricia Venard, July 6, 1956; children: Mark, Thomas, Matthew, David. Student, Coll. St. Thomas, 1950; B.A., U. Minn., 1956, M.A., 1965, Ph.D., 1975; postgrad., Georgetown U., 1957. Officer, seaman Isthmian Lines Inc., N.Y.C., 1943-50, 57-60; marine transp. officer Mil. Sea Transp. Ser., Washington, 1956-57; instr., map libr. U. Minn., 1961-64, asst. to dir. univ. librs., 1964-65, research fellow, 1965-66; asst. prof. Wis. State U. River Falls, 1966-68; asst. chief geography and map div. Libr. of Congress, Washington, 1968-78, chief, 1978-91, acting dir. pub. svc. and collections MGMT I, 1989-90; cons. in geography, 1991-93; mem. U.S. Bd. Geog. Names, 1969-83, vice chmn., 1980-81, chmn., 1981-83. Rev. editor cartography div. Surveying and Mapping, 1971-72; mem. editorial bd. Cartographica, 1971-80, Am. Cartographer, 1974-79, Terrae Incognitae, 1973-75, ACSM Bull., 1974-80, Surveying and Mapping, 1972-80; editorial advisor The Partolan, 1986—; contbg. editor Imago Mundi, 1977-91; several radio and TV programs, 1980-91; editor, contbr. several compilations and symposia vols., others; contbr. articles to profl. jours. Served with U.S. Army, 1950-52. Libr. of Congress Disting. Svc. award, 1992, Smithsonian Inst. Cert. of award, 1986. Mem. Internat. Geog. Union (U.S. nat. com. 1972-80, 84-88), Internat. Cartographic Assn. (U.S. mem. commn. on history of cartography 1972-76, corr. 1976-92, Assn. Am. Geographers (editorial bd. Annals 1988-92), Spl. Librs. Assn. (sec.-treas. geog.and map div. 1965), Soc. History Discoveries (sec.-treas. 1972-75, coun. 1976-92, v.p. 1983-85, pres. 1985-87), Can. Nautical Rsch. Soc., Am. Congress Surveying and Mapping (chmn. publs. com. 1978-80, Presdl. citation 1985), N.Am. Soc. Oceanic History, N.Mex. Geog. Soc. (bd. dirs., governing bd.), Washington Map Soc., Soc. Nautical Rsch., Gt. Lakes Hist. Soc., Explorers Club, Theta Delta Chi. Home: 5430 Ring Dove Ln Columbia MD 21044-1716

WOLTERINK, LESTER FLOYD, biophysicist, educator; b. Marion, N.Y., July 28, 1915; s. John and Ruth Lavina (Voorhorst) W.; m. Lillian Ruth Nichols, June 30, 1938; children—Charles Paul, Timothy John. A.B., Hope Coll., 1936; M.A., U. Minn., 1940, Ph.D, 1943. Faculty Mich. State U., East Lansing, 1941—; prof. physiology Mich. State U., 1952-84, prof. emeritus, 1984—; asso. scientist AEC, Argonne Nat. Lab., 1948; cons., then biosatellite project scientist Ames Research Center, NASA, 1965-66; mem. various coms. AEC Conf. on Isotopes in Plant and Animal Research, 1952-59; mem. NASA Manned Space Sta. Commn., 1966; cons. NSF, 1965-70; mem. panel on nitrogen oxides Nat. Acad. Sci./NRC, 1973-75. Contbr. articles to profl. publs., reports to govt. agys. Mem. Mich. Nucleonic Soc.

(pres. 1961), Soc. Exptl. Biology and Medicine (sec. Mich. sect. 1961-63), Am. Astronautic Soc. (chmn. San Francisco sect. 1966), AAUP, Am. Inst. Biol. Scis., Am. Physiol. Soc., N.Y. Acad. Scis., IEEE, Biomed. Engring. Soc., Biophys. Soc., Sigma Xi (jr. scientist Mich. State U. 1954). Club: Torch (pres. 1983, sec. 1985-86). Home: 2277 Kewanee Way Okemos MI 48864-2514 Office: Mich State U Dept Physiology East Lansing MI 48824

WOLTERS, CURT CORNELIS FREDERIK, foreign service officer; b. Nymegen, The Netherlands, Mar. 13, 1938; came to U.S., 1957; s. Frederik and Cornelia Johanna (Jansen) W.; m. Sara J. Daughters, June 10, 1962 (div. 1980); children: Gwyneth, Chad; m. Charlotte Cooper, Sept. 22, 1980 (div. 1988); children: Lottena, Cicely; m. Sylvana K. Perry, Apr. 1989; 1 child, Roger. Student, Wash. State U., 1958-61, U. Bonn, Fed. Republic Germany, 1962-63; BA, U. Oreg., 1964, MA, 1966; MBA, U. Washington, 1976; PhD, Pacific Western U., 1989. Asst. sec. Rep. Botswana Govt., Gaborone, 1966-68; program advisor The Ford Found., N.Y.C., 1968-74; sr. rsch. analyst Seattle C. of C., 1974-76; sr. assoc. Inst. Pub. Administrn. N.Y., N.Y.C., 1976-78; freelance economist Africa, 1978-79; econ. program officer, diplomat (AID) Dept. State, Washington, 1979—; cons. Inst. for Puget Sound Needs, Seattle, 1975-76, Pacific Cons., Washington, 1976. Contbr. numerous articles to profl. jours.; author project evaluations. Mem. civic action com. Congress of Racial Equality, Eugene, Oreg., 1965-66; vol. campaign Dixie Lee Ray Gubernatorial Campaign, Seattle, 1976; treas., chmn. fin. com. Internat. Sch. Islamabad, 1989-92. Carnegie Found. fellow, 1964-65, Africa-Asia pub. svc. fellow Maxwell Sch., 1966-68, fellow German Govt., U. Bonn, 1962-63; recipient Air Def. Command outstanding achievement award USAF, 1960. Mem. Am. Econ. Assn., Air Force Assn., Wilson Ctr. (assoc. of Smithsonian Instn.), Am. Fgn. Svc. Assn., Holland Am. Club (treas. Greater Seattle area 1975-76), Am. Legion. Office: Agy for Internat Devel AFR/SA Rm 3921 NS Dept State Washington DC 20531

WOLTERS, OLIVER WILLIAM, history educator; b. Reading, Eng., June 8, 1915; came to U.S., 1964; s. Albert William and Gertrude (Lewis) W.; m. Euteen Khoo, Apr. 25, 1955; children: Pamela Gwyneth, Nigel Christopher. B.A., Lincoln Coll., Oxford U., 1937; Ph.D., Sch. Oriental and African Studies, London, 1961. With Malayan Civil Service, 1938-57; lectr. Sch. Oriental and African Studies, London, 1957-63; prof. S.E. Asian history Cornell U., Ithaca, N.Y., 1964-74, Goldwin Smith prof. S.E. Asian history, 1974-85; ret., 1985. Author: Early Indonesian Commerce, 1967, The Fall of Srivijaya, 1970, History, Culture, and Region in Southeast Asian Perspectives, 1982, Two Essays on Dai-Viet in the Fourteenth Century, 1988; editor: (with others) Southeast Asian History, 1976; sr. editor: The Vietnam Forum, 1985-93. Trustee Breezewood Found., Md., 1964-84. Decorated Officer Order Brit. Empire, 1952; Guggenheim fellow, 1972-73; Bellagio fellow Rockefeller Found., 1982; recipient Disting. Scholarship award Assn. for Asian Studies, 1990. Episcopalian.

WOLTERS, RAYMOND, historian, educator; b. Kansas City, Mo., July 25, 1938; s. Raymond M. and Margaret G. (Reilly) W.; m. Mary McCullough, June 23, 1962; children—Jeffrey, Kevin, Thomas. B.A., Stanford U., 1960; M.A., U. Calif.-Berkeley, 1962, Ph.D., 1967. Instr. dept. history U. Del., Newark, 1965-67, asst. prof., 1967-70, assoc. prof., 1970-75; prof. U. Del., 1975—. Mem. editorial adv. bd. Acad. Am. Ency. Author: Negroes and the Great Depression, 1970; The New Negro on Campus, 1975; The Burden of Brown, 1984. Fellow NEH, 1971-72, Am. Coun. Learned Socs., 1978-79, Earhart Found., 1989-90; recipient Silver Gavel award ABA. Mem. Am. Hist. Assn., Orgn. Am. Historians, So. Hist. Assn. Home: 20 Bridlebrook Ln Newark DE 19711-2061 Office: U Del Newark DE 19711

WOLTING, ROBERT ROY, city official; b. Faulkton, S.D., Dec. 29, 1928; s. George and Minnie (Meeter) W.; m. Nancy Catherine O'Brien, Nov. 26, 1953; children: Robert Roy, Linda Marie. Acct. Wolting Implement and Motor Co., Wessington Springs, S.D., 1954-60; city auditor City of Wessington Springs, 1960-64, City of Brookings, S.D., 1964-68; dir. fin. City of Fairbanks, Alaska, 1968-77, city mgr., 1977-79, 90-93; dir. fin., treas., 1984-90; city mgr., 1990-93; elected mem. City Coun., 1994—; city administr., clk. City of Union Springs, Ala., 1980-84. Mem. S.D. Retirement Bd., 1966-68. Sgt. USAF, 1950-54. Mem. Alaska Mcpl. Mgrs. Assn., Mcpl. Fin. Officers Assn. (pres. S.D. chpt. 1965-67, sec. Fairbanks chpt. 1976-78, bd. dirs. 1985-90). Democrat. Methodist. Avocation: photography. Home: 431 Le Ann Dr Fairbanks AK 99701-3232 Office: City of Fairbanks 410 Cushman St Fairbanks AK 99701-4683

WOLTZ, HOWARD OSLER, JR., steel and wire products company executive; b. Mt. Airy, N.C., Apr. 2, 1925; s. Howard Osler and Louise (Elliott) W.; m. Joan Elizabeth Moore, Dec. 29, 1949; children: Louise, Joan Woltz Robins, Howard O. III, Edwin Moore. LLB, U. Va., 1948. Bar: N.C., 1948. Ptnr. law firm Mt. Airy, 1948-54; pres., founder Dixie Concrete Products, Inc., Mt. Airy, 1953-69; founder Dixie Eposaic, Inc., Mt. Airy, 1963; pres., chmn. bd. Insteel Industries (formerly Eposaic Industries, Inc.), Mt. Airy, 1969-89, chmn., CEO, 1989-91; v.p., bd. dirs. Quality Mills, Inc., Mt. Airy. Mem. N.C. Ho. of Reps., 1951-53; chmn. Mt. Airy-Surry County Airport Authority, 1987-93; former pres. Greater Mt. Airy United Fund; former chmn. Surry C.C.; vice-chmn. Hospice Surry County; past bd. dirs. Old Hickory Coun. Boy Scouts Am.; bd. dirs. Triad United Meth. Home. Mem. Nat. Concrete Masonry Assn. (pres. 1965), N.C. Concrete Masonry Assn. (pres. 1959), Wire Reinforcement Inst. (chmn. 1982), Am. Wire Producers Assn. (bd. dirs. 1987-91), N.C. State Bar Assn., Mt. Airy C. of C. (Citizen of Yr. 1991). Rotary (past pres. Mt. Airy). Republican. Home: 819 Greenhill Rd Mount Airy NC 27030-9240 Office: Insteel Industries Inc 1373 Boggs Dr Mount Airy NC 27030-2145

WOLTZ, KENNETH ALLEN, consulting executive; b. Phila., Mar. 2, 1943; s. Herman and Florence (Varell) W.; m. Barbara Hand, June 18, 1966; children: Karyn, Diane, Kenneth. BS, U.S. Mil. Acad., 1966; MBA, Xavier U., 1971. Cert. mgmt. cons. Commd. 2d lt. U.S. Army, 1966, advanced through grades to capt., 1968, resigned, 1968; various mgmt. positions GE, Evansdale, Ohio and Bethesda, Md., 1968-73; mgr. systems Xerox Corp., Rochester, N.Y., 1973-75; dir. info. svcs. McGraw Edison, Des Plaines, Ill., 1975-77; mng. dir., mgmt. cons. Peat, Marwick, Mitchell, Chgo., 1977-80; mgmt. cons., CEO, Woltz & Assoc., Inc., Barrington, Ill., 1980—; mgmt. cons. Speaker at various Univs. Mem. Soc. Mgmt. Info. Systems, Inst. Mgmt. Cons., West Point Soc. (treas. 1975), Assn. Corp. Growth, Assn. Mgmt. Consulting Firms, Ind. Computer Cons. Assn., Forest Grove Club. Home: RR 2 Barrington Hi IL 60010-9802 Office: Woltz & Assocs Inc Barrington Pl 18-5 E Dundee Rd Barrington IL 60010-7412

WOLVERTON, ROBERT EARL, classics educator; b. Indpls., Aug. 4, 1925; s. Robert N. and Vivian (Lefflar) W.; m. Margaret Jester, Sept. 13, 1952; children: Robert Earl, Laurie Ann, Edwin J., Gary A. AB, Hanover Coll., 1948; MA, U. Mich., 1949; PhD, U. N.C., 1954; LittD, Coll. Mt. St. Joseph on the Ohio, 1977; postdoctoral, Oxford (Eng.) U., 1986. Asst. prof. classics U. Ga., 1954-59; asst. prof. classics, history Tufts U., 1959-62; asst. prof., assoc. prof. classics assoc. dean U. Ill. Grad. Coll., 1967-69; dean Grad. Sch. and Research; prof. classics Miami U., Oxford, Ohio, 1969-72; pres., prof. classics Coll. Mt. St. Joseph on Ohio, Cin., 1972-77; prof. Miss. State U., Starkville, 1977—, v.p. acad. affairs, 1977-86, prof. classics, 1986—; interim head dept. fgn. langs., 1991-92, head dept., 1992—; vis. lectr. U. Perugia, Italy, 1985; fellow Acad. Adminstrn. Internship Program, 1965-66; field reader U.S. Office Edn.; cons., reviewer North Cen. Assn. Colls. and Schs., So. Assn. Colls. and Schs.; mem. exec. com. Coun. Grad. Schs. U.S., 1970-73; chmn. Midwest Assn. Grad. Schs., 1971; mem. Regents Adv. Com. Grad. Edn., Ohio, 1969-72, chmn., 1971-72; mem. Medford (Mass.) Edn. Coun., 1961-62. Author: Classical Elements in English Words, 1965, An Outline of Classical Mythology, 1966; contbg. translator: A Life of George Washington in Latin Prose (Francis Glass), 1976; editor: (with others) Graduate Programs and Admissions Manual, 1971, 72; contbr. (with others) articles to profl. jours. and encys. Trustee, v.p. Greater Cin. Consortium Colls. and Univs., St. Francis Hosp., Ohio; mem. Cin. coun. on econ. edn.; bd. dirs. Starville Arts Alliance, pres., 1989—, Starkville-Miss. State U. Symphony Assn., 1985—, pres., 1987—; Miss. Opera Assn.; mem. Miss. Com. Humanities, 1982-86, Miss. Arts Commn., 1986-87; pres. coun. of laity St. Mary's of Oxford, 1969-70; mem. Starkville Community Theatre, 1978-79, pres., 1982-82, 82-83; pres. parish coun. St. Joseph Ch., 1979, 89-90; pres. diocesan pastoral coun. Diocese of Jackson, Miss., 1983-84, 86-87. Recipient

Outstanding Undergraduate Teaching award Miss. State U., 1990. Mem. Am. Classical League (pres. 1972-76), Am. Philol. Assn., Classical Assn. Middle West and South, Vergilian Soc., Am. Assn. Higher Edn., Assn. Ind. Colls. and Univs. Ohio (sec. 1973-75, vice chmn. 1975-77), Nat. Council Chief Acad. Officers (exec. com. 1981-84, chmn. 1983-84), Council Basic Edn., Nat. Faculty Humanities Arts and Scis., Acad. Polit. Sci., Ohio Program in Humanities, Sigma Chi, Omicron Delta Kappa, Eta Sigma Phi, Phi Kappa Phi (nat. editorial advisor 1984-89), Phi Delta Kappa, Phi Eta Sigma. Home: 102 Colonial Circle Starkville MS 39759-4201

WOLYNES, PETER GUY, chemistry researcher, educator; b. Chgo., Apr. 21, 1953; s. Peter and Evelyn Eleanor (Etter) W.; m. Jane Lee Fox, Nov. 26, 1976 (div. 1980); m. Kathleen Cull Bucher, Dec. 22, 1984; children: Margrethe Cull, Eve Cordelia. AB with highest distinction, Ind. U., 1971; AM, Harvard U., 1972, PhD in Chem. Physics, 1976; DSc (hon.), Ind. U., 1988. Research assoc. MIT, Cambridge, 1975-76; asst. prof., assoc. prof. Harvard U., Cambridge, 1976-80; vis. scientist Max Planck Inst. für Biophysikalische Chemie, Gottingen, Fed. Republic Germany, 1977; assoc. prof. chemistry U. Ill., Urbana, 1980-83, prof., 1983—, prof. physics, 1985—, prof. physics and biophysics U. Ill., 1989—; permanent mem. Ctr. for Advanced Study U. Ill., Urbana, 1989—; William H. and Janet LyCan prof. chemistry Ctr. for Advanced Study U. Ill., Urbana, 1993—; vis. prof. Inst. for Molecular Sci., Okazaki, Japan, 1982, 87; vis. scientist Inst. for Theoretical Physics, Santa Barbara, Calif., 1987, Ecole normale Supérieure, Paris, 1992, Merski lectr. U. Nebr., 1986, Denkewalter lectr., Loyola U., 1986. Contbr. numerous articles to profl. jours. Sloan fellow, 1981-83, J.S. Guggenheim fellow, 1986-87; Beckman assoc. Ctr. for Advanced Study, Urbana, 1984-85. Fellow Am. Phys. Soc., Am. Acad. Arts and Scis.; mem. NAS, AAAS, Am. Chem. Soc. (Pure Chemistry award 1986), N.Y. Acad. Scis., Biophys. Soc., Phi Beta Kappa, Sigma Xi, Phi Lambda Upsilon (Fresenius award 1988), Sigma Pi Sigma, Alpha Chi Sigma. Home: 311 W Oregon St Urbana IL 61801-4125 Office: U Ill Sch of Chem Scis 505 S Mathews Ave Urbana IL 61801-3617

WOLYNIC, EDWARD THOMAS, specialty chemicals technology executive; b. Bklyn., May 29, 1948; s. Edward Joseph and Fortunata Wolynic; m. Loraine Cynthia Ciardullo. BS ChemE, Poly. Inst. N.Y., 1969; MS ChemE, Princeton U., 1972, PhD ChemE, 1974. Staff engr. Union Carbide Corp., Bound Brook, N.J., 1974-75; supr. Union Carbide Corp., Tarrytown, N.Y., 1975-77, mgr. mfg. tech., 1977-82, assoc. dir. tech., 1982-85, dir. tech., 1985-88; v.p. rsch. UOP, Tarrytown, 1988-90; v.p. devel. UOP, Des Plaines, Ill., 1990-92; dir. process R&D Internat. Specialty Products Corp., Wayne, N.J., 1993, v.p. R&D, 1993—. Contbr. tech. articles to profl. jours.; patentee in field. Mem. AIChe, Indsl. Rsch. Inst., Com. Devel. Assn., N.Am. Catalyst Soc. Avocations: fishing, tennis, skiing. Office: Internat Specialty Products Isp Bldg 1 1361 Alps Rd Wayne NJ 07470

WOLZ, HENRY GEORGE, philosophy educator; b. Kornwestheim, Germany, Sept. 10, 1905; came to U.S., 1930; s. John and Catherin (Pflueger) W.; m. Barbara L. Dertwinkel, Mar. 20, 1955; 1 dau., Ursula. B.S., Fordham U., 1936, M.A., 1938, Ph.D., 1946. Columbia Coll., 1947; Tutor Bklyn. Coll., 1947, Hunter Coll., 1947-49; asst. prof. Wagner Coll., 1947-51; asst. prof. Queens Coll., City U. N.Y., 1951-56, assoc. prof., 1956-64, prof., 1964—. Author: Plato and Heidegger: In Search of Selfhood, 1981; contbr. numerous articles to profl. jours. Served with AUS, 1942-45. Mem. Am. Philos. Assn., Metaphys. Soc. Am. Home: 25 Ryan St Syosset NY 11791-2129 Office: 65-30 Kissena Blvd Flushing NY 11367

WOLZENSKI, BEN H., insurance company executive; b. St. Louis, Oct. 23, 1949; s. Ben H. Wolzenski and Betty O. (O'Leary) Stieb; m. Jeanne Ann DuFaux, Aug. 21, 1971; children: Michael, David. MS, BA, St. Louis U., 1971. CLU. Sr. actuarial asst. Gen. Am. Life Ins. Co., St. Louis, 1971-76, mgr. product dept., 1976-77, assoc. actuary, 1977-84, traditional products v.p., 1984-86; v.p., ptnr. Ironwood Fin. Svcs., St. Louis, 1986-89; v.p. life product mgmt. Gen. Am. Life Ins. Co., St. Louis, 1989-91, exec. v.p. ind. ins., 1991—. Bd. dirs. St. Louis Hunger Coalition, 1991—. Fellow Soc. Actuaries. Office: Gen Am Life Ins Co 700 Market St Saint Louis MO 63101

WOMACH, EMILY HITCH, retired banker and marketing and public relations executive; b. Laurel, Del., Jan. 27, 1927; d. Elon G. and Jennie (Neal) Hitch; m. William S. Womach, Mar. 13, 1943 (Oct. 1982); 1 son, William Richard. Student, Salisbury (Md.) Bus. Inst., 1948; grad. Sch. Fin. Pub. Rels., Northwestern U., 1957; grad. Sch. Fin. Pub. Relations, Am. Inst. Banking, 1958, Stonier Grad. Sch. Banking, Rutgers U., 1968. With Sussex Trust Co., Laurel, 1945-68; sec., asst., cashier Sussex Trust Co., 1956-62, asst. v.p., sec., 1962-67, v.p., sec., 1967-68; adminstrv. asst. to gov. Del., 1968-69; sales rep. Robinson Real Estate, 1969-71; treas. State of Del., 1971-73; also dir. treasury dept. finance; v.p., mem. sr. mgmt. Farmers Bank State Del., Wilmington, 1973-76; chmn. bd., pres., chief exec. officer Women's Nat. Bank, Washington, 1976-83; chmn. bd., pres. Internat. Fin. Adv. Svcs., 1983-88; dir. mktg., pub. rels. Asbury Meth. Village, Gaithersburg, Md., 1986-92; pres. First WNB Corp., bank holding co., 1981-83; bd. dirs. Penjerdel Corp.; lectr. in field, 1958—; econ. commentator Spectrum on Economy, WCAV Radio, 1975-76; fin. cons. Past mem. nat. adv. coun. Small Bus. Adminstrn.; mem. Del. Bank Adv. Bd., 1963-71; participant Internat. Workshop Women Leaders in Banking and Fin., Amsterdam and San Remo, Italy. Chmn. budget com., auditor Laurel LWV, 1959-71; bd. dirs. Music at Noon, D.C. Performing Arts Soc., 1978-82; mem. edn. com., also fund drive com. Delmarva Poultry Industry, 1963-66; sec.-treas. Overall Econ. Devel. Program Com., 1967-71; mem. Del. State Small Bus. Adv. Council, 1965-71, Laurel Planning Commn., 1965-68, D.C. Employment Security Bd., 1978-80; v.p. Del. div. Am. Cancer Soc., 1964-68, mem. Del. exec. com. and bd., 1957-71; mem. Sussex County unit bd., 1957-71; bd. dirs. Nat. Capital Area region NCCJ, 1978-81; chmn. Del. Heart Fund, 1972; bd. dirs., treas. Community Fund. Greater Washington, 1978-81; mem. adv. coun. The Women's Inst./Am. U., 1978-83; trustee Wesley Coll., 1973-83. Recipient Outstanding Woman Who Works award Downtown Assn. Memphis, 1964, Merit award Del. Fed. Bus. and Profl. Women's Club, 1966; named Outstanding Citizen of Laurel, Outstanding Person of Yr. in Mktg. Washington Fin. Coun., 1981. Mem. Nat. Assn. Bank Women (v.p. Middle Atlantic div. 1960-61, nat. v.p. 1962-63, nat. pres. 1963-64), Am. Inst. Banking (pres. Sussex chpt. 1958-59), Am. Bankers Assn. (exec. com. savs. div. 1966-67, communication com. mktg. div. 1974-75, mem. adminstrv. com. govtl. rels. coun. 1975-76, 80-83), Del. Bankers Assn. (chmn. pub. rels. com. 1959-63, vice chmn. legis. com.), D.C. Bankers Assn. (adminstrv. coun. 1980-83), Friends of Women's World Banking/USA (pres. 1980-83), Am. Newspaper Women's Club (asso.), Del. C of C. (dir. 1974-76, Josiah Marvel cup award 1967), Bus. and Profl. Women's Club (pres. Laurel 1951), Am. Acad. Polit. and Social Sci., Internat. Women's Forum, Rehoboth Art League, Nat. Audubon Soc. (bd. dirs. 1985-87), Delta Kappa Gamma (hon.). Democrat. Methodist.

WOMACK, EDGAR ALLEN, JR., technology executive; b. Humboldt, Tenn., Oct. 29, 1942; s. Edgar Allen Sr. and Lucy Opal (George) W.; m. Linda Jane Cochran, Dec. 28, 1963; children: Constance Elaine, Cynthia Lynn. BS, MIT, 1963, MS, 1965, PhD, 1969. Project engr. U.S. Atomic Energy Commn., Washington, 1968-73, br. chief, 1973; div. asst., dir. U.S. Energy Research and Devel. Adminstrn., Washington, 1973-75; program mgr. Babcock and Wilcox Co., Lynchburg, Va., 1975-78, mgr. plant engring., 1978-80, mgr. reactor and fuel mgmt., 1980-82, mgr. field tech. services, 1982-83, v.p. sales and mktg., 1983-85; v.p. R&D Babcock and Wilcox Co., Alliance, Ohio, 1985-93; sr. v.p., chief tech. officer McDermott Internat., New Orleans, 1993—; bd. dirs. Ceramatec Corp., Indsl. Rsch. Inst., Washington, 1989—, pres., 1994—. Patentee in field. Served to lt. USNR, 1968-70. Hon. Woodrow Wilson Found. fellow. Mem. ASME (ind. adv. bd. 1988—), Am. Mgmt. Assn. (rsch. and devel. coun. 1988-94), Indsl. Research Inst., AAAS, Soc. Sigma Xi. Presbyterian. Avocations: photography, diving, golf. Home: 7412 Jade St New Orleans LA 70124-3539 Office: McDermott Internat Inc PO Box 61961 New Orleans LA 70161-1961

WOMACK, MARY PAULINE, lawyer; b. Chattanooga, Tenn., Dec. 3, 1942; d. Abner and Lucille (Thomas) W. BS, U. Chattanooga, 1964; JD, Woodrow Wilson Coll. Law, 1984. Bar: Ga. 1988, U.S. Dist. Ct. (no. dist.) Ga. 1988. Pvt. practice Clarkston, Ga. Mem. DeKalb County Dems., 66th dist., regional com. State of Ga. Mem. Ga. Bar Assn., Sigma Delta Kappa (past regional v.p.). Home: 892 Glynn Oakes Dr Clarkston GA 30021

Office: The Equitable Bldg Ste 1000 100 Peachtree St NW Atlanta GA 30303

WOMACK, RICHARD MARVIN, manufacturing company executive; b. New Orleans, Jan. 21, 1936; s. David Ray and Amoret Donelson (Gates) W.; m. Eva Robuck, June 8, 1957; children: Ray (dec.), Mike, Deanna. B.S. in Engring., U. Tex.- U.-Austin, 1957, M.B.A., 1959. Mgr. bar soap and household cleaning products div. Procter & Gamble Co., Cin., 1978-79, v.p. U.S. mfg., 1980-81, v.p. engring., 1982-84, v.p. purchases, 1985-86, v.p. purchases and quality, 1987—, v.p. product supply, purchases, 1989; v.p. nat. govt. rels. Washington, 1989—. Bd. dirs. Jr. Achievement, Inc., 1979-89; bd. dirs. Jobs for Cin. Grads., 1982-89, Nat. Minority Supply Devel. Coun., 1986-89. Recipient Neil H. McElroy award Community Chest of Greater Cin., 1983. Mem. Nat. Assn. Mfrs. (bd. dirs. 1990—). Episcopalian. Club: Queen City (Cin.).

WOMACK, SAMUEL EDWARD, computer company executive; b. Covington, Ga., Nov. 16, 1942; s. Oscar Ellis and Mary Lylian (Smith) W.; m. Margaret Fay O'Berry, Dec. 15, 1969 (div. 1978); 1 child, Benjamin Jay; m. Patsy McCamey, June 30, 1979 (div. 1995); stepchildren: Greg Carson, Scott Carson. AA in Bus. and Data Processing, DeKalb Coll.; grad. exec. devel. program, George Mason U. Computer specialist, sys. analyst, programmer U.S. Govt., Dept. Army, Atlanta, 1969-80; supr., computer specialist, sys. analyst U.S. Govt., Dept. Army, Alexandria, Va., 1980-82; dir. Army Regional Data Ctr. U.S. Govt., Dept. Army, Norcross, Ga., 1982-88; pres. Ind. Computer Cons., Inc., Covington, 1988—. With U.S. Army, 1960-65, Vietnam and Germany. Mem. Elks, Masons. Roman Catholic. Avocations: golf, fishing, hunting. Home and Office: PO Box 1084 Covington GA 30209

WOMACK, THOMAS HOUSTON, manufacturing company executive; b. Gallatin, Tenn., June 22, 1940; s. Thomas Houston and Jessie (Eckel) W.; Linda Walker Womack, July 20, 1963 (div. Dec. 1989); children: Britton Ryan, Kelley Elizabeth; m. Pamela Ann Reed, Apr. 20, 1991. BSME, Tenn. Tech. U., Cookeville, 1963. Project engr. U.S. Gypsum Co., Jacksonville, Fla., 1963-65; project mgr. Maxwell House Div. Gen. Foods Corp., Jacksonville, 1965-68; mfg. mgr. Maxwell House Div. Gen. Foods Corp., Hoboken, N.J., 1968-71, div. ops. planning mgr., 1971-73; industry sales mgr. J.R. Schneider Co., Tiburon, Calif., 1973-79; pres. Womack Internat., Inc., Novato, Calif., 1979—. Holder 4 U.S. patents. Mem. Soc. Tribologists and Lubrication Engrs., Am. Filtration Soc., Soc. Mfg. Engrs., Am. Soc. Chem. Engrs. Avocations: skiing, vintage exotic sports cars. Office: Womack Internat Inc One Digital Dr Novato CA 94949

WOMBLE, WILLIAM FLETCHER, lawyer; b. Winston-Salem, N.C., Oct. 29, 1916; s. Bunyan Snipes and Edith (Willingham) W.; m. Jane Payne Gilbert, Oct. 11, 1941; children: William Fletcher, Jr., Jane Womble Haver, Russell G., Ann Womble Strader. AB, Duke U., 1937, JD, 1939. Bar: N.C. 1939. Assoc. Womble Carlyle Sandridge & Rice P.L.L.C. and predecessors, Winston-Salem, 1939-47; ptnr. Womble Carlyle Sandridge & Rice P.L.L.C. and predecessors, 1947—. Campaign chmn. Forsyth County Community Chest, 1948; mem. N.C. Gen. Statutes Commn., 1953-55; mem. N.C. Bd. Higher Edn., 1955-57, 60-63; mem. N.C. Adv. Budget Commn., 1957-58; mem. N.C. Ho. of Reps., 1953-58, chmn. com. higher edn., 1957, vice chmn. fin. com., 1957; life trustee, past chmn. High Point U.; trustee Winston-Salem State U., 1953-55; past trustee, past pres. Children's Home; bd. dirs. Triad United Methodist Home, 1976-87, 89—, treas., 1975-79, pres., 1979-85; mem. People-to-People Citizen Ambassador Program, 1981, 86; chmn. adminstrv. bd. Centenary United Meth. Ch., 1961-63, chmn. bd. trustees, 1983-85. Served to maj. USAAF, 1941-46. Named Trustee of Yr., Gen. Bd. Global Mins. of United Meth. Ch., Health and Welfare Mins. Dept., 1989. Fellow Am. Bar Found. (life, state chmn. 1984-89, Fifty Yr. award 1995); mem. ABA (ho. of dels. 1978-87, bd. govs. 1982-85, ethics com. 1985-91, exec. coun. Nat. Conf. Bar Pres. 1985-88, resource devel. coun. 1986-92, chair affiliate outreach com. sr. lawyers divsn. 1994-95), N.C. Bar Assn. (pres. 1966-67, jud. code subcommittee, chmn. endowment founders campaign 1986-87, chair sr. lawyers divsn. 1994-95, The Judge John J. Parker award 1984), N.C. State Bar (trustee Interest on Lawyers Trust Accounts 1983-91, vice chmn. 1989-91), Forsyth County Bar Assn. (pres. 1962), Am. Judicature Soc., U.S. Supreme Ct. Hist. Soc., N.C. Supreme Ct. Hist. Soc., Winston-Salem C. of C. (pres. 1960-61), Soc. of Cin., Old Town Club, Twin City Club, Piedmont Club, Rotary (local pres. 1964). Democrat. Methodist. Home: 2027 Virginia Rd Winston Salem NC 27104-2319 Office: Womble Carlyle Sandridge & Rice PO Box 84 1600 So Nat Fin Ctr Winston Salem NC 27102-0084

WOMELDORFF, PORTER JOHN, utility executive; b. Milw., Feb. 26, 1933; s. Virgil Leslie and Leorra (Porter) W.; B.S.E.E., U. Ill., 1954; m. Marilyn Sapp, Jan. 7, 1966; children—John Porter, Michael Wayne. With Ill. Power Co., Decatur, 1954—, beginning as elec. engr., successively results supr., instrumentation engr., supr. system planning, mgr. planning, 1954-79, v.p., 1979-93, global climate program exec., 1993—; mem. Ill. Coal Devel. Bd., 1982—, chair. Chair adv. bd. U. Ill. Coll. Engring., 1986-89; chair sci. com. Global Climate Coalition; lay mem. Central Ill. Ann. Conf., United Methodist Ch., 1968—, lay leader, 1976-79, lay mem. North Central Jurisdictional Conf., 1972—, lay mem. Gen. Conf., 1976—; lay mem. Gen. Bd. Pubs., 1992—. Served to lt. C.E., AUS, 1955-57. Decorated Army Commendation Medal. Mem. Instrument Soc. Am. (v.p. 1971-73, Power Div. Achievement award 1983), IEEE, ASME, U. Ill. Elec. Engring. Alumni Assn. (pres., dir. Outstanding Alumni award 1994), Phi Kappa Phi, Tau Beta Pi, Sigma Tau, Eta Kappa Nu, Alpha Kappa Lambda. Home: 735 Country Manor Dr Decatur IL 62521-2524 Office: Ill Power Co 500 S 27th St Decatur IL 62521-2200

WOMER, CHARLES BERRY, retired hospital executive, management consultant; b. Cleve., Mar. 30, 1926; s. Porter Blake and Margaret (Berry) W.; m. Elizabeth Benson, Oct. 7, 1950; children: Richard B., Carol E., John C. M.S. in Hosp. Adminstrn., Columbia U., 1953; B.S. in Mech. Engring., Case Inst. Tech., 1949. Asst. dir. Univ. Hosps., Cleve., 1957-61; assoc. dir. Univ. Hosps., 1961-65, exec. dir. Univ. Hosps.; mgmt. cons., 1982-90, ret., 1990; adminstr. Yale-New Haven Hosp., 1965-67, dir., 1968-76, pres., 1976; lectr. Yale U., 1965-78, 87-91; adj. asst. prof. Case Western Res. U., 1976-83; mem. Comn. Commn. on Hosps. and Health Care, 1973-76; bd. dirs. New Haven Savings Bank, 1969-76. Bd. govs. U. New Haven, 1972-76. Served with AUS, 1944-46. Fellow Am. Coll. Healthcare Execs. (life); mem. Am. Hosp. Assn. (chmn. coun. on mgmt. and planning 1977-79), Conn. Hosp. Assn. (trustee 1970-74, pres. 1972-73, Disting. Svc. award 1976), Assn. Am. Med. Colls. (exec. coun. 1974-77, 78-80, treas. 1975-76, chmn. 1979-80, adminstrv. bd. coun. org. hosps. 1972-77, chmn. 1975-76). Home: 184 Rimmon Rd Woodbridge CT 06525-1920

WOMMACK, W(ILLIAM) W(ALTON), retired manufacturing company executive; b. Winston-Salem, N.C., Dec. 12, 1922; s. Sidney LaMar and Ada (Culler) W.; m. Jean Emery, Sept. 14, 1951; children: Judith J., Kent W., Lynne E., Mary E. B.Chem. Engring, N.C. State Coll., 1943; M.B.A., Harvard U., 1948. Engr. thru div. controller Libbey-Owens-Ford, Toledo, 1948; treas., controller Ottawa River Paper Co., Toledo, 1955-58; asst. gen. mgr. Mead. Corp., 1958-64; v.p. bd. Mead. Corp., Dayton, Ohio, 1964-66; group v.p. bd. Mead. Corp., Dayton, 1966-69, exec. v.p., 1969-71, vice chmn. bd., 1971-81, also dir. bd. dirs. Robbins & Myers, Inc., Rand McNally Co. Lt. USNR, 1943-46.

WON, KYUNG-SOO, symphony conductor, director; b. Korea, Dec. 4, 1928; m. Hae-Ja (Won). Jan. 9, 1944; children: Alisa, Justin. Mus.M., Cin. Conservatory, 1957; diploma Mozarteum, Salzburg, Austria, protege of Pierre Monteux; postgrad. Ind. U. Cert. tchr., Calif. Formerly dir. Seoul (Korea) Nat. U., music dir. Modesto (Calif.) Symphony, Seoul Philharm. Orch.; music dir., condr. Stockton (Calif.) Symphony; now spl. prof. Kyung-Won U.; violin soloist Cin. Symphony. Seoul Philharm., Manila Symphony, Korean Broadcasting System Orch., Korea; guest condr. orchs., London, Berlin, Paris, Vienna, Austria, Ireland, Mexico City, S. Am. cities, Orient. Served with Korean Navy. Recipient Bartok award, Emeel Hermann award, Star award. Mem. Am. Symphony League. Office: Stockton Symphony 37 W Yokuts Ave Ste 4C Stockton CA 95207-5725

WONDER, STEVIE (STEVLAND MORRIS), singer, musician, composer; b. Saginaw, Mich., May 13, 1950; m. Syreeta Wright, 1971 (div. 1972);

children: Aisha, Keita, Mumtaz. Student pub. schs. in Detroit until age 12; then transferred to, Mich. Sch. for Blind. Solo singer, Whitestone Bapt. Ch., Detroit, 1959, rec. artist, Motown Records, Detroit, 1963-70; founder, pres. music pub. co., Black Bull Music, Inc., 1970—, Wondirection Records, Inc., 1982—; recs. include Fingertips, 1963, Uptight/Purple Raindrops, 1965, Someday At Christmas/The Miracles of Christmas, 1966, I'm Wondering/ Everytime I See You I Go Wild, 1966, I Was Made To Love Her/Hold Me, 1967, Shoo-Be-Doo-Be-Doo-Da-Day/Why Don't You Lead Me To Love, 1968, You Met Your Match/My Girl, 1968, For Once In My Life, I Don't Know Why, My Cherie Amour, Yester-Me, Yester-You, Yesterday, Never Had a Dream Come True, Signed, Sealed, Delivered I'm Yours, Heaven Help Us All, I Wish (Grammy award 1977), Don't You Worry 'Bout a Thing, You Haven't Done Nothin', Boogie on Reggae Woman, (Grammy award 1975), Isn't She Lovely, Sir Duke, Another Star, As, You Are the Sunshine of My Life, (Grammy award 1974), Superstition, (Grammy award 1974), Higher Ground, Living For the City, (Grammy award 1975); albums include Little Stevie Wonder: The Twelve-Year Old Genius, 1963, Tribute to Uncle Ray, 1963, Jazz Soul of Little Steve, 1963, At The Beach, 1965, For Once in My Life, 1969, My Cheric Amour, 1970, Talk of The Town, 1970, Portrait, 1976, Uptight, 1966, Down To Earth, 1966, I Was Made To Love Her, 1967, Someday At Christmas, 1967, Stevie Wonder's Greatest Hits, 1968, Music of My Mind, 1972, Innervisions, 1973 (Grammy award 1974), Fulfillingness' First Finale (Grammy award 1975), Songs In the Key of Life, 1976 (Grammy award 1977), Stevie Wonder Live, Where I'm Coming From, 1972, Talking Book, 1972, Journey Through the Secret Life of Plants, 1979, Hotter than July, 1980, Woman in Red (Acad. award, Golden Globe award for single I Just Called to Say I Love You), 1984, In Square Circle (best soul/ R&B album of yr., Down Beat mag. Readers' poll) 1986, Characters, 1987, Jungle Fever, 1991, Inner Peace, 1995, numerous others; appeared in films: Bikini Beach, 1964, Muscle Beach Party, 1964; frequent TV appearances include Mike Douglas Show, guest host Saturday Night Live; named (Musician of Year, Down Beat mag. Rock/Blues Poll 1973-75, 77-78, Best Selling Male Soul Artist of Year, Nat. Assn. Rec. Merchandisers 1974), recipient numerous Grammy awards, also numerous awards for best singer/ songwriter; Rock Music award 1977, Am. Music award 1978, Am. Video award for best rhythm and blues video for Ebony and Ivory 1982, Inducted Songwriters Hall of Fame 1982. Named to: Rock and Roll Hall of Fame, 1989; recipient Nelson Mandela Courage award, 1991. Office: 4616 W Magnolia Blvd Burbank CA 91505-2731*

WONDERS, WILLIAM CLARE, geography educator; b. Toronto, Apr. 22, 1924; s. George Clarence and Ann Mary (Bell) W.; m. Lillian Paradise Johnson, June 2, 1951; children—Karen Elizabeth, Jennifer Anne, Glen William. B.A. with honors, Victoria Coll., U. Toronto, 1946; M.A., Syracuse U., 1948; Ph.D., U. Toronto, 1951; Fil. Dr. h.c., Uppsala U., 1981. Teaching asst. dept. geography Syracuse U., 1946-48; lectr. dept. geography U. Toronto, 1948-53; asst. prof. geography dept. polit. economy U. Alta., 1953-55, assoc. prof. geography, 1955-57, prof., head dept. geography, 1957-67, prof. dept. geography, 1967-87, Univ. prof., 1983—, prof. emeritus, 1987—; vis. prof. geography U. B.C., 1954, U. Okla., 1965-66, St. Mary's U., 1977, U. Victoria, 1989, J.F. Kennedy Inst., U. Free Berlin, 1990; guest prof. Inst. Geography, Uppsala (Sweden) U., 1962-63; rsch. fellow in Geography U. Aberdeen, Scotland, 1970-71, 78; vis. fellow in Can. Studies, U. Edinburgh, Scotland, 1987. Author: Looking at Maps, 1960, The Sawdust Fusiliers, 1991, Norden and Canada-A Geographer's Perspective, 1992, Alaska Highway Explorer, 1994; (with T. Drinkwater et al) Atlas of Alberta, 1969, (with J.C. Muller et al) Junior Atlas of Alberta, 1979; contbr., editor: Canada's Changing North, 1971, The North, 1972, The Arctic Circle, 1976, Knowing the North, 1988; contbr. articles to jours. and encys., chpts. to books. Mem. Nat. Adv. Com. on Geog. Rsch., 1965-69; mem. Can. Permanent Com. on Geog. Names, 1981-94, Alta. Historic Sites Bd., 1978-83; mem. policy bd. Can. Plains Rsch. Centre, U. Regina (Sask.), 1975-86; mem. adv. bd. Tyrrell Mus. Paleontology, 1984-89; bd. dirs. The Muttart Found., 1986-93, 95—, v.p. 1991-93, mem. 1993—. NSF sr. fge. scientist fellow, 1965-66; Canada Council leave fellow, 1969-70, 77-78; Nuffield Found. fellow, 1970-71. Fellow Arctic Inst. N.Am., Royal Soc. Can.; mem. Canadian Assn. Geographers (past. pres.), Royal Scottish Geog. Soc., Canadian Assn. Scottish Studies (councillor 1974-77), Scottish Soc. Northern Studies, Champlain Soc. (councillor 1981-86), Sigma Xi, Gamma Theta Upsilon.

WONG, ALFRED YIU-FAI, physics educator; b. Macao, Portugal, Feb. 4, 1937; s. Ka Ku and Wai Fong (Mak) W.; m. Lydia Yun Li, June 19, 1965; children: Alan C., Christopher C. BA in Sci., U. Toronto, 1958, MA, 1959; MSc, U. Ill., 1961; PhD, Princeton U., 1963. Research assoc. Princeton U., 1962-64; asst. prof. physics UCLA, 1964-68, assoc. prof. physics, 1968-72, prof., 1972—; cons. TRW Systems, Redondo Beach, Calif., 1965-79; bd. dirs. Hipas Observatory, Ark. Contbr. articles to profl. jours. A.P. Sloan fellow UCLA, 1966-67. Fellow Am. Phys. Soc. (Excellence in Plasma Physics award 1985), Sigma Xi, Sigma Pi Sigma. Baptist. Office: UCLA Dept of Physics 405 Hilgard Ave Los Angeles CA 90024-1301

WONG, CHAK-KUEN, computer scientist; b. Macao, China, Mar. 4, 1938. B.A. with first class honors, U. Hong Kong, 1965; M.A., Columbia U., 1966, Ph.D., 1970. Research staff mem. IBM T.J. Watson Research Ctr., Yorktown Heights, N.Y., 1969-95, mgr. design algorithms, 1985-95; vis. prof. computer sci. U. Ill.-Urbana, 1972-73, Columbia U., N.Y.C., 1978-79; prof., chmn. Dept. Computer Sci. Chinese U. Hong Kong, 1995—. Author: Algorithmic Studies in Mass Storage Systems, 1983; editor-in-chief Algorithmica, 1985—; assoc. editor Networks; contbr. articles to profl. jours.; mem. editorial bd. Fuzzy Sets and Systems. Fellow IEEE (editor Transactions on Computers 1981-85, Transactions on VLSI Systems 1992—), Assn. Computing Machinery. Office: IBM TJ Watson Research Ctr PO Box 218 Yorktown Heights NY 10598-0218 also: Dept Computer Sci, Rm 1028 HSH Eng Bldg, Chinese U Hong Kong, Shatin NT Hong Kong

WONG, CHI-HUEY, chemistry educator; b. Taiwan, Aug. 13, 1948; came to U.S., 1979; m. Ying-Lii, Mar. 26, 1975; children: Heather, Andrew. BS in Biochemistry, Nat. Taiwan U., 1970, MS in Biochemistry, 1977; PhD in Chemistry, MIT, 1982. Asst. rsch. fellow Inst. Biol. Chemistry Academia Sinica, Taipei, Taiwan, 1974-79; from asst. prof. to prof. chemistry Tex. A&M U., 1983-89; Ernest W. Hahn prof. chemistry Scripps Rsch. Inst., La Jolla, Calif., 1989—; cons. Miles Labs., 1985-88, Dow Chem., 1985-90, G. D. Searle, 1988-90; sci. advisor Amylin, San Diego 1989-92, Cytel, 1990—; head lab. glycosci. frontier rsch. program Riken, Japan, 1991—. Author: Enzymes in Synthetic Organic Chemistry, 1991; editl. bd. Bicatalysis; contbr. over 250 articles to profl. jours.; patentee in field. Lt. Taiwan Army, 1970-71. Recipient Presdl. Young Investigator in Chemistry award NSF, Washington, 1986; Searle scholar, 1985. Fellow AAAS, Am. Inst. Chemists; mem. Am. Chem. Soc. (Arthur C. Cope scholar award 1993, Internat. Carbohydrate award 1994), Am. Soc. Biochemistry and Molecular Biology, N.Y. Acad. Sci. Office: Scripps Rsch Inst Dept Chemistry 10666 N Torrey Pines Rd La Jolla CA 92037-1027

WONG, CHING-PING, chemist; b. Canton, China, Mar. 29, 1947; came to U.S., 1966; s. Kwok-Keung and Yun-Kwan (Lo) W.; m. Lorraine Homnack, May 27, 1978; children: Michelle, David. BS in Chemistry, Purdue U., 1969; PhD in Organic and Inorganic Chemistry, Pa. State U., 1975. Postdoctoral scholar Stanford (Calif.) U., 1976, mem. tech. staff AT&T Bell Labs., Princeton, N.J., 1977-82, sr. mem. tech. staff, 1982-87, disting. mem. tech. staff, 1987-92; AT&T Bell Labs. fellow, 1992—; program chmn. 39th Electronic Components Conf., 1989; gen. chmn. 41st Electronic Components and Tech. Conf., 1991; bd. govs. IEEE-Components, Hybrids and Mfg. Tech. Soc., 1987-89, tech. v.p., 1990-91, pres., 1992-93. Author, editor: Polymers for Electronic and Photonic Applications, 1993; contbr. articles to profl. jours. Recipient Outstanding Papers and Contbns. award IEEE-Components, Hybrids and Mfg. Tech. Soc., 1990, 91, 94. Fellow IEEE. Achievements include over 30 U.S. and numerous internat. patents for integrated device passivation and encepsulation area; pioneer in application of polymers for device reliability without hermeticity, a new application on electronic device packaging. Home: 11 Wexford Dr Lawrenceville NJ 08648 Office: AT&T Bell Labs PO Box 900 Princeton NJ 08540

WONG, DAVID T., biochemist; b. Hong Kong, Nov. 6, 1935; s. Chi-Keung and Pui-King W.; m. Christina Lee, Dec. 28, 1963; children: Conrad, Melvin, Vincent. Student, Nat. Taiwan U., 1955-56; BS, Seattle Pacific U., 1961; MS, Oreg. State U., 1964; PhD, U. Oreg., 1966. Postdoctoral fellow U. Pa., Phila., 1966-68; sr. biochemist Lilly Rsch. Labs., Indpls., 1968-72, rsch. biochemist, 1973-77, sr. rsch. scientist, 1978-89; rsch. advisor, 1990—; adj. prof. biochemistry and molecular biology Ind. U. Sch. Medicine, 1986—, adj. prof. neurobiology, 1991—. Contbr. numerous articles to sci. jours. Alumnus of Growing Vision Seattle Pacific U., 1989. Recipient Scientist of Yr. award, Pres. award Chinese Neuroscience Soc., 1991, Discoverers award Pharm. Mfr. Assn., 1993. Mem. Am. Coll. Neuropsychopharmaeology, Am. Soc. Pharmacology and Exptl. Therapeutics, Internat. Soc. Neurochemistry, Am. Soc. Neurochemistry, Soc. Neurosci. (pres. Indpls. chpt. 1987, 88), Soc. Chinese Bioscientists in Am., Indpls. Rsch. Assn. Chinese Ams. (pres. 1987), Sigma Xi. Rsch. on biochemistry and pharmacology of neurotransmission; discovery and development of antidepressant drug, Prozac (Fluoxetine) and drug candidates including Dapoxetine, selective inhibitors of serotonin uptake, Tomoxetine, a selective inhibitor of norepinephrine uptake; duloxetine, an inhibitor for uptake of serotonin and norepinephrine; studies of potentially useful substances which activate transmission of norepinephrine, dopamine (Permax (pergolide), an agent for treatment of Parkinson's disease), serotonin, acetylcholine and GABA-neurons; studies of natural products led to the discovery of carboxylic ionophores: Narasin and A204, which increase transport of cations across biomembranes. Office: Lilly Rsch Labs Eli Lilly and Co Lilly Corp Ctr Indianapolis IN 46285

WONG, DAVID YUE, academic administrator, physics educator; b. Swatow, China, Apr. 16, 1934; came to U.S., 1953; s. Fan and Wen (Tsang) W.; m. Katherine Young, Sept. 3, 1960 (div. Mar. 1988); children: Amy, Eric; m. Elizabeth Lewis, Mar. 26, 1988. BA, Hardin Simmons U., 1954; PhD, U. Md., 1957. Theoretical physicist Lawrence Radiation Lab., U. Calif., Berkeley, 1958-59; asst. prof. physics U. Calif., San Diego, 1960-63, assoc. prof., 1963-67, prof., 1967—; chair dept. physics, 1977-80, provost Warren Coll., 1985-94. Alfred P. Sloan fellow, 1966-68. Mem. Am. Inst. Physics.

WONG, EUGENE, engineering educator; b. Nanking, Peoples Republic of China, Dec. 24, 1934; came to U.S., 1949; s. Jennings and May (Yang) W.; m. Joan Chang, Sept. 8, 1956; children: Linda, David, Michael. BS, Princeton U., 1955, AM, 1958, PhD, 1959. Staff researcher IBM Corp., Yorktown, N.Y., 1960-62; asst. prof. elec. engring. U. Calif., Berkeley, 1962-65, assoc. prof., 1965-69, prof., 1969-83, Miller prof., 1983—, chmn. dept. elec. engring and computer sci., 1985—; cons. Ampex Corp, Redwood City, Calif., 1963-79, Computer Corp. Am., Cambridge, Mass., 1976-80; founder, cons. Relational Tech. Inc. Alameda, Calif., 1980—. Author: Stochastic Processes, 1971, Introduction to Random Processes, 1983; also articles. Guggenheim fellow, 1968, Sci. Research Council sr. fellow, 1973, Vinton Hayes fellow, 1976. Fellow IEEE; mem. Assn. Computing Machinery, Nat. Acad. Engring. Home: 97 Stonewall Rd Berkeley CA 94705-1414 Office: Dept EECS U Calif Berkeley CA 94720

WONG, HENRY LI-NAN, bank executive, economist; b. Rangoon, Burma, Nov. 3, 1940; s. Chew King and Jenny (Yu) W.; came to U.S., 1946. m. Laurie Yap, Apr. 11, 1968; children: Rachael S.Y., Remle S.W. BS, Waynesburg Coll., 1965; MS, U. Hawaii, 1968, PhD, 1969. Economist, Econ. Research Service U.S. Dept. Agr., Washington, 1969-70; economist Hawaii Dept. Budget and Fin., Honolulu, 1970-73; dir. Hawaii film office Hawaii Dept. Planning and Econ. Devel., Honolulu, 1973-84; exec. v.p. and chief adminstr., office of chmn. CB Bancshares Inc., Honolulu, 1984—; vice chmn., dir. Hawaii Strategic Devel. Corp., Honolulu, 1991—; v.p., bd. dirs. Friends of East West Ctr., Honolulu, 1983-84. NDEA fellow, 1965-69. Mem. Assn. Film Commrs. (pres. 1980), Am. Econ. Assn., Am. Agrl. Econs. Assn., Hawaii Internat. Film Festival, Chinese C. of C., Hawaii Soc. Corp. Planners, Lanakila Rehab. Ctr. (trustee), Alpha Kappa Psi, Theta Chi. Democrat. Presbyterian. Lodges: Elks, Masons (trustee), Shriners. Office: City Bank City Fin Tower 201 Merchant St Honolulu HI 96813-2929

WONG, JOE, physical chemist; b. Hong Kong, Aug. 8, 1942; arrived in U.S., 1966; s. Po-lim and Mildred (Tam) W.; m. Mei-Ngan, Dec. 20, 1969; children: Glenn, Christina, Theresa. BSc, U. Tasmania, Australia, 1965; BSc with honors, U. Tesmania, Australia, 1966, DSc, 1986; PhD, Purdue U., 1970. Rsch. chemist Electolytic Zinc of Australia, Tasmania, 1966; lectr. in phys. chemistry Electrolytic Zinc of Australia, Tasmania, 1966; rsch. chemist GE R&D Ctr. Schenectady, N.Y., 1970-86; sr. rsch. chemist Lawrence Livermore (Calif.) Nat. Lab., 1986—; adj. prof. chemistry SUNY, Albany, 1981-86; cons. prof. Stanford Synchronization Rad. Lab., 1993—. Author: Glass: Structure by Spectroscopy, 1976; contbr. articles to profl. jours.; 7 patents in field. Sr. fellowship Sci. and Tech. Agy., 1991; recipient Humboldt Rsch. award Humboldt Found., 1991, RD-100 awards, 1990, 91. Fellow Am. Inst. Chemists; mem. AAAS, Am. Chem. Soc., Am. Phys. Soc. Materials Rsch. Soc., Sigma Xi. Home: 871 El Cerro Blvd Danville CA 94526-2704 Office: Lawrence Livermore Nat Lab PO Box 808 L-369 Livermore CA 94551

WONG, KUANG CHUNG, anesthesiologist; b. Chung King, People's Republic China, Nov. 12, 1936; m. Janny Wu; children: Jade, Shale, Amber. BS in Chemistry, Iowa State U., 1959; MS in Pharmacology, State U. Iowa, 1962; PhD in Pharmacology, U. Nebr., Omaha, 1966, MD, 1968. Diplomate Am. Bd. Anesthesiology (assoc. examiner 1979—). Instr. then asst. prof. pharmacology U. Nebr., Omaha, 1965-69; intern Bishop Clarkson Hosp., Omaha, 1968; intern U. Nebr. Coll. Medicine, Omaha, 1968, resident in anesthesia, 1968-69; resident, then fellow U. Wash. Sch. Medicine, Seattle, 1969-70; mem. assoc. grad. faculty U. Nebr., Omaha, 1968-69; asst. to assoc. prof. anesthesiology and pharmacology U. Washington, Seattle, 1970-74; assoc. prof. anesthesiology and pharmacology U. Utah, Salt Lake City, 1974-76, chmn. dept., assoc. prof. anesthesiology and pharmacology, 1976-77, chmn. dept., prof. anesthesiology and pharmacology, 1977—; vis. prof. numerous univs. throughout world, also various hosps.; mem. adv. com. anesthetic and life support drugs FDA, 1982-83; attending anesthesiologist U. Wash. Med. Ctr. and affiliated hosps., Seattle, 1970-74; staff anesthesiologist U. Utah Med. Ctr., Salt Lake City, 1974—; mem. surgery, anesthesia and trauma study sects. NIH, 1982-86. Mem. editorial bd. Anesthesia and Analgesia, 1980-89. Served with U.S. Army, 1955-57. Recipient Dr. Ernest Tibbets Manning Meml. Scholarship, 1965-66, U. Nebr. Upper Regents' Scholarship, 1966-67; grantee NIH, 1969-72, 80-85, Wash. State Heart Assn., 1972-74, Utah Heart Assn., 1975-76, 78-80, U. Utah, 1975-76, 76-77, Knoll Pharm. Co., 1976-79; Riker Labs., Inc., 1976-78, Smith Kline and French, 1979-89. Mem. AMA, Am. Heart Assn., Am. Soc. Anesthesiologists (ad hoc com. self-evaluation 1979), Am. Soc. Clin. Pharmacology and Chemotherapy, Am. Soc. Pharmacology and Exptl. Therapeutics, Assn. Cardiac Anesthesiologists, Assn. Univ. Anesthesiologists, Internat. Anesthesia Rsch. Soc. (trustee 1989—), Salt Lake County Med. Soc., Utah Heart Assn., Utah Med. Soc., Utah State Anesthesiologists, Soc. Acad. Anesthesia Chairmen, Sigma Xi, Alpha Omega Alpha. Office: Univ of Utah Sch of Medicine Dept of Anesthesiology Salt Lake City UT 84132

WONG, KWAN SHUT, art appraiser, artist; b. Taishan, China, Aug. 27, 1934; came to U.S., 1971; s. Shew Lem and Mary (Lee) W.; m. Violetta C. Pong; children: Judy, Tony. BA in Chinese Lit., Chung Chi Coll., Chinese U., Hong Kong, 1963; MA in Ancient Chinese Lit., Kyoto U., Japan, 1969; MA in Chinese Art History, U. Kans., 1975. Instr. Chinese poetry Chinese U., Hong Kong, 1964-65; rsch. assoc. Nelson Gallery of Art, Kansas City, Mo., 1975-81; cons. Chinese paintings Christie, Manson & Woods, N.Y.C., 1981-84, v.p. Chinese paintings, 1984-87, sr. v.p. Chinese paintings, dir. Christie's Swire Hong Kong, 1987—; head Chinese paintings dept. internat. Christie's, 1992—. Author: Masterpieces of Sung and Yuan Dynasty Calligraphy from the John M. Crawford Jr. Collection, 1981, (with Marc Wilson) Friends of Wen Cheng-ming: a View from the Crawford Collection, 1974, (with Shigemi Komatsu) Chinesische und Japanische Kalligraphie aus Zwei Jahrtausenden: Die Sammlung Heinz Gotze, Heidelberg, 1987; contbr. to Artists and Patrons, Bull. of the Mus. of Fine Arts, Houston; one-man shows include Nelson Atkins Art Gallery, 1977, 79; exhibited in group shows Hanart Gallery, N.Y.C., Taipei, Taiwan, Cleve. Mus. of Art, exhbn. of Chinese Calligraphy, U. Rochester, St. Louis U., Ky. U., Cicada Gallery of Fine Arts, Singapore, 1995. Office: Christie Manson & Woods 502 Park Ave New York NY 10022-1108

WONG, MA-LI, psychiatrist; b. Hong Kong; came to U.S., 1985; d. Kowk Keung and Yin Shang (Lau) W.; m. Julio Licinio, Nov. 15, 1985. MD, U. Sao Paulo, Brazil, 1982. Resident in medicine, then neurology U. Sao Paulo Med. Ctr., 1983-85; rsch. assoc. Albert Einstein Coll. Medicine, Bronx, N.Y., 1985-86; resident in psychiatry Albert Einstein Coll. Medicine, 1986-89; rsch. fellow Clin. Neuroendocrinology br. NIMH, Bethesda, Md., 1989-90; chief resident in psychiatry Yale U. Sch. Medicine, New Haven, 1990-91, instr. in psychiatry, 1991-93; vis. scientist clin. neuroendocrinology br. NIMH, Bethesda, Md., 1993—. Contbr. to profl. jours. Mem. N.Y. Acad. Scis., Am. Psychiat. Assn., Am. Fedn. Clin. Rsch., Soc. Neuroscience, Assn. Women Psychiatrists, Endocrine Soc. Avocations: poetry, photography. Office: 8135 N Brook Ln # 907 Bethesda MD 20814

WONG, NANCY L., dermatologist; b. Chung King, China, Aug. 23, 1943; came to U.S., 1947; d. Alice (Lee) Wong; m. Robert Lipshutz; children: Seth, Alison, David. BS, Pa. State U., 1963; MS in Physics magna cum laude, Columbia U., 1965; MD, Jefferson Med. Coll., Phila., 1971. Diplomate Am. Bd. Dermatology. Intern Wilmington Med. Ctr., 1992; resident Jackson Meml. Hosp., Miami, Mount Sinai Med. Ctr., Miami, 1977; physician Kaiser Med. Ctr., Redwood City, Calif., 1987—. NSF fellow, AEC fellow, Woodrow Wilson fellow. Fellow Am. Acad. Dermatology, Woodrow Wilson, Atomic Enery Commn. Avocations: tennis, music, writing, painting. Office: 910 Maple St Redwood City CA 94063-2034

WONG, PO KEE, research company executive, educator; b. Canton City, Kwangtung, China, May 5, 1934; came to U.S., 1959; s. Kum Fun Wong and Wai Chi Lum; m. Ruby Chuen Wah, Aug. 1965; children: Adam, Anita. BS, Taiwan Provincial Cheng Kung U., Tainan, 1956; MS, U. Utah, 1961; PhD Mech. Engring., Calif. Inst. Tech., 1966; PhD in Aeronaut. and Astronaut. Engring., Stanford, 1970. Lic. mech. profl. engr., Taiwan; cert. tchr., Mass. Sr. scientist Lockheed Missile & Space Co., Palo Alto, Calif., 1966-68; lectr. U. Santa Clara, Calif., 1970-71; researcher NASA Ames Rsch. Ctr., Moffet Field, Calif., 1970-71; engr. G.E. Breeder Reactor Dept., Sunnyvale, Calif., 1972-73; specialist engr. Nuclear Svcs. Co., Campbell, Calif. 1973; engr. Stone & Webster Engring. Co., Boston, 1974-76; pres., chief exec. officer Systems Rsch. Co., Somerville, Mass., 1976—; tchr. Boston Public Schs., 1979—. Author, presenter tech. papers; patentee in field. Mem. ASME, AAAS, Internat. Assn. Structural Mechanics in Reactor Tech., N.Y. Acad. Scis. Achievements include patents in field. Avocations: tennis, table tennis, Chinese chess, Western chess, go-game. Home: 50 Bradley St Somerville MA 02145-2930 Office: Charlestown High Sch 240 Medford St Somerville MA 02143-1957

WONG, VICTOR KENNETH, physics educator, academic administrator; b. San Francisco, Nov. 1, 1938; m. Nancy Wong; children: Cassandra, Pamela, Lianna. BS in Engring. Physics, U. Calif., Berkeley, 1960, PhD in Physics, 1966. Postdoctoral fellow Ohio State U., Columbus, 1966-68; lectr., asst. prof. U. Mich., Ann Arbor, 1968-76, adj. prof. physics, 1992—; assoc. prof. physics U. Mich., Dearborn, 1976-82, prof. physics, 1982-86, chmn. dept. natural sci., 1980-83, dean Coll. Arts, Sci. and Letters, 1983-86; provost, vice chancellor acad. affairs U. Mich., Flint, 1986—, prof. physics, 1986—. Assoc. editor: Math. Revs., 1980; contbr. articles to profl. jours. Mem. Am. Phys. Soc., Am. Assn. Higher Edn. (1st chmn. Asian caucus 1986-88), Nat. U. Continuing Edn. Assn. (mem. minority com. 1989), North Ctrl. Assn. Colls. and Schs. (cons. evaluation com. 1989—), Am. Coun. Edn. (mem. commn. on minorities in higher edn. 1993—), Phi Beta Kappa, Tau Beta Pi. Office: Univ Mich Office of Provost Flint MI 48502

WONG, WALLACE, medical supplies company executive, real estate investor; b. Honolulu, July 13, 1941; s. Jack Young Hung and Theresa (Goo) W.; m. Amy Ju, June 17, 1963; children: Chris, Bradley, Jeffery. Student, UCLA, 1960-63. Chmn., pres. South Bay Coll., Hawthorne, Calif., 1985-86; chmn. Santa Barbara (Calif.) Bus. Coll., 1975—; gen. ptnr. W B Co., Redondo Beach, Calif., 1982—; CEO Cal Am. Med. Supplies, Rancho Santa Margarita, Calif., 1986—, Cal Am. Exports, Inc., Rancho Santa Margarita, 1986—, Pacific Am. Group, Rancho Santa Margarita, 1991—; chmn., CEO Alpine, Inc., Rancho Santa Margarita, Calif., 1993—; bd. dirs. Metrobank, L.A. FFF Enterprises; chmn. bd. 1st Ind. Fin. Group., Rancho Santa Margarita. Acting sec. of state State of Calif., Sacramento, 1982; founding mem. Opera Pacific, Orange County, Calif., 1985; mem. Hist. and Cultural Found., Orange County, 1986; v.p. Orange County Chinese Cultural Club, Orange County, 1985. Named for Spirit of Enterprise Resolution, Hist. & Cultural Found., Orange Country, 1987; recipient resolution City of Hawthorne, 1973. Mem. Westren Accred Schs. & Colls. (v.p. 1978-79), Magic Castle (life), Singapore Club. Avocations: traveling, skiing. Office: Alpine Inc 23042 Arroyo Vis Rancho Santa Margarita CA 92688

WONG, WARREN JAMES, mathematics educator; b. Masterton, N.Z., Oct. 16, 1934; came to U.S. 1964; s. Ken and Jessie (Ng) W.; m. Nellie Gee, May 12, 1962; children: Carole Frances, Andrea. BSc, U. Otago, Dunedin, N.Z., 1955, MSc, 1956; PhD, Harvard U., 1959. Lectr. U. Otago, Dunedin, 1960-64, sr. lectr., 1964; assoc. prof. math. U. Notre Dame, Ind., 1964-68, prof., 1968—. Proceedings editorial bd. Am. Math. Soc., Providence, R.I., 1988-90; contbr. articles to profl. jours. Vestryman St. Michael and All Angels Episcopal Ch., South Bend, 1988-90. Mem. Am. Math. Soc., Math. Assn. Am., Australian Math. Soc. Avocation: Episcopalian. Office: Dept Math Univ Notre Dame Notre Dame IN 46556-5683

WONG, WILLIE, mayor, automotive executive; b. Mesa, Ariz., Oct. 12, 1948; m. Cobina Wong; children: Kevin, Jeremy. Grad., Ariz. State U. Vice mayor City of Mesa (Ariz.), 1988-90; councilmen., 1990-91; mayor City of Mesa (Ariz.), 1992—; pres. Wilky's Performance Ctr., Mesa, Ariz.; prev. employment with AT&T. Treas. Regional Pub. Transp. Authority; chmn. Williams Redevel. Ptnrship., Maricopa Assn. Govts. Regional Devel. Policy Com.; vice-chmn. Williams Gateway Airport Authority, Mesa Sister Cities; exec. com. League of Ariz. Cities and Towns; bd. dirs. YMCA (past pres.), Child Crisis Ctr., Southwest Pub. Recycling Assn. Named Outstanding Young Man Mesa Leadership, Tng., & Devel. Assn., 1989. Mem. MAG Regional Coun., Econ. Devel. Adv. Bd., Rotary Club-Mesa West. Avocations: baseball, fishing, travel, reading. Home: 1343 E McLellan Mesa AZ 85203 Office: Office of the Mayor 55 N Center St PO Box 1466 Mesa AZ 85211-1466 also: Wilky's Performance Ctr 402 E Main Mesa AZ 85203*

WONG, WING KEUNG, trading, electronics company executive, physician; b. Hong Kong, Jan. 5, 1933; s. Lai Cho Wong and Sut Mui Chung; m. Ban Cho, May 28, 1957; children: Hoi Ling, Hoi Yin. MB, BS, Beijing Med. Coll., 1955. Lic. Med. Coun. Hong Kong. Physician 1st Hosp. of Beijing Med. Coll., 1955-69; hosp., Ganshu, People's Republic China 1970-73; pvt. practice Hong Kong, 1979—; dir. Cheung Tai Hong Ltd., Hong Kong, Hong Kong, 1974-86, exec. dir., 1987—; dep. chmn. Cheung Tai Hong Holdings Ltd., Bermuda, 1994—; chmn. bd. dirs. Computime Ltd., Hong Kong, 1979-93; dir. Computime Internat. Ltd., British Virgin Islands, Brit. V.I., 1993—. Mem. Hong Kong Med. Assn., Dynasty Club, Tower Club. Avocations: travel, music, diving, photography. Office: Cheung Tai Hong Ltd, 31/F Singga Comml Ctr, 144-151 Connaught Rd W Hong Kong Hong Kong

WONHAM, WALTER MURRAY, electrical engineer, educator; b. Montreal, Que., Can., Nov. 1, 1934; m. Vera Anne Hale; children—Marjorie Jane, Cynthia Margaret. B of Engring., McGill U., Montreal, 1956; PhD, U. Cambridge, Eng., 1961. Asst. prof. elec. engring. Purdue U., Lafayette, Ind., 1961-62; research scientist Research Inst. for Advanced Studies, Balt., 1962-64; assoc. prof. Brown U., Providence, 1964-69; research assoc. NASA, Cambridge, Mass., 1967-69, cons., 1969; prof. elec. engring. U. Toronto, Ont., Can., 1970—; J. Roy Cockburn Prof. U. Toronto, 1991—, Cockburn chair, 1991. Author: Linear Multivariable Control: A Geometric Approach, 1974, 3d edit., 1985 (Russian transl. 1980, Chinese transl. 1984); assoc. editor Soc. for Indsl. and Applied Math., Jour. on Control and Optimization, 1965-79, Systems Control Letter, 1981-85. Athlone fellow, Gt. Britain, 1956-58; spl. scholar Nat. Rsch. Coun. Can., 1958-60; sr. postdoctoral resident rsch. assoc. NAS U.S.A., 1967-69. Recipient Brouwer medal Netherlands Math Soc., 1990. Fellow Royal Soc. Can., IEEE (Control Systems Sci. and Engring. award 1987). Office: U Toronto Dept Elec Engring, 35 St George St, Toronto, ON Canada M5S 1A4

WONNACOTT, (GORDON) PAUL, economics educator; b. London, Ont., Can., Mar. 16, 1933; s. Gordon Elliott and Muriel Johnston Wonnacott; m.

Donna Elizabeth Cochrane, July 2, 1960; children: David, Ann, Alan, Bruce. BA, U. Western Ont., 1955; MA, Princeton U., 1957, PhD, 1959. Instr., asst. prof. econs. Columbia U., N.Y.C., 1958-62; assoc. prof. then prof. econs. U. Md., College Pk., 1962-91; mem. Pres.'s Coun. Econ. Advisers, 1991-93; vis. fellow Inst. Internat. Econs., 1993-94; Alan Holmes vis. prof. econs. Middlebury Coll., 1994—; mem. rsch. staff Royal Commn. Banking and Fin., Toronto, 1962; sr. staff economist Coun. Econ. Advisers, Washington, 1968-70; assoc. dir. divsn. internat. fin. Fed. Res. Bd., Washington, 1974-75; vis. scholar Office Internat. Monetary Rsch., U.S. Treasury, 1980; econ. adviser to Under Sec. of State, 1990-91. Author: The Canadian Dollar, 1960, 2d rev. edit., 1965, (with R.J. Wonnacott) Free Trade between the United States and Canada: The Potential Economic Effects, 1967, (with H.G. Johnson and H. Shibata) Harmonization of International Economic Policies under Free Trade, 1968, Macroeconomics, 1974, 3d rev. edit., 1984, (with R.J. Wonnacott) Economics, 1979, 4th rev. edit. 1990, Spanish edit., 1981, 3d rev. edit., 1987, (with Y. and C. Crusius) Portuguese edit., 1982, 2d rev. edit., 1985, (with A. Blomquist) Can. edit., 1983, 4th rev. edit., 1994, The United States and Canada: The Quest for Free Trade, 1987; contbr. numerous articles to profl. jours. Fellow Brooking Insti., 1957-58, Ford Found., 1963-64; vis. fellow Inst. Internat. Econs., 1986. Mem. Am. Econ. Assn., Can. Econ. Assn. Avocations: skiing, tennis. Home: 10100 Bevern Ln Rockville MD 20854-2130

WONNACOTT, RONALD JOHNSTON, economics educator; b. London, Ont., Can., Sept. 11, 1930; s. Gordon and and Muriel (Johnston) W.; m. Eloise Howlett, Sept. 11, 1954; children: Douglas, Robert, Cathy Anne. BA., U. Western Ont., 1955; A.M., Harvard U., 1957, Ph.D., 1959. Mem. faculty U. Western Ont., London, 1958—, prof. econs., 1964—, chmn. dept., 1969-72; vis. assoc. prof. U. Minn., Mpls., 1961-62; cons. Resources for the Future, Econ. Council Can., Can.-Am. Com., Nat. Planning Assn., C.D. Howe Inst. Author: Canadian-American Dependence: An Interindustry Analysis of Production and Prices, 1961, Canada's Trade Options, 1975, Selected New Developments in International Trade Theory, 1984, The Economics of Overlapping Free Trade Areas and the Mexican Challenge, 1991, (with G.L. Reuber) The Cost of Capital in Canada, 1961, (with Paul Wonnacott) Free Trade Between the U.S. and Canada, 1967, Economics, 1979, 4th edit., 1990, (with Thomas H. Wonnacott) Introductory Statistics, 1969, 5th edit., 1990, Econometrics, 1970, 2d edit., 1979, Regression, 1981. Fellow Royal Soc. Can.; mem. Am. Econ. Assn., Can. Econ. Assn. (pres. 1981), London Hunt Club, Sunningdale Golf Club (Eng.), Hon. Co. Edinburgh Golfers, Craigleith Ski Club. Home: 171 Wychwood Park, London, ON Canada N6G 1S1

WONSER, MICHAEL DEAN, retired public affairs director, art educator; b. Long Beach, Calif., Mar. 12, 1940; s. Franklin Henry and Dorothy Mae (Harris) W.; children: Therice Michele, Sherice Michele, Christopher Franklin; m. Mary L. Van Epps, Dec. 22, 1990. BS, U. Oreg., 1963, MFA, 1965; postgrad., U. Colo., 1976. Instr. Cen. Oreg. Coll., Bend, 1966-68; prof. Adams State Coll., Alamosa, Colo., 1969-82, dir. pub. affairs, 1982—; pres. Colo. Faculty Com. Trustees, 1980-82. Mem. Chamber Edn. Com., Monte Vista, Colo., 1982-88; treas. Chamber of Commerce Ambassador, Alamosa, 1982; chmn. C. of C. Tourism Bd., Alamosa, 1987-89; pres. Luth. Ch. Alamosa, 1980-85; bd. dirs. Creede Repertory Theatre Bd., 1989—; mem. Commerce Comm. and Resources Comm., 1995. Mem. Higher Edn. Assn. of Rockies (pres. Colo. chpt. 1985-88), Rotary (pres. Alamosa chpt. 1990—). Republican. Avocations: golf, skiing. Home: 65016 Hwy 20 W Bend OR 97701

WOO, FRANCES MEI SOO, lawyer; b. San Francisco, Feb. 23, 1949; d. On Lung and Lai Shou (Wong) W.; m. Gary Duane Hoppe, May 3, 1986. BA, Wash. State U., 1971; JD, U. Wash., 1975; LLM in Tax, NYU, 1977. Bar: Wash. 1975, U.S. Dist. Ct. (we. dist.) Wash. 1975, U.S. Tax Ct. 1977, N.Y. 1978, U.S. Dist. Ct. (so. and ea. dist.) N.Y. 1978, U.S. Supreme Ct. 1982. Assoc. Brown & Wood, N.Y.C., 1977-80; employee benefits, tax counsel Westvaco Corp., N.Y.C., 1980-83, SCM Corp., N.Y.C., 1983-87; employee benefits, cons. Mercer Meidinger Hansen, Inc., 1987-88; employee benefits, tax counsel CBS Records, Inc., N.Y.C., 1988-91; employee benefits counsel BASF Corp., Parsippany, N.J., 1991-93; employee benefits cons. N.Y.C., 1993—; bd. dirs. Gramont Owners Corp. Contbr. articles to profl. jours. Mem. ABA, WEB, Wash. State Bar Assn., N.Y. State Bar Assn., Assn. Bar City N.Y., Tax Execs. Inst. Avocation: real estate investment. Home: 215 W 98th St Apt 10D New York NY 10025-5635 Office: 757 3rd Ave Ste 700 New York NY 10017

WOO, S. B. (SHIEN-BIAU WOO), former lieutenant governor, physics educator; b. Shanghai, China, Aug. 13, 1937; came to U.S., 1955; s. C.K. and Kuo-Ying (Chang) W.; m. Katy K.N. Wu, July 20, 1963; children: Chih-I, Chih-Lan. B.S in Physics and Math. summa cum laude, Georgetown Coll., Ky., 1956; M.S. in Physics, Washington U., St. Louis, 1962, Ph.D. in Physics, 1964. Prof. physics U. Del., Newark, 1966—; lt. gov. State of Del., Dover, 1985-89; pres. Del. State Senate; chmn. Bd. Pardons; cons. E.I. DuPont Co., Wilmington, Del., 1968, Del. State Coll., Dover, 1980-81. Contbr. articles to profl. jours. Chmn. bd., chief exec. officer Chinese Am. Community Ctr., Hockessin, Del., 1982-83; sec. Asian-Am. caucus Democratic Nat. Conv., 1983—; pres., co-chmn. Gov.'s Internat. Trade Council, 1985—; chmn. Gov.'s task force on High Tech., 1985—. Recipient Highest Achievement award Asian Am. High Tech. Conv., 1985; Army Rsch. grantee, 1972-87, NSF grantee, 1978-81; Inst. fellow Kennedy Sch., Harvard U. Mem. Am. Phys. Soc., AAAS, AAUP (exec. com. nat. council 1974-77), Orgn. Chinese Ams. (bd. dirs. 1977-79, nat. pres. 1990—), Sigma Xi. Home: 5 Farm House Rd Newark DE 19711-7458

WOO, SAVIO LAU-YUEN, bioengineering educator; b. Shanghai, China, June 3, 1942; s. Kwok Chung and Fung Sing (Yu) W.; m. Patricia Tak-kit Cheong, Sept. 6, 1969; children: Kirstin Wei-Chi, Jonathan I-Huei. BSME, Chico State U., 1965; MS, U. Wash., 1966, PhD, 1971. Research assoc. U. Wash., Seattle, 1968-70; asst. research prof. U. Calif.-San Diego, La Jolla, 1970-74, assoc. research prof., 1974-75, assoc. prof., 1975-80, prof. surgery and bioengring., 1980-90; prof. orthopaedic surgery, vice-chmn. orthopaedic surgery U. Pitts., 1990-92, prof. mech. engring., 1990—, Albert B. Ferguson Jr. prof. orthopaedic surgery, 1993—; prof. civil engring., 1993—; prin. investigator VA Med. Ctr., San Diego, 1972-90, Pitts., 1990—; cons. bioengr. Children's Hosp., San Diego, 1973-80; cons. med. implant cos., 1978-85; vis. prof. biomechanics Kobe (Japan) U., 1981-82; dir., CEO M&D Coutts Inst. for Joint Reconstrn. and Rsch., 1984-90; mem. sci. adv. com. Whitaker Found., 1986—, Steadman-Hawkins Sports Medicine Found., 1990—, OsteoArthritis Scis. Inc., 1992—. Assoc. editor Jour. Biochem. Engring., 1979-87, Jour. Biomechanics, 1978—, Jour. Orthpedic Rsch., 1983-92, Materials Sci. Reports, 1990—, Proc. Inst. Mech. Engrs. (Part H), 1990-94; mem. editorial adv. bd. Jour. Orthopedic Rsch., 1993—; internat. adv. bd. Jour. ESSKA, Knee Surgery, Sports Traumatology, Arthroscopy, 1993—. Recipient Elizabeth Winston Lanier Kappa Delta award, 1983, 85, awards for excellence in basic sci. Am. Orthopaedic Soc. Sports Medicine, 1983, 86, 90, 94, O'Donoghue award, 1990, Wartenweiler Meml. Lectureship, 1987, Citation award Am. Coll. Sports Medicine, 1988, Rsch. Career Devel. award NIH, 1977-82; Japan Soc. Promotion of Sci. fellow, 1981. Fellow Am. Inst. Med. and Biol. Engring (founding fellow, chmn. coll. fellows 1992-94, bd. dirs. 1992-94), ASME (sec., chmn. biomechanics com., chmn. honors com. biomechanics div., mem. exec. com., 1983-88, sec. 1985-86, chmn. 1986-87, H.R. Lissner award 1991); mem. NAE, Inst. Medicine NAS, Western Orthopaedic Assn. (hon.), Internat. Soc. Biomed. (mem. coun. 1992—), Biomed. Engring. Soc. (bd. dirs. 1984-86), Am. Acad. Orthopedic Surgeons, Orthopaedic Research Soc. (exec. com. 1983-88, chmn. program com. 1985-86, pres. 1986-87), Am. Soc. Biomechs. (pres. 1985-86, sec. 1977-80, exec. com. 1984-87, Alfonso Borelli award 1993), Internat. Soc. Fractures Repair (bd. dirs. 1984-94, v.p. 1987-90, pres. 1990-92), Can. Orthopedic Rsch. Soc. (hon.), European Orthopedic Rsch. Soc., U.S. Nat. Commn. Biomechanics (chmn. 1994—, exec. com. 1992—). Home: 47 Pleasant View Ln Pittsburgh PA 15238-1859 Office: U Pitts Dept Ortho Surg Liliane Kaufmann Bldg 3471 5th Ave Ste 1010 Pittsburgh PA 15213-3221

WOO, WILLIAM FRANKLIN, newspaper editor; b. Shanghai, China, Oct. 4, 1936; came to U.S., 1946; s. Kyatang and Elizabeth Louise (Hart) W.; m. Patricia Ernst, Dec. 18, 1964 (div. June 1980); m. Martha Richards Shirk, Sept. 15, 1981; children—Thomas Shenton, Bennett Richards, Peter Snowdon. B.A., U. Kans., 1960. Reporter Kansas City Star, Mo., 1957-62;

feature writer St. Louis Post-Dispatch, 1962-68, editorial writer, 1968-73, asst. editor, 1973-74, editorial page editor, 1974-86, editor, 1986—. Served to staff sgt. USAFR, 1962. Nieman fellow Harvard U., 1966-67. Mem. Am. Soc. Newspaper Editors (bd. dirs. 1993—), Am. Press Inst. (bd. dirs. 1995). Home: 156 S Gray Ave Saint Louis MO 63119-2914 Office: Pulitzer Pub Co 900 N Tucker Blvd Saint Louis MO 63101-1069

WOOD, ALLEN JOHN, electrical engineer, consultant; b. Milw., Oct. 1, 1925; s. Alfred John and Kathleen Francis (Welch) W.; m. Barbara Ann Cook, Oct. 29, 1949; children: John Scott, Susan Beth Wood Richmond. BEE, Marquette U., 1949; MS in Elec. Engring., Ill. Inst. Tech., 1951; PhD, Rensselaer Poly. Inst., 1959. Registered profl. engr., N.Y. Engr. Allis Chalmers Mfg. Co., West Allis, Wis., 1949-50; engr. GE, Lynn, Mass., 1951-52; engr. GE, Schenectady, N.Y., 1952-59, sr. engr., 1960-69; mem. tech. staff Hughes Aircraft Co., Culver City, Calif., 1959-60; cons., prin., dir. Power Techs., Inc., Schenectady, N.Y., 1969-91, treas., chief fin. officer, 1989-91; also bd. dirs. Power Techs., Inc., 1969-91; ind. cons., 1991—; adj. prof. Rensselaer Poly. Inst., Troy, 1966—; cons. in field, 1992—. Author: Power System Reliability Calculations, 1973, Power Generation Operation and Control, 1984; contbr. numerous articles to profl. jours. With U.S. Army, 1942-46, ETO, PTO. Fellow IEEE (life); mem. AAAS, Am. Nuclear Soc. Republican. Mem. Reformed Ch. in Am. Avocations: amateur radio, photography.

WOOD, ARTHUR MACDOUGALL, retired retail executive; b. Chgo., Jan. 27, 1913; s. R Arthur and Emily (Smith) W.; m. Pauline Palmer, Nov. 17, 1945; children: Pauline, Arthur MacDougall Jr. AB, Princeton U., 1934, LLD (hon.), 1976; LLB, Harvard U., 1937; LHD (hon.), DePaul U., 1977; D in Humanics (hon.), Springfield Coll., 1978; HHD (hon.), Beloit Coll., 1981. Bar: Ill. 1937. Atty. Bell, Boyd & Marshall, Chgo., 1937-40; atty. Sears, Roebuck & Co., 1946-52, sec., 1952-59, v.p., 1956-68, dir., 1959-83, comptroller, 1960-62, v.p. charge Pacific Coast ter., 1962-67, v.p. midwestern ter., 1967, pres., 1968-72, chmn., chief exec. officer, 1973-77. Gen. chmn. United Crusade, Los Angeles County, 1966; co-founder Chgo. United, 1975; gov. United Way Am., 1977; trustee Art Inst. Chgo., 1949—, also chmn., 1978-80; life trustee Rush-Presbyn.-St. Luke's Med. Ctr., Chgo.; former trustee Calif. Inst. Tech., U. Chgo.; mem. Chgo. Hort. Soc., trustee, 1992-93; active Pres. Nixon's Labor-Mgmt. Com., 1975, Pres. Coun. Minority Bus. Enterprises, 1970-74. With F.A. AUS; lt. col. USAAF, 1941-45. Decorated Legion of Merit. Mem. Bus. Coun. Office: Sears Towers Ste 9800 Chicago IL 60684

WOOD, BARBARA LOUISE CHAMPION, state legislator; b. Swampscott, Mass., Jan. 10, 1924; d. John Duncan and Eva Louise (Moore) Champion; m. Newall Arthur Wood, June 12, 1948; children: Gary Duncan, Craig Newall, Brian Scott, Dennis Michael, Joan Wood Unger. Diploma in Nursing, Mary Hitchcock Meml. Hosp. Sch. Nursing, Hanover, N.H., 1945; student, Simmons Coll., 1947-48. RN. Rep., mem. ho. com. Vt. Gen. Assembly, Montpelier, 1981—, vice chmn. edn. com., 1983-87; trustee Vt. State Colls., Waterbury, 1986-90, Gifford Meml. Hosp., Randolph, Vt., 1986—; commr., Vt. rep. Edn. Commn. of the States, Denver, 1981-86. Sch. dir. Bethel Sch. Bd., Vt., 1963-85; mem.-at-large Vt. Sch. Bds. Assn., Montpelier, 1982-85. Served to 2d lt. U.S. Army, 1945-46. Mem. Am. Legion, Vis. Nurse Alliance Vt.-N.H. (bd. dirs. 1991—). Republican. Congregationalist. Clubs: Bethel Women's (pres. 1976-78); Vt. Fedn. Women's Clubs (dist. pres. 1978-80). Home: Woodland Rd Bethel VT 05032 Office: Vt House of Reps State House Montpelier VT 05602

WOOD, BETTY A., utilities executive; b. Atlanta, May 22, 1943; d. William Robert and Ethleen (Beard) W. BS, U. Ga., 1965. Home economist Ga. Power Co., Lawrenceville, 1965-75; sr. home economist Ga. Power Co., Athens, 1975-77, customer edn. rep., 1977-79, residential rep., 1979-81, sr. residential rep., 1981-85, field mktg. rep., 1985-90, sr. mktg. rep., 1990—; coord. div. speaker's bur. Ga. Power Co., 1985—, Adopt-A Sch. chmn., 1987. Chmn. pub. edn. Clarke-Oconee unit Am. Cancer Soc., 1986—; mem. Women of Ga. Power; state chmn. Ga. Energy and Aging Consortium, 1990-92. Recipient Woman of Achievement award Athens Bus. and Profl. Women's Club, 1977, Electrical Sales Residential cert., 1992. Mem. Nat. Assn. Women in Constrn., U. Ga. Alumni Assn., Am. Home Econ. Assn., Ga. Home Econ. Assn. (Silver Circle award 1990), Mountain Energy Consortium, Athens Home Builders, Athens Bd. Realtors, Women's Coun. of Realtors, C. of C.'s Women In Mgmt., Interlink. Democrat. Avocation: photography. Home: 3192 Atlanta Hwy Ste 438 Athens GA 30606-3386 Office: Ga Power Co PO Box 1312 1001 Prince Ave Athens GA 30606-5801

WOOD, BYARD DEAN, mechanical engineering educator and researcher; b. Cardston, Alta, Can., Mar. 30, 1940; married, 1965; 3 children. BS, Utah State U., 1963, MS, 1966; PhD in Mech. Engring., U. Minn., 1970. Assoc. prof. heat transfer & exptl. methods Ariz. State U., Tempe, 1970-80, prof. mech. engring., 1980—; cons. Solar Energy Rsch. & Edn. Found., 1977—, Solar Rating & Cert. Corp., Nat. Bur. Standards, ERG, Inc. Fellow ASME; mem. Am. Soc. Heating, Refrigeration and Air-Conditioning Engrs., Combustion Inst., Internat. Solar Energy Soc. Achievements include research in heat transfer and experimental methods in thermal and photovoltaic solar heating and cooling systems, heat and mass transfer associated with large turbulent flames. Office: Ariz State U Dept Mech Engring Tempe AZ 85287*

WOOD, CHARLES MARTIN, III, food company executive; b. New Orleans, May 31, 1943; s. Charles Martin and Veva Penick (Miller) W.; m. Daphne Howard Flowers, June 4, 1966. B.A., Princeton U., 1965; M.B.A., Colgate Darden Sch. Bus. Adminstrn., 1970. Dir. product devel. Flowers Industries, Inc., Thomasville, Ga., 1970-71, dir. mktg., 1971-73, dir. fin., 1973-76, v.p. fin., 1976-78, sr. v.p., chief fin. officer, 1978—, dir., 1975—; chmn. bd. Flower Employees Credit League, Thomasville, Ga., 1978; trustee Flowers Industries Retirement Trust, Thomasville, Ga., 1977-; chmn. bus. adv. bd. Valdosta State Coll., Ga., 1980-82. Trustee John D. Archbold Meml. Hosp., Thomasville, Ga., 1977—; dir. Masters of Foxhounds Assn. Am., Boston, 1981—, pres., 1990-93, chmn. Edn. Found., 1993—; jr. warden vestry All Saints Episcopal Ch., Thomasville, Ga., 1982; nat. trustee Ducks Unltd., Chgo., 1977-81; state chmn. of yr. Hilton Head, S.C., 1980. Served to 1st lt. U.S. Army, 1966-68. Republican. Episcopalian. Clubs: Ivy (Princeton, N.J.); The Brook (N.Y.), Live Oak Hounds (master, huntsman) (1974—). Home: RR 2 Box 191 Monticello FL 32344-9541 Office: Flowers Industries Inc PO Box 1338 US Hwy 19 S Thomasville GA 31799

WOOD, C(HARLES) NORMAN, air force officer; b. Dallas, Mar. 7, 1938; s. Charles Camp Wood and Mary Louise (Wheatley) Ferguson; m. Jerre Louise Jones, June 10, 1961 (div. Sept. 1967); 1 child, Wende Louise; m. Elizabeth Burwell Dillard, June 27, 1969; 1 child, Elizabeth Burwell. BBA, U. Tex., 1960; MPA, Auburn U., 1974. Commd. 2d lt. USAF, 1960, advanced through grades to lt. gen., 1990; electronic warfare officer Strategic Air Command, Kans. and Okinawa, 1962-69; intelligence staff officer Hdqrs. Strategic Air Command, Offutt AFB, Nebr., 1969-72; chief def. analysis br. Hdqrs. Mil. Assistance Command, Saigon, Republic of Vietnam, 1972-73; air staff officer Hdqrs. USAF, Washington, 1974-76; exec. officer Office of Air Force History, Washington, 1976-77; student Nat. War Coll., Washington, 1978-79; dep. comdr. for ops. 544th Strategic Intelligence Wing, Offutt AFB, 1979, wing comdr., 1980; asst. dep. chief of staff intelligence Strategic Air Command, Offutt AFB, 1981-82; exec. officer Pres.'s Fgn. Intelligence Adv. Bd., The White House, Washington, 1982-83; dep. dir. Nat. Strategic Target List, Joint Strategic Planning Staff, Offutt AFB, 1984; dep. asst. chief of staff intelligence USAF, Washington, 1985; dir. intelligence J-2 Hdqrs. U.S. European Command, Fed. Republic Germany, 1986-87; asst. chief of staff intelligence Air Force Hdqrs., Washington, 1988-90; dir. Intelligence Community Staff, Washington, 1990-92; sr. v.p., gen. mgr. BDM Federal. Decorated D.S.M., Legion of Merit, Def. Superior Svc. medal. Mem. Nat. Mil. Intelligence Assn., Security Affairs Support Assn., Armed Forces Communications and Electronics Assn., Air Force Assn. Republican. Mem. Christian Sci. Ch. Home: 5440 Mt Corcoran Pl Burke VA 22015-2147

WOOD, CHARLES TUTTLE, history educator; b. St. Paul, Oct. 29, 1933; s. Harold Eaton and Margaret (Frisbie) W.; m. Susan Danielson, July 9, 1955; children: Lucy Eaton, Timothy Walker, Martha Augusta, Mary Frisbie. A.B., Harvard, 1955, A.M., 1957, Ph.D., 1962. Investment analyst, trader Harold E. Wood & Co., St. Paul, 1955-56; teaching fellow gen. edn.

Harvard, 1959-61, instr. history, 1961-64; mem. faculty Dartmouth, 1964—, prof. history, 1971—, Daniel Webster prof. history, 1980—, Daniel Webster prof. history and comparative lit., 1991—, chmn. dept. history, 1976-79, chmn. dept. comparative lit., 1977; vis. Keeney prof. of history Brown U., 1992-93. Author: The French Apanages and the Capetian Monarchy, 1224-1328, 1966, Philip the Fair and Boniface VIII, 2d edit, 1971, reprint, 1976, Felipe el Hermoso y Bonifacio VIII: Mexico: UTEHA, 1968, The Age of Chivalry: Manners and Morals 1000-1450, 1970, The Quest for Eternity, reprint edit., 1983, Joan of Arc and Richard III, 1988, The Trial of Charles I, 1989; also articles. Chmn. Dresden Bd. Sch. Dirs., 1972-74. Guggenheim fellow, 1986-87; recipient Disting. Service award N.H. Sch. Bds. Assn., 1975; Am. Council Learned Socs. fellow, 1980-81; Am. Bar Found. fellow, 1981-82. Fellow Medieval Acad. Am. (treas. 1989—, fin. com. 1979—, council 1985-87); mem. Am. Hist. Assn. (chmn. nominating com. 1977, Adams prize com. 1976-78), Conf. Brit. Studies, Soc. for French Hist. Studies, N.H. Sch. Bds. Assn. (2d v.p. 1974-75), New Eng. Medieval Conf. (pres. 1978-79), Am. Soc. Legal History, Phi Beta Kappa. Club: St. Botolph (Boston). Home: 7 N Balch St Hanover NH 03755

WOOD, CHRISTOPHER L. J., real estate consulting firm executive; b. London, Jan. 20, 1947; came to U.S., 1983; s. Sidney John and Lillian Ballantine (Pollock) W.; m. Pamela Wood, Dec. 14, 1978; 1 child, Alexander Wood. BSC, London U., 1969. Ptnr., dir. Debenham, Tewson & Chinnocks, London, U.S., 1972—. Fellow Royal Instn. Chartered Surveyors; mem. Am. Soc. Real Estate Counselors, St. George's Soc. N.Y., Thames Rowing Club, Union League Club (Phila.). Office: DTZ Debenham Thorpe Internat 20th Flr 560 Lexington Ave New York NY 10022-6828

WOOD, DAVID CHARLES, lawyer, finance company executive; b. Kansas City, Mo., Aug. 25, 1943; s. Charles O'Brien and Anne Marie (Lohmeyer) W.; m. Rosalie Lidner, Aug. 27, 1966; children—David, Michael, Jennifer. A.B. with honors in History, (curators' scholar 1961-62, 62-63), U. Mo., 1965, J.D. (Omar E. Robinson Meml. scholar 1965-66, Law Sch. Found. scholar 1966-67), 1968. Bar: Mo. 1968, Iowa 1977. Assoc. Welliver, Porter & Cleaveland, Columbia, Mo., 1968-70; asst. counsel Norwest Fin. Svcs., Inc., Des Moines, 1970-74, asst. gen. counsel, 1974-78, asst. v.p., dir. legal affairs, 1978-79, v.p., gen. counsel, 1979-84, sr. v.p., sec., 1984-88, pres., chief operating officer, 1988-94; chmn., CEO, 1995—; bd. dirs., v.p. Centurion Life Ins. Co., Centurion Casualty Co., Des Moines.; v.p. Dial Bank, Sioux Falls, S.D., Dial Nat. Bank, Des Moines; bd. dirs. Norwest Fin. Services, Inc., Des Moines; faculty Nat. Installment Banking Sch., U. Colo-Boulder, 1982-83. Bd. editors: Mo. Law Review, 1966-68; contbr. articles to legal publs. Bd. dirs. Des Moines Ballet Assn., 1989—, United Way of Central Iowa, 1992—, Grand View Coll., 1993—, Civic Music Assn., 1993—. Mem. ABA, Iowa Bar Assn., Mo. Bar Assn., Am. Fin. Svcs. Assn. (law com. 1979-84, ops. com. 1988-93), Conf. on Personal Fin. Law (mem. emeritus gen. com.), Iowa Fin. Svcs. Assn. (pres. 1983-87), Metro Bus. Assn. (pres. 1982-83), Phi Eta Sigma. Republican. Methodist.

WOOD, DAVID KENNEDY CORNELL, choreographer, educator; b. Fresno, Calif., Feb. 24, 1925; s. Earl Warner and Elsie Bliss (Kennedy) W.; m. Marni Pope Thomas, Dec. 28, 1958; children—Marina, Raegan, Ellis. B.A., U. Calif.; 1945; student, Neighborhood Playhouse, N.Y.C., 1947-48, also other theatre and dance schs. Choreographer Broadway musicals, TV, N.Y.C. Opera Ballet, Met. Opera Ballet, 1950-58; soloist, Hanya Holm Co., 1948-50, soloist, rehearsal dir., Martha Graham Co., 1953-68, prof. dance, U. Calif., 1968—; artistic dir., Bay Area Repertory Dance Co., guest soloist, Belles Artes of Mexico, 1958-59, Sweden Ballet Akademien, 1960-61 (choreographic award Nat. Endowment for Arts 1973-74, 77-78); choreographer: Pre-Amble, 1971, Post Script, 1974, Cassandra, 1974, Changelings, 1970, The Immigrant, 1974, In the Glade, 1977, Jeux, 1978, Prometheus, 1980; Dusty Pools and Puddles, 1983, Rim of Heaven, 1984, Duad, 1985, Nova's prodn. Electrical Super Conductivity, 1986, Quiet Interludes, 1987, Graffitti, 1987, Persephone, 1988, American Decades, 1989, Dojoji, 1993. Served with USNR, 1943-46. Mem. Am. Guild Musican Artists, Actors Equity, AFTRA, Calif. Dance Educators Assn., Am. Assn. Dance Cos. Home: 3090 Buena Vista Way Berkeley CA 94708-2020 *The enjoyment of the act of doing, the willingness to accept the discipline of the moment and an awareness of one's individual growth all contribute to a total sense of achievement as well as a pleasure in it.*

WOOD, DAVID L., entomologist, educator; b. Jan. 8, 1931. BS, SUNY, 1952; PhD, U. Calif., Berkeley, 1960. Lic. forester, Calif. Prof. entomology, emeritus dept. Environ. Sci. Policy, Mgmt. U. Calif., Berkeley, 1970—; lectr., reviewer, cons. in field. Contbr. articles to profl. jours. Recipient Silver medal Swedish Coun. for Forestry and Agril. Rsch., 1983. Fellow Entomological Soc. Can. (Founder's award Lectr. Entomological Soc. Am. 1986, Founder's award Western Forest Insect Work Conf. 1992); mem. AAAS, AIBS, Entomol. Soc. Am., Entomol. Soc. Chem. Ecology, Soc. Am. Foresters, Sigma Xi. Home: 26 Hardie Dr Moraga CA 94556-1134 Office: U Calif Envir Biology Berkeley CA 94720

WOOD, DIANE PAMELA, lawyer; b. Plainfield, N.J., July 4, 1950; d. Kenneth Reed and Lucille (Padmore) Wood; m. Dennis James Hutchinson, Sept. 2, 1978; children: Kathryn, David, Jane. BA, U. Tex.-Austin, 1971, JD, 1975. Bar: Tex. 1975, D.C. 1978. Law clk. U.S. Ct. Appeals (5th cir.), 1975-76, U.S. Supreme Ct., 1976-77; atty.-advisor U.S. Dept. State, Washington, 1977-78; assoc. law firm Covington & Burling, Washington, 1978-80; asst. prof. law Georgetown U. Law Ctr., Washington, 1980-81, U. Chgo., 1981-88, prof. law, 1988—, assoc. dean, 1989-92, Harold J. and Marion F. Green prof. internat. legal studies, 1990— (on leave); spl. cons. antitrust divsn. internat. guide U.S. Dept. Justice, 1986-87, dep. asst. atty. gen. antitrust divsn., 1993—. Bd. dirs. Hyde-Park-Kenwood Community Health Ctr., 1983-85. Mem. ABA (sec. antitrust and internat. law, chmn. internat. law sect. BIT com., co-chmn. internat. antitrust com., ILP coun. 1989-91, internat. legal scholar officer 1991-93, chmn., antitrust sec. subcom. on internat. unfair trade, vice-chair, sec. internat. antitrust com. 1991, standing com. on law and nat. security 1991-93), Am. Soc. Internat. Law, Am. Law Inst., Internat. Acad. Comparative Law. Democrat.

WOOD, DONALD CRAIG, marketing professional; b. Wilmington, Del., June 24, 1937; s. Thomas Henry and Madelyn (Brehm) W.; m. Elizabeth Haring, Apr. 28, 1962; children: Craig Standish, Allison Jean. BA, U. Del., 1959; MBA, Northwestern U., 1967. Sales engr. NVF Corp., Broadview, Ill., 1960-62, Synthane Corp., Morton Grove, Ill., 1962-68; account exec., mgr. sales Donnelley Mktg. subs. Dun and Bradstreet Corp., Oakbrook, Ill., 1968-69; from dir. to v.p. market devel. to v.p. mktg. Donnelley Mktg. subs. Dun and Bradstreet Corp., Stamford, Conn., 1977-1980; from v.p., gen. mgr. to pres. Info. Services Div. Donnelley Mktg. subs. Dun and Bradstreet Corp., Stamford, 1980-86, sr. v.p., 1987-90; v.p., gen. mgr. info. svcs. Triad Systems Corp., Livermore, Calif., 1990—. Served to 1st lt. U.S. Army, 1959-60. Home: 215 Viking Pl Danville CA 94526-5723 Office: Triad Systems Corp Livermore CA 94550

WOOD, DONALD EURIAH, lawyer; b. Guymon, Okla., May 27, 1935; s. Theodore and Lula Elizabeth (Rider) W.; m. Lynda Sharon Harris, Sept. 30, 1960; children—Donald Craig, Tana Dawn, Kristen Lynn. B.A., Panhandle A. and M. Coll., 1958; LL.B., Okla. U., 1964, J.D., 1970. Bar: Okla. bar 1964. Asst. county atty. Texas County, 1964; county atty., 1965-67; dist. atty. Okla. 1st Jud. Dist., Guymon, 1967—; mem. adv. com. Okla. Commn. Criminal and Traffic Enforcement Systems, 1972; mem. Gov.'s Commn. Community Affairs and Planning, 1972-75; mem. faculty Panhandle State Coll., 1974-92; mem. Okla. Dist. Atty. Tng. Council, 1976—; mem. Okla. Bur. Narcotics and Dangerous Drugs Commn., 1992—. Served with inf. AUS, 1958-60. Mem. Okla. Bar Assn. (legal ethics com. 1971—), Texas County Bar Assn. (pres. 1966, 1970-71), Nat. Dist. Attys. Assn., Okla. Dist. Attys. Assn. (pres. 1972, exec. com. 1971—), Phi Alpha Delta. Presbyn. Clubs: Elk, Rotarian. Home: 605 Hillcrest Dr Guymon OK 73942-3345 Office: 319 N Main St Guymon OK 73942-4843

WOOD, DONALD FRANK, transportation educator, consultant; b. Waukesha, Wis., Feb. 22, 1935; s. Frank Blaine and Uilah (Mathson) W.; m. Doreen Johnson, July 5, 1968; children: Frank, Tamara. BA, U. Wis., 1957, MA, 1958; PhD, Harvard U., 1970. Transp. planner State of Wis., Madison, 1960-70; prof. San Francisco State U., 1970—. Author: El Camino, 1982; (with others) Motorized Fire Apparatus of the West, 1991, Contemporary

Tansportation, 1993, Contemporary Logistics, 1993, American Volunteer Fire Trucks, 1993, Commercial Trucks, 1993, International Logistics, 1994; contbr. Ency. Britannica. 2d lt. U.S Army, 1958. Mem. Coun. of Logistics Mgmt. (chpt. pres. 1975-76), Transp. Rsch. Forum (chpt. pres. 1974), Am. Truck Hist. Soc. Presbyterian. Home: 321 Riviera Cir Larkspur CA 94939-1508 Office: San Francisco State U. Coll Bus San Francisco CA 94132

WOOD, DONALD W., chemical company executive; b. Toledo, June 14, 1925; s. Eldred K. and Alma L. (Rutchow) W.; m. Karin M. Von Owstein, Jan. 22, 1966; children: Gregory, Claudia, Nicola, Julia. PhD, U. Ill. 1952. V.p. Exxon Chems. Europe, Brussels, 1963-72, Exxon Chem. USA, Houston, 1972-78; pres. Oxirane Corp., London, 1978-81; sr. v.p. Arco Chems. Co., Phila., 1981-87; pres. Arco Chem. Asia-Pacific, Hong Kong, 1988—; bd. dirs. Arco Chems. Co., Inroads of Phila. Bd. dirs. Netherlands-Am. Amity Trust, Washington, 1985-88, Pa. Opera Theater, Phila., 1984—, Phila. World Affairs Council, 1983—. Sgt. U.S. Army, 1943-46, ETO. Mem. Phila. Union League, Merion (Pa.) Cricket Club. Avocations: sports, opera. Home: 500 Hillbrook Rd Bryn Mawr PA 19010-3636 Office: Arco Chem Co 3801 W Chester Pike Newtown Square PA 19073-2320

WOOD, DOUGLAS, author, composer, musician; b. N.Y.C., Dec. 10, 1951; s. James Henry and Joyce Adelle (Wilton) W.; m. Kathryn Ann Sokolowski, May 26, 1973; children: Eric, Bryan. MusB, Morningside Coll., 1973. Tchr. Meriden-Cleghorn (Iowa) Sch., 1973-75, Morris (Minn.) Pub. Schs., 1975-77; speaker at convs. and confs. on wilderness and human spirit. Author: Old Turtle, 1992 (Minn. Book award 1992, named Best Children's Book by Midwest Pubs. 1992, Book of Yr. award Internat. Reading Assn. 1993, ABBY award Am. Booksellers Assn. 1993), Paddle Whispers, 1993, Minnesota: The Spirit of the Land, 1995; composer: (album) Earth Songs, Solitary Shores. Named one of Ten Outstanding Young Minnesotans by Minn. Jaycees, 1991. Avocations: canoeing and wilderness exploration, fishing, reading, tennis. Home: 3835 Pine Point Rd Saint Cloud MN 56303 Office: Pfeifer-Hamilton Whole Persons Assn 1702 Jefferson St Duluth MN 55812-2029

WOOD, DOUGLAS L., medical educator. BS in Zoology, U. Mich., 1961; OD, Kansas City Coll. Osteo. Med., 1966; PhD, Wayne State U., 1986. Intern Mt. Clemens (Mich.) Gen. Hosp., 1966-67, resident in internal medicine, 1967-70, jr. mem. dept. internal medicine, 1970-71, co-dir. hemodyalisis unit, 1970-74, chmn. divsn. cardiopulmonary medicine/respiratory therapy, 1971-80, dir. med. edn., 1971-73, dir. med. affairs, 1972-75, dir. hemodyalisis unit, 1974-87, dir. med. edn., 1982-87; clin. assoc. prof. medicine Coll. Osteo. Medicine Mich. Stae U., East Lansing, 1972-87; sr. cons. dept. internal medicine Harrison Cmty. Hosp., Mt. Clemens, 1970-78, dept. internal medicine Mt. Clemens Gen. Hosp., 1971-92; attending staff, cons. in nephrology St. Joseph Mercy Hosp., Mt. Clemens, 1976-82, dir. acute hemodyalisis, 1981-82; attending staff dept. med. svcs. William Beaumont Hosp., Troy, Mich., 1977-82; presenter in field; mem. adv. com. Mich. Health Policy Forum, 1988—; bd. dirs. Mich. State U. Kalamazoo Ctr. for Med. Studies, 1988. Contbr. articles to profl. publs., chpt. to book. Appd., chmn. Cert. of Need Commn., State of Mich., 1992. Mem. Am. Osteo. Assn., Am. Coll. Osteo. Internists, Am. Ednl. Rsch. Assn., Mich. Kidney Found., Mich. Assn. Osteo. Physicians and Surgeons (chmn. unity com. 1990, editl. com. TRIAD 1979), Mich. Soc. Osteo. Internists, Ingham County Osteo. Assn., Mich. Assn. Med. Edn., Mich. Assn. Osteo. Dirs. Med. Edn., Acad. Osteo. Dirs. Med. Edn., Lansing City Club (bd. govs. 1989). Office: Mich State U Coll Osteo Medicine Rm A308 East Fee Hall East Lansing MI 48824-1316

WOOD, EARL HOWARD, physiologist, educator; b. Mankato, Minn., Jan. 1, 1912; s. William Clark and Inez (Goff) W.; m. Ada C. Peterson, Dec. 20, 1936; children: Phoebe, Mark Goff, Guy Harland, Earl Andrew. B.A., Macalester Coll., 1934, D.Sc., 1950; B.S., U. Minn., 1939, M.S., M.B., Ph.D., 1941, M.D., 1942. Teaching fellow physiology U. Minn., 1936-39, instr., 1940; NRC fellow med. scis., dept. pharmacology U. Pa., 1941; instr. pharmacology Harvard Med. Sch., 1942; research asst. acceleration lab. Mayo Aero Med. Unit, 1943; asst. prof. physiology Mayo Found., U. Minn. Grad. Sch., 1944, prof. physiology and medicine, 1950—; staff mem. sect. physiology Mayo Clinic, 1947—; chmn. biophys. scis. unit Mayo Med. Sch.; career investigator Am. Heart Assn., 1967—; Sci. cons. air surgeon USAF Aero Med. Ctr., Heidelberg, Germany, 1946; vis. prof. U. Bern, 1965-66; vis. scientist dept. physiology Univ. Coll., London, 1972-73; rsch. cons. Canadian Air Force, DCIEM, Toronto, 1993-94. Contbr. articles to profl. jours., chpts. to books. Recipient Presdl. certificate of merit, Disting. Lectr. award Am. Coll. Chest Physicians, 1974, Sr. U.S. Scientist Humboldt award Kiel, Fed. Republic Germany, 1985, Phillips Meml. award ACP, 1983, Lucian award for research in cardiovascular diseases McGill U., 1985, Stewart Meml. lectr. Royal Aero. Soc., 1987, Outstanding Achievement award U. Minn., 1991. Fellow Aerospace Med. Assn. (Disting. Research award 1983); mem. Am. Physiol. Soc. (past chmn. circulation group, pres. 1980-81, Daggs award 1995), Am. Soc. Pharmacology and Exptl. Therapeutics, Am., Central socs. clin. investigation, Soc. Exptl. Biology and Medicine, Am. Heart Assn. (Research Achievement award 1973, past chmn. basic sci. sect.), AAAS, Nat. Acad. Medicine Mex., Nat. Acad. Arts and Scis. (Netherlands), Federated Am. Socs. Exptl. Biology (pres. 1981—), German Soc. for Heart and Circulation Rsch., Carl-Ludwig Ehrenmünze, Phi Beta Kappa, Sigma Xi, Alpha Omega Alpha (Outstanding Achievement award 1991). Research, numerous publs. on devel. instrumental techniques and procedures for study heart and circulation in health and disease; applications of these procedures to detection and quantitation of various types of acquired and congenital heart disease, study of effects and compensatory reaction of heart and circulation to various types of circulatory stress. Home: 211 2nd St NW Apt 1918 Rochester MN 55901

WOOD, ELIJAH, actor; b. Cedar Rapids, Iowa, Jan. 28, 1981. Appeared in films Back to the Future Part II, 1989, Internal Affairs, 1990, Avalon, 1990, Paradise, 1991, Radio Flyer, 1992, Forever Young, 1992, The Adventures of Huck Finn, 1993, The Good Son, 1993, North, 1994, The War, 1994; TV movies include Child in the Night, 1990, Day-O, 1992; also appeared in music video Paula Abdul's Forever Your Girl. Office: William Morris Agency 151 El Camino Beverly Hills CA 90212*

WOOD, ELWOOD STEVEN, III, chemical company executive; b. Norfolk, Va., Mar. 8, 1934; s. Elwood Steven Jr. and Margaret (Schlegel) W.; m. Jean Elizabeth Abbott, Dec. 21, 1961; children: Michael Scott, Tracy Lee. S.B. MIT, 1956, S.M., 1957; M.B.A., U. Pa., 1962. With W.R. Grace & Co., 1961-95; asst. plant mgr. Organic Chems. div. W.R. Grace & Co., Owensboro, Ky., 1964-66; plant mgr. Polyfibron div. W.R. Grace & Co., Adams, Mass., 1966-67; v.p. W.R. Grace & Co., Lexington, Mass., 1967-77; exec. v.p. Constrn. Products div. W.R. Grace & Co., Cambridge, Mass., 1977-82; pres. Polyfibron div., v.p. parent co. W.R. Grace & Co., Lexington, Mass., 1982-95, worldwide GM printing products 1993-95; ret., 1995. Served to 1st lt. U.S. Army, 1958.

WOOD, ERIC FRANKLIN, earth and environmental sciences educator; b. Vancouver, B.C., Can., Oct. 22, 1947; s. Lorne George and Olga Eugena (Hryvnak) W.; m. Katharine Holding Schwed; children: Eric Alexander, Emily Holding. BASc with hons., U. B.C., 1970; SM, MIT, 1972, MSCE, 1973, ScD, 1974. Rsch. assoc. MIT, Cambridge, 1970-73; rsch. scholar Internat. Inst. for Applied Systems Analysis, Vienna, Austria, 1974-76; prof. civil engring. Princeton (N.J.) U., 1976—; EOS sci. steering com. NASA, 1984-87, sci. adv. working group, 1992, land surface processes adv. com., 1985-90, Landsat sci. working group, 1992-93; GCIP sci. steering com. World Climate Rsch. Program, 1993—. Co-author: An Introduction to Groundwater Contamination from Hazardous Wastes, 1984; assoc. editor: Water Resources Research, 1977-82, Applied Math. and Computation, 1983—, Jour. of Forecasting, 1984—, Rev. in Geophysics, 1988—; editor (books) Recent Developments in Real-Time Forecasting/Control of Water Resources Systems, 1980, Scale Effects in Hydrology, 1986, Land Surface-Atmospheric Interactions for Climate Models: Observations, Modeling and Analysis, 1990; contbr. numerous articles to profl. jours. Recipient Rheinstein award Princton U., 1980. Fellow Am. Geophys. Union (mem. editl. bd. Water Resources Monographs, 1980-85, exec. mem. hydrology sect. 1984-85, 88-92, 94-95, union fellows com. 1994-96, union meeting com. 1988-90, chmn. remot sensing com. 1988-92, Horton rsch. com. 1992-95, Robert E. Horton award 1977); mem. AAAS, Ops. Rsch. Soc., NAS (com. on

flood levee policy), NSF (mem. com. of flood hazard mitigation 1979-80, panel on engring. and global climate change 1991), Am. Meteor Soc. (hydrology com. 1987-90). Avocations: squash, sailing, skiing. Office: Princeton U Dept of Civil Engring Princeton NJ 08544

WOOD, EVELYN NIELSEN, reading dynamics business executive; b. Logan, Utah, Jan. 8, 1909; d. Elias and Rose (Stirland) Nielsen; m. Myron Douglas Wood, June 12, 1929 (dec. May 1987); 1 child, Carolyn Wood Evans. BA, U. Utah, 1929, MA, 1947; postgrad., Columbia U., 1956-57. Tchr. Weber Coll., Ogden, Utah, 1931-32; girls counselor Jordan High Sch., Sandy, Utah, 1948-57, tchr. jr. and sr. high schs., 1948-59; instr. U. Utah, 1957-59; founder, originator Evelyn Wood Reading Dynamics, 1959—; tchr. rapid reading U. Del., 1961; guest lectr. NEA, 1961, Internat. Reading Assn., Tex. Christian U., 1962; faculty Brigham Young U., research specialist for reading, 1973-74. Author, conductor radio programs, 1947; author: (With Marjory Barrows) Reading Skills, 1958, A Breakthrough in Reading, 1961, A New Approach to Speed Reading, 1962, Speed Reading for Comprehension, 1962, also articles. Home: 6024 E Wendrew Ln Tucson AZ 85711-2517

WOOD, F. RUSSELL, broadcast executive; b. Farmington, N.Mex., Aug. 21, 1947; s. William R. and Lorna Mae (Richey) W.; m. Ilene Elfors, Jan. 29, 1971; children: Jonathon, Jeremy, Thelissa, Tamilisa. BA in Broadcasting, Brigham Young U., 1971; MA in Communications, U. Mo., Kansas City, 1982. Announcer KRGO Radio, Salt Lake City, 1971-72, KLAK Radio, Denver, 1972-73; agy. acct. exec., announcer Intermark Inc./KSL Radio, Salt Lake City, 1973-74; acct. exec. KSL Radio, Salt Lake City, 1974-75, sales mgr., 1975-80, announcer, 1980-84, gen. mgr., 1987—; gen. mgr. KMBZ/KMBR Radio, Kansas City, Mo., 1980-84; mktg. devel. dir. KSL Radio/TV, Salt Lake City, 1986-87. Bd. dirs. City Repertory Theatre, Salt Lake City, 1989—. Mem. Utah Broadcasters Assn (legis. liaison 1987—), Nat. Assn. Broadcasters (bd. dirs. 1988—), CBS Racio Affiliates Assn. (bd. dirs. 1989). Mormon. Avocations: entertaining, musical performance, drama. Office: Sta KSL(AM) KSL Broadcasting House Salt Lake City UT 84110-1160 Office: KSL Radio Broadcast House Salt Lake City UT 84110-1160

WOOD, FERGUS JAMES, geophysicist, consultant; b. London, Ont., Can., May 13, 1917; came to U.S., 1924, naturalized, 1932; s. Louis Aubrey and Dora Isabel (Elson) W.; student U. Oreg., 1934-36; AB, U. Calif., Berkeley, 1938, postgrad., 1938-39; postgrad. U. Chgo., 1939-40, U. Mich., 1940-42, Calif. Inst. Tech., 1946; m. Doris M. Hack, Sept. 14, 1946; children: Kathryn Celeste Wood Madden, Bonnie Patricia Wood Ward. Teaching asst. U. Mich., 1940-42; instr. in physics and astronomy Pasadena City Coll., 1946-48, John Muir Coll., 1948-49; asst. prof. physics U. Md., 1949-50; assoc. physicist Johns Hopkins U. Applied Physics Lab., 1950-55; sci. editor Ency. Americana, N.Y.C., 1955-60; aero. and space rsch. scientist, sci. asst. to dir. Office Space Flight Programs, Hdqrs., NASA, Washington, 1960-61; program dir. fgn. sci. info. NSF, Washington, 1961-62; phys. scientist, chief sci. and tech. info. staff U.S. Coast and Geodetic Survey, Rockville, Md., 1962-66, phys. scientist Office of Dir., 1967-73, rsch. assoc. Office of Dir., 1973-77, Nat. Ocean Svc.; cons. tidal dynamics, Bonita, Calif., 1978—; mem. Am. Geophys. Union, ICSU-UNESCO Internat. Geol. Correlation Project 274, Working Group #1-Crescendo Events in Coastal Environments, Past and Future (The Millennium Project), 1988—. Capt. USAAF, 1942-46. Recipient Sci. Achievement award Dept. Commerce, NOAA, 1970, 74, 76, 77. Mem. Sigma Pi Sigma, Pi Mu Epsilon, Delta Phi Alpha. Democrat. Presbyterian. Author: The Strategic Role of Perigean Spring Tides in Nautical History and North American Coastal Flooding, 1635-1976, 1978; Tidal Dynamics: Coastal Flooding, and Cycles of Gravitational Force, 1986, Synergetic Gravitational Forces in Tides and the Solar System, 2 vols., 1995; contbr. numerous articles to encys., reference sources, profl. jours.; writer, tech. dir. documentary film: Pathfinders from the Stars, 1967; editor-in-chief: The Prince William Sound, Alaska, Earthquake of 1964 and Aftershocks, vols. 1-2A and sci. coordinator vols. 2B, 2C and 3, 1966-69. Home: 3103 Casa Bonita Dr Bonita CA 91902-1735

WOOD, FRANK BRADSHAW, retired astronomy educator; b. Jackson, Tenn., Dec. 21, 1915; s. Thomas Frank and Mary (Bradshaw) W.; m. Elizabeth Hoar Pepper, Oct. 5, 1945; children—Ellen, Eunice, Mary, Stephen. B.S., U. Fla., 1936; postgrad., U. Ariz., 1938-39; A.M., Princeton, 1940, Ph.D., 1941; postgrad., U.S. Naval Acad., 1943. Research asso. Princeton, 1946; NRC fellow Steward Obs., U. Ariz., also Lick Obs., U. Calif., 1946-47; asst. prof. U. Ariz., 1947-50; asso. prof. U. Pa., 1950, prof. astronomy, 1954-64, chmn. dept., 1954-57, 58-68; exec. dir. Flower and Cook Obs., 1950-54, dir., 1954-68, Flower prof., 1958-68; prof. astronomy, dir. optical astron. observatory U. Fla., Gainesville, 1968-87, assoc. chmn. dept., 1971-77, prof. emeritus, 1989—; established South Pole obs. sta., U. Fla., 1985—. Author: (with J. Sahade) Interacting Binary Stars, 1978; Editor: Astronomical Photoelectric Photometry, 1953, Present and Future of Telescope of Moderate Size, 1958, Photoelectric Astronomy for Amateurs, 1963; Contbr. articles to profl. jours. Col., aide de camp, gov.'s staff, State of Tenn.; served with USNR, 1941-46. Decorated Air medal; Fulbright fellow Australian Nat. U., 1957-58; NATO sr. fellow in sci. U. Canterbury, Christchurch, New Zealand, 1973; Fulbright fellow Instituto de Astronomia y Fisica del Espacio, Buenos Aires, 1977; recipient plaques of appreciation, Govt. South Korea, 1988, Yonsei U., Korean Astron. Soc. Mem. AAAS (sec. sect. D com. on coun. affairs 1970), Am. Astron. Soc. (coun. 1958-61), Royal Astron. Soc. New Zealand (hon.), Internat. Astron. Union (pres. commn. 42 1967-70, v.p. commn. 38 1979-82, pres. 1982-85), Royal Astron. Soc., Fla. Acad. Sci. (chmn. phys. scis. sect. 1974-75, pres 1983-84, gold medal 1989), Astron. Soc. Can., Astron. Soc. Pacific, Ret. Officers Assn., Internat. Amateur and Profl. Photoelectric Photometry (hon.), Navy League, Explorers Club, Phi Beta Kappa, Sigma Xi, Phi Kappa Phi. Episcopalian. Home: 714 NW 89th St Gainesville FL 32607-1453 Office: Dept Astronomy U Fla Gainesville FL

WOOD, FRANK PREUIT, educator, former air force officer; b. Greenville, Tex., Feb. 28, 1916; s. William L. and Ethel (Preuit) W.; m. Harriet Louise Brawner, Oct. 25, 1941; 1 son, Frank M. B.S. in Elec. Engring, U. Tex., 1939; grad., USAF pilot tng. schs., 1941. Commd. 2d lt. USAAF, 1941; advanced through grades to brig. gen. USAF, 1964; dep. chief staff personnel Air Tng. Command, Randolph AFB, Tex., 1962-66; comdr. Air Force Mil. Tng. Ctr. Lackland AFB, San Antonio, 1966-67; chief Mil. Assistance Adv. Group, Italy, 1967-69; dep. chief staff for personnel Tactical Air Command, Langley AFB, Va., 1969-70; ret., 1970; apptd. assoc. dir. Bur. Engring. Research, U. Tex. Coll. Engring., Austin, 1970; dir. Bur. Engring. Research, U. Tex. Coll. Engring., 1971-78. Chmn. bd. equalization City of Austin, 1979—; elder Cen. Christian Ch., Austin, 1975-83, chmn. ofcl. bd, 1977; elder Cen. Christian Ch., San Antonio, 1985-89, 91—. Decorated Legion of Merit with 4 oak leaf clusters; named Disting. Grad., U. Tex. Coll. Engring., 1968. Club: Headliners (Austin). Home: 7400 Crestway Dr Apt 1003 San Antonio TX 78239-3094

WOOD, FREDERICK S., manufacturing company executive; b. 1928. BS, U. Dayton, 1952; postgrad., U.S. Naval Acad., 1970. Internat bus. advisor U.S. Govt., 1961-78; with Gen. Dynamics Corp., St. Louis, 1978— now exec. v.p. Office: Gen Dynamics Corp Pierre Laclede Ctr Saint Louis MO 63105-1861

WOOD, GEORGE H., investment executive; b. Kansas City, Mo., Sept. 7, 1946; s. George H. and Helen Lee (Hansen) W. BSBA, U. Mo., 1968, MBA, 1972. Securities analyst Kansas City Life Ins. Co., 1972-75, asst. dir. securities, 1975-76; sr. trust officer Commerce Bank of Kansas City, N.A., 1976-79, v.p., fixed income and portfolio group mgr., 1979-80, v.p., mgr. investment dept., 1980-82, sr. v.p., 1982-88, chief investment officer, 1988-90; mng. dir. Merus Capital Mgmt., 1990-94; v.p. Pacific Investment Mgmt. Co., 1994—. Past bd. dirs., pres. Young Audiences, Inc. With AUS, 1969-71. Chartered fin. analyst . Mem. Inst. Chartered Fin. Analysts (past chmn. curriculum com.), Assn. Investment Mgmt. and Rsch., Fin. Analysts Fedn., San Francisco Soc. Fin. Analysts (bd. dirs.), U. Mo. Alumni Assn., Phi Delta Theta. Home: 2616 Temple Hills Dr Laguna Beach CA 92651 Office: Pacific Investment Mgmt Co 840 Newport Ctr Dr Newport Beach CA 92658

WOOD, GORDON STEWART, historian, educator; b. Concord, Mass., Nov. 27, 1933; s. Herbert G. and Marion (Friberg) W.; m. Louise Goss, Apr.

30, 1956; children: Christopher, Elizabeth, Amy. AB, Tufts U., 1955; AM, Harvard, 1959; PhD, Harvard U., 1964. Fellow Inst. Early Am. History and Culture, Williamsburg, Va., 1964-66; asst. prof. Harvard U., Cambridge, Mass., 1966-67; assoc. prof. U. Mich., Ann Arbor, 1967-69; prof. history, Univ. prof. Brown U., Providence, 1969—; Pitt. prof. Cambridge U., 1982-83; bd. trustees Tufts U.; Bancroft lectr. U.S. Naval Acad., 1986; Anson G. Phelps lectr. NYU, 1986; Charles Edmundson lectr. Baylor U., 1987; Samuel Paley lectr. Hebrew U., Jerusalem, 1987; presdl. lecture series on presidency, 1991. Author: The Creation of the American Republic, 1776-1787, 1969, The Rising Glory of America, 1760-1820, 1971; co-author: The Great Republic, 1977, The Radicalism of the American Revolution, 1992 (Pulitzer Prize for history 1993). Mem. coun. Inst. Early Am. History and Culture, 1980-83; bd. trustees Colonial Williamsburg. With USAF, 1955-58. Recipient Bancroft prize Columbia U., 1970, Disting. Visitor award Australian-Am. Ednl. Found., 1976, Douglass Adair prize, 1984; Emerson prize Phi Beta Kappa, 1992; Sunderland fellow U. Mich. Law Sch., 1990; All Souls Coll. fellow, 1991; Woodrow Wilson Ctr. guest-scholar, 1993-94. Mem. Am. Hist. Assn. (John Dunning prize), Orgn. Am. Historians, Soc. Am. Historians, Nat. Hist. Soc. (chmn. bd. advisors), Soc. Historians of the Early Am. Republic (pres.), Am. Acad. Arts and Scis., Am. Philos. Soc. Home: 77 Keene St Providence RI 02906-1507 Office: 142 Angell St Providence RI 02912-0001

WOOD, HARLESTON READ, retired manufacturing executive; b. Phila., Oct. 18, 1913; s. Alan and Elizabeth Fitz Simons (Read) W.; m. Emily Newbold Campbell, June 21, 1942; children—Harleston R., Alan IV, Ross G., Morrow, Anthony. Student, Haverford Sch., 1929-31; A.B., Princeton, 1936. Various positions Alan Wood Steel Co., 1938-52, asst. v.p., 1952-54, v.p., 1954, pres., 1955-72, chmn., 1962-79. Gen. chmn. Phila. United Fund Torch drive, 1972; bd. dirs. Ursinus Coll.; Del. Rep. Nat. Conv., 1972; mem. Council on Fgn. Relations, 1961-84. Episcopalian. Home: 4149 SE Old Saint Lucie Blvd Stuart FL 34996-5124

WOOD, HARLINGTON, JR., federal judge; b. Springfield, Ill., Apr. 17, 1920; s. Harlington and Marie (Green) W. A.B., U. Ill., 1942, J.D., 1948. Bar: Ill. 1948. Practiced in Springfield, 1948-69; U.S. atty. So. Dist. Ill., 1958-61; mem. firm Wood & Wood, 1961-69; assoc. dep. atty. gen. for U.S. attys. U.S. dept. Justice, 1969-70; assoc. dep. atty. gen. Justice Dept., Washington, 1970-72; asst. atty. gen. civil div. Justice Dept., 1972-73; U.S. dist. judge So. Dist. Ill., Springfield, 1973-76; judge U.S. Ct. Appeals (7th cir.), 1976—; adj. prof. Sch. Law, U. Ill., Champaign, 1993. Chmn. Adminstrv. Office Oversight Com., 1988-90; mem. Long Range Planning Com., 1991—. Office: US Ct Appeals PO Box 299 600 E Monroe St Springfield IL 62701-1626

WOOD, HENRY AUSTIN, architect; b. Waltham, Mass., June 18, 1929; s. Henry Austin Jr. and Dagmar (Lundholm) W.; m. Joan Klawans, Oct. 22, 1962 (div. 1983); children: Paul F., Joshua W., Daniel L.; m. Diane Sargent, May 24, 1987. BA, Harvard U., 1951, MArch, 1960. Registered arch., Mass., N.Y., R.I., N.J., Mo., Pa., Conn., Ohio, U.K. Jr. architect Samuel Glaser Assoc., Boston, 1960-62; architect Campbell, Aldrich & Nulty, Boston, 1962-65; project mgr. Kallmann & McKinnell, Boston, 1965-67 assoc., 1967-70, ptnr., 1970-73; prin. Kallmann, McKinnell & Wood Architects, Inc., Boston, 1973—. Office: Kallmann McKinnell & Wood 939 Boylston St Boston MA 02115-3104

WOOD, HOWARD GRAHAM, banker; b. Balt., July 27, 1910; s. Howard and Etta (Graham) W.; m. Florence Tottle, Apr. 2, 1977; children by previous marriage—Robert Graham, Virginia B. Delauney. B.A., Johns Hopkins, 1932; LL.B., U. Md., 1936. Bar: Md. bar 1936. With First Nat. Bank Md., 1932—. Author: (with Robert H. Burgess) Steamboats Out of Baltimore, 1969. Mem. Commn. on Revision Balt. City Charter, 1965; treas. S.S. Hist. Soc. Am.; bd. dirs. Presbyn. Home Md. Served to maj. Intelligence Div. AUS, 1942-46. Mem. Phi Beta Kappa, Phi Gamma Delta. Clubs: Elkridge, Johns Hopkins (Balt.). Home: 919 Bellemore Rd Baltimore MD 21210-1206 Office: First Md Bldg Baltimore MD 21202

WOOD, IVAN, JR., lawyer; b. Corpus Christi, Tex., Oct. 1, 1947. AA, Del Mar Jr. Coll., 1967; BBA, U. Tex., 1969, JD, 1972. Bar: Tex. 1972, U.S. Ct. Military Appeals, 1974, U.S. Supreme Ct. 1991. Ptnr. Baker & Hostetler, Houston. Lt. JAGC, USN, 1972-76. Mem. ABA, State Bar Tex., Am. Acad. Hosp. Attys., Nat. Health Lawyers Assn., Beta Alpha Psi, Phi Delta Phi. Office: Baker & Hostetler 1000 Louisiana Ste 2000 Houston TX 77002-5008

WOOD, JACK CALVIN, health care consultant, lawyer; b. Greenwood, Ind., Jan. 9, 1933; s. Earl Leon and Gertrude Ruby (Stott) W. A.B., DePauw U., Greencastle, Ind., 1954; J.D., Harvard U., 1961. Bar: Ill. 1961, Tex. 1965, D.C. 1978, Colo. 1983. Assoc. firm Hopkins-Sutter, Chgo., 1961-65; gen. counsel Sisters of Charity Health Care System, Houston, 1965-73; sr. partner firm Wood, Lucksinger & Epstein, Houston, 1973-87, of counsel, 1987-91; of counsel Vinson & Elkins, 1991—; editor-in-chief Topics In Health Care Financing, 1974-94; clin. prof. law St. Louis U. Med. Sch., 1976—; adj. prof. health care administrn. Tex. Women's U., 1977—; Pres. St. Joseph Hosp. Found., Houston, 1966-68; chmn. governing com. Am. Bar Assn. Health Law Forum, 1981-84. Author: Financial Management, 1973, Medicare Reimbursement, 1974, Private Third Party Reimbursement, 1975. Served to lt. comdr. USNR, 1954-65. Mem. Am. Soc. Hosp. Attys. (pres. 1974-75), Nat. Health Lawyers Assn. (bd. dirs. 1981-85), Am. Soc. Law and Medicine (bd. dirs. 1981-85). Home: 9216 Cliffwood Dr Houston TX 77096-3511 Office: 9218 Cliffwood Dr Houston TX 77096-3511

WOOD, JAMES, supermarket executive; b. Newcastle-upon-Tyne, Eng., Jan. 19, 1930; came to U.S., 1974; s. Edward and Catherine Wilhelmina (Parker) W.; m. Colleen Margaret Taylor, Aug. 14, 1954; children: Julie, Sarah. Grad., Loughborough Coll., Leicestershire, England; hon. LHD, St. Peter's Coll., N.J. Chief food chain Newport Coop. Soc., S. Wales, U.K., 1959-62, Grays Food Coop. Soc., Eng., 1962-66; dir., joint dep. mng. dir. charge retailing Cavenham, Ttd., Hayes, Eng., 1966-80; pres. Grand Union Co., Elmwood Park, N.J., 1973-79; chief exec. officer, dir. Grand Union Co., Inc., 1973, chmn. bd., 1979-80; chmn. bd., CEO Gt. Atlantic & Pacific Tea Co., Inc., 1980—; bd. dirs. Asarco, Inc., Irma Fabrikerne A/S, Denmark, Schering-Plough Corp. Active World USO, UNICEF, United Jersey Bank. With Brit. Army, 1948-50. Mem. Food Mktg. Inst. (bd. dirs.). Roman Catholic. Office: Gt Atlantic & Pacific Tea Co 2 Paragon Dr Montvale NJ 07645-1718

WOOD, JAMES, broker; b. Mt. Kisco, N.Y., May 2, 1927; s. L. Hollingsworth and Martha (Speakman) W.; m. Frances Randall, May 2, 1953; children: Emily Morris, Stephen H. Grad., Deerfield (Mass.) Acad., 1945; B.A., Haverford (Pa.) Coll., 1950. Mfrs. rep. distbn. fertilizers, 1950-54; with Bank of N.Y., 1954-82, asst. v.p., 1960-61; broker Prescott Ball & Turben, 1982-93, v.p., 1986-93; broker Smith Barney, Mt. Kisco, 1993—; bd. dirs. Trans-Wasatch Co., Park City Consolidated, Oakwood Cemetery, Mt. Kisco. Trustee Bryn Mawr Coll., Jewish Found. for Edn. Women; bd. mgrs. Haverford Coll.; chmn. Am. Bible Soc.; v.p., bd. dirs. Howard Meml. Fund. With USNR, 1945-46. Home: Braewold 153 Wood Rd Mount Kisco NY 10549 Office: Smith Barney 100 S Bedford Rd Mount Kisco NY 10549-3443

WOOD, JAMES ALLEN, lawyer; b. McMinnville, Tenn., Jan. 14, 1906; s. Ira and Emma (Calhoun) W.; m. Eva Beth Sellers, Dec. 28, 1941; 1 son, Eben Calhoun. AB, U. Tenn., 1929; LL.B., U. Tex., 1934. Bar: Tex. 1934. Tchr. Bolton High Sch., Alexandria, La., 1929-32; since practiced in Corpus Christi; of counsel Wood, Burney, Cohn & Viles and predecessor firms, 1971—; state dist. judge, Corpus Christi, 1941-43; mem. rules adv. com. Supreme Ct. Tex., 1949-86. Author 6 vols. deprec. contract; articles to profl. jours. Bd. dirs. Nueces River Authority, 1972-89, pres., 1981-84, life time hon. dir., 1989—. Lt. USNR, 1943-45. Fellow Am. Coll. Trial Lawyers; mem. ABA, Tex. Bar Assn., Nueces County Bar Assn. (pres. 1941). Home: 458 Dolphin Pl Corpus Christi TX 78411-1514

WOOD, JAMES CLARENCE, lawyer; b. Cameron, Mo., Oct. 1, 1923; s. Clarence L. and Fanny Florina F. (Crall) W.; m. Mary Bennett, Sept. 17, 1946; children: Judy Lee, Betty Jean, James Bennett, Mary Joanne. BS in

Civil Engring., U. Ill., 1945, LLB, 1948, JD, 1948. Bar: Ill. 1949, U.S. Dist. Ct. (no. dist.) Ill. 1950, U.S. Ct. Appeals (7th, 9th, 6th, 2nd and 10th cirs.). Ptnr. Wood, Dalton, Philips, Mason & Rowe, Chgo., 1955—. Bd. dirs., pres. Deerfield (Ill.) Sch. Dist. 110, 1962-68. Mem. ABA, Chgo. Bar Assn., 7th Cir. Bar Assn. (pres. 1978-79), Am. Intellectual Property Bar Assn., Thorngate Country Club (pres. 1972, 86). Office: Wood Dlaton Phillips Mason & Rowe 20 N Wacker Dr Chicago IL 60606-2806

WOOD, JAMES E., JR., religion educator, author; b. Portsmouth, Va., July 29, 1922; s. James E. and Elsie Elizabeth (Bryant) W.; m. Alma Leacy McKenzie, Aug. 12, 1943; 1 son, James Edward III. BA, Carson-Newman Coll., 1943; MA, Columbia U., 1949; BD, So. Bapt. Theol. Sem., 1947, ThM, 1948; PhD, So. Baptist Theol. Sem., 1957; postgrad., U. Tenn., 1943-44; cert. in Chinese, Yale U., 1949-50; Japanese diploma, Naganuma Sch. Japanese Studies, Tokyo, 1950-51, Oxford, U., Eng., 1983; LLD hon., Seinan Gakuin U., Japan, 1983. Ordained to ministry So. Bapt. Ch., 1942. Pastor So. Bapt. chs., Tenn. and Ky., 1942-48; Bapt. missionary to Japan, 1950-55; prof. religion and lit. Seinan Gakuin U., Japan, 1951-55; prof. history of religions Baylor U., Waco, Tex., 1955-73, dir. honors program, 1959-64; dir. J.M. Dawson Inst. Ch.-State Studies Baylor U., 1957-73, 80—, chmn. interdeptl. grad. degree program in ch.-state studies, 1962-73, 80—; Simon and Ethel Bunn Disting. prof. ch.-state studies, 1980—, chmn. faculty-student Far Eastern exchange program, 1970-72; exec. dir. Bapt. Joint Com. on Public Affairs, Washington, 1972-80; mem. central panel Bapt. World Alliance Commn. on Religious Liberty and Human Rights, 1965-75, Commn. on Freedom, Justice and Peace, 1976-80, Commn. Human Rights, 1981—; chmn. Bapt. Com. on Bicentennial, 1973-76; mem. So. Bapt. Inter-Agy. Council, 1972-80, vice chmn., 1975-76, sec., 1976-77; vis. prof. So. Bapt. Theol. Sem., Louisville, 1974, Okla. Bapt. U., Shawnee, 1977, N.Am. Bapt. Sem., Sioux Falls, S.D., 1974, 79, Naval Coll. of Chaplains, Providence, 1988—; vis. lectr. Ashland (Ohio) Theol. Sem., 1971, ecumenical consultation on edn. Nat. Coun. Chs., 1974 ; Vernon Richardson lectr. Univ. Bapt. Ch., Balt., 1975; lectr. First World Congress on Religious Liberty, Amsterdam, 1977, 2d congress, Rome, 1984; co-chmn. internat. consultation on Religious Rights, Religious Liberty and Ethnic Identity for the New Europe, Budapest, 1992; co-chair consultation on Freedom of Conscience and Belief, Moscow, 1993; lectr. Stetson U., 1976, Wake Forest U., 1976, Notre Dame U., 1980; Carver-Barnes lectr. Southeastern Bapt. Theol. Sem., 1981; Asian Found. lectr. Seinan Gakuin U., Japan, 1983, Univ. Faculty of Law, Warsaw, Poland, 1984, Inst. Religion Chinese Acad. Social Scis., Beijing, 1986, Duquesne U., 1987; lectr. Campbell U., 1985, Brigham Young U., 1986, U. Kans., 1987, Union Theol. Sem. Va., 1989, Faculty of Law U. Oviedo, Spain, 1989, Southwestern Bapt. Theol. Sem., 1992, U. Tirana, Albania, 1992, New Orleans Bapt. Theol. Seminary, 1994, Emory U., U. Malta, 1994; vice chmn. Nat. Com. for Amish Religious Freedom, 1960-68; mem. Nat. Com. for Restoration Blue Lake Lands to Taos Indians, 1963-70; cons. asst. secretariat on religious liberty World Coun. Chs., 1963-65; co-chair Internat. Conf. Religious Freedom, Moscow, 1993; mem. internat. adv. bd. World Report on Freedom Conscious Human Rights Ctr., U. Sussex, U.K. Author: A History of American Literature: An Anthology, 1952, (co-author) Church and State in Scripture, History and Constitutional Law, 1958, The Problem of Nationalism, 1969, Nationhood and the Kingdom, 1977, Secular Humanism and the Public Schools, 1986, Reflections on Church and State, 1995; (edited by Derek H. Davis) The Separation of Church and State Defended: Selected Writings of James E. Wood, Jr., 1995; editor: Markham Press Fund, Baylor U. Press, 1970-72; founding editor: Jour. Ch. and State, 1959-73, 80—, mem. editorial coun., 1973-80; mem. editorial bd. Religion and Pub. Edn., Religious Freedom Reporter; editor, contbr.: Church and State, 1960, Jewish-Christian Relations in Today's World, 1971, Baptists and the American Experience, 1977, Religion and Politics, 1983, Religion, the State, and Education, 1984, Religion and the State, 1985, Report from the Capital, 1975-80, Ecumenical Perspectives on Church and State, 1989, The First Freedom: Religion and the Bill of Rights, 1990, The Role of Religion in the Making of Public Policy, 1991, The Role of Government in Monitoring and Regulating Religion in Public Life, 1993, Problems and Conflicts Between Law and Morality in a Free Society, 1994; area editor, contbr. to Ency. So. Bapts., 1982; contbr. We Hold These Truths, 1964, The Teacher's Yoke, 1964, The Best of Church and State, 1948-75, Issues in Church and State, 1977, Taxation and the Free Exercise of Religion, 1978, First World Congress on Religious Liberty, 1978, The Church, The State and Human Rights, 1980, The Minister's Manual: 1982-83, Freedom of Religion in America, 1982, Government Intervention in Religious Affairs 1982, Dictionary of Theology, 1982, Religion, Education and the First Amendment, 1986, Taking Sides: Clashing Views on Controversial Political Issues, 1986, Church and State in American History, 1987, Global Outreach: Global Congress of the World's Religions, 1987, Dictionary of Christianity in America, 1988, Faith, Life and Witness, 1990, Why We Still Need Public Schools: Church-State Relations and Visions of Democracy, 1992, Changing Trends in Education, 1992, Religious Trends in the 1990s, 1994; contbr. over 300 articles to profl. jours. Sponsor Ams. for Public Schs., 1963-68; bd. dirs. Waco (Tex.) Planned Parenthood, 1966-72, pres., 1971-72; sponsor Christians Concerned for Israel, 1968—, Tex. Conf. Chs. Consultation on Religion and Public Edn., 1971, Nat. Christian Leadership Conf. for Israel, 1978—; pres. Waco area ACLU, bd. dirs. Tex. unit, 1968-72; pres. Nat. Council Religion and Public Edn., 1979-83, exec. com., 1975—, bd. dirs., 1972—; chmn. exec. com. Council Washington Reps. on UN, 1977-80, mem. council exec. com., 1973-80; exec. com. Nat. Coalition on Public Edn. and Religious Liberty, 1973—; mem. religious liberty com. Nat. Council Chs. U.S.A., 1972—, also mem. com. internat. concerns on human rights; Am. rep. Chs. Montreux Colloquium on Helsinki Final Act, 1977; v.p Waco Conf. Christians and Jews, 1983-86, Internat. Acad. for Freedom of Religion and Belief, 1985-90, pres., 1990—; mem. internat. adv. bd. World Report on Freedom of Conscience, Human Rights Ctr., U. Sussex, Eng.; trustee Internat. Devel. Conf., 1974-80; nat. coun. Am.-Israel Friendship League, 1977—; founder, chmn. Waco Human Rights Week, 1981—; mem. ch. rels. com., U.S Holocaust Meml. Coun., 1990—. Recipient Disting. Alumnus award Carson-Newman Coll., 1974, Religious Liberty award Alliance for Preservation of Religious Liberty, 1980, Henrietta Szold award Tex. region Hadassah, 1981, Human Rights award Waco Conf. Christians and Jews, 1986, Cir. of achievement award Baylor U. Mortar Bd., 1991, Religious Freedom Lifetime award Ams. United Ctrl. Tex., 1993; hon. Tex. col., 1969. Mem. Am. Soc. Ch. History, Am. Acad. Religion, Am. Soc. Internat. Law, Am. Soc. Sci. Study of Religion, N. Am. Soc. Ecumenists, NCCJ (ad. com. on ch. state and taxation 1979-85), ACLU, Phi Eta Sigma, Pi Kappa Delta, Alpha Psi Omega. Democrat. Home: 3306 Lake Heights Dr Waco TX 76708-1543 Office: Baylor U PO Box 97308 Waco TX 76798-7308

WOOD, JAMES MICHAEL, lawyer; b. Oakland, Calif., Mar. 22, 1948; s. Donald James and Helen Winifred (Reiman) W.; div.; children: Nathan, Sarah, Ruth. BA, St. Mary's Coll., 1970, JD, U. San Francisco, 1973. Bar: Calif. 1973, U.S. Dist. Ct. (no., cen. and so. dists.) Calif. 1973. Rsch. atty. Alameda County Superior Ct., Oakland, 1973-76; ptnr. Crosby, Heafey, Roach & May, Oakland, 1976—; presenter at profl. confs. Contbr. articles to profl. jours. Chair alumni-faculty devel. fund St. Mary's Coll. Alumni Bd. Dirs., 1990-94. Mem. ABA (litigation sect., health law litigation com., litigation products liability com.), Assn. Trial Lawyers Am. (assoc.), State Bar Calif., Trial Lawyers Assn. (assoc.), No. Calif. Assn. Def. Counsel, Alameda County Bar Assn., Def. Rsch. and Trial Lawyers Assn., Am. Acad. Hosp. Atty's., Am. Soc. Pharmacy Law, Nat. Health Lawyers Assn., Drug Info. Assn. Office: Crosby Heafey Roach & May 1999 Harrison St Oakland CA 94612

WOOD, JAMES NOWELL, museum director and executive; b. Boston, Mar. 20, 1941; s. Charles H. and Helen N. (Nowell) W.; m. Emese Forizs, Dec. 30, 1966; children: Lenke Hancock, Rebecca Nowell. Diploma, Universita per Stranieri, Perugia, Italy, 1962; B.A., Williams Coll., Williamstown, Mass., 1963; M.A. (Ford Mus. Fng. fellow), NYU, 1966. Asst. to dir. Met. Mus., N.Y.C., 1967-68, asst. curator dept. 20th century art, 1968-70; curator Albright-Knox Art Gallery, Buffalo, 1970-73, assoc. dir., 1973-75; dir. St. Louis Art Mus., 1975-80, Art Inst. Chgo., 1980—; vis. com. visual arts U. Chgo., 1980-94; head com. Nat. Endowment Arts. Mem. Intermuseum Conservation Assn. (past pres.), Assn. Art Mus. Dirs. Office: Art Inst Chgo 111 S Michigan Ave at Adams St Chicago IL 60603-6110

WOOD, JANE, dancer. Attended, Washington Sch. Ballet, Acad. Washington Ballet; studied with Patricia Neary, Geneva Ballet. Dancer Geneva Ballet, until 1978; dancer Ballet West, Salt Lake City, 1978-87, soloist, 1987-89, prin. artist, 1989—. Dance performances include Romeo & Juliet, Sleeping Beauty, Swan Lake, Giselle. Office: Ballet West 50 West 200 South Salt Lake City UT 84101*

WOOD, JEANNE CLARKE, charitable organization executive; b. Pitts., Dec. 21, 1916; d. Joseph Calvitt and Helen Caroline (Mattson) Clarke; m. Herman Eugene Wood, Jr., May 6, 1936 (dec.); children: Helen Hamilton (Mrs. John Harry Mortenson), Herman Eugene III. Student, Collegiate Sch. for Girls, Richmond, Va., 1932-33. Asst. to Dr. and Mrs. J. Calvitt Clarke, Christian Children's Fund, Inc., Richmond, 1938-64; founder Children, Inc., Richmond, 1964; pres., internat. dir. Children, Inc., 1964—. Author: (with Helen C. Clarke) In Appreciation: A Story in Pictures of the World-Wide Family of Christian Children's Fund, Inc, 1958, Children's Christmastime Around the World, 1962, Children's Games Around the World, 1962, Children-Hope of the World-Their Needs, 1965, Children-Hope of the World-Their Friends, 1966; Editor: CI News, 1964. Recipient citation Eastern Council Navajo Tribe, 1970, citations Mayor of Pusan (Korea), 1971, citations Mayor of Seoul, 1971, citations Gov. of Kanagawa Prefecture (Japan), 1972, commendation Pres. of U.S., 1972, citation Stephen Philibosian Found., 1975, citation Santa Ana (El Salvador) Dept. Edn., 1975, citation Nat. Sch. for Blind, Dominican Republic, 1982, citation Navajo Tribal Council of Navajo Nation, Window Rock, Ariz., 1982. Office: Children Inc PO Box 5381 1000 Westover Rd Richmond VA 23220-6624 *While there are many things about which we can make no choice in this volatile world where change is constant and sometimes disastrous, it has seemed to me that one can make the choice between accepting things positively or negatively. I have chosen to accept them positively.*

WOOD, JEANNINE KAY, state official; b. Dalton, Nebr., Apr. 22, 1944; d. Grover L. and Elsie M. (Winkelman) Sanders; m. Charles S. Wood, Dec. 7, 1968; children: Craig C., Wendi L. Wood Armstrong. Exec. sec. Idaho Hosp. Assn., Boise, 1966-71; com. sec. Idaho State Senate, Boise, 1976-81, jour. clk., 1981-85, asst. to sec. of senate, 1985-91, sec. of senate, 1991—; pvt. practice typing svc. Boise, 1979-86. Precinct committeeman Rep. Party. Mem. Am. Soc. Legis. Clks. and Secs. (vice chmn. legis. adminstr. com.), Nat. Assn. Parliamentarians, Idaho Assn. Parliamentarians. Methodist. Home: 3505 S Linder Meridian ID 83642 Office: Idaho State Capitol PO Box 83720 Boise ID 83720-0081

WOOD, JOHN ARMSTEAD, planetary scientist, geological sciences educator; b. Roanoke, Va., July 28, 1932; s. John Armstead and Lillian Cary (Hall) W.; m. Elisabeth Mathilde Heuser, June 12, 1958 (div.); children: Crispin S., Georgia K.; m. Julie Marie Nason, Sept. 9, 1989. B.S. in Geology, Va. Polytech. Inst., 1954; Ph.D. in Geology, Mass. Inst. Tech., 1958; post-doctoral study, U. Cambridge, Eng., 1959-60. Staff scientist Smithsonian Astrophys. Obs., Cambridge, Mass., 1959, 61-62, 65—; research asso. Enrico Fermi Inst. U. Chgo., 1962-65; prof. dept. geol. scis. Harvard, 1976—; asso. dir. Harvard-Smithsonian Center for Astrophysics, 1981-86; Vice chmn. Lunar Sample Analysis Planning Team, 1971-72. Author: Meteorites and the Origin of Planets, 1968, The Solar System, 1979. Recipient NASA medal for exceptional sci. achievement, 1973, J.L. Smith medal NAS, 1976, G.K. Gilbert award Geol. Soc. Am., 1992. Fellow AAAS, Am. Geophys. Union, Meteoritical Soc. (pres. 1971-72, Leonard medal 1980); mem. NAS, Am. Acad. Arts and Scis., Cosmos Club. Asteroid no. 4736 named in his honor Johnwood. Home: 1716 Cambridge St Apt 15 Cambridge MA 02138-4343 Office: 60 Garden St Cambridge MA 02138-1596

WOOD, JOHN DENISON, utility company executive; b. Calgary, Alta., Can., Sept. 28, 1931; s. Ernest William and Ellen Gartshore (Pender) W.; m. Christena Isabel; 1 dau., Donna M. BSCE, U. B.C., 1953; MSCE, Stanford U., 1954, PhDCE and Engring. Mechs., 1956. Research asst. in civil engring. and engring. mechs. Stanford U., Palo Alto, Calif., 1953-56; assoc. mgr. dynamics dept. Engring. Mechs. Lab. Space Tech. Labs., Inc., Redondo Beach, Calif., 1956-63; pres., dir. Mechs. Research, Inc., El Segundo, Calif., 1963-66; sr. v.p. engring. and research ATCO Ind. Ltd., Calgary, Alta., 1966-68, sr. v.p. eastern region, 1968-75, sr. v.p. planning, 1975-77; pres., chief exec. officer ATCO Industries N.A., Ltd., Calgary, Alta., 1977-82, ATCOR Resources Ltd., Calgary, 1982-84; pres., chief operating officer Can. Utilities, Ltd., Edmonton, Alta., 1984-88, pres., chief exec. officer, 1988—; bd. dirs. ATCO Ltd., Can. Utilities Ltd., ATCOR Ltd., ATCO Enterprises Inc., Thames Power Ltd., Barking Power Ltd., Vencap Equities Alta. Ltd.; chmn. bd., CEO Can. Western Natural Gas Co. Ltd., Northwestern Utilities Ltd., Alta. Power Ltd., Northland Utilities Enterprises Ltd.; chmn. bd. Frontec Logistics Corp. Co-author: Ballistic Missile and Space Vehicle Systems, 1961. Mem. Pres.'s Club adv. com. U. Alta.; bd. dirs. Jr. Achievement Can., Western Orthopaedic and Arthritis Rsch. Found., Coun. for Can. Unity; bd. govs. Jr. Achievement No. Alta.; mem. adv. coun. Calgary Econ. Devel. Authority, Econ. Devel. Edmonton Bus. Adv. Coun. Athlone fellow, Can. Acad. Engring. fellow. Mem. Engring. Inst. of Can., Sci. Rsch. Soc., Assn. Profl. Engrs. Alta., Sigma Xi, Tau Beta Pi. Baptist. Clubs: Glencoe, Earl Grey, Calgary Petroleum, Mayfair Golf and Country. Avocations: golf, badminton. Office: Can Utilities Ltd, 10035 105th St, Edmonton, AB Canada T5J 2V6 also: Can Western Natural Gas Co Ltd, 909-11 Ave S W, Calgary, AB Canada T2R 1L8*

WOOD, JOHN MARTIN, lawyer; b. Detroit, Mich., Mar. 29, 1944; s. John Francis and Margaret Kathleen (Lynch) W.; m. Judith Anne Messer; children—Timothy Peter, Meagan Anne. B.A., Boston Coll., 1966; J.D., Cath. U. Am., 1969. Bar: D.C. 1970, U.S. Dist. D.C. 1970, U.S. Ct. Appeals (D.C. cir., 3d cir., 4th cir.), U.S. Supreme Ct. 1973. Trial atty. tax div. Dept. Justice, Washington, 1969-73; assoc. Reed Smith Shaw & McClay, Washington, 1973-80, ptnr., 1980-89, mng. ptnr., 1989—. Dir. adv. bd. The Salvation Army, Va., Metro Washington. Mem. D.C. Bar, ABA, Phi Alpha Delta, Delta Sigma Pi. Club: Barristers (Washington), Univ. Club, River Bend Golf & C.C. Home: 9490 Oak Falls Ct Great Falls VA 22066-4142 Office: Reed Smith Shaw & McClay 1301 K St NW Washington DC 20005

WOOD, JOSEPH GEORGE, neurobiologist, educator; b. Victoria, Tex., Dec. 8, 1928; s. Harold Robert and Frances Josephine (Marcak) W.; 1 dau., Marian. B.S., U. Houston, 1954, M.S., 1958; Ph.D., U. Tex., Galveston, 1962. Teaching asst. biology U. Houston, 1956-58; instr. anatomy U. Tex. Dental Br., Houston, 1961, Yale U., 1962-63; asst. prof. U. Ark. Med. Sch., Little Rock, 1963-66; assoc. prof. U. Tex., San Antonio, 1966-70; asst. dean acad. devel. U. Tex., 1967-69; prof. and chmn. dept. neurobiology and anatomy U. Tex., Houston, 1970-84; prof. neurobiology and anatomy U. Tex., 1984-88; prof., chmn. dept. anat. sci. U. Okla. Coll. Medicine, 1988-93; dir. Okla. Ctr. Neurosci., 1990-95; guest prof. dept. pathobiology U. Minn. Served with AUS, 1954-56. Recipient Basic Sci. Teaching award U. Tex. Houston, 1972, 75, 86, Disting. Alumnus award U. Tex. Med. Br., 1976. Mem. Internat. Brain Research Orgn., Am. Assn. Anatomists (exec. com. 1974-78), Neurochem. Soc., Soc. Neurosci. (exec. com. Houston chpt. 1971-77, pres. 1973-77), Am. Soc. Cell Biology, Assn. Am. Med. Colls., Soc. Exptl. Biology and Medicine, Cajal Club, Histochem. Soc., Electron Microscope Soc. Am., Anatomy Chmn., Tex. Soc. Electron Microscopy (pres. 1977-78; exec. council 1971-79), Houston Neurol. Soc., Gesellschaft für Histochemie, Sigma Xi (research award 1962), Phi Kappa Phi, Alpha Omega Alpha. Home and Office: 5009 Park Ave South Minneapolis MN 55417

WOOD, JOSHUA WARREN, III, lawyer, foundation executive; b. Portsmouth, Va., Aug. 31, 1941; s. Joshua Warren and Mary Evelyn (Carter) W.; m. Marcia Neal Ramsey, Feb. 29, 1964; children: Lauren Elaine, Joshua Warren IV. A.B., Princeton U., 1963; J.D., U. Va., 1971. Bar: Va. 1971, N.J. 1976, U.S. Supreme Ct. 1977, N.Y. 1982. Comml. banking asst. Bankers Trust Co., N.Y.C., 1967-68; assoc. McGuire, Woods & Battle, Richmond, Va., 1971-75; v.p., gen. counsel, sec. The Robert Wood Johnson Found., Princeton, N.J., 1975—; spl. counsel Smith, Lambert, Hicks & Miller, Princeton, 1985-87, Drinker, Biddle & Reath, Princeton, N.J. and Phila., 1987-89; of counsel Lankenau & Bickford, N.Y.C., 1989-92; spl. counsel Lane & Mittendorf, N.Y.C. and Edison, N.J., 1993—. Mem. editorial bd. Va. Law Rev., 1969-71. Capt. arty. U.S Army, 1963-67. Decorated Army Commendation medal. Mem. ABA, Princeton Bar Assn.,

N.Y. Bar Assn., Va. Bar Assn., N.J. Bar Assn., Nat. Health Lawyers Assn., Am. Arbitration Assn. (panel of arbitrators), Order of Coif., Princeton Club (N.Y.C.). Office: College Rd PO Box 2316 Princeton NJ 08543-2316

WOOD, KAREN SUE, theatre manager, stage producer, consultant; b. Artesia, Calif., May 14, 1950; d. Frank Leon and Edith Jeanette (DeLong) Wray; m. Lawrence Anthony Wood (div. 1972); 1 child, Kimberly. BA in Theatre Arts, Calif. State U., Fullerton, 1975; MFA in Theatre Mgmt., UCLA, 1977. Assoc. mgr. Huntington Hartford Theatre, L.A., 1978-81; gen. mgr. Sch. Drama, U. So. Calif., L.A., 1986-88, Mark Taper Forum, Ctr. Theatre Group, L.A., 1988—; lectr. dept. theatre Irvine Coll. and UCLA, 1989-93; mgr. theatre co. USIA, Czechoslovakia and Poland, 1988; chair mgmt. com. Music Ctr. Oper. Co., L.A., 1989—, burning tissues com. Theatre L.A., 1992-94; participant Gov.'s Conf. on Arts, Sacramento, 1992-95; founding mem. L.A. Theatre Ctr. Coop., 1992. Producer: (play) Buglips, 1978-79, Uncommon Women and Others, 1982; line producer: 1984 Olympic Arts Festival Theatre du Soleil, 1984, Piccolo Teatro di Milano, 1984, Robert Wilson/King Lear, 1985; assoc. producer 50/60 Vision, 1989-90 (Spl. Prodn. award L.A. Drama Critics Cir. 1989); author: Ambassador Auditorium Box Office Procedures, 1985; also theatre overviews. Trustee, bd. dirs. Odyssey Theatre, L.A., 1980; bd. dirs. Open Fist Theatre, 1995; spkr. Nat. Assn. Schs. of Theatre, 1987. Recipient L.A. Weekly Theatre award, 1979, Dramalogue Theatre award, 1979. Mem. NOW, NAFE, Women in Theatre, Assn. Theatrical Press Agts. and Mgrs., League of Resident Theatres (legue of resident theatres exec. com.), Theatre Commn. Group (charter mem.). Democrat. Office: Ctr Theatre Group Mark Taper Forum 135 N Grand Ave Los Angeles CA 90012-3013

WOOD, KENNETH ARTHUR, newspaper editor emeritus, writer; b. Hastings, Sussex, Eng., Feb. 25, 1926; came to U.S., 1965; s. Arthur Charles and Ellen Mary (Cox) W.; m. Hilda Muriel Harloe, Sept. 13, 1952. Educated in Eng. Editor Stamp Collector newspaper Van Dahl Publs., Albany, Oreg., 1968-80, editor emeritus, 1980—. Author (ency.) This Is Philately, 1982, (atlas) Where in the World, 1983, Basic Philately, 1984, Post Dates, 1985, Modern World, 1987; author several hundred articles and columns published in the U.K. and U.S.A., 1960—. Served with Brit. Army WW II. Recipient Disting. Philatelist award Northwest Fedn. Stamp Clubs, 1974, Phoenix award Ariz. State Philatelic Hall of Fame, 1979, Disting. Philatelist award Am. Topical Assn., 1979. Fellow Royal Philatelic Soc. (London); mem. Am. Philatelic Soc. (Luff award 1987, Hall of Fame Writers Unit, 1984). Avocations: philately, aviation history, modern history, gardening. Office: Van Dahl Pub PO Box 10 520 E First Albany OR 97321-0006

WOOD, KIMBA M., judge; b. Port Townsend, Wash., Jan. 2, 1944. BA cum laude, Conn. Coll., 1965; MSc, London Sch. Econs., 1966; JD, Harvard U., 1969. Bar: U.S. Dist. Ct. D.C. 1969, U.S. Ct. Appeals D.C. 1969, N.Y. 1972, U.S. Dist. Ct. (ea. and so. dists.) N.Y. 1974, U.S. Ct. Appeals (2d cir.) 1975, U.S. Supreme Ct. 1980, U.S. Dist. Ct. (we. dist.) N.Y. 1981. Assoc. Steptoe & Johnson, Washington, 1969-70; with Office Spl. Counsel, OEO Legal Svcs., Washington, 1970-71; assoc., then ptnr. LeBoeuf, Lamb, Leiby & MacRae, N.Y.C., 1971-88; judge, U.S. Dist. Ct. (so. dist.) N.Y., N.Y.C., 1988—. Mem. ABA (chmn. civil practice, procedure com. 1982-85, mem. coun. 1985-88, jud. rep. 1989-91), N.Y. State Bar Assn. (chmn. antitrust sect. 1983-84), Fed. Bar Coun. (trustee from 1978, 1984-85), Am. Law Inst. Office: US Dist Ct US Courthouse 500 Pearl St New York NY 10007

WOOD, LARRY (MARY LAIRD), journalist, author, university educator, public relations executive, environmental consultant; b. Sandpoint, Idaho; d. Edward Hayes and Alice (McNeel) Small; children: Mary, Marcia, Barry. BA summa cum laude, U. Wash., 1939, MA summa cum laude, with highest honors, 1940; postgrad. Stanford U., 1941-42, U. Calif., Berkeley, 1946-47; cert. in photography, U. Calif., Berkeley, 1971; postgrad. journalism, U. Wis., 1971-72. U. Minn., 1971-72, U. Ga., 1972-73; postgrad. in art, architecture and marine biology, U. Calif., Santa Cruz, 1974-76, Stanford Hopkins Marine Sta., Santa Cruz, 1977-80. Lifetime secondary and jr. coll. teaching cert., Wash., Calif. Feature writer and columnist Oakland Tribune and San Francisco Chronicle, Calif., 1939—; archtl. and environ. feature and travel writer and columnist San Jose (Calif.) Mercury News (Knight Ridder), 1972-94; teaching fellow Stanford U., 1940-43; dir. pub. rels. 2-counties, 53-parks East Bay Regional Park Dist., No. Calif., 1948-68; pres. Larry Wood Pub. Rels., 1946—; prof. (tenure) pub. rels., mag. writing, journalism and investigative reporting, San Diego State U., 1974, 75; disting. vis. prof. journalism San Jose State U., 1976; assoc. prof. journalism Calif. State U., Hayward, 1978; prof. sci. and environ. journalism U. Calif. Berkeley Extension grad. div., 1979—; press del. nat. convs. Am. Geophys. Union Internat. Conf., 1986—, AAAS, 1989—, Nat. Park Svc. VIP Press Tour, Yellowstone after the fire Nat. Pk. Svc. VIP Press Tour, 1989, Nat. Assn. Sci. Writers, 1989, George Washington U./Am. Assn. Neurol. Surgeons Sci. Writers Conf., 1990, Am. Inst. Biol. Scis. Conf., 1990, Nat. Conf. Sci. Writers Am. Heart Assn., 1995, Internat. Cardiologists Symposium for Med./Sci. Writers, 1995; EPA del. to USSR and Ea. Europe; mem. Am. Bd. Forensic Examiners, 1994; expert witness on edn., affirmative action, pub. rels., journalism and copyright; cons. sci. writers interne project, Stanford U., 1989—; spl. media guest Sigma Xi, 1990—; mem. numerous spl. press corps; selected White House Special Media, 1993—; internat. press guest Swiss Nat. Tourist Offices, Lake Geneva Region Celebration, 1994, Can. Consulate Gen. Dateline Can., 1995, Ministerio delle Risorse Agricole Alimentari e Forestali and Assocs. Conf., 1995; mem. Am. Bd. Forensic Examiners, 1994; appeared in TV documentary Larry Wood Covers Visit of Queen Elizabeth II. Contbr. over 5,000 articles on various topics for newspapers, nat. mags. nat. and internat. newspaper syndicates including L.A. Times-Mirror Syndicate, Washington Post, Phila. Inquirer, Chgo. Tribune, Miami Herald, Oakland Tribune, Seattle Times, San Francisco Chronicle, Parade, San Jose Mercury News (Nat. Headliner award), Christian Sci. Monitor, L.A. Times/Christian Monitor News Syndicate, Hawaiian Airlines In Paradise and other in-flight mags., MonitoRadio, Sports Illus., Mechanix Illus., Popular Mechanics, Parents, House Beautiful, Am. Home (awards 1988, 89), National Geographic World, Travel & Leisure, Chevron USA/ Odyssey (Calif. Pub.'s award 1984), Xerox Edn. Publs., Europe's Linguapress, PSA Mag., Hawaiian Airlines In Paradise Mag., Off Duty, Oceans, Sea Frontiers, AAA Westways, AAA Motorland, Travelin', others. Significant works include home and garden columnist and editor, 5-part series Pacific Coast Ports, 5-part series Railroads of the West, series Immigration, Youth Gangs, Endangered Species, Calif. Lighthouse Chain, Elkhorn Slough Nat. Estuarine Res., Ebey's Landing Nat. Hist. Res., Calif. Water Wars, BLM's Adopt a Horse Program, Mt. St. Helen's Eruption, Loma Prieta Earthquake, Oakland Firestorm, Missing Children, Calif. Prison Reform, Columbia Alaska's Receding Glacier, Calif. Underwater Parks, and many others; author: Wonderful U.S.A.: A State-by-State Guide to Its Natural Resources, 1989; co-author over 21 books including: McGraw-Hill English for Social Living, 1944, Fawcett Boating Books, 1956-66, Fodor's San Francisco, Fodor's California, 1982-les Merrill Focus on Life Science, Focus on Physical Science, Focus on Earth Science, 1983, 87, Earth Science 1987; contbr. Earth Science 1987; 8 works selected for use by Europe's Woltors-Nordoff-Longman English Language Texts, U.K., Netherlands, 1988; author: (with others) anthology West Winds, 1989; reviewer Charles Merrill texts, 1983-84; book reviewer Profl. Communicator, 1987—; selected writings in permanent collections Oakland Pub. Libr., U. Wash. Main Libr.; environ. works included in Dept. Edn. State of Md. textbook; contbr., author Journalism Quar.; author script PBS/AAA America series, 1992. Nat. chmn. Internat. writing contest for U.S. univ. journalism students Assn. For Edn. in Journalism/Soc. Am. Travel Writers, 1979-83; judge writing contest for Nat. Assn. Real Estate Editors, 1982—; Italy; press del. 1st Internat. Symposium Volcanism and Aviation Safety, 1991, Coun. for the Advancement of Science Writing 1977—, Rockefeller Media Seminar Feeding the World-Protecting the Earth, 1992, Global Conf. on Mercury as Pollutant, 1992, Earth Summit Global Forum, Rio de Janeiro, 1992; invited Nat. Park Svc. Nat. Conf. Sci. Writers, 1985, Postmaster Gen.'s 1992 Stamps, 1991, Internat. Geophysical Union Cong., 1982-95, The Conf. Bd. Cong., 1992, Corp. Comm. Conf., Calif. Inst. Tech.'s Media and Sci. Sem., 1995, EPA and Dept. Energy Tech. Conf., 1992, Am. Soc. Photogrammetry and Remote Sensing Internat. Conv. Mapping Global Change, 1992, N.Y. Mus. Mod. Art Matisse Retrospective Press Rev., 1992, celebration 50th anniversary Oreg. Trail 1993, coun. advancement sci. writing 1993, 94, Sigma Xi Nat. Conf. 1988—, PRSA Travel and Tourism Conf. 1993, Internat. Conf. Environment, 1994, 95, Quality Life Europe, Prague, 1994, and many others; press guest State of Conn., 1993; mem. Gov.'s Conf. Tourism N.C., 1993, 94, 95,

Calif., 1976—, Fla., 1987—; mem. planning com. U. Wash. Purple and Gold Soc., 1995. Recipient numerous awards, honors, citations, speaking engagements, including induction into Broadway Hall of Fame, U. Wash., 1984, Broadway Disting. Alumnus award, 1995; citations for environ. writing Nat. Park Svc., U.S. Forest Svc., Bur. Land Mgmt., Oakland Mus. Assn., Oakland C. of C., Chevron USA, USN plaque and citation, best mag. articles citation Calif. Pubs. Assn., 1984; co-recipient award for best Sunday newspaper mag. Nat. Headliners, citation for archtl. features Oakland Mus. 1983; honoree for achievements in journalism Nat. Mortar Bd., 1988, 89; selected as one of 10 V.I.P. press for Yellowstone Nat. Park field trip on "Let Burn" rsch., 1989; named one of Calif.'s top 40 contemporary authors for writings on Calif. underwater parks, 1989, nat. honoree Social Issues Resources Series, 1987; invited V.I.P. press, spl. press guest numerous events worldwide. Mem. Am. Bd. Forensic Examiners, Calif. Acad. Scis., San Francisco Press Club, Nat. Press Club, Pub. Rels. Soc. Am. (charter mem. travel, tourism, environment and edn. divs.), Nat. Sch. Pub. Rels. Assn., Environ. Cons. N.Am., Am. Assn. Edn. in Journalism and Comm. (exec. bd. nat. mag. div. 1978, panel chmn. 1979, 80, author Journalism Quar. jour.), Women in Comm. (nat. bd. officer 1975-77, book reviewer Prof. Communicator), Soc. Profl. Journalists (nat. bd. for hist. sites 1980—), Nat. Press Photographers Assn. (hon. life, cons. Bay Area interne project 1989—, honoree 1995), Investigative Reporters and Editors (charter), Bay Area Advt. and Mktg. Assn., Nat. Assn. Sci. Writers, Calif. Writers Club (state bd., Berkeley bd. 1989—, honoree ann. conv. Asilomar, Calif. 1990), Am. Assn. Med. Writers, Internat. Assn. Bus. Communicators, Am. Film Inst., Am. Heritage Found. (citation 1986, 87, 88), Soc. Am. Travel Writers, Internat. Oceanographic Found., Oceanic Soc., Calif. Acad. Environ. News Writers, Seattle Advt. and Sales Club (former officer), Nature Conservancy, Smithsonian Audubon Soc., Nat. Wildlife Fedn., Nat. Parks and Conservation Assn., Calif. State Parks Found., Fine., San Francisco, Seattle Jr. Advt. Club (charter), U. Wash. Comm. Alumni (Sch. Comm. alumni, life, charter mem. ocean scis. alumni, Disting. Alumni 1987), U. Calif., Berkeley Alumni (life, v.p. scholarship chmn. 1975-81), Stanford Alumni (life), Mortar Board Alumnae Assn. (life, honoree 1988, 89), Am. Mgmt. Assn., Nat. Soc. Environ. Journalists (charter), Phi Beta Kappa (v.p., bd. dirs. Calif. Alumni Assn., statewide chmn. scholarship awards 1975-81), Annenberg Washington D.C. Program Electronic Media Symposium, U. Wash. Purple and Gold Soc. (planning com., charter, 1995—), Pi Lambda Theta, Theta Sigma Phi. Home: Piedmont Pines 6161 Castle Dr Oakland CA 94611-2737 *A creed I follow is Ralph Waldo Emerson's statement: "Nothing great was ever achieved without enthusiasm."*

WOOD, LAWRENCE CRANE, medical association administrator, educator; b. Phila., May 7, 1945; s. Francis Clark and Mary Louise (Woods) W.; m. Emma Mathis Hollingsworth, Aug. 29, 1959 (div. 1975); children: Lawrence C. Jr., Clinton Tyler; m. Shirley Ann Jacobsen, July 1, 1977; 1 child, Marianna Redd. AB, Princeton U., 1957; MD, U. Pa., 1961. Asst. physician Mass. Gen. Hosp., Boston; instr. Harvard U. Med. Sch., Boston; pres., med. dir. Thyroid Found. Am., Boston, 1985—. Author: Your Thyroid: A Home Reference, 1982. Capt. USMC, 1965-68. Mem. Am. Thyroid Assn., Am. Assn. Clin. Endocrinologists, Am. Coll. Physiology., Mass. Med. Soc., Endocrine Soc. Avocations: fishing, sailing, banjo, guitar. Office: Mass Gen Hosp ACC 635 Parkman St Boston MA 02114

WOOD, LINDA MAY, librarian; b. Fort Dodge, Iowa, Nov. 6, 1942; d. John Albert and Beth Ida (Riggs) Wiley; m. C. James Wood, Sept. 15, 1964 (div. Oct. 1984). BA, Portland State U., 1964; M in Librarianship, U. Wash., 1965. Reference libr. Multnomah County Libr., Portland, Oreg., 1965-67, br. libr., 1967-72, adminstrv. asst. to libr., 1972-73, asst. libr., asst. dir., 1973-77; asst. city libr. L.A. Pub. Libr., 1977-80; libr. dir. Riverside (Calif.) City and County Pub. Libr., 1980-91; county libr. Alameda County Libr., Fremont, Calif., 1991—; adminstrv. coun. mem. Bay Area Libr. and Info. Svcs., Oakland, 1992; bd. dirs. Inland AIDS Project, Riverside, Calif., 1990-91; vol. United Way of Inland Valleys, Riverside, 1986-87, Bicentennial Competition on the Constitution, 36th Congl. Dist., Colton, Calif., 1988-90. Mem. ALA (CLA chpt. councilor 1992-95), Calif. Libr. Assn. (pres. 1985, exec. com., ALA chpt. councilor 1992-95), Calif. County Librs. Assn. (pres. 1984), League of Calif. Cities (cmty. svcs. policy com. 1985-90), OCLC Users Coun. (Pacific Network del. 1986-89). Democrat. Avocations: folk dancing, opera, reading. Office: Alameda County Libr 2450 Stevenson Blvd Fremont CA 94538-2326

WOOD, MARCUS ANDREW, lawyer; b. Mobile, Ala., Jan. 18, 1947; s. George Franklin and Helen Eugenia (Fletcher) W.; m. Sandra Lee Pellonari, July 25, 1971; children: Edward Alan, Melinda Janel. BA cum laude, Vanderbilt U., 1969; JD, Yale U., 1974. Bar: Oreg. 1974, U.S. Dist. Ct. Oreg. 1974, U.S. Ct. Appeals (9th cir.) 1982. Assoc., then ptnr. Rives, Bonihadi & Smith, Portland, Oreg., 1974-78; ptnr. Stoel Rives Boley Jones & Grey, Portland, 1974—. Pres., bd. dirs. Indochinese Refugee Ctr., Portland, 1980, Pacific Ballet Theatre, Portland, 1986-87; bd. dirs. Outside In, Portland, 1989—. Lt. USNR, 1969-71. Mem. ABA, Phi Beta Kappa. Home: 3707 SW Cullen Blvd Portland OR 97221-3525 Office: Stoel Rives Boley Jones & Grey 900 SW 5th Ave Ste 2300 Portland OR 97204-1232

WOOD, MARGARET GRAY, dermatologist, educator; b. Jamaica, N.Y., May 23, 1918; d. C.W. Bromley and B. Eleanor (Niblack) Gray; m. Alfred Conard Wood, Mar. 24, 1950; children: Margaret Diana, M. Deirdre Harper, Moira Dorothy. BA, U. Ala., Tuscaloosa, 1941; MD, Med. Coll. Pa., 1948, DMS, 1989, D in Med. Scis. (hon.), 1990, emeritus prof. medicine, 1993. Diplomate Am. Bd. Dermatology, Am. Bd. Dermatopathology. Intern Phila. Gen. Hosp., 1948-50; resident U. Pa. Hosp., 1950-53; instr. dept. dermatology U. Pa. Sch. Medicine, Phila., 1952-53, assoc., 1953-67, asst. prof., 1967-71, assoc. prof., 1971-75, clin. prof., 1975-80, prof. and chmn. dept. dermatology, 1980-82, prof., 1982-88, prof. emeritus, 1988—; assoc. prof. grad. Sch. Medicine U. Pa., Phila., 1957-71, cons. Sch. Dental Medicine, Med. Vet. Medicine U. Pa., Phila.; asst. prof. Med. Coll. Pa., Phila., 1957-93, prof. emeritus, 1993—, vice chmn. bd. dirs. 1984—, vice chmn. bd. dirs. Med. Coll. Hosps., Phila., 1991—, Hahnemann U. Hosp., 1993—; mem. exec. com. Am. Med. Women's Hosp. Svc. Com., Washington, 1970—; dir. Alleghany Health Systems, Pitts., 1987-91, Alleghany Health Edn. and Rsch. Found., 1991-94; bd. dirs. St. Christophers Hosp. for Children. Author (with others) 4 books; contbr. numerous articles to med. jours. Recipient Rose Hershfeld award Women's Dermatology Soc., 1989. Mem. AMA, Internat. Dermatology Assn., Internat. Dermatopathology Assn., Phila. Dermatology Soc. (pres. 1978-79), Alpha Omega Alpha. Republican. Episcopalian. Avocations: gardening, medical research.

WOOD, MARIAN STARR, publishing company executive; b. N.Y.C., Mar. 30, 1938; d. Edward James and Betty (Starr) Markow; m. Anthony Stuart Wood, Mar. 21, 1963. B.A., Barnard Coll., 1959; postgrad., Columbia U., 1959-64. Teaching asst., lectr. Columbia U., N.Y.C., 1960-64; editor Praeger Pubs., N.Y.C., 1965-71; sr. editor Henry Holt & Co., N.Y.C., 1972-81, exec. editor, 1981—

WOOD, MARION DOUGLAS, state legislator, lawyer; b. Detroit, Aug. 15, 1942; s. Marion Douglas and Kathryn Louise (Johnson) W.; m. Crystal Anne McAllister, Jan. 20, 1962; children: Gregory D., Jeffrey B. BS in Edn., Ark. State U., 1964; JD, U. Ark., 1974. Bar: Ark. 1974, U.S. Dist. Ct. Ark. 1974, U.S. Ct. Appeals (8th cir.) 1982. Trust officer Comml. Nat. Bank, Little Rock, 1972-74; pvt. practice law North Little Rock, 1974-89, Sherwood, Ark., 1989—; mem. Ark. Gen. Assembly, Little Rock, 1977—. Maj. U.S. Army, 1964-70. Mem. Sherwood C. of C. (pres. 1993), Am. Legion, Vietnam Helicopter Pilots Assn., VFW, Rotary. Democrat. Methodist. Avocations: fishing, flying, woodworking. Office: Wood Law Firm PO Box 7078 Sherwood AR 72124

WOOD, MARTHA OAKWELL, obstetrics-gynecology nurse practitioner; b. Chester, Pa., Apr. 19, 1941; d. Albert Edward Jr. and Gertrude Cecelia (Morgan) Warburton; m. Lawrence Dakin Wood, Nov. 22, 1957; children: Lawrence Dakin Jr., Thomas C., Elizabeth W., Michael L., Kathryn M., Scott G. BSN, Neumann coll., 1981; MSN, U. Pa., 1987. RN, Pa. Staff nurse Sacred Heart Med. ctr., Chester, Pa., 1981-84, Crozer-Chester Med. Ctr., 1984-88; clin. instr. obstetrics Neumann Coll., Aston, Pa., 1988, adj. faculty, 1991; instr. maternal-child health Chester County Hosp. Sch. Nursing, West Chester, Pa., 1989-90; adj. clin. instr. Widener U., Chester,

1991; staff devel. specialist Episcopal Hosp., Phila., 1992-93; ob.-gyn. nurse practitioner Camcare Health Corp., Camden, N.J., 1993—, interim nurse mgr., 1994—; supr. women and children nursing Bryn Mawr (Pa.) Hosp., 1988-89; perinatal nursing support Home Care Obstetrics, Bryn Mawr, 1991-93; manuscript reviewer Lippincott Pub. Co., Phila.; lectr. in field. Educator women's health Women's Assn. for Women's Alternatives, Wawa, Pa., 1990-91; big sister Del. County Pregnancy Ctr.; deaconess North Chester Bapt. Ch., 1991-94. Mem. Pa. Perinatal Assn., Acad. Nurse Practitioners, Assn. Reproductive Health Profls., Assn. Women's Health, Obstetrics, Neonatal Nurses, Sigma Theta Tau (Delta Tau chpt.). Baptist. Avocations: interior design, gourmet cooking, crafts, music. Home: 103 W Mowry St Chester PA 19103 Office: Camcare Health Corp 3 Cooper Plaza Ste 104 Camden NJ 08103

WOOD, MARY MARIE, secondary education educator; b. Enon, Mo., Aug. 16, 1928; d. Ely Emerson and Maggie Mae (Campbell) W. AA, Southwest Bapt. Coll., 1951; BSBA, Cen. Mo. State U., 1955, MS in Edn., 1962. Cert. bus. educator, Mo. Tchr. bus. Cole R-1 Schs., Russellville, Mo., 1955-67; tchr. vocat. bus. edn. California (Mo.) R-1 Schs., 1967—. Recipient Most Influential Tchr. award U. Mo., 1991-92; named Calif. R-1 Outstanding Educator, 1987, 93-94. Mem. Nat. Bus. Edn. Assn., Mo. Tchrs. Assn., Mo. Bus. Edn. Assn., California Cmty. Tchrs. Assn. (past officer), Mo. Vocat. Assn., Moniteau County Hist. Soc., Daus. Am. Colonists (libr.). Home: 800 S Randolph St California MO 65018-2011 Office: California R-1 Sch 205 Owen St California MO 65018

WOOD, NANCY ELIZABETH, psychologist, educator; d. Donald Sterret and Orne Louise (Erwin) W. B.S., Ohio U., 1943, M.A., 1947; Ph.D., Northwestern U., Evanston, Ill., 1952. Prof. Case-Western Res. U., Cleve., 1952-60; specialist, expert Dept. HEW, Washington, 1960-62; chief of research Pub. Health, Washington, 1962-64; prof. U. So. Calif., Los Angeles, 1965—; learning disabilities cons., 1960-70; assoc. dir. Cleve. Hearing and Speech Ctr., 1952-60; dir. licensing program Brit. Nat. Trust, London. Author: Language Disorders, 1964, Language Development, 1970, Verbal Learning, 1975 (monograph) Auditory Disorders, 1978, Levity, 1980, Stoneskipping, 1989, Bird Cage, 1994. Pres. faculty senate U. So. Calif., 1987-88. Recipient Outstanding Faculty award Trojan Fourth Estate, 1982, Pres.' Svc. award U. So. Calif., 1992. Fellow Am. Speech and Hearing Assn. (elected, legis. council 1965-68), Am. Psychol. Assn. (cert.), AAAS; mem. Internat. Assn. of Scientists. Republican. Methodist. Office: U So Calif University Park University Park CA 90089

WOOD, NATHANIEL FAY, editor, writer, public relations consultant; b. Worcester, Mass., June 23, 1919; s. Henry Fletcher and Edith (Fay) W.; m. Eleanor Norton, Dec. 19, 1945; children: Gary Nathaniel, Janet Ann. BS in Journalism, Bus. Adminstrn., Syracuse U., 1946. Editor, writer various publs., various cities, 1946-51; mng. editor Butane-Propane News, L.A., 1951-52; editor Western Metalworking Mag., L.A., 1952-62; western editorial mgr. Penton Pub. Co. Cleve., L.A., 1962-71; editor Orange County Illustrated, Orange County Bus., Newport Beach, Calif., 1971-72; western editor Hitchcock Pub., L.A., 1972-75; co-owner, mgr. Norton-Wood Pub. Rels. Svcs., Pasadena, Calif., 1975—; editorial dir. Security World, SDM and SCA Mags., Culver City, Calif., 1975-80; mgr. trade show Cahners Pub. and Expo Group, L.A., 1979-82; sr. editor Alarm Installer Dealer Mag., L.A., 1982-89; editor CNC West Mag., Long Beach, Pasadena, Calif., 1982—. Freelance indsl. writer miscellaneous bus. pubs. Organizer Willkie Presdl. Campaign, Syracuse, N.Y., 1940; advisor various GOP campaigns, L.A., Washington, 1940-92; donor L.A. Civic Light Opera; mem., donor L.A. Mus. Art, 1989—; founding mem. Western Heritage Mus., L.A., 1989—; active Met. Opera Guild, Colonial Williamsburg Found., Mus. Natural History L.A. 2d lt. U.S. Army, 1943-45, PTO. Decorated Purple Heart; recipient Silver, Bronze and Gold medals for Editorial Excellence Gov. of Calif., 1959, 60, 62. Mem. Am. Legion. Scabbard and Blade, L.A. World Affairs Coun., Smithsonian Instn., Alpha Epsilon Rho, Sigma Delta Chi. Avocations: swimming, boating, tennis, photography, gardening. Home: 1430 Tropical Ave Pasadena CA 91107-1623 Office: Norton-Wood Pub Rels Svcs 1430 Tropical Ave Pasadena CA 91107-1623

WOOD, NEIL RODERICK, real estate development company executive; b. Winnipeg, Man., Can., Aug. 22, 1931; s. Reginald and Pearl (Beake) W.; m. Jean Mitchell Hume, Aug. 10, 1957; children: Barbara, David, John, Brian. B.Com., U. Man., 1952; M.B.A., Harvard U., 1955. Asst. mgr. Ont. real estate investment office Gt. West Life Assurance Co., 1955-59; with Cadillac Fairview Corp. Ltd. (and predecessor), Willowdale, Ont., 1959-61, 63-81; exec. v.p. Cadillac Fairview Corp. Ltd. (and predecessor), 1968-71, pres., 1971-81, vice chmn., 1980-81; pres. N.R. Wood Devel. Co. Ltd. 1982—; exec. v.p., dir. Campeau Corp., 1985-86; pres., CEO, dir. Markborough Properties Inc., Toronto, Ont., Can., 1986—; bd. dirs. Gentra Inc.; past pres., trustee Internat. Coun. Shopping Ctrs.; pres., dir. Can. Inst. Pub. Real Estate Cos.; bd. govs. Olympic Trust, Roy Thompson Hall. Mem. Urban Land Inst., Met. Toronto Bd. Trade, Toronto Club, Rosedale Golf Club, Craigleith Ski Club, Beaumaris Club, Lost Tree Club, Loxahatchee Golf Club, Beacon Hall Club. Home: RR # 3, Newmarket, ON Canada L3Y 4W1 Office: Markborough Properties Inc, 1 Dundas W # 2800, Toronto, ON Canada M5G 2J2

WOOD, PAUL F., national health agency executive; b. Lockport, N.Y., Dec. 7, 1935; s. Dwight Edward and Frances (Fletcher) W.; m. Kathleen Frances Stretton, May 27, 1958; children: Paul S., Richard F. BA, Western Res. Univ., 1964; MA, Kent State U., 1970; PhD, Case Western Res. U., 1975. Assoc. exec. dir. United Way of Stark County, Canton, Ohio, 1967-70; owner Paul Wood Co., N. Canton, Ohio, 1970-86; dir. devel. The Salvation Army, N.Y.C., 1986-90; pres. Nat. Coun. on Alcoholism and Drug Dependence, Inc., N.Y.C., 1990—. Bd. dirs. Fairfield (Conn.) Chorale, 1991-94; chmn. fin. com. Westport United Meth. Ch., 1993—. Avocations: sailing, computer programming. Office: Nat Coun On Alcoholism & Drug Dependence 12 W 21st St New York NY 10010

WOOD, PRESNALL HANSEL, editor, minister; b. Vernon, Tex., May 7, 1932; s. J. Hansel and Bertha Lee (Brock) W.; m. Joyce Ann Middlebrook, May 28, 1953; children: Jeffery Brooks, Jed Hansel. BA, Baylor U., 1953; BD, Southwestern Bapt. Sem., Ft. Worth, 1956, ThD, 1964. Pastor Bapt. Chs., Coryell County, Tex., 1953-56, 1st Bapt. Ch., Goldthwaite, Tex., 1956-61, Crestview Bapt. Ch., Midland, Tex., 1961-68, Park Pl. Bapt. Ch., Houston, 1968-77; editor Bapt. Standard, Dallas, 1977—; chmn. bd. trustees Sunday Sch. Bds. So. Bapt. Conv., 1979-80. Author: Prophets with Pens, 1969. Mem. So. Bapt. Press Assn. (pres. 1987-88).

WOOD, QUENTIN EUGENE, oil company executive; b. Mechanicsburg, Pa., Mar. 5, 1923; s. Lloyd Paul and Greta (Myers) W.; m. Louise Lowe, Apr. 14, 1958. B.S., Pa. State U., 1948. Petroleum engr. Quaker State Oil Refining Corp., Parkersburg, W.Va., 1948-52; chief engr. Quaker State Oil Refining Corp., Bradford, Pa., 1952-55; mgr. prodn. Quaker State Oil Refining Corp., 1955-68; v.p. prodn. Quaker State Oil Refining Corp., Oil City, Pa., 1968-70; exec. v.p. Quaker State Oil Refining Corp., Oil City, 1970-73, pres., chief ops. officer, 1973-75; pres., chief exec. officer Quaker State Oil Refining Corp., 1975-82, chmn., chief exec. officer, 1982-88, chmn. bd., 1988-90, dir., 1990-93; bd. dirs. Pa. Mfrs. Ins. Co.; chmn. industry tech. adv. com. U.S. Bur. Mines, 1960-70, Penn Grade Tech. Adv. Com., 1955-69, Pa. Oil and Gas Conservation Commn., 1961-71. Trustee Pa. State U., 1976-94, pres., 1979-87. 1st lt. USAAF, 1943-46. Mem. Am. Inst. Metall. Engrs., Pa. Grade Crude Oil Assn. (dir.), Pa. Oil Producers Assn. (past pres., dir. Bradford dist.), Am. Petroleum Inst. (dir.), Nat. Petroleum Refiners Assn. (dir.). Home: 160 Sea Hammock Way Ponte Vedra Beach FL 32082-4414 Office: Quaker State Corp PO Box 989 Oil City PA 16301-0989

WOOD, R. STEWART, bishop; b. Detroit, June 25, 1934; s. Raymond and Marjorie Wood; m. Kristin Lie Miller, June 25, 1955; children: Lisa, Raymond, Michael. AB, Dartmouth Coll., 1956; MDiv, Va. Theol. Seminary, 1969; MA in Counseling and Sociology, Ball State U., 1973; postgrad., Va. Seminary. Ordained to diaconate and priesthood Episc. Ch., 1959. Vicar Episc. Ch., Seymour and Bean Blossom, Ind.; assoc. rector Grace Ch., Muncie, Ind., rector, 1966-70; exec. dir. Episc. Community Svcs., Indpls., 1970-76; rector All Saint's Episc. Ch., Christ Ch., Glendale, Ind., 1976-84, St. John's Ch., Memphis, 1984-88; elected Bishop Coadjutor Diocese Mich.,

Detroit, 1988—; dir. summer camps, conf. ctr.; dep. Gen. Conv. 1970, 73, 76, 82; exec. coun. Coalition for Ordination of Women, bd. dirs. Avocations: camping, golf, tennis, photography, motorcycling. Office: 4800 Woodward Ave Detroit MI 48201-1310

WOOD, RAYMUND FRANCIS, retired librarian; b. London, Nov. 9, 1911; came to U.S., 1924; s. George S. and Ida A. (Lawes) W.; m. Margaret Ann Peed, Feb. 26, 1943; children: Paul George, Gregory Leo, David Joseph. AB, St. Mary's U., Balt., 1931; MA, Gonzaga U., 1939; PhD, UCLA, 1949; MS in Libr. Sci., U. So. Calif., L.A., 1950. Instr. English U. Santa Clara (Calif.), 1939-41; rehab. officer VA, L.A., 1946-48; reference libr. Fresno (Calif.) State Coll., 1950-66; prof. libr. sci. UCLA, L.A., 1966-77, prof. emeritus, 1977—; from asst. dean to assoc. dean Grad. Sch. Libr. & Info. Sci., 1970-77. Author: California's Augua Fria, 1952, Life and Death of Peter Lebec, 1954, The Saints of the California Landscape, 1987; coauthor: Librarian and Laureate: Ina Coolbrith of California, 1973, many others. Vol. driver ARC, Van Nuys, Calif., 1977—; pres. Friends of the Encino/Tarzana Br. Libr., Tarzana, Calif., 1977-80, Jedediah Smith Soc., Stockton, Calif., 1987-90, knight comdr. Order of St. Gregory, 1994. With U.S. Army, 1942-46, ETO. Travel grantee Am. Book Found., 1964, Del. Amo Found., 1974. Mem. ALA (book reviewer 1974—), Calif. Libr. Assn. (many offices), Mariposa County Hist. Assn. (life), Oral History Assn. (life), Fresno County Hist. Soc. (editor 1959-66), Westerners L.A. Corral (editor of Brand Book 1982). Democrat. Byzantine Catholic. Avocations: lecturing, writing, reading, traveling. Home: 18052 Rosita St Encino CA 91316-4217

WOOD, RICHARD COURTNEY, library director, educator; b. Spartanburg, S.C., Aug. 8, 1943; s. Herman Alva and Mildred Eloise (Porter) W.; m. Amy Louise Black, Aug. 16, 1974. BA, U. Tex., 1966; MLS, U. S.C., 1977. Head cataloging Wofford Coll. Libr., Spartanburg, 1969-78; hosp. libr. John Peter Smith Hosp., Ft. Worth, 1978-80; reference libr. Tex. Coll. Osteo. Medicine, Ft. Worth, 1980-82, assoc. dir. libr., 1982-91; dir. librs., assoc. prof. Sch. Medicine, Tex. Tech U. Health Scis. Ctr., Lubbock, 1991—; cons. Tarrant County Med. Libr. Assn., Fort Worth, 1978-82, 84, Med. Plaza Hosp., Fort Worth, 1979-82, Grand Prairie (Tex.) Community Hosp., 1980-81, Cook-Fort Worth Children's Hosp., 1988—. Patron Kimball Art Mus. Fort Worth, 1987—; spokesman Neighborhood Assn., Fort Worth, 1989; vis. exec. United Way, Fort Worth, 1990. Mem. Dallas-Tarrant County Consortium (chmn. 1980-81), Metroplex Consortium Health Scis. (chmn. 1980-81), South Cen. Regional Group, Med. Libr. Assn. (chmn. osteo. librs. sect. 1986-87), South Cen. Acad. Med. Librs. (bd. dirs. 1991—), Nat. Network Librs. Medicine (bd. dirs. South Cen. region 1991-93), Deutsche Gesellschaft für Heereskunde, Sigma Tau Delta. Republican. Presbyterian. Avocations: languages, travel, history, gardening, music. Home: 1805 Bangor Ave Lubbock TX 79416-5518 Office: Libr of Health Scis Tex Tech U Scis Ctr Lubbock TX 79430

WOOD, RICHARD DONALD, pharmaceutical company executive; b. Brazil, Ind., Oct. 22, 1926; s. Howard T. and Dorothy F. (Norfolk) W.; m. Billie Lou Carpenter, Dec. 29, 1951; children: Catherine Ann Wood Lawson, Marjorie Elizabeth Wood Brentlinger. BS, Purdue U., 1948; MBA, U. Pa., 1950; LLD, Purdue U., 1973, De Pauw U., 1972, Phila. Coll. Pharmacy and Sci., 1975, Ind. State U., 1978, Ind. U., 1989; DSc, Butler U., 1974. Gen. mgr. ops. in Argentina Eli Lilly & Co., 1961; pres. Eli Lilly Corp., 1970-72; mem. bd. dirs. Eli Lilly and Co., 1971—, pres., chmn. of bd., CEO, 1973-91, chmn. of bd., 1991—. Bd. dirs. Lilly Endowment, Inc.; pres., bd. trustees Indpls. Mus. of Art; trustee De Pauw U., Am. Enterprise Inst. for Pub. Policy Rsch., Com. Econ. Devel.; bd. dirs. U.S.-USSR Trade and Econ. Coun., Indpls. Symphony Orch. Found. Mem. The Conf. Bd., Meridian Hills Country Club. Presbyterian. Office: Eli Lilly & Co Lilly Corporate Ctr Indianapolis IN 46285

WOOD, RICHARD J., college president. A.B., Duke U., 1959; B.D., Union Theol. Sem., 1962; M.A., Yale U., 1963, Ph.D., 1965. Pres. Earlham Coll., Richmond, Ind., 1985—. Office: Earlham Coll Office of President Richmond IN 47374

WOOD, RICHARD ROBINSON, real estate executive; b. Salem, Mass., Nov. 8, 1922; s. Reginald and Irene Margaret (Robinson) W.; m. Pamela Vander Wiele, Mar. 8, 1951 (div. Apr. 1969); children: Christopher Robinson, Bryant Cornelius, Marcella Wood Mackenzie; m. Jane Philbin, Sept. 19, 1970. AB, Harvard U., 1944; postgrad., Mass. Inst. Tech., 1947-48. V.p. Hunneman & Co., Boston, 1959-72; trustee, sec. Mass. Real Estate Investment Trust, Boston, 1967-69; trustee Suffolk Franklin Savings Bank, 1967-74; pres., chmn. Continential Real Estate Equity, Boston, 1972-74; exec. v.p. ITEL Real Estate Corp., San Francisco, 1974-75; v.p. Baird & Warner, Chgo., 1976-80; pres., chmn. Renwood Properties, Inc., Peabody, Mass., 1981—; v.p., dir. Common Goal Capitol Group, Balt., 1986—; gen. ptnr. Common Goal Mortgage Fund, Balt., 1986—; v.p., bd. dirs. St. Katherines Care Ctrs., 1990—; pres., chmn. ILCO Properties, Chgo., 1981-87; mem. COun. for Rural Housing and Devel., 1988—. Mem. mayor's citizen adv. bd., Boston, 1965-67; pres. Boston Rep. city com., 1965-67; committeeman, treas. Mass. Rep. State Com., Boston, 1964-72. With U.S. Army med. corps, 1943-44. Mem. Nat. Leased Housing Assn., Harvard Club Boston, Longwood Cricket Club, Harvard Club of U.S. Avocations: tennis, skiing. Home: 19 Chauncy St Cambridge MA 02138 Office: Renwood Properties Inc 100 Corp Pl Ste 403 Peabody MA 01960

WOOD, ROBERT COLDWELL, political scientist; b. St. Louis, Sept. 16, 1923; s. Thomas Frank and Mary (Bradshaw) W.; m. Margaret Byers, Mar. 22, 1952; children—Frances, Margaret, Frank Randolph. AB, Princeton U., 1946; MA, Harvard U., 1947, MPA, 1948, PhD, 1950; LLD (hon.), St. Bonaventure Coll., U. Pitts., 1965, Bklyn. Poly. Inst., 1966, Princeton U., 1969, Rhode Island Coll., U. Mass., 1970, Worcester Poly. Inst., 1971, U. Maine, 1972, Hokkaido U., Japan, 1975, North Adams Coll., 1977, Boston U., 1978, Stonehill Coll., 1979. Assoc. dir. Fla. Legis. Reference Bur., Tallahassee, 1949-51; mgmt. orgn. expert U.S. Bur. Budget, Washington, 1951-54; lectr. govt. Harvard U., 1953-54, asst. prof., 1954-57; asst. prof. polit. sci. MIT, 1957-59, assoc. prof., 1959-62, prof., 1962-66, head dept., 1965-66, 69-70; undersec. HUD, Washington, 1966-68; sec. HUD, 1969; chmn. Mass. Bay Transp. Authority, Boston, 1969-70; dir. Harvard U.-MIT Joint Center for Urban Studies, Cambridge, 1969-70; pres. U. Mass., 1970-77; supt. Boston Public Schs., 1978-80; prof. U. Mass., Boston, 1981-83; Henry Luce prof. Dem. Instns. and the Social Order Wesleyan U., Middletown, Conn., 1983-93, John E. Andrus prof. govt., 1993; prof. emeritus U. Mass., Boston, 1994—; vis. fellow McCormack Inst. Pub. Affairs, U. Manchester, Boston. Author: Suburbia, Its People and Their Politics, 1958, Metropolis Against Itself, 1959, 1400 Governments, The Political Economy of the New York Region, 1960, The Necessary Majority, Middle America and Urban Crisis, 1972, Whatever Possessed the President? Academic Experts and Presidential Policy, 1960-88, 1993; (with others) Schoolmen and Politics, 1962, Government and Politics of the U.S, 1965; author, editor: Remedial Law: When Courts Become Administrators, 1990. Trustee Coll. Bd., 1979-83, Kettering Found., 1971-76; mem. Commn. on Acad. Health Ctrs. and Economy New Eng.; bd. dirs. Lincoln Inst. Land Policy, 1976-80; chmn. Inst. for Resource Mgmt., 1982-84, 20th Century Task Force Fed. Ednl. Policy, 1983, Conn. Gov.'s Coalition on Adult Literacy, 1986-89; mem. Gov.'s Commn. on Quality and Integrated Edn., 1989-90. Served with inf. AUS, World War II, ETO. Decorated Bronze Star; recipient Hubert H. Humphrey award, 1985. Fellow Am. Acad. Arts and Scis., Am. Polit. Sci. Assn. (Career Achievmenet award 1989), Cosmos Club Washington, Phi Beta Kappa.

WOOD, ROBERT ELKINGTON, II, financial services company executive; b. Houston, May 7, 1938; s. Robert Whitney and Elizabeth Cushing (Neville) W.; m. Susan Mayer, Jan. 5, 1963; children: Katherine Hardwick, Elizabeth Neville. BA, Princeton U., 1960. Various merchandising and oper. positions Sears, Roebuck & Co., Chgo., 1960-78, various other positions, 1978-85; chmn., chief oper. officer Sears Consumer Fin. Corp. (subs. Dean Witter), Riverwoods, Ill., 1985-88; sr. exec. v.p., chief adminstrv. officer Dean Witter Fin. Svcs. Group (subs. Sears, Roebuck & Co.), N.Y.C., 1988—; Trustee Chgo. Dock and Canal Trust, 1985—. Trustee Lyric Opera Chgo., 1980—, Hull House Assn., Chgo., 1972-78, Rehab. Inst. Chgo., 1982—. Republican. Episcopalian. Home: 1430 N Lake Shore Dr Chicago IL 60610-1627 Office: Dean Witter Fin Svcs Group Ste 7701 2921 N Leisure World Blvd Silver Spring MD 20906-1372

WOOD, ROBERT WINFIELD, science administrator, biophysicist; b. Detroit, Mich., Dec. 31, 1931. BS, U. Detroit, 1953; MA, Vanderbilt U., 1955; PhD Biophysics, Cornell U., 1961. Sci. fellow Nat. Inst. Gen. Medicine, 1961-62; radiation physicist AEC, 1962-73; dir. phys. and tech. rsch. divsn.Office of Health and Environmental Rsch. U.S. Dept. Energy, Washington, 1973-91, dir. med. applications and biophysics dvsn., 1991—. Recipient Presidential Meritorious Rank award, 1990, Meritorious Svc. award Dept. Energy, 1990. Mem. Health Physics Soc., Radiation Rsch. Soc., Sigma Chi. Office: Office Health & Environ Rsch U S Dept Energy Mail Stop Er # 70 Gtn Washington DC 20585*

WOOD, RONALD, musician; b. London, June 1, 1947. Owner Woody's on the Beach (nightclub), Miami, 1987—. Guitarist and bassist with Jeff Beck Group, 1966-69, Faces, 1969-75, Rolling Stones, 1975—, New Barbarians, 1979; solo albums include Gimme Some Neck, 1979; albums (with Rolling Stones) Black and Blue, 1976, Love You Live, 1977, Some Girls, 1978, Sucking in the Seventies, 1981, Emotional Rescue, 1979, Tattoo You, 1981, Still Life, 1982, Undercover, 1983, Between the Sheets, 1985, Dirty Work, 1986, Rewind, 1986, Steel Wheels, 1988, Flashpoint, 1991, Voodoo Lounge, 1994 (Grammy award Best Rock Album); (with Faces) Long Player, A Nod's As Good As A Wink..., To a Blind Horse, Ooh-La-La; (with Small Faces) First Step, Ogden's Nut Gone Flake, There Are But Four Small Faces, 1991, All or Nothing, 1992; (solo) I've Got My Own Album To Do, Now Look; films include Let's Spend the Night Together, 1982, Digital Dreams, 1983. Office: care Columbia Records CBS Records 51 W 52nd St New York NY 10019-6119*

WOOD, SHARON, mountaineer; b. Halifax, N.S., Can., May 18, 1957; d. Stan and Peggy Wood. LLD (hon.), U. Calgary, 1987. Climbed peaks Mt. McKinley (Alaska), Mt. Logan (Can.), Mt. Aconcagua (Argentina), Mt. Makalu (Himalayas), Mt. Everest (Himalayas, 1st N.Am. woman to climb); Can. Light Everest Expedition, 1986; lectr. in field. Recipient Tenzing Norgay Trophy, 1987. Address: Box 1481, Canmore, AB Canada T0L 0M0

WOOD, STEPHANNIE ANNE, lawyer; b. N.Y.C., Apr. 18, 1958; d. Charles D. and Joan (Darcey) W.; m. Dale Robert McHenry, June 19, 1993. BA, Wellesley Coll., 1980; JD, Georgetown U., 1993. Asso. Tucker, Flyer, Sanger & Lewis, Washington, 1985-88; corp. counsel Cordant, Inc., Reston, Va., 1988—. Office: Cordant Inc 11400 Commerce Park Dr Reston VA 22091

WOOD, STEPHEN, minister. Dir. Native Am. Ministry Dist. of the Christian and Missionary Alliance. Office: 5664 Corinth Dr Colorado Springs CO 80918

WOOD, STEPHEN WRAY, minister; b. Winston Salem, N.C., Oct. 6, 1948; s. D.W. and Annie Lee (Harris) W.; m. Starr Smith, June 18, 1978; children: Allyson, Joshua. BTh., John Wesley Coll., 1973; BA, Asbury Coll., 1973; MA, U. N.C., 1979; DMin, Luther Rice Sem., Fla., 1980; MDiv, Houston Grad. Sch. Theology, 1990. Ordained to ministry Soc. of Friends, 1980. Asst. dean, asst. prof. John Wesley Coll., High Point, N.C., 1975-81; assoc. pastor Glenwood Friends Ch., Greensboro, N.C., 1979-81; pastor Deep River Friends Ch., High Point, 1981-84, Battle Forest Friends, 1986-92; adj. prof. Luther Rice Sem.; assoc. prof. Houston Grad. Sch. Theology; pres. Triad Christian Counseling, Greensboro, 1979. Contbr. articles to religious jours., Dictionary of N.C. Biography; composer, singer religious music. Trustee John Wesley Coll., High Point, 1981—; bd. dirs. Friends Ctr.-Guilford Coll., Greensboro, 1982-89; vice-chmn. Guilford County Rep. Party, N.C., 1981-85; rep. N.C. State Ho. of Reps., 1985-86, 89-90, 90-91, 92-93, 94-95; chaplain High Point Jaycees. With U.S. Army, 1970-71; capt. N.C. State Militia. Mem. BMI (affiliate songwriter 1978—). Avocations: golf, book collecting, reading. Office: 1221 E North Main St High Point NC 27262 *I often reflect upon the maternal advice proffered me as a child, "Steve, if at first you don't succeed, try, try again." We may be down but not out. There is no such thing as the good old days because the future is just as bright as the promises of God. We conquer by continuing.*

WOOD, STUART KEE, retired engineering manager; b. Dallas, Mar. 8, 1925; s. William Henry and Harriet (Kee) Wood; m. Loris V. Poock, May 17, 1951 (dec. June 1990); children: Linda S. Kuehl, Thomas N., Richard D.; m. Lois H. Morton, Nov. 25, 1994. BS in Aero. Engring., Tex. A&M U., 1949. Aircraft sheet metal worker USAF SAC, Kelly Field, San Antonio, Tex., 1942-45; structural design engr. B-52, 367-80, KC-135, 707 Airplanes Boeing, Seattle and Renton, Wash., 1949-55; thrust reverser design engr. 707 and 747 Airplanes Boeing, Renton, 1955-66; supr. thrust reverser group 747 Airplane Boeing, Everett, Wash., 1966-69; supr. rsch. basic engine noise 727 airplane FAA, NASA, 1969-74; supr. jetfoil propulsion Jetfoil Hydrofoil Boeing, Renton, 1974-75; supr. rsch. basic engine performance loss JT9D Pratt & Whitney, 1975-79; supr. propulsion systems 757 Airplane Boeing, Renton, 1979-90; supr., propulsion systems thrust reverser 737, 747, 757, 767 Boeing, Kent, Wash., 1990-94, ret., 1994. Patentee in field. Recipient Ed Wells award AIAA, N.W. chpt., Bellevue, Wash., 1992. Republican. Presbyterian. Avocations: photography, computers, travel. Home: 3831 46th St SW Seattle WA 98116

WOOD, THOMAS E., lawyer; b. L.A., Apr. 20, 1939; s. Louis Earl and Youda (Hays) W.; m. Sally Ann, June 22, 1963; children: Julia E. and Melissa H. BA, Amherst Coll., 1961; LLB, U. Pa., 1966. Bar: Pa. 1966. Assoc. Drinker Biddle & Reath, Phila., 1966-72, ptnr., 1972—. Chmn. Easttown Zoning Hearing Bd., Easttown Twp., Pa., 1976—. Mem. Phila. Club. Office: Drinker Biddle & Reath 1000 Westlakes Dr Ste 300 Berwyn PA 19312

WOOD, VIVIAN POATES, mezzo soprano, educator, author; b. Washington, Aug. 19, 1923; d. Harold Poates and Mildred Georgette (Patterson) W.; studies with Walter Anderson, Antioch Coll., 1953-55, Denise Restout, Saint-Leu-la-Fôret, France and Lakeville, Conn., 1960-62, 64-70, Paul A. Pisk, 1968-71, Paul Ulanowsky, N.Y.C., 1958-68, Elemer Nagy, 1965-68, Vyautas Marijosius, 1967-68; MusB Hartt Coll. Music, 1968; postgrad. (fellow) Yale U., 1968; MusM (fellow), Washington U. St. Louis, 1971, PhD (fellow), 1973. Debut in recital series Internat. Jeunesse Musicals Arts Festival, 1953, solo fellowship Boston Symphony Orch., Berkshire Music Ctr., Tanglewood, 1964, St. Louis Symphony Orch., 1969, Washington Orch., 1949, Bach Cantata Series Berkshire Chamber Orch., 1964, Yale Symphony Orch., 1968; appearances in U.S. and European recitals, oratorios, operas, radio and TV, 1953-68; appeared as soloist in Internat. Harpsichord Festival, Westminster Choir Coll., Princeton, N.J., 1973; appeared as soloist in meml. concert, Landowska Ctr., Lakeville, 1969; prof. voice U. So. Miss., Hattiesburg, 1971—, asst. dean Coll. Fine Arts, 1974-76, acting dean, 1976-77; guest prof. Hochschule für Musik, Munich, 1979-79; prof. Italian Internat. Studies Program, Rome, 1986; Miss. coord. Alliance for Arts Edn., Kennedy Ctr. Performing Arts, 1974—; mem. Miss. Gov.'s Adv. Panel for Gifted and Talented Children, 1974—; mem. 1st Miss. Gov.'s Conf. on the Arts, 1974—; bd. dirs. Miss. Opera Assn. Author: Polenc's Songs: An Analysis of Style, 1971. Recipient Young Am. Artists Concert award N.Y.C., 1955; Wanda Landowska fellow, 1968-72. Mem. Miss. Music Tchrs. Assn., Nat. Assn. Tchrs. of Singing, Music Tchrs. Nat. Assn., Am. Musicology Soc., Golden Key, Mu Phi Epsilon, Delta Kappa Gamma, Tau Beta Kappa (hon.), Pi Kappa Lambda. Democrat. Episcopalian. Avocation: sailing. Office: U So Miss Sch Music South Pt # 8264 Hattiesburg MS 39406-9539

WOOD, WAYNE W., state legislator; b. Janesville, Wis., Jan. 21, 1930. Gen. high sch., Janesville. Formerly builder, contractor, factory worker; mem. Janesville City Coun., 1972-76, pres., 1974-75; mem. Wis. State Assembly, Madison, 1976—; mem. criminal justice and corrections com., mem. ways and means com., 1985—, vice chair 1989-95; mem. state affairs com., 1987—. Mem. State VTAE Bd., 1975-76; mem. Coun. of State Govts. Legis. Oversight Task Force, 1973, Janesville Housing Authority, 1971-77; former mem. Children's Svc. Coun. Adv. Bd., Rock County Sr. 4-H Coun., Sinnissippi Coun. Boy Scouts Am. Mem. UAW. Home: 2429 Rockport Rd Janesville WI 53545-4445

WOOD, WENDY DEBORAH, filmmaker; b. N.Y.C., Oct. 4, 1940; d. John Meyer and Marion Emily (Peters) W.; m. William Dismore Chapple, Dec. 7, 1963; 1 child, Samuel Eliot. BA cum laude, Vassar Coll., 1962; MA,

Stanford U., 1964. Teaching asst. Stanford U., 1962-64; photographer, film editor Bristol (Eng.) U., 1964-66, asst. dir. Internat. Conf. Film Schs., 1966; rsch. asst. biology dept. U. Conn., Storrs, 1970-72; sr. media specialist Aetna Life & Casualty Co., Hartford, Conn., 1972-89; media writer, prodr., dir. U. Conn. Ctr. for Media and Tech., Storrs., 1989—; pres. Chapple Films, Inc., 1972—. Films include: Yankee Craftsman, 1972; Alcoholism, Industry's Costly Hangover, 1974; Draggerman's Haul, 1975; Flight Without Wings, 1977; Auto Insurance Affordability (2 awards), 1981; Where Rivers Run to the Sea (award), 1981; Our Town is Burning Down (6 awards), 1982; Wellness at the Worksite, 1984 (4 awards); Welcome to the Aetna Institute, 1985 (4 awards); Aenhance, 1989 (3 awards). Mem. peer rev. com. Conn. Commn. Higher Edn., 1992—. Recipient CINE Golden Eagle award Council on Internat. Non-theatrical Events, 1972, 76, 84, 1st Place award Indsl. Photography, 1974, cert. Outstanding Creativity U.S. TV Commls. Festival, 1974, EFLA award Am. Film Festival, 1974, 76, Dir's. Choice award Sinking Creek Film Festival, 1975, award Columbus Film Festival, 1975, award Excellence Life Ins. Advtrs. Assn., 1975, Silver Screen award U.S. Indsl. Film Festival, 1976, 81, 1st place award Conn. Film Festival, 1977, 1st prize Nat. Outdoor Travel Film Festival, 1978, 1st pl. Houston Film Festival, 1982, CINE Golden Eagle, 1982, 84, award Am. Film Festival, 1982, N.Y. Film Festival, 1982, 83, Silver CINDY award Assn. Visual Communicators, 1985, others. Bd. dirs. Windham Regional Arts Council, 1987, 88, 89; mem. jury N.Y. Internat. Video and Film Festival. Mem. Info. Film Producers Am. (nat. dir., pres. chpt. 1981-82, Cindy award 1971, 72, 81, 82, 85, 87), Internat. Quorum Motion Picture Producers, Audio Visual Communicators (pres. Conn. chpt. 1985, treas. 1988). Democrat. Quaker. Home: 604 Phoenixville Rd Chaplin CT 06235-2211 Office: U Conn Media Ctr # U-1 Storrs CT 06269

WOOD, WILLIAM DEAN, accountant; b. Indianola, Iowa, July 5, 1947; s. Donald Ruble and Ruby Marie (Smith) W.; m. Nancy Ann Doane, Sept. 13, 1969; children: John Patrick, Michelle Lynne. BBA, U. Iowa, 1973. CPA, Iowa. Staff auditor McGladrey, Hausen, Dunn & Co., Cedar Rapids, Iowa, 1973-75; mgr. McGladrey, Hendrickson & Co., Dubuque, 1975-81; mgr. Arthur Young & Co., Tulsa, 1981-84, prin., 1984-88, dir. entrepreneurial services, 1986-88; chief fin. officer Okla. Fixture Co., Tulsa, 1988—. Chmn. budget com. Dubuque United Way, 1980-81; mem. allocation exec. com. Tulsa United Way, 1986-89; bd. dirs. Palmer Drug Abuse Program, 1988—. Mem. Am. Inst. CPA's, Iowa Soc. CPA's, Okla. Soc. CPA's, Nat. Assn. Accts. Presbyterian. Club: Tulsa Country. Avocations: golf, referee for youth soccer. Office: Okla Fixture Co 924 S Hudson Ave Tulsa OK 74112-2945

WOOD, WILLIAM JEROME, lawyer; b. Indpls., Feb. 14, 1928; s. Joseph Gilmore and Anne Cecilia (Morris) W.; m. Joann Janet Jones, Jan. 23, 1954; children: Steven, Matthew, Kathleen, Michael, Joseph, James, Julie, David. Student, Butler U., 1945-46; AB with honors, Ind. U., 1950, JD with distinction, 1952. Bar: Ind. bar 1952. Mem. firm Wood, Tuohy, Gleason, Mercer & Herrin (and predecessor), Indpls., 1952—; bd. dirs. Grain Dealers Mut. Ins. Co., Indpls., Am. Income Life Ins. Co., Waco, Tex.; gen. counsel Ind. Cath. Conf.; city atty., Indpls., 1959-60; instr. Ind. U. Sch. Law, 1960-62. Author: Indiana Pastors' Legal Handbook, 2nd edit., 1992, Realtors' Indiana Legal Handbook, 2d edit., 1991. Mem. Ind. Corp. Survey Commn., 1963—, chmn., 1977-86; mem. Ind. Corp. Law Study Commn., 1985-87; mem. Ind. Non Profit Corp. Law Study Commn., 1989-91; past bd. dirs. Alcoholic Rehab. Center, Indpls., Indpls. Lawyers' Commn., Community Svc. Coun. Indpls. Served with AUS, 1946-48. Recipient Brotherhood award Ind. region NCCJ, 1973. Mem. Ind. Bar Assn. (award 1968, sec. 1977-78), Indpls. Bar Assn. (pres. 1972-73, coun. bd. mgrs. 1992-93), Indpls. Bar Found., St. Thomas More Legal Soc. (pres. 1970), Indpl. Lit. Club (pres. 1973-74). Democrat. Roman Catholic. Home: 3619 E 75th Pl Indianapolis IN 46240-3674 Office: 3400 Bank One Ctr Tower Indianapolis IN 46204-5134

WOOD, WILLIAM MCBRAYER, lawyer; b. Greenville, S.C., Jan. 27, 1942; s. Oliver Gillan and Grace (McBrayer) W.; m. Nancy Cooper, 1973 (dec. 1993); children: Walter, Lewis; m. Jeanette Dobson Haney, June 25, 1994. BS in Acctg., U. S.C., 1964, JD cum laude, 1972; LLM in Estate Planning (scholar), U. Miami, 1980. Bar: S.C. 1972, Fla. 1979, D.C. 1973, U.S. Tax Ct. 1972, U.S. Ct. Claims 1972, U.S. Supreme Ct. 1977. Intern ct. of claims sect., tax div. U.S. Dept. Justice, 1971; law clk. to chief judge U.S. Ct. Claims, Washington, 1972-74; ptnr. firm Edwards Wood, Duggan & Reese, Greer and Greenville, 1974-78; asst. prof. law Cumberland Law Sch., Samford U., Birmingham, Ala., 1978-79; faculty Nat. Inst. Trial Advocacy: N.E. Regional Inst., 1979, 83-90, Fla. Regional Inst., 1989; teaching team 5th intensive trial techniques course Hofstra U., 1983; assoc. then capital ptnr. firm Shutts & Bowen, Miami, 1980-85; sole practice, Miami, 1985—; also Rock Hill, S.C., 1994—. Contbg. editor: The Lawyers PC; Fla. editor: Drafting Wills and Trust Agreements; substantive com. editor ABA: The Tax Lawyer, 1983—. Pres. Piedmont Heritage Fund., Inc. 1975-78; del. State Rep. Conv., 1985, 1987, 90; exec. committeeman Dade County Republicans, 1988-94, co-gen. counsel, 1990-91; apptd. Dade County Indsl. Devel. Authority, 1990-94; mem. vestry Episc. Ch., 1993-94. With USAF, 1965-69, Vietnam. Decorated Air Force Commendation medal; recipient Am. Jurisprudence award in real propery and tax I, 1971; winner Grand prize So. Living Mag. travel photo contest, 1969. Mem. ABA (taxation sect., teaching law com., 1994—), Greer C. of C. (pres. 1977, Outstanding leadership award 1976), Greater Greenville C. of C. (dir. 1977), Order Wig and Robe, Estate Planning Council South Fla., Omicron Delta Kappa. Club: Bankers (bd. govs. 1989—). Lodge: Masons, Rotary. Office: 5345 Wilgrove Mint Hill Rd Charlotte NC 28227-3467

WOOD, WILLIAM PHILLER, lawyer; b. Bryn Mawr, Pa., Oct. 3, 1927; s. Clement Biddle and Emily (Philler) W.; m. Maud Isabel Atherton, Dec. 30, 1950 (dec. 1970); children: William P., Maude H., Louisa B.; m. 2d Sara Elizabeth Wadsworth, Mar. 19, 1977; stepchildren: Jeremy B. Grace Eric W. Grace. A.B., Harvard U., 1949, J.D., 1955. Bar: Pa. 1956. Assoc. firm Morgan, Lewis & Bockius, Phila., 1955-64; ptnr. Morgan, Lewis & Bockius, 1964-91, counsel, 1991-95; bd. dirs. McArdle Desco Corp., New Castle, Del. Trustee Grundy Foun., Bristol, Pa., 1980—, chmn., 1993-95; trustee Genesee Valley Conservancy, 1990—, pres., 1992—; pres. Phila. Mus. of Art, 1976-80, chmn. exec. com., 1980—, v.p., 1972-76, treas., 1968-72; trustee Fairmount Park Art Assn., 1972—, v.p., 1985—; trustee Louis I. Stott Found., Phila., 1969-94, Bryn Mawr Hosp., 1962-76, Phila. Lyric Opera Co., 1960-70; treas. Phila. Art Alliance, 1960-66; pres. La Napoule (France) Art Found. Henry Clews Meml., 1984-86, chmn. 1986—. Served to 1st lt. U.S. Army, 1950-52. Mem. ABA, Pa. Bar Assn. Clubs: Phila., State-in-Schuykill, Knickerbocker. Home: Woodbine Farm 457 E London Grove Rd West Grove PA 19390 Office: Morgan Lewis & Bockius 2000 One Logan Sq Philadelphia PA 19103

WOOD, WILLIAM RANSOM, retired university president, city official, corporate executive; b. nr. Jacksonville, Ill., Feb. 3, 1907; s. William James and Elizabeth (Ransom) W.; m. Margaret Osborne, 1930 (dec. 1942); 1 son, William Osborne (dec. 1978); m. Dorothy Jane Irving, Mar. 18, 1944; children: Mark Irving, Karen Jane Parrish. A.B., Ill. Coll., 1927, LL.D., 1960; M.A., U. Iowa, 1936, Ph.D., 1939; LLD, U. Alaska, 1989. Tchr., coach pubs. schs. Mich., Iowa, Ill., 1928-46; asst. Supt. Evanston Twp. Schs., Ill., 1948-50; specialist jr. colls. and lower divs. U.S. Office Edn., 1950-53, program planning officer, 1953; dean statewide devel. higher edn. U. Nev., 1954-55, acting president dept. English, 1955-56, acad. v.p., 1955-60, acting pres., 1958-60; pres. U. Alaska, 1960-73; mayor Fairbanks, Alaska, 1978-80; pres. Pacific Alaska Assocs., Ltd.; exec. v.p. Fairbanks Indsl. Devel. Corp., Festival Fairbanks '84; mem. staff study needs and resources higher edn. FAO, Libya, 1955; mem. study group off-duty ednl. program armed forces in Europe, U.S. Dept. Def., 1955; del. Am. Assembly Rgn. Rels., 1957-58; chmn. Nev. com. Fulbright scholarships, 1957-58; mem. chancellor's panel SUNY; mem. sci. group traveling to Antarctica, New Zealand, Australia; presenter sesquicentennial address Sigma Pi Literary Soc. of Ill. Coll., 1993. Editor: Looking Ahead, 1953, From Here On, 1954, All Around the Land, 1954, Youth and The World, 1955, To Be an American, 1957; author, editor: On Your Own, 1953; co-editor: Short Stories as You Like Them, 1940, Youth Thinks It Through, 1941, Just for Sport, 1943, Fact and Opinion, 1945, Short Stories, 1951, Study of Financing of Higher Education in Asia, 1968; author (verse): Not From Stone, 1983, Legacy of Dreams, 1993. Chmn. Alaska Am. Cancer Soc.; v.p. Alaska council Boy Scouts Am.; mem. bd. Rampart Dam adv. com.; mem. Gen. Med. Scis. Nat. Adv. Council,

Alaska Higher Edn. Facilities Commn., 1967, Alaska Small Bus. Adv. Council, 1968, Satellite Communications Task Force; spl. asst. to mayor for trade and devel. Fairbanks North Star borough, 1984—; chmn. Greater Fairbanks Community Hosp. Found.; mem. White House Fellows Selection Panel, Nat. Adv. Council on Edn. Professions Devel.; chmn. Alaska Heart Assn.; mem. Alaskan Command Civilian Adv. Bd., 1962—; bd. dirs. U. Alaska Found., exec. dir. Fest. Fairbanks '84, 1981—. Served to lt. USNR, 1943-46; capt. USNR, ret. 1968. Recipient Outstanding Alaskan award, 1984, Alaskan of Yr. award, 1985, Centennial award Alexis de Tocqueville Soc., 1987, Disting. Citizen award Alaska coun. Boy Scouts Am., 1992; named to Ill. Coll. Athletic Hall of Fame, 1993. Fellow Arctic Inst. N. Am.; mem. Am. Geog. Soc., Assn. Higher Edn. (exec. com.), Nat. Univ. Extension Assn., N.W. Assn. Secondary and Higher Schs., Western Assn. Colls., Navy League, AAAS, Assn. Applied Solar Energy (adv. council 1959), Am. Assn. Land-grant colls. and State Univs., Internat. Assn. Univ. Presidents (exec. com.). Methodist. Clubs: Explorers, Fairbanks Petroleum, Washington Athletic. Lodge: Rotary (gov. dist. 503 1985-86). Home: 665 10th Ave Apt 305 Fairbanks AK 99701-4664

WOOD, WILLIS BOWNE, JR., utility holding company executive; b. Kansas City, Mo., Sept. 15, 1934; s. Willis Bowne Sr. and Mina (Henderson) W.; m. Dixie Gravel, Aug. 31, 1955; children: Bradley, William, Josh. BS in Petroleum Engring., U. Tulsa, 1957; grad. advanced mgmt. program, Harvard U., 1983. Various positions So. Calif. Gas Co., L.A., 1960-74, v.p. then sr. v.p., 1975-80, exec. v.p., 1983-84; pres., CEO Pacific Lighting Gas Supply Co., L.A., 1981-83; sr. v.p. Pacific Enterprises, L.A., 1984-85, exec. v.p., 1985-89, pres., 1989-91, pres., CEO, 1991-92, chmn., pres., CEO, 1992-93, chmn., CEO, 1993—; bd. dirs. Gt. Western Fin. Corp., Gt. Western Bank, L.A.; dir. Automobile Club of So. Calif.; trustee U. So. Calif.; mem. com. visitors Rand Grad. Sch. Trustee, vice chmn. Harvey Mudd Coll., Claremont, Calif., 1984—; Calif. Med. Ctr. Found., L.A., 1983—, vice chmn.; trustee, past pres. S.W. Mus., L.A., 1988—; bd. dirs. L.A. World Affairs Coun., 1994—; dir., past chmn. bus. coun. for Sustainable Energy Future, 1994—; trustee U.S.C. Mem. Soc. Petroleum Energy Engrs., Am. Gas Assn., Pacific Coast Gas Assn. (past bd. dirs.), Pacific Energy Assn., Calif. Bus. Roundtable, Calif. State C. of C. (bd. dirs.), Nat. Assn. of Mfrs. (bd. dirs.), Hacienda Golf CLub, Ctr. Club, Calif. Club. Republican. Office: Pacific Enterprises 633 W 5th St Ste 5400 Los Angeles CA 90013-1011

WOODALL, DAVID MONROE, research engineer; b. Perryville, Ark., Aug. 2, 1945; m. Linda Carol Page, June 6, 1966; 1 child, Zachary Page. B.A., Hendrix Coll., 1967; M.S., Columbia U., 1968; Ph.D., Cornell U., 1974. Registered profl. engr., N.Mex. Nuclear engr. Westinghouse Corp., Pitts., 1968-70; asst. prof. U. Rochester, N.Y., 1974-77; asst. prof. U. N.Mex., Albuquerque, 1977-79, assoc. prof., 1979-83, prof., 1984-86, chair dept., 1980-83; group physics mgr. Idaho Nat. Engring. Lab., Idaho Falls, 1986-92; cons. to govt. Contbr. articles to sci. jours. Grantee NSF, Office Naval Research, others. Mem. Am. Phys. Soc., Am. Nuclear Soc. (chpt. chair 1982-83), IEEE. Home: 2449 Moscow Mountain Rd Moscow ID 83843*

WOODALL, JACK DAVID, manufacturing company executive; b. Ferndale, Mich., Aug. 1, 1936; s. William John and Florence Gladys (Feyen) W.; m. Janice Tracy Lanier, July 6, 1958; children: David Lanier, Kevin Langford, Elizabeth Tracy, Matthew Thomas. BS in Bus., Stetson U., 1958; MS in Internat. Affairs, George Washington U., 1969. Commd. 2d lt. U.S. Army, 1958, advanced through grades to lt. gen., 1989; comdr. 1st Brigade, 2d Inf. Div., Camp Casey, Republic of Korea, 1978-79; chief officer distbn. Mil. Pers. Ctr., Alexandria, Va., 1979-81, dir. plans and ops., 1981-82; chief plans and policy Allied Forces So. Europe, Naples, Italy, 1982-84; asst. div. comdr. 4th Inf. Div., Colorado Springs, Colo., 1984-86; comdg. gen. Berlin Brigade, 1986-87; dep. comdg. gen. V Corps, Frankfurt, Fed. Republic Germany, 1987-88; comdg. gen. 2d Inf. Div., Camp Casey, Korea, 1988-89, U.S. Army Japan, IX Corps, Camp Zama, 1989-92; pres. Innovative Tech., Brooksville, Fla., 1992—. V.p. West Pacific Girl Scouts Japan, Republic of Korea, The Philippines, 1989-92, Far East coun. Boy Scouts Am., 1990-92. Recipient Disting. Alumni award Stetson Alumni Assn., 1985, numerous mil. awards. Mem. Assn. U.S. Army (chpt. pres. 1986-88), Greater Hernando County C. of C. (dir.), Barnett Banks of the Sun Coast (dir.). Avocation: jogging.

WOODALL, LOWERY A., hospital administrator; b. Lincoln County, Miss., June 10, 1929; s. Clem and Ruth (Smith) W.; m. Pat Pack; children: Linda Woodall Sullivan, Lowery A., Margaret Michelle Rowell. BS, U. So. Miss., 1951; postgrad. Baylor U., 1956, U. Chgo., 1959. Bus. mgr. Miss. Bapt. Hosp., Jackson, 1953-56, adminstrv. asst., 1956-58, asst. adminstr., 1958-62; exec. dir. Forrest Gen. Hosp., Hattiesburg, Miss., 1962—; dir. Blue Cross/Blue Shield, Jackson, 1975—, Hattiesburg Community Blood Ctr.; pres., dir. AAA Ambulance Service, Inc., 1967—; past chmn. Southeastern Hosp. Conf. 11-state, 1981-82, Miss. Hosp. Assn., Jackson, 1970-71. Bd. dirs. Indsl. Park Commn., Hattiesburg, 1981—; mem. Forrest County Indsl. Bd., Hattiesburg, 1972—; pres. 1972-73. Named Exec. of Yr., Sales and Mktg. Assn., 1977, Profl. Secs. Internat., 1981; Hub award Community Leaders, 1981; Liberty award South Central Miss. Bar Assn., 1982; recipient Disting. Svc. Award for Excellence, Southeastern Hosp. Conf., 1992. Fellow Am. Coll. Hosp. Adminstrs. Baptist. Lodge: Rotary (pres. 1978-79). Home: 1 Bristol Ln Hattiesburg MS 39402-2368 Office: Forrest Gen Hosp PO Box 16389 Hattiesburg MS 39404-6389

WOODALL, NORMAN EUGENE, banker; b. Miss., June 10, 1916; s. Albert Edward and Annie (Smith) W.; m. Virginia Dale Willard, Aug. 12, 1967. BSBA, Miss. State U., 1939; postgrad., Am. Inst. Banking, 1962; grad., Sch. Banking of South, La. State U., 1964, Advanced Inf. Sch., 1959, Command and Gen. Staff Coll., 1965, Indsl. Coll. Armed Forces, 1970. Adjuster Comml. Credit Co., Jackson, Miss., 1939-41; loan examiner RFC, Birmingham, Ala., 1946-55; sr. v.p. First Nat. Bank Birmingham, 1955—. Bd. dirs Birmingham chpt. ARC, 1974-78; treas. Muscular Dystrophy Assn. Jefferson County Chpt., 1958, pres. 1959-60. Served to col., infantry AUS, 1941-46, ret. 1972. Decorated Bronze Star with V devise, Legion of Merit. Mem. Res. Officers Assn., Assn. U.S. Army, Am. Inst. Banking, Miss. State U. Alumni Assn., Birmingham C. of C.S.R. in State of Ala. (treas. 1990-91, v.p. 1992-93, pres. 1993-94), Ams. Royal Descent, Sovereign Colonial Soc., Newcomen Soc. N.Am., Magna Carta Barons, Colonial Order of the Crown, Birmingham Exch. Club (bd. govs. 1960-62, 71-72, 75-76, v.p. 1973-74, pres. 1974-75), Vestavia Club (Vestavia Hills, Ala.), The Club, Sigma Chi. Home: 3422 Loch Ridge Trl Birmingham AL 35216-4406 Office: 1900 5th Ave N Birmingham AL 35203-2610

WOODALL, SAMUEL ROY, JR., trade association executive; b. July 8, 1936; s. Samuel Roy W.; m. Jane Marvin Brock, Aug. 5, 1958; children—Samuel Roy III, Lawrence B., Claiborne A., George G. B.A., U. Ky., 1958, LL.B., 1962; postgrad. (Woodrow Wilson fellow), Yale U., 1959. Bar: Ky. bar 1962. Atty. Ky. Dept. Ins., 1962-64, gen. counsel, 1965-66; comml. ins. Commonwealth Ky., 1966-68; assoc. firm Wyatt, Grafton and Sloss, Louisville, 1968-69; ptnr. Wyatt, Grafton and Sloss, 1969-72; pres. Western Pioneer Life Ins. Co. (and predecessors), Louisville, 1972-76; asst. to pres. Am. Life & Accident Ins. Co., Louisville, 1976-80; pres. Nat. Assn. Life Cos., Washington, 1980-93; v.p. and director state rels. Am. Coun. Life Ins., Washington, 1993—; guest instr. ins. law U. Louisville, 1968-69. Note editor: U. Ky. Law Rev, 1961-62. Pres. Citizen's Met. Planning Council, Louisville, 1970-71; chmn. City of Louisville Riverfront Commn., 1970-75, Ky. Heritage Commn., 1964-77; bd. dirs. Bingham Child Guidance Clinic, Louisville, 1969-76, Youth Performing Arts Council, 1979-80. Recipient Sullivan medallion U. Ky., 1958; named 1 of Ky.'s 3 Outstanding Young Men Ky. Jr. C. of C., 1968. Mem. ABA, Ky. Bar Assn., D.C. Bar Assn., Fedn. Ins. Counsel, Phi Beta Kappa, Phi Alpha Delta (pres. 1961-62). Home: 2851 29th St NW Washington DC 20008-4111 Office: Am Coun Life Ins 1001 Pennsylvania Ave NW Washington DC 20004

WOODALL, WILLIAM LEON, retired insurance executive; b. Kirby, Ark., July 29, 1923; s. Ocie Doan and Hazel Cornelia (Paslay) W.; m. Patricia Ann Reese, Sept. 30, 1950; children: Michael Reese, David William, Stacy Ann. BS, Miami U., Oxford, Ohio, 1947. CPCU. Home office underwriter Ohio Casualty Group Ins. Cos., Hamilton, 1947-52, underwriter Mpls. br. office, 1952-53, field rep., Des Moines, 1953-54, underwriter Detroit br. office, 1962-64, mgr. Indpls. br. office, 1964-68, company v.p., Hamilton,

1968-77, sr. v.p., 1977-84, exec. v.p., sec., 1984-88, pres., chief oper. officer, 1988-91, also bd. dirs.; ptnr. Cady Ins. Agy., Burlington, Iowa, 1954-62. Republican. Methodist. Lodge: Elks. Home: 910 Macewen Dr Osprey FL 34229-9293

WOODARD, ALFRE, actress; b. Tulsa, Nov. 8, 1953; m. Roderick Spencer; 2 adopted children. Student, Boston U. Appeared in (films) Remember My Name, 1976, Health, Cross Creek, 1983 (Acad. award nomination), Extremities, 1986, Scrooged, 1988, Mandela, 1988, Miss Firecracker, 1989, Grand Canyon, 1991, The Gun in Betty Lou's Handbag, 1992, Passion Fish, 1992, Heart and Souls, 1993, Rich in Love, 1993, Bopha!, 1993, Blue Chips, 1994, Crooklyn, 1994, How to Make an American Quilt, 1995, (TV series) Tucker's Witch, 1982-83, Sara, 1985, St. Elsewhere, 1985-87, Hill Street Blues (Emmy award for guest appearance in drama series 1984), L.A. Law (Emmy award for guest appearance in drama series 1987), (TV spls.) For Colored Girls Who Have Considered Suicide/When the Rainbow is Enuf, Trial of the Moke, Words by Heart, (TV films) A Mother's Courage: The Mary Thomas Story, Child Saver, Ambush Murder, Freedom Road, 1979, Sophisticated Gents, 1981, The Killing Floor, Unnatural Causes, 1986, Mandela, 1987, The Child Saver, Sweet Revenge, 1990, Blue Bayou, 1990, Bopho, 1993, (plays) For Colored Girls Who Have Considered Suicide, When the Rainbow is Enuf, (off-Broadway plays) A Map of the World, 1985, A Winter's Tale 1989, So Nice They Named Twice, Horatio. Recipient Emmy awards for guest appearance in drama series. Office: ICM 8942 Wilshire Blvd Beverly Hills CA 90211*

WOODARD, ALVA ABE, business consultant; b. Roy, N.Mex., June 28, 1928; s. Joseph Benjamin and Emma Lurania (Watkins) W.; m. Esther Josepha Kaufmann, Apr. 5, 1947 (div. Sept. 1991); children: Nannette, Gregory, Loreen, Arne, Mark, Kevin, Steven, Curtis, Marlee, Julie, Michelle; m. Margaret Adele Evenson, Oct. 1, 1994. Student, Kinman Bus. U., 1948-49, Whitworth Coll., 1956, Wash. State U., 1953-54. Sec.-treas., dir. Green Top Dairy Farms, Inc., Clarkston, Wash., 1948-52; v.p., treas., sec., dir. ASC Industries, Inc. (subs. Gifford-Hill and Co.), Spokane, Wash., 1953-75; dir. Guenther Irrigation, Inc., Pasco, Wash., 1966-71; mng. dir. Irrigation Rental, Inc., Pasco, 1968-75, Rain Chief Irrigation Co., Grand Island, Nebr., 1968-75; sec., dir. Keeling Supply Co., Little Rock, 1969-72; pres., dir. Renters, Inc., Salt Lake City, 1971-75, Woodard Western Corp., Spokane, 1976-86, Woodard Industries, Inc., Auburn, Wash., 1987-90; cons. Woodard Assocs., Spokane, Wash., 1985—; pres., dir. TFI Industries, Inc., Post Falls, Idaho, 1989-90; v.p., sec., treas., dir. Trans-Force, Inc., Post Falls, 1989-90, TFI Computer Scis., Inc., Post Falls, 1989-90. Newman Lake (Wash.) Rep. precinct committeeman, 1964-80; Spokane County del. Wash. Rep. Conv., 1968-80. Mem. Adminstrv. Mgmt. Soc. (bd. dirs. 1966-68), Optimists. Avocations: fishing, theater, golf, reading, dancing. Home and Office: PO Box 30333 Spokane WA 99223-3005

WOODARD, CAROL JANE, educational consultant; b. Buffalo, Jan. 19, 1929; d. Harold August and Violet Maybelle (Landsittel) Young; m. Ralph Arthur Woodard, Aug. 19, 1950; children—Camaron Jane, Carsen Jane, Cooper Ralph. BA, Hartwick Coll., 1950; MA, Syracuse U., 1952; PhD, SUNY, Buffalo, 1972; LHD (hon.), Hartwick Coll., 1991; postgrad., Bank St. Coll., Harvard U. Cert. tchr., N.Y. State. Tchr. Orchard Park, N.Y., 1950-51, Danville, Ind., 1951-52, Akron, N.Y., 1952-54; dir. Garden Nursery Sch., Williamsville, N.Y., 1955-65; tchr. Amherst (N.Y.) Coop. Nursery Sch., 1967-69; asst. prof. early childhood edn. SUNY, Buffalo, 1969-72; lab. demonstration tchr. and student teaching supr. SUNY, 1969-76, assoc. prof., 1972-79, prof., 1979-88, prof. emeritus, 1988—; co-dir. Consultants in Early Childhood, 1988—; cons. Lutheran Ch. Am., Villa Maria Coll., Buffalo Pub. Schs., Buffalo Mus. Sci., Headstart Tng. Programs, Erie Community Coll., N.Y. State Dept. Edn., numerous workshops.; cons. sch. systems, indsl. firms, pubs., civic orgns. in child devel.; vis. prof. The Netherlands and East China Univ., Shanghai, People's Republic of China; sci. trainer The Wright Group, 1995. Author 7 books for young children, 2 textbooks in field; co-author Physical Science in Early Childhood, 1987, 2d edit., 1995; co-author nat. curriculum for ch. sch. for 3-yr.-olds; author: (booklet) You Can Help Your Baby Learn; author/coord. TAKE CARE child protection project, 1987; contbr. chpt. to When Children Play, 1985; cons. EPIC Birth to Three Program, 1992; design cons. for indoor playground Noah's Ark, Jewish Ctr., Buffalo, 1992, sites project Buffalo Pub. Schs., 1994-95; contbr. numerous articles in field to profl. jours. Bd. trustees Hartwick Coll., Oneonta, N.Y., 1978-87. Mem. Nat. Assn. Edn. Young Children, Early Childhood Edn. Council Western N.Y., Assn. Childhood Edn. Internat., Phi Delta Kappa, Pi Lambda Theta. Home: 1776 Sweet Rd East Aurora NY 14052-3028

WOODARD, CLARENCE JAMES, manufacturing company executive; b. Conde, S.D., May 8, 1923; s. Wayne W. and Sarah (Halley) W.; m. Patricia Ann Roberts, Jan. 12, 1946; children—Charles D., Sarah H., Scott D., Thomas J. Student, Stanford U., 1941-43; BS with honors in Mech. Engring, Calif. Inst. Tech., 1944; LHD (hon.), John F. Kennedy U., 1986. Pres. Baldwin-Lima-Hamilton Co., Los Angeles, 1946-53; with Rucker Co., Oakland, Calif., 1953-77, chmn. bd., chief exec. officer, 1965-77; office of chmn., cons. to bd. dirs., dir., mem. audit and fin. coms. NL Industries, Inc., N.Y., 1977-82; pres., chief exec. officer Woodard Industries, Inc., San Francisco, 1982—; chmn. Woodard Found., San Francisco; past chmn. West Coast exec. council Nat. Indsl. Conf. Bd.; past chmn. exec. com., bd. dirs., audit com. Delta Calif. Industries, San Francisco; bd. dirs. Informatics Inc., Los Angeles, Systron Donner Corp., Concord, Calif. Bd. dirs., trustee U. Calif. Sch. Bus. Adminstrn., Berkeley; mem. nat. council Salk Inst., La Jolla, Calif.; vice chmn. bd. regents John F. Kennedy U., Orinda, Calif.; chmn. Calif. Found. for the Retarded, Oakland; life nat. trustee Boys Clubs Am., N.Y.C.; bd. dirs., pres. Oakland Boys Clubs; bd. dirs. Children's Hosp., Oakland; trustee Orinda Found.; bd. dirs., vice chmn. United Way, San Francisco; bd. dirs. exec. com. chmn., chmn. fin. com. San Francisco Mus. Modern Art; donor Woodard treatment rm. St. Luke Hosp., San Francisco. Served to lt. USNR, 1943-46. Endowed Woodard Chair in Mech. Engring. at Stanford U.; Patricia R. Woodard Disting. Lecture Series on Cancer, St. Francis Hosp., San Francisco, donor New Patient Pavilion, Children's Hosp. of Oakland; named Man of Yr., Easter Seal Soc., 1986, Am. Cancer Soc., 1989, Episcopal Charities, 1991. Mem. ASME (life), Am. Petroleum Inst., Inst. Environ. Scis., Tau Beta Pi. Clubs: Pacific Union, St. Francis Yacht, Villa Taverna, Commonwealth (San Francisco); Claremont Country, Lakeview (Oakland); Orinda Country; Les Ambassadeurs (London). Office: PO Box 7357 San Francisco CA 94120-7357

WOODARD, HAROLD RAYMOND, lawyer; b. Orient, Iowa, Mar. 13, 1911; s. Abram Sylvanus and Grace Lenora (Brown) W.; m. Clara F. Jarrell, Apr. 30, 1986; children: Walter J., Turner J., Laurel C. BS, Harvard U., 1933, LLB, 1936. Bar: Ind. 1936. Since practiced in Indpls.; ptnr. Woodard, Emhardt, Naughton, Moriarty & McNett; adj. prof. patent law Ind. U. Sch. Law, Indpls., 1957-88. Served as lt. USNR, 1942-46. Named Sagamore of the Wabash, Gov. of Ind., 1991. Fellow Am. Coll. Trial Lawyers; mem. ABA, Ind. 7th Cir. Bar Assn. (past pres.), Am. Patent Law Assn., Lawyers Assn. Indpls. (past pres.), Ind U. Sch. Law-Indpls. Alumni Assn. (1st hon. mem.). Methodist. Clubs: Columbia (past pres.), Woodstock (past pres.), University (past pres.), 100 Club (past pres.). Office: Woodard Emhardt Naughton Moriarty & McNett 3700 Bank One Tower Indianapolis IN 46204-5137

WOODARD, JOHN ROGER, urologist; b. Hawkinsville, Ga., Dec. 18, 1932; s. John Alton and Mary Louise (Williams) W.; m. Inga Lou Harper, Sept. 3, 1955; children—John Roger, Susan, Stephen, Honor. Student, Emory U., Atlanta, 1950-53; M.D. Med. Coll. Ga., Augusta, 1957. Diplomate: Am. Bd. Urology. Intern in surgery Med. Coll. Va., 1957-58, resident in surgery, 1958-59; resident in urology N.Y. Hosp.-Cornell Med. Center, 1959-63; postgrad. fellow in pediatric urology Great Ormand St. Hosp. for Sick Children, London, 1963-64; instr. surgery, surgeon to outpatients N.Y. Hosp.-Cornell Med. Center, 1964; asso. in surgery Emory U., 1964-68; asso. prof. surgery U. Ala. Med. Center, 1968-69; prof. urol. surgery, dir. pediatric urology Emory U., 1969—; chief urology Henrietta Eggleston Hosp. for Children, 1970—; numerous vis. professorships. Contbr. articles to sci. jours., chpts. to med. textbooks. Fellow ACS (bd. govs. 1986-92), Am. Acad. Pediatrics (chmn. urology sect. 1987-88); mem. AMA, Med. Assn. Atlanta (dirs. 1986-89), Med. Assn. Ga., Soc. Pediatric Urology, Am. Urol. Assn., Am. Assn. Gen. Urol. Surgeons, Soc. Pediatric Urol. Surgeons, Nat. Urol. Forum, Cherokee Town and Country Club. Home: 1022

Lullwater Rd NE Atlanta GA 30307-1244 Office: 1901 Century Blvd NE Ste 14 Atlanta GA 30345-3300

WOODARD, JOSEPH LAMAR, law librarian, law educator; b. Auburndale, Fla., Dec. 28, 1937; s. Wilbur Allen and Florence Virginia (Ladd) W.; m. Eleanor Eugenia Cummings, Aug. 7, 1964; children: Robert Edward, James Frederick. BA, U. Fla., 1959, J.D., 1962; MS in Libr. Sci., Columbia U., 1964. Bar: Fla. 1962, U.S. Dist. Ct. (mid. dist.) Fla. 1970. Asst. reference libr. Columbia U., N.Y.C., 1962-64; asst. libr.Cahill, Gordon, Reindel and Ohl, N.Y.C., 1964-65; law libr. Tulane U., 1965-69; ptnr. Schuh, Schuh and Woodard, St. Petersburg, Fla., 1969-71; law librarian Stetson U., 1971—, prof. law, 1979—. Pres. Tampa Bay Library Consortium, 1981, 88-89. Served with USAR, 1957-63. Mem. Fla. Bar, Am. Assn. Law Librs. (sec.-treas. S.E. chpt. 1975-78), Pinellas Pub. Lib. Coop. (sec.-treas. 1993-94, pres. 1994—). Republican. Presbyterian. Office: 1401 61st St S Saint Petersburg FL 33707-3299

WOODARD, LARRY L., Bible college official; b. Lebanon, Oreg., Apr. 16, 1936; s. Hugh Frank and Ima Ellen (Bilyeu) W.; m. Bette Jeanette Brown, Aug. 10, 1956; children: Perry, Craig, Stacy. BS in Forestry, Oreg. State U., 1957. Forester Bur. of Land Mgmt., Oreg., 1957-69, Washington, 1969-72; dist. mgr. Bur. of Land Mgmt., Coeur d'Alene, Idaho, 1972-76; assoc. state dir. Bur. of Land Mgmt., Boise, Idaho, 1976-78, Santa Fe, 1978-82, Boise, 1982-86; state dir. Bur. of Land Mgmt., Santa Fe, 1987-93; dir. devel. Boise Bible Coll., 1993—. Author: A to Z, The Biography of Arthur Zimmerman, 1988, Before the First Wave, 1994. Bd. dirs. Boise Bible Coll., 1977-87; trustee N.Mex. Nature Conservancy, 1987-90. Recipient Disting. Svc. award U.S. Dept. Interior, 1986, Sec.'s Stewardship award U.S. Dept. Interior, 1989, Pres.'s Meritorious Exec. award, 1991. Republican. Avocations: teaching history, writing, hunting, gardening. Home: PO Box 365 Meridian ID 83680 Office: Boise Bible Coll 8695 Marigold Boise ID 83714

WOODARD, NINA ELIZABETH, banker; b. L.A., Apr. 3, 1947; d. Alexander Rhodes and Harriette Jane (Power) Mathews; m. John David Woodard, Mar. 17, 1966 (div.); children: Regina M., James D. Grad. Pacific Coast Banking Sch., 1987; BS in mgmt., Calif. Coast U., 1993. Lifetime cert. sr. profl. in human resources. Dental asst. Donald R. Shire DDS, L.A., 1965-66; with Security Pacific Nat. Bank, Marina Del Rey, Calif., 1968-69; with First Interstate Bank, Casper, Wyo., 1971—; adminstr. asst. personnel, 1975-78, asst. v.p., asst. mgr. pers., 1978-82, v.p., dir. mktg. and pers., 1982-84, v.p., mgr. human resources, 1984-88; v.p., mgr. employee rels. First Interstate Bank Ltd., L.A., 1988-93, v.p. mgr. employee rels. Americas Region; instr. mktg. Am. Inst. Banking, 1983, Casper Coll., 1982. Mem. Civil Svc. Commn., City of Casper, 1983-88; bd. dirs. YMCA, 1984-87, Downtown Devel. Assn.; pres. Downtown Casper Assn. Named Bus. Woman of Yr., Bus. and Profl. Women, 1982, Young Career Woman, 1975. Mem. Nat. Assn. Bank Women, Bus. and Profl. Women (dist. dir.), Am. Soc. Pers. Adminstrn. (regional v.p., state coun. Wyo. 1987-88), Pers. and Indsl. Rels. Assn. (chmn. govt. affairs com. 1989-90, Fast Track award 1991, Pres.'s Achievement award 1993, conf. chmn. 1991, 92, dist. vice chair 1992, dist. chair 1993, 2d v.p. 1994). Fin. Women Internat. (Wyo. state chair 1986, regional adn. and tng. chair 1987, dist. coord. L.A. 1993, L.A. group chair 1994), St. Patrick's Parish Religious Edn. (instr. 1991-92, parish coun. 1993-94). Republican. Roman Catholic.

WOODARD, ROBERT E., bishop. Bishop, Ch. of God in Christ, S.E. Tex., Houston. Office: Ch of God in Christ 2614 Wichita St Houston TX 77004-7714

WOODBERRY, PAUL FRANCIS, real estate executive; b. Boston, Dec. 23, 1927; s. Ronald S. and Elsie E. (Carney) W.; m. Margery Ann Brennan, May 7, 1955; children: Laura, Seth, Lesley, Sarah, Sturgis. B.A., Dartmouth Coll., 1949, M.B.A., 1950. Group exec. W.R. Grace & Co., N.Y.C., 1955-69; pres. Winston Industries, Birmingham, Ala., 1969-70; v.p. Alleghany Corp., N.Y.C., 1970-76, now dir.; exec. v.p. Centex Corp., Dallas, 1976-86; chief fin. officer, exec. v.p. BF Enterprises, Inc., San Francisco, 1986—, also bd. dirs.; cons. Alleghany Corp., 1991—. Bd. dirs. Alleghany Corp., Alleghany Properties Inc., World Minerals, Inc., Harborlite Corp., URC Holdings Co. BF Enterprises, Inc. 1st lt. USAF, 1951-55. Decorated Air medal, Commendation medal. Republican. Roman Catholic. Club: University (N.Y.C.). Home: 1855 Tularosa Rd Lompoc CA 93436-9643 Office: PO Box 639 Lompoc CA 93438

WOODBRIDGE, HENRY SEWALL, management consultant; b. N.Y.C., Sept. 20, 1906; s. George and Harriet (Manley) W.; m. Dorothy Steese White, Jan. 8, 1928 (dec. May 1981); children: Henry Sewall, Anne Sidney (Mrs. William Pickford), Victoria (Mrs. Richard G. Hall). Student, Harvard U., 1923-26. With Stone & Webster, Inc., 1926-27; gen. mgr., dir. Raymond Whitcomb, Inc., 1927-40; bus. mgr., asst. to pub. Boston Evening Transcript, 1940-41; former v.p. Am Optical Co., Southbridge, Mass.; dir. Am. Optical Co., 1941-77; pres. Todd-AO Corp., N.Y.C., 1954-58; fin. and mgmt. cons., 1958—; chmn. bd. True Temper Corp., 1960-66, pres., 1964-65; cons. Editoria Guias LTB SA, Rio de Janeiro and São Paulo, Brazil, 1966-83, Barwick Industries, 1967—. Internat. Horizons, Inc., 1975-85, Learning Techs., Inc., 1985—; pres., mng. dir. Hillwood Corp., 1966-84; also dir.; bd. dirs. Hambro Am. Bank & Trust Co., Vesper Corp., Union Labor Life Ins. Co. Chmn., Sch. Bldg. Com. Pomfret (Conn.), 1943-47, 58-60; mem. Fin. Com. Brookline (Mass.), 1936-39; chmn. Fire, Safety, Pub. Welfare Sub-Com., 1938-39; mem. Conn. Devel. Commn., 1948-55; industry rep. Nat. War Labor Bd., 1942-45; mem. safety equipment adv. com WPB, 1942-46; trustee Old Sturbridge Village, 1941—, chmn., 1965-66; trustee Middlesex Sch., Day-Kimball Hosp. Mem. Indsl. Relations Research Assn., New Eng. Soc. N.Y. (pres. 1962-65), Soc. Cincinnati in State of N.H. (pres. 1989-92). Episcopalian. Clubs: Harvard U., Union (N.Y.C.); Harvard U., Tavern (Boston); Harvard U. Faculty (Cambridge, Mass.); Met., Cosmos (Washington). Home: Drumlin-Ho Pomfret CT 06258 Office: PO Box 156 Pomfret CT 06258-0156

WOODBRIDGE, HENSLEY CHARLES, retired foreign languages educator, librarian; b. Champaign, Ill., Feb. 6, 1923; s. Dudley Warner and Ruby Belle (Mendenhall) W.; m. Anne Emma Smith, Aug. 28, 1953; 1 dau., Ruby Susan Woodbridge Jung. A.B., Coll. William and Mary, 1943; M.A., Harvard, 1946; Ph.D., U. Ill., 1950, M.S. in L.S. 1951; student, U. Nacional de Mexico, summer 1941, 45; D.Arts, Lincoln Meml. U., 1976. Corr. Worldover Press, Mexico, 1945; instr. French and Spanish U. Richmond, 1946-47; teaching asst. U. Ill., 1948-50; reference librarian Ala. Poly. Inst., 1951-53; librarian Murray (Ky.) State Coll., 1953-65; Latin-Am. bibliographer, asso. prof. fin. langs. So. Ill. U., Carbondale, 1965-71, prof., 1971-93, prof. emeritus, 1993—. Author: (with Paul Olson) Tentative Bibliography of Ibero-Romance Linguistics, 1952, Jesse Stuart: a bibliography, 1960, (with Gerald Moser) Rubén Darío y el Cojo ilustrado, 1964, (with John London and George Tweney) Jack London: a bibliography, 1966, rev. edit., 1973, Jesse Stuart and Jane Stuart: a bibliography, 1969, rev. edit., 1979, Rubén Darío: A selective critical bibliography, 1975, Rubén Darío: una bibliografía selectiva, clasificada y anotada, 1975, Benito Pérez Galdós: A selective annotated bibliography, 1975, (with David Zubatsky) Pablo Neruda: An Annotated Bibliography of Biographical and Critical Studies, 1988; co-author: Printing in Colonial Spanish America, 1976; editor Ky. Library Assn. Bull, 1959-60, Ky. Folklore Record, 1963-64, Am. Assn. Tchrs. Spanish and Portuguese-Scarecrow Press Bibliographical Series; contbg. editor: Am. Book Collector, 1965-73; assoc. editor: Hispania, 1967-81; editor, pub.: Jack London Newsletter, 1967-91; mem. editorial bd.: Modern Lang. Jour, 1971-73, Hispanic Linguistics, 1983—; co-editor: (with Dan Newberry) Basic List of Latin American Materials in Spanish, Portuguese and French, 1975; co-compiler: (with Annie Woodbridge) The Collected Short Stories of Mary Johnston, 1982, Spanish and Spanish American Literature: An Annotated Guide to Selected Bibliographies, 1983, Guide to Reference Works for the Study of the Spanish Language and Literature, 1987; contbr. to: Ency. Info. and Library Scis., vol. 36. Mem. Ky. Folklore Soc., Medieval Soc. Am., Cervantes Soc. Am., MLA, Am. Assn. Tchrs. Spanish and Portuguese, Bibiog. Soc. Am., Ky. Hist. Soc.; Instituto de estudios madrileños, Asociación española de bibliografía, Hispanic Soc. Am. (corr.). Club: Filson. Home: 1804 W Freeman St Carbondale IL 62901-2106

WOODBRIDGE, JOHN MARSHALL, architect, urban planner; b. N.Y.C., Jan. 26, 1929; s. Frederick James and Catherine (Baldwin) W.; m. Sally Byrne, Aug. 14, 1954; children: Lawrence F., Pamela B., Diana B.; m. Carolyn Kizer, Apr. 8, 1975. B.A. magna cum laude, Amherst Coll., 1951; M.F.A. in Architecture, Princeton U., 1956. Designer John Funk, architect, San Francisco, 1957-58; designer, assoc. partner Skidmore, Owings & Merrill, San Francisco, 1959-73; staff dir. Pres.'s Adv. Council and Pres.'s Temporary Commn. on Pennsylvania Ave., Washington, 1961-63; exec. dir. Pennsylvania Ave. Devel. Corp., Washington, 1973-77; lectr. architecture U. Calif., Berkeley; vis. prof. U. Oreg., Washington U., St. Louis. Co-author: Buildings of the Bay Area, 1960, A Guide to Architecture in San Francisco and Northern California, 1973, Architecture San Francisco, 1982, San Francisco Architecture, 1992. Chmn. Commn. on Architecture Episc. Ch. Recipient Fed. Design Achievement award Nat. Endowment for Arts, 1988; Fulbright scholar to France, 1951-52. Fellow AIA; mem. Nat. Trust Historic Preservation, Soc. Archtl. Historians, Phi Beta Kappa. Democrat. Episcopalian. Home and Office: 19772 8th St E Sonoma CA 95476-3803

WOODBRIDGE, LINDA, English language educator; b. Chelsea, Mass., Mar. 23, 1945; d. Richard Lord and Viola Beatrice (MacDougall) Taylor; married; children: Dana Louise, Rachel Amelia. BA with honors, UCLA, 1966, MA, 1968, PhD, 1970. Asst. prof. U. Alta., Edmonton, Can., 1970-76, assoc. prof. English, 1976-82, prof., 1982-94, chmn. dept., 1986-89; prof. Penn. State U., Pa., 1994—. Author: Women and the English Renaissance, 1984, The Scythe of Saturn: Shakespeare and Magical Thinking, 1994, numerous articles; compiler: Shakespeare: A Selective Bibliography, 1987; co-editor True Rites & Maimed Rites: Ritual and Anti-Ritual in Shakespeare and His Age, 1992. Rsch. grantee Social Sci. and Humanities Rsch. Coun. Can., 1980, 91-94, 94—. Mem. MLA, Shakespeare Assn. Am. (v.p. 1991-92, pres. 1992-93), Assn. Can. U. Tchrs. of English, Renaissance Soc. Am. Office: Penn State U 117 Burrowes Bldg University Park PA 16802

WOODBURN, RALPH ROBERT, JR., lawyer; b. Haverhill, Mass., Nov. 3, 1946; s. Ralph Robert and Josephine Marie (McClure) W.; m. Janet M. Smith, Sept. 15, 1985. BA, Mich. State U., 1967; JD, Harvard U., 1972; LLM, Boston U., 1981. Bar: Mass. 1972, U.S. Tax Ct. 1987. Assoc. Bowers, Fortier & Lakin, Boston, 1972-76; ptnr., assoc. Haussermann, Davison & Shattuck, Boston, 1976-83; ptnr. Palmer & Dodge, Boston, 1983—; tchr. Harvard Ctr. for Lifelong Learning, Cambridge, Mass., 1986-89. Contbr. articles to Boston Bar Jour. and Estate Planning. Treas. Exeter Assn. of New Eng., Boston, 1985-89, v.p. 1989-91, pres., 1991-93. Fellow Am. Coll. Trust and Estate Counsel; mem. ABA, Boston Bar Assn. (chmn. probate legislation 1983-93, chmn. Wellesley Cable Access bd. 1993-95). Club: Brae Burn Country (Newton, Mass.). Home: 25 Cypress Rd Wellesley MA 02181-2918 Office: Palmer & Dodge 1 Beacon St Boston MA 02108-3106

WOODBURY, ALAN TENNEY, lawyer; b. Milw., July 7, 1943; s. Isaiah Tenney and Maxine Arvilla (Hooper) W.; m. Deborah Carson Eayre, Jan. 27, 1968; children: Jeffrey Tenney, Alison Eayre. BA, Bowdoin Coll., 1965; JD, Temple U., 1968. Bar: Pa. 1968; CLU, ChFC. Atty. Fidelity Mut. Life Ins. Co., Phila., 1968-74, assoc. counsel, 1974-76, asst. v.p., assoc. counsel, 1976-78, 2nd v.p., assoc. counsel, 1978-79, 2nd v.p., sec., assoc. counsel, 1979-84; v.p., sec., assoc. counsel Fidelity Mut. Life Ins. Co., Radnor, Pa., 1984-91, sr. v.p., sec., gen. counsel, 1991-93, sr. v.p. ins. coun., 1994—. Mem. ABA, Phila. Bar Assn., Assn. Life Ins. Counsel, Ins. Fedn. Pa. (trustee pension plan). Republican. Office: Fidelity Mut Life Ins Co 250 King Of Prussia Rd Wayne PA 19087-5295

WOODBURY, LAEL JAY, theatre educator; b. Fairview, Idaho, July 3, 1927; s. Raymond A. and Wanda (Dawson) W.; m. Margaret Lillian Swenson, Dec. 19, 1949; children: Carolyn Enz (Mrs. Donald Hancock), Shannon Margaret (Mrs. Michael J. Busenbark), Jordan Ray, Lexon Dan. BS, Utah State U., 1952; MA, Brigham Young U., 1953; PhD (Univ. fellow), U. Ill., 1954. Teaching asst. U. Ill., 1953; assoc. prof. Brigham Young U., 1954-61; guest prof. Colo. State Coll., 1962; asst. prof. Bowling Green State U., 1961-62; asso. prof. U. Iowa, 1962-65; producer Ledges Playhouse, Lansing, Mich., 1963-65; prof. speech and dramatics, chmn. dept. Brigham Young U., 1966-70, assoc. dean Coll. Fine Arts and Communications, 1969-73, dean Coll. Fine Arts and Communications, 1973-82; vis. lectr. abroad; bd. dirs. Eagle Systems Internat.; bd. dir. workshop Fedn. for Asian Cultural Promotion, Republic of China; dir. European study tour. Author: Play Production Handbook, 1959, Mormon Arts, vol. 1, 1972, Mosaic Theatre, 1976, also articles, original dramas; profl. actor PBS and feature films. Chmn. gen. bd. drama com. Young Men's Mut. Improvement Assn., 1958-61; bd. dirs. Repertory Dance Theatre, Utah ARC; chmn. Utah Alliance for Arts Edn.; mem. adv. coun. Utah Arts Festival; missionary LDS Ch., N.Y.C., 1994. With USN, 1942-46. Recipient Creative Arts award Brigham Young U., 1971, Disting. Alumni award, 1975, Tchr. of Yr. award, 1988, Excellence in Rsch. award, 1992, Disting. Svc. award, 1992. Mem. Rocky Mountain Theatre Conf. (past pres.), Am. Theatre Assn. (chmn. nat. com. royalties 1972—, mem. fin. com. 1982—), NW Assn. Univs. and Colls. (accrediting officer), Am. Theatre Assn. (v.p. Univ. and Coll. Theatre Assn.), Theta Alpha Phi, Phi Kappa Phi. Home: 1303 Locust Ln Provo UT 84604-3651

WOODBURY, MARION A., insurance company executive; b. Wilmington, N.C., 1923; m. Alice Battey Bryson; children—Sheldon, Marion A., Frank, Spencer, Alice. Student, U. N.C., 1949; LLB, Woodrow Wilson Coll., 1956. With exec. tng. program Chubb and Son, N.Y.C., 1949; asst. to pres. Bankers Fire & Marine Ins. Co., 1957, exec. v.p. to pres., 1958; v.p. Reins. Corp. of N.Y., 1959-62, exec. v.p., 1962-65, pres., 1965—, also bd. dirs.; chmn. bd., chief exec. officer, dir. United Reins. Corp. N.Y.; bd. dirs. Piedmont Mgmt. Co., Inc., Navigators Ins. Co., POHJOLA A. Ins. Corp.; trustee Coll. of Ins., 1970-75. Served with C.E. U.S. Army, 1945, PTO. Decorated Bronze Star; recipient Good Scout award Greater N.Y. Council Boy Scouts Am., 1977. Mem. Reins. Assn. Am. (chmn. 1974-75, bd. dirs.), U.S. Srs. Golf Assn. Clubs: Wall St. (gov.); Baltrusol Golf. Home: 14 Delegal Rd The Landings Savannah GA 31411 Office: Reins Corp NY 80 Maiden Ln New York NY 10038-4811

WOODBURY, MAX ATKIN, polymath, educator; b. St. George, Utah, Apr. 30, 1917; s. Angus Munn and Grace (Atkin) W.; m. Lida Gottsch, May 30, 1947; children—Carolyn, Max TenEyck, Christopher, Gregory. B.S., U. Utah, 1939; M.S., U. Mich., 1941, Ph.D., 1948; M.P.H., U. N.C., Chapel Hill, 1977. Mem. faculty U. Mich., 1947-49; mem. Inst. for Adv. Study, Princeton, N.J., 1949-50; mem. faculty Princeton U., 1950-52, U. Pa., 1952-54; prin. investigator logistics research project Office Naval Research, George Washington U., 1954-56; faculty NYU, 1956-66; prof. computer sci. Duke U., prof. biomath. Med. Ctr., 1966-88, sr. fellow Ctr. for Study of Aging and Human Devel., 1975—, sr. fellow, sr. scientist Ctr. Demographic Studies, 1985—, prof. emeritus, 1987—; pres. Biomed. Information-processing Orgn., 1961-62, Inst. for Biomed. Computer Research, 1961-71; cons. WHO, UNIVAC, CBS on computer election forecasts, 1952-62, sci. orgns., univs., govt. agys., corps. Contbr. articles to profl. jours. Served with USAAF, 1941-46, MTO. USPHS, NIH grantee, also other govt. agys., 1947—; recipient MERIT award Nat. Inst. on Aging, NIH, June 1, 1988-May 31, 1998. Fellow AAAS, Am. Statis. Assn., Inst. Math. Statistics; mem. numerous sci., profl. socs., Phi Beta Kappa, Sigma Xi, Phi Kappa Phi (inventor of GoM methodology). Home: 4008 Bristol Rd Durham NC 27707-5403 Office: Duke U Ctr Demographics 2117 Campus Dr Durham NC 27708-0408

WOODBURY, RICHARD BENJAMIN, anthropologist, educator; b. West Lafayette, Ind., May 16, 1917; s. Charles Goodrich and Marion (Benjamin) W.; m. Nathalie Ferris Sampson, Sept. 18, 1948. Student, Oberlin Coll., 1934-36; BS in Anthropology cum laude, Harvard U., 1939, MA, 1942, PhD, 1949; postgrad., Columbia U., 1939-40. Archeol. research Ariz., 1938, 39, Fla., 1940, Guatemala, 1947-49, El Morro Nat. Monument, N.Mex., 1953-56, Tehuacan, Mex., 1964; archaeologist United Fruit Co. Zaculeu Project, Guatemala, 1947-50; assoc. prof. anthropology U. Ky., 1950-52, Columbia U., 1952-58; rsch. assoc. prof. anthropology interdisciplinary arid lands program U. Ariz., 1959-63; curator archeology and anthropology U.S. Nat. Mus., Smithsonian Instn., Washington, 1963-69, acting. head office anthropology, 1965-66, chmn. office anthropology 1966-67; prof., chmn. dept. anthropology U. Mass., Amherst, 1969-73; prof. U. Mass. 1973-81, prof.

emeritus, 1981—, acting assoc. provost, dean grad. sch., 1973-74; mem. divsn. anthropology and psychology NRC, 1954-57; bd. dirs. Archaeol. Conservancy, 1979-84, Valley Health Plan, Amherst, 1981-84, Mus. of No. Ariz., 1983-90; liason rep. for Smithsonian Instn., Com. for Recovery of Archeol. Remains, 1965-69; assoc. seminar on ecol. systems and cultural evolution Columbia U., 1964-73; mem. exec. com. bd. dirs. Human Relations Area Files, Inc., New Haven, Conn., 1968-70; cons. Conn. Hist. Commn., 1970-72. Author (with A.S. Trik) The Ruins of Zaculeu, Guatemala, 2 vols., 1953, Prehistoric Stone Implements of Northeastern Arizona, 1954, Alfred V. Kidder, 1973, Sixty Years of Southwestern Archaeology, 1993; editor: (with I.A. Sanders) Societies Around the World (2 vols.), 1953, (with others) The Excavation of Hawikuh, 1966, Am. Antiquity, 1954-58, Abstracts of New World Archaeology; editor-in-chief: Am. Anthropologist, 1975-78; mem. editorial bd.: Am. Jour. Archeology, 1957-72. Mem. sch. com., Shutesbury, Mass., 1979-82, chmn., 1980-82, bd. assessors, 1982-85; chmn. finance com. Friends of Amherst Stray Animals, 1983-85. With USAF, 1942-45. Fellow Mus. No. Ariz., 1985. Fellow Am. Anthrop. Assn. (exec. bd. 1963-66, A.V. Kidder award 1989), AAAS (coun. rep. Am. Anthrop. Assn. 1961-63, com. on desert and arid zones rsch. Southwest and Rocky Mountains divsn. 1958-64, vice-chair 1962-64, com. arid. lands 1969-74, sec. 1970-72), Archaeol. Inst. Am. (exec. com. 1965-67); mem. Soc. Am. Archeology (treas. 1953-54, pres. 1958-59, chmn. fin. com. 1987-89, Fiftieth Anniversary award 1985, Disting. Svc. award 1988), Ariz. Archeol. and Hist. Soc., Kroeber Anthrop. Soc., Archeol. Conservancy (life), Sigma Xi. Office: U Mass Dept Anthropology Machmer Hall Amherst MA 01003

WOODBURY, THOMAS BOWRING, II, public utility executive, lawyer; b. Salt Lake City, Sept. 15, 1937; s. Thomas Bowring and Beulah B. Woodbury; m. Kathleen Thompson, June 15, 1965; children—Leslie, Thomas, Todd, Matthew, Ashley. A.B. cum laude, Brigham Young U., 1962; J.D., U. Utah, 1966; postgrad. Oxford U. (Eng.), 1961, U. London, 1959-60. Bar: Utah, 1966, N.Y. 1974, Pa. 1982. Assoc. McKay & Burton, Salt Lake City, 1966-72; assoc. gen. counsel Am. Re-Ins. Co., N.Y., 1972-78; sr. v.p., gen. counsel Ins. Co. of N.Am., Phila., 1978-82; exec. v.p., gen. counsel, sec. Home Ins. Co., N.Y., 1982-87; sr. v.p., gen. counsel Comml. Union Ins. Co., Boston, 1987-89; sr. v.p., gen. counsel Edison Co. N.Y., Inc., 1989—. Mem. N.Y. State Bar Assn., Pa. Bar Assn., Utah Bar Assn., Assn. of Bar of City of N.Y. Republican. Mormon. Office: Consol Edison Co of NY Inc 4 Irving Pl New York NY 10003-3502

WOODCOCK, DAVID GEOFFREY, architect, educator; b. Manchester, Eng., May 28, 1937; s. Herbert Edwin and Constance Mary (Bristol) W.; m. Kathleen Mary Bishop, Oct. 1, 1960 (dec. 1964); 1 child, Jonathan Alfred; m. Valerie Frances Gubbins, July 4, 1964; children: Frances Mary, Penelope Jane. BA with 1st class honors in Architecture, U. Manchester, 1960, D in Town Planning, 1966. Chartered architect, U.K.; registered architect, Tex. Lectr. U. Manchester, 1961; asst. prof. Tex. A&M U., College Station, 1962-66, assoc. prof., 1970-76, prof., 1976—; sr. lectr. Kent. Inst. Art & Design, Canterbury, England, 1966-70; pvt. practice, College Station, 1980—, Canterbury, 1966-70. Bd. dirs. Opera and Performing Arts Soc. Tex. A&M U., 1980-83, 88-91, pres., 1993-94, adv. bd. Hammons Sch. Architecture Drury Coll., Mo., 1990-93, Savannah (Ga.) Coll. Arts and Design/Architecture, 1987-93; active Episc. Diocese Tex. Archtl. Commn., 1987—. Recipient Rsch. Excellence award Tex. Hist. Commn., 1991. Fellow AIA; mem. Royal Inst. British Architecturs, Assn. for Preservation Tech. Internat. (bd. dirs. 1990—), Nat. Coun. for Preservation Edn. (bd. dirs.), Assn. Collegiate Schs. Architecture (regional dir. 1981-84, Disting. Prof. 1991). Avocations: drawing, creative and gifted education, choral singing. Office: Tex A&M U Dept Architecture College Station TX 77843

WOODCOCK, LEONARD, humanities educator, former ambassador; b. Providence, Feb. 15, 1911; s. Ernest and Margaret (Freel) W.; m. Sharon Lee Tuohy, Apr. 14, 1978; children—Leslie, Janet, John. Ed., St. Wilfred's Coll.; student, Wayne State U., 1928-30, Walsh Inst. Accountancy, Detroit, 1928-30; numerous hon. degrees. Staff rep. internat. union UAW, 1940-46, adminstrv. asst. to pres., 1946-47, internat. v.p., 1955-70, pres., 1970-77, pres. emeritus, 1977—; chief of mission with rank of amb. U.S. Liaison Office, Peking, 1977-79; amb. to People's Republic of China, 1979-81; adj. prof. U. Mich., 1981—; bd. dirs. ATC Internat. Inc., Houston; dynamometer operator Continental Aviation & Engring. Co., 1947. Bd. govs. emeritus Wayne State U., 1970. Mem. Am.-China Soc. (bd. dirs.). Home: 2404 Vinewood Blvd Ann Arbor MI 48104-2768

WOODCOCK, RICHARD BEVERLEY, health facility administrator; b. Leeds, Yorkshire, Eng., June 7, 1945; arrived in Can., 1948; s. Stanley Walter and Jessica Stretton (Coyne) W.; children: Matthew, Christopher, Jeffrey, Lindsay. Honors BA in Bus. Adminstrn., Waterloo (Ont.) Luth. U., 1970. Cert. hosp. adminstr. Dir. fin. Northwestern Gen. Hosp., Toronto, 1973-76; asso. adminstr. Brantford Gen. Hosp., Ont., 1976-81, pres., 1982—; sec., treas. Brantford Gen. Hosp. Found., 1977—. Fellow Am. Coll. Healthcare Execs., Can. Coll. Health Svc. Execs., Rotary (bd. dirs. Brantford chpt. 1981-84). Avocations: alpine skiing, boating. Office: Brantford Gen Hosp, 200 Terrace Hill St, Brantford, ON Canada N3R 1G9

WOODDELL, PHILO GLENN, fine arts educator, radio broadcaster and producer; b. Hutchinson, Kans., Sept. 3, 1941; s. Philo Davis and Jean Elise Wooddell. B of Music Edn., Southwestern Coll., Winfield, Kans., 1963; MM, Crane Sch. Music, Potsdam, N.Y., 1985; MA, NYU, 1989. Cert. in music and speech edn., N.Y. Tchr., chmn. fine arts/humanities dept. Jeffersonville (N.Y.)-Youngsville Ctrl. Sch. Dist. 1, 1965—; local host N.P.R.'s Morning Edition, WJFF-FM; producer, host Sunday Brunch for WJFF-FM, N.P.R. show Music of the Cinema; mem. programming and adv. bds. Radio Catskill; also mem. bd. trustees, 1991-92, v.p. bd. trustees, 1993; clinician on film music MOMA, N.Y.C.; mem. adv. com. Cities as Schs. Bldg. Leadership Team. Dir. profl. and semi-profl. prodns. for dinner, proscenium, exptl. and children's theatre; performed with Central City (Colo.) Opera Assn., Kansas City Starlight Theatre, Dallas Summer Musicals, N.P.R. Playhouse; shows at various Catskill resorts; vocalist with Phila. Orch., Saratoga Performing Arts Ctr., Saratoga Springs, N.Y.; voice over/narration experience; editor The Collegian; contbr. articles to profl. jours. Founder Sullivan County (N.Y.) Help Line; founder, bd. dirs. Sullivan County Festival of the Arts Program. Mem. Am. Guild of Variety Artists, Music Educators Nat. Conf., Am. Choral Dirs. Assn., Am. Film Inst. (charter), Arts Alliance Assn., Arts in Edn. Assn., N.Y. State United Tchrs., Sullivan County Dramatic Workshop, N.Y. State Music Educators Assn., Soc. for Preservation of Film Music, Lions Club Internat., Phi Mu Alpha Sinfonia. Home: 50 Durr Rd Box 88 Jeffersonville NY 12748-0088 Office: Sta WJFF-Radio Catskill Box 797 Jeffersonville NY 12748-0797

WOODEN, JOHN ROBERT, former basketball coach; b. Martinsville, Ind., Oct. 14, 1910; s. Joshua Hugh and Roxie (Rothrock) W.; m. Nellie C. Riley, Aug. 8, 1932; children: Nancy Anne, James Hugh. B.S., Purdue U., 1932; M.S., Ind. State U., 1947. Athletic dir., basketball and baseball coach Ind. State Tchrs. Coll., 1946-48; head basketball coach UCLA, 1948-75; lectr. to colls., coaches, business. Author: Practical Modern Basketball, 1966, They Call Me Coach, 1972; Contbr. articles to profl. jours. Served to lt. USNR, 1943-46. Named All-Am. basketball player Purdue U., 1930-32, Coll. Basketball Player of Yr., 1932, to All-Time All-Am. Team Helms Athletic Found., 1943, Nat. Basketball Hall of Fame, Springfield (Mass.) Coll., as player 1960, as coach, 1970, Ind. State Basketball Hall of Fame, 1962, Calif. Father of Yr., 1964, 75, Coach of Yr. U.S. Basketball Writers Assn., 1964, 67, 69, 70, 72, 73, Sportsman of Yr. Sports Illustrated, 1973, GTE Acad. All-Am., 1994; recipient Whitney Young award Urban League, 1973, 1st ann. Velvet Covered Brick award Layman's Leadership Inst., 1974, 1st ann. Dr. James Naismith Peachbasket award, 1974, medal of excellence Bellarmine Coll., 1987. *I have tried to live the philosophy of my personal definition of success which I formulated in the middle thirties shortly after I entered the teaching profession. Not being satisfied that success was merely the accumulation of material possessions or the attainment of a position of power or prestige, I chose to define success as "peace of mind which can be attained only through the self-satisfaction that comes from knowing you did your best to become the best that you are capable of becoming."*

WOODEN, REBA FAYE BOYD, guidance counselor; b. Washington, Ind.; Sept. 21, 1940; d. Lester E. and Opal M. (Burch) Boyd; m. N. Nuel Wooden, Jr., Dec. 23, 1962 (div. 1993); children: Jeffrey Nuel, Cynthia Faye. BA, U.

Indpls., 1962; MS, Butler U., 1968, Ind. U., 1990. Cert. tchr., counselor, Ind. Tchr. Mooresville (Ind.) High Sch., 1962-66; tchr. Perry Meridian High Sch., Indpls., 1974-92, counselor, 1992—; part-time instr. Ind. U.-Purdue U. at Indpls., 1994—. Named Outstanding High Sch. Psychology tchr. APA, 1987. Mem. AACD, NEA, Ind. State Tchrs. Assn., Perry Edn. Assn. Methodist. Avocations: reading, travel. Home: 113 Severn Dr Greenwood IN 46142-1880 Office: Perry Meridian High Sch 401 W Meridian School Rd Indianapolis IN 46217-4215

WOODEN, RUTH A., public service advertising executive; b. Madison, Wis., Aug. 4, 1946. BA, U. Minn., 1968, postgrad. Project dir. Lee Creative Rsch., St. Louis, 1970-72; project mgr. Ralston Purina, St. Louis, 1972-78; sr. v.p., account dir. N.W. Ayer, N.Y.C., 1978-88; pres. The Advt. Coun., Inc., N.Y.C., 1988—. Bd. dirs. CARE Inc., N.Y.C., 1980—, U.S. Trust Corp.; trustee Edna McConnell Clark Found., St. Luke's/Roosevelt Hosp. Ctr. Mem. Internat. Radio & TV Soc. (bd. dirs.). Office: The Advt Coun Inc 261 Madison Ave New York NY 10016-2303

WOODFIELD, CLYDE VERNON, senator; b. Hot Springs, Ark., Feb. 11, 1932; s. Ozy V. and Bessie L. (Robertson) W.; m. Sharon Jean McCoy, Mar. 1, 1966; children: John, David, Kelly, Michael. BBA, U. So. Miss., 1955; postgrad., U. Ark., U. So. Miss. Owner, operator Sahara Motel, Gulfport, Miss., Woodfield Farms, Gulfport; asst. mayor City of Gulfport; mem. Ho. of Reps., Jackson, Miss., 1967-71, 82-86; mem. Miss. State Senate, Jackson, 1987—, vice chmn. rules com., 1993—, chmn. bus. and fin. instns. com., 1993—. Bd. dirs. Salvation Army, 1983, Cheshire Home, 1992-94, Natural Sci. Found., 1993; pres. Arts Fair for Handicapped, 1992; mem. exec. bd. Miss Teen USA, 1991-94. Mem. Masons, Shriners. Home: Woodfield Farms 11452 County Farm Rd Gulfport MS 39503 Office: Miss State Senate PO Box 1018 Jackson MS 39215-1018

WOODFORD, ARTHUR MACKINNON, library director, historian; b. Detroit, Nov. 23, 1940; s. Frank Bury and Mary-Kirk (MacKinnon) W.; children: Mark, Amy; m. Reneé Ann Skuba, Apr. 25, 1990; stepchildren: Brandon, Christopher. Student, U. Wis., 1958-60; BA in History, Wayne State U., 1963; AM in LS, U. Mich., 1964. Libr. Detroit Pub. Libr., 1964-74; asst. dir. Grosse Pointe (Mich.) Pub. Libr., 1974-77; dir. St. Clair Shores (Mich.) Pub. Libr., 1977—. Author: All Our Yesterdays, 1969, Detroit and Its Banks, 1974, Detroit: American Urban Renaissance, 1979, Charting The Inland Seas, 1991, Tonnancour, 1994. Mem. Mich. Libr. Assn. (v.p. 1988-89), Gt. Lakes Maritime Inst.; Prismatic Club Detroit (pres. 1982), Algonquin Club (treas. 1983-93). Methodist. Avocations: tennis, bridge, reading, model shipbuilding. Home: 22401 Lakeland Dr Saint Clair Shores MI 48081 Office: Saint Clair Shores Pub Libr 22500 Eleven Mile Rd Saint Clair Shores MI 48081-1399

WOODHOUSE, DERRICK FERGUS, ophthalmologist; b. Sutton, Surrey, U.K., May 29, 1927; s. Sydney Carver and Erica (Ferguson) W.; m. Jocelyn Laira Perry, Mar. 9, 1957; children: Karen Tace, Iain Kenrick, Gillian Erica. BM, BCh., Oxford U., Eng.; 1951; DO, London Coll., 1956. Intern in medicine, surgery, ophthalmology St. Thomas Hosp., Plymouth, Exeter Hosps., London, 1952-53; registrar in ophthalmology Birmingham (Eng.) Eye. Hosp., 1958-60; sr. registrar in ophthalmology Bristol (Eng.) Eye Hosp., 1960-63; cons. eye surgeon Wolverhampton & Midland Counties Eye Infirmary, Eng., 1963-89; staff opthalmologist Liverpool Hosp., NSW, Australia, 1989—. Contbr. articles to profl. jours.; author: Ophthalmic Nursing, 1980. Mem. Wolverhampton Health Authority, 1970-77; treas. Ophthalmic Nursing Bd., 1970-84, chmn., 1984-88. With RAF, 1953-57. Recipient Gold medal, Nepal Med. Assn., 1989. Fellow Royal Coll. Surgeons, Royal Soc. Medicine, Royal Coll. Ophthalmologists; mem. Irish Coll. Ophthalmologists, Brit. Computer Soc. Mem. Soc. of Friends.

WOODHOUSE, JOHN FREDERICK, food distribution company executive; b. Wilmington, Del., Nov. 30, 1930; s. John Crawford and Anna (Houth) W.; m. Marilyn Ruth Morrow, June 18, 1955; children: John Crawford II, Marjorie Ann Woodhouse Purdy. BA, Wesleyan U., 1953; MBA, Harvard U., 1955. Bus. devel. officer Can. Imperial Bank of Commerce, Toronto, Ont., 1955-59; various fin. positions Ford Motor Co., Dearborn, Mich., 1959-64, Cooper Industries, Inc., Mount Vernon, Ohio, 1964-67; treas. Houston, 1967-69, Crescent-Niagara Corp., Buffalo, 1968-69; exec. v.p., chief fin. officer Sysco Corp., Houston, 1969-71, pres., chief operating officer, 1972-83, pres., chief exec. officer, 1983-85, chief exec. officer, chmn. bd., 1985—, mem. exec. and fin. coms., also bd. dirs.; bd. dirs. Shell Oil Co., Winrock Internat. Chmn. Mich. 16th Dist. Rep. Club, 1962-64; treas. Cooper Industries Found., 1967-69; trustee Wesleyan U., 1976-92, vice-chmn., 1986-92; ruling elder Presbyn. Ch. Mem. Nat. Am. Wholesale Grocer's Assn. (bd. dirs. 1990—, vice chmn. 1992, chmn. 1994—), Internat. Foodservice Distbrs. Assn. (bd. dirs. 1988—), Houston Soc. Fin. Analysts, Fin. Execs. Inst.; Harvard Bus. Sch. Club (bd. dirs.), Sigma Chi. Avocations: backpacking, canoeing, tennis. Office: Sysco Corp 1390 Enclave Pky Houston TX 77077-2025

WOODHULL, JOHN RICHARD, electronics company executive; b. LaJolla, Calif., Nov. 5, 1933; s. John Richard Woodhull and Mary Louise (Fahey) Hostetler; m. Barbara Adams; children: Elizabeth A., John A. BS in Engring. Physics, U. Colo., 1957, MS in Applied Math., 1960. Engr. Space Tech. Labs. (now TRW Systems), Redondo Beach, Calif., 1960-63; mgr., engr. Northrop Corp., Hawthorne, Calif., 1964; mem. tech. staff Logicon, Inc., San Pedro, Calif., 1964-69, pres., chief exec. officer, Torrance, Calif., 1969—, also bd. dirs.; instr. physics U. Colo., 1959-60; bd. dirs. 1st Fed. Fin. Corp. Bd. mgrs. San Pedro (Calif.) and Peninsula YMCA; bd. dirs. Los Angeles YMCA, 1985—, Sunrise Med., Torrance, 1986—. With USN, 1956-59. Mem. Chief Execs.' Orgn., World Bus. Coun., Nat. Indsl. Security Assn. (bd. dirs. 1986—). Avocations: sailboat racing, tennis, skiing. Office: Logicon Inc 3701 Skypark Dr Ste 200 Torrance CA 90505

WOODHULL, NANCY JANE, publishing executive; b. Perth Amboy, N.J., Mar. 1, 1945; d. Harold and May (Post) Cromwell; m. William Douglass Watson, Sept. 24, 1976; 1 child, Tennessee Jane. Student, Trenton State Tchrs. Coll., 1963-64. Dept. editor News Tribune, Woodbridge, N.J., 1964-73; reporter Detroit Free Press, 1973-75; mng. editor Times-Union, Rochester, N.Y., 1975-80, Democrat & Chronicle, Rochester, 1980-82; mng. editor USA Today, Arlington, Va., 1982-83, sr. editor, 1983-87; pres. Gannett New Media, Washington, 1986-90, Gannett News Svc., Washington, 1988-90; exec. v.p., editor-in-chief So. Living Mags., Birmingham, Ala., 1990-92; pres. Nancy Woodhull & Assoc., Inc., Washington and Pittsford, N.Y., 1991—; chmn. bd. Peabody Radio and TV awards; trustee The Freedom Forum. Office: Nancy Woodhull & Assoc Inc 5 Durham Way Pittsford NY 14534

WOODHURST, ROBERT STANFORD, JR., architect; b. Abbeville, S.C., July 12, 1921; s. Robert Stanford and Eva (Ferguson) W.; m. Dorothy Ann Carwile, Aug. 4, 1945; 1 son, Robert Stanford III. BS in Architecture, Clemson U., 1942. Registered arch., S.C. Ga. Designer Harold Woodward, Arch., Spartanburg, S.C., 1946-47; assoc. architect F. Arthur Hazard, Arch., Augusta, Ga., 1947-54; ptnr. Woodhurst & O'Brien, Architects, Augusta, 1954-83, Woodhurst Partnership, 1983—; v.p. Southeastern Architects and Engrs., Inc., Augusta, 1964-83; lectr. history architecture N. Augusta Community Coll.; mem. nat. exam. com. Nat. Council Archtl. Regis. Bds.; pres. Ga. State Bd. Arches. Chmn. Augusta-Richmond County Planning Commn., 1966-68; trustee Hist. Augusta, Inc.; active Mayor's Adv. Com., 1965-68; mem. Augusta Bldg. Code Bd. Appeals, 1955-58. Served to capt. U.S. Army, 1942-45. Decorated Air medal with 7 oak leaf clusters; Croix de Guerre avec palms (France); prisoner ofwar, Germany. Fellow AIA (Bronze medal 1942); mem. Ga. Assn. AIA (pres. 1977, Bronze medal 1977, Rothchild Silver Medal 1987), Soc. Archtl. Historians, Nat. Council Archtl. Registration Bds., Augusta Country Club, Pinnacle Club, Elks. Democrat. Baptist. Designed and built: 1st Baptist Ch., Augusta, Univ. Hosp. Med. Ctr., Augusta, Peabody Apts. and Irwin Towers, Augusta, W. Lake Country Club, Augusta, Med. Library, Med. Coll. Ga., Library Voorhees Coll., Denmark, S.C., Ambulatory Care Ctr., Univ. Hosp. Augusta, Married Students Apartments, Med. Coll. Ga., Covenant Presbyn. Ch., Augusta, Student Ctr. Voorhees Coll., Pres.' Home Voorhees Coll., others. Home: 810 Dogwood Ln Augusta GA 30909-2704 Office: Woodhurst Partnership 607 15th St Augusta GA 30901-2601

WOODIN, MARTIN DWIGHT, retired university system president; b. Sicily Island, La., July 7, 1915; s. Dwight E. and Gladys Ann (Martin) W.; m. Virginia Johnson, Sept. 7, 1939 (dec.); children: Rebecca Woodin Johnson, Pamela Woodin Fry, Linda Woodin Middleton; m. Elisabeth Wachalik, Oct. 8, 1968. B.S., La. State U., 1936; M.S., Cornell U., 1939, Ph.D., 1941; L.H.D. (hon.), U. New Orleans, 1985. Faculty La. State U., 1941-85, prof. agrl. econs., head dept., 1957-59; dir. resident instrn. Coll. Agr., 1959-60; dean La. State U. at Alexandria, 1960-62; exec. v.p. La. State U. System, Baton Rouge, 1962-72; pres. La. State U. System, 1972-85; Cons. agr. and planning, Nicaragua, Taiwan, Thailand. Contbr. articles to profl. jours. Dep. dir. La. Civil Def. Agy., 1961-72; v.p., exec. com. United Givers Baton Rouge; sec. La. State U. Found., 1962-72; mem. La. Constn. Revision Commn., Arts and Humanities Coun. of Greater Baton Rouge; mem. pres.'s coun. Nat. Assn. State Univs., 1972-85; mem. coun. trustees Gulf South Rsch. Inst., 1972-85; pres. Coun. So. Univs., 1975-76. With USNR, 1942-46, PTO. Named Alumnus of Yr., La. State U., 1985; named to Order of Jose Cecilio Del Valle, Republic of Honduras, 1985. Mem. Am. Agrl. Econ. Assn., Am. Mktg. Assn., Am. Legion (post comdr.), Internat. House, So. Assn. Land Grant Colls. and State Univs. (pres. 1977-78, 83-84), Acacia, Elks, Rotary, Sigma Xi, Omicron Delta Kappa, Phi Kappa Phi (pres.), Beta Gamma Sigma, Phi Eta Sigma, Gamma Sigma Delta, Alpha Zeta, Pi Gamma Mu. Presbyterian. Home: 234 Court St Baton Rouge LA 70810-4801

WOODING, PETER HOLDEN, interior and industrial designer; b. N.Y.C., Nov. 15, 1940; s. Edmund von Richen and Barbara (Holden) W.; m. Joanna Stypula; 1 child, Robert. BS in Design, U. Mich., 1963; student, Art Ctr. Coll., Los Angeles, 1962. Designer Herman Miller Co., Ann Arbor, 1962-63; account designer Gen. Electric Co., Louisville, 1963-71; design dir. Research and Design Inst., Providence, 1971-76, prin., 1976-78; owner, dir. Peter Wooding Design Assocs., Providence, 1978—; lectr., critic RISD, 1976—, Taipei Inst. Tech.; mem. juries for internat. design competitions, 1985-92; named U.S. del. internat. Design Congress, Amsterdam, 1987, Nagoya, Japan, 1989, U.S. del. to Hungary USIA, U.S. del. USSR/USA Designers Esch., del. to Ljubliana, Yugoslavia, 1991. Contbr. articles to various profl. jours. Bd. dirs. Leuthi-Peterson Camps for Internat. Understanding, Switzerland, 1978-79; pres. Worldesign Found., 1989-90. Recipient I.D. Designers Choice, 1974, Hatch award Boston Art Dirs. Club, 1981, Am. Inst. Graphic Arts award, 1981, Designer's Choice award Indsl. Design Mag., 1982, Idea award in environments, 1989, Internat./Inter-Design on Environ., 1992. Fellow Indsl. Designers Soc. Am. (pres. 1987-88, exec. v.p. 1985-86, chmn. 1988-90); mem. Human Factors Soc., Am. Soc. Interior Designers (interior design project award 1991, 1st place nat. competition award 1991). Avocations: running, biking, travel. Home: 28 Arnold St Providence RI 02906-1002 Office: 369 Ives St Providence RI 02906-3926

WOODING, WILLIAM MINOR, medical statistics consultant; b. Waterbury, Conn., Aug. 24, 1917; s. George Lee and Ella Elizabeth (Asher) W.; m. Nina C. Peaslee, May 30, 1940; children: Barbara Lee Wooding Bose, Elizabeth Ann Wooding Kontur. B Chem. Engring. cum laude, Poly. Inst. Bklyn., 1953. Lab. asst. Am. Cyanamid Co., Stamford, Conn., 1941-44, chemist, 1947-50, rsch. chemist, 1950-56, rsch. adminstrv. svcs. coord., 1956-57; asst. chief chemist Revlon Rsch. Ctr., N.Y.C., 1957-60, assoc. rsch. dir., 1960-65; assoc. rsch. dir. Carter-Wallace, Inc., Cranbury, N.J., 1965-67. dir. tech. svcs., 1967-75; dir. statis. svcs. Carter-Wallace, Inc. and Wallace Labs., Cranbury, 1975-82; cons. med. statis. and clin. trials BioStatistics, Swanton, Vt., 1982—; instr. Stat-a-Natrix Inst., Edison, N.J., 1983-86. Author: Planning Pharmaceutical Clinical Trials, 1994. Home and Office: BioStatistics RR 1 Box 4690 Maquam Shore Swanton VT 05488-9736

WOODLOCK, DOUGLAS PRESTON, federal judge; b. Hartford, Conn., Feb. 27, 1947; s. Preston and Kathryn (Ropp) W.; m. Patricia Mathilde Powers, Aug. 30, 1969; children: Pamela, Benjamin. BA, Yale U., 1969; JD, Georgetown U., 1975. Bar: Mass. 1975. Reporter Chgo. Sun-Times, 1969-73; staff mem. SEC, Washington, 1973-75; law clk. to Judge F.J. Murray, U.S. Dist. Ct. Mass., Boston, 1975-76; assoc. Goodwin, Procter & Hoar, Boston, 1976-79, 83-84, ptnr., 1984-86; asst. U.S. atty., Boston, 1979-83; judge U.S. Dist. Ct., Boston, 1986—; instr. Harvard U. Law Sch., 1981, 82; mem. U.S. Jud. Conf. Com. on Security, Space and Facilities, 1987—; chmn. New Boston Fed. Courthouse Bldg. Com., 1987—. Contbr. articles to profl. jours. Articles editor Georgetown Law Jour., 1973-75. Chmn. Commonwealth of Mass. Com. for Pub. Counsel Services, 1984-86, Town of Hamilton Bd. Appeals, 1978-79. Recipient Dir.'s award U.S. Dept. Justice, 1983. Mem. ABA, Mass. Bar Assn., Boston Bar Assn., Am. Judicature Soc., Am. Bar Found. Office: US Dist Ct McCormack PO & Courthouse Rm 1502 Boston MA 02109

WOODMAN, HAROLD DAVID, historian; b. Chgo., Apr. 21, 1928; s. Joseph Benjamin and Helen Ruth (Sollo) W.; m. Leonora Becker; children—Allan James, David Edward. B.A., Roosevelt U., 1957; M.A., U. Chgo., 1959, Ph.D., 1964. Lectr. Roosevelt U., 1962-63; asst. prof. history U. Mo., Columbia, 1963-66; assoc. prof. U. Mo., 1966-69, prof., 1969-71; prof. Purdue U., West Lafayette, Ind., 1971—, Louis Martin Sears disting. prof., 1990—; chmn. Com. on Am. Studies, 1981-94. Author: Conflict and Consensus in American History, 1966, 8th rev. edit., 1993, Slavery and the Southern Economy, 1966, King Cotton and His Retainers, 1968, Legacy of the American Civil War, 1973; mem. editorial bd. Jour. So. History, 1972-75, Wis. Hist. Soc., 1972-76, Bus. History Rev., 1971-77, Agrl. History, 1976-82, Am. Hist. Rev., 1981-84, Jour. Am. History, 1985-88. Served with U.S. Army, 1950-52. Recipient Otto Wirth award Roosevelt U., 1990; Woodrow Wilson Internat. Center for Scholars fellow, 1977; Social Sci. Rsch. Coun. faculty grantee, 1969-70; Nat. Humanities Ctr. Fellow, 1983-84. Mem. Am. Hist. Assn., Orgn. Am. Historians, Econ. History Assn., Agrl. History Soc. (pres. 1983-84, Everett E. Edwards award 1963), Soc. Am. Historians, Bus. History Conf. (pres. 1981-82), Ind. Assn. Historians (pres. 1983-84), So. Hist. Assn. (exec. coun. 1982-85, Ramsdell award 1965). Home: 1100 N Grant St West Lafayette IN 47906-2460 Office: Purdue U Dept History West Lafayette IN 47907

WOODMAN, HARRY ANDREWS, retired life insurance company executive, consultant; b. Orange, N.J., June 15, 1928; s. Harry Andrews and Mildred Amelia (Woods) W.; m. Betty Jo Pulsford, July 1, 1950; children: Richard Cushman, Andrea Ellen, Lynn Adele, Thomas Gordon. BA, Amherst Coll., 1950. With N.Y. Life Ins. Co., N.Y.C., 1950-89, 2d v.p., 1968-71, v.p., 1971-89; pvt. practice underwriting, actuarial cons. Cos Cob, Conn., 1989—. With USN, 1952-53. Mem. Soc. Actuaries, Home Office Life Underwriters Assn. (former pres.). Home and Office: 58 N Old Stone Bridge Rd Cos Cob CT 06807-1510

WOODMAN, TIMOTHY, artist; b. Concord, N.H., Mar. 4, 1952; s. Timothy Walker and Lucy Newton (Metcalf) W. Student, RISD, 1970-71; BFA, Cornell U., 1974; MFA, Yale U., 1976. One-man shows, 1977—, including N.Y.C., Zabriskie Gallery, San Francisco, St. Louis, L.A., Zabriskie Gallery, 1981, 83, 85, 87, 89, 91, 93, 95, Greenberg Gallery, St. Louis, 1983, 87, Fuller Goldeen Gallery, San Francisco, 1984, Asher Faure Gallery, L.A., 1986; exhibited in group shows Palm Springs (Calif.) Desert Mus., 1984, Contemporary Arts Ctr., Cin., 1985, Phoenix Art Mus., 1986, Wellesley Coll. Mus., 1986, Whitney Mus. at Phillip Morris, 1986, Met. Mus. Art, N.Y., 1988, Montclair Art Mus., N.J., 1989, Nassau County Mus. Art, N.Y., 1991; represented in permanent collections Australian Nat. Gallery, Canberra, Hirshhorn Mus. and Sculpture Garden, Washington, Memphis Brook Mus. Art, Met. Mus. Art, N.Y.C., Newark Mus., N.Y., W.K. Kellogg Found., Battle Creek, Mich., Ribicoff Fed. Bldg., Hartford, Conn. Office: Zabriskie Gallery 724 5th Ave New York NY 10019-4106

WOODMAN, WALTER JAMES, lawyer; b. Talara, Peru, Jan. 21, 1941; s. Walter James and Nora Carmen (Wensjoe) W.; m. Ruth Meyer, Dec. 19, 1970; children: Justin Meyer, Jessica Hilary. BA, U. Miami, 1964; JD, So. Meth. U., 1967. Bar: Tex. 1967, La. 1969, U.S. Supreme Ct. 1971. Lawyer Dallas, 1967-72, Waxahachie, Tex., 1972-79; lawyer in sole practice Shreveport, La., 1979—; bd. dirs. N.W. La. Legal Svcs., Shreveport, 1993—. Author book revs. and articles. Candidate Tex. Ho. of Reps., 1972; bd. dirs Gov.'s Pan Am. Commn., Baton Rouge, 1993—. Home: Nonesuch Farm 12250 Ellerbe Rd Shreveport LA 71115 Office: 535 Olive St Shreveport LA 71104-2311

WOODMAN, WILLIAM E., theater, opera and television director; b. N.Y.C.; s. William E. and Ruth (Cornwall) W. BA, Hamilton Coll.; MFA, Columbia U. Stage mgr. Am Shakespeare Festival, Stratford, Conn., 1957-61; co-producer Robin Hood Theater, Arden, Del., 1961-64; drama educator (founding mem.) Julliard Sch. Lincoln Ctr. Drama Div., N.Y.C., 1968-73; artistic dir. Goodman Theater, Chgo., 1973-78; drama educator U. So. Calif., 1993, Hamilton Coll., 1994. Dir. The Freedom of the City (Brian Friel) on Broadway and at the Goodman Theatre, Chgo.; producer, dir. premieres by Edward Bond, Sam Shepard, Christopher Hampton, David Rabe, Studs Terkel, others; dir. ABC ARTS Cable TV Long Day's Journey into Night, 1982, Shakespeare Video Richard II, Romeo and Juliet, The Tempest 1981-83, Phila. Drama Guild, 1981-84, Dramski Teatar, Skopje, Yugoslavia, Buried Child, 1987, Man & Superman, Roundabout Theater, N.Y.C., 1988, (PBS American Playhouse) The Diaries of Adam & Eve, 1988, Saint Joan, Repertory Theatre of St. Louis, 1989, The Lighthouse, Chgo. Opera Theater, 1990, Die Fledermaus, June Opera Festival of N.J., 1990, Moon for The Misbegotten, Mo. Repertory, 1990, Cocktail Hour, Syracuse Stage, 1990, The Miser, Who's Afraid of Virginia Woolf, Playmaker's Repertory Co., 1991-92, The Gigli Concert, Court Theatre, 1992, The Tempest, Shakespeare in the Park, Westerly, R.I., 1992, The Glass Menagerie, Vt. Stage Co., 1994. Served with U.S. Army, 1954-56. Mem. Dirs. Guild of Am., Soc. Stage Dirs. and Choreographers. Office: Apt 29S 205 West End Ave New York NY 10023

WOODRELL, FREDERICK DALE, health care executive; b. St. Charles, Mo., Sept. 4, 1954; s. Robert Lee and Jeananne Monique (Daily) W.; m. Brenda Kay Justice, Aug. 10, 1974; children: Sara, Grace, Evan. BS in Acctg., Emporia State U., 1976; MPA, U. Mo., 1977. Cons. Robert Brown Consulting, Kansas City, 1976-78; asst. administr. Lee's Summit (Mo.) Community Hosp., 1978-79; asst. administr. Leesburg (Fla.) Regional Med. Ctr., 1979-82, administr., 1982-86; pres., CEO Ctrl. Fla. Heathcare Devel., Leesburg, Fla., 1986-92; dir. U. Miss. Hosp. & Clinic, Jackson, Miss., 1992—; healthcare exec. and cons. Quorum Health Resources, Nashville, 1979—. Active Friends of Children's Hosp., Jackson, 1992—; chmn. Assn. Retarded Citizen, Lake Tavares, Fla., 1990-92. Named Lake County Citizen of Yr. by Orlando (Fla.) Sentinel, 1988. Mem. Am. Hosp. Assn., Am. Coll. Healthcare Execs., Jackson Rotary. Avocations: golf, reading, horseback riding, fishing. Home: 2164 Brackenshire Cir Jackson MS 39211 Office: U Hosps & Clinics U Miss Med Ctr 2500 N State St Jackson MS 39216

WOODRESS, JAMES LESLIE, JR., English language educator; b. Webster Groves, Mo., July 7, 1916; s. James Leslie and Jessie (Smith) W.; m. Roberta Wilson, Sept. 28, 1940. A.B., Amherst Coll., 1938; A.M., NYU, 1943; Ph.D., Duke U., 1950. News editor Sta. KWK, St. Louis, 1939-40; rewriteman, editor UPI, N.Y.C., 1940-43; instr. English, Grinnell (Iowa) Coll., 1949-50; asst. prof. English, Butler U., Indpls., 1950-53; asso. prof. Butler U., 1953-58; asso. prof. English, San Fernando Valley (Calif.) State Coll., 1958-61, prof., 1961-66, chmn. dept., 1959-63, dean letters and scis., 1963-65; prof. English, U. Calif.-Davis, 1966-87, chmn. dept., 1970-74; vis. prof. Sorbonne, Paris, 1974-75, 83. Author: Howells and Italy, 1952, Booth Tarkington: Gentleman from Indiana, 1955, A Yankee's Odyssey: The Life of Joel Barlow, 1958, Dissertations in American Literature, 1957, 62, 68, Willa Cather: Her Life and Art, 1970, 75, 81, American Fiction 1900-50, 1974, Willa Cather: A Literary Life, 1987; editor: Eight American Authors, 1971, American Literary Scholarship: An Annual, 1965-69, 75-77, 79, 81, 87, Critical Essays on Walt Whitman, 1983, Cather's The Troll Garden, 1983, (with Richard Morris) Voices from America's Past, anthology, 1961-62, 75. Served to lt. AUS, 1943-46. Ford Fund for Advancement Edn. fellow, 1952-53; Guggenheim fellow, 1957-58; Fulbright lectr. France, 1962-63; Fulbright lectr. Italy, 1965-66; recipient Hubbell medal, 1985. Mem. MLA (sec. Am. Lit. group 1962-63), AAUP, Phi Beta Kappa. Address: 824 Sycamore Ln Davis CA 95616-3225 Office: U Calif Dept English Davis CA 95616

WOODRING, DEWAYNE STANLEY, religion association executive; b. Gary, Ind., Nov. 10, 1931; s. J. Stanley and Vera Luella (Brown) W.; m. Donna Jean Wishart, June 15, 1957; children: Judith Lynn (Mrs. Richard Bigelow), Beth Ellen. B.S. in Speech with distinction, Northwestern U., 1954, postgrad. studies in radio and TV broadcasting, 1954-57; M.Div., Garrett Theol. Sem., 1957; L.H.D., Mt. Union Coll., Alliance, Ohio, 1967; D.D., Salem (W.Va.) Coll., 1970. Asso. youth dir. Gary YMCA, 1950-55; ordained to ministry United Methodist Ch., 1955; minister adminstrn. and program 1st Meth. Ch., (Ind.) Meth. Ch., 1955-57; minister adminstrn. and program 1st Meth. Ch., Eugene, Oreg., 1957-59; dir. pub. relations Dakotas area Meth. Ch., 1959-60, dir. pub. relations Ohio area, 1960-64; adminstrv. exec. to bishop Ohio East area United Meth. Ch., Canton, 1964-77; asst. gen. sec. Gen. Council on Fin. and Adminstrn., United Meth. Ch., Evanston, Ill., 1977-79; assoc. gen. sec. Gen. Council on Fin. and Adminstrn., 1979-84; exec. dir., chief exec. officer Religious Conf. Mgmt. Assn., 1982—; mem. staff, dept. radio svcs. 2d assembly World Coun. Chs., Evanston, 1954; vice chmn. commn. on entertainment and program North Ctrl. Jurisdictional Conf., 1968-72, chmn., 1972-76; mem. commn. on gen. conf. United Meth. Ch., 1972-93, bus. mgr., exec. dir., 1976-93, mem. divsn. interpretation, 1969-72; commn. commn. Ohio Coun. Chs., 1961-65; mem. exec. com. Nat. Assn. United Meth. Founds., 1968-72; del. World Meth. Conf., London, Eng., 1966, Dublin, Ireland, 1976, Honolulu, 1981, Nairobi, 1986, Singapore, 1991, exec. com. World Meth. Coun., 1986—; del. White House Conf. on Travel and Tourism, 1995; bd. dirs. Ohio East Area United Meth. Found., 1967-78, v.p., 1967-76; chmn. bd. mgrs. United Meth. Bldg., Evanston, 1977-84; lectr. cons. on fgn. travel. Creator: nationally distbd. radio series The Word and Music; producer, dir.: TV series Parables in Miniature, 1957-59. Adviser East Ohio Conf. Communications Commn., 1968-76; pres. Guild Assocs., 1971—; trustee, 1st v.p. Copeland Oaks Retirement Ctr., Sebring, Ohio, 1969-76; bd. dirs. First Internat. Summit on Edn., 1989. Recipient Cert. Meeting Profl. award, 1985, Cert. Expt. Mgr. award, 1988; named to Ky. Cols., 1989, Conv. Liaison Coun. Hall of Leaders honoree, 1994. Mem. Am. Soc. Assn. Execs., Ind. Soc. Assn. Execs. (Mtg. Planner of Yr. award 1990), Mtg. Profl. Internat., Conv. Liaison Coun. (bd. dirs., past chmn.), Def. Orientation Conf. Assn. (chaplain), Cert. Mtg. Profls. (bd. dirs. 1983-91), Internat. Assn. Exposition Mgmt., Found. for Internat. mtgs. (bd. dirs.). Home: 7224 Chablis Ct Indianapolis IN 46278-1540 Office: One RCA Dome Ste 120 Indianapolis IN 46225

WOODRING, JAMES H., lawyer; b. Johnstown, Pa., 1942. BA, Dickinson Coll., 1964; LLB, Yale U., 1967. Bar: Ohio 1967. Atty. Squire Sanders & Dempsey, Cleve. Mem. ABA, Cleve. Bar Assn., Ohio State Bar Assn. Office: Squire Sanders & Dempsey 4900 Society Ct 127 Public Sq Cleveland OH 44114

WOODRUFF, BRUCE EMERY, lawyer; b. Mason City, Iowa, June 23, 1930; s. Frederick Bruce and Grace (Emery) W.; m. Carolyn Clark, Aug. 18, 1956; children: David. C., Douglas B., Lynn M., Daniel R. BS in Bus., U. Ill., 1952; JD, Washington U., St. Louis, 1959. Bar: Mo. 1959, D.C. Dist. Ct. (ea. dist). Mo. 1959, U.S. Ct. Appeals (8th cir.) 1960, U.S. Supreme Ct. 1979. Assoc. Armstrong, Teasdale, Schlafly, Davis & Dicus, St. Louis, 1959-65; ptnr. Armstrong Teasdale, Schlafly & Davis (and predecessor firms), St. Louis, 1966—; counsel, sec. Credit Systems, Inc., St. Louis, 1970—; prin. counsel St. Louis C. C., 1962-89; bd. dirs. Christian Health Svcs. Devel. Corp., St. Louis, Barnes Jewish Christian Health System, St. Louis; city atty. Kirkwood, Mo., 1986. Named Kirkwood Citizen of Yr., 1983. Mem. ABA (banking law com.), Mo. Bar Assn., Bar Assn. Met. St. Louis, Am. Acad. Hosp. Attys. Republican. Presbyterian. Clubs: Algonquin (Glendale, Mo.); Noonday (St. Louis (bd. dirs. 1988-91). Avocations: golf, swimming, sailing, photography. Home: 333 Dickson Ave Saint Louis MO 63122-4631 Office: Armstrong Teasdale Schlafly & Davis 1 Met Sq Ste 2600 Saint Louis MO 63102

WOODRUFF, C(HARLES) ROY, professional association executive; b. Anniston, Ala., Sept. 27, 1938; m. Kay Carolyn Jernigan, June 26, 1962; children: Charles R. Jr., Earl David. BA, U. Ala., 1960; BD, So. Bapt. Theol. Sem., 1963, PhD in Psychology of Religion and Pastoral Care, 1966. Lic. profl. counselor, Va. Asst. pastor Ft. Mitchell Bapt. Ch., South Ft. Mitchell, Ky.; V., 1960-63; Protestant chaplain Silvercrest Hosp., New Albany, Ind., 1963-66; dir. dept. pastoral care and edn. Bryce State Hosp., Tuscaloosa, Ala., 1966-71; assoc. prof., chaplain supr. dept. patient counseling Med. Coll. Va., Richmond, 1971-76; assoc. prof., chmn. dept. psychology of religion and pastoral care Midwestern Bapt. Theol. Sem., Kansas City, Mo.,

1976-78; exec. dir. Peninsula Pastoral Counseling Ctr., Newport News, Va., 1978-88, Am. Assn. Pastoral Counselors, Washington, 1988—; lecturing fellow Interpreter's House, Lake Junaluska, N.C., 1968-78; pastoral counselor, clin. supr. Psychol. Clinic, U. Ala., Tuscaloosa, 1969-71; adj. staff mem. The Counseling Inst., Kansas City, 1976-78. Author: Alcoholism and Christian Experience, 1968; (with others) Alcohol, In and Out of the Church, 1968, Work Adjustment: The Goal of Rehabilitation, 1973, Pastoral Theology and Ministry, Key Resources, 1983, The Dictionary of Pastoral Care and Counseling, 1990; also articles. Apptd. by Gov. of Va. to Bd. Profl. Counselors, Commonwealth of Va., 1987-95 (chmn. 1993-95); mem. Nat. Mental Health Leadership Forum, 1990-93. United Meth. Ch. Gen. Bd. Christian Social Concerns grantee, 1965; So. Bapt. Theol. Sem. teaching fellow, 1965-66. Fellow Coll. Chaplains of Am. Protestant Hosp. Assn.; mem. Assn. for Clin. Pastoral Edn. (cert. supr.), Assn. Couples for Marriage Enrichment (cert.). Home: 10827 Burr Oak Way Burke VA 22015-2416 Office: Am Assn Pastoral Counselors 9504A Lee Hwy Fairfax VA 22031-2393

WOODRUFF, DAVID SCOTT, biologist, educator; b. Penrith, England, June 12, 1943; married, 1972; 2 children. BSc, U. Melbourne, Australia, 1965, PhD in Zoology, 1973. Rsch. fellow biologist Mus. Comp. Zoology, 1973-74; asst. prof. biology Purdue U., 1974-80; assoc. prof., 1980-86; prof. biology U. Calif., San Diego, 1986—; lectr. ecology Comn. Extension Courses Harvard U., 1972-74; dir. Rsch. Initiative & Support Program Devel. Ecology Purdue U., 1977-79; coord. Project in Conservation Sci. U. Calif., San Diego, 1987—. Fellow AAAS; mem. Soc. Sys. Biol., Ecological Soc. Am., Soc. Conservation Biology. Research in genetics, ecology and evolution of land snails; evolution of animal species including gibbons and chimpanzees; host-parasite coevolution; schistosomiasis; conservation biology with field projects in Thailand. Office: U Calif San Diego Dept Bio & Ctr Molec Genetics La Jolla CA 92093-0116[*]

WOODRUFF, DONALD B., art director, production designer. Prodn. designer: (films) Barbarosa, 1982; art dir.: (films) Ruthless People, 1986, Harry and the Hendersons, 1987, Jaws-the Revenge, 1987, Who's That Girl?, 1987, The Naked Gun: From the Files of Police Squad!, 1988, Fletch Lives, 1989, The Hunt for Red October, 1990, For the Boys, 1991. Office: care Art Directors Guild 11365 Ventura Blvd #315 Studio City CA 91604[*]

WOODRUFF, FAY, paleoceanographer, geological researcher; b. Boston, Jan. 23, 1944; d. Lorande Mitchell and Anne (Fay) W.; m. Alexander Whitehill Clowes, May 20, 1972 (div. Oct. 1974); m. Robert G. Douglas, Jan. 27, 1980; children: Ellen, Katerina. RN, Mass. Gen. Hosp. Sch. Nursing, Boston, 1965; BA, Boston U., 1971; MS, U. So. Calif., 1979. Rsch. assoc. U. So. Calif., L.A., 1978-81, rsch. faculty, 1981—; keynote spkr. 4th Internat. Symposium on Benthia Foraminiferi, Sendai, Japan, 1990. Contbg. author: Geological Society of America Memoir, 1985; contbr. articles to profl. jours. Life mem. The Nature Conservancy, Washington, 1992. NSF grantee, 1986-88, 88-91, 91-94. Mem. Am. Geophys Union, Geol. Soc. Am., Internat. Union Geol. Scis. (internat. commn. on stratigraphy, subcommn. on neogene stratigaphy 1991-92), Soc. Women Geographers (sec. So. calif. chpt. 1990-96), Soc. Econ. Paleontologists and Minerologists (sec., editor North Am. Micropaleontology sect. 1988-90), Oceanography Soc. (chpt. mem.), Sigma Xi. Episcopalian. Avocation: birding. Office: Dept Geol Scis U So Calif Los Angeles CA 90089-0740

WOODRUFF, GENE LOWRY, nuclear engineer, university dean; b. Greenbrier, Ark., May 6, 1934; s. Clarence Oliver and Avie Erscilla (Lowry) W.; m. Marylou Munson, Jan. 29, 1961; children—Gregory John, David Reed. B.S. with honors, U.S. Naval Acad., 1956; M.S. in Nuclear Engring., MIT, 1963, Ph.D. in Nuclear Engring., 1966. Registered profl. engr., Wash. Asst. prof. nuclear engring. U. Wash., Seattle, 1965-70, assoc. prof., 1970-76, prof., 1976-93, chmn. dept., 1981-84, dir. nuclear engring. labs., 1973-76, dean Grad. Sch., 1993-94, prof. chem. engring. environ. studies, 1989-94; vice-chair, chair-elect Grad. Record Exam., 1991-92, chair, 1992-93; cons. to govt. and industry. Contbr. numerous articles to sci. and tech. jours. Served to lt. USN, 1956-60. Mem. Nat. Soc. Profl. Engrs. (Achievement award 1977), Am. Nuclear Soc. (Achievement award 1977, chmn. honors/awards com. 1981-84, nat. program com. 1971-75, exec. com. fusion div. 1976-80, vice chmn. edn. div. 1983-84, Arthur Holly Compton award 1986), Am. Soc. Engring. Edn., Assn. Grad. Schs. (v.p./pres.-elect 1990-91, pres. 1991-92). Democrat. Home: 2700 123rd St SE Bellevue WA 98005 Office: U Wash BF-10 355 Benson Hall # Bf-10 Seattle WA 98195

WOODRUFF, HARRISON D., JR., principal. Prin. Keith Valley Middle Sch., Horsham, Pa. Recipient Blue Ribbon award U.S. Dept. Edn., 1990-91. Office: Keith Valley Mid Sch 227 Meetinghouse Rd Horsham PA 19044

WOODRUFF, JOHN DOUGLAS, non-profit association administrator, retired air force officer; b. Bonham, Tex., Feb. 12, 1944; s. Alexander Campbell and Lois Kathryn (Turner) W.; m. Carol Lynne Thompson, June 11, 1966; children: Keith Byron, Jill Marie, David Kent. BS in Sociology/Psychology, East Tex. State U., 1966; grad. with distinction, AFROTC, 1966; MS in Edn., U. So. Calif., 1970; grad. with distinction, Air Command and Staff Coll., 1977; USAF exch. student, U.S. Army War Coll., 1980-81. Commd. 2d lt. USAF, 1966; advanced through grades to col. USAF Air Rescue Svc., 1990; comdr. USAF Air Rescue Svc., McClellan AFB, Calif., 1990-93; vice comdr. 314th Airlift Wing, Little Rock, 1993-95; field svc. manager ARC, Little Rock, 1995—; adj. instr. psychology Golden Gate U., Pope AFB, N.C., 1975-76; com. chmn. Sec. of Air Force's Blue Ribbon Panel on Space, Maxwell AFB, Ala., 1988. Contbr. articles to USAF mag. Mil. sponsor for civic leader program Mil. Affairs Com., Abilene, Tex., 1982-83, Logstar Civilian Hon. Comdr. Program, Sacramento, 1990-93; mem. Cmty. Coun., Jacksonville, Ark., 1993-95. Decorated Legion of Merit with 2 oak leaf clusters, Meritorious Svc. medal with 3 oak leaf clusters, Air Force Commendation medal. Mem. Air Force Assn. (Citation of Honor 1989), Airlift/Tanker Assn., Air Rescue Assn., Jolly Green Pilots Assn., Order of Daedalians. Episcopalian. Avocations: antique refinishing and restoration, military history. Home: 7305 Yuma Ct North Little Rock AR 72116 Office: Amer Red Cross 401 S Monroe Little Rock AR 72205

WOODRUFF, JUDSON SAGE, lawyer; b. Birmingham, Ala., May 18, 1925; s. Ernest Wrigley and Margaret (Martin) W.; m. Ruth Eleanor Dick, June 16, 1949 (div.); 1 child, Jennifer; m. Millicent Imel Coats, Oct. 25, 1974. BS in Physics, U. Okla., 1948, LL.B., 1950; Sterling fellow in grad. law, Yale U., 1950-51. Bar: Okla. 1950, Ohio 1960. With CIA, Washington, 1951-52; asst. econ. attache Fgn. Service, State Dept., Washington, 1952, Tokyo, Japan, 1952-54, Seoul, Korea, 1955; law clk. U.S. Dist. Ct., Ea. Dist. Okla., Muskogee, 1955-56; atty. Marathon Oil Co., Tulsa, 1956-60, Findlay, Ohio, 1960-62, Geneva, Switzerland, 1962-63, London, Eng., 1962-63, Tripoli, Libya, 1962-63; ptnr. firm McAfee & Taft (formerly McAfee, Taft, Mark, Bond, Rucks & Woodruff), Oklahoma City, 1964-90; of counsel McAfee & Taft (formerly McAfee, Taft, Mark, Bond, Rucks & Woodruff), 1990—; instr. Tulsa U. Law Sch., 1958-60; assoc. bar examiner, State of Okla., 1967-69; mem. Okla. Mandatory Continuing Legal Edn. Commn., 1986-89. Okla. editor Oil & Gas Reporter, Southwestern Legal Found., 1964-90; contbr. articles to profl. jours. Chmn. Gov.'s Com. Ad Valorem Taxation, 1967-68; mem. Okla. Alcoholic Beverages Control Bd., 1968-69, Okla. Hwy. Commn., 1969-71; mem. lawyers del. People for People Citizen Ambassadors Program, People's Republic of China, 1986; trustee Westminster Day Sch., 1988—; deacon Westminster Presbyn. Ch., 1994—; dir. Citizens Caring for Children, 1995—. Lt. (j.g.) USNR, 1942-46. Fellow Okla. Bar Found., Am. Bar Found.; mem. Sigma Pi Sigma, Phi Delta Phi, Order of Coif. Republican. Presbyterian (deacon). Office: 10th Fl Two Leadership Sq Oklahoma City OK 73102

WOODRUFF, JUDY CARLINE, broadcast journalist; b. Tulsa, Nov. 20, 1946; d. William Henry and Anna Lee (Payne) W.; m. Albert R. Hunt, Jr., Apr. 5, 1980; children: Jeffrey Woodruff, Benjamin Woodruff, Lauren Ann Lee. Student, Meredith Coll.; 1966; B.A., Duke U., 1968. News announcer, reporter Sta. WAGA-TV, Atlanta, 1970-75; news corr. NBC News, Atlanta, 1975-76; White House corr. NBC News, Washington, 1977-83; anchor Frontline, PBS documentary series, 1983-90; corr. MacNeil-Lehrer News Hour, PBS, Washington, 1983-93; anchor and sr. corr. CNN, Washington, 1993—; mem. bd. advisors Henry Grady Sch. Journalism, U. Ga., 1979-82; bd. visitors Wake Forest U., 1982-89; mem. bd. advisors Benton

Fellowship in Broadcast Journalism, U. Chgo., 1984-90, Knight Fellowship in Journalism, Stanford U., 1985—; trustee Duke U., 1985—; founding bd. dirs. Internat. Women's Media Found., 1989—. Author: This is Judy Woodruff at the White House, 1982. Mem. Commn. on Women's Health, The Commonwealth Fund. Recipient award Leadership Atlanta, Class of 1974, Atlanta chpt. Women in Communications, 1975, Edward Weintal award for excellence in fgn. policy reporting, 1987, Joan Shorenstein Barone award for series on def. issues, 1987, Helen Bernstein award for excellence in journalism N.Y. Pub. Libr., 1989, Pres.'s award Nat. Women's Hall of Fame, 1994, CableAce award for best newscaster, 1995. Mem. NATAS (Atlanta chpt. Emmy award 1975), White House Corrs. Assn. Office: Cable News Network 820 1st St NE Washington DC 20002

WOODRUFF, KAY HERRIN, pathologist, educator; b. Charlotte, N.C., Sept. 22, 1942; d. Herman Keith and Helen Thelma (Tucker) Herrin; m. John T. Lyman, May 3, 1980; children: Robert, Geoffry, Carolyn. BA in Chemistry, Duke U., 1964; MD, Emory U., 1968. Diplomate Am. Bd. Pathology (trustee 1993—). Medicine and pediat. intern U. N.C., Chapel Hill, 1968-69, resident in anatomic pathology, 1969-70; chief resident in anatomic pathology, instr. U. Okla., Oklahoma City, 1970-71, fellow in electron microscopy-pulmonary pathology, instr., 1971-72; chief resident in clin. pathology U. Calif., San Francisco, 1972-74, asst. clin. prof. dept. anatomic pathology, 1974-91, assoc. clin. prof., 1991—; chief electron microscopy VA Hosp., San Francisco, 1974-75, attending clin. cons. dept. anatomic pathology, 1986—; pvt. practice, San Pablo, Calif., 1981—; assoc. pathologist Children's Hosp., San Francisco, 1979-81, St. Joseph's Hosp., San Francisco, 1977-79; cons. pathologist Lawrence Berkeley (Calif.) Lab., 1974-93; med. dir. Bay Area Tumor Inst. Tissue Network, San Pablo, 1989—; dir. Brookside Hosp. Regional Cancer Ctr., San Pablo, 1994; asst. clin. prof. dept. pathology health and med. scis. program U. Calif. Berkeley, and U. Calif., San Francisco Joint Med. Program, 1985-91, assoc. clin. prof., 1991—, others. Contbr. articles and abstracts to med. jours. Mem. exec. bd. Richmond (Calif.) Quits Smoking, 1986-90, Bay Area Tumor Inst., Oakland, Calif., 1987—; mem. exec. bd. Contra Costa unit Am. Cancer Soc., Walnut Creek, Calif., 1985-87, mem. profl. edn. com., 1985—, mem. pub. edn. com., 1985-86, mem. task force on breast health Calif. div., 1992-93; mem. transfusion adv. com. Irwin Meml. Blood Bank, San Francisco, 1977-83; chmn. transfusion adv. com. Alameda Contra County Blood Bank, 1989-92; commr. Calif. Bd. Med. Quality Assurance, 1978-80. Recipient young investigator award Am. Lung Assn., 1975-77; Outstanding Svc. awards Am. Cancer Soc., 1986, 87, Disting. Svc. award, 1988; Disting. Clin. Tchg. award U. Calif., San Francisco and Berkeley Joint Med. Program, 1987, Outstanding Tchg. award, 1988, Excellence in Basic Sci. Instrn. award, 1990, Excellence in Tchr. Clin. Scis. award, 1993; cert. of recognition Cmty. Svc. Richmond, 1989. Mem. AMA, Coll. Am. Pathologists (editl. bd. CAP Today 1986-90, bd. govs. 1990-96, chair coun. on practice mgmt. 1994), Am. Med. Women's Assn. (exec. bd. 1984-87, regional bd. govs. 1984-87), No. Calif. Women's Med. Assn. (pres. 1982-84), Calif. Soc. Pathologists (bd. dirs. 1988-90), No. Calif. Oncology Group, South Bay Pathology Soc., Am. Assn. Blood Banks, Calif. Med. Assn., Alameda-Contra Costa County Med. Soc., Am. Soc. Clin. Pathology, Calif. Pathology Soc., Brookside Hosp. Med. Staff (pres. 1994). Avocations: classical piano, bicycle touring, distance running, reading, wind surfing. Office: Brookside Hosp Dept Pathology 2000 Vale Rd San Pablo CA 94806-3808

WOODRUFF, LAURIE, oil industry executive. Chmn. bd. Canadian Ultramar Ltd., North York, Ont., Can. Office: Canadian Ultramar Ltd, 2550 Victoria Park Ave Ultramar Pl, North York, ON Canada M2J 5A9

WOODRUFF, NEIL PARKER, agricultural engineer; b. Clyde, Kans. July 25, 1919; s. Charles Scott and Myra (Christian) W.; m. Dorothy Adele Russ, June 15, 1952; children—Timothy C., Thomas S. B.S., Kans. State U., 1949, M.S., 1953; postgrad., Iowa State U., 1959. Agrl. engr. Agrl. Research Service, Dept. Agr., Manhattan, Kans., 1949-63; research leader Agrl. Research Service, Dept. Agr., 1963-75; cons. engr. Manhattan, 1975-77; civil engr. Kans. Dept. Transp., Topeka, 1977-79; prof., mem. grad. faculty Kans. State U., civil engr. facilities planning, 1979-84; mem. sci. exchange team to Soviet Union, 1974; with W/PT Cons., 1984—. Contbr. articles to tech. jours. and books. Fellow Am. Soc. Agrl. Engrs. (Hancor Soil Water Engring. award 1975); mem. Sigma Xi, Gamma Sigma Delta. Home and Office: 12906 W Blue Bonnet Dr Sun City West AZ 85375-2538

WOODRUFF, PAUL HARRISON, civil engineer, consultant; b. Harbor Springs, Mich., Oct. 10, 1937; s. Leon A. and Nelda (Harrison) W.; m. Marcia Jane Misteli, June 27, 1959; children: Paula, Daniel, Janet, Mark, Joy, Tama. BSCE, Mich. State U., 1959, MSCE, 1961. Registered profl. engr. Del., Fla., Ill., Ind., Iowa, Ky., Mich., Minn., N.J., Ohio, Pa., R.I., Wis., Mo. Waste control engr. Dow Chem. Co., Midland, Mich., 1961-64; project engr., project mgr. Roy F. Weston, West Chester, Pa., 1964-67, v.p., 1967-71, pres., 1971-77; pres., CEO ERM, Inc., Exton, 1977-93, chmn. bd., 1993—; bd. dirs. Core States Bank, N.A. Author more than 30 papers on environ. mgmt., waste control and resource recovery. Div. chmn. United Way Chester County, 1981-82, 92-93, chmn., 1988, 89; bd. dirs. YMCA West Chester, 1988—, pres. 1991-93; chmn. Water Quality 2000; mem. Del. Valley Earth Week Coalition Adv. Bd.; mem. adv. bd. Chester County Citizens to Save Open Space; founder, chmn. Chester County Youth Exposition, 1990—; trustee Am. Acad. Environ. Engr. (diplomate). Named Entrepreneur of Yr., Delaware Valley Svcs. Category, 1989. Mem. ASCE, ASME, Water Environment Fedn. (Willem Rudolphs medal 1967), Water Pollution Control Assn. Pa., Air and Waste Mgmt. Assn., World Pres.'s Assn., Am. Pub. Works Assn., TAPPI, Rotary (past pres. West Chester club), Tech. Coun. Greater Phila. (bd. dirs.). Republican. Presbyterian. Avocations: swimming, skiing, travel, photography, numismatism. Home: 774 S Warren Ave Malvern PA 19355-3410 Office: Environ Resources Mgmt Inc 855 Springdale Dr Exton PA 19341-2843[*]

WOODRUFF, TERESA K., cell biologist; b. Dec. 7, 1963. BA in Zoology and Chemistry summa cum laude, Olivet Nazarene U., 1985; PhD in Molecular Biology, Cellular Biological and Biochemistry, Northwestern U., Evanston, Ill., 1989. Postdoctoral fellow dept. cell structure R&D Genentech, Inc., South San Francisco, 1989-91, scientist dept. cell structure R&D, 1991—; teaching asst. Olivet Nazarene U., 1983-85, Northwestern U., 1987-88; vis. lectr. Nat. Inst. Sci., Beijing, 1991; speaker in field. Author: (with others) Growth Factors and the Ovary, 1989; contbr. articles to profl. jours.; pub. abstracts. Recipient Grad. Fellow award Abbott Labs., 1987, Cornelia Post Channing Meml. award VII Ovarian Workshop, Ares Serono, 1988, NRSA Tng. award NIH, 1988. Mem. AAAS, Am. Chem. Soc., Am. Fertility Soc., Women in Endocrinology, Endocrine Soc., Phi Delta Lamda, Sigma Xi (Grad. Scientist award 1988). Achievements include patent (with others) for Method of Increasing Fertility in Females, Method of Inhibiting Follicular Maturation in Females, TGF-beta Supergene Family of Receptors. Office: Northwestern U Dept Medicine 303 Chgo Ave Chicago IL 60657

WOODRUFF, THOMAS ELLIS, electronics consulting executive; b. Stockton, Calif., Feb. 8, 1921; s. Ennis Casselberry and Gracella (Scotford) W.; m. Doris Elaine Walters, Jan. 14, 1947 (div. Aug. 1962); children: Mary Ann Woodruff Mahaffy, Patricia Lee; m. Ruth Elizabeth Craik, Feb. 25, 1964; 1 child, Robert Peter; stepchildren: Gordon Lee Vickers, Barbara Ann Vickers, Mary Jean Vickers. AA, Stockton Jr. Coll., 1941; BSEE, U. Calif., Berkeley, 1943. Registered profl. engr., Calif. Engr. GE, Syracuse, N.Y., 1944-47; staff engr. Hughes Aircraft Co., Culver City, Calif. 1947-56; mgr. electronics design Sanders Assocs., Nashua, N.H., 1956-58, chief engr. preliminary design, 1958-60, mgr. of systems programs div., 1960-62, corp. dir. systems, 1962-65, v.p., gen. mgr. corp. systems group, 1965-73, v.p. antisubmarine weapons and communications, 1966-72, dir., 1968-70, sr. dir., 1970-76, v.p. gen. mgr. ocean systems group, 1972-76, v.p. sci. and tech., 1976-88, corp. cons., 1989—; v.p. Sanders Nuclear Corp., Nashua, 1966-71; mem. adv. com. Def. Intelligence Agy., Washington, 1978-83; joint adv. com. MIT Lincoln Lab., Bedford, Mass., 1988-89; cons. Superconductor Tech., Inc., Santa Barbara, Calif., 1988—, Oryx, Inc., Paramus, N.J., 1989—, Sanders/Lockheed, 1988-91, ret. 1992. Patentee, co-patentee 14 inventions in electronics for computers, control systems, video displays, submarine detection devices, others. Mem. IEEE (sr.). Republican. Avocations: skiing, photography, motorcycling, swimming. Home and Office: 8 Berkeley St Nashua NH 03060-2309

WOODRUFF, TOM, JR., special effects designer; b. Williamsport, Pa., Jan. 20, 1959; s. Thomas Howard and Shirley Joanne (Boyer) W.; m. Tami H. Spitler, Aug. 22, 1981; children: David Thomas, Taylor Jon. BA (cum laude), Lycoming Coll., 1980. Artist, technician Burman Studios, Van Nuys, Calif., 1983; co-designer, artist Stan Winston Studio, Inc., Northridge, Calif.; designer, ptnr. Amalgamated Dynamics, Inc., Chatsworth, Calif., 1988—. Designer and performer (film) Tremors, 1989, Alien III, 1990; co-designer, performer (film) Pumpkinhead, 1987, Leviathan, 1988, Alien Nation, 1988, Death Becomes Her, 1992 (Academy award, Visual Effects, 1993); dir., writer (short films) The Demon with 3 Tales, 1987; lab technician (film) Predator, 1987; artist and performer (film) Monster Squad, 1986,(films) The Terminator, 1985, Aliens, 1986; (TV) Amazing Stories, 1986. Avocations: photography, time with family. Home: 8057 Valley Flores Dr Canoga Park CA 91304-6121 Office: Amalgamated Dynamics Inc 21604 Marilla St Chatsworth CA 91311-4123

WOODRUFF, TRUMAN O(WEN), physicist, emeritus educator; b. Salt Lake City, May 26, 1925; s. Wilford Owen and Evelyn (Ballif) W.; m. Ambrosina Lydia Solaroli, Sept. 14, 1948 (dec. June 1991). A.B., Harvard, 1947; B.A., Oxford (Eng.) U., 1950; Ph.D., Calif. Inst. Tech., 1955. Nat. scholar Harvard, 1942-44, 46-47, Sheldon traveling fellow, 1947-48; Rhodes scholar Oxford U., 1948-50; Dow Chem. Co. fellow, Howard Hughes fellow Calif. Inst. Tech., 1950-54; research asso. physics U. Ill., 1954-55; physicist Gen. Elec. Research Lab., 1955-62; prof. physics Mich. State U., 1962-85, prof. emeritus, 1985—, chmn. dept., 1972-75; sr. scientist research labs. Hughes Aircraft Co., Malibu, Calif., 1986-87; cons. in physics Los Angeles 1987—; vis. prof. Scuola Normale Superiore, Pisa, Italy, 1982—. Contbr. articles to sci. jours. Served with USNR, 1944-46. Fulbright fellow U. Pisa, 1968-69. Fellow Am. Phys. Soc.; mem. Am. Harvard Chemists, Phi Beta Kappa, Sigma Xi. Office: 11 Thronwood Irvine CA 92714-3227

WOODRUFF, WILLIAM JENNINGS, theology educator; b. Vassar, Kans., Sept. 30, 1925; s. Kenneth Arthur and Carrie (Brecheisen) W.; m. Wanda Lea Shuck, Aug. 18, 1962; children: Teresa Kaye, Bruce Alan, Neal Wayne. BA, Ottawa U., 1954; MDiv, Fuller Theol. Sem., Pasadena, Calif., 1958; MRE, Asbury Theol. Sem., Wilmore, Ky., 1963, ThM, 1964; postgrad., U. Pa., 1965-68, Concordia Theol. Seminary, 1976-84, Trinity Theol. Seminary, 1993-95. Youth dir. Hyde Park EUB Ch., Wichita, 1958-59; tchr. Lenora (Kans.) Rural High Sch., 1959-60; pastor Attica (Kans.) EUB Ch., 1960-62, Jersey City EUB Ch., 1964-65, Phila. EUB Ch., 1965-68; with Olivet Nazarene U., Kankakee, Ill., 1968—, prof.; ret., 1991. Contbr. to Religious and Theol. Abstracts, 3 jours., 1968-94; contbr. articles to profl. jours. Cpl. U.S. Army, 1951-53, Republic of Korea. Mem. Evang. Theol. Soc., Evang. Tchrs. Tng. Assn., Wesleyan Theol. Soc., Near East Archaeol. Soc., Phi Delta Lambda, Theta Pi, Kappa Delta Pi. Avocations: photography, travel, camping. Home: 2373 Mountain Dr Bartlesville OK 74003-6926

WOODRUM, CLIFTON A., III, lawyer, state legislator; b. Washington, July 23, 1938; s. Clifton A. Jr. and Margaret (Lanier) W.; m. Emily Abbitt, Aug. 10, 1963; children—Robert, Meredith, Anne. A.B., U. N.C., 1961; LL.B., U. Va., 1964. Bar: Va. 1964, U.S. Dist. Ct. (we. dist.) Va. 1964, U.S. Ct. Appeals (4th cir.) 1968, U.S. Supreme Ct. 1970. Assoc. Dodson, Pence & Coulter, Roanoke, Va., 1964-68; ptnr. Dodson, Pence, Viar, Woodrum & Mackey, 1968—; mem. Va. Ho. of Dels., 1980—. Chmn. 6th Dist. Democratic Com., Va., 1972-76; mem. State Water Commn., 1981—; Justice Crime Commn., 1982—; chmn. Med. Malpractice Study, Va., 1984-85. Mem. ABA, Assn. Trial Lawyers Am., Va. Bar Assn., Roanoke Bar Assn. Episcopalian. Home: 2641 Cornwallis Ave SE Roanoke VA 24014-3339 Office: Dodson Pence Viar Young Woodrum & Mackey PO Box 1371 Roanoke VA 24007-1371

WOODRUM, PATRICIA ANN, librarian; b. Hutchinson, Kans., Oct. 11, 1941; d. Donald Jewell and Ruby Pauline (Shuman) Hoffman; m. Clayton Eugene Woodrum, Mar. 31, 1962; 1 child, Clayton Eugene, II. BA, Kans. State Coll., Pittsburg, 1963; MLS, U. Okla., 1966. Br. libr. Tulsa City-County Libr. System, 1964-65, head brs., 1965-66, head reference dept., 1966-67, chief extension, chief pub. svcs., 1967-73, asst. dir., 1973-76, exec. dir., 1976—; bd. dirs. Local Am. Bank Tulsa. Mem. editorial bd. Jour. of Library Administration. Active Friends of Tulsa Libr., Leadership Tulsa Alumni; trustee U. Ctr., Tulsa, chmn., 1992-94. Recipient Disting. Libr. award Okla. Libr. Assn., 1982, Leadership Tulsa Paragon award, 1987, Women in Comm. Newsmaker award, 1989, Outstanding Alumnus award U. Okla. Sch. Libr. Info. Studies, 1989; inducted into Tulsa City-County Libr. Hall of Fame, 1989, Okla. Womens Hall of Fame, 1993. Mem. ALA, Pub. Libr. Assn. (pres. 1993-94), Okla. Libr. Assn. (pres. 1978-79, Disting. Libr. award 1982), Tulsa C. of C. Democrat. Episcopalian. Avocations: backpacking, swimming, gardening. Office: Tulsa City-County Libr 400 Civic Ctr Tulsa OK 74103-3830

WOODRUM, ROBERT LEE, executive search consultant; b. Merkel, Tex., Mar. 3, 1945; s. Bill and Norma (Shea) W.; m. Linda Mary Larkin, July 20, 1968; children: Jennifer, Michael. BA, Calif. State U., Northridge, 1967; postgrad., U. Okla., 1974. Press sec. U.S. Senate, Washington, 1977-78; dir. pub. affairs U.S. Office Personnel Mgmt., Washington, 1979-80; pres. Corp. Communications, Washington, 1980-82; v.p. Norton Simon Inc., N.Y.C., 1982-83; spl. asst. to the commr. NFL, N.Y.C., 1983-84; exec. dir. Ritz Paris Hemingway Award, 1984-87; pres. Ritz Paris Internat., 1984-86; sr. v.p. AmBase Corp., 1986-91; v.p., ptnr. Korn/Ferry Internat., N.Y.C., 1991—; advisor USIA, Washington, 1980-93, ARC, 1983, White House Vets. Com., 1979-80. Trustee N.Y.C. Meals on Wheels, Inc. Lt. comdr. USN, 1968-77. Decorated Navy Achievement medal (2). Mem. N.Y. Sky Club. Home: 6 Plumbridge Ln Hilton Head Island SC 29928-3360 Office: Korn/Ferry Internat 237 Park Ave New York NY 10017-3142

WOODS, ALAN CHURCHILL, JR., retired surgery educator; b. Balt., July 1, 1918; s. Alan Churchill and Anne Powel (Byrd) W.; m. Julie Reiner; children: Alan Churchill III, Runyon Colie, Richard C.B., Louise Huntington. AB, Princeton U., 1940; MD, Johns Hopkins U., 1943. Diplomate Am. Bd. Surgery. Intern Johns Hopkins Hosp., Balt., 1943-44, asst. resident in surgery, 1944-45, 48-49, Halsted fellow in surgery, 1949-50; resident Henry Ford Hosp., Detroit, 1948-49; from instr. to assoc. prof. Johns Hopkins U. Sch. Medicine, 1950-88, assoc. prof. emeritus, 1988—; cons. surgeon Union Meml. Hosp., Balt., 1953—; Greater Balt. Med. Ctr., 1953—. Contbr. articles to med. jours. Capt. M.C., AUS, 1946-48. Fellow ACS. Democrat. Episcopalian. Avocations: fishing, sailing, travel. Home: 207 Wendover Rd Baltimore MD 21218

WOODS, BOBBY JOE, transportation executive; b. Frederick, Okla., June 20, 1935; s. Vivin Richard and Mattie Marie (Malone); divorced; children: Donald B., Kathryn M., David R., Lynda J. Student, U. Calif., Berkeley, 1955-56; AA, Phoenix Coll., 1955; student, Glendale (Ariz.) Coll., 1968, 75. Pres. Southwest Prorate Inc., Phoenix, 1967—, TCAB Registration Cons. Inc., 1993—; office mgr. Menke Transp., Phoenix, 1967-68; dist. exec. Boy Scouts Am., Phoenix, 1968-76; pres. Facing E's Enterprises, Inc., Yarnell, Ariz., 1991—. Commr. Boy Scouts Am., Ariz., N.Mex. Mem. Profl. Trucking Svcs. Assn. (pres. 1989-90), Lions Club (dist. gov. 1992-93, zone chmn. 1983-84, dep. dist. gov. 1984-85, lt. gov. 1991-92, dist. sight and hearing chmn. 1985-91, Sight and Hearing Found. state hearing chmn. 1985-89). Republican. Avocations: hiking, camping, stamp collecting, computers, collecting 78 RPM records. Home: 918 W Cochise Dr Phoenix AZ 85021-2343 Office: TCAB Registrtion Cons Inc 2045 W Glendale Ave Phoenix AZ 85015

WOODS, BRUCE WALTER, editor, poet; b. Dunkirk, N.Y., Apr. 13, 1947; s. Walter Gerald Woods and Alma (Johnson) Rice. B.A., SUNY-Fredonia, 1969. Assoc. editor Dirt Rider, Canoga Park, Calif., 1972, editor, 1972-75; exec. editor Dirt Bike, Encino, Calif., 1975-76, editor, 1976; asst. editorial dir. Daisey Pub., Encino, Calif., 1976-78; editor The Mother Earth News, Hendersonville, N.C., 1978-87; editor-in-chief The Mother Earth News and Am. Country, Hendersonville, N.C., 1987-90; editor Writer's Digest, Cin., Writer's Yearbook, Cin. Author: From the Carp of Good Hope, 1970, How Far?, 1971, Food, 1973, Fieldbook, 1976; editor: Back Country Handbook, 1989. Avocations: hunting; fishing; bicycling; motorcycling. Office: F&W Pubs Writer's Digest 1507 Dana Ave Cincinnati OH 45207

WOODS, DANIEL JAMES, lawyer; b. Bklyn., Nov. 12, 1952; s. James J. and Elinor (Masten) W.; m. Kathryn Anne Morris, Dec. 27, 1974; children: Meghan M., Alexandra K., Shauna E. AB cum laude, U. So. Calif., 1974, JD, 1977. Bar: Calif. 1977, U.S. Dist. Ct. (cen., ea., so., and no. dists.) Calif., U.S. ct Appeals (9th cir.) 1978, U.S. Supreme Ct. 1981. Law clk. to judge U.S. Dist. Ct. (ctrl. dist.), Calif., 1977-78; assoc. Brobeck, Phleger & Harrison, L.A., 1978-84, ptnr., 1984—; vol. pro tem L.A. Mcpl. Ct., 1985—, L.A. Superior Ct., 1989—. Mem. ABA (jud. adminstrn. sect.), Maritime Law Assn., Assn. Trial Lawyers Am. (assoc.). Roman Catholic. Avocations: tennis, bicycling, travel. Office: Brobeck Phleger & Harrison 550 S Hope St Los Angeles CA 90071-2627

WOODS, DAVID FITZWILLIAM, insurance, estate and financial planner; b. Balt., Aug. 2, 1936; s. David Forster and Mona (Thomas) W.; m. Elizabeth Virginia Gans, Oct. 18, 1958; children: David O'Brien, Sarah Woods Bates, Margaret Woods Heffernan, Jennifer Roaslie. BS in Econs., Loyola Coll., Balt., 1964. CLU, ChFC. Agt. Mass. Mut. Life Ins. Co., Springfield, 1966—; ptnr. Woods & Livingston Fin. Group, Springfield, 1992—. Contbr. numerous articles to profl. jours. Trustee, chmn. Baystate Health Systems, Springfield, 1991—; trustee Frank Stanley Beverdige Foudn., Boca Raton, Fla., 1988—; chmn. Baystate Med. Ctr., Springfield, 1992-94; numerous other civic activities. 1st lt. USAF, 1956-63. Mem. NALU (pres. 1986-87), Mass. Assn. Life Underwriters (John P. Meehan award 1981), Springfield Assn. Life Underwriters (David F. Woods award 1986), Assn. for Advanced Life Underwriting (dir.), Am. Coll. (trustee), Life and Health Ins. Found. for Edn. (trustee). Avocations: running, tennis, skiing, hiking, sailing. Office: Woods & Livingston Fin Grp 1500 Main St Ste 604 Springfield MA 01115-0001

WOODS, GEORGE EDWARD, federal judge; b. 1923; m. Janice Smith. Student, Ohio No. U., 1941-43, 46, Tex. A&M Coll., 1943, Ill. Inst. Tech., 1943; JD, Detroit Coll. Law, 1949. Sole practice, Pontiac, Mich., 1949-51; asst. pros. atty. Oakland City, Mich., 1951-52; chief asst. U.S. atty., Ea. Dist. Mich., 1953-60, U.S. atty., 1960-61; assoc., Honigman, Miller, Schwartz and Cohn, Detroit, 1961-62; sole practice, Detroit, 1962-81; judge U.S. Bankruptcy Ct., 1981-83, U.S. Dist. Ct. (ea. dist.) Mich., Detroit, 1983—. Served with AUS, 1943-46. Fellow Internat. Acad. Trial Lawyers, Am. Coll. Trial Lawyers; mem. Fed. Bar Assn., State Bar Mich. Office: US Dist Ct 277 US Courthouse 231 W Lafayette Blvd Detroit MI 48226-2719

WOODS, GERALDINE PITTMAN, health education consultant, educational consultant; b. West Palm Beach, Fla.; d. Oscar and Susie (King) Pittman; m. Robert I. Woods, Jan. 30, 1945; children: Jan, Jerri, Robert I. Student, Talladega Coll., 1938-40, D.Sc. (hon.), 1980; B.S. in Zoology, Howard U., 1942; M.A., Radcliffe Coll. and Harvard U., 1943, Ph.D. in Neuroembryology, 1945; D.Sc. (hon.), Benedict Coll., 1977; HHD (hon.), Howard U., 1989; LHD (hon.), Meharry Med. Coll., 1988; DSc (hon.), Fisk U., 1991, Bennett Coll., 1993. Instr. Howard U., Washington, 1945-46; pres. L.A. chpt. Jack and Jill, 1954-56; pres. Aux. to Med., Dental and Pharm. Assn. of So. Calif., 1951-55, state pres., 1955; past mem. local met. bd. YWCA; mem. nat. adv. council Gen. Med. Scis. Inst. NIH, 1964-68; cons. Nat. Inst. Gen. Med. Scis., 1969-87; mem. gen. research support program adv. com., div. research resources NIH, 1970-73, 77-78. Mem. regional com. Girl Scouts USA, 1969-75, nat. bd., 1975-78; exec. bd. Community Relations Conf. So. Calif., 1968-72; exec. com. Leadership Conf. Civil Rights, 1967-70; chmn. Def. Adv. Com. Women in Services, 1968; mem. air pollution manpower devel. adv. com. EPA, 1973-75; mem. fgn. services officers selection bds. Dept. State, 1967; mem. Calif. Com. on Public Edn.; mem. Calif. Post secondary Edn. Commn., 1974-78, vice chmn., 1976; chmn. bd. trustees Howard U., 1975-88; chmn. Howard U. Found., 1984-88; trustee Calif. Mus. Found.; trustee Atlanta U., 1974-86; bd. dirs. Center for Edn. Opportunity at Claremont Colls., Robert Wood Johnson Health Policy Fellowships; mem. Inst. Medicine of NAS, 1974—, Nat. Commn. for Cert. of Physicians Assts., 1974-81; initiated Minority Access to Research Careers, also, Minority Biomed. Rsch. Program, NIH; co-chmn. internat. conf. Woman to Woman: Single Parenting from a Global Perspective, 1987; video Re: MARC and MBRS programs A Time for Celebration, 1987; bd. dirs. Charles R. Drew U. Medicine and Sci., 1990-93; founder Head Start, L.A., 1965 (award 1985). Named Woman of Yr. Zeta Phi Beta, 1954, one of 20 Famous Black Scientists Nabisco; Black Woman of Achievement Smithsonian Instn., 1989; recipient Meritorious Achievement award Nat. Panhellenic Council, 1966, Merit award Nat. Med. Assn., Inc., 1979, Mary church Ferrell award, 1979, Leadership Achievement award Nat. Assn. Equal Opportunity in Higher Edn., 1987, awards from Pres.'s Council of Youth Opportunity, Iota Phi Lambda, Nat. Pan-Hellenic Council, Howard U. Alumni Assn., So. Calif., Nat. Assn. Colored Women, Calif. Mus. Found., Ch. Christian Fellowship, NIH, Howard U., Delta Sigma Theta, Delta Headstart, 1985, award Calif. State U., 1993, others; one of honorees Dollars and Sense mag. Salute to Am.'s Top 100 Black Business and Profl. Women, 1985; Morehouse Coll. program Rsch. Extravaganza dedicated to her, 1988; named to Gallery of Honor, Assn. Minority Health Profl. Schs., 1990. Mem. NAACP (life), Nat. Coun. Negro Women (life), Golden Key, Phi Beta Kappa, Delta Sigma Theta (pres. R & D Found. 1983-88, nat. pres. 1963-67, Geraldine P. Woods sci. award from Fed. City Alumnae chpt. established in her honor, Geraldine Pittman Woods Headstart/State Presch. Ctr. dedicated 1993). Congregationalist.

WOODS, GRANT, state attorney general; m. Marlene Galán; children: Austin, Lauren, Cole. Grad., Occidental Coll., Ariz. State Coll., 1979. Atty. gen. Ariz., 1990—. Founder Mesa Boys and Girls Club. Office: Atty Gen Office 1275 W Washington St Phoenix AZ 85007-2926

WOODS, GURDON GRANT, sculptor; b. Savannah, Ga., Apr. 15, 1915; s. Frederick L. and Marion (Skinner) W. Student, Art Student's League N.Y.C., 1936-39, Bklyn. Mus. Sch., 1945-46; Ph.D. (hon.), Coll. San Francisco Art Inst., 1966. exec. dir. San Francisco Art Inst., 1955-64; dir. Calif. Sch. Fine Arts, 1955-65; prof. Adlai E. Stevenson Coll., U. Calif. at Santa Cruz, 1966-74; dir. Otis Art Inst., Los Angeles, 1974-77; asst. dir. Los Angeles County Mus. Natural History, 1977-80; Sculptor mem. San Francisco Art Commn., 1954-56; mem. Santa Cruz County Art Commn., Regional Arts Council of Bay Area. Exhibited: N.A.D., 1948, 49, San Francisco Art Assn. anns., 1952-54, Denver Mus. Anns., 1952, 53, Whitney Mus. Ann., 1953, Sao Paulo Biennial, 1955, Bolles Gallery San Francisco 1969, 70, 72, Los Angeles Mcpl. Gallery, 1977, San Jose Inst. Contemporary Art (Calif.), Washington Project for the Arts retrospective, 1968-1985, Washington, 1985, Retrospective Art Mus. Santa Cruz County, Calif., 1987, d.p. Fong Gallery, 1993, 94; commns. include: cast concrete reliefs and steel fountain, IBM Center, San Jose, Calif., fountain, Paul Masson Winery, Saratoga, Calif., McGraw Hill Pubs. (now Birkenstock), Novato, Calif.; work in permanent collection Oakland (Calif.) Mus.; papers in Archives of Am. Art, Smithsonian Instn., Washington. Recipient citation N.Y.C., 1948; prize N.A.D., 1949; Chapelbrook Found. research grantee, 1965-66; Sequoia Fund grantee, 1967; Research grantee Creative Arts Inst., U. Calif., 1968; grantee Carnegie Corp., 1968-69. Mem. Artists Equity Assn (pres. No. Calif. chpt. 1950-52, nat. dir. 1952-55). Address: 133 Seascape Ridge Dr Aptos CA 95003-5890

WOODS, HARRIETT RUTH, state official; b. Cleve., June 2, 1927; d. Armin and Ruth (Wise) Friedman; student U. Chgo., 1945; B.A., U. Mich., 1949; LLD (hon.) Webster U., 1988; m. James B. Woods, Jan. 2, 1953; children: Christopher, Peter, Andrew. Reporter, Chgo. Herald-Am., 1948, St. Louis Globe-Democrat, 1949-51; producer Star. KPLR-TV, St. Louis, 1964-74; moderator, writer Sta. KETC-TV, St. Louis, 1962-64; council mem. University City, Mo., 1967-74; mem. Mo. Hwy. Commn., 1974, Mo. Transp. Commn., 1974-76; mem. Mo. Senate, 1976-84, lt. gov. State of Mo., 1985-89; pres. Inst. for Policy Leadership, U. Mo., St. Louis, 1989-91; pres. Nat. Women's Polit. Caucus, 1991-95; dir. Federal Home Loan Mortgage Corp., 1995—; fellow inst. politics J.F. Kennedy Sch. Govt., Harvard U., 1988. Bd. dirs. LWV of Mo., 1963, Nat. League of Cities, 1972-74; Dem. nominee for U.S. Senate, 1982, 86. Jewish. Office: 1211 Connecticut Ave NW Washington DC 20036

WOODS, HENRY, federal judge; b. Abbeville, Miss., Mar. 17, 1918; s. Joseph Neal and Mary Jett (Wooldridge) W.; m. Kathleen Mary McCaffrey, Jan. 1, 1943; children—Mary Sue, Thomas Henry, Eileen Anne, James Michael. B.A., U. Ark., 1938, J.D. cum laude, 1940. Bar: Ark. bar 1940.

Spl. agt. FBI, 1941-46; mem. firm Alston & Woods, Texarkana, Ark., 1946-48; exec. sec. to Gov. Ark., 1949-53; mem. firm McMath, Leatherman & Woods, Little Rock, 1953-80; judge U.S. Dist. Ct. (ea. dist.) Ark., 1980—; referee in bankruptcy U.S. Dist. Ct., Texarkana, 1947-48; spl. assoc. justice Ark. Supreme Ct., 1967-74, chmn. com. model jury instrns., 1973-80; chmn. bd. Ctr. Trial and Appellate Advocacy, Hastings Coll. Law, San Francisco, 1975-76; mem. joint conf. com. ABA-AMA, 1973-78, Ark. Constl. Revision Study Commn., 1967-68. Author treatise comparative fault.; Contbr. articles to legal jours. Pres. Young Democrats Ark., 1946-48; mem. Gubernatorial Com. Study Death Penalty, 1971-73. Mem. ABA, Ark. Bar Assn. (pres. 1972-73, Outstanding Lawyer award 1975), Pulaski County Bar Assn. Assn. Trial Lawyers Am. (gov. 1965-67), Ark. Trial Lawyers Assn. (pres. 1965-67), Internat. Acad. Trial Lawyers, Internat. Soc. Barristers, Am. Coll. Trial Lawyers, Am. Bd. Trial Advocates, Phi Alpha Delta. Methodist. Home: 42 Wingate Dr Little Rock AR 72205-2556 Office: US Dist Ct PO Box 3683 Little Rock AR 72203-3683

WOODS, JAMES DUDLEY, manufacturing company executive; b. Falmouth, Ky., July 24, 1931; s. Alva L. and Mabel L. (Miller) W.; m. Darlene Mae Petersen, Nov. 8, 1962; children: Linda, Debbie, Jeffrey, Jamie. AA, Long Beach City Coll., 1958; BA, Calif. State U.-Fullerton, 1967, postgrad., 1968-70. Mgr. planning and control Baker Internat. Corp., Los Angeles, 1965-68, v.p. fin. and adminstrn. Baker div., 1968-73, corp. v.p.; group fin. officer, 1973-76, corp. v.p., 1977, past exec. v.p.; pres., chief exec. officer Baker Internat. Corp., Houston; also dir. Baker Internat. Corp.; pres. Baker Packers, Houston, 1976-77, Baker Oil Tools, Orange, Calif., 1977-87; now chmn., pres., chief exec. officer Baker Hughes Inc., Houston. Served with USAF, 1951-55. Republican. Lutheran. Office: Baker Hughes Inc 3900 Essex Ln Houston TX 77027-5111*

WOODS, JAMES HOWARD, actor; b. Vernal, Utah, Apr. 18, 1947; m. Sarah Marie Owen. Student, MIT, 1965-69. Performances include (Broadway prodns.) Borstal Boy, Trial of the Catonsville 9, Finishing Touches, Moonchildren (Theatre World award), off-Broadway prodn. Saved (Obie award, Clarence Derwent award); (films) The Gambler, 1974, Night Moves, 1975, Alex & the Gypsy, 1976, The Choirboys, 1977, The Onion Field, 1979 (Golden Globe award nomination), The Black Marble, 1980, Eyewitness, 1981, Split Image, 1982, Fast-Walking, 1982, Videodrome, 1983, Against All Odds, 1984, Once Upon a Time in America, 1984, Cat's Eye, 1985, Joshua Then and Now, 1985, Salvador, 1986 (Acad. award nomination, 1987), Best Seller, 1987, Cop, 1988, The Boost, 1988, True Believer, 1989, Immediate Family, 1989, Straight Talk, 1992, Diggstown, 1992, Chaplin, 1992, The Getaway, 1994, The Specialist, 1994, Curse of the Starving Class, 1994, Casino, 1995; (TV miniseries) Holocaust, 1978; (TV movies) All the Way Home, 1971, Footsteps, 1972, A Great American Tragedy, 1972, The Disappearance of Aimee, 1976, Raid on Entebbe, 1977, The Gift of Love, 1978, And Your Name is Jonah, 1979, Badge of the Assassin, 1985, Promise, 1986 (Emmy award, Golden Apple award, Golden Globe award), In Love and War, 1987 (Golden Globe award nomination), (Hallmark TV) My Name Is Bill W. (Emmy award 1989), Citizen Cohn, HBO, 1992 (Emmy nomination, Lead Actor - Miniseries, 1993), Jane's House, 1994, Indictment, 1995; guest on The Simpsons, 1994 (voice only). Mem. Acad. Motion Picture Arts and Scis., Internat. Platform Assn., Players Club, Mountaingate Country Club. Office: ICM 8942 Wilshire Blvd Beverly Hills CA 90211*

WOODS, JAMES ROBERT, lawyer; b. San Francisco, Aug. 3, 1947; s. Robert H. and Grace (Snowhill) W.; 1 child, Heather F. AB with honors, U. Calif., Berkeley, 1969; JD, U. Calif. Davis, 1972. Bar: Calif. 1972, N.Y. 1973, U.S. Dist. Ct. (so. & ea. dists.) N.Y. 1975, U.S. Ct. Appeals (2d cir.) 1975, U.S. Dist. Ct. (no. dist.) Calif. 1984. Assoc. LeBoeuf, Lamb, Leiby & MacRae, N.Y.C., 1972-76; ptnr. Maloney, Chase Fisher & Hurst, San Francisco, 1976-83, leBoeuf, Lamb, Greene & MacRae, San Francisco, 1983—. Co-author: California Insurance Law and Practice; contbr. articles to profl. jours. Office: LeBoeuf Lamb Greene & MacRae 1 Embarcadero Ctr San Francisco CA 94111-3600

WOODS, JAMES WATSON, JR., cardiologist; b. Lewisburg, Tenn., Feb. 20, 1918; s. James Watson and Sara Frances (Watson) W.; m. Marion Briner, Nov. 26, 1944; children: Diane, James Watson III, Martin Briner. B.A., U. Tenn., 1939; M.D., Vanderbilt U., 1943. Diplomate: Am. Bd. Internal Medicine. Intern, then resident in medicine U. Pa. Hosp., 1943, 44, 46-47, fellow in cardiology, 1947-48; mem. faculty U. N.C. Med. Sch., Chapel Hill, 1953—; prof. medicine U. N.C. Med. Sch., 1964-87, prof. of medicine emeritus, 1987—, chief hypertension unit, 1964—; mem. sr. attending staff N.C. Meml. Hosp. Contbr. papers in field; contbr. chpts. to books. Served as officer M.C., USNR, 1944-46. Fellow ACP; mem. Am. Fedn. Clin. Research, Am. Clin. and Climatological Assn., Council High Blood Pressure Research, Internat. Soc. Hypertension, So. Soc. Clin. Investigation, N.C. Heart Assn. (pres. 1971-72, Bronze medallion 1970, Silver medallion 1972), Sigma Xi, Alpha Omega Alpha, Phi Eta Sigma, Phi Kappa Phi. Democrat. Presbyterian. Home: 631 Quarterstaff Rd Winston Salem NC 27104

WOODS, JOE ELDON, general contractor; b. Hammon, Okla., Apr. 24, 1933; s. Joseph W. and Gertrude E. (Martin) W.; student Ariz. State U., 1955-61; O.P.M. Program Harvard U., 1984-87; m. Nina Jo Shackelford, July 5, 1952; 1 son, J. Grant. Vice-pres. Kitchell Corp., Phoenix, 1965-69; v.p. devel. Doubletree, Inc., Phoenix, 1969-78; pres., owner Joe E. Woods, Inc., Mesa, Ariz., 1977—; bd. dirs. Price-Woods, Inc., Mesa, 1985—; chmn., bd. dirs. Joe Woods Devel., Mesa, 1986—. Bd. dirs. Mesa United Way, 1983-84; v.p., bd. dirs. East Valley Partnership, Mesa, 1985. With U.S. Army, 1953-55, Korea. Mem. Associated Gen. Contractors, Mesa C. of C. (bd. dirs. 1983-87, chmn. 1985-86, v.p. 1984-85, pres. 1985-86), Harvard Bus. Sch. Republican. Presbyterian. Clubs: Mesa Country, White Mountain Country (Pinetop, Ariz.). Lodge: Rotary. Avocations: golf, fishing, skiing. Office: Joe E Woods Inc 63 E Main St Ste 401 Mesa AZ 85201-7417

WOODS, JOEL GRANT, state attorney general; b. Elk City, Okla., May 19, 1954; s. Joe E. and Nina Jo W.; m. Marlene Galan; children: Austin, Lauren, Cole. BA in Pol. Sci., Occidental Coll., 1976; JD, Ariz. State U., 1979. Bar: Ariz. 1979, U.S. Ct. Appeals (9th cir.), 1985, U.S. Dist. Ct. Ariz., 1985. Atty. Maricopa County Pub. Defender's Office, Phoenix, 1979-82; adminstrv. asst. Office of Congressman John McCain, Mesa, Ariz., 1982-84; pvt. practice law Mesa, 1984-91; atty. gen. State of Ariz., Phoenix, 1991—. Recipient Fair Housing award Ariz. Assn. Realtors, Phoenix, 1991. Fellow Rotary Internat.; mem. Phi Beta Kappa. Republican. Avocations: reading, writing, sports. Office: Office of Atty Gen 1275 W Washington St Phoenix AZ 85007-2926

WOODS, JOHN ELMER, plastic surgeon; b. Battle Creek, Mich., July 5, 1929; m. Janet Ruth; children: Sheryl, Mark, Jeffrey, Jennifer, Judson. BA, Asbury Coll., 1949; MD, Western Res. U., 1955; PhD, U. Minn., 1966. Intern Gorgas Hosp., Panama Canal Zone, 1955-56, resident in gen. surgery, 1956-57; resident in gen. surgery Mayo Grad. Sch., Rochester, Minn., 1960-65, resident in plastic surgery, 1966-67; resident in plastic surgery Brigham Hosp., Boston, Mass., 1968; fellow, transplant cons. Harvard Med. Sch., Cambridge, Mass., 1969; mem. cons. in gen. and plastic surgery Mayo Clinic, Rochester, 1969—, vice chmn. Dept. Surgery; asst. prof. Mayo Med. Sch., Rochester, 1973-76, assoc. prof., 1976-80, prof. plastic surgery, 1980—, Stuart W. Harrington prof. surgery; vis. prof. Yale Sch. Medicine, New Haven, 1984, Harvard Sch. Medicine, Cambridge, 1984. Contbr. over 200 articles to profl. jours.; also 26 book chpts. and 1 film. Recipient Disting. Mayo Clinician award, 1991. Mem. AMA (council on sci. affairs 1985—), ACS (grad edn. com. 1985—), Am. Bd. Med. Specialties, Am. Bd. Plastic Surgery (sec.-treas. 1985-88, chmn. 1988-89), Am. Soc. Plastic Surgeons Ednl. Fedn. (pres. 1984-85). Avocations: skiing, sailing, reading, the arts. Office: Mayo Clinic E 6-B 200 1st St SW Rochester MN 55905

WOODS, JOHN JOSEPH, executive director; b. Syracuse, N.Y., Nov. 10, 1926; s. John Joseph and Agnes C. (Mooney) W.; m. Gertrude B. Fuchs, June 16, 1956 (div. Oct. 15, 1976); m. Ann M. Sorheide, Dec. 15, 1976; children: Gregory, Douglas, Lori, Carrie. BS, SUNY, Rochester, 1981; MS, SUNY, Brockport, 1982; Cert. of Advanced Studies, SUNY, 1982; EdD, U. Rochester, 1987; student, Harvard U., 1988-91. Cert. sch. dist. adminstr., N.Y. Dir. pers. and pub. rels. Alliance Tool Corp., Rochester, N.Y., 1956-78; pres. N.Y. State Sch. Bds. Assn., 1975-76, Woods Pers. Cons. Svcs.,

1978-79; sch. supt. Rochester Tooling & Machining Inst., 1979-85; exec. dir. Monroe County Sch. Bds. Assn., Rochester, 1986—; Speaker in field; lectr. U. Rochester, Grad. Sch. of Edn. and Human Devel.; adj. prof., lectr. SUNY Coll. at Brockport; tutor SUNY Empire State Coll. of Rochester; lectr. Rochester Inst. Tech., Roberts Wesleyan Coll.; chmn. Fed. Elem. Secondary Edn. Act Title III State Adv. Coun., 1973-75. Contbr. articles to profl. jours. Trustee grad. sch. edn. U. Rochester, 1990-96. Recipient Scholar fellowship U. Rochester, Monroe County Sch. Bds. Assn. "Good Guy" award. Mem. ASCD, Monroe County Bar Assn. (sch. atty's com.), Kappa Delta Pi Edn. Hon. Soc. Home: 626 Rumson Rd Rochester NY 14616-1249

WOODS, JOHN WILLIAM, electrical, computer and systems engineering educator, consultant; b. Washington, Dec. 5, 1943; s. John Gill and Margaret (McHugh) W.; m. Harriet Hemmerich, June 17, 1972; children: Anne, Christopher. BSEE, MIT, 1965, MSEE, 1967, PhD, 1970. Sr. rsch. engr. Lawrence Livermore (Calif.) Nat. Lab., 1973-76; asst. prof. Rensselaer Poly. Inst., Troy, N.Y., 1976-78, assoc. prof., 1978-84, prof., 1985—; vis. prof. Delft Tech. U., The Netherlands, 1985; program dir. NSF, Washington, 1987-88; assoc. dir. Ctr. for Image Processing Rsch., 1992—; cons. Kodak, Rochester, N.Y., 1985-86, Johns Hopkins Applied Physics Lab., Laurel, Md., 1987, Calian Comms. Ltd., 1990-91; co-founder Focus Interactive Tech., Inc., 1993. Co-author: Probability and Random Processes for Engineers, 1986, 2d edit., 1994; editor: Subband Image Coding, 1991; co-editor: Handbook of Visual Communications, 1995; mem. editl. bd. Graphical Models and Image Processing, 1989-93; contbg. author book chpts., articles to profl. jours. Mem. Com. Acad. Excellence, Clifton Park, N.Y., 1984. Capt. USAF, 1969-73. Grantee NSF, Air Force Office Sci. Rsch., Advanced Rsch. Projects Agy., Ctr. Advanced TV Studies, 1978-94. Fellow IEEE (editl. bd. Trans. on Video Tech. 1990—); mem. IEEE Signal Processing Soc. (com. chmn. 1983-85, ednl. com. chmn 1987-93, ad com. mem. 1986-88, assoc. editor jour. 1979-82, co-chmn. tech. program com. 1st Internat. Conf. on Image Processing 1994, Best Paper award 1977, 86, Meritorious Svc. award 1989, Tech. Achievement award 1993). Roman Catholic. Home: 43 Longview Dr Clifton Park NY 12065-2318 Office: Rensselaer Poly Inst ESCE Dept Troy NY 12180-3590

WOODS, JOHN WILLIAM, lawyer; b. Ft. Worth, Dec. 10, 1912; s. John George and Eugenia (Smith) W.; m. Gertie Leona Parker, Apr. 15, 1954. B.S., North Tex. State U., 1951, M.Ed., 1952; J.D., St. Mary's U., San Antonio, 1967; postgrad., Fresno State Coll., 1952, West Tex. State U., 1959. Bar: Tex. bar 1966. Tchr. Corcoran, Calif., 1952-53, Pampa, Tex., 1953-63; Tchr. Harlandale Sch. Dist., San Antonio, 1963-67; practicing atty. Amarillo, Tex., 1967-68; county atty. Sherman County, Tex., 1969-72, county judge, 1988, ret.; justice of peace, 1975-88; pvt. practice law Stratford, Tex., 1968—. Served to ensign USN, 1930-47, ETO. Mem. Tex. Bar Assn., 69th Jud. Bar Assn., Am. Legion, Masons, Shriners. Democrat. Mem. Disciples of Christ. Home: 1115 Putnam St Stratford TX 79084

WOODS, JOHN WITHERSPOON, banker; b. Evanston, Ill., Aug. 18, 1931; s. J. Albert and Cornelia (Witherspoon) W.; m. Loti Moultrie Chisolm, Sept. 5, 1953; children: Loti, Cindy, Corrie. BA, U. of South, 1954. With Chem. Bank, N.Y.C., 1954-69; v.p., head Chem. Bank (So. div.), 1965-69; chmn., CEO, AmSouth Bancorp., Birmingham, Ala., 1972—; chmn., CEO Am South Bank N.A., Birmingham, 1983—; bd. dirs. Protective Life INs. Co., Birmingham, Ala. Power Co., Birmingham, McWane, Inc. Trustee So. Rsch. Inst., Birmingham, Tuskegee U.; bd. dirs. Community Chest-United Way Jefferson County, past pres.; past chmn. working com. of 35, Gov.'s Ednl. Reform Commn., trustee Ala. Inst. for Deaf and Blind Found.; past co-chmn. bd. dirs. Ala. Mgmt. Improvement Program. 1st lt. USAF, 1955-57. Named to Ala. Acad. Honor. Mem. The Bankers Roundtable, Birmingham Area C. of C. (pres. 1978, bd. dirs., exec. com.). Office: Am-South Bancorp PO Box 11007 1900 5th Ave N Ste 1400 Birmingham AL 35203-2617*

WOODS, LAURIE, lawyer; b. N.Y.C., Nov. 18, 1947; d. William M. and Sylvia Leona (Bottstein) W.; m. John W. Corwin, June 1, 1968; children—Robert Woods-Corwin, James Woods-Corwin. B.A., New Sch.-N.Y.C., 1969; J.D., Boston U., 1973. Bar: N.Y., 1974. Staff atty. MFY Legal Services, N.Y.C., 1973-79; exec. dir. Nat. Ctr. on Women and Family Law, N.Y.C., 1979—. Contbr. articles in field to jours. Mem. ABA, N.Y. State Bar Assn., Assn. Bar City N.Y., N.Y. Women's Bar Assn. Office: Nat Ctr on Women & Family Law 799 Broadway Rm 402 New York NY 10003-6863

WOODS, LAWRENCE MILTON, airline company executive; b. Manderson, Wyo., Apr. 14, 1932; s. Ben Ray and Katherine (Youngman) W.; m. Joan Frances Van Patten, June 10, 1952; 1 dau., Laurie. B.Sc. with honors, U. Wyo., 1953; M.A., N.Y. U., 1973, Ph.D., 1975; LL.D., Wagner Coll., 1973. Bar: Mont. 1957. C.P.A., Colo., Mont. Accountant firm Peat, Marwick, Mitchell & Co. (C.P.A.'s), Billings, Mont., 1953; supervisory auditor Army Audit Agy., Denver, 1954-56; accountant Mobil Producing Co., Billings, Mont., 1956-59; planning analyst Socony Mobil Oil Co., N.Y.C., 1959-63; planning mgr. Socony Mobil Oil Co., 1963-65; v.p. North Am. div. Mobil Oil Corp., N.Y.C., 1966-67; gen. mgr. planning and econs. North Am. div. Mobil Oil Corp., 1967-69, v.p., 1969-77, exec. v.p., 1977-85; also dir.; pres., chief exec. officer, dir. Centennial Airlines, Inc., 1985-87; pres., dir. Woshakie Travel Corp., 1988—, High Plains Pub. Co. Inc., 1988—; bd. dirs. The Aid Assn. for Lutherans Mutual Funds. Author: Accounting for Capital, Construction and Maintenance Expenditures, 1967, The Wyoming Country Before Statehood, 1971, Sometimes the Books Froze, 1985, Moreton Frewen's Western Adventures, 1986, British Gentlemen in the Wild West, 1989; editor: Wyoming Biographies, 1991; co-author: Takeover, 1980; editor: Wyoming Biographies, 1991; contbr.: Accountants' Encyclopedia, 1962. Bd. dirs. U. Wyo. Research Corp. Served with AUS, 1953-55. Mem. ABA, Mont. Bar Assn., Am. Inst. CPA's, Chgo. Club. Republican. Lutheran. Office: High Plains Pub Co PO Box 1860 Worland WY 82401-1860

WOODS, MARCUS EUGENE, electric utility company executive, lawyer; b. Huntington, Ind., June 11, 1930; s. Harry Milton and Birtha Marie (Becker) W.; m. Jean Ann Vickers, Nov. 27, 1965; children: Marcus Eugene, Patrick Douglas, Edith Marie. B.B.A., Marquette U., 1952; J.D., Ind. U., 1960. Bar: Ind., U.S. Dist. Ct. (so. dist.) Ind. 1960, U.S. Ct. Appeals (7th cir.) 1963. Dep. atty. gen. State of Ind., Indpls., 1960-65; atty. Indpls. Power & Light Co., 1965-67, asst. sec., 1967-73, sec., gen. counsel, 1973—, v.p., 1980—; sec., gen. counsel IPALCO Enterprises, Inc., 1983—; dir. Property and Land Co., Inc., Indpls. Served with USAF, 1952-56. Mem. Ind. State Bar Assn., Indpls. Bar Assn., Edison Electric Inst. (legal com.), Am. Soc. Corp. Secs. Republican. Roman Catholic. Clubs: Athletic; Columbia (Indpls.). Home: 59 Carnaby Dr Brownsburg IN 46112-1059 Office: Indpls Power & Light Co 25 Monument Cir Indianapolis IN 46204-2936

WOODS, MILLICENT WASELL, federal official; b. Durham, N.C., Mar. 8, 1946; d. Michael William and Mary (Turner) W. BA, Mary Baldwin Coll., 1968. Legis. analyst U.S. Ho. Reps., Washington, 1968-72; exec. asst. to dep. undersec. U.S. Dept. Labor, Washington, 1975-76; assoc. dir. U.S. C. of C., Washington, 1977-80; v.p. corp. planning and evaluation Nat. Alliance Bus., Washington, 1980-83, ARC, Washington, 1983-89; dep. asst. sec. Dept. Def. for Pers. Support, Families and Edn., Washington, 1989—. With Leadership Washington, 1987-91; mem. adv. coun. CETA, 1978-82; mem. adv. bd. vis. Mary Baldwin Coll., Staunton, Va., 1986-90; bd. dirs. Bur. Rehab., Washington, 1981-84; mem. exec. com., bd. dirs Iona House Sr. Svcs. Ctr., Washington, 1987-91. Named one of Outstanding Young Women of Am., 1978. Republican. Methodist. Avocations: tennis, piano, theater. Office: Dept of Def Rm 3E784 The Pentagon Washington DC 20301

WOODS, PENDLETON, college official, author; b. Ft. Smith, Ark., Dec. 18, 1923; s. John Powell and Mabel (Hon) W.; m. Lois Robin Freeman, Apr. 3, 1948; children: Margaret, Paul Pendleton, Nancy Cox. BA in Journalism, U. Ark., 1948. Editor, asst. pub. mgr. Okla. Gas & Electric Co., Oklahoma City, 1948-69; dir. Living Legends of Okla., Okla. Christian Univ., Oklahoma City, 1969-82, project, promotion dir. Enterprise Square and Am. Citizenship Ctr., 1982-92, dir. Nat. Edn. Program and Am. Citizenship Ctr., 1992—; arbitrator BBB; leader youth seminars in field. Bd. dirs. Campfire Girls Council, Okla. Jr. Symphony (past pres.), Boy Scout Council, Zoo Amphitheater of Oklahoma City, Will Rogers Centennial Commn., Greater Oklahoma City Tree Bank Found.; bd. dirs., co-founder Ctrl. Park

WOODS, ROBERT A., chemical company executive. Pres. ICI Americas Inc., Wilmington, Del.; pres. ag products Zeneca Inc., Wilmington, 1993—. Office: Zeneca Inc 1800 Concord Pike Wilmington DE 19897

WOODS, ROBERT ARCHER, investment counsel; b. Princeton, Ind., Dec. 28, 1920; s. John Hall and Rose McCall W.; m. Ruth Henrietta Diller, May 27, 1944; children—Robert Archer III, Barbara Diller (Mrs. Gregory Alan Klein), Katherine Heilman (Mrs. John E. Glennon), James Diller. A.B., U. Rochester, 1942; M.B.A., Harvard, 1946. Account exec. Stein Roe & Farnham (investment counsel), Chgo., 1946-53, ptnr., 1954-90; gov. Investment Co. Inst. Trustee U. Rochester; bd. dirs. Chgo. Juvenile Protective Assn., Chgo. Infant Welfare Soc., Chgo. Assn. Retarded Citizens. Served to lt. (s.g.) USNR, 1943-46. Mem. Am. Mgmt. Assn. (trustee 1973), Harvard Bus. Sch. Club Chgo. (pres. 1961), Phi Beta Kappa, Delta Upsilon. Clubs: Univ. Chgo, Glenview, Commonwealth. Home: 470 Orchard Ln Winnetka IL 60093-4222 Office: 1 S Wacker Dr Chicago IL 60606-4614

WOODS, ROBERT EDWARD, lawyer; b. Albert Lea, Minn., Mar. 27, 1952; s. William Fabian and Maxine Elizabeth (Schmit) W.; m. Cynthia Anne Pratt, Dec. 26, 1975; children: Laura Marie Woods, Amy Elizabeth Woods. BA, U. Minn., 1974, JD, 1977; MBA, U. Pa., 1983. Bar: Minn. 1977, U.S. Dist. Ct. Minn. 1980, U.S. Ct. Appeals (8th cir.) 1980. Assoc. Moriarty & Janzen, Mpls., 1977-81, Berger & Montague, Phila., 1982-83; assoc. Briggs and Morgan, St. Paul and Mpls., 1983-84, ptnr., 1984—; adj. prof. William Mitchell Coll. Law, St. Paul, 1985; exec. com., bd. dirs. LEX MUNDI, Ltd., Houston, 1989-93, chmn. bd. 1991-92; bd. dirs. Midwest Asia Ctr., 1993—, chmn. bd. 1994—. Author (with others) Business Torts, 1989; sr. contbg. editor: Evidence in America: The Federal Rules in the States, 1987. Mem. ABA, Minn. State Bar Assn., Hennepin County Bar Assn., Ramsey County Bar Assn. (chmn. corp., banking and bus. law sect. 1985-87), Assn. Trial Lawyers Am., Wharton Club of Minn., Phi Beta Kappa. Home: 28 N Deep Lake Rd North Oaks MN 55127 Office: Briggs & Morgan 2400 IDS Ctr 80 S 8th St Minneapolis MN 55402-2113

WOODS, RODNEY IAN, banker; b. Maidstone, Kent, Eng., Feb. 25, 1941; came to U.S., 1965; s. James and Gladys Irene (Radmall) W.; m. Carole Turnbull, Mar. 21, 1970 (div. Jan. 1974); 1 child, Ian Radmall; m. JoAnne Regina Miceli, Sept. 25, 1975; 1 child, Samantha. Acct. supr. Doyle Dane Bernbach, Toronto and N.Y.C., 1966-73; exec. v.p. Siegel & Gale, N.Y.C., 1973-76; mgr. Merrill Lynch, Pierce, Fenner & Smith, N.Y.C., 1976-78; v.p. U.S. Trust Co. N.Y., N.Y.C., 1978-80, sr. v.p., mktg. dir., 1980-87; 1st v.p. dir. mktg. svcs. Merrill Lynch, Pierce, Fenner & Smith, 1987-88; pres., chief exec. officer Merrill Lynch Trust Co., Princeton, N.J., 1988-92; 1st v.p. mktg. eastern divsn. Merrill Lynch Pvt. Client Group, N.Y.C., 1993—; nat. adv. bd. Outward Bound. Bd. dirs. Kane Lodge Found., Madison Square Boys and Girls Club. Mem. St. George's Soc. N.Y. (life). Republican. Episcopalian. Club: Union League (N.Y.C.). Lodge: Kane (master 1982, dist. dep. grand master 1984-85, trustee 1986—). Home: 101 Old Academy Rd Fairfield CT 06430-7161 Office: Merrill Lynch World Fin Ctr N Tower New York NY 10281

WOODS, ROSE MARY, consultant, former presidential assistant; b. Sebring, Ohio, Dec. 26, 1917; d. Thomas M. and Mary (Maley) W. Ed. high sch.; L.D.H., Pfeiffer Coll., 1971. With Royal China, Inc., Sebring, 1935-43, Office Censorship, 1943-45, Internat. Tng. Adminstrn., 1945-47, Herter Com. Fgn. Aid, 1947, Fgn. Service Ednl. Found., 1947-51; sec. to senator, then v.p. Nixon, 1951-61; asst. Mr. Nixon with firm Adams, Duque & Hazeltine, Los Angeles, 1961-63, firm Nixon, Mudge, Rose, Guthrie, Alexander & Mitchell, N.Y.C., 1963-68; exec. asst. to former Pres. Nixon, 1969-75; now consultant. Named 1 of 10 Women of Year Los Angeles Times, 1961, 1 of 75 Most Important Women in Am. Ladies Home Jour., 1971. Home: 1194 W Cambridge St Alliance OH 44601-2169

WOODS, SUSANNE, college president; b. Honolulu, May 12, 1943; d. Samuel Ernest and Gertrude (Cullom) W. BA in Polit. Sci., UCLA, 1964, MA in English, 1965; PhD in English and Comparative Lit., Columbia U., 1970; MA (hon.), Brown U., 1978. Staff Senator Daniel K. Inouye, 1963; asst. editor Rand Corp., Calif., 1963-65; instr. Ventura Coll., Calif., 1965-66; lectr. CUNY, 1967-69; asst. prof. U. Hawaii, 1969-72; asst. prof. English Brown U., Providence, 1972-77, assoc. prof., 1977-83, prof., 1983-93, dir. grad. studies, 1986-88, assoc. dean faculty, 1987-90; v.p., dean Franklin and Marshall Coll., Lancaster, Pa., 1991-95; pres. Coll. of Wooster, Ohio, 1995—; vis. assoc. prof. U. Calif., 1981-82; dir. NEH-Brown Women Writers Project, 1988—. Author: Natural Emphasis, 1984; gen. editor: Women Writers in English, 1350-1850, 1992—; editor: The Poetry of Aemilia Lanyer, 1993; contbr. numerous articles to profl. jours. and scholarly books; reviewer for various profl. jours., including Renaissance Quar., Jour. of English and Germanic Philology; reader for PMLA Jour., SEL Jour., also others; editorial bd. Hunting Libr. Quar., 1987-90, Ben Jonson Jour., Duquesne U. Press. Pres. Cultural Coun. of Lancaster County, 1993-95, bd. dirs., 1990-95; bd. dirs. Lancaster Gen. Hosp. Found., 1992-95; active various polit. campaigns, 1960-64, 68-76, 84, 92. Bronson fellow, 1976, Huntington Library, 1979-80, 81, Clark Library, 1981, Huntington-NEH, 1984-85, Woodrow Wilson Found., 1968-70. Mem. Am. Council Edn. (R.I. women's coord. 1988-90), MLA (chmn. div. 17th Century English lit. 1982), N.E. MLA (chmn. English Renaissance sect. 1978, Milton sect. 1983), Am. Assn. Higher Edn., Nat. Women's Studies Assn., Renaissance Soc. Am., Milton Soc. (exec. com. 1987-89), Lyrica Soc. (pres. 1987-90), Alpha Gamma Delta. Democrat. Episcopalian. Home: 433 E University St Wooster OH 44691 Office: Coll of Wooster Wooster OH 44691

WOODS, WALTER EARL, biomedical manufacturing executive; b. Phila., Sept. 26, 1944; s. Walter Earl and Janet I. (Ferguson) W.; m. Anna Maria Gianfreda, Dec. 4, 1975; children: Jeffrey, Elaine, Roberto, Carlo. BS in Biology, Del. Valley Coll. Sci. and Agr., 1966. Pilot plant operator Shell Chem., Woodbury, N.J., 1966-67; virologist, tissue culturist 1st U.S. Med. Lab., N.Y.C. and Ft. Meade, Md., 1967-69; virologist Merck, Sharpe & Dohme, West Point, Pa., 1969-70; quality control and assurance supr. Richardson-Merrell Inc., Swiftwater, Pa., 1970-74; cons., dir. influenza vaccine mfg. Richardson-Merrell Inc., Naples, Italy, 1974-75; mgr. biol. prodn. Richardson-Merrell Inc., Swiftwater, 1976-78; mgr. biol. prodn. Connaught Labs., Inc., Swiftwater, 1978-81, dir. vaccine mfg., 1982-84, dir. mfg. resource planning, class A rating, 1984-88, dir. product devel. and mgmt., 1989-91; dir. project mgmt., chmn. HIB and Pertussis bus. groups Pasteur Mérieux Connaught, 1991—; bd. dirs. Connaught-Daiichi Joint Venture, Tokyo; project dir. licensing Acellular Pertussis and Japanese Encephalitis Vacines, 1992, HIB vaccine, 1993, licensed acP vaccine, Germany, 1994. Bd. dirs. Northeastern Pa. Indsl. Resource Ctr., Wilkes-Barre, Pa., 1988-91. Mem. ASM, Pharm. Mfr.'s. Avocations: soccer, music, gardening, reading. Home: 53 Deerfield Way Scotrun PA 18355 Office: Connaught Labs Inc Box 187 Swiftwater PA 18370

WOODS, WALTER RALPH, animal scientist, research administrator; b. Grant, Va., Dec. 2, 1931; s. John Wythe and Hazel Gladys (Hash) W.; m. Jacqulyn Rose Miller, Sept. 14, 1953; children: Neal Ralph, Diana Lyn. B.S., Murray (Ky.) State U., 1954; M.S., U. Ky., 1955; Ph.D., Okla. State U., 1957. Instr. animal sci. Okla. State U., 1956-57; asst. prof., then assoc. prof. Iowa State U., 1957-62; assoc. prof., then prof. U. Nebr., 1962-71; prof. animal sci., head dept. Purdue U., 1971-85; dean Kans. State U., Manhattan, 1985-92; dir. Agrl. Expt. Sta., 1985-92, dir. Coop. Ext. Svc., 1987-92; asst. adminstr. for regional rsch. CSRS USDA, Washington, 1993-94; dep. adminstr. Coop. States, Rsch., Ednl. Svcs. USDA, Washington, 1994—; dir. Agr. Rsch. Inst., 1992—. Author papers, articles in field. Bd. dirs. Ind. 4-H Found., 1979-81, Kans. 4-H Found., 1987-92, Agr. Rsch. Inst., 1992-95; mem. leadership coun. Kans. Value Added Ctr., 1990-92; mem. exec. com. Kans. Rural Devel. Coun., 1990-93; chair Coun. Adminstrv. Head Agr., 1992, Great Plains Agr. Coun., 1990-92. Recipient Disting. Agrl. Alumni award Murray State U., 1969, Meritorious Service award Ind. Pork Producers Assn., 1975. Mem. Am. Soc. Animal Sci. (sec.-treas. Midwest sect. 1979-81, pres. Midwest sect. 1983-84), Sigma Xi, Gamma Sigma Delta. Mem. Disciples of Christ Ch. Home: 5904 Mount Eagle Dr Apt 318 Alexandria VA 22303-2536 Office: USDA CSREES Adminstrn Bldg 338A Washington DC 20250-0005

WOODS, WILLIAM ELLIS, lawyer, pharmacist, association executive; b. Ballinger, Tex., Sept. 25, 1917; s. Cary Dysart and Gertrude Mae (Ellis) W.;

WOODS, PHILIP WELLS (PHIL WOODS), jazz musician composer; b. Springfield, Mass., Nov. 2, 1931; s. Stanley J. and Clara (Markley) W.; m. Beverly Berg, 1957 (div. 1973); children: Garth Darryl, Aimee Francesca; m. Jill Goodwin, Dec. 20, 1985; stepchildren: Allisen, Tracey Trotter. Student, Juilliard Sch., N.Y.C., 1948-52; LLD (hon.), East Stroudsburg U., 1994. Alto saxophone and clarinet with Dizzy Gillespie and Quincy Jones, alto saxophone with Benny Goodman, Gene Krupa, Thelonious Monk, Buddy Rich, Charlie Barnet, Michel Legrand, many others; leader European Rhythm Machine, 1968-73, Phil Woods Quartet, 1974-84, Phil Woods Quintet, 1984—; composer Rights of Swing, Three Improvisations, Sonata for Alto and Piano (Four Moods), The Sun Suite, I Remember, Deer Head Sketches, numerous others; recs. with own bands include Rights of Swing, 1971, Phil and Quill (3 albums with Gene Quill), Images (with Michel Legrand) (Grammy award 1976), (with Benny Carter) My Man Benny, My Man Phil, I Remember: A Tribute to Some of the Great Jazz Musicians, 1979, More Live (Grammy award 1982), At the Vanguard (Grammy award 1983), (as the Phil Woods Quintet) Gratitude, Heaven, Bop Stew, All Bird's Children (as Phil Woods' Little Big Band), Evolution, Bouquet, Flash, Real Life; played saxophone on many other recs. including Clark Terry and Ben Webster's Happy Faces, Symbiosis by Bill Evans, A New Album with Lena Horne, Just the Way You Are with Billy Joel, Dr. Wu with Steely Dan; also played on motion picture soundtracks The Hustler, 1961, Blow-Up, 1966, Twelve Angry Men, 1957, It's My Turn, 1980, Boy In A Tree. Co-founder, bd. dirs. Delaware Water Gap (Pa.) Celebration of the Arts, 1978—. Named New Star of 1956 Downbeat mag.; winner Down Beat Critics' Poll, 1975-79, 81-90, 92-93, Down Beat Readers' Poll, 1975-94; recipient Golden Feather award for best group Phil Woods Quartet Downbeat Critics' Poll, 1978, Downbeat Readers Poll award for best acoustic group Phil Woods Quintet, 1988-91, Downbeat Critics' Poll award for best acoustic group Phil Woods Quintet, 1990, Jazz Times Readers Poll award for best alto sax, 1990, 92; elected to Am. Jazz Hall of Fame, 1994. Mem. Am. Fedn. Musicians. Avocations: reading, cooking, movies, computers. Office: PO Box 278 Delaware Water Gap PA 18327-0278

WOODS, PHYLLIS MICHALIK, elementary school educator; b. New Orleans, Sept. 12, 1937; d. Philip John and Thelma Alice (Carey) Michalik; 1 child, Tara Lynn Woods. BA, Southeastern La. U., 1967. Cert. speech and English tchr., elir. sci., La. Tchr. speech, English and drama St. Charles Parish Pub. Schs., Luling, La., elem. tchr., secondary tchr. remedial reading, Chpt. I reading specialist; Wicat tchr. coord.; tchr. cons. St. Charles parish writing project La. State U. Writing Project. Author: Egbert, the Egret, Angel Without Wings; songwriter; contbr. articles and poems to River Parish Guide. Active 4-H; sch. rep. United Fund, St. Charles Parish Reading Assn. Mem. ASCD, Internat. Reading Assn., St. Charles Parish Reading Coun., Newspaper in Edn. (chmn., historian), La. Assn. Newspapers in Edn. (state com.).

WOODS, REGINALD FOSTER, management consulting executive; b. Charleston, W.va., Sept. 25, 1939; s. Reginald Foster and Jean Lee (Hill) W.; m. Katharine Terry Norden, May 11, 1963; children: Eric Arthur, Elizabeth Terry, Tracy Lee. BME, Cornell U., 1961, MME, 1962, MBA, 1963. Mktg. specialist Gen. Electric Co., N.Y.C., 1963-64; dir. flight equipment and facilities planning Eastern Airlines, N.Y.C., 1964-70; v.p. planning Butler Internat., Inc., Montvale, N.J., 1970, sr. v.p. fin., 1971-80, exec. v.p., 1980-86, pres., 1986-87; chmn. Mgmt. Resources Group, Inc., Saddle River, N.J., 1987—; pres., ceo The Advantage Ptnrs., Chatham, N.J., 1992—; bd. dirs. Benedetto, Gartland & Greene, Inc., N.Y.C., DCG Corp., Roseville, Calif., Damon G. Douglas Co., Cranford, NJ.; pres. DCG Corp., 1994—. Mem. Knollwood Country Club, Glenmore Country Club. Office: The Advantage Ptnrs Inc 466 Southern Blvd Chatham NJ 07928-1406

WOODS, RICHARD DALE, lawyer; b. Kansas City, Mo., May 20, 1950; s. Willard Dale and Betty Sue (Duncan) W.; m. Cecelia Ann Thompson, Aug. 11, 1973; children: Duncan Warren, Shannon Cecelia. BA, U. Kans., 1972; JD, U. Mo., 1975. Bar: Mo. 1975, U.S. Dist. Ct. (we. dist.) Mo. 1975. Assoc. Shook, Hardy & Bacon P.C., Kansas City, Mo., 1975-79, shareholder, 1980—; gen. chmn. Estate Planning Symposium, Kansas City, 1985-86; chair Northland Coalition, 1993. Chmn. fin. com. North Woods Ch., Kans. City, 1986-88, 93—; mem. sch. bd. Norh Kans. City Sch. Dist., 1990—, treas. 1992—; chmn. planned giving com. Truman Med. Ctr., 1992—; mem. Clay County Tax Increment Financing Commn., 1990—. Fellow Am. Coll. Trust and Estate Counsel; mem. ABA, KC, Mo. Bar Assn., Kans. City Met. Bar Assn., Lawyers Assn. Kans. City (mem. 2 pres. young lawyers sect 1981-94), Kans. City Estate Planning Soc. (bd. dirs. 1985-88, 93-95). Democrat. Office: Shook Hardy & Bacon PC One Kansas City Place 1200 Main St Kansas City MO 64105-2100

WOODS, RICHARD SEAVEY, accountant, educator; b. Albion, N.Y., Mar. 1, 1919; s. Stanley Taylor and Helen Saxe (Seavey) W.; m. Dorothy Signor Blake, Dec. 19, 1945; children: David Blake, Michael Signor, Martha Seavey, Catherine Hardie. A.B., U. Rochester, 1941; M.B.A., U. Pa., 1947, Ph.D., 1957. C.P.A., Pa. Tchr. English pub. schs. Shortsville, N.Y., 1941-42; instr. accounting U. Pa. Wharton Sch., Phila., 1947-52; asst. prof. U. Pa. Wharton Sch., 1952-58, assoc. prof., 1958-64, prof., 1964-87, prof. emeritus, 1987—, asso. chmn. dept., 1961-63, acting chmn., 1961-62, 75-76, chmn., 1963-69. Author (with O.S. Nelson) Accounting Systems and Data Processing, 1961; cons. editor: Accountant's Handbook, 1970; editor, contbr.: Audit Decisions in Accounting Practice, 1973, Audit Decision Cases, 1973. Served to lt. USNR, 1942-46. Mem. Am. Accounting Assn., Am. Inst. C.P.A.s. Home: 62 Snyder Ln Springfield PA 19064-1627 Office: Steinberg-Dietrich Hall Univ of Pa Philadelphia PA 19104

m. Martha Brockman, May 28, 1954. B.S., U. Tex. Sch. Pharmacy, 1938; J.D., Sch. Law, 1953. Bar: Tex. bar 1954, U.S. Supreme Ct 1957. Dir. emergency med. service Tex. State Health Dept., 1942-43, USPHS, 1943-47; asst. dir. Nat. Pharm. Survey Office, 1947-48; with Eli Lilly & Co., 1948-51; first dir. U. Tex. Pharmacy Extension Service, Austin, 1953-54; pvt. practice law Corpus Christi, Tex., 1954-58; asst. to exec. v.p. Nat. Pharm Council, N.Y.C., 1958-64; sec. Nat. Pharm Council, 1964-65; Washington rep., assoc. gen. counsel Nat. Assn. Retail Druggists, 1965-76, exec. v.p., 1976-84, hon. past pres., 1984; presenter testimony on health, pharmacy and small bus. before coms. of U.S. Congress and various fed. agys.; mem. Joint Commn. on Pharmacy Practitioners; chmn. Nat. Small Bus. Legis. Coun., 1981; pres. Nat. Drug Trade Conf., 1981; del. U.S. Pharmacopoeial Conv., 1975, 80. Contbr. articles to pharmacy publs. Recipient Achievement Medal award Alpha Zeta Omega, 1975, Lubin Prof. Pharmacy award U. Tenn., 1982. Mem. ABA, Tex. Bar Assns., Law Sci. Acad., Phi Delta Phi, U. Tex. Chancellor's Coun. Methodist. Clubs: Internat., Capitol Hill, Nat. Assn. Execs. (Washington); Can. (N.Y.C.). Home: PO Box 1045 Easton MD 21601-1045

WOODSIDE, LISA NICOLE, academic administrator; b. Portland, Oreg., Sept. 7, 1944; d. Lee and Emma (Wenstrom) W. Student Reed Coll., 1962-65; MA, U. Chgo., 1968; PhD, Bryn Mawr Coll., 1972; cert. Harvard U. Inst. for Ednl. Mgmt., 1979; MA, West Chester U., 1994. Mem. dean's staff Bryn Mawr Coll., 1970-72; asst. prof. Widener U., Chester, Pa., 1972-77, assoc. prof. humanities, 1978-83, asst. dean student services, 1972-76, assoc. dean, 1976-79, dean, 1979-83; acad. dean, prof. of humanities Holy Family Coll., Phila., 1983—; v.p., dean acad. affairs, prof. humanities, 1990—; cons. State N.J. Edn. Dept., 1990; accreditor Commn. on Higher Edn., Middle States Assn., 1979-83, 94. Co-author: New Age Spirituality: An Assessment. City commr. for community rels. Chester, 1980-83; mem. Adult Edn. Council Phila. Am. Assn. Papyrology grantee Bryn Mawr Coll.; S. Maude Kaemmerling fellow Bryn Mawr Coll. Mem. Am. Assn. Higher Edn., Coun. Ind. Colls., Eastern Assn. Coll. Deans, Pa. Assn. Colls. and Tchr. Educators, AAUW (univ. rep. 1975-83), Nat. Assn. Women in C. of C., Am. Psychol. Assn., Transpersonal Assn., Audubon Soc., Del. Valley Orienteering, Phi Eta Sigma, Alpha Sigma Lambda, Psi Chi. Home: 360 Saybrook Ln # A Media PA 19086-6761 Office: Holy Family Coll Torresdale Philadelphia PA 19114

WOODSIDE, ROBERT ELMER, lawyer, former judge; b. Millersburg, Pa., June 4, 1904; s. Robert E. and Ella (Neitz) W.; m. F. Fairlee Habbart, July 11, 1931 (dec.); children—William Edward, Robert James, Jane Fairlee; m. Anna C. Woodside, June 27, 1987. A.B., Dickinson Coll., 1926, LL.B., 1928, LL.D. (hon.), 1951. Bar: Pa. 1928. Practiced in Millersburg and Harrisburg, Pa., 1928-42; judge Ct. Common Pleas, Dauphin Co., 1942-51; became atty. gen. Commonwealth of Pa., 1951; judge Superior Court Pa., 1953-65; ptnr. Mette, Evans and Woodside, Harrisburg, 1965-87; ret., 1987; adj. prof. Dickinson Sch. Law, Carlisle, Pa., 1969-87; legislator Pa. State House of Reps., 1932-42, Rep. house leader, 1939, 41; mem. Joint State Govt. Commn., 1939-42; del. 16th congl. dist. Rep. Nat. Conv., 1952; chmn. Pa. Little Hoover Comm.; chmn. Pa. Council Juvenile Ct. Judges, 1947-49. Pres. bd. trustees Pa. Industrial Sch., White Hill, Pa., 1945-55; chmn. on Commn. on Constl. Revision; mem. Pa. Constl. Conv., 1967-68. Mem. Omicron Delta Kappa, Phi Kappa Sigma, Tau Kappa Alpha. Methodist. Clubs: Mason (33 deg., Shriner), Red Man, Royal Arcanum. Home: 351 Union St Millersburg PA 17061

WOODSIDE, WILLIAM STEWART, service company executive, museum official; b. Columbus, Ohio, Jan. 31, 1922; s. William Stewart and Frances (Moorman) W. BSBA, Lehigh U., 1947; MA in Econs, Harvard, 1950. With Am. Can Co., 1950-87, exec. v.p. operations, 1974-75, pres., chief operating officer, 1975-80, CEO, 1980-86, chmn. exec. com., 1987-88; chmn. Sky Chefs, Inc., N.Y.C., 1987—; bd. dirs. Am. Capital; bd. visitors CUNY Grad. Sch. and Univ. Ctr., Acad. Polit. Sci.; dir. Pub. Edn. Fund Network, Fund for N.Y.C. Pub. Edn. Manpower Demonstration and Rsch. Corp.; trustee, former pres. Whitney Mus. Am. Art, Ctr. Budget and Policy Priorities, Com. for Econ. Devel.; active dean's coun. Harvard Sch. of Pub. Health. Home: 863 Park Ave New York NY 10021-0342

WOODSON, BENJAMIN NELSON, III, insurance executive; b. Altoona, Kans., June 5, 1908; s. Benjamin Nelson and Mary Ola (Burke) W.; m. Grace Cook, Jan. 25, 1930 (dec. Apr. 1981); 1 child, Mary Burnett Crowell; m. Audrey Haney Watson, Apr. 1, 1983. Student pub. schs. Omaha. Stenographer, salesman, officer Mut. Trust Life Co., Chgo., 1928-37; exec. Life Ins. Mgmt. Rsch. Assocs., Hartford, Conn., 1937-44; exec. v.p. Commonwealth Life, Louisville, 1944-50; mng. dir. Nat. Assn. Life Underwriters/Life Underwriters Tng. Coun., Washington, 1950-53; pres. Am. Gen. Life, Houston, 1953-72; v.p., then pres., Am. Gen. Corp., Houston, 1954-72, chmn. chief exec. officer, 1972-78, also bd. dirs.; dir. Mitchell Energy & Devel., Houston, 1976—, Am. Capital Mutual Funds, Houston, 1969—; ptnr., spl. counsel exec. com. John L. Wortham & Son, Houston, 1958—; CLU. Author: More Power to You, 1950; The Set of The Sail, 1968; Simple Truth, 1980, The Best of Woody, 1993; contbr. essays to Life Assn. News, 1937—. Bd. dirs. Tex. Med. Ctr., Houston, 1981—; Up With People, Tucson, 1972—, Sch. Ins. and Fin. Svcs. Mktg., U. Houston, 1983—; regent, vice chmn. U. Houston, 1977-83; gov. Rice U., Houston, 1962-74, overseer Jones Grad. Sch. Bus., 1977-83, overseer emeritus, 1983—; founder, life trustee Houston Found. for Retarded. Named Disting. Citizen Goodwill Industries, 1973, Man of Yr., Fedn. Ins. Counsel, 1980, Houston Honoree of Yr., NCCJ, 1976; recipient Solomon Huebner Gold award, 1988. Mem. Million Dollar Round Table (life), Nat. Assn. Life Underwriters (John Newton Russell award 1963), Tex. Assn. Life Underwriters, Houston Assn. Life Underwriters, Life Underwriter Tng. Council (founder, life trustee), Life Ins. Mktg. and Research Assn., Houston C. of C. (chmn. 1972-73, named Outstanding Leader 1972). Republican. Mem. Oahu Country (Honolulu); Houston (pres. 1970-72), River Oaks Country (v.p., bd. dirs. 1978-81) Forum (founding chmn. 1979—) (Houston), Metropolitan (N.Y.C.), Woodlands Country. Home: 2727 Allen Pkwy # 460 Houston TX 77019

WOODSON, HERBERT HORACE, electrical engineering educator; b. Stamford, Tex., Apr. 5, 1925; s. Herbert Viven and Floy (Tunnell) W.; m. Blanche Elizabeth Sears, Aug. 17, 1951; children: William Sears, Robert Sears, Bradford Sears. SB, SM, MIT, 1952, ScD in Elec. Engring., 1956. Registered profl. engr., Tex., Mass. Instr. elec. engring., also project leader magnetics div. Naval Ordnance Lab., 1952-54; mem. faculty M.I.T., 1956-71, prof. elec. engring., 1965-71, Philip Sporn prof. energy processing, 1967-71; prof. elec. engring., chmn. dept. U. Tex., Austin, 1971-81, Alcoa Found. prof., 1972-75, Tex. Atomic Energy Research Found. prof. engring., 1980-82, Ernest H. Cockrell Centennial prof. engring., 1982-93, dir. Center for Energy Studies, 1973-88, assoc. dean devel. and planning Coll. Engring., 1986-87, acting dean, 1987-88, dean' chair for excellence in engring., 1988—; staff engr. elec. engring. div. AEP Service Corp., N.Y.C., 1965-66; cons. to industry, 1956—. Author: (with others) Electromechanical Dynamics, parts I, II, III. Served with USNR, 1943-46. Recipient Fed. Engr. Yr. Awd., Nat Soc. Profl. Engr., 1990. Fellow IEEE (life; pres. Power Engring. Soc. 1978-80); mem. Am. Soc. Engring. Edn., Nat. Acad. Engring., AAAS. Achievements include patents in field. Home: 7603 Rustling Rd Austin TX 78731-1333 Office: U Tex Coll Engineering Austin TX 78712

WOODSON, RICHARD PEYTON, III, entrepreneur; b. Albuquerque, Mar. 1, 1923; s. Richard Peyton and Katherine (McMillen) W.; m. Martha Avison, Sept. 18, 1954; children: Sheila Prentice, Richard Peyton, Martha Winslow. BA cum laude, Princeton U., 1945; postgrad., Stanford U. Sch. Bus., 1949-50. Ret. chmn. bd., CEO Occidental Life Ins. Co. N.C., Raleigh, 1962-69; chmn. bd. dirs. Peninsular Life Ins. Co., Jacksonville, 1977-85, MCM Corp., Raleigh, 1977-85, Brit.-Am. Ins. Co. Ltd., Nassau, Bahamas, 1974-86; vice-chmn. Bus. Telecom, Inc., Raleigh, N.C., 1986-88; with Enterprise Holdings, Raleigh. Chmn. Raleigh Cmty. Rels. Comm., 1965-69; bd. visitors Davidson Coll., 1967-71; trustee Shaw U., 1964-71, St. Mary's Coll., Raleigh, 1980-83; trustee N.C. Symphony, 1977-86, chmn., 1983-85; active Family Health Internat. Bd., 1982—; chmn. Found. for Internat. Family Health, 1991—, Triangle Cmty. Found., 1990—. Maj. USAAF, 1943-46. Decorated Air medal with three bronze oak leaf clusters. Mem. Life Office Mgmt. Assn. (bd. dirs. 1966-70, chmn. 1969-70), Chief Execs. Forum, World Bus. Coun., Inst. Life Ins. (bd. dirs. 1970-72), Capital City Club, Sphinx Club, Carolina Country Club, Marco Polo Club (N.Y.C.), Princeton Club, Rotary. Democrat. Presbyterian. Home: 2805 Lakeview

Dr Raleigh NC 27609-7636 Office: Enterprise Holdings PO Box 12346 Raleigh NC 27605-2346

WOODSON, RODERICK KEVIN, professional football player; b. Fort Wayne, Ind., Mar. 10, 1965. Student, Purdue U. Cornerback Pittsburgh Steelers, 1987—. Named kick returner The Sporting News Coll. All-Am. Team, 1986, Sporting News NFL All-Pro Team, 1989, cornerback, 1990, 92, 93, NFL 75th Anniversary "All Time Team", 1994. Played in Pro Bowl, 1989-93. Office: Pittsburgh Steelers Three Rivers Stadium Pittsburgh PA 15212*

WOODSON-HOWARD, MARLENE ERDLEY, former state legislator; b. Ford City, Pa., Mar. 8, 1937; d. James and Susie (Lettrich) Erdley; m. Francis M. Howard; children: George Woodson, Bert Woodson, Robert Woodson, Daniel Woodson, David Woodson. BS, Ind. U. of Pa., 1958; MA, U. South Fla., 1968; EdD, Nova U., 1981. Prof. math. Manatee Community Coll., 1970-82, dir. Inst. Advancement, 1982-86; exec. dir. Manatee Community Coll. Foundation, 1982-86; pres. Pegasus Enterprises, Inc., 1986—; state senator Fla., 1986-90. Candidate for gov. of Fla., 1990; bd. dirs. New Coll. Libr. Assn.; past pres. Manatee Symphony. Mem. Nat. Assn. Women Bus. Owners, Women Owners Network, Manatee C. of C., Sarasota Tiger Bay Club, Kiwanis. Republican. Roman Catholic. Home: 12 Tidy Island Blvd Bradenton FL 34210-3301

WOODSWORTH, ANNE, university dean, librarian; b. Fredericia, Denmark, Feb. 10, 1941; d. Thorvald Ernst and Roma Yrsa (Jensen) Lindner; 1 child, Yrsa Anne. BFA, U. Man., Can., 1962; BLS, U. Toronto, Ont., Can., 1964, MLS, 1969; PhD, U. Pitts., 1987. Edn. libr. U. Man., 1964-65; reference libr. Winnipeg Pub. Library, 1965-67; reference libr. sci. and medicine dept. U. Toronto, 1967-68; med. librarian Toronto Western Hosp., 1969-70; research asst. to chief librarian U. Toronto, 1970-71, head reference dept., 1971-74; personnel dir. Toronto Pub. Library, 1975-78; dir. librs. York U., Toronto, 1978-83; assoc. provost for librs. U. Pitts., 1983-88, assoc. prof., 1988-91; dean Palmer Sch. Libr. and Info. Sci. L.I. U., 1991—; pres. Anne Lindner Ltd., 1974-83; bd. dirs. Population Rsch. Found. Toronto, 1980-83, Ctr. for Rsch. Libraries, 1987-88; mem. rsch. libraries adv. coun. OCLC, 1984-87. Author: The Alternative Press in Canada, 1972, Leadership and Research Libraries, 1988, Patterns and Options for Managing Information Technology on Campus, 1990, Library Cooperation and Networks, 1991, Managing the Economics of Leasing and Contracting Out Information Services, 1993, Reinventing in the Information Job Family, 1993, The Future of Education for Librarianship: Looking Forward from the Past, 1994. Trustee Long Island Librs. Resources Coun., 1993-98. Can. Coun. grantee, 1974, Ont. Arts Coun. grantee, 1974, Coun. on Libr. Resources grantee, 1986, 88, 91, 93; UCLA sr. fellow, 1985. Mem. ALA (com. on accreditation 1990-94, councillor 1993—), Can. Assn. Rsch. Librs. (pres. 1981-83), Assn. Rsch. Librs. (bd. dirs. 1981-84, v.p. 1984-85, pres. 1985-86), Assn. Coll. and Rsch. Librs. (chmn. K.G. Saur award com. 1991-93), Assn. for Libr. and Info. Sci. Edn., N.Y. Libr. Assn., Internat. Soc., Am. Soc. Info. Sci., Archons of Colophon. Office: LI U CW Post Campus Brookville NY 11548

WOODWARD, ANNE SPIVEY, museum director; b. Atlanta, Apr. 4, 1949; d. Albert Guy and Jane Davidson (Knapp) S.; m. Roland Henry Woodward, Aug. 11, 1973; children: Elizabeth Rebecca, Hannah Carlisle, Sarah Margaret. BA, Mount Holyoke Coll, 1971; MA, U. Del., 1973. Cert. Mus. Studies. Curatorial cons. Valley Forge (Pa.) State Pk., 1973-76; curatorial cons. Pa. Hist. & Mus. Commn., Harrisburg, 1976-77, field curator, 1977-80; site administr. Brandywine Battlefield, Chadds Ford, Pa., 1985-89; mus. dir. Hist. Soc. Del., Wilmington, 1989—; lectr. in field. Producer: (video) Opening the Door to Freedom,1990. Mem. Am. Assn. Museums, Am. Assn. for State and Local History. Mem. Soc. of Friends. Office: Hist Soc Del 505 N Market St Wilmington DE 19801-3091

WOODWARD, C. VANN, historian; b. Vanndale, Ark., Nov. 13, 1908; s. Hugh Allison and Bess (Vann) W.; m. Glenn Boyd MacLeod, Dec. 21, 1937 (dec.); 1 child, Peter Vincent (dec.). PhB, Emory U., 1930; MA, Columbia U., 1932; PhD, U. N.C., 1937; hon. doctoral degrees, U. Ark., Brandeis U., Cambridge U., Colgate U., Columbia U., Dartmouth Coll., Dickinson Coll., Emory U., Henderson State U., Johns Hopkins U., U. Mich., U. N.C., Northwestern U., Pa. U., Princeton U., Rhodes Coll., Rutgers U., Tulane U., Washington and Lee U., William and Mary Coll. Instr. English Ga. Sch. Tech., 1930-31, 1932-33; asst. prof. history U. Fla., 1937-39; vis. asst. prof. history U. Va., 1939-40; assoc. prof. history Scripps Colls., 1940-43; assoc. prof. history Johns Hopkins U., 1946, prof., 1947-61; Commonwealth lectr. U. London, 1954; Harmsworth prof. Am. history Oxford U., 1954-55; Sterling prof. history Yale U., 1961-77, prof. emeritus, 1977—, Jefferson lectr. in humanities, 1978. Author: Tom Watson: Agrarian Rebel, 1938, The Battle for Leyte Gulf, 1947, Origins of the New South, 1951, (Bancroft prize), Reunion and Reaction, 1951, The Strange Career of Jim Crow, 1955, The Burden of Southern History, 1960, American Counterpoint, 1971, Thinking Back, 1986, The Future of the Past, 1989, The Old World's New World, 1991; editor: The Comparative Approach to American History, 1968, Responses of the Presidents to Charges of Misconduct, 1974, Mary Chesnut's Civil War, 1981 (Pulitzer prize 1982), (series) The Oxford History of the United States, 11 vols., 1982—; co-editor: The Private Mary Chesnut, 1984. Served as lt. USNR, 1943-46. Recipient Nat. Acad. Inst. Arts and Letters Lit. award, 1954, Gold medal for history, 1990, Am. Coun. Learned Socs. prize, 1962, Life Work award Am. Hist. Soc., 1986, Life Work Bobst. award, NYU, 1989; Guggenheim Found. fellow, 1946-47, 60-61. Mem. Am. Philos. Soc., Am. Acad. Arts and Letters, Am. Hist. Assn. (pres. 1969), So. Hist. Assn. (pres. 1952), Orgn. Am. Historians (pres. 1968, Disting Svc. award 1989), Am. Acad. Arts and Scis. (v.p. 1987-88), Brit. Academy, Royal Hist. Soc., Phi Beta Kappa. Home: 83 Rogers Rd Hamden CT 06517-3533

WOODWARD, CLINTON BENJAMIN, JR., civil engineering educator; b. El Paso, Tex., Mar. 4, 1943; s. Clinton Benjamin and Iris Elizabeth (Zant) W.; m. Willie Ann Shollenbarger, June 14, 1969 (div. June 1976); m. Deon Bennett Speir, Nov. 22, 1979; 1 child, Clinton Benjamin III. BSET, N.Mex. State U., 1976; MS, Colo. State U., 1978; MSCE, N.Mex. State U., 1984, PhD, 1986. Asst. mgr. Woodward Lumber Co., Inc., Las Cruces, N.Mex., 1968-73; v.p. Woodward Lumber Co., Inc., Las Cruces, 1973-75; pres. Woodward Enterprises, Inc., Las Cruces, 1975-82; asst. prof. N.Mex. State U., 1987—. Contbr. articles to profl. jours. With USN, 1962-66,. Mem. ASCE, Am. Soc. for Engring. Edn., Soc. for Exptl. Mechanics, Forest Products Rsch. Soc., Am. Soc. Wood Sci. and Tech. Avocations: camping, fly fishing.

WOODWARD, DANIEL HOLT, librarian, researcher; b. Ft. Worth, Oct. 17, 1931; s. Enos Paul and Jessie Grider (Butts) W.; m. Mary Jane Gerra, Aug. 27, 1954; children: Jeffrey, Peter. BA, U. Colo., 1951, MA, 1955; PhD, Yale, 1958; MSLS, Cath. U. Am., 1969. Mem. faculty Mary Washington Coll. of U. Va., 1957-72, prof. English, 1966-72, librarian, 1969-72; librarian Huntington Library, Art Collections and Bot. Gardens, San Marino, Calif., 1972-90, sr. rsch. assoc., 1990—. Editor: The Poems and Translations of Robert Fletcher, 1970; co-editor: New Ellesmere Chaucer Facsimile, Ellesmere Chaucer: Essays in Interpretation, 2 vols., 1995. Served with AUS, 1952-54. Mem. Bibliog. Soc., Am. Phi Beta Kappa, Beta Phi Mu. Home: 1540 San Pasqual St Pasadena CA 91106-3546 Office: Huntington Libr Art Collections and Bot Gardens 1151 Oxford Rd San Marino CA 91108-1299

WOODWARD, FREDERICK MILLER, publisher; b. Clarksville, Tenn., Apr. 15, 1943; s. Felix Grundy and Laura Henrietta (Miller) W.; m. Elizabeth Louise Smoak, Mar. 23, 1967; children: Laura Claire, Katherine Elizabeth. BA cum laude, Vanderbilt U., 1965; postgrad., Tulane U., 1965-70. Manuscript editor U.S.C. Press, Columbia, 1970-73, mktg. dir., 1973-81; dir. U. Press of Kans., Lawrence, 1981—; mem. adv. com. Kans. Ctr. for the Book, Topeka, 1987—; lectr. pub. U. Kans., Lawrence, Kans. State U., Manhattan, 1983—; book judge Western Heritage Ctr., Oklahoma City, 1988. Mem. Assn. Am. Univ. Presses (bd. dirs. 1988-91, pres. 1995—), Kans. State Hist. Soc. (life), Phi Beta Kappa. Democrat. Avocations: racquetball, reading, music. Home: 2220 Vermont St Lawrence KS 66046-3066 Office: U Press Kans 2501 W 15th St Lawrence KS 66049-3905

WOODWARD, GRETA CHARMAINE, construction company executive, rental and investment property manager; b. Congress, Ohio, Oct. 28, 1930; d.

Richard Thomas and Grace Lucetta (Palmer) Duffey; m. John Jay Woodward, Oct. 29, 1949; children: Kirk Jay, Brad Ewing, Clay William. Bookkeeper Kaufman's Texaco, Wooster, Ohio, 1948-49; office mgr. Holland Furnace Co., Wooster, 1948-49; acctg. clk. Columbus and So. Ohio Electric, 1949-50; interviewer, clk. State Ohio Bur. Employment Services, Columbus, 1950-51; clk. Def. Constrn. Supply Ctr. (U.S. Govt.) (formerly Columbus Gen. Depot), 1951-52; treas. Woodward Co., Inc. Reynoldsburg, Ohio, 1963—. Newspaper columnist Briarcliff News, 1960-63. Active Reynoldsburg PTA, 1960-67; Reynoldsburg United Meth. Ch.; mem. women's service bd. Grant Hosp. Avocations: bike riding, crocheting, writing poetry, stock market, financial mags. Office: Woodward Excavating Co Inc 7340 Tussing Rd Reynoldsburg OH 43068-4111

WOODWARD, HALBERT OWEN, federal judge; b. Coleman, Tex., Apr. 8, 1918; s. Garland A. and Helen (Halbert) W.; m. Dawn Blair, Sept. 28, 1940; children: Halbert Owen, Garland Benton. BBA, U. Tex., 1940, LLB, 1946. Bar: Tex. 1941. Mem. Woodward & Johnson, Coleman, 1949-68; mem. Tex. Hwy. Commn., 1959-68, chmn., 1967-68; judge U.S. Dist. Ct. No. Dist. Tex., 1968—, chief judge, 1977-86; dir. S.W. State Bank, Brownwood, Tex. Bd. dirs. Overall Meml. Hosp., Coleman. Served with USNR, 1942-45. Mem. ABA, Tex. Bar Assn., Am. Judicature Soc., Beta Theta Pi. Office: Fed Bldg C-210 US Courthouse 1205 Texas Ave Lubbock TX 79401-4096

WOODWARD, JAMES HOYT, university chancellor, engineer; b. Sanford, Fla., Nov. 24, 1939; s. James Hoyt and Edith Pearl (Breeden) W.; m. Martha Ruth Hill, Oct. 13, 1956; children: Connie, Tracey, Wade. BS in Aero. Engring. with honors, Ga. Tech. Inst., 1962, MS in Aero. Engring., 1963, PhD in Engring. Mechanics, 1967; MBA, U. Ala.-Birmingham, 1973. Registered profl. engr., Ala. Asst. prof. engring. mechanics USAF Acad., Colo., 1965-67, assoc. prof., 1967-68; asst. prof. engring. mechanics N.C. State U., 1968-69; assoc. prof. engring. U. Ala., Birmingham, 1969-70, assoc. prof., 1973-77, prof. civil engring., 1977-89, asst. v.p., 1973-78, dean engring., 1978-84, acad. v.p., 1984-89; chancellor U. N.C., Charlotte, 1989—; dir. tech. devel. Rust Engring. Co., Birmingham, 1970-73; cons. in field. Contbr. articles to profl. jours. With USAF, 1965-68. Mem. ASCE, ASME, Am. Soc. Engring. Edn., Am. Concrete Inst., Am. Mgmt. Assn., Sigma Xi. Methodist. Office: U NC Charlotte Office of Chancellor Charlotte NC 28223

WOODWARD, JOANNE GIGNILLIAT, actress; b. Thomasville, Ga., Feb. 27, 1930; d. Wade and Elinor (Trimmier) W.; m. Paul Newman, Jan. 29, 1958; children: Elinor Terese, Melissa Stewart, Clea Olivia. Student, La. State U., 1947-49; grad., Neighborhood Playhouse Dramatic Sch., N.Y.C. First TV appearance in Penny, Robert Montgomery Presents, 1952; understudy broadway play Picnic, 1953; appeared in plays Baby Want a Kiss, 1964, Candida, 1982, The Glass Menagerie, Williamstown Theatré Festival, 1985, Sweet Bird of Youth, Toronto, 1988; motion pictures include Three Faces of Eve, 1957 (Acad. award Best Actress, Nat. Bd. Rev. award, Fgn. Press award), Count Three and Pray, 1955, Long Hot Summer, 1958, No Down Payment, 1957, Sound and the Fury, 1959, A Kiss Before Dying, 1956, Rally Round the Flag Boys, 1958, The Fugitive Kind, 1960, Paris Blues, 1961, The Stripper, 1963, A New Kind of Love, 1963, A Big Hand for the Little Lady, 1965, A Fine Madness, 1965, Rachel, Rachel, 1968, Winning, 1969, WUSA, 1970, They Might Be Giants, 1971, The Effect of Gamma Rays on Man-in-the-Moon Marigolds, 1972 (Cannes Film Festival award), Summer Wishes, Winter Dreams, 1973 (N.Y. Film Critics award), The Drowning Pool, 1975, The End, 1978, Harry and Son, 1984, Glass Menagerie, 1987, Mr. & Mrs. Bridge, 1990, Philadelphia, 1993; TV appearances include All the Way Home; TV-film appearances in Sybil, 1976, Come Back, Little Sheba, 1977, See How She Runs, 1978 (Emmy award), Streets of L.A., 1979, The Shadow Box, 1980, Crisis at Central High, 1981, Do You Remember Love?, 1985 (Emmy award), Blind Spot, 1993 (Emmy nomination, Lead Actress - Miniseries, 1993), Breathing Lessons, 1994 (Emmy nomination, Lead Actress - Special, 1994, Golden Globe award, Best Actress); narrator film documentary Angel Dust, TV documentary on Group Theatre, 1989. Co-recipient (with Paul Newman) Kennedy Ctr. Honors for Lifetime Achievement in the Performing Arts. Democrat. Episcopalian. *

WOODWARD, JOHN TAYLOR, III, lawyer; b. N.Y.C., Sept. 10, 1940; s. John Taylor Jr. and Helen (Ashbrook) W.; divorced; children: John Taylor IV, Seth Warner, Anne Dulles. BA cum laude, Princeton U., 1962; JD, Harvard U., 1965. Bar: N.Y. 1966. Assoc. Cadwalader, Wickersham & Taft, N.Y.C., 1965-68; gen. atty. Johnson & Johnson, New Brunswick, N.J., 1969-78, internat. counsel, asst. gen. counsel, 1978-86, corp. sec., 1986—. Mem. ABA, Assn. of Bar of City of N.Y., Am. Soc. Corp. Secs., Stockholder Rels. Soc. of N.Y., Princeton Charter Club (gov. 1969—), Phillips Exeter Acad. Alumni Coun., Bedens Brook Club, Princeton Club (N.Y.C.). Republican. Office: Johnson & Johnson 1 Johnson & Johnson Plz New Brunswick NJ 08933*

WOODWARD, KAREN CALLISON, school system administrator; Supt. Adnerson (S.C.) Sch. Dist. 5. State finalist Nat. Supt. Yr., 1992. Office: Anderson Sch Dist 5 PO Drawer 439 400 Pearman Dairy Rd Anderson SC 29625-3100

WOODWARD, KATHERINE ANNE, secondary education educator; b. Detroit, Apr. 6, 1942; d. Walter E. and Helen (Leuer) Roberts; m. Clifford Edward Woodward, July 1, 1967; children: Ted, Bob, Chris, John-Paul. BA in History, Webster U., 1964; student, St. Louis U., 1966; MA in History, Sam Houston State U., 1991. Cert. tchr., Tex., Mo. Tchr. world history Oxford (Ala.) High Sch., 1967-69; tchr. English Santa Fe Jr. High Sch., Altaloma, Tex., 1969; tchr. world history Jersey Village High Sch., Houston, 1985—. Co-founder, pres. Brazoria County Cay Care, Alvin, Tex., 1970-73; co-founder Cypress Creek Emergency Med. Svc., Houston, 1975. Named Outstanding Young Women in Am., 1976. Mem. ASCD, AAUW (pres. North Harris County 1976-77), Tex. Coun. Social Studies, Cypress-Fairbanks Coun. Social Studies (pres. 1994-95, scholarship 1990), Nat. Coun. Social Studies. Avocations: travel, reading, Dutch painting, music, boating. Office: Jersey Village High Sch 7600 Solomon St Houston TX 77040-2199

WOODWARD, KENNETH EMERSON, retired mechanical engineer; b. Washington, Oct. 30, 1927; s. George Washington and Mary Josephine (Compton) W.; m. Mary Margaret Eungard, Mar. 29, 1956; children: Stephen Mark, Kristi Lynn. BME, George Washington U., 1949, M Engring. Adminstrn., 1960; MS, U. Md., 1953; PhD, Am. U., 1973. Mech. engr. Naval Rsch. Lab., Washington, 1950-54; value engring. program mgr. Harry Diamond Labs., Washington, 1955-74; sci. adviser U.S. Army Med. Bioengring. R & D Lab., Ft. Detrick, Md., 1974-75; mech. engr. Woolcott & Co., Washington, 1975-90; ret., 1990. Author: Solar Energy Applications for the Home, 1978; contbr. to profl. pubs. With U.S. Army, 1946-47. Recipient Dept. of the Army Decoration for Exceptional Civilian Svc., Engring. Alumni Achievement award The George Washington U., Washington, 1987. Mem. ASME, Am. Soc. for Artificial Internal Organs. Republican. Baptist. Achievements include 12 U.S. and 2 foreign patents, development of artifical human heart. Home: 1701 Hunts End Ct Vienna VA 22182

WOODWARD, LESTER RAY, lawyer; b. Lincoln, Nebr., May 24, 1932; s. Wendell Smith and Mary Elizabeth (Theobald) W.; m. Marianne Martinson, Dec. 27, 1958; children: Victoria L. Woodward Eisele, Richard T., David M., Andrew E. BSBA, U. Nebr., 1953; LLB, Harvard U., 1957; LLD (hon.), Bethany Coll., 1974. Bar: Colo. 1957. Assoc. Davis, Graham & Stubbs, Denver, 1957-59, 60-62, ptnr., 1962—; Teaching fellow Sch. Law Harvard U., 1959-60. Bd. dirs. Bethany Coll., Lindsborg, Kans., 1966-74, 87-95, chmn., 1989-92; bd. dirs. Pub. Edn. Coalition, Denver, 1985-92, chmn., 1988-89; mem. Colo. Commn. Higher Edn., Denver, 1977-86, chmn., 1979-81. Mem. ABA, Colo. Bar Assn., Am. Law Inst. Republican. Lutheran. Home: 680 Bellaire St Denver CO 80220-4935 Office: Davis Graham & Stubbs 370 17th St Ste 4700 Denver CO 80202-5682

WOODWARD, M. CABELL, JR., financial executive; b. Pitts., Jan. 29, 1929; s. M. Cabell and Anne (Cary) W.; m. Helen Boushee, July 24, 1954; children: Margaret Beale, Anne Cary. B.A., Princeton U., 1951; M.B.A., NYU, 1962. Asst. v.p. The Hanover Bank, N.Y.C., 1954-61; asst. treas. Continental Baking Co., Rye, N.Y., 1961-62; treas. Continental Baking Co., 1962-66, v.p. fin., dir., 1966-69; exec. v.p. ITT Continental Baking Co., Rye,

1969; pres. ITT Continental Baking Co., 1969, chief exec. officer, 1971-78; exec. v.p., chief fin. officer ITT Corp., N.Y.C., 1978-85; vice chmn., chief fin. officer ITT Corp., 1985—, dir., 1980—; dir. Melville Corp., Capital Cities/ABC, Inc. Served to capt. USMCR, 1951-53. Republican. Episcopalian. Office: ITT Corp 1330 Ave Of The Americas New York NY 10019-5422

WOODWARD, MADISON TRUMAN, JR., lawyer; b. New Orleans, Feb. 15, 1908; s. Madison Truman and Maude W.; m. Elvina Bernard, June 30, 1937 (dec. Sept. 26, 1964); children: Anne Carol Woodward Baker, Elizabeth H. Woodward Ryan, Lucie B. Woodward Cavaroc, Margaret E., Madison Truman III; m. Ethel Dameron, June 24, 1977. LLB, Tulane U., 1927; postgrad., U. Mich., 1927-28. Bar: La. 1929. Asso. firm Milling, Benson, Woodward, Hillyer, Pierson & Miller (and predecessors), New Orleans, 1929-36, ptnr., 1937—. Author: Louisiana Manual, 1953, 2d edit., 1962, Supplement, 1973; contbr. articles to legal jours. Trustee Trinity Episcopal Sch., New Orleans, 1965-71. Fellow Am. Bar Found.; Am. Coll. Trial Lawyers, Am. Coll. Probate Counsel; mem. ABA (state del. 1982-87, ho. of dels. 1979-92, bd. of govs. 1987-90), La. Bar Assn. (pres. 1973-74), New Orleans Bar Assn., Am. Law Inst., La. State Law Inst. (council 1957—, pres. 1980-81, vice chmn. 1982-87, chmn. 1989-90), Nat. Conf. Bar Pres. (exec. council 1973-75), 5th Cir. Jud. Conf. (del. and invitee 1966-80, lawyers adv. com. 1982-84), Am. Judicature Soc. (bd. dirs 1973-76), La. Bar Found. (chmn. 1980-85), Valencia Inc. (gov. 1960-78, pres. 1963-64), U.S. Supreme Ct. Hist. Soc. (trustee 1985—, mem. exec. com. 1989—), Garden Dist. Assn. (pres. 1964-65), Soc. Colonial Wars in La. (mem. council 1973—, gov. 1983-85), S.R. (pres. La. soc. 1990—), Hugenot Soc., Royal Order of St. George, Order St. Lazarus (comdr. so. commandery 1986-88), Pickwick Club, New Orleans Country Club, Plimsoll Club, Stratford Club, Internat. House, Pi Kappa Phi. Home: 1234 6th St New Orleans LA 70115-3325 Office: 909 Poydras St New Orleans LA 70112-4000

WOODWARD, RALPH LEE, JR., historian, educator; b. New London, Conn., Dec. 2, 1934; s. Ralph Lee and Beaulah Mae (Suter) W.; m. Sue Dawn McGrady, Dec. 30, 1958; children: Mark Lee, Laura Lynn, Matthew McGrady. A.B. cum laude, Central Coll., Mo., 1955; M.A., Tulane U., 1959, PhD, 1962. Asst. prof. history Wichita (Kans.) U., 1961-62, U. S.W. La., Lafayette, 1962-63; asst. prof. history U. N.C., Chapel Hill, 1963-67; asso. prof. U. N.C., 1967-70; prof. history Tulane U., New Orleans, 1970—; head dept. history Tulane U., 1973-75, chmn. dept. history, 1986-88; dir. Tulane Summer in C. Am., 1975-78; prof. in charge Tulane Jr. Year Abroad, Paris, 1975-76; Fulbright lectr. Universidad de Chile, Universidad Catolica de Valparaiso, Chile, 1965-66, Universidad del Salvador, Universidad Nacional, Buenos Aires, 1968; vis. prof. U.S. Mil. Acad., West Point, N.Y., 1989; regional liaison officer Emergency Com. to Aid Latin Am. Scholars, 1974. Author: Class Privilege and Economic Development, 1966, Robinson Crusoe's Island, 1969, Positivism in Latin America, 1850-1900, 1971, Central America: A Nation Divided, 1976, 2d edit., 1985, Tribute to Don Bernardo de Galvez, 1979, Belize, 1980, Nicaragua, 1983, 2d edit., 1994, El Salvador, 1988, Guatemala, 1992, Rafael Carrera and the Emergence of the Republic of Guatemala, 1993 (Alfred A. Thomas Book award); editor: Central America: Historical Perspectives on the Contemporary Crises, 1988; assoc. editor: Revista del Pensamiento Centroamericano, 1975, Research Guide to Central America and the Caribbean, 1985, Encyclopedia of Latin American History, 1995; contbg. editor: Handbook of Latin American Studies, 1987-90; series editor: World Bibliographical Series, 1987-; contbr. articles to profl. jours. Served to capt. USMC, 1955-58. Henry L. and Grace Doherty Found. fellow Tulane U., 1962. Mem. Am. Hist. Assn. (mem. Conf. L.Am. History, pres. 1989, mem. gen. coun. 1974-76), La. Hist. Assn., Southeastern Conf. L.Am. Studies (program chmn. 1975, pres. 1975-76), L.Am. Studies Assn., Com. on Andean Studies (chmn. 1972-73), Geography and History Acad. Guatemala. Office: Tulane U Dept History New Orleans LA 70118

WOODWARD, RICHARD HOLLIS, JR., utility company executive, lawyer; b. Jackson, Tenn., July 18, 1947; s. Richard Hollis and Opal (Dawson) W.; children: Richard Hollis, Rebecca Jayne. B. Indsl. Engring., Ga. Tech., 1969; J.D., John Marshall Law Sch., 1978. Bar: Ga. 1978; registered profl. engr., Ga. Mgr. div. sales Atlanta Gas Light Co., Savannah, Ga., 1978-80; atty. Atlanta Gas Light Co., Atlanta, 1980-82, asst. sec., 1982, corp. sec., 1982-84, v.p. govtl., regulatory affairs, 1984—; dir. Bus. Devel. Corp., Atlanta. Active Leadership Atlanta, 1981; chmn. div. United Way, 1980; treas. Atlanta Gas Polit. Action Commn., 1981—. Served with U.S. Army, 1970-72. Recipient Young Engr. of Yr. award Ga. Soc. Profl. Engrs., 1978. Mem. Ga. State Bar Assn., Atlanta Bar Assn., Bus. Council Ga. (govt. council 1982—), Am. Gas Assn. (legal mng. com. 1982—), So. Gas Assn. (sec. govt. relations com.). Baptist. Clubs: Cherokee Town and Country, Atlanta City, Lawyer Atlanta. Office: Atlanta Gas Light Co PO Box 4569 Atlanta GA 30302-4569

WOODWARD, RICHARD JOSEPH, JR., geotechnical engineer; b. Pueblo, Colo., Dec. 16, 1907; s. Richard Joseph and Anna Catherine (Earley) W.; m. Mary Irene Campbell, Aug. 29, 1932 (dec.); children: Rita Ann, Sue Marie, Richard Joseph, Patricia Irene. BS, Colo. Coll., 1930; MS, U. Calif., Berkeley, 1947. Naval architect U.S. Navy, 1941-45; lectr. civil engring. U. Calif., Berkeley, 1946-50; ptnr. Woodward-Clyde Cons.'s (and predecessor firms), Oakland, Calif., 1950-53; chmn. bd. Woodward-Clyde Cons.'s (and predecessor firms), 1954-73, chmn. emeritus 1973—; founding pres. Design Profl.'s Ins. Co., 1972. Co-author: Earth and Earth-Rock Dams, 1963, Drilled Pier Foundations, 1972; Contbr. tech. articles to profl. jours. Mem. state tech. svcs. com. U.S. Dept. Commerce, 1967-70; bd. regents Holy Names Coll., Oakland, 1964-72. Decorated knight magistral grace Sovereign Mil. Order Malta Western Assn.; named Disting. Engring. Alumnus U.Calif.-Berkeley Engring. Alumni Assn., 1983. Fellow ASCE (life mem., chmn. exec. com. soil mechanics and founds. div. 1966-70, Middlebrooks award 1964), Am. Cons. Engrs. Coun. (Past Pres.'s award for outstanding contbns. 1972); mem. Internat. Fedn. Cons. Engrs. (chmn. standing com. profl. liability 1971-76), Structural Engrs. Assn. No. Calif. (bd. dir. 1958-60), Sigma Xi, Chi Epsilon, Delta Epsilon, Kiwanis, Serra Club (Berkeley, Calif.), Athens Club (Oakland, Calif.), Commonwealth Club (San Francisco). Roman Catholic. Home and Office: 1860 Tice Creek Dr Apt 1339 Walnut Creek CA 94595-2451

WOODWARD, ROBERT A., radio broadcasting executive; b. Lakewood, Ohio, Aug. 29, 1947; s. Roy and Mamie (Brady) W.; m. Nancy R. Woodward, June 20, 1970; children: Kelly, Christian, Tom. BS in Mktg., U. Dayton, 1969. Intern Sta. WMAL TV/Radio, Washington, 1972-73; acct. exec. Sta. WMOD/Sonderling Broadcasting, Washington, 1973, Sta. WASH/Metromedia, Washington, 1973-80; gen. sales mgr. Sta. WCXR/Metroplex, Washington, 1980-86; ptnr., oper. officer U.S. Radio, Washington, 1987—. Recipient Master Strategist award Rsch. Group, 1988. Mem. Potomac Woods Swim and Tennis Club (v.p. 1988—). Home: 6 Monterra Ct Rockville MD 20853 Address: WWIN(AM) 200 S President St 6th flr Baltimore MD 21202

WOODWARD, ROBERT FORBES, retired government official, consultant; b. Mpls., Oct. 1, 1908; s. Charles Emerson and Ella (Robertson) W.; m. Virginia Parker Cooke, Feb. 20, 1943 (dec. Jan. 1990); children: Robert Forbes, Mary Cooke. A.B., U. of Minn., 1930; student, George Washington U., 1941; LL.D., U. of Pacific, 1962. Joined U.S. Fgn. Service, 1931; vice consul at Winnipeg, Man., Can., 1932-33; student Fgn. Service Tng. Sch., Dept. of State, Washington, 1933; vice consul Buenos Aires, 1933-36; temp. vice consul Asuncion, Paraguay, 1935; 3d sec. legation and vice consul Bogota, Colombia, 1936-37; vice consul Rio de Janeiro, Brazil, 1937-38; assigned div. Latin Am. Affairs, Dept. State, Washington, 1938-42, 44; 2d sec. of embassy and consul La Paz, Bolivia, 1942-44; dep. chief mission, 1942-44; dep. chief mission Guatemala, 1944-46, Habana, 1946-47; dep. dir. Inter-Am. Affairs, Dept. State, Washington, 1947-49; assigned Nat. War Coll., 1949-50; deputy chief mission Stockholm, Sweden, 1950-52; chief fgn. service personnel Dept. State, 1952-53; dep. asst. sec. state for Inter-Am. Affairs, 1953-54; ambassador to Costa Rica, 1954-58, to Uruguay, 1958-61, to Chile, 1961, to Spain, 1962-65; asst. sec. state for Inter-Am. affairs, 1961-62; adviser to spl. negotiators (Canal Treaties with Panama), 1965-67; interim dir. Office of Water for Peace, 1967; ret., 1968; cons. Dept. State, 1968—, Research Analysis Corp., 1969—; Youth for Understanding, 1972—; acting provost Elbert Covell (Spanish-lang.) Coll., U. of Pacific, Stockton, Calif., 1970; Chmn. U.S. del. Econ. Commn. Latin Am., Santiago, Chile, 1961; vice chmn. U.S. del. Alliance for Progress Conf., Punta del Este, 1961,

U.S. del. Fgn. Ministers meeting, Punta del Este, 1962; chmn. U.S. del. Internat. Red Cross Conf., Vienna, 1965; chmn. U.S. del. Conf. for Revision of OAS Charter, Panama, 1966; conducted study on Panama Canal for Dept. Army, Research Analysis Corp., 1971; conducted study on usefulness of UNESCO to U.S. for Dept. State, 1972; coordinator, chief U.S. del. to Working Group with Latin Am. and Caribbean OC on transnat. enterprises, 1974-75. Mem. Inter-Am. Commn. on Human Rights, 1972-76, Am. Acad. Diplomacy, Washington Inst. Fgn. Affairs. Recipient Distinguished Service award U. Minn., 1963. Mem. Met. Club, Chevy Chase Club, Sulgrave Club, Ret. Diplomatic and Consular Officers Club. Home: 1642 Avon Pl NW Washington DC 20007-2958

WOODWARD, ROBERT J., JR., insurance executive; b. 1941; married. BA, Capital U., 1964, JD, 1971. With Nationwide Gen. Ins. Co., Columbus, 1964—, v.p., 1975—; v.p. Nationwide Life Ins. Co., Columbus, Nationwide Mut. Ins. Co., Columbus, Nationwide Mut. Fire Ins. Co., Columbus. Office: Nationwide Mut Ins Co One Nationwide Pla Columbus OH 43216

WOODWARD, ROBERT UPSHUR, newspaper reporter, writer; b. Geneva, Ill., Mar. 26, 1943; s. Alfred E. and Jane (Upshur) W.; m. Elsa Walsh, Nov. 25, 1989; 1 child, Tali. B.A., Yale U., 1965. Reporter Montgomery County (Md.) Sentinel, 1970-71; reporter Washington Post, 1971-78, met. editor, 1979-81, asst. mng. editor, 1981—. Author: (with Carl Bernstein) All the President's Men, 1974, The Final Days, 1976, (with Scott Armstrong) The Brethren, 1979, Wired, 1984, Veil: The Secret Wars of the CIA, 1987, The Commanders, 1991, (with David S. Broder) The Man Who Would Be President, 1991, The Agenda: Inside the Clinton White House, 1994. Served with USN, 1965-70. Office: Washington Post Co 1150 15th St NW Washington DC 20071-0002

WOODWARD, STEPHEN RICHARD, newspaper reporter; b. Fukuoka City, Japan, July 27, 1953; came to U.S., 1954; s. Leonard Edwin and Etsuko (Okumura) W.; m. Sandra Elizabeth Richardson, Dec. 31, 1979; children: Daniel Joseph, Elizabeth Etsuko. BA in English, Wright State U., 1975, MA in Journalism, U. Mo., 1979. Advt. coordinator Wright State U., Dayton, Ohio, 1976-77; reporter Kansas City (Mo.) Star, 1979-82; assoc. editor then editor Kansas City Bus. Jour., 1982-83; editor then gen. mgr. Portland (Oreg.) Bus. Jour., 1984-86; exec. bus. editor The Hartford (Conn.) Courant, 1986-87; editor San Francisco Bus. Times, 1987-88; bus. editor The Oregonian, Portland, 1989-93, reporter, 1993—. Recipient 1st Place Investigative Reporting award Assn. Area Bus. Publs., 1983, 1st Place Column Writing award Assn. Area Bus. Publs., 1985. Mem. Investigative Reporters and Editors Inc. Avocations: astronomy, chess, creative writing. Home: 3309 NE Irving St Portland OR 97232-2538 Office: The Oregonian 1320 SW Broadway Portland OR 97201-3469

WOODWARD, SUSAN ELLEN, economist, federal official; b. Loma Linda, Calif., June 14, 1949; d. Frank Colwin and Dollie Dorothy (O'Kane) W.; 1 child, Sonja Stenger Weissman. BA in Econs., UCLA, 1970, PhD in Mgmt./Fin., 1978. Instr. U. Wash., Seattle, 1975, U. Toronto, 1975-77, UCLA, 1983-85, 84-85, U. Calif., Santa Barbara, 1977-79, U. Rochester (N.Y.), 1983-84; sr. staff economist Coun. Econ. Advisers, Washington, 1985-87; dep. asst. sec., chief economist HUD, Washington, 1987-92; chief economist SEC, Washington, 1992—. Mem. Am. Econ. Assn. (editor 1983-87), Am. Fin. Assn. Home: 2122 California St NW # 252 Washington DC 20008-1803 Office: US SEC 450 5th St NW Washington DC 20549

WOODWARD, THEODORE ENGLAR, medical educator, internist; b. Westminster, Md., Mar. 22, 1914; s. Lewis Klair and Phoebe Helen (Neidig) W.; m. Celeste Constance Lauve, June 24, 1938; children: William E., R. Craig, Celeste L. Woodward Applefeld. BS, Franklin and Marshall Coll., 1934, DSc (hon.), 1954; MD, U. Md., 1938; DSc (hon.), Western Md. Coll., 1950, Hahnemann U., 1993. Diplomate Am. Bd. Internal Medicine. Asst. prof. medicine U. Md. Sch. Medicine, Balt., 1946-48, assoc. prof., also dir. sect. infectious disease, 1948-54, prof., 1954-83, prof. emeritus, 1983—, chmn. dept., 1954-81; attending physician Balt. VA Med Ctr., 1949—; with Armed Forces Epidemiol. Bd., Washington, 1952-92, mem. commns., 1952-72, pres. bd., 1976-78, 80-92; mem. U.S./Japan Coop. Med. Sci. Program, Washington, 1965—; disting. physician Cen. VA, Washington, 1981-87. Author: Chloramphenicol, 1958, 200 Years of Medicine in Baltimore, 1976, A History of the Department of Medicine, University of Maryland, 1807-1981, 1987, A History of Armed Forces Epidemiological Board, 1940-90, 1990, Carroll County (Md.) Physicians of the 19th and Early 10th Centuries, 1990, The Armed Forces Epidemiological Board: The History of the Commissions, 1995; contbr. chpts. in textbooks. Life trustee Gilman Sch., Balt., 1955—. Lt. col. Medical Svc. Corp U.S. Army, 1941-46, ETO, PTO. Decorated Order of the Sacred Treasure Gold and Silver Star Govt. of Japan; recipient U.S.A. Typhus Commn. medal Dept. Def., 1945, also Exceptionally Disting. Svc. award, 1990, Distinguished Teacher awd., Am. Coll. of Physicians, 1992, Outstanding Civilian Svc. medal with oak leaf cluster Dept. Army, 1981. Mem. ACP (master, gov. Md. regent 1970-90, James D. Bruce Meml. award 1970, Disting. Tchr. award 1992), Am. Clin. and Climatol. Assn. (pres. 1969-70), Infectious Disease Soc. Am. (pres. 1976-77, Finland award 1972, Bristol award, Kass award 1991), Inst. Medicine NAS, Elkridge Club (Towson, Md.), Mayo Fellows Assn. (hon.), Hamilton St. Club. Republican. Avocations: photography, gardening, raising wild fowl. Home: 1 Merrymount Rd Baltimore MD 21210-1908 Office: Balt VA Med Ctr 10 N Green St Baltimore MD 21210

WOODWARD, THOMAS AIKEN, lawyer; b. Beatrice, Nebr., June 28, 1933; s. Thomas Aiken and Jessie (Griggs) W.; m. Sara Hubka, Dec. 27, 1962; children: Thomas A., Hewett G. BA, U. Nebr., 1955; JD, U. Mich., 1960; LLM in Taxation, NYU, 1961. Bar: N.Y. 1961, Nebr. 1963, Pa. 1987. Ptnr. Kutak, Rock & Campbell, Omaha, 1969-87; ptnr., chmn. tax dept. Eckert, Seamans, Cherin & Mellott, Pitts., 1987-92; spl. counsel Weller, Wicks & Wallace, Pitts., 1992—. Served to lt. USN, 1955-58. Mem. ABA, N.Y. Bar Assn., Nebr. Bar Assn., Pa. Bar Assn., Allegheny County Bar Assn. Republican. Presbyterian. Office: Weller Wicks & Wallace Benedum-Trees Bldg Ste 1800 Pittsburgh PA 15222

WOODWARD, THOMAS MORGAN, actor; b. Ft. Worth, Sept. 16, 1925; s. Valin Ridge and Francis Louise (McKinley) W.; m. Enid Anne Loftis, Nov. 18, 1950; 1 child, Enid Anne. AA, Arlington State Coll., 1948; BBA, U. Tex., 1951. Motion picture and TV actor, 1955—; numerous TV appearances include Dallas; motion pictures include The Great Locomotive Chase, 1955, Slaughter on 10th Ave., 1957, The Gun Hawk, 1962, Cool Hand Luke, 1966, The Wild Country, 1973, Which Way Is Up, 1977, Speed Trap, 1978, Battle Beyond the Stars, 1980, Girls Just Want to Have Fun, 1985, Dark Before Dawn, 1987, Gunsmoke III, 1991. With USAAF, 1944-45; to capt. USAF, 1951-53. Recipient Golden Boot award Motion Picture and TV Fund, 1988, Golden Lariat award Nat. Western Film Festival, 1988, Lifetime Achievement award in the arts Arlington Tex. Arts Coun., 1994; named Disting. Alumnus of Arts U. Tex., 1969; inducted into the Walk of Western Stars William S. Hart Mus., L.A., 1990. Mem. Acad. Motion Picture Arts and Scis., SAR, Pi Kappa Alpha (Disting. Achievement award 1981, inducted into Order of West Range 1988).

WOODWELL, GEORGE MASTERS, ecologist, educator, author, lecturer; b. Cambridge, Mass., Oct. 23, 1928; s. Philip McIntire and Virginia (Sellers) W.; m. Alice Katharine Rondthaler, June 23, 1955; children: Caroline Alice, Marjorie Virginia, Jane Katharine, John Christopher. AB, Dartmouth Coll., 1950; AM, Duke U., 1956, PhD, 1958; DSc (hon.), Williams Coll., 1977, Miami U., 1984, Carleton Coll., 1988, Muhlenberg Coll., 1990, Duke U., 1994. Mem. faculty U. Maine, 1957-61, assoc. prof. botany, 1960-61; vis. asst. ecologist, biology dept. Brookhaven Nat. Lab., Upton, N.Y., 1961-62; ecologist Brookhaven Nat. Lab., 1965-67, sr. ecologist, 1967-75; founder, dir. Ecosystems Center, 1975-85; dep. and asst. dir. Marine Biol. Lab., Woods Hole, Mass., 1975-76; pres. and dir. Woods Hole Research Ctr., 1985—; lectr. Yale Sch. Forestry, 1967—; chmn. Conf. on Long Term Biol. Consequences of Nuclear War, 1982-83. Editor: Ecological Effects of Nuclear War, 1965, Diversity and Stability in Ecological Systems, 1969, (with E.V. Pecan) Carbon and the Biosphere, 1973, The Role of Terrestrial Vegetation in the Global Carbon Cycle: Measurement by Remote Sensing, 1984, The Earth in Transition: Patterns and Processes of Biotic Impoverishment, 1990, (with K. Ramakrishna) Forest for the Future, 1993, (with F.T. Mackenzie)

Biotic Feedbacks in the Warming of the Earth, 1995. Founding trustee Environ. Def. Fund, 1967; founding trustee Natural Resources Def. Council, 1970, vice chmn., 1974—; founding trustee World Resources Inst., 1982—; bd. dirs. World Wildlife Fund, 1970-84, chmn., 1980-84; bd. dirs. Conservation Found., 1975-77, Ruth Mott Fund, 1984-91, chmn. 1989-91; bd. dirs. Ctr. for Marine Conservation, 1990—; adv. com. TMI Pub. Health Fund., 1980—. Recipient Joseph Priestley award Dickerson Coll., 1993, Hutchinson medal Garden Club of Am., 1993. Fellow AAAS, Am. Acad. Arts and Scis.; mem. NAS, Brit. Ecol. Soc., Ecol. Soc. Am. (v.p. 1966-67, pres. 1977-78), Sea Edn. Assn. (bd. dirs. 1980-85), Sigma Xi. Rsch., pub. on structure and function of natural communities, biotic impoverishment, especially ecological effects of ionizing radiation, effects of persistent toxins, world carbon cycle and warming of the earth. Office: Woods Hole Research Ctr Box 296 13 Church St Woods Hole MA 02543-1007

WOODWELL, MARGOT BELL, broadcasting executive; b. Pitts., Mar. 5, 1936; d. Davitt Stranahan and Marian (Whieldon) Bell; m. William Herron Woodwell, June 24, 1960; children: Davitt Bell, William Herron, James Ross. A.B., Vassar Coll., 1957. Dir. community support Sta. WQED, Pitts., 1978-84, v.p., sta. mgr., from 1984, now v.p., gen. mgr. Pres. bd. trustees St. Edmunds Acad., Pitts., 1972-75; pres. bd. trustees Episcopal Diocese Pitts., 1975-78; bd. dirs Union Nat. Bank of Pitts., Cen. Blood Bank, County Bd. of Health, Lemington Home for Aged, Greater Pitts. Literacy Coun., Pitts. Literacy Initiative; mem. standing com., 1982—; chmn. Episcopal Diocese Renewal Fund, Pitts., 1980—; trustee Vassar Coll., Poughkeepsie, N.Y., 1982—, chmn. devel. com.; mem. Allegheny County Bd. of Health, Health Edn. Ctr. adv. com., steering com. co-chmn. program com. Leadership Pitts., The Mayor's Commn. on Families, women's com. Mus. of Art of the Carnegie, community adv. bd. Jr. League of Pitts., adv. bd. Pa. State Coalition for Literacy, adv. coun. Pa. Dept. Edn. Workplace; bd. dirs. Greater Pitts. Literacy Coun., Pitts. Salvation Army; mktg. com. United Way of Allegheny County. Recipient A Celebration of Excellence award for Media Mgmt. Triangle Corner Ltd., 1986, Outstanding Svc. award Pa. Assn. Adult and Continuing Edn., 1987; named YWCA Woman of Yr. in Communications, 1988, Bishop's award Episcopal Diocese of Pitts., 1988. Office: Sta WQED 4802 5th Ave Pittsburgh PA 15213-2956

WOODWORTH, HARRY EADES, III, brokerage house executive; b. Honolulu, Sept. 26, 1941; s. Harry Eades Woodworth Jr. and Catherine Rose (Maier) Williams. AA, Hartnell Coll., 1966; BSBA, Armstrong Coll., 1968. Stockbroker Dean Witter, Anchorage, 1973-76; sr. v.p. Dean Witter Reynolds (formerly Dean Witter), Anchorage, 1981—; stockbroker Merrill Lynch, Anchorage, 1976-81; Prin. Eagle Land Assocs, Anchorage, 1983—, prin. Eagle Investments, Anchorage, 1983; bd. dirs. L. Nebel and Assocs. Landscape Architects, Anchorage, 1983—, bd. dirs Eagle Broadcasting, Inc., Anchorage, 1983-85, bd. dirs. Pacific Rim Broadcasting, Inc., Anchorage, 1985—. Recipient Pacesetters award Dean Witter Reynolds, Inc., 1983-85. Mem. N.Y. Stock Exchange (registered rep.), Nat. Assn. Security Dealers (registered rep.), N.Y. Commodities Exchange (registered rep.), Chgo. Commodities Exchange (registered rep.), Chgo Bd. Options Exchange (registered rep.), Ducks Unltd., Nat. Rifle Assn., Ferrari Owners Club, Mercedes Owners Club. Republican. Roman Catholic. Club: U.S. Boat, Ducks Unltd. Lodge: Elks. Avocations: travel, skiing, fishing, skeet, boating. Home: 13900 Jarvi Dr Anchorage AK 99515-3940 Office: Dean Witter Reynolds Inc 3601 C St Anchorage AK 99503-5925

WOODY, JOHN FREDERICK, secondary education educator; b. Indpls., Apr. 27, 1941; s. Ralph Edwin and Crystal Oleta (Thomas) W.; m. Nancy Ann Henry, July 7, 1963; children: Michael, Laura. BS in Secondary Sch. Teaching, Butler U., 1963, MS in Edn., 1967, adminstrn. lic., 1979, postgrad., 1991—; postgrad., UCLA, 1980-82, Ind. U., 1990, U. Amsterdam, The Netherlands, 1985, Mont. State U., 1993, Purdue U., 1994. Tchr. Pub. Sch. 90, Indpls., 1963-66, Broad Ripple High Sch., Indpls., 1966-89; tchr., head social studies dept. Arlington H.S., Indpls., 1989—. Author: (resource kits for hist. events) Cram, Inc., 1976-81, (filmstrips) Lowe Sheldrew, 1976-81; contbr. articles to profl. jours. and sch. materials. Sponsor Rep. Nat. Com., 1982—; deacon Heritage Bapt. Ch., 1983—; mem. U.S. Congress German Bundestag Select Com. Ind., 1986-93. Fulbright scholar U.S. Info. Agy., 1985. Mem. ASCD, Nat. Coun. Social Studies, Ind. Coun. Social Studies. Avocations: reading, writing, swimming, lifting weights. Home: 7362 Woodside Dr Indianapolis IN 46260-3137 Office: Arlington High Sch 4825 N Arlington Ave Indianapolis IN 46226-2499

WOODY, MARY FLORENCE, nursing educator, university administrator; b. Chambers County, Ala., Mar. 31, 1926; d. Hugh Ernest and May Lillie (Gilliland) W.; diploma Charity Hosp. Sch. Nursing, 1947; BS, Columbia U., 1953, M.A., 1955. Staff nurse Wheeler Hosp., Lafayette, Ala., 1947-48; polio nurse Willard Parker Hosp., N.Y.C., 1949; staff nurse, supr. VA Hosp., Montgomery, Ala., 1950-53; faculty mem., field supr., nursing dept. Tchrs. Coll., Columbia U., N.Y.C., 1955-56; asst. dir. nursing Emory U. Hosp., clin. asst. prof. Emory U. Sch. Nursing, Atlanta, 1956-68; asst. dir., founding dean, dir. nursing Grady Meml. Hosp., Atlanta, 1968-79; dean, prof. Sch. Nursing, Auburn (Ala.) U., 1979-84; assoc. dir., dir. nursing Emory U. Hosp., Atlanta, 1984-93; interim dean Sch. Nursing, Emory U., 1992-93; chmn. Ga. Statewide Master Planning Com. for Nursing and Nursing Edn., 1971-75; faculty preceptor patient care adminstrn. Sch. Public Health, U. Minn., 1977-79. Recipient Spl. Recognition, 5th Dist. and Ga. Nurses Assn. 1978, Disting. Achievement in Nursing Svc. award Columbia U. Tchrs. Coll. Alumni Assn., 1992, Jane Van de Vrede Outstanding Svc. to Citizens of Ga. award Ga. League Nursing. Fellow Am. Acad. Nursing (charter); mem. Am. Nurses Assn., Nat. League Nursing, Am. Heart Assn., Sigma Theta Tau. Democrat. Chmn. bd. dirs. Am. Jour. Nursing Co., 1978-83. Address: 907 Lenox Hill Atlanta GA 30324-2957

WOOFTER, R. D., utilities company executive; b. Weston, Va., 1923; married. BEE, W.Va. U., 1950. With Tex.-N.Mex. Power Co. (formerly Community Pub. Service Co.), Ft. Worth, 1950—, v.p., mgr. communications, 1967-73, v.p. ops., 1973-74, exec. v.p., 1974-75, pres., chief exec. officer, from 1975, chmn., 1977—, also bd. dirs.; chmn. TNP Enterprises Inc., Ft. Worth. Served with USAF, 1940-45. Office: TNP Enterprises Inc 4100 International Plz Fort Worth TX 76109-4817

WOOL, IRA GOODWIN, biochemist, molecular biologist, educator; b. Newark, Aug. 22, 1925; s. Abraham Herman and Edith (Jacobs) W.; m. Glorye Needlman, Sept. 14, 1950 (div. Oct. 1989); children: Christopher Douglas, Jonathan Andrew; m. Barbara Mirecki, Apr. 22, 1991. A.B., Syracuse U., 1949; M.D., U. Chgo., 1953, Ph.D., 1954. USPHS postdoctoral fellow in physiology U. Chgo., 1953-54, Commonwealth fellow dept. physiology, 1956-57, asst. prof. physiology, 1957-62, asso. prof., 1962-65, prof. depts. physiology, biochemistry, 1965-73, A.J. Carlson prof. biol. scis., dept. biochemistry and molecular biology, 1973—; intern Beth Israel Hosp., Boston, 1954-55; asst. resident in internal medicine Beth Israel Hosp., 1955-56; teaching fellow in physiology Harvard U., 1955-56; mem. molecular biology study sect. NIH, 1974-79. Editor: Vitamins and Hormones: Endocrinology, 1963-68; overseas adv. bd.: Biochem. Jour., 1973-77, Jour. Biol. Chemistry, 1975-79, 82-87, Archives Biochem. Biophys., 1976-80; contbr. articles sci. jours. Served with AUS, 1943-46. Fellow AAAS; mem. Am. Soc. Cell Biology, Biochem. Soc. (Eng.), Am. Soc. Biol. Chemists, Phi Beta Kappa, Sigma Xi, Alpha Omega Alpha. Home: 4950 Chgo Beach Dr Chicago IL 60615

WOOLAM, GERALD LYNN, surgeon; b. Lubbock, Tex., Apr. 16, 1937; s. Rawson Harp and Christine Leta (Rampy) W.; m. Nan Kelly, Feb. 28, 1959; children—Kelly Ann, Gerald Lynn, Gregory Alan. B.A., Tex. Tech. U., 1958; M.D., Baylor U., 1962. Diplomate Am. Bd. Surgery. Intern Parkland Meml. Hosp., Dallas, 1962-63; resident gen. surgery Mayo Clinic and Mayo Grad. Sch. Medicine, U. Minn., Rochester, 1963-67; chief resident asso. in surgery Mayo Clinic and Mayo Grad. Sch. Medicine, U. Minn., 1967-68; practice medicine specializing in surgery Lubbock, 1968—; assoc. clin. prof. surgery Tex. Tech. U. Sch. Medicine, 1972-74, clin. prof., 1975—, prof. interim chmn. dept. surgery, 1980-81. Contbr. articles to profl. jours. Bd. dirs. Community Concert Assn. of Lubbock, 1968-71, 1st United Meth. Ch. Lubbock, 1970-75, 76—, South Plains Health Systems, 1976-81; trustee West Tex. Found., 1971-74. Served with USNR, 1954-62. Recipient Outstanding Clin. Prof. award Tex. Tech. U., 1977. Fellow ACS; mem. AAAS, Priestley Soc. (dir. 1970-73, pres. 1981-82), Lubbock Surg. Soc. (pres. 1972), AMA,

Lubbock-Crosby-Garza County Med. Soc. (treas., exec. com. 1971—, pres. 1986), Osler Soc., Am. Cancer Soc. (pres. Lubbock unit 1972-73, pres. Tex. div. 1978-79, nat. del. 1980-88, nat. dir. 1988—), Am. Heart Assn. (pres. Lubbock County div. 1973-74), Tex. Surg. Soc., Soc. Surgery Alimentary Tract, Soc. for Surg. Oncology, Central Assn. Dentists and Physicians, So. Surg. Assn., Sigma Xi, Phi Chi, Alpha Omega Alpha, Phi Kappa Phi, Phi Eta Sigma, Alpha Epsilon Delta. Home: 4007 69th St Lubbock TX 79413-5945 Office: 3702 21st St Lubbock TX 79410-1230

WOOLARD, EDGAR S., JR., chemical company executive; b. Washington, N.C., Apr. 15, 1934; s. Edgar Smith and Mamie (Boone) W.; m. Peggy Harrell, 1956; children: Annette, Lynda. BS, N.C. State U., 1956. Indsl. engr. DuPont, Kinston, N.C., 1957-59, group supr. indsl. engring., 1959-62, supr. mfg. sect., 1962-64, planning supr., 1964-65; staff asst. to profn. mgr. DuPont, Wilmington, Del., 1965-66; product supr. DuPont, Old Hickory, Tenn., 1966-69, engring. supt., 1969-70; asst. plant mgr. DuPont, Camden, S.C., 1970-71; plant mgr. DuPont, Kinston, S.C., 1971-73; dir. products mktg. div. DuPont, Wilmington, Del., 1973-75, mng. dir. textile mktg. div., 1975-76, mgr. corp. plans dept., 1976-77, gen. dir. products and planning div., 1977-78, gen. mgr. textile fibers, 1978-81, v.p. textile fibers, 1981-83, exec. v.p., 1983-85, vice chmn., 1985-87, pres., COO, 1987-89, chmn., CEO, 1989—, also bd. dirs.; bd. dirs. N.C. Textile Found., Citicorp, IBM Corp., Seagram Co. Ltd. Trustee Med. Ctr. Del., N.C. State U., Winterthur Mus. Lt. U.S. Army. Office: DuPont 1007 N Market St Wilmington DE 19898-0001

WOOLARD, WILLIAM LEON, lawyer, electrical distributing company executive; b. Bath, N.C., Aug. 26, 1931; s. Archie Leon and Pearl Irene (Boyd) W.; m. Virginia Harris Stratton, June 17, 1961; children: William Leon Jr., Margaret Anne. AB, Duke U., 1953, LLB, JD, 1955. Bar: N.C. 1955, U.S. Dist. Ct. (we. and mid. dists.) N.C. 1960. Claims analyst Md. Casualty Co., Charlotte, N.C., 1955-56; dist. mgr. Chrysler Corp., Charlotte, 1956-60; ptnr. Jones, Hewson & Woolard, Charlotte, 1960-86, of counsel, 1986—; pres. Armature Winding Co., Inc., Charlotte, 1970—, also bd. dirs.; v.p. Power Products Mfg. Co., Charlotte, 1970—, also bd. dirs. Mem. adminstrv. bd. 1st United Meth. Ch., Charlotte, 1961-78, trustee, 1984-87; trustee Lawyers Ednl. Found., Charlotte, 1970-78; bd. dirs. Christian Rehab. Ctr., Charlotte, 1972-73, N.C. Eye and Human Tissue Bank, Winston-Salem, 1978-79. Recipient Order of Civil Merit Moran award Republic of Korea, 1990, Disting. Svc. medal Republic of China, 1990, Medal of Friendship Pope John Paul II, 1990, Humanitarian Citizen of Merit medal Republic of China, 1990, Humanitarian medal France, 1990, Outstanding Svc. medal Mayor of Paris, 1990, numerous others; Angier B. Duke scholar Duke U., 1949-53; Carnegie Found. fellow Duke U., 1951-52, Melvin Jones fellow Lions Found., 1978. Mem. ABA, N.C. Bar Assn., N.C. State Bar Assn., 26th Jud. Dist. Bar Assn., Am. Judicature Soc., Lions (pres. Charlotte Cen. club 1972-73, pres. trustee ednl. found. 1973-87, dist. gov., chmn. coun. govs. internat. orgn. 1978-79, internat. bd. dirs. 1981-85, Ambassador of Goodwill award 1983, internat. 3d v.p. 1986-87, 2d v.p. 1987-88, 1st v.p. 1988-89, internat. pres. 1989-90, immediate past pres. 1990-91, chmn. bd. trustee 1990-91), Masons, Shriners, Phi Kappa Sigma, Delta Theta Phi. Avocations: collecting antique and rare books, opera, boating, fishing. Home: 638 Hempstead Pl Charlotte NC 28207-2320 Office: PO Box 32277 Charlotte NC 28232-2277

WOOLDREDGE, WILLIAM DUNBAR, investment banker; b. Salem, Mass., Oct. 27, 1937; s. John and Louise (Sigourney) W.; m. Johanna Marie; children: John, Rebecca Wistar. B.A., Colby Coll., 1961; M.B.A., Harvard, 1964. Staff assoc. Sun Oil Co., Phila., 1964-67; treas. Ins. Co. N.Am., Phila., 1967-72; treas. B.F. Goodrich Co., Akron, Ohio, 1972-84, sr. v.p., 1978-79, exec. v.p., chief fin. officer, mem. mgmt. com., 1979-84; chief fin. officer, exec. v.p., dir. Belden & Blake Corp., North Canton, Ohio, 1984-89; sr. v.p., chief fin. officer, dir. Belden & Blake Oil Prodn., Inc., 1984-89; prin. dir. Carleton Group, Cleve., 1989-92; CFO, v.p. King's Med. Co., Hudson, Ohio, 1993—, also bd. dirs.; bd. dirs. Freeway Corp., Cleve. Bd. dirs. Salvation Army; trustee Children's Hosp. Med. Ctr., Akron. With U.S. Army, 1956-58. Mem. Fin. Execs. Inst. (bd. dirs.). Episcopalian. Club: Country of Hudson. Home: 100 College St Hudson OH 44236-2925 Office: King's Med Co 1920 Georgetown Rd Hudson OH 44236

WOOLDRIDGE, DEAN EVERETT, engineering executive, scientist; b. Chickasha, Okla., May 30, 1913; s. Auttie Noonan and Irene Amanda (Kerr) W.; m. Helene Detweiler, Sept. 1936; children—Dean Edgar, Anna Lou, James Allan. A.B., U. Okla., 1932, M.S., 1933; Ph.D., Calif. Inst. Tech., 1936. Mem. tech. staff Bell Telephone Labs., N.Y.C., 1936-46; co-dir. research and devel. labs Hughes Aircraft Co., Culver City, Calif., 1946-52, v.p. research and devel., 1952-53; pres., dir. Ramo-Wooldridge Corp., Los Angeles, 1953-58, Thompson Ramo Wooldridge, Inc., Los Angeles, also Cleve., 1958-62; research assoc. Calif. Inst. Tech., 1962-79. Author: The Machinery of the Brain, 1963, The Machinery of Life, 1966, Mechanical Man, 1968, Sensory Processing in the Brain, 1979, also articles. Recipient Citation of Honor Air Force Assn., 1950, Raymond E. Hackett award, 1955, Westinghouse Sci. Writing award AAAS, 1963, Disting. Svc. Citation U. Okla, Disting. Alumnus award Calif. Inst. Tech., 1983. Fellow AAAS, Am. Acad. Arts and Sci., Am. Phys. Soc., IEEE, AIAA; mem. Nat. Acad. Scis., Nat. Acad. Engring., Calif. Inst. Assos., Am. Inst. Physics, Phi Beta Kappa, Sigma Xi, Tau Beta Pi, Phi Eta Sigma, Eta Kappa Nu. Address: 4545 Via Esperanza Santa Barbara CA 93110-2319

WOOLEVER, NAOMI LOUISE, retired editor; b. Williamsport, Pa., Sept. 17, 1922; d. Samuel Bruce and Kathryn Elizabeth (Schmidt) W. B.S., Pa. State U., 1944, M.A., 1966, postgrad., 1974-76. Reporter, women's editor Gazette & Bulletin, Williamsport, 1944-53; women's editor Sun-Gazette, Williamsport, 1953-72, assoc. city editor, 1972-74; prof. journalism Williamsport Area Community Coll., 1974-76; nat. editor, mng. editor Grit Pub. Co., Williamsport, 1976-81, editor in chief, 1981-88; career cons. high sch. and coll. journalism classes, Pa. Contbr. articles to profl. jours. Active Williamsport Home Bd. Mgrs. Named Woman of Yr., Williamsport Univ. Women, 1967. Mem. Pa. Women's Press Assn. (pres. 1960-62, Pa. Newswoman of Yr. 1958), Nat. Fedn. Press Women (bd. dirs. 1960-62), Soroptimist Club (pres. Williamsport chpt. 1958-60), Univ. Women's Club (pres. 1961-63), Friends of James V. Brown Libr. (bd. dirs.), Williamsport Country Club, Williamsport Woman's Club, Lycoming County Hist. Soc., Clio Club (pres. 1991-93), Phi Kappa Phi, Kappa Tau Alpha, Zeta Tau Alpha. Republican. Mem. United Methodist Ch. Avocations: music, duplicate bridge, photography, sports. Home: 326 N Montour St Montoursville PA 17754-1832

WOOLEY, BRUCE ALLEN, electronics engineer, educator; b. Milw, Oct. 14, 1943; s. Stanley Allen and Viola Beatrice (Lyster) W.; m. Ariel Starr, Sept. 20, 1969; children: Kevin Lyster, Adam David, Eric Allen. B.S., U. Calif.-Berkeley, 1966, M.S., 1968, Ph.D., 1970. Acting asst. prof. U. Calif.-Berkeley, 1969-70; mem. tech. staff Bell Labs., Holmdel, N.J., 1970-84; prof. elec. engring. Stanford U., Calif., 1984—; vis. lectr. U. Calif.-Berkeley 1980; chmn. Internat. Solid-State Circuits Conf., 1981; program chmn. Internat. Symposium VLSI Cirs., 1990. Editor Jour. Solid-State Circuits, 1986-89; contbr. articles to profl. jours.; inventor integrated circuits for communications, arithmetic and tactile sensing. Recipient Univ. medal U. Calif. Berkeley, 1966; Fortescue fellow, 1966-67. Fellow IEEE; mem. Sigma Xi, Tau Beta Pi, Eta Kappa Nu. Home: 12375 Melody Ln Los Altos CA 94022-3213 Office: Stanford U Dept Elec Engring Stanford CA 94305

WOOLF, HARRY, historian, educator; b. N.Y.C., Aug. 12, 1923; s. Abraham and Anna (Frankman) W.; children: Susan Deborah, Alan, Aaron, Sara Anna. BS, U. Chgo., 1948, MA, 1949; PhD, Cornell U., 1955; DSc (hon.), Whitman Coll., 1979, Am. U., 1982; LHD (hon.), Johns Hopkins U., 1983, St. Lawrence U., 1986. Instr. physics Boston U., 1953-55; instr. history Brandeis U., 1954-55; asst. prof. history U. Wash., 1955-58, assoc. prof., 1958-59, prof. history of sci., 1959-61; Willis K. Shepard prof. history of sci. Johns Hopkins U., 1961-76, chmn. dept. history of sci., 1961-72, provost, 1972-76; dir. Inst. for Advanced Study, Princeton U., 1976-87, prof., 1987—; trustee Cluster C Funds Merrill Lynch, 1982—; mem. adv. coun. Sch. Advanced Internat. Studies, Washington, 1973-76; adv. bd. Smithsonian Rsch. awards, 1975-79; trustee Assoc. Univs., Inc., Brookhaven Nat. Labs., 1972-82; mem. vis. com. student affairs MIT, 1973-77, mem. corp. vis. com. dept. linguistics and philosophy, 1977-83, mem. corp. vis.

com. dept. physics, 1979-85; mem. Nat. Adv. Child Health and Human Devel. Coun. NIH, 1977-80; mem. vis. com. Rsch. Ctr. for Lang. Scis., Ind. U., 1977-80; com. visitors Vanderbilt Grad. Sch., Nashville, 1977-79; adv. coun. dept. philosophy Princeton U., 1980-84, adv. coun. dept. comparative lit., 1982-94; mem. adv. panel WGBH, NOVA, 1979—; bd. dirs. Westmark Internat., 1987-92; mem. adv. coun. NSF, 1984-89; pres., chmn. bd. dirs. Johns Hopkins Program Internat. Edn. Gynecology and Obstetrics, Inc., 1973-76, trustee 1976—. Author: Transits of Venus, 1959, 81, Quantification, 1961, Science as a Cultural Force, 1964, Some Strangeness in the Proportion, 1980, The Analytic Spirit, 1981; contbr. articles, revs. to profl. publs.; editor: Isis Internat., rev. devoted to history of sci. and its cultural influences, 1958-64; series editor The Sources of Sci., 1964—; assoc. editor: Dictionary of Scientific Biography, 1970-80; editorial bd. Interdisciplinary Sci. Revs., 1975—; editorial adv. bd. The Writings of Albert Einstein, 1977—. Trustee Hampshire Coll., Amherst, Mass., 1977-79, Winterthur Mus., 1978-83, Reed Coll., 1992—, Family Health Internat., 1992—, Dibner Inst. for the History of Sci. and Tech., 1992—, Advanced Tech. Labs., 1992—, Spacelabs Med., Inc., 1992—; bd. govs. Tel-Aviv U., 1977-92; trustee-at-large Univs. Rsch. Assn., Inc., 1978-89, chmn. bd., 1979-89; mem. adv. coun. John F. Kennedy Inst. for Handicapped Children, 1979-87; mem. Internat. Rsch. and Exchs. Bd., 1980-94; chmn. MX Missile basing adv. panel Office Tech. Assessment U.S. Congress, 1980-81; trustee Rockefeller Found., 1984-94; bd. dirs. Alex. Brown Mut. Funds, Balt., 1981—; dir. at large Am. Cancer Soc., 1982-86; mem. sci. adv. bd. Wissenschaftskolleg zu Berlin, 1981-87; mem. adv. bd. Stanford Humanities Ctr., 1981-87; bd. dirs. W. Alton Jones Cell Sci. Ctr., 1982-85. NSF sr. postdoctoral fellow, Europe, 1961-62. Fellow AAAS (v.p. 1960), Acad. Internat. d'Histoire des Scis.; mem. History of Sci. Soc., Am. Philos. Soc., Coun. on Fgn. Rels., Am. Acad. Arts and Scis., Phi Beta Kappa, Sigma Xi, Phi Alpha Theta. Office: Inst for Advanced Study Olden Ln Princeton NJ 08540

WOOLF, KENNETH HOWARD, architect; b. N.Y.C., Aug. 19, 1938; s. Howard Walter and Elizabeth Ann (Levy) W.; B.Arch., Cornell U., 1961; m. Elizabeth Adair Rainwater, July 3, 1965; children—Robert Gregg, Susan Adair, Jennifer Adair. Staff architect Look & Morrison, Architects, Pensacola, Fla., 1965-72; pvt. practice architecture, Pensacola, 1972—; instr. architecture Pensacola Jr. Coll., part-time 1967-76. Chmn., Pensacola Archtl. Rev. Bd., 1970-81; mem. Gulf Breeze Planning Bd., 1976-78. Served with USN, 1961-65. Named Jaycee of Yr., 1970. Mem. AIA (sec. N.W. Fla. chpt. 1976-77, 1977-78, pres. N.W. Fla. 1979-81; Comml. Design Honor award 1975). Prin. works include: Coca-Cola Bottling Co. Plant, Pensacola, 1974, 3 profl. office bldgs. towers, Pensacola, 1976, 84, 92, Bapt. Hosp. addition, 1977, The Village, Housing for Elderly, 1978, 81, Azalea Trace Retirement Cmty. Complex, 1980, Northview Cmty. 1981, Coca-Cola Bottling Plant, Beaumont, Tex., 1983, Episcopal Day Sch., Pensacola, 1993. Mem. AIA (sec. N.W. Fla. chpt. 1976-77, 77-78, pres. N.W. Fla. 1979-81, Comml. Design Honor award 1975), Rotary. Episcopalian. Home: 15 N Sunset Blvd Gulf Breeze FL 32561-4051 Office: 100 W Gadsden St Pensacola FL 32501-3910

WOOLF, MICHAEL E., lawyer; b. Phoenix, Mar. 17, 1949. BS, Ariz. State U., 1971, JD cum laude, 1974. Bar: ariz. 1974. Ptnr. O'Connor, Cavanagh, Anderson, Westover, Killingsworth & Beshears, P.A., Phoenix. Mem. ABA, Scottsdale Bar Assn., Maricopa County Bar Assn., State Bar Ariz. Office: O'Connor Cavanagh Anderson Westover Killingsworth & Beshears 1 E Camelback Rd Ste 1100 Phoenix AZ 85012-1656

WOOLF, WILLIAM BLAUVELT, association executive; b. New Rochelle, N.Y., Sept. 18, 1932; s. Douglas Gordon and Katharine Hutton (Blauvelt) W. A.A., John Muir Jr. Coll., 1951; student, U. Calif. at Berkeley, 1951; B.A., Pomona Coll., 1953; M.A., Claremont (Calif.) Grad. Sch., 1955; Ph.D., U. Mich., 1960. Instr., asst. prof., asso. prof. U. Wash. Seattle, 1959-68; assoc. sec., dir. adminstrn. AAUP, Washington, 1968-79; mng. editor Math. Revs., Am. Math. Soc., Ann Arbor, Mich., 1979-90, acting exec. editor, 1984-85; assoc. exec. dir. Am. Math. Soc., Providence, 1990—. Bd. dirs. Nat. Child Research Center, Washington, 1975-77; trustee Friends Sch., Detroit, 1985-90, treas., 1986-90. Fulbright Research fellow U. Helsinki, Finland, 1963-64. Fellow AAAS; mem. Am. Math. Soc., Math. Assn. Am., ACLU (life; treas. Washington 1966-68, bd. dirs. Washtenaw County and Mich. State 1989-90, bd. dirs. R.I. State 1993—, treas. 1994—). Quaker. Home: 35 Halsey St Providence RI 02906-1414 Office: PO Box 6248 Providence RI 02940-6248

WOOLFENDEN, JAMES MANNING, nuclear medicine physician, educator; b. L.A., Nov. 8, 1942. BA with distinction, Stanford U., 1964; MD, U. Wash., 1968. Diplomate Am. Bd. Nuclear Medicine (chmn. credentials com. 1993-94, vice chmn. examinations com. 1993—), Nat. Bd. Med. Examiners; lic. physician Calif., Ariz., Wash. Med. intern L.A. County-U. So. Calif. Med. Ctr., 1968-69; med. resident West L.A. VA Med. Ctr., 1969-70; nuclear medicine resident L.A. County-U. So. Calif. Med. Ctr., 1972-74; from asst. prof. radiology to assoc. prof. radiology U. Ariz., Tucson, 1974-84, prof. radiology, 1984—; mem. med. staff Univ. Med. Ctr., Tucson, 1974—; cons. VA Med. Ctr., 1974—; cons. med. staff Tucson Med. Ctr., 1975—, Carondelet St. Joseph's Hosp., 1974—, St. Mary's Hosp., Tucson, 1976-90; mem. Nat. Cancer Inst. site visit team NIH, 1976, mem. NHLB Inst. site visit team, 1979, mem. diagnostic radiology study sect., 1993—; mem. med. liaison officer network EPA, 1983—; cons.-tchg. med. staff Kino Cmty. Hosp., 1984-94; med. officer Clin. Ctr., NIH, Bethesda, 1984-85; mem. Ariz. Cancer Ctr., U. Ariz., 1988—, sr. clin. scientist Univ. Heart Ctr., 1990—; Ariz. bd. regents U. Ariz. Presdl. Search Com., 1990-91; chmn. Ariz. Atomic Energy Commn., 1979-80, Ariz. Radiation Regulatory Hearing Bd. 1981—; bd. dirs. Calif. Radioactive Materials Mgmt. Forum, 1989—, chmn.-elect, 1993-94, chmn., 1994—, Western Forum Edn. in Safe Disposal of Low-Level Radioactive Waste, 1990—, vice chmn., 1991-92, chmn. 1992-94. Manuscript reviewer: Noninvasive Med. Imaging, 1983-84, Jour. Nuclear Medicine, 1985—, Investigative Radiology, 1989—, Archives of Internal Medicine, 1990—; contbr. book chpts.: Diagnostic Nuclear Medicine, 2d edit., 1988, Adjuvant Therapy of Cancer, 1977, Fundamentals of Nuclear Medicine, 1988, others; contbr. articles and book revs. to profl. publs. Mem. Am. Heart Assn. Coun. on Cardiovasc. Radiology. Maj. U.S. Army, 1970-72, Vietnam. Fellow Am. Coll. Nuclear Physicians (long range planning com. 1981-83, govt. affairs com. 1984—, exec. com. 1987-91, sec. 1989-91, parliamentarian 1991—, mem. publs. com. 1993—, chmn. publs. com. 1993-94, and many others); mem. AMA (diagnostic and therapeutic tech. assessment reference panel 1982—), Am. Fedn. Clin. Rsch., Am. Nuc. Soc., Soc. Nuclear Medicine (com. on audit 1992—, bd. trustees 1992—, Bronze medal for sci. exhibit 1984, bd. dirs., sec.-treas. So. Calif. chpt. 1993—), Assn. Univ. Radiologists, Pima County Med. Soc., Radiol. Soc. N.Am. Office: Ariz Health Scis Ctr 1501 N Campbell Ave Tucson AZ 85724

WOOLFORD, DONNELL, professional football player; b. Balt., Jan. 6, 1966. Student, Clemson U. Cornerback Chgo. Bears, 1989—. Named to Sporting Coll. All-Am. Team, 1988, to Pro Bowl Team, 1993. Office: Chgo Bears Halas Hall 2550 N Washington Rd Lake Forest IL 60045*

WOOLHISER, DAVID ARTHUR, hydrologist; b. LaCrosse, Wis., Jan. 21, 1932; s. Algie Duncan and Blanche Lenore (Jasperson) W.; m. Kathryn Brown, Apr. 21, 1957; children: Carl David, Curt Fredric, Lisa Kathryn. B.S. in Agr., U. Wis.-Madison, 1955, BSCE, 1955, PhD, 1962; MS, U. Ariz., 1959. Instr. U. Ariz., Tucson, 1955-58; hydraulic engr. Agrl. Research Service, USDA, Madison, Wis., 1959-61, Columbia, Mo., 1961-63; asst. prof. Cornell U., Ithaca, N.Y., 1963-67; research hydraulic engr. Agrl. Research Service, Ft. Collins, Colo., 1967-81, Tucson, 1981-91, collaborator, 1991-92; vis. scientist Inst. Hydrology, Wallingford, Eng., 1977-78; vis. prof. Imperial Coll., London, 1977-78; faculty affiliate Colo. State U., 1967-84; adj. prof. U. Ariz., 1981-92; vis. prof. Va. Polytech. and State U., 1992, sr. rsch. sci. Colo. State U. 1993—; vis. prof. U. Córdoba, Spain, 1993-94. Contbr. articles to profl. jours. Fellow Am. Geophys. Union (Robert E. Horton award 1983); mem. NAE, ASCE (Hunter Rouse Lectr. 1994, Arid Lands Hydraulic Engring. award 1988), Common Cause. Office: 1631 Barnwood Dr Fort Collins CO 80525-2069

WOOLLAM, JOHN ARTHUR, electrical engineering educator; b. Kalamazoo, Mich., Aug. 10, 1939; s. Arthur Edward and Mildred Edith (Hakes) W.; children: Catherine Jane, Susan June. BA in Physics, Kenyon Coll., 1961; MS in Physics, Mich. State U., 1963, PhD in Solid State Physics, 1967; MSEE, Case-Western Res. U., 1978. Rsch. scientist NASA Lewis

Rsch. Ctr., Cleve., 1967-80; prof. U. Nebr., Lincoln, 1979—; dir. Ctr. Microelectronic and Optical Materials Rsch., 1988—; pres. J.A. Woollam co., Inc., Lincoln, 1987—. Editor Jour. Applied Physics Com., 1979—. Grantee NASA, NSF, USAF, Def. Advanced Rsch. Projects Agy., Physics Com., 1979-94. Fellow Am. Phys. Soc.; mem. Am. Vacuum Soc. (chmn. thin film div. 1989-91). Office: U Nebr Dept Elec Engring 209NWSEC Lincoln NE 68588-0511

WOOLLEN, EVANS, architectural firm executive; b. Indpls., Aug. 10, 1927; s. Evans Jr. and Lydia (Jameson) Ritchey; m. Nancy Clarke Sewell, July 16, 1955 (dec. 1992); children: Ian, Malcolm Sewell. B.A., Yale U., 1952, M.Arch., 1952. Lic. architect, Ind., Conn., Del., N.Y., Ill., Ohio., Mass., Ala., N.C. Chmn. Woollen, Molzan & Ptnrs., Indpls., 1955—. Architect: Pilot Ctr., Cin. (Nat. HUD 1975), St. Mary's Coll. Library (Nat. AIA-ALA 1983), Grainger Libr., U. Ill., Urbana. Mem. bd. Ind. State Welfare Bd., 1956-59, Art Assn., 1956-66, Indpls. Capital Improvement Bd., 1965-69. With Signal Corps U.S. Army, 1946-47. Fellow AIA. Democrat. Address: 43 W 43rd St Indianapolis IN 46208-3721 Office: Woollen Molzan & Ptnrs Inc 47 S Pennsylvania St Indianapolis IN 46204-3622

WOOLLEY, CATHERINE (JANE THAYER), writer; b. Chgo., Aug. 11, 1904; d. Edward Mott and Anna L. (Thayer) W. AB, UCLA, 1927. Advt. copywriter Am. Radiator Co., N.Y.C., 1927-31; freelance writer, 1931-33; copywriter, editor house organ Am. Radiator & Standard San. Corp., N.Y.C., 1933-40; desk editor Archtl. Record, 1940-42; prodn. editor SAE Jour., N.Y.C., 1942-43; pub. relations writer NAM, N.Y.C., 1944-47; condr. workshop on juvenile writing Truro Ctr. for Arts, 1977, 78, 92, Cape Cod Writers Conf., 1990, 91, 92; instr. writing for juveniles Cape Cod Writers Conf., 1965, 66, 92. Author: juvenile books (under name Catherine Woolley) I Like Trains, 1944, rev., 1965, Two Hundred Pennies, 1947, Ginnie and Geneva, 1948, paperback edit., 1988, David's Railroad, 1949, Schoolroom Zoo, 1950, Railroad Cowboy, 1951, Ginnie Joins In, 1951, David's Hundred Dollars, 1952, Lunch for Lennie, 1952 (pub. as L'Incontentabile Gigi in Italy), The Little Car That Wanted a Garage, 1952, The Animal Train and Other Stories, 1953, Holiday on Wheels, 1953, Ginnie and the New Girl, 1954, Ellie's Problem Dog, 1955, A Room for Cathy, 1956, Ginnie and the Mystery House, 1957, Miss Cathy Leonard, 1958, David's Campaign Buttons, 1959, Ginnie and the Mystery Doll, 1960, Cathy Leonard Calling, 1961, paperback edit., 1988, Look Alive, Libby!, 1962, Ginnie and Her Juniors, 1963, Cathy's Little Sister, 1964, paperback edit., 1988, Libby Looks for a Spy, 1965, The Shiny Red Rubber Boots, 1965, Ginnie and the Cooking Contest, 1966, paperback 1979, Ginnie and the Wedding Bells, 1967, Chris in Trouble, 1968, Ginnie and the Mystery Cat, 1969, Libby's Uninvited Guest, 1970, Cathy and the Beautiful People, 1971, Cathy Uncovers a Secret, 1972, Ginnie and the Mystery Light, 1973, Libby Shadows a Lady, 1974, Ginnie and Geneva Cookbook, 1975, adult book Writing for Children, 1990, paperback, 1990; (under name Jane Thayer) The Horse with the Easter Bonnet, 1953, The Popcorn Dragon, 1953, rev. edit. 1989, Where's Andy?, 1954, Mrs. Perrywinkle's Pets, 1955, Sandy and the Seventeen Balloons, 1955, The Chicken in the Tunnel, 1956, The Outside Cat, 1957, English edit., 1958, 83, Charley and the New Car, 1957, Funny Stories To Read Aloud, 1958, Andy Wouldn't Talk, 1958, The Puppy Who Wanted a Boy, 1958, rev., 1986, paperback edition, 1988, French translation Le Petit Chien Qui Voulait Un Garcon, 1991, The Second-Story Giraffe, 1959, Little Monkey, 1959, Andy and His Fine Friends, 1960, The Pussy Who Went To the Moon, 1960, English edit., 1961, A Little Dog Called Kitty, 1961, English edit., 1962, 75, The Blueberry Pie Elf, 1961, English edit., 1962, revised edit., 1994, Andy's Square Blue Animal, 1962, Gus Was a Friendly Ghost, 1962, English edit., 1971, Japanese edit., 1982, A Drink for Little Red Diker, 1963, Andy and the Runaway Horse, 1963, A House for Mrs. Hopper; the Cat that Wanted to Go Home, 1963, Quiet on Account of Dinosaur, 1964, English edit., 1965, 74, paperback edit., 1988, Emerald Enjoyed the Moonlight, 1964, English edit., 1965, The Bunny in the Honeysuckle Patch, 1965, English edit., 1966, Part-Time Dog, 1965, English edit. 1966, The Light Hearted Wolf, 1966, What's a Ghost Going to Do?, 1966, English edit. 1972, Japanese edit., 1982, The Cat that Joined the Club, 1967, English edit. 1968, Rockets Don't Go To Chicago, Andy, 1967, A Contrary Little Quail, 1968, Little Mr. Greenthumb, 1968, English edit., 1969, Andy and Mr. Cunningham, 1969, Curious, Furious Chipmunk, 1969, I'm Not a Cat, Said Emerald, 1970, English edit. 1971, Gus Was A Christmas Ghost, 1970, English edit. 1973, Japanese edit., 1982, Mr. Turtle's Magic Glasses, 1971, Timothy And Madam Mouse, 1971, English edit., 1972, Gus And The Baby Ghost, 1972, English edit. 1973, Japanese edit., 1982, The Little House, 1972, Andy and the Wild Worm, 1973, Gus Was a Mexican Ghost, 1974, English edit. 1975, Japanese edit., 1982, I Don't Believe in Elves, 1975, The Mouse on the Fourteenth Floor, 1977, Gus Was a Gorgeous Ghost, 1978, English edit., 1979, Where Is Squirrel?, 1979, Try Your Hand, 1980, Applebaums Have a Robot, 1980, Clever Raccoon, 1981, Gus Was a Real Dumb Ghost, 1982, Gus Loved His Happy Home, 1989; contbr. stories to juvenile anthologies in U.S., Great Britain, France, Germany, and Holland, sch. readers, juvenile mags. Trustee Truro Pub. Libraries, 1974-84; Mem. Passaic (N.J.) Bd. Edn., 1953-56, Passaic Redevel. Agy., 1952-53; pres. Passaic LWV, 1949-52. Named mem. N.J. Literary Hall of Fame, 1987; recipient Phantom Friends Lifetime Achievement award, 1992. Mem. Authors League Am., Friends of Truro Libraries, Truro Hist. Soc., Amnesty Internat. U.S.A., Kenilworth Soc. Democrat. Home: PO Box 71 Truro MA 02666-0071

WOOLLEY, GEORGE WALTER, biologist, geneticist, educator; b. Osborne, Kans., Nov. 9, 1904; s. George Aitcheson and Nora Belle (Jackson) W.; m. Anne Geneva Collins, Nov. 2, 1936; children: George Aitcheson, Margaret Anne, Lawrence Jackson. B.S., Iowa State U., 1930; M.S., U. Wis., 1931, Ph.D., 1935. Fellow U. Wis., 1935-36; mem. staff Jackson Meml. Lab., Bar Harbor, Maine, 1936-49; bd. dirs. Jackson Meml. Lab. 1937-49, v.p. bd., 1943-47, asst. dir. and sci. adminstr., 1947-49. vis. research assoc., 1949—; mem. chief div. steroid biology Sloan-Kettering Inst., N.Y.C., 1949-58, prof. biology, 1949-58; prof. biology Sloan-Kettering Inst. div. Cornell U. Med. Coll., Ithaca, N.Y., 1951—, chief div. human tumor exptl. chemotherapy, 1958-61; chief div. tumor biology, 1961-66; assoc. scientist Sloan-Kettering Inst. Cancer Research, 1966—; health sci. adminstr., program coordinator, head biol. scis. sect. Nat. Inst. Gen. Medical Scis., NIH, 1966-85; cons. Nat. Edn. Service U.S. Washington, 1961—; spl. cons. to Nat. Cancer Inst., NIH, 1956—; Mem. Expert Panel on Carcinogenicity, unio intern. contra cancerum, 1962—; mem. panel mem. on growth NRC 1945-51; mem. several internat. med. congresses. Author chpts. in med. books; mem. editorial bd. Jour. Nat. Cancer Inst., 1947-50. Trustee Dalton Schs., N.Y.C. Fellow AAAS, N.Y. Acad. Sci.; mem. Am. Mus. Natural History, Nat. Sci. Tchrs. Assn. (cons. 1961—), Am. Assn. Cancer Research (dir. 1951-54), Am. Soc. Human Genetics, Mt. Desert Island Biol. Lab., Soc. Exptl. Biology and Medicine, Am. Inst. Biol. Scis., Am. Assn. Anatomists, Am. Genetic Assn., Wis. Acad. Arts Sci. and Letters, Jackson Lab. Assn., Genetics Soc. Am., Environ. Mutagen Soc., Sigma Xi. Clubs: Bar Harbor, Bar Harbor (Maine) Yacht. Achievements include advanced research, teaching and administration in genetics, from the beginnings of the field to present; contributions to fields of cancer, virology, endocrinology and molecular biology. Home: 5301 Westbard Cir Apt 336 Bethesda MD 20816-1427

WOOLLEY, MARGARET ANNE (MARGOT WOOLLEY), architect; b. Bangor, Maine, Feb. 4, 1946; d. George Walter and Anne Geneva (Collins) W.; m. Gerard F. Vasisko, June 22, 1985. BA, Vassar Coll., 1969; MArch, Columbia U., 1974. Registered architect, N.Y. Urban designer Mayor's Office Lower Manhattan Devel., 1974-76, Mayor's Office Devel., N.Y.C., 1976-78; project mgr. Office Econ. Devel., N.Y.C., 1978-81, dep. dir. design and engring., 1981-83; dep. dir. design N.Y.C. Pub. Devel. Corp., 1983-85, asst. v.p. design, 1985-86, v.p. design, 1986-91; v.p. design N.Y.C. Econ. Devel. Corp., 1991-94; mem. N.Y. State Licensing Bd. Architecture, 1994—. Mem. assoc. bd. regents L.I. Coll. Hosp. Bklyn., 1982-93 mem. planning and devel. com., 1983-93; pres. assoc. bd. regents, 1988-89. William King Fellows scholar, 1973. Mem. AIA (bd. dirs. N.Y.C. chpt. 1988-90, nat. pub. architects steering com. 1993—), N.Y. State Assn. Architects (bd. dirs. 1990-92), Heights Casino Club, Vassar Club, Jr. League. Home: 135 Willow St Brooklyn NY 11201-2255

WOOLLEY, MARY ELIZABETH, research administrator; b. Chgo., Mar. 16, 1947; John Joseph and Ellen Louise (Bakke) McEnerney; m. John Stuart Woolley, Dec. 6, 1969 (div. 1985); children: George Newsom, Nora Ellen; m.

Michael Howland Campbell, Jan. 1, 1989. BS, Stanford U., 1969; MA, San Francisco State U., 1972; postgrad., U. Calif., San Francisco and Berkeley, 1974-75. Assoc. dir. Inst. Epidemiology and Behavioral Medicine, San Francisco, 1979-81; adminstr. Med. Rsch. Inst. of San Francisco, 1981-82, v.p., adminstr., 1982-86, v.p., exec. dir., 1986-90; pres. Research! Am., Alexandria, Va., 1990—; cons. in fin. and mgmt. NIH, Bethesda, Md., 1984-92; adj. faculty U. Calif. Sch. Pub. Health, Berkeley, 1983-92; lectr. to profl. assns. Editor Jour. of Soc. Rsch. Adminstrs., 1986-89, mem. editorial rev. bd., 1989—; mem. editorial bd. Jour. Women's Health, 1992—, Science Communication, 1994—; contbr. articles and editorials to profl. jours. Bd. dirs. Kensington (Calif.) Edn. Found., 1986-89, Enterprise for High Sch. Students, 1990-92; mem. capital campaign com. Calif. Shakespeare Festival, 1989-91, v.p. Med. Rsch. Assns. Am., 1993—. Recipient Silver Touchstone award Am. Hosp. Assn., 1994, Disting. Svc. award Columbia Coll. Physicians and Surgeons, 1994. Mem. AAAS, Assn. Ind. Rsch. Insts. (pres.-elect 1987-89, pres. 1989-90), Soc. Rsch. Adminstrs. (bd. dirs. 1986-90, bd. advisors 1993-93, Hartford-Nicholson Svc. award 1990, Disting. Contbn. to Rsch. Adminstrn. award, 1993), Calif. Biomedical rsch. Assn. (bd. govs. 1986-90), Md. Gov.'s Commn. on Women's Health, 1993—. Democrat. Office: Research! Am 1522 King St Alexandria VA 22314-2717

WOOLLIAMS, KEITH RICHARD, arboretum and botanical garden director; b. Chester, Eng., July 17, 1940; s. Gordon Frank and Margaret Caroline W.; m. Akiko Narita, Apr. 11, 1969; children: Frank Hiromi, Angela Misako. Grad., Celyn Agrl. and Hort. Inst., North Wales, 1955; student, U. Liverpool, various horticultural insts., 1956-59; Kew Cert., Royal Bot. Gardens, Kew, U.K., 1963. Cert. Horticulture Union Cheshire and Lancs. Insts., 1955, Royal Hort. Soc., 1956, 57, 58, Kew Cert. Horticulture, 1958, Cert. Arboriculture, 1962. Supt. field sta. U. London Queen Mary Coll., Brentwood, Essex, Eng., 1963-65; horticulturist Horizons Ltd., Bermuda, 1965-67; dept. forests, supt. botanic gardens Papua, New Guinea, 1967-68; instr. Eng. staff indsl. cos., Japan, 1968-71; supt., horticulturist Nat. Tropical Bot. Garden, Kauai, Hawaii, 1971-74; horticulturist Waimea Arboretum and Botanical Garden, Haleiwa, Hawaii, 1974-80, dir., 1980—; Contbr. articles to profl. jours., New Royal Horticultural Society's Dictionary of Gardening, 1992. Field assoc. botany Bishop Mus., Honolulu, 1981—; bd. dirs. Friends of Honolulu Bot. Gardens, 1980—; v.p. founder Waimea Arboretum Found., 1977—; bd. dirs. Condominium Estate, Wahiawa, Hawaii, 1990—. Mem. Am. Assn. Botanical Gardens and Arboreta, Am. Hort. Soc., Hawaii Audubon Soc., Hawaiian Botanical Soc. (pres. 1979), Internat. Assn. Plant Taxonomists, Royal Hort. Soc., Kew Guild. Avocations: fishing, home repairs, music, reading, travel. Office: Waimea Arboretum & Bot Garden 59-864 Kamehameha Hwy Haleiwa HI 96712

WOOLLS, ESTHER BLANCHE, library science educator; b. Louisville, Mar. 30, 1935; d. Arthur William and Esther Lennie (Smith) Sutton; m. Donald Paul Woolls, Oct. 21, 1953 (div. Nov. 1982); 1 son, Arthur Paul. AB in Fine Arts, Ind. U., 1958, MA in Libr. Sci., 1962, PhD in Libr. Sci., 1973. Elem. libr. Hammond Pub. Schs., Ind., 1958-65, libr. coord., 1965-67; libr. coord. Roswell Ind. Schs., N.Mex., 1967-70; prof. libr. sci. U. Pitts., 1973—; exec. dir. Beta Phi Mu, 1981—. Author: The School Library Media Manager, 1994; editor: Continuing Professional Education and IFLA: Past, Present, and a Vision for the Future, 1993. Recipient Disting. Svc. award Pa. Sch. Librs. Assn., 1993. Mem. ALA (mem. coun. 1985-89, 91-94), Am. Assn. Sch. Librs. (bd. dirs. 1983-8, pres. 1993-94), Pa. Learning Resources Assn. (pres. 1984-85), Internat. Assn. Sch. Librs. (bd. dirs. 1991—), Internat. Fedn. Libr. Assns. (mem. standing com. sch. librs. sect. 1991—, editor Continuing Profl. Edn. Roundtable Newsletter). Office: U Pitts Sch Libr and Info Sci Pittsburgh PA 15260

WOOLSEY, DAVID ARTHUR, leasing company executive; b. Oakland, Calif., Nov. 27, 1941; s. Stanley Arthur Woolsey and Jane Bernadette (Gallagher) Woolsey-Weyler; m. Kathleen Marie McDonnell, June 26, 1965; children: Anne C., Matthew J., Jane K. BS, U. San Francisco, 1963; MBA, U. Calif., Berkeley, 1965. Mgr. lease and spl. projects financing Kaiser Aluminum & Chem. Corp., Oakland, Calif., 1965-68; v.p. U.S. Leasing International., Inc., San Francisco, 1968-78; exec. v.p. GATX Capital Corp., San Francisco, 1978, exec. v.p. 1982-88, also bd. dirs.; exec. v.p. Orix U.S.A. Corp., 1988—, also bd. dirs. Mem. Equipment Leasing Assn. Am. (bd. dirs.), Orinda Country Club (Calif., pres. 1981), Commonwealth Club (Calif.). Republican. Roman Catholic. Home: 40 Charles Hill Rd Orinda CA 94563-1523 Office: ORIX USA Corp 1 Bush St Ste 250 San Francisco CA 94104-4412

WOOLSEY, FREDERICK WILLIAM, retired journalist, music critic; b. Miles City, Mont., Oct. 7, 1919; s. Fred W. and Louise (Gaylord) W.; m. Mary Lou Hubbard, Apr. 27, 1957 (dec. June 1976); m. Jane R. Towery, Oct. 15, 1983. B.J., U. Mo., 1943. Radio news writer Sta. KXOK, St. Louis, 1943; telegraph desk The Times, Shreveport, La., 1946; reporter, features writer Nashville Tennessean, 1947-55, night city editor, 1955; reporter, rewrite desk Louisville Times, 1956-65, music critic, 1960-85; feature writer Courier-Jour. Sunday mag., 1965-85. Author: radio series Tall Tales of Tenn; folklore, Sta. WSM, Nashville, 1954-55; contbr. articles to journalism anthologies. Mem. Louisville Human Rights Com., 1960; chmn. pub. rels. com. City-County Human Rels. Commn., 1961-62; mem. Ky. Civil Liberties Union, 1956—; bd. dirs. Louisville Urban League, 1958-68, Widowed Persons Svc., 1978-80, Louisville Chamber Music Soc., 1982—, U. Louisville Libr. Assocs., co-founder, exec. bd. Friends of U. Louisville Sch. Music, 1991-93. With USAF, 1943-46. Recipient certificate of merit for mag. writing Am. Bar Assn., 1974. Democrat. Episcopalian. Home: 2416 Dundee Rd Louisville KY 40205-2047

WOOLSEY, JOHN MUNRO, JR., lawyer; b. N.Y.C., Apr. 22, 1916; s. John M. and Alice B. (Bacon) W.; m. Ledlie Laughlin, Dec. 27, 1948; children: John, Alice, Henry, Mary. B.A., Yale U., 1938, LL.B., 1941. Bar: N.Y. 1941, Mass. 1947. Assoc. Debevoise, Stevenson, Plimpton & Page, N.Y.C., 1941-42; with Bd. Econ. Warfare, Washington, 1942; with firm Herrick & Smith and predecessor firms, Boston, 1946-86, ptnr., 1956-83, of counsel, 1984-86; of counsel Palmer & Dodge, 1986—; with Office of U.S. Chief of Counsel, Nürnberg Trials, Germany, 1945-46. Former mem. Trustees of Reservations, Shady Hill Sch. Served to lt. USNR, 1942-46. Decorated Order of White Lion (Czechoslovakia). Mem. Am. Antiquarian Soc., Am. Law Inst., Tavern Club, Century Club (N.Y.C.). Office: Palmer & Dodge One Beacon St Boston MA 02108

WOOLSEY, LYNN, congresswoman; b. Seattle, Nov. 3, 1937. BA, U. San Francisco, 1980. Mem. 103rd-104th Congresses from 6th Calif. dist., 1993—; mem. Ho. Reps. coms. on budget, & econ. & edul. opportunity. Office: US House of Reps 439 Cannon Washington DC 20515-0506*

WOOLSEY, R. JAMES, JR., federal agency administrator; b. Tulsa, Sept. 21, 1941; s. Robert James and Clyde (Kirby) W.; m. Suzanne Haley, Aug. 15, 1965; children—Robert Nathaniel, Daniel James, Benjamin Haley. BA with great distinction, Stanford U., 1963; M.A. (Rhodes scholar), Oxford (Eng.) U., 1965; LL.B., Yale U., 1968. Bar: Calif. bar 1969, D.C. bar 1970. Program analyst Office Sec. Def., Washington, 1968-70, NSC, Washington 1970; gen. counsel Com. Armed Services, U.S. Senate, 1970-73; assoc. firm Shea & Gardner, Washington, 1973-77; ptnr. Shea & Gardner, 1979-89; ambassador and U.S. rep. to negotation on conventional armed forces in Europe, 1989-91; ptnr. with Shea & Gardner, 1991-93; dir. CIA, Washington, 1993—; undersec. of navy, 1977-79; advisor U.S. del. SALT, Helsinki and Vienna, 1969-70. Mem. Pres.'s Commn. on Strategic Forces, 1983-84, Fed. Ethics Law reform, 1989; Blue Ribbon Commn. on Defense Mgmt. 1985-86; del.-at-large Soviet Arms Talks, Geneva, 1983-86; trustee Stanford U., 1972-74, Regent Smithsonian Instution, 1989-93; dir. Martin Marietta, 1991-93. Served with U.S. Army, 1968-70. Mem. Council Fgn. Relations, Phi Beta Kappa. Presbyterian. Office: Cia Washington DC 20001

WOOLSEY, ROBERT EUGENE DONALD, mineral economics, mathematics and business administration educator; b. Fort Worth, Oct. 31, 1936; s. Eugene Ralph W. and Ruby Ruth (White) Binder Woolsey; m. Ronita Elaine Packer, Sept. 17, 1958; children: Wysandria W.W., Darrell E. B.A., U. Tex., 1959, M.A., 1967, Ph.D., 1969. Staff mem. Sandia Corp., Albuquerque, 1966-68; assoc. dir. Computer Center U. Tex., Austin, 1968-69; assoc. prof. math. Colo. Sch. Mines, Golden, Colo., 1969-72, prof. math.,

1972-74, prof. mineral econs., 1974-79, prof., head dept., 1979-81, MAPCO Found. prof., 1981-84, prof., program dir. Ops. Rsch./Mgmt. Sci. program, math dept., 1988—; vis. coll. Colo. Women's Coll., Denver, 1979-81; adj. prof. U. Waterloo, Ont., Can., 1972—; Instituto Technologico de Monterrey, Nuevo Leon, Mexico, 1974—, U. Witwatersrand, Johannesburg, S. Africa, 1984—; vis. prof. dept. engring. U.S. Mil. Acad., West Point, N.Y., 1986-87; prof. core faculty Walden U., 1990—; bd. dirs. Southland Energy Corp., Tulsa, New Tech. Devel. Co., Inc., Vancouver, B.C., Can. Author: Operations Research for Immediate Application, 1975, Applied Management Science, 1980; editor: Transactions of the Institute of Industrial Engineering, 1981-84, Production and Inventory Management, 1984—, Interfaces, 1975-82, Jour. Ops. Mgmt., 1986-87; contbr. articles to profl. jours. Pres. Rocky Mountain Fire Brigade, Inc., Golden, Colo., 1972-83. Served to capt. USAF, 1959-62. Named tchr. of year Standard Oil Ind., 1972; recipient 1st Harold Larnder Meml. prize Can. Operational Research Soc., 1986, Disting. Civilian Service medal U.S. Dept. Army, 1987, Comdrs. medal, 1991, Outstanding Civilian Svc. medal, 1994; named Hon. Col. 115 Engr. Regiment U.S. Army, 1987. Fellow Am. Inst. Decision Sci. (v.p. 1981-83); mem. Inst. Mgmt. Scis. (council 1976-78, pres. 1983-84), Instl. Indsl. Engrs. (sr. mem., editor 1981-84), Ops. Rsch. Soc. Am. (editor 1975-82), Newcomen Soc. Republican. Episcopalian. Home: 1826 Smith Rd Golden CO 80401-1756 Office: Colo Sch Mines Dept Math Golden CO 80401

WOOSLEY, STANFORD EARL, astrophysicist; b. Texarkana, Tex., Dec. 8, 1944; s. Homer Earl and Wanda Faye (Fisher) W.; m. Susan Marie Haas, Aug. 12, 1993. BA in Physics, Rice U., 1966, PhD in Space Sci., 1971. Rsch. assoc. Rice U., Houston, 1971-73; rsch. fellow in physics Kellogg Radiation Lab. Calif. Tech., Pasadena, Calif., 1973-75; asst. prof. U. Calif., Santa Cruz, 1975-78, assoc. prof., 1978-83, prof. astronomy and astrophysics, 1983—, chmn. dept., 1984-87, 89-91. Editor: High Energy Transients, 1984, Supernova, 1991, Nuclear Astrophysics, 1993; contbr. over 170 articles to profl. jours. Grantee NASA, NSF, Calif. Space Inst., 1977—. Fellow Am. Phys. Soc.; mem. Am. Astron. Soc. (coun. 1990-93, chair com. to aid astronomy in the FSU). Achievements include research into the lives and deaths of massive stars and supernova, nucleosynthesis and x-ray and gamma ray bursts. Home: 115 Auburn Ave Santa Cruz CA 95060-6231 Office: U Calif Astronomy Dept Santa Cruz CA 95064

WOOSNAM, IAN HAROLD, professional golfer; b. St. Martins Shropshire, U.K., Mar. 2, 1958; s. Harold and Joan Woosnam; m. Glendryth Mervyn Pugh, Nov. 12, 1983; children: Daniel Ian, Rebecca Louise, Amy Victoria. Ed., St. Martins Modern Sch. Profl. golfer, 1976—; tournament winner News of the World under 23 match-play, 1979, Cacharel under 25 Championship, 1982, Swiss Open, 1982, Silk Cut Masters, 1983, Scandinavian Enterprise Open, 1984, Zambian Open, 1985, Lawrence Batley TPC, 1986, 555 Kenya Open, 1986, Hong Kong Open, 1987, Jersey Open, 1987, Cepsa Madrid Open, 1987, Bell's Scottish Open, 1987, 90, Lancome Trophy, 1987, 93, Suntory World Match-Play Championship, 1987, 90, World Cup (Wales) Team and Individual, 1987, Million Dollar Challenge, 1987, Volvo PGA Championship, 1988, Carrols Irish Open, 1988, 89, Panasonic Euro Open, 1988, Am. Express Med Open, 1990, 91, Monte Carlo Open, 1990, 91, 92, Epson Grand Prix, 1990, U.S. Masters, 1991, USF&G Classic, 1991, PGA Grand Slam of Golf, 1991, World Cup Individual, 1991, Murpheys English Open, 1993, Air France Cannes Open, 1994, Brit. Masters, 1994, ranked 1st Sony world rankings, 1991, Ryder Cup Team Member, 1983, 85, 87, 89, 91, 93. Avocations: snooker, sports, water skiing.

WOOSTER, ROBERT, history educator; b. Beaumont, Tex., Aug. 27, 1956; s. Ralph Ancil and Edna Lee (Jones) W.; m. Catherine Cox, 1992. BA, Lamar U., 1977, MA, 1979; PhD, U. Tex., 1985. Scholar in residence Tex. State Hist. Assn., Liberty, 1985-86; asst. prof. Corpus Christi (Tex.) State U., 1986-90, assoc. prof., 1990—. Author: Soldiers, Sutlers and Settlers (Bates award 1987), U.S. Military and Indian Policy, 1988, History of Fort Davis, 1990, Nelson A. Miles and The Twilight of the Frontier Army, 1993; editorial adv. bd. Southwestern Hist. Quar., Austin, Tex., 1989—. Dep. dir. U.S. Mil. Acad./ROTC fellowship U.S. Mil. Acad., West Point, N.Y., 1990. Mem. Tex. State Hist. Assn., Western Hist. Assn., Orgn. Am. Historians. Democrat. Home: 4600 Ocean Dr # 708 Corpus Christi TX 78412 Office: Texas A&M Univ 6300 Ocean Dr Corpus Christi TX 78412-5599

WOOSTER, WARREN S(CRIVER), marine science educator; b. Westfield, Mass., Feb. 20, 1921; s. Harold Abbott and Violet (Scriver) W.; m. Clarissa Pickles, Sept. 13, 1948; children: Susan Wooster Allen, Daniel, Dana Wooster Pawka. Sc.B., Brown U., 1943; M.S., Calif. Inst. Tech., 1947; Ph.D., UCLA, 1953. From research asst. to prof. Scripps Instn. Oceanography, U. Calif., 1948-73; dir. UNESCO Office Oceanography, 1961-63; dean Rosenstiel Sch. Marine Atmospheric Sci., U. Miami, 1973-76; prof. marine studies and fisheries U. Wash., Seattle, 1976-91, prof. emeritus, 1992; dir. Inst. Marine Studies U. Wash., 1979-82. Contbr. to books, profl. jours. Served with USNR, 1943-46. Fellow Am. Geophys. Union, Am. Meterol. Soc.; mem. Sigma Xi. Office: U Wash Sch Marine Affairs Seattle WA 98195

WOOTAN, GERALD DON, osteopathic physician, educator; b. Oklahoma City, Nov. 19, 1944; s. Ralph George and Corrinne (Loafman) W. BA, Cen. State U., Edmond, Okla., 1970, BS, 1971; MEd, Cen. State U., 1974; MB, U. Okla., Oklahoma City, 1978; DO, Okla. State U., 1985. Dir. mfg. engring. lab. GE, Oklahoma City, 1965-70; counseling psychologist VA Hosp., Oklahoma City, 1970-76; physician asst. Thomas (Okla.) Med. Clin., 1978-81; pvt. practice, Jenks, Okla., 1986—; intern Tulsa Regional Med. Ctr., 1985-86; assoc. prof. Okla. State U. Coll. Osteo. Medicine, 1986—; sec. Green Country Physicians Group, Inc., Tulsa, 1990-91; chmn. gen. practice quality assurance Tulsa Regional Med. Ctr., 1989-91; v.p. New Horizons Counseling Ctr., Clinton, Okla., 1977-81; sr. aviation med. examiner FAA, Tulsa, 1991—, pres. S.W. Diagnostics, Inc., Tulsa, 1991, Okla. Edn. Found. Osteo Medicine, Tulsa, 1988-89; pres., bd. trustees Tulsa Long Term Care Authority. Contbr. articles to profl. jours.; patentee for human restraint. Advancement chmn., chmn. Eagle bd. rev. Boy Scouts Am., Tulsa, 1987-88; trustee Tulsa Long Term Care Authority, 1988-91; trustee Tulsa Community Found. for Indigent Health Care, Inc., 1988-91. With USN, 1962-64. Named Clin. Preceptor of Yr., U. Okla., 1980, Outstanding Alumni award Okla. State U. Coll. Osteo. Medicine, 1990. Mem. Am. Osteo. Assn., Okla. Osteo. Assn., Tulsa Dist. Osteo. Soc. (pres. 1991-92), Am. Acad. Physician Assts., Am. Coll. Gen. Practitioners, Okla. Acad. Gen. Practitioners (v.p.), Am. Coll. Osteo. Family Physicians (bd. cert. 1993, pres. Okla. chpt. 1993-94), Okla. State U. Coll. Osteo. Medicine Alumni Assn. (pres. 1988-89). Avocations: scuba diving, aviation medicine. Home: 4320 E 100th St Tulsa OK 74137-5305 Office: Jenks Health Team 324 W Main St Jenks OK 74037-3774

WOOTEN, CECIL AARON, religious organization administrator; b. Laurel, Miss., March 3, 1924; s. Cecil A. and Alice (Cox) W.; m. Helen Moss, Apr. 4, 1947; children: Michael, Margaret, Martin, Marsha, Mark. BS in Mech. Engring, U. Ala., 1949. With CBI Industries, 1941—, bd. dirs., 1965-83; mng. dir. CBI Constructors Ltd., London, 1957-62; mgr. (Houston sales dist.), 1962-64; v.p., mgr. corp. services Oak Brook, Ill., 1968-69; sr. v.p.-gen. sales mgr., 1969-78; sr. v.p. comml. devel. Chgo. Bridge & Iron Co. (subs. CBI Industries), 1978-79; sr. v.p. corp. adminstrn. CBI Industries, Oak Brook, 1980-83; dir. devel. Christian Family Services, Gainesville, Fla., 1983-86, Denver Ch. of Christ, 1986-88, Boston Ch. of Christ, 1988-92; pres. Internat. Chs. of Christ, Inc., L.A., 1994—; bd. dirs. Oak Brook (Ill.) Bank. Former trustee Elmhurst (Ill.) Coll.; former bd. sponsors Good Samaritan Hosp., Downers Grove, Ill. Served to 1st lt. AUS, 1943-46. Mem. ASME, Nat. Soc. Profl. Engrs. Lodge: Rotary. Home: 3902 Quailwood St Moorpark CA 93021 Office: Los Angeles Church of Christ 3530 Wilshire Blvd Ste 1750 Los Angeles CA 90010

WOOTEN, FRANK THOMAS, research facility executive; b. Fayetteville, N.C., Sept. 24, 1935; s. Frank Thomas and Katherine (McRae) W.; m. Linda Walker, July 14, 1962; children: Laurin Walker, Patrick Thomas, Ashley Tripp. BSEE, Duke U., 1957, PhD, 1964. Engr. Corning Glass Works, Raleigh, N.C., 1964-66; engr. Research Triangle Inst., Research Triangle Park, N.C., 1966-68, mgr. biomed. engring., 1968-75, exec. asst. to pres., 1975-80, v.p. 1980-89; pres. Research Triangle Inst., Research Triangle Park, 1989—; mem. tech. application rev. panel Ballistic Missile Def. Orgn., 1990-94. Contbr. articles on semiconductors and biomed. engring. to profl. publs., 1966-83; patentee semiconductors tech. Bd. dirs. N.C. Biotech. Ctr.,

1989—, MCNC, 1989-94; corp. mem. Nat. Inst. Statis. Scis., 1990—. Served to lt. (j.g.) USN, 1957-59. Shell fellow, 1961; recipient Disting. Engring. Alumnus award Duke U., 1991. Mem. IEEE, Assn. for Advancement Med. Instrumentation (chmn. com. on aerospace tech. 1971-77). Baptist. Office: Research Triangle Inst PO Box 12194 3040 W Cornwallis Rd Research Triangle Park NC 27709

WOOTEN, FREDERICK (OLIVER), applied science educator; b. Linwood, Pa., May 16, 1928; s. Frederick Alexander and Martha Emma (Guild) W.; m. Jane Watson MacPherson, Aug. 30, 1952; children: Donald, Bartley. BS in Chemistry, MIT, 1950; PhD in Chemistry, U. Del., 1955. Sr. scientist Lawrence Livermore (Calif.) Lab., 1957-72; prof. applied sci. U. Calif., Davis, 1972—, chmn. dept. applied sci., 1973-93; vis. prof. physics Drexel U., Phila, 1964, Chalmers Tekniska Hogskola, Goteborg, Sweden, 1967-68, Heriot-Watt U., Edinburgh, Scotland, 1979, Trinity Coll., Dublin, Ireland, 1986, Mich. State U., East Lansing, 1993; vis. scholar math. U. Mass., Amherst, 1991; staff physicist All-Am. Engring. Co., Wilmington, Del., 1955-57; cons. in field. Author: Optical Properties of Solids, 1972. Mem. AAAS, AM. Phys. Soc., N.Y. Acad. Sci., Materials Rsch. Soc., Sigma Xi. Home: 2328 Alameda Diablo Diablo CA 94528 Office: Univ Calif Dept Applied Sci Davis CA 95616

WOOTEN, HOLLIS DARWIN, engineer; b. South Pittsburg, Tenn., Sept. 29, 1939; s. Lawson Wade and Lila Mae (Hill) W.; m. Elserean Phelps, June 26, 1976. BS in Engring., U. Tenn., 1975. Advanced engr. Westinghouse, Richland, Wash., 1975-79; sr. engr. Westinghouse, Oak Ridge, Tenn., 1979-84; sr. design engr. Los Alamos Tech. Assn., Oak Ridge, 1984-86; devel. assoc. Oak Ridge Gaseous Diffusion Plant, 1987-89; devel. staff mem. Oak Ridge Nat. Lab., 1989-92, devel. group leader, 1992—. Scoutmaster Boy Scouts Am., South Pittsburg, 1960; pres. McReynolds PTA, South Pittsburg, 1960; mem. South Pittsburg Aux. Police, 1967. Mem. ASHRAE, Tenn. Soc. Profl. Engrs., Order of Engr., K.C. (mem. coun.), Chattanooga Engrs. Club. Roman Catholic. Avocation: hunting. Office: Martin Marietta Energy Sys Oak Rigde Nat Lab K-25 Site PO Box 2003 Oak Ridge TN 37831-7294

WOOTEN, JAMES TERRELL, journalist; b. Detroit, July 13, 1937; s. J.R. and Clara Charlene (Richmond) W.; m. Katherine Joanne Richardson, Aug. 26, 1958 (dec. 1978); children: Karen, Kristen, Katie, Elizabeth; m. Patience Jean O'Connor, Sept. 27, 1980; 1 dau., Jacqueline DeLacie O'Connor. B.A., Bethel Coll., McKenzie Tenn., 1958; B.D., Presbyn. Theol. Sem., Memphis, 1961. Reporter Huntsville Times, Ala., 1965-68, N.Y. Times. N.Y.C., 1968-73, 74-78; columnist Phila. Inquirer, 1973-74; writer Esquire mag., N.Y.C., 1978-79; nat. corr. ABC News, Washington, 1979—. Author: Soldier, 1972, Dasher, 1978. Recipient Ernie Pyle Meml. award Scripps-Howard, 1974; recipient Blue Pencil award Columbia U., 1979. Office: ABC News Washington Bur 1717 Desales St NW Washington DC 20036-4407

WOOTEN, ROBERT JAMES, executive; b. Siebert, Colo., Mar. 2, 1921; s. Clyde Walter and Fama Helen (Humphrey) W.; children: Robert C., Pamela G. Wooten McBride, Dennis R. Student, U. Wash., 1939-40; BS, U.S. Naval Acad., 1940-43. Commd. ensign USN, 1943, advanced through grades to capt., 1964, ret., 1967; founder, pres. Internat. Nutronics, Los Altos, Calif., 1968-71; pres., chmn. Shaklee Corp., Emeryville, Calif., 1971-76; founder, pres., chmn. Enhance Corp., San Ramon, Calif., 1978-82; cons. various orgns., San Ramon, 1982-89; chief fin. officer Nutek Corp., Palo Alto, Calif., 1989-91, also bd. dirs.; pres. Global Visions, Inc., Livermore, Calif., 1991-93; chmn., CEO Intracal Corp., Walnut Creek, Calif.; bd. dirs. E-Beta Svcs., Inc., Palo Alto. Internat. Synsys Corp., Huntington Beach, Calif.; founder, pres., chmn. Epoch Industries, Ltd., San Ramon. Decorated Disting. Flying Cross with Gold Star and Oak Leaf Cluster. Mem. Soc. Experimental Test Pilots, U.S. Naval Inst. Avocations: flying, farming, writing. Home: 110 Regency Dr Clayton CA 94517-1717

WOOTTON, JOHN FRANCIS, physiology educator; b. Penn Yan, N.Y., May 31, 1929; s. John Edenden and Margaret Eliza (Smith) W.; m. Joyce Albertine Mac Mullen, Aug. 28, 1959; children: J. Timothy, David M., Barbara H., Bruce C. BS, Cornell U., 1951, MS, 1953, PhD, 1960. Grad. rsch. asst. Cornell U., Ithaca, N.Y., 1956-60; post doctoral fellow U. Coll., London, 1960-62; from asst. prof. to assoc. prof. dept. physiology Cornell U., 1962-70, prof. dept. physiology, 1970—, assoc. dean Grad. Sch., 1980-83; grad. faculty rep. field of physiology Cornell U., 1990-92, 93—; vis. scientist MRC Molecular Biology, Cambridge, Eng., 1969-70, Nat. Inst. Med. Rsch., London, 1985-86, 92-93; teporary sr. rsch. assoc. Stanford (Calif.) U., 1977-78. Contbr. articles to profl. jours. 1st lt. USAR, 1954-56. Rsch. and Travel grantee NIH, USDA Burroughs Wellcome Fund, Cornell Biotech. Program. Mem. AAAS, Am. Soc. Biochemistry, Molecular and Cell Biology, Am. Chem. Soc., Biophys. Soc., Sigma Xi (v.p., pres. Cornell chpt.). Avocations: travel, choral singing, gardening, art, fishing. Office: Cornell U Dept Physiology T8-022 Veterinary Rsch Tower Ithaca NY 14853-5908

WOOTTON, MACK EDWARD, food products company executive; b. Lafayette, Ind., Sept. 4, 1937; s. Ralph Edward and Thelma Athel (McCarty) W.; m. Linda Nell Spence, June 19, 1960; children: Jeffrey David, Kella Linn. AB, Ind. U., 1959. Employment supr. Cen. Soya Co. Inc., Ft. Wayne, Ind., 1964-65, ting. dir., 1965-66, product control mgr., 1971-73, corp. compensation dir., 1973-77, dir. personnel services, 1977-83, dir. sales chemurgy div., 1983-84, gen. mgr. chemurgy div., 1984-85, v.p. adminstrn., 1985—; plant personnel mgr. Cen. Soya Co. Inc., Chattanooga, 1966-71. Bd. dirs. United Way, Ft. Wayne, Parkview Meml. Hosp., Ft. Wayne, Lugar Fund for Hoosier Excellence, Indpls.; mem. adv. com. Ind. Vocat. Tech. Coll., Ft. Wayne, 1978-85; adv. bd. Leadership Ft. Wayne; pres. bd. dirs. McMillen Health Ctr., Ft. Wayne, Ft. Wayne Ednl. Found. Capt. USAF, 1959-64. Mem. Am. Mgmt. Assn. (human resources coun. 1986—), Ind. C. of C. (pers. and labor rels. com 1978-83), Ft. Wayne C. of C. (bd. dirs.). Republican. Methodist. Avocations: tennis, woodworking.

WOOTTON, ROBERT RAY, lawyer; b. Binghamton, N.Y., Nov. 3, 1952; s. Earle Edwards and Alburta (Andre) W.; m. Carol Ann Jansto; m. Oct. 8, 1982; children: Anne Andre, Samuel Earle, Nathaniel John. BA, Yale U., 1974, JD, 1979; BPhil, Oxford U., 1976. Bar: Ill. 1979, U.S. Dist. Ct. (no. dist.) Ill. 1979. Assoc. Sidley & Austin, Chgo. 1979-86, ptnr., 1986-89, 92—; tax legis. counsel U.S. Treasury Dept., 1989-91; adj. prof. sch. law Northwestern U., Chgo., 1988-89. Office: Sidley & Austin 1 First National Plz Chicago IL 60603

WORCESTER, ANNE PERSON, sports association executive; married. Degree in Econs. and Internat. Pub. Policy with honors, Duke U., 1982. Asst. ticket mgr. racquet sports divsn. Internat. Mgmt. Group, 1983-84; dir. corp. sales Lipton Championships, 1984-86, head corp. sales Phila. men's tournament, 1986-87; tournament mgr. various events Lipton Championships, Spain, 1987-88; dir. worldwide ops. Va. Slims Tennis, 1988-91; mng. dir. Women's Tennis Coun., 1991-94; CEO WTA Tour, 1994—. Named one of Most Powerful Women in Tennis, Tennis Week Mag., 1993, one of Power 25, Racquet Mag., 1994. Office: WTA Tour 1266 E Main St 4th Fl Stamford CT 06902-3546*

WORCESTER, DONALD EMMET, history educator, author; b. Tempe, Ariz., Apr. 29, 1915; s. Thomas Emmet and Maud (Worcester) Makemson; m. Barbara Livingston Peck, July 5, 1941; children: Barbara Livingston and Elizabeth Stuart (twins), Harris Eugene. A.B., Bard Coll., 1939; M.A., U. Calif., 1940, Ph.D., 1947. Lectr. Calif. Coll. Agr., Davis, 1946, U. Calif. 1947; asst. prof. U. Fla., 1947-51, assoc. prof., 1951-55, head dept., 1955-59, prof. history, 1955-63; chmn. dept. history Tex. Christian U., 1963-72, Lorin A. Boswell prof. history, 1971-80, Ida and Cecil Green emeritus tutor, 1981-94; vis. prof. U. Madrid, 1956-57; chmn. bd. Univ. Press Mgrs., 1961-63. Author: The Interior Provinces of New Spain, 1786, 1951, (with Wendell G. Schaeffer) The Growth and Culture of Latin America, 1956, 2d edit., 1971, Sea Power and Chilean Independence, 1962, Spanish edit., 1971, The Three Worlds of Latin America, 1963, (with Maurice Boyd) American Civilization, 1964, (with Robert and Kent Forster) Man and Civilization, 1965, Makers of Latin America, 1966, Brazil: From Colony to World Power, 1973; editor: Forked Tongues and Broken Treaties, 1975, Bolivar, 1977, The Apaches: Eagles of the Southwest, 1979, German edit., 1982, The Chisholm Trail: High Road of the Cattle Kingdom, 1981, Pioneer Trails West, 1985, The Spanish Mustang: From the Plains of Andalusia to the Prairies of Texas, 1986, The Texas Cowboy, 1986, The Texas Longhorn: Relic of the Past,

Asset of the Future, 1987, (fiction) The War in the Nueces Strip, 1989, A Visit from father and other Tales of the Mojave, 1990, Brazos Scout, 1991, Man on Two Ponies, 1992, Gone to Texas, 1993, Western Horse Tales, 1994; also children's books; mng. editor: Hispanic Am. Hist. Rev, 1960-65; editor TCU Monographs in History and Culture, 1966-73; mem. editl. bd. The Am. West. Served to lt. comdr. USNR, 1941-45. Recipient Golden Spur award Western Writers Am., 1975, 80; C.L. Sonnichsen Book award, 1985. Mem. Western Hist. Assn. (v.p. 1972-73, pres. 1973-74, pres. 1974-75), Western Writers Am. (v.p. 1972-73, pres. 1973-74, Saddleman award 1988), N.Mex. Hist. Soc., Westerners Internat. (dir. 1975-80, pres. 1978, 79), Tex. Inst. Letters, Phi Beta Kappa, Phi Alpha Theta (pres. 1960-62). Home: 9321 Bear Creek Rd Aledo TX 76008-4004 Office: Texas Christian U Dept History Fort Worth TX 76129

WORD, THOMAS S., JR., lawyer; b. Christiansburg, Va., June 29, 1938; s. Thomas Scott and Mary Anita (Privett) W.; m. Patricia Ann Amburn, May 7, 1960; children—Thomas Scott, David McClanahan. B.S., Va. Tech., 1959; LL.B., U. Richmond, 1961. Bar: Va. 1961. Assoc. McGuire, Woods, Battle & Boothe, Richmond, Va., 1961-66, ptnr., 1966—. Fellow Am. Coll. Trust and Estate; mem. Am. Law Inst., Richmond Bar Assn. (pres. 1984-85). Episcopalian. Clubs: Country of Va., Commonwealth. Office: McGuire Woods Battle & Boothe 1 James Ctr 901 E Cary St Richmond VA 23219

WORDEN, ALFRED MERRILL, former astronaut, research company executive; b. Jackson, Mich., Feb. 7, 1932; s. Merrill Bangs and Helen Crowell) W.; m. Jill Lee Hotchkiss, July 9, 1982; children: Merrill Ellen, Alison Pamela, Tamara Lynn. BS, U.S. Mil. Acad., 1955; MS in Aeros., Astronautical and Instrumentation Engring., U. Mich., 1963, DSc in Astronautical Engring., 1972. Commd. 2nd lt. USAF, 1955, advanced through grades to lt. col., 1971; stationed at Andrews AFB, Md., 1956-61, U. Mich., 1961-63, Farnborough, Eng.; with RAF, 1963-65; instr. Aerospace Rsch. Pilots Sch., Edwards AFB, Calif., 1965-66; astronaut Manned Spacecraft Ctr., NASA, Houston, 1966-72; command module pilot Apollo XV, 1971; sr. aerospace engr., test pilot, dir. systems studies divsn. Ames Rsch. Ctr., Moffett Field, Calif., 1972-75, ret., 1975; v.p. High Flight Found., Colorado Springs, Colo., 1975—; pres. MW Aerospace, Inc., 1985—, Jet Electronics and Tech., Inc., 1990-93; staff v.p. BF Goodrich Aerospace, Brecksville, Ohio, 1993—. Author: poetry Hello Earth-Greetings from Endeavour, 1974; children's book A Flight to the Moon, 1974. Bd. dirs. Boys' Clubs Am., Palm Beach County, Salvation Army. Inducted into Mich. Aviation Hall of Fame, 1990. Mem. AIAA, Soc. Exptl. Pilots, Am. Astron. Soc., Explorers Club, Circumnavigators Club. Episcopalian (sr. warden 1969-71). Office: BF Goodrich Rsch Ctr 9921 Brecksville Rd Brecksville OH 44141-3201

WORDEN, JOAN M., public relations executive. BA, St. John's U.; postgrad., NYU, Georgetown. V.p Palmer Wilson & Worden, pres., 1970-88; v.p. Hill & Knowlton, 1988-90; v.p., dep. group supr. Edelman Pub. Rels. Worldwide, 1990-91; sr. cons. Capitoline Internat., 1991—. Mem. Nat. Press Club, Nat. Press Found., Washington Internat. Trade Assn., World Affairs Coun., Am. Women in Radio and TV (former officer, bd. dirs.), Washington and Am. Newswomen's Club (former officer, bd. dirs.). Office: Capitoline Internat Group Ltd 1615 L St NW # 1150 Washington DC 20036-5610

WORDEN, LARRY LEE, lawyer; b. Temple, Tex., Apr. 17, 1952; s. Ryman Knight and Marcia (Matthews) W.; m. Cheryl Kay DeArman, May 19, 1973; children: Ryan Matthew, Kelly Paige, Timothy Andrew. BA, North Tex. State U., 1974, MA, 1976; JD, U. Tex., 1978. Bar: Tex. 1979, U.S. Dist. Ct. (no. and we. dists.) Tex., U.S. Ct. Appeals (5th and 11th cirs.). Assoc. Law, Snakard & Gambill, Ft. Worth, 1979-83; div. counsel Nat. Gypsum Co., Dallas, 1983—; lectr. polit. sci. U. Tex., Arlington, 1982-86. Chmn. ann. fund raiser Am. Cancer Soc., Ft. Worth, 1981, 82. Mem. ABA (bus. and banking sects., securities litigation com.), Tex. Bar Assn., Dallas County Bar Assn., Dallas Assn. Young Lawyers, Tarrant County Young Lawyers Assn. (bd. dirs. 1982-83), Phi Delta Phi. Democrat. Methodist. Avocations: coaching youth sports activities, sailing. Home: 6315 Saffron Hills Dr Spring TX 77379-7536 Office: King Ranch Holdings Inc 16825 Northchase Dr Houston TX 77060

WORDEN, WILLIAM MICHAEL, city agency administrator, preservation consultant; b. Detroit, Nov. 4, 1942; s. Scott Buell and Virginia Alexandra (Moynihan) W.; m. Barbara Williams, Mar. 27, 1976. Student, Ohio U., 1961-63; BA in Art History, Ohio State U., 1967, postgrad., 1967-68. Sole propr. William M. Worden, Organbuilder, Detroit, 1970-76; adminstrv. coord. Detroit Urban Conservation Project, Wayne State U., Detroit, 1976-77; staff dir. Historic Designation Adv. Bd. of Detroit, 1977—; bd. dirs. Mich. Historic Preservation Network, 1988—, sec. 1988-95, chmn., 1995—; bd. dirs. Steamship Hist. Soc. Am., 1994—; planner, tour guide for hist. ch. and organ tours Detroit Hist. Soc., 1976—; mem. bd. advisors nat. Trust for Hist. Preservation, 1978-87, advisor emeritus; pres. The Steamer Columbia Found.; owner, operator Nat. Historic Landmark steamboat. Contbr. articles to profl. jours. Trustee Cass Cmty. Meth. Ch., Detroit, 1988-93; bd. dirs., corp. sec. Maintenance Ctrl. for Srs., Detroit, 1981-85; bd. dirs., sec., pres. Indian Village Assn., Detroit, 1977-82; bd. dirs., sec. Gt. Lakes Maritime Inst., 1959-74; mem. archtl. rev. com. Roman Cath. Archdiocese of Detroit, 1993—. Recipient Career Civil Servant award Am. Soc. Pub. Adminstrn., 1985, Testimonial resolution Detroit City Coun., 1985, Samaritan of the Yr. award Most Holy Trinity Ch., 1986. Mem. Steamship Hist. Soc. Am. (bd. dirs. 1994—), Organ Hist. Soc., numerous orgns. in preservation and maritime history. Roman Catholic. Avocations: antiques, maritime history, music. Office: Historic Designation Adv Bd 204 City County Bldg Detroit MI 48226

WORELL, JUDITH P., psychologist, educator; b. N.Y.C.; d. Moses and Dorothy Goldfarb; m. Leonard Worell, Aug. 11, 1947 (div.); children—Amy, Beth, Wendy; m. H.A. Smith, Mar. 23, 1985. B.S. magna cum laude, Queens Coll., 1950; M.A., Ohio State U., 1952, Ph.D. in Clin. Psychology, 1954; DHL (hon.), Colby-Sawyer Coll., 1993. Research assoc. Iowa Psychopathic Hosp., Iowa City, 1957-59; research assoc. Okla. State U., 1960-66; asst. prof. U. Ky., Lexington, 1969-71; assoc. prof. U. Ky., 1971-75, prof. ednl. and counseling psychology, 1976—, dir. counseling psychology tng. program, 1980-93, chairperson dept. ednl. and counseling psychology, 1993—. Author: (with C.M. Nelson) Managing Instructional Problems, 1981; (with W.E. Stilwell) Psychology for Teachers and Students, 1981; Psychological Development in the Elementary Years, 1982; (with Fred Danner) The Adolescent as Decision-maker: Applications to Development and Education, 1989, (with Pam Remer) Feminist Perspectives in Therapy: An Empowerment Model for Women, 1992; assoc. editor Jour. Cons. and Clin. Psychology, 1976-79, mem. editorial bd., 1984-89; assoc. editor Psychol. Women Quar., 1984-89, editor, 1989-95; mem. editorial bd. Sex Roles, 1984—, Psychol. Assessment, 1991—, Clin. Psychology Rev., 1991—, Women and Therapy, 1992—; cons., reviewer 10 jours.; contbr. articles to profl. jours. Named U. Ky. Campus Woman of Yr., 1976, Disting. Univ. Grad. prof., 1991, Disting. Ky. psychologist, 1990; USPHS fellow, 1953; NIMH rsch. grantee, 1962-69. Fellow APA (pres. Clin. Psychology of Women 1986-88, chmn. com. state assn. rels. 1982-83, fellow selection divsn. 35 com. 1983-84, policy and planning bd. 1989-92, publs. and communications bd. 1992—, chair jours. com., Disting. Leader for Women in Psychology 1990), Ky. Psychol. Assn. (pres. 1981-82), Southeastern Psychol. Assn. (exec. coun. mem.-at-large, pres.-elect 1993-94 pres. 1994-95), Am. Women in Psychology, Phi Beta Kappa. Home: 3892 Gloucester Dr Lexington KY 40510-9729 Office: U Ky Dept Ednl and Counseling Psychology 235 Dickey Hall Lexington KY 40506

WORENKLEIN, JACOB JOSHUA, lawyer; b. N.Y.C., Oct. 1, 1948; s. Abraham and Cela (Zyskind) W.; divorced; children: David, Daniel, Laura. BA, Columbia U., 1969; MBA, JD, NYU, 1973. Bar: N.Y. 1974. Assoc. Milbank, Tweed, Hadley & McCloy, N.Y.C., 1973-81, ptnr., 1982—; chmn. firm planning com., 1988-90, mem. exec. com., 1990-93; sr. advisor to exec. com., 1993—; mng. dir., group head of global project fin. group Lehman Bros., N.Y.C., 1993—; mem. investment banking mgmt. com. Lehman Bros., 1993—; chmn. Utility Leasing Conf., 1990, McGraw-Hill Non-Power Projects Conf., 1991-92, Financing Internat. Power Projects, 1993. Contbr. articles to profl. jours. Pres. Old Broadway Synagogue, N.Y.C., 1978—; trustee Fedn. Jewish Philanthropies, N.Y.C., 1984-86; bd. overseers United Jewish Appeal/Fedn. Jewish Philanthropies, 1987, chmn. lawyer's div. major gifts, 1989-91, chmn. lawyers div., 1991-93, bd. dirs.,

1991—. Mem. ABA (electricity and utility financing com.), N.Y. State Bar Assn. (sec. action unit toward more effective legislature 1975), Assn. of Bar of City of N.Y., Fed. Energy Bar Assn., Down Town Assn., Phi Beta Kappa. Office: Lehman Bros 3 World Fin Ctr 200 Vesey St Fl 16 New York NY 10285-0001

WORK, BRUCE VAN SYOC, business consultant; b. Monmouth, Ill., Mar. 20, 1942; s. Robert M. and Evelyn (Rusken) W.; m. Janet Kay Brown, Nov. 12, 1966; children: Bruce, Terra. B.A., Monmouth Coll., 1964; B.S., U. Mo.-Rolla, 1966; postgrad., U. Chgo., 1978-79. Registered profl. engr., Ill. Various mgmt. positions Midcon Corp. (and subs.), 1966-79; pres. Indsl. Fuels Corp., Troy, Mich., 1979-85, Costain Coal Inc., Troy, Mich., 1985-89; pvt. practice small bus. cons., 1989-92; bus. cons. Wallis Oil Co., 1992—. Mem. various coms. Cuba United Meth. Ch. Mem. Detroit Athletic Club, Forest Lake Country Club, Blue Key. Office: 1732 Lakeshore Dr Cuba MO 65453-9603

WORK, CHARLES ROBERT, lawyer; b. Glendale, Calif., June 21, 1940; s. Raymond P. and Minna M. (Fricke) W.; m. Linda S. Smith, Oct. 4, 1965 (div.); children: Matthew Keehn, Mary Lucila Landis, Benjamin Reed; m. Veronica A. Haggart, Apr., 1985. B.A., Wesleyan U., 1962; J.D., U. Chgo., 1965; LL.M., Georgetown U., 1966. Bar: D.C. 1965, Utah 1965. Asst. U.S. atty. D.C., 1966-73; dep. adminstr. law enforcement assistance adminstrn., U.S. Dept. Justice, 1973-75; ptnr. Peabody, Lambert & Meyers, Washington, 1975-82, McDermott, Will & Emery, Washington, 1982—. Recipient Rockefeller Pub. Service award 1978. Mem. D.C. Bar (pres. 1976-77). Office: McDermott Will & Emery 1850 K St NW Washington DC 20006-2213

WORK, HENRY HARCUS, physician, educator; b. Buffalo, Nov. 11, 1911; s. Henry Harcus and Jeannette (Harcus) W.; m. Virginia Codington, Oct. 20, 1945 (dec. Nov. 1991); children—Henry Harcus III, David Codington, William Bruce, Stuart Runyon. A.B., Hamilton Coll., Clinton, N.Y., 1933; M.D., Harvard, 1937. Intern, resident Boston Children's Hosp., 1937-40, Emma P. Bradley Home Providence, 1940, Buffalo Children's Hosp., 1940-42, N.Y. Hosp., 1945-47; psychiat. services adviser, chief U.S. Children's Bur., Washington, 1948-49; assoc. prof. pediatrics U. Louisville, 1949-55; mem. faculty UCLA, 1955-72, prof. psychiatry and pub. health, 1966-72; chief profl. svcs. Am. Psychiat. Assn., Washington, 1972-83; clin. prof. George Washington U., Georgetown U., Uniformed Svcs. U. of Health Scis., U. Md., 1973—. Author: A Guide to Preventive Child Psychiatry, 1965, Minimal Brain Dysfunction: A Medical Challenge, 1967, Psychiatric Emergencies in Childhood, 1967, Crisis in Child Psychiatry, 1975, also articles. Served to capt. AUS, 1942-45. Recipient Simon Wile Award, Amer. Acad. of Child and Adolescent Psychiatry, 1984. Mem. So. Calif. Psychiat. Assn. (pres. 1966-67), Am. Orthopsychiat. Assn. (v.p. 1968-69), Am. Coll. Psychiatry (sec.-gen. 1979-93), Group for Advancement of Psychiatry (pres. 1982-85). Home: 4986 Sentinel Dr Apt 504 Bethesda MD 20816

WORK, JANE MAGRUDER, professional society administrator; b. Owensboro, Ky., Mar. 30, 1927; d. Orion Noel and Willie May (Stallings) Magruder; m. William Work, Nov. 26, 1960; children: Paul MacGregor, Jeffrey William. BA, Furman U., 1947; MA, U. Wis., 1948; PhD, Ohio State U., 1959. Dir. radio U. South Miss., Hattisburg, 1948-51; pub. relations assoc. Ohio Fuel Gas Co./Columbia Gas, Columbus, 1952-62; adj. prof. communications Pace U., N.Y.C., 1963-75; dir. speechmodule ERIC, Washington, 1975-76; mgr. orgn. liaison, dir. legis. analysis Nat. Assn. Mfgs., Washington, 1977-84, asst. v.p. legis. analysis, 1984-87, v.p. legis. analysis, 1987-93, v.p. mem. comm., 1993—; adv. bd. public affairs NYU Grad. Bus. Sch., 1983-87; adv. bd. Procon. Mag., 1984-87; cons. IBM, Xerox, 1963-77. Contbr. articles to profl. jours. Transition team Consumer Product Safety Commn., Washington, 1979-80; mem., chmn. No. Va. Pvt. Industry Council, Fairfax County, 1979-85; co-chair Va. Gov.'s Employment & Tng. Task Force, Richmond, 1983; active in other civic activities. Named to Acad. Women Achievers YWCA, 1987. Mem. Future Homemakers of Am. (bd. dirs. 1985-88), Issue Mgmt. Assn. (bd. dirs. 1985-88), Nat. Assn. Industry-Edn. Coop. (bd. dirs. 1983—), Am. Soc. Assn. Execs. (tech. adv. com. 1989—), Speech Communication Assn. (sect. chmn. 1980-82), The Planning Forum (bd. dirs. Capital chpt. 1990-93), World Future Soc. (steering network 1993 Gen. Assembly), Alpha Psi Omega (hon.), Pi Kappa Delta (hon.). Republican. Presbyterian. Avocations: gardening, tennis. Home: 6245 Cheryl Dr Falls Church VA 22044-1809 Office: Nat Assn Mfrs 1331 Pennsylvania Ave NW Ste 1 Washington DC 20004-1703

WORK, WILLIAM, retired association executive; b. Ithaca, N.Y., Aug. 10, 1923; s. Paul and Helen Grace (Nichols) W.; m. Jane Noel Magruder, Nov. 26, 1960; children: Paul Magregor, Jeffrey William. AB, Cornell U., 1946; MA, U. Wis., 1948, PhD, 1954; D Arts (hon.), Eastern Mich. U., 1986; LLD (hon.), Emerson Coll., 1987. Cert. assn. exec. Instr., asso. dir theatre Purdue U., 1948-50; from instr. to prof., dir. theatre Eastern Mich. U., 1951-63; exec. sec. Speech Communication Assn., Annandale, Va., 1963-88, ret., 1988; mem. faculty U. Wis., 1950-51, So. Ill. U., 1959; cons., reader, review panelist U.S. Office Edn., 1966-71; del. White House Conf. Children, 1970; pres. Alliance Assn. Advancement Edn., 1977, Coun. Communication Assn., 1974-77; past. mem. AAAS, AAUP, Internat. Communication Assn., Internat. Inst. Communications. Contbr. articles, revs. profl. jours. Mem. Mich. Cultural Commn., 1959-60; mem. Hastings-on-Hudson (N.Y.) Bd. Edn., 1972-75. Recipient Alex Drier award, 1962. Mem. Phi Kappa Phi. Democrat. Unitarian. If, as George Santayana wisely noted, those who cannot remember the past are condemned to repeat it, then it must be equally true that those who fail to prepare for the future are condemned to endure it.

WORKMAN, MARGARET LEE, state supreme court justice; b. May 22, 1947; d. Frank Eugene and Mary Emma (Thomas) W.; m. Edward T. Gardner III; children: Lindsay Elizabeth, Christopher Workman, Edward Earnshaw. AB in Polit. Sci., W.Va. U., 1969, JD, 1974. Bar: W.Va. 1974. Asst. counsel to majority, pub. works com. U.S. Senate, Washington, 1974-75; law clk. 13th jud. cir., W.Va. Ct., Charleston, 1975-76, judge, 1981-88; pvt. practice Charleston, 1976-81; justice W.Va. Supreme Ct. Appeals, Charleston, 1989—, chief justice, 1993. Advance person for Rosalyn Carter, Carter Presdl. Campaign, Atlanta, 1976. Democrat. Episcopalian. Office: State Supreme Ct 317 State Capitol Charleston WV 25305-0001*

WORKMAN, WILLIAM DOUGLAS, III, mayor; b. Charleston S.C., July 3, 1940; s. William Douglas, Jr. and Rhea (Thomas) W.; BA, The Citadel, 1961; grad. U. S.C., 1993; m. Marcia Mae Moorhead, Apr. 23, 1966; children: William Douglas IV, Frank Moorhead. Reporter, Charleston News & Courier, 1965-66, Greenville (S.C.) News, 1966-70; tchr., adminstr., dean allied health scis. Greenville Tech. Coll., 1967-75; exec. asst. to Gov. of S.C., Columbia, 1975-78; mktg. exec. Daniel Internat. Corp., Greenville, 1978-90, dir. of facilities Fluor Daniel, 1991-93; v.p. S.C. ops. Piedmont Natural Gas, 1994—; mayor City of Greenville, 1983—. Chmn. Greenville County Rep. Conv., 1980, 82, 87, 89, 91, S.C. 4th Congl. Dist. Rep. Conv., 1980, 82, 84; chmn. S.C. Rep. Conv., 1984, 89, vice chmn., 1982, 87; Rep. nominee U.S. Congress 4th Dist. S.C., 1986; mem. S.C. Adv. Commn. on Intergovtl. Rels., 1990—; bd. dirs. S.C. Appalachian Coun. of Govts., 1991—; mem. Mcpl. Assn. S.C. 1981— (bd. dirs. 1990—); trustee S.C. Dist. Greenville County, 1969-75, also vice chmn.; bd. dirs. YMCA Camp Greenville, 1973-83, 90—, chmn. 1975; chmn. S.C. Health Coordinating Coun., 1976-78; founder S.C. Literacy Assn., treas., 1969-73; mem. Greenville City Council, 1981-83; mem. Southern Growth Policies Bd., 1992—, S.C. Adv. Commn. on Intergovtl. Rels., 1991—. Served with AUS, 1962-64; lt. col. Res. Decorated Army Commendation medal with 2 oak leaf clusters, Legion of Merit; named Outstanding State Chmn., S.C. Jaycees, 1969, Order of Palmetto. Mem. Res. Officers Assn., Assn. U.S. Army, U.S. Conf. Mayors, Southeastern Assn. Nat. Mgmt. Assn. (mgr. yr. award Greenville chpt. 1985), Newcomen Soc. (S.C. com.), S.C. Downtown Devel. Assn. (bd. dirs.), Greenville Country Club, Commerce Club (bd. dirs.), Greenville-Piedmont Citadel Club (past pres.), Greenville Open Club (bd. dirs.), Poinsett Club. Home: 30 Craigwood Rd Greenville SC 29607-3652 Office: PO Box 2207 Greenville SC 29602

WORLEY, BLAND WALLACE, banker; b. Kinston, N.C., Aug. 14, 1917; s. Bland W. and Ida Ruth (Gooding) W.; m. Ada Harvey, June 28, 1941; children: Anne, Ada, Bland W. B.S., U. N.C., 1938; grad. exec. program, 1955; grad., Grad. Sch. Banking, Rutgers U., 1954. Insp. Hooper Holmes

Bur., Greensboro, N.C., 1938-39; mgr. CIT Corp., Salisbury, N.C., 1939-42; mgr. time payment dept. Wachovia Bank & Trust Co., High Point, N.C., 1946-50; v.p., also High Point office exec. Wachovia Bank & Trust Co., 1951-56; sr. v.p. charge Wachovia Bank & Trust Co. (Greensboro operations), 1956-69; exec. v.p. charge statewide banking div. Wachovia Bank & Trust Co., Winston-Salem, N.C., 1969-70, also dir.; vice-chmn., dir., 1970-75; past trustee Wachovia Realty Investments; former CEO, dir. Barclays Am. Corp., chmn., 1976-84; dir., chmn. First Fed. Savs. & Loan Assn., Charlotte, N.C.; dir. Culp Inc., High Point, N.C.; past vol. chmn. for N.C. U.S. Savs. Bond Program. Past chmn. nat. exec. com. for vol. state chmn. 1969-77; pres. Greater Greensboro United Fund, 1975-77; past treas., mem. nat. exec. bd. Boy Scouts Am., 1970-85; past bd. dirs. N.C. Citizens Assn.; bd. dirs. N.C. Coun. Mgmt. and Devel., 1979-84; bd. dirs., past pres. Bus. Found. of N.C.; trustee, former chmn. bd. trustees Greensboro Coll.; past trustee Atlantic Christian Coll., Wilson, N.C.; past bd. visitors Guilford Coll., Greensboro; trustee U. N.C., Charlotte, 1981-85. Named High Point Young Man of Yr., 1953, Outstanding Young Businessman N.C., 1958; recipient Silver Beaver, Silver Antelope, Silver Buffalo awards Boy Scouts Am., Disting. Citizens award N.C. Citizens for Bus. and Industry, 1987. Mem. N.C. Bankers Assn. (past pres.), Nat. Consumer Fin. Assn., Greensboro C. of C. (past pres., disting. citizen award 1968), Greater Charlotte C. of C. (chmn. 1980-81), Piedmont Club, Old Town Country Club. Home: 1244 Arbor Rd Apt 232 Winston Salem NC 27104-1136

WORLEY, GORDON ROGER, retail chain financial executive; b. Arlington, Nebr., Oct. 13, 1919; s. Carl H. and Zella E. (Ludwig) W. B.S., U. Nebr., 1945; M.B.A., Northwestern U., 1956. C.P.A., Ill. With Aldens, Inc., Chgo., 1940-67; asst. treas. Aldens, Inc., 1956-57, v.p., treas., 1957-67; v.p., controller Gamble-Skogmo, Inc., Mpls., 1967; v.p. fin. Montgomery Ward & Co., Inc., 1967-68; exec. v.p. fin. Montgomery Ward & Co., Inc., Chgo., 1975-83; also dir.; v.p. fin. Marcor Inc., Chgo., 1968-75; also dir. Marcor Inc.; dir. Signature Fin./Mktg. Inc., Montgomery Ward Ins. Group, Ill. Power Co., Decatur, Axia, Inc, Stein, Roe & Farnham Funds, Am. Mgmt. Systems, Inc., Arlington, Va. Bd. dirs. Northwestern Meml. Hosp.; trustee Garrett-Evang. Theol. Sem., chmn., 1984-89; mem. adv. com. Ill. Capital Devel. Bd., 1973-77; mem. Nat. Commn. on Electronic Fund Transfers, 1975-77. Served with USAAF, 1943-46. Mem. Conf. Bd. Coun. of Fin. Execs., Fin. Execs. Inst., Nat. Retail Mchts. Assn., Execs. Club, Econ. Club, Mid-Am. Club, Chgo. Club, Oak Park Country Club, Hole-In-The-Wall Club (Naples, Fla.). Methodist.

WORLEY, JOAN HIETT, library director; b. Houston, Jan. 2, 1939; d. Fred W. and Silvia Marie Hiett; m. William C. Worley (div. 1973); 1 child, Margaret Claire. Student, U. Colo., 1956-57, U. Tex., 1957-59; BA in History, Tex. Tech. U., 1961; MSLS, U. Tenn., 1975. Sales rep. Ency. Brit., Knoxville, 1971-75; reference librarian U. Tenn., Knoxville, 1975-84; libr. dir. Maryville (Tenn.) Coll., 1984-94. Editor jour. Tenn. Librarian, 1980-82; contbr. articles to library jours. Dir. LWV, Knoxville, 1969-71, Tenn. ACLU, 1991—. Mem. ALA, Assn. Coll. and Rsch. Librs. (dir. bibliographic instrn. sect. 1981-82), Tenn. Libr. Assn. (pres. coll., univ. librs. sect. 1986-87). Methodist. Home: 131 Indiana Ave Maryville TN 37801-5935

WORLEY, LLOYD DOUGLAS, English educator; b. Lafayette, La., Sept. 11, 1946; s. Albert Stiles and Doris (Christy) W.; m. Maydean Ann Mouton, Apr. 4, 1966; children: Erin Shawn, Albert Stiles II. BA, U. SW La., 1968, MA, 1972; PhD, So. Ill. U., 1979. Ordained priest, Liberal Cath. Ch. Tchr. Lafayette H.S., 1969-74; vis. asst. prof. dept. English So. Ill. U., Carbondale, 1979-80; asst. prof. dept. English Pa. State U., DuBois, 1980-87; assoc. prof., assoc. dir. composition dept. English U. No. Colo., Greeley, 1987-88, prof. dept. English, 1988—; acting dir. Writing Component Ctr. Basic Skills, So. Ill. U., 1980. Editor: Ruthven Literary Bull., 1988-92; contbr. book chpts. articles. Rector Parish of St. Albertus Magnus, sec-treas. Am. Province; mem. Am. Clerical Synod Chpt. Decorated Knight Comdr. Star of Order of Merit St. Angilbert, 1993, Prelate Comdr. Order of Noble Companions of Swan, 1993; created hereditary Baron of Royal and Serene House of Alabona-Ostrogojsk by HRSH Prince William I Fedn. of Princes of Holy Roman Empire-in-Exile, 1993. Fellow Philalethes Soc.; mem. ASCD, Internat. Assn. for Fantastic in Arts (divsn. head Am. Lit. 1987-93), Lord Ruthven Assembly (pres. 1988-94), Conf. Coll. Composition and Commn., Nat. Coun. Tchrs. English, Am. Conf. Irish Studies, Sigma Tau Delta (bd. dirs. 1990—, high plains regent various states 1992—), Masons (century lodge #190), Order of DeMolay (chevalier, corss of honor, legion of honor), Knights Holy Sepulchre (Sov. Grand Master), Rose Crox Martinist Order (pres. premier nat. coun.). Democrat. Office: 2644 11th Ave D-109 Greeley CO 80631

WORLEY, MARVIN GEORGE, JR., architect; b. Oak Park, Ill., Oct. 10, 1934; s. Marvin George and Marie Hyancinth (Donahue) W.; B.Arch., U. Ill., 1958; m. Maryalice Ryan, July 11, 1959; children—Michael Craig, Carrie Ann, Alissa Maria. Project engr. St. Louis area Nike missile bases U.S Army C.E., Granite City, Ill., 1958-59, architect N.Cen. div. U.S. Army C.E., Chgo., 1960; architect Yerkes & Grunsfeld, architects, Chgo., 1961-65, asso., 1965; asso. Grunsfeld & Assos., architects, Chgo., 1966-85; ptnr. Marvin Worley Architects, Oak Park, Ill., 1985—. Dist. architect Oak Park Elementary Schs., Dist. 97, 1973-80. Mem. Oak Park Community Improvement Commn., 1973-75; mem. exec. bd. Oak Park Council PTA, 1970-73, pres., 1971-72. Served with AUS, 1959. Mem. AIA (corporate), Chgo. Assn. Commerce and Industry, Oak Park-River Forest C. of C. Office: 37 South Blvd Oak Park IL 60302-2777

WORLEY, ROBERT WILLIAM, JR., lawyer; b. Anderson, Ind., June 13, 1935; s. Robert William and Dorothy Mayhew (Hayler) W.; m. Diana Lynn Matthews, Aug. 22, 1959; children—Nathanael, Hope. B.S. in Chem. Engring., Lehigh U., 1956; LL.B, Harvard U., 1960. Bar: Conn. 1960, Fla. 1977, U.S. Supreme Ct. 1966. Assoc. then ptnr. Cummings & Lockwood, Stamford, Conn., 1960-91; gen. counsel Consol. Asset Recovery Corp. sub. Chase Manhattan Corp., Bridgeport, Conn., 1991-94; v.p., sr. assoc. counsel The Chase Manhattan Bank, N.A., N.Y.C., 1994—. Mem. trustees com. on bequests and trusts Lehigh U., 1979—; mem. Conn. Legis. Task Force on Probate Court System, 1991-93; chmn. Greenwich Arts Council, 1981-82; v.p., bd. dirs. Greenwich Choral Soc., 1962-77, 80, mem., 1960—; bd. dirs. Greenwich Ctr. for Chamber Music, 1981-85, Greenwich Symphony, 1986-89; commnr. Greenwich Housing Authority, 1972-77; past mem. Republican Town Com. Greenwich; mem. bldg. com. for sr. ctr. Greenwich Bd. Selectmen, 1980-81. Served to capt. JAGC, AUS, 1965. Mem. ABA, Conn. Bar Assn. (exec. com. probate sect. 1980), Fla. Bar Assn., Stamford Bar Assn. (sec.), Greenwich Bar Assn., Palm Beach County Bar Assn., Am. Arbitration Assn. Republican. Christian Scientist. Club: Landmark. Home: 316 Sound Beach Ave Old Greenwich CT 06870-1932 Office: The Chase Manhattan Bank NA Legal Dept 25th Fl 1 Chase Manhattan Plz New York NY 10081

WORMAN, HOWARD JAY, physician, educator; b. Paterson, N.J., May 21, 1959; s. Louis and Dora (Rubin) W. BA, Cornell U., 1981; MD, U. Chgo., 1985. Diplomate Am. Bd. Internal Medicine. Intern The N.Y. Hosp., N.Y.C., 1985-86, resident, 1986-87; guest investigator The Rockefeller U., N.Y.C., 1987-90; asst. prof. The Mt. Sinai Sch. Medicine, N.Y.C., 1990-94; asst. attending physician The Mt. Sinai Hosp., N.Y.C., 1990-94; asst. prof. Coll. Physicians & Surgeons Columbia U., N.Y.C., 1995—; asst. attending physician The Presbyn. Hosp., N.Y.C., 1995—. Contbr. articles to profl. jours. Recipient Physician-Scientist award NIH, 1987-92; Charles E. Culpeer scholar in Med. Scis., 1994—. Mem. AAAS, ACP, Am. Chem. Soc., Am. Fedn. Clin. Rsch. (Trainee award in clin. rsch. 1989, Henry Christian award 1990), Am. Soc. Cell Biology, Am. Assn. Study of Liver Diseases, N.Y. Acad. Scis. (vice chmn. biol. scis. sect. 1992-93, chmn. 1993-94), Hon. Order Ky. Cols., Phi Beta Kappa. Democrat. Jewish. Avocations: music, golf, reading. Office: Coll Physicians Columbia U 10th fl rm 508 630 W 168th St New York NY 10032

WORMAN, RICHARD W., insurance company executive, state senator; b. Noble County, Ind., July 3, 1933; s. William D. and Leah M. W.; m. Marna Jo Neuhouser, Sept. 29, 1951; children—Terry Jo, Renny, Denny, Rex, Tammy. Buyer, Neuhouser Poultry, Leo, Ind., 1951-53; salesman Allen Dairy, Ft. Wayne, Ind., 1953-57; with Nationwide Ins. Co., Columbus, Ohio, 1951—, dist. sales mgr.; mem. Ind. Ho. of Reps., 1972-76, Ind. Senate,

1978—; trustee, assessor County of Allen, Ind., 1970-72. C.L.U. Mem. Life Underwriters Assn., Republican. Methodist. Clubs: Lions (past pres.), Mason (past master), Shriner. Office: Box 320 Leo IN 46765

WORNER, LLOYD EDSON, retired college president; b. Mexico, Mo., Sept. 13, 1918; s. Lloyd Edson and Letitia (Owen) W.; m. Mary Haden, Aug. 24, 1945; children: Linda Lou, Mary Susan. Student, Washington and Lee U., 1936-38, LL.D., 1972; A.B., Colo. Coll., 1942, LL.D., 1981; postgrad., Princeton U., 1942-43; M.A., U. Mo., 1944, Ph.D., 1946, L.H.D. (hon.), 1983; L.H.D. (hon.), U. No. Colo., 1975. Instr. history Colo. Coll., 1946-47, asst. prof., 1947-50, assoc. prof., 1950-55, prof., dean coll., 1955-63, pres., 1963-81, pres. emeritus, 1981—. Trustee emeritus Fountain Valley Sch.; bd. visitors Mo. Mil. Acad. Congregationalist. Home: 1985 Mesa Rd Colorado Springs CO 80904-1812

WORRELL, ALBERT CADWALLADER, forest economics educator; b. Phila., May 14, 1913; s. Pratt Bishop and Bertha May (Cadwallader) W.; m. Helen Haffner Diefendorf, July 31, 1937; children: Kathleen Worrell Weigel, Frederick Strayer, Nancy WorrellShumaker. B.S., U. Mich., 1935, M.F., 1935, Ph.D., 1953. Asso. prof. U. Ga., 1947-55; asso. prof. Yale, 1955-63, prof. forest econs., 1963-67; Edwin Weyerhaeuser Davis prof. forest policy, 1967-83, Edwin W. Davis prof. emeritus, 1983—; forest economist U.N. Econ. Commn. for Latin Am., Santiago, Chile, 1960-61; guest prof. U. Freiburg, Germany, 1970. Author: Economics of American Forestry, 1959, Principles of Forest Policy, 1970, Unpriced Values, 1979. Mem. Soc. Am. Foresters. Home: 134 Meadowbrook Dr Nacogdoches TX 75964-6568

WORRELL, ANNE EVERETTE ROWELL, newspaper publisher; b. Surry, Va., Mar. 7, 1920; d. Charles Gray and Ethel (Roache) Rowell; student Va. Intermont Coll., 1939, LittD (hon.), U. Richmond, 1965; m. Thomas Eugene Worrell, Sept. 12, 1941; 1 son, Thomas Eugene. Founding stockholder Worrell Newspapers Inc., 1949, v.p., dir., 1969-73; pres. Bristol Newspapers, Inc., Va., pubs. Bristol Herald-Courier, Bristol Va.-Tennessean, 1979—; v.p., sec. Worrell Investment Co., Charlottesville, Va. Pres., Bristol Jr. League, 1959; bd. dir. The Corp. for Thomas Jefferson's Poplar Forest Found., Assn. for the Preservation of Va. Antiquities; trustee Va. Intermont Coll., 1973—; Preservation Alliance Va.; chmn. Centennial Campaign, 1982—; active State Rev. Bd., Bayly Mus., Friends of Bacon's Castle. Named Outstanding Alumna, 1981. Mem. DAR (Shadwell chpt.), Nat. Trust for Hist. Preservation. Clubs: Contemporary, Farmington Country. Episcopalian. Home: Seven Sunset Circle Farmington Charlottesville VA 22901 Office: Pantops PO Box 5386 Charlottesville VA 22905-5386 also: Bristol Newspapers Inc 320 Morrison Blvd Bristol VA 24201

WORRELL, AUDREY MARTINY, geriatric psychiatrist; b. Phila., Aug. 12, 1935; d. Francis Aloysius and Dorothy (Rawley) Martiny; m. Richard Vernon Worrell, June 14, 1958; children: Philip Vernon, Amy Elizabeth. MD, Meharry Med. Coll., 1960. Diplomate Am. Bd. Psychiatry and Neurology. Intern Misericordia Hosp., Phila., 1960-61; resident SUNY-Buffalo Affiliated Hosp., 1961-63, Buffalo Psychiat. Ctr., 1963-64; dir. capitol region Mental Health Ctr., Hartford, Conn., 1974-77; acting regional dir. Region IV, State Dept. Mental Health, 1976-77; asst. chief psychiatry VA Med. Ctr., Newington, Conn., 1977-78, acting chief psychiatry, 1978-79, chief psychiatry, 1978-80; dir. Capitol Regional Mental Health Facilities, Hartford, Conn., 1980-87; clin. prof. psychiatry U. Conn., 1981-87; commr. State Dept. Mental Health, Hartford, 1981-86; chief exec. officer and med. dir. Vista Sandia Hosp., Albuquerque, 1986-88; dir. consultation liason Lovelace Med. Ctr., Albuquerque, 1988-89, geriatric psychiatrist, 1989—. Contbr. articles to profl. jours. Bd. dirs. Transitional Services, Buffalo, 1973-74, ARC, Buffalo, 1973-74, Child and Family Services, Hartford, 1972-73; co-chmn. United Way/Combined Health Appeal, State of Conn., 1983, 84; active Child Welfare Inst. Adv. Bd., Hartford, 1983—, Conn. Prison Bd., Hartford, 1984-85. Recipient Leadership award Conn. Council Mental Health Ctrs., 1983; Outstanding Contbn. award to Health Services YWCA, Hartford, 1983; chmn. Gov.'s Task Force on Mental Health Policy, 1982-85; mem. Gov.'s Task Force on Homeless, 1983-85. Mem. New Eng. Mental Health Commrs. Assn., Am. Med. Women's Assn., Conn. Assn. Mental Health and Aging, Conn. Coalition for Homeless Inc., Conn. Rehab. Assn., Am. Assn. Psychiat. Adminstrs., Am. Hosp. Assn., AMA, Am. Orthopsychiat. Assn., Am. Pub. Health Assn., Assn. Mental Health Adminstrs., Hosp. and Community Psychiatry Service, Corporators of Inst. of Living of Hartford, Am. Psychiat. Assn., Conn. Psychiat. Soc., NASMHPD (sec., bd. dirs. 1982-86), Am. Coll. Psychiatrists, Am. Coll. Mental Health Adminstrs. Democrat. Office: Lovelace Med Ctr 5400 Gibson Blvd SE Albuquerque NM 87108-4763

WORRELL, DAVID CHARLES, lawyer; b. Indpls., Nov. 16, 1951; s. David Earl and Patricia Elizabeth (Pfau) W.; m. Laura B. Bowman, May 7, 1977; children: Rebecca Elizabeth, Matthew Davis. AB, Wabash Coll., 1973; JD, U. Chgo., 1976. Bar: Ind. 1976, U.S. Dist. Ct. (so. dist.) Ind. 1976. Assoc. Baker & Daniels, Indpls., 1976-82, ptnr., 1983—. Mem. ABA, Ind. State Bar Assn., Indpls. Bar Assn. Office: Baker & Daniels 300 N Meridian St Ste 2700 Indianapolis IN 46204

WORRELL, RICHARD VERNON, orthopedic surgeon, college dean; b. Bklyn., June 4, 1931; s. John Elmer and Elaine (Martin) W.; BA, NYU, 1952; MD, Meharry Med. Coll., 1958; m. Audrey Frances Martiny, June 14, 1958; children: Philip Vernon, Amy Elizabeth. Intern Meharry Med. Coll., Nashville, 1958-59; resident gen. surgery Mercy-Douglass Hosp., Phila., 1960-61; resident orthopedic surgery State U. N.Y. Buffalo Sch. Medicine Affiliated Hosps., 1961-64; resident in orthopedic pathology Temple U. Med. Ctr., Phila., 1966-67; pvt. practice orthopedic surgery, Phila., 1964-68; asst. prof. acting head div. orthopedic surgery U. Conn. Sch. Medicine 1968-70; attending orthopedic surgeon E.J. Meyer Meml. Hosp., Buffalo, Millard Fillmore Hosp., Buffalo, VA Hosp., Buffalo, Buffalo State Hosp.; clin. instr. orthopedic surgery SUNY, Buffalo, 1970-74; chief orthopedic surgery VA Hosp., Newington, Conn., 1974-80; asst. prof. surgery (orthopedics) U. Conn. Sch. Medicine, 1974-77, assoc. prof., 1977-83, asst. dean student affairs, 1980-83; prof. clin. surgery SUNY Downstate Med. Ctr., Bklyn., 1983-86; dir. orthopedic surgery Brookdale Hosp. Med. Ctr., Bklyn., 1983-86; prof. of orthopedics U. N.Mex. Sch. of Medicine, 1986—; dir. orthopedic oncology U. N.Mex. Med. Ctr., 1987—; mem. med. staff U. N.Mex. Cancer Ctr., 1987—; chief orthopedic surgery VA Med. Ctr., Albuquerque, 1987—; cons. in orthopedic surgery Newington (Conn.) Children's Hosp., 1968-70; mem. sickle cell disease adv. com. NIH, 1982-86. Bd. dirs. Big Bros. Greater Hartford. Served to capt. M.C., U.S. Army Res., 1962-69. Diplomate Am. Bd. Orthopedic Surgery, Nat. Bd. Med. Examiners. Fellow ACS, Am. Acad. Orthopedic Surgeons, Royal Soc. Medicine, London; mem. AMA, Am. Orthopaedic Assn., Orthopedic Rsch. Soc., Internat. Soc. Orthopedic Surgery and Traumatology, Internat. Fedn. Surg. Colls. (assoc.), Alpha Omega Alpha. Office: U NMex Sch Medicine Albuquerque NM 87131-5296

WORSECK, RAYMOND ADAMS, economist; b. Providence, Mar. 25, 1937; s. Wilford Howe and Florence Marie (Dillmann) W.; m. Mary Elizabeth Lottes, July 15, 1972; children: Andrew Wilford, David Edward. BS in Math., St. Louis U., 1959, MA in Econs., 1970. Registered rep. N.Y. Stock Exchange. Commodity analyst Longstreet-Abbott & Co., St. Louis, 1959-65, dir. basic rsch., 1965-67; sr. price analyst Doane Agrl. Svc., St. Louis, 1967-69; dir. commodity rsch. A.G. Edwards & Sons, Inc., St. Louis, 1969-85, mgr. econ. rsch., 1985—, chief economist, 1989—. Mem. Am. Econ. Assn., Nat. Assn. Bus. Economists (chpt. pres. 1984-85), Fin. Analysts Soc. (bd. govs. St. Louis chpt. 1994-97), St. Louis Com. on Fgn. Rels., Futures Industry Assn. (nat. pres. rsch. divsn. 1983-84). Avocations: history, music, cycling. Home: 331 Elm Valley Dr Saint Louis MO 63119-4574 Office: AG Edwards & Sons Inc 1 N Jefferson Ave Saint Louis MO 63103-2287

WORSHAM, BERTRAND RAY, psychiatrist; b. Atkins, Ark., Feb. 14, 1926; s. Lewis Henry and Emma Lavada (Burris) W.; m. Margaret Ann Dickson, June 4, 1947 (div. 1960); children: Eric Dickson, Vicki Gayle; m. Lynne Ellen Reynolds, Aug. 27, 1976; children: Mary Ellen Clarice, Richard Andrew (dec.). BA, U. Ark., 1951; MD, U. Ark., Little Rock, 1955. Intern Hillcrest Med. Ctr., Tulsa, 1955-56; resident in psychiatry Menninger Sch. Psychiatry, Topeka, 1956-59; pvt. practice, 1959-78; clin. instr. U. Okla. Sch. Medicine, 1965-78; coord. drug and alcohol treatment unit Washington D.C. VA Med. Ctr., 1978-84; med. dir. Norman divsn. Okla. State Vets. Ctr.,

1984-89; psychiat. cons. Comty. Counselling Ctr., Oklahoma City, 1989—; cons. Oklahoma City Vets. Hosp., 1959-72, State Dept. Pub. Health, 1960-65; dir. Cmty. Mental Health Ctr., Shawnee, Okla., 1965-72; mem. staff Coyne Campbell Hosp., 1960-78, Bapt. Med. Ctr., 1960-78, Mercy Health Ctr., 1960-78, Deaconess Hosp., 1963-78, Dr.'s Gen. Hosp., 1963-78, Presbyn. Hosp., 1962-78, U. Health Sci. Ctr., 1962-78, Children's Meml. Hosp., 1968-78, Oklahoma City VA Hosp., 1960-78, Washington D.C. Va. Hosp., 1978-84, Okla. Vets. Ctr., Norman, 1984-89. Mem. Civil Disaster Com., Oklahoma City, 1966, USN League, Okla., 1972— With USAF, 1944-46; capt. USNR, 1957-86, ret. Fellow Menninger Found., Charles F. Menninger Found; mem. AMA, Am. Psychiat. Assn. (Okla. dist. br. 1959-78, 84—), Assn. Mil. Surgeons of U.S., Ret. Officers Assn., World Fedn. for Mental Health, Washington D.C. Psychiat. Assn., No. Va. Mental Health Assn., Masons (32 degree). Republican. Episcopalian. Avocations: golf, church activities. Home: 9915 N Kelley Ave Oklahoma City OK 73131-2022 Office: Comty Counseling Ctr 1140 N Hudson Ave Oklahoma City OK 73103-3906

WORSHAM, ERNEST LEE, lawyer; b. Miami, Fla., Sept. 21, 1946; s. Edward Lee and Susan Jane (Billheimer) W.; m. Annette Louise Pearce, Oct. 30, 1972; children—Eric Lee, Lindsay Carmita. B.S., Colo. State U., 1968; J.D. with honors, U. Fla., 1974. Bar: Fla. 1975, U.S. Dist. Ct. (no. dist.) Fla. 1975, U.S. Dist. Ct. (mid. dist.) Fla. 1981. Law clk. U.S. Dist. Ct. judge, Miami, Fla., 1975; legal writing instr. U. Fla. Law Coll., Gainesville, Fall 1975; assoc. Clayton, Duncan et al, Gainesville, 1975-78; ptnr. LaCoe & Worsham, P.A., Gainesville, 1978-83; gen. counsel St. Johns River water Dist., Palatka, Fla., 1980-83; sr. atty. Dept. Community Affairs, Tallahassee, 1983—; vice chmn. agrl. law com. Fla. Bar, Tallahassee, 1978-82. Chmn., bd. dirs. City of Gainesville Bd. Adjustment, 1978-81. Served to capt. USAF, 1969-72. Mem. Am. Water Resources Assn. Democrat. Methodist. Club: Jaycees (bd. dirs. 1975-80) (Gainesville). Home: 12910 La Rochelle Cir West Palm Beach FL 33410-1405 Office: Honigman Miller Schwartz & Cohn 222 Lakeview Ave West Palm Beach FL 33401-6145

WORSLEY, JAMES RANDOLPH, JR., lawyer; b. Rocky Mount, N.C., July 28, 1924; s. James Randolph and Helen Marie (Killian) W.; m. Cornelia Cheston, Feb. 11, 1956; children: Cornelia Worsley Newell, Julia Worsley Neilson, Charlotte Cheston Worsley. BS, E. Carolina U., 1944; postgrad., Harvard U., 1944-45, LLB, 1949. Bar: N.C. 1949, D.C. 1949. Assoc. Klagsbrunn, Hanes & Irwin, Washington, 1949-54; ptnr. Ober, Kaler, Grimes & Shriver (and predecessor firm), Washington, 1955-94, coun., 1995—. Chmn. Md. Potomac Water Authority, 1969-71, Montgomery County (Md.) Charter Revision Commn., 1967; mem. pastoral coun. Archdiocese of Washington, 1975-78; bd. dirs. Madeira Sch., Greenway, Va., 1975-81. Fellow Am. Bar Found.; mem. Chevy Chase Club, Met. Club. Democrat. Roman Catholic. Avocations: sailing, tennis. Home: 11 Quincy St Chevy Chase MD 20815 Office: Ober Kaler Grimes & Shriver 1401 H St NW Ste 500 Washington DC 20005-2110

WORSLEY, JOHN CLAYTON, architect; b. Providence, Apr. 8, 1919; s. Harold Rollin and Elise (Clay) W.; m. Helen Elizabeth Hauss, Nov. 29, 1940; children: Katherine, Madeleine, John, David, Paul, Nina. AB, Stanford U., 1941; postgrad., Harvard U., 1949-51. Mem. planning office staff Stanford U., 1951-54; architect Ernest Kump, 1954-59; prin. John C. Worsley (Architect), Menlo Park, Calif., 1959-73; state architect of Calif., 1973-76; cons. architect State Capitol of Calif., 1976-82; exec. dir. Calif. Bldg. Standards Commn., 1982-85, cons. architect, 1986—, claims review bd. pub. employees retirement system, 1986-88; hist. cons. for restoration of legis. bldg., Agana, Guam, 1990-91; lectr. Stanford U., 1951-70, asst. dir. divn. architecture and urban design, 1971-72; mem. faculty NSF/AIA Rsch. Found. Seismic Inst. Stanford U., 1977. Editor: California State Capitol Restoration-A Pictorial History, 1983; contbr. articles to profl. jours. Mem. Downtown Planning Com., Menlo Park, Calif., chmn. beautification com., Menlo Park; treas. Devel. Disabilities Svc. Orgn., 1989—, v.p., 1990, pres., chmn. bd., 1991-94. With USNR, 1942-46. Recipient award Sacramento Mus. and History Commn., 1981. Fellow AIA (pres. Santa Clara Valley chpt. 1965, treas. Calif. council 1970-72, mem. joint common. on hazardous bldgs. with Structural Engrs. Calif. and Calif. council AIA 1978-79, presdl. award 1986). Home and Office: 1267 Hide A Way Ln Lake Oswego OR 97034-1646

WORTH, GARY JAMES, communications executive; b. Berkeley Township, N.J., Dec. 13, 1940; s. Melvin Raymond and Viola Vista (Landis) W. Student, Trenton State Coll., 1964, Palm Beach Jr. Coll., 1958-59. Dir. sta. relations MBS, Inc., N.Y.C., 1972; v.p. sta. relations MBS, Inc., 1972; exec. v.p. MBS, Inc., Washington, 1972-79; dir. Mut. Reports, Inc., 1972-79; v.p. dir. WCFL, Inc., Chgo., 1979, Mut. Radio N.Y., Inc., N.Y.C., 1979; pres. Robert Wold Co. Inc. and subs. Wold Communications, Inc., L.A., 1980-85, also dir.; pres., chief exec. officer, dir. WesternWold Inc. and subs. WesternWold TV, L.A., 1986-93, The Video Tape Co., North Hollywood, Calif., 1987—; sec. dir. WesternWorld Video Inc., L.A., 1986-87; chmn., CEO, dir. Starcom TV Svcs., Inc., 1993—; chmn., CEO Starcom Entertainment, Inc., 1993—. Producer, dir.: USAF movie Assignment McGuire. Served to capt. USAF, 1960-66, Vietnam. Decorated Air Force Commendation medal, Armed Forces Expeditionary medal; recipient Chief Herbert H. Almers Meml. award Bergen County (N.J.) Police Acad., 1972. Mem. Nat. Assn. Broadcasters, Nat. Assn. TV Program Execs., Nat. Informercial Mktg. Assn. Methodist.

WORTH, GEORGE JOHN, English literature educator; b. Vienna, Austria, June 11, 1929; came to U.S., 1940, naturalized, 1945; s. Adolph and Theresa (Schmerzler) W.; m. Carol Laverne Dinsdale, Mar. 17, 1951; children: Theresa Jean (Wilkinson), Paul Dinsdale. AB, U. Chgo., 1948, MA, 1951; PhD, U. Ill., 1954. Instr. English U. Ill., Urbana, 1954-55; faculty U. Kans., Lawrence, 1955—, assoc. prof., 1962-65, prof. English lit., 1965—, asst. chmn. dept., 1961-62, assoc. chmn., 1962-63, acting chmn., 1963-64, chmn., 1964-79. Author: James Hannay: His Life and Work, 1964, William Harrison Ainsworth, 1972, Dickensian Melodrama, 1978, Thomas Hughes, 1984, Great Expectations: An Annotated Bibliography, 1986; editor: (with Harold Orel) Six Studies in Nineteenth Century English Literature and Thought, 1962, The Nineteenth Century Writer and His Audience, 1969, (with Edwin Eigner) Victorian Criticism of the Novel, 1985. Mem. AAUP, MLA, Am. Dickens Fellowship, Internat. Ass. U. Profs. English, Dickens Soc., Midwest Victorian Studies Assn., Rsch. Soc. for Victorian Periodicals. Office: U Kans Dept English Wescoe Hall Lawrence KS 66045-2115

WORTH, IRENE, actress; b. Nebr., June 23, 1916. B.Edn., U. Calif. at Los Angeles, 1937; pupil, Elsie Fogarty, London, 1944-45. Formerly tchr. Debut as Fenella in: Escape Me Never, N.Y.C. 1942; Broadway debut as Cecily Harden in: The Two Mrs. Carrolls, 1943; London debut in The Time of Your Life, 1946; following roles, mostly on London stage, include Anabelle Jones in Love Goes to Press, 1946; Ilona Szabo in: The Play's The Thing, 1947; as Eileen Perry in: Edward my Son, 1948; as Lady Fortrose in: Home is Tomorrow, 1948; as Mary Dalton in: Native Son, 1948; title role in: LaCrece, 1948; as Olivia Raines in: Champagne for Delilah, 1949; as Celia Coplestone in: The Cocktail Party, 1949, 50; various roles with Old Vic Repertory Co., London, including Desdemona in Othello; Helena in Midsummer Night's Dream and Lady Macbeth in Macbeth; also Catherine de Vausselles in: on tours The Other Heart, S. Africa, 1952; as Portia in: The Merchant of Venice, 1953; joined, Shakespeare Festival Theatre, Stratford, Ont., Can., 1953; as Helena in: All's Well That Ends Well; Queen Margaret in: Richard III; appeared as Frances Farrar in: A Day by the Sea, 1953-54; leading roles in: The Queen and the Rebels, 1955, Hotel Paradiso, 1956; as Mary Stuart, 1957, The Potting Shed, 1958; appeared as Albertine Prine in: Toys in the Attic, 1960 (Page One award); mem., Royal Shakespeare Co., 1962-64; including world tour King Lear, 1964; star: including world tour Tiny Alice, N.Y.C., 1964, Aldwych, 1970; appeared in: Noel Coward trilogy Shadows of the Evening; also appeared as Hilde in: A Song at Twilight; Anna-Mary in: Come into the Garden Maud (Evening Standard award); Hesione Hushabye in: Heartbreak House (Variety Club Gt. Britain award 1967); Jocasta in: Oedipus, 1968; Hedda in: Hedda Gabler, 1970; with internat. Co., Theatre Research, Paris and Iran, 1971; leading role in: Notes on a Love Affair, 1972; Mme. Arkadina in: The Seagull, 1973; Gertrude in: Hamlet; Mrs. Alving in: Ghosts, 1974; Princess Kosmonopolis in: Sweet Bird of Youth, 1975-76 (Jefferson award, Tony award); Lina in: Misalliance, 1976;

Mme. Ranevskaya in: The Cherry Orchard, 1977 (Drama Desk award); Kate in: Old Times, 1977, After the Season, 1978, Happy Days, 1979, Eyewitness, 1980, Coriolanus, 1988, Lost In Yonkers, (Tony award, 1991); films include; role of Leonie in: Orders to Kill, 1958 (Brit. Film Acad. award), The Scapegoat, 1958, King Lear, 1970, Nicholas and Alexandra, 1971, Rich Kids, 1979, Eyewitness, 1981, Death Trap, 1982, Fast Forward, 1985, Lost in Yonkers, 1993, also numerous radio, TV appearances, Eng., Can., U.S., including; Stella in: The Lake; Ellida Wangel in: The Lady from the Sea (Daily Mail Nat. TV award); also Candida, Duchess of Malfi, Antigone, Prince Orestes, Variations on a Theme, The Way of the World, The Displaced Person; (with Brit. Broadcasting Co.) Coriolanus, 1984; poetry recitals, recs.; (recipient Whitbread Anglo-Am. award outstanding actress 1967). Decorated comdr. Brit. Empire (hon.). Address: Internat Creative Mgmt care Sam Cohn 40 W 57th St Fl 6 New York NY 10019-4001*

WORTH, MARY PAGE, mayor; b. Balt., Jan. 23, 1924; d. Christian Allen and Margaret Pennington (Holbein) Schwarzwaelder; m. William James Worth, Nov. 4, 1947 (dec. May 1986); children: Margaret Page, William Allen, John David III. Student, Ladycliff Coll., Highland Falls, N.Y., 1941-42, Abbott Sch. Art, Washington, 1942-44. Selectman Town of Searsport, Maine, 1973-75; mayor City of Belfast, Maine, 1986—; recreation chmn. Town of Searsport, 1970-72. Del. Rep. State Conv., Maine, 1970-94; pres. Searsport Reps., 1974-76; active ARC Overseas Assn., 1976—; pres. Searsport C. of C., 1976-79; mem. exec. bd. Waldo County Com. for Social Action, Belfast, 1986—; mem. Abnacki coun. Girl Scouts U.S.; tutor Literacy Vols. Am.; recreation specialist ARC, Camp Haugen, Japan, 1946-47; bd. dirs. RSVP-Waldo County, Head Start Waldo County; vol. tchr. Sch. for Blind, Cholon, Republic Vietnam, 1959-61, Am. School at Saigon, Republic Vietnam, 1959-61; club dir. USAF Spl. Services, Fort Meyer, Va., 1962-63, U.S. Army Spl. Services, Fort Belvoir, Va., 1963-64; mem. Congresswoman Olympia Snow's Mcpl. Adv. Bd.; town chair Rep. Party. Mem. DAR (officer Maine 1986—), Internat. Platform Assn., Ret. Officers Assn. (life), 11th Airborne Assn./511th Parachute Infantry Regiment Korea War Vets. Assn., Waldo County Humane Soc. (pres. 1990—), Waldo County Law Enforcement (v.p. 1990—), VFW Aux., Am. Legion Aux., Belfast Garden Club (parliamentarian 1984—), Rotary (bd. govs. com. Maine St. '90). Avocations: Great Dane breeding, antiques. Home: 16 Church St Belfast ME 04915-1601 Office: City of Belfast Mayor's Office 71 Church St Belfast ME 04915-1796

WORTHAM, THOMAS RICHARD, English language educator; b. Liberal, Kans., Dec. 5, 1943; s. Tom and Ruth (Cavanaugh) W. AB, Marquette U., 1965; PhD, Ind. U., 1970. From asst. prof. to assoc. prof. UCLA, 1970-82, prof., 1982—, vice-chmn. and dir. undergrad. studies, 1993—; vis. prof. Am. lit. U. Warsaw, Poland, 1976-77; sr. rsch. fellow Am. Coun. of Learned Socs., 1983-84. Editor: James Russell Lowell's The Biglow Papers: A Critical Edition, 1977, Letters of W. D. Howells, vol. 4, 1892-1901, 1983, The Early Prose Writings of William Dean Howells, 1853-1861, 1990; asst. editor Nineteenth-Century Fiction, 1971-75, mem. adv. bd., 1976-83, co-editor, 1983-86; co-editor Nineteenth-Century Literature, 1986-95, editor, 1995—. Regent's faculty fellow in the humanities U. Calif., 1971; travel grantee Nat. Endowment for the Humanities, 1985-86, 88-89; grants-in-aid of rsch. Am. Philos. Soc., 1976, 81. Mem. Modern Lan. Assn. of Am. (Norman Foerster prize com. of Am. Lit. sect. 1973, chmn. Pacific coast region, com. on manuscript holdings of Am. Lit. sect. 1972-78, mem. Hubbell prize com. of Am. Lit. sect. 1989-91), Am. Studies Assn., Ralph Waldo Emerson Soc. (bd. dirs. 1992-95). Republican. Episcopalian. Avocations: breeding and training Arabian horses. Office: U Calif Dept English 405 Hilgard Ave Los Angeles CA 90095

WORTHEN, JOHN A., insurance executive. From v.p. to sr. v.p. John Hancock Mut. Life Ins. Co. Office: John Hancock Mut Life Ins Co PO Box 111 Boston MA 02117-0111

WORTHEN, JOHN EDWARD, university president; b. Carbondale, Ill., July 15, 1933; s. Dewey and Annis Burr (Williams) W.; m. Sandra Damewood, Feb. 27, 1960; children: Samantha Jane, Bradley Edward. BS in Psychology (Univ. Acad. scholar), Northwestern U., 1954; MA in Student Pers. Adminstrn., Columbia U., 1955; EdD in Adminstrn. in Higher Edn. (Coll. Entrance Exam. Bd. fellow), Harvard U., 1964; PhD (hon.), Yeungnam U., Daegu, Korea, 1986. Dean of men Am. U., 1959-61; dir. counseling and testing and asst. prof. edn., 1963-66, asst. to provost and asst. prof., 1966-68, acting provost and v.p. acad. affairs, 1968, assoc. provost for instrn., 1969, v.p. student affairs, 1970-75, v.p. student affairs and adminstrn., 1976-79; pres. Ind. U. of Pa., 1979-84, Ball State U., Muncie, Ind., 1984—; cons. to public schs. Aviator USN, 1955-59. Mem. Am. Assn. Counseling and Devel., Rotary Internat., Phi Delta Kappa, Kappa Delta Pi, Ind. C. of C., Ind. Bus. Modernization and Tech. Corp.

WORTHEY, CAROL, composer; b. Worcester, Mass., Mar. 1, 1943; d. Bernard Krieger and Edith Lilian (Cramer) Symonds; m. Eugene Worthey III, June 1969 (div. 1980); 1 child, Megan; m. Raymond Edward Korns, Sept. 21, 1980. BA in Music Composition, Columbia U., 1965; grad., Dick Grove Sch. Music., L.A., 1979; grad. filmscoring prog., UCLA, 1978; music studies with Darius Milhaud, Walter Piston, Elliot Carter, Vincent Persichetti, Grant Beglarian, Karl Korte, Otto Luening, Eddy Lawrence Manson, Dick Grove; studied, RISD, 1948-54, Columbia U. 1965. Sr. composer, arranger Celebrity Ctr. Internat. Choir, Hollywood, Calif., 1985—. Composer, arranger The Hollywood Chorale; composer ballets Athena, 1963, The Barren, 1965; composer, lyricist, librettist full-length musical The Envelope Please, 1988; composer piano works performed in France, Italy, Germany, Can., U.S. and Eng. by Mario Feninger, 1982; composer Pastorale performed in Mex., 1994, Neighborhood of the Heart, 1994, (choir) Unquenchable Light, 1993; composer film score The Special Visitor, 1992; compositions performed at Aspen Music Festival, 1963, Carnegie Hall, 1954, Dorothy Chandler Pavilion, 1986-89; appeared as singer-songwriter on L.A. Songwriter's Showcase, 1977; arranger Merv Griffin Show, 1981, The Night Before Christmas, L.A. Children's Theatre, 1988-91, Capistrano Valley Symphony, 1994, Very Old Merry Old Christmas, Dorothy Chandler Pavillion, 1994; author: Treasury of Holiday Magic, 1992, (poems) The Lonely Wanderer Comes Home, 1994; art work exhibited RISD, 1952, Folk and Craft Mus., L.A., 1975, 1st Internat. Art Exhibit Celebrity Ctr. Pavillion, 1992. Vol. performer various childcare ctrs., old folks homes, etc. Recipient Silver Poet award World of Poetry, 1987, 2nd place winner, 1st BarComposers and Songwriters Competition for "Fanfare for Joy & Wedding March", 1990, Golden Poet award World of Poetry, 1992. Mem. Nat. Assn. Composers, USA, Broadcast Music Inc., Nat. Acad. Songwriters, Songwriters and Composers Assn., Toastmasters Internat. Jewish. Avocations: gourmet cooking, films, macrame, creative writing, calligraphy.

WORTHING, CAROL MARIE, minister; b. Duluth, Minn., Dec. 27, 1934; d. Truman James and Helga Maria (Bolander) W.; children: Gregory Alan Beatty, Graydon Ernest Beatty. BS, U. Minn., 1965; Master of Divinity, Northwestern Theol. Seminary, 1982; D of Ministry, Grad. Theol. Found., Notre Dame, Ind., 1988; MBA in Ch. Mgmt., Grad. Theol. Found., Donaldson, Ind., 1993. Secondary educator Ind. (Minn.) Sch. Dist., 1965-78; teaching fellow U. Minn., 1968-70; contract counselor Luth. Social Svc., Duluth, 1976-78; media cons. Luth. Media Svcs., St. Paul, 1978-80; asst. pastor Messiah Luth. Ch., Fargo, N.D., 1982-83; vice pastor Messiah Luth. Ch., Fargo, 1983-84; assoc. editor Luth. Ch. Am. Ptnrs., Phila., 1982-84; editorial assoc. Luth. Ptnrs. Evang. Luth. Ch. Am., Phila. and Mpls., 1984—; parish pastor Resurrection Luth. Ch., Pierre, S.D., 1984-89; assoc. pastor Bethlehem Luth. Ch., Cedar Falls, Iowa, 1989-90; exec. dir. Ill. Conf. Chs., Springfield, 1990—; mem. dept. rels. and interpretation com. Red River Valley Synod, Fargo, 1984-86, mem. ch. devel., Pierre, 1986-87; mem. mgmt. com. office comm. Luth. Ch. in Am., N.Y.C., Phila., 1984-88; mem. mission ptnrs. S.D. Synod, 1988, chmn. assembly resolutions com., 1988; mem. pre-assembly planning com., ecumenics com., chmn. resolutions com. N.E. Iowa Synod, 1989-90; mem. ch. and society com., 1990—; ecumenical com., 1995—; Luth. Ecumenical Rep. Network, 1995—; Cen. and So. Ill. Synod., nat. edn. cons. Am. Luth. Inst., Washington, 1967-70; chaplain state legis. bodies, Pierre, 1984-89. Author: Cinematics and English, 1967, Peer Counseling, 1977, Tischrede Lexegete, 1986, 88, 90, Way of the Cross, Way of Justice Walk, 1987, Introducing Collaboration as a Leadership Stance and Style in an Established Statewide Conference of Churches, 1993. Co-facilitator Parents of Retarded Children, 1985; bd. dirs. Countryside Hospice, 1985; cons. to adminstrv. bd. Mo. Shores Women's Ctr., 1986. Mem. Nat. Assn. Ecumenical Staff (chair of site selection com. 1991-92, chair of scholarship com. 1993-94, mem. profl. devel. com. 1993-94, program planning com. 1995, bd. mem. 1995—), Pierre-Ft. Pierre Ministerium (v.p. 1986-87, pres. 1987-88), NAFE. Democrat. Avocations: writing prose and poetry, concerts, theater, art, photography. Home: 1520 Seven Pines Rd Apt J Springfield IL 62704-6617 Office: Ill Conf Churches 615 S 5th St Springfield IL 62703-1604 *Ecumenism, I believe, about convergence, not consensus. The Spirit of God calls the church to come together for a compassionate purpose: to respond to all who suffer, so that the world might be transformed into God's own vision of peace, justice, and love.*

WORTHINGTON, GEORGE RHODES, naval officer; b. Louisville, July 11, 1937; s. William Bowman and Elizabeth (Frost) W.; m. Sydna Anne Alexander, Mar. 28, 1981 (div. Oct. 1990); children: Rhodes Ballard, Graham Rankins, Greer Anne. BS, U.S. Naval Acad., 1961; postgrad., USMC, Quantico, Va., 1975-76, Nat. War Coll., 1978-79. Commd. ensign USN, 1961, advanced through grades to rear adm., 1989; communications officer USS Halsey Powell USN, San Diego, 1961-63, flag lt., aide comdr. cruiser-destroyer Flotilla Seven, 1963-65; exec. officer Underwater Demolition Team Eleven USN, Coronado, Calif., 1965-68; ops. officer USS Strong USN, Charleston, S.C., 1969-71; exec. officer Naval Spl. Warfare Group USN, Saigon, Vietnam, 1971-72; comdg. officer Seal Team One USN, Coronado, 1972-74; naval attache Def. Attache Office USN, Phnom Penh, Cambodia, 1974-75; comdg. officer Undersea Warfare Group One USN, Coronado, 1976-78; program sponsor Office of Chief of Naval Ops. USN, Washington, 1979-85; comdr. Naval Spl. Warfare Group One USN, Coronado, 1985-87; chief of staff Spl. Ops. Command Europe USN, Stuttgart, Fed. Republic Germany, 1987-88; dep. asst. sec. of def. (spl. ops.) Def. Dept., Washington, 1988-89; comdr. Naval Spl. Warfare Command, Coronado, 1989-92; mktg. agent, cons. PIDEAC Inc., Coronado, 1992—; cons. IFG Ltd., Vantage Systems, Inc., Burdeshaw Assoc., Inc., Spec Ops Expo, Fayetteville, N.C. Decorated D.S.M., Legion of Merit (2), Def. Superior Svc. medal, Meritorious Svc. medal, Navy Combat Action ribbon. Mem. Mayflower Soc. D.C., Naval Acad. Alumni Assn., Naval Inst., Navy League San Diego MILMEC, Army-Navy Club, Army-Navy Country Club. Republican. Episcopalian. Avocations: masters swimming, skiing. Address: Adella Ave # 4 Coronado CA 92118

WORTHINGTON, JANET EVANS, academic director, English language educator; b. Springfield, Ill., Jan. 30, 1942; d. Orville Ray and Helen May (Tuxhorn) Evans; m. Gary H. Worthington; children: Rachael Allene, Evan Edmund, Adam Nicholas Karl. Student, Blackburn Coll., 1960-62; BA in English Lang. and Lit., U. Chgo., 1965; MA in English, U. Iowa, 1969; PhD in English Edn., Fla. State U., 1977; postgrad., W. Va. Inst. Tech., 1981-82, Rensselaer Poly. Inst., 1984. Teaching. fellow Fla. State U., Tallahassee, 1971-72, grad. assistant, 1972-73; coord. lang. arts rsch. Piedmont Schs. Project, Greer, S.C., 1973-76; English instr. Woodrow Wilson High Sch., Beckley, W.Va., 1976-77; Reading specialist, adj. instr. in English W. Va. Inst. Tech., Montgomery, W.Va., 1977-78; asst. prof. W.Va. Inst. Tech., Montgomery, 1979-82, assoc. prof., 1983-87, prof. English, 1987-88; dir. W.Va. Inst. Tech., Oak Hill, 1988-90; tech. writing program coord. Community and Tech. Coll. W.Va. Inst. Tech., Montgomery, 1983-88; dir. continuing edn. Nicholls State U., Thibodaux, La., 1990—; tech. writing cons., various bus., 1986—; Dept. of Mines, State of W.Va., 1980-81; reading cons. Dept of Mines, 1980-81, Mt. Hope (W.Va.) High Sch., 1980-81, Reading Tchrs. Study Group, Kanawha County, W.Va., 1981-83; project mgr. Dept. of Mines, State of W.Va., 1981-83, Dept. of Nat. Resources, State of W.Va., 1984-85; involved in curriculum devel. for various depts., W.Va. Inst. Tech., 1973-90, Raleigh County Schs., Beckley, W.Va., Piedmont Schs. Project, Greer, S.C., English and reading instr. Upward Bound Program, W.Va. Inst. Tech., 1980-85; adj. instr. W.Va. Coll. Grad. Studies, 1979, 81, 83. Author (with William Burns): Practical Robotics: Systems, Interfacing, and Applications, 1986, (with A.B. Somers): Candles and Mirrors: Response Guides for Teaching Novels and Plays in Grades Six through Twelve, 1984, Response Guides for Teaching Children's Books, 1979; editorial bd.: W.Va. Community Coll. Jour.; reviewer: Macmillan Pub. Co. texts, 1985; editor: Diamond Shamrock, 1985; co-producer, host (TV series): About the Author; contbr. numerous articles to profl. jours.; participated in numerous presentations. Mem. W.Va. Community Coll. Assn.; bd.dirs., Curtain Callers, 1979-89, Fayette Fine Arts Coun., 1986-87; promotions chair, W.Va. Children's Book award com., 1984-85. Mem. AAUW (recording sec. 1983-85, pres. 1985—), Assn. for Tchrs. of Tech. Writing, Nat. Assn. for Devel. Edn., Soc. for Tech. Comm. Home: 112 E Garden Dr Thibodaux LA 70301-3750 Office: Nicholls State U Continuing Edn PO Box 2011 Thibodaux LA 70310

WORTHINGTON, JOHN RICE, communications company executive, lawyer; b. 1930; married. BA, U. Mich., 1952, MBA, 1954, JD, 1955. With Jenner & Block, 1955-71; sec. gen. counsel MCI Communications Corp., Washington, 1971-75, v.p. sec. gen. counsel, 1975-79, sr. v.p. gen. counsel, 1979—, also bd. dirs. Office: MCI Comm Corp 1801 Pennsylvania Ave NW Washington DC 20036-3695

WORTHINGTON, MELVIN LEROY, minister, writer; b. Greenville, N.C., June 17, 1937; s. Wilbur Leroy and Alma Lee (Braxton) W.; m. Anne Katherine Wilson, Sept. 12, 1959; children: Daniel Edward, Lydia Anne. Diploma, Imperial Detective Acad., Cin., 1965; B.Bibl.Edn., Columbia Bible Coll., S.C., 1959; B.Th., Luther Rice Sem., Jacksonville, Fla., 1967, B.Div., 1969, M.Th., 1970, D.Th., 1974; M.Ed., Ga. State U.-Atlanta, 1979. Ordained to ministry, Central Conf. Free Will Baptists, 1957. Pastor Union Chapel Free Will Bapt. Ch., Chocowinity, N.C., 1959-62, Palmetto Free Will Bapt. Ch., Vanceboro, N.C., 1959-62, First Free Will Bapt. Ch., Darlington, S.C., 1962-66, Wesconnett Free Will Bapt. Ch., Jacksonville, Fla., 1967; pastor First Free Will Bapt. Ch., Amory, Miss., 1967-72, Albany, Ga., 1972-79; exec. sec. Nat. Assn. Free Will Bapt., Inc., Nashville, 1979—, chmn. Sunday Sch. bd., 1975-77, asst. moderator, 1977-79, chmn. grad. study com., 1976-77; clk. S.C. State Assn. Free Will Bapt., Florence, 1966-67; asst. moderator Ga. State Assn. Free Will Bapt., Moultrie, 1973-74, moderator, 1975-79; pres. Ga. Bible Inst., Albany, 1978. Editor in chief: Contact mag., 1979—, author editorial, 1980—; contbr. articles to profl. jours. Adv. bd. Nat. Fedn. Decency, 1985; nat. bd. dirs. Christian Leaders for Responsible TV, 1986. Mem. Evang. Press Assn., Religious Conf. Mgmt. Assn. (dir. 1983, v.p. 1986, pres. 1989-92), Nashville C. of C., Future Farmers Am. (N.C. Farmer degree 1955, Am. Farmer degree 1957). Democrat. Home: 3308 Timber Trail Dr Antioch TN 37013-1011 Office: Nat Assn Free Will Bapt Inc 5233 Mount View Rd Antioch TN 37013-2306 *The basic principle which has guided, governed and guarded my life has been a burning desire to find, follow and finish the will of God.*

WORTHLEY, HAROLD FIELD, minister, educator; b. Brewer, Maine, Nov. 3, 1928; s. Herbert Morrison and Aline May (Field) W.; m. Barbara Louise Bent, June 25, 1955; children—Susan Louise Rieksts, Laura May, David Bruce. A.B., Boston U., 1950, M.A., 1951; S.T.B., Harvard Div. Sch., 1954, S.T.M., 1956, Th.D., 1970. Ordained to ministry United Ch. of Christ, 1954. Minister Congl. chs., Maine, N.H., Mass., 1951-62; assoc. prof. religion and chaplain Wheaton Coll., Norton, Mass., 1963-77; exec. sec., archivist Congl. Christian Hist. Soc., Boston, 1971—; librarian Congl. Library, Boston, 1977—; editor Bull. of Congl. Library, 1976—, Hist. Intelligencer, 1980-86. Author: Inventory of the Records of the Particular Churches of Massachusetts, 1620-1805, 1970; contbr. articles to profl. jours. Fellow Pilgrim Soc.; Congl. Christian Hist. Soc.; mem. United Ch. of Christ Hist. Council. Home: 14 Mansfield Ave Norton MA 02766-2212 Office: The Congregational Libr 14 Beacon St Boston MA 02108-3704

WORTHY, JAMES AGER, former professional basketball player; b. Gastonia, N.C., Feb. 27, 1961; m. Angela Worthy. Grad., U. N.C., 1985. Basketball player L.A. Lakers, 1982-94. Named to Sporting News All-Am. First Team, 1982; named MVP, NCAA Divsn. I Tournament, 1982, MVP, NBA playoffs, 1988, mem. All-Star team, 1986-92; mem. NCAA Divsn. I Championship Team, 1982, NBA All-Rookie Team, 1983. Mem. NBA Championship Teams, 1985, 87, 88. Office: LA Lakers Great Western Forum 3900 W Manchester Blvd Inglewood CA 90306*

WORTHY, JAMES CARSON, educator; b. Midland, Tex., Jan. 8, 1910; s. James Arthur and Minnie (Gressett) W.; m. Mildred Leritz, June 20, 1934; 1

dau., Joan (Mrs. Robert Wood Tullis). Student, Northwestern U., 1929-33; AB, Lake Forest Coll., 1952, LLD (hon.), 1961; LLD, Chgo. Theol. Sem., 1960; LittD (hon.), Sangamon State U., 1991. Employment mgr. Schuster & Co., Milw., 1936-38; mem. personnel staff Sears, Roebuck & Co., Chgo., 1938-50; dir. employee relations Sears, Roebuck & Co., 1950-53, asst. to chmn. bd., 1955, vice pres. pub. relations, 1956-61; v.p. Cresap, McCormick & Paget, 1962-72; prof. Sangamon State U., Springfield, Ill., 1972-78, J.L. Kellogg Grad. Sch. Mgmt. Northwestern U., Evanston, Ill., 1978—; asst. dep. adminstr. NRA, Washington, 1933-36; asst. sec. commerce, 1953-55; Industry mem. spl. panel WSB, 1952; mem. President's Com. on Govt. Contracts, 1953-55, President's Commn. on Campaign Costs, 1961-62; Mem. Ill. Bd. of Higher Edn., 1967-69. Bd. dirs. Nat. Merit Scholarship Corp., 1958-63; mem. exec. bd. Indsl. Relations Research Assn., 1952-54; pres. Sears-Roebuck Found., 1956-61; trustee Latin Sch. Chgo., 1968-72, Chgo. Theol. Sem., 1953-73; dir. Selected Am. Shares, 1961-79,Comml. Credit Co., 1975-81, Control Data Corp., 1979-87, William C. Norris Inst., 1987—; cochmn. Ill. Citizens for Eisenhower-Nixon, 1952; v.p. United Rep. Fund of Ill., 1955-59, pres., 1959-60, exec. com., 1961-72; mem. Nat. Rep. Finance Com., 1958-60; del. Rep. Nat. Conv., 1960; pres. Republican Citizens League Ill., 1961-62. Fellow Acad. Mgmt. (Dean of Fellows 1987-90), Internat. Acad. Mgmt. Congregationalist. Clubs: Commercial, Chicago, University (Chgo.); Indian Hill (Winnetka, Ill.). Home: 23 Calvin Cir Evanston IL 60201-1911 Office: Northwestern U JL Kellogg Grad Sch Mgmt Evanston IL 60201

WORTHY, K(ENNETH) MARTIN, lawyer; b. Dawson, Ga., Sept. 24, 1920; s. Kenneth Spencer and Jeffrie Pruett (Martin) W.; m. Eleanor Vreeland Blewett, Feb. 15, 1947 (dec. July 1981); children: Jeffrie Martin, William Blewett; m. Katherine Teasley Jackson, June 17, 1983. Student, The Citadel, 1937-39; B.Ph., Emory U., 1941, J.D. with honors, 1947; MBA cum laude, Harvard U., 1943. Bar: Ga. 1947, D.C. 1948. Assoc. Hopkins & Sutter (formerly Hamel & Park), Washington, 1948-51, ptnr., 1952-69, 72-90, sr. counsel, 1991—; asst. gen. counsel Treasury Dept., 1969-72; chief counsel IRS, 1969-72; dir. Beneficial Corp., 1977—; mem. Nat. Council Organized Crime, 1970-72; cons. Justice Dept., 1972-74. Author: (with John M. Appleman) Basic Estate Planning, 1957; contbr. articles to profl. jours. Del. Montgomery County Civic Fedn., 1951-61, D.C. Area Health and Welfare Coun., 1960-61; mem. Emory Law Sch. Coun., 1976—, chmn., 1993—; trustee Chelsea Sch., 1981—; trustee St. John's Coll., Annapolis, Md. and Santa Fe, 1987-93; trustee Sherman Found., Newport Beach, Calif., 1991—; chmn. dept. fin. Episc. Diocese, Washington, 1969-70; fellow Aspen Inst., 1982-92. Capt. AUS, 1943-46, 51-52. Recipient Treasury Exceptional Service award and medal, 1972, IRS Commrs. award, 1972, Disting. Alumnus award Emory U., 1992. Fellow Am. Bar Found., Am. Coll. Tax Counsel (bd. regents 1980-88, chmn. 1985-87), Atlantic Coun. (counselor); mem. ABA (coun. taxation sect. 1965-69, 72-75, chmn. 1973-74, del. Nat. Conf. Lawyers and CPAs 1981-87, ho. of dels. 1983-89, chmn. audit com. 1985-90), Fed. Bar Assn. (nat. coun. 1969-72, 77-79), Ga. Bar Assn., D.C. Bar, Am. Law Inst., Nat. Tax Assn., Am. Tax Policy Inst. (trustee 1989—), Chevy Chase Club, Met. Club, Sea Island Club, Harvard Club, Phi Delta Theta, Phi Delta Phi, Omicron Delta Kappa. Home: PO Box 30264 189 W Gascoigne Ave Sea Island GA 31561 also: 604 Somerset House II 5610 Wisconsin Ave Chevy Chase MD 20815 Office: Hopkins & Sutter 888 16th St NW Fl 7 Washington DC 20006-4103

WORTHY, PATRICIA MORRIS, municipal official, lawyer; b. Fort Benning, Ga., May 28, 1944; d. Walter and Ruby Mae (Lovett) Morris. AA, Queensborough Community Coll., 1964; BA, Bklyn. Coll., 1966; JD, Howard U., 1969. Bar: D.C. 1971. Trial atty. NLRB, Washington, 1969-71; dep. gen. counsel ACTION, Washington, 1971-74; assoc. Dolphin, Branton, Stafford & Webber, Washington, 1974-77; dep. asst. sec. for regulatory functions HUD, Washington, 1977-80; adj. prof. Howard U. Sch. Law, 1979-92; chmn. D.C. Pub. Service Commn., 1980-91, Occupational Safety and Health Bd., Washington, 1979-80, Washington Met. Area Transit Commn., 1980-91; chief of staff Office of Mayor Sharon Pratt Kelly, Washington, 1991-92; vis. prof. law Howard U., Washington, 1992—; bd. dirs. Anacostia Econ. Devel. Corp.; chmn. D.C. Jud. Nomination Commn.; mem. adv. bd. Afro-Am. Datanamics, Inc. Bd. dirs. Nat. Black Child Devel. Inst., 1975-80; trustee WETA-TV Channel 26. Mem. ABA, Nat. Conf. Black Lawyers, Nat. Conf. Bar Examiners (multistate profl. responsibility com. 1986-89), World Peace Through Law (chairperson young lawyers sect. 1973-75). Office: Howard U Sch Law Van Ness & Connecticut Ave NW Washington DC 20001

WORTIS, AVI See AVI

WORTLEY, GEORGE CORNELIUS, business consultant, investor; b. Syracuse, N.Y., Dec. 8, 1926; s. George C. and Arlene (Hirsh) W.; m. Barbara Jane Hennessy, May 13, 1950; children: George C. IV, Ann Wortley Lavin, Elizabeth Wortley Ring. B.S., Syracuse U., 1948. Newspaper pub., pres. Manlius Pub. Corp., Fayetteville, N.Y., 1950-92; pres. Nat. Editorial Found., 1968-73; mem. 97th-100th Congresses from 27th N.Y. Dist., 1981-89, mem. Banking, Fin. and Urban Affairs com., mem. Select Com. on Aging, Select Com. on Children, Youth and Family; pvt. bus. cons., investor Washington, 1989—; Sunrise Holdings, Inc., Washington, 1993—; pres. Am. Newspapers Reps., 1966-68. Pres. Hiawatha council Boy Scouts Am., 1972-75; mem. Nat. Commn. on Hist. Publs. and Records, 1977-80, Fayetteville Sr. Citizen Housing Commn., 1977-80; mem. allocations com. United Way of Central N.Y., 1979-81; mem. public relations com. St. Camillus Health Care Center, 1971-78; mem. fed. legis. com. Am. Lung Assn., 1974-77; bd. dirs. Crouse-Irving Meml. Hosp. Found., 1975-87, pres., 1979-81; bd. dirs. Am. Heart Assn., N.Y., 1960-80, chmn. public relations com., 1970-74, chmn. legis. com., 1977, mem. fund raising adv. com., 1974-79; trustee Cazenovia Coll., 1981-94; bd. dirs. Onondaga Hist. Assn., 1980-89; dir. Global Econ. Action Inst., 1987—. Served with MMR, USNR, World War II. Recipient Silver Beaver award Boy Scouts Am., 1973, Silver Antelope award, 1981. Mem. Nat. Newspaper Assn. (legis. com. 1976-80), Greater Syracuse C. of C. (dir. 1979-81), Upstate Coun. Indsl. Editors, LeMoyne Coll. Pres.'s Assocs., Syracuse U. Alumni Assn. (nat. treas. 1973-77), Chavaliers du Testavin, Cosmos Club, Century Club, Georgetown Club, Lions, KC, Kappa Sigma (pres. 1957-59). Republican. Roman Catholic. Office: 1350 I St NW Ste 200 Washington DC 20005-3305

WORTMAN, RICHARD S., historian, educator; b. N.Y.C., Mar. 24, 1938; s. Joseph R. and Ruth (Nacht) W.; m. Marlene Stein, June 14, 1960; 1 child, Leonie. B.A., Cornell U., 1958; M.A., U. Chgo., 1960, Ph.D., 1964. Instr. history U. Chgo., 1963-64, asst. prof., 1964-69, assoc. prof., 1969-76, prof., 1976-77; prof. history Princeton U., 1977-88, dir. Russian studies, 1982-88; prof. history Columbia U., 1988—; trustee Nat. Council for Soviet and Eastern European Research, 1983-89; sr. fellow Harriman Inst., 1985-86. Author: The Crisis of Russian Populism, 1967, The Development of a Russian Legal Consciousness, 1976, (with Leopold Haimson and Ziva Galilii) The Making of Three Russian Revolutionaries: Voices from the Menshevik Past, 1987, Scenarios of Power: Myth and Ceremony in Russian Monarchy, vol. I, 1995. Social Sci. Research Council grantee, 1975-76; Guggenheim fellow, 1981-82. Mem. Am. Assn. Advancement Slavic Studies (pres. Mid-Atlantic Slavic Conf. 1982-83), AAUP., Am. Hist. Assn. Home: 410 Riverside Dr Apt 91 New York NY 10025-7924

WORTON, RONALD GIBERT, geneticist, educator; b. Winnipeg, Man., Can., Apr. 2, 1942; s. William Keller and Winnifred Pitt (Barber) W.; m. Helen Margaret Dixon, June 4, 1966; 1 child, Scott Robert. BS with honors, U. Man., 1964, MS, 1965; PhD, U. Toronto, 1969; Doctorate honoris causa, U de Louvain, Belgium, 1991. Asst. prof. U. Toronto, 1973-80, assoc. prof., 1980-84, prof., 1985—; staff geneticist, Hosp. for Sick Children, Toronto, 1971-85, sr. scientist rsch. inst., 1984—, geneticist-in-chief, 1985—. Contbr. articles to profl. jours.; patentee in field. Decorated Order of Can.; recipient internat. award Gairdner Found., 1989, award of distinction Muscular Dystrophy Assn. Can., 1989, Mead Johnson award, 1991. Fellow Royal Soc. Can. (Centenary medal 1990), Can. Coll. Med. Geneticists (bd. dirs. 1980-85), Am. Soc. Human Genetics (chmn. program com. 1984-87, bd. dirs. 1988-91), Genetics Soc. Can., Can. Soc. for Cell Biology. Avocations: skiing, curling. Home: 23 Budgell Terr, Toronto, ON Canada M6S 1B3 Office: Genetics Dept. 555 University Ave, Toronto, ON Canada M5G 1X8

WORTZEL, LAWRENCE HERBERT, marketing educator; b. Newark, Sept. 28, 1932; s. Charles and Sadie (Bornstein) W.; m. Heidi Pamela

Vernon, Dec. 23, 1956; children: Joshua Charles, Jennifer Rachel. BS, Rutgers U., 1954; MBA with distinction, Harvard U., 1963, D.B.A., 1967. Ptnr., owner two pharmacies N.J., 1957-61; rsch. asst., then rsch. assoc. Harvard U., 1963-65; mem. faculty Boston U., 1965—, prof. mktg., 1969—, chmn. dept., 1968-72, 73-75; faculty assoc. Mgmt. Analysis Ctr. Group/ Gemini, 1978—; faculty assoc. in residence Mgmt. Analysis Ctr., 1982-83, 89-90; vis. rsch. prof. Mktg. Sci. Inst., 1976; cons. World Bank, 1976—, Inst. for Internat. Econ. Mgmt., Beijing and Shanghai, People's Republic of China, 1981—; sr. faculty mem. Prasetiya Mulya Grad. Sch. Bus., Jakarta, Indonesia, 1994—. Co-author: The Development of Financial Managers, 1971; co-editor: Marketing to the Changing Household, 1984, Strategic Managment of Multinational Corporations: The Essentials, 1984, Global Strategic Management: The Essentials, 1991. Bd. dirs. Boston Concert Opera Assn., 1981-87; pres. Boston U. Hillel Found., 1985-87. Served with U.S. Army, 1956-57. Mem. Am. Mktg. Assn., Assn. Consumer Rsch. Acad., Acad. Internat. Bus., Am. Econ. Assn., Strategic Mgmt. Soc., Acad. Mgmt. Jewish. Home: 39 Stafford Rd Newton MA 02159-1818 Office: 704 Commonwealth Ave Boston MA 02215-2404 *We are responsible for our own successes and our own failures. There's no mysterious 'they' out there who are keeping us from success or causing us to fail.*

WORZALA, FRANK JOHN, metallurgical engineering educator and researcher; b. Milw., Nov. 13, 1933; married 1954; 9 children. BS, U. Wis., 1956, MS, 1958; MS, Carnegie Inst. Tech., 1962, PhD in Metall. Engring., 1965. Engr. Hanford Labs., GE Co., Wash., 1956-57; engr. Bettis Atomic Power Lab., Westinghouse Electric Corp., 1958-65, rsch. scientist, 1966-67; assoc. prof. nuclear materials U. Wis., Madison, 1967-77, prof. metall. engring. & mining engring., 1977—; NSF fellow, rsch. scientist Grenoble Nuclear Rsch. Ctr., France, 1965-66. Mem. Am. Nuclear Soc., Am. Inst. Mining, Metall. and Petrol Engrs., Am. Soc. Metals. Achievements include research in nuclear materials, irradiation damage in metals, fracture mechanics, applied superconductivity and superconducting materials. Office: U Wis Madison Dept Metallurgy 222 Minerals & Metals 1505 University Ave Madison WI 53706-1512*

WORZEL, JOHN LAMAR, geophysicist, educator; b. West Brighton, S.I., N.Y., Feb. 21, 1919; s. Howard Henry and Marie Alma (Wilson) W.; m. Dorothy Crary, Nov. 22, 1941; children: Sandra, Howard, Richard, William P. B.S. in Engring. Physics, Lehigh U., 1940; M.A. in Geophysics (grad. resident scholar), Columbia U., 1948, Ph.D., 1949. Research assoc. Woods Hole (Mass.) Oceanographic Inst., 1940-46; geodesist Columbia U., N.Y.C., 1946-48; research assoc. Columbia U., 1948-49, instr. geology, 1949, asst. prof., 1950-52, assoc. prof., 1952-57, prof., 1957-72; asst. dir. Lamont Geol. Obs., Palisades, N.Y., 1951-64; acting dir. Lamont Geol. Obs., 1964-65, assoc. dir., 1965-72; prof., dep. dir. earth and planetary scis. div. Marine Biomed. Inst., U. Tex. Med. Br., Galveston, 1972-74; acting dir. geophys. lab. Marine Sci. Inst., 1974-75, dir. geophys. lab., 1975-79; also prof. geol. sci. dept. U. Tex. at Austin, 1972-79; adj. prof. Rice U., 1974-78; ret., 1979; Bd. dirs. Palisades Geophys. Inst., 1970—, treas., 1970-74, pres., 1974—. Bd. dirs. Rockland County council Boy Scouts Am., 1964-72. Recipient USN Meritorious Pub. Service citation Dept. of Navy, 1964; Guggenheim Found. fellow, 1963. Fellow Internat. Assn. Geodesy, Am. Geophys. Union, Geol. Soc. Am.; mem. Am. Assn. Petroleum Geologists, Soc. Exploration Geophysicists (chmn. com. 1974-76, v.p. 1978-79), Pi Mu Epsilon, Tau Beta Pi. Republican. Lutheran. Research on gravity and seismic refraction and reflection at sea, sound transmission of sea water. Home: Apt A-308 8117 Blue Heyon Dr E Wilmington NC 28405

WÖSSNER, MARK MATTHIAS, business executive; b. Berlin, Oct. 14, 1938; m. Anna Hvastija, Mar. 30, 1991. Dr. Ing., Tech. U., Stuttgart, Germany, 1968. Mgmt. asst. Bertelsmann, Gütersloh, Germany, 1968; with tech. works mgmt. Bertelsmann/Mohndruck, Gütersloh, Germany, 1970, tech. dir., 1972, gen. mgr., 1974; exec. mem. Bertelsmann, Gütersloh, 1976, bd. dir., dep. chmn., 1981, pres., chief exec. officer, 1983. Office: Bertelsmann AG, Postfach 111, 33311 Gütersloh Germany

WOSZCZYK, WIESLAW RICHARD, audio engineering educator, researcher; b. Czestochowa, Poland, Jan. 9, 1951; arrived in Can., 1974; s. Waclaw Konstanty and Krystyna Maria (Malek) W.; m. Trudy Elizabeth Erickson, Dec. 28, 1978; children: Jake, Magda. MA, State Acad. Music, Warsaw, Poland, 1974; PhD, Chopin Acad., Warsaw, 1984. Rsch. asst. McGill U., Montreal, Can., 1974-75; recording engineer Basement Recording Co. Inc., N.Y.C., 1975-76; sound dir. Harry Belafonte Enterprises Inc., N.Y.C., 1977; chief engr. Big Apple Recording Studios, N.Y.C., 1976-78; asst. prof. McGill U., Montreal, 1978-84, chmn. grad. studies in sound recording, 1979—, assoc. prof., 1984-91, full prof., 1991—; tech. dir. McGill Records, Montreal, 1987—; owner, cons. Sonologic Registered, Montreal, 1988—; chmn. internat. conf. TV Sound Today and Tomorrow, 1991; vis. prof. Bang and Olufsen A/S, Denmark, 1994. Recording engr. over 50 records and films, 1975-85; prodr. over 30 compact discs, 1985—; mem. rev. bd. Jour. Audio Engring., 1992; contbr. articles to profl. jours. Recipient Grand Prix du Disque award Can. Coun. for Arts, 1978, Bd. Govs. award Audio Engring. Soc., 1991; Major Rsch. SSHRC grantee Rsch. Coun. Can., 1986, 93; Indsl. grantee Sony Classical, 1992, Bruel & Kjaer, 1991. Mem. Audio Engring. Soc. (gov., chmn. com. 1991—), Acoustical Soc. Am., Sigma Xi. Roman Catholic. Achievements include 3 patents on audio transducers; majro rsch. on the design and application of transducers for music recording, auditory design in sound recording, multi-channel sound recording, reproduction and audio-visual interactions. Office: McGill U Faculty Music, 555 Sherbrooke St W, Montreal, PQ Canada H3A 1E3

WOTEKI, CATHERINE ELLEN, nutritionist; b. Fort Leavenworth, Kans., Oct. 7, 1947; d. Joseph Jeremiah and Catherine (Costello) O'Connor; m. Thomas Henry Woteki, June 7, 1969. BS, Mary Washington Coll., 1969; MS, Va. Poly. Inst. and State U., 1971, PhD, 1973. Registered dietitian. Asst. prof. Drexel U., Phila., 1975-77; project dir. Congl. Office of Tech. Assessment, Washington, 1977-80; group leader USDA, Washington, 1980-83; dep. dir. Nat. Ctr. for Health Statis., Washington, 1983-90; dir. Food and Nutrition Bd., Washington, 1990-93; dep. assoc. dir. for sci. Office of Sci. and Tech. Policy, Washington, 1994—. Contbr. over 43 articles to profl. jours. Named Outstanding alumna Va. Poly. Inst. and State U., 1987; recipient Elijah White award Nat. Ctr. for Health Statis., 1987, Spl. Recognition award USPHS, 1987, Staff Achievement award Inst. of Medicine, 1991. Mem. Am. Inst. Nutrition, Am. Dietetic Assn. Coun. on Rsch., Inst. Food Technologists, Am. Pub. Health Assn. Office: Office Sci and Tech Policy 0E0B Washington DC 20500

WOTISKA, SISTER DORITA, school system administrator. Supt. schs. Diocese of Lansing, Mich. Office: Office Supt Schs 228 N Walnut St Lansing MI 48933-1577

WOTIZ, JOHN HENRY, chemist, educator; b. Moravska Ostrava, Czechoslovakia, Apr. 12, 1919; came to U.S. 1939, naturalized, 1944; s. Berthold B. and Bertha (Kauder) W.; m. Kathryn Erdody, Feb. 23, 1945; children: Anita, Karen, Vivian. Student, Czech Polytechnicum, Prague, 1937; B.S., Furman U., 1941; M.S., U. Richmond, 1943; Ph.D., Ohio State U., 1948. Instr. U. Pitts., 1948-50, asst. prof., 1950-54, assoc. prof., 1954-57; group leader research center Diamond Alkali Co., Painesville, Ohio, 1957-59; sr. group leader Diamond Alkali Co., 1959-62; prof., chmn. chemistry dept. Marshall U., Huntington, W.Va., 1962-67, So. Ill. U., Carbondale, 1967-68; prof. So. Ill. U., 1968-89, prof. emeritus, 1989—; Nat. Acad. Scis. vis. prof., USSR, 1969, Eastern Europe, 1972; vis. prof., lectr., East Asian and Pacific Ocean countries, 1974, Japan, 1982, Gt. Britain, Fed. Republic Germany, Norway, Sweden, Czechoslovakia, Poland, Hungary, 1987, Peoples Republic China, 1988, Can., India, 1990; past cons. Air Reduction Co., Watson Standard Co.; pres. Glenview Press, Carbondale, Ill. Editor: The Kekulé Riddle: A Challenge for Chemists and Psychologists, 1993. contbr. articles to profl. jours. Served with lt., Chem. Corps AUS, 1946-48. Recipient Univ. gold medal Vysoká Škola Báňská in Ostrava, Czech Republic, 1992. Mem. Am. Chem. Soc. (chmn. div. history of chemistry 1979-80, chmn. of So. Ill. Section, 1992, dir. its. Ctr. for History of Chemistry, Internat. Dexter award for outstanding contbn. to history of chemistry 1982), History of Sci. Soc., AAUP, Am. Contract Bridge League, Sigma Xi. Unitarian-Universalist. Home: 903 S Glenview Dr Carbondale IL 62901-2438

WOTMAN, STEPHEN, dentistry educator; b. N.Y.C., Aug. 5, 1931; s. Jacob Abraham and Rose (Aronson) W.; m. Joyce Ruth Greenberg (div. 1983); children: Russell (dec.), Joshua; m. Sara Dedman Rouse. Student, Franklin and Marshall Coll., 1948-51; DDS, U. Pa., 1956. Pvt. practice dentistry West Nyack, N.Y., 1959-70; rsch. asst., then instr. div. stomatology Sch. Dental and Oral Surgery, Columbia U., N.Y.C., 1962-68, asst. clin. prof. div. preventive dentistry, 1968-70, assoc. prof., 1970-81, spl. asst. to dean, 1970-74, asst. dean for adminstrn. and planning, 1974-77, coord. for dental sch. reconstruction, 1975-77, acting dir. Office of Edn. and Behavioral Scis., 1975-79; assoc. prof. dentistry in pub. health, asst. dean for acad. affairs Sch. Pub. Health, Columbia U., 1981-85, acting dean Sch. Pub. Health, acting assoc. dean faculty of medicine, 1985-86, assoc. dean. pub. health and dental and oral surgery, 1986-87; prof. community dentistry Case Western Res. U., Cleve., 1987–, dean Sch. Dentistry, 1987-88, prof. epidemiology and biostats, dir. MPH degree program, 1993–. Author: (with others) Dental Fluorosis in Diseases of the Mouth and Jaw, 1969, Diseases of the Salivary Glands, 1976, The Pennsylvania Experiment, 1985; contbr. articles to profl. jours. V.p., trustee Bd. Edn. Ramapo Cen. Sch., Spring Valley, N.Y., 1964-70; chmn. bd. trustees Rockland Country Day Sch., Congers, N.Y., 1977-79. Capt. U.S. Army, 1956-58. Recipient Meritorius Svc. award Rockland County Dental Soc., 1975; named to Pierre Fauchard Acad., 1988; grantee Nat. Inst. Dental Rsch., 1968-72, Nat. Heart and Lung Inst., NIH, 1971-75, Sch. Dental and Oral Surgery Columbia U., 1974, U. Pa., 1977, 78, Cleve. Found., 1987, 88, others. Mem. ADA, AAAS, Am. Pub. Health Assn., Ohio Dental Assn., Cleve. Dental Assn., Internat. Assn. Dental Rsch., Ohio Pub. Health Assn., Sigma Xi, Omicron Kappa Upsilon. Rsch. interest in salivary chemistry in systemic diseases such as hypertension, cystic fibrosis, also, health adminstrn. planning in acad. instns., health policy and ambulatory care. Home: 13415 Shaker Blvd Cleveland OH 44120-1548 Office: Case Western Res U Sch Dentistry Cleveland OH 44106-2624*

WOTT, JOHN ARTHUR, arboretum and botanical garden executive, horticulture educator; b. Fremont, Ohio, Apr. 10, 1939; s. Arthur Otto Louis and Esther Wilhelmina (Werth) W.; children: Christopher, Timothy, Holly. BS, Ohio State U., 1961; MS, Cornell U., 1966, PhD, 1968. Mem. staff Ohio State Coop. Extension Svc., Bowling Green, 1961-64; rsch. asst. Cornel U., Ithaca, N.Y., 1964-68; prof. Purdue U., West Lafayette, Ind., 1968-81; prof. Ctr. Urban Horticulture U. Wash., Seattle, 1981–; assoc. dir. Ctr. Urban Horticulture U. Wash., Seattle, 1990–; dir. arboreta Washington Park Arboretum, Seattle, 1993–. Contbr. numerous papers to profl. jours. Mem. Am. Soc. Horticultural Sci. (com. chmn. 1967-82), Am. Assn. Botanic Gardens and Arboreta, Internat. Plant Propagators Soc. (pres. 1984, sec.-treas. 1985–). Avocations: music, antiques. Office: U Wash Washington Park Arboretum XD-10 Seattle WA 98195

WOU, LEO S., architect, planner; b. Tianjin, Republic of China, Sept. 4, 1927; s. Henri and Irene (Chu) W.; m. Mary Fong, Apr. 15, 1955; children—Loring, Jacqui, Tia. B.Arch., U. Pa., 1950; postgrad., Yale U., 1952-54; M.Arch., UCLA, 1984. Pres. Leo S. Wou & Assoc., Inc., Honolulu, 1960, San Francisco, 1968-78; pres. Wou Internat. Inc., Houston, 1978-82; ptnr. Ross/Wou Internat., Los Angeles, 1982–; cons. Golemon & Rolfe, Houston, 1978-79, Pierce, Goodwin, Alexander, Houston, 1978-79. Prin. works include: Master Plan for downtown Honolulu, 1963, Fin. Plaza of Pacific, Hdqrs. of Castle & Cooke and Bank of Hawaii, Honolulu, 1968, Houston Internat. Airport, Terminal D., 1978, Tex. A&M Stadium, 1978, The Crystal Palace Hotel, Tianjin, People's Republic China, 1984, Long Beach (Calif.) World Trade Ctr., 1984, USN 700 sta. Weapons System Lab., Calif., 1985, UCLA Ambulatory Care Complex, Calif., 1986, 400 bed Presbyn./St. Luke's Med. Ctr., Denver, 1987, USN 550 Sta. Automatic Data Processing Ctr., Calif., 1990, Proposed 56-story Office Tower, Singapore, 1992, Proposed Master Plan for Nanyang Polytechnic U., Singapore, 1993, 36-story Tianjin News Bldg., Tianjin, China, 1994. Served with U.S. Army, 1954-56. Fellow AIA. Home: 3600 Montrose Blvd Houston TX 77006-4647 Office: RossWou Inc 2450 Broadway St Ste 650 Santa Monica CA 90404-3064

WOUCH, GERALD, materials scientist; b. Phila., Nov. 21, 1939; s. Abraham and Anna (Goloff) W.; m. Lois Lipkin, Dec. 25, 1977; 1 child, Kimberley. BS, Drexel U., 1962, PhD, 1978; MA, Temple U., 1966. Rsch. scientist GE, Phila., 1964-78, Mobil, Princeton, N.J., 1978-81; sr. rsch. scientist R.R. Donnelley & Sons Co., Chgo., 1981–. Contbr. articles to jours., Encyclopedia of Physics, 1991, chpt. to book. Mem. AIAA, ASTM (printing ink com. 1991–), Am. Chem. Soc., Am. Soc. Materials, Gravure Assn. Am., Am. Inst. Met. Engring., Fed. Soc. Coatings Tech., Met. Soc., Tech. Assn. Pulp and Paper Industry. Achievements include 6 patents; research in containerless processing of materials, crystal growth, thermodynamic properties of metals, materials processing, printing materials, inks, papers, fountain solutions, gravure cylinder engraving, others. Home: 634 Aster Ct Lisle IL 60532 Office: R R Donnelley & Sons Co 750 Warrenville Rd Lisle IL 60532

WOUK, HERMAN, writer; b. N.Y.C., May 27, 1915; s. Abraham Isaac and Esther (Levine) W.; m. Betty Sarah Brown, Dec. 9, 1945; children: Abraham Isaac (dec.), Nathaniel, Joseph. AB with gen. honors, Columbia U., 1934; LHD (hon.), Yeshiva U., 1954; LLD (hon.), Clark U., 1960; LittD (hon.), Am. Internat. Coll., 1979; PhD (hon.), Bar-Ilan U., 1990. Writer radio programs for various comedians N.Y.C., 1935; asst. writer weekly radio scripts comedian Fred Allen, 1936-41; Presdl. cons. to U.S. Treasury, 1941; vis. prof. English Yeshiva U., 1952-57; scholar-in-residence Aspen Inst. Humanistic Studies, 1973-74. Author: novels: Aurora Dawn, 1947, The City Boy, 1948, Slattery's Hurricane, 1949, The Caine Mutiny, 1951 (Pulitzer Prize award for fiction 1952), Marjorie Morningstar, 1955, Youngblood Hawke, 1962, Don't Stop the Carnival, 1965, The Winds of War, 1971, War and Remembrance, 1978, Inside, Outside, 1985 (Washingtonian Book award 1986), The Hope, 1993, The Glory, 1994; dramas: The Traitor, 1949, The Caine Mutiny Court-Martial, 1953; comedy: Nature's Way, 1957; non-fiction: This is My God, 1959; screenplays for TV serials: The Winds of War, 1983, War and Remembrance, 1986. Trustee Coll. of V.I., 1961-69; bd. dirs. Washington Nat. Symphony, 1969-71, Kennedy Ctr. Prodns., 1974-75. Exec. officer U.S.S. Southard USNR, 1942-46, PTO. Recipient Richard H. Fox prize, 1934, Columbia U. medal for Excellence, 1952, Alexander Hamilton medal, 1980, U. Calif.-Berkeley medal, 1984, Golden Plate award Am. Acad. Achievement, 1986, USN Meml. Found. 'Lone Sailor' award, 1987, Yad Vashem KaZetnik award, 1990. Mem. Naval Res. Assn., Dramatists Guild, Authors Guild, Internat. Platform Assn. (Ralph Waldo Emerson award 1981), PEN. Jewish. Clubs: Bohemian (San Francisco); Cosmos, Metropolitan (Washington); Century Assn. (N.Y.C.). Office: care BSW Literary Agy 3255 N St NW Washington DC 20007-2845

WOURMS, MARK KENNETH, zoological park director; m. Patricia Johnson. BS in Biology, Ohio U., 1979; cert. in bus. adminstrn., NYU, 1986; PhD in Ecology and Animal Behavior, Boston U., 1985. Teaching fellow, mgr. biology dept. greenhouse program Boston U., 1980-84; prof. genetics crop improvement Nat. U. Benin, West Africa, 1984-85; asst. dir. exhibits and graphics N.Y. Zool. Soc., 1986-91, assoc. dir. exhibits and graphics, 1991-92; dir. Kansas City (Mo.) Zool. Gardens, 1992–; project coord. World of Birds Renovation, Propagation II, Plant Nursery-Browse Prdn. Ctr., Energy Efficient Greenhouse and zoo-wide safety improvements; fundraiser, lectr., tour guide Great Gorilla Forest, Pierrepont Wildfowl Marsh, N.Y. Zool. Soc. Ann. Meeting and City Reps. dinner; com. mem. long range planning of vis. svcs., zoo ops. and exhibits; mem. Mission Evaluation Com.; cons. Montreal Biodome Project, 1989, Tropical Bldg. at Franklin Park Zoo, 1988; horticulture cons. Tropical Bldg. at Franklin Park Zoo, 1988; panel mem. environ. planning N.Y.C. Parks and Recreation Dept., 1989; value engring. study team Nat. Aquarium, 1989; tchr. edn. programs N.Y. Zool. Soc., 1991; exhibits design and prodn. coord., Ethiopian Baboon Reserve, Pierrepont Wildfowl Marsh, Northern Ponds, Reptile House; tchr., lectr. in field. Contbr. articles on zoology, horticulture and plant-animal interactions to profl. jours and procs.; editor guides and manuscripts Barrons Edn. Series, Inc., 1987–. Tour leader Ecol. Tour of Belize, 1991; judge N.Y. Acad. Scis. Sci. Fair, Bronx, N.Y., 1990, 91, N.Y. Flower Show, N.Y.C., 1991. Recipient Best Grad. Presentation award Am. Orthithologists Union Conf., N.Y. Mem. Am. Assn. Zool. Parks and Aquariums (participant regional confs. 1987, 91), Assn. Zool. Horticulture (presenter confs. 1987, 88, 89, 90), Soc. for Ecol. Restoration, Nat. Trust for

Hist. Preservation. Office: Kansas City Zool Garden 6700 Zoo Dr Kansas City MO 64132-4200

WOVSANIKER, ALAN, lawyer; b. Newark, Mar. 19, 1953; s. Harold and Sally (Gooen) W.; m. Susan Orme, Aug. 23, 1987. AB, Brown U., 1974; JD, Harvard U., 1977. Bar: N.J. 1977. Law clk. to presiding judge U.S. Dist. Ct. N.J., Camden, 1977-78; ptnr. Lowenstein, Sandler, Kohl, Fisher & Boylan, Roseland, N.J., 1978–; adj. prof. law Seton Hall Law Sch., 1988–, Rutgers Law Sch., 1989–;mem. Supreme Ct. Dist. Ethics Com. Contbr. articles to profl. jours. Mem. exec. com. N.J. chpt. Anti-Defamation League. Mem. Essex County Bar Assn. (chair banking law com. 1994-95). Office: Lowenstein Sandler Kohl Fisher & Boylan 65 Livingston Ave Roseland NJ 07068-1725

WOWCHUK, ROSANN, provincial legislator; b. Swan River, Man., Can., Aug. 15, 1945; d. Wasyl and Mary (Pilipchuk) Harapiak; m. Silvestor Wowchuk, June 5, 1965; children: Kimberlie, Pamela, Michael. Cert. in teaching, Man. Tchr.'s Coll., Winnipeg, 1964. Tchr. Cowan, Man., 1964-66; farmer with husband Winnipeg, 1965–; substitute tchr. various schs., 1966-84; polit. organizer Man. New Dem. Party, Winnipeg, 1986-90; elected mem. Man. Govt., Winnipeg, 1990–. Mcpl. councillor Local Govt. Dist. of Mountian, Swan River, 1982-90. Roman Catholic. Office: Manitoba Legislature, Legis Bldg, Winnipeg, MB Canada R3C OV8

WOYCZYNSKI, WOJBOR ANDRZEJ, mathematician, educator; b. Czestochowa, Poland, Oct. 24, 1943; came to U.S., 1970; s. Eugeniusz and Otylia Sabina (Borkiewicz) W.; m. Elizabeth W. Holbrook; children: Lauren Pike, Gregory Holbrook, Martin Wojbor. MSEE, Wroclaw (Poland) Poly., 1966; PhD in Math., Wroclaw U., 1968. Asst. prof. Inst. Math. Wroclaw U., 1968-72, assoc. prof., 1972-77; prof. dept. math. Cleve. State U., 1977-82; prof., chmn. dept. math. and stats. Case Western Res. U., Cleve., 1982-91, dir. Ctr. for Stochastic and Chaotic Processes in Sci. and Tech., 1989–; rsch. fellow Inst. Math. Polish Acad. Scis., Warsaw, 1969-76; postdoctoral fellow Carnegie-Mellon U., Pitts., 1970-72; vis. assoc. prof. Northwestern U., Evanston, Ill., 1976-77; vis. prof. Aarhus (Denmark) U., 1972, U. Paris, 1973, U. Wis., Madison, 1976, U. S.C., 1979, U. N.C., Chapel Hill, 1983-84, Gottingen (Germany) U., 1985, 91, U. NSW, Sydney, Australia, 1988, Nagoya (Japan) U., 1992, 93, 94, U. Minn., Mpls., 1994. Dep. editor in chief: Annals of the Polish Math. Soc., 1973-77; assoc. editor: Chemometrics Jour., 1987–, Probability and Mathematical Statistics, 1988–, Annals of Applied Probability, 1989–, Stochastic Processes and their Applications, 1993–; co-editor: Martingale Theory and Harmonic Analysis in Banach Spaces, 1982, Probability Theory and Harmonic Analysis, 1986, Nonlinear Waves and Weak Turbulence, 1993, Nonlinear Stochastic PDE's: Hydrodynamic Limit and Burgers' Turbulence, 1995; author: (monograph) Martingales and Geometry in Banach Spaces I, 1975, part II, 1978; co-author: Random Series and Stochastic Integrals: Single and Multiple, 1992. Rsch. grantee NSF, Washington, 1970, 71, 76, 77, 81, 87–, Office of Naval Rsch., Washington, 1985–. Fellow Inst. Math. Stats.; mem. Am. Math. Soc., Am. Statis. Assn., Polish Math. Soc. (Gt. prize 1972), Polish Inst. Arts and Scis., Racquet Club East, Rowfant Club. Roman Catholic. Avocations: tennis, music, skiing, sailing, rare books collecting. Home: 3296 Grenway Rd Cleveland OH 44122-3412 Office: Case Western Res U Dept Statistics Case Western Res U Cleveland OH 44106

WOYSKI, MARGARET SKILLMAN, retired geology educator; b. West Chester, Pa., July 26, 1921; d. Willis Rowland and Clara Louise (Howson) Skillman; m. Mark M. Woyski, June 19, 1948; children: Nancy Elizabeth, William Bruno, Ronald David, Wendelin Jane. BA in Chemistry, Wellesley (Mass.) Coll., 1943; MS in Geology, U. Minn., 1945, PhD in Geology, 1946. Geologist Mo. Geol. Survey and Water Resources, Rolla, 1946-48; instr. U. Wis., Madison, 1948-52; lectr. Calif. State U., Long Beach, 1963-67; lectr. to prof. Calif. State U., Fullerton, 1966-91, assoc. dean Sch. Natural Sci. and Math., 1981-91, emeritus prof., 1991–. Contbr. articles to profl. jours.; author lab. manuals; editor 4 guidebooks. Fellow Geol. Soc. Am. (program chmn. 1982); mem. South Coast Geol. Soc. (hon. pres. 1974), Mineral Soc. Am. Home: 1843 Kashlan Rd La Habra CA 90631-8423

WOZNIAK, RICHARD MICHAEL, SR., city and regional planner; b. rural Fullerton, Nebr., Nov. 28, 1928; s. Theo Charles and Monica (Lesiak) W.; m. Evalyn Louise Pickett, Sept. 9, 1951; children: Debra, Karen, Richard Michael, Steve. BS, Iowa State U., 1954. Cert. landscape architect. Landscape architect Rockford (Ill.) Nurseries, 1954-55; landscape architect, city planner Harland Bartholomew & Assocs., St. Louis, 1955-58; sr. planner Springfield/Sangamon County Regional Planning Commn., Springfield, Ill., 1958-60; city planner City of Omaha, 1960-64; owner, cons. Richard M. Wozniak & Assocs., Fremont, Nebr., 1964-74; exec. v.p. Mits Kawamoto & Aassocs., Omaha, 1974-76; owner, planning cons., racher Richard M. Wozniak & Assocs., Long Pine, Nebr., 1976-84; dir. planning and community devel. City of Norfolk (Nebr.)/Madison County, 1984–; cons. to more than 45 cities and counties in Ill., Mich. and Nebr., 1955-84; v.p., pres. Nebr. State Bd. Landscape Artchitects, Lincoln, 1980; treas. Nat. Coun. Landscape Architecture Bds., 1976. Author numerous studies and reports, comprehensive plans; designer land planning for parks and subdivs. With U.S. Army, 1949-49, USAFR, 1954-68. Recipient numerous awards. Mem. Am. Planning Assn. (charter), Am. Inst. Cert. Planners (charter), Nebr. Assn. County Ofcls. (v.p., pres. 1985-91), Am. Legion, VFW, Nebr. Planning and Zoning Assn. Avocations: woodworking, farming, fishing, sculpturing. Home: Rte 1 Box 410 Madison NE 68748 Office: Madison County Dept Planning and Zoning PO Box 864 Norfolk NE 68702

WRAASE, DENNIS RICHARD, utilities company executive, accountant; b. Washington, Mar. 15, 1944; s. Richard Harold and Esther Morelle (Cowan) W.; m. Cecilia Anne Kirby, Dec. 30, 1987; children: Richard Reid, Elisabeth Kirby. BS, U. Md., 1966; MS, George Washington U., 1975. CPA, Md. Acct. Exxon Corp., Balt., 1966-70; fin. analyst Exxon Corp., Houston, 1970-74; mgr. fin. systems Potomac Electric Power Co., Washington, 1974-78, asst. comptr., 1978-81, dir. computer and gen. svcs., 1981-83, comptr., 1983-92, v.p., 1986-89, sr. v.p., 1989–. Pres. Olney Jaycees, Md., 1978; bd. dirs., v.p. Nat. Capital area Boy Scouts Am., Washington, 1987–, Better Bus. Bur., Washington Bd. Trade. With USAR, 1967-73. Mem. Am. Inst. CPAs, Fin. Execs. Inst. Democrat. Lutheran. Office: Potomac Electric Power Co Rm 800 1900 Pennsylvania Ave NW Washington DC 20068-0002

WRABL, CAROL A., nursing administrator; b. Davenport, Iowa, July 26, 1940; d. Elmer Glenn and Amy Ellen (Olive) Gidel; m. Otto Wrabl, May 26, 1962; children: James, Karl. BSN, Augustana Coll., 1963; MSN, U. Ill., Chgo., 1971. Asst. DON Forest Hosp., Des Plaines, Ill., 1965-72; asst. prof. William Rainey Harper Coll., Palatine, Ill., 1971-75; DON Northwestern Meml. Hosp., Chgo., 1977-78, Loyola U. Med. Ctr., Chgo., 1978-85; v.p. patient care svcs. St. John's Regional Med. Ctr., Joplin, Mo., 1985-89; v.p. nursing Grant Hosp., Chgo., 1989-92; v.p. patient care svcs. St. Joseph's Hosp., Marshfield, Wis., 1992–. Home: 11356 Robin Rd Marshfield WI 54449

WRAGG, JOANNA DICARLO, public relations executive, newspaper editor; b. Batavia, N.Y., Nov. 3, 1941; d. Anthony Joseph and Josephine (Ruffino) DiCarlo; m. Otis O. Wragg, III, Dec. 21, 1963; children—Otis O. IV, LaMae. B.A., Fla. State U., 1963. Journalist Lakeland Ledger, 1969-72; editorial writer, then chief editorial writer Miami News, 1972-78; editorial dir. Sta. WPLG-TV, Miami, 1978; editorial writer Miami Herald, 1978-80, assoc. editor, 1980-92; v.p. Wragg & Casas Pub. Rels., 1992–; pub. speaker Am. Press Inst. Contbr. articles newspapers. Recipient Pulitzer prize, 1983, Robert F. Kennedy award Robert F. Kennedy Journalism Found., 1971, Disting. Service award Sigma Delta Chi, 1971. Mem. Nat. Conf. Editorial Writers (pres. 1991), Women in Communications, Pub. Rels. Soc. Am. Unitarian. Clubs: Zonta, Miami Forum. Office: Wragg & Casas Pub Rels 1110 Brickell Ave Ste 302 Miami FL 33131-3106

WRANGHAM, RICHARD WALTER, anthropology educator; b. Leeds, Yorkshire, Eng., Nov. 8, 1948; came to U.S., 1980; s. Geoffrey Walter and Dorothy Joan (Boyle) W.; m. Elizabeth Alison Ross, May 31, 1980; children: Ross Geoffrey, David Wilberforce, Ian Arthur. MA in Zoology, Oxford (Eng.) U., 1970; PhD in Zoology, Cambridge (Eng.) U., 1975. Lectr. Harvard U., Cambridge, Mass., 1976-77, prof., 1989–; rsch. fellow King's Coll., Cambridge U., 1977-80; asst. prof. U. Mich., Ann Arbor, 1980-84,

assoc. prof., 1984-89; sci. trustee Leakey Found., San Francisco, 1980-84; pres. Dolphins of Shark Bay Rsch. Found., Albuquerque, 1987-90, dir. Kibale Chimpanzee Project, Uganda, 1987–; trustee Digit Fund, Denver, 1990–. MacArthur Found. fellow, 1987. Home: 110 Concord Rd Weston MA 02193 Office: Harvard U Peabody Mus 11 Divinity Ave Cambridge MA 02138

WRAY, CECIL, JR., lawyer; b. Memphis, Nov. 19, 1934; s. Thomas Cecil and Margaret (Malone) W.; m. Gilda Gates, Sept. 11, 1964; children: Christopher A., Kathleen Wray Baughman. Student, U. Va., 1952-53; BA magna cum laude, Vanderbilt U., 1956; LLB, Yale U., 1959. Bar: Tenn. 1959, N.Y. 1961, U.S. Supreme Ct. 1964. Registered counseil juridique, France, 1978-82. Law clk. to justice Tom C. Clark U.S. Supreme Ct., Washington, 1959-60; assoc. Debevoise & Plimpton, N.Y.C., 1960-67, ptnr., 1968–; resident ptnr. Debevoise & Plimpton, Paris, 1976-79. Co-author: Innovative Corporate Financing Techniques, 1986. Pres. Search & Care, Inc., N.Y.C., 1981-87; vestryman St. James' Ch., N.Y.C., 1982-87, warden, 1988-94; mem. bd. trustees Fondation des Etats-Unis, Paris, 1976-79. Fellow Am. Coll. Investment Counsel (trustee 1981-86, pres. 1983-84); mem. ABA, Am. Law Inst., N.Y. State Bar Assn., Assn. Bar City N.Y., Internat. Bar Assn., Union Internat. Avocats, Am. Soc. Internat. Law, Coun. Fgn. Rels., Ausable Club (St. Huberts, N.Y.), Union Club, Century Club, Order of Coif, Phi Beta Kappa. Episcopalian. Home: 47 E 88th St New York NY 10128-1152 Office: Debevoise & Plimpton 875 3rd Ave New York NY 10022

WRAY, GAIL MILLER, environmentalist, government agency administrator; b. Milw., Feb. 23, 1939; d. Frederic C. Miller and Adele E. (Kanaley) O'Shaughnessy; children: Jennifer, Edward, Hillary. BA in Polit. Sci., Trinity Coll., Washington, 1961; spl. degree, Montessori Soc., Chgo., 1963. Office mgr. asst. plant mgr. Americology Can Co., 1978-81; recycling dir. Village of Shorewood, Wis., 1981-89; recycling coord. U.S. EPA, Washington, 1989-91; chair Presidential Coun. on Fed. Recycling and Procurement Policy, Washington, 1991-94; apptd. by gov. Wis. as exec. dir. Wis. Recycling Market Devel. Bd., 1994—. Polit. affairs chair Jr. League of Am., 1976-77; founder Shorewood (Wis.) Conservation Com.; 1980; chair LWV Nat. Resources Portfolio, 1987-86, pres. Greater Milw. LWV, 1980-82; mem. program com. Pub. Policy Forum, Milw., 1985-89; founder and pres. Associated Recyclers of Wis., 1987-89; bd. dirs. Midwest Recycling Coalition. Recipient Cert. Appreciation Am. Field Svc. Internat./Inter-cultural., People on the Move award, Milw. Bus. Jour., 1988, Nat. Govs. Assn. Recognition award, 1990; Named to Most Interesting People, Milw. Mag., 1990. Mem. Worldwide Women in the Environment (chair EPA forum), Friends of UN Environment Program, Nat. Recycling Coalition (mkt. devel. com.). Roman Catholic. Avocations: sports, animal owner, travel. Home: 12144 N Ridge Rd Mequon WI 53092-1025

WRAY, GILDA GATES, foundation administrator; b. Washington, Jan. 15, 1943; d. Samuel Eugene and Philomene (Asher) Gates; m. Cecil Wray, Jr., Sept. 11, 1964; children: Christopher, Kathleen Wray Baughman. BA cum laude, Smith Coll., 1964; MA in Internat. Affairs, Columbia U., 1966. Exec. dir. Horizon Concerts, N.Y.C., 1981-87; from program officer to sr. program officer Charles Hayden Found., N.Y.C., 1987-92, v.p., 1992—, trustee, 1993—; mem. rels. com. N.Y. Regional Assn. Grantmakers, 1990-93. Trustee Brearley Sch., N.Y.C., 1979-88, Yorkville Civic Coun., N.Y.C., 1979-81; bd. mgrs. N.Y. Jr. League, 1973-76, 79-81; chmn. grants com. St. James Ch., N.Y.C., 1979-87, mem .gov. com. Babcock-Michel Fund, 1988-92; mem. adv. bd. DeKay Found., N.Y.C., 1991—; mem. gov. bd. Fgn. Policy Assn., N.Y.c., 1982-90; trustee Adirondack Mus., 1994—. Mem. Cosmopolitan Club (bd. govs. 1992—). Episcopalian. Avocations: hiking, tennis, skiing, gardening, reading. Office: Charles Hayden Found One Bankers Trust Plz 130 Liberty St New York NY 10006-1105

WRAY, MARC FREDERICK, minerals company executive; b. Evanston, Ill.; s. George M. and Anabelle (Moriarity) W.; m. Suzanne Elliott, June 16, 1965; children—Marc Thomas, Andrew Elliott. BSc, Loyola U., Chgo., 1955; MBA, Harvard U., Chgo., 1964. With Nicholas Salgo & Co., Pitts, 1964-68; v.p. Bangor Punta Corp., Pitts., 1968-70; exec. v.p. Manati Industries, N.Y.C., 1970-72; corp. v.p., group exec. Internat. Paper Co., Purchase, N.Y., 1972-89; pres., CEO Joy Techs. Inc., Pitts., 1989—, also chmn. bd. dirs.; cons. Stoddard Quirk Mfg., Cudahy, Wis., 1958-60; cons. Jacksonville Paper, Fla., 1960-63; exec. v.p. Nicolas Salgo & Co., N.Y.C., 1963-68; v.p. corp. devel. Bangor Punta Corp., N.Y.C., 1968-70; exec. v.p. Manati Industries, N.Y.C., 1970-72; dir. corp. diversification Internat. Paper Co., N.Y.C., 1972-75, v.p., group exec., 1979—; pres. GCO Minerals Co., Houston, 1975—; chmn., CEO Joy Techs., Inc., Pitts.; dir. Union Bank, Houston. Served with U.S. Army, 1955-56. Mem. Houston C. of C. Roman Catholic. Clubs: Petroleum, Forest, Harvard Bus. Sch. (Houston); Harvard (N.Y.C.). Home: PO Box 4258 Houston TX 77210-4258 Office: GCO Minerals Co 2600 Allen Pky # 1 Houston TX 77019-2106 also: Joy Techs Inc 301 Grant St Pittsburgh PA 15219

WRAY, THOMAS JEFFERSON, lawyer; b. Nashville, July 17, 1949; s. William Esker and Imogene (Cushman) W.; m. Susan Elizabeth Wells, Aug. 19, 1972; children: William Clark, Caroline Kell. BA, Emory U., 1971; JD, U. Va., 1974. Bar: Tex. 1974, U.S. Dist. Ct. (so., no. and ea. dists.) Tex. 1976, U.S. Ct. Appeals (5th and 11th cirs.) 1976, U.S. Supreme Ct. 1987. Assoc. Fulbright & Jaworski, L.L.P., Houston, 1974-82; ptnr. Fulbright & Jaworski, Houston, 1982—. Mem. ABA, Houston Bar Assn., Houston Mgmt. Lawyers Forum (chmn. 1981-82), Houston Club, Briar Club, Phi Beta Kappa. Republican. Episcopalian. Home: 3662 Ella Lee Ln Houston TX 77027-4105 Office: Fulbright & Jaworski LLP 1301 Mckinney St Ste 5100 Houston TX 77010-3095

WREFORD, DAVID MATHEWS, magazine editor; b. Perth, Australia, Dec. 17, 1943; emigrated to Can. 1966; s. Peter Mathews and Mary Lichfield (Edquist) W.; m. Donna Diane Campbell, Sept. 28, 1970; children—Elizabeth Mary, Catherine Anne. B.Sc. in Agr. with honours, U. Western Australia, 1966. Field editor Southam Bus. Publns. Ltd., Winnipeg, Man., 1967-73; field editor Country Guide, Public Press Ltd., Milton, Ont., 1973-75; editor Country Guide, United Grain Growers Ltd., Winnipeg, 1975—. Mem. Man. Mang. Agrologists, Agrl. Inst. Can., Canadian Fedn. Farm Writers and Broadcasters. Mem. Ch. of Eng. Home: 294 Elm St, Winnipeg, MB Canada R3M 3P3 Office: United Grain Growers Ltd, PO Box 6600, Winnipeg, MB Canada R3C 3A7 also: Toronto-Dominion Centre 25th Fl, 201 Portage Ave, Winnipeg, MB Canada R3C 3A7

WREGE, JULIA BOUCHELLE, tennis professional, physical education educator; b. Charleston, W.Va., Apr. 11, 1944; d. Dallas Payne and Mary Louise (Hagan) Bouchelle; m. Douglas Ewart Wrege, July 13, 1968; children: Dallas Ewart, Shannon Bouchelle. B.S. in Physics, Ga. Inst. Tech., 1965, M.S. in Physics, 1967. Systems analyst GE Apollo Systems, Daytona Beach, Fla., 1967-68; med. scientist Space Instruments Research, Atlanta, 1968-70; head tennis profl. Riverside Tennis Club, Atlanta, 1971-72, Am. Adventures, Roswell, Ga., 1972-75, Hampton Farms Tennis Club, Marietta, Ga., 1975-79; head women's tennis coach Ga. Inst. Tech., Atlanta, Ga., 1979-86, 91-92; v.p. Sirius Software, Inc., 1988—; instr. physics So. Coll. Tech., 1990—; stadium chmn., umpire, referee USTA, Atlanta, 1977—. Author: Tournament Manual, 1977, 3d edit., 1989; co-developer software TMS Tennis Tournament, 1989. Pres. Dickerson Mid. Sch. Parent-Tchr.-Student Assn., Marietta, 1982-85. Named Umpire of Yr., Ga. Tennis Assn., 1978, So. Tennis Assn., 1978; Ga. Tennis Coach of Yr., Assn. Intercollegiate Athletics for Women-Ga. Tennis Coaches Assn., 1981, 82, 83. Mem. U.S. Profl. Tennis Assn. (pres. 1980), U.S. Tennis Assn., Intercollegiate Tennis Coaches Assn., Ga. Tennis Assn. (pres. 1976-81, 94—, v.p. 1974-76, 91-92), Atlanta Lawn Tennis Assn., Atlanta Profl. Tennis Assn., Alpha Xi Delta, Sigma Pi Sigma. Republican. Episcopalian. Home: 1366 Little Willeo Rd Marietta GA 30068-2135

WREN, HAROLD GWYN, arbitrator, lawyer, legal educator; b. Big Stone Gap, Va., May 19, 1921; s. James H. and Jessie M. (Reeve) W.; m. Beryl E. Bird, Nov. 20, 1948; children: James H., II, Geoffrey G. A.B., Columbia U. 1942, LL.B., 1948; J.S.D., Yale U., 1957. Bar: N.Y. 1948, Okla. 1956, Tex. 1959, Ky. 1983. Assoc. firm Willkie Farr & Gallagher, N.Y.C., 1948-49; assoc. prof. law U. Miss., Oxford, 1949-54; prof. law U. Okla., Norman, 1954-57, So. Meth. U., Dallas, 1957-65, Boston Coll., 1965-69; dean, prof. law Lewis and Clark Law Sch., Portland, Oreg., 1969-72, U. Richmond, Va.,

1972-76; prof. law U. Louisville, 1976-91, dean, 1976-81; arbitrator Am. Arbitration Assn., 1958—, Fed. Mediation and Conciliation Service, 1958—; of counsel Voyles and Johnson, P.S.C., Louisville, 1991—. Author: Creative Estate Planning, 1970, Problems in Corporate Changes, 1958, Problems in Texas Estates, 1961, (with Gabinet and Carrad) Tax Aspects of Marital Dissolution, 1987, (with Glascock) The Of Counsel Agreement, 1991. Served to capt. USNR, 1942-80. Fulbright scholar, 1953-54. Fellow Am. Coll. Trust and Estate Counsel, Am. Coll. Tax Counsel, Am. Bar Found. (life); mem. ABA, Louisville Bar Assn., Conversation Club, Order of Coif, Phi Beta Kappa, Phi Kappa. Democrat. Episcopalian. Home: 1500 SW 5th Ave Unit 2201 Portland OR 97201 Office: Ste 930 520 SW 6th Ave Portland OR 97204

WREN, ROBERT JAMES, aerospace engineering manager; b. Moline, Ill., May 12, 1935; children: James, Patrick, Kiley. BSCE, U. Tex., 1956; MSCE, So. Meth. U., 1962; doctoral candidate, U. Houston. Registered profl. engr. Tex. Engring. aide Ctrl. Power and Light Co., Corpus Christi, 1954; sta. clk. City of Austin (Tex.) Power Plant, 1954-55; assoc. engr., hydraulic engr. U.S. Bur. of Reclamation, Austin, 1955-57; structural test engr. Gen. Dynamics, Ft. Worth, 1957-62; sr. structural dynamics engr., mgr. vibration and acoustic test facility NASA-Manned Spacecraft Ctr., Houston, 1962-63, 63-66, head exptl. dynamics sect., 1965-70; mgr. Apollo Spacecraft 2TV-1 CSM Test Program, 1966-68, Apollo Lunar Module-2 Drop Test Program, 1968-70; mgr. structural design space sta., space base, lunar base, mars mission NASA-Manned Spacecraft Ctr., Houston, 1970-73; mgr. structural design and devel., space shuttle carrier aircraft-747 NASA Johnson Space Ctr., Houston, 1973-74, mgr. structural div. space shuttle payload systems, 1974-84; mgr. engring. directorate for space shuttle payload safety NASA-Johnson Space Ctr., Houston, 1984—, alternate chmn. space shuttle payload safety review panel, 1990—. Pres. Friendswood Little League Baseball, 1980-83; bd. dirs. Bay Area YMCA, Houston, 1982—, chmn., 1983-84. Recipient Sustained Superior Performance award NASA, Personal Letter of Commendation, George Low NASA Apollo Program, Outstanding Svc. award NASA, Group Achievement awards NASA; Paul Harris fellow Rotary. Mem. Space Ctr. Rotary (dir., treas., sec., v.p. 1979-85, 1986-87, Rotary dist. 5890/govt. rep. 1986-87, area coord. 1987-89, zone leader 1988-89, gov.'s aide 1989-90, chmn. dist. assembly 1989-90, 93-94, fin. com. 1989-91, Rotary Nat. award for Space Achievement Found./co-founder, bd. dirs. 1984—), Rotary World Health Found. Plastic Surgery for Children (co-founder, bd. dirs. 1985—), Rotary Space Meml. Found. (co-founder, bd. dirs. 1986—). Methodist. Avocations: snow and water skiing, running, scuba diving, tennis, sailing. Home: PO Box 1466 Friendswood TX 77546-1466 Office: NASA Johnson Space Ctr Houston TX 77058

WRENN, JAMES JOSEPH, East Asian studies educator; b. New Haven, Conn., July 7, 1926; s. James Joseph and Mariea (Enright) W.; m. Harriet Huddleston Calhoun, July 7, 1953; children: Annemarie Wrenn-Bessmer, James Joseph, Michael Enright, Christopher David. BA, Yale U., 1953, PhD, 1964. Lectr. in Chinese Grad. Sch., Yale U., New Haven, 1961-62, Brown U., Providence, 1962-64; asst. prof. Brown U., 1964-67, assoc. prof. linguistics, 1967-73, prof., 1974-91, co-chmn. East Asian Studies, 1987-95, dir. Ctr. for Lang. Studies, 1987-90. Contbr. articles to profl. jours. Platoon sgt. USMCR, 1944-46, PTO, 1950-52, Korea. Fgn. area fellow Ford Found., Republic of China, 1958-59. Mem. AAUP, MLA, Am. Council Tchrs. Fgn. Langs., Assn. Asian Studies, Chinese Lang. Tchrs. Assn. Club: Faculty. Home: 22 Rhode Island Ave Providence RI 02906-5506 Office: Brown U Brown Sta Box 1850 Providence RI 02912

WRIGHT, ABRAHAM, English language educator, college lecturer; b. Wedgefield, S.C., June 6, 1946; s. Glen and Marion (Green) W. BA, Morris Coll., 1969; MA, Howard U., 1974. Advanced Profl. English Secondary Level, Md. English tchr. North Dist. H.S., Varnville, S.C., 1969-70, Howard County Pub. Sch. Sys., Columbia, Md., 1974—; English lectr. Prince George's C.C., Largo, Md., 1974—. Sec. The Consultation on Church Union, Princeton, N.J., 1992—; mem., bd. trustees The Intern. Coun. of Cmty. Churches, Mokena, Ill., 1986— (sec. 1991—). With U.S. Army, 1970-72, Korea. Mem. Howard County (Md.) Tchrs. Assn., 1974—, Md. State Tchrs. Assn., 1974—, NEA, 1974—. Democrat. Avocations: reading, editing, shopping for old furniture. Home: 1912-3 Rosemary Hills Dr Silver Spring MD 20910 Office: Oakland Mills HS 9410 Kilimanjaro Rd Columbia MD 21045

WRIGHT, ALFRED GEORGE JAMES, band symphony orchestra conductor, educator; b. London, June 23, 1916; came to U.S., 1922, naturalized, 1936; s. Alfred Francis and Elizabeth (Chapman) W.; m. Bertha Marie Farmer, Aug. 6, 1938; children: Adele Marie Wright Needham, Cynthia Elaine Wright Williams; m. Gladys Violet Stone, June 28, 1953. BA, U. Miami, 1937, MEd, 1947; PhD (hon.), Troy State U., 1980. Dir. music Miami Sr. High Sch., 1938-54; prof., head dept. bands Purdue U., Lafayette, Ind., 1954-85; founder, condr. U.S. Coll. Wind Band Tours, 1971—; pres. Internat. Music Tours, Inc.; v.p., exec. sec. Music Tour Svcs., Inc.; dir. prerace pageant Indpls. 500 Mile Automobile Race, 1957-82; mem. advisory coun. Performing Arts Abroad, 1972—; chmn. N.Am. Band Dirs. Coordinating Commn., 1974-75, Nat. High Sch. Honors Band, 1975-76, 77—; jury World Music Contest, Holland, 1974, 79, 81, 85, Bd. dirs. 500 Festival Assocs., 1961-81; founder, chmn. bd. dirs. Hall of Fame Disting. Band Condrs.; pres. All Am. Hall of Fame Band Found.; pres., chief exec. officer John Philip Sousa Meml. Found., 1979. Founding condr. Purdue U. Symphony Orch., 1971-81; Author: The Show Band, 1957, Marching Band Fundamentals, 1960, Bands of the World, 1970; marching band editor: Instrumentalist mag, 1953-81; contbr. articles to profl. mags. Mem. bd. advisors Internat. Music Festivals, 1989; bd. dirs. World Assn. Wind Bands and Ensembles Found., 1991-94. Decorated Star of the Order John Philip Sousa; recipient Disting. Svc. award Purdue U., 1993. Mem. Nat. Band Assn. (founder, pres. 1960-63, hon. life pres. 1973), Coll. Band Dirs. Nat. Assn., Am. Sch. Band Dirs. Nat. Assn., Japan Marching Band Assn. (hon. bd. dirs. 1971-77), Big Ten Band Dirs. Assn. (pres. 1977), Am. Bandmasters Found. (bd. dirs. 1987-89), Am. Bandmasters Assn. (pres. 1979-80), Nat. Acad. Wind and Percussive Arts (founder, chmn. 1961-81), Phi Mu Alpha, Kappa Kappa Psi (Disting. Svc. award 1981), Phi Beta Mu. Home and Office: 345 Overlook Dr West Lafayette IN 47906-1249

WRIGHT, ANDREW, English literature educator; b. Columbus, Ohio, June 28, 1923; s. Francis Joseph and Katharine (Timberman) W.; m. Virginia Rosemary Banks, June 27, 1952; children: Matthew Leslie Francis, Emma Stanbery. A.B., Harvard U., 1947; M.A., Ohio State U., 1948, Ph.D., 1951. Prof. English lit. U. Calif., San Diego, 1963—; chmn. dept. lit. U. Calif., 1971-74; dir. U. Calif. Study Center, U.K. and Ireland, 1980-82; vis. prof. U. Queensland, Australia, 1984, Colegio de la Frontera Norte, San Antonio del Mar, Baja, Calif., 1991-92. Author: Jane Austen's Novels: A Study In Structure, 1953, Joyce Cary: A Preface to His Novels, 1958, Henry Fielding: Mask and Feast, 1965, Blake's Job: A Commentary, 1972, Anthony Trollope: Dream and Art, 1983; Fictional Discourse and Historical Space, 1987; contbg. author numerous books, articles to profl. jours.; editorial bd. Nineteenth Century Fiction, 1964-86. Bd. dirs. Calif. Coun. Humanities, 1983-87. Guggenheim fellow, 1960, 70; Fulbright Sr. Research fellow, 1960-61. Fellow Royal Soc. Lit.; mem. MLA, Jane Austen Soc., Athenaeum (London), Trollope Soc., Santayana Soc., Phi Beta Kappa. Home: 7227 Olivetas Ave La Jolla CA 92037-5335 Office: U Calif San Diego Dept Lit La Jolla CA 92093-0410

WRIGHT, ANN ELIZABETH, physicist, consultant; b. Mooringsport, La., Feb. 20, 1922; d. James Aloysius and Mary Louise (Ghenning) Foley; 1 child, Charles Wright Jr. BS in Physics cum laude, U. Houston, 1965; MS in Med. Physics, U. Tex., Houston, 1967; PhD in Radiol. Physics, U. Tex., 1970. Supr. treasury Shell Oil Co., Houston, 1944-59; clinical prof. U. Tex. Med. Br., Galveston, 1975—; cons. physicist various hosps. nationwide, 1970—; mem. Tex. Bd. Licensure for Med. Physicists, 1991—, Am. Bd. Med. Physicists, 1992—. Fellow Am. Assn. Physicists in Medicine (pres. 1982), Am. Coll. Med. Physics (chmn. bd. chancellors 1984), Am. Inst. Physics (bd. dirs. 1982-86). Avocation: golf.

WRIGHT, BARBARA EVELYN, microbiologist; b. Pasadena, Calif., Apr. 6, 1926; d. Gilbert Munger Wright and Leta Luella (Browne) Deery; m. Kenneth Fremont-Smith, May 25, 1974. AB, Stanford U., 1947, MA, 1948, PhD, 1951. Biologist NIH, Bethesda, Md., 1953-61; assoc. biochemist Mass.

Gen. Hosp., Boston, 1961-69; asst. prof. microbiology Harvard Med. Sch., Boston, 1966-75, assoc. prof., 1975-82; rsch. dir. Boston Biomed. Rsch. Inst., 1967-82; rsch. prof. divsn. biol. scis. U. Mont., Missoula, 1982—; dir. Stella Duncan Rsch. Inst., Missoula, 1982—; cons. Miles Lab., Elkhart, Ind., 1980-84. Author: Critical Variables in Differentiation, 1973; editor: Control Mechanisms in Respiration and Fermentation, 1963; contbr. articles to profl. jours. Grantee NIH, NSF, 1961-95. Mem. AAAS (pres. Pacific div. 1984-85), Am. Soc. for Microbiology (divisional lectr. 1978), Am. Soc. of Biol. Chemists. Avocations: board sailing, skiing, kayaking. Home: 1550 Trotting Horse Ln Missoula MT 59801-9220 Office: U Mont DBS Missoula MT 59812

WRIGHT, BENJAMIN DRAKE, psychology, statistics, education educator; b. Wilkes Barre, Pa., Mar. 30, 1926; s. Harold St. Clair and Dorothy Lynde (Wadhams) W.; m. Claire Marie Engelmann, Sept. 9, 1948; children: Amy Engelmann, Sara Dobbs, Christopher Edward, Andrew Wadhams. BS, Cornell U., 1947; cert., Chgo. Inst. Psychoanalysis, 1953; PhD, U. Chgo., 1957. Lic. psychologist, Ill. Physics rsch. Bell Telephone Lab., Murray Hill, N.J., 1947; physics researcher U. Chgo., 1947-50, therapist Orthogenic Sch., 1950-56, prof. edn., 1960—, prof. psychology, 1960—; cons. Nat. Bd. Med. Examiners, Phila., 1975—, Hines VA Hosp., Chgo., 1980-85, Nat. Coun. State Bds. Nursing, Chgo., 1985—, Am. Soc. Clin. Pathologists, 1986—. Author: Best Test Design, 1979, Rating Scale Analysis, 1982, Conversational Statistics, 1984, Hero, Villain, Saint, 1990; editor: Learning Environments, 1974, Sch. Rev., 1969-78. Served with USN, 1944-46. Mem. Am. Ednl. Research Assn.; Rasch Measurement Spl. Interest Group. Club: Quadrangle. Home: 5721 S Harper Ave Chicago IL 60637-1840 Office: U Chgo MESA Lab 5835 S Kimbark Ave Chicago IL 60637-1608

WRIGHT, BETTY REN, children's book writer; b. Wakefield, Mich., June 15, 1927; d. William and Revena Evelyn (Trezise) W.; m. George Albert Frederiksen, Oct. 9, 1976. BA, Milw.-Downer Coll., 1949. With Western Pub. Co., Inc., 1949-78, mng. editor Racine Editl., 1967-78. Author numerous juvenile and jr. novels, including The Doll House Murders, 1983, Christina's Ghost, 1985, The Summer of Mrs. MacGregor, 1986, A Ghost in the Window, 1987, The Pike River Phantom, 1988, Rosie and the Dance of the Dinosaurs, 1989, The Ghost of Ernie P., 1990, A Ghost in the House, 1991, The Scariest Night, 1991, The Ghosts of Mercy Manor, The Ghost of Popcorn Hill, 1993, The Ghost Witch, 1993, Out of the Dark, 1994, A Ghost Comes Calling, 1994; also numerous picture and ednl. books; contbr. fiction to mags. Recipient alumni svc. award Lawrence U. (merged with Milw.-Downer Coll.), numerous awards for books, including Mo. Mark Twain award, 1986, Tex. Bluebonnet award, 1986, 88, young readers award Pacific N.W. Libr. Assn., 1986, reviewer's choice Booklist, Ala. Young Readers award, 1987, Ga. Children's Choice award, 1988, Ind. Young Hoosier Book award, 1989, children's choice book Internat. Reading Assn.-CBC, 1984, S.C. Children's Choice award, 1988, Okla. Sequoyah Children's Choice award, 1988. Mem. AAUW, Allied Authors, Coun. for Wis. Authors (juvenile book award 1985), Phi Beta Kappa. Avocations: reading, travel. Home and Office: 611 47th Ave Kenosha WI 53144

WRIGHT, BURTON, sociologist; b. Detroit, Jan. 31, 1917; s. Burton and Hazel Marie (Thomas) W.; A.A., C.Z. Coll., 1944; B.A., U. Wash., Seattle, 1947, M.A., 1949; Ph.D., Fla. State U., 1972; m. Marie Fidelis Gallivan, Jan. 26, 1942; children: Burton III, Catherine Margaret (dec.). Enlisted U.S. Navy, 1937, commd. and advanced through grades to comdr., 1957; dir. Naval Res. Recruiting, 1960-64; ret., 1964; mem. faculty U. Wash., 1947-49, Northwestern U., summers 1956-59, George Washington U., Washington, 1954-60, Rollins Coll., Winter Park, Fla., 1966-69; cons. Ford Found., 1951, Dept. Air Force, 1955, U.S. Army Chem. Corps, 1956; prof. dept. sociology U. Central Fla., Orlando, 1972-82, prof. emeritus, 1982-89; ret., 1989; vis. prof. Troy State U., Dothan; dir. Am. Sociol. Assn. Nat. Honors Program, 1981-89. Decorated Navy Commendation medal. Fellow Am. Anthrop. Assn.; mem. Am. Sociol. Assn. (membership com. 1983-86), Soc. Psychol. Study Social Problems, AAUP, Am. Acad. Arts and Scis., Soc. Study Social Problems, So. Sociol. Soc., North Central Sociol. Soc. Roman Catholic. Club: Univ. (Winter Park). Author: (with John P. Weiss and Charles M. Unkovic) Perspective: An Introduction to Sociology, 1975; (with Vernon Fox) Criminal Justice and the Social Sciences, 1978; (with John P. Weiss) Social Problems, 1980. Home: 502 Dunleith Blvd Dothan AL 36301-4221

WRIGHT, CHARLES ALAN, lawyer, educator, author; b. Phila., Sept. 3, 1927; s. Charles Adshead and Helen (McCormack) W.; m. Mary Joan Herriott, July 8, 1950 (div. Jan. 1955); 1 child, Charles Edward; m. Eleanor Custis Broyles Clarke, Dec. 17, 1955; children: Henrietta, Cecily; stepchildren: Eleanor Custis Clarke, Margot Clarke. BA, Wesleyan U., Middletown, Conn., 1947; LL.B., Yale U., 1949; LHD (hon.), Episcopal Theol. Sem. S.W., 1992. Bar: Minn. 1951, Tex. 1959. Law clk. to Hon. Charles E. Clark, U.S. Ct. Appeals (2d cir.), New Haven, 1949-50; asst. prof. law U. Minn., Mpls., 1950-53, assoc. prof., 1953-55; assoc. prof. law U. Tex., Austin, 1955-58, prof., 1958-65, McCormick prof., 1965-80, Bates prof., 1980—; Arthur Goodhart vis. prof. legal sci. Cambridge (Eng.) U., 1990-91, Hayden W. Head regents chair, 1990-91; vis. prof. U. Pa., 1959-60. Harvard U., 1964-65, Yale U., 1968-69; vis. fellow Wolfson Coll., Cambridge U., 1984; reporter study div. of juridstiction between state and fed. cts. Am. Law Inst., 1963-69; mem. adv. com. on civil rules Jud. Conf. U.S., 1961-64, standing com. on rules of practice and proc., 1964-76, 87-93; cons., counsel for Pres., 1973-74; mem. com. on infractions NCAA, 1973-83, chmn., 1978-83, chmn. adminstrv. rev. panel, 1993-94; mem. permanent com for Oliver Wendell Holmes Devise, 1975-87; mem. Commn. on Bicentennial of U.S. Constn., 1985-92. Author: Wright's Minnesota Rules, 1954, Cases on Remedies, 1955, (with C.T. McCormick and J.H. Chadbourn) Cases on Federal Courts, 9th edit., 1992, Handbook of the Law of Federal Courts, 5th edit., 1994, (with H.M. Reasoner) Procedure-The Handmaid of Justice, 1965, Federal Practice and Procedure: Criminal, 2d edit., 1982, (with A.R. Miller) Federal Practice and Procedure: Civil, 1969-73, 2d edit. (with A.R. Miller and M.K. Kane), 1983—, (with A.R. Miller and E.H. Cooper) Federal Practice and Procedure: Jurisdiction and Related Matters, 1975-82, 2d edit., 1986—, (with K.W. Graham and V.J. Gold) Federal Practice and Procedure: Evidence, 1977—; mem. editorial bd. Supreme Ct. Hist. Soc. Yearbook, 1987—. Trustee St. Stephen's Episc. Sch., Austin, Tex., 1962-66, St. Andrew's Episc. Sch., Austin, 1971-74, 77-80, 81-84, chmn. bd., 1973-74, 79-80; trustee Capitol Broadcasting Assn., Austin, 1966—, chmn. bd., 1969-90; trustee Austin Symphony Orch., 1966—, mem. exec. com., 1966-70, 72-83, 86—; trustee Austin Choral Union, 1984-90, Austin Lyric Opera Soc., 1986—; bd. dirs. Am. Friends of Cambridge (Eng.) U., 1994—. Hon. fellow Wolfson Coll. Cambridge U., 1986—. Mem. ABA (commn. on standards jud. adminstrn 1970-77), AAAS, Am. Law Inst. (coun. 1969—, 2d v.p. 1987-88, 1st v.p. 1988-92, pres. 1993—), Am. Bar Found. (Rsch. award 1989), Inst. Jud. Adminstrn., Am. Judicature Soc., Philos. Soc. Tex., Am. Friends Cambridge U. (bd. dirs. 1994—), Country Club, Tarry House Club, Headliners Club, Ridge Harbor Yacht Club, Barton Creek Lakeside Club (Austin), Century Club, Yale Club (N.Y.C.), Mid Ocean Club (Bermuda). Republican. Episcopalian. Avocations: reading and reviewing mysteries, railroads, fishing, coaching Legal Eagles (intramural touch football team). Home: 5304 Western Hills Dr Austin TX 78731-4822 Office: U Tex Sch Law 727 E 26th St Austin TX 78705-3224

WRIGHT, CHARLES EDWARD, lawyer; b. Portland, Oreg., Mar. 21, 1906; s. Archibald Robert and Grace May (Springer) W.; m. Elisabeth Knowlton Strong, Oct. 28, 1937; children—Frederick Pares, Hilda Wright Rhodes, Elisabeth Wright Ritchie. A.B., Yale U., 1929, LL.B., 1932. Bar: Oreg. 1933. Assoc. firm Platt, Platt, Fales, Smith & Black, Portland, 1933-37; sr. atty. Seattle regional office SEC, 1937-43; practice in Portland, 1943—; partner firm Bullivant, Wright, Johnson, Pendergrass and Hoffman, 1947-90; ptnr. Bullivant, Houser, Bailey, Pendergrass & Hoffman, 1990-94; retired, 1994. Bd. dirs. Portland Jr. Symphony; trustee, v.p. Catlin Hillside Schs. Mem. ABA, Oreg. Bar Assn., Am. Judicature Soc., Travelers Aid Soc. (dir. 1946), Portland Art Assn. (past dir.), Oreg. Yale Alumni Assn. (pres. 1961), City Club (past dir.). Home: 7226 NW Penridge Rd Portland OR 97229-6806

WRIGHT, CHARLES PENZEL, JR., poet; b. Pickwick Dam, Tenn., Aug. 25, 1935; s. Charles Penzel and Mary Castleman (Winter) W.; m. Holly McIntire, Apr. 6, 1969; 1 child, Luke Savin Herrick. B.A., Davidson (N.C.) Coll., 1957; M.F.A., U. Iowa, 1963; postgrad., U. Rome, 1963-64. Mem.

faculty U. Calif., Irvine, 1966-83; prof. English U. Calif., 1976-83; mem. faculty U. Va., Charlottesville, 1983—; Fulbright vis. prof. U. Am. lit. U. Padua, Italy, 1968-69; disting. vis. prof. U. Degli Studi, Florence, Italy, 1992. Author: The Dream Animal, 1968, The Grave of the Right Hand, 1970, The Venice Notebook, 1971, Hard Freight, 1973, Bloodlines, 1975, Colophons, 1977, China Trace, 1977, Wright: A Profile, 1979, The Southern Cross, 1981, Country Music: Selected Early Poems, 1982, The Other Side of the River, 1984, Zone Journals, 1988, Halflife, 1988, Xionia, 1990, The World of the 10,000 Things, 1990, Chickamauga, 1995, Quarter Notes, 1995; trans.: The Storm and Other Poems (Eugenion Montale), 1978, Orphic Songs (Dino Campana), 1994. Served with AUS, 1957-61. Recipient Pen Translation Prize, 1979, Nat. Book award for poetry, 1983, citation in poetry Brandeis U. Creative Arts Awards, 1987, Merit medal Am. Acad. and Inst. Arts and Letters, 1992, Ruth Lilly Poetry prize, 1993; Fulbright scholar, 1963-65; Guggenheim fellow, 1976, Ingram Merrill fellow, 1980, 93. Mem. Fellowship of So. Writers, Am. Acad. Arts and Letters. Home: 940 Locust Ave Charlottesville VA 22901-4030 Office: English Dept Univ Va Charlottesville VA 22901

WRIGHT, CHARLES RICHARD, insurance executive; b. Yankton, S.D., June 17, 1941; s. Ray C. and Agness (Weiland) W.; m. Mary M. Adrian; children: Charles A., Anne B., Jane E. BS, Yankton Coll., 1963. CLU. Agt. State Farm Ins., Mpls., 1963-67; agy. mgr., 1967-73; agy. dir. State Farm Ins., N.Y.C., 1973-76; exec. asst. State Farm Ins., Bloomington, Ill., 1976-78; dep. regional v.p. State Farm Ins., Phoenix, 1978-81; v.p. agy. State Farm Ins., Bloomington, 1981-88, regional v.p., 1988-92, agy. v.p., 1992—; mem. ins. adv. bd. Manactony Vehicle; bd. dirs. David Davis Found., Lexington Community Ctr.; bd. trustees Eureka Coll. Mem. Nat. Assn. Life Underwriters, Internat. Platform Assn., Kiwanis. Republican. Methodist. Avocations: antiques, tennis, historic restoration. Home: 10 Spencer Lexington IL 61753-1177 Office: State Farm Ins Co One State Farm Plz Bloomington IL 61710

WRIGHT, CHATT GRANDISON, academic administrator; b. San Mateo, Calif., Sept. 17, 1941; s. Virgil Tandy and Louise (Jeschien) W.; children from previous marriage: Stephen Brook, Jon David, Shelley Adams; m. Janice Tepley, Nov. 28, 1993. Student, U. Calif., Berkeley, 1960-62; BA in Polit. Sci., U. Calif., Davis, 1964; MA in Econs., U. Hawaii, 1968. Instr. econs. U. Hawaii, Honolulu, 1968-70; mgr. corp. planning Telecheck Internat., Inc., Honolulu, 1969-70; economist State of Hawaii, Honolulu, 1970-71; adminstr. manpower City & County of Honolulu, 1971-72; bus. adminstr., dean. Hawaii Pacific U., Honolulu, 1972-74, v.p., 1974-76, pres., 1976—. Commr. City and County of Honolulu Manpower Area Planning Commn., 1976-82; Mayor's Salary Commn. City and County of Honolulu, 1977-80; ethics commr. Honolulu City Ethics Commn., 1978-84; coun. mem. City and County of Honolulu Labor Mkt. Adv. Coun., 1982-84; bd. dirs. Hawaii Econ. Devel. Corp.; trustee Queen's Med. Ctr., Honolulu, 1986-92, Honolulu Armed Svcs. YMCA, 1984-86, Hawaii Maritime Ctr., 1990-92, St. Andrew's Priory Sch., 1994—; chmn. bd. trustees Hist. Hawaii Found., 1990—; mem. adv. bd. Cancer Rsch. Ctr. Hawaii, 1987; bd. dirs. Downtown Improvement Assn., 1988—; bd. govs. Hawaii Med. Libr., 1989-92; mem. adv. bd. Aloha coun. Boy Scouts Am., 1991—; trustee Molokai Gen. Hosp., 1991-92. With USN, 1967-80. Recipient Pioneer award Pioneer Fed. Savs. Bank, 1982. Mem. Am. Assn. Higher Edn., Assn. Governing Bds. of Univs. and Colls., Japan-Am. Soc. Honolulu, Social Sci. Assn., Nat. Assn. Intercollegiate Athletics (vice chair, bd. dirs. coun. pres. 1985-90), Hawaii Joint Coun. Econ. Edn. (bd. dirs. 1982-92), Hawaii Assn. Ind. Colls. and Univs. (chmn. 1986), Assn. Governing Bds. Univs. and Colls., Japan-Am. Soc. Honolulu, Social Sci. Assn., Hawaii C. of C., Sales and Mktg. Execs. Club of Honolulu, Outrigger Canoe Club, Pacific Club (Honolulu), Plaza Club (bd. govs. 1992—), Dahu Country Club, Rotary (Paul Harris fellow 1986). Republican. Episcopalian. Avocations: hunting, fishing, reading, travel. Office: Hawaii Pacific U Office Pres 1166 Fort St Honolulu HI 96813-2717

WRIGHT, CLARK PHILLIPS, computer systems specialist; b. Orange, Tex., Aug. 30, 1942; s. Madison Brown and Mary Elizabeth (Phillips) W.; m. Stacy Charlotte Klutz, June 5, 1965 (div. Oct. 1979); m. Cora Lou Alexandria Schelling, Oct. 31, 1979; 1 child, Isaac Schelling. BA, U. Tex., 1965. Computer programmer Lockheed Electronics Co., Houston, 1965-67; prin. analyst Control Data Corp., St. Paul, 1967-76; computer scientist DBA Systems, Inc., Lanham, Md., 1976-79; engring. specialist Ford Aerospace Corp., Houston, 1979-90, Loral Aerospace Corp., 1990—. Precinct chmn. Rep. Party of Tex., 1982-86. Mem. IEEE, Math Assn. Am., Data Processing Mgmt. Assn., Assn. Computing Machinery, SAR (chartered, sec., treas.), Sons Republic Tex., Info. System Security Assn., Masons, Rotary. Avocations: travel, photography. Home: 5000 Park Ave Dickinson TX 77539-7013 Office: Loral Aerospace Corp PO Box 58487 Houston TX 77258-8487

WRIGHT, DAVID BURTON, retired newspaper publishing company executive; b. Fowler, Ind., Aug. 29, 1933; s. Claude Matthew and Rose Ellen (Lavelle) W.; m. Geraldine F. Gray, May 9, 1964; children—David Andrew, Anne Kathleen. A.B., Wabash Coll., 1955. C.P.A., Ind. Audit staff George S. Olive & Co. C.P.A.s, Indpls., 1958-63, mgmt. cons., 1963-65; controller Herff Jones Co., Indpls., 1965-69, corp. controller, asst. sec., 1970-71; asst. bus. mgr. Indpls. Newspapers Inc., 1971-77, asst. sec., treas., 1975-93, bus. mgr., 1977-93, v.p., 1982-93; asst. sec., treas. Central Newspapers Inc., Indpls., 1975-79 sec., treas., 1979-89; asst. sec., treas. Muncie Newspapers Inc., Ind., 1975-93; mem. St. Francis Hosp. Adv. Bd., Indpls., 1983—. Sec. St. Francis Hosp. Adv. Bd., 1986-87, v.p., 1987-91, pres., 1991-93. Served with U.S. Army, 1956-58. Mem. Ind. Assn. CPAs, Indpls. Econ. Club, KC. Roman Catholic. Home: 6713 Forrest Commons Blvd Indianapolis IN 46227-2396

WRIGHT, DAVID L, food and beverage company executive; b. Wenatchee, Wash., Mar. 12, 1949; s. Franklin Sven and Mary Elizabeth (Collins) W.; m. Karen Sue Rice, Mar. 28, 1981; children: Kara, Erin, Jonathan, Anna Catherine. BA, U. Calif., Davis, 1971. Chief of rsch. dept. of benefit payments State of Calif., Sacramento, 1972-75; profl. staff mem. com. on agr. U.S. Ho. Reps., Washington, 1975-77; adminstrv. asst. Rep. William C. Wampler, Washington, 1977-81; spl. asst. for legis. affairs to Pres. The White House, Washington, 1981-84; dir. govt. affairs Pepsico Inc., Purchase, N.Y., 1984-87; v.p., govt. affairs Pepsico, Inc., Purchase, N.Y., 1987—. Dir., v.p. Nat. Conf. State Legislatures Found., Denver, 1989—. Capt. USAR, 1971-79. Mem Capitol Hill Club, Redding Country Club. Republican. Office: Pepsico Inc 700 Anderson Hill Rd Purchase NY 10577-1444

WRIGHT, DEIL SPENCER, political science educator; b. Three Rivers, Mich., June 18, 1930; s. William Henry and Gertrude Louise (Buck) W.; m. Patricia Mae Jaffke, Aug. 22, 1953; children: David C., Mark W., Matthew D., Lois L. BA, U. Mich., 1952, M in Pub. Adminstrn., 1954, PhD, 1957. Asst. prof. polit. sci. Wayne State U., Detroit, 1956-59; from asst. to assoc. prof. U. Iowa, Iowa City, 1959-67; assoc. prof. U. Calif., Berkeley, 1965-66; prof. U. N.C., Chapel Hill, 1967-83, alumni disting. prof., 1983—; Carl Hatch vis. prof. U. N.Mex., Albuquerque, 1987; adj. prof. U. Okla., Norman, 1972—; lectr. USIA, Washington, various dates; cons. Office Mgmt. and Budget, Washington, 1979-80. Author: Understanding Intergovernmental Relations, 3d edit., 1988; editor: Federalism and Intergovernmental Relations, 1984; contbr. over 60 articles to various polit. sci. and pub. adminstrn. jours. Mem. dir's adv. com. NIH, Bethesda, Md., 1970-74, N.C. Coun. on State Goals and Policies, Raleigh, 1973-77, N.C. State Internship Coun., Raleigh, 1985-93. Internat. Inst. Mgmt. research fellow, Berlin, 1977. Mem. Nat. Acad. Pub. Adminstrn., AAAS, Am. Polit. Sci. Assn., Am. Soc. Pub. Adminstrn., Midwest Polit. Sci. Assn., Policy Studies Orgn., So. Polit. Sci. Assn. (pres. 1981-82). Republican. Methodist. Lodge: Rotary (Chapel Hill). Avocations: (Chapel Hill club 1981, 84, 90). Home: 204 Velma Rd Chapel Hill NC 27514-7601 Office: U North Carolina Dept Polit Sci Campus Box 3265 Chapel Hill NC 27599-3265

WRIGHT, DONALD CONWAY, editorial cartoonist; b. Los Angeles, Jan. 23, 1934; s. Charles C. and Sally (Olberg) W.; m. Rita Rose Blondin, Oct. 1, 1960 (dec. June 1968); m. Carolyn Ann Jay, Feb. 5, 1969. Student, Fla. pub. schs. Staff photographer, copy boy Miami News, Fla., 1952-56, graphics editor, 1958-60, polit. cartoonist, 1960-63, editorial cartoonist, 1963—; with The Palm Beach Post, West Palm Beach, Fla., 1989—; syndicated by Washington Star Syndicate, 1970, N.Y. Times Syndication Sales Service, 1976-82, Chgo. Tribune Co. Syndicate, 1982—; prod. animated cartoons for nat. TV distbn. Newsweek Broadcasting Service, 1978, for "Sunday" Today Show, NBC, 1987, 88; lectr. Miami-Dade Community Coll., 1985. Author: Wright On!, 1971, Wright Side Up, 1981; co-author: Gang of Eight, 1985; exhibited in one-man shows at Inst. for Contemporary Art, Fla. State U., Tallahassee, 1982, Lowe Art Mus., U. Miami, Coral Gables, Fla., 1979, U. Miami Lowe Art Mus., 1968; group show, Dayton, Ohio, 1969; represented in permanent collection Syracuse U., N.Y.; created theme artwork From the Hip (Dino De Laurentiis), 1987. Bd. overseers Emerson Coll., Boston U., 1976-79; AUS 1956-58. Recipient Outstanding Young Man in Communications Media award Young Democrats Fla., 1965, award Nat. Cath. Press, 1965, citation Freedoms Found., Valley Forge, Pa., 1966, Pulitzer prize, 1966, 80, Sch. Bell award Fla. Edn. Assn., 1968, Grenville Clark Editorial Page Cartoon award The Stanley Found. Iowa, 1969, Scripps-Howard Edward J. Meeman Conservation award Scripps-Howard Found., 1971, 1st place award Fla. Better Newspaper Daily Contest Fla. Press Assn., 1972, 1st prize Population Inst. Cartoon Contest Awards, N.Y.C., 1975, Editorial Category award Population Inst. Cartoon Contest Awards, N.Y.C., 1975, Nat. Headliner award Press Club Atlantic City, N.J., 1980, Tom Wallace award Inter Am. Press Assn., 1983, 86, 90, Robert F. Kennedy Meml. Journalism award, Washington, 1983, 88, 1st recipient Cox Newspapers award, 1988, David Brinkley award Barry U., 1989. Mem. Overseas Press Club Am. (awards 1969, 72, 80, 82, 85, 92), Nat. Cartoonists Soc. (Reuben award 1985, 86), Soc. Profl. Journalists (award for disting. svc. in journalism 1978, 90). Democrat. Office: The Palm Beach Post 2751 S Dixie Hwy West Palm Beach FL 33405-1233*

WRIGHT, DONALD EUGENE, retired librarian; b. Boulder, Colo., July 25, 1930; s. Kelley E. and Iva Bell (Winkle) W.; m. Verna Venetta Vorpahl, June 18, 1953 (dec.); children: Sara, Amy, John Kelley. A.B., U. Colo., 1952; A.M., U. Denver, 1953. Library asst. U. Colo., 1948-52, Denver Pub. Library, 1952; reference asst. Ft. Wayne (Ind.) Pub. Library, 1953, Detroit Pub. Library, 1953-54, No. Platte (Nebr.) Pub. Library, 1956-58; library cons. Nebr. Pub. Library Commn., 1958-60; asst. dir. Lincoln (Nebr.) City Libraries, 1960-61; dir. project to aid small pub. libraries ALA, 1961-63, exec. sec. reference services div., 1963-64, exec. sec. trustee assn., 1963-64; chief bur. library services Conn. Dept. Edn., 1964-65; assoc. state librarian, also chief library devel. Ill. State Library, Springfield, 1965-67; librarian Evanston (Ill.) Pub. Library, 1967-92; adminstrv. librarian Niles (Ill.) Pub. Library Dist., 1992-93; ret., 1993; Chmn. Gov. Nebr. Conf. Library Trustees, 1958; co-chmn. for Ill. White House Conf. on Library and Info. Svc., 1977-78, vice chmn. nat. task force, 1985, nat. transition team, 1992. Contbr. profl. jours. Mem. Nebr. Library Assn. (bd. dirs. 1958-61, pres. elect 1961), ALA (life, pres. library adminstrv. div. 1978-79), Ill. Library Assn. (pres. 1972). Presbyterian. Clubs: Rotary; University (Evanston). Home: 1715 Chancellor St Evanston IL 60201-1513

WRIGHT, DONALD FRANKLIN, newspaper executive; b. St. Paul, July 10, 1934; s. Floyd Franklin and Helen Marie (Hansen) W.; m. Sharon Kathleen Fisher, Dec. 30, 1960; children: John, Dana, Kara, Patrick. BME, U. Minn., 1957, MBA, 1958. With Mpls. Star & Tribune Co., 1958-77, research planning dir., then ops. dir., 1971-75, exec. editor, 1975-77; exec. v.p., gen. mgr. Newsday, Inc., L.I., 1977-78, pres., chief operating officer, 1978-81; pres., chief operating officer Los Angeles Times, 1981-87; sr. v.p. Times Mirror Co., Los Angeles, 1988—. Mem. exec. com., bd. fellows Claremont Grad. Sch. and Univ. Ctr.; former chmn. Los Angeles area council Boy Scouts Am., dir. Western region area pres. Boy Scouts Am.; vice chmn., 1989—; dirs. Assocs. of Calif. Inst. Tech.; former chmn. telecommunications com. and prodn. mgmt. com. Am. Newspaper Pubs. Assn.; former mem. Am. Soc. Newspaper Editors; former dir. United Way Long Island, Calif.; bd. dirs. U. Minn. Found. Mem. U. Minn. Alumni Club, City Club Bunker Hill. Presbyterian. Office: Los Angeles Times Times Mirror Co Times Mirror Sq Los Angeles CA 90053

WRIGHT, DOUGLAS TYNDALL, former university president, company director, engineering educator; b. Toronto, Oct. 4, 1927; s. George C. and Etta (Tyndall) W.; B.A.Sc. with honors in Civil Engring, U. Toronto, 1949; M.S. in Structural Engring, U. Ill., 1952; Ph.D. in Engring. U. Cambridge, 1954; D.Eng. (hon.), Carleton U., 1967; LL.D. (hon.), Brock U., 1967, Concordia U., 1982; D.Sc. (hon.), Meml. U. Nfld., 1969; DHL (hon.), Northeastern U., 1985; D.Univ. (hon.), Strathclyde U., Glasgow, 1989; D de L'Université, Compiegne U., France, 1991; D Univ. (hon.), Université de Sherbrooke, 1992; DSc, McMaster U., 1993, Queen's U., 1993. Lectr. dept. civil engring. Queen's U., 1954-55, asst. prof., 1955-58, assoc. prof., 1958; prof. civil engring. U. Waterloo, 1958-67, chmn. dept. civil engring., 1958-63, dean engring., 1959-66; chmn. Ont. Com. on Univ. Affairs Govt. of Ont., 1967-72; chmn. Ont. Commn. Post-Secondary Edn., Toronto, 1969-72, dep. provincial sec. for social devel., 1972-79; dep. minister culture and recreation, 1979-80; pres. U. Waterloo, Ont., Ont., 1981-93; prof. engring. U. Waterloo, Ont., 1981—; vis. prof. Universidad Nacional Autónoma de México, 1964, 66, Université de Sherbrooke, 1966-67; cons. engr. Netherlands and Mexican pavilions Expo 1967, Olympic Sports Palace, Mexico City, 1968, Ont. Place Dome and Forum, 1971; tech. adviser Toronto Skydome, 1984-92; dir. ElectroHome Ltd., 1983, Bell Can., 1985—, Westinghouse Can., Can. Venture Founders Ltd., London Life Ins. Co., London Ins. Group, Com. Dev. Ltd., Geometrica Inc., Visible Decisions, Inc., Meloche, Monnex, Inc., Dantec Systems Corp.; mem. Premier's Coun. on Sci. and Tech., Ont., 1985-91, Prime Minister's Nat. Adv. Bd. for Sci. and Tech., 1985-91; Can. rep. Coun. for Internat. Inst. Applied Systems Analysis, Laxenburg, Austria; Prime Min.'s personal rep. to Coun. Mins. of Edn., 1990-91. Contbr. articles to profl. jours. Bd. dirs. African Students Found., Toronto, 1961-66; bd. dirs. Ont. Curriculum Inst., 1964-67; bd. govs. Stratford Shakespearian Festival, 1984-86, mem. senate, 1987. Athlone fellow, 1952-54; named Officer of Order of Can., 1991, Chevalier L'Ordre National du Mérite of France, 1992; recipient Gold medal Ont. Profl. Engrs., 1990, Can. Engrs. Gold Medal award Can. Coun. Profl. Engrs., 1992. Fellow ASCE, Can. Acad. Engring., Engring. Inst. Can. (del. Engrs. Coun. Profl. Devel., N.Y.C. 1961-70); mem. Assn. Profl. Engrs. Province Ont., Internat. Assn. Bridge and Structural Engring., Internat. Assn. Shell Structures, Can. Assn. Latin Am. Studies, Am. Acad. Mechanics, Can. Inst. Internat. Affairs, Can. Inst. Pub. Adminstrv. Clubs: Royal Can. Yacht, Univ. (Toronto). Office: U Waterloo, Waterloo, ON Canada N2L 3G1

WRIGHT, DOUGLASS BROWNELL, judge, lawyer; b. Hartford, Conn., May 30, 1912; s. Arthur Brownell and Sylvia (Stephens) W.; m. Jane Hamersley, Sept. 24, 1938; children: Jane C., Douglass B., Hamersley S., Elizabeth B., Arthur W. A.B., Yale U., 1933; LL.B., Hartford Coll. Law, 1937. Bar: Conn. 1937. Legal dept. Aetna Life Ins. Co., 1937-39; partner Davis, Lee, Howard & Wright, Hartford, 1939—; lectr. law U. Conn., 1946—; asst. state's atty. State of Conn., 1952-59; judge Conn. Circuit Court, 1959-65, Conn. Superior Ct., 1965—; leader orch. Judge Wright and the Four Wrongs. Author: Connecticut Law of Torts, 1956, Connecticut Legal Forms 5 vols., 1958, Connecticut Jury Instructions, 3 vols., 1960, 76. Sec., dir. Captioned Films for the Deaf, Inc.; bd. dirs., pres. Am. Sch. for Deaf, 1942—; trustee Hartt Mus. Found., 1949—, Good Will Boys Club Hartford, 1950—; regent U. Hartford; bd. dirs. Vis. Nurse Assn., Newington Home for Crippled Children, Hartford Times Farm, Loomis Sch.; incorporator Conn. Inst. for Blind. Served as lt. USNR, 1942-45. Mem. Phi Beta Kappa, Psi Upsilon. Conglist. Clubs: University (Hartford), Hartford Golf (Hartford), Hartford Tennis (Hartford), 20th Century (Hartford); Coral Beach and Tennis (Bermuda); Hillsboro (Pompano Beach, Fla.). Home: 30 Sycamore Rd West Hartford CT 06117-2834 Office: 95 Washington St Hartford CT 06106-4406

WRIGHT, EARL JEROME, pastor, bishop; b. Altheimer, Ark., Dec. 10, 1929; s. Frank Lee and Emma Ophelia (Tillman) W.; m. Geraldine Marvel Miller, Aug. 16, 1952; children: Earl Jerome, Michael Ellis, Marvel Sheryl. Grad., William Tyndale Bible Coll., Detroit, 1953; DDiv (hon.), Trinity Hall Div. Sch., 1961. Ordained min. Ch. of God in Christ, 1953. Postal clk. U.S. Post Office, Detroit, 1952-67; pastor Miller Meml. Ch. of God in Christ, Detroit, 1963—; bishop 2d Eccles. Jurisdiction S.W. Mich., Detroit, 1985—; chair adv. com. Bd. of Bishops, 1986—; chmn. ways and means com. Gen. Assembly, 1991—; nat. sec. youth dept. United Nat. Auxs. Conv. 1970-76, nat. registrar, 1976-82. Mem. exec. bd. dirs., NAACP, Detroit, 1983-87; mem. bd. dirs. FEMA, Detroit, 1983—; vice chmn. Mayor's Clergy

Com., Detroit, 1987-91. Avocations: fishing, health spa activities, bike riding, horseback riding.

WRIGHT, EDWARD S., materials technology administrator. Dir. U.S. Army Materials Tech. Lab., Watertown, Mass. Office: US Army Materials Tech Lab ATTN SLZMT-D Watertown MA 02172

WRIGHT, ERIK OLIN, sociology educator; b. Berkeley, Calif., Feb. 9, 1947; s. Martin Erik and Beatrice Ann (Posner) W.; m. Marcia Kahn, Mar. 28, 1971; children: Jennifer Beatrice, Rebecca Sonia. BA summa cum laude, Harvard U., 1968; BA with 1st class honours, Oxford (Eng.) U., 1970; PhD, U. Calif., Berkeley, 1976. Asst. prof. sociology U. Wis., Madison, 1976-80, assoc. prof., 1980-83, prof., 1983—, C. Wright Mills. prof., 1990, dir. Havens Ctr. for Study Social Structure-Social Change, 1985—; vis. prof. U. Calif., 1987-88. Author: Politics of Punishment, 1973, Class, Crisis and the State, 1978, Classes, 1985, Reconstructing Marxism, 1992, Interrogating Inequality, 1994. Fellow German Marshall Fund, 1982. Mem. Am. Sociol. Assn. Office: U Wis Dept Sociology Madison WI 53706

WRIGHT, ERNEST MARSHALL, physiologist, consultant; b. Belfast, Ireland, June 8, 1940; came to U.S., 1965; BSc, U. London, 1961, DSc, 1978; PhD, U. Sheffield, Eng., 1964. Research fellow Harvard U., Boston, 1965-66; from asst. prof. to full prof. physiology UCLA Med. Sch., 1967—, chmn. dept. physiology, 1987—; cons. NIH, Bethesda, Md., 1982—, Senator Jacob K. Javits neurosci. investigator, 1985. Office: UCLA Sch Med Dept Physiology 10833 Le Conte Ave Los Angeles CA 90024

WRIGHT, EUGENE ALLEN, federal judge; b. Seattle, Feb. 23, 1913; s. Elias Allen and Mary (Bailey) W.; m. Esther Ruth Ladley, Mar. 19, 1938; children: Gerald Allen, Meredith Ann Wright Morton. AB, U. Wash., 1935, JD, 1937; LLD, U. Puget Sound, 1984. Bar: Wash. 1937. Assoc. Wright & Wright, Seattle, 1937-54; judge Superior Ct. King County, Wash., 1954-66; v.p., sr. trust officer Pacific Nat. Bank Seattle, 1966-69; judge U.S. Ct. Appeals (9th cir.), Seattle, 1969—; acting municipal judge, Seattle, 1948-52; mem. faculty Nat. Jud. Coll., 1964-72; lectr. Sch. Communications, U. Wash., 1965-66, U. Wash. Law Sch., 1952-74; lectr. appellate judges' seminars, 1973-76, Nat. Law Clks. Inst., La. State U., 1973; chmn. Wash. State Com. on Law and Justice, 1968-69; mem. com. on appellate rules Jud. Conf., 1978-85, mem. com. on courtroom photography, 1983-85, com. jud. ethics, 1984-92, com. Bicentennial of Constn., 1985-87. Author: (with others) The State Trial Judges Book, 1966; also articles; editor: Trial Judges Jour., 1963-66; contbr. articles to profl. jours. Chmn. bd. visitors U. Puget Sound Sch. Law, 1979-84; mem. bd. visitors U. Wash. Sch. Law, 1989—; bd. dirs. Met. YMCA, Seattle, 1955-72; lay reader Episc Ch. Served to lt. col. USAR, 1941-46, col. Res., ret. Decorated Bronze Star, Combat Inf. badge; recipient Army Commendation medal, Disting. Service award U.S. Jr. C. of C., 1948, Disting. Service medal Am. Legion. Fellow Am. Bar Found.; mem. ABA (coun. div. jud. adminstrn. 1971-76), Fed. Bar Assn. (Disting. Jud. Svc. award 1984), Wash. Bar Assn. (award of merit 1983), Seattle-King County Bar Assn. (Spl. Disting. Svc. award 1984), Appellate Judges Conf., Order of Coif, Wash. Athletic Club, Rainier Club, Masons (33 deg.), Shriners, Delta Upsilon (Disting. Alumni Achievement award 1989), Phi Delta Phi. Office: US Ct Appeals 9th Cir 902 US Courthouse 1010 5th Ave Seattle WA 98104-1179

WRIGHT, FELIX E., manufacturing company executive; b. 1935; married. Student, East Tex. State U., 1958. With Leggett & Platt, Inc., Carthage, Mo., 1959—, sr. v.p., from 1976, chief operating officer, exec. v.p., 1979, now pres., chief operating officer, 1985—. Office: Leggett & Platt Inc 1 Leggett Rd Carthage MO 64836-9649

WRIGHT, FRANK GARDNER, newspaper editor; b. Moline, Ill., Mar. 21, 1931; s. Paul E. and Goldie (Hicks) W.; m. Barbara Lee Griffiths, Mar. 28, 1953; children: Stephen, Jeffrey, Natalie, Gregory, Sarah. B.A., Augustana Coll., Rock Island, Ill., 1953; postgrad., U. Minn., 1953-54. Suburban reporter Mpls. Star, 1954-55; with Mpls. Tribune, 1955-82, N.D. corr., 1955-56, Mpls. City Hall reporter, 1956-58, asst. city editor, 1958-63, Minn. polit. reporter, 1963-68, Washington corr., 1968-72, Washington bur. chief, 1972-77, mng. editor, 1977-82; mng. editor/news Mpls. Star and Tribune, 1982-84, assoc. editor, 1984—; juror for Pulitzer Awards, 1983-84. Chmn. Golden Valley Human Rights Commn., 1965-67; Bd. dirs. Luth. Social Services, Washington. Recipient several Page 1 awards Twin Cities Newspaper Guild, 1950's, 60's, Worth Bingham prize Worth Bingham Meml. Fund, 1971; runnerup Raymond Clapper award for Washington correspondence, 1971; Outstanding Achievement award Augustana Alumni Assn., 1977; citation for excellence in internat. reporting Overseas Press Club, 1989; Minn. SPJ/SDX 1st Place Page One award for in-depth reporting, 1988. Mem. Am. Newspaper Guild (chmn. Mpls. unit 1961-63, editorial v.p. Twin Cities 1963-67), Minn. AP Editors Assn. (pres. 1981), Phi Beta Kappa. Home: 4912 Aldrich Ave S Minneapolis MN 55409-2353 Office: 425 Portland Ave Minneapolis MN 55488-0001

WRIGHT, FRANKLIN LEATHERBURY, JR., lawyer, banker; b. Phila., Mar. 22, 1945; s. Franklin L. and Victoria M. (Douglas) W.; m. Willette C. Pedrick, June 21, 1969; children: Geoffrey, Stephen. AB, Coll. William and Mary, 1967; JD, Temple U., 1967. Bar: Pa. 1973, D.C. 1978. Atty.-advisor Fed. Home Loan Bank Bd., Washington, 1973-77; assoc. dir. Nat. Assn. Mut. Savs. Banks, Washington, 1977-83; dep. counsel, sr. v.p. Dime Savs. Bank N.Y., Garden City, 1983-85, spl. counsel, 1986—, 1st sr. v.p., 1986-90, exec. v.p., 1987-90, external affairs exec., dep. gen. counsel, 1990-95; external affairs exec., dep. gen. counsel Dime Bancorp Inc. (formerly Dime Savs. Bank N.Y.), N.Y.C., 1995—. Editor Temple U Law Rev., 1972. Bd. dirs. Family Life Ctr., Garden City, 1987—. With U.S. Army, 1968-70. Mem. Spray Beach Yacht (N.J.). Episcopalian. Office: Dime Bancorp Inc 589 Fifth Ave New York NY 10017

WRIGHT, GEORGE CULLEN, electronics company executive; b. Anderson, S.C., June 28, 1923; s. Benjamin Norman and Essie Floride (Cole) W.; m. Kathleen Ashe, Oct. 19, 1947; children: Carol Ann (Mrs. John C. Marquardt), George Cullen, Florenda Jean, William Norman. BS, Clemson U., 1948. Asst. supt. Duke Power Co., 1949-56; city mgr. Gaffney, S.C., 1956-60; v.p. mktg. Hubbard & Co., Chgo., 1960-63; dir. Methode Electronics, Inc., Rolling Meadows, Ill., 1956—; v.p., dir. Anchor Coupling Co., Inc., Libertyville, Ill., 1973-76; pres., dir. Exec. Extension & Ventures, Inc., Barrington, Ill., 1976-78, White Marlin Marine, Inc., Anderson, S.C., 1976—, Piedmont Corp., 1986—. Patentee in field. Pres. Barrington East Ass., 1968-70. Served with AUS, 1942-45. Mem. AIEE Electron Industry Assn., Am. Mgmt. Assn. Lodges: Rotary, Sertoma (pres. 1963-65). Home: 224 Jolly Rd Townville SC 29689-3540

WRIGHT, GEORGE NELSON, counselor, educator; b. Earlington, Ky., Dec. 10, 1921; s. James Nelson and Jennie Mae (Carr) W.; m. Patricia Adele Gilmer, June 8, 1952; children: John, Elizabeth, Robert, James. BS, Ind. U., 1947; MS, Purdue U., 1954, PhD, 1959. Cert. rehab. counselor, Wis. Pers. interviewer Mo. Iron Co., Evansville, Ind., 1942-45; rsch. asst. psychology dept. Ind. U., Bloomington, 1946-47; rehab. counselor Ind. Vocat. Rehab. Div., West Lafayette, 1947-58; nat. program dir. Nat. Epilepsy League, Chgo., 1959-62; mem. faculty, dir. rehab. counseling U. Wis., Madison, 1962-92, prof., 1969-92, rsch. dir. Rehab. Rsch. Inst., 1963-92; cons. Philippine Disability Found., Govt. Israel, others. Author: Rehabilitation Research, 1968, Wisconsin Studies in Vocational Rehabilitation, 1968, 73, 76, Epilepsy Rehabilitation, 1975, Total Rehabilitation, 1980; contbr. articles to profl. jours. Recipient Disting. Scholar award Am. Assn. Counseling and Devel., 1989, Pres.'s silver medal Govt. of Israel, 1969, Corbin. award Philippine Disability Found., 1976, Disting. Scholar award Chi Sigma Iota, 1988. Fellow Am. Psychol. Assn. (life, past pres. rehab. psychology div., Disting. Career award 1988, Lifetime Contbns. award 1989), Am. Psychol. Soc.; mem. Nat. Coun. Rehab. Edn. (dir. rsch., Nat. award 1986), Nat. Rehab. Assn. (Founders award 1982), Am. Pers. and Guidance Assn. (bd. dirs., Nat. Svc. award 1975), Am. Rehab. Counseling Assn. (Disting. Rsch. award 1989, Ann. Rsch. award 1971, 73, 74, 87), Sigma Xi. Democrat. Presbyterian. Avocations: travel, rsch., social svcs. Home: 492 Presidential Ln Madison WI 53711-1154 Office: U Wis Rehab Rsch Inst 432 N Murray St Rm 413 Madison WI 53706-1496

WRIGHT, GEORGE SEARCY, federal judge, educator; b. Tuscaloosa, Ala., Nov. 1, 1925; s. Reuben H. and Camille (Searcy) W.; children: Stella Wright Martin, Camille Searcy Brannon, Maxine Wellborn Hudson. B.S. in Engring., U.S. Naval Acad., 1948; J.D., U. Ala., 1956. Bar: Ala., U.S. Dist. Ct. (no. dist.) Ala., U.S.C. Appeals (11th cir.). Commd. ensign U.S. Navy, advanced through grades to lt. (j.g.), 1954; ret. comdr., 1973; ptnr. Rosen, Wright & Harwood, Tuscaloosa, 1966-81; chief judge for no. dist. of Ala., U.S. Bankruptcy Ct., Tuscaloosa, 1961-94; instr. U. Ala. Law Sch., 1973—. Mem. editorial bd. Ala. Law Rev., 1954-56; author casenotes and legal commentaries. Mem. Ala. Law Sch. Found., 1981—. Recipient Outstanding Alumnus award Bench and Bar Legal Honor Soc., 1984; Lawyers Title award U. Ala. Faculty, 1955; Miree award Ala. Title & Abstract Co., 1956. Mem. ABA, Farrah Order of Jurisprudence, Comml. Law League Am., Nat. Conf. Bankruptcy Judges (bd. govs. 1993—), Tuscaloosa Bar Assn. (pres. 1970), Tuscaloosa C. of C., Navy League, Phi Delta Phi. Episcopalian. Club: Exchange. Office: US Bankruptcy Ct PO Box 3226 Tuscaloosa AL 35403-3226

WRIGHT, GEORGE WALTER, aeronautical engineer, state legislator; b. Boston, July 20, 1923; s. George Wright and Ethel Maude (Alward) W.; widowed; 4 children. BA, Boston Coll., 1950; postgrad., Northeastern U., 1952-54; DD (hon.), Cooper State U., 1962. Aircraft mechanic N.E. Airlines, Presque Isle, Maine, 1942-43; airline pilot N.E. Airlines, Boston, 1947-57, Delta Airlines, Boston and Atlanta, 1957-77; antique aircraft restorer Penguin Aeroplane Co., Brookline, N.H., 1977-94; surveyor State of N.H., 1984-91; mem. from Hillsborough County N.H. Ho. of Reps., Concord, 1989—; flight instr. Airline Pilots Assn., N.H., 1952—; asst. minister Enoch Ch. Br. Davidian, Idaho and Tex., 1976-81; mechanic for restoration of various vintage cars. Author I Told You I Was Sick, 1960 (Ugliest Book of Yr. 1961) newspaper column Under the Golden Dome, 1960—. Pres. Granite State Bus. Assn., Nashua, N.H., 1981-84; operator N.H. Recycling Orgn., Concord, 1980-81; brother NAACP, New Eng., 1960-63. Lt. (s.g.) USNR, 1943-45. Recipient Gold medal for decathalon Sr. Olympics, 1972; named Businessman of Yr., 1952;. Republican. Avocations: skeet shooting, swimming, hockey, billiards, embroidery. Home: 53 Flint Pond Dr Hollis NH 03049-6045

WRIGHT, GLADYS STONE, music educator, composer, writer; b. Wasco, Oreg., Mar. 8, 1925; d. Murvel Stuart and Daisy Violet (Warren) Stone; m. Alfred George Wright, June 28, 1953. BS, U. Oreg., 1948, MS, 1953. Dir. bands Elmira (Oreg.) U-4 High Sch., 1948-53, Otterbein (Ind.) High Sch., 1954-61, Klondike High Sch., West Lafayette, Ind., 1962-70, Harrison High Sch., West Lafayette, 1970-84; organizer, condr. Musical Friendship Tours, Cen. Am., 1967-79; v.p., condr. U.S. Collegiate Wind Band, 1975—; bd. dirs. John Philip Sousa Found. 1984—; chmn. Sudler Cup, 1986—, Sudler Flag, 1982; pres. Internat. Music Tours, 1984—, Key to the City, Taxco, Mex., 1975. Editor: Woman Conductor, 1986—; composer: marches Big Bowl and Trumpets and Tabards, 1987; contbg. editor: Informusica (Spain). Bd. dirs. N. Am. Wildlife Park, Battleground, Ind. 1985. Recipient Medal of the order John Philip Sousa Found., 1988, Star of Order, 1991; 1st woman guest conductor U.S. Navy Band, Washington D.C., 1961, Goldman Band, N.Y.C., 1958, Kneller Hall Band, London, 1975, Tri-State Music Festival Massed Orch., Band, Choir, 1985; elected to Women Bd. Dirs. Hall of Fame of Disting. Women Conductor, 1994. Mem. Am. Bandmasters Assn. (bd. dirs. 1993, 1st woman mem.), Women Band Dirs. Nat. Assn. (founding pres. 1967, sec. 1985, recipient Silver Baton 1974, Golden Rose 1990, Hall of Fame 1995), Am. Sch. Band Dirs. Assn., Nat. Band Assn. (Citation excellence 1970), Tippecanoe Arts Fedn. (bd. dirs. 1986-90), Tippecanoe Fife and Drum Corps. (bd. dirs. 1984), Daughters of Am. Revolution, Col. Dames-Pre Quitanen Chpt., New England Women, Tau Beta Sigma (Outstanding Svc. to Music award 1970), Phi Beta Mu (1st hon. women mem. 1972), North Am. Wildlife Park (bd dirs 1990—). Avocations: historic preservation, environ. activities.

WRIGHT, GORDON BROOKS, musician, conductor, educator; b. Bklyn., Dec. 31, 1934; s. Harry Wesley and Helen Philomena (Brooks) W.; m. Inga-Lisa Myrin Wright, June 13, 1958 (div. 1979); children: Karin-Ellen Blindenbacher, Charles-Eric, Daniel Brooks. MusB, Coll. Wooster, 1957; MA, U. Wis., 1961; postgrad., Salzburg Mozarteum, 1972, Loma Linda U. 1979; studied with, René Leibowitz, Carl Melles, Wilfred Pelletier, Herbert Blomstedt, Hans Swarowsky. Founder, music dir. Wis. Chamber Orch., 1960-69; music dir. Fairbanks (Alaska) Symphony Orch., 1969-89; prof. emeritus, 1989—; founder, music dir. Arctic Chamber Orch., Fairbanks, 1970-89; exec. dir. The Reznicek Soc., Indian, Alaska, 1982—. Guest condr. Philharmonia Hungarica, Philomusica London, Norwegian Radio Orch., Orch. St. Luke's, Anchorage Symphony Orch.; composer: Suite of Netherlands Dances, 1965, Six Alaskan Tone Poems, 1974, Symphony in Ursa Major, 1979 (Legis. award 1979), 1984 Overture, Scott Joplin Suite, 1987, Toccata Festiva, 1992; columnist Alaska Advocate. Founder, bd. dirs. No. Alaska Environ. Ctr., Fairbanks, 1971-78. Served as pvt. AUS, 1957-59. Mem. Am. Musicol. Soc., Royal Musical Assn., Am. Symphony Orch. League, Condr.'s Guild, Arturo Toscanini Soc., Am. Fedn. Musicians, Royal Mus. Assn., Sierra Club (lchmn. Fairbanks Group 1969-71), Friends of Earth-Alaska (bd. dirs. 1982—), Wilderness Soc., Audubon Soc., Alaska Conservation Soc. (editor Rev. 1971-78), Ctr. for Alaskan Coastal Studies (bd. dirs. 1982—). Avocations: hiking, kayaking, collecting books, photography. Home: HC 52 Box 8899 Indian AK 99540

WRIGHT, GORDON PRIBYL, management, operations research educator; b. Crosby, Minn., May 18, 1938; s. Kenneth Eugene and Verla Emily (Pribyl) W.; m. Judith Ann Hill, Aug. 19, 1961; 1 dau., Teresa Ann. B.A., Macalester Coll., 1960; M.A., U. Mass., 1963; Ph.D., Case Western Res. U., 1967. Systems analyst Conn. Gen. Life Ins. Co., Bloomfield, 1960-61; instr. dept. math. U. Mass., 1961-63; statistician, mgmt. scis. group Goodyear Tire & Rubber Co., Akron, Ohio, 1963-64; instr., research asst., ops. research dept. Case Inst. Tech., Cleve., 1964-67; asst. prof. dept. indsl. engring. and mgmt. scis. Technol. Inst., Northwestern U., 1967-70; assoc. prof. mgmt. and statistics Krannert Grad. Sch. Mgmt. and Sch. of Sci., Purdue U., West Lafayette, Ind., 1970-75; assoc. dean Krannert Grad. Sch. Mgmt. and Sch. of Sci., Purdue U., 1979-81, dir. prof., 1982—, Krannert disting. prof., 1982—, dir. of research, 1985-89, dir. doctoral programs, 1985-89; prof., chmn. mgmt., dir. profl. programs Krannert Grad. Sch. Mgmt., Purdue U., 1978-79; Basil Turner prof. mgmt. Purdue U., 1987—; vis. prof. bus. adminstrn. and stats. Amos Tuck Sch. Bus. Adminstrn., Dartmouth Coll., 1976-77; vis. prof. Bradley U.; vis. prof. mgmt. sci. Grad. Sch. Mgmt. UCLA, 1984-85; cons. Okamura Mfg. Co., Yokohama, Japan. Author: (with David G. Olson) Designing Water Pollution Detection Systems, 1974, (with Andrew B. Whinston and Gary J. Koehler) Optimization of Leontief Systems, 1975, (with Herbert M. Moskowitz) An Experiential Approach to Management Science, 1975, Introduction to Management Science, 1979, Statistics for Business and Economics, 1982, (with Frank M. Bass) Stochastic Brand Choice and Brand Switching: Theory Analysis and Description, 1980; contbr. (with Frank M. Bass) articles on ops. research and mgmt. to profl. jours. Served with USAF Res., 1961-67. Recipient Salgo-Noren Found. award for outstanding teaching in bus. adminstrn., 1975; NSF research grantee, 1968-70; Dept. Transp. research grantee, 1972-74; HEW research grantee, 1969-70; Sloan Found. research grantee, 1972-75; Fulbright scholar to Ger., 1986; Vis. Erskine fellowship U. Canterbury, New Zealand, 1985. Mem. Ops. Research Soc. Am., Inst. Mgmt. Scis., Sigma Xi, Beta Gamma Sigma. Home: 136 Seminole Dr West Lafayette IN 47906-2116 Office: Krannert Sch Mgmt Purdue U West Lafayette IN 47907

WRIGHT, GWENDOLYN, art center director, writer, educator; b. Chgo., May 14, 1946; d. William Kemp and Mary Ruth (Brown) W.; m. Paul Rabinow, Nov. 18, 1980 (div. 1982); m. Thomas Bender, Jan. 14, 1985; children: David, Sophia. BA, NYU, 1969; MArch, U. Calif., Berkeley, 1974, PhD, 1980. Assoc. prof. Columbia U., N.Y.C., 1983-87, prof., 1988—; dir. Buell Ctr. for Study Am. Architecture, N.Y.C., 1988-92; cons. Fulbright Scholars, Coun. Internat. Exch. Scholars, Washington, 1988-91. Author: Building the Dream: A Social History of Housing in America, 1980, Moralism and the Model Home, 1981, The History of History in American Schools of Architecture, 1990, The Politics of Design in French Colonial Urbanism, 1991. Fellow Ford Found., 1979-80; Stanford Inst. for Humanities, 1982-83, Mich. Inst. for Humanities, 1991, Getty Ctr. for History of Art and the Humanities, 1992—. Fellow Soc. Am. Historians, N.Y. Inst. for Humanities; mem. Soc. Archtl. Historians, Coll. Art Assn., Am. Hist. Assn.,

Orgn. Am. Historians. Democrat. Home: 54 Washington Mews New York NY 10003-6608 Office: Columbia U Avery Hall New York NY 10027

WRIGHT, HARRISON MORRIS, historian, educator; b. Phila., Oct. 6, 1928; s. Sydney L. and Catharine W. (Morris) W.; m. Josephine Stearns Cole, July 20, 1957; children—Rebecca H., J. Rodman, Thomas F., Daniel H., James L. B.A., Harvard, 1950, M.A., 1953, Ph.D., 1957. Teaching fellow Harvard, 1955-57; mem. faculty Swarthmore Coll., 1957—, prof. history, 1968-87, Isaac H. Clothier prof. history and internat. relations, 1987-93, chmn. dept., 1968-79, provost, 1979-84, Clothier prof. and provost emeritus, 1993—, acting pres., 1982. Author: New Zealand, 1769-1840: Early Years of Western Contact, 1959, The Burden of the Present: Liberal-Radical Controversy over Southern African History, 1977; Editor: The New Imperialism—Analysis of Late Nineteenth-Century Expansion, 1961, 2d edit., 1976, Sir James Rose Innes: Selected Correspondence (1884-1902), 1972. Fulbright scholar New Zealand, 1950-51; Ford Found. fgn. areas fellow Eng. and Ghana, 1961-62; grantee Am. Philos. Soc., S. Africa, 1966-67; grantee Old Dominion Fund, S. Africa, 1971. Mem. Am. Hist. Assn., Newport Hist. Soc. (bd. dirs. 1973-88), Hist. Soc. Pa. (coun. 1984-91, coun. emeritus 1992—, v.p. 1986-88, chmn. 1989-91), Rhode Island Hist. Soc., African Studies Assn, Phi Beta Kappa. Home: 86 Clarke St Jamestown RI 02835 Office: History Dept Swarthmore Coll Swarthmore PA 19081

WRIGHT, HARRY, III, lawyer; b. Lima, Ohio, Apr. 27, 1925; s. Harry Jr. and Marjorie (Riddle) W.; m. Louise Forbes Taylor, Dec. 15, 1956; children: Harry IV, Whitaker Wilson, Priscilla W. Nicholson. Student, The Citadel, 1942-43; B.S., U. Ky., 1948; LL.B., Harvard, 1951. Bar: Ohio 1951. With Porter, Wright, Morris & Arthur, Columbus, 1951—; ptnr. Porter, Wright, Morris & Arthur, 1956-88, of counsel, 1988—; adj. prof. law Japan Law Ctr., 1986. Mem. adv. bd. Salvation Army, 1958-74; pres. bd. trustees Six Pence Sch., Columbus, 1965-75; trustee Bradford Coll., 1957-75, pres. bd., 1972-74; trustee Columbus Acad., 1975-81, pres. bd., 1978-80; trustee Columbus Coun. World Affairs, 1979-82 Opera/Columbus, 1980-88, 89—, Ballet Met., 1987-91; trustee Green Lawn Cemetery, 1992—, Neighborhood Ho., 1993—. With USAAF, 1943-46. Mem. ABA (chmn. gen. practice sect. 1976-77, ho. of dels. 1978-87), Ohio Bar Assn. (Supreme Ct. Commn. on CLE 1988-94), Columbus Bar Assn., Columbus Club, Rocky Fork Hunt and Country Club. Episcopalian. Home: 292 N Drexel Ave Columbus OH 43209-1429 Office: 41 S High St Columbus OH 43215-6101

WRIGHT, HARRY FORREST, JR., retired banker; b. Woodbury, N.J., Nov. 9, 1931; s. Harry Forrest and Bertha (Strumpfer) W.; m. Lorraine Catherine McLaughlin, Oct. 16, 1954; children: Harry Forrest III, Lonni Caryn, Gregory William, Douglas Carl. Student, Temple U., 1949-50, Am. Inst. Banking, 1950-52; accounting certificate, Wharton Sch., U Pa., 1960, asso. degree, 1962. Clk. First Nat. Bank, Phila., 1951-60; asst. comptroller, then asst. v.p. First Pa. Co., 1960- 64; v.p. Md Nat. Bank, Balt., 1964-66; v.p., comptroller Md. Nat. Bank, 1966-70, sr. v.p., comptroller, 1970-73, exec. v.p., 1973-81, exec. v.p., 1981-89, also bd. dirs., ret., 1989; v.p., treas. Md. Nat. Corp., 1974-77, sr. v.p., 1977-83; exec. v.p., chief fin. officer MNC Fin. Inc., 1983-88, ret., 1989; treas., dir. Md. Nat. Optimation Svcs., Inc., 1969-76, chmn., 1976-79; sec. Md. Switch, Inc., 1976-79; treas., dir. Manab Properties, Inc.; pres., dir. 10 Light St. Corp., 1973-82; affiliate Property Tax Cons., San Diego, 1990—. Treas. Cub Scouts Am., Severna Park, Md., 1965-66, St. Martin's Kindergarten, 1967-72, Bayberry Hill Property Owners Assn., 1985—; bd. dirs. Greater Balt. chpt. Nat. Found. March of Dimes, 1972—, v.p. 1977-79, pres., 1979-81, chmn., 1981-84, Nat. Coun. Vols., 1983-85, 89—, Nat. Fin. Task Force, 1989—; bd. dirs. Md. Sch. for Blind, 1975—, v.p., 1981-88, pres., 1988-94, chmn. Bd., 1994—; chmn. Richard E. Hoover Commn. for Low Vision and Blindness at Greater Balt. Med. Ctr., 1990-92, treas., 1992—. Mem. Bank Adminstrn. Inst. (pres. Balt. 1970-71, state dir. 1971-73, dist. dir. 1977-79), Fin. Execs. Inst. (dir. 1976-78), Sigma Kappa Phi. Club: Mchts. (Balt.) (bd. dirs. 1974-87, v.p. 1976-79, pres. 1979-82). Home and Office: 1314 St Josephs Ct Crownsville MD 21032 *Success in life is not measured in material wealth, but in diversity of accomplishment, contribution to social good, and respect from peers, subordinates, and superiors alike. The greatest joys are in children and grandchildren and their growth and achievements, and in teaching them continually to strive harder to be successful and happy.*

WRIGHT, HASTINGS KEMPER, surgeon, educator; b. Boston, Aug. 28, 1928; s. Donald M. and Lucia (Durand) W.; m. Nancy E. Howell, June 19, 1954; children: Mark, Kenneth, Barbara, Donald. AB, Harvard U., 1950, MD, 1954, MA, 1973. Diplomate: Am. Bd. Surgery. Intern Univ. Hosps. Cleve., 1954, resident, 1957-61; asst. prof. surgery Western Res. U., Cleve., 1961-66; assoc. prof. surgery Med. Sch. Yale U., New Haven, 1967-72, prof. Med. Sch., 1972-95; prof. surgery emeritus, 1995—; chief gen. surgery Yale-New Haven Hosp., 1968-79, asst. chief surgery, 1979-95. Author: Complications of GI Surgery, 1972; asst. chief editor Archives of Surgery, Chgo., 1977-89. Capt. U.S. Army, 1955-57. Fellow ACS, Am. Surg. Assn.; mem. Soc. Univ. Surgeons (program dir. 1972), Am. Gastroent. Assn., Soc. Surgery Gastrointestinal Tract. Republican. Episcopalian. Clubs: Mory's Assoc. (New Haven); Yale (N.Y.C.). Home: 35 Wood Rd Branford CT 06405-4935 Office: Yale U Med Sch Dept Surgery 333 Cedar St New Haven CT 06510-3289

WRIGHT, HELEN PATTON, association executive; b. Washington, Jan. 15, 1919; d. Raymond Stanton and Virginia (Mitchell) Patton; m. James Skelly Wright, Feb. 1, 1945 (dec. 1988); 1 son, James Skelly; m. John H. Pickering, Feb. 3, 1990. Student, Sweet Briar Coll., 1936-38; grad., Washington Sch. Secretaries, 1939, Am. U., 1989. Tchr. Washington Sch. Secretaries, N.Y.C., 1939-40; sec. The White House, 1941-43, Am. embassy, London, Eng., 1943-45; asst. to exec. dir. Senate Atomic Energy Com., 1946-47. V.p., mem. budget and admissions com. United Fund New Orleans, 1960-62; chmn. met. div., campaign; v.p. Dept. Pub. Welfare, Orleans Parish and City New Orleans, 1960-62, Milne Asylum for Destitute Orphan Boys, New Orleans, 1958-62; mem. bd. New Orleans Social Welfare Planning Coun., 1954-62, New Orleans Cancer Soc., 1958-60; v.p. Juvenile Ct. Adv. Com. New Orleans, 1961; successively sec., v.p., pres. Parents' Assn. Metairie Park Country Day Sch., 1956-59; v.p. La. Assn. Mental Health, 1960-62; del. dir. to Nat. Assn. Mental Health, 1960-62; bd. mem. Washington Health and Welfare Coun., 1962-64, Hillcrest Children's Ctr., Washington, 1963-69, D.C. Mental Health Assn., 1962-72, 73-76; bd. dirs. Hospice Care of D.C., 1981-88, 90—, pres. 1986-88; mem. adv. bd. civil commitment project Nat. Ctr. for State Cts., 1981; bd. dirs. Nat. Assn. Mental Health, 1966-70, 67-74, sec., 1968-70, pres.-elect, 1970-71, pres., 1972-73, cons. on assn. film, 1972; mem. Commn. on Mentally Disabled, Am. Bar Assn., 1973-80; chmn. altar guild Christ Ch. Cathedral, New Orleans, 1960 Little Sanctuary of St. Albans Sch., Washington, 1965; mem. Altar Guild, St. Alban's, Chgo., 1976, 77; chmn. Washington com. Nat. Cathedral Assn., 1976, 77, 78, 79, trustee, 1976-90, sec., 1980-83, v.p., 1984-87; bd. dirs. Nat. Ctr. Voluntary Action; mem. task panel Mental Health Problems, Scope and Boundaries, Pres.'s Commn. Mental Health, 1977; mem. tech. rev. com. Md. Psychiat. Rsch. Ctr., 1979-81. Address: 5317 Blackistone Rd Bethesda MD 20816-1822

WRIGHT, HELENE SEGAL, editor; b. L.A., Jan. 31, 1955; d. Alan and Lila E. (Hambro) Segal; m. David Scott Wright, May 6, 1979. Student, Calif. State U., Fullerton, 1973-75; BA in English, U. Calif., Santa Barbara, 1978. Library asst. ABC-CLIO, Santa Barbara, 1979-80, editorial asst., 1980-81, asst. editor, 1981-83; mng. editor ABC-CLIO, ABC POL SCI, Santa Barbara, 1983—. Mem. Am. Polit. Sci. Assn., Current World Leaders (adv. bd. 1989—). Avocations: reading, collecting, swimming. Home: 142 La Vista Grande Santa Barbara CA 93103-2817 Office: ABC-CLIO 130 Cremona Dr Santa Barbara CA 93117-3075

WRIGHT, HERBERT E(DGAR), JR., geologist; b. Malden, Mass., Sept. 13, 1917; s. Herbert E. and Annie M. (Richardson) W.; m. Rhea Jane Hahn, June 21, 1943; children—Richard, Jonathan, Stephen, Andrew, Jeffrey. AB, Harvard U., 1939, MA, 1941, PhD, 1943; DSc (hon.), Trinity Coll., Dublin, Ireland, 1966; PhD (hon.), Lund U., Sweden, 1987. Instr. Brown U., 1946-47; asst. prof. geology U. Minn., Mpls., 1947-51, asso. prof., 1951-59, prof., 1959-74, Regents' prof. geology, ecology and botany, 1974-88; dir. Limnological Research Center, 1963-90. Served to maj. USAAF, 1942-45. Decorated D.F.C., Air medal with 6 oak leaf clusters; recipient Pomerance award Archeol. Inst. Am., 1985, Ann. award Sci. Mus. Minn., 1990; Gug-

genheim fellow, 1954-55, Wenner-Gren fellow, 1954-55. Fellow AAAS, Geol. Soc. Am. (Ann. award archeol. divsn. 1989, Disting. Career award geology and geomorphology divsn. 1992), Soc. Am. Archeology (Fryxell award 1993); mem. NAS, Ecol. Soc. Am., Am. Soc. Limnology, Oceanography, Am. Quaternary Assn., Arctic Inst., Brit. Ecol. Soc. Research on Quaternary geology, paleoecology, paleolimnology and environ. archaeology in Minn., Wyo., Sweden, Yukon, Labrador, Peru, eastern Mediterranean. Home: 1426 Hythe St Saint Paul MN 55108-1423 Office: U of Pillsbury 221 Pillsbury Hall 310 Pillsbury Dr SE Minneapolis MN 55455

WRIGHT, HUGH ELLIOTT, JR., association executive, writer; b. Athens, Ala., Nov. 20, 1937; s. Hugh Elliott and Martha Angeline (Shannon) W. A.B., Birmingham-So. Coll., 1959; M.Div., Vanderbilt U., 1962, D.Ministry, 1967; postgrad., Harvard U., 1963. Ordained to ministry Methodist Ch., 1963; pastor Baxter (Tenn.) Meth. Ch., 1963-64; assoc. pastor Waverly Pl. Ch., Nashville, 1965-66; field sec. Tenn. Heart Assn. Nashville, 1964-65; editorial asst. Motive mag., Nashville, 1965-67; Protestant-Orthodox editor Religious News Service, N.Y.C., 1967-75; research fellow Auburn Theol. Sem., N.Y.C., 1976; editor project on mediating structures and public policy Am. Enterprise Inst., 1979-80; coordinator project on ch., state and taxation NCCJ, N.Y.C., 1980-83, v.p. for program, 1983-88, sr. v.p., dep. to pres., 1988-91; program cons. N.Y.C., 1992—; cons. Hartford Sem. Found., 1972, United Meth. Bd. Global Ministries, 1975-78, United Meth. Communications, 1979-81; bd. dirs. Internat. Coun. Christians and Jews, DePaul Coll. Law Ctr. on Ch. State Rels., Nat. Coun. Chs. Com. on Religious Liberty, Nat. Coun. Religious and Pub. Edn. Host: Challenge to Faith, Sta. WOR, 1973-77; author: (with R. Lecky) Can These Bones Live, 1969, The Big Little School, 1971, (with R. Lynn) Go Free, 1973, Challenge to Mission, 1973, (with Juanita Wright) Viewers Guide to Six American Families, 1977, (with Howard Butt) At the Edge of Hope, 1978, (with Douglas McGaw) A Tale of Two Congregations, 1980, Holy Company: Christian Heroes and Heroines, 1980, RNS Reporting...Sixty Years of Religious News Service, 1993; editor: (with Robert Lecky) Black Manifesto: Religion, Racism and Reparations, 1969. Recipient award Birmingham Council Indsl. Editors, 1959, Founders medal Vanderbilt U., 1962, Shepherd prize Vanderbilt, 1962, Religious Heritage of Am. award in journalism, 1972, Asso. Ch. Press Feature Article award, 1980. Mem. Authors League and Guild, Am. Acad. Religion, Phi Beta Kappa, Sigma Delta Chi, Alpha Tau Omega, Alpha Psi Omega, Eta Sigma Phi. Democrat. Home: 1346 Midland Ave Bronxville NY 10708-6832 Office: 475 Riverside Dr Rm 300 New York NY 10115

WRIGHT, IRVING SHERWOOD, physician, retired educator; b. N.Y.C., Oct. 27, 1901; s. Harry J. and Cora Ann (Hassett) W.; m. Grace Mansfield Demarest, Oct. 15, 1927; children: Barbara Mansfield, Alison Sherwood; m. Lois Elliman Findlay, Oct. 31, 1953. A.B., Cornell U., 1923, M.D., 1926. Diplomate: Am. Bd. Internal Medicine (mem. adv. bd. 1940-49), subcert. in cardiovascular diseases. Intern N.Y. Post Grad. Med. Sch. and Hosp. of Columbia, 1927-29, asst. and assoc. vis. physician, 1929-39, prof. clin. medicine, dir. and exec. officer dept. medicine, 1939-46; asst. physician Bellevue Hosp. (Cornell Div.), 1931-34, assoc., 1934-37; assoc. prof. Cornell Med. Coll. and assoc. attending physician N.Y. Hosp., 1946-48; prof. clin. medicine Cornell Med. Coll., 1948-68, emeritus clin. prof., 1968—; attending physician Drs. Hosp., N.Y.C., 1934-80, N.Y. Hosp., 1948-80; investigator into biomed. problems of aging; hon. staff dept. medicine N.Y. Hosp., 1980—; physician Met. Opera, 1935-62; dir. medicine Cornell Div.) Welfare Hosp. Chronic Disease, 1937-40 (1st pres. its med. bd. 1937-39), cons. physician, 1940-46; cons. to Orange Meml. Hosp., East Orange, N.J., Monmouth Meml. Hosp., Long Branch, N.J., Hackensack (N.J.) Hosp., Mt. Vernon (N.Y.) Hosp.; chief of med. service Army and Navy Gen. Hosp., Hot Springs (Ark.) Nat. Park, 1942-43; cons. in medicine U.S. Army, 6th Service Command, 1944-45, 9th Service Command, 1945; coordinator health survey Am. prisoners of war from Far East, 1945; chmn. Internat. Com. on Blood Clotting Factors, 1954-63, sec. gen., 1963-68; chmn. com. on cerebral vascular diseases NIH, 1961-65; mem. Pres.'s Comm. Heart Disease, Cancer and Stroke, 1966-68; nat. chmn. Commn. Heart Disease Resources, 1968-76. Author and editor numerous books on cardiovascular diseases.; Editor-in-chief: Modern Medical Monographs; Contbr. articles to med. jours. Chmn. Josiah Macy, Jr. Found. Conf. Blood Clotting, 1947-52; Trustee Cornell U. 1960-65. Served as lt. comdr. USNR, 1935-39; lt. col. to col. AUS, 1942-46; civilian cons. in medicine to surgeon gen. U.S. Army, 1946-74; mem. civilian adv. com. to sec. navy, 1946-47. Recipient Albert and Mary Lasker award Am. Heart Assn., 1960, Gold Heart award, 1958, Disting. Service award, 1976; Irving Sherwood Wright professorship in geriatrics at Cornell U. Med. Coll., 1976. Fellow Royal Coll. Physicians (London), ACP (regent, pres. 1965-66, pres. emeritus 1987—), Acad. Medicine (chmn. geriatrics sect. 1976-79, outstanding Contbrs. to Sci. and Medicine award medal 1986); mem. Am. Assn. Physicians, AMA (chmn. sect. exptl. med. and therapeutics 1939-40), Am. Heart Assn. (chmn. sect. for study peripheral circulation 1939-40, mem. exec. com., bd. dirs. 1935-57, pres. 1952-53, mem. Nat. Adv. Heart Council 1954-58, 60-61), Cornell U. Med. Coll. Alumni Assn. (pres 1953), NRC (sub-com. cardiovascular diseases 1947-51), Am. Soc. Clin. Investigation, Soc. Exptl. Biology and Medicine, N.Y. Acad. Scis., Am. Geriatrics Soc. (pres. 1971-72, Herman award 1970, Thewlis award 1974), Am. Fedn. for Aging Research (founding pres. 1980-86, AFAR Distinction award 1987), Harvey Soc., Sigma Xi, Alpha Omega Alpha; corr. mem. of Acad. Columbian de Ciencas Exactas Fisico-Quimicas Y Naturales (Bogota); hon. mem. Royal Soc. Medicine of London, med. socs. Brazil, Chile, Peru, Argentina, Cuba, Switzerland, Sweden and USSR; also hon. faculty of U. Chile. Presbyn (bd. sessions 1935-36). Clubs: Bedford Golf and Tennis; St. Nicholas Society (N.Y.). Home: 25 East End Ave New York NY 10028-7052 *My aim in life has been to improve the quality of medical care in the fields of internal medicine, geriatric cardiovascular diseases by research, teaching at undergraduate, graduate, and international levels, the development of standards and guidelines, and the application of the best of modern knowledge to the care of patients. In light of the technology of recent years I have placed particular emphasis on the role of a primary physician for the patient, who will apply his scientific knowledge with compassion and an understanding of the total illness-including the social and emotional aspects of the patient's problem rather than his disease alone. This, as I see it, is the challenge of the modern physician*

WRIGHT, J. CRAIG, state supreme court associate justice; b. Chillicothe, Ohio, June 21, 1929; s. Harry and Marjorie (Riddle) W.; m. Jane LaFollette, Nov. 3, 1951; children: Marjorie Jane, Alice Ann. B.A., U. Ky., 1951; LL.B., Yale U., 1954. Ptnr. Wright, Gilbert & Jones, Columbus, 1957-70; judge Franklin County Common Pleas Ct., 1971-84, adminstrv. and presiding judge, 1980-84; assoc. justice Ohio Supreme Ct., Columbus, 1985—. Trustee Columbus Area Coun. on Alcoholism, 1959-83; chmn. bd. House of Hope-Halfway House, Columbus, 1960-68, trustee emeritus; trustee Grace Brethren Ch., Columbus, 1986-81, Worthington Christian Sch., Ohio, 1974-78, St. Anthony's Med. Ctr., Shepherd Hill Hosp. With CIC, U.S. Army, 1955-56. Recipient cert. of excellence Ohio Supreme Ct., 1972-83. Mem. ABA (mem. commn. on impaired lawyers 1988-91, state rep. jud. div. 1975-83), Ohio Bar Assn. (chmn. lawyers assistance com. 1977-84), Ohio Common Pleas Judges Assn. (exec. bd. 1972-83, pres.-elect 1984), Columbus Bar Assn., Am. Judicature Soc., Columbus Country Club, Athletic Club of Columbus. Avocations: golf; duplicate bridge. Home: 443 Country Club Dr Columbus OH 43213-2587 Office: Ohio Supreme Ct 30 E Broad St Fl 2D Columbus OH 43266

WRIGHT, J. RAYMOND, manufacturing company executive; b. Pensacola, Fla., May 19, 1943; s. James F. and Georgia T. (Tennant) W.; m. Marion H. Hagerty, Jan., 1976 (dec. 1980); m. B. Ann Simpson, Aug. 29, 1993. BS in Acctg., U. Ala., 1967. CPA, Ala. From staff acct. to mgr. Haskins & Sells, Birmingham, Ala., 1967-73; contr. Liles Constrn. Co., Montgomery, Ala., 1973-77; mgr. Hill & Flurry, CPAs, Montgomery, 1977-78; asst. contr. to tax mgr. BE & K Inc., Birmingham, 1987-90; CFO Polar-Bek Co., Birmingham, 1990—. chair budget subcom. United Way, Birmingham, 1985—. Mem. AICPA., Nat. Assn. Accts. (pres. Montgomery chpt. 1977-78), Ala. Soc. CPAs, Inst. Mgmt. Accts. Office: Polar-Bek Co 1900 International Park Ste 50 Birmingham AL 35243

WRIGHT, JAMES CORWIN, international management consultant; b. Watertown, S.D., 1959; s. Patrick and Delores Wright; m. Susan Kathleen Mohr, Nov. 7, 1981 (div. Oct. 1983); m. Lynda Renelle Prettyman, Jan. 4, 1986. HHD (hon.), 1993, D in Internat. Mgmt. (hon.), 1993. With delivery

dept. San Juan (P.R.) Star Newspaper, 1972-74; asst. diving instr. Caribbean Sch. of Aquatics, San Juan, 1973-74; freelance musician various locations, 1975-81; detail draftsman AiResearch Mfg. Co. of Ariz., Phoenix, 1977-79; project designer McMartin Industries, Inc., Omaha, 1980-82; chief exec. officer Aztron Corp., Council Bluffs, Iowa, 1982-86; pres. Aztron Prodns., Fountain Hills, Ariz., 1986-88; chief exec. officer Jalyn Entertainment Group, Scottsdale, Ariz., 1988—; pub. Roadrunner Mag., Phoenix, 1988-89; v.p. Zent & Assocs., 1989-93; cons. Tripp and Assocs., Inc., Blair, Nebr., 1982-85, Control Data Corp., Omaha, 1984, Fast Lane Mag., Omaha, 1984-87, Salt River Project, Ariz., 1986-87, MEMCON, Nebr., 1984, Tricon, Ltd., Iowa, 1982-84, Doane Western Co., Ariz., 1986-87, Continental Power Svcs. Co. Inc., Nebr., 1984; gen. mgr. Tight Fit Enterprises, Council Bluffs, 1984-85; trustee Jalyn Internat. Trust, 1991-94, Bus. Intercontinental Trust, 1991—, West African Devel. Trust, 1991-93; writer syndicated column, 1984-89. Author: Newsletters: A Report, 1985, Developing Presentation Skills; editor: (jour.) The Wintight Letter, 1985; contbr. articles to profl. jours. Active Nat. Congl. Com., 1985-86, Rep. Nat. Com., 1985; chmn. G.P.V. Community Assistance Team, Inc., 1990-92. Recipient Cert. of Merit Pres. Ronald Reagan, 1984, Cert. of Merit Presdl. Task Force, 1986, Cert. of Appreciation Nat. Congl. Com., 1985-86, World Decoration Excellence award, 1990, Disting. Leadership award, 1991, Medal of Honor, 1993; named Cert. Internat. Financier Internat. Soc. of Financiers, 1987, 89; Decorated titled knight Paupers Commilitones Christi Templique Solomonis, cpt. Légion de L'Aigle de Mer Baron. Mem. Internat. Traders, Internat. Parliment for Safety and Peace, Internat. Platform Assn., Inst. des Affaires Internat. (assoc.), Maison Internat. des Intellectuels-Academie Midi (sec., pres.), Am. Mgmt. Assn., Nat. Assn. of Underwater Instrs., Liberia-Am. C. of C. (trustee 1991-93). Avocations: sailing, scuba diving. Office: Jalyn Internat Trust PO Box 5065 Scottsdale AZ 85261-5065

WRIGHT, JAMES DAVID, sociology educator, writer; b. Logansport, Ind., Nov. 6, 1947; s. James Farrell and Helen Loretta (Moon) W.; m. Christine Ellen Stewart, July 25, 1987; children: Matthew James, Derek William. BA, Purdue U., 1969; MS, U. Wis., 1970, PhD, 1973. Cert. specialist social policy and evaluation rsch. Asst. prof. sociology U. Mass., Amherst, 1973-76, assoc. prof., 1976-79, prof., 1979-88; Favrot prof. human rels. Tulane U., New Orleans, 1988—. Author/co-author 14 books including: The Dissent of the Governed, 1976, Under the Gun, 1983, The State of the Masses, 1986, Homelessness and Health, 1987 (commendation Nat. Press Club 1988), Address Unknown: Homeless in America, 1989, The Greatest of Evils: Urban Poverty and the Urban Underclass, 1993; editor: (book series) Social Institutions and Social Change, 1984—; editor Social Sci. Rsch. jour., 1978—; contbr. over 100 articles, essays, book chpts. to profl. publs. Mem. Am. Sociol. Assn., Soc. for Study Social Problems, Am. Polit. Sci. Assn. Democrat. Avocations: cooking, gardening, travel.

WRIGHT, JAMES EDWARD, judge; b. Arlington, Tex., Jan. 15, 1921; s. James Robert and Clairette (Smith) W.; m. Eberta Adelaide Slataper, June 25, 1946; 1 child, Patricia Diane Wright Rogers. JD, U. Tex., 1949. Bar: Tex. 1949. Practice in Ft. Worth, 1949-69; city atty. Arlington, 1951-61; judge 141st Dist. Ct., Ft. Worth, 1970-88, sr. dist. judge, 1988—. Served with USAAF, World War II. Paul Harris fellow, 1981; named Disting. Alumnus U. Tex.-Arlington, 1982; named to Mil. Sci. Dept. Hall of Honor, U. Tex.-Arlington, 1985. Fellow Tex. Bar Found. (life); mem. ABA, Ft. Worth-Tarrant County Bar Assn. (pres. 1958-59), Tex. Bar Assn., Sons of the Rep. of Tex., Rotary (pres. Downtown Ft. Worth club 1966-67), Masons (32 deg.), Shriners, Phi Alpha Delta. Baptist. Home: 717 Briarwood Blvd Arlington TX 76013-1502

WRIGHT, JAMES EDWARD, dean, history educator; b. Madison, Wis., Aug. 16, 1939; s. Donald J. and Myrtle (Hendricks) W.; m. Joan Bussah, Sept. 3, 1962 (div.); children: James J., Anne Marie, Michael J.; m. Susan DeBovoise, Aug. 18, 1984. BS, Wis. State U., 1964; MS, U. Wis., 1966, PhD, 1969; MA (hon.), Dartmouth Coll., 1980. From asst. prof. to assoc. prof. history Dartmouth Coll., Hanover, N.H., 1969-80, prof. history, 1980—, assoc. dean faculty, 1981-85, dean faculty, 1989—, acting pres., 1995; sr. historian U. Mid Am., Lincoln, Nebr., 1976-77; humanist-in-residence Colo. Humanities Coun., Georgetown, 1975. Author: Galena Lead District, 1966, Politics of Populism, 1974, Progressive Yankees, 1987; author, co-editor: Great Plains Experience, 1978. Trustee Kimball Union Acad., Meriden, N.H., 1990—; dir. Sherman Fairchild Found., Greenwich, Conn., 1991—; chair Hanover Dem. Town Com., 1970-74. Cpl. USMC, 1957-60. Danforth fellow, 1964-69, Guggenheim fellow, 1973-74, Charles Warren fellow Harvard U., 1980-81. Mem. Orgn. Am. Historians (chair film, media com. 1983-85), Western History Assn. (chair Caughey prize 1986-87), Phi Beta Kappa (hon.). Home: 7 Quail Dr Etna NH 03750 Office: Dartmouth College Dean of Faculty Hanover NH 03755

WRIGHT, J(AMES) LAWRENCE, lawyer; b. Portland, Oreg., Apr. 12, 1943; s. William A. and Esther M. (Nelson) W.; m. Mary Aileene Roche, June 29, 1968; children: Rachel, Jonathan, Christopher. BBA, Gonzaga U., 1966, JD, 1972; LLM, NYU, 1977. Bar: Wash. 1972, U.S. Ct. Mil. Appeals 1974, U.S. Tax Ct. 1976, U.S. Supreme Ct. 1976. Prin. Halverson & Applegate, P.S., Yakima, Wash., 1972-74, 77—. Mem. St. Elizabeth Hosp. Found., Yakima, 1986-89, Yakima Meml. Hosp. Found., 1990—; pres. fin. bd. St. Paul's Cathedral, Yakima, 1979—; mem. fin. coun. Diocese of Yakima, 1994—; v.p. Apple Tree Racing Assn., 1986-87; bd. dirs Capital Theatre, Yakima, 1985—. Capt. U.S. Army, 1966-68, 74-76. Mem. ABA, Wash. Bar Assn., Yakima County Bar Assn., Rotary. Roman Catholic. Avocations: tennis, golf. Office: Halverson & Applegate PS PO Box 22730 311 N 4th St Yakima WA 98907-2715

WRIGHT, JAMES ROSCOE, chemist; b. White Hall, Md., July 7, 1922; s. James Grover and Rose Adele (Hulshart) W.; m. Blanca Zulema Guerrero, June 4, 1950; children: James Alfred, Ronald Keith. BS in Edn., Md. State U., Salisbury, 1946; B.S., Washington Coll., 1948; M.S., U. Del., 1949, Ph.D. in Chemistry, 1951; grad., Program Mgmt. Devel., Harvard, 1967, Fed. Execs. Inst., U. Va., 1972. Asst. prof. Trinity U., San Antonio, 1951-52; research chemist S.W. Research Inst., San Antonio, 1951-52, Chevron Research Corp., Richmond, 1952-60; with Nat. Bur. Standards, 1960—; chief bldg. research div., 1967-72, dir. center bldg. tech., 1972-74; dep. dir. Inst. for Applied Tech., 1974-76, acting dir., 1976-78; dep. dir. Nat. Engring Lab., 1978-85; head U.S. del. industrialized bldg. to USSR, 1969; U.S. del. Internat. Union Testing and Rsch. Labs. for Materials and Structures, 1969-74, 75-85, mem. bur., 1970-73, 74-78, 79—, pres., 1971-72, v.p., 1979-82, pres., 1982-85, hon. mem., 1985—; mem. bldg. rsch. adv. bd. NRC, 1976-80; vice chmn., mem. exec. com. U.S. nat. com. Internat. Coun. Bldg. Rsch., Studies and Documentation, 1973-79; rep. Nat. Bur. Standards to Fed. Constrn. Coun., 1967-70; mem. fire coun. Underwriters Labs., 1969-73; mem. U.S.-Egypt working group Tech. Rshc. and Devel., 1976-80; hon. mem. Producers Coun.; guest worker Nat. Bur. Standards, 1985-88; dir., treas. St. Mark Elderly Housing Corp., 1987—; mem. Smithsonian Exhibit Group, 1989—. Author. Served as officer AUS, 1943-46, ETO. Decorated Bronze Star, Purple Heart, Combat Infantry Badge; recipient Gold medal award for exceptional svc. Dept. Commerce, 1975. Mem. Am. Chem. Soc. (emeritus), ASTM (dir. 1977-80, chmn. com. on soc. devel. 1979-80), Chem. Soc. Washington (chmn. auditing com. 1965-66, chmn. profl. rels. and status com. 1964, chmn. long-range planning com. 1967, assoc. editor Capital Chemist 1963-65), Buick Club Am. (bd. dirs. Washington chpt. 1991—, pres. 1990—), Sigma Xi, Kappa Alpha. Patentee in field. Home: 6204 Lone Oak Dr Bethesda MD 20817-1744

WRIGHT, JANE BROOKS, university foundation professional; b. Athens, Ga., Oct. 31, 1935; d. Joseph Welchel and Sophia (Porter) Brooks; m. Fred Hamilton Wright, June 26, 1956 (div. Nov. 1969); children: Judy Anne Wright Cusick, Gary Allen (dec. Oct. 1993), Mark. BA in Edn., U. Fla., 1971, MA in Edn., 1972. Bookkeeper Paul Smith Constrn. Co., Cape Canaveral, Fla., 1956-57; owner, dir. Children's Corner Sch., Cocoa, Fla., 1964-69; sec. U. Fla. Found., Inc., Gainesville, 1972-73, staff asst., 1973-86, mgr. prospect rsch., 1986-95, part-time asst. mgr., 1995—. Jehovah's Witness. Avocation: gardening. Office: U Fla Found Inc 2012 W University Ave Gainesville FL 32603-1735

WRIGHT, JANE COOKE, physician, educator, consultant; b. N.Y.C., Nov. 30, 1919; d. Louis T. and Corinne (Cooke) W.; m. David D. Jones. A.B., Smith Coll., 1942; M.D. with honors, N.Y. Med. Coll., 1945; Dr. Med. Scis.,

Women's Med. Coll. Pa., 1965; Sc.D., Denison U., 1971. Intern Bellevue Hosp., N.Y.C., 1945-46, resident, 1946, mem. staff, 1955-67; resident Harlem Hosp., 1947, chief resident, 1948; clin. Cancer Rsch. Found., Harlem Hosp., 1949-52; dir., 1952-55; mem. staff Harlem Hosp., 1949-55; practice medicine specializing in clin. cancer chemotherapy N.Y.C.; mem. faculty dept. surgery Med. Ctr., N.Y. U., N.Y.C., 1955-67; adj. assoc. prof. Med. Ctr., N.Y. U., 1961-67, also dir. cancer chemotherapy services research, 1955-67; prof. surgery N.Y. Med. Coll., N.Y.C., 1967-87, prof. surgery emeritus, 1987—, assoc. dean, 1967-75; mem. staff Manhattan VA Hosp., 1955-67, Midtown, Met., Bird S. Color, Flower-Fifth Ave. Hosps., all N.Y.C., 1967-79, Westchester County Med. Center, Valhalla, N.Y., 1971-87, Lincoln Hosp., Bronx, N.Y., 1979-87; cons. Health Ins. Plan of Greater N.Y., 1962-94; cons. Blvd. Hosp., 1963—, St. Luke's Hosp., Newburgh, N.Y., 1964—; pelvic malignancy rev. com. N.Y. Gynecol. Soc., 1965-66, St. Vincent's Hosp., N.Y.C., 1966—. Dept. Health, Edn. and Welfare, 1968-70, Wyckoff Heights Hosp., N.Y.C., 1969—, NIH, 1971—; others; adv. bd. Skin Cancer Found. Contbr. articles to profl. jours. Mem. Manhattan coun. State Commn. Human Rights, 1949—, Pres.'s Commn. Heart Disease, Cancer and Stroke, 1964-65, Nat. Adv. Cancer Coun. NIH, 1966-70, N.Y. State Women's Coun., 1970-72; bd. dirs. Medico-CARE, Health Svcs. Improvement Fund Inc.; trustee Smith Coll., Northampton, Mass., 1970-80. Recipient numerous awards, including; Mademoiselle mag. award, 1952; Lady Year award Harriet Beecher Stowe Jr. High Sch., 1958; Spirit Achievement award Albert Einstein Sch. Medicine, 1965; certificate Honor award George Gershwin Jr. High Sch., 1967; Myrtle Wreath award Hadassah, 1967; Smith medal Smith Coll., 1968; Outstanding Am. Women award Am. Mothers Com. Inc., 1970; Golden Plate award Am. Acad. Achievement, 1971; Exceptional Black Scientists Poster Ciba Geigy, 1980. Fellow N.Y. Acad. Medicine; mem. Nat. Med. Assn. (edit. bd. jours.), Manhattan Ctrl. Med. Soc., N.Y. County Med. Soc. (nominating com.), AMA, AAAS, Am. Assn. Cancer Rsch. (dir. Rsch. Salute 1971-74), N.Y. Acad. Scis., N.Y. Cancer Soc., Internat. Med. and Rsch. Found. (v.p.), Am. Cancer Soc. (dir. div.), N.Y. Cancer Soc. (pres. 1970-71), Am. Soc. Clin. Oncology (sec. treas. 1964-67), Contin Soc., Sigma Xi, Lambda Kappa Mu, Alpha Omega Alpha. Club: The 400 (N.Y. Med. Coll.). Address: 315 West End Ave New York NY 10023-8158

WRIGHT, JEAN NORMAN, elementary education educator; b. Norristown, Pa., June 20, 1931; d. John Rich and Mildred (Hitchcock) Norman; m. John A. Wright (dec. Mar. 1979); children: Lori Wright Lutter, Larry. BA cum laude, Cedar Crest Coll., Allentown, Pa., 1953. Cert. tchr., Pa. Elem. tchr. Upson Sch., Euclid, Ohio, 1953-55; tchr. art and music Schuylkill Elem. Sch., Phoenixville, Pa., 1965-70, elem. tchr., 1970—. Mem. alumni bd. dirs. Cedar Crest Coll., 1980-84; mem. Phoenixville Community Concert Bd., 1986—. Mem. NEA, Pa. Edn. Assn., Cedar Crest Coll. Alumnae Club (pres. 1962-64), Delta Kappa Gamma (pres. 1990-92). Republican. Presbyterian. Avocations: barbershop singing, tennis. Office: Schuylkill Elem Sch Whitehorse Rd Phoenixville PA 19460

WRIGHT, JEANETTE TORNOW, college president; b. Milw., Sept. 8, 1927; d. Julius and Ida Tornow; m. Wilfred D. Wright, June 5, 1948. B.A., George Washington U., 1956, M.A., 1959; Ed.D., Boston U., 1967. Lic. psychologist, Mass. Tchr. emotionally disturbed children Arlington County (Va.) Public Schs., Arlington, 1956-58; instr. psychology Bay Path Coll., Longmeadow, Mass., 1958-60, chmn. dept. behavioral sci., 1959-62, dean students, 1960-62, v.p., dean of coll., 1962-79, pres., 1979—; mem. various evaluation teams, Mass. and Conn.; pres. Nat. Council Ind. Jr. Colls., 1982-83, bd. dirs., 1983-88; bd. dirs. New Eng. Jr. Coll. Coun.; corporator Heritage Bank, 1980-83, dir., 1983-93; ednl. cons. Mem. Gov.'s Commn. on Status of Women, 1973-74; chmn. bd. Carew Hill Girls' Club, Springfield, Mass., 1967-70; New Eng. regional chmn., mem. nat. bd. dirs. Girls' Clubs Am., 1970-71; corporator, mem. ethics com. use of human subjects Baystate Med. Ctr., 1980-87, mem. med. care and edn. com., 1981-84; corporator The MacDuffie Sch., 1985—; bd. dirs. Automobile Club Pioneer Valley, 1977—, pres., 1987-89; v.p. Springfield Mental Health Assn., 1968-69; bd. dirs. Nat. Assn. Ind. Colls. and Univs., 1988-90. Recipient Golden Boy award Boys' Clubs Am., 1974, Nat. award on Advocacy for Girls' Clubs Am., 1988; named One of Am.'s Most Effective Coll. Pres. in Country, 1986; Fulbright scholar, China, 1986. Fellow Mass. Psychol. Assn.; mem. Am. Psychol. Assn., Am. Personnel and Guidance Assn. (pres. Western Mass. 1961-62), Nat. Coun. Ind. Jr. Colls. (bd. dirs. 1980—, pres. 1982-83). Office: Bay Path Coll Office of the President 588 Longmeadow St Longmeadow MA 01106-2292

WRIGHT, JEANNE ELIZABETH JASON, advertising executive; b. Washington, June 24, 1934; d. Robert Stewart and Elizabeth (Gaddis) Jason; m. Benjamin Hickman Wright, Oct. 30, 1965; stepchildren: Benjamin (dec.), Deborah, David, Patricia. B.A., Radcliffe Coll., 1956; M.A., U. Chgo., 1958. Psychiat. social worker Lake County Mental Health Clinic, Gary, Ind., Psychiat. and Psychosomatic Inst., Michael Reese Hosp., Chgo., Jewish Child Care Assn., N.Y.C., 1958-70; gen. mgr. Black Media, Inc. (advt. rep. co.), N.Y.C., 1970-74; pres. Black Media, Inc. (advt. rep. co.), 1974-75; pres., exec. editor, syndicator weekly editorial features Black Resources, Inc., N.Y.C., 1975—. Mem. planning com. First Black Power Conf., Newark, 1966, Second Black Power Conf., Phila., 1967, First Internat. Black Cultural & Bus. Expn., N.Y.C., 1971; nat. bd. dirs. Afro-Am. Family & Community Svcs., Inc., Chgo., 1971-75; founding coun. mem. Nat. Assault on Illiteracy Program, 1980—; pres. Metro-N.Y. chpt. Nat. Assn. Media Women, Inc. 1986-89. Recipient Pres.' award Nat. Assn. Black Women Attys., 1977, 2d ann. Freedom's Jour. award Journalism Students and Faculty of U. D.C. Dept. Communicative and Performing Arts, 1979, Communication award Harlem Svc. Ctr., ARC, 1988, Spl. award Beta Omicron chpt. Phi Delta Kappa, 1982; named Disting. Black Woman in Industry, Nat. Coun. Negro Women, 1981. Mem. AAAS, Nat. Assn. Social Workers, Acad. Cert. Social Workers, Nat. Assn. Media Women (pres. Met. N.Y. chpt. 1986-89, Nat. Media Woman of Yr. award 1984, 86, Founders award 1986), Newswomen's Club N.Y., U. Chgo. Alumni Assn., NAACP, Radcliffe Club, Alpha Kappa Alpha. Democrat. Office: 231 W 29th St Ste 1205 New York NY 10001-5209 Home and Office: 19620 W Saint Andrews Dr Hialeah FL 33015-2340

WRIGHT, JEFF REGAN, civil engineering educator; b. Spokane, Wash., Nov. 25, 1950; s. Harold U. and Gail Virginia (Hodgson) W.; m. Delores Jeanne Finch, Sept. 14, 1972; children: Kelly Hodgson, Myka Kristine. BA, U. Wash., 1975, BS, 1976, MSCE, 1977; PhD, Johns Hopkins U., 1982. Asst. prof. civil engring. Purdue U., West Lafayette, Ind., 1982-86, assoc. prof., 1986-90; prof., 1990—; dir. Ind. Water Resources Rsch. Ctr. Purdue U., West Lafayette, Ind., 1989—; v.p. OMTEK Engring., West Lafayette, 1986—. Author: Expert Systems Applications to Urban Planning, 1989; contbr. numerous articles to profl. publs. Mem. ASCE (editor-in-chief jour.), Ops. Rsch. Soc. Am., Inst. Mgmt. Scis. Office: Purdue U WRRC Sch Civil Engring West Lafayette IN 47907-1284

WRIGHT, JEFFREY, actor. stage appearances include (with Arena Stage, Washington D.C.) Les Blancs, She Stoops to Conquer, Juno and the Paycock (with Yale Repertory) Search and Destroy, Playboy of the West Indies, Daylight in the Exile, N.Y. Shakespeare Festival prodn. of Othello, Millennium Approaches, 1993, Angels in America: Perestroika, 1994 (Antoinette Perry award for Featured Actor in a Play 1994); T.V. appearances include The Young Indiana Jones Chronicles, Seperate But Equal; films include Jumpin' at the Bone Yard, 1992. Office: Walter Kerr Theater 219 W 48th St New York NY 10019*

WRIGHT, JERRY JAYE, physical education educator; b. Richmond, Ind., July 30, 1944; s. Robert Evan and Janet W. (Jay) W.; m. Mary Lee Cathey, Dec. 27, 1980. AA, Art Acad., Cin., 1964; BA, Saginaw Valley State U., 1974; MEd, Bowling Green State U., 1976; PhD, The Ohio State U., 1980. Illustrator Advt. Svcs., Richmond, Ind., 1964-71; asst. baseball coach Bowling Green (Ohio) State U., 1974-75; asst. baseball and basketball coach Saginaw (Mich.) Valley State U., 1975-77; asst. prof. U. No. Iowa, Cedar Falls, 1980-81, U. Wis., Milw., 1981-86; head tennis coach Penn State U., Altoona, Pa., 1986-91; assoc. prof. Penn State U., Altoona, 1986—; chair dept. exercise and sports sci. sport historian Penn State U., Altoona, 1989—. Author: Phys. Educator Jour., 1986, Jour. of Sport History, 1988, Strategies Jour., 1991, 1992, Baseball Rsch. Jour., 1992, The National Pastime, 1993, Encyclopedia of Major League Baseball Teams, 1993, Nine: A Journal of Baseball History and Social Policy Perspectives, 1994, 95, Canadian Journal

---

of the History of Sport, 1994, International Journal of the History of Sport, 1994. Sport historian Blair County Hist. Soc., Altoona, 1989—. Sgt. U.S. Army, 1965-67. Mem. North Am. Soc. for Sport History, Orgn. for Am. Historians, Soc. for Am. Baseball Rsch., Am. Alliance for Phys. Edn., Phys. Edn. in Higher Edn. Avocations: coll. sport memorabilia, baseball cards, tennis, golf, sport historian rsch. Office: Pa State U 3000 Ivyside Park Altoona PA 16601-3760

WRIGHT, JOHN, classics educator; b. N.Y.C., Mar. 9, 1941; s. Henry and Dorothy (Chaya) W.; m. Ellen Faber, June 16, 1962; children: Jennifer, Emily. B.A., Swarthmore Coll., 1962; M.A., Ind. U., 1964, Ph.D., 1971. Instr. classics U. Rochester, 1968-72, asst. prof., 1972-75; asso. prof. Northwestern U., Evanston, Ill., 1975-77; prof. Northwestern U. 1977-83, John Evans prof. Latin lang. and lit., 1983—, chmn. dept., 1978—. Author: The Play of Antichrist, 1967, Dancing in Chains: The Stylistic Unity of the Comoedia Palliata, 1974, The Life of Cola di Rienzo, 1975, Essays on the Iliad: Selected Modern Criticism, 1978, Plautus: Curculio, Introduction and Notes, 1981, rev. edit., 1993, Ralph Stanley and the Clinch Mountain Boys: A Discography, 1983, The Five-String Banjo Stanley Style, 1984, rev. edit. (Clyde Pharr) Homeric Greek: A Book for Beginners, 1985, It's the Hardest Music in the World to Play: The Ralph Stanley Story in His Own Words, 1987, Traveling the High Way Home: Ralph Stanley and the World of Traditional Bluegrass Music, 1993; album Everything She Asks For, 1993; columnist: Banjo Newsletter; contbr. articles to profl. jours. Fellow Am. Acad. Rome, 1966-68; Nat. Endowment Humanities Younger humanist fellow, 1973-74; named to Honorable Order of Ky. Colonels. Mem. Am. Acad. in Rome Soc. of Fellows, Am. Philol. Assn., Ill.Classical Conf., Petronian Soc., Met. Opera Guild, Chgo. Area Bluegrass Assn., Minn. Bluegrass and Old-Time Music Assn., Internat. Bluegrass Music Assn. (print media personality of yr. 1994), BMI. Club: Ralph Stanley Fan. Home: 1137 Noyes St Evanston IL 60201-2633 Office: Northwestern U Dept Classics Evanston IL 60208-2200

WRIGHT, JOHN, film editor. Editor: (films) (with Graeme Clifford and Garth Craven) Convoy, 1978, Separate Ways, 1981, Only When I Laugh, 1981, Frances, 1982, Mass Appeal, 1984, Explorers, 1985, (with Mark Roy Warner and Edward A. Warschilka) The Running Man, 1987, Gleaming the Cube, 1989, (with Dennis Virkler) The Hunt for Red October, 1990 (Academy award nomination best film editing 1990), (with Steve Mirkovich) Teenage Mutant Ninja Turtles II: The Secret of the Ooze, 1991, Last Action Hero, 1993, Speed, 1994 (Academy award nomination best film editing 1994), Die Hard with a Vengeance, 1995, (TV movies) Heartsounds, 1984, My Name Is Bill W., 1989, Sarah, Plain and Tall, 1991. Office: Broder Kurland Webb Uffner Agency 9242 Beverly Blvd Ste 200 Beverly Hills CA 90210*

WRIGHT, JOHN CHARLES YOUNG, oil and gas company executive; b. Mercer, Pa., May 18, 1925; s. Paul Hatfield and Helen (Munnel) W.; m. Becky Bell Lewis, June 9, 1951; children: John Charles, William Lewis, Mary Carolyn. B.A., Denison U., 1947; B.S. in Mining Engring, Ohio State U., 1949, M.Sc. in Petroleum Engring, 1950. Roustabout Stanolind Oil & Gas Corp., Beaumont, Tex., 1948; roustabout So. Petroleum Exploration, Inc., Wichita Falls, Tex., 1949; asst. to pres. Wiser Oil Co. and assoc. cos., 1950-53, v.p., 1953-61, pres., dir., 1961-81, pres., chief exec. officer, dir., 1981-91, chmn. of bd., 1991—; dir. Wiser Oil Co., 1960—, treas., 1961-81; also treas.; asst. to pres. Wittmer Oil & Gas Corp., 1950-53, petroleum engr., 1953—; pres., treas., dir. So-Petroleum, Inc., 1961—; pres., dir. Basin Oil Co., Mich.; pres., dir. Basin Oil Co. Mich.; bd. dirs., chmn. First Tyler Bank & Trust Co., Sistersville; chmn. bd. WesBanco Bank, Sistersville; adv. bd. WesBanco Bank, Wheeling, W.Va. Mem. engrs. com. of 100 Ohio State U. Served to ensign USNR, 1943-46; lt. (s.g.) Res. Recipient Texnokoi award Ohio State U., 1957; named W. Va. Oil and Gas Man of Yr., 1976; honoree Ohio Oil and Gas Assn. Hall of Fame, 1989. Mem. Ind. Petroleum Assn. Am. (dir., v.p. for W.Va.-exec. com. 1968—, Ohio trustee, dir. 1968—, pres. 1970—), Ohio Oil and Gas Assn. (pres. 1968), W.Va. C. of C. (v.p. no. region), Ky. Oil and Gas Assn. (v.p., dir. 1974), W.Va. Oil and Gas Assn., AIME, Am. Legion, Ohio State U. Assn., Sigma Chi, Sigma Gamma Epsilon. Presbyn. (elder). Lodges: Masons; Shriners. Home: 252 Oxford St Sistersville WV 26175-1029 Office: The Wiser Oil Co PO Box 192 210 Charles St Sistersville WV 26175

WRIGHT, JOHN COLLINS, chemistry educator; b. Oak Hill, W. Va., Aug. 5, 1927; s. John C. and Irene (Collins) W.; m. Margaret Ann Cyphers, Sept. 11, 1949; children: Jeffrey Cyphers, John Timothy, Curtis Scott, Keith Alexander. B.S., W.Va. Wesleyan Coll., 1948, LL.D. (hon.), 1974; Ph.D., U. Ill., 1951; D.Sc. (hon.), U. Ala., 1979. W.Va. Inst. Tech., 1979. Research chemist Hercules, Inc., 1951-57; mem. faculty W.Va. Wesleyan Coll., 1957-64; asst. program dir. NSF, 1964-65; dean Coll. Arts and Scis., No. Ariz. U., 1966-70, W.Va. U., Morgantown, 1970-74; vice chancellor W.Va. Bd. Regents, Charleston, 1974-78; pres. U. Ala., Huntsville, 1978-88, prof. chemistry, 1988—; interim pres. W.Va. Coll. Grad. Studies, Institute, 1975-76; hon. research asso. Univ. Coll., London, Eng., 1962-63; cons. NSF, 1965—, Army Sci. Bd., U.S. Army, 1979-82. Served with USNR, 1945-46. Mich. fellow Center Study Higher Edn., U. Mich., 1965-66. Mem. Am. Chem. Soc., AAAS, Assn. Higher Edn., Am. Assn. State Colls. and Univs. (com. chmn. on sci. and tech. 1987). Office: 4724 Panorama Dr SE Huntsville AL 35801-1215

WRIGHT, JOHN D. R., oil industry executive; b. 1937. Pres., CEO Indian Refining Partnership, Lawrenceville, Ill. Office: Indian Refining Partnership S 7th St Lawrenceville IL 62439

WRIGHT, JOHN MACNAIR, JR., retired army officer; b. L.A., Apr. 14, 1916; s. John MacNair and Ella (Stradley) W.; m. Helene Tribit, June 28, 1940; children: John MacNair III, Richard Kenneth. B.S., U.S. Mil. Acad., 1940; grad., Airborne Sch., 1947, Strategic Intelligence Sch., 1948; advanced course, Inf. Sch., 1951, Command and Gen. Staff Coll., 1953; M.B.A., U. So. Calif., 1956; grad., Army Logistics Mgmt. Sch., 1957, Advanced Mgmt. Program, U. Pitts., 1959, Nat. War Coll., 1961, Army Aviation Sch., 1965; M.S. in Internat. Affairs, George Washington U., 1973. Enlisted U.S. Army, 1935, comd. 2d. lt., 1940, advanced through grades to lt. gen., 1970; comdr. Battery Wright Corregidor, P.I., 1942; with intelligence div. War Dept. Gen. Staff, 1946-48; mil. attache am. embassy, Paraguay, 1948-50; bn. comdr. 508th Airborne Regtl. Combat Team, 1951-52; asst. chief of staff for pers. 7th Inf. Div., Korea, 1953, asst. chief staff logistics, 1954; assigned office U.S. Army Chief of Staff, 1956-60; chief staff 8th Inf. Div., 1961-62, asst. chief staff plans and ops. 7th Corps, 1962-63, asst. chief staff plans and ops. 7th Army, 1963-64, asst. div. comdr. 11th Air Assault Div., 1964-65; asst. div. comdr. 1st Cav. Div. (Airmobile) Vietnam, 1965-66; assigned office asst. Chief Staff Force Devel., 1966-67; comdg. gen. U.S. Army Inf. Ctr., 1967-69; comdt. U.S. Army Inf. Sch., 1967-69; comdg. gen. 101st Airborne Div. (Airmobile), Vietnam, 1969-70; controller of the Army Washington, 1970-72; ret., 1973. Dir. R&D Boy Scouts Am., 1973, nat. dir. program support, 1974-77, nat. dir. program support, 1977-78; nat. dir. exploring, 1978-81, mem. nat. exploring com., 1981—; pres. Chattahoochee (Ga.) coun. Boy Scouts Am., 1968-69, mem. exec. bd. region 5, 1967-69; nat. coun., 1964-73; tech. adviser Vietnamese Boy Scout Assn., 1965-66; Regent for Life Nat. Eagle Scout Assn., 1988—; exploring chmn. five nations dist. Calif. Inland Empire Coun., 1992—. Decorated D.S.M. with 2 oak leaf clusters, Silver Star with oak leaf cluster, Legion of Merit with oak leaf cluster, D.F.C., Bronze Star with oak leaf cluster, Air medal with 59 oak leaf clusters, Army Commendation medal, Prisoner of War medal, Purple Heart with oak leaf cluster, Combat Inf. badge, Master Parachutist, Sr. Army Aviator, numerous area and campaign ribbons, fgn. decorations; recipient Silver Beaver award Boy Scouts Am., 1961, Silver Antelope award, 1969, Distinguished Eagle Scout award, 1971, Disting. Svc. award Founders and Patriots Am., 1988, Freedoms Found. at Valley Forge Hon. medal, 1992; elected Army Aviation Hall of Fame, 1986. Mem. Assn. U.S. Army, Army Aviation Assn. Am. (pres. 1974-76), 101st Airborne Divsn. Assn., 1st Cavalry Divsn. Assn., SAR (pres. Tex. Soc. 1987-88, pres. Inland Empire chpt. 1992-93, Silver Good Citizenship medal 1984, 87, Meritorious Svc. medal 1986, Patriot, Liberty and Gold Good Citizenship medals 1988), Ret. Officers Assn., West Point Soc., Mil. Order World Wars (Patrick Henry award medal 1986, 90, comdr. Dallas chpt. 1985-86, vice comdr. dept. ctrl. Calif. 1991-92, comdr. Inland Empire chpt. 1992-93), Nat. Order Founders and Patriots of Am. (sec.-gen. 1986-88,

---

gov. gen. 1988-90, councillor gen. Calif. Soc. 1990-95), Soc. Descendants of Colonial Clergy, Flagon and Tchr. Soc., Soc. Colonial Wars (lt. gov. Calif. soc. 1992—), Sons of the Revolution in State of Calif. (pres. 1993-94), Soc. War of 1812 (dist. dep. pres. gen. 1991—, v.p. Calif. soc. 1993-94, pres. 1994-95), Nat. Huguenot Soc., Soc. Sons and Daus. of Pilgrims, Order Ams. Armorial Ancestry, Soc. Descendants Founders of Hartford, Old Plymouth Colony Descendants, Mil. Order of the Loyal Legion of the U.S., Mil. Order Fgn. Wars of the U.S., Hereditary Order of First Families of Mass., Masons, Shriners, Sojourner, Phi Kappa Phi, Beta Gamma Sigma, Alpha Kappa Psi. Prisoner of war of Japanese, 1942-45. Home: 21227 George Brown Ave Riverside CA 92518-2881

WRIGHT, JOHN PEALE, retired banker; b. Chattanooga, Mar. 27, 1924; s. Robert T. and Margaret (Peale) W.; m. Ruth Garrison, Sept. 11, 1948; children: Margaret Shapard, John Peale, Ruth Garrison, Mary Ivens. Student, Davidson Coll., 1941-43, U. N.C., 1943; B.S. in Phys. Sci, U. Chgo., 1944; M.B.A. Harvard U., 1947. With Am. Nat. Bank & Trust Co., Chattanooga, 1947-82; pres. Am. Nat. Bank & Trust Co., 1962-82, also dir.; dir. spl. projects Third Nat. Corp., Nashville, 1983-85; chmn. bd., dir. Third Nat. Bank of Anderson County, 1980-84. Served to lt. USAAF, 1943-46. Mem. Robert Morris Assocs. (pres. 1968-69), Tenn. Bankers Assn. (bd. dirs., pres. 1973-74). Presbyterian (elder, treas.). Home: PO Box 1667 Santa Rosa Beach FL 32459-1667

WRIGHT, JOHN ROBERT, pathologist; b. Winnipeg, Man., Can., Aug. 18, 1935; came to U.S., 1961, naturalized, 1968; s. Ross Grant and Anna Marie (Crispin) W.; m. Deanna Pauline Johnson, June 25, 1960; children—Carolyn Deanna, David John. M.D. with honors, U. Man., 1959. Diplomate: Am. Bd. Pathology. Intern Winnipeg Gen. Hosp., 1959-60, resident, 1960-61; resident Balt. City Hosp., 1961-63, Buffalo Gen. Hosp., 1963-64; teaching fellow in medicine U. Man., 1960-61; instr. in pathology, Buswell fellow SUNY-Buffalo, 1965-67, prof. pathology, chmn. dept. pathology, 1974—; asst. chief pathology Balt. City Hosps. and; asst. prof. Johns Hopkins U., 1967-74; cons. Roswell Park Meml. Inst., 1975—, bd. visitors, 1981—; interim dir. 1985-86, chmn. bd. visitors, 1987—. Recipient Louis A. and Ruth Siegel Disting. Teaching award SUNY-Buffalo, 1977, 78, 88, Deans award SUNY, 1987. Mem. AMA, AAAS, Coll. Am. Pathologists, Am. Soc. Investigative Pathologists, Am. Soc. Clin. Pathologists, U.S. and Can. Acad. Pathology, Assn. Pathology Chairmen (pres. 1994-96), Am. Heart Assn., Alpha Omega Alpha. Research in amyloidosis and aging, pathology of amyloidosis, characterization of clin. amyloid syndromes. Home: 46 Wynngate Ln Buffalo NY 14221-1840 Office: SUNY 204 Farber Hall Buffalo NY 14214

WRIGHT, JON ALAN, physicist; b. Tacoma, Wash., Jan. 18, 1938; s. Edward S. and Peggy (Hawley) W.; m. Barbara McCulley, Jan. 27, 1962; children: Jeffrey, Allison, Dana. BS, Cal Tech, 1959; PhD in Physics, U. Calif., Berkeley, 1965. Staff physicist Aerospace Corp., L.A., 1965; postdoctoral physicist U. Calif., San Diego, 1965-67; prof. physics U. Ill., Urbana, 1967-82; dir. Ctr. for Studies of Non-Linear Dynamics, San Diego, 1982—; rsch. physicist U. Calif., San Diego, 1990—; vis. prof. U. Utrecht, Netherlands, 1976; vis. assoc. prof. Stanford U., Palo Alto, Calif., 1973. Contbr. tech. papers to profl. jours. Achievements include specialization in nonlinear dynamics, nonlinear waves, semiclassical methods, ocean waves and remote sensing of ocean. Office: INLS U Calif 0402 San Diego CA 92093-0402

WRIGHT, JOSEPH ROBERT, JR., corporate executive; b. Tulsa, Sept. 24, 1938; s. Joe Robert and Ann Helen (Cech) W. B.S., Colo. Sch. Mines, 1961; M.I.A., Yale U., 1964. Vice pres. Booz, Allen & Hamilton, 1965-71; dep. dir. Bur. Census, Dept. Commerce, 1971-72; dep. administ. Social and Econ. Statis. Adminstrn., 1972-73, acting asst. sec. econ. affairs, 1973; asst. sec. adminstr. Dept. Agr., 1973-76; pres. Citicorp Retail Inc. and Retail Consumer Services Inc., N.Y.C.; v.p. Citicorp, Inc., 1976-81; dep. sec. Dept. Commerce, Washington, 1981-82; dep. dir. Office Mgmt. and Budget, Washington, 1982-88; chmn. Pres.'s Council on Integrity and Efficiency, 1982-89; chmn. Pres.'s Coun on Mgmt. Improvement, 1984-89; dir. Office Mgmt. and Budget, 1988-89; exec. v.p., vice chmn. W.R. Grace & Co., N.Y.C., 1989-94; chmn. Grace Environmental, Inc., 1989-94, Avic Internat., 1995—; Jefferson Capital, 1995—; bd. dirs. Travelers Corp., Harcourt, Brace, Jovonavich, Inc., 1990-91, W.R. Grace & Co., 1989-91, Canonie Environ., Inc., 1989-94, Grace Energy, Inc., 1990-94, Productora de Papeles, S.A., La Posta Recycling Ctr., Inc., Nat. Assn. Mfg.; co-chmn. Baker & Taylor, 1992—; bd. advs. Ardshiel, Inc.; fed. co-chmn. Coastal Plains Regional Commn., 1981-82, Four Corners Regional Commn., 1981-82, New Eng. Regional Commn., 1981-82, Old West Regional Commn., 1981-82, Ozarks Regional Commn., 1981-82, Pacific N.W. Regional Commn., 1981-82, S.W. Border Regional Commn., 1981-82; ptnr. Gulfstream Capital, 1995—, Austin Trading Co., 1995—. Mem. adv. bd. Coun. for Excellence in Govt., 1988—, The Jefferson Group, 1993—; trustee Hampton U., 1990—. 1st lt. AUS, 1963-65. Recipient Pres.'s Citizens award and medal, 1989; named Govt. Exec. of Yr., Govt. Computer News Mag., 1988, medal disting. achievement Colo. Sch. Mines, 1985. Mem. Young Pres. Orgn., Nat. Acad. Pub. Adminstrn., Colo. Sch. Mines Alumni Assn., Pres.'s Export Coun., Chief Execs. Orgn., World Bus. Coun., Reagan Alumni Assn., Palm Beach (Fla.) Golf and Polo Club. Home: 2 Ocean Ln Lake Worth FL 33462-3337 Office: 2100 W Sample Rd Ste 300 Pompano Beach FL 33064 also: Jefferson Capital 1341 G St NW Washington DC 20005 also: Avic Internat 599 Lexington Ave New York NY 10022

WRIGHT, JUDITH MARGARET, law librarian, educator; b. Jackson, Tenn., Aug. 16, 1944; d. Joseph Clarence and Mary Catherine (Key) Wright; m. Mark A. Johnson, Apr. 17, 1976; children—Paul, Michael. B.S., Memphis State U., 1966; M.A., U. Chgo., 1971; J.D., DePaul U., 1980. Bar: Ill. 1980. Librarian Oceanway Sch., Jacksonville, Fla., 1966-67; program dir. ARC, South Vietnam, 1967-68; documents and reference librarian D'Angelo Law Library, U. Chgo., 1970-74, reference librarian, 1974-77, dir., lectr. in law, 1980—; mem. adv. bd. Legal Reference Svcs. Quar., 1981—. Mem. ABA, Am. Assn. Law Libraries, Chgo. Assn. Law Libraries. Democrat. Methodist. Home: 5525 S Harper Ave Chicago IL 60637-1829 Office: U Chgo D'Angelo Law Libr 1121 E 60th St Chicago IL 60637-2745

WRIGHT, KENNETH BROOKS, lawyer; b. Whittier, Calif., June 5, 1934; s. Albert Harold and Marian (Schwey) W.; m. Sandra Beryl Smith, June 20, 1959; children: Margo Teresa, Daniel Brooks, John Waugh. B.A. cum laude, Pomona Coll., 1956; J.D., Stanford U., 1960. Bar: Calif. 1961, U.S. Supreme Ct. 1976. Assoc., then prtnr. Lawler, Felix & Hall, 1961-77; prtnr. Morgan, Lewis & Bockius, Los Angeles, 1978—; teaching team leader Nat. Inst. Trial Advocacy, 1978-80; mem. governing com. Calif. Continuing Edn. of Bar, 1971—, 1975-76; nat. panel arbitrators Am. Arbitration Assn., 1970—; lectr. ABA Sect. Litigation Nat. Inst., 1979-87; bd. dirs. L.A. Internat. Comml. Arbitration Ctr. Chmn. bd. editors: Am. Bar Jour, 1977-81. Pres. Pomona Coll. Alumni Assn., 1970-71; pres. Campbell Hall Sch., 1973-74, bd. dirs., vice chmn., 1994—; counsel Vol. League San Fernando Valley, 1979-81; chmn. sect. adminstrn. of justice Town Hall of Calif., 1970-71; sr. warden Episcopal Ch., 1973-74. Served with U.S. Army, 1956-57. Mem. ABA (dir. programs litigation sect. 1977-81, mem. council 1982-88, mem. standing com. on communication 1978-88, chmn. 1987-88, chmn. sect. litigation book publishing com. 1986-89, pres. fellows young lawyers 1985-86, bd. dirs 1980-89), Los Angeles County Bar Assn. (com. on judiciary 1981-93, chmn. continuing legal edn. com. 1989-91, vice-chmn. Continuing legal Edn. com. 1991-93, bd. dirs. L.A. Lawyer, 1989-94), State Bar Calif. (mem. com. continuing edn. of the bar 1972-77, chmn. 1975-76), Conf. Barristers (exec. com. 1966-69, 1st v.p. 1969), L.A. County Bar Found. (bd. dirs. 1993—), Assn. Bus. Trial Lawyers (chair com alternative dispute resolution, 1991-93, bd. dirs. 1993—), Am. Law Inst., Am. Bar Found., Am. Bd. Trial Advs., Internat. Bar Assn., Assn. So. Calif. Def. Counsel, Def. Rsch. Inst., U.S. Supreme Ct. Hist. Soc., Jonathan Club, Chancery Club, Phi Beta Kappa. Republican. Avocations: skiing, tennis. Home: 3610 Longridge Ave Sherman Oaks CA 91423-4918 Office: Morgan Lewis & Bockius 801 S Grand Ave 22d Fl Los Angeles CA 90017-3189

WRIGHT, KENNETH OSBORNE, retired astronomer; b. Ft. George, B.C., Can., Nov. 1, 1911; s. Charles Melville and Agnes Pearl (Osborne) W.; m. Margaret Lindsay Sharp, Sept. 25, 1936 (dec. June 1969); 1 child, Nora Louise Wright Osborne; m. Jean May MacLachlan, Mar. 21, 1970. B.A., U.

Toronto, Ont., Can. 1933, M.A., 1934; Ph.D., U. Mich., 1940; D.Sc. (hon.), Nicholas Copernicus U., Torun, Poland, 1973. With Dominion Astrophys. Obs., Victoria, B.C., 1936-84, asst. dir., 1960-66, dir., 1966-76, guest worker, 1976-84; hon. prof. physics U. Victoria, 1965-80, bd. govs., 1973-75; lectr. U. B.C., 1943-44; spl. lectr. in astronomy U. Toronto, 1959-60; research asso. Mt. Wilson and Palomar Obs., 1962; chmn. asso. com. on astronomy NRC Can., 1972-74. Decorated Can. Centennial medal. Fellow Royal Soc. Can.; mem. Internat. Astron. Union, Am. Astron. Soc., Can. Astron. Soc., Royal Astron. Soc. Can. (Gold medal 1933), Royal Astron. Soc., Astron. Soc. Pacific., Round Table, Rotary. Mem. United Ch. of Can. Research, publs. in field. Home: #202 1375 Newport Ave, Victoria, BC Canada V8S 5E8

WRIGHT, KIETH CARTER, librarian, educator; b. Billings, Mont., Nov. 11, 1933; s. Donald DeWitt and Isabella Sarah W.; children from previous marriage: Cynthia Jean, Elizabeth Anne. BA, Willamette U., 1955; MDiv, Union Theol. Sem., N.Y.C., 1958; MS In Libr. Scis, Columbia U., 1968, D of Libr. Scis., 1972. Chaplain intern Big Spring (Tex.) State Hosp., 1958-59; pastoral care worker N.C. Bapt. Hosp., Winston-Salem, N.C., 1960-64; adminstr. Nat. Council Chs., N.Y.C., 1964-70; librarian Gallaudet U., Washington, 1972-75; mem. faculty Cath. U. Am., Washington, 1976; dean Dept. Libr. and Info. Studies U. Md., College Park, 1977-79; chmn. dept. libr. sci. and ednl. technology Sch. Edn. U. N.C., Greensboro, 1980-86, prof. Sch. Edn., 1986—. Author: Library and Information Services for Handicapped Individuals, 1979, 3d edit., 1989, Workstations and Local Area Networks for Libraries, 1990, Serving Disabled, 1991, The Challenge of Technology, 1993, Computer-related Technologies in Library Operation, 1995. Office Edn. grantee, 1992-94. Mem. ALA. Home: 1605 Bearhollow Rd Greensboro NC 27410-3501 Office: U NC Sch Edn Greensboro NC 27412-5001

WRIGHT, LAURALI R. (BUNNY WRIGHT), writer; b. Saskatoon, Sask., Can., June 5, 1939; d. Sidney Victor and Evelyn Jane (Barber) Appleby; m. John Herbert Wright, Jan. 6, 1962 (separated 1986); children: Victoria Kathleen, Johnna Margaret. Student, Carleton U., 1958-59, U.B.C., 1960, 62-63, U. Calgary, 1970-71, Banff Sch. Fine Arts, 1976, Simon Fraser U., Burnaby, B.C., Can. Reporter Saskatoon Star-Phoenix, 1968-69, Calgary Albertan, 1969-70; reporter, columnist Calgary Herald, 1970-76, 1970-76, asst. city editor, 1976-77; freelance writer Calgary, 1977—. Author: (novels) Neighbours, 1979 (New Alta. Novelist award Alta. Culture and Multiculturalism 1978), The Favorite, 1982, Among Friends, 1984, The Suspect, 1985 (Edgar Allan Poe award Mystery Writers Am. 1986), Sleep While I Sing, 1986, Love in the Temperate Zone, 1988, A Chill Rain in January, 1989 (Arthur Ellis award Crime Writers Can. 1990), Fall from Grace, 1991, Prized Possessions, 1993. Mem. Writers Union Can., Authors' Guild of U.S., Internat. P.E.N., Mystery Writers of Am., Authors League Am., Periodical Writers Assn. Can., Writers Fedn. B.C. Avocations: gardening, reading, movies, theater, concerts, jogging. Office: Virginia Barber Lit Agy Inc 101 Fifth Ave New York NY 10003-1008*

WRIGHT, LAWRENCE A., federal judge; b. Stratton, Maine, Dec. 25, 1927; m. Avis Leahy, 1953; children: Michael, David, James, Stephen, Douglas. BA, U. Maine, 1953; JD, Georgetown U., 1956; LLM, Boston U., 1962. Bar: D.C. 1956, Maine 1956, Mass. 1968, Vt. 1971. Sr. trial counsel chief counsel office IRS, Boston, 1958-69; tax commr. State of Vt., 1969-71; ptnr. Gravel, Shea & Wright Ltd., Vt., 1971-84; judge U.S. Tax Ct., Washington, 1984—. 2d lt. U.S. Army, 1945-48; ret. col. JAG, USAR, 1978. Decorated Legion of Merit, others. Home: 1844 Northbridge Ln Annapolis MD 21401 Office: US Tax Ct 400 2d St NW Washington DC 20217

WRIGHT, LINDA JEAN, government relations executive; b. Chgo., Dec. 14, 1949; d. Eugene P. and Rosemary Margaret (Kiley) Kemph; m. Kelly W. Wright, Jr., Feb. 1979 (div. 1984); m. Samuel Neuwirth Klewans, Aug. 28, 1986 (div. 1991). Student Loretto Heights Coll., 1967-69, U. Ill., 1970-71. Asst. to v.p. Busey 1st Nat. Bank, Urbana, 1969-72; spa mgr., supr. sales tng. Venus and Apollo Health Club, San Antonio, 1973-76; owner Plant Shop, San Antonio, 1976-77; with Enterprise Bank, Falls Church, Va., 1977-84, comml. lending officer, 1978-84, sr. v.p., 1979-84, corp. sec. of bd. dirs., 1980-84; pres., CEO Fairfax Savs. Bank, 1984-87, Bankstar, N.A. (formerly Bank 2000 of Reston, N.A.), 1988-90; v.p Ryan-McGinn Inc., Arlington, Va., 1991—; bd. dirs. INOVA Inst. Rsch. and Edn., 1990-94. Apptd. pub. ofcl., chmn. Va. Small Bus. Fin. Authority, Richmond, 1984-88; trustee Inova Health System, 1992—; mem. exec. com. Fairfax-Falls Ch., United Way, United Way Capital Area, Washington, 1984-85; Fairfax County Spl. Task Force, 1986; bd. dirs. Fairfax Com. of 100, 1993—; mem., bd. dirs. Hospice No. 1, Arlington, 1985-86, chmn. No. Va. Local Devel. Corp., 1986; mem. oper. bd. Fairfax Hosp., 1987-94; pres. No. Va. Transp. Alliance, 1987-92; bd. dirs Va. Found. for Rsch. and Econ. Edn., 1989-91, No. Va. coun. Am. Heart Assn., 1989-94. Mem. Fairfax County C. of C. (dir., v.p., pres. 1987-88), Nat. Assn. Bank Women (chmn. No. Va. group 1980-81), Fairfax Hunt Club, Tower Club (bd. govs. 1989—). Roman Catholic. Avocations: aviation, fox hunting.

WRIGHT, MARIA GLORIA, nursing administrator; b. San Martin, Guatemala, Oct. 10, 1940; d. Miguel A. and Enriqueta (Martinez) Linares; m. George Wright, Nov. 26, 1963 (div. Oct. 1981); 1 child, Mary Deborah Wright Dunaway. Diploma in nursing, Mercy Hosp., Vicksburg, Miss., 1965; AA, Hinds Jr. Coll., Raymond, Miss., 1986; BSN, Miss. Coll., 1988; MSN, U. Miss., 1992. Staff nurse Mercy Hosp. Vicksburg, 1965-70, insvc. instr., 1970-73; head nurse orthopedics Hinds Gen. Hosp., Jackson, 1973-77, surg. area supr., 1977-78; DON Meth. Med. Ctr. (formerly Hinds Gen. Hosp.), Jackson, 1978—. Mem. Rep. Com., Miss., 1984—, San Martinecos Unidos, L.A., 1990—. Mem. ANA, Miss. Nurses Assn., Miss. Hosp. Assn. Orgn. Nurse Execs. (sec.). Roman Catholic. Avocations: reading, drawing, traveling. Home: 104 Red Oak Rd Clinton MS 39056-5514 Office: Meth Med Ctr 1850 Chadwick Dr Jackson MS 39204-3404

WRIGHT, MARSHALL, retired manufacturing executive, former diplomat; b. El Dorado, Ark., July 14, 1926; s. John Harvey and Helen Vaughan (Williams) W.; m. Mable Olean Johnson, Sept. 12, 1950 (dec. June 1989); children: William Marshall, Jefferson Vaughan; m. Lind Groseclose Vaughan, Mar. 31, 1990. Student, U. Ark., 1946-48, Cornell U., 1957-58; B.S. in Fgn. Service, Georgetown U., 1951. Joined U.S. Fgn. Service, 1953; vice consul Egypt, 1953-55; adminstrv. officer Can., 1956; econ. officer Burma, 1958-60; polit. officer Thailand, 1966-67; spokesman for State Dept., 1964-66; country dir. for Philippines, 1969; sr. mem. NSC, 1967-68, dir. long range planning, 1970-72; asst. sec. state for congl. relations, 1972-74; sr. fellow Nat. War Coll., 1969-70; v.p. govt. affairs Eaton Corp., 1974-76, v.p. pub. affairs, 1976-80, v.p. corp. affairs, 1980-91. Chmn. Cleve. ARC; trustee Cleve. Orch., Cleve. Inst. Music; chmn. Cleve. Com. Fgn. Rels.; vice chmn. Govtl. Rsch. Inst.; mem. Conf. Bd. Pub. Affairs Rsch. Coun., MAPI. Pub. Affairs Coun.; bd. dirs Cleveland Town Hall, Bus. Industry Polit. action Com. With USMC, 1944-46. Recipient Meritorious Service award State Dept., 1966, Distinguished Service award, 1972. Mem. Am. Fgn. Svc. Assn., Columbia Country Club, Met. Club, Dacor, Mayfield Country, Union, Moss Creek Golf Club. Home (summer): 304 Corning Dr Cleveland OH 44108-1014 Home (winter): Moss Creek Plantation 80 Toppin Dr Hilton Head SC 29926

WRIGHT, MARY R., state park superintendent; b. Hartford, Conn., Jan. 12, 1949; d. J. William and Eileen J. (Walsh) Bigoness; m. Roy C. Gunter III, June 24, 1972 (div. Feb. 1988); m. Kenneth Ross Wright, Dec. 1, 1988. BA, Marquette U., 1970; MS, U. Mo., 1972. Prgram analyst State Calif. Dept. Health, Sacramento, 1972-76; tng. ctr. dir. State Calif. Dept. Parks and Recreation, Pacific Grove, 1976-81; visitor svcs. mgr. State Calif. Dept. Parks and Recreation, Monterey, 1981-83, Monterey dist. supr., 1983-92, dep. dir., 1992-93; Monterey dist. supt. Calif. Dept. Parks and Recreation, 1991—; hist. preservation commr. City of Monterey, 1984-92. Bd. dirs. Big Sur Health Ctr., 1993—. Office: Monterey Dist Calif State Parks 2211 Garden Rd Monterey CA 93940

WRIGHT, MICHAEL GEORGE, science administrator, research metallurgist; b. Bristol, U.K., Apr. 15, 1939; s. Frank E. Crozier; children: Craig, Graeme. BS, U. Wales, 1960; MSc, McMaster U., 1964. Metallurgist GE-Simon Carves Atomic Energy Group, Kent, U.K., 1961-62; Inland Steel Co. Ind., 1964-66; rsch. sci. Atomic Energy Can. Ltd., Pinawa, Man., Can., 1966-77, br. mgr., 1977-82; sr. adv. and asst., 1982-84, mgr. engring. divsn.,

1984-86, gen. mgr., 1986—. Office: Atomic Energy Can Ltd Rsch, Whiteshell Nuclear Rsch Labs, Pinawa, MB Canada R0E 1L0*

WRIGHT, MICHAEL WILLIAM, wholesale food company executive; b. Mpls., June 13, 1938; s. Thomas W. and Winifred M. Wright. B.A., U. Minn., 1961, J.D. with honors, 1963. Ptnr. Dorsey & Whitney, Mpls., 1966-77; sr. v.p. Supervalu Inc., Mpls., 1977-78; pres., chief operating officer Super Valu Stores, Inc., Mpls., 1978—, chief exec. officer, 1981—, chmn., 1982—; bd. dirs., past chmn. Fed. Res. Bank, Mpls.; bd. dirs. Norwest Corp., Honeywell, Inc., The Musicland Group, Shopko, Inc., Internat. Assn. Chain Stores, Food Mktg. Inst., Nat. Am. Wholesale Grovers Assn., Inc.; vice-chmn. Food Mktg. Inst. 1st lt. U.S. Army, 1964-66. Office: Supervalu Inc PO Box 990 Minneapolis MN 55440-0990 Office: Cub Foods PO Box 9 127 Water Street Stillwater MN 55082*

WRIGHT, MILDRED ANNE (MILLY WRIGHT), conservator, researcher; b. Athens, Ala., Sept. 9, 1939; d. Thomas Howard and Anne Louise (Ashworth) Speegle; m. William Paul Wright, Nov. 20, 1965; children: Paul Howard, William Neal. BS in Physics, U. Ala., Tuscaloosa, 1963. Researcher in acoustics Wyle Labs., Huntsville, Ala., 1963-64; tchr. physics, English Huntsville High Sch., 1964-67; ptnr. Flying Carpet Oriental Rugs, Florence, Ala., 1974—; adj. mem. faculty U. North Ala., Florence, 1988, lectr. Inst. for Learning in Retirement, 1991—. Columnist Times Daily, 1992—; photojournalist, writer River Views Mag., 1993—; contbr. articles to profl. jours. (1st pl. award 1986, 87). Pianist, organist Edgemont Meth. Ch., Florence, 1987-90 (Outstanding Svc. award 1990); mem. steering com. Melton Hollow Nature Ctr., Florence, 1990—, Design Ala., Florence, 1991, River Heritage Discovery Camp, 1993—; mem. River Heritage Com., Florence, 1991—; accompanist Shoals Boy Choir, Muscle Shoals, Ala., 1992-93; bd. dirs. Heritage Preservation, Inc., 1989—, Capital award 1992, pres., 1990-92, treas. 1995—, Tenn. Valley Hist. Soc., pres., 1991-95, Ala. Preservation Alliance, treas., 1993—, Florence Main Street program, 1992-94, Maud Lindsay Free Kindergarten, Frank Lloyd Wright Rosenbaum House Found., Inc., 1992—, Gen. Joseph Wheeler Home Found., 1994—, treas. 1995—, Friends of the Ala. Archives, 1995—; mem. adv. coun. Human Environ. Scis. Dept.; mem. Coby Hall steering com. U. North Ala., 1992—, Kennedy-Douglass Ctr. Arts. Recipient Disting. Svc. award Ala. Hist. Commn., 1991. Mem. AAUW, Ala. Writers' Conclave (Creative Works award 1986, 87), Ala. Hist. Assn., Ala. Archeol. Soc., Natchez Trace Geneal. Soc., Colbert County Hist. Landmarks Found., Nat. Trust for Hist. Preservation, Tenn. Valley Art Assn., La Grange Living History Assn., Trail of Tears Assn., Firenze Club (past pres.), Optimist Club, Sigma Pi Sigma. Avocations: bridge, photography, travel, discovering old buildings, gardening. Home: PO Box 279 Florence AL 35631

WRIGHT, MINTURN TATUM, III, lawyer; b. Phila., Aug. 7, 1925; s. Minturn T. and Anna (Moss) W.; m. Nonya R. Stevens, May 11, 1957; children: Minturn T., Richard S., Robert M., Marianne F. BA, Yale U., 1949; LLB, U. Pa., 1952. Bar: Pa. 1953, U.S. Ct. Appeals (3d cir.) 1953, U.S. Supreme Ct. 1962. Law clk. U.S. Ct. Appeals (3d cir.), 1952-53; assoc. Dechert, Price & Rhoads, Phila., 1953-61, ptnr., 1961—, chmn., 1982-84; bd. dirs. Penn Va. Corp., Phila. Contributionship, Vector Inc., Cotiga Devel. Co.; vis. prof. U. Pa. Law Sch., 1965-69, 93—. Contbr. articles to profl. jours. Trustee Acad. Nat. Scis. Phila., 1958—, chmn., 1976-81; trustee Hawk Mountain Sanctuary Assn., chmn. bd. dirs., 1992—, Rare Ctr., The Nature Conservancy (Pa. chpt.). Served with U.S. Army, 1943-46. Mem. ABA, Pa. Bar Assn., Phila. Bar Assn., Nat. Coal Lawyers Assn., Eastern Mineral Law Assn. (trustee), Phila. Club, Milldam Club. Episcopalian. Office: Dechert Price & Rhoads 4000 Bell Atlantic Tower 1717 Arch St Philadelphia PA 19103-2713

WRIGHT, MURIEL DEASON See WELLS, KITTY

WRIGHT, NANCY JANE, English language educator; b. Springfield, Ill., Feb. 28, 1939; d. William Joseph and Elizabeth (Walton) Lucasey; m. Arthur Lee Wright, Aug. 21, 1960; 1 child, John Arthur. BS magna cum laude, Western Ill. U., 1961; MS summa cum laude, So. Ill. U., 1963; PhD, Tex. A&M U., 1975. Tchg. asst. So. Ill. U., Carbondale, 1961-62; instr. Ferris State Coll., Big Rapids, Mich., 1962-65, Christian Coll., Columbia, Mo., 1965-70; tchg. asst. then instr. Tex. A&M U., College Station, 1971-76; instr. lit. Blinn Coll., Bryan, Tex., 1977—; mem. Am. Disabilities Task Force, Blinn Coll., Bryan, 1994—, mem. curriculum com., 1993-94, acad. advisor, 1992—; workshop leader. Co-author: How to Prepare for the Tasp, 1991, 2d edit., 1994. Vol. instr. LIFT Program, Dallas, 1970-71; dir. music, pianist/accompanist First Christian Ch., Bryan. Mem. Blinn Coll. Profl. Assn. (founding pres.), Nat. Coun. Tchrs. English, Tex. Jr. Coll. Tchrs Assn. Republican. Mem. Disciples of Christ Ch. Home: 1008 Holt College Station TX 77840

WRIGHT, NORMAN HAROLD, lawyer; b. N.Y.C., Mar. 7, 1947; s. Donald H. and Georgianna (Reinert) W.; m. Julie K. Angert, May 29, 1971; children: Zane H., Anne V. BS in Engring., U. Toledo, 1969; JD, Creighton U., 1978. Bar: Nebr. 1978, U.S. Ct. Appeals (8th cir.) 1978, U.S. Supreme Ct. 1989. Engr. E.I. DuPont de Nemours & Co., Inc., Columbus, Ohio, 1969-75, El Paso, Tex., 1975-78; assoc. Fraser, Stryker, Vaughn, Meusey, Olson, Boyer & Bloch, P.C., Omaha, 1978-84, ptnr., 1984—; dir. Nebr. Tax Rsch. Coun., Lincoln, 1989—. Author: Nebraska Legal Forms, Real Estate, 1983. Chmn. bd. Am. Diabetes Assn., Omaha, 1991; bd. trustees Trinity Cathedral Episcopal Ch., Omaha, 1984. Mem. ABA, Nebr. Bar Assn., Inst. Property Taxation, Nebr. Tax Forum, Cosmopolitan Club (sec. 1990-92, treas. 1987-88). Republican. Episcopalian. Avocations: golf, skiing, baseball. Home: 8910 Frances St Omaha NE 68124 Office: Fraser Stryker Vaughn Meusey Olson Boyer & Bloch PC 409 S 17th St Ste 500 Omaha NE 68102

WRIGHT, SIR (JOHN) OLIVER, retired diplomat; b. U.K., Mar. 6, 1921; m. Lillian Marjory Osborne, Sept. 19, 1942; children: Nicholas, John, Christopher. Ed., Solihull Sch., Christ's Coll., Cambridge, Eng.; D.H.L. (hon.), U. Nebr., 1983; LL.D., Rockford Coll., 1984. Joined Diplomatic Service, 1945; Brit. ambassador to Denmark, 1966-69, to Fed. Republic Germany, 1975-81, to U.S., 1982-86; vis. prof. U. St. Louis, Berkeley Hotel; dir. Enviromed P.L.C.; Tobin Lewin vis. prof. Wash. U., St. Louis. Trustee Brit. Mus., 1986-91; bd. dirs. Brit. Council; chmn. Anglo-Irish Encounter, 1986-91. With Royal Navy, 1941-45. Decorated D.S.C., knight grand cross Royal Victorian Order, knight grand cross Order of St. Michael and St. George, grand cross German Order of Merit; named hon. fellow Christ's Coll., 1981; Clark fellow, Cornell U., 1987. Mem. German C. of C. London (pres.). Club: Travellers' (London). Avocations: theatre; gardening.

WRIGHT, PATRICIA DONOVAN, communications executive; b. Rhinelander, Wis., Mar. 10, 1952; d. Stanley Timothy and Evelyn Mae (Smith) Donovan; m. Larry James Wright, May 17, 1980; children: Lindsay Mae, Molly Donovan. BS, U. Wis., 1974. Writer Amoco Corp., Chgo., 1974-77; rep. pub., community rels. Amoco Oil, Texas City, 1977-81; sr. pub. affairs advisor Amoco Corp., Kansas City, Mo., 1981-84; supr. media relations Amoco Corp., Chgo., 1984-86; dir. pub., govt. affairs Amoco Oil Co., Chgo., 1986-89; regional dir. pub. & govt. affairs Midwest Amoco Corp., Chgo., 1989-91, dir. corp. media rels., 1991-92; exec. dir. corp. rels Amoco Found., Chgo., 1992—. Recipient Award of Excellence Internat. Assn. Bus. Communicators, 1992, honors Arthur Page Soc., 1992. Mem. Women In Communications (bd. dirs. Chgo. chpt., chmn. 1985-86, regional meeting chmn.; Clarion award 1977, Cub's Cup award 1977), Publicity Club of Chgo. (Silver Trumpet 1992). Avocations: golf, biking, tennis. Home: 30 Citation Cir Wheaton IL 60187-1117 Office: Amoco Corp 200 E Randolph Dr # 3707 Chicago IL 60601-6401

WRIGHT, PATRICK E., grain company executive; b. 1936. With Owensboro (Ky.) Grain Co., 1955—, now pres. Office: Owensboro Grain Co 719 E 2nd St Owensboro KY 42303

WRIGHT, PAUL, JR., banker; b. Birmingham, Ala., Aug. 21, 1911; s. Paul and Carolyn (Felder) W.; m. Melba Brown Chamblee, Nov. 15, 1935; children: Hazel Elizabeth Wright Kearns, Paul III. B.S. in Bus. Adminstrn., Duke U., 1932; grad., Rutgers Coll. Grad. Sch. Banking, 1940, Exec. Program, U. N.C., 1958. Examiner N.C. Banking Dept., 1932-41; v.p.

Wachovia Bank & Trust Co., Winston-Salem, N.C., 1941-49, Bank of Va., Richmond, 1949-53; pres. Central Carolina Bank & Trust Co., Durham, N.C., 1953-74; vice chmn. bd. Central Carolina Bank & Trust Co., 1974-82; Mem. N.C. Banking Commn., 1966-82; trustee Found. Comml. Banks, 1958—. Served to lt. USNR, World War II. Recipient Durham Civic Honor award, 1965. Mem. Alpha Tau Omega. Democrat. Episcopalian. Home: 19 Old Oak Ct Durham NC 27705-5644 Office: Central Carolina Bank Bldg Durham NC 27702

WRIGHT, P(AUL) BRUCE, lawyer; b. N.Y.C., Aug. 26, 1946; s. Leon and Ruth (Cohen) W.; m. Eta Jacobson, June 28, 1969; children: Matthew, Jason. BS in Acctg., Bklyn. Coll., 1967; JD cum laude, Bklyn. Law Sch., 1971; LLM in Taxation, Georgetown U., 1974. Bar: N.Y. 1971, U.S. Dist. Ct. N.Y. 1974, D.C. 1974, U.S. Ct. Appeals (D.C. cir.) 1974. Atty. advisor IRS, Washington, 1971-75; assoc. Trubin, Sillocks, Edelman & Knapp, N.Y.C., 1975-78, ptnr., 1978-84; ptnr. LeBoeuf, Lamb, Leiby & MacRae (now LeBoeuf, Lamb, Greene & MacRae), N.Y.C., 1984—. Office: LeBoeuf Lamb Greene & MacRae 125 W 55th St New York NY 10019

WRIGHT, PETER MELDRIM, lawyer; b. Charlottesville, Va., Apr. 10, 1946; s. David McCord and Caroline Wallace (Jones) W.; m. Astrid Gabriella Mercedes Sandberg, June 4, 1972; children: David Habersham, Christian Langdon. AB, U. Ga., 1967, JD, 1972. Bar: Ga. 1972, U.S. Dist. Ct. (no. dist.) Ga. 1972. Assoc. Jones, Bird & Howell, Atlanta, 1972-77, ptnr., 1977-82; ptnr. Alston & Bird, Atlanta, 1982—. Author: A Survey of State Blue Sky Laws Applicable to Tax Exempt Bonds, 1987. Sec. Atlanta Coun. Soc. Colonia Wars in Ga., 1975-88, dep. gov., 1989-91; mem. Soc. Cin. S.C., Charleston. Mem. ABA, Ga. Bar Assn., Atlanta Bar Assn., Nat. Assn. Bond Lawyers (chmn. blue sky laws and legal investment law coms. 1982-85, bd. dirs. 1985-86), Ga. Hist. Soc. (bd. curators 1993-94, sec. 1994—), Oglethorpe Club (Savannah, Ga.), St. Andrew's Soc. Savannah. Home: 3502 Woodhaven Rd NW Atlanta GA 30305-1011 Office: Alston & Bird 1 Atlantic Ctr 1201 W Peachtree St NW Atlanta GA 30309-3424

WRIGHT, RANDOLPH EARLE, retired petroleum company executive; b. Brownsville, Tex., Dec. 22, 1920; s. William Randolph and Nelle Mae (Earle) W.; m. Elaine Marie Harris, May 9, 1943; 1 son, Randolph Earle. B.S., U. Tex., 1942. With Texaco Inc., 1946-82; mgr. gas div. Texaco Inc., Houston, 1968-70; gen. mgr. producing dept. Texaco Inc., 1970-71, v.p. gas dept., 1971-82; v.p., sr. officer Texaco Inc., Houston, 1972-80; past pres., dir. Sabine Pipe Line Co.; v.p., asst. to pres. Texaco U.S.A., 1980-82, ret., 1982; past v.p. Texaco Mineral Co.; past chmn. engring. found. adv. council U. Tex., Austin. Past mem. exec. bd. Sam Houston Area council Boy Scouts Am.; past bd. dirs., past pres. Jr. Achievement S.E. Tex.; past bd. dirs. Houston Symphony Soc., Tex. Research League, Houston C. of C.; past trustee U. St. Thomas; trustee S.W. Research Inst. Served with USNR, World War II. Mem. Tex. Research League. Clubs: Lakeside.

WRIGHT, RICHARD G., optical and health care company executive; b. Syracuse, N.Y., Mar. 11, 1934; s. Herbert G. and Marguerite (Wood) W.; m. Barbara Ann Lutzy, Aug. 18, 1954; children: Linda, Richard Jr., Pamela, Michelle, Craig. Student, Colgate U., 1953-54; BS, Syracuse U., 1957. Dir. mktg. soft contact lens div. Am. Optical Co., Southbridge, Mass., 1976-79, gen. mgr. soft contact lens div., 1979-81; exec. v.p. Barnes-Hind div. Revlon, Inc., N.Y.C., 1981-83, pres., 1983-85; pres. Revlon Vision Care Internat., N.Y.C., 1985-86; pres., COO Foster-Grant Corp., Leominster, Mass., 1986-89; pres., CEO Xenon Vision Inc., Princeton, N.J., 1989-91; v.p., gen. mgr. Storz Instruments, Co. divsn. Am. Cyanamid Co., 1991-94; chmn., CEO Celgene Corp., Warren, N.J., 1994—. Home: 90 Stone Run Rd Bedminster NJ 07921 Office: Celgene Corp 7 Powder Horn Dr Warren NJ 07059

WRIGHT, RICHARD JOHN, business executive; b. Bklyn., June 17, 1951; s. David Francis and Mary Catherine W.; m. Linda Marie Green, May 24, 1975; children: Sean, Bridget. B.S. in Physics with honors, Bates Coll., 1973; M.B.A., Rutgers U., 1974. C.P.A. Mgr. Coopers & Lybrand, N.Y.C., 1975-81; chief fin. officer Drexel Burnham Lambert, N.Y.C., 1981-92; pres., dir. DP Investments G.P. Corp., N.Y.C., 1992—; pres. DPI-A Corp. N.Y.C., 1992—, DPI-B Corp., N.Y.C., 1992—; mng. dir. Viking Group, Ltd., Whittredge Capital, L.P. Mem. Fin. Exec. Inst., AICPA, N.Y. State Soc. CPAs, Securities Industry Assn. (tax policy com.), Williams Club, Spring Lake Bath and Tennis Club. Office: DP Investments GP Corp 450 Lexington Ave New York NY 10017

WRIGHT, RICHARD NEWPORT, III, civil engineer, government official; b. Syracuse, N.Y., May 17, 1932; s. Richard Newport and Carolyn (Baker) W.; m. Teresa Rios, Aug. 23, 1959; children—John Stannard, Carolyn Maria, Elizabeth Rebecca, Edward Newport. B.C.E., Syracuse U., 1953, M.C.E. (Parcel fellow), 1955; Ph.D., U. Ill., 1962. Jr. engr. Pa. R.R., Phila., 1953-55; instr. civil engring. U. Ill., Urbana, 1957-62; asst. prof. U. Ill., 1962-65, assoc. prof., 1965-70, prof., 1970-74, adj. prof., 1974-79; chief structures sect. Bldg. Research div. U.S. Bur. Standards, Washington, 1971-72; pres. Internat. Council for Bldg. Research, Studies and Documentation, 1983-86; dep. dir. tech. Ctr. Bldg. Tech., 1972-73, dir., 1974-91; dir. Bldg. and Fire Rsch. Lab., 1991—. Contbr. articles to profl. jours. Pres. Montgomery Village Found., 1989-90, bd. dirs., 1985—. Served with AUS, 1955-57. Named Fed. Engr. of Yr. Nat. Soc. Profl. Engrs., 1988. Fellow ASCE. Home: 20081 Doolittle St Montgomery Village MD 20879-1354 Office: Dept of Commerce Nat Inst Standards & Tech Bldg and Fire Research Labs Gaithersburg MD 20899

WRIGHT, ROBERT BURROUGHS, financial consultant; b. Hillside, N.J., Dec. 21, 1916; s. Herbert M. and Adele (Emmerich) W.; m. Jeanne G. Smith, June 9, 1956; children—Jeanine A., Susan A. A.B., Montclair State Coll., 1939, M.A., 1941; Chem. Engr., Newark Coll. Engring., 1944. Acct. Gen. Motors Corp., Harrison, N.J., 1940-43; asst. controller Mennen Co., Morristown, N.J., 1943-47; controller Mennen Co., 1947-63, asst. treas., 1963-68, treas., chief financial officer 1968-71; also dir.; financial dir.; treas. Ronson Corp., Wood Bridge, N.J., 1971-72; v.p. fin. Ronson Corp., 1972-76, Timeplex, Inc., Rochelle Park, N.J., 1976-81; sr. v.p. Timeplex, Inc., 1981-83; treas., dir. Mennen; v.p., dir. Timeplex Ltd., Scannon Ltd.; dir. Cermetek Inc. Treas.; past dir. Morris County Community Chest and Council, 1955-58. Mem. Am. Mgmt. Assn., Nat. Indsl. Conf. Bd., Financial Execs. Inst. Nat. Assn. Accountants, Financial Execs. Inst. (pres. N.J. chpt. 1963-64; nat. dir. 1970-73, adv. council 1974-76), Montclair State Coll. Alumni Assn. (exec. bd. 1974-77). Home: Winding Way Convent Station NJ 07960-6956

WRIGHT, ROBERT C., broadcasting executive; b. Rockville Center, N.Y., Apr. 23, 1943; m. Suzanne Werner, Aug. 26, 1967; children: Kate, Christopher, Maggie. A.B. in History, Coll. Holy Cross, 1965; LL.B., U. Va., 1968. Bar: N.Y. 1968, Va. 1968, Mass. 1970, N.J. 1971. With Gen. Electric Co., 1969-70, 73-80, gen. mgr. plastics sales dept., 1978-80; law sec. to chief judge U.S. Dist. Ct., N.J., 1970-73; pres. Cox Cable Communications, Atlanta, 1980-83; exec. v.p. Cox Communications, 1980-83; v.p., gen. mgr. housewares, audio and cable TV ops. GE, 1983-84; pres., chief exec. officer GE Fin. Svcs. Inc., 1984-86, NBC, N.Y.C., 1986—. Office: NBC Inc 30 Rockefeller Pl New York NY 10112-0100

WRIGHT, ROBERT F., petroleum products company executive. Previously exec. v.p. Amerada Hess Corp., N.Y.C., pres., chief oper. officer, 1986—, also bd. dirs. Office: Amerada Hess Corp 1185 Avenue Of The Americas New York NY 10036-2601*

WRIGHT, ROBERT JOSEPH, lawyer; b. Rome, Ga., Dec. 13, 1949; s. Arthur Arley and Maude T. (Lacey) W.; m. Donna Ruth Bishop, Feb. 18, 1972; children: Cynthia Ashley, Laura Christine. BA cum laude, Ga. State U., 1979; JD cum laude, U. Ga., 1983. Bar: GA. 1983, U.S. Dist. Ct. (no. dist.) Ga. 1983, U.S. Dist. Ct. (mid. dist.) Ga. 1985. Assoc. Craig & Gainer, Covington, Ga., 1983-84; Heard, Leverett & Adams, Elberton, Ga., 1984-86; gen. counsel Group Underwriters, Inc., Elberton, 1987—. Editorial staff Ga. Jour. Internat. and Comparative Law, 1981-82. Mem. State Bar Ga. (sec. legal econs. sect. 1987-88, chmn. legal econs. sect. 1988-90), Order of the Coif, Masons, Phi Alpha Delta. Baptist. Home: 1030 E Canyon Creek Ct Watkinsville GA 30677-1500

WRIGHT, ROBERT PAYTON, lawyer; b. Beaumont, Tex., Feb. 15, 1951; s. Vernon Gerald and Huberta Read (Nunn) W.; m. Sallie Chesnutt Smith, July 16, 1977; children: Payton Cullen, Elizabeth Risher. AB, Princeton U., 1972; JD, Columbia U., 1975. Bar: Tex. 1975. Ptnr. Baker & Botts, L.L.P., Houston, 1975—. Author: The Texas Homebuyer's Manual, 1986. Mem. State Bar Tex. (chmn. coun. real estate, probate, trust law sect. 1994-95), Houston Bar Assn. (chmn. real estate sect. 1989-90), Tex. Coll. Real Estate Lawyers, Houston Real Estate Lawyers Coun., Houston Club (mem. com. young mems. 1987). Episcopalian. Office: Baker & Botts LLP 3000 One Shell Plz 910 Louisiana St Houston TX 77002

WRIGHT, ROBERT ROSS, III, lawyer, educator; b. Fort Worth, Nov. 20, 1931; children: Robert Ross IV, John, David, Robin. BA cum laude, U. Ark., 1953, JD, 1956; MA (grad. fellow), Duke U., 1954; SJD (law fellow), U. Wis., 1967. Bar: Ark. 1956, U.S. Supreme Ct. 1968, Okla. 1970. Instr. polit. sci. U. Ark., 1955-56; mem. firm Forrest City, Ark., 1956-58; partner firm Norton, Norton & Wright, Forrest City, 1959; asst. gen. counsel, asst. sec. Crossett Co., Ark.; atty. Crossett div. Ga.-Pacific Corp., 1960-63; asst. sec. Pub. Utilities Co., Crossett, Triangle Bag Co., Covington, Ky., 1960-62; mem. faculty law sch. U. Ark., 1963-70; asst. prof., dir. continuing legal edn. and research, then asst. dean U. Ark. (Little Rock div.), 1965-66, prof. law, 1967-70; vis. prof. law U. Iowa, 1969-70; prof. U. Okla., 1970-77; dean U. Okla. (Coll. Law); dir. U. Okla. (Law Center), 1970-76; vis. prof. U. Ark., Little Rock, 1976-77; Donaghey Disting. prof. U. Ark, 1977—; Ark. commr. Nat. Conf. Commrs. Uniform State Laws, 1967-70; past chmn. Com. Uniform Eminent Domain Code; past mem. Com. Uniform Probate Code, Ark. Gov.'s Ins. Study Commn.; chmn. Gov. Commn. on Uniform Probate Code; chmn. task force joint devel. Hwy. Research Bd.; vice chmn. Okla. Jud. Council, 1970-72, chmn., 1972-75; chmn. Okla. Center Criminal Justice, 1971-76. Author: Arkansas Eminent Domain Digest, 1964, Arkansas Probate Practice System, 1965, The Law of Airspace, 1968, Emerging Concepts in the Law of Airspace, 1969, Cases and Materials on Land Use, 3d edit., 1982, supp., 1987, 4th edit., 1991, Uniform Probate Code Practice Manual, 1972, Model Airspace Code, 1973, Land Use in a Nutshell, 1978, 2d edit., 1985, 3d edit., 1994, The Arkansas Form Book, 1979, 2d edit., 1988, Zoning Law in Arkansas: A Comparative Analysis, 1980; contbr. numerous articles to legal jours. Mem. Little Rock Planning Commn., 1978-82, chmn., 1982. Named Ark. Man of Year Kappa Sigma, 1958. Fellow Am. Law Inst., acad. fellow Am. Coll. Probate Counsel; mem. Ark. Bar Assn. (exec. council 1985-88, ho. of dels. life mem., chmn. eminent domain code com., past mem. com. new bar center; past chmn. preceptorship com.; exec. com. young lawyers sect.), Okla. Bar Assn. (past vice-chmn. legal internship com.; former vice chmn. gen. practice sect.), ABA (exec. council chair elect gen. practice sect., former chmn. publ. bd., sect. gen. practice, former chmn. new pubs. editorial bd., former mem. standing com. on profl. career devel., mem. house of dels., mem. standing com. on solo and small firm practitioners), Pulaski County Bar Assn., Ark. Bar Found., U. Wis., U. Ark., Duke alumni assns., Order Coif, Phi Beta Kappa, Phi Alpha Delta, Omicron Delta Kappa. Episcopalian. Home: 249 Pleasant Valley Dr Little Rock AR 72212 Office: U Ark Law Sch 1201 McAlmont St Little Rock AR 72202

WRIGHT, ROBIN, actress; b. 1966; d. Fred W., children: Dylan Frances, Hopper Jack. television appearances include: The Yellow Rose, 1983-84, Santa Barbara, 1984-87 (Emmy awards Best Ingenue in a Daytime Drama series 1985-87); films include: Hollywood Vice Squad, 1986, The Princess Bride, 1987, State of Grace, 1990, Denial, 1991, The Playboys, 1992, Toys, 1992, Forrest Gump, 1994, The Crossing Guard, 1995. Office: Care CAA 9830 Wilshire Blvd Beverly Hills CA 90212-1804*

WRIGHT, RODNEY H., architect; b. Valparaiso, Ind., June 2, 1931; s. George and Lena May (Cahoon) W.; m. Sydney Sullivan Goelitz, Feb. 16, 1966; children by previous marriage: Weston, Julie-An; stepchildren: Louise Goelitz, Ann Marie Goelitz, Thomas Goelitz. Grad. high sch. With various archtl. firms, 1953-60, pvt. practice architecture, 1960—; architect Hawkweed Group Ltd., Chgo., 1978-85; sole propr. Rodney Wright, Architect; lectr Northwestern U., 1971; keynote speaker First Solar Symposium, Sao Paulo, Brasil, 1976; presenter 1987 European Conf. on Architecture, Munich, 1st/2d conf. How Successful Directors Manage, 1986-93; speaker for various child care mtgs. and workshops. Author: Hawkweed, 1975, Passive Solar House Book, 1980, Urban Brickyard, Saving Energy Serving Children, 1993. Bd. dirs. Lake County Urban League, 1961-69, chmn., 1961-65; bd. dirs. Uptown Devel. Ctr., Chgo., 1969-73. With U.S. Army, 1950-53. Design fellow Nat. Endowment for Arts, 1975; recipient award U. Wis./Early Childhood Edn. Conf. Fellow AIA (chpt. dir. 1971, co-chmn. task force 1 1969-72, mem. nat. com. community devel. ctrs. 1970-72). Pioneer in design of passive solar and superinsulated bldgs. Research design of child care environments, including use of color, equipment, natural nonpolluting materials. Address: Rte 4 Box 175A Osseo WI 54758-8947

WRIGHT, ROSALIE MULLER, newspaper and magazine editor; b. Newark, June 20, 1942; d. Charles and Angela (Fortunata) Muller; m. Lynn Wright, Jan. 13, 1962; children: James Anthony Meador, Geoffrey Shepard. BA in English, Temple U., 1965. Mng. editor Suburban Life mag., Orange, N.J., 1960-62; assoc. editor Phila. mag., 1962-64, mng. editor, 1969-73; founding editor Womensports mag., San Mateo, Calif., 1973-75; editor scene sect. San Francisco Examiner, 1975-77; exec. editor New West mag., San Francisco and Beverly Hills, Calif., 1977-81; features and Sunday editor San Francisco Chronicle, 1981-87, asst. mng. editor features, 1987—; tchr. mag. writing U. Calif., Berkeley, 1975-76; participant pub. procedures course Stanford U., 1977-79; chmn. mag. judges at conf. Coun. Advancement and Support of Edn., 1980, judge, 1984. Contbr. numerous mag. articles, critiques, revs., Compton's Ency. Mem. Am. Assn. Sun and Feature Editors (treas. 1984, sec. 1985, 1st v.p. 1986, pres. 1987), Am. Newspaper Pub. Assn. (pub. task force on minorities in newspaper bus. 1988-89, Chronicle minority recruiter 1987—), Calif. Soc. Newspaper Editors, Internat. Women's Forum, Women's Forum West (bd. dirs. 1993—, sec. 1994). Office: Chronicle Pub Co 901 Mission St San Francisco CA 94103-2905

WRIGHT, SCOTT OLIN, federal judge; b. Haigler, Nebr., Jan. 15, 1923; s. Jesse H. and Martha I. Wright; m. Shirley Frances Young, Aug. 25, 1972. Student, Central Coll. Fayette, Mo., 1940-42; LLB, U. Mo., Columbia, 1950. Bar: Mo. 1950. City atty. Columbia, 1951-53; pros. atty. Boone County, Mo., 1954-58; practice of law Columbia, 1958-79; U.S. dist. judge Western Dist. Mo., Kansas City, from 1979. Pres. Young Democrats Boone County, 1950, United Fund Columbia, 1965. Served with USN, 1942-43; as aviator USMC, 1943-46. Decorated Air medal. Mem. ABA, Am. Trial Lawyers Assn., Mo. Bar Assn., Mo. Trial Lawyers Assn., Boone County Bar Assn. Unitarian. Clubs: Rockhill Tennis, Woodside Racquet. Lodge: Rotary (pres. Columbia 1965). Office: US Dist Ct US Courthouse 811 Grand Ave Rm 741 Kansas City MO 64106-1983

WRIGHT, STEPHEN GAILORD, civil engineering educator, consultant; b. San Diego, Aug. 13, 1943; s. Homer Angelo and Elizabeth Videlle (Ward) W.; m. Ouida Jo Kennedy; children: Michelle, Richard. BSCE, U. Calif., Berkeley, 1966, MSCE, 1967, PhD CE, 1969. Prof. civil engring. U. Tex., Austin, 1969—. Contbr. numerous tech. papers & research reports, 1969—. Mem. ASCE. Republican. Presbyterian. Home: 3406 Shinoak Dr Austin TX 78731-5739 Office: U Tex Dept Civil Engring Austin TX 78712

WRIGHT, SUSAN WEBBER, federal judge; b. Texarkana, Ark., Aug. 22, 1948; d. Thomas Edward and Betty Jane (Gary) Webber; m. Robert Ross Wright, III, May 21, 1983; 1 child, Robin Elizabeth. BA, Randolph-Macon Woman's Coll., 1970; MPA, U. Ark., 1972, JD with high honors, 1975. Bar: Ark. 1975. Law clk. U.S. Ct. Appeals 8th Circuit, 1975-76; asst. prof. law U. Ark.-Little Rock, 1976-78, assoc. prof., 1978-83, prof., 1983-90, asst. dean, 1976-78; dist. judge U.S. Dist. Ct. (ea. dist.) Ark., Little Rock, 1990—; vis. assoc. prof. Ohio State U., Columbus, 1981, La. State U., Baton Rouge, 1982-83; mem. adv. com. U.S. Ct. Appeals 8th Circuit, St. Louis, 1983-88. Author: (with R. Wright) Land Use in a Nutshell, 1978, 2d edit., 1985; editor-in-chief Ark. Law Rev., 1975; contbr. articles to research jours. Mem. ABA, Ark. Bar Assn., Pulaski County Bar Assn., Ark. Assn. Women Lawyers (v.p. 1978-79). Episcopalian. Office: US Courthouse 600 W Capitol Ave Ste 302 Little Rock AR 72201-3329

WRIGHT, THEODORE OTIS, forensic engineer; b. Gillette, Wyo., Jan. 17, 1921; s. James Otis and Gladys Mary (Marquiss) W.; m. Phyllis Mae Reeves,

June 21, 1942 (div. 1968); children: Mary Suzanne, Theodore Otis Jr., Barbara Joan; m. Edith Marjorie Jewett, May 22, 1968; children: Marjorie Jane, Elizabeth Carter. BSEE, U. Ill., 1951, MS in Engring., 1952; postgrad., Air Command and Staff Coll., 1956-57, UCLA, 1958. Registered profl. engr. Wash. 2d lt. U.S. Air Force, 1942-65, advanced through grades to lt. col., 1957, ret., 1965; dep. for engring. Titan SPO, USAF Sys. Command, L.A., 1957-65; rsch. engr. The Boeing Co., Seattle, 1965-81; pres. The Pretzelwich, Inc., Seattle, 1981—; cons., forensic engr. in pvt. practice Bellevue, Wash., 1988—; adj. prof. U. Wash., Greenriver Jr. Coll., both 1967-68. Contbr. articles to nat. and internat. profl. jours. Decorated Purple Heart, Air medal. Mem. NSPE (v.p. western region 1985-87), ASTM (com. E-43 metric practice 1988-), Nat. Coun. Weights and Measures, Wash. Soc. Profl. Engrs. (state pres. 1981-82, Disting. Svc. award 1980), U.S. Metric Assn. (life, cert. advanced metrication specialist), Am. Nat. Metric Coun. (bd. dirs. 1978-94), Air Force Assn. (life, state pres. 1974-76, 90-91, Jimmy Doolittle fellow 1975), Order of Daedalians (life), Sigma Tau, Eta Kappa Nu, Pi Mu Epsilon, Tau Beta Pi. Democrat. Presbyterian. Avocations: flying, photography, classical music, archaeology. Home: 141 140th Pl NE Bellevue WA 98007-6939

WRIGHT, THEODORE PAUL, JR., political science educator; b. Pt. Washington, N.Y., Apr. 12, 1926; s. Theodore Paul and Margaret (McCarl) W.; m. Susan Jane Standfast, Feb. 18, 1967; children: Henry Sewall, Margaret Standfast, Catherine Berrian. BA magna cum laude, Swarthmore Coll., 1949; MA, Yale U., 1951, PhD, 1957. Instr. govt. Bates Coll., Lewiston, Maine, 1955-57; asst. prof., 1957-64, assoc. prof., 1964-65; assoc. prof. polit. sci. Grad. Sch. Public Affairs, SUNY, Albany, 1965-71; prof. Grad. Sch. Public Affairs, SUNY, 1971—. Author: American Support of Free Elections Abroad, 1964; contbr. articles on Indian Muslims and Pakistan to profl. jours., chpts. to books. Trustee Am. Inst. Pakistan Studies, 1973-82. Served with USNR, 1944-46. Carnegie intern Indian civilization U. Chgo., 1961-62; Fulbright rsch. prof. India, 1963-64; Am. Inst. Indian Studies rsch. fellow India, 1963-64; Am. Coun. Learned Socs. grantee on South Asia in London, 1974-75; Am. Inst. Pakistan Studies/Fulbright rsch. fellow, Pakistan, 1983-84, Fulbright lectr., 1990-91. Mem. South Asian Muslim Studies Assn. (pres. 1988—), Assn. Asian Studies (chmn. N.Y. Conf. on Asian Studies 1988-89), AAUP, Dutch Settlers Soc. of Albany (pres. 1988-90), Adirondack Mountain Club, Phi Beta Kappa (chpt. pres. 1992-93), Phi Delta Theta. Republican. Unitarian. Home: 27 Vandenburg Ln Latham NY 12110-1190 Office: SUNY Grad Sch Pub Affairs 109 Milne Bldg Albany NY 12222

WRIGHT, THEODORE ROBERT FAIRBANK, biologist, educator; b. Kodaikanal, Tamil Nadu, India, Apr. 10, 1928; s. Horace Kepler and Adelaide Caskey (Fairbank) W.; m. Eileen Marie Yongen, Jan. 6, 1951. ABin Biology, Princeton U., 1949; MA in Biology, Wesleyan U., 1954; PhD in Zoology, Yale U., 1959. Asst. professor biology Johns Hopkins U., Balt., 1959-65; assoc. prof. biology U. Va., Charlottesville, 1965-75, prof. biology, 1975-95; prof. emeritus, 1995—; vis. scientist Max Planck Inst. for Biology, Tubingen, 1975-76, Devel. Biology Ctr., U. Calif., Irvine, 1982. Editor: The Genetics and Biology of Drosophila, vol. 2a-c, 1978, vol. 2d, 1980, Genetic Regulatory Hierarchies in Development, 1990; co-editor: Advances in Genetics, 1988-92. With U.S. Army, 1950-52. NIH postdoctoral fellow Max Planck Inst. for Biology, Tubingen, Fed. Republic Germany, 1958-59; NSF grantee, 1961-72, 90-93; NIH grantee, 1972-93; Am. Cancer Soc. grantee, 1988-90. Fellow AAAS; mem. AAUP, Genetics Soc. Am., Soc. for Devel. Biology, Va. Acad. Sci., Sigma Xi. Office: U Va Dept Biology Gilmer Hall Charlottesville VA 22903-2477

WRIGHT, THOMAS DAVID, lawyer, entrepreneur; b. Ellwood City, Pa., Dec. 4, 1937; s. Russell Oran and Bertha Elizabeth (Davis) W.; m. Virginia Hills Penrose, Aug. 18, 1962; children: Thomas David Jr., Melissa Penrose, Steven Bingham. AB, Dickinson Coll., 1959; LLB, Harvard U., 1962. Bar: Pa. 1963, U.S. Dist. Ct. (we. dist.) Pa 1963, U.S. Tax Ct. 1964. Sr. ptnr., mem. fin. com. Eckert Seamans Cherin & Mellott, Pitts., 1962—; pres. The Hawthorne Group, Pitts., 1986—; bd. dirs. Bus. Records Mgmt. Inc., Pitts., The Bantry Group Corp., Jupiter, Fla., Bradford Schs., Inc., Pitts., Enamel Products & Plating, Inc., Pitts., Hawthorne Sports Mktg., Inc., Pitts., Star Cable Assocs., Pitts., Am. Mobilphone, Inc., Birmingham, Ala., Pepsi Cola Madison, Wis., Werner-Donaldson Moving Svcs., Ind., Pitts., Tampa, West Point Realty, Pitts. Bd. dirs. Nat. Multiple Sclerosis Soc., Pitts., 1987—. Mem. ABA, Pa. Bar Assn., Allegheny County Bar Assn., Pitts. Tax Club, Duquesne Club, St. Clair Country Club, Phi Beta Kappa, Omicron Delta Kappa, Pi Gamma Mu. Republican. Presbyterian. Home: 2351 Golfview Dr Pittsburgh PA 15241-3307 Office: The Hawthorne Group 500 GreenTree Commons 381 Mansfield Ave Pittsburgh PA 15220-2751

WRIGHT, THOMAS H., JR., lawyer; b. Lexington, Va., Nov. 7, 1939; s. Thomas H. and Hannah (Knowlton) W.; m. Martha Otis, Aug. 14, 1963; children: Sally F., Thomas K. BA magna cum laude, Princeton U., 1962; postgrad., Cambridge U., Eng., 1963; JD cum laude, Harvard U., 1966. Bar: D.C., N.J. 1972, U.S. Dist. Ct. N.J. 1966. Assoc. Covington & Burling, Washington, 1966-69; asst. gen. counsel Ford Found., N.Y.C., 1969-72; v.p., gen. counsel, sec. Princeton U., N.J., 1972—; lectr. Dept. Politics Princeton U., 1975-76; assoc. Debevoise, Plimpton, Lyons & Gates, N.Y.C., 1978-79. Bd. dirs. McCarter Theatre, 1973—, Trinity Ch., N.Y.C., 1970-77, 79-81, Princeton U. Press, 1976—, Seabury Press, 1976—, Sarah Lawrence Coll, 1979—, Coun. Libr. Resources, 1982—. Mem. Am. Friends of Cambridge U. (bd. dirs. 1977—), Phi Beta Kappa. Home: Journeys End Princeton NJ 08540 Office: Princeton U 318 Nassau Hall Princeton NJ 08544

WRIGHT, THOMAS HENRY, bishop; b. Wilmington, N.C., Oct. 16, 1904; s. John Maffitt and Josie Young (Whitaker) W.; m. Hannah Hagans Knowlton, Dec. 1, 1937; children—Thomas Henry, Hannah K., James K., John M. A.B., U. of South, 1926, D.D., 1946; B.D., Va. Theol. Sem., Alexandria, Va., 1930, D.D., 1946; D.D., Washington and Lee U., 1940, U. N.C., 1965. Clk. Standard Oil Co. of N.J., Wilmington, 1926-27; ordained to ministry P.E. Ch., 1929, nat. acting sec. of coll. work, 1933-34; Episcopal chaplain U. of N.C., 1931-32, Va. Mil. Inst., 1934-41, Washington and Lee U., 1934-41; rector Robert E. Lee Meml. Ch., Lexington, Va., 1934-41; dean Grace Cathedral, San Antonio, Tex., 1941-43; rector St. Mark's Ch., San Antonio, Tex., 1941-43; consecrated bishop of Diocese of East Carolina, St. James Ch., Wilmington, N.C., Oct. 1945; Pres. of Province.; U.S. rep. to World Christian Student Fed. Meeting, Holland, 1932; Regional dir. Ch. Soc. for Coll. work; asso. mem. Forward Movement Commn., P.E. Ch.; chmn. overseas dept. Nat. Council of Episcopal Ch. Contbr. to jours. Trustee U. of South. Mem. Sigma Nu (former grand chaplain), Sigma Upsilon, Alpha Phi Epsilon; hon. mem. Omicron Delta Kappa. Democrat. Address: The Bishop's House 1625 Futch Creek Rd Wilmington NC 28405-9377

WRIGHT, THOMAS JAMES, chemical company executive; b. Livingston, Mont., June 13, 1932; s. William James and Mary Doreen (Smyth) W.; m. Sandra Gray Church, Jan. 29, 1962; children: James Bland, Jacqueline Doreen. BS in Metall. Engring., Mont. Sch. Mines, 1959. With minerals research lab. N.C. State U., Ashville, 1959-64; project engr. Texasgulf, Inc., Aurora, N.C., 1964-65, process engr., 1965-67, mill supt., 1967-71, acid plant supt., 1971-73, asst. gen. mgr., 1975-78; gen. mgr. Texasgulf Chems. Co., Aurora, 1978-79; sr. v.p. prodn. Texasgulf Chems. Co., Raleigh, N.C., 1979-81, pres., 1981-89; pres., chief operating officer, 1989—; plant mgr. Agrico Chem. Co., South Pierce, Fla., 1973-75; bd. dirs. Texasgulf, Inc., Stamford, Conn., Elf Aquitaine, Inc., Stamford, Compania Exploradora Del Istmo, Mexico City. Served with U.S Army, 1954-56. Mem. Am. Mining Congress, N.C. Engring. Found. (past bd. dirs.), Sulphur Inst. (bd. dirs.), Fertilizer Inst. (bd. dirs.), Phosphate Chem. Export Assn. (bd. dirs.), Potash and Phosphate Inst. (past bd. dirs.), Internat. Fertilizer Assn., N.C. Water Resources Rsch. Inst., Farm Care U.S.A., Raleigh C. of C. Roman Catholic. Clubs: North Ridge Country, MacGregor Downs Country, Capital City (Raleigh). Avocation: golf. Office: Texasgulf Inc PO Box 30321 Raleigh NC 27622-0321

WRIGHT, THOMAS JOE, electric utility executive; b. Monticello, Ark., June 5, 1946; s. Aubrey A. and Christine (Veasey) W.; m. Valerie Fairfield, July 27, 1968; children: Thomas Joe Jr., Jon Christopher. BSEE, U. Ark., 1968, MSEE, 1969. Registered profl. engr., Ark., Miss., Mo., La. Asst. engr. Ark. Power & Light Co., Pine Bluff, 1969-72; div. mgr. Ark. Power &

Light Co., Blytheville, 1981-86; mgr. system planning Ark.-Mo. Power Co., Blytheville, 1972-73, dir. planning and engring., 1973-78, dir. engring. and ops., 1978-79, gen. mgr., 1979-81; pres., chief exec. officer Assoc. Natural Gas Co., Blytheville, 1986-87; group v.p. div. ops. La. Power & Light Co., New Orleans, 1987-88, v.p. customer svc., 1988-92; v.p. Transmission and Distbn. System Entergy Corp., 1992-6; past pres. Profl. Engrs. Exec. Offices Ark. Past pres. Blytheville Unltd., Blytheville C. of C.; v.p. Presbyn. Christian Acad.; past bd. dirs. Blytheville Internat. Visitors Coun., Miss. County Community Coll. Recipient Vol. Econ. Developer of Yr. award So. Indsl. Devel. Coun., 1987. Mem. IEEE, Southeastern Elec. Exch. (engring. and ops. exec. com.), Edison Electric Inst. (customer svc. and mktg. com.), Metairie Country Club. Presbyterian. Home: 164 Ridgewood Dr Metairie LA 70005 Office: Entergy Corp Mail Unit TLC 2301 PO Box 61000 New Orleans LA 70161-1000

WRIGHT, THOMAS WILLIAM, automotive parts company executive; b. Pineland, Tex., Aug. 13, 1941; s. Stonewall Obed Wright and Mary Lois (Williams) Barkley; m. Judy Ann Andrews, Nov. 29, 1968; children: Thomas Wesley, Daniel Scott. BA, U. Tex., 1964; MS, Tex. Christian U., 1968; MBA, U. Dallas, 1976. CPA, Tex.; cert. in data processing. Computer programmer Gen. Dynamics, Ft. Worth, 1964-68; dir. data processing Gen. Automotive Parts Corp., Dallas, 1968-82, v.p. data processing, 1982-84; mgr. acctg. and data processing Genuine Parts Co., Dallas, 1984-85; v.p., treas. Genuine Parts Co., Atlanta, 1985—. Instr. Jr. Achievement Atlanta, 1987. Mem. Am. Inst. CPA's. Avocations: reading, running.

WRIGHT, THOMAS WILLIAM DUNSTAN, architect; b. Rome, Jan. 12, 1919; s. Charles Will and Helen Bree (Dunstan) W.; m. Penelope Ladd, Aug. 6, 1942 (dec. June 1988); children: Peter W.D., Felicity Wright Evans, Allegra. A.B., Harvard U., 1941, M.Arch., 1950. Designer Joseph Saunders (architect), Alexandria, Va., 1950; assoc. Leon Brown (architect), Washington, 1950-53; ptnr. firm Brown and Wright, Washington, 1953-80; sole propr. Thomas W. D. Wright, FAIA, Architects, 1980—; pres. Wright & Rubin Architects, P.C., 1985-89, Wright & Heyne Architects, 1990-91; prin. Thomas W.D. Wright, FAIA, Washington, 1991—; past mem. Old Georgetown bd. U.S. Commn. Fine Arts; past 1st v.p. D.C. Commn. Arts; past mem. D.C. Commrs. Planning and Urban Renewal Adv. Council; arbitrator Am. Arbitration Assn. Served on coll. U.S. national sabre, 1941-46. Am. Sabre Fencing champion, gold medallist sr. age group (70-74); mem. U.S. Sr. Fencing Team, gold medallist sabre 70, 1995. Fellow AIA (past pres. Washington Met. chpt., past nat. chmn. com. on Nat. Capital City, past mem. com. on design, com. on housing); mem. Soc. Archtl. Historians, Nat. Assn. Intergroup Relations Ofcls., Nat. Assn. Housing and Redevel. Ofcls., Nat. Com. against Discrimination in Housing, ACLU. Democrat. Clubs: Cosmos (Washington), Harvard (Washington). Home: 7500 Exeter Rd Bethesda MD 20814-6108 Office: 1400 20th St NW Washington DC 20036-5906 *Since the essential origin of creativity is knowing the sources, then the fundamental source of design is the human being—its body, its mind, its senses and reactions, individually and collectively.*

WRIGHT, VERNON HUGH CARROLL, bank executive; b. Bronxville, N.Y., Sept. 24, 1942; s. Dudley Hugh and Helen Margurite (Carroll) W. m. Lucy Hiss Babb, June 7, 1966; children: Dudley Hugh II, Katherine Babb. BS in acctg., U. Balt., 1969. Sr. v.p. Maryland Nat. Bank, Balt., 1969-90, 91, MNC Fin., Balt., 1990-91; sr. exec. v.p., chief corporate fin. officer MBNA Am. Bank, N.A., Newark, Del., 1991—; bd. dirs. MBNA Am. Bank, Newark, Del.; exec. v.p., chief corp. fin., Newark, with USN, 1962-66. Avocations: farming, teaching. Office: MBNA Am Bank NA 400 Christiana Rd Newark DE 19713-4217

WRIGHT, WALLACE MATHIAS, lawyer; b. Johnston, S.C., Sept. 29, 1928; s. Luther Sloan and Kathleen (Barre) W.; m. Sally Ann Nelson, May 2, 1959; children: Wendy, Russell, Todd. AB, Wofford Coll., 1949; LLB, U. S.C., 1955. Bar: S.C. 1955, Ohio 1962, Tex. 1981. Trial atty. Dept. Justice, Washington, 1955-56; sr. tax trial atty. Office of Regional Counsel IRS, Atlanta, 1956-61; assoc., then ptnr. Jones, Day, Reavis & Pogue, Cleve. and Dallas, 1961-87; v.p., gen. counsel Qwest Microwave Cos., Dallas, 1987-92. Served to 2d lt. USAF, 1950-53, Korea. Mem. ABA, State Bar Tex., Dallas Bar Assn. Presbyterian. Home: 6848 Midcrest Dr Dallas TX 75240

WRIGHT, WILEY REED, JR., lawyer; b. Seattle, Jan. 31, 1932; s. Wiley Reed and Gertrude Ellen (Datson) W.; m. Sally Harrison Clarke, 1955 (div. 1963); children: Wiley III, Margaret, Andrew; m. Roberta Hostinsky, Oct. 18, 1963; children: Cathryn, Amy, Susan. BS in Commerce, Washington and Lee U., 1954, LLB, 1956. Bar: Va. 1956, U.S. Dist. Ct. (ea. dist.) Va. 1956, U.S. Ct. Appeals (4th cir.) 1956, U.S. Supreme Ct. 1993. Law clk. to hon. judge U.S. Dist. Ct., Alexandria, Va., 1958-59; ptnr. Clarke, Richard, Moncure & Whitehead, Alexandria, 1959-68; judge corp. and cir. cts. Alexandria, 1968-79, chief judge cir. ct., 1979-84; ptnr. Hazel & Thomas P.C., Alexandria, 1984—; mem. at large Va. State Bar Coun., 1984-90; mem. Jud. Coun. Va., 1982-84, vice chmn. jud. conf. Va., 1980-82. Assoc. editor: Virginia Circuit Judges Benchbook, 1987. Legal counsel to Alexandria C. of C., 1984-88. 1st lt. U.S. Army, 1956-58. Fellow Va. Law Found.; mem. ABA, Va. Bar Assn., Alexandria Bar Assn., 4th Cir. Conf., George Mason Inn of Ct., Phi Delta Phi, Omicron Delta Kappa. Avocations: sailing, fishing. Home: 2023 Scroggins Rd Alexandria VA 22302-3122 Office: Hazel & Thomas P.C. 3110 Fairview Park Dr Ste 1400 Falls Church VA 22042-4505

WRIGHT, WILLARD JUREY, lawyer; b. Seattle, Feb. 25, 1914; s. Raymond Garfield and Elizabeth (McPherson) W.; m. Alice Ostrander, Dec. 27, 1939 (dec. Dec. 1969); children: Susan, Alice, Rosemary, Raymond Garfield II; m. Katharyn Stubbs Little, July 18, 1970; children: Anne, Gwendolyn, Kathy. AB with honors, Princeton, 1936; cert., Woodrow Wilson Sch. Pub. and Internat. Affairs, 1936; JD with honors, U. Wash., 1939; grad., Navy. Lang. Sch., U. Colo., 1944. Bar: Wash. 1939, U.S. Dist. Ct. 1939, U.S. Ct. Appeals (9th cir.) 1958, U.S. Supreme Ct. 1954. Editor Wash. Law Rev., 1937-39; practice of law Wash., 1939—; partner Wright, Innis, Simon & Todd, Seattle, 1939-69, Davis, Wright, Todd, Riese & Jones, 1969-85; counsel Davis Wright & Jones, 1986-89, Davis Wright Tremaine, Seattle, 1990—; spl. asst. atty. gen. State of Wash., 1953; acting prof. fed. income taxation U. Wash. Law Sch., 1956; pres. Assoc. Vintners, Inc., 1979-81; pres. 1223 Spring St. Owners Assn., 1986-93; officer, dir. or gen. counsel various U.S. bus. corps.; chmn. King County Rep. Rules Com., 1950-58; chmn. 37th Dist. Rep. Orgn., 1949-52; del. Rep. Nat. Conv., Chgo., 1952. Contbr. articles to profl. jours. Trustee Seattle Found., 1954-63, pres., 1961-63, Seattle Com. Fgn. Rels., 1959-62, Lakeside Sch., 1938-67, pres., 1951-55, hon. trustee, 1967—; trustee Princeton U., 1957-61; vis. com. U. Wash. Coll. Bus. Adminstrn., 1963-70, U. Wash. Law Sch., 1974-78; pres. U. Wash. Ann. Fund, 1973-74, U. Wash. Law Sch. Found., 1974-75; trustee Helen Bush Parkside Sch., 1946-63, pres., 1959-62; mem. governing bd. Univ. Hosp., Seattle, 1978-87, chmn., 1980-82; trustee Seattle Art Mus., 1958-88, hon. trustee, 1988—; vestryman Epiphany Episcopal Ch., 1959-64, 68-70, 73-76, 89-92, sr. warden 1970, 74-76, chancellor 1976-94, trustee ch. pension fund, N.Y., 1970-76. Lt. USNR, 1943-46. Recipient Vivian Carkeek prize, 1939, Disting. Svc. award Lakeside Sch., 1964, Bishop's Cross, Epiphany Episcopal Ch., 1977, Disting. Alumnus award Lakeside Sch., 1980. Fellow Am. Bar Found., Am. Coll. Trust and Estate Counsel; mem. ABA, Wash. State Bar Assn. (chmn. real estate, probate and trusts sect. 1958-61), Seattle-King County Bar Assn. (trustee 1955-58, 64-67, pres. 1966-67), Am. Judicature Soc., Nat. Assn. Estate Planning Councils (dir. 1969-71), Estate Planning Council Seattle (pres. 1968-69, dir.), Alumni Assn. U. Wash. Law Sch. (pres. 1957-58), Seattle World Affairs Council (charter trustee, sec. 1949-57), Urban League Seattle (trustee 1959-60, 68-70, pres. bd. trustees 1956-58), Order of Coif, Princeton Quadrangle Club (pres. 1935-36), Seattle Golf Club (sec., trustee 1968-71), Phi Delta Phi. Home: 1630 43d Ave E # 1022 Seattle WA 98112 Office: Davis Wright Tremaine Century Sq Seattle WA 98101

WRIGHT, WILLIAM BIGELOW, financial executive; b. Rutland, Vt., Dec. 21, 1924; s. Earl Smith and Christine (Bigelow) W.; m. Polly Pardee, Aug. 27, 1949; children: Christine, Henry, John, Lucy. Graduated, Phillips Exeter Acad., 1943; AB, Princeton U., 1950. With Chubb & Son, N.Y.C., 1950-53; various positions Am. Internat. Group, N.Y.C., Havana, Tokyo, Seoul, Hong Kong, 1953-57; asst. to the pres. Johnson & Higgins, Caracas, Venezuela, 1957-63; pres. Marble Bank, Rutland, 1968-83; chmn. bd. Marble

Bank, Marble Fin. Corp., Rutland, 1983-94; bd. dirs. Bunbury Co., Princeton, N.J. V.p., treas. Windham Found., Grafton, Vt.; sch. commr. City of Rutland, 1966-75; chmn. Vt. Blue Cross and Blue Shield, 1980-83; pres. Northeast chpt. 10th Mountain Div. Assn., 1993—; trustee, treas. Green Mountain Coll., Poultney, Vt.; pres. Princeton Alumni Assn. of Vt., 1989—; trustee Calvin Coolidge Meml. Found., Plymouth, Vt., 1992—. With U.S. Army, 1943-46, ETO. Mem. Ivy Club, Princeton Club N.Y.C., Alumni Coun. Princeton U. (exec. com. 1992—), v.p., exec. com. Class of '47 1992—). Republican. Congregationalist. Avocations: skiing, golfing, sailing, traveling. Home: Mendon VT 05701 Office: Marble Fin Corp PO Box 978 Rutland VT 05702-0978

WRIGHTON, MARK STEPHEN, chemistry educator; b. Jacksonville, Fla., June 11, 1949; s. Robert D. and Doris (Cutler) W.; children: James Joseph, Rebecca Ann. BS, Fla. State U., 1969; PhD, Calif. Inst. Tech., 1972; DSc (hon.), U. West Fla., 1983. Asst. prof. chemistry MIT, Cambridge, 1972-76, assoc. prof., 1976-77, prof., 1977-95, Frederick G. Keyes prof. chemistry, 1981-89, head dept. chemistry, 1987-90, Ciba-Geigy prof. chemistry, 1989-95, provost, 1990-95; prof., chancellor Washington U., St. Louis, 1995—; bd. dirs. Ionics, Inc., Helix Tech. Corp., OIS (Optical Imaging Sys.), Inc. Author: Organometallic Photochemistry, 1979; editor books in field; cons. editor, Houghton-Mifflin. Recipient Herbert Newby McCoy award Calif. Inst. Tech., 1972, Disting. Alumni award, 1992, E.O. Lawrence award Dept. Energy, 1983, Halpern award in photochemistry, N.Y. Acad. Scis., 1983, Fresenius award Phi Lambda Upsilon, 1984, Dreyfus tchr.-scholar, 1975-80; Alfred P. Sloan fellow, 1974-76, MacArthur fellow, 1983-88. Fellow AAAS; mem. Am. Acad. Arts and Scis., Am. Chem. Soc. (award in pure chemistry 1981, award in inorganic chemistry 1988), Electrochem. Soc. Office: Washington Univ Office of Chancellor 1 Brookings Dr Box 1192 Saint Louis MO 63130

WRIGHT-RIGGINS, AIDSAND F., religious organization executive. Exec. dir. ABC Bd. of Nat. Ministries, Valley Forge, Pa. Office: ABC Bd of Nat Ministries PO Box 851 Valley Forge PA 19482

WRIGLEY, ROBERT ERNEST, museum director, ecologist; b. Buenos Aires, Argentina, May 2, 1943; s. Ernest and Eva (Muir) W.; m. Gail Trueman, May 20, 1967 (dec. 1984); children: Mark E., Robert A.; m. Arlene Dahl, May 24, 1986. BS, McGill U., Montreal, Que., Can., 1965; MS, McGill U., 1967; PhD, U. Ill., 1970. Curator Man. (Can.) Mus. of Man and Nature, Winnipeg, 1970-80; mus. dir. Man. (Can.) Mus. of Man and Nature, 1980-86, dir. rsch. and collections, 1986-88; assoc. prof. Natural Resources Ins. U. Man., 1988-89; dir. Oak Hammock Marsh Interpretive Ctr., Can., 1989—; bd. dirs. Ft. Whyte Centre, Winnipeg, 1983-90, Friends of Assiniboine Park Conservatory, 1988—. Author: 12 books including Reptiles and Amphibians, 1989, Mammals in North America , 1986, Large Mammals, 1984 (Gold award 1984), Manitoba's Big Cat, 1982; mng. editor Manitoba Nature, 1972-82; contbr. articles to profl. jours. Mem. Manitoba Conservation Awards Ecological Resources and Endangered Species Com., 1982-91. Mem. Am. Soc. Mammalogists, The Can. Field-Naturalist, Ducks Unlimited Can., Cactus and Succulent Soc. Am., Manitoba Naturalists Soc. Avocations: natural history book and stamp collecting, raising succulent plants and fish. Home: 505 Boreham Blvd, Winnipeg, MB Canada R3P 0K2 Office: Oak Hammock Marsh Intrp Ctr, PO Box 1160, Oak Hammock Marsh, MB Canada R0C 2Z0

WRIGLEY, WILLIAM, corporation executive; b. Chgo., Jan. 21, 1933; s. Philip Knight and Helen Blanche (Atwater) W.; m. Alison Hunter, June 1, 1957 (div. 1969); children: Alison Elizabeth, Philip Knight, William Jr.; m. Julie Burns, Nov. 28, 1981. Grad., Deerfield Acad., 1950; B.A., Yale, 1954. With Wm. Wrigley Jr. Co., Chgo., 1956—, v.p., 1960-61, pres., CEO, 1961—, also bd. dirs.; dir. Wrigley Philippines, Inc., Wrigley Co. Ltd. (U.K.), The Wrigley Can (N.Z.) Ltd., Wrigley Co. Pty. Ltd., Australia, The Wrigley Co. (H.K.) Ltd., The Wrigley Co. (P.N.G) Pty. Ltd., New Guinea, Wrigley & Co. Ltd., Japan, Wrigley Poland S.P.Z.O.O., Wrigley Chewing Gum Co. Ltd., China, Wrigley d.o.o., Slovenia, Blvd. Bancorp, Inc., Chgo., mem. compensation com.; chmn., trustee William Wrigley Jr. Co. Found.; chmn., mem. pension com., mem. fin. com. Texaco Inc.; bd. dirs., mem. com. non-mgmt. dirs. mem. nominating com. Texaco Inc.; bd. dirs., exec. com., chmn., CEO Santa Catalina Island Co.; mem. corp. issues com., nominating com. Am. Home Products Corp. Bd. dirs. Wrigley Meml. Garden Found.; life trustee Northwestern Meml. Hosp.; benefactor, mem. Santa Catalina Island Conservancy; mem. Geneva. Nat. Bd. Govs.; trustee U. So. Calif., CEO bd. advisor, mem. devel. com.; life mem. Cataline Island Mus., Art Inst. Chgo.; founding mem. Cowboy Artists Am. Mus. Lt. (j.g.) USNR, 1954-56; lt. comdr. Res., 1956-77. Mem. Navy League U.S., Chgo. Hist. Soc. (hon. life) Field Mus. Nat. Hist. (life), Wolf's Head Soc., U. So. Calif. Oceanographic Assocs. (hon. life), Catalina Island Mus. Soc. (life), The Calif. Club, Saddle and Cycle Club, Racquet Club, Chgo. Yacht Club, Tavern Club, Comml. Club, 410 Club (chmn.), Catalina Island Yacht Club (hon. life), Tuna Club of Santa Catalina Island, L.A. Yacht Club, Lake Geneva Country Club (Wis.), Lake Geneva Yacht Club, Brook Club (N.Y.C.), Delta Kappa Epsilon. Office: Wm Wrigley Jr Co 701 N Loara St Anaheim CA 92803-9000

WRINKLE, JOHN NEWTON, lawyer; b. Chattanooga, July 31, 1929; s. John Stuart and Anne (Ownbey) W.; m. Louise Rucker Agee, Feb. 1, 1958; children: Anne Blair, Margaret Rucker. BA, Vanderbilt U., 1951; LLB, Yale U., 1955. Bar: Ala. 1955, U.S. Dist. Ct. (no. dist.) Ala. 1956, U.S. Ct. Appeals (5th cir.) 1958, U.S. Ct. Appeals (11th cir.) 1981, U.S. Tax Ct. 1957. Assoc. White, Bradley, Arant, All & Rose, Birmingham, Ala., 1955-63; ptnr. Bradley, Arant, Rose & White, 1963-92, counsel, 1993—; coord. prelaw students Birmingham So. Coll., 1989—. Trustee Birmingham Symphony Assn., 1970-79, 80-83, Episcopal Found. Jefferson County, 1994—; mem. bd. advisors St. Andrew's Sewanee Sch., 1985—. With USAF, 1951-52. Disting. fellow Birmingham-Southern Coll., 1995—. Fellow Am. Coll. Trust and Estate Counsel; mem. ABA, So. Employee Benefits Conf. (steering com. 1970-73), Birmingham Bar Assn., Assn. of Bar of City of N.Y., Birmingham Com. Fgn. Rels., Redstone Club, Mountain Brook Club, Country Club of Birmingham, Summit Club, Knickerbocker Club (N.Y.C.), Yale Club (N.Y.C.), Phi Beta Kappa, Phi Alpha Delta. Episcopalian. Home: 2 Beechwood Rd Birmingham AL 35213-3914 Office: Bradley Arant Rose & White 2001 Park Pl Ste 1400 Birmingham AL 35203-2709

WRISLEY, ROBERT LYMAN, business educator; b. Montique, Mass., Nov. 28, 1941; s. Lyman A. Jr. and Mildred (Vachula) W.; m. Mary Ellen Davis, June 10, 1967; children: Robert Jr., Scott, Ellen. B of Edn., Mid. Tenn. State U., 1966, MEd, 1968; EdD, U. Ga., 1978. Tchr. English, sci., social studies Walker County Schs., Chickamauga, Tenn., 1967-68, instr., 1967-72; tchr., chmn. bus. office edn. Chickamauga (Ga.) City Schs., 1968-74; adminstrv. asst. to. chmn. of div. vocat. edn. U. Ga., Athens, 1975-78; asst. prof. bus. edn. Fayetteville (N.C.) State U., 1978-85; cons. bus. edn. N.C. State Dept. Pub. Instruction, Raleigh, 1985-89; asst. prof. dept. bus., vocat. and tech. edn. East Carolina U., Greenville, N.C., 1989—; researcher and presenter in field. Contbr. articles to profl. jours. State chpt. advisor Future Bus. Leaders of Am., 1985-89. Mem. Nat. Bus. Edn. Assn., Am. Vocat. Assn., So. Bus. Edn. Assn. (exec. bd 1992—), N.C. Bus. Edn. Assn. (chmn. 1991, chmn. ann. conf. 1991, chmn. bylaws com. 1984-85, 2d v.p. 1983-84, chmn. pub. rels. com. 1982-83, bd. dirs. 1992—), N.C. Vocat. Assn. (chmn. audit com. 1989—, chmn. nominating com. 1988-89, bd. dirs. 1982-85, chmn. bud. edn. divsn. 1984-85), Delta Pi Epsilon (nat. svc. projects com. 1980-84, historian Beta Delta chpt. 1977-79), Pi Omega Pi, Phi Delta Kappa. Lutheran. Office: East Carolina U 2313 Gen Classroom Bldg Greenville NC 27858

WRIST, PETER ELLIS, pulp and paper company executive; b. Mirfield, Eng., Oct. 9, 1927; arrived in Can., 1952; s. Owen and Evelyn (Ellis) W.; m. Mirabelle Harley, Sept. 3, 1955; children: Denise Wrist Parson, Philip, Lydia Wrist Schweizer, Richard; m. Kathryn Idelson. BA, Cambridge (Eng.) U., 1948, MA, 1952; MS, London U., 1952; cert. advanced mgmt. program, Harvard U., 1967; DSc (hon.), U. B.C., 1993. Rsch. physicist Brit. Paper & Bd. Industry Rsch. Assn., Kenley, Eng., 1949-52, Que. North Shore Paper Co., Baie Comeau, Can., 1952-56; rsch. physicist Mead Corp., Dayton, Ohio, 1956-60, assoc. dir. rsch., 1960-61, dir. rsch., 1961-66, mgr. rsch. and engring., 1966-68, v.p. rsch. and engring., 1968-72, v.p. tech., 1972-83; exec. v.p. Pulp and Paper Research Inst. Can., Pointe Claire, Que., 1983-86; pres., chief

exec. officer Pulp and Paper Rsch. Inst. Can., Pointe Claire, Que., 1986-94, dep. chmn. bd., 1994—; ret., 1994; chmn. prize selection com. Marcus Wallenberg Found.; chmn. Nat. Coun. for Air and Stream Improvement, 1972-75; past mem., chmn. rsch. adv. com. Inst. Paper Chemistry, 1971-83. Contbr. articles to profl. jours. Fellow Tech. Assn. Pulp and Paper Industry (bd. dirs. 1971-74, v.p. 1975-77, pres. 1977-79, Engring. award 1969, Gold medal 1983); mem. Can. Pulp and Paper Assn. (tech. sect., Howard Smith award 1954, Weldon Gold medal 1956), N.Y. Acad. Sci. Avocations: sailing, gardening. Home: 7778 SE Country Estates Way Jupiter FL 33458 Office: Pulp & Paper Rsch Inst Can, 570 Saint John's Blvd, Pointe Claire, PQ Canada H9R 3J9

WRISTON, WALTER BIGELOW, retired banker; b. Middletown, Conn., Aug. 3, 1919; s. Henry M. and Ruth (Bigelow) W.; m. Barbara Brengle, Oct. 24, 1942 (dec.); 1 dau., Catherine B.; m. Kathryn Ann Dineen, Mar. 14, 1968. B.A. with distinction, Wesleyan U., Middletown, Conn., 1941; LL.D. Wesleyan U., 1984; postgrad., Ecole Francaise Middlebury, Vt., 1941, Am. Inst. Banking, 1946; M.A., Fletcher Sch. Internat. Law and Diplomacy, 1942; LL.D., Lawrence Coll., 1962, Tufts U., 1963, Brown U., 1969, Columbia U., 1972, Morehouse Coll., 1985; D.C.S., Pace U., 1974, St. John's U., 1974; D.H.L., Lafayette Coll., 1975; LL.D., Fordham U., 1977; D.C.S., N.Y. U., 1977. Officer spl. div. Dept. State, Washington, 1941-42; jr. insp. comptrollers div. Citibank (N.A.), 1946-50, asst. cashier, 1950-52, asst. v.p., 1952-54, v.p., 1954-58; sr. v.p., 1958-60, exec. v.p., 1960-67, pres., 1967-70, chmn., 1970-1984, also dir.; chmn., bd. dirs. Citicorp, until 1984; bd. dirs. York Internat. Corp., Tandem Computers Inc., United Meridan Corp., ICOS Corp., AEA Investors Inc., Bio-Rsch. Labs. Ltd., Cygnus Therapeutic Sys., WMNB Acquisition Corp.; trustee Rand Corp., 1973-83; mem. Nat. Commn. on Productivity, 1970-74, Nat Commn. for Indsl. Peace, 1973-74; chmn. President's Econ. Policy Adv. Bd., 1982-89. Author: Risk and Other Four-Letter Words, 1986, The Twilight of Sovereignty, 1992. Life gov. N.Y. Hosp.; bd. visitors Fletcher Sch. Law and Diplomacy; trustee Manhattan Inst. for Policy Rsch. Inc. Served with AUS, 1942-46. Mem. Bus. Coun., Links Club, Univ. Club, River Club, Sky Club, Met. Club (Washington), Palm Beach Bath and Tennis Club, Ocean Club Fla. Office: Citicorp Ctr 153 E 53rd St Ste 4000 New York NY 10043-0001

WROBLESKI, JEANNE PAULINE, lawyer; b. Phila., Feb. 14, 1942; d. Edward Joseph and Pauline (Popelak) W.; m. Robert J. Klein, Dec. 3, 1979. BA, Immaculata Coll., 1964; MA, U. Pa., 1966; JD, Temple U., 1975. Bar: Pa. 1975. Pvt. practice law, Phila., 1975—; ptnr. Kohn, Nast & Graf, P.C. Mem. Commn. on Women and the Legal Profession, 1986-89; v.p. Center City Residents' Assn. Eisenhower Citizen Amb. del. to Soviet Union. Rhea Liebman scholar, 1974; bd. dirs. South St. Dance Co.; bd. dirs., mem. exec. com. Temple Law Alumni; del. to Moscow con. on law and econ. coop., 1990; del. to jud. conf. for 3d cir. U.S. Ct. Appeals, 1991. Mem. AAUW, ABA, Pa Bar Assn., Phila. Bar Assn. (chmn. women's rights com. 1986, com. on jud. selection and reform 1986-87, chmn. appellate cts. com. 1992, bus. cts. task force), Pa. Acad. Fine Arts, Nat. Mus. Women in the Arts, Am. Judicature Soc., Jagiellonian Law Soc., Alpha Psi Omega, Lambda Iota Tau. Democrat. Clubs: Lawyers, Founders, Peale, Penn. Office: Kohn Nast & Graf PC 2400 One Reading Ctr 1101 Market St Philadelphia PA 19107-2934

WROBLEY, RALPH GENE, lawyer; b. Denver, Sept. 19, 1935; s. Matthew B. and Hedvig (Lyon) W.; m. Madeline C. Kearney, June 13, 1959; children: Kirk Lyon, Eric Lyon, Ann Lyon. BA, Yale U., 1957; JD, U. Chgo., 1962. Bar: Mo. 1962. With Bell Telephone Co., Phila., 1957-59; assoc. Stinson, Mag & Fizzell, Kansas City, Mo., 1962-65, mem. 1965-88; ptnr. Bryan, Cave, McPheeters & McRoberts, Kansas City, 1988-92; ptnr., exec. com. Blackwell, Sanders, Matheny, Weary & Lombardi, 1992—. Bd. dirs. Human Resources Corp., 1971; mem. Civic Coun. Kansas City, 1988—; chmn. Pub. Housing Authority of Kansas City, 1971-74; vice chmn. Mayor's Adv. Commn. on Housing, Kansas City, 1971-74; bd. govs. Citizens Assn., 1965—, vice chmn., 1971-75, chmn., 1978-79; bd. dirs. Coun. on Edn., 1975-81, v.p., 1977-79; bd. dirs., pres. Sam E. and Mary F. Roberts Found., 1974—; trustee Clearinghouse for Mid Continent Founds., 1977—, chmn. 1987-89; bd. dirs. Bus. Innovation Ctr., 1984-91, vice-chmn. 1987-91, adv. bd. dirs., 1993—, Midwest Regional Adv. Bd. Inst. Internat. Edn., 1989-93, Internat. Trade Assn., 1989-92, v.p., 1990; chmn. bd. dir. Mid-Am. Coalition on Healthcare, 1991—. Mem. Mo. Bar Assn. Republican. Presbyterian (elder). Club: Yale (pres. 1969-71, outstanding mem. award 1967). Home: 1015 W 67th Ter Kansas City MO 64113-1942 Office: 2300 Main St Kansas City MO 64108

WRONG, DENNIS HUME, sociologist, educator; b. Toronto, Nov. 22, 1923; s. Humphrey Hume and Mary Joyce (Hutton) W.; m. Elaine L. Gale, Nov. 24, 1949 (div. Oct. 1965); 1 child, Terence Hume; m. Jacqueline Conrath, Mar. 26, 1966. BA, U. Toronto, 1945; PhD, Columbia U., 1956. Tchr. Princeton U., 1949-50, Rutgers U., 1950-51, U. Toronto, 1954-56, Brown U., 1956-61; mem. grad. faculty New Sch. Social Research, 1961-63; prof. sociology, chmn. dept. Univ. Coll., NYU, 1963-65; prof. sociology NYU, 1966-94, prof. emeritus, 1994—; vis. prof. U. Nev., 1965-66; vis. fellow Oxford U., 1978. Author: American and Canadian Viewpoints, 1955, Population, 1956, 59, Population and Society, 1961, 67, 77, Skeptical Sociology, 1976, Power: Its Forms, Bases and Uses, 1979, 88, 95, Class Fertility Trends in Western Nations, 1980, The Problem of Order: What Unites and Divides Society, 1994, 95; editor: Social Research, 1961-64, (with Harry L. Gracey) Readings in Introductory Sociology, 1967, 72, 77, Contemporary Sociology: A Journal of Reviews, 1972-74, Max Weber, 1970; mem. editl. bd. Dissent, 1966—; contbg. editor Partisan Rev., 1981-87. Guggenheim fellow, 1984-85, Woodrow Wilson Internat. Ctr. for Scholars fellow, 1991-92. Mem. Am. Sociol. Assn., Eastern Sociol. Soc. Home: 144 Drakes Corner Rd Princeton NJ 08540-7519 Office: NYU Dept Sociology Washington Sq N New York NY 10003

WRONSKI, STANLEY PAUL, education educator; b. Mpls., Apr. 8, 1919; s. John and Katherine (Kotvis) W.; m. Geraldine Breslin, May 27, 1943; children: Linda A., Mary Jo Twenkel, Sandra J., John S., Paul S. BS in Edn., U. Minn., 1942, MA, 1947, PhD, 1950. Counselor Bur. Vet. Affairs U. Minn., Mpls., 1946-47, instr. Coll. Edn., 1948-49; tchr. Marshall High Sch., Mpls., 1947-48; asst. prof. Ctrl. Wash. Coll. Ellensburg, 1950-51; from asst. to assoc. prof. Boston U., 1951-57; from assoc. prof. to prof. Mich. State U. East Lansing, 1957-84, prof. emeritus, 1984—; advisor Ministry Edn., Bangkok, Thailand, 1964-66; pres. New Eng. Assn. Social Studies Tchrs., Boston, 1955-56, Mich. Coun. for Social Studies, 1960-61, Nat. Coun. for Social Studies, 1974. Co-author: Teaching Social Studies in High School, 1958, 73, Modern Economics, 1964, School and Society, 1964, Social Studies and Social Sciences, 1986. Active U.S. Nat. Commn. for UNESCO, Washington, 1974-76, mil. adv. coun. Ctr. for Def. Info., Washington, 1988—; pres. Greater Lansing UN Assn., 1986-88. Combat. USN, 1944-62. Recipient Internat. Educator award Pacific Rim Consortium, 1992, Glen Taggart award Mich. State U., 1995; named Outstanding Social Studies Educator, Social Studies Tchr. Jour., 1981. Mem. NEA (life), Nat. Peace Found. (charter), Univ. Club (charter), Mich. U. Nat. Fifty com. (chair, 1995). Avocations: golf, reading, volunteer work. Home: 4520 Chippewa Dr Okemos MI 48864-2008 Office: Mich State U Erickson Hall East Lansing MI 48824

WROTH, JAMES MELVIN, former army officer, computer company executive; b. Lincoln, Nebr., Feb. 2, 1929; s. Charles M. and Reba (Sharp) W.; m. Donna Mae Benson, June 4, 1951 (dec.); children: Mark, David S., Mary E. Bannon; m. Molly B. Mullan, June 15, 1975; stepchildren: Edward H. Mullan (dec.), Philip C. Mullan. B.S., U. Nebr., 1951; M.B.A., Syracuse U., 1963; postgrad., F.A. Sch., 1957, Command and Gen. Staff Coll., 1962, Armed Forces Staff Coll., 1967, Army War Coll., 1968; grad., Advanced Mgmt. Program, Harvard, 1972. Commd. 2d lt. U.S. Army, 1951, advanced through grades to brig. gen., 1973; 40th inf. divsn. Korea, 1952-53; instr. A.A.A. Sch., Ft. Bliss, Tex., 1954-56; with 3d Inf. Div., Ft. Benning, Ga. and, Germany 1957-61, Office Chief of Staff, U.S. Army, 1963-66; comdg. officer 1st Bn. 31st Arty., Korea, 1967; exec. asst. to asst. sec. Army, 1968-70; exec. officer I Field Force Vietnam Arty., 1970; comdg. officer 52d Arty. Group, Vietnam, 1971; with Office Dep. Chief Staff for Personnel, Dept. Army, 1972-75; comdg. gen. VII Corps Arty. and Augsburg Germany Mil. Community 1975-77; comdr. 2d ROTC region, Ft. Knox, Ky., 1977-79; ret., 1979; v.p., dir. mgmt. scis. ops. Gen. Research Corp., McLean, Va., 1979-82;

group v.p Info. Systems & Network Corp., Bethesda, Md., 1982-93; chmn., pres. J-Tech, Inc., White Stone, Va., 1993—. Trustee Washington Adventist Hosp. Found., 1989-93. Decorated D.S.M., Legion of Merit, Bronze Star, Air Medal with V device, Army Commendation medal; Vietnamese Gallantry Cross with palm.; Recipient John J. Pershing award, 1951, 40 and 8 award, 1951, F.A. Assn. award, 1950. Mem. Nat. Soc. Pershing Rifles (past nat. comdr.), Alpha Kappa Psi, Beta Gamma Sigma. Home: Rt 2 Box 4320 White Stone VA 22578 Office: PO Box 1287 White Stone VA 22578

WROTH, L(AWRENCE) KINVIN, lawyer, educator; b. Providence, July 9, 1932; s. Lawrence Counselman and Barbara (Pease) W.; m. Susan Collins, May 2, 1958 (div. 1972); children: Ann K., Caroline D., Eliza H.; m. Deborah Bethell, Aug. 10, 1972; 1 dau., Katharine L.; stepchildren—John H., David H., Elizabeth T. and Sarah B. Zobel. B.A., Yale U., 1954; LL.B., Harvard U., 1960. Bar: Mass. 1960, Maine 1974. Teaching fellow, asst. prof. law Dickinson Sch. Law, 1960-62; research assoc. Harvard U., 1962-64; asso. prof. law U. Maine Sch. Law, Portland, 1964-66; prof. U. Maine Sch. Law, 1966—; assoc. dean Sch. Law U. Maine, 1977-78, acting dean, 1978-80, dean, 1980-90; rsch. fellow Charles Warren Center Studies in Am. History, Harvard U., 1968-74; cons. civil and probate procedure, profl. and jud. responsibility, and ct.-bar rels. Maine Supreme Jud. Ct., 1967—; cons. civil and criminal procedure and evidence Vt. Supreme Ct., 1969—. Author: (with R.H. Field and V.L. McKusick) Maine Civil Practice, 2d edit., 1970; editor-in-chief: Province in Rebellion, 1975; editor: (with H.B. Zobel) Legal papers of John Adams, 1965; reporter: Vermont Rules of Civil Procedure, 1971, Vermont Rules of Criminal Procedure, 1974, Maine Rules of Probate Procedure, 1980, (with J. Dooley) Vermont Rules of Evidence, 1982, Maine Code of Judicial Conduct, 1993, Vermont Code of Judicial Conduct, 1994. Pres. Greater Portland Landmarks, Inc., 1966-69, adv. trustee, 1969-85; adv. coun. Nat. Trust Hist. Preservation, 1967-70; bd. dirs. Maine Bar Found., 1983-89, sec., 1983-86, v.p., 1987, pres. 1988, fellow 1991; bd. dirs. Pine Tree Legal Assistance Inc., 1985—; mem. bd. dirs. Nat. Assn. IOLTA Programs, Inc., 1988-90; bd. dirs. Portland Symphony Orch., 1990, v.p. for ops. and resources, 1991-95, pres. 1995—; mem. Maine Commn. on Legal Needs, 1989-90, Commn. to Study Future of Maine's cts., 1991-93. Recipient Littleton-Griswold prize Am. Hist. Assn., 1966, Howard H. Dana award Maine Bar Found., 1991, Justice Louis Scolnik award Maine Civil Liberties Union, 1992, Herbert Harley award Am. Judicature Soc., 1994. Fellow ABA, Am. Bar Found.; mem. Maine Bar Assn. (Disting. Svc. award 1990), Am. Law Inst., Colonial Soc. Mass., Mass. Hist. Soc. Home: Cobbs Bridge Rd RR 2 Box 575 New Gloucester ME 04260 Office: U Maine Sch Law 246 Deering Ave Portland ME 04102-2837

WRUBLE, BERNHARD KARP, lawyer; b. Wilkes-Barre, Pa., Mar. 21, 1942; s. Maurice and Ruth Yvonne (Karp) W.; m. Judith Marilyn Eyges, Nov. 16, 1968 (div. 1987); children: Justine, Vanessa, Alexis; m. Jill Diamond, Nov. 24, 1990; children: Mattia, Austin. BA in Polit. Sci., Williams Coll., Williamstown, Mass., 1963; LLB, U. Pa., 1966; postgrad., NYU, 1972-74, Harvard U., 1978. Bar: U.S. Dist. Ct. (so. dist.) N.Y. 1969, U.S. Dist. Ct. (ea. dist.) N.Y. 1972, U.S. Ct. Appeals (2d cir.) 1972, U.S. Supreme Ct. 1972, U.S. Ct. Appeals (7th cir.) 1974, U.S. Ct. Appeals (D.C. and 4th cirs.) 1984, U.S. Ct. Appeals (5th cir.) 1985, U.S. Ct. Appeals (11th cir.) 1986. Law clk. to presiding judge U.S. Ct. Appeals (3d cir.), 1966-67; assoc. Simpson, Thacher & Bartlet, N.Y.C., 1968-73; prin. Simpson, Thatcher & Bartlet, N.Y.C., 1974-77; prin. dep. gen. counsel U.S. Dept. Army, Washington, 1977-79; dir. Office Govt. Ethics, Washington, 1979; exec. asst. to sec. and dep. sec. U.S. Dept. Energy, Washington, 1979-81; dir. Pres.'s Interagy. Coal Export Task Force, Washington, 1980-81; ptnr. Verner, Liipfert, Bernhard, McPherson and Hand, Washington, 1981—. Bd. dirs. Epilepsy Found. Am., 1983, chmn., 1991. Mem. ABA, D.C. Bar Assn., N.Y. State Bar Assn., Williams Coll. Alumni Assn. (pres. Washington chpt. 1986-91). Williams Coll. Soc. Alumni Assn. (exec. com. 1988-91). Democrat. Office: Verner Liipfert Bernhard McPherson and Hand 901 15th St NW Ste 700 Washington DC 20005-2310

WRUBLE, BRIAN FREDERICK, investment management company executive; b. Kalamazoo, Apr. 18, 1943; s. Milton and Rose Muriel (Nathanson) W.; m. Susan Roberta Shifrin, June 23, 1968 (div. Oct. 1984); children: Amy Carolyn, Jordan Todd; m. Kathleen Wilson Bratton, Apr. 20, 1985; 1 child, Henrietta Zane Bratton. BEE, Cornell U., 1965, MEE, 1966; MBA with distinction, NYU, 1976. Field engr. Sperry Corp., Lake Success, N.Y., 1966-69; v.p. Alliance One Instl. Services, Inc., N.Y.C., 1970-76, H. C. Wainwright and Co., Inc., N.Y.C., 1976-77, Wainwright Securities, Inc., N.Y.C., 1977; v.p., co-mgr. fundamental equities research Smith Barney, Harris Upham & Co.'s, N.Y.C., 1977-79; exec. v.p. chief fin. ops. Equitable Life Assurance Soc. U.S., N.Y.C., 1979-92; chmn., chief exec. officer Equitable Capital Mgmt. Corp., N.Y.C., 1985-92; chief investment officer Equitable Life Assurance Soc. U.S., N.Y.C., 1991-92; pres. chief oper. officer, dir. Delaware Mgmt. Holdings, Inc., 1992—; pres., CEO The Delaware Group, 1992—; pres., chief oper. officer Delaware Mgmt. Co., 1992—; chmn. Delaware Distributors, Inc., 1992—; chmn., chief exec. officer Delaware Svc. Co., Inc., 1992—; chmn., pres. Equitable Realty Assets Corp., Atlanta, 1983-92; v.p., dir. TELMARI, Inc., N.Y.C., 1982-83, Equitable Variable Life Ins. Co., 1987-92; chmn. Equico Capital Corp., N.Y.C., 1984-92, CEO Equitable Gen. of Okla., Oklahoma City, 1985-86; bd. dirs. Advanced System Applications Inc., 1985-87, Frye Copysystems Inc., N.Y.C., 1988-90, Supermkts. Gen. Corp., 1990-92, The Jackson Lab., Inc., 1990—; trustee Equitable Retirement Plans, N.Y.C., 1980-86, Inst. Advanced Study, 1992—; gov. Assn. Investment Mgmt. and Rsch., 1992—; pres. Hudson River Trust, 1991-92, Equitable Funds, 1991-92. Author: The Pollution Revolution, 1971. Vice chmn. Boys Choir of Harlem, N.Y.C., 1984-92; bd. dirs. Harlem Youth Devel. Found., 1989-92, Corp. Ptnrs. Phila. Art Mus., 1992—, vice chmn., 1992—; bd. govs. Jerome Levy Econ. Inst., 1990—. Recipient Heroes award Boys Choir Harlem, 1990, Founders award, 1993. Mem. IEEE, Assn. Investment Mgmt. and Rsch., Phila. Soc. Security Analysts, Inst. CFAs (CFA, vice chmn. 1993, chmn. 1994, bd. trustees rsch. found. 1994—, assoc. editor CFA Digest 1983—), Phila. C. of C. (bd. dirs. 1992—), mem. exec. com. 1993—). Republican. Jewish. Avocations: running, skiing, sailing, amateur radio. Office: Delaware Mgmt Holdings Inc One Commerce Sq Philadelphia PA 19103

WRUCK, ERICH-OSKAR, foreign language educator, administrator; b. Gr. Kroessin/Pomerania, Germany, Oct. 29, 1928; came to U.S., 1952, naturalized, 1954; s. Erich Albert and Erna (Kroening) W.; m. Esther Emmy Schmidt, Oct. 3, 1953; children: Eric Gordon, Karin Esther, Krista Elisabeth. BA magna cum laude, Rutgers U., 1959, MA, 1961, PhD, 1969. Asst. instr. Rutgers U., New Brunswick, N.J., 1959-62; asst. prof. Davidson Coll., N.C., 1962-69, assoc. prof., 1969-73, prof., chmn. dept. German, 1983-87, dir. Davidson Abroad Program, Marburg, Fed. Republic German, 1966-67, 71-72, Jr. Year Abroad Program, Wuerzburg, Fed. Republic Germany, 1986-87, 89-92 (ret. 1994). Served to 1st lt. U.S. Army, 1953-57, to col. USAR, 1986. Recipient Meritorious Service medal Dept. Army, 1983, 86, 88. Mem. Goethe Gesellschaft, Freies Deutsches Hochstift, Schiller Gesellschaft, Goethe Soc. of N. Am., Soc. for German Am. Studies, Julius Maximilians medal U. Wuerzburg, 1987. Republican. Lutheran. Avocations: painting, photography, soaring, skiing, running.

WRUCKE-NELSON, ANN C., elementary school educator; b. Mankato, Minn., Nov. 5, 1939; d. G.F. and Dorothy (Thomas) Wrucke; children: Chris, Dor-Ella. BS, Mankato State U., 1961; MLA, So. Meth. U., 1974; postgrad., U. Minn., 1963, Tex. Woman's U.; EdD in Early Childhood Edn., Tex. Woman's U., 1992. Cert. elem., kindergarten, bilingual-ESL, history tchr., Tex. Tchr. Rochester (Minn.) Pub. Schs., Christ the King Sch., Dallas; dir., tchr. Norway Christian Presch., Dallas; Every Student Learns Lang. program kindergarten tchr. Dallas Ind. Sch. Dist.; tchr. summer session Tex. Woman's U., 1991; presenter in field. Producer video: A Year of Language Learning, 1990. Sunday sch. tchr. Holy Trinity Ch. Recipient Tchr. of Yr. award, 1989, Tex. TESOL scholarship, 1990; scholar Mankato State U., Bill Martin Literacy Conf.; named ESL Tchr. Yr., 1991. Mem. Assn. for Childhood Edn. Internat. So. Assn. on Children Under Six, Tchrs. English to Speakers Other Lang., Tex. Tchrs. English to Speakers Other Lang., Dallas Assn. for Edn. of Young Child.

WU, CHIEN SHIUNG, physicist; b. Shanghai, May 31, 1912; naturalized citizen, U.S.; married, 1942; 1 child. BS, Nat. Cent. U., China, 1934; PhD, U. Calif., 1940; DSc (hon.), Princeton U., 1958, Smith Coll., 1959, Goucher

Coll., 1960, Rutgers U., 1961, Yale U., 1967, Russell Sage Coll., 1971, Harvard U., 1974, Bard Coll., 1974, Adelphi U., 1974, Dickinson Coll., 1975; LLD (hon.), Chinese U., Hong Kong, 1969. Rsch. fellow, lectr. U. Calif., 1940-42; asst. prof. Smith Coll., 1942-43; instr. Princeton U., 1943-44; sr. scientist Columbia U., 1944-47, assoc., 1947-52, from assoc. to full prof., 1952-72, Pupin prof. physics, 1972-81; ret.; mem. adv. com. to dir. NIH, 1975-82; hon. prof. Nanking U., Sci. & Tech. U., Beijing U., Tsao Hwa U., Nan Kai U., People's Republic China & Padua U., Italy; Nishina Meml. lectr. Univs. Tokyo, Osaka and Kyoto, 1983. Recipient Rsch. award Rsch. Corp., 1959, AAUW award, 1960, Achievement award Chi-Tsin Cult Found., 1965, Nat. Sci. Medal, 1975, Wolf Prize in Physics, 1978, Pupin medal Columbia Engring. Sch. Alumni Assn., 1991, Ettore Majorana-Erice-Sci. for Peace prize, 1992; named Scientist of Yr., Indsl. Rsch. Mag., 1974; asteroid named in honor, 1990. Fellow AAAS, Royal Soc. Edinburgh (hon.); mem. NAS (Comstock award 1964), Am. Phys. Soc. (pres. 1975, Tom Bonner prize 1975), Chinese Acad. Sci., Am. Acad. Arts & Sci. Achievements include research in nuclear physics, non-conservation of parity in beta decay. Home: 15 Claremont Ave Apt 73 New York NY 10027-6814 Office: Columbia Univ Dept of Physics Morningside Heights New York NY 10027*

WU, HARRY PAO-TUNG, librarian; b. Jinan, Shandong, China, May 1, 1932; came to U.S., 1960; s. James Ching-Mei and Elizabeth Hsiao (Lu) W.; m. Irene I-Len Sun, June 23, 1961; children: Eva Pei-Chen, Walter Pei-Liang. BA, Nat. Taiwan U., Taipei, 1959; student Ohio State U., 1962; MLS, Kent State U., 1966. Archive and library asst. Taiwan Handicraft Promotion Center, Taipei, 1959-60; student asst. Kent State U. Library, 1960-61; reference librarian Massillon (Ohio) Pub. Library, 1964-65, acting asst. dir., 1965, asst. dir., head adult services, 1966; dir. Flesh Pub. Library, Piqua, Ohio, 1966-68; dir. St. Clair County Library System, Port Huron, Mich., 1968—; founder and dir. Blue Water Library Fedn., Port Huron, 1974—; pres. Mich. Library Film Circuit, Lansing, 1977-79; mem. St. Clair County Literacy Project Com., 1986—; bd. dirs. Blue Water Reading Coun., 1987-88, Mich. Waterways council Girl Scouts U.S.A., Port Huron, 1985-86; bd. dirs. United Way St. Clair County, Mich., 1990-91; bd. trustees Libr. Mich., 1992—. Mem. Am., Mich. (chmn. library systems roundtable 1974-75) library assns., Am. Mgmt. Assn., Assn. Ednl. Communications and Tech., Detroit Suburban Librarians Roundtable, Chinese-Am. Librarians Assn. Clubs: Port Huron Internat. (pres. 1988), Rotary (dir. 1972-74, 88-90, Paul Harris fellow 1988). Home: 1518 Holland Ave Port Huron MI 48060-1511 Office: 210 Mcmorran Blvd Port Huron MI 48060-4098

WU, HSIU KWANG, economist, educator; b. Hankow, China, Dec. 14, 1935; came to U.S., 1952, naturalized, 1963; s. Kuo Cheng and Edith (Huang) W.; m. Kathleen Gibbs Johnson, Aug. 17, 1968. Grad., Lawrenceville Sch., 1954; A.B., Princeton U., 1958; M.B.A., U. Pa., 1960, Ph.D., 1963. Prof., group coordinator fin., econs. and internat. bus. Boston U., 1968-72; prof., chmn. fin., econs. and legal studies faculty U. Ala., 1972-81, Lee Bidgood prof. fin. and econs., 1978—, Ala. Banker Edn. Found. Banking Chair prof., 1973-78; econ. adviser Office of Comptroller of Currency, U.S. Treasury, 1966-69, 75-80; dir. Ala. Fed., 1984-88; dir. SECOR Bank FSB, 1988-93, chmn. bd., 1992-93; cons. instl. investor study SEC, 1969-70; mem. com. examiners undergrad. program for counseling and evaluation test in bus. Ednl. Testing Service, 1971, 77. Co-editor: Elements of Investments, 2d rev. edit, 1972; Contbr. articles to law and econ. jours. Sloan Faculty fellow Sloan Sch. Mgmt., Mass. Inst. Tech., 1965-66. Mem. Am. Econ. Assn., Am. Fin. Assn., Am. Statis. Assn., Fin. Mgmt. Assn. Home: 3332 Arcadia Dr Tuscaloosa AL 35404-4361 Office: U Ala Coll Commerce Tuscaloosa AL 35487

WU, JAMES CHEN-YUAN, aerospace engineering educator; b. Nanking, China, Oct. 5, 1931; came to U.S., 1953, naturalized, 1963; s. Chien Lieh and Cheng-Ling (Hsia) W.; m. Mei-Ying Chang, Sept. 7, 1957; children—Alberta Yee-Hwa, Norbert Mao-Hwa. Student, Nat. Taiwan (Formosa) U., 1949-52; BS, Gonzaga U., 1954; postgrad., Columbia U., 1954; MS (univ. fellow), U. Ill., 1955, PhD, 1957. Engr. Wah Chang Corp., N.Y.C., 1954; researcher Mass. Inst. Tech. at Cambridge, 1957; asst. prof. Gonzaga U., Spokane, Wash., 1957-59; research specialist Douglas Aircraft Co., 1959-65, group leader, 1960-61, supr., 1961-62, br. chief, 1963-65; prof. aerospace engring. Ga. Inst. Tech., 1965—; cons. N.Am. Aviation Co., Geophys. Tech. Corp., European Atomic Energy Commn., Ispra, Italy, European Atomic Energy Commn. (research center), U.S. Army Research Office, Durham, S.C. Contbr. articles to profl. jours. Chmn. bd. dirs. Chinese-Am. Inst. Recipient profl. achievement award Douglas Aricraft Co., 1963, Outstanding Tchrs. award Gonzaga U., 1959; Asso. fellow Am. Inst. Aeros. and Astronautics. Mem. Am. Soc. Engring. Edn. (founding), Soc. Indsl. and Applied Math. (vice-chmn. Pacific N.W. 1958-59), Am. Astron. Soc. (sr.), Am. Phys. Soc., Nat. Assn. Chinese Ams. (pres. Atlanta chpt.), Sigma Xi, Tau Beta Pi, Sigma Alpha Nu. Office: Sch Aerospace Engring Georgia Inst Tech Atlanta GA 30332

WU, JIN, oceanographer, educator, engineer; b. Nanking, China, Apr. 9, 1934; came to U.S., 1959, naturalized, 1972; s. Shiang-San and Aei-Feng (Chen) W.; m. Tzu-Chen Chang, Sept. 9, 1961; children: Victor Hua-Teh, Abraham Hua-Chung, Marvin Hua-Wei. B.Sc., Nat. Cheng Kung U., 1956; M.Sc., U. Iowa, 1961, Ph.D., 1964. Instr. physics Taitung Sr. High Sch., 1958-59; research asst., research assoc. U. Iowa, 1959-63; research scientist Hydronautics, Inc., Laurel, Md., 1963-66, sr. research scientist, then prin. research scientist, 1966-74, head geophys. fluid dynamics div., 1966-74, cons. 1974-80; mem. faculty U. Del., Newark, 1974—; prof. marine studies and civil engring. U. Del., 1977-80, H. Fletcher Brown prof. marine studies and civil engring., 1980—, coordinator phys. oceanography program Coll. Marine Studies, 1974-75, 79-80, dir. Air-Sea Interaction Lab., 1981—; vis. lectr. von Karman Inst. Fluid Dynamics, Brussels, 1970; hon. research cons. Nat. Sci. Council, Taiwan, 1983—; adviser Tainan Hydraulic Lab., Nat. Cheng Kung U., 1977—; expert-cons. Naval Research Lab., 1980—; NSF vis. prof. Nat. Taiwan U., 1970, 79, 84, Nat. Cheng Kung U., Taiwan, 1974, 75, 76; hon. prof. Ocean Univ. of Qingdao, 1983—; vis. prof. U. Calif., 1985; nat. invitation chair Nat. Taiwan U., 1986, Nat. Cheng Kung U., 1987. Contbr. numerous articles to profl. jours. Served with Chinese Navy, 1956-58. Recipient Achievement award Nat. Cheng Kung U., 1986, Ocean Sci. Educator award Office Naval Rsch., 1991-94. Mem. ASCE (Publ. award 1988), Am. Geophys. Union, Academia Sinica, Am. Meteool. Soc., Sigma Xi. Home: 1822 Greenplace Ter Rockville MD 20850-2942 Office: Univ Del Grad Coll Marine Studies Newark DE 19716

WU, LI-PEI, banker; b. Changhwa, Taiwan, Sept. 9, 1934; came to U.S., 1968; s. Yin-Su and Chiao-Mei (Hsiao) W.; m. Jenny S. Lai, Mar. 24, 1963; children: George T., Eugene Y. BA, Nat. Taiwan U., 1957; MBA, Kans. State U., Ft. Kays, 1969; Comml. Banking Exec. Program, Columbia U., 1974. Staff acct., asst. controller, asst. v.p., v.p. Nat. Bank Alaska, Anchorage, 1969-73, v.p. controller, 1973-76, sr. v.p. chief fin. officer, 1976-78; chmn. exec. com. Alaska Nat. Bank of the North, Anchorage, 1978-79, chief adminstrv. officer, 1979-80, pres., 1980-81; pres., chief exec. officer Gen. Bank, Los Angeles, 1982-84, chmn., pres, chief exec. officer, 1984—; fin cons. alaska '84, 1981-82, Western Airlines, Los Angeles, 1981-82, Microsci. Internat. Assn, San Jose, Calif., 1986-87; bd. dirs. Simons, Li & Assocs., Ft. Collins, Colo. Pres. Taiwanese United Fund, 1991. Recipient Outstanding Entrepreneur award Nat. Assn. Investment Cos. Mem. Taiwanese Am. Citizens League (life mem.). Avocations: reading, sports. Office: Gen Bank 800 W 6th St Los Angeles CA 90017-2704

WU, NAN FAION, pediatrician; b. Malaysia, July 13, 1943; came to U.S., 1969; m. Chia F. Wu, June 22, 1969; children: Edwin, Karen. MD, Nat. Taiwan U., 1969. Diplomate Am. Bd. Pediatrics. Intern Atlantic City Med. Ctr., 1969-70; resident in pediatrics Martland Hosp. U. Medicine and Dentistry of N.J., N.J. Med. Sch., Newark, 1970-73; pvt. practice pediatrics West Orange, N.J. Fellow Am. Acad. Pediatrics. Office: 35 Park Ave West Orange NJ 07052-5526

WU, NELSON IKON, art history educator, author, artist; b. Peking, China, June 9, 1919; came to U.S., 1945, naturalized, 1956; s. Aitchen K. and Lu-Yü (Yang) W.; m. Mu-lien Hsüeh, Dec. 1, 1951; children: Chao-ming, Chao-ting, Chao-ping, Chao-ying. B.A., Nat. Southwest Asso. U., Kunming, China, 1942; M.A., Yale U., 1949; Ph.D., 1954. Instr. Nat. S.W. Asso. U. Kunming, China, 1942-43; asst. prof. history of art San Francisco State Coll., 1954-55; instr. Yale U., 1955-59, asst. prof., 1959-65; prof. history of art and

Chinese culture Washington U., St. Louis, 1965-68, Edward Mallinckrodt Disting. Univ. prof., 1968-84, emeritus, 1984—, chmn. dept. art and archaeology, 1969-70; founder-adviser Asian Art Soc. Washington U., St. Louis, 1972—; fellow Davenport Coll., Yale, 1956-65; vis. prof. Tokyo U., 1972; Founder art festivals Yenling Yeyuan Picnic, 1952-65, Ashiya Seminar, Japan, 1966-67. Cinematographer, assoc. dir., editor motion picture The Flop, 1952; dir., writer music The Finger Painting of Wu Tsai-yen, 1955; author: (pseudonym Lu-ch'iao): Wei-yang Ko (Song Never to End, voted Most Profoundly Influential Book of 1950's by readers of China Times, 1991), 1959 (over 50 printings), Tung Ch'i-ch'ang: Apathy in Government and Fervor in Art, 1962, Chinese and Indian Architecture: City of Man, Mountain of God, and Realm of Immortals, 1963, (Italian and German transls.) Jen-tzu Tales, 1974, over 20 printings, Ch'an-ch'ing-shu, 1975, over 10 printings; contbg. author: Renditions, 1976, (with Kohara and Ch'en) Hsu/Wei and Tung Ch'i-ch'ang China Times, 1988, 89, 92, 95, China Times Weekly, 1992; adv. editor Tsing-hua Jour Chinese Studies, 1982—; exhibited at Faculty Show, Washington U., 1985, St. Louis Art Mus., 1985; featured on Pub. Broadcasting System show Living Treasures, 1987. Trustee Yale-in-China Assn., 1959-65; hon. trustee Nankai Sch., Tientsin, China, 1993. Tsing-hua Research fellow, 1954-55; Morse fellow Yale, 1958-59; Am. Council Learned Socs. fellow, 1958-59; Guggenheim Found. fellow, 1965-66; Fulbright research scholar, 1965-67; research scholar Kyoto U., Japan, 1965-67; Nat. Endowment for Humanities sr. fellow, 1972; New Haven Art Festival Lit. award, 1960; Calligraphy prize Ashiya, Japan, 1966; Living Treasures plaque St. Louis Older Adult Services and Info. System, 1985; hon. in Taipei, Taiwan at a conf. on contemporary Chinese lit., 1990. Mem. St. Louis Chinese Soc. (pres. 1969-70), League of Chinese Americans (dir. 1974-77). Home: 6306 Waterman Ave Saint Louis MO 63130-4707 also: 1530 Notch Rd Cheshire CT 06410-1070

WU, RAY JUI, biochemistry educator; b. Peking, China, Aug. 14, 1928; came to U.S., 1949, naturalized, 1961; s. Hsien and Daisy (Yen) W.; m. Christina Chan, Aug. 11, 1956; children: Albert, Alice. B.S., U. Ala., 1950; Ph.D., U. Pa., 1955. Asso. mem. Pub. Health Research Inst. City of N.Y., 1957-66; asso. prof. biochemistry, molecular and cell biology Cornell U., Ithaca, N.Y., 1966-72; prof. Cornell U., 1972—, chmn. sect., 1975-79; vis. rsch. scientist Stanford U., 1965-66; NSF sr. fellow MRC Lab., Cambridge, Eng., 1971; vis. assoc. prof. MIT, 1972. Contbr. chpts. to books, articles to profl. jours. NIH grantee, 1960—; NSF grantee, 1967—; Am. Cancer Soc. grantee, 1976—; Rockefeller Found grantee, 1985—. Mem. Am. Soc. Biol. Chemists, Am. Chem. Soc., AAAS, Academia Sinica, Internat. Soc. Plant Molecular Biology. Democrat. Home: 111 Christopher Cir Ithaca NY 14850-1701 Office: Cornell U Biotechnology Bldg Ithaca NY 14853

WU, ROBERT CHUNG YUNG, space sciences educator; b. Kao-hsiung, Taiwan, Republic of China, Oct. 16, 1943; came to U.S., 1969; s. Liang-Cheng and grace (Huang) W.; m. Grace S.J. Lee, June 20, 1970; children: David, John, Michael. MS, U. Ill., 1970, PhD, 1973. Postdoctoral fellow U. Iowa, Iowa City, 1976-77; postdoctoral fellow U. So. Calif., L.A., 1973-75, rsch. scientist, 1977-78, asst. rsch. prof., 1978-88, assoc. rsch. prof., 1988-94; rsch. prof., 1995—; cons. Rockwell Internat., L.A., 1984, Jet Propulsion Lab., Pasadena, 1985, 89. Contbr. articles to Jour. Chem. Physics, Jour. Geophys. Rsch., Optical Communs., Applied Physics B, Jour. Quantitative Spectroscopy and Radiative Transfer, Jour. Planetary Space Sci. Mem. Am. Geophys. Union, Optical Soc. Am. Office: U So Calif Space Scis Ctr Los Angeles CA 90089

WU, SENG-CHAI, financial planner, life insurance agency official; b. Amoy, Fuchian, China, Oct. 19, 1930; came to U.S., 1954; s. Eng-Hwa and Lian-Hoe (Iu) W.; m. Evelyn M. Mangaser, Sept. 9, 1975; children: Patrick O., Michael L., Andrew J. BA, Union Coll., Lincoln, Nebr. CLU; ChFC. Sales rep., also regional sales mgr. Home Health Edn. Svc., Richardson, Tex., 1959-68; sales rep., mgr. Met. Life Ins. Co., N.Y.C., 1968-85; sales mgr. Met. Life Ins. Co., Arcadia, Claremont, Calif. 1982-85; fin. cons. Fin. Design, Rancho Cucamonga, Calif., 1985—; gen. agy. mgr. Franklin Fin. Svcs. Corp., Springfield, Calif., 1988—, Am. Mut. Life Ins. Co., Des Moines, 1991—. Active Philippines and Chinese Assn., Dallas, 1969-75; nominated to participate LIMRA Internat. Rsch. Mem. Pomona Valley Life Underwriter Assn., Arrowhead CLU Assn. Republican. Adventist. Avocations: volleyball, photography, gardening, walking. Home: 10988 Wilson Ave Alta Loma CA 91737-2438

WU, TAI TE, biological sciences and engineering educator; b. Shanghai, China, Aug. 2, 1935; m. Anna Fang, Apr. 16, 1966; 1 son, Richard. M.B., B.S., U. Hong Kong, 1956; B.S. in Mech. Engring. U. Ill., Urbana, 1958; S.M. in Applied Physics, Harvard U., 1959, Ph.D. in Engring. (Gordon McKay fellow), 1961. Rsch. fellow in structural mechanics Harvard U., 1961-63; rsch. fellow in biol. chemistry Harvard U. (Med. Sch.), 1964, rsch. assoc., 1965-66; rsch. scientist Hydronautics, Inc., Rockville, Md., 1962; asst. prof. engring. Brown U., Providence, 1963-65; asst. prof. biomath. Grad. Sch. Med. Scis., Cornell U. Med. Coll., N.Y.C., 1967-68; assoc. prof. Grad. Sch. Med. Scis., Cornell U. Med. Coll., 1968-70; assoc. prof. physics and engring. scis. Northwestern U., Evanston, Ill., 1970-73, prof., 1973-74, prof. biochemistry and molecular biology and engring. scis., 1973-85, acting chmn. dept. engring. scis., 1974, prof. biochem., molecular biology, cell biology and biomed. engring., engring. scis., applied math., 1985-94, prof. biochemistry, molecular biology, cell biology, biomed. engring., 1994—. Author: (with E.A. Kabat and others) Variable Regions of Immunoglobulin Chains, 1976, Sequences of Immunoglobulin Chains, 1979, Sequences of Proteins of Immunological Importance, 1983, Sequences of Proteins of Immunological Interest, 1987, 5th edit., 1991; editor: New Methodologies in Studies of Protein Configuration, 1985; contbr. articles to profl. jours. Recipient progress award Chinese Engrs. and Scientists Assn. So. Calif., Los Angeles, 1971; C.T. Loo Scholar, 1959-60; NIH Research Career Devel. awardee, 1974-79. Mem. Am. Soc. Biochem. & Molecular Biology, Biophys. Soc., Chgo. Assn. Immunology, Sigma Xi, Tau Beta Pi, Pi Mu Epsilon. Office: Northwestern U Dept Biochem Molecular Biology & Cell Biology Evanston IL 60208

WU, TAI TSUN, physicist, educator; b. Shanghai, China, Dec. 1, 1933; came to U.S., 1950, naturalized, 1964; s. King Ching and Wei Van (Tsang) W.; m. Sau Lan Yu, June 18, 1967. B.S., U. Minn., 1953; S.M., Harvard U., 1954, Ph.D., 1956. Jr. fellow Soc. Fellows Harvard U., 1956-59, asst. prof., 1959-63, assoc. prof., 1963-66, Gordon McKay prof. applied physics, 1966—, prof. physics, 1966—; mem. Inst. Advanced Study, Princeton, 1958-59, 60-61, 62-63; vis. prof. Rockefeller U., 1966-67; sci. assoc. Deutsches Elektronen-Synchrotron, Hamburg, Ger., 1970-71, 82-83; Kramers prof. U. Utrecht, Netherlands, 1977-78; sci. assoc. CERN, Geneva, Switzerland, 1977-78, 86—. Author: (with Ronold W.P. King) Scattering and Diffraction of Waves, 1959, (with Barry M. McCoy) Two-Dimensional Ising Model, 1973, (with Ronold W.P. King, Glenn S. Smith and Margaret Owens) Antennas in Matter: Fundamentals, Theory and Applications, 1981, (with Hung Cheng) Expanding Protons: Scattering at High Energies, 1987, (with Raymond Gastmans) The Ubiquitous Photon: Helicity Method for QED and QCD, 1990, (with Ronold W.P. King and Margaret Owens) Lateral Electromagnetic Waves: Theory and Applications to Communications, Geophysical Exploration, and Remote Sensing, 1992. Recipient Alexander von Humboldt award, 1985; Putnam scholar, 1953; fellow A.P. Sloan Found., 1960-66; fellow NSF, 1966-67; Guggenheim Found., 1970-71. Mem. Am. Acad. Arts and Sci., Sigma Xi, Eta Kappa Nu, Tau Beta Pi. Home: 35 Robinson St Cambridge MA 02138-1403 Office: Harvard U 204B Pierce Hall Cambridge MA 02138-2901 *A person's strength is, simultaneously, his weakness.*

WU, THEODORE YAO-TSU, engineer; b. Changchow, Kiangsu, China, Mar. 20, 1924; came to U.S., 1948, naturalized, 1962; s. Ren Fu and Gee-Ing (Shu) W.; m. Chin-Hua Shih, June 17, 1950; children: Fonda Bai-yueh, Melba Bai-chin. B.S., Chiao-Tung U., 1946; M.S., Iowa State U., 1948, Ph.D. Calif. Inst. Tech., 1952. Mem. faculty Calif. Inst. Tech., Pasadena, 1952—; assoc. prof. Calif. Inst. Tech., 1957-61; prof. engring. sci., 1961—; vis. prof. Hamburg (Germany) U., 1964-65; cons. numerous indsl. firms. Editorial bd.: Advances in Applied Mechanics series, 1970; Contbr. profl. jours. Guggenheim fellow, 1964-65. Fellow Am. Phys. Soc. (Fluid Dynamics prize 1993), AIAA (asso.); mem. Sigma Xi, Nat. Acad. Engring.,

Phi Tau Phi. Office: Calif Inst Tech Engring & Applied Science 128-95 1201 E California Blvd Pasadena CA 91125*

WU, TUNG, curator, art historian, art educator, artist; b. Foochow, Fukien, China, Dec. 10, 1940; came to U.S., 1965; s. Chin-Wen and Jingrong (Chen) W.; m. Ying Chin, July 16, 1974. BA, Normal U., Taipei, Taiwan, 1962; postgrad., U. Mich., 1967-70, Harvard U., 1979—. Rsch. asst. Nat. Palace Mus., Taichung, Taiwan, 1962-65; photographer Archive U. Mich., 1966-68; rsch. asst. Cleve. Mus. Art, 1968, Nelson-Atkins Mus. Art, Kansas City, Mo., 1969; rsch. fellow Mus. Fine Arts, Boston, 1971-79, asst. curator, 1980-85, assoc. curator, 1985-86, curator Asian art, 1986-92, Matsutaro Shoriki curator Asian art, 1992—; teaching asst. U. Kans., Lawrence, 1969, Harvard U., 1978; vis. lectr. Harvard U., Cambridge, Mass., 1975, Emmanuel Coll., Boston, 1992, Simmons Coll., Boston, 1993; advisor Chinese Inst. Am., N.Y.C., 1985—; Chinese Cultural Found., San Francisco, 1985-87; cons. Project Emperor-One, Boston, 1983-86. Mem. Nat. Com. on U.S.-China Rels., Washington, 1985—; curator Nat. Devel. Seminar Taipei, 1989, 92; advisor dept. Asian trade art Peabody Mus., Salem. Mass., 1991—; trustee W.A. Compton Found. Oriental Arts; mem. Nat. Edn. Reform, Taipei, 1994. Nat. Mus. History fellow (Taipei), 1984—; grantee Freer Found. U. Mich. 1968, Ford Found., Kansas City, 1969, Smithsonian Instn., Washington, 1978. Mem. Taoist Soc. Japan, Soc. Chinese Kunqu Opera, Soc. Chinese Calligraphy. Office: Mus Fine Arts Asiatic Dept 465 Huntington Ave Boston MA 02115-5519

WU, WILLIAM LUNG-SHEN (YOU-MING WU), aerospace medical engineering design specialist, foreign intelligence analyst; b. Hangchow, Chekiang Province, China, Sept. 1, 1921; came to U.S., 1941, naturalized, 1955; s. Sing-Chih and Mary (Ju-Mei) Wu. AB in Biochemistry, Stanford U., 1943, MD, 1946; MS in Chemistry and Internal Medicine, Tulane U., 1955; diploma, U.S. Naval Sch. Aviation Medicine, Pensacola, Fla., 1956, USAF Sch. Aviation Medicine, USAF Aerospace Med. Ctr., 1961; cert. of tng. in aviation medicine. U. Calif., Berkeley, 1962, 1964. Diplomate Am. Bd. Preventive Medicine, Am. Bd. Internal Medicine, Am. Bd. Psychiatry, Am. Bd. Pathology. Gen. rotating intern U. Iowa Hosps., Iowa City, 1945-46; resident Lincoln (Nebr.) Gen. Hosp., 1946-47, resident in pathology, 1947-48; resident in pathology Bryan Meml. Hosp., Lincoln, 1947-48; fellow, instr. in internal medicine Tulane U., New Orleans, 1948-54; asst. vis. physician Charity Hosp. and Hutchinson Meml. Teaching and Diagnostic and Cancer Detection Clinics, New Orleans, 1948-51; vis. physician Charity Hosp. and Hutchinson Meml. Teaching and Diagnostic Clinics, New Orleans, 1951-54; staff physician Holderman (Army) Hosp., Napa, Calif., 1958; staff physician Aviation Space and Radiation Med. Group Gen. Dynamics/Convair, San Diego, 1958-61; aerospace med. specialist, med. monitor for Life Sciences Sect. Gen. Dynamics/Astronautics, San Diego, 1961-65; aerospace med. and bioastronautic specialist Lovelace Found. for Med. Edn. and Rsch., Albuquerque, 1965-68; staff physician Laguna Honda Hosp., San Francisco, 1968-74; ret.; staff physician Kaiser-Permanente Hosp. all-night med. clinic, San Francisco, 1971-73; safety rep. and med. examiner U.S. Civil Aeronaut. Adminstrn., 1959; med. examiner Fed. Aviation Adminstrn., 1961; expert witness in forensic medicine and/or medicolegal jurisprudence for cts. Author 8 books and 100 tech. papers in field. Active mem. Planning, Rsch. and Devel. Commn. Redwood City; bd. dirs. Legal Aid Soc. Santa Clara County, U.S. Congl. Adv. Bd., Am. Security Coun. Found., Little House Sr. Multipurpose Ednl. Ctr.; Life Fellow Royal Soc. of Lichtenstein, Zurich, Switzerland, Oxford Club (N.Y. and Fla.), Royal Coll. of Heraldry. Comdr., flight surgeon M.C., USN, 1954-57. Recipient Gold medal Internat. Inst. Community Svc., 1976, J. Edgar Hoover Gold Disting. Pub. Svc. award Am. Police Hall of Fame, 1991, Albert Einstein Bronze medal, 1986, Cambridge Gold medal, Dedication Insignia. Fellow San Diego Biomed. Rsch. Inst. (bd. dirs. 1961-65, sec. of fellows 1961-62, chmn. of fellows 1963), Inst. Environ. Scis. (chmn. specifications and standards com.), AIAA (mem. nominating com. San Diego sect., plant rep. life sci. sect. 1963-65); mem. IEEE (vice chmn. San Diego chpt. profl. tech. group on biomed. electronics 1962-65), N.Y. Acad. Scis., Internat. Univ. Found. (hon. pres.), Internat. Acad. Found. (hon. registrar-sec.), Computer Club, Sigma Xi, U.S. Naval Inst. (life), Naval League of U.S. West-pac (life). Achievements include research of theroetical aspects of cold catalyzed hydrogen fusion nuclear-rocket warm super-conductor hyper-magnetic, hydrogen-fusion space stations; patentee S(RAM-PANT)S. Home: 250 Budd Ave Campbell CA 95008-4063

WU, YING CHU LIN SUSAN, engineering company executive, engineer; b. Beijing, June 23, 1932; came to U.S., 1957; d. Chi-yu and K.C. (Kung) Lin; m. Jain-Ming Wu, June 13, 1959; children: Ernest H., Albert H., Karen H. BSME, Nat. Taiwan U., 1955; MS in Aero. Engring., Ohio State U., 1959; PhD in Aeros., Calif. Inst. Tech., 1963. Sr. engr. Elecro-Optical Systems, Inc., Pasadena, Calif., 1963-65; asst. prof. aero. engring. U. Tenn. Space Inst., Tullahoma, 1965-67, assoc. prof., 1967-73, prof., 1973-88; adminstr. Energy Conversion R&D Programs, Tullahoma, 1981-88; pres., chief exec. officer ERC, Inc., Tullahoma, 1987—; presdl. appointee adv. bd. Nat. Air and Space Mus., Smithsonian Inst., 1993—. Contbr. over 90 articles to profl. jours. Mem. Better Sch. Task Force, Tullahoma, 1985-86; founding mem. Tullahoma Edn. Found. for Excellence; trustee Rochester Inst. Tech., 1992—. Recipient Chancellor's Rsch. award U. Tenn., 1978, Outstanding Educator of Am. award, 1973, 75; Amelia Earhart fellow, 1958, 59, 62. Fellow ASME, AIAA (assoc., chmn. Tenn. sect., H.H. Arnold award 1984, Plasmodynamics and Lasers award 1994); mem. Soc. Women Engrs. (life mem., achievement award 1985), Rotary, Sigma Xi (chmn. U. Tenn. Space Inst. club). Home: 1451 Rocky Ridge Dr Apt 809 Roseville CA 95661-3006 Office: ERC Inc PO Box 417 Tullahoma TN 37388-0417

WUDL, FRED, chemistry educator, consultant; b. Cochabamba, Bolivia, Jan. 8, 1941; came to U.S., 1958; s. Robert and Bertha (Schorr) W.; m. Linda Raimondo, Sept. 2, 1967. BS, UCLA, 1964, PhD, 1967. Postdoctoral rsch. fellow Harvard U., 1967-68; asst. prof. dept. chemistry SUNY, Buffalo, 1968-72; mem. tech. staff AT&T Bell Labs., Murray Hill, N.J., 1972-82; prof. chemistry and materials U. Calif., Santa Barbara, 1982—. Recipient Arthur C. Cope scholar award Am. Chem. Soc., 1993, Natta medal Italian Chem. Soc., 1994, Wheland medal U. Chgo., 1994. Fellow AAAS. Office: Dept Chemistry U Calif Santa Barbara CA 93106

WUDUNN, SHERYL, journalist, correspondent; b. N.Y.C., Nov. 16, 1959; d. David and Alice (Mark) W.; m. Nicholas D. Kristof, Oct. 8, 1988. BA, Cornell U., Ithaca, N.Y., 1981; MBA, Harvard U., 1986; MPA, Princeton U., 1988. Lending officer Bankers Trust Co., N.Y.C., 1981-84; intern reporter Wall St. Jour., L.A., 1986; bus. reporter South China Morning Post, Hong Kong, 1987; corr. N.Y. Times, Beijing, 1989-93, Tokyo, 1995—. Co-author: China Wakes, 1994. Recipient Pulitzer Prize for fgn. reporting, 1990, George Polk award L.I. U., N.Y., 1990, Hal Boyle award Overseas Press Club, 1990. Avocations: aerobics, singing. Home: NY Times Asahi Shumbun Bldg, 3-2 Tsukiji 5-chome, Chuo-ku Tokyo 104-11, Japan Office: NY Times 229 W 43rd St New York NY 10036-3913

WUEBKER, VIRGINIA ANN, retired elementary school educator, program director; b. Waco, Tex., Oct. 29, 1928; d. Oliver Ernest and Bertha Elizabeth Blume; m. William Herbert Wuebker, Sept. 21, 1954; children: Robin Battershell, Bonnie, Cardinal. BS in Edn., Baylor U., 1951, MS in Edn., 1957. Cert. elem. tchr., Tex. Primary tchr. Connally Ind. Sch., Lacy-Lakeview, Tex., 1958-60, Midway Ind. Sch., Woodway, Tex., 1960-65; 2d, 4th grade tchr. Robinson (Tex.) Sch., 1965-89; ret. from teaching, 1989; dir. Summer Reading Inst., Waco, Tex., 1980—; dir. Univ. Interscholastic Competition, Waco, West, Whitney, Tex., 1987-89; tchr. evaluator Robinson Ind. Sch. Dist., 1982-83; supr. student tchrs. Baylor U., Waco, 1990-91. Author: You, Your Child and Reading, 1975, Mud Is Nice, 1994, The Tale of Yip, 1994, Blockhead, 1994; contbr. column to newspaper publs. Pres. C. of C., Robinson, 1970, Cemetery Assn., Robinson, 1974; founder Sr. Citizens Ctr., Robinson, 1966. Mem. NEA, Tex. State Tchrs. Assns., Robinson PTA, Tex. Reading Coun., Internat. Reading Assn., Tex. Classroom Tchrs. Assn. United Ch. of Christ. Avocations: gardening, guitar, reading. Home: 604 N Robinson Dr Waco TX 76706-5312

WUENSCH, BERNHARDT JOHN, ceramic engineering educator; b. Paterson, N.J., Sept. 17, 1933; s. Bernhardt and Ruth Hannah (Slack) W.; m. Mary Jane Harriman, June 4, 1960; children: Stefan Raymond, Katrina Ruth. SB in Physics, MIT, 1955, SM in Physics, 1957, PhD in Crystallography, 1963. Rsch. fellow U. Bern, Switzerland, 1963-64; asst. prof. ceramics MIT, Cambridge, 1964-69, assoc. prof. ceramics, 1969-74, prof., 1974—, TDK chair materials sci. and engring., 1985-90, dir. Ctr. Materials Sci. and Engring., 1988-93, acting dept. head dept. materials sci. and engring., 1980; vis. prof. Crystallographic Inst., U. Saarland, Fed. Republic Germany, 1973; physicist Max Planck Institut für Festkorperforschung, Stuttgart, Fed. Republic Germany, 1981; mem. U.S. nat. com. for crystallography NRC, NAS, 1980-82, 89—; mem. N.E. regional com. for selection of Marshall Scholars, 1970-73, chmn., 1974-80. Co-editor: Modulated Structures, 1979; adv. editor Physics and Chemistry of Minerals, 1976-85; assoc. editor Can. Mineralogist, 1978-80; editor Zeitschrift fuer Kristallographie, 1981-88. Ford Found. postdoctoral fellow, 1964-66. Fellow Am. Ceramic Soc. (Outstanding Educator award 1987), Mineral. Soc. Am.; mem. Am. Crystallographic Assn., Mineral. Assn. Can., Materials Rsch. Soc., Electrochem. Soc. Episcopalian. Home: 190 Southfield Rd Concord MA 01742-3432 Office: MIT Rm 13-4037 Cambridge MA 02139

WUERL, DONALD W., bishop; b. Pittsburgh, Nov. 12, 1940; s. Francis J. and Mary A. (Schiffbauer) W. BA, Cath. U. Am., 1962; MA, Cath. U. Am., Rome, 1963; ThM, Pontifical Gregorian U., Rome, 1967; ThD, Pontifical U. St. Thomas, Rome, 1974; DD (hon.), Duquesne U., 1989, Washington and Jefferson Coll., 1990; HLD (hon.), La Roche Coll., 1990; LHD (hon.), St. Vincent Coll., 1992. Ordained priest Roman Cath. Ch., 1966. Asst. pastor, parochial vicar St. Rosalia Ch., Pitts., 1967-69; sec. to Cardinal John Wright Congregation for Clergy, Rome, 1969-79; vice-rector St. Paul Sem., Pitts., 1980-81, rector, 1981-85; Ord. aux. bishop of Seattle, titular bishop of Rosmarkaeum, 1986, bishop of Pittsburgh, 1988—; sec. to Bishop of Pitts., 1967-69; lectr. Duquesne U., 1968-69, 80-85, Pontifical U. St. Thomas, 1975-79; lectr. adult theology program Diocese of Pitts., 1967-69, dir. Inst. Continuing Edn. for Priests, 1982-84, assoc. gen. sec., 1985; ofcl. Congregation for Clergy, Rome, 1969-79; mem. alumni bd. govs. Cath. U. Am., 1977-84, vice-pres. for religious, 1981-82; exec. sec. to Papal rep. for Study of Sems. in U.S., 1982-85. Author: The Forty Martyrs, 1971, Fathers of the Church, 1975, The Catholic Priesthood Today, 1976, A Visit to the Vatican, 1981, The Church and Her Sacraments: Making Christ Visible, 1990; co-author: The Teaching of Christ: A Catholic Catechism for Adults, 1976, rev., 1984, 91, abridged, 1979, study guide, 1977, A Catholic Catechism, 1986; contbg. author: New Catholic Ency.; contbr. articles to religion publs.; author religious cassette programs. Recipient Disting. Pennsylvanian award Gannon U., 1989, Brotherhood award NCCJ, 1991, Treee of Life award Jewish Nat. Fund, 1992, Disting. Alumni award Cath. U. Am., 1992; named Vectors/Pitts. Man of Yr. in religion, 1988. Mem. Am. Cath. Hist. Assn., Cath. Theol. Soc. Am., Fellowship Cath. Scholars, Acad. Romana Universale, Phi Kappa Theta (Man of Achievement award 1988). Office: Diocese of Pitts 111 Blvd Of The Allies Pittsburgh PA 15222-1618

WUEST, GEORGE W., retired state supreme court justice; b. Lake Andes, S.D., Feb. 3, 1925; m. Sandra Wuest, June 25, 1956; children: Linda, Douglas. LLB, U.S.D., 1949. Atty. State of S.D., Lake Andes; asst. atty. gen. State of S.D.; judge U.S. Ct. Appeals (4th cir.), S.D., 1965-86; assoc. justice S.D. Supreme Ct., Pierre, 1986-95; ret., 1995. Address: 500 E Capitol Ave Pierre SD 57501

WULBERT, DANIEL ELIOT, mathematician, educator; b. Chgo., Dec. 17, 1941; s. Morris and Anna (Greenberg) W.; children: Kera, Noah. BA, Knox U., 1963; MA, U. Tex., Austin, 1964, PhD, 1966. Research assoc. U. Lund (Sweden), 1966-67; asst. prof. U. Wash., Seattle, 1967-73; prof. U. Calif.-San Diego, La Jolla, 1973—; vis. prof. Northwestern U., Evanston, Ill., 1977. Contbr. articles in field. World champion cyclist Masters World Cup Track Points Race, 1990. Office: U Calif San Diego Dept Math # 0112 La Jolla CA 92093

WULF, MELVIN LAWRENCE, lawyer; b. N.Y.C., Nov. 1, 1927; s. Jacob and Vivian (Hurwitz) W.; m. Deirdre Howard, Dec. 18, 1962; children: Laura Melissa, Jane Miranda. B.S., Columbia U., 1952, LL.B., 1955. Bar: N.Y. 1957. Asst. legal dir. ACLU, 1958-62, legal dir., 1962-77; Distinguished vis. prof. Hofstra Law Sch., 1975, spl. prof. law, 1976-77; mem. firm Clark Wulf & Levine, 1978-83, Beldock, Levine & Hoffman, 1983—. Author articles. Served to lt. (j.g.) USNR, 1955-57. Ford Found. fellow, 1967. Home: 340 Riverside Dr New York NY 10025 Office: 99 Park Ave New York NY 10016-1503

WULF, WILLIAM ALLAN, computer information scientist, educator; b. Chgo., Dec. 8, 1939; s. Otto H. and Helen W. (Westermeier) W.; m. Anita K. Jones, July 1, 1977; children: Karin, Ellen. BS, U. Ill., 1961, MSEE, 1963; PhD in Computer Sci., U. Va., 1968. Prof. computer sci. Carnegie-Mellon Univ., Pitts., 1968-81; chmn., chief exec. officer Tartan Labs., Pitts., 1981-87; AT&T prof. computer sci. Univ. Va., Charlottesville, 1988—; asst. dir. Nat. Sci. Found., Washington, 1988-90; chair bd. on computer sci. and telecommunications NRC; bd. dirs. Baker Engrs., Beaver, Pa.; cons. various computer mfrs. Author: Fundamental Structures of Computer Science, 1981. Bd. dirs. Pitts. High Tech. Coun., 1982-88; trustee Charles Babbage Inst. Fellow IEEE, AAAS, Am. Acad. Arts and Scis., Assn. Computing Machinery (coun.); mem. NAE. Avocations: woodworking, photography. Office: U Va Dept Computer Sci Charlottesville VA 22903

WULFF, HARALD P., chemicals executive. Pres., ceo Henkel Corp., Gulph Mills, Pa. Office: Henkel Corp 2200 Renaissance Blvd King Of Prussia PA 19406

WULFF, JOHN KENNETH, controller; b. L.A., Oct. 15, 1948; s. Kenneth A. and Grace L. (Pinkerton) W.; m. Linda Carol Coffman, June 20, 1970; children: Kenneth E., J. Christopher, Jason D. BS, U. Pa., Phila., 1971. CPA, Conn. Staff acct. Peat Marwick Main & Co. and predecessors, N.Y.C., 1971-74; mgr. Peat Marwick Main & Co. and predecessors, 1974-77; ptnr. Peat Marwick Main & Co. and predecessors, 1977-87; deputy controller Union Carbide Corp., Danbury, Conn., 1987-88; v.p., controller Union Carbide Corp., 1988—. Mem. Fin. Execx. Inst., AICPA, and vairous other profl. orgns.

WÜMPELMANN, KNUD AAGE ABILDGAARD, clergyman, religious organization administrator; b. Odense, Denmark, Aug. 7, 1922; s. Heinrich Christian and Helga P.P. (Abildgaard) W.; m. Karen M. Petersen, Aug. 23, 1947; children: Jørgen, Mogens. BD, Cen. Bapt. Theol. Sem., Kansas City, Kans., 1953, MRE, 1954; DD (hon.), William Jewell Coll., Liberty, Mo., 1985. Ordained to ministry Bapt. Union Denmark, 1948. Asst. pastor Jetsmark Bapt. Ch., Denmark, 1947-50; asst. pastor Købner Meml. Ch., Copenhagen, 1950-55, min., 1955-64; gen. sec. Bapt. Union Denmark, Copenhagen, 1964-80; sec., treas. European Bapt. Fedn., Copenhagen, 1980-89; regional sec. for Europe Bapt. World Alliance, Copenhagen, 1980-89; pres. Bapt. World Alliance, McLean, Va., 1990-95. Author: Vi tror, 1966; editor: Baptistsamfundene i Rwanda-Burundi, 1968. Recipient Disting. Svc. award Ctrl. Bapt. Theol. Sem., Scroll of Honor, Bapt. Theol. Sem., Rüschlikon-Zürich, Switzerland, 1991. Home: Villavej 8, DK-4340 Toelloese Denmark Office: Bapt World Alliance 6733 Curran St Mc Lean VA 22101-3804

WUNDER, CHARLES C(OOPER), physiology and biophysics educator, gravitational biologist; b. Pitts., Oct. 2, 1928; s. E(dgar) Douglas and Annabel (Cooper) W.; m. Marcia Lynn Barnes, Apr. 4, 1962; children: Edgar Douglas, David Barnes, Donald Charles. A.B. in Biology, Washington and Jefferson Coll., 1949; M.S. in Biophysics, U. Pitts., 1952, Ph.D. in Biophysics, 1954. Assoc. U. Iowa, Iowa City, 1954-56, asst. prof. physiology and biophysics, 1956-63, assoc. prof. physiology and biophysics, 1963-71, prof. physiology and biophysics, 1971—; cons. for biol. simulation of weightlessness U.S. Air Force, 1964; vis. scientist Mayo Found., Rochester, Minn., 1966-67. Author: Life into Space: An Introduction to Space Biology, 1966; also chpts., numerous articles, abstracts. Recipient Research Career Devel. award NIH, 1961-66; AEC predoctoral fellow U. Pitts., 1951-53; NIH spl. fellow, 1966-67; grantee NIH, NASA. Mem. Am. Physiol. Soc., The Biophys. Soc. (charter), Aerospace Med. Assn., Iowa Acad. Sci. (chmn. physiology sect. 1971-72, 83-84, co-chmn. 1982-83), Soc. Exptl. Biology and Medicine, Am. Soc. Biomechanics (founding), Aerospace Physiologist Soc. Presbyterian. Achievements include the establishment of chronic centrifugation as an approach for investigating gravity's role as a biological determi-

nant. Home: 702 W Park Rd Iowa City IA 52246-2425 Office: U Iowa BSB Iowa City IA 52242

WUNDERLICH, ALFRED LEON, artist, art educator; b. Salem, Oreg., June 26, 1939; s. Joseph Anthony and Anna Margaret (Meyer) W.; children: Annelise, Jonathan Resor. Cert., Cooper Union, 1961; B.F.A., Yale U., 1962, M.F.A., 1968. Dir. visual studies program Hopkins Ctr., Dartmouth Coll., Hanover, N.H., 1965-66; asst. prof. art Hopkins Ctr., Darmouth Coll., Hanover, N.H., 1966-74; assoc. prof. R.I. Sch. of Design, Providence, 1983-94; prof. R.I. Sch. of Design, Providence, 1994—; adj. lectr. Hunter Coll. CUNY, 1973; adj. prof., vis. artist Pahlavi U., Shiraz, Iran, 1978, vis. artist U. Edinburgh, Scotland, Edinburgh Internat. Arts Festival, 1973, Kansas City Art Inst., Art Inst. Chgo., Ohio State U., 1986, Carnegie Mellon U., 1987; fine arts advisor Inst. for Internat. Edn.; mem. U.S. Art in Space team, met with Soviet Artists Union team, Moscow, 1990; owner, artistic dir. GAS-523 project to fly aboard NASA Space Shuttle, 1996. One-man shows Dartmouth Coll., 1969, Kyoto, Japan, 1969, Pahlavi U., 1978, Kwanghow Mus., Canton, China, 1979, Chang-tu Mus., Szechwan, China, 1978, MIT, 1981, Swarthmore Coll., 1985, also numerous group exhbns.; represented in permanent collections Mus. Modern Art, N.Y.C., Art Inst. Chgo., Yale U. Art Gallery, Nat. Gallery Scotland, 1st Nat. Bank Boston, Dartmouth Coll., Smithsonian-Cooper Hewitt Mus., Stanford U. Art Mus., also others. Recipient Bocour Color award, 1960; Yale ALumni fellow, 1962-63; Yaddo fellow, 1973; Dartmouth Faculty fellow, 1968; Fulbright grantee to India, 1963-64; Dartmouth Coll. research grantee, 1970-72; SUNY research grantee, 1983. Home: 151 Pratt St Providence RI 02906-1412 Office: RISD 2 College St Providence RI 02903-2717

WUNDERLICH, BERNHARD, physical chemistry educator; b. Brandenburg, Germany, May 28, 1931; came to U.S., 1954, naturalized, 1960; s. Richard O. and Johanne (Wohlgefahrt) W.; m. Adelheid Felix, Dec. 28, 1953; children: Caryn Cornelia, Brent Bernhard. Student, Humboldt U., Berlin, Germany, 1949-53, Goethe U., Frankfurt, Germany, 1953-54, Hastings Coll., 1954-55; Ph.D., Northwestern U., 1957. Instr. chemistry Northwestern U., Evanston, Ill., 1957-58; instr. chemistry Cornell U., Ithaca, N.Y., 1958-60, asst. prof., 1960-63; assoc. prof. phys. chemistry Rensselaer Poly. Inst., Troy, N.Y., 1963-65, prof. phys. chemistry, 1965-88, prof. emeritus, 1988—; prof. chemistry U. Tenn., Knoxville, 1988—; Disting. scientist div. chemistry Oak Ridge Nat. Lab., 1988—; cons. E.I. duPont de Nemours Co., 1963-88; dir. Lab. for Advanced Thermal Analysis; rsch. in solid state of linear high polymers. Author: Macromolecular Physics, Vol. 1, 1973, Vol. 2, 1976, Vol. 3, 1980, Thermal Analysis, 1990; author computer and audio courses on Crystals of Linear Macromolecules and Thermal Analysis; contbr. over 350 articles to profl. jours.; mem. editorial bd. Chemistry, 1965-68, Makromolekulare Chemie, Jour. Thermal Analysis; adv. bd.: Jour. Polymer Sci., Macromolecules 1984-88, Polymers for Advanced Tech. Recipient Humboldt award, 1987-88; award for applied chem. thermodynamics Swiss Soc. for Thermal Analysis and Calorimetry, 1993. Fellow Am. Phys. Soc., N.Am., Thermal Analysis Soc. (Mettler award in thermal analysis 1971); mem. Am. Chem. Soc. Home: 200 Baltusrol Dr Knoxville TN 37922-3707 Office: U Tenn Dept Chemistry Knoxville TN 37996

WUNDERLICH, RENNER, film producer, cinematographer; b. St. Louis, May 5, 1947; s. Harry Joseph and Erlynne (Renner) W.; m. Margaret Lazarus; children: Michael, Matthew. BA, Boston Coll., 1968. Prodr., dir., cinematographer, editor Cambridge (Mass.) Documentary Films, 1974—; freelance videographer and sound tech. NBC, ABC, CBS, PBS, BBC and ind. prodrs., 1984—. Prodr., dir., cinematographer, editor: (TV show) Mr. Goodman, 1972-73, (documentaries) Taking Our Bodies Back, 1974, Rape Culture, 1975, Eugene Debs and the American Movement, 1977, Killing Us Softly, 1978, Pink Triangles, 1982, Calling the Shots, 1982, 91, The Last Empire, 1986, Still Killing Us Softly, 1987, Hazardous Inheritance, 1991, Not Just a Job, 1991, Life's Work, 1993, Defending Our Lives, 1993 (Academy Award, Best Documentary Short Subject 1994). Recipient Silver Hugo award Chgo. Internat. Film Festival, 1972, Red Ribbon award Am. Film and Video Festival, 1983, 92, 1st Pl. award Nat. Coun. Family Rels. Film and Video Festival, 1984, 93, Blue Ribbon award Am. Film and Video Festival, 1986, 87, 91, Bronze Apple award Nat. Ednl. Film and Video Festival, 1988, 1st Pl. award Chicagoland Ednl. Film and Video Festival, 1988, Chris award Columbus Internat. Film Festival, PASS award Nat. Coun. Crime and Delinquency, 1993, Silver Apple award Nat. Ednl. Film and Video Festival, 1991, Cert. of Merit, AAAS, 1991, Silver placque Chgo. Internat. Film Festival, 1993, Outstanding Film of Yr. award New England Film and Video Festival, 1993, Exceptional Merit in Media award Nat. Women's Polit. Caucus, 1994. Avocation: electric cars. Office: Cambridge Documentary Films PO Box 385 Cambridge MA 02139

WUNDERMAN, JAN DARCOURT, artist; b. Winipeg, Man., Can., Jan. 22, 1921; d. Rene Paul and Georgette Marie (Guionet) Darcourt; m. Frank Joseph Malina, 1938 (div. 1945); m. Lester Wunderman (div. 1967); children: Marc, Geroge, Karen Renee. BFA, Otis Art Inst., L.A., 1942. One man show Easthampton Guild Hall, L.I., 1977; represented in numerous permanent pub., corp. and pvt. collections including Zimmerli Mus., Nat. Assn. of Women Artists, Rutgers U., 1994. Recipient Ohashi award Pan Pacific Exhbn., Tokyo and Osaka, 1962, Emily Lowe award 1965, J.J. Akston Found. prize, 1965, Canaday Meml. prize, 1979, Marian De Solo Mendes prize, 1981, Charles Horman Meml. prize, 1983, Amelia Peabody award Nat. Assn. Women, 1991, Grumbacher Gold medal of honor, 1992, Doris Kreindler award 1992. Mem. Nat. Assn. Women ARtists (medal of honor 1966, Marcia Brady Tucker award 1965, E. Holzinger prize 1966, Jane C. Stanley prize 1977, Marge Greenblatt award 1990, Amelia Peabody award 1991), Am. Soc. Contemporary Artists (corr. sec. 1977-78, Bocour award 1980, Elizabeth Erlanger Meml. award 1990, Kreindler award 1992), Contemporary Artists Guild. Avocations: music, tennis, skiing. Studio: 41 Union Sq W Rm 516 New York NY 10003-3208

WUNDERMAN, LESTER, advertising agency executive; b. N.Y.C., June 22, 1920; s. Harry and Dorothy (Horowitz) W.; m. Suzanne Oksman Cott, 1975; children: Marc, Karen. Student, Bklyn. Coll., 1936-38, New Sch. Social Research, 1952-55, Columbia U., 1957, 72-73; LHD (hon.), CUNY, 1984. Vice pres., then exec. v.p. Maxwell Sackheim & Co., Inc., N.Y.C., 1947-58; pres. Wunderman Worldwide, N.Y.C., 1958-77; chmn. Wunderman Cato Johnson, 1977—; exec. v.p. Young & Rubicam Inc., from 1975, dir., 1980—; lectr. to major trade groups worldwide, on creativity and mktg. NYU, New Sch. Social Research, Boston U., MIT; lectr. primitive art Columbia U., Bklyn. Mus., New Orleans Mus. Fine Arts; spl. researcher primitive art, Mali; Pres. Wunderman Found., 1962—; chmn. vis. com. Primitive Wing, Met. Mus. Art, N.Y.C., 1979—; lectr., adj. prof., chmn. ESSEC, Cergy-Pontoise, France, in the Lester Wunderman Chair, 1985-90; adj. prof. mktg. NYU, 1993—; founder Lester Wunderman Inst., Amsterdam, 1987—; founding chmn. Internat. Strategic Forum on Direct Mktg., 1985—; chmn. exec. com. for Direct Mktg., NYU, 1984—; dir. Dentsu Wunderman Direct, Tokyo, 1985—. Wunderman collection African art exhibited at 13 maj. mus., U.S., 1973-75 and at The Met. Mus. Art, N.Y.C., 1988, now in permanent collection at Met. Mus. Art, Musée Dapper, Paris; author: Frontiers of Direct Marketing, 1981; mem. editorial bd. Jour. Direct Mktg., Jour. Consumer Mktg., 1983—; contbr. articles on mktg. in major publs. worldwide. Trustee Internat. Ctr. of Photography; mem. adminstrv. coun. Internat. Fund for Promotion of Culture for UNESCO; bd. dirs. mem. exec. com. U.S. Com. for UNICEF, 1984-92; trustee Children's TV Workshop, 1986—. Named Mail Order Man of Yr. N.Y. Advt. Club, 1967, Direct Marketer of Yr., Direct Mktg. Day, 1982; named to Hall of Fame, Direct Mktg. Assn., 1983; Focus award Montreaux Symposium Direct Mktg., 1985. Mem. Am. Mktg. Assn. Advt. Agys. (past bd. dirs.), Direct Mktg. Assn. (bd. dirs. 1979-85), East Hampton Tennis Club (N.Y.C.), Town Tennis (N.Y.C.), Alta Delta Sigma. Home: 900 5th Ave New York NY 10021-4157 Office: Wunderman Cato Johnson 675 Avenue Of The Americas New York NY 10010-5100

WUNNICKE, BROOKE, lawyer; b. Dallas, May 9, 1918; d. Rudolph von Falkenstein and Lulu Lenore Brooke; m. James M. Wunnicke, Apr. 11, 1940; (dec. 1977); 1 child, Diane B. BA, Stanford U., 1939; JD, U. Colo., 1945. Bar: Wyo. 1946, U.S. Dist. Cty. Wyo. 1947, U.S. Supreme Ct. 1958, Colo. 1969. Pvt. practice law, 1946-56; ptnr. Williams & Wunnicke, Cheyenne, Wyo., 1956-69; of counsel Calkins, Kramer, Grimshaw & Harring, Denver, 1969-73; chief appellate dep. atty. Dist. Atty's Office, Denver, 1973-86; of

counsel Hall & Evans, Denver, 1986—; adj. prof. law U. Denver, 1978—; lectr. Internat. Practicum Inst. Denver, 1978—. Author: Ethics Compliance for Business Lawyers, 1987; co-author: Standby Letters of Credit, 1989, Supplement, 1994, Corporate Financial Risk Management, 1992, Legal Opinion Letters Formbook 1994, UCP 500 and Standby Letters of Credit-Special Report, 1994, How to Survive Derivatives, 1995; columnist Letters of Credit Report; contbd. articles to profl. jours. Pres. Laramie County Bar Assn., Cheyenne, Wy., 1967-68; Dir. Cheyenne C. of C., Cheyenne, Wy., 1965-68. Recipient awards for Outstanding Svc., Colo. Dist. Attys. Coun., 1979, 82, 86, Disting. Alumni award U. Colo. Sch. of Law, 1986, 93, Lathrop Trailblazer award Colo. Women's Bar Assn., 1992. Fellow Colo. Bar Found. (hon.); mem. ABA, Wyo. State Bar, Denver Bar Assn. (trustee 1977-80), Colo. Bar Assn., Am. Arbitration Assn. (nat. panel, regional panel large complex cases), William E. Doyle Inn of Ct. (hon.), Order of Coif, Phi Beta Kappa. Republican. Episcopalian. Avocations: reading, writing, teaching, lecturing. Office: Hall & Evans L L C 1200 17th St Denver CO 80202-5800

WUNSCH, CARL ISAAC, oceanographer, educator; b. Bklyn., May 5, 1941; s. Harry and Helen (Gellis) W.; m. Marjory Markel, June 6, 1970; children—Jared, Hannah. S.B., MIT, 1962, Ph.D., 1967. Asst. prof. phys. oceanography MIT, Cambridge, 1967-70; assoc. prof. MIT, 1970-75, prof., 1975-76, Cecil and Ida Green prof., 1976—; Sec. of Navy rsch. prof., 1985-89, head dept. earth and planetary scis., 1977-81; vis. fellow U. Cambridge, Eng., 1969, 74-75, 81-82; sr. vis. scientist geophys. Fluid Dynamics Lab., Princeton, 993-94; vis. rschr. CNES/CNRS, Toulouse, France, 1994; cons. NAA, NSF, NAS, JPL. Author: The Ocean Circulation Inverse Problem, 1995; co-author: Ocean Acoustic Tomography, 1995; assoc. editor Jour. Phys. Oceanography, 1977-80, Revs. of Geophysics and Space Physics, 1981-85; co-editor: Evolution of Physical Oceanography, 1981; editor Cambridge U. Press Monographs on Mechanics and Applied Mathematics, 1984-88; contbr. articles to profl. jours. Recipient Tex. Instruments Found. Founders prize, 1975, Huntsman prize Bedford Inst. Oceanography and Govt. of N.S., Can., 1988, Pub. Svc. medal NASA, 1993, Fulbright sr. scholar, 1981-82; Guggenheim fellow, 1981-82. Fellow Am. Geophys. Union (James R. Macelwane award 1971, Maurice Ewing medal 1990), Am. Meterol. Soc., Royal Astron Soc., Am. Acad. Arts and Scis.; mem. NAS (chmn. bd. ocean studies 1991-94), Soc. Indsl. and Applied Math., OCeanography Soc. Home: 75 Washington Ave Cambridge MA 02140-2708 Office: MIT Dept of Earth Atmospheric and Planetary Scis Cambridge MA 02139

WUNSCH, JAMES STEVENSON, political science educator; b. Detroit, Sept. 27, 1946; s. Richard Ellis and Jane Rolston (Stevenson) W.; m. Lillian C. Richards, Mar. 29, 1969 (div. Feb. 1983), 1 child, Kathryn; m. Mary Gayle Gundlach, Aug. 19, 1983; children: Hallie, Hannah. BA, Duke U., 1968; MA, Ind. U., 1971, PhD, 1974. Rsch. fellow U. Ghana, Accra, 1971-72; asst. prof. Creighton U., Omaha, 1974-78, assoc. prof., 1978-86, prof. polit. sci., 1986—, chmn. dept., 1983-93; social sci. analyst, cons. Ghana, Liberia, Kenya, Sudan, Thailand, Philippines, USAID, Washington, 1978-80; vis. assoc. prof. Ind. U., Bloomington, 1985-86; sr. project mgr. Assocs. in Rural Devel., Burlington, Vt., 1987-88, cons. Bangladesh, Zambia, Nigeria, 1985-94, South Africa, 1993. Author: The Failure of the Centralized State, 1990, (monograph) Rural Development, Decentralization and Administrative Reform, 1988; contbr. articles to profl. jours., chpts. to books. Bd. dirs. Omaha Symphony Chorus, 1977-78, Nebr. Choral Arts Soc., 1982-86, Voices of Omaha 1982-85, Trinity Cathedral, Omaha, 1980-83; participant Leadership Omaha, 1982-83; mem. Omaha Com. Fgn. Rels., 1975—; mem. govt. affairs com. Greater Omaha C. of C., 1980-85; mem. issues and interests com. Nebr. Rep. party, 1985-88. Recipient R.F. Kennedy Quality Tchg. award Creighton U., 1985, Burlington No. award, 1992, Dean's award for excellence in tchg., 1994; rsch. award NSF, NEH, USAID, USIA; Fulbright-Hays fellow in Ghana, 1971-72, Internat. Affairs fellow N.Y. Coun. Fgn. Rels., 1978-79. Mem. ASPA, Am. Polit. Sci. Assn., Midwest Polit. Sci. Assn., African Studies Assn., Internat. Studies Assn., Phi Beta Kappa, Pi Sigma Alpha, Phi Beta Delta. Republican. Episcopalian. Avocations: vocal music, camping, cross-country skiing. Home: 1631 N 53rd St Omaha NE 68104-4947 Office: Creighton U Dept Polit Sci 30th And California Omaha NE 68178

WUNTCH, PHILIP SAMUELS, journalist, film critic; b. Austin, Tex., Aug. 2, 1945; s. David and Lillian (Samuels) W.; m. Mimi West, Apr. 27, 1986. BA in Journalism, So. Meth. U., 1968. Journalist, entertainment writer Dallas Times Herald, 1968-69; entertainment writer Dallas Morning News, 1969-74, film critic, 1974—. Contbr. articles to World Book Year Book, 1981—. Avocation: constant reading. Office: Dallas Morning News PO Box 655237 Dallas TX 75265

WUORINEN, CHARLES P., composer; b. N.Y.C., June 9, 1938; s. John Henry and Alfhild (Kalijarvi) W. BA, Columbia U., 1961, MA, 1963; DMus (hon.), Jersey City State Coll., 1971. Lectr. Columbia U., 1964-65, instr., 1965-69, asst. prof., 1969-71, co-dir. Group Contemporary Music, 1962—; vis. lectr. Princeton U., 1967-68, New Eng. Conservatory, 1968-71, Yale U., 1983; adj. lectr. U. South Fla., 1971-72; faculty Manhattan Sch. Music, 1972-79, U. So. Calif., 1981; artistic dir., chmn. Am. Composers Orch., 1977-87; composer-in-residence Ojai Festival, 1975, Santa Fe Chamber Music Festival, 1993; San Francisco Symphony, 1984-89; condr. Cleve. Orch., 1976, Finnish Radio Orch., 1979, Helsinki Philharm., 1979; disting. prof. Rutgers U., 1984—; vis. prof. SUNY, Buffalo, 1989-94, NYU, 1990. Author: Simple Composition; mem. editorial bd. Perspectives of New Music; bd. mem. Composers Recs. Inc., 1962-89; composer numerous works including Music for Orchestra, 1956, Be Mery All That Be Present, mixed chorus, 1957, Concert for Four Trombones, 1960, Madrigale Spirituale, 1960, Turetzky Pieces, 1960, Evolutio: organ, 1961, Evolution Transcripta for chamber orch., 1961, Tiento Sobre Cabezon, 1961, Concert for Double Bass Alone, 1961, Trio No. 1 for flute, cello and piano, 1961, Invention for percussion quintet, 1962, Octet, 1962, Duuiensela for cello and piano, 1962, Bearbeitungen über das Glogauer Liederbuch, 1962, The Prayer of Jonah, 1962, 2d Flute Trio: Piece for Stefan Wolpe, 1962, Chamber Concerto for cello and 10 players, 1963, Piano Variations, 1963, Flute Variations, 1963, Composition for violin and 10 instruments, 1964, Chamber Concerto for flute and 10 players, 1964, Orchestral and Electronic Exchanges, 1965, Composition for oboe and piano, 1965, Chamber Concerto for oboe and 10 players, 1965, Super Salutem for male voices and instruments, 1964, Piano Concerto, 1966, The Bells for carillon, 1966, Bicinium, 2 oboes, 1966, Janissary Music for 1 percussionist, 1966, Harpsichord Divisions, 1966, Making Ends Meet for piano four-hands, 1966, John Bull: Salve Regina Versus Septem, 1966, Duo for violin and piano, 1967, The Politics of Harmony: A Masque, 1967, String Trio, 1968, Flute Variations II, 1968, Time's Encomium (electronic), 1969, Adapting to the Times for cello and piano, 1969, The Long and the Short for violin, 1969, Contrafactum for orch., 1969, Nature's Concord trumpet and piano, 1969, Piano Sonata, 1969, Ringing Changes for percussion, 1970, A Song, 1970, Tuba Concerto, 1970, A Message to Denmark Hill, 1970, Cello Variations, 1970, String Quartet, 1971, Canzona for 12 instruments, 1971, Grand Bamboula for string orch., 1971, Amplified Violin Concerto, 1972, Harp Variations, 1972, Bassoon Variations, 1972, Violin Variations, 1972, On Alligators for 8 instruments, 1972, Speculum Speculi for 6 players, 1972, Third Trio for flute, cello and piano, 1973, 12 Short Pieces for piano, 1973, Grand Union for cello and drums, 1973, Arabia Felix for 6 Instruments, 1973, Second Piano Concerto, 1974, Fantasia for violin and piano, 1974, Reliquary for Igor Stravinsky for orch., 1975, The W. of Babylon (opera), 1975, TASHI, 1975, Hyperion for 12 instruments, 1975, Cello Variations 2, 1975, 2d Piano Sonata, 1976, Percussion Symphony, 1976, The Winds, 1977, Fast Fantasy for cello and piano, 1977, Archangel for trombone and string quartet, 1977, Six Pieces for violin and piano, 1977, Six Songs for two voices, Wind Quintet, Self Similar Waltz for piano, Ancestors for chamber ensemble, 1978, Two-Part Symphony, 1978, Archaeonpteryx for bass trombone and chamber ensemble, 1978, The Magic Art, A Masque for chamber orch., 1979, Fortune for 4 instruments, 1979, 2d String Quartet, 1979, The Celestial Sphere for chorus and orch.; 1979, Psalm 39 for baritone and guitar, 1979, Percussion Duo, 1979, Joan's for 5 instruments, 1979, Blue Bamboula for piano, 1980, Capriccio for piano, 1981, Horn Trio, 1981, Short Suite for orch., 1981, Trio for bass instruments, 1981, New York Notes for 6 players, 1982, Mass, 1982, Divertimento for alto sax and piano, 1982, Divertimento for string quartet, 1982, Spinoff for violin, double bass and congas, 1983, Trio for violin, cello and piano, 1983, Third Piano Concerto, 1983, Rhapsody for violin and orch., 1984, Concertino, 1984, Crossfire for orch., 1984, Movers and Shakers for orch., 1984, Bamboula Squared for orch. and computer-generated sound, 1984, Natural Fantasy for organ, 1985, Horn Trio Continued, 1985, Trombone Trio, 1985, Prelude to Kullervo for tuba and orch., 1985, Double Solo for Horn Trio, 1985, Fanfare for the Houston Symphony, 1986, The Golden Dance for orch., 1986, Third Piano Sonata, 1986, Third String Quartet, 1987, Galliard for chamber orch., 1987, Bamboula Beach for orch., 1987, FIVE: Concerto for amplified cello and orch., 1987, Sonata for violin and piano, 1988, Bagatelle for piano, 1988, Ave Christe for piano, 1988, Another Happy Birthday for orch., 1988, Machault Mon Chou for orch., 1988, String Sextet, 1989, Twang for soprano and piano, 1989, A Solis Ortu for chorus, 1989, Genesis for chorus and orch., 1989, Astra for orch., 1990, Delight of the Muses for orch., 1991, Missa Brevis, 1991, A Winter's Tale for Soprano and Six Instruments, 1992, Microsymphony, 1992, Missa Renovata for Chorus and Orch., 1992, Saxophone Quartet, 1992, Concerto for Saxophone Quartet and Orch., 1993, The Mission of Virgil for orch., 1993, Percussion Quartet, 1994, Piano Quintet, 1994, Christes Crosse, 1994, Lightenings VIII, 1994, Guitar Variations, 1994. Recipient Philharmonic Young Composers award, 1954; Bennington Composers Conf. scholar, 1956-60; Bearns prize, 1958-59, 61; MacDowell Colony fellow, 1958; Alice M. Ditson fellow, 1959; Arthur Rose teaching fellow, 1960; Broadcast Music-Student Composers award, 1961, 62, 63; Lili Boulanger Meml. award, 1963; Festival fellow Santa Fe Opera, 1962; Festival fellow World's Fair Music and Sound, 1962; commd. by Koussevitzky Found., 1964, Berkshire Music Center, 1963, Fromm Found., 1963-71, Ford Found., 1962, Orch. of Am., 1958, Columbia U., 1956, Washington and Lee U., 1964, Fine Arts Quartet, 1969, Naumberg Found., 1971, U. South Fla., 1972, Nat. Opera Inst., 1973, Light Fantastic Players, 1973, N.Y. State Council on the Arts, 1974, N.Y. Philharm., 1974, Balt. Chamber Music Soc., 1974, Buffalo Philharm., 1974, Ojai Festival, 1974, Contemporary Chamber Ensemble, 1974, TASHI, 1974, Beethoven Festival, Bonn, 1978, Albany Symphony, 1981, San Francisco Symphony, 1984, 86, 88, 89, Cleve. Orch., 1984, Balt. Symphony, 1984, Houston Symphony, 1986, N.Y.C. Ballet, 1987, 90, Libr. of Congress, 1988, New World Symphony, 1987, Chamber Music Soc. Lincoln Ctr., 1989, 92, Am./ Soviet Youth Orch., 1990, Phila. Orch., 1992, Beethorenhalle Orch., Bonn Mönchengladbach and Ludwig Forum, Germany; grantee Nat. Inst. Arts and Letters, 1967, Nat. Endowment Arts, 1974, 76; Guggenheim fellow, 1968, 72; Ingraham Merrill fellow, 1972, Rockefeller Found. fellow, 1979, 80, 81, John D. and Catherine T. MacArthur fellow, 1986-91; recipient Pulitzer prize, 1970, Brandeis U. creative arts award, 1970, Creative Artists Pub. Svc. award, 1976; Arts and Letters award Finlandia Found., 1976, Koussevitzky Internat. Rec. award, 1970, 72. Mem. AAAS, Am. Soc. Univ. Composers, Am. Composers Alliance (dir.), Am. Music Ctr. (dir.), Internat. Soc. Contemporary Music (dir.), Am. Acad. and Inst. Arts and Letters, Phi Beta Kappa. Office: care Howard Stokar Mgmt 870 W End Ave New York NY 10025-4948

WURMFELD, SANFORD, artist, educator; b. N.Y.C., Dec. 6, 1942; s. Charles Jacob and Esther (Witzling) W.; m. Rella Stuart-Hunt, Dec. 11, 1971; children: Jeremy Philip, Treva. BA in Art with honors, Dartmouth Coll., 1964; ind. study, Rome, 1964-65. Lectr. Hunter Coll., N.Y.C., 1967-72, asst. prof., 1972-77, assoc. prof., 1977-80, chmn. dept. art, 1978—, prof. art, 1980—; vis. artist lectr. Calif. State Coll., Hayward, Cooper Union, N.Y., Bard Coll., Arondale-on-Hudson, N.Y., Livingston Coll., New Brunswick, N.J., 1973, SUNY, Fredonia, 1971, Drexel U., Phila., 1970, Whitney Mus., 1982, Met. Mus. Art, 1987, Princeton U., 1990, The Slade U. Coll., 1991, Chelsea Coll. Art, London, 1991. One man shows include Susan Caldwell Gallery, Inc., N.Y., 1978, Bard Coll. Invitational Exhibit, 1977, Susan Caldwell Gallery, 1976-77, Galarie Denise Rene, 1974, Rockefeller Meml. Gallery, Fredonia, N.Y., 1971, Tibor de Nagy Gallery, 1968, Bryant Park, N.Y., Fischbach Gallery, 1969; group shows include Mus. Modern Art, N.Y., 1968, Grank Palais, Paris, 1968, Kunsthaus, Zurich, 1968, Tate Gallery, London, 1968, Ft. Worth Art Ctr., 1969, Galerie de Gestlo, Kunstfair, Basel Switzerland, 1970, 72, Columbia Film Festival, 1973, Galerie Denise Rene, 1974, Hopkins Ctr. Galleries, 1974, Lehigh U., 1976, Susan Caldwell Gallery, 1977-79, Toni Birckhard Gallery, Cin., 1980, Carnegie Internat., 1983, others; represented in permanent collections at Met. Mus. Art., N.Y., Guggenheim Mus., N.Y., SUNY, Fredonia, Cen. Trust Co., Cin., Am. Telephone and Telegraph, N.Y., Baxter Travenol Labs., Deerfield, Ill., Gen. Electric Corp., Fairfield, Conn., Sprengler Mus., Hanover, Fed. Republic of Germany, City of Hannover, Fed. Republic of Germany, Shreve, Lamb, & Harmon Corp., N.Y., Silkscreeners Guild, W. Ger., Warner Nat. Corp., Cin., U.N.C. William Hayes Ackland Meml. Art Ctr., Chapel Hill, others; contbr. articles to profl. jours. Recipient Ames award Dartmouth Coll., 1964; fellow Guggenheim Found., 1974, Nat. Endowments for the Arts Individual Artist's, 1987-88; CUNY faculty rsch. grantee. Home: 18 Warren St New York NY 10007-1066 Office: Hunter Coll Dept Art 695 Park Ave New York NY 10021-5085

WÜRSIG, BERND GERHARD, marine biology educator; b. Barsinghausen, Hanover, Fed. Republic of Germany, Nov. 9, 1948; s. Gerhard Paul and Charlotte Annemarie (Yorkowski) W.; m. Melany Anne Carbalaira, Nov. 19, 1969; children: Kim, Paul. BS, Ohio State U., 1971; PhD, SUNY, Stony Brook, 1978. Postdoctoral researcher U. Calif., Santa Cruz, 1978-81; prof. Moss Landing (Calif.) Marine Labs., 1981-89; dir. Marine Mammal Lab. Tex. A&M U., Galveston, 1989—; govt. cons. Minerals Mgmt. Service, Washington, 1980—. Contbr. articles to profl. jours.; contbr. seven-part miniseries to TV on lives of dolphins, dolphin problems induced by humans, also Discovery Channel show on Life of B. Würsig. Recipient Dean's award for excellence in teaching, 1986, Alban-Heiser award for excellence in Tex. conservation rsch. Zool. Soc. Houston, 1991. Mem. Marine Mammal Soc. (pres. 1991-93), N.Y. Acad. Scis., Soc. Cryptozoology, Am. Behavior Soc., Am. Mus. Natural History, Soc. Archimedes. Club: Explorers (N.Y.C.) (fellow of research). Avocations: photography, diving, airplane piloting, skiing, hiking. Home: 2400 Taylor Ln Pearland TX 77581-5744 Office: Tex A&M U Marine Mammal Rsch Program 4700 Ave U Bldg 303 Galveston TX 77551

WURSTER, CHARLES FREDERICK, environmental scientist, educator; b. Phila., Aug. 1, 1930; s. Charles Frederick and Helen B. (Schmitberger) W.; m. Eva M. Tank-Nielsen, Aug. 26, 1970; children—Steven Hadley, Nina F., Erik Frederick. S.B., Haverford Coll., 1952; M.S., U. Del., 1954; Ph.D., Stanford U., 1957. Teaching asst. U. Del., 1952-54; research asst. Stanford U., 1954-57; Fulbright fellow Innsbruck, Austria, 1957-58; research chemist Monsanto Research Corp., 1959-62; research assoc. biol. scis. Dartmouth Coll., 1962-65; asst. prof. biol. scis. State U. N.Y. at Stony Brook, 1965-70; assoc. prof. environ. scis. Marine Scis. Research Center, 1970-94; vis. prof. Macquarie U., Sydney, Australia, 1988; founding trustee, sec., mem. exec. com. Environ. Def. Fund, Inc., 1967—; mem. adminstr's. pesticide policy adv. com. EPA, 1975-78. Contbr. numerous articles to profl. publs. Fellow AAAS; mem. Defenders of Wildlife (dir. 1975-84, 87—), Nat. Parks and Conservation Assn. (trustee 1970-79). Research on DDT, PCBs, other chlorinated hydrocarbons, effects on phytoplankton, birds; relationship between environmental sciences and public policy; instrumental in banning several insecticides, including DDT, Dieldrin and Aldrin. Ecol. tourism. Office: SUNY Marine Scis Research Ctr Stony Brook NY 11794-5000

WURSTER, DALE ERWIN, pharmacy educator, university dean emeritus; b. Sparta, Wis., Apr. 10, 1918; s. Edward Emil and Emma Sophia (Steingraeber) W.; m. June Margaret Peterson, June 16, 1944; children: Dale Eric, Susan Gay. BS, U. Wis., 1942, PhD, 1947. With faculty U. Wis. Sch. Pharmacy, 1947-71, prof., 1958-71; prof., dean N.D. State U. Coll. Pharmacy, 1971-72, U. Iowa Coll. Pharmacy, Iowa City, 1972-84, prof., 1972—, interim dean, 1991-92, dean emeritus, 1984—; George B. Kaufman Meml. lectr. Ohio State U., 1968; cons. in field; phys. scis. adminstr. U.S. Navy, 1960-63; sci. adv. Wis. Alumni Rsch. Found., 1968-72; mem. revision com. U.S. Pharmacopoeia, 1961-70, pharmacy rev. com. USPHS, 1966-72. Contbr. articles to profl. jours., chpts. to books; patentee in field. With USNR, 1944-46. Recipient Superior Achievement citation Navy Dept., 1964, merit citation U. Wis., 1976; named Hancher Finkbine Medallion Prof. U. Iowa, 1984; recipient Disting. Alumni award U. Wis. Sch. Pharmacy, 1984. Fellow Am. Assn. Pharm. Scientists (founder, sponsor Dale E. Wurster Rsch. award 1990—, Disting. Pharm. Sci. award 1991); mem. Am. Assn. Colls. Pharmacy (exec. com. 1964-66, chmn. conf. tchrs. 1960-61, vis. scientist 1963-70, recipient Disting. Educator award 1983), Acad. Pharm. Scis. (exec. com. 1967-70, chmn. basic pharmaceutics sect. 1965-67, pres. 1975, Indsl. Pharm. Tech. award 1980), Am. Pharm. Assn. (chmn. sci. sect. 1964-65, Rsch. Achievement award 1965), Wis. (Disting. Service award 1971),

Iowa Pharmacists Assn. (Robert G. Gibbs award 1983), Wis. Acad. Scis., Arts and Letters, Soc. Investigative Dermatology, Rumanian Soc. Med. Sci. (hon.), Am. Found. Pharm. Edn. (bd. grants 1987-92), Ea. Va. Med. Sch. Contraceptive Rsch. and Devel. Program (tech. adv. com. 1989—), Am. Assn. Pharm. Scientists (Disting. Scientist award 1991), Sigma Xi, Kappa Psi (past officer), Rho Chi, Phi Lambda Upsilon, Phi Sigma. Home: 16 Brickwood Knolls NE Iowa City IA 52240-9144

WURTELE, CHRISTOPHER ANGUS, paint and coatings company executive; b. Mpls., Aug. 25, 1934; Valentine and Charlotte (Lindley) W.; m. Heather Campbell (div. Feb. 1977); children: Christopher, Andrew, Heidi; m. Margaret Von Blon, Aug. 21, 1977. BA, Yale U., 1956; MBA, Stanford U., 1961. V.p. Minn. Paints, Inc. (merged with Valspar Corp. 1970), Mpls., 1962-65; exec. v.p., 1965, pres., CEO The Valspar Corp., Mpls., 1973—; dir. Gen. Mills Inc., Donaldson Co., Bemis Co., IDS Mutual Fund Group. Mem. adv. coun. Grad. Sch. Bus. Stanford U.; bd. dirs. Bush Found., Walker Art Ctr. With USN, 1956-59. Mem. Am. Bus. Conf., Mpls. Club, Nat. Paint & Coatings Assn. (bd. dirs.). Episcopalian. Home: 2409 E Lake Of The Isles Pky Minneapolis MN 55405 Office: Valspar Corp 1101 S 3rd St Minneapolis MN 55415-1211

WURTELE, MORTON GAITHER, meteorologist, educator; b. Harrodsburg, Ky., July 25, 1919; s. Edward Conrad and Emily Russell (Gaither) W.; m. Zivia Syrkin, Dec. 31, 1942; children—Eve Syrkin, Jonathan Syrkin. S.B., Harvard, 1940; M.A., UCLA, 1944, Ph.D., 1953. Asst. prof. meteorology Mass. Inst. Tech., Cambridge, 1953-58; asso. prof. meteorology U. Calif. at Los Angeles, 1958-64, prof., 1964—, chmn. dept., 1971-76; vis. prof. U. Buenos Aires, 1962, U. Jerusalem, 1965; cons. in field. Prin. contbr.: Glossary of Meteorology; co-editor: Progress in Desert Research; contbr. articles to profl. jours. Trustee Univ. Corp. for Atmospheric Rsch.; pres., dir. Sage Resources, Inc. With USNR, 1940-41. Fulbright grantee, 1949-50, 65; NATO sr. fellow, 1961-62. Fellow Am. Meteorol. Soc.; mem. Am. Profs. for Peace in Middle East (nat. exec. 1974—), Royal Meteorol. Soc., Am. Geophys. Union, Phi Beta Kappa, Sigma Xi. Club: Harvard So. Calif. Home: 432 E Rustic Rd Santa Monica CA 90402-1114 Office: UCLA Los Angeles CA 90024-1565

WURTMAN, JUDITH JOY, research scientist; b. Bklyn., Aug. 4, 1939; d. Alexander Mordecai and Jeanette Teicher Hirschhorn; m. Richard Jay Wurtman; children: Rachael, David. BA, Wellesely (Mass.) Coll., 1959; M in Biology Edn., Harvard U., 1960; PhD, George Washington U., 1973. Tchr. Malden Sch. System, 1959-60; rsch. asst. Microbiol. Assocs., Bethesda, Md., 1962-67; exhibit researcher Boston Mus. Sci., 1973-74; asst. prof. Newton (Mass.) Coll., 1974-76; postdoctoral fellow dept. nutrition MIT, Cambridge, 1976-78, rsch. scientist dept. nutrition, dept. brain and cognitive sci., 1987—; mem. scientific adv. bd. NutriSystem, Phila. 1988-89, Interneuron Pharms., Boston, 1989—; bd. dirs. Walden Labs. Author: Eating Your Way Through Life, 1979, The Carbohydrate Craver's Diet, 1983, The Carbohydrate Craver's Diet Cookbook, 1984, Managing Your Mind and Mood Through Food, 1987; editor: Nutrition and the Brain (8 vols.), 1983—. Mem. Am. Inst. Nutrition, Am. Dietitic Assn., Am. Soc. for Clin. Nutrition, Boston Soc. Psychiatry and Neurology, Soc. for Light Treatment and Biol. Rhythms, Sigma Xi (MIT chpt.). Office: MIT Dept of Brain and Cognitive Scis E25-604 Cambridge MA 02139

WURTMAN, RICHARD JAY, physician, educator; b. Phila., Mar. 9, 1939; s. Samuel Richard and Hilda (Schreiber) W.; m. Judith Joy Hirschhorn, Nov. 15, 1959; children: Rachael Elisabeth, David Franklin. A.B., U. Pa., 1956; M.D., Harvard U., 1960. Intern Mass. Gen. Hosp., 1960-61, resident, 1961-62, fellow medicine, 1965-66, clin. assoc. in medicine, 1985—; research associate, med. research officer NIMH, 1962-67; mem. faculty MIT, Cambridge, 1967—, prof. endocrinology and metabolism, 1970-80, prof. neuroendocrine regulation, 1980-84, Cecil H. Green disting. prof., 1994—; dir. Clin. Rsch. Ctr., MIT, Cambridge, 1985—; prof. neuroscience MIT, 1984-94, Cecil H. Green disting. prof., 1994—; lectr. medicine Harvard Med. Sch., 1969—; prof. Harvard-MIT Div. Health Scis. and Tech., 1978—; sci. dir. Ctr. for Brain Scis. and Metabolism Charitable Trust, 1981—; invited prof. U. Geneva, 1981; Sterling vis. prof. Boston U., 1981; mem. small grants study sect. NIMH, 1967-69, preclin. psychopharmacolgy study sect., 1971-75; behavioral biology adv. panel NASA, 1969-72; council basic sci. Am. Heart Assn., 1969-74; research adv. bd. Parkinson's Disease Found., 1972-80, Am. Parkinson's Disease Assn., 1978—; com. phototherapy in newborns NRC-Nat. Acad. Scis., 1972-74, com. nutrition, brain devel. and behavior, 1976, mem. space applications bd., 1976-82; mem. task force on drug devel. Muscular Dystrophy Assn., 1980-87; chmn. life scis. adv. com. NASA, 1979-82; mem. adv. bd. Alzheimer's Disease Assn., 1981-84; asso. neuroscis. research program MIT, 1974-82; chmn. life scis. adv. bd. USAF, 1985—; Bennett lectr. Am. Neurol. Assn., 1974; Flexner lectr. U. Pa., 1975; chmn. sci. adv. bd. Interneuron Pharms., 1989—; founder, chmn. sci. adv. bd. Interneuron Pharms. Inc., 1989—; Hans Lindler Meml. lectr. Weizmann Inst., 1993. Author: Catecholamines, 1966, (with others) The Pineal, 1968; editor: (with Judith Wurtman) Nutrition and the Brain, Vols. I and II, 1977, Vols. III, IV, V 1979, Vol. VI, 1983, Vol. VII, 1986; also articles; mem. editorial bd. Endocrinology, 1967-73, Jour. Pharmacology and Exptl. Therapeutics, 1968-75, Jour. Neural Transmission, 1969-88, Neuroendocrinology, 1969-72, Metabolism, 1970-80, Circulation Research, 1972-77, Jour. Neurochemistry, 1973-82, Life Scis., 1973-81, Brain Research, 1977—. Holder of approximately 40 U.S. patents on new treatments for diseases and conditions. Recipient Alvarenga prize and lectureship Phila. Coll. Physicians, 1970, CIBA-Geigy Drew award in Biomed. Research, 1982, Roger Williams award in Preventative Nutrition, 1987, Roger J. Williams award in Preventive Medicine, 1989, NIMH Merit award, 1989—, Internat. Prize for Modern Nutrition, 1989, Hall of Fame Disting. Alumni award Ctrl. High Sch. Phila., 1992; Disting. lectr. Purdue U., 1984; Rufus Cole lectr. Rockefeller U. 1985; Pfizer lectr. NYU Med. Sch., 1985; Grass Fedn. lectr. U. Ga., 1985, Alan Rothballer Meml. lectr., N.Y. Med. Coll., Valhalla, N.Y., 1989, Gretchen Kerr Green lectr. in the neurosciences, 1989; Chevalier de Malte, Order of the Knights of Malta, 1987; Wellcome Vis. Prof. Washington State U., Pullman, 1989; Julius Axelrod Disting. lectr. in neurosci., CUNY, 1990, Sigma Tau Found. lectr. on aging, Rome, 1990, Disting. lectr. in neurosci., La. State U., 1991, McEwen lectr. Queen's U., Ont., 1991; Plenary lectr. 3d Internat. Symposium on Microdialysis, 1993; Hans Lindner Meml. lectr. Weizmann Inst., 1993. Mem. Am. Soc. Clin. Investigation, Endocrine Soc. (Ernst Oppenheim award 1972), Am. Physiol. Soc., Am. Soc. Biol. Chemists, Am. Soc. Pharmacology and Exptl. Therapeutics (John Jacob Abel award 1968), Am. Soc. Neurochemistry, Soc. Neuroscis., Am. Soc. Clin. Nutrition, Am. Inst. Nutrition (Osborne & Mendel award 1982). Club: Harvard (Boston). Home: 300 Boylston St Boston MA 02116-3923 Office: Mass Inst Tech E25-604 45 Carlton St Cambridge MA 02142

WURTZ, ROBERT HENRY, physiologist, scientist; b. St. Louis, Mar. 28, 1936; s. Robert Henry and Alice Edith (Popplwell) W.; m. Sally Smith, Dec. 20, 1958 (div.); children: William, Erica; m. Emily Otis, Apr. 23, 1983. AB, Oberlin Coll., 1958; PhD, U. Mich., 1962. Rsch. assoc. Ctr. for Nuclear Info., St. Louis, 1962-63; fellow Sch. Medicine, Washington U., 1962-65; rsch. biophysicist NIH, Bethesda, Md., 1965-66, physiologist, 1966-78, chief lab. sensorimotor rsch., 1978—; vis. scientist Cambridge U., Eng., 1975-76. Editor: Neurobiology of Saccadic Eye Movement, 1989. Fellow AAAS; mem. NAS, Am. Acad. Arts and Scis., Soc. Neurosci. (pres. 1991), Am. Physiol. Soc., Assn. for Rsch. in Vision and Opthalmology, Soc. Exptl. Psychologists. Office: 9000 Rockville Pike Bethesda MD 20892-0001

WURTZEL, ALAN LEON, retail company executive; b. Mount Vernon, N.Y., Sept. 23, 1933; s. Samuel S. and Ruth (Mann) W.; m. Irene C. Rosenberg, Oct. 9, 1988; children from previous marriage: Judith Halle, Daniel Henry, Sharon Lee. AB, Oberlin Coll., 1955; postgrad., London Sch. Econ., 1955-56; LLB cum laude, Yale, 1959. Bar: Conn. 1959, D.C. 1960, Va. 1968. Law clk. Chief Judge David L. Bazelon, U.S. Ct. Appeals, D.C. 1959-60; assoc. Fried, Frank, Harris, Shriver & Kampelman, Washington, 1960-65; legisl. asst. to Senator Joseph Tydings, 1965-66; with Cir. City Stores, Inc. (formerly Wards Co., Inc.), Richmond, 1966—, v.p., 1968-70, pres., 1970-83, chief exec. officer, 1973-86, chmn., 1983—; pres. NATM Buying Corp., 1978-86; pres. Operation Independence, 1987-88; bd. dirs. Office Depot, Inc., Boca Raton, Fla., Nat. Alliance of Bus., Washington; mem. Nat. Skills Standards Bd. Bd. visitors Va. Commonwealth Ednl. U., 1985-92; trustee Oberlin Coll.; dir. Washington Ednl. Television Assn.; pres.

Jewish Community Fedn., Richmond, 1983-85. Mem. Va. State Bd. Edn., Gov.'s Econ. Adv. Coun. Office: 2134 R St NW Washington DC 20008-1907 Office: Cir City Stores Inc 9950 Mayland Dr Richmond VA 23233-1463

WURZBURG, RICHARD JOSEPH, health insurance executive; b. Chicago, Ill., Mar. 12, 1947; s. Max and Babette (Strasburger) W.; m. Ruth Lea Goldhaber, Apr. 8, 1979; children: Jeffrey Joseph, Robert Ian. BJ, U. Mo., 1970; MBA, U. Pa., 1972. Comml. banking asst. 1st Nat. Bank Chgo./ Continental Ill. Nat. Bank Chgo., 1972-75; sr. product mgr. Citicorp Subs., St. Louis, 1975-77; v.p. CNA Health Plans, chgo., 1977-82; exec. v.p. Bank Adminstrn. Inst., Rolling Meadows, Ill., 1982-85; sr. v.p. 1st Fed. Savs. and Loan, Rochester, N.Y., 1985-86; pres., CEO Partners Health Plan, South Bend, Ind., 1986-94; chmn. Partners Health Adminstrs., Inc., South Bend, 1992-94; pres. Michiana Healthnet, South Bend, 1994; COO N.Am. Med. Mgmt. Tex., Houston, 1995—. Trustee Temple Beth-El, South Bend, 1990-95, chmn. endowment comm., 1990-95; v.p. St. Joseph Valley Jewish Fedn., 1994-95; mem. adv. bd. Jr. League, 1992-95. Mem. Knollwood Country Club, Summit Club (bd. dirs. 1993-95), St. Joseph Valley Jewish Fedn. (dir. 1993-95). Avocations: golf, reading. Office: NAm Med Mgmt Tex 1235 N Loop W Ste 450 Houston TX 77008

WURZBURGER, WALTER SAMUEL, rabbi, philosophy educator; b. Munich, Germany, Mar. 29, 1920; s. Adolf W. and Hedwig (Tannenwald) W.; m. Naomi C. Rabinovitz, Aug. 19, 1947; children—Benjamin W., Myron I., Joshua J. BA, Yeshiva U., 1944, DD (hon.), 1987; MA, Harvard U., 1946, PhD, 1951. Ordained rabbi, 1944. Rabbi Congregation Chai Odom, Boston, 1944-53, Shaarei Shomayim Congregation, Toronto, Ont., Can., 1953-67; rabbi Shaaray Tefila Congregation, Lawrence, N.Y., 1967-94, Rabbi emeritus, 1994—; editor Tradition, N.Y.C., 1961-87; columnist Toronto Telegram, 1957-67; adj. assoc. prof. philosophy Yeshiva U., 1967-80, adj. prof., 1980—. Author: Ethics of Responsibility, 1994; editor: A Treasury of Tradition, 1967; contbg. editor Sh'ma; contbr. articles to profl. jours., chpts. to books, Ency. Judaica, Ency. of Religion, Ency. of Bioethics. Mem. exec. com. United Jewish Welfare Funds of Toronto, 1965-67; past chmn. commn. on adoptions, synagogue commn., trustee Fedn. Jewish Philanthropies N.Y.; bd. dirs. Union Orthodox Jewish Congregations Am.; chmn. com. on interreligious affairs Synagogue Coun. Am., 1973-75, 83-87, pres., 1981-83, hon. pres., 1983-85; mem. interfaith com. United Community Funds of Toronto, 1960-67; v.p. synagogue commn. Fedn. Philanthropies, 1973-75; mem. nat. adv. com. United Jewish Appeal Am., 1971-78. Recipient Nat. Rabbinic Leadership award Union Orthodox Jewish Congregations Am., 1983, Samuel Belkin Lit. award Yeshiva Coll. Alumni Assn., 1994. Mem. Rabbinical Coun. Am. (past pres.), Rabbinical Coun. Can. (past pres.). Home: 138 Hards Ln Lawrence NY 11559-1315

WURZEL, LEONARD, retired candy manufacturing company executive; b. Phila., Feb. 4, 1918; s. Maurice L. and Dora (Goldberg) W.; m. Elaine Cohen, Aug. 18, 1949; children—Mark L., Lawrence J. B.S., Washington and Jefferson Coll., 1939; M.B.A., Harvard, 1941. With Loft Candy Corp., Long Island City, N.Y., 1946-64; v.p. Loft Candy Corp., 1949-56, exec. v.p., 1956-57, pres., 1957-64, dir., 1949-64; chmn., dir. Calico Cottage Candies, Inc., 1964-94; ret., 1994; mayor Village of Sands Point, N.Y., 1989—. Capt. Adj. Gen.'s Dept., AUS, 1941-46. Decorated Bronze Star. Mem. Assn. Mfrs. Confectionery and Chocolate (bd. dirs., past pres., chmn.), Candy Chocolate and Confectionery Inst. (bd. dirs., treas.), Retail Confectioners Internat. (bd. dirs., past pres.). Home: 25 Woodland Dr Sands Point NY 11050-1136 Office: 393 Sagamore Ave Mineola NY 11501-1919

WURZEL, MARY V., past association executive; b. Newport, R.I., July 17, 1918; d. William James and Mary Josephine (Dennis) Veach; m. Edward Milton Wurzel, Sept. 2, 1945; children: William D., David L., Edward Michael, Donald J., James D. BA, Brown U., 1939. Pres. Ex-Ptnrs. of Servicemen/Women for Equality, Alexandria, Va., 1984-90, 92-94. Docent Kennedy Ctr.; alumni chair Brown U., Providence, R.I.; Navy Arlington Lady. Home: 203 Yoakum Pkwy # 903 Alexandria VA 22304-3723

WUSSLER, ROBERT JOSEPH, broadcasting executive, media consultant; b. Newark, Sept. 8, 1936; s. Walter and Anna (MacDonald) W.; children: Robert Joseph, Rosemary, Sally, Stefanie, Christopher, Jeanne. BA in Communication Arts, Seton Hall U., 1957, LLD (hon.), 1978; LLD (hon.), Emerson Coll., 1976. With CBS News, N.Y.C., 1957-72; v.p., gen. mgr. Sta. WBBM-TV, Chgo., 1972-74; v.p. CBS Sports, N.Y.C., 1974-76, pres., 1977-78; pres. Sta. CBS-TV, N.Y.C., 1976-77, Pyramid Enterprises Ltd., N.Y.C., 1978-80; exec. v.p. Turner Broadcasting System Inc., Atlanta, 1980-87, sr. exec. v.p., from 1987, bd. dirs.; pres. Atlanta Sports Teams, Inc., 1981-87; pres., chief exec. officer COMSAT Video Enterprises, Inc., Washington, 1989-92, ret., 1992; pres. Wussler Group, 1992—; bd. dirs. Nat. Acad. TV Arts and Scis., 1986-90; bd. dirs. Atlanta Hawks Ltd., Atlanta Braves Nat. League Baseball Club, Inc.; co-owner Denver Nuggets, NBA, 1989-92. Bd. regents Seton Hall U., 1978-84; trustee Marymount Manhattan Coll. 1977-81. Recipient Emmy awards, numerous other nat. and internat. news and sports awards. Mem. Dirs. Guild Am., Internat. Radio and TV Soc., Ariz. Heart Inst., Cable Advt. Bur., Nat. Cable TV Assn. (satellite network com.), European Broadcasting Union. Roman Catholic.

WUST, CARL JOHN, microbiology and medical biology educator; b. Providence, R.I., July 2, 1928; s. Louis August and Ida (Jauernig) W.; m. Barbara Marion Russin, Sept. 5, 1951 (dec.); children: Carl John, Stephen Louis, Catherine Joanne, Gregory Harold, Elizabeth Diane. BS, Providence Coll., 1950; MS, Brown U., 1953; PhD, Indiana U., 1957. Ordained deacon Roman Cath. Ch. Post-doctoral fellow Yale U., New Haven, Conn., 1957-59; biologist, biochemist Oak Ridge (Tenn.) Nat. Lab., 1959-70; assoc. prof. U. Tenn., Knoxville, Tenn., 1970-74; prof. of Microbiology U. Tenn., Knoxville, 1974—; prof. med. biology, prof. emeritus, 1994—. Contbr. articles to profl. jours. Mem. Am. Assn. Immunologists, Am. Soc. for Microbiology, Soc. for Fractl. Biology& Medicine, K.C., Sigma Xi. Roman Catholic. Home: 132 Iroquois Rd Oak Ridge TN 37830-4934 Office: U Tenn Dept Microbiology Knoxville TN 37996

WUTHNOW, ROBERT, sociology educator; b. Sterling, Kans., June 23, 1946; s. Victor Robert and Kathryn Clare (Huey) W.; m. Sara Margery Wilcox, June 15, 1968; children—Robyn Elizabeth, Kathryn Brooke, Joel Robert. B.S., U. Kans., 1968; Ph.D., U. Calif., Berkeley, 1975. Instr. U. Ariz., Tucson, 1974-76; asst. prof. Princeton (N.J.) U., 1976-79, assoc. prof., 1979-84, prof. sociology, 1984-92, Gerhard R. Audlinger prof. social scis., 1992—; bd. trustees Princeton U. Press, 1985-89; bd. advisors Princeton Religion Research Ctr., 1979—; cons. Gallup Orgn., 1980—. Author: The Consciousness Reformation, 1976, Experimentation in American Religion, 1978, Meaning and Moral Order, 1987, The Restructuring of American Religion, 1988, The Struggle for America's Soul, 1989, Communities of Discourse, 1989, Acts of Compassion, 1991, Rediscovering the Sacred, 1992, Christianity in the 21st Century, 1993, Sharing the Journey, 1993, Producing the Sacred, 1993, God and Mammon in America, 1994, Learning to Care, 1995; co-author: Adolescent Prejudice, 1975, Cultural Analysis, 1984. Spl. career fellow Ford Found., 1969-72; William Paterson preceptor Princeton U., 1976-79. Mem. Am. Sociol. Assn., Soc. for Sci. Study of Religion (exec. council 1979-80). Home: 4 Highland Rd Princeton NJ 08540-4710 Office: Princeton U Dept Sociology 2N2 Green Hall Princeton NJ 08544

WYAND, MARTIN JUDD, economics educator, retired military officer; b. Greenwich, Conn., May 28, 1931; s. Charles Samuel and Marian (Winter) W.; m. Margaret Alison Knox, May 26, 1974. BA in Social Sci., Pa. State U., 1953, MA in Econs., 1954; JD in Law, U. Denver, 1969; PhD Econs., U. Ill., 1964. Graduate teaching asst. Pa. State U., Univ. Park, 1953-54; grad. teaching asst. U. Ill., Urbana, 1960-64; from asst. prof. to prof. U. Denver, 1964-82; adj. prof. econs. Metro State Coll., Denver, 1982-84; adj. prof. Coll. Bus. Adminstrn., U. Colo. Denver, 1984-90; lectr. Coll. Bus. Adminstrn., Pa. State U., 1990—; instr. Armed Forces Intelligence Trng. Ctr. 1974-76. Contbr. articles to profl. jours. Adminstrv. bd. dirs. Washington Park Meth. Ch., Denver, 1977-85. Served to col. USAFR, 1953-83, ret. 1991. Grantee Shell Oil Co., 1966, U. Denver, 1976. Mem. Am. Econ. Assn., Am. Collegiate Sch. Bus., Rocky Mountain Social Sci. Assn., Res. Officers Assn. (pres. Geddes chpt. 1978-82, etc.), Ret. Officers Assn., Air Force Assn., Alpha Kappa Psi, Pi Gamma Mu, Alpha Phi Omega. Avocations: reading, chess, classical music, swimming. Home: 1066 Crabapple Dr State College PA 16801-4252 Office: Pa State U 427 Beam Bldg University Park PA 16802

WYANT, CORBIN A., newspaper publisher; m. Donna Lee Humphrey, Oct. 5, 1963; children: Mrs. Blair Milliken, Corbin W., Beth Ashley. BA, Bucknell U., 1958; student Grad. Sch. Journalism, Pa. State U., 1973-74. Reporter/photographer Daily Leader-Times, Kittanning, Pa., 1958-69, advt. sales rep., circulation mgr., 1960-61, co-pub., gen. mgr., 1961-73; pres. Daily Dispatch, Douglas, Ariz., 1965-73; pub. Daily Herald News, Punta Gorda, Fla., 1974-76; v.p., gen. mgr. Naples (Fla.) Daily News, 1977-85, pub., 1985—, pres., 1986—. Former treas. and founder Mental Health Clinic Armstrong County, Pa.; former bd. dirs. Mental Health and Mental Retardation Assn. Armstrong and Ind. Counties, Med. Ctr. Hosp., Punta Gorda, Fla.; former chmn. Armstrong County Airport Authority; former v.p., building chmn. YMCA Charlotte County; elder First Presbyn. Ch., Naples, Fla.; asst. coach Babe Ruth Baseball, Naples, 1983; coach Little League, Naples, 1979; bd. dirs. Naples/Marco (Fla.) Philharm., Inc., 1987—; Community Concert Assn., 1978-84; mem. adv. bd. Salvation Army, Naples, 1987—; v.p. Collier Cultural Ctr., Inc., 1978-82, YMCA Collier County, 1977-87. Mem. Fla. Press Assn. (bd. dirs. 1986-92, pres. 1993-94, chmn. 1994-95), Fla. Newspaper Advt. Network (founder, bd. dirs. 1987—), Gulf Coast Sailing Assn., Collier Athletic Club, Forum Club, Collier Country Club (pres. 1988-89), Rotary (pres. Naples 1982-83). Office: Naples Daily News 1075 Central Ave Naples FL 33940-6295

WYATT, DORIS FAY CHAPMAN, English language educator; b. Del Rio, Tex., July 12, 1935; d. Cecil Cornelius and Lola Wade (Veazey) Chapman; m. Jimmy Trueman Wyatt, June 2, 1956 (div. Nov. 1977); children: Abra Natasha Smith, Garret Colin Wyatt, Garrett Bret Wyatt. BS in Edn., S.W. Tex. State U., 1956; MA in English, U. North Tex., 1969; MA in Counseling, East Tenn. State U., 1983. Cert. profl. tchr. career ladder III, Tenn.; cert. marriage and family therapist. Elem. tchr. Clover Pk. Pub. Schs., Tacoma, 1957-58; jr. high reading tchr. Levelland (Tex.) Pub. Schs., 1964-67; tchr. English Denton (Tex.) Pub. Schs., 1967-70; tchr. reading & English Vets. Upward Bound, East Tenn. State U., Johnson City, 1981-87; tchr. English Johnson City (Tenn.) Pub. Schs., 1970—; beauty cons. Mary Kay Cosmetics, Johnson City, 1971—; adj. faculty mem. Tusculum Coll., Greeneville, Tenn., 1993—; pine plantation owner. Area dir. People-to-People Student Ambassador Program, Washington County, Tenn., 1975-94, tchr.-leader, Johnson City, 1974-84. Named to Nat. Dean's list, 1982-83. Mem. NEA, AAUW, Johnson City Edn. Assn. (pres., bd. dirs. 1989-90), Tenn. Edn. Assn., Nat. Coun. Tchrs. English, Assembly on Lit. for Adolescents, Alpha Delta Kappa (pres. 1994-95), Phi Kappa Phi. Democrat. Methodist. Avocations: people, travel, photography, reading. Home: 1805 Sundale Rd Johnson City TN 37604-3023 Office: Johnson City Pub Schs Sci Hill High Sch John Exum Pky Johnson City TN 37604-4553

WYATT, FOREST KENT, university president; b. Berea, Ky., May 27, 1934; s. Forest E. and Almeda (Hymer) W.; m. Janice Collins, Mar. 4, 1956; children: Tara Janice Wyatt Mounger, Elizabeth Pharr Wyatt Mitchell. BS in Edn., Delta State U., Cleveland, Miss., 1956; MEd, U. So. Miss., 1960; EdD, U. Miss., 1970; postgrad., Harvard Inst. Ednl. Mgmt., 1975. Instr., coach Univ. Mil. Sch., Mobile, Ala., 1956-60; tchr., adminstr. Bolivar County dist. schs., Cleveland, Miss., 1960-64; alumni sec. Delta State U., 1964-69, adminstrv. asst. to pres., dir. adminstrv. services, asso. prof. edn., 1969-75, pres., 1975—; dir. Grenada Bank. Contbr. articles to profl. jours. Past bd. dirs. United Givers Fund, Cleveland Beautification Commn.; past bd. dirs., past v.p. Miss. Com. for Humanities, Delta Area coun. Boy Scouts Am. Friends of State Libr. Commn.; past chmn. Indsl. Devel. Found.; past pres. Cleveland Crosstie Arts Coun.; past trustee So. Bapt. Theol. Sem.; past bd. dirs. Miss. Econ. Coun.; past pres. Gulf South Conf.; bd. dirs. Southeastern Regional Vision for Edn. With U.S. Army, 1957-58. Recipient Kossman award for Outstanding Community Svc. C. of C., 1987. Mem. Miss. Assn. Educators, Am. Coun. on Edn. (mem. com. on govtl. rels.), Am. Coun. on Tchrs. Edn., Miss. Assn. Sch. Adminstrs., Am. Assn. State Colls. and Univs. (chmn. athletic com., com. governance, com. profl. devel. task force on athletics), NCAA (coun., past chmn. student-athlete adv. com., pres's. commn., gender equity com., exec. dir. search com., chmn. athletics cert. study com. divsn. II), Miss. Assn. Colls. (past pres.), So. Assn. Colls. and Schs. (Commn. on Colls.), Inter-Alumni Coun., Cleve. C. of C. (past pres.), Cleve. Country Club (dir.), Lions, Phi Delta Kappa, Omicron Delta Kappa, Kappa Delta Pi. Address: Delta State U Cleveland MS 38733

WYATT, GERARD ROBERT, biology educator, researcher; b. Palo Alto, Calif., Sept. 3, 1925; came to Can., 1935; s. Horace Graham and Mary Aimee (Strickland) W.; m. Sarah Silver Morton, Dec. 19, 1951 (dec. Mar. 1981); children—Eve Morton, Graham Strickland, Diana Silver; m. Mary Evelyn Rogers, Mar. 16, 1985. B.A., U. B.C., 1945; postgrad, U. Calif.-Berkeley, 1946-47; Ph.D., Cambridge U., 1950. Research scientist Can. Dept. Agr., Sault Ste. Marie, Ont., 1950-54; asst. prof. biochemistry Yale U., New Haven, 1954-60, assoc. prof., 1960-73; prof. biology Queen's U., Kingston, Ont., 1973-94, prof. emeritus, 1994—; sci. dir. Insect Biotech Can., 1990-93. Contbr. articles to profl. jours. Guggenheim fellow, 1956; Killam Research fellow, 1985. Fellow Royal Soc. Can.; mem. Can. Soc. Cell Biology, Am. Entomol. Soc. Avocation: natural history. Home: 114 Earl St, Kingston, ON Canada K7L 2H1 Office: Queen's Univ, Dept Biology, Kingston, ON Canada K7L 3N6

WYATT, JAMES FRANK, JR., lawyer; b. Talladega, Ala., Dec. 1, 1922; s. James Frank and Nannie Lee (Heaslett) W.; m. Rosemary Barbara Slone, Dec. 21, 1951; children: Martha Lee, James Frank III. B.S., Auburn U., 1943; J.D., Georgetown U., 1949, postgrad., 1950. Bar: D.C. 1949, Ala. 1950, Ill. 1953, U.S. Supreme Ct 1953. Atty. Office Chief Counsel, IRS, 1949-51; tax counsel Universal Oil Products Co., Des Plaines, Ill., 1951-63; asst. treas. Universal Oil Products Co., 1963-66, v.p. fin., treas., 1966-75; treas. CF Industries, Inc., Long Grove, Ill., 1976-78; v.p. fin., treas. CF Industries, Inc., 1978-82; assoc. Tenney & Bentley, 1983-85, Arnstein, Gluck, Lehr, Barron & Milligan, 1985-88; pvt. practice, 1989—; dir. 1st Nat. Bank, Des Plaines. Village trustee, Barrington, Ill., 1963-75; bd. dirs. Buehler YMCA, Barrington Twp. Republican Orgn., 1962—; Barrington Area Rep. Workshops, 1962-63. Served to capt., Judge Adv. Gen. Corps AUS, 1944-47. Mem. Tax Execs. Inst. (v.p. 1966-66, chpt. pres. 1961-62), Fed. Am., Chgo. bar assns., Barrington Home Owners Assn. (pres. 1960-61), Newcomen Sco., Assn. U.S. Army, Scabbard and Blade, Phi Delta Phi, Sigma Chi. Episcopalian. Clubs: Barrington Hills Country; Economics, University (Chgo.). Home: 625 Concord Pl Barrington IL 60010-4508 Office: 200 Applebee St Barrington IL 60010-3063

WYATT, JAMES FRANKLIN, librarian; b. Mullins, W.Va., July 4, 1934; s. Lennie V. and Fannie A. (Brown) W.; m. Mary Walters, July 26, 1955; 1 child, Whitney Brown. B.A., U. Richmond, 1956; postgrad., Colgate Rochester Div. Sch., 1956-57, 63-65; M.S., U. N.C.-Chapel Hill, 1966; Ph.D., Fla. State U., 1973. Dir. library Mars Hill Coll., N.C. 1966-73; dean libraries U. Ala., Tuscaloosa, 1973-80; dir. libraries U. Rochester, N.Y., 1980—; bd. govs. Research Libraries Group, Palo Alto, Calif., 1984-89. Bd. overseers Am. Baptist Hist. Soc., Rochester, 1984-86. Served to lt. USCG, 1958-63. Higher Edn. Act fellow, 1970-73. Mem. ALA, Assn. Coll. and Research Libraries, Assn. Research Libraries (bd. dirs. 1978-81). Democrat. Baptist. Avocations: music; skiing; tennis. Home: 155 Danbury Cir N Rochester NY 14618-2717 Office: U Rochester Rush Rhees Library Rochester NY 14627

WYATT, JAMES LUTHER, drapery hardware company executive; b. Williamsburg, Ky., May 13, 1924; s. Jesse Luther and Grace Edwina (Little) W.; m. Barbara Christman, Aug. 28, 1946; children—Linda Lou, William Charles Christman (dec.). B.S., U. Ky., 1947, M.S., 1948; Sc.D., Mass. Inst. Tech., 1952. Registered profl. engr., Ohio, Pa. Devel. engr. titanium div. Nat. Lead Co., Sayreville, N.J., 1948-50; tech. mgr., head, dept. metall. engrng., mgr. new products Horizons, Inc., Cleve., 1953-57; cons. asso. Booz, Allen & Hamilton, N.Y.C., 1957-61; v.p. program devel. Armour Research Found., Chgo., 1961-63; v.p. new product devel. Joy Mfg. Co., Pitts., 1963-67; v.p. corp. devel. Nat. Gypsum Co., Buffalo, 1967-69, Max Factor & Co., Hollywood, Calif., 1969-71; pres. Wyatt & Co., 1971—, Jimbabs, Inc., 1983—. Ambassador Industries, Inc. Los Angeles, 1988—; U.S. del. 1st World Metall. Congress. Contbr. tech., mgmt. papers to profl. lit. Mem. Pompano Beach Power Squadronm, adminstr. officer, 1991, exec.

officer, 1992, comdr., 1993; chmn. bd. trustees Meth. Ch., 1992, mem. fin. com., 1993, mem. adminstrv. bd. Lt. col. USAAF, 1942-46. Mem. AIME, Am. Soc. Metals, Sigma Phi Epsilon, Alpha Chi Sigma. Clubs: Econs. (Chgo.), Execs. (Chgo.); Univ. (N.Y.C.); Calif. Yacht. Patentee in field. Home: 510 NE Golden Harbour Dr Boca Raton FL 33432-2942 Office: Bunker Hill Towers 800 W 1st St Unit 507 Los Angeles CA 90012

WYATT, JOE BILLY, university chancellor; b. Tyler, Tex., July 21, 1935; s. Joe and Fay (Pinkerton) W.; m. Faye Hocutt, July 21, 1956; children: Joseph Robert, Sandra Faye. B.A., U. Tex., 1956; M.A., Tex. Christian U., 1960. Systems engr. Gen. Dynamics Corp., 1956-65; mgr. Digital Computer Lab., 1961-65; dir. computer ctr., assoc. prof. computer sci. U. Houston, 1965-72; dir. Office Info. Tech. Harvard U., 1972-76, sr. lectr. computer sci., 1972-82, v.p. adminstrn., 1976-82; chancellor Vanderbilt U., Nashville, 1982—; mem. faculty Kennedy Sch. of Harvard U., 1976-82; bd. dirs., chmn. com. on math/sci., Am. Coun. of Edn.; bd. dirs. Reynolds Metals Co., Advanced Networking and Sys. Corp. Author (with others) Financial Planning Models for Colleges and Universities, 1979; editor-in chief: Jour. Applied Mgmt. Systems, 1983; contbr. articles to profl. jours.; patentee in field of data processing. Trustee Harvard U. Press, 1976-83, pres., 1975-76, chmn. bd., 1976-79; trustee EDUCOM, Princeton, N.J., 1973-81, Leadership Nashville, 1983-93; bd. dirs. Nashville Inst. Arts, 1982-83, Ingram Industries, 1990—; chmn. adv. com. IST, NSF, 1978-85; vice chmn. bd. Mass. Tech. Devel. Corp., Boston, 1977-83; mem. Coun. Competitiveness; fellow Gallaudet Coll., 1981-83; mem. alumni bd. dirs. Harvard Bus. Sch., 1982-92. Recipient award for exemplary leadership CAUSE, Hilton Head, S.C., 1982, Nat. Tree of Life award Jewish Nat. Fund, 1988; named Outstanding Tennessean Gov. of Tenn., 1986. Fellow AAAS; mem. IEEE, Assn. Am. Univs. (chair exec. com. 1990-91), Hosp. Corp. Am. (bd. dirs. 1984-92), Nat. Assn. Ind. Colls. and Univs. (policy bd. 1980-82), Am. Coun. edn. (chair adv. com. on tech. edn. 1980-81, bd. dirs. 1990-92), Assn. Computing Machinery (pres. Dallas and Ft. Worth chpt. 1963-65), U. Rsch. Assn. (bd. trustees 1988—), So. U. Rsch. Assn., Inc. (chmn. coun. pres. 1988-89), Bus. Higher Edn. Forum (exec. com. 1990-93), Aircraft Owners and Pilots Assn., Nashville C. of C. (bd. dirs. 1983-86, pres.-elect 1995), Experimental Aircraft Assn. (pres. adv. com.), Govt. Univ. Industry Rsch. Roundtable, Sigma Xi, Beta Gamma Sigma, Phi Beta Kappa (hon.), Harvard Club (N.Y.C.). Methodist. Office: Vanderbilt U Office of Chancellor 211 Kirkland Hall Nashville TN 37240

WYATT, JOSEPH LUCIAN, JR., lawyer, educator; b. Chgo., Feb. 21, 1924; s. Joseph Lucian and Cecile Gertrude (Zadico) W.; m. Marjorie Kathryn Simmons, Apr. 9, 1954; children: Daniel, Linn, Jonathan. AB in English Lit. with honors, Northwestern U., 1947; LLB, Harvard U., 1949. Bar: Calif. 1950, U.S. Dist. Ct. (cen. dist.) Calif. 1950, U.S. Ct. Appeals (9th cir.) 1950, U.S. Tax Ct., U.S. Supreme Ct. 1965. Assoc. firm Brady, Nossaman & Walker, Los Angeles, 1950-58; ptnr. Brady, Nossaman & Walker, L.A., 1958-61; pvt. practice L.A., 1961-71; sr. mem. Cooper, Wyatt, Tepper & Plant, P.C., L.A., 1971-79; of counsel Beardsley, Hufstedler & Kemble, L.A., 1979-81; ptnr. Hufstedler & Kaus, L.A., 1981-85; sr. of counsel Morrison & Foerster, L.A., 1995—; mem. faculty Pacific Coast Banking Sch., Seattle, 1963-92, Southwestern Grad. Sch. Banking, 1988-89; adviser Am. Law Inst., 1988—, Restatement, Trusts 3d. Author: Trust Administration and Taxation, 4 vols., 1964—; editor: Trusts and Estates, 1962-74. Lectr. continuing legal edn. programs, Calif. and Tex.; trustee Pacific Oaks Coll. and Children's Sch., 1969—; counsel, parliamentarian Calif. Democratic party and presdl. conv. dels., 1971—; mem. Calif. State Personnel Bd., 1961-71, v.p., 1963-65, pres., 1965-67; bd. dirs. Calif. Pub. Employees Retirement System, 1963-71. Served with USAAF, 1943-45. Fellow Am. Coll. of Trust and Estate Counsel; mem. ABA, Internat. Acad. Estate and Trust Law (treas.), Am. Law Inst., Calif. Bar Assn. (del. state conf. 1956, 62-67), L.A. Bar Assn. (trustee 1956). Democrat. Christian Scientist. Avocations: poetry, fishing. Home: 1119 Armada Dr Pasadena CA 91103-2805 Office: Morrison & Foerster Ste 3500 555 W 5th St Los Angeles CA 90013-1024

WYATT, LENORE, civic worker; b. N.Y.C., June 12, 1929; d. Benedict S. Rosenfeld and Ora (Copel) Kanner; m. Bernard D. Copeland, May 17, 1953 (dec. March 1968); children: Harry (dec.), Robert (dec.); m. C. Wyatt Unger, Mar. 26, 1969 (dec. Feb. 1992); 1 child, Amy Unger; m. F. Lowry Wyatt, Sept. 12, 1992. Student, Mills Coll., 1946-48; BA, Stanford U., 1950, MA, 1952; postgrad., NYU, 1952-53. Instr. Stanford U., Palo Alto, Calif., 1952, Hunter Coll., N.Y.C., 1052-53, Calif. State U., Sacramento, 1056-60, U. Calif., Davis, 1965-69; property mgr. Unger, Demara & Markakis, Sacramento, 1974-83; former actress and model. Pres. Sacramento Opera Assn., 1972-73; treas. Sacramento Children's Home, 1990-92, v.p., 1992—; former mem. bd. dirs. Sutter Hosp. Aux., Sutter Hosp. Med. Rsch. Found., Sacramento Symphony League, Temple B'nai Israel Sisterhood, Sacramento chpt. Hadassah, Crocker Soc. of Crocker Art Gallery, Sacramento Symphony Assn., Sacramento Reportory Theater Assn.; founding mem. Tacoma Communities Art Sch.; mem. Temple Beth El of Tacoma. Mem. Joint Adventure Investment Club, Am. Contract Bridge League, Sacramento Pioneer Assn., Stanford U. Alumni Assn. (past bd. dirs. Sacramento) Sutter Club, Kandahar Ski Club, Sutter Lawn Tennis Club, DelPaso Country CLub (capt. women's golf 1983), Tacoma Country and Golf Club, Maui Country Club, Wash. Athletic Club, Tacoma Club. Republican. Jewish. Avocations: golf, duplicate bridge.

WYATT, MARY JEAN (M.J. WYATT), public relations executive. Acct. exec. Burson-Marsteller; acct. supr. Rowland Co.; acct. exec., acct. supr. Manning, Selvage & Lee, 1980-85, v.p., dep. group mgr., 1985-86; v.p., group mgr. Ketchum, 1986-87, sr. v.p., 1988, sr. v.p., group mgr., dir. healthcare, 1989-90; pres. Ruder Finn Healthcare, 1990—. Bd. dirs. Nat. Hemophilia Found. Mem. Am. Med. Writers Assn., Women in Comm. Inc. Office: Ruder Finn Inc 301 East 57th Street New York NY 10022*

WYATT, OSCAR SHERMAN, JR., energy company executive; b. Beaumont, Tex., July 11, 1924; s. Oscar Sherman Sr. and Eva (Coday) W.; m. Lynn Sakowitz; children: Carl, Steven, Douglas, Oscar Sherman III, Brad. BS in Mech. Engring., Tex. Agrl. and Mech. Coll., 1949. With Kerr-McGee Co., 1949, Reed Roller Bit Co., 1949-51; ptnr. Wymore Oil Co. 1951-55; founder Coastal Corp., Corpus Christi, Tex., 1955; now chmn. bd., CEO Coastal Corp., Houston. Served with USAAF, World War II. Office: Coastal Corp Coastal Tower 9 Greenway Plz Houston TX 77046-0995

WYATT, RICHARD JED, psychiatrist, educator; b. Los Angeles, June 5, 1939; children: Elizabeth, Christopher, Justin. B.A., Johns Hopkins U., 1961, M.D., 1964; M.D. (hon.), Central U. Venezuela, 1977. Intern in pediatrics Western Res. U. Hosp., Cleve., 1964-65; resident in psychiatry Mass. Mental Health Center, Boston, 1965-67; with NIMH, 1967—, asst. dir. intramural research, 1977-87, chief neuropsychiatry br., chief Neurosci. Ctr., 1972—; clin. prof. psychiatry Stanford U. Med. Sch., 1973-74, Duke U. Med. Sch., 1975—, Uniformed Svcs. Sch. Medicine, 1980—, Columbia U., 1987—; practice medicine specializing in psychiatry Washington, 1968—; cons. Psychiatry Shelter Program for the Homeless, Columbia U., 1987—; mem. sci. adv. bd. Nat. Alliance for Rsch. Schizophrenia and Depression, 1991. Mem. editorial bd. Advances in Neurosci., 1989, Harvard Rev. Psychiatry, 1992. Recipient Harry Solomon Research award Mass. Mental Health Center, 1968, A.E. Bennett award Soc. Biol. Psychiatry, 1971, Psychopharm. award Am. Psychiat. Assn., 1971, Superior Achievement award USPHS, 1980, Dean award Am. Coll. Psychiatrists, McAlpin Research Achievement award Nat. Mental Health Assn., 1986, Arthur P. Noyes award Commonwealth of Pa., 1986, Arieti award Am. Acad. Psychoanalysts, 1989, Robert L. Robinson award for Moods in Music, 1990, Mental Health Bell Media award for Moods in Music Mental Health Assn. Atlanta, 1991, Media award for To Paint the Stars Nat. Mental Health Assn. , 1991. Fellow Am. Psychiat. Assn. (task force on local arrangements 1991—), Am. Coll. Neuropsychopharmacology (nominating com. 1991, Efron award 1983); mem. Washington Psychiat. Assn., Soc. Psychophysiol. Study Sleep, Soc. Biol. Psychology, Am. Assn. Geriatric Psychiatry, Psychiat. Research Soc., Soc. Neuroscis., AMA. Office: NIMH Neurosci Rsch Ctr 2700 Martin Luther King Ave SE Washington DC 20032

WYATT, ROBERT ODELL, journalism educator; b. Jackson, Tenn., Feb. 7, 1946; s. Odell and Sera Mae (Mebane) Wyatt; m. Judith Gail Caplan, Sept. 5, 1976. B.A., U. of the South, 1968; MA, Northwestern U., 1970, PhD, 1973; MS, U. Tenn., 1977. Asst. to assoc. prof. U. Tenn., Nashville,

1973-79; assoc. prof. Mid. Tenn. State U., Murfreesboro, 1979-84, prof., 1984—, dir. Office Communication Rsch., 1989—; vis. prof. comm. U. Caen, France, 1994; cons. in comm.; mem. Pulitzer Prize Jury, 1980, 85, 91, 93, chair jury, 1985, 91, 93; rsch. cons. Freedom Forum First Amendment Ctr., Vanderbilt U. Author: Free Expression and the American Public, 1991 (Sigma Delta Chi award for rsch. on journalism 1992); editor book sect. The Nashville Tennessean, 1978-93; contbr. articles to profl. jours. Mem. Soc. Profl. Journalists, Assn. for Edn. in Journalism and Mass Comm., Internat. Comm. Assn., Am. Assn. Pub. Opinion Rsch., Speech Comm. Assn. Democrat. Episcopalian. Home: 720 Adkisson Ln Nashville TN 37205-1202 Office: Middle Tenn State U PO Box 391 Murfreesboro TN 37133-0391

WYATT, WILSON WATKINS, lawyer; b. Louisville, Nov. 21, 1905; s. Richard H. and Mary (Watkins) W.; m. Anne Kinnaird Duncan, June 14, 1930; children: Mary Anne, Nancy Kinnaird, Wilson Watkins Jr. J.D., U. Louisville, 1927; LL.D. (hon.), Knox Coll., 1945, U. Louisville, 1948, Centre Coll., 1979, Bellarmine Coll., 1988, Transylvania U. 1989; LHD (hon.), Hanover Coll., 1990. Bar: Ky. 1927. Pvt. practice law Louisville, 1927-41; mayor of Louisville, 1941-45; housing expediter and adminstr. Nat. Housing Agy., 1946; founding ptnr. firm Wyatt, Grafton & Sloss, 1947-80; founding ptnr. firm Wyatt, Tarrant & Combs, 1980-82, of counsel, 1982—; lt. gov. of, Ky., 1959-63; Presdl. emissary oil negotiations from Pres. U.S. to Pres. Indonesia, 1963; mem. law faculty Jefferson Sch. Law, 1929-35; dir. Courier Jour. and Louisville Times Co., WHAS, Inc., Standard Gravure Co., 1939-86, Ky. Center for Arts Endowment Fund. Presdl. emissary oil negotiations from Pres. U.S. to Pres. Indonesia, 1963; mem. law faculty Jefferson Sch. Law, 1929-35; dir. Courier Jour. and Louisville Times Co., WHAS, Inc., Standard Gravure Co., 1939-86, Ky. Ctr. for Arts Endowment Fund, 1980-94. Spl. rep. Bd. Econ. Warfare, N. Africa, March-May 1943; chmn. Louisville Met. Area Def. Council (twice awarded citation of Merit), 1942-45; pres. Am. Soc. Planning Ofcls., 1943-44, Ky. Mcpl. League, 1944, Am. Mcpl. Assn., 1945, Louisville Area Devel. Assn., 1944-45; pres. Nat. Mcpl. League, 1972-75, chmn. council, 1978-81; chmn. Nat. Conf. on Govt., 1975-78; mem. bd. U.S. Conf. Mayors, 1942-45; mem. Louisville Sinking Fund Commrs., 1936-38, Louisville Com. on Fgn. Relations (chmn. 1940-41); chmn. Ky. Econ. Devel. Commn., 1960-63; trustee Bellarmine Coll., 1975-82, chmn., 1979-82; trustee U. Louisville, 1950-58, chmn., 1951-55; Ky. chmn. Treasury adv. com. U.S. Savs. Bonds Program, 1948-55; mem. Commn. on Future of South, 1974, 86, Commn. on Operation U.S. Senate, 1975-76; founding chmn. bd. Regional Cancer Ctr. Corp., 1977-84; chmn. Louisville Community Found., 1984-92, sr. advisor, 1992—; vice chmn. Ky. Cancer Commn., 1978-79, Ky. Econ. Devel. Corp., 1984—, Ky. Council Sci. and Tech., 1987-90; founding chmn. Leadership Ky., 1984-86, chmn. emeritus; chmn. Judicial Nominating Com. 6th Circuit, 1977-80, Shakertown Roundtable, 1985—, U. Louisville Found. Devel. Cabinet, 1988-91; founding chmn. Leadership Louisville, 1979-81; trustee Bingham Fund for Excellence in Teaching, Transylvania U., 1987—; bd. dirs. Nat. Ctr. for Family Literacy, 1989-92, Shakertown at Pleasant Hill, Ky. Inc., 1990—; chmn. Gov.'s Higher Edn. Nominating Com., 1992-93; 1st pres. Young Dem. Club, Louisville Jefferson County; nat. chmn. Jefferson-Jackson Day Dinners, 1948, 49; del at large 7 nat. Dem. convs., 1944-68; nat. campaign mgr. for Stevenson, 1952, co-ordinator campaign divs., 1956; Dem. nat. committeeman for Ky., 1960-64. Recipient U.S. Treasury Disting. Service award, 1955, Brotherhood award NCCJ, 1974, Gold Cup for Community Service Louisville Area C. of C., 1974; Gov.'s Disting. Service Medallion, 1980; named Kentuckian of Yr., Sta. WHAS-TV, 1952, Citizen of Yr. Louisville Jaycees, 1972, Man of Yr., Louisville Advt. Club, 1973-74, Lawyer of Year, Ky. Bar Assn., 1976, Male High Sch. Alumni Hall of Fame, 1976, Lawyer of Yr., Louisville Bar Assn., 1980, Alumnus of Yr., U. Louisville, 1987, Bus. Hall of Fame, Jr. Achievement, 1994; Ottenheimer award Jewish Community Ctr., 1987, Mcpl. Leadership award Ky. Mcpl. League, 1987, Brennan-Haly Lecture award U. Louisville, 1989, Cmty. Svc. award Cath. Schs., 1991, Citizen Laureate award Younger Woman's Club Louisville, 1991, First Amendment prize Soc. Profl. Journalists, 1991, Wilson W. Wyatt award established by U. Louisville, 1987, Fleur-de-lis award Louisville Forum, 1993. Mem. ABA, Ky. Bar Assn. (sec. 1930-34, commr. 1958), Louisville Bar Assn., Am. Law Inst. (life), Ky. C. of C. (dir. 1974), Louisville Area C. of C. (pres. 1972), Pendennis Club, University Club, Louisivlounntry Club, Jefferson Club, Century Club (N.Y.C.), Rotary. Presbyterian. Home: The 1400 Willow Louisville KY 40204 Office: Citizens Pla 28th Fl Wyatt Tarrant Combs Louisville KY 40202

WYATT, WILSON WATKINS, JR., finance association and public relations executive; b. Louisville, Dec. 3, 1943; s. Wilson Watkins Sr. and Anne (Duncan) W.; m. Jane Clay, Aug. 15, 1964 (dec. 1975); children: Carol, Wilson III, Sarah Wyatt. Student, U. of the South, 1961-65. Reporter The Courier-Jour., Louisville, 1965-67; pub. rels. account exec. Doe-Anderson Advt., Louisville, 1967-68; account exec. Zimmer-McClaskey-Lewis, Louisville, 1968-70; ptnr. Bennett & Wyatt Pub. Rels., Louisville, 1970-71; state rep., vice chair appropriations and revenue com. Ky. Gen. Assembly, Frankfort, 1969-71; exec. dir. Louisville Cen. Area Inc., 1971-77; dir. corp. affairs and communications Brown & Williamson Tobacco Corp., Louisville, 1977-82; v.p. pub. policy BATUS Inc., Washington, 1982-86; v.p. corp. affairs BATUS Inc., Louisville, 1986-90; sr. v.p. corp. affairs PNC Fin. Corp., Pitts., 1990-92; sr. v.p. corp. comm. and govt. rels. The Travelers Cos., Hartford, 1992-94; exec. dir., CEO Am. Acad. of Actuaries, Washington, 1995—; lead U.S. def. pub. rels. activities against hostile takeover for B.A.T. Industries, U.K., 1989-90; chmn. Travelers Found., Travelers Good Govt. Com. Mem. youth adv. com. Atlantic Inst., 1967-68; del. North Atlantic Treaty Assn. Young Leaders Conf., 1967; chmn. Leadership Effort for All Dems., Ky., 1967-68; regional campaign coord. for Robert F. Kennedy, Ky.-Ind., 1968; mem. Pres.'s Forum, Washington, 1988-91; trustee Conn. Policy 2nd Econ., 1992-95; mem. exec com Hartford Downtown Coun., 1992-94; mem. adv. bd. Dem. Leadership Coun., Washington. Named one of Outstanding Young Men in Am., Ky. Jaycees, 1973. Mem. Pub. Rels. Seminar, The Vice President's Forum, 1993—, Pub. Affairs Rsch. Coun. (conf. bd. 1986—), Pub. Affairs Coun. (bd. dirs. 1982—, exec. com. 1982-86), Speaker's Club (Washington), Greater Hartford C. of C. (exec. com. 1992-94), Hartford Stage (bd. dirs. 1993—). Avocations: boating, photography, writing, tennis. Home: 7291 Bozman-Neavitt Rd Bozman MD 21612 Office: Am Acad Actuaries 1100 Seventeenth St NW 7th Fl Washington DC 20036

WYATT-BROWN, BERTRAM, historian, educator; b. Harrisburg, Pa., Mar. 19, 1932; s. Hunter and Laura Hibbler (Little) Wyatt-B.; m. Anne Jewett Marbury, June 30, 1962; children: Laura (dec.), Natalie. B.A., U. of South, 1953, LL.D. (hon.), 1985; B.A. with honours, King's Coll., Cambridge (Eng.), U., 1957, M.A., 1961; Ph.D., Johns Hopkins U., 1963. Mem. faculty Colo. State U., Ft. Collins, 1962-64, U. Colo., Boulder, 1964-66; mem. faculty Case Western Res. U., Cleve., 1966-83; prof. history Case Western Res. U., 1974-83; Richard J. Milbauer prof. history U. Fla., Gainesville, 1983—; Fleming lectr. La. State U., Baton Rouge, 1995; vis. prof. U. Wis.-Madison, 1969-70. Author: Lewis Tappan and the Evangelical War Against Slavery, 2d edit., 1971, Southern Honor: Ethics and Behavior in the Old South, 1982, paperback edit., 1983, Yankee Saints and Southern Sinners, 1985, paperback edit., 1990, Honor and Violence in the Old South, 1986; The House of Percy: Honor, Melancholy and Imagination in a Southern Family, 1994, The Literary Percys: Family History, Gender, and the Southern Imagination, 1994; also articles; editor: The American People in the Antebellum South, 1973. Served to lt. USNR, 1953-55. Grantee Am. Philos. Soc., 1968-69, 72-73, NEH, summer 1975; Guggenheim fellow, 1974-75; assoc. Woodrow Wilson Internat. Ctr. Scholars, 1975; fellow Davis Ctr. Princeton U., 1977-78, NEH fellow, 1985-86, NEH fellow Nat. Humanities Ctr., 1989-90; recipient Ramsdell award So. Hist. Assn., 1971, History prize Ohio Acad. History, 1983, ABC/Clio, 1989, Jefferson Davis Meml. prize for History, 1983; finalist Am. Book award and Pulitzer prize for History, 1983; Commonwealth Fund lectr. Univ. Coll., London, 1985, Lamar lectr. Mercer U., 1993, Webb lectr. U. Tex., Arlington, 1994. Mem. Orgns. Am. Historians (mem. exec. coun. 1990-93), Soc. Am. Historians, So. Hist. Assn. (exec. coun. 1994-96), Soc. for History of Early Am. Republic (pres.-elect 1995—), Phi Beta Kappa, Phi Alpha Theta (History prize 1983). Episcopalian. Home: 3201 NW 18th Ave Gainesville FL 32605-3705

WYCHE, SAMUEL DAVID, professional football coach; b. Atlanta, GA, Jan. 5, 1945; m. Jane Wyche; children—Zak, Kerry. B.A., Furman U., 1966; Masters degree, U. S.C. Profl. football player Continental Football League, Wheeling Ironmen, 1966; profl. football player Cin. Bengals, 1968-70, Washington Redskins, 1971-73, Detroit Lions, 1974-75, St. Louis Cardinals, 1976, Buffalo Bills, 1976; owner sporting goods store, Greenville, S.C., 1974-92; asst. coach San Francisco 49ers, 1979-82; head coach Ind. U., Bloomington, 1983, Cin. Bengals, 1984-91, Tampa Bay (Fla.) Buccaneers, 1992—. Named Coach of Yr. NFL, 1988, Nat. Football Conf., 1988. Office: care Tampa Bay Buccaneers One Buccaneer Place Tampa FL 33607

WYCKOFF, EDWARD LISK, JR., lawyer; b. Middletown, N.J., Jan. 29, 1934; m. Elizabeth Ann Kuphal; 1 child, Jenny Adele. B.A., Duke U., 1955; J.D., U. Mich., 1960. Ptnr. Kramer, Levin, N.Y.C.; lectr. Practising Law Inst., 1970—, World Trade Inst., various profl. and bus. orgns. in U.S. and abroad; spl. counsel N.Y. State Bankers Assn., 1974—; counsel N.Y. State Senate Com. Housing and Urban Renewal, 1969-71, N.Y. State Senate Com. Judiciary 1963-64, Com. Affairs of the City of N.Y., 1962; mem. N.Y.C. Mayor's Taxi Study Commn., 1967. Directing editor, commentator West's McKinney's Forms on Estates and Trusts, 1974—; mng. editor, 1982-84; commentator McKinney's Not-For-Profit Corp. law, 1993—; contbr. articles to profl. jours. Bd. dirs., pres. 1652 Wyckoff House and Assn., Inc., 1982—; trustee Soc. for Preservation of L.I. Antiquities, 1988—, N.Y.C.; Historic House Trust, 1993—; trustee, pres. Homeland Found., 1989—; trustee Inner-City Scholarship Fund, Inc., 1993—, The Band Ctr. Bard Coll., 1994—; bd. advisors Wildlife Conservation Soc.; mem. Concilium Sodalium to Vatican Mus., 1991—. Lt. USNR, 1955-57. Fellow Am. Coll. Trust and Estate Counsel, Am. Bar Found.; mem. ABA (chair com. on internat. property, estate and trust of law sect. real property, probate and trust law, taxation 1991—), Internat. Fiscal Assn., Internat. Bar Assn., N.Y. State Bar Assn. (exec. com. tax sect., chmn. com. income taxation estates and trusts 1976-80, com. internat. estate planning 1980—), Assn. of Bar of City of N.Y. (mem. com. lectures and continuing edn., com. trusts, estates and surrogate cts. 1970-73, com. corp. Clubs: Holland Soc., St. Nicholas Soc., Knickerbocker, Racquet and Tennis (N.Y.C.), Mashomack Fish and Game Preserve, Pine Plains, N.Y., Essex (Conn.) Yacht Club. Avocations: tennis, sailing. Office: Kramer Levin 919 3rd Ave New York NY 10022

WYCKOFF, MARGO GAIL, pyschologist; b. Omaha, Jan. 30, 1941; d. Winfield Jennings and Gail Claudia (Leach) Hartland; m. Tom Lawrence Wyckoff, Mar. 17, 1971; children: Ted, Elizabeth. BA, U. Wash., 1973, MSW, 1975; PhD, Union Grad. Sch., Seattle, 1978; cer. Licensed psychologist. Clin. lectr. U. Wash. Med. Sch., Seattle, 1976-78, asst. prof. univ. Pain Ctr., 1980-87; assoc. dir. pain ctr. Swedish Med. Ctr., Seattle, 1979-83, dir. behavioral svcs., 1979-83; pvt. practice Seattle, 1983—; psychology cons. Providence Med. Ctr., Seattle, 1979-83. Contbr. articles to jours., chpts. to books. Mem. Wash. Psychol. Assn. (bd. dirs. 1986-87), Nat. Orgn. Soc. Workers, Internat. Assn. for the Study of Pain, Psychoanalytic Assn. (bd. dirs. 1982-84), Wash. Environ. Council. Democrat. Avocations: history, environmental work, fishing, music.

WYCKOFF, SUSAN, astronomy researcher; b. Santa Cruz, Calif., Mar. 18, 1941; d. Stephen and Jean (Taft) W.; m. Peter Augustus Wehinger, July 29, 1967. BA in Astronomy, Mount Holyoke, 1962; postgrad., Swarthmore Coll., 1962-63; PhD in Astronomy, Case Inst. Technology, 1967. Postdoctoral fellow U. Mich., Ann Arbor, 1967-68; asst. prof. Albion (Mich.) Coll., 1968-70; rsch. assoc. U. Kans., Lawrence, 1970-72; sr. lectr. Tel-Aviv U., Israel, 1972-75; prin. rsch. fellow Royal Greenwich Observatory, Sussex, Eng., 1975-78; vis. prof. Ohio State U., Columbus, 1978-79; assoc. prof. Ariz. State U., Tempe, 1979-82, prof.. 1982—; adj. prof. Sussex U., 1975-77, U. Heidelberg Theoretical Astrophysics Inst., 1980, U. Ariz., Tucson, 1984—; vis. astronomer Royal Grennwich Observatory, Sussex, Eng., 1983, Mt. Stromlo Observatory, Australian Nat. U., Canberra, 1987, Smith Coll., 1989; Shapley lectr., 1985-86; vis. com. Aura, Inc., Tucson, 1985-88; mem. Internat. Astron. Union Working Group High Resolution Spectra Comets, 1982—; space telescope working group key projects Extragalactic Astronomy, 1984-85. Contbr. articles profl. jours. Mem. Gov.'s Disease Control Commn., Phoenix, 1985-87. Named Woman of Achievement Yr. Phoenix Jr. League, 1983. Fellow Royal Astronomical Soc. (Eng.); mem. NSF adv. com. 1983—, Nat. Acad. Sci. space sci. bd. 1984—, Ariz. State U. Faculty Women's Coun. (pres. 1983-84, exec. bd. 1983—), Am. Astron. Soc. Coun. (A.J. Cannon award comm. 1982-87), Internat. Astron. Union, Mt. Graham Internat. Observatory (citizen's coun.), Am. Astronomical Soc. (mem. coun. 1985-88), Sigma Xi. Avocations: jogging, swimming. Home: 2135 E Loma Vista Dr Tempe AZ 85282-2927 Office: Ariz State U Physics/Astronomy Dept Tempe AZ 85287-1504

WYCLIFF, NOEL DON, journalist, newspaper editor; b. Liberty, Tex., Dec. 17, 1946; s. Wilbert Aaron and Emily Ann (Broussard) W.; m. Catherine Anne Erdmann, Sept. 25, 1982; children: Matthew William, Grant Erdmann. BA, U. Notre Dame, 1969. Reporter Houston Post, 1970-71, Dayton (Ohio) Daily News, 1972-73, Seattle Post-Intelligencer, 1978, Dallas Times-Herald, 1978-79, Chgo. Sun-Times, 1981-85; reporter, editor Chgo. Daily News, 1973-78; editor N.Y. Times, N.Y.C., 1979-81, editorial writer, 1985-90; dep. editor editorial page Chgo. Tribune, 1990-91, editor editorial page, 1991—; occasional instr. journalism Columbia Coll., Chgo., Roosevelt U., Chgo. Woodrow Wilson fellow, 1969. Mem. Am. Soc. Newspaper Editors, Nat. Assn. Black Journalists, Nat. Assn. Minority Media Execs. Roman Catholic. Office: Chicago Tribune 435 N Michigan Ave Chicago IL 60611

WYCOFF, ROBERT E., petroleum company executive; b. Tulsa, 1930; married. B.S.M.E., Stanford U., 1952, M.S.M.E., 1953. With Atlantic Richfield Co., L.A., 1953—, various engring. and mgmt. positions, 1957-70, mgr. western region Internat. div., 1971-73, v.p., resident mgr. Alaska region N.Am. Producing div., 1973-74, corp. planning v.p., 1974-77, sr. v.p. planning and fin., 1977-80, exec. v.p., 1980-84, chief corp. officer, 1984, vice chmn., 1985, pres., chief operating officer, 1988-93, also dir.; chmn. Lyondell Petrochem. Co., Houston. Mem. ASME, Am. Petroleum Inst. Office: Atlantic Richfield Co PO Box 2579 515 S Flower St Los Angeles CA 90071

WYCZALKOWSKI, MARCIN ROMAN, retired economist; b. Pieskowa Skala, Poland, Apr. 20, 1910; came to U.S., 1946, naturalized, 1965; s. Josef J. and Zofia K. (Wyczalkowski) W.; m. Maria M. Anisko, July 15, 1938; children: Anna M. (Mrs. Richard Furnival), Andrew V., Carin T. (Mrs. Brian Carter). MA in Econs., Warsaw (Poland) Acad. Commerce, 1936, D. of Econs., 1938; postgrad., London Sch. Econs.-Polit. Sci., 1938-39. From asst. prof. to prof. econs. Warsaw Acad. Commerce, 1936-38, lectr., 1942-44, dep. prof., 1945-46, dep. rector, 1946; sr. advisor IMF, Washington, 1946-75, ret.; dir. econ. rsch. dept. Nat. Bank Poland, 1945-46; govt. advisor Union of Burma, 1958-59; advisor Govt. of Cyprus, 1962-64; advisor Karl Carribean Monetary Authority, 1975-76. Author: (Polish) Money in Market and in Planned Economy, clandestine edit., 1944; Economic Organizations of the UN, 1946; chief editor econ. monthly, Poland, 1945-46. Served with Polish Armed Forces, 1939, Polish Underground Army (Armia Krajowa), 1942-45. Mem. Polish-Am. Arts Assn. Avocation: writing. Home: 6303 Beachway Dr Falls Church VA 22044

WYDEN, RONALD LEE, congressman; b. Wichita, Kans., May 3, 1949; s. Peter and Edith W.; m. Laurie Oseran, Sept. 5, 1978; 1 child, Adam David. Student, U. Santa Barbara, 1967-69; A.B. with distinction, Stanford U., 1971; J.D., U. Oreg., 1974. Campaign aide Senator Wayne Morse, 1972, 74; co-founder, co-dir. Oreg. Gray Panthers, 1974-80; dir. Oreg. Legal Services for Elderly, 1977-79; instr. gerontology U. Oreg., 1976, U. Portland, 1980, Portland State U., 1979; mem. 97th-104th Congresses from 3d Oreg. dist., Washington, D.C., 1981—; mem. Commerce com., subcom. telecom. and fin., health and environment, small bus. com. Recipient Service to Oreg. Consumers award Oreg. Consumers League, 1978, Citizen of Yr. award Oreg. Assn. Social Workers, 1979, Significant Service award Multnomah County Area Agy. on Aging, 1980; named Young Man of Yr. Jr. C. of C., 1980. Mem. Am Bar Assn., Iowa Bar Assn. Democrat. Jewish. Office: 1111 Longworth House of Representatives Washington DC 20515-3703*

WYDICK, RICHARD CREWS, lawyer, educator; b. Pueblo, Colo., Nov. 1, 1937; s. Charles Richard and Alice (Marsh) W.; m. Judith Brandil James, 1961; children—William Bruce, Derrick Cameron. B.A., Williams Coll. ·1959; LL.B., Stanford U., 1962. Bar: Calif. Bar 1962. Asso. firm Brobeck, Phleger & Harrison, San Francisco, 1966-71; mem. faculty U. Calif. Law Sch., Davis, 1971—; prof. law U. Calif. Law Sch., 1975—, dean, 1978-80.

Author: Plain English for Lawyers, 3d edit., 1994. Served to capt. USAR, 1962-66. Office: Sch Law U Calif Davis CA 95616

WYER, JAMES INGERSOLL, lawyer; b. Denver, June 9, 1923; s. William and Katherine (Rolfe) W.; m. Joan Best Connelly, Aug. 13, 1960; children: Joan Connelly Tatnall, Peter Ford, June Wyer Nugent. B.A., Yale U., 1945, LL.B., 1949. Bar: N.Y. 1950, N.J. 1987. Assoc. Dewey, Ballantine, Bushby, Palmer & Wood, N.Y.C., 1949-56, Am. Cyanamid Co., Wayne, N.J., 1956; v.p., gen. counsel Am. Cyanamid Co., 1973-86; of counsel Robinson, St. John & Wayne, Newark, 1987—; Bd. dirs. Solomat Enterprises, Inc., William Penn Life Ins. Co. N.Y., PharmaGenics, Inc. Bd. dirs. Nat. Legal Ctr. for the Pub. Interest. Served with USNR, 1943-46. Mem. Assn. Gen. Counsel (1st v.p. 1982-84, pres. 1985-86), ABA, Assn. of Bar of City of N.Y., Atlantic Legal Found. (chmn. 1986—). Republican. Clubs: Jupiter Island (Hobe Sound, Fla.); Seabright (N.J.) Beach, Seabright Lawn, Tennis and Cricket (Rumson, N.J.); Coral Beach and Tennis (Bermuda), Hobe Sound (Fla.) Yacht. Office: Robinson St John & Wayne 2 Penn Plz E Newark NJ 07105-2249

WYER, WILLIAM CLARKE, management consultant, development executive; b. Portland, Maine, Dec. 8, 1946; s. John A. and Evelyn (Clarke) Petruccelli; m. Barbara D. Judge; 1 child, Melissa K. AAS, Corning (N.Y.) Community Coll., 1968; postgrad., Russell Sage Coll., 1969. Dir. pub. rels. N.Y. State Rep. Com., 1968-71; exec. asst. to co-chmn. Rep. Nat. Com., 1972; asst. to pres. Rollins Internat. Co., 1972-74; spl. asst., campaign dir. to U.S. Senator William V. Roth, Jr., Del., 1975-77; exec. asst. to U.S. Congressman Thomas B. Evans, Jr., Del., 1977-78; pres. Del. C. of C., 1978-89; mng. dir. Wilmington 2000, Inc., 1993—; pres. Wyer Group Inc., 1993—; bd. dirs. Beneficial Nat. Bank, Artesian Resources Corp. Board dirs. Port Wilmington Maritime Soc., 1978—; mem. adv. bd. Nature Conservancy; trustee Goldey Beacon Coll., Med. Ctr. of Del. Found. Mem. Del. C. of C. (life, hon. sr. coun.), Rodney Square Club (founding bd. govs.), Univ. and Whist Club, Northport Yacht Club (Maine chpt.), Ocean Reef Club (Key Largo, Fla.). Republican. Methodist. Home: 1980 Superfine Ln Unit 501 Wilmington DE 19802-4913

WYETH, ANDREW, artist; b. Chadds Ford, Pa., July 12, 1917; s. Newell Converse and Carolyn (Bockius) W.; m. Betsy Merle James, May 15, 1940; children: Nicholas, James Browning. Educated pvt. tutors; DFA (hon.), Colby Coll., Maine, 1954, Harvard U., 1955, Dickinson Coll., 1958, Swarthmore Coll., 1958, Nasson Coll., 1963, U. Md., U. Del., Northeastern U., Temple U., 1964; LHD (hon.), Tufts U., 1963; DFA (hon.), Princeton U., 1965; LHD (hon.), Franklin and Marshall Coll., 1965, Lincoln U., 1966, Amherst Coll., 1967; DFA (hon.), Bowdoin Coll., 1970; LHD (hon.), Ursinus Coll., 1971; DFA (hon.), U. Pa., 1972; LHD (hon.), West Chester U., 1984; DFA (hon.), Dartmouth Coll., 1984, Bates Coll., 1987; LHD (hon.), U. Vt., 1988. Artist, landscape painter, 1936—; first one-man show William Macbeth Gallery, N.Y.C., 1937, first solo exhbn. ever held in White House, 1970, first exhbn. by living Am. artist Royal Acad. Arts, London, 1980; exhibited Doll & Richards, Boston, 1938, 40, 42, 44, Cornell U., 1938, Macbeth Gallery, 1938, 41, first tempera show, 1943, 45, Currier Gallery, Manchester, N.H., 1939, room of watercolors, Art Inst. Chgo. 1941; room at Realist and Magic Realist show, Mus. Modern Art, N.Y.C., 1943; one-man exhbn., M. Knoedler & Co., N.Y.C., 1953, 58, Mass. Inst. Tech., Cambridge, 1960, Fogg Art Mus., William Farnsworth Library and Mus., 1963, Helga Pictures at numerous art museums, other univs. and museums; also exhbns. Arnot Mus., Elmira, N.Y., 1986, Seibu-Pisa, Tokyo, 1986, Kenesaw (Ga.) Mus. Art, 1986, Thomasville (Ga.) Art Ctr., 1987, Acad. of the Arts of USSR, Leningrad, 1987, Acad. of the Arts USSR, Moscow, 1987, Nat. Gallery of Art, Washington, 1987, Corcoran Gallery Art, Washington, 1987, An American Vision: Three Generations of Wyeth Art, various mus., 1987, Dallas Mus. Art, 1987, Mus. Fine Arts, Boston, 1988, Terra Mus. Am. Art, Chgo., 1988, Mus. Fine Arts, Houston, 1988, Setagaya Art Mus., Tokyo, 1988, L.A. County Mus. Art, L.A., 1988, Palazzo Reale, Milan, Italy, 1988, Fitzwilliam Mus., Cambridge, Eng., 1988, Fine Arts Mus. San Francisco, 1988, Brandywine River Mus., Chadds Ford, Pa., 1988, Detroit Inst. Arts, k1989, Sezon Mus. Art, Tokyo, 1991, Heckscher Mus., Huntington, N.Y., 1989, Gilcrease Mus., Tulsa, 1989, Portland (Maine) Mus. Art, 1989, Nukaga Gallery, Japan, 1990, Marcelle Fine Art Inc., N.Y.C., 1990, Takuji Kato Modern Art Mus., Tokyo, 1991, Takuji Kato Modern Art Mus.. Chichibu City, Japan, 1991, Jacksonville (Fla.) Art Mus., 1992, Portland (Maine) Mus. Art, 1993, Fanworth Art Mus. à Rockland, Maine, 1994; represented in permanent collections Met. Mus. Art, Nat. Gallery Art. Awarded 1st prize Wilmington Soc. Fine Arts, 1939, Obrig prize Am. Watercolor Soc., 1945, award of Merit, Am. Acad. Arts and Letters and Nat. Inst. Arts and Letters, 1947, 1st prize in watercolor Nat. Acad., 1946, Gold medal Nat. Inst. Arts and Letters, 1965, George Walter Dawson Meml. medal Phila. Watercolor Club, 1957, Mellon Gold medal of Achievement Pa. Artists Exhibit, Ligonier Valley, Pa., 1958, Arts Festival award and Citation for bringing dignity to Am. art Phila. Mus. Art, 1959, Percy M. Owens Meml. award Fellowship of Pa. Acad. Fine Arts, Phila., 1960, Presdl. Medal of Freedom, 1963, citation LaSalle Coll., Phila., 1965, Gold medal of honor Pa. Acad. Fine Arts, 1966, Carnegie Inst. award, award for excellence 1st award recognize outstanding performance in arts, Washington Coll., Chestertown, Md., 1976; Gold medal Nat. Arts Club, 1978, first Am. artist awarded Presdl. award Gold Congl. medal, 1988. Mem. Am. Watercolor Soc. (certificate of merit 1962), Nat. Inst. Arts and Letters, Soviet Acad. Arts (hon.), Academie des Beaux-Arts, Chester County Art Assn. (dir.), Audubon Soc. (dir.), N.Y. Watercolor Soc., Wilmington Soc. Fine Arts, Phila. Watercolor Club (dir.), Washington Watercolor Club (dir.), Balt. Watercolor Club (dir.), Am. Acad. Arts and Letters. Nat. Academician elect May 1945, Gold medal preeminence in painting 1965), Am. Acad. Arts and Scis., Royal Soc. Painters and Watercolours (London). Office: care Frank E Fowler PO Box 247 Lookout Mountain TN 37350-0247

WYETH, JAMES BROWNING, artist; b. Wilmington, Del., July 6, 1946; s. Andrew and Betsy (James) W.; m. Phyllis Overton Mills, Dec. 12, 1968. Privately tutored. One man shows include: M. Knoedler & Co., N.Y.C., 1966, William A. Farnsworth Mus., Rockland, Maine, 1969, Coe Kerr Gallery, N.Y.C., 1974, Brandywine River Mus., Chadds Ford, Pa., 1974, Joslyn Art Mus., Omaha, 1976, Pa. Acad. Fine Arts, 1980, Greenville County Art Mus., Greenville, S.C., 1981, Amon Carter Mus., Ft. Worth, 1981, Anchorage Fine Arts Mus., 1983; touring exhbn. An American Vision: Three Generations of Wyeth art, various mus. worldwide, 1987—. Mem. stamp adv. com. U.S. Postal Service, 1969—; mem. Nat. Endowment for Arts, 1972—; bd. govs. Nat. Space Inst., 1975—. Served with Del. Air N.G., 1966-71. Office: care Frank E Fowler PO Box 247 Lookout Mountain TN 37350-0247

WYGANT, FOSTER LAURANCE, art educator; b. Dayton, Ohio, Oct. 30, 1920; s. Harold F. and M. Esther (Weber) W.; m. Rae E. Hoyt, 1 child, Nancy Laura. Profl. diploma, Juilliard Sch. Music, 1942; B.A., Columbia U., 1949, M.A., 1956, Ed.D., 1959; postgrad., Am. Art Sch., Artists League, 1951-53. Clarinetist Dallas Symphony and free-lance clarinetist N.Y.C., 1945-47, publicity, fund-raising positions, and free-lance artist, 1952-56, tchr. art, pub. schs., 1956-59; asst. prof. Montclair State Coll., N.J., 1959-63, assoc. prof., 1963-68; prof. art edn. U. Cin., 1968-87, chmn. dept., 1968-84, dir. Sch. Art Edn. and Art History, 1984-86, emeritus prof., 1987—; vis. sr. lectr. Leeds Coll. Art, Eng., 1966; regional chmn. Scholastic Awards Program, 1968-84; chmn. Action for Arts in Ohio Schs., 1974-75. Author: Art in American Schools in the Nineteenth Century, 1983, School Art in American Culture 1820-1970, 1993; editor, prin. author: Standards for Art Teacher Preparation Programs, 1979, Principals, Purposes and Standards for School Art Programs, 1982. Served with U.S. Army, 1941-45. N.Y. State and Juilliard Sch. Music scholar, 1939-41; Kellogg Found. fellow Columbia U., 1955-56. Mem. Nat. Art Assn. (nat. dir. higher edn. divsn. 1975-79, Recognition award 1980, Disting. Svc. award 1982, Disting. fellow 1995), Ohio Art Edn. Assn. (pres. 1972-74), Seminar for Rsch. in Art Edn., Coun. for Policy Studies in ARt Edn., Am. Fedn. Musicians. Home: 3562 Interwood Ave Cincinnati OH 45220-1824

WYGANT, JAMES PETER, food company executive; b. Montreal West, Que., Can., Oct. 31, 1926; s. Samuel Edwin and Louise (Biersach) W.; m. Ruth Evelyn Mitchell, June 11, 1948; children: Margaret, Patricia, Sally. Student, McGill U., 1945-46, U. Syracuse, 1960-61. Various positions

Campbell Sales Co. and Campbell Soup Co., 1948-61; gen. sales mgr. Campbell Soup Co., Toronto, 1961-66; v.p. in charge grocery div. Standard Brands Ltd., Montreal, Que., 1966-69; v.p., dir. Standard Brands Ltd., 1969-72; pres., chief exec. officer Gen. Bakeries Ltd., Don Mills, Ont., 1972-81; pres. Stroehmann Bros. Co., Williamsport, Pa., 1981—; also chmn. Stroehmann Bros. Co.; dir. Quality Bakers of Am. Bd. govs. St. Joseph's U. Acad. Food Mktg. Served with Royal Can. Navy, 1944-45. Mem. Am. Bakery Assn. (bd. govs. 1975—). Mem. United Ch. Can. Clubs: Williamsport Country, Donalda. Office: Stroehmann Bakery Inc 1685 Four Mile Dr Williamsport PA 17701-1938

WYGNANSKI, ISRAEL JERZY, aerospace engineering educator; b. Warsaw, Poland, June 3, 1935; came to U.S., 1965; s. Herman Zvi and Deborah (Freidstern) W.; m. Renate Wissemann; children: Tamara, Dorit. B.Engring., McGill U., Montreal, Que., Can., 1961, M.Engring., 1962, PhD, 1964. Prof. U. B.C., Vancouver, Can., 1964-65; sr. rsch. scientist Boeing Sci. Rsch. Labs., Seattle, 1965-72; prof. U. Tel Aviv, 1972—, head dept. engring. 1972-76, dean faculty engring., 1977-81; prof. U. Ariz., 1983—; vis. prof. U. So. Calif., L.A., 1976-77, U. Ariz., Tucson, 1981-83. Contbr. articles to profl. jours.; patentee enhancement of mixing, delaying of separation and jet noise suppression. Inst. for Advanced Study fellow, Berlin, 1990-91. Fellow Am. Phys. Soc.; assoc. fellow AIAA; mem. NAE. Office: U Ariz AME Dept Tucson AZ 85721

WYGOD, MARTIN J., pharmaceuticals executive; b. N.Y.C. BS, N.Y.U., 1961. Chmn., pres., chief exec. officer Medco Containment Inc., Montvale, N.J., 1983-94; chmn. Synetic, Inc., Elmwood Park, N.J., 1994—. Office: Synetic Inc 669 River Dr Elmwood Park NJ 07407 Office: National RX Services Inc PA 5073 Ritter Rd Mechanicsburg PA 17055

WYKES, DAVID, English educator; b. Nuneaton, Warwickshire, U.K., Jan. 14, 1941; came to U.S., 1972; s. Frank Perry and Joyce (West) W.; m. Viva (Pat) Corrington, Aug. 24, 1963; 1 child, Cassian Tristram. BA, Oxford U., U.K., 1962; MA, Miami U., 1964; PhD, U. Va., 1967. Asst. lectr. U. Nottingham, U.K., 1967-68; lektor U. Trondheim, Norway, 1968-69; jr. rsch. fellow Trinity Coll., Oxford, U.K., 1969-72; asst. prof. Dartmouth Coll., Hanover, N.H., 1972-77, assoc. prof., 1977-85, prof., 1985—; mem. editorial com. Studies in Short Fiction, Newberry Coll., 1989—. Author: A Preface to Dryden, 1977, A Preface to Orwell, 1987; contbr. articles to scholarly jours. Avocations: recorded music, French. Office: Dartmouth Coll Dept English 6032 Sanborn House Hanover NH 03755

WYKES, EDMUND HAROLD, retired insurance company executive; b. Newcastle-on-Tyne, Eng., July 19, 1928; s. Cyril Edmund and Sylvia (Glover) W.; m. Joan Nightingale, Oct. 1, 1955; children—Julie, Christopher. LL.B., Durham U. 1949; postgrad., Gibson and Weldon Coll. Law, 1953. Bar: Ont. 1958. Solicitor H.E. Ferens & Son, Durham City, Eng., 1953-57; sec., counsel Imperial Life Assurance Co. of Can., Toronto, 1971-77, gen. counsel, sec., 1977-80, v.p., gen. counsel, sec., 1980-91, v.p., sec., 1991-93, ret., 1993. Solicitor Supreme Ct. Eng., 1953. Served with RAF, 1949-51. Mem. English Law Soc., Assn. Life Inst. Counsel, Am. Soc. Corp. Secs. Inc. Home: 86 Wimbleton Rd, Islington, ON Canada M9A 3S5

WYKOFF, FRANK CHAMPION, economics educator; b. Oakland, Calif., Feb. 20, 1942; s. Victor Clifton and Clarisse (Champion) W.; m. Jane Pierpont Humphreys, Sept. 11, 1965; children: Victor Clifton, Elisabeth Pierpont. AB, U. Calif., Berkeley, 1963, MA, 1965, PhD, 1968. Instr. U. Calif., Berkeley (part-time), 1966-68, 74; prof. econs. Pomona Coll., Claremont, Calif., 1968—, Elden Smith prof., 1979—; dir. Ctr. for Study of Economics; vis. prof. U. B.C., Vancouver, 1976-77; fin. economist U.S. Treasury Dept., Washington, 1972-73; cons., 1973-81; instr. U. Wis.-Madison, 1971; speaker Found. for Am. Communications, 1982—; expert cons. GAO, Washington, 1980—. Author: Macroeconomics, 1981, Understanding Economics Today, 1986; editor Econ. Inquiry Jour. Faculty fellow GAO, 1980; fellow Brookings Instn., 1972-73, NSF, 1976; faculty fellow Haynes Found., 1969, 71; fellow Ford Found., 1968, 70. Mem. Am. Econ. Assn., Western Econ. Assn., Inst. on Advanced Econs. for Journalists (dir. FACS). Home: 1001 Richmond Dr Claremont CA 91711-3351 Office: Pomona Coll Econ Inquiry 109 Seaver North 645 N College Ave Claremont CA 91711-6333

WYKURZ, IRENEUSZ WOJCIECH, stage director, actor; b. Kłodzko, Poland, July 8, 1952; came to U.S., 1990; d. Czesław and Natalia (Dopp) W. Grad., Polish Nat. Theatrical Acad., Krakow, 1976. Actor State Theatre, Zielona Gora, 1976-78, Stupsk, 1978-82; actor, dir., tchr. State Theatre, Kalisz, 1982-86, Czestochowa, 1986-90; founder and pres. Polish Theatre Group of N.Y., Inc., 1992—; lectr. Polish Nat. Acad. Cinema, Theatre and TV, psychiatric divsn. United Province Hosp., Unitas, dept. communication arts NYU. Author: Theory of the Six Postures; contbr. articles to profl. jours.; played leading stage roles Britannic, Vaclav Story, Hamlet, Three Sisters, Session, Short Night, Kiss of the Spider Woman; appeared in films Był Jazz, Stan Wyjatkowy, Gdziekolwiek Jestes, Tulipan, Pan Kleks, Komediantka, Crimen; appeared on TV Polish Television Network, Polish Sunday, Polish & Slavic World; actor, announcer Green Mountain Radio; dir. plays Kajtus Czarodziej, Snow White, Dwunastu, Agrypina, Getting Out, Noc Trybad, A Prawda nas Wyswobodzi, Serenada, The Party, The Shop of Songs, Jaselka Polskie, Maestro, St. John's Eve on the River, Robinson Cruzoe, Juvenalia 1986, Juvenalia 1987. Mem. U.S. Profl. Tennis Registry, Polish Inst. Arts and Scis. Am. Roman Catholic. Avocations: tennis, reflexology, guitar, horseback riding, fencing. Home and Office: 73-54 53d Ave Apt 4 Maspeth NY 11378

WYLE, FREDERICK S., lawyer; b. Berlin, Germany, May 9, 1928; came to U.S., 1939, naturalized, 1944; s. Norbert and Malwina (Mauer) W.; m. Katinka Franz, June 29, 1969; children: Susan Kim, Christopher Anthony, Katherine Anne. B.A. magna cum laude, Harvard U., 1951, LL.B., 1954. Bar: Mass. 1954, Calif. 1955, N.Y. 1958. Teaching fellow Harvard Law Sch., 1954-55; law clk. U.S. Dist. Ct., No. Dist. Calif., 1955-57; assoc. firm Paul, Weiss, Rifkind, Wharton & Garrison, N.Y., 1957-58; pvt. practice San Francisco, 1958-62; spl. asst. def. rep. U.S. del. to NATO, Paris, 1962-63; mem. Policy Planning Council, Dept. State, Washington, 1963-65; dep. asst. sec. def. for European and NATO affairs Dept. Def., Washington, 1966-69; v.p. devel., gen. counsel Schroders, Inc., N.Y.C., 1969-71; atty., cons. Schroders, Inc., 1971-72; chief exec. officer Saturday Rev. Industries, Inc., San Francisco, 1972-76; individual practice law San Francisco, 1976—; internat. counsel to Fed. States Micronesia, 1974-82; cons. Rand Corp., Dept. of Def., Nuclear Regulatory Commn.; trustee in bankruptcy, receiver various corps since 1974. Contbr. to: Ency. Brit, 1972, also articles in profl. publs., newspapers. Served with AUS, 1946-47. Mem. World Affairs Coun., Internat. Inst. Strategic Studies, Phi Beta Kappa. Office: 2500 Russ Bldg 235 Montgomery St San Francisco CA 94104-2902

WYLIE, CLARENCE RAYMOND, JR., mathematics educator; b. Cin., Sept. 9, 1911; s. Clarence Raymond and Elizabeth M. (Shaw) W.; m. Sikri M. Aho, June 27, 1935 (dec. 1956); children: Chris Raymond (dec.), Charles Victor; m. Ellen F. Rasor, June 25, 1958. B.S., Wayne State U., 1931, M.S., Cornell U., 1932, Ph.D, 1934; DSc (hon.), Furman U., 1994, U. Utah, 1995. Instr. Ohio State U., 1934-40, asst. prof., 1940-46; cons. mathematican Propeller Lab., Wright Field, Dayton, Ohio, 1943-46; chmn. dept. math. and acting dean Coll. of Engring., Air Inst. Tech., Wright Field, Dayton, 1946-48; prof. math. U. Utah, Salt Lake City, 1948-69; chmn. dept. U. Utah, 1948-67; prof. math. emeritus, 1991—; prof. math. Furman U., Greenville, S.C., 1969-78; William R. Kenan, Jr. prof. math. Furman U., 1971-78, Kenan prof. emeritus, 1978—, chmn. dept. math., 1970-76; part-time cons. math. Gen. Electric Co., Schenectady, Briggs Mfg. Co., Detroit, Aero Products div. Gen. Motors Corp., Dayton; Humble lectr. in sci. Humble Oil Co., 1955; disting. visitor Westminster Coll., Salt Lake City, 1981; cons. mathematican Holloman Air Base, N.Mex., 1955, 56. Author: 101 Puzzles in Thought and Logic, 1958, Advanced Engineering Mathematics, 6th edit., 1995, Introduction to Projective Geometry, 1969, (limericks) The Wisdom of Eric Lim, 1974, Differential Equations, 1979, The World of Eric Lim, 1991, Strange Havoc; poems, 1956, also miscellaneous poetry; other books, papers, articles, pub. in math. jours. Recipient Disting. Alumni award Wayne State U., 1956, Disting. Engring. Alumni Achievement award, 1985, named to Engring. Coll. Hall of Fame, 1985; Algernon Sydney Sullivan award Furman U., 1982; Bell Tower award Furman U., 1986.

Fellow AAAS; mem. Math. Assn. Am. (chmn. Rocky Mountain sect. 1955-56, bd. govs. 1957-60, sect. lectr. Southeastern sect. 1983), Am. Math. Soc., Am. Soc. Engring. Edn. (chmn. math. div. 1949-50, 1957-58), Utah Acad. Sci. Arts and Letters, S.C. Acad. Sci., Phi Beta Kappa, Sigma Xi, Pi Mu Epsilon, Sigma Pi Sigma, Pi Kappa Delta, Delta Sigma Rho, Sigma Delta Psi, Sigma Rho Tau, Phi Kappa Phi, Tau Kappa Alpha. Methodist.

WYLIE, EVAN BENJAMIN, civil engineering educator, consultant, researcher; b. Donavon, Sask., Can., Jan. 14, 1931; came to U.S., 1950; s. Mansel and Florence (Riddell) W.; m. Frances Eleanor Miller, Feb. 4, 1955; children—Brian Douglas, Scott Cameron, Karen Louise. B.S. in Civil Engring., U. Denver, 1953; M.S. in Civil Engring., U. Colo., 1955; Ph.D. in Civil Engring., U. Mich., 1964. Registered profl. engr., Mich. Engr. Ford Motor Co. of Can., Toronto, Ont., 1956-59; asst. prof. civil engring. U. Denver, 1959-62; asst. prof. civil engring. U. Mich., Ann Arbor, 1965-66, assoc. prof. civil engring., 1966-70, prof. civil engring., 1970—, chmn. dept. civil engring., 1984-90, chmn. dept. civil and environ. engring., 1991-94. Author: (with V.L. Streeter) Hydraulic Transients, 1967, Fluid Mechanics, 1975, 8th edit., 1985, Fluid Transients, 1978, Fluid Transients in Systems, 1993. Fellow ASME, ASCE; mem. Am. Soc. Engring. Edn., Internat. Assn. Hydraulic Rsch. Republican. Avocations: tennis; skiing; woodworking. Home: 1070 Chestnut St Ann Arbor MI 48104-2824 Office: Univ Mich Dept Civil Environ Engring Ann Arbor MI 48109-2125

WYLIE, MARY EVELYN, anesthesiologist, educator; b. Huntington, W.Va., Jan. 28, 1947; d. Herman E. and Charlotte (Toney) Smith; m. John K. Ostlund, June 14, 1987; 1 child, Sarah Johnson. BS in Biology, U. Ill., Chgo., 1973, MD, 1977. Diplomate Am. Bd. Anesthesiology. Intern Northwestern U. Med. Ctr., Chgo., 1977-78, resident in anesthesiology, 1978-80; fellow in adult and pediatric cardiac anesthesia Tufts-New Eng. Med. Ctr., Boston, 1980-81; anesthesiologist Waltham (Mass.)-Weston Hosp., 1981-88, Boston City Hosp., 1988-90, Presbyn. Univ. Hosp., Pitts., 1991—; asst. prof. anesthesiology Boston U. Med. Sch., 1988-90, U. Pitts. Med. Sch., 1991—. Mem. AMA, Pa. Med. Soc., Am. Soc. Anesthesiologists, Pa. Soc. Anesthesiologists, Soc. for Neurosurgical Anesthesia and Critical Care, Soc. for Ambulatory Anesthesia, Internat. Trauma Anesthesia and Critical Care Soc. Baha'i. Avocation: ballroom dancing. Office: Presbyn Univ Hosp Dept Anesthesia DeSoto St Pittsburgh PA 15261

WYLLIE, PETER JOHN, geologist, educator; b. London, Feb. 8, 1930; came to U.S., 1961; s. George William and Beatrice Gladys (Weaver) W.; m. Frances Rosemary Blair, June 9, 1956; children: Andrew, Elizabeth (dec.), Lisa, John. B.Sc. in Geology and Physics, U. St. Andrews, Scotland, 1952, B.Sc. with 1st class honours in Geology, 1955, Ph.D. in Geology, 1958, D.Sc. (hon.), 1974. Glaciologist Brit. W. Greenland Expdn., 1950; geologist Brit. N. Greenland Expdn., 1952-54; asst. lectr. geology U. St. Andrews, 1955-56; research asst. geochemistry Pa. State U., State College, 1956-58, asst. prof. geochemistry, 1958-59, assoc. prof. petrology, 1961-65, acting head, dept. geochemistry mineralogy, 1962-63; research fellow chemistry Leeds (Eng.) U., 1959-60, lectr. exptl. petrology, 1960-61; prof. petrology geochemistry U. Chgo., 1965-77, Homer J. Livingston prof., 1978-83, chmn. dept. geophys. scis., 1979-82, master phys. scis. collegiate div., asso. dean coll., asso. dean phys. scis. div., 1972-73; chmn. div. geol. and planetary scis. Calif. Inst. Tech., Pasadena, 1983-87, prof. geology, 1987—; chmn. commn. exptl. petrology high pressures temperatures Internat. Union Geol. Scis.; mem. adv. panel earth scis. NSF, 1975-78, chmn. adv. com. earth scis. div., 1979-82; mem. U.S. Nat. Com. on Geology, 1978-82; mem. U.S. Nat. Com. Internat. Union Geodesy and Geophysics, 1980-84, U.S. Nat. Com. Geochemistry, 1981-84; chmn. com. on objectives in solid-earth scis. NRC, 1988-93. Author: The Dynamic Earth, 1971, The Way the Earth Works, 1976; editor: Ultramafic and Related Rocks, 1967; chmn. editorial & writing com. Solid-Earth Sciences and Society, 1993; editor Jour. Geology, 1967-83; editor-in-chief Minerals Rocks (monograph series), 1967—. Served with RAF, 1948-49. Recipient Polar medal H.M. Queen Elizabeth, Eng.; Quantrell award, 1979; Wollaston medal Geol. Soc. London, 1982, Abraham-Gottlob-Werner-Medaille German Mineral. Soc., 1987. Fellow Am. Acad. Arts and Sci., Royal Soc. London, Edinburgh Geol. Soc. (corr.), Mineral. Soc. Am. (pres. 1977-78, award 1965), Am. Acad. Scis. (fgn. assoc.), Am. Geophys. Union, Indian Geophys. Union (fgn.), Nat. Acad. Sci. India (fgn.), Russian Acad. Scis. (fgn.), Russian Mineral. Soc. (fgn., hon.), Indian Nat. Sci. Acad. (fgn.), Geol. Soc. Am.; mem. Mineral. Soc. Gt. Britain and Ireland (hon.), Internat. Mineral. Assn. (2d v.p. 1978-82, 1st v.p. 1982-86, pres. 1986-90), Internat. Union of Geodesy and Geophysics (v.p. 1991—). Office: Calif Inst Tech Geol Planetary Scis 17 # 25 Pasadena CA 91125

WYLLY, BARBARA BENTLEY, performing arts association administrator; b. Bala-Cynwyd, Pa., June 10, 1924; d. William Henry and Virginia (Barclay) Bentley; m. William Beck Wylly, Apr. 26, 1947; children: Virginia Wylly Johnson, Barbara L., Thomas C. II. A. Briarcliff Jr. Coll., 1943. Pres. bd. dirs. Hillside Hosp. Inc., Atlanta, 1982, mem. adv. coun., 1982—; pres. Atlanta Symphony Assocs., 1975-76, mem. adv. bd., 1976—; chmn. bd. dirs. Ctr. for Puppetry Arts, Atlanta, 1988—. Republican. Episcopalian. Avocations: walking, reading, music. Home: 940 Foxcroft Rd NW Atlanta GA 30327 Office: Ctr Puppetry Arts 1404 Spring St NW Atlanta GA 30309-2851

WYLLYS, RONALD EUGENE, information science educator, dean; b. Phoenix, May 14, 1930; s. Rufus Kay and Eugenia (Dunsmore) W.; m. Jean Mary Graham, Nov. 2, 1957 (div. 1988); children—A. Erika, R.K. Graham, Athala Lucy, Kaila B; m. Martha E. Richardson, Sept. 1, 1989. B.A., Ariz. State U., 1950; postgrad. U. Calif.-Berkeley, 1950-52, Am. U., 1953-57, Georgetown U., 1957-59, UCLA, 1959-64; Ph.D. U. Wis.-Madison, 1974. Mathematician, Dept. Def., Washington, 1954-59; assoc. in math. George Washington U., Washington, 1954-59; assoc. info. retrieval Planning Research Corp., Los Angeles, 1959-61; computer systems specialist System Devel. Corp., Santa Monica, Calif., 1961-66; chief systems analyst Univ. Libraries, U. Wis.-Madison, 1966-69, lectr. computer scis. dept., 1966-72; from asst. prof. to prof. Grad. Sch. Library and Info. Sci., U. Tex., Austin, 1972—, acting dean, then dean, 1982-90; cons. in field. Co-author: National Document Handling Systems for Science and Technology, 1967. Contbr. articles to profl. jours., chpts. to books. Served to lt. (j.g.) USN, 1948-49, 52-54. Mem. AAAS, ALA, Am. Soc. Info. Sci., Am. Statis. Assn., Assn. Library and Info. Sci. Edn., Tex. Library Assn. Unitarian. Avocations: opera; bird-watching. Home: 1306 Belmont Pky Austin TX 78703-1416 Office: U Tex at Austin Grad Sch Libr & Info Sci Austin TX 78712-1276

WYLY, CHARLES JOSEPH, JR., corporate executive; b. Lake Providence, La., Oct. 13, 1933; s. Charles Joseph and Flora (Evans) W.; m. Caroline Denmon; children: Martha, Charles Joseph III, Emily, Jennifer. B.S., La. Tech. U., 1956. Sales rep. IBM Service Bur. Corp., 1956-64; v.p. Wyly Corp., Dallas, 1964-65, exec. v.p., 1965-69, pres., 1969-73, chmn. exec. com., 1973-76, dir., 1964-76; chmn. bd. Earth Resources Co., 1968-80; vice chmn. bd. dirs. USACafes, Inc. (Bonanza Internat., Inc.), 1968-89, Sterling Software, Inc., Michaels Stores, Inc.; chmn. Tex. High-Speed Rail Authority, 1990-91, Maverick Capital. Mem. Pres.'s Advisory Council on Mgmt. Improvement, 1970-73; vice-chmn. Devel. Council So. Methodist U. Found. Sci. and Engring., 1970-71; Mem. Republican Nat. Fin. Com., 1970—; Bd. dirs. Dallas County United Way Fund; pres. Dallas Theater Center., 1972-79. Mem. Am. Mgmt. Assn., Pi Kappa Alpha, Omicron Delta Kappa, Delta Sigma Pi, Beta Gamma Sigma. Clubs: City, Crescent, Brookhollow (Dallas); Willow Bend Polo and Hunt. Office: 8080 N Central Expy Ste 1100 Dallas TX 75206-1806

WYMAN, DAVID SWORD, historian, educator; b. Weymouth, Mass., Mar. 6, 1929; s. Hollis Judson and Ruth (Sword) W.; m. Mildred Louise Smith, Sept. 13, 1950; children: James Nayler, Teresa Carol. AB, Boston U., 1951; EdM, Plymouth State Coll., 1961; AM, Harvard U., 1962, PhD, 1966; DHL (hon.), Hebrew Union Coll. Jewish Inst. Religion, 1986, Yeshiva U., 1988. Various positions, 1951-57; tchr. pub. schs. Tilton, N.H., 1957-60; tchr. pub. high sch. Penacook, N.H., 1960-61; prof. history U. Mass., Amherst, 1966-91, Josiah DuBois prof. history, 1986-91, Josiah DuBois prof. emeritus, 1991—, chmn. Judaic Studies Program, 1977-78, 82-84; acad. advisor Simon Wiesenthal Ctr., L.A., 1983—; nat. coun. Nat. Christian Leadership Conf. for Israel, 1986, numerous radio and TV appearances; historian advisor to films. Author: Paper Walls: America and the Refugee Crisis, 1938-41, 1968, The Abandonment of the Jews: America and the Holocaust, 1941-45, 1984 (Anisfield-Wolf award 1984, Stuart Bernath award 1984, Theodore Saloutos

book award 1984, Present Tense Lit. award 1984, Boston Hadassah Myrtle Wreath award 1985, Nat. Jewish Book award 1985); editor: America and the Holocaust, 13 vols. documents, 1989-90; contbr. articles to profl. jours., chpts. to books. Recipient Chancellor's medal, U. Mass., 1986, Achievement award Isaac M. Wise Temple, Cin. 1986, Humanitarian award Bklyn. Holocaust Meml. Com., 1986; elected to Boston U. Collegium Disting. Alumni, 1986; Woodrow Wilson fellow, 1961-62, 65-66; grantee Social Sci. Rsch. Coun., 1969-70, Am. Coun. Learned Socs., 1969-70, Charles Warren Ctr. at Harvard U., 1969-70. Mem. Soc. for Am. Baseball Rsch., N.H. Hist. Soc., Friends Hist. Assn., Phi Beta Kappa. Avocations: baseball, greyhounds as pets, local N.H. history. Home: 61 Columbia Dr Amherst MA 01002-3105

WYMAN, JAMES THOMAS, petroleum company executive; b. Mpls., Apr. 9, 1920; s. James Claire and Martha (McChesney) W.; m. Elizabeth Winston, May 6, 1950; children: Elizabeth Wyman Wilcox, James Claire, Steven McChesney. Grad., Blake Prep. Sch., Mpls., 1938; B.A., Yale U., 1942. With Mpls. Star and Tribune, 1946-50; advt. mgr. Super Valu Stores, Inc., Eden Prairie, Minn., 1951-54; store devel. mgr. Super Valu Stores, Inc., 1955-56, gen. sales mgr., 1956-57, sales v.p., 1957-60, dir., 1959-87, exec. v.p., 1961-64, pres., chief exec. officer, 1965-70, chmn. exec. com., 1970-76, ret., 1976; chmn. bd., bd. dirs. Marshall & Winston, Inc. Served to lt. (s.g.) USNR, World War II. Clubs: Minneapolis; Woodhill Country (Wayzata). Home: 2855 Woolsey Ln Wayzata MN 55391-2752 Office: 1105 Foshay Tower Minneapolis MN 55402

WYMAN, JAMES VERNON, newspaper executive; b. Brockton, Mass., Nov. 17, 1923; s. George Dewey and Christine Laverne (Skinner) W.; m. Viola Marie Bousquet, June 24, 1950; children—J. Vernon, Douglas Phillip, Carolyn Anne. Student, Northeastern U., Boston, 1946-48; B.S. in Journalism, Boston U., 1951. With Providence Jour.-Bull., 1951—, asst. city editor, 1960-63, city editor, 1963-74, exec. city editor, 1974, metro mng. editor, 1974-79, exec. news editor, 1979-85, dep. exec. editor, 1985-88, v.p., exec. editor, 1989—. Served with AUS, 1942-46, PTO. Recipient Yankee Quill award, 1989. Mem. New Eng. Soc. Newspaper Execs. Assn. (past pres.), AP Mng. Editors Assn., New Eng. Soc. Newspaper Editors, Acad. New Eng. Journalists (past dir.), New Eng. Newspaper Assn., Sigma Delta Chi (past pres. New Eng. chpt.). Roman Catholic. Home: 6 Barway Ln Cumberland RI 02864-4914 Office: The Providence Journal 75 Fountain St Providence RI 02902-0050 *Success comes in many packages and is gauged in myriad ways. But it must be most rewarding when it can be measured in terms of simple, effective service to others—in terms of sincere endeavors to foster hope and to ignite the human spirit in those around you.*

WYMAN, JANE (SARAH JANE FULKS), actress; b. St. Joseph, Mo., Jan. 4, 1914; d. R. D. and Emme (Reise) Fulks; m. Myron Futterman, 1937; m. Ronald Reagan, 1940 (div. 1948); children: Maureen Reagan Revell, Michael; m. Fred Karger (div.). Student, U. Mo., 1935. Formerly radio singer, chorus girl in movie musicals, actress. Chorus girl: Gold Diggers of 1937; actress: (featured roles) films My Man Godfrey, 1936, Brother Rat, 1938, Lost Weekend, 1945 (Acad. award nomination), The Yearling, 1946 (Acad. award nomination), Johnny Belinda, 1948 (Acad. award winner), Stage Fright, 1950, The Glass Menagerie, 1950, The Blue Veil, 1951 (Acad. award nomination), Magnificent Obsession, 1954 (Acad. award nomination), All That Heaven Allows, 1956, Miracle in the Rain, 1956, Holiday for Lovers, 1959, Pollyanna, 1960, Bon Voyage, 1962, How to Commit Marriage, 1969; TV shows Fireside Theater, 1955, Jane Wyman Theater, Falcon Crest, 1981-90 (recipient Golden Globe awardBest Actress in Series-Drama, 1984). *

WYMAN, LOUIS CROSBY, state justice, former senator, former congressman; b. Manchester, N.H., Mar. 16, 1917; s. Louis Eliot and Alice Sibley (Crosby) W.; m. Virginia Elizabeth Markley, Aug. 20, 1938; children—Jo Ann, Louis Eliot. B.S. with honor, U. N.H., 1938; LL.B. cum laude, Harvard U., 1941. Bar: Mass. bar 1941, N.H. bar 1941, D.C. bar 1947, Fla. bar 1957. Asso. firm Ropes, Gray, Best, Coolidge & Rugg, Boston, 1941-42; mem. firm Wyman, Starr, Booth, Wadleigh & Langdell, Manchester, N.H., 1949-52; gen. counsel to U.S. Senate investigating com., 1946; sec. to U.S. Senator Styles Bridges, 1947; counsel to joint congl. com. on Fgn. Econ. Cooperation, 1948-49; atty. gen. N.H., 1953-61; legis. counsel to gov. N.H., 1961; partner Wyman, Bean & Stark, Manchester, 1957-78; asso. justice Superior Ct. N.H., 1978—; mem. 88th, 90th-94th congresses from 1st dist. N.H., mem. com. appropriations, subcom. on def.; apptd. U.S. senator, 1974; chmn. N.H. Commn. on Interstate Cooperation; mem. Jud. Council of N.H.; chmn. Nat. Com. on Internal Security, 1958-61. Served as lt. USNR, 1942-46. Fellow Am. Coll. Trial Lawyers; mem. ABA (chmn. standing com. jurisprudence and law reform 1961-63), Mass. Bar Assn., N.H. Bar Assn., Fla. Bar Assn., D.C. Bar Assn., Nat. Assn. Attys. Gen. U.S. (pres. 1957), Phi Kappa Phi, Theta Chi, Kappa Delta Pi. *In a mixed up world each person needs a goal—something he or she can strive for, work toward and measure progress against. Mine has always been to try to help make this world a better place to live for all—with dignity, privacy, security and reasonable comforts. Toward greater progress in this goal I forsook the practice of law for years of public service during which it was more clearly possible to do much for people. Less money but more action if you will. Throughout everything in life it is vital to believe in something greater than man alone and to seek guidance from prayer. Faith that sincere effort will be rewarded, if not in this life in the next, also helps.*

WYMAN, RALPH MARK, corporate executive; b. Usti, Czechoslovakia, Feb. 7, 1926; came to U.S., 1941, naturalized, 1946; s. Hans and Stella (Parnas) W.; m. Lotte Ann Novak, Oct. 25, 1947; 1 dau., Leslie Andrea Wyman Cooper. Student, Upper Can. Coll., 1942, Bucknell U., 1942-43; B.S. in Bus. Adminstrn., NYU, 1945; postgrad., Columbia U., 1945-46. Asst. mgr. export dept. Liebermann Waelchi & Co., N.Y.C., 1946-47; trainee White Weld Co. (investment brokers), 1947-48; v.p. H.O. Canfield Co., 1948-65, sec. 1949-53, vice chmn. bd., 1965-79, dir., 1953-79; dir. Pantasote Inc., 1960-89, vice chmn. bd., 1967-89; mng. partner United Eagle Mgmt. Co., Eagle Mgmt. Co., 1960—; pres. Veritas Co., 1960—; dir., vice chmn. United Way of Greenwich, 1980-86, The Youth Shelter, Greenwich, 1993—; trustee Princeton Theol. Sem., 1976—. Mem. Greenwich Country Club, Lambda Chi Alpha. Presbyterian (elder, trustee Synod of N.E. 1974-76). Home: Baldwin Farms North Greenwich CT 06831 Office: Greenwich Office Park 9 10 Valley Dr Greenwich CT 06831-5206

WYMAN, RICHARD VAUGHN, engineering educator, exploration company executive; b. Painesville, Ohio, Feb. 22, 1927; s. Vaughn Ely and Melinda (Ward) W.; m. Anne Fenton, Dec. 27, 1947; 1 son, William Fenton. B.S., Case Western Res. U., 1948; M.S., U. Mich., 1949; Ph.D., U. Ariz., 1974. Registered profl. engr., Nev.; registered geologist, Ariz., Calif.; lic. water right surveyor, Nev. Geologist N.J. Zinc Co., 1949, 52-53, Cerro de Pasco Corp., 1950-52; chief geologist Western Gold & Uranium, Inc., St. George, Utah, 1953-55, gen. supt., 1955-57, v.p., 1957-59; pres. Intermountain Exploration Co., Boulder City, Nev., 1959-93; tunnel supt. Reynolds Electric & Engring. Co., 1961-63, mining engr., 1965-67; asst. mgr. ops. Reynolds Electric and Engring. Co., 1967-69; constrn. supt. engr. Sunshine Mining Co., 1963-65; lectr. U. Nev., Las Vegas, 1969-73, assoc. prof., 1973-80, dept. chmn., 1976-80, prof., 1980-92, prof. emeritus, 1992—; chmn. dept. civil and mech. engring., 1984-90, chmn. dept. civil and environ. engring., 1990-91; mineral rep. Ariz. Strip Adv. Bd., 1976-80, U.S.B.L.M.; peer rev. com. Nuclear Waste Site, Dept. of Energy, LAs Vegas, 1978-82; pres. Ariz. Juno Resources, Boulder City, 1980-83, v.p. 1990—; pres. Wyman Engring. Cons., 1987—; cons. Corp. Andina de Fomento, Caracas, Venezuela, 1977-78; v.p. Comstock Gold, Inc., 1984-93. Contbr. articles to profl. jours. Sec. Washington County Republican Party, Utah, 1958-60; del. Utah Rep. Conv., 1958-60; scoutmaster Boy Scouts Am., 1959-69. Served with USN, 1944-46. Fellow ASCE (edn. divsn. 1990, local rep. nat. conv. Las Vegas 1990), Soc. Econ. Geologists (life); mem. AIME (chmn. So. Nev. sect. 1971-72, dir. 1968—, sec.-tres. 1974-92, chmn. Pacific S.W. Minerals Conf. 1972, gen. chmn. nat. conv. 1980, Disting. Mem. award 1989), Assn. Engring. Geologists (dir. S.W. sect. 1989-91), Am. Inst. Minerals Appraisers, Nev. Mining Assn. (dir. 1968—, life), Am. Soc. Engring. Edn., Sigma Xi, Assn. Ground Water Scientists and Engrs., Arctic Inst. N. Am. (life), Am. Soc. Engring. Edn., Sigma Xi, Las Vegas sect. 1986-910, Phi Kappa Phi (pres. U. Nev. Las Vegas chpt. 100 1982-83), Sigma Gamma Epsilon. Congregationalist. Home: 610 Bryant Ct Boulder

City NV 89005-3017 Office: Wyman Engring PO Bxo 60473 Boulder City NV 89006-0473

WYMAN, ROBERT J., biology educator, neurophysiologist, neurogeneticist; b. Syracuse, N.Y., June 8, 1940; s. Ralph M. and Selma (Franklin) W. A.B., Harvard U., 1960; M.S., U. Calif.-Berkeley, 1963, Ph.D., 1965; M.A. hon., Yale U., 1980. Math. analyst Tech. Research Group, Syosset, N.Y., 1959; NSF research fellow Calif. Inst. Tech., Pasadena, 1966; asst. prof. biology Yale U., New Haven, 1966-71, assoc. prof., 1971-80, prof., 1980—; vis. scientist Nobel Inst., Stockholm, 1970-71, Med. Research Council, Cambridge, Eng., 1974, Biozentrum, Basel, Switzerland, 1977; bd. sci. advs. MicroGeneSys Corp., New Haven. Contbr. articles to profl. jours. Bd. dirs. Urban League Conn., Nat. Abortion Rights Action League, Planned Parenthood of Conn.; bd. sponsors Nat. Com. for Effective Congress; mem. Fedn. Am. Scientists. Harvard Club scholar, 1956-60; NIH predoctoral fellow, 1960-65; NSF postdoctoral fellow, 1966; NASA research grantee NASA, 1968-70, NIH research grantee, 1967—, NSF grantee, 1986—. Mem. Soc. Neurosci., Internat. Brain Rsch. Orgn., Soc. Exptl. Biology, Genetics Soc. Am., Conn. Acad. Arts and Scis. (coun.), Sigma Xi. Home: 135 Gaylord Mountain Rd Bethany CT 06524-3129 Office: Yale U Biology Dept New Haven CT 06511

WYMAN, STANLEY MOORE, radiologist; b. Cambridge, Mass., Aug. 3, 1913; s. John Palmer and Lelia (Moore) W.; m. Jessie Elinor Brooks, July 23, 1945 (dec. Apr. 1978); children—Stephen Brooks, Jean Wyman Beebe, Martha Wyman Bermingham, Barbara Wyman Samett; m. Evelyn S. Stigger, Apr. 26, 1980. A.B., Harvard, 1935, M.D., 1939. Radiologist Mass. Gen. Hosp., Boston, 1946-68, 76-80; vis. radiologist Mass. Gen. Hosp., 1969-76, sr. radiologist, 1980—; cons. U.S. Naval Hosp., Chelsea, Mass., 1961-74; clin. prof. radiology Harvard Med. Sch., 1978-82, emeritus clin. prof. radiology, 1982—; Cons. radiol. tng. com. NIH. Contbr. articles to profl. jours. Served to maj., M.C. AUS, 1942-46. Decorated Bronze Star. Mem. AMA (former del.), Radiol. Soc. N.Am. (past pres., Gold medal 1974), Am. Coll. Radiology (pres. 1970-71, gold medal 1971), Am. Roentgen Ray Soc. (Silver medal 1952), New Eng. Roentgen Ray Soc. (hon. mem. past pres.), Mass. Radiol. Soc. (past pres.), Mass. Med. Soc. (pres. 1981-82), Aesculapian Club, Harvard Club (Boston), Economy Club (Cambridge, Mass.) (pres. 1989-90). Home: 987 Memorial Dr Cambridge MA 02138-5737 Office: Mass Gen Hosp Boston MA 02114

WYMAN, THOMAS H., food products executive; b. 1930. Bachelors, Amherst Coll., 1951. With Nestle, Switzerland, 1961-63; with Polaroid, Cambridge, Mass., 1963-75, sr. v.p., gen. mgr., 1972-75; with Green Giant Co., Mpls., 1975-79; vice chmn. Pillsbury Co., Mpls., 1979-80; with CBS Inc., N.Y.C., 1980-83, chmn., 1983; chmn., pres. United Biscuits (Holdings) U.S., Ltd.; UB Investments US Inc., Elmhurst, Ill., 1992—. Office: UB Investments US Inc 1 Hollow Tree Ln Elmhurst IL 60126

WYMAN, WILLARD G., headmaster. Headmaster Thacher Sch., Ojai, Calif. Office: Thacher Sch 5025 Thacher School Ojai CA 93023

WYMAN, WILLIAM GEORGE, musician; b. London, Oct. 24, 1941. Owner Ripple Records, Ripple Music, Ripple Publs., Ripple Prodns. Bassist with musical group, The Rolling Stones, 1962-92; albums include: 12 x 5, 1964, The Rolling Stones Now, 1965, Out of Our Heads, 1965, December's Children, 1965, Big Hits, 1966, Aftermath, 1966, Got Live If You Want It, 1967, Between the Buttons, 1967, Their Satanic Majesties Request, 1967, Flowers, 1967, Beggar's Banquet, 1968, Through the Past Darkly, 1969, Let it Bleed, 1969, Get Yer Ya Yas Out, 1970, Sticky Fingers, 1971, Hit Rocks: 1964-1971, 1972, Exile on Main Street, 1972, More Hot Rocks (Big Hits & Fazed Cookies), 1972, Goats Head Soup, 1973, It's Only Rock n' Roll, 1974, Made in the Shade, 1975, Metamorphosis, 1975, Black and Blue, 1976, Love You Live, 1977, Some Girls, 1978, Sucking in the Seventies, 1981, Tattoo You, 1981, Still Life, 1981, Undercover, 1983, Rewind: 1971-1984, Between the Sheets, 1985, Dirty Work, 1986, Emotional Rescue, 1988, Steel Wheels, 1989, Flashpoint, 1991, Voodoo Lounge, 1994, numerous others; solo recs. include Stone Alone, Monkey Grip, Bill Wyman; films Sympathy for the Devil, 1970; Gimme Shelter, 1970, Ladies and Gentlemen the Rolling Stones, 1974, Let's Spend the Night Together, 1982, Digital Dreams, 1983; author: photographs Chagall Mediterranè, 1984, (with Ray Coleman) Stone Alone: The Story of a Rock 'n' Roll Band, 1991. Address: Ripple Records Ltd care Panacea Entertainment Mgmt 2705 Glendower Ave Los Angeles CA 90027-1116*

WYMBS, NORMAN ELWOOD, author, researcher; b. Perth Amboy, N.J., Oct. 24, 1923; s. Elwood F. and Mary A. (Woitscheck) W.; m. Harriet L. Stevens, July 14, 1945; children: Paul S., Ellen L. Wymbs Golston. BS in Aero. Engring., St. Louis U., 1948. CLU. Salesman Johns Manville Corp., Chgo., 1948-51; owner, mgr. WHSL Grocer, Chgo., 1951-63, ins. agy., Boca Raton, Fla., 1965-85; columnist Gold Coast News, Palm Beach County, Fla., 1972-80. Author: A Place To Go Back To, 1987, Sold to the Highest Bidder, 1991. Mayor City of Boca Raton, 1971; mem. Fla. Rep. Com., 1976-90, Fla. Coun. on Aging, Washington, 1989-92; chmn. Ronald Reagan Found., Dixon, Ill., 1984—. Author: A Place to Go Back To, 1987, Ronald Reagan's Crusade, 1994. Presbyterian.

WYMORE, LUANN COURTNEY, elementary education educator; b. Kansas City, Mo., Feb. 22, 1942; d. Clifford Willis and Lola (Moore) Courtney; m. George Philip Wymore, Dec. 27, 1964; children: Courtney, Kristin, Ryan. BA, William Jewell Coll., 1964; MA, U. Mo., Kansas City, 1969; PhD, Mo., 1989. Cert. elem., biology, Englisy tchr., Mo. Elem. tchr. Sch. Dist. North Kansas City, Mo., 1964-69; asst. prof. elem. edn. Mo. Valley Coll., Marshall, Mo., 1989—; presenter in field. Contbr. articles to profl. jours. Leader Girl Scouts U.S.A., Slater, Mo., 1980's, 4-H Club, Orearville, Mo., 1980's. Mem. ASCD, PEO, Internat. Reading Assn. Democrat. Avocations: reading, piano, organ, travel. Home: 820 Rich St Slater MO 65349-1258 Office: Mo Valley Coll 500 E College St Marshall MO 65340-3197

WYNAR, BOHDAN STEPHEN, librarian, author, editor; b. Lviv, Ukraine, Sept. 7, 1926; came to U.S., 1950, naturalized, 1957; s. John I. and Euphrosina (Doryk) W.; m. Olha Yarema, Nov. 23, 1992; children: Taras, Michael, Roxolana, Yarynka. Diplom-Volkswirt Econs., U. Munich, Germany, 1949, Ph.D., 1950; M.A., U. Denver, 1958. Methods analyst, statistician Tramco Corp., Cleve., 1951-53; freelance journalist Societ Econs., Cleve., 1954-56; adminstrv. asst. U. Denver Libers., 1958-59, head tech. svcs. div., 1959-62; assoc. prof. Sch. Librarianship, U. Denver, 1962-66; dir. div. libr. edn. State U. Coll., Geneseo, N.Y., 1966-67; dean Sch. Libr. Sci. State U. Coll., Geneseo; prof. State U. Coll., 1967-69; pres. Libraries Unlimited Inc., 1969—. Author: Soviet Light Industry, 1956, Economic Colonialism, 1958, Ukrainian Industry, 1964, Introduction to Bibliography and Reference Work, 4th edit, 1967, Introduction to Cataloging and Classification, 8th edit, 1992, Major Writings on Soviet Economy, 1966, Library Acquisitions, 2d edit, 1971, Research Methods in Library Science, 1971, Economic Thought in Kievan Rus', 1974; co-author: Comprehensive Bibliography of Cataloging and Classification, 2 vols., 1973, Ukraine: A Bibliographic Guide to English Language Publications, 1990; editor Ukrainian Quar., 1953-58, Preliminary Checklist of Colorado Bibliography, 1963, Studies in Librarianship, 1963-66, Research Studies in Library Science, 1970—, Best Reference Books, 3d edit., 1985, 4th edit., 1992, Colorado Bibliography, 1980; gen. editor: American Reference Books Ann., 1969—; editor: ARBA Guide to Subject Encyclopedias and Dictionaries, 1985, ARBA Guide To Biographical Dictionaries, Reference Books in Paperback, An Annotated Guide, 2d edit., 1976, 3rd edit., 1991, Dictionary of Am. Library Biography, 1978, Ukraine-A Bibliographic Guide to English-Language Publications, 1990, International Writings of Bohdan S. Wynar 1949-1992, 1993, Recommended Reference Books for Medium-Sized and Small Libraries, 1981—; co-editor, contbr. Ency. Ukraine, 1955—;editor Wynar Libr. Series, 1981-90. Mem. exec. bd. ZAREVO, Inc. Mem. ALA (pres. Ukrainian Congress com. br., Denver 1976), Colo. Library Assn., N.Y. Library Assn., Am. Assn. Advancement Slavic Studies (pres. Ukrainian Research Found. 1976-90), AAUP, Ukrainian Hist. Assn. (exec. bd.), Sevčenko Societe Scientifique (Paris), Ukrainian Acad. Arts and Scis. (N.Y.C.). Office: Librs Unltd Inc 6931 S Yosemite St Englewood CO 80112-1400

WYNBLATT, PAUL PINHAS, materials science educator, researcher; b. Alexandria, Arab Republic of Egypt, June 30, 1935; came to U.S. 1962; s. Jean Weinblatt and Selma (Daniel) Weinblatt Pollock; m. Elizabeth Ann Whitehouse, May 2, 1959; children—Deborah Ann, Michael John. B.Sc.Tech., U. Manchester, Eng. 1956; M.S., Israel Inst. Tech., Haifa, 1958; Ph.D., U. Calif.-Berkeley, 1966; hon. doctorate, U. Aix-Marseille, France, 1987. Rsch. metallurgist Israel Atomic Energy Commn., Dimona, 1958-62; staff scientist Ford Motor Co., Dearborn, Mich., 1966-81; prof. materials sci. and engring. Carnegie-Mellon U., Pitts., 1981—, head dept., 1991—, dir. Ctr. for Study of Materials, 1985-88, assoc. dean Carnegie Inst. Tech., 1989-91; vis. prof. Ecole Nat. Supérièure de Chimie de Paris, 1987, U. d'Aix-Marseille, France, 1988. Mem. editorial bd. Jour. Rsch. Mgmt. and Tech., 1983—; Computational Materials Sci., 1993—; contbr. articles to profl. jours. Fellow Am. Soc. Metals; mem. Am. Vacuum Soc., Metall. Soc. of AIME (bd. dirs. 1977-80, chmn. chemistry and physics of metals com. 1983-84), Materials Rsch. Soc. Avocations: hiking; tennis; music; fine arts. Office: Carnegie-Mellon U Dept Materials Sci & Engring Pittsburgh PA 15213

WYNDER, ERNST LUDWIG, science foundation director, epidemiologist; b. Herford, Germany, Apr. 30, 1922; came to U.S. 1938, naturalized 1943; s. Alfred and Therese (Godfrey) W.; m. Sandra Miller, 1993. BA, NYU, 1943; B in Med. Sci., Washington U., 1950, MD, 1950; DSc (hon.), N.Y. Med. Coll., 1992; MD (hon.), Med. Faculty U. Hamburg, 1992; DSc (hon.), Washington U., St. Louis, 1994. Lic. doctor and surgeon, N.Y. Asst. Sloan-Kettering Inst. for Cancer Rsch., N.Y.C., 1952-54, assoc., 1954-60, assoc. mem., 1960-69, assoc. scientist, 1969-83, adj. mem., 1984—; pres., med. dir. Am. Health Found., N.Y.C., 1969—. Contbr. 700 articles to profl. jours. Decorated officer's cross Order of Merit (Germany), 1991; recipient Bordon Undergrad. Rsch. award Washington U., 1950, N.Y. State Health Edn. and Illness Prevention award N.Y. State, 1981, Max von Pettenkofer medal Max von Pettenkofer Inst., 1988, Alton Ochsner award Alton Ochsner Med. Found., 1988, Lucy Wortham James Clin. Rsch. award Soc. Surg. Oncology, 1989, medal Surgeon Gen. U.S., 1989, Mayor's Ethnic award City of N.Y., 1989, Nathan Pritikin Pioneer award Nathan Pritikin Rsch. Found., 1989, Medal of Honor for clin. rsch. Am. Cancer Soc., 1989, Robert-Koch Gold medal Robert-Koch Stiftung, 1990, Disting. Clinician award Milken Family Med. Found., 1990, CliniOncol Rsch., Julia Hudson Freund lecture award, Wash. U., 1990. Mem. Am. Assn. Cancer Rsch. (hon.), Am. Coll. for Preventive Medicine, Am. Pub. Health Assn., Max Planck Soc. Germany, N.Y. Acad. Scis. (Sarah L. Poiley Meml. award 1979), Am. Soc. Preventive Oncology (Disting. Achievement award 1984). Office: Am Health Found 320 E 43d St New York NY 10017

WYNDRUM, RALPH W., JR., communications company executive; b. N.Y.C., Apr. 20, 1937; s. Ralph W. and Virginia M. (Woolley) W.; m. Meta Schmidt, Apr. 23, 1960; children: Dorothy, Jeanne, Ralph, Joan. B.S., Columbia U., 1959, M.S. in Elec. Engring., 1960, M.S. in Bus. Adminstrn., 1978; Sc.D., NYU, 1963. Mem. tech. staff Bell Labs., Murray Hill, N.J., 1963-65; supr. exploratory circuit design Bell Labs., 1965-69; head loop transmission tech. dept. Bell Labs., Holmdel and Whippany, N.J., 1969-79; head advanced loop transmission systems dept. Bell Labs., Whippany, 1979-87, head internat. loop systems dept., 1987, dir. systems analysis ctr., 1987-90, dir. quality process ctr., 1990-92, dir. quality, engring., software and techs., 1993-94; v.p. AT&T World Svcs., 1994—, dir. process engr. ctr., 1995—; adj. prof. N.J. Inst. Tech., 1965, Stevens Inst. Tech., 1980-88. Contbr. articles to profl. jours. Fellow IEEE (bd. dirs. 1988-90, v.p. pubs. 1990-91, President's Leadership award 1991); mem. IEEE Comm. Soc. (chmn. conf. bd. 1981-87), Assn. MBA Execs., Sigma Xi, Eta Kappa Nu, Beta Gamma Sigma. Republican. Roman Catholic. Patentee in field. Home: 35 Cooney Ter Fair Haven NJ 07704-3001 Office: Bell Labs Rm 3l324 Holmdel NJ 07733

WYNER, AARON DANIEL, mathematician; b. N.Y.C., Mar. 17, 1939; s. Alvin and Mary (Jacobson) W.; m. Nusha Zukerman, June 9, 1963; children—Tamar, Abraham, Dena, Yael. BS, Queens Coll., 1960, Columbia U., 1960; MS, Columbia U., 1961, PhD, 1963. Asst. prof. elec. engring. Columbia U., 1963; mem. tech. staff AT&T Bell Labs., Murray Hill, N.J., 1963—; head communications analysis research dept. AT&T Bell Labs., 1974-93; adj. and vis. prof. Columbia U., Polytech. U., Technion, Haifa, Israel, Weizmann Inst. Sci., Rehovot, Israel., Princeton U. Assoc. editor: IEEE Transactions on Info. Theory, 1970-72, editor-in-chief, 1983-86. Guggenheim Found. fellow, 1966. Fellow IEEE (past pres. Info. Theory Soc., Centennial medal 1984), AAAS; mem. Internat. Sci. Radio Union (chmn. U.S. commn. on signals and systems 1987-90, vice-chmn. internat. commn. 1990-93), Nat. Acad. Engring. Patentee in field. Home: 33 Oakview Ave Maplewood NJ 07040-2213 Office: AT&T Bell Labs 600 Mountain Ave New Providence NJ 07974-2010

WYNER, JUSTIN L., laminating company executive; b. Boston, Aug. 6, 1925; s. Rudolph H. and Sara G. Wyner; m. Genevieve Gloria Geller, July 3, 1955; children: George Michael, Daniel Mark, James Henry. BS cum laude, Tufts Coll., 1946; MBA, Harvard U., 1948. Pres. Shawmut Mills div. R.H. Wyner Assocs., West Bridgewater, Mass. Mem. Brookline Rep. Town Com., 1964—; trustee Beth Israel Hosp., Boston, 1966—, mem. fin. com., 1972-82; trustee Temple Israel, Boston, 1964—, pres., 1979-82, chmn. bd. mgrs., 1983-94; trustee Am. Jewish Hist. Soc., 1987—, pres., 1992—; trustee Hebrew Coll., 1967—, chmn. cultural affairs com., 1977-78, Temple Kehillath Israel, 1967—; trustee Combined Jewish Philanthropies, Boston, 1966—, Roxbury Latin Sch., 1985-89; moderator Town of Brookline, Mass., 1970-82, 91-94, chmn. fin. com., 1961-64; nat. chmn. Reps. for Eugene McCarthy, 1968; chmn. Brookline United Fund, 1960; pres. Jewish Community Rels. Coun., 1971-73, mem. adminstrv. com., 1967—; dir. Brookline Taxpayer's Assn. 1956-61, Brookline Community Council, 1957-61; gov. Hebrew Union Coll.-Jewish Inst. Religion, 1987-92; bd. dirs. Mass. div. Am. Cancer Soc., 1987—; pres. Hebrew Free Loan Soc. Boston, 1972-88; moderator Town of Brookline, 1970-82, 91-94; active various other civic and religious orgns. Mem. Nat. Assn. for Textile Tech. (nat. bd. govs. 1970-73), Nat. Knitwear Mfrs. Assn. (past dir., bd. dirs., present hon. life dir.), New Bedford Yacht Club, Harvard (Boston and N.Y.C.), Belmont Country Club, Thorny Lea Golf Club, Norfolk Trout. Avocations: sailing, amateur radio, golf. Home: 830 Newton St Chestnut Hill MA 02167-2643 Office: Shawmut Mills 208 Manley St West Bridgewater MA 02379-1086

WYNER, YEHUDI, composer, pianist, conductor, educator; b. Calgary, Alta., Can., June 1, 1929; s. Lazar and Sarah Naomi (Shumiatcher) Weiner; m. Nancy Joan Braverman, Sept. 16, 1951 (div. 1967); children: Isaiah, Adam, Cassia; m. Susan M. Davenny, June 15, 1967. Diploma, Juilliard Sch. Music, 1946; A.B., Yale U., 1950, B.Mus., 1951, M.Mus., 1953; M.A., Harvard U., 1952. Vis. assoc. prof. Hofstra Coll., 1959; lectr. Queens Coll., N.Y.C., 1959-60; instr. Hebrew Union Coll., N.Y.C., 1957-59; music dir. Westchester Reform Temple, N.Y.C., 1959-68; asst. prof. theory Yale U., 1963-69, assoc. prof. theory, 1969-77, chmn. composition dept., 1969-73; prof. music SUNY, Purchase, 1978-89, dean music, 1978-82; faculty Berkshire Music Ctr., 1975-85; faculty Tanglewood Music Ctr., 1975—; vis. prof. composition Cornell U., 1987; Ziskind vis. prof. composition Brandeis U., 1987-88, Walter Naumburg prof. composition, dir. contemporary ensemble, 1989—; vis. prof. Harvard U., 1991-93. Mus. dir., New Haven Opera Soc., 1968-77, Turnau Opera Assn., 1961-64; mem., Bach Aria Group, 1968—; composer-condr., Tanglewood, 1961; composer-in-residence, Santa Fe Chamber Music Festival, 1982, Am. Acad. in Rome, spring 1991; composer: Two Chorale Preludes for Organ, 1951, Partita for Piano, 1952, Dance Variations for Wind Octet, 1953, rev., 1959, Psalm 143, chorus, 1952, Sonata for Piano, 1954, Concert Duo for Violin and Piano, 1955-57, Dedication Anthem, 1957, Serenade for Seven Instruments, 1958, Passover Offering, 1959, Three Informal Pieces for Violin and Piano, 1961, Friday Evening Service for Cantor, Chorus, Organ, 1963, Incidental Music for play The Old Glory, 1964, Torah Service with Instruments, 1966, Da Camera for Piano and Orch, 1967, Cadenza for Clarinet and Harpsichord, 1969, De Novo for cello and small ensemble, 1971, Liturgy for the High Holidays, 1971, Three Short Fantasies for Piano, 1963-71, Songs, 1950-79, Canto Cantabile for Soprano and Concert Band, 1972, music for play The Mirror, 1972-73, Memorial Music for Soprano and 3 Flutes, 1971-73, Intermedio for Soprano and String Orchestra, 1974, Wedding Music, 1976, Dances of Atonement for Violin and Piano, 1976, Fragments from Antiquity; 5 songs for soprano and symphony orch., 1978; Piano Quartet, 1980, All the Rage for flute and piano, 1980; Processionals and Marches, 1979, 80, Tanz and Maissele, 1981,

On This Most Voluptuous Night, 1982, Passage for 7 Instruments, 1983, Wind Quintet, 1984, String Quartet, 1985, Composition for Viola and Piano, 1987, Toward the Center for piano, 1988, Sweet Consort for flute and piano, 1988, Leonardo Vincitore for 2 sopranos, string bass and piano, 1988, O To Be a Dragon, four songs for women's chorus and piano, 1989, Trapunto Junction for brass trio and percussion, 1991, Changing Time for small ensemble, 1991, New Fantasies for piano, 1991, Amadeus' Billiard for small ensemble, 1991, Il Cane Minore for 2 clarinets and bassoon, 1992, Wedding Dances: From the Notebook of Suzanne de Venné, 1993, Post Fantasies for Piano, 1993, Prologue and Narrative for cello and orch., 1994, Song Cycle for soprano, baritone and piano, Restaurants, Wines-Bistros, Shrines, 1994, More Fantasies for Piano, 1994, Lyric Harmony for orch., 1995. Recipient Inst. Arts and Letters grant, 1961, Brandeis Creative Arts award, 1963; commns. from Yale U., 1958, Mich. U., 1959, Fromm Found., 1960, Koussevitzsky Found. at Library Congress, 1960, Ford Found., 1971, Yale Band, Yale Repertory Theater, Cantilena Chamber Players, Aeolian Chamber Players, Santa Fe Chamber Music Festival, Collage of Boston, N.Y. Woodwind Quintet, Frank Taplin project, NEA Consortium, Boston Symphony Chamber Players, Atlantic Sinfonietta, Carnegie Hall Am. Composers Orch., RNCM Manchester Internat. Cello Festival; Rome Prize fellow, 1953-56; Alfred E. Hertz fellow U. Calif., 1953-54; Guggenheim fellow, 1960, 76-77; NEA grantee, 1976. Mem. Internat. Soc. Contemporary Music (mem. bd.), Am. Composers Alliance (exec. bd.), Am. Music Center (exec. bd.). Office: Music Dept Brandeis U Waltham MA 02254

WYNETTE, TAMMY, singer; b. Red Bay, Ala., May 5, 1942; d. William Hollis Pugh; m. George Jones, Sept. 1968 (div.); m. George Richey, 1978; children: Gwen, Jackie, Tina. Former beauty operator. Rec. artist Epic Records, 1967—; regular appearances on Grand Ole Opry; tours U.S., Can., Europe; recs. include: Womanhood, Stand By Your Man, Run Woman Run, 1970, Woman to Woman, 1974, Womanhood, 1978, Crying In The Rain, 1981, Sometimes When We Touch, 1985, From the Bottom of my Heart, 1986, Higher Ground, 1987, Next To You, 1989, Heart Over Mind, 1990, Best Loved Hits, 1991, (with others) Tears of Fire: The 25th Anniversary Collection, 1992; author autobiography Stand By Your Man, 1982. Named Female Vocalist of Year Country Music Assn., 1968, 69, 70. Office: care Epic/CBS Records Inc 51 W 52nd St New York NY 10019-6119*

WYNGAARDEN, JAMES BARNES, physician; b. East Grand Rapids, Mich., Oct. 19, 1924; s. Martin Jacob and Johanna (Kempers) W.; m. Ethel Vredevoogd, June 20, 1946 (div. 1977); children: Patricia Wyngaarden Fitzpatrick, Joanna Wyngaarden Gandy, Martha Wyngaarden Krauss, Lisa Wyngaarden Rolland, James Barnes Jr. Student, Calvin Coll., 1942-43, Western Mich. U., 1943-44; MD, U. Mich., 1948; DSc (hon.), U. Mich. and Med. Coll. of Ohio, 1984, U. Ill., 1985, George Washington U., 1986; PhD (hon.), Tel Aviv U., 1987; DSc (hon.), U. S.C., West Mich. U., 1989. Diplomate: Am. Bd. Internal Medicine. Intern Mass. Gen. Hosp., Boston, 1948-49; resident Mass. Gen. Hosp., 1949-51; vis. investigator Pub. Health Rsch. Inst., N.Y.C., 1952-53; investigator NIH, USPHS, Bethesda, Md., 1953-56; asso. prof. medicine and biochemistry Duke U. Med. Sch., 1956-61, prof., 1961-65; vis. scientist Inst. de Biologie-Physiochemique, Paris, 1963-64; prof., chmn. U. Pa. Med. Sch., 1965-67; physician-chief Svc. Hosp. U. PA., Phila., 1965-67; Frederic M. Hanes prof., chmn. dept. medicine Duke U. Sch. of Medicine, Durham, N.C., 1967-82; physician-in-chief Med. Svc. Duke U. Hosp., Durham, 1967-82; chief of staff Duke U. Hosp., Durham, 1981-82; dir. NIH, Bethesda, MD, 1982-89; assoc. dir. life scis. Office of Sci. and Tech. Policy, Exec. Office of Pres., The White House, 1989-90; dir. Human Genome Orgn., 1990-91; fgn. sec. NAS, 1990-94; prof. medicine, assoc. vice chancellor for health affairs Duke U., Durham, N.C., 1990-94, ret., 1994; mem. staff VA, Durham County Hosps.; cons. Office Sci. and Tech. Exec. Office of Pres., 1966-72; Mem. Pres.'s Sci. Adv. Com., 1972-73; mem. Pres.'s Com. for Nat. Medal of Sci., 1977-80; mem. adv. com. biology and medicine AEC, 1966-68; mem. bd. sci. counselors NIH, 1971-74; mem. adv. bd. Howard Hughes Med. Inst., 1969-82; mem. adv. council Life Ins. Med. Research Fund, 1967-70; adv. bd. Sci. Yr., 1977-81; vice chmn. Com. on Study Nat. Needs for Biomed. and Behavioral Research Personnel, NRC, 1977-81; bd. dirs. Marion Merrell Dow Corp., Hybridon Corp., Human Genome Scis. Author: (with W.N. Kelley) Gout and Hyperuricemia, 1976; mem. editorial bd. Jour. Biol. Chemsitry, 1971-74, Arthritis and Rheumatism, 1959-66, Jour. Clin. Investigation, 1962-66, Ann. Internal Medicine, 1964-74, Medicine, 1963-90; editor: (with J.B. Stanbury, D.S. Fredrickson) The Metabolic Basis of Inherited Disease, 1960, 66, 72, 78, 83, (with O. Sperling and A. DeVries) Purine Metabolism in Man, 1974, (with L.H. Smith, Jr.) Cecil Textbook of Medicine, 16th edit., 1982, 19th edit., 1992. Bd. dirs. Royal Soc. Medicine Found., 1971-76, The Robert Wood Johnson Found. Clin. Scholar Program, 1973-78. Ensign USNR, 1943-46; sr. surgeon USPHS, 1951-56, rear adm. USPHS, 1982-90. Recipient Borden Undergrad. Research award, U. Mich., 1948, N.C. Gov.'s award for sci., 1974, Disting. Alumnus award We. Mich. U., 1984, Robert Williams award Assn. Profs. Medicine, 1985, Dalton scholar in medicine, Mass. Gen. Hosp., 1950, Richard Schweiker Excellence in Govt. award, 1985, Fedn. of Am. Socs. of Exptl. Biology Pub. Svc. award, 1989, Humanitarian award Nat. Orgn. for Rare Diseases, 1990; Royal Coll. Physicians fellow, 1984. Mem. Am. Rheumatism Assn., Am. Fedn. Clin. Research, Soc. Soc. Clin. Investigation (pres. 1974, founder's medal 1978), ACP (John Phillips Meml. award 1980), Am. Soc. Clin. Investigation, AAAS, Am. Soc. Biol. Chemists, Assn. Am. Physicians (councillor 1973-77, pres. 1978), Endocrine Soc., Nat. Acad. Scis., Royal Acad. Scis. Sweden, Am. Acad. Arts and Sci., Inst. Medicine, Sigma Xi. Democrat. Presbyterian. Club: Interurban Clinical (Balt.). Avocations: tennis, skiing, painting.

WYNKOOP, DONAL BROOKE, electric power company executive; b. Denver, July 10, 1945; s. Francis Yates and Marylynn Frances (Koogle) W.; m. Sheila Ann Bell, Dec. 17, 1961; children: Donal B. Jr., David Brian, Cheryl Lynn. Grad. high sch., Denver; cert. electric meter course, I.C.S., 1970, cert. electrical distrbn. engr., 1980. Journeyman Pub. Svc. Co. Colo., Denver, 1971-79, sr. meterman, 1979-86, unit mgr., 1986—. Avocations: camping, fishing, travel. Office: Pub Svc Co Colo 1123 W 3rd Ave Denver CO 80223-1351

WYNN, ALBERT RUSSELL, congressman; b. Phila., Sept. 10, 1951; m. Alice Johnson. BS, U. Pitts., 1973; student, Howard U.; JD, Georgetown U., 1979. Intern African Regional Affairs, U.S. State Dept., 1972-73; exec. dir. consumer protection divsn. Prince George's County, 1977-81; mem. Md. Ho. of Dels., 1982-86; lawyer Albert R. Wynn & Assocs., 1982-86; mem. Md. State Senator from Dist. 25, 1986-92, 103d-104th Congresses from 4th Md. Dist., 1993—; mem. banking & fin. svcs com., internat. rels. com., Patuxent Inst. reform task force, 1988—; joint com. econ. devel. strategy, 1989—; del. Dem. Nat. Conv. 1984, 88; pres. Metro. Washington coun. consumer agenices. Mem. NAACP legal assistance program, coalition on black affairs, voter registration, edn. coalition, gov.'s task force drunk & drugged driving; 1st vice chmn. legis. black caucus; chmn Prince George's County black elected officials alliance. Mem. J. Franklin Bourne Bar Assn., Kappa Alpha Psi (past pres.). Democrat. Baptist. Office: US Ho of Reps 418 Condon Ter SE Washington DC 20515-2004*

WYNN, COY WILTON, journalist; b. Prescott, Ark., Aug. 9, 1920; s. Ota Gilbert and Kate (Ward) W.; m. Leila Birbari, June 2, 1947. B.A., La. Coll., Pineville, 1941; M.A., La. State U., 1942. Chmn. dept. journalism Am. U., Cairo, Egypt, 1945-47; dir. div. journalism Lehigh U., Bethlehem, Pa., 1947-50; free-lance writer Middle East, 1950-51; corr. AP, Beirut, Lebanon, 1951-55; bur. chief AP, Cairo, 1955-61; corr. Time mag., Rome, 1962-74; chief bur. Time mag., Cairo, 1974-78; chief Rome Bur. Time mag., 1979-85, cons. on Vatican affairs, 1985-91, ret., 1991. Author: Nasser of Egypt: The Search for Dignity, 1959, Keepers of the Keys, 1988; also articles. Former mem. Associazione della Stampa Estera in Italia; hon. trustee John Cabot U., Rome. Mem. The Authors Guild. Roman Catholic. Clubs: American (Rome) (past pres.). Home: 52 Viale Liegi, Rome Italy 00198

WYNN, JOHN CHARLES, clergyman, retired religion educator; b. Akron, Ohio, Apr. 11, 1920; s. John Francis and Martha Esther (Griffith) W.; m. Rachel Linnell, Aug. 27, 1943; children: Mark Edward, Martha Lois Borland, Maryan Kay Ainsworth. BA, Coll. Wooster, 1941; BD, Yale U., 1944; MA, Columbia U., 1963, EdD, 1964; DD, Davis and Elkins Coll., 1958. Ordained to ministry Presbyn. Ch., 1944. Student asst. pastor Trinity Luth. Ch.: New Haven, 1943-44; assoc. minister First Presbyn. Ch., Evanston, Ill.,

1944-47; pastor El Dorado, Kans., 1947-50; dir. family edn. and research United Presbyn. Bd. Christian Edn., Phila., 1950-59; prof. Colgate Rochester/Bexley Hall/Crozer Theol. Sem., 1959-85, prof. emeritus, 1985—; pvt. practice family therapy; adj. prof. U. Rochester, San Francisco Theol. Sem., St. Bernard's Sem., Wesley Theol. Sem.; postdoctoral fellow Cornell U., 1973-74, St. John's U., 1980; lectr. Sch. Continuing Edn. Johns Hopkins U.; mem. summer faculty Union Theol. Sem., N.Y.C.; del. study conf. World Coun. Chs., 1953, 57, 64, 65, 67, 75, 80; lectr. 5 univs., Republic of South Africa, 1968; chmn. com. on sexuality in human cmty. U.P. Ch.; vol. mem. chaplaincy staff Charlestown Care Ctr., Balt. Author: How Christian Parents Face Family Problems, 1955, Pastoral Ministry to Families, 1957, Families in the Church, A Protestant Survey, 1961, Christian Education for Liberation and Other Upsetting Ideas, 1977, Family Therapy in Pastoral Ministry, 1982 (rev. and expanded as Family Therapy in Pastoral Ministry: Counseling for the Nineties, 1991), The Family Therapist, 1987; Editor: Sermons on Marriage and Family Life, 1956, Sex, Family and Society in Theological Focus, 1966, Sexual Ethics and Christian Responsibility, 1970; Contbr. articles to mags. and religious jours. Bd. dirs. Presbyn. Life, Planned Parenthood League Rochester and Monroe County, Family Service Rochester, Pastoral Counseling Ctr. Fellow Am. Assn. Marriage and Family Therapy (approved supr.); mem. Religious Edn. Assn., Nat. Coun. Chs. of Christ in U.S.A. (chmn. com. family life 1957-60), Nat. Coun. Family Rels., Family Svc. Assn. Am., Rochester Coun. Chs. (dir.). Address: 717 Maiden Choice Ln Apt 523 Catonsville MD 21228-6116

WYNN, KENNETH RICHARD, design and furnishings company executive; b. Utica, N.Y., June 22, 1952; s. Michael and Zelma (Kutner) W.; children: Jennifer, Ashley, Michael. B.A. in French Lit., Swarthmore Coll., 1973; M.B.A. in Fin., U. Nev., 1977. Dir. purchasing Golden Nugget, Inc., Las Vegas, 1973—, v.p. design and constrn., 1977—; pres. Atlandia Design. Mem. devel. planning group property Swarthmore Coll. (Pa.), 1983—. Recipient Harvard Club award (Syracuse), 1969. Republican. Jewish. Office: Atlandia Design 3260 Industrial Rd Las Vegas NV 89109-1132

WYNN, ROBERT E., retired career officer, electronics executive; b. Dallas, Jan. 31, 1942; s. Wendell W. and Thelma (Smart) W.; m. Lavenia K. Davis, Mar. 25, 1972; children: Leslie, Lauren. Bachelors degree, West Point, 1964; MEE, U. Tenn., 1971. Commd. 2d lt. U.S. Army, 1964, advanced through grades to commdg. gen., 1990; chief comm. Ops. Divsn. 5th Signal Command, Heidelberg, Germany, 1979-81; chief of staff 5th Signal Command, Worms, Germany, 1984-85; chief plans and programs, dep. chief staff Ops. and Plans DCS for OPS and PLANS, Washington, 1981-84; comdr. 2d Signal Brigade, Mannheim, Germany, 1986-88, U.S. Army Info. Systems Command/Tng. Doctrine Command, Ft. Monroe, Va., 1988-90; commdg. gen. 7th Signal Command, Ft. Ritchie, Md., 1990-92, U.S. Army Info. Systems Engring. Command, Ft. Huachuca, Ariz., 1992—; ret., 1995; dir. tech. staff Electrospace sys., Inc., Richardson, Tex., 1995—. Decorated Bronze Star, Legion of Merit, Silver Order of Mercury. Mem. Assn. U.S. Army Assn. Grads. (life), Armed Forces Comm. and Electronics Assn. (life, bd. dirs.), Sky Soldier (life, 173d airborne brigade), Signal Corps Regiment (life). Avocations: golf, tennis. Home: 703 Laredo Cir Allen TX 75002

WYNN, STEPHEN A., hotel, entertainment facility executive; b. 1941; married. Pres., chief exec. officer Best Brands, Inc., 1969-72; chmn. bd. dirs., pres., CEO Mirage Resorts Inc. (formerly Golden Nugget Inc.) 1973—. Office: Mirage Resort Inc PO Box 7777 Las Vegas NV 89177-0777 Office: G N L V 3260 Industrial Rd Las Vegas NV 89109-1132*

WYNN, THOMAS JOSEPH, county judge, educator; b. Chgo., Aug. 30, 1918; s. Phillip H. and Delia B (Madden) W.; m. Bernadette L. Lavelle, Apr. 17, 1948; children: Thomas Joseph, John P. AB, DePaul U., 1941, JD, 1942. Bar: Ill. 1942. Spl. investigator Phoenix & Murphy, Chgo., 1942; pvt. practice law Chgo., 1946-59; ptnr. Wynn & Ryan, Chgo., 1959-79; assoc. judge Cir. Ct. Cook County, Ill., 1979-83, judge chancery div. mechanic's lien sect., 1983—; lectr. bus. law Latin Am. Inst., Chgo., 1946-47; mem. faculty Coll. Commerce, DePaul U., Chgo., 1947—, assoc. dean Evening div., 1957-73, prof., 1972-79, part-time faculty, 1979-83, adj. prof. bus. law, 1983—; asst. atty. gen. Ill., 1957-58; bd. dirs., gen. counsel Suburbanite Bowl, Inc., 1958-79; gen. legal counsel Chgo. Consortium Colls. and Univs., GM Tool Corp.; pres., bd. dirs. Metroplex Leasing and Financing, Inc. Candidate for alderman Chgo. City Coun., 1951; candidate for judge Mcpl. Ct. Chgo., 1956; exec. sec., bd. dirs. Ill. Good Govt. Inst., 1958-79; mem. adv. bd. to dean Coll Law DePaul U., 1992—. Ensign-lt. (S.G.) USNR, 1942-46. Mem. Ill. Bar Assn., Chgo. Bar Assn. (mem. arbitration and alternative dispute resolution com. and civil practice coms.), Ill. Judges Assn. (com. mandatory arbitration alt. dispute resolution, com. pubs.), Assn. Univ. Evening Colls. (past chmn.), Am. Bus. Law Assn. (pres. 1972-73), Am. Real Estate and Urban Econs. Assn., Chgo. Area Evening Deans and Dirs. Assn., U.S. Adult Edn. Assn., Ill. Adult Edn. Assn., Am. Right-of-Way Assn. (advisor chmn., nat. edni. com., 1963-64), St. Vincent DePaul Soc., DePaul Law Alumni Assn. (past pres.), Smithsonian Inst., Pres.'s Club, (DePaul U. 1986—), Blue Key, Gamma Eta Gamma, Beta Gamma Sigma, Delta Mu Delta. Home: 225 S Rohlwing Rd Palatine IL 60067-6441 Office: Cir Ct Cook County Daley Civic Ctr Chicago IL 60606

WYNN, WILLIAM HARRISON, union official; b. South Bend, Ind., July 17, 1931; s. William and Effie (Welch) W.; m. Bonnie Day, Oct. 20, 1962; children: Mark and Brad (twins). Student public schs., South Bend. Dept. head A&P Tea Co., South Bend, 1949-54; bus. rep. Local 37, Retail Clks. Internat. Union, South Bend, 1954-59, rep. Dist. Council 12, 1959-61; sec-treas. Dist. Council 12, Retail Clks. Internat. Union, 1962-66; internat. rep. Retail Clks. Internat. Union, Washington, 1961-62; asst. divisional dir. Retail Clks. Internat. Union, 1966-69, asst. to internat. dir. orgn., 1969, adminstrv. asst. to pres., 1969-71, divisional dir., 1971-76, internat. v.p., 1972-76, internat. sec.-treas., 1976-77, pres., 1977-79; pres. United Food and Comml. Workers Internat. Union, Washington, 1979—; v.p. AFL-CIO; mem. exec. com. Internat. Fedn. Comml., Clerical and Tech. Employees, Joint Labor Mgmt. Com. of Retail Food Industry; mem. exec. bd. Maritime Trades Dept., AFL-CIO; pres. Food and Beverage Trades Dept., AFL-CIO; dir. Union Labor Life Ins. Co.; mem. labor policy adv. com. for multilateral trade negotiations. Corp. mem. Muscular Dystrophy Assn., Inc.; mem. Pres.'s Com. on Employment of Handicapped, Com. for Nat. Health Ins.; mem. exec. bd. A. Philip Randolph Inst. Recipient Medal award Israel Prime Minister, 1978. Office: UFCW 1775 K St NW Washington DC 20006-1502*

WYNNE, BRIAN JAMES, former association executive, consultant; b. N.Y.C., Dec. 2, 1950; s. Bernard and Dolores (Doyle) W. Student, Institute des Sciences Politiques, Paris, 1970-71; B.A., Coll. Holy Cross, 1972; M.A., U. So. Calif. 1974. Mem. staff Exec. Cons., Inc., McLean, Va., 1974-76; prin., 1976-78; exec. dir. Indsl. Designers Soc. Am., Washington, 1978-89; cons. to various non-profit orgns.; dir. Worldesign 85, founder Worldesign Found. Mem. Am. Soc. Assn. Execs., Indsl. Designers Soc. Am. (hon.), Phi Sigma Iota. Home: 5200 N Ocean Blvd Fort Lauderdale FL 33308-3037

WYNNE, BRUCE, tribal administrator, artist; b. Wellpinit, Wash., June 14, 1944; s. William and Gertrude (Flett) W.; m. Marie Jacob (dec. Sept. 1970); m. Mary Eaves, Apr. 1, 1973; children: John (dec.), Angela, Duane, Jena. Grad., Inst. Am. Indian Arts, Santa Fe, 1964; BFA, U. Colo., 1975. Exhibits designer Heard Mus., Phoenix, 1968-70; asst. dir. Indian Ednl. Opportunity Program U. Colo., Boulder, 1970-73; prof. artist, primarily in sculpture, 1975-84; mem. Spokane Indian Tribal Coun., 1984—, vice chmn., 1985-87, tribal chmn., 1989—. Exhibited in shows, including Scottsdale Nat. Indian Arts Exhbn., 1967, 75, 76, Red Cloud Nat. Indian Art Exhibit, Pine Ridge, S.D., 1970, Heart Mus., 1971, 75, 76, Santa Fe Indian Art Market, 1975, Gallup (N.Mex.) Intertribal Exhbn., 1976, Philbrook Ann. Indian Arts Exhbn., Tulsa, 1976, 77, Native Am. Ctr. for Living Arts, Niagara Falls, N.Y., 1980; represented in collections including Heard Mus., Philbrook Art Ctr., Diamond L. Found., Snyder, Tex., Buffalo Bill Mus. and Western Art Ctr., Cody, Wyo. Mem. Pres. Clinton Transition Team, 1992-94; mem. N.W. Portland Area Indian Health Bd.; mem. Wash. State Gov.'s Adv. Com. on Social and Health Svcs., 1992—. Mem. Affiliated Tribes of N.W. Indians (pres. 1991—), Nat. Congress of Am. Indians (v.p. 1991—, bd. dirs., mem. health com.), Upper Columbia United Tribes (chmn. 1989-94), Inland Tribal Consortium. Office: Spokane Bus Coun PO Box 477 Wellpinit WA

99040 Office: Spokane Tribe of Indians Alex Sherwood Meml Ctr 6208 Ford/Wellpinit Rd Wellpinit WA 99040

WYNNE, JAMES EARL, lawyer; b. Chgo., Sept. 3, 1950; s. Conrad Joseph and Irene F. (Spengler) W.; m. Cathy Mantay, July 27, 1974; children: Alison Kauri, Ashley Erin, Michael James. BA in Econs., Mich. State U., 1972; JD, Ill. Inst. Tech.-Chgo.-Kent, 1975. Bar: Ill. 1975, Mich. 1978, U.S. Dist. Ct. (no. dist.) Ill. 1975, U.S. Dist. Ct. (ea. dist.) Mich. 1978, U.S. Ct. Appeals (6th cir.) 1985. Atty. Coghlan & Joyce, Chgo., 1975-78, Milmet & Vecchio, Detroit, 1978-83; ptnr. Milmet & Vecchio, 1983-86, Butzel Long, Detroit, 1986—; hearing panelist Mich. Atty. Discipline Bd., Detroit, 1987—; adj. prof. trial advocacy U. Detroit Law Sch., 1989—. Author: (with others) Tolling Statues of Limitation, 1988, (with another) REmedies of Buyers and Sellers under the UCC. Mem. ABA, Am. Trial Lawyers Assn., Chgo. Bar Assn., Mich. Bar Assn., Detroit Bar Assn. Republican. Roman Catholic. Club: Detroit Golf. Avocations: golf, home renovation. Office: Butzel Long 150 W Jefferson Ave Ste 900 Detroit MI 48226-4415

WYNNE, JOHN OLIVER, newspaper, broadcast and cable executive; b. Norfolk, Va., July 6, 1945; s. Oliver Jr. and Margaret (Klasman) W.; m. Susan Stribling (Snodgrass), Dec. 23, 1972; children: John Oliver Jr., Lee Stribling (dec.), Bradford Annan. BA, Princeton U., 1967; JD, U. Va., 1971. Bar: Va. 1971. Atty. Willcox, Savage, Lawrence, Dickson & Spindle, Norfolk, 1971-74; corp. sec. Landmark Comm., Inc., Norfolk, 1974-77, v.p. broadcast and cable, 1977-78; v.p., gen. mgr. Sta. KNTV-TV subs. Landmark Comm., Inc., Norfolk; pres. broadcasting and video enterprises Landmark Comm., Inc., 1980-90, COO, pres. newspapers and broadcasting group, 1990-91, pres., CEO, 1991—. The Weather Channel, 1981—, The Travel Channel, 1992—; bd. dirs. Cabletelevision Advt. Bur., N.Y.C., 1983-90. Trustee Norfolk Acad., 1980—; trustee Va. Found. for Ind. Colls., 1990—; bd. dirs., vice chmn. Children's Health System, Inc., Norfolk, 1987-93; chmn. Jr. Achievement, Norfolk, 1987; chmn. capital campaign South Hampton Rds. United Way, Norfolk, 1986. Served with U.S. Army, 1968-74. Mem. Nat. Cable TV Assn. Bd. dirs. 1988—), Harbor Club. Episcopalian. Club: Harbor (Norfolk). Avocations: golf, tennis, skiing, walking, reading. Office: Landmark Communications Inc 150 W Brambleton Ave Norfolk VA 23510-2018

WYNNE, JOHNNY CALVIN, university dean, plant breeding researcher; b. Williamston, N.C., May 17, 1943; s. James Harry and Rachel Loraine (Ayers) W.; m. Diane Louise Sawyer, 1961 (div. Feb. 1989); children: Debbie Ann, Donna Carol; m. Jacqueline Crawford Creech, Nov. 25, 1989; children: John Christopher, James Alexander. BS, N.C. State U., 1965, MS, 1968, PhD, 1974. Instr. crop sci. dept. N.C. State U., Raleigh, 1968-74, asst. prof., 1974-78, assoc. prof., 1978-83, prof., 1983-91, acting tchg. administr., 1987-89, head dept., 1989-91, assoc. dean, dir. N.C. agr. rsch. svc., 1992—. Recipient rsch. award Nat. Peanut Coun., 1992. Fellow AAAS, Am. Peanut Rsch. and Edn. Soc. (pres. 1990, Bailey award 1977); mem. Crop Sci. Soc. Am., Coun. for Agrl. Sci. and Tech., So. Assn. Expt. Sta. Dirs. (chmn. 1994), Sigma Iota Rho. Office: N Carolina State Univ PO Box 7643 Raleigh NC 27695

WYNNE, LYMAN CARROLL, psychiatrist; b. Lake Benton, Minn., Sept. 17, 1923; s. Nels Wind and Ella C. (Pultz) W.; m. Adele Rogerson, Dec. 22, 1947; children: Christine, Randall, Sara, Barry, Jonathan. War certificate, Harvard, 1943, MD, 1947, PhD in Social Psychology, 1958; MD (hon.), Oulu U., Finland, 1989. Med. intern Peter Bent Brigham Hosp., Boston, 1947-48; grad. fellow social relations dept. Harvard, 1948-49; resident neurology Queen Square Hosp., London, Eng., 1950; resident psychiatry Mass. Gen. Hosp., Boston, St. Elizabeth's Hosp., Washington, also NIMH, 1951-54; psychoanalytic tng. Washington Psychoanalytic Inst., 1954-60, teaching analyst, 1965-72; cons., investigator WHO, 1965—; staff NIMH, 1954-57, chief sect. family studies, 1957-61, chief adult psychiatry br., 1961-72; mem. faculty Washington Sch. Psychiatry, 1956-72; prof. U. Rochester Sch. Medicine and Dentistry, 1971—, chmn. dept. psychiatry, 1971-77, dir. div. family programs, 1971-83; psychiatrist-in-chief Strong Meml. Hosp., Rochester, N.Y., 1971-77; vis. lectr. Am. U., Beirut, Lebanon, 1963-64. Chmn. bd. dirs. Family Process; mem. editorial adv. bd. Jour. Nervous and Mental Diseases; sr. editor: The Nature of Schizophrenia, 1978; editor: The State of the Art in Family Therapy Research; co-editor: Psychosocial Intervention in Schizophrenia, 1983, Children at Risk for Schizophrenia, 1984, The Language of Family Therapy, 1985; sr. editor Systems Consultation, 1986. Chmn. AAMFT Rsch. & Edn. Found., 1992-94. Med. dir. USPHS, 1961-72; mem. NRC, 1969-72. Recipient Commendation medal USPHS, 1965; Hofheimer prize Am. Psychiat. Assn., 1966; Frieda Fromm-Reichmann award Am. Acad. Psychoanalysis, 1966; Meritorious Service medal USPHS, 1966; Stanley Dean award Am. Coll. Psychiatrists, 1976; McAlpin Research Achievement award, 1977, Disting. Achievement in Family Therapy Research, Am. Family Therapy Assn., 1981; Disting. Research Achievement award Assn. Marriage and Family Therapy, 1982, Disting. Profl. Contbn. award Am. Assn. for Marriage and Family Therapy, 1985, Disting. Contbn. to Family Therapy award Am. Family Therapy Assn., 1989. Fellow Am. Psychiat. Assn. (life), Am. Acad. Psychoanalysis; mem. Am. Psychosomatic Soc. (mem. council 1969-72), Psychiat. Research Soc., Western N.Y. Psychoanalytic Soc. (pres. 1986-87), Am. Coll. Psychoanalysts, Am. Family Therapy Assn. (pres. 1986-87), Am. Assn. for Marriage and Family Therapy (bd. dirs. 1992-94), Am. Psychoanalytic Assn., Assn. for Clin. Psychosocial Rsch. (coun. 1984-91). Home: 17 Tobey Brook Pittsford NY 14534 Office: Strong Meml Hosp Rochester NY 14642

WYNNE-EDWARDS, HUGH ROBERT, entrepreneur, scientist; b. Montreal, Que., Can., Jan. 19, 1934; s. Vero Copner and Jeannie Campbell (Morris) W.-E.; married; children from previous marriages: Robin Alexander, Katherine Elizabeth, Renée Elizabeth Lortie, Krista Smyth, Jeannie Elizabeth, Alexander Vernon. B.Sc. with 1st class honors, U. Aberdeen, Scotland, 1955; M.A., Queen's U., 1957, Ph.D., 1959; D.Sc. (hon.), Meml. U., 1975. With Geol. Survey Can., 1958-59; lectr. Queen's U., Kingston, Ont., 1968-72; asst. prof., then assoc. prof., 1961-68, prof., head dept. geol. scis., 1968-72; prof., then Cominco prof., head dept. geol. scis. U. B.C., Vancouver, 1972-77; asst. sec. univ. Ministry of State for Sci. and Tech., Ottawa, 1977-79; sci. dir. Alcan Internat. Ltd., Montreal, 1979-80, v.p. R&D, chief sci. officer, 1980-89; CEO Moli Energy Ltd., Vancouver, 1989-90; pres. Terracy Inc., Vancouver, 1989—; sci. advisor Teck Corp., Vancouver, 1989-91; pres., CEO B.C. Rsch. Inc., Vancouver, 1993—; adviser Directorate Mining and Geology, Uttar Pradesh, India, 1964, Grenville project Que. Dept. Natural Resources, 1968-72; vis. prof. U. Aberdeen, 1965-66, U. Witwatersrand, Johannesburg, South Africa, 1972; UN cons., India, 1974, SCITEC, 1977-78; mem. sci. adv. com. CBC, 1980-84; mem. Sci. Coun. Can., 1983-89, Nat. Adv. Bd. on Sci. and Tech., 1987; indsl. liaison com. UN Ctr. for Sci. and Tech. in Devel., 1982-84; vice chmn. tech. adv. group Bus. Coun. for Sustainable Devel., Geneva, 1991. Bd. dirs. Royal Victoria Hosp., Montreal, 1984-89; dir. Soc. Quebecoise d'initiatives petrolière, 1983-87; dir. CS Resources Ltd., 1993—. Decorated officer Order of Can., 1991; recipient Spendiarov prize 24th Internat. Geol. Congress, Montreal, 1972. Fellow Can. Acad. Engring., Royal Soc. Can.; mem. Can. Rsch. Mgmt. Assn. (vice chmn. 1982-84, chmn. 1984-85, assn. medal 1987), Univ. Club (Montreal). Mem. United Ch. Avocations: tennis, skiing, carpentry. Office: Terracy Inc, 2030 27th St, West Vancouver, BC Canada V7V 4L4 also: BC Rsch Inc, 3650 Wesbrook Mall, Vancouver, BC Canada V6S 2L2

WYRICK, CHARLES LLOYD, JR., publisher, writer, editor; b. Greensboro, N.C., May 5, 1939; s. Charles Lloyd and Edythe Ellen (Ellis) W.; m. Constance Michelle Hooper, Aug. 22, 1964; children—Charles Lloyd, III, Christopher Conrad Hooper. B.A., Davidson (N.C.) Coll. 1961; M.F.A., U. N.C., 1967. Instr. Stephens Coll., Columbia, Mo., 1964-66; asst. head programs div. Va. Museum, Richmond, 1966-68; exec. dir. Assn. Preservation Va. Antiquities, Richmond, 1968-70; pres. Research & Restoration, Inc. Richmond. 1970-73; dir. Del. Art Mus., Wilmington, 1973-79, Gibbes Mus. Art, Charleston, S.C., 1980-86; pres. Wyrick & Co., Charleston, 1986—. Dixie Media, Inc., Charleston, 1989—; editor, pub. "Omnibus", 1989-94; mem. Richmond Commn. Archt. Rev., 1969-72, New Castle County (Del.) Hist. Rev. Bd., 1977-88, also vice chmn.; mem. Bd. Archtl. Rev. City of Charleston, 1988-94, chmn., 1992-94; mem. Charleson Consortium on Higher Edn.; cons. in field. Author: "The 17th Street Market", 1972; contbr. articles to profl. jours. Bd. visitors Davidson Coll., 1993—; mem. Econs. of Amenities City of Charleston, 1978; chmn. S.C. Coastal Conservation

League, 1989-94, Charleston Area Arts Coun., 1989-91, Friends of Charleston County Courthouse, 1989-94, Pub. Art Trust, 1988-90; adv. com. S.C. Dept. Natural Resources, 1992—. Recipient 1st award spl. column writing Va. Press Assn., 1973. Mem. Assn. Am. Pubs., Pubs. Assn. of South (bd. dirs. 1990-92, pres. 1991-92), S.C. Acad. Authors (bd. dirs. 1990-92), Carolina Yacht Club. Home: 34 Legare St Charleston SC 29401-2336 Office: 1-A Pinckney St Charleston SC 29401-2626

WYRICK, PRISCILLA BLAKENEY, microbiologist; b. Greensboro, N.C., Apr. 28, 1940; d. Carnie Lee and Prestine (Blakeney) W. BS in Med. Tech., U. N.C., Chapel Hill, 1962; MS in Bacteriology, U. N.C., 1967, PhD in Bacteriology, 1971. Technologist Clin. Microbiology Lab., N.C. Meml. Hosp., Chapel Hill, 1962-64; asst. supr. Clin. Microbiology Lab., N.C. Meml. Hosp., 1964-65, supr., 1965-66; sci. staff fellow Nat. Inst. Med. Rsch., Mill Hill, London, 1971-73; asst. prof. dept. microbiology U. N.C. Sch. Medicine, Chapel Hill, 1973-79; assoc. prof. U. N.C. Sch. Medicine, 1979-88, prof., 1988—. Grantee, NIH. Mem. Am. Acad. Microbiology, Am. Soc. Microbiology (pres. N.C. br. 1981-82, chmn. div. gen. med. microbiology 1981-82), AAAS, Soc. Infectious Diseases, Sigma Xi. Office: U NC Sch Medicine CB 7290 816 FLOB Chapel Hill NC 27599

WYRSCH, JAMES ROBERT, lawyer, educator, author; b. Springfield, Mo., Feb. 23, 1942; s. Louis Joseph and Jane Elizabeth (Welsh) W.; m. B. Darlene Wyrsch, Oct. 18, 1975; children: Scott, Keith, Mark, Brian, Marcia. BA, U. Notre Dame, 1963; JD, Georgetown U., 1966; LLM, U. Mo., Kansas City, 1972. Bar: Mo. 1966, U.S. Ct. Appeals (8th cir.) 1971, U.S. Supreme Ct. 1972, U.S. Ct. Appeals (10th cir.) 1974, U.S. Ct. Appeals (5th cir.) 1974, U.S. Ct. Mil. & Appeals 1978, U.S. Ct. Appeals (6th cir.) 1982, U.S. Ct. Appeals (11th cir.) 1984, U.S. Ct. Appeals (7th cir.) 1986, U.S. Ct. Appeals (4th cir.) 1990. Assoc. Wyrsch, Atwell, Mirakian, Lee and Hobbs, P.C. and predecessors, Kansas City, Mo., 1970-71, of counsel, 1972-77, ptnr., 1978—, pres., shareholder, 1988—; adj. prof. U. Mo., 1981—; mem. com. instrns. Mo. Supreme Ct., 1983—. Capt. U.S. Army, 1966-69; named to Who's Who in Kansas City Law, Kansas City Bus. Jour., 1991, 1994; recipient U. Mo. Kansas City Svc. award Law Found., 1991-92. Fellow Am. Coll. Trial Lawyers, Am. Bar Found.; mem. ABA, Am. Arbitration Assn. (panel arbitrators), Mo. Bar Assn. (vice chmn. criminal law com. 1978-79), Kansas City Bar Assn. (chmn. anti-trust com. 1981), Assn. Trial Lawyers Am., Am. Bd. of Trial Advocates (adv.), Nat. Assn. Criminal Def. Attys. Mo. Assn. Criminal Def. Attys. (sec. 1982), Phi Delta Phi. Democrat. Roman Catholic. Co-author: Missouri Criminal Trial Practice, 1994; contbr. articles to profl. jours. Home: 811 W Hearnes Ave Blue Springs MO 64015-3003 Office: Wyrsch Atwell Mirakian Lee & Hobbs PC 1101 Walnut 13th Flr Kansas City MO 64106-2281

WYRTKI, KLAUS, oceanography educator; b. Tarnowitz, Germany, Feb. 7, 1925; came to U.S., 1961; s. Wilhelm and Margarete (Pacharzina) W.; m. Helga Kocher, June 6, 1954 (div. 1970); children: Undine, Oliver; m. Erika Maassen. PhD magna cum laude, U. Kiel, Germany, 1950. With German Hydrographic Inst., Hamburg, 1950-51; German Rsch. Coun. postdoctoral rsch. fellow U. Kiel, 1951-54; head Inst. Marine Rsch., Djakarta, Indonesia, 1954-57; sr. rsch. officer, then prin. rsch. officer div. fisheries and oceanography Commonwealth Sci. and Indsl. Rsch. Orgn., Sydney, Australia, 1958-61; assoc. rsch. oceanographer, then rsch. oceanographer Scripps Instn. Oceanography, U. Calif., 1961-64; prof. oceanography U. Hawaii, Honolulu, 1964—; chmn. North Pacific Expt., 1974-80, com. on climate changes and ocean Internat. Assn. Phys. Scis. of the Oceans; mem. Spl. Com. on Ocean Rsch. Working Group on Prediction of El Nino, Sci. Working Group on Topography Expt., panel on climate and global change NOAA. Author: The Horizontal and Vertical Field of Motion in the Peru Current, 1963; editor: Oceanographic Atlas of the International Indian Ocean Expedition, 1988; mem. editorial bd. Jour. Phys. Oceanography, 1971-79. Recipient Excellence in Rsch. award U. Hawaii, 1980, Rosenstiel award U. Miami, 1981. Fellow Am. Geophys. Union (Maurice Ewing medal 1989), Am. Meteorol. Soc. (Harald Ulrick Sverdrup Gold medal 1991), Deutsche Meteorologische Gesellschaft (Albert Defant medal 1992). Office: U Hawaii 1000 Pope Rd Honolulu HI 96822-2336*

WYSCHOGROD, EDITH, philosophy educator; b. N.Y.C.; d. Morris and Selma Shurer; m. Michael Wyschogrod, Mar. 9,1955; children: Daniel, Tamar. AB, Hunter Coll., 1957; PhD, Columbia U., 1970. Prof. philosophy Queens Coll., Flushing, N.Y., 1967-92; J. Newton Rayzor prof. philosophy and religious thought Rice U., Houston, 1992—. Author: Emmanuel Levinas: The Problem of Ethical Metaphysics, 1974, Spirit in Ashes, 1985, Saints and Postmodernism, 1990; co-author: Lacan and Theological Discourse, 1989. Fellow Nat. Humanities Ctr., 1981, Woodrow Wilson Ctr., 1987-88. Mem. Am. Acad. Religion (pres. 1992-93). Office: Rice University PO Box 1892 6100 South Main Houston TX 77251

WYSE, BONITA W(ENSINK), nutrition educator, researcher; b. Lorain, Ohio, Oct. 2, 1945; d. Norbert B. and Ruth B.(DeChant) Wensink. BS, Notre Dame of Ohio, 1967; MS, Mich. State U., 1970; PhD, Colo. State U., 1977. Registered dietitian. Clin. dietitian St. Lawrence Hosp., Lansing, Mich., 1968-69; instr. nutrition Utah State U., Logan, 1970-73, asst. prof., 1973-77, assoc. prof., dir. coordinated undergrad. med. dietetics program, 1977-81, prof., 1981—, acting dean Coll. Family Life, 1984-86, dean, 1986—; bd. dirs. Gerber Products Co., Fremont, Mich.; cons. Met. Life Found., N.Y.C., 1983-86; mem. adv. bd. Heart, Blood, Lung Inst., NIH, Bethesda, Md., 1984-87. Author: Nutritional Quality Index of Foods, 1979; contbr. articles to profl. jours. Bd. dirs. Citizens Against Phys. and Sexual Abuse, Logan, 1984. Recipient Outstanding Alumna award Dept. Food Sci. and Nutrition, Mich. State U., 1982. Mem. Am. Dietetic Assn. (council on research 1982-87, bd. dirs. 1984-87, Frances E. Fischer Meml. Nutrition Lectr., 1984), Utah Dietetic Assn. (pres. 1976-77), Am. Inst. Nutrition, Am. Home Econs. Assn. (Borden award for research 1981). Republican. Roman Catholic. Office: Utah State U Dean's Office Family Life Logan UT 84322-2900

WYSE, LOIS, advertising executive, author; b. Cleve.; d. Roy B. Wohlgemuth and Rose (Schwartz) Weisman; m. Marc Wyse (div. 1980); m. Lee Guber (dec. 1988). Pres. Wyse Advt. Inc., N.Y.C., 1951—; bd. dirs. Consol. Natural Gas, Pitts.; ptnr. City & Co. Author 54 books; contbg. editor Good Housekeeping; syndicated columnist Wyse Words, publisher. Trustee Beth Israel Med. Ctr., N.Y.C. Mem. Woman's Forum (bd. dirs.), Com. 200, PEN. Office: Wyse Advt Inc 22 W 23d St 5th Fl New York NY 10010

WYSE, WILLIAM WALKER, lawyer; b. Spokane, Wash., July 20, 1919; s. James and Hattie (Walker) W.; m. Janet E. Oswalt, Jan. 30, 1944; children: Wendy L., Scott C., Duncan E. AB, U. Wash., 1941; JD, Harvard U., 1948. Bar: Oreg. 1948. Pvt. practice Portland; ptnr. Stoel, Rives, Boley, Jones & Gray, 1953-88; pres. Wyse Investment Services, 1988—; past dir. Treasureland Savs. and Loan Assn.; past trustee, sec. Pacific Realty Trust; past trustee Holladay Park Plaza. Bd. dirs. Cmty. Child Guidance Clinic, 1951-57, pres., 1956-57; chmn. ctrl. budget com. United Fund, 1958-60; 1st v.p. United Good Neighbors; chmn. bd. dirs. Portland Sch. Bd., 1969-66; bd. dirs. Oreg. Symphony Soc., 1973-74, 93—, pres. 1968-70; pres. Tri-County Cmty. Coun., 1970-71; bd. dirs. Portland Mental Health Assn.; bd. dirs., sec. Oreg. Parks Found. Mem. ABA, Oreg. Bar Assn., Multnomah County Bar Assn., Am. Coll. Real Estate Lawyers, Univ. Club, Arlington Club, Portland City Club (past gov.), Wauna Lake Club, Delta Upsilon. Republican. Presbyterian. Home: 3332 SW Fairmount Ln Portland OR 97201-1446 Office: 806 SW Broadway Portland OR 97205

WYSER-PRATTE, JOHN MICHAEL, lawyer; b. Paris, Sept. 4, 1936; came to U.S., 1950; s. Eugene John and Marguerite (von Prattes) W.-P.; m. Jean Doughty Templeton, Aug. 22, 1964 (div. Jan. 1976); children: Michèle Marguerite, Renée Christine; m. Maryse Sisitan, Jan. 23, 1976; 1 child, Anne Catherine. BA, Coll. of the Holy Cross, 1958; JD, Georgetown U., 1963; cert. in internat. law studies, U. Geneva, 1964, Institut Universitaire des Hautes Etudes Internationales. Bar: N.Y. 1965, U.S. Ct. Appeals (2d crct.) 1974, U.S. Dist. Ct. (so. and ea. dists.) N.Y. 1975. Assoc. Coudert Bros., N.Y.C., 1964-71, ptnr., 1972-86; ptnr. Schnader, Harrison, Segal & Lewis, N.Y.C., 1987-95, Ross & Hardies, N.Y.C., 1995—; rsch. asst. Inst. for Internat. Trade Law, Georgetown U. Law Ctr., 1962-63; guest lectr., seminar speaker local C. of C.s, France, 1986—; guest speaker ann. Round Table

Groupement des Industries Françaises Aéronautiques et Spatiales, Paris, 1986-92. Capt. USMC, 1958-62, USMCR, 1962-71. Schulte Zur Hausen fellow, 1963-64. Mem. ABA, Union Internationale des Avocats, Assn. Bar City of N.Y., French-Am. C. of C. (U.S.), Paris Am. Club. Republican. Roman Catholic. Office: Ross & Hardies Park Ave Towers 65 E 55th St New York NY 10022

WYSK, RICHARD A., engineering educator, researcher; b. Holyoke, Mass., Sept. 22, 1948; s. Stanley and Sophia Dorothy (Mazurowski) W.; m. Caryl Lynne Ray, Jan. 18, 1969; children: Richard Patrick, Rebecca Jeanne, Robyn Caryl. BS in Indsl. Engring. & Ops. Rsch., U. Mass., 1972, MS in Indsl. Engring. & Ops. Rsch., 1973; PhD in Indsl. Engring., Purdue U., 1977. Prodn. control mgr. Gen. Electric, Erie, Pa., 1975-76; assoc. prof. Va. Polytechnic Inst., Blacksburg, 1977-83; prof. Pa. State U. State College, 1983-90, William Leonhard chair engring., 1995—; Royce Wisenbaker chair Tex. A&M U., College Station, 1990-94; William Lionhard chair in engring. Pa. State U. State College, 1995—; dir. Inst. Mfg. Systems, College Station, 1990-94. Co-author: A Study Guide for the P.E. in I.E., 1982, An Intro to Automated Proc. Plan., 1985, Modern Manufacturing Process Engineering, 1989, Computer-aided Manufacturing, 1991 (Book-of-the-Yr. award Inst. Indsl. Engrs. 1992, E. Eugene Merchant Mfg. Textbook award Soc. Mfg. Engrs. 1992). Pks. commr. Montgomery County Pks. & Recreation, Blacksburg, 1982-83; adv. mem. Inst. Systems Rsch. U. Md., 1991—. With U.S. Army, 1969-71, Vietnam. Decorated Army Commendation medal with 2 oak leaf clusters. Fellow Inst. Indsl. Engrs. (chpt. pres. 1990—, Region III Award of Excellence 1982, D. Baker award 1993); mem. Soc. Mfg. Engrs. (sr., Outstanding Young Mfg. Engr. 1981), Engring. Accreditation Commn. (commr. 1990-92), Sigma Xi. Avocations: racquetball, basketball. Office: Pa State U 207 Hammond Bldg State College PA 16802

WYSLOTSKY, IHOR, engineering company executive; b. Kralovane, Czechoslovakia, Dec. 22, 1930; s. Ivan and Nadia (Alexiew) W.; came to U.S., 1958, naturalized, 1961; M.E., Sch. Aeros., Buenos Aires, Argentina, 1955; m. Marta Farion, 1983; children: Katria, Bohdan, Roman, Alexander. Design engr. Kaiser Industries, Buenos Aires, 1955-58; cons. design engr., Newark, 1959-64; chief engr. Universal Tool Co., Chgo., 1964-69; pres. CBC Devel Co., Inc., Chgo., 1969-74; pres. TEC, Inc., Chgo., 1972-83; pres. REDEX Corp., 1983-89, chmn. 1993—; engring. adviser to bd. Biosystems Insts., Inc., La Jolla, Calif.; vis. com. mem. Harvard Univ., 1993—. Co-founder Ukrainian Univ. Studies, U. Ill.; co-founder, pres. Am. Ukrainian Bus. Coun., 1991-93; mem. Ukrainian working com. Ctr. Strateqic Internat. Studies, Washington. Vis. com. mem. Harvard U. Mem. Packaging Inst. U.S.A., Am.-Israeli C. of C. (v.p.), Brit. Engring. Assn. River Plate. Mgmt. adv. bd. Modern Plastics Publs. Patentee in field. Home: 6133 N Forest Glen Ave Chicago IL 60646-5015 Office: 860 E State Pky Schaumburg IL 60170

WYSOCKI, F(ELIX) MICHAEL, lawyer; b. Phila., Sept. 12, 1947; s. Felix and Helen (Kuzmik) W.; m. Lois Barbara Abramson, Aug. 23, 1970; 1 child, Dana. BA with highest distinction, George Washington U., 1969; JD cum laude, U. Pa., 1972. Bar: Pa. 1972, U.S. Dist. Ct. (ea. dist.) Pa. 1972. Assoc. Goodis, Greenfield, Henry, Shaiman & Levin, Phila., 1972-75, Garfinkel & Volpicelli, Phila., 1975-79; ptnr. Garfinkel & Volpicelli, 1979-80, Rawle & Henderson, Phila., 1980-86, Saul, Ewing, Remick & Saul, Phila., 1987—; lectr. Pa. Bar Inst. Bd. dirs., pres. Radnor A Better Chance. Mem. ABA, Pa. Bar Assn., Phila. Bar Assn. (vice chmn. real property sect. 1988, chmn. real property sect. 1989, bd. govs. 1989, exec. com. real property sect.), Phi Beta Kappa. Avocations: reading, running, cycling, skiing, tennis. Office: Saul Ewing Remick & Saul 3800 Centre Sq W Philadelphia PA 19102

WYSS, DAVID ALEN, financial service executive; b. Ft. Wayne, Ind., Nov. 14, 1944; s. Alen G. and Anne W. (Winicker) W.; m. Grace H. Hawes, June 11, 1966; children: Sarah J., Alen D. BS, MIT, 1966; PhD, Harvard U., 1971. Economist Fed. Res., Washington, 1970-74, sr. economist, 1975-77; advisor Bank Eng., London, 1974-75; sr. staff economist Council Econ. Advisers, Washington, 1977-79; v.p. DRI Ltd., London, 1979-83; rsch. dir. DRI/McGraw Hill, Lexington, Mass., 1983—. Contbr. numerous articles to profl. jours. Mem. Am. Econ. Assn., Am. Statis. Assn., Nat. Assn. Bus. Economists. Office: DRI/McGraw Hill 24 Hartwell Ave Lexington MA 02173-3144

WYSS, JOHN BENEDICT, lawyer; b. Evanston, Ill., Nov. 23, 1947; s. Walther Erwin and Caroline Nettie (Benedict) W.; m. Dianne Dunlop, Aug. 12, 1978 (div. Aug. 1993); children: John Christian, Kirsten Dunlop. BS in Physics summa cum laude, Stanford U., 1969; JD, Yale U., 1972. Bar: Calif. 1972, D.C. 1974, U.S. Supreme Ct. 1976. Trial atty. antitrust div. U.S. Dept. Justice, Washington, 1972-74; assoc. Kirkland & Ellis, Washington, 1974-78, ptnr., 1978-83; ptnr. Wiley, Rein & Fielding, Washington, 1983—. Mem. ABA, Phi Beta Kappa. Office: Wiley Rein & Fielding 1776 K St NW Washington DC 20006-2304

WYTON, ALEC, composer, organist; b. London, Aug. 3, 1921; came to U.S., 1950, naturalized, 1968; s. Gilbert and Jessie (Burrage) W.; m. Mary Thornton Broman; children: Vaughan, Richard, Patrick, Christopher. B.A., Oxford U., 1945, M.A., 1949; Mus.D. (hon.), Susquehanna (Pa.) U., 1970. Asst. organist Christ Church Cathedral, Oxford U., 1943-46; organist St Mathews Ch., Northampton, Eng., 1946-50, Christ Church Cathedral, St. Louis, 1950-54, Cathedral St. John the Divine, N.Y.C., 1954-74, St. James's Ch., N.Y.C., 1974-87, St. Stephen's Ch., Ridgefield, Conn., 1987—; chair dept. music Manhattan Sch. Music, 1984-93; adj. prof. music Union Theol. Sem., N.Y.C., 1960-73; chmn. dept. ch. music Manhattan Sch. Music, 1984-93; coord. standing commn. on ch. music Episcopal Ch., 1974-85. Composer numerous pieces.; Contbr. articles to profl. jours. Served with Brit. Army, 1941-42. Fellow Royal Coll. Organists, Am. Guild Organists (hon. fellow, pres. 1964-69), Royal Canadian coll. Organists, Royal Acad. Music, Royal Sch. Ch. Music. Republican. Episcopalian. Home: 75 Danbury Rd Apt B-1 Ridgefield CT 06877

WYVILL, J. CRAIG, research engineer, program director; b. Washington, May 8, 1951; s. Andrew J. and Rach C. Wyvill; m. Peggy T. Wyvill. BSME, Ga. Tech., 1973; MBA, Ga. State U., 1981. Registered profl. engr., Ga. Va. Energy systems engr. Union Carbide Corp., Charleston, W.Va., 1973-75; project officer EPA, Washington, 1975-79; rsch. engr. Ga. Tech Rsch. Inst., Atlanta, 1979—, dir. agrl. tech. rsch. program, 1982—. Mem. ASME, Soc. Mfg. Engrs. (chpt. pres. 1990, 93-94), Inst. Food Technologists, Ga. Agribus Coun. Office: Ga Inst Tech Ga Tech Res Inst MARC Bldg Rm 335 Atlanta GA 30332-0800

XENAKIS, STEPHEN NICHOLAS, psychiatrist, army officer; b. Washington, July 5, 1948; s. Stanley Steve and Mary Alexandria (Poulos) X.; m. Mary Elizabeth Boddie, Jan. 19, 1974; children: Nicholas John, Lea Elizabeth. AB, Princeton U., 1970; MD, U. Md., Balt., 1974; postgrad., Balt.-D.C. Psychoanalytic Inst., 1972-75, Armed Forces Staff Coll., 1984-85, U.S. Army War Coll., 1989-90. Diplomate Am. Bd. Psychiatry and Neurology. Commd. U.S. Army, 1972, advanced through grades to brig. gen., 1994; resident U. Md., Balt., 1974; intern Letterman Army Med. Ctr., Presidio of San Francisco, 1974-75, resident in psychiatry, 1975-78; fellow in child and adolescent psychiatry Letterman Army Med. Ctr., U. Calif., San Francisco, 1978-80; chief dept. psychiatry Darnell Army Community Hosp., Ft. Hood, Tex., 1980-82; div. surgeon 1st Cav. Div., Ft. Hood, Tex., 1982-84; chief child, adolescent, family psychiatry Eisenhower Army Med. Ctr., Ft. Gordon, Ga., 1985-86, dep. comdr. clin. svcs., dir. med. edn., 1986-89; comdr. Blanchfield Army Community Hosp., 1990-93; project mgr. AMEDD Vanguard, Fairfax, Va., 1993, TRICARE S.E., Augusta, Ga., 1994—; clin. prof. Uniformed Svcs. of Health Scis., Bethesda, Md., 1985—; Med. Coll. of Ga., Augusta, 1985—; lectr., author Porter Lecture, 1989. Contbr. articles to profl. jours. Bd. dirs. Augusta Regional AIDS Coun., 1987-89. Fellow Am. Acad. and Adolescent Psychiatry, Am. Psychiat. Assn., Am. Coll. Physician Execs., Assn. Mil. Surgeon U.S. Greek Orthodox. Office: TRICARE Eisenhower Army Med Ctr Fort Gordon GA 30905

XIE, GANQUAN, mathematician, computational geophysical scientist, educator; b. Changsha, Hunan, People's Republic of China, July 2, 1943; s. Shuming Xie and Sumen Liu; m. Jianhua Li, Sept. 29, 1969; children: Feng, Lee. BCS, Hunan U., ChangSha City, 1966; PhD, SUNY, 1984;

postdoctoral rsch., NYU, 1984-86. Asst. prof. Hunan Computer Research Inst., 1967-80; vice-chmn. Soc. Computational Math., Hunan, 1979-81; postdoctoral research Courant Inst. Math., N.Y.C., 1984—; prof., dir. Hunan Computer Rsch. Tech. Inst., 1987-88; staff scientist Lawrence Berkely lab., 1991—; chmn. Chinese Computational Math. Soc., 1986-88; vis. rscher SUNY, 1989; vis. prof. KSU, 1990. Mem. editorial com. Jour. Computational Math., Beijing, 1987-88; inventor in field; contbr. to profl. jours. Nat. Sci. Found. grantee, 1986-87, recipient Chinese Scientific prize, 1978. Mem. Soc. Indsl. Applied Math., SEG (Soc. of Exploration Geophysicists), AGU (Am. Geophys. Union). Avocations: applied math., numerical inversse tomography of the seismic exploration and electromagnetic exploration. Home: 1413 Glendale Ave Berkeley CA 94708 Office: Lawrence Berkeley Lab 50E Earth Scis Divsn Berkeley CA 94720

XU, ZHIFU, chemist, researcher; b. Qichun, Hubei, China, Nov. 17, 1962; came to U.S. 1988; s. Sixiong Xu and Hanjiao Zhang; m. Suzhen Ruan, Aug. 12, 1987; 1 child, Angela Ruan. BS, Wuhan U., China, 1982; MS, Wuxi Inst. Light Industry, China, 1985; PhD, U. Mich., 1992. Rsch. fellow Zhengzhou Inst. Tech., China, 1985-88; rsch. asst. U. Mich., Ann Arbor, 1988-92, postdoctoral fellow, 1993; rsch. chemist PPG Industries, Inc., Allison Park, PA, 1993—. Co-author: Adv. Dendritic Macromolecules, 1993. Mem. Am. Chem. Soc. Achievements include synthesis and unambiguous characterizations of the world's largest pure hydrocarbon molecule: C1134H1146; efficient synthesis of large-size dendritic molecules up to 12.5 nanometers in diameter. Office: PPG Industries Rsch Ctr 4325 Rosanna Dr Allison Park PA 15101-1413

YABLANS, FRANK, film company executive, motion picture producer; b. N.Y.C., Aug. 27, 1935; s. Morris and Annette Y.; m. Ruth Edelstein, Dec. 21; children: Robert, Sharon, Edward. Student, CCNY, U. Wis. Salesman, Warner Bros., 1956-58; br. mgr. Walt Disney Prodns., 1958-66; v.p. Filmways Prodns., 1966-69; successively v.p. sales, v.p. marketing, exec. v.p., pres. Paramount Pictures Corp., N.Y.C., 1969-75; pres. Frank Yablans Presentations, Inc., N.Y.C., 1975—; dir. Dirs. Co., Cinema Internat. Corp.; chmn. bd. MGM/UA Entertainment Co., 1983-85; founder Northstar Entertainment, 1985—; pres. Epic Records, 1989—; pres., chief exec. officer Nova Internat. Films, Inc. Films include Silver Streak, 1976, The Other Side of Midnight, 1977, The Fury, 1978, (also co-author screen play) North Dallas Forty, 1979, Mommie Dearest (producer, co-author screen play), Monsignore, 1982, The Star Chamber, 1983, Kid Co, 1983, Boy and Cell, 1989, Lisa, 1990. Chmn. entertainment div. Fedn. Jewish Philanthropies; bd. dirs. Boys' Clubs Am., Will Rogers Hosp.; trustee Am. Film Inst. Served with AUS, 1954-56. Decorated commendatore Repubblica Italiana. Mem. Variety Club Internat. (chmn.), Motion Picture Assn. (dir.). Club: Fairview Country. Office: Epic Productions Inc 3330 Cahuenga Blvd W Ste 500 Los Angeles CA 90068-1351

YABLON, JEFFERY LEE, lawyer; b. Chgo., June 28, 1948; s. Robert R. and Faye I. (Goldberg) Y.; m. Jean C. LaPrade, Apr. 17, 1983. BA with honors, U. Wis., 1970; JD, Stanford U., 1973. Bar: Calif. 1974, D.C. 1975. Law clk. to Judge Cynthia Holcomb Hall, U.S. Tax Ct., Washington, 1973-75; Fulbright scholar U. Florence, Italy, 1975-76; assoc. Covington & Burling, Washington, 1976-80, Lee, Toomey & Kent, Washington, 1980-82; assoc. Shaw, Pittman, Potts & Trowbridge, Washington, 1982-84, ptnr., 1984—. Contbr. articles to legal jours. Bd. dirs. Am. Friends Hebrew U., Washington, 1991—. Mem. ABA, State Bar Calif., D.C. Bar. Jewish. Office: Shaw Pittman Potts & Trowbridge 2300 N St NW Washington DC 20037

YABLON, LEONARD HAROLD, publishing company executive; b. N.Y.C., June 3, 1929; s. Philip A. and Sarah (Herman) Y.; m. Carolyn Sydney Torgan, June 8, 1950; children—Scott Richard, Bonnie Michele. B.S., L.I. U., 1950; M.B.A., Coll. City N.Y., 1969. C.P.A., N.Y. Acct., 1950-63; exec. v.p., dir. Forbes Inc., N.Y.C., 1963—; pres. Sangre de Cristo Ranches, Fiji Forbes; v.p. Forbes Investors Adv. Inst.; pres. Forbes Trinchera; sec.-treas. Forbes Found.; pres. Forbes Europe. Home: Pleasant Ridge Rd Harrison NY 10528 Office: 60 5th Ave New York NY 10011-8802

YACK, PATRICK ASHLEY, editor; b. Little Rock, Oct. 25, 1951; s. Leo Patrick and Sarah Ann (Dew) Y.; m. Susan Marie Courtney, June 7, 1980; children: Alexander Ryan, Kendall Elizabeth. BFA, So. Meth. U., 1974. Staff asst. U.S. Rep. Alan Steelman, Washington, 1975-76; press aide U.S. Senator Charles Percy, Chgo., 1977-78; reporter Fla. Times-Union, Jacksonville, 1979-80; regional reporter Fla. Times-Union, Atlanta, 1981-82; reporter The Denver Post, 1983-85, Washington bur. chief, 1985-87; nat. editor Atlanta Constitution, 1987-89; mng. editor The Register-Guard, Eugene, Oreg., 1989-94; editor News & Record, Greensboro, N.C., 1994—. Mem. Am. Soc. Newspaper Editors, AP Mng. Editors Assn., Nat. Assn. Black Journalists.

YACKEL, JAMES WILLIAM, mathematician, academic administrator; b. Sanborn, Minn., Mar. 6, 1936; s. Ewald W. and Marie E. (Heydlauff) Y.; m. Erna Beth Seecamp, Aug. 20, 1960; children: Jonathan, Juliet, Carolyn. BA, U. Minn., 1958, MA, 1960, PhD, 1964. Rsch. instr. dept. math. Dartmouth Coll., Hanover, N.H., 1964-66; asst. prof. dept. stats. Purdue U., West Lafayette, Ind., 1966-69, from assoc. prof. to prof., 1969-76, assoc. dean sci., 1976-87; vice chancellor acad. affairs Purdue U. Calumet, Hammond, Ind., 1987-90, chancellor, 1990—; rsch. mathematician Inst. Def. Analysis, Washington, 1969. Author: Applicable Finite Mathematics, 1974; editor Statistical Decision Theory, 1971; contbr. articles to profl. jours. Fellow AAAS; mem. Am. Math. Soc., Math. Assn. Am., Inst. Math. Stats. Research on Ramsey's theorem and finite graphs, stochastics processes, density estimation. Office: Purdue U Calumet Office of Chancellor Hammond IN 46323

YACKIRA, MICHAEL WILLIAM, power company executive; b. N.Y.C., Aug. 14, 1951; s. Alan Israel and Lillian (Landau) Y.; m. Roberta Guido, July 24, 1977; children: Steven, Andrew. BS in Acctg., Herbert H. Lehman Coll., CUNY, 1972. Sr. acct. Arthur Andersen, N.Y.C., 1972-75; v.p. St. Joe Petroleum, Houston, 1975-83; mgr. fin. analysis U.S. Industries, Stamford, Conn., 1983-84; dir. bus. analysis and research GTE Svc. Corp., Stamford, 1984-85, dir. bus. devel. and analysis, 1985-86, asst. controller budget planning and analysis, 1986-87; v.p. fin. and revenues GTE Fla., Tampa, 1987-88; v.p. fin. and info. mgmt. GTE Info. Svcs., Tampa, 1988-89; v.p. corp. devel. and planning FPL Group, Inc., Juno Beach, Fla., 1989-91; chief planning officer Fla. Power and Light Co., 1990-91; sr. v.p. market and regulatory svcs. Fla. Power & Light Co., Juno Beach, 1991—. Bd. dirs. Ctr. for Family Svcs., West Palm Beach, Fla. Office: Fla Power & LIght Co PO Box 14000 No Palm Beach FL 33408-0420

YACKTMAN, DONALD ARTHUR, financial executive, investment counselor; b. Chgo., Sept. 12, 1941; s. Victor and Matilda (Chamberlain) Y.; m. Carolyn I. Zuppann, June 15, 1965; children:Donald, Stephen, Jennifer, Melissa, Brian, Robert, Michael. B.S., U. Utah, 1965; M.B.A., Harvard U., 1967. Chartered investment counselor. Trainee, Continental Bank, Chgo., 1967-68; ptnr. Stein Roe & Farnham, Chgo., 1968-82; pres. Selected Am. Shares; sr. v.p. Prescott Asset Mgmt., 1982-92; pres. Yacktman Asset Mgmt. Co. and Yacktman Fund, 1992—; mem. exec. bd. N.W. Suburban coun. Boy Scouts Am., 1984—; mem. high coun. Ch. Jesus Christ Latter Day Saints. Mem. Fin. Analysts Soc. Office: Yacktman Asset Mgmt Co 303 W Madison St Ste 1925 Chicago IL 60606

YACONETTI, DIANNE MARY, business executive; b. Chgo., Dec. 16, 1946; d. Anthony and Dora Marie (Mazzoni) Pontillo. Student, Mallinckrodt Coll., 1984-85; Advanced Mgmt. Program, Harvard U., 1990. Various positions Brunswick Corp., Skokie, Ill., 1964-80, mgr. legal support services, 1980-83, asst. sec., 1984-86, corp. sec., 1986-88, v.p. adminstrn., corp. sec., 1988—; bd. dirs. The Lambs, Libertyville, Ill. Mem. Am. Soc. Corp. Secs. Roman Catholic. Office: Brunswick Corp 1 N Field Ct Lake Forest IL 60045-4810

YACOUB, IGNATIUS I., university dean; b. Dwar Taha, Syria, Jan. 5, 1937; came to U.S. 1978; s. Immanuel and Martha (Kharma) Y.; m. Mary Haddad, Sept. 14, 1961; children—Hilda, Lena, Emile. A.B., Middle East Coll., Beirut, Lebanon, 1960; M.A., Pacific Union Coll., Angwin, Calif., 1964; Ph.D., Claremont Grad. Sch., Calif., 1976. Dean studies Middle East

Coll., Beirut, Lebanon, 1967-73, 75-78; dir. dept. edn. Afro-Mideast div. Seventh-Day Adventist Ch., 1970-73, dir. dept. pub. affairs, 1975-78; prof., chmn. dept. bus. econs. Southwestern Union Coll., Keene, Tex., 1978-80; prof., chmn. dept. bus. and econs. Loma Linda U., Riverside, Calif., 1980-86, dean Sch. of Bus. and Mgmt., 1986-90; dean Sch. Bus. and Mgmt., La Sierra U., Riverside, Calif., 1990—; bd. dirs. Riverside Nat. Bank. Mem. Exec. 2000 Coun. Riverside Comty. Hosp. Found., 1991—. Recipient Gov.'s Appreciation award, Lions, Club; Lions Club award, Beirut. Mem. Am. Mgmt. Assn., Acad. Mgmt., Greater Riverside C. of C., Corona C. of C. Seventh-day Adventist. Home: 2722 Litchfield Dr Riverside CA 92503-6213

YACOVONE, ELLEN ELAINE, banker; b. Ithaca, N.Y., Aug. 4, 1951; d. Wilfred Elliott and Charlotte Frances (Fox) Drew; m. Richard Daniel Yacovone, June 2, 1979; stepchildren: Christopher Daniel, Kimberly Marie. Student Broome Community Coll., 1973-80; cert. Inst. Fin. Edn., Chgo., 1974. Sec. to exec. v.p. Ithaca Savs., N.Y., summer 1968; mortgage clk. Citizens Savs. Bank, 1968-69; with Lincoln Bank, Van Nuys, Calif., 1970-71; asst. bookkeeper Henry's Jewelers, Binghamton, N.Y., 1971-74; teller, br. supt., br. mgr. First Fed. Savs., Binghamton, N.Y., 1974-82, v.p., cen. regional sales mgr., 1982-86, dist. sales mgr., 1986-88; br. mgr. Great Western Bank, Pensacola, Fla., 1988-89, v.p., regional mgr. San Diego east region, 1989-95; br. v.p. Gateway Ctr., San Diego, 1995—; owner, operator EYE Shuts, 1995—. Mem. Gov.'s Commn. on Domestic Violence, Albany, N.Y., 1983-87; bd. dirs. S.O.S. Shelter, Inc., Endicott, N.Y., 1979-88, pres., 1982-83, treas., 1985-86; vol. United Way of Broome County, Binghamton, 1976-88, Sta. WSKG Pub. TV, Conklin, N.Y., 1974-88; mem. Found. State U. Ctr. at Binghamton; bd. dirs. Interfaith Shelter Network, San Diego, 1992—, Schs. for Success, San Diego, 1995—. Named Woman of Achievement, Broome County Status of Women Coun., 1981. Mem. Triple Cities Bus. and Profl. Women (pres. 1979-81, young careerist award 1977), Sales and Mktg. Execs., Broome County C. of C., Broome County Bankers Assn. (bd. dirs. 1979-88, pres. 1983-84), Inst. Fin. Edn. (bd. dirs. 1976-88, pres. 1984-85, winner N.Y. State speech contest 1984). Republican. Methodist. Avocations: exercise, camping, wood working, gardening, needlecrafts. Home: 602 Myra Ave Chula Vista CA 91910-6230 Office: Great Western Bank 652 Gateway Ctr Dr San Diego CA 92102

YACOWITZ, HAROLD, biochemist, nutritionist; b. N.Y.C., Feb. 17, 1922; s. Louis and Clara (Kurtzberg) Y.; m. Ann Ruth Barnett, Dec. 31, 1941; children: Caryn R., Richard S., Suzanne Yacowitz Dragan. BS, Cornell U., 1947, M in Nutritional Sci., 1948, PhD, 1950. Rsch. biochemist Parke-Davis Inc., Detroit, 1950-51; assoc. prof. Ohio State U., Columbus, 1951-55; head nutrition rsch. dept. Squibb Inst. for Med. Rsch., New Brunswick, N.J., 1955-59; dir. rsch. Nopco Chem. Co. Inc., Harrison, N.J., 1959-61, Amburgo Co. Inc., Phila., 1961-80; rsch. assoc. Fairleigh Dickinson U., Madison, N.J., 1961-80; pres., dir. rsch. Dr. H. Yacowitz & Co., Piscataway, N.J., 1961—, Animal Identification & Marking Systems Inc., Piscataway, 1982—; pres. Peninsula Investment & Devel. Inc., Cambridge, Md., 1961—; pres., bd. dirs. rsch. Drug Delivery Devices Inc., Piscataway, 1991—. Contbr. articles to profl. jours.; patentee in field. Leader Boy Scouts Am., Ithaca, N.Y., 1946-50, Piscataway, 1955-59. With U.S. Army, 1943-46, ETO, PTO. Grange League Fedn. fellow Cornell U., 1947-48, Robert Gould rsch. fellow, Cornell U., 1949-50, Coun. on Arteriosclerosis fellow Am. Heart Assn., 1970. Fellow N.Y. Acad. Scis. (chmn. sect. biology and medicine 1972-76); mem. Am. Chem. Soc., Am. Inst. Nutrition, Am. Assn. Lab. Animal Scientists, Exptl. Investors Club (New Brunswick, pres. 1955-59). Jewish. Avocations: gardening, sailing, fishing, swimming. Office: Animal Ident Marking Syst Inc 221 2nd Ave Piscataway NJ 08854

YAFFE, BARBARA MARLENE, journalist; b. Montreal, Que., Can., Mar. 4, 1953; d. Allan and Ann (Freedman) Y.; m. Wilson E. Russell, Aug. 30, 1985. Student, McGill U., 1970-73; BA, U. Toronto, 1974; B in Journalism, Carleton U., 1974. Reporter Montreal Gazette, 1975-76, Toronto Globe and Mail, 1976-79; reporter, columnist Toronto Globe and Mail, Halifax, N.S., 1979-81; TV bur. chief CBC-TV, St. Johns, Nfld., 1981-84, Edmonton, Alta., 1983; reporter Toronto Globe and Mail, St. John's, 1984-86; editor Sunday Express, St. John's, 1987-88; editor Vancouver Sun, 1988-93, columnist, 1993—. Recipient Gov. Gen.'s award Roland Michener Found., 1977. Jewish. Office: c/o Vancouver Sun, 2250 Granville St, Vancouver, BC Canada V6H 362

YAFFE, JAMES, author; b. Chgo., Mar. 31, 1927; s. Samuel and Florence (Scheinman) Y.; m. Elaine Gordon, Mar. 1, 1964; children: Deborah Ann, Rebecca Elizabeth, Gideon Daniel. Grad., Fieldston Sch., 1944; B.A. summa cum laude, Yale U., 1948. Prof. Colo. Coll., Colo. Springs, 1968—; dir. gen. studies Colo. Coll., 1981—. Author: Poor Cousin Evelyn, 1951, The Good-for-Nothing, 1953, What's the Big Hurry?, 1954, Nothing But the Night, 1959, Mister Margolies, 1962, Nobody Does You Any Favors, 1966, The American Jews, 1968, The Voyage of the Franz Joseph, 1970, So Sue Me!, 1972, Saul and Morris, Worlds Apart, 1982, A Nice Murder for Mom, 1988, Mom Meets Her Maker, 1990, Mom Doth Murder Sleep, 1991, Mom Among the Liars, 1992; play The Deadly Game, 1960, (with Jerome Weidman) Ivory Tower, 1967, Cliffhanger, 1985; also TV plays, stories, essays, revs. Served with USNR, 1945-46. Recipient Nat. Arts Found award, 1968. Mem. P.E.N., Authors League, Writers Guild of Am., Dramatists Guild, A.A.U.P., Mystery Writers of Am., Phi Beta Kappa. Jewish. Club: Elizabethan (Yale). Avocations: music, bridge, movies. Address: 1215 N Cascade Ave Colorado Springs CO 80903-2303 Office: Colo Coll Colorado Springs CO 80903

YAFFE, SUMNER JASON, pediatrician, research center administrator, educator; b. Boston, May 9, 1923; s. Henry H. and Ida E. (Fisher) Y.; m. Anita Yaffe; children: Steven, Kris, Jason, Noah, Ian, Zachary. A.B., Harvard U., 1945, M.A., 1950; M.D., U. Vt., 1954. Diplomate Am. Bd. Pediatrics. Intern Children's Hosp., Boston, 1954-55, resident, 1955-56; resident in pediatrics St. Mary's Hosp., London, 1956-57; instr. pediatrics Stanford U., Palo Alto, Calif., 1959-60, asst. prof., 1960-63; assoc. prof. pediatrics SUNY-Buffalo, 1963-66, prof., 1966-75, adj. prof. biochem. pharmacology, 1968-75, acting chmn. dept. pediatrics, 1974-75; prof. pediatrics and pharmacology U. Pa., Phila., 1975-81; dir. Ctr. for Research for Mothers and Children, NIH, Bethesda, Md., 1981—; clin. prof. pediatrics Georgetown U. Med. Ctr., 1986, Johns Hopkins Hosp., 1986; attending physician Palo Alto-Stanford Hosp., 1959-63; attending physician Children's Hosp., Buffalo, 1963-75, Phila., 1975-81; vis. prof. pharmacology Karolinska Inst., Stockholm, 1969-70; dir. Pediatric Renal Clinic, Stanford Med. Ctr., 1960-63; dir. newborn nursery service Palo Alto-Stanford Hosp., 1960-63, program dir. Clin. Research Ctr. for Premature Infants, 1962-63; dir. Clin. Research Ctr. for Children Children's Hosp., Buffalo, 1963-70, dir. Poison Control Ctr., 1967-75, dir. div. clin. pharmacology, Phila., 1975-81; program cons. Nat. Inst. Child Health and Human Devel., NIH, 1963-71, mem. tng. grant com., 1963-65, mem. reproductive biology com., 1965-67; mem. adv. panel on maternal and child health WHO, Geneva, 1970—; liaison rep. drug research bd. NRC, 1971-75, com. on drug dependence, 1972-75, mem. com. on problems of drug safety, 1972-75; mem. adv. panel in pediatrics U.S. Pharmacopeia, 1970—, in toxicology, 1974-75; cons. Am. Found. for Maternal and Child Health, Inc., 1973—; pres. Maternal and Child Health Research Found., Children's Hosp., 1974—; Wall Meml. lectr. Children's Hosp., Washington, 1968—; Dr. W.E. Upjohn lectr. Can. Med. Assn., 1974; Louisville pediatric lectr. Sch. Medicine U. Louisville, 1974; William N. Creasy vis. prof. clin. pharmacology SUNY, 1976; advisor Internat. Childbirth Assn. Greater Phila., 1979-83; guest lectr. Dept. Pediatrics Georgetown U. Hosp., Washington, 1988—; lectr. in pediatrics Johns Hopkins Sch. Medicine, Balt., 1988—. Author: Clinics in Perinatology, 1974, Drug Assessment: Criteria and Methods, 1979, Pediatric Pharmacology, 1980, 2d edit. 1992; co-author: (with R. Galinsky) Clinical Therapeutics, 1978; editor: (with R. H. Schwartz) Drug and Chemical Risks to the Fetus and Newborn, 1980, (with G.G. Briggs, T.W. Bodendorfer, R.K. Freeman) Drugs in Pregnancy and Lactation, A Reference Guide to Fetal and Neonatal Risk, 1983, 2d edit., 1986, 4th edit., 1994, (J.V. Aranda) Pediatric Phyarmacology, 2nd edit., 1993; mem. editorial bd. Pediatric Alert, 1977—, Pharmacology 1977—, Devel. Pharmacology and Therapeutics, 1979—; mem. editorial adv. bd. Drug Therapy, 1979—; cons. editor Clin. Pharmacokinetics, 1977; co-editor Developmental Pharmacology, 1979-94; contbr. chpts. to profl. books., articles to profl. jours. Served with U.S. Army, 1943-44. Recipient Lederle Med. Faculty award Lederle Found., 1962; Fulbright scholar, 1956-57. Fellow Acad. Pharm. Scis.; mem. AMA (com. on drugs 1963-68), Am. Acad. Pediatrics (chmn. com. on drugs 1967-76), AAUP, Am. Coll. Clin.

Pharmacology and Chemotherapy, Am. Fedn. for Clin. Rsch., Am. Pediatric Soc., Am. Pharmaceutics Assn., Am. Pub. Health Assn., Am. Soc. for Clin. Pharmacology and Therapeutics (chmn. sect. on pediatric pharmacology 1977-83), Am. Soc. Pharmacology and Exptl. Therapeutics, Fedn. Am. Socs. for Exptl. Biology, Perinatal Rsch. Soc., Soc. for Pediatric Research, Sigma Xi, Alpha Omega Alpha. Home: 6417 Tilden Ln Rockville MD 20852-3742 Office: Nat Inst of Child Health & Human Devel 6100 Executive Blvd Bethesda MD 20892-7510

YAGER, HUNTER, advertising executive; b. Bklyn., Sept. 29, 1929; s. Jules and Lucille (Kornblum) Y.; m. Gertrude Kathryn Johnson, Feb. 17, 1960; children—Leslie Jeanne, Andrew Hunter, Phoebe Hildreth. BA, N.Y. U., 1950; MBA, Harvard U., 1955. Copywriter Donahue & Coe, Inc., N.Y.C., 1951-53; account exec. Foote, Cone & Belding, N.Y.C., 1955-58; account exec., account supr., v.p. mgmt. supr. exec. v.p. mgmt com. Grey Advt., Inc., N.Y.C., 1958-85; dir. Grey Advt., Ltd., Can., 1970-79; mktg. and advt. cons., 1985-91, retired, 1992; instr. mktg. NYU, 1961-62; bd. trustees Manchester Music Festival. Dir., sec., mem. exec. com., devel. com., mktg. com. Chamber Music Soc. of Lincoln Ctr., 1986-90; dir., mktg. com. Manhattan Theatre Club, 1987-92; bd. dirs., pres. West Lyon Farm Condominium Assn., Greenwich, Conn., 1985-90; v.p. Powder Mill Owners Assn., Londonberry, Vt.; bd. dirs. Harvard Bus. Sch. Club Fairfield County, 1986-91; bd. dirs. Manchester Music Festival, 1993—. Mem. Camp Rising Sun Alumni Assn., Harvard Bus. Sch. Alumni Assn. (bd. dirs. 1993—). Unitarian. Clubs: Harvard, Harvard Business School (N.Y.C., dir. Fairfield County). Home: West Fields RR 2 Box 3190 Manchester VT 05255

YAGER, JOHN WARREN, retired banker, lawyer; b. Toledo, Sept. 16, 1920; s. Joseph A. and Edna Gertrude (Pratt) Y.; m. Dorothy W. Merki, July 25, 1942; children: Julie M., John M. AB, U. Mich., 1942, JD, 1948. Bar: Ohio 1948. Pvt. practice law Toledo, 1948-64; trust officer Toledo Trust Co., 1964-69; v.p., trust officer Fifth Third Bank, 1969-91; sec. First Ohio Bancshares, Inc., 1980-85; ret. Pres. Toledo Met. Park Dist., 1971-85, Neighborhood Health Assn., 1974-75, councilman, Toledo, 1955-57, 60-61, mayor, 1958-59; bd. dirs. Toledo-Lucas County Library, 1968-70, Riverside Hosp., Downtown Toledo Assn.; past pres. Toledo Legal Aid Soc., Toledo Council Chs., Toledo Mcpl. League, Econ. Opportunity Planning Assn., Toledo, Com. on Relations with Toledo, Spain. Maj. USMC, 1942-46, 50-52. Decorated Bronze Star; named one of 10 Outstanding Young Men in Toledo, 1952, 54, 55. Mem. Toledo Bar Assn., Delta Tau Delta. Home: 29301 Bates Rd Perrysburg OH 43551-3808

YAGER, JOSEPH ARTHUR, JR., economist; b. Owensville, Ind., Apr. 14, 1916; s. Joseph Arthur and Edna (Pratt) Y.; m. Virginia Estella Berost, Sept. 2, 1938; children: Thomas, Martha. A.B., U. Mich., 1937, J.D., 1939, M.A., 1940; grad. Nat. War Coll., 1955. Economist OPA, 1942-44; economist State Dept., 1946-47, chief China research br., 1949-50; chief div. research for State Dept., Far East, 1952-57; attaché U.S. consulate gen. Canton, China, 1947-48; consul U.S. consulate gen., Hong Kong, 1950-51; econ. counselor Taipei, 1957-59; dep. chief of mission, 1959-61; dir. Office Chinese Affairs, 1961, Office East Asian Affairs, 1961-63; mem. Policy Planning Council, 1963-66, vice chmn., 1966-68; dep. dir. internat. and social studies div. Inst. Def. Analyses, 1968-72; sr. fellow Brookings Instn., 1972-83, guest scholar, 1983-86; resident cons. Sci. Applications Internat. Corp., 1986-89, sr. fellow, 1989—. Author: Transforming Agriculture in Taiwan, 1988, Prospects for Nuclear Weapons Proliferation in a Changing Europe, 1992; co-author: Energy and U.S. Foreign Policy, 1974, New Means of Financing International Needs, 1978, Military Equation in Northeast Asia, 1979, Nonproliferation and U.S. Foreign Policy, 1980, International Cooperation in Nuclear Energy, 1981, Energy Balance in Northeast Asia, 1984, Energy Policy Experience of Asia Countries, 1987. Served in AUS, 1944-45. Mem. Phi Delta Phi, Delta Tau Delta. Home: 10006 Woodhill Rd Bethesda MD 20817-1218 Office: Sci Applications Internat Corp 1710 Goodridge Dr Mc Lean VA 22102-3701

YAGER, MILAN P., government agency administrator; b. Estherville, Iowa, Mar. 3, 1954; s. Melvin O. and Maxine (Jensen) Y.; m. Barbara E. Steakley; children: Austin, Reid. B Liberal Arts, U. Iowa, 1977; MPA, Am. U., 1984. Sr. legis. asst. U.S. Rep. Berkley Bedell, Washington, 1978-84; legis. dir. United Fresh Fruit & Vegetable Assn., Alexandria, Va., 1984-85; chief of staff U.S. Rep. Dick Durbin, Washington, 1985-88; pres. Yager co., Middlebury, Vt., 1988-89; dir. environ. policy Nat. Assn. Home Builders, Washington, 1989-93; dir. office econ. analysis ICC, Washington, 1993—. Candidate for dist. 4 Iowa State Legislature, 1978. Democrat. Methodist. Office: ICC 12th and Constitution Washington DC 20423

YAGER, VINCENT COOK, banker; b. Chgo., June 15, 1928; s. James Vincent and Juanita (Cook) Y.; m. Dorothy Marie Gallagher, Sept. 28, 1957; children: Susan Marie, Sheila Ann. B.A., Grinnell Coll., 1951. Asst. cashier Chgo. Nat. Bank, 1954-60, Harris Trust & Savs. Bank, Chgo., 1960-63; v.p. comml. loan dept. Madison Bank & Trust, Chgo., 1963-68; v.p. fin. Cor-Plex Internat. Corp., Chgo., 1968-70; pres., chief exec. officer, dir. First Nat. Bank of Blue Island, Ill., 1970-89; pres., CEO, dir. Great Lakes Fin. Resources, Inc., Matteson, Ill., 1982—; vice-chmn., dir. Bank of Matteson, Ill., 1992—; chmn. GL Mortgage Corp., Wheeling, Ill. Mem. adv. bd. St. Francis Hosp., Blue Island, others. With U.S. Army, 1951-53, ETO. Mem. Robert Morris Assocs. (pres. chpt. 1981-82), Bankers Club of Chgo. Mem. United Ch. of christ. Clubs: Midlothian Country; Econ. of Chgo. Lodge: Rotary. Home: 1032 S Rand Rd Villa Park IL 60181-3145 Office: Gt Lakes Fin Resources Inc 4600 Lincoln Hwy Matteson IL 60443-2315

YAGIELA, JOHN ALLEN, dental educator; b. Washington, July 23, 1947; s. Stanley and Kathryn Marie (Gilkeson) Y.; m. Dolores Jean Mitchell, Mar. 21, 1970; children: Gregory, Leanne. Student, U. Calif., Riverside, 1965-67; DDS, UCLA, 1971, postgrad., 1982-83; PhD in Pharmacology, U. Utah, 1975. Asst. prof. dentistry Emory U., Atlanta, 1975-78, assoc. prof., 1978-82; assoc. prof. UCLA, 1982-83, prof., 1983—, assoc. dean acad. and adminstrv. affairs, 1984-89; cons. Astra Pharm. Products Inc., Worcester, Mass., 1982—, VA Wadsworth divsn., L.A., 1983-92, Gen. Med. Co., L.A., 1988—, ADA, Chgo, 1991—. Co-author: Regional Anesthesia of the Oral Cavity, 1981, Local Anesthesia of the Oral Cavity, 1995; co-editor: Pharmacology and Therapeutics for Dentistry, 3d edit., 1989; editor Anesthesia Progress; contbr. articles on dental therapeutics to profl. jours. Recipient Award of Achievement Am. Coll. Dentists, 1971; Regents scholar UCLA, 1968-71; Alpha Omega award, 1971. Fellow Am. Dental Soc. Anesthesiology; mem. ADA, AAAS, Internat. Assn. Dental Rsch. (sec.-treas. PTTG group 1984-88, pres.-elect 1989-90, pres. 1990-91), Am. Assn. Dental Schs. (chmn. pharmacology therapeutics sect. 1983), Omicron Kappa Upsilon. Methodist. Avocations: photography, hiking. Home: 7956 Glade Ave Canoga Park CA 91304-4718 Office: UCLA Sch Dentistry Ctr for Health Scis Los Angeles CA 90095

YAGODA, HARRY NATHAN, system engineering executive; b. Bklyn., May 19, 1936; s. Hyman and Sylvia (Yoskowitz) Y.; m. Myrna Rita Yagoda; children: Michelle Robin, Randi Noelle. BSEE, CUNY, 1958; MSEE, NYU, 1960; PhDEE, Poly. U. N.Y., 1963. Registered profl. engr. 19 states including N.Y., N.J., Calif. Mem. tech. staff AT&T Bell Labs., Whippany, N.J., 1958-62; prof. Poly. U. N.Y., Bklyn., 1962-70; pres. Computran Systems Corp., Hackensack, N.J., 1970—; bd. dirs. Randelle Inc., Wayne, N.J., Klfc Systems, Raleigh, N.C. Named Disting. Alumnus, Poly. U. N.Y., 1980. Fellow Inst. Transp. Engring. (bd. dirs. 1982-84). Home: 75 Anderson Dr Wayne NJ 07470 Office: Computran Systems Corp 100 1st St Hackensack NJ 07601

YAHIL, AMOS, astrophysicist, educator; b. Tel Aviv, Nov. 28, 1943; came to U.S. 1966, naturalized, 1987; s. Chaim and Helena (Westphal) Y. BS, Hebrew U., 1966; PhD, Calif. Inst. Tech. 1970. Staff Inst. Advanced Study, Princeton, N.J., 1971-73; lectr. Astrophysics Tel Aviv U. 1970-71, 73-75, sr. lectr., 1975-77; asst. prof. SUNY, Stony Brook, 1977-79, assoc. prof., 1979-83, prof., 1983—. Recipient Fullam award Dudley Obs., 1982, Guggenheim fellow, 1984. Mem. Am. Astronomy Soc., Internat. Astronomy Union. Office: SUNY Astronomy Program Stony Brook NY 11794-2100

YAHN-KRAMER, BETTIE LYNN, forester, horticulturist; b. St. Charles, Mo., Aug. 11, 1953; d. Glendon Henry and Lillian Stevenson (Kessler) Yahn; m. Harold Anthony Kramer, Mar. 31, 1984. BS in Agr., U. Mo.,

1975. Horticulture park supr. I Jackson County Parks and Recreation, Blue Springs, Mo., 1978-79, horticulture and natural resources park supr II, 1980-83, maintenance and ops. dist. mgr., 1984-86, Ctrl. dist. park supt., 1987, Ea. dist. park supt., 1988-90, asst. dir. parks and recreation, 1990-92, acting dir., 1992, dir., 1992—; participant Pikes Peak Ascent Trail Run, SEMO 24-hr. Track Run, Kansas City Marathon, St. Louis Marathon, Ark. Gov.'s Cup 25-Mile Run; race dir. for triathlon and biathlon events Kansas City Corp. Challenge. Bd. dirs. Longview Recreation Ctr., Heart of Am. Sr. Olympics, 1992; mem. adv. bd. Sch. Natural Resources U. Mo.; mem. forest stewardship adv. com. Mo. Dept. Conservation. Mem. Nat. Recreation and Park Assn., Mo. Park and Recreation Assn. (sec.-treas. mgmt. sect. 1992, pres.-elect 1992-93, pres. 1993-94, legis. issues com. 1993, 94, exec. bd. dirs., sec. 1994-95), Mo. State Sr. Sports Orgn. (charter, bd. dirs. 1994). Avocations: fishing, camping, hiking, cross-country skiing, gardening. Office: Jackson County Parks & Rec 22807 Woods Chapel Rd Blue Springs MO 64015

YAHR, MELVIN DAVID, physician; b. N.Y.C., Nov. 18, 1917; s. Isaac and Sarah (Reigelhaupt) Y.; m. Felice Turtz, May 9, 1948; children—Carol, Nina, Laura, Barbara Anne. A.B., N.Y. U., 1939, M.D., 1943. Diplomate: Am. Bd. Psychiatry and Neurology (pres.). Intern Lenox Hill Hosp., N.Y.C., 1943-44; resident Lenox Hill Hosp., also Montefiore Hosp., Bronx, N.Y., 1947-48; staff Columbia, 1948-73, asso. prof. clin. neurology, 1957-62, prof. neurology, 1962-70, H.H. Merritt prof. neurology, 1970-73, asst. dean grad. medicine, 1959-67, assoc. dean, 1967-73; asst. neurologist N.Y. Neurol. Inst., 1948-53, assoc. attending neurologist, 1953-60, attending neurologist, 1960-73; Goldschmidt prof. neurology, chmn. dept. neurology Mt. Sinai Med. Center, 1973-92; Aidekman Family Prof. Neurological Rsch., 1992—; exec. dir. Parkinson's Disease Found., 1957-73; panel neurologist N.Y.C. Bd. Edn., 1958-59; mem. com. evaluation drugs in neurology NIH, 1959-60, panel mem. neurol. study sect., 1959-80; mem. com. revisions U.S. Pharmacopea. Assoc. editor: Internat. Jour. Neurology; editor-in-chief Jour. Neural Transmission, 1989—; Archives Neurology, 1964-89. Fellow Am. Acad. Neurology, N.Y. Acad. Medicine, Harvey Soc.; mem. A.M.A. (chmn. com. neurol. disorders in industry), Am. Neurol. Assn. (sec.-treas. 1959-68, pres. 1969), Assn. Research Nervous and Mental Disease, N.Y. State Neurol. Soc., New York County Med. Soc., Am. Epilepsy Soc., Eastern Assn. Electroencephalographers. Office: Mt Sinai Med Ctr 1 Gustave L Levy Pl New York NY 10029-6504

YAKELEY, JAY B., III, naval officer; b. Phoenix, Ariz.; m. Mary Lou Murray; 1 child, Kelly. Student, Loras Coll.; grad., Naval War Coll.; M of Econs., SUNY, Stony Brook. Commd. ensign USN, advanced through grades to rear adm.; instr. tng. squadron 9 (VT-9) Meridian, Mass., 1967-69; with Fighter Squadron 101, 1969; with Fighter Squadron 74 USS FORRESTAL (CV 59); with F-47 USS AMERICA (CV 66), asst. ops. and quality assurance officer; 1st fleet prodn. acceptance test pilot F-14 TOMCAT, Calverton, N.Y., 1973-76; safety, maintenance and ops. officer Fighter Squadron 2 USS ENTERPRISE (CVN 65, 1976-78; flight instr. Fighter Squadron 124 F-14 Fleet Replacement Squadron, 1978-80, exec. officer Fighter Squadron 114, 1980-83; head air warfare analysis Office of Navy Planning and Program Divsn., 1983-85; commdr. Fighter Squadron 124 Fleet Replacement Squadron, NAS Miramar, Calif., 1985-87; commdng. officer Navy Fighter Weapons Sch., 1987-89; commdr. Carrier Air Wing 14 USS Independence (CV62), 1989-91; dep. dir. White House Mil. Office, 1991-93; dep. commdr. Joint Task Force, Riyadh, Saudi Arabia, 1993-94; comdr. Carrier Group Three USS Abraham Lincoln (CVN 72), 1994—. Decorated Def. D.S.M., Legion of Merit with gold star, Meritorious Svc. medal with 2 gold stars, Air Medal, Navy Commendation medal with combat "V", Vietnam Cross of Gallantry. Office: Navy Dept Washington DC 20370

YALDEN, MAXWELL FREEMAN, Canadian diplomat; b. Toronto, Ont., Can., Apr. 12, 1930; s. Frederick and Marie (Smith) Y.; m. Janice Shaw, Jan. 28, 1952; children: Robert, Cicely (dec.). B.A., Victoria Coll., U. Toronto, 1952; M.A., U. Mich., 1954, Ph.D., 1956; D.U. (hon.), U. Ottawa, 1982. With Can. Dept. External Affairs, 1956-69, asst. undersec. state, 1969-73, dep. minister communications, 1973-77, commr. ofcl. langs., 1977-84; Can. amb. to Belgium and Luxembourg, 1984-87; chief Can. Human Rights Comms., Ottawa, 1987—. Office: Canadian Human Rights Commission, 320 Queen St #1300, Ottawa, ON Canada K1A 1E1

YALE, JEFFREY FRANKLIN, podiatrist; b. Derby, Conn., Jan. 18, 1943; s. Irving and Bernice (Blume) Y.; m. Lenore Bernsley, Apr. 23, 1987; children: Brian Joseph, Andrew Malcolm. U. Fla., 1960-62; D of Podiatric Medicine, Ill. Coll. Podiatric Medicine, 1966. Diplomate Am. Bd. Podiatric Surgery, Am. Bd. Podiatric Orthopedics, Am. Bd. Med. Quality Assurance and Utilization Rev. Surg. resident Highland Gen. Hosp., Oakland, Calif., 1966-67; capt. U.S. Army Med. Svc., Fort Ord, Calif., 1967-71; instr. masters level Quinnipiac Coll., Hamden, Conn., 1981; cons. surgeon VA Med. Ctr., West Haven, Conn., 1982—; chmn. podiatric surgery Griffin Hosp., Derby, Conn., 1974—; assoc. clin. prof. U. Osteo. Health Scis., Des Moines, 1982—; chmn. Podiatric Medicine Test Com. Nat. Bd. Podiatric Med. Examiners, 1977-94; pres. Ct. Examining Bd. in Podiatry, 1979, Am. Acad. Podiatric Sports Medicine, 1986; pres. Yale Podiatry Group, P.C., Ansonia, Conn., 1976—; bd. dirs. Podiatry Ins. Co. Am., Brentwood, Tenn., also chmn. underwriting com.; editl. adv. bd. Am. Podiatric Med. Assn., 1992-95. Author: Firm Footings For the Athlete, 1984, The Arthritic Foot, 1984, Yale's Podiatric Medicine, 3d edit., 1987; contbr. numerous sci. articles to profl. jours. Corporator Griffin Hosp., Derby, Conn., 1982. Capt. U.S. Army, 1967-71. Fellow Am. Acad. Podiatric Sports Medicine, Am. Assn. Hosp. Podiatrists, Am. Coll. Foot and Ankle Surgeons; mem. New Haven County Podiatric Med. Assn., Conn. Podiatric Med. Assn., Am. Podiatric Med. Assn., Conn. Pub. Health Assn., Am. Pub. Health Assn. Jewish. Avocations: marble collecting, swimming, gardening. Home: 18 Inwood Rd Woodbridge CT 06525-2558 Office: Yale Podiatry Group PC 364 E Main St Ansonia CT 06401-1995

YALE, SEYMOUR HERSHEL, dental radiologist, educator, university dean, gerontologist; b. Chgo., Nov. 27, 1920; s. Henry and Dorothy (Kulwin) Y.; m. Muriel Jane Cohen, Nov. 6, 1943; children: Russell Steven, Patricia Ruth. B.S., U. Ill., 1944, D.D.S., 1945, postgrad., 1947-48. Pvt. practice of dentistry, 1945-54, 56—; asst. clin. dentistry U. Ill., 1948-49, instr. clin. dentistry, 1949-53, asst. prof. clin. dentistry, 1953-54, assoc. prof. dept. radiology Coll. Dentistry, 1956, prof., head dept. Coll. Dentistry, 1957-65, adminstrv. asst. to dean Coll. Dentistry, 1961-63, asst. dean Coll. Dentistry, 1963-64, acting dean Coll. Dentistry, 1964-65, dean, 1965-87, dean emeritus, 1987—; also mem. grad. faculty dept. radiology Coll. Medicine U. Ill., Chgo., prof. dentistry and health resources mgmt. Sch. Pub. Health, 1987—; sr. dental dir. Dental Care Plus Mgmt. Corp., Chgo.; pres., dir. dental edn. Dental Care Plus Mgmt. Ednl. Svcs., Ltd.; health care facilities planner; dir. tng. Dental Technicians Sch., U.S. Naval Tng. Center, Bainbridge, Md., 1954-56; Mem. subcom. 16 Nat. Com. on Radiation Protection; mem. Radiation Protection Adv. Bd., State of Ill., 1971, City of Chgo. Health Systems Agy.; founder Ctr. for Rsch. in Periodontal Disease and Oral Molecular Biology, 1977; organizer, chmn. Nat. Conf. on Hepatitis-B in Dentistry, 1982; organizer, dir. Univ. Taskforce Primary Health Care Project, U. Ill., Chgo.; chmn. U. Ill.-U. Stockholm-U. Gothenberg Conf. on Geriatrics, 1985; dir. planning AMVETS/UIC Teaching Nursing Home Project, 1987; co-sponsor 1st Egyptian Dental Congress, 1984; adj. prof. Ctr. for Exercise Sci. and Cardiovascular Rsch., Northeastern Ill. U., Chgo., 1991. Bd. dirs., co-benefactor (with wife) World Heritage Mus., U. Ill., Urbana, 1985; mem. Hillel Bd., U. Ill.-Chgo.; life mem. (with wife) Bronze Circle of Coll. Liberal Arts, U. Ill., Urbana; mem. (with wife) Pres.' Council, U. Ill. Recipient centennial research award Chgo. Dental Soc., 1959; Distinguished Alumnus award U. Ill., 1973; Harry Sicher Meml. Lecture award Am. Coll. Stomologic Surgeons, 1983. Fellow Acad. Gen. Dentistry (hon.), Am. Coll. Dentists; mem. Ill. Dental Soc. (mem. com. on radiology), Chgo. Dental Soc., Internat. Assn. Dental Rsch., Am. Acad. Oral Roentgenology, Am. Dental Assn., Odontographic Soc. Chgo. (Award of Merit 1982), Council Dental Deans State Ill. (chmn.), N.Y. Acad. Scis., Gerontol. Soc. Am., Pierre Fauchard Acad. (Man of Yr. award Ill. sect. 1988), Am. Pub. Health Assn., Gerontol. Soc. Am., American Kappa Upsilon, Sigma Xi, Alpha Omega (hon.). Established (with wife) collection of Coins of Ottoman Empire and Related Mohammedan States and supplemental antique map collection at World Heritage Mus. Home: 155 N Harbor Dr Chicago IL 60601-7328 Office: 25 E Washington St Chicago IL 60602-1702

YALEN, GARY N., insurance company executive; b. N.Y.C., May 17, 1942; s. Sidney Leo and Mildred (Epstein) Y.; m. Rena Lynn Gear, Nov. 3, 1968; children—Robert, Lesley. BEE, Rensselaer Poly. Inst., 1964; MBA, U. Mich., 1965. Chartered fin. analyst. Mktg. engr. N.Y. Telephone Co., N.Y.C., 1965-69; security analyst Merrill Lynch, N.Y.C., 1969-74; security analyst Irving Trust Co., N.Y.C., 1974-80, research dir., 1980-83, sr. v.p., chief investment officer, 1983-87, exec. v.p., 1987-89; exec. v.p. Bank of N.Y., 1989-90; chief investment officer, exec. v.p. Fortis Asset Mgmt. (formerly Amev), 1990—. Served with U.S. Army, 1966-68, Vietnam. Mem. N.Y. Soc. Security Analysts, Beta Gamma Sigma. Avocations: golf, bridge. Home: 175 Nancy Ln Wyckoff NJ 07481-2522 Office: Fortis Asset Mgmt One Chase Manhattan Plz New York NY 10005

YALMAN, ANN, judge; b. Boston, June 9, 1948; d. Richard George and Joan (Osterman) Y. BA, Antioch Coll., 1970; JD, NYU, 1973. Trial atty. Fla. Rural Legal Svcs., Immokalee, Fla., 1973-74; staff atty. EEO, Atlanta, 1974-76; pvt. practice Santa Fe, N.Mex., 1976—; part time U.S. Magistrate, N.Mex., 1988—. Commr. Met. Water Bd., Santa Fe, 1986-88. Mem. N.Mex. Bar Assn. (commr. Santa Fe chpt. 1983-86). Home: 441 Calle La Paz Santa Fe NM 87501-2821 Office: 304 Catron St Santa Fe NM 87501-1806

YALOW, ROSALYN SUSSMAN, medical physicist; b. N.Y.C., N.Y., July 19, 1921; d. Simon and Clara (Zipper) Sussman; m. A. Aaron Yalow, June 6, 1943; children: Benjamin, Elanna. A.B., Hunter Coll., 1941; M.S., U. Ill., Urbana, 1942, Ph.D., 1945; D.Sc. (hon.), U. Ill., Chgo., 1974, Phila. Coll. Pharmacy and Sci., 1976, N.Y. Med. Coll., 1976, Med. Coll. Wis., Milw., 1977, Yeshiva U., 1977, Southampton (N.Y.) Coll., 1978, Bucknell U., 1978, Princeton U., 1978, Jersey City State Coll., 1979, Med. Coll. Pa., 1979, Manhattan Coll., 1979, U. Vt., 1980, U. Hartford, 1980, Rutgers U., 1980, Rensselaer Poly. Inst., 1980, Colgate U., 1981, U. So. Calif., 1981, Clarkson Coll., 1982, U. Miami, 1983, Washington U., St. Louis, 1983, Adelphi U., 1983, U. Alta. (Can.), 1983, SUNY, 1984, Tel Aviv U., 1985, Claremont (Calif.) U., 1986, Mills Coll., Oakland, Calif., 1986, Cedar Crest Coll., Allentown, Pa., 1988, Drew U., Madison, N.J., 1988, Lehigh U., 1988; L.H.D. (hon.), Hunter Coll., 1978; DSc. (hon.), San Francisco State U., 1989, Technion-Israel Inst. Tech., Haifa, 1989; DSc (hon.), Med. Coll. Ohio Toledo, 1991; L.H.D. (hon.), Sacred Heart U., Conn., 1978, St. Michael's Coll. Winooski Park, Vt., 1979, Johns Hopkins U., 1979, Coll. St. Rose, 1988, Spertus Coll. Judaica, Chgo., 1988; D. honoris causa, U. Rosario, Argentina, 1980, U. Ghent, Belgium, 1984; D. Humanities and Letters (hon.), Columbia U., 1984; DSc (hon.), Fairleigh Dickinson U., 1992, Conn. Coll., 1992, Smith Coll., Northampton, Mass., 1994, Union Coll., Schenectady, 1992. Diplomate: Am. Bd. Scis. Lectr., asst. prof. physics Hunter Coll., 1946-50; physicist, asst. chief radioisotope service VA Hosp., Bronx, N.Y., 1950-70, chief nuclear medicine, 1970-80, acting chief radioisotope service, 1968-70; research prof. Mt. Sinai Sch. Medicine, CUNY, 1968-74, Disting. Service prof., 1974-79, Solomon A. Berson Disting. prof.-at-large, 1986—; Disting. prof.-at-large Albert Einstein Coll. Medicine, Yeshiva U., 1979-85, prof. emeritus, 1986—; chmn. dept. clin. scis. Montefiore Med. Ctr., Bronx, 1980-85; cons. Lenox Hill Hosp., N.Y.C., 1956-62, WHO, Bombay, 1978; sec. U.S. Nat. Com. on Med. Physics, 1963-67; mem. nat. com. Radiation Protection, Subcom. 13, 1957; mem. Pres.'s Study Group on Careers for Women, 1966-72; sr. med. investigator VA, 1972-92, sr. med. investigator emeritus, 1992—. Co-editor: Hormone and Metabolic Research, 1973-79; editorial adv. council: Acta Diabetologica Latina, 1975-77, Ency. Universalis, 1978—; editorial bd.: Mt. Sinai Jour. Medicine, 1976-79, Diabetes, 1976, Endocrinology, 1967-72; contbr. numerous articles to profl. jours. Bd. dirs. N.Y. Diabetes Assn., 1974. Recipient VA William S. Middleton Med. Research award, 1960; Eli Lilly award Am. Diabetes Assn., 1961; Van Slyke award N.Y. met. sect. Am. Assn. Clin. Chemists, 1968; award A.C.P., 1971; Dickson prize U. Pitts., 1971; Howard Taylor Ricketts award U. Chgo., 1971; Gairdner Found. Internat. award, 1971; Commemorative medallion Am. Diabetes Assn., 1972; Bernstein award Med. Soc. State N.Y., 1974; Boehringer-Mannheim Corp. award Am. Assn. Clin. Chemists, 1975; Sci. Achievement award AMA, 1975; Exceptional Service award VA, 1975; A. Cressy Morrison award N.Y. Acad. Scis., 1975; sustaining membership award Assn. Mil. Surgeons, 1975; Distinguished Achievement award Modern Medicine, 1976; Albert Lasker Basic Med. Research award, 1976; La Madonnina Internat. prize Milan, 1977; Golden Plate award Am. Acad. Achievement, 1977; Nobel prize for physiology/medicine, 1977; citation of esteem St. John's U., 1979; G. von Hevesy medal, 1978; Rosalyn S. Yalow Research and Devel. award established Am. Diabetes Assn., 1978; Banting medal, 1978; Torch of Learning award Am. Friends Hebrew U., 1978; Virchow gold medal Virchow-Pirquet Med. Soc., 1978; Gratum Genus Humanum gold medal World Fedn. Nuclear Medicine or Biology, 1978; Jacobi medallion Asso. Alumni Mt. Sinai Sch. Medicine, 1978; Jubilee medal Coll. of New Rochelle, 1978; VA Exceptional Service award, 1978; Fed. Woman's award, 1961; Harvey lectr., 1966; Am. Gastroenterol. Assn. Meml. lectr., 1972; Joslin lectr. New Eng. Diabetes Assn., 1972; Franklin I. Harris Meml. lectr., 1973; 1st Hagedorn Meml. lectr. Acta Endocrinologica Congress, 1973; Sarasota Med. award for achievement and excellence, 1979; gold medal Phi Lambda Kappa, 1980; Achievement in Life award Ency. Brit., 1980; Theobald Smith award, 1982; Pres.'s Cabinet award U. Detroit, 1982; John and Samuel Bard award in medicine and sci. Bard Coll., 1982; Disting. Research award Dallas Assn. Retarded Citizens, 1982, Nat. Medal Sci., 1988; Abram L. Sachar Silver Medallion Brandeis U., Waltham, Mass., 1989, Disting. Scientist of Yr. award ARCS, N.Y.C., 1989; Golden Scroll award The Jewish Advocate, Boston, 1989, spl. award Clin. Ligand Assay Soc., Washington, 1988, numerous others. Fellow N.Y. Acad. Scis. (chmn. biophysics div. 1964-65), Am. Coll. Radiology (asso. in physics), Clin. Soc. N.Y. Diabetes Assn.; mem. Nat. Acad. Scis., Am. Acad. Arts and Scis., Am. Phys. Soc., Radiation Research Soc., Am. Assn. Physicists in Medicine, Biophys. Soc., Soc. Nuclear Medicine, Endocrine Soc. (Koch award 1972, pres. 1978), Am. Physiol. Soc. (hon.) Harvey Soc., (hon.) Med. Assn. Argentina, (hon.) Diabetes Soc. Argentina, (hon.) Am. Coll. Nuclear Physicians, (hon.) The N.Y. Acad. Medicine, (hon.) Am. Gastroent. Assn., (hon.) N.Y. Roentgen Soc., (hon.) Soc. Nuclear Medicine, Phi Beta Kappa, Sigma Xi, Sigma Pi Sigma, Pi Mu Epsilon, Sigma Delta Epsilon, Tau Beta Pi. Office: VA Hosp 130 W Kingsbridge Rd Bronx NY 10468-3904

YAMABE, SHIGERU, medical educator; b. Tokyo, July 7, 1923; s. Hiroshi and Jyo (Mihara) Y.; m. Takako Naoi, Apr. 2, 1967; 1 child, Yoko. MS, Osaka (Japan) U., 1946, PhD, 1952. Lectr. Osaka U. Med. Sch., 1953-58; prof. Kobe Coll., Nishinomiya, Japan, 1958-89, hon. prof., 1989—; system dir. Drug Rsch. System Internat., Kobe, 1989—; rsch. exec. mbr. Osaka Seijinbyo Med. Ctr., Higashinariku, Osaka, Japan, 1991—; vis. lectr. Tokyo U., Kyoto (Japan) U., 1966-84; vis. rsch. dept. microbiology London Hosp. Med. Coll., 1978—, Case Western Res. U., Cleve., 1982, 84, Harvard Med. Sch., Boston, 1988-89; hon. vis. lectr. London Hosp. Med. Coll., 1990—; invited lectr. U. Paris VI, 1992—; vis. sr. scientist Inst. Pathology, Oxford, 1992—; vis. prof. Grad. Sch. Pub. Health U. Pitts., 1993—; sci. advisor Taiho Pharm. Co., Tokyo, 1991—. Author: Bioenergetics, 1968 (award 1970); editor: Research and Development of New Drugs, 1994; internat. jour. editor Antiviral Chemistry and Chemotherapy, 1993—, Jour. Chemotherapy, 1988—; drug designer, inventor Tazobactam antiobiotic, 1991, Zaltoprofen anti-inflammatory drug, 1993; 40 patents for cancer and AIDS drugs. Fellow Royal Soc. Medicine; mem. N.Y. Acad. Sci. Avocation: poetry. Home: 1-2-7 Kamokogahara, Higashinada, Kobe 658, Japan Office: ESS, Hotel Okura Kobe Chuo-ku, Kobe 650, Japan

YAMADA, KEIICHI, engineering educator, university official; b. Dec. 23, 1931. M in Engring., U. Tokyo, 1956; DSc, U. Göttingen, Fed. Republic of Germany, 1958, U. Freiburg, Fed. Republic of Germany, 1959; D in Engring., U. Tokyo, 1964. Asst. prof. U. Tokyo, 1959-68; assoc. prof. Tokyo Inst. Tech., 1968-75, prof., 1975-77; prof. U. Tsukuba, 1977—; dir. Inst. Socio-Econ. Planning U. Tsukuba, Ibaraki, 1984-86, dir. Rsch. Ctr. for Univ. Studies, 1986-90, provost of colls., 1991-93; vice-dir. Inst. for Policy Scis., Tokyo, 1984—. Author: Life Cycles of Scientific Research, 1986, The World Mountains from the Air, 1981; editor-in-chief Jour. Sci. Policy and Rsch. Mgmt., 1985-88; one-man photog. show Le Montagna del Cielo, Italy, 1989. Mem. Japanese Soc. for Sci. Policy and Rsch. Mgmt. (councilor 1988—), Japan-China Soc. Avocation: alpine aerial photography. Office: U Tsukuba, Tsukuba-shi, Ibaraki 305, Japan

YAMADA, KENNETH MANAO, cell biologist; b. Mpls., Sept. 18, 1944; s. Paul Manao and Masaye (Uriu) Y.; m. Susan Jane Sleeper, July 1, 1973. BA

in Biol. Scis., Stanford U., 1966, PhD in Biol. Scis., 1971, MD, 1972. Intern Mary's Help Hosp./Seton Med. Ctr., Daly City, Calif., 1972-73; commd. lt. USPHS, 1974, advanced through grades to capt., 1982—; sect. chief Nat. Cancer Inst., Bethesda, Md., 1987-90; lab. chief Nat. Inst. Dental Rsch., Bethesda, Md., 1990—; mem. NIH Cell Biology Study Sect., 1979-83; mem. external adv. com. Howard U. Cancer Rsch. Ctr., 1979-88; co-chmn. Gordon Conf. on Fibronectin, 1982; Stadtler lectr. U. Tex. Sys. Cancer Ctr., M.D. Anderson Hosp., 1988; Swerling lectr. Dana-Farber Cancer Inst., Harvard Med. Sch., 1988. Contbr. more than 200 articles to profl. jours. Postdoctoral fellow U. Oreg., Dept. Biology, Eugene, 1973-74; recipient Eli Luke and Jacob David Rsch. award, 1972. Fellow AAAS; mem. Am. Soc. Cell Biology (coun. mem. 1993—), Am. Soc. Biochemistry and Molecular Biology, Internat. Soc. Matrix Biology (coun. mem. 1994—), Southeastern Cancer Rsch. Assn. (bd. dirs. 1980-83), Soc. Devel. Biology, Sigma Xi, Phi Beta Kappa (Undergrad. Rsch. award). Office: Natl Inst of Dental Rsch Bldg 30 Rm 421 9000 Rockville Pike Bethesda MD 20892-4370

YAMADA, SHINICHI, mathematician, computer scientist, educator; b. Nagoya, Japan, Jan. 10, 1937; s. Umekichi and Nami (Kawashima) Y.; m. Atsuyo Yamamoto, Oct. 10, 1964; 1 child, Atsushi. BS, U. Tokyo, 1959, DSc, 1988; SM, Harvard U., 1970. System analyst Nippon Univac Co., Tokyo, 1959-70, tech. advisor, 1970-90; lectr. Keio U., Tokyo, 1980-85, Waseda U., Tokyo, 1982—, Chiba U., 1989—, prof. dept. info. sci. Hirosaki U., Japan, 1990-93, prof. dept of information scis., Science U. of Tokyo, 1993—. Author: Sciences of Information Processing, 1984, Micro-Prolog Collection, 1986, Kowalski Logic for Problem Solving, 1987, Encyclopedia of Artificial Intelligence, 1988, Encyclopedia of Computer Systems, 1989. Mem. editorial staff Info. Processing Soc. Japan, 1983-87; contbr. articles to profl. jours. Mem. IEEE, AAAS, Am. Math. Soc., Math. Soc. Japan, Assn. Symbolic Logic, Assn. Computing Machinery, N.Y. Acad. Scis. Clubs: Harvard of Japan. Home: 821-19 Nishi-Fukai, Nagareyama-Shi Chiba 270-01, Japan Office: Sci U Tokyo Dept Info Sci, Yamasaki 2641 Noda-SHI, Chiba 278, Japan

YAMAGUCHI, KRISTI TSUYA, ice skater; b. Hayward, Calif., July 12, 1971; d. Jim and Carole (Doi) Y. Gold medalist, Figure Skating Albertville Olympic Games, 1992; U.S. Skating champion, 1992, World Skating champion, 1991, 1992, World Junior champion, 1988, world profl. figure skating champion, 1994. Recipient Women First award YWCA, 1993. Avocations: tennis, rollerblading, reading, and dancing. Address: U.S. Figure Skating Assn. 20 First St. Colorado Springs CO 80906*

YAMAGUCHI, TAMOTSU, bank executive; b. Hokkaido, Japan, Oct. 11, 1930; came to U.S., 1986; s. Chuji and Nami (Inouye) Y.; m. Noriko Kogishi; children: Takashi, Masako. BS in Econs., U. Tokyo, 1953. With Bank of Tokyo, 1953-63; dept. mgr. Bank of Tokyo, Dusseldorf, 1963-66; dept. mgr. fgn. exchange and funds ops. Bank of Tokyo, London, 1966-70; acting gen. mgr. Bank of Tokyo, 1970-79; pres., dir. Bank of Tokyo, Sao Paulo, Brazil, 1979-82; gen. mgr. bd. dirs. Mfg. & Tech. Conversion, Internat., Tokyo, 1982-84; sr. v.p. Bank of Tokyo Ltd., Tokyo, 1984-87, resident mng. dir. Am.; chmn. bd. Bank Tokyo Trust Co., New York, 1986—; dep. pres. Bank Tokyo, 1988-92; bd. dirs. Bank Tokyo Can., Toronto, Ont.; chmn. bd. Union Bank, L.A., 1992—. Elder Hope Chapel, Torrance, Calif., 1990-91. Mem. Asia Soc. (bd. dirs.), Japan Am. Soc. (bd. dirs.), Calif. Bus. Roundtable, L.A. World Affairs Coun. (bd. dirs.), Mountaingate Country Club, Jonathan Club. Clubs: Nippon (N.Y.C.). Home: 5937 Peacock Ridge Rd Palos Verdes Estates CA 90274

YAMAGUCHI, YUKIO, chemistry research scientist; b. Hiroshima, Japan, Feb. 22, 1941; came to U.S., 1970; s. Tameo and Miyuki (Kodama) Y.; m. Masako Iwamura, Aug. 3, 1994. BE, Kyushu U., Fukuoka, Japan, 1964, ME, 1966; PhD, U. Tex., Austin, 1978. Research assoc. Kyushu U., Fukuoka, 1966-70; postdoctoral fellow U. Tex., Austin, 1979-80; postdoctoral fellow U. Calif. and Lawrence Berkeley Lab., Berkeley, 1980-82, chemistry rsch. scientist, 1982-87; chemistry rsch. scientist U. Ga., Athens, 1987—. Author: (with Y. Osamura, J.D. Goddard and H.F. Schaefer) A New Dimension to Quantum Chemistry: Analytic Derivative Methods in Ab Initio Molecular Electronic Structure Theory; contbr. articles to profl. jours. Mem. Am. Chem. Soc., Chem. Soc. of Japan. Avocations: reading, travel, swimming. Office: U Ga Ctr Computational Quantum Chem Athens GA 30602

YAMAKAWA, ALLAN HITOSHI, university administrator; b. San Francisco, Oct. 18, 1938; s. Victor Tadashi and Alice Tsugie (Sato) Y.; m. Nancy Ann Habel, Apr.17, 1977 (div. Mar 1987); children: Bryan Allan, David Scott. BS, Roosevelt U., 1962, MEd, 1970. Tech. svcs. dir. audio visual libr. Roosevelt U., Chgo., 1958-60; dean, exec. dir. Ency. Britannica Schs., Inc., Chgo., 1960-67; curriculum svcs. dir. Field Enterprises Newspaper Div., Chgo., 1967-70; edn. svcs. dir. Chgo. Tribune Co., 1970-76; tng. svcs. dir. Dialogue Systems Inc., N.Y.C., 1976-79; orgn. devel. dir. U. Ill., Chgo., 1979—; cons., trainer Can. Daily Newspaper Pub. Assn., Toronto, 1973-84, Am. Newspaper Pub. Found., Reston, Va., 1972-80, Gifted Students Found. Dallas, 1974-75; cons. Cedars Sinai Med. Ctr., Beverly Hills, Calif., 1983—, W. K. Kellogg Found., 1987—. Author: Handbooks of Teaching Methods, 1974, Communicate, 1975, Catalysts For Change, 1976, Evaluation of Senior Administrators, 1994; patentee experiential learning method. Instr. ARC, Chgo., 1954—; bd. dirs. Edison Regional Gifted Ctr. Sch., Chgo., pres., 1989-93; distt. program chmn. Boy Scouts Am., 1985—. Mem. ASTD, ASCD, Soc. Programmed and Automated Learning, Toastmasters (pres. 1974-76). Avocations: photography, computer programming, electronics, pyrotechnics, film production. Office: U Ill 1140 S Paulina St Chicago IL 60612-7216

YAMAKAWA, DAVID KIYOSHI, JR., lawyer; b. San Francisco, Jan. 25, 1936; s. David Kiyoshi and Shizu (Negishi) Y. BS, U. Calif., Berkeley, 1958, JD, 1963. Bar: Calif. 1964, U.S. Supreme Ct. 1970. Prin. Law Offices of David K. Yamakawa Jr., San Francisco, 1964—; dep. dir. Cmty. Action Agy., San Francisco, 1968-69; dir. City Demonstration Agy., San Francisco, 1969-70; mem. adv. coun. Calif. Senate Subcom. on the Disabled, 1982-83; chmn. cmty. residential treatment system adv. com. Calif. Dept. Mental Health, 1980-85, San Francisco Human Rights Commn., 1977-80; pres. Legal Assistance to the Elderly, 1981-83; 2d v.p. Nat. Conf. Social Welfare, 1983—; v.p. Region IX, Nat. Mental Health Assn., 1981-83; vice-chmn. Mt. Zion Hosp. and Med. Ctr., 1986-88; bd. dirs. United Neighborhood Ctrs. of Am., 1977-83, ARC Bay Area, 1988-91, Mt. Zion Inst. on Aging, 1993—, v.p., 1994—; bd. trustees Mt. Zion Med. Ctr., 1994-95, San Francisco, 1993—; chmn. bd. trustees United Way Bay Area, 1983-85; chief fin. officer Action for Nature, Inc., 1987—; v.p. Friends of Legal Assistance to the Elderly, 1984—; bd. dirs. Inst. Sector, 1986-92, Friends of the San Francisco Human Rights Commn., 1980—; CFO, 1980-85, vice chmn., 1985-94, CFO, 1994—, La Madre de los Pobres, 1982—, v.p., 1994—, Nat. Concilio Am., 1987—, Hispanic Community Found. of the Bay Area, 1989—, legal coun. 1989—; bd. dirs. Internat. Inst. San Francisco, 1989—, pres., 1990-93, Non-Profit Svcs., Inc., 1987—; sec. 1987-90, chmn., 1990—; pres. Coun. Internat. Programs, San Francisco, 1987-89; mem. citizens adv. com. San Francisco Hotel Tax Fund Grants for the Arts Program, 1991—. Recipient John B. Williams Outstanding Planning and Agy. Rsch. award United Way of the Bay Area, 1980, Mortimer Fleishhacker Jr. Outstanding Vol. award United Way, 1985, Spl. Recognition award Legal Assistance to the Elderly, 1983, Commendation award Bd. Suprs. City and County of San Francisco, 1983, cert. honor, San Francisco Found. award, 1985, 1st Mental Health Awareness award Mental Health Assn. San Francisco, 1990; David Yamakawa Day proclaimed in San Francisco, 1985. Mem. ABA (Liberty Bell award 1986). Office: 582 Market St Ste 410 San Francisco CA 94104-5305

YAMAMOTO, DONALD YUKIO, diplomat; b. Seattle, Mar. 13, 1953; s. Hideo and Lillian Yamamoto; m. Margaret Darling, Dec. 11, 1982; 1 child, Michael. BA, Columbia Coll., 1975; East Asian cert., Columbia U., 1978, MIA, 1978. Diplomat Dept. State, Washington, 1980—. Office: Unit 45004 Box 242 APO AP 96337-5004 Office: Unit 45004 Box 242 APO NY 96337

YAMAMOTO, HARRY YOSHIMI, research institute director, educator; b. Honolulu, Nov. 26, 1933; s. Isami and Takeno (Morita) Y.; m. Millie Y. Wakugawa, Jan. 31, 1957; children: Craig A., Joanne V. BS, U. Hawaii, 1955; MS, U. Ill., 1958; PhD, U. Calif., 1962. Prof. U. Hawaii, Honolulu,

1961—; dir. Hawaii Inst. Tropical Agr. and Human Resources, Honolulu, 1993—; cons. HYCON, Honolulu, 1970—; bd. dirs. Hawaii Biotechnology Group, Inc., Honolulu, 1983—. Contbr. rsch. articles to profl. jours. Rsch. grantee NSF, USDA, DOE industry. Mem. Am. Soc. Plant Physiology, Inst. Food Technologists, Am. Chem. Soc., AAAS. Office: U Hawaii at Manoa Hawaii Inst of Tropical Agr and Human Re Honolulu HI 96822

YAMAMOTO, JOE, psychiatrist, educator; b. Los Angeles, Apr. 18, 1924; s. Zenzaburo and Tomie (Yamada) Y.; m. Maria Fujitomi, Sept. 5, 1947; children: Eric Robert, Andrew Jolyon. Student, Los Angeles City Coll., 1941-42, Hamline U., 1943-45; B.S., U. Minn., 1946, M.B., 1948, M.D. 1949. Asst. prof. dept. psychiatry, neurology, behavioral sci. U. Okla. Med. Center, 1955-58, asst. prof., 1958-60; assoc. prof. dept. psychiatry U. So. Calif. Sch. Medicine, Los Angeles, 1961-69; prof. U. So. Calif. Sch. Medicine, 1969-77, co-dir. grad. edn. psychiatry, 1963-70; prof. UCLA, 1977—; dir. Psychiat. Outpatient Clinic, Los Angeles County-U. So. Calif. Med. Center, 1958-77; dir. adult ambulatory care services UCLA Neuropsychiat. Inst., 1977-88, chief Lab. for Cross Cultural Studies. Contbr. articles in field to profl. jours. Served to capt., M.C. U.S. Army, 1953-55. Fellow Am. Psychiat. Assn. (life), Pacific Rim Coll. Psychiatrists, Am. Acad. Psychoanalysis (trustee, mem. exec. com., pres. 1978-79), Am. Coll. Psychiatrists, Am. Orthopsychiatric Assn. (pres. elect 1993-94, pres. 1994—), Am. Assn. for Social Psychiatry (trustee 1981-84, v.p. 1984-86); mem. So. Calif. Psychoanalytic Inst. and Soc. (pres. 1972-73), Soc. for Study of Culture and Psychiatry, Group for Advancement Psychiatry (bd. dirs. 1992—), Kappa Phi, Alpha Omega Alpha. Office: UCLA Neuro-psychiat Inst 760 Westwood Plz Los Angeles CA 90024-1759 *Learning about the diverse peoples of America, I have been fascinated with how we can be Asian, Hispanic, Black, European, and Native American and still identify with our national values. We value our freedom, individual rights and our ability to be someone different but equal. In mental health also there is a need for recognition of cultural differences and the need of treatment response to the individual.*

YAMAMOTO, KAORU, psychology, education educator; b. Tokyo, Mar. 28, 1932; came to U.S., 1959; s. Saburo and Hideko (Watanabe) Y.; m. Etsuko Hamazaki, Apr. 6, 1959 (div. 1986); m. Carol-Lynne Moore, Oct. 4, 1986; children: Keita Carey Moore, Kiyomi Lynne Moore. BS in Engring., U. Tokyo, 1953; MA, U. Minn., 1960, PhD, 1962. Engr. Toppan Printing Co., Tokyo, 1953; engr., rsch. chemist Japan Oxygen Co., Tokyo, 1954-57, 58-59; asst. prof. Kent (Ohio) State U., 1962-65; from asst. to assoc. prof. U. Iowa, Iowa City, 1965-68; prof. Pa. State U., University Park, 1968-72, Ariz. State U., Tempe, 1972-87, U. Colo., Denver, 1987—; vis. prof. U. Minn., Mpls., 1974, Simon Fraser U., Burnaby, B.C., Can., 1984, U.Victoria, B.C., 1986, U. Wash., Seattle, 1987, Zhejiang Normal U., Jinhua, China, 1991; Fulbright lectr. U. Iceland, 1985. Author: The Child and His Image, 1972, Their World, Our World, 1993; author, editor: 6 books; co-author: Beyond Words, 1988; editor Am. Ednl. Rsch. Jour., 1972-75, Ednl. Forum, 1984-92; contbr. over 125 articles to profl. jours., 8 chpts. to books. Landsdowne scholar U. Victoria, 1985. Fellow APA; mem. Am. Sociol. Assn., Am. Anthrop. Assn., Motus Humanus. Avocations: winter sports, travel, classical music, reading. Office: U Colo Denver Box 106 PO Box 173364 Denver CO 80217-3364

YAMAMOTO, MICHAEL TORU, journalist; b. San Francisco, July 9, 1960; s. Harry Naoto and Noriko (Yoshitomi) Y.; m. Marianne Chin, Oct. 9, 1993. BA Psychology, San Francisco State U., 1981, BA Journalism, 1981. Editor San Francisco State U. Phoenix, 1980; news editor Hayward (Calif.) Daily Rev., 1979-80, Long Beach (Calif.) Press-Telegram, 1981; nat. desk editor L.A. Times, 1981-85; night news editor L.A. Times, Washington, 1986-87, investigative projects editor, 1988; dep. city editor San Francisco Chronicle, 1989-92, exec. projects editor, 1993, city editor, 1993—; adj. prof. Am. U., Washington, 1987, Calif. State U. at Northridge, Calif., 1984-85; vis. faculty mem. Am. Press Inst., Reston, Va., 1994, Poynter Inst. for Media Studies, St. Petersburg, Fla., 1995, San Francisco Unified Sch. Dist., 1994; fellow Coro Found., San Francisco, 1990-91. Recipient Dow Jones Newspaper Fund scholarship, Princeton, N.J., 1980. Mem. Asian Am. Journalism Assn., White House Corr. Assn., Soc. Profl. Journalists., World Affairs Coun. Office: San Francisco Chronicle 901 Mission St San Francisco CA 94103

YAMAMOTO, RICHARD KUMEO, physics educator; b. Honolulu, June 29, 1935; s. Minoru and Edith Hatsuko (Ogawa) Y.; m. Lily Marie Chin, June 11, 1961; children: Cara-Jean, Lani, Sharon. SB, MIT, 1957, PhD, 1963. Rsch. assoc. MIT, Cambridge, 1963-64; instr., 1964-65, asst. prof., 1965-68, assoc. prof., 1968-75, prof. physics, 1975—. Fellow Am. Phys. Soc.; mem. AAAS, N.Y. Acad. Scis., AAUP. Office: MIT 77 Massachusetts Ave Cambridge MA 02139-3594

YAMAMOTO, TAMOTSU, art educator, artist, architectural illustrator; b. Kyoto, Japan, Jan. 28, 1946; came to U.S., 1972; s. Kyuichi Mitsuyori-Yamamoto and Koume Yamamoto; m. Selene Rate Hunter, July 26, 1977. BFA, Kyoto U. Fine Arts, 1969, MFA, 1971; postgrad. diploma, Sch. Museum Fine Arts, 1975, 76. Prin. Yamamoto Archtl. Illustration, Boston, 1976—; prof. Mt. Ida Coll., Newton, Mass., 1994—; adj. prof. Chamberlayne Jr. Coll., 1979-88, Mass. Coll. Art, 1983-88, Boston Archtl. Ctr., 1988—, Wentworth Inst. Tech., 1994—. Contbr. Architecture in Perspective, vol. 4, 1989, vol. 7, 1992, vol. 8, 1993, vol. 9, 1994, Architecture in Perspective: Retrospective, 1992, Architectural Rendering, 1992, The Art of Architectural Illustration, 1994, KAPA Retrospective, 1995; exhbns. include Mus. Fine Arts, Kyoto, 1966-71, 72, Gallery 16, Kyoto, 1969m, Gallery Shinanobashi, Osaka, 1969, Hartford Mus. Fine Arts, 1972, Ctr. Advanced Visual Studies, Cambridge, Mass., 1972, 75, Avant Garde Fesitval N.Y., 1975, 78, Boston Mus. Fine Arts, 1977, Charles River, Cambridge, 1978, Artists Found., 1978, 80, Tokyo Express, 1981, JARA ann. exhbn., Tokyo, Nagoya and Osaka, Japan, 1986—, Chgo. Art Inst., 1989, Nev. Mus. Art, Reno, 1990, John B. Aird Gallery, Toronto, 1990, Japan Archtl. Renderers Assn. Japan Inst. Architects Nat. Conv., Kobe, 1993, Robert W. Woodruff Arts Ctr., Atlanta, 1993, Gwenda Jay Gallery, Chgo., 1993, World Conv., Chgo., AIA NeoCon93, The Internat. Architects, AIA Chpt. Gallery, San Francisco, Architecture II Gallery, U. Manitoba, Can., Design Exchange, Toronto, 1992, Boston Archtl. Ctr., 1994, AIA Nat. Conv., L.A., 1994, Coll. Art and Design, Detroit, 1994, Chgo. Architecture Found., 1994, Contract Design Ctr., San Francisco, 1994, Galerie Aaedes, Berlin, Architekturforum Macular Aedesm Vienna, AIA Nat. Conv., Atlanta, ACSA European Conf., Lisbon, Portugal, 1995; contbr. articles to profl. jours. Recipient Excellence in Design award Boston Soc. Architects, 1973, Comp. Winning award Internat. Archtl. Artist, 1989, 92, 93, 94. Mem. Am. Soc. Archtl. Perspectivists (treas. exec. bd. dirs. 1989-93, adv. coun. 1994—, internat. coord., pres.), Japan Archtl. Renderers Assn. (hon.), Inst. Contemporary Arts, Boston Archtl. Ctr. (grantee faculty expense fund 1994). Avocations: golf, ski, classical experimental music. Home: 15 Sleeper St Boston MA 02210-1225

YAMANE, GEORGE MITSUYOSHI, oral diagnosis and radiology educator; b. Honolulu, Aug. 9, 1924; s. Seigi and Tsuta (Moriwaki) Y.; m. Alice Matsuko Nemoto, July 6, 1951; children: Wende Michiko, Linda Keiko, David Kiyoshi. Student, U. Hawaii, 1944; A.B., Haverford Coll., 1946; D.D.S., U. Minn., 1950, Ph.D., 1962. Teaching, research asst. U. Hawaii, Honolulu, 1943-44; teaching asst. div. oral pathology, oral diagnosis Sch. Dentistry, U. Minn., Mpls., 1951-53; asst. prof. oral pathology Coll. Dentistry U. Ill., Chgo., 1957-59; dir. tissue lab. Sch. Dentistry U. Wash., Seattle, 1960-63; asst. prof. oral pathology Sch. Dentistry U. Wash., 1959-63; grad. faculty mem. U. Minn., Mpls., 1963-70; prof., chmn. div. oral diagnosis, oral medicine and oral roentgenology U. Minn., 1963-70; prof., chmn. dept. oral diagnosis and radiology Dental Sch. Univ. of Medicine and Dentistry of N.J., 1970-83; prof. dept. biodental sci. Dental Sch. Coll. of Medicine and Dentistry of N.J., 1983-88, assoc. dean research and patholgoist programs, 1976-79, div. div. oral and pathobiology, 1988-92, prof. dept oral pathology, biology and diagnosis sci., 1988-92, prof. emeritus, 1992—; cons. Children's Orthopedic Hosp. and Med. Ctr., Seattle, 1960-63, VA Hosp., American Lake, Wash., 1961-63, Mpls., 1966-70; cons. Minn. State Dept. Health, 1965-70, Wyo. State Bd. Health, 1966-70. Contbr. articles to med. and dental jours. Served with AUS. USPHS fellow, 1953-55; recipient Nell S. Talbot Instructorship award Coll. Dentistry U. Ill., 1958; Excellence in Teaching award U. Medicine and Dentistry N.J., 1984, Exceptional Merit award U.

Medicine and Dentistry N.J., 1986. Fellow Am. Acad. Oral Pathology, AAAS, Am., Internat. colls. dentists, N.J. Acad. Medicine; mem. Am. Dental Assn., Orgn. Teachers. Oral Diagnosis (sec.-treas. 1970-73, pres. 1974-75), Am. Acad. Periodontology, Internat. Assn. Dental Research, Am. Assn. Dental Schs., Sigma Xi (pres. Newark chpt. 1985), Omicron Kappa Upsilon, Xi Psi Phi.

YAMANE, STANLEY JOEL, optometrist; b. Lihue, Kauai, Hawaii, Mar. 13, 1943; s. Tooru and Yukiko (Miura) Y.; m. Joyce Mitsuko Tamura; children—Stanley Tooru Aiichi, Karen Margaret. B.S. in Optometry, Pacific U., 1966, O.D., 1966. Diplomate Am. Acad. Optometry. Practice optometry Waipahu, Hawaii, 1967-73; ptnr. with Dr. Dennis M. Kuwabara, 1973-81; ptnr. Drs. Kuwabara & Yamane, Optometrists, Inc., Waipahu, 1981-91; with br. office Drs. Kuwabara & Yamane, Optometrists, Inc., Honolulu; with DBA Eye Care Assocs. of Hawaii, Honolulu, 1989-91; dir. profl. affairs Vistakon, Inc., 1991-92; v.p. profl. affairs Vistakon Inc., 1992—; lectr., cons. in field; sec.-treas. Hawaii Bd. Examiners in Optometry, 1975-76, v.p., 1976-78, pres., 1978-80; mem. adj. faculty Coll. Optometry, Pacific U, 1977-91, Pa. Coll. Optometry, 1981-91, So. Coll. Optometry, 1982-91, U. Mo., St. Louis, 1990-91; bd. dirs. Hawaii Vision Svc. Plan, 1984-91. Cons. editor Optometric Mgmt. Jour., 1981-91, Contact Lens Forum Jour., 1987-91, editor, 1991; contbr. articles to profl. jours. Bd. mgrs. Leeward Oahu Br. YMCA, 1967-70, Hi-Y advisor, 1967-71, mem. Century Club, 1967-91, bd. mgrs. West Oahu Br., 1971-78, gen. chmn. sustaining membership, 1976; 2d v.p. August Ahrens Elem. Sch. PTA, 1969; mem. Leeward Mental Health Adv. Council, 1975-76, Friends of Waipahu Cultural Garden Park Found., 1976—, Aloha council Boy Scouts Am., 1976-91; mem. bus. adv. council Waipahu High Sch., 1976-81, Parent-Tchr.-Community Adv. Council, 1978-80; bd. dirs. Central/Leeward unit Am. Cancer Soc., 1977-80, pub. edn. dir., 1978-79, v.p., 1979-80, founder, chmn. Celebrity Auction, 1980, dir. Oahu Baseline Survey, 1978; bd. dirs. Barbers Point council Navy League Am., 1981-85; profl. bd. advisors U. Houston Inst. for Contact Lens Research. Recipient Merit award Nat. Eye Research Found., 1974, Disting. Service award, 1976. Fellow Am. Acad. Optometry (cornea and contact lens diplomate, vice chair cornea and contact lens sect. 1992-94, chair cornea and contact lens sect. 1994—, sec., 1990-92, vice chair ethics com. 1991-92, corp. support for Jour. com. 1981, chair diplomate awards com. 1988-90), AAAS, Am. Optometric Assn. (ann. congress del. 1978, pub. health com. 19738, optometric paraoptometric personnel com. 1978-79, contact lens project team 1979-80, task force on R&D 1984-87, contact lens sect. coun. 1988-92, sec., 1989-90, vice chair 1990-91, chair elect 1991-92, numerous coms.), Leeward Oahu Jaycees (Disting. Service award 1969, Top Outstanding Young Man award 1975), Hawaii State Jaycees, Am. Optometric Found. (bd. dirs. 1981-91, chmn. task force clin. research 1981-83, nominations com. 1982, treas. 1985-86, sec., 1987-88, pres.-elect, 1988-89, pres. 1989-90), Am. Pub. Health Assn., Better Vision Inst., Contact Lens Soc., Optometrists in Vision Devel., Hawaii Optometric Assn. (corr. sec. 1968-70, state newsletter editor 1968-70, rec. sec. 1971, 2d v.p. 1972, pres. 1974-75; Man of Yr. 1975, Optometrist of Yr. 1979), Internat. Optometric & Optical League, Internat. Soc. Contact Lens Rsch., Brit. Contact Lens Assn., Japan Contact Lens Acad., Nat. Assn. of the Professions, Nat. Eye Research Found. (fellow Internat. Orthokeratology sect.; editorial bd. Contacto Jour. 1979, contact lens cert. com. 1981-85), Nat. Fedn. Ind. Bus., Optometric Cons. in Contact Lens Optometric Extension Program Found. (chmn. study group 1969-70, state dir. 1971-73), Optometric Hist. Soc., Optometric Polit. Action Coms., Soc. Contact Lens Specialists, Hawaii Assn. Children with Learning Disabilities, Hawaii Assn. Intellectually Gifted Children (pub. relations chmn. 1st Ann. State Conf. 1975, legis. lobbyist 1975-76), Waipahu Bus. Assn. (bd. dirs. 1974-78, chmn. pub. relations 1974-75, legis. lobbyist 1974-75, pres. 1974-75), Nat. Acad. Practice in Optometry (mem.-at-large on exec. com., disting. practitioner in optometry). Democrat. Baptist. Home: 8609 Autumn Green Dr Jacksonville FL 32256-9560 Office: Vistakon Inc Vp Profl Affairs 4500 Salibury Rd Ste 300 Jacksonville FL 32216-0954

YAMANO, DONALD, engineering executive. BS in Mech. Engring., Calif. State Polytechnic Coll., 1966. Various positions Shell Chem. Co., Houston, 1966-72; sr. engr. Bechtel Power Corp., Norwalk, Calif., 1972-75; dir. project mgmt. and engring. CE Miller Corp., Irvine, Calif., 1975-82; pres. LG&E Power Constructors, Inc., Irvine, Calif., 1982—. Office: LG&E Power Engineers & Constrs 2030 Main St Irvine CA 92714-7240*

YAMAOKA, SEIGEN HARUO, bishop; b. Fresno, Calif., Aug. 21, 1934; s. Haruichi and Rika (Ogawa) Y.; m. Shigeko Masuyama, Apr. 3, 1966; children—Jennifer Sae, Stacy Emi. B.A., Calif. State U.-Fresno, 1956; M.A., Ryukoku U., Kyoto, Japan, 1961; M.R.E., Pacific Sch. Religion, Berkeley, Calif., 1969, D.Min., 1979. Ordained to ministry Buddhist Chs. Am., 1961. Minister Oakland Buddhist Ch., Calif., 1964-71; registrar Inst. Buddhist Studies, Berkeley, 1969-71, lectr.; mem. Curriculum com., 1969-81, pres., 1981—; minister Stockton Buddhist Temple, Calif., 1971-81; treas. No. Calif. Radio Ministry, 1975-76; cons. ethnic studies Stockton Unified Sch. Dist., 1974-76; chmn. Buddhist Chs. Am. Ministers Assn., 1979-81; bishop Buddhist Chs. Am., San Francisco, 1981—, research com., 1970-79; English sec. Ministerial Assn., 1972-75; assoc. in doctrinal studies Hokyo, Kyoto, 1974; mem. Bd. Buddhist Edn., 1975-77; vice chmn. No. Calif. Ministers Assn., 1974; trustee Numata Ctr. for Buddhist Translation and Research, Buddhist Dharma Kyokai Soc. of Am. Author: Compassion in Encounter, 1970, Teaching and Practice Jodo Shinshu, 1974, Jodo Shinshu: Religion of Human Experience, 1976, Meditation-Gut-Enlightenment... Way of Hara, 1976, Awakening of Gratitude in Dying, 1978; editor, advisor, writer: Dharma School Teachers Guide, 1979. Mem. Japan Karate Fedn., Shinshu Acad. Soc., San Francisco-Japanese Am. Citizens League, Calif. State U.-Fresno Alumni Assn., Pacific Sch. Religion Alumni Assn., Internat. Assn. Shin Buddhist Studies, Internat. Translation Ctr. Kyoto, Hongwanji Bishops Council Kyoto. Home: 37 Waterloo Ct Belmont CA 94002-2936 Office: Buddhist Chs of Am 1710 Octavia St San Francisco CA 94109-4341

YAMARONE, CHARLES ANTHONY, JR., aerospace engineer, consultant; b. Bronxville, N.Y., Oct. 30, 1936; s. Charles Anthony and Mildred (La Manna) Y.; m. Catherine MacMullan, May 31, 1957; children: Charles Anthony III, Thomas, Stephen, Mark, James. BSEE, Manhattan Coll., 1958. Design engr. Gen. Precision Inc., Pleasantville, N.Y., 1958-62; engr. supr. Jet Propulsion Lab., Calif. Inst. Tech., Pasadena, 1962-69, sect. mgr., 1969-76, data processing mgr., 1976-80, project mgr., 1980—. Recipient Laurels award, Space/Missiles, Aviation Week & Space Tech., 1993. Mem. Am. Geophys. Union, Am. Inst. for Advancement of Science. Office: Jet Propulsion Lab Topex Project Office 4800 Oak Grove Dr Pasadena CA 91109-8001*

YAMATO, KEI C., international business consultant; b. Honokaa, Hawaii, Sept. 21, 1921; s. Kango and Shizuka (Tanaka) Y.; m. Sherrie Keiko Inamine; children: Karen, Marla, Kei Tracy. B.A., U. Hawaii, 1946; LL.B., Yale, 1950. Pres. Internat. Bus. Mgmt. Co., 1950; founder Pacific-Asia Bus. Council, 1950; pres. Orchids of Hawaii Internat., Inc., 1951, Polynesian Products, Inc., Holiday Promotions Internat., Inc., 1952, Orchawaii Internat. Travel Corp., 1962, Pacific Area Landscaping, Inc., 1970—, Hawaii Hort. Enterprises, Inc., 1970—, Agrisystems, Inc., 1971—; v.p., dir. Sperry & Hutchison Travel Awards, Inc., 1964, Copley Internat. Corp., 1967; all N.Y.C.; pres. Internat. Cons. Co., 1968, Asia-Pacific Corp., 1968; chmn. Asia Internat. Group of Cos., Asia Internat. Cons.; mng. dir. Internat Cons. Assocs., 1993. Bd. dirs. Internat. Execs. Assn., World Trade Club N.Y.C., Sales Execs. Club N.Y.C.; mem. Regional Export Expansion Council, U.S. Dept. Commerce; organizer Asia Pacific Inst.; pres. Saudi Arabia Pacific Asia Bus. Council, Arab Assian Assocs. Served in U.S. AUS, World War II, ETO. Decorated Silver Star, Purple Heart with 2 oak leaf clusters. Mem. Advt. Club N.Y.C., Nat. Indsl. Conf. Bd., Profl. Mgmt. Cons. Assn., Am. Sales Promotion Execs. assn., Chgo. Execs. Club, Sales and Marketing Execs. Internat., N.Y. Hort. Soc., Asia Soc., Japan Soc., Am. Mgmt. Assn. (lectr.), 442d Regimental Combat Team Assn., Landscape Contractors Assn. Hawaii, Gen. Contractors Assn. Hawaii, Friends East-West Center, East-West Philosophers Conf., Hawaii Assn. Nurserymen, Hawaii Bot. Soc., Honolulu Execs. Assn., U. Hawaii Alumni Assn., Navy League, Nat. Fedn. Ind. Bus., Am. Assn. Nurserymen, Pacific Area Travel Assn., Assn. U.S. Army, Hawaii Visitors Bur., Hawaii C. of C., U.S. Arab C. of C., Saudi Arabia Bus. Council. Clubs: Rotary, Bankers. Home: PO Box 781 Honolulu HI 96808

YAMAYEE, ZIA AHMAD, engineering educator, dean; b. Herat, Afghanistan, Feb. 2, 1948; came to U.S., 1974; s. Sayed and Merjan Ahmad. BSEE, Kabul (Afghanistan) U., 1972; MSEE, Purdue U., 1976, PhD, 1978. Registered profl. engr., Calif., Wash. Mem. faculty of engring. Kabul U., 1978; dir. engr. Systems Control, Inc., Palo Alto, Calif., 1979-81; sr. engr. Pacific N.W. Utilities, Portland, Oreg., 1981-83; assoc. prof. elec. engring. Clarkson U., Potsdam, N.Y., 1983-85; assoc. prof. Gonzaga U., Spokane, 1985-87, dean Sch. Engring., 1988—; part-time rsch. engr. La. Power and Light Co., New Orleans, 1987-88; sr. cons. Engring. and Cons. Svcs., Spokane, 1989—. Contbr. articles, reports to profl. jours. Bd. dirs. Wash. State Math., Engring. Sci. Achievement, Seattle, 1989—; mem. Spokane Intercollegiate Rsch. and Tech. Inst. Adv. Coun., 1990—. NSF grantee. Mem. Am. Soc. Engring. Edn., IEEE (sr.). Office: Gonzaga U Sch Engring 502 E Boone Ave Spokane WA 99258-1774

YAMMINE, RIAD NASSIF, oil company executive; b. Hammana, Lebanon, Apr. 12, 1934; s. Nassib Nassif and Emilie (Daou) Y.; came to U.S., 1952, naturalized, 1963; m. Beverly Ann Hosack, Sept. 14, 1954; children: Kathleen Yammine Gross, Cynthia Yammine Rotman, Michael. BS in Petroleum Engring., Pa. State U., 1956; postgrad. Advanced Mgmt. Program, Harvard U., 1977. Registered profl. engr., Ohio. Engr. Trans-Arabian Pipe Line Co., Saudi Arabia, 1956-61; with Marathon Pipe Line Co., 1961-75, mgr. Western div., Casper, Wyo., 1971-74, mgr. Eastern div., Martinsville, Ill., 1974-75; mktg. ops. div. mgr. Marathon Oil Co., 1975-83; pres. Marathon Pipeline Co., 1983-84; v.p. supply and transp. Marathon Petroleum Co., 1984-88, dir., 1984-90; pres. EMRO Mktg. Co., 1988—; also officer, bd. dirs. various subs. Patentee in field. Trustee, Wright State Univ. Found.; past trustee, Fisk U. Mem. ASME, Am. Petroleum Inst. Republican. Club: Findlay Country. Home: 624 Winterhaven Dr Findlay OH 45840-6841 Office: 539 S Main St Findlay OH 45840-3242 also: 500 Speedway Dr Enon OH 45323-1056

YAMNER, MORRIS, lawyer; b. Passaic, N.J., Sept. 5, 1938; s. Sam and Edna (Halpern) Y.; 1 child, Laura; m. Gail Garber, Oct. 23, 1975; children: Laura, Amy, Lisa. BS in Bus., Ohio State U., 1959; JD, Georgetown U., 1962. Bar: N.J. 1962, N.Y. 1983. Law sec. Superior Ct., Somerville, N.J., 1962-63; dep. atty. gen. Atty. Gen. Office, Trenton, N.J., 1963-66; ptnr. Cole, Yamner & Bray, Paterson, N.J., 1966-90, Sills, Cummis, Newark, 1990—. Bd. dirs. Jewish Fedn., Clifton, N.J., 1985—, YM/YMHA, 1980—. Mem. Daus. of Miriam (bd. dirs. 1985—), Preakness Hills Country Club (bd. dirs. 1992—). Office: Sills Cummis 1 Riverfront Plz Newark NJ 07102-5401

YAN, SAU-CHI BETTY, biochemist; b. Hong Kong, Nov. 25, 1954; d. Ming Yan and Choo-Chen Woo; m. Victor J. Chen, Feb. 29, 1980; 1 child, Heidi I. BS, Ctrl. Mo. State U., 1975; PhD, Iowa State U., 1980. Postdoctoral fellow St. Paul-Ramsey Med. Ctr., 1980-82; postdoctoral fellow med. sch. U. Tex., Houston, 1982-84; sr. biochemist Eli Lilly & Co, Indpls., 1985-88, sr. scientist, 1989-93, sr. rsch. scientist, 1993—. Patentee in field; contbr. articles to profl. jours. Bd. dirs. A Children's Habitat, Indpls., 1994. Mem. AAAS, Am. Soc. Biochemistry, Molecular Biology, Protein Soc., Soc. Chinese Bioscientists Am. Office: Eli Lilly & Co DC1543 307 E McCarty St Indianapolis IN 46240

YANAGISAWA, SAMUEL TSUGUO, electronics executive; b. Berkeley, Calif., Feb. 18, 1922; s. Jusaku George and Mitsuyo (Mochizuki) Y.; m. Fernande Gerardine Renar, July 10, 1952; children: Shane Henry, Steven Kim, Ian Gerard. BS. with honors in Elec. Engring., U. Calif.-Berkeley, 1942. Product line mgr. Machlett Labs. Inc., Springdale, Conn., 1943-63; v.p. ops. Warnecke Electron Tubes, Inc., Des Plaines, Ill., 1963-67; with Varo Inc., Garland, Tex., 1968-87, pres., 1971-84, chief exec. officer, 1974-85, chmn., 1976-87, also bd. dirs., ret., 1987; pres. Yanagisawa & Assocs., Dallas, 1989—; dir. Republic Bank, Garland; mem. Army Sci. Bd., 1986-90. Contbr. articles to profl. jours.; patentee electron devices. bd. dirs. So. Meth. U. Found. for Sci. and Engring.; mem. adv. coun., chmn. bd. visitors McDonald Obs., U. Tex., Austin; mem. adv. coun. Communities Found. of Tex.; bd. dirs. Dallas Council on World Affairs; adv. coun. Sch. Engring., U. Tex. at Dallas. Served to lt. AUS, 1945-46. Mem. IEEE (sr.), AAAS, Am. Def. Preparedness Assn., U.S. Night Vision Assn., Soc. Info. Display, Am. Electronic Assn., Am. Vacuum Soc., Assn. U.S. Army, Assn. Old Crows, Japanese Am. Citizens League, Nat. Japanese Am. Hist. Soc., Phi Beta Kappa, Sigma Xi, Tau Beta Pi, Eta Kappa Nu. Office: Yanagisawa & Assocs 7708 Chalkstone Dr Dallas TX 75248-5320

YANAGITANI, ELIZABETH, optometrist; b. Ogden, Utah, Nov. 24, 1953; d. Katsuyoshi and Yaeko (Watanabe) Y. AS, Weber State Coll., Ogden, Utah, 1974; BA magna cum laude, U. Utah, 1976; OD, Pacific U., Forest Grove, Oreg., 1980. Externship Tripler Army Med Ctr., Schofield Barracks, Hawaii, 1979; staff optometrist Gen. Med., San Diego, 1984-89, San Ysidro Health Ctr., Calif., 1985-87, 91—, Logan Heights Family Health Ctr., San Diego, 1989-91; assoc. of pvt. office Chula Vista, Calif., 1985—; asst. instr. Am. Bus. Coll., San Diego, 1982. Recipient Gates Meml. award Nat. Eye Rsch. Found., 1980; scholar Weber State Coll., 1972-73, U. Utah, 1975, Project award Beta Sigma Kappa, 1980. Mem. San Diego County Optometric Soc. (v.p. 1985), Calif. Optometric Soc. (del. to leadership conf. 1985), Achievement Through Vision/COVD (pres. 1990), Phi Kappa Phi. Avocations: travel, photography.

YANCEY, ELEANOR MARGARET GARRETT, crisis intervention clinician; b. Ga., Oct. 24, 1933; adopted d. Overton LaVerne Garrett; m. Robert Grady Yancey, Nov. 10, 1961 (div. Apr. 1968); children: Katherine La Verne, David Shawn. Student, High Mus. Art Inst., 1952-53, Ga. State U., 1953-55, 78; BA, La Grange Coll., 1958. Social worker, case worker Fulton County Dept. Family and Children's Svcs., Atlanta, 1957-61; asst. tchr. Atlanta (Ga.) Bd. Edn., 1973-85; mental health crisis intervention clinician Dekalb County Bd. Health, Decatur, 1985—, acting dir. crisis intervention, 1988-90. Performed summer stock, 1966-70. Performed with Rogers & Co., 1969, 70; band booster pres. Henry Grady High Sch., Atlanta, 1977-78, v.p. PTA, 1978-79; pres. PTA Morningside Elem. Sch., Atlanta, 1977; grand juror Dekalb County, Decatur, 1983; active Sesquicentennial Celebration of Ala. Statehood. Mem. Kappa Kappa Iota (Lambda chpt. state pres. 1987-88, Eta pres. local chpt. 1992—). Democrat. Avocations: drawing, gardening, travel, music. Home: 3425 Regalwoods Dr Doraville GA 30340-4019

YANCEY, JIMMIE ISAAC, marketing professional; b. Ripley, Miss., Dec. 11, 1935; s. Charlie Edward and Overa (Wilbanks) Y.; m. Jonell Smith, Mar. 1, 1958; children: Angela Jo, Jamie Lorraine, Cynthia Overa, Melanie Ann. BS, Miss. State U., 1963, MBA, 1966. Editor univ. rels. Miss. State. U., Starkville, 1963-65, editor coll. bus., 1965-66; editor Miss. Extension Svc., Starkville, 1966-67, Nat. Cotton Coun., Memphis, 1967-71; pub. rels. dir. Cotton Inc., Raleigh, N.C., 1971, Am. Soybean Assn., Hudson, Iowa, 1971-78; gen. mgr. Prog. Farmer Network, Starkville, 1978-86; owner, mgr. Yancey Agrl. Network, Starkville, 1986—; mktg. cons. Wyffel's Hybrids, Inc., Atkinson, Ill., 1987-93. Bd. dirs. Agri-Bus. Edn. Found.; sr. adv. com. Coll. Bus. and Industry, Miss. State U. Mem. Nat. Agrl. Mktg. Assn., (pres. 1986-87, Meritorious Svc. award 1986), Nat. Assn. Farm Broadcasters, Am. Advt. Fedn., Starkville C. of C. (venture capital com. 1990), Am. Soybean Assn. (Mertorious Svc. award 1974, Broadcaster of Yr. 1984), Hudson C. of C. (pres. 1972, Iowa chpt.), Nat. Alliance of Ind. Corp. Cons., Miss. Rotary, Pres.'s Club. Presbyterian. Avocations: gardening, fishing. Office: Yancey Agrl Network 1004 N Jackson PO Box 2000 Starkville MS 39759-7000

YANCEY, PHILIP DAVID, editor, author; b. Atlanta, Nov. 4, 1949; s. Marshall Watts and Mildred Sylvania (Diem) Y.; m. Janet Elenor Norwood, June 2, 1970. BA magna cum laude, Columbia (S.C.) Bible Coll., 1970; MA with highest honors, Wheaton (Ill.) Coll., 1972; MA, U. Chgo., 1990. Writer, then mng. editor Campus Life mag., Wheaton, 1970-75; editor Campus Life mag., 1974-80; editor-at-large Christianity Today, 1980—. Author: After The Wedding, 1976, Where Is God When It Hurts?, 1977 (Gold medallion award Evang. Christian Pubs. Assn. 1978), Growing Places, 1978, Unhappy Secrets of the Christian Life, 1979, Fearfully and Wonderfully Made, 1980 (Gold Medallion award), Insight, 1982, In His Image (Gold Medallion award), 1984, Open Windows, 1984, The Student Bible, 1986 (Gold Medallion award), Disappointment with God, 1988 (Gold

Medallion award), I Was Just Wondering, 1989, Reality and the Vision, 1990, Praying with the KGB, 1992, Pain: The Gift Nobody Wants, 1993 (Gold Medallion award); also articles. Mem. Evang. Press Assn. (Periodical of Year award 1975). Office: Campus Life Mag Christianity Today 465 Gundersen Dr Carol Stream IL 60188-2415

YANCEY, RICHARD CHARLES, investment banker; b. Spokane, Wash., May 28, 1926; s. George R. and M. Ruth (Yenney) Y.; m. Mary Anne Shaffer, Feb. 5, 1956; children: Leslie, Jennifer, Richard C. Jr. BA in Econs., Whitman Coll., Walla Walla, Wash., 1949; MBA with distinction, Harvard U., 1952. Assoc. Dillon, Read & Co. Inc., N.Y.C, 1952-63; v.p. Dillon, Read & Co., Inc., N.Y.C., 1963-75, mng. dir., 1975-89, dir., 1990; sr. adv., 1992; ret. Dillon, Read & Co., Inc., N.Y.C., 1992; bd. dirs. Composite Group Mut. Funds, Spokane, Wash., Ad Media Corp. Advisors, Inc., N.Y.C., The Score Bd., Inc., Cherry Hill, N.J., Capmac Holdings, Inc., N.Y.C.; former mem. partnership bd. Whittle Communications L.P., Knoxville, Tenn. Former bd. overseers Whitman Coll.; former trustee, former pres. Plymouth Ch. of Pilgrims, Bklyn.; former trustee N.Y. Infirmary-Beekman Downtown Hosp. Served with USNR, 1944-46, PTO. Mem. N.Y. Soc. Security Analysts. Republican. Clubs: Harvard, Metropolitan (N.Y.C.); Wintergreen (Windham, N.Y.) . Home: 42 Monroe Pl Brooklyn NY 11201-2603 Office: Dillon Read & Co Inc 535 Madison Ave Fl 15 New York NY 10022-4212

YANCEY, ROBERT EARL, JR., oil company executive; b. Ashland, Ky., June 16, 1945; s. Robert E. Sr. and Estelline (Tackett) Y.; m. Nina McGee, June 16, 1962; children: Rob, Yvonne, Elizabeth. BS in Chem. Engring., Cornell U., 1967. Sr. v.p., group operating officer; supt. Catlettsburg (Ky.) Refinery, 1976-79; exec. asst. Ashland (Ky.) Petroleum Co., 1979-80, group v.p., 1980-81, sr. v.p., 1981-86, pres., 1986—; sr. v.p., group operating officer Ashland Inc., 1988—. Republican. Avocations: golf, hunting, fishing. Home: 504 Amanda Furnace Dr Ashland KY 41101-2193 Office: Ashland Petroleum Co PO Box 391 Ashland KY 41105-0391

YANCIK, JOSEPH JOHN, government official; b. Mt. Olive, Ill., Dec. 1, 1930; s. Joseph John and Anna (Gubach) Y.; m. Rosemary Panich, Feb. 19, 1955; children—Geri Anne, Ellen Marie. B.S., U. Ill., 1954; M.S. in Mining Engring., Mo. Sch. Mines, 1956; Ph.D., U. Mo.-Rolla, 1960. Mining research engr. St. Joe. Lead Co., Bonne Terre, Mo., 1955-58; mgr. research and devel. Monsanto Co., St. Louis, 1960-70; asst. dir. mining U.S. Bur. Mines, Washington, 1970-77; v.p. research Nat. Coal Assn., Washington, 1977-82; pres. Bituminous Coal Research, Inc., Washington, 1980-82; dir. Coal Export Office U.S. Dept. Commerce, Washington, 1982-84; dir. Office of Energy Internat. Trade Adminstrn., Washington, 1984—. Contbr. articles to profl. jours. Served with C.E. U.S. Army, 1950-52. Recipient Alumni Achievement award U. Mo.-Rolla, 1975, Silver Medal award U.S. Dept. Commerce, 1986, Gold Medal award Dept. Commerce, 1992. Roman Catholic. Club: Cosmos (Washington). Home: 1703 James Payne Cir Mc Lean VA 22101-4223 Office: Main Commerce Bldg #4413 14th and Constitution Washington DC 20230

YANCY, CECIL HENTON, JR., editor; b. Payne, Ala., June 25, 1962; s. Cecil H. and Clydia Lucille (Thacker) Y.; m. Kimberly Ann Harris, Sept. 19, 1987; children: April Marie, Sarah Lucille. BA, Auburn U., 1985. Farm editor The Cullman (Ala.) Times, Inc., 1985-87; wire editor The Dothan (ala.) Eagle, 1987-89; editor Ga. Farm Bur. Fedn., Macon, 1990-94; assoc. editor Specialized Agrl. Publs., Juliette, Ga., 1994—. Contbr. articles to Progressive Farmer, The New Farm. Mem. Assemblies of God. Avocations: music, history. Home: Rt 1 Box 2839 Juliette GA 31046 Office: PO Box 235 Juliette GA 31046

YANDELL, CATHY MARLEEN, foreign language educator; b. Anadarko, Okla., Dec. 27, 1949; d. Lloyd O. and Maurine (Dunn) Y.; m. Mark S. McNeil, Sept. 7, 1974; children: Elizabeth Yandell McNeil, Laura Yandell McNeil. Diplome d'etudes, Inst. des Professeurs de Français à l'Etranger, Sorbonne, 1970; BA, U. N.Mex., 1971; MA, U. Calif., Berkeley, 1973, PhD, 1977. Teaching asst. U. Calif., Berkeley, 1971-75, acting instr., 1976-77; asst. prof. Carleton Coll., Northfield, Minn., 1977-83, assoc. prof., 1983-89, prof. French, 1989—; chair commn. on the status of women, Carleton Coll., Northfield, 1983-85, ednl. policy com., 1983-88, romance langs. and lits., 1990-94, pres. of faculty, 1991-94. Contbr. to Art & Argumentation: The Sixteenth Century Dialogue, 1993, French Texts/American Contexts: French Women Writers, 1994; editor: Pontus de Tyard's Solitaire Second, ou prose de la musique, 1980; contbr. articles to profl. jours. Active exec. com., then mem. Amnesty Internat., Northfield, 1980—. Regents' Travelling fellow U. Calif. at Berkeley, 1975-76; Faculty Devel. grantee Carleton Coll., 1988, 91; NEH Rsch. fellow., 1994-95. Mem. MLA (del. 1989-92). Democrat. Avocations: dance, music, hiking, biking, cross-country skiing. Home: 514 E 5th St Northfield MN 55057 Office: Carleton College 1 N College St Northfield MN 55057

YANDERS, ARMON FREDERICK, biological sciences educator, research administrator; b. Lincoln, Nebr., Apr. 12, 1928; s. Fred W. and Beatrice (Pate) Y.; m. Evelyn Louise Gatz, Aug. 1, 1948; children: Mark Frederick, Kent Michael. A.B., Nebr. State Coll., Peru, 1948; M.S., U. Nebr., 1950, Ph.D., 1953. Research asso. Oak Ridge Nat. Lab. and Northwestern U., 1953-54; biophysicist U.S. Naval Radiol. Def. Lab., San Francisco, 1955-58; asso. geneticist Argonne (Ill.) Nat. Lab., 1958-59; prof. zoology Mich. State U., 1959-69; prof., asst. dean Mich. State U. (Coll. Natural Sci.), 1963-69; prof. biol. scis. U. Mo., Columbia, 1969—, dean Coll. Arts and Scis., 1969-82, research prof., dir. Environ. Trace Substances Research Ctr., 1983-93, dir. Alzheimer's Disease and Related Disorders Program, 1994—; research prof., dir. Environ. Trace Substances Research Ctr. and Sinclair Comparative Medicine Research Farm, Columbia, 1984-94; prof. emeritus, 1994—; Trustee Argonne Univs. Assn., 1964-75, v.p., 1969-73, pres., 1973, 76-77, chmn. bd., 1973-75; bd. dirs. Coun. Colls. Arts and Scis., 1981-82; mem. adv. com. environ. hazards VA, Washington, 1985—, chmn. sci. coun., 1988—, chmn. of com., 1990—. Contbr. articles to profl. jours. Trustee Peru State Coll., 1992. Served from ensign to lt. USNR, 1954-58. Recipient Disting. Svc. award Peru State Coll., 1989. Fellow AAAS; mem. AAUP (Robert W. Martin acad. freedom award 1971), Am. Inst. Biol. Scs., Environ. Mutagen Soc., Genetics Soc. Am., Radiation Research Soc., Soc. Environ. Toxicology and Chemistry. Home: 2405 Ridgefield Rd Columbia MO 65203-1531 Office: U of Mo 521 Clark Hall Columbia MO 65211

YANDLE, STEPHEN THOMAS, law school dean; b. Oakland, Calif., Mar. 7, 1947; s. Clyde Thomas and Jane Walker (Hess) Y.; m. Martha Anne Welch, June 26, 1971. BA, U. Va., 1969, JD, 1972. Bar: Va. 1972. Asst. dir. admissions U. Va. Law Sch., Charlottesville, 1972-76; from asst. to assoc. dean Northwestern U. Sch. Law, Chgo., 1976-85; assoc. dean Yale U. Law Sch., New Haven, 1985—. Served to capt. U.S. Army, 1972. Mem. Law Sch. Admission Coun. (programs, edn. and prelaw com. 1978-84), Assn. Am. Law Schs. (chmn. legal edn. and admissions sect. 1979, nominations com. 1987, chmn. adminstrn. of law schs. sect. 1991), Nat. Assn. for Law Placement (pres. 1984-85, co-chair Joint Nat. Assn. com. on placement 1986-88). Office: Yale U Sch Law PO Box 208215 New Haven CT 06520-8215

YANDLE, SYLVESTER ELWOOD, II, sales executive, inventor; b. Lafayette, La., Sept. 14, 1932; s. Arthur Ray and Marie (Delhomme) Y.; m. Gretchen Ehrensing, June 28, 1957; children: Gretchen Marie, Sylvester E. III, Gladys Anne, Henry Arthur. Student, Southwestern La. Inst. Well logger Core Labs., Lafayette, La., 1954-56; salesman Security Rock Bits, Lafayette, La., 1956-61, Orbit Valve, New Orleans, 1961-62, So. Engine & Pump, New Orleans, 1962-66; owner, pres. Indsl. Pump Sales, Inc., Belle Chasse, La., 1967—, Commodore Boat Stores, Belle Chasse, La., 1978—, Hydro Damp Inc., Belle Chasse, La., 1992—. Inventor: Air bag for airlines (patent 1991), Hydro Damp (patent 1989), Indicators Studs for Railroads (patent pending). Active mem. Aurora Civic Assn., La. Sgt. 1st class, M.C., USAR, 1948-59. Mem. New Orleans C.C., Airplane Owners & Pilots Assn. Republican. Roman Catholic. Avocations: duck carving, knife making, painting, inventing, flying. Home: 5883 Rhodes Ave New Orleans LA 70131 Office: Indsl Pump Sales Inc 2814 Engineers Rd Belle Chasse LA 70037

YANEY, GEORGE, history educator; b. Teaneck, N.J., Oct. 30, 1930; s. Arthur J. and Frances (Levings) Y.; m. Ann Hinrichs, June 7, 1952; children: Brian, Dale, Carolyn, Tara. B in Mgmt. Engring., Rensselaer Poly. Inst.,

1952; MA, U. Colo., 1956; PhD, Princeton U., 1961. Instr. Coll. Wooster, Ohio, 1957-58; prof. history U. Md., College Park, 1960—. Author: Systematization of Russian Government, 1973, Urge to Mobilize, 1982, World of the Manager, 1994. Served to capt. USMC, 1952-54, Korea. Rsch. fellow Harvard U., 1969-70, fellow Slavic Rsch. Ctr., U. Hokkaido, Japan, 1990-91; Fulbright grantee, 1975, 77, 85, Internat. Rsch. Exchanges Bd. grantee 1965, 75, 77, 85, 89. Home: 7303 Baylor Ave College Park MD 20740-3001 Office: Univ of Maryland Dept Of History College Park MD 20742

YANG, CHEN NING, physicist, educator; b. Hofei, Anhwei, China, Sept. 22, 1922; naturalized, 1964; s. Ke Chuan and Meng Hwa Lo; m. Chih Li Tu, Aug. 26, 1950; children: Franklin, Gilbert, Eulee. BS, Nat. S.W. Assoc. U., China, 1942; PhD, U. Chgo., 1948; DSc (hon.), Princeton U., 1958, Bklyn. Poly. Inst., 1965, U. Wroclaw, Poland, 1974, Gustavus Adolphus Coll., 1975, U. Md., 1979, U. Durham, Eng., 1979, Fudan U., 1984, Swiss Fed. Inst. Tech., Switzerland, 1987, Moscow State U., 1992, Drexel U., 1995. Instr., U. Chgo., 1948-49; mem. Inst. Advanced Study, Princeton U., 1949-55, prof., 1955-66; Albert Einstein prof. SUNY, Stony Brook, 1966—; dir. Inst. Theoretical Physics SUNY, 1966—. Trustee Rockefeller U., 1970-76, Salk Inst., 1978—, Ben Gurion U., 1980—. Recipient Nobel prize for physics, 1957, Rumford prize, 1980, Nat. Medal of Sci., 1986, Benjamin Franklin medal, 1993, Bower prize, 1994. Mem. AAAS (bd. dirs. 1975-79), NAS, Am. Phys. Soc., Royal Soc. London (fgn.), Chinese Acad. Scis., Academia Sinica, Brazilian Acad. Scis., Venezuelan Acad. Scis., Royal Spanish Soc. Scis., Polish Acad. Scis., Russian Acad. Scis., Am. Philos. Soc., Sigma Xi. Office: SUNY Dept Physics Stony Brook NY 11794-3840

YANG, CHIN-PING, chemist, engineering educator; b. Penghu Hsien, Taiwan, Republic of China, Dec. 25, 1931; s. Yee Yang and Chi Chao; m. Ye-ho Hwang, Oct. 10, 1961; children: Chung-Sheng, Chung-Chen, Chung-Cheng. BS in Chemistry, Taiwan Normal U., Taipei, Republic of China, 1956; M. Engring., Tokyo U., 1973; D. Engring., Tokyo Inst. Tech., 1986. Chmn., prof. chem. engring. dept. Tatung Inst. Tech., Taipei, 1970-89, prof. chem. engring. dept., 1990—; chmn. grad. sch. chem. engring. Tatung Inst. Tech., Taipei, 1980-89; cons. Tatung Co., Taipei, 1963—. Contbr. articles to profl. jours.; patentee in field. Mem. Am. Chem. Soc., Japan Chem. Soc., Chinese Chem. Soc., Soc. Polymer Sci. Japan, Soc. Chinese Inst. Chem. Engrs. Home: 126-1 Chien St Shihlin, Taipei Taiwan Office: Tatung Inst of Tech, 40 Chungshan N Rd 3d Sec, Taipei Taiwan

YANG, EDWARD S., electrical engineering educator; b. Nanking, Peoples Republic of China, Oct. 16, 1937; s. Joseph L. and York-Shih (Lung) Y.; m. Ruth Chu; children: David K., Grace S. BS, Nat. Cheng-Kung U., Taiwan, 1957; MS, Okla. State U., 1961; PhD, Yale U., 1966. Engr. IBM Corp., Poughkeepsie, N.Y., 1961-63; asst. prof. elec. engring. Columbia U., N.Y.C., 1965-70, assoc. prof., 1970-75, prof., 1975—, chmn. dept., 1987-89, 93—. Author: Fundamental Semiconductor Devices, 1978, Microelectronic Devices, 1988; contbr. over 140 articles to profl. jours. Fellow IEEE. Office: Columbia U Dept Of Elec Engring New York NY 10027

YANG, HENRY T., university chancellor, educator; b. Chungking, China, Nov. 29, 1940; s. Chen Pei and Wei Gen Yang; m. Dilling Tsui, Sept. 2, 1966; children: Maria, Martha. BSCE, Nat. Taiwan U., 1962; MSCE, W.Va. U., 1965; PhD, Cornell U., 1968. Rsch. engr. Gilbert Assocs., Reading, Pa., 1968-69; asst. prof. Sch. Aeros. and Astronautics, Purdue U., West Lafayette, Ind., 1969-72, assoc. prof., 1972-76, prof., 1976-94, Neil A. Armstrong Disting. prof., 1988-94, sch. head, 1979-84; dean engring. Purdue U., 1984-94; chancellor U. Calif., Santa Barbara, 1994—; mem. scientific adv. bd. USAF, 1985-89; mem. aero. adv. com. NASA, 1985-89; mem. engring. adv. com. NSF, 1988-91; mem. mechanics bd. visitors ONR, 1990-93. mem. def. mfg. bd. DOD, 1988-89, def. sci. bd., 1989-91; mem. acad. adv. bd. Nat. Acad. Engring., 1991-94; mem. tech. adv. com. Pratt & Whitney, 1993—; bd. dirs. Space Industries Internt., 1993—. Recipient 12 Best Teaching awards Purdue U., 1971-94. Fellow AIAA, ASEE (Centennial medal 1993); mem. Nat. Acad. Engring., Academia Sinica. Home: University House University Calif Santa Barbara CA 93106 Office: Chancellor's Office U California Santa Barbara CA 93106

YANG, JACKSON, aerospace engineering company executive. Pres. Advanced Tech. and Rsch. Corp., Burtonsville, Md. Office: Advanced Tech & Rsch Corp Springpoint Executive Ctr 15210 Dino Dr Burtonsville MD 20866-1172*

YANG, LINDA TSAO, financial executive; b. Shanghai, China, Sept. 5, 1926; came to U.S., 1946; d. Ying Yung and Yu-shun (Ng) Tsao; m. An Tzu Yang, June 20, 1953; children—Yuelin T., Eton Y. B.A., St. John's U., Shanghai, 1945; M.S., Grad. Sch. Bus., Columbia U., 1948, M.Phil. in Econs., 1975. Econ. analyst Am. Overseas Fin. Corp., N.Y.C., 1955-58; founder, dir. Mother Lode Savs., Sacramento, 1977-80; savs. and loan commr. State of Calif., San Francisco and Los Angeles, 1980-82; prin. Linda Tsao Yang & Assocs., Davis, Calif., 1983—; dir. The Hong Kong Assn. of No. Calif.; bd. dirs., mem. budget and fin. com. Blue Cross Of Calif.; vice chmn. investment com., v.p. bd. adminstrn. Pub. Employees Retirement System, State of Calif., 1977-80; invited expert on restructuring fin. instrn. Senate Banking Com., Senate Fin. Com., Washington, 1981-82. Mem. policy adv. com. Coll. Agrl. and Environ. Scis., U. Calif.-Davis, 1979-85; mem. policy adv. com. Ctr. for Real Estate and Urban Econs., Grad. Sch. Bus., U. Calif.-Berkeley, 1980-82; mem. fairness commn. Dem. Nat. Com., 1984-85, compliance assistance commn. 1986-88; commr. Calif. Commn. on Teaching Profession, 1984-86. Recipient award Am. Savs. and Loan League, 1982, Achievement award Los Angeles YWCA, 1982, Outstanding Service award United Chinese-Am. League, 1982. Mem. Am. Econ. Assn., Acad. Polit. Sci., Orgn. Chinese-Ams., Trusteeship for Betterment of Women, Los Angeles, Asian-Pacific Women's Network Calif., Nat. Assn. State Savs. and Loan Suprs. (bd. dirs., nat. legis. com. 1980-82), Nat. Economists Club (Washington), Downtown Economists Luncheon Group (N.Y.C.). Office: 1619 Holly Ln Davis CA 95616-1010

YANG, RALPH TZU-BOW, chemical engineering educator, researcher; b. Chung King, China, Sept. 18, 1942; came to U.S., 1965, naturalized, 1976; s. Chen Pei and Wei (Gee) Y.; m. Frances H. Chang, Dec. 23, 1972; children—Michael, Robert. BS, Nat. Taiwan U., 1964; MS, Yale U., 1968, PhD, 1971. Rsch. assoc. Argonne Nat. Lab., Ill., 1972-73; sci. Aluminum Co. of Am., Pitts., 1973-74; group leader Brookhaven Nat. Lab., Upton, N.Y., 1974-78; assoc. prof. SUNY-Buffalo, 1978-82, prof., 1982—, chmn. chem. engring. dept., 1990-95; Praxair prof. chem. engring., chair, 1993-95, prof., chmn. chem. engring. dept. U. Mich., 1995—; cons. in field. Author: Gas Separation by Absorption Processes, 1987. Contbr. articles to profl. jours. Patentee in field. Research grantee NSF, 1980—, Dept. Energy, 1980—, Alcoa Found., 1979-81. Fellow Am. Inst. Chem. Engring. (William H. Walker award for excellence in contbn. to chem. engring. lit., 1991); mem. Am. Chem. Soc. (Ind. Engring. Chem. Rsch. jour. adv. bd. 1991-93), Am. Carbon Soc. (adv. bd. 1985—), Am. Soc. Engring. Edn., Internat. Adsorption Soc. (adv. bd. Jour. of Adsorption 1993—), Adsorption Sci. and Tech. (adv. bd. 1986—). Office: U Mich Dept Chem Engring Ann Arbor MI 48109

YANG, SHANG FA, biochemistry educator; b. Tainan, Taiwan, Nov. 10, 1932; came to U.S., 1959, naturalized, 1971; s. Chian-Zuei and En-Liu (Lu) Y.; m. Eleanor Shou-yuan, Sept. 16, 1964; children: Albert, Bryant. BS, Nat. Taiwan U., 1956, MS, 1958; PhD, Utah State U., 1962. Rsch. assoc. U. Calif., Davis, 1962-63, NYU Med. Sch., N.Y.C., 1963-64, U. Calif.-San Diego, La Jolla, 1964-65; asst. biochemist U. Calif.-Davis, 1966-69, assoc. biochemist, 1969-74, prof., biochemist, 1974—, chmn., 1989-90 ; vis. prof. U. Konstanz, Germany, 1974, Nat. Taiwan U., Taipei, 1983, U. Cambridge, U.K., 1983, Nagoya U., Japan, 1988-89. Assoc. editor Jour. Plant Growth Regulation, 1981—. Mem. editorial bd. Plant Physiology, 1974-92, Plant Cell Physiology, 1987-91, Plant Physiology and Biochemistry, 1988—; Acta Phytophysiologica Sinica, 1988—. Recipient Campbell award Am. Inst. Biol. Sci., 1969; Guggenheim fellow, 1982; recipient Internat. Plant growth Substance Assn. Research award, 1985, Wolf Found. prize agriculture, 1991, Outstanding Rsch award Am. Soc. Horticultural Sci., 1992. Mem. NAS, Academia Sinica, Am. Soc. Biochemistry and Molecular Biology, Am. Soc. Plant Physiologists (chmn. Western sect. 1982-84). Home: 1118 Villanova Dr Davis CA 95616-1753 Office: U Calif Dept of Vegetable Corps Davis CA 95616

YANG, TONY TIEN SHENG, engineering educator; b. Tainan, Formosa, May 26, 1928; came to U.S., 1957; s. Tsang and Shih Y. (Cheng) Y.; m. Hsiu-Ying Tsai, Aug. 7, 1959; 1 son, Joseph. B.S., Nat. Taiwan U., 1953; M.S., U. Okla., 1959, Ph.D., 1968. Registered profl. engr., D.C. Md., Okla. Project engr. Okla. Dept. Hwys., Oklahoma City, 1958-66, sr. structural engr. 1968-70; prof., chmn. civil and mech. engring. program Fed. City Coll., Washington, 1970-73, prof., chmn. engring. and computer sci. dept., 1973-78; prof., chmn. civil and mech. engring. dept. U. D.C., Washington, 1978-86, prof. civil engring., 1987—. Mem. ASCE, Am. Soc. Engring. Edn., Am. Concrete Inst. Home: 6108 Beech Tree Dr Alexandria VA 22310-2240 Office: 4200 Connecticut Ave NW Washington DC 20008-1174

YANG, WEN-CHING, chemical engineer; b. Taipei, Taiwan, Nov. 11, 1939; came to U.S., 1964; s. Ting-Lien and Ho (Lee) Y.; m. Rae Tien, Aug. 24, 1968; children: Evonne R., Peter T. BSChemE, Nat. Taiwan U., Taipei, 1962; MSChemE, U. Calif., Berkeley, 1965; PhD in Chem. Engring., Carnegie Mellon U., 1968. Sr. engr. rsch. and devel. ctr. Westinghouse Electric Co., Pitts., 1968-76, fellow engr., 1976-93, adv. engr. sci. and tech. ctr., 1993—; instr. U. Pitts., 1980, 83; chair rsch. rev. panel Office Fossil Energy, Dept. Energy, Washington, 1990. Author: (with others) Encyclopedia of Fluid Mechanics, 1986, 92; editor spl. vol. Powder Tech. jour., 1987; contbr. over 75 papers to sci. jours. Lt. Army Tank Corp., 1962-63. Fellow AIChE (programming chair and sec. group 3, editor 4 symposium series vols. 1987-88, 92-93, sec. particle tech. forum 1993—, Fluidized Processes Recognition award 1993); mem. Am. Chem. Soc., Chinese Am. Chem. Soc. (pres. Pitts. chpt. 1994), Orgn. Chinese Am. Achievements include patents in field; development of widely-used correlations and design equations in pneumatic transport and fluidization areas. Avocations: Chinese calligraphy, painting, tennis, gardening. Home: 236 Mt Vernon Ave Export PA 15632 Office: Westinghouse Electric Co Sci & Tech Ctr 1310 Beulah Rd Pittsburgh PA 15235*

YANG, XIANGZHONG, research scientist, administrator, educator; b. Weixian, Hebei, China, July 31, 1959; came to U.S., 1983; s. Wukui Yang and Fengrong Zhang; m. Xiuchun Tian, Jan. 5, 1986; 1 child, Andrew Chun. BS in Animal Sci. with honors, Beijing Agrl. U., 1982; diploma, Nanjing (China) Agrl. U., 1982; MS in Reproductive Physiology, Cornell U., 1986, PhD in Reproductive Physiology, 1990. Rsch. asst. Cornell U., Ithaca, N.Y., 1983-89, lab. program coord., 1987-90, postdoctoral fellow, 1990-91, sr. rsch. assoc., dir. Embryo Engring. Program, 1992—; adj. prof. Beijing Agrl. U., 1992—; hon. prof. Chinese Acad. Agrl. Scis., Beijing, 1991—, Beijing Agrl. U., 1992—; Xinjiang (China) Acad. Animal Scis., 1993—; dir. China-Cornell Fellowship Programs, Ithaca, 1992-95; chmn. local arrangement com. Reproduction in Farm Animals Symposium, Ithaca, 1992; mem. internat. program com. Ann. M.C. Chang Meml. Conf., 1992; cons. sci. dir. Baylor Ctr. Reproductive Health, Dallas, 1993—; cons. Gencyme Transgenics, Inc., Framingham, Mass., 1993—. Author: Biotechnology of Preimplantational Embryos, 1993; editor-in-chief Agr. Scis. Overseas, 1990—; contbr. numerous articles to sci. jours., abstracts, tech. papers to conf. procs. Grantee CU Biotech, 1993—, EAIC Inc., 1993—, USDA, 1991-94, 92-95, Rockefeller Found., 1991-95, 92-95, Rockefeller Found., 1991-95, 92-95, Lingnan Found., 1995-97, Vet Sch., 1993-94, 94-96, Transpharm. Inc., 1994—, Baylor U., 1994-96; fellow China State Edn. Commn., 1983-85, Cornell U. Grad. Sch., 1985; recipient 1st place award Nat. Entrance Exam. Graduate Study, Beijing Agrl. U., 1981. Mem. Internat. Embryo Transfer Soc. (edn. com. mem. 1992-94), Soc. Study of Reproduction (com. chair 1991-93), The N.Y. State Acad. of Scis., Chinese Agrl. Assn. Students and Scholars (founder, pres. 1988-89, conf. chair 1989), Am. Fertility Soc., Chinese Soc. and Tech. Assn., Sigma Xi.

YANG, ZHEN, research scientist; b. Shenyang, Liaoning, People's Republic of China, Aug. 16, 1959; came to U.S., 1992; s. Gue-Fu Yang and Jing-Ren Han; m. Su-Ling Lu, Aug. 10, 1986; 1 child, Lu-Ning. BS in Pharm. Chemistry, Shenyang Coll. Pharmacy, 1982, MS in Pharm. Chemistry, 1986; PhD in Organic Chemistry, Chinese U. of Hong Kong, 1992. Asst. engr. Pharm. Factory of Baoto, Inner Mongolia Autonomous Region, China, 1982-83; teaching asst. pharm. dept. Shenyang Coll. Pharmacy, 1986-89; rsch. asst. Chinese U. of Hong Kong, 1989, teaching asst., 1989-92; rsch. scientist Scripps Rsch. Inst., La Jolla, Calif., 1992—. Contbr. articles to profl. jours. Fellow Hong Kong Jockey Club, 1989-92. Achievements include patents pending for strategy for ABC taxoid ring synthesis, synthesis of taxol and taxol analogs. Home: 4158 Decoro St # 21 San Diego CA 92122 Office: The Scripps Rsch Inst Dept Chemistry MB 10A 10666 N Torrey Pines Rd La Jolla CA 92037

YANKELOVICH, DANIEL, social researcher, public opinion analyst; b. Boston, 1924; married. BA, Harvard U., 1946, MA, 1950; postgrad., Sorbonne, Paris, 1952. Chmn. Yankelovich, Skelly & White, Inc., N.Y.C., 1959-86; rsch. prof. psychology NYU; v.p., dir. Reliance Group Holdings, Inc.; dir. Meredith Corp., Loral Corp., Reliance Ins. Co., Harper's Mag. Found.; pres. Pub. Agenda Found., N.Y.C.; vis. prof. psychology, grad. faculty New Sch. Social Research; spl. adv. Aspen Inst.; Bd. dirs. Work in Am. Inst., Charles F. Kettering Found., Inst. for World Order, U.S. West; vis. com. Harvard U.; mem. Council Fgn. Relations; pres. Public Agenda Found.; commr. Sloan Commn. Author: The Changing Values on Campus, 1972, (with William Barrett) Ego and Instinct: Psychoanalysis and the Science of Man, 1969, The New Morality: A Profile of American Youth in the Seventies, 1974, New Rules: Searching for Self-Fulfillment in a World Turned Upside Down, 1981, Coming to Public Judgement: Making Democracy Work in a Complex World, 1991; co-editor: Beyond the Beltway: Engaging the Public in U.S. Foreign Policy, 1994. Dir. Carnegie Found. for Advancement of Teaching. Office: Pub Agenda Found 6 E 39th St Fl 9 New York NY 10016-0112*

YANKOVICH, JAMES MICHAEL, education educator; b. Richmond, Va., Mar. 15, 1935; s. Michael James and Edna Mae (Mann) Y.; m. Ann Page Richardson, Aug. 11, 1956; children: Kathy, Julie, Michael. B.A., U. Richmond, 1957; M.Ed., U. Va., 1961; Ed.D., U. Mich., 1971. Tchr. Henrico County, Va., 1958-60; guidance counselor, 1960-61; prin. Glen Echo Elem. Sch., 1961-62, Varina Elem. Sch., 1962-64, Johnson Elem. Sch. Charlottesville, Va., 1964-65; asst. supt. schs. Charlottesville, 1965-66; asst. prof. U. Mich., Flint, 1968-71; assoc. prof. U. Mich., 1971-74, dean acad. affairs, 1971-74; dean Sch. Edn., Coll. of William and Mary, Williamsburg, Va., 1974-83, 93-95, prof. edn., 1983-92; dean Sch. Edn., 1992—. Bd. dirs. Inst. Ednl. Mgmt., Harvard U. 1973. C.S. Mott leadership fellow, 1966-67. Mem. Phi Delta Kappa. Home: 116 Yorkshire Dr Williamsburg VA 23185-3983 Office: Coll William and Mary Williamsburg VA 23187-8795

YANKWICH, PETER EWALD, chemistry educator; b. L.A., Oct. 20, 1923; s. Leon Rene and Helen (Werner) Y.; m. Elizabeth Pope Ingram, July 14, 1945; children: Alexandra Helen Yankwich Capps, Leon Rene II, Richard Ingram. BS, U. Calif., Berkeley, 1943, PhD, 1945. Mem. sci. staff Radiation Lab., U. Calif., Berkeley, 1944-48; faculty U. Calif., 1947-48; mem. faculty U. Ill., Urbana, 1948-88, prof. chemistry, 1957-88; head div. phys. chemistry, 1958-73. Fellow AAAS, Am. Phys. Soc.; mem. Am. Chem. Soc. (chmn. phys. chemistry div. 1971-72, chem. edn. planning and coordinating com. 1974-77, chmn. edn. commn. 1977-81, bd. dirs. 1982-91), Phi Beta Kappa, Sigma Xi. Home: 4512 4th Rd N Arlington VA 22203-2343

YANNAS, IOANNIS VASSILIOS, polymer science and engineering educator; b. Athens, Apr. 14, 1935; s. Vassilios Pavlos and Thalia (Sarafoglou) Y.; m. Stamatia Frondistou (div. Oct. 1984); children: Tania, Alexis. AB, Harvard U., 1957; SM, MIT, 1959; MS, Princeton U., 1965, PhD, 1966. Asst. prof. mech. engring. MIT, Cambridge, 1966-68, duPont asst. prof., 1968-69, assoc. prof., 1969-78, prof. polymer sci. and engring. dept. mech. engring., 1978—, prof., chem. materials sci. and engring., 1983—; prof. Harvard-MIT Div. Health Scis. and Tech., Cambridge, 1978—; vis. prof. Royal Inst. Tech., Stockholm, 1974. Mem. editorial bd. Jour. Biomed. Materials Rsch., 1986—, Jour. Materials Sci. Materials Medicine, 1990—, Tissue Engineering, 1994—; contbr. over 100 tech. articles to profl. jours.; 13 patents in field. Recipient awards for design of first successful artificial skin for treatment of massively burned patients, including Founders award

Soc. for Biomaterials, 1982, Clemson award Soc. for Biomaterials, 1992, Fred O. Conley award Soc. Plastics Engrs., 1982, award in medicine and genetics Sci. Digest/Cutty Sark, 1982, Doolittle award Am. Chem. Soc., 1988; fellow Pub. Health Svc., Princeton U., 1963, Shriners Burns Inst., Mass. Gen. Hosp., Boston, 1980-81. Fellow Am. Inst. Chemists, Am. Inst. Med. and Biol. Engrs. (founder), Biomaterials Sci. and Engring.; mem. Inst. Medicine of Nat. Acad. Scis. Office: MIT Bldg 3-334 77 Massachusetts Ave Cambridge MA 02139-3594

YANNONI, COSTANTINO SHELDON, research chemist; b. Boston, May 20, 1935; s. Costantino Salvatore and Raffaela Yolanda (Fiorentino) Y.; m. Susan Elizabeth Taylor, Aug. 13, 1966 (div. Dec. 1990); children: Dominic, Michael, Philip, Elizabeth, Scott. BA, Harvard U., 1957; MA, Columbia U., 1961, PhD in Chemistry, 1967. Mem. rsch. staff rsch. div. IBM, Yorktown Heights, N.Y., 1967-71, IBM Almaden Rsch. Ctr., San Jose, Calif., 1971—; mem. editl. adv. bd. Brazilian Jour. Physics, 1992—. Contbr. articles to profl. jours. Recipient Herman S. Bloch award U. Chgo., 1994, award in magnetic resonance Ea. Analytical Symposium, 1994, Louis B. Strait award No. Calif. Spectographic Soc., 1994. Mem. Am. Chem. Soc., Internat. Soc. Magnetic Resonance (coun., nominating com. 1986—). Research in structure and dynamics of reactive intermediates; structure of molecules at interfaces. Office: IBM Rsch Div Almaden Rsch Ctr 650 Harry Rd San Jose CA 95120-6099

YANNUCCI, THOMAS DAVID, lawyer; b. Springfield, Ohio, Mar. 30, 1950; s. David Marion and Patricia (Wilson) Y.; m. Lisa Marie Copeland, June 30, 1972; children: Teresa, Andrea, Thomas D. Jr. AB, U. Notre Dame, 1972, JD, 1976. Bar: Ohio 1977, U.S. Ct. Appeals (D.C., 1st, 2d, 5th, 7th, 8th, 11th and 10th cirs.) 1980, U.S. Supreme Ct. 1980, D.C. 1981. Law clk. to presiding justice U.S. Ct. Appeals (D.C. cir.), Washington, 1976-77; trial atty. U.S. Dept. Justice, Washington, 1977-80; ptnr. Kirkland & Ellis, Washington, 1980—. Editor-in-chief U. Notre Dame Law Rev., 1975-76. Roman Catholic. Office: Kirkland & Ellis 655 15th St NW Ste 1200 Washington DC 20005-5701

YANNUZZI, WILLIAM A(NTHONY), conductor; b. Balt., July 30, 1934; s. Carmine and Maria Rosaria (Capparelli) Y. A.B. cum laude, Johns Hopkins U., 1957, M.A., 1958; M.A., St. Johns Coll., Santa Fe, 1969. Tchr. French Balt. City Coll., 1958-66; mem. faculty Peabody Conservatory, 1977—. Asst. condr., Balt. Opera Co., Inc., 1962-73; music dir., 1973—. Served with U.S. Army, 1951-54. Mem. Phi Beta Kappa. Office: Balt Opera Co Inc 1202 Maryland Ave Baltimore MD 21201-4915

YANOFF, MYRON, ophthalmologist; b. Phila., Dec. 21, 1936; s. Jacob and Lillian S. (Fishman) Y.; m. Karin Michelle Lindblad, Aug. 8, 1980; 1 dau., Alexis A.; children by previous marriage: Steven L., David A., Joanne M. A.B., U. Pa., 1957; M.D., 1961. Prof. ophthalmology and pathology U. Pa. Med. Sch., Phila.; William F. Norris and George E. de Schweinitz prof. ophthalmology, chmn. dept., dir. Scheie Eye Inst., 1977-86; chmn., prof. ophthalmology Med. Coll. Pa. and Hahnemann U., Phila., 1988—; 1st exchange vis. prof. U. Vienna, 1992. Author: Ocular Pathology, Textbook of Ophthalmology; contbr. articles to profl. jours. Served to maj. M.C. USAR. Recipient Humboldt award, 1988. Mem. Am. Ophthalmologic Soc., Verhoeff Soc., Am. Acad. Ophthalmology. Office: Hahnemann U Feinstein Bldg Dept Ophthalmology Broad & Race Sts Philadelphia PA 19102

YANOFSKY, CHARLES, biology educator; b. N.Y.C., Apr. 17, 1925; s. Frank and Jennie (Kopatz) Y.; m. Carol Cohen, June 19, 1949, (dec. Dec. 1990); children: Stephen David, Robert Howard, Martin Fred; m. Edna Crawford, Jan. 4, 1992. BS, CCNY, 1948; MS, Yale U., 1950, PhD, 1951, DSc (hon.), 1981; DSc (hon.), U. Chgo., 1980. Rsch. asst. Yale U., 1951-54; asst. prof. microbiology Western Res. U. Med. Sch., 1954-57; mem. faculty Stanford U., 1958—, prof. biology, 1961—, Herzstein prof. biology, 1966—; career investigator Am. Heart Assn., 1969—. Served with AUS, 1944-46. Recipient Lederle Med. Faculty award, 1957; Eli Lilly award bacteriology, 1959; U.S. Steel Co. award molecular biology, 1964; Howard Taylor Ricketts award U. Chgo., 1966; Albert and Mary Lasker award, 1971; Townsend Harris medal Coll. City N.Y., 1973; Louisa Gross Horwitz prize in biology and biochemistry Columbia U., 1976; V.D. Mattia award Roche Inst., 1982; medal Genetics Soc. Am., 1983; Internat. award Gairdner Found., 1985; named Passano Laureate Passano Found., 1992. Mem. NAS (Selman A. Waksman award in microbiology 1972), Am. Acad. Arts and Scis., Genetics Soc. Am. (pres. 1969, Thomas Hunt Morgan medal 1990), Am. Soc. Biol. Chemists (pres. 1984), Royal Soc. (fgn. mem.), Japanese Biochem. Soc. (hon.). Home: 725 Mayfield Ave Stanford CA 94305-1016 Office: Stanford U Dept Of Biological Sci Stanford CA 94305

YANOWITCH, MICHAEL H., lawyer; b. Phila., Jan. 23, 1949. BA cum laude, Yale U., 1973; MBA with honors, U. Chgo., 1976, JD with honors, 1977. Bar: Ill. 1977, N.Y. 1984; CPA Ill. Law clerk to Hon. Harlington Wood U.S. Ct. Appeals 7th cir., 1977-78; ptnr. Sidley & Austin, N.Y.C. Mem. Order Coif, Beta Gamma Sigma. Office: Sidley & Austin 875 3rd Ave New York NY 10022-6225

YANTIS, PHILLIP ALEXANDER, audiologist, educator; b. Portland, Ore., Mar. 30, 1928; s. George Alexander and Katharine Grace (Fisher) Y.; m. Elna Margaret Mattila, June 11, 1954; children: Steven George, Michael John, Jeffrey Scott. B.A., U. Wash., 1950; M.A., U. Mich., 1952, Ph.D., 1955. Research asso. physiol. acoustics U. Mich. at Ann Arbor, 1955-58, instr. otolaryngology, 1957-60; asst. prof. audiology Case Western Res. U., Cleve., 1960-63; assoc. prof. Case Western Res. U., 1963-65; dir. clin. audiology Cleve. Hearing and Speech Center, 1960-65; assoc. prof. audiology U. Wash., Seattle, 1965-69; prof. U. Wash., 1969-91, prof. emeritus, 1991—, dir. program in speech pathology and audiology, dept. speech, 1968-74, assoc. chmn. dept. speech and hearing scis., 1983-89; Bd. dirs. Am. Bd. Examiners in Speech Pathology and Audiology, 1968-70, 78-80; bd. dirs. Deafness Speech and Hearing Publs., Inc., 1978-81, pres., 1980; mem. Council on Profl. Standards in Speech-Language Pathology and Audiology, 1981, 83-85, chmn., 1983-84. Asst. editor for hearing: Deafness, Speech and Hearing Abstracts, 1960-64; asso. editor for hearing: Jour. Speech and Hearing Research, 1966-69; editorial bd.: Archives of Otolaryngology, 1979-85. Trustee Am. Speech and Hearing Found., 1969-71, 74-75. Served with AUS, 1950-51. Fellow Am. Speech-Lang.-Hearing Assn. (v.p. planning 1969-71, pres. 1975, honors 1987), Am. Acad Audiology; mem. Am. Auditory Soc., Wash. Speech and Hearing Assn. (honors 1980). Home: 1434 NW 204th Pl Seattle WA 98177-2155 Office: Dept Speech and Hearing Sciences U Wash Seattle WA 98195

YANTIS, RICHARD WILLIAM, investments executive; b. Tipp City, Ohio, Nov. 19, 1923; s. Guy Everett and Frances (Barnhart) Y.; m. Marjorie Louise Gray, May 11, 1943; children: Cheryl Ann, Sandra Lee, Susan Elizabeth. Student, U. Dayton, 1942-44. Regional mgr. Gen. Finance Corp., Chgo., 1946-53; v.p. Fruehauf Trailer Finance Co., Detroit, 1953-56; pres. Delta Acceptance Corp., Ltd., London, Ont., Can., 1956-64; exec. v.p., dir. Avco Corp., Greenwich, Conn., 1965-73; pres. Avco Community Developers, Inc., La Jolla, Calif., 1973-75; cons. Avco Community Developers, Inc., 1975-80; pres. Cathedral Mortgage Co., Inc., Palm Springs, Calif., 1980-82. Served with USNR, 1941-45. Clubs: Masons, Shriners, Seven Lakes Country; London, London Hunt and Country. Home: 331 Westlake Ter Palm Springs CA 92264-5534

YAO, DAVID DA-WEI, engineering science educator; b. Shanghai, China, July 14, 1950; came to U.S. 1983, naturalized, 1990; s. William Kang-Fu and Nancy Yun-Lan (Lu) Y.; m. Helen Zhi-Heng Chen, Jan. 31, 1979; children: Henry, John. MASc, U. Toronto, Ont., Can., 1981, PhD, 1983. Assoc. prof. systems engring. Harvard U., Cambridge, Mass., 1986-88; asst. prof. indsl. engring. and ops. rsch. Columbia U., N.Y.C., 1983-86, prof., 1988—, Thomas Alva Edison prof., 1992—; acad. visitor AT&T Bell Labs., Holmdel, N.J., 1989, T.J. Watson Rsch. Ctr., IBM, Yorktown, N.Y., 1990—. Co-author: Monotone Structure in Discrete-Event Systems, 1994; editor: Stochastic Modeling and Analysis of Manufacturing Systems, 1994; contbr. more than 100 articles to sci. jours. including Maths. Ops. Rsch., Jour. of Assn. Computing Machinery, Advances in Applied Probability, 1983—. Recipient Presdl. Young Investigator award NSF, Washington, 1987-92, Guggenheim fellow John Simon Guggenheim Meml. Found.,

N.Y.C., 1991-92. Mem. IEEE, Soc. Indsl. and Applied Math., Ops. Rsch. Soc. Am. (George Nicholson prize 1983). Achievements include development of theory of algebraic structures in discrete event systems, theory of stochastic convexity and its applications in queuing networks, stochastic network models for computer integrated manufacturing systems, methodologies in the optimization and control of stochastic discrete event systems. Home: 1261 Underhill Ave Yorktown Heights NY 10598 Office: Columbia U 302 Mudd Bldg New York NY 10027-6699

YAO, JAMES TSU-PING, civil engineer; b. Shanghai, China, July 7, 1933; came to U.S. 1953; s. C.C. and Mae Jane (Wang) Y.; m. Anna Lee, June 14, 1958; children: Tina Lee, Timothy H.J., Shana Lynn. BSCE, U. Ill., 1957, MSCE, 1958, PhD, 1961. Registered profl. engr. Tex., N.Mex. Postdoctoral preceptor Columbia U., N.Y.C., 1964-65; asst. prof. civil engring. U. N.Mex., Albuquerque, 1961-64, assoc. prof., 1965-69, prof., 1969-71; prof. Purdue U., W. Lafayette, Ind., 1971-88, asst. head dept. civil engring., 1983-88, asst. dean grad. sch., 1984-87; prof. Tex. A&M U., College Station, 1988—, head dept. civil engring., 1988-93. Editor Jour. Structural Engring., 1990-92. Recipient Max Planck Rsch. award Alexander Von Humboldt Found., 1990, Civil Engring. Disting. Alumnus award U. Ill., Urbana, 1991, Centennial medallion Am. Soc. Engring. Edn., 1993. Fellow ASCE (State-of-the-Art of Civil Engring. award 1973, 83, Alfred M. Freudenthal medal 1990, Richard R. Torrens award 1992). Avocations: volleyball, paperfolding. Office: Tex A&M Univ Dept Civil Engring College Station TX 77843-3136

YAPLE, HENRY MACK, library director; b. Vicksburg, Mich., May 30, 1940; s. Henry J. and Pauline B. (Spencer) Y.; m. Marilyn Lou Bales, Dec. 31, 1971; children: Sean H., Kendra S. BA in English with hons., Kalamazoo Coll., 1963; MA, U. Idaho, 1966; postgrad., U. d'Aix-Marselle, France, 1965-66, U. Toronto, 1966-69; MLS, W. Mich. U., 1972. Order libr. Mich. State U., E. Lansing, 1972-74, humanities bibliographer, 1974-78; acquisitions libr. U. Wyo., Laramie, 1978-87; libr. dir. Whitman Coll., Walla Walla, Wash., 1987—; Mem. Wyo. Coun. for the Humanities, 1982-86. U. Toronto scholar, 1966-69; Rotary fellow, 1965, 66; U. Wyo. rsch. grantee, 1982, 86. Mem. ALA, Wyo. Libr. Assn. (pres. 1984-85), Nat. Ski Patrol System (sr. patroller 1978—, nat. #6946 1988), Wash. Libr. Assn., Northwest Assn. of Pvt. Colls. and U. Libnrs. (pres. 1987-88, 94-95), Rotary (Walla Walla), Beta Phi Mu. Avocations: book collecting, skiing, kayaking. Home: 1889 Fern St Walla Walla WA 99362-9393 Office: Whitman Coll Office Libr 345 Boyer Ave Walla Walla WA 99362-2083

YARAR, BAKI, metallurgical engineering educator; b. Adana, Turkey, Feb. 28, 1941; came to U.S., 1980; s. Salih and Sidika Yarar; m. Ruth G. Yarar; children: Deniz, Defne. BSc in Chemistry, Mid. East Tech. U., Ankara, Turkey, 1965, MSc in Chemistry, 1966; PhD in Surface Chemistry, U. London, 1969; DIC in Mineral Tech., Imperial Coll. London, 1969. Instr. Mid. East Tech. U., 1970-71, asst. prof., 1971-76, assoc. prof., 1976-79; vis. prof. U. B.C., Vancouver, Can., 1979-80; assoc. prof. Colo. Sch. of Mines, Golden, 1980-86, prof., 1986—; pvt. practice cons. in mineral processing, worldwide, 1980—. Author chpts. to books, over 100 papers; editor books; mem. editorial bd. 4 jours. Lt. Turkish Army, 1970-71. Holder numerous awards and certificates of recognition. Mem. Soc. Mining Engrs. (chmn. fundamental com. 1989), Am. Chem. Soc., Materials Rsch. Soc., Sigma Xi (life). Achievements include pioneering work in selective flocculation; invention of the gamma floation process; patent for superconductivity meter device. Home: 13260 Braun Rd Golden CO 80401 Office: Colo Sch Mines Dept Metal Engring Golden CO 80401

YARBOROUGH, WILLIAM CALEB, former professional stock car race driver; b. Timmonsville, S.C., Mar. 27, 1939. Named Grand Nat. Champion Nat. Assn. Stock Car Auto Racing, 1976. Winner Atlanta 500, 1967, 68, 74, Cam 2 Motor Oil 400, 1977, Capital City 400, 1976, Carolina 500, 1975, Daytona 500, 1968, 77, 83, 84, Mason-Dixon 500, 1969, Nat. 500, 1973, So. 500, 1968, 73, 74, 78, Va. 500, 1974, 77, Wilkes 400, 1974, Winston Western 500, 1974; champion Winston Cup, 1976-78, many others. Office: care Nat Assn Stock Car Auto Racing 1801 Volusia Ave Daytona Beach FL 32114-1215*

YARBOROUGH, WILLIAM PELHAM, writer, lecturer, retired army officer, consultant; b. Seattle, May 12, 1912; s. Leroy W. and Addessia (Hooker) Y.; m. Norma Mae Tuttle, Dec. 26, 1936; children: Norma Kay (dec.), William Lee, Patricia Mae. BS, U.S. Mil. Acad., 1936; grad., Command and Gen. Staff Coll., 1944, Brit. Staff Coll., 1950, Army War Coll., 1953. Commd. 2nd lt. U.S. Army, 1936, advanced through grades to lt. gen., 1968, ret., 1971; various assignments U.S. Army, U.S., Philippines and ETO, 1936-42; exec. officer Paratroop Task Force, North Africa, 1942; comdr. 2d Bn., 504th Par. Inf. Regt., 82d Airborne Div., Sicily invasion, 1943, 509th Parachute Inf., Italy and France, 1943-44; comdg. officer 473 Inf., Italy, 1945; provost marshal 15th Army Group, ETO, 1945, Vienna Area Command and U.S. Forces, Austria, 1945-47; mem. staff, faculty U.S. Army Info. Sch., 1948-49; operations officer, gen. staff Joint Mil. Assistance Adv. Group, London, Eng., 1951-52; mem. faculty Army War Coll., 1953-56, 57; dep. chief Mil. Assistance and Adv. Group, Cambodia, 1956-57; comdg. officer 66th CIC Group, Stuttgart, Germany, 1958-60, 66th M.I. Group, Stuttgart, 1960; comdg. gen. U.S.A. Spl. Warfare Ctr.; also comdt. U.S. Army Spl. Warfare Sch., Ft. Bragg, 1961-65; sr. mem. UN Command Mil. Armistice Commn., Korea, 1965; asst. dep. chief staff DCSOPS for spl. operations Dept. Army, Washington; chmn. U.S. delegation Inter-Am. Def. Bd., Joint Brazil U.S. Def. Commn., Joint Mexican-U.S. Def. Commn.; Army mem. U.S. sect. permanent Joint Bd. on Def., Can.-U.S. Def. Commn., Washington, 1965; asst. chief of staff intelligence Dept. Army Washington, 1966-68; comdg. gen. I Corps Group, Korea, 1968-69; chief staff, also dep. comdr.-in-chief U.S. Army, Pacific, Hawaii, 1969-71. Contbr. Internat. Mil. and Def. Ency., 1993, MacMillan Ency. of the Am. Mil., 1994; William P. Yarborough collection papers and artifacts donated to Mugar Meml. Librs., Boston U. Decorated Disting. Svc. medal with three oak leaf clusters, Silver Star, Legion of Merit with three oak leaf clusters, Bronze Star, Joint Svc. Commendation medal with oak leaf clusters, Croix de Guerre with Palm (France), Cross for Valor and Diploma (Italy), Order of Merit Second Class (Korea), Order of Ulchi (Korea). Fellow Co. Mil. Historians, Explorers Club; mem. Kiwanis Club. Home: 160 Hillside Rd Southern Pines NC 28387-6727

YARBRO, ALAN DAVID, lawyer; b. Huntington, W.Va., Sept. 16, 1941; s. John David and Bernice (Bulette) Y.; m. Lee Merryman Myers, July 1961; children: Wendy, Jennifer, Caroline. AB magna cum laude, Harvard U. 1962, LLB cum laude, 1966. Bar: Md. 1966, U.S. Ct. Appeals (4th cir.) 1966, U.S. Dist. Ct. Md. 1966. Assoc. Venable Baetjer & Howard, Balt., 1966-72, ptnr., 1973—. Trustee Children's Hosp., Balt., 1986—, pres. 1988-89. Fellow Am. Bar Found., Md. Bar Found.; mem. ABA, Md. Bar Assn., Bar Assn. of Balt. (chmn. ethics com. 1988-89).

YARBRO, JAMES WESLEY, financial executive; b. Woodbury, Tex., Mar. 30, 1920; s. Daniel Fore and Annie Belle (Hunt) Y.; m. Mary Elise Alderdice, Aug. 17, 1944; children: Suzanne Elise, James Wesley Jr., Rosemary. BS, North Tex. State Coll., 1940. CPA, Tex. Instr. high sch. Crane, Tex., 1940-42; aviator USN, South Pacific Theater, 1942-45; internal revenue agt. U.S. Treasury Dept., Ft. Worth, 1946-51; asst. sec.-treas., tax mgr. So. Prodn. Co., Ft. Worth, 1951-57; with Tex. Pacific Coal & Oil Co., Ft. Worth, 1957-63, fin. v.p., bd. dirs., 1959-63; fin. v.p. King Resources Co., Denver, 1963-66; fin. v.p., bd. dirs., treas. Western Co., Ft. Worth, 1967-69; pvt. practice fin. svc. Ft. Worth, 1969-88; ret., 1988. Lt. USNR, 1942-45. Mem. AICPAs, Tex. Soc. CPAs, Ind. Petroleum Assn. Am., Petroleum Club Ft. Worth, Rotary. Christian Ch. Home: 1417 Westover Ln Fort Worth TX 76107

YARBROUGH, JERRY A., transportation company executive; b. 1938. BSCE, MIT, 1960; MBA, U. Chgo., 1967. With Crane Supply Co., Chgo., 1965-67; with ABF Freight Sys., Inc., Ft. Smith, Ark., 1968—, sr. v.p. ops., 1979—. Office: ABF Freight System Inc 301 S 11th St Fort Smith AR 72901-3798

YARBROUGH, MARILYN VIRGINIA, lawyer, educator; b. Bowling Green, Ky., Aug. 31, 1945; d. William Ottoway Yarbrough and Merca Lee

(Hardin) Toole; m. Walter James Ainsworth, Sept. 3, 1967 (div. Oct. 1980); children: Carmen Virginia, Carla Renee; m. David A. Didion, Dec. 31, 1987. BA, Va. State U., 1966; JD, UCLA, 1973. Bar: Calif. 1973, Kans. 1982. Instr. Boston Coll. Law Sch., Newton, Mass., 1975-76; prof. law U. Kans., Lawrence, 1976-87, assoc. vice chancellor, 1983-87; prof. Law Sch. U. Tenn., Knoxville, 1987-93; dean Law Sch U. Tenn., Knoxville, 1987-91; William J. Maier Jr. chair law W.Va. U., Morgantown, 1991-92; prof. U. N.C. Law Sch., Chapel Hill, 1992—, assoc. provost, 1994—. Editor in chief Black Law Jour. 1972-73; contbr. articles to profl. jours. Bd. dirs. Knox County Endl. Enrichment Fund, Knoxville, 1989-92, Knoxville Housing Partnership, 1989-92, United Way of Knoxville, 1990-92; trustee Law Sch. Admission Coun., pres., 1986-88; trustee Webb Sch. of Knoxville, 1988-91; mem. Pulitzer Prize Bd., 1990—. Mem. ABA (reporter Am. Law Inst.-ABA com. continuing profl. edn. 1988-90, sect. legal edn. and admissions to bar 1989-94), Poynter Inst. for Media Studies (adv. bd. 1984-90, bd. dirs. 1990-92). Democrat. Mem. United Ch. of Christ.

YARBROUGH, MARTHA CORNELIA, music educator; b. Waycross, Ga., Feb. 8, 1940; d. Henry Elliott and Jessie (Sirmans) Y.; B.M.E., Stetson U., 1962; M.M.E., Fla. State U., 1968, Ph.D., 1973. Choral dir. Ware County High Sch., Waycross, Ga., 1962-64, Glynn Acad., Brunswick, Ga., 1964-70; asst. choral dir. Fla. State U., 1970-72; cons. in music Muscogee County Sch. Dist., Columbus, Ga., 1972-73; cons. in tchr. edn. Psycho-Edno. Cons., Inc., Tallahassee, 1972-73; asst. prof. music edn., dir. univs. choruses and oratorio soc. Syracuse U., 1973-76, assoc. prof. music edn., 1976-83, prof., 1983-86, acting asst. dean Coll. Visual and Performing Arts, 1980-82, acting dir. Sch. Music, 1980-82, chmn. music edn., 1982-86; prof. music La. State U., Baton Rouge, 1986—, coordinator music, edn., 1986—; artist in residence Sch. Music U. Ala., Tuscaloosa, 1989-90. Chair exec. com. Music Edn. Rsch. Coun., 1992-94. Mem. Music Educators Nat. Conf., N.Y. State Sch. Music Assn., Am. Ednl. Research Assn., Soc. Research Music Edn. (mem. exec. com. 1988-90, program chair 1990-92, chair, 1992-94), AAUP, Pi Kappa Lambda, Phi Beta, Kappa Delta Pi. Co-author: Competency-Based Music Education, 1980; mem. editorial com. Jour. Research in Music Edn.; contbr. articles to profl. jours., chpts. in books. Office: Sch Music La State U Baton Rouge LA 70803

YARD, RIX NELSON, former athletic director; b. Ocean County, N.J., July 1, 1917; s. George Rix and Lena (Nelson) Y.; m. Adra Gehrett, Sept. 12, 1941; children: Rix Nelson, Constance. BS, U. Pa., 1941, MS, 1947, EdD, 1956. Tchr. Swissvale (Pa.) High Sch., 1946; instr., asst. football coach, head basketball coach Denison U., 1947-49, chmn. dept. phys. edn., dir. athletics, lacrosse coach, 1953-63; asst. football coach U. Pa., 1949-53; dir. athletics Tulane U., 1963-76, prof. phys. edn., 1968-82, prof. emeritus, 1982—, dir. club and intramural sports, 1976-82, also adminstr. phys. edn. major program. Pres. New Orleans Football Hall of Fame, 1965-76; Vice pres. Granville (Ohio) Bd. Edn., 1961-63; asst. fire chief Granville Vol. Fire Co., 1958-63; mem. Granville Zoning Com., 1961; Bd. dirs. New Orleans chpt. A.R.C. Served with USNR, 1941-46; ret. capt. Res. Named Nat. Lacrosse Coach of Yr., 1963; named to Sports Hall of Fame Denison U., 1983, Ohio Lacross Hall of Fame, 1995. Mem. Nat. Collegiate Athletic Assn. (chmn. TV com. 1958, 60, rep. to Sugar Bowl 1964-78, chmn. ins. com. 1971-76, chmn. acad. and testing requirements com.), Nat. Assn. Coll. Dirs. Athletics (exec. com.); (named to Hall of Fame 1977); Mem. Navy League (dir. New Orleans chpt.). Club: New Orleans Quarterback (dir. 1967-78). Home: 6 Roberts Landing Dr Poquoson VA 23662-1026

YARDIS, PAMELA HINTZ, computer consulting company executive; b. N.Y.C., Sept. 23, 1944; d. Edward F. and Isabella (Sawers) Hintz; m. J.A. Yardis, Apr. 2, 1966 (div. July 1980); children: Bradley, Brent, Tricia, Todd, Ryan, Kara, Melissa. BA, Bethany Coll., 1966; MA, Columbia U., 1983, MEd, 1983. Cert. mgmt. cons. Tchr. Yonkers (N.Y.) Pub. Schs., 1966-68; cons. PHY, Inc., Stamford, Conn., 1978-83; account exec. Mgmt. Systems, Stamford, 1982-84; sr. account exec., cons. Mgmt. Dynamics, Yonkers, 1984-86; v.p. GMW Assn., Inc., N.Y.C., 1986-87; pres. Chestnut Hill Cons. Group, Inc., Stamford, 1987—. Chmn. Mayor's Commn. Prevention Youth Drug and Alcohol Abuse, Stamford, 1986-91; mem. Dem. Cen. Com., Stamford, 1984—; bd. dirs., pres. Alcohol and Drug Coun., Inc., Conn. Communities for Drug Free Youth, Childcare, Inc., Youth Shelter. Recipient Gov.'s Cmty. Svc. award, 1988, Golden Rule award J.C. Penney, Bravo award YWCA, 1992, Women of Enterprise award SBA & Avon, Inc. 1993, Sacian award S.W. Area Commerce and Bus., 1994. Mem. Women in Mgmt. (v.p. 1986-88, Ann. Recognition award), Data Processing Mgmt. Assn., Advt. Rsch. Found., Inst. Mgmt. Cons. (pres. Fairfield Westchester chpt. 1990-93, chmn. 1993—, nat. bd. dirs., chmn. 1993-95), Sales and Mktg. Execs. (bd. dirs.). Presbyterian. Avocations: travel, camping, politics. Home: 125 Chestnut Hill Rd Stamford CT 06903-4029 Office: Chestnut Hill Cons Group PO Box 15755 Stamford CT 06901-0755

YARDLEY, JOHN FINLEY, aerospace engineer; b. St. Louis, Feb. 1, 1925; s. Finley Abna and Johnnie (Patterson) Y.; m. Phyllis Steele, July 25, 1946; children: Kathryn, Robert, Mary, Elizabeth, Susan. B.S., Iowa State Coll., 1944; M.S., Washington U., St. Louis, 1950. Structural and aero. engr. McDonnell Aircraft Corp., St. Louis, 1946-55, chief strength engr., 1956-57; project engr. Mercury spacecraft design, 1958-60; launch ops. mgr. Mercury and Gemini spacecraft, Cape Canaveral, Fla., 1960-64; Gemini tech. dir. Mercury and Gemini spacecraft, 1964-67; v.p., dep. gen. mgr. Eastern div. McDonnell Douglas Astronautics, 1968-72, v.p., gen. mgr., 1973-74, pres., 1981-88, sr. corp. v.p., 1989, ret.; assoc. adminstr. for manned space flight NASA, Washington, 1974-81. Served to ensign USNR, 1943-46. Recipient Achievement award St. Louis sect. Inst. Aerospace Scis., 1961, John J. Montgomery award, 1963, Pub. Service award NASA, 1963, 66 ; profl. achievement citation Iowa State Coll., 1970, Spirit of St. Louis medal, 1973, Alumni citation Washington U., 1975, Disting. Achievement citation Iowa State U., 1976, Presdl. citation as meritorious exec. Sr. Exec. Service, 1980, NASA Disting. Service medal, 1981, Goddard Meml. trophy, 1983, Achievement award Washington U. Engring. Alumni, 1983, Elmer A. Sperry award, 1986; named Engr. of Yr. NASA, 1982; Von Karman Astronautics Lectureship award, 1988. Fellow AIAA (Goddard award 1982), Am. Astronautical Soc. (Space Flight award 1978); mem. Internat. Acad. Astronautics, NASA Alumni League (bd. dirs.), Nat. Acad. Engring., Nat. Space Club (bd. govs.), Tau Beta Pi, Phi Kappa Phi, Phi Eta Sigma, Phi Mu Epsilon. Presbyterian. Home: 14319 Cross Timbers Ct Chesterfield MO 63017-5718

YARDLEY, JONATHAN, journalist, columnist; b. Pitts., Oct. 27, 1939; s. William Woolsey and Helen (Gregory) Y.; m. Rosemary Roberts, June 14, 1961 (div. 1975); children: James Barrett, William W. II.; m. Susan L. Hartt, Mar. 23, 1975. AB, U. N.C., Chapel Hill; DHL (hon.), George Washington U., 1987. Writer N.Y. Times, 1961-64; editorial writer, book editor Greensboro (N.C.) Daily News, 1964-74; book editor Miami (Fla.) Herald, 1974-78, Washington Star, 1978-81; book critic, columnist Washington Post, 1981—. Author: Ring: A Biography of Ring Lardner, 1977, Our Kind of People: The Story of an American Family, 1989, Out of Step: Notes from a Purple Decade, 1991, States of Mind: A Personal Journey Through the Mid-Atlantic, 1993; editor: My Life as Author and Editor (H.L. Mencken), 1993. Recipient Pulitzer prize for criticism, 1981, Disting. Alumnus award U. N.C., 1989; Nieman fellow in journalism Harvard U., 1968-69. Episcopalian. Home: 223 Hawthorne Rd Baltimore MD 21210-2503 Office: Washington Post 1150 15th St NW Washington DC 20071-0002

YARDLEY, ROSEMARY ROBERTS, journalist, columnist; b. Albertville, Ala., Apr. 1, 1938; d. James Bailey Jr. and Mildred (Smith) Roberts; m. Jonathan Yardley, June 14, 1961 (div. 1975); children: James B., William W. II; m. Donald Arthur Boulton, Apr. 30, 1988. BA, U. N.C., 1960; MA, U. N.C., Greensboro, 1978. Staff writer The Charlotte (N.C.) Observer, 1960-61; editorial asst. The N.Y. Times, N.Y.C., 1962-64; staff writer The Greensboro (N.C.) News and Record, 1974-78, editorial writer, 1978-88, editorial columnist, 1988—; mem. faculty English dept. U. N.C., Greensboro, 1990—. Contbr. articles, book revs. to various publs. Bd. dirs. Weatherspoon Art Mus. U. N.C. Greensboro, 1986—, U. N.C. Journalism Found. 1985-93, Weatherspoon Art Found., 1989—, Friends U. Libr., Greensboro, 1988-90, Ea. Music Festival, Greensboro, 1984-88; bd. dirs. English Speaking Union Greensboro, 1995—. Recipient 2d prize N.C. Press Assn., 1976, 1st prize 1987, 2d prize 1995; John S. Knight fellow Stanford U., 1980-81; Bosch Found. travel fellow, 1990, Atlantik Bruke Found. travel fellow, 1988.

Democrat. Presbyterian. Home: 223 Elmwood Dr Greensboro NC 27408-5829 Office: The Greensboro News and Record 200 E Market St Greensboro NC 27401-2910

YARGER, SAM JACOB, dean, educator; b. Pontiac, Mich., Oct. 8, 1937; s. Ralph And Eva L. (Little) Y.; m. Gwen Polk (div. 1982); 1 child, Mark Alan; m. Sally K. Mertens. BS in Elem. Edn., Eastern Mich. U., 1959; MA in Sch. Psychology, U. Mich., 1962; PhD in Ednl. Psychology, Wayne State U., 1968. Assist. prof. Oakland (Mich.) Community Coll., 1967-68, U. Toldeo, 1968-71; assoc. prof. Syracuse (N.Y.) U., 1971-77, prof., 1977-84, assoc. dean, 1980-84; dean, prof. U. Wis., Milw., 1984-92, U. Miami, Fla., 1992—; researcher Assessment Pre-Vocat. Skills Mentally Retarded Youth, 1964-65, Tchr. Attitude Change in Relations to Program Input, 1968, Leader Behavior in a Task Oriented Setting in Relation to Group Activity, 1968, Attitudes Inner-City Residents Toward Ednl. Programs and Tchrs., 1970, Dimensions Tchr. Ctr. Movement in Am. Edn., 1972-75, Dimensions Field Derived Content in Tchr. Edn. Programs, 1973-75, Nat. Study Inservice Edn., 1976-77, Nat. Study Preservice Edn., 1976-77, Nat. Study Federally-Funded Tchr. Ctr., 1979-82, Nat. Study Tchr. Edn., 1985—; developer, dir. tchr. edn. programs, various U.S. locations; mem., chmn. various univ. coms.; cons., speaker in field. Author: Improving Teacher Education, 1978, Documenting Success - A Guidebook for Teacher Centers, 1979, Inservice Teacher Education, 1980; author monographs; contbr. articles to profl. jours., chpts. to books. Mem. Am. Ednl. Rsch. Assn. (assoc. editor 1983-85, chair elect Orgn. Instl. Affilliates 1994-95), Am. Assn. Colls. for Tchr. Edn. (bd. dirs. 1984-87, exec. com. 1985-87). Office: U Miami Sch Edn PO Box 248065 Coral Gables FL 33124-8065

YARINGTON, CHARLES THOMAS, JR., surgeon, administrator; b. Sayre, Pa., Apr. 26, 1934; s. C.T. and Florence (Hutchinson) Y.; m. Barbara Taylor Johnson, Sept. 28, 1963; children: Leslie Anne, Jennifer Lynne, Barbara Jane. Grad., Hill Sch., 1952; A.B., Princeton, 1956; M.D. Hahnemann Med. Coll., 1960; grad., Army Command and Gen. Staff Coll., 1969, Air War Coll., 1973, Indsl. Coll. Armed Forces, 1974. Intern Rochester (N.Y.) Gen. Hosp., 1960-61; resident Dartmouth Hosp., 1961-62, U. Rochester Strong Meml. Hosp., 1962-65; instr. otolaryngology U. Rochester Sch. Medicine, 1962-65; asst. prof. surgery W.Va. U. Sch. Medicine, 1967-68; assoc. prof., chmn. dept. otorhinolaryngology U. Nebr. Med. Center, 1968-69, prof., chmn. dept. otorhinolaryngology, 1969-74; clin. prof. otolaryngology U. Wash., Seattle, 1974—; clin. prof. surgery Uniformed Services U. Health Scis., Bethesda, 1985—; chief otolaryngology Virginia Mason Med. Ctr., Seattle, 1978-88, 92—, chief dept. surgery, 1988-91; cons. Surg. Gen. USAF; pres. Virginia Mason Rsch. Ctr., Seattle, 1983-85; trustee Mason Clinic, 1988-91; mem. adv. coun. Nat. Inst. Neurol. Diseases, Communicative Diseases, Stroke of NIH, Bethesda, Md., 1986-90; bd. dirs. Virginia Mason Hosp., Virginia Mason Med. Ctr., bd. govs., 1989—. Author books and articles in field.; Mem. editorial bd. Aviation, Space, Environ. Med. Jour., Otol. Clinics of N. Am., Mil. Medicine, Otolaryngology-Head and Neck Surgery. Trustee Seattle Opera Assn., 1983-89. Served to maj., M.C. AUS, 1965-67; brig. gen. USAF Res., to 1986. Decorated D.S.M.; Legion of Merit; named Commdr. Venerable Order St. John (Gt. Britain); recipient Sir Henry Wellcome medal, 1984. Fellow ACS, Royal Soc. Medicine, Am. Acad. Otolaryngology (Barraquer Meml. award 1968, mem. standing com., bd. govs. 1982-88, Honor award 1974); mem. Am. Broncho-Esophagological Assn. (council, treas. 1982-86, pres. 1987-88), Am. Laryngol. Assn., Pacific Coast Oto. Ophthalmology and Otolaryngology (coun., pres. 1987-88), Soc. Med. Cons. to Armed Forces, Am. Soc. Head and Neck Surgery, N.W. Acad. Head and Neck Surgery (pres. 1984-86), Am. Soc. Otology, Rhinology and Laryngology (v.p. 1992-93), Res. Officers Assn. (pres. Seattle chpt., nat. officer), Pan-Pacific Surg. Assn., AMA, Sons of Revolution (pres. Wash. 1985-87), Seattle Yacht Club, Princeton Quadrangle Club, RAF Club (London), Cosmos Club (Washington), Rainier Club (Seattle), Sigma Xi. Office: Mason Clinic 1100 9th Ave Seattle WA 98101-2799

YARIV, AMNON, electrical engineering educator, scientist; b. Tel Aviv, Israel, Apr. 13, 1930; came to U.S., 1951, naturalized, 1964; s. Shraga and Henya (Davidson) Y.; m. Frances Pokras, Apr. 10, 1972; children: Elizabeth, Dana, Gabriela. B.S., U. Calif., Berkeley, 1954, M.S., 1956, Ph.D., 1958. Mem. tech. staff Bell Telephone Labs., 1959-63; dir. laser research Watkins-Johnson Co., 1963-64; mem. faculty Calif. Inst. Tech., 1964—, Thomas G. Myers prof. elec. engring. and applied physics, 1996—; chmn. bd. ORTEL Inc., Accuwave Corp.; cons. in field. Author: Quantum Electronics, 1967, 75, 85, Introduction to Optical Electronics, 1971, 77, 89, Theory and Applications of Quantum Mechanics, Propagation of Light in Crystals. Served with Israeli Army, 1948-50. Recipient Pender award U. Pa., Harvey prize Technion, Israel, 1992. Fellow IEEE (Quantum Electronics award 1980), Am. Optical Soc. (Ives medal 1986), Am. Acad. Arts and Scis.; mem. NAS, NAE, Am. Phys. Soc. Office: 1201 E California Blvd Pasadena CA 91125-0001

YARKONY, GARY MICHAEL, physician, researcher; b. N.Y.C., May 22, 1953; m. Kirsten Kohlmeyer; children: Judith, Rachel, Seth, Lauren. BA in Biology, SUNY, Buffalo, 1974; MD, SUNY, Syracuse, 1978; M Mgmt, Northwestern U., 1994. Diplomate Am. Bd. Phys. Medicine and Rehab. Intern, then resident in physical medicine, rehab. Northwestern U., Chgo., 1978-81, chief resident dept. rehab. medicine, 1980; asst. dir. head trauma program Rehab. Inc. Chgo., 1981-84, attending staff, 1981-94; v.p. clin. program devel. Schwab Rehab. Hosp., Chgo., 1994—; attending phsyician Northwestern Meml. Hosp., Chgo., 1984-94; assoc. prof. Dept. of Rehab. Medicine, Northwestern U. Med. Sch., 1985-94; adj. assoc. prof. Pritzker Inst. for Med. Engring., Ill. Inst. of Tech., 1991—; dir. rehab. Midwest Regional Spinal Cord Injury Care System, Chgo., 1984-94; clin. prof. med., 1995—. Contbr. articles to profl. jours. and chpts. to book. Fellow Am. Acad. Physical Medicine and Rehab.; mem. Assn. Academic Physiatrists, Am. Spinal Injury Assn., Internat. Med. Soc. Paraplegia, Internal Rehab. Medicine Assn., Phi Beta Kappa, Phi Eta Sigma. Office: Schwab Rehab Hosp 1401 S California Blvd Chicago IL 60608

YARLOW, LORETTA, art museum director; b. N.Y.C., Sept. 26, 1948; d. Albert and Sylvia (Seligsohn) Y.; m Gregory Salzman, June 5, 1977; children: Nina, Alexander. BA, Sarah Lawrence Coll., 1970; EdM, Harvard U., 1971. Curator Inst. Contemporary Art, Boston, 1972-74; co-dir. Yarlow/Salzman Gallery, Toronto, Ont., Can., 1974-84; dir./curator Art Gallery York U., Toronto, 1988—. Office: Art Gallery York U, 4700 Keele St, North York, ON Canada M3J 1P3

YARMOLINSKY, ADAM, lawyer, educator, university administrator; b. N.Y.C., Nov. 17, 1922; s. Avrahm and Babette (Deutsch) Y.; m. Harriet Leslie Rypins, Mar. 24, 1945 (div. 1981); children: Sarah Franklin, Tobias, Benjamin Levi, Matthew Jonas; m. Jane Cox Vonnegut, Oct. 20, 1984 (dec Dec. 1986); m. Sarah Ames Ellis, Feb. 3, 1990. A.B., Harvard U., 1943; LL.B., Yale U., 1948. Bar: N.Y. 1949, D.C. 1952; U.S. Supreme Ct. 1955. Law clk. to Judge C.E. Clark U.S. Ct. Appeals (2d cir.), 1948-49; assoc. Root, Ballantine, Harlan, Bushby & Palmer, N.Y.C., 1949-50; law clk. to Justice Stanley Reed U.S. Supreme Ct., 1950-51; assoc. Cleary, Gottlieb, Friendly & Ball, Washington, 1951-55; dir. Washington office Fund for the Republic, Inc., 1955-56, sec., 1956-57; pub. affairs editor Doubleday & Co., Inc., 1957-59; cons. pvt. founds., 1959-60, spl. asst. sec. of def., 1961-64; dep. dir. Pres.'s Anti-Poverty Task Force, 1964; chief U.S. Emergency Relief Mission to Dominican Republic, 1965; prin. dep. asst. sec. def. for internat. security affairs, 1965-66; prof. law Harvard U.; mem. inst. politics John F. Kennedy Sch. Govt., 1966-71; on leave, 1970-72; chief exec. officer Welfare Island Devel. Corp., 1971-72; Ralph Waldo Emerson univ. prof. U Mass., 1972-77; counselor ACDA, 1977-79; of counsel Fort & Schlefer, Washington, 1979—; prof. policy scis. grad. program U. Md. Balt. County, Balt., 1985-93, acting provost, 1986-87, provost, 1987-93; regents prof. pub. policy U. Md. System, 1993—; lectr. Am. U. Law Sch., 1951-56, Yale U. Law Sch., 1958-59; adj. prof. Georgetown U. Law Sch., 1984-85; cons. Office Tech. Assessment, 1974-77; mem. gov.'s adv. coun. Mass. Comprehensive Health Planning Agy., 1972-74; mem. inst. for Rsch. on Poverty, 1972-77; mem. adv. coun. inter-univ. seminar on Armed Forces and Soc.; mem. Governing Coun. Wye Faculty Seminar; moderator Aspen Inst. Exec. Seminars, 1976—; Troutbeck Ednl. Leadership Program, 1984—; Oxford Aspen Seminars, 1986-89. Author: Recognition of Excellence, 1960, The Military Establish-

ment, 1971, Paradoxes of Power, 1983; also articles in periodicals.; Editor: Case Studies in Personnel Security, 1955, Race and Schooling In the City, 1980; Spl. corr.: The Economist, London, 1956-60. Trustee Bennington Coll., 1984—, chmn., 1986-88; trustee Robert F. Kennedy Meml., Vera Inst. Justice, 1967—, New Directions Edn. Fund, 1979-82, Ctr. for Nat. Policy, 1984—, Am. Sch. Tangiers, 1979-89, Ocean Rsch. and Edn. Soc., 1980-85, Coalition for Nat. Svc., 1986—; Coun. Econ. Priorities, 1990-93, Hospice Care of D.C., 1990—; trustee Ind. Sector, 1980-84, 89—, chmn. govt. rels. com., 1989-92, vice chmn. bd., 1994—; trustee Com. for Nat. Security, 1983, chmn. bd., 1986-91; chair Lawyers Alliance for World Security, 1994—. Recipient Distinguished Pub. Service medal Dept. Def., 1966. Fellow Am Acad. Arts and Scis.; mem. Assn. Bar City of N.Y. (chmn. com. sci. and law 1984-87), Am Law Inst. (life), Hudson Inst., Internat. Inst. Strategic Studies, Inst. Medicine of NAS (charter mem., coun. 1970-77, com. on human rights 1978-89), Coun. on Fgn. Rels., Century Assn. (N.Y.C.), Hamilton St. Club (Balt.). Office: U Md Balt County 5401 Wilkens Ave Baltimore MD 21228

YARNALL, D. ROBERT, JR., entrepreneur, investor; b. Phila., Feb. 11, 1925; s. D. Robert and Elizabeth (Biddle) Y.; m. Rie Gabrielsen, June 24, 1954 (dec. Oct. 1980); children: Joan, Sara, Kristina; m. Anne Gates, July 3, 1982; stepchildren—Sarah, Michael, Amy Gates. B.M.E., Cornell U., 1948. Mech. engr. Westinghouse Electric Co., Phila., 1947; dir. relief mission to Poland Am. Friends Service Com., 1948-49; with Yarnall Waring Co. (name changed to Yarway Corp. 1965), Phila., 1949-86, v.p., 1957-62, pres., chief exec. officer, 1962-78, chmn. bd., 1968-86; founder, chmn. bd. Envirite Corp., Plymouth Meeting, Pa., 1975—; dir. James G. Biddle Co., Plymouth Meeting, Pa., 1957-78, chmn. bd., 1976-78; dir. Fed. Res. Bank of Phila., 1965-72, dep. chmn., 1971-72; dir. S.K.F. Industries, King of Prussia, Pa., Quaker Chem. Co., Phila., Meritor Fin. Group (PSFS), Keystone Internat. Inc., Houston; Cons. UN Indsl. Devel. Orgn. mission to Indonesia, 1968; exec.-in-residence on faculty Centre d'Etudes Industrielles, Geneva, Switzerland, 1971-72; Bd. dirs. World Affairs Council, Pa., 1957-61, 64-68, 74—, chmn. bd., 1978-80. Trustee Internat. House, Phila., chmn., 1972-76; trustee U. Pa., 1981—, Phila Art Mus., 1978—, Greater Phila. Partnership, 1975—; trustee St. John's Coll., Annapolis, Md., 1975-86, vice chmn., 1978-82; bd. dirs. Pa. Environ. Council, 1976—, WHYY, Phila., Greater Phila. First Corp., 1984-86, Chestnut Hill Hosp., 1986—. Served with Am. Field Service with Brit. Army, World War II. Mem. ASME, Chief Execs. Orgn. Clubs: Philadelphia, Union League, Divotee Golf (Phila.). Home: 6706 Springbank Ln Philadelphia PA 19119-3713 Office: Envirite Corp Plymouth Meeting PA 19462

YARNELL, JEFFREY ALAN, regional credit executive; b. Columbus, Ohio, Oct. 23, 1941; s. Russell Lester and Grace Wilma (Adams) Y.; m. Carroll Ginevra Meier, July 6, 1982; children: Natalie, Brian. Student, Ohio State U., 1963. Cert. credit exec. Nat. Assn. Credit Mgmt. Teller Huntington Nat. Bank, Columbus, Ohio, 1965-66; credit mgr. janitrol divsn. Midland Ross, Columbus, 1966-68; asst. credit mgr. Marlite divsn. Masonite, Dover, Ohio, 1968-72; v.p., gen. credit mgr. wholesale fl. coverings Carson Pirie Scott, Chgo., 1972-88; regional credit mgr. Ga.-Pacific Corp., Des Plaines, Ill., 1988—; bd. dirs. Chgo.-Midwest Credit Mgmt. Assn., 1991-94. Author: Credit Manual, 1978. Advisor Jr. Achievement, Dover, Ohio, 1969-70; mem. Toastmasters Internat., Columbus, Ohio, 1965-67; councilor Boy Scouts Am., Palos Heights, Ill., 1980-81. With USNR, 1963-65. Mem. Chgo.-Midwest Credit Mgmt. Assn. (bd. dirs. 1991-94). Republican. Lutheran. Avocations: golf, skiing, chess, reading, stock market analysis, bowling. Office: Ga Pacific Corp 2350 E Devon Ave Ste 350 Des Plaines IL 60018

YARNELL, MICHAEL ALLAN, lawyer; b. Chgo., Sept. 10, 1944; s. Howard Winfred and Mary Elizabeth (Card) Y.; m. Karen Alice Hockenyos, June 12, 1971 (div. Mar. 1994); children: Sarah Munro, Jacob Rainey. BS, Ariz. State U., 1967; JD with honors, U. Ill., 1971. Bar: Ariz. 1971. Ptnr. Streich, Lang, Weeks & Cardon, Phoenix, 1971-91, also bd. dirs.; mem. Myers, Barnes & Jenkins, Phoenix, 1991; judge Maricopa County Superior Ct., Phoenix, 1991—. Author: Ins and Outs of Foreclosure, 1981, 8th edit., 1990; projects editor Law Rev. U. Ill. Law Forum, 1970. Chairperson Phoenix Children's Theatre, 1987. 1st lt. U.S. Army, 1971-72, Korea. Fellow Ariz. Bar Found.; mem. ABA, Maricopa Bar Assn., State Bar Ariz. (Outstanding Contbn. to Continuing Legal Edn. award 1988), Order of Coif, Phi Kappa Phi. Republican. Avocations: computers, small boat sailing, white water rafting. Office: Maricopa County Superior Ct 201 W Jefferson St Phoenix AZ 85003-2205

YARNELL, RICHARD ASA, anthropologist; b. Boston, May 11, 1929; s. Sidney Howe and Floy Mae (Wilson) Y.; m. Meredith Jean Black; children—Karen Lyn, Anne Chesson, William Sidney, Susan Lynn. Student, Tex. A&M Coll., 1946-47; B.S., Duke U., 1950; M.A., U. N.Mex., 1958; Ph.D., U. Mich., 1963. Mem. faculty Emory U., Atlanta, 1962-71, asso. prof., 1967-71; mem. faculty U. N.C., Chapel Hill, 1971—, prof. anthropology, 1975—. Contbr. papers, reports to profl. jours., books. With USAF, 1951-55. Fellow AAAS; mem. Soc. for Econ. Botany, Soc. Ethnobiology, Southeastern Archaeol. Conf., Soc. Am. Archaeology (Fryxell medal 1992). Office: U North Carolina Dept Anthropology Clb # 3115 Chapel Hill NC 27514

YAROSEWICK, STANLEY J., academic administrator, physicist; b. Epping, N.H., Sept. 10, 1939. BS, U. N.H. 1961; MS, Clarkson Coll. Tech., 1963, PhD in Physics, 1966. Asst. prof. physics Clarkson Coll. Tech., Potsdam, N.Y., 1966-69, assoc. prof. physics, 1969-74; prof. physics West Chester (Pa.) Univ., 1974-87, v.p. acad. affairs, provost, 1987-94, interim pres., 1991-92; pres. Keene (N.H.) State Coll., 1994—. Mem. Am. Assn. Physics Tchrs., Am. Assn. State Colls. and Univs. Office: Keene State Coll Keene NH 03431

YAROWSKY, JONATHAN R., lawyer; b. Kansas City, Mo., May 23, 1949. AB summa cum laude, U. Mich., 1971; MS, Cornell U., 1974; JD, UCLA, 1977. Teaching instr. Cornell U., Ithaca, N.Y., 1972-74; assoc. Fed. Pub. Defender's Office, L.A., 1975, Rosenfeld, Meyer & Susman, Beverly Hills, Calif., 1976, Covington & Burling, 1977-82; majority counsel Subcom. on Econ. and Comml. Law, Washington, 1982-90; gen. counsel House Com. on Judiciary, Washington, 1991—. Chief comment editor UCLA Law Rev., 1977. Mem. Phi Beta Kappa. Office: Judiciary 2138 Rayburn House Ofc Buil Washington DC 20515

YARROW, PETER, folksinger; b. N.Y.C., May 31, 1938. B.A., Cornell U. Mem. group, Peter, Paul and Mary, from 1962, 78—, also solo performer, recording artist, Warner Bros.; albums with Peter, Paul and Mary include: Peter Paul and Mary-Moving, In the Wind, In Concert, A Song Will Rise, See What Tomorrow Brings, Peter Paul and Mary Album, Album 1700, Late Again, Peter Paul & Mommy, 10 Years Together The Best Of, Reunion, 1978, Peter, Paul & Mommy, No Easy Walk to Freedom, 1987, Too, 1993 (Emmy nominee 1993); solo album: Peter, 1972, That's Enough for Me, 1963 (Grammy award 1963), Hard Times, 1975, Love Songs, 1975; on Broadway appearance: Peter, Paul and Mary "From Bleecker to Broadway", 1986. Bd. dirs. Newport Folk Found., Kerrville (Tex.) Folk Festival, Ctr. for Global Edn., Augsberg Coll. Recipient Emmy nominee for "Puff the Magic Dragon", 1979, Citizen Action Leadership award, Vista, 1979, Alfred Lowenstein award, 1982, Hospice Care of R.I. award, 1987, Nat. Emergency Civil Liberties Com. award, 1988, Interlochen Disting. Alumnus Arts award, 1992, Conn. Hospice award, 1993, Grammy award for prodr. Peter Paul & Mommy, too, 1994, Kate Wolf Meml. award for the World Folk Music Assn., 1994. *

YARWOOD, DEAN LESLEY, political science educator; b. Decorah, Iowa, Mar. 17, 1935; s. Harold Nicholas and Elsie Mabel (Roney) Y.; m. Elaine Delores Bender, Sept. 2, 1956; children: Lucinda, Kent, Keith, Douglas, Dennis. BA, Iowa U., 1957; MA, Cornell U., 1961; PhD, U. Ill., 1966. Tchr. social studies, acting jr. high prin. Mid-Prairie Community Sch., Wellman, Iowa, 1957-59; asst. prof. Coe Coll., Cedar Rapids, Iowa, 1963-66, U. Ky., Lexington, 1966-67; asst. prof. U. Mo., Columbia, 1967-70, assoc. prof., 1970-78, prof., 1978—, dir. grad. studies dept. polit. sci., 1970-72, 88, 94—, chmn. dept. polit. sci., 1988-91, Frederick A. Middlebush prof. polit. sci., 1992-95. Editor: The National Administrative System: Selected Readings, 1971, Public Administration, Politics, and the People: Selected Readings for Managers, Employees and Citizens, 1987; author, co-author

numerous articles in polit. sci. jours. Recipient Bradish Meml. scholarship, 1953-57, Iowa Merit scholarship, 1956-57, Woodrow Wilson fellowship, 1959-60, James Garner fellowship, 1961-62, Woodrow Wilson Dissertation fellowship, 1962-63. Mem. Am. Soc. Pub. Adminstrn. (chmn. sect. on pub. administrn. edn. 1986-87, publs. com. 1986-89), Am. Polit. Sci. Assn., Midwest Polit. Sci. Assn., So. Polit. Sci. Assn., Mo. Polit. Sci. Assn. (v.p. 1990-91, pres. 1991-92), Mo. Inst. for Pub. Administrn. (coun. 1976-77, v.p. 1977-78, pres. 1978-79), Cen. Mo. Chpt. of Am. Soc. Pub. Administrn. (coun. 1979-80, pres. 1978-79), ex-officio mem. coun. 1981-83), Phi Beta Kappa. Home: 304 Mumford Dr Columbia MO 65203-0230 Office: U Mo Dept Polit Sci 314 Professional Bldg Columbia MO 65211

YARYMOVYCH, MICHAEL IHOR, manufacturing company executive; b. Bialystok, Poland, Oct. 13, 1933; came to U.S., 1951, naturalized, 1956; s. Nicholas Joseph and Olga (Kruczowy) Y.; m. Roxolana Abramiuk, Nov. 21, 1951; children—Tatiana, Nicholas. B.Aero. Engring., NYU, 1955; M.S. in Engring. Mechanics, Columbia U., 1956, D. Engring. Sci., 1969. Dep. asst. sec. research and devel. U.S. Air Force, Washington, 1967-70; dir. AGARD, NATO, Paris, 1970-73; chief scientist U.S. Air Force, 1973-75; asst. administr. field ops. ERDA, 1975-77; v.p. engring. N.Am. aerospace ops. Rockwell Internat. Corp., Seal beach, Calif., 1977-81; v.p. advanced systems devel. Rockwell Internat. Corp., El Segundo, Calif., 1981-86, v.p., assoc. dir. Sys. Devel. Ctr., 1986—; mem. Air Force Sci. Adv. Bd., 1990—; chmn. NATO Adv. Group for Aerospace R&D, 1994—; cons. in field. Author papers in field. Translator Russian books and periodicals. Recipient Exceptional Civilian Svc. award Dept. Air Force, 1968, 73, 75, 94, Disting. Svc. award ERDA, 1977; Guggenheim fellow, 1956-58. Fellow AIAA (dir., pres., gen. chmn. ann. meeting 1978); mem. Air Force Assn., Nat. Mgmt. Assn., Nat. Security Industries Assn., AAAS, Am. Astronautical Soc., Aerospace Industry Assn., Internat. Acad. Astronautics (v.p. sci. programs). Office: Rockwell Internat Sys Devel Ctr 2800 Westminster Ave Seal Beach CA 90740-5606

YASHER, MICHAEL, accountant; b. United, Pa., Aug. 17, 1928; s. Michael and Mary (Sasik) Y.; m. Margaret Jean Wallace, June 23, 1956 (dec. July 12, 1987); 1 child, Michael. BS, Penn State U., 1956; diploma, Air Command & Staff Coll., 1972, Nat. Defense U., 1977; MA, Ctrl. Mich. U., 1983. CPA, Washington; cert. profl. contract mgr., Washington. Area and audit mgr. U.S. Gen. Acctg. Office, Washington, 1956-84; auditor Haskins & Sells, CPAs, Phila., 1956; acct. to the comptroller U.S. Air Materials Command, 1979-83; acct., cons. E. K. Williams Co., Lanham, Md., 1985—. Contbr. numerous papers and articles to profl. publs. Treas. Boy Scouts of Am., Rockville, Md., 1970s; bd. dirs. Sr. Softball Assn. Montgomery County, Md., 1992-94; pres. Leisure World (Md.) Billiards Club, 1994. Col. USAF, 1948-88. Recipient Bronze medal for softball Md. Sr. Olympics, 1992, 1994, Gold medal, 1994, Silver medal for volleyball, Meritorious Svc. award U.S.G.A.O., 1975, Data Systems Design Ctr. Outstanding Officer Mobilization Augmentee, 1978. Mem. AICPA, Res. Officers Assn., Billiards Club. Democrat. Roman Catholic. Avocations: coin collecting, sports. Home: 15107 Interlachen Dr Silver Spring MD 20906-5625 Office: E K Williams Co 1700 Elton Rd Silver Spring MD 20903

YASHON, DAVID, neurosurgeon, educator; b. Chgo., May 13, 1935; s. Samuel and Dorothy (Cutler) Y.; children—Jaclyn, Lisa, Steven. B.S. in Medicine, U. Ill., 1958, M.D., 1960. Diplomate Am. Bd. Neurol. Surgery. Intern U. Ill., 1961, resident, 1961-64, asst. in neuroanatomy, 1960; clin. instr. neurosurgery U. Chgo., 1965-66; asst. prof. neurosurgery Case Western Res U., Cleve., 1966-69; assoc. prof. neurosurgery Ohio State U., Columbus, 1969-74, prof., 1974-89, prof. emeritus, 1989—; mem. staff St. Ann's Hosp., Children's Hosp., Park Med. Ctr.; cons. Med. Research and Devel. Command, U.S. Army; mem. Neurology B Study Sect NIH. Author: Spinal Injury; contbr. articles to med. jours. Served as capt. U.S. Army, 1960-68. Fellow Royal Coll. Surgeons Can. (cert.), A.C.S.; mem. AMA, Am. Physiol. Soc., Congress Neurol. Surgeons, Am. Assn. Anatomists, Canadian, Ohio neurosurg. socs., Am. Assn. Neurol. Surgeons, Research Soc. Neurol. Surgeons, Acad. Medicine Columbus and Franklin County, Soc. for Neurosci., Soc. Univ. Surgeons, Am. Acad. Neurology, Assn. for Acad. Surgery, Am. Acad. Neurol. Surgery, Am. Assn. for Surgery of Trauma, Central Surg. Soc., Ohio Med. Soc., Columbus Surg. Soc., Sigma Xi, Alpha Omega Alpha. Office: Park Med Ctr 1492 E Broad St Ste 121 Columbus OH 43205-1500

YASINSKY, JOHN BERNARD, nuclear scientist; b. Shenandoah, Pa., June 10, 1939; s. Joseph and Helen Y.; m. Marlene A. Tuladziecki, Apr. 28, 1962; children: Diane L., Karen A., Mark J. B.S. in Physics, Wheeling (W.Va.) Coll., 1961; M.S., U. Pitts., 1963; Ph.D in Nuclear Sci, Carnegie Mellon U., 1966. Scientist, sr. scientist, then mgr. electric systems and plant analysis Westinghouse Bettis Lab., Pitts., 1963-71; White House fellow, spl. asst. to sec. U.S. Dept. Commerce, Washington, 1971-72; mgr. bus. devel. breeder reactor divs. Westinghouse Corp., Pitts., 1973-74, mgr. mktg. advanced reactors div., 1974-75, dir. dept. advanced coal conversion, 1975-77; pres. Westinghouse Hanford Co., Richland, Wash., 1979-80; gen. mgr. advanced power systems divs. Westinghouse Electric Corp., Pitts., after 1980, then pres. Europe, Africa and Middle East; evening instr. nuclear engring. div. Carnegie Mellon U., 1966-72; Bd. dirs. Wheeling Coll., 1981, Wash. State Council Econ. Edn., 1979-80, Tri-City Nuclear Industry Council, 1979-80, Kadlec Med. Center, 1979-80; mem. adv. com. Wash. State Joint Grad. Center, 1979-80, Hanford Energy Center, 1979-80; mem. steering com. Wash. State Energy Council, 1979-80. Contbr. over 50 articles to profl. jours. Mem. Am. Nuclear Soc., Nat. Security Indsl. Assn., White House Fellows Assn., Atomic Indsl. Forum. Club: Pitts. Field. Office: Westinghouse Nuclear Ctr PO Box 355 Pittsburgh PA 15230-0355

YASSIN, ROBERT ALAN, museum administrator, curator; b. Malden, Mass., May 22, 1941; s. Harold Benjamin and Florence Gertrude (Hoffman) Y.; m. Marilyn Kramer, June 9, 1963; children: Fredric Giles, Aaron David. BA (Rufus Choate scholar), Dartmouth Coll., 1962; postgrad., Boston U., 1962-63; M.A., U. Mich., 1965, postgrad. (Samuel H. Kress Found. fellow), 1968-70, Ph.D. candidate, 1970; postgrad (Ford Found. fellow), Yale U., 1966-68. Asst. to dir. Mus. Art U. Mich., 1965-66, asst. dir., 1970-72, asso. dir., 1972-73, acting dir., 1973, instr. dept. history of art, 1970-73; co-dir. Joint Program in Mus. Trng., 1970-73; chief curator Indpls. Mus. Art, 1973-75, 87-89, acting dir., 1975, dir., 1975-89; exec. dir. Tucson Mus. Art, 1990—; adj. prof. Herron Sch. Art Ind. U./Purdue U., 1975-89. Contbr. to mus. publications. Mem. Ariz. Hist. Soc., Ariz. Mus. Assn., Tucson Mus. Assn., Tucson Arts Coalition., Tucson Downtown Adv. Coun. Mem. Am. Assn. Mus. (bd. dirs. Internat. Coun. Mus. 1986-89), Assn. Art Mus. Dirs., Coll. Art Assn. Am., Intermus. Conservation Assn. (chmn. exec. com. 1977-78), Tucson C. of C. (cultural affairs com., econ. devel. com.), Nat. Trust Historic Preservation, Rotary. Jewish. Home: 3900 N Calle Casita Tucson AZ 85718-5873 Office: Tucson Mus Art 140 N Main Ave Tucson AZ 85701-8290

YASSKY, LESTER, lawyer, banker; b. N.Y.C., July 19, 1941; s. Leo and Ida (Tauss) Y.; m. Harriet Anne Rose, June 30, 1963; children—David, Evan, Rachel. B.A., Columbia U., 1963; LL.B., Harvard U., 1966. Bar: N.Y. 1967. Assoc. Shea & Gould, N.Y.C., 1966-75; ptnr. Shea & Gould, 1975-90; sec. Toys "R" Us, Inc., Paramus, N.J., 1978-90; sr. v.p., gen. counsel Dai-Ichi Kangko Bank, Ltd., 1990—. Mem. ABA, N.Y.C. Bar Assn., N.Y. State Bar Assn., Phi Beta Kappa. Democrat. Avocations: sports; travel. Office: Dai-Ichi Kangko Bank Ltd 1 World Trade Ctr New York NY 10048-0202

YASTRZEMSKI, CARL MICHAEL, former baseball player, public relations executive; b. Southampton, N.Y., Aug. 22, 1939; m. Carolann Casper, Jan. 30, 1960. Student, Notre Dame U.; B.S. in Bus. Administrn. Merrimack Coll. Second baseman, shortstop Raleigh (N.C.), Carolina League, 1959; outfielder Mpls. (Am. Assn.), 1960; left fielder Boston Red Sox (Am. League), 1961-83, cons., instr., 1983—; with Eaton Vance Company, Boston, 1968—, Kahn's & Co. (subs. Sara Lee Corp.), Cincinnati, 1978—. Chosen most valuable player Carolina League, 1959; chosen most valuable player Am. League, 1967; inducted into Baseball Hall of Fame, 1989. Mem. Am. League All-Star Team, 1963, 65-77, 79, 83. Office: Eaton Vance Corp 24 Federal St Fl 5 Boston MA 02110-2507*

YASUDA, HIROTSUGU KOGE, chemical engineering professor; b. Kyoto, Japan, Mar. 24, 1930; s. Mitsuo and Kei (Niwa) Y.; m. Gerda Lisbeth Schmidtke, Apr. 6, 1968; children: Ken Eric, Werner Akira, Lisbeth Kay. BSChemE, Kyoto U., 1953; MS in Polymer Chemistry, SUNY, Syracuse, 1959, PhD in Polymer and Phys. Chemistry, 1961. Rsch. assoc. Ophthalmic Plastic Lab., Mass. Eye & Ear Infirmary, Boston, 1962-63; head biomaterial sect. eye rsch. Cedar-Sinai Med. Ctr., L.A., 1963-65; vis. scientist Royal Inst. Tech., Stockholm, 1965-66; sr. chemist Rsch. Triangle Inst., Rsch. Triangle Pk., N.C., 1966-72, mgr. Polymer Rsch. Lab., 1972-78; prof. chem. engring. U. Mo., Rolla, 1978-88, dir. Thin Films Inst., 1974-88; prof. chem. engring. U. Mo., Columbia, 1988—, chmn. dept., 1988-90, dir. Ctr. for Surface and Plasma Techs., 1989—. Author: Plasma Polymerization, 1985. Home: 1004 Lake Point Ln Columbia MO 65203-2900 Office: U Mo Ctr for Surface Sci and Plasma Tech Columbia MO 65211

YATES, ALBERT CARL, university administrator, chemistry educator; b. Memphis, Sept. 29, 1941; s. John Frank and Sadie L. (Shell) Y.; m. Ann Young; children: Steven, Stephanie, Aerin Alessandra. B.S., Memphis State U., 1965; Ph.D. Ind. U., 1968. Research assoc. U. So. Calif., Los Angeles, 1968-69; prof. chemistry Ind. U., Bloomington, 1969-74; v.p. research, grad. dean U. Cin., 1974-81; exec. v.p., provost, prof. chemistry Washington State U., Pullman, 1981-90; pres. Colo. State U., Fort Collins, 1990—; chancellor Colo. State U. System, Fort Collins, 1990—; mem. grad. record exam. bd. Princeton (N.J.) U., 1977-80, undergrad. assessment program council, 1977-81; cons. NRC, 1975-82, Office End., HEW, 1978-80; mem. exec. council acad. affairs NASULGC, 1983-87, ACE, 1983-87,. nat adv. council gen. med. scis. NIH, 1987—. Contbr.: research articles to Jour. Chem. Physics; research articls to Phys. Rev.; research articles to Jour. Physics, Phys. Rev. Letters, Chem. Physics Letters. Served with USN, 1959-62. Recipient univ. and State honors and awards. Mem. Am. Phys. Soc., Am. Chem. Soc., AAAS, Nat. Assn. State Univs. and Land Grant Colls. (mem. exec. council academic affairs), Am. Council Edn. (mem. exec. com. academic affairs), Sigma Xi, Phi Lambda Upsilon. Home: 1744 Hillside Dr Fort Collins CO 80524-1965 Office: Colo State U 102 Administration Bldg Fort Collins CO 80523

YATES, BROCK WENDEL, editor, journal; b. Buffalo, N.Y., Oct. 21, 1933; s. Raymond Francis and Marguerite (Wendel) Y.; m. Sally Kingsley, June 13, 1955 (div. 1978); children: Brock Jr., Daniel, Claire; m. Pamela Reynolds Russomanno, Feb. 18, 1978; stepchildren: Sean, Stacy. B.A. Hobart Coll., 1955. Editor Car and Driver Mag., N.Y.C., 1964-66; sr. editor Car and Driver Mag., Wyoming, N.Y., 1966—; writer TV documentaries, 1976—. Author: Decline and Fall of the American Automobile Industry, 1982, Enzo Ferrari, The Man, The Cars, the Races, 1990, Sunday Driver, 1972, (motion picture screenplays) Smokey and the Bandit II, Cannonball Run; columnist Boating Mag., 1990-93; contbr. numerous articles to profl. jours. Lt. USN, 1955-60. Recipient Ken Purdy award Internat. Motor Press Assn., 1976, Mobility award Nat. Auto Dealers Assn., 1987, Ace award Cable TV Acad., 1988, Journalism Excellence award, Detroit Press Club, 1993. Mem. Kappa Alpha Soc. Republican. Protestant. Avocations: boating, travel, golf, motor racing. Home: Farmstead Rt 19 Wyoming NY 14591 Office: Car and Driver Mag 2002 Hogback Rd Ann Arbor MI 48105-9732

YATES, CHARLES RICHARDSON, former arts center executive; b. Atlanta, Sept. 9, 1913; s. Presley Daniel and Julia (Richardson) Y.; m. Dorothy Malone May 20, 1944; children: Dorothy Y. Kirkley, Charles R., Sarah F. (Mrs. Michael Baker), J. Comer. B.S. with honors, Ga. Inst. Tech., 1935. With 1st Nat. Bank Atlanta, 1935-47, asst. v.p., 1940-47; with Joshua L. Baily & Co., Inc., Atlanta, 1947-60; v.p. Joshua L. Baily & Co., Inc., 1956-60; v.p. finance Atlantic Coast Line R.R. Co. and L. & N. R.R. Co., 1960-67; v.p. Seaboard Coast Line R.R. Co., 1967-71, v.p. finance, 1971-73; v.p. finance L. & N. R.R. Co., 1967-73; pres. Atlanta Arts Alliance, 1973-83; trustee Profile Fund I, Sacramento; dir. Technology Park/Atlanta. Trustee Ga. Tech. Found., Woodruff Arts Ctr. Served with AUS, 1943-46. Mem. Ga. C. of C. (dir., pres. 1965-67). Episcopalian. Clubs: Augusta (Ga.) Nat. (sec.); Atlanta Athletic (Atlanta), Peachtree Golf (Atlanta), Capital City (Atlanta); Royal and Ancient Golf (St. Andrews, Scotland).

YATES, DAVID JOHN C., chemist, researcher; b. Stoke-on-Trent, Staffordshire, Eng., Feb. 13, 1927; came to U.S., 1958; s. Eric John and Beatrice Victoria (Street) Y.; m. Natalie Chmelnitsky, June 22, 1983. B.S. with honors, U. Birmingham, U.K., 1949; Ph.D. U. Cambridge, Eng., 1955, Sc.D., 1968. Rsch physicist Kodak Labs., Wealdstone, London, 1949-50; rsch. chemist Brit. Ceramic Rsch. Assn., Stoke-on-Trent, 1950-51; rsch. assoc. dept. colloid sci. U. Cambridge, 1951-58; lectr. Sch. Mines and dept. chemistry Columbia U., N.Y.C., 1958-60; sr. rsch. fellow Nat. Phys. Lab., Teddington, U.K., 1960-61; rsch. assoc. corp. labs. Exxon Rsch. and Engring., Annandale, N.J., 1961-86; rsch. prof. dept. of chem. engring. Lafayette Coll., Easton, Pa., 1986-87; rsch. prof. dept. materials sci. Rutgers U., Piscataway, N.J., 1987-88; cons. San Diego, 1988—. Contbr. over 70 articles to profl. jours., chpts. to books; 13 U.S. patents, numerous fgn. patents. Fellow Inst. of Physics (U.K.), Royal Soc. Chemistry (U.K.), N.Y. Catalysis Club (chmn. 1966-67). Club: N.Y. Catalysis (chmn. 1965-66). Avocations: photography, bicycling, gliding, travel, sports cars.

YATES, ELLA GAINES, library consultant; b. Atlanta, June 14, 1927; d. Fred Douglas and Laura (Moore) Gaines; m. Joseph L. Sydnor (dec.); 1 child, Jerri Gaines Sydnor Lee; m. Clayton R. Yates (dec.). A.B., Spelman Coll., Atlanta, 1949; M.S. in L.S. Atlanta U., 1951; J.D., Atlanta Law Sch., 1979. Asst. br. librarian Bklyn. Pub. Library, 1951-54; head children's dept. Orange (N.J.) Pub. Library, 1956-59; br. librarian E. Orange (N.J.) Pub. Library, 1960-69; med. librarian Orange Meml. Hosp., 1967-69; asst. dir. Montclair (N.J.) Pub. Library, 1970-72; dir. Atlanta-Fulton Pub. Library, 1972-76, dir., 1976-81; dir. learning resource ctr. Seattle Opportunities Industrialization Ctr., 1982-84; asst. dir. adminstrn. Friendship Force, Atlanta, 1984-86; state librarian Commonwealth of Va., 1986-90; library cons. Price Waterhouse, 1991; adv. bd. Library of Congress Center for the Book, 1977-83; cons. in field; vis. lectr. U. Wash., Seattle, 1981-83; mem. Va. Records Adv. Bd., 1986-90; mem. Nagara Exec. Bd., 1987-91. Contbr. to profl. jours. Vice chmn. N.J. Women's Coun. on Human Rels., 1957-59; chmn. Friends Fulton County Jail, 1973-81; bd. dirs. United Cerebral Palsy Greater Atlanta, Inc., 1979-81 Coalition Against Censorship, Washington, 1981-84, YMCA Met. Atlanta, 1979-81, Exec. Women's Network, 1979-82, Freedom To Read Found., 1979-85, Va. Black History Mus., Richmond, 1990-91; sec., exec. dir. Va. Libr. Found. Bd., 1986-90. Recipient Meritorious award Alfanta U., 1977, Phoenix award City of Atlanta, 1980, Serwa award Nat. Coalition 100 Black Women, 1989, Black Caucus award, 1989, Disting. Svc. award Clark-Atlanta U., 1991, Ednl. Support Svc. award Tuskegee Airmen, 1993; named Profl. Woman of Yr. NAACP, N.J., 1972, Outstanding Chum of Yr., 1976, Outstanding Alumni Spelman Coll., 1977. Mem. ALA (exec. bd. 1977-83, commn. freedom and access to info.), NAACP, Southeastern Libr. Assn., Nat. Assn. Govt. Archives and Records Adminstrn. (exec. bd. 1987-91), Delta Theta Phi, Delta Sigma Theta. Baptist. Home and Office: 1171 Oriole Dr SW Atlanta GA 30311-2424

YATES, ELTON G., retired petroleum industry executive; b. Slidell, La., July 31, 1935; s. Elton O. and Leona E. (Sollberger) Y.; m. Jo Ellen Levy, Apr. 11, 1955; children—Sherlyn, Michele, Steven. B.S. in Petroleum Engring, La. State U., 1957. Petroleum engr. Texaco Inc., various locations, 1957-68; dist. engr. Texaco Inc., Corpus Christi, Tex., 1968-70; div. devel. engr. Texaco Inc., Houston, 1970-71; coordinator joint ops. Texaco Inc., N.Y.C., 1971-75; pres., gen. mgr. Texaco Iran, London, 1975-77; asst. gen. mgr. producing Eastern Hemisphere Texaco Inc., N.Y.C., 1977-78; gen. mgr. producing Harrison, N.Y., 1978-79, corp. v.p., dept. head producing, 1979-82; div. pres. Texaco Oil Trading and Supply, 1981-82; pres. Texaco Middle East/Far East, 1982-84, Texaco Latin Am./West Africa, 1984-87; corp. sr. v.p. Texaco Inc., White Plains, N.Y., 1987-94, ret., 1994; bd. dirs. wholly owned Texaco Inc. Co. subs., Coast Guard Found.; former dir. Arabian Am. Oil Co.; dir. Caltex Corp. and Anncessas. Mem. dean's adv. coun. Coll Engring. La. State U. Elected to La. State U. Coll. Engring. Hall of Distinction. Mem. Soc. Petroleum Engrs. of AIME, 25 Yr. Club of Petroleum Industry, Country Club of N.C., Country Club of Darien (Conn.), Country Club of Pinehurst (N.C.), Phi Epsilon Tau. Methodist.

YATES, JEFFREY MCKEE, trade association executive; b. N.Y.C., Feb. 18, 1948; s. Richard George Yates and Marie Rose (McKee) Correll; m. Lauran Boakes, July 1, 1972; children: Christopher, Matthew, Alison. B.A. in History, Yale U., 1971; J.D., Nat. Law Ctr. George Washington U., 1974. Bar: N.J. 1974, Fla. 1975, N.Y. 1976. Assoc. Boakes, Lindsay & Smith, Woodbury, N.J., 1974-75; asst. gen. counsel Ind. Ins. Agents of Am. Inc., N.Y.C., 1975-78; gen. counsel Ind. Ins. Agents of Am. Inc., N.Y.C., 1978-81; exec. v.p., gen. counsel Ind. Ins. Agents of Am. Inc., Alexandria, Va., 1981—. Mem. Fla. Bar Assn., Am. Soc. Assn. Execs. Home: 4207 Kimbrelee Ct Alexandria VA 22309-3000 Office: Ind Ins Agts of Am Inc 127 S Peyton St Alexandria VA 22314-2803

YATES, JERE EUGENE, business educator, management consultant; b. Memphis, Apr. 4, 1941; s. Emmett Eugene and Naomi Christine (Whitfield) Y.; m. Carolyn Kay Hall, June 8, 1962; children: Camille, Kevin, Brian. BA, Harding U., 1963, MTh, 1964, 1966; PhD, Boston U., 1968. Instr. Harding U., Searcy, Ark., 1967-69; prof. bus. Pepperdine U., Malibu, Calif., 1969—; cons. Hughes Aircraft Co., L.A., 1973—, Allied-Signal Corp., North Hollywood, Calif., 1985-90, Pacific Physican Svcs., 1988—. Author: Managing Stress, 1979 (membership book award, 1979); contbr. articles to profl. jours. Mem. AAUP, Acad. Mgmt., UCP/Spastic Children's Found. (bd. dirs., exec. com.), Westlake Tennis and Swim Club, North Ranch Country Club. Republican. Mem. Ch. of Christ. Office: Pepperdine U Malibu CA 90263

YATES, JOHN MELVIN, diplomat; b. Superior, Mont., Nov. 25, 1939; s. Leon Glen and Violet May (McPheeters) Y.; m. Peggy Maureen Simpson, Mar. 26, 1961 (dec. Apr. 1986); children: Catherine Diener, John Simpson, Maureen Cole, Paul Marion, Leon Gregory; m. Mary Barbara Carlin, Jan. 30, 1988. A.B. Stanford U., 1961; M.A., Fletcher Sch. Law and Diplomacy, 1962, M.A.L.D., 1963, Ph.D., 1972. Fgn. service officer U.S. Dept. State, Washington, 1964—, Algiers, Algeria, 1964-66, Blantyre, Malawi, 1967-68, Bamako, Mali, 1969-71, New Delhi, India, 1973-75, Ankara, Turkey, 1975-77, Libreville, Gabon, 1977-80, Washington, 1971-73, 80-82; U.S. amb. to Republic of Cape Verde, 1983-86; counselor for Polit. Affairs, Manila, Philippines, 1986-89; dep. chief of mission Lagos, Nigeria, 1989-91; dep. chief of mission Kinshasa, Zaire, 1991-93, chief of mission, 1993—. Recipient Presdl. award for sustained superior accomplishment in conduct of fgn. policy. Mem. Am. Fgn. Service Assn. Disciple of Christ. Office: Am Embassy Unit 31550 APO AE 09828

YATES, JOHN THOMAS, JR., chemistry educator, researcher; b. Winchester, Va., Aug. 3, 1935; s. John Thomas and Kathryn (Barnett) Y.; m. Kerin Joyce Narbut, Oct. 18, 1958; children: Geoffrey, Nathan. BS, Juniata Coll., 1956; PhD, MIT, 1960. Asst. prof. chemistry Antioch Coll., Yellow Springs, Ohio, 1960-63; NRC fellow, research chemist Nat. Bur. Standards, Washington, 1963-82; R.K. Mellon prof. chemistry U. Pitts., 1982—, dir. Surface Sci. Ctr., 1982—; co-dir. materical rsch. U. Pitts., 1994. Co-author: The Surface Scientist's Guide to Organometallic Chemistry, 1987; co-editor: Vibrational Spectroscopy of Molecules on Surfaces, 1987, Chemical Perspectives of Microelectronic Materials, Vol. 131; assoc. editor: Studies in Surface Science and Catalysis, 1986; series editor: Methods of Surface Characterization, 1987; bd. editors Ann. Rev. Phys. Chemistry, 1983-85, Jour. Phys. Chemistry, 1983-88, Jour. Chem. Physics, Jour. Catalysis, Chem. Revs., Langmuir, Surface Sci., Applications of Surface Sci., Accounts Chem. Rsch.; co-editor Langmuir; contbr. revs. and articles to profl. jours.; inventor desorption spectrometer, 1981. Recipient Silver medal Dept. Commerce-Nat. Bur. Standards, 1973, Stratton award, 1981, Pres.' Disting. rsch. award U. Pitts., 1989, Proctor and Gamble award, 1989, Von Humboldt Sr. Rsch. award, 1994; Sherman Fairchild Disting. scholar Calif. Inst. Tech., 1977-78. Fellow Am. Phys. Soc. (bd. dirs. divsn. chem. physics 1991—, chmn. divsn. chem. physics 1989), Am. Vacuum Soc. (chmn. surface sci. divsn. 1973, 92, trustee 1975, bd. dirs. 1982-85, M.W. Welch award 1994); mem. Am. Chem. Soc. (chmn. divsn. colloid and surface chemistry, Langmuir lectr. 1979, Kendall award in colloid of surface chemistry 1986, Morley prize Cleve. chpt. 1990, Peter Debye lectr. Cornell U. 1993, von Humboldt Sr. Rsch. award 1995). Office: U Pitts Surface Sci Ctr Dept Chemistry Pittsburgh PA 15260

YATES, KATHLEEN BARRETT, newspaper executive; b. Washington, July 28, 1954; d. William Kirby and Beatrice Mabel (Robinson) Y.; m. Peter Andrew Troop, July 6, 1986; children: Jay Robinson, Tora Ballad. BA, Trinity Coll., 1976; MBA, Stanford U., 1981. Economist Gordian Assocs., Washington, 1976-79; asst. to pub. San Jose (Calif.) Mercury News, 1981-82, dir. fin., 1982-86, sr. v.p., gen. mgr., 1988—; asst. to pres. Knight Ridder Inc., Miami, Fla., 1986-88. Trustee San Jose Repertory Theater, 1984-86, San Jose Mus. of Art, 1988-90, Sta. KTEH Pub. TV, San Jose, 1988—, Health Dimension, Inc., San Jose, 1989—. Recipient Twin award YWCA, 1985. Office: San Jose Mercury News 750 Ridder Park Dr San Jose CA 95190

YATES, KEITH, chemistry educator, writer; b. Preston, Eng., Oct. 22, 1928; came to Can., 1948; s. Harold and Elizabeth Ann (Wilson) Y.; m. Norma June Charter, Aug. 21, 1953; children: Alison, Robyn, Nicola. B.A., U. B.C., Vancouver, 1956, M.Sc., 1957, Ph.D., 1959; D.Phil., Oxford U., England, 1961. Asst. prof. U. Toronto, 1961-64, assoc. prof., 1964-68, prof., 1968-90, prof. emeritus, 1990—, asst. dean, 1967-70, chmn., 1974-85. Author: Huckel Molecular Orbital Theory, 1977, Graf Spee's Raiders, 1995; contbr. articles to profl. jours. Served with Royal Navy, 1946-48. Recipient Gen.'s Gold medal Gov. of B.C., 1956; Royal Soc. Can. fellow, 1984. Fellow Chem. Inst. Can. (recipient Syntex award 1984, Palladium medal 1991, Chem. Inst. Can. medal 1991). Avocations: bridge, naval history. Home: 536 Arbutus Dr, Mayne, BC Canada V0N 2J0 Office: U Toronto, Dept Chemistry, Toronto, ON Canada M5S 1A1

YATES, KEITH LAMAR, retired insurance company executive; b. Bozeman, Mont., Oct. 29, 1927; s. Thomas Bryan and Altha (Norris) Y.; m. Dolores Hensel, Aug. 30, 1948; children: Thomas A., Molly Yates McIntosh, Richard A., Nancy Yates Sands, Penny Dannielle Yates, Pamela Yates Beeler. BA, Eastern Wash. State U., 1953. Salesman Ancient Order United Workmen, Spokane, Wash., 1952-53, sales mgr., 1953-56, corp. sec., 1956-73; corp. sec. Neighbors of Woodcraft, Portland, Oreg., 1973-89, pres., 1989-92; ret., 1992. Author: Life of Willie Willey, 1966, The Fogarty Years, 1972, History of The Woodcraft Home, 1975, An Enduring Heritage, 1992. Pres. Wash. State Christian Mens Fellowship, Seattle, 1965-67; pres. Met. Area Assn. Christian Chs., 1981-83; mem. regional bd. Christian Chs. Oreg., 1990-94. Command sgt.-maj., ret., 1987; served with USN, USAF, USANG, 1946-87. Mem. Wash. State Frat. Cong., (cert. Commendation 1969, sec. 1957-68, pres., mem. exec. bd., chmn. conv. program advt. com. 1960-73), Oreg. State Frat. Cong. (Outstanding Frat. 1975-76, Spl. Appreciation award 1984, Frat. Family of Yr. 1986, sec. 1975-87, pres., mem. exec. bd. 1974—), Nat. Fraternal Congress Am. (conv. arrangement com. 1964, 90, publicity com. 1964, 65, 68, 90, credentials com 1970, 77, 78, pres. press & pub. rels. sec. 1971-72, pub. rels. com. 1973-74, chmn. 1972, co-chmn. press and pub. rels. frat. seminar 1972, frat. monitor com. 1974-75, mem. com. 1975-76, family life com. 1978-80, constitution com. 1980, pres. state frat. congs. sec. 1981-82, historian 1987—, Washington County's Disting. Patriot, 1988), Portland Ins. Acctg. and Statis. Soc. Assn. Records Mgrs. and Adminstrs. (Oreg. chpt.), Portland C. of C., Wash. Ins. Coun., Wash. Claims Assn., Seattle Underwriting Assn. Home: 29860 SW Buckhaven Rd Hillsboro OR 97123-8706

YATES, PETER, director, producer; b. Ewshoot, Surrey, England, July 24, 1929; s. Robert L. and Constance Yates; m. Virginia Pope; 3 children. Student, Royal Acad. of Dramatic Art. Entered film industry, 1956. Films directed: Summer Holiday, 1962, One Way Pendulum, 1964, Robbery, 1966, Bullitt, 1968, John and Mary, 1969, The Hot Rock, 1971, The Friends of Eddie Coyle,1972, for Pete's Sake, 1973, The Deep, 1976, Krull, 1982, Eleni, 1985, Suspect,1987, An Innocent Man, 1989; dir. producer Murphy's War, 1970, Mother, Jugs and Speed, 1975, Breaking Away, 1979 (nominated Acad. award 1980), Eyewitness, 1980, The Dresser, 1983 (nominated Acad. award 1984), The House on Carroll Street, 1988, Year of the Comet, 1991, Roommates, 1994. Mem. Acad. Motion Pictures Arts & Scis., Dirs. Guild Am., Garrick Club. Office: United Talent Agy 9560 Wilshire Blvd Beverly Hills CA 90212-1825*

YATES, ROBERT DOYLE, anatomy educator; b. Birmingham, Ala., Feb. 28, 1931; s. James William, Jr. and Mildred (Doyle) Y.; m. Jane Congleton, 1955; children: Robert Lee, Pamela C. BS, U. Ala., 1954, MS, 1956, PhD, 1959. Student anatomy dept. U. Ala., Birmingham, postdoctoral fellow, 1959-60; with U. Tex., Galveston, 1961-72; prof. anatomy Tulane U. Med. Sch., New Orleans, 1972—, chmn. dept. anatomy, 1972—; vis. investigator Harvard U. Med. Sch., Boston, 1962-63, Yale U. Med. Sch., New Haven, 1965-67. Mem. editorial bd.: Am. Jour. Anatomy, Anat. Record; contbr. articles to profl. jours. and chpts. to books. Vestryman Trinity Episc. Ch., Galveston, 1965-68; vestryman, jr. warden Trinity Episc. Ch., New Orleans, 1985-89, sr. warden, 1989-92. With inf. U.S. Army, 1960-61. Recipient numerous awards NIH, 1965-72, Research Career Devel. award, Golden Apple teaching award AMA Student Assn., 1971. Mem. Am. Assn. Anatomists (chmn. nominating com. 1980, sec.-treas. 1988—), Internat. Fedn. Assn. Anatomists (treas. 1989—), Assn. Anatomy Cell Biology and Neurobiology Chairpersons (sec.-treas. 1976—), Am. Soc. Cell Biology. Republican. Avocations: tennis, stained glass, beveled glass, hunting. Office: Tulane U Sch of Medicine 1430 Tulane Ave New Orleans LA 70112-2699

YATES, ROBERT LYNN, utilities executive; b. Kuttawa, Ky., May 17, 1947; s. Eugene and Lillie Mae (Thomas) Y.; m. Sally Marie Buckingham, Feb. 17, 1973; children: Jeffrey L., Robert Joseph. BS, Murray (Ky.) State U., 1969; MBA, So. Ill. U., Edwardsville, 1973. CPA, Tenn. Contr. TVA, Knoxville, 1982-87, v.p., treas., 1987—. Recipient Donald L. Scartlebury Meml. award Joint Fin. Mgmt. Improvement Program, 1991. Mem. AICPA, Assn. Govt. Accts. (pres. East Tenn. chpt. 1982-83, Employee of Yr. 1982), Knoxville C. of C., Beta Alpha Psi. Avocations: camping, hiking, gardening, reading. Office: TVA 400 W Summit Hill Dr Knoxville TN 37902-1415

YATES, ROBIN DAVID SEBASTIAN, Chinese history educator; b. Oxford, Eng., July 30, 1948; came to U.S., 1970; s. Joseph Ronald St. John and Mary Violet (Eliot) Y.; m. Grace Sieugit Fong, June 29, 1991. BA, Oxford U., 1970, MA, 1974; MA, U. Calif., Berkeley, 1975; PhD, Harvard U., 1980. Lectr. Harvard U., Cambridge, Mass., 1980-82, asst. prof., 1984-87, assoc. prof., 1987-88, Harris K. Weston assoc. prof. humanities, 1988-89; Burlington No. Found. prof. Asian studies Dartmouth Coll., Hanover, N.H., 1989-93, chair Asian studies program, 1992-93; prof. Chinese history McGill U., Montreal, Que., Can., 1993—, dir. Ctr. East Asian studies, 1993—, chair dept. East Asian studies, 1993—; cons. Nova, WGBH, Terra Nova TV, Discovery Channel, Project Emperor I, Voyager Co. Author: Washing Silk: The Life and Selected Poetry of Wei Chuang (834-910), 1988, (with W. Joseph Needham) Science and Civilization in China, Vol. 5, Part 6, 1995; mem. editl. bd. China Rev. Internat., 1993—. Fellow NEH, 1982-83, Am. Coun. Learned Socs., 1988-89, Com. on Scholarly Comm., People's Republic China NSF, 1992, Chiang Ching-Kuo Found., 1994—. Mem. Assn. for Asian Studies (pres. New Eng. regional conf. 1990-91, bd. dirs., chair China and Inner Asia Coun. 1991-93). Achievements include discovery of earliest representation of a gun in the world in Buddhist cave temple. Avocations: gardening, cooking. Office: McGill U Ctr East Asian Studies, 3434 McTavish, Montreal, PQ Canada H3A 1X9

YATES, RONALD WILBURN, air force officer; b. Memphis, Oct. 3, 1938; s. Mose Wilburn and Maggie Josephine (Dunehew) Y.; m. Constance Siegrist, July 2, 1960; children: Wade, Dawn, Kristen. BS, USAF Acad., 1960; MS, U. So. Calif., 1970; postgrad., Def. Sys. Mgmt. Coll., 1973, Indsl. Coll. Armed Forces, 1977. Commd. 2d lt. USAF, 1960, advanced through grades to gen., 1990; A-10 dir. devel. test. aero. systems div. USAF, Wright-Patterson AFB, Ohio, 1973-76; F-16 program element monitor USAF, Washington, 1977-79; F-15 system program dir. aero. systems div. USAF, Wright-Patterson AFB, 1980-81; comdr. aero. sys. div. 4950th Test Wing, Wright-Patterson AFB, 1981-83; F-16 system program dir. aero systems div. USAF, Wright-Patterson AFB, 1983-86; dir. tactical programs, then principle dep. Office Asst. Sec. Air Force Acquisition, 1986-90; comdr. Air Force Systems Command, Andrews AFB, Md., 1990-92; with Air Force Materiel Command, Wright-Patterson AFB, 1992—. Author: Lateral Directional Stability Roll Coupling, 1968. Decorated Legion of Merit with oak leaf cluster, DFC, Air medal with three oak leaf clusters, D.S.M. Mem. Air Force Assn., Order of Daedalians. Avocations: skiing; jogging. Office: HQ Air Force Materiel Command 4375 Chidlaw Rd Dayton OH 45433

YATES, SIDNEY RICHARD, congressman; lawyer; b. Chicago, Ill., Aug. 27, 1909; s. Louis and Ida (Siegel) Y.; m. Adeline Holleb, June 24, 1935; 1 child, Stephen R. Ph.B., U. Chgo., 1931, J.D., 1933. Bar: Ill. bar 1933. Practiced as sr. mem. Yates & Holleb; asst. atty. gen. Ill. State Bank Receiver, 1935-37; asst. atty. gen. attached to traction atty. Ill. Commerce Commn., 1937-40; mem. 80th-87th, 89th-104th Congresses from 9th Dist. Ill., 1949-62, 1965—; ranking minority mem. Appropriations subcoms. on the Interior; U.S. del. UN Trusteeship Council with rank of ambassador. Served to lt. USN, 1944-46. Mem. Am., Ill. State, Chgo. bar assns., Am. Vets. Com., Chgo. Council Fgn. Relations, Decalogue Soc. Lawyers. Democrat. Jewish. Clubs: City, Bryn Mawr Country. Office: US House of Reps 2109 Rayburn House Bldg Washington DC 20515-1309*

YATES, WALTER HARVEY, JR., career officer; b. Hattiesburg, Miss., Nov. 6, 1941; s. Walter Harvey and Mary (Mordica) Y.; m. Donna Jo Everett, Mar. 22, 1964; children: Walter III, Hope, Michelle. BS, U. So. Miss., 1963; MS, George Washington U., 1973; student, Naval Coll. Command and Staff, 1973, U.S. Army War Coll., 1983. Commd. 2d lt. U.S. Army, 1963, advanced through grades to maj. gen., 1992; rifle platoon leader Company A U.S. Army, Ft. Carson, Colo., 1963-64, anti-tank platoon leader, 1964; fixed wing aviator U.S. Army, Vietnam, 1965-66; flight instr. fixed wing br. dept. tactics Flight Aviation Sch. Regiment U.S. Army, Ft. Rucker, Ala., 1966-68; aircraft maintenance officer U.S. Army, Vietnam, 1968-69; comdr.hdqs. co. U.S. Army, Ft. Carson, 1970, with ops., 1970-72; with ops. U.S. Army, Ft. Hood, Tex., 1973-75, comdr. Troop A, 1975-76; logistics staff officer, then sr. exercise officer, plans and ops. divsn., Office Dep. Chief of Staff for Logistics U.S. Army Europe, 1976-78, aviation staff officer, Office Dep. Chief of Staff, Ops., comdr., 1979-82; dep. comdr. 6th cav. brigade Ft. Hood, 1983-84, comdr. Apache Tng. Brigade, 1984-85, comdr. 6th Cavalry Brigade, 1986-88; chief conventional plans divsn. The Joint Staff, Washington, 1988-89, dep. dir. ops. Nat. Mil. Commd. Ctr., 1989-90; ADC, 3d armored divsn. and comdr. Giessen Mil. Community U.S. Army Europe, 1990-91; commdg. gen. U.S. Army, Berlin, 1991—. Decorated Def. D.S.M., Legion of Merit with oak leaf cluster, Disting. Flying Cross, Bronze Star, Air medals, Master Army Aviator Badge. Roman Catholic. Avocations: golf, racquetball, horseback riding, hunting. Office: US Army Berlin Unit 26704 Box 430 APO AE 09235

YATSEVITCH, GRATIAN MICHAEL, retired army officer, diplomat, engineer; b. Kiev, Russia, Nov. 16, 1911; s. Michael Gratian and Margaret (Thomas) Y.; A.B., Harvard U., 1933, M.A., 1934, postgrad. (J.B. Woodworth fellow), 1935-40; m. Barbara Stewart Francis, July 2, 1973; children by previous marriage—Gael Yatsevitch McKibben, Peter, Kara, Gratian. Mining engr. Zlot Mines Ltd., also Beshina Gold Mines Ltd. of London in Yugoslavia, 1935-40, mgr. gold mine, 1936-40; commd. 2d lt. field arty.-U.S Army, 1933, advanced through grades to col., 1951; chief cannon and aircraft armament br. devel. prodn. cannon, Office of Chief of Ordnance, 1940-45; mil. attache, Moscow, 1945-46; U.S. del. Allied Control Commn., Sofia, Bulgaria, 1946-47; mil. attache, Sofia, 1947-49; attache and spl. asst. to U.S. Amb., Turkey, 1952-53, Iran, 1953-57; sr. staff officer, Washington, 1950-52, 53-57; ret., 1969; hon. chmn. Star Trading and Marine Co., Washington; econ. cons. Middle E. Decorated Legion of Merit with oak leaf cluster. Clubs: Met. (Washington); Carlton, Lansdowne (London); Camden Yacht. Contbr. articles on arty. and mineral. subjects to mags. Home: Easterly Shermans Pt Camden ME 04843 Office: 1050 17th St NW Ste 450 Washington DC 20036-5500

YAU, SHING-TUNG, mathematics educator; b. Swatow, China, Apr. 4, 1949; came to U.S., 1969; m. Yu-Yun Kuo; children: Isaac, Michael. PhD, U. Calif., Berkeley, 1971; PhD (hon.), Chinese U. Hong Kong, 1980, Harvard U., 1987. Mem. Inst. Advanced Study, Princeton, N.J., 1971-72; asst. prof. math. SUNY, Stony Brook, 1972-73; prof. math. Stanford (Calif.) U., 1974-79, Inst. Advanced Study, Princeton, 1979-84, U.Calif.-San Diego, La Jolla, 1984-87, Harvard U., Cambridge, Mass., 1987—; vis. scholar, chair math. dept. U. Tex., Austin, 1986; spl. chair Nat. Tsing Hua U., Hsinchu,

Taiwan, 1991—; Wilson T.S. Wang Disting. Vis. Prof. Chinese U. Hong Kong, 1991—. Contbr. numerous articles to profl. publs. Named Honorable prof., Fudan U. China, Academia Sinica China; recipient Sr. Scientist award, Humboldt Found. fellow, 1985; Crafoord prize 1994, recipient Veblen prize, 1981, Fields medal, 1982, Certy prize, 1980. Mem. NAS, AAAS, N.Y. Acad. Scis., Acad. Arts and Scis. Boston, Am. Math. Soc., Am. Phys. Soc., Soc. Indsl. Applied Math. Office: Harvard U Dept Math 3d Fl Sci Ctr 1 Oxford St Cambridge MA 02138-2901

YAU, STEPHEN SIK-SANG, computer science and engineering educator, computer scientist, researcher; b. Wusei, Kiangsu, China, Aug. 6, 1935; came to U.S., 1958, naturalized, 1968; s. Pen-Chi and Wen-Chum (Shum) Y.; m. Vickie Liu, June 14, 1964; children: Andrew, Philip. BS in Elec. Engring, Nat. Taiwan U., China, 1958; MS in Elec. Engring, U. Ill., Urbana, 1959, PhD, 1961. Rsch. asst. elec. engring. rsch. lab. U. Ill., Urbana, 1959-61; asst. prof. elec. engring. Northwestern U., Evanston, Ill., 1961-64, assoc. prof., 1964-68, prof., 1968-88, prof. computer scis., 1970-88, Walter P. Murphy prof. Elec. Engring. and Computer Sci., 1986-88, also chmn. dept. computer scis., 1972-77; chmn. dept. elec. engring. and computer sci. Northwestern U., 1977-88; prof. computer and info. sci., chmn. dept. U. Fla., Gainesville, 1988—; conf. chmn. IEEE Computer Conf., Chgo., 1967; symposium chmn. Symposium on feature extraction and selection in pattern recognition Argonne Nat. Lab., 1970; gen. chmn. Nat. Computer Conf., Chgo., 1974, First Internat. Computer Software and Applications Conf., Chgo., 1977; Trustee Nat. Electronics Conf., Inc., 1965-68; chmn. organizing com 11th World Computer Congress, Internat. Fedn. Info. Processing, San Francisco, 1989; gen. co-chmn. Internat. Symposium on Autonomous Decentralized Systems, Japan, 1993. Editor-in-chief Computer mag., 1981-84; assoc. editor Jour. Info. Scis., 1983—; editor IEEE Trans. on Software Engring., 1988-91; contbr. numerous articles on software engring., distributed and parallel processing systems, computer sci., elec. engring. and related fields to profl. publs.; patentee in field. Recipient Louis E. Levy medal Franklin Inst., 1963, Golden Plate award Am. Acad. of Achievement, 1964, The Silver Core award Internat. Fedn. Info. Processing, 1989, Spl. award, 1989. Fellow IEEE (mem. governing bd. Computer Soc. 1967-76, pres. 1974-75, dir. 1976-77; Richard E. Merwin award Computer Soc. 1981, Centennial medal 1984, Extraordinary Achievement 1985, Outstanding Contbn. award Computer Sci. Soc. 1985), AAAS, Franklin Inst.; mem. Assn. for Computing Machinery, Am. Fedn. Info.-Processing Socs. (mem. exec. com. 1974-76, 79-82, dir. 1972-82, chmn. awards com. 1979-82, v.p. 1982-84, pres. 1984-86; chmn. Nat. Computer Conf. Bd. 1982-83), Am. Soc. Engring. Edn., Sigma Xi, Tau Beta Pi, Eta Kappa Nu, Pi Mu Epsilon. Office: AZ State U Computer Sci & Eng GWC 206 Tempe AZ 85287

YAU, TE-LIN, corrosion engineer; b. Ton-Chen, Anhuei, China, Apr. 9, 1945; s. Chiu-Ho and Chih (Yang) Y.; m. Jue-Hua Tsai, Mar. 19, 1979; children: Kai-Huei, Ian-Huei, Jean-Huei. BS in Engring. Sci., Cheng Kung U., Taiwan, 1969; MS in Engring. Sci., Tenn. Technol. U., 1972; PhD in Metall. Engring., Ohio State U., 1979. Mech. engr. Taiwan Shipbuilding Corp., Keelung, Taiwan, 1970-71; corrosion group head Teledyne Wah Chang, Albany, Ore., 1979—; cons. Fontana Corrosion Ctr., Ohio State U., Columbus, 1979. Author: ASTM STP, 1984, 85, 86, 90, 92, 95, ASM Metals Handbook, 1987, ASM Stress Corrosion Cracking, 1992; contbr. over 60 articles to profl. jours. Mem. Nat. Assn. Corrosion Engrs. Internat. (chmn. T-5A-38 task group on reactive metals 1993—), Electrochem. Soc., TAPPI, Sigma Xi. Achievements include a patent on novel liquid metal seal on zirconium or hafnium reduction apparatus; devel. of new applications for reactive metals, improving the performance of reactive metals by employing metall., electrochem. and mech. techs. Home: 1445 Belmont Ave SW Albany OR 97321-3765 Office: Teledyne Wah Chang Albany 1600 Old Salem Rd NE Albany OR 97321-0460

YAVAS, UGUR, marketing educator; b. Istanbul, Turkey, Oct. 3, 1947; came to U.S., 1970; s. Hasan Sinan and Mebrure (Sakman) Y.; m. Ayse Aytul Ozkes, Aug. 3, 1970; children: Zeynep, Sinan. BA, Robert Coll., Istanbul, 1970; MBA, Fla. State U., 1972, GA. State U., 1974; PhD, Ga. State U., 1976. Assoc. prof. Bogazici U., Istanbul, 1976-77, 78-79; asst. prof. Ball State U., Muncie, Ind., 1977-78, asst./assoc. prof., 1979-81; assoc. prof., prof. Univ. of Petroleum and Minerals, Dhahran, Saudi Arabia, 1981-87; prof. E. Tenn. State U., Johnson City, 1987—; cons. Marsh, Muncie, 1976-79, Datotek/Cukurova, Istanbul, 1980. Contbr. numerous articles to profl. jours. Served with Turkish Air Force, 1976. Mem. Acad. Mktg. Sci. (bd. dirs. 1982-84), Assn. for Consumer Research (rep. 1984-87), European Mktg. Acad. (coordinator 1985-87), Am. Mktg. Assn. Avocations: soccer, tennis, traveling. Home: 1903 Woodland Ave Johnson City TN 37601-2285 Office: E Tenn State U Coll of Bus Dept Mktg and Mgmt PO Box 70625 Johnson City TN 37614-0625

YAVITZ, BORIS, business educator and dean emeritus; b. Tbilisi, USSR, June 4, 1923; came to U.S., 1946, naturalized, 1950; s. Simon and Miriam (Mindlin) Y.; m. Irene Bernhard, July 17, 1949; children—Jessica Ann, Judith, Emily. M.A., Columbia (Eng.) U., 1943; M.S., Columbia U., 1948, Ph.D., 1964. Economic cons. Jewish Agy. for Palestine, N.Y.C., 1944-49; mgmt. cons. Werner Mgmt. Cons., Larchmont, N.Y., 1949-54; owner, mgr. Simbar Devel. Corp., N.Y.C., 1954-61; faculty Columbia U., N.Y.C., 1964-94; prof. mgmt. Columbia U., 1964-94; dean Columbia U. (Grad. Sch. Bus.), 1975-82, Paul Garrett prof. pub. policy and bus. responsibility, 1982-94; dep. chmn., dir. Fed. Res. Bank N.Y., 1976-82; dean emeritus, Paul Garrett prof. emeritus Columbia U., 1994—; bd. dirs. J.C. Penney Co. Inc., Barnes Group Inc., Israel Discount Bank of N.Y., Crane Co., Medusa Corp.; trustee Am. Assembly, N.Y.C., 1975-82. The Inst. for the Future, 1984—; bd. govs. Media and Soc. Seminars, 1983-84; mem. nat. adv. coun. W. Averill Harriman Inst. Advanced Study of Soviet Union, 1983—; chmn. Nat. Assn. Corp. Dirs. Blue Ribbon Commn. on Corp. Governance. Author books; contbr. articles in field to profl. jours. Served to lt. British Royal Navy, 1943-46. Mem. ASME, Inst. Mgmt. Sci. Home and Office: Old Canoe Place Rd Hampton Bays NY 11946

YAWORSKY, GEORGE MYROSLAW, physicist, technical and management consultant; b. Aug. 4, 1940; s. Myroslaw and Mary (Yaworsky) Y.; m. Zenia Maria Smishkewych, Sept. 9, 1972; 1 child, Maria Diana. BS in Physics, Rensselaer Poly. Inst., 1962, MBA, 1977, PhD in Physics, 1979; MS in Physics, Carnegie-Mellon U., 1964. Physicist Republic Steel Research Ctr., Independence, Ohio, 1966-68; tech. and mgmt. cons. in ops. research, mktg. analyses, computer modeling, sci. programming and other areas to state govt., pvt. cos., 1972-81; internat. tech. assessment and analysis cons. EG&G, Inc., Rockville, Md., 1981-82; program dir.-computer integrated mfg. Eagle Research Group, Arlington, Va., 1982-83; prin. investigator high volume mfg. Scl. Applications, Inc., McLean, Va., 1983-84; cons. computer integrated mfg., design of experiments, quality engring., materials sci., tech. transfer, defense conversion, Eastern Europe bus. ventures, internat. bus. and mgmt., 1984—; mem. U.S. del. to Coordinating Com. for Multilateral Export Controls, Paris, 1982; adj. assoc. prof. biomed. engring., U. Tenn., Memphis, 1992—. Contbr. articles to profl. jours.; guest book reviewer, author and contbr. Recipient Physics Teaching award Rensselaer Poly. Inst., 1971; John Huntington scholar; Rensselaer Alumni scholar. Mem. N.Y. Acad. Scis., Robotics Internat. of Soc. Mfg. Engrs. (sr.), Computer and Automated Systems Assn. of Soc. Mfg. Engrs. (sr., chmn. Greater Washington chpt. 1985-93), Am. Phys. Soc., Am. Assn. Physics Tchrs., Am. Prodn. and Inventory Control Soc., AAAS, Rensselaer Alumni Assn., Sigma Xi. Home and Office: 5121 Clinton Rd Alexandria VA 22312-2117

YAXLEY, JACK THOMAS, secondary education educator; b. Detroit, June 30, 1943; s. Thomas William Yaxley and Evelyn Dora (Chandler) Dahlman. AS, Broward Community Coll., 1964; BS, Fla. Atlantic U., 1965, MEd, 1966, postgrad., 1968, 70-73; postgrad., Brown U., 1969, Bowdoin Coll., 1972, B.C.C. Field Sch., Mex., 1979-80, Hope Coll., 1986, English for Speakers of Other Langs. Inst., 1991-92, Broward Schs. Macintosh Computer Tng. Inst., 1992. Cert. assoc. master tchr., tchr. English for speakers of other langs. Tchr. chemistry N.E. High Sch., Ft. Lauderdale, Fla., 1966-70; tchr. honors chemistry, chemistry, advanced placement chemistry South Plantation (Fla.) High Sch., 1971—, instr. gifted and honors earth/space sci., 1990—; tchr. mentor chemistry Plantation High Sch., 1990-91; chem. analyst Alfinco/Russell-Anaconda, Oakland Park, Fla., 1966-70; part-time instr. Fla. Atlantic U., 1970-71; cons. Broward Dist. Schs., Ft. Lauderdale, 1971-87, tchr. gifted summer camp, 1983-85; lab. instr. Broward C.C., 1982-83, lectr.

chemistry, 1988-90; cons. textbooks Modern Chemistry, CBS/Holt-Rinehart, 1983, Holt. Phys. Sci., 1984, Modern Phys. Sci., 1984-85, Exploring Matter and Energy: Phys. Sci., 1990; presenter, editor workshop NSF, Broward Sch., 1986; presenter Dist. VIIa Leadership Tng. Inst. Phi Delta Kappa, 1991, 93; mem. bd. advisors, bd. dirs. com. Lake Emerald Svcs. Co., Inc.; panel mem. Home Testing Inst., Port Washington, N.Y.; instr. Sch. Tech. Inservice, 1995. Columnist Reflections of Lake Emerald, 1985-88. Mem., bd. dirs. Lake Emerald Owners Assn., 1983-93, chairperson activities com., 1985-88, security com., 1985-86, 89-92, handicapped facilities com., 1992, beautification com., 1993, v.p. bd. dirs., 1989-91, pres., 1991, v.p, 1992, mem. negotiations com., 1992-93, corp. sec., 1993—, mem. budget and fin. com., 1994. Named Tchr. of Yr., Fla. Engring. Soc., 1985; recipient Tchr. of 3d Acad. Quarter award Fla. Power and Light, 1989, Outstanding Tchr. award Tandy Tech. Scholars, 1991-92, 92-93; fellow NSF, 1969, 72, 86. Mem. NEA (life, Broward faculty rep. 1987—), Fla. Assn. Sci. Tchrs. (life), Fla. Teaching Profession-NEA, Fla. Atlantic U. Alumni Assn. (bd. dirs. 1966-71), Fla. Atlantic U. Coll. Edn. Alumni Assn. (founding benefactor), Planetary Soc., Phi Delta Kappa (scholarship fund raising com. auction, treas. 1990-93, bd. dirs. 1990—, Victoria C.T. Reed Adopt a Scholar program com. 1991—, v.p. for programs 1993-94, mem. scholarship ball com. 1993, mem. juvenile diabetes project com. 1994-95, rsch. rep. 1994-95, Disting. Svc. award 1987, 88, 91, 93). Republican. Roman Catholic. Avocations: cultural anthropology, ethnographic research in Mex. Home: 112 Lake Emerald Dr Apt 110 Fort Lauderdale FL 33309-6215 also (summer): Can Lakes Club 6663 110th Ave # 298 Stanwood MI 49332 Office: South Plantation High Sch 1300 Paladin Way Fort Lauderdale FL 33317-5402

YAZHE, HERBERT, national monument superintendent; b. Naschitti, N.Mex., Feb. 8, 1938; m. Helena Yazhe, May 26, 1959; children: Lucinda, Herman. Student, Colo. State U., 1966-69. Navajo ranger Navajo Nation, Window Rock, Ariz., 1959-64, asst. chief ranger, 1964-66, asst. dept. head, 1969-72, asst. dir., 1982-85; tng. coordinator Nat. Park Service, Grand Canyon, Ariz., 1972-74; chief interpreter Canyon de Chelly Nat. Monument, Chinle, Ariz., 1974-78, asst. supt., 1985-86, supt., 1986—; program officer Bur. Indian Affairs, Chinle, Ariz., 1978-82. Active Chinle Planning Bd., 1985—, Joint Mgmt. Plan, Chinle, 1985—, Navajo Studies Conf., Tsaile, Ariz., 1987—. Mem. Rotary (spl. recognition, 1973). Democrat. Roman Catholic. Home: PO Box 2191 Chinle AZ 86503-2191 Office: Canyon de Chelly Nat Monument PO Box 588 Chinle AZ 86503-0588

YEAGER, ANDREA WHEATON, editor; b. Baytown, Tex., Apr. 17, 1951; d. Virgil Jerry Jr. and Billy Ruth (Leslie) Wheaton; m. Danny Rhea Bowen, Feb. 21, 1976 (div. Sept. 1985); m. Hubert Allen Yeager, Jr., Dec. 21, 1985. BA in Teaching, Sam Houston State U., Huntsville, Tex., 1973. Assoc. editor The Houstonian, Sam Houston State U., Huntsville, Tex., 1970-73; reporter The Orange (Tex.) Leader, 1973-74, lifestyle editor, 1974-78; editor The Suburbia Reporter, Houston, 1978-79; copy editor The Houston Chronicle, 1979-81, features copy desk chief, 1981-85; copy editor The Sun Herald, Biloxi, Miss., 1986-88, features editor, 1988-91, mng. editor, 1991—. Crisis vol. Gulf Coast Women's Ctr., Biloxi, 1991—; bd. dirs. Am. Heart Assn., Gulfport, 1990-92, Boys & Girls Clubs of Gulf Coast, Biloxi, 1992—, Crimestoppers; mem. Leadership Gulf Coast Class, 1991-92, class rep., 1995—; pres. Altrusa Internat. of Biloxi, 1992—; mem. nutrition adv. bd. Gulfport Sch. Dist./Am. Cancer Soc., 1993—. Mem. La.-Miss. AP Mng. Editors (2d v.p. 1994—), Harrison County Home Econs. Coun. (v.p. 1991—), Miss. Press Assn., Pub. Rels. Assn. Miss., Gayfers Career Club. Republican. Methodist. Avocations: dance, reading, needle arts, computers, travel. Home: 12297 Windward Dr Gulfport MS 39503-5501 Office: The Sun Herald 205 Debuys Rd Gulfport MS 39507-2838

YEAGER, CAROLINE HALE, radiologist, consultant; b. Little Rock, Sept. 5, 1946; d. George Glenn and Crenor Burnelle (Hale) Y.; m. William Berg Singer, July 8, 1978; children: Adina Atkinson Singer, Sarah Rose Singer. BA, Ind. U., Bloomington, 1968; MD, Ind. U., Indpls., 1971. Diplomate Am. Bd. Radiology; med. lic. State of Calif. Intern Good Samaritan Hosp., Los Angeles, 1971-72; resident in radiology King Drew Med. Ctr. UCLA, Los Angeles, 1972-76; dir. radiology Hubert Humphrey Health Ctr., Los Angeles, 1976-77; asst. prof. radiology UCLA, Los Angeles, 1977-84; asst. prof. radiology King Drew Med. Ctr. UCLA, Los Angeles, 1977-85, dir. ultrasound, 1977-84; ptnr. pvt. practice Beverly Breast Ctr., Beverly Hills, Calif., 1984-87; cons. Clarity Communications, Pasadena, Calif., 1981—; pvt. practice radiology Claude Humphrey Health Ctr., 1991-93; dir. sonograms and mammograms Rancho Los Amigos Med. Ctr., 1993-94; trustee Assn. Teaching Physicians, L.A., 1976-81; cons. King Drew Med. Ctr., 1984, Gibraltar Savs., 1987, Cal Fed Inc., 1986, Medical Faculty At Home Professions, 1989—, Mobil Diagnostics, 1991-92, Xerox Corp., 1990-91, Frozen Leopard, Inc., 1990-91. Author: (with others) Infectious Disease, 1978, Anatomy and Physiology for Medical Transcriptionists, 1992; contbr. articles to profl. jours. Trustee U. Synagogue, Los Angeles, 1975-79; mem. Friends of Pasadena Playhouse, 1987-90. Grantee for innovative tng. Nat. Fund for Med. Edn., 1980-81. Mem. Am. Inst. Ultrasound in Medicine, L.A. Radiology Soc. (ultrasound sect.), Nat. Soc. Performance and Instrn. (chmn. conf. Database 1991, publs. L.A. chpt. 1990, info. systems L.A. chpt. 1991, dir. adminstrn. L.A. chpt. 1992, Outstanding Achievement in Performance Improvement award L.A. chpt. 1990, bd. dirs. 1990-93, Pres. award for Outstanding Chpt. 1992, v.p. programs 1993), Stanford Profl. Women L.A. Jewish. Avocations: geneology, writing, humor. Home and Office: 3520 Yorkshire Rd Pasadena CA 91107-5440

YEAGER, CHARLES ELWOOD (CHUCK YEAGER), retired air force officer; b. Myra, W.Va., Feb. 13, 1923; s. Albert Hal and Susie May (Sizemore) Y.; m. Gennis Faye Dickhouse, Feb. 26, 1945; children: Sharon Yeager Flick, Susan F., Donald C., Michael D. Grad., Air Command and Staff Schs., 1952, Air War Coll., 1961; DSc (hon.), W.Va. U., 1948, Marshall U., Huntington, W.Va., 1969; D in Aero. Sci., Salem Coll., W.Va., 1975. Enlisted in USAAF, 1941; advanced through grades to brig. gen. U.S. Air Force, 1969, fighter pilot, ETO, 1943-46, exptl. flight test pilot, 1945-54; various command assignments U.S. Air Force, U.S., Germany, France and Spain, 1954-62; comdr. 405th Fighter Wing, Seymour Johnson AFB, N.C., 1968-69; vice comdr. 17th Air Force, Ramstein Air Base, Fed. Republic Germany, 1969-71; U.S. def. rep. to Pakistan, 1971-73; spl. asst. to comdr. Air Force Inspection and Safety Ctr., Norton AFB, Calif., 1973, dir. aerospace safety, 1973-75; ret., 1975. Author: (with Leo Janos) Yeager: An Autobiography, 1985, (with Charles Leerhsen) Press On!, 1988. Decorated DSM with oak leaf cluster, Silver Star with oak leaf cluster, Legion of Merit with oak leaf cluster, DFC with 2 oak leaf clusters, Bronze star with V device, Air medal with 10 oak leaf clusters, Air Force Commendation medal, Purple Heart; recipient Presdl. medal of Freedom, 1985. First man to fly faster than speed of sound. Home: PO Box 128 Cedar Ridge CA 95924-0128

YEAGER, CHARLES WILLIAM, lawyer, newspaper publisher; b. Frederick, Md., Sept. 18, 1921; s. Ralph A. and Ina Jane (Nuckles) Y.; m. Charlotte L. Matthews, Nov. 26, 1958; children: Gretchen A. Murphy, Kristin A. Bridge, Charles W. Yeager Jr., Matthew R. Yeager. BA, W.Va. U., 1943; LLB, U. Va., 1948. Bar: W.Va. 1948, Fla. 1969, U.S. Supreme Ct. 1968. Ptnr. Steptoe & Johnson, Charleston, W.Va., 1948-93; of counsel Rose and Atkinson, Charleston, 1993—. Pub., editor The Nicholas CHronicle. Maj. U.S. Army, 1942-46. Democrat. Office: Nicholas Chronicle 605 Church St Summersville WV 26651-1411

YEAGER, DAVID P., management consultant; b. 1953. Grad., U. Dayton, 1975; Masters, U. Chgo., 1988. With affiliated cos. Hub Group, Inc., 1975—; vice chmn. bd. Hub Group, Inc., Lombard, Ill., 1985—. Office: Hub Group Inc 377 E Butterfield Rd Lombard IL 60148

YEAGER, ERNEST BILL, physical chemist, electrochemist, educator; b. Orange, N.J., Sept. 26, 1924; s. Ernest Frederick and Olga (Wittwer) Y. BA, Montclair State Coll., N.J., 1944.5; LLD (hon.), Montclair State Coll., 1983; MS in Chemistry, Case Western Res. U., 1946; PhD in Phys. Chemistry, Western Res. U., 1948. Instr. Case Western Res. U., 1948-51, asst. prof., 1951-56, assoc. prof., 1956-58, prof. chemistry, 1958-83, Frank Hovorka prof. chemistry, 1983-90, prof. emeritus, 1990—, acting chmn. dept. chemistry, 1964-65, chmn. dept. chemistry, 1969-72, chmn. faculty senate, 1972-73; dir. Case Ctr. for Electrochem. Scis., 1976-91; vis. prof. U. Southampton, Eng., 1968; cons. Union Carbide Corp., 1954-85, Inst. Def. Analyses, 1963-66, 91-92, NASA, 1964-68, Argonne Nat. Lab., 1965-67,

Gen. Motors Corp., 1969-76, Eveready Battery Co., 1985-93; mem. com. undersea warfare NRC, 1961-73; adv. bd. Office Critical Tables, 1964-69, mem. phys. scis. div., 1968-73; mem. power panel Advanced Research Project Agy., 1972-75; chmn. Gordon Research Conf. Electrochemistry, 1966; mem. internat. commn. electrochemistry Internat. Union Pure and Applied Chemistry, 1971-76; mem. vis. com. Brookhaven Nat. Lab., 1979-81; mem. adv. com. on USSR-Eastern Europe Nat. Acad. Scis., 1979-85; mem. com. on battery materials tech. Nat. Materials Adv. Bd., 1980-88; mem. com. on fuel cells, 1981-83; mem. rev. com. chem. tech. div. Argonne Nat. Lab., 1984-88; mem. com. on electrochem. aspects of energy conservation and prodn. Nat. Materials Adv. Bd. NRC, 1985-86; mem. advanced fuel cell working group Dept. Energy, 1984; mem. com. on electrochem. aspects of energy conservation and prodn. of the nat. materials adv. bd. NRC, 1985-86; mem. NSF com. for internat. programs, 1988-90; mem. bd. visitors Chemistry Div. Office of Naval Rsch., 1988-90. Editor: Transactions of the Symposium on Electrode Processes, 1959, 66, Techniques of Electrochemistry, Vol. I, 1972, Vol. II, 1973, Vol. III, 1977, Comprehensive Treatise of Electrochemistry, Vol. I, 1980, Vols. II, III, IV, 1981, Vols. V, VI, VII, 1983, Vols. VIII, IX, X, 1984, Electrochemistry in Industry: New Directions, 1982; mem. editorial bd. Jour. Advanced Energy Conversion, 1964-66; sect. editor Electrochem. Acta, 1972-76; contbr. articles to profl. jours. Elder area Presbyn. ch. Coffin fellow, 1947-48, NATO sr. fellow, 1968; recipient Ann. Tech. award Cleve. Tech. Socs. Coun., 1954, Ann. award Chem. Professions, 1967-68, Ann. Alumni citation Montclair State Coll., 1968, Commendation cert. USN, 1972. Fellow AAAS; mem. AAUP, Acoustical Soc. Am. (v.p. 1969-70, Biennial award), Electrochem. Soc. (hon., v.p. 1962-65, pres. 1965-66, Acheson medal 1980, Heise award Cleve. sect. 1965, de Nora medal 1992), Am. Chem. Soc. (Morley medal 1981), Soc. Applied Spectroscopy (pres. Cleve. chpt. 1953-54), Internat. Soc. Electrochemists (hon., v.p. 1967-69, pres. 1969-70), Optical Soc. Am., Chem. Soc. London, Sigma Xi (pres. Case Western Res. U. chpt. 1959-60). Home: 2 Bratenahl Pl Apt 5F Cleveland OH 44108-1167

YEAGER, JACQUES STALDER, SR., construction company executive; b. Riverside, Calif., Oct. 26, 1921; s. Ernest Louis and Emma (Leah) Y.; m. Mary Barbara Gibbs, July 1, 1948 (dec. May 1990); 5 children. BSCE, U. Calif., Berkeley, 1947. With E.L. Yeager Constrn. Co. Inc., Riverside, 1947-56, pres., 1956-93, chmn. bd., CEO, 1993—; bd. dirs. Bank of Am.; appointed bd. regents U. Calif., 1988. Bd. dirs. Riverside Community Hosp., 1960-70, chmn. bd. dirs. 1959-60, mem. exec. com. 1979—, nominating com., 1979—, spl. contributions com., 1979-80, Founder's Club, (charter), 1974—, Monday Morning Group, 1960—, pres. Monday Morning Group, 1974-75; bd. dirs. Riverside Community Hosp. found. Ventures Corp., 1985—; bd. dirs. United Fund Riverside, 1966-74, chmn. 1975-76, mem. 1965—; active U. Calif. Riverside, 1969—; mem. Riverside County Energy Task Force, 1974-75, Riverside and San Bernardino Counties Transp. Support Group, 1974-80, Met. Water Dist. Blue Ribbon Task Force, 1993—; chmn. Riverside Civic Ctr. Art Fund Raising Com., 1974-76; bd. dirs. Riverside Internat. Raceway, 1975-78; mem. Inland Empire Cultural Found., 1980-84; mem. Loma Linda (Calif.) U. Community Adv. Com., 1981-84; dir. at large Calif. Water Resources Assn., 1983—; hon. com. mem. ARC, 1984—; mem. needs assessment steering com. Riverside County Local Streets and Hwys., 1984-85, Riverside Transp. Com., 1984—; bd. dirs. Regional Inst. So. Calif., 1985-89. Served with USN, WWII. Named Entrepreneur of Yr., Ernst & Young Inc. mag., 1990, Businessman of Yr., Valley Group, 1991. Mem. Greater Riverside C. of C. (2% Club 1982-90, co-chmn. econ. devel. partnership 1983—, Citizen of Yr. award 1984), U. Calif.-Berkeley Alumni Assn. (steering com. Coll. Engring. 1979—, Inland Colls. chpts. Alumni Assocs. 1979—), Calif. C. of C. (bd. dirs. 1978-88, chmn. transp. com. 1982-84, statewide indsl. safety and health com. 1984-89), Exch. Club (Book of Golden Deeds award Riverside 1984, Kiwanis. Office: E L Yeager Constrn Co Inc PO Box 87 1995 Agua Mansa Rd Riverside CA 92502-0087

YEAGER, JANICE SKINNER, library director; b. Corbin, Ky., July 3, 1945; d. Raymond and Eula (Reeves) Skinner; m. Thomas A. Yeager, Nov. 11, 1988. BA, Berea Coll., 1966; MLS, U. Ky., 1969. Cert. libr., Ind. Extension libr. Rock County Libr. Systems, Janesville, Wis., 1969-71; serial bibliographer Ohio State U. Librs., Columbus, 1971-74; adminstr. Arrowhead Libr. System, Janesville, 1974-85; asst. dir. Monroe County Pub. Libr., Bloomington, Ind., 1985-91, assoc. dir. support svcs., 1991—; adj. instr. Ind. U., Bloomington, 1987. Mem. ALA (coun. 1995—), AAUW (named to ednl. found. program 1985, pres. Bloomington br. 1989-91), Ind. Libr. Fedn. (sec. 1990-91, bd. dirs. 1992—), South Cen. Ind. Pers. Assn. (sec. 1987, pres. 1988), Stone Hills Libr. Network (pres. 1990-91), Network Career Women (sec. 1986), Pub. Libr. Assn. (pres. pub. libr. sys. sect. 1982-83). Office: Monroe County Pub Libr 303 E Kirkwood Ave Bloomington IN 47408-3534

YEAGER, MARK L., lawyer; b. Chgo., Apr. 7, 1950. BA, U. Mich., 1972; JD, Northwestern U., 1975. Bar: Ill. 1975, Fla. 1985. Ptnr. McDermott, Will & Emery, Chgo., 1975—. Mem. ABA (vice-chmn. Robinson-Patman Act com.).

YEAGER, PHILLIP CHARLES, transportation company exeuctive; b. Bellevue, Ky., Nov. 15, 1927; s. Ferd A. and Helen (Koehler) Y.; m. Joyce E. Ruebusch, June 2, 1951; children: David P., Debra A. Yeager Jensen, Mark A. BA, U. Cin., 1951. Warehouse mgr. Pure Carbonic Co., Cin., 1950-52; trace clk., rate clk., asst. office mgr. Pa. R.R., Chgo., 1952-56; salesman Pa. R.R., Kansas City, Mo., 1956-59; asst. dir. Trailvan Pa. R.R., Phila., 1959-65; div. sales mgr. Pa. R.R., Milw., 1965-68; dir. Trailvan Penn-Ctrl. R.R., N.Y.C., 1968-71; pres. Hub City Terminals, Chgo., 1971-85; chmn. The Hub Group, Chgo., 1985—; bd. dirs. 30 Hubcity terminals. Cpl. U.S. Army, 1946-47. Recipient Achievement award Intermodal Transp. Assn., 1991, Harry E. Salzberg medallion for outstanding achievement in transp.; named Chgo. Transp. Man of Yr., Chgo. Transp. Assn., 1990. Mem. N.Y. Traffic Club, Chgo. Traffic Club. Republican. Lutheran. Avocations: golf, biking, swimming. Office: The Hub Group Inc 377 E Butterfield Rd Ste 700 Lombard IL 60148-5659

YEAKEL, JOSEPH HUGHES, clergyman; b. Mahanoy City, Pa., Mar. 12, 1928; s. Claude Harrison and Florence Mae (Hughes) Y.; m. Lois Josephine Shank, Mar. 26, 1948; children—Claudia Jo, Joseph Douglas, Joanna Irene, Mary Jo, Jody Lucile. A.B., Lebanon Valley Coll., 1949, D.D. (hon.), 1968; M.Div., United Theol. Sem., 1952; LL.D. (hon.), Otterbein Coll.; S.T.D. (hon.), Keuka Coll. Ordained to ministry United Methodist Ch., 1952; student asst. pastor Euclid Ave. Evang. United Brethren Ch., Dayton, Ohio, 1949-52; asst. pastor Otterbein Evang. United Brethren Ch., Hagerstown, Md., 1952-55; pastor Messiah Evang. United Brethren Ch., York, Pa., 1955-61, Meml. Evang. United Brethren Ch., Silver Spring, Md., 1961-63; asst. sec. Gen. Bd. Evangelism, Evang. United Brethren Ch., 1963-65, exec. sec., 1965-68; gen. sec. Gen. Bd. Evangelism United Meth. Ch., Nashville, 1968-72; bishop N.Y. West area United Meth. Ch., 1972-84, bishop Washington area, 1984—. Served with USNR, Seabees, 1945-46, PTO. Home: 8684 Doves Fly Way Laurel MD 20723-1248 Office: 9226 Colesville Rd Silver Spring MD 20910-1605

YEARGIN-ALLSOPP, MARSHALYN, medical epidemiologist, pediatrician; b. Greenville, S.C., May 17, 1948; d. Grady Andrew and Willie Mae (Blocker) Yeargin; m. Ralph Norman Allsopp, Apr. 5, 1975; children: Timothy Chandler, Whitney Marisha. Student Bennett Coll., 1964-66; BA, Sweet Briar Coll., 1968; MD, Emory U., 1972. Diplomate Am. Bd. Pediatrics. Intern Montefiore Hosp., Bronx, N.Y., 1972-73, resident, 1973-75; instr. pediatrics Albert Einstein Coll. Medicine, Bronx, 1975-77, asst. prof. pediatrics, 1977-78, 80-81; pediatrician Montefiore-Morrisania Comprehensive Health Care Ctr., Bronx, 1975-78, Louise Wise Adoption Agy., N.Y.C., 1975-80, Children's Evaluation and Rehab. Ctr., Rose F. Kennedy Ctr., Bronx, 1980-81; officer USPHS, 1981—, comdr., 1983—; epidemiologic intelligence surveillance officer birth defects br. Ctrs. for Disease Control, Atlanta, 1981-83, preventive medicine resident, 1982-84, med. epidemiologist, 1984—; pediatric cons. Clayton County Early Intervention Program, Jonesboro, Ga., 1983—; med. dir. Easter Seal Presch. Program, Atlanta, 1981-83; physician Com. on Handicapped, N.Y.C., 1979-81, United Cerebral Palsy Program, Bronx, 1980-81. Bd. overseers Sweet Briar Coll., 1981-89; bd. dirs. Neighborhood Arts Ctr., Atlanta, 1984-87; mem. prevention edn. com. Retarded Citizens, Atlanta, 1984—; mem. fundraising campaign Greater Atlanta YWCA, 1985; bd. trustees Pace Acad., 1986—; co-chmn. Minority

Atlanta Families in Ind. Schs., Inc., 1986—; chair, Bd. dirs. profl. adv. com. Cerebral Palsey Ctr., Reach, Inc., Atlanta, 1988—; Recipient Disting. Alumna award, Sweet Briar Coll., 1992. mem. State of Ga. Interagy. Coun. for Edn. of the Handicapped Act., 1988—. Fellow Am. Acad. Pediatrics, Am. Acad. Cerebral Palsy and Devel. Medicine; mem. AMA, Atlanta Med. Assn., Jack and Jill of Am., Phi Beta Kappa, Delta Sigma Theta. Home: 3783 Paces Ferry West NW Atlanta GA 30339-4138 Office: Ctrs for Disease Control 1600 Clifton Rd NE Atlanta GA 30329-4046

YEARLEY, DOUGLAS CAIN, mining and manufacturing company executive; b. Oak Park, Ill., Jan. 7, 1936; s. Bernard Cain and Mary Kenny (Howard) Y.; m. Elizabeth Anne Dunbar, Feb. 8, 1958; children: Sandra, Douglas Jr., Peter, Andrew. BMetE, Cornell U., 1958; postgrad., Harvard U., 1968. Engr. welding Gen. Dynamics, Groton, Conn., 1958-60; dir. rsch., project engr. Phelps Dodge Copper Products, Elizabeth, N.J., 1960-68; mgr. ops. Phelps Dodge Internat. Co., N.Y.C., 1968-71; v.p. ops. Phelps Dodge Tube Co., L.A., 1971-73; exec. v.p. Phelps Dodge Cable and Wire Co., Yonkers, N.Y., 1973-75; pres. Phelps Dodge Brass Co., Lyndhurst, N.J., 1975-79; pres. Phelps Dodge Sales Co., N.Y.C., 1979-82, v.p. mktg., 1979-82; sr. v.p. Phelps Dodge Corp., N.Y.C., 1982-87, exec. v.p., 1987-89; chmn., chief exec. officer Phelps Dodge Sales Co., N.Y.C., 1989-91; chmn., pres., CEO Phelps Dodge Sales Co., Phoenix, 1991—; also bd. dirs. Phelps Dodge Corp., N.Y.C.; bd. dirs. USX Corp., Pitts., J.P. Morgan and Co., Inc. and Morgan Guaranty Trust Co., N.Y.C., Lockheed Corp., Calabasas, Calif., So. Peru Copper Co. Mem. Ariz. Econs. Coun., 1989—, Conf. Bd., 1989—; bd. dirs. Am. Grad. Sch. Internat. Mgmt., 1990-92, Phoenix Symphony, 1988-94; chmn. Arts Coalition, 1989-90; trustee Phoenix Art Mus., 1994—. Mem. Nat. Elec. Mfrs. Assn. (bd. dirs. 1983-92), Internat. Cooper Assn. (bd. dirs. 1987—, chmn. 1990—), Am. Mining Congress (vice chmn.), Copper Devel. Assn. (chmn. 1989-93, dir. 1993—), Nat. Assn. Mfrs. (bd. dirs. 1988-94), Bus. Roundtable, Bus. Coun., Skyu Club, Echo Lake Country Club, Paradise Valley Country Club, Ariz Club, Blinf Brook Country Club. Republican. Congregationalist. Avocations: tennis, golf, classical music. Home: 8201 N Via De Lago Scottsdale AZ 85258-4215 Office: Phelps Dodge Corp 2600 N Central Ave Phoenix AZ 85004-3050

YEARWOOD, DONALD ROBERT, oil and shipping executive; b. Bklyn., Sept. 16, 1939; s. John Kirton and Helen Agnes (Schoenaker) Y.; m. Marie Louise Piovano, Oct. 20, 1962; children: Adam, Christopher, Jennifer, Katherine. Student, Bklyn. Coll., 1958; BS in Marine Engring., U.S. Mcht. Marine Acad., 1961; postgrad., Cooper Union for Advancement Sci. & Art, 1963; MBA in Mgmt., CUNY, 1968; postgrad., World Trade Inst., 1980. Cert. marine engr., U.S. Coast Guard, 1961. Marine engr. Cities Svc. Oil Co., at sea, 1961-62; sr. project engr. M. Rosenblatt & Son, Inc., N.Y.C., 1962-65; mgr. Mgmt. Info. Systems John J. McMullen Assocs., N.Y.C., 1965-70, v.p. mgmt. scis., 1972-75; v.p., gen. mgr. Pacific Marine Corp., Tokyo, 1970-72; pres. Pacific Marine Corp., N.Y.C., 1976-78; cons. Inter-Maritime Group, Geneva, 1978-81; pres. Am. Trading Transp., N.Y.C., 1981-89; sr. v.p. Am. Trading & Prodn., Balt., 1989-92; chmn., chief exec. officer Attransco Inc., 1992—; bd. dirs. Attransco, Inc., Am. Trading and Prodn. Corp., 1989-92, Crown Cen. Petroleum Corp., 1990-92, North Am. Petroleum Co., 1992—. Author: Graduate Records Exam: Business, 1967; patentee liquified natural gas inventions. Chmn. U.S. Mcht. Marine Acad. Found., Kings Point, N.Y., 1988-89; bd. visitors Mass. Maritime Acad., 1986—. Lt. USN, 1961-67. Mem. U.S. Mcht. Marine Academy Alumni Assn. (exec. v.p., pres. 1994—, Outstanding Profl. Achievement award 1986, Meritorious Alumni Svc. award 1986, Disting. Svc. award 1991), Soc. Nav. Architect and Marine Engrs., Nat. Cargo Bur., Soc. Marine Port Engrs., Am. Bur. Shipping, N.Y. Yacht Club, Harbor Hills Yacht Club.

YEARWOOD, TRISHA, country music singer, songwriter; b. Monticello, Ga., 1964; m. Chris Latham (div.); m. Robert Reynolds, May 21, 1994. Degree in Music Bus., Belmont Coll. Intern MTM Records, demo singer, commercial jingles singer; recording artist MCA Records. Albums include Trisha Yearwood, 1991 (platnium), Hearts in Armor, 1992 (Grammy nomination: Best Country Female Vocal, 1994 for "Walkaway Joe"), The Song Remembers When, 1993; back-up vocalist Garth Brooks albums; opening act Garth Brooks Tour, 1991; TV appearances on TNN American Music Shop. Named Best New Country Artist by Am. Music Awards, 1992, Top New Female Vocalist by Acad. Country Music, 1992; first female in country music history to have debut single reach #1 on charts with She's in Love with You, 1991. Office: MCA Records Internat 70 Universal City Plaza Universal City CA 91608*

YEATES, ZENO LANIER, retired architect; b. Atlanta, Jan. 9, 1915; s. Zeno Epps and Louise (Ames) Y.; m. Elsie Lankford, June 12, 1947; children—Zeno Ames, Arthur Lankford, Laura. B.S. in Civil Engring, Miss. State U., 1937; B.Arch., U. Pa., 1942, M.Arch. 1976. Asso. J. Frazer Smith & Assos., Memphis, 1947-57; partner Zeno Yeates & Assos., Memphis, 1957-63; pres. Yeates & Gaskill, Inc. (Architects), Memphis, 1963-79, Yeates Gaskill Rhodes (Architects, Inc.), 1980-85; ret., 1983; chmn. Tenn. Br. Arch. and Engring. Examiners, 1963-67; vol. Internat. Exec. Svc. Corp.; designer 11 hosps. in S.Am., Ctrl. Am., Eastern Europe. Fellow AIA (dir. 1975-77); mem. Tenn. Soc. Architects (pres. 1958), Constrn. Specifications Inst. Presbyterian. Clubs: Kiwanis (Memphis), Univ. (Memphis). Home: 2992 Gardens Way Memphis TN 38111-2647

YEATMAN, HARRY CLAY, biologist, educator; b. Ashwood, Tenn., June 22, 1916; s. Trezevant Player and Mary (Wharton) Y.; m. Jean Hansford Anderson, Nov. 24, 1949; children—Henry Clay, Jean Hansford. A.B., U. N.C., Chapel Hill, 1939, M.A., 1942, Ph.D., 1953; student, Cornell U., summer 1937. Asst. prof. biology U. of South, Sewanee, Tenn., 1950-54; asso. prof. U. of South, 1954-60, prof., 1960—, Kenan prof., 1980—, chmn. dept., 1972-76; eiderhostel tchr., 1987-88; vis. prof. marine biology Va. Inst. Marine Sci., Gloucester Point, summer 1967; cons. Smithsonian Instn., Sci. Applications, Inc., La Jolla, Calif., Ctrs. for Disease Control, Atlanta, WHO, Ecol. Analysts, Inc., Balt., Duke Power Co., Charlotte, N.C. Contbr. articles to profl. jours. Served with AAAS, 1942-46. Gen. Edn. Bd. fellow, 1941-42; Brown Found. fellow, 1984. Fellow AAAS; mem. Soc. Systematic Biology (charter), Soc. Limnology and Oceanography (charter), Soc. Ichthyology and Herpetology, Tenn. Acad. Sci., Am. Micros. Soc., Am. Ornithologists Union, Tenn. Ornithol. Soc., Tenn. Archeol. Soc., Nat. Speleological Soc., Blue Key, Phi Beta Kappa, Sigma Xi, Omicron Delta Kappa, Sigma Nu. Republican. Episcopalian. Home: Jumpoff Rd PO Box 356 Sewanee TN 37375 Office: Woods Lab Sewanee TN 37383-1000

YEATMAN, HOYT, special effects expert, executive. BA, UCLA, 1977. Mem. spl. effects crews for various movies; mem. animation and spl. effects teams NBC-TV, N.Y.C.; mem. prodn. team Paramount Pictures; co-founder, v.p., supr. visual effects Dream Quest Images, Simi Valley, Calif.; guest speaker, U.S. and overseas. Visual effects works include: (TV) Laugh-In Spls., Buck Rogers, Battlestar Gallactica, (movies) Close Encounters of the Third Kind, The Abyss (Oscar 1989), Star Trek: The Motion Picture, (projects) Michael Jackson's Moonwalker, John Badham's Blue Thunder, Short Circuit, Steven Spielberg's Amazing Stories; also dir. TV commls. for Proctor & Gamble, Taco Bell. Office: Dream Quest Images 2635 Park Center Dr Simi Valley CA 93065-6212

YEATS, ROBERT SHEPPARD, geologist, educator; b. Miami, Fla., Mar. 30, 1931; s. Robert Sheppard and Carolyn Elizabeth (Rountree) Y.; m. Lillian Eugenia Bowie, Dec. 30, 1952 (dec. Apr. 1991); children: Robert Bowie, David Claude, Stephen Paul, Kenneth James, Sara Elizabeth; m. Angela M. Hayes, Jan. 7, 1993. B.A., U. Fla., 1952; M.S., U. Wash., 1956, PhD, 1958. Registered geologist, Oreg., Calif. Geologist, petroleum exploration and prodn. Shell Oil Co., Ventura and Los Angeles, Calif., 1958-67; Shell Devel. Co., Houston, 1967; assoc. prof. geology Ohio U., Athens, 1967-70; prof. Ohio U., 1970-77; prof. geology Oreg. State U., Corvallis, 1977—; prof. oceanography Oreg. State U., 1991—, chmn. dept., 1977-85; geologist U.S. Geol. Survey, 1968, 69, 75; Glomar Challenger scientist, 1971, co-chief scientist, 1973-74, 78; mem. Oreg. Bd. Geologist Examiners, 1981-83; chmn. Working Group 1 Internat. Lithosphere Program, 1987-90; mem. geophysics study com. NRC, 1987-94; chmn. task force group on paleoseismology Internat. Lithosphere Program, 1990—; chmn. subcom. on Himalayan active faults Internat. Geol. Correlation Program, Project 206, 1984-92; researcher on Cenozoic tectonics of So. Calif., Oreg., New Zealand and Pakistan; active faults of Calif. Transverse Ranges, deep-sea drilling in

Ea. Pacific; vis. scientist N.Z. Geol. Survey, 1983-84, Geol. Survey of Japan, 1992, Inst. de Phys. du Globe de Paris, 1993. Mem. Ojai (Calif.) City Planning Commn., 1961-62, Ojai City Council, 1962-65. 1st lt. U.S. Army, 1952-54. Named Richard H. Jahns Disting. Lectr. in Engring. Geology, 1995; Ohio U. rsch. fellow, 1973-74; grantee NSF, U.S. Geol. Survey. Fellow AAAS, Geol. Soc. Am. (chmn. structural geology and tectonics divsn. 1984-85, Cordilleran sect. 1988-89, assoc. editor bull. 1987-89); mem. Am. Assn. Petroleum Geologists (Outstanding Educator award Pacific sect. 1991), Am. Geophys. Union, Seismol. Soc. Am., European Union of Geoscis., Oreg. Acad. Sci. Home: 1654 NW Crest Pl Corvallis OR 97330-1812 Office: Oreg State U Dept Geoscis Corvallis OR 97331

YEAZELL, RUTH BERNARD, English language educator; b. N.Y.C., Apr. 4, 1947; d. Walter and Annabelle (Reich) Bernard; m. Stephen Z. Yeazell, Aug. 14, 1969 (div. 1980). BA with high honors, Swarthmore Coll., 1967; MPhil (Woodrow Wilson fellow), Yale U., 1970, PhD, 1971. Asst. prof. English Boston U., 1971-74, UCLA, 1975-77, assoc. prof., 1977-80, prof., 1980-91, Yale U, 1991—, dir. grad. studies, 1993—, Chace family prof., 1995—. Author: Language and Knowledge in the Late Novels of Henry James, 1976, Death and Letters of Alice James, 1981, Fictions of Modesty: Women and Courtship in the English Novel, 1991; assoc. editor Nineteenth-Century Fiction, 1977-80; editor: Sex, Politics, and Science in the 19th Century Novel, 1986, Henry James: A Collection of Critical Essays, 1994. Woodrow Wilson fellow, 1967-68, Guggenheim fellow, 1979-80, NEH fellow, 1988-89, Pres.'s Rsch. fellow U. Calif., 1988-89. Mem. MLA (exec. coun. 1985-88), English Inst. (supervising com. 1983-86). Office: Yale U Dept English New Haven CT 06524

YEE, ALBERT HOY, retired psychologist, educator; b. Santa Barbara, Calif., June 14, 1929; children: Lisa Diane, Hoyt Brian, Cynthia Rae. B.A., U. Calif., Berkeley, 1952; M.A., San Francisco State U., 1959; Ed.D., Stanford U., 1965. Post-doctoral research fellow U. Oreg., Eugene, 1966-67; assoc. prof. edn. U. Wis., Madison, 1967-70, prof., 1970-73; prof. ednl. psychology, dean grad. studies and research Calif. State U., Long Beach, 1973-79, originating founder Grad. Ctr., 1974; prof. edn. U. Mont., 1979-83, dean Sch. Edn., 1979-82; sr. lectr. psychology Chinese U. of Hong Kong, 1985-89; dean, prof. psychology Am. Coll., Singapore; sr. lectr. psychology Nat. U., Singapore, 1980-90; dir. program U. Md., Hongkong, 1990; disting. vis. prof. ednl. psychology spl. adviser coll. grad. studies and internat. programs Marist Coll., 1990-92; prof. ednl. psychology Fla. Internat. U., Miami, 1992-94; intern. 1st Fed. Adv. Com. for Asian and Pacific Island Ams., Bur. Census, 1976-81. Author: Man, Society and the World, 1968; co-author: Comprehensive Spelling Instruction: Theory, Research and Application, 1971; editor: Social Interaction in Educational Settings, 1971, Perspectives on Management Systems Approaches to Education: A Symposium, 1973, Search for Meaning, 1984, A Study on Possible Future Developments for Hong Kong: Strategic Planning and Innovations, 1985, A People Misruled: Hong Kong and the Chinese Stepping-Stone Syndrome, 1989, 2d edit., 1992; editor: East Asian Higher Education: Traditions and Transformations. With AUS, 1952-55, Korea, Japan. Recipient Civic Commendation Madison, 1973; sr. Fulbright lectr. Tokyo and Tamagawa Univs., Japan; also 1st Fulbright scholar to People's Republic China, 1972. Fellow AAAS, Nat. Conf. Research in English, Am. Psychol. Assn., Am. Psychol. Soc.; mem. Calif. Coll. and Univ. Faculty Assn. (founder 1961), Am. Ednl. Research Assn., Chinese Hist. Soc. Am. and Orgn. of Chinese Americans (Bicentennial speaker), Asian-Am. Psychol. Assn. (pres. 1979-82, jour. editor 1981-82), Brit. Psychol. Soc., Hong Kong Psychol. Soc.

YEE, ALFRED ALPHONSE, structural engineer, consultant; b. Honolulu, Aug. 5, 1925; s. Yun Sau and Kam Ngo (Lum) Y.; m. Janice Ching (div.); children: Lailan, Mark, Eric, Malcolm, Ian; m. Elizabeth Wong, June 24, 1975; children: Suling, Trevor, I'Ling. BSCE, Rose Hulman Inst. Tech., 1948, Dr. of Engring. (hon.), 1976; MEng in Structures, Yale U., 1949. Registered profl. engr., Hawaii, Calif., Guam, Fla., Tex., Minn., Ohio., Northern Mariana Islands. Officer civil engring. dept. Dept. Pub. Works, Terr. of Hawaii, Honolulu, 1949-51; structural engr. 14th Naval Dist., Pearl Harbor, Hawaii, 1951-54; pvt. practice structural engring. cons. Honolulu, 1954-55; structural engring. cons. Park & Yee Ltd., Honolulu, 1955-60; pres. Alfred A. Yee & Assocs. Inc., Honolulu, 1960-82; v.p., tech. adminstr. Alfred. A. Yee div. Leo A. Daly, Honolulu, 1982-89; pres. Applied Tech. Corp., Honolulu, 1984—. Patentee in concrete tech., land and sea structures; contbr. articles to profl. jours. Served with U.S. Army, 1946-47. Named Engr. of Yr., Hawaii Soc. Profl. Engrs., 1969, one of Men Who Made Marks in 1970, Honolulu, 1970. Fellow Yale Engring. Assn.; mem. NAE, Prestressed Concrete Inst. (Martin P. Korn award 1965), NSPE, Soc. Naval Architects and Marine Engrs., Fla. Engring. Soc., Internat. Assn. Bridge and Structural Engring., Post-Tensioning Inst., ASCE (hon.), Am. Concrete Inst. (hon.). Avocations: golfing, swimming. Office: 1441 Kapiolani Blvd Ste 810 Honolulu HI 96814-4404

YEE, EDMOND, church administrator. Exec. dir. Committee for Multicultural Ministries of the Evangelical Lutheran Church, Chgo. Office: Evangelical Lutheran Church Am 8765 W Higgins Rd Chicago IL 60631-4101

YEE, STEPHEN, airport executive. Adminstrv. asst. health dept. City of L.A., 1958-63, sr. adminstrv. asst. dept. airports, 1963-72, fed. aid coord., 1972-75, project mgr., 2d level roadway and terminal improvements, airport facilities planner, 1975-83, staff asst. to bd. airport commrs., 1983-85, airport mgr. L.A. Internat. Airport, 1985—. Office: Los Angeles Intl Airport Los Angeles Dept of Airports 1 World Way Los Angeles CA 90045-5803*

YEGEN, CHRISTIAN CONRAD, JR., lawyer, business executive; b. N.Y.C., Oct. 5, 1943; s. Christian Conrad and Gladys Claire (Winter) Y.; m. Lonna Kane, July 11, 1970; children—Christopher, Hilary. B.A., Brown U., 1965; J.D., NYU, 1968. Bar: N.Y. 1969. Pres., then chmn. Integrity Fin. Group, Inc., Paramus, N.J., 1970—; prin. Yegen Assocs., Fairlawn, N.J., 1970—. Vol. VISTA, 1968-69; mem. N.J. Health Care Fin. Facilities Authority, Trenton, 1975-80; chmn. Pvt. Industry Council, Hackensack, N.J., 1979-83; bd. mgrs. Mid Bergen Mental Health Commn., Paramus, 1982, Bergen Pines Hosp., Paramus, 1985; mem. Tenafly Town Council, N.J., 1982-85; chmn. bd. Roundabout Theatre Co., N.Y.C., 1978—; trustee Edison State Coll., Trenton, 1981—. Mem. Sierra Club, ACLU, Nature Conservancy. Democrat. Avocations: tennis, reading, theatre. Office: Integrity Fin Group Mack Centre Dr Paramus NJ 07652 also: Roundabout Theatre Co 1530 Broadway New York NY 10036-4002

YEGGE, ROBERT BERNARD, lawyer, college dean emeritus, educator; b. Denver, June 17, 1934; s. Ronald Van Kirk and Fairy (Hill) Y. A.B. magna cum laude, Princeton U., 1956; M.A. in Sociology, U. Denver, 1958, J.D., 1959. Bar: Colo. 1959, D.C. 1978. Ptnr. Yegge, Hall and Evans, Denver, 1959-78; with Harding & Ogborn successor to Nelson and Harding, 1979—; prof. U. Denver Coll. Law, 1965—, dean, 1965-77, dean emeritus, 1977—; asst. to pres. Denver Post, 1971-75; v.p., exec. dir. Nat. Ctr. Preventive Law, 1986-91. Author: Colorado Negotiable Instruments Law, 1960, Some Goals; Some Tasks, 1965, The American Lawyer: 1976, 1966, New Careers in Law, 1969, The Law Graduate, 1972, Tomorrow's Lawyer: A Shortage and Challenge, 1974, Declaration of Independence for Legal Education, 1976. Mng. trustee Denver Ctr. for Performing Arts, 1972-75; chmn. Colo. Coun. Arts and Humanities, 1968-80, chmn. emeritus, 1980—; mem. scholar selection com. Henry Luce Found., 1975—; Active nat. and local A.R.C., chmn. Denver region, 1985-88; trustee Denver Symphony Soc., Inst. of Ct. Mgmt., Denver Dumb Friends League, 1992—, Met. Denver Legal Aid Soc., 1994—, Colo. Acad.; trustee, vice chmn. Nat. Assembly State Arts Agys.; vice chmn. Mexican-Am. Legal Edn. and Def. Fund, 1970-76. Recipient Disting. Svc. award Denver Jr. C. of C., 1965; Harrison Tweed award Am. Assn. Continuing Edn. Adminstrs., 1985, Alumni Faculty award U. Denver, 1993. Mem. Law and Soc. Assn. (life, pres. 1965-70), ABA (chmn. lawyers conf. 1987-88, chmn. accreditation commn. for legal assistant programs 1980-90, standing com. legal assts. 1987-92, standing com. delivery legal svcs. 1992—, del. to jud. adminstrv. coun. 1989—), Colo. Bar Assn. (bd. govs. 1965-77), Denver Bar Assn., D.C. Bar Assn., Am. Law Inst., Am. Judicature Soc. (bd. dirs. 1968-72, 75-85, Herbert Harley award 1985), Am. Acad. Polit. and Social Sci., Am. Sociol. Soc., Assn. Am. Law Schs., Order St. Ives, Phi Beta Kappa, Beta Theta Pi, Phi Delta Phi, Alpha Kappa Delta, Omicron Delta

Kappa. Home: 3472 S Race St Englewood CO 80110 Office: Harding & Ogborn Ste 1950 1200 17th St Denver CO 80202-5810

YEGULALP, TUNCEL M., mining engineer, educator; b. Konya, Turkey, Nov. 5, 1937; came to U.S., 1963; s. Faik Suleyman and Selma Safiye (Karatay) Y.; m. Sevinc Guneri, July 5, 1963; children—Ali, Serdar. B.S., Tech. U., Istanbul, 1961; D.Engring. Sci., Columbia U., 1968. Mining engr. M.T.A., Ankara, Turkey, 1961-63, chief feasibility studies group, 1971; research engr. Mobil Research, Paulsboro, N.J., 1967-69; chief systems cons. Sisag Ltd., Ankara, 1971-72; asst. prof. Columbia U., N.Y.C., 1972-75, assoc. prof. Henry Krumb Sch. Mines, 1975-85, prof., 1985—; dir. N.Y. Mining and Mineral Resources Inst. Rsch., 1987—; elected permanent mem. U.S. del. World Mining Congress, 1993. Author articles in field. Served to 2d lt. C.E. Turkish Army, 1969-71. Internat. AEC fellow, Vienna, 1963; Krumb fellow, Columbia U., 1964, Campbell fellow, 1965. Mem. AIME, Inst. Mgmt. Scis., Ops. Research Soc. Am., Turkish Studies Assn., Sigma Chi. Moslem. Office: Columbia U 805-1 SWM New York NY 10027

YEH, CHAI, electrical engineer, educator; b. Hangchow, China, Sept. 21, 1911; came to U.S., 1933, naturalized, 1956; s. Yun Ching and Ai Hwa (Ho) Y.; m. Ida Chiang, June 20, 1936; children—Yin, Jen. B.S., Chekiang U., Hangchow, 1931; Ph.D., Harvard U., 1936. Prof. elec. engring. Pei Yang U., Tientsin, China, 1936-37, Tsing Hwa U. Peking, China, 1937-48; chmn. dept. elec. engring. Tsing Hwa U., 1945-47; vis. prof. Univ. Kans., 1948-56; prof. elec. and computer engring. U. Mich., Ann Arbor, 1956-81, prof. emeritus, 1981—. Author: Handbook of Fiber Optics, Theory and Applications, 1990, Applied Photonics, 1994; contbr. articles to profl. jours. Mem. IEEE, Sigma Xi. Home: 1821 Alhambra Dr Ann Arbor MI 48103-5006 Office: U Mich Ann Arbor MI 48109

YEH, GREGORY SOH-YU, physicist, educator; b. Shanghai, Peoples Republic of China, Apr. 11, 1933; came to the U.S., 1953; BS, Holy Cross U., 1957; MS, Cornell U., 1960; PhD, Case Inst. Tech., Cleve., 1966. Rsch. physicist Goodyear, Akron, Ohio, 1960-61; sr. rsch. physicist Gen. Tire, Akron, 1961-64; asst. prof. U. Mich., Ann Arbor, 1967-69, assoc. prof., 1969-72, prof., 1972—; vis. scientist Ford Motor Co., Dearborn, Mich., 1970, Dow Corning, Midland, Mich., 1981; vis. prof. U. Calif., Berkeley, 1982, U. Ulm, Germany, 1973, 83. Avocations: photography, skiing. Office: U Mich Dow Bldg 3042 Ann Arbor MI 48109

YEH, JAMES KUEN-JANN, nutritionist; b. Kuen-Ming, Yuen Nang, China, June 27, 1942; came to U.S., 1967; s. Jin Gee-shan Yeh and Shing (Lan) Tsao; m. Jenny Ming, Feb. 1, 1969; children: Berhan S., Bervan Y. BS, Nat. Taiwan U., 1965; MS, U. Wis., 1968, PhD, 1974. Rsch. asst. U. Wis., Madison, 1969-74; rsch. assoc. Brookhaven Nat. Lab., Upton, N.Y., 1974-76; rsch. biochemist Nassau County Med. Ctr., East Meadow, N.Y., 1976-78; dir. metabolism lab. Winthrop-Univ. Hosp., Mineola, N.Y., 1978—; asst. prof. SUNY, Stony Brook, 1980-87; assoc. prof. SUNY, 1988—; adj. prof. L.I. U., Brookville, N.Y., 1980-83; nutrition cons. Life Health Ctr., West Babylon, N.Y., 1986-88; dir. metabolism lab. Winthrop-Univ. Hosp., Mineola, 1978—. Contbr. articles to profl. jours. Grantee NIH, 1975, Retirement Rsch. Found., 1986. Fellow Am. Coll. Nutrition; mem. Am. Soc. of Bone Mineral Rsch., Internat. Conf. on Calcium Regulating Hormones, Am. Coll. Sports Medicine, N.Y. Acad. Sci., Soc. Chinese Bioscientists in Am. Home: 10 Wisteria Pl Syosset NY 11791 Office: Winthrop-Univ Hosp 259 First St Mineola NY 11501

YEH, KUNG CHIE, electrical engineer; b. Hangchow, China, Aug. 4, 1930; came to U.S., 1950, naturalized, 1970; s. Su-Chung and Ae-Shian (Hsu) Y.; m. Margaret Mao-Shu Yung, Sept. 14, 1957; children: Joanna, Lisa, David, Richard. B.S., U. Ill., 1953; M.S., Stanford U., 1954, Ph.D., 1958. Research asst. Stanford U., 1954-58; research assoc. U. Ill., Urbana, 1958-59; mem. faculty U. Ill., 1959-92, prof. elec. engring., 1967-68, assoc. Center Advanced Study, 1973-74; dean Coll. Engring. Nat. Sun Yat-Sen U., Kaohsiung, Taiwan, 1993—; vis. fellow U. Hawaii, 1967; vis. chair prof. Nat. Taiwan U., 1976; lectr. Space Rsch. Ctr., Polish Acad. Scis., Warsaw, 1977; vis. scientist Max Planck Inst. Aeronomy, 1979; head dept. elec. engring. and chair prof. Nat. Sun Yat-sen U., Taiwan, 1981-82; U.S. mem. electromagnetic wave propagation panel AGARD (achievement award, 1992), NATO, 1984-92. Co-author: Theory of Ionospheric Waves, 1972; editor or co-editor: Radar Returns from the Clear Air, 1980, Scattering and Propagation in Random Media, 1987, Target and Clutter Scattering and Their Effects on Military Radar Performance, 1991, Radio Propagation in the Ionosphere and Magnetosphere: Theory and Application, 1992; mem. editorial bd. Waves in Random Media, 1990-93; assoc. editor Radio Sci., 1979-81, editor-, 1983-86; contbr. articles to profl. jours. Recipient Scientific Achievement award AGARD, 1992; named Hon. Guest prof. Wuhan U.; China. Fellow IEEE (cert. of achievement award for paper 1968); mem. Am. Geophys. Union, Am. Phys. Soc., Am. Meteorol. Soc., U.S. Nat. Com. of Internat. Union Radio Sci. (vice chmn. commn. G. 1981-84, chmn. 1985-87). Home: 4 Regent Ct Champaign IL 61820-7619 Office: Nat Sun Yat-Sen U, Office Dean Coll Engring, Kaohsiung Taiwan 80424

YEH, LIAN-TUU, mechanical engineer; b. Keelung, Republic of China, Dec. 12, 1944; came to U.S.; s. Chin-Chih and Chenn (Lin) Y.; m. Arlene Yao-Lee Wang, Oct. 3, 1945; children: Joseph Jer-Haw, Jennifer Jer-Fen. BSME, Cheng Kung U., Tainwan, Republic of China, 1967; MSME, U. Akron, 1972, PhD, 1976. Prin. engr. Babock & Wilcox Co., Barberton, Ohio, 1977-82; mem. group tech. staff Tex. Instruments, Inc., Dallas, 1982-90; mech. R&D engr. Compaq Comp. Corp., Houston, 1991-92; sr. engring. specialist Loral Vought Systems Corp., Dallas, 1992—; adj. prof. U. Tex., Arlington, 1994. Contbr. 36 articles on heat transfer to tech. jours.; co-patentee in field; speaker in field, tech. reviewer for jours., NSF. Del. seminar on heat transfer in high tech. and power engring., San Diego, 1985; session co-chmn. Internat. Symposium on Cooling Tech., Honolulu, 1987, and other heat transfer confs. Fellow ASME (mem. nat. com. on heat transfer in electronic equipment); mem. AIAA (sr. mem.), Internat. Electronic Packaging Soc. (reviewer), Sigma Xi. Home: 5810 Brushy Creek Trl Dallas TX 75252-2342

YEH, PAUL PAO, electrical and electronics engineer, educator; b. Sung Yang, Chekiang, China, Mar. 25, 1927; came to U.S., 1956, naturalized, 1963; s. Tsung Shan and Shu Huan (Mao) Y.; m. Beverley Pamela Eng, May 15, 1952; children: Judith Elaine, Paul Edmond, Richard Alvin, Ronald Timothy. Student, Nat. Cen. U., Nanking, China, 1946-49; BA Sc in Elec. Engring., U. Toronto (Ont., Can.), 1951; MSEE, U. Pa., 1960, PhD, 1966. Registered profl. engr., Ont. Design engr. Can. Gen. Electric Co., Toronto, 1951-56; asst. prof. SUNY, Binghamton, 1956-57; sr. engr. H.K. Porter, ITE & Kuhlman, Phila. and Detroit, 1957-61; assoc. prof. N.J. Inst. Tech., Newark, 1961-66; supr. rsch. and devel. Am. Rockwell, Anaheim, Calif., 1966-70; sr. R&D engr. Lockheed Advanced Devel. Co., Burbank, Calif., 1970-72, 78-89; mem. tech. staff The Aerospace Corp., El Segundo, Calif., 1972-78; chief scientist Advanced Systems Rsch., Pasadena, Calif., 1989—; cons. Consol. Edison Co., N.Y.C., 1963-64; sr. lectr. State U. Calif., Long Beach, 1967-73; vis. prof. Chung Shan Inst., 1989-92, Tsinghua U., 1993—, S.E. U., 1994—, Zhejiang U., 1994—; hon. prof. Northwestern Poly. U., 1993—, Shanghai U., 1994—; hon. prof. Beijing U. Aeros. and Astronautics, 1993—, Zhejiang U. Sci. and Tech., 1994—; rsch. power sys. design and control, 1951-66; investigator R&D Stealth tech. electronic warfare, avionics, nuclear hardening, anti-submarine warfare,. Recipient Achievement award for anti-submarine warfare/magnetic anomaly detection sys. Lockheed Corp. Mem. IEEE (sr., life), Nat. Mgmt. Assn., Am. Def. Preparedness Assn., Assn. Old Crows, Chines Am. Engring./Sci. Assn. So. Calif. (pres. 1969-71), Nat. Ctrl. U. Alumni Assn. (pres. 1977), Nat. Security Indsl. Assn., Beijing Assn. for Sci. and Tech. Exchs. with Fgn. Countries (hon. dir.), Assn. Profl. Engrs. of Ont. Can., N.Y. Acad. Scis., Air Force Assn. Republican. Presbyterian. Achievements include patent for Non-Capacitive Transmission Cable. Home: 5555 Via De Campo Yorba Linda CA 92687-4916 Office: Advanced Systems Rsch Inc 33 S Catalina Ave Ste 202 Pasadena CA 91106-2426

YEH, RAYMOND WEI-HWA, architect, educator; b. Shanghai, China, Feb. 25, 1942; came to U.S., 1958, naturalized, 1976; s. Herbert Hwan-Ching and Joyce Bo-Ding (Kwan) Y.; m. Hsiao-Yen Chen, Sept. 16, 1967; children—Bryant Po Yung, Clement Chung-Yung, Emily Su-Yung. B.A., U. Oreg., 1965, B.Arch., 1967; M.Arch., U. Minn., 1969. Cert. Nat. Coun.

Archtl. Registration Bds.; registered architect, Okla., Calif., Hawaii. Draftsman, designer various archtl. firms, 1965-68; design architect Ellerbe Architects, St. Paul, 1968-70; v.p., dir. design Sorey, Hill, Binnicker, Oklahoma City, 1973-74; prin. architect Raymond W.H. Yeh & Assos., Norman, Okla., 1974-80; asst. prof. to profl. U. Okla., Norman, 1970-79; head dept. architecture, prof. Calif. Poly. State U., San Luis Obispo, 1979-83; dean Coll. Architecture U. Okla., Norman, 1983-92; prin. architect W.H. Raymond Yeh, Norman, 1983-93; dean sch. architecture U. Hawaii at Manoa, Honolulu, 1993—; profl. adviser Neighborhood Conservation and Devel. Center, Oklahoma City, 1977 79. Works include: St. Thomas More U. Parish and Student Center, Norman, Summit Ridge Center Retirement Community, Harrah, Okla., (recipient Nat. Design award Guild Religious Architecture 1978). Bd. dirs. Internat. Alumni Assn., 1978-80. Nat. Endowment for Arts fellow, 1978-79. Fellow AIA (dir., pres. Okla. chpt. 1986, design awards, nat. com. chmn. 1989); mem. Calif. Coun. Archtl. Edn. (dir., pres 1982-83), Okla. Found. for Architecture (founding chair bd. 1989-90), Asian Soc. Okla. (award of Excellence 1992). Presbyterian. Office: U Hawaii Manoa Sch Architec Sch Architecture Honolulu HI 96813

YEH, TSUNG, orchestral conductor; b. Shanghai, People's Republic China, May 17, 1950; came to U.S., 1981; s. Zu-Jiu and Ren-Qing (Zhang) Ye; m. Sau-Lan Wong, Apr. 8, 1983; 1 child, Mona. B. Music, The Mannes Coll. Music, 1983; postgrad., Yale U., 1983-84. Exxon/Arts Endowment condr. St. Louis Symphony Orch., 1984-87; prin. condr. St. Louis Youth Orch., 1986-87; resident condr. Fla. Orch., Tampa and St. Petersburg, Fla., 1987-89; music dir., condr. South Bend (Ind.) Symphony Orch., 1988—; prin. guest condr. Albany (N.Y.) Symphony Orch., 1991—; guest condr. Rochester (N.Y.) Philharm., 1987, Minn. Orch., Mpls., 1987, Traverse (Mich.) Symphony Orch., 1989, Taiwan (Republic of China) Symphony Orch., 1989, San Francisco Symphony Orch., 1989, Albany (N.Y.) Symphony Orch., 1990, Taipei (Republic of China) Symphony Orch., 1991, Hong Kong Philharm. Orch., 1991. Mem. Fischoff Chamber Music Assn. (bd. dirs. 1989—), Am. Symphony Orch. League, Conductors' Guild. Office: South Bend Symphony Orch PO Box 267 South Bend IN 46624-0267

YEH, WILLIAM WEN-GONG, civil engineering educator; b. Szechwan, China, Dec. 5, 1938; s. Kai-Ming and Der-Chao (Hu) Y.; m. Jennie Pao, Mar. 25, 1967; children: Michael, Bobby. B.S.C.E., Nat. Cheng-Kung U., Taiwan, 1961; M.S.C.E., N.Mex. State U., 1964; Ph.D. in Civil Engring., Stanford U., 1967. Acting asst. prof. Stanford U., 1967; asst. research engr. UCLA, 1967-69, asst. prof. civil engring., 1969-73, assoc. prof., 1973-77, prof., 1977—, chmn. dept., 1985-88; cons. Office of Hydrology, UNESCO, Paris, 1974, Jet Propulsion Lab., Pasadena, Calif., 1975-78, U.S. Bur. Reclamation, Phoenix, 1977-81, Dept. Water and Power, São Paulo, Brazil, 1981-83, Rockwell Internat., 1983-88, U.S. AID, 1987-91, Met. Water Dist. of So. Calif., 1989—. Contbr. numerous articles to scholarly jours. Recipient Disting. Faculty award UCLA Engring. Alumni Assn., 1975; recipient Engring. Found. Fellowship award United Engring. Trustees, 1981, numerous research grants including NSF, 1967—. Fellow Am. Geophys. Union (Robert E. Horton award 1989), ASCE (editor Jour. Water Resources Planning and Mgmt. 1988-93, Julian Hinds award 1994), Am. Water Resources Assn. Home: 822 Hanley Ave Los Angeles CA 90049-1914 Office: U Calif 4531 C BH 405 Hilgard Ave Los Angeles CA 90095-1593

YELLE, RICHARD WILFRED, artist, product designer; b. Attleboro, Mass., July 22, 1951; s. Joseph Edward and Margaret Jeanne (Hickland) Y.; m. Johanna Sarah Gotheil, Apr. 12, 1986; children: Marc Gotheil Weinstock, Scott Richard. BFA, Mass. Coll. Art, 1974; MFA, RISD, 1976; MA, NYU, 1983. Prin. Richard Yelle Design, N.Y.C., 1976—; co-founder, dir. N.Y. Exptl. Glass Workshop, N.Y.C., 1977-80; dir. Clayworks Studio Workshop, N.Y.C., 1978-80; co-founder, pub. Craft Internat. Mag., N.Y.C., 1980-83; adminstr. Mus. Mile, N.Y.C., 1982-84; asst. v.p. Mass. Coll. Art, Boston, 1984-86; chmn. product design Parsons Sch. Design, N.Y.C., 1986—; panelist Nat. Endowment for Arts, Washington, 1983, site visitor, 1983-84; clk. Mass. Coll. Art Found., Boston, 1985-86. Exhibited in numerous glass art and design shows; in permanent collections Met. Mus. Art, N.Y.C., Mus. Fine Arts, Boston, others; founder, editor Glass mag., 1978-81, mem. editorial bd., 1981—. Recipient Disting. Alumnus award NYU, 1984; RISD teaching fellow, 1974-76. Mem. Glass Art Soc., Am. Craft Coun., N.Y. Exptl. Glass (chmn. 1980-85, bd. dirs.), Indsl. Designers Soc. Am. Office: Parsons Sch Design Product Design Dept 66 5th Ave New York NY 10011

YELLE, ROGER V., physical chemist; b. Taunton, Mass., July 19, 1957. BS, Worcester Polytechnic Inst., 1978; MS, U. Wis., 1980, PhD in Physics, 1984. Mem. profl. staff plasma physics lab. Princeton U., N.J., 1980-82; res. assoc., 1984-88, sr. res. assoc., 1988-89; asst. res. scientist lunar & planetary lab. U. Ariz., 1989—; prin. investigator NSF, 1985-87, NASA, 1987—. Mem. Am. Geophys. Union, Am. Astronomical Soc. (Harold C. Urey prize 1993). Research in physical and chemical processes in planetary atmospheres; role of readiation in the initiation of chemical cycles and in the thermal balance in planetary atmospheres. Office: NASA Ames Rsch Center Moffett Field CA 94035 also: Dept Planetary Sci U Ariz Tucson AZ 85721-0001*

YELLEN, JANET LOUISE, government official, economics educator; b. Bklyn., Aug. 13, 1946; d. Julius and Anna Ruth (Blumenthal) Y.; m. George Arthur Akerlof, July 8, 1978; 1 child, Robert Joseph. BA in Econs. summa cum laude, Brown U., 1967; PhD, Yale U., 1971. Asst. prof. econs Harvard U., Cambridge, Mass., 1971-76; lectr. London Sch. Econs. and Polit. Sci., Washington, 1978-80; asst. prof. econs. Sch. Bus. Adminstrn., U. Calif., Berkeley, 1980-82, assoc. prof., 1982-85, prof. Haas Sch. Bus., 1985—, Bernard T. Rocca Jr. prof. internat. bus. and trade, 1992—; cons. div. internat. fin., Bd. Govs. of FRS, Washington, 1974-75, economist trade and fin. studies sect., 1977-78, mem., 1994—; rsch. fellow MIT, Cambridge, 1974; cons. Congl. Budget Office, 1975-76, mem. panel econ. advisers, 1993—; rsch. affiliate Yale U., New Haven, 1976; mem. adv. panel in econs. NSF, 1977-78, 91-92; mem. Brookings Panel on Econ. Activity, 1987-88, 90-91, sr. adviser, 1989—; Yrjö Jahnsson Found. lectr. on macroecon. theory, Helsinki, 1977-78; mem. Coun. on Fgn. Rels., 1976-81. Author: (monograph) (with Arrow and Shavell) The Limits of the Market in Resource Allocation, 1977; assoc. editor Jour. Econ. Perspectives, 1987-91; contbr. articles to profl. jours. Hon. Woodrow Wilson fellow, 1967, grad. fellow NSF, 1967-71, Guggenheim fellow, 1986-87; grantee NSF, 1975-77, 90-94. Mem. Am. Econ. Assn. (assoc. mem. to Pres. 1986-87, nominating com. 1988-90), Phi Beta Kappa. Home: 3201 Leland St Chevy Chase MD 20815 Office: Bd Govs of FRS 20th and Constitution Ave Washington DC 20551

YELLEN, LINDA, film director, writer, producer; b. Forest Hills, N.Y., July 13; d. Seymour and Bernice (Mittelman) Y. BA magna cum laude, Barnard Coll.; MFA in Film, Columbia U., PhD in Lang., Lit. and Communications. Mem. film faculty Columbia U., N.Y.C., Barnard Coll., Yale U., CUNY; prin. Chrysalis-Yellen Prodns., Inc., N.Y.C., 1982—; pres. The Linda Yellen Co., N.Y.C., 1988—; represented by William Morris Agy. Producer, dir.: (films) Prospera; Come Out, Come Out; Looking Up, 1978; exec. producer (film) Everybody Wins, 1989; producer, dir., co-writer (film) Prisoner Without a Name, Cell Without A Number, NBC-TV, 1984 (Peabody award, Writers Guild nominee for best screenplay); exec. producer, producer (CBS network spls.): Hard Hat and Legs, 1980; Mayflower: The Pilgrims Adventure, 1979; Playing For Time, 1981 (Emmy award for best dramatic spl., Peabody award, Christopher award); exec. producer, producer, co-writer (CBS network spl.) The Royal Romance of Charles and Diana, 1982; exec. producer, producer (TV movies): Second Serve: The Renee Richards Story, CBS-TV, 1986 (Luminous award), Liberace, CBS-TV, 1988; exec. producer Hunt for Stolen War Treasures, syndicated TV, 1989, Sweet Bird of Youth, NBC-TV, 1989; dir., writer, prodr. Chantilly Lace, 1993, Parallel Lives, 1994, The End of Summer, 1995, (Showtime); contbr. articles to N.Y. Times, Village Voice, Interview, Hollywood Reporter. Mem. Dirs. Guild Am. (exec. council), Writers Guild Am., Acad. TV Arts and Scis., Women in Film.

YELLIN, THOMAS GILMER, broadcast executive; b. N.Y.C., Jan. 2, 1953; s. David and Carol Lynn (Gilmer) Y.; m. Anne Locksley, July 30, 1982; children: Chloe Locksley Yellin, Isabel Locksley Yellin. BA, Harvard U., 1975. Producer Sta. WQED, Pitts., 1975-76; assoc. producer CBS Reports, CBS News, N.Y.C., 1976-80, sr. producer, 1985-89; producer, pres. sr. producer Nightline ABC News, N.Y.C., 1980-84, sr. producer ABC World

News Tonight, 1984-85; sr. producer West 57th mag. CBS News, N.Y.C., 1985-89; exec. producer Peter Jennings Reporting ABC News, N.Y.C., 1989-92, exec. producer Day One Mag., 1992—. Office: Day1One 147 Columbus Ave 8th FL New York NY 10023

YELLIN, VICTOR FELL, composer, music educator; b. Boston, Dec. 14, 1924; s. Mendl and Sarah (Fell) Y.; m. Isabel Joseph, May 26, 1948; 1 son, David. A.B. cum laude, Harvard U., 1949, A.M., 1952, Ph.D., 1957. Teaching fellow Harvard U., Cambridge, Mass., 1952-56; asst. prof. NYU, N.Y.C., 1956-58, assoc. prof., 1961-64, prof., 1964—; asst. prof. Williams ., Williamstown, Mass., 1958-60; assoc. prof. Ohio State ., Columbus, 1960-61; coordinator N.Y. Metro-Fulbright-Hayes Vis. Scholars, 1978-82; mem. editorial adv. bd. Am. Music. Composer: (opera) Abaylar, 1974 (song cycle) Dark of the Moon, 1986; conductor: Mrs. H.H.A. Beach's Grand Mass in E-flat, N.Y.C., 1982; author: Chadwick, Yankee Composer, 1990, Bye Bye Blues Variations for Violin and Piano, Tully Hall, N.Y.C., 1992; contbr. Early Melodrama in Am., The Aethiop, Orchestral Restoration. Served with U.S. Army, 1943-46, ETO. Recipient grant Nat. Endowment Humanities, 1978. Mem. Am. Musicol. Soc., Sonneck Soc. Home: 52 Washington Mews New York NY 10003-6608 Office: NYU 100 Washington Sq E New York NY 10003-6688

YELTON, ELEANOR O'DELL, reading specialist; b. Maryville, Tenn., Jan. 21, 1929; d. Rondie Bliss and Maxie (Williams) O'Dell; m. Doran Yelton, Aug. 26, 1951; children: Doran II, Marshall, David, Holly. BS, East Tenn. State U., 1951. Cert. tchr., Fla. Tchr. Rozelle Sch., Memphis, 1952-55; tchr. English Clay High Sch., Green Cove Springs, Fla., 1963-66, reading specialist, 1966—; reading specialist The Bolles Sch., Jacksonville, Fla., 1966-84; chair adv. coun. Clay High Sch., Green Cove Springs, 1991-92. Author: (newsletters) PERKS, 1990 (Secondary Reading Coun. Fla. award 1991), Parents' Link, 1993. Mem. Internat. Reading Assn., Fla. Reading Assn., Secondary Reading Coun. Fla., Tchr. Acad. for Excellence, Clay County Reading Coun. (founder Books for Babies program Humana Hosp. 1990, pres. 1990-91). Avocations: traveling, reading, computers. Home: PO Box 8 Green Cove Springs FL 32043 Office: Clay High Sch 2025 Hwy 16 W Green Cove Springs FL 32043

YEMMA, JOHN, newspaper editor. Fgn. editor Boston Globe. Office: Globe Newspaper Co 135 Morrissey Blvd Boston MA 02107*

YEN, SAMUEL S(HOW)-C(HIH), obstetrics and gynecology educator, reproductive endocrinologist; b. Beijing, Feb. 22, 1927; s. K.Y. and E.K. Yen; children: Carol Amanda, Dolores Amelia, Margaret Rae. BS, Cheeloo U., China, 1949; MD, U. Hong Kong, 1954, DSc, 1980. Diplomate Am. Bd. Ob-Gyn (bd. examiners 1973-78), Am. Bd. Reproductive Endocrinology (bd. examiners 1976-82). Intern Queen Mary Hosp., Hong Kong, 1954-55; resident Johns Hopkins U., Balt., 1956-60; assoc. prof. reproductive biology Case Western Res. U., Cleve., 1970—; prof. ob-gyn U. Calif., San Diego, 1972-83, chmn. dept. reproductive medicine, 1972-83, prof. reproductive medicine, 1983—; dir. reproductive endocrinology U. Calif. Med. Ctr., San Diego, 1983—, W.R. Persons chair, 1987; assoc. dir. obstetrics Univ. Hosp., Cleve., 1968-70; DeGroof lectr., 1987. Editor: Reproductive Endocrinology Physiology, Pathophysiology and Clinical Management, 1978, 2d rev. edit., 1986, 3d edit., 1991; mem. editorial bd. Endocrine Revs., 1984—. Recipient Axel Munthe Found. award, 1982; Oglebay fellow 1968-69. Fellow Royal Coll. Ob/Gyn; mem. NAS Inst. Med., Am. Assn. Physicians, Soc. for Gynecol. Investigation (pres. 1981, Disting. Scientist award 1992, Rorer Clin. Investigator award 1992). Office: U Calif-San Diego Reproductive Medicine # 0633 La Jolla CA 92093

YEN, TEH FU, civil engineering and environmental educator; b. Kun-Ming, China, Jan. 9, 1927; came to U.S. 1949; s. Kwang Pu and Ren (Liu) Y.; m. Shiao-Ping Siao, May 30, 1959. B.S., Cen. China U., 1947; M.S., W.Va. U., 1953; Ph.D., Va. Poly. Inst. and State U., 1956; hon. doctoral degree, Pepperdine U., 1982. Sr. research chemist Good Yr. Tire & Rubber Co., Akron, 1955-59; fellow Mellon Inst., Pitts., 1959-65; sr. fellow Carnegie-Mellon U., Pitts., 1965-68; assoc. prof. Calif. State U., Los Angeles, 1968-69; assoc. prof. U. So. Calif., 1969-80, prof. civil engring. and environ. engring., 1980—; hon. prof. Shanghai U. Sci. and Tech., 1986, U. Petroleum, Beijing, 1987, Daqing Petroleum Inst., 1992; cons. Universal Oil Products, 1968-76, Chevron Oil Field Rsch. Co., 1968-75, Finnigan Corp., 1976-77, GE, 1977-80, United Techs., 1978-79, TRW Inc., 1982-83, Exxon, 1981-82, DuPont, 1985-88, Min. Petroleum, Beijing, 1982—; Biogas Rsch. Inst.-UN, Chengdu, 1991. Author numerous tech. books; contbr. articles to profl. jours. Recipient Disting. Svc. award Tau Beta Pi, 1974, Imperial Crown Gold medal, Iran, 1976, Achievement award Chinese Engring. and Sci. Assocs. So. Calif. 1977, award Phi Kappa Phi, 1982, Outstanding Contbn. honor Pi Epsilon Tau, 1984, Svc. award Republic of Honduras, 1989, Award in Petroleum Chemistry ACS, 1994. Fellow Royal Chem. Soc., Inst. Petroleum, Am. Inst. Chemists; mem. Am. Chem. Soc. (bd. dirs. 1993, councillor, founder and chmn. geochemistry divsn. 1979-81, Chinese Acad. Scis. (standing com.), Acad. Scis. Russian Fedn. (academician, fgn. mem.). Home: 2378 Morslay Rd Altadena CA 91001-2716 Office: U So Calif University Park KAP 224A Los Angeles CA 90089

YEN, WILLIAM MAO-SHUNG, physicist; b. Nanking, Kiangsu, China, Apr. 5, 1935; came to U.S., 1952; s. Wanli and Jane Hsanlin (King) Y.; m. Delane Robinson, Aug. 16, 1968 (div. May 1974); m. Laurel Frances Curtis, Aug. 18, 1978; 1 child, Jane Luhsan Bess. BS, U. Redlands, 1956; PhD, Washington U., 1962. Rsch. assoc. Stanford (Calif.) U., 1962-65; asst. prof. U. Wis., Madison, 1965-68, assoc. prof., 1968-72, prof., 1972-90; mem. Graham Perdue prof. U. Ga., Athens, 1986—; cons. Lawrence Livermore (Calif.) Nat. Labs., 1975-84, Argonne (Ill.) Nat. Labs., 1976-82, Rosemount Corp., Eden Prairie, Minn., 1988—. Editor: Laser Spectroscopy of Solids I, 1981, II, 1988, Dynamical Processes in Disordered Solids, 1989; contbr. more than 190 articles to scholarly and profl. jours. Washington U. fellow, 1960, J.S. Guggenheim Found. fellow, 1979, Fulbright Sr. fellow, 1995; recipient Sr. U.S. Scientist award A.V. Humboldt Found., 1985, 90; named hon. prof. U. St. Antonio de Abad, Cusco, Peru, 1983, hon. prof. Inst. Physics, Acad. Sinica, 1995. Fellow AAAS, Am. Physical Soc., Optical Soc. Am.; mem. Electro Chem. Soc., Sigma Xi. Achievements include pioneering establishment of laser spectroscopy as a tool to study optical properties of solids. Home: 180 River Oak Way Athens GA 30605-2677 Office: U Ga Dept Physics and Astronomy Athens GA 30602

YENKIN, BERNARD KALMAN, paint company executive; b. Columbus, Ohio, Dec. 2, 1930; s. Abe I. and Eleanore G. (Weiner) Y.; m. Miriam Schottenstein, Mar. 31, 1957; children: Leslie Mara, Jonathan, Allison Katsev, Amy. BA, Yale U., 1952; MBA, Harvard U., 1954. V.p. Yenkin-Majestic Paint Corp., Columbus, 1968-77, pres., 1977-85, chmn. bd., 1985—. Pres. Columbus Jewish Fedn., 1980-82, Pro Musica Chamber Orch., Columbus, 1983-85, Columbus Torah Acad., 1977-79; bd. v.p. Jewish Ednl. Svc. N.Am., 1992—. Recipient Mayor's award for Vol. Svc. City of Columbus, 1984, Young Leadership award Columbus Jewish Fedn., 1965. Mem. Yale Club of Cen. Ohio (pres. 1979-81), Yale Club of N.Y., U. Club (Columbus). Office: Yenkin-Majestic Paint Corp 1920 Leonard Ave Columbus OH 43219-2591

YENSON, EVELYN P., lottery official; b. Johannesburg, Republic of South Africa, Dec. 20, 1944; came to U.S., 1963; d. T. and P.F. Yenson; children: Megan Y. Sun, Elliot H. Sun. BA, Coll. New Rochelle, 1967; MA, U. Wis., Milw., 1968. Planner/evaluator Seattle Pub. Schs., 1971-73; dir. planning divsn., various other positions Dept. Cmty. Devel., Seattle, 1973-83; planning dir. Seattle Ctr., 1983-84; pvt. practice as cons. Seattle, 1984-85; dir., dep. commr. Expo '86, Vancouver, B.C., Can., 1985-86; dir. Wash. State Lottery, Olympia, 1987—; presenter in field. Mem. Mcpl. League Bd. Seattle, 1991-92; bd. dirs. Seattle Arts Commn., 1989-93; bd. dirs. Camp Brotherhood, Seattle, 1994—, treas., 1995; sec. bd. dirs. Sunhill, Inc. Seattle. Mem. N.Am. Assn. State and Provincial Lotteries (pres. 1991-93, past pres.), Intertoto (bd. dirs.). Roman Catholic. Avocations: arts, music, swimming, golfing, walking. Home: 2350 34th St Seattle WA 98144 Office: Wash State Lottery PO Box 43001 Olympia WA 98504-3001

YEO, EDWIN HARLEY, III, bank executive; b. Youngstown, Ohio, May 23, 1934; s. Edwin H. and Virginia (Blevins) Y.; children: Andrew Houston, Douglas Farrier, Claire Manger; m. Margaret L. G. Greene. B.A., U. Md.,

1959. With Pitts. Nat. Bank, 1959-75, sr. v.p., 1968-72, vice chmn., 1972-75; also dir.; under sec. treasury for monetary affairs Treasury Dept., Washington, 1975-77; exec. v.p. First Nat. Bank Chgo., 1977-80; chief fin. advisor City of Chgo., 1980-81; mng. dir. Morgan Stanley, 1981-85; counselor to pres. Fed. Res. Bank N.Y., N.Y.C., 1985-93; counselor to chmn. bd. govs. Fed. Res. Sys., Washington, 1993—. Served with USMC, 1952-55. Clubs: Duquesne (Pitts.); Cosmos (Washington); Stone Horse Yacht Club (Harwichport, Mass.). Office: 1270 6th Ave New York NY 10020

YEO, RON, architect; b. Los Angeles, June 17, 1933; s. Clayton Erik and Rose G. (Westman) Y.; m. Birgitta S. Bergkvist, Sept. 29, 1962; children: Erik Elov, Katarina Kristina. B.Arch., U. So. Calif., 1959. Draftsman Montierth & Strickland (Architects), Long Beach, Calif., 1958-61; designer Gosta Edberg S.A.R. Arkitekt, Stockholm, 1962; partner Strickland & Yeo, Architects, Garden Grove, Calif., 1962-63; pres. Ron Yeo, Architect, Inc., Corona del Mar, Calif., 1963—; cons., lectr. in field. Archtl. works include Garden Grove Civic and Community Center, 1966, Hall Sculpture Studio, 1966, Garden Grove Cultural Center, 1978, Gem Theater, 1979, Festival Amphitheatre, 1983, Los Coyotes Paleontol. Interpretive Ctr., 1986. Mem. Orange County Planning Commn., 1972-73, 1975-76; chmn. Housing and Community Devel. Task Force, 1978, Orange County Fire Protection Planning Task Force, City of Newport Beach City Arts Commn., 1970-72; pres. Orange County Arts Alliance, 1980-81. Fellow AIA; mem. Constrn. Specifications Inst. Democrat. Office: Ron Yeo FAIA Architect Inc 500 Jasmine Ave Corona Del Mar CA 92625-2308

YEO, RONALD FREDERICK, librarian; b. Woodstock, Ont., Can., Nov. 13, 1923; s. Frederick Thomas and Jugertha Aleda (Vansickle) Y.; m. Margaret Elizabeth Horsley, Oct. 12, 1953; children: Joanne, Peter. BA, U. Toronto, 1948, BLS, 1966; LLD (hon.), U. Regina, 1990. Mgr. book dept. Am. News Co., Toronto, 1948-53; sales mgr., dir. Brit. Book Service, Toronto, 1953-63; mgr. trade div. Collier-Macmillan Can., Toronto, 1963-65; pub. services coordinator North York (Ont.) Pub. Library, 1966-71; chief librarian Regina (Sask.) Pub. Library, 1971-88; mem. Nat. Library Adv. Bd., 1982-87, chmn., 1986-87. Served with RCAF, 1942-45. Recipient Silver Jubilee medal, 1977. Mem. Can. Libr. Assn. (pres. 1978-79), Can. Assn. Pub. Librs. (chmn. 1975-76), Sask. Libr. Assn., Adminstrs. of Large Pub. Librs. (chmn. 1973-74), Kiwanis (pres. Regina chot. 1981-82).

YEOMANS, DONALD KEITH, astronomer; b. Rochester, N.Y., May 3, 1942; s. George E. and Jessie (Sutherland) Y.; m. Laurie Robyn Ernst, June 20, 1970; children: Sarah, Keith. BA, Middlebury (Vt.) Coll., 1964; MS, U. Md., 1967, PhD, 1970. Supr. Computer Scis. Corp., Silver Spring, Md., 1973-76; rsch. astronomer Jet Propulsion Lab., Pasadena, Calif., 1976-92, supr., 1993—; discipline specialist Internat. Halley Watch, 1982-89; prin. investigator NASA Comet Mission, 1987-91, Near-Earth Asteroid Rendezvous Mission, 1994—. Author: Comet Halley: Once in a Lifetime, 1985, The Distant Planets, 1989, Comets: A Chronological History of Observation, Science, Myth, and Folklore, 1991. Recipient Space Achievement award AIAA, 1985, Exceptional Svc. medal NASA, 1986, Achievement award Middlebury Coll. Alumni, 1987; named NASA/JPL Sr. Rsch. Scientist, 1993. Mem. Internat. Astron. Union, Am. Astron. Soc., Astron. Soc. Pacific. Democrat. Presbyterian. Avocations: tennis, history of astronomy. Office: Jet Propulsion Lab 301-150G 4800 Oak Grove Dr Pasadena CA 91109-8099

YEOMANS, DONALD RALPH, Canadian government official, consultant; b. Toronto, Ont., Can., Mar. 25, 1925; s. Ralph and Louise (Weismiller) Y.; m. Catherine Simpson Williams, May 13, 1950; children: Patricia Ann, Nancy Louise, Jane Elizabeth. B.A.Sc., U. Toronto, 1947. Registered profl. engr., Ont.; cert. mgmt. acct. Mem. Bur. of Govt. Orgns., Ottawa, Ont., 1962-64; dep. sec. Treasury Bd., Ottawa, 1964-69; asst. dep. minister Dept. Supply and Services, Ottawa, 1969-75; assoc. exec. dir. Anti-Inflation Bd., Ottawa, 1975-76; asst. dep. minister Dept. Nat. Health-Welfare, Ottawa, 1976-77; commr. Correctional Services of Can., Ottawa, 1977-85; chmn. Tariff Bd., 1985-89; spl. advisor Can. Jud. Centre, 1989-92; mem. bd. govs. Carleton U., 1980-93, chmn., 1989-91; spl. advisor Royal Com. Govt. Orgns., 1961, Royal Com. Fin. Accountability, 1977; assoc. Cons. and Audit Can., 1992—; exec. counsellor Pub. Svc. Commn., 1990—; mem. bd. govs. Can. Comprehensive Audit Found., 1989-94; mem. nid. adv. com. Auditor Gen. Can., 1989—; chmn. Coun. Adminstrv. Tribunals, 1986; chmn. Coun. Chairs Ont. Univs., 1991-93; mem. Expert Com. on AIDS in Prisons, 1992-94; chmn. awrds com. Am. Correctional Assn., 1992—. Recipient Centennial medal Govt. Can., 1967, Jubilee medal Govt. Can., 1977, E.R. Cass award Am. Corr. Assn., 1991; Australian Commonwealth fellow, 1985. Fellow Soc. Mgmt. Accts. Can (pres. 1977); mem. Assn. State Correctional Adminstrs (pres. 1983), Inst. Pub. Administrn. Can. (pres. 1974). Clubs: Five Lakes (pres. 1975); Canadian (Ottawa, pres. 1978). Home and Office: 310 Clemow Ave, Ottawa, ON Canada K1S 2B8

YEOMANS, RUSSELL ALLEN, lawyer, translator; b. Vancouver, B.C., Can., May 13, 1944; came to U.S., 1951; s. Douglas Allen and Mabel Jean (Maguire) Y.; m. Minako Hara, July 7, 1981; children: Megumi Kay, Ken Douglas. BA, U. Calif., Berkeley, 1966, postgrad.; LLB, U. Ottawa, Ont., Can., 1985; LLM, U. Wash., 1986; postgrad., Hiroshima (Japan) U., York U., Toronto, 1990-92. Bar: N.Y. 1988, Calif. 1992; called to Ont. bar, 1991. Mem. rsch. dept. Japan External Trade Orgn., San Francisco, 1967-69; translator Office State. Ottawa, Ont., 1971-73, 84-85; head fgn. trade dept. Tanaka Shoji, Hiroshima, Japan, 1973-76; head tchr. Brit. Japan, Tokyo, 1977-81; fgn. law cons. Tokyo Aoyama Law Office, 1986-88; assoc. Baker & McKenzie, Toronto, 1989-91, L.A., 1991-92; pvt. practice, Rancho Palos Verdes, Calif., 1992-93; ptnr. Sanders and Yeomans, Torrance, Calif., 1993-94; pvt. practice Rancho Palos Verdes, Calif., 1994—. With USN, 1961-65. Mem. N.Y. State Bar Assn., York Bar Assn., Law Soc. Upper Can., Indonesian Bus. Soc., U. Calif. Berkeley Alumni Assn., U. Wash. Law Alumni Assn., Tokyo Can Club (v.p.'s, pres. 1987-89). Home: 6746-2 Los Verdes Dr Palos Verdes Peninsula CA 90275 Office: PO Box 3214 Palos Verdes Peninsula CA 90274-9214

YEOSOCK, JOHN JOHN, army officer; b. Wilkes-Barre, Pa., Mar. 18, 1937; s. John A. and Elizabeth B. (Petras) Y.; m. Betta Lynn Hoffner, July 20, 1960; children—John John, Elizabeth John. BS in Indsl. Engring., Pa. State U., 1959; MS in Ops. Rsch., U.S. Naval Postgrad. Sch., Monterey, Calif., 1969; postgrad., Nat. War Coll., 1974. Commd. officer U.S. Army, 1959, advanced through grades to lt. gen.; brigade commdr. 194th Armored Brigade, Ft Knox, Ky., 1978-80; chief of staff 1st Cavalry div. U.S. Army, Ft. Hood, Tex., 1980-81, asst. div. commdr. 1983-84; project mgr. Saudi N.G., Riyadh, Saudi Arabia, 1981-83; dep. chief of staff ops. Forces Command., Atlanta, 1984-86; commdr. 1st Cavalry Div., Ft. Hood, 1986-88; asst. dep. chief of staff for ops. The Pentagon, Washington, 1988-89; commdr. 3d Army and dep. commdg. gen. Forces Command, Ft. McPherson, Ga., 1989—&; commdr. U.S., U.K., French Army Forces, Kuwaiti Theater Ops., Desert Storm, Saudi Arabia, 1990-91; internat. cons., 1993—. Decorated D.S.M. (3), Legion of Merit (2), Bronze Star, French Legion of Honor, King Faisal award Class II, King Abdul Aziz medal Class II (Saudi Arabia), Combat Infantryman badge; recipient Nat. Vets. award, 1994, AUSA Inspiration award Atlanta, 1992; named Outstanding Engring. Alumnus, Pa. State U., 1990, Disting. Alumni, 1992, Disting. Alumnus, Valley Forge Mil. Acad., 1994; named to Pi Kappa Phi Hall of Fame. Mem. Wilkes-Barre C. of C. (hon.), Achievement award 1991. Home: 411 Taberon Rd Peachtree City GA 30269

YEPSEN, DAVID ARLON, reporter; b. Jefferson, Iowa, Oct. 12, 1950; s. Arlon Eugene and Marjorie Mae Yepsen; m. Mary Hamilton Stuart, June 11, 1982; 1 child, Elizabeth. B Gen. Studies, U. Iowa, 1972; MPA, Drake U., 1985. Reporter Quad City Times, Davenport, Iowa, 1973-74; reporter Des Moines Register, 1974-82, chief polit. reporter, 1983—. 2d lt. Army N.G., 1972-78. Fellow Joan Shorenstein Barone Ctr. on Press, Politics and Pub. Policy, John F. Kennedy Sch. Govt., Harvard U., 1989. Congregationalist. Office: The Des Moines Register 715 Locust St Des Moines IA 50309

YERGIN, DANIEL HOWARD, writer, consultant; b. Los Angeles, Feb. 6, 1947; s. Irving H. and Naomi Y.; m. Angela Stent, Aug. 10, 1975; children: Alexander George, Rebecca Isabella. BA with first class honors, Cambridge U., Eng., 1968, MA, 1970, PhD, 1974; PhD (hon.), U. Mo., 1980, U.

Houston, 1994. Contbg. editor New York mag., 1968-70; research fellow Harvard U., Cambridge, Mass., 1974-76; lectr. bus. sch. Harvard U., 1976-79, lectr. Kennedy Sch. Govt., 1979-83; research assoc. Harvard U., Cambridge, 1983—; pres. Cambridge Energy Research Assoc., Cambridge, 1982—; mem. policy adv. com. Program on U.S.-Japan Rels., Harvard U.; mem. bd. energy experts Dallas Morning News; mem. internat. panel advisors Asia-Pacific Petroleum Conf.; fellow World Econ. Forum, Davos. Author: Shattered Peace: The Origins of the Cold War and the National Security State, 1977, rev. edit., 1990, The Prize: Epic Quest for Oil, Money and Power, 1991 (Pulitzer Prize for non-fiction 1992); co-author: Cold War, 1977, Energy Future, 1979, Global Insecurity, 1982, Future of Oil Prices: Perils of Prophecy, 1984, Russia 2010: And What It Means for the World, 1993; contbg. editor Atlantic Monthly, 1977-83. Mem. adv. bd. Solar Energy Rsch. Inst., Golden, Colo., 1979-81; sec. Energy Adv. Bd. Fellow Univ. Consortium for World Order Studies, 1974-75, Rockefeller Found., 1975-79, German Marshall Fund, 1980-81; Marshall scholar Cambridge U., 1974. Fellow Atlantic Inst. Internat. Affairs; mem. PEN, Lehrman Inst. (assoc.), Coun. on Fgn. Rels., Nat. Petroleum Coun., Internat. Assn. for Energy Econs., Am. Hist. Assn., Am. Polit. Assn., Royal Inst. Internat. Affairs, Am. Marshall Scholars (bd. dirs. 1988-91), U.S. Energy Assocs. (bd. dirs.), Offshore No. Seas Found. Internat. Coun., The Nature Conservancy (Last Great Places com.), Yale Club (N.Y.C.), Harvard Club (N.Y.C.). Office: Cambridge Energy Rsch Assocs 20 University Rd Ste 450 Cambridge MA 02138-5756*

YERKES, DAVID NORTON, architect; b. Cambridge, Mass., Nov. 5, 1911; s. Robert Mearns and Ada (Watterson) Y.; m. Catharine Noyes, Oct. 7, 1939 (dec. 1969); 1 dau., Catharine; m. Sarah Hitchcock Satterlee, July 9, 1972. B.A., Harvard U., 1933; M.F.A., Yale U., 1935. Draftsman, designer Chgo. and Washington, 1937-39, Deigert & Yerkes and Assos., Washington, 1945-69, David N. Yerkes & Assos., Washington, 1970-80, Yerkes, Pappas and Parker, 1980-83; Mem. panel archtl. advisers Nat. Commn. Fine Arts, 1961-63, 79-82; vice chmn. Presdl. Inaugural Parade Com., 1965. Prin. works include Voice of America Studios, Washington, 1958, Nat. Arboretum Hdqrs. Bldg, Am. Embassy, Somalia, also Madeira Sch. Auditorium, 1969; 4 stas. Washington subway system, 1971-81, hdqrs., Nat. Trust Historic Preservation, Washington, 1977, suite, Time, Inc., Washington, 1980, also various schs., labs. Served to capt. AUS, 1943-45. Firm recipient numerous regional and nat. awards; recipient Kemper award AIA, 1972. Fellow AIA (bd. dirs. 1965-68, v.p. 1968-69, chmn. nat. honor awards jury 1966, chmn. Reynolds Meml. award jury 1969, pres. found. 1974-76). Home: 1527 30th St NW Washington DC 20007-3088

YERKES, SUSAN GAMBLE, newspaper columnist; b. Evanston, Ill., Sept. 5, 1959; d. Charles Tyson and Darthea (Campbell) Higgins. BA in Liberal Arts (hon.), U. Austin, 1974; MA in Mass Comms., Wichita State U., 1976. Pub. affairs dir. anchor KAKE-TV, Wichita, Kans., 1977-81; freelance writer pub. rels. YS Comms. Global, 1981-84; metro columnist San Antonio Light, 1986-93; lifestyle columnist S.A. Express News, San Antonio, 1993—; radio TV host KTKR-AM, San Antonio, 1993—; nat. assn. broadcast editorials, Boston, 1978-81. Recipient 1st Place Column Writing Nat. Press Women, 1988. Mem. Internat. Womens Forum, Women in Communications, Public Relation Soc. Am. Episcopalian. Avocations: horseback riding, travel, reading, friends. Home: 7711 Broadway # 29B San Antonio TX 78209 Office: San Antonio Express News Ave E 3rd St San Antonio TX 78205

YERMAN, FREDRIC WARREN, lawyer; b. N.Y.C., Jan. 8, 1943; s. Nat W. and Tina (Barotz) Y.; m. Ann R. Rochlin, May 31, 1965; children: Emily, Deborah. BA, CUNY, 1963; LLB, Columbia U., 1966. Bar: N.Y. 1967. Assoc. Kaye, Scholer, Fierman, Hays & Handler, N.Y.C., 1966-74, ptnr., 1974—, chmn. exec. com., 1990-92; bd. dirs. Lawyer's Com. for Civil Rights under Law, N.Y. Bd. dirs. United Way Tri-State, N.Y., Legal Aid Soc., N.Y.C.; chmn. Jewish Bd. Family and Children Svcs., N.Y.C., 1994—. Fellow Am. Coll. Trial Lawyers. Home: 31 Sheridan Rd Scarsdale NY 10583-1523 Office: Kaye Scholer Fierman Hays & Handler 425 Park Ave New York NY 10022-3506

YERUSHALMI, JOSEPH, chemical engineer, researcher, educator; b. Israel, Aug. 12, 1938; m. Zahava Yerushalmi; children: Aire, Chen, Tal. B-SChemE, CCNY, 1965, MSChemE, 1967; PhD in engring., CUNY, 1969. Project mgr. Electric Power Rsch. Inst., Palo Alto, Calif., 1975-76, tech. mgr., 1978-80; prof. CCNY, 1977-78; gen. mgr. PAMA (Energy Resources Dev., Ltd.), Israel, 1980-89; pres. BCR Nat. Lab., Pitts., 1989—. Mem. Am. Inst. Chem. Engrs. Office: BCR Nat Lab 500 William Pitt Way Pittsburgh PA 15238-1331

YERUSHALMI, YOSEF HAYIM, historian, educator; b. N.Y.C., May 20, 1932; s. Leon and Eva (Kaplan) Y.; m. Ophra Pearly, Jan. 4, 1959; 1 child, Ariel. B.A., Yeshiva U., 1953; M.Hebrew Lit., Jewish Theol. Sem. Am., 1957, DHL (hon.), 1987; M.A., Columbia, 1961, Ph.D., 1966; M.A. (hon.), Harvard, 1970. Instr. Jewish history Rutgers U., New Brunswick, N.J., 1963-66; asst. prof. Hebrew and Jewish History Harvard, 1966-70, prof., 1970-78, Jacob E. Safra prof. Jewish history and Sephardic civilization, 1978-80, chmn. dept. near eastern langs. and civilizations, 1978-80; Salo Wittmayer Baron prof. Jewish history, culture and soc., and dir. Center for Israel and Jewish Studies, Columbia U., 1980—. Author: From Spanish Court to Italian Ghetto: Isaac Cardoso, A Study in Seventeenth-Century Marranism and Jewish Apologetics, 1971, Haggadah and History, 1975, The Lisbon Massacre of 1506, 1976, Zakhor: Jewish History and Jewish Memory, 1982, Freud's Moses: Judaism Terminable and Interminable, 1991, Ein Feld in Anatot: Versuche uber judische Geschichte, 1993; author (in Hebrew): Spinoza on the Survival of the Jews, 1983; contbr. articles to profl. publs. on Spanish and Portuguese Jewry and history of psychoanalysis; chmn. publs. com., Jewish Publ. Soc., 1972-84; pres. Leo Baeck Inst., 1986-91. Bd. dirs. Conf. Jewish Social Studies, Psycho analytic Research and Devel. Fund, Editorial Bd., History and Memory. Recipient Newman medal CUNY, 1975, Nat. Jewish Book award, 1983, 92, Ansley award Columbia U. Press, 1968; Kent fellow, 1963, traveling fellow Nat. Found. Jewish Culture, 1964, NEH fellow, 1976-77, Rockefeller fellow in humanities, 1983-84, Guggenheim fellow, 1989-90. Fellow Am. Jewish Research, Am. Acad. Arts and Scis., Academia Portuguesa da História (hon.). Home: 450 Riverside Dr New York NY 10027 Office: Columbia University 511 Fayerweather Hall 116th St & Broadway New York NY 10027

YESAWICH, PETER CHARLES, advertising executive; b. Ithaca, N.Y., Oct. 28, 1950; s. Paul Joseph Jr. and Elizabeth (Larkin) Y.; m. Cara Euiler, May 24, 1980; children: Peter Charles, Paul Christopher. BS, Cornell U., 1972, MS, 1974, PhD, 1976; AMP, Yale U., 1994. Dir. rsch. Robinsons, Inc., Orlando, Fla., 1976-78, v.p., 1978-81, exec. v.p., 1981-83; pres., chief exec. officer Robinson, Yesawich & Pepperdine, Inc., Orlando, 1983—; vis. assoc. prof. Cornell U., Ithaca, 1977—, U. Ctrl. Fla., Orlando, 1988—; chmn. Pope Tourism Inst., Orlando, 1988-90. Contbr. articles to profl. jours. Recipient World Travel award Am. Assn. Travel Editors, 1985, Silver Medal award Am. Assn. Advt. Agencies, Adrian award Hospitality Sales and Mktg. Assn. Internat.; named Author of Yr., Cornell Quar., 1986. Mem. Cornell Hotel Soc., Am. Hotel & Motel Assn., Caribbean Hotel Assn., Hotel Sales Mktg. Assn., Am. Mktg. Assn. Avocations: jogging, travel. Office: Robinson Yesawich & Pepperdine Inc 1900 Summit Tower Blvd Ste 600 Orlando FL 32810-5913

YESTON, MAURY, composer, lyricist, educator; b. Jersey City, Oct. 23, 1945; s. David and Frances (Haar) Y.; m. Anne Sheedy, 1982; children: Jake, Max. BA, Yale U., 1967, PhD, 1974; MA, Clare Coll., Cambridge (Eng.) U., 1972. Assoc. prof. dept. music Yale U., New Haven, 1974-82; dir. undergrad. studies in music, 1976-82; tchr. BMI Mus. Theatre Workshop, 1982—. Composer, lyricist: off-Broadway play Cloud 9 - Music, 1981; Broadway play Nine - The Musical, 1982 (Tony award 1982, Grammy award nominee 1982, Drama Desk award 1982), One Two Three Four Five, 1987, Grand Hotel, 1989 (Tony award nominee 1990), (rec.) Goya: A Life in Song, 1989, December Songs, 1990, Phantom, 1991; composer: Movement for Cello and Orchestra, 1967; author: The Stratification of Musical Rhythm, 1975; author, editor: Readings in Schenker Analysis, 1977. Recipient BMI award, 1982, 89. Office: Flora Roberts 157 W 57th St New York NY 10019-2210

YETMAN, LEITH ELEANOR, administrator, educator; b. Kellits, Clarendon, Jamaica, West Indies; came to U.S., 1967; d. 2nd child of 12

children of Percival Augustus and Grace Elizabeth (Anderson) Y.; m. Noel W. Miller, Apr. 8, 1961 (div. 1977); children: Donovan, Jo-Ann, Kirk, Lori-Anne; adopted children: LaFara, Samantha, Brandon Ryan. Attended, Bethlehem Teachers Coll., St. Elizabeth, Jamaica, 1960; BSC, Baruch Coll., 1976; MA, Columbia U., 1978. Cert. tchr., N.Y. Legal sec. various law firms, N.Y.C., 1969-76; instr. Taylor Bus. Inst., N.Y.C., 1977-79; founder, pres., dir. N.Y. Inst. Bus. Tech., N.Y.C., 1981—. Recipient Outstanding Achievement award Baruch Coll. Alumni Assn., 1989; Leith E. Yetman Day proclaimed June 1, 1994 by Manhattan Borough Pres. Mem. Better Bus. Bur. N.Y.C. Office: NY Inst Bus Tech 401 Park Ave S New York NY 10016

YEUNG, EDWARD SZESHING, chemist; b. Hong Kong, Feb. 17, 1948; came to U.S., 1965; s. King Mai Luk and Yu Long Yeung; m. Anna Kunkwok Seto, Sept. 18, 1971; children: Brad, Gregg, Kim, Van. BS, U. Nebr., 1952, JD, 1963, PhD in Agrl. Econs., 1966, hon. doctorate; hon. doctorate, Clemson U.; Georgetown U., Santa Clara U., Nebr. Wesleyan U., U. Md., DePaul U. Bar: Nebr. 1963, D.C. 1977. Farmer, rancher Nebr., 1957-75; mem. faculty dept. agrl. econs. U. Nebr., Lincoln, 1960-66; dir. U. Nebr. Mission in Colombia, South Am., 1968-70; exec. asst. Gov. Nebr., 1966-68; adminstr. consumer and mktg. svcs. USDA, Washington, 1970-71; regional dir. Com. for Reelection of Pres., 1972; asst. sec. Agr. for Mktg. and Consumer Svcs., Washington, 1973-74, Agr. for Internat. Affairs and Commodity Programs, Washington, 1974-75; dep. spl. trade rep. Exec. Office of Pres., Washington, 1975-77; sr. ptnr. Nelson, Harding, Yeutter & Leonard, Lincoln, Nebr., 1977-78; pres., chief exec. officer Chgo. Mercantile Exchange, 1978-85; U.S. trade rep., 1985-89; sec. U.S. Dept. Agriculture, 1989-91; chmn. Rep. Nat. Com., Washington, 1991-92; counsellor to the President for domestic policy The White House, Washington, 1992—; bd. dirs. Caterpillar, FMC Corp., Oppenheimer Funds. Contbr. numerous articles to profl. jours. Former trustee Garrett-Evangelical Theol. Sem., Evanston, Ill.; past bd. dirs. Chgo. Coun. on Fgn. Rels.; past bd. visitors Sch. Bus. Adminstrn. Georgetown U.; former trustee, mem. exec. com. Farm Found., Oak Brook, Ill. Served with USAF, 1952-57, USAFR, 1957-87. Recipient Israel Prime Minister's medal, Master Builder of Men award FarmHouse, Leadership award Fowler-McCracken Commn., Consumers for World Trade award. Mem. Nebr. Bar Assn. Republican. Methodist. Avocations: snow skiing, water skiing, weight lifting.

YGLESIAS, HELEN BASSINE, author, educator; b. N.Y.C., Mar. 29, 1915; d. Solomon and Kate (Goldstein) Bassine; m. Bernard Cole, 1938 (div. 1950); children: Tamar Cole, Lewis Cole; m. Jose Yglesias, Aug. 19, 1950 (div. 1992); 1 child, Rafael. Student pub. schs. Literary editor Nation Mag., 1965-70; adj. assoc. prof. writing Columbia Sch. Arts, N.Y.C., 1973—; vis. prof. creative writing Writers Workshop, U. Iowa, Iowa City, 1980. Author: (novels) How She Died (Houghton Mifflin award), 1972, Family Feeling, 1976, Sweetsir, 1981, The Saviors, 1987, (non-fiction) Starting: Early, Anew, Over and Late, 1978, Isabel Bishop, 1989. Home: HC 64 Box 2075 Brooklin ME 04616-9801

YHOUSE, PAUL ALAN, manufacturing executive; b. Grand Rapids, Mich., June 23, 1949; s. Keith E. and Elaine (Laraway) Y.; m. Elizabeth Orlyk, Aug. 21, 1971. BBA, U. Mich., 1971. With Arthur Andersen & Co., various locations, 1971-76, mgr., 1976-82, ptnr., 1982-91; sr. v.p., CFO Holnam Inc., Dundee, Mich., 1991-93; pres., CEO, 1993—. Active adv. bd. Paton Acctg. Ctr., U. Mich., Ann Arbor. Mem. AICPA (chmn. healthcare com. 1980-91), Fin. Execs. Inst., Mich. Anssn. CPAs. Office: Holnam Inc 6211 Ann Arbor Rd Dundee MI 48131

YIANNOPOULOS, ATHANASSIOS NICHOLAS, law educator; b. Thessaloniki, Greece, Mar. 13, 1928; came to U.S., 1953, naturalized, 1963; s. Nicholas A. and Areti T. (Alvanos) Y.; m. Mirta Valdes, May 9, 1982; children—Maria, Nicholas, Alexander, Philip. LL.B., U. Thessaloniki, 1950; M.C.L., U. Chgo., 1954; LL.M. (Walter Perry Johnson fellow in law), U. Calif., Berkeley, 1955, J.S.D., 1956; J.D., U. Cologne, W. Ger., 1961; LLD, U. Thessaloniki, Greece, 1995. Bar: Greece 1958. Mem. faculty La. State U., Baton Rouge, 1958-79; Prof. of comparative law, Eason-Weinmann Tulane U. Law Sch., New Orleans, 1979—; in charge revision La. Civil Code, Law Inst., 1962—. Author: Civil Law Property, 3d edit., 1991, Personal Servitudes, 3d edit., 1989, Predial Servitudes, 1983; (with T. Schoenbaum) Admiralty and Maritime Law, 1984; editor: Louisiana Civil Code, annually, 1980—; contbr. articles to various periodicals Ency. Brit. Pres. Baton Rouge Symphony Assn., 1972-73; bd. dirs. Music Soc., 1961-79. Served to 2d lt. Greek Army, 1950-53. Mem. Order of Phoenix, Am. Acad. Fgn. Law, Internat. Acad. Comparative Law, Am. Law Inst., Phi Alpha Delta. Mem. Greek Orthodox Ch. Club: Baton Rouge City. Office: 662 Sunset Blvd Baton Rouge LA 70808

YIELDING, K. LEMONE, physician; b. Auburn, Ala., Mar. 25, 1931; s. Riley Lafayette and Bertie (Dees) Y.; m. Lerena Wade Hauge, Dec. 7, 1973; children: K. Lemone, Michael Lafon, Teresa Louise, Riley Lafayette, Katrina Elizabeth, Elaine Louise Blodgett, Laura Carlen Blodgett. B.S., Ala. Poly. Inst., 1949; M.S., U. Ala., 1952, M.D., 1954. Intern U. Ala. Med. Center, 1954-55; clin. assoc. Nat. Inst. Arthritis and Metabolic Diseases, NIH, 1955-57, sr. investigator, 1958-64; resident med. service USPHS Hosp., Balt. 1957-58; adj. asst. prof. medicine Georgetown U. Med. Sch., 1958-64; cons. USPHS, 1964-68, 75—; prof. biochemistry, assoc. prof. medicine, chief lab. molecular biology U. Ala. Med. Center, Birmingham, 1964-80; prof. and chmn. dept. anatomy, prof. medicine U. So. Ala. Coll. Medicine, Mobile, 1980-87, dean grad. sch., U. Tex. Med. Br., Galveston, 1987—; cons. Am. Heart Assn., Arthritis Found., NIH, NASA. Contbr. to profl. jours., books. Served with USPHS, 1955-64. Grantee USPHS, Am. Cancer Soc., Nat. Found.-March of Dimes, U.S. Army, Am. Inst. Cancer Research. Mem. Am. Soc. Biol. Chemistry, Am. Assn. Cancer Research, Am. Assn. Photobiology, Assn. Research Vision and Ophthalmology, Soc. Exptl. Biology and Medicine, Am. Soc. Pharm. and Exptl. Therapeutics, Am. Assn. Pathologists, So. Soc. Clin. Investigation, Am. Assn. Anatomy, Soc. Toxicology, Sigma Xi.

YIH, CHIA-SHUN, fluid mechanics educator; b. Kweiyang, Kweichow, China, July 25, 1918; s. Ting-Jian and Wan-Lan (Shiao) Y.; m. Shirley Gladys Ashman, Feb. 17, 1949; children: Yiu-Yo, Yuen-Ming David, Weiling Katherine. B.S. Nat. Central U., 1942; M.S., U. Iowa, 1947, Ph.D., 1948. Instr. Nat. Kweichow U., 1944-45; instr. math. U. Wis., 1948-49; lectr. U. B.C., 1949-50; assoc. prof. Colo. State U., 1950-52; research engr. U. Iowa, 1952-54, assoc. prof., 1954-56; assoc. prof. U. Mich., Ann Arbor, 1956-58; prof. U. Mich., 1958-68, Stephen P. Timoshenko Disting. univ. prof. fluid mechanics, 1968-88, S.P. Timoshenko Disting. univ. prof. emeritus, 1988—; grad. rsch. prof. U. Fla., 1987-90, grad. rsch. prof. emeritus, 1990—; vis. prof. U. Paris, U. Grenoble, France, 1970-71; Henry Russel lectr. U. Mich., 1974; lectr. Chinese Acad. Sc., Beijing, 1981, von Kármán Inst., Brussels, 1981, Internat. Ctr. of Theoretical Physics, Trieste, Italy, 1994; G.I. Taylor lectr. U. Fla., 1992; cons. Huyck Felt Co., 1960-64; trustee Rocky Mountain Hydraulic Lab, 1976-85; attaché de recherche in math. French Govt., 1951-52. Author: Dynamics of Nonhomogeneous Fluids, 1965, Fluid Mechanics, An Introduction to the Theory, 1969, 79, 88, Stratified Flows, 1980; editor: Advances in Applied Mechanics, 1970-82; mem. editl. bd. Advances in Applied Mechanics, Physics of Fluids, 1969-72, SIAM Jour. Applied Math. 1971-72, Ann. Revs. of Fluid Mechanics, 1969-72, Advances in Mechanics of China, Acta Mechanica Sinica, Applied Math. and Mechanics, to 1989, Jour. Hydrodynamics to 1989; contbr. articles to profl. jours. Recipient Achievement award Chinese Inst. Engrs. N.Y., 1968, Achievement award Chinese Engrs. and Scientists Assn. So. Calif., 1973, Sr. Scientist award Humboldt Found., Fed. Republic Germany, 1977-78, The-

odore von Kármán medal ASCE, 1981, Stephen S. Attwood award U. Mich., 1984; sr. postdoctoral fellow NSF, 1959-60, Guggenheim fellow, 1964. Fellow Am. Phys. Soc. (chmn. exec. com. fluid dynamics divsn. 1973-74, Fluid Dynamics prize 1985, Otto Laporte award 1989); mem. U.S. Nat. Acad. Engring., Academia Sinica, Sigma Xi, Pi Mu Epsilon, Tau Beta Pi, Phi Kappa Phi. Home: 3530 W Huron River Dr Ann Arbor MI 48103-9417 Home (winter): 4084 NW 23rd Cir Gainesville FL 32605

YIM, JOAN B., federal agency administrator; b. Aug. 14, 1944. BA in History, Conn. Coll., 1966; postgrad., U. Hawaii, 1975-79. Chair cmty. planning com. Kaneohe (Hawaii) Cmty. Coun., 1972-74; exec. sec. neighborhood commn. City and County of Honolulu, 1974-75; planner Office State Planning Office of Gov., State of Hawaii, Honolulu, 1975-92; supervising planner Parsons Brickerhoff Quade & Douglas, Inc., Honolulu, 1992-93; dep. adminstr. Maritime Adminstrn. U.S. Dept. Transp., Washington, 1993—. Nat. committeewoman Dem. Party of Hawaii, 1988—; mem. nat. com. Women Working for Clinton/Gore; mem. exec. bd. Women's Caucus of Dem. Nat. Com.; contbr. Clinton Primary Campaign and Clinton/Gore Fed. Election Compliance Fund; co-chair Apple Pie and Sisterhood; mem. 27-member Nat. Rules and By-law com. Dem. Presdl. Del. Selection Process; regional vice chmn. Dem. Task Force, Nat. Women's Polit. Caucus, 1989-91; legis. co-chair Hawaii Women's Polit. Caucus, 1990-92; mem. at large Nat. Conv. Rules Com., 1992, active Spkrs. Bur. Women Leaders, Clinton/Gore, Hawaii. Mem. LWV, Am. Planning Assn. (Hawaii chpt.), Hawaii Govt. Employees Assn. (assoc.), Assn. Advancement Marine Policy Edn. and Rsch. (mem. ad hoc com.), The Coastal Soc. Home: 3101 New Mexico Ave NW # 819 Washington DC 20016

YIN, GERALD ZHEYAO, technology and engineering executive; b. Beijing, Jan. 29, 1944; came to U.S., 1980; s. Huaixing and Halumi Yin; m. Junling June Yen, Feb. 28, 1971; 1 child, John Chengjiang. BS in Chem. Physics, U. Sci. & Tech. China, Beijing, 1967; postgrad., Beijing U., 1978-80; PhD in Chemistry, UCLA, 1984. Process engr. Lanzhou Oil Refinery, Lanzhou, People's Republic of China, 1968-73; mgr. research staff Chinese Acad. Sciences, Lanzhou, 1973-78; sr. process engr. Intel Corp. Santa Clara TD, Santa Clara, Calif., 1984-86; mgr., staff engr. Lam Rsch. Corp., Rsch. & Devel., Fremont, Calif., 1986-91; dir. etch tech. and engring. new product devel. Applied Materials, Inc., Santa Clara, Calif., 1991. Author: Introducing Orthogonal Design to Semiconductor Industry, 1985; inventor multistep power reduction plasma etching, Rainbow oxide etcher, 200mm enhanced Electron Cyclotron Resonance reactor, High Density Plasma oxide and Decoupled Plasma Source metal etch plasma source and reactors. Recipient Nat. Acad. award People's Republic of China, 1979, Nat. Acad. Invention award, People's Republic of China, 1980. Mem. Electrochem. Soc., Am. Chem. Soc., Am. Vacuum Soc., Silicon Valley Chinese Engring. Assn. (founder, first pres.). Achievements include 6 U.S., Japanese and German patents; 12 patent applications in process. Office: Applied Materials Inc 3320 Scott Blvd M/S 1111 Santa Clara CA 95054

YINGLING, WILLIAM E., III, retail company executive; b. Balt., 1944; married. BS, U. Md., 1971. With Grand Union Stores, 1966-83; with Bi-Lo, Inc., Mauldin, S.C., 1983—, from v.p. store ops. to pres., chief exec. officer, also bd. dirs. Office: Bi-Lo Inc Industrial Blvd Mauldin SC 29662 Office: Thrifty Drug Stores 3424 Wilshire Blvd Los Angeles CA 90010-2241

YNTEMA, MARY KATHERINE, retired mathematics educator; b. Urbana, Ill., Jan. 20, 1928; d. Leonard Francis and M. Jean (Busey) Y. BA in Math., Swarthmore Coll., 1950; MA in Math., U. Ill., 1961, PhD in Math., 1965. Tchr., secondary math. Am. Coll. for Girls, Istanbul, Turkey, 1950-54, Columbus (Ohio) Sch. for Girls, 1954-57; computer programmer MIT Lincoln Lab. Lexington, Mass., 1957-58; tchr., secondary math Roundup (Mont.) High Sch., 1959-60; asst. prof. math U. Ill., Chgo., 1965-67; asst. prof. computer sci. Pa. State U., University Park, 1967-71; assoc. prof. to prof. math. Sangamon State U., Springfield, Ill., 1971-91; ret., 1991. Avocation: enjoyment of nature.

YOAKAM, DWIGHT, country western musician; b. Pikeville, Ky., 1956. Albums include Guitars, Cadillacs, Etc. Etc., 1985, Hillbilly Deluxe, 1987, Buenas Noches From A Lonely Room, 1988, Just Lookin' for a Hit, 1989, If There Was a Way, 1990, This Time, 1993 (2 Grammy nominations); duet with Buck Owens Streets of Bakersfield, 1988 (#1 single); co-prodr. stage appearance Southern Rapture, 1993. Named Top Male Vocalist by Acad. Country Music, 1986. *

YOCAM, DELBERT WAYNE, communication company executive; b. Long Beach, Calif., Dec. 24, 1943; s. Royal Delbert and Mary Rose (Gross) Y.; m. Janet McVeigh, June 13, 1965; children—Eric Wayne, Christian Jeremy, Elizabeth Janelle. B.A. in Bus. Adminstrn., Calif. State U.-Fullerton, 1966; M.B.A., Calif. State U., Long Beach, 1971. Mktg.-supply changeover coordinator Automotive Assembly div. Ford Motor Co., Dearborn, Mich., 1966-72; prodn. control mgr. Control Data Corp. Hawthorne, Calif., 1972-74; prodn. and material control mgr. Bourns Inc., Riverside, Calif., 1974-76; corp. material mgr. Computer Automation Inc., Irvine, Calif., 1976-78; prodn. planning mgr. central staff Cannon Electric div. ITT, World hdqrs., Santa Ana, Calif., 1978-79; exec. v.p., chief ops. officer Apple Computer, Cupertino, Calif., 1979-91; pres., COO Textronix Inc., Wilsonville, Oreg., 1992-95; mem. faculty Cypress Coll., Calif., 1972-79; bd. dirs. Adobe Sys. Inc., Mountain View, Calif., 1991—, Oracle Corp., Redwood Shores, Calif., 1992—, AST Rsch. Inc., Irvine, Calif., 1992—, Tech. Ctr. of San Jose, Calif. 1987-93, vice chmn., 1989, 90. Mem. Am. Electronics Assn. (bd. dirs. 1988-89), Control Data Corp. Mgmt. Assn. (co-founder 1974), L.A. County Heart Assn. (active 1966).

YOCHELSON, BONNIE ELLEN, museum curator, art historian; b. Buffalo, Nov. 6, 1952; d. Samuel and Kathryn (Mersey) Y.; m. Paul Lewis Shechtman, Sept. 3, 1972; children: Emily, Anna. BA in History, Swarthmore Coll., 1974; MA, NYU, 1979, PhD, 1985. Asst. curator dept. prints and drawings Nat. Gallery Art, Washington, 1979-81; lectr. dept. art history U. Pa.q, Phila., 1985-87; curator prints and photographs Mus. of the City of N.Y., 1987-91, cons. curator, 1991—; faculty M of Photography program Sch. Visual Arts, N.Y.C., 1988—; adj. assoc. prof. dept. art history NYU, 1987. Mem. Coll. Art Assn.

YOCHELSON, ELLIS LEON, paleontologist; b. Washington, Nov. 14, 1928; s. Morris Wolf and Fannie (Botkin) Y.; m. Sally Witt, June 10, 1950; children: Jeffrey, Abby, Charles. B.S., U. Kans., 1949, M.S., 1950; Ph.D., Columbia U., 1955. Paleontologist U.S. Geol. Survey, 1952-85, scientist emeritus, 1991; biostratigrapher, specializing in Paleozoic gastropods and minor classes of extinct mollusks; lectr. night sch. George Washington U., 1962-65; lectr. Univ. Coll. U. Md., 1964-74, U. Del., 1981; vis. prof. U. Md., 1986-87; organizer N.Am. Paleontol. Conv., 1969, editor proc, 1970-71; Co-editor: Essays in Paleontology and Stratigraphy, 1967; editor: Scientific Ideas of G.K. Gilbert, 1980; editorial bd. Nat. Geog. Rsch. and Exploration; contbr. numerous articles to profl. jours. Co-editor: Essays in Paleontology and Stratigraphy, 1967; editor: Scientific Ideas of G.K. Gilbert, 1980; contbr. numerous articles to profl. jours. Fellow AAAS (chmn. sect. E 1971); mem. Soc. Systematic Zoology (sec. 1961-66, councilor 1973), Internat. Paleontol. Assn. (treas. 1972-76), Paleontol. Soc. (pres. 1976), History of Earth Scis. Soc. (sec.-treas. 1982-85, sec. 1986-87, pres.-elect 1988, pres. 1989), N.Am. Paleontol. Soc. (sec. VI sect.), Sigma Xi. Office: Smithsonian Instn E-304 E Mus Natural History Washington DC 20560

YOCHELSON, JOHN, political economist; b. New Brunswick, N.J., Jan. 2, 1944; s. Samuel and Kathryn (Mersey) Y.; m. Diane Kamino, Aug. 19, 1950; children: Lisa R., Laura S. BA magne cum laude, Yale U., 1965; MPA, Princeton U., 1967. Polit. economist Ctr. for Strategic and Internat. Studies, Washington; pres. Edmond de Rothschild Found., 1992—; mem. adv. bd. Internat. Inst. Geopolitics, Paris, 1995—, European Inst., Washington, 1989—; mem. adv. com. internat. investment U.S. Dept. of State, Washington, 1990-92, Coun. of Fgn. Rels., N.Y.C., 1991. Editor: Keeping Pace: U.S. Policies and Global Economic Change, Under Pressure: U.S. Industry and the World Economy. 2d lt. U.S. army, 1967-70. Mem. Phi Beta Kappa. Republican. Office: Ctr for Strategic Studies 1800 K St NW Washington DC 20006-2200

YOCHEM, BARBARA JUNE, sales executive, lecturer; b. Knox, Ind., Aug. 22, 1945; d. Harley Albert and Rosie (King) Runyan; m. Donald A. Yochem (div. 1979); 1 child, Morgan Lee; m. Don Heard, Dec. 12, 1987. Grad. high school, Knox, Ind., 1963. Sales rep. Hunter Woodworks, Carson, Calif., 1979-84, sales mgr. 1984-87; sales rep. Comml. Lumber and Pallet, Industry, Calif., 1987-92; owner By By Prodns., Glendora, Calif., 1976—. Author: Barbara Yochem's Inner Shooting; contbr. articles to profl. jours. Head coach NRA Jr. Olympic Shooting Camp, 1989-94; foster parent, 1992-94. Recipient U.S. Bronze medal U.S. Olympic Com., 1976, World Bronze medal U.S Olympic Com., 1980; nominated Calif. Trapshooting Hall of Fame, 1994. Avocation: trapshooting. Address: By By Prodns PO Box 1676 Glendora CA 91740-1676

YOCHIM, MARIE HIRST, retired association executive; b. Washington; d. Herbert Nelson and Ellen (Mankin) Hirst; m. Eldred Martin Yochim, Dec. 24, 1942. Student, Strayer Coll., 1939-40. Exec. officer Jesse Johnson, Inc., Lakewood Builders & Glenbrook Corp., Arlington, Va., 1940-56; regent DAR Falls Ch. (Va.) Chpt., 1956-62; dir. dist. V Va. DAR, 1962-65, state rec. sec., 1965-68, state regent, 1977-80, mem. fin. com. bd. trustees, 1987—; chief of Corresponding Gen.'s Office Nat. Soc. DAR, Washington, 1962-77, organizing sec. gen., 1980-83, 1st v.p. gen., 1983-86, 89-92, pres. gen., 1989—. Recipient Bronze medal Chapel of Four Chaplains, 1980, Medal of Aprpeaciation, Va. chpt. SAR, 1980, Va. Honor Pin, Va. chpt. Children of Revolution, 1981, Gold Good Citizenship medal SAR, 1990, Martha Washington medal SAR, 1991. Mem. Jamestown Soc., U.S. Daus. of 1812, Colonial Dames of XVII Century, Dames of Ct. of Honor, Nat. Gavel Soc., Order of Eastern Star. Lutheran. Home: 7314 Hughes Ct Falls Church VA 22046-1923 Office: 1776 D St NW Washington DC 20006-5392

YOCHUM, PHILIP THEODORE, retired motel and cafeteria chain executive; b. Quakertown, Pa., Sept. 20, 1924; s. Theodore J. and Margaret (Scheetz) Y.; m. Connie Petrillose, June 23, 1947; children: Cynthia, Philip Theodore. B.S. in Hotel Adminstrn., Cornell U., 1948. Engaged in hotel and restaurant work Quakertown, Pa.; engaged in hotel and restaurant work Ithaca, N.Y., 1948-51; various positions to regional mgr. Slater System, Inc., Balt., 1951-57; asst. v.p. ops. A.L. Mathias Co., Towson, Md., 1957-59; v.p. A.L. Mathias Co., 1959-61, exec. v.p., 1961-65; exec. v.p. (merger A.L. Mathias Co. and Servomation Corp. 1964); pres. Servomation Mathias, Inc. (merger into Servomation Corp., 1964), 1965-74, regional mgr. for food service mgmt. and vending, 1974-76; also dir.; dir. corp. devel. S & S Enterprises (operating Golden Plough Restaurants in Md. and N.J.), 1977-80; dist. mgr. Canteen Corp., Landover, Md., 1980-81; v.p., gen. mgr. Davis Bros., Inc., Hdqrs. Atlanta, 1981-91. Trustee Food Service Execs. Assn. Edn. Trust Fund. Served with AUS, World War II, ETO. Decorated Purple Heart. Mem. Internat. Food Service Execs. Assn. (Food Exec. of Year award Balt. br. 1972, 1990, city chmn. So. region sec., publicity chmn. Atlanta br.), Food Service and Lodging Inst. (dir.), Cornell Soc. Hotelmen, Ga. Hospitality and Travel Assn., Nat. Restaurant Assn. Home: 158 77th St Avalon NJ 08202-1019

YOCK, ROBERT JOHN, federal judge; b. St. James, Minn., Jan. 11, 1938; s. William Julius and Erma Idella (Fritz) Y.; m. Carla Marie Moen, June 13, 1964; children: Signe Kara, Torunn Ingrid. B.A., St. Olaf Coll., 1959; J.D., U. Mich., 1962; postgrad., U. Strasbourg, France, 1961, Old Dominion Coll., 1964-65, U. Minn., 1966-67. Bar: Minn. 1962, U.S. Supreme Ct. 1965, D.C. 1972. Asso. Thomas, King, Swenson & Collatz, St. Paul, 1966-69; chief counsel Nat. Archives, Office Gen Counsel, GSA, Washington, 1969-70, exec. asst. to adminstr., 1970-72; asst. gen. counsel GSA, 1972-77; trial judge U.S. Ct. Claims, Washington, 1977-82; judge U.S. Claims Ct., Washington, 1982-92, U.S. Ct. Fed. Claims, Washington, 1992—. Served with JAGC USN, 1962-66. Mem. ABA, Minn., Fed., D.C. Bar Assns. Home: 4200 Webster Ct Annandale VA 22003-3424 Office: US Ct Fed Claims 717 Madison Pl NW Washington DC 20005-1086

YOCKIM, JAMES CRAIG, state senator, oil and gas executive; b. Williston, N.D., Feb. 13, 1953; s. Daniel and Doris (Erickson) Y.; m. Donna Jean Erickson, Apr. 21, 1985; children: Jenna, Ericka. BSW, Pacific Luth. U., 1975; MSW, San Diego State U., 1979. Caseworker Dyslin Boys Ranch, Tacoma, 1975-77; landman Fayette Oil & Gas, Williston, 1980-82; head caseworker, program dir. Pyslin Boys Ranch, 1979-80; owner Hy-Plains Energy, Williston, 1982-87; city fin. commr. City of Williston, 1984-88; therapist Luth. Social Svcs., Williston, 1983—; senator N.C. State Senate, 1986—; owner James C. Yockim Resources, Williston, 1987—. Del. N.D. Dem. Conv., 1984, 86, 88, 90, 92; dist. chmn. Dem. Party, Williston, 1988; caucus chmn. Dem. Caucus N.D. State Senate. Recipient Ruth Meiers award N.D. Mental Health Assn., 1989, Legislator of Yr. award N.D. Children's Caucus, 1989; named Outstanding Young North Dakotan N.D. Jaycees, 1988. Mem. NASW. Avocations: racquetball, softball, golf. Home: 1123 2nd Ave E Williston ND 58801 Office: 322 Main Ste 202 Williston ND 58802-2344

YOCUM, CHARLEEN ELAINE, educational administrator, counselor; b. Denver, June 21, 1941; d. Charles Marston and Margie Ellen (Terwilliger) Macy; m. Gilbert Lee Yocum, Mar. 22, 1964; children: David, Dean, Danielle. AB in Teaching, U. No. Colo., 1963; MEd, Colo. State U., 1984, postgrad., 1991—. Cert. tchr., job devel. specialist, Colo. Sec. various cos., Denver, 1957-63; tchr. North High Sch., Denver, 1963, Metro Youth Ctr., Denver, 1966; instr. Red Rocks C.C., Lakewood, Colo., 1971-78; tchr. Jefferson County Schs., Arvada, Colo., 1978-89; adminstr. Jefferson County Schs., Lakewood, 1989-93; career counselor Standley Lake High Sch., 1993—; facilitator numerous curriculum guides, 1988—. Co-chmn. Arvada West Bus. Adv. Coun., 1980-88; mem. Exec. Bus. Coun., Golden, Colo., 1985-88; mem., co-facilitator Jeffco County Adv. Com., Golden, 1988-92; charter mem. Eldorado Homeowners Assn., 1971-75; block organizer Am. Heart Assn., Diabetes Found., 1980-88; participant Ronald MacDonald House; mem. Leaders Industry, Bus., Edn. Relating To Youth, Lakewood, 1991-92. Named Outstanding Bus. Tchr., Nat. Mgmt. Assn., Instr. of Excellence, Women's Leadership Inst., 1990; scholar Leadership Lakewood, 1991. Mem. Am. Vocat. Assn., Colo. Vocat. Assn., Jefferson County Adminstrs. Assn., Colo. Mktg. Assn., Colo. For and About Bus., Leadership Lakewood Alumnae Assn. Avocations: bridge, golf, bowling, watching football, baseball and soccer, church activities. Office: Standley Lake High Sch 9300 W 104th Ave Westminster CO 80021

YOCUM, CHARLES FREDRICK, biology educator; b. Storm Lake, Iowa, Oct. 31, 1941; s. Vincent Cary and Olive Lucille (Cammack) Y.; m. Patricia Joan Bury, Jan. 1, 1981; 1 son, Erik Charles. BS, Iowa State U., 1963; MS, Ill. Inst. Tech., 1968; PhD, Ind. U., 1971. Research biochemist Ill. Inst. Tech. Research Inst., Chgo., 1963-68; grad. fellow Ind. U., Bloomington, 1968-71; postdoctoral fellow Cornell U., Ithaca, N.Y., 1971-73; asst. prof. U. Mich., Ann Arbor, 1973-77, assoc. prof., 1978-82, prof. biol. scis. and chemistry, 1983—, chmn. dept. biology, 1985-91; vis. prof. Mich. State U., East Lansing, 1980-81; cons. NSF, Washington, 1982—. Editorial bd. Plant Physiology, Photosynthesis Research, Biochimica et Biophysica Acta.; contbr. articles to various pubs. Recipient Henry Russel award U. Mich., 1977; research grantee NSF, 1978—, USDA, 1978—. Mem. AAAS, Am. Chem. Soc., Am. Soc. Plant Physiologists, Am. Soc. Biol. Chemists, Am. Soc. Photobiology. Avocations: classical music, travel. Office: Dept Biology Univ of Mich Ann Arbor MI 48109-1048

YOCUM, HARRISON GERALD, horticulturist, botanist, educator, researcher; b. Bethlehem, Pa., Apr. 2, 1923; s. Harrison and Bertha May (Meckes) Y. BS, Pa. State U., 1955; MS, Rutgers U., 1961. Horticulture instr. U. Tenn., Martin, 1957-59; biology tchr., libr. asst. high schs., El Paso, Tex., 1959-60; rsch. asst. geochronology lab. U. Ariz., Tucson, 1960-67, rsch. asst. environ. rsch. lab., 1969-76; landscaping supt. Tucson Airport Authority, 1976-82; instr. Pima C.C., Tucson, 1976—. Contbr. articles to profl. jours. Founder Tucson Bot. Gardens, 1964. Mem. Am. Hort. Soc., Men's Garden Club Tucson Inc. (pres. 1991), Tucson Cactus & Succulent Soc. (pres. 1991, 92), Internat. Palm Soc. (charter), El Paso Cactus & Rock Club, Tucson Gem & Mineral Soc., Old Pueblo Lapidary Club, Deming Mineral Soc., Nat. Geog. Soc., Ariz.-Sonora Desert Mus., Huachuca Vigilantes, Penn State Alumni Assn., Pa. Club Tucson, Fraternal Order Police Assocs., N.Am. Hunting Club (life), Shriners, Masons, Scottish Rite. Lutheran. Home: 1628 N Jefferson Ave Tucson AZ 85712-4204

YOCUM, RONALD HARRIS, chemical company executive; b. Darby, Pa., June 2, 1939; s. Jacob Harris and Gladys (Phillips) Y.; m. Martha Virginia Meitzner, July 6, 1963; children—Beth Ann, James Eric. B.A., Gettysburg Coll., Pa., 1961; Ph.D., U. Pa., 1965. With Dow Chem. Co., 1965—; dir. research and devel. Dow Latin Am. Coral Gables, Fla., 1973-77; dir. research and devel. designed products dept. Midland, Mich., 1977-78, dir. product research Dow USA, 1978-80, dir. research Mich. div., 1980-85; group v.p. Norchem, Rolling Meadows, Ill., 1985-87; group v.p. Quantum Chem. Corp., Cin., 1987-89, pres. USI div., 1989-90, exec. v.p., 1990—. Editor: (with others) Functional Monomers, Vols. I and II, 1974. Active Boy Scouts Am. Mem. Am. Chem. Soc., Chem. Industry Inst. of Tech. (bd. dirs. 1985-86). Republican. Episcopalian. Office: Quantum Chem Corp USI Division 11500 Northlake Dr Cincinnati OH 45249-1642

YODER, AMOS, university research official; b. Falls City, Nebr., Mar. 2, 1921; s. Amos Howard and Mildred Ann (Johnson) Y.; m. Janet Lee Tatman, June 15, 1946; children: James Amos, Barbara Ann Yoder Gorga, Sally Irene Yoder Ramseyer. BA, Ohio Wesleyan U., 1942; PhD, U. Chgo., 1949. Jr. econs. editor Bd. of Econ. Warfare, Washington, 1942-43; fgn. svc. officer Dept. of State, Washington, 1949-74; Borah Disting. prof. polit. sci. U. Idaho, Moscow, 1974-91; Fulbright prof. Lajos Kossuth U., Debrecen, Hungary, 1991; rsch assoc. Mershon Ctr., Ohio State U., Columbus, 1993—; vis. lectr. U. Calif., Davis, 1964-65; Fulbright prof. Fgn. Affairs Coll., Beijing, 1986-87. Author: International Politics and Policymakers Ideas, 1982, The Conduct of American Foreign Policy Since World War II, 1986, World Politics and the Causes of War Since 1914, 1986, The Evolution of the United Nations, 1989, rev. edit., 1993, Communist Systems and Challenges, 1990, Communism in Transition, 1993; guest editor Terrorism-An Internat. Jour., summer 1983; contbr. articles to profl. jours. With USAF, 1943-46. Recipient Commendation ribbon War Dept., 1946, Merit Honor award Dept. State, 1967. Mem. Internat. Studies Assn., Idaho Polit. Sci. Assn. (v.p., pres. 1980-81), Amnesty Internat., Kiwanis (pres. Moscow, Idaho chpt. 1981-82). Democrat. Presbyterian. Home: 127 S Hempstead Rd Westerville OH 43081-2514 Office: Ohio State U Mershon Ctr 1501 Neil Ave Columbus OH 43201 *Whatever success and satisfaction I have attained in my life have been based on playing the games with principles and persistence.*

YODER, EDGAR PAUL, education educator; b. Millersburg, Ohio, June 20, 1946; s. Albert Daniel Yoder and Ella Marie (Bontrager) Erb; m. Deborah Jean Barnhart, June 12, 1971; children: Scott, Suzan. BSA, Ohio State U., 1968, MS, 1972, PhD, 1976. Cert. tchr., counselor, prin., Ohio, Va. Tchr. agr. and sci. Conotton Valley Schs., Bowerston, Ohio, 1968-69, East Holmes Schs., Berlin, Ohio, 1969-72; curriculum specialist Ohio State U., Columbus, 1972-74, project dir., 1974-76; asst. prin. Montgomery County Schs., Blacksburg, Va., 1976-77; asst. prof. Va. Poly. Inst. and State U., Blacksburg, 1977-78; asst. prof. Pa. State U., University Park, 1978-84, assoc. prof. tchr. edn., 1984-94, prof., 1994—; cons. Poland Ministry Edn., Warsaw, 1994, Swaziland Ministry Agr., Mbane, 1985, 87, U. Peredenyia, Kandy, Sri Lanka, 1984. Author text: Ag Supplies and Services, 1974, (with others) Undergraduate Education in Agriculture, 1989, also chpt. to book. Chmn. community svc. Sertoma Internat., Columbus, 1975; asst. dir. Va. HSA Assn., Blacksburg, 1978; sect. chmn. Am. Heart Assn., State College, Va., 1981; pres. Ferguson Twp. PTO, State College, 1983-84; bd. dirs. RAFT Drug Rehab. Ctr., Radford, 1976-78, Nat. Future Farmers Am., Alexandria, Va., 1981-83. Recipient Hon. Degree, Nat. Future Farmers Am., 1983. Mem. Nat. Assn. Coll. Tchrs. Agr. (teacher fellow 1987, Regional Outstanding Teaching award 1992), Am. Assn. Agr. Educators (legis. chmn. 1985), Am. Assn Ednl. Rsch., Am. Vocat. Edn. Rsch. Assn., Assn. Internat. Agr. and Extension Edn., Phi Delta Kappa, Gamma Sigma Delta (Teaching award of Merit 1987). Avocations: collecting sports memorabilia, restoring antiques, classic cars. Office: Penn State U Coll Agricultural Scis University Park PA 16802

YODER, EDWIN MILTON, JR., columnist, educator, editor, writer; b. Greensboro, N.C., July 18, 1934; s. Edwin M. and Mytrice M. (Logue) Y.; m. Mary Jane Warwick, Nov. 1, 1958; children: Anne Daphne, Edwin Warwick. B.A., U. N.C., 1956; BA, MA (Rhodes scholar), Oxford (Eng.) U., 1958; D.H.L. (hon.), Grinnell Coll., 1980, Elon Coll., 1986; DLitt (hon.), U. N.C., 1993. Editorial writer Charlotte (N.C.) News, 1958-61; editorial writer Greensboro Daily News, 1961-64, assoc. editor, 1965-75; asst. prof. history U. N.C., Greensboro, 1964-65; editorial page editor Washington Star, 1975-81; syndicated columnist Washington Post Writers Group, 1982—; prof. journalism and humanities Washington and Lee U., 1992—. Author: Night of the Old South Ball, 1984, The Unmaking of a Whig, 1990, Joe Alsop's Cold War, 1995; contbr. articles to periodicals. Recipient awards editorial writing N.C. Press Assn., 1958,· 61, 66, Walker Stone award Scripps-Howard Found., 1978, Pulitzer prize editorial writing, 1979; Disting. Alumnus award U. N.C., Chapel Hill, 1980. Mem. Nat. Conf. Editorial Writers, Am. Soc. Newspaper Editors. Democrat. Episcopalian. Home: 4001 Harris Pl Alexandria VA 22304-1720

YODER, FREDERICK FLOYD, fraternity executive; b. Wilkinsburg, Pa., Oct. 7, 1935; s. Floyd Elvin and Mary Viola (Stahl) Y. B.S. in Journalism, Ohio U., 1957. Mem. hdqrs. staff Sigma Chi, Evanston, Ill., 1957—, coordinator chpt. visitation and installations program, 1964-72, leadership tng. adminstr., 1962-76, editor mag., 1972-91, dir. commn., 1991-93, dir. alumni participation and cmty. svc., 1994—. Editor The Norman Shield, 1973-91, Sigma Chi Membership Directory, 1977, 87; contbr. articles to interfrat. jours. Served with AUS, 1958. Mem. Coll. Frat. Editors Assn. (past pres., Varner Outstanding Frat. Communicator award, Ford Outstanding Svc. award), Chgo. Headline Club, Soc. Profl. Journalists, Omicron Delta Kappa. Home: 2603 Sheridan Rd Evanston IL 60201-1752 Office: 1714 Hinman Ave Evanston IL 60201-4517

YODER, HATTEN SCHUYLER, JR., petrologist; b. Cleve., Mar. 20, 1921; s. Hatten Schuyler and Elizabeth Katherine (Knieling) Y.; m. Elizabeth Marie Bruffey, Aug. 1, 1959; children: Hatten Schuyler III, Karen Marianne. AA, U. Chgo., 1940, SB, 1941; student, U. Minn., summer 1941; PhD, Mass. Inst. Tech., 1948; D honoris causa, U. Paris VI, 1981; D in eng. (hon.), Colo. Sch. Mines, 1995. Petrologist Geophys. Lab., Carnegie Instn., Washington, 1948-71, dir., 1971-86, dir. emeritus, 1986—; cons. Los Alamos (N.Mex.) Nat. Lab., 1972—. Author: Generation of Basaltic Magma, 1976; editor: The Evolution of the Igneous Rocks: Fiftieth Anniversary Perspectives, 1979; co-editor Jour. of Petrology, 1959-69; assoc. editor Am. Jour. Sci, 1972-90; contbr. articles to sci. jours. Trustee Culver Trust, 1992—. Served to lt. comdr. USNR, 1942-58. Recipient Bicentennial medal Columbia U., 1954, A.G. Werner medal German Mineral Soc., 1972; named to Disting. Alumni Hall of Fame, Lakewood (Ohio) H.S., 1990; mineral yoderite named in his honor. Fellow Geol. Soc. Am. (mem. council 1966-68, A.L. Day medal 1962), Geol. Soc. London (hon. Wollaston medal 1979, Hallimond lectr. 1979), Geol. Soc. South Africa (du Toit lectr. 1987), Am. Acad. Arts and Scis., Mineral. Soc. Am. (council 1962-64, 69-73, pres. 1971-72, Roebling medal 1992), Am. Geophys. Union (pres. volcanology, geochemistry and petrology sect. 1962-64); mem. Mineral Soc. London (hon. 1983—), Geol. Soc. Finland, Russian Mineralogical Soc. (hon.), Geochem. Soc. (organizer, founding mem., council 1965-58), Am. Chem. Soc., Mineral Assn. Can., NAS (chmn. geology sect. 1973-76, A.L. Day prize and lectureship 1972), Washington Acads. Sci., Geol. Soc. Washington, Chem. Soc. Washington, French Soc. Mineralogy and Crystallography (hon. 1986—), Am. Philos. Soc. (council 1983-85), Public Members Assn. of the Fgn. Svc. (mem. bd. dirs 1992—, v.p. 1994), History Earth Scis. Soc. (pres. 1995—), SAR, Sigma Xi, Phi Delta Theta Golden Legion. Home: 6709 Melody Ln Bethesda MD 20817-3152 Office: Geophys Lab 5251 Broad Branch Rd NW Washington DC 20015-1305

YODER, JOHN CHRISTIAN, state senator, lawyer, insurance company executive; b. Newton, Kans., Jan. 9, 1951; s. Gideon G. and Stella (Hostetler) Y.; m. T. Irene Sanders, Apr. 23, 1984 (div. Nov. 1991). BA, Chapman Coll., Orange, Calif., 1972; JD, U. Kans., 1975; MBA, U. Chgo., 1976. Bar: Kans. 1975, Ind. 1976, D.C. 1985, W.Va. 1991. Assoc. prof. bus. Goshen (Ind.) Coll., 1975-76; chmn. bd. Stone Mill Bakeries, Inc., 1977-81; dist. ct. judge Wva. jud. dist. State of Kans., Newton, 1977-80; chmn. bd., v.p., dir. Jay Energy Devel. Co., 1978-81; jud. fellow U.S. Supreme Ct., Washington, 1980-81, spl. asst. to chief justice of the U.S., 1981-83; dir. Asset Forfeiture Office, U.S. Dept. Justice, Washington, 1983-84; pvt. practice, Harpers Ferry, W.Va., 1984—; mem. W.Va. Senate, Charleston, 1993—,

minority whip, 1993-94; exec. v.p., dir. Patriot Life Ins. Co., Tampa, Fla., 1985—; bd. dirs. Kinderhook Oil and Gas Inc., Waukee, Iowa. Rep. nominee for U.S. Senate, 1990. Mem. FBA, W.Va. Bar, D.C. Bar, Ind. Bar Assns., Kans. Bar Assn., U.S.C. of C. (coun. on trends and perspectives 1982-90). Mennonite. Avocations: hiking, bicycling. Home: RR 3 Box 109 Harpers Ferry WV 25425-9728 Office: WVa Senate 1900 Kanawha Blvd E Charleston WV 25305-0800

YODER, JOHN HOWARD, theology educator; b. Smithville, Ohio, Dec. 29, 1927; s. Howard C. and Ethel (Good) Y.; m. Anne Marie, July 14, 1952; children: Rebecca, Marthe, Daniel, Elisabeth, Esther, John-David. Dr. Theol., U. Basel, 1957. Prof. Goshen Bibl. Sem., Elkhart, Ind., 1965-84, U. Notre Dame (Ind.), 1977—. Author: Politics of Jesus, 1972, Priestly Kingdom, 1985. Mem. Soc. of Christian Ethics (pres. 1987-88). Office: U Notre Dame Dept of Theology Dept Theology Notre Dame IN 46556

YODER, LAUREN WAYNE, foreign language educator; b. Newport News, Va., Mar. 9, 1943; s. Lauren Aquilla and Nina Viola (Stemen) Y.; m. Rita Suzanne Frey, June 27, 1964; children—Reinald, Jocelyn. B.A., Eastern Mennonite Coll., 1964; M.A., U. Iowa, 1969, Ph.D. 1973. Tchr. Ecole Secondaire Pedagogique, Kikwit, Zaire, 1966-68; prof. French, dir. Ctr. for Spl. Studies Davidson Coll. Fulbright lectr. U.S. Info. Agy., Paris, 1971-72, Libreville, Gabon, 1980-81; participant NEH summer seminar, Miami, Fla., 1979, Lawrence, Kans., 1991. Mem. SAMLA, African Lit. Assn., Caribbean Studies Assn., Assn. Caribbean Studies. Democrat. Mennonite. Avocations: bee-keeping, skiing, gardening, volleyball. Home: PO Box 1604 Davidson NC 28036-1604 Office: Davidson Coll PO Box 1719 Davidson NC 28036-1719

YODER, PATRICIA DOHERTY, public relations executive; b. Pitts., Oct. 30, 1939; d. John Addison and Camella Grace (Conti) Doherty; children: Shari Lynn, Wendy Ann. BA, Duquesne U., 1961. Press sec. U.S. Ho. of Reps., 1965-69; dir. office of pub. info. City of Ft. Wayne, 1973-76; asst. mgr. pub. and corp. communications Mellon Bank N.A., Pitts., 1977-79; v.p. pub. affairs Am. Waterways Operators Inc., Washington, 1980-83; sr. v.p., gen. mgr. 1983-86, exec. v.p., dir. internat. banking, 1989-91, Hill and Knowlton Inc., Pitts.; sr. v.p. corp. and pub. affairs PNC Bank, Pitts., 1987-89; v.p., mgr. corp. pub. rels. and advt. GE Capital, 1991—. Trustee Shadyside Hosp., Pressley Ridge Sch., Pitts.; bd. dirs. Children's Mus., Civic Light Opera, Pitts. Ballet Theatre, Stamford, (Conn.) Symphony; mem. communications bd. visitors U. Pitts. Mem. Pitts. Field Club, Duquesne Club, Landmark Club, Century Club of Disting. Duquesne U. Alumni. Roman Catholic. Home: 13 Brown House Rd Old Greenwich CT 06870 Office: 260 Long Ridge Rd Stamford CT 06927-0001

YODER, RONDA ELAINE, nursing educator; b. Indpls., Oct. 7, 1963; d. Charles Stewart and Sarah Angeline (Pfaff) Bower; m. Robert Paul Yoder, July 22, 1989; 1 child, Robert Andrew. BSN, Pensacola Christian Coll., 1985; MSN, Ind. U., Indpls., 1988; DSN, U. Ala., Birmingham, 1994. Emergency staff nurse Westview Hosp., Indpls., 1986-88, West Fla. Regional Med. Ctr., Pensacola, 1988-89; DON Pensacola Christian Coll., 1988-93, mem. nursing faculty, 1993—. Mem. Sigma Theta Tau. Home: 1245 Langley Ave Pensacola FL 32504

YODER, RONNIE A., federal administrative law judge; b. Knoxville, Tenn., July 10, 1937; s. Raymond Abraham and Veryl Hope (Hostetler) Y.; m. Shirley Mae Grimes, June 28, 1961; children: Susan Elizabeth, Mary Amanda, Elizabeth Anne, John Anthony Gerhard. BA in Polit. Sci. with honors, U. Va., 1958, JD, 1961. Bar: Va. 1961, N.Y. 1963, D.C. 1965, U.S. Dist. Ct. D.C. 1965, U.S. Dist. Ct. (so. dist.) N.Y. 1969, U.S. Ct. Claims 1964, U.S. Supreme Ct. 1968. Assoc. Mudge Rose Guthrie & Alexander, N.Y.C. and Washington, 1962-70; of counsel Zuckert Scoutt & Rasenberger, Washington, 1970-72, ptnr., 1972-75; adminstrv. law judge U.S. Dept. Labor, Washington, 1976, CAB, Washington, 1976-84, U.S Dept. Transp., Washington, 1985—; adminstrv. law judge Nat. Transp. Safety Bd., 1979-80, Maritime Adminstrn., 1982, FDIC, 1982-83. Small Bus. Adminstrn., 1983. Mem. editorial bd. U. Va. Law Rev., 1959-61; contbr. articles to profl. jours. Sec., co-counsel Capital Headstart, 1966-68; narrator Lincoln Commn., 1985, 86. Rockefeller fellow, 1961. Mem. ABA (mem. jud. adminstrn. div. coun. 1994—, nat. conf. adminstrv. law judges exec. com. 1980-83, 85-89, 90—, sec., 1991-92, vice chair, 1992-93, chair-elect, 1993-94, chair 1994—, parliamentarian, 1991-92, reporter Model Code Judicial Conduct for Fed. Adminstrv. Law Judges 1989, adminstrv. law sect. com. on internat. and comparative adminstrv. law, sect. of sect. officers chair task force on participation in profl. assns. by govt. employees 1991-92), Am. Judicature Soc., SAR, Fed. Adminstrv. Law Judges Conf. (exec. com. 1976-81, 85, 87), Nat. Assn. Adminstrv. Law Judges, Va. Bar Assn. (adminstrv. law sect. bd. govs. 1981-87), D.C. Bar Assn., Am. Judges Assn., Fed. Bar Assn., Nat. Capital Presbytery (permanent jud. commn.), Phi Eta Sigma, Phi Beta Kappa. Home: 1400 Summit Ave Alexandria VA 22302-2735 Office: Dept Transp 400 7th St SW Rm 9228 Washington DC 20590-0002

YODER WISE, PATRICIA SNYDER, nurse, educator; b. Wadsworth, Ohio, July 2, 1941; d. Belford Grant and Leona Cora (Mohler) Snyder; m. Robert Thomas Wise, Feb. 17, 1973; children: Doreen Ellen, Deborah Ann. BS in Nursing, Ohio State U., 1963; MS in Nursing, Wayne State U., 1968; EdD, Tex. Tech. U., 1984. Cert. gerontol. nurse and nursing adminstr., RN, Tex., Ohio. Rsch. asst. Wayne State U., Detroit, 1968; ednl. dir. Ohio Nurses' Assn., Columbus, 1968-72; asst. dir. nursing Mt. Clemens (Mich.) Gen. Hosp., 1972-73; assoc. prof., head of nursing Ferris State Coll., Big Rapids, Mich., 1975-77; asst. prof., assoc. prof., dir. continuing edn. U. Colo., Denver, 1977-79; assoc. dean, assoc. prof. Sch. Nursing, Tex. Tech U. Health Scis. Ctr., Lubbock, 1979-86, assoc. dean, prof., 1986-87, interim assoc. dean grad. program, 1986-89, exec. assoc. dean, prof. nursing, 1989-92, interim dean, prof., 1992-93; dean, prof. Sch. Nursing, 1993—; prin. p.t. Wylan Assocs., Lubbock, 1989—; mem. acad. adv. panel on nursing Health and Scis. Network, 1983-92, Nurses Coalition, 1982-92; bd. dirs. RN Polit. Action Com., 1989-93. Editor Jour. Continuing Edn. in Nursing, 1986—. Recipient Teaching Excellence award Am. Nurses Found., Fellow Am. Acad. Nursing; mem. ANA (site visitor continuing edn. 1982-88), Tex. Nurses Assn. (bd. dirs. 1989-93, pres. dist. 18 1987-89, pres. 1995-97), Coun. Countinuing Edn., Tex. Nurses Found. (pres. 1992-95), Sigma Theta Tau (grantee). Home: 3713 95th St Lubbock TX 79423-3811

YOE, HARRY WARNER, retired agricultural economist; b. Martinsburg, W. Va., Oct. 20, 1912; s. Horace George and Mary Morrow (Van Metre) Y.; m. Barbara Virginia Fultz, Mar. 22, 1936; children—Harry Warner, Robert Boyd, Paul Michael. B.S., W. Va. U., 1935, grad. study, 1940. Agriculturist U.S. Dept. Agr., Red House Homesteads, W. Va., 1935-38; dir. spl. project U.S. Dept. Agr., Princeton, W.Va., 1938-40; dist. supr. Farm Security Adminstrn. U.S. Dept. Agr., Morgantown, W. Va., 1940-42; econ. cons. Supreme Comdr. Allied Power, Tokyo, Japan, 1947-51; agrl. adminstr. Inter-Am. Affairs, 1951-53; dir. div. Western S.A., ICA, 1953-57; dir. USOM to Haiti, 1957-61, ICA West Indies and Eastern Caribbean Mission, Port-of-Spain, Trinidad, W.I., 1961-62; with AID, Dept. State, Wash., 1962-64; dir. AID mission Georgetown, British Guiana, 1964-68; assoc. mem. firm, dir. econs. and planning div. Miller-Warden-Western, Inc., 1968-69; dir., v.p. Hoskins-Western-Sonderegger, Inc., 1969-82; ret., 1982. Author: Fisheries Cooperatives in Japan, 1950. Served from lt. (j.g.) to comdr. USNR, 1942-46. Recipient commendation for econ. rehab. Yokohama area, Japan U.S. Army, 1946, meritorious award for econ. reforms Japanese Fishing Industry, 1951; spl. commendation ICA, 1953; superior honor award AID, 1967. Mem. Alpha Zeta, Pi Kappa Alpha. Episcopalian (vestryman). Clubs: Rotary, Internat. (Washington). Home: RR 3 Martinsburg WV 25401-9803

YOERGER, ROGER RAYMOND, agricultural engineer, educator; b. LeMars, Iowa, Feb. 17, 1929; s. Raymond Herman and Crystal Victoria (Ward) Y.; m. Barbara M. Ellison, Feb. 14, 1953; 1 child, Karen Lynne; m. Laura M. Summitt, Dec. 23, 1971; stepchildren—Daniel L. Summitt, Linda Summitt Canull, Anita Summitt Smith. B.S., Iowa State U., 1949, M.S., 1951, Ph.D., 1957. Registered profl. engr., Ill., Pa., Iowa. Instr., asst. prof. agrl. engring. Iowa State U. 1949-56; assoc. prof. agrl. engring. Iowa State U., 1956-58; prof. agrl. engring. U. Ill., Urbana, 1959-85; head agrl. engring. dept. U. Ill., 1978-85, prof. emeritus agrl. engring., 1985—. Contbr. articles to profl. jours. Patentee in field. Mem. Ill. Noise Task Force, 1974-80. Fellow Am. Soc. Agrl. Engrs. (Massey-Ferguson medalist 1989); mem. Am.

Soc. Engring. Edn., Phi Kappa Phi (dir. fellowships, dir. 1971-83, pres. elect 1983-86, pres. 1986-89), Rotary, Moose. Roman Catholic. Home: 107 W Holmes St Urbana IL 61801-6614 Office: 1304 W Pennsylvania Ave Urbana IL 61801-4726

YOGANATHAN, AJIT PRITHIVIRAJ, biomedical engineer, educator; b. Colombo, Sri Lanka, Dec. 6, 1951; came to U.S., 1973; s. Ponniah and Mangay (Navaratnam) Y. BSChemE with honors, Univ. Coll., U. London, 1973; PhDChemE, Calif. Tech. U., 1978. Engring. asst. Shell Oil Refinery, Stanlow, Eng., 1972; teaching asst. Calif. Inst. Tech., 1973-74, 1976, rsch. fellow, 1977-79; asst. prof. Ga. Inst. Tech., 1979-83, assoc. prof., 1983-88, chmn. bioengring. com., 1984-88, prof. chem. engring., 1988—, co-dir. Bioengring. Ctr., 1989—, prof. mech. engring., 1989—, co-dir. Emory U.-Ga. Tech. Biomed. Tech. Ctr., 1992—, Regents prof., 1994—; adj. assoc. prof. U. Ala., 1985—. Founding fellow Am. Inst. Med. & Biol. Engring., 1992; recipient Edwin Walker prize Brit. Inst. Mech. Engrs., 1988, Humboldt fellowship, 1985, Am. Heart Assn.-Ga. Affiliate Rsch. Investigatorship award, 1980-83, Calif. Inst. Tech. fellowship, 1973-77, Goldsmid Medal and prize Univ. Coll., 1973, 72, Brit. Coun. scholarship, 1971-73. Mem. AICE, ASME, Biomed. Engring. Soc., Am. Soc. Echocardiography (dir. 1987-91). Office: Sch of Chem Engring Ga Tech U Atlanta GA 30332

YOH, HAROLD L., III, company executive; b. L.A., Dec. 22, 1960; s. Harold L. Jr. and Mary Michael (Milus) Y.; m. Sharon Lynn Crucher, Oct. 13, 1984; children: Kristen, Catherine, Samantha. BSME, Duke U., 1983; MBA, U. Pa., 1990. Various positions to v.p., 1983-89; pres. Day Products, Bridgeport, N.Y., 1992-93; sr. v.p. Day & Zimmermann Internat., Phila., 1993-94; pres. Day & Zimmermann Internat.-Process & Indsl., Inc., Phila., 1995—. Office: Day & Zimmermann Internat 1818 Market St Philadelphia PA 19103-3638

YOH, HAROLD LIONEL, JR., engineering, construction and management company executive; b. Bryn Mawr, Pa., Dec. 12, 1936; s. Harold Lionel and Katherine (Hulme) Y.; m. Mary Michael Milus, June 20, 1959; children: Harold Lionel III, Michael Hulme, Karen Bogart, Jeffrey Milus, William Courtlandt. B.S. in Mech. Engring. Duke, 1958; M.B.A., U. Pa., 1962. Vice pres. H.L. Yoh Co. subs. Day & Zimmerman, Inc., Phila., 1960-63, sr. v.p. div. mgr., 1963-64, pres., 1964-76; v.p. adminstrn. Day & Zimmermann, Inc., Phila., 1961-69, sec., 1966-70, v.p., treas., 1969-76, vice chmn., chief exec. officer, 1976-80, chmn. bd., chief exec. officer, 1980—; also bd. dirs. Day & Zimmermann, Inc.; past pres., past dir. Nat. Tech. Services Assn.; bd. dirs. Continental Bancorp. Greater Phila First Corp. and several other privately held cos. Bd. dirs. Phila. Coll. Arts, Bryn Mawr Civic Assn., Phila. Indsl. Devel. Corp., The Haverford Sch.; past chmn. bd. dirs. Pop Warner Little Scholars; past Pa. State chmn. U.S. Savs. Bonds.; chmn. dean's council Sch. Engring. Duke U., chmn. univ. Greater Phila. Area Capital Campaign; Mid-Atlantic regional chmn. U.S. Olympics. Named Ambassador City of Phila., Silver Knight of D&Z Lone Star chpt. Mgmt. Nat. Mgmt. Assn., 1979-80; recipient Blue Devil award Duke U., Disting. Alumnus award Duke U., Robert Morris award Boy Scouts Am. Mem. ASME, Am. Def. Preparedness Assn. (dir.), Phila. C. of C. (chmn. dir.), Young President's Orgn. (internat. dir.), Phila. Pres.' Orgn., Chief Execs. Orgn., Navy League (life), Newcomen Soc., World Bus. Council, Sigma Nu. Republican. Episcopalian. Clubs: Union League, Phila. Country (Phila.); Merion Golf (Ardmore, Pa.); University (Washington); Seaview Country (N.J.). Avocations: golf, fishing. Home: 116 Summit House West Chester PA 19382-6518 Office: Day & Zimmermann Inc 280 King Of Prussia Rd Radnor PA 19087-5110

YOHALEM, HARRY MORTON, lawyer; b. Phila., Jan. 21, 1943; s. Morton Eugene and Florence (Mishnun) Y.; m. Martha Caroline Remy, June 9, 1967; children: Seth, Mark. BA with honors, U. Wis., 1965; JD cum laude, Columbia U., 1969, M in Internat. Affairs., 1969. Bar: N.Y. 1969, D.C. 1981, Calif. 1992, U.S. Supreme Ct. 1985. Assoc. Shearman & Sterling, N.Y.C., 1969-71; asst. counsel to gov. State of N.Y., Albany, 1971-73, counsel office planning svcs., 1973-75; asst. gen. counsel FEA, Washington, 1975-77; mem. staff White House Energy Policy and Planning Office, Washington, 1977; dep. gen. counsel for legal svcs. Dept. Energy, Washington, 1978-80, dep. under sec., 1980-81; ptnr. Rogers & Wells, Washington, 1981-91; gen. counsel Calif. Inst. Tech., Pasadena, 1991—. Editor comments Columbia Jour. Transnat. Law, 1967-68, rsch. editor, 1968-69. Prin., Coun. for Excellence in Govt., Washington, 1990—; pres. Opera Bel Canto, Washington, 1984-87; mem. Lawyers Com. for Arts, Washington, 1981-88; mem. adv. bd. Pasadena Conservatory of Music, 1994—. Harlan Fiske Stone scholar Columbia U., 1967, 69. Mem. ABA, Calif. Bar Assn., D.C. Bar Assn. Atheneum, Phi Kappa Phi. Home: (bd. dirs. 1977-79), Sci. Fiction Writers Am. (pres. 1986-88), Nat. Assn. for Preservation and Perpetuation of Storytelling, Bay State Writers Guild, Western New Eng. Storytellers Guild (founder), Mystery Writers Am., Horror Writers Am., Authors Guild. Democrat. Jewish/Quaker. Home: 31 School St Hatfield MA 01038-9701

YOHE, JAMES LYLE, art gallery director, art dealer; b. San Francisco, Aug. 9, 1944; s. Lyle Arthur and Winifred Wanda (Wilson) Y.; m. Chong Ae Yun, June 16, 1971; 1 child, Yujin Lyle. BFA, U. N.Mex., 1968; postgrad., Rutgers U., 1970-72. Exec. dir. Andre Emmerich Gallery, N.Y.C., 1990—. Office: Andre Emmerich Gallery 41 E 57th St New York NY 10007

YOHN, DAVID STEWART, virologist, science administrator; b. Shelby, Ohio, June 7, 1929; s. Joseph Van and Agnes (Tryon) Y.; m. Olivetta Kathleen McCoy, June 11, 1950; children: Linda Jean, Kathleen Ann, Joseph John, David McCoy, Kristine Renee. B.S., Otterbein Coll., 1951; M.S., Ohio State U., 1953, Ph.D, 1957; M.P.H., U. Pitts., 1960. Research fellow, scholar in microbiology Ohio State U., 1952-56, prof. virology Coll. Veterinary Medicine, 1969-95, prof. emeritus, 1995—, dir. Comprehensive Cancer Ctr., 1973-88; dep. dir. Comprehensive Cancer Ctr., 1988-94; research assoc., asst. prof. microbiology U. Pitts., 1956-62; assoc. cancer research scientist Roswell Park Meml. Inst., Buffalo, 1962-69; mem. nat. med. and sci. adv. com. Leukemia Soc. Am., 1970-91, trustee, 1971-91; pres. Ohio Cancer Research Assocs., 1982—; mem. cancer research centers rev. com. Nat. Cancer Inst., 1972-77. Pres. bd. deacons North Presbyn. Ch., Williamsburg, N.Y., 1967-68. Recipient Pub. Service award Lions, 1968. Mem. Am. Assn. Cancer Rsch., Am. Soc. Microbiology, Am. Assn. Immunologists, Internat. Assn. Comparative Rsch. on Leukemia and Related Diseases (sec.-gen. 1974—), Ohio Valley-Lake Erie Assn. Cancer Ctrs. (sec. 1978—), Sertoma (pres 1992-93, chmn. bd. dirs. 1993-94, Dist. Sertoman of Yr. award 1987). Home: 1237 Norwell Dr Columbus OH 43220-3958 Office: Ohio State U Comprehensive Cancer Ctr 300 W 10th Ave Ste 1132 Columbus OH 43210-1240

YOHN, WILLIAM HENDRICKS, JR., federal judge; b. Pottstown, Pa., Nov. 20, 1935; s. William H. and Dorothy C. (Cornelius) Y.; m. Jean Louise Kochel, mar. 16, 1963; children: William H. III, Bradley G., Elizabeth J. AB, Princeton U., 1957; JD, Yale U., 1960. Bar: Pa. 1961, U.S. Dist. Ct. D.C. 1961. Ptnr. Wells Campbell Reynier & Yohn, Pottstown, 1961-71; mem., chmn. coms. Pa. House of Reps. Harrisburg, 1968-80; ptnr. Binder Yohn & Kalis, Pottstown, 1971-81; judge Montgomery County Ct. of Common Pleas, Norristown, Pa., 1981-91, U.S. Dist. Ct., ea. dist., Pa., 1991—; asst. D.A., Montgomery County D.A. Office, 1962-65; instr. Am. Inst. of Banking, 1963-66. Bd. dirs. Greater Pottstown Drug Abuse Prevention Program, 1970-76, Pottstown Meml. Med. Ctr., 1974—, chmn., 1984—. Cpl. USMCR, 1960-66. Mem. Pa. Bar Assn., Montgomery Bar Assn. (bd. dirs. 1967-70). Republican. Office: US Dist Ct 3809 US Courthouse 601 Market St Philadelphia PA 19106-1723

YOHO, ROBERT WAYNE, company executive; b. Ardmore, Md., Jan. 26, 1936; s. Wilbert Wiley Sr. and Effie Pauline (Bowen) Y.; m. Alice Pilar Tenorio, Aug. 29, 1952; children: Robert Jr., Gary W., Dana M. BSME, Md. U., 1959; BA in Bus., Southeastern U., 1961. Lic. mech. contractor, Calif., Ga., Fla., Mich., N.C. Asst. to pres. Griffith Consumers, Washington, 1955-63; pres. Triple A Corp., College Park, Md., 1963-66; exec. v.p. Howdeshell Mech., Clearwater, Fla., 1967-71; pres. Schneider-Yoho Corp. (Fla. and Calif.), 1971-76; pres., founder Tropic-Kool Engring., Clearwater, Fla., 1977-87; pres. New Thermal Techologies, Clearwater, 1988—. Patentee roof curbs, control panels, hoods, desiccant air conditioners, others. Mem. Krew of Neptune, Treasure Island, 1992; active various civic orgns., St. Petersburg, Fla., 1987-93. Recipient Gov.'s award State of Fla., 1993, Fla. award Fla. Dept. Commerce, 1993, Tech. award Tampa Bay Planning Coun., 1993, award Dept. of Energy. Mem. ASHRAE, Assn. Energy Engrs. (sr.), Fla. Soc. Profl. Engrs. Avocations: sailing, racquetball, bowling. Home:

5812 Toucan Pl Clearwater FL 34620 Office: New Thermal Tech 12900 Automobile Blvd Clearwater FL 34622

YOKEN, MEL B., French language educator, author; b. Fall River, Mass., June 25, 1939; s. Albert Benjamin and Sylvia Sarah (White) Y.; m. Cynthia Stein, June 20, 1976; children: Andrew Brett, David Ryan, Jonathan Barry. B.A., U. Mass., 1960, Ph.D., 1972; M.A.T., Brown U., 1961. Instr. French U. Mass., Dartmouth, 1966-72, asst. prof., 1972-76, assoc. prof., 1976-81 prof., 1981—; dir. French summer study program French Inst., 1981-88; vis. prof. Wheaton Coll., 1987, U. of Montreal, 1981-88, translator New Bedford Superior Ct., New Bedford, Mass., 1985—, Fall River Superior Ct., Fall River, Mass., 1985—; mem. nominating com. Nobel prize for lit., 1972—. Pres. Friends of Fall River Pub. Libr., 1972-80, pres. bd. dirs., 1972-80; pres. New Bedford Pub. Libr., 1980-82, Am. Field Svc., 1985—. Recipient Disting. Svc. award City Fall River, 1974, 80, Excellence in Teaching French award, 1984, 85, Gov.'s citation, 1986, Nat. Disting. Leadership award, 1990, Dist. Svc. award Mass. Foreign Lang. Assn., 1992, Medaille de Vermeil du Rayonnement de la Langue Française, L'Academie Francaise, 1993; Mel Yoken Day proclaimed by Mayor of New Bedford, 1990; Govt. of Que. grantee, 1981-85, 87-89, Can. Embassy grantee, 1986,87, Southeastern Mass. U. grantee, 1985, 89, 90. Mem. MLA (life), Am. Assn. Tchrs. French (life), Am. Coun. Tchrs. Fgn. Langs., Middlebury Amicale (life), N.E. MLA (coord. 1987—), New Eng. Fgn. Lang. Assn., Mass. Fgn. Lang. Assn. (bd. dirs. 1985—, disting. svc. award 1992), N.Y. State Assn. Fgn. Lang. Tchrs., Internat. Platform Assn., Francophone Assn. (v.p. 1990—), Fall River C. of C., Brown U. Alumni Assn. (rep.), Richelieu Internat. Universal Manuscript Soc. (v.p. 1993—). Author: Claude Tillier, 1976, Speech is Plurality, 1978, Claude Tillier (1801-44): Fame and Fortune in His Novelistic Work, 1978, Entretiens Quebecois I, 1986, Entretiens Quebecois II, 1989, Letters of Robert Molloy, 1989, Festschrift in Honor of Stowell Goding, 1993; contbr. articles to profl. jours. Avocations: traveling, languages, baseball, postcards, meteorology. Home: 261 Carroll St New Bedford MA 02740-1412 Office: U Mass Dartmouth Lang Dept Old Westport Rd North Dartmouth MA 02747-2512

YOKUBAITIS, ROGER T., lawyer; b. Wharton, Tex., Jan. 9, 1945. Attended, St. Louis U.; BA, JD, U. Houston, 1969. Bar: Tex. 1969. Ptnr. Dula, Carmody & Yokubaitis, L.L.P., Houston. Mem. ABA, Houston Bar Assn., State Bar of Tex., Houston Bankruptcy Conf., Am. Bankruptcy Inst. Office: Dula Carmody Yokubaitis LLP 5718 Westheimer Ste 1515 Houston TX 77057-5733

YOLEN, JANE, author; b. N.Y.C., Feb. 11, 1939; d. Will Hyatt and Isabelle (Berlin) Y.; m. David Wilber Stemple, Sept. 2, 1962; children: Heidi Elisabet, Adam Douglas, Jason Frederic. B.A., Smith Coll., 1960; M.Ed., U. Mass., 1978; LL.D. (hon.), Coll. of Our Lady of the Elms, 1980. Asst. editor This Week mag., 1960; mem. staff Saturday Rev., 1960; asst. editor Gold Medal Books, 1961, Rutledge Press, 1961-63; asst. juvenile editor A.A. Knopf, Inc., 1963-65; free-lance writer, 1965—; lectr. dept. edn. Smith Coll., 1979-84; editor Jane Yolen books, imprint Harcourt Brace Jovanovich, 1988—; tchr. writers confs. Centrum, Cape Cod Writers Conf., Soc. Children's Book Writers, U. Mass.; mem. Mass. Council on Arts, 1974. Author: Pirates in Petticoats, 1963, The Witch Who Wasn't, 1964, The Emperor and the Kite, 1968, Writing Books for Children, 1973, The Girl Who Cried Flowers, 1974, The Hundredth Dove, 1978, The Dream Weaver, 1979, Commander Toad in Space, 1980, The Gift of Sarah Barker, 1981, Touch Magic, 1981, Dragon's Blood, 1982, Tales of Wonder, 1983, Heart's Blood, 1984, Cards of Grief, 1984, Dragonfield, 1985, Merlin's Booke, 1986, The Lullabye Songbook, 1986, Ring of Earth, 1986, Favorite Folktales From Around the World, 1986, Piggins, 1987, Owl Moon, 1987, Three Bears, 1987, A Sending of Dragons, 1987, The Devil's Arithmetic, 1988, Sister Light/Sister Dark, 1988, White Jenna, 1989, Dove Isabeau, 1989, Baby Bear's Bedtime Book, 1990, Tam Lin, 1990, Bird Watch, 1990, Sky Dogs, 1990, Wizard's Hall, 1991, All those Secrets of the World, 1991, Wings, 1991, Hark! A Christmas Sampler, 1991, Encounter, 1992, Briar Rose, 1992, Letting Swift River Go, 1992, What Rhymes with Moon, 1993, Welcome to the Greenhouse, 1993, Honkers, 1993, Here There Be Dragons, 1993, Grandad Bill's Song, 1994, Good Griselle, 1994, The Girl in the Golden Bower, 1994, Old Dame Counterpane, 1994, Old Macdonald's Songbook, 1994, Here There Be Unicorns, 1994, Beneath the Ghost Moon, 1994, The Wild Hunt, 1995, Ballad of the Pirate Queens, 1995, And Twelve Chinese Acrobats, 1995, Water Music, 1995, Among Angels, 1995, Here They Be Witches, 1995, others. Mass. del. Democratic Nat. Conv., 1972; town coordinator Robert Drinan's campaign, 1970; chmn. bd. trustees Hatfield (Mass.) Library, 1978-83. Mem. Soc. Children's Book Writers (bd dirs 1974—), Children's Lit. Assn. (bd. dirs 1977-79), Sci. Fiction Writers Am. (pres. 1986-88), Nat. Assn. for Preservation and Perpetuation of Storytelling, Bay State Writers Guild, Western New Eng. Storytellers Guild (founder), Mystery Writers Am., Horror Writers Am., Authors Guild. Democrat. Jewish/Quaker. Home: 31 School St Hatfield MA 01038-9701

YOLTON, JOHN WILLIAM, philosopher, educator; b. Birmingham, Ala., Nov. 10, 1921; s. Robert Elgene and Ella Maude (Holmes) Y.; m. Jean Sebastian, Sept. 5, 1945; children: Karin Frances Yolton Griffith, Pamela Holmes Yolton Smith. BA with honors, U. Cin., 1945, MA, 1946; postgrad., U. Calif., Berkeley, 1946-50; DPhil (Fulbright fellow), Balliol Coll., Oxford, Eng., 1952; LL.D. (hon.), York U., 1974; D.Litt. (hon.), McMaster U., 1976. Vis. lectr. philosophy Johns Hopkins U., 1952-53; asst. prof. Princeton U., 1952-57; assoc. prof. Kenyon Coll., 1957-61; prof. U. Md., 1961-63; prof. philosophy York U., Toronto, 1963-78; chmn. dept. York U., 1963-73, acting dean grad. studies, 1967-68, acting pres., 1973-74; prof. philosophy Rutgers U., New Brunswick, N.J., 1978—; dean Rutgers Coll., Rutgers U., 1978-85, John Locke prof. history of philosophy, 1989-92, prof. emeritus philosophy, 1992—; cons. Bertrand Russell Archives, McMaster U., 1973-86. Author: John Locke and the Way of Ideas, 1956, Metaphysical Analysis, 1967, Locke and the Compass of Human Understanding, 1970, Thinking Matter, 1983, Perceptual Acquaintance from Descartes to Reid, 1984, Locke and French Materialism, 1991, other books; gen. editor Clarendon Edit. of Works of John Locke, Oxford U. Press, 1984-92, Blackwell's Companion to the Enlightenment, 1992, Locke Dictionary (Blackwell), 1993, Library of the History of Ideas, 1989—; editor: (with wife) Locke's Some Thoughts Concerning Education, 1989, 5 books in field; mem. editorial bd. jours. in field; v.p., bd. dirs. Jour. of the History of Ideas, 1991—; contbr. articles to profl. jours. Mem. N.J. Com. for Humanities, 1978-85, treas., 1980-85. Am. Council Learned Socs. fellow, 1960-61; Can. Council fellow, 1968-69. Mem. Mind Assn., Can. Philos. Assn., Am. Soc. for 18th Century Studies, Hume Soc.

YON, EUGENE T., process control company executive; b. Mt. Hope, W.Va., Dec. 29, 1936; s. Gildo Yon; m. Rosemary Yon, Aug. 20, 1960; children: Steven, Kevin. BSEE, U. Cin., 1960; MSEE, Case Inst. Tech., 1962, PhD, 1965. Registered profl. engr. Assoc. prof. engring. Case Western Res. U., Cleve., 1966-76; v.p. Booz-Allen Hamilton, Cleve., 1976-84; group v.p. Commn. Engring., Stamford, Conn., 1984-88; ptnr., v.p. Booz-Allen Hamilton, N.Y.C., 1988-91; pres., COO Bailey Controls Co., Cleve., 1991—; group v.p. U.S. ops. Elsace Bailey, Cleve., 1994—. Contbr. articles to profl. jours. Home: 316 Green Oak Ct Longwood FL 32779

YONAS, ALBERT, psychology educator; b. Cleve., Apr. 13, 1942; s. Bernard and Blanche (Simon) Y.; children: Aaron, Rachel Phipps-Yonas, Benjamin, Hannah Phippen-Yonas. BA in Psychology, U. Mich., 1964; PhD in Psychology, Cornell U., 1968. Rsch. asst. U. Mich., Ann Arbor, 1964; rsch. asst. Cornell U., Ithaca, N.Y., 1964-67, tchg. asst., 1966-67, NIMH predoctoral fellow, 1967-68; asst. prof. psychology Inst. Child Devel. U. Minn., Mpls., 1968-73, assoc. prof., 1973-79, prof., 1979—, dir. Ctr. for Rsch. in Learning, Perception and Development, 1991—. Editor: Minnesota Symposium on Child Psychology, Vol. 20, 1988. Pres. bd. dirs. Hillel Found., U. Minn., 1985-90. Jewish. Achievements include description of development of depth perception in human infants; discovered that infants perceive pictorial depth cues at 7 months. Home: 1596 Vincent Ave Saint Paul MN 55108 Office: U Minn Inst Child Devel 51 E River Rd Minneapolis MN 55455-0280

YONDA, ALFRED WILLIAM, mathematician; b. Cambridge, Mass., Aug. 10, 1919; s. Walter and Theophelia (Naruscewicz) Y.; B.S., U. Ala., 1952, M.A. in Math., 1954; m. Mary Jane McManus, Dec. 19, 1949 (dec.); chil-

dren—Nancy, Kathryn, Elizabeth, John; m. Peggy A. Terrel, June 22, 1975. Mathematician rocket research Redstone Arsenal, Huntsville, Ala., 1953, U.S. Army Ballistic Research Labs., Aberdeen, Md., 1954-56; instr. math. U. Ala., Tuscaloosa, 1954, Temple U., Phila., 1956-57; asso. scientist, research and devel. div. Avco Corp., Wilmington, Mass., 1957-59; sr. mem. tech. staff RCA, Camden, N.J., 1959-66; mgr. computer analysis and programming dept. Raytheon Co. space and information systems div., Sudbury, Mass., 1966-70, mgr. software systems lab., 1969-70, prin. engr. missiles systems div., 1970-73; mgr. systems analysis and programming GTE Govt. Systems Corp., 1973-77, mgr. software engring. Atlantic ops., 1977-82, sr. mem. tech. staff Command Control & Communications Sector, 1983-91; software systems engr. Yonda Software Systems Cons., 1991—. Pres., Milford Area Assn. Retarded Children, 1972-73; vice-chmn. fin. com. Town of Medway, 1973; bd. dirs. Blackstone Valley Mental Health and Retardation Area , 1970-76; trustee Medway Libraries, 1973-82, chmn., 1974-81. Served with USAAF, 1943-46. Hon. fellow Advanced Level Telecommunications Tng. Center, Ghaziabad, India, 1981. Registered profl. engr. Mem. AAAS, IEEE, Math. Assn. Am., N.Y. Acad. Scis., Sigma Xi, Phi Eta Sigma, Pi Mu Epsilon (pres. Ala. chpt. 1953-54), Sigma Pi Sigma. Contbr. articles to profl. jours. Office: 12 Sunset Dr Medway MA 02053-2008

YONG, RAYMOND NEN-YIU, civil engineering educator; b. Singapore, Apr. 10, 1929; naturalized, 1966; s. Ngim Djin and Lucy (Loh) Y.; m. Florence Lechensky, July 8, 1961; children—Raymond T.M., Christopher T.K. B.A. in Math. and Physics, Washington and Jefferson Coll., 1950; B.S., M.I.T., 1952; M.S., Purdue U., 1954; M.Engring., McGill U., Montreal, Que., Can., 1958, Ph.D., 1960. Mem. faculty McGill U., 1959—, prof. civil engring., 1965—, William Scott prof. civil engring. and applied mechanics, dir. Geotech. Research Centre, 1973—, assoc. mem. Ctr. for Medicine, Ethics and Law, 1991—; adj. prof. civil engring U. Fla., Gainesville, 1984—; adj. rsch. prof. civil engring. Carleton U., Ottawa, 1990. Author: Soil Properties and Behavior, 1975 (Japanese edit. 1977), Introduction to Soil Behavior, 1966 (Japanese edit. 1974), Vehicle Traction Mechanics, 1985, Principles of Contaminant Transport in Soils, 1992. Decorated chevalier Ordre National du Que., 1985; recipient Killam prize Can. Coun., 1985, ASTM Charles B. Dudley award, 1988, Can. Environ. Achievement award, Lifetime Achievement Environment Can., 1991. Fellow Royal Soc. Can. Engring. Inst. Can., Can. Soc. for Civil Engring.; mem. ASCE, ASTM (Charles B. Dudley award 1988), Inst. Civil Engrs., Soc. Rheology, Clay Minerals Soc., Internat. Soc. Terrain-Vehicle Systems (pres. 1993—), Can. Geotech. Soc. (R.F. Legget award 1993). Office: McGill U-Geotech Rsch Ctr, 817 Sherbrooke St w, Montreal, PQ Canada H3A 2K6

YONKMAN, FREDRICK ALBERS, lawyer, management consultant; b. Holland, Mich., Aug. 22, 1930; s. Fredrick Francis and Janet Dorothy (Albers) Y.; m. Kathleen VerMeulen, June 9, 1953 (div. Sept. 22, 1980); children: Sara, Margriet, Nina.; m. Barbara Anne Sullivan, Aug. 22, 1981; 1 child, Fredrick Ryan. B.A., Hope Coll., Holland, 1952; J.D., U. Chgo., 1957. Bar: N.Y. 1958, Mass. 1968, D.C. 1984. With firm Winthrop, Stimson, Putnam & Roberts, N.Y.C., 1957-64; sec., gen. counsel Reuben H. Donnelley Corp., N.Y.C., 1964-66, Dun & Bradstreet, Inc., N.Y.C., 1966-68; mem. law firm Sullivan & Worcester, Boston, 1968-72; gen. counsel Am. Express Co., N.Y.C., 1972-78; exec. v.p. Am. Express Co., 1975-80; pres. Buck Cons., N.Y.C., 1980-81; mgmt. cons. and psychoanalyst, 1981—; counsel Peabody, Lambert & Myers, Washington, 1983-84; chmn. Outward Bound, Inc., 1980-81; mem. bd. and chmn. audit com. Kennecott Corp., 1978-81; adj. prof. law Georgetown U., 1976-78; chmn. Georgetown Internat. Law Inst., 1980-81; vis. com. U. Chgo. Law Sch., 1980-82. Bd. dirs. Washington Campus Program, 1976-81; With AUS, 1952-54. Recipient Silver Anniversary award Nat. Coll. Athletic Assn., 1977. Mem. ABA, N.Y. State Bar Assn., Mass. Bar Assn., Rsch. Soc. for Process Oriented Psychology (Zurich) (diplomate), Union Club (Boston). Presbyterian. Home: 34 Beekman Pl New York NY 10022

YONTZ, KENNETH FREDRIC, medical and chemical company executive; b. Sandusky, Ohio, July 21, 1944; s. Kenneth Willard and Dorothy (Kromer) Y.; m. Jean Ann Marshall, July 21, 1962 (div. Aug. 1982); children: Terri, Christine, Michael, Jennifer; m. Karen Glojek, July 7, 1984 (wid. Dec. 1995). BSBA, Bowling Green State U., 1971; MBA, Eastern Mich. U., 1979. Fin. planning mgr. Ford Motor Co., Rawsonville, Mich., 1970-74; fin. mgr. Chemetron Corp., Chgo., 1974-76, pres. fire systems div., 1976-80; pres. electronics div. Allen Bradley Co., Milw., 1980-83, group. pres. electronics, 1983-85, exec. v.p., 1985-86; chmn. bd., pres., chief exec. officer Sybron Corp., Milw., 1986—, also bd. dirs.; bd. dirs. Playtex Corp., N.Y.C. Bd. dirs. Greater Milw. Open., Boys and Girls Club. Mem. Nat. Assn. Mfrs. (bd. dirs.), Bluemound Country Club, PGA West, Milw. Athletic Club, The Milwaukee Club (bd. dirs.), Montclair Golf Club. Roman Catholic. Office: Sybron Corp 411 E Wisconsin Ave Milwaukee WI 53202 *Positive results are seldom achieved from negative thoughts.*

YOOD, HAROLD STANLEY, internist; b. Plainfield, N.J., Feb. 23, 1920; s. Raphael and Netta (Newcorn) Y.; m. Helen H. Hull, Nov. 8, 1941; children: Pamela, Patricia Yood Herskovitz, Paula Yood Peterson, Andrew H. BA, U. Va., 1940, MD, 1943. Intern Syracuse (N.Y.) U. Med. Ctr., 1943; pvt. practice Plainfield, N.J., 1946-91; med. dir. Cen. Jersey Individual Physicians Assn.; staff dept. medicine Muhlenberg Hosp., 1976—, pres., staff, 1980-86, cons., 1991-95, emeritus, 1995—. Contbr. articles to Jour. Med. Soc. N.J., Communication for Ciba, others. Bd. govs. Muhlenberg Regional Med. Ctr., 1980-86, exec. com.; trustee, v.p. United Way Plainfield/Fanwood, 1975-81; bd. dirs. United Way Union County, 1978-81; pres. Jewish Community Ctr., Plainfield, 1970-71; v.p. Jewish Fedn. Cen. N.J., 1971-73, Cen. N.J. Jewish Home for Aged, 1973-80. Capt. M.C. AUS, 1944-45, ETO. Decorated Purple Heart, Croix de Guerre (France), Croix de Guerre (Belgium). Fellow Am. Coll. Gastroenterology (sr.); mem. AMA, Med. Soc. N.J. (governing coun. hosp. med. sect. 1983-92, chmn. 1988-90, trustee 1989-90), Union County Med. Soc., Plainfield Area Med. Assn., N.Y. Acad. Sci., Am. Coll. Physician Execs., Lions (life) N.J. Bridge League. Office: CJIPA 1133 Park Ave Plainfield NJ 07060

YOON, JI-WON, virology, immunology and diabetes educator, research administrator; b. Kang-Jin, Chonnam, Korea, Mar. 28, 1939; came to U.S., 1965; s. Baek-In and Duck-Soon (Lee) Y.; m. Chungja Rhim, aug. 17, 1968; children: Dr. John, James W. MS, U. Conn., 1971, PhD, 1973. Sr. investigator NIH, Bethesda, Md., 1978-84; prof., chief div. virology U. Calgary, Alta., Can., 1984—, prof., assoc. dir. diabetes rsch. ctr., 1985-90, prof., dir. diabetes rsch. ctr., 1990—; mem. edit. bd. Annual Review Advances Present Rsch. Animal Diabetes, 1990—, Diabetes Rsch. Clin. Practice, 1989—; scientific coord. 10th Internat. Workshop on Immunology Diabetes, Jerusalem, 1989-90; sr. investigator NIH, 1976-84. Contbg. author: Current Topics in Microbiology and Immunology, 1990, Autoimmunity and Pathogenesis of Diabetes, 1990; contbr. articles to New England Jour. Medicine, Jour. Virology, Sci., Nature, The Lancet, Jour. Diabetes. Rsch. fellow Sloan Kettering Cancer Inst., 1973-74, Staff fellow, Sr. Staff fellow NIH, 1974-76, 76-78; recipient NIH Dir. award, 1984, Heritage Med. Scientist award, Alberta Heritage Found. Med. Rsch., 1984, Lectrship. award, 3d Asian Symposium Childhood Diabetes, 1989, 8th Annual Meeting Childhood Diabetes, Osaka, Japan, 1990, 9th Korean/Can. Heritage award, 1989. Mem. Am. Soc. Immunologists, Am. Diabetes Assn., Am. Soc. Microbiology, N.Y. Acad. Sci., Soc. Virology, Internat. Diabetes Fedn. Baptist. Achievements include first isolation of diabetogenic virus from patients with recent onset of IDDM; first demonstration of prevention of virus-induced diabetes by vaccination with nondiabetogenic virus in animals; discovery that autoimmune IDDM can be prevented by depletion of macrophages in diabetic animals; certain viral glycoproteins (rubella virus E2 glycoprotein) can induce organ-specific autoimmune disease; research on molecular identification of diabetogenic viral gene in animal models, discovery of a nontoxic organic compound with no side effects that completely prevents type I diabetes in NOD mice, discovery that bacterial superantigens such as staphylococcal enterotoxins (SEC1, SEC3) can prevent autoimmune type I diabetes by activation of CD4+ suppressor T cells in NOD mice; research on the role of cloned T-Cells in the pathogenesis of autoimmune Type I diabetes at cellular and molecular level. Home: 206 Edgeview Dr NW, Calgary, AB Canada T3A 4W9 Office: Julia McFarlane Diabetes Rsch Ctr, 3330 Hospital Dr NW, Calgary, AB Canada T2N 4N1

YORBURG, BETTY (MRS. LEON YORBURG), sociology educator; b. Chgo., Aug. 27, 1926; d. Max and Hannah (Bernstein) Gitelman; m. Leon Yorburg, June 23, 1946; children: Harriet, Robert. PhB, U. Chgo., 1945, MA, 1948; PhD, New Sch. Social Rsch., 1968. Instr., Coll. New Rochelle, 1966-67; lectr. City Coll. and Grad. Center, City U. N.Y., 1967-69, asst. prof., 1969-73, assoc. prof. sociology dept., 1973-77, prof., 1978—; asst. Prof. Clifford Shaw, Chgo. Area Project, 1946-47. Author: Utopia and Reality, 1969, The Changing Family, 1973, Sexual Identity: Sex Roles and Social Change, 1974, The New Women, 1976, Introduction to Sociology, 1982, Families and Societies, 1983, Family Relationships, 1993, Sociological Reality, 1995. Mem. AAAS, Am. Sociol. Assn., Ea. Sociol. Assn., Am. Coun. Family Rels., N.Y. Acad. Scis. Home: 20 Earley St Bronx NY 10464-1512 Office: CCNY Sociology Dept 138th Convent Ave New York NY 10031-9127

YORDAN, CARLOS MANUEL, foreign service officer; b. P.R., Nov. 27, 1925; s. Nicholas and Octavia (Baez) Y.; m. Hilda Bordas, Aug. 16, 1946; 1 son, Carlos Manuel. Student, Gregg Bus. Coll., 1940-42; M.A. in Polit. Sci., U. Chgo. (corr.), 1960, M.A. in Am. History, 1962. Joined U.S. Fgn. Service, 1947; chief clk. engring. dept. Unifruitco, Dominican Republic, 1944-47; adminstrv. officer State Dept., Santo Domingo, Dominican Republic, 1947-50, Quito, Ecuador, 1950-52; 2d sec., vice consul State Dept., Lima, Peru, 1953-55, Rangoon, Burma, 1956-58, London, 1958-60, Budapest, Hungary, 1960-61, Washington, 1961-65; 1st sec., consul State Dept., Warsaw, Poland, 1965-67, West Berlin, 1967-70, Dublin, 1970-73, Brasilia, Brazil, 1973-77; counselor embassy Santo Domingo, Dominican Republic, 1977-81. Mem. Fgn. Svc. Assn., Royal Dublin Soc., Am. Soc. Natural History, Country Tennis Ctr. of Sarasota (Fla.), TPC Prestancia. Office: 3697 Gleneagle Dr Sarasota FL 34238-2812

YORINKS, ARTHUR, children's author; b. Roslyn, N.Y., Aug. 21, 1953; s. Alexander and Shirley (Kron) Y.; m. Adrienne Berg, Oct. 23, 1983. Writer, tchr. performer Am. Mime Theatre, 1969-79; instr. theatre arts Cornell U., Ithaca, N.Y., 1972-79; assoc. dir. New Works Project, N.Y.C., 1977—; founder, artistic dir. Moving Theatre, N.Y.C., 1979; founder, assoc. artistic dir. The Night Kitchen, N.Y.C., 1990—. Author: (children's books) Sid and Sol, 1977, The Magic Meatballs, 1979, Louis the Fish, 1980 (Sch. Libr. Jour. Best Book Yr. Citation 1980), It Happened in Pinsk, 1983 (Booklist Children's Editor's Choice 1984, Biennale of Illustration plaque 1985), Hey, Al, 1986 (ALA Notable Book citation 1986, Caldecott medal 1987, Ky. Bluegrass award 1988), Bravo Minski, 1988 (Sch. Libr. Jour. Best Book Yr. Citation 1988), Company's Coming, 1988 (ALA Notable Book citation 1986), Oh, Brother, 1989 (Sch. Libr. Jour. Best Book Yr. Citation 1989), Ugh, 1990 (Sch. Libr. Jour. Best Book Yr. citation 1990), Christmans in July, 1991, Whitefish Will Rides Again, 1994, (plays) Six, 1973, The Horse, 1978, Crackers, 1979, The King, 1980, Kissers, 1980, Piece for a Small Cafe, 1981, Piece for a Larger Cafe, 1982, It's Alive!, 1994, So, Sue Me, 1994, (opera librettos) Leipziger Kerzenspiel, 1984, The Juniper Tree, 1985, (with adaptor Philip Glass) The Fall of the House of Usher, 1988, (screenplay) Sid and Sol, 1982. Office: The Night Kitchen 10 E 53d St New York NY 10022

YORK, ALEXANDRA, lawyer; b. Jersey City, Feb. 9, 1939; d. Daniel Simpson and Regina (Norwich) S. BA, Tulane U., 1960; JD, Fordham U., 1976. Bar: N.Y. 1978, U.S. Dist. Ct. (so. and ea. dists.) N.Y. 1978, N.J. 1984, U.S. Dist. Ct. N.J. 1984, U.S.C. Appeals (2d cir.) 1987. Vol. Peace Corps, Philippines, 1961-63; legis. adviser Speaker of the Philippines House of Reps., Manila, 1964; speechwriter Mems. U.S. Congress, Washington, 1965; compliance officer U.S. Equal Employment Opportunity Commn., Washington, 1966-68; cons. N.Y.C. Dept. Consumer Affairs, 1969; cons., speechwriter N.Y.C. Dept. Air Resources, 1970-72; assoc. Shea and Gould, N.Y.C., 1977-79, Leopold Kaplan P.C., N.Y.C., 1980-86; asst. atty. gen. N.Y. State Dept. of Law, N.Y.C., 1987-93; spl. counsel external affairs Congress of Federated States of Micronesia, Pohnpei, 1993—; mem. Practicing Law Inst., N.Y.C., 1991—, adv. com. environ. law; guest lectr. internat. environ. law Law Sch. Pace U., White Plains, N.Y.; ofcl. del. UN Conf. on Environ. and Devel., Rio de Janiero, 1992. Contbr. articles on internat. environ. law and climate change to profl. jours. Mem. ABA (natural resources sect., energy and environ. sect., internat. law and practice sect. 1990—; program chair ann. meeting 1991, 92, chair subcom. on Human Rights and Environ.), Assn. of Bar of City of N.Y. (mem. internat. law com. 1990-93, originator spl. com. internat. environ. law 1991), Am. Soc. Internat. Law (environ. sect. 1991—).

YORK, DONALD GILBERT, astronomy educator, researcher; b. Shelbyville, Ill., Oct. 28, 1944; s. Maurice Alfred and Virginia Maxine (Huntwork) Y.; m. Anna Sue Hinds, June 12, 1966; children: Sean, Maurice, Chandler, Jeremy. BS, MIT, 1966; PhD, U. Chgo., 1971. Rsch. asst. Princeton (N.J.) U., 1970-71, rsch. assoc., 1971-73, rsch. astronomer, 1973-78, sr. rsch. astronomer, 1978-82; assoc. prof. U. Chgo., 1982-86, prof., 1986-92, Horace B. Horton prof. astronomy and astrophysics, 1992—; dir. Apache Point Obs., Astrophys. Rsch. Consortium, Seattle, 1984—, Sloan Digital Sky Survey, 1990—. Contbr. articles to profl. jours. Recipient Pub. Svc. award NASA, 1976; grantee NASA, 1978—, NSF, 1984—. Mem. Internat. Astron. Union, Am. Astron. Soc. (publs. bd. 1980-83). Republican. Avocations: squash, white water canoeing, science history, religion history. Office: 5640 S Ellis Ave Chicago IL 60637-1433

YORK, E. TRAVIS, JR., academic administrator, former university chancellor, consultant; b. Mentone, Ala., July 4, 1922; s. E. Travis and Leila (Hixon) Y.; m. Vermelle Cardwell, Dec. 26, 1946; children: Lisa Carol, Travis Loften. BS., Auburn U., 1942, M.S., 1946, D.Sc. (hon.), 1982; Ph.D. (research fellow 1946-49), Cornell U., 1949; postgrad., George Washington U., 1957-59; D.Sc. (hon.), U. Fla., 1984. Assoc. prof. agr. N.C. State Coll., 1949-52, prof., 1952-56, head dept. agronomy, 1953-56; Eastern dir. Am. Potash Inst., 1956-59; dir. Ala. Extension Service, Auburn U., 1959-61; adminstr. Fed. Extension Service, U.S. Dept. Agr., 1961-63; provost for agr. U. Fla., 1963-71, v.p. agrl. affairs, 1971-73, exec. v.p., interim pres., 1973-74, Disting. Svc. prof., 1988—; chancellor State U. System of Fla., 1975-80, chancellor emeritus, 1980—. Mem. Author for Peace Coun., 1961-62, Freedom from Hunger Com., 1961-62, Pres.'s. Panel Vocat. Edn., 1961-62; chmn. coun. grad. edn. in agrl. scis. So. Regional Edn. Bd., 1964-66, mem., 1975-80, exec. com., 1978-80, mem. pres. coun., Pres.' Sci. Adv. Coun. Task Force on World Food Problems, 1966-67; mem. senate, exec. com. Nat. Assn. State Univs. and Land Grant Colls., 1967-70; mem. Edn. Commn. of States, 1975-79, steering com., 1977-79, treas., exec. com., 1978-79; bd. dirs. Nat. 4-H Svc. Com., 1963-75, AV Med. Corp., Sante Fe, 1987—; trustee, mem. exec. com. Nat. 4-H Found., 1968-73; mem.-at-large nat. coun. Boy Scouts Am., 1962-75; dir., pres. Alpha Gamma Rho Edn. Found., 1965-72; bd. dirs. Nat. Ctr. for Voluntary Action, 1970-74; mem. Bd. for Internat. Food and Agrl. Devel., 1980-86, chmn., 1983-86; trustee Escuela Agrícola Panamericana, 1980-88, Found. for Agronomic Rsch., 1980-92; tech. adv. com., cons. Group for Internat. Agrl. Rsch., 1983-89; trustee Agronomic Sci. Found., 1989-92. Officer AUS, 1943-45. Recipient B.B. Comer award excellence natural sci. Auburn U., 1942; Disting. Svc. award Fla. Vet. Med. Assn., 1966; Nat. 4-H Alumni award, 1967; George Washington honor medal award Freedoms Found., 1967; Nat. Partner in 4-H award, 1970; Disting. Faculty award U. Fla., Fla. Blue Key, 1972; E.T. York, Jr. Disting. Svc. award Fla., 1973; Honors medal Fla. Acad. Scis., 1974; E.T. York Svc. award Fla. Bd. Regents, 1983, Disting. Svc. award Am. Farm Bur., 1991, Disting. Svc. award Rotary Internat., 1994; named Fla. Agrl. Hall of Fame, 1990, Ala. Agrl. Hall of Fame, 1992. Fellow AAAS, Am. Soc. Agronomy, Soil Sci. Soc. Am., Am. Crop Sci. Soc.; mem. Am. Soc. Hort. Sci. (hon.), Am. Soc. Agrl. Scientists (pres. 1968), Blue Key, Rotary (dist. gov. 1981-82), Sigma Xi, Phi Kappa Phi, Alpha Zeta, Gamma Sigma Delta (Internat. Disting. Svc. award 1973), Omicron Delta Kappa, Phi Delta Kappa, Epsilon Sigma Phi, Alpha Gamma Rho (named to Hall of Fame 1982). Methodist. Address: 4020 SW 78th St Gainesville FL 32608

YORK, GARY ALAN, lawyer; b. Glendale, Calif., Aug. 29, 1943; m. Lois York, 1987; 1 child, Jonathan Alan. BA, Pomona Coll., 1965; LLB, Stanford U., 1968. Bar: Calif. 1969. Ptnr. Dewey Ballantine, L.A. Buchalter, Nemer, Fields & Younger, L.A., 1995—; instr. law sch. UCLA, 1968-69. Bd. editors Stanford Law review, 1966-68. Mem. ABA (chmn. real estate fin. com., real property probate and trust sect. 1987-89, chmn. usury com. 1992-93), L.A. County Bar Assn. (chmn. real estate fin. sect. 1993-95),

State Bar Calif.; Am. Coll. Real Estate Lawyers. Office: Buchalter Nemer Fields & Younger 601 S Figueroa St Los Angeles CA 90017

YORK, HERBERT FRANK, physics educator, government official; b. Rochester, N.Y., Nov. 24, 1921; s. Herbert Frank and Nellie Elizabeth (Lang) Y.; m. Sybil Dunford, Sept. 28, 1947; children: David Winters, Rachel, Cynthia. AB, U. Rochester, 1942, MS, 1943; PhD, U. Calif. Berkeley, 1949; DSc (hon.), Case Inst. Tech., 1960; LL.D., U. San Diego, 1964, Claremont Grad. Sch., 1974. Physicist Radiation Lab., U. Calif., Berkeley, 1943-58, assoc. dir., 1954-58; asst. prof. physics dept. U. Calif., Berkeley, 1951-54, assoc. prof., 1954-59, prof., 1959-61; dir. Lawrence Radiation Lab., Livermore, 1952-58; chief scientist Advanced Rsch. Project Agy., U.S. Dept. Def., 1958; dir. advanced rsch. projects divsn. Inst. for Def. Analyses, 1958; dir. def. rsch. and engring. Office Sec. Def., 1958-61; chancellor U. Calif.-San Diego, 1961-64, 70-72, prof. physics, 1964—, chmn. dept. physics, 1968-69, dean grad. studies, 1969-70, dir. program on sci., tech. and pub. affairs, 1972-88; dir. Inst. Global Conflict and Cooperation, 1983-88, dir. emeritus, 1988—; amb. Comprehensive Test Ban Negotiations, 1979-81; trustee Aerospace Corp., Inglewood, Calif., 1961-87; mem. Pres.'s Sci. Adv. com., 1957-58, 64-68, vice chmn., 1965-67; trustee Inst. Def. Analysis, 1963—; gen. adv. com. ACDA, 1962-69; mem. Def. Sci. Bd., 1977-81; spl. rep. of sec. def. and space arms control talks, 1978-79; mem. coun. nat. labs. Pres. U. Calif., 1991—; mem. task force future nat. labs. Sec. Energy, 1994-95; cons. Stockholm Internat. Peach Rsch. Inst.; researcher in application atomic energy to nat. def., problems of arms control and disarmament, elementary particles. Author: Race to Oblivion, 1970, Arms Control, 1973, The Advisors, 1976, Making Weapons, Talking Peace, 1987, Does Strategic Defense Breed Offense?, 1987, (with S. Lakoff) A Shield in the Sky, 1989, Arms and the Physicist, 1994; also numerous articles on arms or disarmament; bd. dirs. Bull. Atomic Scientists. Trustee Bishop's Sch., La Jolla, Calif., 1963-65. Recipient E.O. Lawrence award AEC, 1962; Guggenheim fellow, 1972. Fellow Am. Phys. Soc. (forum on physics and soc. award 1976, Leo Szilard award 1994), AAAS; mem. Internat. Acad. Astronautics, Fedn. Am. Scientists (chmn. 1970-71, exec. com. 1969-76, 95—, pub. svc. award 1992), Phi Beta Kappa, Sigma Xi. Home: 6110 Camino De La Costa La Jolla CA 92037-6520 Office: U Calif-San Diego Mail Code 0518 La Jolla CA 92093

YORK, JAMES MARTIN, lawyer; b. Abilene, Tex., Feb. 22, 1939; s. James Orville and Hazel Mae (Martin) Y.; m. Sandra L. Zunker, June 5, 1959 (div. 1967); children: Debra Lynn, James Martin Jr.; m. Nora Darlene Buechman, Nov. 3, 1972; 1 child, Victoria Lee. Student, Baylor U., 1957-60, LLB, 1962. Bar: Tex. 1962. Atty. Matthew & Matthews, Dallas, 1962-63, Ross, Banks, May & Cron, Houston, 1963-64, Law Offices of Fred W. Moore, Houston, 1964-65; pvt. practice Houston, 1965—. Sect. editor Baylor Law Rev., 1962. State Rep. primary candidate Rep. Party, Houston, 1970; del.-at-large Rep. State Conv., Houston, 1971; Rep. primary cand. for judge 310th Dist. Ct., 1994; coach Westbury Nat. Little League, Houston, 1967, Voss West Little League, Houston, 1969, 70; apptd. assoc. judge 246th Dist. Ct., 1995. Named Boss of Yr. Houston Assn. Legal Secs., 1973. Mem. Rotary Club of Houston, Inwood Forest Golf Club, Houston Bar Assn., State Bar of Tex., Baylor Alumni Assn., Baylor Lettermen's Assn. Baptist. Avocations: golf, swimming, reading. Office: 246th Dist Ct 7th Fl Family Law Ctr 1115 Congress Ave Houston TX 77002

YORK, JAMES ORISON, real estate executive; b. Brush, Colo., June 27, 1927; s. M. Orison and Marie L. (Kibble) Y.; m. Janice Marie Sjoberg, Aug. 1, 1959; children—Douglas James, Robert Orison. Student, U. Calif. at Berkeley, 1945-46; B.A. cum laude, U. Wash., 1949. Teaching fellow U. Wash., Seattle, 1950-52; econ. research analyst Larry Smith & Co. (real estate), Seattle and N.Y.C., 1953-60; partner Larry Smith & Co. (real estate), Seattle, 1960-66; pres. Larry Smith & Co. (real estate), San Francisco, 1966-71; pres., chief exec. officer R.H. Macy Properties, N.Y.C., also sr. v.p. planning and devel., dir. R.H. Macy & Co., Inc., 1971-88; pres. James York Assocs. (real estate), 1988—; trustee HRE Properties, Corp. Property Investors; chmn., N.Y.C. retail div. Am. Cancer Soc. Contbg. author: Shopping Towns-USA, 1960. Trustee ICSC Ednl. and Rsch. Found. With USNR, 1945-47. Mem. Am. Soc. Real Estate Counselors, Urban Land Inst., Internat. Real Estate Fedn., Internat. Council Shopping Centers, Phi Beta Kappa, Lambda Alpha. Episcopalian. Clubs: Olympic (San Francisco); American Yacht (Rye, N.Y.); Corinthian Yacht (Seattle); Union League (N.Y.C.); Knights of Malta, Order St. John, Washington Athletic (Seattle), Royal Victoria (B.C.) Yacht. Home and Office: 4 Riverstone Laguna Niguel CA 92677-5309

YORK, JAMES WESLEY, JR., theoretical physicist, educator; b. Raleigh, N.C., July 3, 1939; s. James Wesley and Mary Smedes (Poyner) Y.; m. Betty Louise Mattern, Aug. 19, 1961; children: Virginia York Setzer, Guilford Mattern. B.S. with high honors in Physics, N.C. State U., Raleigh, 1962, Ph.D. in Physics, 1966. Asst. prof. N.C. State U., Raleigh, 1965-68; rsch. assoc. Princeton (N.J.) U., 1968-69, lectr., 1969-70, asst. prof., 1970-73; assoc. prof. U. N.C., Chapel Hill, 1973-77, prof. dept. physics, 1977-89, Agnew H. Bahnson, Jr. disting. prof. physics, 1989—, dir. Inst. Field Physics, 1984-90; vis. asst. prof. U. Md., College Park, 1972; prof. associe U. Paris, 1976; vis. scientist Harvard U., Cambridge, 1977; vis. prof. U. Tex., Austin, 1979, 87; speaker Internat. Symposium on Methods of Differential Geometry in Physics and Mechanics, Warsaw, Poland, 1976; Alfred Schild Meml. lectr., U. Tex., 1979; del. Seventh Internat. Congress on Math. Physics, Boulder, Colo., 1983, Tex. Symposium on Relativistic Astrophysics, Jerusalem, 1984, Marcel Grossman Meeting, Rome, 1985, NATO Advanced Study Inst., Les Houches, France, 1982, Huelva, Spain, 1992, Paris, 1992, Banff, Can., 1992, other internat. and nat. meetings; co-organizer sci. meetings including Neutron stars and pulsars, Princeton, 1969, Spacetime dynamics, Aspen Ctr. for Theoretical Physics, 1981, Classical Problems in Gravitation, 1990, Cosmic Censorship, 1992; mem. com. of visitors physics div. NSF, 1991; plenary lectr. Fifth Can. Conf. on Gen. Relativity and Astrophysics, Waterloo, 1993. Directions in Gen. Relativity, College Park, Md., 1993. Mem. editorial bd. Jour. Math. Physics, 1989-92; contbr. chpts. to books, articles to sci. jours. Decorated Companion of St. Patrick, 1960; recipient 3d prize Gravity Rsch. Found. Essay award, 1975; Ford Found. fellow, 1962-65; Battelle Found. grantee, 1967, NSF postdoctoral fellow, 1969-70, Nat. Rsch. Com. France grantee, 1976, NSF grantee, 1974—; travel grantee, 1971, 76, 83, 84; U.S.A.-Israel Binat. Sci. Found. grantee, 1987-90, 90-93. Fellow Am. Phys. Soc.; mem. AAAS, Internat. Soc. Gen. Relativity and Gravitation, Rotary, Sigma Xi, Phi Kappa Phi, Tau Beta Pi, Sigma Pi Sigma, Pi Mu Epsilon, Phi Lambda Sigma. Episcopalian. Avocations: literature, music, sports. Office: U NC Dept Physics and Astronomy Chapel Hill NC 27599-3255

YORK, JEROME B., computer company executive; b. Memphis, June 22, 1938. BS, U.S. Mil. Acad.', 1960; MS, MIT, 1961; MBA, U. Mich., 1966. Various engring. positions GM Corp., Pontiac, Mich., 1962-67; various managerial positions Ford Motor Co., Deerborn, Mich., 1967-70; dir. strategic planning RCA Corp., Hertz Corp. (subs.), 1970-72 v.p., 1972-75; group v.p. Baker Industries, Inc., Parsippany, N.J., 1976-78; pres. Delta Truck Body Co., Inc., Montgomeryville, Pa., 1978-79; asst. contr. Chrysler de Mex. Chrysler Corp., Highland Park, Mich., 1979-82, mng. dir. Chrysler de Mex., 1982-85, v.p., gen. mgr. Dodge divsn., 1986-90, v.p., contr., 1989-90, exec. v.p., CFO, 1990-93; sr. v.p., CFO IBM Corp., Armonk, N.Y., 1993—; also bd. dirs. Office: IBM Corp Old Orchard Rd Armonk NY 10504*

YORK, JOSEPH STAFFORD, secondary gifted and talented education educator; b. Memphis, Oct. 13, 1944; s. Benjamin Preston and Ora Belle (Stafford) Y. BA, Lambuth Coll., Jackson, Tenn., 1966; postgrad., Memphis State U., 1970, St. John's Grad. Inst., Santa Fe, U. Tenn. Cert. English, history and Bible tchr., Tenn. Instr. English, Dyersburg (Tenn.) State Community Coll., Memphis State U.; tchr. English gifted and talented edn. Fayette County Schs., Somerville, Tenn., McNairy County Schs., Adamsville, Tenn.; dep. chief adv. probation officer Juvenile Ct. Memphis and Shelby County; mem. adv. coun. on tchr. edn. and cert. Tenn. Bd. Edn. Author: Handbook for Written Expression, (poem) The Other Side of the Mirror, 1976. Named Tchr. of Yr., Millington (Tenn.) High Sch., 1976, Tenn. SE Dist., 1989, Fayette County Sch. System and Fayette-Ware High Sch., 1989, 90, Outstanding Tenn. Tchr., 1985, Edn. of Yr. Fayette County C. of C., Tenn. Tchr. of Yr., 1991, S.E. Dist. Tenn. Tchr. of Yr., 1990;

recipient Excellence in Teaching award U. Tenn. at Knoxville, 1990, 91, 92; charter inductee Nat. Tchrs. Hall of Fame, 1992. Mem. NEA, Nat. Coun. Tchrs. English, Nat. State Tchrs. Yr. (exec. dir. Tenn. chpt. 1991—), Tenn. Coun. Tchrs. English, Coun. on Coll. Composition and Communication, Tenn. Edn. Assn., Assn. Supervision and Curriculum Devel., Fayette County Edn. Assn., McNairy County Edn. Assn., Kappa Delta Pi, Phi Delta Kappa, Kappa Sigma. Home: PO Box 203 Adamsville TN 38310-0203

YORK, MICHAEL (MICHAEL YORK-JOHNSON), actor; b. Fulmer, Eng., Mar. 27, 1942; s. Joseph Gwynne and Florence Edith (Chown) Johnson; m. Patricia McCallum, Mar. 27, 1968. BA with honors in English, Univ. Coll., Oxford U. (Eng.), 1964; DFA (hon.), U. S.C. Profl. debut with Dundee Repertory Theatre, Scotland, 1964; mem. Nat. Theatre Co., London, 1965-66; TV film or miniseries appearances include: Much Ado About Nothing, The Forsyte Saga, Rebel in the Grave, True Patriot, Jesus of Nazareth, 1977, A Man Called Intrepid, 1979, The Phantom of the Opera, 1983, The Master of Ballantrae, 1984, Sword of Gideon, The Far Country, 1985, Are You My Mother, 1986, Ponce de Leon, 1987, 1987, Till We Meet Again, 1989, The Road to Avonlea, 1991, Gardens of the World, 1993; The Four Minute Mile, The Lady and the Highway Man, 1988, The Heat of the Day, 1988, The Hunt for Stolen War Treasure, 1989, The Night of the Fox, 1990, Duel of Hearts, September, 1995, A Young Connecticut Yankee in King Arthur's Court, 1995; animated films The Magic Paintbrush, 1993; TV appearances: David Copperfield's Christmas, 1994, Teklab, 1994, Fall From Grace, 1994, Not of This Earth, 1995; TV series appearance: Knots Landing, 1987, September, 1994; stage appearances include: Any Just Cause, 1967, Hamlet, 1970, Broadway prodns. of Outcry, 1973, Ring Round the Moon, 1975, Bent, 1980, Cyrano de Bergerac, 1981, Whisper in the Mind, 1990, The Crucible, 1991, Someone Who'll Watch Over Me, 1993, Nora, 1993; appeared in motion pictures including: The Taming of the Shrew, 1966, Accident, 1966, Red and Blue, 1967, Smashing Time, 1967, Romeo and Juliet, 1967, The Strange Affair, 1967, The Guru, 1968, Alfred the Great, 1968, Justine, 1969, Something for Everyone, 1969, Zeppelin, 1970, La Poudre D'Escampette, 1971, Cabaret, 1971, England Made Me, 1971, Lost Horizon, 1972, The Three Musketeers, 1973, Murder on the Orient Express, 1974, Great Expectations, 1974, Conduct Unbecoming, 1974, The Four Musketeers, 1975, Logan's Run, 1976, Seven Nights in Japan, The Last Remake of Beau Geste, 1977, The Island of Dr. Moreau, 1977, Fedora, 1977, The Riddle of the Sands, 1978, Final Assignment, 1980, The White Lions, Success is the Best Revenge, 1984, Dawn, 1985, Vengeance, 1986, The Secret of the Sahara, 1987, Imbalances, 1987, Lethal Obsession, 1987, Midnight Cop, 1988, The Return of the Musketeers, 1989, The Long Shadow, 1991, Eline Vere, 1991, Wide Sargasso Sea, 1991, Rochade, 1991, Discretion Assured, Shadow of a Kiss, 1993, Gospa, 1994; radio performances The Dark Tower, 1977, (recipient Peabody award), A Matter of Honor, 1986, Babbitt, 1987, The Crucible, 1988, Are You Now, UTZ, 1989, McTeague, 1992, Make and Break, 1993; recs. include: Mere Christianity, 1982, Anna Karenina, 1985, Don Quixote, 1986, The King Must Die, 1988, British Rock: The First Wave, UTZ, 1989, The Modigliani Scandal, 1989, The Mummy, 1989, Candide, 1989, The Vampire Lestat, 1989, The Berlin Stories, 1990, The Remains of the Day, 1990, City of Joy, 1991, Beyond Love, 1991, Memories, Dreams, Reflections, 1991, A Poet's Bible, 1992, Einstein's Dreams, 1993, Accidentally on Purpose, 1993, The English Patient, 1993, Fortune's Favorite, 1993, The Three Musketeers, 1993, Paradise Lost, 1993, The Book of Psalms, 1994, The Book of Virtues, 1994, The Magic Paw-Paw, 1994; contbr.(books) The Courage of Conviction, 1985, Voices of Survival, 1987; author: Accidentally on Purpose, 1992; (recording) The Rubaiyat of Omar Khayyam, 1995. Avocations: travel, music, art. Office: ICM 8942 Wilshire Blvd Beverly Hills CA 90211-1908

YORK, RICHARD TRAVIS, art dealer; b. Nashville, Oct. 22, 1950; s. James Samuel and Jeane (Townes) Y. BA, Vanderbilt U., 1972. Dir. Am. art Hammer Galleries, N.Y.C., 1974-76; in charge Am. dept. M. Knoedler & Co., N.Y.C., 1976-77; assoc. Hirschl & Adler Galleries, N.Y.C., 1977-81; dir., owner Richard York Gallery, N.Y.C., 1981—. Author: (exhbn. catalogues) The Eye of Stieglitz, 1978 (Arlis award), Buildings Architecture in American Modernism, 1980, Ellen Day Hale, 1981 (Arlis award), The Natural Image: Plant Forms in American Modernism, 1982, An American Gallery, 1986, vols. I & II, 1987, III & IV, 1988, V, 1989, VI, 1990, VII, 1992, Charles G. Shaw: Abstractions of the Thirties, 1987, Will Henry Stevens: A Modernist's Response to Nature, 1987, Joseph Stella: The Tropics, 1988, Joseph Goldyne: Twenty Years of Work, 1992, American Paintings from the Collection of James H. Ricau, 1993. Mem. art adv. com. Colby Coll., 1990; mem. art adv. panel IRS, 1991—. Mem. Art Dealers Assn. Am. (bd. dirs. 1992—). Office: Richard York Gallery 21 E 65th St New York NY 10021-6524

YORK, THEODORE, electronics executive; b. 1942. BS mgmt. engering., Rensselaer Polytechnic Inst., Troy, N.Y. Pres., ceo Burndy Corp., Norwalk, Conn., 1986. Office: Burndy Internat Inc 51 Richards Ave Norwalk CT 06854-2318

YORK, THEODORE ROBERT, consulting company executive; b. Mitchel Field, N.Y., May 4, 1926; s. Theodore and Helen (Zierak) Y.; m. Clara Kiefer, Jan. 3, 1952; children: Theodore R. II, Sharon L., Scott K., Krista A. Jarman. BS, U.S. Mil. Acad., 1950; MBA, George Washington U., 1964; MPA, Nat. U., 1984. Commd. 2d lt. USAF, 1950, advanced through grades to col., 1970, ret., 1974; pres. T. R. York Cons., Fairfax, Va., 1974-79, T. R. Cons., San Diego 1979-85, ULTRAPLECS Intelligent Bldgs., Sandy, Utah, 1991—; dir. Software Productivity Consortium, Herndon, Va., 1985-90. Mem. Loudoun County Rep. Com., Leesburg, Va., 1990-91. Decorated DFC, Air medal (5), Meritorius Svc. medal, Joint Svcs. Commendation medal (5). Mem. Internat. Facilities Mgmt. Assn., Intelligent Bldgs. Inst. (advisor), Instituto Mexicana Del Edificios Intelegente (hon.), Office Planners and Users Group, Shriners, Masons. Avocations: computers, electronics. Office: ULTRAPLECS Intelligent Bldg 1289 S Bluff View Dr Sandy UT 84092-5922

YORKIN, BUD (ALAN YORKIN), producer, director; b. Washington, Pa., Feb. 22, 1926; s. Maurice A. and Jessie (Sachs) Y.; children: Nicole, David. BS in Elec. Engring., Carnegie-Mellon U., 1948; postgrad. in English Lit., Columbia U., 1951; LHD, Washington and Jefferson Coll., 1974. ptnr. Tandem Prodns., Inc., L.A., 1959-74. With engring. staff, NBC, N.Y.C., 1949-50, stage mgr., NBC, 1950-52; assoc. dir. Colgate Comedy Hour, 1952-53; dir. TV shows including Dinah Shore Show, Tony Martin Show, Ernie Ford Show, George Gobel Show, N.Y.C. and L.A., 1948-52; writer, producer, dir. An Evening With Fred Astaire, 1958, Another Evening With Fred Astaire, 1959, Jack Benny spls., 1959; exec. producer TV series All in the Family, 1971-79, Sanford and Son, 1972-77, Maude, 1972-78, Good Times, 1974-79, Diff'rent Strokes, 1978-86, What's Happening, 1976-79, Carter Country, 1977-79, Archie Bunker's Place, 1980-83, The Night They Raided Minsky's, Cold Turkey, Deal of the Century, Blade Runner, also numerous spls.; dir. (films) Come Blow Your Horn, 1965, Never Too Late, 1966, Divorce, American Style, 1967, Inspector Clouseau, 1968; producer, dir. (films) Start the Revolution Without Me, 1970, The Thief Who Came to Dinner, 1971, Twice in a Lifetime, 1985, Arthur on the Rocks, 1988, Love Hurts, 1990, Intersection, 1993. Trustee Am. Film Inst., Mus. Contemporary Art, L.A., Carnegie-Mellon U., Am. Heart Assn., UCLA. Recipient several Emmy awards, Sylvania award, Look award, Dirs. Guild award, Harvard Lampoon's Golden Jester award, Peabody award. Mem. TV Acad. Arts and Scis. (past gov.), Dirs. Guild Am. (past gov.). Office: Bud Yorkin Prodns Inc 345 N Maple Dr Ste 206 Beverly Hills CA 90210-3856

YORKS, RICHARD ALAN, investment banker; b. Boston, Mar. 28, 1940; s. David and Bella (Burstein) Y.; m. Ellen Barbara Roberts, Oct. 25, 1964; children: Laura Elyse, Andrew Michael. BA, U. Pa., 1961; MBA, Harvard U., 1963. CLU, ChFC. V.p. Bankers Leasing Corp., Boston, 1972-75; sr. v.p. Prulease, Inc., Boston, 1975-77; exec. v.p. Prulease, Inc., Cambridge, Mass., 1978-80; v.p. product planning The Prudential, Newark, 1981-82; pres. Pruco Life Ins. Co., Newark, 1983-86; v.p. The Prudential, Newark, 1986-87; v.p. Prudential Capital Corp., Newark, 1987; chmn. bd., chief exec. officer Prudential Asset Sales & Syndications, Inc., Newark, 1988-91; chmn. Prudential Specialized Fin. Group, Newark, 1992, Prudential Instl. Investors, Newark, 1993-94; pres. Prudential Asset Mgmt. Group-Real Estate, Newark, 1994—; bd. dirs. N.J. Gov.'s Awards, Prudential Equity Investors, Prudential Home Bldg. Investors, Prudential Trust Co., Prudential

Asset Mgmt. Parties, Inc. Avocations: golf, travel. Home: 16 Hemlock Rd Short Hills NJ 07078 Office: Prudential Asset Mgmt Group 51 JFK Parkway Short Hills NJ 07078

YORSZ, STANLEY, lawyer; b. Norwich, Conn., June 5, 1953; s. Stanley and Helen (Chimilewski) Y.; m. Margaret A. McLean, June 14, 1986. BA, Colgate U., 1975; JD, Dickinson U., 1978. Bar: Pa. 1978, U.S. Dist. Ct. (we. dist.) Pa. 1978, U.S. Ct. Appeals (3d cir.) 1980, U.S. Supreme Ct. 1980. Law clk. to judge Pa. Superior Ct., Pitts., 1978-80; assoc. Buchanan Ingersoll P.C., Pitts., 1980-86, ptnr., 1986—. Editor comments Dickinson Law Rev., 1978. Mem. ABA, Allegheny County Bar Assn., Pa. Bar Assn., Rivers Club. Roman Catholic. Avocations: tennis, squash, golf. Office: Buchanan Ingersoll PC 5800 USX Tower 600 Grant St Pittsburgh PA 15219

YORTY, SAMUEL, lawyer, former mayor; b. Lincoln, Nebr., Oct. 1, 1909; s. Frank Patrick and Johanna (Egan) Y.; m. Elizabeth Hensel, Dec. 1, 1938 (dec. Fev. 1984; 1 son, William Egan (dec. Oct. 1983); m. Gloria Haig, June 8, 1986. Student law sch., Southwestern U., U. So. Calif., U. Calif. Extension. Bar: Calif. bar 1939. Since practiced in Los Angeles; mem. 82d Congress from 14th Dist. Calif., 83d Congress from 26th Dist. Calif.; mayor Los Angeles, 1961-73; Mem. Calif. State Assembly, 1936-40, 49-50. Served to capt. USAAF, 1942-45. Decorated Encomienda medal Spain; comdr. Finnish Lion; Nat. Order So. Cross Brazil; comdr.'s cross German Order Merit; Gt. Silver Insignia of Honor with Star Austria; Order Civil Merit Korea; Knight Legion of Honor France; Order Homayoun medal Iran; Order Sun of Peru. Republican. Home and Office: 12979 Blairwood Dr Studio City CA 91604-4031

YOSELOFF, JULIEN DAVID, publishing company executive; b. N.Y.C., June 25, 1941; s. Thomas and Sara (Rothfuss) Y.; m. Darlene Starr Carbone, Aug. 6, 1967; children—Michael Ian, Anthony Alexander. B.A., U. Pa., 1962; student, London Sch. Econs., 1962-63; MA, Rutgers U., 1994. With A.S. Barnes and Co., Inc., Cranbury, N.J., 1963-80; dir. Associated Univ. Presses, Inc., 1966—; pres. Rosemont Pub. and Printing Corp., 1985—. Served with AUS, 1964. Mem. Phi Beta Kappa Assos, Phi Beta Kappa. Avocations: amateur radio, photography. Office: 440 Forsgate Dr Cranbury NJ 08512

YOSELOFF, THOMAS, publisher; b. Sioux City, Iowa, Sept. 8, 1913; s. Morris and Sarah (Rosansky) Y.; m. Sara Rothfuss, Apr. 30, 1938; children: Julien David, Mark Laurence; m. Lauretta Sellitti, Apr. 23, 1964; 1 dau., Tamar Rachel. A.B., U. Iowa, 1934; Litt.D. (hon.), Bucknell U., 1982; L.H.D. (hon.), Fairleigh Dickinson U., 1982. Chmn. Rosemont Pub. & Printing Corp., 1969—, Associated Univ. Presses, 1969—, Golden Cockerel Press, London, 1979—. Author: A Fellow of Infinite Jest, 1946, (with Lillian Stuckey) Merry Adventures of Till Eulenspiegel, 1944, Further Adventures of Till Eulenspiegel, pub. 1957, The Time of My Life, 1979; Editor: Seven Poets in Search of an Answer, 1944, Voyage to America, 1961, Comic Almanac, 1963, The Man from the Mercury, 1986. Pres. Center for War/Peace Studies, 1977-91. Recipient award of merit Bucknell U., 1975, award of merit U. Del., 1987. Mem. Phi Beta Kappa, Sigma Delta Chi, Delta Sigma Rho. Home: Box 289 68 Cedar Dr Colts Neck NJ 07722-1672 Office: 440 Forsgate Dr Cranbury NJ 08512

YOSHIKAWA, THOMAS T., internist; b. L.A., Feb. 26, 1941. MD, U. Mich., 1966. Diplomate Am. Bd. Internal Medicine, Am. Bd. Infectious Disease. Intern Harbor Gen. Hosp., Torrance, Calif., 1966-67, resident, 1967-70, fellow in infectious disease, 1972; mem. staff med. ctr. George Washington U., Washington, adj. prof. health care scis. Recipient Milo D. Leavitt Meml. Lecture award Am. Geriat. Soc., 1994. Mem. ACP, Am. Gynecol. Soc., Genetics Soc. Am. Office: ACMD Geriatrics & Extended Care (114), Dept Veteran Affairs 810 Vermont Ave NW Washington DC 20420*

YOSHINO, GEORGE, food products executive; b. Kennewick, Wash., June 25, 1928; s. Frank H. and Kazuye (Hada) Y.; m. Frances T. Kaku, Dec. 29, 1951 (div. 1979); children: Jean Frances, Frankie Jo, Michael Stanton, Harry Walter; m. Marguerite Shirley Mosley, Dec. 8, 1990. Grad. high sch., Weiser, Idaho. Owner Yoshino Farms, Quincy, Wash., 1948—; pres. Columbia Growers Inc, Quincy, 1956-62, Yoshino Western, Inc., Quincy, 1962-68, Wyco, Inc., Seattle, 1968-74; asst. sr. v.p. U & I Inc., Pasco, Wash., 1974-79; dir. gen. mgr. Spad Distributing, Inc., Pasco, 1979-86; pres. Century 21 Products, Inc., Pasco, 1987—; bd. dirs. Am. Nat. Bank, Kennewick; exec. bd. Benton-Franklin Govtl. Conf., 1993—; dir. Associate Wash. Bus. Mem. City Coun. Quincy, 1964-66; bd. dirs. Columbia Basin Commn., Olympia, Wash., 1964-68; dir. Associated Wash. Bus., 1994—; dir. exec. com. Benton Franklin Regional Coun., 1993—. Mem. Produce Mktg. Assn., Associated Wash. Bus. Republican. Office: Century 21 Products Inc 1917 N 2nd Pasco WA 99301

YOSHIZUMI, DONALD TETSURO, dentist; b. Honolulu, Feb. 18, 1930; s. Richard Kiyoshi and Hatsue (Tanouye) Y.; BS, U. Hawaii, 1952; DDS, U. Mo., 1960, MS, 1963; m. Barbara Fujiko Iwashita, June 25, 1955; children: Beth Ann E., Cara Leigh S., Erin Yuri. Clin. instr. U. Mo. Sch. Dentistry, Kansas City, 1960-63; pvt. practice Santa Clara, Calif., 1963-70, San Jose, Calif., 1970—. With USAF, 1952-56. Mem. Am. Dental Assn., Calif. Dental Assn., Santa Clara County Dental Soc., Omicron Kappa Upsilon, Delta Sigma Delta. Contbr. articles to profl. jours. Home: 5054 Parkfield Ave San Jose CA 95129-3225 Office: 2011 Forest Ave San Jose CA 95128

YOSKIN, JON WILLIAM, II, insurance company executive; b. Phila., Oct. 16, 1939; s. Lewis William and Louise (Houck) Y.; m. Dorothea James, Sept. 25, 1961 (div. Mar. 1992); children: Nicholas, Dorothea, Maurice P.; m. Elizabeth Anne Groves, Sept 26, 1992. Pvt. practice Phila., 1959-74; sr. v.p. Middle Atlantic Gen. Investment Co., Phila., 1974-80; assoc. v.p. Transatlantic Life Assurance Co., Phila., 1980-85, Meritor Life Ins. Co., Phila., 1985-88; owner, CEO Tri-Arc Fin. Svcs., Phila., 1988—; bd. dirs. Nat. Media Corp. Bd. mem. Concerto Soloist, Phila., 1990-92; mem. Spl. Olympics Adv. Com. Mem. Nat. Assn. Life Underwriters, Nat. Assn. Ins. Brokers (bd. dirs.), Profl. Assn. Ins. Agts., Sons of Am. Revolution, Mil. Order Loyal Legion of U.S. Republican. Episcopalian. Avocation: big game hunting. Home: 1606 Pine St Philadelphia PA 19103 Office: Tri-Arc Fin Svcs PO Box 6745 983 Old Eagle School Rd Ste 616 Wayne PA 19087

YOSKOWITZ, IRVING BENJAMIN, lawyer, manufacturing company executive; b. Bklyn., Dec. 2, 1945; s. Rubin and Jennie Y.; m. Carol L. Magil, Feb. 11, 1973; children: Stephen M., Robert J. BBA, CCNY, 1966; JD, Harvard U., 1969; postgrad., London Sch. Econs., 1971-72. Bar: N.Y. 1970, D.C. 1970, Conn. 1982. Programmer IBM, East Fishkill, N.Y., 1966; systems analyst Office Sec. Def., Washington, 1969-71; asso. firm Arnold & Porter, Washington, 1972-73; atty. IBM, 1973-79; regional counsel IBM, Bethesda, Md., to 1979; dep. gen. counsel United Technologies Corp., Hartford, Conn., 1979-81; v.p. and gen. counsel United Technologies Corp., 1981-86, sr. v.p., gen. counsel, 1986-90, exec. v.p., gen. counsel, 1990—; bd. dirs. BBA Group, plc. 1995—. Mem. editorial bd. Harvard Law Rev., 1968-69. With U.S. Army, 1969-71. Knox fellow, 1971-72. Mem. ABA, Am. Corp. Counsel Assn., Assn. Gen. Counsel (bd. dirs. 1982-85), Assn. Gen. Counsels. Office: United Techs Corp United Techs Bldg Hartford CT 06101

YOSOWITZ, SANFORD, lawyer, metal sales and fabricating executive; b. Cleve., July 26, 1939; s. Joseph and Esther (Moss) Y.; m. Ruth A. Goodman, June 24, 1962; children: Jeffrey Seth, Mark Robert, Chari Beth. B.S., Ohio State U., 1961; J.D., Case Western Res. U., 1964. Bar: Ohio 1964. Assoc. Lane, Krotinger & Santora, Cleve., 1964-66; law practice Cleve., 1966-69; corp. atty., asst. sec. Alcan Aluminum Corp., Cleve., 1969-73, sr. atty., asst. sec., 1979-80, v.p., gen. counsel, sec., 1980—; also dir. Alcan Aluminum Corp.; div. counsel Alcan Bldg. Products, Cleve., 1973-79; lectr. Ohio Legal Ctr. Inst., 1969-70, Greater Cleve. Bar Assn., 1972—; adv. bd. Can.-U.S. Law Inst. Editor-in-chief: Western Res. Law Rev., 1963-64; pub., editor: Industrial Concentration, 1979; editorial chmn.: Antitrust Law Jour., 1977-84. Am. show producer Boy Scouts Am., 1982; auctioneer pub. TV auction, 1974-81, community theatre actor, party entertainment producer and lyricist. Recipient of merit Ohio Legal Ctr. Inst., 1969. Mem. ABA (coun. mem. antitrust law sect. 1984-87), Bar Assn. Greater Cleve. (chmn. corp. law dept sect. 1973), Ohio Bar Assn., Cuyahoga County Bar Assn., adv. bd. Can.-U.S.

Law Inst., Sigma Alpha Mu. Home: 2585 Larchmont Dr Cleveland OH 44122-1515 Office: Alcan Aluminum Corp 100 Erieview Cleveland OH 44114

YOST, LYLE EDGAR, farm equipment manufacturing company executive; b. Hesston, Kans., Mar. 5, 1913; s. Joseph and Alma (Hensley) Y.; m. Erma Martin, July 31, 1938; children: Byron, Winston, Susan, Cameron. B.S. B.A, Goshen Coll., 1937; postgrad., U. Ind., 1940. With St. Joseph Valley Bank, Elkhart, Ind., 1938-41; tchr. Wakarusa (Ind.) High Sch., 1942-45; founder Hesston Corp., Kans., 1947, pres., 1949-83; now chmn. bd. Hesston Corp.; ret., 1991. Bd. dirs., past pres. Farm and Indsl. Equipment Inst.; mem. Gov.'s Com. for Ptnrs. for Progress Kans.-Paraguay; chmn. com. establishing creamery in Uruguay, 1967; mem. Stat Dept. cultural del. to USSR, 1967; chmn. pres.'s adv. coun. Hesston Coll. (Kans.); chmn. Prince of Peace Chapel, Aspen, Colo. Named Farmarketing Man of Year Nat. Agrl. Advt. and Marketing Assn., 1969; Kansan of Achievement in Bus., 1972; Kansan of Year, 1974. Mem. Alpha Kappa Psi (hon.). Home: 123 Kingsway Hesston KS 67062-9610 Office: PO Box 909 Hesston KS 67062-0909

YOST, NICHOLAS CHURCHILL, lawyer; b. Washington, Aug. 15, 1938; s. Charles Woodruff and Irene Ravitch (Oldakowska) Y.; m. Sandra Moore Rennie; children: Robert, Scott, Daniel. AB, Princeton U., 1960; LLB, U. Calif., Berkeley, 1963. Bar: Calif. 1964, U.S. Supreme Ct. 1972, D.C. 1978. Dep. atty. gen. adminstrv. law Calif. Dept. Justice, 1965-69; counsel Calif. State Environ. Quality Study Coun., 1969-71; dep. atty. gen. in charge environ. unit Calif. Dept. Justice, 1971-77; gen. counsel Coun. Environ. Quality, Exec. Office of Pres., Washington, 1977-81; vis. scholar Environ. Law Inst., Washington, 1981-82; ptnr. Dickstein, Shapiro & Morin, Washington, 1982-85; ptnr. Dickstein, Shapiro & Morin, Washington, 1985-94, Sonnenschein Nath & Rosenthal, San Francisco, 1994—; U.S. dir. legal and adminstrv. aspects of environ. protection agreement between U.S. and USSR, 1977-81; dir. Pres.'s Task Force on Global Resources and Environ. 1980-81; mem. U.S. Del. to UN Conf. Environ. and Devel., Rio, 1992; mem. Calif. EPA Blue Ribbon Commn. on a Unified Environ. Statute, 1994—. Contbr. articles to profl. jours. Capt. U.S. Army, 1963-65. Mem. ABA (chmn. standing com. on environ. law 1989-91), State Bar Calif. (chmn. com. on environ. 1975-76), D.C. Bar Assn. (co-chmn. environ., energy and natural resources sect. 1985-86, 88-89), Environ. Law Inst. (bd. dirs. 1986-92), UN Assn. L.A. (v.p. 1969-71), UN Assn. Washington (bd. dirs. 1987-93). Home: 901 Powell St Apt 8 San Francisco CA 94108-2024 Office: Sonnenschein Nath 685 Market St Fl 10 San Francisco CA 94105-4200

YOST, PAUL ALEXANDER, JR., foundation executive, retired coast guard officer; b. Phila., Jan. 3, 1929; s. Paul Alexander Sr. and Jeanne Moore (Bailey) Y.; m. Jan Worth, June 2, 1951; children: Linda L., Paul Alexander III, David J., Lisa L., Christopher J. BS, USCG Acad., 1951; MS, U. Conn., 1959; MA, George Washington U., 1964; grad., Naval War Coll., 1964. Commd. ensign USCG, 1951, advanced through grades to adm., 1986; comdr. 8th dist. USCG, New Orleans, 1978-81; chief staff hdqrs. USCG, Washington, 1981-84; comdr. 3d dist., maritime Atlantic def. zone, and Atlantic area USCG, N.Y.C., 1984-86; commandant USCG, Washington, 1986-90, ret., 1990; pres. James Madison Found., Washington, 1990—. Decorated D.S.M. with gold star, Silver Star, Legion of Merit combat "V" with gold star, Meritorious Service Medal. Office: James Madison Meml Fellowship Found 2000 K St NW Washington DC 20590-0001

YOST, WILLIAM ALBERT, psychology educator, hearing researcher; b. Dallas, Sept. 21, 1944; s. William Jacque and Gladys (Funk) Y.; m. Lee Prater, June 15, 1969; children—Kelley Ann, Alyson Leigh. B.A., Colo. Coll., 1966; Ph.D., Ind. U., 1970. Assoc. prof. psychology U. Fla., Gainesville, 1971-77; dir. sensory physiology and perception program NSF, Washington, 1982-83; prof. psychology Loyola U., Chgo., 1977-89; dir. Parmly Hearing Inst., 1977—, prof. hearing scis., 1990—; adj. prof. psychology and otolaryngology Loyola U., Chgo., 1990—; individual expert bio-acoustics Am. Nat. Stds. Inst., 1983—; mem. study sect. Nat. Inst. Deafness and Other Communication Disorders, 1990-94; mem. hearing bioacoustics and biomechanics com. Nat. Rsch. Coun., 1992—. Author: Fundamentals of Hearing, 1977, 84, 94; editor (with others) New Directions in Hearing Science, 1985, Directional Hearing, 1987, Auditory Processing of Complex Sounds, 1987, Classification of Complex Sounds, 1989, Psychoacoustics, 1993; assoc. editor Auditory Neurosci., 1994—; ad hoc reviewer NSF, Air Force Office Sci. Rsch., Office Naval Rsch., 1981—; contbr. chpts. to books, articles to profl. jours. Pres. Evanston Tennis Assn., Ill., 1984, 90. Grantee NSF, 1974—, NIH, 1975—, AFOSR, 1983—. Fellow Acoustical Soc. Am. (assoc. editor jour. 1984-91); mem. NAS (exec. com. on hearing, bioacoustics and biomechanics 1981-87, chmn. 1993-97), Assn. Rsch. in Otolaryngology (sec.-treas. 1984-87, pres.-elect 1987-88, pres. 1988-89), Acoustics Soc. Am. (chmn. com. psychol. and physiol. acoustics 1990—), Nat. Inst. Deafness and Other Comm. Disorders (task force, rev. panel 1990—), Acoustical Soc. Am. (chmn. tech. com. 1990—).

YOST, WILLIAM ARTHUR, III, lawyer; b. Greensburg, Pa., Apr. 7, 1935; s. William Arthur Jr. and Virginia (Penny) Y.; m. Katherine Luedke, Apr. 20, 1963; children: Virginia, Alexander. AB, Haverford Coll., 1957; LLB, Yale U., 1960. Bar: Wis. 1960, Tex 1984. Corp. counsel, sec., v.p. adminstrn. Will Ross Inc., Milw., 1972-78; pres. Yost, Krombach & Schmitt, S.C., Cedarburg, Wis., 1978-83; sr. v.p. legal and sec. Pearle Inc., Dallas, 1983-92; chmn. Pearle Vision Found., 1992—; bd. dirs. Arthritis Found, Tex., 1993—. Mem. ABA, Internat. Bar Assn., Tex. Bar Assn., Wis. Bar Assn., Dallas Bar Assn., Yale Club, Town Club, T-Bar Racquet Club, Univ. Club.

YOTHER, MICHELE, publisher; b. Atlanta, Aug. 25, 1965; d. Carole (Spence) Marsh; m. Michael B. Yother, Mar. 17, 1990. BA in acctg. cum laude, Ga. State U., 1990. Asst. v.p. Bank Am., Atlanta, 1986-90; pres. Gallopade Pub. Group, Atlanta, 1990—; pres. Carole Marsh Family Interactive Multimedia, 1993—. Pub. over 2500 children's books, computer disks and activities. Equifax Bus. scholar Ga. State U., 1989. Mem. Women's Nat. Book Assn. (bd. dirs. 1994-95), Bank Am. Club (pres. 1989), Golden Key. Methodist. Home: 359 Milledge Ave Atlanta GA 30312 Office: Gallopade Pub Group 359 Milledge Ave Ste 100 Atlanta GA 30312

YOUMAN, LILLIAN HOBSON LINCOLN, building services contractor; b. Powhatan, Va., May 12, 1940; d. Willie David and Arnetha (Hobson) Hobson; children: Darnetha LaRoi, Tasha Renee'. BA, Howard U., 1966; MBA, Harvard U., 1969. Account exec. Ferris & Co., 1972-76; exec. v.p. Unified, 1973-76; pres. Centennial One, Lanham, Md., 1976—. Bd. dirs. Citizens Bank of Md. Named Small Bus. Person of Yr., State of Md., 1981, Female Minority Contractor of Yr., Dept. of Commerce, 1984, Nat. Minority Entrepreneur of Yr., 1988; finalist Arthur Young/Inc. Entrepreneur of Yr., 1989. Mem. Bldg. Svc. Contractors Assn. (v.p.), Capitol Assn. Bldg. Svc. Contractors (dir.); Prince George C. of C. (bd. dirs.). Republican. Baptist. Avocations: reading, traveling, golfing. Home: 1305 Lavall Dr Davidsonville MD 21035-1136 Office: Centennial One Inc 9600 Martin Luther King Jr Hwy Suite E Lanham Seabrook MD 20706

YOUMAN, ROGER JACOB, editor, writer; b. N.Y.C., Feb. 25, 1932; s. Robert Harold and Ida (Kellner) Y.; m. Lillian Frank, June 22, 1958; children: Nancy, Laura, Joshua, andrew. B.A., Swarthmore Coll., 1953. Desk asst. CBS News, N.Y.C., 1953; program editor TV Guide, N.Y.C., 1956; regional editor TV Guide, Memphis, 1956-57, Houston, 1957; asst. programming editor TV Guide, N.Y.C., 1957-60; assoc. editor TV Guide, Radnor, Pa., 1960-65, asst. mng. editor, 1965-72, mng. editor, 1972-76, exec. editor, 1976-79, 80-81, co-editor 1981-90, editor, 1990-93; editor Panorama, 1979-80; editl. dir. TV Guide On Screen, 1993—; del. U.S.-Soviet Bilateral Info. Talks, 1988, 90. Author: (with Arthur Shulman) How Sweet It Was, 1966, The Television Years, 1973; contbr. articles to various pubs. Served with AUS, 1954-55. Mem. NATAS, Am. Soc. Mag. Editors. Home: 752 Mancill Rd Wayne PA 19087-2043 Office: TV Guide 4 Corporate Ctr Radnor PA 19088

YOUMANS, JULIAN RAY, neurosurgeon, educator; b. Baxley, Ga., Jan. 2, 1928; s. John Edward and Jennie Lou (Milton) Y.; children—Reed Nesbit, John Edward, Julian Milton. B.S., Emory U., 1949, M.D., 1952; M.S., U. Mich., 1955, Ph.D., 1957. Diplomate: Am. Bd. Neurol. Surgery. Intern U. Mich. Hosp., Ann Arbor, 1952-53; resident in neurol. surgery U. Mich.

Hosp., 1953-55, 56-58; fellow in neurology U. London, 1955-56; asst. prof. neurosurgery U. Miss., 1959-62, assoc. prof., 1962-63; assoc. prof. Med. U. S.C., 1963-65, prof., 1965-67, chief div. neurosurgery, 1963-67; prof. U. Calif., Davis, 1967-91, 1991—; chmn. dept. neurosurgery U. Calif. 1967-82; cons. USAF, U.S. VA, NRC. Editor: Neurological Surgery, 1973, 3d edit., 1989; contbr. articles to profl. jours. No. vice chmn. Republican State Central Com. of Calif., 1979-81. Served with U.S. Navy, 1944-46. Mem. ACS (bd. govs. 1972-78), Congress of Neurol. Surgeons (exec. com. 1967-70), Am. Acad. Neurology, Am. Assn. Neurol. Surgeons, Am. Assn. Surgery of Trauma, Pan-Pacific Surg. Assn., Western Neurosurg. Soc., Neurosurg. Soc. Am., Soc. Neurol. Surgeons, Soc. Univ. Neurosurgeons, N. Pacific Soc. Neurology and Psychiatry, Royal Soc. Medicine, Am. Trauma Soc., U.S. C of C., Bohemian Club, Sutter Club, Capital Club of Sacramento, Rotary. Republican. Episcopalian. Office: Ste 10 502 Mace Blvd Davis CA 95616

YOUNG, A. THOMAS, defense, aerospace, energy and information systems company executive; b. Wachapreague, Va., Apr. 19, 1938; s. William Thomas and Margaret (Colonna) Y.; m. Page Carter Hayden, June 24, 1961; children: Anne Blair, Thomas Carter. BMechE, B in Aero. Engring., U. Va., 1961; M in Mgmt., MIT, 1972. Designer Newport News (Va.) Shipbldg. & Drydock Co., 1961; with NASA, 1961-82; various positions Langley Research Ctr., Hampton, Va., 1961-69; staff mem. and mission dir. Viking Project Hampton, 1969-76; dir. Hdqrs. Planetary Program Washington, 1976-79; dep. dir. Ames Research Ctr., Moffett Field, Calif., 1979-80; dir. Goddard Space Flight Ctr., Greenbelt, Md., 1980-82; with Martin Marietta Corp., 1982—; v.p. aerospace rsch. and engring. Bethesda, Md., 1982-83; v.p., gen. mgr. Balt. Aerospace, 1983-84, pres., 1984-85; exec. v.p., then. pres. Orlando (Fla.) Aerospace, 1985-87; pres. Electronics & Missiles Group, Orlando, 1987-89; sr. exec. v.p. Martin Marietta Corp., 1989-90, pres., chief operating officer, 1990—; bd. dirs. Cooper Industries, Inc., Dial Corp.; chmn. Gov.'s Space Commn., Tallahassee, Fla., 1987-88. Bd. dirs. Va. Engring. Found. of U. Va. Sch. Engring. and Applied Scis.; prin. Ctr. for Excellence in Govt., Washington, 1987; trustee U. Cen. Fla., 1987-89; mem. Orange County (Fla.) Sch. Bd. Found., 1987-89. Sloan fellow MIT, 1971-72; decorated DSM Viking Project NASA, 1977; recipient Outstanding Leadership medal Voyager Program NASA, 1980, Meritorious Exec. Presdl. Rank award Pres. Jimmy Carter, 1980, Disting. Exec. award Pres. Ronald Reagan, 1981. Fellow AIAA, Am. Astronautical Soc.; mem. Nat. Assn. Engrs. Republican. Methodist. Avocations: boating, fishing. Office: Martin Marietta Corp 6801 Rockledge Dr Bethesda MD 20817-1877*

YOUNG, ALICE, lawyer; b. Washington, Apr. 7, 1950; d. John and Elizabeth (Jen) Y.; m. Thomas L. Shortall, Sept. 22, 1984; children: Amanda, Stephen. AB magna cum laude, Yale U., 1971; JD, Harvard U., 1974. Bar: N.Y. 1975. Assoc. Coudert Bros., N.Y.C., 1974-81; mng. ptnr. Graham & James, N.Y.C., 1981-87; ptnr. Milbank, Tweed, Hadley & McCloy, N.Y.C., 1987-93; ptnr., chair Asia Pacific Practice (U.S.) Kaye, Scholer, Fierman, Hays & Handler, N.Y.C., 1994—; mem. Coun. on Fgn. Rels., 1977—. Contbr. articles to profl. jours. Trustee Aspen (Colo.) Inst., 1988—, Pan-Asian Repertory Theatre, N.Y.C., 1987-90, Lingnan Found., N.Y.C., 1984-91; mem. bus. com. Met. Mus. Art, N.Y.C., 1989-94, Nat. Com. on U.S.-China Rels., 1993—, U.S.-China Bus. Coun., 1993—, Com. of 100, 1993—; mem. bd. overseers visitation com. to Law Sch., Harvard U., 1994—. Named one of 40 Under 40 Crain's Bus., N.Y.C., 1989; Bates fellow Yale U., 1970, NDFL fellow Harvard U., 1967-68; recipient Star award N.Y. Women's Agenda, 1992. Mem. ABA, N.Y. State Bar Assn. (fgn. investment com.), Assn. Bar City N.Y. (spl. com. on rels. with Japanese bar, Union Internat. des Avocats), Nat. Asian Pacific Am. Bar Assn., Asian Am. Bar Assn. N.Y., Harvard Law Sch. Assn. N.Y.C. (trustee 1990—), Japan Soc. (sec. 1989—), Asia Soc. (pres.'s coun. 1984—). Office: Kaye Scholer Fierman Hays & Handler 425 Park Ave New York NY 10022-3598

YOUNG, ANDREW, clergyman, civil rights leader, former mayor, former ambassador, former congressman; b. New Orleans, Mar. 12, 1932; s. Andrew J. and Daisy (Fuller) Y.; m. Jean Childs, June 7, 1954; children—Andrea, Lisa Dru, Paula Jean, Andrew J. III. Student, Dillard U., 1947-48; B.S., Howard U., 1951; B.D.. Hartford Theol. Sem., 1955; D.D. (hon.), Wesleyan U., 1970, United Theol. Sem. Twin Cities, 1970; LL.D. (hon.), Wilberforce U., 1971, Clark Coll., 1973, Yale U., 1973, Swarthmore Coll., Atlanta U., others; numerous other hon. degrees. Ordained to ministry Congl. Ch., 1955; pastor in Thomasville, Ga., 1955-57; assoc. dir. dept. youth work Nat. Council Chs., 1957-61; mem. staff So. Christian Leadership Conf., 1961-70, administr. citizen edn. program, 1961-64, exec. dir., 1964-70, exec. v.p., 1967-70; now bd. dirs.; mem. 93d-95th Congresses from 5th Ga. Dist.; mem. Rules com.; U.S. ambassador to UN, 1977-79; mayor of Atlanta, 1982-89. Chmn. Atlanta Community Relations Commn., 1970-72; chmn. bd. Delta Ministry of Miss.; bd. dirs. Martin Luther King, Jr. Center for Social Change, Robert F. Kennedy Meml. Found., Field Found., So. Christian Leadership Conf. Recipient Pax-Christi award St. John's U., 1970; Springarn medal.; Medal of Freedom, 1980, French Legion of Honor medal, 1982; co-recipient, Martin Luther King, Jr., Award for Public Svc. (Ebony mag.), 1990. Mem. Ams. Dem. Action. Office: Law Internat Inc 1000 Abernathy Rd NE Atlanta GA 30328-5603

YOUNG, ANDREW BRODBECK, lawyer; b. Phila., Feb. 8, 1907; s. Edward E. and Estelle (Brodbeck) Y.; m. Olive C. Sherley, Apr. 22, 1933; children: Andrew Oliver (dec.), Sherley (Mrs. Paul A. Hollos). A.B., Princeton U., 1928; LL.B., Harvard U., 1931. Bar: Pa. 1931. Ptnr. Stradley, Ronon, Stevens & Young, Phila., 1935—; v.p., bd. dir. W.W. Interests (formerly Warren Webster & Co.); bd. dirs. M. A. Bruder & Sons, Inc., Welex Inc., Holmes Investment Co., Phila. Belt LineRy. Co.; lectr. finance U. Pa., 1939-66; lectr. various tax insts., 1953-80; mem. Mayor's Com. Exec. and Elective Salaries Phila. City Govt., 1959, Mayor's Com. Port Promotion Phila., 1959-63; mem. adv. council Phila. Community Renewal Program, 1964-66; chmn. Phila. Indsl. Devel. Corp., 1963-68, pres., 1963-70, chmn. 1970-86; mem. Mayor's Tax Study Commn., 1960, mem. Commr. Internal Revenue's Adv. group., 1965; trustee Phila. Belt Line Ry. Co. Chmn. bd. trustees Mary Jacobs Meml. Libr. Found., Rocky Hill, N.J.; trustee Lovett Found., Michael Bruder Found., Frank Michaels Scholarship Found., Penjerdel Found.; mem. coun. pres.'s advisers LaSalle Coll., 1969-74. With Surgeon Gen.'s Office, AUS, 1942-45. Fellow Am. Bar Found.; mem. ABA (mem. ho. of dels. 1966-70, mem. council tax sect. 1958-70, chmn. sect. 1963-65), Pa. Bar Assn., Am. Law Inst. (tax adv. group, corps.-stockholders project 1957-59), Am. Coll. Tax Counsel, Am. Law Inst. (estate and gift tax project 1964-67), Phila. C. of C. (pres. 1958-60, chmn. bd. 1960-62, dir.), Am. Arbitration Assn. (nat. panel arbitrators), Phi Beta Kappa. Episcopalian. Clubs: Philadelphia, Sunday Breakfast, Sunnybrook Golf, Tunkhannock Creek Assn. (Phila.); Commanderie de Bordeaux, Penn, Wilderness, Angler's. Home: 613 Foulkeways Gwynedd PA 19436-1024 Office: 2600 One Commerce Sq 2005 Market St Philadelphia PA 19103

YOUNG, ANN ELIZABETH O'QUINN, historian, educator; b. Waycross, Ga.; d. James Foster and Pearl Elizabeth (Sasser) O'Quinn; student Shorter Coll.; BA, MA, U. Ga., PhD, 1965; m. Robert William Young, Aug. 18, 1968; children: Abigail Ann, Leslie Lynn. Asst. prof. history Kearney (Nebr.) State Coll. (name now U. Nebr. at Kearney 1991), 1965-69, assoc. prof., 1969-72, prof., 1972—; participant Inst. on Islam, Middle East and World Politics, U. Mich., summer 1984, Coun. on Internat. Ednl. Exch., London, 1990, NEH Seminar NYU, 1993. Mem. NEA, PEO, Phi Alpha Theta, Delta Kappa Gamma (chpt. pres. 1978-79), Phi Mu. Republican. Presbyterian. Contbg. author Dictionary of Georgia Biography; contbr. articles to profl. revs. Office: U Nebr at Kearney Dept History Kearney NE 68849-1285

YOUNG, ARTHUR PRICE, librarian, educator; b. Boston, July 29, 1940; s. Arthur Price and Marion (Freeman) Y.; m. Patricia Dorothy Foss, June 26, 1965; children: John Marshall, Christopher Price. B.A., Tufts U., 1962; M.A.T., U. Mass., 1964; M.S. in L.S., Syracuse U., 1969; Ph.D., U. Ill., 1976. Head reader services, social sci. bibliographer SUNY-Cortland, 1969-72; rsch. assoc. U. Ill. Libr. Rsch. Ctr., Urbana, 1972-75; asst. dean pub. services, assoc. prof. U. Ala., Tuscaloosa, 1976-81; dean librs., prof. U. R.I., Kingston, 1981-89; dir. Thomas Cooper Libr., U. S.C., Columbia, 1989-93; sr. fellow UCLA, 1991; dir. librs. No. Ill. U., DeKalb, 1993—; mem. adj. faculty Syracuse (N.Y.) U., 1970-71, Rosary Coll., River Forest, Ill., 1994—; pres. Consortium R.I. Acad. and Rsch. Librs., 1983-85; bd. govs. Univ. Press New Eng., 1987-89. Author: Books for Sammies: American Library

Association and World War I, 1981, American Library History: A Bibliography of Dissertations and Theses, 1988, Higher Education in American Life, 1636-1986: A Bibliography of Dissertations and Theses, 1988, Cities and Towns in American History: A Bibliography of Doctoral Dissertations, 1989, Academic Libraries: Research Perspectives, 1990, Religion and the American Experience, 1620-1900: A Bibliography of Doctoral Dissertations, 1992, Religion and the American Experience, the Twentieth Century: A Bibliography of Doctoral Dissertations, 1994; editl. bd. various jours. Served to capt. USAF, 1964-68. Recipient Berner Nash award U. Ill., 1976. Mem. ALA (chmn. editorial bd.), Assn. Coll. and Rsch. Librs. (publs. in librarianship 1982-88, chmn. Jesse H. Shera Endowment Fund com. 1991-94), S.C. Libr. Assn. (chmn. libr. adminstrn. sect. 1991-92), Assn. Rsch. Librs. (scholarly commn. com. 1991-93), Orgn. Am. Historians, Am. Hist. Assn., Phi Kappa Phi, Beta Phi Mu, Phi Delta Kappa. Episcopalian. Home: 310 Ridge Dr De Kalb IL 60115-1742

YOUNG, BARBARA, psychiatrist, psychoanalyst, psychiatry educator, photographer; b. Chgo., Oct. 27, 1920; d. William Harvey and Blanche Katherine (DeBra) Y. A.B., Knox Coll., 1942; M.D., Johns Hopkins U., 1945; grad., Balt. Psychoanalytic Inst., 1955. Intern Univ. Hosps., Iowa City, Iowa, 1945-46, asst. resident in neurology, 1945-47; asst. resident in psychiatry Phipps Clinic, Johns Hopkins U. Hosp., Balt., 1947-49; staff psychiatrist Perry Point (Md.) VA Hosp., 1949-51; practice medicine specializing in psychiatry/psychoanalysis Balt., 1951—; instr. Johns Hopkins U., 1953-69, asst. prof. psychiatry, 1969—; photographer, 1958—. Works represented in, Mus. Modern Art, (locat.) N.Y.C., Balt. Mus. Art, Santa Barbara (Calif.) Mus. Art, Eastman House, Rochester, N.Y., Yale U. Gallery of Art. Mem. Am. Psychoanlytic Assn., Am. Psychiat. Assn., Balt.-Washington Soc. for Psychoanalysis. Democrat. Address: 5307 Herring Run Dr Baltimore MD 21214-1937

YOUNG, BARNEY THORNTON, lawyer; b. Chillicothe, Tex., Aug. 10, 1934; s. Bayne and Helen Irene (Thornton) Y.; m. Sarah Elizabeth Taylor, Aug. 31, 1957; children: Jay Thornton, Sarah Elizabeth, Serena Taylor. BA, Yale U., 1955; LLB, U. Tex., 1958. Bar: Tex. 1958. Assoc. Thompson, Knight, Wright & Simmons, Dallas, 1958-65; ptnr. Rain, Harrell, Emery, Young & Doke, Dallas, 1965-87; mem. firm Locke Purnell Rain Harrell (A Profl. Corp.), 1987—; bd. dirs. Jones-Blair Co. Mem. adv. coun. Dallas Cmty. Chest Trust Fund, Inc., 1964-66; bd. dirs. Mental Health Assn. Dallas County, Inc., 1969-72, Summerhill Crow Family Found., 1984-87; trustee Hockaday Sch., Dallas, 1971-77, 90—, chmn., 1994—; trustee Dallas Zool. Soc., 1986-92, Lamplighter Sch., Dallas, 1976—, chmn., 1983-86, St. Mark's Sch., Dallas, 1970—, pres., 1976-78, The Found. for Latter Ctr. and Comm. Disorders, 1988—, Friends of Ctr. for Human Nutrition, 1986, Shelter Ministries of Dallas Found., 1993—, Dallas Hist. Soc., 1993—; mem. Yale Devel. Bd., 1984-91. Fellow Tex. Bar Found., Dallas Bar Found.; mem. ABA, Tex. Bar Assn., Dallas Bar Assn., Am. Judicature Soc., Order of Coif, Phi Beta Kappa, Phi Sigma Alpha, Phi Gamma Delta, Phi Delta Phi, Dallas Country Club, Dallas County Rep. Men's Club (bd. dirs. 1977-79), Petroleum Club (Dallas), Yale Club (Dallas, N.Y.C.). Home: 6901 Turtle Creek Blvd Dallas TX 75205-1251 Office: Locke Purnell Rain Harrell 2200 Ross Ave Dallas TX 75201-2708

YOUNG, BLESS STRITAR, lawyer; b. Mar. 17, 1947. Student, Marietta Coll., 1965-68; BA, Temple U., 1969, JD, 1973. Bar: Pa. 1973, U.S. Dist. Ct. (ea. dist.) Pa. 1975, D.C. 1978, U.S. Ct. Appeals (D.C. cir.) 1978, N.Y. 1979, U.S. Supreme Ct. 1979, Calif. 1983, U.S. Dist. Ct. (no. dist.) Calif. 1983, U.S. Dist. Ct. (so. and cen. dists.) Calif. 1985. Assoc. Arthur S. Kafrissen & Assocs., Phila., 1973-74; atty. Bell of Pa., Phila., 1974-77, AT&T, N.Y.C., 1977-83; gen. atty. AT&T, San Francisco, 1983-87, L.A., 1987-88; ptnr. Fulbright & Jaworski, L.A., 1988—; judge pro tem Contra Costa County Superior Ct., Martinez, Calif., 1985-87, L.A. Mcpl. Ct., 1988—. Atty. Vol. Lawyers for Arts, N.Y.C., 1977-83. Named one of Outstanding Young Women Am., 1977. Mem. ABA (sect. litigation, mem. labor and employment commn., chairperson trade secrets litigation subcom. 1994—, editor Model Jury Instructions: Employment Litigation 1994), Pa. Bar Assn., N.Y. State Bar Assn., Calif. Bar Assn., Pi Kappa Delta. Office: Fulbright & Jaworski 865 S Figueroa St Los Angeles CA 90017-2543

YOUNG, BRYANT LLEWELLYN, lawyer, business executive; b. Rockford, Ill., Mar. 9, 1948; s. Llewellyn Anker and Florence Ruth Y. AB, Cornell U., 1970; JD, Stanford U., 1974. Bar: Calif. 1974, Nev. 1975, D.C. 1979. Law clk. U.S. Dist. Ct. (no. dist.) Calif., San Francisco, 1974-75; assoc. Dinkelspiel, Pelavin, Steefel & Levitt, San Francisco, 1975-77; White House fellow, spl. asst. to sec. HUD, Washington, 1977-78, spl. asst. to sec., 1978-79, acting dep. exec. asst. for ops. Office of Sec., 1979; dep. gen. mgr. New Community Devel. Corp., 1979, acting gen. mgr., 1979-80; mgmt. cons. AVCO Corp., 1980; spl. asst. to chmn. bd. and chief exec. officer U.S. Synthetic Fuels Corp., Washington, 1980-81, project dir., 1981; pres. Trident Mgmt. Corp., San Francisco, 1981-87; of counsel Pelavin, Norberg, Harlick & Beck, San Francisco, 1981-82, ptnr., 1982-87; mng. ptnr. bus. section Carroll, Burdick & McDonough, San Francisco, 1987-90; founding ptnr. Young, Vogl & Harlick, San Francisco, 1990-93, Young, Vogl, Harlick & Wilson, San Francisco, 1993—. Mem. pub. affairs com. San Francisco Aid Retarded Citizens, Inc., 1977; U.S. co-chmn. New Towns Working Group, U.S.-USSR Agreement on Cooperation in Field of Housing and Other Constrn., 1979-80; treas., bd. dirs. White House Fellows Found., 1980-84; prin. Coun. Excellence in Govt., Washington, 1986-94; mem. adv. com. Nat. Multi-Housing Coun., 1987-92; mem. Ross Sch. Found., 1994—. Mem. ABA (real property, trust and probate law sects.), White House Fellows Assn. (chmn. ann. meeting 1979, del. China 1980), Am. Field Svc. Returnees Assn., Can.-Am. C. of C. No. Calif. (v.p., bd. dirs. 1992—), The Netherlands C. of C. in U.S., Chile-Calif. Found. (mem. exec. com., bd. dirs. 1993—). Office: 425 California St Ste 2500 San Francisco CA 94104-2210

YOUNG, C. CLIFTON, judge; b. Nov. 7, 1922, Lovelock, Nev.; m. Jane Young. BA., Nev., 1943; LLB, Harvard U., 1949. Bar: Nev. 1949, U.S. Dist. Ct. Nev. 1950, U.S. Supreme Ct. 1955. Justice Nev. Supreme Ct., Carson City, 1985—, former chief justice, from 1989. Office: Nev Supreme Ct 201 S Carson St Carson City NV 89701

YOUNG, C. W. (BILL YOUNG), congressman; b. Harmarville, PA, Dec. 16, 1930; m. Beverly Angello; children: Pamela Kay, Terry Lee, Kimber, Robert, William, Patrick. Mem. Fla. Legislature, 1960-70, 92nd-104th Congresses from 10th dist. Fla., 1971—; mem. Appropriations com., subcom. Defense, Labor, HHS and Edn., legis.; mem. Fla. Constn. Revision Commn., 1965-67; chmn. So. Hwy. Policy Com., 1966-68; mem. Electoral Coll., 1968; del. Rep. Nat. Conv., 1968, 72, 76, 80, 84, 88. Named Most Valuable Senator, Capitol Press Corps, 1969. Methodist. Office: US Ho Reps 2407 Rayburn Ho Office Bldg Washington DC 20515-0910

YOUNG, CHARLES EDWARD, university chancellor; b. San Bernardino, Calif., Dec. 30, 1931; s. Clayton Charles and Eula May (Walters) Y. AA, San Bernardino Coll., 1954; AB, U. Calif., Riverside, 1955; MA, UCLA, 1957, PhD, 1960; DHL (hon.), U. Judaism, L.A., 1969. Congl. fellow Washington, 1958-59; adminstrv. analyst Office of the Pres., U. Calif., Berkeley, 1959-60; asst. prof. polit. sci. U. Calif., Davis, 1960; asst. prof. polit. sci. UCLA, 1960-66, assoc. prof., 1966-69, prof., 1969—, asst. to chancellor, 1960-62, asst. chancellor, 1962-63, vice chancellor, adminstrn., 1963-68, chancellor, 1968—; bd. dirs. Intel Corp.; cons. Peace Corps., 1961-62, Ford Found. on Latin Am. Activities, 1964-66; mem. bd. govs. L.A. Met. Project. Mem. Knight Found. Commn. on Intercollegiate Athletics, Calif. Coun. on Sci. and Tech., NCAA Pres.'s Commn., Coun. for Govt.-Univ.-Industry Rsch. Roundtable and the Nat. Rsch. Coun. Adv. Bd.-Issues in Sci. and Tech., Nat. Com. on US-China Rels., chancellor's assocs. UCLA, coun. trustees L.A. Ednl. Alliance for Restructuring Now; past chair. Assn. Am. Univs., Nat. Assn. State Univs. and Land-Grant Colls.; mem. adminstrv. bd. Internat. Assn. Univs.; bd. govs. Found. Internat. Exchange Sci. and Cultural Info. by Telecommunications, The Theatre Group Inc.; v.p. Young Musicians Found.; bd. dirs. Los Angeles Internat. Visitors Council, Greater Los Angeles Energy Coalition, Los Angeles World Affairs Coun.; trustee UCLA Found. With USAF, 1951-52. Named Young Man of Year Westwood Jr. C. of C., 1962. Fellow AAAS. Office: UCLA Office of Chancellor Office of Chancellor 405 Hilgard Ave Los Angeles CA 90095

YOUNG, CHRISTOPHER, composer. Scores include (films) The Dorm That Dripped Blood, 1982, Robbie, 1982, The Power, 1983, Savage Hunter, 1984, Highpoint, 1984, Wheels of Fire, 1984, Avenging Angel, 1984, Def-Con 4, 1985, Wizards of the Lost Kingdom, 1985, Barbarian Queen, 1985, Nightmare on Elm Street Part II: Freddy's Revenge, 1985, Godzilla 1985, 1985, Torment, 1986, Getting Even, 1986, Invaders from Mars, 1986, Trick or Treat, 1986, Hellraiser, 1987, Flowers in the Attic, 1987, The Telephone, 1987, Bat-21, 1988, Haunted Summer, 1988, Hellbound: Hellraiser II, 1988, The Fly II, 1989, Hider in the House, 1989, Bright Angel, 1991, The Five Heartbeats, 1991, The Vagrant, 1992, The Dark Half, 1992, Rapid Fire, 1992, Jennifer Eight, 1992, Sliver, 1993, Dream Lover, 1994, Murder in the First, 1995, (TV movies) American Harvest, 1987, Last Flight Out, 1990, Max and Helen, 1990. Office: Marks and Vangelos Mgt 19301 Ventura Blvd Ste 206 Tarzana CA 91356*

YOUNG, DALE LEE, banker; b. Palmyra, Nebr., Mar. 13, 1928; s. Mike P. and Grace (Clutter) Y.; m. Norma Marie Shalla, June 18, 1950; children—Shalla Ann, Philip Mike. B.B.A., U. Nebr., 1950. With FirsTier Bank N.A. (formerly First Nat. Bank & Trust Co.), Lincoln, Nebr., 1950-91, cashier, 1966-91, v.p., 1966-76, exec. v.p., 1976-92; sec. ISCO, Inc., Lincoln, 1991—, also bd. dirs.; bd. dirs. Woodmen Accident and Life Co.; sec., bd. dirs. Leasing Corp. Treas. Lincoln City Library Found.; Treas., mem. exec. com. Nebr. Republican Com., 1968—; bd. dirs., v.p. Lincoln Symphony; bd. dirs. Lincoln Community Services, ARC, Lincoln Found.; trustee Bryan Meml. Hosp., 1976-80; mem. Lincoln City Coun., 1991—. Served with AUS, 1946-48, 50-51. Mem. Nebr. Art Assn., Omaha-Lincoln Soc. Fin. Analysts, Lincoln C. of C. (pres.), Theta Xi. Presbyterian. Clubs: Nebraska, Lincoln Country, Univ. Home: 2627 Park Ave Lincoln NE 68502-4023 Office: PO Box 81008 Lincoln NE 68501-1008

YOUNG, DAVID MICHAEL, biochemistry and molecular biology educator, physician; b. Bluffton, Ind., Oct. 11, 1935; s. Eli and Ruth (Comer) Y.; m. Diane Tangeman, Dec. 28, 1957 (div. 1971); children: Peter Michael, Amy Katherine; m. Lucia Virginia Patat, Sept. 2, 1972; children: David Michael II, Allison Amelia. B.S., Duke U., 1957, M.D., 1959. Diplomate: Nat. Bd. Med. Examiners. Intern pediatrics dept. Duke U. Med. Ctr., Durham, N.C., 1958-60; staff scientist Lab Cellular Physiology and Metabolism Nat. Heart Inst., NIH, 1960-62; vis. scientist McCollum-Pratt Inst., Johns Hopkins U., Balt., 1962-63, asst. prof. biology, 1963-64; asst. prof. Harvard U. Med. Sch., Boston, 1965-72, assoc. prof. Biol. chemistry, 1972-79, tutor biochem. scis., 1966-76; mem. grad. program for advanced study in immunology, 1971-76, assoc. chmn. div. med. scis., chmn. program for cell biology, 1972-76; head Lab Phys. Biochemistry Mass. Gen. Hosp., Boston, 1965-79; prof. biochemistry U. Fla. Coll. Medicine, Gainesville, 1979—, prof. medicine, 1979-86, chmn. dept. biochemistry and molecular biology, 1979-81, prof. molecular biology, 1981-86, prof. pediatrics, 1986—; mem. cell physiology study sect. NIH, Bethesda, Md., 1978-82, sect. chmn., 1980; acad. assoc. Nichols Inst., San Juan Capistrano, Calif., 1976—; vis. prof. biology Johns Hopkins U., 1994, 95. Editor-in-chief: Jour. Molecular and Cellular Biochemistry, 1983—; patentee nerve growth factor, nerve growth factor antibody. Served to sr. surgeon USPHS, 1959-63. USPHS spl. fellow, 1962; recipient career devel. award USPHS, 1967-72; NIHresearch grantee, 1964—; grantee John A. Hartford Found., 1968-73. Mem. Am. Soc. Biol. Chemists, Am. Chem. Soc., AAAS, Biophys. Soc., Am. Soc. for Clin. Investigation, Am. Heart Assn. (research allocations com. 1976-79), Am. Soc. for Cell Biology, Alpha Omega Alpha. Home: 2106 NW 27th Ter Gainesville FL 32605-3873 Office: Dept Biochemistry and Molecular Biology Coll Medicine U Fla Gainesville FL 32610

YOUNG, DAVID POLLOCK, humanities educator, author; b. Davenport, Iowa, Dec. 14, 1936; s. Cecil T. and Mary Ella (Pollock) Y.; m. Chloe Hamilton, June 17, 1963 (dec. Feb. 1985); children—Newell Hamilton, Margaret Helen; m. Georgia L. Newman, Dec. 31, 1989. B.A., Carleton Coll., 1958; M.A., Yale, 1959, Ph.D., 1965. Faculty dept. English Oberlin Coll., 1961—, prof., 1973—; Longman prof. of English, 1986—; Translator. Author: Something of Great Constancy: the Art of "A Midsummer Night's Dream", 1965, Sweating Out the Winter, 1969, The Heart's Forest: Shakespeare's Pastoral Plays, 1972, Boxcars, 1973, Work Lights: 32 Prose Poems, 1977, Rilke's Duino Elegies, 1978, The Names of A Hare in English, 1979, (with Stuart Friebert) A Field Guide to Contemporary Poetry and Poetics, 1980, Four T'ang Poets, 1980, (with Stuart Friebert and David Walker) Valuable Nail: Selected Poems of Günter Eich, 1981, (with Dana Hábová) Interferon, or On Theater, Poems by Miroslav Holub, 1982, (with Keith Hollaman) Magical Realist Fiction, 1984; editor: (with Stuart Friebert and David Walker) Field: Contemporary Poetry & Poetics, (with Stuart Friebert) The Longman Anthology of Contemporary American Poetry, 1983, Foraging, 1986, Troubled Mirror: A Study of Yeats's The Tower, 1987, Sonnets to Orpheus, Rainer Maria Rilke, 1987, THe Heights of Macchu Picchu, 1987, Earthshine, 1988, Five T'ang Poets, 1990, The Action to the Word: Structure and Style in Shakespearean Tragedy, 1990, (with Dana Hábová) Vanishing Lung Syndrome Poems by Miroslav Holub, 1990, The Planet on the Desk: Selected and New Poems, 1960-90, 1991, Shakespeare's Middle Tragedies: New Century Views, 1992, The Book of Fresh Beginnings: Selected Poems of Rainer Maria Rilke, 1994, Night Thoughts and Henry Vaughan, 1994, (with Stuart Friebert) Models of the Universe, an Anthology of the Prose Poem, 1995; editor: FIELD, Contemporary Poetry and Poetics, 1969—, contbr. poetry to lit. publs. Recipient U.S. award Internat. Poetry Forum, 1969, Ohio Individual Artist award, 1990; Guggenheim fellow, NEA fellow. Office: Oberlin Coll Dept English Oberlin OH 44074

YOUNG, DAVID WILLIAM, accounting educator; b. L.A., Feb. 8, 1942; s. William Albert and Hilda Mary (Cook) Y.; m. Ernestine M.L. Van Schaik, Oct. 4, 1968 (div. 1975); m. Francesca Michela Larson, Jan. 28, 1984; children: Christian William, Anthony Edwin. BA, Occidental Coll., 1963; MA, UCLA, 1966; D in Bus. Administrn., Harvard U., 1977. Systems engr. IBM, Glendale, Calif., 1963-64; asst. to pres. Lundberg Survey, Inc., Hollywood, Calif., 1964-66; program economist U.S. Agy. Internat. Devel., El Salvador, 1966-69; cons. Thomas Goldsmith & Assoc., Cambridge, Mass., 1969-71; mng. dir. Commonwealth Mgmt. Systems, Cambridge, 1971—; assoc. prof. mgmt. Harvard U. Sch. Pub. Health, Boston, 1976-85, consulting faculty mem., 1985—; prof. acctg. and control Boston U. Sch. Mgmt., 1985—, chmn. dept. acctg., 1986-91, dir. acctg. MBA program, 1989-93, dir. inst. acctg. rsch. and edn., 1989-93, dir. health care mgmt. program, 1991-94; mng. ptnr. The Crimson Group, Cambridge, 1994—; vis. prof. mgmt. control Instituto de Estudios Superiores de la Empresa, Barcelona, Spain, 1984. Author: The Managerial Process in Human Service Agencies, 1979, Financial Control in Health Care, 1984, The Hospital Power Equilibrium, 1985, Management Control in Nonprofit Organizations, 1984, 88, 94, Introduction to Financial and Management Accounting: A User Perspective, 1994; contbr. articles to profl. jours. Trustee Art Inst., Boston, 1990—, Symmes Hosp., Arlington, 1993-94, Mass. Eye and Ear Infirmary, Boston, 1980-92, Roxbury Comprehensive Cmty. Health Ctr., 1983-86; chmn. Mass. Hosp. Payment Sys. Adv. Commn., 1992—. Milton Fund fellow Harvard Med. Sch., 1984. Mem. Am. Acctg. Assn., Am. Econ. Assn. Democrat. Office: Boston U Sch Mgmt 704 Commonwealth Ave Boston MA 02215-2404

YOUNG, DAVIS, public relations executive; b. Montclair, N.J., Apr. 12, 1939. BA in Journalism, U. N.C. Acct. extc. Walker & Co., 1963-65; acct. extc. Carr Liggett Adv. Inc., 1965-68, acct. supr., 1968-70, v.p., 1970-75; pres. Young-Liggett Pub. Rels., 1975-88; exec. v.p., dir. Edward Howard & Co., Cleve., 1988-89, pres., COO, 1990—; v.p. Internat. Pub. Rels. Group of Cos., 1986. Recipient Disting. Svc. award Kent State U. Mem. Pub. Rels. Soc. Am. (chmn. nat. com. edn. 1975, pres. Greater Cleve. chpt. 1977, gen. chmn. spring conf., 1982, co-chair nat. conf. 1985, chmn. nat. membership 1986, chmn. nat. conf. 1991, pub. rels. com. 1992, Pres. Citation award). Office: Edward Howard & Co 1 Erieview Plz 7th Fl Cleveland OH 44114-1716

YOUNG, DENNIS EUGENE, financial services executive; b. Wahoo, Nebr., May 18, 1943; s. Donald W. and Grace B. (Spittgerber) Y.; m. Diane M. Johnson, July 10, 1965; children: Lisa, David, Darren. B.A. magna cum laude, Buena Vista Coll., Storm Lake, Iowa, 1965. With Norwest Fin. Corp., Des Moines, 1965—, treas., 1976—, v.p., chief fin. officer, 1979-83, sr. v.p., treas., 1983—, also bd. dirs.; pres. Norwest Fin. Can., Inc.; treas. Centurion Casualty Co., Des Moines; v.p., treas., bd. dirs. Centurion Life Ins. Co., Des Moines. Trustee, vice chmn. Buena Vista Coll., 1979—;

trustee, treas. Des Moines Art Ctr.; bd. govs. Iowa Coll. Found. Mem. Fin. Execs. Inst., Iowa Soc. Fin. Analysts, Nat. Assn. Corp. Treasures. Clubs: Des Moines, Wakonda (Des Moines). Office: Norwest Fin Inc 206 8th St Des Moines IA 50309-3805

YOUNG, DON J., federal judge; b. Norwalk, Ohio, July 13, 1910; s. Don J. and Elaine (Dennis) Y.; m. Seville Beatrice Shagrin, June 27, 1936; children—Don J., Patricia C. A.B. cum laude, Western Res. U., 1932, LL.B., 1934; student, Cleve. Art Sch., 1932-34. Bar: Ohio bar 1934. Pvt. practice Norwalk, 1934-52; judge Ct. Common Pleas, Huron County, Ohio, 1952-53, Probate and Common Ct., Huron County, 1953-65; U.S. judge No. Dist. Ohio for Western Div., 1965—; instr., lectr. juvenile ct. laws at seminars and insts. for judges, 1959—; v.p. Ohio Assn. Probate Ct. Judges, 1958-60; pres. Ohio Assn. Juvenile Ct. Judges, 1960-62; law reporter Nat. Juvenile Ct. Found., 1959-73, sec.-treas., 1960-61, sec., 1961-62; sec. Nat. Council Juvenile Ct. Judges, 1962-65, exec. com., 1966-69. Contbr. articles to profl. jours.; exhibited jewelry, Cleve. Mus. Art, Butler Art Inst., Nat. Ceramic Exhbn. Exec. dir. Norwalk CD Corps, 1942-46; pres. Firelands Hist. Soc., 1945-46, Norwalk Cemetery Assn., 1951-57; sec. Norwalk Recreation Com., 1946-53; trustee Young Men's Library and Reading Room Assn., 1955-65, 86—, Whittlesey Acad. Arts and Scis., 1955-65. Mem. ABA, Ohio Bar Assn., Order of Coif, Phi Beta Kappa, Pi Epsilon Delta. Episcopalian. Office: US Dist Ct 220 US Courthouse 1716 Spielbusch Ave Toledo OH 43624-1332 Personal philosophy: I try to be guided by the law; as expressed by Hillel nearly 2000 years ago: What thou hatest for thyself, do not unto thy fellow man. That is the whole of the law. All else is explanation.

YOUNG, DONALD ALAN, physician; b. Oakland, Calif., Feb. 8, 1939; s. Leo Alan and Pearl Anita (Walker) Y.; children: Jennifer, Karen. B.A., U. Calif., Berkeley, 1960, M.D., 1964. Diplomate Am. Bd. Internal Medicine. Intern, then resident in internal medicine U. Calif. Hosp., San Francisco, 1964-66; resident in internal medicine Parkland Hosp., Dallas, 1966-67; fellow chest diseases U. Calif. Hosp., San Francisco, 1967-68; mem. staff Palo Alto (Calif.) Med. Clinic, 1970-75; med. dir. Am. Lung Assn., 1975-77; scholar administry. scholars program VA, Washington, 1977-80; dep. dir. policy Bur. Program Policy, Health Care Financing Adminstrn. HHS, Washington; exec. dir. Prospective Payment Assessment Commn., Washington, 1984—; clin. instr. U. Calif. Med. Sch., San Francisco, 1968-70, Stanford U. Med. Sch., 1970-75. Trustee Vt. Lung Center; bd. dirs. Mid-Md. Lung Assn. Served with M.C. AUS, 1968-70. Decorated Commendation medal.; Recipient Borden award, 1964. Home: 5495 Vantage Point Rd Columbia MD 21044-2637 Office: 300 7th St SW Suite 301B Washington DC 20024

YOUNG, DONALD E., congressman; b. Meridian, Calif., June 9, 1933; m. Lula Fredson; children—Joni, Dawn. AA, Yuba Jr. Coll., 1952; BA ., Chico (Calif.) State Coll., 1958. Former educator, river boat capt.; mem. Fort Yukon City Council, 6 years, mayor, 4 years; mem. Alaska Ho. of Reps., 1966-70, Alaska Senate, 1970-73, 93rd-104th Congresses from Alaska, 1973—; mem. transp. & infrastructure com., chmn. resources com. With U.S. Army, 1955-57. Republican. Episcopalian. Office: US House of Representatives 2331 Rayburn House Office B Washington DC 20515*

YOUNG, DONALD E., computer manufacturing company executive; b. Pitts., July 23, 1920; s. William P. and Helen (Bollenberg) Y.; m. Pauline Schloesser; children: Leigh, Anna Dey, Lance. B.A., George Washington U., 1948; M.B.A., Harvard U., 1951. Spl. agt. FBI, 1948-49, with Office Spl. Investigations, 1951-55; asst. to pres. G.H. Packwood Co., 1955-56; asst. to v.p. and treas., bank sales rep., regional bank mgr. Todd Co., 1956-60; with Unisys Corp. (merger Burroughs Corp. and Sperry Rand Corp.), Detroit, 1960—, v.p. corp. communications, 1966-76; sr. v.p. Burroughs Corp., 1976-79, exec. v.p., 1980—; chmn. bd. Systems Devel. Corp., A Burroughs Co., Camarillo, Calif.; dir. Mich. Bank Bank, Detroit, Blue Cross/Blue Shield Mich. Bd. dirs. Detroit Conv. Bur., Boys Club Met. Detroit, Police Athletic League Detroit; bd. govs. Nat. Invest-in-Am., Greater Mich. Found.; mem. bd. mems. Mich. Coll. Found.; trustee Met. Fund Detroit, Founders Soc. of Detroit Inst. Arts, William Beaumont Hosp., Detroit, Detroit Renaissance. Served to capt. USAAF, 1941-46, ETO. Decorated D.F.C. with oak leaf cluster, Air medal with 5 oak leaf clusters. Mem. Soc. Former Agts. FBI, Mich. C. of C. (charter), Computer and Bus. Equipment Mfrs. Assn. (dir.), Econ. Club Detroit (v.p. 1975—). Clubs: Adcraft (Detroit), Detroit (Detroit), Detroit Athletic (Detroit), Harvard Bus. Sch. (Detroit); Harvard (N.Y.C.); Bloomfield Hills Country (pres. dir. 1979). Office: Burroughs Corp Burroughs Pl Detroit MI 48202 Office: System Devel Corp 5151 Camino Ruiz Camarillo CA 93012-8601

YOUNG, DONALD FREDRICK, engineering educator; b. Joplin, Mo., Apr. 27, 1928; s. Oral Solomon and Blanche (Trent) Y.; m. Gertrude Ann Cooper, Apr. 15, 1950; children: Michael, Pamela, Susan, Christopher, David. B.S., Iowa State U., 1951, M.S., 1952, Ph.D., 1956. Research engr. AEC Ames Lab., 1952-55; asst. prof. Iowa State U., Ames, 1955-58, assoc. prof., 1958-61, prof. engring. sci. and mechanics, 1961-74, Anson Marston Disting. prof. engring., 1974—. Author: Introduction to Applied Mechanics, 1972, (with others) Essentials of Mechanics, 1974, (with others) Fundamentals of Fluid Mechanics, 1990, 2d edit., 1994; contbr. articles to profl. jours. Recipient Outstanding Tchr. award Standard Oil, 1971; recipient Faculty citation Iowa State Alumni Assn., 1972. Fellow ASME (chmn. bioengring. div. 1973-74); mem. Am. Heart Assn., Am. Soc. Engring. Edn., Pi Tau Sigma, Pi Mu Epsilon, Phi Kappa Phi, Sigma Xi. Home: 2042 Prairie Vw E Ames IA 50010-4558 Office: Iowa State U 3023 Black Engr Ames IA 50010

YOUNG, DONALD STIRLING, clinical pathology educator; b. Belfast, N. Ireland, Dec. 17, 1933; s. John Stirling and Ruth Muir (Whipple) Y.; m. Silja Meret; children: Gordon, Robert, Peter. MB, ChB, U. Aberdeen, Scotland, 1957; PhD in Chem. Pathology, U. London, 1962. Terminable lectr. materia medica U. Aberdeen, 1958-59; fellow Postgrad. Med. Sch., U. London, 1959-62, registrar, 1962-64; vis. scientist NIH, Bethesda, Md., 1965-66; chief clin. chemistry service NIH, 1966-77; head clin. chemistry sect. Mayo Clinic, Rochester, Minn., 1977-84; prof. pathology and lab. medicine U. Pa., 1984—; dir. William Pepper Lab. Hosp. of U. Pa., 1984—; past bd. dirs. Nat. Com. Clin. Lab. Standards. Co-editor: Drug Interference and Drug Metabolism in Clinical Chemistry, 1976, Clinician and Chemist, 1979, Chemical Diagnosis of Disease, 1979, Drug Measurement and Drug Effects in Laboratory Health Science, 1980, Interpretation of Clinical Laboratory Tests, 1990, Effects of Preanalytical Variables on Clinical Laboratory Tests, 1993. Recipient Dir.'s award NIH, 1977, Gerard B. Lambert award, 1974-75, MDS Health Group award Can. Soc. Clin. Chemists, 1978; Roman lectr. Australian Assn. Clin. Biochemists, 1979; Jendrassik award Hungarian Soc. Clin. Pathologists, 1985, ATB award Italian Soc. Clin. Biochemistry 1987. Mem. Am. Assn. Clin. Chemistry (J.H. Roe award Capital sect. 1973, Bernard Gerulat award N.J. sect. 1977, Ames award 1977, Van Slyke award N.Y. met. sect. 1985, past pres.), Internat. Fedn. Clin. Chemists (past pres.), Acad. Clin. Lab. Physicians and Scientists (past exec. com.), Assn. Clin. Biochemists (Ciba-Corning lectr. 1985). Achievements include research in clinical chemistry; development and application of high resolution analytical techniques in the clinical laboratory; optimized use of the clinical laboratory. Home: 1116 Remington Rd Wynnewood PA 19096-4045 Office: U Pa William Pepper Lab 3400 Spruce St Philadelphia PA 19104-4238

YOUNG, DOUGLAS, Canadian government official; b. Tracadie, Sept. 20, 1940. Min. transport Canada, 1993— provincial first elected to N.B. Legislature g.e., 1978, reelected g.e., 1982, 87; apptd. Min. Fisheries and Aquaculture, 1987; elected to the H. of C. g.e., 1987. Office: Transport Canada, Twr C Place de Ville 28th Fl, Ottawa, ON Canada K1A 0N5 also: PO Box 3635, Tracadie, NB Canada E1X 165*

YOUNG, DOUGLAS RYAN, technology company executive; b. Bronxville, N.Y., Apr. 30, 1945; s. Harold Sydney and Edith Isabelle (Ryan) Y.; m. Anne Honora Jennings, May 23, 1970; children: Amanda Jennings Young, Christina Crawford Young, Ryan Townsend Young, Kielley Kavanaugh Young. BA, Princeton (N.J.) U., 1967; MBA, NYU, 1978. Various sales, mktg. and planning positions IBM, N.Y., 1970-82; regional mgr. Storage Tech. Corp., N.Y., 1982-84; pres. Unilease Computer Corp., London and N.Y.C., 1984-87; v.p. sale, mktg. and svc. Data Switch Corp., Shelton, Conn., 1987-89; dir. ins. vertical Oracle Corp., N.Y.C., 1989-91; v.p. enterprise mktg. Data Gen. Corp., Westboro, Mass., 1991—. Lt. (j.g.) USN, 1967-70. Avocations: computers, motocycles, sailing, photography, stunt kite exhibitions. Office: Data Gen Corp 4400 Computer Dr Westborough MA 01580

YOUNG, DWIGHT WAYNE, ancient civilization educator; b. Lambert, Okla., Dec. 15, 1925; s. Maurice Leonard and Freda Flora (Polson) Y.; m. Barbara Louise Pirtle, May 25, 1946; children: Terry Wayne, Cecilia Ann. B.A. magna cum laude, Hardin-Simmons U., Abilene, Tex., 1949; Th.M. Dallas Theol. Seminary, 1956; Ph.D., Dropsie Coll., 1955; postgrad., Brown U., 1959-60. Asst. prof. Brandeis U., Waltham, Mass., 1958-63, assoc. prof., 1963-67, 69-72, prof., 1972-87, prof. emeritus, 1987—; cons. Harper & Row Pubs., N.Y.C., 1958-60; vis. prof. Hebrew U., Jerusalem, Israel, 1965, Cornell U., Ithaca, N.Y., 1967-69; chief editor Pirtle Polson Pubs., Gloucester, Mass., 1980—. Author: Coptic Manuscripts from the White Monastery: Works of Shenute, 1993; editor: Studies Presented to Hans Jakob Polotsky, 1981, The Future of Coptic Studies, 1978; contbr. numerous articles and revs. on ancient civiliations to profl. jours. Served with USMC, 1943-46. Recipient Solomon award in Hebrew, Dallas Theol. Seminary, 1951; fellow in Arabic, U. Mich., 1960. Mem. Internat. Assn. for Coptic Studies. Home: 5555 N Sheridan Rd Apt 617 Chicago IL 60640-1619 Office: Brandeis U Dept Nr Ea Studies South St Waltham MA 02154

YOUNG, ED (TSE-CHUN), illustrator, children's author; b. Tientsin, China, Nov. 28, 1931; came to U.S., 1951; s. Qua-Ling and Yen Teng Young; married, 1962 (div. 1969); m. Natasha Gorky, June 1, 1971. Student, City Coll. San Francisco, 1952, U. Ill., Urbana-Champaign, 1952-54; BPA, Art Ctr. Coll. Design, 1957; postgrad., Pratt Inst., 1958-59. Illustrator, designer Mel Richman Studio, N.Y.C., 1957-62; instr. visual comm. Pratt Inst., Bklyn., 1960-66; sec., instr. Shr Jung Tai Chi Chuan WSch., N.Y.C., 1964-73, bd. dirs.; instr. Sarah Lawrence Coll., Bronxville, N.Y., 1975—. Author, illustrator: The Rooster's Horns: A Chinese Puppet Play to Make and Perform, 1978, The Terrible Nung Gwama: The Chinese Folktale, 1978, High on a Hill: A Book of Chinese Riddles, 1980, Up a Tree, 1983 (N.Y. Times Best Illustrated Children's Book award 1984), Lon Po Po, 1989 (Caldecott medal 1990), Seven Blind Mice, 1992 (Caldecott honor book 1993), Red Thread, 1993, Little Plum, 1994; illustrator: The Mean Mouse and Other Mean Stories, 1962 (Am. Inst. Graphic Arts award 1962), Poetry for Young Scientists, 1964, The Yellow Boat, 1966, The Emperor and the Kite, 1968 (Caldecott honor book 1968), Chinese Mother Goose Rhymes, 1968 (Horn book honor list 1969, Child Study Assn. Book award 1969), The Golden Swans, 1969, The Tiniest Sound, 1969, The Seventh Mandarin, 1970, The Girl Who Loved the Wind, 1972, The Horse From Nowhere, 1973, Young Fu of the Upper Yangtze, 1973, The Red Lion, 1977, The Cricket Boy, 1977, Tales From the Arabian Nights, 1978, White Wave, 1979, The Lion and the Mouse, 1979, Bo Rabbit Smart for True, 1981, Yeh-Shen: A Cinderella Story From China, 1982, Foolish Rabbit's Big Mistake, 1985 (Horn Book Honor List 1986), The Double Life of Pocahontas, 1985, Eyes of the Dragon, 1987, In the Night, Still Dark, 1988, Cats Are Cats, 1988, Birches, 1988, Moon Tiger, 1988, The Happy Prince, 1989, The Voice of the Great Bell, 1989, High in the Mountains, 1989, Mice are Nice, 1990, Goodbye Geese, 1991, All of You Was Singing, 1991, While I Sleep, 1992, What Comes in Spring?, 1992, Whale Song, 1992, The Rime of the Ancient Mariner, 1992, Dreamcatcher, 1992, Sadako, 1993, Iblis: An Islamic Tale, 1993, Bicycle Rider, 1993, Bitter Bananas, 1994. Office: Shr Jung Tai Chi Chuan Sch 87 Bowery New York NY 10003*

YOUNG, EDWIN HAROLD, chemical and metallurgical engineering educator; b. Detroit, Nov. 4, 1918; s. William George and Alice Pearl (Hicks) Y.; m. Ida Signe Soma, June 25, 1944; children—David Harold, Barbara Ellen. B.S. in Chem. Engring. U. Detroit, 1942; M.S. in Chem. Engring, U. Mich., 1949, M.S. in Metall. Engring. 1952. Chem. engr. Wright Air Devel. Center, Dayton, Ohio, 1942-43; instr. U. Mich., Ann Arbor, 1946-52; asst. prof. U. Mich., 1952-56, assoc. prof., 1956-59, prof. chem. and metall. engring., 1959-89, prof. emeritus chem. and metall. engring., 1989—, chmn. Mich. Bd. Registration for Profl. Engrs., 1963-78, chmn., 1969-70, 72-73, 75-76; mem. Mich. Bd. Registration for Architects, 1963-78. Author: (with L.E. Brownell) Process Equipment Design, 1959; contbr. articles to profl. jours. Dist. commr. Boy Scouts Am., 1961-64; mem. Wolverine coun., 1965-69. Served with USN, 1943-46, capt. Res. ret. 1978. Fellow ASME, ASHRAE, Am. Inst. Chemists, Am. Inst. Chem. Engrs. (Donald Q Kern award 1979), Engring. Soc. Detroit; mem. Am. Chem. Soc., Am. Soc. Engring. Edn., Nat. Soc. Profl. Engrs. (pres. 1968-69, award 1977), Mich. Soc. Profl. Engrs. (pres. 1962-63, Engr. of Year award 1976), Mich. Assn. of Professions (pres. 1966, Distinguished award 1970), Nat. Council Engring. Examiners, Naval Res. Assn., Res. Officers Assn., Sigma Xi, Tau Beta Pi, Phi Kappa Phi, Phi Lambda Upsilon, Alpha Chi Sigma. Republican. Baptist. Home: 609 Dartmoor Rd Ann Arbor MI 48103-4513

YOUNG, EDWIN REYNOLDS, JR., urologist, missionary; b. Nov. 28, 1926; s. Edwin Reynolds Sr. and Ivy (Boyd) Y.; m. Cecil McEachern, Feb. 6, 1954; children: Edwin R. III, Mayhoward Y. Johnston, Jennifer Y. Jurkowski, Mason P., Cecile Y. Whitten, Matthew D. BA, Erskine Coll., 1949; MD, Vanderbilt U., 1954. Cert. Am. Bd. Urology. Intern Phila. Gen. Hosp., 1954-55; resident U. Colo. Med. Ctr., 1955-56; gen. practitioner Young and Perry, Anderson, S.C., 1956-57; gen. physician Miners Meml. Hosp. Pikeville, Ky., 1957-59; resident urology U. Miami Jackson Meml. Hosp., 1964-65, Chatham County Meml. Hosp., Savannah, Ga., 1965-67; physician urology Bowie and Walker, Anderson, 1972-73, pvt. practice, Abbeville, S.C., 1973-86; urologist Kilimanjaro Christian Med. Ctr., Moshi, Tanzania, 1986-89; med. missionary assoc. Reformed Presbyn. Ch. Mission Hosp., Sahiwal, Pakistan, 1959-64, med. supt., chief surgery, 1967-72, missionary-at-large, 1992—. Fellow Am. Coll. Surgeons; mem. AMA, Am. Urological Assn. (southeast sect.), Pakistan Med. Assn., Med. Assn. Tanzania, East African Assn. Surgeons, So. Med. Assn., S.C. Med. Assn., Abbeville County Med. Assn. Home: 221 Holly St Flat Rock NC 28731-9535 Office: World Witness 1 Cleveland St Greenville SC 29601-3628

YOUNG, ESTELLE IRENE, dermatologist; b. N.Y.C., Nov. 2, 1945; d. Sidney D. and Blanche (Krosney) Young. BA magna cum laude, Mt. Holyoke Coll., 1963; MD, Downstate Med. Ctr., 1971. Intern, Lenox Hill Hosp., N.Y.C., 1971-72, resident in medicine, 1972-73; resident in dermatology Columbia Presbyn. Hosp., N.Y.C., 1973-74, NYU Med. Ctr., 1974-75, Boston U. Hosp., 1975-76; asst. dermatologist Harvard U. Health Services, Cambridge, Mass., 1975-76; assoc. staff mem. dermatology Boston U. Med. Ctr., 1976-77; practice medicine specializing in dermatology, Petersburg, Va., 1976—; mem. staff Poplar Springs Hosp., 1976—, Southside Regional Med. Ctr. (formerly Petersburg Gen. Hosp.), 1976—, Cen. State Hosp., 1984—; clin. instr. dept. dermatology Med. Coll. Va., 1976—, asst. clinic prof., 1988-94, assoc. clin. prof., 1994—; sec. med. staff Petersburg Gen. Hosp., 1982—. Fellow Am. Acad. Dermatology; mem. Va. Med. Soc., Va. Dermatology Soc., Tidewater Dermatology Soc. (pres. 1982-83), Physicians for Social Responsiblity Soc., Tidewater Physicians for Social Responsibility (pres. 1990—), Internat. Physicians for Prevention of Nuclear War, Southside Va. Med. Soc., Sigma Xi. Contbr. articles to profl. jours. Home: 2319 Monument Ave Richmond VA 23220-2603 Office: 612A S Sycamore Petersburg VA 23803

YOUNG, FRANCIS ALLAN, psychologist; b. Utica, N.Y., Dec. 29, 1918; s. Frank Allan and Julia Mae (McOwen) Y.; m. Judith Wadsworth Wright, Dec. 21, 1945; children—Francis Allan, Thomas Robert. B.S., U. Tampa, 1941; M.A., Western Res. U., 1945; Ph.D., Ohio State U., 1949. Instr. Wash. State U., Pullman, 1948-50; asst. prof. Wash. State U., 1950-56, assoc. prof., 1956-61, prof. psychology, 1961-88, dir. primate rsch. ctr., 1957-88, prof., dir. emeritus, 1988—; vis. prof. ophthalmology U. Oreg., Portland, 1964; asst. dir. U. Wash. Regional Primate Ctr., dir. primate field sta., 1966-68; vis. prof. pharmacology U. Uppsala (Sweden) Med. Sch., 1971; vis. prof. optometry U. Houston, 1979-80. Editor: (with Donald B. Lindsley) Early Experience and Visual Information Processing in Perceptual and Reading Disorders, 1970; contbr. chpts. to books, numerous articles to profl. jours. Named Disting. Psychologist State of Wash.. Wash. Psychol. Assn., 1973; recipient Paul Yarwood Meml. award Calif. Optometric Assn., 1978; Apollo award Am. Optometric Assn., 1980; Nat. Acad. Sci.-NRC sr. postdoctoral fellow in physiol. psychology U. Wash., 1956-57; research grantee NSF, 1950-53; research grantee USAF, 1965-72; research grantee NIH, 1960-78.

Home: 344 NW Webb St Pullman WA 99163-3150 Office: Wash State U Pullman WA 99164-1170

YOUNG, FRANK NELSON, JR., biology educator, entomologist; b. Oneonta, Ala., Nov. 2, 1915; s. Frank Nelson and Mary (Loe) Y.; m. Frances Norman, July 2, 1943; children—Elizabeth Von Herrmann, Frank Nelson III. B.S., U. Fla., 1938, M.S., 1940, Ph.D., 1942. Asst. prof. biology U. Fla., Gainesville, 1946-49; asst. prof. Ind. U., Bloomington, 1949-51; assoc. prof. Ind. U., 1951-62, prof., 1963-86, prof. emeritus, 1986—; assoc. Smithsonian Instn., 1989—; rsch. assoc. Fla. Dept. Agriculture. Author: Water Beetles of Florida, 1954; contbr. articles on aquatic insects to profl. jours. Served with U.S. Army, 1942-46, col. Res. ret., 1976. Recipient Phi Sigma medal, 1940, Guggenheim fellow, 1960-61; La. State U. fellow, 1963. Fellow Ind. Acad. Sci., Royal Entomol. Soc.; mem. AAAS, Am. Inst. Biol. Scis. Baptist. Home: 405 S Mitchell St Bloomington IN 47401-5169 Office: 201 Morrison Hall Ind Univ Bloomington IN 47405

YOUNG, FREDDIE GILLIAM, educational administrator; b. Miami, Fla., Nov. 1, 1939; d. Thomas and Myrtle (Gibson) Gilliam. BS, Fla. A&M U., 1961; MS, Hunter Coll., 1970; postgrad., U. Ghana, 1970; EdD, Nova U., 1990; cert. Prin.'s Exec. Tng. Program, Dade County Pub. Schs. Cert. supervision and adminstrn., African studies, elem. and jr. coll. Tchr. Collier County Pub. Schs., Naples, Fla., N.Y.C. Pub. Schs., Bronx, N.Y.; tchr. Dade County Pub. Schs., Miami, prin.; adj. lead prof. Nova U.; presenter Am. Assn. Ethnic Studies Conf., Fla. Atlantic U., 1991, Assn. Carribean Studies Cairo, 1993, Georgetown, Guyana, 1994. Del. 19th congl. dist. Dem. conv., 1988; mem. Am. Jewish Com. Named Most Outstanding Black Woman, S. Fla., Women's C. of C., Educator of Yr. Zeta Phi Beta; recipient 50 outstanding svc. awards Prin. Ctr. Harvard U. Sch. Edn., 1989; finalist for Adminstr. of Yr., 1991, DCAA. Mem. AAUW, ASCD, Am. Jewish Com., Nat. Alliance Black Educators, S. Fla. Exec. Educators, Miami Alliance Black Educators, Dade County Adminstrs. Assn. (chair), Fla. Reading Assn., Dade Reading Coun., Fla. A&M U. Alumni Assn. (pres. Miami-Dade chpt.), Nova U. Alumni Assn. (sec. Miami chpt.), Phi Delta Kappa. Home: 12390 SW 144th Ter Miami FL 33186-7419

YOUNG, GENEVIEVE LEMAN, publishing executive, editor; b. Geneva, Sept. 25, 1930; came to U.S., 1945, naturalized, 1968; d. Clarence Kuangson and Juliana Helen (Yen) Y.; m. Cedric Sun, 1955 (div. 1972); m. Gordon Parks, Aug. 26, 1973 (div. 1979). BA (Wellesley Coll. scholar), Wellesley Coll., 1952. Asst. editor Harper & Row (pubs.), N.Y.C., 1960-62; editor Harper & Row (pubs.), 1962-64, asst. mng. editor, 1964-66, mng. editor, 1966-70; exec. editor J.B. Lippincott Co., N.Y.C., 1970-77; v.p. J.B. Lippincott Co., 1972-77; sr. editor Little, Brown & Co., N.Y.C., 1977-85; editor-in-chief Lit. Guild Am., N.Y.C., 1985-88; v.p., editorial dir. Bantam Books, N.Y.C., 1988-92. Alumna trustee Phillips Acad., Andover, Mass., 1975-78, class agt., 1979-85; mem. Wellesley Bus. Leadership Coun., 1989—; mem. Youth Counseling League, 1986—, pres., 1989—, mem. com. of 100, 1990-93; mem. Literacy Vols. N.Y.C., 1992—, Andover Devel. Bd., 1993—. Recipient Alumna Achievement award Wellesley Coll., 1982, Matrix award, 1988. Mem. Assn. Am. Pubs. (exec. coun. gen. pub. div. 1975-78, 85-87, freedom to read com. 1972-75), Women's Media Group (pres. 1981-82, 2d v.p. 1994—), Century Assn. Home: 30 Park Ave New York NY 10016

YOUNG, GEORGE BERNARD, JR., professional football team executive; b. Balt., Sept. 22, 1930; s. George Bernard and Frances Marie (Kauders) Y.; m. Kathryn M.L. Reddington, Sept. 4, 1965. A.B., Bucknell U., 1952; M.B.A., Loyola U., Balt., 1967; CASE, Johns Hopkins U., 1971. Tchr. history, head football coach Calvert Hall High Sch. and Balt. City Coll., 1953-68; asst. dir. player personnel Balt. Colts, 1968-70, offensive line coach, 1970; dir. player personnel, 1971-73, offensive coordinator, line coach, 1973-74; dir. profl. scouting Miami (Fla.) Dolphins, 1975-79; gen. mgr. N.Y. Football Giants, 1979—, now also v.p. Democrat. Roman Catholic. Office: NY Giants Giants Stadium East Rutherford NJ 07073*

YOUNG, GEORGE CRESSLER, federal judge; b. Cin., Aug. 4, 1916; s. George Philip and Gladys (Cressler) Y.; m. Iris June Hart, Oct. 6, 1951; children: George Cressler, Barbara Ann. A.B., U. Fla., 1938, LL.B., 1940; postgrad., Harvard Law Sch., 1947. Bar: Fla. 1940. Practice in Winter Haven, 1940-41; assoc. firm Smathers, Thompson, Maxwell & Dyer, Miami, 1947; adminstrv., legislative asst. to Senator Smathers of Fla., 1948-52; asst. U.S. atty. Jacksonville, 1952; partner firm Knight, Kincaid, Young & Harris, Jacksonville, 1953-61; U.S. dist. judge No., Middle and So. dists. Fla., 1961-73; chief judge Middle Dist., 1973-81, sr. judge, 1981—; Mem. com. on adminstrn. fed. magistrates system Jud. Conf. U.S., 1973-80. Bd. dirs. Jacksonville United Cerebral Palsy Assn., 1953-60. Served to lt. (s.g.) USNR, 1942-46. Mem. Rollins Coll. Alumni Assn. (pres. 1968-69), ABA (spl. com. for adminstrn. criminal justice), Fla. Bar Assn. (gov. 1960-61), Jacksonville Bar Assn. (pres.), Am. Judicature Soc., Am. Law Inst., Order of Coif, Fla. Blue Key, Phi Beta Kappa, Phi Kappa Phi, Phi Delta Phi, Sigma Alpha Epsilon. Home: 2424 Shrewsbury Rd Orlando FL 32803-1334 Office: US Dist Ct 635 US Courthouse 80 N Hughey Ave Orlando FL 32801-2207

YOUNG, GORDON ELLSWORTH, composer, organist; b. McPherson, Kans., Oct. 15, 1919; s. Benjamin Warden and Rose Esther (Johnson) Y. Mus.B., Southwestern Coll., 1940, Mus.D., 1960; attended, Curtis Inst. Music, 1944-46; studies with Powell Weaver, Kansas City Conservatory; studies with Joseph Bonnet, Paris. Organist First Meth. Ch., Tulsa, 1940-44; staff organist Radio Sta. KVOO, 1941-44; music writer Tulsa Daily World, 1942-44; organist First Presbyn. Ch., Lancaster, Pa., 1944-48; faculty, glee club dir. Franklin and Marshall Coll., 1946-47; organist Arch St. Presbyn. Ch., Phila., 1949-50, First Presbyn. Ch., Detroit, 1952-72; concert artist.; music tchr.; mem. faculty Tex. Christian U., 1950-52; mem. coop. faculty Wayne State U., 1954-60. Composer numerous organ, choir, solo voice and instrumental works; performer in 12 fgn. countries; contbr. to Bapt. Hymnal, 1991, Seventh-day Adventist Hymnal, Hymns for the Family of God. Recipient Special Tribute award State of Mich., biographical tribute Nat. Fedn. Music Clubs, 1992. Mem. ASCAP (several awards), Am. Guild of Organists (life, hon.). Republican. Presbyn. Office: PO Box 256 Detroit MI 48231-0256 A positive attitude in all things makes the whole difference between success and failure in a career.

YOUNG, HARRISON, II, software development and marketing executive; b. Bklyn., Feb. 11, 1944; s. Harrison and Bobbie Aline (King) Y.; m. Shirley Gene Stanfield, Aug. 31, 1967 (div. Sept. 21, 1992); children: Melanie Marie, Tracy Lea; m. Emelie Martha Mannweiler, Dec. 18, 1993. BBA, Pacific Western U., L.A., 1990; MBA, U. Leicester, Eng., 1993. Cert. computer profl. Sr. systems engr. and account mgr. Info. Systems divsn. RCA, Houston, 1967-70; sr. scientist and program mgr. Tetra Tech Inc., San Diego, 1970-74; co-founder, exec. v.p. and sr. program mgr. Atlantic Analysis Corp., Norfolk, Va., 1974-85; program mgr. Comarco Inc., Anaheim, Calif., 1985-86, v.p., divsn. gen. mgr., 1986-87; pres. Washington-based subs. Comarco Inc., 1987-88; pres., CEO, dir. Comarco Inc., Anaheim, 1985-90; pres., CEO Tetra Tech Systems Integration subsidiary Honeywell, San Diego, 1990-92; pres., COO NW Internat. Corp., Annandale, Va., 1992-94; exec. v.p., COO Advanced Programming Concepts, Austin, Tex., 1994—. Bd. dirs. Blue Cross Blue Shield of Va., 1976-81. With USN, 1961-67. Mem. Am. Mgmt. Assn., Armed Forces Comms. and Electronics Assn. Nat. Contract Mgmt. Assn., Data Processing Mgmt. Assn., Instrumentation Soc. Am. Avocations: fishing, computers, foreign travel. Home: 12633 Pony Ln Austin TX 78727 Office: Advanced Programming Concepts 7004 Bee Caves Rd Austin TX 78746

YOUNG, HARRISON HURST, III, banker; b. Pitts., Dec. 15, 1944; s. Harrison Hurst Jr. and Margaret Ann (Knappen) Y.; m. Susan Parish, Feb. 15, 1969 (div.); m. Kirsty Hamilton, Jan. 29, 1994; 1 child, Angus Harrison Hamilton Young. AB, Harvard U., 1966. Reporter Washington Post, Washington, 1966; lending officer Citibank, N.Y., N.Y., 1971-75; assoc., v.p., prin. Morgan Stanley & Co., Inc., N.Y.C., Bahrain and London, 1975-86; mng. dir. Prudential Securities, Inc., N.Y.C., 1986-89, Dean Witter Reynolds, N.Y.C., 1989-91; chief oper. officer, dep. to chmn. FDIC, Washington, 1994—; sr. advisor, mng. dir. Morgan Stanley & Co., Inc., Hong Kong, 1994—. Served to capt. U.S. Army, 1966-71, Vietnam. Mem. River Club, Brooks' (London), Ladies Recreation Club (Hong Kong). Democrat. Episcopalian. Avocation: writing. Office: Morgan Stanley Asia Ltd 1251 Ave of the Americas New York NY 10020

YOUNG, HOWARD SETH, chemist, researcher; b. Birmingham, Ala., July 7, 1924; s. Tilden Hendricks and Annie Lou (McGaugh) Y.; m. Anne Reid Maven, Aug. 29, 1945; children: Alice McGaugh, Glenn Reid, Margaret Reid, George Maven, Ralph Hendricks, Elizabeth Anne, Joan McGaugh. BS in Chemistry, Birmingham Southern Coll., 1942; PhD, Brown U., 1948. Chemist Tenn. Eastman Co., Kingsport, 1948-51, sr. rsch. chemist, 1951-62, rsch. assoc., 1963-67, sr. rsch. assoc., 1967-70, dir. engring. rsch., 1970-74; dir. phys. and analytical chemistry rsch. Eastman Chems. Div., Kingsport, 1976-84, asst. dir. rsch., 1984-85, dir. rsch., 1985-89, ret., 1989. Contbr. articles to profl. jours.; patentee in field. Served to corp. U.S. Army, 1945-46. Mem. Am. Chem. Soc., Sigma Xi. Avocations: reading, walking, birdwatching. Home: 1909 E Sevier Ave Kingsport TN 37664-3231

YOUNG, HOWARD THOMAS, foreign language educator; b. Cumberland, Md., Mar. 24, 1926; s. Samuel Phillip and Sarah Emmaline (Frederick) Y.; m. Carol Osborne, Oct. 5, 1949 (div. 1966); children—Laurie Margaret, Jennifer Anne; m. Jennifer Bunker, July 15, 1966 (div. 1980); m. Edra Lee Airheart, May 23, 1981; 1 child, Timothy Howard. B.S. summa cum laude, Columbia U., 1950, M.A., 1952, Ph.D., 1954. Lectr. Columbia U., N.Y.C., 1950-54; asst. prof. Romance langs. Pomona Coll., Claremont, Calif., 1954-60; assoc. prof. Pomona Coll., Claremont, 1960-66, Smith prof. Romance langs., 1966—; vis. prof. Middlebury Program in Spain, Madrid, 1986-87, U. Zaragoza, 1967-68; chief reader Spanish AP Edni. Testing Service, Princeton, 1975-78, chmn. Spanish lang. devel. commn., 1976-79; mem. fgn. lang. adv. commn. Coll. Bd., N.Y.C., 1980-83; mem. West Coast selection commn. Mellon Fellowships for Humanities, Princeton, 1984-86, European selection com., 1987, 90. Author: The Victorious Expression, 1964, Juan Ramón Jiménez, 1967, The Line in the Margin, 1980; contbr. numerous articles and book revs. to profl. jours. Dir. NEH summer seminar for Sch. tchrs., 1993. Served with USNR, 1944-46, ETO. Fellow Del Amo Found., 1960-61, NEH, 1975, 89-90; Fulbright fellow; 1967-68; Rockefeller Study Ctr. scholar, 1976. Mem. MLA, Assn. Tchrs. Spanish and Portuguese, Am. Comparative Lit. Assn., Acad. Am. Poets. Avocation: tennis. Home: 447 W Redlands Ave Claremont CA 91711-1638 Office: Pomona Coll Modern Lang Dept 550 N Harvard Ave Claremont CA 91711

YOUNG, HUGH DAVID, physics educator, writer, organist; b. Ames, Iowa, Nov. 3, 1930; s. Hugh Surber and Nellie Sibella (Peters) Y.; m. Alice Carroll, June 25, 1960; children: Gretchen Carroll, Rebecca Susan. B.S. in Physics, Carnegie-Mellon U., 1952, M.S. in Physics, 1953, Ph.D. in Physics, 1959, B.F.A. in Music, 1972. Instr. physics Carnegie-Mellon U., Pitts., 1956-59; asst. prof. Carnegie-Mellon U., 1959-65, assoc. prof., 1965-77, prof., 1977—; head dept. natural scis. Margaret Morrison Carnegie Coll., Carnegie-Mellon U., 1962-67, acad. coordinator, lectr. modern engring. mgrs. program, 1966-82; vis. assoc. prof. physics U. Calif., Berkeley, 1967-68, vis. prof. physics, 1974; asst. organist St. Paul's Cathedral, Pitts., 1978-82. Author: Statistical Treatment of Experimental Data, 1962, Fundamentals of Mechanics and Heat, 2d edit., 1974, Fundamentals of Optics and Modern Physics, 2d edit., 1976; (with Sears and Zemansky) College Physics, 7th edit., 1990, University Physics, 8th edit., 1992. Bd. dirs. Renaissance and Baroque Soc., 1980-86. Recipient Ryan teaching award Carnegie Inst. Tech., 1965. Mem. Am. Assn. Physics Tchrs., Am. Phys. Soc., Am. Guild Organists (assoc.). Democrat. Avocations: organ, rock climbing. Home: 5746 Aylesboro Ave Pittsburgh PA 15217-1412 Office: Carnegie-Mellon Univ Dept Physics Pittsburgh PA 15213

YOUNG, J. A., bishop. Bishop of N.W. Okla. Ch. of God in Christ, Lawton. Office: Ch of God in Christ PO Box 844 Lawton OK 73502-0844

YOUNG, J. ANTHONY, entertainment company executive. Student, Edinburgh U., 1967-70. With Arthur Andersen & Co., Glasgow, Scotland, 1970-74, P.A. Mgmt. Cons., Ltd., London, 1974-76; v.p. fin. EMI Films, Inc., 1976-78; with Lorimar Prodns., Inc., Culver City, Calif., 1979-88, past sr. v.p. fin.; former exec. v.p., chief fin. officer Lorimar Telepictures Corp., Culver City; pres. MCA Enterprises Internat. MCA Inc., Universal City, Calif., 1988-93; exec., v.p. ICS Comm. Inc., Century City L.A., 1994—. Office: ICS Comm Inc 10100 Santa Monica Blvd 15th Fl Los Angeles CA 90067

YOUNG, J. LOWELL, soil chemist, biologist; b. Perry, Utah, Dec. 13, 1925; s. I.A. and Elzada (Nelson) Y.; m. Ruth Ann Jones, Sept. 15, 1950; children: Gordon, LoAnn, Colene, Kathryn. BS, Brigham Young U., 1953; PhD, Ohio State U., 1956. Rsch. asst. Ohio Agrl. Expt. Sta., Columbus, 1953-56, postdoctoral fellow, 1956-57; chemist Agrl. Research Service USDA, Corvallis, Oreg., 1957-64, rsch. chemist, 1964-78; asst. prof. Oreg. State U., Corvallis, 1957-63, assoc. prof., 1963-78, prof. soil sci., 1978-90, Courtesy prof. soil sci., 1990—; rsch. chemist Horticultural Crops Rsch. Unit USDA, Corvallis, 1978-88; collaborator Horticultural Crops Rsch. Unit U.S. Dept. Agrl., Corvallis, 1988-91. Contbr. articles to profl jours. Served with USAAF, 1944-46. Mem. AAAS, Internat. Soil Sci. Soc., Internat. Humic Substances Soc. (soil Sci. Soc. of Am. officer 1972-75, assoc. editor jour. 1975-80), Am. Soc. Agronomy (officer western 1966-72), Western Soc. Soil Sci. (officer 1966-71), Inst. for Alternative Agrl. Office: Oreg State U Crops & Soil Sci Dept Corvallis OR 97331

YOUNG, J. WARREN, magazine publisher. Pub. Boy's Life mag., Irving, Tex. Office: Boys' Life PO Box 152079 Irving TX 75015-2079*

YOUNG, JACK ALLISON, financial executive; b. Aurora, Ill., Dec. 31, 1931; s. Neal A. and Gladys W. Young; m. Virginia Dawson, Jan. 24, 1959; children: Amy D., Andrew A. BS in Journalism, U. Ill., 1954. CLU; chartered fin. cons.; registered security rep. Advt. writer Caterpillar Tractor Co., 1956-58; ins. agent Equitable Life Assurance Soc., St. Geneva, Ill., 1958—, ins. broker, 1972—; pres. Jack A. Young and Assocs., 1978—, Tax Sav Inc., 1983—; pres. Creative Brokerage, Inc., 1982—; pres., gen. securities prin. Chartered Planning, Ltd., 1985—; v.p. Old Mill Leasing Co., 1985—; past trustee Equitable CLU Assn.; past chmn. Equitable Nat. Agents Forum. Bd. dirs. Tri-City Family Services, 1975-83, pres., 1979-81; trustee Delnor Community Health System, 1985—, chmn., 1988-91; bd. dirs. St. Charles Ctr. Phys. Rehab., 1991—; chmn., pres. Delnor Community Health Care Found., 1986-88. Served to lt. (j.g.), USN, 1954-56. Named to Equitable Hall of Fame, 1978. Mem. Million Dollar Round Table (life), Am. Soc. C.L.U.s. Am. Coll. C.L.U. Golden Key Soc., Fox Valley Estate Planning Council, Internat. Assn. for Fin. Planning, Inc., Aurora Assn. Life Underwriters (past pres., nat. committeeman), Nat. Assn. Securities Dealers (registered prin.). Club: Geneva Golf (pres. 1994). Home: 18 Campbell St Geneva IL 60134-2732 Office: 28 N Bennett St Geneva IL 60134-2207

YOUNG, JAMES EARL, ceramics educator, educational administrator; b. Chgo., Dec. 20, 1922; s. James Alexander and Ellen (Chedister) Y.; children: Hugh Parker, Katherine Sue. BS, U. Ill., 1948; PhD, State U. N.Y. Coll. Ceramics Alfred U., 1962. Ceramic engr. Republic Steel Co., Chgo., 1948-52; ceramic engr. Armour Research Found., Chgo., 1952-55; research supr. Structural Clay Research Found., Geneva, Ill., 1955-57; research fellow State U. N.Y. Coll. Ceramics at Alfred U., 1957-61, asst. prof., 1961-63, assoc. prof., 1963-67, prof., chmn. dept., 1967-70; dean Coll. Arts and Scis., Rutgers U., Camden, N.J., 1970-73; provost Rutgers U., Newark, 1973-82; exec. dir. Commn. on State Colls. of N.J., 1982—; prof. Rutgers U., 1984—. Contbr. articles to tech. jours. Served with AUS, 1943-46. Am. Council Edn. fellow acad. adminstrn., 1966-67. Mem. Am. Ceramic Soc. Home: 130 Kingsberry Dr Somerset NJ 08873-4309 Office: PO Box 909 Piscataway NJ 08855-0909

YOUNG, JAMES EDWARD, lawyer; b. Painesville, Ohio, Apr. 20, 1946; s. James M. and Isabel P. (Rogers) Y. BBA, Ohio U., 1968; JD, Ohio State U., 1972. Bar: Ohio 1972; Law clk. to chief judge U.S. Ct. Appeals, Nashville, 1972-73; chief counsel City of Cleve. 1980-81, law dir. 1981-82; assoc. Jones, Day, Reavis & Pogue, 1973-79, ptnr., 1983—. Office: Jones Day Reavis & Pogue 901 Lakeside Ave E Cleveland OH 44114-1116

YOUNG, JAMES FRED, college president; b. Burnsville, N.C., Nov. 11, 1934; s. James Ray and Nina (Briggs) Y.; m. Phyllis Elizabeth Johnson, Apr. 15, 1962; children: Alan James, David Barden, Jane Elizabeth. AAS, Mars Hill Coll., 1954; BS, Wake Forest U., 1956; MEd, U. N.C. 1957; EdD, Columbia U., 1964. Tchr. Micaville (N.C.) High Sch., 1957-58; research asst. Columbia U., 1959; prin. Enfield Sch., Halifax County, N.C., 1959-61; asst. supt. Halifax County (N.C.) Schs., 1961-64, Burlington (N.C.) City Schs., 1964-68; supt. Lynchburg (Va.) public schs., 1968-71; dep. supt. public instr. Commonwealth (Va. Richmond, 1971-73; pres. Elon Coll., Elon College, N.C., 1973—; chmn. bd. N.C. Nat. Bank, Burlington.; Bd. dirs. Burlington Day Sch., 1974—, Appalachian Regional Edn. Lab., Charleston, W.Va., 1972-73; chmn. Gov.'s Task Force on Financing Standards of Quality for Public Schs. in Va., 1972-73; sec. exec. com. Ind. Coll. Fund N.C., 1976-78; mem. exec. com. United Ch. of Christ Council for Higher Edn., 1977—. Served with AUS, 1958. Mem. N.C. Edn. Assn. (pres. Halifax County unit 1960-61, Burlington unit 1967-68), N.C. Assn. Ind. Colls. and Univs. (sec. exec. com. 1978—, chmn. 1985-89), Nat. Assn. Intercollegiate Athletics (pres.'s adv. coun. 1977—, com. on eligibility and acad. standards, chmn. coun. pres.'s 1988-90), Internat. Assn. Univ. Pres. (v.p. southeastern region), Alamance County C. of C. (dir. 1974-75). Club: Rotary. Office: Elon Coll Office Pres E Haggard Ave Elon College NC 27244-9344

YOUNG, JAMES HARVEY, historian, educator; b. Bklyn., Sept. 8, 1915; s. W. Harvey and Blanche (DeBra) Y.; m. Myrna Goode, Aug. 25, 1940; children: Harvey Galen, James Walter. B.A., Knox Coll., 1937, D.H.L., 1971; M.A., U. Ill., 1938, Ph.D., 1941; D.Sc., Rush U., 1976. Mem. faculty Emory U., 1941-84, prof. history, 1958-80, Charles Howard Candler prof. Am. social history, 1980-84, prof. emeritus, 1984—, chmn. dept., 1958-66; vis. assoc. prof. Columbia U., 1949-50; mem. nat. adv. food and drug council FDA, 1964-67; mem. Consumers Task Force, White House Conf. on Food, Nutrition and Health, 1969; mem. history life scis. study sect. NIH, 1970-73, 79-80, 91-93, chmn., 1992-93; vis. lectr. Am. Assn. Colls. Pharmacy Vis. Lectrs. Program, 1970-73; cons.-panelist NEH, 1970-83; cons. in history Centers for Disease Control; Logan Clendening lectr. U. Kans. Med. Ctr., 1973; Samuel X. Radbill lectr. Phila. Coll. Physicians, 1978; Beaumont lectr. Yale U., 1980; vis. hist. scholar Nat. Library Medicine, 1986; Harold J. Lawn lectr. U. Minn., 1990; David L. Cowen lectr. Rutgers U., 1990; James Campbell lectr. Rush U., 1992; Waring lectr. Med. U. S.C., 1993. Author: The Toadstool Millionaires, 1961, The Medical Messiahs, 1967, expanded edit., 1992, American Self-Dosage Medicines, An Historical Perspective, 1974, Pure Food: Securing the Federal Food and Drugs Act of 1906, 1989, American Health Quackery: Collected Essays, 1992; editor: (with W.A. Beardslee and T.J.J. Altizer) Truth, Myth and Symbol, 1962, (with T.L. Savitt) Disease and Distinctiveness in the American South, 1988. Served with AUS, 1943-45. FDA rsch. appointee, 1977-85; Carnegie Rsch. grantee, 1947, USPHS grantee, 1960-65, Nat. Libr. Medicine grantee, 1990-94; Faculty fellow Fund Advancement Edn., 1954-55, Social Sci. Rsch. Coun. fellow, 1960-61, Guggenheim fellow, 1966-67. Mem. Am. Hist. Assn., So. Hist. Assn. (pres. 1982), Orgn. Am. Historians, Soc. Am. Historians, Am. Assn. History of Medicine (coun., Fielding H. Garrison lectr. 1979, William H. Welch medal 1982, Continuing Lifetime Achievement award 1992), Am. Inst. History of Pharmacy (coun., hon. pres. 1993-95, Edward Kremers award 1962), Phi Beta Kappa, Sigma Xi, Phi Kappa Phi, Omicron Delta Kappa, Phi Alpha Theta. Congregationalist. Home: 272 Heaton Park Dr Decatur GA 30030-1027

YOUNG, JAMES HERBERT, agricultural engineer; b. LaFayette, Ky., Mar. 19, 1941; s. James Monroe and Mary Holmes (Allen) Y.; m. Adrienne Lou Scott, July 20, 1963; children: Leigh Ann Young Sanders, James Scott Young. BS in Agrl. Engring., U. Ky., 1962, MS in Agrl. Engring., 1964; PhD, Okla. State U., 1966. Asst. prof. N.C. State U., Raleigh, 1966-70, assoc. prof., 1970-76, prof., 1976—. Fellow Am. Soc. Agrl. Engrs. (pubs. dir. 1988-90, electric power and processing dir. 1982-84), Am. Peanut Rsch. and Edn. Soc.; mem. ASHRAE, Am. Soc. Engring. Edn., Alpha Epsilon (Outstanding Alumnus 1986). Republican. Baptist. Home: 4104 Pepperton Dr Raleigh NC 27606-1734 Office: NC State U PO Box 7625 Raleigh NC 27695-7625

YOUNG, JAMES JULIUS, university administrator, former army officer; b. Fort Ringgold, Tex., Nov. 28, 1926; s. John Cooper and Violet Thelma (Ohl) Y.; m. June Agnes Hillstead, Dec. 17, 1948; children: Robert Michael, Steven Andrew, Patrick James, Mary Frances. B.S., U. Md., 1960; M.H.A., Baylor U., 1962; Ph.D. in Hosp. and Health Adminstrn. U. Iowa, 1969. Commd. 2d lt. U.S. Army, 1947, advanced through grades to brig. gen., 1977; comdr., med. ops. officer, dir. tng. field med. units in European Command, 1949-53; comdr. Mil. Med. Leadership Sch., 1953-54; med. advisor (Nationalist Army of China), 1955-57; asst. adminstr. Fitzsimons Army Med. Center, 1957-60; med. plans and ops. officer (US Forces), Korea, 1962-63; sr. field med. instr., chief field med. service Med. Field Service Sch., 1963-66; dir. health care orgn. and mgmt. analysis Office of Surgeon Gen., 1969-71; dir. med. plans and ops. directorate Office of the Surgeon, Military Assistance Command, Vietnam, 1971-72; exec. officer, chief adminstrv. services Silas Hays Army Hosp., 1973-74; military health analyst, military health care study OMB, Exec. Office of Pres., 1974-76; dep. dir. resources mgmt. and cons. for health care adminstrn. Office of Surgeon Gen., 1976-77; chief Med. Services Corps, U.S. Army and; dir. resources mgmt. Office of Surgeon Gen., 1977-81; ret., 1981; instr. U. Iowa, 1967-69; asst. prof., preceptor Baylor U., 1973-74; vice chancellor for health affairs W.Va. Bd. Regents, Charleston, 1982-87; dean sch. of allied health scis. U. Tex. Health Sci. Ctr., San Antonio, 1987-90, interim dean Sch. Medicine, 1988-89, dean Sch. Medicine, 1989—; cons. to Minister of Health, Republic of Vietnam, 1972-73; adj. prof. Baylor U., 1977-81, George Washington U., 1975-76, W.Va. U., 1986; prof. U. Tex. Health Sci. Ctr., San Antonio, 1989—. Contbr. articles to profl. jours. Decorated D.S.M., Legion of Merit, Meritorious Service medal and; others; recipient Walter Reed medallion for service, 1981; Army Med. Dept. medallion for contribution to health service, 1981. Mem. APHA, Coun. Deans, Assn. of Am. Med. Colls., Assn. Mil. Surgeons (chmn. med. svc. sect. 1978), Assn. U.S. Army, Interagy. Inst. Fed. Health Execs., Phi Kappa Tau. Roman Catholic. Home: 1610 Anchor Dr San Antonio TX 78213-1943 Office: U Tex Health Sci Ctr Office Of Dean Med Sch San Antonio TX 78284

YOUNG, JAMES MORNINGSTAR, physician, naval officer; b. Massillon, Ohio, Oct. 28, 1929; s. Ralph Louis and Pauline Louise (Morningstar) Y.; m. Bettylu Jones, July 3, 1952; children: Anne Christine, Mark Andrew, Patricia Jane, Elizabeth Lynne, Judith Pamela, Claudia Dianne; m. Mariette M. Aubuchon, Oct. 11, 1970; children: Gretchen Camille, Jason Paul. AB, Duke U., 1951, MD, 1955. Diplomate Am. Bd. Internal Medicine. Intern Bethesda Naval Hosp., 1955-56, resident, 1958-61; commd. lt. (j.g.) USN, 1955, advanced through grades to lt. comdr., 1961, promoted to temporary rank capt., 1963; staff Oakland (Calif.) Naval Hosp., 1966-69; chief medicine Naval Hosp. Boston, Chelsea, Mass., 1969-74; med. officer Naval Air Sta. South Weymouth, Mass., 1974-75; assoc. clin. prof. medicine Boston U. Sch. Medicine, 1969-75; v.p. med. affairs Mass. Blue Shield/Blue Cross, 1975-87; lectr. Harvard Sch. Pub. Health, 1987-90; sr. advisor Beijing Coll. Traditional Chinese Medicine, 1987-88; med. advisor U.S.-China People's Friendship Assn., Washington, 1988-90; cons. USPHS, Office Asst. Sec. for Health, Nat. Ctr. for Health Svcs., Rsch. and Health Care Tech. Assessment, HHS, 1985-90; v.p. for med. affairs Greenery Rehab. Group, Inc., 1988-90; assoc. med. dir. New. Eng. Rehab. Hosp., 1992-95, chief medicine, 1992-95. Contbr. articles to med. publs. Decorated knight comdr. with star Equestrian Order of the Holy Sepulchre of Jerusalem, 1986—; named Citizen of Washington H.S., Massillon, Ohio, 1993. Fellow ACP, AMA, Alpha Omega Alpha, Omicron Delta Kappa, Beta Omega Sigma, Sigma Alpha Epsilon. Home: 340 Chestnut St Newton MA 02165-2951

YOUNG, JANIE CHESTER, museum consultant; b. Port Huron, Mich., Apr. 19, 1949; d. Leonard Arthur and Ruth Elizabeth (Brown) Chester; m. Maximilian L. Ferro, Nov. 12, 1988. BA, U. Mich., 1971, M Mus. Practice, 1975. Fellowship coord. Toledo Mus. Art, 1973-75; curator edn. Rutgers U. Art Gallery, New Brunswick, N.J., 1975-77; dir. Saginaw (Mich.) Art Mus., 1977-80, Polk Pub. Mus., Lakeland, Fla., 1980-81, New Bedford (Mass.) Glass Mus., 1982-91; cons. Nantucket (Mass.) Hist. Assn., 1987, Sutton (Mass.) Hist. Soc., 1989, Tex. A&M U., 1990. Author: Queen's Choice, Burmese 1885-1985, 1985, Evolution of Decoration in Burmese Glass, 1989. Nettie Poe Ketcham fellow, Toledo Mus. Art, 1972-73. Mem. The Glass Assn., Nat. Early Am. Glass Club. Episcopalian. Avocation: art glass. Office: New Bedford Glass Mus 50 N 2nd St New Bedford MA 02740-6249

YOUNG, JAY ALFRED, chemical safety and health consultant, writer, editor; b. Huntington, Ind., Sept. 8, 1920; s. Jacob Phillip and Marie (Skully)

Y.; m. Anne Elizabeth Neff, June 29, 1942 (dec. June 1962); children: John, Paul, Cecelia, Michael, Joseph, Andrea, Therese, Gregory, Thomas, Lucy, Margaret, Antonia; m. Mary Ann Owens, Aug. 15, 1962; children: James, Laurence; 4 stepchildren. BS, Ind. U., 1939; AM, Oberlin Coll., 1940; PhD, U. Notre Dame, 1950. Chief chemist Asbestos Mfg. Co., Huntington, Ind., 1941-42; ordnance engr. U.S. War Dept., Washington, 1942-44; from instr. to prof. chemistry King's Coll., Wilkes-Barre, Pa., 1949-69; vis. prof. Carleton U., Ottawa, Ont., Can., 1969-70, Fla. State U., Tallahassee, 1975-77; Hudson prof. Auburn (Ala.) U., 1970-75; mgr. tech. publs. Chem. Mfrs. Assn., Washington, 1977-80; chem. safety and health cons. Silver Spring, Md., 1980—; pro bono cons. Occupational Safety and Health Adminstrn., EPA, Consumer Product Safety Commn., Washington, 1980—. Author: Practice in Thinking, 1958, Chemical Concepts, 1963, Selected Principlesof Chemistry, 1963, Arithmetic for Students of Science, 1968, Keys to Chemistry,1973, Keys to Oxidation-Reduction, 1974, Things That Last, 1977, Fire!, 1977, Actions and Reactions, 1978, Chemistry. A Human Concern, 1978, Kitchen Chemistry, 1980, Improving Safety in the Chemical Laboratory, 1987, 2d edit., 1991, Chemical Safety Manual for Small Businesses, 1989, Developing a Chemical Hygiene Plan, 1990, Laboratory Safety, 1992, Interactive Media Communications; contbr. to Ency. Britannica and over 100 articles to profl. jours. Tech. resource person on chem. hazards, precautions, transp. incidents involving chems. to media. Lt. USNR, 1944-46. Recipient Disting. Chemistry Alumnus award U. Notre Dame, 1968, Excellence in Chemistry Teaching award Mfg. Chemists Assn., 1970. Fellow AAAS; mem. Am. Chem. Soc. (councilor 1963-87, policy com. 1970-81, chmn. div. chem. health and safety 1979-80, chem. health and safety award 1991). Roman Catholic. Avocations: wood and metalworking, gardening. Home and Office: 12916 Allerton Ln Silver Spring MD 20904

YOUNG, JEFFRY JOHN, psychologist, gerontologist, educator, statistician; b. Harvey, Ill., Aug. 23, 1952; s. Harold Joyce and Marion June (Krismer) Y.; m. Rosalind Michelle Lloyd Sheridan, Jan. 25, 1992. Student, St. Patrick's Coll., Mountain View, Calif., 1971-73; BA in Philosophy & Psychology, San Jose State U., 1977, MA in Gen. Psychology, 1978; PhD in Social/Environ. Psychology, Claremont (Calif.) Grad. Sch., 1986. Coord. Ctr. for Applied Social Rsch. Claremont Grad. Sch., 1979-86; postdoctoral intern, behavioral scis. svc. sect. L.A. Police Dept., 1986-87; assoc. dir. Ruby Gerontology Ctr. Calif. State U., Fullerton, 1988-89, dir. Gerontology Rsch. Inst., 1989-92, rsch. prof. Sch. Humanities and Social Scis., 1986-93; assoc. dir. Roybal Inst. for Applied Gerontology Calif. State U., L.A., 1991-94, dir. Gerontology Rsch. Ctr., 1991-94; dir. advocacy and demonstration projects Nat. Asian Pacific Ctr. Aging, Seattle, 1994—; adj. asst. prof. Sch. Gerontology, U. So. Calif., L.A., 1991-94; adj. mem. dept. psychology Calif. State U., L.A., 1991-94; co-prin. investigator Alzheimer's Outreach Project Nat. Inst. on Aging, UCLA, 1992-95; cons. health resources and svcs. adminstrn. Alzheimer's Demonstration project East L.A., Calif., 1992-94; project dir. Alzheimer's Disease Rsch. Ctr., Nat. Inst. on Aging, U. So. Calif. and U. Calif., Irvine, 1991-94; dir. Adminstrn. Aging Project, 1994—; prin. investigator Agy. Health Care Policy and Rsch., 1995; facilitator White House Conf. on Aging. Author abstracts and articles. Chair adv. bd. com. Rancho Los Amigos Med. Ctr., Downey, Calif., 1993—; touch judge uni. div. So. Calif. Rugby Football Union, 1988-91; pres. Meals on Wheels of Fullerton, Calif., 1993-94; chmn. instl. rev. bd. Calif. State U., L.A., 1994. Recipient Cert. of Recognition, L.A. Police Dept., 1987, Points of Light award, 1992, others; named to Outstanding Young Men of Am. 1986. Mem. Am. Evaluation Assn. (charter mem.), Am. Bd. Forensic Examiners, N.Am. Mycological Soc. (life), Phi Beta Delta, Sigma Phi Omega (life). Roman Catholic. Avocations: mycology, rare books, rugby, cross-country skiing, microscopy. Home: 11520 Sunrise Dr NE Bainbridge Island WA 98110-1379 Office: Nat Asian Pacific Ctr Aging 1511 3d Ave Ste 914 Seattle WA 98101-1622

YOUNG, JERE ARNOLD, lawyer, management consultant; b. Sinking Spring, Pa., Nov. 29, 1936; s. Herbert M. and Helen (Bock) Y.; m. Constance Werkheiser, June 28, 1958; children—Jere Arnold, Karen Denise, Tracy Lynn. BS in Econs., U. Pa., 1958; JD, Yale U., 1961. Bar: Pa. 1961, U.S. Supreme Ct. 1976. With firm Dechert, Price and Rhoads, Phila., 1961-65; sr. v.p., gen. corp. counsel, sec. Indsl. Valley Bank and Trust Co., Phila., 1965-79; v.p. fin., sec. Tasty Baking Co., Phila., 1980; exec. v.p. SE Nat. Bank of Pa., 1980-82, pres., 1983-84; pres. HP Investors Ltd., 1985-87; chmn., chief exec. officer Hansen Bancorp, Inc., 1988-92; chmn. Hansen Savs. Bank, 1988-92, Hansen Savs. Bank Fla., 1987-92; pres. Capital Adv. Group, Inc., 1992—; bd. dirs. First Comml. Bank of Phila., 1992—. Pres. Radnor Twp. Sch. Authority, 1983. Mem. Del. County Bar Assn. Home: 646 Malin Rd Newtown Square PA 19073-2613 Office: 4 Sentry Pkwy Ste 325 Blue Bell PA 19422

YOUNG, JERRY WESLEY, animal nutrition educator; b. Mulberry, Tenn., Aug. 19, 1934; s. Rufus William and Annie Jewell (Sweeney) Y.; m. Charlotte Sullenger, July 8, 1959; children: David, Jeretha. BS, Berry Coll. 1957; MS, N.C. State U., 1959, PhD, 1963. Asst. prof. Iowa State U., Ames, 1965-70, assoc. prof., 1970-74, prof. in animal sci. & biochemistry, 1974—. Contbr. articles to profl. jours. Postdoctoral fellow NIH, 1963-65. Mem. Am. Dairy Sci. Assn. (Outstanding Dairy Nutrition Rsch. 1987), Am. Inst. Nutrition, Am. Soc. Animal Sci., Am. Chem. Soc., Sigma Xi, Phi Kappa Phi, Gamma Sigma Delta. Baptist. Office: Iowa State U 313 Kildee Hall Ames IA 50010*

YOUNG, JESS R., physician; b. Fairfield, Ill., Feb. 4, 1928; s. Edgar S. and Clara B. (Musgrave) Y.; m. Gloria Wynn, July 10, 1953; children—James C., Patricia A. BS, U. Steubenville, 1951; MD, St. Louis U., 1955. Intern Highland Alameda County Hosp., Oakland, Calif., 1955-56; resident in internal medicine Cleve. Clinic Hosp., 1956-59, mem. staff dept. peripheral vascular disease, 1959—, chmn. dept., 1976-94. Co-author: Leg Ulcer, 1975, Peripheral Vascular Diseases, 1991; contbr. articles to profl. jours., chpts. to books. Served with AUS, 1946-47. Mem. AMA, Am. Heart Assn. (stroke council), Am. Coll. Cardiology, Internat. Cardiovascular Soc., ACP, Am. Fedn. Clic. Research, Ohio Soc. Internal Medicine, Soc. for Vascular Medicine and Rsch., Inter-Urban Club. Methodist. Home: 1503 Burlington Rd Cleveland OH 44118-1216 Office: 9500 Euclid Ave Cleveland OH 44195-0002

YOUNG, JOAN CRAWFORD, advertising executive; b. Hobbs, N.Mex., July 30, 1931; d. William Bill and Ora Maydelle (Boone) Crawford; m. Herchelle B. Young, Nov. 23, 1971 (div.). BA, Hardin Simmons U., 1952; postgrad. Tex. Tech. U., 1953-54. Reporter, Lubbock (Tex.) Avalanche-Jour., 1952-54; promotion dir. Sta. KCBD-TV, Lubbock, 1954-62; account exec. Ward Hicks Advt., Albuquerque, 1962-70; v.p. Mellekas & Assocs., Advt., Albuquerque, 1970-78; pres. J. Young Advt., Albuquerque, 1978—. Bd. dirs. N.Mex. Symphony Orch., 1970-73, United Way of Greater Albuquerque, 1985-89; bd. trustees N.Mex. Children's Found., 1994—. Recipient Silver medal N.Mex. Advt. Fedn., 1977. Mem. N.Mex. Advt. Fedn. (bd. dirs. 1975-76), Am. Advt. Fedn., Greater Albuquerque C. of C. (bd. dirs. 1984), Albuquerque Petroleum Club (membership chmn. 1992-93, bd. dirs. 1993—, sec. 1994—). Republican. Author: (with Louise Allen and Audre Lipscomb) Radio and TV Continuity Writing, 1962. Home: 1638 Tierra Del Rio NW Albuquerque NM 87107 also: 500 Marquette NW Albuquerque NM 87102

YOUNG, JOHN ALAN, electronics company executive; b. Nampa, Idaho, Apr. 24, 1932; s. Lloyd Arthur and Karen Eliza (Miller) Y.; m. Rosemary Murray, Aug. 1, 1954; children: Gregory, Peter, Diana. B.S. in Elec. Engring, Oreg. State U., 1953; M.B.A., Stanford U., 1958. Various mktg. and finance positions Hewlett Packard Co. Inc., Palo Alto, Calif., 1958-63, gen. mgr. microwave div., 1963-68, v.p. electronic products group, 1968-74, exec. v.p., 1974-77, chief oper. officer, 1977-78, pres., 1977-92, chief exec. officer, 1978-92; ret., 1992; bd. dirs. Wells Fargo Bank, Wells Fargo and Co., Chevron Corp., SmithKline Beecham Plc, Affymetrix, Inc., Shaman Pharms., Inc., Abiotic Sys. (name now Ciphergen, Novell) and Gen. Magic; chmn. Smart Valley, Inc. Chmn. an fund Stanford U., 1966-73, nat. chmn. corp. gifts, 1973-77, mem. adv. coun. Grad. Sch. Bus., 1967-73, 75-80, Univ. trustee, 1977-87; bd. dirs. Mid-Peninsula Urban Coalition, 1971-80, co-chmn., 1983-85; chmn. Pres.'s Commn. on Indsl. Competitiveness, 1983-85, Nat. Jr. Achievement, 1983-84; pres. Found. for Malcolm Baldrige Nat. Quality Award; mem. Adv. Com. on Trade Policy and Negotiations, 1988-92. With USAF, 1954-56. Mem. Nat. Acad. Engring., Coun. on Competi-

tiveness (founder, founding chair computer systems policy project 1986), Bus. Coun.

YOUNG, JOHN EDWARD, lawyer; b. Tulsa, July 11, 1935; s. Russell Edward and Frances Lucille (Wetmore) Y.; m. Mary Moore Nason, Dec. 27, 1966; children: Cynthia Nason, Abigail Brackett. BS with honors, Calif. Inst. Tech., 1956; LLB magna cum laude, Harvard U., 1959. Bar: N.Y. 1961, U.S. Dist. Ct. (so. dist.) N.Y. 1973. Assoc. Cravath, Swaine & Moore, N.Y.C., 1960-67, ptnr., 1968—; resident ptnr. Cravath, Swaine & Moore, Paris, 1971-73, London, 1990—. Editor Harvard Law Rev., 1958-59. Sheldon Traveling fellow Harvard U., 1959-60. Mem. ABA, N.Y. State Bar Assn., Assn. of Bar of City of N.Y., Century Assn., Harvard Club of N.Y.C. Democrat. Episcopal. Home: 1088 Park Ave New York NY 10128-1132 also: 5 Cresswell Pl, London SW1O 9RB, England Office: Cravath Swaine & Moore 825 8th Ave New York NY 10019-7416 also: 33 King William St, London EC4R 9DU, England

YOUNG, JOHN HARDIN, lawyer; b. Washington, Apr. 25, 1948; s. John D. and Laura Virginia (Gwathemey) Y.; m. Mary Frances (Farley) Crosby. AB, Colgate U., 1970; JD, U. Va., 1973; BCL, Oxford U., Eng., 1976. Bar: Va. 1973, D.C. 1974, U.S. Dist. Ct. (ea. dist.) Va. 1974, U.S. Dist. Ct. D.C. 1974, Internat. Trade Ct. 1974, U.S. Ct. Fed. Claims 1974, U.S. Ct. Appeals (4th, Fed. and D.C. cirs.), U.S. Supreme Ct. 1977. Ptnr. Porter Wright Morris & Arthur, Washington, 1988-92, of counsel, 1992—; gen. counsel The Smoot Corp., 1992—; v.p. law Q Star Technologies, Inc., 1992—; mem. adv. bd. The Antitrust Bulletin and Jour. of Antitrust Law and Econs.; mem. U.S. Sec. State's adv. com. Pvt. Internat. Law, 1987-94; chmn. Va. Retirement Sys. Rev. Bd., 1989-91; asst. atty. gen. Commonwealth of Va., 1976-78; mem. master plan task force City of Alexandria, Va., 1987-88, mem. budget and fiscal affairs adv. com., 1989-91; moderator Alexandria Forum, 1993—, Fedn. Forum/TV Channel 10, 1989-91; gen. counsel CAPAccess, 1992—. Contbr. articles to profl. jours. and books on litigation, evidence and trial tactics. Gen. counsel Dem. Party of Va., 1993—; consel Gov. Wilder recount, 1989, Gov. Glendenny recount, 1995. Mem. ABA (coun. 1986-89, adminstrv. law sect., chmn. trade regulation and competition com. 1983-86, chair continuing legal edn. com. 1991-94, chair dispute resolution com. 1994—, vice chair nominating com. 1994-95), Nat. Lawyers Coun., Am. Law Inst., George Mason Am. Inn of Ct. (master), Hon. Soc. Mid. Temple, Comml. Bar Assn. U.K. (overseas mem.), Phi Alpha Theta (history hons.). Episcopalian. Home: 5146 Woodmire Ln Alexandria VA 22311-1301 Office: 5201 Leesburg Pike Ste 1100 Falls Church VA 22311

YOUNG, J(OHN) MICHAEL, philosophy educator; b. Waterloo, Iowa, Jan. 5, 1944; s. Robert James and Loa Belle (LaBarre) Y.; m. Carolyn Elizabeth Bryan, Jan. 26, 1963; children—Jason, Michelle, Bryan. B.A., Grinnell Coll., 1965; M.A., Yale U., 1967, Ph.D., 1969. Asst. prof. philosophy U. Kans., Lawrence, 1969-76, assoc. prof. philosophy, 1976-84, prof. philosophy, 1984—; vis. scholar Coll. Liberal Arts and Scis., 1982-85, 90—; vis. assoc. prof. SUNY, Stony Brook, 1979-80. Editor, translator: Immanuel Kant: Logic Lectures, 1992; contbr. articles to profl. jours. Mem. Am. Philos. Assn. Home: 803 Highland Dr Lawrence KS 66044-2431 Office: U Kans Dept Philosophy Lawrence KS 66045

YOUNG, JOHN WATTS, astronaut; b. San Francisco, Sept. 24, 1930; s. William H. Y.; m. Susy Feldman; children by previous marriage: Sandra, John. BS in Aero. Engring, Ga. Inst. Tech., 1952; D Applied Sci. (hon.), Fla. Technol. U., 1970; LLD (hon.), Western State U., 1969; DSc (hon.), U. S.C., 1981, Brown U., 1983. Joined USN, 1952, advanced through grades to capt.; test pilot, program mgr. F4 weapons systems projects, 1959-62; then maintenance officer Fighter Squadron 143, Naval Air Sta., Miramar, Calif.; chief astronaut office Flight Ops. Directorate, 1975-87, spl. asst. dir. JSC for engring. ops., safety, 1987—; comdr. 54-hour, 36-orbit 1st flight of Shuttle Space, 1981, and 10 day orbital shuttle 1st flight Space Lab., 1983. Decorated DFC (3), D.S.M. (2); recipient NASA Disting. Svc. medal (3), NASA Exceptional Svc. medal (2), NASA Engring. Achievement medal, 1988, NASA Outstanding Leadership medal, 1992, NASA Outstanding Achievement medal, 1994, Congl. Space medal of honor, 1981; named Disting. Young Alumni Svc. award Ga. Tech. Acad. Disting. Engrs., 1994; named to Nat. Aviation Hall of Fame, 1988. Fellow Am. Astronautical Soc. (Flight Achievement award 1972, 81, 83, Space Flight award 1993), Soc. Exptl. Test Pilots (Iven Kincheloe award 1972, 81), AIAA (HAley Astronautics award 1972, 83, 84); mem. Sigma Chi. Astronaut NASA, made 1st two-man 3 orbit flight, Gemini 3, Mar. 1965, Gemini 10 3 day flight, 1966, Apollo 10 8-day flight lunar landing dress rehearsal, 1969, Apollo 16 11 day lunar landing and surface exploration, 1972; dir. space shuttle br., astronaut office, 1973-75. Office: NASA Johnson Space Ctr Houston TX 77058

YOUNG, JON NATHAN, archeologist; b. Hibbing, Minn., May 30, 1938; s. Robert Nathan Young and Mary Elizabeth (Barrows) Roy; m. Karen Sue Johnson, June 5, 1961 (div. May 1980); children: Shawn Nathan, Kevin Leigh; m. Tucker Heitman, June 18, 1988. BA magna cum laude, U. Ariz., 1960, PhD, 1967; MA, U. Ky., 1962. Archeologist Nat. Park Svc. Southwest Archeol. Ctr., Globe and Tucson, Ariz., 1967-75; exec., camp dir. YMCA of Metro. Tucson, 1976-77; asst. dir. Kit Carson Meml. Found., Taos, N.Mex., 1978; co-dir. Las Palomas de Taos, 1979; archeologist Nat. Forest Svc., Carson Nat. Forest, Taos, 1980—; exec. order cons. U.S. Sec. Interior, 1973-75. Author: The Salado Culture in Southwestern Prehistory, 1967; co-author: Excavation of Mound 7, 1981, First-Day Road Log in Techtonic Development of the Sangre de Cristo Mountains, 1990. Advisor Boy Scouts Am.; active YMCA White Rag Soc. Grantee NEH, 1978; Ariz. Wilson Found., NSF, Ky. Rsch. Found. fellow, 1960-62; Baird Found., Bausch and Lomb, Elks; recipient cert. merit USDA, 1987, 89. Fellow AAAS, Am. Anthrop. Assn., Explorers Club, Royal Anthrop. Inst.; mem. Current Anthropology (assoc.), Ariz. Archaeol. and Hist. Soc., Ariz. Hist. Soc., Coun. on Am.'s Mil. Past, Soc. Hist. Archaeology, Soc. Am. Archaeology, Harwood Found., Millicent Rogers Mus., Taos Archaeol. Soc., Taos County Hist. Soc., Sigma Xi, Phi Beta Kappa, Alpha Kappa Delta, Phi Kappa Phi, Delta Chi. Home: PO Box 2207 Taos NM 87571-2207 Office: Nat Forest Svc Suprs Office PO Box 558 Taos NM 87571-0558

YOUNG, JOSEPH H., federal judge; b. Hagerstown, Md., July 18, 1922; s. J. Edgar and Mabel K. (Koser) Y.; m. Doris Oliver, Sept. 6, 1947; children: Stephen A., William O., J. Harrison. A.B., Dartmouth Coll., 1948; LL.B., U. Va., 1951. Bar: Md. 1951. Assoc. firm Marbury Miller & Evans, Balt., 1951-52; assoc. firm Piper & Marbury, Balt., 1952-58, ptnr., 1958-71, mng. ptnr., 1968-71; judge U.S. Dist. Ct. Md., from 1971, now sr. judge; instr. Johns Hopkins U. (McCoy Coll.), 1954-62. Bd. dirs. Legal Aid Soc. Balt., 1958-71, CICHA (Health Appeal), 1964-71; bd. dirs. exec. com. Md. div. Am. Cancer Soc., 1958—, chmn. div. bd. dirs. 1969-71, bd. dirs. 1966—, chmn. nat. svcs. com. 1970-73, chmn. exec. com. 1976-77, dir.-at-large 1973-83, vice-chmn. nat. bd. dirs. 1975-77, chmn. nat. bd. 1977-80, chmn. pub. issues com. 1981-83, past officer dir. 1984; mem. Found. for Malcolm Baldrige Nat. Quality Award; worldwide fight com. 1987-90, also mem. trust adv. bd.; mem. oncology adv. coun. Johns Hopkins U.; chmn. com. on campaign orgn. & pub. edn. Internat. Union Contra Cancer, Geneva, Switzerland, 1981-90, mem. fin. com., chmn. 1993—, exec. com. 1993—. Decorated Bronze Star, Purple Heart. Recipient Disting. Service Award Am. Cancer Soc., 1983; Dartmouth Coll. Alumni award, 1983; James Ewing Soc. award, 1983. Mem. 4th Circuit Jud. Conf., Assn. Alumni Dartmouth Coll. (pres. 1984-85). Republican. Presbyterian (elder, deacon, trustee). Clubs: Hamilton Street, Rule Day, Lawyers Round Table. Office: US Dist Ct 101 W Lombard St Baltimore MD 21201

YOUNG, JOSEPH LAURIE, architecture educator; b. Huntsville, Tex., Sept. 23, 1924; s. Benjamin Wiley and Margaret (Cater) Y. BArch, U. Tex., 1950; MArch, Ga. Inst. Tech. 1955. Registered architect S.C. Teaching fellow U. Tex., Austin, 1948-50; prof. emeritus architecture Clemson U., S.C., 1950—, Univ. marshall, 1985-88; Hayes Fulbright fellow Middle East Tech. U., Ankara, Turkey, 1963-64; cons. to bus.; artist drawings of hist. bldgs., 1950—; resident teacher Charles E. Daniel Clemson U. Centre Bldg. Rsch. and Urban Study, Genova, Italy, 1985-86, 88-89; dir. Clemson U. Ctr. for Archtl. Study, Coll. of Charleston, S.C., 1988. Elder Ft. Hill Presbyn. Ch. With USNR, 1943-46. Recipient Student Adviser award Clemson U. 1989. Fellow AIA (pres. S.C. chpt. 1971-72, Svc. awards 1969, 71, 84; bd. dir. S.C. chpt. 1966-69); mem. S.C. AIA, Tiger Brotherhood, Rotary Internat.,

Tau Sigma Delta, Paul Harris Fellow Rotary. Home: 705 Clemson House PO Box 712 Clemson SC 29631

YOUNG, JOSEPH LOUIS, artist; b. Pitts., Nov. 27, 1919; s. Louis and Jennie (Eger) Y.; m. Millicent Goldstein, June 19, 1949; children: Leslie Sybil, Family Leslie. Grad., Westminster Coll., New Wilmington, Pa., 1941, D. Litt., 1960; Edwin Austin Abbey mural painting scholar, 1949; grad., Boston Mus. Sch. Fine Arts, 1951; Albert H. Whitin traveling fellow, Am. Acad. in Rome, 1951-52. Newspaperman Pitts. and N.Y.C., 1941-43; lectr. Tufts Coll., 1949; painting instr. Boston Mus. Sch., 1950; Idylwild Arts Found., 1959, Brandeis Camp Inst., 1962-74; founder, dir. Joseph Young Mosaic Workshop, 1953—; founding chmn. dept. archtl. arts Brooks Santa Barbara (Calif.) Sch. Fine Arts, 1969-75; head mus. exhibits Bowers Mus., Santa Ana, Calif., 1977-78; head visual arts CETA program, City of Los Angeles, 1978-80; organized internat. sculpture competition for city of Huntington Beach, Calif., 1974; art cons. Allied Arts Commn., City of Huntington Beach, 1973-74; cons. Art in Public Bldgs. Program, Calif. Arts Council, 1976-77; field adminstr. CCA/CETA Program, Los Angeles.; Invited prin. speaker at nat. convs. A.I.A., Am. Craftsmen Council, 4th Congress I.A.P.A., 7th Nat. Sculpture Conf., Council of Am., U. Kans.; lectr. Rome, Venice, Florence (as guest) Italian govt., 1959. Restoration of mosaics from Greek and Roman periods and Della Robbia sculpture, 1972-73; author: A Course in Making Mosaics, 1957, Mosaics, Principles and Practice, 1963, also articles in profl. jours.; pub. mural painting bibliography, 1946; asso. founding editor: Creative Crafts mag, 1960-64; concept and design: ARTSMARKET, 1979; work featured 16mm documentary film The World of Mosaic; true fresco, oil and mosiac mural commns. in, Boston, Chgo., Pitts., Los Angeles, survey govt. sponsored mural painting programs, 1951; one man show, Pitts. Arts and Crafts Center, 1950, Falk-Raboff Gallery, Los Angeles, 1953, ten year retrospective exhbn. archtl. art work, Desert Mus., Palm Springs, Calif., 1963, Calif. council A.I.A. Fine Arts Architecture Exhbn., 1964, Nat. Gold Medal Exhbn. of N.Y. Archtl. League, 1951; work reproduced in numerous books, mags., newspapers throughout the world; invited to submit designs for Nebr. State Capitol murals, paintings and mosiacs in numerous pvt. collections; executed mosiac murals Los Angeles Police Facilities Bldg., 1955, Don Bosco Tech. High Sch., 1956, Temple Emanuel, 1957, Southland Shopping Center, 1958, Our Lady of Lourdes Ch., 1959, Cameo residence, Beverly Hills, Calif., 1961, Santa Barbara Stock Exchange, 1960, St. Martins Ch., La Mesa, Calif., 1966, stained glass windows, liturgical art program, Congregation Beth Sholom, San Francisco, 1966, West Apse of Nat. Shrine of Immaculate Conception, Washington, 1966, mosiac arch, Eden Meml. Park, San Fernando, Calif., 1960; commd. to execute mural, Los Angeles County Hall of Records, Shalom Meml. Park, Chgo., B.V.M. Presentation Ch., Midland, Pa., 1961, Hollenbeck Police Sta., Los Angeles, 1963, Beth Emet Temple, Anaheim, Calif., 1963, Temple Sinai, Glendale, Calif., 1963, Sinai Temple, Los Angeles, 1963, Valley Beth Israel, Sun Valley, Calif., 1964, Beth Tikvah, Westchester, Calif., 1964, Belmont High Sch., Los Angeles, 1972; commd. to design and execute 14 bas-relief concrete-mosaic murals for exterior of, Math. Scis. Bldg. at UCLA, bronze sculpture, La Mirada (Calif.) Civic Theatre, 1979; did liturgical art programs for, Congregation B'nai B'rith, Santa Barbara, Temple Beth Torah, Alhambra, Temple Beth Ami, West Covina, Temple Menorah, Redondo Beach, Temple Solael, Canoga Park, Temple Bamidbar, Lancaster, Temple Beth Jacob, Redwood City (all Calif.), other congregations in Calif., concrete bas reliefs, Southgate County Pub. Library, 1973, mosaics for, St. Mary of Angels, Hollywood, Calif., 1973, Triforium polyphonoptic, kinetic tower, Los Angeles Mall, 1969-75; multimedia presentations for, 400th Anniversary Michelangelo, Italian Trade Commn., Casa de Maria, Santa Barbara, Hancock Coll., Santa Maria, Los Angeles County Mus. Art, U. Calif., Los Angeles and Irvine., designs for Holocaust Monument for Pan-Pacific Park in Los Angeles won national competition and dedicated in 1992; appointed to City of West Hollywood Arts Commn.; chmn. Fine Arts Bd., U. of Judaism, L.A.; completed cycle of Stained Glass windows for Ventura County Jewish Community Ctr. devoted to theme of Seven Days of Creation, 12 tribes stained glass for Temple Beth Israel, West Hollywood, Calif., 1991; work subject of restrospective exhbn. at the Jewish Community Galleries, 1986; commd. projects now represented by Yanov & Gold, Ltd. of Los Angeles, Calif. Served with USAAF, 1943-46. Recipient Nat. Army Arts contest award, 1945; Huntington Hartford Found. fellow, 1952-53. Fellow Internat. Inst. Arts and Letters (life); mem. Nat. Soc. Mural Painters (nat. v.p. 1969—), Artists Equity Assn. (pres. So. Calif. chpt. 1956, nat. v.p. 1960), Calif. Confedn. Arts (founding pres. 1976). Home and Studio: Art in Architecture 7917 1/2 W Norton Ave Los Angeles CA 90046

YOUNG, JOSEPH RUTLEDGE, JR., lawyer; b. Charleston, S.C., Mar. 28, 1943; s. Joseph Rutledge and Elizabeth Evans (Jenkins) Y.; m. Kathleen Baldwin Kimmell, Aug. 10, 1968; children—Joseph Rutledge, Simons Waring. B.A. with distinction in History, U. Va., 1965, LL.B., 1968. Bar: S.C. 1968, U.S. Dist. Ct. (so. dist.) S.C. 1968, U.S. Ct. Appeals (4th cir.) 1972. Assoc. Young, Clement, Rivers & Tisdale, Charleston, 1970-75, ptnr. 1975—. pres. Cen. R.R. of S.C., 1988—; bd. dirs. So. Nat. Bank of S.C., 1988-95, BB & T of S.C., 1995—. Contbr. articles to profl. jours. Mem. Charleston City Council, 1975-80; v.p. Historic Charleston Found., 1993—; trustee Middleton Place Found., 1987—, Charleston Day Sch., 1985-91. Served to capt. U.S. Army, 1968-70, Vietnam. Decorated Bronze Star. Fellow Am. Coll. Trial Lawyers; mem. S.C. Bar Assn. (chmn. CLE 1982-84, bd. govs. 1984-88, sec. 1991, treas. 1992-93, pres.-elect 1993-94, pres 1994-95, exec. com. bd. commrs. on grievances and discipline 1983-86), Am. Bd. Trial Advocates (diplomate), Fedn. Ins. and Corp. Counsel, St. Andrews Soc., St. George's Soc., Preservation Soc., U.S. Supreme Ct. Hist. Soc. (state chmn.), Carolina Yacht Club, Farmington Country Club, Yeamans Hall Club. Office: Young Clement Rivers & Tisdale 28 Broad St Charleston SC 29401-3070

YOUNG, KATHERINE ANN, education educator; b. Castleford, Idaho, Apr. 9, 1941; d. Ross and Norna (Scully) Stoner; m. Virgil Monroe Young, Dec. 20, 1964; 1 child, Susan Annette. BS in Elem. Edn., U. Idaho, 1965; MEd, Ea. Washington U., 1969; EdD, Utah State U., 1980. Cert. advanced elem. tchr., Idaho. Tchr. spl. edn. Coeur d'Alene (Idaho) Sch. Dist., 1965-66; tchr. elem. grades Coeur d' Aleue (Idaho) Sch. Dist., 1966-67, Boise (Idaho) Sch. Dist., 1967-88; assoc. prof. edn. Boise State U., 1988-93, prof., 1993—. Co-author: (resource book) The Story of Idaho Author's, 1977, The Story of Idaho Guide and Resource Book, 1993; author: The Utah Activity Book, 1980, Constructing Buildings, Bridges, and Minds, 1993; cons., contbr. (nat. edn. jour.) Learning, 1991—; named Idaho Tchr. of Yr., State Dept. of Edn., Boise, 1983; invited to luncheon at White House, Pres. Ronald Reagan, Washington, 1983; Recipient Outstanding Young Educator award Boise Jaycees, 1983; profiled in Idaho Centennial pub., 1990; travel to Japan grantee Rocky Mountain Region Japan Project, 1990. Mem. ASCD, Nat. Coun. for Social Studies, Idaho Law Found., Alliance Idaho Geographers (state coord.). Avocations: travel, reading. Office: Boise State U Dept Tchr Edn 1910 University Dr Boise ID 83725-0001

YOUNG, KATHERINE CURTIN, manufacturing executive; b. Beacon, N.Y., Apr. 29, 1939; d. Daniel Francis and Thea Marie (Haak) Curtin; m. Robert R. Young (div. 1976); children: Timothy Robert, Thomas Alexander. Student, Dutchess Coll., 1960-72, U. Rochester, 1956-58, Skidmore Coll., 1989—. With IBM Corp., 1959-88; procurement mgr. IBM Corp., Boca Raton, Fla., 1982-87, site quality mgr. 1987-88; v.p. materials Conner Peripherals, San Jose, Calif., 1988—. Bd. dirs. YMCA, Boca Raton, 1986; speaker Congl. Forum, Monte Visa, Calif., 1990. Mem. IEEE, Am. Soc. for Quality Control. Republican. Roman Catholic. Office: Conner Peripherals 3081 Nanker Rd San Jose CA 95134

YOUNG, KENNETH EVANS, educational consultant; b. Toronto, Ont., Can., Mar. 21, 1922; s. John Osborne Wallace and Gwendolyn May (Evans) Y.; m. Mae Catherine Wittenmyer, July 1, 1945; 1 child, Bruce Kenneth. AB, San Francisco State Coll., 1943; MA, Stanford U., 1947, PhD, 1953; LLD (hon.), U. Nev., 1972. Prin. journalism and speech San Francisco State Coll., 1946-48; instr. journalism and English Calif. State Poly. Coll., San Luis Obispo, 1949-50; from asst. prof. to acting dean Coll. Arts and Scis. Kellogg-Voorhis Campus, Pomona, 1951-57; dean faculty U. Alaska, College, 1957-59; fellow in coll. adminstrn. U. Mich., Ann Arbor, 1959-60; exec. v.p. U. Nev., Reno, 1960-64; pres. SUNY, Cortland, 1964-68; v.p., dir. Washington office Am. Coll. Testing Program, 1968-75; pres. Council on Postsecondary Accreditation, Washington, 1975-80; exec. dir. Nat. Univ. Continuing Edn. Assn., Washington, 1980-84; dir. Inst. for

Learning in Retirement, Am. U., Washington, 1984-89; sr. assoc., cons. Diane U. Eisenberg Assocs., Washington, 1984—. Prin. editor: Understanding Accreditation, 1983; contbr. articles to profl. jours. Sgt. U.S. Army, 1943-45. Republican. Club: Cosmos (Washington). Home: Apt 512 4200 Cathedral Ave NW Washington DC 20016

YOUNG, KENNETH LAURENCE, union official; b. N.Y.C., Oct. 20, 1927; s. Laurence E. and Rosalie M. Y.; m. Charlotte Harrison, Aug. 4, 1951; children: Michael, Lauren, Eric. B.A., Antioch Coll., 1950. Editor, organizer Ins. and Allied Workers Organizing Com., CIO, Washington, 1951-55; publicity and research dir. Ins. Workers Am., CIO, 1955-57; asst. dir. publicity and public relations AFL-CIO Indsl. Union Dept., Washington, 1957-63; publicity dir. Internat. Union Elec., Radio and Machine Workers, 1963-65; legis. rep. AFL-CIO, Washington, 1965-73; asso. dir. legis. dept. AFL-CIO, 1973-79, dir. legis. dept., 1979-80, exec. asst. to pres., 1980-91; ret., 1991. bd. dirs. Nat. Endowment for Democracy, Leadership Conf. Edn. Fund, Advocacy Inst., Nat. Capitol area regional of NCCJ, Fed. Prison Industries, Inc.; mem. ABA Commn. on Access to Justice/2000; former mem. exec. com. Leadership Conf. on Civil Rights. Chmn. Democratic precinct, Silver Spring, Md., 1958-61. Served with U.S. Army, 1946-47. Mem. Newspaper Guild AFL-CIO, United Food and Comml. Workers AFL-CIO, NAACP, ACLU, Coalition Labor Union Women. Home: 801 Buckingham Dr Silver Spring MD 20901-3616

YOUNG, KEVIN, track and field athlete. Olympic track and field participant Barcelona, Spain, 1992. Recipient 400m Hurdles Gold medal Olympics, Barcelona, 1992; world recorder holder in 400m hurdles. Office: US Olympic Com 1750 E Boulder St Colorado Springs CO 80909-5746*

YOUNG, LAURA, dance educator, choreographer; b. Boston, Aug. 5, 1947; d. James Vincent and Adelaide Janet (Coupal) Y.; m. Anthony Charles Catanzaro, Sept. 26, 1970 (div. Nov. 1981); m. Christopher Edward Mehl, Aug. 23, 1987. Grad. high sch., Cohasset, Mass. Dancer Met. Opera Ballet, N.Y.C., 1971-73; dancer Boston Ballet Co., 1963-65, prin. dancer, 1965-71, 73-89, ballet mistress, 1989-91; guest tchr. Dance Tchrs. Club Boston, 1978-82, Dance Masters Assn., 1979, 90, 92, 93, Walnut Hill Sch., Natick, Mass., 1984-87, 90-91; tchr., asst. dir. Boston Ballet II, 1986—; dir. summer dance program, 1986-94; 1st hon. mem. Dance Masters Assn. Chpt. 5, 1992; bd. dirs. Boston Dance Alliance; mem. faculty Boston Conservatory, 1990-94; prin. Boston Ballet Sch., 1993—. Choreographer (ballets) Occasional Waltzes, 1984, Albinoni Suite, 1986, Champ Dances, 1987, A Place of Sound and Mind, 1988, Deadlock, 1989, Rumpelstiltskin, 1989. Recipient Leadership award Greater Boston C. of C., 1987; named Disting. Bostonian, Boston's 350th Jubilee Com., 1980. Mem. Am. Guild Mus. Artists, Dance Masters Am. (hon.). Office: Boston Ballet Co 19 Clarendon St Boston MA 02116-6107

YOUNG, LAWRENCE, electrical engineering educator; b. Hull, Eng., July 5, 1925; arrived in Can., 1955; naturalized, 1972; s. Herbert and Dora Y.; m. Margaret Elisabeth Jane, Jan. 5, 1951. B.A., Cambridge U., 1946, Ph.D., 1950, Sc.D., 1963. Asst. lectr. Imperial Coll., London, 1952-55; mem. research staff B.C. Research Council, 1955-63; prof. dept. elec. engring. U. B.C., Vancouver. Author: Anodic Oxide Films, 1961; contbr. articles to profl. jours. Recipient Callinan award Dielectrics div. Electrochemical Soc., 1983, Can. Electrochem. Gold medal, 1990. Fellow IEEE, Royal Soc. Can. Office: Dept Electrical Engineering, U BC, Vancouver, BC Canada V6T 1W5

YOUNG, LEO, electrical engineer; b. Vienna, Austria, Aug. 18, 1926; came to U.S., 1953, naturalized, 1958; s. Samuel and Marie Y.; m. Fay Merskey, Jan. 4, 1953 (dec. May 1981); children—Philip Michael, Sarah Anne, Joseph David; m. Ruth Breslow, Jan. 2, 1983. BA, Cambridge U., 1946, MA, 1950; MS, Johns Hopkins U., 1956, D.Engring. (Westinghouse-B.G. Lamme grad. scholar), 1959, D.H.L. (hon.), 1989. Lab. mgr. Decca Radar, Ltd., Surbiton, Eng., 1951-53; adv. engr. Westinghouse Electric Corp., Balt., 1953-60; staff scientist, program mgr. Stanford Research Inst., Menlo Park, Calif., 1960-73; staff cons., asst. Naval Research Lab., Washington, 1973-81; dir. research Office of Undersec. for Def. Research and Engring., Dept. Def., 1981-94; cons. to dir. def. rsch. and engring. Dept. Def., 1994—; bd. dirs. Filtronic-Comtek (U.K.). Author: Microwave Filters, 1964, Systems of Units in Electricity and Magnetism, 1969, Advances in Microwaves, Vols. 1-8, 1966-74, Everything You Should Know About Pensions Plans, 1976; also articles. Fellow AAAS, IEEE (pres. 1980, pres. Microwave Soc. 1969, Microwave prize 1963, Microwave Career award 1988, Disting. Contbns. to Engring. Professionalism IEEE-USA 1993, Pinnacle award 1995); mem. Sigma Xi. Patentee in field. *It has been my goal to serve the public and my belief that engineering and science improve the quality of life. I have enjoyed doing engineering research and am fortunate in receiving recognition.*

YOUNG, LESLIE TOWNER, state legislator, stockbroker; b. N.Y.C., May 26, 1930; s. Leslie Bernard and Constance (Towner) Y.; m. Patricia Cutler, May 18, 1955; children: William, Anne. BA, Yale U., 1952; MS, Columbia U., 1957. Fin. analyst Union Carbide Corp., N.Y.C., 1957-68; v.p., dir. Laird Bissell Meeks, N.Y.C., 1968-74; stockbroker, mgr. Dean Witter Reynolds, Greenwich, Conn., 1974—; mem. Conn. Ho. of Reps., Hartford, 1984—. Bd. dirs., pres. New Canaan (Conn.) United Way, 1960s; bd. dirs., v.p. Lower Fairfield Alcohol and Drug Abuse Coun., Stamford, Conn., Weir Farm Heritage Trust, Wilton, Conn.; chmn. Republican Town Com., New Canaan, 1968-74. With U.S. Army, 1953-55. Mem. New Canaan Country Club (greens chmn. 1978—), New Canaan Exch. Club. Avocations: golf, sailing, travel. Home: Lone Tree Farm Rd New Canaan CT 06840 Office: State of Conn Legislative Office Bldg Hartford CT 06106

YOUNG, LOIS CATHERINE WILLIAMS, university agency consultant; b. Wakeman, Ohio, Mar. 10, 1930; d. William McKinley and Leona Catherine (Woods) Williams; m. William Walton Young; children: Ralph, Catherine, William. BS, NYU, 1957; MS, Hofstra U., 1962, profl. diploma, 1967, EdD, 1981; M Pub. Adminstrn., Fla. Internat. U., 1988. Cert. tchr., sch. supr., N.Y., pub. mgmt., Fla. Tchr. Copiaque (N.Y.) Schs., 1957-59; research assoc. Columbia and Hofstra Univs., Hempstead, N.Y., 1964-69; tchr. Half Hollow Hills Pub. Schs., Dix Hills, N.Y., 1970-72; instr. Conn. Coll., New London, 1972-73; tchr., supr., reading coordinator Hempstead (N.Y.) Pub. Schs., 1975-85; cons. South African project AID Fla. Meml. Coll., Miami, Fla., 1987-88; clinician Hofstra U., Hempstead, 1962-64; tchr. trainer Amityville (N.Y.) Pub. Schs., 1965, Hofstra Univ., 1982; key speaker Internat. Reading Assn., N.Y., Calif., Caribbean Islands, 1982-86. Author numerous poems. Sec. Nassau County (N.Y.) chpt. Jack and Jill of Am., 1960-62; pres. PTA, Uniondale, N.Y., 1962-68; active Boy Scouts Am., Uniondale, N.Y., 1963-65; bd. dirs. Miami chpt. UN Assn./USA, 1987-92, 1st v.p. 1989-91, Broward Fort Lauderdale chpt., 1993—; active multilateral project, 1987-90; contbr. Procs. South African Project, 1987. Recipient Lifetime Membership award PTA, 1964, rsch. grant N.Y. State Fed. Programs, 1978, Laurel Wreath award Doctoral Assn. of N.Y. Educators, 1982, Cert. of award UN Assn./USA, 1987, 88, Outstanding Achievement award Fla. Internat. U., 1988, Golden Poet award World of Poetry, 1990, 91; fellow Fla. Internat. U., 1987. Mem. Internat. Soc. Poets (life, lifetime adv. panel 1993—, award, Nat. Libr. of Poetry award 1994), Fla. Internat. U. Alumni Assn., NYU Alumni Assn. (bd. dirs. 1983-90, 2d v.p. 1986-87), Hofstra U. Alumni Assn., Tuskegee Airmen, Inc., Weston (Fla.) Toastmasters Club (charter), Toastmasters Internat., Kappa Delta Pi, Kappa Kappa Alpha, Theta Iota Omega (global affairs com. 1984-86), Phi Delta Kappa. Avocations: creative writing, travel, tennis, radio reading for unsighted, golf. Home: 1345 Sunset Spgs Fort Lauderdale FL 33326-2936

YOUNG, LORETTA (GRETCHEN YOUNG), actress; b. Salt Lake City, Jan. 6, 1913; M. Thomas Lewis (div.). Grad., Ramona Convent, Alhambra, Calif.; student, Immaculate Heart Coll., Hollywood, Calif. Motion picture appearances include Laugh Clown Laugh, 1928, Loose Ankles, 1929, The Squall, 1930, Kismet, 1930, The Devil to Pay, 1930, I Like Your Nerve, 1931, Platinum Blonde, 1932, The Hatchet Man, 1932, Big Business Girl, 1932, Life Begins, 1932, Zoo in Budapest, 1933, Man's Castle, 1933, The House of Rothschild, 1934, Midnight Mary, 1935, The Crusaders, 1935, Clive of India, 1935, Call of the Wild, 1935, Shanghai, 1936, Ramona, 1936, Ladies in Love, 1937, Wife, Doctor and Nurse, 1937, Second Honeymoon, 1938, Four Men and a Prayer, 1938, Suez, 1938, Kentucky, 1938, Three Blind Mice, 1938, The Story of Alexander Graham Bell, 1939, The Doctor Takes a Wife, 1939, He Stayed for Breakfast, 1940, Lady from Cheyenne,

1941, The Men in Her Life, 1941, A Night to Remember, 1942, China, 1943, Ladies Courageous, 1944, And Now Tomorrow, 1944, The Stranger, 1945, Along Came Jones, 1946, The Perfect Marriage, 1946, The Farmer's Daughter, 1947 (Acad. award 1947), The Bishop's Wife, 1948, Rachel and the Stranger, 1948, Come to the Stable, 1949, Cause for Alarm, 1951, Half Angel, 1951, Paula, 1952, Because of You, 1952, It Happens Every Thursday, 1953, others; appeared in TV series Loretta Young Show (Emmy awards 1954, 56, 59, Acad. Television Arts & Scis.), 1953-61, in TV films Christmas Eve (Golden Globe Award for best actress in a TV movie), 1986, Lady in a Corner, 1989; stage appearance in An Evening with Loretta Young, 1989. Active in Cath. charity orgns. Roman Catholic. Office: care Studio Fan Mail 1122 S Robertson Blvd Los Angeles CA 90035*

YOUNG, LORETTA, government official; b. Emporia, Va., Mar. 22, 1939; d. Robert Washington and Lillie Mae (Moore) Y. BS in Bus. Edn. cum laude, St. Paul's Coll., Lawrenceville, Va.; MBA, George Washington U. Acting chief comm. divsn. Minority Bus. Devel. Agy., U.S. Dept. Commerce, Washington, chief Office Planning and Evaluation Divsn., chief mgmt. divsn., acting asst. dir. Office Ops., chief planning and evaluation divsn., acting dir., 1993—; tchr. Va. State U., Petersburg. Mem., chairwoman bd. trustees Shiloh Bapt. Ch., Alexandria, Va. Mem. NAACP, Am. Soc. Pub. Adminstrn., Nat. Bus. League, Va. State Office Minority Bus. Enterprise, St. Paul's Nat. Alumni Assn. Democrat. Baptist. Avocations: tennis, bowling, dancing, basketball, cards. Home: Dept of Commerce Minority Business Devel Agency 3139 M St SE Washington DC 20019 Office: Dept Commerce 14th & Constitution Ave NW Washington DC 20230

YOUNG, LOWELL SUNG-YI, medical administrator, educator; b. Honolulu, Dec. 5, 1938. AB, Princeton U., 1960; MD, Harvard U., 1964. Di;omate Am. Bd. Internal Medicine with subspecialty in infectious diseases. Intern, jr. asst. resident, sr. asst. resident Med. divsn. Bellevue Hosp. and Meml. Hosp., N.Y.C., 1964-67; fellow in medicine Cornell U. Med. Coll., 1965-67; epidemic intelligence officer bacterial diseases br. Nat. Communicable Disease Ctr., Atlanta, 1967-69, chief spl. pathogens sect., 1968-69; spl. postdoctoral rsch. fellow Nat. Inst. Allergy and Infectious Diseases, 1969-70; rsch. fellow in medicine Meml. Hosp./Cornell U. Med. Coll., 1969-70; clin. asst. physician infectious disease svc. dept. medicine Meml. Hosp., 1970-72, assoc. dir. microbiology lab., 1971-72; instr. in medicine Cornell U. Med. Coll., 1970-72; asst. clinician Sloan-Ketterin Inst. for Cancer Rsch., 1971-72; adj. prof. pharmacy U. of Pacific, San Francisco, 1989—; mem. microbiology and invectious diseases adv. com. Nat. Inst. Allergy and Infectious Diseases, 1981-85, mem. allergy and immunology rsch. com., 1975-79; mem. staff Calif. Pacific Med. Ctr., Mt. Zion Hosp. and Med. Ctr., U. Calif., San Francisco; mem. sci. adv. bd. Am. Found. for AIDS Rsch. Mem. editl. bd. Infection, Infectious Diseases in Clin. Practice, Antimicrobic Newsletter, Diagnostic Microbiology and Infectious Diseases, Antimicrobial Agts. and Chemotherapy; contbr. numerous articles to profl. jours., chpts. to books. Recipient Alexander D. Langmuir prize Epidemic Intelligence Svc., 1970, Garrod medal Brit. Soc., 1992. Fellow ACP (mem. med. self-assessment com.), Infectious Diseases Soc. Am. (councillor 1983-85); mem. Am. Soc. for Clin. Investigation, Am. Fedn. for Clin. Rsch., Am. Soc. for Microbiology, Western Soc. for Clin. Rsch., Internat. Immunocompromised Host Soc., Brit. Soc. Antimicrobial Chemotherapy. Office: Calif Pacific Med Ctr Kuzell Inst 2200 Webster St Ste 305 San Francisco CA 94115

YOUNG, LUCY CLEAVER, physician; b. Wheeling, W.Va., Aug. 8, 1943. B.S. in Chemistry, Wheaton Coll. (Ill.), 1965; M.D., Ohio State U., 1969. Diplomate Am. Bd. Family Practice, Bd. of Ins. Medicine. Rotating intern Riverside Meth. Hosp., Columbus, Ohio, 1969-70; resident Trumbull Meml. Hosp., Warren, Ohio, 1970-71; practice medicine specializing in family practice, West Chicago, Ill., 1971-73, Paw Paw and Mendota, Ill., 1973-78; cofounder and med. dir. Wholistic Health Ctr. of Mendota, 1976-78; asst. med. dir. Met. Life Ins. Co., Gt. Lakes Head Office, Aurora, Ill., 1979-80; med. dir. Commonwealth Life Ins. Co., Louisville, 1980-85; assoc. prof. U. Ill. Abraham Lincoln Sch. Medicine, 1976-79; faculty monitor MacNeal Meml. Hosp. Family Practice Ctr. (Ill.), 1979-80; faculty preceptor U. Louisville Family Practice Dept., 1981-85; Locum Tenens Family Practice for Kron Med. Corp. of Chapel Hill, N.C., 1986-89; physician Red Bird Mission & Med. Ctr., Beverly, Ky., 1989-90; family practice floater Ochsner Clinic satellites, New Orleans, 1990—; clin. faculty preceptor La. State U. Sch. Medicine, 1992—; mem. staffs Central DuPage Hosp., Winfield, Ill., 1971-73, Mendota Community Hosp., 1973-80. Vol. Red Bird Med. Ctr., 1985—. Fellow Am. Acad. Family Practice; mem. Am. Med. Women's Assn. (pres. New Orleans br. 1992-93, reg. V reg. gov. 1993—), Christian Med. and Dental Soc. (del. to House 1995—). Home: PO Box 0730 Madisonville LA 70447-0730 Office: Ochsner Clinic 1514 Jefferson Hwy New Orleans LA 70121

YOUNG, MALCOLM EUGENE, JR., social studies secondary educator; b. Sulphur Springs, Tex., Sept. 27, 1943; s. Malcolm Eugene Sr. and Cleo Lessie (Wilson) Y.; m. Frances Jeane Tatum, Aug. 27, 1966; children: Robert, Kerri, Scott. BS, Howard Payne U., 1967; MEd, North Tex. State U., 1969. Lic. tchr., Tex. Tchr., coach Travis Jr. High Sch., Irving, Tex., 1967-69, MacArthur High Sch., Irving, 1969-71, North Jr. High Sch., Richardson, Tex., 1971-72, Westwood Jr. High Sch., Richardson, 1972-75; tchr., coach J.J. Pearce High Sch., Richardson, 1975-78, tchr., 1978—. Tchr. participant Close Up, Washington, 1989, Law-Related Edn. Summer Inst., Austin, 1993; sponsor, participant Close Up-Citizen Bee regional competition, Dallas, 1990-95. Taft Seminar for Tchrs. fellow, Austin, Tex., 1995. Mem. Nat. Coun. Social Studies, Assn. Tex. Profl. Educators, Tex. Coun. Social Studies, Richardson Assn. Tex. Profl. Educators. Methodist. Avocations: leather work, hunting, fishing, camping. Office: Richardson Ind Sch Dist 1600 N Coit Rd Richardson TX 75080-2805

YOUNG, MARGARET BUCKNER, civic worker, author; b. Campbellsville, Ky.; d. Frank W. and Eva (Carter) Buckner; m. Whitney M. Young, Jr., Jan. 2, 1944 (dec. Mar. 1971); children: Marcia Elaine, Lauren Lee. BA, Ky. State Coll., 1942, MA, U. Minn., 1946. Instr. Ky. State Coll., 1942-44; instr. edn. and psychology Spelman Coll., Atlanta, 1957-60; dir. emeritus N.Y. Life Ins. Co.; alt. del. UN Gen. Assembly, 1973. Mem. pub. policy com. Advt. Coun. Trustee emerita Lincoln Ctr. for Performing Arts; chmn. Whitney M. Young, Jr. Meml. Found., 1971-92; trustee Met. Mus. Art, 1976-90; bd. govs. UN Assn., 1975-82; bd. visitors U.S. Mil. Acad., 1978-80; dir. Philip Morris Cos., 1972-91. Author: The First Book of American Negroes, 1966, The Picture Life of Martin Luther King, Jr., 1968, The Picture Life of Ralph J. Bunche, 1968, Black American Leaders-Watts, 1969, The Picture Life of Thurgood Marshall, 1970, pub. affairs pamphlet.

YOUNG, MARGARET CHONG, elementary education educator; b. Honolulu, May 8, 1924; d. Henry Hon Chin and Daisy Kyau (Tong) Chong; m. Alfred Y.K. Young, Feb. 21, 1948; children: Robert S.W., Richard S.K., Linda S.K. EdB, 5th yr. cert., U. Hawaii, 1945. Cert. tchr., Hawaii. Tchr. Waipahu (Hawaii) Elem. Sch., Manoa Housing Sch., Hawaii Dept. Edn., Honolulu, Pauoa Elem. Sch., Honolulu. Author: And They Also Came, History of Chinese Christian Association, Hawaii's People From China; contbr. numerous articles to profl. jours. Ch. sch. tchr., supt. United Ch. Christ-Judd St. Grantee San Francisco State Coll. Mem. NEA, Hawaii State Tchrs. Assn., Hawaii Congress of Parents and Tchrs. (hon. life mem.), Kappa Kappa Iota (Disting. Educator award 1986-87), Delta Kappa Gamma (internat.).

YOUNG, MARILYN RAE, school system adminstrative secretary, mayor; b. Muskegon, Mich., Dec. 29, 1934; d. Albert Henry Cribley and Mildred Ida (Johnson) Raby; m. Peter John Young, May 21, 1955; children: Pamela Lynn Young-Walker, Lane Allen. Grad. high sch., Calumet City, Ill., 1952. Dep. pub. fiduciary Yuma County, Ariz., 1979-83; adminstrv. sec. Yuma Sch. Dist. One, 1983—; councilman City of Yuma, 1990-93, mayor, 1993—. Pres. bd. dirs. Behavioral Health Svcs. of Yuma, 1979-90; vice chmn. Yuma Planning and Zoning Commn., 1985-89; v.p. bd. dirs. Children's Village, Yuma, 1983-89; lay leader Trinity United Meth. Ch., 1986—; grad. Yuma Leadership, Inc., 1985; treas. bd. dirs. Yuma Leadership, Inc., 1986-89; participant Ariz. Women's Town Hall, 1989, various Yuma County Town Halls, 1987-90; adv. bd. mem. Friends of KAWC; chmn Yuma Pub. Safety Police Bd., 1990—, Yuma Fire Pub. Safety Bd., 1990—, Yuma Youth Leadership Com., 1991-92; mem. allocation panel United Way, 1991-93; charter mem. Friends of Roxaboxen; active High Sch. Ad Hoc Com.,

1991—; exec. bd. mem., Yuma Met. Planning Orgn., 1990—, Western Ariz. Coun. of Govts., 1990—; corp. bd. dir. Yuma Econ. Devel., 1990—; hon. chmn. Yuma County San Luis Rio Colo.Commn., 1990—; mem. Nat. League of Cities FAIR Com., 1990—, Binational Border Health Task Force, 1990—, resolution com. League of Ariz. Cities and Towns, 1990—, mem. com. U.S. Conf. of Mayors, 1990—. Mem. Yuma County C. of C. (mem. mil. affairs com. 1988-90). Avocations: community involvement, reading, travel, needlework. Home: 1288 W 18th St Yuma AZ 85364-5313 Office: City of Yuma 180 W 1st St Yuma AZ 85364-1495

YOUNG, MARVIN OSCAR, lawyer; b. Union, Mo., Apr. 4, 1929; s. Otto Christopher and Irene Adelheide (Barlage) Y.; m. Sue Carol Mathews, Aug. 23, 1952; children: Victoria Leigh, Kendall Marvin. A.B., Westminster Coll., 1951; J.D., U. Mich., 1954; LLD, Westminster Coll., 1989. Bar: Mo. 1954. Practice law firm Thompson, Mitchell, Thompson Douglas, St. Louis, 1954-55, 57-58; atty. Mo. Farmers Assn., Columbia, 1958-67; exec. v.p. First Mo. Corp., Columbia, 1965-68; v.p. ops. MFA-Central Coop., Columbia, 1967-68; v.p., gen. counsel, sec. Peabody Coal Co. St. Louis, 1968-82; gen. counsel Peabody Holding Co., Inc., St. Louis, 1983-85; also dir., sec. subs. and affiliates Peabody Coal Co.; ptnr. Gallop, Johnson & Neuman, St. Louis, 1986—, chmn. corp. dept., 1988-90, chmn. energy dept., 1990—; city atty. Warson Woods, Mo., 1990—; speaker at legal insts. Assoc. editor Mich. Law Rev., 1953-54; contbr. articles to profl. jours. Pres. Warson Woods PTA, 1974-75; trustee Met. Sewer Dist. St. Louis, 1974-80, chmn. 1978-80; mem. Mo. Energy Coun., 1973-77, Mo. Environ. Improvement and Energy Resources Athority, 1983-87, vice chmn. 1986-87; trustee Eastern Mineral Law Found., 1983—; pres. Alumni Assn. Westminster Coll., Fulton, Mo., 1978-80, trustee coll., 1977—, exec. com., 1978—, chmn. 1986-90; chmn. Churchill Meml. and Libr., Fulton, 1992—; mem. Chancellor's Coun. Adv. Bd. U. of Mo., St. Louis, 1992—; mem. lawyers adv. coun. Gt. Plains Legal Found., Kansas City, Mo., 1976-84; mem. Rep. Com. Boone County, Mo., 1962-68, chmn. legis. dist. com., 1962-64, 66-68; alt. del. Rep. Nat. Conv., 1968; pres. Clayton Twp. Rep. Club, 1973-77; sr. warden Episc. Ch., 1988-89. Served to capt. USAF, 1955-57. Recipient alumni award of merit, 1972; Churchill fellow, 1990; named Coal Lawyer Yr. Nat. Coal Assn., 1994. Mem. ABA, Mo. Bar Assn., Bar Assn. Met. St. Louis, Barristers Soc., Round Table Club of St. Louis, John Marshall Rep. Lawyers Club (pres. 1977), Mo. Athletic Club, Rotary (bd. dirs. St. Louis club 1993-95), Masons, Order of Coif. Home: 555 Flanders Dr Saint Louis MO 63122-1617 Office: Gallop Johnson & Neuman LC Ste 1600 101 S Hanley Rd Saint Louis MO 63105-3489

YOUNG, MARY ELIZABETH, history educator; b. Utica, N.Y., Dec. 16, 1929; d. Clarence Whitford and Mary Tippit Y. B.A., Oberlin Coll., 1950; Ph.D. (Robert Shalkenbach Found. grantee, Ezra Cornell fellow), Cornell U., 1955. Instr. dept. history Ohio State U., Columbus, 1955-58; asst. prof. Ohio State U., 1958-63, assoc. prof., 1963-69, prof., 1969-73; prof. history U. Rochester, N.Y., 1973—; cons. in field. Author: Redskins, Ruffleshirts, and Rednecks: Indian Allotments in Alabama and Mississippi, 1830-1860, 1961; co-editor, contbr.: The Frontier in America! Development: Essays in Honor of Paul Wallace Gates, 1969. Recipient Pelzer award Miss. Valley Hist. Assn., 1955, Award Am. Studies Assn., 1982, Ray A. Billington award, 1982; Social Sci. Research Council grantee, 1968-69. Mem. Am. Hist. Assn., Orgn. Am. Historians, Am. Studies Assn., Soc. Ethnic History, Soc. for Historians of the Early Am. Republic, Am. Antiquarian Soc. Home: 2230 Clover St Rochester NY 14618-4124 Office: U Rochester Dept History Rochester NY 14627

YOUNG, MATT NORVEL, JR., university chancellor emeritus; b. Nashville, Oct. 5, 1915; s. Matt Norvel and Ruby (Morrow) Y.; m. Helen Mattox, Aug. 31, 1939; children: Emily Lemley, Matt Norvel III, Marilyn Stewart, Sara Jackson. B.A., Abilene Christian U., 1936; M.A., Vanderbilt U., 1937; Ph.D., George Peabody Coll., Vanderbilt U., 1943; L.H.D., Calif. Coll. Medicine, 1964; LL.D., Lubbock Christian U., 1982, Pepperdine U., 1987. Minister College Ch. of Christ, David Lipscomb Coll., 1941-43, Broadway Ch. Christ, Lubbock, Tex., 1944-57; pres. Pepperdine U., Los Angeles, 1957-71; chancellor Pepperdine U., 1971-84, chancellor emeritus, 1985—, also regent.; chmn. bd. 20th Century Christian Pub. Co., Nashville, also dir.; dir. Imperial Bank, Los Angeles; co-founder Lubbock Christian U., 1957, Lubbock Children's Home, 1953, Tex. Tech U. Bible chair, 1950. Author: History of Christian Colleges, 1949, The Church is Building, 1956; co-founder: 21st Century Christian mag., 1938, editor, pub., 1945-76; editor Power for Today, 1955-70, Preachers of Today, Vol. I, 1952, Vol. II, 1959, Vol. III, 1964, Vol. IV, 1970, Vol. V, 1982, Churches of Today, Vol. I, 1960, Vol. II, 1969, Stress is a Killer, 1978. Bd. govs. L.A. County Mus. Natural History, 1960—, trustee, 1970—; bd. dirs. Nat. Coun. on Alcoholism, 1981-83, Calif. M-2 Prisoner Rehab. Assn., 1986-90, Forest Lawn Meml. Parks, Christian Higher Edn. Found.; vice chmn. bd. Union Rescue Mission. Recipient George Washington medal Freedom Found., 1962, 64. Mem. Los Angeles Area C. of C. (dir.), Phi Delta Kappa. Clubs: Bohemian, California. Lodge: Rotary. Home: 24420 Tiner Ct Malibu CA 90265-4705 Office: Pepperdine U Malibu CA 90265

YOUNG, MAURICE ISAAC, mechanical and aerospace engineering educator; b. Boston, Feb. 10, 1927; s. Joseph J. and Alice (Lifshitz) Y.; m. Eleanor Cooper, Sept. 25, 1954; children: Rochelle, Gerald, Rosalind. Student, Worcester Poly. Inst., 1944-45; Ph.B., U. Chgo., 1949, B.S., 1949; M.A., Boston U., 1950; Ph.D., U. Pa., 1960. Sr. dynamics engr. Bell Aircraft Corp., Buffalo, 1951-52; Sr. dynamics engr. Bell Aircraft Corp., Ft. Worth, 1952-53; group engr. Jacobs Aircraft Engine Co., Pottstown, Pa., 1953-54; prin. tech. engr. Piasecki Helicopter and Aircraft Corp., Morton, Pa., 1954-56, Phila., 1956-58; sr. engring. specialist communications and weapons div. Philco Corp., Phila., 1958-61; mgr. applied mechanics Philco Corp., 1958-61; mgr. helicopter research and advanced tech. Vertol Div. Boeing Co., Phila., 1961-68; prof. mech. and aerospace engring. U. Del., 1968-88, prof. emeritus, 1988; mem. internat. organizing com. for modeling and simulation Internat. Assn. Sci. and Tech. for Devel., 1982; cons. Vigyan Rsch. Assocs., Hampton, Va., 1988-90; also cons. in field; NASA-Am. Soc. Engring. Edn. faculty fellow, NASA Langley Rsch. Ctr., 1987. Mem. editorial bd. Powered Lift Aircraft, 1975-83. Served with USAAF, 1946-47. DuPont Faculty fellow, 1969-70; U.S. Army grantee, 1971-74. Fellow AIAA (assoc.); mem. Soc. Engring. Sci., Sigma Xi. Home: 852 Brompton Ct Newport News VA 23602-9344

YOUNG, MERWIN CRAWFORD, political science educator; b. Phila., Nov. 7, 1931; s. Ralph Aubrey and Louise (Merwin) Y.; m. Rebecca Conrad, Aug. 17, 1957; children: Eva Colcord, Louise Conrad, Estelle Merwin, Emily Harriet. BA, U. Mich., 1953; postgrad., Inst. Hist. Rsch. U. London, 1955-56, Inst d'Etudes Politiques, U. Paris, 1956-57; Ph.D., Harvard U., 1964. Asst. prof. polit. sci. U. Wis., Madison, 1963-66, assoc. prof., 1966-69, prof., 1969—, Rupert Emerson prof., 1983; H. Edwin Young prof., 1994; chmn. African Studies Program U. Wis., Madison, 1964-68, chmn. dept. polit. sci., 1969-72, 84-87, assoc. dean Grad. Sch., 1968-71, acting dean Coll. Letters and Sci., 1992-93; vis. prof. Makerere U. Coll., Kampala, Uganda, 1965-66; dean Faculty of Social Sci. Nat. U., Lubumbashi, Zaire, 1973-75; Fulbright prof. U. Dakar, Senegal, 1987-88. Author: Politics in the Congo, 1965, The Politics of Cultural Pluralism, 1976 (Herskovits prize 1977, Ralph Bunche prize 1979, Ideology and Development in Africa, 1982, The African Colonial State in Comparative Perspective, 1994; co-author: Cooperatives and Development, 1981, The Rise and Decline of the Zairian State, 1985; editor: The Rising Tide of Cultural Pluralism: The Nation-State at Bay?. Served to 1st lt. U.S. Army, 1953-55. Social Sci. Rsch. fellow, 1967-68; Ford Faculty fellow, 1967-68; Guggenheim fellow, 1972-73; vis. fellow Inst. for Advanced Study, Princeton, 1980-81; fellow Woodrow Wilson Internat. Ctr. for Scholars, 1983-84; recipient Disting. Africanist award, 1990. Mem. Am. Polit. Sci. Assn., African Studies Assn. (pres. 1982-83, Disting. Africanist award 1990). Home: 639 Crandall St Madison WI 53711-1836 Office: U Wis Dept Polit Sci North Hall 1050 Bascom Mall Madison WI 53706-1389

YOUNG, MICHAEL KENT, lawyer, educator; b. Sacramento, Nov. 4, 1949; s. Vance Lynn and Ethelyn M. (Sowards) Y.; m. Suzan Kay Stewart, June 1, 1972; children: Stewart, Kathryn, Andrew. BA summa cum laude, Brigham Young U., 1973; JD magna cum laude, Harvard U., 1976. Bar: Calif. 1976, N.Y. 1985. Law clk. to Judge Benjamin Kaplan, Supreme Jud. Ct. Mass., Boston, 1976-77; law clk. to Justice William H. Rehnquist, U.S. Supreme Ct., Washington, 1977-78; from assoc. prof. law to Fuyo Prof. of

Japanese law Columbia U., N.Y.C., 1978—, dir. Ctr. for Japanese Legal Studies, 1985—, dir. Program Internat. Human Rights and Religious Liberties, 1995—; dep. legal advisor U.S. Dept. State, Washington, 1989-91, dep. under sec. for econ. affairs, 1991-93, amb. for trade and environ. affairs, 1992-93; vis. scholar, mem. law faculty U. Tokyo, 1978-80, 83; vis. prof. Waseda U., 1989; chmn. bd. advisors Japan Soc. Fellow Japan Found., 1979-80; Fulbright fellow, 1983-84. Mem. Coun. of Fgn. Rels. Mem. LDS Ch. Avocations: skiing, photography.

YOUNG, MICHAEL WARREN, geneticist, educator; b. Miami, Fla., Mar. 28, 1949; s. Lloyd George and Mildred (Tillery) Y.; m. Laurel Ann Eckhardt, Dec. 27, 1978; children: Natalie, Arissa. BA, U. Tex., 1971, PhD, 1975. NIH postdoctoral fellow Med. Sch., Stanford (Calif.) U., 1975-77; asst. prof. genetics The Rockefeller U., N.Y.C., 1978-83, assoc. prof., 1984-88, prof., 1988—; investigator Howard Hughes Med. Inst., N.Y.C., 1987—; mem. adv. panel on genetic biology NSF, Washington, 1983-87; spl. advisor Am. Cancer Soc., N.Y.C., 1985—; spl. reviewer genetics study sect. NIH, Bethesda, Md., 1990—, mem. cell biology study sect., 1993—. Contbr. articles to profl. jours. Meyer Found. fellow, N.Y.C., 1978-83. Fellow N.Y. Soc. Fellows; mem. AAAS, Genetics Soc. Am., Am. Soc. Microbiologists, N.Y. Acad. Scis., Harvey Soc. Achievements include research on transposable DNA elements, molecular genetics of nerve and muscle development, biological clocks. Home: PO Box 37 Saddle River NJ 07458-0037 Office: The Rockefeller Univ 1230 York Ave New York NY 10021-6341

YOUNG, MILTON EARL, retired petroleum production company executive; b. San Angelo, Tex., Dec. 3, 1929; s. Edward Earl and Annie Mae (North) Y.; m. Clara Louise Sens, June 1, 1957; children—Vanessa, Bradley. A.A., San Angelo Coll., 1950; B.S. in Petroleum Engring, U. Tex., 1953. Various positions Continental Oil Co., 1953-73; v.p. for prodn., drilling, engring. Tesoro Petroleum Corp., San Antonio, 1973-74, sr. v.p., 1974-85, group v.p. exploration and prodn., 1985-86, retired, 1986. Served with USNR, 1948-49. Mem. Soc. Petroleum Engrs. Republican. Lutheran. Home: 1802 Frazar Rd Sealy TX 77474

YOUNG, MORRIS, electrical engineering consultant; b. Alexandria, Egypt, Aug. 28, 1937; came to U.S., 1949; s. Nessim and Anna Yahia; m. Susan Slater, Dec. 22, 1962; children: Bruce Leonard, Amy Ellen. Student, CUNY, 1953-58, 63-67. Assoc. and chief elec. engr. I.M. Robbins, P.C., 1973-94; v.p. Joseph R. Loring & Assocs., N.Y.C., 1994; sr. elec. engr. Lilker Assocs., N.Y.C., 1994—. Trustee bd. edn. Wantagh Schs., dist. liaison to B.O.C.E.S., chmn. subcom. citizen's adv. com. for capital improvement project, budget adv. com., guest lectr. in indsl. arts dept.; appointee Nassau County Exec. Francis Purcell's Task Force; officer L.I. Planning Coun.; coach, mgr., Am. league pres. Wantagh Little League; chmn. cub pack 185 Boy Scouts Am.; v.p. Wantagh/Seaford Homeowners Assn.; mem. L.I. R.R. Commuter's Coun.; vol. Friends in Svc. to Humanity. Mem. Nat. Soc. Archtl. Engrs., Wantagh Rep. Club, Am. Legion, Jewish War Vets. of the U.S. Home: 3452 Beltagh Ave Wantagh NY 11793 Office: Lilker Assocs 15 West 36th St New York NY 10018

YOUNG, NANCY, lawyer; b. Washington, Dec. 3, 1954; d. John Young and Byounghye Chang; m. Paul Brendan Ford, Jr., May 28, 1983; children: Paul Brendan III, Ian A., Hunter Chang Young, Jade Augustine Young. BA, Yale U., 1975, MA, 1976; JD, Columbia U., 1979. Bar: N.Y. 1981. Assoc. Simpson Thacher & Bartlett, N.Y.C., 1979-82, Richards O'Neil & Allegaert, N.Y.C., 1982-86; ptnr., chair internat. practice group Richards & O'Neil, N.Y.C., 1986—; lectr. Am. corp. and securities law Tokyo U. Faculty of Law, 1992. Contbr. articles to legal pubs. Named Internat. Woman of Yr., 1992-93. Mem. ABA (co-chmn. conf. minority ptnrs. in corp. majority law firms 1992), Asian-Am. Bar Assn., Assn. Bar City of N.Y. (com. on Asian affairs, com. on fgn. comparative law), Internat. Bar Assn., Am. Fgn. Law Assn., Coun. on Fgn. Rels., Yale U. Alumni Assn. (bd. govs. 1989-92), Columbia U. Law Sch. Assn. (bd. dirs. 1991-92), Columbia U. Alumni Assn. (bd. dirs. 1991-92), Yale Club Japan (bd. dirs. 1991-92), Internat. Lawyers Club. Home: One East End Ave New York NY 10021 Office: Richards & O'Neil 885 3rd Ave New York NY 10022-4802

YOUNG, NANCY HENRIETTA MOE, elementary education educator; b. Athens, Ohio, June 25, 1936; d. Charles N. Moe and Mary E. (Sams) Moe-Oyler; m. Henry O. Young, May 13, 1956; children: Pamela Sue Young Paustenbach, Patrick H. BA in Elem. Edn., Ohio U., 1973, degree in elem. edn., 1983. Tchr. 3rd grade Berne Union Sch., Sugar Grove, Ohio, 1968-86, tchr. 4th grade, 1987-94, head dept., 1992-94, tchr. 8th grade English, social studies, reading, 1994-95. Jennings scholar Capital U., 1980-81. Mem. NEA, Ohio Edn. Assn., Berne Union Edn. Assn. Republican. Mem. 1st Ch. of God. Avocations: music, reading, traveling, family. Home: 2410 Blue Valley Rd SE Lancaster OH 43130-9019 Office: Berne Union Middle Sch 506 N Main St Sugar Grove OH 43155-9500

YOUNG, NEIL, musician, songwriter; b. Toronto, Ont., Can., Nov. 12, 1945; m. Pegi Young; children: Ben, Amber; 1 child (with Carrie Snodgrass), Zeke. Formed rock group Buffalo Springfield (with Stephen Stills), with group until 1968; solo performer, also joined group Crosby, Stills & Nash (became Crosby, Stills, Nash & Young), 1969-70, 74-75; as solo artist and with bank Crazy Horse, 1968-69, 70—. Albums include (with Crosby, Stills, Nash & Young) Déja Vu, 1970, Four-Way Street, 1971, So Far, 1974, American Dream, 1988; (solo albums) Neil Young, 1969, After the Goldrush, 1970, Harvest, 1972, Journey Through the Past, 1972, Time Fades Away, 1973, On the Beach, 1974, Zuma, 1975, American Stars 'n' Bars, 1977, Decade, 1977, Comes a Time, 1978, Hawks and Doves, 1980, Reactor, 1981, Trans, 1983, Neil and The Shocking Pink: Everybody's Rocking, 1983, Old Ways, 1985, Landing on Water, 1986, Freedom, 1989, Harvest Moon, 1992, (4 Grammy nominations), Lucky Thirteen, 1993, Unplugged, 1993; (with Crazy Horse) Everybody Knows This is Nowhere, 1969, Tonight's the Night, 1975, Rust Never Sleeps, 1979, Live Rust, 1979, Life, 1987, Ragged Glory, 1990, Weld, 1991, Arc, 1991, Arc Weld, 1991, Sleeps With Angels, 1994; (with Buffalo Springfield) Buffalo Springfield Again, 1967, Last Time Around, 1968, Retrospective, 1969; (with the Bluenotes) This Note's For You, 1988; (with Stills-Young Band) Long May You Run, 1976; composed film soundtrack Journey Through the Past, 1973, Where the Buffalo Roam, 1980, Human Highway, 1982; writer, dir., performer film Rust Never Sleeps. Academy award nominee, Best Original Song, 1993 (for "Philadelphia" from Philadelphia). Office: Geffen Records 9126 W Sunset Blvd West Hollywood CA 90069-3110*

YOUNG, OLIVIA KNOWLES, retired librarian; b. Benton, Ark., Sept. 3, 1922; d. Wesley Taylor and Med Belle (Crawford) Knowles; m. Calvin B. Young, Oct. 6, 1951; 1 child, Brigham Taylor. BA, Tenn. Tech. U., 1942; BS in Libr. Sci., George Peabody Coll. for Tchrs., 1946. Head periodicals and documents dept. Peabody Coll. Library, Nashville, 1946-49; area librarian U.S. Army, Austria, 1949-51; librarian Cairo Pub. Library, Ga., 1955-57, Caney Fork Regional Library, Sparta, Tenn., 1957-58; chief librarian Fort Stewart Ft. Stewart (Ga.) U.S. Army, 1959-63; dir. Watauga Regional Library, Johnson City, Tenn., 1963-70; dir. devel. and extension Tenn. State Library and Archives, Nashville, 1971-82, state librarian and archivist, 1982-85; ret., 1985. Mem. Tenn. Library Assn. (treas. 1970, Honor award 1985), Southeastern Library Assn., ALA, Boone Tree Library Assn. (pres. 1968). Methodist. Club: Altrusa (sec. 1967). Home: PO Box 160444 San Antonio TX 78280-2644

YOUNG, ORAN REED, political scientist, educator; b. Yonkers, N.Y., Mar. 15, 1941; s. John A. and Eleanor (Wiggin) Y.; children: Linda Katrin, Naomi Frankel. AB, Harvard U., 1962; MA, Yale U., 1964, Ph.D, 1965. Mem. staff Hudson Inst., 1962-64; research asso. Harvard, 1965; prof. polit. sci. Princeton, 1966-71; prof. govt. U. Tex., Austin, 1972-76; prof. govt. and politics U. Md., College Park, 1976-82; co-dir. Center for No. Studies, 1980-82, dir., 1983-86, sr. fellow, 1986—; sr. fellow Dickey Endowment; dir. Inst. Arctic Studies, Inst. Internat. Environ. Governance; rsch. prof. govt.; adj. prof. environ. studies Dartmouth Coll., 1987—; mem. polar rsch. bd. NRC, 1989—; U.S. del. Internat. Arctic Sci. Com., 1993—. Author: The Intermediaries: Third Parties in International Crises, 1967, Systems of Political Science, 1968, (with others) Neutralization and World Politics, 1968, The Politics of Force: Bargaining During International Crises, 1968, (with others) Political Leadership and Collective Goods, 1971, Bargaining: Formal Theories of Negotiation, 1975, Resource Management at the International Level,

1977, Compliance and Public Authority, A Theory with Applications to International Politics, 1979, Natural Resources and the State: The Political Economy of Resource Management, 1981, Resource Regimes: Natural Resources and Social Institutions, 1982, International Cooperation: Building Regimes for Natural Resources and the Environment, 1989; co-author: The Age of the Arctic: Hot Conflicts and Cold Realities, 1989; (with others) Global Environmental Changes: Understanding the Human Dimensions, 1992; Arctic Politics: Conflict and Cooperation in the Circumpolar North, 1992; (with others) Polar Politics: Creating International Environment Regimes, 1993, International Governance: Protecting the Environment in a Stateless Society, 1994; sr. editor: World Politics, 1968-76; mem. editorial bd. Internat. Orgn., 1968-76, 90—. Chmn. com. on the human dimensions of global change NRC, 1989-95, mem. com. on global change rsch., 1995—. Mem. Internat. Studies Assn., Am. Soc. Polit. and Legal Philosophy, Public Choice Soc., Am. Polit. Sci. Assn. Club: Cosmos. Home: PO Box 1594 Norwich VT 05055-0663 Office: Dartmouth Coll 6193 Murdough Ctr Hanover NH 03755-3560

YOUNG, PATRICK, editor; b. Ladysmith, Wis., Oct. 19, 1937; s. Rodney and Janice (Wolf) Y.; m. Leah Ruth Figelman, Oct. 8, 1966; 1 child, Justine Rebecca. BA, U. Colo., 1960. Reporter UPI, Washington, 1961-62; journalist USN, 1963-64; staff writer Nat. Observer, Silver Spring, Md., 1965-77; free-lance writer Laurel, Md., 1977-79; mem. sr. staff Pres.'s Commn. on the Accident at Three Mile Island, Washington, 1979; chief sci. and med. writer Newhouse News Svc., Washington, 1980-88; editor Sci. News, Washington, 1988—; sci. writer in residence U. Wis., 1986. Author: Asthma and Allergies, 1980, Drugs and Pregnancy, 1987, Schizophrenia, 1988; co-author: Keeping Young Athletes Healthy, 1991. With USN, 1963-64. Recipient Howard W. Blakeslee award Am. Heart Assn., 1971, Sci. Writing award in physics and astronomy Am. Inst. Physics, 1974, James T. Grady award Am. Chem. Soc., 1977. Mem. Nat. Assn. Sci. Writers, Am. Soc. Mag. Editors, Nat. Press Club. Office: Sci News 1719 N St NW Washington DC 20036

YOUNG, PAUL ANDREW, anatomist; b. St. Louis, Oct. 3, 1926; s. Nicholas A. and Olive A. (Langford) Y.; m. Catherine Ann Hofmeister, May 14, 1949; children—Paul, Robert, David, Ann, Carol, Richard, James, Steven, Kevin, Michael. B.S. St. Louis U., 1947, M.S., 1953; Ph.D., U. Buffalo, 1957. Asst. in anatomy U. Buffalo, 1953, instr. anatomy, 1957; asst. prof. anatomy St. Louis U., 1957, assoc. prof., 1966, prof., 1972—, chmn. dept., 1973—. Author: (with B.D. Bhagat and D.E. Biggerstaff) Fundamentals of Visceral Innervation, 1977, also computer assisted neurological anatomy tutorials; contbr. articles to profl. publs. Recipient Golden Apple award Student AMA, 1974, Teaching award Acad. Sci. St. Louis, 1993. Mem. Am. Assn. Anatomists, Am. Assn. Clin. Anatomists, Soc. Neurosci., Sigma Xi, Alpha Omega Alpha. Office: St Louis U Dept Anatomy & Neurobiology 1402 S Grand Blvd Saint Louis MO 63104-1004

YOUNG, PAUL RAY, medical board executive, physician; b. Fairfield, Nebr., June 27, 1932; s. Earl Edward and Louisa May (Saunders) Y.; m. Irene Marie Gray (div. 1971); children: Michael, Susan, Jean, James; m. Faye Elizabeth Hall, Oct. 28, 1972. BA, U. Nebr., Lincoln, 1953; MD, U. Nebr., Omaha, 1958. Diplomate Am. Bd. Family Practice. Intern Rsch. Hosp., Kansas City, Mo., 1958-59; pvt. practice, Raytown, Mo., 1961-67; dir. continuing med. edn. Rsch. Hosp., Kansas City, Mo., 1967-71; assoc. prof. family practice U. Mo. Coll. Medicine, Columbia, 1971-75; chmn. dept. U. Nebr. Coll. Medicine, 1975-80, U. Tex. Med. Br., Galveston, 1980-88; dep. dir. Am. Bd. Family Practice, Lexington, Ky., 1988-90, exec. dir., 1990—; mem. RRC for Family Practice, Chgo., 1976-87, chmn., 1979-87. Founding editor Family Practice Recert., 1979, Jour. Am. Bd. Family Practice, 1987. Pres. Nicholas J. Piscano Meml. Found., Lexington, 1990—. Capt. M.C., USAF, 1959-61. Fellow Am. Acad. Family Physicians; mem. Soc. Tchrs. Family Practice (bd. dirs. 1970-72), Alpha Omega Alpha. Office: Am Bd Family Practice Inc 2228 Young Dr Lexington KY 40505-4219

YOUNG, PAUL RUEL, computer scientist, administrator; b. St. Marys, Ohio, Mar. 16, 1936; s. William Raymond and Emma Marie (Steva) Y.; children: Lisa Erin, Neal Eric. BS, Antioch Coll., 1959; PhD, MIT, 1963. Tchr. math. Harley Sch., Rochester, N.Y., 1957; asst. prof. Reed Coll., 1963-66; NSF postdoctoral fellow in math. Stanford U., 1965-66; asst. prof. computer sci. and math. Purdue U., Lafayette, Ind., 1966-67, assoc. prof., 1967-72, prof., 1972-83; chmn., prof. computing and info. scis., prof. math. U. N.Mex., 1978-79; chmn., prof. computer sci. U. Wash., 1983-88, prof. computer sci. and engring., 1988—; assoc dean engring. U. Wash., Seattle, 1991-94; asst. dir. computer info. scis. & engrs. NSF, Arlington, Va., 1994—; vis. prof. elec. engring. and computer sci. U. Calif.-Berkeley, 1972-73, 82-83; Brittingham vis. prof. U. Wis., Madison, 1988-89; mem. adv. com. computer scis. NSF, 1977-80, chmn., 1979-80. Author: (with Michael Machtey) An Introduction to the General Theory of Algorithms, 1978. NSF and Woodrow Wilson fellow, MIT, 1959, 63. Fellow IEEE (chmn. tech. com. on math. founds. of computing 1981-83), Assn. Computing Machinery; mem. Computing Rsch. Assn. (chmn. 1989-91). Office: NSF Computer & Info Sci & Egrng 4201 Wilson Blvd Arlington VA 22203

YOUNG, PETER HOLDEN, JR., wholesale food company executive; b. L.A., Jan. 26, 1932; s. Peter Holden and Marian (Hockensmith) Y.; m. LUanna Gregson, Aug. 26, 1953; children: VAlerie, Wendy, Peter, Gregson. Student, Stanford U., 1950; BA, Occidental Coll., 1953. Mgmt. trainee Young's Market Co., L.A., 1953-55, liquor salesman, 1955-57, sales mgr. meat div., 1957, mgr. splty. foods, 1958-85; pres. splty. Young Splty. Foods (now part of Con-Agra), L.A., 1985—; advisor to gen. trade pubs. Mem. Nat. Assn. for Splty. Food Trade (hon. show chmn. 1983, show mgr. Anaheim, Calif. 1984). Republican. Avocations: audio, music, photography.

YOUNG, PETER ROBERT, librarian; b. Washington, Aug. 13, 1944; s. Ju Chin and Jane Kathrine (Lybrand) Y.; m. Mary Sue Townsend, Mar. 25, 1978; children: Kathryn, Timothy; children from previous marriage: Robert, Jonathan. AB Philosophy, Coll. Wooster, Ohio, 1966; grad. George Washington U., 1967; MSLS Libr. Svc., Columbia U., 1968. Adminstrv. libr. Am. U. Libr., Washington, 1968; head cataloger, reference libr. Franklin & Marshall Coll. Libr., Lancaster, Pa., 1971-74; asst. libr. pub. svcs. Rice U. Librs., Houston, Tex., 1974-76; asst. dir. Grand Rapids (Mich.) Pub. Libr., 1978; sales support libr. CL Systems Inc., Newtonville, Mass., 1976-78; libr. systems analyst, 1978-80; customer svcs. officer Cataloging Distbn. Svc. Libr. Congress, Washington, 1980-84, asst. chief Marc edit. divsn., 1984-85, chief Copyright Cataloging divsn., 1985-88; dir. acad. info. svcs. The Faxon Co., Westwood, Mass., 1988-89, dir. Faxon Inst. Advanced Studies Scholarly and Sci. Communication, 1989-90; exec. dir. U.S. Nat. Commn. Librs. and Info. Sci., Washington, 1990—; exec. bd. Fed. Libr. and Info. Ctr. com., 1993—; adv. bd. Highsmith Press, 1991—; co chair libr. stats. standard revision com. Nat. Standards Info. Office, 1988-93; libr. adminstrs. devel. program U. Md.; implementation task force libr. data Nat. Ctr. Edn. Stats. U.S. Office Edn., 1988, adv. coun. edn. stats. Office Edn. Rsch. and Improvement, 1990—; lectr. in field. Edit. bd. Serials Review, 1990—; contbr. articles to profl. jours. With U.S. Army, 1968-70, Vietnam. Mem. ALA (pub. policy for pub. librs. com. 1993—, com. rsch. and stats. 1990—, various coms., assns.), Chinese Am. Libr. Assn. (chair pub. rels. com. 1987-88, pres. 1989-90), Ont. Libr. Assn. (planning com., del. mem.), U.S. Nat. Commn. Librs. and Info. Sci. (stats. task force 1988-89). Office: Natl Commission on Libraries 1110 Vermont Ave Ste 820 Washington DC 20005

YOUNG, PHILIP HOWARD, library director; b. Ithaca, N.Y., Oct. 7, 1953; s. Charles Robert and Betty Irene (Osborne) Y.; m. Nancy Ann Stutsman, Aug. 18, 1979. BA, U. Va., 1975; PhD, U. Pa., 1980; MLS, Ind. U., 1983. Asst. prof. history Appalachian State U., Boone, N.C., 1980-82; reference asst. Lilly Library, Ind. U., Bloomington, 1982-83; adminstr., info. specialist Ind. Corp. for Sci. & Tech., Indpls., 1983-85; dir. Krannert Meml. Library, U. Indpls., 1985—. Mem. Am. Library Assn., Ind. Libr. Fed. Archaeological Inst. Am., Phi Beta Kappa, Phi Alpha Theta, Beta Phi Mu. Democrat. Methodist. Home: 1944 Patton Dr Speedway IN 46224-5355 Office: U Indpls Krannert Meml Libr 1400 E Hanna Ave Indianapolis IN 46227-3697

YOUNG, PHYLLIS CASSELMAN, music educator; b. Milan, Kans., Oct. 20, 1925; d. Phillip James and Velma (Stewart) Casselman; m. James M. Young, July 14, 1945 (dec. Sept. 1991). MusB with high honors, U. Tex.,

1949, MusM, 1950. Tchr. string instruments Kansas City (Kans.) Pub. Schs., 1951-52; prof. cello and string pedagogy U. Tex., Austin, 1953—; dir. U. Tex. String Project, Austin, 1958-93; Parker C. Fielder Regents prof. music U. Tex., Austin, 1991—; presenter numerous workshops and master classes, 1976—. Author: Playing the String Game, 1978, The String Play, 1986; also articles. Mem. Am. String Tchrs. Assn. (state pres. 1972-74, nat. pres. 1978-80, Nat. citation 1974, 82, Disting. Svc. award 1984), European String Tchrs. Assn., Music Educators Nat. Conf., Suzuki Assn. Ams., Tex. Music Educators Assn. Home: 7304 W Rim Dr Austin TX 78731 Office: Sch Music Univ Tex Austin TX 78712

YOUNG, RALPH ALDEN, soil scientist, educator; b. Arickaree, Colo., July 14, 1920; s. Edmond Birdsall and Lottie Opal (Payne) Y.; m. Helen Augusta Claudon, Aug. 28, 1942; children—Gregg, Gayle. B.S., Colo. State U., 1942; M.S., Kans. State U., 1947; Ph.D., Cornell U., 1953. Instr. soils Kans. State U., 1947-48; asst. prof. soils N.D. State U., 1948-50, 53-55, assoc. prof., 1955-59, prof., 1959-62; vis. soil chemist U. Calif. at Davis, 1962-63; prof. soil sci., chmn. div. plant, soil and water sci. U. Nev., Reno, 1963-75; assoc. dir. Nev. Agrl. Expt. Sta., 1975-82; prof. soil sci. U. Nev., 1982-84, prof. emeritus, 1985—. Contbr. articles to profl. jours. Served to capt. AUS, 1943-46. Fellow AAAS; mem. Soil Conservation Soc. Am. (pres. chpt. 1968), Am. Soc. Agronomy, Soil Sci. Soc. Am., Western Soil Sci. Soc. (pres. 1972-73), Sigma Xi, Alpha Zeta, Gamma Sigma Delta, Phi Kappa Phi. Home: 2229 Stagecoach Rd Grand Junction CO 81503-2614

YOUNG, RAYMOND HENRY, lawyer; b. Boston, Sept. 28, 1927; s. Raymond H. and Clara Elms (Oakman) Y.; m. Louisa Breda, Sept. 1, 1951; children: Christopher, Pamela, Amy. AB, Yale U., 1947, LLB, 1950. Bar: Mass. 1951. Assoc. Warner, Stackpole, Stetson & Bradlee, Boston, 1950-52; pvt. practice Boston, 1952-64; ptnr. Young & Bayle, Boston, 1964—. Mem. ABA (past sec. sect. real property, probate and trust law, mem. commn. legal problems of the elderly), Am. Coll. Trust and Estate Counsel (mem. joint editorial bd. for uniform probate code), Am. Law Inst. (advisor for restatement property 3d donative transfers), Nat. Commn. on Nat. Probate Ct. Standards, Internat. Acad. Trust and Estate Law (pres.), Mass. Bar Assn., Boston Bar Assn. (past pres.), Boston Estate Planning Coun. (past pres., Estate Planner of Yr. award 1991), Boston Probate and Estate Planning Forum. Home: 122 Garfield St Watertown MA 02172-4916 Office: Young & Bayle 150 Federal St Boston MA 02110

YOUNG, REBECCA MARY CONRAD, state legislator; b. Clairton, Pa., Feb. 28, 1934; d. Walter Emerson and Harriet Averill (Colcord) Conrad; m. Merwin Crawford Young, Aug. 17, 1957; children: Eve, Louise, Estelle, Emily. BA, U. Mich., 1955; MA in Teaching, Harvard U., 1963; JD, U. Wis., 1983. Bar: Wis. 1983. Commr. State Hwy. Commn., Madison, Wis., 1974-76; dep. sec. Wis. Dept. of Adminstrn., Madison, 1976-77; assoc. Wadsack, Julian & Lawton, Madison, 1983-84; elected rep. Wis. State Assembly, Madison, 1985—. Translator: Katanga Secession, 1966. Supr. Dane County Bd., Madison, 1970-74; mem. Madison Sch. Bd., 1979-85. Recipient Pub. Interest award Ctr. for Pub. Representation, 1980, Woman of Distinction award YWCA, 1981, Clean 16 Environ. award WI Environ. Decade, Inc., 1985-94, Outstanding Contbns. in Supporting Women Nat. Women's Polit. Caucus Wis., 1985, Exemplary Work award Congress for Working Am., 1986, Wis. Pro-Choice Community award, 1987, Community Bldg. award Wis. Coalition for Advocacy, 1988, Legis. Leadership award Maternal & Child Health Coalition, 1988, 89, WISCAP Gaylord Nelson Human Svc. award, 1989, Outstanding Contbn. in Supporting Women's Right to Choice, Nat. Women's Polit. Caucus Wis., 1989, Support Network award Transitional Employment Program, 1989, Outstanding Community Svc. Recognition, Rainbow Project Child and Family Mental Health Clinic, 1989, NAACP award, 1990, Planned Parenthood of Wis., Inc. award, 1990, Wis. Alliance of Cities Cert. of Merit., 1990, Key to the City of Madison, 1990, Dane County Alliance for the Mentally Ill Disting. Svc. award, 1991, Wis. Dept. of Health and Social Svcs. Head Start Bar. cert., 1991, Legis. of Yr. award Fair Housing of Dane County, 1991, Best of Madison Legis. award Madison Mag. 1991, Met. Milw. Fair Housing Coun. honor, 1991, Bus. Forum Dane County Ann. award, 1992, Stateswoman of Yr. award Wis. Women's Network, 1992, Partnership award Wis. Coun. Community Corrections, 1993, Recovery Options for Mothers and Children award 1993, Legislator of the Yr. award Wis. Child Support Enforcement Assn., 1993, Golden Triangle award Wis. Farmers Union, 1993-94, Family Svc. Picada, Madison Met. Sch. Dist., Fast Parents commendation, 1994, Merit cert. Wis. Alliance of Cities, 1994. Mem. ABA. Democrat. Avocations: board games, hiking. Home: 639 Crandall St Madison WI 53711-1836 Office: State Legislature-Assembly PO Box 8953 Madison WI 53708-8953

YOUNG, RICHARD, religious organization executive. General secretary suffragan Pentecostal Assemblies of the World, Indpls. Office: Pentecostal Assemblies of the World 3939 Meadows Dr Indianapolis IN 46205-3100

YOUNG, RICHARD ALAN, publishing company executive; b. Oak Park, Ill., Mar. 17, 1935; m. Carol Ann Schellinger, June 28, 1958; children: Steven, Karen, Christopher. Student, Colo. Sch. Mines, 1954-56; B.A., U. Iowa, 1958. Registered profl. engr.; registered environ. assessor; cert. environ. auditor. Chief engr. Cardox Corp., Chgo., 1958-61; asst. chief engr. Goodman Mfg. Co., Chgo., 1961-63; plant and environ. engr. Signode Corp., Glenview, Ill., 1963-68; editor Pollution Engring. Tech. Pub. Co., Barrington, Ill., 1968-81; exec. dir. Nat. Registry of Environ. Profls., 1988—; pub. Cahners Pub. Co., Des Plaines, Ill., 1990-95, Stevens Pub. Co., Waco, Tex., 1995—; prof. Nat. Ctr. for Environmental Communication, 1994—; adj. prof. George Williams Coll.; mcpl. pollution control adviser and enforcement officer for 24 cities and state govts.; ofcl. rep. and pollution control expert U.S. Govt. at meeting with Socialist countries in Bulgaria. Editor 26 books on environ. engring.; pollution engring.; series editor, Marcel Dekker Inc., N.Y.C; Contbr. articles to profl. jours. Recipient Jesse H. Neal certificate for outstanding editorial writing Am. Bus. Press, Inc., 1971, Outstanding Service award Western Soc. Engrs., Charles Ellet award as Most Outstanding Engr. of Yr. 1970; Environ. Quality award EPA, 1976. Mem. Internat. Assn. for Pollution Control (dir.), Assn. Local Air Pollution Control Ofcls., Am. Soc. Bus. Press Editors (Editl. Excellence award 1980, Design Excellence award 1982), Am. Inst. Plant Engrs. (past nat. chmn. environ. quality), Internat. Congress Environ. Profls. (mng. dir.), Nat. Inst. Hazardous Materials Mgmts. (dir. 1984-88, cert. hazardous materials mgr.). Soc. Environ. Mgmt. (nat. dir.). Patentee in field. Office: 1253 Roosevelt Ave Glenview IL 60025-2831

YOUNG, RICHARD STUART, technical services executive; b. Southampton, N.Y., Mar. 6, 1927; s. P. Stuart and Myrtle F. (Terrell) Y.; m. Nancy J. Mayer, June 7, 1955; children: Dee Ann, Sandra, Mark. A.B. Gettysburg Coll., 1948, Sc.D., 1966; postgrad., U. N.C., 1951-53; Ph.D., Fla. State U., 1955. With FDA, Washington, 1956-58; with NASA, Army Ballistic Missile Agency, Huntsville, Ala., 1958-59, NASA-Ames Research Center, Moffett Field, Calif., 1960-67; chief exobiology program-hdqrs., chief program scientist Viking NASA, Washington, 1969-77; chief of bioscis. div. NASA Hdqrs., 1975-79; v.p. Rockefeller U., N.Y.C., 1979-82; exec. dir. Am. Soc. Cell Biology, Bethesda, Md., 1982-85; mgr. Mgmt. and Tech. Svcs. Co., Washington, 1985—; sr. scientist Kennedy Space Ctr., Fla., 1987—. Contbr. articles to profl. jours., also books. Served with USN, 1944-46. Mem. Internat. Soc. for Study Origin of Life (sec. 1970-77, v.p. 1977-82). Home: 661 Adams Ave Cape Canaveral FL 32920-2165 Office: MD RES Kennedy Space Center FL 32920

YOUNG, RICHARD WILLIAM, corporate director; b. Ridgewood, N.Y., Oct. 17, 1926; s. Charles Michael and Louise Margaret (Baust) Y.; m. Sheila deLisser, Sept. 11, 1949; children: Christine, Noreen, Brian, Eileen. A.B., Dartmouth Coll., 1946, A.M., 1947; Ph.D., Columbia U., 1950. Sr. rsch. chemist Chemotherapy div. Am. Cyanamid Co., Conn., 1950-56, group leader pesticide chems. Agrl. div., 1956-58, dir. chem. Agrl. div., 1958-60, dir. chem. rsch. cen., rsch. div., 1960-62; asst. dir. rsch. Polaroid Corp., Cambridge, Mass., 1962-69, v.p. rsch. 1963-69, sr. v.p. rsch. and devel., 1969-72, sr. v.p. pres. Internat. div., 1972-80, exec. v.p. dir. worldwide mktg., 1980-82; pres. Houghton Mifflin Co., Boston, 1982-85; chmn., CEO Mentor O & O, Inc., Norwell, Mass., 1985-92; bd. dirs. Bay State Milling Corp., Quincy, Mass., Instron Corp., Canton, Mass., Oceantrawl Inc., Seattle, Mentor Corp., Santa Barbara, Calif. Patentee in field. Chmn. bd. trustees Regis Coll., Weston, Mass., Mass. Eye and Ear Infirmary, Boston, Trinitas Found.,

Quincy; mem. corp. Northeastern U., Boston. Mem. Am. Chem. Soc. Home: 100 Royalston Rd Wellesley MA 02181-1244 Office: Trinitas Found 100 Congress St Quincy MA 02169

YOUNG, ROBERT (GEORGE YOUNG), actor; b. Chgo., Feb. 22, 1907; m. Elizabeth Louise Henderson, 1933; children: Carol Anne, Barbara Queen, Elizabeth Louise, Kathleen Joy. Grad. high sch. pres. Cavalier Prodns., 1947—. Studied and acted with Pasadena Community Playhouse, 4 years; toured in stock, 1931; actor in motion pictures, 1931—; pictures include It's Love Again, Eng.; Secret Agent, Eng., The Bride Wore Red, Northwest Passage, Western Union, The Trial of Mary Dugan, H.M. Pulham, Esq., Western Union; radio broadcasts, 1936—; co-star pictures including Mr. and Mrs. North, 1942, And Baby Makes Three, 1949, Bride for Sale, 1949, That Forsythe Woman, 1949, Goodbye My Fancy, 1951, Secret of the Incas, 1954; regular on series Father Knows Best, 1954-62; TV program Window on Main Street, 1961-62; TV series Marcus Welby, M.D. 1969-76; appeared in TV films Vanished, 1971, All My Darling Daughters, 1972, My Darling Daughters' Anniversary, 1973, The Father Knows Best Reunion, 1977, Mercy or Murder?, 1987, Conspiracy of Love, Little Women, Marcus Welby M.D.-A Holiday Affair. Recipient Emmy award, 1956, 1957. Address: care Herb Tobias & Assocs Inc 1901 Avenue of the Stars Ste 840 Los Angeles CA 90067*

YOUNG, ROBERT A., III, freight systems executive; b. Ft. Smith, Ark., Sept. 23, 1940; s. Robert A. and Vivian (Curtis) Y.; m. Mary Carleton McRae; children—Tracy, Christy, Robert A. IV, Stephen. BA in Econs., Washington and Lee U., 1963. Supr. terminal ops. Ark. Best Freight, Ft. Smith, 1964-65; pres. Data-Tronics Inc, Ft. Smith, 1965-67; sr. v.p. Nat. Bank of Commerce, Dallas, 1967-70; v.p. fin. Ark. Best Freight Systems, Inc., 1970-73, exec. v.p., 1973, pres., chief operating officer, 1973-88, chief exec. officer, 1988—; pres. ABF Freight Systems, Inc., Ft. Smith, 1979—; bd. dirs. First Nat. Bank, Ft. Smith, Mosler Corp., Hamilton, Ohio. Pres. United Way, Ft. Smith, 1981; vice chmn. bd. dirs. Sparks Regional Med. Ctr., Ft. Smith, 1985; chmn. bd. trustees Ark. Coll.; bd. dirs. ATA Found., Inc., Ft. Smith Boys Club. Served with USAF, 1963. Recipient Silver Beaver award Boy Scouts Am. Mem. Am. Trucking Assn. (vice chmn.), Ark. State C. of C. (pres., bd. dirs.), Phi Delta Theta. Presbyterian. Home: PO Box 48 Fort Smith AR 72902-0048 Office: ABF Freight Systems Inc 301 S 11th St Fort Smith AR 72901-3721 also: Ark Best Corp 1000 S 21st St Fort Smith AR 72901-4098*

YOUNG, ROBERT ANTHONY, association director; b. Syracuse, N.Y., May 21, 1943; s. Frank A. and Grace (Farnett) Y. BS, Le Moyne Coll., 1965; MS, Long Beach State Coll., 1966. Exec. dir. Cystic Fibrosis Found., Syracuse, 1974-75; dir. pub. rels. & programs Am. Heart Assn., New Orleans, 1975-76; dir. programs La. State Bar Assn., New Orleans, 1976-84; exec. dir. Am. Coll. Trial Lawyers, Irvine, Calif., 1984—. With USAF, 1966-67. Mem. Am. Soc. Assn. Execs., Nat. Assn. Bar Execs. (leadership award 1986, chmn's. award pub. rels. sect. 1984). Avocations: travel, golf, tennis. Office: Am Coll of Trial Lawyers 8001 Irvine Center Dr Ste 960 Irvine CA 92718-2921

YOUNG, ROBERT B., JR., engineering company executive. Pres. Lockheed Engring. & Sci. Co., Houston. Recipient Leadership in Quality Mgmt. award AIAA, 1992. Office: Lockheed Engineering & Science Comp PO Box 58561 Houston TX 77258*

YOUNG, ROBERT CRABILL, medical researcher, science facility administrator, internist; b. Columbus, Ohio, 1940. MD, Cornell U., 1965. Diplomate Am. Bd. Internal Medicine. Intern N.Y. Hosp., N.Y.C., 1965-66, resident, 1966-67; sr. researcher Yale-New Haven Med. Ctr., 1969-70; sr. investigator, attending physician med. br. Nat. Cancer Inst., Bethesda, Md., from 1971, chief med. br., 1974-88; pres. Fox Chase Cancer Ctr., Phila., 1988—; clin. prof. medicine Georgetown U., from 1974, assoc. prof., 1976-84; clin. prof. medicine George Washington U., 1984—. Sr. surgeon USPHS, 1967-69. Fellow ACP; mem. Am. Soc. Hematology, Am. Assn. Cancer Rsch., Am. Soc. Clin. Oncology. Office: Fox Chase Cancer Ctr 7701 Burholme Ave Philadelphia PA 19111-2497

YOUNG, ROBERT DONALD, physicist, educator; b. Chgo., Apr. 20, 1940; s. Robert Joseph and Nellie (Krik) Y.; children: Robert Gerald, Jennifer Ann Young Rolinski; m. BJ Marymont, Feb. 14, 1981; 1 child, Emily Marymont. BS in Physics, Ill. Inst. Technology, 1962; MS in Physics, Purdue U., 1965, PhD in Physics, 1967. Devel. engr. Western Elec., Cicero, Ill., 1962; process engr. Nat. Video Corp., Chgo., 1963; asst. prof. physics Ill. State U., Normal, 1967-73, assoc. prof., 1974-78, prof., 1979—, dir. rsch. Coll. Arts and Scis., 1994—; adj. prof. physics U. Ill., Urbana, 1986—. Contbr. articles to Proceedings Nat. Acad. Sci., Ann. Rev. Biophysics, Phys. Rev. Letters, Chemica Scripta, Jour. Phys. Chemistry, Jour. Chem. Physics, Computers in Physics, Physical Rev., Biophysical Jour. Named Researcher of Yr., Ill. State U., 1989. Mem. Am. Phys. Soc., Am. Chem. Soc., Biophys. Soc., Am. Assn. Physics Tchrs. Achievements include research on glassy properties of proteins, usage of computer techniques in physics education, individualized modular approach in physics education. Home: 4 Turner Rd Normal IL 61761-4218 Office: Ill State U CAS Rsch Office Normal IL 61790-4590

YOUNG, ROBERT FRANCIS, publisher; b. N.Y.C., Dec. 14, 1919; s. Frank and Johanna (Wecklein) Y.; m. Patricia Burrage, Mar. 31, 1950 (div. Oct. 1989); children: Melinda, Julie, Steven, Christopher; m. Judith Ann Guardino, June 1990. B.B.A, City Coll., N.Y., 1941. Salesman Street & Smith Pub. Co., 1947-49, Look mag., 1949-55; account exec. Benten & Bowles, 1955-59, account supr., 1959-63, sr. v.p., mgmt. supr., 1963-68; pub. Family Circle, 1968-84, pres., 1975-84; exec. dir. SCC Council, 1986-88; sr. v.p Ubbermeyer Mace Investment Banking, 1988-90; spl. cons. to pub. Bus. Tokyo, N.Y.C, 1989-90; cons. to under sec. state, the advisor to sec. state for pub. diplomacy, 1984; cons. to Official Guide Edn. '88, Brisbane, Australia, 1986.; bd. dirs. N.Y. Times Media Co., Australian Family Circle, Modern Medicine Australia, Clear Pool Camp, Carmel, N.Y.; sr. v.p. Untermeyer and Mace, Investments Brokers, 1989—. Served to maj. USAAF, 1941-46, CBI. Decorated DFC, Air medal. Club: Gypsy Trail (Carmel, N.Y.). Office: 3 W 51st St New York NY 10019-6909

YOUNG, ROGER AUSTIN, natural gas distribution company executive; b. Boston, Feb. 2, 1946; s. Robert Harris McCarter and Gloria Bond (Tenney) Y.; m. Linda Furste, Sept. 6, 1975; children: Catherine Simms, Geoffrey Furste. B.A., Princeton U., 1968. Systems analyst Orange and Rockland Utilities, Inc. Spring Valley, N.Y., 1968-72; asst. v.p. Bay State Gas Co., Boston, 1972-75, v.p., 1975-80; exec. v.p. Bay State Gas Co., Canton, Mass., 1980-81; pres. Bay State Gas Co., Westborough, Mass., 1981-90, pres., chief exec. officer, 1990—; bd. dirs., mem. exec. com. Inst. Gas Tech.; regional bd. dirs. Baybanks, Inc. Bd. dirs. New Eng. Council. Mem. Am. Gas Assn., New Eng. Gas Assn. (bd. dirs., chmn. 1984-85), Newcomen Soc., Associated Gas Distbrs. Congregationalist. Clubs: The Country (Brookline, Mass.); Colonial (Princeton, N.J.). Home: 125 Mill St PO Box 95 Sherborn MA 01770 Office: Bay State Gas Co 300 Friberg Pky Westborough MA 01581-3920

YOUNG, RONALD FARIS, commodity trader; b. Schenectady, Dec. 17, 1939; s. James Vernon and Dorothy (Girod) Y.; m. Anne Randolph Kendig, Feb. 23, 1963; children: Margaret Randolph Reynolds, Anne Corbin. B.A., U. Va., 1962; M.B.A., Harvard U., 1966. Grain trader Continental Grain Co., 1966-70; pres. Conti-Commodities, Chgo., 1970; v.p. commodity sales DuPont, Glore Forgan, Chgo., 1971-72; self-employed commodity trader Chgo. Bd. Trade, 1972-78; ind. trader Va. Trading Co., 1978-90, pres., 1978-84, dep. chmn., 1984-89; pres. Randolph Ptnrs., Ltd., 1983-91; chmn. bd. Chgo. Bd. Trade, 1978, dir., 1975-77, 80. Bd. dirs. Princeton Fund, 1981-82, Lake Forest Hosp., 1981-84, Lake Forest Country Day Sch. 1981-86. Served with USMCR, 1959-65. Mem. Casino Club, Racquet Club (bd. dirs. 1989—), Onwentsia Club (Lake Forest, Ill. bd. dirs. 1981-90, pres. 1991-93), Everglades Club (Palm Beach, Fla.), Bath and Tennis Club (Palm Beach, Fla.). Republican. Episcopalian. Home: 1448 N Lake Shore Dr Chicago IL 60610-1625 Office: 141 W Jackson Blvd Ste 1520A Chicago IL 60604-2904

YOUNG, ROY ALTON, university administrator, educator; b. McAlister, N.Mex., Mar. 1, 1921; s. John Arthur and Etta Julia (Sprinkle) Y.; m. Marilyn Ruth Sandman, May 22, 1950; children: Janet Elizabeth, Randall Owen. BS, N.Mex. A&M Coll., 1941; MS, Iowa State U., 1942, PhD, 1948; LLD (hon.), N.Mex. State U., 1978. Teaching fellow Iowa State U., 1941-42, instr., 1946-47, Indsl. fellow, 1947-48; asst. prof. Oreg. State U., 1948-50, assoc. prof., 1950-53, prof., 1953—, head dept. botany and plant pathology, 1958-66, dean research, 1966-70, acting pres., 1969-70, v.p. for research and grad. studies, 1970-76, dir. Office for Natural Resources Policy, 1986-90; chancellor U. Nebr., Lincoln, 1976-80; mng. dir., pres. Boyce Thompson Inst. Plant Research, Cornell U., Ithaca, N.Y., 1980-86; mem. Commn. on Undergrad. Edn. in Biol. Scis., 1963-68; Gov.'s Sci. Council, 1987-90; cons. State Expt. Stas. div. USDA; chmn. subcom. plant pathogens, agriculture bd. Nat. Acad. Scis.-NRC, 1965-68; mem. exec. com. study on problems of pest control, 1972-75; mem. exec. com. Nat. Govs.' Council on Sci. and Tech., 1970-74; mem. U.S. com. man and biosphere UNESCO, 1973-82; mem. com. to rev. U.S. component Internat. Biol. Program, NAS, 1974-76; mem. adv. panel on post-doctoral fellowships in environ. sci. Rockefeller Found., 1974-78; bd. dirs. Pacific Power & Light Co., 1974-91, PacifiCorp., 1984-91, Boyce Thompson Inst. for Plant Research, 1975-93, Boyce Thompson Southwestern Arboretum, 1981-92, Oreg. Grad. Inst., 1987—; mem. adv. com. Directorate for Engring. and Applied Sci., NSF, 1977-81; mem. sea grant adv. panel, 1978-80; mem. policy adv. com. Office of Grants, USDA, 1985-86. Trustee Ithaca Coll., 1982-89. Lt. USNR, 1943-46. Recipient Disting. Svc. award Oreg. State U., 1978. Fellow AAAS (exec. com. Pacific div. 1963-67, pres. div. 1971), Am. Phytopathology Soc. (pres. Pacific div. 1957, chmn. spl. com. to develop plans for endowment 1984-86, bd. dirs. 1986-88); mem. Oreg. Acad. Sci., Nat. Assn. State Univs. and Land Grant Colls. (chmn. coun. for rsch. policy and adminstrn. 1970, chmn. standing com. on environment and energy 1974-82, chmn. com. on environment 1984-86), Sigma Xi, Phi Kappa Phi, Phi Sigma, Sigma Alpha Epsilon. Home: 3605 NW Van Buren Ave Corvallis OR 97330-4950

YOUNG, RUSSELL DAWSON, physics consultant; b. Huntington, N.Y., Aug. 17, 1923; s. C. Halsey and Edna (Dawson) Y.; m. Carol Vaughn Jones, Aug. 14, 1954; children: Bessmarie, Gale, Janet, Shari. BS in Physics, Rensselaer Poly. Inst., Troy, N.Y., 1953; PhD in Physics, Pa. State U., 1959. Rsch. assoc. Pa. State U., State College, 1959-61; project leader Nat. Bur. Stds., Gaithersburg, Md., 1961-73, chief optics and micrometrology, 1973-78; chief mech. processing div. Nat. Bur. Stds., Gaithersburg, 1975-80, ind. sys. div. chief, 1980-81, chief mech. prodn. div., 1980-81; pres. R.D. Young Cons., Pasadena, Md., 1981—. Contbr. articles to profl. jours.; inventor in field of instrumentation. 1st lt. Signal Corps, U.S. Army, 1943-46. Recipient Edward V. Condon award Dept. Commerce, 1974, Silver medal 1979, Gaede-Langmuir award 1977, Presdl. citation 1986, Wash. Acad. Scis. award 1988. Fellow Internat. Inst. Prodn. Engring. Rsch., Nat. Inst. Standards and Tech. Avocation: boating. Home: 852 Riverside Dr Pasadena MD 21122-1730

YOUNG, SCOTT ALEXANDER, television journalist, author; b. Man., Can., Apr. 14, 1918; s. Percy Andrew and Jean Ferguson Y.; m. Edna Blow Ragland, June 18, 1940; children: Robert, Neil; m. Astrid Carlson Mead, May 20, 1961; children: Deirdre, Astrid; m. Margaret Burns Hogan, May 9, 1980. Grad. high sch.; LittD honoris causa, Trent U., Can., 1990. Columnist Toronto (Ont., Can.) Globe and Mail, 1957-69, 71-80; sports editor Toronto Telegram, 1969-71; TV writer and personality, 1957—; pres. Ascot Prodns. Ltd. Author: Red Shield in Action, 1949, Scrubs on Skates, 1952, reissue, 1985, Boy on Defense, 1953, reissue, 1985, (novel) The Flood, 1956, HMCS, text for Gilbert Milne's photos, 1960, (with Astrid Young) (biography) O'Brien, 1967, Silent Frank Cochrane, 1973, (with Punch Imlach) Hockey is a Battle, 1969, (with George Robertson), (novel) Face-Off, 1971, Clue of the Dead Duck, 1962, reissue, 1981, Boy at the Leaf's Camp, 1963, reissue, 1985, (with Astrid Young) (novel) Big City Office Junior, 1964, Scott Young Sports Stories, 1965, The Leafs I Knew, 1966, We Won't Be Needing You, Al, and Other Stories, 1968, (with Leo Cahill) Goodbye Argos, 1973, War on Ice, 1976, Canada Cup of Hockey 1976, 1976, (with Margaret Hogan) Best Talk in Town, 1980, (with Conn Smythe) Memoirs of the Late Conn Smythe, 1981, (with Punch Imlach) Heaven and Hell in the NHL, 1982, (novel) That Old Gang of Mine, 1982, Neil and Me, 1984, (biography) Hello Canada, 1985, Gordon Sinclair-A Life and Then Some, 1987, (novel) Murder in a Cold Climate, 1988, Face-Off in Moscow, 1989, 100 Years of Dropping the Puck, 1989, (short stories) Home for Christmas, 1989, The Boys of Saturday Night, 1990, (with alan Eagleston) Power Play, 1991, (novel) The Shaman's Knife, 1993, (autobiography) A Writer's Life, 1995, short stories in several anthologies. Mem. Province Ont. Royal Commn. Violence in Communications Industry, 1975-77. Served with Royal Canadian Navy, World War II. Recipient Can. Nat. Newspaper award, 1959, Wilderness award for TV script, 1963, U.S. Eclipse award, 1971; named to NHL Hall of Fame, 1988, Man. Hockey Hall of Fame, 1992. Address: 1 Middleton Dr, Peterborough, ON Canada K9J 4Z1

YOUNG, SEAN, actress; b. Louisville; m. Robert Lujan; 1 child: Rio Kelly Lujan. Grad., Interlochen Arts Acad., Mich. 1978. Actress: (feature films) Jane Austen in Manhattan, 1980, Stripes, 1981, Blade Runner, 1982, Young Doctors in Love, 1982, Dune, 1984, Baby - Secret of the Lost Legend, 1985, No Way Out, 1987, Wall Street, 1987, The Boost, 1988, Cousins, 1989, Fire Birds, 1990, A Kiss Before Dying, 1991, Once Upon a Crime, 1992, Love Crimes, 1992, Fatal Instinct, 1993, Ace Ventura: Pet Detective, 1994, Even Cowgirls Get the Blues, 1994, Dr. Jekyll and Ms. Hyde, 1995; TV appearances include Under the Biltmore Clock, Tender is the Night, Blood and Orchids, 1986, Blue Ice, 1994, Witness to the Execution, 1994. Office: UTA 9560 Wilshire Blvd 5th Fl Beverly Hills CA 90212*

YOUNG, SHIRLEY, automotive industry executive, strategic marketing consultant; b. Shanghai, China, May 25, 1935; d. Clarence and Juliana (Koo) Y.; divorced; children: David W., William C., Douglas H.L. Hsieh. B.A. in Econs., Wellesley Coll., 1955; postgrad., NYU, 1956-57; Dr. Letters (hon.), Russell Sage Coll., 1982. Research assoc. Alfred Politz Research, N.Y.C., 1955-57; research mgr. Hudson Paper Corp., N.Y.C., 1957-59; research assoc. Grey Advt. Inc., N.Y.C., 1959-69, dir. mktg. and research, 1969-71, exec. v.p. mem. agy. policy coun., 1971-79, exec. v.p. mktg., planning and strategy devel., 1980-83; pres. Grey Strategic Mktg. Inc., N.Y.C., 1983-88, chmn., 1988-90; v.p. consumer market devel. Gen. Motors, Detroit, 1988—; mem. bus. adv. coun. U.S. State Dept. Aid; bd. dirs. Promus Corp., Bell Atlantic, Phila.; vice chmn. nominating com. N.Y. Stock Exch., 1980-81; cons., bd. dirs. dayton Hudson Corp., 1987—. Chmn. Com. 100, Chinese Am. Leadership Resource; bd. dirs. United Way of Tri-State, N.Y.C., 1981, Catalyst, 1980-86, Am. Pub. Radio, Detroit Symphony Orch., Interlochen Corp. Coun.; trustee Founders Soc. of Detroit Inst. Art, Wellesley Coll.; mem. Com. of 200; bd. dirs. Assocs. Harvard Bus. Sch.; bd. dirs. Jr. Achievement, Inc., 1993—; mem. bus. adv. coun. U.S. AID; trustee Wellesley Coll.; mem. Citizen's Adv. Coun. U. Mich., Dearborn; bd. dirs. WTVS/Channel 56, Detroit Symphony Orch. Named Advt. Woman of Yr., Am. Advt. Fedn., 1974, Woman of Achievement, Am. Parkinson Disease Assn., 1980, Outstanding Corp. Dir., Catalyst, 1981; recipient WEAL Award in Advt., 1982, Alumna Achievement award Wellesley Coll., 1986, Alumna of Yr. award Chinese Am. Planning Coun., 1987. Mem. Advt. Research Found., Am. Assn. Advt. Agencies, Am. Mktg. Assn., Phi Beta Kappa. Office: GM Corp GM Bldg 14-117 3044 W Grand Blvd Detroit MI 48202

YOUNG, STEVEN, professional football player; b. Salt Lake City, Oct. 11, 1961. JD, Brigham Young, 1993. With L.A. Express, USFL, 1984-85, Tampa Bay Buccaneers, 1985-87; quarterback San Francisco 49ers, 1987—. Davey O'Brien Award, 1983, All-America team quarterback, The Sporting News, 1983; Named NFL's Top-rated quarterback, 1991, named NFL Most Valuable Player, The Sporting News, 1992, NFL All-Pro team quarterback, The Sporting News, 1992, Superbowl Most Valuable Player, 1995. Played in Pro Bowl 1992, 93; highest rated passer NFL, 1991-93. Office: San Francisco 49ers 4949 Centennial Blvd Santa Clara CA 95054-1229*

YOUNG, THOMAS DANIEL, retired humanities educator, author; b. Louisville, Miss., Oct. 22, 1919; s. William Allen and Lula (Wright) Y.; m. Arlease Lewis, Dec. 21, 1941; children: Thomas Daniel, Terry Lewis, Kyle David. B.S., Miss. So. Coll., 1941; M.A., U. Miss., 1948; Ph.D., Vanderbilt U., 1950; postgrad., U. Oxford, 1962, The Sorbonne, 1974. Instr. English U.

Miss., 1946-48; asst. Vanderbilt U., Nashville, 1948-50, dean admissions, asst. to vice-chancellor, 1961-64, prof., chmn. dept. English, 1964-72, Gertrude C. Vanderbilt prof. English, 1972-85, Gertrude C. Vanderbilt prof. emeritus, 1985—; asst. prof. English Miss. So. Coll., 1950-51, prof., chmn. dept., 1951-54, dean basic coll., 1954-57; prof. English, dean Delta State Coll., Cleveland, Miss., 1957-61; Pres. So. Lit. Festival Assn., 1952-53; chmn. English commn. Miss. Assn. Coll., 1952-55; coordinator Gen. Edn. Conf., 1953. Author: Jack London and the Era of Social Protest, 1950, The Literature of the South, 1952, rev. edit., 1968, Donald Davidson: An Essay and a Bibliography, 1965, American Literature: A Critical Survey, 1968, John Crowe Ransom; Critical Essays and a Bibliography, 1968, John Crowe Ransom, 1970, Donald Davidson, 1971, The Literary Correspondence of Allen Tate and Donald Davidson, 1974, The New Criticism and After, 1976, Gentleman in a Dustcoat: A Biography of John Crowe Ransom, 1977, The Past in the Present: Studies in the Modern American Novel, 1981, Tennessee Writers, 1981, John Crowe Ransom: An Annotated Bibliography, 1982, The Vocation of Letters in America: The Literary Correspondence of Allen Tate and John Peale Bishop, 1982, Selected Essays of John Crowe Ransom, 1983, Selected Letters of John Crowe Ransom, 1985, Singin' Billy, 1985, (with Louis D. Rubin and others) The History of Southern Literature, Conversations with Malcolm Cowley, 1986, The Lytle-Tate Letters, 1987, Fabulous Provinces: A Memoir, 1988, Modern American Fiction, 1989, Selected Essays, 1990; gen. editor: The Fugitive Bibliographies. Mem. AAUP, South Atlantic MLA (chmn. Am. lit. sect. 1971, chmn. lit. criticism sect. 1969, mem. exec. com. 1969-72), MLA (chmn. So. Lit. sect. 1969, 80, 82), Am. Studies Assn. Lower Miss. (pres. 1956-57), Phi Delta Kappa, Omicron Delta Kappa. Address: PO Box 31 Rose Hill MS 39356-0031

YOUNG, TOMMIE MORTON, social psychology educator, writer; b. Nashville. BA cum laude, Tenn. State U., 1951; MLS, George Peabody Coll. for Tchrs., 1955; PhD, Duke U., 1977; postgrad. U. Okla., 1967, U. Nebr., 1968. Coord., Young Adult Program, Lucy Thurman br. YWCA, 1951-52; instr. edn. Tenn. State U., Nashville, 1956-59; instr., coord. media program Prairie View Coll. (Tex.), 1959-61; asst. prof. edn., assoc. prof. English, dir. IMC Ctr., U. Ark.-Pine Bluff, 1965-69; asst. prof. English and edn., dir. learning lab., N.C. Central U., Durham, 1969-74; prof., dir./ chairperson litr. media svcs. and dept. ednl. media, dir. Afro-Am. Family Project, N.C. Agrl. and Tech. State U., Greensboro, 1975—; adj. prof. langs., lit. and philosophy, dir. schs. history project Tenn. State U., Nashville, 1994—; dir. workshops, grants; pres., dir. Ednl. Cons. Svcs. Author: Afro American Genealogy Sourcebook, 1987, Oral Histories of Former All-Black Public Schools, 1991, After School Programs for At-Risk Youth and Their Families, 1994; contbr. poem to Poetry: American Heritage; contbr. rsch. papers, articles to profl. jours. Nat. chmn. Com. to Re-Elect the Pres.; past sec. Fedn. Colored Women's Clubs; bd. dirs. Southwestern div. ARC, Nashville area, 1994—, dir. Volun-Teens; chairperson learning resources com. Task Force Durham Day Care Assn.; bd. dirs., chairperson schs. div. Durham County Unit Am. Cancer Soc.; past mem. adv. bd., bd. dirs. YMCA, Atlanta; chair Gilford County Commn. on Needs of Children; bd. advisors NIH, N.C. Coun. of the Arts; mem. Guilford County Involvement Coun.; chmn. N.C. adv. com. U.S. Civil Rights Com.; mem. exec. planning com. Greensboro. Recipient awards ARC, 1968, 73, NAACP, 1973, HEW, 1978, U.S. Commn. on Civil Rights, 1982; named Disting. Alumni Tenn. State U., 1994. Mem. AAUW (honor award 1983, pres. Greensboro br., chairperson internat. rels. com.), ALA (divsn. coll. and rsch. librs., past chair), NAACP (life, 1st v.p. Durham br., exec. bd. Greensboro br., dir. parent edn./child advocacy program, Woman of Yr. 1992), NEA, Assn. Childhood Ednl. Internat., Comparative and Internat. Edn. Assn., Archives Assoc., Internat. Platform Assn., Nat. Hist. Soc., Greensboro Jr. League (community adv. bd. 1991—), Zeta Phi Beta (chairperson polit. action com. eastern region, nat. grammateus, Polit. and Civic Svc. award 1974, Outstanding Social-Polit. Svc. award 1982, Woman of Yr. 1977), Commn. on Status of Women (Woman of Achievement 1991), Phi Kappa Phi (Disting. State U. Alumni award 1994, Disting Alumni NAFEO award, 1995, Carl Rowan-Oprah Winfrey lectr. Tenn. State U., 1995), Excellence in Jerusalem award SPJ, 1995. Home: PO Box 17684 Nashville TN 37217

YOUNG, TZAY Y., electrical and computer engineering educator; b. Shanghai, China, Jan. 11, 1933; came to U.S., 1958; s. Chao-Hsiung and Chiu-Ming (Chu) Y.; m. Lily Liu, Dec. 27, 1965; children: Debbie Chia-Pei, Arthur Chia-Kai. BS, Nat. Taiwan U., Taipei, 1955; MS, U. Vt., 1959; DEng, Johns Hopkins U., 1962. Rsch. assoc. Johns Hopkins U., Balt., 1962-63; mem. tech. staff Bell Labs., Murray Hill, N.J., 1963-64; asst. prof. Carnegie-Mellon U., Pitts., 1964-68, assoc. prof., 1968-74; prof. elec. and computer engring. U. Miami, Coral Gables, Fla., 1974—, acting chmn. dept., 1988-91, chmn. dept., 1991—; sr. postdoctoral rsch. assoc. NAS, NASA, Goddard Space Flight Ctr., Md., 1972-73. Author: (with T.W. Calvert) Classification, Estimation and Pattern Recognition, 1974; editor: (with K.S. Fu) Handbook of Pattern Recognition and Image Processing, 1986; editor: Handbook of Pattern Recognition and Image Processing, vol. 2, Computer Vision, 1994; also numerous articles. Rsch. grantee NSF, NASA, FHTIC, also indsl. grants. Fellow IEEE (assoc. editor Trans. Computers 1974-76; editorial bd. Trans. Pattern Analysis and Machine Intelligence 1979-84, adv. bd. 1984-90); mem. Sigma Xi, Eta Kappa Nu. Office: U Miami Dept Elec & Computer Engring Coral Gables FL 33124

YOUNG, VIRGIL M., education educator; b. Santa Rosa, Calif., Sept. 24, 1936; s. Virgil M. and Vesta May (Huyett) Williams; stepson Louis H. Young; m. Katherine Ann Young, Dec. 20, 1964; 1 child, Susan Annette. BS, U. Idaho, 1958, EdD, 1967. Cert. advanced secondary sch., sch. supt., Idaho. Tchr. Moscow (Idaho) Sch. Dist.; adminstrv. asst. to supt. Coeur d'Alene (Idaho) Sch. Dist.; prof. edn., dept. head Boise (Idaho) State U. Author: (elem., jr. high textbook) The Story of Idaho, 3 editions; coauthor: The Story of the Idaho Guide and Resource Book, 1993. Capt. USAR. Mem. N.W. Assn. Tchr. Educators (past pres.), Idaho Assn. Colls. Tchr. Edn. (past pres.), Phi Delta Kappa (past pres.).

YOUNG, WALTER RICHARD, controller; b. Danville, Ky., Aug. 7, 1947; s. Harold Basil and Dorothy (Devine) Y.; B.S. in Acctg., Western Ky. U., 1969; MS (Haggin fellow), U. Ky., 1972; MBA So. Miss. U., 1993; m. Lisette Rowley, June 19, 1971; children: Walter Richard, Ralph Martin, Katharine Elizabeth. With Price Waterhouse & Co., 1972-81, audit mgr., Little Rock, 1977-81; with Fairfield Cmtys., Inc., 1981-87, v.p., corp. contr.; v.p., contr. Union Life Ins., 1988-89; v.p. acctg., chief acctg. officer Nat. Am. Corp./Thousand Trails, Inc., 1989-92; CFO Rabex Resorts, Biloxi, Miss., 1992-94; fin. adminstr. Kare-In-Home Health Svcs., Inc., 1994—. Treas. Friends Ark. Ednl. TV, 1978-82, chmn. acctg. div. for festival, 1978, 79, 80; active United Way; youth soccer coach. Served with USAR, 1969-71. Decorated Army Commendation medal; C.P.A., Ark., Tenn. Mem. AICPA, Cen. Ark. Soccer Assn. (treas. 1986-89), Ark. Soc. CPAs, Inst. Internal Auditors (past chpt. pres.), Nat. Assn. Accts., Western Ky. U. Alumni Assn., U. Ky. Alumni Assn., Miss. Coast Futbal Assn., Lions. Democrat. Baptist. Club: Western Ky. U. Ark. (past chpt. pres.) Home: 815 Magnolia Bayou Blvd Ocean Springs MS 39564-8515 Office: 221 Beaunoir Rd Biloxi MS 39531

YOUNG, WILLIAM BENJAMIN, special education educator; b. Wichita, Kans., Jan. 30, 1929; s. Ernest William and Florence Belle (McCann) Y.; m. La Vona P., Feb., 1949 (div. 1973); children: Lynda, David, Timothy; m. Patricia Sue Reber, Aug., 1974. Student, Southwestern Coll., Winfield, Kans., 1947-48; B in Gen. Edn., U. Omaha, 1961; MS in Pers. Counseling, Miami U., Oxford, Ohio, 1965; PhD in Exceptional Edn., Adminstrn. and Counseling, Ohio State U., 1972. Cert. elem. and secondary adminstr., tchr., counselor, psychologist, psychometrist, spl. edn., mental retardation, learning disabled/behavior disordered, emotionally handicapped, Ind.; cert. K-12 guidance counselor and edn. leadership, Fla.; lic sexologist, flight instr.; lic Coast Guard capt. Enlisted USAF, 1948; dir. commd. 2nd lt. commd. 2d lt. 1955; advanced through grades to capt. USAF, 1960, ret. 1966; numerous teaching and counseling positions as civilian, 1966-91; co-owner, instr. Ft. Wayne (Ind.) Ground Schs., 1984-88; marriage and family counselor, pvt. practice, 1966-91; tchr., counselor, behavior specialist Broward County Schs., Ft. Lauderdale, Fla., 1989—; adj. prof. grad. spl. edn. Nova U. Mem. ACA, Coun. for Exceptional Children, Coun. Behavior Disorders, Fla. Counseling Assn., 32 degree Masons. Avocations: flying, sailing, traveling, golf, swimming. Home: 2548 Gulfstream Ln Fort Lauderdale FL 33312-4704

YOUNG, WILLIAM F., legal educator; b. 1925. B.A., U. Tex., 1947, LL.B., 1949. Bar: Tex. 1949. Grad. fellow Harvard U., 1951-52; prof. U. Tex., 1949-56, Columbia U., 1956—. Mem. Am. Law Inst., Order of Coif. Office: Columbia U Sch Law 435 W 116th St New York NY 10027-7201

YOUNG, WILLIAM FIELDING, lawyer; b. N.Y.C., Jan. 6, 1948; s. Charles Fielding and Josephine Cope (Roig) Y.; m. Mary Anne Silver, June 13, 1970. BA, U. Va., 1970; JD, Harvard U., 1977. Bar: Va. 1977, U.S. Dist. Ct. (ea. and we. dists.) Va. 1977, U.S. Ct. Appeals (4th cir.) 1977, D.C. 1988, U.S. Dist. Ct. D.C. 1988, U.S. Ct. Appeals (D.C. cir.) 1988. Assoc. Hunton & Williams, Richmond, Va., 1977-85; ptnr. Hunton & Williams, Washington, 1985—, Fairfax, Va., 1985—. Mem. Va. Dist. Export Coun., Richmond, 1983—. Lt. USN, 1970-74. Mem. Va. Bar Assn. (bd. govs. antitrust sect. 1985—, chmn. elect. internat. law sect. 1985-87), Phi Beta Kappa, Downtown Club (Richmond). Democrat. Episcopalian. Home: 1215 Mottrom Dr Mc Lean VA 22101-2721 Office: Hunton & Williams 2000 Pennsylvania Ave PO Box 19230 Washington DC 20036

YOUNG, WILLIAM GLOVER, federal judge; b. Huntington, N.Y., Sept. 23, 1940; s. Woodhull Benjamin and Margaret Jean (Wilkes) Y.; m. Beverly June Bigelow, Aug. 5, 1967; children: Mark Edward, Jeffrey Woodhull, Todd Russell. A.B., Harvard U., 1962, LL.B., 1967. Bar: Mass. 1967, U.S. Supreme Ct. 1970. Law clk. to chief justice Supreme Jud. Ct., Mass., 1967-68; spl. asst. atty. gen. Mass., 1969-72, chief legal counsel to gov., 1972-74; asso. firm Bingham, Dana and Gould, Boston, 1968-72; ptnr. Bingham, Dana and Gould, 1975-78; assoc. justice Superior Ct., Commonwealth of Mass., Boston, 1978-85; judge U.S. Dist. Ct. Mass., Boston, 1985—; lectr. part time Harvard Law Sch., 1979-90, Boston Coll. Law Sch., Boston U. Law Sch. Served to capt. U.S. Army, 1962-64. Mem. Am. Law Inst., Mass. Bar Assn., Boston Bar Assn., Harvard Alumni (pres. 1976-77). Office: US Dist Ct Rm 1903 McCormack PO & Courthouse Boston MA 02109

YOUNG, WILLIAM JOHN, French language educator, retired university president; b. Toronto, Ont., Can., Apr. 24, 1925; came to U.S., 1955; s. George Samuel and Dorothy Helen (Moroney) Y. BA, U. Toronto, 1948, MA, 1952; postgrad., U. Paris, 1955; PhD, U. Laval, Que., Can., 1956. Ordained priest Roman Cath. Ch., 1951. Head modern langs. St. John Fisher Coll., Rochester, N.Y., 1955-58; head modern langs. U. St. Thomas, Houston, 1958-62, v.p., dean, 1962-66, pres., 1966-67, 1979-85, chancellor, 1985-87, pres. emeritus, 1987—; mem. gen. adminstrn. Congregation St. Basil, Toronto, 1967-77. Translator: Basilian History to 1864, 1975. Pres. Houston Coun. Fgn. Lang. Tchrs., 1965-66; mem. equity-quality-audit com. Houston Ind. Sch. Dist., 1985-89; mem. Cert. Adv. Coun., Austin, 1984-90. Decorated chevalier Palmes Académiques (France). Mem. Alliance Francaise de Houston (pres. 1964-65), Forum Club of Houston (bd. dirs.1980-86). Home: 4019 Yoakum Blvd Houston TX 77006-4833 Office: U St Thomas Dept Modern Langs 3800 Montrose Blvd Houston TX 77006-4626

YOUNG, WILLIAM VICTOR, banker; b. Albany, Calif., Apr. 25, 1937; s. Victor Albert and Nina Barbara (McNamara) Y.; B.A., San Jose State U., 1959; M.A., U. Oreg., 1966; postgrad. Grad. Sch. Credit and Fin. Mgmt., London U., 1978; A.M.P., Harvard U., 1983; m. Genevieve Murphy, Sept. 22, 1962; children—William Mark, Michael Patrick, Sarah Elizabeth. With Bank of America, 1966—, v.p., mgr., Rotterdam, Netherlands, 1973-76, regional v.p. Central Am./Caribbean Area, Guatemala City, Guatemala, 1976-78, sr. v.p. Central Europe Area, Frankfurt, W. Ger., 1978-81, exec. v.p. Latin Am./Caribbean div., Caracas, Venezuela, 1981-86, exec. v.p., internat. div., San Francisco, 1986—, Europe, Middle East, Africa divs., Lodnon, 1988; mem. mgmt. adv. council Bank of Am. N.T. and S.A.; mem. world banking div. exec. council Bank of Am.; dep. chmn. European Brazilian Bank Ltd., London. Served to 1st lt. U.S. Army, 1959-61. Mem. Council of Ams., Brazil-U.S. Bus. Council, Argentine-U.S. Bus. Council, Venezuelan-Am. C. of C., Found. for Mgmt. Edn. in Central Am. Home: PO Box 37000 San Francisco CA 94137 Office: Bank of America Nat Trust & Sav Assn 555 California St San Francisco CA 94104-1502

YOUNGBERG, ROBERT STANLEY, principal, consultant; b. Chgo., Apr. 21, 1932; s. Holger Raymond and Eva Boyd (Carr) Y.; m. Catherine Jane Fitzpatrick, June 19, 1954; children: Kevin, Melissa, Margo Jenkins, Brian. BS, U. Ill., 1954; MEd, Wayne State U., 1959; PhD, U. Mich., 1975. Tchr. Hanneman-Herman-Dixon, Detroit, 1956-62; counselor Barbour Jr. High/Ruddman Jr. High Sch., Detroit, 1962-67, Redford High Sch., Detroit, 1967-70; prin. mid. sch. Novi, Mich., 1970-79, prin. high sch., 1979-92; pvt. practice edn. cons. Clearwater, Fla., 1992—; site evaluator secondary recognition program U.S. Dept. Edn., Mich. Dept. Edn., 1988-90; immigration and customs inspector U.S. Dept. Justice, 1961-64; summer camp dir. Mich. and Wis., 1965-70; cons. in field. Chmn. citizens adv. com. Sch. Facilities, Detroit, 1958-59; chmn. Citizens Adv. Com. on Mid. Schs., Novi, 1972-74, Citizens Adv. Com. on Humanities and Arts, 1975, Great Cities Sch. Improvement Project, Detroit, 1962-64, Dist. Curriculum Coun., Novi, 1972-80; bd. dirs. Youth Assistance Bd., Novi, 1975-79; site vis. North Ctrl. Assn., 1968-91; bus. cons. Mgmt. Style for Retail Merchants, Novi, 1988-91. With U.S. Army, 1954-56. Mem. Mich. Assn. Sch. Adminstrs., Mich. Assn. Secondary Sch. Prins., Nat. Assn. Secondary Sch. Prins., Nat. ASCD, Kensington Valley Activities Conf. (bd. dirs.), Phi Delta Kappa. Avocations: physical fitness, senior games, racquetball, basketball, track and field events. Office: 2427 Bond Ave Clearwater FL 34619-1204

YOUNGBLOOD, BETTY J., academic administrator; b. Detroit; m. Ralph P. Youngblood; 1 child. BS in Political Sci., Oakland U., Rochester, Mich.; MA in South Asian Studies, U. Minn., PhD in Political Sci. Formerly mem. faculty West Ga. Coll., Tex Tech U.; various adminstrv. positions Kennesaw State Coll., Marietta, Ga.; v.p. acad. affairs MacMurray Coll., Jacksonville, Ill., Wesley Coll., Dover, Del.; vice chancellor acad. affairs, dean faculty, prof. polit. sci. U. Wis.-Superior, 1990-91, acting chancellor, 1991-92, chancellor, 1992—; cons., evaluator North Ctrl. Assn. Colls. and Schs. Contbr. articles to profl. jours. Bd. dirs. United Way, Superior. Rsch. grantee for study in N.W. India. Mem. Superior C. of C., Rotary. Office: U Wis-Superior Office of the President 1800 Grand Ave Superior WI 54880

YOUNGBLOOD, J. CRAIG, lawyer; b. Ft. Worth, July 6, 1947; s. Angus O'Neal and Kathleen (Hill) Y.; m. Linda Gilman, Apr. 17, 1982; children: Jesica Caye, Jaclyn Cristine. Student, Rice U., 1965-66; BA in Polit. Sci. and Math, U. Tex., San Antonio, 1977; JD, U. Tex., Austin, 1980. Bar: Tex. 1982, U.S. Dist. Ct. (so. dist.) Tex. 1982, U.S. Ct. Appeals (D.C., 3rd, 5th and 11th cirs.) 1982, U.S. Ct. Appeals (10th cir.) 1983. Assoc. Vinson & Elkins, Houston, 1981-87, ptnr., 1988—; adv. bd. grad. program in energy and natural resources U. Houston Law Ctr. Mem. Tex. Law Rev.; contbr. chpt. to book; contbr. articles to profl. jours., lectr. in field. Mem. ABA, Tex. Bar Assn., Houston Bar Assn., Fed. Energy Bar Assn. (pres. bd. dirs. Houston chpt. 1989-90), Tex. Law Rev. Assn. Republican. Avocations: hunting, fishing, snow skiing, personal computers. Home: 11 Red Sable Pt The Woodlands TX 77380-2687 Office: Vinson & Elkins 2300 First City Tower 1001 Fannin St Houston TX 77002-6760

YOUNGBLOOD, MICHELLE KAREN WOLSTEIN, judge; b. Killeen, Tex., Jan. 14, 1958. BBA, Tex. A&M U., 1980; JD, Baylor U., 1983. Bar: Tex. 1983, U.S. Ct. Appeals (5th, 11th cirs.) 1986, U.S. Supreme Ct., 1986. Asst. city atty. City of Dallas, 1983-85; atty. advisor HUD, Ft. Worth, 1985-87; adminstrv. judge EEOC, Dallas, 1987-91; adminstv. law judge City of Arlington, Tex., 1991—; adj. prof. Tarrant County Jr. Coll., Ft. Worth, 1986—, Dallas Community Coll., 1987—, U. Tex., Arlington, 1992—, Dallas Community Colls., 1991—; pub. speaker various community orgns. and events, 1983—; profl. mediator/arbitrator, 1990—; meadiator Dispute Resolution Svcs. Contbr. articles to profl. jours. V.p. Ft. Worth metro chapter Sweet Adelines Internat., 1985—; arbitrator BBB, Ft. Worth, 1986—. Named Woman of the Yr. Meadowbrook Bus. and Profl. Women, Ft. Worth, 1987-88, Outstanding Young Women of Am., 1988, Young Career Women of the Yr., Bus. & Profl. Women, 1989, 91. Mem. Coll. State Bar Tex., Fed. Bar Assn. (pres. Ft. Worth chpt. 1988-87, sec. nat. young lawyers div. 1988—, nat. coun. 1988—), Tarrant County Young Lawyers Assn. (bd. dir. 1986-87), Tarrant County Women's Bar Assn. (bd. dirs. 1986-88), Tarrant County Women's Bar Assn. (bd. dirs 1986-88), Tarrant County Bar Assn., Tex. Young Lawyers Assn. (Cert. of Spl. Achievement), Bus. and Profl. Women (Young Career Woman of Yr. 1987, 88, 91, Woman of Yr.

Meadowbrook-Ft. Worth chpt. 1987). Home: PO Box 265 Fort Worth TX 76101-0265 Office: EEOC F303 Elmbrook Dallas TX 75247

YOUNGBLOOD, RAY WILSON, publishing company executive; b. Tulia, Tex., Feb. 18, 1931; s. Burk Richard and Jenny (Lucile) W.; BBA, Tex. Tech. U., 1952; MBA, U. Tex., 1958; m. Imogene Price, June 7, 1959; children: Michael Ray, Janet Lynn. CPA, Tex. Auditor, Peat, Marwick, Mitchell & Co., CPAs, Houston, 1958-65; chief acct. Houston Chronicle Pub. Co., 1965-66, controller, asst. treas., 1966-83, treas., 1983—. Served to 1st lt. USAF, 1952-57. Mem. Internat. Newspaper Fin. Execs., (dir. 1971-77), Am. Inst. CPAs, Tex. Soc. CPAs, Planning Execs. Inst., Nat. Assn. Accts., Fin. Execs. Inst. Methodist. Club: Exchange (treas. 1971, 74-75). Office: Houston Chronicle Publ Co `801 Texas St Houston TX 77002-2906

YOUNGBLOOD, RICHARD NEIL, columnist; b. Minot, N.D., May 9, 1936; s. Edward Anthony and Helen (Condo) Y.; m. Adele Henley, May 4, 1957 (div. 1983); children: Kent Jay, Ruth Adele, Beth Alise; m. Mary Dinneen, July 14, 1984. B.A. U. N.D., 1958. Reporter Grand Forks (N.D.) Herald, 1955-63; reporter Mpls. Star Tribune, 1963-67, asst. city editor, 1967-69, bus./fin. editor, 1969-84, columnist, 1984—. Recipient Excellence award in bus. and fin. journalism John Handcock Mut. Life, 1974; named Newspaper Farm Editor of Yr. Newspaper Farm Editors of Am., 1965. Avocations: reading, crossword puzzles, boating. Office: Mpls Star Tribune 425 Portland Ave Minneapolis MN 55488

YOUNG-BRUEHL, ELISABETH, philosophy educator; b. Elkton, Md., Mar. 3, 1946; d. Herbert Gibbons Young and Lois (Williams) Sutton. BA, New Sch. for Social Rsch., 1968, MA, 1974, PhD, 1974. Prof. philosophy Wesleyan U., Middletown, Conn., 1974-91; prof. psychology Haverford (Pa.) Coll., 1992—. Author: Freedom and Karl Jaspers Philosophy, 1981, Hannah Arendt, 1982, Anna Freud, 1988, Mind and The Body Politic, 1989, Freud on Women, 1990, Creative Characters, 1991, Global Cultures, 1994. NEH fellow, 1984-85, Guggenheim Found. fellow, 1986-87. Mem. Authors Guild. Democrat. Office: Haverford Coll Haverford PA 19041

YOUNGDAHL, JAMES EDWARD, lawyer; b. Mankato, Minn., Nov. 17, 1926; s. Benjamin Emanuel Lincoln and Livia (Bjorkquist) Y.; children—Jay Thomas Armstrong, Jan Kristi, Lincoln Anders Morton, Sara Lise. Student, Washington U., St. Louis, 1944-45; A.B., U. Mo., 1947; LL.B., U. Ark., 1959. Bar: Ark. bar 1959. Field sec. League for Indsl. Democracy, N.Y.C., 1947-48; nat. rep., asst. regional dir. Amalgamated Clothing Workers Am., CIO and AFL-CIO, St. Louis, Paducah, Ky., New Orleans, 1948-56; since practiced in Little Rock, Memphis, New Orleans and Albuquerque; ptnr. McMath, Leatherman, Woods & Youngdahl, 1959-68, Youngdahl & Larrison, 1968-80, Youngdahl & Youngdahl P.A., 1980—, Youngdahl, Sadin & McGowan, 1985—; instr. labor law U. Ark. Sch. Law, 1963, 69-71, U. Ark. Sch. Law (Ark. Law Sch.), 1964-66; mem. arbitration services adv. com. Fed. Mediation and Conciliation Service, 1978-84. Editor-in-chief: Ark. Law Rev, 1958-59; contbg. editor: Ark. Advocate, 1972-74; contbr. articles to profl. jours. Vice chmn. New Orleans Forum, 1953-54; pres. Ark. Assn. for Mental Health, 1960-61; chmn. Ark. adv. com. U.S. Commn. on Civil Rights, 1962-65; mem. exec. com. So. Regional Council, 1969-74; mem. nat. exec. bd. Workers Def. League, 1965-75; bd. dirs. Voter Edn. Project, Inc., 1971-74. Home: 2046 Royal St New Orleans LA 70356 Office: Ste 201 2929 Coors Blvd NW Albuquerque NM 87120 also: Ste 1805 124 W Capitol Little Rock AR 72203

YOUNGER, JUDITH TESS, lawyer, educator; b. N.Y.C., Dec. 20, 1933; d. Sidney and Kate (Greenbaum) Weintraub; m. Irving Younger, Jan. 21, 1955; children: Rebecca, Abigail M. B.S., Cornell U., 1954; J.D., NYU, 1958; LL.D. (hon.), Hofstra U., 1974. Bar: N.Y. 1958, U.S. Supreme Ct 1962, D.C. 1983, Minn. 1985. Law clk. to judge U.S. Dist. Ct., 1958-60; asso. firm Chadbourne, Parke, Whiteside & Wolff, N.Y.C., 1960-62; mem. firm Younger and Younger, and (successors), 1962-67; adj. asst. prof. N.Y. U. Sch. Law, 1967-69; assoc. prof. State of N.Y., 1969-70; assoc. prof. Hofstra U. Sch. Law, 1970-72, prof., assoc. dean, 1972-74; dean, prof. Syracuse Coll. Law, 1974-75; dep. dean, prof. law Cornell Law Sch., 1975-78, prof. law, 1975-85; vis. prof. U. Minn. Law Sch., Mpls., 1984-85, prof., 1985—; of counsel Popham, Haik, Schnobrich & Kaufman, Ltd., Mpls., 1989—; cons. NOW, 1972-74, Suffolk County for Revision of Its Real Property Tax Act, 1972-73; mem. N.Y. Gov.'s Panel To Screen Candidates of Ct. of Claims Judges, 1973-74; mem. Minn. Lawyers' Profl. Responsibility Bd., 1991-93. Contbr. articles to profl. jours. Trustee Cornell U., 1973-78. Mem. ABA (council legal edn. 1975-79), Am. Law Inst. (adv. restatement property 1982-84), AAUP (v.p. Cornell U. chpt. 1978-79), N.Y. State Bar Assn., Assn. of Bar of City of N.Y., Minn. Bar Assn. Home: 3520 W Calhoun Pky Minneapolis MN 55416-4657 Office: U Minn Law Sch Minneapolis MN 55455

YOUNGER, KENNETH G., freight carrier corporation executive; b. 1925; grad. Duke U., 1949. Eastern div. mgr. Roadway Express Inc., 1949-62; exec. v.p. and gen. mgr. Sea Land Services Inc., 1962-72; pres. Hennis Freight Lines, 1972-75, Spector Freight Systems, 1975-76; chief operating officer Carolina Freight Carriers Corp., Cherryville N.C., from 1976, now chmn., chief exec. officer, also dir.; pres., chief exec. officer Carolina Freight Corp., Cherryville, now vice chmn.; dir. Trucking Employers Inc. Served with USAAF. Office: Carolina Freight Corp PO Box 697 NC Hwy 150 E Cherryville NC 28021-0697 also: Carolina Freight Corp PO Box 1000 Cherryville NC 28021-1000

YOUNGER, KENNETH MAURICE, military officer; b. Altavista, Va., Nov. 30, 1952; s. Herbert Hoover and Delma Edith (Miller) Y.; m. Sharon Jameta Stinson, Mar. 25, 1979; 1 child, Sean. BS, Va. State U., 1975; grad., Army Command and Staff Coll., 1984, Naval Command and Staff Coll., 1988; MS, Salve Regina Coll., 1989. Commd. U.S. Army, 1975, advanced through grades to lt. col.; Chaparral and Vulcan platoon leader U.S. Army, Republic of Korea, 1976-77; battery comdr. bn. S-4 U.S. Army, Fed. Republic of Germany, 1980-83; logistics plans officer, aide-de-camp U.S. Army, Ft. Hood, Tex., 1983-87, maj. bn. S-3, 1986-87; info. mgmt. officer J4 HQ Forscom, 1988-90; col. assignment officer PERSCOM, 1990-92; pers. policy integrator Pentagon, Washington, 1992-93. Named one of Outstanding Young Men Am., 1985. Baptist. Avocations: jogging, stamp collecting, golf. Home: 11 Dupont Plz Fort Bragg NC 28307-2012 Office: HQ 3D Bn # 4th Ada Fort Bragg NC 28307

YOUNGERMAN, JACK, artist, sculptor; b. Louisville, Mar. 25, 1926; s. Guy Arthur and Margaret Anne (Everhart) Y.; m. Delphine Seyrig, July 3, 1950; 1 son, Duncan Pierre. Student, U. N.C., 1944-46; B.A., U. Mo., 1947; postgrad., Ecole des Beaux Arts, Paris, 1947-48. instr. Yale U., New Haven, 1974-75, Hunter Coll., N.Y.C., 1981—, Sch. Visual Arts, N.Y.C., 1981—. One-man shows include Betty Parsons Gallery, N.Y.C., 1958, 60, 61, 64, 65, 68, Paris, 1951, 62, 63, Milan, 1965, Los Angeles, 1963, Worcester Art Mus., 1965, MIT, 1966, Galerie Adrien Maeght, Paris, 1966, Phillips Collections, Washington, 1968, Galerie Denise Rene, Galerie Rive Gauche, Paris, 1973, Pace Gallery, N.Y.C., 1971, 73, 75, Central Park, N.Y.C., 1981, Washburn Gallery, N.Y.C., 1981, 84-87, Guggenheim Mus., 1986, Heland Wetterling Gallery, Stockholm, 1989; exhibited in group shows at Carnegie Internat., 1958, 61, Mus. Modern Art, 1959, Corcoran Mus., Washington, 1958, 63, 79, Kimura Gallery, Tokyo, 1960, Whitney Mus., 1960, 65, 74, 77, 88, 89, Guggenheim Mus., 1961, 64, 66, 81, 82, 86, 88, Art Inst. Chgo., 1962, Mus. Bousmans van Beuningen, Rotterdam, The Netherlands, 1966, Jewish Mus., N.Y.C., 1967, 68, 69, Carnegie Instn., 1971, Hirshhorn Mus., 1980, Haus der Kunst, Munich, W.Ger., 1981, Nat. Gallery Art, Washington, 1981, 83, 89, Found. Nat. des Artes Graphiques et Plastiques, Paris, 1983, Mus. Fine Arts, Budapest, Hungary, 1985, L.A. County Mus. Art, 1986, U.S. Embassy, Moscow, 1988, Szepmuveszeti Muzem, Budapest, 1988, Nat. Gallery of Art, Washington, D.C., 1989, Whitney Mus., N.Y.C., 1989, Ferie Internacional de Arte Contemporaneo, Madrid, Spain, 1991; represented in permanent collections, Mus. Modern Art, N.Y.C., Knox-Albright Mus., N.Y.C., Worcester Art Mus., Smithsonian Instn., Washington, Whitney Mus., Corcoran Mus., Carnegie Inst. Mus. Art, Phillips Collections, Washington, La. Mus. Modern Art, Humlebach, Denmark, New Sch. for Social Rsch., Olympic Sculpture Park, Seoul, S. Korea, Solomon R. Guggenheim Mus., N.Y.C., Univ. Art Mus., Berkeley, Calif., Vassar Coll., Poughkeepsie, N.Y., Yale U. Art Ctr., New Haven, Conn.; stage designs Histoire de Vasco, Paris, 1956; stage design Deathwatch, N.Y.C., 1958. Recipient Nat. Council Arts and Sci., 1966; NEA fellow, 1972; Guggenheim Found. fellow, 1977. Address: 130 W 3rd St New York NY 10012 Office: Washburn Gallery 41 E 57th St 8th floor Fuller Bldg New York NY 10022

YOUNGKEN, HEBER WILKINSON, JR., former university administrator, pharmacy educator; b. Phila., Aug. 13, 1913; s. Heber Wilkinson and Clara (Eastman) Y.; m. Daphne Goodwin, Mar. 28, 1942; children: John R., Richard C. A.B., Bucknell U., 1935; B.S., Mass. Coll. Pharmacy, 1938; M.S., U. Minn., 1940, Ph.D., 1942; student, Harvard Grad. Sch., 1938-39; DSc (hon.), U. R.I., 1992. Asst. biology and pharmacognosy Mass. Coll. Pharmacy, 1935-39; teaching asst. pharmacognosy Coll. Pharmacy, U. Minn., 1939-42; from. instr. to prof. pharmacognosy U. Wash., Seattle, 1942-57; chmn. dept., dir. med. plant lab. U. Wash., 1946-57; prof. pharmacognosy, dean Coll. Pharmacy, U. R.I., 1957-81, v.p. acad. affairs, 1967-68, provost health sci. affairs, 1969-81; vis. prof. U. London, 1970, U. Cairo, Egypt, 1977, 79, 81, 85. Author: (with R. Pratt) Pharmacognosy, 2d edit, 1956, Organic Chemistry in Pharmacy, 1949, Natural Products in Pharmacy; also numerous papers in field. Mem. R.I. Health Care Coordinating Coun., R.I. Gov.'s Justice Commn.; pres. R.I. Health Sci. Edn. Coun., 1976-77; chmn. sect. pharmacognosy/natural products Acad. Pharm. Scis., 1976-77; bd. dirs. R.I. Soc. for Prevention Blindness, Health Data Resources, Inc., R.I. Search; bd. dirs URI Found., pres. 1984-87. With USNR, 1943-46; now capt. Res. Recipient Edwin L. Newcomb award research pharmacognosy Am. Found. Pharm. Edn., 1951. Fellow Am. Pharm. Assn., Am. Assn. Coll. Pharmacy, AAAS; mem. Soc. Exptl. Biology and Medicine, N.Y. Acad. Sci., Am. Soc. Hosp. Pharmacists, R.I. Pharm. Assn. (Toxicology award 1964, Man of Yr. award 1979, Bowl of Hygeia award 1989), Am. Coll. Apothecary, Soc. Econ. Botany, R.I. Soc. Hosp. Pharmacists, Am. Soc. Pharmacognosy (pres. 1970), Rotarian Club, Sigma Xi, Phi Kappa Phi, Phi Sigma, Rho Chi, Kappa Psi, Phi Kappa Psi. Baptist. Home: 188 Oakwoods Dr Peace Dale RI 02883-2533 Office: U RI Coll Pharmacy Kingston RI 02881

YOUNG LIVELY, SANDRA LEE, nurse; b. Rockport, Ind., Dec. 31, 1943; d. William Cody and Flora Juanita (Carver) Thorpe; m. Kenneth Leon Doom, May 4, 1962 (div. 1975); children: Patricia, Anita, Elizabeth. AS, Vincennes U., 1979, student, U. So. Ind., 1987—. Nursing aide, nurse Forest Del Nursing Home, Princeton, Ind., 1975-80; charge nurse Welborn Bapt. Hosp., Evansville, Ind., 1979-80, 82-83; staff nurse Longview Regional Hosp., Tex., 1980-82; dir. home health Roy H. Laird Meml. Hosp., Kilgore, Tex., 1984-86; med. post-coronary nurse Mercy Hosp., Owensboro, Ky., 1987, Dept. of Corrections charge nurse, Branchville Tng. Ctr., Tell City, Ind, 1987-90; charge nurse dept. mental health Evansville (Ind.) State Hosp., 1990—; staff nurse, asst. dir. Leisure Lodge Home Health, Overton, Tex., 1983-84. Grantee Roy H. Laird Meml. Hosp., 1986. Mem. NAFE, Menniger Found., Vincennes U. Alumni Assn., Internat. Platform Assn. Avocations: writing, research, cake decorating, house plants. Home: R #1 Box 2115 Jefferson TX 75657 Office: Evansville State Hosp 3400 Lincoln Ave Evansville IN 47714-0147

YOUNGMAN, HENNY, comedian; m. Sadie Cohen (dec.); children: Gary, Marilyn. Appeared regularly on: radio show Kate Smith, during 1930's; now nightclub and concerts comedian; appears on TV; appeared in: TV series Henny and Rocky, 1955, Joey and Dad, 1975; film Silent Movie, 1976, History of the World, Part I, 1981, The Comeback Trail, 1982, Goodfellows, 1990; recs. include Take My Album . . . Please, 1978, 128 Greatest Jokes, In Concert, 1987, Bits & Pieces, 1992; author 10 books including: How Do You Like Me So Far?, Take My Wife Please, 400 Traveling Salesmen's Jokes, 500 All Time Greatest One-Liners, Don't Put My Name on This Book, Take My Life, Please. Office: care of Peter Mallon 8051 Shalom Dr Spring Hill FL 34606-6939 *Life should be like a one liner--good to the last word.*

YOUNGMAN, OWEN RALPH, newspaper editor; b. Chgo., Apr. 24, 1953; s. Ralph Elmer and Charlotte Earldine (Ottoson) Y.; m. Linda Ann Erlandson, Aug. 24, 1975. Sportswriter Ashtabula Star-Beacon, Ohio, 1969-71; office clerk Chgo. Tribune, 1971-73, transcriber, 1973-75, copy editor, slotman, 1976-79, copy chief, news editor, 1979-83, dep. sports editor, 1984-86, assoc. met. editor, 1986-88, assoc. features editor, 1988-90, dep. fin. editor, 1990-91, assoc. mng. editor, 1991-93, features editor, 1993-95, mng. editor, features, 1995—. Mem. Evangelical Covenant Ch., Am. Soc. Newspaper Editors, President's Club of North Park Coll., Arts Club of Chgo. Avocations: philately; personal computing. Home: 40 Kenmore Ave Deerfield IL 60015-4750 Office: Chicago Tribune 435 N Michigan Ave Chicago IL 60611

YOUNGNER, JULIUS STUART, microbiologist, educator; b. N.Y.C., Oct. 24, 1920; m. Tula Liakakis, 1943 (dec. 1963); children—Stuart, Lisa; m. Rina C. Balter, Aug. 3, 1964. B.A., NYU, 1939; M.S., U. Mich., 1941, Sc.D., 1944. Diplomate: Am. Acad. Microbiology. Teaching asst. dept. microbiology Sch. Medicine, U. Mich., 1941-43; instr. 1946-47; scientist Nat. Cancer Inst., Bethesda, Md., 1949; asst. prof. Virus Research Lab., U. Pitts., 1949-56, asso. prof. dept. microbiology, Sch. Medicine, 1956-60, prof., 1960—; chmn. dept. microbiology Virus Research Lab., U. Pitts. (Sch. Medicine), 1966-85, chmn. dept. microbiology, biochemistry, and molecular biology, 1985-89, Disting. Svc. prof., 1989—; vis. prof. dept. microbiology, Faculty Medicine U. Athens, Greece, 1963; F.G. Novy meml. lectr. Sch. Medicine, U. Mich., 1965; nat. lectr. Found. for Microbiology, 1972-73; 6th ann. Lippard meml. lectr. Coll. Physicians and Surgeons, Columbia U., 1980; mem. study sect. virology and rickettsiology USPHS, NIH, 1965-69; mem. bd. sci. councilors Nat. Inst. Allergy and Infectious Diseases, 1970-74, chmn., 1973-74; mem. task force on virology, 1976-77; mem. clin. a fellowship study sect. NIH, 1979-80; mem. adv. group to microbiology program Am. Inst. Biol. Scis., 1970-73; asso. mem. commn. on influenza Armed Forces Epidemiol. Bd., Dept. Def., 1959-69, mem., 1970-73; com. on biomed. research and research tng. Am. Assn. Med. Colls., 1973-75; cons. to surgeon gen. Dept. Army, 1973-76. Contbr. chpts. to books, articles to sci. jours. Referee Macy faculty scholar award program Josiah Macy, Jr., Found., 1977; mem. study group immunology and infectious diseases Health Research Services Found., 1959-79, chmn., 1978-79; mem. microbiology and virology study group Am. Cancer Soc., 1981-85, chmn. 1985. Served with U.S. Army, 1944-46; with USPHS, 1947-49. E.I. du Pont de Nemours & Co. ednl. aid grantee, 1973. Fellow Hellenic Soc. Microbiology and Hygiene (hon. fgn.); mem. Am. Soc. for Microbiology (chmn. sect. T 1981—, mem. com. med. microbiology and immunology, bd. public and sci. affairs 1981—), Am. Soc. Virology (pres.-elect 1985-86, pres. 1986-87), Soc. for Gen. Microbiology, Am. Assn. Immunologists, Infectious Diseases Soc. Am., AAAS, AAUP, Assn. Med. Microbiology Chairmen (pres.), Am. Acad. Microbiolog (bd. govs. 1985-91), Am. Type Culture Collection (bd. dirs. 1992—), Internation Soc. Interferon and Cytokine Rsch. (hon.). Office: U Pitts Dept Molecular Genetics & Biochemistry Pittsburgh PA 15261

YOUNGQUIST, ALVIN MENVID, JR., publisher, editor; b. Toledo, Oct. 9, 1925; s. Alvin Menvid and Elsie W. (Bostock) Y.; m. Judith Jackett, June 13, 1953. B.S., Northwestern U. Sch. Bus., 1950; postgrad., Sch. Journalism, 1951. Editor: Bankers Monthly, Skokie, Ill., 1953-70; editor, pres., pub.: Bankers Monthly, Inc, Northbrook, Ill., 1971-85, cons. editor, 1985—. Served with USNR, 1943-46. Mem. U.S. Power Squadrons (Skokie Valley), U.S. Sailing Assn., White Lake Yacht Club. Republican. Episcopalian. Home and Office: 1410 S Mears Ave Whitehall MI 49461-1737

YOUNGQUIST, ANDREW LANCE, construction executive; b. Newport Beach, Calif., Nov. 30, 1940; s. Vincent R. and Elizabeth (Tebbs) Y.; children: Bill, Jennifer; m. Linda Kay, May 17, 1980. Student, Orange Coast Coll. Pres. Decco Constrn., Orange, Calif., 1970-78; v.p. Capitol Systems, Newport Beach, 1976-77; with Saffell & McAdam, Irvine, Calif., 1977-79; pres. Birtcher Constrn. Ltd., Laguna Niguel, Calif., 1979—. Dir. Girl Scout Coun., Orange Empire, Girl Scouts U.S, 1991; bd. mem. Orange County Together. Mem. Nat. Assn. Indsl. Office Pks., Internat. Coun. Shopping Ctrs., Associated Gen. Contractors (bd. mem. Orange County dist.), Bldg. Industry Assn., Balboa Bay Club, Pacific Anglers. Republican. Home: 1851 Braemer Way Newport Beach CA 92660-3724 Office: Birtcher Constrn Ltd 24051 Shelley Rd Laguna Beach CA 92656-3912

YOUNGREN, RALPH PARK, architect; b. Cloquet, Minn., Dec. 26, 1924; s. Andrew Frederick and Eunice (Park) Y.; m. Ann Henderson, June 28, 1962; children: Todd Park, Malcolm Park. AB, Harvard U., 1948, BArch,

MArch, 1950. Assoc. ptnr. Skidmore, Owings & Merrill, Chgo., 1950-67; pres. Metz, Train, Youngren, Chgo., 1967-84; sr. v.p., dir. design Smith, Hinchman & Grylls, Detroit, 1985-93; sr. cons. designer Smith, Hinchman & Grylis, Detroit, 1994—; archtl. advisor Chgo. Dept. Urban Renewal, 1962. Designer Regenstein Library, Chgo., Rush Med. Coll., Chgo., Beckman Inst., Urbana, Ill., Chrysler Corp., Auburn Hills Corp. Hdqs. Bd. dirs. Greening of Detroit Commn. Staff sgt. U.S. Army, 1943-45, ETO. Fellow AIA (bd. dirs. Chgo. chpt. 1976-78, R.J. Reynolds award 1964), Chgo. Archtl. Found. (trustee 1969-85), Thomas Jefferson Found. (trustee 1972-74), Friends of Modern Art (bd. dirs.), Detroit Inst. Art. Home: 1045 Cedar Bend Dr Ann Arbor MI 48105 Office: Smith Hinchman & Grylls Assoc Inc 150 W Jefferson Ave Ste 100 Detroit MI 48226-4415

YOUNGWOOD, ALFRED DONALD, lawyer; b. N.Y.C., Apr. 27, 1938; s. Milton and Lillian (Ginsburg) Y.; m. Judith Goldfarb, June 24, 1963; children: Jonathan David, Stephen Michael. BA magna cum laude, Yale U., 1959; LLB magna cum laude, Harvard U., 1962. Bar: N.Y. 1962, D.C. 1970, U.S. Tax Ct. 1964, U.S. Ct. Appeals (2d cir.) 1969. Law clk. to judge U.S. Dist. Ct. N.Y., 1962-63; assoc. Paul, Weiss, Rifkind, Wharton & Garrison, N.Y.C., 1964-70, ptnr., 1970—. Fulbright scholar, London, 1963-64. Mem. ABA, N.Y. State Bar Assn. (chmn. tax sect. 1978-79, exec. com. 1971—, ho. of dels. 1979-80), Assn. of Bar of City of N.Y. Home: 1125 Park Ave New York NY 10128-1243 Office: Paul Weiss Rifkind Wharton 1285 Ave Of The Americas New York NY 10019-6028

YOUNKIN, C. GEORGE, archivist; b. Great Bend, Kan., Oct. 13, 1910; s. Charles Franklin and Nannie Sylvia (Wilson) Y.; student Washburn U., 1932-35, Southeastern U., Washington, 1936-37; m. Ruth Ward, Dec. 27, 1939 (dec. 1980); children: Karen (Mrs. John R. Postma), Eleta (Mrs. Stephen B. McElroy), Cheryl (Mrs. Thomas R. Gamble), Chip G. With U.S. Dept. Agr., Washington, 1935-51; with Nat. Archives, Ft. Worth, 1951-75, regional archivist for Ark., La., N.Mex., Okla. and Tex., 1968-75; ret., 1975; pres. S.W. Archives Cons., 1975—; archive cons. Kiowa Hist. and Research Assn., Carnegie, Okla. Mem. council exec. com. and historian Boy Scouts Am., Ft. Worth, 1975-80; mem. Gov.'s Adv. Com. on Aged for Tarrant County, 1976-80; mem. Tarrant County Hist. Commn.; trustee Ch. of Good Shepherd, 1980-83; pres. Sr. Citizens Alliance Tarrant County, Inc., 1992-94; legis. chmn. Nat. Assn. Retired Fed. Employees, Arlington, Tex., 1978-93; mem. NEH, 1986-94; mem. Am. Indian Vet.'s Soc. North Tex., 1992—. Served with AUS, 1943-45. Recipient Silver Beaver award Boy Scouts Am., 1966, Order of Arrow, Boy Scouts Am., 1966; pub. service award GSA, 1967, spl. service award Fed. Bus. Assn., 1967, Cross and Flame award United Meth. Ch. and Boy Scouts Am., 1988. Fellow Tex. State Geneal. Soc.; mem. Soc. S.W. Archivists (sec.-treas. 1971-80), Internat. Council Archives, Soc. Am. Archivists (regional activities com.), Nat. Trust Historic Preservation, Kiowa Tia-Piah Soc. Carnegie (Okla.), Westerners Internat., Western History Assn., Tex. Hist. Assn. Dir., Llano Estacado Heritage Quar., 1974-82. Home and Office: 3501 Quail Ln Arlington TX 76016-3304

YOUNT, DAVID EUGENE, physicist, university official; b. Prescott, Ariz., June 5, 1935; s. Robert Ephram and Jeannette Francis (Judson) Y.; m. Christel Marlene Notz, Feb. 22, 1975; children—Laura Christine, Gregory Gordon, Steffen Jurgen Robert, Sonja Kate Jeannette. B.S. in Physics, Calif. Inst. Tech., 1957; M.S. in Physics, Stanford U., 1959, Ph.D in Physics, 1963. Instr. Princeton U., 1962-63, asst. prof. physics, 1963-64, Minn. Mining and Mfg. fellow, 1963; NSF postdoctoral fellow U. Paris, Orsay, France, 1964-65; rsch. assoc. Stanford Linear Accelerator Ctr. Stanford U., 1965-69; assoc. prof. U. Hawaii, 1969-73, prof., 1973—, chmn. dept. physics and astronomy, 1979-85, acting asst. v.p. for acad. affairs, 1985-86, v.p. rsch. and grad. edn., 1986-95. Mem. Am. Phys. Soc., Undersea and Hyperbaric Med. Soc., Am. Chem. Soc., U.S. Tennis Assn., Sigma Xi. Republican. Lutheran. Achievements include development (with J. Pine) of first high-energy positron beam, (with others) of SLAC two-meter streamer chamber; discovery (with others) of rho (1600) and psi (3772) mesons; development and experimental verification of theoretical model describing the nuclei which initiate bubble formation in aqueous media, including blood and tissue. Home: 5468 Opihi St Honolulu HI 96821-1914 Office: U Hawaii 2505 Correa Rd Honolulu HI 96822-2219 *Actualizing my potential is the central theme of my life. I have the potential to work, to play, to learn, to love, to teach, and to understand. These are not conscious goals so much as forces which motivate my behavior. I work very hard, not for success, but because fulfillment requires an effort. I try to be honest, not as a goal, but because dishonesty interferes with learning, loving, teaching and understanding. I enjoy children, not because I'm an affectionate adult, but because I see that we are involved in the same process.*

YOUNTS, SANFORD EUGENE, university administrator; b. Davidson County, N.C., Aug. 29, 1930; m. Ruth Wilson; children—Gregory Sanford, Leslie Joan. B.S., N.C. State U., 1952, M.S., 1955; Ph.D., Cornell U., 1957. Asst. prof. agronomy U. Md., College Park, 1957-59; eastern agronomist Am. Potash Inst., 1959-60; assoc. prof. N.C. State U., Raleigh, 1960-64; southern regional dir. Potash Inst. N.Am., 1964-67, v.p., 1967-69; dir. rural devel. ctr. U. Ga., Tifton, 1969-72; v.p. for services U. Ga., Athens, 1972—. Editor: (with others) Potassium in Agriculture, 1966, monographs on soil fertility; contbr. articles to profl. jours. Co-chmn., bd. trustees Ctr. for PVO/Univ. Collaboration in Devel., Cullowhee, N.C.; chmn. State Heart Fund Campaign, Ga., 1983, 84; chmn. bd. trustees South-East Consortium, Chapel Hill, N.C. 1981. Named Outstanding Prof., N.C. State U., 1963, Disting. Alumnus, N.C. State U. Coll. Agr. and Life Scis.; recipient Order of May Decoration, Argentine Govt., 1994. Fellow Soil Sci. Soc. Am., Am. Soc. Agronomy, Crop Sci. Soc. Am.; mem. AAAS, Phi Kappa Phi. Lodge: Kiwanis (pres. 1976, disting. pres. 1977). Office: U Ga 300 Old College Athens GA 30602

YOUREE, BEVERLY B., library science educator; b. Jackson, Tenn., Mar. 29, 1948; d. Beverly Durward and Rebecca Wade B.; m. Mack Moore Youree, May 26, 1973; 1 child, Roderick Buford. BA, Union U., 1969; MLS, Peabody Coll., 1970; EdD, Vanderbilt U., 1984. Reserves circulation libr. Mid. Tenn. State U. Murfreesboro, 1970-74, instr. libr. sci., 1974—, mem. faculty senate, 1984-90, sec.-treas., 1987-88; chmn. vis. coms. So. Assn. Evaluation Teams, 1989—; pres. Concerned Faculty and Adminstrv. Women, 1986-90. Contbr. articles to profl. jours. State founder, coord. Tenn. Exhibitors' and Media Profls. Tour; mem. adv. bd. John Wiley & Sons Pub. Co., 1991—; active Middle Tenn. State U.; mem. faculty senate, 1984-90, sec.-treas., 1987-88, mem. unvi. libr. com., 1981-83, sec. 1981-82; mem. ad hoc com. on edn., curriculum svc. and facilities, 1975-76; mem. faculty senate legis. com., 1980-83, sec. 81-83; mem. non-instructional assignment semester com., 1988-90, sec. 88-89, chair 89-90; mem. com. on status of women, 1988-94; mem. grad. coun., 1988-90; active So. Assn. Evaluation Teams, chair vis. coms., 1989-90, 91, 92, 93, 94; pres. Concerned Faculty and Adminstrv. Women, 1986-90; chmn. Commn. on Status of Women, 1994—. Mem. ALA (mem. state liaison to young adult svcs. divsn. 1988—, mem. outstanding theatre for the college bound list revision com. 1988), NEA, Tenn. Libr. Assn. (chmn. coll. libr. sect. 1979-80, 88-89, chair vol. state book award com. 1980—, co-chair exhibits for state conv. 1985—, Frances Neal Cheney award 1993), Southeastern Libr. Assn. (sec. sch. libr. sect. 1986-88, chair-elect sch. libr. sect. 1988-90, chair, 1990-92, co-chair exhibits for conv. 1988-90, 90-92), Tenn. Edn. Assn. (sec. higher edn. dept. 1989-93, pres. 1993—, mem. instructional and profl. devel. commn. 1991-94, past pres. and sec. Middle Tenn. State U. chpt.), Tenn. Assn. Sch. Librs., Middle Tenn. Edn. Assn., Assembly Literature for Adolescents, Soc. Sch. Librs. Internat. (mem. legis. task force 1988-89), Kappa Delta Pi (mem. nominating com. mem. 1991-92, mem. Theta Omicron chpt., treas. 1981—, assoc. counselor 1983-86, counselor 1987-94, Svc. to Edn. award), Phi Delta Kappa. Democrat. So. Baptist. Avocations: knitting, reading, needlepoint. Home: 3567 Castlewood Dr Murfreesboro TN 37129-4605 Office: Middle Tenn State U Dept Ednl Leadership PO Box 184 Murfreesboro TN 37132-0184

YOUREE, GENE TASSEY, tool design engineer; b. Murfreesboro, Tenn., June 23, 1930; s. Buford Henry and Daisy Mae (Dennis) Y.; m. Lois Jean Ragan, Mar. 23, 1951; children: Pamela Joyce, Stephen Harold. Student, U. Tenn., 1966-69. Machinist Hamm Tool & Die Co., Nashville, 1966-69; purchasing agt. Dolphin Industry, Nashville, 1969-70; tool designer Peterson Tool Co., Nashville, 1970-76, design engr., 1977-80, head dept. engring., 1980—. Patentee in field. With U.S. Army, 1951. Mem. Masons, Order of

Ea. Star. Baptist. Avocation: woodworking. Office: Peterson Tool Co 739 Fesslers Ln Nashville TN 37210-4300

YOURZAK, ROBERT JOSEPH, management consultant, engineer, educator; b. Mpls., Aug. 27, 1947; s. Ruth Phyllis Sorenson. BCE, U. Minn., 1969; MSCE, U. Wash., 1971, MBA, 1975. Registered profl. engr., Wash., Minn. Surveyor N.C. Hoium & Assocs., Mpls., 1965-68, Lot Surveys Co., Mpls., 1968-69; site layout engr. Sheehy Constrn. Co., St. Paul, 1968; structural engring. aide Dunham Assocs., Mpls., 1969; aircraft and aerospace structural engr., program rep. Boeing Co., Seattle, 1969-75; engr., estimator Howard S. Wright Constrn. Co., Seattle, 1976-77; dir. project devel. and adminstrn. DeLeuw Cather & Co., Seattle, 1977-78; sr. mgmt. cons. Alexander Grant & Co., Mpls., 1978-79; mgr. project systems dept., project mgr. Henningson, Durham & Richardson, Mpls., 1979-80; dir. project mgmt., regional offices Ellerbe Assocs., Inc., Mpls., 1980-81; pres. Robert Yourzak & Assocs., Inc. Mpls., 1982—; lectr. engring. mgmt. U. Wash., 1977-78; lectr., adj. asst. prof. dept. civil and mineral engring. and mech./indsl. engring. Ctr. For Devel. of Tech. Leadership, Inst. Tech.; mgmt. scis. dept. Sch. Mgmt. U. Minn., 1979-90, bd. adv. inst. tech., 1989—; founding mem., membership com., mem. Univ. of Minn. com. Minn. High Tech. Coun., 1983—; speaker in field. Author: Project Management and Motivating and Managing the Project Team, 1984. Chmn. regional art group experience Seattle Art Mus., 1975-78; mem. Pacific N.W. Arts Council, 1977-78, ex-officio adviser Mus. Week, 1976; bd. dirs. Friends of the Rep. Seattle Repertory Theatre, 1973-77; mem. Symphonics Seattle Symphony Orch., 1975-78. Scholar Boeing Co., 1967-68, Sheehy Constrn. Co., summer 1967. Named An Outstanding Young Man of Am., U.S. Jaycees, 1978. Mem. Am. Soc. Tng. and Devel. (So. Minn. chpt.), Project Mgmt. Inst. (cert. project mgmt. profl., speaker, founding pres. 1985, chmn., adv. com. 1987-89, bd. dirs 1984-86, program com. chmn. and organizing com. mem. Minn. chpt. 1984, speaker, project mgr. internat. mktg. program 1985-86, chmn. internat. mktg. standing com. 1986, long range and strategic planning com. 1988-93, chmn., 1992, v.p. pub. rels. 1987-88, ex-officio dir. 1989, 1992, internat. pres. 1990, chmn. bd. 1991, ex-officio chmn. 1992, internat. bd. dirs., chmn. nominating com. 1992), Am. Cons. Engrs. Coun. (peer reviewer 1986-89), Am. Arbitration Assn. (mem. Mpls. panel of constrn. arbitrators), Minn. Surveyors and Engrs. Soc., ASCE (chmn. continuing edn. subcom. Seattle chpt. 1976-79, chmn. program com. 1978, mem. transp. and urban planning tech. group 1978, Edmund Friedman Young Engr. award 1979, chmn. continuing edn. subcom. 1979-80, chmn. energy com. Minn. chpt. 1980-81, bd. dir. 1981-89, sec. 1981-83, v.p. profl. svcs. 1983-84, v.p. info. svcs. 1984-85, pres. 1986-87, past pres. 1987-89, fellow 1988—, speaker), Inst. Indsl. Engrs. (pres. Twin Cities chpt. 1985-86, chmn. program com. 1983-84, bd. dirs. 1985-88, awards com., chmn. 1984-89, speaker), Cons. Engrs. Council Minn. (chmn. pub. rels. com. 1983-85, vice chmn., 1988, chmn., 1989, program com. chmn. Midwest engrs. conf. and exposition 1985-90, speaker, Honor award 1992), Inst. Mgmt. Cons. (cert. mgmt. cons.), Mpls. Soc. Fine Arts, Internat. Facility Mgmt. Assn., Am. Soc. Engring. Edn., Rainer Club (co-chmn. Oktoberfest), Sierra Club, Chowder Soc., Mountaineers, North Star Ski Touring, Chi Epsilon (life). Office: 7320 Gallagher Dr Ste 325 Minneapolis MN 55435-4510

YOUSTEN, ALLAN ARTHUR, microbiologist, educator; b. Racine, Wis., Nov. 9, 1936; s. Albert Andrew and Alice Emily (Standiford) Y.; m. Anna Richardson; children: Joanne E., Kenneth A. BS, U. Wis., Madison, 1958; PhD, Cornell U., 1963. Microbiologist Internat. Minerals and Chem. Corp., Libertyville, Ill., 1965-69; spl. NIH postdoctoral fellow U. Wis., Madison, 1969-71; prof. microbiology Va. Poly. Inst. and State U., Blacksburg, 1971—; vis. prof. Ariz. State U., 1987, Heriot-Watt U., Edinburgh, U.K., 1994. 1st lt. U.S. Army, 1963-65. Fulbright-Hayes fellow Pasteur Inst., Paris, 1980. Office: Va Poly Inst and State U Biology Dept Blacksburg VA 24061

YOVICH, DANIEL JOHN, educator; b. Chgo., Mar. 5, 1930; s. Milan D. and Sophie (Dorociak) Y.; m. Anita Barbara Moreland, Feb. 7, 1959; children: Daniel, Amy, David, Julie Ann. Ph.B., DePaul U., 1952; M.A., Governors State U., 1975, M.S., 1976. Cert. reality therapist, cert. profl. mgr., PMA instr. Formulator Nat. Lead Co., 1950-52, 56-59; researcher Montgomery Ward, Chgo., 1959-62; tech. dir. Riley Bros., Inc., Burlington, Iowa, 1962-66, Mortell Co., Kankakee, Ill., 1966-70; exec. dir. Dan Yovich Assos., 1970-79; asst. prof. Purdue U., Hammond, Ind. 1979-84, assoc. prof., 1984-90, prof., 1990—; instr. Army Security Agy. Sch., 1954-56; instr. Napoleon Hill Acad., 1965-66; cons. Learning House, Inc., 1964—; instr. Kankakee C. C. Continuing Edn., 1976; assoc. Hill, Zediker & Assocs. Psychologists, Kankakee, 1975-79; mem. adv. bd. Nat. Congress of Inventor Orgns., 1984. Author: Applied Creativity; prdr., moderator: (program) Careers Unlimited, Sta. WCIU-TV, Chgo., 1967; contbr. articles to profl. jours. Mem. community adv. council Governors State U., 1978. Served to 1st lt. AUS, 1952-56. Recipient Outstanding Citizen Award News Pub. Co. Am., 1971, Outstanding Tchr. award Purdue U., 1980, 82, 83, Faculty Service award Nat. U. Continuing Edn. Assn., 1984, Disting. Service award Purdue U.-Calumet Alumni Assn., 1988, Arthur Young award Venture Mag., 1988. Mem. World Future Soc., Nat. Mgmt. Assn., Am. Soc. Tng. and Devel., Am. Soc. Profl. Supervision (exec. sec. 1986), Inventors and Entrepreneurs Soc. Ind. (founder, exec. dir. 1984), Global Intuition Network, Internat. Creativity Network, Infantry Officer Cand. Sch. Alumni Assn. (life), Napoleon Hill Found., Inst. Reality Therapy, Inst. Contemporary Living, Soc. Am. Inventors (life), Am. Legion, K.C. Patentee game Krypto, coating Sanitane. Home: 6736 Waveland Hammond IN 46323 Office: Purdue U (Calumet) 2200 169th St Hammond IN 46323-2094

YOVICICH, GEORGE STEVEN JONES, civil engineer; b. Belgrade, Yugoslavia, June 2, 1929; s. Steven and Draginja (Djurdjevic) Y.; m. Sofija Sckulic, Feb. 3, 1960; 1 son, Steven. B.S. in Civil Engring, High Tech. Sch., Belgrade; M.S.C.E., U. Darmstadt, Germany, 1956; Ph.D. in Bus. and Adminstrn, U. Fla. Registered profl. engr., Ill. and other states. Civil engr. Hollabird & Root, Chgo., 1956-58; bridge engr. Div. Hwys. Ill. Dept. Transp., Chgo., 1958-70; v.p.-project mgr. Arcadia Internat. & Co., Skokie, Ill., 1956-70, chmn. bd., pres. 1970—; chmn. bd. Arcadia Engring. Internat. Inc.; pres. Arcadia Internat. Inc., 1977—; v.p. Hoppmann & Assocs. Inc., Evanston, Ill., 1987—; projects mgr. Midwest, Granite Constrn. Co.; Prof. structural engring. Northwestern U.; prof. math. and structural engring. U. Ill. at Chgo. and Urbana; v.p. Arcadia Nat. Builders; mem. bd. trustees Mchts. Funds Bank, Internat. Bank, Miami, Fla. Legis. asst., mem. hwys. com., mem. traffic safety com., utilities com., r.r. and aviation com., welfare com., Ill. Ho. of Reps., 1970—; advisor Internat. Parliment for Safety and Peace, UN; bd. dirs. Oakton C.C., Skokie, Sch. Dist. 68, Skokie. Maj. AUS, 1954-56. Mem. ASCE, Registered Profl. Engrs. Soc.

YOVITS, MARSHALL CLINTON, computer and information science educator, university dean; b. Bklyn., May 16, 1923; s. Louis Frederick and Rebecca (Gerber) Y.; m. Anita S. Friedman, Aug. 2, 1952; children: Bruce J., Mara F., Steven. B.S., Union Coll., Schenectady, 1944, M.S., 1948; M.S., Yale U., 1949, Ph.D., 1951. Sr. physicist John Hopkins U., 1951-56; physicist electronics br. Office Naval Rsch., Washington, 1956, head info. systems br., 1956-62; dir. Naval Analysis Group, 1962-66; prof., chmn. dept. computer and info. sci. Ohio State U., 1966-78, prof., 1978-79; prof. computer and info. sci. Sch. of Sci., Ind. U., Purdue U., Indpls., 1980—, dean., 1980-93, prof. emeritus Ind. U., Purdue U., Indpls., 1993—; gen. chmn. Computer Sci. conf. NSF, 1973. Editor: (with Scott Cameron) Self-Organizing Systems, Proc. Interdisciplinary Conf., 1960, Large-Capacity Memory Techniques for Computing Systems, 1961 (with George T. Jacobi, Gordon D. Goldstein) Self-Organizing Systems, 1962, (with D.M. Gilford, R.H. Wilcox, E. Staveley, H.D. Lerner) Research Program Effectiveness, 1966, Advances in Computers. Vol. 11, 1971; editor: series Advances in Computers, Vols. 13-40; contbr. rsch. articles to profl. jours. AEC fellow, 1950-51, Indpls. Ctr. Advanced Rsch. fellow, 1988-89; recipient Navy Superior Civilian Service award, 1964; Navy Outstanding Performance award, 1961. Fellow AAAS (chmn. coun. sect T 1985-88, chmn.-elect 1995), IEEE (computer soc. chmn. awards com. 1989, bd. govs. 1988-89, Computer Pioneer award 1990); mem. Assn. for Computing Machinery (coun., gen. chmn. Computer Sci. conf. 1982), EDUCOM (nominating com.), Sigma Xi. Home: 9016 Dewberry Ct Indianapolis IN 46260-1527

YOW, JOHN STUART, JR., retired internist; b. Mt. Vernon, Ind., Sept. 15, 1926; s. John Stuart and Helen (Keck) Y.; m. Cecelia McGowin, June 6,

1950 (dec. Aug. 14,1 988); children: Tere, Cecelia, John III. Student, Newberry Coll., 1944-45, Ga. Tech, 1945-46; BS, Auburn U., 1948; MD, U. Ala. Sch. Medicine, 1953. Chief resident internal medicine U. Ala., Birmingham, 1958-59; asst. chief internal medicine 3380 USAF Hosp. Biloxi, Miss., 1955-56; chief internal medicine St. Margaret's Hosp., Montgomery, Ala., 1965-67; internist Montgomery, Ala., 1959-93; ret., 1993; standing com. Episcopal Diocese of Ala., Birmingham, 1989—, commn. of ministry, 1989—; admissions com. U. Ala. Sch. Medicine, 1979—. Capt. USAF, 1955-57. Mem. AMA, Med. Soc. Ala., So. Med. Soc., Am. Soc. Internal Medicine, Ala. Soc. Internal Medicine, Am. Coll. Sports Medicine, Montgomery Country Club, Capital City Club. Episcopalian. Avocations: photography, music. Home: 2177 Allendale Rd Montgomery AL 36111-1017

YOW, RAYMOND MURRAY, insurance company executive, retired physician; b. Raleigh, N.C., Apr. 12, 1924; s. Vernon Spencer and Nell P. Yow; m. M.L. Collins, Feb. 3, 1951 (div. 1988); children: Patricia, Margaret, Norman; m. Cathaleen F. Tawes, Apr. 27, 1988. Student, Va. Mil. Inst., 1941-43, U. Chgo., 1944; BS, U. Ill., 1945, MD, 1948. Diplomate Am. Bd. Urology. Practice medicine specializing in urology. Salisbury, Md., 1955-87, ret., 1987; sr. v.p. Med. Mutual Liability Ins. Soc. Md., Hunt Valley, Md., 1975-83, chief exec. officer, 1983—, also chmn. bd., 1983—. Served to lt. (j.g.) USN, 1949-51. Mem. ACS, Am. Urol. Assn. (pres. mid-Atlantic sect. 1973), Soc. Internat. de Urologie. Republican. Methodist. Avocations: golf, boating. Home: 412 Pine Bluff Rd Salisbury MD 21801-7111 Office: Med Mutual Liability Ins Soc 225 International Cir Hunt Valley MD 21030

YOW, THOMAS SIDNEY, III, college administrator; b. Raleigh, N.C., July 12, 1943; s. Thomas Sidney Jr. and Christine (Southerland) Y.; m. Julia Bryson; children: Robert, Steve. BA, Meth. Coll., 1966; MDiv, Duke U., 1971, EdD, 1982; DD, Meth. Coll., 1989. Dir. admissions, fin. aid Meth. Coll., Fayetteville, N.C., 1973-77; asst. to pres. Louisburg (N.C.) Coll., 1977-85; pres. Martin Meth. Coll., Pulaski, Tenn., 1985-91, Young Harris (Ga.) Coll., 1991—; bd. dirs. Towns County Bank, Hiawassee, Ga. Bd. dirs. Blue Ridge EMC, Young Harris, Ga., 1994—, Cub Scouts, Louisburg, 1977; mem. commn. on colls. JACS, 1994—; mem. nat. adv. com. Atlanta Com. Olympic Games, 1992—. Paul Harris fellow, 1988. Mem. Towns County C. of C. (bd. dirs. 1992-95). Office: Young Harris Coll Young Harris GA 30582

YRIGOYEN, CHARLES, JR., church denomination executive; b. Phila., Dec. 9, 1937; s. Charles and Erma Mae (Suters) Y.; m. Jeanette Alice Brittingham, Dec. 13, 1958; children: Debra Jean, Charles III. BS in Econs., U. Pa., 1959; BD, Lancaster (Pa.) Theol. Sem., 1962; ThM, Ea. Bapt. Theol. Sem., Phila., 1964; PhD, Temple U., 1973; DD (hon.), Albright Coll., 1987. Ordained to ministry United Meth. Ch., 1960. Pastor various chs. Meth. Ch., Pa., 1958-66; campus min. Meth. Ch., Phila., 1966-68; chaplain, prof. religion Albright Coll., Reading, Pa., 1968-82; gen. sec. Gen. Com. on Archives and History, United Meth. Ch, Madison, N.J., 1982—; vis. scholar Union Theol. Sem., N.Y.C., 1980, adj. prof., 1982-93; adj. prof. ch. history Drew U., Madison, 1982—; adj. prof. Moravian Theol. Sem., Bethlehem, Pa., 1994—; mem. exec. com. World Meth. Coun., 1986—; bd. dirs. Wesley Works Editl. Project. Author: Acts for Our Time, 1987; editor: Reformed and Catholic, 1978, Catholic and Reformed, 1979; editor Meth. History Jour., 1982—. Masland fellow Union Theol. Sem., 1975, 80. Mem. World Meth. Hist. Soc. (gen. sec. 1987—), Wesley Hist. Soc., Wesleyan Theol. Soc., Am. Soc. Ch. History, Charles Wesley Soc. Republican. Home: 2 Hemlock Ln Morristown NJ 07960 Office: Gen Com on Archives and History PO Box 127 Madison NJ 07940

YSSELDYKE, JAMES EDWARD, psychology educator, research center administrator; b. Grand Rapids, Mich., Jan. 1, 1944; 2 children. Student in psychology, Calvin Coll., 1962-65; BA in Psychology, Biology, Western Mich. U., 1966; MA in Sch. Psychology, U. Ill., 1968, PhD, 1971. Lic. consulting psychologist, Minn. Tchr. spl. edn Kent County Juvenile Ct. Ctr., Grand Rapids, 1966-67; research asst. U. Ill. Inst. Research on Exceptional Children, 1969-70, teaching asst. dept. ednl. psychology, 1970; sch. psychology intern Oakland County Schs., Pontiac, Mich., 1970-71; asst. prof. sch. psychology Pa. State U., 1971-75, assoc. prof., 1975; assoc. prof. U. Minn., Mpls., 1975-79, prof., 1979-91, dir. Inst. Research on Learning Disabilities, 1977-83, dir. Nat. Sch. Psychology Inservice Tng. Network, 1977-83; dir. sch. psychology program U. Minn., 1987-93, dir. Nat. Ctr. on Ednl. Outcomes, 1991—; advisor, cons. and researcher in field. Author: (with J. Salvia) Assessment in Special and Remedial Education, 1985, 5th edit., 1991, (with B. Algozzine and M. Thurlow) Critical Issues in Special and Remedial Education, 1992, Strategies and Tactics for Effective Instruction, 1992, (with) S.L. Christenson) The Instructional Environment System-II, 1993; editor: Exceptional Children, 1984-90; assoc. editor: The School Psychologist, 1972-75; mem. editorial bd., cons. editor numerous jours.; contbr. chpts. to books and articles to jours. Dir. Nat. Ctr. on ednl. outcomes, 1991—. Recipient Disting. Teaching award U. Minn., 1988; fellow NIMH, 1967-69; grantee in field. Fellow APA (Lightner Witmer award 1973); mem. ASCD, Am. Psychol. Soc., Am. Ednl. Rsch. Assn., Coun. for Exceptional Children (Rsch. award 1995), Nat. Assn. Sch. Psychologists, Coun. for Learning Disabilities, Coun. for Ednl. Diagnostic Svcs. Office: Nat Ctr on Ednl Outcomes 350 Elliott Hall 75 E River Rd Minneapolis MN 55455-0280

YTTERBERG, RALPH WARREN, company executive; b. Chgo., Sept. 15, 1927; s. Victor E. and Ruby E. (Liljestrom) Y.; m. Janet P. Gustafson, Sept. 11, 1948; children: Steven, Charles, Alan. B.A., Albion Coll., 1950. Various supervisory positions Corning Glass Works, Bradford, Pa., 1950-57, Albion, Mich., 1950-57, Corning, N.Y., 1950-57; prodn. control mgr. Dresser Clark, Olean, N.Y., 1957-59; pres. Dresser Europe, Brussels, Belgium, 1969-72; div. gen. mgr. Singer Co., S.C., 1960-69; corp. v.p. Singer Co., N.Y.C., 1960-69; group pres. Rockwell Internat., Pitts., 1969-72; sr. v.p. human resources, sr. v.p. ops. Dresser Industries, Inc., Dallas, 1972—. Bd. dirs. Dallas Opera, 1978—, Dallas Symphony. Fellow Machinery & Allied Products Inst.; mem. Am. Mgmt. Assn. (planning council), Northwood Country Club, Petroleum Club. Republican. Avocations: golfing, fishing. Home: 6562 Briarmeade Dr Dallas TX 75240-7912 Office: Indresco Inc 2121 San Jacinto St Dallas TX 75201

YTTREHUS, ROLV BERGER, composer, educator; b. Duluth, Minn., Mar. 12, 1926; s. Chris and Petra (Andal) Y. BA, U. Minn., Duluth, 1950; MusM, U. Mich., 1953; studies with Goffredo Petrassi, Acad. Santa Cecilia, Rome, 1962; studies with Nadia Boulanger, Paris, 1954-55; studies with Roger Sessions, Princeton, N.J., 1957-60; studies with, Aaron Copland, Tanglewood, 1958. Instr. music U. Mo., Columbia, 1963-68; asst. prof. Purdue U., West Lafayette, Ind., 1968-69; assoc. prof. U. Wis., Oshkosh, 1969-77; prof. Rutgers U., New Brunswick, N.J., 1977—; recorded with Composers Recs., Inc., 1st Edition Records, Centaur Records; lectr. Internat. Ferienkurse Für Neue Musik, Darmstadt, Germany, 1994. Composer: Music for Winds, Percussion and Viola, 1961, Expressioni Per Orchestra, 1962, Music for Winds, Percussion, Cello and Voices, 1969, Quintet, 1973, Sextet, 1974, Gradus Ad Parnassum, 1979, Sonata for Percussion and Piano, 1983, Explorations for Solo Piano, 1985, Sonata for Cello and Piano, 1988, Raritan Variation (solo piano), 1989, Symphony No. 1, 1995. Served with USN, 1944-46, PTO. Recipient award Minn. Fedn. Music Clubs, 1957, Margaret Lee Crofts award, Tanglewood, Mass., 1958, award N.J. Coun. on Arts, 1989; Fulbright scholar, 1954, scholar Govt. of Italy, 1960-62; fellow Composers Conf., 1971, 72, 75; grantee Nat. Endowment for Arts, 1976. Mem. Internat. Soc. Contemporary Music (bd. dirs. 1979—), Am. Composers Alliance (rec. award 1985), Composers Guild N.J. (pres. 1985-92). Avocation: reading. Home: One Woods Circle East Brunswick NJ 08816 Office: Rutgers U Music Dept New Brunswick NJ 08903

YU, AITING TOBEY, engineering executive; b. Chekiang, China, Jan. 6, 1921; came to U.S., 1945, naturalized, 1978; s. H.K. and A. (Chow) Y.; m. Natalie Kwok, Nov. 10, 1951; children: Pamela, Leonard T. BS, Nat. Cen. U., Chungking, China, 1943; SM, MIT, 1946; PhD, Lehigh U., 1949; MBA, Columbia U., 1972. Registered profl. engr., Fla. Asst. prof. engring. NYU, 1949-51; design engr. Hewitt-Robins Inc., 1951-54, chief design engr., 1955-58, engring. mgr., 1958-59; dir. systems engring. Hewitt-Robins Inc., Totowa, N.J., 1967-68, v.p. ops. Hewitt-Robins Inc.; tech. dir. West S.Am. Overseas Corp., N.Y.C., 1959-67; prin. A.T. Yu Cons. Engrs., 1971-72; co-founder, chmn. Orba Corp., Mountain Lakes, N.J., 1972—, now chmn. emeritus.

Contbr. articles to profl. jours; patentee in field. Recipient nat. outstanding engring. achievement awards by ASCE, NSPE, AIME, ASME. Mem. NAE, AIME (chmn. minerals processing div., SME pres. 1986), NSPE, Nat. Acad. Forensic Engrs., Nat. Acad. Engring., Sigma Xi. Home: 962 Gullane Dr Cypress Run Tarpon Springs FL 34689 Office: Orba Corp 1250 W Sam Houston Pky S Houston TX 77251-1281

YU, ANTHONY C., religion and literature educator; b. Hong Kong, Oct. 6, 1938; came to U.S., 1956, naturalized, 1976; s. P.C. and Norma (Au) Y.; m. Priscilla Tang, Sept. 18, 1963; 1 son, Christopher Dietrich. B.A., Houghton Coll., 1960; S.T.B., Fuller Theol. Sem., 1963; Ph.D., U. Chgo., 1969. Instr. U. Ill.-Chgo., 1967-68; asst. prof. U. Chgo., 1968-74, assoc. prof., 1974-78, prof., 1978-88, Carl Darling Buck disting. svc. prof. humanities Div. Sch., Dept. East Asian Langs., Comparative Lit. and Civilizations, English, 1988—; assoc. vis. prof. Ind. U., Bloomington, 1975; Whitney J. Oates short-term vis. fellow Princeton U., 1986; Disting. vis. prof. Faculty of Arts, U. Alta., Can., 1992; mem. joint com. on study Chinese civilization Am. Coun. Learned Socs., 1980-86, bd. dirs., 1986-94; regional chmn. Mellon Fellowship in Humanities, 1982-92. Asst. editor Jour. Asian Studies, 1975-78; co-editor Jour. Religion, 1980-89; author, editor: Parnassus Revisited, 1973; editor, translator: The Journey to the West, 4 vols., 1977-83, Essays on The Journey to the West and Other Studies (in Chinese), 1989; co-editor (with Mary Gerhart) Morphologies of Faith: Essays on Religion and Culture in Honor of Nathan A. Scott, Jr., 1990. Recipient Gordon J. Laing prize, 1983; Danforth fellow, 1960-67; Guggenheim fellow, 1976-77; NEH translation grantee, 1977-82; Am. Coun. Learned Socs. fellow, 1986-87; Masterworks Study grantee NEH Seminar for Pub. Sch. Tchrs., 1992. Mem. Assn. for Asian Studies, Am. Acad. Religion, MLA, Am. Comparative Lit. Assn., Milton Soc. Am. Club: The Arts. Home: Pentnouse 8 950G N Clark St Chicago IL 60610 Office: U Chicago 1025 E 58th St Chicago IL 60637-1509

YU, ELEANOR NGAN-LING, advertising company executive; b. Hong Kong, July 28, 1958; d. Seong Yuon and Esther (Lam) Chan. Student, Oxford U., 1976; BA with honors, U. Ottawa, 1979; MBA, Golden Gate U., 1986. Copywriter, intern Ogilvy & Mather, Ottawa, Can.; asst. account exec. DDB, N.Y.C.; account exec. JWT, N.Y.C.; account supr. Mktg. Group, Phila.; chief exec. officer, pres. AdLand, San Francisco. Mem. com. San Francisco Grandprix Assn., 1988; bd. dirs. Chinatown Youth Ctr., San Francisco, 1986, United Way, San Francisco, 1986, San Francisco C. of C., 1995, Inter Assn. Advertising Agys., 1995, Asian Am. Arts Found., 1995; mem. San Francisco Econ. Vitality Com., 1994; bd. overseers U. Calif., San Francisco Med./Nursery Sch.; bd. advisor Nat. Asian and Pacific Am. Coalition. Named Entrepreneur of Yr. SBA, 1995. Mem. NAFE, Asian Bus. Assn. (pres. 1985-86), Pacific Affairs Council (chmn. 1988—), San Francisco C. of C. (mem. bd. dirs. 1994), Golden Gate U. Alumni Assn. (bd. dirs. 1986—), Inter Assn. of Advt. Agy's. Office: AdLand Advertising Inc 2728 Hyde St San Francisco CA 94109

YU, GEORGE TZUCHIAO, political science educator; b. London, May 16, 1931; s. Wangteh and Ying (Ho) Y.; m. Priscilla Chang, Aug. 11, 1957; children: Anthony, Phillip. A.B., U. Calif., Berkeley, 1954, M.A., 1957, Ph.D., 1961. Asst. prof. polit. sci. U. N.C. Chapel Hill, 1961-65; assoc. prof. polit. sci. U. Ill., Urbana, 1965-70; prof. U. Ill., 1970—, head dept., 1987-92, dir. Ctr. for East Asian and Pacific Studies, 1992—; dir. grad. studies, 1981-85; vis. sr. lectr. polit. sci. Univ. Coll., Nairobi, 1968; chair U.S.-China African Studies Exchange Com., 1985—. Author: The Chinese Anarchist Movement, 1961, 65, Party Politics in Republican China, 1966, China and Tanzania, 1970, China's African Policy, 1975, Intra-Asian International Relations, 1977, Modern China and Its Revolutionary Process, 1985, American Studies in China, 1993, China in Transition, 1994. Grantee Social Sci. Rsch. Coun., 1967-68, 70-71, NEH, 1978-81, 84-86, Earhart Found., 1976-77, 81-83, 88, Ford Found., 1985-87, 89, 92. Mem. Assn. Asian Studies, African Studies Assn. Office: 702 S Wright St Urbana IL 61801-3631

YU, HYUK, chemist, educator; b. Kapsan, Korea, Jan. 20, 1933; s. Namjik and Keedong (Shin) Y.; m. Gail Emmens, Jan. 20, 1964; children: Jeffrey, Steven, Douglas. BS in Chem. Engring., Seoul Nat. U., 1955; MS in Organic Chemistry, U. So. Calif., 1958; PhD in Phys. Chemistry, Princeton U., 1962. Rsch. assoc. Dartmouth Coll., Hanover, N.H., 1962-63; rsch. chemist Nat. Inst. Sci. and Tech., Washington, 1963-67; asst. prof. U. Wis., Madison, 1967-69, assoc. prof., 1969-78, prof. chemistry, 1978—, Evan P. Helfaer chair chemistry, 1991—; cons. polymer sci. and standards div. Nat. Inst. Standards and Tech., Gaithersburg, Md., 1967—, Eastman Kodak Co., various locations, 1969—, Procter and Gamble Co., Cin., 1988—, Japan Synthetic Rubber Co., Tsukuba, 1991—; Fulbright-Hays lectr. Inha U., Inchon, Korea, 1972; chmn. Gordon Rsch. Conf. Polymer Physics, 1986, 93. Contbr. articles to refereed pubs. John Simon Guggenheim Found. fellow, 1984; recipient Alexander von Humboldt award Humboldt Found., 1992; High Polymer Physics award Am. Phys. Soc., 1994. Fellow Am. Phys. Soc.; mem. Am. Chem. Soc. (exec. com. polymer chemistry div., editorial adv. bd. 1988-91), N.Y. Acad. Scis., Biophys. Soc., Materials Rsch. Soc., Korean Chem. Soc. (life), Polymer Soc. Korea (life), Sigma Xi (chpt. pres. 1987-88). Office: Univ Wis 1101 University Ave Madison WI 53706-1322

YU, JEN, medical educator; b. Taipei, Taiwan, Jan. 23, 1943; came to U.S., 1969; s. Chin Chuan and Shiu Lan (Lin) Y.; m. Janet Chen, June 16, 1973; children—Benjamin, Christopher. M.D., Nat. Taiwan U., 1968; Ph.D. in Physiology, U. Pa., 1972. Diplomate Am. Bd. Phys. Medicine and Rehab. Intern. Phila. Gen. Hosp., 1972-73; resident in phys. medicine and rehab Hosps. U. Pa., 1973-75; asst. prof. dept. phys. medicine and rehab. U. Pa. Sch. Medicine, Phila., 1975-76, U. Tex. Health Sci. Ctr., San Antonio, 1976-79, assoc. prof., 1979-81; prof. dept. phys. medicine and rehab. U. Calif.-Irvine Coll. Medicine, 1981-82, prof., chmn. dept. phys. medicine and rehab., 1982—. Contbr. articles to med. jours. Mem. Am. Acad. Phys. Medicine and Rehab., Am. Congress Rehab. Medicine, Assn. Acad. Physiatrists, Am. Assn. Anatomists, Soc. for Neurosci. Office: U Calif Irvine Med Ctr Dept Phys Medicine and Rehab 101 City Dr Orange CA 92668-2901

YU, ROBERT KUAN-JEN, biochemistry educator; b. Chungking, China, Jan. 27, 1938; came to U.S., 1962; s. Shin-cheng and June Chien-yu (Tsao) Y.; m. Helen Chow, July 1, 1972; children: David S., Jennifer S. BS, Tunghai U., Taiwan, 1960; PhD, U. Ill., 1967; Med.ScD. (hon.), Tokyo, 1980; MA (hon.), Yale U., 1986. Rsch. assoc., instr. Albert Einstein Coll. Medicine, Bronx, 1967-72; asst. prof. Yale U., New Haven, 1973-75, assoc. prof., 1975-82, prof., 1983-88; prof. biochemistry, chmn. dept. Va. Commonwealth U., Richmond, 1988—; mem. study sect. NIH, Washington, 1980-84; mem. Bd. Lab. Svcs., Va., 1994—. Editor: Ganglioside Structure Function and Biomedical Potential, 1984, New Trends in Ganglioside Research, 1988; contbr. over 450 articles to profl. publs. Josiah Macy scholar, 1979; grantee NIH, 1975—; recipient Jacob Javits award NIH, 1984-91, Alexander von Humboldt award, 1990, Va. Outstanding Scientist of Yr. award, 1995. Mem. AAAS, Am. Soc. Neurochemistry (mem. coun. 1983-86, 91—), Internat. Soc. Neurochemistry, Soc. Neurosci., Am. Soc. Biochemistry and Molecular Biology, Am. Chem. Soc., Am. Soc. Cell Biology, N.Y. Acad. Sci. Home: 306 Cheswick Ln Richmond VA 23229-7660 Office: Va Commonwealth U Med Coll Va Richmond VA 23298-0614

YU, VICTOR LIN-KAI, physician, educator; b. Mpls., Jan. 9, 1943; s. Robert S.H. and Victoria (Hsiao) Y.; m. Deborah Lin, June 19, 1971; children: Chen Ming, Kwan Ting. BA, Carleton Coll., 1965; MD, U. Minn., 1970. Internship and residency U. Colo., Denver, 1970-72; residency Stanford U., Palo Alto, Calif., 1974, postdoctoral fellow, 1975-77; prof. medicine U. Pitts., 1978—; chief bd. sci. counsels NIH, 1986-92; chief infectious disease sect. VA Med. Ctr., Pitts., 1981—; disting. lectr. Am. Soc. Microbiology, 1988; Malia lectr. Shadyside Hosp., 1992; Berris lectr. U. Toronto, 1993; Rubin lectr. Berkshire AHEC. Contbr. rsch. on Legionnaires' disease to sci. publs. Recipient Disting. Rsch. award Am. Legion, 1982, Health Svcs. Rsch. Found., 1984; named disting. scientist Chinese Med. Soc., Taipei, Taiwan, 1988; recipient Gold medal for Outstanding Contbn. to Sci., Fed. Exec. Bd., 1993, Citation of Merit, Allegheny County, Pa., 1993. Fellow ACP; mem. Am. Chinese Ams. (officer Pitts. sect. 1978—). Home: 87 Longue Vue Dr Pittsburgh PA 15228-1538 Office: U Pitts Divsn Infectious Disease W931 Montefiore Pittsburgh PA 15213

YU, YING SHIH, history educator, researcher; b. Tientsin, China, Jan. 22, 1930; s. Hsieh-chung and Ya-yen (Yew) Y.; m. Monica Shu-ping Chen, June 6, 1964; children: Sylvia, Judy. BA, New Asia Coll., Hong Kong, 1952; PhD, Harvard U., 1962; LL.D. (hon.), Chinese U. Hong Kong, 1977; LittD, Middlebury Coll., 1984. Asst. prof. history U. Mich., Ann Arbor, 1962-66; assoc. prof. Chinese history Harvard U., Cambridge, 1966-69, prof. Chinese history, 1969-77; pres. New Asia Coll., Hong Kong, 1973-75; Charles Seymour prof. history Yale U., New Haven, 1977-87; Michael Henry Strater univ. prof. Princeton (N.J.) U., 1987—; overseas cons. Project of Confucian Ethics, Singapore, 1983-88. Author: Trade and Expansion in Han China, 1967, History and Thought, 1976, Religious Ethic and Merchant Class in Early Modern China, 1986; author, editor: Early Chinese History in People's Republic of China, 1981; co-editor Milton Jour. Asian Studies, 1987—. Mem. Academia Sinica. Home: 4588 Province Line Rd Princeton NJ 08540-2212 Office: Princeton U 211 Jones Dr Princeton NJ 08540

YU, YI-YUAN, mechanical engineering educator; b. Tiejin, China, Jan. 29, 1923; came to U.S., 1947, naturalized, 1962; s. Tsi-Chi and Hsiao-Kung (Wang) Y.; m. Eileen Hsiu-Yung Wu, June 14, 1952; children: Yolanda, Lisa. BS, Tienjin U., 1944; MS, Northwestern U., 1950, PhD, 1951. Prof. mech. engring. (Poly Inst. Bklyn.), 1957-66; cons. engr. Gen. Electric Space Div., Valley Forge, Pa., 1966-70; Disting. prof. aero. engring. (Wichita State U.), 1972-75; mgr. components and analysis Rockwell Internat. (Rocketdyne, , Canoga Park, Calif., 1975-79, exec. engr. Energy Systems, 1979-81; dean engring. N.J. Inst. Tech., Newark, 1981-85, prof. mech. engring., 1981-93, prof. emeritus, 1993—; vis. prof. Cambirdge U., 1960; advisor Middle East Tech. U., Ankara, Turkey, 1966; lectr. Gen. Electric Co., 1963-73; mem. ad hoc com. on dynamic analysis USN, 1968-69; cons. internat. adv. panel Chinese U. Devel. Project, 1983, David W. Taylor Naval Ship Rsch. and Devel. Ctr., 1987-88; cons. Atty. Gen.'s Office State N.J., 1982-84. Author: Vibrations of Elastic Plates, 1995; co-author: Handbook in Engineering Mechanics, 1962. Guggenheim fellow, 1960; Air Force Office Sci. Research grantee, 1956-66; NASA grantee, 1967-69, 74-75. Fellow AIAA (assoc.), ASME (life); mem. Am. Soc. Engring. Edn., Am. Soc. for Composites, Am. Acad. Mechanics (chmn. com. mech. edn. 1993-94), Sigma Xi, Phi Kappa Phi, Pi Tau Sigma, Tau Beta Pi. Presbyterian. Home: 24 Gordon Rd Essex Fells NJ 07021-1604 Office: 323 King Blvd Newark NJ 07102 *At the end of each day, let everyone of us ask the question: Have I done the best I can this day to make the world a better place to live for myself and for my fellow human beings? As long as the answer is yes, it does not matter whether one is a teacher, farmer, worker, businessperson or homemaker.*

YUAN, SHAO WEN, aerospace engineer, educator; b. Shanghai, China, Apr. 16, 1914; came to U.S., 1934, naturalized, 1954; s. Ti An and Chieh-huang (Chien) Y.; m. Hui Chih Hu, Nov. 5, 1950. B.S., U. Mich., 1936; M.E., Stanford U., 1939; M.S., Calif. Inst. Tech., 1937, Ph.D., 1941. Rsch. engr. Glenn Martin Co., 1942-43; chief of rsch. Helicopter div. McDonnell Aircraft Corp., 1943-45; instr. Washington U. St. Louis, 1944-45; asst. prof. Poly. Inst. Bklyn., 1946-49, assoc. prof., 1949-54, prof., 1954-57; ptnr. von Kármán, Yuan & Arnold Assocs., 1955-63; prof. aerospace engring. U. Tex., 1958-68; prof., chmn. mech. engring. div. George Washington U., 1968-78, chmn. civil, mech. and environ. dept., 1973-78, 80-81, prof. emeritus, 1984—; pres. RISE, Inc., 1977-85; Canadair Chair prof. U. Laval, Can., 1957-58; chmn. adv. com. Joint Inst. for Advancement of Flight Sci., 1970-84; hon. prof. Zhejiang U., 1987—; cons. Edo Aircraft Corp., Aerojet Corp., Cornell Aero. Lab., Dept. of Interior, Oak Ridge Nat. Lab., N.Am., Aviation, Inc., Fairchild-Hiller Corp., McDonnell-Douglas Corp., The World Bank; hon. adviser Nat. Center Research of China, Taiwan, 1958-68; chmn., founder 1st U.S.-China Conf. on Energy, Resources, and Environment, 1982; founder Consortium of Univs. for Promoting Grad. Aerospace Studies, 1984; founder Disting. Lecture Series on Founds. of Aerospace Research and Devel., 1986. Author: Foundations of Fluid Mechanics, 1967; Contbr. to: High Speed Aerodynamics and Jet Propulsion series, 1959, Energy, Resources, and Environment: Procs. at 1st U.S.-China Conf., 1982. Recipient Outstanding Achievements award George Washington U., 1981; named Outstanding Educator of Am., 1970, Outstanding Chinese American, 1983. Fellow AAAS, AIAA; mem. ASME (life), Am. Soc. Engring. Edn., Soc. Engring. Sci. (bd. dirs. 1973-78, pres. 1977), Torchbearers Caltech, Founding Grant Soc. of Stanford U. (charter), John Montieth Soc. of U. Mich. (charter), Sigma Xi, Phi Kappa Phi, Pi Tau Phi, Sigma Gamma Tau, Pi Tau Sigma, Tau Beta Pi, Tau Xi Sigma. Achievements include patents in field. Home: 1400 Geary Blvd Apt 1505 San Francisco CA 94109-6570 *As engineers and scientists, we are concerned with that "something beyond"; consequently, the utmost achievement of an engineer is to create what has never been, for the improvement of quality of life.*

YUAN, SIDNEY WEI KWUN, cryogenic engineer, consultant; b. Hong Kong, July 30, 1957; came to U.S., 1975; s. Chia Chi and Tso Tak (Wong) Y.; m. Katherine K.Y. Dai, Sept. 8, 1981; children: Jacquelyn Kate, Chrystal Sidney. BSc, UCLA, 1980, MSc, 1981, PhD, 1985. Rsch. asst. UCLA, 1980-81, rsch. engr., 1981-85, teaching asst., 1984-85; rsch. sci. Lockheed Missiles & Space Co., Palo Alto, Calif., 1985—; cons. Toyo Sanso Inc. Japan, 1990—, Applied Aerotek Inc., 1991—, Compliance Engring. and Tech., 1992—, Applied Scis. Labs., 1992—; lectr. fundamentals of super-conductivity UCLA, 1989. Contbr. over 30 articles on cryogenics, thermodynamics, heat and mass transport to profl. jours. Recipient Nat. Excellence Recognition award Space Found., 1985, Superior Performance Team award Lockheed, 1990. Mem. AIAA (Engr. of Yr. award 1991), Am. Inst. Chem. Engrs. (Indsl. Rsch. award 1994), Cryogenic Soc. Am. (vice chmn. no. Calif.), Sigma Xi, Tau Beta Pi. Republican. Avocations: table tennis, go. Home: 4964 Adagio Ct Fremont CA 94538-3201 Office: Lockheed Missiles & Space Co 3251 Hanover St Bldg 205 Palo Alto CA 94304-1121

YUDOF, MARK G., lawyer, educator, academic administrator; b. Phila., Oct. 30, 1944; s. Jack and Eleanor (Parris) Y.; m. Judith Lynn Gomel, July 11, 1965; children: Seth Adam, Samara Lisa. BA, U. Pa., 1965, LLB, 1968. Bar: Pa. 1970, U.S. Supreme Ct. 1974, U.S. Dist. Ct. (we. dist.) Tex. 1975, U.S. Ct. Appeals (5th cir.) 1976, Tex. 1980. Law clk. to judge U.S. Ct. Appeals (5th cir.), 1968-69; assoc. gen. counsel to ABA study FTC, 1969; research assoc. Harvard Ctr. Law and Edn., 1969-70; sr. staff atty., 1970-71; lectr. Harvard Grad. Sch. Edn., 1970-71; asst. prof. law U. Tex., Austin, 1971-74, prof., 1974—, assoc. dean, 1979-84, James A. Elkins Cent. Chair in Law, 1983—, dean, 1984-94, exec. v.p., provost, 1994—, John Jeffers Rsch. Chair in Law, 1991-94; of counsel Pennzoil vs. Texaco, 1987; mem. adv. bd. Inst. for Transnat. Arbitration, 1988—. Am. Jour. Edn., 1991—; chmn. bd. contbrs. to Tex. Lawyer, 1988—; mem. nat. bd. contbrs. Am. Lawyer Newspapers Group, Inc., 1988—. Author: When Government Speaks, 1983 (Scribes Book award 1983, cert. merit ABA 1983), (with others) Educational Policy and the Law, 1992, (with others) Gender Justice, 1986. Mem. Tex. Gov.'s Task Force on Sch. Fin., 1989-90, Tex. Gov.'s Select Com. on Edn., 1988; bd. dirs. Freedom to Read Found., 1989-91; mem. adv. bd. Austin Diagnostic Clinic Community, 1989—; mem. Austin Cable Commn., 1981-84, chmn., 1982; mem. nat. panel on sch. desegregation rsch. Ford Found., 1977-80; mem. state exec. com. Univ. Interscholastic League, 1983-86; mem. rsch. adv. com. Ctr. for Policy Rsch. in Edn., 1985—; bd. dirs. Jewish Children's Regional Svc., 1980-86. Recipient Teaching Excellence award, 1975, Most Meritorious Book award Scribes, 1983, Humanitarian award Austin region NCCJ, 1988, Antidefamation League Jurisprudence award, 1991; fellow Queen Mary and Westfield Coll., U. London. Fellow Tex. Bar Found., Am. Bar Found.; mem. ABA (legal edn. and admissions to bar sect. 1984—), Am. Law Inst., Tex. Bar Assn., Assn. Am. Law Schs. (chmn. law and socn. sect. 1983-84, mem. exec. com. 1988-90), Univ. Club, Headliners Club, Met. Club. Avocation: collecting antique maps. Office: U Tex Exec Vice Pres/Provost MAI 201 Austin TX 78712

YUE, AGNES KAU-WAH, otolaryngologist; b. Shanghai, Peoples Republic China, Dec. 1, 1947; came to U.S., 1967; d. Chen Kia and Nee Yuan (YingO ; m. Gerald Kumata, Sept. 25, 1982; children: Julie, Allison Benjamin. BA, Wellesley Coll., 1970; MD, Med. Coll. Pa., 1974; postgrad., Yale U., 1974-78. Intern Yale-New Haven Hosp., 1974-75, resident, 1975-78; fellow U. Tex. M.D. Anderson Cancer Ctr., Houston, 1978-79; asst. prof. U. Wash., Seattle, 1979-83; physician Pacific Med. Ctr., Seattle, 1979-90; pvt. practice Seattle, 1990—. Fellow Am. Acad. Otolaryngology, Am. Coll. Surgeons; mem. Northwest Acad. Otolaryngology. Avocations: sailing, opera, profl. voice, cooking. Office: 1801 NW Market St Ste 410 Seattle WA 98107-3909

YUE, ALFRED SHUI-CHOH, metallurgical engineer, educator; b. China, Nov. 12, 1920; s. Choy Noon-woo and Sze Man-hun (Tom) Y.; m. Virginia Chin-wen Tang, May 21, 1944; children: Mary, Raymond Yuan, John, Ling Tsao, David, Nancy Chang. B.S., Chao-tung U., 1942; M.S., Ill. Inst. Tech., 1950; Ph.D., Purdue U., 1956. Assoc. engr. Taiwan Aluminum Co., 1942-47; instr. Purdue U., 1952-56; research engr. Dow Chem. Co., Midland, Mich., 1956-62; sr. mem. Lockheed, Palo Alto Research Lab., 1962-69; now cons.; prof. engring. and applied sci. U. Calif., Los Angeles, 1969—; hon. prof. Xian Jiao-tong U., China, 1980; cons. LTV Aerospace Co., Lockheed Missile & Space Co., Atlantic Richfield Co.; Sec.-gen. Chinese Culture Assn. in U.S.A., 1967, also; bd. dirs. Chinese scholar to U.S.A. Fellow AIAA (assoc.); mem. AAAS, AIME, Assn. Soc. Metals, Materials Rsch. Soc., Sigma Xi, Sigma Pi Sigma, Tau Beta Pi, Phi Tau Phi (pres. 1978-82). Office: U of Calif Los Angeles CA 90095-1595

YUECHIMING, ROGER YUE YUEN SHING, mathematics educator; b. Mauritius, Feb. 25, 1937; s. James and Marie Yuechiming; m. Renée Bethery, Nov. 9, 1963; children: Françoise, Marianne, Isabelle. BSc with 1st class honours, U. Manchester, Eng., 1964, PhD, 1967. Asst. U. Strasbourg, France, 1967-69; lectr. math. U. Paris VII, 1970—; participant math. confs. and seminars in numerous countries; referee various math. jours. Contbr. over 70 articles on ring theory to sci. jours. of numerous countries. Mem. French Math. Soc., Am. Math. Soc., London Math. Soc., Belgian Math. Soc. Achievements include introduction of concept of p-injective modules, new approaches in ring and module theory leading to a better understanding of von Neumann regular rings, V-rings, self-injective rings and generalizations. Home: 38 rue du Surmelin, 75020 Paris France Office: U Paris VII Unite de Recherche Associée 212, Nat Ctr Sci Rsch 2 Pl Jussieu, 75251 Paris France

YUELYS, ALEXANDER, former cosmetics company executive; b. Bronx, N.Y., Aug. 12, 1926; s. Dionisyus and Anastasia (Stathes) Y.; m. Nicoletta Lardas, Dec. 9, 1950; 1 son, Jordan. B.A., Hunter Coll., 1952. C.P.A., N.Y. With Arthur Young, 1952-56, Haskins & Sells, 1950-52; with Fabergé, Inc., N.Y.C., 1956-83, exec. v.p., chief fin. officer, dir.; dir. Brut Prodns., Inc., Am. Stage Co. Bd. dirs. St. Michael's Home for Aged, v.p., 1984—. Served with USAAF, 1945-46. Mem. Fin. Execs. Inst., Nat. Assn. Accountants. Home: PO Box 836 Alpine NJ 07620-0836

YUEN, DAVID ALEXANDER, geophysics and computational physics educator; b. Hong Kong, June 14, 1948; s. Joseph A. and Angela (Luk) Y. BS, Calif. Inst. Tech., 1969; MS, Scripps U., 1973; PhD, UCLA, 1977. NATO and NSF postdoctoral fellow U. Toronto, 1978-80; postdoctoral fellow, then asst. prof. to assoc. prof. Ariz. State U., Tempe, 1980-85; assoc. prof. U. Colo., Boulder, 1985; assoc. prof. to prof. U. Minn., Mpls., 1985—. Fulbright fellow, 1991-92, von Humboldt sr. fellow, 1992. Office: U Minn Supercomputer Inst 1200 Washington Ave S Minneapolis MN 55415-1284

YUEN, THOMAS CHI KWAN, business executive; b. Shanghai, China, Sept. 10, 1951; children: Jennifer, Connie. Student, Wah Yan Coll., Kowloon, Hong Kong, 1969; BSEE, U. Calif., 1974. With Hughes Aircraft-MTS, Oceanside, Calif., 1974-75; sr. engr. Computer Automation, Irvine, Calif., 1975-77, 78-79; sr. design engr. Sperry Univac, Irvine, Calif., 1977-78; co-founder, chief ops. officer AST Rsch., Inc., Irvine, Calif., 1980-92. Mem. bd. overseers U. Calif. Irvine; bd. dirs. Hist. and Cultural Found. Orange County. Recipient award of Excellence Asian Am. High Tech. Conv., 1986, Spirit of Enterprise award Chinese Am. Coun. of Hist. and Cultural Found. Orange County, 1987; named Hon. Prof. China's Cen. Inst. Nationalities, Beijing, 1991. Mem. U. Calif. Irvine Chancellor's Club. Office: AST Rsch Inc PO Box 19658 Irvine CA 92713-9658

YUENGER, JAMES LAURY, journalist; b. Green Bay, Wis., June 13, 1939; s. David Anthony and Carol Jeanette (Haines) Y.; m. Blanche Schulz, Nov. 9, 1963 (div. 1985); 1 child, Jay Noel; m. Mary Catherine Henry, Oct. 5, 1985. BA, St. Norbert Coll., DePere, Wis., 1961. Corr. Moscow Chgo. Tribune, 1971-72, fgn. news editor, 1972-74, corr. London, 1974-76, asst. news editor, 1976-77, roving corr. Middle East, Europe, 1977-81, corr. Poland, 1986-87, editorial writer, 1987-88, nat. news editor, 1988-89, fgn. news editor, 1989-94, sr. writer, 1995—; news U. Chgo., 1981-85;. With U.S. Army, 1957-61. Recipient Alumni award humanities St. Norbert Coll., 1977. Mem. Press Club (Chappaquiddick, Mass.), Am. Kite Club. Avocation: kite flying. Office: Chgo Tribune Co 435 N Michigan Ave Chicago IL 60611-4001

YUHAS, ALAN THOMAS, investment management executive; b. Ashland, Pa., Nov. 27, 1948; s. George Jacob and Elizabeth Jane (Belfonti) Y.; married; children: Daisy Mariella, Alan George. BA, Temple U., 1973, JD, 1980. Statistician Ct. Common Pleas, Phila., 1974-76; mktg. rep. Control Data Corp., Phila., 1976-77; mgr. Chase Econometrics, Bala Cynwyd, Pa., 1977-80; prin. Sparrowhawk Ltd., Phila., 1980-86; prin. Rolland Ross Asset Mgmt., Blue Bell, Pa., 1986—, also bd. dirs.; bd. dirs. RYQ, BIRR, AARR; cons. Gifford Fong Assocs., Walnut Creek, Calif., 1980-83, Fidelity Bank N.A., Phila., 1983-87. Served to capt. U.S. Army, 1966-69, Vietnam. Mem. Phi Beta Kappa. also: Roll & Ross Asset Mgmt 587 Skippack Pike Ste 400 Blue Bell PA 19422-2158

YUILL, THOMAS MACKAY, academic administrator, microbiology educator; b. Berkeley, Calif., June 14, 1937; s. Joseph Stuart and Louise (Dunlop) Y.; m. Ann Warnes, Aug. 24, 1960; children: Eileen, Gwen. BS, Utah State U., 1959; MS, U. Wis., 1962, PhD, 1964. Lab. officer Walter Reed Army Inst. Rsch., Washington, 1964-66; med. biologist SEATO Med. Research Lab., Bangkok, Thailand, 1966-68; asst. prof. U. Wis.-Madison, 1968-72, assoc. prof., 1972-76, prof., 1976—; dept. chmn., 1979-82, assoc. dean., 1982-93; dir. Inst. Environ. Studies, 1993—; cons. NIH, Bethesda, 1976-86; chmn. Viral Diseases Panel, U.S.-Japan Biomed. Scis. Program, 1979-86, Am. Com. Arbovirology, 1982—; bd. dirs. Cen. Tropical Agrl. Res. Teaching, Turrialba, Costa Rica, 1988—. Contbr. chpts. to books, articles to profl. jours. Served to capt. U.S. Army, 1964-66. Recipient grants state and fed. govts., 1968—. Mem. Orgn. Tropical Studies (pres. 1979-85), Wildlife Disease Assn. (treas. 1980-85, pres. 1985-87, editl. bd. 1989—), Am. Soc. Tropical Medicine and Hygiene (editorial bd. 1984-92), Am. Soc. Microbiology, Am. Soc. Virology, Wildlife Soc., Sigma Xi. Avocations: flying; cross-country skiing; music. Office: U Wis Inst Environ Studies 40 Sci Hall 550 N St Madison WI 53706

YUKEI, HASEBE YOSHIKAZU, religious studies educator; b. Tokyo, July 7, 1929; s. Yoichi Koyu and Shii (Watanabe) H.; m. Reiko H. Nobuta, Oct. 28, 1963. B degree, Komazawa U., Tokyo, 1955, MA, 1957, PhD, 1989. Lectr. Zen culture Shogen Jr. Coll., Minokama, Gifu, Japan, 1963-65; asst. prof. Aichigakuin U., Nagoya, Aichi, Japan, 1965-75, prof. Buddhist and Zen culture lit., 1975—. Author: Introduction to the Studies of Ming and Ching Buddhism, 1979, Historical Studies of Buddhist Orders in the Ming and Ching Dynasties, 1993. Mem. Japanese Assn. Indian and Buddhist Studies, Japanese Assn. for Religious Studies, The Nippon Buddhist Rsch. Assn., Tokai Assn. of Indian and Buddhist Studies, The Japan Art History Soc. Office: Aichigakuin U, 12 Araike, Iwasaki, Nishin-cho, Aichi-ken Japan

YULE, JOE, JR. See ROONEY, MICKEY

YULISH, CHARLES BARRY, public affairs executive; b. Cleve., Oct. 14, 1936; s. Isadore and Minna (Scott) Y.; m. Barbara Pearlman, Aug. 22, 1973 (div. 1983); 1 child, Alexi Jules-Nicholas. AA in Govt., U. Fla., 1957; BS in Polit. Sci., Kent State U., 1959; MPA, Syracuse U., 1961; postgrad., NYU, 1961-63, New Sch. Social Rsch., 1963-64. Spl. projects officer U.S. Atomic Energy Commn., Washington and N.Y.C., 1961-63; pub. affairs mgr. Atomic Indsl. Forum, N.Y.C., 1963-66; pres., chief exec. officer Charles Yulish Assocs. Inc., N.Y.C., 1966-83; exec. v.p. Wesley, Brown & Bartle Inc., N.Y.C., 1984-87; voice chmn., pitnr. Holt, Ross & Yulish, Edison, N.J., 1988-92; exec. v.p., mng. dir. E. Bruce Harrison Co., Washington, 1993-95; v.p. corp. comm. U.S. Enrichment Corp., Bethesda, Md., 1995—; bd. dirs. Intermedia News and Feature Svcs. Writer, dir. (film) Energy: We Have the Choices, 1978 (Golden Eagle award); editor: Hard vs. Soft Energy Paths, 1980; author over 60 articles on classical music. Founder, bd. dirs. Serge Koussevitsky Archives Soc., N.Y.C., 1977; bd. dirs. Imperial Russia Hist. Soc., 1986, U.K. and U.S. Friends of Benjamin Franklin. Maxwell fellow Syracuse U., 1960. Mem. Internat. Assn. Pub. Participation Practitioners, Pub. Rels. Soc. Am.,

Counselors Acad., Soc. Profl. Mgmt. Cons. (cert.). Home: 1438 Q St NW Washington DC 20009

YUN, PETER SUBUENG, economics educator; b. Yong-Wol, Korea, June 7, 1936; s. Sea Young and Soon Oak (Kim) Y.; m. Sandy J. Forsythe, June 21, 1970; children: Amy Rebecca, Peter Jung. B.A., U. Ga., 1966, Ph.D., 1975; M.A., U. Okla., 1968. Asst. prof. econs. Clinch Valley Coll., Wise, Va., 1974-79, assoc. prof., 1979-86, prof., 1986—; chmn. bus. div., 1979-86. Pres., Universal Bus. Services, Wise, 1981-88, East West Quality Assocs., 1991—; dir. Va. Gov's. Sch for the gifted Clinch Valley Coll., 1987—. Invest-in-America grantee, 1979, 80, NSF grantee, 1991; recipient Outstanding Alumni award Emmanuel Coll., 1984. Mem. Am. Econ. Assn., So. Econ. Assn., Bibl. Archaeology Soc. Home: PO Box 2620 Wise VA 24293-2620 Office: Clinch Valley Coll College Ave Wise VA 24293

YUN, SAMUEL, minister, educator; b. Ulsan, Republic of Korea, June 19, 1958; came to U.S., 1984; s. Eungoh and Chanho (Kim) Y.; m. Kyungim Martha Mah, Jan. 10, 1984; children: Miriam, Joseph, Mikyung. BTh, Yonsei U., Seoul, Republic of Korea, 1980, MTh, 1984; MA in Religion, U. Dubuque, 1985; ThM, Harvard U., 1987; postgrad., Boston U., 1987—. Ordained to ministry Korean Presbyn. Ch. in Am., 1987. Preacher Carmel-Peniel Presbyn. Ch., Rewey, Wis., 1984-85; assoc. pastor, dir. edn. Korean Presbyn. Ch. in Boston, Cambridge, Mass., 1985-88; pastor The Peace Ch., Brockton, Mass., 1988-90, Korean Presbyn. Garden Ch., Hackensack, N.J., 1990-93, Princeton (N.J.) Korean Presbyn. Ch., 1993—; prof., dean acad. affairs Presbyn. Theol. Sem. in Am., Corona, N.Y., 1986—; sec. gen. Coun. Korean Chs. in New Eng., Boston, 1989-90; rec. sec. Coun. Korean Chs. in N.J., 1991-93. Author: Living the Word, 1990, Living the Prayer, 1994; translator The Black Gold and Isram, 1985. Mem. Am. Acad. Religion, Soc. Bibl. Lit. Home: 9 Sayre Dr Princeton NJ 08540 Office: 500 Plainsboro Rd Plainsboro NJ 08536

YUNCKER, BARBARA, science writer; b. Greencastle, Ind.; d. Truman George and Ethel (Claflin) Y. A.B., DePauw U., D.Litt., 1976. Copyreader Wall St. Jour.; various editing positions N.Y. Post; asst. dep. commnr. commerce N.Y. State, 1956-57; medicine and sci. editor N.Y. Post, 1959-84; med. columnist Good Housekeeping mag., 1963-76. Contbr. to nat. mags. Recipient Page One award Newspaper Guild N.Y., 1961; Adolf Meyer award, 1961; Alumni citation DePauw U., 1963; Page One award Newspaper Women's Club N.Y., 1963, 68; Albert Lasker med. journalism award, 1967, 69; Am. Psychiat. Assn. award, 1974; Silurians award, 1975; Matrix award Women in Communications, 1979. Mem. Newspaper Guild (exec. com. local 3 1976-82), v.p. 1981-82, chmn. N.Y. Post unit 1976-79, internat. v.p. 1981-83), Nat. Assn. Sci. Writers, Soc. Journalists and Authors. Democrat. Home: Tunnel Hill Canaan NY 12029 Office: 235 E 22nd St New York NY 10010

YUNICH, DAVID LAWRENCE, consumer goods consultant; b. Albany, N.Y., May 21, 1917; s. Max A. and Bess (Fellman) Y.; m. Beverly F. Blickman, June 11, 1941; children: Robert Hardie, Peter B. AB, Union Coll., 1939, LLD, 1964; postgrad., Harvard U., 1939-40. Mdse. councilor L. Bamberger & Co., Newark, 1947-48, pres., dir., 1955-62; v.p. Macy's, N.Y.C., 1941-51, sr. v.p., 1951-62; pres. Macy's, 1962-71; vice chmn. bd. R. H. Macy & Co. Inc., 1971-73, dir., 1958-73; chmn. Met. Transp. Authority, 1974-1977; bd. dirs. W.R. Grace & Co., East River Savs. Bank, Dean & DeLuca Inc., Caswell-Massey Co. Ltd., Fidelity Charitable Gift Trust, Fidelity Advisor Emerging Asia Fund, Inc., Fidelity Advisor Korea Fund, Inc. Chmn. Mayor's Coun. Econ. and Bus. Advisers, N.Y.C., 1973-74; mem. N.Y. State Banking Bd., 1968-74; bd. dir. Regional Plan Assn.; chmn. Gov.'s Commn. Financing Mass Transp., 1970-72; mem. Grace Commn.; pres. Greater N.Y. coun. Boy Scouts Am., 1972-1976; trustee Union Coll., 1965-72, Skidmore Coll., 1966-73, Albany Med. Coll., 1967-74, Carnegie Hall Corp., Saratoga Performing Arts; bd. dirs. Ednl. Broadcasting Corp., 1960-68, Nat. Jewish Hosp., Denver, 1960-68; bd. govs., trustee Rutgers U., New Brunswick, N.J., 1958-62. Decorated chevalier confrerie de Chevaliers du Tastevin. Mem. N.Y. C. of C. and Industry (chmn. bd. 1971-74), Retail Dry Goods Assn. (pres. 1964-69), Am. Pub. Transp. Assn. (v.p.), Nat. Retail Mchts. Assn. (bd. dir.), Am. Mgmt. Assn. (bd. dir. 1958-68). Clubs: Harvard Bus. Sch., Harvard, Recess, Univ., Econ. (N.Y.C.); Blind Brook, Scarsdale (Westchester); Saratoga Golf and Polo (Saratoga Springs, N.Y.); Sandy Lane Golf (Barbados, W.I.). Home: 5 Birches Cooper Rd Scarsdale NY 10583 Office: 1114 Avenue Of The Americas New York NY 10036-7701 *I admire those men who, whatever their motives, whatever their goals, are inspired to uncommon levels of accomplishment.*

YUNICH, PETER B., publishing executive; b. N.Y.C., May 9, 1946; s. David Lawrence and Beverly Fay (Blickman) Y.; m. Bonnie Dawn Heiderer, Feb. 17, 1980; children: Whitney, Shannon. BA in Classics, Brown U., 1968; MBA, Harvard U., 1970. Product mgr. Clairol, Inc., N.Y.C., 1970-73; dir. book clubs Doubleday & Co., N.Y.C., 1973-76; exec. v.p. The Charter Co., Jacksonville, Fla., 1977-82; exec. dir. AT&T, Basking Ridge, N.J., 1983-87; pres. Global Transactions Svcs. Co., Basking Ridge, 1987-88, Simon & Schuster Interactive, N.Y.C., 1988—. Home: 7 Highview Ave Basking Ridge NJ 07920 Office: Simon and Schuster 1230 Avenue Of The Americas New York NY 10020-1513

YUNIS, JORGE JOSE, geneticist, pathologist, educator, poet; b. Sincelejo, Colombia, Oct. 5, 1933; s. José and Victoria (Turbay) Y.; m. Malvina Torbay, Jan. 15, 1994; children by previous marriage: George, Olga, Karl, Amira, Omar. MD, Compluiense U., Madrid, 1956, PhD, 1957. Gen. practice medicine Barranquilla, Colombia, 1957-59; resident in clin. pathology U. Minn., Mpls., 1959-62, resident in anat. pathology, 1962-64, mem. faculty, 1965-89, prof., 1969-89, dir. grad. studies of lab. medicine, 1969-74, dir. grad. studies of pathology, 1972-74, chmn. human genetics com. for health scis., 1972-77; mem. faculty Hahnemann U., Phila., 1989-92, prof. dept. neoplastic diseases, 1989-92, vice chmn., assoc. dir. Inst. for Cancer and Blood Diseases, 1989-92, dir. Human Genetics and Molecular Biology Div., 1989-92, prof. dept. pathology, 1991-92; prof. depts. anatomy, pathology, microbiology & immunology Thomas Jefferson U. Med. Coll., Phila., 1993—; dir. cancer biol. dept. anatomy, pathology, cell biology Thomas Jefferson U. Med. Col., Phila., 1993—; vis. prof. numerous univs. Author: Human Chromosome Method, 1965, 75, Biochemical Methods in Red Cell Genetics, 1969, Molecular Pathology, 1975, New Chromosomal Syndromes, 1977, Molecular Structure Human Chromosomes, 1977, Esencia Humana, 1995; contbr. more than 250 articles to profl. jours. Named Clin. Prof. of Yr. Harvard Med. Sch., 1987; honored by Colombian Parliament, Bogota, 1986, 93, Colombian Med. Schs. Assn., 1993. Mem. Leukemia Soc. Am. (trustee 1983-88), Colombian Acad. Medicine. Avocations: poetry, literature, photography. Office: Thomas Jefferson U Jefferson Med Coll 1020 Locust St Philadelphia PA 19107

YURA, JOSEPH ANDREW, civil engineering educator, consulting structural engineer; b. Hazelton, Pa., Apr. 11, 1938; s. Michael and Anna (Sokol) Y.; m. Joan Marie Seman, Aug. 22, 1964; children: Thomas, Christine, Paul, Elizabeth. B.S., Duke U., 1959; M.S., Cornell U., 1961; Ph.D., Lehigh U., 1965. Registered profl. engr., Tex., Pa., Fla. Asst. prof. Lehigh U., Bethlehem, Pa., 1965-66; asst. prof. U. Tex., Austin, 1966-70, assoc. prof., 1970-75, prof., 1975-82, Warren Bellows prof., 1982—. Recipient Gen. dynamics Teaching award U. Tex., 1972; recipient T.R. Higgins Lectureship award Am. Inst. Steel Constrn., 1974, Hussein M. Alharthy Centennial Professorship award U. Tex., Austin, 1987. Mem. ASCE (Raymond C. Reese Rsch. prize 1991), Structural Stability Rsch. Coun., Rsch. Coun. on Structural Connections, Structural Engrs. Assn. Tex., Am. Soc. for Engring Edn., Phi Beta Kappa, Tau Beta Pi. Democrat. Roman Catholic. Home: 5308 Bull Run Austin TX 78727-6608 Office: U Tex Dept Civil Engring 10100 Burnet Rd Austin TX 78758-4445

YURCHENCO, HENRIETTA WEISS, ethnomusicologist, writer; b. New Haven, Mar. 22, 1916; d. Edward and Rebecca (Bernblum) Weiss; m. Basil Yurchenco, June 1936 (div. 1955); 1 child, Peter; m. Irving Levine, 1965 (div. 1979). Student, Yale U., 1935-36; student piano scholarship, Mannes Coll. Music, 1936-38. Radio producer WNYC, WBAI, others, 1939-69; writer, critic, tchr., folk music editor Am. Record Guide and Musical Am., 1959-70; prof. music Coll. City N.Y., 1962-86, Bklyn. Coll., 1966-69, New Sch. for Social Research, 1961-68; co-dir. project for study of women in music, Grad. Ctr. CUNY. Author: A Fiesta of Folk Songs From Spain and Latin

America, 1967, A Mighty Hard Road: A Biography of Woody Guthrie, 1970, !Hablamos! Puerto Ricans Speak, 1971; contbr. articles to profl. jours.; 11 field recs. from Mexico, P.R., John's Island, S.C., Guatemala, Ecuador, Morocco, issued by Libr. Congress, Folkways, Nonesuch, Folkways/Smithsonian Global Village; collections in Libr. Congress, Discoteca Hebrew U., Jerusalem, Arais Montana Inst., Madrid, Inst. Nacional Indigenista, Mexico City. Recipient grants-in-aid Am. Philos. Soc., 1954, 56, 57, 65, 67, 89, grants-in-aid CUNY Faculty Research Fund, 1970, 83, 87; NEH grantee, 1984. Mem. Internat. Council Traditional Music (com. on women's studies), Soc. Ethnomusicology, Soc. Asian Music, Sonneck Soc., Internat. Assn. Study of Popular Music, Am. Musicologists Soc. Research in folk, tribal and popular music for Library of Congress, Mexico, Guatemala, P.R., Spain, Morocco, Balearic Islands, John's Island, S.C., Ireland, 1941-83. Home: 360 W 22nd St New York NY 10011-2600 Office: 139th St And Convent Ave New York NY 10031

YURCHUCK, ROGER ALEXANDER, lawyer; b. Amityville, N.Y., June 9, 1938; s. Alexander and Ella Marie (Munley) Y.; m. Sally Ward, Apr. 14, 1961 (div. 1972); children: Scott, Lauren; m. Susan Holland, June 1, 1985. AB cum laude, Northwestern U., 1959; LLB, Harvard U., 1962. Bar: Ohio 1962. Assoc. Vorys, Sater Seymour and Pease, Columbus, Ohio, 1962-68, ptnr., 1969-71, 73—; ptnr. in charge Cin. office Vorys, Sater Seymour and Pease, 1984—; v.p., gen. counsel Fed. Home Loan Mortgage Corp., Washington, 1971-73; vice chmn., bd. dirs. Securities Investors Protection Corp., Washington, 1982-88. Del. Rep. Nat. Conv., 1980, 84. Mem. ABA, Fed. Bar. Assn., Ohio Bar Assn., Phi Beta Kappa. Republican. Episcopalian. Clubs: Queen City (Cin.); Univ. (Columbus). Office: Vorys Sater Seymour and Pease 221 E 4th St Cincinnati OH 45202-4124

YURCISIN, JOHN, church official; m. Ann Popovich, July 16, 1944; 1 child, Ann Melanie. Grad., N.J. State Coll., 1940, Christ the Saviour Sem., 1944. Ordained, 1944. Asst. pastor St. John's Ch., Hawk Run, Pa.; administr. St. Mary's Ch., Clarence, Pa.; pastor Sts. Peter and Paul Ch., Windber, Pa., 1944-52, Christ the Saviour Parish, Johnstown, Pa., 1952; diocesan chancellor; dean Cathedral Parish, Christ the Saviour Sem., 1951-75; elevated to dignity of Protopresbyter, 1962; prof. Orthodox Christian ethics, Carpatho-Russian history and lang., Ch. Slavonic Christ the Saviour Sem.; vicar gen. Am. Carpatho-Russian Orthodox Diocese, 1990—. Editor The Ch. Messenger, 1949-65, A.C.R.Y. Ann. and Ch. Almanac.; contbr. numerous articles and leaflets in field. Decorated Czech. Orthodox Ch.; Carpatho-Russian Studies chair named in his honor. Mem. Orthodox Soc. of Am. Office: 249 Butler Ave Johnstown PA 15906-2137

YUROW, JOHN JESSE, lawyer; b. Washington, Jan. 30, 1931; s. Louis and Lauretta (Jedeikin) Y.; m. Bette Hilary Troshinsky, Aug. 1, 1953; children—Michael Jay, Gary Alan, Diane Ruth Yurow Beckwith, Lois Anne. A.B., George Washington U., 1953, J.D., 1958. Bar: D.C. 1958, Mich. 1961. Trial atty. Office Regional Counsel, IRS, Detroit, 1958-62; assoc. Arent, Fox, Kintner, Plotkin & Kahn, Washington, 1962-68, ptnr., 1969—; professorial lectr. in law George Washington U., Washington, 1974-76. Past mem. editorial bd. George Washington U. Law Rev.; contbr. articles on tax subjects to profl. publs. Served with U.S. Army, 1953-55. Mem. D.C. Bar Assn. (chmn. taxation div. 1977-78), ABA, Fed. Bar Assn. (chmn. taxation com. 1972-73), Order of Coif, Phi Delta Phi. Democrat. Club: Indian Spring Country (Silver Spring, Md.). Lodge: B'nai B'rith. Avocations: tennis; travel. Home: 931 Clintwood Dr Silver Spring MD 20902-1724 Office: Arent Fox Kintner Plotkin & Kahn 1050 Connecticut Ave NW Washington DC 20036-5303

YURT, ROGER WILLIAM, medical educator, physician; b. Louisville, June 8, 1945; s. Albert William and Mary Louise (McGrath) Y.; m. Joan A. Terry, Sept. 3, 1971; children: Jennifer, Daniel, Gregory. BS in Biology, Loyola U., New Orleans, 1967; MD, U. Miami, 1972. Diplomate Nat. Bd. Med. Examiners. Intern Parkland Meml. Hosp.-Southwestern Med. Sch., U. Tex.-Dallas, 1972-73, resident in surgery, 1973-74; postdoctoral fellow in medicine Robert B. Brigham Hosp.-Harvard U. Med. Sch., Boston, 1974-77; postdoctoral trainee NIH, 1975-77; resident in surgery, then chief resident in surgery N.Y. Hosp.-Cornell Med. Ctr., N.Y.C., 1977-79, acting dir. Burn Ctr., dir. research, 1982-83, dir. Trauma Ctr., 1984—, assoc. prof. surgery, 1982—, vice chmn. dept. surgery Cornell U. Med. Coll., 1987—, acting chmn., 1991-93; acting surgeon-in-chief, The N.Y. Hosp., 1991-93; clin. asst. prof. surgery Uniformed Services U. of Health Sci., Bethesda, Md., 1980-82; clin. asst. prof. gen. surgery Health Sci. Ctr., U. Tex.-San Antonio, 1981-82; chmn. burn com., mem. bd. dirs. Regional Emergency Med. Services of N.Y., 1982-84, mem. trauma ctr. adv. com., 1984—, chmn., N.Y. Bklyn. ACS Com. Trauma, 1994—; dir. Mulhearn Research Lab., N.Y.C., 1982—. Editor: Infections in Surgery, 1981—; contbr. articles to med. jours. Served to maj. M.C., U.S. Army, 1979-82. Grantee United Health Found., 1968-69, NIH, 1984-87; fellow Sch. Medicine, U. Miami, summer 1969-71, USPHS, 1973-75; Irma Hirschl Trust Career Scientist award, 1984-88. Mem. Am. Surg. Assn. Surg. Infection Soc. (charter, chmn. membership com., sec. 1987-90, pres. 1991-92), Assn. Acad. Surgery, Soc. Univ. Surgeons, Internat. Surg. Soc., Am. Assn. for Surgery of Trauma, Ea. Assn. for Surgery of Trauma, Alpha Omega Alpha, Omicron Delta Kappa. Roman Catholic. Office: Cornell U Medical Coll 1300 York Ave New York NY 10021

YUSPEH, ALAN RALPH, lawyer; b. New Orleans, June 13, 1949; s. Michel and Rose Fay (Rabenovitz) Y.; m. Janet Horn, June 8, 1975. B.A., Yale U., 1971; M.B.A., Harvard U., 1973; J.D., Georgetown U., 1978. Bar: D.C. 1978. Mgmt. cons. McKinsey & Co., Washington, 1973-74; adminstrv. asst., legis. asst. Office of U.S. Senator J. Bennett Johnston, Washington, 1974-78; atty. Shaw, Pittman, Potts & Trowbridge, Washington, 1978-79, Ginsburg, Feldman, Weil and Bress, Washington, 1979-82; gen. counsel Com. on Armed Services-U.S. Senate, Washington, 1982-85; ptnr. Preston, Thorgrimson, Ellis & Holman, Washington, 1985-88, Miller & Chevalier, Washington, 1988-91, Howrey & Simon, Washington, 1991—. Editor Law and Policy in Internat. Business jour., 1978-79, Nat. Contract Mgmt. Jour., 1988-92; assoc. editor Pub. Contract Law jour., 1987-91. Chmn. bd. of ethics, City of Balt., 1988—. Served to 1st lt. USAR, 1971-77. Home: 1812 South Rd Baltimore MD 21209-4506 Office: Howrey & Simon 1299 Pennsylvania Ave NW Washington DC 20004-2400

YUSSOUFF, MOHAMMED, physicist, educator; b. Cuttack, India, Aug. 14, 1942; came to U.S., 1991; s. Haji and Nurunnisa Fakhruddin; m. Farhana Begum, Apr. 6, 1969; children: Ashraf, Zeenat, Mustafa. MSc, Delhi U., 1963; PhD, Indian Inst. Tech., Kanpur, 1967. Prof. physics Indian Inst. Tech., Kanpur, 1967-90; vis. prof. physics Mich. State U., East Lansing, 1991—; vis. scientist U. Köln, Germany, 1972-74, U. Western Ont. London, Can., 1990-91; Humboldt scientist Atomic Energy Agy., Jülich, Germany, 1979-81; vis. prof. U. Konstanz, Germany, 1986-89; guest scientist Ford Rsch., Dearborn, Mich., 1991—; mem. physics examination Pub. Svc. Commn., Delhi, India, 1976-86, rsch. grants Univ. Grants Commn., Delhi, 1985-90; bd. dirs. Aligarh (India) Muslim U., 1989-90; dir. Internat. Sch. on Band Structure, Indian Inst. Tech., 1986. Editor: Electronic Band Structure and Its Applications, 1987, The Physics of Materials, 1987; developer of Slow Pace program for teaching science and engineering to deficient students with poor social, economic or school backgrounds. Mem. Am. Phys. Soc., Indian Phys. Soc. Islam. Achievements include pioneering work on theory of freezing, theory of disordered systems, chaneling, clusters, electronic structure, ionic conductors, exhaust gas sensors, and foundations of quantum theory. Home: 31011 Grandview Westland MI 48185-5065 Office: Mich State Univ Dept Physics East Lansing MI 48824-1116 also: Ford Motor Co Scientific Rsch Lab Dept Physics Dearborn MI 48121-2053

YUZEITIS, JAMES RICHARD, information specialist; b. Chgo., Nov. 11, 1942; s Stanley J. and Amy B. (English) Y.; m. Susan C. London, Oct. 7, 1967; children: Timothy, David, Amy. BA in Econs., Loyola U., Chgo., 1965, MS in Personnel Mgmt., 1968. Personnel adminstr. Chgo. Police Dept., 1965-67; personnel asst. McDonald's Corp., Chgo., 1967-69; ops. trainee McDonald's Corp., Washington, 1969-70; personnel mgr. McDonald's Corp., Detroit, 1970-72; licensing mgr. McDonald's Corp., Columbus, Ohio, 1972-73; internat. personnel cons. McDonald's Corp., Oakbrook, Ill., 1973-80, dir. of human resources, 1980-86, dir. human resources devel., 1986-91; pres. Quality Surveys, Inc., Big Timber, Mont., 1991—; cons. Ronald McDonald Children's Charities, Chgo., 1986-88.

Cons. and vol. Ronald McDonald Houses, Chgo., 1987; vol. Crazy Mont. Mus. Soc., Big Timber, 1991-92; bd. dirs. Pioneer Med. Ctr., Big Timber, 1993—. Recipient medal of Merit Cath. Youth Orgn., Chgo., 1960. Mem. Soc. for Human Resource Mgmt., Human Resource Planning Soc., Indsl. Rels. Rsch. Soc. Avocations: ranch mgmt., fishing, music. Home: PO Box 1244 Big Timber MT 59011-1244 Office: Quality Surveys Inc PO Box 1089 Big Timber MT 59011-1089

YZAGUIRRE, RAUL HUMBERTO, civil rights administrator; b. San Juan, Tex., July 22, 1939; s. Ruben Antonio and Eva Linda (Morin) Y.; m. Audrey H. Bristow, Jan. 2, 1965; children: Regina Dolores, Raul Humberto, Elisa Almalinda, Roberto Hayse, Rebecca Morin, Benjamin Ruben. Student, U. Md., 1963-64; B.S., George Washington U., 1968. Registered med. technologist. Student and community activist, 1963-65; active War on Poverty, 1969-74; founder, exec. dir. Interstate Research Assocs (Hispanic cons. firm), Washington, 1969-73; v.p. Center for Community Change, Washington, 1974; community organizer in S.Tex., 1974; pres. Nat. Council of La Raza, Washington, 1974—; lectr. Harvard U., U. Notre Dame, U. Tex., others.; commr. U.S. Nat. Commn. for UNESCO, 1983—; chmn. bd. dirs. Associated SW Investors, 1976—. Editor-in-chief: Agenda, 1974-81. Co-chmn. Nat. Urban Coalition, 1975-83; co-chmn. Working Com. on Concerns of Hispanics and Blacks, 1979—; sec. ind. sector, 1983-84; sec., chmn. Forum of Nat. Hispanic Orgns., 1976-79; chmn. adv. com. I.N.S.; former trustee Common Cause; co-founder, chmn. Nat. Neighborhood Coalition, 1977—. Served with USAF, 1959-62. Recipient Rockefeller Public Service award, 1979, Common Cause Pub. Service award, 1986. Mem. Am. GI Forum, Hispanic Assn. Corp. Responsibility (co-founder, chmn. bd. dirs.). Democrat. Roman Catholic. Office: Nat Council of La Raza 810 1st St NE Fl 3 Washington DC 20002-4227 *The civil rights struggle of the 80's will be the transformation of America to a truly pluralistic society where cultural differences will not only be tolerated, but indeed valued.*

YZERMAN, STEVE, professional hockey player; b. Cranbrook, B.C., Can., May 9, 1965. With Detroit Red Wings, 1983—. Recipient Lester B. Pearson award, 1988-89; named Sporting News NHL Rookie of Yr., NHL All-Rookie Team, 1983-84, 1988-93. Youngest person ever to play in NHL All-Star game, 1984. Office: Detroit Red Wings 600 Civic Center Dr Detroit MI 48226-4419*

ZABAN, ERWIN, diversified manufacturing company executive; b. Atlanta, Aug. 17, 1921; s. Mandle and Sara Unis (Feidelson) Z.; m. Judy Zaban; children: Carol Zaban Cooper, Laura Zaban Dinerman, Sara Kay Franco. Officer Zep Mfg. Co., 1942-62; exec. v.p. Nat. Service Industries, Atlanta, 1962-66, pres., 1966-79, chief exec. officer, 1972-87, chmn., 1975—, also dir.; bd. dir. Engraph, Inc., Wachovia Corp.; elected mem. bd. visitors Berry Coll. Bd. dirs. Atlanta Symphony Orch., 1982, Jewish Home for the Aged, 1985; trustee Atlanta Hist. Soc., 1985. Named Man of Yr. B'nai B'rith, 1977, Father of Yr. Father's Day Coun.; recipient Disting. Svc. award Atlanta Urban League, 1979, NCCJ, 1988, Human Rels. award Anti-Defamation League, 1981, Bd. Govs. award 11-Alive Community Svc. Awards, 1990; named to Ga. State U. Coll. Bus. Adminstrn. Hall of Fame, 1989. Mem. Standard Club, Commerce Club (bd. dirs.). Office: Nat Svc Industries Inc 1420 Peachtree St NE Atlanta GA 30309-3002

ZABCIK, DANIEL D., manufacturing executive; b. Barclay, Tex., Nov. 24, 1928; s. John Alfred and Eleanora (Baletka) Z.; m. Joyce C. Wells, June 7, 1956 (dec. May 1986); children: Carol Zabcik DeWitt, Daniel E., Robert A.; m. Rosemary Ligon, Apr. 11, 1987. BCE, U. Tex., 1950. Registered profl. engr., Tex. Engr. Stran Steel Corp., Houston, 1961-69; v.p. Metallic Bldg. Co., Houston, 1969-78; exec. v.p. Mid-West Steel Bldg. Co., Houston, 1978-82, pres., 1983-86; dir.; exec. v.p. Nat. Components, Inc., Houston, 1989—; pres. Mid-West Metallic, Houston, 1989—; pres., dir. Southwest Bus. Co., Houston, 1987—. Contbr. articles to profl. jours. Maj. USAF, 1950-53. Mem. Gulf Coast Conservation Assn., Pine Forest Country Club. Avocations: golf, racquet ball, hunting, fishing, gardening. Home: 11502 S Kolbe Dr Cypress TX 77429-3303 Office: NCI Bldg Systems Inc 7301 Fairview St Houston TX 77041

ZABEL, EDWARD, economist, educator; b. Orange, N.J., Oct. 17, 1927; s. Otto and Helen (Katzenberger) Z.; m. Norma Nicholson, June 23, 1956; children: Jeffrey, David, Richard. B.A., Syracuse U., 1950; M.A., Princeton U., 1953, Ph.D., 1956. Research asst. Princeton U., 1954-56; economist Rand Corp., Santa Monica, Calif., 1956-58; mem. faculty U. Rochester, N.Y., 1958-81; prof. econs. U. Rochester, 1967-81; prof. econs. U. Fla., Gainesville, 1981-83, Matherly prof. econs. and decision scis., 1983—; assoc. editor Mgmt. Sci., 1969-73; bd. editors Applied Econs., 1973—; Applied Econs. Letters, 1993—. Contbr. to profl. jours. Served with AUS, 1945-47. Ford Found. fellow, 1964-65; NSF rsch. grantee, 1960-81. Mem. Am. Econ. Assn., Econometric Soc., Econometric Soc. Inventory Rsch., Western Econ. Assn., Inst. mgmt. Scis., AAUP, Phi Beta Kappa. Democrat. Home: 1926 NW 27th St Gainesville FL 32605-3863 Office: U Fla Dept Econs Gainesville FL 32611

ZABEL, SHELDON ALTER, lawyer; b. Omaha, Apr. 25, 1941; s. Louis Julius and Anne (Rothenberg) Z.; m. Roberta Jean Butz, May 10, 1975; children: Andrew Louis, Douglas Patrick, Robert Stewart Warren. AB cum laude, Princeton U., 1963; JD cum laude, Northwestern U., 1966. Bar: Ill. 1966, U.S. Supreme Ct. 1976. Law clk. to presiding justice, Ill. Sup. Ct., 1966-67; assoc Schiff, Hardin & Waite, Chgo., 1967-73, ptnr., 1973—; instr. environ. law Loyola U., Chgo. Mem. bd. dirs. Chgo. Zool. Soc. Mem. ABA, Chgo. Bar Assn., Chgo. Council Lawyers, Order of Coif. Jewish. Clubs: Union League, Metropolitan (Chgo.). Avocations: skiing, squash. Office: Schiff Hardin & Waite 7200 Sears Tower 233 S Wacker Dr Chicago IL 60606

ZABEL, VIVIAN ELLOUISE, secondary education educator; b. Randolph AFB, Tex., July 28, 1943; d. Raymond Louis and Dolly Veneta (Lyles) Gilbert; m. Robert Lee Zabel, Feb. 18, 1962; children: René Lynne, Robert Lee Jr., Randel Louis, Regina Louise. BA in English and Speech, Panhandle State U., 1977; postgrad., U. Cen. Okla., 1987-92. Cert. tchr., Okla. Tchr. English, drama, speech, debate Buffalo (Okla.) High Sch., 1977-79; tchr. English, drama, speech Schulter (Okla.) High Sch., 1979-80; tchr. English Morris (Okla.) High Sch., 1980-81; tchr. speech, drama, debate Okla. Christian Schs., Edmond, 1981-82; tchr. English, drama, debate, speech/debate coach Braman (Okla.) High Sch., 1982-83; debate coach Pawhuska (Okla.) High Sch., 1983-84; tchr. English, French, drama, speech and debate coach Luther (Okla.) High Sch., 1984—; dir. drama Nazarene Youth Impact Team, Collinsville, Okla., 1979-81; tchr. high sch. Sunday sch. class Edmond Ch. of the Nazarene, 1992—. mem. community-sch. rels. com. Luther Pub. Schs., 1991-92, supt.'s adv. com., 1992—; adjudicator and tournament dir. tournaments OSSAA. Editor Potpourri mag., 1975-76; author poetry, short stories. Adult supr. Texas County 4-H, Adams, Okla., 1975-77; double diamond coach NFL; adjudicator and tournament dir. qualifying OSSAA Tournaments. Recipient Disting. Svc. award NFL, 1994. Mem. Nat. Debate Coaches Assn., Nat. Fedn. Interscholastic Speech and Debate Assn., Okla. Speech Theatre Communications Assn., Okla. Coun. Tchrs. Engl. Republican. Nazarene. Home: 2912 Rankin Ter Edmond OK 73013-5344

ZABEL, WILLIAM DAVID, lawyer; b. Omaha, Dec. 14, 1936; s. Louis J. and Anne I. Z.; m. Deborah M. Miller, Oct. 31, 1979; children by previous marriage: Richard, David. AB summa cum laude, Princeton U., 1958; LLB cum laude, Harvard U., 1961. Bar: N.Y. 1961, U.S. Supreme Ct. 1966, Fla. 1975. Ptnr. Schulte Rothe & Zabel, N.Y.C., 1969—; ptnr. firm Schulte, Roth & Zabel, Palm Beach, Fla., 1975—; lectr. Cornell Law Sch.; So. Fed. Tax Inst., U. Miami Inst. Estate Planning, Great Plains Tax Inst., Assn. of Bar of City of N.Y., Practising Law Inst., profl. orgns.; N.Y. State adv. com. U.S. Civil Rights Commn. 1969-73; vol. civil rights litigator Lawyers Constl. Def. Com., Miss., summer 1965; bd. dirs. Del. Mgmt. Holdings Inc. Author: Estate Planning for the Large Estate, 1976, Domicile, Wills and Tax Problems of Migrating Clients Transplanted to Florida, 1976, Income, Estate and Gift Tax Consequences of Marital Settlements, 1979, Estate Planning for Interests in a Closely Held Business, 1981, Use of Trusts in Connection with Marital Dissolutions, 1983, Thy Will Be Done?, 1991; Am. editor: The Lawyer, Eng., 1963-66; mem. editorial adv. bd. Trusts & Estates mag.; contbr. articles to periodicals. Pres. Merlin Found.; mem. Lymphoma Found., Soros Founds., Open Soc. Fund, Inc., Human Rights Watch/Hel-

sinki, Doctors of World, Winston Found. World Peace, Ottinger Found., David H. Cogan Found., The Picower Med. Rsch. Inst., Samuel Waxman Cancer Rsch. Found., Lymphoma Found., Lawson Valentine Found.; Am. Friends of the Israel Mus., Am. Com. For Weizmann Inst. Sci.; legal counsel Internat. Confedn. Art Dealers; bd. dirs. Tauber Inst., Brandeis U.; trustee The New Sch. for Social Rsch., 1994—; adv. bd. Project on Death in Am.; chmn. Princeton U. Planned Giving com., 1991—. Recipient Disting. Community Svc. award Brandeis U., 1986, U.S. Masters Squash Team Bronze medal 14th Maccabiah Games, 1993; fellow Brandeis U., 1987—. Fellow Am. Coll. Trust and Estate Coun., Internat. Acad. Estate and Trust Law; mem. ABA, Am. Law Inst., N.Y. State Bar Assn., Assn. of Bar of City of N.Y. (internat. human rights com.), Lawyers Com. for Human Rights (bd. dirs.), Vol. Lawyers for Arts (bd. dirs.), Estate Planning Coun. N.Y.C. (bd. dirs. 1975-79), Fla. Bar Assn., Harmonie Club (pres. 1989-91), Phi Beta Kappa. Home: 850 Park Ave New York NY 10021-1845 Office: Schulte Roth & Zabel 900 3rd Ave New York NY 10022-4728 also: Phillips Point W Tower 10th Fl 777 S Flagler Dr West Palm Beach FL 33401

ZABRISKIE, JOHN L., healthcare and agricultural products manufacturing company executive; b. 1940. -. With Merck & Co., Inc., Whitehouse Station, N.J., 1965-93, past exec. v.p., past pres. mfg. divsn.; chmn., CEO Upjohn Co., Kalamazoo, 1993—, also bd. dirs. Office: Upjohn Co 7000 Portage Rd Kalamazoo MI 49001*

ZABRISKIE, VIRGINIA M., art dealer; b. N.Y.C.. Student, Washington Sq. Coll.; BA, NYU, MA. Dir. Zabriskie Gallery, 1954—, Paris, 1978—. Mem. Art Dealers Assn. (bd. dirs.). Address: Zabriskie Gallery 724 5th Ave New York NY 10019-4106 also: 37 rue Quincampoix, 75004 Paris France

ZABSKY, JOHN MITCHELL, engineering executive; b. Joplin, Mo., Apr. 18, 1933; s. Joseph Anthony and Joan (Lucas) Z. AS, Joplin Jr. Coll., 1953; BSME, U. Mo., 1956; MSME, U. Kans., 1965. Profl. engr., Mo. System engr. Bendix KCD, Kansas City, Mo., 1958-62; rsch. engr. Rocketdyne, Neosho, Mo., 1962-65, Boeing Co., Huntsville, Ala., 1965-66; prin. rsch. engr., scientist Honeywell Inc., St. Paul, 1966-71; chief engr. Pressure Tank & Pipe Fabrication Co., Nashville, 1971-72, Engring. for Industry, Danville, Va., 1972-73; area mgr. fluid machinery Dresser Adv. Tech. Ctr., Irvine, Calif., 1973-85; v.p. ops. ATI, Laguna Niguel, Calif., 1985-93; pres. Cytoprobe, San Diego, 1993-94, v.p. ops., 1994—; cons. Oral Care Products, L.A., 1990-92. Patentee in field. Pres. Mpls.-St. Paul Singletons, 1969-72. Mem. AIAA, ASME, Mo. Profl. Engrs. Home: 3640C S Main St Santa Ana CA 92707-5720

ZACCAGNINO, JOSEPH ANTHONY, hospital administrator; b. New Rochelle, N.Y., June 16, 1946. BA, U. Conn., 1968; MA, Yale U., 1970. Adminstrv. resident Yale-New Haven (Conn.) Hosp., 1970-71, adminstrv. asst., 1971-72, asst. dir., 1972-75, assoc. dir., 1975-77, v.p. adminstrn., 1977-78, exec. v.p., COO, 1978-91, pres., CEO, 1991—. Mem. NEHA, Am. Hosp. Assn. (mem. com. svc.), Conn. Hosp. Assn. (trustee). Office: Yale-New Haven Hosp 20 York St New Haven CT 06504

ZACCARIA, ADRIAN, utilities executive; b. 1944. BS, U.S. Merchant Marine Acad., 1966. Engr. Raytheon Co., Lexington, Mass., 1967-68, Gen. Dynamics Corp., Falls Ch., Va., 1968-71; with Bechtel Power Corp., San Francisco, 1974—, now pres. Office: Bechtel Power Corp PO Box 193965 50 Beale St San Francisco CA 94105-1813

ZACCHINO, NARDA, newspaper editor. Ass. editor L.A. Times, Calif. Office: Los Angeles Times Times Mirror Sq Los Angeles CA 90053*

ZACEK, JOSEPH FREDERICK, history educator, international studies consultant, East European affairs specialist; b. Stickney, Ill., Dec. 18, 1930; s. Joseph and Emilie (Dvorak) Z.; m. Judith Ellen Cohen (div. 1975); 1 child, Natalie Ann; m. Jane Perlberg Shapiro; stepchildren: Leslie Helen, Peter Carl. BA summa cum laude, U. Ill. at Urbana-Champaign, 1952, MA in History, 1953, PhD in History, 1962; cert., Columbia U. Inst. on East Cen. Europe, 1962. Asst. prof. history Occidental Coll., L.A., 1962-65; asst. prof., dir. Russian & East European Programs UCLA, 1965-68; assoc. prof. SUNY at Albany, 1968-71, dir. Russian & East European Programs, 1968-77, 91-92, prof., 1971—, chair dept. history, 1974-77; mem. selection com. for East Europe Internat. Rsch. and Exch. Bd., Princeton, N.J., 1978-81, nat. bd. cons. NEH, Washington, 1975—; vis. scholar IREX Charles U., Prague, Czechoslovakia, 1973, Columbia U., 1977-78, U. Ill., Urbana and Champaign, 1987. Author: Palacky: The Historian as Scholar and Nationalist, 1970; editor, co-author: Frantisek Palacky, 1798-1876: A Centennial Appreciation, 1981, The Enlightenment and the National Revivals in Eastern Europe, 1983, The Intimate Palacky, 1984; also numerous periodical articles and chpts. in multi-authored books. With M.I., U.S. Army, 1954-57. Fgn. Area Tng. fellow Ford Found., Columbia U., 1960-62, Sr. Humanities fellow Rockefeller Found., 1977-78, fellow Russian Rsch. Ctr. Harvard U., 1986-91; rsch. grantee Am. Coun. Learned Socs. Sci./Soc. Rsch. Coun., 1965, Am. Philos. Soc., 1968; recipient Comenius medal Govt. of Czech and Slovak Fed. Republic, 1992, Medal of Comenius Pedagogical Inst. in Prague, 1992, Josef Hlávka medal of Czechoslovak Acad. of Scis. in Prague, 1992; also other grad. and postdoctoral awards and grants. Mem. Am. Hist. Assn., Am. Assn. for Advancement of Slavic Studies, Czechoslovak History Conf., Slovak Studies Assn., Consortium on Revolutionary Europe, Assn. for Study of Ethnicity and Nationalism, Phi Beta Kappa. Avocations: travel, gardening, music. Office: SUNY Dept History Albany NY 12222

ZACHARIAS, DONALD WAYNE, university president; b. Salem, Ind., Sept. 28, 1935; s. William Otto and Estelle Mae (Newlon) Z.; m. Tommie Kline Dekle, Aug. 16, 1959; children: Alan, Eric, Leslie. BA, Georgetown (Ky.) Coll., 1957, LLD (hon.), 1983; MA, Ind. U., 1959, PhD, 1963. Asst. prof. communication and theatre Ind. U., 1963-69; assoc. prof. U. Tex., Austin, 1969-72; prof. U. Tex., 1972-79, asst. to pres., 1974-77; exec. asst. to chancellor U. Tex. System, 1978-79; pres. Western Ky. U., 1979-85, Miss. State U., 1985—; bd. dirs. First Fed. Savs. & Loan Assn., Bowling Green, Ky., Inst. for Tech. Devel., Sanderson Farms, Inc., Miss. econ. Coun. Author: In Pursuit of Peace: Speeches of the Sixties, 1970. Bd. dirs. Greenview Hosp.; pres. Southeastern Conf., 1989-91. With U.S. Army, 1959-60. Named Mississippian of Yr. Data Processing Mgmt. Assn.; recipient Teaching award Ind. U. Found., 1963, Cactus Teaching award U. Tex., 1971, Justin Smith Morrill award U.S. Dept. Agriculture, 1992. Mem. Inst. Tech. Devel. (bd. dirs. 1985-92), Nat. Assn. State Univs. and Land-Grant Colls. (exec. com. 1990-92), Phi Kappa Phi (pres. 1978). Democrat. Episcopalian. Office: Miss State U Office of Pres PO Box J Mississippi State MS 39762

ZACHARIASEN, FREDRIK, physics educator, consultant; b. Chgo., June 14, 1931; s. William Houlder and Ragni (Durban-Hansen) Z.; m. Nancy Walker, Jan. 27, 1957; children—Kerry, Judith. B.S., U. Chgo., 1951; Ph.D., Calif. Inst. Tech., 1956. Instr. MIT, Cambridge, 1955-56; research physicist U. Calif.-Berkeley, 1956-57; asst. prof. physics Stanford U., Calif., 1957-60; prof. Calif. Inst. Tech., Pasadena, 1960—; assoc. dir. Los Alamos Nat. Lab., 1982-83. Author: Structure of Nucleons, 1960; Hadron Physics, 1973; Sound Fluctuation, 1979. Sloan fellow, 1960-64; Guggenheim fellow, 1970. Home: 2235 Villa Heights Rd Pasadena CA 91107-1142 Office: Calif Inst Tech 1201 E California Blvd Pasadena CA 91125-0001

ZACHARIUS, WALTER, publishing company executive; b. N.Y.C., Oct. 16, 1923; s. Abraham and Sara (Cohen) Z.; m. Alice M. Riesenberg, Dec. 19, 1948; children—Steven Bruce, Judith Helen. Certificate, Coll. City N.Y. Sch. Bus.; 1948; student, N.Y.U., 1949-50; certificate pub. relations and publicity, New Sch. Social Research, 1949; B.A., Empire State U., 1977. With circulation dept. MacFadden Pubs., Inc., 1947—, Popular Library Book, Inc., 1948-49, Am. Mercury, Inc., 1949-51; circulation dir. Ace News Co., N.Y.C., 1951-61; pres. Magnum Royal Pubs., Inc., N.Y.C., 1961—, Magnum Communications, N.Y.C., 1961—; v.p. Lancer Book, Inc., N.Y.C., 1961-75; pres. Walter Zacharius Assoc., Inc., 1966—; chmn. bd. Kensington Pub. Corp. Mem. Com. World Human Rights, 1968—, Friends Hofstra Mu. Fine Arts, 1969—, Friends Inst. Fine Arts NYU, 1989; Democratic committeeman, 1969; v.p. Reform Dem. Assn. Great Neck, N.Y., 1970—; trustee United Cerebral Palsy of Queens, v.p., 1975—; pres. United Cerebral Palsy of Queens, 1986-89; pres. North Shore Community Art Ctr.; chmn. dubs. div. United Jewish Appeal Fedn., 1988-90. With AUS, 1942-45, ETO.

MTO. Recipient Pub. Rels. award United Cerebral Palsy Queens, 1970, award of honor United Jewish Appeal Fedn. Campaign, 1987, Disting. Svc. award United Jewish Appeal, 1992, Appreciation award United Jewish Appeal-Fedn. N.Y. Pub. Divsn., 1993, cert. distinction Gallatin divsn. NYU, 1993. Mem. Am. Book Pubs. Assn., Periodicals Book Assn. Am., Ind. Newspaperstand Circulators of Am., Assn. Am. Pubs. Jewish (trustee congregation 1960-64). Home: 440 E 56th St New York NY 10022-4147 Office: Zebra Books 850 3rd Ave New York NY 10022

ZACHEM, HARRY M., oil company executive; b. Ironton, Ohio, Aug. 14, 1944; s. Charles Russell and Millie (Norris) Z.; m. Mary M. Hamilton, 1987; children: Nancy Kathryn, Mary Elizabeth; m. Mary U. Hamilton, Apr. 1987. B.A., U. Ky., 1968; A.M.P., Harvard U., 1985. Sales rep. State Govt., Frankfort, 1968-71; sales rep. Ashland Oil Inc., Balt., 1972-74; pub. relations rep. Ashland Oil Inc., Ashland, Ky., 1974-75; Washington rep. Ashland Oil Inc., 1975-81, v.p. fed. govt. relations, 1981-86; adminstrv. v.p. Ashland Oil Inc., Ashland, 1986-88, sr. v.p. external affairs, 1988—, also bd. dirs. Pub. Affairs Council, Washington, 1984—. Mem. NAM. Episcopalian. Avocations: golf; tennis; sailing. Office: Ashland Oil Inc PO Box 391 Ashland KY 41105-0391

ZACHERT, MARTHA JANE, retired librarian; b. York, Pa., Feb. 7, 1920; d. Paul Rodes and Elizabeth Agnes (Lau) Koontz; m. Edward G. Zachert, Aug. 25, 1946; 1 child, Lillian Elizabeth. AB, Lebanon Valley Coll., 1941; MLS, Emory U., 1953; DLS, Columbia U., 1968. Asst. Enoch Pratt Free Library, Balt., 1941-46; head librarian Wood Research Inst., Atlanta, 1947; sch. librarian DeKalb (Ga.) County Schs., 1950-52; head librarian, prof. history of pharmacy So. Coll. Pharmacy, Mercer U., Atlanta, 1952-63; instr. Ga. State Coll., 1962-63, Emory U., summers 1955-59, 1956-57, 59-60; mem. faculty Library Sch., Fla. State U., 1963-78, prof., 1973-78; prof. Coll. Librarianship U. S.C., Columbia, 1973-74, 78-84; vis. fellow Brit. Library, 1980; cons. So. Regional Med. Library, Emory U., 1976-77, Nat. Library Medicine, 1977, others. Assoc. editor: Jour. Library History, 1966-71, 73-76; mng. editor, 1971-73; cons. editor: Jour. Library Adminstrn., 1979-86; contbr. numerous articles to profl. jours. Fellow Med. Libr. Assn.; mem. ALA, Spl. Librs. Assn. (past pres. Fla. chpt., spl. citation 1977, Hall of Fame 1985), Southwestern Libr. Assn. (Hall of Fame 1985), Am. Printing History Assn., Beta Phi Mu (pres. 1974-75). Home and Office: 2018 W Randolph Cir Tallahassee FL 32312-3349

ZACHERT, VIRGINIA, psychologist, educator; b. Jacksonville, Ala., Mar. 1, 1920; d. R.E. and Cora H. (Massee) Z. Student, Norman Jr. Coll., 1937; A.B., Ga. State Woman's Coll., 1940; M.A., Emory U., 1947; Ph.D., Purdue U., 1949. Diplomate: Am. Bd. Profl. Psychologists. Statistician Davison-Paxon Co., Atlanta, 1941-44; research psychologist Mil. Contracts, Auburn Research Found., Ala. Poly. Inst.; indsl. and research psychologist Sturm & O'Brien (cons. engrs.), 1958-59; research project dir. Western Design, Biloxi, Miss., 1960-61; self-employed cons. psychologist Norman Park, Ga., 1961-71, Good Hope, Ga., 1971—; rsch. assoc. med. edn. Med. Coll. Ga., Augusta, 1963-65, assoc. prof., 1965-70, rsch. prof., 1970-84, rsch. prof. emerita, 1984—, chief learning materials div., 1973-84, mem. faculty senate, 1976-84, mem. acad. coun., 1976-82, pres. acad. coun., 1983, sec., 1978; mem. Ga. Bd. Examiners of Psychologists, 1974-79, v.p., 1977, pres., 1978; adv. bd. Comdr. Gen. ATC USAF, 1967-70; cons. Ga. Silver Haired Legislature, 1980-86, senator, 1987-93, pres. protem, 1987-88, pres. 1989-93, rep. 1993—, speaker protem, 1993—; gov.'s appointee Ga. Coun. on Aging, 1988—; U.S. Senate mem. Fed. Coun. on the Aging, 1990-93. Author: (with P.L. Wilds) Essentials of Gynecology-Oncology, 1967, Applications of Gynecology-Oncology, 1971. Del. White House Conf. on Aging, 1981, senator appointee, 1995. Served as aerologist USN, 1944-46; aviation psychologist USAF, 1949-54. Fellow AAAS, Am. Psychol. Assn.; mem. AAUP (chpt. pres. 1977-80), Sigma Xi (chpt. pres. 1980-81). Baptist. Home: 1126 Highland Ave Augusta GA 30904-4628 Office: Med Coll Ga Dept Ob-Gyn Augusta GA 30912 *It's really quite simple—I find, if I wish to be understood or heard, that simplicity is necessary but not ever easy. Simplicity is basic, essential and always the major factor in my search for truth.*

ZACHOS, KIMON STEPHEN, lawyer; b. Concord, N.H., Nov. 20, 1930; s. Stephen and Sophia (Bacogiannis) Z.; m. Anne Colby, July 5, 1959; children: Ellen, Elizabeth, Sarah. BA, Wesleyan U., 1952; JD, NYU, 1955; LLM, Boston U., 1968; LLD (hon.), N.H. Coll., 1992, St. Anselm Coll. 1994. Bar: N.H. 1955, U.S. Dist. Ct. N.H. 1957, U.S. Supreme Ct. 1963. Ptnr. Sheehan, Phinney, Bass & Green, Manchester, N.H., 1957—; White House fellow, spl. asst. to atty. gen. Nicholas deB. Katzenbach, Washington, 1965-66; bd. dirs. New Eng. Tel., Bank of Ireland 1st Holdings Inc., 1st NH Bank Inc., Hitchiner Mfg. Co., Inc., also others. Dep. speaker N.H. Ho. Reps., 1969-74; active various charitable and ednl. orgns. Named Man of Yr., Manchester C. of C., 1985, Disting. Citizen, Boy Scouts Am., 1987, Bus. Leader of Yr., New Hampshire Assn. C of C., 1994; recipient Brotherhood award NCCJ, 1966. Mem. ABA, N.H. Bar Assn. Republican. Greek Orthodox. Avocation: stamp collecting. Home: 2093 Elm St Manchester NH 03104-2316 Office: Sheehan Phinney Bass & Green 1000 Elm St Manchester NH 03101-1730

ZACHRY, HENRY BARTELL, JR., construction company executive; b. 1933; married. BSCE, Tex. A&M U., 1954. With H.B. Zachry Co., San Antonio, 1957—, pres., chief exec. officer, 1965-86, chmn., dir., 1984—; pres. Zachry, Inc., San Antonio. Office: H B Zachry Co 527 W Harding Blvd San Antonio TX 78221 also: Zachry Inc 527 Logwood Ave San Antonio TX 78221

ZACK, ARNOLD MARSHALL, lawyer, mediator, arbitrator; b. Lynn, Mass., Oct. 7, 1931; s. Samuel George and Bess Ethel (Freedman) Z.; m. Norma Eta Wilner, Aug. 10, 1969; children: Jonathan Samuel, Rachel Anne. AB, Tufts Coll., 1953; LLB, Yale U., 1956; MPA, Harvard U., 1961. Asst. to Saul Wallen (arbitrator), 1956-63; cons. UN Mission to Congo, 1960, U.S. Peace Corps, 1961-63, Labor Dept., 1962-79, Pres.'s Study Commn. on Nat. Service Corps, 1962-63, U.S. AID, 1963—, Friedrich Ebert Stiftung, 1963-64, Nat. Center for Dispute Settlement, 1968-76; vis. Fulbright lectr. Haile Selassie U., Addis Ababa, 1963-64; referee Nat. R.R. Adjustment Bd., 1964—; mem. faculty Harvard U. Trade Union Program, 1985—; dir. Labor-Mgmt. Inst., Am. Arbitration Assn., 1966-68; full time mediator/arbitrator, Boston, 1968—; bd. dirs. ctr. for socio-legal studies faculty of law U. Natal, 1986-92; mem. Fgn. Service Labor Relations Bd., 1981-84, Presdl. Emergency Bds. 221 and 222; cons. Internat. Labor Orgn., 1961—; chair Essential Industries Dispute Settlement Bd. Bermuda, 1993—; permanent arbitrator, Am. Airlines & APA, Gen. Dynamics, IAM, Greyhound Bus Lines and Amal. Transit Union, TWA and Air Line Pilots Assn., TWA and IAM; Yale U. and Fedn. Univ. Employees, Procter & Gamble and Ind. Oil and Chem. Workers, Commonwealth Mass. Author: Labor Training in Developing Countries, 1964, Ethiopia's High Level Manpower-Analysis and Projections, 1964, Handbook on Grievance Arbitration in the Public Sector, 1974, Handbook on Fact Finding and Arbitration in the Public Sector, 1974, Grievance Arbitration, A Practical Guide, 1977; (with R. Bloch) Arbitration of Discipline and Discharge Cases, 1979, (with R. Bloch) The Agreement in Negotiation and Arbitration, 1983; Arbitration in Practice, 1984, Mediation in the Public Sector, 1985, Grievance Arbitration: Cases on the Merits in Discipline Discharge and Contract Interpretation, 1989, Handbook on Grievance Arbitration: Issues on Procedure and Ethics, 1992; contbr. articles to profl. jours. Recipient Whitney North Seymour medal for outstanding contbn. to arbitration, 1980, Cushing Gavin award, 1986, Mildred Spaulding award, 1987, Disting. Svc. award for arbitration of labor-mgmt. disputes, 1989. Fellow African Studies Assn.; mem. ABA, Nat. Acad. Arbitrators (treas. 1972-75, bd. govs. 1977-79, v.p. 1980-82, pres. 1994-95, pres. Rsch. and Edn. Found. 1989-91), Am. Arbitration Assn., Indsl. Rels. Rsch. Assn., Internat. Soc. for Labor Law and Social Securities (bd. dirs.), Harvard Club, Yale Club (N.Y.C.). Address: 170 W Canton St Boston MA 02118-1216

ZACK, DANIEL GERARD, library director; b. Waukegan, Ill., Oct. 1, 1943; s. Raymond Gerard and Rosanna Marie (Atkinson) Z.; m. Mary Frances Anthony, Aug. 25, 1966; children: Jennifer Lee, Rebecca Jane. BA in Psychology, Western Ill. U., 1967; MS in Libr. Sci., U. Ill., 1975. Director IBM Corp., Rochester, Minn., 1968-70 Memorex Corp., Mpls., 1970-74; rsch. assoc. Libr. Rsch. Ctr. U. Ill., Urbana, 1974-75; asst. dir. Portage

County Pub. Libr., Stevens Point, Wis., 1976-78; dir. Burlington (Iowa) Pub. Libr., 1978-87, Gail Borden Pub. Libr., Elgin, Ill., 1987—. Founder Friends of Ill. Librs., 1991; mem. adv. com. Ctr. City Devel. Corp., Elgin, 1992. Mem. ALA, ACLU, Ill. Libr. Assn. (mgr. pub. libr. forum 1991-92, exec. bd. dirs. 1992—), Pub. Libr. Assn. (intellectual freedom com. 1993—), Kiwanis. Office: Gail Borden Pub Libr Dist 200 N Grove Ave Elgin IL 60120

ZACK, GEORGE J., conductor, music director; b. Pine Bluff, Ark., July 8, 1936; s. George Peter and Eugenia (Paschal) Z.; m. Kerry Sheehan, Oct. 4, 1970; children: Katherine Eugenia, Melissa Sheehan. Student, Am. Conservatory Music, Chgo., 1957, 58; MusB cum laude in Music Theory and Composition, Wichita State U., 1958; MusM in Music Theory and Viola, U. Mich., 1960; PhD in Music Theory, Fla. State U., 1972; studies with Dr. Richard Lert, Stella Roberts, Gustav Meier. Instr. music U. Mich., Ann Arbor, 1962-64; assoc. prof. Hiram (Ohio) Coll., 1964-72; music dir. Music Theater Soc., Lexington, Ky., 1972-75, Lexington Philharm., 1972—, Wooster (Ohio) Symphony, 1973-75, Warren (Ohio) Chamber Orch., 1967—; artist-in-residence Ea. Ky. U., James Madison U.; guest condr. State Orch. Salonika, Greece, 1981, 83-84, 84-85, Louisville Orch., 1978; condr. N.E. Ohio All State Orch., 1969, Men and Boy's Choir Festival, 1975, 76, N.Y. All-State Orch., 1975, Ky. All-State Orch., 1974, 76, South Bend, Inc., Youngstown, Ohio, Albuquerque Chamber Orch., Monterey County Symphony, Calif., Amarillo, Tex., Bridgeport, Conn., Santa Cruz, Calif., Stockton, Calif., Charleston, S.C., Modesto, Calif., Las Vegas, Nev.; guest speaker various civic orgns. Dir. (radio program) George Zack's Enhancement of Music, Sta. WEKU-FM, 1975—; dir., producer (radio program) The Enhancement of Music, Sta. WBKY-FM, 1973-75, (TV program) Form in Music, NBC, 1965; co-host (TV program) Ky. Morning, 1979. Commr. Picnic with the Pops, Lexington, 1982—. Recipient Orpheus award Phi Mu Alpha, 1976, Hellenic award, 1993. Mem. Am. Symphony Orch. League, Condr.'s Guild, Am. Fedn. Musicians (hon. mem. chpt. 554-635 local 118), Cen. Ky. Youth Music Soc. (bd. dirs., condr.), NCCJ (bd. dirs.-co-chmn.). Greek Orthodox. Home: 237 Woodspoint Rd Lexington KY 40502-1905

ZACKHEIM, ADRIAN WALTER, editor; b. N.Y.C., Sept. 19, 1951; s. Albert Alex and Mary Elizabeth (Cooper) Z.; m. Sarah Babst Parsons, Sept. 1, 1985; children: Adrian Alex, David Parsons. BA, Grinnell Coll., 1973; MA, U. Toronto, Ont., Can., 1975. Editor St Martins Press, N.Y.C., 1977-79; editor Doubleday & Co., Inc., N.Y.C., 1979-84, sr. editor, 1984-85; sr. editor William Morrow & Co., Inc., N.Y.C., 1986-89, sr. editor, v.p., 1989-90, exec. editor, v.p., 1990-91, editorial dir., v.p., 1991-94; publishing dir., v.p. Harper Bus., 1994—; exec. editor, v.p. Harper Collins, 1994—. Office: Harper Collins 10 E 53d St New York NY 10022-5299

ZACKS, GORDON BENJAMIN, manufacturing company executive; b. Terre Haute, Ind., Mar. 11, 1933; s. Aaron and Florence Melton (Spurgeon) Z.; married; children: Catherine E., Kimberly A. B.A., Coll. Commerce, Ohio State U. With R.G. Barry Corp., Pickerington, Ohio, 1955—, exec. v.p., 1964-65, pres., 1965—, chmn. bd., 1979—, now also chief exec. officer, chmn. Mem. Nat. Republican Senatorial Com.; hon. chmn. United Jewish Appeal; bd. dirs. numerous Jewish orgns., locally and nationally. Mem. Chief Exec. Officer Orgn., Am. Mgmt. Assn. Republican. Home: 140 N Parkview Ave Columbus OH 43209-1436 Office: R G Barry Corp 13405 Yarmouth Dr NW Pickerington OH 43147-9257 also: PO Box 129 Columbus OH 43216-0129

ZACKS, SUMNER IRWIN, pathologist; b. Boston, June 29, 1929; s. David and Rose Z.; m. Marilyn Garfinkel, June 28, 1953; children—Nancy Alice, Charles Matthew, Susan Esther. B.A. cum laude, Harvard Coll., 1951, M.D. magna cum laude, 1955; M.A. (hon.), U. Pa., 1975, Brown U., 1977. Diplomate Am. Bd. Pathology. Intern Mass. Gen. Hosp., Boston, 1956; resident Mass. Gen. Hosp., 1956-58; teaching fellow Harvard U., 1956; asst. prof. pathology U. Pa., 1962-64, assoc. prof., 1964-71, prof., 1971-76; prof. pathology Brown U., 1976-89, chmn. pathology, 1977-82; pathologist in chief Miriam Hosp., Providence, R.I., 1976-88, ret., 1989. Author: The Motor Endplate, 1964, 74, Atlas of Neuropathology, 1971; contbr. chpts. to books and articles in profl. jours. Served to capt. USAR, 1958-60. Fellow Am. Coll. Pathology; mem. Histochem. Soc. (sec. 1965-68), Am. Coll. Pathologists, Assn. Am. Pathologists, Am. Soc. Cell Biology, Am. Soc. Neuropathologists, Internat. Acad. Pathology, Sigma Xi.

ZAENGLEIN, WILLIAM GEORGE, JR., lawyer; b. Orange, N.J., Jan. 31, 1929; s. William George Sr. and Elsie May (Traenkle) Z.; m. Elizabeth J. Skinner, Dec. 18, 1954; 1 son, William George, III; m. Joyce A. Moffit, Oct. 18, 1968; 1 son, Eric Hunter. B.A., Yale U., 1952, J.D., 1955. Bar: D.C. 1957, Calif. 1969, U.S. Dist. Ct. (cen. dist.) Calif. 1969. With gen. counsel's office GSA, 1956-59; contract adminstr. Lear Siegler Corp., 1959-63; sr. contract adminstr. Northrop Corp., 1963-66; legal asst. law firm Orange, Calif., 1966-69; v.p., corp. counsel First Am. Title Ins. Co., The First Am. Fin. Corp., Santa Ana, Calif. 1969-77; v.p., sec., corp. counsel First Am. Title Ins. Co., 1977-91; v.p., sec., counsel The First Am. Fin. Corp., 1977-91; retired, 1991; dir. First Am. Trust Co., 1976—. Mem. Orange County Bar Assn., Am. Soc. Corporate Secs., Yale Club of So. Calif., Phi Delta Phi, Chi Phi. Office: First Am Fin Corp 114 E 5th St Santa Ana CA 92701-4642

ZAENTZ, SAUL, motion picture producer; b. Passaic, N.J.. Producer films: One Flew Over the Cuckoo's Nest, 1975 (Oscar for Best Picture), Three Warriors, 1977, Lord of the Rings, 1978, Amadeus, 1984, The Unbearable Lightness of Being, 1988, At Play in the Fields of the Lord, 1991; exec. producer The Mosquito Coast, 1986. Office: Saul Zaentz Co Film Ctr 2600 10th St Berkeley CA 94710-2522

ZAFFARONI, ALEJANDRO C., biochemist, medical research company executive; b. Montevideo, Uruguay, Feb. 27, 1923; came to U.S., 1944; s. Carlos and Luisa (Alfaro) Z.; m. Lyda Russomanno, July 5, 1946; children—Alejandro A., Elisa. B., U. Montevideo, 1943; Ph.D. in Biochemistry, U. Rochester, 1949; Doctorate (hon.), U. Republic, Montevideo, 1983; M.Divinity, Cen. Bapt. Seminary, 1987. Dir. biochem. research Syntex S.A., Mexico City, 1951-54, v.p., dir. research, 1954-56; exec. v.p., dir. Syntex Corp., Palo Alto, Calif., 1956-68; pres. Syntex Labs. Inc., Palo Alto, Calif., 1962-68, Syntex Research, Palo Alto, Calif., 1962-68; founder, co-chmn. ALZA Corp., Palo Alto, Calif., 1968—, also CEO; founder, mem. policy bd. and exec. com. DNAX Research Inst. of Molecular and Cellular Biology, Inc., Palo Alto, Calif., 1980—, chmn., 1980-82; founder, chmn., chief exec. officer Affymax, N.V., Palo Alto, Calif., 1989—; chmn. Internat. Psoriasis Research Found.; bd. dir. incorporator Neuroscis. Research Found. MIT, Brookline, Mass.; bd. govs. Weizmann Inst. Sci., Rehovot, Israel; mem. pharm. panel of com. on tech. and internat. econs. and trade issues Nat. Acad. Engring. Office of Fgn. Sec. and Assembly of Engring., Washington; hon. prof. biochemistry Nat. U. Mex., 1957, U. Montevideo, 1959. Contbr. numerous articles to profl. jours.; patentee in field. Recipient Barren medal Barren Found., Chgo., 1974; Pres.'s award Weizmann Inst. Sci., 1978; Chem. Pioneer award Am. Inst. Chemists, Inc., 1979. Fellow Am. Acad. Arts and Scis., Am. Pharm. Assn.; mem. AAAS, Am. Chem. Soc., Am. Found. Pharm. Edn., Am. Inst Chemists, Inc., Am. Soc. Biol. Chemists, Inc., Am. Soc. Microbiology, Am. Soc. Pharmacology and Exptl. Therapeutics, Biomed. Engring. Soc., Calif. Pharmacists Assn., Internat. Pharm. Fedn., Internat. Soc. Chronobiology, Internat. Soc. Study of Biol. Rhythms, Soc. Exptl. Biology and Medicine, Sociedad Mexicana de Nutricion y Endocrinologia, Biochem. Soc. Eng., Endocrine Soc., Internat. Soc. Research in Biology of Reproduction, N.Y. Acad. Scis., Christian Legal Soc. (Mo. bd. dirs. 1973—), Tau Kappa Epsilon (internat. pres. 1953-57). *

ZAFREN, HERBERT CECIL, librarian, educator; b. Balt., Aug. 25, 1925; s. Morris and Sadie Mildred (Edlavitch) Z.; m. Miriam Koenigsberg, Feb. 11, 1951; children: Ken, Edie. A.B., Johns Hopkins U., 1944, postgrad., 1946-49; diploma, Balt. Hebrew Coll., 1944, Litt.D. (hon.), 1969; A.M. in Library Sci., U. Mich., 1950. Jr. instr. Johns Hopkins U., Balt., 1947-49; bibliog. searcher Law Libr. U. Mich., Ann Arbor, 1949-50; libr. Hebrew Union Coll.-Jewish Inst. Religion, Cin., 1950-91, prof. Jewish bibliography, 1968—; exec. dir. Am. Jewish Periodical Ctr., Cin., 1956-80, co-dir., 1980—; dir. librs. Cin., L.A., N.Y.C., Jerusalem, 1966-95; mem. exec. bd. Jewish Book Council Am. 1979—. Editor Studies in Bibliography and Booklore, 1953—, Bibliographica Judaica, 1969—; compiler: A Gathering of Broadsides, 1967. Served with USN, 1944-46. Mem. ALA, Assn. Jewish Librs.

(founder, nat. pres. 1965-66), World Coun. on Jewish Archives (v.p. 1977-81), Assn. Jewish Studies, Spl. Librs. Assn. (pres. Cin. chpt. 1953-54), Coun. Archives and rsch. Librs. in Jewish Studies (pres. 1974-78, 89-91), Am. Hist. Assn., Am. Printing Hist. Assn., Israel Bibliophiles, Typophiles, World Union Jewish Studies, AAUP (chpt. pres. 1964-68), Grolier Club (N.Y.C.), Phi Beta Kappa, Beta Phi Mu. Office: Hebrew Union Coll Jewish Inst Religion 3101 Clifton Ave Cincinnati OH 45220-2488

ZAGEL, JAMES BLOCK, federal judge; b. Chgo., Mar. 4, 1941; s. Samuel and Ethel (Samuels) Z.; m. Margaret Maxwell, May 27, 1979. BA, U. Chgo., 1962, MA in Philosophy, 1962; JD, Harvard U., 1965. Bar: Ill. 1965, U.S. Dist. Ct. (no. dist.) Ill. 1965, U.S. Supreme Ct. 1970, U.S.C. Ct. Appeals (7th cir.) 1972. Asst. atty. gen. criminal justice div. State of Ill., Springfield, 1970-77; chief prosecuting atty. Ill. Jud. Inquiry Bd., Springfield, 1973-75; exec. dir. Ill. Law Enforcement Commn., Springfield, 1977-79; dir. Ill. Dept. Revenue, Springfield, 1979-80, Ill. Dept. State Police, Springfield, 1980-87; judge U.S. Dist. Ct. (no. dist.) Ill., Chgo., 1987—. Co-author: Criminal Law and Its Administration, 1989, Cases and Comments on Criminal Procedure, 1992. Named Outstanding Young Citizen, Chgo. Jaycees, 1977 ; recipient Disting. Service Merit award Assn. Commerce and Industry, 1983. Mem. Chgo. Bar Assn., Jud. Conf. of U.S. (codes of conduct com. 1987-92). Office: US Dist Ct 219 S Dearborn ST Ste 1978 Chicago IL 60904

ZAGORIA, SAM D(AVID), arbitrator, author, educator; b. Somerville, N.J., Apr. 9, 1919; s. Nathan and Rebecca (Shapiro) Z.; m. Sylvia Bomse, Dec. 21, 1941; children: Paul, Marjorie Zagoria Isacks, Ronald. B.L. in Journalism, Rutgers U., 1941. With New Brunswick Daily Home News, N.J., 1940-41, N.J. Def. Council, Trenton, 1941-42; Fed. Office Govt. Reports, Newark, 1942; reporter Washington Post, 1946-55; adminstrv. asst. to Senator Clifford P. Case, Washington, 1955-65; mem. NLRB, Washington, 1965-69; dir. Labor-Mgmt. Rels. Svc. U.S. Conf. of Mayors, Washington, 1970-78; mem. U.S. Consumer Product Safety Commn., 1978-84; ombudsman Washington Post, 1984-86; arbitrator, writer, 1986—; Fulbright lectr., Copenhagen, 1987; vis. prof. Fla. Atlantic U., Boca Raton, 1988-91; adj. prof. Wake Forest U., Winston-Salem, N.C., 1993—. Author: Public Workers, Public Unions, 1972, The Ombudsman: How Good Governments Handle Citizens' Grievances, 1988. Campaign mgr. reelection Senator Case, 1960; campaign mgr. race for gov., former Sec. of Labor James P. Mitchell, 1961. With USAAF, 1942-45. Nieman fellow Harvard, 1954. Mem. Common Cause, Nat. Consumers League, Rutgers U. Alumni Assn. Jewish. Home and Office: 2864 Wynfield Crossing Ln Winston Salem NC 27103 also: 3221 S Ocean Blvd # 204 Highland Beach FL 33487

ZAGORIN, PEREZ, historian, educator; b. Chgo., May 29, 1920; s. Solomon Novitz and Mildred (Ginsburg) Z.; m. Honoré Desmond Sharrer, May 29, 1947; 1 son, Adam. A.B., U. Chgo., 1941; A.M., Harvard U., 1947, Ph.D., 1952. Various positions OWI, U.S. Govt., U.P. Syndicate, CIO, 1942-46; instr. Amherst Coll., 1947-49; lectr. Vassar Coll., 1951-53; from asst. prof. to prof. history McGill U., 1955-65; prof. U. Rochester, 1965—, Joseph C. Wilson prof. history, 1982-90, Joseph C. Wilson prof. history emeritus, 1990—, chmn. dept., 1968-69, acting chmn. dept., 1988-89; vis. prof. Johns Hopkins, 1964-65; Amundsen vis. prof. U. Pitts., 1964; William Andrews Clark Meml. Library prof. UCLA, 1975-76; Mem. adv. coun. Yale Ctr. Study Parliamentary History; Thompson lectr. history Vassar Coll., 1987. Author: A History of Political Thought in the English Revolution, 1954, The Court and the Country, 1969, Culture and Politics from Puritanism to the Enlightenment, 1980, Rebels and Rulers 1500-1660, 2 vols., 1982, Ways of Lying: Dissimulation, Persecution, and Conformity in Early Modern Europe, 1990, Milton Aristocrat and Rebel: The Poet and His Politics, 1992; co-editor: Philosophy Science and Religion in England 1640-1700, 1991, Guide to Historical Literature, 1994; contbr. numerous articles in hist. jours.; mem. editorial bd. Jour. of the History of Ideas. Sheldon traveling fellow Harvard U., 1949-50, Fulbright fellow 1949-50, faculty rsch. fellow Social Sci. Rsch. Coun., 1958-59, sr. rsch. fellow Folger Shakespeare Libr., 1964-65, fellow Inst. Advanced Study, Princeton, N.J., 1972-73, sr. fellow Nat. Humanities Ctr., 1978-79, fellow Ctr. Advanced Study in Behavioral Scis., 1983-84, Edgar F. Shannon Ctr. for Advanced Studies fellow U. Va., 1994—. Fellow Royal Hist. Soc., Am. Acad. Arts and Scis.; mem. Am. Hist. Assn. (chmn. Gershoy prize com. 1982-84). Home: 2990 Beaumont Farm Rd Charlottesville VA 22901 Office: U Rochester Dept History Rochester NY 14627

ZAH, PETERSON, american indian tribal executive; b. Low Mountain, Ariz., Dec. 2, 1937; s. Henry and Mae (Multine) Z.; m. Rosalind Begay; children: Elaine, Eileen, Keeyonnie. BA, Ariz. State U. Journeyman carpenter Ariz. Vocat. Edn. Dept., Phoenix, 1963-64; constrn. estimator design and constrn. dept. Navajo Tribe, Fort Defiance, Ariz., 1964-65; field coordinator VISTA Indian Tng. Ctr. Ariz. State U., Tempe, 1965-67; exec. dir. DNA People's Legal Services Inc., Window Rock, Ariz., 1967-81; chmn. Navajo Tribal Council, Window Rock, 1983-87, chmn. Navajo Edn. and Scholarship, 1989-90; now mem. The Navajo Nation, Window Rock; dir. West regional office Save The Children Fedn., 1989-90. Mem. Ariz. adv. com. U.S. Civil Rights Commn., 1983—; pres. Window Rock Sch. Bd., 1973—. Mem. Nat. Assn. Indian Legal Services. Democrat. Office: Navajo Nation PO Box 9000 Window Rock AZ 86515-0308

ZAHARIA, ERIC STAFFORD, developmental disabilities program administrator; b. Pomona, Calif., Aug. 24, 1948; s. Edgar A. and Dorothy (Stafford) Z.; m. Caryle Koentz, Dec. 23, 1967; children: Tye W., Tieg A. BA, Pomona Coll., 1970; MEd, U. Ariz.-Tucson, 1973; PhD, George Peabody Coll., 1978; postgrad., Govt. Execs. Inst. U. N.C., Chapel Hill, 1981. Mental retardation worker Ariz. Tng. Program, Tucson, 1970-71, unit dir., 1971-73; dir. residential svcs Willmar State Hosp., (Minn.), 1973-76; rsch. asst. Inst. on Mental Retardation and Intellectual Devel., Nashville, 1976-78; dir. mental retardation program svcs Dept. Mental Health/Mental Retardation, State of Tenn., Nashville, 1978-79; dir. Caswell Ctr., Kinston, N.C., 1979-86; program adminstr. Colo. Div. of Devel. Disabilities, Denver, 1986-90; dir. Utah div. Svcs. for People with Disabilities, Salt Lake City, 1990—; mem. adj. faculty East Carolina U., Greenville, 1979-86; bd. dirs Neuse Enterprises Inc., Kinston. Chmn. Big Bros./Sisters Kinston Inc., 1980-83; mem. N.C. Coalition for Community Svc., 1987-88. Mem. Am. Assn. Mental Retardation, Nat. Assn. Supts., Pub. Residential Facilities, Assn. Retarded Citizens, Kinston C. of C. (bd. dirs. 1983-86). Home: 8010 Juniper Dr Park City UT 84060-5370 Office: 120 N 200 W Salt Lake City UT 84103-1550

ZAHN, CARL FREDERICK, museum publications director, designer, photographer; b. Louisville, Mar. 9, 1928; s. Fred Joseph and Myrtle (Fulks) Z.; m. Betty Jane Woodrow, Nov. 18, 1950 (div. July 1977); children: Lisa, Karen, Richard; m. Felicitas Magdalena Fuhlrott, July 30, 1979. BA, Harvard Coll., 1948. Asst. in conservation Fogg Art Mus., Cambridge, Mass., 1949-50; with art dept. Benton & Bowles Inc., N.Y.C., 1950-51; design asst. Inst. Contemporary Art, Boston, 1951-56; dir. publs. Mus. Fine Arts, Boston, 1956—; also exhbn. designer, 1995—. exhibitions include: Addison Gallery Am. Art, Andover, Mass., 1959, Am. Inst. Graphic Arts, N.Y.C., 1960—, Rose Art Mus. Brandeis U., Waltham, Mass., 1969; author: Introduction to Hermann Zapf and His Design Philosophy, 1987; co-author Weston's Westons: Portraits and Nudes, 1989. Mem. Am. Inst. Graphic Arts (v.p. 1971-72), Soc. Printers, Bund Deutscher Buchkünstler, Mink Meadows Golf Club, East Chop Tennis Club (bd. dirs. 1970-72), Longwood Cricket Club. Home: 39 Cedarwood Rd Jamaica Plain MA 02130-3021 Office: Mus Fine Arts 479 Huntington Ave Boston MA 02115-5599

ZAHN, DONALD JACK, lawyer; b. Albany, N.Y., Oct. 24, 1941; s. Jerome and Clara (Zinsher) Z.; m. Laurie R. Hyman, Aug. 19, 1966; children: Lawrence, Melissa. AB, NYU, 1963; LLB, Union U., 1966; LLM in Taxation, NYU, 1967. Bar: N.Y. 1966, U.S. Dist. Ct. (no. dist.) N.Y. 1966, U.S. Tax Ct. 1969, U.S. Ct. Appeals (2d cir.) 1970, Tex. 1972, U.S. Ct. Appeals (5th and 11th cirs.). Assoc., Bond, Schoeneck and King, Syracuse, N.Y., 1967-71; ptnr. Haynes and Boone, Dallas, 1971-82, Akin, Gump, Strauss, Hauer & Feld, Dallas, 1982-92; assoc. prof. internat. taxation, fed. income taxation, bus. assns., corp. taxation Tex. Wesleyan Sch. Law , Irving, Tex., 1992—; adj. prof. Sch. Law, So. Meth. U., Dallas, 1972-87, 90-91. Trustee, sec. mem. exec. and fin. com., nominating com. Greenhill Sch., Addison, Tex., 1980-90; trustee, chmn. budget com., mem. fin. com. Jewish Fedn. Greater Dallas, 1978-89; trustee, chmn. Found. Jewish Fedn., Dallas, 1980-

89; trustee, v.p., pres. Dallas chpt. Am. Jewish Com., 1980-92; mem. Tex. World Trade Council, 1986-87, Dallas Mayor's Internat. Com. Mem. State Bar Tex. (sec. 1982-83, chmn. tax sect. 1984-85, newsletter taxation sect. editor 1980-81), Internat. Bar Assn., Internat. Comte (N. Tex. commn.), Southwestern Legal Found. (adv. bd., treas. Internat. and Comparative Law Ctr., lectr. Acad. in Internat. Law), N.Y. State Bar Assn. Jewish. Office: Tex Wesleyan U Sch of Law 2535 E Grauwyler Irving TX 75061-3400

ZAHN, MARKUS, electrical engineering educator; b. Bergen-Belsen, Germany, Dec. 3, 1946; s. Irving and Maria (Fischer) Z.; m. Linda Ruth Jasen, June 1, 1969; children: Laura Michelle, Daniel Jacob, Jeffrey David, Amy Elizabeth. BSEE, MSEE, MIT, 1968, cert. in Elec. Engring., 1969, DS, 1970. Prof. elec. engring. U. Fla., Gainesville, 1970-80; prof. elec. engring. MIT, Cambridge, 1980—, dir. VI-A internship program. Author (book) Electromagnetic Field Theory: A Problem Solving Approach, 1979; co-author (videotapes) Demonstrations of Electromagnetic Fields and Energy, 1989. Fellow IEEE. Avocation: stamp collecting. Office: MIT Rm 10-174 Cambridge MA 02135

ZAHN, PAULA, newscaster; b. Feb. 24, 1956; m. Richard Cohen; 1 child, Haley. With Sta. WHDH, Boston, 1983-85; anchor, reporter Sta. KCBS, L.A., 1985-87; co-anchor World News Now ABC News, N.Y.C., 1987-90; co-anchor CBS This Morning CBS News, N.Y.C., 1990—; contbr. CBS news mag. 48 Hours; co-host CBS broadcast Winter Olympics, Albertville, France, 1992. Office: CBS News CBS This Morning 524 W 57th St New York NY 10019-2902

ZAHN, TIMOTHY, writer; b. Chgo., Sept. 1, 1951; s. Herbert William and Marilou (Webb) Z.; m. Anna L. Romo, Aug. 4, 1979; 1 child, Corwin Jame. BA, Mich. State U., 1973; MA, U. Ill., 1975. Author: The Blackcollar, 1983, A Coming of Age, 1983, Cobra, 1985, Spinneret, 1985, Blackcollar: The Backlash Mission, 1986, Cobra Strike, 1986, Triplet, 1987, Deadman Switch, 1988, Cobra Bargain, 1988, Warhorse, 1990, Heir to Empire, 1991, Dark Force Rising, 1992, Star Wars: The Last Command, 1993, Conquerors' Pride, 1994, Conquerors' Heritage, 1995; also sci. fiction short stories. Recipient Hugo award nomination for short story World Sci. Fiction Conv., 1983, Hugo award for best novella Cascade Point, 1984, Hugo award nomination short story, 1985. Office: c/o Bantam Books Inc 1540 Broadway New York NY 10036

ZAHND, RICHARD HUGO, professional sports team executive, lawyer; b. N.Y.C., July 22, 1946; s. Hugo and Rose (Genovese) Z.; m. Phyllis Beth Workman, Aug. 13, 1978; children: Andrew Richard, Melissa Dawn. A.B., NYU, 1968, J.D., 1971. Bar: N.Y. 1972. Assoc. Paul, Weiss, Rifkind, Wharton & Garrison, N.Y.C., 1971-74; staff atty. Madison Square Garden Corp., N.Y.C., 1974-75; v.p. legal affairs Madison Square Garden Center, Inc., N.Y.C., 1975-79; v.p., gen. counsel Madison Square Garden Corp., N.Y.C., 1979-86; v.p. N.Y. Knickerbockers Basketball Club, N.Y.C., 1979-86, N.Y. Rangers Hockey Club, N.Y.C., 1979-86; v.p., gen. counsel Nat. Hockey League Ent., Inc., N.Y.C., 1992—, now sr. v.p., gen. counsel. Served to capt. U.S. Army, 1972. John Norton Pomeroy scholar NYU Law Sch., 1969; Mortimer Bishop scholar NYU Law Sch., 1969; Judge Jacob Markowitz scholar NYU Law Sch., 1970; recipient Am. Jurisprudence prize NYU Law Sch., 1969. Mem. ABA, N.Y. State Bar Assn. Episcopalian. Office: 1251 Ave Americas Fl 47 New York NY 10020*

ZAHORIAN, STEPHEN GLEN, banker; b. Elmira, N.Y., Aug. 24, 1938; s. Stephen and Kathryn E. (Anderson) Z.; m. Linda J. Cole, June 6, 1959 (div. 1982); children: Laurie Lee, Stephen G. Jr.; m. Barbara Ann Sica, Feb. 26, 1983 (div. 1987); m. Janet Burger, Nov. 27, 1987. Student Bentley Coll. Acctg., 1959; postgrad. N.Y. State Bus. Adminstrn. Consumer Credit Sch., 1964; Am. Banking Assn. Comml. Lending Sch., 1969; Stonier Grad. Sch. Banking, 1975. Asst. cashier, v.p. First Nat. Bank, Ithaca, N.Y., 1963-71; exec. v.p. Edison Nat. Bank, Ft. Myers, Fla., 1971-72; pres., chief exec. officer Barnett Bank of Lee County, N.A., 1972—; past dir. Fed. Reserve Bank of Atlanta, Miami Br. Former mem. City of Ft. Myers Planning Bd.; former chmn. Downtown Redevel. Agy.; past dir. and pres. Lee County YMCA; past pres. Pres's Roundtable; mem. exec. com. Bus. Devel. Corp; Chamber of S.W. Fla.; bd. dirs. Downtown Property Owners Assn. Mem. ABA, Royal Palm Yacht Club, Fiddlesticks Country Club, Edison Pageant of Light Club, Rotary (bd. dir. 1974). Roman Catholic. Home: 2711 E 1st St Fort Myers FL 33916-1844 Office: Barnett Bank Lee County NA PO Box 12288 Saint Petersburg FL 33733-2288

ZAHUMENY, JANET MAE, secondary education educator; b. Rahway, N.J., Mar. 23, 1945; d. Richard Evans and Elsie Mae (Walling) Franklin; m. Edward Zahumeny, Dec. 21, 1966 (div. 1987); 1 child, Carole Ann. BA, Newark State Coll., 1967; MEd, William Paterson Coll., 1990; MA, Kean Coll., 1994. Cert. secondary tchr., N.J. Math. tchr. Hunterdon Cen. High Sch., Flemington, N.J., 1967-68; math., computer tchr. Roselle Park (N.J.) High Sch., 1968—; instr. computers Roselle Park Adult Sch., 1987-88; instr. computer tech. William Paterson Coll., 1993—; cons. Gray's Appraisal, Cranford, N.J., 1987; textbook editor Prentice Hall, 1989; computer group asst. Bell Labs., Whippany, N.J., summers 1972-73; chmn. Dist. Computer Study Com., 1988; in svc. tchr. tng. 1988—, 8th grade computer coord., 1988-89; mem. Mid. States Evaluation Team, 1972, 82, 85; liason com. RPHS, 1985—, cooperating tchr. Kean Coll., 1990—, Montclair State U.; adminstrv. asst. to v.p. Alpha Wire, summer 1991—; participant Computing Inst., 1983, Woodrow Wilson Inst., 1991, NSF Inst., 1991. Active Cranford PTA, Roselle Park PTSA. Named Outstanding Math. tchr., Cittone Inst., Edison, N.H., 1988, Outstanding Tchr., N.J. Gov.'s Recognition Program, 1989, Outstanding Computer/Math. Tchr. Tandy Techs., 1991; recipient Grad. Scholarship Kean Coll., Union, N.J., 1992, Computer Grant award 1993, Presdl. award for excellence in tchg. maths. and sci., 1994, 95. Mem. Mem. NEA, Nat. Coun. Tchrs. Math., Assn. Math. Tchrs. N.J., N.J. Edn. Assn., Roselle Park Edn. Assn., Mensa, Kean Coll. Alumni Assn., William Paterson Coll. Alumni Assn., Ednl. Tech. Network, Pi Lambda Theta, Kappa Delta Pi, Phi Kappa Phi. Avocations: computers, embroidering, sailing, bowling, bridge. Office: Roselle Park High Sch 185 W Webster Ave Roselle Park NJ 07204-1699

ZAILLIAN, STEVEN, screenwriter, director; b. Calif., Jan. 30, 1953. BA, San Francisco State U., 1975. Scripts include: The Falcon and the Snowman, 1985, Awakenings, 1990 (Acad. award nominee for best adapted screenplay, 1990), Jack the Bear, 1993, Schindler's List, 1993 (Acad. award best adapted screenplay 1993); co-writer (with Donald Stewart and John Milius) Clear and Present Danger, 1994; scriptwriter, dir.: Searching for Bobby Fisher, 1993.

ZAIMAN, JOEL HIRSH, rabbi; b. Chgo., Mar. 10, 1938; s. Solomon and Ruth (Levy) Z.; m. Ann Shanok, July 1, 1959; children: Elana Beth, Sarina, Ari Lev. BS, DePaul U., 1957; Master of Hebrew Letters, Jewish Theol. Sem., N.Y.C., 1962. Assoc. rabbi Temple Emanu-El, Providence, 1962-73, sr. rabbi, 1973-80; sr. rabbi Chizuk Amuno Congregation, Balt., Md., 1980—; pres. Balt. Bd. Rabbis, 1985-87; 1st v.p. Synagogue Coun. Am., 1988, pres. 1989-91. Contbr. articles to profl. jours. Chmn. Solomon Schecter Day Sch. Edn. Com. Balt., 1983; bd. dirs. Levindale Hebrew Geriatric Ctr. and Hosp., Balt., 1984—, mem. long range planning com.; bd. dirs. Balt. Bd. Jewish Edn., Md. Commn. on Hereditary and Congenital Disorders, Assoc. Jewish Charities and Welfare Fund; v.p. Balt. Jewish Coun., 1992-94, pres., chmn.; mem. chancellor's rabbinic cabinet Jewish Theol. Sem.; mem. bd. patient care adv. com. Sinai Hosp., 1991; bd. dirs., mem. program com. Inst. Christian and Jewish Studies; mem. adv. coun. Md. Health Care Decisions Act, 1994—. Fellow Pearlstone Inst. Jewish Living (program planning com.); mem. Rabbinical Assembly (exec. council, long range planning com.), United Synagogue Commn. Jewish Edn. (chmn.), Md. Jewish Hist. Soc. (bd. dirs.), Associated Jewish Fedn. Balt. (bd. dirs. 1991—). Home: 7912 Winterset Ave Baltimore MD 21208-3109 Office: Chizuk Amuno Congregation 8100 Stevenson Rd Baltimore MD 21208-1899

ZAISER, KENT AMES, lawyer; b. St. Petersburg, Fla., June 10, 1945; s. Robert Alan and Marion (Brown) Z. AB Duke U., 1967; postgrad. U. Calif.-Berkeley, 1971; JD, U. Fla., 1972. Bar: Fla. 1973, U.S. Dist. Ct. (no. dist.) Fla. 1974, U.S. Supreme Ct. 1978, U.S. Dist. Ct. (so. dist.) Fla. 1980, U.S. Dist. Ct. (mid. dist.) Fla. 1981, U.S. Ct. Appeals (11th cir.) 1981. Rsch. aide Fla. Supreme Ct., Tallahassee, 1973-75, adminstrv. asst. to chief justice,

1975-76; asst. gen. counsel Fla. Dept. Natural Resources, Tallahassee, 1976-80; asst. atty. gen. Fla. Dept. Legal Affairs, Tallahassee, 1980-85; dep. gen. counsel S.W. Fla. Water Mgmt. Dist., Brooksville, 1985-89, gen. counsel, 1989-92; ptnr. Foley and Lardner, Tallahassee, 1992-93; prin. Kent A. Zaiser, P.A., Tallahassee, 1994—; cons. Fla. State Cts. Adminstr., Tallahassee, 1975. Contbg. author: Environmental Regulation and Litigation in Florida, 1980-84. Campaign chmn. Vince Fechtel for State Rep. of Fla., Leesburg, 1972. Mem. Tallahassee Bar Assn., Jefferson County Bar Assn. Democrat. Episcopalian. Club: Governors. Home: 3286 Longleaf Rd Tallahassee FL 32310-6406 Office: PO Box 6045 Tallahassee FL 32314-6045

ZAITZEFF, ROGER MICHAEL, lawyer; b. Detroit, June 25, 1940; s. Peter and Mary (Fedchenia) Z.; m. Amine Erma Wefali, Jan. 30, 1970; children: Zachary, Natasha, Zoe, Peter. BA with high honors and high distinction, U. Mich., 1962; MA with distinction, U. Calif., Berkeley, 1963, JD, 1969. Bar: N.Y. 1974, U.S. Dist. Ct. (so. dist.) N.Y. 1975, U.S. Ct. Appeals (2nd cir.) 1975, D.C. 1985. Assoc. Seward & Kissel, N.Y.C., 1969-77, ptnr., 1977-94; ptnr. Latham & Wakins, N.Y.C., 1994—. Contbr. articles to U. Fla. Law Rev., The Bus. Lawyer, Internat. Bus. Lawyer, Touro Law Rev., Internat. Tax and Bus. Lawyer, Nat. Law Jour. Mem. Tribar Opinion Com., 1990-93. Heller grantee U. Mich., 1962. Mem. ABA, Internant. Bar Assn., Assn. of Bar of City of N.Y., N.Y. State Bar Found., Southwestern Legal Found. (adv. bd.), N.Y. County Lawyers Assn. (spl. com. legal opinions in comml. transactions), Phi Beta Kappa. Office: Latham & Watkins 885 3rd Ave New York NY 10022-4802

ZAJAC, JACK, sculptor, painter; b. Youngstown, Ohio, Dec. 13, 1929; s. John and Elizabeth Z.; m. Corda Eby, Sept. 19, 1956; children: Aaron John, Christian Rafael. Student, Scripps Coll., 1949-53, Am. Acad., in Rome, 1954-55, 57-58, 58-59. prof. art U. Calif., Santa Cruz. One-man shows include, San Diego Mus., 1975, Public Gardens Orveito, 1976, group exhbns. include, Pitts. Internat., 1955-65, Biennale di Roma, 1968, Stephen Wirtz Gallery, San Francisco, 1984; represented in permanent collections, Mus. Modern Art, N.Y.C., Whitney Mus., Hirshhorn Mus., Jan Turner Gallery, L.A., Forum Gallery, N.Y.C. Rome Prize fellow, 1954; Guggenheim fellow, 1959; am. Acad. Arts and Letters grantee, 1958. Fellow Am. Acad. in Rome; mem. NAD.

ZAJICEK, JERONYM, music educator; b. Krasne, Brezno, Czechoslovakia, Nov. 10, 1926; came to U.S., 1952; s. Frantisek Zajicek and Emilie (Lauterkranz) Zajickova. Student, Charles U., Prague, Czechoslovakia, 1946-49; MusB, Roosevelt U., 1957, MusM, 1958; studies with K.B. Jirak, Paul A. Pisk; PhD, Charles U., Prague, 1990. Music program dir. for Czechoslovak sect. Radio Free Europe, Munich, 1950-52; prof. theory and composition Loop Coll., Chgo., 1964—. Composer numerous works including Clarinet Sonata, 1958, Sinfonietta for Large Orch., 1958, Cello Sonata, 1975; recorded Concertino for Flute and String Orch., 1963, Willie Schwegler Flute and Cologne Radio Orch., String Quartet, 1963. Oliver Ditson fellow, 1956, 57; 1st prize Internat. Soc. for Contemporary Music (Chgo. chpt. 1964). Roman Catholic. Home: 4230 Prescott Ave Lyons IL 60534-1537 Office: Harold Washington Coll 30 E Lake St Chicago IL 60601-2420

ZAJONC, ROBERT B(OLESLAW), psychology educator; b. Lodz, Poland, Nov. 23, 1923; came to U.S., 1949, naturalized, 1953; s. Mieczyslaw and Anna (Kwiatkowska) Z.; m. Donna Benson, June 20, 1953 (div. 1981); children: Peter Clifford, Michael Anton, Joseph Robert; m. Hazel Markus, May 25, 1982; 1 child, Krysia Courcelle Rose. Ph.D., U. Mich., 1955; Dr. hon. causa, U. Louvain, 1984, U. Warsaw, 1989. Asst. prof. psychology U. Mich., 1955-60, assoc. prof., 1960-63, prof., 1963-94, Charles Horton Cooley Disting. prof. psychology, 1983-94, rsch. scientist Inst. for Social Rsch., 1960-83, dir., 1989; prof. psychology Stanford (Calif.) U., 1994—; directeur d'études Maison des Sciences de L'Homme, Paris, 1985-86; vis. prof. U. Oxford, 1971-72. Author: Social Psychology: An Experimental Approach, 1965; editor: Animal Social Psychology, 1970; assoc. editor: Jour. Personality and Social Psychology, 1960-66. Guggenheim fellow, 1978-79; Fulbright fellow, 1962-63; recipient Disting. Prof. award of social sci., 1983. Fellow AAAS (co-recipient Psychol. prize 1976), APA (Disting. Sci. Contbrn. award 1978), Japan Soc. Promotion of Sci., N.Y. Acad. Scis.; mem. Soc. for Exptl. Social Psychology (Disting. Scientist award 1986), Polish Acad. Scis. (fgn.). Office: Stanford U Dept Psychology Jordan Hall Stanford CA 94305

ZAKAIB, LORNE, industrial technology executive; b. Montreal, Que., Can., June 11, 1932; s. Jesse Charles Zakaib and Rea Yvonne Brodeur; m. Viola Kouri, Sept. 3, 1961; children: Janice, Jay. B in Engring., McGill U., Montreal, 1956, diploma in bus., 1974. Program mgr. FIIID Navigation Systems Canadian Marconi, 1965-70, oper. mgr. Marine and Land Communications, 1970-73; mfg. site mgr. IBM Can., Bromont, Que., 1973-89; exec. v.p. S.N.C Group, Montreal, 1989—; pres., chief oper. officer S.N.C. Indsl. Techs. Inc., Le Gardeur, Que., Can. Past pres. Assn. for Mentally Retarded. Named Nouveau Performant, City of Montreal, 1986; recipient 3 Mercuriades awards. Mem. IEEE, Order Engrs., Montreal of C. Home: 421 Saint Thomas Circle, Saint Lambert, PQ Canada J4R 1Y3 Office: SNC Defence Products Ltd, 2 Pl Felix-Martin, Montreal, PQ Canada H2Z 1Z4 also: SNC Industrial Tech Inc, 5 montée des Arsenaux, Le Gardeur, PQ Canada J5Z 2P4

ZAKANITCH, ROBERT RAHWAY, artist; b. Elizabeth, N.J., May 24, 1935; s. Andrew and Mary Z. Student, Newark (N.J.) Sch. Fine and Indsl. Art, 1954-57. vis. artist, lectr. Sch. Art Inst. Chgo., 1976, U. Calif., San Diego, 1974; lectr. numerous univs. One man shows include Henri Gallery, Alexandria, Va., 1965, Reese Palley Gallery, N.Y.C., 1970, 71, Cunningham Ward, N.Y.C., 1973, 74, Holly Solomon Gallery, N.Y.C., 1977, Robert Miller Gallery, N.Y.C., 1978, 79, 81, 84, 85, 88, Galerie Liatowitsch, Basel, Switzerland, 1978, Galerie Rudolf Zwirner, Cologne, Fed. Republic Germany, 1979, Daniel Templon Gallery, N.Y.C., 1980, Bruno Bischofberger Gallery, Zurich, 1980, James Mayor Gallery, London, 1981, Marcus Gallery, 1984, Inst. Contemporary Art, Phila., 1981, Akira Ikeda Gallery, Nagoya, Japan, 1981, Daniel Templon Gallery, Paris, 1982, 87, 91, McIntosh-Drysdale Gallery, Washington, 1983, Harcus Gallery, Boston, 1984, 87, 89, Delahunty Gallery, Dallas, 1984, Helander/Rubinstein Gallery, Palm Beach, Fla., 1985, 89, Asher Faure Gallery, L.A., 1985, Yares Gallery, Scottsdale, Ariz., 1987, Sidney Janis Gallery, N.Y.C., 1990, Jason McCoy Gallery, N.Y.C., 1994, 1995 (John Simon Guggenheim fellowship grant), Guild Hall, East Hampton, N.Y., 1995, others; group shows include Franklin Gallery, Cornell U., 1978, Va. Mus. Fine Arts, 1979, Palais des Beaux-Arts, Brussels, 1979, Inst. Contemporary Art, U. Pa., 1979, New Mus., N.Y., 1979, Galerie Daniel Templon, Paris, 1980, Nat. Gallery Art, Washington, 1980, Indpls. Mus. Art, 1980, San Francisco Art Inst., 1980, Whitney Mus. Am. Art, N.Y., 1981, Jacksonville Art Mus., 1981, Galeria Civica, Italy, 1982, Mus. Fine Arts, Boston, 1982, Fay Gold Gallery, Atlanta, 1982, High Mus. Art, Atlanta, 1983, Meml. Art Gallery, Rochester, N.Y., 1983, Kuntsmus., Luzern, 1983. Served with U.S. Army, 1958-60. John Simon Guggenheim fellowship grant, 1995. Office: 78 Greene St New York NY 10012-5100

ZAKARIAN, ALBERT, lawyer; b. Pawtucket, R.I., May 3, 1940; m. Barbara Ann Zakarian, May 28, 1967; children: Adam, Dana. BA, Trinity Coll., 1962; LLB, Columbia U., 1965. Bar: Conn. 1965, U.S. Dist. Ct. Conn. 1965, U.S. Ct. Appeals (2d cir.) 1971. Assoc. Day, Berry & Howard, Hartford, Conn., 1965-74, ptnr., 1975—; panelist Conn. Alt. Disp. Resolution, Ctr. for Pub. Resources, 1988—; co-chair Fed. Spl. Masters Program for Dist. of Conn. Contbr. articles to profl. jours. Mem. town com. Simsbury (Conn.) Dems., 1974-86; chmn. Simsbury Human Rels. Commn., 1985. Capt. JAGC USAF, 1965-68, Vietnam. Decorated Bronze Star. Fellow Am. Coll. Trial Lawyers, Am. Bar Found.; mem. Nat. Bd. Trial Advocacy, Am. Bd. Trial Advs. (diplomate), Conn. Bar Assn. (chmn. civil justice sect. 1979-82, fed. judiciary com.), Hartford County Bar Assn. (pres. 1985-86). Democrat. Office: Day Berry & Howard Cityplace Hartford CT 06103

ZAKARIAN, JOHN J., journalist; b. Jerusalem, Oct. 26, 1937; came to U.S., 1957; s. Ivan and Arsha (Aghabekian) Z.; m. Kay Holder, Sept. 14, 1963; children—Paul, David. B.S. in Journalism, U. Ill., 1961; M.A. in Mass Communication, U. Iowa, 1965. Reporter AP, Chgo., 1961; reporter Register-Mail, Galesburg, Ill., 1962-64; legis. corr., editorial editor Lindsay-Schaub Newspapers, Decatur, Ill., 1965-69; assoc. editor Herald Traveler, Boston, 1970-71; editorial writer Post-Dispatch, St. Louis, 1971-77; editor

editorial page Hartford Courant, Conn., 1977—. Named Alumnus of Yr., So. Ill. U., Carbondale, 1972; recipient Walker Stone Editorial Writing award Scripps-Howard Found., Cin., 1984, 1st prize for Editls. New England Associated Press, 1986, Citation for Excellence Overseas Press Club Am., 1987, Tom Wallace award for Interpretative Commentary Inter Am. Press Assn., 1989; Nieman fellow Harvard U., 1968-69; Am. Leadership Forum, Fellow, founder Hartford and Houston, 1984-85. Mem. Nat. Conf. Editorial Writers (pres. 1976), Am. Soc. Newspaper Editors (mem. internat. press com.). Mem. Armenian Orthodox Ch. Avocations: tennis; chess; gardening; mountain climbing. Office: Hartford Courant 285 Broad St Hartford CT 06115-2510

ZAKHEIM, DOV SOLOMON, economist, government official; b. Bklyn., Dec. 18, 1948; s. Zvi Hirsh and Bella (Rabinowitz) Z.; BA summa cum laude, Columbia U., 1970; student London Sch. Econs., 1968-69; DPhil, Oxford U., 1974; m. Barbara Jane Portnoi, Aug. 20, 1972 (div. 1990); children: Keith Samuel, Roger Israel, Scott Elisha; m. Deborah Bing Lowy, May 26, 1991. Rsch. fellow St Antony's Coll., U. Oxford, Eng., 1974; asst. to mng. dir. U.K. br. Internat. Credit Bank Geneva, 1974-75; asso. analyst Nat. Security and Internat. Affairs, Congl. Budget Office, Washington, 1975-78, prin. analyst, 1978-81; spl. asst. to asst. sec. def. (internat. security policy) Dept. Def., 1981-82, spl. asst. to under sec. def. (policy), 1982-83; asst. under sec. def. (policy and resources), 1983-85; dep. undersec. def. for planning and resources, 1985-87; exec. v.p. System Planning Corp., Arlington, Va., 1987-90, corp. v.p., 1990—; CEO SPC Internat. Inc., 1988—; cons. to sec. def. and under sec. def. (policy), 1987-93, ABC News, 1991; adj. prof. Nat. Def. U., 1992, Columbia U., 1995; guest lectr. War Coll., others. Contbr. articles to profl. jours. V.p. S.E. Hebrew Congregation, Silver Spring, Md., 1978-80; bd. dirs. Yeshiva H.S. of Greater Washington, 1979-82, Young Israel Shomrai Emunah, 1983-85; hon. bd. dirs. Hebrew Acad. of Greater Washington, 1980-82; bd. deps. of Brit. Jews, 1971-72; mem. Chief Rabbi's Chaplaincy Bd., U.K., 1971-72; mem. U.S. Commn. for Preservation of Am.'s Heritage Abroad, 1991-95. Recipient Dirs.'s Award for outstanding svc. Congressional Budget Office, 1979, Disting. Pub. Service medal, Dept. Def., 1986, Bronze Palm to Disting. Pub. Svc. medal Dept. Def. 1987; NSF fellow, 1970-73; Columbia Coll. Kellett fellow, 1974. Mem. Council Fgn. Relations, Internat. Inst. Strategic Studies, U.S. Naval Inst., Royal Inst. Internat. Affairs (U.K.), Soc. Govt. Economists, Phi Beta Kappa. Club: Columbia, Capitol Hill, United Oxford and Cmbridge U. Contbr. articles to profl. jours. Home: 817 Lamberton Dr Silver Spring MD 20902-3038 Office: System Planning Corp 1500 Wilson Blvd Arlington VA 22209-2454

ZAKHEM, SAM HANNA, diplomat; b. Beirut, Nov. 25, 1935; s. Hanna Y. and Matilda (Khozami) Z.; m. Merilynn Rosina Gillis; children: John Stuart, Charles Samir, James Paul. BA in Econs., Am. U., Cairo, 1957; MBA, U. Detroit, 1959; MA in Polit. Sci., U. Colo., 1968, PhD, 1970; postgrad., Wayne State U., Detroit, 1960-62. Prof. polit. sci. U. Colo., Denver, 1968-72; dir. ctr. for internat. students U. Denver, 1972-73; rsch. analyst Heritage Found., Washington, 1973-74; dir. corp. rels. and econs. Rocky Mountain Orthodontics, Denver, 1976-82, v.p. corp. relations, 1982-86; amb. to Bahrain Manama, 1986-89; pres. Zakhem and Assocs. Consulting, 1993—; rep. Colo. Ho. of Reps., Denver, 1974-78; senator Colo. State Senate, 1979-83. Bd. dirs. Harvard U., John F. Kennedy Sch. Govt., 1990—; chmn. Freedom Task Force, 1990—; pres. I Love Am. Edn. Found., 1992—. Named Am. by Choice, State of Colo., 1972, Citizen of Yr., VFW, 1994; recipient George Washington Freedom medal Freedom Found. Valley Forge, 1978. Republican. Eastern Orthodox. Avocations: tennis, volleyball. Home: 2530 S Gray Ct Denver CO 80227-4017

ZAKI, ABDELMONEIM EMAM, dental educator; b. Cairo, Egypt, Dec. 18, 1933; came to U.S., 1959; naturalized, 1976; s. Emam Badr El Din and Fatima Hussein (Kamel) Z. DDS, Cairo U., 1955, MS in Radiology, 1958; MSc in Dentistry, Ind. U., Indpls., 1962; PhD in Anatomy, U. Ill., Chgo., 1969. Dental surgeon Demonstration Tng. Ctr., Qalyb, Egypt, 1955-59; instr., then asst. prof. Cairo U., 1962-67; rsch. asst., assoc. U. Ill., Chgo., 1967-69, asst. prof., 1970-72, assoc. prof., 1972-75, prof. dentistry, 1975—, head dept. oral biology, 1994—; sr. investigator, Nat. Inst. Dental Rsch., Bethesda, Md., 1981-82; cons., Cairo U., Alexandria U., Tanta U., all in Egypt, 1976—. Author: Human Dentition, 1965, rev. edit., 1968; contbr. 43 articles and 88 abstracts to dental publs. Mem. Arab-Am. Anti-Discriminatin Com., Washington. Fellow Internat. Coll. Dentists; mem. Am. and Internat. Assns. Dental Rsch. (officer Chgo. chpt. 1982—), Am. Assn. Anatomists, Electron Microscope Soc. Am., N.Y. Acad. Scis., Chgo. Acad. Sci., Egyptian-Am. Club Chgo., Arab Am. Univ. Grads., Chgo. Health Club, Sigma Xi. Moslem. Office: U Ill Chgo 801 S Paulina St Chicago IL 60612-7213

ZAKIM, DAVID, biochemist; b. Paterson, N.J., July 10, 1935; s. Sam and Ruth (Sorokin) B.; m. Nancy Jane Levine, June 12, 1957 (div. 1976); children: Michael, Eric, Thomas; m. Dagmar Auralia Stanke, July 30, 1978; children: Tamara, Robert. AB in Chemistry, Cornell U., 1956; MD summa cum laude, SUNY, Bklyn., 1961. Diplomate Am. Bd. Internal Medicine. Intern N.Y. Hosp., N.Y.C., 1961-62, asst. resident, 1962-63, fellow, 1963-65; asst. prof. to prof. medicine and pharmacology U. Calif., San Francisco, 1968-83; Vincent Astor Disting. prof. medicine Cornell U. Med. Coll., N.Y.C., 1983—; prof. biochemistry Cornell U. Grad. Sch. Med. Sci., 1983—. Contbr. over 150 articles to profl. jours.; editor: Hepatology: A Textbook of Liver Disease, 1982, 2d edit., 1990, Disorders of Acid Secretion, 1991; editor series: Current Topics in Gastroenterology, 1985—; editor Gastroenterology Medicine Today, 1992—. Capt. U.S. Army, 1965-68. Named Disting. Alumnus, SUNY-Bklyn., 1986. Mem. Am. Assn. Physicians, Am. Soc. Biol. Chemists, Biophysics Soc. Achievements include patent on fusion of proteins with lipid vesicles; demonstration of the lipid-dependence of UDP-glucuronology transferase; elucidation of mechanism for uptake of fatty acids and bilirubin into cells. Home: 15 Cole Dr Armonk NY 10504-3004 Office: Cornell U Med Coll Medicine-Gastroenterology 1300 York Ave New York NY 10021-4805

ZAKIN, JACQUES LOUIS, chemical engineering educator; b. N.Y.C., Jan. 28, 1927; s. Mordecai and Ada Davies (Fishbein) Z.; m. Laura Pienky, June 11, 1950; children: Richard Joseph, David Fredric, Barbara Ellen, Emily Anne, Susan Beth. B.Chem. Engring., Cornell U., 1949; M.S. in Chem. Engring., Columbia U., 1950; D.Engring. Sci., N.Y. U., 1959. Chem. engr. Flintkote Research Labs., Whippany, N.J., 1950-51; research technologist, research dept. Socony-Mobil, Bklyn., 1951-53, sr. research technologist, 1953-56, supervising technologist, 1959-62; assoc. prof. chem. engring. U. Mo., Rolla, 1962-65; prof. U. Mo., 1965-77, dir. minority engring. program, 1974-77, dir. women in engring. program, 1975-77; chmn. dept. chem. engring. Ohio State U., Columbus, 1977-94, Helen L. Kurtz profl, 1994—; chmn. sci. manpower and resources com. Coun. Chem. Rsch., 1984-86, mem. governing bd., 1986-89, exec. com., 1988-89; mem. adv. bd. State of Ohio Alternative Fuels, 1992-93; vis. prof. Technion, 1968-69, 94-95, Hebrew U., 1987. Co-editor: Proc. Turbulence Symposium, 1969, 71, 73, 75, 77, 79, 81, 83; contbr. articles to profl. jours. Bd. dirs. Rolla Community Concert Assn., 1966-77, 2d v.p., 1975-77; bd. dirs. Ozark Mental Health Assn., 1976-77; trustee Ohio State Hillel Found., 1981-84, treas., 1984-89, pres., 1989-92; trustee Congregation Beth Tikvah, 1983; bd. trustees Columbus Jewish Fedn., 1989-92; co-chmn. Academics and Scientists for Soviet Refusenhiks. With USNR, 1945-46. Recipient Outstanding Rsch. award U. Mo., Rolla, 1970, Josef Hlavka Meml. medal Czechoslovakian Acad. Sci., 1992, Outstanding Educator of Yr. award Ohio Soc. Profl. Engrs., 1994; mem. Tech. Person of Yr., Columbus Tech. Coun., 1987; Am. Chem. Soc. Petroleum Rsch. Fund Internat. fellow, 1968-69, Socony-Mobil Employee Incentive fellow NYU, 1956-59; sr. Fulbright rsch. fellow Technion, 1994-95. Fellow Am. Inst. Chem. Engrs.; mem. Am. Chem. Soc., Soc. of Rheology, Am. Soc. Engring. Edn., Sigma Xi, Phi Lambda Upsilon, Phi Eta Sigma, Alpha Chi Sigma, Tau Beta Pi, Phi Kappa Phi. Jewish. Patentee in field. Office: Ohio State U 140 W 19th Ave Columbus OH 43210-1110

ZAKIN, JONATHAN NEWELL, computer industry executive; b. Suffern, N.Y., Aug. 18, 1949; s. Paul Peter and Shirley Ruth (Friedman) Z.; m. Esther Karlinsky, Jan. 1972 (div. Aug. 1976); m. Andrea Elisabeth Schutze, June 9, 1984; children: Carl Hartwig, Hans Christopher. BS in Mgmt., NYU, 1971; MBA, Harvard U. 1976. Mgr. fin. planning Prudential Lines Inc., N.Y.C., 1971-74, asst. to pres., 1976-77; assoc. J. Henry Schroder Corp., N.Y.C., 1977-78; gen. mgr. Brisk & Kindle Ltd., London, 1978-80;

pres. Cosma Internat., Brussels, 1980-84; v.p. sales and mktg. Winterhalter, Inc., Ann Arbor, Mich., 1984-86; exec. v.p. mktg. and sales U.S. Robotics, Inc., Skokie, Ill., 1987—. Mem. Monroe Club, Harvard Club. Avocations: jogging, photography, art collecting. Home: 794 Dean Ave Highland Park IL 60035-4724 Office: US Robotics 8100 Mccormick Blvd Skokie IL 60076-2999*

ZAKKAY, VICTOR, aeronautical engineering educator, scientist; b. Baghdad, Iraq, Sept. 8, 1927; came to U.S., 1946, naturalized, 1956; s. Haron and Massouda Isac (David) Zakkai. B.A.E., Poly Inst. Bklyn., 1952, M.Ae.E., 1953, Ph.D.Ae.E., 1959. Research assoc. prof. Poly Inst. Bklyn., 1962-64; assoc. prof. aeronautics NYU, Bronx, 1964-65, prof. aero. and astron. engring., asst. dir. Aero. Lab., 1965-73; prof. applied sci., dir. Antonio Ferri Labs. NYU, Westbury, N.Y., 1973, 75—; chmn. dept. applied sci. NYU, N.Y.C., 1977-84, Astor prof. aero. sci., 1980—; cons. TRW Environ. Engring., Research Triangle Park, N.C., 1980-81, Advanced Tech. Labs., Westbury, 1977-81, b.v. Neratoom, The Hague, Netherlands, 1981—. Editor: (with Olfe) Supersonic Flow, Chemical Processes and Radiation Transfer, 1963; contbr. articles to profl. jours. Mem. AIAA, Sigma Xi, Tau Beta Pi, Sigma Gamma Tau. Home and Office: NYU Barney Building 34 Stuyvesant St New York NY 10003-7506

ZAKS, JERRY, theatrical director, actor; b. Stuttgart, Fed. Republic of Germany, Sept. 7, 1946; came to U.S., 1948, naturalized, 1954; s. Sy and Lily (Gliksman) Z.; m. Jill P. Rose, Jan. 14, 1979; children: Emma Rose, Hannah Lily. AB, Dartmouth Coll., 1967; MFA, Smith Coll., 1969. Guest artist, vis. prof. Dartmouth Coll., 1977, 83-84. Actor: (Broadway plays) Grease, 1974, Once in a Lifetime, 1977, 1940's Radio Hour, 1978, Tintypes, 1980, (off-Broadway plays) including Ensemble Studio Theatre, 1971-81, O'Neill Center, Conn., 1975, Phoenix Theatre, 1976-78, Arena Stage, Washington, 1978, N.Y. Shakespeare Festival, 1975, Manhattan Theatre Club, 1980, Roundabout Theatre, (TV and/or films) including Tuscaloosa's Calling Me, 1979, Attica, 1979; star: (CBS-TV movie) Gentleman Bandit, 1981; appeared in: (TV spl.) Yankee Doodle Dandy, Kennedy Center Tribute to James Cagney, 1980; dir.: (plays, musicals) The Foreigner, 1984 (Obie award 1985), The Marriage of Bette and Boo, 1985 (Obie award 1985, Drama Desk award 1985), (nat. tour) Tintypes, Tap Dance Kid, 1985 (Dramalogue award 1985), Beyond Therapy, Sister Mary Ignatius, Baby with the Bathwater, 1984, House of Blue Leaves, 1986 (Antoinette Perry award), Anything Goes, 1987, Lend Me A Tenor, 1989 (Antoinette Perry award), Six Degrees of Separation, 1990 (Antoinette Perry award), Guys and Dolls, 1992 (Tony award), Smokey Joe's Café, 1994-95 (Tony nomination - Direction of a Musical, 1995); dir. Ensemble Studio, 1978-80, Phoenix Theatre, N.Y.C., 1980-81, Playwrights Horizons, 1981, Phila. Drama Guild, 1981, Denver Ctr. Theater, 1984, N.Y. Pub. Theater, 1984, Assassins, 1990. Bd. dirs. Ensemble Studio Theatre, N.Y.C., 1976—. Mem. AFTRA, Actors Equity Assn., Screen Actors Guild, Soc. Stage Dirs. and Choreographers. Office: c/o Helen Merrill 337 W 22nd St New York NY 10011*

ZALAZNICK, SHELDON, editor, journalist; b. Bronx, N.Y., Aug. 6, 1928; s. Samuel and Esther Leah (Schneiderman) Z.; m. Vera Altobelli, Apr. 4, 1953; 1 dau., Andrea. B.A., Univ. Coll. N.Y. U., 1948; M.A., Tchrs. Coll. Columbia, 1950. Tchr. English Benjamin Franklin High Sch., N.Y.C., 1950-52; assoc. editor Newsweek mag., 1952-56; v.p. Manning Pub. Relations Co., 1956-59; sr. editor Forbes mag., 1959-63, mng. editor, 1976-89; founding editor New York mag. sect. N.Y. Herald Tribune, N.Y.C., 1963-64; Sunday editor N.Y. Herald Tribune, 1964-66; staff writer Gen. Learning Corp., 1966-67; assoc. editor Fortune mag., 1967-69; v.p., editorial dir. New York mag., 1969-76. Home: 458 W 246th St Bronx NY 10471-3330

ZALESKI, MAREK BOHDAN, immunologist; b. Krzemieniec, Poland, Oct. 18, 1936; came to U.S., 1969, naturalized, 1977; s. Stanislaw and Jadwiga (Zienkowicz) Z. M.D., Sch. Medicine, Warsaw, 1960, Dr. Med. Sci., 1963. Instr. dept. histology Sch. Medicine, Warsaw, 1955-60; asst. prof. Sch. Medicine, 1960-69; research asst. prof. (Henry C. and Bertha H. Buswell fellow) dept. microbiology SUNY, Buffalo, 1969-72; assoc. prof. SUNY, 1976-78, prof., 1978—; vis. scientist Inst. Exptl. Biology and Genetics, Czechoslovak Acad. Sci., Prague, 1965; Brit. Council's scholar, research lab. Queen Victoria Hosp., East Grinstead, Eng., 1966-67; asst. prof. dept. anatomy Mich. State U., East Lansing, 1972-75, assoc. prof., 1975-76. Contbg. author: Transplantation and Preservation of Tissues in Human Clinic, 1966, The Man, 1968, Cytophysiology, 1970, Principles of Immunology, 1978, Medical Microbiology, 1982, Molecular Immunology, 1984; co-author: Immunogenetics, 1983, co-editor: Immunobiology of Major Histocompatibility Complex, 1981; co-translator: Spirit of Solidarity, 1984, Marxism and Christianity: The Quarrel and the Dialogue in Poland (J. Tischner), 1987; mem. editorial com. Immunology Investigations, Polish Jour. of Immunology; contbr. articles to med. jours. Former mem. adv. com. for Internat. Rescue Com., Amnesty Internat., Raul Wallenberg Com. USA; bd. dirs., Permanent Chair Polish Culture, Canisius Coll., Bufallo. NIH grantee, 1976-88; NEH grantee, 1985-87. Mem. Polish Anat. Soc., Transplantation Soc., Internat. Soc. Exptl. Hematology, Ernest Witebsky Center Immunology, Am. Assn. Immunologists, Buffalo Collegium of Immunology, N.Y. Acad. Scis., Solidarity and Human Rights Assn. Roman Catholic. Office: SUNY Dept Microbiology Buffalo NY 14214

ZALESKI, MICHAEL LOUIS, state official, lawyer; b. Kenosha, Wis., Jan. 11, 1941; s. Louis Edward and Lena Louise (Bellotti) Z.; m. Sue Alyce Householder, Nov. 24, 1967; children—Sara, David. B.S. in Psychology, U. Wis., 1963, J.D. in Law, 1966. Bar: Wis. 1966, U.S. Dist. Ct. (we. dist.) Wis. 1966, U.S. Dist. Ct. (ea. dist.) Wis. 1970, U.S. Supreme Ct. 1982. Asst. dist. atty. Dane County, Wis., 1967-70; asst. atty. gen. State of Wis. Madison, 1970-86; atty. Quarles & Brady, Madison, 1986—. Served to capt. JAG, USAR, 1968-72. Mem. Wis. State Attys. Assn. (exec. bd. 1978-86), Roman Catholic. Home: 4710 Deerpath Rd Middleton WI 53562-2324 Office: Quarles & Brady PO Box 2113 1 S Pinckney St Madison WI 53703-2808

ZALEZNIK, ABRAHAM, psychoanalyst, management specialist, educator; b. Phila., Jan. 30, 1924; s. Isadore and Anna (Appelbaum) Z.; m. Elizabeth Ann Aron, June 24, 1945; children: Dori Faith, Ira Harry. AB in econs, Alma Coll., 1945, DLitt (hon.), 1992; MBA, Harvard U., 1947, DCS, 1951; grad., Boston Psychoanalytic Soc. and Inst. 1965. Research asst. Harvard U. Grad. Sch. Bus. Adminstrn., 1947-48, instr., 1948-51, asst. prof., 1951-56, assoc. prof., 1956-61, prof., 1961—, Cahners-Rabb prof. social psychology of mgmt., 1967-83, Konosuke Matsushita prof. leadership, 1983-90, Konosuke Matsushita prof. leadership emeritus, 1990—; research fellow Boston Psychoanalytic Soc. and Inst., 1965-68, mem. faculty, 1972—; pvt. practice psychoanalysis Boston, 1968—; cons. to mgmt.; vice chmn. bd. Ogden Corp.; bd. dirs. Ardco, Inc., King Ranch, Inc., Timberland Co., Le Chateau Stores, Ltd., Freedom Newspapers, Inc., Am. Greetings, Butchers, Inc., TJX Corp. Author: Human Dilemmas of Leadership, 1966, (with Manfred F.R. Kets de Vries) Power and the Corporate Mind, 1975, The Managerial Mystique, 1989, An Executive Guide to Motivating People, 1990, Learning Leadership, 1992; contbr. articles to profl. jours. Trustee Beth Israel Hosp., Boston, 1968—. Served with USN, 1942-46. Mem. Boston Psychoanalytic Soc., Am. Psychoanalytic Assn. (cert.), Am. Sociol. Assn., Tavern Club (Boston), Belmont Country Club (Mass.). Home: 170 N Ocean Blvd Palm Beach FL 33480-3946 Office: Harvard University Business School Boston MA 02163 also: Ogden Corp 2 Pennsylvania Plz New York NY 10121

ZALINSKI, EDMUND LOUIS GRAY, insurance executive, mutual funds and real estate executive, investor; b. Salt Lake City, Aug. 18, 1915; s. Edward Robins and Agnes (de Schweinitz) Z.; m. Matilde Eleanor Mittendorf, July 15, 1939; children: Nancy Zalinski Johnson, Matilde Zalinski Davidson, Susanne Zalinski Williams. AB, Cornell U., 1937; MBA, Harvard, 1938; PhD summa cum laude, NYU, 1944. Mgr. sales offices N.Y. Life Ins. Co., 1938-47; asst. v.p., 1951-52, 2d v.p., 1953-54, v.p., 1954-55; instr. NYU, 1944-46; 1st mng. dir. Life Underwriter Tng. Coun., 1947-51, pres., 1954, dir., 1951—; exec. v.p. Nat. Assn. Life Underwriters, 1949-51; v.p., chmn. agy. com. John Hancock Mut. Life Ins. Co., Boston, 1953-57; pres., chief exec. officer Life Ins. Co. N.Am., 1957-71; pres. dir. INA Life Ins. Co. N.Y., 1968-72; v.p., dir. INA Properties, Inc., INA Trading Corp., Phila. Investment Corp.; dir. chmn. exec. com. Bryn Mawr Trust Co., 1963-88; chmn. Greit Realty Trust, 1966-79; chmn., gen. ptnr., bd. dirs. leasing cos.; bd. dirs. Transwall Corp., B.G. Balmer Co.; chmn. bd. dirs. Am. Capital Mut. Funds, 1973-92; mem. adv. coun. Underwriter Edn. and Tng.,

1947-50, Joint Com. Mgmt. Tng., 1948-51; mem. research adv. com. Life Ins. Agy. Mgmt. Assn., 1951-57; Huebner Found. lectr., 1956; mem. vis. com. Harvard Grad. Sch. Bus. Adminstrn., NYU; trustee Am. Coll. Life Underwriters, 1954-72, chmn. mgmt. edn. com., 1957-72; also chmn. devel. com.; treas., founder, chmn. Life Underwriters Tng. Coun., 1947—, life trustee, 1968—. Author publs. relating to field. Trustee, mem. exec. com., v.p. Phila. Mus. Art, 1965-72; bd. dirs. Bur. Mcpl. Rsch., Phila.; bd. dirs., chmn. exec. com. Pa. Economy League, 1963-72. Recipient Huebner Gold Medal award for professionalism in fin. edn. and tng. Am. Coll., 1993. Mem. Life Inst. Assn. Am. (dir. 1970-72), Ins. Fedn. Pa. (dir., chmn. 1970-72), Newcomen Soc., Loyal Legion, SAR, Cornell Club Phila. (dir.), Harvard Bus. Sch. Club Phila. (past pres.), Merion Cricket Club, Palmbrook Country Club. Home: 100 Grays Ln Apt 401 Haverford PA 19041-1754 also: 9701 W Sandstone Dr Sun City AZ 85351-2058 Office: 410 Lancaster Ave Haverford PA 19041-1329

ZALIOUK, YUVAL NATHAN, conductor; b. Haifa, Israel, Feb. 10, 1939; s. Israel Nahum and Ahuda (Nathanson) Z.; m. Susan Marlys Davies, May 5, 1972; children: Eyal, Adam, Tamar. LL.B., Hebrew U., Jerusalem, 1964; student, Rubin Acad. Music, Jerusalem, 1960-63, Guildhall Sch. Music, London, 1965-67. Founder YZ Enterprises, Inc., Maumee, Ohio. Condr. Royal Ballet of London, 1966-70; music dir., Opera Studio, Paris, 1973-74, Haifa Symphony, 1975-77; interim chief condr. Edmonton (Alta., Can.) Symphony Orch, 1980-81; music dir., condr. Toledo Symphony Orch, 1980-89, condr. laureate, 1989—. Recipient 1st prize Am.-Israel Cultural Found. Competition, 1965; 2d prize Internat. Condrs. Competition, Besancon, France, 1966; 1st prize Internat. Condrs. Competition, Besancon, 1967; 1st prize for progressive programming ASCAP, 1984, Entrepreneur of Yr. award, 1992; winner Mitropoulos Condrs. Competition, N.Y.C., 1970. Jewish. Club: Rotary. *

ZALK, ROBERT H., lawyer; b. Albert Lea, Minn., Dec. 1, 1944; s. Donald B. and Juliette J. (Erickson) Z.; m. Ann Lee Anderson, June 21, 1969; children: Amy, Jenna. BA, Carleton Coll., 1966; JD, U. Minn., 1969. Bar: Minn. 1969, U.S. Dist. Ct. Minn. 1969. Atty. Popham, Haik, Schnobrich, Kaufman & Doty, Mpls., 1969-72, No. States Power Co., Mpls., 1972-73, Wright, West & Diessner, Mpls., 1973-84, Fredrikson & Byron P.A., Mpls., 1984-94, Zalk & Assocs., Mpls., 1994-95, Zalk & Eayrs, Mpls., 1995—. Fellow Am. Acad. Matrimonial Lawyers bd. mgrs. Minn. chpt. 1989-92), Minn. State Bar Assn. (co-chmn. maintenance guideline com. 1991-94), Hennepin County Bar Assn. (co-chmn. family law sect. 1990-91). Office: Zalk & Eayrs 5861 Cedar Lake Rd Minneapolis MN 55416-1481

ZALL, PAUL MAXWELL, retired English language educator, consultant; b. Lowell, Mass., Aug. 3, 1922; s. Nathan and Bertha (Rubin) Z.; m. Elisabeth Weisz, June 21, 1948; children: Jonathan, Barnaby, Andrew. BA, Swarthmore Coll., 1948; AM, Harvard U., 1950, PhD, 1951. Teaching fellow Harvard U., 1950-51; instr. Cornell U., 1951-55, U. Oreg., 1955-56; research editor Boeing Co., 1956-57; asst. prof. Calif. State Coll., Los Angeles, 1957-61; asso. prof. Calif. State Coll., 1961-64, prof. English, 1964-86; research scholar, cons. to library docents Huntington Library, San Marino, Calif., 1986—; acting chmn. dept. Calif. State Coll., 1969-71; cons. in report writing, proposal preparation and brochures to industry and govt. agys., 1957—. Author: Elements of Technical Report Writing, 1962, Hundred Merry Tales, 1963, Nest of Ninnies, 1970, Literary Criticism of William Wordsworth, 1966, (with John Durham) Plain Style, 1967, Simple Cobler of Aggawam in America, 1969, (with J.R. Trevor) Proverb to Poem, 1970, Selected Satires of Peter Pindar, 1971, Comical Spirit of Seventy-Sic, 1976, Ben Franklin Laughing, 1980, (with J.A.L. Lemay) Autobiography of Benjamin Franklin, 1981, (with Leonard Franco) Practical Writing, 1978, Norton Critical Edition of Franklin's Autobiography, 1986, Abe Lincoln Laughing, 1983, 95, (with E. Birdsall) Descriptive Sketches, 1984, Mark Twain Laughing, 1985, Being Here, 1987, George Washington Laughing, 1989, Franklin's Autobiography: A Model Life, 1989, Founding Mothers, 1991, Becoming American, 1993, Lincoln's Legacy, 1994. Pres. Friends of South Pasadena Library, 1967-70. Served with USAAF, 1942-45, ETO. Am. Philos. Soc. fellow, 1964, 66; John Carter Brown Libr. rsch. grantee, Huntington Libr. rsch. grantee, fellow, 1993. Home: 1911 Leman Ln South Pasadena CA 91030-4628 Office: Huntington Libr San Marino CA 91108

ZALL, ROBERT ROUBEN, food scientist, educator; b. Lowell, Mass., Dec. 6, 1925; s. Samuel and Sarah (Cohen) Z.; m. Mollie Leah Wiseblood, June 8, 1949; children—Linda Tajll Sheffield, Judy Zall Kusek, Jonathan J. B.S., U. Mass., 1949, M.S., 1950; Ph.D., Cornell U., 1968. Gen. mgr. Grandview Dairies, Bklyn. and Arkport, N.Y., 1950-66; dairy industry cons. Ithaca, N.Y., 1968-71; prof. food sci. Cornell U., 1971-92; prof. emeritus, 1992—; past trustee Milk Industry Pension and Welfare Fund; dairy industry cons., project dir. EPA-Industry demonstration whey processing plant. Author: (with Bela G. Liptak) Environmental Engineers Handbook, 1972; co-contbr. to Food Processing Waste Management, 1979, Food Processing, 15 vols., 1979, Dairy Microbiology, 1981, rev. edit., 1990; contbr. numerous articles to profl. jours., popular mags. Served with AUS, 1944-46. Recipient Cert. Appreciation EPA, 1975, 79; Howard B. Marlott award N.Y. State Milk and Food Sanitarians. Mem. Internat. Assn. Milk, Food and Environ. Sanitarians, Internat. Dairy Fedn., Inst. Food Technologists, Am. Soc. Agrl. Engrs., Masons, Phi Kappa Phi. Patentee automatic cleaning apparatus, stabilization of milk and improved cheese yield, Rennin-like enzymes from clams, a process for preserving fish and microbial production of acetaldeyde. Home: 54 Woodcrest Ave Ithaca NY 14850-6241 Office: Cornell U Dept Food Sci Stocking Hall Ithaca NY 14853-7201 *Most people I know, never made a success of themselves by just working forty hours a week. It takes hard work, the love of a good wife, and the willingness to accept challenges.*

ZALLEN, HAROLD, corporate executive, scientist, former university official; b. Boston, Apr. 7, 1926; s. Joseph and Lillian L. (Stahl) Z.; m. Eugenia Malone, Aug. 23, 1959. BS in Pharmacy, Northeastern U., Boston, 1951; EdM in Sci. and Math., Boston U., 1954; MS in Organic Synthetic Medicinal Chemistry, Purdue U., 1959, PhD in Analytical Medicinal Chemistry and Nucleonics, 1960. Registered pharmacist, Mass. With USAAF, 1943-46; combat flier, sgt. 487 Bomb Group 839 Bomb Squadron 8th U.S. Army Air Force; commd. 1st lt. U.S. Army, 1955, advanced through grades to col., 1986; ret.; mgr. Shoppers World Pharmacy, Inc., Framingham, Mass., 1951-53; asst. prof. phys. sci. Portia Law Sch. Calvin Coolidge Coll., Boston, 1952-54; tchr. physics and chemistry Natick (Mass.) High Sch., 1955-56; grad. instr., asst. radiol. control officer Purdue U., Lafayette, Ind., 1957-58; assoc. prof. chemistry Coll. Pharmacy Mercer U., Atlanta, 1960-61; assoc. prof. to prof., head dept. radiol. sci., dir. Office Radiol. Safety Auburn U., Ala., 1961-66; specialist phys. sci. rsch. div. higher edn. rsch. Bur. Rsch., U.S. Office Edn., 1966-67, head curriculum higher edn. rsch., 1967; head instructional sci. equipment program, assoc. program dir., then dir. spl. projects program NSF, Washington, 1967-72; asst. dean, dir. rsch. and grad. studies Okla. State U., Stillwater, 1972-73, prof. chemistry, 1972-73, rsch. prof. biochemistry and molecular biology, 1973-75; assoc. v.p. for adminstrn. and fin., chief adminstrv. officer Health Scis. Ctr. Campus U. Okla., Oklahoma City and Tulsa, 1973-75; assoc. v.p. for systems planning, procedure devel. and spl. projects, cen. adminstrn. U. Okla., Norman, from 1975; exec. v.p. Acad. World Inc., 1975—; pres. Malone, Zallen & Assocs. div. AcaWorld Corp., Greenville, N.C.; v.p., dir. nuclear div. Vachon, Nix & Assocs., Atlanta; pres., chief exec. officer Computer Profls. Inc., Computer Distbrs. Corp.; pres. Malone Group Internat., Columbus, Ga.; sci. advisor Litton Corp./Army Rsch. Inst., 1991, Omega Tng. Group Inc./GIAT Industries, France, 1992—, Wetzel Internat., Inc., 1994—; analytical chemist Communicable Diseases Ctr. USPHS, Atlanta, 1962; spl. lectr. Radiobiology Inst., NSF, 1963-64; mem. Pres.'s Sci. and Technol. Adv. Commn., Washington; bd. dirs. Internat. Sci. and Engring. Fairs, Sci. Svc., Inc., 1973-85; v.p. Okla. Coll. Osteo. Medicine and Surgery, Tulsa; cons. Okla. State Regents for Higher Edn.; Gov. N.C. primary alt. to So. States Energy Bd., 1984-90, mem. exec. com. bd., 1986, cons. in field. Author 4 books in field, 1986-89; editor, pub. Jour. Internat 6800 Computer Ctr.; contbr. numerous articles to profl. jours. Republican candidate N.C. Gen. Assembly, 1986. Recipient Mayoralty cert. merit for outstanding svc. and Key to City of New Orleans, 1973; GE sci. fellow Union U., Schenectady, N.Y., 1955; fellow Purdue Rsch. Found., 1958, Elks Cancer Soc., 1959, Am. Cancer Soc., 1960. Mem. Am. Chem. Soc. (bd. dirs., chmn. Auburn sect. 1966), Am. Soc. Engring. Edn. (long range planning com.), Nat. Coun. Univ. Adminstrs., Soc. Rsch. Adminstrs. (pres. So. sect. from 1974, chmn. publs. com.), Health

---

Physics Soc., Greenville (N.C.) Area C. of C. (chmn. rsch.), Columbus Club, Rotary (chmn. bull. com. Auburn 1963, bd. dirs. Auburn 1964, bd. dirs. Stillwater 1972-73, Greenville 1981-86, charter pres. Greenville, N.C. Morning club 1986, Paul Harris fellow), Masons (32 degree), Shriners, Sigma Xi, Phi Lambda Upsilon, Rho Chi, Phi Delta Kappa, Delta Sigma Theta, Beta Pi (past nat. sec.). Baptist. Office: Malone Group Internat PO Box 8767 Columbus GA 31908-8767

ZALOKAR, ROBERT H., bank executive; b. 1927. BS, Univ. Kans., 1950. Examiner FDIC, Washington, 1950-55; asst. v.p. Old Dominion Bank, 1955-58; exec. v.p. Bank of Annadale, 1958-65; pres. Falls Ch. Bank, 1965-69; exec. v.p. First Va. Bank, 1969-74, pres., chief adminstrv. officer, 1974-78, pres., chief exec. officer, 1978—, also chmn. bd., dir., 1984—. With USN, 1945-46. Office: First Va Banks Inc 6400 Arlington Blvd Falls Church VA 22042-2336

ZALUTSKY, MORTON HERMAN, lawyer; b. Schenectady, Mar. 8, 1935; s. Albert and Gertrude (Daffner) Z.; m. Audrey Englebardt, June 16, 1957; children: Jane, Diane, Samuel. BA, Yale U., 1957; JD, U. Chgo., 1960. Bar: Oreg. 1961. Law clk. to presiding judge Oreg. Supreme Ct., 1960-61; assoc. Hart, Davidson, Veazie & Hanlon, 1961-63, Veatch & Lovett, 1963-64, Morrison, Bailey, Dunn, Cohen & Miller, 1964-69; prin. Morton H. Zalutsky, P.C., 1970-76; ptnr. Dahl, Zalutsky, Nichols & Hinson, 1977-79, Zalutsky & Klarquist, P.C., Portland, Oreg., 1980-85, Zalutsky, Klarquist & Johnson, Inc., Portland, 1985-94; Zalutsky & Klarquist, P.C., Portland, 1994—; instr. Portland State U., 1961-64, Northwestern Sch. of Law, 1969-70; assoc. prof. U. Miami Law Sch.; lectr. Practicing Law Inst., 1971—; Oreg. State Bar Continuing Legal Edn. Program, 1970, Am. Law Inst.-ABA Continuing Legal Edn. Program, 1973—, 34th, 37th NYU ann. insts. fed. taxation, So. Fed. Tax Inst., U. Miami Inst. Estate Planning, Southwestern Legal Found., Internat. Foun. Employee Benefit Plans, numerous other profl. orgns. Author: (with others) The Professional Corporation in Oregon, 1970, 82; contbg. author: The Dentist and the Law, 3d edit.; editor-in-chief (retirement plans) Matthew Bender's Federal Tax Service, 1987—; contbr. to numerous publs. in field. Mem. vis. com. U. Chgo. Law Sch. Mem. ABA (vice chair profl. svcs. 1987-89, mem. coun. tax sect. 1987-89, spl. coord. 1980-85), Am. Law Inst., Am. Bar Retirement Assn. (trustee, bd. dirs., vice chair 1990-92, chair 1991-92), A-E-F-C Pension Plan, 1994—, Multnomah, Multnomah County Bar Assn., Am. Coun. Tax Lawyers (charter mem.), Oreg. Estate Planning Coun. Jewish. Home: 3118 SW Fairmount Blvd Portland OR 97201-1466 Office: 215 SW Washington St Fl 3D Portland OR 97204-2636

ZAMBIE, ALLAN JOHN, lawyer; b. Cleve., June 9, 1935; s. Anton J. and Martha (Adamski) Z.; m. Nancy Halt, Sept. 22, 1973. Student, Ohio U., 1953-54; B.A., Denison U., 1957; LL.B., Western Res. U. (now Case Western Res. U.), 1960. Bar: Ohio bar 1960. Asso. firm Hribar and Conway, Euclid, Ohio, 1961-63; staff atty. The Higbee Co., Cleve., 1963-67; asst. sec. The Higbee Co., 1967-69, sec., 1969-74, v.p.-sec., 1974-88, gen. counsel 1978-88; v.p., sec., gen. counsel The Lamson & Sessions Co., Cleve., 1989-94; of counsel Conway, Marken, Wyner, Kurant & Kern Co., LPA, Cleve., 1994—. Trustee Cleve Music Sch. Settlement, pres. bd. trustees, 1980-82; trustee N.E. Ohio affiliate Am. Heart Assn. Served with AUS, 1960-61. Mem. ABA (corp., banking and bus. law sect.), Ohio Bar Assn., Cleve. Bar Assn., Am. Soc. Corporate Secs. (nat. v.p. 1977—). Home: 2953 Litchfield Rd Cleveland OH 44120-1738 Office: Ste 300 30195 Chagrin Blvd Cleveland OH 44124

ZAME, WILLIAM R., economist, educator, mathematician; b. Long Beach, N.Y., Nov. 4, 1945; s. Herbert and Miriam Zame; m. Elaine Bennett, Sept. 13, 1989. BS, Calif. Inst. Tech., Pasadena, 1965; PhD, Tulane U., 1970. Instr. Rice U., Houston, 1970-72; from asst. prof. to prof. SUNY, Buffalo, 1972-91; assoc. prof. Tulane U., New Orleans, 1975-78; prof. Johns Hopkins U., Balt., 1990-93, UCLA, 1991—. Contbr. over 55 articles to profl. jours. NSF grantee, 1970-93. Office: UCLA Dept Econs 405 Hilgard Ave Los Angeles CA 90024

ZAMECNIK, PAUL CHARLES, oncologist, medical research scientist; b. Cleve., Ohio, Nov. 22, 1912; m.; 3 children. AB, Dartmouth Coll., 1933; MD, Harvard U., 1936; DSc (hon.), U. Utrecht, 1966, Columbia U., 1971, Harvard U., 1982, Roger Williams Coll., 1983, Dartmouth Coll., 1988, U. Mass., 1994. Resident C.P. Huntington Meml. Hos., Boston, MA, 1936-37; intern. U. Hosps., Cleve., Ohio, 1938-39; Moseley traveling fellow, 1939-40; Finney-Howell fellow Rockefeller Inst., 1941-42; instr., assoc. prof. Harvard U., 1942-56, Collis P. Huntington prof., 1956-79; dir. J.C. Warren Labs., 1956-79; emeritus prof. oncological medicine Sch. Medicine, 1979—; prin. sci. Worcester Found. Experimental Biology, 1979—; physician Mass. Ge. Hosp., 1956-79; hon. physician Mass. Gen. Hosp., 1979—; vis. fellow dept. chemistry Calif. Tech. U., 1952; vis. scholar U. Cambridge, 1962. Recipient Warren Triennial prize, 1946, 50, Ewing award, 1963, Borden award, 1965, Am. Cancer Soc. Nat. award, 1968, Passano award, 1970, Nat. Medal of Sci. NSF, 1991, Hudson Hoagland award, 1992; Fogarty fellow NIH, 1975, 78. Mem. NAS, Am. Acad. Arts and Sci., Am. Soc. Biol. Chemists, Am. Assn. Cancer Rsch. (pres. 1964-65), Assn. Am. Physicians. Office: Worcester Found Exptl Biology 222 Maple Ave Shrewsbury MA 01545-2732

ZAMES, GEORGE DAVID, electrical engineer, educator; b. Poland, Jan. 7, 1934; s. Sam Simha and Leona Z.; m. Eva Eisenfarb, July 21, 1964; children: Ethan, Jonathan. B.Eng., McGill U., 1954; Sc.D. in Elec. Engring, MIT, 1960. Asst. prof. MIT, 1960-62, 63-65, Harvard U., 1962-63; sr. scientist NASA, Cambridge, Mass., 1965-71; vis. prof. Technion, Haifa, Israel, 1972-74; prof. elec. engring. McGill U., Montreal, 1974—, Macdonald chair. elec. engring., 1983—. Assoc. editor So. Indsl. and Applied Math. Jour. on Control, 1968-84, Systems and Control Letters, 1981-84, Internat. Math. Assn. Jour. Math. Control and Info., 1983—, Math. of Control Signals and Systems, 1987—; editor at large Jour. Robust and Non-linear Control, 1990—; contbr. articles to profl. jours. Athlone fellow Imperial Coll., London U., 1954-56; Nat. Acad. Scis. Resident Research Assoc., 1966-67; Guggenheim fellow, 1967-68; Killam fellow, 1984-86; sr. fellow Can. Inst. Advanced Research, 1984—; recipient Brit. Assn. medal, McGill U., 1954; Outstanding Paper award Am. Automatic Control Council, 1968; classic paper citation Inst. Sci. Info., 1981; Control Sci. Field award IEEE, 1985, Outstanding Paper awards Control Systems Soc., 1977, 80, 82, 86. Fellow IEEE, Royal Soc. Can. Home: 4996 Circle Rd, Montreal, PQ Canada H3W 1Z7 Office: McGill U Dept Elec Engring, 3480 University St, Montreal, PQ Canada H3A 2A7

ZAMIR, FRANCES ROBERTA (FRANCES ROBERTA WEISS-SWEDE), assistant principal; b. Bklyn., Nov. 6, 1944; d. Martin and Jean (Roskosky) Swede. BA in English, Calif. State U, Northridge, 1967, MA in Spl. Edn., 1975; MA in Edni. Adminstrn., Calif. State U., L.A., 1987. Credential adminstrv. svcs., stdl. elem, spl. edn.-learning handicapped, Calif; cert. resource specialist. Childrens' ctr. tchr. L.A. Unified Sch. Dist., 1966-68, elem. tchr., 1968-76, spl. edn. tchr., 1976-80, resource specialist tchr., 1980-86, mentor tchr., 1984-86, program specialist/region advisor, 1986-90, asst. prin., 1990—; owner, ptnr. Best Bet Ednl. Therapy/Tutoring Referral Svc., 1979-81; cons. Academics Plus Tutoring Referral Svc., 1984-86; asst. prof. resource specialist cert. program Calif. State U., Dominguez Hills, 1987-90; instr. early and regular edn. credential program UCLA, 1990—; mem. asst. prin. steering com. L.A. Unified Sch. Dist., Region C, 1992—; adminstr. portfolio documentation subcom. Adminstrv. Tng. Acad., 1991; sch. site rev. coms. Calif. State Dept. Edn., 1985-87, ad hoc com. on quality indicators, 1985. Mem. Speakers Bur. Commn. on Jews With Disabilities, 1985-86. Mem. NEA, Assoc. Adminstrs. L.A. Rep. Coun. (elem. asst. prin. rep. 1992-94), Friends of Cal State, Calif. Assn. Program Specialists (So. Calif. regional rep. 1988-90), Calif. Assn. Sch. Adminstrs. (spl. edn. com. L.A. chpt. 1985-86, 87-88), Calif. Assn. Resource Specialists (state pres. 1984-85, bd. dirs. 1983-86), Calif. Tchrs. Assn., Women in Ednl. Leadership, Kappa Delta Pi, Phi Beta Kappa. Office: L A Unified Sch Dist 450 N Grand Ave Los Angeles CA 90012-2100

ZAMMITT, NORMAN, artist; b. Toronto, Ont., Can., Feb. 3, 1931. AA, Pasadena City Coll., 1957; MFA, Otis Art Inst., Los Angeles. One man exhbns. include Felix Landau Gallery, Los Angeles, 1962, 66, 68, Los Angeles County Mus. Art, 1977, Corcoran Gallery, Washington, 1978, Flow-Ace Gallery, 1984, Loma Linda U., Riverside, Calif., 1987; included in

---

group exhbns. at Los Angeles County Mus. Art, 1987, Haags Gemeentemus. Arts, The Hague, 1987, Bronx Mus. Arts, N.Y., 1987, Ace Contemporary Exbns., Los Angeles, 1988; represented in permanent collections at Library of Congress, Corcoran Gallery, Nat. Gallery, Hirschhorn Collection, Washington, Mus. Modern Art, N.Y.C., Los Angeles County Mus. Modern Art, San Francisco Mus. Modern Art, Larry Aldrich Found. Mus., Conn., Rowland Inst. Sci., Cambridge, Mass., Seattle Art Mus., Stanford U. Hosp., Palo Alto, Calif.; also represented in pvt. collections including Edwin H. Land, Maurice Tuchman, Norman Lear, John Kluge. Guggenheim fellow, 1968; Pollock-Krasner grantee, 1991. Home: 233 N Wilson Ave Pasadena CA 91106-1422

ZAMORA, MARIO DIMARUCUT, anthropologist, educator; b. Angeles, Pampanga, The Philippines, July 27, 1935; came to U.S., 1959, naturalized, 1978; s. Leon Biag and Caridad (Dimarucut) Z.; m. Ducella Norma Parmalee, Nov. 22, 1963 (div.); children: Gregory, Nerissa, Morris, Lili, Sarah Elizabeth; m. Maria Luz Mercado, 1982; children: Jovito Jose, Maria Gracia. AB, U. Philippines, 1956, MA, 1959; PhD, Cornell U., 1963. Mem. faculty U. Philippines, 1962-72, prof. anthropology, 1971-72, chmn. dept., 1964-70, acad. dean, 1970-72; vis. prof. Eastern Mont. Coll., 1972-73, Coll. William and Mary, Williamsburg, Va., 1973-75; prof. anthropology Coll. William and Mary, 1975-86; Fulbright/Hays prof. U. Trondheim, 1986—; organizer/chair internat. symposia on anthropology of war and peace, mgmt. anthropology and third world anthropology Internat. Congress Anthrop. and Ethnol. Scis., Zagreb, Yugoslavia, 1988; chair numerous internat. meetings in field; lectr., paper reader, reviewer in field; chmn. subcom. on Asia and Oceania, Commn. on Devel., charter mem. Commn. on Study of Peace, apptd. mem. Commn. on Futurology; elected exec. mem. Internat. Union Anthrop. and Ethnol. Scis., 1983-88; founder, mem. Internat. Ctr. Asian Studies Ranch U., v.p. for rsch. and acad. affairs Internat. Multidisciplinary Inst., 1985; hon. dir.-gen. Internat. Rsch. Ctr. for Iloko-Philippines, Mariano Marcos State U., Batac, Ilocos Norte, 1980—; external examiner Ranchi U., India, Karnatak U., India, Venkateswaran U., India, U. Toronto.; grants reviewer Wenner Gren Found. Anthrop. Rsch., NSF; founding dir. Mahatma Gandhi Freedom Lecture Series; nat cons. Silliman U. Rsch. Ctr., 1985-1990; cons. Ilocano Rsch. and Info. Ctr., Fulbright lectr. New U. Lisbon, Portugal, 1986; organizer, chair internat. symposium pioneers in anthropology from Asia, Africa, Latin Am., 13th Internat. Cong. of Anthropology and Ethnology, Scis., Mexico City, 1993.; PhD external examiner anthropology U. Madras, India, Karnatak U., India, Utkal U., India, Lucknow U., India, Mysore U., India; founding chair Benigno Aquino Meml. Lectr, Dag Hammarksjold Lectrs. World Affairs. author: Los Indigenas delas Islas Filipinas, 1992; co-author, editor: Themes in Culture, 1971, Studies in Philippine Anthropology, 1967, Anthropology: Range and Relevance, 1969; co-author, co-editor Human Intervention: Fieldwork in Cultural Anthropology, 1986; co-author: Politics and Social Change, 1966, The Human Dimensions in South Asian Research, Changing Identities in Modern Southeast Asia, Anthrop. Research: Perspectives and Fieldwork, 1986, Humanistic Approaches in Social Anthropology, 1986, (with T. Hamada) The State of the Art in World Anthropology: A Report on the 12th International Congress of Anthropology and Ethnological Sciences The Eastern Anthropologist, vol. 43, number 3, 1989; sr. editor: Social Change in Modern Philippines: Perspectives, Problems, and Prospects, 2 vols., The Panchayat Tradition: A North Indian Village Council in Transition, Internat Education and the Social Sciences: Selected Readings, 1988, The Social Sciences and International Education: A Reader, 1989; iFieldwork: The Human Experience, Studies in Third World Societies; major editor Social Change in Modern Philippines, 2 vols.; editor Anthropological Research: Perspectives and Fieldwork, Social Change in India, Pakistan and Bangladesh, Anthropological Research: Perspectives and Fieldwork, 1984, Social Change in Modern South Asia; assoc. editor Jour. Asian and African Studies; mem. editorial internat. bd. Internat. Jour. Asian Studies, Internat. Multidisciplinary Sci. Inst., Scandinavian Jour. of Dev. Alternatives, Tambara, Colegium Antropologicum, Croatian Anthrop. Soc.; contbr. articles and revs. to Current Anthropology; articles and revs. to numerous other profl. jours.; corr. editor for Philippines: Current Anthropology, 1984-85, Grad. Research Jour. of Found. U.; mem. internat. editorial and adv. bd.: Asian Profile, Jour. Social Studies (Bangladesh), Jour. Luzon (Philippines), Jour. Social Studies (Nigeria), S.E. Asia Perspectives (India 1985), South Asia Social Scientist (India); columnist Tarlac Star, 1985-86; co-editor, co-author The Anthropology of Peace (essays in honor of E. Adamson Joebel), 2 vols., Studies in Third World Societies, 1992, Perspectives on Cultural Changes in the Philippines: Focus on the Philippines, 1993; gen. edit. 2 internat. book series Anthropological Perspectives, Issues in Anthropology: Focus on Asia, Africa, Latin Am. Hon. sec., regional adviser for U.S. Ethnographic and Folk Culture Soc. India; chmn. symposium Anthropology and Internat. Rels. Inter-Congress, 5-12, 1990, Lisbon, Internat. Union Anthropological and Ethnological Scis.; external examiner for PhD Karnatek U., Utkal U., 1990, BA honors thesis Seet Briar Coll., Va.; nominations com. mem. Va. Social Sci. Assn., 1990; organizer, chair student honors session, 1990, All-Va. Undergrad. Essay Competition, 1990. Recipient Outstanding Filipino Overseas award Pres. of Philippines, 1980, Scholar award Va. Social Sci. Assn. 1985, Disting. Svc. award; First Adlai Stevenson fellow, 1967; Fulbright/Smith Mundt scholar, 1959-63; UP fellow, 1962-63; Fulbright prof. U. Trondheim, 1986; Norwegian Marshall Fund scholar, 1985-86; Excellence medal in anthropology and Filippine studies Philippine Govt., 1987, Gorjanovic-Kramberger medal Croation Anthrop. Soc. Yugoslavia, 1988; Rsch. grantee Va. Social Sci. Assn., Travel grantee Am. Anthropological Assn./Nat. Sci. Found., Portugal Exec. Meeting Internat. Union Anthro and Ethnological Scis., 1988-90, Presdl. award Assn. Third World Studies, Disting. Svc. award U. Philippines Alumni Assn. others. Fellow Am. Anthrop. Assn. (life), Assn. Asian Studies (life), Royal Anthrop. Inst. Gt. Britain and Ireland, Royal Soc. for Asian Affairs; life mem. Indian Anthrop. Assn., Indian Social Soc., Indian Ethnographic and Folk Culture Soc. (hon. regional sec. and advisor for U.S.), Indian Inst. Public Adminstrn., Indian Polit. Sci. Assn.; mem. Assn. for Polit. and Legal Anthropology, Canadian Sociol. and Anthrop. Assn., So. Anthrop. Soc., Va. Social Sci. Assn. (v.p. 1985-86, pres. 1987, mem. nomination com. 1987—; chmn. essay com., chmn. scholar award com. in anthropology, chmn. anthropology and student sessions, Presdl. citation 1987), Internat. Assn. Anthropology Editors (mem. exec. bd. 1979—), Assn. Third World Anthropologists (founding chmn., founding editor Bull.), Assn. for Anthrop. Diplomacy (founding pres. 1980—), U.S. Assn. Philippine Anthropologists (founding chmn. 1980, founding editor Newsletter 1980), Profs. World Peace Acad. U.S. (founding mem.), Internat. Ctr. for Asian Studies, Soc. Applied Anthropology (mem. ethics com. 1987), Internat. Congress Anthrop. and Ethnol. Scis. (organizer, chmn. Zagreb, Yugoslavia), NAACP, Soc. for Anthropology of Europe (founding mem.), Soc. for Advancement Scandinavian Ethnographical Assn., Internat. Union Anthrop. and Ethnol. Scis. (v.p. 1988—), ex-officio exec. mem. Commn. on Latin Am Devel. Studies), Danish Ethnographical Assn., Third World Studies, Inc. Lodge: Rotary. Home: 3009 E Brittington Williamsburg VA 23185-8701 Office: Coll of William & Mary Dept Anthropology Williamsburg VA 23185

ZAMORA, MARJORIE DIXON, retired political science educator; b. Farm Randolph, N.Y., Nov. 8, 1933; d. Wendell Hadley and Jessie (Mercer) Dixon; m. Cornelio Raul Zamora, Dec. 20, 1969; 1 child, Daniel Cornelio. BA, Earlham Coll., 1956; MA, U. Ill., 1968; postgrad., U. Ill., Chgo., 1989—. Tchr. Ridge Sch., Godsman Sch., Stenson Sch., various cities, 1956-62; with U.S. Peace Corps, tchr. Palmares High Sch., Costa Rica, 1963-64; reporter Lerner Newspaper, Chgo., 1965; dormitory counselor, researcher Univ. Ill., Urbana, 1966-68, 86; instr. Chgo. City Coll., 1968-69; prof. polit. sci. Moraine Valley CC v., Palos Hills, Ill., 1969-94, prof. emeritus, 1994—; researcher, Univ. Ill., Chgo., 1985-88. Contbr. articles on Costa Rican polit. bus. cycle and economy, land reform to various publs. in U.S., Cen. Am. Campaign dir. Polit. State Legis., 1974-76. Mem. AAUW, Moraine Valley Community Coll. Faculty Assn., Am. Polit. Sci. Assn. (chair profl. and community activities). Avocations: skiing, swimming, hiking, symphonic music, scuba. Home: 3820 Lawn Ave Western Springs IL 60558-1141

ZAMPAGLIONE, ARTURO, newspaper publishing executive. U.S. bureau chief La Repubblica, N.Y.C., 1994—. Office: La Repubblica 444 Madison Ave Ste 2105 New York NY 10022

ZAMPANO, ROBERT CARMINE, federal judge; b. New Haven, Mar. 18, 1929; s. Anthony N. and Marie (Fusco) Z.; m. Dorothea Mea Gilbride, Nov. 23, 1950; children: Deborah Lee, Robert Anthony. B.A., Yale U., 1951, LL.B., 1954. Bar: Conn. 1954. Law clk. to U.S. dist. judge Conn., 1954-55;

with Thompson, Weir & MacDonald, New Haven, 1955-57, Zampano & Mager, East Haven, 1959-61; judge East Haven, 1959-60; counsel, 1956-61; exec. sec. rev. div. Superior Ct. Conn., 1956-61; U.S. dist. atty. Conn., 1961-64; judge U.S. Dist. Ct., 1964—; now sr. judge U.S. Dist. Ct. Dist. Conn. Co-chmn. bar sect. New Haven United Fund, 1956-57; commr. Quinnipiac council Boy Scouts Am., 1953; pres. East Haven 175th Anniversary Comm., 1960; chmn. East Haven Democratic party, 1956-61; bd. dirs. New Haven ARC, Community Health Care Plan, 1978-79, East Haven Community Ctr.; bd. govs. U. New Haven; trustee Gunnery Sch., 1966-76, Hamden Hall Country Day Sch., 1966-76; mem. adv. bd. Conn. Mental Health Ctr., 1969-74, New Haven Regional Ctr. for Mentally Retarded, 1966-73. Mem. Am., New Haven County bar assns., Am. Justinian Soc. Jurists (dist.). Clubs: K.C. Melebus (New Haven), Yale (New Haven) (dir. 1960-63), Amity (New Haven) (sec. 1961). Office: US Dist Ct 141 Church St New Haven CT 06510-2030

ZAMPIELLO, RICHARD SIDNEY, metals and trading company executive; b. New Haven, May 7, 1933; s. Sidney Nickolas and Louise Z.; B.A., Trinity Coll., 1955; M.B.A., U. Bridgeport, 1961; m. Helen Shirley Palsa, Oct. 10, 1961; 1 son, Geoffrey Richard. With Westinghouse Elec. Corp., Pitts., 1955-64; exec. v.p. Ullrich Copper Corp., subs. Foster Wheeler, Kenilworth, N.J., 1964-71; sr. v.p. Gerald Metals, Inc., Stamford, Conn., 1971-85; group v.p. Diversified Industries Corp., St. Louis, 1985-90; pres. Plume and Atwood Brass Mill div. Diversified Industries Corp., Thomaston, Conn., 1985-90; pres. Upstate Metals Corp., Canastota, N.Y., 1990—. Mem. ASME, Soc. Mfg. Engrs., AIME. Clubs: Yale, Mining (N.Y.C.); Lake Waramug Country (Washington, Conn.), Washington Country. Home: Woodbury Rd Washington CT 06793-1814 Office: 20 E Main St Waterbury CT 06702-2302

ZANAKIS, STEVE H., management/science/information systems educator; b. Athens, Greece, Nov. 16, 1940; came to U.S., 1968; m. Helen Avagianou, 1968; children: Aliki, Christina, Helena. BS in Mech./Elec. Engring., Nat. Tech. U., Athens, 1964; MBA, Pa. State U., 1970, MS in Stats., 1972, PhD in Bus. Adminstrn., 1973. Registered engr., Greece. Indsl. engr. Greek Productivity Ctr., Athens, 1967-68; asst. prof. indsl. engring. and systems analysis W.Va. Coll. Grad. Studies, Charleston, 1972-76, assoc. prof. and dir. indsl. engring. and systems analysis, 1976-80; assoc. prof. mgmt. Coll. of Bus. Adminstrn. Fla. Internat. U., Miami, 1980-82, prof. and founding chmn. dept. decision scis. and info. systems, 1982-86, prof. decision scis. and info. systems., 1986—; cons. Union Carbide Corp., W.Va. Dept. Hwys., Charleston Area Med. Ctr., Key Pharm. Ryder, U.S. Acad. for Ednl. Devel.; instr. exec. mgmt. devel. programs, U.S., Europe, S.Am. Author: Production Operations Management Software for IBM, PC, 1989, Production Planning and Scheduling, 1984, Engineering Economy, 1975, Optimization in Statistics, 1983, Stat-ez: An Easy to Use Statistical Software, 1987, Decision Support System for Conflict Resolution and Strategy Selection, 1991, Decision Support System for Stock Market Trading & Portfolio Management; editor Mgmt. Sci. Jour., 1983, European Jour. Ops. Rsch. 1986; assoc. editor Decision Scis. Jour., 1990—; contbr. numerous articles to profl. jours. Recipient Fla. Bd. Regents Teaching award, 1994, Fla. Internat. U. Awards for excellence in research, 1993, teaching, 1991, outstanding achievement, 1990 and svc., 1986; State of Fla. Hwy. Adminstrn. Rsch. grantee, 1984-85, Fed. grantee, 1976-77. Mem. The Inst. of Mgmt. Scis., Decision Scis. Inst., Tech. Chamber of Greece. Greek Orthodox. Office: Fla Internat U Dept Decision Scis/Info Sys Miami FL 33199

ZANARDELLI, JOHN JOSEPH, healthcare services executive; b. Monongahela, Pa., July 27, 1950; s. John and Linda (Lazzari) Z.; m. Suzanne King, Jan. 29, 1972; children: Brandon John, Stephen William, Robyn Lynn. AA, Community Coll. Allegheny Cty, Pitts., 1970; AS in Acctg., Community Coll. Allegheny Cty., Pitts., 1991; BS in Edn., California U. Pa., 1972; MPH, U. Pitts., 1979, cert. acct., 1994. Rsch. asst. grad. sch. pub. health U. Pitts., 1973-78; adminstrv. resident Cen. Med. Ctr. & Hosp., Pitts., 1978-79; vice chmn., sec., dir. Allegheny Mountain Health Enterprises, Inc. Oil City, Pa., 1985-88; exec. v.p. Oil City Area Health Ctr. Inc., 1979-88; exec. v.p., chief oper. officer Grane Healthcare, Inc., Pitts., 1988-90; adminstr., chief oper. officer Southwood Psychiat. Hosp., Inc., Pitts., 1990-91; exec. dir. Allegheny Sr. Care, Pitts., Pa., 1991-92; exec. dir., CEO United Meth. Svcs. for the Aging, 1993—; preceptor health adminstrn. program grad. schs. in pub. health and bus. U. Pitts., 1980—; pres. HCPP, Inc., Pitts., 1983—. Fellow Am. Coll. Healthcare Execs. Home: 2997 Greenwald Rd Bethel Park PA 15102-1615 Office: Asbury Heights 700 Bower Hill Rd Pittsburgh PA 15243-2040

ZAND, DALE EZRA, business management educator; b. N.Y.C., July 22, 1926; m. Charlotte Edith Rosenfeld, Oct. 16, 1949; children—Fern, Mark, Karen, Jonathan, Matthew. B.Elec. Engring., Cooper Union, 1945; M.B.A., N.Y.U., 1949, Ph.D., 1954. Asst. to v.p. Spectator Bags, 1947-49; v.p. Glo-Cold Co., 1949-50; mem. faculty N.Y. U. Stern Sch. Bus., 1950—, prof. mgmt., 1963—, chmn. dept., 1968—; cons. to industry, 1951—; Bd. dirs. Newfield Exploration Co., Nat. Tng. Labs. Inst. Applied Behavioral Sci. Author: Information, Organization, and Power, 1981, also articles. Served with USNR, 1945. Ford Found. fellow, 1959-60. Mem. Am. Psychol. Assn., Inst. Mgmt. Sci., Acad. Mgmt., Internat. Assn. Applied Social Scientists. Office: NYU Stern Sch Bus 40 W 4th St (T7-16) New York NY 10012

ZANDE, RICHARD DOMINIC, civil engineering firm executive; b. Battle Creek, Mich., Apr. 29, 1931; s. Dominic and Maria O. (Bombassei) Z.; m. Marilyn Sue Love, Feb. 15, 1958; children: Michael, Michelle, Brent, Patrick. BSCE, Mich. State U., 1955. Registered profl. engr. Ohio, Fla., Ky., W.Va., Mich., Pa., Ind., Ill., N.J., S.C. Prin. Martin & Zande, Columbus, Ohio, 1966-68; chief exec. officer R.D. Zande & Assoc., Columbus, 1968—, Zande Environ. Svc., Columbus, 1988—, Zande-Garrod, Inc., Cin., 1990—; bd. dirs. Franklin County Solid Waste Mgmt. Authority, Columbus, 1985-87; mem. engring. adv. bd. Ohio State U., Columbus, 1988—; mem. small bus. adv. com. Cleve. Fed. Res. Bank, 1992—. Bd. dirs. St. Stephen's Community House, Columbus, 1988—, Bus. Exec. Coun. for the Ctr. for Applied and Profl. Edn., Franklin U., 1990-92, Purchasing Procedures Task Force City of Columbus, Jr. Achievement, 1989-92; dir. small bus. solicitations United Way. Mem. ASCE, NSPE, Ohio Assn. Cons. Engrs., Am. Cons. Engrs. Coun., Greater Columbus Devel. Com., Columbus C. of C. (bd. dirs. 1987-92). Roman Catholic. Home: 901 Bluffview Dr Columbus OH 43235-1727 Office: RD Zande & Assocs Inc 1237 Dublin Rd Columbus OH 43215-1071

ZANDER, ALVIN FREDERICK, social psychologist; b. Detroit, Oct. 13, 1913; s. Hugo Helmuth and Frieda Wilhemenia (Miesler) Z.; m. Patience Clare, Dec. 19, 1939; children—Constance, Christopher, Judith; m. Marion Cranmore, Aug. 11, 1980. BS, U. Mich., 1936, MS in Pub. Health, 1937, PhD, 1942. Asst. dir. research service Boy Scouts Am., N.Y.C., 1943-45; asst. prof. psychology Springfield (Mass.) Coll., 1946-47; prof. psychology, dir. Research Center for Group Dynamics, U. Mich., Ann Arbor, 1959-79; asso. v.p. U. Mich., 1973-80. Author: Group Dynamics, 1953, 3d edit., 1968, Motives and Goals in Groups, 1971, Groups at Work, 1977, Making Groups Effective, 1982, 2d edit., 1994, The Purposes of Groups and Organizations, 1985, Effective Social Action by Community Groups, 1990, Making Boards Effective, 1993. Served with USPHS, 1944-46. U. Chgo. fellow, 1938-39; Fulbright fellow. Oslo, Norway, 1957-58; Japanese Govt. fellow, 1980-81; Gen. Edn. Bd. fellow U. Iowa, 1942. Mem. Am. Psychol. Assn. (div. secs.), Am. Psychol. Soc., Soc. Psychol. Study Social Issues (pres.), Soc. Exptl. Social Psychology. Home: 2841 Ptarmigan Dr # 4 Walnut Creek CA 94595-3136

ZANDER, BENJAMIN, conductor, educator; b. London, Mar. 9, 1939. Diploma, State Conservatory, Cologne, 1960; BA, London Univ., 1964; studied cello with, Gaspar Cassadó. Prof. chamber music, performance and analysis New Eng. Conservatory of Music, Boston, 1967—; condr. Youth Chamber Orch., 1972—; mus. dir., condr. Boston Philharm. Orch., 1979—; artistic dir. Walnut Hill High Sch. for the Performing Arts. Office: Boston Philharm PO Box 354 Newton MA 02258-0181

ZANDER, GAILLIENNE GLASHOW, psychologist; b. Bklyn., Apr. 7, 1932; d. Saul and Anna (Karasik) G.; m. A.J. Zander, Aug. 5, 1952; children: Elizabeth L, Caroline M., Catherine A. MusB, U. Wis., 1953, MS, 1970; PhD, Marquette U., 1984. Music tchr. Wis. Sch. Systems, 1953-65;

psychol. asst. Vernon Psychol. Labs., Chgo., 1965-70; psychologist Milw. Pub. Schs., 1970-92, CESA 19, Kenosha, Wis., 1977-78; pvt. practice psychology Milw., 1980—. Fellow Am. Orthopsychiat. Assn.; mem. APA, Wis. Psychol. Assn., Psychologists Assn. in Milw. Pub. Schs. (rep., v.p., pres.), Am. Acad. Pain Mgmt. (diplomate). Home: 13750 Carson Ct Brookfield WI 53005-4989 Office: Performance Enhancement 12630 W North Ave Brookfield WI 53005-4626 also: Cooper Resource Ctr 20860 WaterTown Rd Waukesha WI 53186

ZANDER, GLENN R., airline company executive; b. 1951. Joined TWA, Mt. Kisco, N.Y., 1971—, from various mgmt. positions to v.p. and overseas contr., 1971-87, sr. v.p. fin., CFO, 1987—, co-CEO, 1992—. Office: TWA Inc 100 S Bedford Rd Mount Kisco NY 10549

ZANDER, JANET ADELE, psychiatrist; b. Miles City, Mont., Feb. 19, 1950; d. Adelbert William and Valborg Constance (Buckneberg) Z.; m. Mark Richard Ellenberger, Sept. 16, 1979; 1 child, Evan David Zander Ellenberger. BA, St. Olaf Coll., 1972; MD, U. Minn., 1976. Diplomate Am. Bd. Psychiatry and Neurology. Resident in psychiatry U. Minn., Mpls., 1976-79, fellow in psychiatry, 1979-80, asst. prof. psychiatry, 1981—; staff psychiatrist St. Paul (Minn.) Ramsey Med. Ctr., 1980—, dir. edn. in psychiatry, 1980—, dir. inpatient psychiatry, 1986—; vice chair Dept. Psychiatry St. Paul Ramsey Med. Ctr., 1991—; bd. dirs. Perry Assurance. Contbr. research articles to sci. jours. Sec. Concentus Musicus Bd. Dirs., St. Paul, 1981-89; mem. property com. St. Clement's Episcopal Ch., St. Paul, 1985. Mem. Am. Psychiat. Assn., Am. Med. Women's Assn., Minn. Psychiat. Soc. (ethics com. 1985-87, women's com. 1985-87, mem. coun. 1994—), Minn. Med. Assn., Ramsey County Med. Soc. (bd. dirs. 1994—). Democrat. Avocations: singing, skiing. Home: 230 Crestway Ln West Saint Paul MN 55118-4424 Office: St Paul Ramsey Med Ctr 640 Jackson St Saint Paul MN 55101

ZANDIN, KJELL BERTIL, management consulting executive; b. Morlanda, Sweden, Mar. 14, 1937; came to U.S., 1975; s. Sven G. and Hildur D. (Johansson) Z.; m. Sonja A. Johansson, Nov. 21, 1964; children: Michael, Christin. MS in Mech. Engring., Chalmers U. of Tech., 1962. Devel. engr. SKF, Gothenburg, Sweden, 1962-64; cons. Maynard MEC AB, Gothenburg, 1964-68; cons. mgr. H.B. Maynard & Co., Inc., Gothenburg, 1969-71, Dusseldorf, Fed. Republic Germany, 1972-75; sr. v.p. H.B. Maynard & Co., Inc., Pitts., 1975—, also ptnr., bd. dirs. Author: MOST Work Measurement Systems, 1980, 2d edit., 1990. Served with Swedish Army, 1957-58. Received First Tech. Innovation award Inst. Indsl. Engrs., 1986. Mem. Inst. Indsl. Engrs. (sr.), World Affairs Council of Pitts., Scandinavian Soc. Western Pa. Lutheran. Avocations: tennis, golf, skiing. Home: 105 Alleyne Dr Pittsburgh PA 15215-1401 Office: H B Maynard & Co Inc 400 Edith St Pittsburgh PA 15211-1148

ZANDMAN, FELIX, electronics executive; b. 1928. PhD, U. Paris The Sorbonne, U. Nancy, France, 1953. With French Nat. Ctr. Sci. Rsch., Paris, 1950-53; with engring. and consulting SNECMA, 1953-57; dir. basic rsch. Tatnall Measuring Systems Co., Phoenixville, Pa., 1957-62; founder, pres., CEO, chmn. bd. Vishay Intertech., Inc., Malvern, Pa., 1962—; also dir. Vishay Intertech., Inc. Office: Vishay Sprague Holdings Corp 678 Main St Sanford ME 04073*

ZANE, RAYMOND J., lawyer, state senator; b. Woodbury, N.J., July 23, 1939; s. Clarence R. and Veronica (Levy) Z.; children—Marybeth, Raymond II, Kenneth. B.S. in Bus. Adminstrn., St. Joseph's U., 1965; J.D., Rutger's U., 1974. Bar: N.J. 1974, N.Y. 1989. Freeholder, Gloucester County, Woodbury, N.J., 1971-73; mem. N.J. Senate, 1973—, dep. asst. minority leader. Mem. N.J. Bar Assn., Gloucester County Bar Assn. Home: 509 Sharp Dr Mickleton NJ 08056-1441 Office: 39 S Broad St Woodbury NJ 08096-7920 Other: NJ State Senate State Capital Trenton NJ 08608

ZANETTI, JOSEPH MAURICE, JR., corporate executive; b. San Francisco, Aug. 3, 1928; s. Joseph Maurice and Lillian Mary (Solari) Z.; m. Marilyn Ruth Parker, Aug. 11, 1956; children: Pamela, Gregory, Geoffrey, Regina. BA, Saint Mary's Coll., 1950; postgrad., U. Calif., Berkeley, 1950-51, 53-55, 56-57; postgrad. in Edn., San Francisco State Coll., 1955-56. Cert. secondary tchr., Calif. Tchr. Piedmont (Calif.) High Sch., 1956-57, Pleasant Hill (Calif.) High Sch., 1957-58; supr. Sandia Labs., Albuquerque, 1958-64; mktg. dir. Ednl. Research Assocs., Albuquerque, 1964-66; exec. asst. Sandia Labs., Albuquerque, 1966-73; pres. U. of Albuquerque, Albuquerque, 1973-75; dir. area devel. Pub. Svc. Co. of N.Mex., Albuquerque, 1975-86; pres., chmn. bd. dirs. Rio Grande Trading Co. Inc., Albuquerque, 1986-88; pres. Foresight, Inc., Albuquerque, 1988-90; v.p. Summa Med. Corp., Albuquerque, 1988-91; sr. v.p. Summa Med. Corp., Vienna, Va., 1991-92; v.p. Systems Support Agy. Inc., Vienna, Va., 1992-93; pres. Complexus, Inc., Albuquerque, N.Mex., 1993—; cons. Pub. Service Co. N.Mex., Albuquerque 1986-88; ; pres. N.Mex. Internat. Trade and Investment Council Inc., Albuquerque, 1984-89; active Adv. Bd. Coll. and U. Partnership Program, Memphis, 1984—. Chmn. adv. bd. N.Mex. Mus. Natural History, Albuquerque, 1985-90; vice chmn., bd. govs. Albuquerque Tech. Vocat. Inst., 1971-77; mem. Bd. Edn., Albuquerque Pub. Schs., 1971-77. Capt. USNR, 1948-83. Mem. Res. Officers Assn. (life), Resource Devel. Com., Albuquerque Pub. Schs. (chmn.). Republican. Roman Catholic.

ZANGERLE, JOHN A., lawyer; b. Lakewood, Ohio, Jan. 24, 1942. BA, Haverford Coll., 1964; JD, Case Western Res. U., 1967. Bar: Ohio 1967. Ptnr. Baker & Hostetler, Cleve. Office: Baker & Hostetler 3200 Nat City Ctr 1900 E 9th St Cleveland OH 44114

ZANGGER, RUSSELL GEORGE, organization executive, flying school executive; b. Larchwood, Iowa, Feb. 22, 1922; s. Charlie and Lina Bell (Sharp) Zangger; m. Marie Unruh, May 24, 1944; 1 child, James Russell. Student pub. schs., Larchwood; DD (hon.), Ch. Gospel Ministries, Chula Vista, Calif., 1981. Farmer, Larchwood, 1944-79; owner, operator Zangger Flying Svc., Larchwood, 1949—; founder, dir. The Remain Intact ORGANization, Larchwood, 1980—. Spokesperson against infant circumcision. Avocation: teaching the meaning of Christianity. Home and Office: The Remain Intact Organization RR 2 Box 86 1917 135th St Larchwood IA 51241-7712

ZANNIERI, NINA, museum director; b. Summit, N.J., Feb. 1, 1955; d. Angelo Joseph and Louise Mary (Brumm) Z.; m. Douglas M. Vogel, Oct. 29, 1994. BA, Boston Coll., 1977; postgrad., Coll. of William & Mary, 1977-78; MA, Brown U., 1980. Curatorial asst. R.I. Hist. Soc., Providence, 1980-81, asst. curator, 1981-83, curator, 1983-86; dir. Paul Revere Meml. Assn., Boston, 1986—. Gen. editor: (exhbn. catalog) Paul Revere: The Man Behind the Myth, 1988; collaborator: (house guide) A Most Magnificent Mansion; project dir.: (exhbn. catalog) Let Virtue Be A Guide To Thee, 1983. Bd. dirs. Freedom Trail Found., Boston, Slater Mill Hist. Site, Pawtucket, R.I. Mem. Am. Assn. Mus.'s, New Eng. Mus. Assn. (curators com. 1984-86, bd. dirs. 1988—), Am. Assn. State and Local History, Phi Beta Kappa. Office: Paul Revere Meml Assn The Paul Revere House 19 North Sq Boston MA 02113-2405

ZANOTTI, JOHN PETER, broadcasting company executive; b. L.A., June 12, 1948; m. Claudia Jean Haskell, Aug. 8, 1970; children: Jeffrey, Laura, Mark, Christina. AB cum laude, N.Y.U., 1970; JD magna cum laude, Ariz. State U., 1974. Assoc. corp. dept./pub. fin. O'Melveny and Myers, L.A., 1974-78; corp. dir. legal Harte-Hanks Comms. Inc., San Antonio, 1978-79, asst. sec., 1979-80, v.p. legal, sec., 1980-83; pres. Harte-Hanks Mktg./Cen. Group, Cin., 1983-84; asst. to pres. newspaper divsn. Gannett Co., Inc., Rosslyn, Va., 1984-85; pres., pub. The Cin. Enquirer, 1985-90; CEO, exec. v.p. Phoenix (Ariz.) Newspapers, Inc., 1990-91; pub. The Ariz. Republic, The Phoenix Gazette, 1990-91; pres. TV group Gt. Am. Broadcasting Co., 1991-92, pres., COO, 1992-93; CEO, pres. Citicasters Inc. (formerly Gt. Am. Comms. Co.), Cin., 1993—. Contbr. articles to profl. jours. Bd. trustees Children's Hosp. Med. Ctr., 1989-90, 94—, Johnny Bench Scholarship Fund, 1987-90, 91—, Taft Mus., 1992-93, Xavier U., 1989-90; bd. dirs. Neediest Kids of All, 1986-90, 91—, Ariz. State U. Law Soc., 1990—; internat. bd. dirs. "Just Say No," 1991-92; mem. Walter Cronkite Sch. Journalism and Telecomm. Endowment Com., Ariz. State U., 1990-91, Cin. Bus. Com., 1987-90, Phoenix-40, 1990-91; bd. advisors U. Cin.

Coll. Bus. Adminstrn., 1988-90; co-chmn. Last Resort Scholarship Fund, Cin. Youth Collaborative, 1989-90. Mem. Assn. for Maximum Svc. TV, Inc. (bd. dirs. 1992—), Nat. Assn. Broadcasters (bd. dirs. 1994—), TV Operators Caucus, Inc., State Bar Calif., State Bar Tex., Greater Cin. C. of C. (bd. trustees 1988-90), Cin. Country Club, Commonwealth Club, Queen City Club. Office: Citicasters Inc 1 E 4th StSte 600 Cincinnati OH 45202

ZANOTTI, MARIE LOUISE, hospital adminstrator; b. Pitts., May 3, 1954; d. Louis Charles and Josephine Rose (Antoniello) Z. BS, U. Pitts., 1976; M of Pub. Health, Yale U., 1980. Adminstrv. asst. Presbyn.-Univ. Hosp., Pitts., 1980-82; dir. Meml. Hosp. Burlington County, Mt. Holly, N.J., 1982-85; accoc. hosp. dir. The Milton S. Hershey Med. Ctr.-Univ. Hosp., Hershey, Pa., 1985-92; assoc. hosp. dir. Latrobe (Pa.)Area Hosp., 1993; workshop presenter Healthcare Fin. Mgmt. Assn., 1988-89. Active Hershey Bus. Assn., 1988—; bd. dirs. Ronald McDonald House, 1991-92, chestnut ridge chpt. ARC 1993—, Med. Alliance Ins. Network, Ltd.,1993—. Fellow Am. Coll. Healthcare Execs.; mem. Healthcare Adminstrs. Group (pres. 1989), Hosp. Assn. Pa., Hosp. Coun. Western Pa., Latrobe Area C. of C. Exec. Women Westmoreland County, Yale U. Hosp. Adminstrn., Latrobe Country Club. Avocations: performing arts, sports. Home: 111 Mara Lago Greensburg PA 15601 Office: Latrobe Area Hosp 121 W 2nd Ave Latrobe PA 15650

ZANT, ROBERT FRANKLIN, computer information educator; b. Valdosta, Ga., Sept. 28, 1943; s. John F. and Norma G. (Shadrick) Z.; m. Sue Ann Frazier, Nov. 8, 1961; children—Debra Lynn, Tina Sue. AA, St. John's River Jr. Coll., 1963; BA, U. Fla., 1965, MA, 1970, PhD, 1972. Systems programmer U. Fla., Gainesville, 1966-67; asst. prof. Clemson U., S.C., 1970-74; assoc. prof. North Tex. State U., Denton, 1974-80; prof. computer info. systems North Tex. State U., 1980-88, chmn. dept., 1982-85; prof. computer info. systems U. Ala., Huntsville, 1988—, chmn. dept., 1988—; cons. Riegel Textile Corp., Greenwood, S.C., 1971-73, Dow-Badashe Co., Anderson, S.C., 1972—, Dallas Eye Inst., 1981-83, Cottingham Bearing Co., Dallas, 1981-83. Contbr. articles to profl. jours. NDEA fellow, 1967-70. Mem. Assn. Computing Machinery, Decision Scis. Inst., Assn. Computer Educators, Inst. Mgmt. Scis., Data Processing Mgmt. Assn. Office: U Ala Coll Adminstrv Sci 4701 University Dr Huntsville AL 35899-0100

ZANUCK, RICHARD DARRYL, motion picture company executive; b. Beverly Hills, Calif., Dec. 13, 1934; s. Darryl F. and Virginia (Fox) Z.; m. Lili Gentle; children: Virginia, Janet; Linda Harrison, Oct. 26, 1969; children: Harrison Richard, Dean Francis; m. Lili Fini, Sept. 23, 1978. Grad. Harvard Mil. Acad., 1952; B.A., Stanford, 1956. Story, prodn. asst. Darryl F. Zanuck Prodns., 1956, v.p., 1956-62; president's prodn. rep. 20th Century-Fox Studios, Beverly Hills, 1962-63; v.p. charge prodn. 20th Century-Fox Studios, 1963-69, pres., 1969-71, dir., 1966-71; chmn. 20th Century-Fox Television, Inc.; sr. exec. v.p. Warner Bros., Inc., 1971-72; co-founder, pres. Zanuck/Brown Co., 1972-88; founder, owner The Zanuck Co., 1989—. Producer: The Sting, 1973 (Acad. award), Jaws, 1975, Jaws 2, 1978, The Island, 1980, Neighbors, 1982, The Verdict, 1983, Cocoon, 1985, Target, 1985, Cocoon, the Return, 1988, Driving Miss Daisy, 1989 (Acad. award, Irving G. Thalberg award 1991), Rush, 1991, Rich in Love, 1992, Clean Slate, 1993. Nat. chmn. Fibrosis Assn.; mem. organizing com. 1984 Olympics; trustee Harvard Sch. 2d lt. U.S. Army. Named Producer of Yr., Nat. Assn. Theatre Owners, 1974, '85, Producers Guild Am., 1989; recipient Irving Thalberg award 1991, Lifetime Achievement award, Producers Guild Am., 1993. Mem. Acad. Motion Picture Arts and Scis. (bd. govs.), Screen Producers Guild, Phi Gamma Delta. Office: 202 N Canon Dr Beverly Hills CA 90210-5302

ZAPAPAS, JAMES RICHARD, pharmaceutical company executive; b. Martinsville, Ind., July 15, 1926; s. James K. and Bertha (Gardner) Z.; m. Patricia A. Ryan, Aug. 30, 1947; children: Marianne Zapapas McGriff, Patricia Zapapas Parry, Gail Zapapas Rodecker, James R., Carol, Julie Zapapas Tepper. BS in Pharmacy, Purdue U., 1947, ScD hon., 1979. Dir. dry products ops. Eli Lilly & Co., Indpls., 1967-70, dir. pers., 1970-73, dir. pers. and pub. rels., 1973-74, v.p. prodn. ops., 1974-75, group v.p., dir., 1976-77, pres. Elizabeth Arden Inc., 1975-76. chmn. bd., 1977-87, ret., 1987; bd. dir., group v.p. Eli Lilly & Co., 1976-86; bd. dir. Am. United Life. Republican. Roman Catholic. Home: 5025 Plantation Dr Indianapolis IN 46250-1638

ZAPEL, ARTHUR L., book publishing executive; b. Chgo., 1921; m. Janet Michel (dec.); children: Linda (dec.), Mark, Theodore, Michelle; m. Cynthia Rogers Pisor, 1986; stepchildren: Dawn, Anthony. BA in English, U. Wis., 1946. Writer, prodr. Westinghouse Radio Stas.; film writer Galbreath Studios, Ft. Wayne; creative dir. Kling Studios, Chgo., 1952-54; writer, prodr. TV commls. J. Walter Thompson Advt., Chgo., 1954-73, v.p. TV and radio prodn., 1954-73; founder, pres. Arthur Meriwether, Inc., 1973-83; pres. Meriwether Pub. Ltd., 1969-90; chmn. Arthur Meriwether, Inc., Meriwether Pub. Ltd., 1990-95; pres. Westcliffe (Colo.) Ctr. for the Arts. Illustrator: 'Twas the Night Before, The Jabberwock; created game A Can of Squirms; wrote plays for ednl. use in schs. and chs.; supr. editing and prodn. 1200 plays and musicals, 1970—. Founding pres. Art Students League of Colorado Springs, 1992; past pres. Colo. Springs Symphony Coun.; past bd. dirs. Colorado Springs Opera Festival. Recipient numerous awards Freedoms Found., Valley Forge, Art Dirs. Club N.Y., Art Dirs. Chgo., Hollywood Advt., 1960-67, Gold Records Radio Ad Bur., 1959-60, XV Festival Internat. Du Film Publicitaire Venise, 1968, Gold Camera award U.S. Indsl. Film Festival, 1983, Dukane award, 1983, Gold award Houston Internat. Film Festival, 1984. Office: Meriwether Pub Ltd 885 Elkton Dr Colorado Springs CO 80907

ZAPF, HERMANN, book and type designer; b. Nuremberg, Fed. Republic of Germany, Nov. 8, 1918; s. Hermann and Magdalene (Schlamp) Z.; m. Gundrun von Hesse, Aug. 18, 1951; 1 child, Christine Ludwig. Freelance designer, 1938—; type dir. D. Stempel AG, type foundry, Frankfurt, Fed. Republic of Germany, 1947-56; design cons. Mergenthaler Linotype Co., N.Y.C. and Frankfurt, 1957-74; cons. Hallmark Internat., Kansas City, Mo., 1966-73; v.p. Design Processing Internat. Inc., N.Y.C., 1977-86; prof. typographic computer programs Rochester (N.Y.) Inst. Tech., 1977-87; chmn. Zapf, Burns & Co., N.Y.C., 1987-91; instr. lettering Werkkunstschule, Offenbach, Fed. Republic Germany, 1948-50; prof. graphic design Carnegie Inst. Tech., 1960; instr. typography Technische Hochschule, Darmstadt, Fed. Republic Germany, 1972-81. Author: William Morris, 1948, Pen and Graver, 1952, Manual Typographicum, 1954, 68, About Alphabets, 1960, 70, Typographic Variations, 1964, Orbis Typographicus, 1980, Hora fugit/Carpe diem, 1984, Hermann Zapf and His Design Philosophy, 1987, ABC-XYZapf, 1989, Poetry Through Typography, 1993; designer types, Palatino, Melior, Optima, ITC Zapf Chancery, ITC Zapf Internat., Digiset, Marconi, Digiset Edison, Digiset Aurelia, Pan-Nigerian, URW-Roman and San Serif, Renaissance Roman. Hon. curator Computer Mus., Boston. Recipient Silver medal Brussels, 1962, 1st prize typography Biennale Brno, Czechoslovakia, 1966, Gold medal Type Dirs. Club, N.Y., Frederic W. Goudy award typography Rochester, 1969, Silver medal Internat. Book Exhbn., Leipzig, 1971, Gold medal, 1989; Johannes Gutenberg prize Mainz, Fed. German Republic, 1974, Gold medal Museo Bodoniano, Parma, Italy, 1975, J.H. Merck award, Darmstadt, 1978, Robert Hunter Middleton award, 1987, Euro Design award, 1994; named hon. citizen State of Tex., 1970, hon. royal designer for industry. Mem. Royal Soc. Arts, Am. Math. Soc., Assn. Typographique Internat., Am. Inst. Graphic Arts, Alliance Graphique Internationale, Bund Deutscher Grafik Designer, Internat. Gutenberg Gesellschaft; hon. mem. Type Dirs. Club N.Y.C., Soc. Typographique de France (Paris), Soc. Typographic Arts (Chgo.), Double Crown Club (London), Soc. Scribes and Illuminators (London), Friends of Calligraphy (San Francisco), Soc. Printers (Boston), Soc. Graphic Designers Can., Bund Deutscher Buchkünstler, Grafiska Inst. (Stockholm), Typophiles, Alpha Beta Club (Hong Kong), Soc. of Calligraphy (L.A.), Wynkyn de Worde Soc. (London), Monterey Calligrapher's Guild, Washington Calligraphers Guild, Eesti Kalligraafide Koondis (Tallinn, Estonia), Typographers Internat. Assn., Art Dirs. Club Kansas City, Assocs. Stanford U. Librs., Alcuin Soc. (Vancouver), Goudy Internat. Ctr., Gamma Epsilon Tau.

ZAPPALA, STEPHEN A., state supreme court justice; b. 1932; s. Frank and Josephine Zappala. B.A., Duquesne U.; LL.B., Georgetown U., 1958. Bar: Pa. 1958. Solicitor Allegheny County, Pitts. 1974-76; judge Ct. of

Common Pleas-Allegheny County, 1980-82; assoc. justice Pa. Supreme Ct., 1982—. Served with U.S. Army. Office: Pa Supreme Ct 330 Grant St Pittsburgh PA 15219-2202

ZAPPE, JOHN PAUL, city editor, educator; b. N.Y.C., July 30, 1952; s. John Paul and Caroline (Pikor) Z.; m. Siobhan Bradshaw, May 30, 1982. AA, Dutchess Community Coll., Poughkeepsie, 1971; BA, Marist Coll., 1973; JD, Syracuse (N.Y.) U., 1978. Reporter Poughkeepsie Jour., 1973-75, Nev. State Jour., Reno, 1979-80; freelance reporter Am. Media Bold, Oakland, Calif., 1981-83; reporter Press-Telegram, Long Beach, Calif., 1983-88, city editor, 1988—; tchr. Syracuse U., 1976-78, Calif. State U., 1985-87; cons. Am. Media Bold, 1981-83. Chmn. Local 69 Newspaper Guild, Long Beach, 1984-87. Mem. Investigative Editors and Reporters. Office: Press-Telegram 604 Pine Ave Long Beach CA 90844-0001

ZAPPULLA, LAWRENCE JOSEPH, bank executive; b. Newark, July 24, 1936; s. Joseph and Josephine (Vitale) Z.; m. Barbara M. Delamater, June 11, 1961; children: Mary, Joseph, Linda, Lawrence J. Jr. BS in Bus. Adminstrn., Seton Hall U., 1957. CPA, N.J. Acct. Lerner, Schuhalter Co., Newark, 1957-68; ptnr. Lerner, Schuhalter & Zappulla, Maplewood, N.J., 1968-77; compt. Howard Savs. Bank, Livingston, N.J., 1977-80, v.p., compt., 1980-89, v.p. acctg., 1989—. Mem. County Com., Essex County, N.J., 1965-67. Mem. Am. Inst. CPA's, N.J. Soc. CPA's, Fin. Mgrs. Soc. for Savs. Instns., Bank Adminstrn. Inst. Roman Catholic. Home: 49 Clark St Glen Ridge NJ 07028-2207 Office: Howard Savs Bank 200 S Orange Ave Livingston NJ 07039-5896

ZAR, JERROLD H(OWARD), biology educator, statistician; b. Chgo., June 28, 1941; s. Max and Sarah (Brody) Z.; m. Carol Bachenheimer, Jan. 15, 1967; children—David Michael, Adam Joseph. BS, No. Ill. U., 1962; MS, U. Ill., Urbana, 1964, PhD, 1967. NSF fellow marine sci. Duke U. Marine Lab., Beaufort, N.C., 1965; research assoc. dept. zoology U. Ill., Urbana, 1967-68; asst. prof. dept. biol. scis. No. Ill. U., DeKalb, 1968-71; assoc. prof. No. Ill. U., 1971-78, prof., 1978—, chmn. dept. biol. scis, 1978-84, assoc. provost grad. studies and research, dean Grad. Sch., 1984—; vis. scientist Argonne Nat. Lab., 1974; cons. EPA, also other govt. agys. and industries; founder, dir. ENCAP, Inc., 1974-93. Author: Biostatistical Analysis, 1974, 2d edit., 1984, (with J.E. Brower and C.N. von Ende) Field and Laboratory Methods for General Ecology, 1977, 3d edit., 1990; also articles, chpts. to books. NIH fellow U. Ill. Urbana, 1965-67. Fellow AAAS; mem. Am. Inst. Biol. Scis., Am. Ornithologists Union, Am. Physiol. Soc., Am. Statis. Assn., Biometric Soc., Cooper Ornithol. Soc., Am. Soc. Zoologists, Ecol. Soc. Am. (cert. sr. ecologist), Nat. Assn. Biol. Tchrs., Nat. Assn. Environ. Profls. (cert. environ. profl.), Wilson Ornithol. Soc. Office: No Ill U Graduate School De Kalb IL 60115-2864

ZARA, LOUIS, author, editor; b. N.Y.C., Aug. 2, 1910; s. Benjamin and Celia (Glick) Rosenfeld; m. Bertha Robbins, Sept. 23, 1930; children: Paul, Philip, Daniel; m. Marlene Brett, Mar. 22, 1958; m. Helen Dillman, Aug. 7, 1987. Student, Hebrew Theol. Coll., 1926-27; ed., Crane Coll., 1927-30, U. Chgo., 1930-31. Chmn. Walt Whitman Fellowship, 1940; Vice pres. Ziff Davis Pub. Co., Chgo., N.Y.C. 1946-61; editor-in-chief Masterpieces, 1950-51, dir. gen. book div., 1959-61; pres. Pub.'s Cons., Inc., N.Y.C., 1955-56. Internat. Communications Corp., N.Y.C., 1955-56; editor in chief gen. trade div. Follett Pub. Co., N.Y.C., 1962-65; editor in chief Mineral Digest, 1969-77; creative dir. George Jensen, Inc., 1974-77; cons. Astro Minerals Ltd., 1968-83. Author: novels Blessed is the Man, 1935, Give Us This Day, 1936, Some for the Glory, 1937, This Land is Ours, 1940, Against This Rock, 1943, Ruth Middleton, 1946, Rebel Run, 1951, In the House of the King, 1952, Blessed is the Land, 1954, Dark Rider, 1961; non-fiction Jade, 1969, Locks and Keys, 1969; also stories, scenarios, radio scripts, dramas, Twentieth Century Fox, 1936, ABC radio-TVshow Stump the Authors, 1945-46; scripts Scattergood Baines, 1941; contbr. fiction, essays and articles to mags. and anthologies, including O'Brien Best Short Stories of 1940. Recipient prose award Chgo. Found. Lit., 1940, Daroff Meml. fiction award, 1955. Fellow Royal Numis. Soc., Am. Numis. Soc.; mem. Authors Guild, Melville Soc., Overseas Press Club, Mineral Soc. Am., Macdowell Colony Fellows, Appraisers Soc. Am. (bd. dirs. 1980-87, pres. 1988-90, hon. life 1994), Nat. Commn. Anti-Defamation League (hon. life). Home: 141 E 56th St New York NY 10022

ZARAFONETIS, CHRIS JOHN DIMITER, physician, emeritus educator; b. Hillsboro, Tex., June 6, 1914; s. James and Helen (Skouras) Z.; m. Sophia Levathes, Mar. 27, 1943; 1 child, John Christopher. AB, U. Mich., 1936, MS, 1937, MD, 1941. Diplomate: Am. Bd. Internal Medicine. Extern Simpson Meml. Inst., U. Mich., 1940-41, research assoc., 1947-50; also asst. prof. medicine at univ.; intern Harvard IV Med. Service, Boston City Hosp., 1941-42; research fellow internal medicine U. Mich. Med. Sch., 1946-47; faculty Temple U. Med. Sch., 1950-60, prof. clin. and research medicine, 1957-60; chief hematology sect. Temple U. Hosp., 1950-60; dir. Simpson Meml. Inst. Med. Research, 1960-78; prof. internal medicine U. Mich., 1960-80, emeritus, 1980—; coord. med. edn. for nat. def., 1966-71; mem. com. on naval med. rsch. NRC-NAS, 1970-74, med. com. on problems of drug dependence, 1970-74; sci. adv. bd. Armed Forces Inst. Pathology, 1970-74; dir. rsch. and engring. Def. Dept., chmn. joint med. rsch. conf., 1968-75; mem. Army Sci. Adv. Panel, 1974-78, Army Sci. Bd., 1978-86; bd. dirs. Medicine in the Pub. Interest, 1973-89, Gorgas Meml. Inst. Tropical and Preventive Medicine, 1982-92. Author numerous articles in field.; asst. editor: Am. Jour. Med. Scis, 1951-60; editor Procs. Internat. Conf. on Leukemia-Lymphoma, 1968; Procs. Internat. Conf. Drug Abuse; mem. editorial adv. bd.: History of U.S Army Medical Service in Vietnam and South Asia. Served to maj. M.C. AUS, 1942-46, col. Res. ret. Decorated Order Ismail Egypt; Legion of Merit U.S.; recipient Sternberg medal U. Mich., 1941, U.S.A. Typhus Commn. medal, 1946, Henry Russel award U. Mich., 1950; Disting. Service award Am. Soc. Clin. Pharmacology and Therapeutics, 1980, Def. Def. medal for disting. pub. service, 1984. Fellow ACP (Physician Laureate award Mich. chpt. 1988), Internat. Soc. Hematology; mem. Am. Soc. Hematology, Am. Micros. Soc. (editorial bd. trans. 1956-65), AMA (vice chmn. sect. exptl. medicine 1968-69, chmn. sect. clin. pharmacology and therapeutics 1969-71, alt. del. 1971-73, del. 1973-75), Am. Fedn. Clin. Research, Am. Soc. Tropical Medicine, Soc. Exptl. Biology and Medicine, N.Y. Acad. Scis., Soc. Med. Scis.— to Armed Forces (v.p 1968-69, pres. 1969-70, alt. del. to AMA 1978-83, del. 1984-88, John R. Seal award, 1986), AAAS, Am., Internat. socs. internal medicine, Midwest Blood Club, Am. Soc. Clin. Pharmacology and Chemotherapy (regent, pres. 1968-69), Internat. Soc. Blood Transfusion, Med. Mycol. Soc. Ams., Assn. Mil. Surgeons U.S., Am. Therapeutic Soc. (pres. 1968-69), Internat. Soc. Toxinology, Associación Médica Argentina, Sociedad de Farmacología y Terapéutica (hon.), Phi Beta Kappa, Sigma Xi, Alpha Omega Alpha, Phi Kappa Phi. Home: 2721 Bedford Rd Ann Arbor MI 48104-4011

ZARANKA, WILLIAM F., academic administrator, author; b. Elizabeth, N.J., Dec. 22, 1944; s. William A. and Anne M. (Paulauska) Z.; m. Ruth Annalea Falchero; children: Jacob, Philip. BA, Upsala Coll., 1966; MA, Purdue U., 1968; PhD, U. Denver, 1974. Instr. Purdue U., West Lafayette, Ind., summer 1969; asst. prof. U. Pa., Phila., 1975-78; teaching fellow U. Denver, 1969-71, instr. English., 1969-71, 74-75, asst. prof., dir. creative writing, 1978-84, dean arts and humanities, 1984-89, provost, 1989—. Author: The Branx X Anthology of Poetry, 1981, The Brand X Anthology of Fiction, 1983, (poetry) A Mirror Driven through Nature, 1981, Blessing, 1986. Fellow Breadd Loaf Writers Conf., 1981. Roman Catholic. Avocation: astronomy. Office: U Denver Office of Provost 2199 S University Blvd Denver CO 80210-4711

ZARB, FRANK GUSTAVE, insurance brokerage executive; b. N.Y.C., Feb. 17, 1935; s. Gustave and Rosemary (Antinora) Z.; m. Patricia Koster, Mar. 31, 1957; children: Krista Ann, Frank, Jr. B.B.A., Hofstra U., 1957, M.B.A., 1962, L.H.D., 1975. Trainee Cities Service Oil Co., N.Y.C., 1957-62; gen. partner Goodbody & Co., N.Y.C., 1962-69; exec. v.p. CBWL-Hayden Stone, Inc. (investment banking), N.Y.C., 1969-71; asst. sec. U.S. Dept. Labor, Washington, 1971-72; exec. v.p. Hayden Stone, Inc., N.Y.C., 1972-73; assoc. dir. Office of Mgmt. and Budget, Washington, 1973-74; asst. to Pres., U.S., 1974-77; adminstr. Fed. Energy Adminstrn., Washington, 1974-77; adv. U.S Congress, 1977-78; gen. ptnr. Lazard Freres & Co., N.Y.C., 1977-88; chmn., pres. chief exec. officer Smith, Barney, Harris, Upham & Co., Inc., N.Y.C., 1988-93; vice chmn., group chief exec. The

Travelers Inc., N.Y.C., 1993-94; chmn., pres., CEO Alexander & Alexander Svcs. Inc., N.Y.C., 1994—; bd. coun. U.S. and Italy. Author: The Stockmarket Handbook, 1969, Handbook of Financial Markets, The Municipal Bond Handbook. Trustee Hofstra U., Gerald R. Ford Found. Recipient Disting. Scholar award Hofstra U., 1974. Mem. Coun. Fgn. Rels. Office: Alexander & Alexander Svcs 1185 Avenue of the Americas New York NY 10036

ZARE, RICHARD NEIL, chemistry educator; b. Cleve., Nov. 19, 1939; s. Milton and Dorothy (Amdur) Z.; m. Susan Leigh Shively, Apr. 20, 1963; children: Bethany Jean, Bonnie Sue, Rachel Amdur. BA, Harvard, 1961; postgrad., U. Calif., Berkeley, 1961-63; PhD (NSF predoctoral fellow), Harvard, 1964; DS (hon.), U. Ariz., 1990, Northwestern U., 1993, ETH, Zürich, 1993. Postdoctoral fellow Harvard, 1964; postdoctoral research asso. Joint Inst. for Lab. Astrophysics, 1964-65; asst. prof. chemistry Mass. Inst. Tech., 1965-66; asst. prof. dept. physics and astrophysics U. Colo., 1966-68, assoc. prof. physics and astrophysics, asso. prof. chemistry, 1968-69; prof. chemistry Columbia, 1969-77, Higgins prof. natural sci., 1975-77; prof. Stanford U., 1977—, Shell Disting. prof. chemistry, 1980-85, Marguerite Blake Wilbur prof. chemistry, 1987—, prof. physics, 1992—; cons. Aeronomy Lab., NOAA, 1966-77, radio standards physics div. Nat. Bur. Standards, 1968-77, Lawrence Livermore Lab., U. Calif., 1974—, SRI, Internat., 1974—, Los Alamos Sci. Lab., U. Calif., 1975—; fellow adjoint Joint Inst. Lab. Astrophysics, U. Colo.; mem. IBM Sci. Adv. Com., 1977-92; chmn. commn. on physical scis., mathematics, and applications Nat. Rsch. Coun., 1992—; researcher and author publs. on laser chemistry and chem. physics. editor Chem. Physics Letters, 1982-85. Recipient Fresenius award Phi Lambda Upsilon, 1974, Michael Polanyi medal, 1979, Nat. Metal Sci., 1983, Spectroscopy Soc. award Pitts., 1983, Michelson-Morley award Case Inst. Tech. Case We. Res. U., 1986, ISCO award for Significant Contbns. to Instrumentation for Biochem. Separations, 1990; nonresident fellow Joint Inst. for Lab. Astrophysics, 1970—, Alfred P. Sloan fellow, 1967-69, Christensen fellow St. Catherine's Coll., Oxford U., 1982, Stanford U. fellow, 1984-86. Fellow AAAS, Calif. Acad. Scis. (hon.); mem. Nat. Acad. Sci. (Chem. Scis. award 1991), Nat. Scis. Bd., Am. Acad. Arts and Scis., Am. Phys. Soc. (Earle K. Plyler prize 1981, Irving Langmuir prize 1985), Am. Chem. Soc. (Harrison Howe award Rochester chpt. 1985, Remsen award Md. chpt. 1985, Kirkwood award, Yale U. New Haven chpt. 1986, Willard Gibbs medal Chgo. chpt. 1990, Peter Debye award in phys. chemistry 1991, Linus Pauling medal 1993, The Harvey prize 1993, Dannie-Heineman Preis 1993), Am. Philos. Soc., Chem. Soc. London, Phi Beta Kappa. Office: Stanford U Dept Chemistry Stanford CA 94305-5080

ZAREFSKY, DAVID HARRIS, academic administrator, communication studies educator; b. Washington, June 20, 1946; s. Joseph Leon and Miriam Ethel (Lewis) Z.; m. Nikki Sheryl Martin, Dec. 23. 1970; children: Beth Ellen, Marc Philip. BS, Northwestern U., 1968, MA, 1969, PhD, 1974. Instr. communication studies Northwestern U., Evanston, Ill., 1968-73, asst. prof., 1974-77, assoc. prof., 1977-82, prof., 1982—, chmn. dept., 1975-83, assoc. dean Sch. Speech, 1983-88, dean, 1988—. Author: President Johnson's War on Poverty, 1986 (Winans-Wichelns award 1986), Lincoln, Douglas and Slavery, 1990 (Winans-Wichelns award 1991); co-author: Contemporary Debate, 1983; editor: Rhetorical Movement, 1993; co-editor: American Voices, 1989, Contemporary American Voices, 1992; contbr. articles to profl. jours. Recipient Best Article award So. Speech Communication Assn., 1985, Midwest Forensic Assn., 1988; named Debate Coach of the Year Georgetown U., 1973, Emory U., 1972. Mem. AAUP, Speech Comm. Assn. (pres. 1993, dist. scholar award 1994), Ctrl. State Comm. Assn., Am. Forensic Assn. (Svc. award 1989), Delta Sigma Rho-Tau Kappa Alpha (Svc. award 1986). Democrat. Jewish. Avocations: stamp collecting, reading, travel. Office: Northwestern U 1905 Sheridan Rd Evanston IL 60208-2260

ZAREFSKY, RALPH, lawyer; b. Houston, Apr. 9, 1950. BA cum laude, Northwestern U., 1972; JD, Stanford U., 1976. Bar: Calif. 1976. Law clk. to Hon. Lawrence T. Lydick U.S. Dist. Ct., 1976-78; ptnr. Baker & Hostetler, L.A. Mem. ABA, State Bar Calif. Office: Baker & Hostetler 600 Wilshire Blvd Los Angeles CA 90017

ZAREM, ABE MORDECAI, management consulting executive; b. Chgo., Mar. 7, 1917; s. I.H. and Lea (Kaufman) Z.; m. Esther Mariam Moskovitz, Oct. 4, 1941; children: Janet Ruth, David Michael, Mark Charles. B.S. in Elec. Engring, Ill. Inst. Tech., 1939, LL.D. (hon.), 1968; M.S. in Elec. Engring, Calif. Inst. Tech., 1940, Ph.D., 1944; LL.D., U. Calif. at Santa Cruz, 1967. Design engr. very high voltage power transmission system Allis Chalmers Rsch. div., 1944; initiator, group mgr. Microtime & Electro Optical Phys. Rsch., U.S. Naval Test Sta., 1945-48; assoc. dir., mgr. L.A. div. Stanford Rsch. Inst., 1948-56; mem. faculty UCLA, 1956-61; founder, chmn., pres. Electro-Optical Systems, Inc., Pasadena, Calif., 1956-67; v.p. Xerox Corp., L.A., 1963-67, sr. v.p., dir. corp. devel., bd. dirs., 1967-69; mgmt. and engring. cons., 1969-79; founder, chmn. Xerox Devel. Corp., L.A., 1975-80; chmn. strategic bus. planning, techno-econ. and venture capital, pres., owner Abe M. Zarem & Co., 1981—; founder, mng. dir., Frontier Assoc., 1980—; mem. adv. com. competitive tech. program State of Calif., 1989; mem. Calif. Coun. Sci. and Tech., chmn. advanced sci. & tech. programs com. Author: Utilization of Solar Energy, 1963. Traffic and parking commr. City of Beverly Hills, 1971-72, planning commr., 1972-73; Bd. dirs. Music Center Opera Assn., Los Angeles, 1968—; nat. trustee City of Hope; trustee Calif. Inst. Arts, 1973-74. Named Outstanding Young Elec. Engr. in U.S. Eta Kappa Nu, 1948; One of America's Ten Outstanding Young Men U.S. Jr. C. of C., 1950; recipient Albert F. Sperry medal Instrument Soc. Am., 1969. Fellow AIAA, IEEE; sci. mem. (a founder) Solar Energy Soc.; mem. Nat. Acad. Engring. Inventor World's fastest high-speed camera, automatic oscillograph. Home: 9640 Lomitas Ave Beverly Hills CA 90210-3333

ZAREMBKA, PAUL, economics educator; b. St. Louis, Apr. 17, 1942. BS, Purdue U., 1964; MS, U. Wis., 1967, PhD, 1967. Asst. prof. U. Calif., Berkeley, 1967-72; vis. prof. Heidelberg (Fed. Republic Germany) U., 1970-71, Gottingen (Fed. Republic Germany) U., 1972; assoc. prof. SUNY, Buffalo, 1973-76, prof., 1976—; sr. rsch. officer Internat. Labor Office, Geneva, 1974-77; researcher Louis Pasteur U., Strasbourg, France, 1978-79; Fulbright-Hayes lectr. Coun. Internat. Exchange of Scholars, Poznan, Poland, 1979. Author: Toward a Theory of Economic Development, 1972; editor: Frontiers in Econometrics, 1974, Research in Political Economy, 1977—; co-editor: Essays in Modern Capital Theory, 1976; contbr. articles to profl. publs. Active Buffalo ctr. chpt. exec. bd. United Univ. Professions, 1981—, pres., 1991-95, greivance officer acad., 1995—; active AFL-CIO Buffalo Labor Coun., 1982-83, Commn. on Quality Edn. in Buffalo for the 1990's, 1990-91; subcom. on capital appropriations citizens adv. com. on cmty. improvement, City of Buffalo, 1990—, bd. dirs. united parents, 1991-94. NSF grantee, 1969-72. Office: SUNY Dept Econs 415 Fronczak Hall Buffalo NY 14260

ZAREMSKI, MILES JAY, lawyer; b. Chgo. Aug. 16, 1948; s. Samuel and Ann (Levine) Z.; m. Elena Cinthia Resnik, July 19, 1970; children: Jason Lane, Lauren Devra. BS, U. Ill., 1970; JD, Case Western Res. U., 1973. Bar: Ill. 1973, U.S. Dist. Ct. (no. dist.) Ill. 1973, U.S. Ct. Appeals (7th cir.) 1973, U.S. Supreme Ct. 1977, U.S. Ct. Appeals (8th cir.) 1988. Spl. asst. state's atty. Lake County, Ill., 1980-82; sr. ptnr., chair health care law dept. Arnstein & Lehr, Chgo., West Palm Beach, Fla. and Milw., 1987—; asst. prof. med. jurisprudence U. Health Scis./Chgo. Med. Sch., 1991-92; arbitrator, mandatory arbitration programs Cook and Lake Counties, Ill., 1990—. Editor: Medical and Hospital Negligence, 4 vols., 1988, supplement, 1993; columnist Jour. Radiology, 1987-88; contbr. chpts. to books and articles to profl. jours. Oversight com. law sch. Case Western Res. U., Cleve., 1985—; mem. exec. com. law sch. ctr for health care Loyola U., Chgo., 1987-89; mem. lakefront commn. City of Highland Park, Ill., 1982-84; bd. dirs., officer Regional Organ Bank Ill., Chgo., 1986-91; bd. dirs. The Lambs, Libertyville, Ill., 1982-84, Jocelyn Cctr. for Mental Health, 1994—. Named one of Outstanding Young Men in Am., U.S. Jaycees, 1979. Fellow Am. Coll. Legal Medicine (assoc. in law 1973-91, chair health law sect. 1989—, mem. editl. bd. Jour. Legal Medicine 1981—, bd. dirs. 1993—); mem. ABA (mem. various coms. tort and ins. practice sec., vice chmn. 1979-90, chmn. med. and law com. 1984-85, editor-in-chief Forum 1979-81, spl. com. on med. profl. liability 1985, 91-95, mem. editl. bd. Forum on Health Law 1989-91), Ill. Bar Assn. (1st and 3d prizes 1978-79), Am. Trial Lawyers Assn.,

Chgo. Trial Lawyers Assn., Chgo. Bar Assn., Lake County Bar Assn., Am. Soc. Law and Medicine (editor-in-chief 1981-83, bd. editors 1983-86), Am. Acad. Hosps. Attys., Am. Soc. Writers on Legal Subjects (scribes), Nat. Health Lawyers Assn., Ill. Assn. Hosps. Attys. Jewish. Avocations: baseball, soccer, coaching athletic teams. Office: Arnstein & Lehr 120 S Riverside Plz Chicago IL 60606-3913

ZARET, BARRY LEWIS, cardiologist, medical educator; b. N.Y.C., Oct. 3, 1940; s. Irving Z. and Beatrice (Fader) Zaret; m. Myrna Zimmerman, June 23, 1963; children: Adam L., Elliot C., Owen M. B.S., Queens Coll., 1962; M.D., NYU, 1966; M.A., Yale U., 1982. Diplomate: Am. Bd. Internal Medicine. Intern Bellevue Hosp., N.Y.C., 1966-67, resident, 1967-79; research fellow John Hopkins U., Balt., 1969-71; asst. prof. medicine Yale U., New Haven, 1973-76, assoc. prof. medicine and diagnostic radiology, 1976, chief sect. cardiology, 1978—, assoc. prof. medicine and diagnostic radiology, 1980-82, prof. medicine and diagnostic radiology, 1982-84; Robert W. Berliner prof. medicine Yale U., 1984—, assoc. chair clin. affairs, 1994—; mem. staff Yale-New Haven Med. Ctr. Mem. editorial bd.: Am. Jour. Cardiology, 1977—, Jour. Cardiovascular Medicine, 1979—, Jour. Am. Coll. Cardiology, 1986-91, 92—, Jour. Cardiac Imaging, 1986—, Circulation, 1993; assoc. editor: Yearbook of Nuclear Medicine, 1980—; editor-in-chief: Jour. Nuclear Cardiology, 1993—; contbr. articles to various publs. Recipient Casimir Funk award Soc. Mil. Surgeons, 1973; recipient Herrman Blumgart Pioneer award New Eng. chpt. Soc. Nuclear Medicine, 1978. Fellow Am. Coll. Cardiology, Coun. Clin. Cardiology, Am. Heart Assn., Coun. Circulation, Am. Heart Assn., Am. Physiology Soc.; mem. Am. Soc. Clin. Investigation, Am. Fedn. Clin. Rsch., Assn. Am. Physicians, Soc. Nuclear Medicine, Am. Soc. Nuclear Cardiology, Assn. Univ. Cardiologists, Assn. Profs. Cardiology (pres. 1992), Phi Beta Kappa, Alpha Omega Alpha, Interurban Clin. Club. Jewish. Home: 15 Cassway Rd Woodbridge CT 06525-1214 Office: Yale U Sch Medicine 333 Cedar St # 3fmp New Haven CT 06510-3289

ZARINS, BERTRAM, orthopaedic surgeon; b. Latvia, June 22, 1942; came to U.S., 1946, naturalized, 1956; s. Richard Arthur and Maria (Rozenbergs) Z. A.B. in Chemistry, Lafayette Coll., 1963; M.D., SUNY-Syracuse, 1967. Diplomate Am. Bd. Orthopaedic Surgery. Clin. instr. orthopaedic surgery Harvard Med. Sch., Boston, 1976—, asst. clin. prof., 1982—; orthopaedic surgeon Mass. Gen. Hosp., Boston, 1976—, chief sports medicine unit, 1982—; team physician Boston Bruins Hockey Team, 1976—; chmn. med. com. Sports Medicine council, U.S. Olympic Com., 1980-92; team physician New Eng. Patriots Football Team, 1982—; head physician USA Olympic teams XIV Winter Olympic Games, Sarajevo, 1984. Contbr. articles to profl. jours. Served to lt. comdr. M.C., USNR, 1973-75. Fellow ACS, Am. Acad. Orthopaedic Surgeons (chmn. com. on sports medicine 1993—), Am. Coll. Sports Medicine; mem. AMA, Internat. Arthroscopy Assn. (bd. dirs. 1991—), Arthroscopy Assn. N.Am., N.Am. Trauma Assn. (pres. 1977), Internat. Soc. of the Knee, Am. Shoulder and Elbow Surgeons, Herodicus Soc., Brookline (Mass.) Country Club. Office: Mass Gen Hosp Ambulatory Care Ctr Ste 514 Boston MA 02114

ZARLE, THOMAS HERBERT, university president. BS, Springfield Coll., 1963; MA, Ohio U., 1965; PhD, Mich. State U., 1970; MPH, Harvard U., 1978. V.p. instl. advancement Bentley Coll., Waltham, Mass., until 1988; pres. Aurora U., Ill., 1988—. Office: Aurora U Office of Pres 347 S Gladstone Ave Aurora IL 60506-4877

ZARNOWITZ, VICTOR, economist, educator; b. Lancut, Poland, Nov. 3, 1919; came to U.S., 1952, naturalized, 1957; s. Leopold and Bertha (Blumenfeld) Z.; m. Lena Engelman, Jan. 12, 1946; children: Steven L., Arthur H. Student, U. Cracow, Poland, 1937-39; M.A. in Econs, U. Heidelberg, Germany, 1949, Ph.D. summa cum laude, 1951. Tutor, instr. econs. U. Heidelberg, also Grad. Sch. Bus., Mannheim, Germany, 1949-51; analyst Nat. Bur. Econ. Research, 1952-59, mem. sr. research staff, 1963-78, research assoc., 1979—; lectr., then vis. prof. Columbia, 1956-59; mem. faculty Grad. Sch. Bus., U. Chgo., 1959—, prof. econs. and fin., 1965-90, prof. emeritus, 1990—; dir. study of bus. cycle indicators, cons. Bur. Econ. Analysis, U.S. Dept. Commerce, 1972-93; rsch. assoc. Ctr. for Internat. Bus. Cycle Rsch., Columbia U., 1979—, co-dir. rsch., 1994—. Author: Unfilled Orders, Price Changes and Business Fluctuations, 1962, An Appraisal of Short Term Economic Forecasts, 1967, Orders, Production and Investment, 1973, (with C. Boschan) Cyclical Indicators: An Evaluation and New Leading Indexes, 1975, An Analysis of Forecasts of Aggregate Income, Output, and the Price Level, 1979, Business Cycles and Growth, 1981, (with G.H. Moore) Sequential Signs of Recession and Recovery, 1982, On Functions, Quality, and Timeliness of Economic Information, 1982, The Accuracy of Individual and Group Forecasts from Business Outlook Surveys, 1984, Recent Work on Business Cycles in Historical Perspective, 1985, Rational Expectations and Macroeconomic Forecasts, 1985, (with G.H. Moore) Major Changes in Cyclical Behavior, 1986, (with L.A. Lambros) Consensus and Uncertainty in Economic Prediction; Business Cycles: Theory, History, Indicators and Forecasting, 1992, What is a Business Cycle?, 1992, Has Macro-Forecasting Failed?, 1993, (with Phillip Braun) Twenty Two Years of the NBER- ASA Quarterly Economic Outlook Surveys, 1993; co-author, editor: The Business Cycle Today, 1972; contbr. to books. Fellow Nat. Assn. Bus. Economists, Am. Statis. Assn.; mem. Am. Econ. Assn., Ciret (hon.). Home: 5752 S Blackstone Ave Chicago IL 60637-1824 Home: 601 W 115 St Apt 55 New York NY 10025

ZARO, BRAD A., research company executive, biologist; b. San Jose, Calif., Dec. 4, 1949; s. Raymond J. and Irene R. (Cunha) Z.; m. Angela M. Greenan, Nov. 20, 1971; children: Amy C., Kristen E. BA in Zoology, San Jose State U., 1974, MA in Biology, 1981. Chemist, Dept. Drug Metabolism Syntex Rsch., Inc., Palo Alto, Calif., 1976-78, chemist II, Dept. Drug Metabolism, 1978-81, chemist III, Dept. Drug Metabolism, 1981-84, clin. rsch. assoc. I, Inst. of Clin. Medicine, 1984-85, clin. rsch. assoc. II, Inst. of Clin. Medicine, 1985-87, sen. clin. rsch. assoc., Inst. of Clin. Medicine, 1985-87; sen. clin. rsch. assoc. Triton Biosciences, Inc., Alameda, Calif., 1988, mgr. clin. trials, 1988; pres. Clinimetrics Rsch. Assoc., Inc., San Jose, 1988—. Contbr. articles to scholarly jours. Mem. Am. Coll. Clin. Pharmacology, Am. Assoc's. for the Advancement of Sci., Assoc's. of Clin. Pharmacology, Prof. Tech. Cons's. Democrat. Roman Catholic. Avocations: scuba diving, skiing, flying airplanes. Office: Clinimetrics Rsch Assocs Ste 403 2025 Gateway Pl San Jose CA 95110

ZARR, MELVYN, lawyer, educator; b. Worcester, Mass., Aug. 29, 1936; m. Gail Sclar, Aug. 29, 1971. A.B., Clark U., 1958; LL.B., Harvard U., 1963. Bar: Mass. bar 1964, Maine bar 1973. Staff atty. NAACP Legal Def. & Edn. Fund, Inc., N.Y.C., 1963-69; co-dir. Mass. Law Reform Inst., Boston, 1970-73; prof. law U. Maine, 1973—; U.S. magistrate, Portland, Maine, 1977-82. Mem. Am. Law Inst. Home: 19 Mckinley Rd Falmouth ME 04105-1913 Office: U Maine Sch Law 246 Deering Ave Portland ME 04102-2837

ZARRELLA, ARTHUR M., superintendent; b. Providence, July 30, 1936; s. Joseph and Flora (Santora) Z.; m. Ann Miletta, Aug. 19, 1960; children: Matthew, Mark, Chris, Paul. BS, U. R.I., 1960; D of Pedagogy (hon.), R.I. Coll., 1985. Cert. bus. edn., history, social studies, guidance and counseling, critic tchr., secondary sch. prin., secondary sch. asst. prin., supt. of schs. Tchr. bus. edn. Cranston High Sch. West, 1961-62; tchr. bus. edn. Mt. Pleasant High Sch., 1962-65, tchr. social studies, 1965-68; social studies dept. head Ctrl. High Sch., 1968-70, guidance dept. head, 1970-72, student rels. adminstr., 1972-76, prin., 1976-87; prin. Classical H.S., 1987-88, acting asst. supt. for secondary edn., 1988-89, asst. supt. for secondary edn., 1989-90, asst. supt. secondary edn./dep., 1990—, acting supt. schs., 1991-92, supt. of schs., 1992—; asst. coach track and field Mt. Pleasant High Sch., 1961-64, head coach track and field, 1964-69; tchr. Brown U., 1970, Providence Coll., 1973-74, 74-75, 86, 86—, advisor administr. internship program, 1976-82; tchr. R.I. Coll., 1980, 82, social worker practicum supervision, 1974-75, 75-76; counselor practicum supervision U. R.I., 1976-78; advisor adminstrv. internship program Harvard U., 1985-86; cons. The Inst. for Ednl. Leadership, Inc., Hartford, 1985; presenter in field; many others. Contbr. articles to profl. jours. Bd. dirs. Mt. Pleasant Little League, 1973-76, treas., 1973-75, pres. 1976; bd. dirs. West End Community Assn., 1978-89, Wiggins Village Tenants Assn., 1980—, Young Vols. of R.I., 1982-84, Urban Edn. Ctr., 1982—, R.I. Leadership Acad., 1983-85, Keep Providenc Beautiful,

1984-85, Providence Edn. Fund, 1985-88, West End Community Ctr., 1986-90, Todd Morsilli Fund, 1987—, chairperson, 1989-91; scholarship chairperson Italian Am. Sports Hall of Fame, 1988-89; others. With USNG, 1959-65. Recipient Delta Sigma Theta Sorority's Community Svc. award, 1986, Mayor's citation for community svc., 1989, R.I. Ho. of Reps. citation for community svc., 1989, Gov.'s citation for community svc., 1989, R.I. Senate citation for community svc., 1989, Youth Dirs. Assn. Community Svc. award, 1989, NAACP Edn. award, 1989, R.I. Ho. of Reps. citation for commitment to substance abuse programs, 1991, Mayor's Citizen citation, 1991, Roberto Clemente Citizen award, 1991, many others. Mem. Nat. Assn. Secondary Sch. Prins., R.I. Assn. Secondary Sch. Prins., R.I. Sch. Adminstrs. Assn., Barnard Club. Roman Catholic. Home: 80 Waller St Providence RI 02908-3822 Office: Providence Sch Dept 797 Westminster St Providence RI 02903-4018

ZARRO, JANICE ANNE, lawyer; b. Newark, June 30, 1947; d. Samuel James and Elma Dora (Monaco) Z.; m. Bobby C. Wood. BA, Rutgers U., 1969; JD, IIT-Chgo.-Kent Coll. Law, 1973. Bar: Pa. 1974. Counsel jud. com. U.S. Ho. Reps., Washington, 1973-77; profl. staff mem. counsel labor and human resources com. U.S. Senate, Washington, 1977-80; dir. Avon Products, Inc., N.Y.C., 1980-81; dir. Avon Products, Inc., Washington, 1982-86, v.p., 1986-90; pres. The Novus Group, Inc., 1990-92; dir. fed. affairs Mallinckrodt Med., 1992—, v.p., 1993-94; v.p. govt. affairs Worldwide Mallinckrodt Group, 1994—; gen. counsel Nat. Italian-Am. Found., 1989—; mem. Bus. Govt. Rels. Coun., Washington, 1987—. Past chmn. Nat. Capital chpt. Multiple Sclerosis Soc. Recipient Leadership Recognition award Nat. Women's Econ. Alliance, 1984. Mem. ABA, Pa. Bar Assn. Home: 6A W Chapman St Alexandria VA 22301-2502

ZARSE, LEIGH BRYANT, architect, architectural engineer; b. Wauwatosa, Wis., Sept. 26, 1930; s. Alfred Henry and Cecile (Moreau) Z.; student U. Wis., Milw., 1948-50, Ohio State U., 1950-52; B. Archtl. Engring., U. Ill., 1954; m. Hannelore Schilling, June 30, 1973. Ptnr. Zarse & Zarse, Inc., Milw., 1957-84, pres., 1967-84; structural project engr. Milw. Met. Sewerage Dist., 1984—; mem. municipal planning com. City Club of Milw., 1965—, sec. bd. dirs., 1971. Served to maj. USAFR, 1954-57. Registered architect and profl. engr., Wis.; certified multi-disaster design protection specialist CD Preparedness Agy., FAA Comml. Multi-Engine Instrument Pilot; Mem. AIA (Top Honor award 1963), ASCE, Am. Concrete Inst., Engrs. and Scientists of Milw., Aircraft Owners Pilots Assn., Am. Bonanza Soc., Alpha Rho Chi, Sigma Delta Omega (pres. local chpt. 1949-50). Designer numerous local, state and fed. govt. bldgs., including: 1500 seat amphitheater for Gen. McCormack, Lackland AFB, San Antonio, 1954, 40 schs. in S.E. Wis., 1957—, Kenosha (Wis.) City Hall, 1971, St. Francis (Wis.) City Hall, 1963, Hales Corners (Wis.) City Hall, 1968, FAA and Weather Bur. Bldg. at Gen. Billy Mitchell Field, Milw., 1970, MMSD Hdqtrs. Office Bldg., 1987, Jones Island Maintenance Facility, 1989, MMSD South, 1993. Home: 1812 Mountain Ave Milwaukee WI 53213-2336

ZARTMAN, DAVID LESTER, animal sciences educator, researcher; b. Albuquerque, July 6, 1940; s. Lester Grant and Mary Elizabeth (Kitchel) Z.; m. Micheal Aline Plemmons, July 6, 1963; children: Kami Renee, Dalan Lee. BS, N.Mex. State U., 1962; MS, Ohio State U., 1966, PhD, 1968. Jr. ptnr. Marlea Guernsey Farm, Albuquerque, 1962-64; grad. rsch. assoc. Ohio State U., Columbus, 1964-68; asst. prof. dairy sci. N.Mex. State U., Las Cruces, 1968-71, assoc. prof., 1971-79, prof., 1979-84; prof., chmn. dept. Ohio State U., Columbus, 1984—; pres. Mary K. Zartman, Inc., Albuquerque, 1976-84; cons. Bio-Med. Electronics, Inc., San Diego, 1984-89, Zartemp, Inc., Northbrook, Ill., 1990, Recom Applied Solutions, 1993—. Contbr. articles to profl. jours.; patentee in field. Recipient State Regional Outstanding Young Farmer award Jaycees, 1963, Disting. Rsch. award N.Mex. State U. Coll. Agr. and Home Econs., 1983; named one of Top 100 Agr. Alumni, N.Mex. State U. Centennial, 1987; spl. postdoctoral fellow NIH, New Zealand, 1973; Fulbright-Hayes lectr., Malaysia, 1976. Fellow AAAS; mem. Am. Dairy Sci. Assn., Am. Soc. Animal Sci., Dairy Shrine Club, Ohio Extension Profs. Assn., Poultry Soc. Am., Sigma Xi, Gamma Sigma Delta, Alpha Gamma Rho (1st Outstanding Alumnus N.Mex. chpt. 1985), Alpha Zeta, Phi Kappa Phi. Home: 7671 Deer Creek Dr Columbus OH 43085-1551 Office: Ohio State U 2029 Fyffe Rd Columbus OH 43210

ZARUBY, WALTER STEPHEN, holding company executive; b. Vegreville, Alta., Can., Mar. 4, 1930; s. William and Annie (Kubon) Z.; m. Margaret Beth Fargey, Sept. 22, 1958; children: Stephen, Jeffrey. B.A.Sc., U. Toronto, 1952. Engr., project mgr. Shell Oil Co. and Shell Can. Ltd., 1952-70; sr. v.p. Westburne Internat. Industries Ltd., Calgary, Alta., 1970-73; pres. Westburne Internat. Industries Ltd., 1973-76, Radium Holdings Ltd., Calgary, 1977-87, Radium Resources Ltd., 1978—, Radium Energy Corp., Las Vegas, Nev., 1981-87; dir. Aberford Resources Ltd., 1981-87; pres. Zaruby & Assocs., Inc., 1987—, Indsl. Minerals Recovery, Inc., 1987—. Mem. Assn. Profl. Engrs., Geologists, and Geophysicists Alta., Assn. Drilling Contractors (bd. dirs. 1971-74). Clubs: Calgary Petroleum, Calgary Golf and Country, Glencoe. Address: 1012 Bel-Aire Dr SW, Calgary, AB Canada T2V 2B9

ZARWYN, BERTHOLD, physical scientist; b. Vienna, Austria, Aug. 22, 1921; came to U.S., 1949, naturalized, 1955; s. Joseph and Bronislawa Regina (Unger) Z.; M.E., Gliwice, Poland, 1946; Sc.D., Munich (W. Ger.) U., 1947; Ph.D., N.Y.U., 1954; Engring. Sc.D., Columbia, 1963. Project engr. Curtiss-Wright Corp., Woodridge, N.J., 1951-55; staff scientist AMF Corp., N.Y.C., 1955-57; chief scientist Link Aviation Co., Binghamton, N.Y., 1957-58; head research staff Am. Bosch-Arma Corp., Garden City, N.Y., 1958-63; corp. cons. Cutler-Hammer Corp., Deer Park, N.Y., 1963-65; chief engr. Bell Aerosystems Corp., Niagara Falls, N.Y., 1965-66; sr. cons. Mitre Corp., Bedford, Mass., 1966-68; spl. asst. to commanding gen., acting chief engr. Hdqrs. U.S. Army Materiel Command, Arlington, Va., 1968-71, chief phys. scis. br., U.S. Army Devel. and Readiness Command, Alexandria, Va., 1971-75, phys. scientist U.S. Army Harry Diamond Labs., Washington, 1975-78; chief system analysis br. U.S. Army Elec. Rsch. and Devel. Command, Adelphi, Md., 1978-79, chief tech. divsn., 1979-81, asst. tech. dir., 1981-85; spl. asst. to dep. chief of staff for tech. and program mgmt. U.S. Army Lab. Command, Adelphi, 1985-87, pres. Pan-Tech. Corp., 1987—; adj. faculty, lectr., cons. in field; dir. Film Microelectronics Co. Inc., Burlington, Mass., 1965-67. Mem. IEEE, Am. Phys. Soc., N.Y. Acad. Scis., Sigma Xi. Editorial bd. Bavarian Soc. Engrs., 1947-49; translation panel Russian Jour. Applied Math. and Mechanics with Pergamon Inst., 1956-57. Inventor nuclear gyroscope, microwave holography, other items. Home and Office: Pan-Tech Corp 7589 Mansfield Hollow Rd Delray Beach FL 33446-3314

ZASLAVSKY, ROBERT, educator; b. Phila., Feb. 26, 1942; s. Harry and Sally (Zwick) Z.; div.; 1 child, Cordelia Helena. AB in Philosophy, English Lit., Temple U., 1964; MA in Philosophy, New Sch. Social Rsch., 1969, PhD in Philosophy, 1978; postgrad., Cabrini Coll., 1989—. Substitute tchr. math. and English Phila. Bd. Edn., 1964; caseworker Phila. Dept. Pub. Assistance, 1964-65, N.Y.C. Dept. Welfare, 1965-68; instr. philosophy Villanova U., 1971-73; instr. philosophy of art Immaculata Coll., 1975; libr. interlibr. loan and reference Bryn Mawr (Pa.) Coll., 1973-86; exec. producer, on-air performer, camera oper. Studio 9 Video Prodns., Ardmore, Pa., 1986—; adj. instr. English and religion, student tchr. adviser Cabrini Coll., 1990; instr. lit. Main Line Sch. Night, 1991—; instr. humanities Akiba Hebrew Acad., Merion Station, Pa., 1990—; job counselor Kingston (N.Y.) Community Ctr., 1968; presenter seminars; guest lectr. Greek lit. Bryn Mawr Coll., 1976-78, Villanova U., 1978-81; assoc. Greater Phila. Philosophy Consortium, 1983-86; instr. Rittenhouse Acad., 1989, Haverford Twp. Adult Sch., 1989, Valley Forge Mil. Acad., 1989-90; instr. Elderhostel program Cabrini Coll., 1990, 91, Valley Forge Hist. Soc., 1991. Contbr. articles, revs. to lit. publs. Mem. ASCD, Nat. Coun. Tchrs. English, Ind. Sch. Tchrs. Assn. (classical langs. div.), Pa. State Edn. Assn., The American Classical League, Mystery Writers Am., Core Knowledge Fdn. Home: Apt 9 9 Station Ave Ardmore PA 19003 Office: Akiba Hebrew Acad 223 N Highland Ave Merion Station PA 19066-1798

ZASLOW, JEFFREY LLOYD, syndicated columnist; b. Phila., Oct. 6, 1958; s. Harry and Naomi (Weintraub) Z.; m. Sherry Lynn Margolis, July 4, 1987; children: Jordan Danielle, Alexandra Nicole. BA with honors, Carnegie-Mellon U., 1980. Reporter/columnist The Orlando (Fla.) Sentinel, 1980-83; staff writer The Wall St. Jour., Chgo., 1983-87; columnist The

Chgo. Sun Times, 1987—, USA Weekend mag., 1995—. Author: (with others) You Can Do Something About AIDS, 1988, Tell Me All About It, 1990, Take It from Us, 1994; contbr. feature articles to The N.Y. Times, Reader's Digest, Phila. Inquirer, Boston Globe, Cosmopolitan mag., Glamour, Business Week, others; writer of liner notes for singer Don McLean's double-live album, 1983; numerous appearances on TV including ABC's Nightline with Ted Koppel, Good Morning Am., NBC's Today Show, CBS's This Morning, Oprah Winfrey Show, The Larry King Show, NBC's Tonight Show, CBS's Saturday Night with Connie Chung; subject of articles in Time, Newsweek, People, Life, Washington Post, others. Jewish. Office: Chgo Sun-Times Inc 401 N Wabash Ave Rm 320 Chicago IL 60611-3532

ZASSENHAUS, HILTGUNT MARGRET, physician; b. Hamburg, Ger., July 10, 1916; came to U.S., 1952, naturalized, 1957; d. Julius and Margret Z. Diploma of Scandinavian Langs., U. Hamburg, 1938; MD, U. Copenhagen, 1952; MD (hon.), Goucher Coll., Towson State U., U. Notre Dame, 1975, U. Md., 1984, Washington Coll. Md., 1984, Western Coll. Md., 1987, U. Md., Balt. County, 1988. With German Dept. Justice, Berlin, 1941-45; secret relief action for Scandinavian polit. prisoners; organizer relief action for German orphans German Dept. Justice, 1945-48; intern, then resident in internal medicine Balt. City Hosp., 1952-54; pvt. practice specializing in internal medicine Balt., 1954—; med. bd. Greater Balt. Med. Center; appointed mem. Md. Council Humanities, 1979—; del. Med. and Chirurgical Faculty of State of Md., 1985-89. Author: biography On Guard in The Dark, 1948; autobiography Walls (Christopher award as best book of year 1975, Best Book of Yr . Book Assn. Evang. Ch. Germany 1981); subject of documentary Woman of Courage, 1989; also articles, essays. Trustee White Rose Found., N.Y., 1988; bd. dirs. Roland Park Country Sch., GBMC, Balt., 1985; bd. dirs. Greater Balt. Medf. Ctr., 1986,; trustee The White Rose Found., N.Y.C., 1988; apptd. hon. senator U. Hamburg, 1990. Decorated knight St. Olav's Order 1st class (Norway); Order Dannebrog 1st class (Denmark), Bundesverdienstkreuz 1st class (Fed. Republic Germany); recipient Danish Red Cross medal, 1948, Norwegian Red Cross medal, 1948, 86, Gold Meml. medal Senate of City of Hamburg, Fed. Republic Germany, 1986, Community Service award Med. Assn. Md., 1986, Gold medal U. Hamburg, 1990; named Outstanding Woman of Year in Balt. County AAUW, 1976; nominated for Nobel Peace Prize, 1974; named to Md. Women's Hall of Fame, 1986; subject of documentary It Mattered to Me, produced by ITV, Yorkshire TV (Eng.), 1981; apptd. hon. sen. U. Hamburg, Fed. Republic Germany, 1990. Mem. Physicians for Social Responsibility (bd. dirs.), Balt. County Med. Soc. Address: 7028 Bellona Ave Baltimore MD 21212 *I know that one person can make the difference. That gives me hope that the walls of hate and prejudice separating man from man one day will fade so that people will cease destroying each other and join to serve life.*

ZASTROW, JOHN THURMAN, judge; b. Wausau, Wis., Dec. 2, 1937; s. Raymond Henry and Helen Octavie (Sanche) Z.; m. Christel Schulz, Nov. 21, 1964; 1 child, Stephen Alexander. AB in Polit. Sci., UCLA, 1961, M of Pub. Adminstrn., 1964; JD, Ariz. State U., 1971. Bar: Ariz. 1971, U.S. Dist. Ct. Ariz. 1971, U.S. Ct. Appeals (9th cir.) 1972, U.S. Supreme Ct., 1975. Asst. dir. League of Ariz. Cities and Towns, Phoenix, 1964-68; assoc. Perry and Head, Phoenix, 1971-73; asst. city atty. City of Scottsdale, Ariz., 1973-76; judge City of Phoenix, 1976-83; judge pro tem Superior Ct. Maricopa County, Phoenix, 1982; immigration judge U.S. Dept. Justice, Phoenix, 1983—; faculty assoc. Ariz. State U., Tempe, 1965; faculty advisor Nat. Jud. Coll., Reno, 1980; pres. Ariz. City Atty.'s Assn., Phoenix, 1974-75. Contbr. numerous articles to profl. jours. Dem. candidate for Ariz. Ho. Reps., 1970. Served to 1st lt. U.S. Army, 1961-67. Recipient Award for Service, Valley Big Bros., 1970. Mem. ABA, Ariz. Bar Assn., Maricopa County Bar Assn., Internat. Platform Assn., Ariz. State U. Law Alumni Assn. (Merit award 1981), Am. Legion, SAR (mem. nat. soc.). Episcopalian. Avocations: traveling, speaking Spanish. Office: US Dept Justice EOIR Office Immigration Judge 230 N 1st Ave PO Box 0090 Room 3114 Phoenix AZ 85025

ZATKOFF, LAWRENCE P., federal judge; m. Nancy L. Chenhall; four children. BSBA, U. Detroit, 1962; JD cum laude, Detroit Coll. Law, 1966. Bar: Mich., U.S. Supreme Ct. Mem. corp. personnel staff Chrysler Corp., 1962-66; asst. prosecuting atty. Macomb County, Mich.; with Moll, Desenberg, Purdy, Glover & Bayer, Detroit, 1966-68; ptnr. LaBarge, Zatkoff & Dinning, Roseville, 1968-78; probate judge Macomb County, 1978-82; judge Macomb County Cir. Ct., 1982-87, U.S. Dist. Ct. (ea. dist.) Mich. 1986—; part-time faculty Detroit Coll. Law; mem. rep. assembly Mich. State Bar, mem. spl. com. on grievances; appointed assoc. appeal agt. SSS, 1969-72. guest lectr., past mem. scholarship ball com. Macomb County Community Coll.; citizen's adv. bd. Macomb-Oakland Regional Ctr., 1978-79; ex officio mem. Macomb County Youthscope; adv. bd. Met. Detroit chpt. March of Dimes; trustee St. Joseph Hosp. of Mt. Clemens; mem. Selfridge Air NG Base Community Council; Rep. candidate 12th dist. U.S. Congress Mich., 1976, party treas. 12 dist. 1975, exec. com., 1975, chmn. Macomb County exec. com., 1976, del. several nat. and regional Rep. Convs., Macomb County campaign coordinator for U.S. Sen. candidate Marvin Esch, 1976. Mem. ABA, Fed. Bar Assn., Mich. Bar Assn., Macomb County Bar. Assn. (dir., treas. Young Lawyers sect., past probate ct. liason to bd. dirs., mem. cir. ct. liason com.), Detroit Bar Assn., Am. Judicare Soc., Am. Arbitration Assn., Nat. Orgn. Legal Problems of Edn., Nat. Council Juvenile and Family Ct. Judges, Mich. Probate and Juvenile Ct. Judges Assn. (mental health com.), Nat. Coll. Probate Judges, Mich. Judges Assn., VFW (legal case rep. 1976, spokesman Vietnamese Embassy Paris 1976,; judge Voice of Democracy programs 1975, state wide scholarships judge, Voice of Democracy awards 1975, 76, Americanism award 1976, Spl. Recognition award 1978). Clubs: 100, Macomb County 300, Rep. Majority (charter). Office: US Dist Ct 257 US Courthouse 231 W Lafayette Blvd Detroit MI 48226-2719

ZATUCHNI, GERALD IRVING, physician, educator; b. Phila., Oct. 5, 1933; s. Samuel and Minnie (Pollack) Z.; m. Bette Ruth Christine, June 15, 1958; children: Cheryl Lee, Bettina, Mimi. AB, Temple U., 1954, MD, 1958, MSc, 1965. Diplomate Am. Bd. Obstetrics and Gynecology. Intern Walter Reed Army Hosp., Washington, 1958-59; residency in ob-gyn Temple U. Med. Ctr., Phila., 1962-65; gen. practice medicine Phila., 1965-66; staff assoc. Population Council, N.Y.C., 1966-69; resident advisor Population Council, New Delhi, 1969-71; cons. World Health Orgn., Geneva, 1971-73; regional advisor Population Council, Tehran, Iran, 1973-75; assoc. med. dir. Population Council, N.Y.C., 1975-76; prof. ob-gyn Northwestern U., Chgo., 1977—; cons. Medico-Legal, 1982—; bd. dirs. Fertility Research Northwestern U. Author books; editor numerous books, jours. Served to capt. USMC, 1958-62. Recipient Phillip Williams prize Phila. Ob. Soc., 1964, Babcock Surg. prize Temple U., 1965; Fertility Research grantee, U.S. Govt., 1981. Fellow Am. Coll. Ob-Gyn.; mem. Soc. Advancement Contraception (pres. 1986). Avocations: painting, sailing, golf, tennis. Office: Prentice Women's Hosp Ste 1000 680 N Lake Shore Dr Chicago IL 60611

ZAUNER, CHRISTIAN WALTER, university dean, exercise physiologist, consultant; b. Phila., July 21, 1930; s. Philip Walter and Margaret Helen (Gilmor) Z.; m. Betty Ann Schwenk, Feb. 1, 1957; children: Beth, Ward, Joe. BS, West Chester State, 1956; MS, Syracuse U., 1957; PhD, So. Ill. U., 1963. Asst. prof. Phila., 1963-65; prof. phys. edn. and medicine U. Fla., Gainesville, 1965-84; dir. Sports Medicine Inst., Mt. Sinai Med. Ctr., Miami Beach, Fla., 1984-87; chmn. exercise sci. Oreg. State U., Corvallis, 1987-94; dean health and human performance East Carolina U., Greenville, N.C., 1994—; cons. in exercise rehab. Hosp. Corp. Am.; cons. in sports medicine State of Kuwait, Arab Gulf; cons. sport sci. curriculum Ministry Edn., Thailand. Contbr. numerous articles to various profl. jours. Served with USN, 1951-54. Grantee U. Fla., 1971, Am. Scandinavian Foun., 1971, Fla. Blue Key, 1978, Nat. Acad. Sci., 1985-86, 88, 90, 94. Fellow Am. Coll. Sports Medicine; mem. Am. Physiol. Soc., N.Y. Acad. Scis., AAHPERD, Sigma Chi. Democrat. Roman Catholic. Office: East Carolina U Sch Health and Human Performance Greenville NC 27858-4353

ZAUSNER, L. ANDREW, lawyer; b. Plainfield, N.J., May 1, 1949; s. Sol and Beatrice (Summer) Z.; m. Nancy J. Zausner, Aug. 10, 1990; children: L. Alexander, Samantha Rae. B.A., Boston U., 1971; M.B.A., U. Pa., 1975, J.D., 1975. Bar: Pa. 1975, D.C. 1979, U.S. Supreme Ct. 1979. Mem. firm Blank, Rome, Comisky & McCauley, Phila., 1975-77; atty., adv. legislation Fed. Energy Adminstrn., Washington, 1977; spl. asst. to acting gen. counsel Dept. Energy, Washington, 1977-78; exec. asst. to dep. sec. Dept. Energy,

1978-79; dir. govt. relations Pennzoil Co., 1979-82, v.p. govt. relations, 1982-85; ptnr. Webster & Sheffield, 1985-90, Dickstein, Shapiro & Morin, Washington, 1990—; bd. dirs. Dauphin Deposit Bank and Trust Co., Harrisburg, Pa., chmn. trust and investment com. Home: 7017 Natelli Woods Ln Bethesda MD 20817-3925 Office: 2101 L St NW Ste 800 Washington DC 20037-1526

ZAVAGLIA, GREG J., management consultant; b. Collinsville, Ill., Mar. 18, 1938; s. Angelo Zavaglia and Theresa (Zampogna) Z.; m. Lorelei Hoga, Nov. 5, 1960; children: Cindy, Mike, Scott, Gregg. Student, Collinsville high sch., Ill., 1956. Electrician McDonnell Douglas, St. Louis, 1956-59; carpenter Blazier Co., East St. Louis, 1959-64; supt. Henges Co., St. Louis, 1964-72; v.p. Guarantee Interiors, St. Louis; pres., owner I.C.S. Ltd, St. Louis, 1980—; mem. AGC St. Louis, 1964, WACI St. Louis 1975. Mem. Shriners Club, Masons Club. Republican. Home: 13009 Bramblewood Acres Ln Saint Louis MO 63141-8560

ZAVARIN, EUGENE, forestry science educator; b. Sombor, Yugoslavia, Feb. 21, 1924; came to U.S., 1950; s. Alexey K. and Iya A. (Shepkin) Z.; m. Valentina S. Kusubov, July 15, 1956; children: Ksenya, Sergey, Michael, Nina, Mavrick. BS, U. Goettingen, Fed. Republic Germany, 1949; PhD, U. Calif., Berkeley, 1954. Sr. lab. technician U. Calif., Berkeley, 1952-54; asst. specialist Forest Products Lab., Richmond, Calif., 1954-57, asst. forest product chemist, 1957-62, assoc. forest product chemist, 1962-68, forest product chemist, 1968—; lectr. wood chemistry U. Calif., Berkeley, 1962-75, prof. forestry, 1975—; Reviewer grant proposals NSF. Mem. editorial adv. bd. Jour. Wood Chemistry and Tech.; contbr. articles to profl. jours. Fellow NIH, Institut de Chimie des Substances Naturelle, Gif-sur-Yvette, France, 1963; NSF grantee, 1965-67. Fellow Internat. Acad. Wood Sci.; mem. AAAS, Am. Chem. Soc., Sigma Xi. Republican. Avocations: travel, gardening, photography. Home: 280 Edgehill Way San Francisco CA 94127-1006 Office: U Calif Forest Products Lab 1301 S 46th St Richmond CA 94804-4698

ZAVIS, MICHAEL WILLIAM, lawyer; b. Chgo., Apr. 19, 1937; s. Herbert and Ruth (Kanes) Z.; m. Joan Gordon, June 1960; children: Amy Zavis Perlmutter, Cathy. BS, U. Pa., Wharton, 1958; JD, U. Chgo., 1961. Bar: Ill., U.S. Dist. (no. dist.) Ill., U.S. Ct. Appeals (7th cir.). Assoc. Peebles, Greenberg & Keele, Chgo., 1961-63, Greenberger, Krauss & Jacobs, Chgo., 1964-69; ptnr. Goldberg, Weigle, Mallin & Gitles, Chgo., 1969-74, Katten, Muchin & Zavis, Chgo., 1974—; bd. dirs. Ill. Devel. Fin. Authority; mem. adv. com. Sch. Social Svcs. U. Chgo. Editor U. Chgo. Law Rev., 1960-61. Fellow ABA, Ill. State Bar Assn., Chgo. Bar Assn.; mem. Bryn Mawr Country Club (Lincolnwood, Ill.) (past pres.), Standard Club, Boca Rio Country Club. Office: Katten Muchin & Zavis 525 W Monroe St Ste 1600 Chicago IL 60661-3693

ZAWACKI, BRUCE E., surgeon, ethicist; b. Northampton, Mass., Dec. 6, 1935. BS, Coll. of the Holy Cross, 1957; MD, Harvard U., 1961; MA, U. So. Calif., 1986. Diplomate Am. Bd. Surgery. Dir. burn study br. U.S. Army Inst. Surg. Rsch., San Antonio, 1968; gen. surgeon So. Calif. Permanente Med. Group, Panorama City, 1969-71; dir. burn ctr. LAC and U. So. Calif. Med. Ctr., L.A., 1971—; assoc. prof. surgery U. So. Calif. Sch. Medicine, L.A., 1975—; prof. medicine, religion U. So. Calif. Sch. Religion, L.A., 1992—; chair ethics resource com. LAC and U. So. Calif. Med. Ctr., L.A., 1988—. Contbr. articles to profl. jours. Served to maj. U.S. Army, 1967-68. Mem. Am. Burn Assn. (2d v.p., bd. trustees 1992-93), Soc. for Health and Human Values, L.A. Surg. Soc., Internat. Soc. for Burn Injuries. Achievements include first to describe the natural history of reversible burn injury, the independence of burn hypermetabolism from evaporative water loss and an autonomous role for burn patients without precedent for survival. Office: LAC and USC Med Ctr 1200 N State St Rm 12-650 Los Angeles CA 90033

ZAWADA, EDWARD THADDEUS, JR., physician, educator; b. Chgo., Oct. 3, 1947; s. Edward Thaddeus and Evelyn Mary (Kovarek) Z.; m. Nancy Ann Stephen, Mar. 26, 1977; children: Elizabeth, Nicholas, Victoria, Alexandra. BS summa cum laude, Loyola U., Chgo., 1969; MD summa cum laude, Loyola-Stritch Sch. Medicine, 1973. Diplomate Am. Bd. Internal Medicine, Am. Bd. Nephrology, Am. Bd. Nutrition, Am. Bd. Critical Care, Am. Bd. Geriatrics, Am. Bd. Clin. Pharm. Intern UCLA Hosp., 1973, resident, 1974-76; asst. prof. medicine UCLA, 1978-79, U. Utah, Salt Lake City, 1979-81; assoc. prof. medicine Med. Coll. Va., Richmond, 1981-83; assoc. prof. medicine, physiology & pharmacology U. S.D. Sch. Medicine, Sioux Falls, 1983-86, Freeman prof., chmn. dept. Internal Medicine, 1987—; chief div. nephrology and hypertension, 1983-88, pres. univ. physician's practice plan, 1992—; chief renal sect. Salt Lake VA Med. Ctr., 1980-81; asst. chief med. service McGuire VA Med. Ctr., Richmond, 1981-83. Editor: Geriatric Nephrology and Urology, 1984; contbr. articles to profl. publs. Pres. Minnehaha div. Am. Heart Assn., 1984-87, pres. Dakota affiliate Am. Heart Assn., 1989-91. VA Hosp. System grantee, 1981-85, 85-88; Health and Human Svcs. grantee Pub. Health Svcs. Rsch. Adminstrn. Bureau Health Profl., 1993—. Fellow ACP, Am. Coll. Chest Physicians, Am. Coll. Nutrition, Am. Coll. Clin. Pharmacology, Internat. Coll. Angiology, Am. Coll. Angiology, Am. Coll. Clin. Pharmacology, Royal Soc. Medicine; mem. Internat. Soc. Nephrology, Am. Soc. Nephrology, Am. Soc. Pharmacology and Exptl. Therapeutics, Am. Physiol. Soc., Am. Inst. Nutrition, Am. Soc. Clin. Nutrition, Am. Geriatric Soc., Westward Ho Country Club. Democrat. Roman Catholic. Avocations: golf, tennis, skiing, cinema, music. Home: 2908 S Duchess Ave Sioux Falls SD 57103-4826 Office: U SD Sch Medicine 1400 W 22d St Sioux Falls SD 57105-1570

ZAWINUL, JOSEF, bandleader, composer, keyboardist, synthesist; b. Vienna, Austria, July 7, 1932; came to U.S., 1959; s. Josef and Maria (Hameder) Z.; m. Maxine Byars, Mar. 16, 1964; children—Anthony, Erich, Ivan. Student, Realtymnasium, Vienna, 1945-49, Vienna Conservatory Music, 1942-47; Dr. honoris Causa, 1969. Appeared with Vienna Radio Orch., 1952-58, Maynard Ferguson, 1959; mem. Fatty George Band, 1956-58; accompanist Dinah Washington, 1959-61, Joe Williams, 1961; mem. Cannonball Adderley Quintet, 1961-70; recs. with Miles Davis include BitchesBrew, In a Silent Way; founder own group Weather Report, 1970-85, Zawinul Syndicate, 1985—; recs. include: Weather Report, Vitous, 1971, I Sing the Body Electric, 1972, Tale Spinnin', Black Market, 1974, Heavy Weather, 1977, Mr. Gone, 1978, Mysterious Traveler, Night Passage, Sportin Life, Weather Report with Jaco Pastorius, 1981, This is This, 1986, (with Miles Davis), In a Silent Way, 1969, Bitches Brew, 1970, (with Salifkeita) Amen, 1992, (solo) Dialects, Zawinul, (with Zawinul Syndicate) Immigrants, Black Water, 1989, Lost Tribes. Recipient Jazz Record of Year award 5 of 8 albums, 1973-78; named Best Synthesizer player Downbeat mag., 1984, 85, 89. Office: Internat Music Network 112 Washington St Marblehead MA 01945*

ZAWISTOWSKI, STEPHEN LOUIS, psychologist, educator; b. Lackawanna, N.Y., July 28, 1955; s. Louis Henry and Alice Theresa (Bartus) Z.; m. Jane Elaine Clark, May 26, 1979; 1 child, Matthew. BA, Canisius Coll., 1977; AM, U. Ill., 1979, PhD, 1983. Vis. asst. prof. Ind. U., Bloomington, 1983-84, postdoctoral fellow, 1984-85; asst. prof. St. John's U., N.Y.C., 1985-88; sr. v.p. ASPCA, N.Y.C., 1988—. Co-author: Animal Rights Handbook, 1990; co-editor: For Kids Who Love Animals, 1991; contbg. editor: Animal Watch mag.; co-exec. producer (film) Question of Respect, 1990 (Silver Apple award 1990); bd. editors Psychologists for the Ethical Treatment of Animals, 1988—; contbr. articles to profl. jours. Scoutmaster Boy Scouts Am., S.I., 1988—; asst. coach S.I. Youth Soccer, 1986—; bd. dirs. Nat. Coun. on Pet Population Study and Policy; mem. steering com. N.Y. State Watchable Wildlife Program. Recipient Stan Lesny scholarship Kosciuszki Found., 1977, U. Ill. Grad. fellowship, 1977, Postdoctoral fellowship NSF, 1984; named Psychologist of Yr., Psychologists for Ethical Treatment of Animals, 1989. Mem. Animal Behavior Soc., Order of Arrow, Sigma Xi. Achievements include research in genetics and animal learning. Office: ASPCA 424 E 92nd St New York NY 10128-6804

ZAX, LEONARD A., lawyer; b. Paterson, N.J., July 16, 1950; s. Harry and Shirley Jeanne (Hollander) Z.; m. Helen Kemp, May 25, 1980; children: David Hollander, Laura Alexandra. BA, U. Calif., 1972; M of City Planning, Harvard U., 1975, JD, 1975. Bar: N.J. 1978, D.C. 1978. Spl. asst. to gen. counsel HUD, 1975-76, spl. asst. to sec. HUD, 1976-77; lectr., mem.

faculty Harvard U., Cambridge, Mass., 1977-78; assoc. Fried, Frank, Harris, Shriver & Kampelman, 1995—, ptnr. Latham & Watkins, 1995—, Washington, 1977-82, ptnr., 1982—, also chmn. dept. real estate; co-chmn. Mayor's Downtown Housing Commn., Washington, 1986-89, D.C. Enterprise Zones Study Commn., 1986-89; co-regional dir. Asian Real Estate Assn., Washington, 1991-92; chmn. Washington adv. comm. Contbg. author Nat. Law Jour., L.A. Times, Harvard Law Bull., Real Estate Fin. Jour., Jour. RTC Real Estate, Urban Land, Washington Business jour., Washington Post; editor: Real Estate and the RTC: A Guide to Asset Purchases and Contracting, 1990. Trustee D.C. Preservation League, Greater Washington Rsch. Ctr.; mem. Fannie Mae Nat. adv. comm.; mem. adv. com. on real estate devel., Harvard U., 1990-92. Mem. ABA (chmn. com. on housing and urban devel. law 1986-89, steering com. representation of the Homeless Project 1988-91, governing bd. forum com. affordable housing and community devel. 1991-94), D.C. Bar Assn., Urban Land Inst. Home: 4511 28th St NW Washington DC 20008-1035 Office: Latham & Watkins Ste 1300 1001 Pennsylvania Ave NW Washington DC 20004-2505

ZAX, MELVIN, psychologist, educator; b. Cambridge, Mass., Apr. 14, 1928; s. Joseph and Sadie (Kirshner) Z.; m. Ruth Leah Vogel, Apr. 23, 1977; children: Jeffrey S., David B., Jonathan B. A.B., Boston U., 1951, A.M., 1952; Ph.D., U. Tenn., 1955. Clin. psychologist U. Tenn., Knoxville, 1955-56; staff psychologist St. Elizabeths Hosp., Washington, 1956-57; asst. prof. psychology U. Rochester, N.Y., 1957-62; asso. prof. U. Rochester, 1962-67, prof., 1967-93; chmn. exptl. and spl. tng. rev. com. NIMH, 1970-71; prof. emeritus, 1993—. Author: (with G. Stricker) Patterns of Psychopathology, 1963, (with E.L. Cowen) Abnormal Psychology: Changing Conceptions, 1972, (with G.A. Specter) An Introduction to Community Psychology, 1974, (with M. Nichols) Catharsis in Psychotherapy, 1977; editor: (with Stricker) The Study of Abnormal Behavior: Selected Readings, 1964, (with Cowen and E.A. Gardner) Emergent Approaches to Mental Health Problems, 1967, (with D. Dorr and J. Bonner) The Psychology of Discipline, 1983; adv. editor Jour. Cons. and Clin. Psychology, 1965-81; contbr. articles to profl. jours. Served with AUS, 1946-47. NIMH spl. research fellow Psykologisk Inst., Copenhagen, 1966-67. Fellow Am. Psychol. Assn.; mem. Eastern Psychol. Assn., AAUP, Phi Delta Kappa, Sigma Xi, Phi Kappa Phi. Home: 27 Sky Ridge Dr Rochester NY 14625-2167 Office: 625 Panorama Trl Bldg 2 Rochester NY 14625

ZAYAS-BAZAN, EDUARDO, foreign language educator; b. Camagüey, Cuba, Nov. 17, 1935; came to U.S., 1962, naturalized, 1969; s. Manuel Eduardo and Aida Modesta (Loret de Mola) m. Carolyn M. Novak, Sept. 12, 1987; children: Eduardo, Elena Maria. Dr. en Derecho, U. Nat. José Martí, 1958; MS, Kans. State Tchrs.' Coll., 1966. Social worker Cuban Refugee Asst. Program, 1962-64; Spanish tchr. Plattsmouth High Sch., 1964-65, Topeka West High Sch., 1965-66; Spanish instr. Appalachian State U., 1966-68; asst. prof. East Tenn. State U., Johnson City, 1968-73; assoc. prof. East Tenn. State U., 1973-79, prof, 1979—, chmn. fgn. lang. dept., 1973-93. Author: (with P. Ferreiro) Cómo dominar la redacción, 1989, (with G. Fernández de la Torriente) Cómo aumentar su vocabulario 3, Cómo escribir cartas eficaces, 1989, (with N.A. Humbach and J.B. Fernández) Nuestro mundo, 1990, (with Fernández) !Arriba!, 1993, (with Carolyn M. Novak) No se equivoque con el inglés, 1993, El inglés que usted no sabe que sabe, Primers 7 Segunda Serie, 1993; editor: (with Anthony G. Lozano) Del amor a la revolución, 1975, (with L. Suárez) De aquí y de allá, 1980 (with Fernández) Asi somos, 1983; translator: Secret Report on the Cuban Revolution, 1981. Pres. Sister Cities Internat., Johnson City, 1971-76. Recipient Disting. Faculty award E. Tenn. State U., 1978. Mem. ACTFL, AAUSC, Am. Assn. Tchrs. Spanish and Portuguese (pres. 1985), Tenn. Fgn. Lang. Teaching Assn. (pres 1980, Jacqueline Elliott award 1989), Nat. Assn. Cuban-Am. Educators (pres. 1991-93, chair bd. dirs. 1994—), Sigma Delta Pi (Premio Martel 1984), Pi Delta Phi. Home: 2310 David Miller Rd Johnson City TN 37604-3510 Office: East Tenn State U Dept Fgn Langs Johnson City TN 37614

ZAYEK, FRANCIS MANSOUR, bishop; b. Manzanillo, Cuba, Oct. 18, 1920; s. Mansour and Mary (Coury) Z. Student, St. Joseph's Catholic U., Beirut, 1938; D.D., U. Propagation of Faith, 1947, Ph.D., 1947; D.C.L., Lateran U., 1951. Ordained priest Roman Catholic Ch., 1946; rector Maronite Cathedral of Holy Family, Cairo, 1951-56; Oriental sec. to Vatican Apostolic Internunciature; mem. Archdiocesan Tribunal, 1951-56; promoter of justice Sacred Roman Rota, 1956-58; prof. Oriental canon law Internat. Coll. St. Anselm, Rome, 1958-60, Lateran U., Rome, 1960-61; aux. bishop to Cardinal James De Barros Camera; archbishop of Rio de Janeiro, 1962; consecrated maronite bishop, 1962; titular bishop of Callinicum, maronite bishop Rio de Janeiro, 1962-64; presided over First Ann. Maronite Conv., Washington, 1964; first maronite exarch of U.S.A., 1966—, first eparch of St. Maron of Detroit, 1972-77, first eparch of St. Maron of Bklyn., 1977—; given title of archbishop, 1982; bishop Pittsburgh, 1988—. Decorated knight comdr. Equestrian Order of Holy Sepulchre of Jerusalem; recipient medal of merit Govt. of Republic Italy, 1966. Address: 111 Blvd of the Allies Pittsburgh PA 15222*

ZAZULIA, IRWIN, retail store executive. Pres., chief exec. officer Hecht's, Arlington, Va. Office: Hecht's 685 N Glebe Rd Arlington VA 22203-2199

ZDANIS, RICHARD ALBERT, academic administrator; b. Balt., July 15, 1935; s. Albert Francis and Elsie (Kral) Z.; m. Barbara Rosenberger, June 5, 1955; children: Michael Richard, Carole Lynn. BA, Johns Hopkins U., 1957, PhD in Physics, 1960. Rsch. assoc. Princeton (N.J.) U., 1960-61, instr., 1961-62; asst. prof., then assoc. prof. Johns Hopkins U., Balt., 1962-69, prof., 1969-88, assoc. provost, 1975-79, v.p. for adminstrv. svcs., 1977-79, vice provost, 1979-88; provost Case Western Res. U., Cleve., 1988—; cons. Naval Ordnance Lab., 1967-68, 69-74. Bd. dirs. Great Lakes Mus., Cleve. Edn. Fund, Cleve. chpt. ARC, Cleve. Commn. Higher Edn.; mem. governing Ohio LINK, 1994—. Mem. AAAS, Am. Phys. Soc., Associated Univs. Inc. (bd. dirs.), Assn. Univs. for Rsch. in Astronomy (bd. dirs.). Office: Case Western Res U Office of Provost 10900 Euclid Ave Cleveland OH 44106-7004

ZDOBYLAK, ANDREW MARTIN, corporate executive, homebuilder; b. Gary, Ind., May 9, 1951; s. John Edward and Frances (Jagoda) Z.; m. Karen Ann Bringol, Oct. 7, 1980; children: Amy Frances, John Claymille. Student, U.S. Mil. Acad., 1970-72; BA, Rutgers U., 1975. Project mgr. Gem Homes, 1976-79; project mgr. Gemcraft Homes, Inc., San Antonio, 1979-80, div. mgr., 1980-82, v.p., 1982, pres., 1983-88, sr. v.p., 1983, 88—. Mem. Greater Houston Builders Assn. (trustee 1988—), San Antonio Builders Assn. Republican. Roman Catholic. Avocations: weightlifting, hunting reading. Home: 4704 Mimosa Cir Richmond TX 77469-9624 Office: Gemcraft Homes Inc 9494 South Fwy Houston TX 77051-3049

ZEA, KRISTINA GWYN, costume and production designer; b. N.Y.C.; d. James Gwyn and Alice Joy (Karl) Z. BS, Columbia U., 1972. Costume designer MGM, N.Y.C., 1979-80, Mabou Mines, N.Y.C., 1982-83, Tristar Pictures, Phila. and San Jose, Calif., 1983-84, Columbia Pictures, Santa Fe, 1984-85; prodn. designer, assoc. producer 20th Century Fox, Chgo., 1985-86; art dir. Tristar Pictures, N.Y.C. and New Orleans, 1986, 20th Century Fox, Washington, 1986-87; production designer Orion Pictures, N.Y.C., 1987—. Prodn. designer (films) Lucas, 1986, Angel Heart, 1987, Married to the Mob, 1988, Miss Firecracker, 1989, New York Stories (Life Lessons segment), 1989, Goodfellas, 1990, The Silence of the Lambs, 1991, The Super, 1992, Lorenzo's Oil, 1992, The War, 1994. Named Outstanding Working Woman Glamour Mag., 1982. Mem. Phi Beta Kappa.

ZEAMER, RICHARD JERE, engineer, executive; b. Orange, N.J., May 13, 1921; s. Jay and Margery Lilly (Herman) Z.; m. Jean Catherine Hellens, July 8, 1944 (div. 1966); children: Audrie Dagna, Richard Warwick, Geoffrey Hellens; m. Theresa Elizabeth Taborsky, Mar. 27, 1969; children: Emily Elizabeth, Charlotte Anne. BSME, MIT, 1943, MSCE, 1948; PhD in Mech. Engring., U. Utah, 1975. Registered profl. engr., Utah. Civil engr. Morton C. Tuttle, Boston, 1949-53; process design engr. Nekoosa Edwards Paper Co., Port Edwards, Wis., 1953-55; process engr. W.Va. Pulp and Paper Co., Luke, Md., 1955-60; rocket engr., supr. Allegany Ballistics Lab., Rocket Ctr., W.Va., 1960-65; engring. supr. Hercules Powder Co., Magna, Utah, 1965-69; engr. structures, heat, flow, combustion & failure analysis Hercules Rocket Plant, Magna, 1969-83; project engring. mgr. Hercules Aerospace

Div., Magna, 1983-89; pres., mgr. Applied Sci. Assocs., Salt Lake City, 1989—; chmn. policy studies UN Assn. Utah, 1990—; project leader world problem analyses, 1990—. Contbr. papers, articles, reports to profl. publs. Judge sci. fair, Salt Lake County, Utah, 1985—; chmn. citizens policy panel Utah chpt. UN Assn., U.S.A., N.Y.C., 1990—; mem. Utah State Hist. Soc., Salt Lake City, 1990-93, Mil. History Soc. Utah, Salt Lake City, 1990—. 1st lt. U.S. Army, 1943-46. Recipient commendation for presentation on world population problem Utah's Forum on Global Environ., 1992. Fellow AIAA (astronautics assoc.); mem. Cons. Engrs. Coun. Utah (article award 1992), League Utah Writers, Wasatch Mountain Club (hike leader 1987—). Achievements include patent for improved artillery ammunition, successful application of engineering approach to analysis of history. Home and Office: Applied Sci Assocs 843 13th Ave Salt Lake City UT 84103-3327

ZEBROSKI, EDWIN LEOPOLD, nuclear engineer consultant; b. Chgo., Apr. 1, 1921; s. Peter Paul and Sophie (Rydz) Z.; m. Gisela Karin Rudolph, Sept. 6, 1969; children: Lars, Zoe, Susan, Peggy. BS, U. Chgo., 1941; PhD, U. Calif., Berkeley, 1947. Registered prof. engr., Calif. Project engr. Gen. Electric Co., Schenectady, N.Y., 1947-53; mgr. devel. engring. Gen. Electric Co., San Jose, Calif., 1958-73; mgr. engring. SRI Internat., Menlo Park, Calif., 1954-58, dir. systems and materials dept., 1974-79; dir. nuclear safety analysis ctr. EPRI, Palo Alto, Calif., 1979-81; v.p. engring. INPO, Atlanta, 1981-83; chief nuclear scientist EPRI, 1983-87; dir. risk mgmt. svcs. APTECH Engring. Svcs., Sunnyvale, Calif., 1988—; vis. prof. Purdue U., West Lafayette, Ind., 1977-78; cons. OTA, Washington, 1980, 82-83, Dept. Energy, Washington, 1985-90, panels Nat. Rsch. Coun., 1982-90, Electricite de France, 1986-87, Dept. Interior, Washington, 1987-89, EPRI, Palo Alto, 1988-94, Acad. Sci., USSR, 1987, Juelich Lab., Germany, 1988; mem. commn. engring. edn. NRC, Washington, 1970-73. Contbr. chpts. to books, numerous articles to profl. jours.; patentee in field. Pres. bd. Unitarian Ch., Palo Alto, 1967-68. Recipient Charles A. Coffin award Gen. Electric Co., Schenectady, 1954. Fellow AAAS, Am. Nuclear Soc. (bd. exec. com. 1969-71), Am. Inst. Chemists; mem. NAE (chmn. energy com. 1984-86, chmn. mem. com. 1986-87, membership com. 1993—), Am. Phys. Soc., Soc. for Risk Analysis. Avocations: safety and risk management, decision analysis, music, writing. Office: APTECH Engring Svcs 1282 Reamwood Ave Sunnyvale CA 94089-2233

ZECCA, JOHN ANDREW, retired association executive; b. Bklyn., June 18, 1914; s. Joseph and Elvira (Orsi) Z.; m. Jean Ann Scott, June 27, 1964; 1 son, John Andrew. Student, Heffley Queensboro Coll., Ridgewood, N.Y., 1931, N.Y. U., 1933-36. Auditor ASCE, 1936-50, comptroller, 1950-60; registered rep. Goodbody & Co., 1960-61; pvt. cons. practice, 1961-64; sec., gen. mgr. United Engring. Trustees, 1965-81; trustee Engring. Index, Inc., 1967-81; sec. Engring. Found., 1965-81. John Fritz Medal Bd. Award, 1965-81; Daniel Guggenheim Medal Bd. Award, 1965-81. Mem. East Side Assn., ASCE, Council Engring. and Sci. Soc. Execs., Am. Soc. Assn. Execs. Home: 15 Hillside Ter Suffern NY 10901-2104

ZECH, WILLIAM ALBERT, manufacturing company executive; b. Buffalo, Aug. 13, 1918; s. William and Mary (Egbert) Z.; m. Ruth C. Koch, Feb. 17, 1945; children: William, Candace. BSME, Purdue U., 1942. Chief engr. Joy Mfg., Buffalo, 1957-63; chief engr. Clark div. Dresser Industries, Inc., Olean, N.Y., 1963-65, gen. mgr., 1965-68, pres., 1968-77; pres. compressor group Dresser Industries, Inc., Houston, 1977—. Mem. ASME. Home: 1307 W Vistawood Dr Houston TX 77077-3232

ZECHELLA, ALEXANDER PHILIP, oil company executive, former naval officer; b. Newport, Ky., 1920; s. Nicholas and Cecila (Rizzi) Z.; m. Jean Bary, June 24, 1942; children: Bary, Pamela, Amy. B.S. in Elec. Engring., U.S. Naval Acad., 1942; B.S., Rensselaer Poly Inst., 1947, M.S. in C.E., 1948. Commd. ensign U.S. Navy, 1942, advanced through grades to comdr., 1953, served, 1939-53, destroyer duty World War II, Korean War; design engr. Nuclear Submarine Bettis Atomic Power Lab., Westinghouse Corp., Pitts., 1953-56; various positions in nuclear power reactors Nuclear Submarine Bettis Atomic Power Lab., Westinghouse Corp., 1961-71; pres. Offshore Power Systems subs. Westinghouse Corp., Jacksonville, Fla., 1972-79; corp. v.p. Westinghouse Corp, N.Y.C., 1979-80; design. mgr. Shippingport Power Sta., Pitts., 1956-59; constrn. mgr. prototype nuclear aircraft carrier USS Enterprise, Idaho Falls, Idaho, 1959-61; exec. v.p. Charter Co., Jacksonville, Fla., 1980-84; pres., chief operating officer, chief exec. officer, dir Charter Co., Jacksonville, 1984-85; chmn., pres. Charter Oil Co., Jacksonville, 1980-83; chmn. bd. dirs. Environ. Recovery Group. Trustee St. Vincent's Hosp., Jacksonville, Jacksonville U.; bd. dirs. Tournament Players Championship Charities, Inc.; chmn. St. Vincent's Found., Inc. Mem. Tu Beta Pi, Chi Epsilon. Republican. Episcopalian. Clubs: River, Sawgrass Country. Lodges: Masons; Shriners. Home: 1301 1st St S Jacksonville FL 32250-6443 Office: PO Box 548 251 Levy Rd Atlantic Beach FL 32233-2613

ZECHMAN, FRED WILLIAM, JR., physiologist, educator, administrator; b. Youngstown, Ohio, Mar. 16, 1928; s. Frederick William and Kathryn S. (Ritz) Z.; m. Nancy Ann Bussard, June 24, 1950; children: Jami Ann, Frederick William III. B.S., Otterbein Coll., 1949; M.S., U. Md., 1951; Ph.D. (Univ. scholar), Duke U., 1957, postgrad. (Univ. fellow), 1956-57. Grad. asst. dept. zoology U. Md., 1949-51; biologist Office Naval Research, Washington, 1951-53; instr. in physiology Duke U., 1953-57; asst. prof. physiology Miami U., Oxford, Ohio, 1957-60; assoc. prof. Miami U., 1960-61; asst. prof. physiology and biophysics U. Ky. Coll. Medicine, 1961-62, assoc. prof., 1963-68, prof. dept. physiology and biophys., 1986-93, chmn. dept. physiology and biophys., research prof., 1980-81, assoc. dean Grad. Sch., 1982-88, vice chancellor research and grad. studies, 1988-90, prof. emeritus, 1993—; vis. lectr. U. Hawaii, 1971; bd. dirs. U. Ky. Research Found.; cons., lectr. in field; mem. internat. symposiums. Contbr. articles to profl. publs. Recipient Outstanding Preclin. Teaching award Student AMA, 1968-69, Faculty Sci. Achievement award Ky. Med. Assn., 1971; Am. Physiol. Soc. summer fellow, 1960; USAF grantee, 1960-66, 67-71; NIH grantee, 1966-71, 74-83. Mem. Aerospace Med. Assn., AAAS, Am. Physiol. Soc. (ednl. materials rev. bd. public affairs), Soc. Exptl. Biology and Medicine, Ky. Acad. Sci., Am. Thoracic Soc., Sigma Xi. Home: 6400 Head Rd Wilmington NC 28409

ZECKENDORF, WILLIAM, JR., real estate developer; b. N.Y.C., Oct. 31, 1929; s. William Zeckendorf and Irma (Levy) Kolodin; m. Guri Lie, Feb. 4, 1956 (div. Aug. 1963); children: William Lie, William Jr.; m. Nancy King, Oct. 24, 1963. Student, U. Ariz., 1948-50; LHD (hon.), L.I.U., 1993. Pres. Webb & Knapp, Inc., N.Y.C., 1950-65; chmn. bd. Gen. Property Corp., N.Y.C., 1965-78, Zeckendorf Co., N.Y.C., 1981—. Bd. dirs. Santa Fe Chamber Music, 1987—; chmn. bd. L.I.U., Greenvale, N.Y., 1987-92; chmn. bd. trustees L.I.U., 1959-94, now emeritus. Served as cpl. U.S. Army, 1952-54. Recipient Weizmann Medallion Weizmann Inst. Sci., N.Y., 1985; named Man of Yr. West Side C. of C., N.Y.C., 1984. Mem. Real Estate Bd. N.Y. (bd. govs. 1984—), Realty Found. N.Y. (bd. dirs. 1976—, Man of Yr. award 1987), Confrerie des Chevaliers du Tastevin (grand senechal 1992—), Commanderie de Bordeaux, Sky Club (N.Y.C.). Republican. Jewish. Home: 502 Park Ave New York NY 10022 Office: Zeckendorf Co Inc 245 Park Ave 16th Fl New York NY 10167

ZECKHAUSER, RICHARD JAY, economist, educator; b. Phila., Nov. 1, 1940; s. Julius Nathaniel and Estelle (Borgenicht) Z.; m. Nancy Mackell Hoover, Sept. 9, 1967; children: Bryn Gordon, Benjamin Rennell. A.B., Harvard U., 1962, Ph.D., 1969. Jr. fellow Soc. Fellows Harvard U., 1965-68, mem. faculty, 1968—; prof. polit. econ. Kennedy Sch., 1972—, now Frank P. Ramsey prof. polit. economy; bd. dirs. Recovery Engring., Inc., Johnson-Grace Co., Comm. Group Ins., founder, bd. dirs. Niederhoffer, Cross & Zeckhauser, 1968-84. Co-author: A Primer for Policy Anaylsis, 1978, Demographic Dimensions of the New Republic, 1981; editor: Benefit-Cost and Policy Analysis, 1974, What Role for Government, 1982, Principals and Agents: The Structure of Business, 1985, Am. Soc. Pub. and Pvt. Responsibilities, 1986; (with) Paul MacAvoy, William Stanbury and George Yarrow) Privatization and State-Owned Enterprise: Lessons from the United Kingdom, Canada and the United States, 1988, Strategy and Choise, 1991; contbr. over 140 articles to profl. jours. Fellow Econometric Soc., Assn. for Pub. Policy and Mgmt., Am. Acad. Arts and Scis. Champion numerous regional and nat. contract bridge competitions. Home: 138 Irving St Cambridge MA 02138-1929 Office: Harvard U John F Kennedy Sch Govt 79 John F Kennedy St Cambridge MA 02138-5800

ZEDILLO PONCE DE LEÓN, ERNESTO, president of Mexico; b. Mexico City, Apr. 27, 1951; m. Nilda Nuñez; 5 children. Student, Instituto Politécnico Nacional, Bradford U., U. Colo.; MA, Yale U., PhD. With Partido Revolucionario Institucional, 1971—, Instituto de Estudios Políticos, Económicos y Sociales; econ. rschr. Dirección Gen. de Programación Económica y Social; lectr. Colegio de Mex., 1978-80; dep. mgr. finance and econ. rsch., advisor to bd. dirs. Banco de Mex.; dep. sec. for planning and budget Govt. Mex., Mexico City, 1985-88, sec. for planning and budget, 1988-92, sec. public edn., 1992-93, pres., 1994—. Campaign mgr. Luis Donaldo Colosio. Office: Office of Pres, Los Pinos Puerta No 1, 11109 Mexico City Mexico*

ZEDLER, JOY BUSWELL, ecological sciences educator; b. Sioux Falls, S.D., Oct. 15, 1943; d. Francis H. and Charlotte (Johnson) Buswell; m. Paul H. Zedler, June 26, 1965; children: Emily and Sarah (twins). BS, Augustana Coll., 1964; MS, U. Wis., 1966, PhD, 1968. Instr. U. Mo., Columbia, 1968-69; prof. San Diego State U., 1969—; mem. Nat. Wetland Tech. Com., Water Sci Tech. Bd. Nat. Rsch. Coun., 1991-94; dir. Pacific Estuarine Rsch. Lab., 1985—, Coastal and Marine Inst., 1991-93. Author: Ecology of Southern California Coastal Wetlands, 1982, Salt Marsh Restoration, 1984; co-author: A Manual for Assessing Natural and Restored Wetlands, 1990, Ecology of Tijuana Estuary, 1992. Fellow San Diego Natural History Mus.; mem. Ecol. Soc. Am. (mem. pub. affairs com. 1988-90), Soc. Wetlands Scientists, Am. Assn. Limnology and Oceanography. Achievements include pioneering studies of impacts of freshwater inflows to coastal wetlands in southwestern U.S. and Australia; contributions to understanding of coastal wetland functioning; development of methods for improving restoration projects in coastal wetlands; identification of shortcomings of ongoing coastal wetland restoration programs. Office: San Diego State U Biology Dept San Diego CA 92182-4614

ZEDROSSER, JOSEPH JOHN, lawyer; b. Milw., Jan. 24, 1938; s. Joseph and Rose (Zollner) Z. AB, Marquette U., 1959; LLB, Harvard U., 1963. Bar: N.Y. 1964, U.S. Dist. Ct. (so. dist.) N.Y. 1966, U.S. Dist. Ct. (ea. dist.) N.Y. 1971, U.S. Ct. Appeals (2d cir.) 1971, U.S. Ct. Appeals (D.C. Cir.) 1975, U.S. Supreme Ct. 1975. Assoc. William G. Mulligan, N.Y.C., 1966-67, Christy, Bauman, Frey and Christy and successors, N.Y.C., 1967-71; dir. community devel. unit Bedford-Stuyvesant Community Legal Svcs. Corp., N.Y.C., 1971-73; assoc. atty. fed. defender svcs. unit Legal Aid Soc., N.Y.C., 1973-74; asst. atty. gen. Environ. Protection Bur., N.Y. State Dept. Law, N.Y.C., 1974-80; regional counsel EPA, N.Y.C., 1980-82; assoc. prof. St. John's U. Sch. Law, N.Y.C., 1982-86; ptnr. Rivkin, Radler, Dunne & Bayh, Uniondale, N.Y., 1986-89; Breed, Abbott & Morgan, N.Y.C., 1989-93, Whitman Breed Abbott & Morgan, N.Y.C., 1993—. Lectr., contbr. to course handbooks for courses sponsored by Practicing Law Inst. and other assns. Lt. USNR, 1965-74, USAR, 1963-65. Mem. ABA, Assn. of Bar of City of N.Y., N.Y. State Bar Assn. (mem. Environ. Law Sect. Exec. Com.), Alpha Sigma Nu. Roman Catholic. Home: 115 E 34th St Apt 10D New York NY 10016-4632 Office: Whitman Breed Abbott & Morgan 200 Park Ave New York NY 10166

ZEFF, OPHELIA HOPE, lawyer; b. Oak Park, Ill., Aug. 19, 1934; d. Bernard Allen and Esther (Levinsohn) Gurvis; m. David Zeff, Dec. 29, 1957 (div. 1983); children: Sally Lyn Zeff Propper, Betsy Zeff Russell, Ellen, Adam; m. John Canterbury Davis, Sept. 18, 1987. BA, Calif. State U., 1956; JD, U. Pacific, 1975. Bar: Calif. 1975. Reporter Placerville (Calif.) Mountain Dem., 1956-57, Salinas Californian, 1957-59; corr. Modesto (Calif.) Bee, 1962-64; atty. ALRB, Sacramento, 1975-76, Yolo County Counsel, Woodland, Calif., 1976-78, Law Office of O.H. Zeff, Woodland, 1978-85; employee rels. officer Yolo County, 1985-87; ptnr. Littler, Mendelson, Fastiff, Tichy & Mathiason, Sacramento, 1987—. Mem. Vallejo (Calif.) Sch. Bd., 1971-74, pres., 1974; mem. Woodland Libr. Bd., 1982; v.p. LWV, Vallejo, 1972; mem. LWV, Sacramento, 1987—. Recipient Am. Jurisprudence Lawyer Coop. Pub., 1974. Mem. Sacramento County Bar, Sacramento Women Lawyers, Indsl. Rels. Assn. No. Calif., Traynor Soc. (life). Democrat. Jewish. Avocations: hiking, skiing, biking, reading, traveling. Office: Littler Mendelson Fastiff Tichy & Mathiason 16th Fl 400 Capitol Mall Sacramento CA 95814

ZEFF, STEPHEN ADDAM, accounting educator; b. Chgo., July 26, 1933; s. Roy David and Hazel (Sex) Z. B.S., U. Colo., 1955, M.S., 1957; M.B.A., U. Mich., 1960, Ph.D., 1962; D in Econs. honoris causa, Turku Sch. Econs. and Bus. Adminstrn., Finland, 1990. Instr. U. Colo., 1955-57; teaching fellow, instr. U. Mich., 1958-61; asst. prof. Acctg. Tulane U., New Orleans, 1961-63, assoc. prof., 1963-67, prof., 1967-77, W.R. Irby prof., 1977-78; prof. acctg. Rice U., 1978-79, Herbert S. Autrey prof., 1979—; prof. acctg. U. Limburg, The Netherlands, 1992-95; vis. assoc. prof. U. Calif.-Berkeley, 1964-65, U. Chgo., 1966; vis. prof. Instituto Tecnológico y de Estudios Superiores de Monterrey, Mex., 1969, Victoria U., Wellington, New Zealand, 1976, Harvard U., 1977-78, Northwestern U., 1982, 83, U. Tex.-Austin, 1986, Free U. Amsterdam, 1990, 91; spl. lectr., hon. sr. Fulbright scholar Monash U., Australia, 1972. Author: Uses of Accounting for Small Business, 1962, American Accounting Association, Its First 50 Years, 1966, Forging Accounting Principles in Five Countries: A History and an Analysis of Trends, 1972, Forging Accounting Principles in Australia, 1973, Forging Accounting Principles in New Zealand, 1979, Company Financial Reporting: A Historical and Comparative Study of the Dutch Regulatory Process, 1992; editor: Business Schools and the Challenge of International Business, 1968, Asset Appreciation, Business Income and Price-Level Accounting: 1918-1935, 1976, The Accounting Postulates and Principles Controversy of the 1960s, 1982, The U.S. Accounting Profession in the 1890s and Early 1900s, 1988; co-editor: Financial Accounting Theory, Vol. II, 1969; Essays in Honor of William A. Paton: Pioneer Accounting Theorist, 1979, Sourcebook on Accounting Principles and Auditing Procedures 1917-1953, 1984; book rev. editor Acctg. Rev., 1962-66, editor, 1977-82; rev. editor Acctg. Horizons, 1995—; founder, editor Boletin Interamericano de Cantabilidad, 1968-71; contbr. articles to profl. jours. Mem. Am. Acctg. Assn. (dir. edn. 1969-71, pres. 1985-86, named Outstanding Acctg. Educator 1988), European Acctg. Assn. (exec. com. 1981—), Tex. Soc. CPAs (hon.), Am. Econ. Assn., Inst. Mgmt. Accts., Fin. Execs. Inst., AAUP. Mem. Am. Acctg. Assn. (dir. edn. 1969-71, pres. 1985-86, named Outstanding Acctg. Educator 1988), European Acctg. Assn. (exec. com. 1981—), Am. Econ. Assn., Inst. Mgmt. Accts., Fin. Execs. Inst., AAUP. Club: Harvard (N.Y.C.). Home: 4545 Acacia St Bellaire TX 77401-3701 Office: Rice University PO Box 1892 Houston TX 77251-1892

ZEFFIRELLI, FRANCO, theater and film director; b. Florence, Italy, Feb. 12, 1923; s. Ottorino Corsi and Alaide Cipriani. Attended, U. Architecture, Florence.; DHL, U. San Diego, 1980; PhD, U. Tel Aviv, 1993. Actor in Crime and Punishment, 1946, Euridyce, 1947; appeared in film Onorevole Angelina, 1948; set designer for various prodns. of Luchino Visconti, 1949-52, A Streetcar Named Desire, The Three Sisters; dir. (films) The Taming of the Shrew, 1966, Romeo and Juliet, 1967, Brother Sun, Sister Moon, 1971, Filumena, 1977, The Champ, 1979, Endless Love, 1981, I Pagliacci, 1981, La Traviata, 1982, Cavalleria Rusticana, 1986, Otello, 1986, The Young Toscanini, 1988, Hamlet, 1990, Sparrow, 1993, (ballet) Swan Lake, 1985; co-screenwriter, dir.(film) Hamlet, 1990; TV dir. Giorni Di Distruzione, 1966, Fidelio conducted by Leonard Bernstein, 1970, Missa Solemnis of Beethoven conducted by Wolfgang Sawallisch in Basilica of St. Peter in presence of Pope Paul VI, 1970, Jesus of Nazareth (epic film), 1976; numerous operas including Cenerentola, La Scala, 1953, I Pagliacci, 1959, Cavalleria Rusticana, 1959, Lucia Di Lammermoor, Covent Garden, 1959, La Bohene, La Scala, 1963, Falstaff, Met. Opera, 1964, Tosca, Covent Garden, 1965, Norma, Paris Opera, 1965, Anthony and Cleopatra, Met. Opera, 1966, Otello, Met. Opera, 1972, Don Giovanni, Staatsoper, Vienna, 1972, Un Ballo in Maschera, La Scala, 1972, Otello, La Scala, 1976, Carmen, Staatsoper, Vienna, 1978, La Traviata, 1979, 83, Tosca, Met. Opera, 1985, Turandot, 1987, Don Giovanni, 1990, Don Carlo, La Scala, 1992, Aida, Rome Opera, 1993; theatre dir. Romeo and Juliet, Old Vic Co., London, 1960, Othello, Stratford-on-Avon, Eng., 1961, Camille, Winter Garden Theatre, N.Y.C., 1962, Who's Afraid of Virginia Woolf?, Festival del Teatro, Venice, and Paris, 1963, Romeo and Juliet, Verona, Italy, Paris, Vienna, Austria, Rome and Milan, Italy, Moscow and Leningrad, 1964, Hamlet, 1964, After The Fall, 1965, Much Ado About Nothing, Old Vic Theatre, 1965, La Lupa, Florence, Rome, Vienna, Zurich, Switzerland, Paris, London and Moscow, 1965, A Delicate Balance, 1966, Black Comedy, 1967, Venti Zecchini D'Oro, 1968, Due Piu Due Non Fanno Quattro, 1969, Sabato, Doemnica, Lunedi,

Nat. Theatre, London, 1973, The Dead City, Italy, 1975, Lorenzaccio, Comedie Française, Paris, 1976, Filumena Marturano, Lyric Theatre, London, 1977; author: Zeffirelli by Zeffirelli, 1986. Recipient Liberty award, 1986. Mem. Dirs. Guild Am. Roman Catholic. Address: Via Lucio Volumnio 37, 00178 Rome Italy

ZEFFREN, EUGENE, toiletries company executive; b. St. Louis, Nov. 21, 1941; s. Harry Morris and Bess (Dennis) Z.; m. Steccia Leigh Stern, Feb. 2, 1964; children: Maryl Renee, Bradley Cruvant. AB, Washington U., 1963; MS, U. Chgo., 1965, PhD, 1967. Research chemist Procter & Gamble Co., Cin., 1967-75, sect. head, 1975-77, assoc. dir., 1977-79; v.p. R & D, Helene Curtis, Inc., Chgo., 1979-95; pres. Helene Curtis USA, Chgo., 1995—. Co-author: The Study of Enzyme Mechanisms, 1973; contbr. articles to profl. jours.; patentee in field of enzymes and hair care. Mem. AAAS, Am. Chem. Soc., Soc. Cosmetic Chemists, Cosmetic Toiletry and Fragrance Assn. (sci. adv. com. 1979-95, vice chmn. 1984-88, chmn. 1988-90), Indsl. Rsch. Inst., Omicron Delta Kappa. Republican. Jewish. Avocations: tennis, swimming, skiing, reading adventure and espionage novels. Office: Helene Curtis Inc 325 N Wells St Chicago IL 60610

ZEGARELLI, EDWARD VICTOR, retired dental educator, researcher; b. Utica, N.Y., Sept. 9, 1912; s. Frank Anthony and Maria Josephine (Ambroselli) Z.; m. Irene Marie Ceconi, June 17, 1939; children: Edward V., David J., Philip E., Peter J. AB, Columbia U., 1934, DDS, 1937, DSc (hon.), 1983; MS, U. Chgo., 1942. Staff Sch. Dental and Oral Surgery, Columbia U., 1937-78, asst. instr., then successively instr., asst. prof., assoc. prof., head diagnosis and roentgenology, 1947-58, chmn. com. dental research, 1956-78, Dr. Edwin S. Robinson prof. dentistry, 1958, prof. dentistry, dir. div. stomatology, 1958-78, acting dean, 1973, dean, 1974-78, dean emeritus, 1979—; Edward V. Zegarelli prof. dentistry, 1993—; chmn. sect. hosp. dental services Columbia-Presbyn. Med. Center; dir. and attending dentist dental service Presbyn. Hosp., 1974-79, also mem. exec. com. of med. bd., 1974-76; police surgeon N.Y.C., 1968-89; chmn. exam. com. N.E. Regional Bd. Dental Examiners, 1969-90; cons. VA, Washington; Weisberger Meml. lectr. Harvard U., 1969, Mershon Meml. lectr., 1970, Ralph L. Spaulding Meml. lectr., 1972; deans com. Montrose VA Hosp.; cons. East Orange, Kingsbridge VA hosps., Westchester Med. Ctr., Valhalla, N.Y., USPHS, Phelps Meml. Hosp., Tarrytown, N.Y., Vassar Bros. Hosp., Poughkeepsie, Bur. Medicine, FDA, Council on Dental Therapeutics; area cons. VA; cons.-lectr. U.S. Naval Dental Sch., Bethesda, Md., 1970-78; pres. N.Y. State Bd. Dental Examiners, 1970-71; chmn. exam. rev. com. N.E. Regional Bd. Dental Examiners, 1969-90; Samuel Charles Miller Meml. lectr., 1976; mem. council deans Am. Assn. Dental Schs., 1973-79; mem. postgrad. edn. com. N.Y.C. Cancer Com.; mem. profl. edn. and grants com. N.Y.C. div. Am. Cancer Soc., 1963-73; chmn. panel on drugs in dentistry NAS, NRC, FDA; mem. N.Y. State Health Research Council, N.Y. Commn. on Health Manpower; mem. bd. govs. (dental) Gen. Health Ins., N.Y.C. Contbg. author: The Thyroid, Medical Roentgenology, Current Pediatric Therapy, Cancer of Head and Neck; author: (with others) Pharmacotherapeutics of Oral Disease, 1964, Clinical Stomatology, 1966, Diagnosis of Diseases of Mouth and Jaws, 1969, 2d edit., 1978; also articles on mouth, jaw bone disease. Bd. dirs. Hist. Soc. Tarrytowns, 1983, United Way Tarrytowns, 1983, YMCA of Tarrytowns, 1984, Phelps Meml. Hosp. Hospice Agy, 1986. Recipient Austin Sniffen medal 9th Dist. Dental Soc., 1961; Columbia U. Dental Alumni Research award, 1963; Jarvie-Burkhart medal N.Y. Dental Soc., 1970; Samuel J. Miller medal Am. Acad. Oral Medicine, 1976; Henry Spenadel award 1st Dist. Dental Soc., 1979; Man of Yr. award C. of C. Tarrytowns and Irvington, 1983; Man of Achievement award Americans for Italian Migration, 1984; named Disting. Practitioner mem. Nat. Acads. Practice, 1986. Fellow Am. Coll. Dentists (William J. Gies medal 1981), N.Y. Acad. Dentistry, Internat. Coll. Dentists, 9th Dist. Dental Soc.; mem. Am. Acad. Oral Pathology, Am. Assn. for Cancer Edn. (charter), Am. Assn. Dental Examiners (Dentist Citizen of Yr. award 1978), Orgn. Tchrs. Oral Diagnosis, N.Y. Acad. Scis., N.Y. Dental Soc. (chmn. council sci. research 1956-71), Greater N.Y. Acad. Prosthodontics (hon.), Guatemala Dental Soc. (hon.), Am. Dental Assn. (mem. council dental therapeutics 1963-69, vice chmn. 1969), Columbia Dental Alumni Assn., William Jarvie Research Soc., Internat. Assn. Dental Research, AAAS, Nat. Italian-Am. Found., Sigma Xi (chpt. pres. 1974-76), Omicron Kappa Upsilon (sec. treas. Columbia chpt. 1944-57, pres. 1959-60), Sigma Phi Alpha, Knight Malta. Lodge: Rotary (pres. 1985-86) (Tarrytown). Home: 120 Gory Brook Rd North Tarrytown NY 10591

ZEHE, ALFRED FRITZ KARL, physics educator; b. Farnstaedt, Halle, Germany, May 23, 1939; came to Mexico, 1990; s. Alfred and Lina Olga (Kuhnt) Z.; m. Ruth Schorrig, July 30, 1960; children: Axel, Peter. MSc, U. Leipzig, Germany, 1964, D Natural Scis., 1969, Habilitation; 1974; D honoris causa, U. Puebla, Mexico, 1980. Researcher U. Leipzig, 1964-68, asst. prof., 1968-71, assoc. prof., 1971-75; prof. Tech. U. Zwickau, Germany, 1975-80, Tech. U. Dresden, Germany, 1980-91; prof. physics U. Puebla, 1991—; dir. dept. math. and scis. Tech. U. Zwickau, Germany, 1975-76; dir. dept. exptl. solid-state physics U. Puebla, 1977-80; dir. vacuum-physics chair Tech. U. Dresden, 1980-90. Author: Zehe-Roepke Rule for Electromigration, 1985, Microelectronics and ASIC's design, 1994, Industrial Metrology, 1995; editor: Fisica y Tecnologia de Semiconductores, 1982; contbr. articles to profl. jours.; patentee in field. Recipient Cincuentenario medal of honor U. PUebla, 1989, Disting. Prof. award Inst. Superior de Informatica, Santo Domingo, 1991; named Disting. Citizen, City Coun., Puebla, 1990. Mem. Phys. Soc. Germany, Phys. Soc. Mex., Math. Soc. Republic Dominicana, Acad. Materials Scis. Mex., Acad. Scis. Republic Dominicana, N.Y. Acad. Scis. Avocations: music, travel, science. Home: Schillerstr 19, 01326 Dresden Germany Office: U Autonoma de Puebla, Apartado Postal # 1505, 72000 Puebla Mexico

ZEHFUSS, LAWRENCE THOMAS, hardware supply company executive; b. Pitts., Feb. 2, 1938. BSBA, Duquesne U., 1960. C.P.A., Pa. Accountant, analyst H.J. Heinz Co., Pitts., 1960-61; public acct. P.A. Love & Co., Pitts., 1961-65; fin. mgr. Am. Hardware Supply Co. (now Servistar Corp.), Butler, Pa., 1965-70, v.p. fin., treas., 1970-79, chief exec. officer, from 1979, pres., 1979—; dir. corp. bank; speaker for industry assns. Vice chmn. Butler Meml. Hosp. Mem. Pres.'s Assn. Office: Servistar Corp PO Box 1510 Butler PA 16003-1510

ZEHM, STANLEY JAMES, education educator; b. Seattle, Dec. 3, 1936; s. Howard Ernest and Rene (Martin) Z.; m. Andrea Sue Johnson, Oct. 25, 1969; children: Kristofor Michael, Erin Jennifer Zehm Burton. BA, St. Edward's Sem., 1959; MDiv, St. Thomas Sem., 1963; MA in English, Gonzaga U., 1966; PhD in English Edn. with distinction, Stanford U., 1973. Tchr. English Carroll High Sch., Yakima, Wash., 1963-67, McFadden Intermediate Sch., Santa Ana, Calif., 1967-71; supr. student interns, then rsch. asst. Stanford (Calif.) U., 1971-73; prof. edn. Wash. State U., Pullman, 1973-81; dir. curriculum Richland (Wash.) Sch. Dist., 1981-82; asst. supt. Selah (Wash.) Sch. Dist., 1982-86; dean div. edn. and psychology Heritage Coll., Toppenish, Wash., 1987-90; prof. and chair dept. instructional and curricular studies U. Nev., Las Vegas, 1990—; marriage, family and child counselor Graden Grove (Calif.) Counseling Ctr., 1967-71; adv. com. Wash. State Lang. Arts Curriculum Com., Olympia, 1985; adv. bd. Wash. State Arts Commn., Olympia, 1989-90. Co-author: On Being A Teacher, 1993, Classrooms Under the Influence, 1993; contbr. to profl. publs. Bd. Trustees St. Jude's Ranch for Children, Boulder City, Nev., 1993—. Named one of 100 Outstanding English Tchrs., State of Calif., 1968; grantee U.S. Dept. Edn., Dept. Labor, NSF, Nat. Endowment for Humanities. Mem. ASCD, Internat. Reading Assn. (media awards chair 1974-76), Nat. Coun. Tchrs. English, Orange County Tchrs. English (v.p. 1969-70), Phi Delta Kappa. Roman Catholic. Avocations: hiking, theater, reading, botany, poetry. Home: 8116 Lake Hills Dr Las Vegas NV 89128-7090 Office: U Nev Las Vegas Instrnl/Curricular Studies 4505 S Maryland Pky Las Vegas NV 89154-9900

ZEHNER, LEE RANDALL, biotechnologist, research director; b. Darby, Pa., Mar. 15, 1947; s. Warren L. and Alycia G. (Van Riper) Z.; m. Susan D. Hovland, June 23, 1973; children: Adam, Erica. BS in Chemistry, U. Pa., 1968; PhD in Organic Chemistry, U. Minn., 1973. Sr. rsch. chemist Arco Chem. Co., Glenolden, Pa., 1973-78; rsch. group leader Ashland Chem. Co., Dublin, Ohio, 1978-82; mgr. organic rsch. W.R. Grace & Co., Clarksville, Md., 1982-85; dir. biotech. programs Biospherics Inc., Rockville, Md.,

1985—, v.p. sci. svcs., 1991—. Author various tech. publs.; patentee in field. Mem. AIChE, Am. Chem. Soc., Inst. Food Technologists, Am. Mgmt. Assn., N.Y. Acad. Scis. Avocations: swimming, gardening, computers. Home: 131 Brinkwood Rd Brookeville MD 20833 Office: Biospherics Inc 4201 Wilson Blvd Arlington VA 22230

ZEHR, CLYDE JAMES, church administrator; b. Valley Ctr., Kans., Oct. 4, 1934; s. John Wesley and Anna Mae (Carithers) Z.; m. Leona Mae Zehr, Nov. 23, 1957; children: Karen Elaine, Mark Wesley. BS, U. Kans., 1957; ThM, Western Evang. Sem., Portland, Oreg., 1961; MBA, Seattle U., 1976. Ordained to ministry Evang. Meth. Ch. Structural engr. Boeing Co., Seattle, 1957-59; pastor Rockwood Evang. Meth. Ch., Portland, 1961-63; missionary OMS Internat., Seoul, Republic of Korea, 1964-80; dir. Christian Leadership Seminars, Kent, Wash., 1980-82; supt. N.W. dist. Evang. Meth. Ch., Kent, 1982-86; gen. supt. Evang. Meth. Ch., Wichita, Kans., 1986—. Author: Study Notes on Leadership, 1982. Trustee Western Evang. Sem., Portland, 1982—. Republican. Office: Evang Meth Ch Hdqrs 3000 W Kellogg Dr Wichita KS 67213-2204

ZEHRING, KAREN, information executive; b. Washington, Dec. 5, 1945; d. Robert William Zehring and Gretchen (Lorenz) Proos; m. George Lang, 1970 (div. 1979); m. Peter Frank Davis, June 10, 1979; children: Jesse, Antonia. BA, U. Denver, 1967; postgrad., Yale U., 1967-68. Assoc. pub. mktg. and sales Instl. Investor Systems, Inc., N.Y.C., 1968-74; co-owner, co-creator Café des Artistes Restaurant, N.Y.C., 1975-79; owner, pub. The Corp. Fin. Letter, N.Y.C., 1976-78; group dir. planning and devel. Bus. Week mag., N.Y.C., 1977-78; owner, pub., exec. editor Corp. Fin. Sourcebook The Corp. Fin. Bluebook, N.Y.C., 1979-84; chmn., pres., pub., editor-in-chief Corp. Fin. mag., N.Y.C., 1986-90; cons. Karen Zehring & Assocs., Castine, Maine, 1990-94; mng. ptnr. Creative Devel. Ptnrs., N.Y.C., 1995—. Mem. The Women's Forum, Am. Soc. Mag. Editors. Unitarian. Office: Ste 20G 100 W 57th St New York NY 10019

ZEICHNER, OSCAR, historian, educator; b. N.Y.C., Jan. 2, 1916; s. Joseph and Lena (Schaeffer) Z.; m. Florence Koenigsberg, June 27, 1942; children: Barbara Ann, Carolyn Sue. B.A. cum laude, CCNY, 1936; M.A., Columbia U., 1938, Ph.D., 1946. Mem. faculty CCNY, 1936—, prof. history, 1960-76, prof. emeritus, 1976—, asst. dean in charge grad. studies Coll. Liberal Arts and Sci., 1957-63, asso. dean in charge Coll. Liberal Arts and Sci., 1963-68; dean grad. studies CCNY (Coll. Liberal Arts and Sci.), 1968-72; assoc. dean grad. studies CUNY, 1963-68; assoc. Columbia U. Seminar Early Am. History and Culture. Author: Connecticut's Years of Controversy, 1750-76, 1949, 70; editorial bd.: Connecticut Am. Revolution Bicentennial Series Publs.; contbr. articles to profl. jours. Recipient hon. mention J.H. Dunning prize Am. Hist. Assn., 1946. Mem. Assn. for Study Conn. History (pres. 1975-76), Phi Beta Kappa (pres. Gamma chpt. 1971-72). Home: 5500 Fieldston Rd Bronx NY 10471-2567

ZEIDENSTEIN, GEORGE, population educator; b. Pitts., July 29, 1929; s. Max and Sophia (Cohen) Z.; m. Sondra F. Auerbach, Jan. 25, 1953; children: Laura, Louis Peter. B.A., U. Pitts., 1951; J.D. cum laude, Harvard U., 1954. Bar: N.Y. 1954. Pvt. practice N.Y.C., 1954-65; vol. lawyer Lawyers Constl. Def. Com., Holly Springs, Miss., 1964; partner firm Spear and Hill, 1962-65; country dir. Nepal Kathmandu, Peace Corps, 1965-68; regional dir. designate Office E. Asia and Pacific, Washington, 1968; pres. Bklyn. Linear City Devel. Corp., N.Y.C., 1968-69; sr. program officer Asia and Pacific Ford Found., 1969-71, dep. head Asia and Pacific, 1971-72; rep. Ford Found., Bangladesh, 1972-76; pres., trustee Population Council, N.Y.C., 1976-93; disting. fellow Harvard Ctr. Population and Devel. Studies, Cambridge, Mass., 1993—; chmn. Himalayas coun. Asia Soc., 1970-72; assoc. seminar tradition and change in South and S.E. Asia, Columbia U., 1971-73, assoc. seminar on tech. and pub. issues, 1981-85; coun. Overseas Devel. Coun., 1979-93; chmn. Appraisal Group Global Com. Parliamentarians on Population and Devel., 1985-86; bd. visitors Grad. Sch. Pub. Health, U. Pitts., 1988—; advisor to chair Ind. Commn. on Population and Quality of Life, 1993-95. Vice chmn. bd. trustees, chmn. program com. Save the Children Fedn., 1991-95, Internat. Ctr. Rsch. on Women, 1993—; chmn. Internat. HIV/AIDS Alliance, 1993—; bd. dirs. Earthforce, 1993-95; active Britton Woods Com., 1992—. Decorated knight commdr. Order of Lion (Finland, Senegal). Mem. Coun. Fgn. Rels., Harvard Club. Home: 795 East St N Goshen CT 06756-1130 Office: Harvard Ctr Population Devel Studies 9 Bow St Cambridge MA 02138-5103

ZEIDLER, FRANK P., former association administrator, mayor, arbitrator, mediator, fact-finder; b. Milw., Sept. 20, 1912; s. Michael and Clara (Nitschke) Z.; m. Agnes Reinke; children: Clara, Dorothy, Michael, Anita, Mary, Jeannette. Student, Marquette U., 1930, U. Wis. Extension Div., 1930-70, U. Chgo., 1937; LLD (hon.), U. Wis., 1958, St. Olaf Coll., 1988; LHD (hon.), Carthage Coll., 1983, Mt. Mary Coll., 1993, U. Wis.-Milw., 1990. Dir. Milw. Pub. Schs., 1941-48; mayor City of Milw., 1948-60; dir. Wis. Dept. Resource Devel., 1963-64; sec. emeritus Pub. Enterprise Com.; mem. U.S. nat. commn. UNESCO, 1953, 56, 59. Author: Shakespeare's plays in modern verse. Pres. Ctrl. North Cmty. Coun.; past pres., co-editor newsletter Greater Milw. UN Assn.; nat. chmn. Socialist Party U.S.A., 1973-83; Socialist Party candidate for Pres. U.S., 1976; convenor Dem. Socialist Conf.; past pres. Luth. Local Action Conf.; bd. dirs. Goethe House, Milw., Milw. Theol. Inst.; mem. exec. coun. Luth. Ch. Am., 1980-82; hon. mem. cabinet Interfaith Conf. Greater Milw.; chmn. Norman Thommas Inst. for Peace and Social Justice. Named One of 10 Outstanding Young Men, Nat. Jr. C. of C., 1949; recipient Eugene V. Debs award, 1977. Mem. Am. Arbitration Assn., Milw. World Federalist Assn. (bd. dirs.), Nat. Model R.R. Assn. (founder). Home: 2921 N 2nd St Milwaukee WI 53212

ZEIDMAN, BENJAMIN, nuclear physicist; b. N.Y.C., Oct. 6, 1931; s. Samuel and Eve (Ellmann) Z.; m. Ruth Leona Goldstein, Dec. 25, 1956 (dec. July 1970); 1 son, Michael; m. Anne Macfarland, June 3, 1972. BS, CCNY, 1952; postgrad. George Washington U., Washington, 1952-54; PhD, Washington U., St. Louis, 1957. Assoc. physicist Argonne Nat. Lab., Ill., 1957-59; Ford fellow Niels Bohr Inst., Copenhagen, 1964; mem. staff, cons. Los Alamos Nat. Lab., N.Mex., 1968—; mem. vis. staff Brookhaven Nat. Lab., Upton, L.I., N.Y., 1972; vis. prof. SUNY-Stonybrook, 1972; Humboldt awardee Max Planck Institute für Kernphysik, Heidelberg, Germany, 1975-76; physicist Argonne Nat. Lab., Ill., 1959-79, sr. physicist, 1979—. Contbr. articles on nuclear physics to profl. jours. Recipient Humboldt award Av Humboldt Found., Bonn, W.Ger., 1975; Ford fellow, Copenhagen, 1963. Fellow AAAS, Am. Phys. Soc., Sigma Xi. Avocations: woodworking, sports. Home: 354 Cumnor Ave Glen Ellyn IL 60137-4840 Office: Argonne Nat Lab 203 Phy Argonne IL 60439

ZEIEN, ALFRED M., consumer products company executive; b. N.Y.C., Feb. 25, 1930; s. Alphonse and Betty (Barthelemy) Z.; m. Joyce Valerie Lawrence, Dec. 26, 1952; children—Scott, Grey, Claudia. B.S., Webb Inst.; M.B.A. postgrad., Harvard U. Group v.p Gillette Co., Boston, 1973-74, sr. v.p., 1978-81, vice chmn., 1981-90, pres., 1990-91, chmn., chief exec. officer, 1991—; div. gen. mgr. Braun AG, Frankfurt, Federal Republic of Germany, 1974-76, chmn. bd., 1976-78; bd. dirs. Polaroid Corp., Cambridge, Mass., Repligen Corp., Cambridge, Raytheon Corp., Lexington, Mass., Bank of Boston, Mass. Mut. Ins. Co., Springfield. trustee Univ. Hosp., Boston, 1983—. Avocations: sailing; tennis. Home: 300 Boylston St Boston MA 02116-3923 Office: Gillette Co Prudential Towers Bldg Boston MA 02199

ZEIFANG, DONALD P., lawyer; b. Niagara Falls, N.Y., Apr. 13, 1936. BA, U. Notre Dame, 1960; JD, Georgetown U., 1963. Bar: D.C. 1965. Law clk. to Hon. John J. Sirica U.S. Dist. Ct. (D.C. dist.), 1963-65; ptnr. Baker & Hostetler, Washington. Mem. ABA, D.C. bar, Fed. Comm. Bar, Nat. Assn. Broadcasters (v.p. 1973-80, sr. v.p. 1976-80 govt. rels.). Office: Baker & Hostetler Washington Sq 1050 Connecticut Ave NW Ste 11 Washington DC 20036-5303

ZEIGER, LARRY See KING, LARRY

ZEIGER, SCOTT LESLIE, commercial theater executive; b. Bklyn., Sept. 25, 1960; s. Martin Zeiger and Phyllis Roberta Miller Iampieri; m. Kathleen Marie Ryan, Dec. 4, 1988; 1 child, Joshua Ryan. BA, U. Fla., 1982. Regional mktg. dir. Ringling Bros. Barnum and Bailey Circus, Washington,

1983; dir. mktg. Pace Theatrical Group, Houston, 1983-86, v.p., 1986-89, exec. v.p., 1989-91; pres. Pace Theatrical Group, N.Y.C., 1991—. Exec. prodr.: The Who's Tommy, 1993 (5 Tony awards). Adv. com. Houston Downtown Theatre Dist., 1986-93; bd. dirs. Story Theatre, Ft. Lauderdale, Fla., 1993—. Mem. League of Am. Theatres and Prodrs. (exec. com. 1992—), bd. govs. 1988-92). Jewish. Avocations: travel, exercise, music.

ZEIGLER, ALAN KARL, lawyer; b. Perry, Fla., Oct. 11, 1949; s. Fred Montgomery and Ora Lee (Saunders) Z. BA, Birmingham-So. Coll., 1971; JD, Vanderbilt U., 1974. Bar: Ala. 1975. Clk. to Judge Walter P. Gewin, U.S. Ct. Appeals, Tuscaloosa, Ala., 1974-75; assoc. Bradley, Arant, Rose & White, Birmingham, Ala., 1975; ptnr. Bradley, Grant, Rose & White, Birmingham, Ala., 1981. Episcopalian. Office: Bradley Arant Rose & White 1400 Park Place Tower 2001 Park Pl Birmingham AL 35203

ZEIGLER, BERNARD PHILLIP, electrical and computer engineering educator; b. Montreal, Que., Can., Mar. 5, 1940; came to U.S. 1962; naturalized, 1985; s. Maurice and Sylvia (Filger) Z.; m. Rebecca Robinson, May 1964 (div. 1984); children: Bianca, Noemi; m. Christine Dymek, Aug. 1985; 1 child, Claire. B in Engring. Physics, McGill U., 1962; MEE, MIT, 1964; PhD in Computer Sci., U. Mich., 1969. Asst. prof. computer sci. U. Mich., Ann Arbor, 1970-73, assoc. prof. computer sci., 1973-75; vis. scientist Weizman Inst. Sci., Israel, 1975-80; prof. computer sci. Wayne State U., Detroit, 1981-85; prof. elec. and computer engring. U. Ariz., Tucson, 1985—; cons. Environ. Research lab. U. Ariz., 1986—, Martin Marietta Corp., McDonell Douglas. Author: Theory of Modelling and Simulation, 1976, Multifacetted Modelling and Discrete Event Simulation, 1984, Object-Oriented Simulation of Hierarchical Modular Models, 1990. Research grantee, NSF, 1982—, NASA, 1987—. Fellow IEEE. Office: U Ariz Dept ECE Tucson AZ 85721

ZEIGLER, CHARLES E., JR., utility company executive; b. Bogota, N.J., 1925; married. With Pub. Service Co. N.C., Inc., Gastonia, 1946—, v.p., 1956-73, pres., 1973—; chief exec. officer, from 1973, now also chmn. bd.; chmn., pres. PSNC Natural Resources Corp., PSNC Exploration Corp., PSNC Prodn. Corp., PSNC Propane Corp., Tar Heel Energy Corp. Office: Pub Svc Co of NC Inc 400 Cox Rd Gastonia NC 28054-0609*

ZEIGLER, EARLE FREDERICK, physical education-kinesiology educator; b. N.Y.C., Aug. 20, 1919; s. Clarence Mattison and Margery Christina (Beyerkohler) Shinkle; m. Bertha M. Bell, June 25, 1941; children—Donald H., Barbara A. A.B., Bates Coll., 1940; A.M., Yale U., 1944, Ph.D., 1951; LL.D., U. Windsor, 1975. Assoc. phys. dir., aquatic dir. Bridgeport (Conn.) YMCA, 1941-43; instr. German U. Conn., Storrs, 1943-47; coach, instr. phys. edn. Yale U., 1943-49; asst. prof. U. Western Ont. (Can.), London, 1949-50; prof., chmn. dept. phys., health and recreation edn. U. Western Ont. (Can.), 1950-56, assoc. prof. Sch. Edn.; supr. phys. edn. and athletics U. Mich., Ann Arbor, 1956-63; chmn. dept. phys. edn. Sch. Edn. U. Mich., 1961-63; prof. dept. phys. edn. for men Coll. Phys. Edn. U. Ill., Urbana, 1963-72; head dept. phys. edn. for men, chmn. grad. dept. Coll. Phys. Edn. U. Ill., 1964-68; prof. dept. phys. and health edn. U. Western Ont., London, 1971-89, prof. emeritus, 1989—; dean U. Western Ont. (Faculty of Phys. Edn.), 1972-77. Author: A History of Professional Preparation for Physical Education in the United States, 1951, Administration of Physical Education and Athletics, 1959, The Case Method Approach: An Instructional Manual, 1959, Philosophical Foundations for Physical, Health, and Recreation Education, 1964, A Brief Introduction to the Philosophy of Religion, 1965, (with H.J. VanderZwaag) Physical Education: Progressivism or Essentialism, 1968, Problems in the History and Philosophy of Physical Education and Sport, 1968, (with M.L. Howell and M. Trekell) Research in the History and Philosophy of Physical Education and Sport, 1971, Personalizing Physical Education and Sport Philosophy, 1975, Physical Education and Sport Philosophy, 1977, Issues in North American Physical Education and Sport, 1979, Decision-Making in Physical Education and Athletics, 1982, (with G.W. Bowie) Management Competency Development in Sport and Physical Education, 1983, Ethics and Morality in Sport and Physical Education, 1984, (with J. Campbell) Strategic Market Planning: An Aid to the Evaluation of an Athletics/Recreation Program, 1984 , Assessing Sport and Physical Education: Diagnosis and Projection, 1986, (with G. Bowie and R. Paris) Competency Development in Sport and Physical Education Management, 1988, (with A. Mikalachki and G. Leyshon) Change Process in Sport and Physical Education Management, 1988, Introduction to Sport and Physical Education Philosophy, 1989, Sport and Physical Education: Past, Present, Future, 1990, Professional Ethics for Sport Managers, 1992, Critical Thinking for the Professions of Health, Physical Education, Recreation, and Dance, 1994, A Selected, Annotated Bibliography of Completed Research on Management Theory and Practice in Physical Education and Athletics to 1972, 1995, (with G.W. Bowie) Developing Management Competency in Sport and Physical Education, 1995; author, editor: A History of Sport and Physical Education to 1900, 1973, A History of Physical Education and Sport in the United States and Canada, 1975, (with M.J. Spaeth) Administrative Theory and Practice in Physical Education and Athletics, 1975, History of Physical Education and Sport, 1979, rev. edit., 1988, Physical Education and Sport: An Introduction, 1982, Physical Education and Kinesiology in North America: Professionalism and Scholarly Foundations, 1994; contbr. articles to profl. jours. Recipient Outstanding Tchr. award U. Western Ont., 1987, Disting. Svc. award Internat. Soc. Comparative Phys. Edn. and Sport, 1988; inducted into Univ. Western Ont.'s Wall of Wrestling Fame, 1991; named first Human Movement Scis. and Edn. scholar, U. Memphis, 1994. Fellow Am. Acad. Kinesiology and Phys. Edn. (pres. 1981-82, Hetherington award 1989); mem. AAHPERD (Alliance scholar 1977-78, Disting. Svc. award 1979, Honor award 1981, Gulick award 1990), Philosophy Edn. Soc., Internat. Assn. Profl. Schs. Phys. Edn., Can. Assn. Health, Phys. Edn. and Recreation (v.p. 1955-56, v.p. 1983-85, honour award 1975, spl. presentation citation 1986), Am. Philos. Assn., Nat. Assn. Phys. Edn. in Higher Edn., N.Am. Soc. Sport History (life), Philosophic Soc. for Study of Sport (pres. 1974-75), N.Am. Soc. for Sport Mgmt. (founding mem., hon. past pres. 1986-87), Canadian Profl. Schs. Conf. (pres. 1953-55), Ont. Recreation Assn. (v.p. and dir. 1955-56), Soc. Municipal Recreation Dirs. Ont. (Honor award 1956), Phi Epsilon Kappa (life). N.Am. Soc. Sport Mgmt. created the Annual Earle Zeigler Lecture, 1988. Home: 25 Berkshire Ct, London, ON Canada N6J 3N8 *Ever since the Platonic tradition split what we once before believed to be a unified organism into mind and body, and then Christianity added a spiritual dimension that shattered a unified concept of the organism even further, purposeful human movement in sport, dance, play, and exercise has been regarded as inferior to so-called intellectual attainments. My life purpose is to work toward redressing that imbalance by promoting a type of education that restores the Greek Classical Ideal.*

ZEIGLER, L(UTHER) HARMON, political science educator; b. Savannah, GA., Mar. 9, 1936; s. Luther H. and Sarah Louise (Betts) Z.; m. Patricia Lynn Duffy, Dec. 20, 1956; children: Michael, Amanda. BA, Emory U., 1957; MA, U. Ill., 1958, PhD, 1960. Asst. prof. Fla. State U., Tallahassee, 1960-61, Emory U., Atlanta, 1961-63, U. Ga., Athens, 1963-64; assoc. prof. U. Oreg., Eugene, 1964-67, prof. dept. polit. sci., 1967-85, chmn., 1982-85; Philip M. Phibbs disting. prof. Am. politics U. Puget Sound, Tacoma, Wash., 1985-92; affiliate prof. U. Wash., 1986-92. Author: The Irony of Democracy, 1970, 9th edit., 1993, 10th edit., 1995, Governing American Schools, 1974, Professionals Versus the Public: Attitudes, Communication and Response in Local School Districts, 1980, American Politics in the Media Age, 1983, Women, Public Opinion and Politics: The Changing Attitudes of American Women, 1984, Pluralism, Corporatism and Confucianism, 1988, The Political Community, 1990, Political Parties in Indsl. Democracies, 1992. Fellow Ford Found., 1969 (spl. fellowship fellow, 1969-70; Fulbright-Hays grantee W. Germ., 1977; sr. scholar Australia, 1978. Mem. Am. Polit. Sci. Assn.

ZEIKEL, ARTHUR, investment company executive; b. Bronx, N.Y., June 1, 1932; s. Sidney and Dorothy (Einhorn) Z.; m. Terrie Ruth Stoops, Dec. 7, 1960; children: Jeffrey, Jill, Judith. B.B.A., CCNY, 1954; M.B.A., NYU, 1960. Research analyst Ira Haupt Co., N.Y.C., 1958-59; research analyst Blair & Co., N.Y.C., 1959-63; portfolio mgr. Dreyfuss Corp., N.Y.C., 1963-68; pres., dir., chief exec. officer S&P Inter-Capital, N.Y.C., 1968-76; pres. Merrill Lynch Asset Mgmt., Inc., Princeton, N.J., 1976—; exec. v.p., Merrill Lynch & Co. Inc.; pres. Merrill Lynch Investment Mgmt. Inc.; exec. v.p., Merrill Lynch Pierce Fenner & Smith Inc.; pres., trustee, Merrill Lysnch Ready Assets Trust Inc. Author: (with others) Guide to Intelligent

Investing, 1977, Investment Analysis and Portfolio Management, 5th edit., 1987; contbr. articles to profl. jours. Served with U.S. Army, 1956-58. Mem. Investment Co. Inst. (bd. govs. 1983—), Fin. Analyst Research Found. (trustee), Fin. Analyst Fedn. Club: Econ. of N.Y. Office: Merrill Lynch & Co World Fin Ctr N Twr New York NY 10281

ZEILIG, NANCY MEEKS, magazine editor; b. Nashville, Apr. 28, 1943; d. Edward Harvey and Nancy Evelyn (Self) Meeks; m. Lanny Kenneth Fielder, Aug. 20, 1964 (div. Dec. 1970); m. Charles Elliot Zeilig, Jan. 6, 1974 (div. Dec. 1989); 1 child, Sasha Rebecca. BA, Birmingham-So. Coll., 1964; postgrad., Vanderbilt U., 1971-73. Editorial asst. Reuben H. Donnelley, N.Y.C., 1969-70; asst. editor Vanderbilt U., Nashville, 1970-74; editor U. Minn., St. Paul, 1975; asst. editor McGraw-Hill Inc., Mpls., 1975-76; mng. editor Denver mag., 1976-80; editor Jour. Am. Water Works Assn., Denver, 1981—; Editor, co-pub.: WomanSource, 1982, rev. edit., 1994; contbr. articles to consumer mags. Editor, co-pub.: WomanSource, 1982, rev. edit. 1984; editor: 100 Years, 1975; contbr. articles to consumer mags. Avocations: travel, reading British and Am. fiction, cooking. Subject of NBC News documentary Women Like Us, 1980. Office: Jour Am Water Works Assn 6666 W Quincy Ave Denver CO 80235-3098

ZEILINGER, PHILIP THOMAS, aeronautical engineer; b. David City, Nebr., Feb. 13, 1940; s. Thomas Leroy and Sylvia Dorothy Zeilinger; m. Elna Rae Simpson, June 13, 1970; children: Shari, Chris. AS, Wentworth Mil. Acad., Lexington, Mo., 1959; BSME, Kans. U., 1962. Estimator, engr. Reynolds Electronics and Engring. Co., El Paso, Tex., 1966-68; accessories coord. ITI Garrrett, Phoenix, 1974-79; cntrl. access engr., 1968—; controls coord. ITEC, 1983-84, integrated support specialist ITEC, 1984-86, mgr. systems software light helo turbine engring. co. div., 1986-91, FAA designated engr. rep. engine div., 1991—; chmn. Light Helicopter Turbine Engine Company Computer Aided Acquistion and Logistics Working Group. V.p. Install. Devel. Authority, Tempe, Ariz., 1979-84; pres. Tempe Royal Garden Homes Assn., Tempe, 1984-90. 1st lt. U.S. Army, 1962-66. Recipient Vol. Svc. award City of Tempe, 1984, Grand Cross of Color, Internat. Order of Rainbow Girls, 1978. Mem. AIAA, Aircraft Owners and Pilots Assn., Explt. Aircraft Assn. (v.p. chpt. 228 1974-79), Masons (master 1990-92, chmn. statewide picnic 1992, Mason of the Yr. 1992). Democrat. Unitarian. Achievements include patent for Airesearch/Garrett. Home: 760 N Sycamore Pl Chandler AZ 85224 Office: 11 S 34th St Phoenix AZ 85010

ZEILLER, WARREN, former aquarium executive, consultant; b. Weehawken, N.J., Nov. 11, 1929; s. Arthur Herman and Ruth (Preusser) Z.; m. Judith Marion Ricciardi, May 27, 1961; children: Dianne Leigh, Todd Kiersted. B.Sc. in Animal Husbandry, Colo. A&M Coll., 1955; M.A. in Bus., Mich. State U., 1957. Mgmt. trainee Grand Union Co., 1956-58; corp. sec., salesman Art Zeiller Co., Inc., Allendale, N.J., 1958-60; salesman Joseph Abraham Ford Co., Miami, Fla., 1960; with Miami Seaquarium, 1960-85, curator, 1962-85, v.p., gen. mgr., 1977-85, ret., 1985; pres. Images of Art, Inc., Coral Gables, Fla.; exec. dir. Tropical Everglades Visitor Assn., 1988—; lectr., cons. bus., mktg., tourism; TV appearances. Author: Tropical Marine Invertebrates of Southern Florida and the Bahama Islands, 1974, Tropical Marine Fishes of Southern Florida and the Bahama Islands, 1975, Introducing the Manatee, 1992; contbr. articles to profl. jours. Treas. Jr. Orange Bowl Com., 1984-85; mem. adv. bd. Coral Gables War Meml. Youth Ctr., 1973-93, pres., 1981-83; mem. Gov.'s tourism adv. coun. Fla. Hospitality Industry Coun., 1983-84; bd. dirs. Dade Marine Inst.; bd. dirs., pres. Humane Soc. Greater Miami, Inc., 1993-94. Served with USN, 1951-55. Mem. Fla. Attractions Assn. (v.p. 1981-82, pres. 1982-83), Mus. and Art Center, Colo. State U. Alumni Assn., Sigma Chi. Republican. Methodist. Club: Rotary (pres. Coral Gables 1978-79). Patentee surg. cast and cast removal saw. Home: 5016 SW 72d Ave Miami FL 33155

ZEISLER, RICHARD SPIRO, investor; b. Chgo., Nov. 28, 1916; s. Erwin Paul and Ruth Henrietta (Spiro) Z. B.A., Amherst Coll., 1937; postgrad., Harvard U., 1937-38; M.Div., Va. Theol. Sem., 1941. Religious work, 1941-47; owner Richard S. Zeisler & Co. (investments), N.Y.C., 1948—; bd. dirs. PEC Israel Econ. Corp., 1949—. Bd. dirs. Chamber Music Soc., Lincoln Center, 1969—, Skowhegan Sch. Painting and Sculpture, 1983—; trustee Mus. Modern Art, 1979—, mem. com. on painting and sculpture, 1972—; architecture and design com., 1989—; trustee, former v.p. Jewish Bd. Family and Children's Services, N.Y.C., 1951—; past pres. Am. Jewish Com. (N.Y. chpt.); past vice-chmn. NCCJ (N.Y. chpt.); mem. com. for dance collection, past chmn. N.Y. Pub. Library, 1967—; mem. creative arts commn. Brandeis U., 1958-94; mem. art adv. com., past chmn. Mt. Holyoke Coll., 1963—; fellow Pierpont Morgan Library, 1963—; governing life mem. Art Inst. Chgo., 1977—, mem. com. on 20th century painting and sculpture, 1981—; life fellow Met. Mus., 1969—; mem. Manhattan Inst., 1990—; mem. adv. coun. Princeton (N.J.) Art Mus., 1993—. Mem. N.Y. Soc. Security Analysts, Am. Coun. on Germany, Asia Soc., U.S.-New Zealand Coun., Ams. Soc., Century Assn. Club (N.Y.C.), Univ. Club (N.Y.C.), Grolier Club (N.Y.C.), Arts Club (London), Reform Club (London), Econ. of N.Y. Home and Office: 980 Fifth Ave New York NY 10021-0126

ZEITLIN, BRUCE ALLEN, superconducting material technology executive; b. N.Y.C., July 31, 1943; s. Lester and Rae (Benson) Z.; m. Amy Joy Kozan, Aug. 29, 1965; children: Laurence, Jessica, Andrea. BS, Rensselaer Poly. Tech., 1965; MS, Stevens Inst. Tech., 1968. Scientist Airco Cen. Rsch. Lab., Murray Hill, N.J., 1965-70; tech. dir. Magnetic Corp. of Am., Waltham, Mass., 1970-72; v.p. IGC/Advanced Superconds., Waterbury, Conn., 1986—, Intermagnetics Gen. Corp., Latham, N.Y., 1986—; bd. dirs. Alsthom Intermagnets SA, Paris. Patentee in field. Mem. Am. Phys. Soc. Avocation: astronomy. Office: IGC/Advanced Supercondrs 1875 Thomaston Ave Waterbury CT 06704-1034

ZEITLIN, FROMA I., classics educator; b. N.Y.C., May 9, 1933; d. Samuel and Dora Inselbuch; m. George E. Zeitlin, Dec. 26, 1953; children—Jonathan, Judith, Ariel. B.A., Harvard U.-Radcliffe Coll., 1954; M.A., Catholic U., 1965; Ph.D., Columbia U., 1970. Instr. Bklyn. Coll., 1969-70; asst. prof. Rutgers U., New Brunswick, N.J., 1970-76; assoc. prof. dept. classics Princeton U., N.J., 1976-83, prof., 1983—. Author: Under the Sign of the Shield, 1982; contbr. articles on classics, Greek tragedy, comedy, myth, religion, and ancient fiction to profl. jours. NEH fellow, 1975-76, 88-89; Guggenheim fellow, 1984-85. Mem. Am. Philol. Assn. (bd. dirs. 1980-82, nominating com. 1983-84). Jewish. Office: Dept Classics Princeton U Princeton NJ 08544

ZEITLIN, HERBERT ZAKARY, retired college president; b. N.Y.C.; s. Leonard and Martha Josephine (Soff) Z.; m. Eugenia F. Pawlik, July 3, 1949; children: Mark Clyde, Joyce Therese Zeitlin Harris, Ann Victoria, Clare Katherine. B.S., N.Y. U., 1947, M.A., 1949; Ed.D., Stanford U., 1956. Tchr. Mepham High Sch., Bellmore, N.Y., 1946-47, Nassau County Vocat. Edn. Extension Bldr., Mineola, N.Y.; electronics instr., adj. faculty Mephan C.C., 1946-49; tchr., counselor, dir. testing Phoenix Union High Sch. and Coll. Dist., 1949-57; dean eve. coll., prin. high sch. Antelope Valley Union High Sch. and Coll. Dist., Lancaster, Calif., 1957-62; dean instrn. Southwestern Coll., Chula Vista, Calif., 1962-64; pres., supt. Triton Coll., River Grove, Ill., 1964-76; pres., dean West L.A. Coll., 1976-80; pres. Trident Consultants; mgmt. cons. Trident Consultants, Los Angeles, 1976—; adj. faculty Ariz. State U., Flagstaff, 1953-55, No. Ill. U., DeKalb, 1971-76, U. Calif., Santa Barbara, 1979. Editor in field. Mayor Upper Woodland Hills, Calif. Served with USAAF, 1942-46. Recipient spl. commendation Chgo. Tribune, spl. commendation Richard Ogilvie, former gov. Ill.; Adminstr. of Yr. award Triton Coll. Faculty Assn., 1974; Adminstr. of Yr. award Ill. Sch. Adminstrs. Assn., 1976. Home: 20124 Phaeton Dr Woodland Hills CA 91364-5633 Office: Bramount Properties 21731 Ventura Blvd Woodland Hills CA 91364-1845 *I always felt that being the president of an organization was like being the quarterback on the football team. You had a choice of running with the ball and taking some bruises or passing it to someone who should score. I was lucky most of the time in selecting some very fine receivers.*

ZEITLIN, MARILYN AUDREY, museum director; b. Newark, July 14, 1941; d. Sidney M. and Theresa Feigenblatt) Litchfield; widowed; children: Charles C. Sweedler, Milo Sweedler. Student, Vanderbilt U., 1963-65; AB in Humanities, Harvard U., 1966, MA in Teaching of English, 1967; postgrad., Cornell U., 1971-74. Dir. Ctr. Gallery, Bucknell U., Lewisburg, Pa., 1975-78; Freedman Gallery, Albright Coll., Reading, Pa., 1978-81, Anderson

Gallery, Va. Commonwealth U., Richmond, 1981-87; curator, acting co-dir. Contemporary Arts Mus., Houston, 1987-90; exec. dir. Washington Projects for the Arts, 1990-92; dir. Univ. Art Mus., Ariz. State U., Tempe, 1992—; juror Dallas Mus. of Arts, McKnight Awards, Mpls.; grant evaluator IMS; grant evaluator, panelist NEH; lectr., cons. in field. Editor, contbr. essays to art pubs. Bd. dirs. Cultural Alliance Washington; curator, commr. for U.S. for 1995 Venice Biennale. Samuel H. Kress fellow, 1972-73. Mem. Assn. Coll. and Univ. Mus. and Galleries (v.p. 1986-88), Am. Assn. Mus., Coll. Art Assn. (U.S. commr. Venice Bieniale 1995). Office: Ariz State U Art Mus PO Box 872911 Tempe AZ 85287-2911

ZEKMAN, PAMELA LOIS (MRS. FREDRIC SOLL), reporter; b. Chgo., Oct. 22, 1944; d. Theodore Nathan and Lois Jane (Bernstein) Z.; m. Fredric Soll, Nov. 29, 1975. B.A., U. Calif. at Berkeley, 1965. Social worker Dept. Public Aid Cook County, Chgo., 1965-66; reporter City News Bur., Chgo., 1966-70; Chgo. Tribune, 1970-75, Chgo. Sun-Times, 1975-81; investigative reporter Sta. WBBM-TV, Chgo., 1981—. Recipient Pulitzer Prize awarded to Chicago Tribune for gen. local reporting on vote fraud series, 1973; Community Service award for vote fraud series UPI, 1972; Feature Series award for nursing home abuses series AP, 1971; Pub. Service award for slumlord series UPI, 1973; Newswriting award AP, 1973; In Depth Reporting award for police brutality series AP, 1974; Investigative Reporting awards Inland Daily Press Assn., 1974, 78; Investigative Reporting award for series on city waste AP, 1975; Pulitzer Prize for pub. service for series on hosp. abuses, 1976; Investigative Reporting award for series on baby selling, 1976; Pub. Service award for series on currency exchange abuses UPI, 1976, Investigative Reporting award for series on abuses in home for retarded children AP, 1977; Soc. Midland Authors Golden Rake award; UPI Public Service award; Ill. AP award; Nat. Headliners Club award; Sweepstakes award for Mirage Tavern investigative project, 1978; Nat. Disting. Service award for series on med. abuses in abortion clinics Sigma Delta Chi, 1979; named Journalist of Yr. No. Ill. U., 1979; recipient George Foster Peabody Broadcasting award, 1982, 85, RTNDA Investigative Reporting award, 1983, DuPont Columbia award 1982, 87. Office: WBBM-TV 630 N Mcclurg Ct Chicago IL 60611-3007

ZEKMAN, TERRI MARGARET, graphic designer; b. Chgo., Sept. 13, 1950; d. Theodore Nathan and Lois (Bernstein) Z.; m. Alan Daniels, Apr. 12, 1980; children: Jesse Logan, Dakota Caitlin. BFA, Washington U., St. Louis, 1971; postgrad., Art Inst. Chgo., 1974-75. Graphic designer (on retainer) greeting cards and related products Recycled Paper Products Co., Chgo., 1970—, Jillson Roberts, Inc., Calif.; apprenticed graphic designer Helmuth, Obata & Kassabaum, St. Louis, 1970-71; graphic designer Container Corp., Chgo., 1971; graphic designer, art dir., photographer Cuerden Advt. Design, Denver, 1971-74; art dir. D'Arcy, McManus & Masius Advt., Chgo., 1975-76; freelance graphic designer Chgo., 1976-77; art dir. Garfield Linn Advt., Chgo., 1977-78; graphic designer Keiser Design Group, Van Noy & Co., Los Angeles, 1978-79; owner and operator graphic design studio Los Angeles, 1979—. Recipient cert. of merit St. Louis Outdoor Poster Contest, 1970, Denver Art Dirs. Club, 1973.

ZELANSKI, PAUL JOHN, art educator, author; b. Hartford, Conn., Apr. 13, 1931; s. John and Sofie (Berkowski) Z.; m. Annette Harding, June 30, 1965; children: John, Noemi, Ruth. Cert., The Cooper Union, 1955; BFA, Yale U., 1957; MFA, Bowling Green (Ohio) State U., 1958. Instr. art North Tex. State U., Denton, 1958-61; prof. art U. Conn., Storrs, 1962—; artist McDowell Art Colony, Peterborough, N.H.; advisor Permanent Pigments; panelist studio talk show Sta. WGHB, Boston, 1963-68; cons. Binnery & Smith; Getty lectr. North Tex. State U., 1989; vis. artist Inst. of Art of Krakow, Poland, 1990, Acad. Visual Arts, Maastricht, 1994. Author: Design Principles and Problems, 1984, Shaping Space, 1987, The Art of Seeing, 1988, Color, 1989; contbr. articles to profl. jours. Mem. com. silver anniversary U. Conn. Sch. Fine Arts, 1985; bd. dirs. Yale U. Art Sch. Alumni Assn., 1979-80. Cpl. U.S. Army, 1952-54. Accademia Italia fellow, 1977. Fellow Am. Commputing Machinery; mem. Computer Art and Design Edn. (chartered), Silvermine Guild Artists, New Eng. Artist Assn. (bd. dirs. 1966-76), Textbooks Authors Am. Roman Catholic. Avocation: reading. Home: 17 Cowles Rd West Willington CT 06279-1705 Office: U Conn # U99 Storrs Mansfield CT 06268

ZELAZNY, ROGER JOSEPH, author; b. Cleve., May 13, 1937; s. Joseph Frank and Josephine Flora (Sweet) Z.; m. Judith Alene Callahan, Aug. 20, 1966; children—Devin, Trent, Shannon. B.A., Case Western Res. U., 1959; M.A., Columbia U., 1962. Claims rep. Social Security Adminstrn., 1962-64, policy specialist, 1965-69; profl. writer, 1969—. Books include This Immortal, 1966, Lord of Light, 1967, Creatures of Light and Darkness, 1969, Damnation Alley, 1969, Nine Princes in Amber, 1970, The Guns of Avalon, 1972, To Die in Italbar, 1973, Sign of the Unicorn, 1975, My Name is Legion, 1976, The Hand of Oberon, 1976, The Courts of Chaos, 1978, The Chronicles of Amber (2 vols.), 1979, The Changing Land, 1981; numerous others; also contbr. numerous short stories and articles to mags., anthologies. Recipient Hugo sci. fiction awards, 1966, 68, 76, 82, 86, 87; Nebula award Sci. Fiction Writers, 1966, 76; Prix Apollo, 1972; Balrog award, 1980, 84.

ZELAZO, NATHANIEL K., engineering executive; b. Lomza, Poland, Sept. 28, 1918; came to U.S., June, 1928; s. Morris and Ida (Kachorek) Z.; m. Helene Fishbein-Ret, June 27, 1943; children—Ronald Elliott, Annette Renee. B.S., CUNY, 1940; postgrad., Columbia U., 1940-42, 52-55; M.S.M.E., U. Wis., 1957, DE (hon.), 1986; D. Engring., Milw. Sch. Engring., 1983. Registered profl. engr., Wis., D.C. Vice pres. Norden Ketay (United Tech.), N.Y.C., 1952-55; dir. research devel. Avionics div. J. Oster Corp., Racine, Wis., 1955-59; pres., chief officer Astronautics Corp. Am., Milw., 1959-84, chief exec. officer, 1984—; chmn. bd. Astronautics C.A. Ltd., 1988—, Kearfott Guidance and Navigation Corp., Wayne, N.J., 1988—; v.p. Fgn. Sales Corp., St. Thomas, V.I., 1988—. Regent, mem. corp. Milw. Sch. Engring., 1984, bd. dirs., 1980—; mem. engring. adv. coun. Marquette U., Milw., 1984, mem. Pres.'s Exec. Senate; mem. indsl. liaison coun. Coll. Engring. and Applied Sch. U. Wis., Milw.; bd. dirs. Greater Milw. Com. Recipient Employer of Yr. award Dept. Def., 1982, Billy Mitchell Meml. award Air Force Assn., 1977, Small Businessman of Yr. award SBA, 1966, Disting. Svc. award U. Wis., Madison, 1985, ECE Centennial medal U. Wis. Madison, 1991, High Tech. Exporter of Yr. award Wis. Dept. Devel., 1989, Entrepreneur of Yr. award in high tech. Arthur Young, Inc., 1989, Wis. Mfr. of Yr. Spl. award Redlin Browne & Co., 1990, Gov.'s New Product award Wis. Soc. Profl. Engrs., 1993; honoree NCCJ, 1990; named Engr. of Yr., 1985, Engrs. and Scientists Milw. Mem. AIAA, IEEE (Centennial medal 1984), Nat. Soc. Profl. Engrs., Am. Soc. Naval Engrs., Am. Helicopter Soc., Engrs. and Scientists of Milw., Inc., Physics Club Milw., Air Force Assn., Navy League U.S., Armed Forces Communications and Electronics Assn., Am. Technion Soc. (Albert Einstein award 1982), Wis. Clubs: Wisconsin, Milw. Yacht, Milw. Athletic. Avocations: music; sailing; skiing. Home: 1610 N Prospect Ave Milwaukee WI 53202-2491 Office: Astronautics Corp Am 4115 N Teutonia PO Box 523 Milwaukee WI 53201-0523

ZELBY, LEON WOLF, electrical engineering educator, consulting engineer; b. Sosnowiec, Poland, Mar. 26, 1925; came to U.S., 1946, naturalized, 1951; s. Herszel and Helen (Wajnryb) Zylberberg; m. Rachel Kupfermintz, Dec. 28, 1954; children: Laurie Susan, Andrew Stephen. BSEE, Moore Sch. Elec. Engring., 1956; MS, Calif. Inst. Tech., 1957; PhD, U. Pa., 1961. Registered profl. engr., Pa., Okla. Mem. staff RCA, Hughes R & D Labs., Lincoln Lab., MIT, Sandia Corp., Argonne (Ill.) Nat. Labs., Inst. for Energy Analysis; mem. faculty U. Pa., 1959-67, assoc. prof., 1964-67; assoc. dir. plasma engring. Inst. Direct Energy Conversion, 1962-67; prof. U. Okla., Norman, 1967—, dir. Sch. Elec. Engring., 1967-71; cons. RCA, 1961-67, Moore Sch. Elec. Engring., 1967-68, also pvt. firms. Editor Tech. and Soc. mags. 1990-93; contbr. articles on energy-associated problems and issues to profl. jours. With AUS, 1946-47. Cons. Electrodynamic Corp. fellow Calif. Inst. Tech., 1957, Mpls.-Honeywell fellow U. Pa., 1957-58, Harrison fellow, 1958. Mem. IEEE, Franklin Inst., Sigma Xi, Tau Beta Pi, Eta Kappa Nu, Phi Beta Kappa, Sigma Tau, Phi Kappa Phi. Home: 1009 Whispering Pines Dr Norman OK 73072-6912 *To learn as much, and to experience as much as possible, without harm to others; read, study, vary professional and recreational activities within constraints of the system.*

ZELDIN, RICHARD PACKER, publisher; b. Worcester, Mass., Aug. 7, 1918; s. M. and Virginia (Gealt) Z.; m. Virginia Graves, Nov. 25, 1950; children—Elizabeth Ann, Richard Shepherd. BS, West Chester U., Pa., 1942; grad. exec. program bus. adminstrn., Columbia U., 1966. Gen. mgr. profl. and reference book dir. McGraw-Hill Book Co., Inc., 1948-68; v.p., publishing dir. Litton Ednl. Pub. Co., Inc., 1968-70; pres. R.R. Bowker Co., 1970-76, Xerox Coll. Pub. Xerox Individualized Pub., 1970-76;; pub. John Wiley & Sons, Inc., 1976-83; v.p. Moseley Assocs. Inc., N.Y.C., 1983—; sec.-treas. sci., tech. and med. book pubs. group Asso. Am. Pubs., 1966-70; mem. adv. com. comml. publs. AEC, 1966-70. Author: A Tennis Guide to the USA, 1980, Business Forms on File, 1984, Personal Forms on File, 1984. Served to lt. USNR, 1942-46. Recipient Disting. Alumni award West Chester U., 1974. Mem. Info. Industry Assn. (sec. 1973—), IEEE, Am. Soc. Info. Sci., Soc. for Scholarly Pub. Clubs: Dutch Treat (N.Y.C.), Pubs. Lunch (N.Y.C.). Home: 20 Fairfield Dr Tinton Falls NJ 07724-3114 Office: Moseley Assocs Inc 270 Madison Ave New York NY 10016-0601

ZELEN, MARVIN, statistics educator; b. N.Y.C., June 21, 1927; m. Thelma Geier, Sept. 10, 1950; children: Deborah, Sandra. BS, CCNY, 1949; MS, U. N.C., 1951; PhD, Am. U., 1957; MA (hon.), Harvard U., 1977. Stat. eng. lab. Nat. Bureau of Standards, 1952-61; assoc. prof. Univ. Md., 1960-61; head, stat. and applied Math. section Nat. Cancer Inst., 1963-66; leading prof. State Univ., Buffalo, N.Y.C., 1967-77; pres. Frontier Sci. and Tech. Rsch. Found., Boston, 1975—; chief div. biostats. Dana Farber Cancer Inst., Boston, 1977—; prof. Harvard U. Sch. Pub. Health, Boston, 1977—; chmn. dept. biostat. Harvard U., 1980-90; vis. prof. Univ. Wis., 1961-63, vis. assoc. prof. Univ. Calif., 1958. Sgt. U.S. Army, 1945-46. Fulbright scholar, 1965-66. Fellow Am. Acad. Arts and Sci., AAAS, Inst. Math. Stats., Am. Statis. Assn.; mem. Internat. Stats. Inst. Home: 230 Eliot St Chestnut Hill MA 02167-1447 Office: Harvard Sch Pub Health 677 Huntington Ave Boston MA 02115-6023

ZELENCIK, STEPHEN J., electronics company executive; b. East Chicago, Ind., Mar. 8, 1935; s. Stephen John and Catherine Edith (Churilla) Z.; m. Harriet Sarnecki, Oct. 18, 1958; 1 child, Mary Kathryn. B.S. in Elec. Engring., Purdue U. Sales mgr. Amphenol Corp., Broadview, Ill., 1961-65; nat. sales mgr. Fairchild Semi condr., Mount View, Calif., 1965-70; area sales mgr. Advance Micro Devices, Sunnyvale, Calif., 1970-76, dir. distbn. ops., 1976-80, sr. v.p. sales mktg., 1980—. Served with U.S. Army, 1956-58. Office: Advanced Micro Devices 901 Thompson Pl Sunnyvale CA 94086-4518

ZELIFF, WILLIAM H., JR., congressman; b. June 12, 1936; m. Sydna Zeliff. BS, Univ. Conn. Exec. DuPont Co., 1959-76; innkeeper; mem. 102nd-104th Congresses from 1st dist. N.H, 1991—; chmn. govt. reform & oversight subcom. on Nat. Security, Internat. Affairs & Criminal Justice; mem. transp. & infrastructure com., small bus. com. Served U.S. Army. Protestant. *

ZELIKOW, HOWARD MONROE, management and financial consultant; b. Bklyn., Apr. 17, 1934; s. Herman and Mae (Rebell) Z.; m. Doris Brown, June 10, 1956 (div. Aug. 1987); children—Lori Ann Zelikow Florio, Daniel M.; m. Marcie Peskin Rosenblum, Dec. 12, 1987. BA, Dartmouth Coll., 1955, MBA, Amos Tuck Sch., 1956. Acct., Ernst & Ernst, N.Y.C., 1956-61; controller Kratter Corp., N.Y.C., 1961-64; mgr. J.H. Cohn, C.P.A.s, Newark, 1964-65; ptnr. Zelikow & Rebell, CPA's, N.Y.C., 1965-70; v.p. Oxbow Constrn. Corp., Port Washington, N.Y., 1970-76; exec. v.p., treas., chief fin. officer Progressive Ins. Cos., Mayfield Village, Ohio, 1976-87; prin. ZKA Assocs., Cleve., 1987—; ptnr. Kayne Anderson & Co., L.A., 1988—; bd. dirs. Capital Guaranty Corp., San Francisco, Victoria Fin. Corp., Cleve. Trustee, Village of Great Neck Estates, Great Neck, N.Y., 1975-76. Mem. AICPA, Fin. Execs. Inst., Oakwood Club, Hillcrest Club, Phi Beta Kappa. Jewish. Home: 17700 Parkland Dr Cleveland OH 44122-3443 Office: ZKA Assocs 24300 Chagrin Blvd Beachwood OH 44122-5679

ZELIN, JEROME, retail executive; b. Bklyn., Dec. 24, 1930; s. Isidore and Ida (Roffman) Z.; m. Muriel Altsher, Dec. 18, 1955; children—Dorothy, Michael, Steven. BS magna cum laude, N.Y.U., 1952. Acct. Seymour Schwartz CPA, 1954-57; partner firm Schwartz, Zelin & Weiss CPAs, N.Y.C., 1958-61; vice chmn., pres., exec. v.p., treas., financial v.p., dir. Unishops, Inc. (retail co.), Jersey City, 1961-74; exec. v.p., dir. Masters, Inc., Westbury, N.Y., 1974—; dir. Market Diners, Inc., N.Y.C. Trustee Temple Sholom of Flatbush. Served with AUS, 1952-54. Mem. N.Y. Soc. CPAs, Am. Inst. CPAs, Beta Gamma Sigma, Tau Alpha Omega. Jewish. Home: 225 Arkansas Dr Brooklyn NY 11234-6901

ZELINSKY, DANIEL, mathematics educator; b. Chgo., Nov. 22, 1922; s. Isaac and Ann (Ruttenberg) Z.; m. Zelda Oser, Sept. 23, 1945; children: Mara Sachs, Paul O., David. BS, U. Chgo., 1941, MS, 1943, PhD, 1946. Rsch. mathematician applied math group Columbia U., N.Y.C., 1941-43; instr. U. Chgo., 1943-44, 46-47; Nat. Rsch. Coun. fellow Inst. Advanced Study, Princeton, N.J., 1947-49; from asst. to assoc. prof. dept. math. Northwestern U., Evanston, Ill., 1949-60, prof., 1960-93, prof. emeritus, 1993—, acting chmn. math. dept., 1959-60, chmn., 1975-78; vis. prof. U. Calif. Berkeley, 1960, Fla. State U., Tallahassee, 1963, Hebrew U., Jerusalem, 1970-71, 85, others; vis. scholar Tata Inst., 1979; mem. various coms. Northwestern U.; lectr. in field. Author: A First Course in Linear Algebra, 1968, rev. edit., 1973; contbr. articles to profl. jours. Fulbright grantee Kyoto U., 1955-56, grantee NSF, 1958-80; Guggenheim fellow Inst. Advanced Study, 1956-57, Indo-Am. fellow, 1978-79. Fellow AAAS (mem. nominating com. sect. A 1977-80, chmn. elect sect. A 1984-85, chmn. 1985-86, retiring chmn. 1986-87), Am. Math. Soc. (mem. coun. 1961-67, editor Transactions of A.M.S. 1961-67 mem. various coms., mem. editorial bd. Notices of A.M.S. 1983-86, chmn. editorial bk. com. 1989, chmn. ad hoc com. 1991-92). Jewish. Home: 613 Hunter Rd Wilmette IL 60091 Office: Northwestern U Dept Math Evanston IL 60208

ZELINSKY, PAUL O., illustrator, painter, author; b. Evanston, Ill., Feb. 14, 1953; s. Daniel and Zelda B. (Oser) Z.; m. Deborah M. Hallen, Dec. 31, 1981; children: Anna H., Rachel L. BA summa cum laude, Yale U., 1974; MFA in Painting, Tyler Sch. Art, 1976. Art instr. San Diego State U., 1976; free lance illustrator/author, 1977—. Illustrator: Dear Mr. Henshaw, 1983 (Caldecott honor 1995), More Rootabagas, 1993; illustrator, adapter: Rumpelstiltskin (Caldecott honor 1987); illustrator, adapter, designer: The Wheels on the Bus (Redbook Mag. award 1990). Recipient Caldecott honor for Hansel & Gretel, Am. Libr. Assn., Chgo., 1985, Best Illustrated Book N.Y. Times Book Rev., N.Y.C., 1981, 85, 94. Mem. Graphic Artists Guild, Children's Illustrators and Authors (charter), Soc. Children's Book Writers and Illustrators, Phi Beta Kappa. Avocations: cooking, reading, child care.

ZELIS, ROBERT FELIX, cardiologist, educator; b. Perth Amboy, N.J., Aug. 5, 1939; s. Felix Andrew and Rita Marie (Jurasz) Z.; m. Gail Ann Heelon, Sept. 10, 1960; children: Robert Felix, Kathleen, Karen, David. B.S. cum laude, U. Mass., 1960; M.D. with honors, U. Chgo., 1964. Diplomate: Am. Bd. Internal Medicine (cardiovascular disease). Intern, then asst. resident in medicine Beth Israel Hosp., Harvard U. Med. Sch., 1964-66; clin. assoc. (lt. comdr. USPHS) cardiology br. Nat. Heart Inst., NIH, Bethesda, Md., 1966-68; mem. faculty U. Calif. Med. Sch., Davis, 1968-74; asst. asso. prof. medicine U. Calif. Med. Sch., 1972-74, chief lab. clin. physiology, 1968-74, asst. chief sect. cardiovascular medicine, 1970-74; prof. medicine and cellular/molecular physiology Milton S. Hershey (Pa.) Med. Center, Pa. State U. Coll. Medicine, 1974—, chief div. cardiology, 1974-84, dir. cardiology research, 1984—. Editor: The Peripheral Circulations, 1975; co-editor: Calcium Blockers, 1982; mem. editorial bd. Annals Internal Medicine, 1976-79, Am. Jour. Physiology, 1976-79, Circulation, 1979-82, Am. Heart Jour., 1980-90, Am. Jour. Cardiology, 1983-86, Jour. C.V. Pharmacology, 1991—, Jour. Am. Coll. Cardiology, 1994—; contbr. articles to med. jours. Mark S. Barr fellow, 1960-64; recipient Borden Research award, 1964. Fellow A.C.P., Am. Coll. Chest Physicians, Am. Coll. Cardiology (gov. Eastern Pa. 1977-80); mem. Am. Fedn. Clin. Research (pres. 1977-78), Am. Soc. Clin. Investigation (nat. council 1981-85, v.p. 1984-85), Am. Physiol. Soc., Assn. Am. Physicians, Assn. Univ. Cardiologists, Am. Soc. Pharmacology and Exptl. Therapeutics, Am. Heart Assn. (nat. fellow councils circulation, arteriosclerosis, clin. cardiology and epidemiology, v.p. for community programs 1979-81, award of merit 1983 v.p., exec. com. Pa. 1976-79, pres. Pa. affiliate 1979-80, Charles T. Mears Humanitarian award

1984), Western Soc. Clin. Research, Sigma Xi, Alpha Omega Alpha, Phi Eta Sigma. Roman Catholic. Home: 227 Homestead Rd Hershey PA 17033-1328 Office: Cardiology Div MS Hershey Medical Center Box 850 Hershey PA 17033

ZELL, SAMUEL, transportation leasing company executive; b. Chgo., Sept. 28, 1941; married. BA, U. Mich., 1963, JD, 1966. With Yates Holleb and Michelson, 1966-68; pres. Equity Fin. and Mgmt. Co., 1968—; chmn. Great Am. Mgmt. and Investment Inc., 1981—, also chief exec. officer; also cochmn. Revco D.S.; chmn. Delta Queen Steamboat Co., New Orleans, 1984—, Eagle Industries Inc.; chmn. Itel Corp., 1985—, bd. dirs. Office: Gt Am Mgmt & Investment Inc 2 N Riverside Plz 6th Fl Chicago IL 60606*

ZELLER, CLAUDE, physicist, researcher; b. Aulnay, France, Dec. 11, 1940; came to U.S., 1976; m. Elisabeth Kreib, 1962 (div. 1967); 1 child, Frederic; m. Florence Labour, Oct. 14, 1967; children: Caroline, Elisabeth. PhD, Univ. Nancy, France, 1968. Rsch. physicist Univ. Nancy, France, 1968-76; visiting rsch. faculty Univ. Pa., Phila., 1976-79; sr. physicist Pitney Bowes R&D, Norwalk, Conn., 1979-84, mgr. applied physics, 1984-91; fellow Pitney Bowes, Shelton, Conn., 1992—; adv. bd. CNRS, Paris, 1969-71; sec. scientific bd. Univ. Nancy, 1971-76; cons. Bruker-Spectrospin, Wissembourg, France, 1970-75. Contbr. articles to profl. jours. Recipient sr. fellowship, NATO, 1976. Mem. IEEE, N.Y. Acad. Scis., Am. Physical Soc., Am. Soc. of Le Souvenir Français, U.S. Jaycees, Soc. for Imaging Sci. & Tech., L'Union Alsacienne (v.p.), Appalachian Mountain Club. Roman Catholic. Achievements include 5 patents and 76 published articles in area of research in U.S. and European journals. Pioneer work in electron beam X-Ray microanalysis, early design of soft cast steel electro-magnet yoke for NMR applications, development of advanced materials such as high electrical conductivity intercalated graphite fibers composite materials and very high magnetic permeability amorphous fibers, investigation of the interferences of electronic articles surveillance systems with pacemakers and reporting to international regulatory commissions. Notable findings include synthetic conductors whose electrical conductivity is comparable to copper, work cited in Physics Today. Home: 97 Fan Hill Rd Monroe CT 06468-1831 Office: Pitney Bowes Inc 35 Waterview Dr Shelton CT 06484-3000

ZELLER, EDWARD JACOB, physics, astronomy and geology educator, consultant; b. Peoria, Ill., Nov. 6, 1925; s. John George and Mabel Gertrude (Singer) Z. A.B., U. Ill., 1946; M.A., U. Kans., 1948; Ph.D., U. Wis.-Madison, 1951. Research assoc. U. Wis.-Madison, 1951-56; asst. prof. U. Kans., Lawrence, 1956-59, assoc. prof., 1959-63, prof. geology, 1963-91, prof. physics and astronomy, 1969—. Contbr. numerous articles to profl. jours.; co-inventor identification markings for gemstones and making selective conductive regions in diamond layers. Recipient Antarctic Service medal Nat. Acad. Sci., 1966, Group Achievement award NASA, 1983; NSF sr. postdoctoral fellow, Bern, Switzerland, 1962; German Acad. exchange fellow, Munster, Fed. Republic Germany, 1975. Fellow Geol. Soc. Am.; mem. AAAS, Am. Geophys. Union, Explorers Club, Antarctican Soc., Am. Polar Soc., Sigma Xi. Home: 2908 W 19th St Lawrence KS 66047-2301 Office: U Kans Space Tech Ctr Irving Hill Rd Lawrence KS 66045

ZELLER, FRANCIS JOSEPH, academic administrator; b. Chgo., July 31, 1943; s. Charles Joseph and Erma J. (Kile) Z.; m. Frances Joan McGrath, Aug. 3, 1968; children: Patrick, Brian. BA in English, Lewis U., 1967; MA in Edn. Adminstrn., No. Ill. U., 1970, EdD in Edn. Adminstrn., 1983. Chmn. Robert Frost Jr. High Sch., Schaumburg, Ill., 1967-69; asst. bus. mgr. Park Ridge (Ill.) Elem. Sch., 1970-71; bus. mgr. Barrington (Ill.) High Sch., 1971-73; dean bus. svcs. Illinois Valley Community Coll., Oglesby, Ill., 1973&. Contbr. articles to profl. jours. Mem. adv. com. State Univ. Retirement System, Champaign, Ill., 1983-87. Named Outstanding Rotarian La Salle (Ill.) Rotary Club, 1976. Mem. NEA, Ill. C.C. Chief Fin. Officers (bd. dirs. 1984-87), Ill. Assn. Sch. Bus. Ofcls. (past pres.), Internat. Assn. Sch. Bus. Ofcls. (chair comm. col. com.), Ottawa C. of C., Golden Triangle Club, Art Inst. Chgo., Delta Sigma Pi. Avocations: tennis, cross-country skiing, bicycling. Office: Ill Valley Community Coll 2578 E 350th Rd Oglesby IL 61348-1074

ZELLER, JOSEPH PAUL, advertising executive; b. Crestline, Ohio, Mar. 19, 1940; s. Paul Edward and Grace Beatrice (Kinstle) Z.; m. Nancy Jane Schmidt, June 17, 1961; children: Laurie, Joe. BA, U. Notre Dame, 1962; MFA, Ohio U., 1963. Radio/television Drewrys Ltd. USA, Inc., South Bend, Ind., 1963-64; media supr. Tatham-Laird & Kudner, Chgo., 1964-67; v.p. assoc. media dir. J. Walter Thompson Co., Chgo., 1967-77; v.p. media dir, v.p. Campbell-Mithun, Chgo., 1977-80; sr. v.p., dir. media, fin. D'Arcy Masius Benton & Bowles, Chgo., 1980—; chmn. media council, D'Arcy Masius Benton & Bowles, Chgp., 1980-86, chmn. Z Prop, 1986—; dir. circle Desert Caballeros Mus., 1994—. Pres. Amateur Hockey Assn. Ill., 1985. Mem. Broadcast Pioneers, Chgo. Advt. Club, Moose. Roman Catholic. Avocations: amateur hockey, country music.

ZELLER, MARILYNN KAY, librarian; b. Scottsbluff, Nebr., Mar. 1, 1940; d. William Harold and Dorothy Elizabeth (Wilkins) Richards; m. Robert Jerome Zeller, May 21, 1966; children: Kevin Jerome and Renae Kay. BS, Calvary Bible Coll., 1985; MLS, U. Mo., Columbia, 1989. Cert. libr. File clk. Waddell & Reed, Kansas City, Mo., 1962-65; payroll clk. Century Fin. Co., Kansas City, Mo., 1965-67, Percy Kent Bag Co., Independence, Mo., 1968-70; accounts receivable Swansons on the Pla, Kansas City, 1971-73; clk. casualty ins. Mill Mutuals, Kansas City, 1977-80; registrar's asst. Calvary Bible Coll., Kansas City, 1980-85, libr. asst., 1985-88, asst. libr., 1988-89, head libr., 1989—; chairperson libr. com. Calvary Bible Coll., Kansas City, 1989—; libr. rep. Friends of the Hilda Kroeker Libr., Kansas City, 1989—. Author: History of the Christian Librarian's Association, 1989. Mem. Christian Librarian's Assn., Spl. Librarian's Assn., Mo. Libr. Assn., Am. Libr. Assn. Avocations: walking, reading, crocheting, sewing, swimming. Home: 401 13th Ave N Greenwood MO 64034-9750 Office: Calvary Bible Coll 15800 Calvary Rd Kansas City MO 64147-1341

ZELLER, MICHAEL EDWARD, physicist; b. San Francisco, Oct. 8, 1939; s. Edward Michael and Marie (Eschen) Z.; m. Linda Marie Smith, June 12, 1960; children: Jeffrey, Daniel. B.S., Stanford U., 1961; M.S., UCLA, 1964, Ph.D., 1968. Research assoc. UCLA, 1968-69; instr. physics Yale U., New Haven, 1969-70, asst. prof., 1970-76, assoc. prof., 1976-82, prof., 1982—, chmn., 1989—. Recipient DeVane medal Phi Beta Kappa, 1980. Fellow Am. Phys. Soc.; mem. N.Y. Acad. Sci., Sigma Xi, Sigma Pi Sigma. Democrat. Jewish. Home: 155 Newton Rd Woodbridge CT 06525-1534 Office: Yale U Physics Dept 260 Whitney Ave New Haven CT 06511-3748

ZELLER, MICHAEL JAMES, psychologist, educator; b. Des Moines, Dec. 3, 1939; s. George and Lila (Fitch) Z. BS, Iowa State U., 1962, MS, 1967. Instr. psychology Mankato (Minn.) State U., 1967-73, asst. prof. psychology, 1974-89, assoc. prof. psychology, 1990—; mem. social sci. edn. coun. Mankato State U., 1976—; ednl. cons. Random House, Scott Foresman, West Pub. Editor: Test Item File to Accompany Introduction to Psychology, 6th edit., 1992; co-author: Test Item File to Accompany Introduction to Psychology, 5th edit., 1989, Test File for Psychology, 3d edit., 1988, Unit Mastery Workbook, 1st, edit., 1974, 2d edit., 1976, Test Item File to Accompany Psychology, 1st edit., 1974, 2d edit., 1976, Psychology: A Personal Approach, 1st edit., 1982, 2d edit., 1984; contbr. chpts. to books. With USAR, 1964-70. Mem. APA, Minn. Psychol. Assn., Inter-Faculty Orgn., Midwestern Psychol. Assn., Psi Chi (award 1988). Achievements include development and research on educational materials, methods of instruction and career opportunities for psychology majors. Home: PO Box 1958 Mankato MN 56002 Office: Mankato State Univ MSU 35 PO Box 8400 Mankato MN 56002

ZELLERBACH, WILLIAM JOSEPH, retired paper company executive; b. San Francisco, Sept. 15, 1920; s. Harold Lionel and Doris (Joseph) Z.; m. Margery Haber, Feb. 25, 1946; children: John William, Thomas Harold, Charles Ralph, Nancy. B.S., Wharton Sch., U. Pa., 1942; grad., Advanced Mgmt. Program, Harvard U., 1958. With Crown Zellerbach Corp. and subs., 1946-85; officer, dir. Crown Zellerbach Corp., 1960-85. Mem. gen. adv. com. fgn. assistance programs AID, 1965-68; pres. Zellerbach Family Fund. Served as lt. USNR, 1942-46. Mem. Nat. Paper trade Assn. (pres. 1970). Clubs: Villa Taverna (San Francisco), Presidio Golf (San Francisco), Pacific Union (San Francisco), Commonwealth (San Francisco); Peninsula

Country (San Mateo, Calif.). Office: 120 Montgomery St Ste 2100 San Francisco CA 94104-4324

ZELLERS, CARL FREDRICK, JR., railway executive; b. Wilmington, N.C., Apr. 25, 1932; s. Carl Fredrick and Bessie Jane (Jackson) Z.; m. Betty B. Burroughs, Dec. 8, 1984; children—Patricia, Carl Fredrick, Pamela. Cert. internal auditor. With Atlantic Coast Line R.R. Co., Wilmington, 1950-62, chief clk., 1958-62; sec.-treas. High Point, Thomasville & Denton R.R. Co. (N.C.), 1963-65; with Fla. East Coast Ry., St. Augustine, 1968—, sec., 1974-76, v.p., 1977—, dir., 1982—, pres. 1992—; pres. Gran Cen. Corp. div. Fla. East Coast Industries, Inc., 1984—, Fla. East Coast Industries, 1995—; bd. dirs. St. Joe Paper Co. Mem. Tax Execs. Inst., Fin. Execs. Inst., Inst. Internal Auditors. Republican. Methodist. Home: 355 Marsh Point Cir Saint Augustine FL 32084-5864 Office: Florida East Coast Industries 1 Malaga St Saint Augustine FL 32084-3583

ZELLIOT, ELEANOR MAE, history educator; b. Des Moines, Oct. 7, 1926; d. Ernest A. and Minnie (Hadley) Z. BA, William Penn Coll., 1948; MA, Bryn Mawr (Pa.) Coll., 1949; PhD, U. Pa., 1969. Assoc. editor The Am. Friend, Richmond, Iowa, 1950-58; tchr. Scattergood Sch., West Branch, Iowa, 1958-60; editor Pendle Hill Pubs., Wallingford, Pa., 1960-62; acting instr., asst. prof. U. Minn., Mpls., 1966-69; researcher South Asia Hist. Atlas, Mpls., 1966-69; from asst. prof. to assoc. prof. Carleton Coll., Northfield, Minn., 1969-79; prof. Carleton Coll., Northfield, 1979—, dept. chair, 1989-92, Laird Bell prof., 1993—; v.p. Midwest Conf. on Asian Affairs, 1994—. Author: From Untouchable to Dalit, 1992; editor: Experience of Hinduism, 1988, (jour. issue) Marathi Sampler, 1982; contbr. articles to profl. jours. Mem. Dem. Farmer Labor Party, Minn., LWV. Fellowship NEH, 1987, Fulbright, 1992. Mem. Minn. Consortium for South Asia, Am. Inst. of Indian Studies (v.p. 1994—, bd. trustees, fellowship 1985, 89), Associated Colls. of Midwest: India Studies, Assn. of Asian Studies. Mem. Soc. of Friends. Avocations: walking, cooking. Office: Carleton Coll Northfield MN 55057

ZELLMAN, ANDE, editor; b. New Haven, Sept. 6, 1952; s. Seymour Zellman and Lillian Shapiro. BS, Boston U., 1974. Features editor Boston Phoenix, 1978-82; mag. editor Dallas Times Herald, 1982; asst. mag. editor Boston Globe, 1983-85, mag. editor, 1985-94, assoc. editor media devel., 1994—; N.E. judge Livingston Awards (journalism), N.Y., 1988—. Mem. Sunday Mag. Editors Assn. (pres. 1988-90). Office: Boston Globe Mag 135 Morrissey Blvd Boston MA 02107*

ZELLNER, BENJAMIN HOLMES, research astronomer; b. Forsyth, Ga., Apr. 16, 1942; 3 children. BS, Ga. Inst. Tech., 1964; PhD in Astronomy, U. Ariz., 1970. Rsch. assoc. Lunar & Planetary Lab., U. Ariz., 1970-76, rsch. fellow, 1976-78, assoc. rsch. prof., 1978-85; staff scientist Space Telescope Sci. Inst., Computer Scis. Corp., Balt.; now mem. dept. physics Ga. So. Univ., Statesboro. Rsch. fellow Observatory Paris, 1972-73. Mem. Internat. Astronomy Union, Am. Astronomists Soc. Achievements include research in astronomical polarimetry, light scattering by circumstellar and interstellar material, physical properties of minor planets. Office: Ga So Univ Dept Physics Statesboro GA 30460*

ZELMANOV, EFIM ISAAKOVICH, mathematician educator. PhD in Math., Novofibirsky U., Russia, 1980; doctoral scientist, Leningrad U., St. Petersburg, Russia, 1985. Recipient Fields medal, 1994. Office: U Chgo Dept Math 5734 University Ave Chicago IL 60637*

ZELMANOWITZ, JULIUS MARTIN, mathematics educator, university administrator; b. N.Y.C., Feb. 20, 1941; s. Morris and Tillie (Holtz) Z.; m. Joan R. Traubel, June 24, 1962; 1 child, Dawn Michèle. AB, Harvard U., 1962; MS, U. Wis., 1963, PhD, 1966. Asst. prof. U. Calif., Santa Barbara, 1966-73, assoc. prof., 1973-77, prof. maths., 1977—, assoc. vice chancellor acad. affairs, 1985-87, assoc. vice chancellor acad. personnel, 1988—; assoc. prof. Carnegie-Mellon U., Pitts., 1970-71; vis. asst. prof. UCLA, 1969-70, vis. assoc. prof. 1973-74; vis. prof. U. Rome, 1977, McGill U., Montreal, Quebec, 1982-83, 87-88, U. Munich, 1983, 88. Contbr. articles to profl. jours. Sr. rsch. grantee Italian Nat. Rsch. Coun., Rome, 1977, Palermo, 1988; named Milw. Prof. of Maths. The Technion, Haifa, Israel, 1979; Fulbright sr. fellow, Munich, 1983. Mem. Am. Math. Soc., Math. Assn. Am. Home: 3215 Laurel Canyon Rd Santa Barbara CA 93105-2015 Office: U Calif Dept Math Santa Barbara CA 93106

ZELMER, AMY ELLIOTT, health science educator; b. Halifax, N.S., Can., Dec. 20, 1935; d. George Thomas and Annie Caroline (Smart) Elliott; m. A.C. Lynn Zelmer, Dec. 16, 1969; 1 child, JenniferLynne. B.Sc.N., U. Western Ont., 1961; M.P.H., U. Mich., 1963; Ph.D., Mich. State U., 1973. Registered nurse, Qld, Australia. Nurse, health educator N.S. Dept. Public Health, Halifax, 1957-65; dir. health edn. Alta. Dept. Health, Edmonton, 1965-67; asst. prof. extension dept. U. Alta., 1967-72, asst. prof., coordinator continuing edn. Sch. Nursing, 1972-74, dean Faculty Nursing, 1976-80, assoc. v.p. acad., 1980-88; dean Sch. Health Sci., Ctrl. Queensland U., Rockhampton, Australia, 1988-92, prof. health sci., 1992—; health edn. specialist S.E. Asia Regional office WHO, New Delhi, 1975-76; cons. Can. Internat. Devel. Agy.; mem. Queensland Cen. Region Health Authority. Mem. editorial bd. Qualitative Health Rsch.; Jour. Clin. Rsch. in Nursing; cons. editor: Group and Orgn. Studies, 1976-82. Pres. Edmonton Internat. Aid Soc., 1981. Fellow Royal Coll. Nursing of Australia.; mem. Can. Assn. Univ. Schs. Nursing (pres. 1980-82), Alta. Pub. Health Assn. (pres. 1983-84), Rotary (Rockhampton). Office: Ctrl Queensland U, Univ Cen Queensland, Rockhampton Queensland 4702, Australia

ZELNICK, CARL ROBERT, Congressional correspondent; b. N.Y.C., Aug. 9, 1940; s. David Isadore and Lillian (Ostrow) Z.; m. Pamela Margaret Sharp, Dec. 30, 1967; children: Eva Michal, Dara Yael, Marni Ruth. B.S., Cornell U., 1961; LL.B., U. Va., 1964. Bar: N.Y. 1965, D.C. 1966. Law assoc. H. Charles Ephraim, Washington, 1966-67; corr./columnist Anchorage Daily News, 1968-76; Assoc. editor Environmental Law Reporter, 1971-72; spl. corr. Christian Sci. Monitor, 1973-77; corr./bur. chief Nat. Pub. Radio, Washington, 1972-76; exec. editor Frost/Nixon Interviews, Washington, 1976-77; dir. news coverage ABC-TV, Washington, 1977-81; dep. bur. chief ABC News, Washington, 1981-82; Moscow bur. chief, corr. ABC News, 1982-84; corr. ABC News, Israel, 1984-86; ABC News Pentagon corr. Washington, 1986-94. Contbr. articles to newspapers and mags. Served with USMC, 1964-65. Recipient Gavel awards Am. Bar Assn., 1969, 74, Du Pont award Columbia U. Sch. Journalism, 1984, Emmy award, 1984, 92. Mem. Council on Fgn. Relations, Radio and TV Corrs. Assn. Internat. Inst. for Strategic Studies, Washington Press Club, Phi Epsilon Pi, Pi Delta Phi. Jewish. Office: ABC News Washington Bureau 1717 DeSales St NW Washington DC 20036-4407

ZELNICK, STRAUSS, entertainment company executive; b. Boston, June 26, 1957; s. Allan Zelnick and Elsa Lee Strauss; m. Wendy Belzberg, 1990; children: Cooper, Lucas. BA summa cum laude, Wesleyan U., Middletown, Ct., 1979; MBA, Harvard U., 1983, JD cum laude, 1983. Bar: N.Y. 1984. Dir. internat. TV Columbia Pictures Internat. Corp., N.Y.C., 1983-85, v.p. internat. TV, 1985-86; sr. v.p. corp. devel. Vestron Inc., Stamford, Conn., 1986-87, exec. v.p., 1987, pres., chief oper. officer, 1988-89; pres., chief oper. officer Twentieth Century Fox, L.A., 1989-93; pres., CEO Crystal Dynamics, Palo Alto, Calif., 1993-95; pres., CEO, BMG Entertainment N.Am., N.Y.C., 1995—. Trustee Wesleyan U., 1992—; mem. contemporary arts coun. Mus. Modern Art, 1989, Young Pres. Orgn.; chmn. Covenant House Calif., 1992-95; bd. dirs. Covenant House, N.Y.C., 1995—. Mem. N.Y. State Bar Assn., Harvard Club, Phi Beta Kappa. Avocations: squash, sailing, skiing. Home: 118 E 65th St New York NY 10021 Office: BMG Entertainment NAm 1540 Broadway New York NY 10036

ZELON, LAURIE DEE, lawyer; b. Durham, N.C., Nov. 15, 1952; d. Irving and Doris Miriam (Baker) Z.; m. David L. George, Dec. 30, 1979; children: Jeremy, Daniel. BA in English with distinction, Cornell U., 1974; JD, Harvard U., 1977. Bar: Calif. 1977, U.S. Ct. Appeals (9th cir.) 1978, U.S. Supreme Ct. 1989. Assoc. Beardsley, Hufstedler & Kemble, L.A., 1977-81; assoc. Hufstedler, Miller, Carlson & Beardsley, L.A., 1981-82, ptnr., 1983-88; ptnr. Hufstedler, Miller, Kaus & Beardsley, L.A., 1988-90, Hufstedler, Kaus & Ettinger, L.A., 1990-91, Morrison & Foerster, L.A., 1991—.

Editor-in-chief: Harvard Civil Rights-Civil Liberties Law Rev., 1976-77. Vol. atty. ACLU of So. Calif., L.A., 1977—; bd. dirs. N.Y. Civil Liberties Union, 1973-74. Mem. ABA (chmn. young lawyers div. pro bono project 1981-83, delivery and pro bono projects com. 1983-85, subgrant competition-subgrant monitoring project 1985-86, chair standing com. on lawyers pub. svc. responsibility 1987-90, chair law firm pro bono project 1989-91, standing com. legal aid and indigent defendants 1991—, chair 1993—), Calif. Bar Assn., L.A. Bar County Assn. (trustee 1989-91, v.p. 1992-93, vice chmn. 1987-88, chmn. 1988-89, chmn. subcom. 1991-92, chair real estate litigation subsect. 1991-92), Women Lawyers Assn. L.A., Calif. Women Lawyers Assn. Democrat. Office: Morrison & Foerster 555 W 5th St Ste 3500 Los Angeles CA 90013-1024

ZEMAITIS, THOMAS EDWARD, lawyer; b. York, Pa., Oct. 16, 1951; s. Leonard Brobst and Ruth Eleanor (Day) Z.; m. Jacqueline Ann Staley, Aug. 18, 1973; 1 child, Daniel Staley. BA magna cum laude, U. Pa., 1973, JD magna cum laude, 1976. Bar: Pa. 1976, U.S. Dist. Ct. (ea. dist.) Pa. 1976, U.S. Ct. Appeals (3d cir.) 1977, U.S. Supreme Ct. 1980, U.S. Ct. Appeals (5th and 11th cirs.) 1981, U.S. Dist. Ct. (ea. dist.) Mich. 1986, U.S. Ct. Appeals (6th cir.) 1986, U.S. Ct. Appeals (D.C. cir.) 1987, U.S. Ct. Appeals (2d cir.) 1990. Assoc. Pepper, Hamilton & Scheetz, Phila., 1976-84, ptnr., 1984-91; gen. atty. Bell Atlantic Corp., Phila., 1992—. Bd. dirs. Support Ctr. for Child Advs., Phila., 1978—, v.p. 1980-83, pres., 1983-85; trustee Women's Law Project, Phila., 1980-88, 90—, treas., 1984-88; mem. Sch. Com. Moorestown Friends Sch., 1992—, sec., 1992—. Mem. ABA, Pa. Bar Assn., Phila. Bar Assn., Order of Coif, Phi Beta Kappa. Democrat. Avocations: theater, reading. Home: 620 Oldershaw Ave Moorestown NJ 08057-3136 Office: Bell Atlantic Network Svcs Inc 1717 Arch St Fl T 32D Philadelphia PA 19103-2713

ZEMAN, JAROLD KNOX, history educator; b. Semonice, Czechoslovakia, Feb. 27, 1926; emigrated to Can., 1948, naturalized, 1955; s. Jaroslav and Jaroslava (Potuckova) Z.; m. Lillian Koncicky, June 18, 1951; children: Miriam, Dagmar, Timothy, Janice. Grad., Charles U., Prague, 1948, Th.Cand., 1948; B.D., Knox Coll., U. Toronto, Ont., Can., 1952; Dr.Theol. U. Zurich, Switzerland, 1966; DD (hon.), McMaster U., Hamilton, Ont., 1985, Acadia U., Wolfville, N.S., 1994. Ordained to ministry Baptist Ch., 1950; pastor in Toronto and Villa Nova, Ont., 1949-59; sec. dept. Can. missions Bapt. Conv. Toronto, 1959-68; prof. ch. history Acadia U., Wolfville, N.S., Can., 1968-91; dir. Acadia Ctr. for Bapt. and Anabapt. Studies, 1991—; vis. prof. Bapt. Theol. Sem., Russlikon, Switzerland, 1965, 84, Mennonite Sem., Elkhart, Ind., 1976-77, Regent Coll., Vancouver, B.C., 1979, Gordon-Conwell Theol. Sem., Boston, 1983, Moravian Theol. Sem., Bethlehem, Pa., 1984, Ontario Theol. Sem., Toronto, 1986, 92; guest lectr., U.S., Can.; mem. religious adv. com. CBC. Author: God's Mission and Ours, 1963, The Whole World At Our Door, 1964, The Anabaptists and the Czech Brethren in Moravia, 1526-1628: A Study of Origins and Contacts, 1969, The Hussite Movement and the Reformation in Bohemia, Moravia and Slovakia, 1350-1650, 1977, Baptist Roots and Identity, 1978, Renewal of Church and Society, 1984; Open Doors: Baptists in Canada 1950-90, 1992; co-author: Baptists in Canada 1760-1990: A Bibliography, 1989; numerous articles.; editor: The Believers' Church in Canada, 1979, Baptists in Canada, 1980, Costly Vision, 1988. Mem. Bapt. Fedn. Can. (pres. 1979-82), Am. Hist. Assn., Am. Soc. Ch. History, Soc. Reformation Research, Can. Soc. Ch. History, Czechoslovak Soc. Arts and Scis. Home: PO Box 164, Wolfville, NS Canada B0P 1X0 Office: Acadia U, Wolfville, NS Canada B0P 1X0

ZEMANIAN, ARMEN HUMPARTSOUM, electrical engineer, mathematician; b. Bridgewater, Mass., Apr. 16, 1925; s. Parsegh and Filor (Paparian) Z.; m. Edna Odell Williamson Zemanian, July 12, 1958; children: Peter, Thomas, Lewis, Susan. BEE, CCNY, 1947; ScD in Engring., NYU, 1953. Registered engr., N.Y. Tutor CCNY, 1947-48; engr. The Maintenance Co., N.Y.C., 1948-52; from asst. to assoc. prof. NYU, 1952-62; prof. SUNY, Stony Brook, 1962-83, leading prof., 1983—. Author: Distribution Theory and Transform Analysis, 1965, Generalized Integral Transformations, 1968, Realizability Theory for Continuous Linear Systems, 1972, Infinite Electrical Networks, 1991; co-author: Electronics, 1961; co-editor and co-founder: (rsch. jour.) Circuits, Systems and Signal Processing, 1982—. NSF faculty fellow in sci., 1975-78; recipient Sci. award Armenian Students Assns. Am., 1982; Academician (fgn. mem.) Armenian Acad. Scis., 1990, Academician (fgn. mem.) Armenian Acad. Engr., 1994. Fellow IEEE; mem. Am. Math. Soc., Soc. for Indsl. and Applied Math. (v.p. publs. 1974-75), Tau Beta Pi, Eta Kappa Nu, Sigma Xi. Democrat. Presbyterian. Office: SUNY Stony Brook NY 11794-2350

ZEMANS, FRANCES KAHN, legal association executive; b. Chgo., May 1, 1943; married; 3 children. BA in zoology, U. Mich., 1965; MA in polit. sci., Northwestern U., 1966, Ph.D.in polit. sci., 1972. Instr. dept. politics Lake Forest (Ill.) Coll., 1973-74; instr. dept. polit. sci. Northwestern U., Evanston, Ill., 1974-75; asst. prof. depts. edn. and polit. sci. U. Chgo., 1975-80; dir. edn., rsch. Am. Judicature Soc., Chgo., 1983-85, asst. exec. dir. programs, 1985-87, exec. v.p., dir., 1987—; cons. ABA, 1980; mem. task force on judicial conduct and ethics of spl. commn. on administrn. of justice in Cook County, 1985-88; vis. lectr. Northwestern U., Chgo., 1986; bd. dirs. Cook County Criminal Justice Project, 1987-90; adjudication working group Bureau Justice Assistance, U.S. Dept. Justice, Washington, 1987, 88; mem. task force gender bias in courts, State of Ill., 1988-90;mem. Ill. Judicial Inquiry Bd., 1988-92. Contbr. articles to profl. jours.; mem. editorial bd. Justice System Journal, 1986-90; presenter in field. Bd. dirs. ACLU, Ill., 1978-87; mem. Police Bd. City of Chgo., 1980-87, chair budget com., office of profl. standards com., rules and regulations revision com.; mem. Chgo. crime survey planning com. Chgo. Community Trust, 1984-86, adv. com. govt. assistance project, 1990—; bd. visitors So. Meth. U. Sch. Law, 1987-90. Scholar ABF, 1974-83. Mem. Am. Polit. Sci. Assn., Law and Soc. Assn. (trustee 1980-83). Office: Am Judicature Soc 25 E Washington St Ste 1600 Chicago IL 60602-1805

ZEMANS, JOYCE PEARL, art historian, arts administrator; b. Toronto, Ont., Can., Apr. 21, 1940; m. Frederick H. Zemans; children: Deborah, David, Marcia. BA, U. Toronto, 1962, MA in Art History, 1966. Co-chair dept. art history Ont. Coll. Art, Toronto, 1970-71, chair dept. liberal arts, 1973-75; chair dept. visual arts York U., Toronto, 1975-81, assoc. prof. art history, 1975—, dean faculty fine arts, 1985-88, co-dir. MBA program in arts and media adminstrn., faculty adminstrv. studies, 1994—, Robarts chair in Can. studies, 1995-96; dir. Can. Coun., Ottawa, Ont., 1989-92. Author: (book) Jock Macdonald, 1986; (catalogue) J.W.G. Macdonald: The Inner Landscape, 1981, Christopher Pratt, 1985, Kathleen Munn and Edna Tacon: New Perspectives on Modernism, 1989; (career series) Art, 1971; contbr. articles to profl. jours. Bd. dirs. Nat. Coun. Art Adminstrn., 1979-82. Mem. Can. Assn. Fine Art Deans (exec.), Internat. Coun. Fine Art Deans (bd. dirs. 1985-89), Internat. Assn. Art Critics, Univ. Art Assn. Can., Coll. Art Assn., Comité International de l'histoire de l'art, Can., Laidlaw Found. (bd. dirs.). Office: York U, Faculty of Fine Arts, Toronto, ON Canada M3J 1P3

ZEMECKIS, ROBERT L., film director; b. Chgo., 1952; m. Mary Ellen Trainor. Ed., U. So. Calif. Cinema Sch. Dir.: (films) I Wanna Hold Your Hand, 1978, Used Cars, 1980, Romancing the Stone, 1984, Back to the Future, 1985, Back to the Future, Part II, 1989, Who Framed Roger Rabbit?, 1988, Back to the Future, Part II, 1989, Back to the Future, PartIII, 1990, Death Becomes Her, 1992, Forrest Gump, 1994 (Best Dir. Acad. award); co-screenwriter: 1941, 1979, Trespass, 1992; exec. prodr. : The Public Eye, 1992. Mem. Dirs. Guild Am. Office: care Gelfand Rennert & Feldman 1888 Century Park E Ste 90 Los Angeles CA 90067 also: CAA 9830 Wilshire Blvd Beverly Hills CA 90212*

ZEMEL, JAY NORMAN, electrical engineer, educator; b. N.Y.C., June 26, 1928; s. Leo and Miriam Esther (Schwartz) Z.; m. Jacqueline Eva Lax, July 21, 1950; children: Alan Raymond, Babette Sharon, Andrea Melanie. B.S., Syracuse U., 1949, M.S., 1953, Ph.D., 1956; M.A. (hon.), U. Pa., 1971. Supervisory research physicist U.S. Naval Ordnance Lab., 1954-66; RCA prof. solid state electronics U. Pa., 1966-93, H. Nedwill Ramsey prof. sensor techs., 1993—, chmn. dept. elec. engring., 1973-77, dir. Ctr. for Chem. Electronics, 1979-85, dir. Ctr. for Sensor Tech., 1985-89; vis. prof. Nat. Poly.

Inst. Mex., 1971, U. Tokyo, 1978, Naval Research Lab., 1977-78, U. Neuchatel, Switzerland, 1987, U. N.C., Charlotte, 1991-92; vis. scientist Instituto Elettronica dello Stato Solido-Centro Nazionale dela Resercha, Rome, 1985; dir. Advanced Study Inst. on Non-destructive Evaluation in Semicondr. Materials and Devices NATO, 1978, dir. Advanced Study Inst. on Chemically Sensitive Electronic Devices, 1980; mem. com. on sci. and the arts Franklin Inst. Editor in chief: Thin Solid Films, 1972-90; contbr. articles to profl. jours. Recipient Meritorious Civilian Service award Navy Dept., 1958, Sustained Superior Performance award, 1960. Fellow IEEE. Home: 223 Meetinghouse Rd Jenkintown PA 19046-2906 Office: U Pa Moore Sch Elec Engring Philadelphia PA 19104-6314

ZEMKE, (E.) JOSEPH, computer company executive. CEO Auto-Trol Tech., Denver, 1981-84; chief operating officer Amdahl Corp., Sunnyvale, Calif., 1985—, pres., 1987—; CEO, 1992—. Office: Amdahl Corp PO Box 3470 1250 E Arques Ave Sunnyvale CA 94086-4730

ZEMM, SANDRA PHYLLIS, lawyer; b. Chgo., Aug. 18, 1947; d. Walter Stanley and Bernice Phyllis (Churas) Z. BS, U. Ill., 1969; JD, Fla. State U., 1974. Bar: Ill. 1975, Fla. 1975. With fin. dept. Sinclair Oil, Chgo., 1969-70; indsl. rels. advisor Conco Inc., Mendota, Ill., 1970-72; assoc. Seyfarth, Shaw, Fairweather & Geraldson, Chgo., 1975-82, ptnr., 1982—. Bd. dirs. Chgo. Residential Inc., 1993-97; mem. Art Inst. Round Table, Chgo., 1993-94. Mem. Ill. State Bar Assn., Fla. State Bar Assn., Univ. Club Chgo. (bd. dirs. 1991-94). Office: Seyfarth Shaw 55 E Monroe St Chicago IL 60603-5863

ZEMMER, JOSEPH LAWRENCE, JR., mathematics educator; b. Biloxi, Miss., Feb. 23, 1922; s. Joseph Lawrence and Hazel (Quint) Z.; m. Joan Kornfield, June 28, 1950; children—Joel Alan, Rachel Lee, Judith Louise. B.S., Tulane U., 1943, M.S., 1947; Ph.D., U. Wis., 1950. Mem. faculty U. Mo., Columbia, 1950—, prof. math., 1961—, chmn. dept., 1967-70, 73-76, prof. emeritus, 1987—; Fulbright lectr. Osmania U., Hyderabad, India, 1963-64. Contbr. articles to profl. jours. Served with AUS, 1944-46. Mem. Am. Math. Soc., Math. Assn. Am. (chmn. Mo. 1960-61), Can. Math. Soc., Phi Beta Kappa, Sigma Xi. Home: 701 Glenwood Ct Columbia MO 65203-2832 Office: U Mo Dept Mathematics Columbia MO 65211

ZEMPLENYI, TIBOR KAROL, cardiologist; b. Part Lupča, Czechoslovakia, July 16, 1916; came to U.S., 1968, naturalized, 1974; s. David Dezider and Irene (Pollak) Z.; m. Hana Bendová, Aug. 13, 1952; 1 son, Jan. MD, Charles U., Prague, Czechoslovakia, 1946, Docent Habilit., 1966; CSc. (PhD), Czechoslovak Acad. Sci., 1960, DSc., 1964. Clin. asst. with dept medicine Prague Motol Clinic, 1946-52; head atherosclerosis rsch. Inst. for Cardiovascular Rsch., Prague, 1952-68; assoc. prof. medicine Charles U., 1966-68; assoc. prof. medicine U. So. Calif., L.A., 1969-75, prof., 1975-92, prof. emeritus, 1992—; attending physician L.A. County- U.So. Calif. Med. Ctr. Author: Enzyme Biochemistry of the Arterial Wall, 1968; editorial bd. Atherosclerosis, 1962-75, Cor et Vasa, 1993—; adv. bd. Advances in Lipid Rsch., 1963-66; contbr. articles to numerous profl. jours. WHO fellow for study in Sweden and Gt. Britain, 1959. Fellow Am. Heart Assn., Am. Coll. Cardiology; mem. Western Soc. for Clin. Rsch., Longevity Assn. (mem. sci. bd.), European Atherosclerosis Group, Italian Soc. for Atherosclerosis (hon.). Office: 3400 Loadstone Dr Sherman Oaks CA 91403-4512

ZEMSKY, ROBERT, educational administrator; b. Tucson, Feb. 26, 1940; s. Boris Zemsky and Josephine (Kalman) Anderson; m. Ann Rosenkrans, May 7, 1960; children: Peter, Tobi, Jeffrey. BA, Whittier Coll., 1962; MA in History, Yale U., 1963, PhD in History, 1966. Asst. prof. U. Pa., Phila., 1966-69, assoc. prof., 1969-82, prof., 1982—; chief planning officer, 1980—; dir. Inst. for Rsch. on Higher Edn., 1981—; bd. trustees Franklin and Marshall Coll., Lancaster, Pa., 1984—; bd. dirs. higher edn. rsch. program Pew Charitible Trusts, Phila., 1986—. Author: Merchants, Farmers and River Gods, 1969, Structure of College Choice, 1983. Woodrow Wilson fellow, 1962-63, 65-66; SSRC fellow, 1973.

ZEN, E-AN, research geologist; b. Peking, China, May 31, 1928; came to U.S., 1946, naturalized, 1963; s. Hung-chun and Heng-chi'h (Chen) Z. AB, Cornell U., 1951; MA, Harvard U., 1952, PhD, 1955. Research fellow Woods Hole Oceanographic Inst., 1955-56, research asso., 1956-58; asst. prof. U. N.C., 1958-59; geologist U.S. Geol. Survey, 1959-80, rsch. geologist, 1981-89; adj. rsch. prof. geology U. Md., 1990—; vis. assoc. prof. Calif. Inst. Tech., 1962; Crosby vis. prof. MIT, 1973; Harry H. Hess sr. vis. fellow Princeton U., 1981; counselor 28th Internat. Geol. Congress. 1986-89. Contbr. articles to profl. jours. Recipient Major John Coke medal Geol. Soc. London, 1992, Outstanding Contbn. to Pub. Understanding of Geology award Am. Geol. Inst., 1994. Fellow AAAS, Am. Acad. Arts and Scis., Geol. Soc. Am. (councillor 1985-88, v.p. 1991, pres. 1992, Day medal 1986), Mineral. Soc. Am. (coun. 1975-77, pres. 1975-76, Roebling medal 1991); mem. NAS, Geol. Soc. Washington (pres. 1973), Mineral. Assn. Can. Office: U Md Dept Geology College Park MD 20742

ZENGER, JOHN HANCOCK, publishing company executive; b. Salt Lake City, Nov. 13, 1931; s. John H. and L. (Hancock) Z.; m. Dixie Robison, June 1, 1955 (div. 1978); children: Mark R., Robin, Todd R., Blake R., Mitchell R., Drew R.; m. Holly Olsen, June 29, 1979; stepchildren: Roger, Kirk, Lori, Michael. BS, Brigham Young U., 1955; MBA, UCLA, 1957; D in Bus. Adminstrn., U. So. Calif., Los Angeles, 1963. Asst. prof. Grad Sch. Bus. U. So. Calif., L.A., 1966-67; exec. v.p. Blanfield-Smith and Co., Pasadena, Calif., 1965-67; v.p. human resources Syntex Corp., Palo Alto, Calif., 1967-77; pres. Zenger-Miller Inc., Cupertino, Calif., 1977-92; group v.p. Times Mirror Co., San Jose, 1992—. Chmn. Palo Alto Human Refs. Coun., 1961-66. Ford Found. fellow, 1962-63; recipient Disting. Svc. award Brigham Young U., 1983; named to Human Refs. Devel. Hall of Fame, 1994. Mem. Am. Soc. Tng. and Devel., Brigham Young U. Alumni Assn. (pres. 1981). Republican. Mormon. Avocation: magic. Home: 27300 Altamont Rd Los Altos Hills CA 94022 Office: 1735 Technology Dr San Jose CA 95110-1313

ZENNER, SHELDON TOBY, lawyer; b. Chgo., Jan. 11, 1953; s. Max and Clara (Goldner) Z.; m. Ellen June Morgan, Sept. 2, 1984; children: Elie, Nathaniel. BA, Northwestern U., 1974, JD, 1978. Bar: U.S. Dist. Ct. (no. dist.) Ill. 1978. Assoc. Shadur, Krupp & Miller, Chgo., 1978-80; law clk. to judge U.S. Dist. Ct. (no. dist.) Ill., Chgo., 1980-81; asst. U.S. atty., dep. chief spl. prosecutions div. No. Dist. of Ill., Chgo., 1981-89; ptnr. Katten Muchin & Zavis, Chgo., 1989—; adj. faculty Medill Sch. Journalism Northwestern U., 1982-89, Sch. of Law, 1986—; instr. Nat. Inst. Trial Attys., 1989—. Mem. Phi Beta Kappa. Office: Katten Muchin & Zavis 525 W Monroe St Chicago IL 60661-3629

ZENO, PHYLLIS WOLFE, association executive, editor; b. Cleve.; d. Oliver MacKenzie and Helen Virginia (Shipley) Wolfe; m. Norman Zeno, June 10, 1960 (dec. Feb. 1983); children: Richard Williams, Linda Williams Aber, Leslie Williams Metzler. Student, U. Wisconsin, 1943-45, New Sch. Social Rsch., N.Y.C., 1948. Staff writer Fred Waring Show, CBS-TV, N.Y.C., 1953-54; indsl. show writer MCA, N.Y.C., 1959-61, MCI, N.Y.C., 1959-74; editor Club Life mag., Manhasset, N.Y., 1970-74; promotion coord. Peninsula Motor Club, Am. Automobile Assn., Tampa, Fla., 1974-86; creative dir. AAA Auto Club South (formerly Peninsula Motor Club), Tampa, 1986—; editor-in-chief AAA Going Places. Composer This Is An Opening, 1975 (pop music award ASCAP 1976), How Do You Open a Show?, 1976, We Never Sing Opening Numbers, 1976. Recipient Silver award of excellence Fla. Mag. Assn., 1988, Bronze award of excellence, 1987, Charlie award 1st pl. for regular column, 1993, Addy award of merit Tampa Ad Fedn., 1986. Mem. ASCAP, Soc. Am. Travel Writers. Christian Scientist. Avocations: travel, photography. Home: 8402 Cherrystone Ct Tampa FL 33615-4913 Office: AAA Auto Club South 1515 N Westshore Blvd Tampa FL 33607-4505

ZENOWITZ, ALLAN RALPH, government official; b. Queens Village L.I. N.Y.; Apr. 18, 1928; s. Ralph and Ann Louise (Brickman) Z. Student, Trinity Coll., 1947-49; spl. studies, Yale U., 1947, Harvard U., 1948; grad., U.S. Army Armor Sch., 1950; spl. studies, U. Va., 1955, U.S. Naval War Coll., U.S. Army War Coll., Nat. Def. Univ. U.S. Army Command and Gen. Staff Coll.; BA in Govt. and Internat. Rels., U. Conn., 1960; JD, New Eng. Sch. Law, 1964; grad., U.S. Army Quatermaster Sch., 1966, U.S. Army

Logistics Mgmt. Coll., 1970. Congl. intern, 1946-47; New Eng. area mgr. F.G. Ludwig Inc., Hartford, Conn., 1953-54; dir. ARZ Pub. Relations and Devel., Hartford, Conn., 1955-56; mgmt. exec. Saks Fifth Ave, N.Y.C., 1956-57; dir. spl. situations Fred Gaertner Jr. & Assoc., mgmt. engrs., bus. cons., N.Y.C., 1957-60; aide to gov. of Mass., 1961-62; state dir. Mass. Civil Def. Agy., Office Emergency Preparedness, 1965-71; chmn. Mass. Emergency Communications Commn.; mem. Mass Radiol. Adv. Protection Coun.; chmn. Mass. Gov's Water Emergency Adv. Com., 1965-71, Mass. Emergency Energy Com., 1970-71; regional dir. U.S. Office of Civil Def., 1971-72, U.S. Def. Civil Preparedness Agy., 1972-79; dir. resources mgmt. Fed. Emergency Mgmt. Agy., Washington, 1980-81, dir. fed. plans, 1981-82, chief Nat. Defense Exec. Res., 1982-83, sr. policy advisor, exec. officer, 1994—; sr. policy advisor Nat. Emergency Tng. Cr., 1983-88; spl. asst. for hazardous material mgmt. Office Sec. Def., Washington, 1988—; mem. exec. com. Christian A. Herter chair in internat. relations; mem. policy com. Boston Fed. Exec. Bd., 1971-79; mem. U.S.-Can Civil Emergency Adv. Com., 1971-79; chmn. adv. council New Eng. Sch. Law, Law Enforcement Legal Edn. Program; del. NATO sr. civil emergency com., 1972; cons. Republican Nat. Com., 1964-65; adj. prof. New Eng. Sch. Law, 1965-71; chmn. Dept. Defense Fire Protection Coordinating Com., 1988-91. Mem. Mass. Rep. State Com., 1964-65; mem. Great Barrington Rep. Town Com., 1964-65. Served as 1st lt. U.S. Army, 1950-52; served to col. (ret.) USAR. Recipient White House Citation for outstanding pub. service, 1967; recipient Disting. Service citation Dept. Def., 1971, 91, Meritorious Service medal U.S. Army, 1976, Legion of Merit U.S. Army, 1977; charter mem. Fed. Exec. Service U.S. Govt., 1979. Mem. Am. Acad. Polit. Sci., Am. Polit. Sci. Assn., Am. Soc. Internat. Law, Nat. Assn. State Dirs. of Disaster Preparedness (pres. 1969-70, exec. com. 1968-71), Am. Soc. Pub. Adminstrn., U. Conn. Alumni Assn. (pres. greater Washington dipt. 1983—), Army and Navy Club (Washington). Home: 2555 Pennsylvania Ave NW Washington DC 20037-1614 Office: 500 C St SW Washington DC 20472-0002

ZENTMYER, GEORGE AUBREY, plant pathology educator; b. North Platte, Nebr., Aug. 9, 1913; s. George Aubrey and Mary Elizabeth (Strahorn) Z.; m. Dorothy Anne Dudley, May 24, 1941; children: Elizabeth Zentmyer Dossa, Jane Zentmyer Fernald, Susan Dudley. A.B., UCLA, 1935; M.S., U. Calif., 1936, Ph.D. 1938. Asst. forest pathologist U.S. Dept. Agr., San Francisco, 1937-40; asst. pathologist Conn. Agrl. Expt. Sta., New Haven, 1940-44; asst. plant pathologist to plant pathologist U. Calif., Riverside, 1944-62, prof. plant pathology, 1962—, prof. emeritus, 1981—, faculty rsch. lectr., 1964, chmn. dept., 1968-73; cons. NSF, Trust Ty. of Pacific Islands, 1964, 66, Commonwealth of Australia Forest and Timber Bur., 1968, AID, Ghana and Nigeria, 1969, Govt. South Africa, 1980, Govt. Israel, 1983, Govt. Western Australia, 1983, Ministry Agriculture and U. Cordoba, Spain, 1989, Govt. Costa Rica, 1993; mem. NRC panels, 1968-73. Author: Plant Disease Development and Control, 1968, Recent Advances in Pest Control, 1957, Plant Pathology, An Advanced Treatise, 1977, The Soil-Root Interface, 1979, Phytophthora Cinnamomi and the Diseases it Causes, 1980, Phytophthora: Its Biology, Taxonomy, Ecology and Pathology, 1983, Ecology and Management of Soilborne Plant Pathogens, 1984, Compendium of Tropical Fruit Diseases, 1994; assoc. editor: Ann. Rev. of Phytopathology, 1971—, Jour. Phytopathology, 1951-54, also jour. articles. Bd. dirs. Riverside YMCA, 1949-58, Friends of Mission Inn, 1981—, pres., 1991-93, Calif. Mus. Photography, 1988—; pres. Town and Gown Orgn., Riverside, 1962; bd. dirs. Riverside Hospice, 1982-85, pres., 1984-85; bd. dirs. Friends U. Calif. Riverside Botanic Garden, 1985-89, 91—, pres., 1987-89; bd. trustees U. Calif. Riverside Found., 1993-94. Recipient award of honor Calif. Avocado Soc., 1954, spl. award of honor, 1981; recipient Emeritus Faculty award U. Calif., Riverside, 1991; Guggenheim fellow, Australia, 1964-65, NATO sr. sci. fellow, Eng., 1971; NSF rsch. grantee, 1963, 68, 71, 74, 78; Bellagio scholar Rockefeller Found., 1985. Fellow AAAS (pres. Pacific div. 1974-75), Am. Phytopath. Soc. (pres. 1966, pres. Pacific div. 1955, found. bd. dirs. 1987—, v.p. 1991—, Award of Distinction 1983, award of Merit Caribbean div. 1972, Lifetime Achievement award Pacific div. 1991), Explorers Club; mem. NAS, Mycol. Soc. Am., Am. Inst. Biol. Scis., Bot. Soc. Am., Brit. Mycol. Soc., Australasian Plant Pathology Soc., Philippine Phytopath. Soc., Indian Phytopath. Soc., Assn. Tropical Biology, Internat. Soc. Plant Pathology (councilor 1973-78), Pacific Assn. Tropical Phytopathology, Sigma Xi, Gamma Sigma Delta. Home: 708 Via La Paloma Riverside CA 92507-6403

ZEPF, THOMAS HERMAN, physics educator, researcher; b. Cin., Feb. 13, 1935; s. Paul A. and Agnes J. (Schulz) Z. BS summa cum laude, Xavier U., 1957; MS, St. Louis U., 1960, PhD, 1963. Asst. prof. physics Creighton U., Omaha, 1962-67, assoc. prof., 1967-75, prof., 1975—, acting chmn. dept. physics, 1963-66, chmn., 1966-73, 81-93, coord. allied health programs, 1975-76, coord. pre-health scis. advising, 1976-81; cons. physicist VA Hosp., Omaha, 1966-71; vis. prof. physics St. Louis U., 1973-74; program evaluator Am. Coun. on Edn., 1988—. Contbr. articles and abstracts to Surface Sci., Bull. Am. Phys. Soc., Proceedings Nebr. Acad. Sci., The Physics Tchr. jour., others. Chmn. physics judging com. Greater Nebr. Sci. and Engring. Fair, 1973-85. Recipient Cert. Recognition award Phi Beta Kappa U. Cin. chpt., 1953, Disting. Faculty Svc. award Creighton U., 1987. Mem. AAAS, Am. Phys. Soc., Am. Assn. Physics Tchrs. (pres. Nebr. sect. 1978), Nebr. Acad. Sci. (life, chmn. physics sect. 1985—), Internat. Brotherhood Magicians, Soc. Am. Magicians (pres. assembly #7, 1964-65), KC, Sigma Xi (Achievement award for rsch. St. Louis chpt. 1963, pres. Omaha chpt. 1993-94), Sigma Pi Sigma. Roman Catholic. Office: Creighton U Dept Physics Omaha NE 68178

ZERBE, ANTHONY, actor; b. Long Beach, Calif.; s. Arthur Le Van and Catherine (Scurlock) Z.; m. Arnette Jens, Oct. 7, 1962; children: Jennet, Jared Le Van. Student, Pomona Coll., 1954-55, Stella Adler Theater Studio, N.Y.C., 1958-60. Pres. prodn. co. Cameo Theater Inc. Actor Fred Miller Theater, Milw., 1962-63, Arena Stage, Washington, 1963-65, Theater Living Arts, Phila., 1965-66, Stratford (Ont. Can.) Theater, 1962, Old Globe Theater, San Diego, 1965-67, 72, Mark Taper Forum, Los Angeles, 1967—, Seattle Repertory Co., 1975—; appeared on Broadway in The Little Foxes, 1981; films include Cool Hand Luke, 1967, Will Penny, 1967, Omega Man, 1970, Liberation of L.B. Jones, 1972, Farewell My Lovely, 1975, Turning Point, 1977, Who'll Stop the Rain, 1978, First Deadly Sin, 1980, Soggy Bottom, U.S.A. 1980, The Dead Zone, 1983, Offbeat, 1985, Steel Dawn, 1987, Private Investigations, 1987; appeared on numerous TV shows, including Harry-O series, 1974-76 (Emmy awd., NATAS, 1976, for continuing performance by a supporting actor in a drama series), Young Riders, 1992-93; TV films include The Priest Killer, 1971, Snatched, 1973, She Lives, 1973, The Healers, 1974, In the Glitter Palace, 1977, Man of Honor, 1980, Attica, 1980, The Return of the Man from UNCLE, 1983 Dream West, 1986, One Police Plaza, 1986; miniseries: George Washington, 1984, North and South, Book II, 1986; one-man show It's All Done With Mirrors, 1977—; (with Roscoe Lee Browne) two-man show Behind the Broken Words, 1977—. Served with USAF, 1959. Recipient Emmy award as best supporting actor Harry-O, 1976. Office: care Susan Smith & Assocs 121 N San Vicente Blvd Beverly Hills CA 90211-2303*

ZERELLA, JOSEPH T., pediatric surgeon; b. Youngstown, Ohio, Mar. 7, 1941; s. Atilio and Ann (Capuzello) Z.; m. Diana Isabelle Talbot, Aug. 5, 1967; children—Ann, Michael, Mark. B.S., Northwestern U., 1962, M.D., 1966. Diplomate Am. Bd. Surgery, Am. Bd. Pediatric Surgery. Intern Med. Coll. Wis., Milw., 1966-67, resident in surgery, 1967-68, 70-73; tng. fellow in pediatric surgery Children's Hosp. Med. Ctr., Cin., 1973-75; staff pediatric surgeon Phoenix Children's Hosp., 1975—, chmn. dept. surgery 1987—; staff Ariz. Children's Hosp., Phoenix, 1975—; pvt. practice medicine specializing in pediatric surgery, Phoenix, 1975—; mem. staff Good Samaritan Hosp., Phoenix, 1975—, sect. chief pediatric surgery, 1979—; mem. staff St. Joseph's Hosp., Phoenix, 1975—, sect. chief pediatric surgery, 1980—; Contbr. articles to profl. jours. Served as capt. U.S. Army, 1968-70. Fellow ACS, Am. Acad. Pediatrics, Am. Pediatric Surg. Assn., Pacific Assn. Pediatric Surgeons. Roman Catholic. Office: Saguaro Children's Surgery Ltd 1301 E Mcdowell Rd Ste 100 Phoenix AZ 85006-2688

ZERETZKE, FREDERICK FRANK H., artist, educator; b. Milw., July 4, 1919; s. Herman and Hertha Hildegarde (Riebow) Z.; m. Marian Louise Elfers, Dec. 7, 1942; children: Frederick J., David L., Mary J., John E. Student, Milw. Art Inst., 1938-39, Layton Sch. of Art, Milw., 1940-41, Rockford (Ill.) Coll., 1947. Art tchr. Burpee Art Gallery, Rockford, Ill., 1946-48; mural artist People's Real Estate Agy., Rockford, 1958, Grace

Luth. Ch., Loves Park, Ill., 1960, Sweden House, Rockford, 1972; artist oil meml. young girl First United Presbyn. Ch., Greeley, Colo., 1963; mural artist Linos, Rockford, 1974; art tchr. pvt. studio, Rockford, Ill., 1968-78; art. tchr. pvt. studio, Burlington, Wash., 1978—; artist and tchr. art in nat. def. Camp Callan, San Diego, 1942-43, Rock Valley Coll. Rockford, Ill., 1970-77, Skagit Valley Coll., Mt. Vernon, Wash., 1978-80. Prin. works include mural in Hadamar, Germany, exhibits in galleries in Wis., Calif., Wash., Ill., Elements Gallery, Bellingham, Wash., 1988-90, Fox Glove Art Gallery, Mt. Vernon, Wash., 1989-92, Twisted Willow Gallery, Mt. Vernon, 1993-94, Arts & Frame Gallerie, Canyon Lake, Calif., 1993, juried show Arts Coun. Snohomish County, Everett, Wash., 1993, Concrete Wash. Art Show (1st prize watercolor 1992), Bald Eagle Art Show, Concrete, 1993 (4 awards), sculpture in Mt. Vernon, 1983, portraits, 1941—. Sec. Loves Park (Ill.) Zoning Bd., 1949-56. With U.S. Army, 1941-45, ETO. Scholar Milw. Art Inst., 1939, Layton Sch. Art, 1940; awarded commission for design for Swedish Tour of Sveas Soner Chorus of Rockford, 1965; named Artist of Yr. Winnebago County, 1974. Mem. Tamaroa Water Color Soc. Rockford (hon. lifetime, founder, pres. 1964), Skagit Art Assn. (pres. 1987-88). Mem. Unitarian Ch. Avocations: photography, psychology, travel, hiking, outdoor life. Home: 722 Peterson Rd Burlington WA 98233

ZERIN, STEVEN DAVID, lawyer; b. N.Y.C., Oct. 1, 1953; s. Stanley Robert and Cecilie Paula (Goldberg) Z.; m. Susan Marilyn Wershba, Oct. 13, 1984; children: Alexander James, J. Oliver. BS, Syracuse U., 1974; JD, St. Johns U., 1977. Bar: N.Y. 1978, U.S. Dist. Ct. (so. dist.) N.Y. 1985, U.S. Supreme Ct. 1986. Assoc. Gladstein & Isaac, N.Y.C., 1981-82, Sperry, Weinberg, Wels, Waldman & Rubenstein, N.Y.C., 1982-85; ptnr. Wels & Zerin, N.Y.C., 1985—. Trustee, mem. bd. govs. Daytop Village. Mem. ABA (exec. mem. and lectr. family law sect.), N.Y. State Bar Assn. (exec. com. family law sect.), Assn. of Bar of City of N.Y. Democrat. Home: 200 E 89th St New York NY 10128-9999 Office: Wels & Zerin 600 Madison Ave 22d Fl New York NY 10022

ZERNER, HENRI THOMAS, art historian; b. France, May 25, 1939; s. Frederick and Elisabeth (Lazarsfeld) Z.; m. Catherine Wilkinson, May 5, 1973; children: Rachel, Charles-Theodore. Student, Columbia Coll., 1957-58; Ph.D., U. Paris, 1969. Mem. faculty dept. art history Brown U., 1966-73; vis. curator prints and drawings Mus. of Art, R.I. Sch. Design, 1965-73; curator prints Fogg Art Mus.; prof. fine arts Harvard U., 1973—. Author: The School of Fontainebleau Etchings and Engravings, 1970, Romanticism and Realism: The Mythology of 19-century Art, 1984. Recipient Prix Achille Fould Académie des Inscriptions et Belles Lettres, 1971; Focillon fellow, 1961; Guggenheim fellow, 1971; Am. Council Learned Socs. fellow, 1978. Mem. Coll. Art Assn. Am., Internat. Council Museums, Société de l'Histoire de l'Art Français. Office: Harvard U Fogg Art Mus Cambridge MA 02138

ZERNER, MICHAEL CHARLES, chemistry and physics educator, consultant, researcher; b. Boston, Jan. 31, 1940; s. Maurice Bernard and Blanche (Deutsch) Z.; m. Anna Gunilla Fojerstam, May 5, 1966; children: Erik Mark, Emma Danielle. BS, Carnegie Mellon Inst., 1961; MS, Harvard U., 1962, PhD, 1966; postdoctoral U. Uppsala, (Sweden), 1968-70. Asst. prof. U. Guelph (Ont., Can.), 1970-74, assoc. prof., 1974-80, prof., 1980-82, adj. prof., 1982-87; prof. chemistry and physics U. Fla., Gainesville, 1981—, chmn. dept. chemistry, 1988-94; cons. in theoretical chemistry; co-organizer Internat. Sanibel Symposium on Theoretical Chemistry, 1983—. Served to U.S. Army, 1966-68. Recipient cert. U.S. Army Materials Command, 1975, Humboldt prize, 1991-94, Achievement award Internat. Soc. Quantum Bio., 1986; named Fulbright Disting. Prof., 1987; NIH fellow, 1968-70; Grantee NSF, Nat. Sci. and Engring. Rsch. Coun. of Can., Office Naval Rsch. Fellow AAAS; mem. Am. Chem. Soc. Am. Inst. Physics, Sigma Xi, others. Patentee in photoconduction and polymer sci.; co-editor Procs. Internat. Conf. Quantum/Biology and Pharmacology, 1978-94; Internat. Congress Quantum Chemistry, 1983-94; editor Adv. Quantum Chemistry; assoc. editor Internat. Jour. Quantum Chemistry; contbr. pubs. to profl. lit. Office: U Fla Dept Of Chemistry Gainesville FL 32611

ZERR, EMIL MARTIN, construction company executive; b. San Antonio, Dec. 3, 1930; s. Emil Martin and Cleo (Grona) Z.; m. Barbara Freeman, May, 1959; children—Sharon Kay Boren, Debra Ann Harris, William Martin. B.S. in Civil Engring., U. Tex, 1957. Registered profl. engr., Tex. Gen. mgr. Brown & Root Inc., Houston, 1959, project mgr., asst. div. mgr., v.p., now sr. v.p. Brown & Root chmn. United Way Tex, Gulf Coast, 1984. Served with USMC, 1951-54, Korea. Decorated Bronze Star. mem. Houston Engring. and Sci. Soc., Assn. Builders and Contractors (bd. dirs. 1972-80), Assn. Gen. Contractors (nat. bd. dirs. 1983-85). Republican. Roman Catholic. Clubs: Houston, Plaza. Home: 14935 Cindywood Dr Houston TX 77079-6364 Office: Brown & Root Tech Svcs 4100 Clinton Dr Houston TX 77020-6237

ZERVAS, NICHOLAS THEMISTOCLES, neurosurgeon; b. Lynn, Mass., Mar. 9, 1929; s. Themistocles and Demetra P. (Stasinopoulos) Z.; m. Thalia Poleway, Feb. 15, 1959; children—T. Nicholas, Christopher Louis, Rhea. A.B., Harvard U., 1950; M.D., U. Chgo., 1954. Intern N.Y. Hosp., 1955; resident in neurology Montreal Neurol. Inst., 1956; resident in neurosurgery Mass. Gen. Hosp., Boston, 1958-62; fellow in stereotaxic cerebral surgery U. Paris, 1960-61; asst. attending surgeon, asso. neurosurgery Jefferson Med. Coll., Phila., 1962-67; asso. prof. surgery Harvard U., 1971-77; also chief neurosurg. service Beth Israel Hosp., Boston, 1967-77; prof. surgery Harvard U., 1977—; also chief neurosurg. service Mass. Gen. Hosp., 1977—; Higgins prof. neurosurgery Harvard U., 1987—. Contbr. numerous articles to sci. jours. Chmn. Mass. Coun. Arts and Humanities, 1983-91; trustee Boston Symphony Orch., 1990—, vice chmn., 1993—, pres., 1994. Capt. M.C. AUS, 1956-58. Mem. Am. Acad. Neurol. Surgery (pres. 1990-91), Am. Assn. Neurol. Surgeons, Soc. Neurol. Surgeons, Am. Neurol. Assn., Am. Bd. Neurol. Surgery (chmn. 1990-91), Inst. Medicine Nat. Acad. Scis., Sigma Xi. Home: 100 Canton Ave Milton MA 02186-3507 Office: Mass Gen Hosp 32 Fruit St Boston MA 02114-2620

ZERWEKH, ROBERT PAUL, engineering administrator, engineering management educator, researcher, consultant, artist; b. Peoria, Ill., Feb. 25, 1939; s. Robert John and Beatrice Emily (Lewis) Z.; m. Marilyn Ann Bevan, May 26, 1974; children—Jeffrey, Robert, Richard, Michael. B.S. in Metall. Engring., U. Mo., 1961; M.S. in Metall. Engring., U. Ill., 1963; Ph.D. in Metallurgy, Iowa State U., 1970. Research asst. U. Ill.-Urbana, 1961-64; jr. metall. Ames Lab, U.S. AEC, Ames, Iowa, 1964-65; sr. materials engr. Gen. Dynamics Corp., Groton, Conn., 1965-67; prof. engring. U. Kans., Lawrence, 1970—, assoc. dean, engring., 1980-86, assoc. vice chancellor research grad. studies, pub. service, 1987—; cons. Industry Legal Profession, Midwest, 1970—; trustee Ctr. for Research, Inc., Lawrence, Kans., 1981—; mem. adv. bd. and exec. com. sch. of engring. U. Kans., 1981-86. Contbr. articles to profl. jours. Bd. dirs. Lawrence Arts Ctr., 1981-83. Named Emerging Artist Am. Artist Mag., 1989; NASA grantee, 1976-78; Atomic Energy Commn. fellow, 1971, NASA-ASEE fellow, 1975. Mem. Am. Soc. Engring. Mgmt., Lawrence C. of C. Republican. Mem. Christian Ch. (Disciples of Christ). Avocations: oil painting; sports; classical music; reading. Office: U Kans Rsch Grad Studies and Pub Svc Lawrence KS 66045

ZETCHER, ARNOLD B., apparel executive; b. 1940. BA, Washington U., 1962. With Federated Dept. Stores, N.Y.C., 1962-76; chmn. bd., CEO Bonwit Teller, N.Y.C., 1976-80; with Kohl's Corp., N.Y.C., 1980-83; chmn bd., CEO Kohl's Food Stores, N.Y.C., John Breuner Co., San Ramon, Calif., 1983-86; pres. The Talbot Inc., Hingham, Mass., 1987—. Office: Talbot's Inc 175 Beal St Hingham MA 02043-1501

ZEUGNER, JOHN FINN, history educator, writer; b. N.Y.C., Oct. 7, 1938; s. Orland Kump and Ethel (Finn) Z.; m. Alice Chatfield Valentine, Sept. 7, 1968; children: Emily Valentine, Maxwell Finn, Laura Ruth. A.B., Harvard U., 1959; M.A., Fla. State U., 1968, Ph.D., 1971. Night mgr. Beach Cart, Sarasota, Fla., 1960-67; asst. prof. history Worcester Poly. Inst., Mass., 1971-74; assoc. prof. Worcester Poly. Inst., 1974-82, prof., 1982—; Fulbright lectr. Osaka U., Kobe U., Japan, 1976-78; vis. prof. Keio U., Tokyo, 1981-83; Bryant Drake guest prof. Kobe Coll., Japan, 1994-95. Contbr. articles, short stores to profl. pubs. Served with USCG, 1961-62. Named Paris Fletcher Disting. Prof. Humanities, Worcester Poly. Inst. 1985; grantee NEA, 1970. Mem. Orgn. Am. Historians, Soc. Historians Am. Fgn. Rels.,

Soc. Historians Tech. Avocations: tennis; chess. Home: 31 William St Worcester MA 01609-2313 Office: Worcester Poly Inst Humanities Dept Worcester MA 01609

ZEUSCHNER, ERWIN ARNOLD, investment advisory company executive; b. Freiburg, Germany, Nov. 17, 1935; came to U.S., 1936; s. Reinhold Hermann and Helene Barbara (Maas) Z.; m. Christa Elfreide Ellmers, June 20, 1959 (dec. Aug., 1971); children—Peter Erwin, Suzanne Christina, Andrea Ellmers; m. Margaret Anne Finn, Mar. 25, 1972; 1 dau., Elizabeth Nora. B.A. in Econs., Queens Coll., 1957; M.B.A. in Fin, NYU, 1964. Sr. v.p. Chase Manhattan Bank, N.Y.C., 1970-72; sr. v.p., dir. Chase Investors Mgmt. Corp., 1972-80; sr. v.p. Chase Manhattan Corp., 1970-80; ptnr. David J. Greene & Co. (investment advs.), N.Y.C., 1980—. Served to capt. USAF, 1958-60. Mem. N.Y. Soc. Security Analysts (dir.). Home: 1 Middle Dr Manhasset NY 11030-1414 Office: 599 Lexington Ave New York NY 10022

ZEVNIK, PAUL A., lawyer; b. Ashland, Wis., Nov. 2, 1950; s. Richard Anton and Barbara Ann (Rohow) z.; m. Cynthia Ann Hargadon, May 15, 1983; children: Daniel Anton, Katherine Ann. AB magna cum laude, AM, Harvard U., 1972, JD cum laude, 1976. Bar: Calif. 1976, D.C. 1978, U.S. Supreme Ct. 1983, Pa. 1985. Assoc. Covington & Burling, Washington, 1977-80; ptnr. Paul Hastings Janofsky & Walker, Washington, 1980-87, Kaye Scholer Fierman Hays & Handler, Washington, 1987—; sec., bd. dirs. Golden Hills Broadcasting Corp., Denver, Lomas de Oro Broadcasting Corp., Denver, Zeus Corp. of Wash., Seattle; bd. dirs. Interspan Communications Corp., Ft. Worth. Democrat. Home: 1616 Riggs Pl NW Washington DC 20009-6417 Office: Winston & Strawn 1400 L St NW # 6 Washington DC 20005-3509

ZEVON, SUSAN JANE, editor; b. N.Y.C., July 23, 1944; d. Louis and Rhea (Alter) Z. BA, Smith Coll., 1966. Asst. editor trends and environments House & Garden, N.Y.C., 1970-80; account supr. Jessica Dee Communications, N.Y.C., 1981-84; editor architecture House Beautiful, N.Y.C., 1985—. Author: (with others) Decorating On The Cheap, 1984. Mem. Archtl. League N.Y., Smith Coll. N.Y. Club (v.p. 1987-88, pres. 1988-89). Avocations: films, lit., gymnastics, art. Office: House Beautiful 1700 Broadway New York NY 10019-5905

ZEVON, WARREN, singer, songwriter; b. Chgo., Jan. 24, 1947; m. Crystal Zevon (div.); 1 child, Ariel; 1 child from previous marriage, Jordan. Folksinger, writer commls., pianist with Everly Bros., 1970-73; albums include Wanted Dead or Alive, 1970, Warren Zevon, 1976, Excitable Boy, 1978 (gold record), Bad Luck Streak in Dancing School, 1980, Stand in the Fire, 1980, The Envoy, 1982, Sentimental Hygiene, 1987, Transverse City, 1989, (with Hindu Love Gods) Hindu Love Gods, 1990, Mr. Bad Example, 1991, Learning to Flinch, 1993, A Quiet Normal Life (the best of Warren Zevon), 1993, Mutineer, 1995; composer: When Johnny Strikes up the Band, Hasten Down the Wind, Werewolves of London, Poor Poor Pitiful Me, Play It All Night Long, Roland the Headless Thompson Gunner. Office: care Virgin Records Am Inc 338 N Foothill Rd Beverly Hills CA 90210-3608*

ZEWAIL, AHMED HASSAN, chemistry and physics educator, editor, consultant; b. Damanhour, Egypt, Feb. 26, 1946; came to U.S., 1969, naturalized, 1982; s. Hassan A. Zewail and Rawhia Dar; m. Dema Zewail; children: Maha, Amani, Nabeel. B.S., Alexandria U., Egypt, 1967, M.S., 1969; Ph.D., U. Pa., 1974; MA (hon.), Oxford U., 1991; DS (hon.), Am. U., Cairo, 1993. Teaching asst. U. Pa., Phila., 1969-70; IBM fellow U. Calif., Berkeley, 1974-76; asst. prof. chemistry and chem engring. Calif. Inst. Tech., Pasadena, 1976-78, assoc. prof., 1978-82, prof., 1982-89, Linus Pauling prof. chem. physics, 1990—; cons. Xerox Corp., Webster, N.Y., 1977-80, ARCO Solar, Inc., Calif., 1978-81. Editor Laser Chemistry, 1980-85, Jour. Phyical Chemistry, 1985-90, Chem. Physics Letters, 1991—, Internat. Series Monographs on Chemistry, 1992—, Advances in Laser Spectroscopy Vol. I, 1977, Vol. 3, 1978, Photochemistry and Photobiology, Vols. I and II, 1983, Ultrafast Phenomena VII, 1990, VIII, 1993, IX, 1994, The Chemical Bond: Structure and Dynamics, 1992, Femtochemistry-Ultrafst Dynamics of the Chemical Bond, Vols. I and II, 1994, Adv. Editl. Bd. Jour. Physical Chemistry, 1980-84, Chemical Physics, 1988—, Laser Focus World, 1992, Am. Men and Women of Sci., 1993—, World Sci., 1994—; contbr. numerous articles to sci. jours. Recipient Tchr.-scholar award Dreyfus Found., 1979-85, Alexander von Humboldt Sr. U.S. Scientist award, 1983, NASA award, 1991, 1st AMM Achievement award, 1991, Nobel Laureate Signature award, 1992, Carl Zeiss award, Cairo U. Medal and Sheld of Honor, 1992, U. Qatar medal, 1993, Niles award of honor, 1994; John Simon Guggenheim Meml. Found. award, 1987, King Faisal Internat. prize in sci., 1989. Mem. NAS, Am. Acad. Arts and Scis. (Royal Netherlands Acad. Arts and Scis. medal 1993), Am. Chem. Soc. (Buck-Whitney medal 1985, Harrison Howe award 1989, Hoechst prize 1990), Am. Physical Soc. (Herbert P. Broida prize 1995), European Acad. Arts, Scis., and Humanities, Third World Acad. Scis., Sigma Xi (Earle K. Plyler prize 1993, Wolf prize 1993). Patentee in solar energy field. Office: Calif Inst Tech Divsn Chemistry and Chem Engring Mail Code 127 72 Pasadena CA 91125

ZEYEN, RICHARD JOHN, plant pathology educator; b. Mankato, Minn., Jan. 17, 1943; s. Clifford John and Eleanor Otilla (Laase) Z.; m. Anita Kozan, June 25, 1967 (div. 1971); m. Carol Breese Van Why, Dec. 10, 1984. Dir. EM facility Minn. Agrl. Exptl. Sta., St. Paul, 1971—; asst. prof. plant pathology U. Minn., St. Paul, 1973-75, assoc. prof., 1976-83, prof., 1983—; cons. Minn. Pollution Control Agy. Contbr. articles to profl. jours. Underwood fellow Agr., Food and Rsch. Coun., U.K., 1993; NATO Scientific Exch. Program fellow, Wales, U.K., 1990-95. Mem. AAAS, Am. Phytopathol. Soc. (chmn. various coms. 1967—), Microscopy Soc. Am., Minn. Microscopy Soc. (past officer, bd. dirs., pres. 1981-82), Mankato State U. Alumni Assn. (bd. dirs. 1974-77), Sigma Xi. Achievements include analytical electron microscopy, X-ray microanalysis applications to biolog. specimens; molecular and biochem. regulation genetically controlled plant disease resistance; plant viruses, their vectors; cytochemistry diseased plants. Home: 2206 Hoyt Ave Saint Paul MN 55108-1341 Office: U Minn Dept Plant Pathology 495 Borlaug Hall Buford Cir Saint Paul MN 55108

ZHANG, XUMU, chemist, educator; b. E Zhou City, Hubei, China, Oct. 30, 1961; came to U.S., 1985; m. Liping Xiong, July 14, 1986; 1 child, Isadora Y. BS, Wuhan U., 1982; MS, Chinese Acad. Scis., Fuzhou, Peoples Republic of China, 1985; postgrad., U. Calif., San Diego, 1985-87; PhD, Stanford U., 1992. Staff rschr. Chinese Acad. Scis., 1982-85; rsch. asst. Stanford (Calif.) U., 1987-92, postdoctoral fellow, 1992-94; asst. prof. chemistry Pa. State U., University Park, 1994—; cons. Adelphi Tech., Inc., 1993-94. Franklin Veatch fellow, 1991; Camille and Henry Dreyfus Found. grantee, 1994. Mem. Am. Chem. Soc. Achievements include transition metal catalyzed asymmetric synthesis for chiral drugs. Office: Pa State U Dept Chemistry University Park PA 16802*

ZHANG, YOUXUE, geology educator; b. Huarong County, Hunan, China, Sept. 17, 1957; came to U.S., 1983; s. Zaiyi Zhang and Dezhen Wu; m. Zhengjiu Xu; children: Dan, Ray. BS in Geol. Scis., Peking U., Beijing, 1982; MA in Geol. Scis., Columbia U., 1985, MPhil, 1985, PhD in Geol. Scis., 1989. Grad. rsch. asst. Columbia U., N.Y.C., 1983-88; postdoctoral fellow Calif. Inst. Tech., 1988-91; asst. prof. geology U. Mich., Ann Arbor, 1991—. Contbr. articles to profl. jours. Named Young Investigator, NSF, 1994. Mem. Am. Geophys. Union, Geochem. Soc. (F.W. Clarke medal 1993), Mineral. Soc. Am., Sigma Xi. Office: Dept Geol Sci U Mich Ann Arbor MI 48109-1063

ZHOU, HUANCHUN, chemist; b. Shanghai, Oct. 1, 1939; came to U.S., 1985; s. Qingyun and Wanxian (Hu) Z.; m. Qingliang Li, Sept. 5, 1967; 1 child, Fugang. BS equivalent, Fudan U., China, 1962; MS, Shanghai U. Tech., China, 1981; PhD equivalent, U. Fla., 1990. Engr. Wuzi Oil Pump Factory, Jiangsu, China, 1971-74; laborer Wuxi Oil Pump Factory, Jiangsu, 1971-74; analytical technician Wuzi Oil Pump Factory, Jiangsu, China, 1974-76; faculty Shanghai U. Tech., 1982-84; rschr. asst. chemistry U. Fla., Gainesville, 1985-91, instr. math., 1988-89, rschr. materials sci. and engring. dept., 1988-90; chemist Fla. Dept. Agrl. and Consumer Svc., 1991—; lab. chief Wuxi Oil Pump Factory, 1964-76; chmn. sect. chem. analysis Wuxi Sci-Tech. Assn., 1963-66; lectr. to 201st Am. Chem. Soc. Meeting, 1991. Editor: Wuxi Chem. Analysis and Phys. Test, 1964-66; corr. editor Jour. Chem.

Analysis and Phys. Test, 1964-66; contbr. articles to profl. jours.; co-developer chem. polymerization polyaniline and polypyrrole on Langmuir-Blodgett trough, first in world; discovered method to monitor polymerizations by Langmuir-Blodgett computerized techniques. Polit. prisoner, China, 1966-71. Co-grantee Office of Naval Rsch., 1991. Home: Temple Ter 7517-C Pitch Pine Cir Tampa FL 33617

ZHOU, MING DE, aeronautical scientist, educator; b. Zhejiang, China, June 26, 1937; s. Pin Xiang and Ang Din (Xia) Z.; m. Zhuang Yuhua, Aug. 12, 1936; children: Zhengyu, Yan Zhuang. BS, Beijing U. Aeros.-Astronautics, 1962; MS, Northwestern U. Tech., 1967; PhD, Internat. Edn. Rsch. Found., 1992. Tchr. Harbin (China) U. Tech., 1962-64, 67-73; from lectr. to prof. Nanjing (China) U. Aeronautics and Astronautics, 1973-86, 86—; dean bd. postgrad. studies Nanjing (China) U. Aeros. and Astronautics, 1985-89; nationally qualified PhD advisor China, 1989—; rsch. scientist U. Ariz., Tucson, 1991-93, rsch. prof., 1993—; vis. scholar Cambridge (England) U., 1980-82; guest scientist Inst. Exptl. Fluid Mechanics, Göttingen, Germany, 1983-84, 85, 87; sr. vis. scientist Tech. U. Berlin, 1988, 90; rsch. assoc. U. So. Calif., L.A., 1989-90. Mem. editorial com. Chinese Jour. Exptl. Mechanics, 1986-89; author: (with others) Viscous Flows and Their Measurements, 1988, (with others) Introduction to Vorticity and Vortex Dynamics, 1992; contbr. articles to Aero. Jour. U.K., Experiments in Fluids, AIAA Jour., Chinese Jour. Aeronautics. Co-recipient Nat. award Progress in Sci. and Tech. first class, Peoples Republic of China, 1985. Mem. AIAA (sr.), Am. Phys. Soc., Chinese Soc. Aeronautics, Chinese Soc. Mechanics (mem. acad. group exptl. fluid mechanics 1986-89), Chinese Soc. Aerodynamic Rsch. (acad. group unsteady flow and vortex control 1985-89). Achievements include patent for techniques and device of artificial boundary layer transition.

ZHOU, XIAOYUAN, paleobiologist, researcher; b. Lingwu, Ningxia, China, Jan. 8, 1965; s. Mingjin Zhou and Guangxia Kong; m. Zhang Bo, June 26, 1992. BS, Beijing U., 1984; MS, Acad. Sinica, Beijing, 1987; PhD, U. Mich., 1995. Rsch. asst. Inst. Vertebrate Paleontology and Paleoanthropology, Acad. Sinica, Beijing, 1987-89, Mus. Paleontology, U. Mich., Ann Arbor, 1989—. Doctoral Dissertation grantee U. Mich., 1992, grantee-in-aid Geol. Soc. Am., 1992. Mem. Soc. Vertebrate Paleontology. Office: U Mich Mus Paleontology Ann Arbor MI 48109

ZHU, AI-LAN, opera singer; b. Nanjing, Jiang Su, Peoples Republic of China, Nov. 29, 1956; came to U.S., 1984; d. De-Chang Zhu and Shu-hua Tsao; m. Chai-Lun Yueh, Oct. 30, 1982. MusB, Cen. Conservatory Music, Beijing, 1977; Artist Diploma in Opera, Hartt Sch of Music, U. Hartford, 1986. Appeared in leading opera houses of N.Am.; leading soprano in Tex. Opera Theater, Houston, 1987, Va. Opera Assn., Norfolk, 1987, Opera Theater St. Louis, 1989, PepsiCo Summerfare and European tour, N.Y., 1989, Lyric Opera of Boston, 1990, Glyndebourne Opera Festival, 1990, 91, Lyric Opera of Kansas City, 1990, Caramoor Festival, N.Y., 1990, Chautauqua Opera and Orch., 1990, Opera Pacific, L.A., 1991, Minn. Opera, 1992, Opera Co. Phila., 1992, Mich. Opera Theater, 1993, Austin Lyric Opera, 1993, 94—, Scottish Opera, 1994, Austin Lyric Opera, 1994-95, Conn. Opera, 1995, Atlanta Opera, 1995; European tour Pelléas et Mélisande, 1992-93; concert singer Chautauqua (N.Y.) Instn., 1987, Liederkranz Found., N.Y.C., 1989; recital The Theatre Musical de Paris, Chatelet, 1991; concert tour with Sherrill Milnes, Beijing, China, 1993. Finalist Luciano Pavarotti internat. vocal competition, Opera Cos. Phila., 1985; recipient 1st prize Sigma Alpha Iota vocal competition, Chautauqua, N.Y., 1986, 5th prize Liederkranz Found. vocal competition, N.Y.C., 1989. Mem. Am. Guild Mus. Artists. Home: 51 King Philip Dr West Hartford CT 06117-2140 Office: Columbia Artists Mgmt 165 W 57th St New York NY 10019-2201

ZHU, MINGDE, chemist; b. Shanghia, Peoples Republic of China, Apr. 5, 1940; came to the U.S., 1986; s. Nianci and Nanyun (Du) Z.; m. Yuxin Jin, Apr. 30, 1967; children: Peter, Norman. MS, Beijing U., 1965. Rsch. assoc. Acad. Agriculture, Beijing, 1965-70; chem. engr. Ganjiang Pharm. Factory, Jian, Peoples Republic of China, 1971-79; rsch. chemist Acad. Chinese Traditional Medicine, Beijing, 1980-83; vis. scholar Uppsala (Sweden) U., 1983-86; sr. rsch. chemist Bio-Rad Labs., Richmond, Calif., 1986—. Patentee IEF in capillary, non-gel sieving. Office: Bio-Rad Labs Life Science Group 2000 Alfred Nobel Dr Hercules CA 94547

ZHUKOV, YURI, ballet dancer; b. Leningrad, Russia. Student, A.Y. Vaganova Sch. Choreography, Leningrad. With Kirov Ballet; soloist San Francisco Ballet, 1989-92, prin. dancer, 1992—. Appeared in ballets Nutcracker, Serenade, The Four Temperaments, Handel-a Celebration, The Sleeping Beauty, Swan Lake, Aurora Polaris, Menuetto, The Four Seasons, Variations de Ballet, Vivaldi Concerto Grosso, Dreams of Harmony, The End, Dark Elegies, Rodin, Job, Cinderella, Giselle, Scotch Symphony. Office: San Francisco Ballet 455 Franklin St San Francisco CA 94102-4471*

ZIADEH, FARHAT J., Middle Eastern studies educator; b. Ramallah, Palestine, Apr. 8, 1917; s. Jacob and Nimeh Farah Z.; m. Suad Salem, July 24, 1949; children—Shireen, Susan, Rhonda, Deena, Reema. B.A., Am. U., Beirut, 1937; LL.B., U. London, 1940. Bar: Barrister-at-law Lincoln's Inn 1946. Instr. Princeton U., 1943-45, lectr. Oriental studies, 1948-54, asst. prof., 1954-58, asso. prof., 1958-66; magistrate Govt. of Palestine, 1947-48; editor Voice of Am., USIA, 1950-54; prof. U. Wash., Seattle, 1966—; prof., chmn. dept. Near Eastern lang. and lit. U. Wash., 1970-82, dir. Ctr. Arabic Study Abroad, 1983-89; adj. prof. U. Wash. Law Sch., 1978-87, prof. emeritus, 1987—; Author: Reader in Modern Literary Arabic, 1964, Lawyers, The Rule of Law and Liberalism in Modern Egypt, 1968, Property Law in the Arab World, 1979; contbr. articles to profl. jours. Mem. Middle East Studies Assn. (pres. 1979-80), Am. Oriental Soc. (past pres. western br.), Am. Research Center in Egypt (past bd. govs., exec. com.), Am. Assn. Tchrs. Arabic (past pres.). Eastern Orthodox. Office: Univ Wash Seattle WA 98195

ZIBART, MICHAEL ALAN, wholesale book company executive; b. Nashville, Mar. 12, 1947; s. Alan Walter and Joy (Hughes) Z.; m. Margaret Anne Boyd, Dec. 27, 1976; children: Emily Joy, Mary Claire. B.A., Vanderbilt U., 1969. Mgmt. trainee Zibart Bros. Books, Nashville, 1961-69; property mgr. Pollack Co., Nashville, 1966-69; buyer Ingram Book Co., Nashville, 1970-75, mgr. trade dept., 1976, v.p., 1976-85, exec. v.p., 1985-88; founder, pres. ProMotion, Inc., Nashville, 1988—. Author: Almanac on Bookselling, 3d edit., 1980. Office: ProMotion Inc 2501 21st Ave S # 5 Nashville TN 37212-5626

ZICHEK, SHANNON ELAINE, secondary school educator; b. Lincoln, Nebr., May 29, 1944; d. Melvin Eddie and Dorothy Virginia (Patrick) Z. AA, York (Nebr.) Coll., 1965; BA, U. Nebr., Kearney, 1968; postgrad., U. Okla., Edmond, 1970, 71, 72, 73, 74, 75, U. Nebr., Kearney, 1980, 81, 82, 89, 92. Tchr. history and English, NW High Sch., Grand Island, Nebr., 1948—. Republican. Christian. Home: 2730 N North Rd Grand Island NE 68803-1143

ZICK, JOHN WALTER, retired accounting company executive; b. Highland Park, Ill., Sept. 21, 1925; s. Walter Ernest and Helen Ann (Wiedenhoeft) Z.; m. Mary Ann Sutter, Dec. 11, 1948; children: Sharon, Catherine, John W. B.S., Northwestern U., 1948. With Price Waterhouse, Chgo., 1948-73, N.Y.C., 1973-86; partner Price Waterhouse, 1960-86, partner in charge N.Y.C. office, 1973-76, regional mng. partner, 1976-78, co-chmn., ops., dept. sr. partner, 1978-86. Bd. dirs. Medic Alert Found., U.S., 1994—; founding mem., elder Winnetka (Ill.) Presbyterian Ch., 1956-67; bd. auditors New Trier Twp., Ill., 1969-73; trustee Carnegie Hall Soc. and Corp., 1980—; mem. corp. Greenwich Hosp. Assn., 1980-89. Served with USN, 1943-46. Mem. AICPA (treas. and dir. 1974-77), Ill. Soc. CPAs (pres. 1971-72). Clubs: Pine Valley Golf; Union League (N.Y.C.); Blind Brook; Burning Tree (Washington).

ZIDEK, JAMES VICTOR, statistician, educator; b. Acme, Alta., Can., Sept. 26, 1939; s. John and Mann (Marik) Z.; m. Patricia Lynne Donald, Aug. 5, 1961. B.Sc. with honors, U. Alta., 1961, M.Sc., 1963; Ph.D., Stanford U., 1967. Mem. faculty U. B.C., Vancouver, 1967—; prof. stats., 1976—, head dept., 1984-89; prof. dept. stats. U. Wash., Seattle, 1983-84;

hon. research fellow Univ. Coll., London, 1971-72; vis. sr. research scientist Commonwealth Sci. and Indsl. Research Orgn., 1976-77; chmn. statis. scis. com. Natural Sci. and Engring. Research Council Can., 1980-81, chmn. math. sci. group, 1988-91. Editor Statis. Sci., 1988-91, Chapman and Hall Math Stat Series; sr. assoc. editor Can. Jour. Stats., 1980; contbr. articles to profl. jours. Fellow Inst. Math. Stats., Am. Statis. Assn.; mem. Internat. Statis. Inst., Internat. Assn. Survey Statisticians, Royal Statis. Soc., Can. Statis. Soc., Elec. Stats. Soc. Can. (pres. 1987-88). Office: U B C, Vancouver, BC Canada V6T 1Z2

ZIEBARTH, E. WILLIAM, news analyst, educator; b. Columbus, Wis., Oct. 4, 1910; s. John and Priscilla (Conrad) Z.; m. Elizabeth Herreid, Dec. 16, 1939; 1 son, John Thomas. B.S., U. Wis., 1933, Ph.M., 1934; Ph.D., U. Minn., 1948, D.H.L. (hon.), 1985. Staff U. of Air, WHA, U. Wis., 1934; instr. speech U. Minn., 1936; acting gen. mgr. sta. WLB, 1944, asso. prof., chmn. dept. speech, 1948, prof., chmn. dept. speech and theatre arts, 1949—, dean summer session, 1954—, dean gen. extension div., 1963-64; dean Coll. Liberal Arts, 1964, interim pres., 1974; cons. for TV World Affairs, 1954; founder, also dir. Min. Sch. of Air, 1938; prodn. mgr. WCCO-CBS, 1945, news analyst, 1947-52, exec. cons., 1948; edit. dir. central div. CBS network, 1946, cons., 1948-51, spl. fgn., corr., internat. affairs analyst, Scandinavia, So. and Western Europe, 1949, fgn. corr.; internat. broadcaster, Scandinavia, Western Europe, Western Asia, 1950, Asiatic analysis, Tokyo, Japan, 1952; exec. v.p., interim gen. mgr. KTCA-TV, KTCI-TV, 1976; exec. v.p., gen. mgr. Twin City Area Pub. TV Corp., 1976-77; radio edn. cons. Hill Found. award study in Soviet Union, 1958, 68; bd. dirs. Midwest Ednl. Television Corp.; trustee Twin City Area TV Corp.; co-chmn. feasibility research Pan-Pacific-Mainland Edn. and Communication Expt. by Satellite, Honolulu, Tokyo, Hong Kong, 1973. Author Six Classic Plays for Radio and How to Produce Them, published in, 1940; contbr.: articles to profl. jours. Mass Media editor Speech Monographs, 1951-53; cons. editor: articles to profl. jours. Central States Speech Jour. Dir. Hennepin County Tb Assn., Minn. Tb and Public Health Asso. Mem. Gov.'s Youth Commn.; mem. Nat. Commn. on Arts and Scis.; Trustee Macalester Coll. Joint winner nat. Peabody award, 1948; recipient citation Nat. English Council, 1949; Radio Council award for distinguished news analysis, 1952, for significant contbns. internat. understanding, 1951; first award Nat. Inst. Edn. by Radio for news interpretation, 1952; Best Commentator award AFTRA, 1955; joint winner Peabody award, internat. affairs, 1960; Nat. Peabody award, 1972; Blakeslee award Nat. Heart Assn., 1972; Mitchell V. Charnley award for Outstanding Contbns. to Broadcast Journalism, 1982; Outstanding Individual award Speech-Communication Assn., 1979; N.W. Area Found. fellow to People's Republic of China, 1976. Mem. Nat. Assn. Edn. by Radio, Fgn. Policy Assn., Minn. Hist. Soc., Nat. Adult Edn. Assn., Nat. Assn. Ednl. Broadcasters and Telecasters, Nat. Soc. Study Communication (Radio council, mass media com.), Central States Speech Assn., Chi Phi, Phi Kappa, Delta Sigma Rho, Phi Delta Kappa, Psi Chi, Alpha Epsilon Rho, Delta Phi Lambda, Lambda Alpha Psi. Clubs: Hesperia, Greyfriars, Campus, Univ. St, Paul. Home: 1596 Northrop Ave Saint Paul MN 55108-1322 Office: N-231 Psychology Elliott Hall # U Minn Minneapolis MN 55455

ZIEBARTH, KARL REX, international transportation consultant; b. Reading, Pa., May 25, 1938; s. Robert Kurt and Leah Evelyn (DuBor) Z.; m. Gisela Hermine Hader, Nov. 13, 1970; children: Viktoria, Alexander, Elena. B.A., Yale U., 1959. Security analyst Bank of N.Y., 1960-63; 2d v.p. Hayden, Stone, Inc., N.Y.C., 1963-70; asst. v.p Dominick and Dominick, N.Y.C., 1970-71; v.p., sec., treas. Mo.-Kans.-Tex. R.R. Co., Dallas, 1970-78; exec. v.p. fin. Mo.-Kans.-Tex. R.R. Co., 1979-88, also bd. dirs.; pres. Atlantic & Western Mgmt., Irving, Tex., 1990, also bd. dirs.; fin. and transp. cons. Dallas, 1990—. Trustee Phila. Soc., 1975-78, Dallas Ballet Assn., 1981-86, Am. Enterprise Forum, 1989—. Capt. USAR, 1960-69. Clubs: Racquet (Chgo.); Petroleum (Dallas); Reform (London); Yale (N.Y.C.). Office: 3626 N Hall St Ste 405 Dallas TX 75219-5129

ZIEFF, RALPH MORRISON, psychologist; b. Boston, Apr. 17, 1940; s. Henry and Anne Ruth (Morrison) Z.; m. Leah Kahalas, Aug. 12, 1962 (div. Aug. 1974); children: Eric Henry, Jonathon Eliot, Julie Rachel. AB cum laude, Harvard U., 1962; PhD, U. N.C., 1971. Lic. psychologist, Maine. Staff psychologist N.C. Meml. Hosp., Chapel Hill, 1967-68, Temple U. Med. Ctr., Phila., 1968-70; staff psychologist, asst. prof. psychology Med. Coll. Pa., Phila., 1970-71; dir. community psychiatry Maine Med. Ctr., Portland, 1971-78; pvt. practice Portland, 1974—; asst. clin. prof. psychiatry Tufts Med. Sch., Boston, 1971-78; cons. Waynflete Sch., Portland, 1974—, Shalom House, Inc., Portland, 1974—. Active Democrat, 1962—. Mem. APA, Am. Assn. Retired Persons, Nat. Register of Health Care Providers in Psychology, New Eng. Psychol. Assn. Jewish. Avocations: tennis, auctions, swimming. Home: 291 Pine Point Rd Scarborough ME 04074 Office: 193 Middle St Portland ME 04101

ZIEGAUS, ALAN JAMES, public relations executive; b. Bremerton, Wash., May 8, 1948; s. Alan Moon and Dorothy (Lamont) Z.; m. Constance Jean Carver, 1972; children: Jennifer, Ashley. BJ, San Diego State U., 1970. Staff writer San Diego Tribune, 1972-77; asst. account exec. San Diego City Council, 1977-78; v.p. Gable Agy., San Diego, 1978-80; pres. Stoorza, Ziegaus & Metzger, San Diego, 1980—. Mem. planning com. County San Diego, 1980-82; mem. sewage task force City of San Diego, 1986-88, civil svc. com., 1992—; trustee armed forces YMCA, San Diego, 1984—. Recipient Best Investigative Series award AP, 1975. Mem. San Diego Press Club (Best News Story award 1973). Home: 12351 Brassica St San Diego CA 92129 Office: Stoorza Ziegaus & Metzger 225 Broadway Ste 1600 San Diego CA 92101-5000*

ZIEGELMAN, ROBERT LEE, architect; b. Detroit, Apr. 20, 1936; s. Samuel Ziegelman and Annabelle (Davis) Benton; m. Esther C. Adelson, June 20, 1957 (div.); children: Shelly Dawn, John David, Adam. M. BArch, U. Mich., 1958, MArch, MIT, 1959. Registered architect, Mich., Pa., Okla., D.C., N.Y., Ga., Tex., Md., Mo., Ark., Toronto, Ont. Project designer Eero Saarinen and Assocs., Birmingham, Mich., 1959-62; project designer Minoru Yamasaki and Assocs., Birmingham, 1962-63; prin. Ziegelman and Ziegelman, Architects, Birmingham, 1963-72, Robert L. Ziegelman, Architects, Birmingham, 1972-80; chmn. bd. Luckenbach/Ziegelman and Ptnrs. Inc., Birmingham, 1980—; mem. dean's adv. com. Lawrence Tech. U.; adj. prof. U. Mich., 1976-85; design lectr. MIT, 1980; chmn. bd. Insta-Drugs, Inc., Birmingham, 1966-80. Prin. works include Guatemala Hosp. and Surg. Ctr. (award of excellence, Am. Inst. Steel Constr.), Westinghouse Electric Pace Control Ctrs (Gov.'s award), William Bell Townhouses (Record Apts. of Yr. award Archtl. Record, award of merit, AIA, Housing Mag., Homes for Better Living award Housing Mag., Handleman Distbn. Ctrs. (award of honor Mich. Soc. Architects), Handleman Corp. Offices (honor award Detroit chpt. AIA), Prefabricated Bank Bldg. (honor award Detroit chpt. AIA), 260 Brown (M award Masonry Inst. Am., Mich. Soc. Architects), Thal residence (M award Mason Inst. Am., Mich. Soc. Architects), U. Mich. (M award Masonry Inst. Am., Mich. Soc. Architects, AIA Honor award); contbr. articles to profl. jours.; patentee in field. Bd. dirs. Boys and Girls Club Am., Detroit, 1980-82, Birmingham, Bloomfield Art Assn., 1990; chmn. Housing Bd. Appeals, Birmingham, 1989; mem. Civic Design Com., Birmingham, Dean Search Com., U. Mich. Fellow AIA (pres. Detroit chpt. 1992); mem. Nat. Coun. Archtl. Registrations Bds. Office: Luckenbach/Ziegelman 115 W Brown St Birmingham MI 48009-6019

ZIEGENHAGEN, DAVID M., healthcare company executive; b. Mpls., May 25, 1936; s. Elmer Herbert Ziegenhagen and Margaret Ruth (Mackenzie) Kruger; m. Mary Ange Kinsella, Nov. 26, 1966 (div. Dec. 1982); children: Marc, Eric. BA, U. Minn., 1962. Assoc. dir. Thailand Peace Corps, Bangkok, 1963-65; Thailand program officer Peace Corps, Washington, 1966-67; dir. Western Samoa Peace Corps, Apia, 1967-70; exec. dir. Mental Health Assn. Minn., Mpls., 1970-76; co-founder, pres. Current Newspapers, Inc., Burnsville, Minn., 1975-84; sr. program officer The St. Paul Found., 1982-84; pres. DMZ Assocs., St. Paul, 1983-85; exec. dir. Minn. Bd. Med. Practice, St. Paul, 1985-88; CEO, pres. Found. for Health Care Evaluation, Bloomington, Minn., 1988—; field dir. Am. Refugee Com., Bangkok, 1979; dir. Health Edn. Rsch. Found., St. Paul, 1993-95; mem. Citizens League, Mpls., 1975—, dir., 1988—; mem. Adminstrs. in Medicine, Washington, 1985-88; dir. Walk-In Counseling Ctr., Mpls., 1988—, Am. Med. Rev. Rsch. Ctr., Washington, 1990—. Mem. Nat. Mental Health Staff Coun. (pres. 1970-76). Avocations: travel, international development, arts.

Office: Found for Health Care Evaluation 2901 Metro Dr Ste 400 Minneapolis MN 55425-1558

ZIEGLER, DANIEL MARTIN, chemistry educator; b. Quinter, Kans., July 6, 1927; s. Anton T. and Clara (Weissbeck) Z.; m. Mary Alice Weir, Aug. 19, 1952; children: Daniel L., Paul W., Mary Claire, James M. BS in Chemistry, St. Benedicts Coll., 1949; PhD in Chemsitry, Loyola U., 1955; postdoctoral, U. Wis., 1955-58. Asst. prof. Inst. Enzyme Rsch. U. Wis., Madison, 1958-61; asst. prof. chemistry U. Tex., Austin, 1961-62, assoc. prof. chemistry, 1962-69, prof. chemistry, 1969—. Editor jour. Biol. Chemistry, 1979-89; mem. editorial bd. Analyt. Biochemistry, 1989-91, Arch. Biochem. Biophys., 1966-71; contbr. articles to profl. jours. Recipient Bernard B. Brodie award Am. Soc. Pharmacol. Experiments, 1990, Alexander von Humboldt award, Germany, 1991. Home: 6704 Shoal Creek Blvd Austin TX 78757-4379 Office: U Tex Dept Chemistry & Biochemist Austin TX 78712

ZIEGLER, DELORES, mezzo-soprano; b. Decatur, Ga.; children: Katie, Adam. Grad., Maryville Coll.; postgrad., U. Tenn. Operatic roles include Dorabella in Cosi Fan Tutti, Octavian in Der Rosenkavalier, Dulcinee in Don Quichotte, Cherubino in Le Nozze di Figaro, Rosina in Barber of Seville, Romeo, in I Capuleti e i Montecchi (first singer to sing the role of Romeo in Moscow and San Francisco), Idamante in Idomeneo, Charlotte in Werther, Adalgisa in Norma, Sextus in La Clemenza di Tito; performances with Atlanta Symphony, Bonn Theater der Stadt, Theater der Stadt Koln, La Scala Opera, Paris Opera, Bolshoi Opera, Moscow, Vienna Stattsopera, Phila. Orch., Met. Opera; recs. include Dorabella in Cosi Fan Tutte, EMI, Mozart Requiem, Mozart Great Mass, Atlanta Symphony, Mahler's 8th Symphony Telark Records, Beethoven 9th Symphony, Phila. Orch., EMI, Bach B Minor Mass, Teldek records, Margared in Le Roi d'ys, Erato Disque, title role in Bertoni's Orfeo, Frequenz records, Mozart's Kronenmesse, Deutsch Grammaphon; debut as Dorabella in Cosi fan tutti, Lyric Opera Chgo., first Carmen at Atlanta Opera; debut at N.Y. Met. as Siebel in Faust, 1990. Office: care Lynda Kay 2702 Crestworth Ln Buford GA 30519 Office: Côté Artists Mngmt Inc 157 W 57th St Ste 803 New York NY 10019*

ZIEGLER, DEWEY KIPER, neurologist; b. Omaha, May 31, 1920; s. Isidor and Pearl (Kiper) Z.; Mar. 30, 1954; children: Amy, Laura, Sara. BA, Harvard U., 1941, MD, 1945. Diplomate: Am. Bd. Psychiatry and Neurology; bd. dirs. 1974-83, exec. com. 1978-82). Intern in medicine Boston City Hosp., 1945-46; asst. resident then chief resident in neurology N.Y. Neurol. Inst.-Columbia U. Coll. Physicians and Surgeons, 1948-51; resident in psychiatry Boston Psychopathic Hosp., 1951-53; asst. chief neurol. service Montefiore Hosp., N.Y.C.; and asst. prof. neurology Columbia U., 1953-55; asst. prof. U. Minn., 1955-56; assoc. clin. prof. U. Kans. Med. Sch., 1956-64, chief dept. neurology, 1968-85; prof. U. Kans. Med. Center, 1964-89, prof. emeritus, 1989—; cons. Social Security Adminstrn., 1975—; mem. com. on certification and co-certification Am. Bd. Med. Specialties, 1979-82. Author: In Divided and Distinguished Words, 1942; Contbr. numerous articles to profl. jours. Served to lt., j.g., M.C USNR, 1946-48. Fellow Am. Acad. Neurology (pres. 1979-81, v.p. 1972-73); mem. AMA, Am. Neurol. Assn., Am. Epilepsy Soc. Jewish. Home: 8347 Delmar Ln Shawnee Mission KS 66207-1821 Office: Kans U Med Center 3900 Rainbow Blvd Kansas City KS 66103-2918

ZIEGLER, DONALD EMIL, federal judge; b. Pitts., Oct. 1, 1936; s. Emil Nicholas and Elizabeth (Barclay) Z.; m. Claudia J. Chermak, May 1, 1965; 1 son, Scott Emil. B.A., Duquesne U., 1958; LL.B., Georgetown U., 1961. Bar: Pa. 1962, U.S. Supreme Ct. 1967. Practice law Pitts., 1962-74; judge Ct. of Common Pleas of Allegheny County, Pa., 1974-78; judge U.S. Dist. Ct. (we. dist.) Pa., Pitts., 1978-94, chief judge, 1994—. Treas. Big Bros. of Allegheny County, 1969-74. Mem. ABA, Pa. Bar Assn., Allegheny County Bar Assn., Am. Judicature Soc., St. Thomas More Soc. Democrat. Roman Catholic. Club: Oakmont Country. Office: US Post Office & Courthouse 6th Fl Courtroom 12 7th & Grant Sts Pittsburgh PA 15219

ZIEGLER, DONALD ROBERT, accountant; b. Lancaster, Pa., Nov. 15, 1932; s. John Jacob and Esther Mae (McKelly) Z.; m. Suzanne Foster, children: D. Rand, Scott F., Kurt J. B.S. in Econ. Acctg., Franklin and Marshall Coll., 1954. CPA, Pa. Mgr., sr. staff mem. Price Waterhouse, Phila., 1954-67, ptnr. 1967-92, sr. practice ptnr., 1978-92, mng. ptnr. Mid-Atlantic area, 1985-88; vice chmn. Southeast Region, 1988-92; mem. policy bd. Price Waterhouse, N.Y.C., 1980-88, mem. mgmt. com., 1986-92. Author: (with others) Managing and Accounting for Inventories, 1980. Contbg. author various books in field. Trustee Franklin and Marshall Coll., 1983—; alumni exec. coun., 1979-83, devel. com., chmn. audit com. 1989—, Phila. alumni coun.; trustee Pa. Ballet, 1988-92, 94—, devel. and fin. coms., vice chmn. bd. trustees, 1989-92, chmn. exec. com. 1989-91. With U.S. Army, 1955-57. Recipient Outstanding Soldier award U.S. Army, 1955, Disting. Svc. Alumni medal Franklin and Marshall Coll. 1991. Mem. AICPA (auditing standards com. 1973-76, chmn. subcom. fraud 1976-80), Pa. Inst. CPAs (Phila. chpt. exec. coun.). Clubs: Sunnybrook Golf (Plymouth Meeting); Rehoboth Beach Country Club; Phila. Aviation (bd. govs. and treas. 1969-90), Royal Blackheath Golf (U.K.). Home: RD 1 700 N Trooper Rd Norristown PA 19403-4502 Office: Price Waterhouse LLP 30 S 17th St Philadelphia PA 19103-4021

ZIEGLER, EARL KELLER, minister; b. Sheridan, Pa., Mar. 4, 1929; s. Abraham Hoffman and Rhoda Bucher (Keller) Z.; m. Vivian Zug Snyder, Aug. 12, 1951; children: Karen Louise Miller, Randall Earl, Doreen Kay Creighton, Michael Wayne, Konnae Lee Manatrakoon, Sulien Nicodemus. BA, Elizabethtown (Pa.) Coll., 1951; MDiv, Bethany Theol. Sem., Chgo., 1954; DDiv, Lancaster (Pa.) Theol. Sem., 1982. Ordained to ministry Ch. of the Brethren, 1950. Pastor Woodbury (Pa.) Congregation, Pa., 1954-60, Black Rock Ch. of Brethren, Brodbecks, Pa., 1960-70, Mechanic Grove Ch. of Brethren, Quarryville, Pa., 1970-83, Atlantic N.E. Dist. Exec., Harrisburg, Pa., 1983-89, Lampeter (Pa.) Ch. of the Brethren, 1989—; moderator Ch. of the Brethren, Elgin, Ill., 1993-94; moderator various dists., Pa., 1959—; mem. Gen. Bd., Ch. of Brethren, 1975-80; chmn. Parish Ministerial Comm., 1979-80; dir. Family Life Inst., 1961, 64, mem. Nat. Korean Com., 1988-91, Denominational Structure Com., 1990-91, others; adj. prof. ch. history Evang. Sem., Myerstown, Pa., 1988—. Author: Divorce Among the Church of the Brethren Clergy, 1981; contbr. articles to profl. jours. Pres. Manheim Elem. PTA, 1964-65; trustee Elizabethtown Coll., 1965-83; dir. Community Choir, Lineboro, Md., 1966-70; dir. Solanco Community Men's Chorus, Quarryville, 1976-83. Recipient Alumni citation, Elizabethtown Coll. Alumni Assn., 1964, award for Outstanding Ch. Planting in Azua Province of Dominican Republic, 1990, Award of Appreciation, Germantown Ch. of Brethren, 1990. Mem. Lampeter Willow St. Ministerium (pres. 1989-91). Republican. Office: Ch of the Brethren Gen Offices 1451 Dundee Ave Elgin IL 60120-1674 *"You shall have what your faith expects," were the words of Jesus to two blind men. These words challenge the potential within each of us, a faith that conquers, a spirit that soars. Between the possible and the impossible is the measure of one's will.*

ZIEGLER, EKHARD ERICH, pediatrics educator; b. Saalfelden, Austria, Apr. 12, 1940; children: Stefan, Gabriele, Lena. M.D., U. Innsbruck, Austria, 1964. Diplomate: Am. Bd. Pediatrics. Intern U. Innsbruck, 1966-67, resident in pediatrics, 1967-68 70-71, resident in pharmacology, 1966-68, asst. dept. pediatrics, 1970-73; vis. instr. pediatrics U. Iowa, Iowa City, 1968-70, asst. prof. pediatrics, 1973-76, assoc. prof., 1976-81, prof., 1981—; dir. program human nutrition, 1989—; mem. nutrition study sect. NIH, 1988-92. Recipient Nutrition award Am. Acad. Pediactrics, 1988. Mem. Am. Soc. Clin. Nutrition, Soc. Pediatric Research, Soc. Exptl. Biology and Medicine, N.Am. Soc. Pediatric Gastroenterology, Midwest Soc. Pediatric Research, Am. Pediatric Soc., The Nutrition Soc., N.Y. Acad. Scis., Am. Acad. Pediatrics. Club: Univ. Athletic (Iowa City). Office: U Iowa Dept Pediatrics Iowa City IA 52242

ZIEGLER, JACK (DENMORE), cartoonist; b. N.Y.C., July 13, 1942; s. John Denmore and Kathleen Miriam (Clark) Z.; m. Jean Ann Rice, Apr. 20, 1968 (div. 1995); children: Jessica, Benjamin, Maxwell. B.A. in Communication Arts, Fordham U., 1964. Free-lance cartoonist N.Y.C., 1972—; cartoonist The New Yorker, N.Y.C., 1974—. Author: Hamburger Madness, 1978, Filthy Little Things, 1981, Marital Blitz, 1987, Celebrity Cartoons of the Rich and Famous, 1987, Worst Case Scenarios, 1990, Mr. Knocky, 1993; illustrator: (children's books) Lily of the Forest, 1987, Flying Boy, 1988, Annie's Pet, 1989, Eli and the Dimplemeyers, 1994, (adult books) Waiting Games, 1983, The Joy of Stress, 1984, That's Incurable!, 1984, Modern Superstitions, 1985, The No-Sex Handbook, 1990, There'll be a Slight Delay, 1991. Mem. Cartoonists Assn. (founding mem.), The Glory Boys, Nat. Cartoonists Soc. Democrat.

ZIEGLER, JOHN AUGUSTUS, JR., lawyer; b. Grosse Pointe, Mich., Feb. 9, 1934; s. John Augustus and Monnabell M. Ziegler; divorced; children—John Augustus III, Laura, Lisa, Adeline. A.B., U. Mich., J.D., 1957. Bar: Mich. 1957. Since practiced in Detroit; assoc. Dickinson, Wright, McKean & Cudlip, 1957-65, ptnr., 1965-68; ptnr. Parsons, Tennent, Hammond, Hardig & Ziegelman, 1969-70, Ziegler, Dykhouse & Wise, 1970-77; pres. Nat. Hockey League, 1977-92, chmn. bd. govs., 1976-78; of counsel Dickinson, Wright, Moon, Van Dusen & Freeman, Detroit, 1992—. Office: 1 Detroit Ctr 500 Woodward Ave Ste 4000 Detroit MI 48226-3425 also: 375 Park Ave Ste 2004 New York NY 10152

ZIEGLER, MANDELL STANLEY, composite sheet manufacturing executive; b. Niles, Mich., Dec. 11, 1921; s. Benjamin M. and Frances Maria (Fox) Z.; m. Marjorie Carolyn Klyne, Aug. 19, 1951; children: Thomas, John. BS in Chemistry, U. Notre Dame, 1943; PhD in Organic Chemistry, Mich. State U., 1950. Chemist E. I. DuPont De Nemours & Co., Wilmington, Del., 1950-60, Russell Reinforced Plastics Corp., Lindenhurst, N.Y., 1960-64; chief exec. officer Am. Acrylic Corp., West Babylon, N.Y., 1964—. Patentee in field. Pres. South Bay Jewish Community Coun., Massapequa, N.Y., 1982-90. Lt. (j.g.) USN, 1944-46. Mem. Am. Chem. Soc. Avocations: tennis, bridge, Am., British and naval history. Office: Am Acrylic Corp 400 Sheffield Ave West Babylon NY 11704-5399

ZIEGLER, MICHAEL LEWIS, lawyer; b. N.Y.C., Apr. 27, 1950. BA, SUNY, Albany, 1972; JD, SUNY, Buffalo, 1976; MPH, Columbia U., 1978. Bar: N.Y. 1976. Asst. prof. Columbia U., N.Y.C., 1977-80; ptnr. Epstein Becker & Green, N.Y.C., 1980-88, Bower & Gardner, N.Y.C., 1988-92, LeBoeuf, Lamb, Leiby & MacRae, N.Y.C., 1992—; adj. prof. Columbia U., 1980—, adj. assoc. prof. NYU, 1980—; adj. prof. SUNY Coll. Optometry, 1988—. Bd. dirs., chmn. N.Y. Found. For Ambulatory Care, 1993—; mem., co-chmn. bylaws com. New Leadership Group United Hosp. Fund, 1992—; gen. counsel Ronald MacDonald House of L.I., 1990—; bd. dirs., gen. counsel Care for the Homeless, Inc., 1992—. Named disting. adj. prof. grad. sch. pub. adminstrn. NYU, 1986. Mem. Nat. Health Lawyers Assn., N.Y. Acad. Scis., Assn. Bar N.Y.C. Office: LeBoeuf Lamb Leiby & MacRae 125 W 55th St New York NY 10019-5369

ZIEGLER, RANDALL KEITH, food service executive; b. Zanesville, Ohio, July 21, 1942; s. Claude M. Jr. and Pearl Pauline (Elliott) Z.; m. Judith Anne Begley, June 12, 1965; children: Dustin Eric, Braeden Keith, McKenzie Anne. BS, Ohio State U., 1965. Sales rep. Ledrele Labs. Pharms., Charleston, W.va., 1965-66; dist. sales mgr. ARA Svcs., Louisville and Dayton, Ohio, 1972-73; mng. dir. Ziegler Foods, Inc., Indpls., 1975-77; v.p. ARA/ARASERV, Phila., 1977-81, Servomation/Svc. Am., Stamford, Conn., 1981-86, Fine Host Internat. Corp., Greenwich, Conn., 1986-89; chmn. of bd. Fine Host Corp., Greenwich, Conn., 1989—. Capt. USAF, 1966-72. Named Ky. Col., Commonwealth of Ky., 1973; recipient Key Man award Great Falls Jaycees, 1968. Mem. Internat. Assn. Auditorium Mgrs. (bd. dirs. 1986-90, chmn. allied com. 1986-88, chmn. Sports Day 1990—, mem. allied com. 1986—), Nat. Assn. Concessionaires (bd. dirs. 1991—), Blue Ribbon Com. (chmn. 1994-95), Mont. Jaycees (chmn. state membership 1968), Jaycees (v.p. 1972),. Avocations: youth coaching, scuba, family activities. Home: 10 Copper Kettle Rd Trumbull CT 06611 Office: Fine Host Internat Corp 3 Greenwich Office Park Greenwich CT 06831

ZIEGLER, RAYMOND STEWART, architect; b. Colorado Springs, Colo., Aug. 18, 1919; s. Edwin L. and Grace (Stewart) Z.; m. Jolene Baddeley, Aug. 22, 1942; children: John, Richard. Student, Ecole De Beaux Arts, Atelier Winslow, U. Calif., San Francisco Archtl. Club. Ptnr. Allison, Rible, Robinson and Ziegler, Architects, Los Angeles, 1958-69; exec. dir., v.p Allison, Rible, Robinson and Ziegler an asso. group of Leo A Daly Co., 1969-74; ptnr. Raymond Ziegler Partnership, Architects, 1974-77; pres., chmn. bd. Ziegler Kirven Parrish Architects, 1978-84; pvt. cons. practice Altadena, Calif., 1984—; mem. Calif. adv. bd. Office Architecture and Constrn., 1968-77, chmn., 1971; vis. prof. sch. architecture U. Hawaii, 1987. Bd. dirs. L.A. Beautiful, 1974-77, 80-86, v.p., 1984, pres.-1985-86, pres.'s coun., 1987-89; bd. dirs. Soc. for Prevention Blindness, 1974-76; hon. lifetime dir. San Gabriel Valley unit Am. Cancer Soc., 1978—, chmn. campaign adv. bd., 1979-80; mem. United Way Health Ptnrs. Coun., 1982-85; mem. L.A. County Architects Evaluation Commn., 1984-95; chmn. profl. practice sect. com. for 1989 licensing exam. Calif. Bd. Archtl. Examiners. 1st lt. inf. AUS, World War II. Fellow AIA (treas. So. Calif. chpt. 1968-69, bd. dirs. Calif. Council 1968-69, trustee Ins. Trust of Calif. Council 1977-81, chmn. 1980-81, bd. dirs. Pasadena and Foothill chpt. 1984, treas. 1985-86); mem. Archtl. Guild (bd. dirs.), Design Profls. Safety Assn. (dir. 1980-85), Los Angeles C. of C. (bd. dirs. 1972-77), Hist. Soc. So. Calif. (bd. dirs. 1982-84, 86-91), Masons, Rotary. Home: 1276 Sunnyoaks Cir Altadena CA 91001-1543

ZIEGLER, RICHARD FERDINAND, lawyer; b. Elizabeth, N.J., Aug. 1, 1949; m. Carolyn Lewis; children: Anna B., David A., Andrew P. D-J. BA in History summa cum laude, Yale u., 1971; JD magna cum laude, Harvard U., 1975. Bar: N.Y. 1976, U.S. Dist. Ct. (so. and ea. dists.) N.Y. 1976, U.S. Dist. Ct. (ea. dist.) Mich. 1982, U.S. Supreme Ct. 1984, U.S. Dist. Ct. (no. dist.) N.Y. 1987. Law clk. to judge U.S. Dist. Ct. (so. dist.), N.Y.C., 1975-76; assoc. Paul, Weiss, Rifkind, Wharton & Garrison, N.Y.C., 1976-77; asst. U.S. atty. U.S. Dept. Justice (so. dist.) N.Y., N.Y.C., 1977-80; assoc. Cleary, Gottlieb, Steen & Hamilton, N.Y.C., 1980-83, ptnr., 1983—. Mem. ABA, Assn. Bar City of N.Y., Fed. Bar Council, N.Y. State Bar Assn. Office: Cleary Gottlieb Steen & Hamilton 1 Liberty Pla New York NY 10006

ZIEGLER, RONALD LOUIS, association executive, former government official; b. Covington, Ky., May 12, 1939; s. Louis Daniel and Ruby (Parsons) Z.; m. Nancy Lee Plessinger, July 30, 1960; children: Cynthia Lee Charas, Laurie Michelle. Student, Xavier U., 1957-58; B.S., U. So. Calif., 1961; DSc. (hon.), Mass. Coll. Pharmacy, 1989 (LE I.U., 1993. With Procter & Gamble Distbg. Co., 1961; account rep. J. Walter Thompson Co., 1962-68; press dir. Calif. Rep. Central Com., 1961-62; press aide to Richard Nixon in Calif. gubernatorial campaign, 1962; press aide staff Richard Nixon, 1968-69; press sec. to Pres. Nixon, 1969-74, asst. to, 1973-74; mng. dir., sr. v.p. internat. services Syska and Hennessy, Inc., Washington, 1975-80; pres. Nat. Assn. Truck Stop Operators, Alexandria, Va., 1980-87; pres., chief exec. officer Nat. Assn. Chain Drug Stores, Alexandria, 1987—; mem. nat. adv. bd. U. Okla., adv. coun. Pharm. Found. U. Tex.; chmn. Pharmacy Direct Network, 1994—. Bd. dirs. Nat. Coun. on Patient Info. and Edn., Nat. Drug Trade Conf., Richard Nixon Libr. and Birthplace. Mem. Nat. Assn. Chain Drug Stores Execs., Nat. Retail Fedn. (bd. dirs.), Pharmacists Against Drug Abuse, Assn. White House Press Secretaries, Nat. Assn. Rare Disorders, Sigma Chi Alumni. Office: Nat Assn Chain Drug Stores 413 N Lee St Alexandria VA 22314

ZIEGLER, R.W., JR., lawyer, consultant; b. Pitts.; children: Caroline, Gretchen, Jeremy, Benjamin, Phoebe, Polly. Student, Carnegie Tech., U. Pitts.; JD, Duquesne U., 1972. Bar: Pa. 1972, Calif. 1981, U.S. Ct. Appeals (3d cir.) 1977, (9th cir.) 1982, U.S. Dist. Ct. (we. dist.) Pa. 1972, Calif., 1982, U.S. Tax Ct. 1978, U.S. Supreme Ct. 1977. Ptnr. Ziegler & Ombres, Pitts., 1973-79; pres. Ziegler Ross Inc., San Francisco, 1979—; lectr. for Bar Assns. Author: Law Practice Management; editor: Law Office Guide in Computing. Mem. ABA, Am. Mgmt. Assn., Pa. State Bar Assn., Calif. State Bar Assn. Office: 1350 Bayshore Hwy Ste 440 Burlingame CA 94010

ZIEGLER, WILLIAM, III, diversified industry executive; b. N.Y.C., June 26, 1928; s. William and Helen (Murphy) Z.; m. Jane Elizabeth Troy, Feb. 22, 1952; children: Melissa Jane, William Troy, Peter Martin, Cynthia Curtis, Helen Matilda, Karl Huttig. B.A., Harvard U., 1950; M.B.A., Columbia U., 1962. Vice pres. GIH Corp., N.Y.C., 1959-64, pres., 1964—, dir., 1955—; dir. Am. Maize Products Co., N.Y.C., 1958—; chmn. bd., dir. Park Ave. Operating Co., Inc., 1958—; chmn.bd., dir. Jno. H. Swisher & Son, Inc. Bd dirs. Foresight, Inc., New Haven; pres. E. Matilda Ziegler Found. for Blind;

sec. Matilda Ziegler Pub. Co. for Blind; bd. dirs. Maritime Ctr. at Norwalk. Served from ensign to lt. USNR, 1952-54. Mem. Southwestern Area Commerce and Industry Assn. Conn. (dir.). Clubs: N.Y. Yacht, Noroton (Conn.) Yacht. Home: 161 Long Neck Point Rd Darien CT 06820-5815 Office: Am Maize Products Co PO Box 10128 250 Harbor Dr Stamford CT 06904-2128

ZIEGLER, WILLIAM ALEXANDER, lawyer; b. N.Y.C., July 15, 1924; s. William Alexander and Sally (Cootes) Z.; m. Glenn Crawley, Feb. 10, 1950; children: Richard S., Daryl A. Henning, Susan G. Barrows, W. Thomas. A.B., Harvard U., 1944, J.D., 1949. Bar: N.Y. 1949, U.S. Tax Ct 1950, U.S. Dist. Ct. (so. dist.) N.Y. 1949, U.S. Dist. Ct. (ea. dist.) N.Y. 1957, U.S. Dist. Ct. (no. dist.) Ohio 1973, U.S. Dist. Ct. (ea. dist.) Mich. 1983, U.S. Ct. Apppeals (1st cir.) 1963, U.S. Ct. Appeals (2d cir.) 1957, U.S. Ct. Appeals (3d cir.) 1986, U.S. Ct. Appeals (4th cir.) 1979, U.S. Ct. Appeals (5th cir.) 1987, U.S. Ct. Appeals (6th cir.) 1984, U.S. Ct. Appeals (7th cir.) 1992, U.S. Ct. Appeals (8th cir.) 1981, U.S. Ct. Appeals (9th cir.) 1973, U.S. Ct. Appeals (10th and 11th cirs.) 1983, U.S. Ct. Appeals (D.C. cir.) 1972, U.S. Supreme Ct. 1972. Assoc. Sullivan & Cromwell, N.Y.C., 1949-56, ptnr., 1957-89, cons., 1990—; chmn. exec. com., bd. dirs. H.W. Wilson Co.; sec., bd. dirs. Std. Commel. Corp. Engring. Info., Inc., H.W. WIlson Found.; bd. dirs. Harvard Club Fairfield County, dirs. Fgn. Policy Assn. Bd. dirs. Fgn. Polisy Assn.; sec., bd. dirs. H.W. Wilson Found. Mem. Assn. Bar City of N.Y., Riverside Country Club (Mont.), Harvard Club of N.Y.C. Office: 125 Broad St New York NY 10004

ZIEHLER, TONY JOSEPH, insurance agent; b. Anderson, Ind., June 20, 1936; s. Joseph Anthony and Julie Ann (Kette) Z.; m. Alice Mae Pattison, Apr. 2, 1956 (div. 1972); children: Susan Z. Brown, Kathryn Z. Dwyer, Jane Z. Bee, Patricia Z. Koty, Michael; m. Barbara Buys Wood, Feb. 28, 1981; stepchildren: David Wayne Wood, Brent Douglas Wood. BSBA, U. Ariz., 1958. CLU. Prin. Ziehler Ins., Tucson, 1958—. Employee edn. chmn. So. Ariz. Div. Am. Cancer Soc.; co-chmn. Medic-Alert Found., Pima County, Ariz.; chmn. Tucson Festival Soc.; mem. Salpointe High Sch. Found., others. Recipient William Wisdom award U. Ariz., Tucson, 1958. Mem. Greater Tucson Assn. Life Underwriters (pres. 1963-64, Agt. of Yr. 1975), Ariz. Assn. Life Underwriters (pres. 1970-71, Agt. of Yr. 1980), So. Ariz. CLU Soc. (pres. 1968-69), Salvation Army (pres. adv. bd. 1984-85), Univ. of Ariz. Found. (mem. planned giving com.), Rotary, (com. chmn.), Tucson Conquistadores (pres. 1985-86), Los Charros del Desierto, Golden Key Soc., MIllion Dollar Round Table, others. Republican. Avocations: travel, trail riding, Belgian draft horses, mountain hiking, sports. Home: 6000 E Calle De Vita Tucson AZ 85715-1957 Office: Ziehler Ins 6420 E Broadway Blvd Ste B102 Tucson AZ 85710-3536

ZIELINSKI, CHARLES ANTHONY, lawyer; b. Buffalo, N.Y., Dec. 24, 1944; s. Charles Walter and Genevieve Teresa (Szczepanik) Z.; m. Kathryn Mary Guercio, May 30, 1969; children: Eden Clare, Jessica Anne. BA, LeMoyne Coll., 1966; JD, SUNY, Buffalo, 1969. Bar: N.Y. 1970, U.S. Ct. Appeals (D.C. and 1st cirs.) 1971, U.S. Ct. Appeals (2d cir.) 1972, U.S. Supreme Ct. 1975. Trial and appellate litigation atty. Fed. Communications Commn., Washington, 1970-73; legal asst. to chmn. N.Y. State Pub. Svc. Commn., Albany, N.Y., 1973-76, commr., 1976-77, chmn., 1977-81; ptnr. Wald, Harkrader & Ross, Washington, 1981-85, Rogers & Wells, Washington and N.Y.C., 1986—; chmn. N.Y. State Bd. on Electric Generation Siting and the Environ., 1977-81, N.Y. State Telecom. Policy Task Force, 1980-81, Nat. Assn. of Regulatory Utility Coms., Ad Hoc Com. on Nat. Energy Act, 1979-81, mem. exec. com., 1978-81. Contbr. articles to profl. jours. Mem. Fed. Communications Bar Assn. Office: Rogers & Wells 607 14th St NW Washington DC 20005-2000

ZIEMANN, EDWARD FRANCES, food service company executive, sales and marketing professional; b. Chgo., July 3, 1944; s. Edward F. and Ethyle (Ruthenbeck) Z.; m. Linda Magarethe Nakamichi Sowka, July 14, 1952; children: Russell, Jeffrey, Robert, Christina. BA, U. Ill., Chgo., 1967. Cert. foodservice profl. Reservations freight clk. Milw. Road. R.R., Chgo., 1965-66; sales adminstr. Robertson Photo Mechanic, Des Plaines, Ill., 1966-68; v.p. and officer Anetsberger Bros., Inc., Northbrook, Ill., 1968—; mem. Tech. Liaison Com., Chgo., 1990-91. Bd. dirs. Village Improvement Com., Round Lake, Ill.; asst. Catholic Charities, Waukegan, Ill., 1990-91. Mem. Am. Mktg. Assn., Nat. Assn. Food Equipment Manufacture, Bakers Club (century mem.), Moose. Republican. Roman Catholic. Avocations: swimming, golfing, writing, cooking, gardening. Office: Anetsberger Bros Inc 180 Anets Dr Northbrook IL 60062-5452

ZIEMANN, G. PATRICK, bishop; b. Pasadena, Calif., Sept. 13, 1941. Attended, St. John's Coll. and St. John's Sem., Camarillo, Calif., Mt. St. Mary's Coll., L.A. Ordained priest Roman Cath., 1967. Titular bishop, aux. bishop Diocese Santa Rosa, Obba, 1986-92; bishop Diocese Santa Rosa, Santa Rosa, Calif., 1992—. Office: Chancery Office PO Box 1297 547 B St Santa Rosa CA 95401-5249*

ZIEMER, RODGER EDMUND, electrical engineering educator, consultant; b. Sargeant, Minn., Aug. 22, 1937; s. Arnold Edmund and Ruth Ann (Rush) Z.; m. Sandra Lorann Person, June 23, 1960; children: Mark Edmund, Amy Lorann, Norma Jean, Sandra Lynn. B.S., U. Minn., 1960, M.S., 1962, Ph.D., 1965. Registered profl. engr., Mo. Research asst. U. Minn., Mpls., 1960-62; research assoc. U. Minn., 1962; prof. elec. engring U. Mo., Rolla, 1968-83; prof. elec. engring. U. Colo., Colorado Springs, 1984—, chmn. dept. elec. engring.-1984-93; cons. Emerson Electric Co., St. Louis, 1972-84, Mid-Am. Regional Coun., Kansas City, Mo., 1974, Motorola, Inc., Scottsdale, Ariz. 1980-84, Martin Marietta, Orlando, 1980-81, TRW, Colorado Springs, summer, 1985, Sperry, Phoenix, 1986, Pericle Communications, summer, 1994; sabbatical at Motorola, Scottsdale, 1991. Author: Principles of Communications, 1976, 2d edit., 1985, 3d edit., 1990, 4th edit., 1995, Signals and Systems, 1983, 2d edit., 1989, 3d edit., 1993, Digital Communications and Spread Spectrum Systems, 1985, Introduction to Digital Communication, 1992, Introduction to Spread Spectrum Communications, 1995; editor: IEEE Jour. on Selected Areas in Communications, 1989, 92, 95, IEEE Communications Mag., 1991. Served to capt. USAF, 1965-68. Scholar Western Electric, 1957-59; trainee NASA, 1962-65. Fellow IEEE; mem. Am. Soc. Engring. Edn., Armed Forces Communications and Electronics Assn., Sigma Xi, Tau Beta Pi, Eta Kappa Nu. Lutheran. Home: 8315 Pilot Ct Colorado Springs CO 80920-4412 Office: Univ Colo PO Box 7150 Colorado Springs CO 80933-7150

ZIEN, DAVID ALLEN, state legislator; b. Chippewa Falls, Wis., Mar. 15, 1950; s. Allen Roy Zien and Orpha Mattix; m. Suzanne Eleanor Bowe, Sept. 8, 1992; children: Travis, Aryan, Kurt, Amber, Lori, Angel-Sky, Rebecca. BS in Geography and Bus. cum laude, U. Wis., Eau Claire, 1974; MS in Guidance and Counseling summa cum laude, U. Wis. Stout, Menomonie, 1975; postgrad., U. Wis., Superior, 1975-80; doctoral studies, U. Wis., 1980-84. Roofer pvt. practice Chippewa Falls, Wis., 1970-75; longshoreman Superior, Wis., 1975-79; vet. outreach counselor State of Wis., Superior, 1975-79; job svc. counselor State of Wis., Medford, Wis., 1980-83; campus adminstr. Northcentral Tech. Coll., Medford, Wis., 1983-88; state rep. 68th Assembly, Eau Claire, Wis., 1988-93; state senator 23rd Dist. Eau Claire, 1993—; Wis. wits. outreach dir. VFW, Madison, Wis., 1975-84. Contbr. articles to profl. jours. Speaker, presenter Rep. Party of Wis., 1984—; advisor Wis. Cmty. Edn. Assn., 1983-89. Sgt. USMC, Vietnam, 1968-70. Named Legislator of Yr. ABATE of Wis., 1990, VFW, 1990, 92-93, State of Wis., 1991, Am. Legion, 1993, Wis. Assn. Concerned Vets., 1993, Wis. Farm Bur. Friend of Agr., 1991-94, NFIB Guardian of Small Bus., 1992; recipient Wis. Counties Assn. Cert. Appreciation 1993-94, Hmong Stout Student Assn. Outstanding Good Friend award, 1993-94, State Hist. Soc. Cert. Appreciation, 1994. Mem. VFW, NRA, DAV, WVV (Vet. of Yr. 1992), VEC (Damn Fine Legislator 1992), VVA (Disting. Achievement award 1993), WACVO, HOG, ALEC, NCSL, AFA, CMA, AMA, BOLT, ABATE, ANY, WVT, Northland VV, USMC League & Club, Eagles, Nat. Motorcycle Hall of Fame, Grandma's Marathon, Christian Outdoorsmen, Nat. Rep. Legislators, Am. Life League, Am. Legion, Iron Bde., Internat. Assn. Employment Security, Am. Legis. Exch., Wis. Wildlife Fedn., Highground Vets. Meml. Project, Wis. Vets. Tribute Com., Elks, Masons. Lutheran. Avocations: motorcycling, hunting, running. Home: 2928 Solem Ln Eau Claire WI 54703-1233

ZIERING, SIGI, medical company executive; b. Kassel, Germany, Mar. 20, 1928; came to U.S., 1949; s. Isaac and Cilly (Frisch) Z.; m. Marilyn Brisman, June 14, 1953; children—Michael, Rosanne, Ira, Amy. B.A., Bklyn. Coll., 1953; M.A., Syracuse U., 1955, Ph.D., 1957. Sr. scientist Raytheon Co., Waltham, Mass., 1957-59; dept. head Allied Research, Boston, 1959-61; pres. Space Scis., Waltham, 1961-68; research dir. Whittaker Corp., Los Angeles, 1968-70; v.p. med. group Dynascis., Los Angeles, 1970-71; pres. Diagnostic Products, Los Angeles, 1972—, also dir. Contbr. articles to physics jours. Pres., Temple Beth Am., Los Angeles, 1979-80. Mem. Am. Phys. Soc., Am. Assn. Clin. Chemists. Office: Diagnostic Products Corp 5700 W 96th St Los Angeles CA 90045-5544

ZIERING, WILLIAM MARK, lawyer; b. New Britain, Conn., Feb. 4, 1931; s. Jacob Max and Esther (Freedman) Z.; m. Harriet Koskoff, Aug. 20, 1958; 1 son, Benjamin. B.A., Yale U., 1952; J.D., Harvard U., 1955. Bar: Conn. 1955, Calif. 1962. Assoc. Koskoff & McMahon, Plainville, Conn., 1959-60; sr. trial atty. SEC, San Francisco, 1960-65; pvt. practice law San Francisco, 1965—; ptnr. Bremer & Ziering, 1972-77; instr. Golden Gate U. Law Sch., San Francisco, 1968-75. Vice pres., bd. dirs. Calif. League Handicapped, 1972—. Served to comdr. USNR, 1955-58. Mem. ABA, Calif. Bar Assn., San Francisco Bar Assn. (past chmn. securities, corps. and banking), Navy League (dir.). Club: Commonwealth. Home: 2027 Lyon St San Francisco CA 94115-1609 Office: 4 Embarcadero Ctr Ste 3400 San Francisco CA 94111-4187

ZIERLER, NEAL, mathematician; b. Balt., Sept. 17, 1926; s. Joseph Nathan and Betsey (Levie) Z.; m. Betty Matsumoto, Dec. 26, 1950 (div. 1981); children: Robert Eugene, Joan Mariye, Ann M. AB, Johns Hopkins U., 1945; AM, Harvard U., 1949, PhD, 1959. Mathematician, physicist Ballistic Rsch. Labs., Aberdeen, Md., 1951; mem. tech. staff instrumentation lab. MIT, Cambridge, Mass., 1952-54; mem. tech. staff Lincoln Lab. MIT, Lexington, Mass., 1954-60; supr. info. processing group of jet propulsion lab. Calif. Inst. Tech., Pasadena, 1960-61; sr. scientist ARCON Corp., Lexington, 1961-62; head sub-dept. process analysis MITRE Corp., Bedford, Mass., 1962-65; tech. staff Ctr. for Comm. Rsch. Inst. Def. Analysis, Princeton, N.J., 1965—. Patentee error-detecting and -correcting devices; contbr. articles to profl. jours. Lt. USN, 1944-46. Fellow IEEE; mem. Am. Math. Soc., Math. Assn. Am. Avocations: tennis, skiing, photography. Office: Inst Def Analysis Ctr Communications Rsch Thanet Rd Princeton NJ 08540-3699

ZIFCHAK, WILLIAM C., lawyer; b. 1948. BA, Columbia U., 1970; JD, Columbia U., 1973. Bar: N.Y. 1974, U.S. Ct. Appeals (2d cir.) 1975, U.S. Ct. Appeals (3d cir., D.C. cir.) 1983, U.S. Dist. Ct. (e. dist.) N.Y. 1984. Ptnr. Kaye, Scholer, Fierman, Hays & Handler, N.Y.C; planning com. NYU Ann. Nat. Conf. Labor, 1991—. Contbr. articles to profl. jours. Mem. ABA (sect. labor and employment law 1975—, subcom. antitrust, RICO and labor rels. law), Assn. Bar City of N.Y. (sec. com. labor and employment law 1984-87), N.Y. State Bar. Office: Kaye Scholer Fierman Hays & Han 425 Park Ave New York NY 10022-3506

ZIFF, LARZER, English language educator; b. Holyoke, Mass., Oct. 2, 1927; s. Isadore Menden and Sara (Rosenbloom) Z.; m. Ruth Rosalind Geisenberger; children—Joshua, Oliver, Joel, Abigail. Student, Middlebury Coll., 1945-47; M.A., U. Chgo., 1951, Ph.D., 1955; M.A. (hon.), U. Oxford, Eng., U. Pa. Prof. English U. Calif., Berkeley, 1956-73; univ. lectr. Oxford U., Eng., 1973-78; prof. English U. Pa., 1978-81; Caroline Donovan prof. English Johns Hopkins U., Balt., 1981—, chair dept., 1991—; dir. U. Calif. Edn. Abroad Program, U.K., Ireland, 1969-71; cons. and lectr. in field. Author: The Career of John Cotton, 1962; The American 1890's, 1968; Puritanism in America, 1973; Literary Democracy, 1981; Writing in the New Nation, 1991; also articles, essays in profl. jours.; mem. editorial bds. including ELH, 1981—. Recipient numerous awards for excellence in English including Christian Gauss award, the American 1890's, 1967; Fulbright fellow, 1959-60, fellow Am. Coun. Learned Socs., 1963-64, Newberry Libr., 1964, NEH, 1967-68, Guggenheim fellow, 1977-78, Woodrow Wilson Internat. Ctr. for Scholars, 1986-87; Fulbright Disting. Sr. Lectr., 1993. Fellow Am. Acad. Arts and Scis.; mem. MLA, Am. Antiquarian Soc., Am. Studies Assn. Office: Johns Hopkins U Dept English Baltimore MD 21218

ZIFF, LLOYD RICHARD, lawyer; b. N.Y.C., Mar. 9, 1942; s. George and Lillian (Gisnet) Z.; m. M. Morrow Cox, Jan. 28, 1967; children: Tina Marie, M. Courtney, Robert G. Grad., Peekskill Mil. Acad.; BA, U. Pa., 1968, JD magna cum laude, 1971. Bar: Pa. 1971, U.S. Supreme Ct. 1975. Assoc. Pepper, Hamilton & Scheetz, Phila., 1971-77, ptnr., 1977-92; founding ptnr. Harkins Cunningham, Phila. and Washington, 1992—; mem. adv. group ea. dist. U.S. Dist. Pa., Phila., 1995—; teaching fellow U. Pa. Sch. Law, 1971, lectr., 1981-82; mem. faculty Acad. Advocacy, 1980—; mem. DeVitt implementation com. U.S. Dist. Ct. (ea. dist.) Pa., 1980-84, cert. arbitrator 1982—, mem. continuing legal edn. com., 1985—, chmn. local rules adv. com., 1991—, mediator, 1992—, mem. adv. group, 1995—; co-chmn. Seminar on Complex Litigation, 1983; invitee Jud. Conf. of 3d Cir., 1986, 89, 91. Contbr. articles to legal jours. Mem. Kent State U. Task Force, Pres.'s Commn. on Campus Unrest, (Ohio), 1970; mem. Inter-disciplinary Com. on Child Abuse S.E. Pa., 1973-75; mem. adv. com. Family Resources Ctr., St. Christopher's Hosp. for Children, Phila., 1976; chmn. Phila. Bail Project, 1969; counsel Phila. Vietnam Vets. Meml. Fund, 1985—. Served with U.S. Army, 1965-67. Warwick Found. scholar U. Pa., 1971; Salzburg Seminar fellow Am. Studies-Am. Law and Legal Instns., (Austria), 1978. Mem. ABA, Pa. Bar Assn., Phila. Bar Assn. (chmn. election procedures com. 1976, chmn. spl. com. on admission attys. to fed. practice 1986, chair Fidelity award com. 1987, chair fed. bench bar conf., 1988, chmn. fed. cts. com. 1989), Am. Judicature Soc., U.S. Supreme Ct. Hist. Soc., U.S. Ct. Appeals for the 3d Cir. Hist. Soc., U.S. Dist. Ct. for Ea. Dist. Pa. Hist. Soc., Order of Coif, Chapel of the Four Chaplains, Legion of Honor, The Penn Club of N.Y. Office: Harkins Cunningham 1800 One Commerce Sq Philadelphia PA 19103-7042

ZIFF, MORRIS, internist, rheumatologist, educator; b. N.Y.C., Nov. 19, 1913; s. Benjamin and Ethel (Seldowitz) Z.; m. Jacqueline Mae Miller, Dec. 10, 1978; children: Edward B., David R. BS, NYU, 1934, PhD, 1937, MD, 1948. Intern Bellevue Hosp., N.Y.C., 1948-49, resident in internal medicine, 1949-50, attending physician, 1950-58; asst. prof. medicine NYU, 1954-57, assoc. prof., 1957-58; Ashbel Smith prof. internal medicine U. Tex. Health Sci. Ctr., Dallas, 1958-87; Ashbel Smith prof. emeritus internal medicine Ashbel Smith prof. emeritus, Dallas, 1987—; Morris Ziff prof. rheumatology U. Tex. Health Sci. Ctr., Dallas, 1982-87; dir. Harold C. Simmons Arthritis Rsch. Ctr., Dallas, 1983-84; attending physician Parkland Meml. Hosp., Dallas, 1958—; mem. med. staff Zale-Lipshy Univ. Hosp., Dallas, 1989—; cons. Dallas VA Hosp., Brooke Army Hosp., 1964-75, William Beaumont Army Hosp., 1965-76. Contbr. over 250 articles to sci. jours., chpts. to books. Recipient Heberden medal Heberden Soc. London, 1964, Rsch. Career award USPHS, 1962-84, Marchman award Dallas So. Med. Soc., 1968, Disting. Svc. award Arthritis Found., 1968, Disting. Alumni Sci. award NYU, 1966, Carol Nachman prize in rheumatology, 1974, World Internat. Conf. on Inflammation prize, 1986. Fellow ACP; mem. Assn. Am. Physicians, Am. Soc. Clin. Investigation, Am. Assn. Immunologists, Am. Coll. Rheumatology (master, Bunim medal 1982, Gold medal 1988), N.Y. Acad. Medicine (Klemperer medal 1991), Harvey Soc., Phi Beta Kappa, Sigma Xi, Alpha Omega Alpha. Home: 11116 Pinocchio Dr Dallas TX 75229-4031 Office: U Tex Health Sci Ctr 5323 Harry Hines Blvd Dallas TX 75235-9030

ZIFF, PAUL, philosophy educator; b. N.Y.C., Oct. 22, 1920; m. Loredana Vanzetto; 3 children. BFA, Cornell U., 1949, PhD, 1951. Instr. philosophy U. Mich., Ann Arbor, 1952-53; from instr. to asst. prof. Harvard U. Cambridge, Mass., 1953-59; from instr. to prof. to assoc. prof. U. Pa., 1959-63; prof. U. Wis., 1964-68, U. Ill., Chgo., 1968-70; Kenan prof. U. N.C., Chapel Hill, 1970-88, prof. emeritus, 1988—; chmn. bd. dirs. Chapel Hill Ctr. Linguistic Rsch.; cons. in field. Contbr. articles to profl. jours. Paul Ziff chair installed in his honor U. N.C., 1994; festschrift Language, Mine and Art pub. in his honor, 1994; grantee Rockefeller Found., spring 1955, Guggenheim Found., Rome, 1962-63. Office: Chapel Hill Ctr for Philosophic Linguistic Rsch 1309 Brigham Rd Chapel Hill NC 27514-3402

ZIFF, WILLIAM BERNARD, JR., publishing executive; b. June 24, 1930; s. William B. and Amelia (Morton) Z.; m. Tamsen Ann Kojis, 1987; children from previous marriage: Dirk Edward, Robert David, Daniel Morton. BA, Rutgers U., 1951; postgrad., Heidelberg U., 1952-53, U. Madrid, 1952-53. Ptnr., then owner and chmn. Ziff Davis Pub. Co., N.Y.C., until 1984; pub. chmn. Ziff Communication Corp., N.Y.C., 1987—. Office: Ziff Communications Co 1 Park Ave New York NY 10016-5802

ZIFFREN, KENNETH, lawyer; b. Chgo., June 24, 1940. BA, Northwestern U., 1962; JD, UCLA, 1965. Bar; Calif. 1967. Law clerk to Chief Justice Warren, 1965-66; ptnr. Ziffren, Brittenham, Branca & Fischer, L.A. Mem. ABA, State Bar Calif., L.A. County Bar Assn., Beverly Hills Bar Assn., L.A. Copyright Soc. (pres. 1977-78). Office: Ziffren Brittenham Branca & Fischer 2121 Ave of the Stars 32nd Fl Los Angeles CA 90067

ZIFFREN, LESTER, lawyer; b. Davenport, Iowa, Apr. 13, 1925; s. Jacob and Belle M. (Rothenberg) Z.; m. Paulette C. Rolando, May 28, 1953; 1 child, Mimi. BA, UCLA, 1949, JD, 1952. Bar: Calif. 1953. Dep. atty. gen. Calif. Dept. Justice, L.A., 1953-59; ptnr. Greenberg, Ziffren and Shafton, L.A., 1959-61, Ziffren and Ziffren, L.A., 1961-79; ret. ptnr., adv. coun. Gibson, Dunn & Crutcher, L.A., 1979—; bd. dirs. Westminster Capital, Inc., Beverly Hills, Calif. Co-author Handling Condemnation Cases, 1960. Trustee UCLA Found., mem. legal com. Sch. Law, founder Chadbourne Fellow Sch. Law, bd. visitors sch. medicine, chancellor's assoc., trustee Ctr. on Aging; mem. pres.'s coun. Brandeis U.; vice-chmn. nat. bd. govs. Hebrew Union Coll., mem. student affairs com. L.A. campus, vice-chmn. bd. overseers, mem. exec. com.; bd. govs. Cedars-Sinai Med. Ctr.; bd. dirs. L.A. Music Ctr. Opera Assn., State of Israel Bonds; vice-chmn., bd. dirs., L.A. exec. commr.,past pres. L.A. chpt. Prime Mins. Club. With U.S. Army, 1943-46. Mem. ABA, State Bar Calif., L.A. County Bar Assn., Hillcrest Country Club (bd. dirs. 1979-82). Democrat. Jewish. Office: Gibson Dunn & Crutcher 2029 Century Park E Ste 4100 Los Angeles CA 90067

ZIGA, KATHLEEN, lawyer; b. Phila., 1947; m. John Ziga; children: John Strand, Jeffrey, Karen. BA magna cum laude, Mich. State U., 1969; MA, U. Mich., 1970, JD, 1977. Ptnr. Dechert, Price & Rhoads, Phila. Office: Dechert Price & Rhoads 4000 Bell Atlantic 1717 Arch St Philadelphia PA 19103-2793

ZIGEL, JAMES M., aircraft manufacturing executive; b. 1947. BA, U. Mo., 1969, JD, 1972. Gen. counsel Astro Industries, 1972-74; atty. U.S. Army Aviation Systems Command, 1974-76; chief counsel NATO, Brussels, 1976-80; asst. gen. counsel Emerson Electric Co., 1980-85; gen. counsel Western Gear Corp., 1985-87; v.p., gen. counsel, sec. Lucas Industries Inc., Reston, Va., 1989—, pres., CEO, 1993. Office: Lucas Industries Inc 11180 Sunrise Valley Dr Reston VA 22091

ZIGER, STEVEN GARY, architect; b. Washington, Aug. 10, 1955. BS in Architecture, U. Ill., 1977. Registered arch., Md. With RTKL, Balt., 1977-79, Hord, Coplan, Macht, Balt., 1979-84; v.p., founding ptnr. Ziger/Snead, Balt., 1984—; active Balt. County Design Rev. Panel, State of Md. Archtl. Design Rev. Bd. Mem. adv. bd. Johns Hopkins U. Sch. Continuing Studies; trustee The Woodbourne Ctr., Learning Independence Through Computers, Mus. Contemporary Art, Parks and People; chair mayor's adv. com. on Howard St. Devel. Mem. AIA (pres. Balt. chpt. 1992), Balt. Found. for Architecture (v.p. programs). Office: Ziger/Snead 1006 Morton St Baltimore MD 21201-5436

ZIGLAR, JAMES W., former federal official, lawyer, investment banker; b. Pascagoula, Miss., Dec. 8, 1945; married; 3 children. BA, George Washington U., 1968, JD, 1972. Bar: Va. 1972, D.C. 1973, N.Y. 1975, Ariz. 1977. Staff asst. Senator James Eastland, Washington, 1964-71; spl. asst. Dept. of Justice, Washington, 1971-72; law clk. to assoc. justice Harry Blackmun U.S. Supreme Ct., Washington, 1972-73; assoc. Mudge, Rose, Guthrie et al, N.Y.C., 1973-77; ptnr. O'Connor, Cavanagh, Anderson et al, Phoenix, 1977-80; sr. v.p. dept. pub. fin. Dillon, Read & Co., N.Y.C., 1980-84; mng. dir. Paine Webber, Inc., Washington, 1984-86, 90—; asst. sec. Dept. of Interior, Washington, 1987-88; mng. dir. Drexel Burnham Lambert Inc., N.Y.C. 1989-90. Bar: Va. 1972, D.C. 1973, N.Y. 1975, Ariz. 1977. Office: Paine Webber Inc 1300 I St NW Ste 1050 E Washington DC 20005

ZIGLER, EDWARD FRANK, educator, psychologist; b. Kansas City, Mo., Mar. 1, 1930; s. Louis and Gertrude (Gleitman) Z.; m. Bernice Gorelick, Aug. 28, 1955; 1 child, Scott. BA, U. Mo.-Kansas City, 1954; PhD, U. Tex., 1958; MA (hon.), Yale, 1967; DSc (hon.), Boston Coll., 1985; LHD (hon.), Bank St. Coll. Edn., 1989, U. New Haven, 1991, St. Joseph Coll., 1991; PhD (hon.), U. Mo., 1993. Psychol. intern Worcester (Mass.) State Hosp., 1957-59; asst. prof. psychology U. Mo., 1958-59; mem. faculty Yale U., 1959—, prof. psychology and child study center, 1967—, Sterling prof., 1976—; dir. child devel. program, 1961-76, chmn. dept. psychology, 1973-74; head psychology sect. Yale Child Study Center, 1967—; dir. Bush Center in Child Devel. and Social Policy, 1977—; dir. Office Child Devel.; chief Children's Bur., HEW, Washington, 1970-72; cons. in field, 1962—; mem. nat. steering com. Project Head Start, 1965-70, chmn. 15th anniversary Head Start com., 1980; mem. nat. adv. com. Nat. Lab. Early Childhood Edn., 1967-70; nat. rsch. adv. bd. Nat. Assn. Retarded Children, 1968-73; nat. rsch. coun. Project Follow-Through, 1968-70; chmn. Vietnamese Children's Resettlement Adv. Com., 1975; mem. Pres.'s Com. on Mental Retardation, 1980; joint appointee Yale U. Sch. Medicine, 1982—; chmn. Yale Infant Care Leave Commn., 1983-85, arents as Tchrs., 1986—; mem. adv. com. Head Start Quality and Expansion, 1993, DHHS adv. com. on svcs. for families with infant and toddlers, 1994. Author, co-author, editor books and monographs; contbr. articles to profl. jours. Served with AUS, 1951-53. Recipient Gunnar Dybwad Disting. scholar in behavioral and social sci. award Nat. Assn. Retarded Children, 1964, 69, Social Sci. Aux. award, 1962, Alumni Achievement award U. Mo., 1965, Alumnus of Yr. award, 1972, C. Anderson Aldrich award Am. Acad. Pediatrics, 1985, Nat. Achievement award Assn. for Advancement Psychology, 1985, Dorthea Lynde Dix Humanitarian award for svc. to handicapped Elwyn Inst., 1987, Sci. Leadership award Joseph P. Kennedy Jr. Found., 1990, Mensa Edn. and Rsch. Found. award for excellence, 1990, Nat. head Start Assn. award, 1990, Bldg. dedication Edward Zigler Head Start Ctr., 1990, As They Grow award in edn. Parents mag., 1990, Excellence in Edn. award Pi Lambda Theta, 1991, Friend of Edn. award Conn. Edn. Assn., 1991, Loyola-Mellon Social Sci. award 1991, President's award Conn. Assn. Human Svcs., 1991, Harold W. McGraw, Jr. prize in Edn., 1992, Disting. Achievement in Rsch. award Internat. Assn. Scientific Study of Mental Deficiency, 1992, Disting. Svc. award Coun. Chief State Sch. Officers, 1993, Outstanding Fed. Leadership in Support of Head Start Rsch., Adminstrn. on Children, Youth and Families, 1993, Child and Family Advocacy award Parents as Tchrs. Nat. Ctr., 1994, Nat. Distinction award U. Pa. Edn. Alumni Assn., 1994; named Hon. Commr. Internat. Yr. of Child, 1979. Fellow Am. Orthopsychiat. Assn. (Blanche F. Ittleson award 1989, pres. 1993-94), Am. Psychol. Assn. (pres. div. 7 1974-75, G. Stanley Hall award 1979, award for disting. contbns. to psychology in pub. interest 1982, Nicholas Hobbs award 1983, award for disting. profl. contbns. to knowledge 1986, Edgar A. Doll award 1986, award for disting. contbn. to community psychology and community mental health 1989); mem. Inst. Medicine of NAS, AAAS, Am. Acad. Mental Retardation (pres. award 1982), Sigma Xi. Home: 177 Ridgewood Ave North Haven CT 06473-4442 Office: Yale U Dept Psychology 2 Hillhouse Ave PO Box 208205 New Haven CT 06520-8205

ZIGMAN, ROBERT S., public relations executive; b. Milw., Sept. 22, 1919; s. Walter A. and Becky (Neisser) Z.; m. Dorothy T. Traver, Apr. 11, 1953; 1 son, Robert W. With Milprint, Inc., Milw., 1947-52; mgr. aluminum foil div. Milprint, Inc., 1952-58; chmn. Zigman-Joseph-Skeen PR, Milw., 1959—; v.p. devel. St. Mary's Hosp., Milw.; bd. dir. emeritus U. Wis.-Milw. Found., St. Rose Residence, Inc., Stearns Chem. Corp. Bd. dirs. United Performing Arts Fund, Harambee Sch. Devel. Corp.; past bd. dirs. Florentine Opera; past pres., past bd. dirs. Friends of Milw. Pub. Mus.; bd. curators State Hist. Soc. Endowment Com.; past bd. dirs. Gov.'s Council on Arts, Youth Opportunities Unlimited; bd. visitors U. Wis. System; trustee U. Wis. Meml. Union; civilian co-chmn. Armed Forces Week, 1985; trustee, pres.-elect Wis. Hist. Soc. Found. With AUS, 1942-46; trustee Performing Arts Ctr. Decorated Bronze Star medal, Combat Inf. badge; recipient 2 Chinese decorationsDisting. Svc. to Music award Wis. Coll. Conservatory Women's

League, 1973, Golden Baton awards Milw. Symphony Orch., citations County and City Milw., Disting. Svc. award to journalism U. Wis.-Madison, 1986, Courtland R. Conlee Community Svc. award Milw. County Hist. Soc., Spirit of Milw. award Met. Milw. Civic Alliance. Fellow Wis. Acad. Scis. Arts and Letters; mem. Wis. Hist. Soc., Co. Am. Mil. Historians, Wis. State Hist. Soc. (curator 1966—), Pub. Rels. Soc. Am., Scabbard and Blade, Sigma Delta Chi, Beta Gamma Sigma. Home: 10246 N Westport Cir Mequon WI 53202 Office: Milw Club 706 N Jefferson St Milwaukee WI 53202

ZIKAKIS, JOHN P., educator, researcher, biochemist; b. Piraeus, Greece, Sept. 16, 1933; came to U.S., 1958; s. Philip J. and Salome J. (Moshou) Z.; m. Kiki K. Matrozos, Aug. 29, 1958; 1 child, Salome J. Assoc. engr. Pythagoras Coll., Piraeus, 1956; BA, U. Del., 1965, MS, 1967, PhD, 1970. Lab. asst. DuPont de Nemours and Co., Newark, Del., 1959-61; research asst. U. Del., Newark, 1965-70, asst. prof. animal sci. dept., 1970-75, assoc. prof. animal sci. dept., 1975-81, prof. animal sci. dept., coll. marine studies, 1981-89; acad. indust. consultant, 1986—; prof. food sci. U. Del., Newark, 1987-89, prof. emeritus, 1989; v.p. United Chitotechnologies, Inc., Newark, 1989-93; cons. U. Thessaloniki, Greece, 1972-80; vis. prof. U. Panama, 1984-85, sci. advisor, 1985-89; sci. advisor Govt. of Greece, 1972-74; organizer numerous nat. and internat. sci. confs. and symposia over past 23 yrs. Author: Chitin, Chitosan and Related Enzymes, 1984, Advances in Chitin and Chitosan, 1992; mem. editorial bd. Jour. Agr. Food Chemistry, 1983-86; contbr. over 125 articles to profl. jours. Patentee in field. Trustee Riverside Hosp., Wilmington, Del., 1977-84; pres. bd. dirs. Maison Grande Condominium Assn., Inc., Miami Beach, Fla., 1990-92; bd. dirs. Holy Trinity Greek Orthodox Ch., Wilmington, 1971-73; pres. bd. govs. Commondore Condominium Assn., Ft. Lauderdale, Fla., 1993-94. 1st lt. Greek Air Force, 1952-56. Sr. Fulbright scholar, U. Panama, 1984-85; recipient Gold medal and cert. U. Patra, 1973, cert. recognition, commendation for excellence in rsch., edn., pub. svc. Pres. of U. Del., 1977. Mem. AAAS, Am. Chem. Soc. (historian div. agrl. and food chemistry 1980-84, chmn. div. agrl. and food chemistry 1986-87, Disting. Svc. award 1991), N.Y. Acad. Scis., Del. Acad. Sci., Inst. Food Technologists, Am. Inst. Biol. Sci., Am. Chitosci. Soc. (co-founder, trustee, pres. 1989—), Am. Dairy Sci. Assn., Sigma Xi. Avocations: tennis, sailing, swimming, gymnastics. Office: 307 SE 14th St Fort Lauderdale FL 33316-1929

ZIKMUND, BARBARA BROWN, minister, seminary president, church history educator; b. Ann Arbor, Mich., Oct. 16, 1939; d. Henry Daniels and Helen (Langworthy) Brown; m. Joseph Zikmund II, Aug. 26, 1961; 1 child, Brian Joseph. BA, Beloit Coll., 1961; BDiv, Duke U., 1964, PhD, 1969; D in Div (hon.), Doane Coll., 1984, Chgo. Theol. Sem., 1985, Ursinus Coll., 1989. Ordained to ministry United Ch. of Christ, 1964. Instr. Albright Coll., Reading, Pa., 1966-67, Temple U., Phila., 1967-68, Ursinus Coll., Collegeville, Pa., 1968-69; assoc. prof. religion studies Albion Coll., Mich., 1970-75; asst. prof. ch. history, dir. studies Chgo. Theol. Sem., 1975-80; dean and assoc. prof. ch. history Pacific Sch. Religion, Berkeley, Calif., 1981-85, dean and prof. ch. history, 1985-90; pres. Hartford (Conn.) Sem., 1990—; chmn. United Ch. of Christ Hist. Coun., 1983-85, mem. coun. for ecumenism, 1983-89; mem. Nat. Coun. Chs. Commn. on Faith and Order, 1979-87, World Coun. of Chs. Programme Theol. Com., 1984-91, Nat. Coun. Chs. Working Group on Inter-Faith Rels., 1992—, World Orgn. Confs. Theol. Instns., sec. treas. 1992—; elector Wadsworth Atheneum, 1994—, corporator St Francis Hosp., 1994—, pres. Greater Hartford Consortium for Higher Edn., 1994—. Author: Discovering the Church, 1983; editor: Hidden Histories in the UCC, 1984, vol. 2, 1987; (with Manschreck) American Religious Experiment, 1976; mem. editorial bd. Jour. Ecumenical Studies, 1987—; Mid-Stream, 1991—; contbr. articles to profl. jours. Mem. City Coun., Albion, Mich., 1972-75; elector Wadsworth Atheneum, 1994—, corporator St. Francis Hosp., 1994—; pres. Greater Hartford Consortium for Higher Edn., 1994—. Woodrow Wilson fellow, 1964-66; NEH grantee, 1974-75; vis. scholar Schlesinger Libr. Women's History, Radcliffe Coll., 1988-89. Mem. Assn. Theol. Schs. (v.p. 1984-86, pres. 1986-88, issues implementation grantee 1983-84), Am. Soc. Ch. History (council 1983-85, pres. elect 1995—), Internat. Assn. Women Ministers (v.p. 1977-79), AAUW (v.p. 1973-75), Greater Hartford of C. (bd. dirs. 1992-95). Democrat. Office: Hartford Sem Office of Pres 77 Sherman St Hartford CT 06105-2260

ZIKORUS, ALBERT MICHAEL, golf course architect; b. Needham, Mass., Apr. 9, 1921; s. Walter Peter and Rose Mary (Smith) Z.; m. Charlene Bradstreet Aldrich; 1 child, Michael; m. Joan Gayle Boone, 1979. Student, Mass. State Coll., 1941. Greenskeeper Ould Newbury Golf Course, Newburyport, Mass., 1942, Wellesley (Mass.) Golf Course, 1946, Woodbtidge (Conn.) Golf Course, 1948-51; assoc. William F. Mitchell Architect, 1951-52, Orin E. Smith Architect, Southington, Conn., 1953-58. Designed Tunxis Plantation Country Club, Farmington, Conn., Twin Hills Country Club, Longmeadow, Mass., Timberlin Golf Course, Berlin, Conn., Tashua Golf Course, Trumbull, Conn., Segalla Country Club, Amenia, N.Y., others. Sgt. USAF, 1942-46. Mem. Am. Soc. Golf Course Architects. Avocations: swimming, fishing, hiking, hunting, golf. Home/Office: PO Box 187 Canaan ME 04924-0187 Office: PO Box 187 Canaan ME 04924-0187

ZILKHA, EZRA KHEDOURI, banker; b. Baghdad, Iraq, July 31, 1925; came to U.S., 1941, naturalized, 1950; s. Khedouri A. and Louise (Bashi) Z.; m. Cecile Iny, Feb. 6, 1950; children: Elias Donald, Donna Zilkha Krisel, Bettina. Grad., Hill Sch., Pottstown, Pa., 1943; AB, Wesleyan U., Middletown, Conn., 1947; LLD (hon.), Wesleyan U., 1987. Pres. Zilkha & Sons, Inc., N.Y.C., 1956—; pres. 3555 Intermediate Corp., Del., 1991—; bd. dirs. Chgo. Milw. Corp., Chgo., Newhall Land & Farming, Calif., CIGNA Corp., Phila., Cambridge Assocs., Boston, Milw. Land Co., Chgo.; gen. ptnr. Heartland Ptnrs., L.P., Chgo. Chmn. Internat. Ctr. for Disabled, N.Y.C.; trustee Brookings Inst., Washington, Lycée Français, N.Y.C.; trustee emeritus Wesleyan U.; former trustee Spence Sch., N.Y.C. Decorated chevalier Legion d'Honneur, officier Ordre Nat. du Merite (France); recipient Freedom of Human Spirit award Internat. Ctr. for Disabled, 1989. Mem. Coun. Fgn. Rels. Clubs: Racquet and Tennis (N.Y.C.), Knickerbocker (N.Y.C.), Meadow (Southampton, N.Y.); Travellers (Paris), Polo (Paris).

ZILLI, HARRY ANGELO, JR., rail transportation executive; b. Cleve., June 8, 1930; s. Harry and Millie (Trunkett) Z.; m. Sharon R. Hobart, Aug. 30, 1974; children: Harry Angelo, Constance Jane Zilli Busser. B.B.A., Western Res. U., 1954. CPA, Ohio. Comptroller Wabush Mines, Sept-Iles, Que., Can., 1966-70; fin. planner Diamond Shamrock Corp., Cleve., 1970-72; with Erie Lackawanna Rlwy. Co., Cleve., 1972-92; treas. Erie Lackawanna Rlwy. Co., 1973-76, exec. officer, 1976-82, pres., treas., 1982-85, exec. v.p., treas., COO, CFO, 1985-87, pres., CEO, treas., 1987-92, also bd. dirs.; trustee Erie Lackawanna Inc. Liquidating Trust, North Olmsted, Ohio, 1992-94; ret., 1995. Trustee Fairview Found., 1985—. With AUS, 1954-56. Mem. Aqua Masters Scuba Club (pres. 1990-92), Case Res. Athletic Club (exec. com. 1987—, 1st v.p. 1991, pres. 1992). Methodist. Home: 24765 Randall Dr North Olmsted OH 44070-3448

ZILLY, THOMAS SAMUEL, federal judge; b. Detroit, Jan. 1, 1935; s. George Samuel and Bernice M. (McWhinney) Z.; divorced; children: John, Peter, Paul, Luke; m. Jane Greller Noland, Oct. 8, 1988; stepchildren: Allison Noland, Jennifer Noland. BA, U. Wash., 1956; LLD, Cornell U., 1962. Bar: Wash. 1962, U.S. Ct. Appeals (9th cir.) 1962, U.S. Supreme Ct. 1976. Ptnr. Lane, Powell, Moss & Miller, Seattle, 1962-88; judge U.S. Dist. Ct. (we. dist.) Wash., Seattle, 1988—; judge pro tem Seattle Mcpl. Ct., 1972-80. Contbr. articles to profl. jours. Mem. Cen. Area Sch. Council, Seattle, 1969-70; scoutmaster Thunderbird Dist. council Boy Scouts Am. Seattle, 1976-84; bd. dirs. East Madison YMCA. Served to lt. (j.g.) USN, 1956-59. Recipient Tuahku Dist. Service to Youth award Boy Scouts Am., 1983. Mem. ABA, Wash. State Bar Assn., Seattle-King County Bar Assn. (treas. 1979-80, trustee 1980-83, sec. 1983-84, 1st v.p. 1984-85, 1st v.p 1985-86, pres. 1986-87). Office: US Dist Ct 410 US Courthouse 1010 5th Ave Seattle WA 98104-1130

ZILVERSMIT, DONALD BERTHOLD, nutritional biochemist, educator; b. Hengelo, Holland, July 11, 1919; came to U.S., 1939, naturalized, 1950; s. Herman and Elizabeth (DeWinter) Z.; m. Kitty Fonteyn, June 28, 1945; children: Elizabeth Ann, Dorothy Susan, Sarah Jo. Student, U. Utrecht, Holland, 1936-39, DSc in Phys. Scis. (hon.), 1980; BS, U. Calif., Berkeley,

1940, PhD, 1948. Mem. faculty U. Tenn. Med. Coll., 1948-66, prof., 1956-66; prof. nutrition, prof. biochemistry, molecular and cell biology divs. nutritional sci. and biol. scis. Cornell U., 1966—, prof. emeritus 1990—; vis. prof. U. Leiden, Holland, 1961-62, Mass. Inst. Tech., 1972-73; vis. fellow Australian Nat. U., Canberra, Australia, 1966; vis. lectr. Venezuela Inst. Sci. Investigations, 1977; career investigator Am. Heart Assn., 1959-89; editor Jour. Lipid Research, 1958-62, Circulation Research, 1962-67, 68-74, Circulation, 1960-65, Biochim. Biophysica Acta, 1969-79, Arteriosclerosis, 1980-90; editor Procs. Soc. Exptl. Biology and Medicine, 1975-87, mem. adv. council, 1978-81; cons. NIH. Editor-in-chief: Jour. of Lipid Research, 1958-61; adv. bd., 1962-72; Contbr. articles to profl. jours. Recipient Borden award, 1976, Disting. Achievement in Nutrition Rsch. award Bristol-Myers Squibb, 1990. Fellow Am. Inst. Nutrition; mem. AAAS, NAS, Am. Physiol. Soc., Am. Soc. Biol. Chemists, Coun. on Arteriosclerosis, Am. Heart Assn. (exec. bd. 1968-70, G. Lyman Duff Meml. award 1978), Soc. Exptl. Biology and Medicine, N.Y. Acad. Scis., Philosophy of Sci. Assn., Soc. Lit. and Sci., Phi Beta Kappa, Sigma Xi. Office: Cornell U Div Nutritional Scis Ithaca NY 14853

ZIM, HERBERT SPENCER, author, educator; b. N.Y.C., July 12, 1909; s. Marco and Minnie (Orlo) Z.; m. Sonia Elizabeth Bleeker, Jan. 16, 1934 (dec. 1971); children: Aldwin Herbert, Roger Spencer; m. Grace Kent Showe, June 4, 1978. Student, CCNY, 1927-29; B.S., M.A., Ph.D., Columbia, 1933-40; D.Sc. (hon.), Beloit Coll., 1967, Fla. State U., 1977. Instr. sci., summer play schs., 1926-31; instr. sci. Bklyn. Ethical Culture Sch., 1930-31, N.Y. Ethical Culture Schs., 1932-50; tchr. edn. dept., head sci. dept., 1937-45; asso. prof. edn. U. Ill., 1950-54, prof. edn., 1954-57; ednl. cons. Manhasset Bay Schs., 1946-48, U.S. Fish and Wildlife Service, 1947-51, Western Pub. Co., 1967-70, Am. Friends Service Com., 1968-78; editorial cons. Individualized Sci. Instrnl. System, 1972-79; pres. Rogewinn Corp., 1968-71; Instr. Columbia, 1935-36; summer field trips, 1937-41; research under Gen. Edn. Bd. Grant for Comm. on Secondary School Curriculum, Progressive Edn. Assn., 1934-37; adj. prof. edn. U. Miami, 1970-82; Mem. Am. Inst. Jr. Activities Com. 1938-42, bd. mgrs., 1940-42, v.p., 1942; mem. steering com. Biol. Scis. Curriculum Study and Intermediate Scis. Curriculum Study, War Dept. (preinduction tng. program), 1942-43; civilian pub. service, 1943-45. Author/editor over 150 books relating to sci. including Life and Death, 1970, Armored Animals, 1971, Your Brain, 1972, Crabs, 1974, Medicine, 1974, Snails, 1975, Caves, 1977, Little Cats, 1978, Your Skin, 1979, New Moon, 1980, Quartz, 1981, Guide to Trees, 1985, Reptiles and Amphibians, 1987, Mammals, 1987, Insects, 1987, Flowers, 1987, Fishes, 1987; rev. edits. Alligators and Crocodiles, Sharks and others, 1978-87; editor-in-chief: Our Wonderful World Ency., 1952-63, Golden Ency. Natural Sci., 1960-70; originator, editor: Golden Guide Series, 1947-70; ednl. dir.: rev. edits. Artists and Writers Press, 1957-69. Recipient Children's Sci. Book awards N.Y. Acad. Scis., 1988. Fellow AAAS; mem. numerous sci. and ednl. socs. Home: 88835 Old Hwy Tavernier FL 33070-2038

ZIMAND, HARVEY FOLKS, lawyer; b. N.Y.C., Aug. 28, 1928; s. Savel and Gertrude (Folks) Z.; m. Ingeborg Rockosch, 1963 (div. 1980); children—Patricia Folks, Stephanie Folks; m. Noel French, Apr. 30, 1983. B.A., Colgate U., 1950; postgrad., Oxford U., Eng., 1950; M.A., U. Chgo., 1951; postgrad., Columbia U., 1952-53; LL.B., Yale U., 1957. Bar: N.Y. 1957. Rapporteur Council for Fgn. Relations, N.Y.C., 1952-53; atty. Dept. Navy, Washington, 1956-70; ptnr. Kelley Drye & Warren, N.Y.C., 1970—; dir. Toronto-Dominion Trust Co., N.Y.C. Bd. dirs. Virginia Day Nursery, N.Y.C., 1980-84. Served to cpl. U.S. Army, 1951-53. Fellow N.Y. Bar Found., Am. Coll. Probate Counsel; mem. ABA, N.Y. State Bar Assn., Assn. Bar City of N.Y., Estate Planning Council. Republican. Episcopalian. Clubs: Yale (N.Y.C.); Randolph Mountain (N.H.). Home: 120 E 81st St New York NY 10028 Office: Kelley Drye & Warren 101 Park Ave New York NY 10178-0062

ZIMBARDO, PHILIP GEORGE, psychologist, educator, writer; b. N.Y.C., Mar. 23, 1933; s. George and Margaret (Bisicchia) Z.; m. Christina Maslach, Aug. 10, 1972; children: Zara, Tanya; 1 son by previous marriage, Adam. AB, Bklyn. Coll., 1954; MS, Yale U., 1955, PhD, 1959. Asst. prof. psychology Yale U., New Haven, 1959-61, NYU, N.Y.C., 1961-67; vis. assoc. prof. psychology Columbia U., N.Y.C., 1967-68; prof. psychology Stanford (Calif.) U., 1968—; pres. P.G. Zimbardo, Inc., San Francisco. Author: Cognitive Control of Motivation, 1969, Canvassing or Peace, 1970, Psychology and You, 1976, Shyness, What It Is, What To Do About It, 1977, Influencing Attitudes and Changing Behavior, rev. edit., 1977, Psychology for Our Times: Readings, 1977, The Shyness Workbook, 1979, A Parent's Guide to the Shy Child, 1981, The Psychology of Attitude Change and Social Influence, 1991, Psychology and Life, rev. edit., 1992, Psychology, 1996. Pres. Montclair Ter. Assn., 1975—; sr. project advisor Exploratorium, 1993; host, writer, gen. acad. advisor PBS-TV series Discovering Psychology, 1987-90. Recipient Peace medal Tokyo Police Dept., 1972, Disting. Tchr. award Am. Psychol. Foundn., 1975, Stanford, Calif., 1994; Ctr. for Advanced Study of Behavioral Scis. fellow, 1971. Mem. APA (Presdl. citation Discovery Psychology series 1994), AAAS, AAUP, Internat. Congress Psychology, Western Psychol. Assn. (pres. 1983), Ea. Psychol. Assn., Calif. Psychol. Assn. (Disting. Contbn. to Rsch. award 1978), Can. Psychol. Assn., Soc. for Psychol. Study of Social Issues, Soc. for Clin. and Exptl. Hypnosis, Sigma Xi, Phi Beta Kappa, Psi Chi. Roman Catholic. Home: 25 Montclair Ter San Francisco CA 94109-1517 Office: Stanford U Psychology Dept Stanford CA 94305 *One of the few virtues of growing up in a poor urban ghetto is the realization that people are the most important resource we have—to be used wisely, well and as often as possible. The second is the tempering of book learning by street wits. The third is to value a career that allows me to contribute to improving the quality of our lives through research and teaching.*

ZIMBLE, JAMES ALLEN, naval officer, physician; b. Phila., Oct. 12, 1933; s. Nathan Norman and Mary Jay (Klaits) Z.; m. Judith Ann Goldberg, Sept. 17, 1961 (div. Apr. 1970); children: Amy B., Jennifer L.; m. Janet Mary Bailey, June 19, 1970; 1 child, Daniel A.; stepchildren: David T., Jennifer G., Melinda S. Richards. BS, Franklin and Marshall Coll., 1955; MD, U. Pa., 1959; ScD, SUNY Sch. Medicine, 1990. Diplomate Am. Bd. Ob-Gyn, Nat. Bd. Med. Examiners. Intern U.S. Naval Hosp., St. Albans, N.Y., 1959-60, resident, 1963-66; commd. ensign U.S. Navy, 1956, advanced through grades to vice adm., 1987, med. officer in USS John Marshall, 1961-63; staff U.S. Naval Hosp., Camp Pendleton, Calif., 1966-70, Phila., 1970-72; chief obstetrics and gynecology, dir. clin. services U.S. Naval Hosp., Lemoore, Calif., 1972-76; dir. clin. services Naval Regional Med. Ctr., Long Beach, Calif., 1976-78; comdg. officer Naval Regional Med. Ctr., Orlando, Fla., 1978-81; med. officer Hdqrs. U.S. Marine Corps, Washington, 1981-83; fleet surgeon to comdr. in chief Atlantic Fleet, med. advisor to Supreme Allied Command, Norfolk, Va., 1983-86; dep. asst. sec. of def. for strategic planning and med. program mgmt. Dept. Def., 1986-87; surgeon gen. USN, Washington, 1987-91; chief Bur. Medicine and Surgery, 1987-91; pres. Uniformed Svcs. U. Health Scis., Bethesda, Md., 1991—; assoc. clin. faculty U. Calif.-Irvine, 1977-78; assoc. prof. dept. mil. medicine Uniformed Svc. U. Health Scis., Bethesda, Md., 1983—. Contbr. articles to profl. jours. Decorated Def. Meritorious Service medal, Legion of Merit (3), Navy Meritorious Service medal, Def. Superior Service medal, Def. Disting. Service medal, Navy Disting. Svc. medal. Disting. fellow Am. Coll. Physician Execs.; fellow Am. Coll. Surgeons, Am. Coll. Ob-Gyn, Assn. Mil. Surgeons U.S.; mem. AMA (del.), Uniformed Svcs. U. Health Scis. (bd. regents), Nat. Libr. Medicine (bd. regents), NRA, Interagy, Inst. for Fed. Health Care Execs., U.S. Naval Inst. Rsch. Officers Assn., Naval Hist. Found. (trustee), Armed Forces Radiol. Rsch. Inst. (bd. govs.), Am. Hosp. Assn. (del.). Republican. Jewish. Office: USUHS 4301 Jones Bridge Rd Bethesda MD 20814-4799

ZIMET, CARL NORMAN, psychologist, educator; b. Vienna, Austria, June 3, 1925; came to U.S., 1943, naturalized, 1945; s. Leon and Gisela (Kosser) Z.; m. Sara F. Goodman, June 4, 1950; children: Andrew, Gregory. BA, Cornell U., 1949; PhD, Syracuse U., 1953; postdoctoral fellow, Standard U., 1953-55. Diplomate in clin. psychology Am. Bd. Profl. Psychology (trustee 1966-74). Instr., then asst. prof. psychology and psychiatry Yale U., 1955-63; mem. faculty U. Colo. Med. Center, 1963—, prof. clin. psychology, 1965—, head div., 1963—; Mem. Colo. Bd. Psychol. Examiners, 1966-72, Colo. Mental Health Planning Commn., 1964-66; mem. acad. adv. com. John F. Kennedy Child Devel. Center, U. Colo., 1966—; chmn. Council for Nat. Register of Health Service Providers in Psychology, 1975-85, pres., mem.

exec. bd. div. psychotherapy, 1970—; chair exec. com. Assn. Psychol. Internship Ctrs., 1988-91. Bd. editors: Jour. Clin. Psychology, 1962—, Jour. Clin. and Cons. Psychology, 1964-73, Psychotherapy, 1967—, Profl. Psychology, 1969-75. With USNR, 1943-46. Recipient Disting. Service award Colo. Psychol. Assn., 1976. Fellow APA (council reps. 1969-72, 73—, bd. dirs. 1985-88, Disting. award for profl. contbn. 1987, div. psychotherapy and div. clin. psychology), Soc. Personality Assessment (pres. 1975-76, bd. dirs.—Current age psychol. services 1987—); mem. Am. Acad. Clin. Psychology (pres. 1993—), Denver Psychoanalytic (trustee 1968-71), Am. Group Psychotherapy Assn., Med. Sch. Profs. Psychology (pres. 1992-94). Home: 4325 E 6th Ave Denver CO 80220-4939

ZIMINSKI, RICHARD WILLIAM, engineering executive; b. Mineola, N.Y., Aug. 23, 1934; s. Peter J. and Anna D. (Clausen) Z.; m. Mary Ann Wechtel, Feb. 1, 1955; children: Ann Regn, Peter, Rick, Julia Konopasek, Matthew. BS in Enging. of Mines, Lehigh U., 1956. Mining engr. N.J. Zinc Co., Treadway, Tenn., 1956-60; plant supt. Martin Marietta, Martinsburg, W.Va., 1960-67; v.p. engring. Precipitat Pollution Control, Bound Brook, N.J., 1967-72; mgr. ESP div. Mikropol, Summit, N.J., 1972-76; owner, pres. Ambient Engr. Inc., Matawan, N.J., 1974—. Contbr. (handbook) APC Handbook and Design. Mem. Am. Inst. of Mining Engrs., Nat. Soc. of Profl. Engrs., Air and Waste Mgmt. Assn. Avocations: scuba diving, horticulture. Office: ENSR Consulting & Engineering 35 Nagog Park Acton MA 01720

ZIMM, BRUNO HASBROUCK, physical chemistry educator; b. Woodstock, N.Y., Oct. 31, 1920; s. Bruno L. and Louise S. (Hasbrouck) Z.; m. Georgianna S. Grevatt, June 17, 1944; children: Louis H., Carl B. Grad., Kent (Conn.) Sch., 1938; A.B., Columbia U., 1941, M.S., 1943, Ph.D., 1944. Research assoc. Columbia U., 1944; research assoc., instr. Polytech. Inst. Bklyn., 1944-46; instr. chemistry U. Calif. at Berkeley, 1946-47, asst. prof., 1947-50, assoc. prof., 1950-51; vis. lectr. Harvard U., 1950-51; research assoc. research lab. Gen. Electric Co., 1951-60; prof. chemistry U. Calif., La Jolla, 1960-91, prof. emeritus, 1991—. Assoc. editor: Jour. Chem. Physics, 1947-49; adv. bd.: Jour. Polymer Sci, 1953-62, Jour. Bio-Rheology, 1962-73, Jour. Biopolymers, 1963—, Jour. Phys. Chemistry, 1963-68, Jour. Biophys. Chemistry, 1973—. Recipient Bingham Medal Soc. Rheology, 1960, High Polymer Physics prize Am. Phys. Soc., 1963; Kirkwood medal Yale U., 1982. Mem. Biophys. Soc., Am. Soc. Biol. Chemists, Am. Chem. Soc. (Baekeland award 1957), Nat. Acad. Scis. (award in Chem. Scis. 1981), Am. Acad. Arts and Scis., Am. Phys. Soc.

ZIMMAR, GEORGE PETER, publishing executive, psychology educator; b. Chgo., Dec. 31, 1937; s. Peter George and Sofia (Kanellis) Z.; m. Doulie J. Pappas; children: Sofia Corrine, Peter David George. BS in Psychology, Roosevelt U., 1960, MS in Exptl. Psychology, 1961; PhD in Neurosci., SUNY, Buffalo, 1966; postgrad., MIT, 1968. Rsch. assoc. Northwestern U. Med. Sch., Chgo., 1960-61; instr. psychology SUNY, Buffalo, 1962-64; asst. prof. Grinnell (Iowa) Coll., 1965-69; prof., chmn. dept. Briarcliff Coll., Briarcliff Manor, N.Y., 1970-77; editor Praeger Pubs., N.Y.C., 1978-81; sr. editor CBS Pub. Group/Elsevier, N.Y.C., 1981-88; editor-in-chief Rowman & Littlefield Pubs., Totowa, N.J., 1988-89; sr. editor Springer-Verlag, N.Y.C., 1989-91; pres. Youth Edn. Systems, Inc., Scarborough, N.Y., 1985—, also chmn. bd. dirs.; adj. prof. Pace U., Pleasantville, N.Y., 1977, NYU, 1991—; v.p., bd. dirs. McGraw Learning Labs. Inc., Dobbs Ferry, N.Y., 1970-774; bd. dirs. Neoclassical Press, Madison, Conn. Author: Chronology of Wars, 1989; contbr. articles to profl. jours. Pres. Ch. of Our Saviour, Rye, N.Y., 1981-82, bd. dirs., 1973—; capital campaign officer Hackley Sch., Tarrytown, N.Y., 1988. Hillman fellow Roosevelt U., 1961, Sloan Found. fellow, 1968; Cattell grantee Grinnell Coll., 1967. Mem. APA, Am. Psychol. Soc. (charter), Cognite Sci. Soc., Sigma Xi. Greek Orthodox. Office: Youth Edn Systems Inc Scarborough Station Briarcliff Manor NY 10510

ZIMMER, ALBERT ARTHUR, education educator; b. Pitts., May 20, 1918; s. Albert Peter and Hilda (Volz) Z.; m. Alma Zimmermann, Mar. 7, 1945; children: Alene Lynne, Alyce Lorraine, Alana Leigh. B.S., Pa. State U., 1942, M.Ed., 1947; Ed.D., U. Pitts., 1951. Tchr. pub. schs. State College, Pa., 1941-42; music supr. pub. schs. Ford City and Monongahela, Pa., 1946-49; instr. U. Pitts., 1949-52; head edn. dept. Susquehanna U., 1952-59, dean students, 1959-62; dean, v.p. Bethany Coll., Lindsborg, Kans., 1962-66; acting pres. coll. Bethany Coll., 1966-67; chmn. dept. edn. Thiel Coll., Greenville, Pa., 1967-83, chmn. emeritus, 1983—; vis. lectr. Bucknell U., Rutgers U., Pa. State U., U. Conn.; Del. Gov. Pa. Conf. Edn., 1954. Contbr. articles to profl. jours. Dir. Snyder County Civil Def., 1952-62; mem. Selinsgrove (Pa.) SSS Bd., 1959-62; Nat. del. Luth Ch. Am., 1956, 60, 62; chief Central Pa. Synod, 1956-62, 64, mem. Christian edn. commn., 1958-62, social welfare commn., 1960-62, church councilman, Selinsgrove, 1952-62, Lindsborg, 1963—, City councilman, Selinsgrove, 1960-62, Greenville, 1980-88, mem. planning commn., 1960-62; fire warden Pa. Forest Commn. 1958-62; Bd. dirs. Snyder County chpt. Am. Cancer Soc., 1956-60; bd. dirs. fund chmn. Snyder County chpt. A.R.C., 1954; bd. dirs. Monongahela Youth Council, 1946-47, Monongahela Concert Bd., 1946-47, Walnut Acres Found., Pa., 1958-62, Lindsborg Community Vol. Ambulance Service, 1966—, Gettysburg Luth. Theol. Sem., 1974-78. Served with AUS, 1942-46. Mem. NEA, AAUP, Music Educators Nat. Conf., Pa. Assn. Liberal Arts Colls. (pres. 1960-61), Pa. Assn. Student Teaching (v.p. 1958-59), Nat. Assn. Deans, Rotary, Phi Delta Kappa, Theta Chi, Phi Mu Alpha, Kappa Phi Kappa, Alpha Phi Omega. Home: 73 N Main St Greenville PA 16125-1781

ZIMMER, HANS, composer; b. Frankfurt, Germany, 1958. Former mem. The Buggles. Scores include (films) (with Stanley Myers) Moonlighting, 1982, (with Myers) Success Is the Best revenge, 1984, Terminal Exposure, 1987, (with Myers) The Wind, 1987, (with Myers) The Zero Boys, 1987, (with Myers) Taffin, 1988, Wonderland, 1988, (with Myers) The Nature of the Beast, 1988, (with Luis Bonfa) Prisoner of Rio, 1988, Burning Secret, 1988, (with Myers) Paperhouse, 1988, Rain Man, 1988 (Academy award nomination best original score 1988), A World Apart, 1988, Arcadia, 1988, Black Rain, 1989, Diamond Skulls, 1989, Driving Miss Daisy, 1989, Twister, 1989, Bird on a Wire, 1990, (with Shirley Walker) Chicago Joe and the Showgirl, 1990, Days of Thunder, 1990, Fools of Fortune, 1990, Green Card, 1990, The Neverending Story II: The Next Chapter, 1990, Pacific Heights, 1990, Backdraft, 1991, Regarding Henry, 1991, Thelma and Louise, 1991, Radio Flyer, 1991, The Power of One, 1992, A League of Their Own, 1992, (with Mark Mancina) Where Sleeping Dogs Lie, 1992, Sniper, 1993, (with Bob Telson) Younger and Younger, 1993, Point of No Return, 1993, True Romance, 1993, Calendar Girl, 1993, Cool Runnings, 1993, The House of the Spirits, 1993, I'll Do Anything, 1994, Renaissance Man, 1994, The Lion King, 1994 (Academy award best original score 1994), Crimson Tide, 1995, Nine Months, 1995, (TV movies) Wild Horses, 1985, First Born, 1989, Millennium: Tribal Wisdom and the Modern World, 1992; music prodr.: The Last Emperor, 1987. Office: Gorfaine Schwartz Agency 3301 Barham Blvd Ste 201 Los Angeles CA 90068*

ZIMMER, JOHN HERMAN, lawyer; b. Sioux Falls, S.D., Dec. 30, 1922; s. John Francis and Veronica (Berke) Z.; student Augustana Coll., Sioux Falls, 1941-42, Mont. State Coll., 1943; LLB, U. S.D., 1948; m. Deanna Langner, 1976; children by previous marriage: Mary Zimmer Quinlin, Robert Joseph, Judith Maureen Zimmer Rose. Bar: S.D. 1948. Pvt. practice law, Turner County, S.D., 1948—; of counsel Zimmer & Duncan, Parker, S.D., 1972—; states atty. Turner County, 1955-58, 62-64; asst. prof. med. jurisprudence U. S.D.; minority counsel U.S. Senate Armed Services Com. on Strategic and Critical Materials Investigation, 1962-63; chmn. Southeastern Council Govts., 1973-75; mem. U. S.D. Law Sch. adv. council, 1973-74. Chmn. Turner County Rep. Com., 1955-56; mem. S.D. Rep. adv. com., 1959-60; alt. del. Rep. Nat. Conv., 1968; pres. S.D. Easter Seal Soc., 1986-87. Served with AUS, 1943-46; PTO. Decorated Bronze Star, Philippine Liberation ribbon. Mem. ABA, Fed. S.D. (commr. 1954-57) Bar Assns., Assn. Trial Lawyers Am., S.D. Trial Lawyers Assn. (pres. 1967-68), VFW, Am. Legion, Phi Delta Phi. Lodges: Elks, Shriners. Home: RRI PO Box 857 Parker SD 57053 Office: Zimmer & Duncan Law Bldg PO Box 550 Parker SD 57053-0547

ZIMMER, PAUL HOWARD, housing and transportation manufacturing company executive; b. Detroit, Apr. 18, 1929; s. Donald R. and Ora E. (Howie) Z.; m. Rosina Procopio, Dec. 1979; children: Mark Louis, Christina

Lee; children by previous marriage: Mallory (Mrs. Carl M. Scholl), Mary J., Robert P. Student, Fla. So. Coll., 1949. With Zimmer Boat & Trailer Co., Detroit, 1946-50; sec., treas., later pres. Zimmer Industries, Elwood, Ind., 1959-61; founder, chmn. bd., pres., chief exec. officer Zimmer Corp., 1961—. Office: Zimmer Corp 777 SW 12th Ave Pompano Beach FL 33069-4527

ZIMMER, PAUL JEROME, publisher, editor, poet; b. Canton, Ohio, Sept. 18, 1934; s. Jerome Francis and Louise Celina (Surmont) Z.; m. Suzanne Jane Koklauner, Apr. 4, 1959; children: Erik Jerome, Justine Mary. BA, Kent State U., 1959. Assoc. dir. U. Pitts. Press, 1967-78; dir. U. Ga. Press, Athens, 1978-84, U. Iowa Press, Iowa City, 1984—. Author: (poetry) Family Reunion, 1983 (AAAL award 1985), The Great Bird of Love, 1989 (Nat. Poetry Series 1989), Big Blue Train, 1993. With U.S. Army, 1954-55. Avocation: collecting antique photography. Home: 420 Fairchild St Iowa City IA 52245 Office: U Iowa Press 119 S Park Rd Iowa City IA 52246

ZIMMER, RICHARD ALAN, congressman, lawyer; b. Newark, N.J., Aug. 16, 1944; s. William and Evelyn (Schlank Rader) Z.; m. Marfy Goodspeed, Dec. 27, 1965; children: Carl William, Benjamin Goodspeed. BA, Yale U., 1966, LLB, 1969. Bar: N.Y. 1971, U.S. Dist. Ct. (so. and ea. dists.) N.Y. 1974, N.J. 1975, U.S. Dist. Ct. N.J. 1975, U.S. Supreme Ct. 1980. Assoc. Cravath, Swaine and Moore, N.Y.C., 1969-75; gen. atty. Johnson & Johnson, New Brunswick, N.J., 1976-91; mem. N.J. Gen. Assembly, 1982-87, chmn. state govt. com., 1986-87; mem. N.J. Senate, 1987-91, 102nd-103rd Congresses from 12th N.J. dist., Washington, D.C., 1991—. Chmn. March of Dimes WalkAmerica, Hunterdon County, N.J., 1984-86; treas. Hunterdon Hospice, Flemington, N.J., 1984-86. Mem. ABA, N.J. State Bar Assn., Hunterdon County Bar Assn. Republican. Home: Locktown-Flemington Rd Flemington NJ 08822-9541 Office: US House of Reps 228 Cannon HOB Washington DC 20515

ZIMMER, ROBERT J., mathematician; b. N.Y.C., Nov. 5, 1947; s. Max S. and Harriet (Brokaw) Z.; m. Terese Schwartzman, Oct. 27, 1974; children—David, Benjamin, Alexander. A.B., Brandeis U., 1968; Ph.D., Harvard U., 1975. Asst. prof. U.S. Naval Acad., Annapolis, Md., 1975-77; instr. U. Chgo., 1977-79, assoc. prof., 1979-80, prof. math, 1980—; prof. math. U. Calif.-Berkeley, 1981-83, chmn. math dept., 1991-95, assoc. provost for rsch. & edn., 1995—. Author: Ergodic Theory and Semisimple Groups, 1984, Essential Results of Functional Analysis; contbr. articles to profl. jours. Sloan Found. fellow, 1979-83. Office: U Chicago Dept Math 5734 S University Ave Chicago IL 60637-1546

ZIMMERER, ANN(A) MORGAN, lawyer, consulting psychologist, genealogist; b. Hillsboro, W.Va., June 29, 1923; d. Edgar R. and Lula M. (Cox) Morgan; m. Robert Ivan Zimmerer, Oct. 15, 1950; children: Sandra Kaye, Gerald Lee, Douglas Allan. Diploma, Charleston Sch. Commerce, 1941; BS in Social Work, U. W.Va., 1947, MA in Psychology, 1954; Ph.D., U. Houston, 1963, J.D., 1972. Bar: Tex. 1972; Cert. psychologist, W.Va., Tex. lic. psychologist, Tex. lic. real estate salesman. Jr. child welfare worker W.Va. Dept. Pub. Assistance, Beckley, summers, 1947, 48; staff psychologist Mental Hygiene Clinic, W.Va. Dept. Health, Charleston, 1949-51; psychol. cons. to pvt. physicians W.Va. Div. Vocat. Rehab., Children's Home Soc. W.Va., 1952-55; counselor U. Houston, 1956-58; sch. psychologist Houston Ind. Sch. Dist., 1958-60, elem. counselor, 1960-63; instr., acting chmn. dept. psychology San Jacinto Coll., Pasadena, Tex., 1963-64; chmn. dept. psychology San Jacinto Coll., 1964-69; cons. psychologist Pasadena, Tex., 1963—; assoc. law firm Jack R. Bailey, Houston, 1972-73; individual practice law, 1973-88; of counsel Zimmerer & Assocs., P.C., 1989—; salesman Brotherton-Beaver 21st Century, 1982-85; genealogist, 1986—. Del. to Pres.'s White House Conf. on Children, 1970, Gov.'s White House Conf. on Children, 1970; mem. Mayor's Commn. on Obscenity, Pasadena, 1971-72, Republican Tex. com., 1987; mem. George Bush Steering Com., Tex.; mem. Rep. Presdl. Task Force, 1989—, Rep. Senatorial Inner Circle, 1992—, Rep. Presdl. Legion Merit, 1993; Pasadena's ambassador of goodwill to China, 1982—; participant del. Tex. attys. invited to study Chinese legal system by minister justice People's Republic China, 1982; research editor Harris County Hist. and Geneal. Soc., 1983, genealogist, 1984-85. Served with WAVES, 1943-45. Mem. Am. Psychol. Assn., Tex. Psychol. Assn., W.Va. Psychol. Assn. (charter mem.), AAUW, Soc. for Rorschach and Projective Techniques, Internat. Congress Psychologists, Am. Tex., Houston, Pasadena Bar Assn., Am. Trial Lawyers Assn., Nat. Genealogical Soc., U. Houston Law Found., Theta Sigma (charter, 1st pres.), Delta Kappa Gamma. Clubs: La Tamba Dance, River Oaks Dance, Pasadena Writers (v.p. 1983). Home: 2208 Fenwood Dr Pasadena TX 77502-3606 Office: PO Box 4344 Pasadena TX 77502-0344

ZIMMERMAN, ADAM HARTLEY, retired mining and forest industries executive; b. Toronto, Ont., Can., Feb. 19, 1927; s. Adam Hartley and Mary Ethelwyn (Ballantyne) Z.; m. Janet Lewis, May, 1951; children: Thomas, Barbara, Mary, Kate. Attended, Upper Can. Coll., Toronto, Ridley Coll., St. Catharines, Ont., Royal Can. Naval Coll., U. Toronto; postgrad. in philosophy, 1951. Chartered acct., Ont. With sales dept. Procter & Gamble, 1950; with Clarkson, Gordon & Co., Toronto, 1950-58; asst. comptroller Noranda Mines Group of Cos., 1958-60; comptroller Noranda Inc., Toronto, 1960-66, v.p., 1966-74, exec. v.p., dir., 1974-82, pres., COO, 1982-87, vice chmn., 1987-92; CEO Noranda Forest Inc., Toronto, 1987-91, chmn. bd., 1987-93, dir., 1987-94; chmn. MacMillan Bloedel Ltd., 1983-90, vice chmn. 1990-93, bd. dirs.; vice chmn. Confederation Life Ins. Co., 1992-93, chmn., 1993-94, bd. dirs.; chmn. C.D. Howe Inst., 1990-93; bd. dirs. Econ. Investment Trust Ltd., The Pittston Co., Toronto-Dominion Bank, Southam Inc., Roy Thomson Hall, Battery Tech. Inc., MacMillan Bloedell Ltd.; mem. adv. bd. Faculty of Foresty U. Toronto, Faculty of Forestry and Environ. U. N.B., Royal LePage Real Estate; bd. govs. Ridley Coll., 1987; mem. adv. bd. Royal Soc. Can., Can. Journalism Found. Past chmn. C. D. Howe Inst.; hon. trustee Hosp. for Sick Children; trustee Hosp. Sick Children Found., 1966-88, hon. trustee, 1988—; bd. dirs.; trustee World Wildlife Fund Can. Lt. Royal Can. Navy Res., 1946-52. Mem. The York Club, Toronto Golf Club, Madawaska Club, Craigleigh Ski Club. Office: 1 Toronto St Ste 500, Toronto, ON Canada M5C 2W4

ZIMMERMAN, BERNARD, lawyer; b. Munich, Bavaria, Fed. Republic Germany, May 31, 1946; came to U.S., 1949; s. Sam and Roza (Spodek) Z.; m. Grace L. Suarez, Oct. 23, 1976; children: Elizabeth, Adam, David, Dara Bylah. AB, U. Rochester, 1967; JD, U. Chgo., 1970. Bar: Calif. 1971, La. 1971, U.S. Supreme Ct. 1975, U.S. Dist. Ct. (no., ea., cen. and so. dists.) Calif., U.S. Dist. Ct. (ea. dist.) La., U.S. Ct. Appeals (9th cir.). Law. clk. chief judge U.S. Dist. Ct. (ea. dist.) La., New Orleans, 1970-71; asst. prof. law La. State U., Baton Rouge, 1971-72; ptnr. Pillsbury, Madison & Sutro, San Francisco, 1972-95; legal cons. 3d Constnl. Convention Commonwealth, Northern Mariana Islands, 1995—; dep. pub. defender City of San Francisco, 1975; arbitrator U.S. Dist. Ct., San Francisco, AAA; judge pro tem San Francisco Superior and Mcpl. Cts. Bd. dirs., mem. exec. com. San Francisco Lawyers' Com. on Urban Affairs, 1984—, treas., 1987; mem. regional bd. Anti-Defamation League. Mem. Phi Beta Kappa. Democrat. Jewish. Club: Olympic (San Francisco). Office: 563 Liberty St San Francisco CA 94114-2820

ZIMMERMAN, BILL J., oil company executive, lawyer; b. Coffeyville, Kans., Aug. 13, 1932; s. Ralph R. and Nellie E. (Brown) Z.; m. Marianne Belt, Nov. 21, 1953 (div. 1980); children—Kurt R., Julie M., Jennifer L.; m. Patsy Cantrell, Dec. 8, 1980. B.B.A., Southern Meth. U., 1954; J.D., Denver U., 1964. Bar: Colo. 1964, Calif. 1967, N.Y. 1969, Tex. 1973, Okla. 1978. Acct., sr. gas agent, atty., regional atty. Shell Oil Co., 1958-76; sr. group counsel NL Industries, Inc., Houston, 1976-77; assoc. gen. counsel Kerr-McGee Corp., Okla. City, 1977-80; v.p., gen. counsel Superior Oil Co., Houston, 1980-83, Union Pacific Resources Co., Fort Worth, 1983—. Mem. Nat. Republican Party, Tarrant County Rep. Com., Tex. Served to sgt. U.S. Army, 1955-57. Mem. ABA, Am. Corp. Counsel Assn. (bd. dirs. 1983—), Am. Petroleum Inst., Am. Petroleum Assn. Am., Petroleum Club, Shady Oaks Country Club, Ft. Worth Club. Republican. Methodist. Clubs: Petroleum, Shady Oaks Country (Fort Worth). Avocations: tennis, swimming; golf. Home: 908 Roaring Springs Rd Fort Worth TX 76114-4453 Office: Union Pacific Resources Co PO Box 7 Fort Worth TX 76101-0007

ZIMMERMAN, BRYANT KABLE, lawyer; b. Mt. Morris, Ill., Nov. 19, 1922; s. Milo D. and Hazel G. (Kable) Z.; m. Harriet Bong, Jan. 20, 1946;

children: Paula, Keith, Craig. A.B., Augustana Coll., 1946; student, Washington U., St. Louis, 1942-43; LL.B., Harvard U., 1948. Bar: Calif. 1949. Assoc. counsel McCutchen, Doyle, Brown & Enersen, San Francisco, 1949-63; v.p., gen. counsel FrancoWestern Oil Co., Bakersfield, Calif., 1963-65; sr. v.p., sec., chief legal officer, dir. Guy F. Atkinson Co., South San Francisco, Calif., 1965-88; of counsel Pettit & Martin, San Francisco, 1988-95. Bd. dirs., v.p. Republican Alliance, 1965-74; bd. dirs., sec. Atkinson Found., 1967-88; trustee Willamette U., 1978-90; chmn. Nat. Constrn. Employers Coun., 1985-86, Californians for Compensation Reform, 1984-88; chmn. Coun. on Multiemployer Pension Security, 1985-86. With USAAF, 1942-46. Mem. Nat. Constructors Assn. (bd. dirs. 1980-83, chmn. 1983). Methodist. Home: 75 Del Monte Dr Burlingame CA 94010-6226

ZIMMERMAN, DIANE LEENHEER, law educator, lawyer; b. Newton, N.J., Apr. 16, 1941; d. Adrian and Mildred Eleanor (Booth) Leenheer; m. Earl A. Zimmerman, Sept. 24, 1960 (div. Aug. 1982); m. 2d, Cavin P. Leeman, Feb. 18, 1984. BA, Beaver Coll., Glenside, Pa., 1963; JD, Columbia U., 1976. Bar: N.Y. 1977, U.S. Supreme Ct. 1983. Reporter, Newsweek mag., N.Y.C., 1963-71; spl. features writer N.Y. Daily News, N.Y.C., 1971-73; law clk. U.S. Dist. Ct. (ea. dist.) N.Y., Bklyn., 1976-77; asst. prof. law NYU, N.Y.C., 1977-80, assoc. prof., 1980-82, prof., 1982—; mem. faculty Practicing Law Inst. N.Y.C., 1979, 84, 90, 92, 94; of counsel Skadden, Arps, Slate, Meagher & Flom. Articles and book rev. editor Columbia Law Rev., 1975-76. Mem. working group on women, censorship and pornography Nat. Coalition Against Censorship. Recipient citation of merit Columbia U. Sch. Journalism, 1972; Kent scholar and Stone scholar, 1973-76; Disting. Lee vis. prof. Coll. William and Mary, 1994. Mem. ABA (vice chmn. tort liability study com. tort and ins. sect. 1986-87, chair 1st amendment rights com. 1989-94), Am. Law Inst., Assn. of Bar of City of N.Y. (chairperson com. civil rights 1981-83), Copyright Soc. USA (trustee 1988-91), Soc. Am. Law Tchrs. Office: NYU Sch Law 40 Washington Sq S New York NY 10012-1005

ZIMMERMAN, DON, film editor. Prodns. include: Coming Home, 1978, Heaven Can Wait, 1978, Uncle Joe Shannon, 1978, Being There, 1979, A Change of Seasons, 1980, Barbarosa, 1982, Rocky III, 1982, Best Friends, 1982, Staying Alive, 1983, Teachers, 1984, Rocky IV, 1985, Cobra, 1986, Over the Top, 1986, Fatal Beauty, 1987, Everybody's All-American, 1988, The Package, 1989, Navy Seals, 1990. Office: The Gersh Agy 232 N Canon Dr Beverly Hills CA 90210

ZIMMERMAN, DON CHARLES, plant physiologist, biochemist; b. Fargo, N.D., Feb. 27, 1934. BS, N.D. State U., 1955, MS, 1959, PhD in Biochemistry, 1964. Rsch. chemist sci. and edn. adminstrn. agrl. rsch. USDA, 1959—, clin. dir. agrl. rsch. svc., 1988—; asst. prof. N.D. State U., 1964-69, adj. prof. biochemistry, 1969—. Mem. AAAS, Am. Soc. Plant Physiology. Office: USDA Red River Valley Agrl Rsch Ctr ND U Sta PO Box 5677 Univ Sta Fargo ND 58105

ZIMMERMAN, D(ONALD) PATRICK, lawyer; b. Albany, N.Y., Mar. 20, 1942; s. Bernard M. and Helen M. (Eshelman) Z. Student Lawrenceville Sch., 1960; BA, Rollins Coll., 1964; JD, Dickinson Sch. Law, 1967. Bars: Pa. 1968, U.S. Supreme Ct. 1971. Atty., Legal Aid, 1968-69; pub. defender, Lancaster County, Pa., 1969-72; sole practice, Lancaster, Pa., 1974—; instr. Ct. Common Pleas for Constables, 1976—; solicitor Lancaster County Dep. Sheriff Assn., 1977—, Lancaster County Constable Assn., 1975—; instr. sheriff's dept. Lancaster County for Dep. Sheriffs, 1978—; of counsel to Dep. Sheriff Assn. Pa., 1979-81; spl. counsel Pa. State Constables Assn., 1981; chmn. Bd. Arbitrators Lancaster County, 1975-81; spl. counsel Legislative Com. to Constable Assn. Pa., 1982; mem. pastoral coun. St. Anthony's Catholic Ch., 1995—. Recipient Ofcl. Commendation of Merit, Lancaster County Sheriff's Dept., 1979, Ofcl. Commendation of Merit Fraternal Order Police State Lodge 66, 1985, Outstanding Svc. award, 1987, Disting. Service award Fraternal Order State Police Pa., 1987, Outstanding Leadership award, 1988. Mem. ABA, Am. Trial Lawyers Assn., Pa. Bar Assn., Lancaster County Bar Assn. Author: The Pennsylvania Landlord and Tenant Handbook, 1982, revised edit., 1993; contbr. articles to profl. jours. Office: 214 E King St Lancaster PA 17602-2977

ZIMMERMAN, EDWIN MORTON, lawyer; b. N.Y.C., June 11, 1924; s. Benjamin and Tobie (Fuchs) Z.; m. Caroline Abbot, July 3, 1956; children: Sarah Abbot, Lyle Benjamin, Miriam Appleton. AB, Columbia U., 1944, LLB, 1949. Bar: N.Y. 1949, D.C. 1969, U.S. Supreme Ct 1969. With Hoover Commn. Reorgn. Exec. Br., 1948; law clk. to Hon. Stanley F. Reed U.S. Supreme Ct., 1950-51; law clk. to Judge Simon H. Rifkind U.S. Dist. Ct., 1949-50; pvt. practice law N.Y.C., 1951-59; prof. law Stanford U., 1959-69; with Justice Dept., 1965-69, asst. atty. gen. charge antitrust div., 1968-69; mem. Covington & Burling, Washington, 1969—; mem. coun. Adminstrv. Conf. U.S., 1975-78; mem. mfg. studies bd. Nat. Acad. Sci., 1983-87. Trustee Textile Mus., 1983—, pres. bd. trustees, 1987—; mem. Folger Poetry Bd., 1990—. 1st lt. AUS, 1944-46. Mem. ABA, Assn. of Bar of City of N.Y., Am. Law Inst., Coun. Fgn. Rels., Phi Beta Kappa. Home: 1820 Kalorama Sq NW Washington DC 20008-4022 Office: Covington & Burling PO Box 7566 1201 Pennsylvania Ave NW Washington DC 20004-2401

ZIMMERMAN, EVERETT LEE, English educator, academic administrator; b. Lancaster, Pa., Dec. 9, 1936; s. Amos Wanner and Anna (Sensenig) Z.; m. Muriel Laden, Apr. 28, 1963, children: Andrew, Daniel. BA, Bob Jones U., 1958; MA, Temple U., 1961, PhD, 1966. Lectr. Temple U., Phila., 1961-62; instr. Rutgers U., Camden, N.J., 1962-66, asst. prof., 1966-69; asst. prof. U. Calif., Santa Barbara, 1969-72, assoc. prof., 1972-80, prof. English, 1980—, dean, 1988-90. Author: Defoe and the Novel, 1975, Swift's Narrative Satires, 1983, also articles. Dem. committeeman, Phila., 1965-66. Jr. Faculty fellow, 1971, Humanities Inst. fellow, 1975 U. Calif.; NEH grantee, 1986; Guggenheim fellow, 1989-90. Mem. MLA, Am. Soc. 18th Century Studies. Home: 1822 Prospect Ave Santa Barbara CA 93103-1950 Office: U of Calif Dept Of English Santa Barbara CA 93106

ZIMMERMAN, GAIL MARIE, medical foundation executive; b. Fort Wayne, Ind., June 23, 1945; d. Albert Douglas and Aina Dorothy (Johnson) Z. B.A., U. Puget Sound, 1967. Intelligence analyst CIA, Washington, 1970-72; research asst. Arthur Young & Co., Portland, Oreg., 1972-74; emergency med. service planner Marion-Polk-Yamhill Counties, Salem, Oreg., 1975-76; health cons. Freedman Assocs., Portland, Oreg., 1976-77; legis. asst. U.S. Senator Bob Packwood, Portland, 1977-78; exec. dir. Nat. Psoriasis Found., Portland, 1979—. Democrat. Avocations: tennis; hiking. Office: Nat Psoriasis Found 6600 SW 92nd Ave Ste 300 Portland OR 97223-7195

ZIMMERMAN, GEORGE ABRAHAM, lawyer; b. Detroit, Mar. 9, 1954; s. Benio and Pola (Zuckerberg) Z.; m. Cathy Schwartz, Aug. 12, 1979; 1 child, Cari Felice. BA, Bklyn. Coll., 1975; JD, NYU, 1979. Bar: U.S. Dist. Ct. (so. and ea. dists.) N.Y. 1980. Assoc. Skadden, Arps, Slate, Meagher & Flom, N.Y.C., 1979-87, ptnr., 1987—. Mem. ABA, N.Y. State Bar Assn. (com. fed. cts. 1987—). Office: Skadden Arps Slate Meagher & Flom 919 3rd Ave New York NY 10022-3903

ZIMMERMAN, GEORGE OGUREK, physicist, educator; b. Poland, Oct. 20, 1935; s. Charles and Carolin Olga (Fisher) Z.; m. Isa Kaftal, Oct. 4, 1964. B.S., Yale U., 1958, M.S., 1959, Ph.D. (Univ. Wilson fellow 1959-60, D.N. Clark fellow 1959-61), 1963. Research assoc. Yale U., 1962-63; asst. prof. physics Boston U., 1963-68, assoc. prof., 1968-74, prof., 1974—, assoc. chmn. dept. physics, 1971-72, chmn. dept., 1973-83, chmn. faculty coun. 1985-86, dir. honors program in sci. and engring. for HS students, 1978—; mem. staff Nat. Magnet Lab., Cambridge, Mass., 1964, vis. scientist, 1964-70; assoc. physicist U. Calif., San Diego, 1973; vis. scientist Brookhaven Nat. Lab., 1980; vis. scholar Harvard U., 1988, Kamerling Onnes Laboratorium, Leiden, The Netherlands, 1988; pres. Zerres Corp.; participant numerous physics teaching improvement programs for secondary sch. tchrs. and students. Contbr. articles on low temperature physics, phase transitions and superconductivity to profl. jours.; patentee in field. Rsch. Corp. grantee, 1964-65, Air Force Office Sci. Rsch. grantee, 1966-86, NSF grantee, 1975—. Mem. Am. Phys. Soc., N.Y. Acad. Sci., AAAS, Phi Beta Kappa, Sigma Xi.

Home: 566 Commonwealth Ave Boston MA 02215 Office: Boston U Dept Physics Boston MA 02215 *Administration is easier than science because in administration one can create one's own reality, while in science reality is unalterable.*

ZIMMERMAN, GIDEON K., minister; b. Lehr, N.D., Aug. 18, 1920; m. Eleanor Pekrul; children: Paul, Mark (dec.), Thomas. Diploma, N.Am. Baptist Sem., Rochester, N.Y., 1943; B.A., Wesley Coll., U. N.D., 1951; postgrad., Bethany Bibl. Sem., 1958-59, Chgo. Lutheran Sem., 1959-61; B.D., N.Am. Bapt. Sem., Sioux Falls, S.D., 1960, D.D. Pastor First Bapt. Ch., Auburn, Mich., 1943-47, Grace Bapt. Ch., Grand Forks, N.D., 1947-51, Temple Bapt. Ch., Milw., 1951-55; gen. sec. dept. Christian edn. N. Am. Bapt. Conf., 1955-68, exec. sec., 1968-79, estate planning counselor, 1979-85. Home: 3721 Bardstown Rd Unit 308 Louisville KY 40218

ZIMMERMAN, HAROLD SEYMOUR, elementary school educator; b. Bklyn., June 3, 1928. BA, Bklyn. Coll., 1950; MA, So. Ill. U., Edwardsville, 1970; postgrad., various, 1950-90. 8th grade English, Social Studies, Reading tchr. Sherwood Day Sch., Chesterfield, Mo., 1956-64; 7th grade core curriculum, English, Social Studies tchr. Nipher Jr. High Sch., Kirkwood, Mo., 1964-70; 7th grade Social Studies, team teaching tchr. Brittany Woods Sch., University City, Mo., 1971-91; tchr. Russian lit. OASIS, 1995; adj. prof. Russian studies Lindenwood Coll., St. Charles, Mo., 1975—, Washington U., 1972-91; limited participant 1st U.S./Russia Joint Conf. on Edn., 1994; cons. in field. Author: Facing Issues of Family Living; contbr. articles to profl. jours. Chairperson bd. trustees Indian Meadows subdivsn., Olivette, Mo.; chairperson Youth Commn., Olivette; vol. OASIS, St. Louis Zoo. Mem. NEA, ASCD, Mo. Edn. Assn., Nat. Coun. Social Studies (spl. interest groups psychology, tchr. edn., religion in schs.), Mo. Geog. Alliance Tchr. Cons. Home: 804 S Hanley Rd Clayton MO 63105

ZIMMERMAN, HELENE LORETTA, business educator; b. Rochester, N.Y., Feb. 26, 1933; d. Henry Charles and Loretta Catherine (Hobert) Z. BS, SUNY, Albany, 1953, MS, 1959; PhD, U. N.D., 1969. Cert. records mgr. Bus. tchr., chmn. bus. dept. Williamson (N.Y.) Cen. Sch., 1953-69; asst. prof. U. Ky., Lexington, 1969-70; assoc. prof. bus. Cen. Mich. U., Mt. Pleasant, 1970-74, prof., 1974—. Author General Business, 1977; contbg. author to records mgmt. text book, 1987. Sec. Isabella County Christmas Outreach, Mt. Pleasant, 1983-94. Mem. Assn. Records Mgmt. and Adminstrn., Inst. Cert. Records Mgrs. (sec. 1985-89, exam. devel. com. 1993—), Internat. Soc. Bus. Edn. (internat. v.p. English speaking nations 1986-88), Nat. Bus. Edn. Assn., Mich. Bus. Edn. Assn. (bd. dirs. 1985-90, 95—, pres. 1988-89), AAUW (pres. 1984-86), Delta Kappa Gamma (state pres. 1987-89, internat. fin. com. 1990-94). Avocations: travel, crafts. Office: Ctrl Mich U Grawn # 337 Mount Pleasant MI 48859

ZIMMERMAN, HERMAN F., motion picture production designer; b. Spingfield, Ill., Apr. 19, 1935; s. Herman and Linnie Belle (Buck) Z.; m. Sandra J. Simmet, Jan. 3, 1976; children: Herman Fredrick, Buffeé Jeanine. BS in Speech, Northwestern U., 1957, MA, 1958. Assoc. prof. drama Northwestern U., Evanston, Ill., 1958-62; entertainment mgr. Harrahs, Reno, Nev., 1962-64; art dir. NBC-TV, Burbank, Calif., 1965-68, Hollywood (Calif.) Video Ctr., 1968-73; freelance art dir. Hollywood, 1973-80; prodn. designer Paramount Pictures, Hollywood, 1980—; theater scene designer, assoc. prof. drama Northwestern U. Prodn. designer for films Star Trek V: The Final Frontier, Star Trek VI: The Undiscovery Country, Star Trek: Generations, TV series Star Trek: The Next Generation, Star Trek: Deep Space Nine (Emmy award nomination 1993); prodr., dir. series The Picture of Health talk/info. show; designer TV programs Cheers, Webster, Black Rain, The Burning Bed, The Tonight Show, A Rumor of War, The Word, The Starmaker, others. Mem. Soc. Motion Picture Art Dirs., Dirs. Guild Am. Avocation: sailing. Office: care Art Directors Guild 2345 Hercules Dr Los Angeles CA 90046 Office: Paramount Pictures Corp 5555 Melrose Ave Los Angeles CA 90038

ZIMMERMAN, HOWARD ELLIOT, chemist, educator; b. N.Y.C., July 5, 1926; s. Charles and May (Cohen) Z.; m. Jane Kirschenheiter, June 3, 1950 (dec. Jan. 1975); children: Robert, Steven, James; m. Martha L. Baylye Kaufman, Nov. 7, 1975 (div. Oct. 1990); m. Margaret J. Vick, Oct. 1991; stepchildren: Peter and Tanya Kaufman. B.S., Yale U., 1950, Ph.D., 1953. NRC fellow Harvard U., 1953-54; faculty Northwestern U., 1954-60, asst. prof., 1955-60; assoc. prof. U. Wis., Madison, 1960-61; prof. chemistry U. Wis., 1961—; Arthur C. Cope and Hilldale prof. chemistry, 1975—; chmn. 4th Internat. Union Pure and Applied Chemistry Symposium on Photochemistry, 972; organizer, chmn. Organic Photochemistry Symposium at Pacifichem 95, Honolulu, 1995. Author: Quantum Mechanics for Organic Chemists, 1975; mem. editorial bd.: Jour. Organic Chemistry, 1967-71, Molecular Photochemistry, 1969-75, Jour. Am. Chem. Soc., 1982-85, Revs. Reactive Intermediates, 1984-89; contbr. articles to profl. jours. Recipient Halpern award for photochemistry N.Y. Acad. Scis., 1979, Chem. Pioneer award Am. Inst. Chemists, 1986, Sr. Alexander von Humboldt award, 1988, Hilldale award U. Wis., 1988-89, 90. Mem. NAS, Am. Chem. Soc. (James Flack Norris award 1976, Arthur C. Cope Scholar award 1991), Chem. Soc. London, German Chem. Soc., Inter-Am. Photochemistry Assn. (co-chmn. organic div. 1977-79, exec. com. 1979-86), Phi Beta Kappa, Sigma Xi. Home: 1 Oconto Ct Madison WI 53705-4925 Office: U Wis Chemistry Dept 1101 University Ave Madison WI 53706-1396

ZIMMERMAN, HYMAN JOSEPH, internist, educator; b. Rochester, N.Y., July 19, 1914; s. Philip and Rachel (Marine) Z.; m. Kathrin J. Jones, Feb. 28, 1943; children: Philip M., David J., Robert L., Diane E. AB, U. Rochester, 1936; MA, Stanford U., 1938, MD, 1943. Diplomate Am. Bd. Internal Medicine. Intern Stanford (Calif.) U. Hosp., 1942-43; asst. resident in medicine Gallinger Mcpl. Hosp. divsn. George Washington U., Washington, 1946-47, chief resident in medicine, 1947-48, clin. instr. in medicine, 1948-51, prof. Sch. Medicine, 1965-68, 71-79, prof. medicine, gastroenterology Sch. Medicine, 1986-89, prof. emeritus, 1989—; asst. chief of med. svc. VA Hosp., Washington, 1949-51; chief of med. svc. VA Hosp., Omaha, 1951-53, Chgo., 1953-57; chief of liver and metabolic rsch. lab. VA Hosp., Washington, 1965-68; chief of med. svc. VA Hosp., Boston, 1968-71; chief of med. svc. VA Hosp., Washington, 1977-78, sr. clinician, 1978-80, disting. physician, 1984-89; disting. scientist Armed Forces Inst. Pathology, Washington, 1989—; asst. prof. medicine Coll. Medicine U. Nebr., Omaha, 1951-53; assoc. prof. of medicine Coll. of Medicine U. Ill., Chgo., 1953-57; prof., chmn. dept. medicine Chgo. Med. Sch., 1957-65; chmn. dept. of medicine Mt. Sinai Hosp., Chgo., 1957-65; prof. of medicine Sch. of Medicine Boston U., 1968-71; clin. prof. Sch. of Medicine Georgetown U., Washington, 1971-78; sr. clinician VA Hosp., Washington, 1978—; clin. prof. medicine Howard U., 1971-78, Uniformed Svcs. U. Health Scis., 1978—; cons. Clin. Ctr. NIH, Bethesda, 1965—, USN Med. Ctr., Bethesda, 1965—; vis. prof., lectr. numerous hosps. and univs. Author: Hepatotoxicity, 1978; contbr. numerous articles to med. jours.; contbg. editor numerous med. pubs. Maj. AUS, 1943-46. Recipient William Beaumont award for clin. rsch., 1981, Disting. Achievement award Am. Assn. for Study Liver Disease, 1986, gold medal Can. Liver Found., 1989. Fellow ACP (mastership 1993); mem. AMA (mem. coun. on drugs, mem. gastroenterology panel 1968-70), AAAS, AAUP, Am. Soc. Clin. Pharmacology and Therapeutics, Am. Fedn. for Clin. Rsch., Am. Diabetes Assn.; Endocrine Soc., Asian-Pacific Assn. for Study of Liver Diseases, Am. Soc. Clin. Investigation, N.Y. Acad. Scis., Cen. Soc. Clin. Rsch., Soc. for Exptl. Biology and Medicine, Am. Gastroenterol. Assn. (named Disting. Educator 1990), Drug Info. Assn.; Cosmos Club, Sigma Xi, Alpha Omega Alpha. Jewish. Home: 7913 Charleston Ct Bethesda MD 20817-1421 Office: Armed Forces Inst Path Hepatic Dept Washington DC 20306-6000

ZIMMERMAN, JACK WALLACE, newspaper editor; b. Seneca, Kans., May 7, 1926; s. Edward Walter and Cleo Lauree (Conlin) Z.; m. Mary Frances Wray, Oct. 4, 1947; children—Miles C., Marc E., Kim, Christine. B.S., U. Kans., 1952. Reporter, city editor Jour.-World, Lawrence, Kans., 1952-68; asst. to exec. editor Gannett Newspapers, Rochester, N.Y., 1968-79; asst. mng. editor Daily Oklahoman, Oklahoma City, 1980-84, mng. editor, 1984—. Author: I Just Closed My Eyes and Swang, 1965. Served with U.S. Army, 1944-46. Mem. AP Mng. Editors Assn. Avocations: gardening; music; wood carving; fishing. Home: RR 1 Box 338 Lead Hill AR 72644-9501 Office: Okla Pub Co Daily Oklahoman 500 N Broadway PO Box 25125 Oklahoma City OK 73125-0125

ZIMMERMAN, JAMES M., retail company executive; b. 1944. Chmn. Rich's Dept. Store div. Federated Dept. Stores, 1984-88; pres., chief operating officer Federated and Allied Dept. Stores, Cin., 1988—. Office: Federated Department Stores Inc 7 W 7th St Cincinnati OH 45202-2424*

ZIMMERMAN, JO ANN, health services and educational consultant, former lieutenant governor; b. Van Buren County, Iowa, Dec. 24, 1936; d. Russell and Hazel (Ward) McIntosh; m. A. Tom Zimmerman, Aug. 26, 1956; children: Andrew, Lisa, Don and Ron (twins), Beth. Diploma, Broadlawns Sch. of Nursing, Des Moines, 1958; BA with honors, Drake U., 1973; postgrad., Iowa State U., 1973-75. RN, Iowa. Asst. head nurse maternity dept. Broadlawns Med. Ctr., Des Moines, 1958-59, weekend supr. nursing svcs., 1960-61, supr. maternity dept., 1966-68; instr. maternity nursing Broadlawns Sch. Nursing, 1968-71; health planner, community rels. assoc. Iowa Health Systems Agy., Des Moines, 1978-82; mem. Iowa Ho. Reps., 1982-86; lt. gov., Senate pres. State of Iowa, 1987-91; cons. health svcs., grant writing and continuing edn. Zimmerman & Assocs., Des Moines, 1991—; ops. dir. Medlink Svcs., Inc., rehab. and work hardening co., Des Moines, 1992—. Contbr. articles to profl. jours. Mem. advanced registered nurse practitioner task force on cert. nurse mid-wives Iowa Bd. Nursing, 1980-81, Waukee, Polk County, Iowa Health Edn. Coordinating Coun., Iowa Women's Polit. Caucus, Dallas County Women's Polit. Caucus; chmn. Des Moines Area Maternity Nursing Conf. Group, 1969-70, task force on sch. health svcs. Iowa Dept. Health, 1982, task force health edn. Iowa Dept. Pub. Instruction, 1979, adv. com. health edn. assessment tool, 1980-81, Nat. Lt. Govs., chair com. on Agrl. and Rural Devel., 1989; Dallas County Dem. Cen. Com., 1972-84; bd. dirs. Iowa PTA, 1979-83, Waukee Community Sch. Bd., 1976-79, pres., 1978-79; chairperson Health Com., 1980-84; bd. dirs. Iowa Parent and Tchrs. Assn.; mem. steering com. ERA, Iowa, 1991, 92; founder Dem. Activist Women's Network (DAWN), 1992. Mem. ANA, LWV (health chmn. met. Des Moines chpt.), Iowa Nurses Assn., Iowa League for Nursing (bd. dirs. 1979-83), Family Centered Childbirth Edn. Assn. (childbirth instr., advisor), Iowa Cattleman's Assn., Am. Lung Assn. (bd. dirs. Iowa 1988-92), Dem. Activist Women's Network (founder 1992). Mem. Christian Ch. Avocations: gardening, sewing, reading, bridge, breeding British White Park cattle. Office: Zimmerman & Assocs 7630 Ashworth Rd West Des Moines IA 50266-5859

ZIMMERMAN, JOHN H., communications company executive; b. Akron, Ohio, Oct. 3, 1932; s. Erle C. and Agnes R. (Lower) Z.; m. LaVonne A. Robertson, July 25, 1953; children: Rebecca Zimmerman Brown, J. Jeffrey, Amy Leigh Zimmerman Larimore. B.A. in Econs., Colgate U., 1954; M.B.A., Kent State U., 1962. Dir. labor relations Firestone Tire and Rubber Co., Akron, Ohio, 1975-78, v.p. employee relations, 1978-82; sr. v.p. human resources MCI Communications, Washington, 1982—; adj. prof. Kent State U., 1963-66, U. Akron, 1970-72; mem. U.S. Gov. Commn. on Achieving Necessary Skills, 1990-92; mem. adv. coun. Ctr. for Workplace Excellence; mem. Work Readiness Adv. Com. V.p. Akron-Canton Regional Airport Bd. Trustees, 1981-82; active Nat. Com. Vietnam POW Reemployment, 1972-73; mem. adv. bd. Nat. Urban League, N.Y.C., 1972-83, U. Akron Ctr. Econ. Edn., 1981-82, Nat. Alliance Businessmen Bd., 1973-82; mem. adv. bd. Sch. Bus. and Pub. Mgmt., George Washington U., 1987—; trustee Akron Gen. Med. Ctr., 1981-82, Akron YMCA, 1980-82; chmn. Summit County Pers. Rev. Commn., 1970. Mem. Am. Mgmt. Assn. (mem. HR adv. coun. 1986-93, chair 1991-93, bd. trustees 1991-93), Phi Beta Kappa. Presbyterian. Home: 7272 Evans Mill Rd Mc Lean VA 22101-3423 Office: MCI Comm Corp 1801 Pennsylvania Ave NW Washington DC 20006-3605

ZIMMERMAN, JOSEPH FRANCIS, political scientist, educator; b. Keene, N.H., June 29, 1928; s. John Joseph and May Veronica (Gallagher) Z.; m. Margaret Bernardette Brennan, Aug. 2, 1958; 1 child, Deirdre Ann. BA, U. N.H., 1950; MA, Syracuse U., 1951, PhD, 1954. Instr. govt. Worcester Poly. Inst., 1954-55, asst. prof., 1955-57, assoc. prof., 1957-62, prof., 1962-65; lectr. Clark U., Worcester, Mass., 1957-65; prof. polit. sci. SUNY, Albany, 1965—; staff dir. N.Y. State Joint Legis. Com. Mass. Transp., 1967-68, research dir., 1968-73; research dir. N.Y. State Select Legis. Com. Transp., 1973-77, N.Y. State Senate Com. on Transp., 1977-82, Legis. Commn. on Critical Transp. Problems, 1982—. Author: State and Local Government, 1962, The Massachusetts Town Meeting: A Tenacious Institution, 1967, The Federated City: Community Control in Large Cities, 1972, Pragmatic Federalism, The Reassignment of Functional Responsibility, 1976, (with Frank W. Prescott) The Politics of the Veto of Legislation in New York, 1980, The Government and Politics of the Empire State, 1981, Local Discretionary Authority, 1981, (with Deirdre A. Zimmerman) The Politics of Subnational Governance, 1983, State-Local Relations: A Partnership Approach, 1983 (CHOICE award as outstanding acad. book 1984), Participatory Democracy: Populism Revived, 1986, Federal Preemption: The Silent Revolution, 1990, Contemporary American Federalism, 1992, (with Wilma Rule) United States Electoral System: Their Impact Upon Women and Minorities, 1992, (with Wilma Rule) Electoral Systems in Comparative Perspective: Their Impact on Women Minorities, 1994, Curbing Unethical Behavior of Government, 1994; contbr. articles to profl. pubs. Pres. Citizens' Plan E Assn., Worcester, 1960-62, Citizens for Neighborhood Improvement Worcester, 1957-59. Served to capt. USAF, 1951-53. Named 1 of 3 Outstanding Young Men Worcester Jr. C. of C., 1959, 61, 1 of 3 Outstanding Young Men Mass, Jr. C. of C., 1961, disting. citizen award Nat. Conf. on Govt., 1986. Mem. Am. Polit. Sci. Assn., Am. Soc. Public Adminstrn., Nat. Mcpl. League. Roman Catholic. Club: German-Am. Social. Home: 82 Greenock Rd Delmar NY 12054-4414 Office: SUNY Grad Sch Public Affairs 135 Western Ave Albany NY 12222

ZIMMERMAN, JUDITH ROSE, art educator; b. Youngstown, Ohio, Jan. 17, 1945; d. Emery and Josephine Leona (Terlecki) Ference; m. William Carl Zimmerman, Jr., Nov 27, 1965; children: Shawn, William III. BFA in Art Edn., Kent State U., 1977, MEd in Curriculum and Instruction, 1992. Cert. art tchr., Ohio. Elem. art tchr. Sandy Valley Sch. Dist., Magnolia, Ohio, 1977—; instr. art Massillon (Ohio) Art Mus. Adv. com. Edn. Enhancement Partnership Coun., Canton, Ohio, 1992; active Little Art Gallery, 1992, Massillon Art Mus. Mem. NEA, Nat. Art Edn. Assn., Ohio Edn. Assn., Ohio Art Edn. Assn. (chairperson east central divsn. 1985-90, elem. divsn 1989-91, Art Educator of Yr. 1983, Featured Art Tchr. of Month 1990), Ohio Alliance for Art Edn., Canton Art Inst. (Art Educator of Yr. 1992), Phi Delta Kappa. Roman Catholic. Avocations: reading, tennis, music, oil painting, walking. Home: 802 Lucille Ave North Canton OH 44720 Office: Sandy Valley Sch Dist Rt 2 Magnolia OH 44643

ZIMMERMAN, LEROY S., lawyer, former state attorney general; b. Harrisburg, Pa., Dec. 22, 1934; s. LeRoy and Amelia (Magaro) Z.; m. Mary Augusta Jaymes, Feb. 9; children: Susan A., Mark J., Amy A. BS in Econs., Villanova (Pa.) U., 1956; JD, Dickinson Sch. Law, Carlisle, Pa., 1959; LLD (hon.), Dickinson Sch. Law, 1989. Bar: Pa. 1960. Pvt. practice law, 1960-81; ptnr. Hepford, Zimmerman & Swartz, 1970-81; asst. dist. atty., then dist. atty. Dauphin County, 1963-80; atty. gen. Commonwealth Pa., Harrisburg, 1981-89; sr. ptnr. in charge of Harrisburg office Eckert Seamans Cherin & Mellott, Harrisburg, 1989—; apptd. White Ho. Conf. for a Drug Free Am.; mem., former chmn. exec. working group Fed.-State-Local Prosecutorial Rels.; past pres. Pa. Dist. Attys. Assn. Trustee Dickinson Sch. Law, The Hall Found.; mem. devel. coun. Villanova U.; bd. dirs. Harrisburg Area YMCA, YMCA of the USA. With USAF. Recipient Man of Yr. award Police Chiefs Assn. Southeastern Pa., 1982, Achievement award Nat. Italian-Am. Found., 1983, Pres.'s award Pa. Chiefs Police Assn., 1986. Mem. Nat. Assn. Attys. Gen. (former chmn. criminal law com., mem. anti-trust, asbestos and environ. control coms.), Pa. Dist. Attys. Assn. (past pres.), Phi Alpha Delta, Sons Italy in Am. Republican. Roman Catholic. Club: K.C. Office: Eckert Seamans Cherin & Mellott 1 S Market Sq 213 Market St Harrisburg PA 17101

ZIMMERMAN, LOUIS SEYMOUR, lawyer; b. Houston, Mar. 17, 1949; s. Robert Eugene and Rosalind (Pincoffs) Z.; m. Janet Whaley, Aug. 9, 1975; children: Patrick, Thomas, Frank. BA, Williams Coll., 1971; JD, U. Tex., 1974. Bar: Tex. 1974, U.S. Dist. Ct. (so. and we. dists.) Tex. 1974, D.C. 1974, U.S Ct. Appeals (5th, 11th and D.C. cirs.) 1974. Law clk. to Hon. judge Owen Cox U.S. Dist. Ct., Corpus Christi, Tex., 1974-76; assoc. Fulbright & Jaworski, Houston, 1976-82; ptnr. Fulbright & Jaworski, Washington, 1983-86, Austin, Tex., 1986—. Office: Fulbright & Jaworski 600 Congress Ave Ste 2400 Austin TX 78701-3234

ZIMMERMAN, MARTIN E., financial executive; b. Chgo., Jan. 28, 1938; s. Joseph and Sylvea Zimmerman; m. Rita Kalifon, June 20, 1961 (div. 1992); children: Jacqueline, Adam. BSEE, MIT, 1955-59; MBA in Fin., Columbia U., 1961. Dir. market research Nuclear-Chgo., Inc. div. G.D. Searle & Co., 1964-67; pres. Telco Mktg. Services, Inc., Chgo., 1967-74; pres., chmn., chief exec. officer Linc Group, Inc., Chgo., 1975—. Contbr. numerous articles on leasing to profl. mags. Bd. overseers Columbia U. Grad. Sch. Bus.; trustee Mus. Contemporary Art, Chgo., Ravenswood Med. Ctr., Chgo. Capt. U.S. Army, 1961-63. McKinsey scholar, Kennecott Copper fellow Columbia U., 1959-61. Mem. Equipment Lessors Assn. (bd. dirs.). Clubs: University, Mid-Am. (Chgo.). Avocations: fishing, bird hunting, skiing, amateur radio. Home: 100 E Bellevue Pl Apt 26D Chicago IL 60611-1125 Office: The Linc Group Inc 303 E Wacker Dr 1000 Chicago IL 60601-5212

ZIMMERMAN, MARY ANN, university purchasing agent; b. Bloomsburg, Pa., Dec. 29, 1956; d. Albert C. Zimmerman and Ethel A. Benninger; m. Kenneth T. Yetman, Mar. 20, 1983; children: Eric Lee, Michael Guy. BS in Biology, Pa. State U., 1978; MS in Marine Sci., U.S.C., 1980. Cert. pub. purchasing buyer Nat. Inst. Govtl. Purchasing. Research asst. zoology dept. U. Md., College Park, 1980-82, purchasing liaison zoology dept., 1982-84, buyer IV, then buyer V, team leader, 1984—. Democrat. Lutheran. Avocations: raising children and plants, reading. Office: U Md Purchasing Dept College Park MD 20742

ZIMMERMAN, MICHAEL DAVID, state supreme court chief justice; b. Chgo., Oct. 21, 1943; s. Elizabeth Porter; m. Lynne Mariani (dec. 1994); children: Evangeline Albright, Alessandra Mariani, Morgan Elisabeth. BS, U. Utah, 1966, JD, 1969. Bar: Calif. 1971, Utah 1978. Law clk. to Chief Justice Warren Earl Burger U.S. Supreme Ct., Washington, 1969-70; assoc. O'Melveny & Myers, L.A., 1970-76; assoc. prof. law U. Utah, 1976-78, adj. prof. law, 1978-84, 89—; of counsel Kruse, Landa, Zimmerman & Maycock, Salt Lake City, 1978-80; spl. counsel Gov. of Utah, Salt Lake City, 1978-80; ptnr. Watkiss & Campbell, Salt Lake City, 1980-84; assoc. justice Supreme Ct. Utah, Salt Lake City, 1984-93, chief justice, 1994—; co-moderator Justice Soc. Program of Snowbird Inst. for Arts and Humanities, 1991, 92; moderator, Tanner lecture panel jud. philosophy U. Utah, 1994; faculty, Judging Sci. Program Duke U., 1992. Editor: Utah Law Rev., 1968-69; contbr. numerous articles to legal publs. Mem. Project 2000, Coalition for Utah's Future. Named Utah State Bar Appellate Ct. Judge of Yr., 1988; Justice and Soc. Program of Aspen Inst. for Humanistic Studies fellow, 1988, co-moderator, 1989; inaugural recipient Excellence in Ethics award Utah Valley State Coll., 1994. Mem. ABA (faculty mem. judges' seminar 1993), Am. Law Inst., Utah Bar Assn., Salt Lake County Bar Assn., Jud. Conf. U.S. (adv. com. civil rules 1985-91), Utah Jud. Coun. (supreme ct. rep. 1986-91, chair 1994—, chair com. on alternative dispute resolution 1993-94), Utah Constnl. Revisions Commn., Snowbird Inst. for Arts and Humanities (bd. dirs.), Am. Inns of Ct. VIII, Am. Judicature Soc., U. Utah Coll. of Law Alumni Assn. (pres. 1991-92), Order of Coif, Phi Kappa Phi. Office: Utah Supreme Ct 332 State Capitol Salt Lake City UT 84114-1181

ZIMMERMAN, MICHAEL GLENN, marketing/communications executive; b. Charlotte, N.C., Nov. 22, 1957; s. Glenn Calvin and Phyllis Ann (Miller) Z.; m. MaryBeth O'Neill, Sept. 2, 1989; 1 child, Abbey Marie. BA in Journalism, Ohio State U., 1980. Acct. supr. Paul Werth Assocs., Columbus, Ohio, 1980-84; acct. mgr. Watt, Roop & Co., Cleve., 1984-85, sr. acct. mgr., 1985-87, v.p., 1987-89, sr. v.p., 1989-92, exec. v.p., dir. client svcs., 1992—; mem. mktg. com. Cleve. regional office Ohio State U., 1990—. Mem. mktg. com. United Way of Cuyahoga County, Cleve., 1990—; trustee, devel. chmn. Ctr. for Mental Retardation, Cleve., 1991—; small bus. alliance Rock & Roll Hall of Fame, Cleve., 1992—. Mem. Am. Advt. Fedn. (mem. Cleve. chpt., Addy award 1989), Pub. Rels. Soc. Am. (Silver Anvil award 1988, 92). Republican. Avocations: Ohio State football, arts, travel, gourmet cooking/dining, golf. Home: 3143 Clark Pkwy Westlake OH 44143 Office: Watt Roop & Co 1100 Superior Ave Cleveland OH 44114

ZIMMERMAN, NANCY PICCIANO, library science educator; b. Jeannette, Pa., July 29, 1951; d. Daniel Joseph and Helen Elizabeth (Lipinski) Picciano; m. Lee W. Zimmerman, Aug. 10, 1974; children: Matthew, Renée. BA in English, Carlow Coll., Pitts., 1973; MLS in Libr. Sci., U. Pitts., 1974; MS in Computer Edn. and Cognitive Sys., U. North Tex., 1992; PhD in Libr. and Info. Studies, Tex. Woman's U., 1992. Lic. libr. media specialist, K-12, lang. arts/English 7-12. Libr. media specialist Fairfield (Calif.)-Suisun Sch. Dist., 1976-78; reference libr. Pikes Peak Libr. Dist., Colorado Springs, Colo., 1983; libr. media specialist North Pole (Alaska) H.S., 1984-85, Prince William County Schs., Woodbridge, Va., 1985-89; dir. info. retrieval lab. Tex. Woman's U., Denton, 1989-91; adj. prof., rsch. assoc. U. North Tex., Denton, 1991-92; asst. prof. Sch. Info. and Libr. Studies SUNY, Buffalo, 1993—. Nat. stroke and turn ofcl. U.S Swimming, 1985—. Recipient ALISE rsch. grant award, 1994. Mem. ALA (chair elect Libr. Rsch. Round Table 1994—), Am. Assn. Sch. Librs., Internat. Assn. Sch. Librs., N.Y. Libr. Assn., Phi Delta Kappa, Beta Phi Mu (nat. exec. coun. 1994—). Office: SUNY at Buffalo Sch Info & Libr Studies 381 Baldy Hall Box 601020 Buffalo NY 14260-1020

ZIMMERMAN, PAUL ALBERT, retired college president, minister; b. Danville, Ill., June 25, 1918; s. Albert Carl and Hanna Marie (Haffner) Z.; m. Genevieve Emmaline Bahls, June 11, 1944; children—Karmin (Mrs. Raymond Philp), Thomas. Student, Concordia Coll., Ft. Wayne, Ind., 1936-39; B.A., Concordia Sem., St. Louis, 1941, M.Div., 1944; M.A., U. Ill., 1947, Ph.D., 1951; D.D., Concordia Sem., Springfield, Ill., 1975; LLD (hon.), Concordia Coll., Ann Arbor, Mich., 1994. Prof. theology and sci. Bethany Coll., Mankato, Minn., 1944-53; prof. Concordia Tchrs. Coll., Seward, Nebr., 1953-54; pres. Concordia Tchrs. Coll., 1954-61, Concordia Luth. Jr. Coll., Ann Arbor, Mich., 1961-73, Concordia Coll., River Forest, Ill., 1973-83, ret., 1983; pastor St. Luke's Luth. Ch., Harrison, Mich., 1983-88. Author and editor: Darwin, Evolution and Creation, 1959, Rock Strata and the Bible Record, 1971, Creation, Evolution and God's Word, 1972. Chmn. Washtenaw County Red Cross, 1968-70; pres. Ann Arbor Found., 1970-71; mem. Citizens Com. Study Taxation, Ann Arbor, 1972; mem. adv. bd. St. Joseph Mercy Community, 1969-72; chmn. Luth. Ch. Mo. Synod's Bd. for Mission Services, 1982-92, Mission Task Force, 1990-91, administrv. asst. pres. Mo. Synod, 1972-73, 93-94, mem. curriculum commn. bd. higher edn., 1963-73, mem. task force constl. revision Mo. Synod, chmn. com. adjudication procedures Mo. Synod. Fellow Creation Rsch. Assn. (bd. dirs., fin. sec.). Lutheran. Home: 2798 Princeton Dr Traverse City MI 49684

ZIMMERMAN, RAYMOND, retail chain executive; b. Memphis, TN, 1933; married. V.p. Service Mdse. Co., Inc., Nashville, from 1959, pres., 1973—, chmn., 1981—, now also chief exec. officer, also bd. dirs. Office: Service Merchandise Co Inc 7100 Service Merchandise Dr Brentwood TN 37027-2927*

ZIMMERMAN, RICHARD ANSON, food company executive; b. Lebanon, Pa., Apr. 5, 1932; s. Richard Paul and Kathryn Clare (Wilhelm) Z.; m. Nancy J. Cramer, Dec. 27, 1952; children: Linda Joan, Janet Lee. BA in Commerce, Pa. State U., 1953; LLD, Lebanon Valley Coll., 1992. Asst. sec. Mellon Bank, Harrisburg, Pa., 1956-58; with Hershey (Pa.) Foods Corp., 1958—, asst. to pres., 1965-71, v.p., 1971-76, pres., chief oper. officer, 1976-84, pres., 1984-85, CEO, 1984-95, chmn., 1985-94; ret., 1994; bd. dirs. Lance, Inc., Westvaco Corp., Eastman Kodak Co. Trustee Pa. State U., United Theol. Sem.; mem. United Way Am. Lt USN, 1953-56. Recipient Alumni fellow award Pa. State U., 1978, Disting. Alumni award Pa. State U., 1987, N.C.C.J. Nat. Brotherhood award, 1988. Mem. Alumni Assn. Pa. State U. (pres. 1982-83), Hershey Country Club, Masons, Rotary (pres. Hershey 1973-74), Phi Kappa Psi. Methodist. Office: Hershey Foods Corp PO Box 810 Hershey PA 17033-0810

ZIMMERMAN, RICHARD GAYFORD, journalist; b. Springfield, Ohio, Sept. 3, 1934; s. Charles Ballard and Dorothy Cubitt (Gayford) Z. B.F.A. cum laude, Wittenberg U., 1956; M.A., Am. U., 1958. Freelance writer and polit. cartoonist, 1959-61; wire editor Urbana (Ohio) Daily Citizen, 1960-61; state house corr. Horvitz Newspapers, Mansfield, Lorain, Dover and Willoughby, Ohio, 1962-64, Dayton (Ohio) Jour. Herald, 1964-67; chief state house bur. Cleve. Plain Dealer, 1967-71, reporter Washington bur., 1971-72, chief Washington bur., 1972-77, nat. corr., 1978-85; freelance writer Africa,

1977. Co-author: Ohio Politics, 1994; contbr. articles to various publs. Served with USAF, 1961-62. Recipient award Ohio A.P., 1971, 83, award Ohio Legis. Corrs. Assn., 1968, 69. Mem. Ohio Press Club (trustee 1969), Nat. Press Club (sec. 1974-75, vice chmn. bd. govs. 1975-76, chmn. speakers com. 1979-80, chmn. house com. 1986-88, chmn. forum com. 1990-91, Washington Corr. award 1982), Ohio Legis. Corrs. Assn. (v.p. 1969-70), Beta Theta Pi. Home: 125 10th St SE Washington DC 20003-3922

ZIMMERMAN, ROBERT ALLEN See DYLAN, BOB

ZIMMERMAN, ROGER JOSEPH, fisherie biologist; b. Alice, Tex., Dec. 2, 1941; s. Walter George and Laura Virgie (Heine) Z.; m. Domenica Marie DeCaro, Dec. 28; children: Katherine, Robert. BS in Biology, Tex. A&I Coll., 1966, MA in Biology and Geology, 1969; PhD in Marine Scis., U.P.R., Mayaguez, 1979. Tchg. asst. biology dept. U. South Fla., Tampa, 1971; rsch. assoc. marine sci. dept. U. South Fla., St. Petersburg, 1971-73; rsch. assoc. P.R. Nuclear Ctr. U. P.R., 1974-75, grad. fellow, 1975-78, marine benthic ecologist Ctr. for Energy & Environ. Rsch., 1978-81; fishery ecologist fishery mgmt. divsn. NOAA/NMFS Galveston (Tex.) Lab., 1981-91, divsn. chief fishery ecology divsn., 1991-93, lab. dir., 1993—; rsch. fellow U.S. Nat. Mus. Natural History, Smithsonian Instn., Washington and Harbor Branch, Fla., summers, 1975, 76; vis. instr. marine biology dept. Tex. A&M U., Galveston, summer 1988, 89; vis. instr. biology dept. Corpus Christi (Tex.) State U., 1986; tchg. asst. biology U. South Fla., 1970; lectr.-counselor Tex. A&I U., 1969, lab. coord., tchg. asst., 1968-69; OAS and U.S. AID advisor to INstuto de Pesca de Ecuador, 1981-89; mem. coastal ocean estuarine habitat rsch. planning com. NOAA, 1987, sci. adv. com., 1989; chair predator-prey com. S.E. Fisheries Sci. Ctr., 1990-91; coord. climate and globan change ecol. sys. and dynamics work group NSMF, 1990, spl. asst. to office of sr. scientist, 1990; mem. sci. adv. com. Galveston Bay project Nat. Estuary Program, 1993-94, mem. mgmt. com. Corpus Christi project, 1994-95; acting dir. SEFSC Galveston Lab., 1993; bd. dirs. Gulf of Mex. regional marine rsch. program NMFS/SEFSC, 1992-93; rep. programs on coastal fisheries and estuarine ecology SERSC, 1992-95; cons., advisor in field; adj. wildlife and fisheries dept. and biology dept. Tex. A&M U., dept. biology Corpus Christi State U., dept. marine scis. La. State U., 1985-89, dept. biology U. Houston, 1983-85; presenter workshops in field. Reviewer for jours. in field, including Fishery Bull., contbns. to Marine Sci., Marine Ecology Progress Series, Jour. Exptl. Marine Biology and Ecology, Marine Biology, Bull. Marine Sci., Jour. Wetlands Ecology and Mgmt., Estuaries, Coastal and Shelf Sci., also various proposals; editl. reviewer SEFSC Galveston Lab., 1984—; contbr. numerous articles to profl. publs.; author abstracts, revs. in field. Mem. Estuarine Rsch. Fedn., Gulf Estuarine Rsch. Soc., Crustacean Soc., Am. Fisheries Soc., Assn. Marine Labs. of the Caribbean. Home: Nat Marine Fisheries Svc SE Fisheries Sci Ctr 3202 Ave N 1/2 Galveston TX 77551

ZIMMERMAN, S(AMUEL) MORTON (MORT ZIMMERMAN), electrical and electronics engineering executive; b. Paterson, N.J., Mar. 18, 1927; s. Solomon Zimmerman and Miriam (Feder) Glatzer; m. Marion Patricia Bogue, Sept. 15, 1951; children: Judy, Suzy, Sharon, Dan. Student, Ga. Inst. Tech., 1942-44, 46-48, Oglethorpe U., 1948-51; BSEE, Pacific Internat. U., L.A., 1958. Pres. Comml. Electronics Corp., Dallas, 1954-56, Electron Corp. subs. LTV Corp., 1956-65; chmn. bd., pres. Capital Bancshares, Inc., 1965-66; chmn. bd. Capital Nat. Bank Tampa (formerly Springs Nat. Bank), Fla., 1965, Capital Nat. Bank Miami (name now Peoples Downtown Bank), Fla., 1966, Merc. Nat. Bank Miami Beach (name now Barnett Bank), Fla., 1967, Underwriters Bank & Trust Co. N.Y. (name now Banco Cen.), 1968; chmn. bd., pres. Capital Gen. Corp., 1967, Comml. Tech., Inc., 1977—; Petro Imperial Corp. and subs. DOL Resources and Tech.-Star, Dallas, 1983—; chmn. bd., pres. Tans Exchange Corp., 1965—, Electric & Gas Tech., Inc., 1985—; also chmn. 8 subs. cos.; chmn. bd. Video Sci. Tech., Inc. 1981-92; Interfed. Capital, Inc., 1990—. Patentee: TV camera video amplifier and blanking circuits, electronic thermometer, video x-ray image system and methods, video system and method for presentation and reproduction x-ray film images, electromagnetic radio frequency lighting system, laser display of electronically generated image signal; patent applied for: new tech. for electronic refrigeration system. Petty officer USN, 1942-45. Recipient Interfaith award City of N.Y. Mem. IEEE, Brookhaven Country Club. Republican. Jewish. Home: 5629 Meaders Ln Dallas TX 75229-6655 Office: Electric & Gas Tech Inc 13636 Neutron Rd Dallas TX 75244-4410

ZIMMERMAN, SCOTT FRANKLIN, lawyer; b. Pitts., June 13, 1935; s. Franklin Prince and Louise (Scott) Z.; m. Judith Kirkpatrick, Aug. 20, 1960; children: Martha, Sarah. BA, Westminster Coll., 1960; LLB, U. Mich., 1963. Bar: Pa. 1963, U.S. Ct. Appeals (3d cir.) 1967, U.S. Ct. Appeals (6th cir.) 1968, U.S. Ct. Appeals (2d cir.) 1972, U.S. Supreme Ct. 1973. Ptnr. Reed Smith Shaw & McClay, Pitts., 1963—; instr. labor econs. Carnegie-Mellon U., Pitts., 1972-78. Trustee Ellis Sch., Pitts., 1987-92. Mem. ABA, Pa. Bar Assn., Allegheny County Bar Assn. Republican. Episcopalian. Clubs: Duquesne, Longue Vue (Pitts.). Avocations: skiing, golf, running, diving. Office: Reed Smith Shaw & McClay James H Reed Bldg 435 6th Ave Pittsburgh PA 15219-1809

ZIMMERMAN, THOM JAY, ophthalmologist, educator; b. Lincoln, Ill., Oct. 5, 1942; s. Kenneth Earl and Georgia Rosemary (Taylor) Z.; m. Tinker Steiner; 1 child, Jessica. BS in Zoology, U. Ill., 1964; MD, U. Ill., Chgo., 1968; PhD in Pharmacology, U. Fla., 1976. Diplomate Nat. Bd. Med. Examiners, Am. Bd. Ophthalmology. Intern St. Lukes Hosp., Chgo., 1968-69; resident U. Fla. Coll. Medicine, Dept. Ophthalmology, Gainesville, 1971-74, corneal fellow, 1974-75, glaucoma fellow, 1976-77; acting chmn. dept. ophthalmology La. State U., New Orleans, 1977; assoc. prof. ophthalmology and pharmacology Ochsner Clinic, New Orleans, 1977-79; prof. pharmacology and toxicology U. Louisville, 1986—, prof., chmn. dept. ophthalmology, 1986—; ophthalmic cons. (glaucoma) USPHS Hosp., New Orleans, 1977-82; cons. Nat. Adv. Eye Council and NEI, 1983; U.S. rep. for exec. com. Pan-Am. Glaucoma Soc., 1983-85; chmn. glaucoma symposium of Nat. Soc. to Prevent Blindness, 1988; guest lectr. numerous profl. socs. and confs. Author 6 books and numerous editorials; contbr. sci. articles to profl. jours.; mem. editorial bd. Jour. Continuing Edn. in Ophthalmology, 1977—; Annals of Ophthalmology, 1978—, Advances in Therapy, 1986—; contbr. book chpts., abstracts. Served with USPHS, 1969-71. Recipient Will F. Lyon award Presbyn.-St. Lukes Hosp., 1969; Robert E. McCormick scholar Research to Prevent Blindness Inc., 1978; grantee Nat. Eye Inst., 1978-84, 85-86; delivered Culler Meml. lecture, Ohio State U., 1986. Fellow Am. Coll. Clin. Pharmacology; mem. AMA (Physician's Recognition award 1971, 73, 75, 77, 79, 81, 83), Assn. for Research in Vision and Ophthalmology, Am. Soc. for Clin. Pharmacology and Therapeutics, Am. Soc. Contemporary Ophthalmology, Internat. Glaucoma Congress, Am. Acad. Ophthalmology, La.-Miss. Ophthalmology Soc., Research to Prevent Blindness Ophthalmologic Assn., So. Med. Assn., Can. Implant Soc., Ky. Med. Assn., Ky. Acad. Eye Physicians and Surgeons, Louisville Acad. Ophthalmology, Jefferson County Med. Soc., Alpha Omega Alpha. Home: 389 Mockingbird Valley Rd Louisville KY 40207-1337 Office: Univ of Louisville Dept Ophthalmology 301 E Muhammad Ali Blvd Louisville KY 40202-1511

ZIMMERMAN, WILLIAM, political science educator; b. Washington, Dec. 26, 1936; s. William III and Isabel Edith (Ryan) Z.; m. Barbara Lamar; children: W. Frederick, Carl L., Alice R.; m. Susan McClanahan, Dec. 10, 1989; 1 child, Rachel Thompson. BA with honors, Swarthmore Coll., 1958; MA, George Washington U., 1959; PhD, Columbia U., 1965. Lectr. dept. polit. sci. U. Mich., 1963-64, from asst. to assoc. prof. dept. polit. sci., 1964-74, assoc. chmn. dept. polit. sci., 1971, dir. Ctr. for Russian and East European studies, 1972-78, 91-92, prof. dept. polit. sci., 1974—, assoc. dean for faculty Coll. of Lit., Sci. and Arts, 1981-84; vis. assoc. prof. Columbia U., summer 1966; rsch. assoc. IPPS, 1994; program dir. Ctr. for Internat. Peace and Security Rsch., 1983—; program dir. Ctr. for Polit. Studies, 1989—; vis. prof. Harvard U., winter 1988; sr. rsch. assoc. Soviet Interview Project, prin. investigator for various confs. and studies; program chmn. comparative communist studies Am. Polit. Sci. Assn. meetings, 1973; mem. adv. coun. Ctr. for Advanced Russian Studies, Woodrow Wilson Ctr., Smithsonian Instn., 1975-84; com. advisor Nat. Coun. Soviet and East European Rsch., 1978-81. Recipient Helen Dwight Reid award Am. Polit. Sci. Assn., 1965; Fgn. Area trng. fellow Ford Found., 1961-62, William Bayard Cutting traveling fellow Columbia U., 1962-63; rsch. grantee Inst. for War and Peace Studies and Russian Inst., Columbia U., 1965, Inter-univ. com. travel grantee

Am./Soviet exch. of young faculty, 1956-66, rsch. grantee Program on Internat. Orgn., U. Mich., 1967, 68, 72, Fulbright-Hays grantee for rsch. in Yugoslavia, 1970, IREX travel grantee to Romania, 1975. Mem. Am. Assn. for Advancement of Slavic Studies (co-chmn. planning com. on Soviet fgn. policy, chmn. rsch. and devel. com.), Nat. Coun. on Soviet and East European Rsch. (exec. com., bd. trustees 1978-81), Coun. on Fgn. Rels., Phi Kappa Phi. Avocation: philately. Office: U Mich 426 Thompson St Ann Arbor MI 48109-1248

ZIMMERMAN, WILLIAM EDWIN, newspaper editor and publisher; b. Bklyn., Feb. 2, 1941; s. George and Ruth (Edelbaum) Z.; m. Teodorina Bello, Dec. 13, 1969; 1 child, Carlota Pastora. BA, Queens Coll., 1962. Pres. Guarionex Press, Ltd., N.Y.C., 1977—; various positions with Am. Banker, N.Y.C., 1962-82, editor, sr. v.p., 1982-89; editor in chief Banking Week, 1986-89; dep. editor. Sunday Bus. sect., The N.Y. Times, 1989; spl. projects editor, editor Student Briefing page Newsday, L.I., N.Y., 1989—. Author: The Little Book of Joy, How to Tape Instant Oral Biographies, 1979, A Book of Questions to Keep Thoughts and Feelings, 1984, Make Beliefs, 1987, Life Lines: A Book of Hope, 1990. Mem. Am. Oral History Assn., N.Y. Fin. Writers Assn., Am. Soc. Bus. Writers, Overseas Press Club, Deadline Club, Am. Soc. Bus. Press Editors, Dowtown Athletic Club, N.Y. Athletic Club, Sigma Delta Chi. Democrat. Jewish. Office: Newsday Inc 2 Park Ave New York NY 10016-5603

ZIMMERMAN, WILLIAM ROBERT, entrepreneur, engineering based manufacturing company executive; b. Cleve., May 11, 1927; s. Irving and Ella (Berger) Z.; m. Nancy Owen, 1963 (div. 1970); 1 child, Amanda; m. Eileen Samuelson, Nov. 11, 1979. BS, MIT, 1948, MS, 1949. Cons. Kurt Salmon Assocs., Washington, 1949-50, A.T. Kearney and Co., Chgo., 1950-52; mill mgr. Am. Envelope Co., West Carrollton, Ohio, 1952-56; exec. v.p. Avery Internat., Pasadena, Calif., 1956-67; pres. Swedlow, Inc., Garden Grove, Calif., 1967-73, Monogram Industries, Inc., Santa Monica, Calif., 1973-78; bd. dirs. Bentley Mills Industry, Calif., Moorhouse Industries, Fullerton, Calif. Council pres. Boy Scouts Am., Painesville, Ohio, 1957-62; exec. com. Jr. Achievement So. Calif., Los Angeles, 1975-77; trustee Los Angeles County Mus. Nat. History, 1987—, Harvey Mudd Coll., Claremont, Calif., 1983—. Republican. Clubs: Calif. (Los Angeles); Valley Hunt, Annendale (Pasadena). Avocations: tennis, jogging. Office: Zimmerman Holdings Inc 2600 Mission St San Marino CA 91108-1638

ZIMMERMANN, GERHARDT, conductor; b. Van Wert, Ohio, June 22, 1945; s. Ervin and Ethel Jane (Allen) Z.; m. Sharon Marie Reher, Mar. 17, 1974; children: Anna Marie, Peter Karl Irum. MusB, Bowling Green State U.; MFA, U. Iowa; student, with James Dixon, Leopold Sipe, Flora Contino, Richard Lert. Tchr. in Genoa (Ohio) Pub. Schs., 1967-70; condr. orch. Augustana Coll., Rock Island, Ill., 1971-72; music dir. Clinton (Iowa) Symphony Orch., 1971-72; asst. prof. music, condr. orchs. Western Ill. U., Macomb, 1972-74; asst. condr. St. Louis Symphony Orch., 1974-78, assoc. condr., 1978-82; music dir., condr. St. Louis Youth Orch., 1975-82, Canton Symphony Orch., 1980—, N.C. Symphony Orch., Raleigh, 1982—; guest condr. Recipient 2d Prize Georg Solti Conducting Competition 1973. Mem. Am. Symphony Orch. League, Nat. Acad. Rec. Arts and Scis., Phi Mu Alpha Sinfonia. Office: NC Symphony Orch Meml Auditorium PO Box 28026 Raleigh NC 27611-8026*

ZIMMERMANN, JOHN, financial consultant; b. Milw., June 10, 1937; s. Elmer Harry and Norman Wihelmina (Bergmann) Z.; m. Mary Sue Lankford, Apr. 9, 1959; children: Elizabeth, John Mark. B.B.A., U. Wis., Milw., 1964; M in Banking, Rutgers U., 1984. CPA, Wis., Ga. Audit mgr./research Price Waterhouse & Co., Milw., 1964-73, N.Y.C., 1971-73; asst. v.p., controller First Nat. Bank of Atlanta, 1973-74, v.p., controller, 1974, group v.p., controller, 1974-77, sr. v.p., controller, 1977-84; sr. v.p., controller First Atlanta Corp., 1985-86; exec. v.p., chief operating officer Enterprise Bank Network Inc., Atlanta, 1986-88; cons. to fin. instns., 1990—; bd. dirs. Vinings (Ga.) Bank and Trust, Monogram Credit Card Bank Ga. (subs. GE). Chmn. three yr. capital expansion campaign New Sch., Atlanta, 1984-87, bd. dirs., 1989-91, 94—, also treas.; v.p. adminstrn., fin. and labor United Way Atlanta, 1984-86, mem. goal setting com., 1982, bd. dirs., 1986-88. With USAF, 1955-59. Named Tinker AFB Airman of Quarter, USAF, 1956. Mem. AICPA, Fin. Execs. Inst. (pres. Atlanta chpt. 1982-83, so. area dir. 1985-87), Ga. Soc. CPAs, Wis. Soc. CPAs, Atlanta Athletic Club, Yacht Club. Office: 2160 Fairfax Dr Alpharetta GA 30201

ZIMMERMANN, JOHN PAUL, plastic surgeon; b. Milw., Mar. 9, 1945; s. Paul August and Edith Josephine (Tutsch) Z.; m. Bianca Maria Schadach Zimmermann, June 13, 1970; children: Veronica, Jean-Paul. BS in Biology, Chemistry, Marquette U., 1966; MD, Med. Coll. Wis., 1970. Diplomate Am Bd. Plastic Surgery. Internship surgery Stanford U. Sch. of Medicine, Calif., 1970-71; flight surgeon USAF, 1971-73; residency in gen. surgery, plastic & reconstructive surgery, 1974-79; fellowship head & neck surgery Roswell Park Meml. Cancer Inst., Buffalo, N.Y., 1977; pvt. practice Napa, Calif., 1979—; dir. Aesthetic Surgery Ctr. of Napa Valley, Calif., 1993—; clinical asst. prof. of plastic surgery Stanford U. Sch. of Medicine, Calif., 1993—; bd. dirs. Interplast, Palo Alto, Calif. (pres., bd. dirs. 1991-94, chmn. bd. dirs. 1994-95). Mem. Am. Soc. Plastic & Reconstructive Surgeons, Am. Soc. Aesthetic Plastic Surgeons, Lipoplasty Soc., Calif. Soc. Plastic Surgeons (bd. dirs.), Calif. Med. Assn., Napa County Med. Assn. Republican. Roman Catholic. Avocations: sailing, golf, direct care of indigent patientsthrough Interplast. Office: 3344 Villa Ln Ste 10 Napa CA 94558

ZIMMERMANN, R. PETER, financial executive; b. Abington, Pa., June 21, 1940; s. Rudolph G. and Josephine (Witt) Zimmermann; m. Mary Elizabeth Kane, Oct. 8, 1971. B.S. in Bus. Adminstrn., Drexel U., 1963. C.P.A. With Ernst & Whinney, Phila., Duesseldorf, Fed. Republic Germany, 1963-71; with Touche Ross & Co., Mexico City, 1971-75; with Touche Ross & Co., N.Y.C., 1975-81, ptnr., 1976-81; v.p., treas. Ford Found., 1981-83; v.p., contr. John Blair & Co., 1983-86; exec. v.p. USGI, Inc., 1987; sr. v.p., chief fin. officer Air Express Internat. Corp., 1988-89; fin. mgmt. cons., 1989-91; CFO Revelation Tech., Inc., 1991-93; v.p.; CFO Decision Servcom, Inc., 1993—; bd. dirs. EV Environ., Inc. Republican. Clubs: Woodway Country (Darien, Conn.), Merion Golf Club (Ardmore, Pa.). Office: Decision Servcom Inc One Progress Ave Horsham PA 19044

ZIMMERMANN, T. C. PRICE, historian, educator; b. Bryn Mawr, Pa., Aug. 22, 1934; s. R.Z. and Susan (Goodman) Z.; m. Margaret Upham Ferris. BA, Williams Coll., 1956, Oxford U., 1958; MA, Oxford U., 1964; AM, Harvard U., 1960, PhD, 1964. Asst. prof. Reed Coll., Portland, Oreg., 1964-67, assoc. prof., 1967-73, prof. history, 1973-77, chmn. dept. history, 1973-75; v.p. acad. affairs Davidson (N.C.) Coll., 1977-86, Charles A. Dana prof. History, 1986—; mem. Oreg. Com. for Humanities NEH, 1971-77; mem. Region 14 selection com. Woodrow Wilson Nat. Fellowship Found., Princeton, N.J., 1967-70. Co-editor of collected works of Paolo Giovio, 1985; contbr. articles to profl. jours. Pres. Am. Alpine Club, N.Y.C., 1979-82, bd. dirs., 1975-83; bd. dirs. Charlotte Opera Assn., N.C., 1980-82, N.C. Outward Bound Sch., Morgantown, 1977-81; bd. advisors Lowell Obs., 1988-93; mem. Rome Prize Jury (Post-Classical Humanistic Studies) Am. Acad. in Rome, 1992. Danforth fellow, 1956-62, Fulbright fellow, Italy, 1962-64, Villa "I Tatti" fellow Harvard U. Ctr., 1970-71; Am. Council of Learned Socs. fellow, N.Y.C., 1975-76. Mem. Am. Hist. Assn., Renaissance Soc. Am., Sixteenth Century Studies Conf., Soc. Italian Hist. Studies, Am. Assn. Italian Studies, Phi Beta Kappa. Office: Davidson College PO Box 1719 Davidson NC 28036-1719

ZIMMERMANN, WARREN, former foreign service officer; b. Phila., Nov. 16, 1934; s. Albert Walter and Barbara (Shoemaker) Z.; m. Corinne Roosevelt Robinson Chubb, Apr. 18, 1959; children: Corinne Alsop, Warren Jr., Elizabeth Beach Metcalfe. BA, Yale U., 1956; BA/MA, Cambridge U., Eng., 1958. Joined Office Fgn. Svc., 1961; consular and polit. officer Am. Embassy, Caracas, Venezuela, 1962-64; student Serbo-Croation lang. Fgn. Svc. Inst., 1964-65; polit. officer Am. Embassy, Belgrade, Yugoslavia, 1965-68; Soviet policy analyst Bur. Intelligence & Rsch., Dept. State, 1968-70; speechwriter to sec. of state Dept. State, Washington, 1970-73; student Russian lang. Fgn. Svc. Inst., Dept. State, 1973; dep. chief, polit. sect. Am. Embassy, Moscow, 1973-75; spl. asst. policy planning Bur. European Affairs, Dept. State, 1975-77; counselor polit. affairs Am Embassy, Paris, 1977-80; dep. chmn. Madrid Conf. on Conf. Security and Cooperation in Europe U.S.

Del., 1980-81; dep. chief mission Am. Embassy, Moscow, 1981-84; dep., with rank of amb., to negotiations on nuclear and space arms with Soviet Union U.S. del., Geneva, 1985-86; chmn., with rank of amb., to Vienna Conf. on Conf. Security and Cooperation in Europe U.S. del., Austria, 1986-89; amb. to Yugoslavia, 1989-92; dir. Bur. Refugee Programs Dept. State, Washington, 1992-94; sr. fellow Rand Corp., 1994; disting. fellow New Sch. Social Rsch., 1994—; vis. prof. Johns Hopkins Sch. Advanced Internat. Studies, 1994—, Sch. Pub. Affairs, U. Md., 1995—; vis. fellow Coun. Fgn. Rels., N.Y.C., 1984-85; chief U.S. delegation negotiations Hotline Upgrade Agreement with Soviet Union, 1983-84; Carnegie teaching fellow Yale U., 1958-59. With U.S. Army, 1959. Mem. Coun. Fgn. Rels., Internat. Inst. Strategic Studies. Democrat. Avocations: history, tennis, skiing, fishing. Home: 96 Interpromontory Rd Great Falls VA 22066

ZIMMETT, MARK PAUL, lawyer; b. Waukegan, Ill., July 4, 1950; s. Nelson H. Zimmett and Roslyn (Yastrow) Zimmett Grodzin; m. Joan Robin Urken, June 11, 1972; children: Nora Helene, Lili Eleanor. BA, Johns Hopkins U., 1972; JD, NYU, 1975. Bar: N.Y. 1976, U.S. Dist. Ct. (so. and ea. dists.) N.Y. 1976, U.S. Dist. Ct. (no. dist.) Calif. 1980, U.S. Ct. Appeals (2d cir.) 1980, U.S. Supreme Ct. 1981, U.S. Ct. Appeals (5th cir.) 1986, U.S. Ct. Appeals (9th cir.) 1988. Assoc. Shearman & Sterling, N.Y.C., 1975-83, ptnr., 1984-90; adj. assoc. prof. internat. law NYU, 1986—. Author: Letters of Credit, New York Practice Guide Business and Commercial Law, 1990; contbr. articles to profl. jours. Mem. ABA (subcom. on letters of credit, com. on uniform comml. code sect. bus. law), N.Y. State Bar Assn., Assn. of Bar of City of N.Y., N.Y. County Lawyers Assn. (com. on bus. bankruptcy law), Citizens Union. Democrat. Jewish. Office: 126 E 56th St New York NY 10022-3613

ZIMMIE, THOMAS FRANK, civil engineer, educator; b. Scranton, Pa., Jan. 24, 1939; s. Thomas and Stella Josephine (Price) Z.; m. Patricia Joyce Kelly, June 8, 1962 (div. 1979); 1 child, David Thomas; m. Judith Anne Braden, July 13, 1989. BSCE, Worcester Poly. Inst., 1960; MSCE, U. Conn., 1962, PhD in Geotech. Engring., 1972. Registered profl. engr., N.Y., Conn. Staff engr. Union Carbide Corp. (Linde div.), Buffalo, 1964-68; profl. engr. Town of Mansfield, Conn., 1968-72; ptnr. Wang and Zimmie Cons., Troy, N.Y., 1973-80; v.p. Arch Engring. Cons., Troy, 1984-88; program dir. NSF, Washington, 1988-90; pres., CEO Civrotech Cons. Engrs., Inc., Troy, 1993—; mem. faculty dept. civil engring Rensselaer Poly. Inst., Troy, 1973—; postdoctoral researcher Norwegian Geotech. Inst., Oslo, 1972-73; geotech. engr. N.Y. Dept. Environ. Conservation, Albany, 1983-85; town engr. Town of North Greenbush, N.Y., 1985-88. Editor: Permeability and Groundwater Contamination, 1981. 1st lt. U.S. Army, 1962-64. Mem. ASCE (Outstanding Svc. award 1986, 87), ASTM (Spl. Svc. award 1980, Charles Dudley award 1984), Transp. Rsch. Bd., Am. Rd. and Transp. Builders Assn. Achievements include research in environmental geotechnology. Home: 39 Zelenke Dr Wynantskill NY 12198 Office: Civil/Environ Engring Dept Soil Mechanics Lab Rensselaer Poly Inst Troy NY 12180

ZIMNY, MARILYN LUCILE, anatomist, educator; b. Chgo., Dec. 12, 1927; d. John and Lucile Ruth (Andryske) Z. BA, U. Ill., 1948; MS, Loyola U., Chgo., 1951, PhD, 1954. Asst. prof. anatomy La. State U. Med. Ctr., New Orleans, 1954-59, assoc. prof., 1959-64, prof., 1964-75, prof., acting head, 1975-76, prof., head, 1976—, acting dean sch. grad. studies, 1989-90, dean sch. grad. studies and vice-chancellor for academic affairs, 1990—; vis. prof. anatomy U. Costa Rica Sch. Medicine, 1961, 62. Grantee, NIH, 1958-72, 88-89, Arthritis Found., 1969-72, Schlieder Ednl. Found., 1972-75, Frost Found., 1975-78, NSF, 1982-83. Mem. AAAS, Am. Assn. Anatomists (mem. exec. com. 1981-85, program sec. 1990-94), Am. Physiol. Soc., Assn. Anatomy Chmn. (pres. 1983), Electron Microscopic Soc. Am., Am. Assn. Dental Schs. (sect. anat. scis.), Assn. Rsch. in Vision and Ophthalmology, Am./Internat. Assn. Dental Rsch., Omicron Kappa Upsilon, Alpha Omega Alpha. Home: 3330 Esplanade Ave New Orleans LA 70119-3132 Office: La State U Med Ctr Resource Ctr New Orleans LA 70112 *My appreciation for people has been a major factor in attaining my professional goals. Other factors include perseverance in the face of challenge, decision-making, warranted aggressiveness, mental curiosity and dealing openly with friends and colleagues.*

ZIMNY, MAX, lawyer; b. Bklyn., Mar. 9, 1925; s. Joseph and Rebecca (Nadelman) Z.; m. Bernice Nelson, June 26, 1948; children—Stuart, Andrew. Student Bklyn. Coll., 1942-47; LL.B. cum laude, 1950; postgrad. NYU Grad. Sch. Labor Law, 1950-52. Bar: N.Y. 1950, U.S. Dist. Ct. (so. and ea. dists.) N.Y. 1951, U.S. Ct. Appeals (2d cir.) 1955, U.S. Supreme Ct. 1962; U.S. Ct. Appeals (D.C. cir.) 1968, U.S. Ct. Appeals (4th cir.) 1969, U.S. Ct. Appeals (9th cir.) 1975, U.S. Ct. Appeals (8th cir.) 1980, U.S. Dist. Ct. (no. dist.) N.Y. 1983, U.S. Ct. Appeals (6th cir.) 1987, U.S. Ct. Appeals (7th cir.) 1988, U.S. Ct. Appeals (3d and 5th cirs.) 1991. Mem. Zimny & Goldberg, N.Y.C., 1950-52; asst. gen. counsel Textiles Workers Union Am., N.Y.C., 1952-58; asst. gen. counsel Internat. Ladies' Garment Workers' Union, N.Y.C., 1958-63, assoc. gen. counsel, 1963-72, gen. counsel, 1972-95, gen. coun. Union of Needletrades, Indsl. and Textile Employees, 1995—; mem. Vladeck, Elias, Vladeck, Zimny and Englehard, N.Y.C., 1976-78. Bd. dirs. Nat. Resources Ctr. for Consumers Legal Services, Lawyers Coord. Com. AFL-CIO; mediator, fact finder N.Y. Pub. Employment Relations Bd., 1968—; mem. steering com. ctr. for Law and Econ. Policy, Columbia U. Sch. Law; chmn. Consumer Adv. Council City of N.Y.; adv. com. N.Y. U. and Fordham Conf. on Labor, 1985—; mem. Levittown (N.Y.) Bd. Edn.; chmn. Profls. for Histadrut, N.Y.C.; bd. dirs. Corsi Labor Mgmt. Inst. Served with U.S. Army, 1943-46. Mem. ABA (chmn. com. on arbitration 1977-81, coun. labor sect. 1989—), Bar Assn. City of N.Y. (labor com.), N.Y. State Bar Assn., Order of Coif. Club: B'nai B'rith (pres. lodge). Author: Labor Arbitrator Development, 1983, Arbitration: A Guide for Advocates, 1990.

ZIMRING, FRANKLIN E., legal educator, lawyer; b. 1942. B.A., Wayne State U., 1963; J.D., U. Chgo., 1967. Bar: Calif. 1968. Asst. prof. U. Chgo., 1967-69, assoc. prof., 1969-72, assoc. dir. Center for Studies in Criminal Justice, 1971-73, prof., 1972-85, co-dir. Ctr. for Studies in Criminal Justice, 1973-75, dir., 1975-86; prof. law, dir. Earl Warren Legal Inst., Univ. Calif., Berkeley, 1985—. Author: Confronting Youth Crime, 1978; (with Newton) Firearms and Violence in American Life, 1969; (with Hawkins) Deterrence, 1973, (with Frase) Criminal Justice System, 1979, The Changing Legal World of Adolescence, 1982, (with Hawkins) Capital Punishment and the American Agenda, 1986, (with Hawkins) The Scale of Imprisonment, 1991, (with Hawkins) The Search for Rational Drug Control, 1992, Incapacitation: Penal Confinement and the Restraint of Crime, 1995. Mem. Am. Acad. Arts and Scis. Office: U Calif Earl Warren Legal Inst Boalt Hall Berkeley CA 94720

ZINBARG, EDWARD DONALD, insurance company executive; b. N.Y.C., Oct. 24, 1934; s. Harry and Esther (Cohen) Z.; m. Barbara Scheffres, Dec. 20, 1956; children—Elizabeth, Allison. B.B.A. magna cum laude, CUNY, 1954; M.B.A., U. Pa., 1955; Ph.D., NYU, 1959. Adj. prof. fin. CUNY, N.Y.C., 1958-73; with Prudential Ins. Co. Am., Newark, 1960—, chief economist, 1967-70, research dir. common stock, 1970-74, corp. fin. dept., 1974-78, v.p. asset mgmt. dept., 1978-88, exec. v.p., 1988—. Author: (with J.B. Cohen and A. Zeikel) Investment Analysis and Portfolio Management, 5th edit., 1987, Guide to Intelligent Investing, 1978. Mem. investment com. United Way of Essex and West Hudson, N.J., 1972—; trustee Trenton (N.J.) State Coll., 1978—, Oheb Shalom Congregation, South Orange, N.J., 1976—. Mem. N.Y. Soc. Security Analysts, Am. Fin. Assn. Home: 5 Hardwell Rd Short Hills NJ 07078-2117 Office: The Prudential Ins Co of Am 213 Washington St Newark NJ 07101-3777

ZINBERG, DOROTHY SHORE, science policy educator; b. Boston, Feb. 25, 1928; m. Norman E. Zinberg, 1956 (dec.); children: Sarah, Anne. Student, U. Wis., 1945-47, U. Buffalo, 1947-48; BA, Boston U., 1949, MA, 1958; PhD, Harvard U., 1966. Teaching and research asst. in biochemistry Harvard Med. Sch., Cambridge, Mass., 1949-50, 52-57; research chemist Lever Bros., Cambridge, 1950-52; sr. research asso. Daniel Yankelovich, Inc., N.Y.C., and; Cambridge Center for Research in Behavioral Scis., 1966-68; lectr. Harvard U., 1960—, sr. rsch. assoc., 1974—; mem. adv. com. Office Sci. Pers. NRC, Washington, 1971-74, bd. on engring. edn., 1991; spl. adviser Aspen Inst.; vis. scholar Nat. Acad. Sci., China, 1987.

Columnist London Times Higher Edn. Supplement, 1993—. Bd. dirs. Fine Arts Workshop, Provincetown, Mass., 1970-86, internat. sci. exchs. NAS, 1974-77, mem. com. on internat. rels., 1977-80, com. on internat. human resources; chmn. adv. coun. internat. divsn. NSF, 1978-81; mem. coun. Internat. Exch. of Scholars, 1978-81, com. internat. exch. of engrs. NAE, 1987-88, adv. panel Office Tech. Assessment Edn. and Employment of Scientists and Engrs., 1986-88; bd. dirs. on Engring. Edn. NRC, 1990—; trustee Simon's Rock Coll., 1971-75, Buckingham, Browne and Nichols Sch., 1971-77; mem. adv. bd. USAF Univ., 1989-93, NATO Com. on Sci. and Tech. Policy, 1995—. Fellow AAAS (com. exchange of scientists with Fed. Republic of Germany 1987, 91, com. on sci. freedom and responsibility 1972-74, com. on opportunities in sci. 1973-76, com. on sci., engring. and pub. policy 1982-88); mem. Fedn. Am. Scientists (council 1980-85), Council on Fgn. Relations, Internat. Sci. Policy Found. (adv. bd. 1988—). Home: 3 Acacia St Cambridge MA 02138-4818 Office: Harvard U JF Kennedy St Cambridge MA 02138

ZINDEL, PAUL, author; b. S.I., N.Y., May 15, 1936; s. Paul and Betty (Frank) Z.; m. Bonnie Hildebrand, Oct. 25, 1973; children: David Jack, Lizabeth Claire. BS, Wagner Coll., 1958, MS, 1959, HHD (hon.), 1971. Chemistry tchr. Tottenville High Sch., S.I., N.Y., 1959-69; playwright-in-residence Alley Theatre, Houston, 1967. Author: (plays) Dimensions of Peacocks, 1959, Euthanasia and the Endless Hearts, 1960, A Dream of Swallows, 1964, The Effect of Gamma Rays On Man-In-The-Moon Marigolds, 1965 (Obie award 1970, N.Y. Drama Critics Circle award 1970, Variety award 1970, Pulitzer Prize in drama 1971, N.Y. Critics award 1971, Vernon Rice Drama Desk award 1971), And Miss Reardon Drinks A Little, 1967 (L.A. Drama Critics award 1968), Let Me Hear You Whisper, 1973, The Secret Affairs of Mildred Wild, 1973, The Ladies Should Be in Bed, 1973, Ladies at the Alamo, 1977, A Destiny with Half Moon Street, 1983, Amulets Against the Dragon Forces, 1989; (screenplays) Up The Sandbox, 1972, Mame, 1973, Maria's Lovers, 1985, Runaway Train, 1986; (TV movies) The Effect of Gamma Rays on Man-In-The-Moon Marigolds, 1966, Let Me Hear You Whisper, 1974, Alice in Wonderland, 1985, Babes in Toyland, 1986, A Connecticut Yankee in King Arthur's Court, 1989; (novels for teenagers) The Pigman, 1968, My Darling, My Hamburger, 1969, I Never Loved Your Mind, 1970, I Love My Mother, 1975, Pardon Me, You're Stepping on My Eyeball, 1976, Confessions of a Teen-Age Baboon, 1977, The Undertaker's Gone Bananas, 1978, (with Bonnie Zindel) A Star for the Latecomer, 1980, The Pigman's Legacy, 1980 (ALA Best Books for Young Adults Selection 1981), The Girl Who Wanted a Boy, 1981, (with Crescent Dragonwagon) To Take a Dare, 1982, Harry and Hortense at Hormone High, 1984, When A Darkness Falls, 1984, The Amazing and Death-Defying Diary of Eugene Dingman, 1987, A Begonia for Miss Applebaum, 1989, The Pigman and Me, 1992, David and Della, 1993, Attack of the Killer Fishsticks, 1993, Fright Party, 1993, Fifth Grade Safari, 1993, One Hundred Percent Laugh Riot, 1994, Loch, 1994, The Doom Stone, 1995. Ford Found. grantee, 1967. Office: care Harper & Row Inc 10 E 53rd St New York NY 10022-5244●

ZINDER, NEWTON DONALD, stock market analyst, consultant; b. N.Y.C., Aug. 12, 1927; s. Paul and Jennie (Feld) Z.; m. Clarice Katz, Dec. 26, 1954; children—Marla, Andrea, Pamela. B.A., NYU, 1948, M.B.A., 1957; M.A., Columbia U., 1949. Securities analyst Ira Haupt & Co., N.Y.C., 1953-60; securities analyst E.F. Hutton & Co., N.Y.C., 1960-63, stock market analyst, 1963-88; stock market analyst Shearson Lehman Bros., N.Y.C., 1988-92; investment cons., 1993—. Served with USN, 1945-46. Mem. Market Technicians Assn. Home: 1734 Roland Ave Wantagh NY 11793-2856

ZINDER, NORTON DAVID, genetics educator, university dean; b. N.Y.C., Nov. 7, 1928; s. Harry Jean and (Gottesman) Z.; m. Marilyn Estreicher, Dec. 24, 1949; children—Stephen, Michael. A.B., Columbia U., 1947; M.S., U. Wis., 1949, Ph.D., 1952. Asst. Rockefeller U., N.Y.C., 1952-56, asso., 1956-58, asso. prof. genetics, 1958-64, prof., 1964—, John D. Rockefeller Jr. prof., 1977—, dean and postgrad. studies, 1993—; cons. genetic-biology NSF, 1962-66, Office Tech. Assessment, Washington, 1979-81, Chas. Pfizer & Co., 1963-67; chmn. ad hoc com. to rev. viral cancer program Nat. Cancer Inst., 1973-74; mem. vis. com. dept. biology Harvard U., 1975-81, sect. virology Yale U., 1975-83, dept. biochemistry Princeton U., 1975-86; mem. sci. adv. bd. Carter-Wallace Inc., 1982-85, Genetic Systems Corp., 1981-86; mem.adv. com. Alliance Internat. Health Care Trust, 1984—; trustee Cold Spring Harbor Lab., 1967-85, sec. to bd., 1980-85; chmn. com. to rev. Army chem. weapons stockpile disposal program, NAS/NRC, 1987-91; chmn. program adv. com. on human genome, NIH, 1988-91, other affiliations. Assoc. editor: Virology; sect. editor Intervirology, 1973-90. Recipient Eli Lilly award in microbiology and immunology, 1962, U.S. Steel Found. award in molecular biology, 1966, medal of excellence Columbia U., 1969, award in sci. freedom & responsibility AAAS, 1982; Am. Cancer Soc. scholar, 1955-58. Fellow Am. Acad. Arts and Scis. (coun. 1984-87); mem. NAS (mem. coun. 1988-91, exec. com. Assembly of Life Scis. 1975-78, bd. army sci. and tech. 1981), Soc. Am. Biol. Chemists, Genetics Soc. Am., Am. Soc. for Microbiology, Council Fgn. Relations, Harvey Soc., Sigma Xi. Spl. research in microbial genetics. Home: 450 E 63rd St New York NY 10021-7928 Office: Rockefeller U 1230 York Ave New York NY 10021

ZINE, LARRY JOSEPH, retail executive; b. Williston, N.D., Dec. 12, 1954; s. Joseph and Olga (Hapip) Z.; m. Nancy Jane Brude, Aug. 14, 1976. BBA in Mktg., U. N.D., 1977, MS in Acctg., 1979. CPA, N.D. Grad. teaching asst. U. N.D., Grand Forks, 1977-78, instr., 1979-81; acct. Circle K Corp., Phoenix, 1981-82, tax and audit supr., 1982-84, fin. reporting mgr., 1984-87, v.p. fin. reporting, 1987, chief fin. officer, 1988. Mem. AICPA, Beta Alpha Psi. Avocation: running. Office: Circle K Corp PO Box 52084 Phoenix AZ 85072-2084

ZINGMAN, EDGAR ALAN, lawyer; b. N.Y.C., Dec. 26, 1923; s. Louis M. and Sarah (Steinberg) S.; m. Barbara Gold, Dec. 17, 1950; children: Aileen Dale, Margaret Lee, Jonathan Alan. BS, CCNY, 1947; LLB, Yale U., 1950. Bar: N.Y. 1950, Ky. 1950, U.S. Dist. Ct. (ea. and we. dists.) Ky. 1951, U.S. Ct. Appeals (6th cir.) 1952, U.S. Supreme Ct. 1965. Assoc. Wyatt, Grafton & Sloss, Louisville, Ky., 1950-57; ptnr. Wyatt, Tarrant & Combs and predecessor firms, Louisville, 1957—. Bd. dirs. ACLU, N.Y., 1965-70; chmn. bd. dirs. Ky. Civil Liberties Union, 1958-70. Recipient Disting. Svc. award Ky. Hosp. Assn., Louisville, 1978, Am. Hosp. Assn., 1988. Mem. Ky. Assn. Hosp. Attys. (bd. dirs., pres.), Am. Acad. Hosp. Attys. (bd. dirs. 1980-87, pres. 1985), Jefferson Club. Avocations: music, theater, sports, travel, reading. Office: Wyatt Tarrant & Combs 2600 Citizens Plz Louisville KY 40202

ZINGRAFF, MICHAEL, JR., magazine editor; b. Phila., July 4, 1920; s. Michael and Barbara (Lux) Z.; m. Nancy Cheney Green, Apr. 5, 1942; 1 child. Elizabeth Michelle Zingraff Alexander. Student, Ursinus Coll., 1945-48. Corp. sec., sales mgr. 63d St. Motors, Inc., Phila., 1955-65; sales, parts and svc. mgr., agy. mgr. various auto dealerships, Phila. area, 1965-72; parts rsch. editor The Chilton Co., Radnor, Pa., 1973, sr. wholesaler editor Motor/Age, 1973-92; paint, body supplies, equipment editor Autobody Repair News, 1990-92; contbtg. editor Automotive Aftermarket News, 1990-91; freelance bus. publs. features writer, rsch. & cons. svcs. Lansdowne, Pa., 1992—; Avocations: travel, fishing, people, reading, community services volunteer. Pres., bd. dirs. Phila. chpt. Automotive Booster Clubs Internat., 1980—, trustee B-18 Scholarship Fund, 1976—; deacon 1st Presbyn. Ch., Lansdowne, 1994—. Staff sgt. U.S. Army and USAF, 1939-45, ETO. Recipient Grand Prize Moto award Internat. Motor Press Assn., Las Vegas, Nev., 1988. Mem. Automotive Engine Rebuilders Assn., Mfrs. Coun. of Automotive Engine Rebuilders Assn. (assoc. 1989-92), Automotive Warehouse Distbrs. Assn. (del. 1975-92), Automotive Svc. Industries Assn. (conv. planning com. 1975-92). Avocations: travel, fishing, people, reading. Home and Office: M & N Consulting 211 Drexel Ave Lansdowne PA 19050-1313

ZINK, CHARLES TALBOTT, lawyer; b. Long Beach, Calif., Oct. 27, 1937; s. William Talbott and Nellie Grace (Hoskins) Z.; m. Deborah Sidney Burks, Nov. 26, 1983. AB, Princeton U., 1959; LLB, U. Va., 1965. Bar: Va. 1965, Ga. 1965. Mng. ptnr. Hansell & Post, Atlanta, 1965-89; ptnr. Jones, Day, Reavis & Poque, Atlanta, 1989-93, Long, Aldridge & Norman, Atlanta, 1993—; lectr. N.W. Ctr. for Profl. Edn., Washington, Atlanta and Tampa,

---

Fla., 1983—; mem. faculty Atlanta Coll. Trial Advocacy, 1985, mem. exec. com., 1984—, pres., 1985, 86. Bd. dirs. internat. Atlanta Humane Soc., 1983—. Lt. (j.g.) USN, 1959-62. Mem. Lawyers Club Atlanta, Atlanta Tax Forum, Capital City Club. Republican. Episcopalian. Office: Long Aldridge & Norman 5300 One Peachtree Ctr Atlanta GA 30308

ZINN, LEE B., academic administrator, economist, educator; b. Salem, Ind., June 7, 1930; s. Otto C. and Lera (Berkey) Z.; m. Patricia Louise Patton, Aug. 16, 1964; children: Kevin Patrick, Barry Lee. BA in Econs. magna cum laude, Ind. U., 1959; PhD in Econs., Okla. State U., 1967. Field rep. GM Acceptance Corp., Louisville, Ky., 1953-54; asst. mgr. Dougherty Motor Sales, Salem, 1954-56; asst. prof. econs. Southeastern State Coll., Durant, Okla., 1964-67; spl. asst. to dir. Tech. Use Studies Ctr. Southwe. State Coll., Durant, Okla., 1964-65, dir., 1965-68, assoc. prof. of Econs., 1967-68; dir., prin. rsch. economist, bur. bus. and econ. rsch. U. N.Mex., Albuquerque, 1968-77; prof. bus. adminstrn. N.Mex. Highlands U., Kirtland, 1974-81; dir. Inst. Applied Rsch. Svcs. U. N.Mex., Albuquerque, 1975—, dir. Nat. Energy Info. Ctr. affiliate/U.S. Dept. Energy, 1978-87, assoc. v.p. rsch., bus. and govt. rels., 1988—; bd. dirs. First Security Bank, N.Mex.; mem. Gov.'s adv. com. statis. standards for Okla., 1964-66, sci. and industry Okla., 1965-66, statewide planning com. implemenation of Tech. Svcs. Act, Okla., 1965-66; cons. majority leader U.S. Ho. Reps., 1964-68, So. Okla. Devel. Assn., 1965-68, Gov. Okla., 1965-68, Kiamichi Econ. Devel. Dist., Okla., 1967-68, N.Mex. Corp. Commn., 1969-74, N.Mex. State Planning Office, 1971, Ohio State U. Evaluation Ctr., 1972, others; mem. Gov.'s adv. com. N.Mex. Dept. Devel., 1971; adv. panel spl. tech. assistance program Office Econ. Opportunity, 1972-74; mem. Albuquerque adv. coun. U.S. Small Bus. Adminstrn., 1974-81, chmn. 1977-79; chmn. Gov.'s Coun. Econ. Advisors, 1975-78; sec. econ. devel. Gov.'s Cabinet, 1975-76, policy advisor, 1976-78; econ. devel. task force We. Interstate Commn. Higher Edn., 1979; bd. dirs. Nat. Tng. Inst. Community Econ. Devel., 1979-82, Inst. Study Community Econ. Devel., 1980-82. Mem. edit. review bd. Review of Regional Economics and Business, 1976-85; bd. edit. contbrs. The Albuquerque Tribune, 1979-82; mem. edit. adv. bd. The Southwest Review of Management and Economics, 1981-85; contbr. articles to profl. jours. Organizing pres. Kiamichi Econ. Devel. Dist., Okla., 1966-67; active Monte Vista Christian Ch., 1968—; exec. dir. N.Mex. Coun. Econ. Edn., 1969-75, chmn. operating com., 1976-86; pres. East Holiday Park Neighborhood Assn., 1978—; adv. coun. city growth and devel. Greater Albuquerque Leadership Devel. Program, 1980-82; adv. bd. U.S. Armed Svcs., 1980-87; adv. bd. econ. devel. City of Albuquerque, 1980-84; community advisor NCAA Vols. for Youth, 1981-85; mem. Bernalillo county Human Svcs. Coalition, 1982-85; apptd. by Gov.-elect Anaya N.Mex. Jobs Task Force, 1982-83; apptd. chmn. by mayor Better Albuquerque Bond Coms., 1983-87; trustee U. Albuquerque, 1983-86; bd. dirs. Albuquerque Conv. and Vis. Bur., 1984-87, Consumer Credit Counseling Svc. N.Mex., 1985-94, pres. 1989-90, Better Bus. Bur. N.Mex., 1992—; pres. adv. coun. UNICEF, Albuquerque, 1985—; mem. employment and tng. needs task force City of Albuquerque, 1987-88; evaluation team Congressman Lujan's South Valley task force, 1987; apptd. chmn. by Mayor Saavedra and city coun. pub. forum com. recycling, 1991. 2d lt. U.S. Army, 1951-53, Germany; lt. col. USAR, 1953-71. Fellow Nat. Defense Edn. Act, 1959-62; grantee Nat. Aeronautics and Space Administrn., 1964-68, N.Mex. Dept. Devel., 1968-80, HEW, 1968-76, 1971-72, Bank N. Mex., 1969-77, The Albuquerque Model Cities Agy., 1969-70, Four Corners Regional Commn., 1969-80, U.S. Forest Svc., 1974-77, U.S. Dept. Commerce, 1975-79, 1976—, N.Mex. Energy Resources Bd., 1976-77, The Navajo Nation, 1976-78, U.S. Army Corps. Engrs., 1976-78, U.S. Dept. Energy, 1978-87. Mem. Am. Assembly Collegiate Schs. Bus. (rsch., statis., publs. com. 1976-77, small bus. adminstrn. liasion com. 1976-78), Am. Soc. Info. Sci. (frontier chpt. exec. com. 1972-73, chmn.-elect 1972, chmn. 1973), Assn. Univ. Bus. and Econ. Rsch. (exec. com. 1971-78, v.p. 1975-76, pres. 1976-77), Mid continh. and Devel. Coun. (bd. dirs. 1965-69), Fedn. Rocky Mountain States (chmn. bus. rsch. com. 1969-75), Rocky Mountain Coun. Burs. Bus. and Econ. Rsch. (chmn. 1969-77), N.Mex. coun. Econ. Edn. (bd. dirs. 1969-90), Greater Albuquerque C. of C. (end. com. 1968-73, bd. dirs. 1970-76, 78-82, chmn. growth com. 1972, v.p. 1973-74, pres. 1981), Phi Kappa Phi, Phi Beta Kappa (alpha chpt. exec. com., sec. 1973-75). Democrat. Avocation: pipe organs. Home: 3741 Mount Rainier Dr NE Albuquerque NM 87111-4399 Office: U NMex Inst Applied Rsch Svcs 1920 Lomas Blvd NE Albuquerque NM 87106-2744

ZINMAN, DAVID JOEL, conductor; b. N.Y.C., July 9, 1936; s. Samuel and Rachel Ilo (Samuels) Z.; m. Leslie Heyman (dec.); children: Paul Pierre, Rachel Linda; m. Mary Ingham, May 19, 1974; 1 child, Raphael. B.Mus., Oberlin (Ohio) Conservatory, 1958; M.A., U. Minn., 1961. Asst. to Pierre Monteux, 1961-64; guest condr. U.S. and Europe; music dir. Netherlands Chamber Orch., 1964-77, Rochester (N.Y.) Philharm. Orch., 1974-85; prin. guest condr. Rotterdam Philharm. Orch., 1977-79, chief condr., 1979-82; prin. guest condr., music dir. designate Balt. Symphony Orch., 1983-85, music dir., 1985—; adj. prof. Eastman Sch. Music, Rochester. Rec. artist Phillips, Nonesuch, Decca/London, Decca/Argo, Angel/EMI, Telarc, Sony Classical. Recipient Grand Prix du Disque, 1967, 82, Edison award 1967, 3 Grammy awards, 1990, Gramophone best selling record awad, 1993, Gramophone award, 1994, Deutschen Schallplaatten prize. Office: Balt Symphony Orch 1212 Cathedral St Baltimore MD 21201-5545

ZINMAN, JACQUES, former insurance agency executive; b. Phila., Nov. 7, 1922; BS, U. Va., 1943; postgrad. U. Pa., 1945. Chmn., The Zinman Group, Ins. Agy., 1950-82. Mem. exec. com. Pa. state Rep. fin. com.; mem. Presdl. Electoral Coll. from Pa., 1972; bd. dirs. Pop Warner Nat. Football League. Ensign USNR, 1943-44. Recipient Outstanding Young Man Phila. award Jewish Nat. Fund, 1961. Mem. Variety Club, Theta Delta Chi. Lodge: Masons. Contbr. articles to profl. jours. Office: Lakes Agy of Fla 627 E Atlantic Blvd Pompano Beach FL 33060-6343

ZINN, GROVER ALFONSO, JR., religion educator; b. El Dorado, Ark., June 18, 1937; s. Grover Alfonso and Cora Edith (Saucke) Z.; m. Mary Mel Farris, July 28, 1962; children: Jennifer Anne, Andrew Grover. BA, Rice U., 1959; BD, Duke U., 1962, PhD, 1969; spl. student, U. Glasgow, Scotland, 1962-63. Asst. minister The Barony Ch., Glasgow, 1962-63; instr. in religion Oberlin (Ohio) Coll., 1966-68, asst. prof., 1968-74, assoc. prof., 1974-79, prof., 1979—, Danforth Prof. religion, 1986—, chmn. dept. religion, 1980-84, 85-86, 1993-94. Translator: Richard of St. Victor: The Twelve Patriarchs, The Mystical Ark, and Book Three of the Trinity, 1979; co-editor Medieval France: An Encyclopedia; mem. editorial bd. Dictionary of Biblical Interpretation; contbr. articles on medieval Christian mysticism and theology. H.H. Powers Travel grantee Oberlin Coll., 1969, 85; Dempster fellow United Meth. Ch., 1965-66, NEH Younger Humanist fellow, 1972-73, Research Status fellow Oberlin Coll., 1972-73, Faculty Devel. fellow Oberlin Coll. 1985, Lilly Endowment fellow U. Pa., 1981-82; recipient ACLS Travel award, 1982. Mem. Medieval Acad. Am. (councillor 1983-86), Am. Soc. Ch. History (coun. mem. 1989-92, 95—), Ecclesiastical History Soc. Democrat. Methodist. Avocations: photography, electronics. Home: 61 Glenhurst Dr Oberlin OH 44074-1423 Office: Oberlin Coll Rice Hall Oberlin OH 44074

ZINN, KEITH MARSHALL, ophthalmologist, educator; b. Bklyn., Oct. 15, 1940; s. Victor Zinn and Eve (Lane) Z.; m. Elaine H. Kirban, Apr. 8, 1979. Student, NYU, Bronx, 1961; M.D., SUNY, Bklyn., 1965. Diplomate Am. Bd. Ophthalmology; lic. physician, N.Y., Calif. Intern St. Lukes Hosp., N.Y.C., 1965-66; research assoc. NIH, Bethesda, Md., 1966-68; post-doctoral fellow Retina Found., Boston, 1968-69; post-doctoral fellow dept. ophthalmology Harvard U. Med. Sch., Boston, 1968; asst. resident to chief resident dept. ophthalmology Mount Sinai Hosp., N.Y.C., 1969-71, ednl. fellow dept. ophthalmology, 1971-72; chief clin. fellow retina service Mass. Eye & Ear Infirmary, Harvard U. Med. Sch., Boston, 1972-73, Heed fellow dept. ophthalmology, 1972-73; research assoc. dept. retina research Retina Found., Boston, 1972-73; mem. faculty Lancaster Post-Grad. Course in Ophthalmology, Harvard U. Med. Sch., Boston, 1970-90; guest faculty dept. ophthalmology Harvard U. Med. Sch., Boston, 1969-84; asst. prof. dept. ophthalmology Mt. Sinai Sch. medicine, N.Y.C., assoc. clin. prof., 1976-80, clin. prof., 1980—; attending ophthalmic surgeon N.Y.C., 1980—; attending ophthalmic surgeon Manhattan Eye Ear & Throat Hosp., N.Y.C., 1981—; surgeon cons. Hosp. Joint Diseases, N.Y.C., 1975-83, Patrolmen's Benevolent Assn., N.Y.C., 1977—; lectr. in field. Author: The Pupil, 1972, Ocular Fine Structure for the Clinician, 1973, The Developing Visual System, 1975, The Retinal Pigment Epithelium, 1975; author-editor: The Retinal Epithelium, 1979, Clinical Atlas of Peripheral Retinal Disorders, 1988;

numerous audio-visual teaching progs. in ophthalmology; contbg. editor Mt. Sinai Jour. Medicine, 1975—; assoc. mem. editorial bd. Ophthalmic Surgery, 1980-89; mem. faculty editorial bd. Clin. Ophthalmology Update, 1982—; inventor in field. Served to lt. comdr. USPHS, 1966-68. Recipient numerous awards for excellence in medicine, including: Joseph Globus award Mount Sinai Jour. Medicine, 1979, Abraham Kornzweig Teaching award Mount Sinai Jour. Medicine, 1982. Fellow Am. Acad. Ophthalmology, Otolaryngology, ACS, Internat. Coll. Surgeons, Internat. Eye Found., Soc. Eye Surgeons, N.Y. Acad. Medicine, N.Y. Diabetes Assn., N.Y. Heart Assn., N.Y. Soc. Clin. Ophthalmology, Soc. Heed Fellows, Retina Soc., Ophthalmic Soc. U.K., Oxford Ophthal. Congress, Brit. Am. Retinal Group; mem. AMA (Physicians Recognition award 1971, 76, 81, 82, 85), Ophthalmic Laser Surg. Soc. (v.p. 1986-88, pres. 1988-90), Am. Intraocular Lens Implant Soc., N.Y. Acad. Medicine (trustee 1989-90, sec. 1985-86, chmn. ophthalmology sect. 1987-88, David Warfield fellowship com. 1990-92), Am. Bd. Laser Surgery (bd. dirs. 1987—), others. Office: 1044 Fifth Ave New York NY 10028-0108

ZINN, ROBERT JAMES, astronomer, educator; b. Chgo., Aug. 4, 1946; s. Walter Henry and Jean Ann (Smith) A.; m. Graziella Anna di Tullio; children—Gabriele, Annalisa, Giovanni. B.S., Case Inst. Tech., 1968; Ph.D., Yale U., 1974. Carnegie fellow Mt. Wilson obs., Pasadena, Calif., 1974-76, Las Campanas fellow, 1976-79; asst. prof. Yale U., New Haven, 1979-82, assoc. prof., 1982-87; prof., 1987—. Mem. Am. Astron. Soc., Internat. Astron. Union. Office: Yale U Dept Astronomy PO Box 208101 New Haven CT 06520-8101

ZINN, WILLIAM, violinist, composer, business executive; b. N.Y.C., Nov. 19, 1924; s. Philip and Anna (Miller) Z.; m. Sophia Kalish, July 11, 1948; children: Karen Louise Heau, David Benjamin. Student, SUNY, 1952-54. Violinist Balt. Symphony, 1944-45, Indpls. Symphony, 1945-46, Ft. Wayne Philharm., 1946-47, Pitts. Symphony, 1947-49, Mpls. Symphony, 1950-51; concertmaster New Britain (Conn.) Symphony, 1968-90, Queens Symphony, 1969-71, Ridgefield (Conn.) Symphony, 1973-76, Chappaqua (N.Y.) Symphony, 1976; soloist with orchs. on records, on radio and in recitals; founder Masterwork Piano Trio, Masterwork Piano Quartet, Classical String Quartet, Zinn's Ragtime String Quartet, Excelsior String Quartet, Queens Festival Orch., Bayside, N.Y., 1965, Assn. Musical William Zinn, Caracas, Venezuela, 1968, Vitametrics of Am., 1976, Internat. Symphony for World Peace, 1978, Big Apple Chamber Pops, 1983, Excelsior Composer's Festival Competition, 1984; tchr. mech. drafting Mondell Inst., 1956; coach ensembles for Chamber Music Assocs., 1973-78; engr. N.Y.C. Bd. Edn. 1951-57, Bodin-Zinn Corp., 1957-58, Chem. Constrn. Corp., 1958-59; pres. Zinn Originals, Inc., 1959-68, Sparx, Inc., Trademark Hall of Fame, Inc., Nice Realty Corp., MFW Restaurant Corp.; co-founder Excelsior Music Pub. Co., Visionary Music Pub. Co., Nat. Music Promotion Agy., Telecommunication Services, 1982, Assoc. Sci. Publs., 1985, Barclay House Pubs., 1985, Excelsior Typographers and Engravers Unltd., 1985, Empco Recs. Internat., 1985, Imperial Editions, 1986, Missing Link Pubs., 1986, Krazy Klassics Kompany, 1986, New Age Pubs., 1987, Krazy Klassics Komix, 1988, Zinn Pub. Group, 1989, Zinn Communications, 1989, 94, Decca Books, 1993, Arlington House, 1993, Zinn Labs, Inc.; sec.-treas. Spark Industries, Inc., Music Clearing House, 1989, Innovation Records, 1991, Krazy Klassics Records, 1991, Hanover House, 1991; pres. Zinn Labs, Inc., 1994; adj. prof. NYU, 1987—. Author: (with Edward Gordon) Themography, 1947, (with George S. Grosser) Vitametrics I, The Human Formula for Self-Evaluation, 1976, Vitametrics II, The Human Formula for Self-Improvement, 1978, (with George S. Grosser) The Lost Chord, 1981; composer: (perpetual movement for woodwinds, strings and percussion) Chromatique, 1946, Piccolo Concerto, 1948, Violin Concerto, 1950, String Quartet, 1963, (piano solo) Chopinesque, 1965, (ballet) Night Creatures, 1966, Andante for Strings, 1967, Concerto for Octahorn, 1976, The International Anthem For World Peace, 1977, String Symphony, 1977, Romance for French Horn or Viola and Piano, 1981, Concerto for Violin/Viola/Cello/Double Bass and Orch., 1985, Kol Nidrei Meml. for String Quartet or String Orchestra, 1985, six concert duos for violin and viola, 1988, also songs including Mia, 1989, Aloha Hawaii, 1989, The Willows, 1990 (winner Hawaiian Nat. Song Contest 1990), Our Song of Love, 1990, Symphony in Ragtime, 1990, In Old Hawaii, 1991, Chistmas in Hawaii, 1991, A Tribute to the Masters for string quartet or string orch. (14 original works in the style of Bach, Vivaldi, Mozart, Beethoven, Brahms, Rossini, Chopin, Schubert, J. Strauss, Jr., Tschaikowksy, Dvorak, Debussy, Mendelssohn, Sousa), 1991; arranger numerous operatic arias for string quartet or string orch.; originator Musiphonics, 1981, 24 Paganini caprices for string quartet, 1992, 10 Sousa marches for string quartet, 1992, The Merry Widow Waltz for string quartet or string orch., 1992; arranger 21 Henry Mancini songs for string quartet/string orchestra, 1992, 16 Duke Ellington songs for string quartet/string orchestra, 1993, Gold and Silver Waltz, Skater's Waltz for string quartet and string orchestra, 1993, 7 arias from Porgy & Bess for string quartet/string orchestra, 1994, A Tribute to Fritz Kreisler for violin and piano, 1994, 15 arrangements of Fritz Kreisler works for String Quartet String Orch., 1994, 12 classic Jewish Favorites for String Quartet/String Orch., 1995, 12 Jewish Songs for String Quartet/String Orch., 995; pioneer multi-styles of music for string quartet and string orch.; composer over 500 works; developer numerous products for home, personal, automobile and novelty use. Chmn. bd. dirs. Let Us Remember to Remember, 1984. Recipient 41st Hawaiian Nat. Song Contest award, 1990. Mem. ASCAP, Internat. Platform Assn., Nat. Council Women of U.S., Am. Fedn. Musicians, N.Y. Humanist Assn. Home: 35-19 215th Pl Bayside NY 11361

ZINNECKER, ROBERT WALLACE, telecommunications company executive; b. Cass City, Mich., Apr. 7, 1938; s. William Wallace and Helen Berniece (Bradford) Z.; m. Elaine Ival Johns, Aug. 9, 1958; children: Tim, Karen, Diana, Brad. Student higher acctg., Northeastern Sch. Commerce, Bay City, Mich., 1957. Treas. Contel of Mich., Pinconning, 1962-66; div. controller Contel of Mo., Wentzville, 1966-68; v.p. Contel Data Services, Wentzville, 1968-77; pres. gen. mgr. Continental Telephone Co., Knoxville, Iowa, 1977-83, Contel of N.Y., Johnstown, N.Y., 1983—; bd. dirs. City Nat. Bank and Trust Co., Gloversville, N.Y. Pres. Fulton County Econ. Devel. Corp., Gloversville, 1986. Mem. N.Y. State Telephone Co. (bd. dirs. 1986-87, v.p. 1986-87, pres. 1988—), Iowa Telephone Assn. (pres. 1982-83), Fulton County C. of C. (bd. dirs., v.p. 1986-89, Outstanding Exec. award 1986), Pine Brook Club, Eccentric Club. Republican. Methodist. Avocations: golfing, photography, writing, gardening. Home: 3 Pennsylvania Ct Rexford NY 12148-1342 Office: Continental Tel Co Inc 850 Harrison Ext Johnstown NY 12095 also: 201 W Service Rd Chantilly VA 22021

ZINNEMANN, FRED, film director; b. Austria, Apr. 29, 1907; emigrated to U.S., 1929, naturalized, 1937; s. Oskar and Anna (Feiwel) Z.; m. Renee Bartlett, Oct. 9, 1936; 1 child, Tim. Student law, Vienna U., 1925-27; student, Sch. Cinematography, Paris, France, 1927-28; DLitt (hon.), Durham U., U.K., 1964. Asst. cameraman Paris and Berlin, Germany, 1928; asst. dir. to Berthold Viertel, Fox Studio, Hollywood, 1929-30; asst. to Robert Flaherty, 1931. 1st directorial assignment: documentary on Mexican fishermen The Wave, 1934; dir. 16 short subjects for Metro-Goldwyn-Mayer, including Story of Dr. Carver, a series on great physicians including Dr. Semmelweis (Acad. award), also several anti-crime shorts, 1937-41, features including The Seventh Cross, The Search, 1946-47 (Screen Dirs. Guild award), Act of Violence, 1948, The Men, 1949, Teresa, 1950, High Noon, 1951 (Screen Dirs. Guild, N.Y. Film Critics awards), The Member of the Wedding, 1952, Benjy, 1951 (Acad. award best documentary), From Here to Eternity, 1953 (Acad. awards including best picture, best dir., N.Y. Film Critics' Screen Dirs. Guild), Oklahoma !, 1956, A Hatful of Rain, 1957, The Nun's Story, 1958 (N.Y. Film Critic's award), The Sundowners, 1959, Behold a Pale Horse, 1964, A Man for All Seasons, 1966 (Acad. awards best picture, best dir., Dir.'s Guild ann. award , N.Y. Film Critics' award for best film, best dir.); dir. The Day of the Jackal, 1972, Julia, 1976 (3 Oscars, Donatello award 1978), Five Days One Summer, 1982; author: A Life in The Movies, 1992; contbr. to: Ency. Brit.; photo exhibition Victoria & Albert Mus., London, 1992. Recipient Golden Thistle award Edinborough Film Festival, 1965, award Moscow Film Festival, 1965, Gold medal City of Vienna, 1967, D. W. Griffith award Dirs. Guild Am., 1971, Donatello (Italy) award, 1976, 3 Golden Globe awards, U.S. Congl. Lifetime Achievement award, 1987, John Huston award Artists Rights Found., 1994; named to Order Arts and Letters, France, 1982. Fellow Brit. Acad. Film and TV (Fellowship award affiliated), Brit. Film Inst.; mem. Acad. Motion Picture Arts and Scis., Am. Film Inst. (co-founder 1961, former trustee). Co-founder sch. of neo-realism in Am. motion pictures. Strongly involved in battle for

federal laws protecting moral rights of authors. Office: 98 Mount St, London W1Y 5HF, England

ZINNEN, ROBERT OLIVER, general management executive; b. Racine, Wis., June 28, 1929; s. Aloys Henry and Mabel Helen (Holy) Z.; m. Darlene Mary Weyers, Aug. 25, 1956; children: Claudia Jane, Robert O. B.B.A., U. Wis., 1951, J.D., 1956. Bar: Wis. 1956, Ill. 1959, Mass. 1982; CPA, Ill. Tax accountant Price Waterhouse, Chgo., 1956-59; mem. firm Tenney & Bentley, Chgo., 1959-64; assoc. dir. taxes Allstate Cos., Skokie, Ill., 1964-65; v.p. fin. Do-All Co., Des Plaines, Ill., 1965-67; dir. taxes Quaker Oats Co., Chgo., 1967-71; internat. atty. Am. Hosp. Supply Corp., 1971-75; fin. cons. Alexander Proudfoot Co., Chgo., 1975-76; v.p. fin. Milton Bradley Co., Springfield, Mass., 1976-82; co-owner, exec. v.p. Roadmaster Corp., Olney, Ill., 1982-88, cons., 1988—. Mem. Housing and Traffic Commns., Highland Park, Ill., 1963-66; chmn. Congl. Action Com., Springfield; bd. dirs. Assoc. Industries, Mass. Served with U.S. Army, 1951-53. Mem. Toy Mfrs. Am. (bd. dirs. 1984-88), Quail Creek Country Club, Longmeadow Country Club. Republican. Roman Catholic.

ZINNER, MICHAEL JEFFREY, surgeon, educator; b. Miami, Fla., Apr. 2, 1945; s. Doran D. and Eve (Wernicoff) Z.; m. Karin Sui, May 22, 1981; children: Darren, Daniel. BEE, Johns Hopkins U., 1967; MD, U. Fla., 1971; postgrad., NIH Found. for Edn. in the Scis., Bethesda, Md., 1973-74. Diplomate Am. Bd. Surgery (bd. dirs. 1988—). Intern The Johns Hopkins Hosp., Balt., 1971-72, jr. asst. resident in surgery, 1972-73, sr. asst. resident, 1976-79, asst. chief of svc. in surgery, 1979-80; registrar thoracic surgery Frenchay Hosp., Bristol, Eng., 1977; instr. The Johns Hopkins U. Sch. Medicine, Balt., 1978-80; asst. prof. surgery Downstate Med. Ctr., Bklyn., 1980-83, assoc. prof., 1983-85; assoc. dir. surg. residency program, coord. residency program The Johns Hopkins Med. Instns., Balt., 1985-88, assoc. prof., vice chmn. dept. surgery, 1985-88, prof., 1988; prof., chmn. dept. surgery UCLA Sch. Medicine, 1988-94; mem. staff Kings County Hosp., Bklyn., 1980-85, chief gen. surgery and oncology, 1983-85; mem. staff Balt. VA Hosp., 1985-88, Johns Hopkins Hosp., 1985-88, Wadsworth VA Hosp., L.A., 1988-94; chief of surgery UCLA Med. Ctr., 1988-94; surgeon-in-chief Brigham and Womens Hosp., Boston, 1994—; prof. Harvard Med. Sch., 1994—; ednl. cons. Cath. Med. Ctr., 1981-84; mem. Clin. Resch. Ctr. Subcom. on Sci. Rev. Protocols, SUNY, Downstate, 1982-84. Author 83 published articles in med. jours.; lectr. to 23 med. meetings, assns. and socs. Maj. M.C., U.S. Army, 1973-76. Rsch. grantee NIH, 1982-86, 88—; merit rev. grantee VA, 1988; grantee numerous univers., founds., pharm. cos. 1978—. Fellow ACS (com. on rsch. and edn. 1988); mem. IEEE, NIH (ad hoc, study sect., surgery and biomed. engring. 1986), Am. Fedn. Clin. Rsch., Assn. Acad. Surgery (com. on issues 1980-82, recorder 1982-84, exec. coun. 1982—, pres. 1985-86), Am. Physiol. Soc., Am. Gastroenterol. Assn., Am. Pancreatic Assn., Soc. Univ. Surgeons (com. on publs. 1984-86, com. on edn., 1986-87, exec. coun. 1986—, pres. 1987-88), Soc. Critical Care Medicine, N.Y. Surg. Soc., Gastroenterology Rsch. Group, Surg. Biology Club, Collegium Internationale Chirugiac Digestival, Conjoint Coun. Surg. Rsch., Soc. Surgery of Alimentary Tract, Soc. Clin. Surgery, Alpha Omega Alpha. Avocations: fishing, boating. Office: Brigham and Womens Hosp Dept Surgery 75 Francis St Boston MA 02115

ZINNER, PETER, film editor and director, music editor; b. Vienna, Austria, July 24, 1919; came to U.S., 1940; s. Alfred and Mimy (Kornfeld) Z.; m. Eleanor Zinner, July 24, 1949 (div. Apr. 1955); m. Christa Heutelbeck, Mar. 20, 1959; children: Nicolas Nelken, Katina Andrea. Grad. high sch., Vienna. Apprentice film editor 20th Century Fox Film Studios, Hollywood, Calif., 1943-47; asst. film editor Universal Studios, Hollywood, 1947-49; music film editor MGM Studios, Culver City, Calif., 1949-60; pres. Zinner Internat., Pacific Palisades, Calif., 1970—; 2d unit dir., film editor on Officer and A Gentleman, Parmount Studios. Recipient Acad. award for film editing Deer Hunter, 1978, Brit. Film Acad. award for Deer Hunter, 1978; Emmy awards for War and Remembrance, 1989, Citizen Cohn, 1989; Acad. award nominations, 1970-72. Democrat. Avocations: skiing, tennis.

ZINSER, ELISABETH ANN, university president; b. Meadville, Pa., Feb. 20, 1940; d. Merle and Fae Zinser. BS, Stanford U., 1964; MS, U. Calif., San Francisco, 1966, MIT, 1982; PhD, U. Calif., Berkeley, 1972. Nurse VA Hosp., Palo Alto, Calif., 1964-65, San Francisco, 1969-70; instr. Sch. Nursing U. Calif., San Francisco, 1966-69; pre-doctoral fellow Nat. Inst. Health, Edn. and Welfare, 1971-72; administr. Sch. Medicine U. Wash., Seattle, 1972-75, Coun. Higher Edn., State of Ky., 1975-77; prof., dean Coll. Nursing U. N.D., Grand Forks, 1977-83; vice chancellor acad. affairs U. N.C., Greensboro, 1983-89; pres. Gallaudet U., Washington, 1988, U. Idaho, Moscow, 1989—; cons. Ctr. Leadership Devel. Am. Coun. Edn., Washington, Boeing Aircraft Co., Seattle, Nat. Workshop Acad. Deans, Higher Edn. Exec. Assocs., Denver, Bush Found., St. Paul; chmn. commn. on outreach and tech. transfer Nat. Assn. State Univs. and Land Grant Colls., 1993—, mem. bd. dirs., 1994—. Author: (with others) Contemporary Issues in Higher Education, 1985, Higher Education Research, 1988; co-author: Nurse: A Changing Word in a Changing World, 1982. Bd. dirs. Humana Hosp., Greensboro, 1986-88; v.p., bd. dirs. Ea. Music Festival, Greensboro, 1987-89; trustee N.C. Coun. Econ. Edn., 1985-89, Greensboro Day Sch., 1987-89. Leadership fellow Bush Found., 1981-82. Mem. Am. Assn. Higher Edn., Assn. Am. Colls. (Coun. Liberal Learning), Am. Assn. Univ. Administrs., AAUP, AAUW, Rotary, Pi Lambda Theta, Sigma Theta Tau. Home: 1026 Nez Perce Dr Moscow ID 83843-4138 Office: U Idaho Office of the President Moscow ID 83843*

ZINSSER, WILLIAM KNOWLTON, editor, writer, educator; b. N.Y.C., Oct. 7, 1922; s. William Herman and Joyce (Knowlton) Z.; m. Caroline Fraser, Oct. 10, 1954; children: Amy Fraser, John William. A.B., Princeton U., 1944; L.H.D., Rollins Coll., 1984; Litt.D., Ind. State U., 1985, Wesleyan U., 1988. Feature writer N.Y. Herald Tribune, 1946-49, drama editor, 1949-54, film critic, 1955-58, editorial writer, 1958-59; free-lance writer, 1959—; commentator on NBC-TV Sunday program, 1964-65; columnist Look mag, 1967, Life mag, 1968-72, N.Y. Times, 1977; faculty Yale U., 1971-79, master Branford Coll., 1973-79; gen. editor, Book-of-the-Month Club, 1979-86 . Author: Any Old Place With You, 1957, Seen Any Good Movies Lately?, 1958, Search and Research, 1961, The City Dwellers, 1962, Weekend Guests, 1963, The Haircurl Papers, 1964, Pop Goes America, 1966, The Paradise Bit, 1967, The Lunacy Boom, 1970, On Writing Well, 1976, Writing with a Word Processor, 1983, Willie and Dwike, 1984, Writing to Learn, 1988, Spring Training, 1989, American Places, 1992, Speaking of Journalism, 1994; co-author: Five Boyhoods, 1962; editor Extraordinary Lives, 1986, Inventing the Truth, 1987, Spiritual Quests, 1988, Paths of Resistance, 1989, Worlds of Childhood, 1990, They Went, 1991. Bd. dirs. Bklyn. Mus., 1967-72. Served with AUS, 1943-45, MTO. Clubs: Century Assn, Coffee House. Home: 45 E 62nd St New York NY 10021

ZIOCK, KLAUS OTTO HEINRICH, physics educator; b. Herchen, Germany, Feb. 4, 1925; came to U.S., 1958, naturalized, 1966; s. Samuel and Elisabeth (Bauer) Z.; m. Ursula E. A. Thierbach, May 31, 1952; children—Hans-Joachim, Klaus-Peter, Robert, Michael. Diplom Physiker, U. Bonn, Fed. Republic Germany, 1949, Dr. rer.nat., 1956. Rsch. physicist E. Leybold's Nachfolger, Cologne, Fed. Republic Germany, 1950-54; rsch. assoc. U. Bonn, Fed. Republic Germany, 1956-58; rsch. assoc. Yale U., New Haven, 1958-60, asst. prof. physics, 1960-62; assoc. prof. physics U. Va., Charlottesville, 1962-72, prof. physics, 1972—. Author: Basic Quantum Mechanics, 1969; contbr. numerous articles to profl. jours.; patentee in field. Recipient Humboldt prize Alexander von Humboldt Stiftung, 1978. Mem. Am. Phys. Soc.

ZIOLKOWSKI, JAN M., English educator; b. New Haven, Nov. 17, 1956; s. Theodore J. and Yetta (Goldstein) Z.; m. Elizabeth Ann Millenius; children: Saskia Elizabeth, Ada Margaret, Yetta Joy. AB summa cum laude, Princeton U., 1977; PhD, U. Cambridge, Eng., 1982; MA (hon.), Harvard U., 1987. Asst. prof. Harvard U. Cambridge, Mass., 1981-84, John L. Loeb assoc. prof. of the humanities, 1984-87, prof. medieval Latin and of comparative lit., 1987—. Editor Comparative Literature Studies. Fellow Guggenheim Found., 1987-88, ACLS, 1986, Rome Prize fellow, Am. Acad. in Rome, 1980-81; Marshall scholar, 1977-80. Mem. Medieval Acad. Am. (councillor 1991—); Phi Beta Kappa. Home: 930 Centre St Newton MA 02159-1266 Office: Harvard Univ Dept. Medieval Latin/Liter Cambridge MA 02138

ZIOLKOWSKI, THEODORE JOSEPH, comparative literature educator; b. Birmingham, Ala., Sept. 30, 1932; s. Mieclslaw and Cecilia (Jankowski) Z.; m. Yetta Bart Goldstein. Mar. 26, 1951; children: Margaret Cecilia, Jan Michael, Eric Josef. AB, Duke U., 1951, AM, 1952; student, U. Innsbruck, Austria, 1952-53; PhD, Yale U., 1957. Instr., then asst. prof. Yale U., New Haven, 1956-62; assoc. prof. Columbia U., N.Y.C., 1962-64; prof. Germanic langs. and lit. Princeton (N.J.) U., 1964-69, chmn., 1973-79, Class of 1900 prof. modern langs., 1969—, prof. comparative Jit., 1975—, dean Grad. Sch., 1979-92; vis. prof. Rutgers U., 1966, Yale U., 1967, 75, CUNY, 1971, Bristol U., 1987, U. Munich, 1992; vis. scholar U. Ctr. in Va., 1971, Piedmont U. Ctr., N.C., 1971; Dancy Meml. lectr. U. Montevallo, 1973; Christopher Longest lectr. U. Miss., 1979; Patten Found. lectr. Ind. U., 1980; vis. lectr. Österreichische Akademie der Wissenschaften, 1992; chmn. N.Y. State Doctoral Evaluation Program in German, 1975-80; nat. rev. panel for U.S. Nat. Grad. Fellows Program, 1985-87, 91—; chmn. overseers vis. com. on German Harvard U., 1982-88; mem. selection com. D for Bennett award, 1988; with German-Am. Acad. Coun., 1993—. Author: Hermann Broch, 1964, The Novels of Hermann Hesse, 1965, Hermann Hesse, 1966, Dimensions of the Modern Novel, 1969, Fictional Transfigurations of Jesus, 1972 (James Russell Lowell prize for criticism), Disenchanted Images, 1977, Der Schriftsteller Hermann Hesse, 1979, The Classical German Elegy, 1980, Varieties of Literary Thematics, 1983, German Romanticism and Its Institutions, 1990, Virgil and the Moderns, 1993; also articles and revs.; editor: Hermann Hesse, Autobiographical Writing, 1972, Hermann Hesse, Stories of Five Decades, 1972, Hesse: A Collection of Critical Essays, 1973, Herman Hesse, My Belief: Selected Essays, 1974, Herman Hesse, Tales of Student Life, 1976, Herman Hesse, Pictor's Metamorphoses and Other Fantasies, 1982, Hermann Hesse, Soul of the Age: Selected Letters, 1891-1962, 1991; mem. editl. bd. Germanic Rev., 1962—, Publs. Modern Lang. Assn., 1971-75, Arbitrium, 1983—, 17th Century Studies, 1985—, Germanistik, 1987—; mem. editl. bd. Princeton U. Press, 1972-75, trustee, 1982—; German series cons. Cambridge U. Press, 1993—; translator: The Poetics of Quotation (Herman Meyer) 1968, Herman Hesse: A Pictorial Biography, 1975. Recipient Howard T. Behrman award for disting. achievement in humanities, 1978, Wilbur Lucius Cross medal Yale U., 1982, Goethe Inst. gold medal, 1987, Henry Allen Moe prize in humanities, 1988; Fulbright rsch. grantee, 1958-59, grantee Am. Philos. Soc., 1959, NEH grantee, 1978, Guggenheim fellow, 1964-65, Am. Coun. Learned Socs. fellow, 1972, 76; resident fellow Bellagio Study Ctr., 1993. Mem. MLA (exec. coun. 1976-77, pres. 1985), Acad. Lit. Studies, Am. Comparative Lit. Assn., Am. Acad. Arts and Scis. Authors Guild, Am. Assn. Tchrs. German, Yale Grad. Sch., pres. 1974-76), Assn. Grad. Schs. (v.p. 1989-90, pres. 1990-91), Heinrich von Kleist Gesellschaft, Goethe-Gesellschaft, Internat. Vereinigung für Germanistik (exec. coun. 1985—, treas. 1990—), Am. Philos. Soc. (councillor 1991—), Göttingen Akademie der Wissenschaften, Austrian, Akademie der Wissenschaften, Phi Beta Kappa. Home: 36 Bainbridge St Princeton NJ 08540-3902 Office: Princeton U 230 E Pyne Bldg Princeton NJ 08544

ZIOMEK, JONATHAN S., journalist, educator; b. Newport News, Va., July 28, 1947; s. Stanley Walter and Joy Carmen (Schmidt) Z.; m. Rosalie Ziomek, Aug. 14, 1971; children: Joseph, Jennifer; 1 stepchild, Daniel. BA in Sociology, U. Ill., 1970, MS in Journalism, 1982. Reporter, feature writer, Sun. fin. editor Chgo. Sun-Times, 1970-78; press sec. Robert Ash Wallace for U.S. Senate campaign, Chgo., 1979-80; assoc. prof., asst. dean Northwestern U., Evanston, Ill., 1982—; dir. grad. editorial programs Medill Sch. Journalism, Northwestern U., Evanston, Ill., 1988—; presenter workshops. Contbr. articles to various mags.; editor: Chgo. Journalist Newsletter, 1991-93. Participant Internat. Visitors Ctr., Chgo., 1988—; fact-finder USIA, Bulgaria and Yugoslavia, 1990. Mem. Assn. for Edn. in Journalism and Mass Communications, Soc. Profl. Journalists, Chgo. Headline Club. Home: 2149 Hartrey Ave Evanston IL 60201-2571 Office: Northwestern Univ Medill Sch Journalism Evanston IL 60208

ZIOMEK, THOMAS JOHN, lawyer; b. Derby, Conn., Dec. 9, 1946; s. Anthony John and Anna (Madura) Z.; m. Nancy Monagan, July 27, 1974; children—Stephanie, Claire, Audrey. A.B., Georgetown U., 1968; J.D., Villanova U., 1971. Bar: Conn. 1971, Pa. 1972. Law clk. Commonwealth Ct. Pa., 1971-73; assoc White & Williams, Phila., 1973-78, ptnr., 1978—; lectr. pub. in law, 1979-81, 93. Contbr. articles to legal publs. Active Com. to Benefit the Children, 1978—. Mem. ABA, Phila. Bar Assn. Club: Racquet (Phila.). Mem. Villanova U. Law Rev., 1972-73; contbg. author The Business Insurance Handbook, 1981, Consequences of Nuclear Accidents, 1986, Liability of Insurance Agents and Brokers, 1987, 93. Office: White & Williams 1650 Market St Philadelphia PA 19103-7301

ZION, JAMES WILLIAM, lawyer; b. Palm Springs, Calif., Feb. 6, 1944; s. James William Sr. and Dortha Mae (Bennett) Z.; m. Rosemary Ann Blanchard, Dec. 26, 1967 (div. 1981); 1 child, Jeannette B.; m. Elsie Bailey, Mar. 23, 1990 (div. 1994). BA, U. St. Thomas, 1966; JD, Cath. U. Am., 1969. Bar: Mont. Sr. staff atty. Neighborhood Legal Svcs., Hartford, Conn., 1969-73; ptnr. Zion Law Firm, 1974-81; solicitor Cts. of Navajo Nation, Window Rock, Ariz., 1981-83; hearing examiner Mont. Human Rights Commn., Helena, 1985-87; asst. atty. gen. Mont. Dept. Labor and Industry/Mont. Human Rights Commn., Helena, 1987-88; gen. counsel Navajo Housing Authority, Window Rock, 1988-90; solicitor Navajo Nation Supreme Ct., Window Rock, 1990—; instr. Nat. Indian Justice Ctr., Petaluma, Calif., 1983—. Author: Navajo Peacemaker Court Manual, 1982; contbr. articles on Indian law and rights to legal publs. Fellow Royal Anthropol. Inst. Gt. Britain and Ireland; mem. Am. Anthropol. Assn., Commn. on Folk Law and Legal Pluralism, Dem. Socialists Am. Roman Catholic. Avocations: writing, travel. Home: PO Box 2429 Window Rock AZ 86515-2429

ZION, ROGER H., consulting firm executive, former congressman; b. Escanba, Mich., Sept. 17, 1921; s. Herschel G. and Helen (Hutchinson) Z.; m. Marjorie Knauss, Feb. 20, 1945; children—Gayle, Scott, Randy. B.A., U. Wis., 1943; postgrad., Grad. Sch. Bus. Adminstrn., Harvard, 1944-45. With Mead Johnson & Co., 1946-66, dir. tng. and profl. relations, 1965-66; internat. marketing mgmt. cons., 1966; mem. 90th-93d congresses from 8th Dist. Ind.; chmn. Republican Task Force on Energy and Resources; pres. Resources Devel., Inc. (cons.), Washington, 1975—. Author: Keys to Human Relations in Selling, 1963, The Hallowed Howls of Congress, 1994. Vice pres. Buffalo Trace council Boy Scouts Am., 1961; Bd. dirs, chmn. Evansville (Ind.) chpt. ARC, 1960-65. Served to lt. USNR, 1943-46, PTO. Named Toastmaster Evansville Press Gridiron dinner, 1963; recipient Citizen of Month award New Image Com. of Evansville's Future, 1962. Mem. VFW, Am. Legion, Nat. Sales and Marketing Execs. Assn. (pres. Evansville 1962), Wabash Valley Assn., AMVETS (life), Rotary (dir. Evansville club 1964), Evansville Country Club (dir. 1960-65), Alpha Delta Phi (pres. Wis. chpt. 1941-43). Republican. Congregationalist. Home: 834 Plaza Dr Evansville IN 47715-6936 Office: 412 1st St SE Washington DC 20003-1804

ZIPERSKI, JAMES RICHARD, lawyer, trucking company executive; b. Milw., May 27, 1932; s. George Felix and Louise (Medema) Z.; m. Patricia Jean Hoag, June 28, 1958; children: Jean Marie, David Carrington, James Patrick. BS, Marquette U., 1953, JD, 1957. Bar: Wis. 1957, U.S. Supreme Ct., 1967, U.S. Ct. Appeals, 1978. Resident counsel Schwerman Trucking Co., Milw., 1957—; assoc., 1962—; exec. v.p. corp., 1977-80, exec. v.p., 1980-86; exec. v.p., corp. and sec. Evergreen Holding Corp. (parent co. Schwerman Trucking Co.), Milw., 1987—; also bd. dirs. Served with AUS, 1953-55. Mem. Transp. Lawyers Assn., Westmoor Country Club, Kiwanis, Alpha Kappa Psi, Phi Delta Phi. Home: 2110 N Swan Blvd Milwaukee WI 53226-2644 Office: Evergreen Holding Corp PO Box 736 611 S 28th St Milwaukee WI 53215-1201

ZIPES, DOUGLAS PETER, cardiologist, researcher; b. White Plains, N.Y., Feb. 27, 1939; s. Robert Samuel and Josephine Helen (Weber) Z.; m. Marilyn Joan Jacobus, Feb. 18, 1961; children: Debra, Jeffrey, David. B.A. cum laude, Dartmouth Coll., 1961, B.Med. Sci., 1962; M.D. cum laude, Harvard Med. Sch., 1964. Diplomate Am. Bd. Internal Medicine (mem. subspecialty bd. cardiovascular disease 1989—, chmn. subspecialty bd. cardiovascular disease 1995—, chmn. com. certification in clin. cardiac electrophysiology 1989—). Intern, resident, fellow in cardiology Duke U. Med. Ctr., Durham, N.C., 1964-68; vis. scientist Masonic Med. Research Lab. Utica, N.Y., 1970-71; asst. prof. medicine Ind. U. Sch. Medicine, Indpls., 1970-73, assoc. prof., 1973-76, prof., 1976-94, prof. pharmacology and toxicology, 1993—, disting. prof. medicine, 1994—; cons.; mem. cardiology adv. com. NIH, 1991-94. Author: Comprehensive Cardiac Care, 7th edit., 1991; editor: Slow Inward Current, 1980, Cardiac Electrophysiology and Arrhythmias, 1985, Nonpharmacological Therapy of Tachyarrhythmias, 1987, Cardiac Electrophysiology From Cell to Bedside, 1990, 2d edit., 1994; co-editor: Treatment of Heart Diseases, 1992, Ablation of Cardiac Arrhythmias, 1994, Antiarrhythmic Therapy: A Pathophysiologic Approach, 1994, Cardiovascular Therapeutics, 1995; editl. bd. Circulation, 1974-78, 83—, Am. Jour. Cardiology, 1979-82, 88T—, Am. Jour. Medicine, 1979-90, Jour. Am. Coll. Cardiology, 1983, Am. Heart Jour., 1977—, PACE, 1977—, Circulation Rsch., 1983-90, Am. Jour. Noninvasive Cardiology, 1985-89, Jour. Electrophysiology, 1987-89, Cardiovascular Drugs and Therapy, 1986—, Japanese Heart Jour., 1989—, Jour. Cardiovascular Pharmacology and Therapeutics, Current Clin. Trials; editor in chief: Progress in Cardiology, 1988-92, Jour. Cardiovascular Electrophysiology, 1990—, Cardiology in Rev., 1992—; contbr. numerous articles to med. publs.; patentee cardioverter, elec. prevention of arrhythmia, discrimination of atrial fibillation and fixation of implantable devices. Pres., bd. dirs. Indpls. Opera Co., 1983-85; mem. study sect. NIH, Washington, 1977-81; mem. nat. merit rev. bd. VA, 1982-85, Cardiology Adv. Com. NHLBL, 1991-94, mem. steering com. AVID. Recipient Disting. Achievement award Am. Heart Assn., 1989. Fellow ACP, Am. Coll. CArdiology (chmn. ACC/AHA subcom. to assess EP studies, chmn. young investigators award com. 1988-94, trustee 1992—, mem. nominating com. 1993—), Am. Heart Assn. (exec. com. 1980-88, sci. sessions program 1983-86, chmn. com. on electrocardiogram and cardiac electrophysiology 1983-86, sci. pub. com. 1986-90, cardiovascular rsch. study com. 1987-90, steering com. for rsch., med. and cmty. programs 1988-90, sci. sessions chmn. XIV congress of internat. soc. cardiology, chmn. sci. sessions 1992, chmn. animals in rsch. task force, mem. corp. rels. rev. com. 1989-94, mem. internat. program com. 1992—, bd. dirs. internat. cardiology found. 1993—, bd. dirs. 1994—); mem. Am. Soc. Clin. Investigation, Assn. Univ. Cardiologists (v.p. 1994), Assn. Am. Physicians, Am. Physiol. Soc., Cardiac Electrophysiology Soc. (pres. 1985-86), N.Am Soc. Pacing and Electrophysiology (pres. 1989-90, trustee 1990—), InterAm. Soc. Cardiology (v.p 1993—), Ind. Cardiac Electrophysiology Soc. (founder). Home: 10614 Winterwood Carmel IN 46032-9688 Office: Ind U Sch Medicine 1000 W Michigan St Indianapolis IN 46223

ZIPF, WILLIAM BYRON, pediatric endocrinologist, educator; b. Dayton, Ohio, Mar. 20, 1946; s. Robert Eugene and Merium (Murr) Z.; m. Joanne Fisher, Sept. 20, 1969; children: William Byron Jr., Thanda Lynn, Robert E. II. BA, Denison U., 1968; MD, Ohio State U., 1972. Diplomate Nat. Bd. Med. Examiners, Am. Bd. Pediatrics, Am. Bd. Pediatric Endocrinology. Intern in pediatrics Mott Children's Hosp./U. Mich., Ann Arbor, 1972-73, resident in pediatrics, 1973-75, clin. fellow in pediatric endocrinology, 1975-76, rsch. fellow, 1976-78; asst. prof. dept. pediatrics and physiology Ohio State U., Columbus, 1978-83, assoc. prof., 1983-89, prof., 1989—; dir. clin. study ctr. Children's Hosp./Ohio State U., Columbus, 1982—, vice-chmn. dept. pediatrics, 1989—, dir. pediatric endocrinology, 1990—. Contbr. chpts. on endocrine diseases of children to books, articles to profl. jours. Grantee NIH, 1980-84, Cystic Fibrosis Found., 1987-92. Fellow Am. Acad. Pediatrics, Nat. Med. Bd.; mem. Soc. Pediatric Rsch., Endocrine Soc., Lawson Wilkins Soc. Pediatric Endocrinology. Achievements include discovery of endocrine abnormalities associated with conditions of altered nutrition in children; definition of role of pancreatic peptide abnormalities in specific appetite disorders. Office: Childrens Hosp 700 Childrens Dr Columbus OH 43205-2696

ZIPP, ARDEN PETER, chemistry educator; b. Dolgeville, N.Y., July 14, 1938; s. Arden Peter and Dorothy Arlene (Killmeier) Z.; m. Kathryn Vernay; children—Allyson Scott, Alaina Ruth. A.B., Colgate U., 1960; Ph.D., U. Pa., 1964. Asst. prof. Drew U., Madison, N.J., 1964-66; asst. prof. SUNY, Cortland, 1966-68, assoc. prof., 1968-73, prof. chemistry, 1973-85, Disting. teaching prof., 1985—; vis. prof. U. Utah, 1972-73, summer 1975, Advanced Placement reader, 1975-80, TL, 1981-88, chief reader, 1989-92, internat. baccalaureate chief examiner, 1986—; rsch. collaborator Brookhaven Nat. Lab., Upton, N.Y., 1979-86, U. Va. spring 1987, SUNY Binghamton fall 1987, U. N.C. Chapel Hill, spring 1988, U. Rochester, fall 1993. Recipient CMA Catalyst award, 1991. Contbr. articles to profl. jours. Mem. Am. Chem. Soc., Phi Beta Kappa, Sigma Xi, Phi Eta Sigma, Phi Kappa Phi. Avocations: bicycling; photography. Home: 587 Babcock Rd Tully NY 13159 Office: Dept Chemistry SUNY-Cortland Cortland NY 13045

ZIPP, JOEL FREDERICK, lawyer; b. Shaker Heights, Ohio, Feb. 12, 1948; s. Jack David and Eleanor Adele Z.; m. Elizabeth Ann Frieden, Dec. 4, 1976; 1 child, Carlyn Leigh. BS, U. Wis., 1970, MS, 1972; JD, Case Western Res. U., 1975. Bar: Ohio 1975, D.C. 1976, U.S. Ct. Claims, 1976, U.S. Ct. Appeals (D.C. cir.) 1976, U.S. Ct. Appeals (5th cir.) 1979, U.S. Ct. Appeals (11th cir.) 1983, U.S. Supreme Ct. 1983. Trial atty. Fed. Energy Regulation Com., Washington, 1975-79, asst. dir. office of enforcement, 1979; assoc. Morley, Caskin & Generelly, Washington, 1979-80, ptnr., 1981—; gen. counsel, sec. Portland Natural Gas Transmission Sys., 1993—. Notes editor Energy Law Jour., 1990—; contbr. articles to profl. jours. Bd. dirs. Westmoreland Children's Ctr., Washington, 1986-88. Smithsonian fellow, 1969. Mem. ABA, Fed. Energy Bar Assn. (bd. dirs., past com. chair, chair 1992 and 1993 ann. meetings), So. Gas Assn. (legal task force 1995—). Jewish. Avocations: sailing, skiing, running. Home: 9216 Burning Tree Rd Bethesda MD 20817-2251 Office: Morley Caskin 1225 I St NW Washington DC 20005-3914

ZIPPER, HERBERT, symphony conductor; b. Vienna, Austria, Apr. 27, 1904; came to U.S., 1946; s. Emil and Regina (Westreich) Z.; m. Trudl Dubsky, Oct. 1, 1939 (dec. July, 1976). Master diploma, Vienna State Acad. for Music and Drama, Vienna, 1926. Prof. Conservatory of Düsseldorf, Fed. Republic Germany, 1931-33; apptd. by Pres. Sergio Osmeñ-a of Philippines as mem. com. for cultural rehab. of Philippines, 1946; lectr. New Sch. for Social Research in opera, symphony, and composition, 1947-52; exec. dir. Nat. Guild Community Mus. Schs., 1967-72; music cons. JDR 3d Fund, N.Y.C.; projects dir. U. So. Calif. Sch. Performing Arts, Los Angeles, 1972-80; invited guest condr. and tchr. conducting and composition People's Republic of China, 1981. Asst. condr. Wiener Burgtheater, 1923-25, condr. Vienna Madrigal Assn., 1927-29, opera condr. Stadttheater Ingolstadt, Bavaria, 1929-30, condr. Mcpl. Music Soc., 1931-33; guest condr. in various cities of Europe, 1933-37; instrumental in found. and orgn. of Vienna Concert Orch., composed mainly of musicians who fled Germany, 1934; composed music for polit. satires in Paris, 1939; mus. dir. Manila Symphony Orch. and head Acad. Music of Manila, 1939-42; gave 130 symphony concerts for armed forces and civilians, 1945-44; mus. dir. Bklyn. Symphony Orch., 1947-50; Fine Arts Quartet Concert series, Chgo., Wilmette, Ill., 1960-67; condr. summer season, Manila Symphony Orch., 1951-69; dir. Community Music Ctr. North Shore, 1953-67, condr. Chgo. Businessmen's Orch., 1955-62, condr. 26 symphony concerts in Beijing, Tienjin and Guangzhou, Peoples Republic China, 1981, 4 months 1982, condr. orchs. in 4 cities, Peoples Republic China, 4 months, 1984; condr. concerts in Beijing, Jinan, Tianjin, Qingdao, Peoples Republic China, 1986, Beijing and Shenyang, China, 1988, Beijing and Changchun, 1989, Beijing Cen. Philharm., Orch. Concerts, 1990; condr. Cen. Philharm. of China, Philharm. Chamber Orch., Radio Broadcast Orch., Beijing, 1991, concerts with Tianjin Philharmonic, 1993; opened Styrian Automn, Graz, Austria, 1988, Zipper's Biography, 1992, Chinese edition, 1992, German edition, 1993; composer revision of choral works by old masters and own choral arrangements, 1948-49; German version of Ernst Toch's opera The Last Tale, 1964. Chmn. Philippine fellowship project, 1966; pres. Nat. Guild Community Music Schs., 1957-62, exec. dir. 1967-72; project dir. U. So. Calif. Sch. of Performing Arts, 1972-80. Prisoner Dachau and Buchenwald concentration camps, 1938-39. Recipient Louis S. Weiss Meml. prize New Sch. of Social Research, N.Y., 1954, Presdl. award medal and citation Pres. of Philippines, 1959, Austrian Cross Honor for Sci. and Art, 1966, Silangan award U. East Manila, Philippines, 1977, Samuel Rosenbaum Meml. award Nat. Guild Community Schs. Arts, Golden Honor Insignia for important achievements Govt. Vienna, Austria, 1993. Reorganized orch. after imprisonment by Japanese and work in underground, 1945. Home: 1091 Palisair Pl Pacific Palisades CA 90272

ZIPPIN, CALVIN, epidemiologist; b. Albany, N.Y., July 17, 1926; s. Samuel and Jennie (Perkel) Z.; m. Patricia Jayne Schubert, Feb. 9, 1964; children: David Benjamin, Jennifer Dorothy. AB magna cum laude, SUNY,

Albany, 1947; ScD, Johns Hopkins U., Balt., 1953. Rsch. asst. Sterling-Winthrop Rsch. Inst., Rensselaer, N.Y., 1947-50; instr. biostats. Sch. Pub. Health, U. Calif., Berkeley, 1953-55; asst. to full rsch. biostatistician Sch. Medicine U. Calif., San Francisco, 1955-67, asst. prof. preventive medicine, 1958-60, prof. epidemiology, 1967-91, prof. emeritus, 1991—; vis. assoc. prof. stats. Stanford U., 1962; adv. WHO, 1969—; vis research worker Middlesex Hosp. Med. Sch., London, 1975; various coms. Am. Cancer Soc. and Nat. Cancer Inst., 1956—; faculty adviser Regional Cancer Centre, Trivandrum, India, 1983—; cons., lectr., vis. prof. in field. Contbr. articles to profl. jours.; editorial advisor Jour. Stats. in Medicine, Boston, 1981-86. Active Dem. Ctrl. Com. Marin County, Calif., 1994—. Recipient Disting. Alumnus award SUNY, Albany, 1969, also awards, fellowships and grants for work in cancer biometry and epidemiology. Fellow Am. Statis. Assn., Am. Coll. Epidemiology, Royal Statis. Soc. Gt. Britain; mem. Biometric Soc. (mem. internat. coun. 1978-81, pres. Western N.Am. region 1979-80), Calif. Cancer Registries Assn. (hon.), Internat. Assn. Cancer Registrars (hon.), B'nai Brith (pres. Golden Gate lodge 1970-71, pres. Greater San Francisco Bay area coun. 1974-75), Phi Beta Kappa, Sigma Xi, Delta Omega. Home: 4 Warren Ct Belvedere Tiburon CA 94920-1117 Office: U Calif San Francisco CA 94143-0746

ZIPPRODT, PATRICIA, costume designer. B.A., Wellesley Coll.; student, Art Inst. Chgo., Art Students League N.Y., Fashion Inst. Tech. Asst. to various theatre designers; costume designer School for Scandal, Shakespeare Co., Washington, 1994; lectr., condr. master classes Yale U., Harvard U., others; vis. lectr. theatre arts NYU; prof. theatre arts Brandeis U., 1985-93; founding mem. Nat. Theater for the Deaf. Designer: (Broadway mus.) Fiddler on the Roof, 1964 (Tony award 1964), Cabaret, 1966 (Tony award 1966), Zorba, 1968 (Drama Desk award 1968), 1776, 1969 (Drama Desk award 1969, Joseph P. Maharam award 1970), Pippin, 1972 (Drama Desk award 1973), Mack and Mable, 1974, Chicago, 1975, King of Hearts, 1978, Alice in Wonderland, 1982 (Joseph P. Maharam award 1983), Smile, 1983, The Accidental Death of an Anarchist, 1984, Sweet Charity, 1985 (Tony award 1986), Big Deal, 1986, Shogun: The Musical, 1990 (Drama Desk award 1990, Joseph P. Maharam award 1990), My Fair Lady, 1993; (Broadway plays) A Period of Adjustment, 1962, Little Foxes, 1967, Plaza Suite, 1968, Scratch, 1971, All God's Chillun' Got Wings, 1975, Poor Murderer, 1976, Kingdoms, 1981, Fools, 1981, Brighton Beach Memoirs, 1983, The Glass Menagerie, 1983, Macbeth, 1988, Cat on a Hot Tin Roof, 1989, My Favorite Year, 1992; (off-Broadway plays) Our Town, 1960, The Balcony, 1960, Camino Real, 1961, Oh Dad Poor Dad Etc., 1962, A Man's a Man, 1963, The Blacks, 1962; (Guthrie Theatre) Waiting for Godot, 1973, Don Juan, 1982 (Joseph P. Maharam award 1983), The Bacchae, 1987; (Nat. Actors Theatre) The Crucible, 1991-92, Hotel Paradiso, 1991-92, The Master Builder, 1991-92; (Boston Opera) Madam Butterfly, 1962, Hippolyte E Aricie, 1966, The Rise and Fall of the City of Mahagonny, 1972; (New York City Opera) Katerina Ismailova, 1967, The Flaming Angel, 1968, Naughty Marietta, 1978; (Guggenheim Mus., N.Y.C.) The Mother of Us All, 1972; (Julliard Opera) Lord Byron, 1973; (Met. Opera) Tannhaüser, 1977, The Barber of Seville, 1982; (Am. Repertory Theatre, Cambridge, Mass.) The Fall of the House of Usher, 1988; (Am. Ballet Theatre) Les Noces, 1969, The Leaves are Fading, 1975, Estuary, 1982, Coppélia, 1991; (New York City Ballet) Watermill, 1972, Dybbuk Variations, 1974, The Sleeping Beauty, 1991; (Houston Ballet) Helgi Tommasen, 1985; (Ballet Hispanico) Cada Noche Tango Jnez de Castro Tres Cantos, 1988; (films) The Graduate, 1967; (television spls.) Anne Bancroft Spl., CBS, 1970, June Moon, WNET, 1973, The Glass Menagerie, ABC, 1973, Alice in Wonderland, WNET, 1983, Chrysler Skating, 1992; (nat. tours) Bette Midler, 1976, Ben Vereen, 1983; designer, advisor: The Seagull (St. Petersburg, Russia), Anna Christie (Beijing, China); exhibitor design sketches Wright-Hepburn, London, 1966, Capicorn Gallery, N.Y.C., 1968, Mus. City N.Y., 1972, U. Calif.-San Diego, 1974, Toneelmuseum, Amsterdam, The Netherlands, 1975, U.S. Internat. Theatre Inst. traveling exhibit, 1974-78, N.Y. City Ballet, 1994. Recipient award for spl. costumes NATAS, 1970, Alumna Achievement award Wellesley Coll., 1971, spl. award New Eng. Conf., 1973, Ritter award Fashion Inst. Tech., 1977, Disting. Career award S.E. Theatre Conf., 1985. Mem. United Scenic Artists, Costume Designers Guild, Motion Picture Acad. Arts and Scis. Inducted into Theatrical Hall of Fame, 1992. Address: 29 King St New York NY 10014-4944

ZIRBES, MARY KENNETH, social justice ministry coordinator; b. Melrose, Minn., Sept. 4, 1926; d. Joseph Louis and Clara Bernadine (Petermeier) Z. BA in History and Edn., Coll. St. Catherine, 1960; MA in Applied Theology, Sch. Applied Theology, Berkeley, Calif., 1976. Joined Order of St. Francis, Roman Cath. Ch., 1945. Tchr. Pub. Grade Sch., St. Nicholas, Minn., 1947-52; prin. Holy Spirit Grade Sch., St. Cloud, Minn., 1953-59, St. Mary's Jr. High Sch., Morris, Minn., 1960-62; coord. Franciscan Mission Team, Peru, South America, 1962-67, Franciscan Missions, Little Falls, Minn., 1967-70; dir. St. Richard's Social Ministry, Richfield, Minn., 1971-80, Parish Community Devel., St. Paul, Mpls., Minn., 1980-85; councillor gen. Franciscan Sisters of Little Falls, 1960-62, 67-70; asst. dir. Renew-Archdiocese of St. Paul-Mpls., 1986-89; coord. Parish Social Justice Ministry-Archdiocese of St. Paul-Mpls., 1990-93; dir. Franciscan Assocs., 1993—; co-developer Assn. of Pastoral Ministers, Mpls., St. Paul, 1979-81, Compañeros/Sister Parishes-Minn. and Nicaragua, 1984-89, Minn. Interfaith Ecology Coalition, 1989-92. Author: Parish Social Ministry, 1985, (manual) Acting for Justice, 1992. Organizer Twin Cities Orgn., Mpls., 1979-80; bd. dirs. Franciscan Sisters Health Care, Inc., Little Falls, 1990-93, Rice-Marion Residents Assn., St. Paul, 1991-92. Named Outstanding chair Assn. Pastoral Ministers, 1981; recipient Five Yrs. of Outstanding Svc. award Companeros, 1989. Mem. Assn. Pastoral Ministers (chair 1979), Amnesty Internat., Voices for Justice-Legis. Lobby, Audubon Soc., Network, Minn. Interfaith Ecology Coalition, Franciscan Sisters of Little Falls. Avocations: water color painting, birding, golf, reading history and biography. Office: Franciscan Sisters 116-8th Ave SE Little Falls MN 56345

ZIRIN, JAMES DAVID, lawyer; b. N.Y.C., Jan. 10, 1940; s. Morris and Kate (Sapir) Z.; m. Marlene Hess, May 18, 1990. AB with honors, Princeton U., 1961; JD with honors, U. Mich., 1964. Bar: N.Y. 1965, U.S. Supreme Ct. 1978. Asst. U.S. atty. U.S. Dist. Ct. (so. dist.) N.Y., N.Y.C., 1967-70; assoc. Breed, Abbott & Morgan, N.Y.C., 1965-67, 70-72, ptnr., 1972-93; ptnr. Brown & Wood, N.Y.C., 1993—. Contbr. articles to London Times, Forbes, Barron's, N.Y. newsday, N.Y. Law Jour. Bd. dirs. Legal Aid Soc., N.Y.C., 1984-89, exec. com., 1986-89. Lt. USNR, 1965-70. Fellow Am. Coll. Trial Lawyers; mem. Fed. Bar Coun. (v.p 1982-84), Assn. of Bar of City of N.Y., University Club. Republican. Office: Brown & Wood One World Trade Ctr New York NY 10048

ZIRINSKY, DANIEL, real estate investor and photographer; b. Bklyn., Mar. 14, 1927; s. David and Gertrude (Coleman) Z.; m. Ellen Reiss Snyder, Apr. 7, 1957 (div. Aug. 1977); children: Steven George, Mark Allen, Laura Reiss; m. Gilda Schiff, Oct. 12, 1980. BS, Syracuse U., 1949. Pres. Bus. Bldgs. of Am., Inc., Great Neck, N.Y., 1969—; real estate developer and owner/investor Great Neck, N.Y., 1950—, photographer, 1950—; judge, lectr. and tchr. photographer. One-man photography shows from 1953-87 include Great Neck House, 1987, Lincoln Savs. Bank, 1987, Gould Electronics, 1987, Bryant Libr., 1986, others; group exhbns. include Great Neck Libr., 1990, 91, 92, 93, Ind. Art Soc., 1990, Long Beach Art League, 1990, Chelsea Mansion, 1989-90, others. Treas. N. Shore Sci. Mus., Port Washington, N.Y., 1970-78; founder N.Y. Inst. Tech., Old Westbury, 1958; v.p.; trustee The Advanced Ctr Psychotherapy, 1987—, Advanced Inst. Analytic Psychotherapy, 1987—. Recipient Photographic Fed. L.I. Color Print of Yr. award, 1992, 1st pl. North Shore Univ. Hosp., 1992, 93. Mem. Photographic Soc. Am. (life, 59 medals, 74 hon. mentions in U.S., Eng., Australia, Japan, Can., Mex., France, Yugoslavia, Germany), Photographic Soc. Hong Kong (assoc.), Leica Hist. Soc. Am., Am. Photographic Hist. Soc., Great Neck Color Camera Club (1991-92 Print of Yr. award, 1990-91 Color Print of Yr. award, 1989-90 Color Print of Yr. award, 28 awards, 42 hon. mentions), Artists Network Great Neck, Real Estate Bd. N.Y. Jewish. Avocations: computer, ham radio, yachting, skiing, cycling. Home: 7 Beech Dr Kings Point NY 11024 Office: 60 Cutter Mill Rd Great Neck NY 11021

ZIRKEL, DON, public information official; b. Ozone Park, N.Y., Aug. 13, 1927; s. George Henry and Frances Anna (Neumann) Z.; m. Marie Margaret Greene, June 28, 1952; children: Jeanne Zirkel O'Connell, Barbara Zirkel Dempsey, Joseph, Thomas, Mary Zirkel Pacifico, Anne Zirkel-Hagopian, John, Paul, Timothy. Student, Fordham U., 1948-50; B.A., St. John's U.,

1955. Mem. editorial staff Cath. newspaper The Tablet, Bklyn., 1948-85; editor Cath. newspaper The Tablet, 1968-85; exec. staff N.Y. State Div. Human Rights, 1985-92; dir. pub. info. Ctr. for Devel. Disabilities, Woodbury, N.Y., 1992—; lectr. in field. Contbr. articles to Cath. newspapers, mags. Rsch. asst. to Congressman James J. Delaney, 1961-63, Congressman Hugh L. Carey, 1963-65; bd. dirs. Citizens for Ednl. Freedom, Cath. Interracial Coun. Intercommunity Ctr. for Justice and Peace. With AUS, 1950-52. Recipient Best News Story award Cath. Press Assn., 1957, Americanism award Cath. War Vets., 1961, Worldmission award U.S. Mission Secretariat, 1963. Roman Catholic (lector 1966—, Eucharistic minister 1973—, ordained deacon 1979). Club: K.C. (State award 1973). Home: 34 Fountain St Hicksville NY 11801-3120 Office: Ctr Devel Disabilities 72 S Woods Rd Woodbury NY 11797

ZIRKEL, GENE, computer science educator and mathematics; b. N.Y.C., Dec. 2, 1931; s. George Henry and Frances Anna (Neumann) Z.; m. Patricia Lou McCormick, Apr. 15, 1968; 1 child, George Stephen. BS, St. John's Coll., Bklyn., 1953; MA, St. John's U., Queens, N.Y., 1960; MS, N.Y. Inst. Tech., 1984. Tchr. Mt. St. Michael's High Sch., Bronx, N.Y., 1955-56, Cardinal Hayes High Sch., Bronx, 1956-60; chair math. Marist High Sch., Bayonne, N.J., 1960-62, prin., 1966-67; tchr. Aquinas High Sch., Augusta, Ga., 1962; chair theology Archbishop Molloy High School, Queens, 1962-66; prof. Nassau Community Coll, Garden City, N.Y., 1967—; lectr. Marist Coll., Poughkeepsie, N.Y., 1959-66, Adelphi U. Garden City, 1973-74; com. create nat. exam Math Assn. Am. Co-author: Understanding Statistics, 1972, Beginning Statistics, 1976, Program CSI, 1990, Understanding Fortran 77 & 90, 1994; contbr. articles to profl. jours.; columnist Standard Deviations. Union rep. Labor and Religion Coalition, L.I., N.Y., 1980s; Cath. chaplain Nassau Community Coll., vol. parish outreach poor, homeless, and hungry. Recipient best articles of 1976 award Matyc Jour., Disting. Faculty award Nassau C.C., 1995; scholar NSF, 1960. Fellow Dozenal Soc. (chmn. bd. dirs. 1991-92, pres. 1977-88, v.p. 1988-90); mem. Nat. Coun. Tchrs. Math. (life). Democrat. Avocation: swimming. Home: 6 Brancatelli Ct West Islip NY 11795-2502 Office: Nassau Community Coll 1 Education Dr Garden City NY 11530-6793

ZIRKIND, RALPH, physicist; b. N.Y.C., Oct. 20, 1918; s. Isaac and Zicel (Lifshitz) Z.; m. Ann Goldman, Nov. 22, 1940; children: Sheila Zirkind Knopf, Elaine Zirkind Gorman, Edward I. B.S., CCNY, 1940; M.S., Ill. Inst. Tech., 1945; postgrad., George Washington U., 1946-47; Ph.D., U. Md., 1950; D.Sc., U. R.I., 1968. Physicist Navy Dept., 1945-50, chief physicist, 1951-60; physicist Oak Ridge Nat. Lab., 1950-51, Advanced Research Project Agy., Washington, 1960-63; prof. Poly. Inst. Bklyn., 1963-70, U. R.I., Kingston, 1970-72; adj. prof. U. R.I., 1972—; physicist Advanced Research Projects Agy., Arlington, Va., 1972-74; cons. Advanced Rsch. Projects Agy., and industry, Arlington, 1974—; lectr. U. Md., 1948-50, George Washington U., 1952-53, U. Mich., 1966; cons. ACDA, Jet Propulsion Lab., Calif. Inst. Tech. Contbg. author: Jet Propulsion Series, 1952, FAR Infrared Properties of Materials, 1968; editor: Electromagnetic Sensing of Earth, 1967; mem. editorial bd.: Infrared Physics, 1963—; contbr. articles profl. jours. Recipient Meritorious Civilian Svc. award Navy Dept., 1957, Meritorious Civilian Svc. award Dept. Def., 1970, Outstanding Educator of Am. medal, 1972, Maj. Contbn. award BMDO/AIAA, 1994. Mem. Am. Phys. Socs., N.Y. Acad. Scis., Sigma Xi, Sigma Pi Sigma, Eta Kappa Nu. Home: 820 Hillsboro Dr Silver Spring MD 20902-3202 Office: 4001 Fairfax Dr Ste 700 Arlington VA 22203-1618

ZIRKLE, DAVID H., data processing company executive; b. 1936. BA, George Washington U., Washington, 1955. With IBM Corp., Washington, 1955-73, Xerox Corp., Stanford, Conn., 1973-80, Northern Telcom Corp., Washington, 1980-82; with Racal Corp., Fort Lauderdale, Fla., 1982-93, pres., 1993—. Office: Racal Corporation PO Box 407044 Fort Lauderdale FL 33340-7044

ZIRKLE, LEWIS GREER, physician, executive; b. Pittsfield, Mass., July 23, 1940; s. Lewis Greer and Vivian (Shaw) Z.; m. Sara K. Zirkle, Aug. 24, 1963; children: Elizabeth, Molly, Julie. BS, Davidson Coll., 1962; MD, Duke U., 1966. Intern Duke U. Hosp., 1966-67, resident, 1968-73; resident U.S. Army, Shriner's Hosp., 1967-68; pvt. practice Richland, Wash., 1973—; bd. dirs. Orthopedics Overseas, chmn. program in Vietnam, 1992—. Contbr. articles to profl. jours. Maj. U.S. Army, 1968-73. Presbyterian. Avocations: reading, sports. Home: 2548 Harris Ave Richland WA 99352-1638 Office: NW Orthopedics 875 Swift Blvd Richland WA 99352-3513

ZIRPOLI, ALFONSO JOSEPH, federal judge; b. Denver, Apr. 12, 1905; s. Vincenzo and Stella (Graziani) Z.; m. Giselda Campagnoli, Sept. 19, 1936; children: Sandra Elena, Jane Amanda. AB, U. Calif., Berkeley, 1926, JD, 1928. Bar: Calif. 1928, U.S. Supreme Ct. 1941. Pvt. practice law, 1928-32, 44-61; asst. dist. atty. City and County San Francisco, 1932-33; asst. U.S. atty. No. Dist. Calif., 1933-44; instr. criminal law Hastings Coll. Law, 1945; sr. judge U.S. Dist. Ct. (no. dist.) Calif., San Francisco., 1961—. Mem. Bd. Suprs. City and County San Francisco, 1958-61. Recipient Star Solidarity, 1953, grand officer Order Merit, 1956; Italy). Fellow Am. Coll. Trial Lawyers; mem. ABA, Fed. Bar Assn., Calif. Bar Assn. Office: US Dist Ct PO Box 36060 16700 Valley View Ave Ste 300 La Mirada CA 90638-5841

ZISCH, WILLIAM E., technical services executive. V. chmn. Science Applications Internat. Corp., San Diego. Office: Sci Applications Internat 10260 Campus Point Dr San Diego CA 92121-1522

ZISCHKE, DOUGLAS ARTHUR, foreign service officer; b. Sioux Falls, S.D., May 24, 1929; s. Arthur Gustav and Alice Minetta (Wedeking) Z.; m. Janice Mae Kuehnemann, June 8, 1957; children: Mark Douglas, Deborah Jan, Todd Lincoln. B.S. in Journalism, U. Wis., 1951, M.S. cum laude, 1952. Joined U.S. Fgn. Svc., 1957; tech. editor Forest Svc., Madison, 1955-57; asst. info. officer USIS, Montevideo, Uruguay, 1957-58, La Paz, Bolivia, 1958-59; asst. cultural affairs officer, br. pub. affairs officer Mexico, 1960-65; info. specialist Washington, 1965-67; pub. affairs officer Tegucigalpa, Honduras, 1967-69; dep. pub. affairs officer Buenos Aires, Argentina, 1969-71; pub. affairs officer Guatemala, Guatemala, 1971-74; assigned to U.S. Army War Coll., 1974-75; dep. pub. affairs officer Am. embassy Tehran, Iran, 1975-78; cultural coord. USICA, Washington, 1979-80; internat. coms., 1980-86; fgn. affairs advisor State Dept., 1986—. Author monograph. Bd. dirs. Boy Scouts Am; dir. Lutheran Ch. 1973-74. Served with Signal Corps, AUS, 1953-55.

ZISK, SHERRY, health facility administrator; b. Johnstown, Pa., June 16, 1951; d. Russell C. and Frieda L. (Garman) Gibson; m. Stephen A. Zisk, May 21, 1977; children: Ryan M., Eric M. BSN, U. Pitts., 1973, MEd in Nursing. With West Pa. Hosp., Pitts., v.p. nursing svc. Mem. ANA, Am. Orgn. Nurse Execs., Forum Nurse Execs., Sigma Theta Tau (Eta chpt.).

ZISKIN, LAURA, film producer. Co-founder Frogwood Films. Films include: (assoc. prodr.) Eyes of Laura Mars, 1978; (prodr.) Murphy's Romance, 1985, No Way Out, 1987, D.O.A., 1988, Everybody's An American, 1988, The Rescue, 1988, What About Bob?, 1991, The Doctor, 1991, Hero, 1992; (exec. prodr.) Pretty Woman, 1990. Office: Laura Ziskin Prodns 10202 W Washington Blvd Culver City CA 90232-3195*

ZISMAN, BARRY STUART, lawyer; b. N.Y.C., Sept. 18, 1937; s. Harry and Florence Rita (Tucker) Z.; m. Maureen Frances Brumond, Dec. 30, 1979; children: Michael Glenn, Marlene Ann. AB, Columbia U., 1958, JD, 1961. Bar: D.C. 1962, N.Y. 1965, Tex. 1986, U.S. Dist. Ct. (ea. and so. dists.) N.Y. 1967, U.S. Ct. Appeals (D.C. cir.) 1967, U.S. Dist. Ct. (no. and so. dists.) Tex. 1986, U.S. Ct. Appeals (5th cir.) 1988, U.S. Supreme Ct. 1967. With U.S. Govt., 1962-66; pvt. practice Syosset, N.Y., 1966-71; sr. counsel CBS Inc., N.Y.C., 1972-75; assn. counsel, asst. sec. M. Lowenstein & Sons, N.Y.C., 1975-79; gen. counsel Grumman Allied Indsl. Inc., Bethpage, N.Y., 1979-83; asst. gen. counsel Grumman Corp., Bethpage, 1982-83; sr. atty. FDIC, Dallas, 1984-87; of counsel Arter & Hadden, Dallas, 1987-88, ptnr. 1988; ptnr. Winstead, McGuire, Sechrest & Minick, Dallas, 1988-90, Arter & Hadden, Dallas and Washington, 1990-91, Rubinstein & Perry, Dallas, 1991-94, Zisman & Assocs., Dallas, 1994—; advisor in field; vice-chmn. Assn. of Bank and Thrift Receivership Coun. Editor and author: Banks and Thrifts: Government Enforcement and Receivership Law, 1991.

With U.S. Army, 1961-62. Home: 905 Murl Dr Irving TX 75062-4441 Office: Zisman and Assocs 2626 Cole Ave Ste 400 Dallas TX 75204

ZISSMAN, LORIN, marketing research, consulting company executive; b. Phila., July 13, 1930; s. Charles Louis and Sarah (Axelman) Z.; m. Beverly Ann Zissman, June 23, 1957 (div. Sept. 1987); children: Nancy Zissman Peters, Jonathan, Eric, Amy; m. Carole Winokur, Oct. 16, 1988. BA, Temple U., 1951. Rsch. analyst Benson & Benson, Princeton, N.J., 1956-56; pres. Opinion Rsch. Corp., ORC Caravan Surveys, Princeton, 1956-69; v.p. Response Analysis Corp., Princeton, 1969-70; pres. Total Rsch. Inc., Princeton, 1970-75; pres. Total Rsch. Corp., Princeton, 1975-86, pres., chief exec. officer, 1986-93, chmn., chief exec. officer, 1993—. Mem. Am. Mktg. Assn. (chmn. standards and practices com. 1973-74), Coun. Am. Survey Rsch. Orgns., Am. Assn. Pub. Opinion Rsch., Am. Contract Bridge League, Princeton Community Players, Villagers Barn Theatre. Jewish. Avocations: theatre, softball, tennis, ping pong, bridge. Home: 7F Marten Rd Princeton NJ 08540-1634 Office: Total Rsch Corp Princeton Corp Ctr 5 Independence Way Princeton NJ 08543-5305

ZITNAY, GEORGE ALBERT, foundation executive; b. Stratford, Conn., Nov. 7, 1938; s. John George and Mary Ann (Mitchell) Z.; m. Lorraine Helen Aldino, Aug. 27, 1960; children: Kevin C. Christopher G. Student, U. Conn., 1956-58; BS, So. Conn. State U., 1961, MS, 1974; PhD, Columbia Pacific U., 1989. Dir. in-svc. tng., dir. social svcs., edn. and tng. New Haven Regional Ctr., 1965-67; supt. Ctrl. Conn. Regional Ctr., Meriden, 1967-73; asst. prof. child psychiatry, dir. Univ. Med. Sch., Ctr. for Exceptional Children, Boston, 1973-75; supt., CEO Pineland Ctr., Pownal, Maine, 1975-76, 79-84; commr. Dept. Mental Health and Corrections, State of Maine, Augusta, 1976-79; ct. monitor State of W.Va., Charleston, 1983-84; asst. commr. for mental retardation Dept. Mental Health, Boston, 1984-85; exec. dir. The Joseph P. Kennedy Jr. Found., Washington, 1985-90; pres., CEO The Nat. Head Injury Found., Washington, 1990—; mem., chmn. Nat. Ctr. for Med. and Rsch., Nat. Inst. Child Health and Devel./NIH, liaison from NCMRR to devel. coun., adv. coun., 1992—; chmn. Nat. Coalition or Rsch. in Neurol. Disorders; mem. neurology panel Social Security Adminstrn.; mem. Found. for Brain Rsch.; tchr., camp dir. and asst. prin. various programs throughout Conn., 1961-65; faculty Grad. Sch. Spl. Edn., So. Conn. State U., New Haven, Lesley Coll., Cambridge, Mass.; asst. prof. dept. child psychiatry Boston U. Med. Sch.; asst. prof. dept. human svcs. U. Maine, Portland; faculty bioethics Georgetown U., Washington; faculty values edn. Summer Inst., U. Colo.; course dir. values edn. U. Va. Sch. Edn.; lectr. in field. Author: The Creation of a Community Setting, Perspectives on Neuropsychological rehabilitation; contbr. articles to profl. jours. Mem. Com. on Aging, Alexandria, Va., 1994-95; mem. Consortium for Citizens with Disabilities, Washington, Spl. Olympics, United Way, Best Buddies, Washington; bd. dirs. Project CHOICE; bd.t. chmn. theol. edn. com. Christ Ch., Alexandria, Va. Recipient Peter W. Townsend Meml. award Am. Assn. on Mental Deficiency/Maine Assn. for Retarded Citizens. Mem. Am. Soc. Assn. Execs., Am. Assn. on Mental Retardation (mem. awards and nomination coms., former nat. counselor regional X), Very Spl. Arts Internat., Coun. on Founds., Nat. Assn. Supts. of Pub. Residential Facilities, Nat. Assn. State Mental Health Dirs., Nat. Assn. State Mental Retardation Program Dirs. Episcopalian. Avocations: gardening, tennis, golf. Home: 400 Madison St #1301 Alexandria VA 22314 Office: National Head Injury Found Ste 100 1776 Massachusets Ave NW Washington DC 20036

ZITO, JAMES ANTHONY, retired railroad company executive; b. Oak Park, Ill., Feb. 5, 1931; s. Bruno and Concetta (Kalasardo) Z.; m. Mary B. De Stasio, July 9, 1983; children: Antony, Antonia. Student, Elmhurst Coll., 1956-57; sr. exec. program, Stanford U., 1981. Sr. v.p. ops. Chgo. & North Western Transp. Co., 1976-90, also bd. dirs.; former chmn. A.A.R. Op. Transp. Co.; pres. Z&B Inc., Campbell St. R.E. Corp. With USCG, 1951-53. Mem. St. Charles Country Club, KC. Home: 1655 Persimmon Dr Saint Charles IL 60174-1328

ZITO, MICHAEL STEVEN, protective services official; b. New Orleans, Oct. 4, 1957. AAS in Fire Protection Tech., Delgado Community Coll., 1993. Emergency med. tech. intermediate/neonatal tech. East Jefferson Gen. Hosp., 1978—; police officer Jefferson Parish Police Dept., 1979-90; firefighter Kenner (La.) Fire Dept., 1979—, fire chief; firefighter instr. Jefferson Parish Fire Acad., 1982-87; pub. info. and edn. officer Kenner Fire Dept., 1985-93; instr. Delgado Community Coll., 1992-93. Producer, dir., host. (TV show) Kenner Fire Report, 1984-88. Named one of Outstanding Young Persons in U Jaycees, 1990; recipient Outstanding Svc. award VFW, 1991, Fgn. Legion, 1992. Roman Catholic. Home: 6 S Lafourche Ct Kenner LA 70065-3930 Office: Kenner Fire Dept 1801 Williams Blvd Kenner LA 70062-6261

ZITRIN, ARTHUR, physician; b. Bklyn., Apr. 10, 1918; s. William and Lillian (Elbaum) Z.; m. Charlotte Marker, Oct. 4, 1942; children—Richard Alan, Elizabeth Ann. B.S., City Coll. N.Y., 1938; M.S., N.Y. U., 1941, M.D., 1945; certificate psychoanalytic medicine, Columbia, 1955. Diplomate: Am. Bd. Psychiatry and Neurology. Research fellow animal behavior Am. Museum Natural History, 1939-42; intern King County Hosp., 1945-46; resident psychiatry Bellevue Hosp., 1948-51; instr. physiology Hunter Coll., N.Y.C., 1948-49; mem. faculty N.Y.U. Sch. Medicine, 1949—, professor psychiatry, 1967—; mem. staff Bellevue Hosp., N.Y.C., 1951—; dir. psychiatry Bellevue Hosp., 1955-68, N.Y.C. Dept. Hosps., 1962- 64; pvt. practice, 1949—; attending psychiatrist Univ. Hosp., N.Y.C.; cons. psychiatrist Manhattan Va Hosp. Author papers in field. Served to capt. M.C. AUS, 1946- 48. Fellow Am. Psychiat. Assn. (life), N.Y. Acad. Medicine; mem. AMA, N.Y. Soc. Clin. Psychiatry (pres. 1966- 67), Am. Psychoanalytic Assn. (life), Sigma Xi, Alpha Omega Alpha. Home: 56 Ruxton Rd Great Neck NY 11023-1529 Office: 550 1st Ave New York NY 10016-6402

ZIVARI, BASHIR, architect, industrial designer; b. Bklyn., Aug. 13, 1961; s. Farajollah and Ingeborg Elfriede (Brügmann) Z.; m. Pamela Lorraine Ray, Feb. 17, 1990. M Indsl. Design with distinction, Pratt Inst., 1991, BArch, 1984. Registered architect, N.Y. With Russo & Sonder Architects, N.Y.C., 1984-88; prt. practice architecture, N.Y.C., 1988; asst. designer Lee Harris Pomeroy Architects, N.Y.C., 1988-91; project mgr. The Phillips Janson Group Architects, N.Y.C., 1991—. Designs in permanent collections of Mus. Modern Art, N.Y.C., Cooper-Hewitt Mus., N.Y.C., patentee for modular stool. Recipient 2d place Shaw-Walker furniture competition, 1987; Roscoe awards for outstanding achievement in product design Interior Design mag., 1993, best of category award for children's furniture, 1993; gold award for consumer product Businesswed mag. and Indsl. Design Soc. Am., 1994. Mem. Baha'i Faith. Avocation: squash. Home: 309 Carroll St Brooklyn NY 11231

ZIVLEY, WALTER PERRY, lawyer; b. Mineral Wells, Tex., Aug. 5, 1931; s. Walter Perry Sr. and Jane (Beeler) Z.; m. Nancy Campbell, Feb. 5, 1955; children: Bruce, Claire Zivley Baker, Lisa Zivley Trujillo, Walter Perry Jr. BBA, So. Meth. U., 1953, LLB, 1955. Bar: Tex. 1955, U.S. Dist. Ct. (so. and ea. dists.) Tex., U.S. Ct. Appeals (5th cir.), U.S. Tax Ct., U.S. Supreme Ct. Assoc. Hutcheson, Taliafeno and Harman, Houston, 1955-62, ptnr.; 1962; ptnr. Liddell, Sapp, Zivley, Hill and LaBoon L.L.P., Houston, 1963—; bd. dirs. Tex. Commerce Bank W. Ctrl., Houston. Pres. Open Door Mission Found., Inc., Houston, 1992. Fellow Am. Coll. Trust and Estate Coun.; mem. ABA, State Bar Tex. (real estate probate and trust sect., chmn. 1975-76), Houston Bar Assn. Republican. Presbyterian. Avocations: hunting, tennis, golf. Office: Liddel Sapp Zivley Hill and LaBoon LLP 3400 Tex Commerce Towers Houston TX 77002

ZIZIC, THOMAS MICHAEL, physician, educator; b. Milw., Dec. 9, 1939; s. Michael Mitchell Zizic and Dorothy (Batas) Ciric; m. Karen Owens, June 15, 1962 (div. Sept. 1967); m. Martha Ann Ardos, Nov. 22, 1967; children: Lara Ann, Kristine Michelle. BS, U. Wis., 1961; MD, Johns Hopkins U., 1965. Intern Johns Hopkins Hosp., Balt., 1965-66, asst. resident, 1966-67, fellow in internal medicine, 1969-71, instr. dept. medicine, 1971-73, asst. prof. medicine, 1971-81, assoc. prof. medicine, 1981—; pvt. practice, Balt., 1988—; co-dir. Chesapeake Osteoporosis Ctr., Balt., 1988—; cons. in field. Contbr. numerous articles and abstracts to profl. jours. V.p Md. chpt. Arthritis Found., Balt., 1976-77; chmn. Md. Commn. on Arthritis and Related Diseases, 1986-90. Fellow Am. Coll. Rheumatology, 1986; Md. Soc. Rheumatic Diseases (pres. 1975-76), D.C. Rheumatism Assn., Balt. City Med. Soc., Johns Hopkins Hosp. Med. Soc., Arthritis Found. (fellow 1971-73, v.p. 1976-77, med. and sci. com. 1977-79, chmn. profl. edn. com. 1977-78, govtl. affairs com. 1979-83), Phi Beta Kappa, Phi Kappa Phi, Phi Eta Sigma. Avocations: skiing, tennis. Office: 5601 Loch Raven Blvd Baltimore MD 21237

ZIZZA, SALVATORE J., diversified company executive; b. Francofonte, Italy, Nov. 19, 1945; came to U.S., 1954; s. Carmelo and Gregoria (Mazzarino) Z.; m. Deborah Ann Bright, Sept. 24, 1983; children: Robert Carl, Gregory Thomas. B.A. in Polit. Sci., St. John's U., 1967, M.B.A., 1972. Asst. mgr. Chem. Bank, N.Y.C., 1967-71; asst. sec. Am. Bank & Trust Co., N.Y.C., 1972-73; pres. Mortgagee Affiliates, N.Y.C., 1973-78; owner, pres. Zizza & Co. Ltd., N.Y.C., 1978—; pres., chief operating officer, dir. Nico, Inc., N.Y.C., 1978—, LVI Group, Inc., N.Y.C., 1985—; dir. Gabelli, Equity-Growth-Asset Funds, Stanley Interiors Corp. First v.p., bd. govs. Columbus Citizens Com., N.Y.C., 1980; bd. dirs. Nat. Italian Am. Found., Washington, 1986. Mem. Young Mortgage Bankers Assn., Real Estate Bd. of N.Y., Young Pres. Orgn. Roman Catholic. Avocations: skiing; tennis; reading.

ZIZZO, ALICIA, concert pianist; b. N.Y.C., Apr. 2, 1945; d. Spiro and Christine (Corda) Theodoratos; m. Thomas Edward Zizzo; children: Peter, Claudia. BA, Hofstra U., 1965; postgrad., C.W. Post U., 1975, L.I. U., 1976, Mannes Coll. Music. performed Eastern Europe; lectr. in field. Debut as concert pianist N.Y.C.; performed in major concert halls throughout Europe, named as one of the great Am. pianists in the world; one of few Am. artists invited to perform by Ea. Bloc countries Europe; discovered lost manuscripts of George Gershwin's classical music; first pianist to record George Gershwin's Rhapsody in Blue and Concerto in "F" from original manuscripts; recorded reconstructed fragments of lost George Gershwin manuscripts of Lullaby and original piano score of his opera Blue Monday; created first authentic version of Preludes and Rhapsody in Blue; feature artist for Jaguar in Concert Series, Vienna and other major internat. concert series and symphony orchs.; recordings for Pro-Arte Records, Fanfare Records, Mastersound Records; music published by Warner Bros. Publs; recordings include Virtuoso Piano Fantasies-Works by Chopin, Debussy et. al. Home: PO Box 294 Glen Head NY 11545 Office: Jeffrey James Arts Consulting 316 Pacific St Massapequa Park NY 11762 Office: c/o Allegro Imports 12630 NE Mary St Portland OR 97230-1059*

ZLATKIS, ALBERT, chemistry educator; b. Pomorzany, Poland, Mar. 27, 1924; came to Can. 1927, U.S., 1949, naturalized, 1959; s. Louis and Zisel (Nable) Z.; m. Esther Shessel, June 15, 1947; children: Lori, Robert, Debra. B.A.Sc., U. Toronto, 1947, M.A.Sc., 1948; Ph.D., Wayne State U., 1952. Rsch. chemist Shell Oil Co., Houston, 1953-55; asst. prof. chemistry U. Houston, 1955-58, assoc. prof., 1958-63, chmn. chemistry dept., 1958-62, prof. chemistry, 1963—; adj. prof. chemistry Baylor Coll. Medicine, 1975—; tour speaker Am. Chem. Soc., 1961, 63, 66, South Africa Chem. Inst., 1971, USSR Acad. Scis., 1973, Polish Acad. Scis., 1977; chmn. Internat. Symposium on Advances in Chromatography, 1963—. Author: Practice of Gas Chromatography, 1967, Preparative Gas Chromatography, 1971, Advances in Chromatography, 25 vols., 1963-88, A Concise Introduction to Organic Chemistry, 1973, High Performance Thin-Layer Chromatography, 1977, 75 Years of Chromatography—A Historical Dialogue, 1979, Instrumental HPTLC, 1980, Electron Capture—Theory and Practice in Chromatography, 1981; contbr. articles to profl. jours.; mem. editorial bd. Jour. High Resolution Chromatography, Jour. Chromatographic Science, Chromatographia, Jour. Chromatography. Recipient award of Yr. award Dallas Soc. Analytical Chemistry, 1977, Tswett Meml. medal USSR Acad. Scis., 1980, Tswett Chromatography medal, 1983, NASA Tech. award, 1975, 80, NASA Patent award, 1978, Disting. Tex. Scientist award Tex. Acad. Sci., 1985, James L. Waters Pioneers in Devel. Analytical Instrumentation award, 1990; grantee USPHS, 1966, NASA, 1964-76, Welch Found., 1969, AEC, 1967, NSF, 1978, EPA, 1979, U.S. Army Rsch. Office, 1982, Gulf Coast Hazardous Substance Rsch. Ctr., 1989, Tex. Advanced Rsch. Program, 1991. Mem. Am. Chem. Soc. (chmn. S.E. Tex. sect. 1964, award in chromatography 1973, S.W. regional award 1988), Groupement pour l'Avancement des Méthodes Spectrographiques (France), Sigma Xi, Phi Lambda Upsilon. Home: 22 Sandalwood Dr Houston TX 77024-7122

ZLATOFF-MIRSKY, EVERETT IGOR, violinist; b. Evanston, Ill., Dec. 29, 1937; s. Alexander Igor and Evelyn Ola (Hill) Z.-M.; m. Janet Dalbey, Jan. 28, 1976; children from previous marriage—Tania, Laura. B.Mus., Chgo. Mus. Coll., Roosevelt U., 1960; M.Mus., Roosevelt U., 1961. Mem. faculty dept. music Roosevelt U., Chgo., 1961-66; founding mem., violinist, violist Music of the Baroque, 1971—. Violinist orch. Lyric Opera of Chgo., 1974—; concert master, personnel mgr., 1974—, violinist, violist, Contemproary Chamber Playsers U. Chgo., 1964-82, solo violinist, Bach Soc., 1966-83; violist, violinist, Lexington String Quartet, 1966-81; founding mem., violinist, violist Music of the Baroque, 1971—; rec. artist numerous recs., radio-TV and films; solo violinist appearing throughout U.S. Recipient Olive Ditson award Franklin Honor Soc., 1961. Mem. Nat. Acad. Rec. Arts and Scis. Republican. Roman Catholic. Home: 41 W 743 Hughes Rd Elburn IL 60119 Office: Lyric Opera Chgo 20 N Wacker Dr Chicago IL 60606-2806

ZLATOPER, RONALD JOSEPH, career officer; b. Cleve., Mar. 21, 1942; s. Joseph M. and Ann Rose (Bayda) Z.; m. Barry Lane Oliver, Aug. 8, 1970; children: Ashley D., Michael J. BS in Math., Rensselaer Poly. Inst., 1963; MSA, George Washington U., 1970; MS in Mgmt., MIT, 1975. Commd. ensign USN, 1963, advanced through grades to vice adm., 1991; disting. grad. Naval War Coll., Newport, R.I., 1973; program coord. Office of Chief of Naval Ops., Washington, 1975-77; comdg. officer Attack Squadron 85, Naval Air Sta., Oceana, Va., 1978-81; exec. asst. Office of Program Appraisal, Sec. of Navy, Washington, 1981-82; comdr. Airwing One on USS America, Norfolk, Va., and Indian Ocean, 1982-83; mil. asst. to Sec. Def. Office of Sec. Def., Washington, 1983-85; Airwing comdr. Carrier Airwing 15, San Diego and Indian Ocean, 1986-87; chief of staff U.S. 7th Fleet, Yokosuka, Japan, 1987-88; dir. distbn. Naval Mil. Pers. Command, Washington, 1988-90; comdr. Carrier Group 7, San Diego and Persian Gulf, 1990-91; chief of naval pers. Bur. Pers., Washington, 1991—. Contbr. articles on naval strategy to profl. jours. Bd. dirs. Ptnrs. in Edn., Navy Pers. Command, Washington, 1988-90, Armed Forces Retirement Home, Washington, 1991—, Navy Marine Corps Relief Soc., Washington, 1991—; vol. So. Others Might Eat, Washington, 1988-90; nominating chair U.S. Naval Inst., 1993—. Decorated D.F.C., D.S.M., Legion of Merit with two oak leaf clusters, Meritorious Svc. medal. Mem. Assn. Naval Aviation, Naval Inst., Pi Kappa Phi (treas. 1963). Roman Catholic. Avocations: reading, running, scuba, skiing, tennis. Home: 3701 Nebraska Ave NW Washington DC 20016-2727 Office: Navy Dept 2 Navy Anx Washington DC 20370-0002

ZLOCH, WILLIAM J., federal judge; b. 1944. BA, U. Notre Dame, 1966, JD, 1974. Assoc. Saunders, Curtis, Ginestra & Gore, Ft. Lauderdale, Fla., 1974-75, Kelley, Tompkins, Frazier & Kelley, Ft. Lauderdale, 1975-81; Patterson & Maloney, Ft. Lauderdale, 1981-85; judge U.S. Dist. Ct. (so. dist.) Fla., Ft. Lauderdale, 1985—. Served to lt. USN, 1967-69. Recipient Disting. Am. award Nat. Football Found., 1987. Mem. Fla. Bar Assn. (various coms., Pres.'s Pro Bono award 1985), Broward County Bar Assn. (various coms., Pres.'s award 1982-83). Office: US Dist Ct 299 E Broward Blvd Fort Lauderdale FL 33301-1944

ZLOWE, FLORENCE MARKOWITZ, artist; b. Allentown, Pa.; d. Morris and Anna (Mandel) Markowitz; m. Irwin Zlowe, May 1, 1936. Student, Pa Mus. Coll. Art, Phila., 1929-33; fine arts courses, NYU, 1950-53. One woman show, Charles Z. Mann Gallery, N.Y.C., 1968, Community Gallery, N.Y.C., 1978; exhibited in group shows, Nat. Acad. Riverside Mus., N.Y., Nat. Arts Club, Pen and Brush Club, Lever House, Jersey City Mus., Norfolk (Va.) Mus., Fort Lauderdale (Fla.) Mus., Joe and Emily Lowe Mus., Fla.; represented in permanent collections, Norfolk Mus., Fort Lauderdale Mus., Joe and Emily Lowe Mus., Wilson Pub. Co., N.Y.C., Phila. Mus. Art, Butler Inst. Am. Art, Minn. Mus. Art, St. Paul, Cooper-Hewitt Mus. Design, Smithsonian Instn., N.Y.C., Tweed Mus., Duluth, Minn., Evansville (Ind.) Mus., Lakeview (Ill.) Center Arts and Scis., Ga. Mus. Art, Athens, Slater Meml. Mus., Norwich, Conn. Mem. Am. Soc. Contemporary Artists (dir., treas.), N.J. Soc. Painters and Sculptors, Nat. Assn. Women Artists (1st prize ann. 1958, 12 additional awards for oils 1958-84), League Present

Day Artists, Artists Equity Assn. N.Y. Home: 440 E 57th St New York NY 10022-3045 Studio: 41 Union Sq W New York NY 10003-3208

ZMUDA, SHARON LOUISE, construction executive; b. Chgo., May 31, 1942; d. Theodore Edward and Virginia (Fleig) Z. Student, Sch. Art Inst. Chgo., 1961-62; BA, Mundelein Coll., Chgo., 1964. In student services dept. La Salle Extension U., Chgo., 1965-69; sales coordinator S.K. Smith Co., Chgo., 1969-71; customer service specialist Am. Express Co., Chgo., 1971-73; office mgr. North Shore Cement, Inc., Chgo., 1975-84; pres. Abacor Rd. Constrn., Inc., Chgo., 1984—; program host, Consumers' Counter, CRIS Radio, 1983—. Fundraiser Sch. Art Inst. of Chgo. 1987—. Mem. Women's Bus. Devel. Ctr., Nat. Assn. Women in Constrn. Roman Catholic. Avocations: interior decorating, catering, collecting. Home and Office: Abacor Rd Constrn Inc 3137 N Davlin Ct Chicago IL 60618-6508

ZOBACK, MARK DAVID, geophysicist, educator; b. N.Y.C., Apr. 13, 1948; s. Larry and Minnie (Greenberg) Z.; m. Mary Lou Chetlain, Sept. 15, 1973; children: Eli Matthew, Megan Lacey. BS, U. Ariz., 1969; MS, Stanford U., 1973, PhD, 1975. Geophysicist Amoco Prodn. Co., Ft. Worth, Tex., 1969-71; rsch. geophysicist U.S. Geol. Survey, Menlo Park, Calif., 1975-84; prof. geophysics Stanford (Calif.) U., 1984—, chair dept., 1992—; chair coord. com. Continental Sci. Drilling, 1990—; cons. in field. Editor 4 books; patentee in field; contbr. articles to profl. jours. Postdoctoral fellow Nat. Rsch. Coun., 1975; recipient Sr. Sci. award von Humboldt Found., 1991. Fellow AAAS, Geol. Soc. Am.; mem. Am. Geophys. Union (pres. technodnophysics sect. 1989-90). Home: 716 Garland Dr Palo Alto CA 94303-3603 Office: Stanford U Dept Geophysics Mitchell Bldg Stanford CA 94305

ZOBEL, DONALD BRUCE, botany educator; b. Salinas, Calif., July 17, 1942; s. Bruce John and Barbara June (Lemon) Z.; m. Priscilla Fay Matthews, July 9, 1966; children: Cheryl, Gregory. BS, N.C. State U., 1964; MA, Duke U., 1966, PhD, 1968. Asst. prof. Oreg. State U., Corvallis, 1968-74, assoc. prof., 1974-82, prof., 1982—; vis. rsch. Taiwan Forestry Rsch. Inst., Taipei, 1976-77; Fulbright lectr. Tribhuvan U., Kathmandu, Nepal, 1984-85; Indo-Am. fellow, Kumaun U., NainiTal, India, 1991. Author: Ecology, Pathology and Management of Port-Orford-cedar (Chamaecyparis lawsoniana), 1985, A Practical Manual for Ecology, 1987; contbr. articles to profl. jours. Grantee NSF, 1974-77, 80-84, 94—. Mem. AAAS, Ecol. Soc. Am., NW Sci. Assn. (trustee 1980-83), Internat. Assn. for Ecology, Brit. Ecol. Soc. Republican. Mem. Christian Ch. Home: 2310 NE Seavy Cir Corvallis OR 97330-4231 Office: Oreg State U Dept Botany & Plant Pathol Cordley Hall # 2082 Corvallis OR 97331-2902

ZOBEL, HILLER BELLIN, judge; b. N.Y.C., Feb. 23, 1932; s. Hiller and Harriet Selma (Bellin) Z.; m. Deborah Bethell, June 21, 1958; children—John H., David H., Elizabeth T., Sarah B.; m. Rya S. Weickert, Nov. 23, 1973. B.A. cum laude, Harvard U., 1953, LL.B., 1959; postgrad., Oxford U., 1956. Bar: Mass. 1959, U.S. Ct. Appeals 1960, U.S. Dist. Ct. 1960, U.S. Supreme Ct. 1966. Assoc. firm Bingham, Dana & Gould, Boston, 1959-67; research assoc. Harvard U., 1962-63; assoc. prof. Boston Coll. Law Sch., 1967-69, prof., 1969-79; assoc. counsel firm Hill & Barlow, Boston, 1971-72; partner, counsel firm Brown, Rudnick, Freed & Gesmer, Boston, 1972-79; assoc. justice Mass. Superior Ct., 1979—; reporter Mass. Advisory Com. on Rules of Civil Procedure; spl. asst. atty. gen. Commonwealth of Mass.; spl. counsel Mass. Dept. Pub. Utilities. Author: The Boston Massacre, 1970, (with J.W. Smith) Massachusetts Rules of Practice, 1974-81, (with S.N. Rous) Doctors and the Law, 1993; editor: (with L.K. Wroth) Legal Papers of John Adams, 1965; contbr. articles to profl. jours. Served with U.S. Navy, 1953-55. Recipient Am. Hist. Assn. Littleton-Griswold prize, 1966. Fellow Soc. Am. Historians; mem. Am. Law Inst., Mass. Hist. Soc., Colonial Soc. Mass., Am. Antiquarian Soc., Mass. Bar Assn., Boston Bar Assn., Maritime Law Assn. U.S., Am. Soc. Legal History (v.p. 1970-71), Nat. Conf. State Trial Judges (exec. com. 1990-93). Democrat. Jewish. Office: Superior Ct Boston MA 02108

ZOBEL, LOUISE PURWIN, author, educator, lecturer, writing consultant; b. Laredo, Tex., Jan. 10, 1922; d. Leo Max and Ethel Catherine (Levy) Purwin; m. Jerome Fremont Zobel, Nov. 14, 1943; children: Lenore Zobel Harris, Janice A., Eunder E. Audrey Zobel Dollinger. BA cum laude, Stanford U., 1943, MA, 1976. Cert. adult edn. and community coll. tchr., Calif. Freelance mag. writer and author Palo Alto, Calif., 1942—; writer, editor, broadcaster UP Bur., San Francisco, 1943; lectr. on writing, history, travel No. Calif., 1964—; lectr.. educator U. Calif. campuses, other colls. and univs., 1969—; writing cons. to pvt. clients, 1969—; editorial asst. Assn. Coll. Unions Internat., Palo Alto, 1972-73; acting asst. prof. journalism San Jose State U., 1976; keynote speaker, seminar leader, prin. speaker at nat. confs. Author: (books) The Travel Writer's Handbook, 1980, (paperback), 1982, 83, 84, 85, rev. edit., 1992; narrator (90 minute cassette) Let's Have Fun in Japan, 1982; contbr. articles to anthologies, nat. mags. and newspapers; writer advertorials. Bd. dirs., publicity chair Friends of Palo Alto Libr., 1985—; officer Santa Clara County Med. Aux., Esther Clark Aux., others; past pres. PTA. Recipient award for excellence in journalism Sigma Delta Chi, 1943, awards Writers Digest, 1967-75, 94, Armed Forces Writers League, 1972, Nat. Writers Club, 1976. Mem. Am. Soc. Journalists and Authors, Travel Journalists Guild, Internat. Food, Wine and Travel Writers Assn., Pacific Asia Travel Assn., Calif. Writers Club (v.p. 1988-89), AAUW (v.p. 1955-57, Nat. writing award 1969), Stanford Alumni Assn., Phi Beta Kappa. Avocations: travel, reading, writing, photography. Home and Office: 23350 Sereno Ct Unit 30 Cupertino CA 95014-6543

ZOBEL, ROBERT LEONARD, state government official; b. Reedsburg, Wis., July 28, 1935; s. Leonard Walter and Kathryn Jennifer (Cleveland) Z.; m. Faith Minnie Weatherwax, Aug. 5, 1961; children: Karl, Paul, Mary. BS in Fin., U. N.D. 1961. Investment banker Loewi & Co., Milw., 1961-65; bank examiner State of Wis., Madison, 1965-68, dir. investment bd., 1968—; mem. adv. bd. Merrill Lynch Capital, N.Y.C., Madison Fund, Boston, Zell/Chillmack, Chgo., Hancock Internat., Boston, Horizon Ptnrs., Milw.; mem. stockholder rep. bd. Burdick, Milton/Madison, A.C. Equipment, Milw.; bd. dirs. Trak Internat., Port Washington, Pa Vera, Madison; presenter nat. and internat. profit. assns., seminars, others. Mem. owners' com. Olympia Resort, Oconomowoc, Wis.; coach youth soccer, baseball and basketball orgns.; lay min. area United Meth. Ch.; participant mission projects, including ch. bldg., Vulcain, Costa Rica, Rio Claro, Costa Rica, Prince Town, Trinidad, Portsmouth, Dominica, hosp. and sch. rehab., Bo, Sierra Leone, Maua, Kenya, Santa Cruz, Bolivia, Cochabamba, Bolivia; vol. Salvation Army. With USN, 1956-58. Mem. Elks. Avocations: mission work, golf, tennis, reading, public speaking. Home: 5312 Healy Ln Monona WI 53716-2519 Office: Wis Investment Bd 121 E Wilson St Madison WI 53703-3455

ZOBEL, RYA WEICKERT, federal judge; b. Germany, Dec. 18, 1931. A.B., Radcliffe Coll., 1953; LL.B., Harvard U., 1956. Bar: Mass. 1956, U.S. Dist. Ct., Mass., 1956, U.S. Ct. Appeals (1st cir.) 1967. Assoc. Hill & Barlow, Boston, 1967-73; assoc. Goodwin, Procter & Hoar, Boston, 1973-76, ptnr., 1976-79; U.S. dist. judge of Mass. Boston, 1979—. Mem. ABA, Boston Bar Assn., Am. Bar Found.; Mass. Bar Assn., Am. Law Inst. Home: 294 Jerusalem Rd Cohasset MA 02025 Office: US Dist Ct John W McCormack PO & Courthouse 90 Devonshire St Rm 1802 Boston MA 02109

ZOBELL, GREGORY GRANT, hospital administrator; b. Billings, Mont., Jan. 29, 1950; s. Rex Scholes and Bernice (Gunnell) Z.; m. Suzanne Taylor, Apr. 19, 1975; children: Gregory Grant Jr., Jeff, Natalie, Stephanie, Joshua. BS, Brigham Young U., 1975; MS, Trinity U., San Antonio, 1979. CEO, Kino Cmty. Hosp., Tucson, 1990-92; assoc. adminstr. Good Samaritan Hosp., Phoenix, 1980-89, 93—. Fellow Am. Coll. Healthcare Execs. Mem. LDS Ch. Home: 1704 E Enrose St Mesa AZ 85203 Office: Good Samaritan Reg Med Ctr 1111 E McDowell Rd Phoenix AZ 85006

ZOBELL, KARL, lawyer; b. La Jolla, Calif., Jan. 9, 1932; s. Claude E. and Margaret (Harding) ZoB.; m. Barbara Arth, Nov. 22, 1968; children: Bonnie, Elizabeth, Karen, Claude, Mary. Student, Utah State U., 1949-51, Columbia U., 1951-52; AB, Columbia U., 1953, student of law, 1952-54; JD, Stanford U., 1958. Bar: Calif., 1959. Assoc., lawyer Gray, Cary, Ames and Frye, San Diego, 1959-64, ptnr., lawyer, 1964—, chmn., 1989-90; dir., officer San Diego Digital Multimedia Assn., San Diego, 1994; bd. dirs., founder La Jolla

(Calif.) Bank and Trust Co.; v.p. bd. dirs. Geisel-Seuss Enterprises, Inc. Trustee La Jolla Town Coun., 1962-87, chmn. bd. trustees, 1967-68, pres. 1976-77, 80-81, v.p., 1986-87; trustee La Jollans Inc., 1964-80, founder, 1964, pres. 1965-68, 73-76, 78-79, Dr. Seuss Found., 1992—; James C. Copley Charitable Found., 1992—; mem. charter rev. com. City San Diego, 1968, 73; chmn. City of San Diego Planning Commn., 1988-93; trustee La Jolla Mus. Art, 1964-72, San Diego Mus. Contemporary Art, 1990-92; pres. 1967-70, bd. dirs Scripps Meml. Hosp. Found., 1980-84, bd. overseers, Stanford Law Sch., 1977-80, U. Calif., San Diego, 1974-76. Served to lt. USCG, 1954-57. Fellow Am. Coll. Trust and Estate Counsel; mem. ABA, Calif. Bar, La Jolla Beach and Volleyball Club (pres. 1982—), La Jolla Beach and Tennis Club, Lambda Alpha. Republican. Home: Po Box 1 1555 Coast Walk La Jolla CA 92037-3731 Office: Gray Cary Ames & Frye 1200 Prospect St Ste 575 La Jolla CA 92037-3645

ZOBER, NORMAN ALAN, health facility administrator; b. Pitts., Mar. 20, 1943; married. B. U. Iowa, 1965; M, Trinity U., 1969. Adminstrv. resident Albany (N.Y.) Med. Ctr. Hosp., 1969-70; asst. adminstr. Arnot-Ogden Meml. Hosp., Elmira, N.Y., 1970-74; administr. Rancocas Valley Hosp., Willingboro, N.J., 1974-76; regional dir. Am. Medicorp, Inc., Ft. Lauderdale, Fla., 1976-78; v.p. Psychiat. Inst. of Washington, 1978-80, sr. v.p. ops., 1980-83, exec. v.p. hosp. ops., 1983-84, CEO, 1984-92; pres. hosp. divsn. Nat. Med. Enterprises, Washington, 1992-93; pres. Medical Rehab., Milw., 1993—. Home: 5809 Nicholson Ln Apt 1603 North Bethesda MD 20852 Office: Med Rehab 1516 W Mequon Rd Milwaukee WI 53092

ZOBRIST, BENEDICT KARL, library director, historian; b. Moline, Ill., Aug. 21, 1921; s. Benedict and Lila Agnas (Colson) Z.; m. Donna Mae Anderson, Oct. 23, 1948; children: Benedict Karl II, Markham Lee, Erik Christian. AB, Augustana Coll., Rock Island, Ill., 1946; postgrad., Stanford U., 1946-47; MA, Northwestern U., 1948, PhD, 1953; postgrad., U. Ill., 1961, Tunghai U., Taiwan, 1962, Columbia U., 1962-63, Fed. Exec. Inst., Charlottesville, Va., 1974, Hebrew U., Israel, 1978; LHD, Avila Coll., 1995. Manuscript specialist in recent Am. history Library of Congress, Washington, 1952-53; asst. reference librarian Newberry Library, Chgo., 1953-54; command historian Ordnance Weapons Command, Rock Island Arsenal, 1954-60; prof. history, chmn. dept. Augustana Coll., 1960-69, asst. dean faculty, 1964-69, asso. dean, dir. grad. studies, 1969; asst. dir. Harry S. Truman Libr., Independence, Mo., 1969-71; dir. Harry S. Truman Libr. 1971-94; exec. sec. Harry S. Truman Libr. Inst., Independence, 1971-94; mem. steering com. Harry S. Truman Statue Com., Independence, 1973-76; dir., regent Harry S. Truman Good Neighbor Award Found., 1974—; mem. Independence Truman Award Commn., 1975-94, Mo. Hist. Records Adv. Bd., 1978—; adj. prof. history U. Mo.-Kansas City, 1975—, Ottawa U., Kansas City, 1977-94, U. Mo. St. Louis, 1987-94; chmn. Independence Commn. Bicentennial of U.S. Constitution, 1987, Uptown Independence, Inc., 1989-94; mem. adv. coun. Truman Little White House State Historic Site, Key West, Fla., 1987-94. Contbr. articles, revs. to profl. jours. Trustee Heritage League of Greater Kansas City, 1981—, Liberty Meml. Assn., Kansas City, Mo., 1990—, Black Archives Mid-Am., Inc., Kansas City, 1992-94; mem. Truman Nat. Centennial Com., 1982-84. Served with AUS, 1942-46. Recipient Outstanding Alumni Achievement award Augustana Coll., 1975, Bronze Good Citizenship medal Kans. SAR, 1986, People's Choice award Independence (Mo.) Neighborhood Councils, 1987, Mid-Am. Regional Council award for contbns. to met. community, 1987, Citizen Achievement award Black Archives of Mid-Am., 1988, Silver Good Citizenship medal Mo. SAR, 1988, Special Recognition award City of Independence, 1988, Outstanding Civic Leader in Independence, 1989, Gold Medal of Honor DAR, 1990, Spl. Commendation award Nat. Park Svc., 1993; named World Citizen of Yr. by Kans. City Mayor's UN Day Com., 1994. Mem. AAUP, Am. Hist. Assn., Jackson County (Mo.) Hist. Soc. (v.p. 1972-82, 93-95), Orgn. Am. Historians, Assn. Asian Studies, Am. Assn. State, Local History, Soc. Am. Archivists, U.S. Power Squadron, Am. Legion, La Societe des 40 Hommes et 8 Chevaux, VFW. Home: 71B T St Lake Lotawana MO 64086

ZOBRIST, GEORGE WINSTON, computer scientist, educator; b. Highland, Ill., Feb. 13, 1934; s. George H. and Lillie C. (Augustine) Z.; m. Freida Groverlyn Rich, Mar. 29, 1955; children: Barbara Jayne, George William, Jean Anne. B.S., U. Mo., 1958, Ph.D., 1965; M.S., Wichita State U., 1961. Registered profl. engr., Mo., Fla. Electronic scientist U.S. Naval Ordnance Test Sta., China Lake, Calif., 1958-59; research engr. Boeing Co., Wichita, 1959-60; instr. Wichita State U., 1960-61; assoc. prof. U. Mo., Columbia, 1961-69, U. So. Fla., Tampa, 1969-70; chmn. elec. engring. dept. U. Miami, Coral Gables, Fla., 1970-71; prof. U. South Fla., Tampa, 1971-72, 73-76; prof., chmn. dept. elec. engring. U. Toledo, 1976-79; dir. computer sci. and engring. Samborn, Steketee, Otis, Evans, Inc., Toledo, 1979-82; prof. computer sci. Grad. Engring. Ctr. U. Mo.-Rolla, St. Louis, 1982-85; prof. computer sci. U. Mo., Rolla, 1985—, chmn. dept., 1994—; research prof. U. Edinburgh, Scotland, 1972-73; cons. Wilcox Electric Co., Bendix Corp., both Kansas City, Mo., 1966-68, ICC, Miami, 1970-71, Def. Communications Agy., Washington, 1971, 72, U.S. Naval Research Labs., Washington, 1971, Med. Service Bur., Miami, 1970-71, NASA, Kennedy Space Ctr., Fla., 1973-76, 88, 89, 93, 94, Prestolite Corp., Toledo, 1977-79, IBM, Lexington, Ky., 1983-86, Wright-Patterson AFB, Ohio, 1986, PAFB, Fla., 1987, McDonnell Douglas, Mo., 1989, Digital Systems Cons., Mo., 1989, Oak Ridge Nat. Labs., 1992. Author: Network Computer Analysis, 1969, Progress in Computer Aided VLSI Design, 1988-90; editor: Internat. Jour. Computer Aided VLSI Design, 1989-91, Computer Sci. and Computer Engring. Monograph series, 1989-91, Internat. Jour. of Computer Simulation, 1990—, VLSI Design, 1992—; contbr. articles to profl. jours. Served with USAF, 1951-53. Named Young Engr. of Yr. ctrl. chpt. Mo. Soc. Profl. Engrs., 1967; NSF summer fellow, 1962, 64; NASA, IBM, DOE, UES/AFOSR, McDonnell Douglas rsch. grantee, 1967-88. Mem. IEEE (sr. mem. Soc. Computer Simulation, Am. Legion, Rotary, Sigma Xi, Tau Beta Pi, Phi Eta Sigma, Eta Kappa Nu, Pi Mu Epsilon, Upsilon Pi Epsilon. Home: 12030 Country Club Dr Rolla MO 65401 Office: U Mo-Rolla Dept Computer Sci Rolla MO 65401

ZOCHOLL, STANLEY ERNEST, electronics executive; b. Phila., July 23, 1929; s. Hugo Ernest and Elsa Elizabeth (Peterson) Z.; m. Edith Ruth Wolf, Aug. 23, 1952; children: Susan Louise, Joanne Edith, Carol Lynn. BSEE, Drexel U., 1958, MSEE, 1973. Various positions ITE Cir. Breaker Co., Phila., 1955-69; sr. devel. engr. Gould-Brown Boveri, Phila., 1969-81; protection engr. BBC Brown Boveri, Horsham and Allentown, Pa., 1981-87; dir. tech. Westinghouse ABB Power T&D Co. (name changed to ABB Power T&D Co., Inc. 1989), Allentown, 1987-91; disting. engr. Schweitzer Engring. Labs., 1991—. Patentee in field. Fellow IEEE (power system relay com. 1985—, instr. seminars 1988-89, Best Paper award Trans. 1988). Home and Office: 71 E Rambler Dr Southampton PA 18966-2034

ZODHIATES, SPIROS GEORGE, association executive; b. Cyprus, Mar. 13, 1922; came to U.S., 1946, naturalized, 1949; s. George and Mary (Toumazou) Z.; m. Joan Carol Wassel, Jan. 10, 1948; children: Priscilla Zodhiates Barnes, Lois Zodhiates Jenks, Philip, Mary. Student, Am. U. Cairo, 1941-45; B.Th., Shelton Coll., 1947; M.A., N.Y. U., 1951; Th.D., Luther Rice Sem., 1978. Ordained to ministry Gen. Assn. Regular Baptist Chs., 1947; gen. sec. Am. Mission to Greeks (name changed to AMG Internat. 1974), Ridgefield, N.J., 1946-65; pres. Am. Mission to Greeks (name changed to AMG Internat. 1974), 1965—. Author: numerous Bible-study books and booklets including Behavior of Belief, 1959, the Pursuit of Happiness, 1966, To Love is to Live, 1967, Getting the Most Out of Life, 1976, Life After Death, 1977, Hebrew Greek Key Study Bible, 1984, Complete Word Study New Testament, 1991 (Gold Medallion 1993), Complete Word Study Dictionary: New Testament, 1992, Complete Word Study Old Testament, 1994; editor in chief: (Greek) Voice of the Gospel, 1946, Pulpit and Bible Study Helps, 1975—. Served with Brit. Army, 1943-46. Served with Brit. Army, 1943-46. Recipient Gold Cross Greek Red Cross, 1951; decorated Order Brit. Empire. Home: 8927 Villa Rica Cir Chattanooga TN 37421-1506 Office: AMG Internat 6815 Shallowford Rd Chattanooga TN 37421-1755

ZOELLER, DAVID LOUIS, lawyer; b. Indpls., Nov. 26, 1949; s. John Louis and M. Maxine (Snoderly) Z.; m. Wesley Anne Carlton, Aug. 14, 1971; children: Laura Anne, David Carlton. BA, Wabash Coll., 1971; JD, Ind. U., 1974. Bar: Ind. 1974, U.S. Dist. Ct. (so. dist.) Ind. 1974. Assoc. sec., legal counsel Stokely-Van Camp Inc., Indpls., 1974-83; sr. v.p., sec., gen.

counsel Merchants Nat. Corp., Indpls., 1983—. Mem. ABA, Ind. Bar Assn., Indpls. Bar Assn. Republican. Presbyterian. Office: Merchants Nat Corp 1 Merchants Plz Ste 845 Indianapolis IN 46255

ZOELLER, DONALD J., lawyer; b. Queens Village, N.Y., Mar. 18, 1930; s. Henry Adolph and Marion Elizabeth (Brodie) Z.; m. Susan Josephine Campisi, Sept. 3, 1955; children—Paul Joseph, Jean Marie, Diane Marie. A.B., Fordham Coll., 1951; LL.B., Fordham Sch. Law, N.Y.C., 1958. Bar: N.Y. 1959, D.C. 1967. Law clk. to judge U.S. Dist. Ct. (so. dist.) N.Y., N.Y.C., 1958-59; assoc. Mudge Rose Guthrie Alexander & Ferdon, N.Y.C., 1959-68, ptnr., 1968—, exec. ptnr., 1991—; adj. prof. law Fordham U. Law Sch., 1989—; lectr. in field. Contbr. articles to legal publs. 1st lt. U.S. Army, 1951-53, Korea. Mem. ABA, N.Y. State Bar Assn., Bar Assn. City of N.Y., Nassau County Bar Assn., Inst. Jud. Adminstrn., Am. Judicature Soc. Republican. Roman Catholic. Avocations: skiing; swimming; tennis; reading. Office: Mudge Rose Guthrie Alexander & Ferdon 180 Maiden Ln New York NY 10038-4925 *Notable cases include: Matsushita Electric Indsl. co. Ltd. et al vs. Zenith Radio Corp. et al, 475 U.S. 574, 89 L. edit. 2d 538, 106, s.ct. 1438.*

ZOELLER, FUZZY, professional golfer; b. New Albany, Ind., 1952. Professional golfer, 1973—; PGA tour victories include San Diego Open, 1979, Masters, 1979, Colonial Nat., 1981, Heritage Classic, 1983, U.S. Open, 1984, Bay Hill Classic, 1985, AT&T Pro Am., 1986, Heritage Classic, 1986, Anheuser-Busch Classic, 1986. Office: care PGA Tour Ponte Vedra Beach FL 32082*

ZOELLER, JACK CARL, financial executive; b. Buffalo, Feb. 26, 1949; s. Ronald Carl and Margaret Lillian (Wademan) Z.; m. Kathryn Louise Helmke, Apr. 25, 1981; children: Andrew, Alexander. BS, U.S. Mil. Acad., 1970; M of Pub. Policy, Harvard U., 1972; M of Letters, Oxford (Eng.) U., 1974. Program budget officer Army Chief of Staff's Office, Pentagon, Washington, 1978-80; v.p. E.F. Hutton & Co., Inc., N.Y.C., 1982; pres. E.F. Hutton Indemnity Group, N.Y.C., 1983-85, Capital Risk Mgmt., Iselin, N.J., 1985-87; exec. v.p. ComFed Mortgage Co., Lowell, Mass., 1987-88, pres., 1988-91; pres. ComFed Savs. Bank, Lowell, 1990-91; chmn. chief exec. officer ComFed Bancorp., Cambridge, Mass., 1990—; pres. The Zoeller Group, Washington, 1993—; bd. dirs. N.Am. Adminstrs., Inc., 1995—; pres. N.Am. Fin. Corp., 1995—. Mem. exec. com. Lowell Devel. and Fin. Corp., 1989-91, class gift com. U.S. Mil. Acad., 1990—; youth sports coach, 1990—. Served to Capt. U.S. Army, 1970-80. Decorated Meritorious Svc. medals; Rhodes scholar Oxford U., 1972. Mem. West Point Soc. N.Y. (bd. govs. 1985-87), West Point Soc. D.C., Fed. Nat. Mortgage Assn. (N.E. regional adv. bd. 1990-91), New Eng. Hist. Geneal. Soc., Mass. Soc. Mayflower Descendants. Home: 2810 31st St NW Washington DC 20008 Office: The Zoeller Group 1101 30th St NW Washington DC 20007-3708

ZOELLICK, ROBERT BRUCE, corporate executive, lawyer; b. Evergreen Park, Ill., July 25, 1953; s. William T. and Gladys (Lenz) Z.; m. Sherry Lynn Ferguson, June 28, 1980. BA with honors, Swarthmore Coll., 1975; M Pub. Policy, JD magna cum laude, Harvard U., 1981. Bar: D.C. 1981. Econs. asst. Coun. on Wage and Price Stability, Exec. Office Pres., Washington, 1975-76; spl. asst. to asst. atty. gen. criminal div. U.S. Dept. Justice, Washington, 1978-79; pvt. practice law, 1981-82; law clk. to Judge Patricia M. Wald, U.S. Ct. Appeals for D.C. Cir., Washington, 1982-83; v.p., asst. to chmn. and chief exec. officer of bd. Fannie Mae, Washington, 1983-85; from spl. asst. to Dep. Sec., Dep. Asst. Sec. for Fin. Instns. Policy, to counselor to sec. and exec. sec. U.S Treasury Dept., Washington, 1985-88; dir. campaign isues George Bush for Pres., Washington, 1988; counselor of Dept. with rank under sec. U.S. Dept. State, Washington, 1989-92, under sec. for econ. and agrl. affairs, 1991-92; dep. chief of staff, asst. to Pres. White House, Washington, 1992-93; exec. v.p., gen. counsel Fannie Mae, Washington, 1993—. Decorated Knight Comdr.'s Cross (for work on German unification, Germany); recipient Alexander Hamilton award U.S Treasury Dept., 1988, Disting. Svc. award U.S. State Dept, 1992; fellow Luce Found., Hong Kong, 1980. Mem. D.C. Bar Assn., Phi Beta Kappa.

ZOFFER, H. JEROME, educator, university dean; b. Pitts., July 23, 1930; s. William and Sarah Leah (Fisher) Z.; m. Maye Rattner, July 19, 1959; children: Gayle Risa, William Michael. BBA, U. Pitts., 1952, MA, 1953, PhD, 1956; CPCU, Am. Inst., Phila., 1954. Sales and mgmt. cons., 1952-60; instr. Sch. Bus. Adminstrn., U. Pitts., 1953-56; asst. prof. Sch. Bus. Adminstrn. U. Pitts., 1956-59, assoc. prof. Joseph M. Katz Grad. Sch. Bus., 1959-66, prof. Sch. Bus. Adminstrn., Grad. Sch. Bus., 1966—, chmn. dept. real estate and ins., 1958-60, dir. spl. studies, 1960-62, asst. dean for acad. affairs, 1962-65, assoc. dean for adminstrn., 1965-68, dean Grad. Sch. Bus., 1968—; bd. dirs. Pennwood Savs. Bank, Homestate Pa. Growth Fund, The Enterprise Corp.; Ford Found. fellow in applied math. U. Pa., Phila., 1961-62; mem. visitation com. Am. Assembly Collegiate Schs. of Bus., 1972—, mem. standards com., 1974-78, mem. exec. com., 1975-87, chmn. accreditation rsch. com., 1974-84, v.p. bd. dirs., 1984-85, pres., 1985-86, mem. Mid. State Evaluation Accrediting Teams, 1967-85. Author: The History of Automobile Liability Insurance Rating: 1900-1958, 1959; also monographs; contbr. articles to profl. jours. Bd. dirs., v.p. Leadership Inst. for Community Devel., 1968-73, Allegheny chpt. Epilepsy Found. Am., 1971-77; bd. dirs. Pitts. Dist. Export Coun., 1974-77; bd. govs. Internat. Ins. Seminars, Inc., 1968-77; pres. Temple Sinai Congregation, 1979-81; mem. festival bd. Three Rivers Art Festival, 1983-93; mem. steering com. Leadership Pitts., 1986-91; sec. Am. Jewish Com., 1993—; bd. dirs. Student Cons. Project, U. Pitts., 1970—; Consortium for Coop. and Competitiveness, 1986—, Moral Force in the Workplace, 1986—; investment com. United Jewish Fedn., 1992—. Named Man of Yr. in Edn., Vectors Pitts., 1986, Disting. Alumnus, 1989, U. Pitts. Alumni Assn. Mem. Soc. Psychol. Study Social Issues, Mid. Atlantic Assn. Colls. Bus. Adminstrn. (pres. 1972-73), Am. Assn. Univ. Adminstrs. (exec. com. 1971-79, pres. 1975-77, dir. 1980-83, pres. found. 1983-95), Univ. Club (bd. dirs. 1988-94, sec. 1990-91, v.p. 1991-92, pres. 1992-93), Omicron Delta Gamma, Beta Gamma Sigma (pres. Beta chpt. 1964-68). Home: 5620 Aylesboro Ave Pittsburgh PA 15217-1402 Office: U Pitts Pitts Campus Katz Grad Sch Bus Pittsburgh PA 15260

ZOHN, HARRY, author, educator; b. Vienna, Austria, Nov. 21, 1923; came to U.S., 1940, naturalized, 1945; s. Abraham Leon and Adele (Awin) Z.; m. Judith Ann Gorfinkle, Sept. 3, 1962; children—Steven David, Marjorie Eve. BA, Suffolk U., Boston, 1946; MA in Edn., Clark U., 1947; AM, Harvard U., 1949, PhD, 1952; LittD (hon.), Suffolk U., 1976. Credit investigator Credit Bur. Greater Boston, 1941-46; teaching fellow German Harvard, 1947-51; mem. faculty Brandeis U., 1951—, prof. German, 1967—, chmn. dept. Germanic and Slavic langs., 1967-77, 87-90, chmn. Sch. Humanities coun., 1978-79, chmn. grad. program in lit. studies, 1981-84; exec. dir. Goethe Soc. New Eng., 1963-68. Author: Wiener Juden in der deutschen Literatur, 1964, Karl Kraus, 1971, German edit., 1990, Jüdisches Erbe in der österreichischen Literatur, 1986, Amerikanische "Thirty-eighters" aus Wien als doppelte Kulturträger, 1994, Austriaca and Judaica, 1995; editor: Liber Amicorum Friderike Zweig, 1952, Wie sie es sehen, 1952, Schachnovelle, 1960, Men of Dialogue, 1969, Der farbenvolle Untergang, 1970, Greatness Revisited, 1971, Deutschland, Deutschland über Alles, 1972, The Saints of Qumran, 1977, Germany? Germany!, 1990, Aus dem Tagebuch eines Emigranten, 1992; translator books by Theodor Herzl, Kurt Tucholsky, Karl Kraus, Jacob Burckhardt, Walter Banjamin, Gershom Scholem, Alex Bein, André Kaminski, Fritz Molden, Manès Sperber, Hermann Langbein, others; mem. editl. bd. Modern Austrian Lit., Cross Currents; gen. editor (series) Austrian Culture. Mem. adv. com. fgn. langs. Commonwealth Mass. 1961-64; trustee Suffolk U., 1978-81, 83—. Decorated officer's cross Order Merit (Fed. Republic Germany) 1960; Cross of Honor for Sci. and Art (Republic of Austria) 1984; Gold Medal of Honor, City of Vienna, 1994; recipient Art prize Wolfgang Altendorf Cultural Found., 1991. Mem. Austro-Am. Assn. Boston (chmn. bd. 1965—), Internat. Stefan Zweig Soc. (v.p. 1957-90), Internat. Arthur Schnitzler Assn. (v.p. 1978—), Austrian PEN Club, Am. PEN Center, Am. Assn. Tchrs. German (pres. Mass. chpt. 1954-59), PEN Centre German-Speaking Writers Abroad, Am. Translators Assn. (dir. 1970-71, 76), New Eng. Modern Lang. Assn. (past sec.-treas., Mass. chmn., dir.). Home: 48 Davis Ave Newton MA 02165-1924 Office: Brandeis U Shiffman Hall Waltham MA 02254-9110

ZOHN, MARTIN STEVEN, lawyer; b. Denver, Oct. 22, 1947; s. William and Alice (Lewis) Z.; m. Carol Falender, June 6, 1980; children: David Joseph, Daniel Robert. BA, Harvard U., 1969; JD, Harvard U., 1972. Bar: Calif. 1972, Ind. 1973, U.S. Ct. Claims 1980, U.S. Supreme Ct. 1980, U.S. Ct. Appeals (9th cir.) 1981. Assoc. Cadick, Burns, Duck & Neighbors, Indpls., 1972-77, ptnr., 1977-80; ptnr. Pacht, Ross, Warne, Bernhard & Sears, Inc., L.A., 1980-86, Shea & Gould, L.A., 1986-89, Proskauer Rose Goetz & Mendelsohn, L.A., 1989—; pres. Indpls. Settlements, Inc., 1977-79. Mem. Fin. Lawyers Conf., L.A. County Bar Assn. (exec. com. prejudgment remedies sect. 1985-92), Beverly Hills Bar Bus. Assn. (exec. com. bus. law sect. 1985-92), Phi Beta Kappa. Office: Proskauer Rose Goetz & Mendelsohn 11755 Wilshire Blvd Ste 1800 Los Angeles CA 90025-1524

ZOIS, CONSTANTINE NICHOLAS ATHANASIOS, meteorology educator; b. Newark, Feb. 21, 1938; s. Athanasios Konstantinos and Asimina (Speros-Blekas) Z.; m. Elyse Stein, Dec. 26, 1971; children: Jennifer, Jonathan. BA, Rutgers U., 1961; MS, Fla. State U., 1965; PhD, Rutgers U., 1980. Draftsman Babcock and Wilcox Corp., Newark, 1956; designer Foster Wheeler Corp., Carteret, N.J., 1956; instr. Rutgers U., New Brunswick, N.J., 1961-62; grad. asst. Fla. State U., Tallahassee, 1962-65; rsch. meteorologist Nat. Weather Svc., Garden City, L.I., N.Y., 1965-67; prof. Kean Coll. N.J., Union, 1967—; founder meteorology program Kean Coll., N.J.; cons. Connell, Foley and Geiser, Roseland, N.J., 1986-88; chmn. Kean Coll. All-Coll. Promotion com., 1991-93. Author, editor: Papers in Marine Science, 1971; author: Observation of the Newark N.J. Nocturnal Heat Island and Its Consideration in Terms of a Physical Model, 1980, Dynamical and Physical Oceanography, 1988, Atmospheric Dynamics: Exercises and Problems, 1988, Climatology Workbook, 1988, Weather Map Folio, 1989; contbg. author: Outcomes Assessment at Kean Coll. of N.J., 1992. Mem. AAAS, Nat. Weather Assn., Am. Meteorol. Soc. (pres. N.J. chpt. 1980-81), N.Y. Acad. Scis. (vice chmn. atmospheric scis. sect. 1986-87, chmn. 1987-88, adv. com. atmospheric sci. sect., 1988—), N.J. Marine Scis. Consortium, Phi Beta Kappa. Republican. Greek Orthodox. Avocations: guitar, banjo, fishing, baseball, snorkeling. Home: 2798 Carol Rd Union NJ 07083-4831 Office: Kean Coll of NJ Morris Ave Union NJ 07083-7117

ZOLA, GARY PHILLIP, religious educational administrator, rabbi,; b. Chgo., Feb. 17, 1952; m. Stefani Paula Rothberg; children: Amanda Roi, Jorin Benjamin, Jeremy Micah, Samantha Leigh. BA in Am. History with distinction, U. Mich., 1973; MA in Counseling Psychology, Northwestern U., 1976; PhD in Am. History, Hebrew Union Coll., Cin., 1991. Ordained rabbi, 1982. Dir. informal edn. and youth activities Temple Israel, Mpls., 1973-74; regional youth dir., asst. camp dir. Olin-Sang-Ruby Union Inst., UAHC, Chgo., 1974-77; student pulpit B'nai Israel Congregation, Williamson, W.Va., 1978-79; mem. student pulpit Anshe Sholom Congregation, Olympia Fields, Ill., 1979-80, Columbus Hebrew Congregation, Columbus, Ind., 1981-82; rabbi for high holy days Chgo. Jewish Experience, Chgo., 1982—; nat. dir. admissions Hebrew Union Coll.-Jewish Inst. Religion, Cin., 1982-89, nat. dean admissions and student affairs, 1989-91, nat. dean admissions, student affairs and alumni rels., 1991—; del. Emerging Leaders Conf., Am. Coun. for Internat. Leadership, 1989, 91; bd. dirs. Am. Jewish Com., Cin., 1982—, mem. exec. com., 1984—; bd. dirs. Hillel U. Cin., 1991—, Jewish Fedn., Cin., 1993—; pres. Greater Cin. Bd. Rabbis, 1993—, Jewish Cmty. Rels. Coun., (bd. dir.,1994—); founding mem. Kehillah of Cin., Jewish Think Tank. Author: Isaac Harby of Charleston, 1994; editor: Hebrew Union College-Jewish Institute of Religion--A Centennial History, 1875-1975, (Michael A. Meyer) 1992; contbr. numerous scholarly articles to profl. jours.; mem. editorial bd. Reform Judaism. Bd. dirs. ethics com. Jewish Hosp., Cin.; life mem. N.Am. Fedn. Temple Youth; active NCCJ. Mem. Ctrl. Conf. Am. Rabbis, Orgn. Am. Historians, Assn. Jewish Studies, So. Jewish Hist. Soc., Am. Jewish Hist. Soc., N.Am. Fedn. Temple Youth (life). Office: Hebrew Union Coll-Jewish Inst Religion 3101 Clifton Ave Cincinnati OH 45220

ZOLBER, KATHLEEN KEEN, nutrition educator; b. Walla Walla, Wash., Dec. 9, 1916; d. Wildie H. and Alice (Johnson) Keen; m. Melvin L. Zolber, Sept. 19, 1937. BS in Foods and Nutrition, Walla Walla Coll., 1941; MA, Wash. State U., 1961; PhD, U. Wis., 1968. Registered dietitian. Dir. food service Walla Walla Coll., 1941-50, mgr. coll. store, 1951-59, asst. prof. food and nutrition, 1959-62, assoc. prof., 1962-64; assoc. prof. nutrition Loma Linda (Calif.) U., 1964-72, prof. nutrition, 1973-91, dir. dietetic edn., 1967-84, dir. dietetics Med. Ctr., 1972-84, dir. nutrition program, 1984-91; retired. Mead Johnson grantee, 1965-67; recipient Alumna of Yr. award Walla Walla Coll., 1977; Delores Nyhus award Calif. Dietetic Assn., 1978. Mem. Am. Dietetic Assn. (pres. 1982-83, Copher award 1992), Am. Pub. Health Assn., AAUP, Omicron Nu, Delta Omega. Home: PO Box 981 Loma Linda CA 92354-0981

ZOLBERG, ARISTIDE RODOLPHE, political science educator, researcher; b. Brussels, Belgium, June 14, 1931; came to U.S., 1948; s. Samuel and Sabina (Fiszhaut) Z.; m. Vera Lenchner, Feb. 1, 1953; children: Erica Wendy, Daniel Robert. B.A., Columbia U., 1953; M.A., Boston U., 1956; Ph.D., U. Chgo., 1961. Lectr. Northwestern U., Evanston, Ill., 1960-61; asst. prof. U. Wis.-Madison, 1961-63; asst. prof. U. Chgo., 1963-66, assoc. prof., 1966-69, prof., 1969-83, chmn. dept. polit. sci., 1969-72; Univ.-in-Exile prof. Grad. Faculty New Sch. Social Research, N.Y.C., 1983—; chmn. dept. polit. sci. New Sch. for Social Rsch., N.Y.C., 1984-87, 92-94; dir. Ctr. for Theory, Politics and Policy, N.Y.C., 1987—, Internat. Ctr. for Migration, Ethnicity, and Citizenry, N.Y.C., 1993—; cons. Dept. State, Washington, 1965-68; vis. prof. Princeton U., 1972, U. Paris, 1978, 79, 80, Collège de France, 1986, Inst. for Advanced Studies, Vienna, 1993; mem. Comité de Rédaction Internat., Actes de la Recherche en Scis. Sociales, Paris, 1990; chmn. com. on We. European Studies New Sch. for Social Rsch.; dir. Internat. Ctr. for Migration, Ethnicity and Citizenship, N.Y.C., 1993—. Author: One Party Government in the Ivory Coast, 1964, Creating Political Order, 1966; co-author: Escape from Violence: Conflict and the Refugee Crisis in the Developing World, 1989; editor: Ghana and Ivory Coast: Patterns of Modernization,, 1971, Working Class Formation: Historical Patterns in Western Europe and North America, 1986; mem. internat. editorial adv. bd. Jour. Refugee Studies, 1990—; editorial bd. Internat. Migration Rev. Chair com. on Western Europe, New Sch., 1991; dir. Internat. Ctr. for Migration, Ethnicity, and Citizenship, N.Y.C., 1994—. Served with U.S. Army, 1954-55. Inst. for Advanced Study fellow, Princeton, 1972; fellow Social Sci. Research Council, 1964, 68; vis. fellow N.Y.U. Soc. Fellows, 1992; chevalier Ordre des Palmes Académiques (France), 1982. Mem. Am. Polit. Sci. Assn., Francaise de Sci. Politique, Internat. Polit. Sci. Assn., Coun. on Fgn. Rels. Office: New Sch Social Rsch Grad Faculty 65 5th Ave New York NY 10003-3003

ZOLIN, FRANK STANLEY, county administrator; b. Chgo., Nov. 18, 1932; s. Eugene H. Zwolinski and Genevieve (Blazak) Z.; m. Beverley M. Vaughn, 1957 (div. 1977); m. Carole Lynn Ervin, Oct. 2, 1978 (div. 1987). AA, L.A. City Coll., 1956; BA, Calif. State U., L.A., 1958; postgrad., Calif. State U., 1958-59. Chief analyst Chief Adminstrv. Office County of L.A., 1962-68, adminstrv. dep. Chief Adminstrv. Office, 1968-69, county clk., exec. officer, jury commr. Superior Ct., 1969—. Bd. dirs. Constl. Rights Found., L.A., 1987-88, Guiding Eyes, Sylmar, Calif. 1988-89; mem. Town Hall, L.A. Recipient Herbert Lincoln Harley award Am. Judicature Soc., 1983. Mem. Superior Ct. Adminstrs. Assn. (pres. 1981-82), L.A. County Mgmt. Council (pres. 1976), Nat. Assn. for Ct. Mgmt. (past regional dir.), Rotary, Phi Alpha Delta. Office: Los Angeles Superior Ct 111 N Hill St RM 204 Los Angeles CA 90012

ZOLLAR, JAWOLE WILLA JO, art association administrator; b. Kansas City, Kans., Dec. 21, 1950; d. Alfred Jr. and Dorothy Delores (Blair) Zollar; 1 child, Elizabeth Herron. BA in Dance, U. Mo., Kansas City, 1975; MFA in Dance, Fla. State U., 1979. Faculty Fla. State U., Tallahassee, 1977-80; artistic dir. Urban Bush Women, N.Y.C., 1984—. Recipient N.Y. Dance and Performance award, 1992; named Outstanding Alumni U. Mo.-Kansas City, 1993; Mankato State U. Worlds of Thought Resident scholar, 1994; Nat. Endowment of Arts Choreography fellow, 1992, 93, 94. Mem. Dance U.S.A., Assn. of Am. Cultures, Internat. Assn. of Blacks in Dance. Home: 339 15th St Brooklyn NY 11215 Office: Urban Bush Women care St Mark's Church 131 E 10th St New York NY 10003 also: care IMG Artists 22 E 71st St New York NY 10021

ZOLLAR, NIKKI MICHELLE, state agency administrator; b. Chgo., June 18, 1956; d. Lowell M. and Doris J. (Lowe) Z.; m. William A. Von Hoene, Jr., June 18, 1983; children: William Lowell Von Hoene, Branden Tracey. BA, Johns Hopkins U., 1977; JD, Georgetown U., 1980. Fed. jud. law clk. U.S. Dist. Ct. (no. dist.) Ill., Chgo., 1980-81; assoc. Lafontant, Wilkins, Jones & Ware, Chgo., 1981-83, Kirkland & Ellis, Chgo., 1983-85; chmn., sec. Chgo. Bd. Election Commrs., 1987-90; dir. Ill. Dept. Profl. Regulation, Chgo., 1991—. Bd. trustees Woodland Acad. of Sacred Heart, Cmty. Youth Creative Learning Experience; mem. Louis R. Lowe women's bd. United Negro Coll. Fund; mem. women's coun. Chgo. Heart Assn.; mem. Chgo. com. Solidarity with So. Africa; mem. women's bd. Jackson Park Hosp.; active Chgo. Urban League, Nat. Coalition of 100 Black Women. Recipient Outstanding Achievement award YWCA, Outstanding Achievement of Svc. to Cmty. award Washington Park YMCA, Youth Svc. award Beatrice Caffrey Found., David C. Hilliard award Chgo. Bar Assn., 1988-89, Kizzy award Revlon Corp./Kizzy Scholarship Fund, African-Am. Women's Achievement award Columbia Coll., Martin Luther Kind Jr. award for dedicated leadership Boy Scouts Am., Outstanding Young Profl. award Chgo. Urban Profls., Svc. and Leadership award United Negro Coll. Fund, Outstanding Achievement cert. Ill. State Atty. Appellate Svc. Commn.; named One of 100 Outstanding Black Bus. and Profl. Women in U.S., Dollars and Sense mag. Mem. Ill. Women in Govt., Women Execs. in State Govt., Alpha Gamma Pi. Mem. United Ch. of Christ. Avocation: long distance running. Office: Ill Dept Profl Regulation Director 320 W Washington St Springfield IL 62786

ZOLLER, RICHARD BERNARD, investment counsel consultant; b. Stillwater, Minn., May 3, 1929; s. Bernard Fredrick Z. and Vivian Montrose (Paul) Palmquist; m. Olive Leane Nilsen, July 12, 1952; children: Eric Thorstein, Kristin Elise. BS, U. Minn., 1953, PhD, 1958. Chartered fin. analyst; registered investment advisor. Dir. econ. research Peavey Co., Mpls., 1958-62; economist Armour & Co., Chgo., 1962-66, mgr. capital appropriation, 1966-68; dir. investments Armour & Co. and Greyhound Corp., Chgo., 1968-79; v.p. investments Greyhound Corp. (now The Dial Corp.), Phoenix, 1979-92; pres. Richard B. Zoller Inc., Phoenix, 1993—. Author research publs. in agrl. econs., 1955-58. Bd. dirs. Phoenix Symphony Assn., 1985-97, exec. com., 1986; bd. dirs. Handicap Village of Ariz., Phoenix, 1975-84; chmn. Ariz. Gov.'s Employment Security Adv. Council, 1980, Ariz. Retirement System Investment Adv. Council, 1987-91. With U.S. Army, 1951-52, Korea. Mem. Phoenix Soc. Fin. Analysts (pres. 1985). Office: The Dial Corp Dial Towers Phoenix AZ 85077

ZOLNO, MARK S., lawyer. BA Polit. Sci., No. Ill. Univ., 1965; JD, John Marshall Law Sch., 1978; MA cum laude Internat. Rels., Universidad de las Américas, Mexico, 1974. Bar: Ill. 1978, U.S. Dist. Ct. (no. dist.) Ill. 1979, U.S. Ct. Internat. Trade 1979, U.S. Ct. Appeals (fed. cir.) 1979. With U.S. Customs Svc., Dept. Commerce, U.S. Trade Rep's. Office, Internat. Trade Commn., Fed. Trade Commn., FDA; ptnr. Katten Muchin & Zavis, Chgo., 1988—; past chmn. Chgo. Bar Assn. Customs and U.S. Trade Law Com.; lectr. in field. Contbr. articles to profl. jours. Office: Katten Muchin & Zavis Ste 1600 525 W Monroe St Chicago IL 60661

ZOLOMIJ, ROBERT WILLIAM, landscape architect, consultant; b. Phila., Oct. 13, 1942; s. William and Anna (Sikacz) Z.; m. Joanne M. Volk, Oct. 2, 1965; children: Nancy Lyn, Christopher John; m. Nancy S. Helfferich, Nov. 21, 1992. BS in Landscape Architecture, Pa. State U., 1965; M Landscape Architecture, U. Ill., 1971. Lic. landscape arch., Ill. Site planner Bucks County Planning Commn., Doylestown, Pa., 1965-67; assoc. prof. U. Ill., Urbana, 1970-78; sr. landscape arch. Skidmore Owings & Merrill, Chgo., 1978-79; sr. assoc. Barton-Aschman Assocs., Evanston, Ill., 1979-84; v.p. Harland Bartholomew Assocs., Northbrook, Ill., 1984-86; ptnr. Land Design Collaborative, Inc., Evanston, 1986—. Co-author: Time Saver Standards for Landscape Architects, 1988. Univ. fellow U. Ill., 1967. Fellow Am. Soc. Landscape Archs. (chpt. treas. 1986-88, v.p. 1988-90, pres. 1990-92). Avocations: golf, travel, reading, woodworking. Home: 3429 Harrison St Evanston IL 60201-4953 Office: Land Design Collaborative 1563 Sherman Ave Evanston IL 60201-4421

ZOLOTOW, CHARLOTTE SHAPIRO, author, editor; b. Norfolk, Va., June 26, 1915; d. Louis J. and Ella F. (Bernstein) Shapiro; m. Maurice Zolotow, Apr. 14, 1938 (div. 1969); children: Stephen, Ellen. Student, U. Wis., 1933-36. Editor children's book dept. Harper & Row, N.Y.C., 1938-44; sr. editor Harper & Row, 1962-70; v.p., assoc. pub. Harper Jr. Books, 1976-81; editorial cons., editorial dir. Charlotte Zolotow Books, 1982-90; pub. emerita, advisor Harper Collins Children's Books, 1991—; tchr. U. Colo. Writers Conf. on Children's Books, U. Ind. Writers Conf.; also lectr. children's books. Author: The Park Book, 1944, Big Brother, 1960, The Sky Was Blue, 1963, The Magic Words, 1952, Indian Indian, 1952, The Bunny Who Found Easter, 1959, In My Garden, 1960, But Not Billy, 1947, 2d edit, 1983, Not a Little Monkey, 1957, 2d edit., 1989, The Man With The Purple Eyes, 1961, Mr. Rabbit and the Lovely Present, 1962, The White Marble, 1963, A Rose, A Bridge and A Wild Black Horse, 1964, 2d edit., 1987, Someday, 1965, When I Have a Little Girl, 1965, If It Weren't for You, 1966, 2d edit., 1987, Big Sister, Little Sister, 1966, All That Sunlight, 1967, When I Have A Son, 1967, My Friend John, 1968, Summer Is, 1968, Some Things Go Together, 1969, The Hating Book, 1969, The New Friend, 1969, River Winding, 1970, 79, Lateef and His World, 1970, Yani and His World, 1970, You and Me, 1971, Wake Up and Goodnight, 1971, William's Doll, 1972, Hold My Hand, 1972, 2d edit., 1987, The Beautiful Christmas Tree, 1972, Janie, 1973, My Grandson Lew, 1974, The Summer Night, 1974, 3d edit. 1991, The Unfriendly Book, 1975, It's Not Fair, 1976, 2d edit., 1987, Someone New, 1978, Say It, 1980, If You Listen, 1980, 2d edit. 1987, The New Friend, 1981, One Step, Two ..., 1981, The Song, 1982, I Know a Lady, 1984, Timothy Too!, 1986, Everything Glistens, Everything Sings, 1987, I Like to be Little, 1987, The Poodle Who Barked at the Wind, 1987, The Quiet Mother and the Noisy Little Boy, 1988, Something's Going to Happen, 1988, This Quiet Lady, 1992, The Seashore Book, 1992, Snippets, 1992, The Moon was the Best, 1993, Peter and the Pigeons, 1993, others; compiler An Overpraised Season, Early Sorrow. Recipient Harper Gold award for editorial excellence, 1974, Kerlan award U. Minn., 1986, Corp. award for children's books Lit. Market Pl., 1990, Silver medallion U. So. Miss., 1990, Tribute for Far Reaching Contbn. to Children's Lit., ALA, 1991. Mem. PEN, Authors League. Home: 29 Elm Pl Hastings Hdsn NY 10706-1703 Office: 10 E 53rd St New York NY 10022

ZONANA, VICTOR F., government agency official, writer, communications executive; b. N.Y.C., Mar. 3, 1954; s. Felix and Nelly Z. BA, Dartmouth Coll., 1975. Staff writer Wall St. Jour., Phila. and San Francisco, 1975-85; spl. writer L.A. Times, San Francisco and N.Y.C., 1985-93; dep. asst. sec. pub. affairs U.S. Dept. Health and Human Svcs., Washington, 1993—. Recipient John Hancock award Outstanding Journalism, 1993. Mem. Soc. Profl. Journalists, Nat. Lesbian and Gay Journalists Assn. (founder 1991), Phi Beta Kappa. Home: 3835 S St NW Washington DC 20007 Office: Dept Health and Human Svcs Rm 638-E 200 Independence Ave SW Washington DC 20201-0004

ZONIS, MARVIN, political scientist, educator; b. Boston, Sept. 18, 1936; s. Leonard and Clara (Barenberg) Z.; m. Lucy Salenger, Jan. 3, 1976; children by previous marriage-Nadia E. Leah; 1 stepdaugher, Brix E. Smith. A.B., Yale U., 1958; postgrad., Harvard Grad. Sch. Bus., 1958-59; Ph.D., M.I.T., 1968; candidate, Inst. for Psychoanalysis, Chgo., 1977-85. Mem. faculty U. Chgo., 1966—, assoc. prof. and prof. behavioral scis., 1973-89—, prof. Grad. Sch. Bus., 1989—; dir. U. Chgo. (Center for Middle Eastern Studies), 1976-79; pres. Marvin Zonis and Assocs., Internat. Cons., 1991—; cons. in field; chmn. com. on Middle East Am. Coun. Learned Socs.-Social Sci. Rsch. Coun., 1970-76; pres. Am. Inst. Iranian Studies, 1969-71; bd. dirs. CNA Fin. Corp. Author: The Political Elite of Iran, 1971, Khomeini, The Islamic Republic of Iran, and The Arab World, 1987, Majestic Failure: The Fall of the Shah, 1991, The East European Opportunity: The Complete Business Guide and Source Book, 1992; contbr. articles to profl. jours. Served with USAF, 1959-60. Recipient Quantrell award for excellence in teaching U. Chgo., 1979. Office: U. Chicago 5828 S University Ave Chicago IL 60637-1515 Psychoanalytic approaches to the study of political phenomena open new vistas to understanding as well as facilitating the design of U.S. policy.

ZOOGMAN, NICHOLAS JAY, lawyer; b. N.Y.C., Apr. 2, 1947; s. Morris William and Hannah (Stern) Z.; m. Carla Ganz, June 7, 1970; children: Sarah Elizabeth, Peter William. BA, NYU, 1967; MA, Harvard U., 1969, JD, 1973. Bar: N.Y. 1974, U.S. Dist. Ct. (so. and ea. dists.) N.Y. 1974, U.S. Ct. Appeals (2d cir.) 1975, U.S. Supreme Ct. 1979, U.S. Dist. Ct. (ea. dist.) Mich. 1988, U.S. Ct. Appeals (D.C. cir.) 1990, U.S. Ct. Appeals (6th cir.) 1993. Assoc. Donovan Leisure Newton & Irvine, N.Y.C., 1973-75; ptnr. Anderson Kill Olick & Oshinsky, N.Y.C., 1976—. Mem. ABA, N.Y. State Bar Assn., Assn. Bar City N.Y., Phi Beta Kappa, Pi Sigma Alpha. Office: Anderson Kill Olick & Oshinsky 1251 Avenue of the Americas New York NY 10020

ZOOK, ELVIN GLENN, plastic surgeon, educator; b. Huntington County, Ind., Mar. 21, 1937; s. Glenn Hardman and Ruth (Barton) Z.; m. Sharon Kay Neher, Dec. 11, 1960; children—Tara E., Leigh A., Nicole L. B.A., Manchester Coll., 1959; M.D., Ind. U., 1963. Diplomate Am. Bd. Surgery, Am. Bd. Thoracic Surgery, Am. Bd. Plastic Surgery. Intern Meth. Hosp., Indpls., 1963-64; resident in gen. and thoracic surgery Ind. U. Med. Center, Indpls., 1964-69; resident in plastic surgery Ind. U. Hosp., Indpls., 1969-71; asst. prof. plastic surgery Ind. U. Hosp., 1971-73; asso. prof. surgery So. Ill. U., Springfield, 1973-75; prof. So. Ill. U., 1975—, chmn. div. plastic surgery, 1973—; mem. staff Meml. Med. Center, St. Johns Hosp., Springfield. Contbr. articles to med. jours. Mem. AMA, Assn. Acad. Surgery, Am. Soc. Plastic and Reconstructive Surgery (sec. 1988-91, v.p. 1991-92, pres.-elect 1992-93, pres. 1993-94), Midwestern Soc. Plastic and Reconstructive Surgery (pres. 1986-87), ACS, Sangamon County Med. Soc. (pres. 1987), Am. Cleft Palate Assn., Am. Assn. Plastic Surgery (trustee 1987-90), Plastic Surgery Rsch. Coun. (chmn. 1981), Am. Burn Assn., Ill. Surg. Soc., Am. Soc. Surgery Hand (coun.), Am. Bd. of Plastic Surgery (sec.-treas. 1988-91, chmn. 1991-92), Am. Soc. Aesthetic Plastic Surgery, Am. Soc. Surgery of Trauma, Assn. Acad. Chmn. Plastic Surgery (pres. 1986-87), Am. Surg. Assn., RRC for Plastic Surgery, Sangamo Club, Springfield Med. Club, Island Bay Yacht Club. Presbyterian. Clubs: Sangamo, Springfield Med, Island Bay Yacht. Home: 42 Hazel Dell Springfield IL 62707-9507 Office: 800 N Rutledge St Springfield IL 62702-4911 Do the best possible in all that is possible.

ZOOK, KAY MARIE, nursing administrator; b. O'Neill, Nebr.; d. Roy W. and Elsie B. Carroll; m. Larry A. Zook, Aug. 17, 1957; children: David, Debra Zook Wickizer. Diploma, Mary Lanning Sch. Nursing, Hastings, Nebr., 1955; BS, Hastings Coll., 1957; MS, St. Francis Coll., Joliet, Ill., 1984. RN, Nebr., Minn., Colo. Instr. nursing Mary Lanning Meml. Hosp., Hastings; instr. med.-surg. nursing Bryan Meml. Hosp., Lincoln, Nebr.; asst. DON Lincoln Gen. Hosp.; charge nurse St. Luke's Hosp., Duluth, Minn.; edn. coord. Rose Med. Ctr., Denver; v.p. patient svcs. St. Joseph Hosp., Denver, 1973—. Author: (bulletin) A New Threat to Health Care Delivery: The Nursing Shortage, 1988. Active Denver Leadership Forum, 1987. Fellow The Wharton Sch. U. Pa., Phila., 1985. Mem. Am. Orgn. Nurse Execs., Colo. Soc. Nurse Execs., Colo. League Nursing. Office: St Joseph Hosp 1835 Franklin St Denver CO 80218

ZOOK, MERLIN WAYNE, meteorologist; b. Connellsville, Pa., July 2, 1937; s. Ellrose Durr and Frances Adeline (Loucks) Z.; m. Maxine Beatrice Hartzler, May 1, 1965; children: Kevin Ray, Kathleen Joy. BA, Goshen (Ind.) Coll., 1959; MS, Pa. State U., 1961. Cert. consulting meteorologist, environ. profl. Rsch. assoc. U. Mich., Ann Arbor, 1958; grad. asst. Pa. State U., University Park, 1960-61; audio-visual asst., staff meteorologist Mennonite Cen. Com., Akron, Pa., 1961-63; air quality program specialist Pa. Dept. Environ. Resources, Harrisburg, 1963—; book reviewer Sci. Edn. Dept. Boston U., 1990-92, Nat. Weather Assn., Temple Hills, Md., 1983-88, book rev. editor, 1988-92; scientist, participant AAAS-Bell Atlantic Found., Washington, 1989-90. Author, contbr.: (chpt.) Behind the Dim Unknown, 1966. Guest lectr. Millersville (Pa.) State U., 1988, 90, Boy Scouts Am., Camp Hill, Pa., 1990, Pa. State U., Middletown, 1990, 91—, Cub Scouts Am., Camp Hill, 1991—. Mem. Am. Meteorol. Soc., Union of Concerned Scientists, Pa. State U. Alumni Assn. Achievements include development of models for the daily prediction of the Pollutant Standards Index in Pa.; of collection of cloud type photographs with classifications for study of cloud characteristics/physics; research in meso-scale meteorology and localized forecasting, on the relationship between solar radiation and formation of ozone in urban areas in Pa., on migratory patterns of local birds influenced by meteorological conditions. Home: 105 June Dr Camp Hill PA 17011-5069 Office: Pa Dept Air Quality Dept Environ Resources 400 Market St Harrisburg PA 17105

ZOOK, RONALD Z., school system administrator. Supt. Parkrose Sch. Dist. # 3, Portland, Oreg. Recipient Nat. Superintendent of the Yr. awd., Oregon, Am. Assn. of School Administrators, 1993. Office: Parkrose Sch Dist 3 10636 NE Prescott St Portland OR 97220

ZOON, KATHRYN EGLOFF, biochemist; b. Yonkers, N.Y., Nov. 6, 1948; d. August R. and Violet T. (Pollock) Egloff; BS, Rensselaer Poly. Inst., 1970; PhD Johns Hopkins U., 1975; m. Robert A. Zoon, Aug. 22, 1970; children: Christine K, Jennifer R. Interferon research fellow NIH, Bethesda, Md., 1975-77, staff fellow, 1977-79, sr. staff fellow, 1979-80; sr. staff fellow div. biochem. biophysics Bur. Biologics, FDA, Bethesda, 1980-83; rsch. chemist divsn. biochem. biophysics, 1983-84, rsch. chemist divsn. virology, 1984-88, rsch. chemist div. cytokine biology, Ctr. for Biologics Evaluation and Rsch., FDA, 1988—, div. dir., 1989-92; dir. Ctr. for Biologics Evaluation and Rsch., 1992—; lectr. NIH, 1994, Reigelman Lecturship, 1994. N.Y. State Regents fellow, 1970; Person of the Yr. award Biopharm, 1992, 95, Pub. Svc. award Genetic Engring. News, 1994. Mem. Am. Soc. Biochemistry and Molecular Biology, Internat. Soc. Interferon Research, Internat. Soc. Cytokine Rsch. Roman Catholic. Contbr. numerous articles on research in biol. chemistry to sci. jours.; sect. editor Jour. Interferon Research, 1980—. Office: CBER 1401 Rockville Pike Rockville MD 20852-1428

ZOON, WILLIAM K., packaging company executive; b. Passaic, N.J., 1943. Student, Fairleigh Dickinson U., 1969. Exec. v.p. Am. Nat. Can Co., Chgo. Office: Am Nat Can Co 8770 W Bryn Mawr Ave Chicago IL 60631-3515

ZOPF, PAUL EDWARD, JR., sociologist; b. Bridgeport, Conn., July 9, 1931; s. Paul Edward and Hilda Ernestine (Russell) Z.; m. Evelyn Lanoel Montgomery, Aug. 5, 1956; 1 child, Eric Paul. B.S., U. Conn., 1953; M.S., U. Fla., 1955, Ph.D., 1966. Asst. prof. sociology Guilford Coll., Greensboro, N.C., 1959-66, assoc. prof., 1966-70, prof., 1970-72, Dana prof. sociology, 1972—; cons. local govt. agys. Author: North Carolina: A Demographic Profile, 1967, Demography: Principles and Methods, 1970, 76, Principles of Inductive Rural Sociology, 1970, Profile of Women in Greensboro: 1990, 1977, Sociocultural Systems, 1978, Cultural Accumulation in Latin America, 1980, Population: An Introduction to Social Demography, 1984, Income and Poverty Status of Women in Greensboro, 1985, America's Older Population, 1986, American Women in Poverty, 1989, Mortality Patterns and Trends in the United States, 1992; editor Guilford Coll. Self-Study Accreditation Report; contbr. articles to profl. jours. Recipient Teaching Excellence award Guilford Coll., 1978; grantee Kenan Found., 1970-79, Guilford Coll., 1979—. Mem. Am. Acad. Polit. and Social Sci., Am. Sociol. Assn., Internat. Union Sci. Study Population, So. Sociol. Soc., Rural Sociol. Soc., Population Reference Bur. Quaker. Home: 815 George White Rd Greensboro NC 27410-3317 Office: Guilford Coll Dept Sociology Greensboro NC 27410 In my role as professor, researcher and author, I have oriented my activities to the service of students, my institution, my professional discipline, and various community agencies. I have found that pursuing various professional processes that I enjoy and can handle adequately, is the real reward. Honors, if they come, are a by-product of that pursuit; they would be elusive and perpetually inadequate if they were the principal reason for my efforts.

ZORE, EDWARD JOHN, insurance company investment executive; b. Milw., July 5, 1945; s. Joseph F. and Marie A. Z.; m. Diane Widemshek, Aug. 19, 1967; children: Annemarie, Kathryn. B.S., U. Wis.-Milw., 1968, M.S., 1970. Exec. v.p., CFO, chief investment officer Northwestern Mut. Life Ins. Co., Milw., 1969—. Republican. Roman Catholic. Home: 129 W Miller Dr Mequon WI 53092-6189 Office: Northwestern Mutual Life Ins Co 720 E Wisconsin Ave Milwaukee WI 53202-4797

ZORIO, JOHN WILLIAM, financial services executive; b. Fayetteville, W.Va., Nov. 17, 1946; s. Nelson and Zelma (Simpson) Z.; m. Mary Ann Helen Dombrowski, Aug. 13, 1966; children: Jennifer Susan, Jonathan David. BSBA in Econs., Concord Coll., 1968. CLU, ChFC. Field underwriter N.Y. Life Ins. Co., McLean, Va., 1971-73, asst. gen. mgr., 1974-79; gen. mgr. N.Y. Life Ins. Co., Cin., 1980-83; v.p. N.Y. Life Ins. Co., N.Y.C., 1984-85; gen. mgr. N.Y. Life Ins. Co., Cleve., 1986-89; sr. v.p, N.Y. Life Ins. Co., Chgo., 1990—. Sgt. U.S. Army, 1969-71. Republican. Roman Catholic. Avocations: woodworking, reading, sports. Home: 540 Turicum Rd Lake Forest IL 60045-3366 Office: NY Life Ins Co 2201 Waukegan Rd # 150W Bannockburn IL 60015-1577

ZORN, ERIC J., newspaper columnist; b. New Haven, Jan. 6, 1958; s. Jens Christian and Frances (Barnhart) Z.; m. Johanna Wolken, Dec. 2, 1985. BA, U. Mich., 1980. With Chgo. Tribune, 1980—, met. reporter, 1985-86, columnist, 1986—; instr. Medill Sch. Journalism Northwestern U., Evanston, Ill., 1985—. Avocation: old-time square dance caller. Office: Chgo Tribune PO Box 25340 435 N Michigan Ave Chicago IL 60611-4001

ZORN, ERIC STUART, retail department store chain executive; b. Newark, Oct. 2, 1948; s. Arthur and Evelyn (Bernstein) Z.; m. Lois Karen Green, Nov. 29, 1979. Student, Fairleigh Dickinson Coll., Wayne, N.J., Upsala Coll., East Orange, N.J. Cash ops. supr. Vornado Inc., Garfield, N.J., 1966-69; corp. auditor Mangel Stores Corp., N.Y.C., 1969-70; sr. v.p. Jamesway Corp., Secaucus, N.J., 1970—; pres. Omnia Protective Services Inc., Ft. Lee, N.J., 1979—, 1530 Owners Corp. (coop. bldg.), Ft. Lee. Mem. Internat. Mass Retailing Inst. (chmn. loss prevention group 1979-82), N.J. Retail Mchts. Assn. (chmn.), Internat. Soc. Stress Analysts, Soc. Strategic Planning. Republican. Jewish. Office: Jamesway Corp 40 Hartz Way Secaucus NJ 07094-2479

ZORNES, MILFORD, artist; b. Camargo, Okla., Jan. 25, 1908; s. James Francis and Clara Delphine (Lindsay) Z.; m. Gloria Codd, 1935; 1 son, Franz Milford; m. Patricia Mary Palmer, Nov. 8, 1942; 1 dau., Maria Patricia. Student, Otis Art Inst., Los Angeles, 1929, Pomona Coll., 1930-34. Instr. art Pomona Coll., 1946-50; art dir. Vortox and Padua Hills Theatre, Claremont, 1954-66. Exhibited, Calif. Watercolor Soc., Met. Mus., Am. Watercolor Soc., Corcoran Gallery, Bklyn. Mus., Denver Mus., Cleve. Mus., L.A. Mus., Brooks Gallery, London, Bombay Art Assn., Chgo. Art Inst., Butler Mus., Gallery Modern Masters, Washington, Santa Barbara (Calif.) Mus., Cin. Mus., Laguna (Calif.) Art Gallery, Oklahoma City Mus., Springville (Utah) Mus.; represented in permanent collections at L.A. Mus., White House Collection, Met. Mus., Pentagon Bldg., Butler Mus., UCLA, Nat. Acad., San Diego Mus., L.A. County Fair, Home Savs. and Loan Assn., L.A., Corcoran Gallery, Washington; mem. art com., Nat. Orange Show, San Bernardino, Calif., 1963-65; author: A Journey to Nicaragua, 1977, The California Style: California Watercolor Artists, 1925-1955, 1985; subject of book by Gordon McClelland: Milford Zornes, Hillcrest Press, 1991. Served with U.S. Army, 1943-45, CBI. RecipientPaul Prescott Barrow award Pomona Coll., 1987, David Prescott Burrows award, 1991, A Most Disting. Citizen award So. Utah State Coll., 1988, Am. Artist Achievement award Am. Artist Mag., 1994. Mem. NAD, Am. Watercolor Soc., Southwestern Watercolor Soc., Watercolor West, Nat. Watercolor Soc., Utah Watercolor Soc. Address: PO Box 176 Orderville UT 84758 It has been my effort in life to have awareness: not to have all knowledge because no one can encompass all knowledge; not to have only wealth or only success, because there is no dimension of completeness of wealth or success; not to achieve complete goodness, because goodness and right are relative; not to enjoy the epitomy in taste because taste is a gratification of self alone; but rather to seek and achieve understanding of relative values and a concept of the completeness of life. With this as my effort and my inner goal, I find success within the areas of my limited abilities, my meager knowledge, and my frail grasp of the infinite.

ZORNOW, DAVID M., lawyer; b. N.Y.C., Mar. 31, 1955; s. Jack and Marion (Gilden) Z.; m. Martha Malkin, July 21, 1985; children: Samuel Morris, Hannah Jane, Ethan Lewis. AB summa cum laude, Harvard U., 1976; JD, Yale U., 1980. Bar: N.Y. 1981, U.S. Ct. Appeals (3d cir.) 1982, U.S. Dist. Ct. (so. dist.) N.Y. 1983, U.S. Ct. Appeals (2d cir.) 1984, U.S. Dist. Ct. D.C. 1989, U.S. Ct. Appeals (D.C. cir.) 1989, U.S. Dist. Ct. Ariz. 1990, U.S. Dist. Ct. (ea. dist.) N.Y. 1993. Law clerk to Judge Herbert J. Stern U.S. Dist. Ct. N.J., Newark, 1980-82; assoc. Kramer Levin Kamin Nessen & Frankel, N.Y.C., 1982-83; asst. U.S. atty. so. dist. N.Y. U.S. Atty.'s Office, N.Y.C., 1983-87; assoc. counsel Office Ind. Counsel-Iran/Contra Investigation, Washington, 1987-89; ptnr. Skadden Arps Slate Meagher & Flom, N.Y.C., 1989—; chmn. N.Y.C. Civilian Complaint Rev. Bd., 1994—; vis. faculty Trial Advocacy Workshop Harvard Law Sch., Cambridge, Mass., 1988. Mem. ABA (com. on white collar crime), Fed. Bar Coun., Assn. of Bar of City of N.Y., N.Y. Assn. Criminal Def. Lawyers, N.Y. Coun. Def. Lawyers. Office: Skadden Arps Slate Meagher & Flom 919 3rd Ave New York NY 10022-3903

ZORNOW, WILLIAM FRANK, historian, educator; b. Cleve., Aug. 13, 1920; s. William Frederick Emil and Viola (Schulz) Z. A.B., Western Res. U., 1942, A.M., 1944, Ph.D. 1952. Vice pres., treas. Glenville Coal & Supply Co., Real Value Coal Corp., Zornow Coal Corp., 1941-45; dep. clk. Probate Ct., Cuyahoga County, Ohio, 1941-43; prodn. planning engr. Hickok Elec. Instrument Co., Cleve., 1943-46; teaching asst. Western Res. U., 1944-47; instr. U. Akron, 1946-47, Case Inst. Tech., 1947-50, Washburn U., 1950-51; lectr. Cleve. Coll., 1948-49; asst. prof. Kans. State U., 1951-58; asst. prof. history Kent (Ohio) State U., 1958-61, asso. prof., 1961-66, prof. history, 1966—; perpetual hon. fellow Harry S. Truman Libr. Inst., Independence, Mo.; collection corr. Berkshire Loan and Fin. Co., Painesville (Ohio) Security Credit Acceptance Corp., Mentor, Ohio, 1951-60; cons. Karl E. Mundt Library, Dakota State Coll., Madison, S.D.; presenter 1st coll. arts and scis. faculty lecture series Kent State U., 1962. Author: Lincoln and the Party Divided, 1954, rev. edit., 1972, Kansas: A History of the Jayhawk State, 1957, America at Mid-Century, 1959; author: (with others) Abraham Lincoln: A New Portrait, 1959, Kansas: The First Century, 1956; contbr. articles to encys. and profl. jours.; editor Shawnee County (Kans.) Hist. Bull, 1950-51; abstractor: America: History and Life: Historical Abstracts, 1964—. Mem. Dir.'s Circle Cleve. Mus. Art, 1989—, Cleve. Clin. Found., 1992—, Soc. Fellows. Faculty rsch. grantee Kans. State U., 1955-57, Kent State U., 1960-64. Mem. AAAS, AAUP, Soc. Fellow of Cleve. Clinic Found., Am. Acad. Polit. and Social Sci., Am. Hist. Assn., Orgn. Am. Historians, Ohio Acad. History (chmn. awards com.), Ohio Hist. Soc. (libr. adv. com. 1969—), Ohio Soc. N.Y., Ctr. Study of Presidency, Acad. Polit. Sci., Sierra Club San Francisco, Delta Tau Delta (4-star coun. 1992—), Pi Gamma Mu, Phi Alpha Theta, Phi Beta Kappa. Home: 7893 Middlesex Rd Mentor OH 44060-7617 Office: Kent State U 305 Bowman Hall Kent OH 44242

ZOROWSKI, CARL FRANK, engineering educator, university administrator; b. Pitts., July 14, 1930; s. Stanley and Mary Josephine (Kozuch) Z.; m. Sarah Jane Crossley, Aug. 7, 1954 (dec. 1983); children: Kathleen Ann, Karl Alan, Kristine Alaine; m. Louise Parrish Lockwood, Apr. 13, 1985. BSME, Carnegie Inst. Tech., 1952, MSME, 1953, PhD, 1956. Instr. Carnegie Inst. Tech., Pitts., 1952-56, asst. prof., 1956-61, assoc. prof., 1961-62; prof. mech. and aero. engrng. dept. N.C. State U., Raleigh, 1964-66, R.J. Reynolds Industries prof., 1966—, assoc. dept. head, 1964-72, dept. head, 1972-79, assoc. dean acad. affairs Sch. Engrng., 1979-85, dir. Integrated Mfg. Systems Inst., 1986-92, dept. head, 1992-93; dir. Succeed/NSF Coalition, 1993—, assoc. dean acad. affairs, 1993-94. Served to 2d lt. USAR, 1952-58. Recipient research award Sigma Xi, 1967. Fellow ASME (Richards Meml. award 1975); mem. Am. Soc. Engring. Edn. (Western Electric award 1968), Fiber Soc. (Achievement award 1970). Contbr. pubs. to profl. jours.; patentee in field. Home: 103 Windyrush Ln Cary NC 27511-9758 Office: NC State U PO Box 7901 Raleigh NC 27695

ZORTHIAN, BARRY, communications executive; b. Kutahia, Turkey, Oct. 8, 1920; naturalized 1930; s. Herbert Peter and Annaly (Markarian) Z.; m. Margaret Aylaian, June 6, 1948; children: Gregory Jannig, Stephen Arnak. BA, Yale U., 1941; LLB, N.Y. U., 1953; LLD (hon.), Ind. Inst. Tech., 1970. Bar: N.Y. 1953. Newspaper reporter, 1936-42, newspaper and radio reporter, 1947-48; news and policy editor USIA, 1948-56, program mgr. Voice of Am., 1956-61; dep. pub. affairs. officer USIS, India, 1961-64;

min.-counselor for info. Am. Embassy, Vietnam, 1964-68; v.p. Time, Inc., 1969-79, v.p. govt. affairs, 1974-79; pres. Time-Life Broadcast, 1969-73, Washington/Balt. Regional Assn., 1979-81; sr. v.p. Gray and Co., Washington, 1981-84; ptnr. Alcalde & Fay, Arlington, Va., 1984—. Bd. dirs. Am. U. of Armenia, Internat. Coll. of Beirut, Armenian Gen. Benevolent Union. With USMCR, 1942-46; col. Res. ret. Mem. Coun. on Fgn. Rels., Am. Fgn. Svc. Assn., Bus.-Govt. Rels. Coun., Marine Corps Res. Officers Assn. Conglist. Clubs: Century Assn. (N.Y.C.); Congressional Country (Washington), Burning Tree (Washington), Metropolitan (Washington), Federal City (Washington). Home: 4201 Cathedral Ave NW Apt 405E Washington DC 20016-4914 Office: Alcalde & Fay 2111 Wilson Blvd Ste 850 Arlington VA 22201-3001

ZOUMAS, BARRY LEE, food products company executive, nutritionist; b. Reading, Pa., July 9, 1942; s. James and Clementine (Foscone) Z.; m. Rosemary Henry, June 25, 1966; children: Christine, Larry, B. Lee. BS in Chemistry, Kutztown (Pa.) State U., 1964; MS in Nutrition, Pa. State U., 1966, PhD in Nutrition, 1969. Sr. scientist Mead Johnson & Co., Evansville, Ind., 1969-70; mgr. nutritional scis. Hershey Foods Corp., Hershey, Pa., 1970-76; dir. R & D Hershey (Pa.) Foods Corp., 1976-81, v.p., sci. and tech., 1981—; bd. dirs. Pa. Rsch. Corp, State College. Patentee in field; contbr. 20 articles to sci. jours. Bd. overseers U. Pa. Dental Sch., Phila., 1986-90. Recipient Disting. Alumni award Kutztown State Coll., 1984, Alumni award Pa. State U., 1985, Alumni fellow, 1989. Mem. AAAS, Am. Inst. Nutrition (chmn. industry adv. com. 1984-86), Inst. Food Technologists, Am. Chem. Soc., Rotary (Hershey, Pa.). Republican. Roman Catholic. Avocation: golf. Home: 425 Elm Ave Hershey PA 17033-1752 Office: Hershey Foods Corp 100 Crystal A Dr Hershey PA 17033-9529

ZOX, LARRY, artist; b. Des Moines, May 31, 1936; s. Oscar and Mildred (Friedman) Z.; m. Jean Marilyn Glover, July 19, 1965; children—Melinda, Alexander Cassidy. Student, Okla. U., 1955-56, Drake U., 1957, Des Moines Art Center, 1955-57. vis. critic Cornell U., summer 1967; faculty (Sch. Visual Arts), 1967-68, 69-70, 70-76, Yale, summer, 1972, Kent State U., summer 1974. Exhibited one man shows at Am. Gallery, N.Y.C., 1962, Kornblee Gallery, N.Y.C., 1964-66, 68, 69, 70, 71, Andre Emmerich Gallery, 1973, 75, 76, Whitney Mus. Am. Art; 1973, Galerie Rocke, Cologne, Germany, 1968, Janie C. Lee Gallery, Houston, 1974, Hokin Gallery, Bay Harbor Islands, Fla., 1981, Meridith Long & Co., Houston, 1981, Hokin Gallery, Palm Beach, 1981, Salander-O'Reilly Galleries, N.Y., 1982, Rubiner Gallery, West Bloomfield, Mich., 1985, 90, Images Gallery, Toledo, 1986, 90, 91, Percival Gallery, Des Moines, 1987, 89, 91, Marsh Gallery U. Richmond, Va., 1992, Robert Strin-St. Louis, Mo., 1992, C.S. Schulte Gallery, Millburn, N.J., 1993-94, Gallery One Toronto, Can., others; exhibited group shows at Am. Gallery, 1963, Am. Fedn. Art, 1963-65, Mus. Modern Art, N.Y.C., 1964, Albright-Knox Art Gallery, Buffalo, 1964, Washington Gallery Modern Art, 1964, Gallery Modern Art, N.Y.C., 1965, Tibor de Nagy, N.Y.C., 1965, ann. Whitney Mus., N.Y.C., 1965-70, one-man retrospective, 1973, Art Inst. Chgo., 1965, Kornblee Gallery, 1966, Guggenheim Mus., N.Y.C., 1966, Expo Am. Pavilion, 1967, Palm Springs Desert Mus., 1973, Daniel Templon Gallery, Paris, 1975, Andre Emmerich Gallery, 1975, Andre Emmerich Gallery, N.Y., 1975, Edmonton (Alta., Can.) Art Gallery, 1977, Old Vanderbilt Mansion, Old Brookville, N.Y., 1979, Allen Rubiner Gallery, Royal Oak, Mich., 1980, Meredith Long & Co. N.Y., 1980, Md. Inst. Coll. Art, Balt., 1980, Meredith Long & Co., Houston, 1980, Mus. Fine Arts, Boston, 1981, Solomion R. Guggenheim Mus., N.Y., 1981, Salander-O'Reilly Gallery, N.Y., 1981, St. Lawrence U., 1985, Rubiner Gallery, West Bloomfield, 1986, Percival Gallery, Des Moines, 1987, Gallery of Art, 1988, Charles H. MacNider Mus., 1988, Sioux City Art Ctr., 1988, Des Moines Art Ctr., 1988, Blanden Meml. Art Mus., 1988, Muscatine Art Ctr., 1988, C.S. Shulte Gallery, N.Y. and N.J., 1991, others; represented in permanent collections Am. Republic Ins. Corp., Des Moines, J. & L. Hudson Co., Detroit, Joseph H. Hirshhorn Mus., U.S. Steel Corp., Mus. Modern Art, N.Y.C., Philip Johnson Collection, Dallas Mus. Fine Arts, Des Moines Art Center, Met. Mus. Art, N.Y.C., Indpls. Mus., Whitney Mus.; artist in residence, Juniata Coll., Huntingdon, Pa., 1964, U. N.C., 1967. Recipient Nat. Council Arts award, 1969; Guggenheim fellow, 1967. Office: care Andre Emmerich Gallery 238 Park Ave S New York NY 10003-1401

ZRAKET, CHARLES ANTHONY, systems research and engineering company executive; b. Lawrence, Mass., Jan. 9, 1924; s. Habib and Martha (Beshara) Z.; m. Shirley Ann Camus, Oct. 13, 1961; children: David C., Suzanne M., Elizabeth A., Caroline A. BSEE, Northeastern U., Boston, 1951; SMEE, MIT, 1953; PhD in Engring. (hon.), Northeastern U., 1988. Mem. rsch. staff digital computer lab. MIT, 1951-53, group leader digital computer lab., Lincoln Lab., 1953-58; tech. dir., then sr. v.p. MITRE Corp., Bedford, Mass. and McLean, Va., 1958-78, exec. v.p., chief oper. officer, 1978-86, pres., chief exec. officer, 1986-90; trustee MITRE; bd. dirs. Bank of Boston, Boston Edison, Scholar-in-Residence, Kennedy Sch. Govt., Harvard U., 1990-94, Aspect Med. Sys., Wyman-Gordon Corp. Contbr. articles to Science, Daedalus, IEEE Jours; co-editor: Managing Nuclear Operations. Trustee Hudson Inst., Northeastern U., Computer Mus. With AUS, 1943-46. Decorated Bronze Star, Purple Heart with oak leaf cluster, Combat Inf. badge; named Disting. Corp. Leader, MIT, 1985, Dept. Def. Medal for Disting. Pub. Svc., 1990. Fellow AAAS, IEEE, AIAA (Reed Aeros. award 1993), Am. Acad. Arts and Scis.; mem. NAE, Coun. on Fgn. Rels., Sigma Xi, Tau Beta Pi, Eta Kappa Nu. Home: 71 Sylvan Ln Weston MA 02193-1027 Office: MITRE Corp Burlington Rd Bedford MA 01730

ZRULL, JOEL PETER, psychiatry educator; b. Detroit, Jan. 10, 1932; s. Arthur Benjamin and Mildred (Bazy) Z.; m. Nancy Jane Eichenlaub, June 19, 1954; children: Mark Christian, Lisa Carol. BA with honors, U. Mich., 1953, MD, 1957. Diplomate Am. Bd. Psychiatry, Am. Bd. Child Psychiatry. From instr. to assoc. prof. psychiatry U. Mich. Med. Sch., Ann Arbor, 1962-73; prof., chief child psychiatry Med. Coll. Ohio, Toledo, 1973-75, prof., chmn. dept. psychiatry, 1975—; cons. Monroe (mich.) County Intermediate Sch. Dist., 1961—; pres. Associated Physicians MCO, Inc., Toledo, 1983-84, 87-90; chief of staff Med. Coll. Hosps., Toledo, 1984-86; mem. com. on cert. in child psychiatry Am. Bd. Psychiatry and Neurology, 1986-91, chmn. 1990-91. Editor: Adult Psychiatry: New Directions in Therapy, 1983; contbr. articles to profl. jours. Grantee NIMH, 1974-76, Ohio Dept. Mental Health, 1978-86. Fellow Am. Psychiat. Assn., Am. Acad. Child and Adolescent Psychiatry (chmn. com. ing. 1984-87, chmn. comm. memls. and awards 1992—), Am. Coll. Psychiatrists, Am. Ortho-Psychiat. Assn.; mem. AMA, Soc. Profs. of Child and Adolescent Psychiatry (sec. treas. 1989-92, pres.-elect 1992-94, pres. 1994-96). Roman Catholic. Avocations: tennis, bridge, golfing. Home: 6133 W Wyandotte Rd Maumee OH 43537-1334 Office: Med Coll Ohio PO Box 10008 Toledo OH 43699-0008

ZSCHAU, MARILYN, singer; b. Chgo., Feb. 9, 1944; d. Edwin Arthur Eugene and Helen Elizabeth (Kelly) Z. BA in Radio, T.V., Motion Pictures, Opera, Theatre, U. N.C.; ed. Juilliard Sch. Music, also studied with John Lester. Toured with Met. Nat. Co., 1965-66; debut, Vienna Volksoper, in Die Tote Stadt, 1967, Vienna Staatsoper, in Ariadne auf Naxos, 1971; with N.Y.C. Opera from 1978; debut Met. Opera, in La Boheme, 1985, La Scala, in Die Frau ohne Schatten, 1986; has toured and sung in many countries. Office: Columbia Artists Mgmt Inc Joyce Arbib Mayer Divsn 165 W 57th St New York NY 10019

ZSIGMOND, VILMOS, cinematographer, director; b. Szeged, Hungary, June 16, 1930; came to U.S., 1957, naturalized, 1962; s. Vilmos and Bozena (Illichmann) Z.; children: Julia, Susi. M.A., U. Film and Theater Arts, Budapest, Hungary, 1955. Free-lance cinematographer for numerous commls., also ednl., documentary and low-budget feature films, 1965-71; now dir., cinematographer on commls. (winner several nat. and internat. awards); feature films, 1971—; films include McCabe and Mrs. Miller, 1971; Images, 1972, Deliverance, 1972, The Long Goodbye, 1973, Scarecrow, 1973, Cinderella Liberty, 1973, The Sugarland Express, 1974, Obsession, 1976, Close Encounters of the Third Kind, 1977 (Acad. award 1977), The Last Waltz, 1978, The Rose, 1978, The Deerhunter, 1978 (Acad. award nomination and Brit. Acad. award), Heavens Gate, 1979, The Border, 1980, Blow Out, 1980, Jinxed, 1981, Table for Five, 1982, The River, 1983 (Acad. award nomination), No Small Affair, 1984, Real Genius, 1985, Witches of Eastwick, 1986, Journey to Spirit Island, 1988, Fatman and Little Boy, 1989, Two Jakes, 1989, Bonfire of the Vanities, 1990, Stalin, 1991 (CableAce

award, Direction of Photography and/or Lighting Direction in a Dramatic/Theatrical Special/Movie or Miniseries, ASC award, Emmy award), Sliver, 1992; dir. The Long Shadow, 1992, Intersection, 1993, Maverick, 1993, The Crossing Guard, 1994. Mem. Acad. Motion Picture Arts and Scis., Dirs. Guild, Am. Soc. Cinematographers. Office: Feinstein & Shorr 16133 Ventura Blvd Ste 800 Encino CA 91436

ZUBAL, JOHN T., book exchange executive, publisher, bibliographer; b. Cleve., Nov. 5, 1939; s. Thomas A. Zubal and Anna R. Kukurudza; m. Marilyn C. Zubal, June 17, 1961; children: Victoria, Michael, Jean Marie, Thomas. BS, Fordham U., 1961; MA, John Carroll U., 1962; DLitt (hon.), Hay (Wales) Inst., 1981. Pres. John T. Zubal, Inc., Cleve., 1962—, U.S Book Exch., Cleve., 1990—; ptnr. Zubal & Dole Pubs., Cleve., 1980—; assoc. prof. Cuyahoga C.C., Cleve., 1963-75. Office: US Book Exch 2969 W 25th St Cleveland OH 44113-5332

ZUBE, ERVIN HERBERT, landscape architect, geographer, educator; b. Milw., Apr. 24, 1931; s. Ervin Louis and Germaine Emma (Petersen) Z.; m. Margaret Jean Pew, June 19, 1954; 1 child, Eric Carl. BS, U. Wis.-Madison, 1954; MLA in Landscape Architecture, Harvard u., 1959; postgrad., FAAR, Am. Acad., Rome, 1961; PhD in Geography, Clark U., 1973. Asst. dean of men U. Wis., Madison, 1953-54, Asst. prof., 1961-64; asst. prof. U. Calif., Berkeley, 1964-65; prin. Zube and Dega Assocs. Landscape Architects, Madison, Wis., 1961-64; pres. Rsch., Planning and Design Assocs., Amherst, 1966-70; prof., dept. head U. Mass., Amherst, 1965-72, dir. environ. research inst., 1972-77; dir. sch. Renewable Natural Resources U. Ariz., Tucson, 1977-83, prof. landscape architecture, 1983-84, 87—, chmn. landscape resources divsn., 1984-87; adj. prof. geography, regional devel. U. Ariz., 1985—; sr. Fulbright Hays Disting. prof. U. Ljubljana, Yugoslavia, 1979; Lansdowne vis. geography scholar U. Victoria, 1986; mem. Nat. Commn. on Rsch. and Resources Mgmt. Policy, Nat. Pk. Sys., 1988-89; lectr. in field; mem. exec. bd. Ency. on Environ., 1991-94; chairperson GAP analysis peer rev. panel U.S Fish and Wildlife Svcs., Nat. Biol. Survey, 1993. Author, editor 11 books; editorial bd. Landscape Rsch., 1974—, Landscape Jour., 1981—, Jour. Archtl. and Planning Rsch., 1983—, Landscape Ecology, 1987-92, New Eng. Landscape, 1987-91, Landscape and Urban Planning, 1988—, Environ. Psychology, 1990—, Jour. Planning Lit., 1990—, Society and Natural Resources, 1991-93; contbr. articles to profl. jours., chpts. to books. Trustee Highland Ednl. Trust, 1969—, Tucson Bot. Garden, 1981-83, 85-87, Ariz. Sonora Desert Mus., Tucson, 1981-85, 86-89, pres., 1987-88, mem. adv. coun., 1985-86, Rsch. Ranch Found., Elgin, Ariz., 1983-95, v.p., 1989-90, pres., 1990-92; active U.S MAB Program, Project 13, 1977-88, chair, 1980-86, mem. U.S nat. com., 1980-83. Fellow NATO, Eng., 1977, NEA, 1983-84; scholar Harvard U., 1983-84. Fellow Udall Ctr. for Studies in Pub. Policy, 1992-93, Am. Soc. Landscape Architects (chmn. coun. edn. 1973-75, dir. profl. practice inst 1982-87, chmn. 1986-87, Bradford Williams medal 1981, Rsch. Honor award 1982, ASLA medal 1995); mem. Nat. Archtl. Accrediting Bd. (dir. 1978-80), Internat. Coun. for Exch. Scholars (mem. adv. com. in architecture and city planning chairperson 1979-82), Eisenhower Consortium Western Environ. Forestry Rsch. (v.p. rsch. 1979-82), Environ. Design Rsch. Assn. (dir. 1982-85, chmn 1984-85), Assn. Am. Geographers, S.W. Pks. and Monuments Assn. (bd. dirs. 1985—, v.p. 1986-89, pres. 1989-92), Landscape Architecture Found. (bd. dirs. 1989-91, Alfred Lagasse medal 1992), Rincon Inst. (mem. bd. advs. 1990—, chairperson 1994—), Nat. Pks. and Conservation Assn. (mem. sci. adv. com. 1991-95, mem. coun. advisors 1993-95), Coun. Nat. Pk. Coop. Assocs. (bd. dirs. 1993—, v.p. 1994—). Office: U Ariz 325 Bio Sci E Tucson AZ 85721

ZUCARO, ALDO CHARLES, insurance company executive; b. Grenoble, France, Apr. 2, 1939; s. Louis and Lucy Zucaro; m. Gloria J. Ward, Oct. 12, 1963; children: Lucy, Louis, Faye. BS in Acctg, Queens Coll., N.Y.C., 1962. C.P.A., N.Y., Ill. Ptnr. Coopers & Lybrand (and predecessor), Chgo. and N.Y.C., 1962-76; exec. v.p., chief fin. officer Old Republic Internat. Corp., Chgo., 1976-81, pres., 1981—, chief exec. officer, 1990—, also chmn. bd. dirs., 1993—, chmn. of the bd., 1993—; pres., bd. dirs. Old Republic Life Ins. Co., Old Republic Life of N.Y., Old Republic Ins. Co., Internat. Bus. and Merc. Reassurance Co., Republic Mortgage Ins. Co., Old Republic Nat. Title Ins. Co., Home Owners Life Ins. Co. Editor: Financial Accounting Practices of the Insurance Industry, 1975, 76. Mem. AICPAs. Roman Catholic. Office: Old Republic Internat Corp 307 N Michigan Ave Chicago IL 60601-5311

ZUCCHINI, MICHAEL RINALDO, banking company executive; b. N.Y.C., Aug. 23, 1946; s. Vincent Anthony and Mildred (Palma) Z.; m. Patricia A. Hayward, Feb. 6, 1988; children from previous marriage: Angela, Vincent, Jeannine. B.P.S., Pace U., 1976, M.B.A., 1982. Cert. in data processing. Sr. systems programmer Avon Products, N.Y.C., 1970-73; mgr. tech. svcs. subs. Westinghouse Electric Corp., New Rochelle, N.Y., 1973; prin. Ind. Data Processing, N.Y.C., 1973-74; v.p. Gen. RE, Stamford, Conn., 1974-87; pres., dir. Elm St. Corp., Stamford, 1974-87, GRE Realty Corp., Stamford, 1974-87; pres., chief exec. officer Gen. RE Svcs. Corp., Stamford, 1984-87; exec. v.p., chief info. officer Fleet/Norstar Fin. Group, Providence, R.I., 1987—; chmn., chief exec. officer, dir. Fleet/Norstar Svcs. Corp., Providence, R.I., 1987—; mem. task force Pres.'s Pvt. Sector Survey-Dept. Edn., 1982. Contbr. articles to profl. jours.; patentee computer terminal portability device, 1984. Served with U.S. Army, 1966-68. Recipient AMS-Carnegie Mellon U. award for mng. info. tech., 1987. Mem. Data Processing Mgmt. Assn., Assn. of Inst. for Cert. Computer Profls., Soc. Mgmt. Info. Systems. Republican. Roman Catholic. Home: Moonraker Farm Chepachet RI 02814 Office: Fleet Norstar Fin Group 50 Kennedy Plz Providence RI 02903-2393

ZUCCHINO, DAVID ALAN, newspaper journalist; b. McPherson, Kans., Nov. 14, 1951; s. Ernest Joseph and Maxine Loree (Jones) Z.; m. Kacey Anne Chapp, June 20, 1981; children: Adrien, Emily, Natalie. BA in Journalism, U. N.C., 1973, BA in English Lit., 1973. Reporter News & Observer, Raleigh, N.C., 1973-78, Detroit Free Press, 1978-80; fgn. corr. Phila. Inquirer, 1980—. Recipient Pulitzer Prize for feature writing, 1989. Recipient award Am. Soc. Newspaper Editors, 1985, award Overseas Press Club, Pulitzer prize Columbia U., 1989. Avocation: coach. Home: 28 Hume Rd, Dunkeld Johannesburg 2196, Republic South Africa Office: Phila Inquirer 400 N Broad St Philadelphia PA 19130-4099*

ZUCCONI, DAVID G., zoo and museum director. Office: Tulsa Zool Pk 5701 E 36th St N Tulsa OK 74115-2100

ZUCCOTTI, JOHN EUGENE, real estate company executive; b. N.Y.C., June 23, 1937. AB in History, Princeton U., 1959; LLB, Yale U., 1963. Bar: N.Y. 1963, D.C. 1970. Asst. to under sec. and sec. HUD, Washington, 1967-69; sec., counsel Nat. Corp. for Housing Partnerships, Washington, 1969-70; spl. counsel to housing subcom. Banking and Currency Com. U.S. Ho. of Reps., Washington, 1970-73; ptnr. Tufo, Johnston and Zuccotti, N.Y.C., 1970-72; chmn. N.Y.C. Planning Commn., 1973-75, mem., 1971-73; 1st dep. mayor City of N.Y., 1975-77; sr. ptnr. Tufo, Johnston, Zuccotti and Allegaert, N.Y.C., 1977-86, Brown & Wood, N.Y.C., 1986-89; pres., chief exec. officer Olympia and York Cos. (U.S.A.), 1989—; impartial arbitrator between MTA/TWU, 1981-90. Home: 36 2nd Pl Brooklyn NY 11231-3403 Office: Olympia & York 237 Park Ave Fl 12 New York NY 10017-3142

ZUCK, ALFRED CHRISTIAN, consulting mechanical engineer; b. Ridgefield, N.J., Dec. 16, 1924; s. Frederick William and Margaret Christine (Umland) Z.; m. Vilma Hudson, May 6, 1951; children: Allyson, Jon, Randall. M.E., Poly. Inst. Bklyn., 1960. Registered profl. engr., 21 states including N.Y.; nat. council engring. examiners; lic. profl. planner, N.J. From designer to sr. v.p. Syska & Hennessy, Inc., N.Y.C., 1946-78; prin. Edwards & Zuck (P.C.), N.Y.C., 1978-91, ret., 1991; mem. nat. panel Am Arbitration Assn, Nat. Council Engring. Examiners. Served with AUS, 1943-46; to 1st lt. USAF, 1951-52; to capt. N.J. Air N.G., 1947-56. Decorated Bronze Star (2). Fellow Am. Cons. Engrs. Council (past mem. Nat. Ethical Practices Com.); mem. NSPE, N.Y. State Soc. Profl. Engrs. (past chmn. profl. engrs. in pvt. practice program), Am. Soc. Mil. Engrs., Nat. Council Engring. Examiners, N.Y. Assn. Cons. Engrs. (past v.p., bd. dirs.), ASHRAE, N.Y. Bldg. Congress. (bd. govs.) Lutheran. Club: N.Y Athletic. Home: 444 Weymouth Dr Wyckoff NJ 07481-1217 Office: Edwards & Zuck PC 330 W 42nd St New York NY 10036-6902

ZUCK, ALFRED MILLER, association executive; b. East Petersburg, Pa., Aug. 27, 1934; s. Walter Newton and Mary (Miller) Z.; m. Geraldine Connelly, July 21, 1957; children: Susan, David. BA, Franklin and Marshall Coll., 1957; MPA, Syracuse U., 1958. Dir. fed. program Presdl. Commn. on Youth Opportunities, Washington, 1967-68; dir evaluation Employment and Tng. Adminstrn., Dept. Labor, Washington, 1968-70, dir adminstrn. and mgmt., 1970-75; comptroller U.S. Dept. Labor, Washington, 1975-77; exec. dir. Commn. on Exec., Legis. and Jud. Salaries, Washington, 1980; asst. sec. Dept. Labor, Washington, 1977-83, acting sec., 1981; asst. adminstr. EPA, Washington, 1983; exec. dir. Nat. Assn. Schs. of Pub. Affairs and Adminstrn., Washington, 1983—; pres. Internat. Inst. Adminstrv. Scis., Brussels, 1989-92, Am. Consortium for Internat. Pub. Adminstrn., Washington, 1984-89; bd. dirs. Pub./Pvt. Venture, Inc., Phila., 1984-90. Recipient Presdl. Disting. Exec. award Pres. of U.S., 1980; Disting. Alumni award Franklin and Marshall Coll., 1980. Fellow Nat. Acad. Pub. Admisstrn. (trustee 1989—, chmn. bd. trustees 1993—); mem. Phi Beta Kappa. Office: NASPAA 1120 G St NW Ste 730 Washington DC 20005-3801

ZUCKER, ALEXANDER, physicist, administrator; b. Zagreb, Yugoslavia, Aug. 1, 1924; came to U.S., 1939; s. William and Bertha (Klopfer) Z.; m. Joan-Ellen Jamieson, Nov. 28, 1953; children: Rebecca, Claire, Susannah. B.A., U. Vt., Burlington, 1947; M.S., Yale U., New Haven, 1948, Ph.D., 1950. Physicist Oak Ridge Nat. Lab., Tenn., 1950-60, assoc. dir. electro-nuclear div., 1972-75, dir. heavy ion project, 1988, assoc. dir. phys. scis.; 1973-88, acting lab. dir., 1988; assoc. dir. for nuclear techs. Oak Ridge Nat. Lab. 1989-93; exec. dir., environ. studies bd. NAS-NAE, Washington, 1970-72; mem. U.S. del. to USSR on Peaceful Uses of Atomic Energy, 1963; Ford prof. physics U. Tenn., Knoxville, 1968-73; U.S. del. to Pugwash Conf., 1971; research coordination council Gas Research Inst., Chgo., 1978-83; com. Army manpower Nat. Research Council, Washington, 1982-83; adv. panel on technologies to reduce U.S. materials import vulnerability Office of Technology Assessment, Washington, 1982-85; council on energy engring. research Dept. of Energy, Washington, 1983—; industry, nat. lab. steel initiative White House, Washington, 1984. Editor Internat. Jour. Nuclear Sci. Applications, 1980—; cons. editor Ency. and Yearbook of Sci. and Tech. McGraw-Hill Pub. Co., 1989; mem. editorial bd. Science, 1981-82; contbr. articles to profl. jours. Guggenheim fellow, 1966-67; Fulbright-Hays Research scholar, 1966-67. Fellow Am. Phys. Soc., AAAS, Sigma Xi; mem. ASME, Nat. Acad. Scis. (nuclear physics del. to People's Republic of China 1979), Internat. Union Pure and Applied Physics (mem.-at-large U.S. nat. com. 1976-78). Research in nuclear physics with heavy ions and protons; accelerators, especially cyclotrons; materials research programs, especially high-temperature materials and surfaces; nuclear power reactors, especially gas-cooled reactors; research reactor with ultra high neutron flux. Office: Oak Ridge Nat Lab PO Box 2008 Oak Ridge TN 37831-2008

ZUCKER, ALFRED JOHN, English educator, academic adminstrator; b. Hartford, Sept. 25, 1940; s. Samuel and Rose (Zucker) Z.; AA, L.A. Valley Coll., 1960; AB in English, UCLA, 1962, AB in Speech, MA in English, 1962, MA in Speech, 1963, PhD, 1966, postgrad., UCLA, U. So. Calif., Harvard U.; m. Sallie Lea Friedheim, Dec. 25, 1966; children—Mary Anne, John James, Jr., James Patrick, Patrick Jonathan, Anne-Marie Kathleen, Kathleen Mary. Lectr. English, Los Angeles City Coll., 1963-68; prof. English, philosophy, chmn. div. humanities Los Angeles Southwest Coll., 1968-72, chmn. English dept., 1972-74, asst. dean instruction, 1974—; prof. English El Camino Coll., 1985—; prof. English L.A. Valley Coll., 1989—. Mem. Los Angeles Coll. Dist. Senate, 1969—. Mem. Los Angeles Coll. Tchrs. Assn. (dir.), Calif. Jr. Coll. Assn., Calif. Tchrs. Assn., AAUP, World Affairs Coun., Mensa, Phi Beta Kappa, Phi Beta Kappa (pres. U. Calif. at Los Angeles chpt. 1966-67, v.p. 1967-68), Tau Alpha Epsilon. Lodge: KC. Contbr. articles to profl. jours. Office: 5800 Fulton Ave Van Nuys CA 91401-4062

ZUCKER, DAVID, director; b. Milw., Oct. 16, 1947. co-founder (with Jerry Zucker and Jim Abrahams) Kentucky Fried Theatre, Madison, WI, 1969, then Los Angeles, CA, 1972. Co-screenwriter: Kentucky Fried Movie, 1977; co-screenwriter, co-dir.: Airplane!, 1980; co-exec. prodr, co-dir., co-screenwriter: Top Secret, 1984, The Naked Gun, 1988, The Naked Gun 2 1/2: The Smell of Fear, 1991, The Naked Gun 33 1/3: The Final Insult, 1994; co-dir.: Ruthless People, 1986; co-exec. prodr.: Brain Donors, 1992; TV series: Police Squad!, 1982; TV spls.: Our Planet Tonight, 1987. Office: Zucker Bros Prodns Sony Studios 10202 Washington Blvd Culver City CA 90232-3119*

ZUCKER, JERRY, energy systems manufacturing executive; b. Tel-Aviv, Israel, Aug. 24, 1946; came to U.S., 1952, naturalized, 1958; s. Leon and Zipora (Shlifkovitz) Z.; m. Anita Goldberg, June 21, 1970; children: Jonathan Michael, Andrea Michelle, Jeffrey Mark. BS, U. Fla., 1968, MEE, 1972. Electronics design engr. Vital Industries, Inc., Gainesville, Fla., 1968-71; devel. engring. group dir. Cons. Engrs., Inc., Gainesville, 1971-73; supt. process engring. and tech. services Hudson Pulp & Paper Corp., Palatka, Fla., 1973-78; dir. mfg. and tech. services Raybestos Manhattan, Inc., North Charleston, S.C., 1978-82; chmn. bd., chief exec. officer InterTech Group, Inc.; bd. dirs. High Tech. Coatings Corp., Advanced Chem. Techs., Inc., Tighitco, Inc., Ecosys, Inc., Polymer Group, Inc., FiberTech Group, Inc., ConX Inc., Tycon Inc., Worthington Products Inc., Aerospace Def. Inc., Technetics Group, Inc., Global Golf, Inc., Fabrene, Inc., Polymer Group, Inc., Daramic, Inc.; cons. phosphate mining, pulp and paper and sugar industries. Bd. dirs. Roper Hosp., Trident United Way, Charleston Jewish Fedn. (pres.), Hotline Inc. (crisis intervention), Hebrew Benevolent Soc., Hebrew Orphan Soc., Jewish Cmty. Assn. Org. Rehab. Tng., S.C. Aquarium. Mem. Med. Soc. S.C. (bd. dir.), TAPPI (mem. nat. elec. engring. com. 1977—), IEEE, Am. Chem. Soc. Jewish. Numerous patents in electrochem., mech. chem. fields. Contbr. articles to tech. jours. Home: 16 Buckingham Dr Charleston SC 29407-3455 Office: The InterTech Group Inc PO Box 5205 4838 Jenkins Ave North Charleston SC 29405

ZUCKER, JERRY, producer, director; b. Milw., Mar. 11, 1950. Student, U. Wis. co-founder Ky. Fried Theatre. Films include: Kentucky Fried Movie, 1977 (co-screenwriter, actor), Rock 'n' Roll High School, 1979 (2nd unit dir.), Airplane!, 1980 (co-dir., co-screenwriter), Top Secret, 1984 (co-dir., co-screenwriter), Ruthless People, 1986 (co-dir.), The Naked Gun, 1988 (exec. prodr., co-screenwriter), Ghost, 1990 (dir.), The Naked Gun 2 1/2: The Smell of Fear, 1991 (exec. co-prodr.), Brain Donors, 1992 (co-exec. prodr.), My Life, 1993 (co-prodr.), The Naked Gun 33 1/3: The Final Insult, 1994 (co-exec. prodr.), First Knight, 1995 (dir.). Address: Zucker Bros Prodns Sony Studios 10202 W Washington Blvd Los Angeles CA 90049*

ZUCKER, MARJORIE BASS, medical researcher, hematologist; b. N.Y.C., June 10, 1919; d. Murray H. and Agnes (Naumburg) Bass; m. Howard D. Zucker, June 25, 1938; children: Andrew A., Ellen Zucker Harrison, Joan, Barbara Zucker-Pinchoff. AB, Vassar Coll., 1939; postgrad., Columbia Coll. Medicine, 1943-45; PhD, Columbia U., 1944. Rsch. asst. Coll. Physicians and Surgeons Columbia U., N.Y.C., 1944-49; asst. to assoc. prof. physiology Coll. of Dentistry NYU, 1949-54; assoc. mem. Sloan Kettering Inst., N.Y.C., 1955-63; asst. rsch. dir. ARC Rsch. Lab NYU Med. Ctr., N.Y.C., 1963-70, assoc. prof. pathology, 1963-71, prof. pathology, 1971-92, prof. emeritus, 1992—; mem. various rev. coms. NIH, Bethesda, Md., 1971-85. Co-author: The Physiology of Blood Platelets, 1965; co-patentee composition containing platelet factor 4, 1988; contbr. numerous articles to profl. jours. Recipient award N.Y. Met. chpt. Am. Women in Sci., 1986. Mem. Internat. Soc. Thrombosis (mem. coun. Marian Barnhart Lecture award 1989), Soc. for Exptl. Biology and Medicine (pres. 1983-85), Choice in Dying (dir., v.p. 1990). Democrat. Avocation: bird-watching. Address: 333 Central Park W New York NY 10025-7145

ZUCKER, NORMAN LIVINGSTON, political scientist, educator, author; b. N.Y.C., Aug. 4, 1933; s. George Meyer and Beatrice Lillian (Livingston) Z.; m. Naomi Judith Flink, June 25, 1961; children: Sara, George. B.A., Rutgers U., 1954, M.A., 1956, Ph.D., 1960. Asst. prof. polit. sci. Tufts U., Medford, Mass., 1962-66; assoc. prof. polit. sci. U. R.I., Kingston, 1966-69; prof. U. R.I., 1969—; cons. Select Commn. on Immigration and Refugee Policy, 1980; manuscript cons. to pubs. Author: George W. Norris: Gentle Knight of American Democracy, 1966, The American Party Process, 1968, The Coming Crisis in Israel: Private Faith and Public Policy, 1973, The Guarded Gate: The Reality of American Refugee Policy, 1987; cons. editor

World Affairs, 1975-84; assoc. editor Jour. Refugee Studies, 1987—; contbr. articles and revs. to profl. jours., chpts. to books. Wurzweiler Found. grantee, 1963; Am. Philos. Soc. grantee, 1964; Rockefeller Found. fellow in human rights, 1980. Mem. Internat. Polit. Sci. Assn., Am. Polit. Sci. Assn., New Eng. Polit. Sci. Assn., AAUP. Office: U RI Dept Polit Sci Kingston RI 02881

ZUCKER, ROBERT A(LPERT), psychologist; b. N.Y.C., Dec. 9, 1935; s. Morris and Sophie (Alpert) Z.; m. Martine Latil; children: Lisa, Alex, Eleanor; m. Kristine Ellen Freeark, Mar. 10, 1979; 1 child, Katherine. B.C.E., CCNY, 1956; postgrad., UCLA, 1956-58; Ph.D., Harvard U., 1966. Lic. psychologist, Mich. From instr. to asst. prof. psychology Rutgers U., 1963-68; from asst. prof. to assoc. prof. to prof. Mich. State U., 1968-94; prof. psychology in psychiatry and psychology U. Mich., 1994—, dir. Alcohol Rsch. Ctr., 1994—, dir. substance abuse divsn. dept. psychiatry, 1994—; vis. prof. U. Tex., Austin, 1975; vis. rsch. prof. psychology in psychiatry U. Mich., 1990-91; vis. scholar Nat. Inst. Alcohol Abuse and Alcoholism, 1980; dir. clin. tng. Mich. State U., 1982-94; lectr. Nebr. Symposium on Motivation, 1986; cons. in field. Editor: Further Explorations in Personality, 1981, Personality and the Prediction of Behavior, 1984, The Emergence of Personality, 1987, Studying Persons and Lives, 1990, Personality Structure in the Life Course, 1992, The Development of Alcohol Problems: Exploring the Biopsychosocial Matrix of Risk, 1994, Alcohol Problems Among Adolescents: Current Directions in Prevention Research, 1995; contbr. chpts. and articles to profl. publs. Bd. dirs. Nat. Coun. on Alcoholism-Mich., 1978-82; mem. Psychosocial Initial Rev. Group, Nat. Inst. Alcohol Abuse and Alcoholism, 1989-92. Fellow AAAS, APA, APS, Am. Orthopsychiat. Assn.; mem. Midwestern Psychol. Assn., Ea. Psychol. Assn., Soc. Personology, Soc. Life History Rsch. in Psychopathology. Office: Univ Mich Alcohol Rsch Ctr Ste 2A 400 E Eisenhower Pky Ann Arbor MI 48108-3318 *Clinical psychology has always appealed to me because of its concern about human trouble as well as for its scientific commitment. Clinical involvement can serve as a counterpoint to scientific and scholarly activity; a firm grounding in the datum of everyday experience is critical to the evolution of the science as well as the profession of psychology.*

ZUCKER, WILLIAM, retired business educator; b. Bridgeport, Conn., July 21, 1917; s. Meyer and Ida Lena (Elovitz) Z.; m. Kathlyn Saltman, Jan. 16, 1944; children—Peter Bayard, Alison Beth, Jeremy Michael, David Laurence. A.B., Johns Hopkins U., 1938; AM. Harvard U., 1940, PhD, 1951. Sec. Commerce and Industry Assn. of N.Y., N.Y.C., 1944-59; v.p. Downtown Lower Manhattan Assn., N.Y.C., 1959-64; pres. Southeastern Pa. Econ. Devel. Corp., Phila., 1964-73; adj. prof. Wharton Sch. U. Pa., Phila., 1972-83, assoc. dir. Entrepreneurial Ctr., Wharton Sch., 1973-83, dir. exec. edn. Wharton Sch., 1977-83, dir. Wharton Real Estate Ctr., 1983-88, Meshulam Riklis prof. creative mgmt. Wharton Sch., 1983-88; prof. emeritus U. Pa., 1988—; pres. Adviserv Co., Phila., 1993-94; lectr. CCNY, 1956-58; vis. prof. Grad. Sch. Bus. Columbia U., 1988-91. Author: Local Development Corporations, 1980, REITS, 1975; editor Real Estate Fin. Jour., 1985—; contbr. articles to profl. jours. Mem. New Canaan Bd. Edn., Conn., 1961-64, New Canaan Bd. Fin., 1958-61. Democrat. Jewish. Home: Cathedral Village 600 E Cathedral Rd # L105 Philadelphia PA 19128-1933 Office: U Pa 2000 Steinberg Dietrich Hal Philadelphia PA 19104

ZUCKERBERG, DAVID ALAN, pharmaceutical company executive; b. Bklyn., Sept. 11, 1946; s. Murray and Selma (Gold) Z.; m. Doris Tavel, May 23, 1971; children: Stephen A., Jonathan P. BS ChemE, Poly. Inst. Bklyn., 1968; MS in Biochemistry, Fairleigh Dickinson U., 1975. Process devel. engr. Procter & Gamble, Cin., 1968-70; with research and devel. Beecham, Clifton, N.J., 1970-77; with research and devel. Block Drug Co., Jersey City, 1977-86, v.p. quality assurance, quality control, 1986-91, v.p. rsch. svcs., 1991—; lectr. in chemistry St. Thomas Aquinas Coll., Sparkill, N.Y., 1978-88. Contbr. articles to profl. jours. Mem. New City Jewish Ctr. Mem. Am. Chem. Soc., Am. Inst. Chem. Engrs., Internat. Assn. Dental Rsch., Nonprescription Drug Mfrs. Assn. (mfg. controls com. 1986-90). Republican. Home: 32 Roslyn Ln New City NY 10956-3643 Office: Block Drug Co Inc 257 Cornelison Ave Jersey City NJ 07302-3113

ZUCKERBERG, ROY J., investment banking executive; b. N.Y.C., July 21, 1936; s. Sam and Gertrude R. (Rabstein) Z.; m. Barbara Hope Schwam, June 21, 1959; children: Lloyd P., Dina R. B.S., Lowell Tech. Inst., 1958. Vice pres. The Zuckerberg Co., Copiague, N.Y., 1959-67; with Goldman, Sachs & Co., N.Y.C., 1967—, v.p. securities sales, 1972, gen. ptnr., 1977, co-head securities sales div., 1988-89, co-head equities div., mem. mgmt. com., 1990—. Trustee L.I. Jewish Med. Ctr., 1981-89, vice chmn., 1989—; trustee Brandeis Sch., 1979-86, ARC Greater N.Y., 1992—, Jewish Communal Fund, 1992—; bd. dirs. The Brookdale Found., 1985—, Am. Jewish Joint Distbn. Com. Inc., 1992—; trustee The Bklyn. Mus., 1987-94; mem. bd. overseer Albert Einstein Coll. Medicine Yeshiva U., 1989—. Clubs: Harmonie, Woodmere, Mashomack. Home: 1249 Veeder Dr Hewlett NY 11557-2512 also: 435 E 52nd St New York NY 10022-6445 Office: Goldman Sachs & Co 85 Broad St New York NY 10004-2434

ZUCKER-FRANKLIN, DOROTHEA, medical scientist, educator; b. Berlin, Aug. 9, 1930; came to U.S., 1949; d. Julian and Gertrude (Feige) Zucker; m. Edward C. Franklin, May 15, 1956 (dec. 1982); 1 child, Deborah Julie. BA, Hunter Coll., 1952; MD, NYU, 1956. Diplomate Am. Bd. Internal Medicine. Intern Phila. Gen. Hosp., 1956-57; resident in internal medicine Montefiore Hosp., N.Y.C., 1957-59, postdoctoral fellow in hematology, 1959-61; with Med. Sch. NYU, N.Y.C., 1962—, prof. Med. Sch., 1974—, dir. lab., 1966—; asst. attending physician Montefiore Hosp., 1961-65; assoc. attending physician Univ. Hosp., 1968-74, attending physician, 1974—; assoc. attending physician Bellevue Hosp., 1968-74, attending physician, 1974—; cons. physician Manhattan (N.Y.) VA Hosp., 1970—, PHS Agy. for Healthcare Policy and Rsch., 1992—; sci. adv. bd., rev. panel Israel Cancer Rsch. Fund, 1982—; mem. U.S.-Israel Binat. Sci. Found., 1980—; bd. dirs. Henry M. and Lillian Stratton Found., Inc., 1987—; AID related Rsch. Rev. Com. NIHLB, 1986-90; mem. allergy immunol. com. NIH, 1974-80, pathological tng. com. NIH, 1971-74, Health Resource Coun., N.Y.C., 1971-74, blood products com. FDA, 1981-87. Mem. editl. bd. Blood, 1973-76, 80-86, Jour. Reticuloendothelial Soc., 1964-74, 80—, Am. Jour. Pathology, 1979—, Blood Cells, 1980—, Ultrastructural Pathology, 1979, Am. Jour. Medicine, 1981—, Hematology Oncology, 1982—, Jour. Immunology, 1986—; author: (with others) The Physiology and Pathology of Leukocytes, 1962, Atlas of Blood Cells, Function and Pathology, 1981, 2d edit., 1989, Amyloidosis, 1990; contbr. 250 articles to sci. publs. and 10 chpts. to med. textbooks. Recipient Career Devel. award NIH, 1965-70; NIH rsch. grantee, 1970—; postdoctoral fellow in electromicroscopy NYU, 1962-63. Fellow N.Y. Acad. Scis.; mem. Am. Fedn. Clin. Rsch., Am. Soc. Clin. Investigation, Am. Assn. Physicians, Am. Soc. Hematology (pres. 1995, chairperson subcom on leukocyte physiology 1977, chairperosn subcom on immunohematology 1984, exec. coun. 1985—, advanced learning resources com. 1987—), Soc. Exptl. Biology and Medicine, Am. Soc. Exptl. Biology, Am. Soc. Immunologists, Am. Soc. Cell Biology, Reticuloendothelial Soc. (pres. program and nominatingcoms. 1984-85), N.Y. Soc. Electron Microscopists (pres. 1962, 84-85), N.Y. Soc. for Study Blood. Office: NYU Med Ctr 550 1st Ave New York NY 10016-6402

ZUCKERKANDL, EMILE, molecular evolutionary biologist, scientific institute executive; b. Vienna, Austria, July 4, 1922; came to U.S., 1975; s. Frederic and Gertrude (Stekel) Z.; m. Jane Gammon Metz, June 2, 1950. M.S., U. Ill., 1947; Ph.D., Sorbonne, Paris, 1959. Postdoctoral research fellow Calif. Inst. Tech., Pasadena, 1959-64; research dir. CNRS, Montpellier, France, 1967-80, dir. Ctr. Macromolecular Biochemistry, 1965-75; pres. Linus Pauling Inst., Palo Alto, Calif., 1980-92, Inst. Molecular Med. Scis., Palo Alto, Calif., 1992—; cons. in genetics Stanford U., 1963, vis. prof., 1964; vis. prof. U. Del., 1976. Contbg. author: Evolving Genes and Proteins, 1965; co-author: Genetique des Populations, 1976; editor Jour. Molecular Evolution, 1971—. Decorated Order of Merit (France). Fellow AAAS; mem. Societe de Chimie Biologique, N.Y. Acad. Scis., Internat. Soc. Study Origin of Life. Home: 565 Arastradero Rd Palo Alto CA 94306 Office: Inst Molecular Med Scis 460 Page Mill Rd Palo Alto CA 94306-2025

ZUCKERMAN, MARTIN HARVEY, personnel director; b. N.Y.C., Feb. 20, 1942; s. Merwin and Helen (Weinstein) Z.; m. Joyce S. Harris, July 26, 1969; children: Lyle, Evan. BA, NYU, 1963; JD, St. John's U., 1965; LLM

NYU, 1966. Bar: N.Y. 1966. Field atty. Nat. Labor Relations Bd., N.Y.C., 1966-70; sr. atty. Simpson, Thatcher & Bartlett, N.Y.C., 1970-80; v.p. compensation and benefits Chemical Banking Corp. (formerly Mfrs. Hanover Trust Co.), N.Y.C., 1980-1983, sr. v.p., asst. personnel dir., 1983-85, exec. v.p., personnel dir., 1985-92; exec. v.p., pers. dir. Chem. Banking Corp. (formerly Mfrs. Hanover Trust Co.), 1992—; mem. mgmt. com. Chem. Banking Corp., 1994—; mem. adv. coun. on human resources mgmt. The Conf. Bd., 1992—. Trustee Drs. Hosp., 1984-92, Beth Israel Hosp., 1987—, Employee Benefit Rsch. Inst., 1989—; treas. Puerto Rican Legal Def. and Edn. Fund, Inc., mem. exec. com., 1985—. Mem. N.Y. State Bar Assn., N.Y. County Lawyers Assn.

ZUCKERMAN, MORTIMER BENJAMIN, real estate developer, publisher, editor; b. Montreal, Que., Can., June 4, 1937; came to U.S., 1961, naturalized, 1977; s. Abraham and Esther Z. B.A. in Econs. and Polit. Theory with 1st class honors, McGill U., Montreal, 1957, LL.B. with honors, 1961; M.B.A. with distinction, U. Pa., 1962; LL.M., Harvard U., 1962. Sr. v.p. Cabot, Cabot & Forbes, Boston, 1965-69; chmn. bd. Boston Properties Co., 1970—; pres., chmn. bd. Atlantic Monthly Co., Boston, 1980—; chmn., editor-in-chief U.S. News & World Report; chmn., co-pub. N.Y. Daily News; dir., exec. com. Stride Rite Corp., 1970-83; dir. Property Capital Trust Co., 1979-80, RET Income Found., 1976-79; public interest dir. Fed. Home Loan Bank of Boston, 1972-73; lectr., then assoc. prof. Harvard U. Grad. Sch. Design, 1966-74; vis. lectr. city and regional planning Yale U., 1967-69. Pres. bd. trustees Sidney Farber Cancer Inst., Boston, 1980; trustee Mus. Sci., 1980, Beth Israel Hosp., 1975, Ford Hall Forum, 1979-83, Urban Inst., Russell Sage Found., 1985-86; chmn. bd. visitors Boston U. Sch. Medicine, 1978-79; adv. bd. Ctr. Strategic and Internat. Studies; adv. bd. Wharton Sch.; bd. dirs. Wolf Trap Found., Tennis Hall of Fame. Mem. Coun. on Fgn. Rels., Internat. Inst. Strategic Studies. Clubs: Harvard (Boston and N.Y.C.); Harmonie (N.Y.C.). Office: New York Daily News 220 E 42nd St New York NY 10017*

ZUCKERMAN, RICHARD ENGLE, lawyer, educator; b. Yonkers, N.Y., Aug. 2, 1945; s. Julius and Roslyn (Ehrlich) Z.; m. Denise Ellen Spoon, July 14, 1968; children: Julie Ann, Lindsay Beth. BA, U. Mich., 1967; JD cum laude, Southwestern U., 1974. Bar: Calif. 1974, Mich. 1976, Nev. 1986, U.S. Dist. Ct. (ea. and we. dists.) Mich. 1977, U.S. Ct. Appeals (6th cir.) 1977, U.S. Ct. Appeals (9th cir.) 1982, U.S. Ct. Appeals (7th and 9th cirs.) 1994, U.S. Tax Ct. 1980, U.S. Supreme Ct. 1985. Spl. atty. organized crime and racketeering sect. U.S. Dept. Justice, Detroit, 1974-77; sr. ptnr. Raymond, Rupp, Wienberg, Stone & Zuckerman, P.C., Troy, Mich., 1977-87, Honigman, Miller, Schwartz & Cohn, Detroit, 1987—; adj. prof. Detroit Coll. Law, 1978—. Served to lt. USN, 1967-71, Vietnam. Mem. ABA (grand jury com. criminal justice sect.), Fed. Bar Assn. (chmn. criminal law sect. Detroit chpt. 1985-90, bd. dirs. 1985-94, co-chair criminal def. atty. com. 1995—), Knollwood Country Club (West Bloomfield, Mich.), Standard Club. Republican. Jewish. Office: Honigman Miller Schwartz & Cohn 2290 First National Bldg Detroit MI 48226

ZUCKERMAN, STUART, psychiatrist, educator; b. Syracuse, N.Y., Feb. 18, 1933; s. George and Cassie (Kolsan) Z. Student, U. Kans., 1950-51; BS, U. Ala., 1954; DO, Phila. Coll. Osteo. Medicine, 1958. Diplomate: Am. Osteo. Bd. Neurology and Psychiatry, Am. Nat. Bd. Psychiatry; cert. correctional health profl. Rotating intern Hosps. Phila. Coll. Osteo. Medicine, 1958-59; psychiat. fellow, resident Phila. Mental Health Clinic, 1959-62, Psychoanalytic Studies Inst., Phila., 1959-62; chief resident, 1962; chief div. neuropsychiatry Grandview Hosp., Dayton, Ohio, 1962-65; asst. med. dir., chief children's and adolescent's unit N.J. State Hosp., Ancora, 1967-70; chief outpatient dept. Atlantic City, 1970-72; practice specializing in neuropsychiatry Atlantic City, 1965—; founding prof. psychiatry, chmn. dept. Ohio U. Coll. Osteo. Medicine, Athens, 1976-77; clin. prof. Ohio U. Coll. Osteo. Medicine, 1977—; mem. faculty U. Pa. Sch. Medicine, Phila. Coll. Osteo. Medicine, 1972-76; lectr. U. Pa., 1977-79; prof. dept. psychiatry, charter faculty Sch. Medicine, Marshall U., 1977-78, clin. prof., 1979-80; clin. prof. N.Y. Coll. Osteo. Medicine, 1979—; chief mental hygiene VA Hosp., Huntington, W.Va., 1977-78; liaison psychiatrist, acting chief VA Med. Center, Perry Point, Md., 1979-80; med. dir. Mental Health Clinic of Ocean County, Toms River, N.J., 1980-85, Ventnor Mental Health Ctr., Atlantic City; chief psychiatrist N.J. Dept. Corrections So. State Correctional Facility, 1985—; attending psychiatrist Atlantic City, Shore Meml., Kessler Meml., Washington Meml., Atlantic County Mental hosps., 1965-76; attending psychiatrist, asst. dir. dept. psychiatry Phila. Gen. Hosp., 1972-76; med. dir. Shawnee Mental Health Center, (Adams, Lawrence, Scioto counties), Portsmouth, Ohio, 1977-78; cons. psychiatrist Athens Mental Health and Mental Retardation Ctr., 1976-77, Scioto Meml., So. Hills, Mercy hosps., Portsmouth, 1977-78, Lansdowne Cmty. Mental Health Center, (Greenup, Carter counties), Ashland, Ky., 1977-78, Atlantic City Med. Ctr., 1984—, Cmty. Meml. Hosp., Toms River, N.J., 1984-91, So. Ocean County Hosp., Manahawkin, N.J., 1984-91, Paul-Kimball Med Ctr., Lakewood, N.J., 1984—, Obleness Meml. Hosp., Clin. Services of Athens, Vinton, Hocking Counties, Hudson Health Ctr., Ohio U.; cons. Bayside State Prison, Leesburg, N.J., Atlantic County Justice System, Mays Landing, N.J., 1992-93, child study spl. svcs. S. Jersey sch. systems; chmn. profl. adv. com. Atlantic County Mental Health Bd.; 1969-71; mem. nominating com. Mental Health Assn., Atlantic County, 1972-75; exam. psychiatrist Jersey Police and Fire depts.; mem. Atlantic County Mental Health Bd.; mem. profl. adv. com. N.J. Dept. Corrections; cons. N.J. Dept. Pub. Advocate. Mem. adv. bd.: Osteo. Physician, 1975—; asso. editor: Bull. Am. Coll. Neuropsychiatrists, 1963-70; contbr. articles to profl. jours. Bd. dirs. Atlantic County Family Svcs. Assn., 1968-74, Cape May County Drug Abuse Coun., 1973-76, Nat. Commn. Correctional Health Care, 1988— Fellow Menninger Found., Am. Coll. Forensic Psychiatry, Am. Coll. Neuropsychiatrists (bd. reps.), Am. Acad. Disability Evaluating Physicians (charter), Acad. Medicine N.J.; mem. AMA (Physicians Recognition award 1985—), AAUP, Am. Bd. Forensic Examiners (cert.), World Psychiat. Assn., Am. Psychiat. Assn., N.J. (confidentiality, pub. psychiatry com., gen. hosp. psychiatry com., law com., mkgt. benefits com.) Psychiat. Assn., Am. Assn. Psychiatrists in Alcohol and Addictions (founder), Am., N.J. pub. health assns., Am. Osteo. Assn. (hosp. inspection team 1971-75, bd. reps.), Am. Assn. CMHC Psychiatrists, Am. Assn. Psychiatrists in Pvt. Practice, Internat. Assn. Med. Specialists, Am. Soc. Law and Medicine, Am. Acad. Clin. Psychiatrists, Corp. Advancement Psychiatry, Am. Med. Writers Assn., Nat. Council Community Mental Health Ctrs., Met. Coll. Mental Health Assn., Am. Soc. Criminology, South Jersey Neuropsychiat. Soc., Psychiat. Outpatients Ctrs. Am., Am. Coll. Legal Medicine, Acad. Psychiatry and Law (pub. info. com., edn. com., internat. affairs com.), Am. Acad. Forensic Scis., Am. Assn. Acad. Psychiatry, Am. Coll. Emergency Physicians, Am. Acad. Psychotherapists, Am. Assn. Mental Deficiency, Am. Assn. Psychiat. Services for Children, Acad. Psychosomatic Medicine, N.J. (chmn. com. on confidentiality), Fla. assns. osteo. physicians and surgeons, N.J. Hosp. Assn., Am. Vocat. Assn., Am. Assn. Group Therapy, Assn. Mil. Surgeons U.S., Nat. Assn. VA Physicians, Am. Assn. Psychiat. Adminstrs., Am. Assn. Adolescent Psychiatry, World Med. Assn., Am. Assn. Mental Health Adminstrs., Am. Assn. Gen. Hosp. Psychiatrists, Human Factors Soc., Orthopsychiat. Assn., Am. Physicians Fellowship, Assn. for Research Nervous and Mental Diseases, Atlantic County Osteo. Med. Soc. (pres. 1970-72), N.J. Assn. Mil. Surgeons U.S (v.p.), Am. Assn. Correctional Health Care, Am. Coll. Forensic Psychiatry (diplomate 1984), charter mem. Soc. of Correctional Physicians. Home: 6700 Atlantic Ave Ventnor City NJ 08406-2618 Office: Ventnor Mental Health Ctr Ventnor City NJ 08406

ZUCKERT, DONALD MACK, marketing executive; b. N.Y.C., Apr. 3, 1934; s. Sidney L. and Doris (Mack) Z.; m. Susan Liefter; children: Andrew, Timothy. AB in Govt. with honors, Bowdoin Coll., 1956; LLB, NYU, 1959. Bar: N.Y., Conn. 1960. With Ted Bates Worldwide, Inc., N.Y.C., 1960-87; pres. Ted Bates US Affiliate Group, N.Y.C., 1974-83, Ted Bates Advt./N.Y., N.Y.C., 1983-86; chmn., chief exec. officer Ted Bates Worldwide, Inc., 1986-87; mem. Backer Spielvogel Bates Worldwide Inc., N.Y.C., 1987; chmn., chief exec. officer Arcature Corp., Stamford, Conn., 1989—; bd. dirs. Calif. & Wash. Co., San Bruno, Calif., Suanti Ltd., Manchester, N.H., F.S.G.S. Inc., Stamford, Conn., Rattlesnake Holdings, Inc., Wilmington, Del. Bd. govs. Bowdoin Coll., Brunswick, Maine. Served to capt. AUS, 1956-57. Mem. Innis Arden Golf Club (Old Greenwich, Conn.), Wentworth by the Sea Country Club (New Castle, N.H.), River Club (N.Y.C.), Alpha Tau Omega. Office: Arcature Corp 3 Stamford Lndg Stamford CT 06902-7235

ZUCKMAN, HARVEY LYLE, legal educator; b. Mpls., Apr. 14, 1934; s. George and Elizabeth (Polinsky) Z.; m. Charlotte Anne Snyder, Jan. 27, 1962; children: Jill Belinda, Beth Nancy, Michael Scott. A.B., U. So. Calif., 1956; LL.B., NYU, 1959. Bar: Calif. 1960, D.C. 1973, U.S. Supreme Ct. 1963. Atty. civil div. appellate sect. U.S. Dept. Justice, Washington, 1963-67; prof. law St. Louis U., 1967-70, Columbus Sch. Law of Cath. U. Am., 1970—; dir. Inst. for Communications Law Studies Columbus Sch. Law, Cath. U. Am., 1981—; adj. prof. communications Am. U., 1976-81; cons. Bur. Nat. Affairs, 1974-81. Producer: Am. Law Inst.-ABA Legal Edn. TV series, 1973-74; co-author: Mass Communications Law, 1977, 4th edit., 1994; editor ABA newsletter Comm. Lawyer, 1981-86. Served with U.S. Army Judge Adv. Gen., 1960-63. Mem. ABA (forum com. on comm. law, co-chmn. nat. celebration of 200th anniversary of 1st amendment 1991), D.C. Bar Assn. (chairperson com. on continuing legal edn. 1975-83), Fed. Comm. Bar Assn., Am. Law Inst., Assn. Am. Law Schs. (sects. family law and mass comm.). Democrat. Office: Cath U Am Columbus Sch Law Leahy Hall Washington DC 20064

ZUEHLKE, RICHARD WILLIAM, technical communications consultant, writer; b. Milw., June 17, 1933; s. Harold Babcock and Phoebe Blanche (Frykman) Z.; m. Carol Sue Yates, Dec. 26, 1955; children: Kenneth Richard, William Woodfill, Deanne Elizabeth. B.S., Lawrence Coll., 1955; Ph.D., U. Minn., 1960. Instr. chemistry Lawrence U., 1958-62, asst. prof., 1962-68; Eliphalet Remington prof. chemistry U. Bridgeport, 1968-79, chmn. dept., 1968-73; vis. prof. U. R.I., 1976-77, 79-80, assoc. marine scientist, 1980-85; owner, pres. The Right Connection, Inc., 1983-91; pres. TetraR Cons., Inc., 1985-88; cons. Kimberly-Clark Corp., 1960-62, United Illuminating Co., 1969-75, Chem. Specialties Corp., 1970-73, Sperry Remington Corp., 1976-79; NSF Sci. Faculty fellow U. Pitts., 1966-67; asst. to dir. Gordon Rsch. Confs., 1990-94; cons., writer in field. Fellow Am. Inst. Chemists; mem. Am. Chem. Soc., AAAS, Sigma Xi, Sigma Phi Epsilon. Congregationalist. Lodge: Rotary. Home: 1410 South Rd Wakefield RI 02879-7641 Office: U RI Gordon RschCtr 1410 South Rd Wakefield RI 02879-7641

ZUERN, DAVID ERNEST, bank executive; b. Erie, Pa., July 5, 1949; s. John H. and Mathilda Zuern; 2 children. BS, Gannon U., 1971; MBA, Case Western Res. U., 1974. Investment officer Marine Bank, Erie, 1972-74, asst. v.p., 1974-76, v.p., 1976-79, sr. v.p., 1979-82, exec. v.p., 1982-84, sr. exec. v.p., 1984-88, pres., 1988-93; pres., CEO PNC Bank N.W. Pa., 1993—. Past chmn. Pub. Broadcasting N.W. Pa., Erie; chmn. Hamot Health Found., Erie; bd. trustees Gannon U., Erie; bd. dirs. Hamot Med. Ctr.; mem. cmty. agenda com. Erie Conf., 1987—; mem. adv. bd. Edinboro U., Erie United Arts Fund, 1985—; fin. chmn. Congressman Tom Ridge, 1982—; chmn. banking and ins. com. Gov.-Elect Ridge Transition Team, 1995; bd. dirs. Pa. Coun. on Econ. Edn.; corporator St. Vincent Health Systems; chmn. United Way Campaign, 1995. Recipient Disting. Alumnus award Gannon U., 1985. Mem. Pa. Bankers Assn. (past chmn. Group VII, 1986-87, chmn. pub. affairs com.). Home: 6521 Pheasant Run Blvd Fairview PA 16415-1721 Office: PNC Bank PO Box 8480 901 State St Erie PA 16501

ZUFRYDEN, FRED S., academic administrator, marketing educator, researcher; b. Grenoble, France, June 13, 1943; came to U.S., 1956; s. Henri and Cecile (Frymer) Z.; m. Toby Marlene Levin, Dec. 24, 1967; 1 child, Ryan. B.A. in Math., UCLA, 1965, M.B.A., 1966, Ph.D. in Bus. Adminstrn., 1971. Rsch. engr. mil. ops. and systems analysis group N.Am. Aviation, Inc., L.A., 1966-67; rsch. assoc. resources rsch. dept. Planning Rsch. Corp., L.A., 1967-68; ops. rsch. specialist data systems div. Litton Systems, Inc., L.A., 1968-70; asst. prof. dept. mgmt. scis. Sch. Bus. and Econs., U. Calif., Northridge, 1970-71; asst. prof. dept. mktg. Grad. Sch. Bus. U. So. Calif., L.A., 1971-75; assoc. prof. U. So. Calif., 1975-82, prof., 1982—, Ernst Hahn prof. mktg., 1991—, chmn. mktg. dept., 1987-90, rsch. dir. internat. bus. econs. and rsch. Grad. Sch. Bus., 1983—. Mem. editorial bd. Jour. Advt. Rsch., 1981—, Mktg. Sci., 1979—, Jour. Mktg., 1978—; mem. cons. and planning com. Mktg. Sci. Jour., 1979; referee Jour. Mktg. Rsch., Mgmt. Sci., Decision Sci., Jour. Internat. Rsch. in Mktg.; mem. abstract writing staff International Abstracts in Operations Rsch./Mgmt. Sci., 1973; contbr. articles to profl. jours. including Jour. Mktg. Rsch., Mktg. Sci., Jour. Operational Rsch. Soc., Mgmt. Sci., Decision Scis., Jour. Mktg., Jour. Advt. Rsch., Jour. Internat. Rsch. in Mktg., Jour. Royal Statis. Soc., Interfaces, Rsch. in Mktg., Jour. of Mktg. Rsch. Soc., Jour. of Bus., others. Rsch. grantee U. So. Calif., 1973, 75, 76, 77, 78, A.C. Nielsen Co., 1988-90. Mem. Am. Mktg. Assn. (cert. recognition 1974), Ops. Rsch. Soc. Am., Inst. Mgmt. Sci., Omega Rho, Beta Gamma Sigma.

ZUHDI, NAZIH, surgeon; b. Beirut, May 19, 1925; came to U.S. 1950; s. Omar and Lutfiye (Atef) Z.; children by previous marriage: Omar, Nabil; m. Annette McMichael; children: Adam, Leyla, Zachariah. BA, Am. U., Beirut, 1946, MD, 1950. Diplomate Am. Bd. Surgery, Am. Bd. Thoracic Surgery. Intern St. Vincent's Hosp., S.I., N.Y., 1950-51, Presbyn.-Columbia Med. Ctr., N.Y.C., 1951-52; resident Kings County SUNY Med. Ctr., N.Y.C., 1952-56; fellow SUNY Downstate Med. Ctr., Bklyn., 1953-54; resident Univ. Hosp., Mpls., 1956; resident Univ. Hosp., Oklahoma City, 1957-58, practice surgery specializing in cardiovascular and thoracic, 1958-87, practice in heart transplantation, lung transplantation and heart-lung transplantation, 1985—; founder, dir. Transplantation Inst. Bapt. Med. Ctr., 1984—, transplantation surgeon in chief Bapt. Hosp., Oklahoma City; founder, chmn. Okla. Cardiovascular Inst., Oklahoma City, 1983-84, Okla. Heart Ctr., Oklahoma City, 1984-85. Contbg. author Cardiac Surgery, 1967, 2d edit., 1972; contbr. articles to profl. jours.; developer numerous med. devices, techniques, rsch. and publs. on cardiopulmonary bypass, internal hypothermia, assisted circulation, heart surgery and transplantation of thoracic organs; developer heart-lung machines; designer, use of exptl. plastic bypass hearts; originator use of banked citrated blood for cardiopulmonary bypass for open heart surgery; of clin. non-hemic primes of heart-lung machines producing intentional hemodilution, at present, the universally accepted principle of cardiopulmonary bypass for partial and total body perfusion; researcher in cardiovascular studies. Named Hon. Citizen Brazil; named to Okla. Hall of Fame, 1994; Muslim scholar, lectr. Fellow ACS; mem. AMA, Am. Thoracic Soc., Okla. Thoracic Soc., So. Med. Assn., Okla. Med. Assn., Internat., Coll. Angiology, Am. Coll. Chest Physicians, Oklahoma City C. of C., Oklahoma County Med. Soc., Oklahoma City Clin. Soc., Okla. Surg. Assn., Oklahoma City Surg. Soc., Southwestern Surg. Congress, Am. Coll. Cardiology, Am. Soc. Artificial Internal Organs, Soc. Thoracic Surgeons (founder mem.), Am. Assn. for Thoracic Surgery, Internat. Cardiovascular Soc., Okla. State Heart Assn., Osler Soc., So. Thoracic Surg. Assn., Lillehei Surg. Soc., Internat. Soc. Heart Transplantation, Dwight Harken's Founder's Group Cardiac Surgery, Internat. Soc. Cardiothoracic Surgery (Japan, founder), Am. Soc. Transplant Surgeons, Milestones of Cardiology of Am. Coll. Cardiology, Okla. City Golf and Country Club, Okla. Hall of Fame. Achievements include first banked citrated blood for cardiopulmonary bypass for open heart surgery; invention of clinical non-hemic primes of heart-lung machines producing intentional hemodilution. Home: 7305 Lancet Ct Oklahoma City OK 73120-1430

ZUICHES, JAMES JOSEPH, academic administrator; b. Eau Claire, Wis., Mar. 24, 1943; s. William Homer and Bronnie Monica (Stich) Z.; m. Carol Ann Kurilo, Aug. 19, 1967; children: James Daniel, Joseph Kurilo. BA in Philosophy, U. Portland, 1967; MS in Sociology, U. Wis., 1969, PhD in Sociology, 1973. Instr., asst. prof. sociology Mich. State U., East Lansing, 1971-82, prof., 1982; assoc. program dir. in sociology NSF, Washington, 1979-80, program dir. in sociology, 1980-82; assoc. dir. rsch. Cornell U., Ithaca, N.Y., 1982-86; assoc. dean Coll. Agr. and Home Econs., Wash. State U., Pullman, 1986-94, dir. Agrl. Rsch. Ctr., 1986-94; program dir. food sys. and rural devel. W.K. Kellogg Found., Battle Creek, Mich., 1994-95; dean Coll. Agr. and Home Econs. Wash. State U., Pullman, 1995—; mem. adv. subcom. NSF, 1977-79; mem. sci. advc. com. USDA Nat. Rsch. Initiative, Washington, 1992-93; mem. com. on future land grant univ. bd. on agr., NRC, Washington, 1994-97; pub. Wash. Land and People mag. 1987-92. Co-editor: The Demography of Rural Life, 1993; contbr. articles to profl. jours. Pres. bd. dirs. Edgewood Village Children's Ctr., East Lansing, 1978-79. Recipient sustained superior performance award NSF, 1981; rsch. grantee NIMH, 1973, ERDA, 1978. Fellow AAAS; mem. Rural Sociol. Soc. (pres. 1992-93, editor 50th Anniversary Rsch. Series, 5 vols. 1988-93), Am. Sociol. Assn., Population Assn. Am. Roman Catholic. Avocations: skiing, swimming, hiking, reading.

ZUKER, MICHAEL, biomathematician; b. Montreal, Que., Can., Apr. 1, 1949; s. Norman and Edith (Diamond) Z.; m. Barbara Ann Boness, Dec. 24, 1978; children—Sandra Esther, Leslie Susan. B.Sc., McGill U., Montreal, Que., Can., 1970; Ph.D. MIT, 1974. Rsch. officer NRC Can., Ottawa, Ont., 1974-94; fellow Can. Inst. for Advanced Rsch., 1988-94; assoc. prof. Inst. for Biomed. Computing Washington U., St. Louis, 1994—; vis. scholar Stanford U., 1991-92. Assoc. editor: Bull. Math. Biology, 1984-86, Computer Applications in Bioscis., 1987—; contbr. research articles to profl. jours. Recipient Silver medal Royal Conservatory of Music, Toronto, 1962; Prince of Wales scholar McGill U., Montreal, Que., Can., 1969; Woodrow Wilson fellow, 1970. Mem. AAAS, Soc. Math. Biology. Avocations: piano playing, windsurfing, cycling. Home: 435 Oakley Dr Saint Louis MO 63105 Office: Washington U Inst for Biomed Computing 700 S Euclid Ave Saint Louis MO 63110

ZUKERMAN, MICHAEL, lawyer; b. Bklyn., Oct. 3, 1940; s. Charles Morris and Gertrude Ethel Zukerman; m. Claire J. Goldsmith, June 25, 1961 (div. 1986); children: Steven, Amy; m. Elaine DeMasi, Nov. 21, 1986; children: Jaclyn, Laura. BS, U. Fla., 1961; LLB, St. John's U., 1964; LLM, NYU, 1966. Bar: N.Y. 1965, Pa. 1983, U.S. Tax Ct. 1984. Credit analyst, loan officer Franklin Nat. Bank, 1964-66; assoc. Jaffin, Schneider, Kimmel & Galpeer, N.Y.C., 1966-67; ptnr. Zukerman, Licht & Friedman and predecessors, N.Y.C., 1967-79, Baskin & Sears, P.C., N.Y.C., 1979-85, Graubard, Moskowitz, Dannett, Horowitz & Mollen, 1985-86, Gersten, Savage, Kaplowitz & Zukerman, 1986-89; of counsel Olshan, Grundman, Frome & Rosenzweig, 1990—; pres. First Ptnrs. Credit Corp., N.Y.C., 1988-93, exec. v.p. Brookhill Group, 1986-88, Real Mark Adv. Corp., 1993—; mem. bd. dirs. Interjurist LTD, internat. law firm. Contbg. editor Real Estate Taxation and Acctg., 1988—; lectr. on various subjects, 1986—. Trustee Temple Beth Torah, Melville, N.Y., 1972-80; bd. dirs. Dayton Mgmt. Corp., 1974—; Suffolk Jewish Community Planning Bd., Hauppague, N.Y., 1982-85, WATSCO, Inc.; Am. Vending Assocs., 1983-86; trustee, treas. YMHA Suffolk County, Hauppague, 1980-85; co-chmn. bus. adv. coun. Town of Greenburgh, 1992; bd. dirs. Congregation Bnai Elohim. Mem. ABA. Home: 6 Thomas St Scarsdale NY 10583-1031 Office: Olshan Grundman Frome & Rosenzweig 505 Park Ave New York NY 10022-1106

ZUKERMAN, MORRIS E., investment banker; b. Vineland, N.J., June 13, 1944; s. Nathan Z.; m. Karen D. Solomon, Dec. 5, 1971; children: Laura B., Sarah B., Alexandra W. Diploma, Phillips Acad., Andover, Mass., 1962; BA, Harvard Coll., 1966; MBA (with high distinction), Harvard Grad. Sch. Bus. Adminstrn., 1970; MA (with honors), Cambridge (Eng.) U., 1968. Economist Internat. Bank for Reconstrn. and Devel., Washington, 1968-70, U.S. Office Mgmt. and Budget, Washington, 1970-72; mng. dir. Morgan Stanley & Co. Inc., N.Y.C. and L.A., 1972-88; pres. M. E. Zukerman & Co. Inc., N.Y.C., 1988—. Trustee Phillips Acad. Andover, 1984-88, Jackson Lab., Bar Harbor, Maine, 1988-90, The Spence Sch., N.Y.C., 1989-93; bd. dirs. L.A. Music Ctr. Opera, 1986-90; vis. com. on faculty recruitment, Harvard U. Sch. of Arts and Scis., 1990-92. Mem. Harvard Club N.Y.C., University Club (N.Y.C.), Regency Club (L.A.), Oxford & Cambridge U. Club (London). Avocation: African affairs. Office: M E Zukerman & Co Inc 535 Madison Ave 19th Fl New York NY 10022

ZUKERMAN, PINCHAS, concert violinist, violist, conductor; b. Tel Aviv, July 16, 1948; came to U.S., 1962; s. Yehuda and Miriam (Lieberman) Z.; m. Eugenia Rich, May 26, 1968 (div.); children: Natalia, Arianna; m. Tuesday Weld, 1985. Student, Juilliard Sch. Music, 1965-68; MusD (hon.), Brown U., 1989. Ind. concert violinist, 1968—. With impresario, Sol Hurok, 1967-76; condr., soloist English Chamber Orch., 1974, Mostly Mozart Festival, N.Y.C., 1975; guest condr., soloist Los Angeles Philharm., Boston Symphony, Phila. Orch., N.Y. Philharm.; music dir. South Bank Festival, London, 1978-80, St. Paul Chamber Orch., 1980-87; prin. festival condr. Dallas Internat. Summer Music Festival, 1990—; prin. guest condr. Dallas Symphony, 1993—; toured with Isaac Stern; mem. trio with Daniel Barenboim and Jacqueline du Pre; (rec. artist) CBS, EMI, Philips Classics labels, RCA Victor Red Seal, BMG Classics. Winner Internat. Levintritt Competition, 1967. Office: care Shirley Kirshbaum & Assoc 711 West End Ave-5 KN New York NY 10025*

ZUKOSKI, CHARLES F., surgeon, educator; b. St. Louis, Jan. 26, 1926; s. Charles F. Jr. and Bernadine (Edom) Z.; m. Elizabeth Paull Jacob, May 9, 1953; children: Helen, Charles, Robin, Ann. Degree, U. N.C., 1947; MD, Harvard U., 1951. Diplomate Am. Bd. Surgery. Intern Roosevelt Hosp., N.Y.C., 1951-52; resident Univ. Hosp., Birmingham, Ala., 1955-58; asst. chief VA Hosp., Birmingham, 1958-59; rschr. Med. Coll. Va., Richmond, 1959-61; asst. prof. Vanderbilt U. Med. Ctr., Nashville, 1961-68; assoc. prof. Coll. Medicine U. N.C., Chapel Hill, 1968-69; prof. surgery Coll. Medicine U. Ariz., Tucson, 1969-95, prof. emeritus dept. surgery Coll. Medicine, 1995—; chief surg. svc. VA Hosp., Tucson, 1990-95. Contbr. 85 articles to profl. publs. Capt. USAF, 1953-55. Fellow NIH, 1959-61, 66-67, Josia Macy Found., 1976-77. Fellow ACS, Am. Surg. Assn.; mem. Soc. Univ. Surgeons, So. Surg. Assn. Achievements include research on immunosuppressive drugs. Home: 1901 E Miraval Cuarto Tucson AZ 85718

ZUKOWSKI, WALTER HENRY, administrative science educator; b. Worcester, Mass., Sept. 28, 1914; s. Frank B. and Helen (Jankowska) Z.; m. Lucille Kathryn Pinette, Dec. 26, 1955; 1 dau., Mary L.A. B.B.A., Clark U., 1948, A.M., 1949; Ph.D., 1956. Instr. Worcester Poly. Inst., 1949-50, Clark U., 1951-52; mem. faculty Colby Coll., Waterville, Maine, 1952—; prof. adminstrv. sci. Colby Coll., 1965-73, Wadsworth prof. adminstrv. sci., 1973-82; emeritus Wadsworth prof. adminstrv. sci., 1982—; chmn. dept. adminstrv. sci. Colby Coll., 1958-80; asst. prof. La. State U. (C.Z. br.), summers 1952-54; vis. prof. Rockefeller Found. grantee Al-Hikma U., Baghdad, Iraq, 1958-59, Robert Coll., Istanbul, Turkey, 1965-66; vis. prof., cons. ednl. policy Iranzamin Coll., Tehran, Iran, 1972-73; cons. in field. Mem. platform com. Maine Republican Party, 1964. Served with USAAF, 1942-46. Mem. Am. Finance Assn., Am. Econ. Assn., Am. Accounting Assn. Home: PO Box 402 Waterville ME 04903-0402

ZUKOWSKY, JOHN ROBERT, curator; b. N.Y.C., Apr. 21, 1948; s. John and Mary (Charchan) Z. BA, Hunter Coll., 1971; MA, SUNY, Binghamton, 1974, PhD, 1977. Archtl. archivist Hudson River Mus., Yonkers, N.Y., 1974-76; archtl. archivist Art Inst. Chgo., 1978-81, architecture curator, 1981—; mem. Historic Sites Adv. Council, Springfield, Ill., 1982-83, Landmarks Preservation Council, Chgo., 1982-83; jury mem. Honor awards AIA, Washington, 1987. Co-author: Hudson River Villas, 1985, The Sky's the Limit Chicago Skyscrapers, 1990, Austrian Architecture and Design, 1991; co-author, editor: Mies Reconsidered, 1986, Chicago Architecture: 1872-1922, 1987, Chicago Architecture and Design, 1923-93, 1993, The Many Faces of Modern Architecture, 1994; editor: A System of Architectural Ornament (Louis H. Sullivan), 1990; contbr. articles to profl. jours. Decorated Chevalier des arts and lettres (France), Ritter Kreuz 2d class, Austria; recipient Honig award Chgo. chpt. Am. Soc. Appraisers, 1989; postdoctoral rsch. fellow NEH, 1977-78, Rsch. fellow, NEA, 1991. Mem. AIA (hon., Disting. Svc. award Chgo. chpt. 1986), Arts Club Chgo. Office: Art Inst Chgo Dept Architecture 111 S Michigan Ave Chicago IL 60603-6110

ZULCH, JOAN CAROLYN, retired medical publishing company executive, consultant; b. Great Neck, N.Y., Apr. 10, 1931; d. Walter Howard and Edna Ruth (Howard) Z. B.S. in Biology, Allegheny Coll., 1952; postgrad., Hunter Coll., 1954. Med. sec. E.R. Squibb & Sons, N.Y.C., 1952; with Macmillan Pub. Co., N.Y.C., 1952-88, editorial asst. med. dept., 1952-56, asst. editor med. dept., 1956-58, editor med. dept., 1958-61, med. editor coll. and profl. div., 1961-75, sr. editor medicine, coll. and profl. div., 1975-78, exec. editor med. books, profl. books div., 1978-79, editor-in-chief, 1979-80, asst. v.p., editor-in-chief profl. books div., 1980-82; v.p., pub. med., nursing, health sci. dept. Macmillan Pub. Co., 1982-85, v.p., pub. med. books, sci., tech., med. dept., 1985-88, cons. med. pub., 1989—. Recipient Best Illustrated Med. Book award Assn. Med. Illustrators, 1977, Outstanding Book in Health Sci. award Assn. Am. Pubs., 1982. Mem. AAAS, AAUW, Post Libr. Assn. L.I.U. (rec. sec. 1990-93, exec. coun. 1990—). Friends of Locust Valley Libr. (pres. 1991-93, 94—), treas. 1993-94), Alpha Gamma Delta, Delta Sigma Rho. Republican. Home and Office: 36 Wood Ln Lattingtown PO Box 547 Locust Valley NY 11560-0547

ZULKER, CHARLES BATES, broadcasting company executive; b. Pleasantville, N.J., Dec. 20, 1926; s. William John and Virginia (Carr) Z.; m. Virginia Wright, June 24, 1949; children: Connie Lee, Timothy Scott Charles. Adminstrv. officer Princeton (N.J.) U., 1950-60; asst. mgr. Sta. WPEL, Montrose, Pa., 1960-65; gen. mgr. Sta. WCHR, Trenton, N.J., 1965—. Trustee Princeton Evang. Fellowship, 1973-83; bd. council Word of Life Internat., Schroon Lake, N.Y., 1974-82; mem. exec. bd. Upper Makefield Community Assn., 1972-79. With U.S. Army, 1944-46. Mem. Wooden Canoe Heritage Assn. of Am., Nat. Religious Broadcasters, Nat. Assn. of Broadcasters. Office: Woodside Rd Yardley PA 19067

ZULKEY, EDWARD JOHN, lawyer, author; b. Chgo., June 10, 1948; s. Edward M. and Virginia (Domecki) Z.; m. Janice Buren, Aug. 12, 1972; children: Claire, Jack. BA, Northwestern U., 1970; JD, U. Ill., 1973. Bar: Ill. 1973, Ariz. 1990, U.S. Ct. Appeals (7th cir.) 1973, U.S. Dist. Ct. (no. dist.) Ill. 1973, U.S. Dist. Ct. (no. dist.) Ariz. 1990. Ptner. Baker & McKenzie, Chgo., 1973—. Contbr. articles to profl. jours. Named to Order of the Coif, 1973. Mem. ABA (co-chair legal malpractice of ins. coverage), Internat. Assn. Def. Counsel. Avocations: Am. history, running, sailing, guitar. Office: Baker & McKenzie 1 Prudential Plz 130 E Randolph Dr Chicago IL 60601-6206

ZUMBRUN, RONALD ARTHUR, lawyer; b. Oak Park, Ill., Dec. 12, 1934; s. Arthur Raymond and Jean (Crandall) Z.; m. Ann Hartley, July 14, 1957; children: Kevin Ronald, Richard Douglas, Heidi Ann. BA in Econs., Pomona Coll., 1957; LLB, U. Calif., Berkeley, 1961. Bar: Calif. 1962, U.S. Dist. Ct. (no. dist.) Calif. 1962, U.S. Ct. Appeals (9th cir.) 1962, U.S. Dist. Ct. (cen. dist.) Calif. 1963, U.S. Supreme Ct. 1974, U.S. Dist. Ct. (ea. dist.) Calif. 1974, U.S. Ct. Appeals (D.C. cir.) 1975, U.S. Dist. Ct. (so. dist.) Calif. 1978, U.S. Ct. Appeals (3d, 5th, 7th, 8th, 9th and 11th cirs.) 1981, D.C. 1985, U.S. Ct. Appeals (fed. cir.) 1994. Sr. trial atty. Calif. State Dept. Pub. Works, Sacramento, 1961-71; dep. dir. legal affairs Calif. State Dept. Social Welfare, Sacramento, 1971-73; spl. counsel HEW, Washington, 1973; legal dir., pres. Pacific Legal Found., Sacramento, 1973-94, pres. emeritus, 1994—; pres., mng. atty. Zumbrun, Best & Findley, Sacramento, 1991—. Mem. Gov. Reagan's Task Force on Pub. Assistance, Sacramento, 1970, exec. office of Pres. Welfare Reform Study Team, 1972, Gov. Reagan's Task Force Project: Safer Calif., 1974, Carmichael (Calif.) adv. commn. on Parks and Recreation, 1969—. Served to capt. U.S. Army, 1957-70.9. Mem. Calif. Bar Assn., Sacramento Bar Assn., Phi Alpha Delta. Republican. Episcopalian. Lodge: Rotary. Office: Zumbrun Best & Findley 2150 River Plz Dr Ste 255 Sacramento CA 95833

ZUMBRUNNEN, DAVID ARNOLD, mechanical engineering educator, consultant; b. Salt Lake City, Sept. 3, 1955; s. Lynn David and Anne Cecilia Z.; m. Elizabeth Buck. B in Mech. Engring., U. Minn., 1977; MS in Mech. Engring., Purdue U., 1984, PhD in Mech. Engring., 1988. Registered profl. engr., Ind., S.C. Rsch. asst. Purdue U., West Lafayette, Ind., 1982-83, rsch. fellow, asst., 1985-88; staff engr. MPR and Assocs., Washington, 1983-85; assoc. prof. Clemson (S.C.) U., 1988—. Lt. USN, 1977-82. Presdl. Faculty fellow The White House/NSF, 1992—. Mem. ASME, AIAA, Soc. of Mfg. engrs., Soc. of Plastics engrs. Avocations: rowing, tennis, jogging, bicycling. Office: Clemson U Sch Mech & Indsl Engring Clemson SC 29634-0921

ZUMETA, BERTRAM WILLIAM, retired economist; b. Rutherford, N.J., Jan. 18, 1919; s. Arthur H. and Bertha A. (Cook) Z.; m. Ruth Spencer Astbury, Apr. 1, 1943; children: William Mark, David Cook. A.B., Franklin and Marshall Coll., 1940; postgrad., U. Pa., 1946-50, 52-53. Lectr., instr. econs. and stats. Wharton Sch. U. Pa., 1945-51, 53-63; economist Fed. Res. Bank of Phila., 1959-66, Phila. Electric Co., 1966-70; sr. v.p., economist 1st Pa. Bank, 1970-72, asst. to pres., 1972; v.p., economist First Pa. Corp., 1973-74, sr. v.p., economist, 1974-78; exec. v.p., economist First Pa. Bank and First Pa. Corp., Phila., 1978-80; sr. lectr. mgmt. Wharton Sch., U. Pa., 1980-81; bd. govs. Pa. Economy League, 1979-83; mem. U.S. Sec. of Commerce's Econ. Adv. Bd., 1967-68, Pa. Gov.'s Econ. Adv. Coun., 1967-70, 74-76. Served to comdr. USNR, 1942-45, 51-53. Home: 511 Foulkeways Gwynedd PA 19436

ZUMINO, BRUNO, physics educator, researcher; b. Rome, Apr. 28, 1923; came to U.S., 1951; naturalized, 1962; divorced. D in Math. Scis., U. Rome, 1945. From asst. prof. to prof. NYU, 1953-69; staff mem. European Orgn. for Nuclear Rsch. (CERN), Geneva, 1969-81; prof. physics U. Calif., Berkeley, 1981—; Alfred C. and Mary Sprague Miller rsch. prof., 1989; Loeb lectr. Harvard U., Cambridge, Mass., spring 1966; vis. prof. Columbia U., N.Y.C., fall 1978; disting. vis. prof. Enrico Fermi Inst., U. Chgo., spring 1983. Recipient Max Planck medal German Phys. Soc., 1989, Wigner medal Found. for Group Theory and Fundamental Physics, Am. Nuclear Soc., 1992; co-recipient Dirac medal Internat. Ctr. for Theoretical Physics, Trieste, Italy, 1987; Guggenheim Found. fellow, 1968-69, 87-88. Fellow Am. Phys. Soc. (co-recipient Heineman prize 1988), Am. Acad. Arts and Scis.; mem. NAS, Italian Phys. Soc. Office: U Calif Dept Physics Berkeley CA 94720*

ZUMPE, DORIS, psychiatry researcher, educator; b. Berlin, May 18, 1940; came to U.S., 1972; d. Herman Frank and Eva (Wagner) Z. BSc, U. London, 1961, PhD, 1970. Asst. to K.Z. Lorenz, Max-Planck-Inst. for Verhaltensphysiologie, Seewiesen, Fed. Republic Germany, 1961-64; rsch. asst. and assoc., lectr. Inst. Psychiatry, U. London, 1965-72; rsch. assoc. Emory U. Sch. Medicine, Atlanta, 1972-74, asst. prof. psychiatry (ethology), 1974-77, assoc. prof., 1977-87, prof., 1987—; reviewer NSF, 7 sci. jours. Contbr. over 140 articles to profl. jours. NIMH grantee, 1971—. Mem. AAAS, Internat. Soc. Psychoneuroendocrinology, Internat. Primatological Soc., Internat. Soc. for Human Ethology, Soc. for Study of Reprodn., Am. Soc. Primatologists, N.Y. Acad. Scis., Earl Music Am., Viola da Gamba Soc. Am. Avocation: music. Office: Emory U Sch Medicine Dept Psychiatry Atlanta GA 30322

ZUMWALT, ELMO RUSSELL, JR., retired naval officer; b. San Francisco, Nov. 29, 1920; s. Elmo Russell and Frances Z.; m. Mouza Coutelais-du-Roche; children: Elmo Russell, James Gregory, Ann F., Mouzetta C. B.S. with distinction, U.S. Naval Acad. 1942; student, Naval War Coll., 1952-53, Nat. War Coll., 1961-62; LL.D., Villanova U., 1972, U. N.C., 1975, Nat. U., 1979; L.H.D., U.S. Internat. U., 1973; Dr. Pub. Service, Central Mich. U., 1974; D.Sc., Mich. Tech. U., 1979. Commd. ensign U.S. Navy, 1942, advanced through grades to adm., 1970; served with U.S.S. Phelps, 1942-43, U.S.S. Robinson, San Francisco and South Pacific, 1943-44; exec. officer U.S.S. Saufley, 1945-46; exec. officer, navigator U.S.S. Zellars, 1946-48; asst. prof. naval sci. U. N.C., Chapel Hill 1948-50; comdg. officer U.S.S. Tills, 1950-51; navigator U.S.S. Wisconsin, Korea, 1951-52; head shore and overseas bases sect. Navy Dept., Washington, 1953-55; comdr. destroyer U.S.S. Isbell, 1955-57; lt. detailer Navy Dept., Washington, 1957; asst. asst. for naval personnel to Asst. Sec. Navy, Washington, 1957-58; exec. asst., sr. aide Office Asst. Sec. Navy, 1958-59; comdr. Frigate U.S.S. Dewey, 1959-61; desk officer for France, Spain and Portugal Office Sec. Def., 1962-63, dir. arms control and contingency planning for Cuba, 1963; exec. asst., sr. aide Sec. of Navy, 1963-65; comdr. Cruiser Destroyer Flotilla, 1965-66; dir. chief naval ops. systems analysis group Washington Office Chief Naval Ops.; dep. sci. officer Center Naval Analyses, 1966-68; comdr. U.S. Naval Forces Vietnam, chief naval adv. group Vietnam, 1968-70; chief naval ops. Washington, 1970-74; pub. gov. Am. Stock Exchange, 1979-85; dir. Transway Internat., Inc., 1976-85, RMI, Inc., 1983-86, Am. Bldg. Maintenance Industries, 1995, Navistar Internat. Corp., Gifford-Hill & Co., Inc., 1979-86, Unicorp Am. Corp., 1994; pres., chief exec. officer, dir. Am. Med. Bldgs., Inc., Milw., 1977-79; vice chmn. bd. Am. Med. Bldgs., Inc., 1980-83, chmn., chief exec. officer, 1983-85, chmn., 1985—; pres. Admiral Zumwalt & Cons. Inc., 1979-86, Admiral Zumwalt & Cons. Inc., 1980—; bd. dirs. Aeronca, Inc., Fleet Aerospace, Inc., NL Industries, Inc. Dallas Semiconductor; vis. prof. Vanderbilt U., 1974-75, U. Nebr., 1975, Whittier Coll., 1975; mem. bd. govs. Am. Stock Exch., 1978-84; chmn. Phelps-Stokes Fund, 1985-93. Author: On Watch, 1976, My Father My Son, 1986. Dem. candidate for U.S. Senate, 1976; chmn. Nat. Marrow Donor Program, 1988-94, Ethics and Pub. Policy Ctr., 1988—. Decorated D.S.M. with Gold Star, Legion of Merit with Gold Star, Bronze Star with combat V, Navy Commendation medal with combat V; Philippine Republic Presdl. citation; Vietnamese Chuong My medal 1st class; Nat. Order Vietnam 3d class; Vietnamese Navy Disting. Service Order 1st class. Address: 1000 Wilson Blvd Ste 3105 Arlington VA 22209-2211

ZUMWALT, RICHARD DOWLING, flour mill executive; b. Amarillo, Tex., Dec. 1, 1912; s. Richard Dowling and Cora Bell (Pate) Z.; m. Florine Anita Nelson, Oct. 23, 1938; 1 dau., Alexandra Anita (Mrs. Klaus Schwabe). Extension student, Tex. Tech. Coll., 1931, Dallas Coll., 1949. With J. C. Crouch Grain Co., 1931-44; with Burrus Mills, Inc., Dallas, 1944-83, exec. v.p., 1956-64, pres., 1964-83; sec.-treas. Zumwalt Inc., 1973—; ret. gen. mgr. Burrus milling dept. Cargill, Inc.; past pres. Bulgur Assos., Washington, Dallas Grain Exchange. Mem. Millers Nat. Fedn., Tex. Mfrs. Assn. (past dir.). Home: 7353 Blairview Dr Dallas TX 75230-5416

ZUMWALT, ROGER CARL, hospital administrator; b. Eugene, Oreg., Oct. 26, 1943; s. Robert Walter and Jean Elaine (Adams) Z.; m. Sharon Marlene Ryan, Aug. 22, 1970; children: Kathryn Nicole, Timothy Robert. Student, Boise State U., 1963-65; BA, Western Oreg. State Coll., 1969; postgrad., U. Iowa, 1969-71; MA cum laude, Oreg. State U., 1973. Adminstr. Coulee Community Hosp., Grand Coulee, Wash., 1973-75, Eastmoreland Hosp., Portland, Oreg., 1975-81; hosp. surveyor Am. Osteopathic Assn., Chgo., 1977—; exec. dir. Community Hosp., Grand Junction, Colo., 1981—; speaker numerous local and nat. presentations on healthcare, hosp. mktg./success/costs, etc., 1981—; bd. dirs. Healthcare Fin. Mgmt. Assn., Portland, 1978-80; chief exec. officer Community Med. Pla., 1984—, Community Health Care Providers Orgn., 1986—, Community Hosp. Found., 1988—; Newspaper columnist, 1973-75; contbr. articles, presentations to profl. publs. Commr. Multnomah County Health Care Commn., Portland, 1978-81; health cons. Grant County Housing Authority, Grand Coulee, 1974-75; mem. park bd. City of Tigard, Oreg., 1976-78; caucus rep. Mesa County Rep. Party, Grand Junction, 1988; mem. adv. com., pres.'s office Mesa State Coll., Grand Junction, 1989; bd. dirs. Hospice of Grand Valley, Grand Junction, Colo., 1992—, mem. devel. com., 1993—. With USAF, 1961-65. Fellow Coll. Osteopathic Healthcare Execs. (bd. dirs. 1985-88, pres. 1987, examiner 1989—, Disting. Svc. award 1989); mem. Am. Osteopathic Hosp. Assn. (bd. dirs. 1987—, treas. 1992-93, 1st v.p. 1994—, 2d v.p. 1993-94), Am. Osteopathic Assn., Bur. Healthcare Facilities Accreditation (v.p., 1994), Joint Commn. on Am. Healthcare Organ. (Task Force on Small and Rural Accreditation, 1994), Colo. Hosp. Assn. (bd. dirs. 1987-92), Grand Valley Hospice (bd. dirs. 1992—), Mountain States Voluntary Hosp. Assn. (bd. dirs. 1984—, exec. com. 1991—, v.p. 1993, vice chmn. bd. 1992—), Western Col. Ind. Practice Assn. (medicine mauls measles com., fin. com. 1991-92), Western Colo. Health Care Alliance (bd. dirs. 1989-94, v.p. 1992, chmn. bd. 1993, past chmn. 1994), Mesa County Mental Health Assn. (bd. dirs. 1988-89, 1991-92), Grand Junction C of C (bd. dirs. 1991-93), Rotary, Masons, Shriners (pres. Grand Junction club 1989, bd. dirs. El Jebel 1986-90, 1st v.p. Western Colo. club 1989). Republican. Methodist. Avocations: golf, camping, fishing, hunting. Home: 2515 Snowmass Ct Grnd Junction CO 81503-1752 Office: Community Hosp 2021 N 12th St Grand Junction CO 81501-2999

ZUMWALT, ROSS EUGENE, forensic pathologist, educator; b. Goodrich, Mich., July 18, 1943; s. Paul Lawrence and Lila Ann (Birky) Z.; m. Theresa Ann Schar, Sept. 12, 1970 (div. Apr. 1988); children: Christopher Todd, Tenley Ann; m. Cheryl Lynn Willmann, Sept. 4, 1988; 1 child, David Willman Zumwalt. BA, Wabash Coll., 1967; MD, U. Ill., 1971. Diplomate in anat. and forensic pathology Am. Bd. Pathology. Intern, resident in pathology Mary Bassett Hosp., Cooperstown, N.Y., 1971-73; resident in anat. and forensic pathology Southwestern Med. Sch., Dallas, 1973-76; asst. med. examiner Dallas County, Dallas, 1974-76; staff pathologist, dir. labs. Naval Regional Med. Ctr., Camp Lejeune, N.C., 1976-78; dep. coroner Cuyahoga County, Cleve., 1978-80, Hamilton County, Cin., 1980-86; assoc. prof. pathology U. Cin. Sch. Medicine, 1980-86; prof. pathology U. N.Mex. Sch. Medicine, Albuquerque, 1987—; chief med. investigator Office of Med. Investigator, Albuquerque, 1987—; trustee Am. Bd. Pathology, Tampa, Fla., 1993—. Lt. comdr. USN, 1976-78. Fellow Am. Acad. Forensic Scis., Coll. Am. Pathologists; mem. AMA, Nat. Assn. Med. Examiners (bd. dirs. 1984—), Am. Soc. Clin. Pathologists (chmn. coun. on forensic pathology), Am. and Can. Acad. Pathologists. Avocation: golf. Office: Office of Med Investigator 700 Camino de Salud Albuquerque NM 87131 Also: 819 El Alhambra Cir NW Albuquerque NM 87107-6301

ZUNDE, PRANAS, information science educator, researcher; b. Kaunas, Lithuania, Nov. 26, 1923; came to U.S., 1960, naturalized, 1964; s. Pranas and Elzbieta (Linajevic) Z.; m. Alge R. Bizauskas, May 29, 1945; children: Alge R., Audronis K., Aurelia R., Aidis L., Gytis J. Dipl. Ing., Hannover Inst. Tech., 1947; MS, George Washington U., 1965; PhD, Ga. Inst. Tech., 1968. Dir. project Documentation Inc., Bethesda, Md., 1961-64; mgr. mgmt. info. system Documentation Inc., Bethesda, 1964-65; sr. research scientist Ga. Inst. Tech., Atlanta, 1965-68, assoc. prof., 1968-72, prof. dept. computer sci., 1973-91, prof. emeritus, 1991—; cons. UNESCO, Caracas, Venezuela, 1970-72, Esquela Polit. Nacional, Quito, Ecuador, 1974-75, State of Ga., Atlanta, 1976-78, Royal Sch. Librarianship, Copenhagen, 1985-87, Clemson (N.C.) U., 1987—; N.Y. State Dept. Edn., 1993; vis. prof. Simon Bolivar U., Caracas, 1976, J. Kepler U., Austria, 1981; vis. scientist Riso Nat. Lab., Roskilde, Denmark, 1983, Lithuanian Acad. Scis., Vilnius, 1988-89. Author: Agriculture in Soviet Lithuania, 1962, National Science Information Systems in Eastern Europe, 1972; editor: Procs. Info. Utilities, 1974, Procs. Founds. of Info. and Software Sci., 1983-90; contbr. articles to tech. and sci. jours. Mem. senate Vitoldus Magnus U., Kaunas, Lithuania, 1990—. NSF grantee; Fulbright prof. NAS, 1975. Mem. Am. Soc. Info. Sci., Semiotic Soc. Am., Soc. Sigma Xi. Roman Catholic. Office: Ga Inst Tech Coll Computing North Ave Atlanta GA 30332

ZUNG, THOMAS TSE-KWAI, architect; b. Shanghai, China, Feb. 8, 1933; came to U.S., 1937, naturalized, 1954; 1 child, Thomas Bates. Student Drew U., 1950-51, (Rose scholar) Va. Poly. Inst., 1951-53, Columbia U., 1955-57; BArch, U. Mich., 1960; MS in Design Sci. (student R. Buckminster Fuller), Internat. Coll., 1982. Project architect Edward Durell Stone, architect, N.Y.C., 1958, 60-65; architect, Cleve., 1967—; pres. Buckminster Fuller, Sadao and Zung, architects, 1979—; prin. archtl. works include City Cleve. Pub. Utilities Bldg., Cleve. State U. Sports Center Dome, Mayfran, Inc., Sawmill Creek Lodge, U. Akron Guzzetta Hall, music, speech and theater arts center, Alumni Center Bowling Green State U., U. Akron Master Plan-West, City of East Cleveland, Superior Euclid beautification plan, student recreation ctr. at Bowling Green State U., Glenville Public Libr., campus bldg. Tex. Wesleyan Coll., recreation, health and phys. edn. bdg. Wittenberg U., Medina Res. Park Office, arena, health, phys. edn. complex U. Akron, Dyke Coll., Lima State Prison, Cleve. Children's Christian Home, State of Ohio Pre-Release Ctr. Cleve., Lorain-Grafton State Prison, Mayfield High Sch., Asian Village Project, Cleve. Metroparks Tropical Rainforest Bldg., Student Union Wittenberg U., YWCA Salem Ohio, China Internat. Trade Ctr. People's Rep. China, additions to Cleve. Hopkins Internat. Airport, Ohio State U. Coll. of Dentistry-Postle Hall and Hist. Costume and Textile Mus., Columbus, Western Res. Psychiat. Hosp. Ohio, Trumbull State Prison; patentee in field. Task force chmn. Greater Cleve. Growth Assn., 1970; mem. Coun. Human Rels., 1972, Leadership Cleve. Class '77; cubmaster local Boy Scouts Am., 1977-79; bd. dirs. Buckminster Fuller Inst., 1983—, Pearl S. Buck Found., 1989—, hist. house com. Pearl S. Buck House, cons. architect; trustee Pace Assn., 1970-73, Karamu House, 1974-80, Cleve. Inst. Music, 1979—, Ohio Arts Coun., 1982-84, Chinese Cultural Assn., 1980-84; vestryman St. Christopher-by-River, 1980-83. Served with Signal Corps, U.S. Army, 1953-55. Decorated 4 medals; recipient Design award Cleve. chpt. AIA, 1972, Korean Inst. Constrn. Tech., 1984; Anicka Design award U. Mich., 1959, Sr. design prize, 1960; Pub. Works award State of Ohio, 1971, Ohio Valley ABC Design Excellence award Wittenberg U. Student Union, 1989, others. Mem. AIA (dir. Cleve. chpt. 1980, design award 1989), Am. Soc. Planning Ofcls., English Speaking Union (trustee 1972-75), Ohio Soc. Architects, Ohio Assn. Minority Architects and Engrs. (trustee 1982—), Hermit Club, City Club (dir. 1972-74, v.p. 1974), Rotary. Office: Buckminster Fuller Sadao & Zung 13000 Shaker Blvd Cleveland OH 44120

ZUNKER, RICHARD E., insurance company executive; b. 1938. BS, U. Wis., 1964. With Employers Ins. Wausau, Wis., 1964-69, Northwestern Nat. Investors Life, 1969-75; with Safeco Life Ins. Co., Seattle, 1975—, pres., also bd. dirs. With U.S. Army, 1956-58. Office: Safeco Life Ins Co PO Box 34690 Seattle WA 98124-1690

ZUNZ, OLIVIER JEAN, history educator; b. Paris, July 19, 1946; s. Jean R. and Monique M. (Blin) Z.; m. Christine M. Crommen, July 3, 1970; children: Emmanuel, Sophie. Licence in history and geography, U. Paris X, 1968, M in History, 1969; Doctorat-ès-Lettres, U. Paris I, Panthéon-Sorbonne, 1982. Scientist Ctr. Nat. de la Recherche Scientifique, Paris, 1976-78; asst. prof. dept. history U. Va., Charlottesville, 1978-83, assoc. prof., 1983-88, prof., 1988—; vis. prof. Ecole des Hautes Etudes en Scis., Sociales, Paris, 1985—; dir. seminar for Coll. Tchrs. NEH, 1989, 92. Author: The Changing Face of Inequality: Urbanization, Industrial Development, and Immigrants in Detroit, 1980-1920, 1982, Making America Corporate, 1870-1920, 1990; editor, co-author: Reliving the Past: The Worlds of Social History, 1985; co-editor: (with David Ward) The Landscape of Modernity: Essays on New York City, 1900-1940, 1992; mem. editorial bd. Revs. in Am. History, 1990—; contbr. articles, book revs. to profl. jours. Jr. fellow Mich. Soc. Fellows, 1973-76, John Simon Guggenheim Meml. Found. fellow, 1986-87; grantee U. Mich.-Ford Found. Population Devel. Fund, 1974-76, NSF, 1976-78, NEH, 1979-81, 84-87; also recipient numerous rsch. grants. Mem. Am. Hist. Assn., Orgn. Am. Historians. Home: 1368 Hilltop Rd Charlottesville VA 22903-1225 Office: U Va Dept History Randall Hall Charlottesville VA 22903-3284

ZUPCOFSKA, PETER F., lawyer; b. Boston, Feb. 18, 1952; s. Patrick P. and Josephine M. (Gnoza) Z.. BA magna cum laude, Boston Coll., 1973, JD, 1976. Bar: Mass. 1977, U.S. Supreme Ct. 1994. Asst. register Norfolk divsn. Probate and Family Ct., Dedham, Mass., 1976-83; assoc. Burns & Levinson, Boston, 1983-88, ptnr., 1989; of counsel Bingham, Dana & Gould, Boston, 1989-92, ptnr., 1992—; mem. Commonwealth Mass. Dept. Social Svcs. No. Code adv. com., 1986-89; lectr. in field. Co-author: Motions and Cases in Family Law Trial Advocacy, Family Law Trial Inst.: Problems and Cases, 1992; author: Drafting Documents to Support a Divorce Action, 1994; contbr. chpt. to Massachussetts Family Law Manual, 1994; contbr. articles to profl. jours. Mem. Law and Child Devel. Project Boston Coll., 1974-76; participant Probate and Family Ct. Lawyer for the Day Project, 1990-95; bd. dirs. Boston Coll. Alumni, 1993—; mem. Boston Coll. Law Sch. Alumni Coun., 1991—, Pres. Cir., 1991—; Dean's Coun., 1986—, Leadership Gifts com., 1987-90, chmn. Alumni Assn. Law Day, 1989, co-chmn. Class 1976 5th Yr., 10th Yr., 15th Yr. Reunion com.; vol. Hole in the Wall Gang Camp, Ashford, Conn., 1991, benefit com., 1992-94; co-chmn. Boston Benefit, 1995. Mem. ABA (family law sect. 1978—, exec. mem. adoption com. 1982-83, vice-chmn. 1980-82, Merit cert. 1981-83), Mass. Bar Assn. (family law sect. 1983—, co-chmn. Norfolk probate and family ct. bench bar com. 1988-89, Cert. Appreciation 1988-89), Boston Bar Assn. (family law sect. 1989—), Boston Estate Planning Coun., Mass. Continuing Legal Edn. (curriculum adv. com., family law 1990-93, 95—). Home: 85 Dartmouth St Boston MA 02116 Office: Bingham Dana & Gould 150 Federal St Boston MA 02110

ZUPKO, ARTHUR GEORGE, consultant to drug industry, retired college administrator; b. Yonkers, N.Y., Nov. 22, 1916; s. George and Julia (Tutko) Z.; m. Lillian Belle Cosner, Dec. 20, 1947; 1 child, Arthur Maynard. Student, N.Y. U., 1936-38; B.S., U. Fla., 1942; M.S., Purdue U., 1948, Ph.D., 1949; D.Sc. (hon.), L.I. U., 1979. Research asst. Burroughs Wellcome Co., Tuckahoe, N.Y., 1936-38; asst. prof., assoc. prof., prof. St. Louis Coll. Pharmacy, 1949-55, assoc. dean, 1955, dean, 1956-60; provost Bklyn. Coll. Pharmacy, L.I. U., 1960-73, pres., 1973-76; pres. Arnold and Marie Schwartz Coll. Pharmacy and Health Scis., 1976-79, pres. emeritus, 1979—; bd. dirs. MedPhone, Inc., U.S. Adapted Names, Biofine Pharm.; mem. bd. pharmacy coms. Chas. Pfizer & Co. Author: (with Otto Ruhmer) Contributions of Jews to Pharmacy, 1959, Drug Interactions, 1979; Contbr. articles to profl. jours. Chmn. spl. gifts Bklyn. chpt. Am. Cancer Soc., 1963; solicitor ARC, 1962-63; merit badge counselor Hutchinson-Bronx River council Boy Scouts Am., 1963-64; solicitor United Fund, 1961-65; mem. Narcotic Addiction Centers Com., 1960-65; bd. dirs. Korean-Am. Found., Tb and Respiratory Assn., Bklyn.; mem. spl. com. Cooley's Anemia Found. Served with U.S. Army, 1934-36; Served with USNR, 1942-46. Decorated Bronze Star medal. Fellow Am. Found. Pharm. Edn.; mem. Am. Pharm. Assn. (hon. chmn. bd. trustees 1988), Am. Coll. Apothecaries, N.Y. State Pharm. Soc. (hon. pres.), Kings County Pharm. Soc., N.Y. Acad. Pharmacy, AAAS, N.Y. Acad. Sci., Sigma Xi, Rho Chi, Phi Kappa Phi, Phi Lambda Upsilon, Delta Sigma Theta, Alpha Zeta Omega. Home: 402 Santa Helena Ln Fort Myers FL 33903-1507

ZUPKO, RAMON, composer, music professor; b. Pitts., Nov. 14, 1932; s. Michael E. and Frances E. (Bartek) Z.; m. Vonette Sarche, Sept. 14, 1969; 1 child, Mischa. BS in Music, Juilliard, 1956, MS in Music, 1957. Asst. prof. music Chgo. (Ill.) Musical Coll., 1967-71; prof. music Western Mich. Univ., Sch. Music, Kalamazoo, 1971—. Recipient composition fellowship Guggenheim Found., 1982, Composers award Am. Acad. & Inst. of Arts and Letters, N.Y., 1982, Disting. Faculty award Mich. Acad. Governing Bds., Lansing, 1984, Composers awards NEA, Washington, 1978, 80, 85. Mem. Soc. Composers Inc., Am. Composers Alliance, Am. Music Ctr., Internat. Soc. Contemporary Music, Phi Kappa Phi. Avocations: biking, photography. Home: RR 1 Kalamazoo MI 49009-9801 Office: Sch Music Dalton Ctr We Mich U Kalamazoo MI 49008

ZURAW, KATHLEEN ANN, special education and physical education educator; b. Bay City, Mich., Sept. 29, 1960; d. John Luke and Clara Josephine (Kilian) Z. AA with high honors, Delta Community Coll., 1980; BS with high honors, Mich. State U., 1984, MA, 1987. Cert. spl. edn., mentally impaired phys. edn. grade K-12, adaptive phys. edn. tchr., Mich. Summer water safety instr. Camp Midicha, Columbia, Mich., 1982, Bay Cliff Health Camp, Big Bay, Mich., 1983; summer spl. edn. tchr. Jefferson Orthopedic Sch., Honolulu, 1984, 85, 86, Ingham Intermediate Sch. Dist., Mason, Mich., 1987; spl. edn. tchr. Bay Arenac Intermediate Sch. Dist., Bay City, 1985-87, Berrien County Intermediate Sch. Dist., Berrien Springs, Mich., 1987—; mem. citizen amb program fitness delegation People's Republic China, 1991. Area 17 coach Mich. Spl. Olympics, Berrien Springs, 1987—; mem. YMCA, St. Joseph, Mich., 1987—, Y-Ptnrs., 1989, Coun. Exceptional Children; participant Citizen Ambassador Delegation to People's Republic of China, 1991. Mem. Am. Alliance Health, Phys. Edn., Recreation and Dance, Phi Theta Kappa, Phi Kappa Phi, Phi Delta Kappa. Roman Catholic. Avocations: sports, crafts. Home: 7306 W S Saginaw Rd Bay City MI 48706

ZURAWSKI, VINCENT RICHARD, JR., biotechnology company executive, research scientist; b. Irvington, N.J., June 10, 1946; s. Vincent Richard and Norma Mary (Alliston) Z.; m. Mary R. Stanziola, Aug. 18, 1968; children: Daniel Vincent, John Alliston. B.A., Montclair State Coll., 1968; Ph.D., Purdue U., 1973. Postdoctoral research fellow chemistry dept. Purdue U., West Lafayette, Ind., 1974; rsch. fellow dept. medicine Harvard Med. Sch., Boston, 1975-78, instr. dept. medicine, 1978-79; rsch. fellow dept. medicine Mass. Gen. Hosp., Boston, 1975-79; co-founder Centocor, Inc., Malvern, Pa., 1979, v.p., tech. dir., 1979-82, sr. v.p., tech. dir., 1982-83, exec. v.p., tech. dir., 1983-86, corporate sec., 1981-86, sr. v.p. tech. affairs, 1986-87, sr. v.p., chief scientific officer, 1987-93; founder, pres., chief exec. officer Apollon Inc., 1992—; lectr. Harvard Med. Sch., Boston, 1985-92; vis. prof. Radiumhemmet and Karolinska Hosp., Stockholm, 1988; mem. adv. com. devel. rsch. in cancer diagnostics Nat. Cancer Inst., 1988-89; mem. biotechnology adv. com. Phila. Tech. Coun., 1992—; bd. dirs. Pa. Biotechnology Assn., 1993—. Contbr. articles to profl. jours. and chpts. to books; assoc. editor Jour. Clin. Lab. Analysis, 1986-87; adv. editor Nuclear Med. Communications, 1986—; patentee in field; pioneer in clin. applications of monoclonal antibodies. With USAR, 1969-76. NIH postdoctoral fellow, 1976-78; Med. Found. research fellow, 1977-78; NIH grantee, 1985, 87-90. Mem. AAAS, Am. Assn. Cancer Rsch., Am. Chem. Soc., Am. Soc. Microbiology, Am. Soc. for Biochemistry and Molecular Biology, Am. Assn. Immunologists. Office: Apollon Inc 1 Great Valley Pky Malvern PA 19355-1423

ZUREK, WOJCIECH HUBERT, physicist; b. Bielsko-Biala, Silesia, Poland, Dec. 19, 1951; came to U.S., 1975; s. Maksymilian Stanislaw and Anna Katarzyna (Piaskowska) Z.; m. Anna Krystyna Debogorska, June 10, 1977; children: Agnes Anna, Maximilian Francis. MSc in Physics, S Staszic Tech. U., Krakow, Poland, 1974; PhD in Physics, U. Tex. Rsch. fellow Dept. Physics, U. Tex., Austin, 1979-81; vis. fellow Astrophysics, U. Oxford, Eng., 1981; rsch. fellow Calif. Inst. Tech., Pasadena, 1981-83; disting. rsch. fellow

---

Los Alamos (N.Mex.) Nat. Lab., 1984-87, staff mem., 1987-91, theoretical astrophysics group leader, 1991—; external assoc. prof. Santa Fe Inst., 1988—, assoc. cosmology program Canadian Inst. for Advanced Rsch., Toronto, 1989—. Editor (with J.A. Wheeler) Quantum Theory and Measurement, 1983, (with W.A. Miller and A. van der Merwe) Between Quantum and Cosmos, 1988, Complexity, Entrophy and Physics Information, 1990; contbr. articles to Astrophys. Jour., Nature, Phys. Rev., Phys. Rev. Letters, Physics Today; editor (with others) Physical Origins of Time Asymmetry, 1994. Richard Chace Tolman fellow Calif. Inst. Tech., 1981-83, J. Robert Oppenheimer fellow Los Alamos Nat. Lab., 1984-87, Fellows Prize, 1988. Achievements include research in the role of decoherence in the transition from quantum to classical, in cosmological phase transitions, in galaxy formation, physics of information, computation, entropy and complexity, Maxwell's demonology. Office: Theoretical Astrophysics T-6 MS B288 Los Alamos Nat Lab Los Alamos NM 87545

ZURHEIDE, CHARLES HENRY, consulting electrical engineer; b. St. Louis, May 9, 1923; s. Charles Henry and Ollie C. (Kirk) Z.; m. Ruth M. Plueck, June 25, 1949; children—Barbara Anne, Pamela S. B.S. in Elec. Engring, U. Mo., Columbia, 1944. Registered profl. engr., Mo. Distbn. engr. Laclede Power & Light Co., St. Louis, 1944-45; sub-sta. engr., then indsl. engr. Union Electric Co., St. Louis, 1945-51; chief elec. engr. Fruin-Colnon Contracting Co., St. Louis, 1951-54; a founder, treas., v.p. Smith-Zurheide, Inc., St. Louis, 1954-65; pres. Zurheide-Herrmann, Inc., St. Louis, 1965—, chmn. bd., 1988—; chmn. Elec. Code Rev. Commn., St. Louis, 1965-93, Mo. Bd. Profl. Engrs., 1977-82, St. Louis Indsl. Devel. Commn., 1965-67; mem. adv. panel region 6 GSA, 1977—; plan commn., City of Ferguson, Mo., 1968-73; tech. adv. com. St. Louis C. of C., 1977. Recipient Distinguished Service in Engring. award U. Mo., 1976. Fellow Am. Cons. Engrs. Council; mem. Mo. Soc. Profl. Engrs. (Engr. of Year award 1970), Cons. Engrs. Council Mo., IEEE, Illuminating Engring. Soc., Engrs. Club St. Louis, Tau Alpha Pi. Clubs: Norwood Hills Country, Mo. Athletic. Home: 25 Lake Pembroke Dr Saint Louis MO 63135-1210 Office: Zurheide-Herrmann Inc 4333 Clayton Ave Saint Louis MO 63110-1621

ZURIER, ROBERT BURTON, medical educator, clinical investigator; b. Passaic, N.J., Feb. 19, 1934; s. Milton and Lillian (Matzner) Z.; m. Catherine Elizabeth Miers, June 3, 1962; 1 child, Adam Wheaton. BS, Rutgers U., 1955; MD, U. Tex. Southwestern Med. Ctr., Dallas, 1962; MA (hon.), U. Pa., 1981. Intern, then resident in medicine Boston City Hosp., 1962-64; fellow in medicine St. Lukes Hosp., N.Y.C., 1964-66; fellow in rheumatology NYU, 1970-73; pvt. practice internal medicine Holden, Mass., 1967-70; asst. prof. medicine U. Conn., Farmington, 1973-76, assoc. prof., 1976-80; prof., chief. rheumatology U. Pa., Phila., 1980-91; prof. medicine, dir. rheumatology div. U. Mass. Med. Ctr., Worcester, 1991—. Served to capt. USAR, 1956-68. Guggenheim Found. fellow, 1986. Mem. AAAS, Am. Coll. Rheumatology, Am. Soc. Clin. Investigation, Interurban Clin. Club (pres. 1989-90). Office: U Mass Med Ctr 55 Lake Ave N Worcester MA 01655-0001

ZURKOWSKI, PAUL GEORGE, information company executive; b. Milw., Nov. 8, 1932; s. Stanley Frank and Martha (Bednarz) Z.; m. Margaret Ann Becker, July 9, 1960; children: Paul Coleman, Pamela Carol, Patricia Christine, Peggy Catherine, Paula Claire, Peter Christopher. B.A., U. Wis., Whitewater, 1954; LL.B., U. Wis., Madison, 1957. Bar: Wis. 1957, U.S. Supreme Ct. 1961. Publisher Our Ads (shopping guide), Palmyra, Wis., 1950-55; investigator legal firm Swingen & Stern, Madison, 1955-58; atty. HHFA, Washington, 1958; examiner ICC, 1958-59; congl. legis. asst., 1959-61, 64-69; individual legal practice, also congl. home sec. Madison, 1961; exec. dir. Info. Industry Assn., Washington, 1969; pres. Info. Industry Assn., 1972-89, Ventures in Info., Chevy Chase, Md., 1989—; bd. dirs. Herner & Co. Publisher Holy Redeemer News, 1984-87, Today's Parish, 1987-90, Our Parish Times, 1990—. Pres. Parish Cmty. Svcs., Inc., Md., 1991—; founder Cath. Bus. Network, 1993, past pres., 1993-94, sec. 1994—. Served with AUS, 1957; as officer USAR, 1961-64. Decorated Army Commendation medal; recipient Disting. Alumni Service award U. Wis., Whitewater, 1974; named to Info. Industry Hall of Fame, 1988. Office: 8027 Ellingson Dr Chevy Chase MD 20815

ZUR LOYE, HANS-CONRAD, research chemist. BSc in Chemistry, Brown U., 1983; PhD in Chemistry, U. Calif., Berkeley, 1988. Postdoctoral fellow dept. chemistry Northwestern U., Evanston, Ill., 1988-89; assoc. prof. dept. chemistry MIT, Cambridge. Exxon Faculty fellow Am. Chem. Soc., 1994. Office: MIT Dept Chemistry 77 Massachusetts Ave Cambridge MA 02139-4307*

ZURMUHLE, ROBERT WALTER, physicist; b. Luzern, Switzerland, Nov. 27, 1933; came to U.S., 1961, naturalized, 1966; s. Otto and Marie (Schmidli) Z. M.S., U. Zurich, 1958, Ph.D., 1960. Asst. prof. physics U. Pa., Phila., 1963-67; assoc. prof. U. Pa., 1967-76, prof., 1976—. Contbr. articles to nuclear physics jours. Fellow Am. Phys. Soc.; mem. New Helvetic Soc., Sigma Xi. Home: 24 University Mews Philadelphia PA 19104-4756 Office: U Pa Dept Physics Philadelphia PA 19104

ZUSPAN, FREDERICK PAUL, obstetrician/gynecologist, educator; b. Richwood, Ohio, Jan. 20, 1922; s. Irl Goff and Kathryn (Speyer) Z.; m. Mary Jane Cox, Nov. 23, 1943; children: Mark Frederick, Kathryn Jane, Bethany Anne. B.A., Ohio State U., 1947, M.D., 1951. Intern Univ. Hosps., Columbus, Ohio, 1951-52; resident Univ. Hosps., 1952-54, Western Res. U., Cleve., 1954-56; Oblebay fellow Western Res. U., 1958-60, asst. prof., 1958-60; chmn. dept. ob-gyn McDowell (Ky.) Meml. Hosp., 1956-58, chief clin. services, 1957-58; prof., chmn. dept. ob-gyn Med. Coll. Ga., Augusta, 1960-66; Joseph Boliver DeLee prof. ob-gyn, chmn. dept. U. Chgo., 1966-75; obstetrician, gynecologist in chief Chgo. Lying-In Hosp., 1966-75; prof., chmn. dept. ob-gyn Ohio State U., Columbus, 1975-87; R.L. Meiling prof. in ob-gyn Ohio State U. Sch. Medicine, Columbus, 1984-90; prof. emeritus Ohio State U., Columbus, 1991—. Founding editor: Lying In, Jour. Reproductive Medicine; editor-in-chief: Am. Jour. Ob-Gyn and Ob-Gyn. Reports, (with Lindheimer and Katz) Hypertension in Pregnancy, 1976; Current Developments in Perinatology, 1977, (with Quilligan) Operative Obstetrics, 1981, 89, Manual of Practical Obstetrics, 1981, 90, Am. Jour. Ob-Gyn., Clin. and Exptl. Hypertension in Pregnancy, 1979-86, (with Rayburn) Drug Therapy in Ob-Gyn., 1981, 2d edit. 1986; editor: (with Christian) Controversies in Obstetrics and Gynecology; editor in chief Ob-Gyn. Reports, 1988-90; editor in chief Am. Jour. Ob-Gyn.; contbr. articles to med. jours., chpts. to books. Pres. Barren Found., 1974-76. Served with USNR, 1942-43; to 1st lt. USMCR, 1943-45. Decorated DFC, Air medal with 10 oak leaf clusters. Mem. Soc. Gynecol. Investigation, Chgo. Gynecol. Soc., Am. Assn. Ob-Gyn, Columbus Ob-gyn Soc. (pres. 1984-85), Am. Acad. Reproductive Medicine (pres.), Am. Coll. Obstetricians and Gynecologists, Assn. Profs. Gynecology and Obstetrics (pres. 1972), South Atlantic Assn. Obstetricians and Gynecologists (Found. prize for research 1962), Central Assn. Ob-Gyn (cert. of merit, research prize 1970), Am. Soc. Clin. Exptl. Hypnosis (exec. sec. 1968, v.p. 1970), So. Gynecol. Investigation, Internat. Soc. Study Hypertension in Pregnancy (pres. 1981-83), Am. Gynecology and Obstetrics Soc. (pres. 1986-87), Soc. Perinatal Obstetrics, Perinatal Research Soc., Sigma Xi, Alpha Omega Alpha, Alpha Kappa Kappa. Home: Upper Arlington 2400 Coventry Rd Columbus OH 43221-3754 *The strength of our nation rests in the quality of our offspring. Every fetus has the privilege of being wellborn.*

ZUSSY, NANCY LOUISE, librarian; b. Tampa, Fla., Mar. 4, 1947; d. John David and Patsy Ruth (Stone) Roche; m. R. Mark Allen, Dec. 20, 1986. BA in Edn., U. Fla., 1969; MLS, U. So. Fla., 1977, MS in Pub. Mgmt., 1980. Cert. librarian, Wash. Adnl. evaluator State of Ga., Atlanta, 1969-70; media specialist DeKalb County Schs., Decatur, Ga., 1970-71; researcher Ga. State Libr., Atlanta, 1971; asst. to dir. reference Clearwater (Fla.) Pub. Libr., 1972-78, dir. libs., 1978-81; dep. state libr. Wash. State Libr., Olympia, 1981-86, state libr., 1986—; chmn. Consortium Automated Librs., Olympia, 1982—; cons. various pub. librs., Wash., 1981—; exec. officer Wash. Libr. Network, 1986-90; v.p. WLN (non-profit org.), 1990-93. Contbr. articles to profl. jours. Treas. Thurston-Mason Community Mental Health Bd., Olympia, 1983-85, bd. dir., 1982-85; mem. race com. Seafair Hydroplane Race, Seattle, 1986—, mem. milk carton derby team, 1994—. Mem. ALA, Assn. Specialized and Coop. Libr. Agys. (legis. com. 1983-86, chmn. legis. com. 1985-87, vice chmn. state libr. agys. sect. 1985-86, chmn.

---

state ibr. agys. sect. 1986-87, chmn. govt. affairs com. Libr. Adminstrn. and Mgmt. Assn. 1986-87), Freedom to Read Found. (bd. dirs. 1987-91), Chief Officers of State Libr. Agys. (dir.-at-large 1987-90, v.p./pres. elect 1990-92, pres. 1992-94), Wash. Libr. Assn. (co-founder legis. planning com. 1982—, fed. rels. coord. 1984—), Fla. Libr. Assn. (legis. and planning com. 1978-81), Pacific N.W. Libr. Assn., Rotary, Phi Kappa Phi, Phi Beta Mu. Avocations: hiking, barbershop chorus/quartet, hydroplane boat racing, cross country skiing. Home: 904 E Bay Dr NE #404B Olympia WA 98506-3970 Office: Wash State Libr PO Box 42464 Olympia WA 98504-2464

ZUSY, CATHERINE, curator; b. Washington, May 4, 1958; d. Frederick John and Mary Jane (Lloyd) Z.; m. Samuel Conant Kendall, Sept. 6, 1992. BA, Bucknell U., 1981; MA in History Mus. Studies, SUNY, Oneonta, 1984. Curator of edn. Deland (Fla.) Mus., 1981-82; asst. curator State Capital Pub. Mus., Guthrie, Okla., 1982-83; rsch. asst., dept. Am. decorative arts Mus. Fine Arts, Boston, 1985-87; curator decorative arts The Bennington (Vt.) Mus., 1989; chief curator N.H. Hist. Soc., Concord, N.H., 1991—; lectr. L.A. County Mus. Arts, M. H. de Young Mus., San Francisco, Mus. Fine Arts, Boston, others. Author: Highlights from the Bennington Museum, 1989, Norton Stoneware and American Redware: The Bennington Museum Collection, 1992; contbr. author to catalogues; contbr. articles to profl. jours. Sec. N.H. Visual Arts Coalition, 1992-94; mem. steering com. N.H. Save Outdoor Sculpture, 1992-94, Sprocket Gallery, Manchester, N.H., 1993-94. Hist. Deerfield Summer fellow, 1981, Nat. Mus. Act and Norse Found. fellow, 1983-84, Louise du Pont Crowninshield Rsch. fellow Winterthur Mus., 1990; grantee Am. Ceramic Cir., 1993-95; recipient Charles F. Montgomery award Decorative Arts Soc., 1993. Office: NH Hist Soc 30 Park St Concord NH 03301

ZVETINA, JAMES RAYMOND, pulmonary physician; b. Chgo., Oct. 14, 1913; s. John and Jennie (Albrecht) Z.; m. Florence Courtney, Feb. 4, 1944. BS, Loyola U., 1940; MD, U. Ill., 1943. Intern West Suburban Hosp., Oak Park, Ill., 1944, resident physician, 1944-45; asst. ward med. officer USNH, NOB, Norfolk, Va., 1945; staff physician Pulmonary TB Svc. VA Med. Hosp., Hines, Ill., 1946-54; asst. chief Pulmonary Svc. VA Med. Hosp., Hines, Ill., 1954-68, sect. chief, 1968-88, attending physician, 1988-91, cons., 1992—; clin. prof. medicine Coll. Medicine, U. Ill., Chgo., 1978—; mem. adv. bd. Coll. Medicine, U. Ill., 1985—; rep. Rsch. Conf. in Pulmonary Disease, VA Armed Forces, 1946-74. Contbr. articles to profl. jours. V.p. Chgo. Cath. Physicians, 1979, pres., 1978. Comdr. USNR, 1945-46, med. officer USNR, ret. Recipient Svc. award 40 Yrs. VA Adminstrn., 1985, Svc. award 30 Yrs. U. Ill. Med. Sch., 1978. Fellow Am. Coll. Chest Physicians; mem. AMA, Ill. State Med. Soc. (Fifty Yr. club), Chgo. Med. Soc. Roman Catholic. Achievements include research in area of pulmonary infections. Home: 96 Forest Ave Riverside IL 60546-1977 Office: VA Hines Hines IL 60141

ZWAHLEN, FRED CASPER, JR., journalism educator; b. Portland, Oreg., Nov. 11, 1924; s. Fred and Katherine (Meyer) Z.; m. Grace Eleanor DeMoss, June 24, 1959; children: Molly, Skip. BA, Oreg. State U., 1949; MA, Stanford U., 1952. Reporter San Francisco News, 1949-50; acting editor Stanford Alumni Rev., Palo Alto, Calif., 1950; successively instr. journalism, news bur. asst., prof. journalism, chmn. journalism dept. Oreg. State U., Corvallis, 1950-91, prof. emeritus, 1991—; Swiss tour guide, 1991—; corres. Portland Oregonian, 1950-67. Author: (with others) Handbook of Photography, 1984. Coord. E.E. Wilson Scholarship Fund, 1964—; active budget com. Corvallis Sch. Dist., 1979. Recipient Achievement award Sch. Journalism U. Oregon, 1988. Mem. Assn. for Edn. in Journalism and Mass Communications (conv. chmn. 1983, pres.' award 1988), Oreg. Newspaper Pubs. Assn. (bd. dirs. 1980-85, student loan fund named in his honor 1988), Soc. Profl. Journalists (nat. svc. citation 1988), Corvallis Country Club, Shriners, Masons, Elks, Moose, Eagles, Delta Tau Delta. Republican. Presbyterian. Avocations: photography, sightseeing, travel. Home: 240 SW 7th St Corvallis OR 97333-4551 Office: Oreg State U Dept Student Activities Corvallis OR 97331

ZWASS, VLADIMIR, computer scientist, educator; b. Lvov, USSR, Feb. 3, 1946; came to U.S., 1970, naturalized, 1979; s. Adam and Friderike (Getzler) Z.; m. Alicia Kogut, Apr. 24, 1977; 1 child, Joshua Jonathan. M.S., Moscow Inst. Energetics, 1969; M.Ph., Columbia U., 1974, Ph.D., 1975. Mem. profl. staff IAEA, Vienna, Austria, 1970; asst. prof. computer sci. Fairleigh Dickinson U., 1975-79, assoc. prof., 1979-84, prof., 1984—, prof. computer sci. and mgmt. info. systems, 1990—, chmn. com. computer sci., 1976—; cons. U.S. Govt., Met. Life Ins. Co., Citibank, Diebold Group; seminar assoc. Columbia U., 1986—; speaker nat. and internat. meetings. Author: Introduction to Computer Science, 1981, Programming in Fortran, 1981, Programming in Pascal, 1985, Programming in Basic, 1986, Management Information Systems, 1992; editor-in-chief Jour. Mgmt. Info. Systems, 1983—; contbr. articles to profl. jours. and publs., Ency. Britannica, N.Y. Times, chpts. to books. Columbia U. fellow, 1970-71; Helena Rubinstein Found. scholar, 1971-75; grantee USN. other agys. Mem. IEEE, Assn. Computer Machinery, Assn. for Info. Sys., Sigma Xi, Eta Kappa Nu. Home: 538 Churchill Rd Teaneck NJ 07666-2900 Office: Fairleigh Dickinson U Teaneck NJ 07666

ZWEBEN, MURRAY, lawyer, consultant; b. Elizabeth, N.J., May 9, 1930; s. Jacob and Anna (Katz) Z.; m. Elaine Tinkelman, Nov. 22, 1950 (div. Apr. 1974); children: M. Lisa, Marc Samuel, John Eric, Harry T.; m. Anne Waggoner, Apr. 23, 1974; 1 child, Suzanne Grady. BS, Albany (N.Y.) State U., 1952, MS, 1953; LLB, George Washington U., 1959. Sec. to parliamentarian U.S. Senate, Washington, 1956-59, asst. parliamentarian, 1963-75, parliamentarian, 1975-81, parliamentarian emeritus, 1983—; law clk. U.S. Claims Ct., Washington, 1959-60; atty. Columbia Gas Systems, N.Y.C., 1960-63; pvt. practice, Washington, 1981-84; cons. atty. Nossaman, Guthmar, Knox & Elliott, Washington, 1984-86, Elliott, Zweben & Steelman, Washington, 1986-90, Elliott & Zweben, Washington, 1990—. Lt. USN, 1953-58. Lt. USN, 1953-56. Avocation: tennis. Home: 4010 Highwood Ct NW Washington DC 20007-2131 Office: 1227 25th St NW # 800 Washington DC 20037

ZWEIBEL, JOEL BURTON, lawyer; b. N.Y.C., Feb. 7, 1935; s. Jacob and Ruth (Fleischner) Z.; m. Lynn Herzog (dec. Nov. 1984); children: Jane, Emily; m. Chrystine Marie Trichter. BBA, CCNY, 1955; LLB, Yale U., 1958. Bar: N.Y. 1959. Ptnr. Kaye, Scholer, Fierman, Hays & Handler, N.Y.C., 1969-79, Gelberg & Kronovet, N.Y.C., 1979-81, Kramer, Levin, Nessen, Kamin & Frankel, N.Y.C., 1981-90, O'Melveny & Myers, N.Y.C., 1990—; lectr. 2d Ann. Uniform Comml. Code Law Inst., 1968. Author: Creditors' Rights Handbook, 1980; co-author: Herzog's Bankruptcy, 6th edit., 1980; contbr. articles to profl. jours. Recipient award Bankruptcy and Reorgn. div. Fedn. United Jewish Appeal, 1989. Mem. ABA, Assn. of Bar of City of N.Y. (chmn. com. on bankruptcy and corp. reorgn. 1981-84), Nat. Bankruptcy Conf. (chmn. com. on avoiding powers 1983—, treas. 1991), Beta Gamma Sigma. Avocations: art, theatre, music, photography. Home: 325 E 72nd St New York NY 10021-4685 Office: O'Melveny & Myers 153 E 53rd St New York NY 10022-4611

ZWEIFEL, DAVID ALAN, newspaper editor; b. Monroe, Wis., May 19, 1940; s. Cloyence John and Uva Lorraine (Skinner) Z.; m. Sandra Louise Holz, Sept. 7, 1968; children: Daniel Mark, Kristin Lynn. BJ, U. Wis., 1962. Reporter The Capital Times, Madison, Wis., 1962-71, city editor, 1971-78, mng. editor, 1978-83, editor, 1983—. V.p. Alliance for Children and Youth, Madison, 1990—; bd. dirs. United Cerebral Palsy Dane County, Madison, 1984-91. Lt. U.S. Army, 1963-65; col. USNG, ret. Named Investigative Reporter of Yr. Madison Press Club, 1972. Mem. Am. Soc. Newspaper Editors (com. freedom info.), Wis. AP (pres. 1987-88), Wis. Freedom Info. Coun. (pres. 1986—), Wis. N.G. Assn. (trustee 1975-81), U. Wis. Alumni Assn., Elks. Avocations: running, bowling, book collecting. Home: 5714 Tecumseh Ave Monona WI 53716 Office: The Capital Times PO Box 8060 Madison WI 53713

ZWEIFEL, DONALD EDWIN, automobile dealer, civic affairs volunteer; b. L.A., Nov. 30, 1940; s. Robert Fredrick and Eugenia Bedford (White) Z.; m. Donna Jean Croslin; 1 son, Phillip Matthew. Student, Orange Coast Coll., 1963-67, UCLA. Coll. Law, Irvine, 1968-70, Western State U. Coll. Law, 1973, Irvine U. Coll. Law, 1974-75, Rancho Santiago Jr. Coll., 1988, Chapman U., 1989, 93—; grad., Aviation Ground Sch., 1990; student, USAF Air U., 1994-

95. Cert. Student Pilot, 1989. Devel. tech. Hughes Aircraft, Newport Beach, Calif., 1963-64; co-founder Sta. KUCI-FM, Irvine, Calif., 1970; owner, mgr. Zweifel Jaguar Car Sales and Svc., Santa Ana, Calif., 1975-76; pres. Zweifel & Assocs. Inc., Santa Ana, 1977-86, Zweifel South Coast Exotic Cars, Orange, Calif., 1987—. Editor: (coll. textbook) The Dream Is Alive, Space Flight and Exploration In Earth Orbit. Vol. emergency coord. emergency mgmt. div. Orange County Fire Dept., 1985-87, Navy Relief Soc., 1993, CAP Squadron, 1993, sr. programs officer, 1993-94, asst. transp. officer Calif. Wing Hdqrs., 1994-95, Group VII Facilities officer, 1994-95, squadron pers. officer, 1993-95, Calif. wing rep. to Orange County Vol. Orgns. Assisting in Disaster, ARC, 1994—, Calif. wing vol. Office Emergency Svcs., Calif., 1994—; grad. Squadron Leadership Sch., 1993, Wings Supply Officers Sch., 1995; program coord. Young Astronaut Coun., 1989-90; cadet CAP, USAF auxiliary, Long Beach, Calif., 1953-60, 62-64; bd. dirs. Orange County Homeless Issues Taskforce, 1994—, Orange County Homeless Svc. Providers for the Reuse of Marine Corps Air Sta., Tustin, Calif., 1994—; mem. restoration adv. bd., chmn. operable unit # 1 subcom. Marine Corps Air Sta., El Toro, Calif., 1994—; apptd. to CALEPA Mil. Environ. Adv. Com., 1995. With Army N.G., 1958-59. Recipient 5 certs. achievement Fed. Emergency Mgmt. Agy., 1989-91, 2 certs. appreciation CAP, 2 certs commendation, 1994. Mem. Air Force Assn. (vice-chmn. civilian recruitment Calif. state membership com. 1988-89, 90-91, v.p. membership, Gen. Doolittle chpt. bd. dirs. 1987-89, 90-92, Exceptional Svc. award Gen. Jimmy Doolittle chpt. 1988, 91, Calif. Meritorious Svc. award 1988), Calif. Assn. for Aerospace Edn. (fellow), Marine Corps Hist. Found. (life), Aerospace Edn. Found. (Gen. Jimmy Doolittle fellow 1988, Gen. Ira Eaker fellow 1989, Pres.'s award 1988), U.S. Naval Inst., AIAA (Cert. of Appreciation 1989, L.A. chpt. hist. com. 1989), Marine Corps Assn. (assoc.), Navy League, Gulf & Vietnam Vet. Hist. Assn. (cons., co-founder, trustee 1983—, exec. dir.), Am. Def. Preparedness Assn., Exptl. Aircraft Assn., Assn. of Old Crows, U.S. Marine Corps Combat Correspondents Assn. (affiliate), Confederate Air Force (col. 1989, adj. 1st Composite Group detachment 1989), Aircraft Owners and Pilots Assn., World Affairs Coun. Orange County. Avocations: sailing, bicycle racing, traveling, flying.

ZWEIFEL, RICHARD GEORGE, curator; b. L.A., Nov. 5, 1926; s. Harold Charles and Kathleen Marguerite (Garland) Z.; m. Frances Ann Wimsatt, July 30, 1956; children: Matthew Karl, Kenneth Paul, Ellen Katrina. B.A., UCLA, 1950; Ph.D., U. Calif. at Berkeley, 1954. Mem. staff Am. Mus. Natural History, N.Y.C., 1954-89, chmn. curator dept. herpetology, 1968-80, curator emeritus, 1989—; sci. attaché Gondwana, 1974-75. Served with AUS, 1945-46. Mem. Soc. Study Evolution, Am. Soc. Icthyologists and Herpetologists. Home: PO Box 354 Portal AZ 85632-9998

ZWEIFEL, TERRY L., aeronautical engineer, researcher; b. Phoenix, Oct. 24, 1942; s. Robert Rudy and Ruby Mae (Toliver) Z.; m. Carol Jean Vogt, June 2, 1965. BS in Aero. Engring., U. Ariz., 1965; student, L.A. Valley Coll., 1971-75. Cert. controls engr., Calif. Tech. mgr. Lockheed Aero. Systems Co., Burbank, Calif., 1965-79; chief engr. Simmonds Precision Products Inc., Vergennes, Vt., 1979-81; sr. fellow Honeywell Inc., Phoenix, 1981—; lectr. to profl. groups. Contbr. numerous articles to profl. jours.; patentee windshield detection, flight guidance in windshear, cruise airspeed control, numerous other patents in field. Mem. AIAA (Atmospheric Environment award 1989). Avocations: computer software, chess, travel. Home: 7250 N 30th Dr Phoenix AZ 85051-7513 Office: Honeywell Inc 21111 N 19th Ave Phoenix AZ 85027-2708

ZWEIG, GEORGE, physicist, neurobiologist; b. Moscow, May 20, 1937; came to U.S., 1938; s. Alfred and Rachael (Frölich) Z. BS in Math., U. Mich., 1959; PhD in Physics, Calif. Inst. Tech., 1963. NAS-NRC fellow European Orgn. for Nuclear Rsch., Geneva, 1963-64; asst. prof. physics Calif. Inst. Tech., Pasadena, 1964-66, assoc. prof., 1966-67, prof., 1967-83; staff mem. Los Alamos (N.Mex.) Nat. Lab., 1981-85, fellow, 1985—; founder, pres. Signition Inc., Los Alamos, 1985—; vis. prof. physics U. Wis., Madison, 1967-68; mem. Jason div. Inst. for Def. Analysis, Arlington, Va., 1965-72. Recipient MacArthur prize MacArthur Found., 1981, Disting. Alumnus award Calif. Inst. Tech., 1984; Alfred P. Sloan Found. fellow in physics, 1966-74, in neurobiology, 1974-78. Mem. IEEE, AAAS, Am. Math. Soc., Am. Phys. Soc., Assn. for Rsch. in Otolaryngology. Discoverer quarks, 1963; creator continuous wavelet transform for signal processing, 1975, active model of coclear mechanics, 1987. Office: LANL MS B276 PO Box 1663 Los Alamos NM 87544-0600

ZWEIMAN, BURTON, physician, scientist, educator; b. N.Y.C., June 7, 1931; s. Charles and Gertrude (Levine) Z.; m. Claire Traig, Dec. 30, 1962; children: Amy Beth, Diane Susan. AB, U. Pa., 1952, MD, 1956. Diplomate Am. Bd. Internal Medicine, Am. Bd. Allergy & Immunology. Intern Mt. Sinai Hosp., N.Y.C.; Hosp. U. Pa., Bellevue Hosp. Ctr. Hosp. U. Pa., Bellevue Hosp. Center, 1957-60; fellow NYU Sch. Medicine, 1960-61; mem. faculty dept. medicine U. Pa. Sch. Medicine, Phila., 1963—; prof. medicine, chief allergy and immunology divsn. U. Pa. Sch. Medicine, 1975—; cons. U.S. Army, NIH; co-chmn. Am. Bd. Allergy and Immunology, 1979-81. Editor Jour. Allergy Clin. Immunology, 1988-93; contbr. articles to med. jours. Served with M.C., USNR, 1961-63. Allergy Found. Am. fellow, 1959-61. Fellow ACP, Am. Acad. Allergy (past pres.); mem. Am. Assn. Immunologists, Am. Fedn. Clin. Rsch., Phi Beta Kappa, Alpha Omega Alpha. Office: U Pa Sch Medicine 512 Johnson Pavilion 36th and Hamilton Walk Philadelphia PA 19104

ZWERDLING, ALEX, English educator; b. Breslau, Germany, June 21, 1932; came to U.S., 1941, naturalized, 1946; s. Norbert and Fanni (Alt) Z.; m. Florence Goldberg, Mar. 23, 1969; 1 son, Antony Daniel. B.A., Cornell U., 1953; postgrad. (Fulbright scholar), U. Munich, Germany, 1953-54; M.A., Princeton U., 1956, Ph.D., 1960. Instr. English Swarthmore Coll., 1957-61; asst. prof. English U. Calif., Berkeley, 1961-67; assoc. prof. U. Calif., 1967-73, prof., 1973-86; prof. English U. Calif., Berkeley, 1988—; chmn. grad. studies U. Calif., 1985-86; univ. prof. George Washington U., 1986-88; vis. prof. Northwestern U., 1977; mem. advanced placement exam. com. Ednl. Testing Service, 1975-79; mem. fellowship panel Nat. Endowment for Humanities, 1977-82, 84-87, Nat. Humanities Ctr., 1989-90; fellow Center for Advanced Study in Behavioral Scis., 1964-65. Author: Yeats and the Heroic Ideal, 1965, Orwell and the Left, 1974, Virginia Woolf and the Real World, 1986; mem. adv. com. PMLA, 1978-82. Am. Coun. Learned Socs. fellow, 1964-65; NEH fellow, 1973-74; Guggenheim fellow, 1977-78; Woodrow Wilson Ctr. fellow, 1991-92; fellow Nat. Humanities Ctr., 1992-93. Mem. MLA (chmn. 20th Century Brit. lit. div. 1969-70, 85-86). Office: U Calif Dept English Berkeley CA 94720

ZWERLING, GARY LESLIE, investment bank executive; b. N.Y.C., Aug. 6, 1949; s. Seymour Joseph and Evelyn Rhoda (Posner) Z.; m. Marierose Miraglia, Aug. 25, 1974; children: Cara Marisa, Craig Harris. BEngring., SUNY, Stony Brook, 1960; MBA, SUNY, Albany, 1972. V.p. Chase Manhattan Bank, N.Y.C., 1972-78; gen. prtnr. Goldman, Sachs & Co., N.Y.C., 1978—. Mem. N.Y. One to One Sponsoring Group, Heritage Soc. of A Living Meml. to the Holocaust-Mus. Jewish Heritage. Jewish. Avocation: skiing. Office: Goldman Sachs & Co 85 Broad St New York NY 10004-2434

ZWERVER, PETER JOHN, linguistics educator; b. Grouw, Friesland, The Netherlands, Sept. 3, 1942; came to U.S., 1959; m. Margot Anne Otters, July 16, 1978. AA in Fgn. Langs., Cerritos Coll., 1963; BA in German and English, Calif. State U. Long Beach, 1963; MA in Edn., Azusa Pacific U., 1971; PhD in Edn., Pacific Western U., 1980; PhD in Linguistics, Clayton U., 1988; BS in Liberal Studies, SUNY, Albany, 1989; BA in Archtl. Arts, Clayton U., 1995. Cert. standard elem., jr. high sch. and gen. secondary tchr., Calif.; cert. in standard supervision and adminstrv. svcs. grades kindergarten through 12, Calif. Tchr. math. and woodworking Monrovia (Calif.) Unified Sch. Dist. 1966—; assoc. prof. applied linguistics Pacific Western U., L.A., 1984-92, prof., 1992—; v.p. adminstrv. svcs. Am. M & N U., Metairie, La., 1993—; fellow in community arts and architecture Am. Coastline U., New Orleans, 1989; mem. acad. adv. coun. Pacific Western U., 1994—; chmn. acad. coun. Am. Coastline U., 1988—. Editor jour. Internat. Inst. for Intl. Scholarship, Pacific Western U., 1983-87; contbg. author: Poetic Voices of America, 1993; columnist Foothill Inter-City Newspapers, 1983-86. Pres. Monroe Sch. PTA, 1975, Santa Anita Family Svc., Monrovia, 1982, Arcadian Christian Sch., Arcadia, Calif., 1974. Recipient Hon. Svc.

award Nat. Congress of Parents and Tchrs., 1976. Mem. NEA, Nat. Assn. Scholars, Calif. Tchrs. Assn., Monrovia Tchrs. Assn., Doctorate Assn. N.Y. Educators, Phi Beta Kappa, Phi Delta Kappa (rsch. rep. U. So. Calif. chpt. 1990-91, Rsch. award 1987, Intrnat. Svc. Key, 1993). Avocations: woodworking, attending concerts, museums, architecture, reading.

ZWICK, CHARLES J., think-tank executive. Chmn. of the board Carnegia Endowment for International Peace, Washington, D.C. Office: Carnegie Endowment Internat Peace 2400 N St NW Washington DC 20037-1153

ZWICK, EDWARD M., director, producer, scriptwriter; b. Chgo., Oct. 8, 1952; s. Allen and Ruth Ellen (Reich) Z.; m. Lynn Liberty Godshall, Oct. 24, 1982. BA, Harvard U., 1974; MFA, Am. Film Inst., 1976. Editor, feature writer The New Republic, Rolling Stone, 1972-74; co-founder Bedford Falls Prodn. Co. Writer, prodr., dir.: (TV series) Family, 1976-80 (Humanitas prize 1980), (TV spl.) Spl. Bull., 1983 (Emmy award for outstanding drama spl. 1983, Dir. Guild award 1983, Writers Guild award 1983, Humanitas prize 1983); dir.: (TV movies) Paper Dolls, 1982, Having It All, 1982, Extreme Close-Up, 1990, (films) About Last Night, 1986, Glory, 1989, Leaving Normal, 1992, Legends of the Fall, 1994; co-creator, exec. prodr.: (with Marshall Herskovitz) thirtysomething, 1987-91 (Emmy award for outstanding drama series 1988), Dream Street, 1989, My So Called Life, 1994-95; author: Literature and Liberalism, 1975. Office: ICM 8942 Wilshire Blvd Beverly Hills CA 90211-1908*

ZWICK, KENNETH LOWELL, lawyer; b. Cleve., Oct. 30, 1945; s. Alvin Albert Zwick and Selma (Mack) Durbin; m. Ruth Winifred Epstein, June 21, 1969; children: Tara, Monica. BSME,BS in Mgmt., MIT, 1969; JD, Temple U., 1976. Bar: Pa. 1976. Engr. Raytheon Corp., Norwood, Mass., 1969-71; tech. mgr. On-Line Systems, Inc., Phila., 1971-76; staff atty. Mead Data Cen., Washington, 1976-83; dir. litigation support office U.S. Dept. Justice, Washington, 1983-88, dir. mgmt. programs office, 1988—. Mem. ABA, D.C. Computer Law Forum, ASME (assoc.). Democrat. Jewish. Home: 9316 Wescott Pl Rockville MD 20850-3452 Office: US Dept Justice 3140 Main Justice Bldg Washington DC 20530

ZWIEP, DONALD NELSON, mechanical engineering educator, administrator; b. Hull, Iowa, Mar. 18, 1924; s. Daniel and Nellie (De Stigter) Z.; m. Marcia J. Hubers, Sept. 3, 1948; children: Donna J., Mary N., Joan L., Helen D. BSME, Iowa State Coll., 1948, MSME, 1951; DEng (hon.), Worcester Polytech. Inst., 1965. Registered profl. engr., Mass. Design engr. Boeing Airplane Co., 1948-50, sr. tool engr., summer 1953, summer faculty asso., 1955; asst. prof. Colo. State U., 1951-56, assoc. prof., 1956-57; cons. engr. aviation div. Forney Mfg. Co., 1956-57; prof., head dept. mech. engring. Worcester Polytech. Inst., 1957-88, acting head mgmt. dept., 1974-76, chmn. Mfg. Engring. Application Ctr., 1981-88, acting provost, v.p. acad. affairs, 1988-90, prof., dept. head emeritus, 1990—; constrn. engr. U.S. C.E., summer 1954; cons. engr., acting chief engr. J.J. Malir, Inc., summer 1956. Chmn. bd. trustees James F. Lincoln Arc Welding Found., 1976—. Served as pilot USAAF, World War II, CBI; lt. col. USAFR; cons. and ednl. specialist. Fellow ASME (life, v.p. edn. 1972-74, pres. 1978-80); mem. Am. Soc. Engring. Soc. (life, pres. Colo. State U. chpt. 1954-55, treas. Rocky Mountain sect. 1955, nat. bd. dirs. 1974-75), Am. Assn. Engring. Socs. (chair coun. pre-coll. edn.), Am. Welding Soc., Soc. Mfg. Engrs., Torch Club, Sigma Xi, Omicron Delta Kappa, Tau Beta Pi, Sigma Tau, Pi Tau Sigma. Methodist. Home: 47 Birchwood Dr Holden MA 01520-1937 Office: Worcester Poly Inst 100 Institute Rd Worcester MA 01609-2247

ZWILICH, ELLEN TAAFFE, composer; b. Miami, Fla., Apr. 30, 1939; d. Edward Porter and Ruth (Howard) Taaffe; m. Joseph Zwilich, June 22, 1969 (dec. June 1979). MusB, Fla. State U., 1960, MusM, 1962; D Mus. Arts, Juilliard Sch., 1975; studies with Roger Sessions and Elliott Carter; MusD (hon.), Oberlin Coll., 1987, Converse Coll., 1994; LHD (hon.), Manhattanville Coll., 1991, Marymount Manhattan Coll., 1994. composer in residence Santa Fe Chamber Music Festival, 1990, Am. Acad., Rome, 1990; bd. dirs. MacDowell Colony; first composer's chair Carnegie Hall, 1995. Premiere, Symposium for Orch., Pierre Boulez, N.Y.C., 1975, Chamber Symphony and Passages, Boston Musica Viva, Richard Pittman, 1979, 82. Symphony 1, Gunther Schuller, Am. Composers Orch., 1982; violinist Am. Symphony, N.Y.C., 1965-73; composer: Sonata in Three Movements, 1973-74; String Quartet, 1974; Clarino Quartet, 1977; Chamber Symphony, 1979; Passages for Soprano and Chamber Ensemble), 1981; String Trio, 1982; Symphony 1:3 Movements for Orch., 1982 (Grammy nomination New World Records, 1987); Divertimento, 1983; Einsame Nacht, 1971; Emlekezet, 1978; Im Nebel, 1972; Passages for Soprano and Orch., 1982; Trompeten, 1974; Fantasy for Harpsichord, 1983; Intrada, 1983; Prologue and Variations, 1983; Double Quartet for Strings, Chamber Music Soc. of Lincoln Ctr., 1984; Celebration for Orch., Indpls. Symphony, John Nelson, 1984; Symphony #2 (Cello Symphony) San Francisco Symphony, Edo De Waart, 1985, Symphony #2 Louisville Orch. recording, L.L. Smith (Grammy nomination 1991); Concerto Grosso 1985, Handel Festival Orch., Steven Simon, 1986; Concerto for Piano and Orch., Detroit Symphony, Gunther Herbig, Marc-André Hamelin, 1986; Images for 2 Pianos and Orch., Nat. Symphony Orch., F. Machetti, 1987; Tanzspiel, Peter Martins N.Y.C. Ballet, 1987; Praeludium Boston chpt. AGO, 1987; Trio for piano, violin and cello; Kalichstein, Laredo, Robinson trio, 1987; Symbolon, Zubin Mehta and the N.Y. Philharm., Leningrad and Moscow (USSR), N.Y.C. (Koussevitsky Internat. Rec. award nominee 1990), 1988; concerto for trombone and orch. J. Friedman, Sir Georg Solti, Chgo. Symphony, 1989, concerto for trombone and orch. Christian Lindberg, James De Priest, Malmö Symphony, concerto for flute and orch. D.A. Dwyer, Seija Ozawa, Boston Symphony, 1990, quintet for clarinet and string quartet David Schiffrin, Chamber Music N.W., 1990; concerto for oboe and orch. John Mack, Christoph von Dohnanyi, Cleve. Orch., 1991; concerto for bass trombone strings, timpani and cymbals Chgo. Symphony Orch.Ch. Vernon, Daniel Barenboim, 1991; concerto for violin, violoncello and orch. Jaime Laredo, Sharon Robinson, Louisville Orch., L. Smith 1991; Immigrant Voices Peter Leonard, St. Lukes Orch. N.Y. Internat. Festival of the Arts Chorus, Ellis Island, 1991, concerto for flute and orch D.A. Dwyer, J. Sedares, London Symphony Orch., 1992, Symphony # 3, J. Ling, N.Y. Philharmonic, 1993, concerto for bassoon and orch., Nancy Goeres, Lorin Maazel, Pitts. Symphony, 1993, concerto for horn and string Orch., David Jolley, Rochester Philharm., L.L. Smith, 1993, Fantasy for Orch., JoAnn Falletta, Long Beach Symphony Orch., 1994; New World Records: Music By Ellen Taaffe Zwilich; N.Y. Philharm. conducted by Zubin Mehta. Recipient Elizabeth Sprague Coolidge Chamber Music prize, 1974, Gold medal G.B. Viotti, Vercelli, Italy, 1975, citation Ernst von Dohnanyi, 1981, Pulitzer prize, 1983, Composers award Lancaster Symphony Orch., Arturo Toscanini Music Critics award, 1987, Alfred I. DuPont award, 1991; Martha Baird Rockefeller Fund rec. grantee, 1977, 79, 82, Guggenheim fellow, 1981. Mem. Am. Fedn. Musicians (hon. life), Am. Music Ctr. (bd. dirs., v.p. 1982-84), Am. Composers Orch. (bd. dirs.), Am. Acad. and Inst. Arts and Letters (Academy award), Internat. League Women Composers, Am. Composers Alliance, Am. Composers Orch. (bd. dirs.), Fla. Artista Hall of Fame. Home: 600 W 246th St Bronx NY 10471-3611 Office: care Music Assocs Am 224 King St Englewood NJ 07631-3026

ZWINGE, RANDALL JAMES HAMILTON See RANDI, JAMES

ZWIRN, ROBERT, architect, architecture educator; b. N.Y.C., Apr. 6, 1948; m. Sharon Kay Hansen, Mar. 19, 1972 (div. Sept. 1979); m. Carolyn Marie Pione, Feb. 20, 1994. BS, Rensselaer Poly. Inst., 1968, BArch, 1969; MArch, U. Oreg., 1970; JD, U. Ala., Montgomery, 1975. Registered architect, Ala., Ohio, La. Asst. prof. architecture Auburn (Ala.) U., 1970-78, assoc. prof., 1978-79; vis. fellow Princeton (N.J.) U., 1979-81; architect I.M. Pei & Ptnrs., N.Y.C., 1981-84; prof. architecture Miami U., Oxford, Ohio, 1984—, chmn. dept., 1984-92; dir. Sch. Architecture La. State U., Baton Rouge, 1994—; archtl. advisor City of Forest Park, Ohio, 1989-90. Contbr. biographies to Ency. Architecture. Numerous archtl. comms., 1976—. Mem. Future of Oxford, 1988-89. Miami U. Sch. Fine Arts grantee, 1988; NEH summer stipend grantee UCLA, 1994. Mem. Assn. Collegiate Schs. Architecture (nat. bd. dirs., bd. dirs. E. Cen. region 1986-89, co-editor 1989), Architects Soc. Ohio (bd. dirs. 1988-89, Profl. Devel. award 1990). Democrat. Jewish. Avocation: gardening. Office: La State U Sch Architecture Baton Rouge LA 70808

ZWISLOCKI, JOZEF JOHN, neuroscience educator, researcher; b. Lwow, Poland, Mar. 19, 1922; came to U.S., 1951; s. Tadeusz and Helena (Moscicki) Z.; m. Ruth Gerber, Oct. 29, 1945 (div. May 1954); m. Sylvia Claire Goldman, July 11, 1954 (dec. July 17, 1992); m. Jadwiga M. Morrison, Dec. 2, 1993. Diploma, Fed. Tech. Inst., Zurich, Switzerland, 1944, Sc.D., 1948; D. honoris causa, U. Adam Mickiewicz, Poznán, Poland, 1991. Research asst. dept. otolaryngology U. Basel, Switzerland, 1945-51; research fellow psychoacoustic lab. Harvard U., Cambridge, Mass., 1951-57; dir. Bioacoustic Lab. Syracuse U., N.Y., 1958-63, founder, dir. Lab. of Sensory Communication, 1963-73, founder dir. Inst. for Sensory Research, 1973-84, prof. neurosci., 1984-88, Disting. prof. neurosci., 1988-92; Disting. rsch. prof. Inst. for Sensory Rsch. Syracuse U., 1992, prof. communicative disorders dept. spl. edn. Sch. Edn., 1982-92; research prof. SUNY Health Sci. Ctr. at Syracuse, 1967—; affiliate prof. bioengring. L.C. Smith Coll. Engring., 1988-96, 1988-92; Carhart Meml. lectr. Am. Auditory Soc., 1992; mem. exec. coun. Com. Hearing, Bioacoustics and Biomechanics, NRC, Washington, 1965-68, chmn. 1967-68; mem. rev. panel on communicative scis. NIH, Bethesda, Md., 1966-70, chmn., 1969-70; mem. Communicative Disorders Program Project rev. com. NIH, Bethesda, 1971-75; chmn. Bd. Sci. Advs. Ctr. Health Scis., U. Wis., Madison, 1975-78. Inventor acoustic ear simulator, acoustic bridge, layered earplugs; contbr. articles to profl. jours. Recipient Faculty Research award Syracuse chpt. Sigma Xi, 1973, Internat. Ctr. Ricerche e Studi Amplifon prize, 1976, Chancellor's citation, Syracuse U., 1980, Javits Neurosci. Investigator award NIH, 1984, Kwiek medal Acoustics Inst., A. Mickiewicz U., Poland, 1991, medal Acoustical Soc. Poland, 1991, Hugh Knowles prize Northwestern U., 1992. Fellow Acoustical Soc. Am. (chmn. tech. com. on psychol. and physiol. acoustics 1962, 63, exec. coun. 1982-85, recipient 1st Bekesy medal 1985, chmn. long-range planning com. 1983-86, nominating com. 1986-87, mem. com. on tutorials 1988-91, com. on meetings 1988-91, chmn. spring meeting, 1989), Am. Speech and Hearing Assn., The Polish Inst. of Arts and Scis. of Am.; mem. NAS, Internat. Soc. Audiology (v.p. 1967-72), Internat. Union of Physiol. Scis. (commn. on auditory physiology 1982-89), Internat. Union Pure and Applied Physics (Commn. on Acoustics 1982-89), Collegium Oto Rhino Laryngologicum Amicitiae Sacrum, Assn. for Research in Otolaryngology (award of merit 1988), Hearing Research (edit. bd.). Clubs: Drumlins Tennis, Onondaga Ski (Syracuse). Avocations: skiing, tennis, trout fishing, inventions.

ZWOYER, EUGENE MILTON, consulting engineering executive; b. Plainfield, N.J., Sept. 8, 1926; s. Paul Ellsworth and Marie Susan (Britt) Z.; m. Dorothy Lucille Seward, Feb. 23, 1946; children: Gregory, Jeffrey, Douglas. Student, U. Notre Dame, 1944, Mo. Valley Coll. 1944-45; BS, U. N.Mex., 1947; MS, Ill. Inst. Tech., 1949; PhD, U. Ill., 1953. Mem. faculty U. N.Mex., Albuquerque, 1948-71, prof. civil engring., dir. Eric Wang Civil Engring. Rsch. Facility, 1961-70; rsch. assoc. U. Ill., Urbana, 1951-53; owner, cons. engr. Eugene Zwoyer & Assocs., Albuquerque, 1954-72; exec. dir., sec. ASCE, N.Y.C., 1972-82; pres. Am. Assn. Engring. Socs., N.Y.C., 1982-84; exec. v.p. T.Y. Lin Internat., San Francisco, 1984-86, pres., 1986-89; owner Eugene Zwoyer Cons. Engr., 1989—; chief oper. officer, treas. Polar Molecular Corp., Saginaw, Mich., 1990, exec. v.p., 1991-92. Trustee Small Bus. Research Corp., 1976-80; trustee Engring. Info., Inc., 1981-84; internat. trustee People-to-People Internat. 1974-86; v.p. World Fedn. Engring. Orgns., 1982-85. Served to lt. (j.g.) USN, 1944-46. Named Outstanding Engr. of Yr. Albuquerque chpt. N.Mex Soc. Profl. Engrs., 1969, One Who Served the Best Interests of the Constrn. Industry, Engring. News Record, 1980; recipient Disting. Alumnus award the Civil Engring. Alumni Assn. at U. Ill., 1979, Disting. Alumnus award Engring. Coll. Alumni Assn., U. N.Mex., 1982, Can.-Am. Civil Engring. Amity award Am. Soc. Civil Engrs., 1988, Award for Outstanding Profl. Contbns. and Leadership Coll. Engring. U. N.Mex., 1989. Mem. AAAS, ASCE (dist. bd. dirs. 1968-71), NSPE, Am. Soc. Engring. Edn., Am. Concrete Inst., Nat. Acad. Code Adminstrn. (trustee, mem. exec. com. 1973-79), Engrs. Joint Coun. (bd. dirs. 1978-79), Engring. Soc. Commn. on Energy (bd. dirs. 1977-82), Sigma Xi, Sigma Tau, Chi Epsilon. Home: 6363 Christie Ave Apt 1326 Emeryville CA 94608-1940 Office: Ste 200C 1172 San Pablo Ave Berkeley CA 94706-2245

ZYLANOFF, PHILLIPA LOUISE, anesthesiologist; b. Indpls., Feb. 2, 1943; d. Joseph David Zylanoff and Phillipa (Schreiber) Moore; divorced; children: Gwendolynn, Ann, Daniel, Aliza, Tamar. BS, Calif. State U., Hayward, 1966; MD, Med. Coll. Pa., 1972. Diplomate Am. Bd. Anesthesiology. Asst. prof. U. Calif., Davis, 1977-79; staff anesthesiologist New Iberia (La.) Parish Hosp., 1979-81; pvt. practice anesthesiology Moorehead, Ky., 1981-84; asst. prof. U. S. Ala., Mobile, 1985-87; dir. anesthesiology Randolph Hosp., Asheboro, N.C., 1987-90; pvt. practice anesthesiology Detroit, 1990—. Contbr. articles to profl. jours. Course dir. Mich. affiliate Am. Heart Assn. Mem. AMA, Mich. Soc. Anesthesiologists, Mich. State Med. Soc., Wayne County Med. Soc. (peer review com. 1991-93), Soc. Cardiovascular Anesthesiologists (presenter 1987). Republican. Jewish. Avocations: gardening, scuba diving, music. Home: 17311 Beechwood Ave Franklin MI 48025-5523

ZYLIS-GARA, TERESA GERARDA, soprano; b. Landwarow, Poland, Jan. 23, 1935; married; 1 child. Student conservatories. Debut, Cracow, Glyndebourne (Eng.) Opera, 1965, Paris Opera, 1966, San Francisco Opera, Met. Opera, 1968, Salzburg (Austria) Festival, leading soprano, Deutsche Oper am Rhein, appearances with Vienna Staatsopera, Royal Opera House-Covent Garden, London, Munich (W.Ger.) Staatsoper, Hamburg (W.Ger.) Staatsoper, La Scala, Milan, Italy, also opera houses of Berlin, Brussels, Paris, San Francisco and Chgo., Teatro Colon, Buenos Aires, Bolshoi-Moscow, soprano soloist with, Boston Symphony Orch., N.Y. Philharm. Orch., Los Angeles Philharm., Cleve. Orch., guest artist on radio and TV in, Europe and U.S.; rec. artist: Angel, Deutsche Grammophon and, Seraphim records; prin. roles in: Il Trovatore; Un Ballo in: Maschera; Desdemona in: Otello; Marschallin in: Der Rosenkavalier; also title role in: Tosca. Winner contest Mozart. German Broadcasters, Internat. Singing Competition, Munich, 1960; recipient Prime Minister's prize, 1979, Mozart gold medal, Mexico City, Polish Nat. award. Fellow Kosciuszko Found., Frederic Chopin Found. Office: c/o Hamburg State Opera, Grosse-Theaterstasse 34, D-2000 Hamburg 36, Germany Address: 16A Blvd de Belgique, Monaco-Ville Monaco L'artiste face a l'oeuvre est comme le roseau dans le vent: c'est lui qui doit plier. La musique est l'expression universelle de l'ame d'un peuple.*

ZYLSTRA, STANLEY JAMES, farmer, food company executive; b. Hull, Iowa, Dec. 18, 1943; s. Jerald S. and Dora (Te Slaa) Z.; m. Ruth Eileen Van Batavia, Jan. 3, 1964; children: Rachel Ann, Carl Dean. BA, Northwestern Coll., 1965; MA, Univ. S.D., 1969. Math tchr., counselor Boyden-Hull Sch., 1965-73; farmer Hull, 1970—; dir. Land O'Lakes, Mpls., 1985—, chmn. bd. dirs., 1988—. Mem. Kiwanis (pres. 1974-75). Republican. Mem. Reformed Church in America. Home: RR 1 Box 200 Hull IA 51239-9763 Office: Land O'Lakes Inc 4001 Lexington Ave N Saint Paul MN 55126-2934

ZYTKOW, JAN MIKOLAJ, computer science educator; b. Warsaw, Sept. 9, 1944; came to U.S., 1982; s. Swiatozar Mikolaj and Maria (Szeruda) Z.; m. Malgorzata Krzywińska, Oct. 14, 1972; children: Nikola, Ania, Andrzej, Michael. MS in Theoretical Physics, U. Warsaw, 1967, MA in Philosophy, 1970, PhD in Philosophy Sci., 1972, habilitation docent, 1979. Asst. prof. U. Warsaw, 1972-80, assoc. prof. 1981-82; vis. prof. Carnegie-Mellon U., Pitts., 1982-84; assoc. prof. Wichita (Kans.) State U., 1984-87, prof., 1987—. Author: (with others) Scientific Discovery, 1987; contbr. articles to profl. jours. Mem. Am. Assn. Artificial Intelligence, Philosophy Sci. Assn. Lutheran. Home: 3636 Armstrong St Wichita KS 67204-3922 Office: Wichita State U. Computer Sci Dept Wichita KS 67260

ZYWICKI, ROBERT ALBERT, electrical distribution company executive; b. Chgo., Sept. 23, 1930; s. Martin Albert and Margaret Irene (Mackowski) Z.; m. Barbara Joan Hagerty; children: Robert, Cheryl, Cindy, Carrie. B in Commerce, Northwestern U., 1966. Teller Chgo. Title and Trust Bank, Chgo., 1949-50; painter Getz Molding Co., Chgo., 1950-51; purchasing agt. Woodworker's Tool Works, Chgo., 1953-54; serviceman Addressograph Multigraph, Chgo., 1954-55; mem. Chgo. Fire Dept., 1955-62; v.p. Anixter Bros. Inc., Skokie, Ill., 1955-87; co-owner A-Z Industries, Northbrook, Ill., 1987-92, A-Z Anicom (formerly A-Z Industries), Northbrook, Ill., 1992—. Served as cpl. U.S. Army, 1951-53. Mem. Am. Legion (comdr.). Republican. Roman Catholic. Avocations: thoroughbred horse racing, classical music, baseball card collecting, tennis. Home: 1330 Sprucewood Ln Deerfield IL 60015-4771